ULRICH'S™ INTERNATIONAL PERIODICALS DIRECTORY

31st Edition

1992-93

Ulrich's International Periodicals Directory
is compiled by
R.R. Bowker
Serials Department

Judith Salk, Executive Editor
Edvika Popilskis, Senior Editor

Frank McDermott, Senior Associate Editor
Egill Halldorsson, Ewa Kowalska, Associate Editors

Lisa Finan, Laura Forbes, Christopher King, Dawn Lombardy, Henry Wessells, Pu Xiang,
Assistant Editors

Mary Crouthers, Editorial Assistant
Ila Joseph, Mail Processing Clerk
Brenda Worthy, Secretary

Barry Barish, Terence Carlson, Karl Dusza, Dorothy Hodges,
Margareta Leon, Inna Levine, Lucy Setteducato, and
Eline van de Poel, Contributing Editors

Max Kobrinsky, Systems Communications Manager
Jack Murphy, Supervisor, Computer Operations
Karen Strong, Senior Account Manager, International Computaprint Corporation

James P. Murray, Senior Vice President and General Manager
Peter Simon, Vice President, Database Publishing Group

31st Edition
ULRICH'S™
INTERNATIONAL PERIODICALS DIRECTORY
1992-93

including
Irregular Serials & Annuals

Volume 3
Indexes

THE BOWKER INTERNATIONAL SERIALS DATABASE

R.R. BOWKER
A Reed Reference Publishing Company
New Providence, New Jersey

Published by R.R. Bowker
A Reed Reference Publishing Company
121 Chanlon Rd., New Providence, NJ 07974

Ulrich's Hotline (U.S. only): 1-800-346-6049
Editorial (Canada only, call collect): 1-908-665-2870, 2875
Serials Fax (overseas users): 908-771-7725

Copyright © 1992 by Reed Publishing (USA) Inc.
All rights reserved.

Ulrich's is a trademark of Reed Properties Inc., used under license.

No part of this publication may be reproduced or transmitted in any form or by any means, stored in any information storage and retrieval system, without prior written permission of R.R. Bowker, 121 Chanlon Rd., New Providence, NJ 07974

International Standard Book Number 0-8352-3264-6
(3 Volume set)
International Standard Book Number 0-8352-3265-4
(Volume 1)
International Standard Book Number 0-8352-3266-2
(Volume 2)
International Standard Book Number 0-8352-3267-0
(Volume 3)
International Standard Serial Number 0000-0175
Library of Congress Catalog Card Number 32-16320

Printed and bound in the United States of America.

No payment is either solicited or accepted for the inclusion of entries in this publication. R.R. Bowker has used its best efforts in collecting and preparing material for inclusion in this publication, but does not warrant that the information herein is complete or accurate, and does not assume, and hereby disclaims, any liability to any person for any loss or damage caused by errors or omissions in this publication, whether such errors or omissions result from negligence, accident or any other cause.

3 Volume Set

ISBN 0-8352-3264-6

Contents

PREFACE vii

USER'S GUIDE ix

INTERNATIONAL STANDARD SERIAL NUMBER xvii

ABBREVIATIONS

    General Abbreviations and Special Symbols xix
    Money Symbols xx
    Micropublishers and Distributors xxi
    Reprint Services xxv
    Country of Publication Codes xxvi
    Abstracting and Indexing Services xxviii

SUBJECT GUIDE TO ABSTRACTING AND INDEXING xl

SUBJECTS xlii

CROSS-INDEX TO SUBJECTS xlviii

VOLUME 1

CLASSIFIED LIST OF SERIALS/SUBJECTS A to H 1

VOLUME 2

CLASSIFIED LIST OF SERIALS/SUBJECTS I to Z 2521

VOLUME 3

REFEREED SERIALS 4863

CONTROLLED CIRCULATION SERIALS 4961

SERIALS AVAILABLE ON CD-ROM 5031

PRODUCER LISTING/SERIALS ON CD-ROM 5043

SERIALS AVAILABLE ONLINE 5045

VENDOR LISTING/SERIALS ONLINE 5109

CESSATIONS 5127

INDEX TO PUBLICATIONS OF INTERNATIONAL ORGANIZATIONS .. 5311

    International Organizations 5311
    International Congress Proceedings 5321
    European Communities 5324
    United Nations 5325

ISSN INDEX 5331

TITLE INDEX 5855

Preface

Ulrich's International Periodicals Directory has been the premier serials reference source since 1932. The 31st edition, which is the 60th anniversary edition of **Ulrich's**, continues to uphold its reputation for excellence in the provision of serials bibliographic information. With the publication of this edition, we not only unveil a new look for this venerable serials authority, but we also include a multitude of new features which will enhance your access to and use of the serials information we provide.

Foremost among the physical changes introduced in this edition of **Ulrich's** is the new typeface which is intended to improve the readability of the text. Boldfaced data elements, particularly in the title field, now appear in each listing to help users locate vital bibliographic information at a glance. Not so obvious to the user are other internal changes, such as improved punctuation between data elements.

Noteworthy new features such as full-page advertising rates and an advertising contact name appear when provided by the publisher; and, when known, years of coverage of serials by specific A&I services are included. We also now note the shelfmark numbers of serials held by the British Library indicating their availability for document delivery through the British Library Document Supply Centre (BLDSC). For a full explanation of the BLDSC and the shelfmark number, please refer to page xiii in the User's Guide in this volume. In addition, we have expanded our coverage of serials reprint services. Such services are an important resource, providing access to back issues and otherwise hard-to-find serials. While many microform publishers also function as reprint services, we have highlighted the reprint services in a separate list on page xxv.

In a year full of enormous political changes, **Ulrich's** has kept pace with the emergence of new nations from the former Soviet Union and Yugoslavia. Entries for publications from these 19 new countries reflect both actual correspondence with publishers in the new nations and revisions according to the latest USMARC Code List for Countries.

Numerous additions and refinements were made to our subject heading file this year, reflecting our acknowledgement of the increasingly specialized nature of serials publishing. New subject classifications in this edition fall into two groups: those with separate headings for publications in such diverse areas as Women's Studies, Men's Studies, Singles' Interests and Lifestyles, Leisure and Recreation, Matrimony, and How-to and Do-It-Yourself; and, as a result of extensive research and discussion, many specialized subheadings such as ten new headings within the Law classification; Pollution, Toxicology and Environmental Safety, and Waste Management within the Environmental Studies category; Bioengineering and Biotechnology within the Biology category; Science Fiction, Fantasy, Horror and Mystery and Detective within the Literature category; and Solar Energy, Wind Energy, Geothermal Energy within the Energy category, to name only a few.

Serials continue to be important as primary sources of current and topical news in all fields of endeavor, as evidenced by the vast number of serials published and their rapid development into electronic formats. The availability of serials in electronic formats, either online or on CD-ROM, continues to grow. This edition of **Ulrich's** includes 2,941 serials available exclusively online or in addition to hardcopy, and 558 serials available on CD-ROM. These serials are indicated by a notation and a bullet (●) in the main entry.

The 31st edition of **Ulrich's** contains information on nearly 126,000 serials published throughout the world, arranged under 788 subject headings. More than 66,000 entries from the 30th edition have been updated to reflect the most current information available and nearly 10,000 serials have been added. Also included in this edition is information on 8,304 titles that are known to have ceased or suspended publication in the last three years. The ceased or suspended titles are preceded by a dagger (†) in the "Title Index" for instant identification. Users can identify newer serials, over 3,800 of which are known to have begun publication since January 1, 1990, by looking for an upside-down solid triangle (▼) preceding entries in both the "Classified List of Serials" and the "Title Index." In addition, over 5,000 refereed serials notations, 42,000 brief descriptions, 30,300 LC Classification Numbers, 14,100 CODEN, and 2,142 vendor file names or numbers for 2,941 titles available in an online format appear in this edition.

International data inquiries are mailed annually to some 67,000 publishers to secure accurate and up-to-date information directly from the publishers on current titles, as well as new titles, titles changes, and cessations. In addition, updating of the database occurs daily from information received from publishers throughout the year. All post office returns are researched, and entries from publishers whose addresses cannot be located are suspended from the file. Information about title changes, cessations, and new titles not received by the deadline for this edition will appear in **Ulrich's Update**; in the online database available through DIALOG Information Services, Inc., BRS Information Technologies, Inc., and the European Space Agency (ESA-ISA); on **Ulrich's *Plus*™** CD-ROM; and on **Ulrich's Microfiche**. In addition, users are encouraged to call our editorial office for help in solving serials questions.

Included in **Ulrich's** are serials which are currently available, issued more frequently than once a year and usually published at regular intervals, as well as publications issued annually or less frequently than once a year, or irregularly. Due to the vast number of serials, we have established certain criteria for inclusion, while maintaining our aim of maximum title coverage that will satisfy the widest range of use. We include all publications that meet the definition of a serial except general daily newspapers, newspapers of local scope or local interest, administrative publications of major government agencies below state level that can be easily found elsewhere, membership directories, comic books, and puzzle and game books. This edition of **Ulrich's** is arranged in eleven sections within three volumes: the first two volumes comprise the "Classified List of Serials;" the third volume contains the "Refereed Serials," "Controlled Circulation Serials," "Serials Available on CD-ROM," "Producer Listing/Serials on CD-ROM," "Serials Available Online," "Vendor Listing/Serials Online," "Cessations," "Index to International Organizations," "ISSN," and "Title" indexes.

Your purchase and use of **Ulrich's** is complemented with some additional services. **Ulrich's Update**, provided free of charge, three times per year—in November, February, and May—is a supplemental service to the annual directory. The **Ulrich's Hotline** is a toll-free number that customers can call to get help in solving their periodicals and serials research problems and questions. Canadian users are asked to call a special number collect, and our overseas users are asked to use a designated fax number. (Please see page iv for our address and telephone and fax numbers.) **Ulrich's News**, previously a free quarterly publication sent to subscribers of **Ulrich's**, was recently merged with a new quarterly newsletter from R.R. Bowker, **The Cornerstone**. (The last issue of of **Ulrich's News** was published in 1992, and the first issue of **The Cornerstone** will debut in September, 1992.) **The Cornerstone** will include not only valuable information about serials and **Ulrich's**, as had **Ulrich's News**, but will also contain news about other Bowker titles and pertinent topics.

As always, we continue to research, plan, and implement enhancements to the **Ulrich's** database and our database maintenance system. The 32nd edition is sure to include some new developments that will enhance your usage of **Ulrich's**. We consider feedback from our users to be essential, so please contact us and let us know your thoughts. We want **Ulrich's** and its family of products to provide all necessary reference information quickly and effectively. Comments and suggestions are encouraged in order to help keep our database and its bibliographic publications of the highest quality.

My sincere appreciation is extended to the senior staff of **Ulrich's**, Edvika Popilskis, Frank McDermott, and Ewa Kowalska, and to our fine staff of serials editors for their unflagging dedication and hard work in updating and maintaining the serials database in preparation of the 31st edition of **Ulrich's**. Thanks also to Peter Simon, Vice President of the Database Publishing Group, and to all others at R.R. Bowker for their contributions toward the completion of this 60th anniversary edition. Profound gratitude goes to Karen Strong, Senior Account Manager at International Computaprint Corporation, for her competence, diligence, and patience in working closely with us this past year to program all the special features contained herein. Finally, I would like to thank the various information specialists throughout the world who have taken it upon themselves to provide us with hard-to-find serials data. We consider their participation and interest in the dissemination of accurate and comprehensive serials information to be of great value to **Ulrich's** and its users.

Judith Salk
Executive Editor

User's Guide

This directory offers two primary access methods for locating periodicals: by subject in the CLASSIFIED LIST OF SERIALS, and alphabetically in the TITLE INDEX. Ceased serials are listed in a separate CESSATIONS section and are also accessible by means of the TITLE INDEX. Other indexes provide listings of selected periodicals in specific categories. These indexes are REFEREED SERIALS, CONTROLLED CIRCULATION SERIALS, SERIALS AVAILABLE ON CD-ROM, PRODUCER LISTING/SERIALS ON CD-ROM, SERIALS AVAILABLE ONLINE, VENDOR LISTING/SERIALS ONLINE, PUBLICATIONS OF INTERNATIONAL ORGANIZATIONS, and ISSN INDEX.

In addition, separate subheadings for "Abstracting, Bibliographies and Statistics" under major subject headings provide convenient access to these types of publications. Page references for these subheadings are given in the "Subject Guide to Abstracting and Indexing" on p. xl. This Subject Guide provides an overview of subjects for which abstracting and indexing publications have been identified.

This "User's Guide" is separated into three divisions for ease of use: (I) Section Descriptions, (II) Full Entry Content Description, and (III) Cataloging Rules for Main Entry Title.

Section Descriptions

CLASSIFIED LIST OF SERIALS

This is the main section of the book, containing bibliographic information for currently published serials classified by subject. Entries are arranged alphabetically by title within each subject heading. Subject cross-references in the text direct the user to the location of subheadings.

Volume 1 contains subjects A-H, from "Abstracting and Indexing" through "Humanities." Volume 2 contains subjects I-Z, "Instruments" through "Zoology."

A complete listing of the "Subjects" used in the CLASSIFIED LIST OF SERIALS appears on p. xlii. To aid international users, this list is translated into four languages. For additional guidance on the subject classification scheme, the user should also consult the "Cross-Index to Subjects" on p. xlviii, which contains additional key word references.

Each serial is listed with full bibliographic information only once. If a serial covers several subjects, title cross-references appear under the related headings, directing the user to the heading where the full entry is listed.

New serials (beginning publication within the last three years) are highlighted by a ▼ in front of the title.

The "Cataloging Rules for Main Entry Title" section of this "User's Guide" explains the title cataloging rules followed in compiling the **Ulrich's International Periodicals Directory.**

REFEREED SERIALS

This section is an alphabetical listing by title of all serials known to be refereed, or peer reviewed. It includes the publisher name, address, and telephone number, if known. The italicized number at the end of each entry is the page number where the full entry appears in the CLASSIFIED LIST OF SERIALS.

CONTROLLED CIRCULATION SERIALS

This section is an alphabetical listing of all serials known to have controlled circulations. It includes the publisher name and address, telephone and fax numbers, and circulation figure, if known. The italicized number at the end of each entry is a reference to the page on which the full entry appears in the CLASSIFIED LIST OF SERIALS.

SERIALS AVAILABLE ON CD-ROM

This section is an alphabetical listing of all serials known to be available on CD-ROM, either in addition to hardcopy, or on CD-ROM only. It includes the publisher name, address, telephone and fax numbers, if known. It also includes the name of CD-ROM producers, when known. The italicized number at the end of each entry is the page number where the full entry appears in the CLASSIFIED LIST OF SERIALS.

PRODUCER LISTING/SERIALS ON CD-ROM

This section is an alphabetical listing of identified producers of serials on CD-ROM. Entries include the producer address, telephone and fax numbers, and an alphabetical listing of all serials titles known to be available. If known, the serial on CD-ROM product name is listed in parentheses after the serial title. All serials listed in this index also have full bibliographic entries in the CLASSIFIED LIST OF SERIALS. Consult the TITLE INDEX or the SERIALS AVAILABLE ON CD-ROM listing for page numbers.

SERIALS AVAILABLE ONLINE

This section is an alphabetical listing of all serials known to be available online, either in addition to hardcopy, or online only. Entries include publisher name, address, telephone and fax numbers, plus names of online vendors and file names or numbers, if known. The number in parentheses at the end of each entry is the page number where the full entry appears in the CLASSIFIED LIST OF SERIALS.

VENDOR LISTING/SERIALS ONLINE

This section is an alphabetical listing of identified vendors of online periodicals. Entries include addresses, telephone and fax numbers for the vendor, and an alphabetical listing of all titles known to be available, with file names or numbers, if known. All serials listed in this index also have full bibliographic entries in the CLASSIFIED LIST OF SERIALS. Consult the TITLE INDEX or the SERIALS AVAILABLE ONLINE listing for page numbers.

CESSATIONS

In this section, entries for serials which have ceased in the past three years are listed alphabetically by title. The cessation entry includes: title, Dewey Decimal Classification number, former frequency of publication, publisher name and address, country-of-publication code, and, if available, other information such as ISSN, CODEN, LC number, subtitle, corporate author, year of first issue and year ceased. Titles which were originally planned as continuing series but which have closed are included in the CESSATIONS section although back issues may still be available.

If a title has "ceased" because a new title is being used, there will not be an entry in the CESSATIONS section. Instead, the entry is maintained in the CLASSIFIED LIST OF SERIALS under the new title, with a "Formerly" or "Former title" indication.

INDEX TO PUBLICATIONS OF INTERNATIONAL ORGANIZATIONS

Complexity of corporate author structure, as well as title page variations in multilingual texts, compound the problems in cataloging international publications. This special index is provided so that the user may have one reference point for these titles. This index consists of four sections:

International Organizations
International Congress Proceedings
European Communities
United Nations

The index contains all current titles listed in the Bowker International Serials Database. The user must consult the CLASSIFIED LIST OF SERIALS for the full bibliographic information pertaining to these titles. Page references are provided.

ISSN INDEX

The ISSN INDEX lists serials in order by ISSN number. It includes all serials contained in the Bowker International Serials Database, whether current, ceased, or inactive, to which an ISSN has been assigned in our file. A dagger symbol (†) indicates that the title is ceased. If an ISSN appears twice, it usually indicates that the serial has split into two or more parts. Titles which have changed, and for which new ISSNs have been assigned, will show cross-references from one ISSN to the new ISSN. If no new ISSN has been assigned, the cross-reference is from ISSN to new title. Entries for inactive titles do not appear in the book.

A full description of the ISSN and its use is provided on p. xvii.

TITLE INDEX

The TITLE INDEX, which is at the end of Volume 3, is the second major access point for serials. To locate a serial by its title, the user should be familiar with title cataloging rules as described in the "Cataloging Rules for Main Entry Title" paragraphs of this "User's Guide."

The TITLE INDEX lists all current and ceased serials included in this directory. **Boldface** type indicates the page number where the complete entry will be found; page numbers in roman type refer to related subject categories.

USER'S GUIDE xi

For serials with identical titles published within a country, the city of publication is added in parentheses, and sometimes the year of first publication is given to further distinguish the titles.

If a serial title consists of or contains an acronym, a cross-reference is provided from the full name to the acronym form of the title.

Cross-references are provided from former titles and variant titles, and from the alternate language titles of multiple-language publications. Recent title changes are noted, with a reference to the current title. The TITLE INDEX also lists the country code for all serials, along with the ISSN, if known.

The ▼ used in the Classified List to indicate new serials also appears in this index, preceding the title. A † appears preceding the title if the publication has ceased.

Full Entry Content Description

Basic Information
The following items are mandatory for listing and appear in all entries: main entry title, frequency of publication, publisher address, country code, and Dewey Decimal Classification number.

Dewey Decimal Classification Number
The Dewey Decimal number is printed at the top left of each entry. More than one Dewey number may have been assigned if a serial covers several subjects.

LC Classification Number
The Library of Congress classification number, if known, appears directly below the Dewey Decimal number. Shelf numbers are not included.

SAMPLE ENTRY

① 930.198 490.996   ② US   ③ ISSN 1055-7644
④ DZ991   ⑤ CODEN: JAAPL9
⑥ **JOURNAL OF ANTARCTIC ARCHAEOLOGY AND PROTOLINGUISTICS;** ⑦ international communications and research. ⑧ (Supplement avail.) ⑨ (Text in English, French, Polynesian languages) ⑩ 1986. ⑪ 2/yr. ⑫ $39 to individuals; institutions $99 (includes Supplement) (effective 1993). ⑬ (Societe d'Archaeologie et de Linguistique Pacifiques—Society of Pacific Archaeology and Linguistics) ⑭ W.A. Translations (Subsidiary of: Temporary Culture), ⑮ Box 43072, Upper Montclair, NJ 07043-7072. ⑯ TEL 908-665-2869. ⑰ FAX 508-555-0010. ⑱ TELEX 123458. ⑲ (Subscr. to: Department of Archaeology and Proto-Linguistics, 7 Old College Walk, Arkham, MA 01901-1011. TEL 508-555-0110. ⑳ Dist. in Europe by: Editions d'Erlette, Ch. de Kerangat, Plumelec 56120, France. TEL 33-76-63-94). (Co-sponsor: Miskatonic University, Department of Archaeology and Proto-Linguistics) ㉑ Eds. A.H. Whateley, J.M. Snyrnat. ㉒ adv. contact: Arthur Dunwich; ㉓ B&W page $400; trim 8⅛ x 10; ㉔ bk.rev.; abstr.; bibl.; illus.; index; ㉕ circ. 500 (paid); 500 (controlled). ㉖ (also avail. in microform from SWZ, UMI; also avail. on diskette; back issues avail.; reprint service avail. from SWZ, UMI). ㉗ **Indexed:** Abstr. Anthropol., Br.Archaeol.Abstr. ㉘ (1991—), Onoma (1986—), Ref.Zh.
㉙ ●Also avail. online. ㉚ Vendor(s): UTOPIA (Miskatonic).
㉛ Also avail. on CD-ROM. ㉜ Producers: TEMPCULT (Miskatonic).
㉝ —BLDSC shelfmark: 4939.001100.
㉞ **Supersedes (1927-1986):** Miskatonic Annals of Antarctic Archaeology and Extraterrestrial Linguistics ㉟ (ISSN 0055-1298).
㊱ **Description:** Publishes archaeological field research on prehistoric civilizations in the Pacific Islands and Antarctica, with relevant contributions discussing worldwide linguistic evidence of contacts among civilizations.
㊲ *Refereed Serial*

KEY

① Dewey Decimal Classification
② Country Code
③ ISSN
④ LC Classification
⑤ CODEN
⑥ Main Entry Title
⑦ Subtitle
⑧ Bibliographic Note
⑨ Language
⑩ First Published
⑪ Frequency
⑫ Price
⑬ Sponsoring Body
⑭ Publisher
⑮ Address
⑯ Telephone
⑰ Fax
⑱ Telex
⑲ Subscription Address & Tel
⑳ Distributor Address & Tel
㉑ Editor
㉒ Advertising Contact
㉓ Advertising Rate
㉔ Special Features
㉕ Circulation
㉖ Format
㉗ Indexed In
㉘ Years of Coverage
㉙ Online Availability
㉚ Online Vendor/File Name
㉛ CD-ROM Availability
㉜ CD-ROM Producer
㉝ British Library Document Supply Centre Shelfmark Number
㉞ Title Changes
㉟ Former ISSN
㊱ Brief Description
㊲ Refereed

xii USER'S GUIDE

Country Code
The Country Code is printed at the top right of each entry following the Dewey Decimal number. A complete list of country codes used will be found on p. xxvi.

ISSN
The ISSN for the main entry title is printed immediately following the country code. Not all publications have been assigned an ISSN, and lack of a number does not render a publication ineligible for listing.

CODEN
The CODEN designation, if known, is printed directly below the country code and ISSN. The CODEN is an alphanumeric code, applied uniquely to a specific publication. Devised by the American Society for Testing and Materials, it is used primarily for scientific and technical titles. New CODEN are assigned by Chemical Abstracts Service.

Title Information
The main title is printed in upper case as the first item in the entry. Titles are cataloged according to rules described below in the "Cataloging Rules for Main Entry Title" section. For multiple-language publications, the parallel language title is also printed in uppercase, immediately following the main entry title, and is separated from it by a slash.

A ▼ printed before the title indicates that the title began publishing within the last three years.

An asterisk printed after the title indicates that the information in the entry was not verified by the publisher for this edition.

The subtitle is printed in lower case after the title.

Variant titles or translated edition titles are given within the entry and are labeled as such.

Former titles are given at the end of the entry, along with publication dates if known. If a former title also had an ISSN, the ISSN is listed in parentheses after the former title. Many entries contain extensive former title information, providing a history of changes which may be useful for bibliographic record-keeping.

The Key Title, which is assigned at the time of ISSN assignment by the responsible center of the International Serials Data System, is given only if it is different from the main entry title.

Year First Published
The year first published is given if provided by the publisher. If information is lacking, a volume number and specific year may be provided to indicate the approximate age of the publication.

Frequency
The frequency of publication is given in abbreviated form, such as "a." for annual, "irreg." for irregular, "m." for monthly, "3/yr." for three times per year. All abbreviations used are listed in the "General Abbreviations" on p. xix.

Price
Unless otherwise indicated, the price given is the annual price for an individual subscription in the currency of the country of origin. The price in U.S. dollars may also be given in parentheses if it is provided by the publisher. No attempt is made to convert foreign currency to U.S. dollars. Separate postage information is not given, since postal rates vary widely.

Publisher Information
Many serials are editorially controlled by a sponsoring organization or corporate author and published by a commercial publisher. In these instances, the commercial publisher's name and address are given, and the name of the corporate author is given in parentheses immediately preceding. In other instances, either a sponsoring organization or a commercial publisher has sole responsibility, and only one name is given. We avoid listing printers as publishers, preferring the name and address of someone with editorial responsibility. For the same reason, we avoid listing distributors as publishers.

If no publisher name is given, it is assumed that the publisher name is the same as the title.

If the publisher is also the editor, the person's name is given with the notation "Ed. & Pub."

Subscription or Distribution Address
A second address is given only if the address for ordering subscriptions is different from the publisher's address. Distributors are listed only if we have been informed that a particular organization is the exclusive distributor. Additional subscription and/or distribution offices of international publishers are listed, if known.

Telephone, Fax and Telex Numbers
Telephone, Fax and Telex numbers are given when provided by the publisher. U.S. and Canadian numbers are given in standard North American format. Numbers

in other countries are provided in the same format as supplied by the publisher, resulting in some inconsistencies. Users are advised to consult an international operator before placing calls. Telephone numbers for subscription and/or distribution offices appear if provided by the publisher.

Editor
Usually only one name is given, preceded by the notation "Ed." Advanced degrees and titles are omitted, except for medical, military and religious titles; absence of a title does not mean that the editor has none. The abbreviation "Ed.Bd." indicates editorship by three or more persons.

Advertising Rates and Contact Name
When provided by the publisher, full-page advertising rates and trim size information are indicated, as is the name of the advertising contact.

Special Features
A listing of special features may include such items as book or other types of reviews, advertising (usually meaning commercial, not classified advertising), charts, illustrations, bibliography section, article abstracts, and an annual index to the periodical's contents.

Reprint Services
If a serial is known to be available from a reprint service, a code referring to the service appears in the entry. More than one code may be listed. For a list of reprint services and a translation of the codes, please refer to p. xxv.

Circulation
All circulation figures used are approximate. Circulation is given only if provided by the publisher. The notation "controlled" indicates that the publication is available only to qualified persons, usually members of a particular trade or profession.

Format
Formats other than standard magazine format are noted in parentheses. Other formats may be looseleaf, duplicated (mimeographed), tabloid, newspaper. If a publication is available in microform, a notation is made which includes a three-letter code for the vendor, if known. A list of names, addresses, telephone and fax numbers of micropublishers is provided on p. xxi.

Abstracting and Indexing
The notation "Indexed:" precedes a list of abbreviations for all abstracting and indexing services known to cover the serial on a regular basis. Years of coverage immediately follow each abstracting and indexing service code, if known. The complete names of the abstracting and indexing services are listed with their abbreviations on p. xxviii. All currently published abstracting and indexing services are also listed as entries in the CLASSIFIED LIST OF SERIALS.

Online Availability and CD-ROM Availability
If a serial is known to be available in a full-text online format and/or on CD-ROM, a bullet symbol (●) precedes the information. Online and CD-ROM availability are noted whether they exist in addition to hardcopy or in one or both formats exclusively. Online vendors and CD-ROM producers are also listed, if known.

For a listing of serials available online, consult the SERIALS AVAILABLE ONLINE index on p. 5045. Complete names and addresses of vendors, with a listing of serials known to be available through them, are in a separate index, VENDOR LISTING/SERIALS ONLINE on p. 5109.

For a listing of serials available on CD-ROM, consult the SERIALS AVAILABLE ON CD-ROM index on p. 5031. Complete names and addresses of producers, with a list of CD-ROMs known to be available through them, are in a separate index, PRODUCER LISTING/ SERIALS ON CD-ROM on p. 5043.

British Library Document Supply Centre (BLDSC)
Serials holdings of the British Library, available for document delivery through the British Library Document Supply Centre (BLDSC), are noted. The British Library shelfmark number, the unique identifier of each serial, is preceded by an em-dash (—) which is followed by the notation "BLDSC shelfmark: 0000.000000." The format of the shelfmark is four digits, a decimal, then 6 digits.

While the **Ulrich's** and BLDSC's titles were matched on the presence of ISSNs, not all titles have ISSNs, and the absence of a shelfmark number in an **Ulrich's** record does not necessarily mean that title is unavailable from the BLDSC. For further information about BLDSC's services, contact: Customer Services, British Library Document Supply Centre, Boston Spa, Wetherby, LS23 7BQ, UK; Tel: +44 (937) 546060, Fax: +44 (937) 546333.

Brief Description
A brief description of the contents and editorial focus of the publication may be provided, preceded by the word "Description:" at the end of the entry. These descriptions were submitted by the publisher or were written by editorial staff after examination of sample copies or publisher catalogs.

Refereed Serial
The manuscript peer review and evaluation system is utilized to protect, maintain and raise the quality of scholarly material published in serials. If a serial is known to be refereed or juried, the notation "Refereed Serial" appears in italics at the end of the entry. This information is generally provided by the serial publisher.

Cataloging Rules for Main Entry Title

The majority of titles in the Bowker International Serials Database were cataloged according to *Anglo-American Cataloging Rules* prior to 1978, the date of the new edition of *Anglo-American Cataloging Rules*. The new *AACR II* reflects a trend toward the Key Title concept of cataloging as used by the International Serials Data System (ISDS) and published in its *International Standard Bibliographic Description for Serials* (1974).

Because recataloging a database the size of Bowker's was not feasible, our cataloging rules were modified but not radically changed. Cross-references are provided in the TITLE INDEX from variant forms of title, such as Key Title, to aid users searching by other methods.

Whenever possible, main entry title cataloging is done from a sample of the title page of the most recent issue, according to the following rules:

Articles at the beginning of titles are omitted, or are bypassed in filing.

Serials with distinctive titles are usually entered under title. For example:

Annual Bulletin of Historical Literature
Business Week
Milton Studies

If a title consists only of a generic term followed by the name of the issuing body, or if the name of the issuing body clarifies the content of the publication, entry is under the name of the issuing body. For example:

Newsletter of the American Theological Library Association
is entered as
American Theological Library Association. Newsletter

Economic Performance and Prospects, issued by the Private Development Corporation of the Philippines
is entered as
Private Development Corporation of the Philippines. Economic Performance and Prospects

A title which consists of a subject modified generic term followed by the name of the issuing body is considered nondistinctive and is entered under the name of the issuing body. For example:

Annual Meeting Scientific Proceedings of the American Animal Hospital Association
is entered as
American Animal Hospital Association. Annual Meeting Scientific Proceedings

Government publications with nondistinctive titles are entered under the name of the government jurisdiction of the issuing body, although distinctive titles of government organizations may be entered directly under title. For example:

Great Britain. Economic and Social Research Council. Annual Report
but
Statistical Abstract of Iceland

Titles which begin with the initials of the issuing body are entered under the initials. Cross-references from the full name are provided in the TITLE INDEX.

If a geographic name is part of the name of the issuing body, entry will be under the common form of the name of the body. For example:

University of the West Indies. Vice-Chancellor's Report
not
West Indies. University. Vice-Chancellor's Report

Note, however, that government publications retain similar cataloging as government jurisdiction.

Canada. Statistics Canada. Field Crop Reporting Series

Multilingual titles are entered under the first title given on the title page, or the first title reported by the publisher if the title page is not available. Titles in other languages are entered directly after the main entry title. Cross-references are provided in the TITLE INDEX for each language title.

FILING RULES
Due to the restrictions imposed by computer filing of titles, the following special filing rules should be noted.

Articles and prepositions within titles are alphabetized as words:

Journal of the West
precedes
Journal of Theological Studies

Hyphenated words are treated as separate words:

Pre-Text
precedes
Preaching

However, words indicating compass points (northeast, southwest, etc.) are filed as one word regardless of how printed:

Northeast Agriculture
North East Coast Institution of Engineers and Shipbuilders Transactions
Northeast Folklore Society Newsletter
North-East India Council for Social Science Research Journal

Titles entered under corporate author or government jurisdiction are sequenced before distinctive titles that begin with the same words:

British Columbia. Ministry of Energy, Mines and Petroleum Resources. Mineral Market Update
precedes
British Columbia Catholic

Acronyms and initials are treated as such and are listed at the beginning of each letter of the alphabet. Exceptions are the abbreviations U.N. (United Nations), U.S. (United States), Gt. Britain (Great Britain), and St. (Saint), which are filed as words:

U W I P A Newsletter
United Mutual Fund Selector
U.S. Environmental Protection Agency. Clean Water: Report to Congress

Titles in excess of 36 characters which are identical may not sort sequentially. The editors suggest that users scan the entire sequence of identical titles to locate specific entries.

Diacritical marks have been omitted. The German and Scandinavian umlaut has been replaced by the letter "e" following the vowels a, e, o, and u. In Danish, Norwegian and Swedish, the letter å is sequenced as "aa" and the letter ø as "oe."

International Standard Serial Number (ISSN)

1. *What is the ISSN?*

An internationally accepted, concise, unique and unambiguous code for the identification of serial publications. One ISSN represents one serial.

The ISSN consists of seven numbers with an eighth check digit calculated according to Modulus 11 and used to verify the number in computer processing. A hyphen is printed after the fourth digit, as a visual aid, and the abbreviation ISSN precedes the number.

A code indicating country of publication may be printed preceding the ISSN as an additional identifier; for example, UK ISSN 1234-5679.

2. *How did the ISSN evolve as an international system?*

The International Organization for Standardization Technical Committee 46 (ISO/TC 46) is the agency responsible for the development of the ISSN as an international standard. The organization responsible for the administration and assignment of ISSN is the International Center (IC) of the International Serials Data System (ISDS). The IC/ISDS, supported by the French government and Unesco, is located in Paris.

The implementation of the ISSN system started with the numbering of the 70,000 titles in the serials database of the R.R. Bowker Company (*Ulrich's International Periodicals Directory* and *Irregular Serials and Annuals*). The next serials database numbered was the *New Serial Titles 1950-70* cumulation listing 220,000 titles, cumulated, converted to magnetic tape and published by the R.R. Bowker Company in collaboration with the Serials Record Division of the Library of Congress. These two databases were used as the starting base for the implementation of the ISSN.

3. *What types of publications are assigned ISSN?*

For assignment of an ISSN, a serial is defined by the International Serials Data System as: "a publication in print or in non-print form, issued in successive parts, usually having numerical or chronological designations, and intended to be continued indefinitely."

4. *How is ISSN used?*

ISSN, the tool for communication of basic information about a serial title with a minimum of error, is used for such processes as ordering, billing, inventory control, abstracting, and indexing. Authors use ISSN for copyright. In library processes, ISSN is used in operations such as acquisitions, claiming, binding, accessioning, shelving, cooperative cataloging, circulation, interlibrary loans, and retrieval of requests.

5. *May a publication have an International Standard Book Number (ISBN) and an ISSN?*

Yes! Monographic series (separate works issued indefinitely under a common title, generally in a uniform format with numeric designations) and annuals or titles planned to be issued indefinitely under the same title may be defined as serials. The ISSN is assigned to the serial title, while an ISBN is assigned to each individual title or monograph in the series.

A new ISBN is assigned to each volume or edition by the publisher, while the ISSN, which is assigned by the International Center, national or regional center, remains the same for each issue. Both numbers should be printed on the copyright page of each volume, with initials or words preceding each number for immediate identification. With the availability of both ISSN and ISBN, the problem of defining the overlap of serials and monographs has been resolved.

SAMPLE TITLE

ADVANCES IN THE BIOSCIENCES
ISSN 0065-3446
Vol. 1 Proceedings: Berlin. Schering Symposium of Endocrinology, Berlin. Ed. by Gerhard Raspe. 1969. 40.00 (ISBN 0-08-013395-9). Pergamon.
Vol. 2 Proceedings. Schering Symposium on Biodynamics & Mechanims of Action of Steroid Hormones, Berlin. Ed. by Gerhard Raspe. 1969. 41.25 (ISBN 0-08-006942-8). Pergamon.
Vol. 3 Proceedings. Schering Workshop on Steroid Metabolism "in Vitro Versus in Vivo," Berlin. Ed. by Gerhard Raspe. 1969. 41.25 (ISBN 0-08-017544-9). Pergamon.
Vol. 4 Proceedings. Schering Symposium on Mechanisms Involved in Conception. Berlin. Ed. by Gerhard Raspe. 1970. text ed. 41.25 (ISBN 0-08-017546-5) Pergamon.
Vol. 25 Development of Responsiveness to Steroid Hormones. Alvin M. Kaye & Myra Kaye et al. LC 79-42938. 1980. 66.00 (ISBN 0-08-024940-X). Pergamon Press.

6. *Where should the ISSN appear on the serial?*

In a prominent position on or in each issue of the serial, such as front cover, back cover, title or copyright pages. ISDS recommends that the ISSN of a periodical be printed, whenever possible, in the upper right corner of the front cover.

Promotional and description materials about the serial should include the ISSN.

7. *When a title changes is a new ISSN assigned?*

In most instances, a new ISSN is assigned when a title changes. However, the determination is made by the International Center or the National or regional center of ISDS. Publishers should report all title changes to their respective centers.

8. *How does a publisher apply for an ISSN?*

The publisher should maintain contact with the national, regional or International Center of ISDS. They require bibliographic evidence of the serial, including a copy of the title page and cover. There is no charge to the publisher for the assignment of ISSN.

For full information, publishers should contact the national library or bibliographic center in the country where they are publishing. The address for the International Center is:

International Serials Data System (ISDS)
International Center (for the Registration of Serial Publications)
20 rue Bachaumont
75002 Paris, France

The address for the National Center in the United States is:

National Serials Data Program
Library of Congress
Washington, DC 20540
(202) 707-6452

9. *What is SISAC?*

SISAC stands for the Serials Industry Systems Advisory Committee. SISAC is an industry group formed to develop voluntary standardized formats for electronically transmitting serial business transaction information. SISAC provides a forum where serial (particularly journal) publishers, library system vendors, and librarians can discuss mutual concerns regarding the electronic transmission of serial information and develop cooperative solutions, in the form of standardized formats, to efficiently address these concerns. *(Reprinted with permission from SISAC.)*

10. *SISAC Codes*

The serial identification code, also called the SIID, is a string of letters and/or numbers which follows the International Standard Serials Number (ISSN) and identifies a particular issue. The identification code and the machine-scannable bar code presentation was tested in libraries in 1986.

The SIID is a new presentation of existing codes. The code begins with the International Standard Serials Number (ISSN) and then adds issue information comprised of the date (chronology) and the volume/issue numbers (enumeration). *(Reprinted with permission from SISAC.)*

Abbreviations
General Abbreviations and Special Symbols

a.	annual	music rev.	music reviews
abstr.	abstracts	N.S.	New Series
adv.	advertising	pat.	patents
approx.	approximately	play rev.	play reviews (theatre reviews)
BLDSC	British Library Document Supply Centre	Prof.	Professor
bi-m.	every two months	q.	quarterly
bi-w.	biweekly	record rev.	record reviews
bibl.	bibliographies	s-a.	twice annually
bk.rev.	book reviews	s-m.	twice monthly
c/o	care of	s-w.	twice weekly
charts	charts (diagrams, graphs, tables)	stat.	statistics
circ.	circulation	subscr.	subscription
contr.	controlled	tele. rev.	television reviews
cum.index	cumulative index	3/m.	3 times a month
Cy.	county	3/yr.	3 times a year
d.	daily	tr. lit.	trade literature (manufacturers' catalogues, reader response cards)
dance rev.	dance reviews		
Dir.	Director	tr. mk.	trade marks
Ed., Eds.	Editor, Editors	video rev.	video reviews
Ed.Bd.	Editorial Board	w.	weekly
film rev.	film reviews	‡	not available from a subscription agency
fortn.	fortnightly		
ISSN	International Standard Serial Number	*	not updated/unverified
illus.	illustrations	●	online and/or CD-ROM availability
irreg.	irregular	▼	new serial
m.	monthly	†	ceased
mkt.	market prices		

Money Symbols

SYMBOL	UNIT	COUNTRY
A.	austral	Argentina
Arg.$	peso	Argentina
Aus.$	dollar	Australia
B.	baht	Thailand
B.$	dollar	Brunei Darussalam, Belize
BEF	franc	Belgium
Bl.	balboa	Panama
Bol.$	peso	Bolivia
Br.	birr	Ethiopia
Bs.	bolivar	Venezuela
BTN	bonus do tesouro nacional	Brazil
BTNF	bonus do tesouro nacional fiscal	Brazil
C.$	cordoba; dollar	Nicaragua, Cayman Islands
Can.$	dollar	Canada
CFPF	franc	New Caledonia
Col.	colon	Costa Rica, El Salvador
Col.$	peso	Colombia
Cr.$	cruzeiro	Brazil
Cz.$	cruzado	Brazil
D.	dalasi	Gambia
DH., Dh.	dirham	Morocco, United Arab Emirates
DKK	krone	Denmark
DM.	mark	Germany
din.	dinar	Algeria, Jordan, Kuwait, Libya, Tunisia, Yugoslavia
$	dollar; peso	various
Dr.	drachma	Greece
E.	emalangeni	Swaziland
EAs.	shilling	East Africa, Somalia, Tanzania, Uganda
EC$.	dollar	Dominica, St. Lucia
ECU	European currency unit	European Communities
Esc.	escudo	Angola, Portugal, Mozambique
F.	franc	Djibouti, France, Guadeloupe, Mali, Martinique, Monaco, Rwanda
F$	dollar	Fiji
FIM	markka	Finland
fl.	guilder; florin	Netherlands, Netherlands Antilles, Surinam
FMG.	franc	Malagasy Republic
Fmk.	mark; markka	Finland
Fr.	franc	Belgium, Liechtenstein, Luxembourg, Switzerland
Fr. CFA	franc	African Financial Community, Benin, Burkina Faso, Burundi, Cameroon, Central African Republic, Chad, Congo, Gabon, Ivory Coast, Niger, Reunion, Senegal, Togo
Ft.	forint	Hungary
g.	guarani	Paraguay
Gde.	gourde	Haiti
G.$	dollar	Guyana
HK$	dollar	Hong Kong
I£	pound	Ireland
I.D.	dinar	Iran, Iraq
IRl.	riyal	Iran
IS	shekel	Israel
ISK	krona	Iceland
J.$	dollar	Jamaica
Jam.$	dollar	Jamaica
K.	kina; kwacha	Malawi, Papua New Guinea, Zambia

SYMBOL	UNIT	COUNTRY
Kcs.	koruny	Czechoslovakia
kip	kip	Laos
Kr.	krona; krone	Scandinavian countries
KShs.	shilling	Kenya
L.	lempira; lira	Honduras, Italy
Le.	leone	Sierra Leone
lei	lei	Rumania
Lit.	lira italiana	Italy
lv.	lev	Bulgaria
M.$	dollar; ringgit	Malaysia
Mex.$	peso	Mexico
$m.n.	moneda nacional	various
mt.	metical	Mozambique
N$	new Uruguay peso	Uruguay
NC.	cedi	Ghana
NOK	krone	Norway
NT.$	dollar	Republic of China (Taiwan)
N.Z.$	dollar	New Zealand
ORI.	riyal	Oman
P.	pula; peso	Botswana, Philippines, various
QRl.	riyal	Qatar
£	pound	Ireland, Gt. Britain, Malta
£C	pound	Cyprus
£E	pound	Egypt
£L	pound; dinar	Lebanon
£N	pound; naira	Nigeria
£S	pound	Syria
ptas.	peseta	Spain
Q.	quetzal	Guatemala
R.	rand	South Africa, Lesotho, Namibia
RD.$	peso	Dominican Republic
Rps.	rupiah	Indonesia
Rs.	riel; rial; rupee	Cambodia, India, Iran, Mauritius, Nepal, Pakistan, Seychelles, Sri Lanka
Rub.	ruble	former U.S.S.R.
S/	sucre; sole	Ecuador, Peru
S.	schilling	Austria
S.$	dollar	Singapore
SEK	krona	Sweden
SFr.	franc	Liechtenstein, Switzerland
SI$	dollar	Solomon Islands
SL.	pound	Sudan
SLT	talar	Slovenia
SRl.	riyal	Saudia Arabia
$T.	dollar	Tonga
TK.	taka	Bangladesh
TL.	pound; lira	Turkey
T.T.$	dollar	Trinidad and Tobago
tugrik	tugrik	Mongolia
UM	ouguiya	Mauritania
Urg.$	peso	Uruguay
vatu	vatu	Vanuatu
VN.$	dollar	Vietnam
Won	won (hwan)	Korea
Y	yuan	People's Republic of China
Yen	yen	Japan
YRl.	rial	Yemen
Z	zaire	Zaire
Z.$	dollar	Zimbabwe
Zl.	zloty	Poland

Micropublishers and Distributors

ACR **A.C.R.P.P.**
(Association pour la Conservation et la Reproduction photographique de la Presse)
B.P. 221, 77313 Marne-La-Vallee
Cedex 2, France
Tel: 331-60177213 **Fax:** 331-60176805

ADL **Advanced Library Systems, Inc.**
100 Brickstone Sq.
Andover, MA 01810-3894
Tel: 508-470-0610 **Fax:** 508-475-1072

AFS **Fertility and Sterility**
2140 11 Avenue South
Suite 200
Birmingham, AL 35205-2800
Tel: 205-933-8494; **Fax:** 205-930-9904

AGU **American Geophysical Union**
2000 Florida Ave., NW
Washington, DC 20009
Tel: 202-462-6903 **Fax:** 202-328-0566

AIP **American Institute of Physics**
335 East 45th St.
New York, NY 10017
Tel: 212-661-9409; **Fax:** 212-949-0473

AIR **Aircraft Technical Publishers**
101 South Hill Dr.
Brisbane, CA 94005
Tel: 415-468-1705; **Fax:** 415-468-1596

AJP **American Jewish Periodical Center**
Hebrew Union College-Jewish Institute of Religion
3101 Clifton Ave.
Cincinnati, OH 45220
Tel: 513-221-1875; **Fax:** 513-221-0321

ALP **Alpha Com**
Ueberseering 9, 2000
Hamburg 60, Germany
Tel: 49-40-513020; **Fax:** 49-40-51302000

AMP **Adam Matthew Publications**
44 Royal Ave., Calcot
Reading, Berkshire RG3 5UP England
Tel: 44-734-422765; **Fax:** 44-0380830300

AMS **AMS Press, Inc.**
56 E. 13th St.
New York, NY 10003
Tel: 212-777-4700; **Fax:** 212-995-5413

ATL **American Theological Library Association, Preservation Board**
820 Church St., Suite 300
Evanston, IL 60201
Tel: 708-869-7788; **Fax:** 708-869-8513

ATP **Appropriate Technology Project**
P.O. Box 4543
Stanford, CA 94309
Tel: 415-326-8581; **Fax:** 415-326-3475

BAR **Barbour Index Plc**
New Lodge, Drift Rd., Windsor
Berkshire SL4 4RQ England
Tel: 44-344884121; **Fax:** 44-344884845

BHP **Brookhaven Press**
P.O. Box 2287
La Crosse, WI 54602-2287
Tel: 608-781-0850; **Fax:** 608-781-3883

BIO **BIOSIS**
2100 Arch St.
Philadelphia, PA 19103-1399
Tel: 215-587-4800, 800-523-4806; **Fax:** 215-587-2041

BKR **Bowker A&I Publishing**
A Reed Reference Publishing Company
121 Chanlon Rd.
New Providence, NJ 07974
Tel: 908-665-2847, 800-227-2477; **Fax:** 908-771-7725

BLC **Bloch & Company**
P.O. Box 18058
Cleveland, OH 44118
Tel: 216-371-0979

BLH **Bell & Howell**
(Micropublishing now operated by UMI)

BLI **Balch Institute**
Research Library
18 S. 7th St.
Philadelphia, PA 19106
Tel: 215-925-8090; **Fax:** 215-922-3201

BNB **British Library National Bibliographic Service**
Boston Spa, Wetherby
West Yorkshire LS23 7BQ England
Tel: 44-71-937546585; **Fax:** 44-71-937546586

BNQ **Bibliotheque national de Quebec**
Service de Microphotographie
1700 St. Denis
Montreal, PQ H2X 3K6 Canada
Tel: 514-873-1100; **Fax:** 514-873-9932

BWC **Butterworth & Co., Ltd.**
88 Kingsway
London WC2B 6AB England
Tel: 44-71-4056900; **Fax:** 44-71-4051332

CCM **Core Collection Micropublishers**
Div. of Roth Publishing, Inc.
185 Great Neck Rd.
Great Neck, NY 11021
Tel: 516-466-3636, 800-327-0295; **Fax:** 516-829-7746

CDS **Current Digest of the Soviet Press**
3857 N. High St.
Columbus, OH 43214
Tel: 614-292-4234; **Fax:** 614-267-6310

CHL	**Chadwyck-Healey Ltd.** Cambridge Place Cambridge CB2 1NR England **Tel:** 223-311479; **Fax:** 223-66440	HAW	**The Haworth Press** 10 Alice St. Binghamton, NY 13904 **Tel:** 607-722-7259; **Fax:** 607-722-1424
	Chadwyck-Healey, Inc. N.A. Distributors 1101 King St. Alexandria, VA 22314 **Tel:** 703-683-4890; **Fax:** 703-683-7589	HPL	**Harvester Press Microfilm Publications Ltd.** (Now wholly owned and operated by Research Publications, Inc.)
		IAM	**SIAM Publications** 3600 University City Science Center Philadelphia, PA 19104-2688 **Tel:** 215-382-9800; **Fax:** 215-386-7999
CIH	**Canadian Institute for Historical Microreproductions** P.O. Box 2428, Station D Ottawa, ON K1P 5W5 Canada **Tel:** 613-235-2628; **Fax:** 613-235-9752	ICS	**Editions I.C.S.** 23 Ave. Villemain 75014 Paris, France **Tel:** 33-1-45392244; **Fax:** 33-1-45434680
CIS	**Congressional Information Services** 4520 East-West Hwy., Ste. 800 Bethesda, MD 20814-3389 **Tel:** 301-654-1550, 800-638-8380; **Fax:** 301-654-4033	IDC	**Inter Documentation Co., AG.** Hoge Woerd 151 Leiden, 2301 EE The Netherlands **Tel:** 31-71142700; **Fax:** 31-71131721
CLA	**Canadian Library Association** (no longer producer) Microfile Program 200 Elgin St., Ste. 602 Ottawa, ON K2P 1L5 Canada **Tel:** 613-232-9625; **Fax:** 613-563-9895	IFA	**International Federation of Film Archives (FIAF)** 113 Canalot Studios 222 Kensal Rd., London W10 5BN England **Tel:** 44-81-9601001; **Fax:** 44-81-960-8907
CLS	**CLASS** (Cooperative Library Agency for Systems & Services) 1415 Koll Circle, Ste. 101 San Jose, CA 95112-4698 **Tel:** 408-453-0444; **Fax:** 408-453-5379	ILO	**ILO Publications** 1828 L St., N.W., Ste 801 Washington, DC 20036 **Tel:** 202-653-7652 **Fax:** 202-653-7687
		IMI	**Irish Microforms, Ltd.** Unit 56 Sandyford Industrial Estate Dublin 18 Ireland **Tel:** 353-1-2893626; **Fax:** 353-1-2954270
CMC	**Computer Microfilm Corp.** 3900 Wheeler Ave. Alexandria, VA 22304 **Tel:** 703-823-0500; **Fax:** 703-823-0505	IPC	**Institute of Paper Science & Technology, Inc.** 575 14th St., N.W. Atlanta, GA 30318 **Tel:** 404-853-9500; **Fax:** 404-853-9510
CML	**Commonwealth Microfilm Products** 3395 American Dr., Unit 11 Mississauga, ON L4V 1T5 Canada **Tel:** 416-671-4173; **Fax:** 416-671-8361		
EDR	**Eric Document Reproduction Service** (See: CMC)	IRE	**International Research and Evaluation** 21098 IRE—Control Center Eagan, MN 55121 **Tel:** 612-888-9635; **Fax:** 612-888-9124
EEE	**Institute of Electrical and Electronics Engineers** 345 East 47th St. New York, NY 10017 **Tel:** 212-705-7900; **Fax:** 212-705-7682	ISI	**Institute for Scientific Information** 3501 Market St. Philadelphia, PA 19104 **Tel:** 215-386-0100; **Fax:** 215-386-6362; 215-386-2911
EMP	**Emmett Publishing, Ltd.** West House 21, West St. Haslemere, Surrey GU27 2AB England **Tel:** 44-428-654443; **Fax:** 44-428-661582	JAI	**JAI Press Inc.** 55 Old Post Rd., No. 2 P.O. Box 1678 Greenwich, CT 06836-1678 **Tel:** 203-661-7602; **Fax:** 203-661-0792
FCM	**Fairchild Microfilms** Fairchild Book Division 7 West 34th St. New York, NY 10001 **Tel:** 212-630-3880; **Fax:** 212-630-3868	JOH	**Johnson Reprint Microeditions** (Microeditions phased out) 111 Fifth Ave. New York, NY 10003 **Tel:** 212-614-3200; **Fax:** 212-614-3221
GCS	**Preston Publications** P.O. Box 48312 7800 Merrimac Ave. Niles, IL 60714 **Tel:** 708-965-0566; **Fax:** 708-965-7639	JSC	**J. S. Canner & Co.** 10 Charles St. Needham Hights, MA 02194 **Tel:** 617-449-9103; **Fax:** 617-449-1767
GMC	**General Microfilm Co.** (acquired by OMNISYS Corp.)		

MICROPUBLISHERS AND DISTRIBUTORS

KGS   **K.G. Saur**
A Reed Reference Publishing Company
121 Chanlon Rd.
New Providence, NJ 07974
Tel: 908-464-6800; **Fax:** 908-771-7725

KHS   **Kansas State Historical Society**
Microfilm Publications
120 West Tenth Ave.
Topeka, KS 66612-1291
Tel: 913-296-3251; **Fax:** 913-296-1005

KTO   **Kraus Microform**
358 Saw Mill River Rd.
Millwood, NY 10546-1035
Tel: 914-762-2200; **Fax:** 914-762-1195

LCP   **The Library of Congress**
Photoduplication Service
10 First St., S.E.
Washington, DC 20540
Tel: 202-707-5650; **Fax:** 202-707-1771

LIB   **Library Microfilms**
1115 E. Arques Ave.
Sunnyvale, CA 94086
Tel: 408-736-7444; **Fax:** 408-736-4397

LOP   **Lomond Publications**
P.O. Box 88
Mt. Airy, MD 21771
Tel: 301-829-1496, 800-443-6299

MCA   **Microfilming Corporation of America**
(Acquired by UMI;
operation phased out)

MCE   **Microcard Editions**
(See: CIS)

MDX   **Micromedex Inc.**
600 Grant St.
Denver, CO 80203
Tel: 303-831-1400; **Fax:** 303-837-1717

MEL   **Metropolitan Library Service Agency**
(MELSA)
S-322 Griggs Midway Bldg.,
1821 University Ave.
St. Paul, MN 55104-3083
Tel: 612-645-5731; **Fax:** 612-649-3169

MIM   **Pergamon Press**
660 White Plains Rd.
Tarrytown, NY 10591-5153
Tel: 914-524-9200; **Fax:** 914-333-2444

MIS   **Moody's Investors Service**
Sales Department
99 Church St.
New York, NY 10007
Tel: 212-553-0300; **Fax:** 212-553-4700

MML   **Micromedia Limited**
20 Victor St.
Toronto, ON M5H 2N8
Canada
Tel: 416-362-5211, 800-387-2689; **Fax:** 416-362-6161

MMP   **McLaren Micropublishing Ltd.**
P.O. Box 972, Station F
Toronto, ON M4Y 2N9
Canada
Tel: 416-960-4801; **Fax:** 416-964-3745

MUE   **University Music Editions, Inc.**
P.O. Box 192, Fort George Station
New York, NY 10040
Tel: 718-569-5340, 5393; **Fax:** 718-601-7226

NBI   **Newsbank, Inc.**
58 Pine St.
New Canaan, CT 06840
Tel: 203-966-1100, 800-243-7694; **Fax:** 203-966-6254

NRP   **Norman Ross Publishing, Inc.**
330 West 58th St.
New York, NY 10019
Tel: 212-765-8200, 800-648-8850; **Fax:** 212-765-2393

NTI   **National Technical Information Service**
5285 Port Royal Rd.
Springfield, VA 22161
Tel: 703-487-4600; **Fax:** 703-321-8547

NYL   **New York Law Publishing Co.**
111 Eighth Ave.
New York, NY 10011
Tel: 212-741-8300; **Fax:** 212-741-3985

NYT   **New York Times Information Bank**
(Operation phased out)
229 W. 43rd St.
New York, NY 10036
Tel: 212-556-1234

OEC   **Organization for Economic Cooperation &**
Development, Publications & Information Center
2001 L St., N.W., Ste. 700
Washington, DC 20036
Tel: 202-785-6323; **Fax:** 202-785-0350

OMN   **OMNISYS Corp.**
211 Second Ave.
Waltham, MA 02154
Tel: 617-684-1234; **Fax:** 617-684-1245

OMP   **Oxford Microform Publication Ltd.**
(Acquired by UMI)

PMC   **Princeton Microfilm Corp.**
P.O. Box 2073
Princeton, NJ 08543
Tel: 609-452-2066, 800-257-9502; **Fax:** 609-275-6201

PSL   **The Pretoria State Library**
P.O. Box 397
Pretoria 0001,
Republic of South Africa
Tel: 27-12-218931; **Fax:** 27-12-3255984

RPI   **Research Publications**
12 Lunar Dr.
Drawer AB
Woodbridge, CT 06525
Tel: 203-397-2600; **Fax:** 203-397-3893

RRI   **Fred B. Rothman & Co.**
10368 W. Centennial Rd.
Littleton, CO 80127
Tel: 303-979-5657, 800-457-1986; **Fax:** 303-978-1457

SAS	Society for Applied Spectroscopy P.O. Box 1438 Frederick, MD 21701 **Tel:** 301-694-8122; **Fax:** 301-694-6860	**VCI**	VCH Publishers, Inc. 303 N.W. 12th Ave. Deerfield Beach, FL 33442-1788 **Tel:** 305-428-5566; **Fax:** 305-428-8201
SOC	Societe Canadienne du Microfilm Inc- Canadian Microfilming Co. Ltd. 464 rue Saint-Jean, Ste. 110 Montreal, PQ H2Y 2S1 Canada **Tel:** 514-288-5404; **Fax:** 514-843-4690	**VFN**	The Voltaire Foundation at the Taylor Institution St. Giles' Oxford OX1 3NA England **Tel:** 44-865270250; **Fax:** 44-865270740
TMI	Tennessee Microfilms P.O. Box 23075 Nashville, TN 37202 **Tel:** 615-242-3632	**WDS**	Dawson Microfiche (Distributor only) Cannon House Parkfarm Rd. Folkestone, Kent CT19 5EE England **Tel:** 303-850-101; **Fax:** 303-850-440
UMI	University Microfilms International (A Bell & Howell Company) 300 N. Zeeb Rd. Ann Arbor, MI 48106 **Tel:** 313-761-4700, 800-521-0600; **Fax:** 313-761-1203	**WMP**	World Microfilm Publications Ltd. Microworld House 2-6 Foscote Mews London, W92 HH England **Tel:** 44-71-2662200; **Fax:** 44-71-2662314
UNM	University of Michigan Library Microform Reading Room 2 South Hatcher c/o Graduate Library Ann Arbor, MI 48109 **Tel:** 313-764-0503; **Fax:** 313-764-0259	**WPI**	Waverly Press, Inc. 428 East Preston St. Baltimore, MD 21202 **Tel:** 410-528-4288 **Fax:** 410-528-4312
UNW	University of Wisconsin Library Interlibrary Loan Department 728 State St., Rm. 231 Madison, WI 53706 **Tel:** 608-262-3193; **Fax:** 608-262-4649	**WSH**	William S. Hein & Co., Inc. Hein Building 1285 Main St. Buffalo, NY 14209 **Tel:** 716-882-2600, 800-828-7571; **Fax:** 716-883-8100
UPD	Updata Publications Inc. 1736 Westwood Blvd. Los Angeles, CA 90024 **Tel:** 310-474-5900; **Fax:** 310-474-4095	**WWS**	Williams & Wilkins 428 East Preston St. Baltimore, MD 21202 **Tel:** 410-528-4309; **Fax:** 410-528-4312

Reprint Services

ISI	Institute for Scientific Information 3501 Market St. Philadelphia, PA 19104 Tel: 215-386-0100; Fax: 215-386-6362; 215-386-2911	SWZ	Swets & Zeitlinger B.V. P.O. Box 810 Heereweg 347 B 2160 SZ Lisse The Netherlands Tel: 31-2521-35111; Fax: 31-2521-15888
JOH	Johnson Reprint Microeditions 111 Fifth Ave. New York, NY 10003 Tel: 212-614-3200; Fax: 212-614-3221	UMI	University Microfilms International (A Bell & Howell Company) 300 N. Zeeb Rd. Ann Arbor, MI 48106 Tel: 313-761-4700, 800-521-0600; Fax: 313-761-1203
KTO	Kraus Microform 358 Saw Mill River Rd. Millwood, NY 10546-1035 Tel: 914-762-2200; Fax: 914-762-1195	WDS	Dawson Microfiche Cannon House Parkfarm Rd. Folkestone, Kent CT19 5EE England Tel: 303-850-101; Fax: 303-850-440
RRI	Fred B. Rothman & Co. 10368 W. Centennial Rd. Littleton, CO 80127 Tel: 303-979-5657, 800-457-1986; Fax: 303-978-1457	WSH	William S. Hein & Co., Inc. 428 East Preston St. Baltimore, MD 21202 Tel: 410-528-4309; Fax: 410-528-4312
SCH	Schmidt Periodicals GmbH Dettendorf D-8201 Bad Feilnbach 2 Germany Tel: 49-8064221; Fax: 49-8064557		

Country of Publication Codes

This list of countries and their codes has been taken from the list used by the Library of Congress in the MARC II format, 1972. The list used here is not the complete list of the MARC II format and is limited to presently existing national entities. The states of the United States, provinces and territories of Canada, and divisions of the United Kingdom are not listed separately.

The codes are mnemonic in most cases. Special codes not in the MARC format are used for publications of two international organizations: EI for European Communities and UN for United Nations and related organizations, and KR for Ukraine, respectively.

Country Code Sequence

Code	Country
AA	ALBANIA
AE	ALGERIA
AF	AFGHANISTAN
AG	ARGENTINA
AI	ARMENIA
AJ	AZERBAIJAN
AN	ANDORRA
AO	ANGOLA
AQ	ANTIGUA
AS	AMERICAN SAMOA
AT	AUSTRALIA
AU	AUSTRIA
AY	ANTARCTICA
BA	BAHRAIN
BB	BARBADOS
BD	BURUNDI
BE	BELGIUM
BF	BAHAMAS
BG	BANGLADESH
BH	BELIZE
BL	BRAZIL
BM	BERMUDA
BN	BOSNIA HERCEGOVINA
BO	BOLIVIA
BP	SOLOMON ISLANDS
BR	UNION OF MYANMAR (FORMERLY BURMA)
BS	BOTSWANA
BT	BHUTAN
BU	BULGARIA
BW	BELARUS
BX	BRUNEI DARUSSALAM
CB	CAMBODIA
CC	CHINA, PEOPLE'S REPUBLIC OF
CD	CHAD
CE	SRI LANKA
CF	CONGO (BRAZZAVILLE)
CH	CHINA, REPUBLIC OF
CI	CROATIA
CJ	CAYMAN ISLANDS
CK	COLOMBIA
CL	CHILE
CM	CAMEROON
CN	CANADA
CR	COSTA RICA
CS	CZECHOSLOVAKIA
CU	CUBA
CV	CAPE VERDE
CX	CENTRAL AFRICAN REPUBLIC
CY	CYPRUS
CZ	CANAL ZONE
DK	DENMARK
DM	BENIN
DQ	DOMINICA
DR	DOMINICAN REPUBLIC
EC	ECUADOR
EG	EQUATORIAL GUINEA
EI	EUROPEAN COMMUNITIES
ER	ESTONIA
ES	EL SALVADOR
ET	ETHIOPIA
FA	FAEROE ISLANDS
FG	FRENCH GUIANA
FI	FINLAND
FJ	FIJI
FK	FALKLAND ISLANDS
FM	FEDERATED STATES OF MICRONESIA
FP	FRENCH POLYNESIA
FR	FRANCE
FT	DJIBOUTI
GD	GRENADA
GH	GHANA
GI	GIBRALTAR
GL	GREENLAND
GM	GAMBIA
GO	GABON
GP	GUADELOUPE
GR	GREECE
GS	GEORGIA
GT	GUATEMALA
GU	GUAM
GV	GUINEA
GW	GERMANY
GY	GUYANA
HK	HONG KONG
HO	HONDURAS
HT	HAITI
HU	HUNGARY
IC	ICELAND
IE	IRELAND
II	INDIA
IO	INDONESIA
IQ	IRAQ
IR	IRAN
IS	ISRAEL
IT	ITALY
IV	IVORY COAST
JA	JAPAN
JM	JAMAICA
JO	JORDAN
KE	KENYA
KG	KYRGYZSTAN
KN	KOREA, NORTH
KO	KOREA, SOUTH
KR	UKRAINE
KU	KUWAIT
KZ	KAZAKHSTAN
LB	LIBERIA
LE	LEBANON
LH	LIECHTENSTEIN
LI	LITHUANIA
LO	LESOTHO
LS	LAOS
LU	LUXEMBOURG
LV	LATVIA
LY	LIBYA
MC	MONACO
ME	MAURITIUS
MG	MALAGASY REPUBLIC (MADAGASCAR)
MH	MACAO
MJ	MONTSERRAT
MK	SULTANATE OF OMAN
ML	MALI
MM	MALTA
MP	MONGOLIA
MQ	MARTINIQUE
MR	MOROCCO
MU	MAURITANIA
MV	MOLDOVA
MW	MALAWI
MX	MEXICO
MY	MALAYSIA
MZ	MOZAMBIQUE
NA	NETHERLANDS ANTILLES
NE	NETHERLANDS
NG	NIGER
NL	NEW CALEDONIA
NN	VANUATU (NEW HEBRIDES)
NO	NORWAY
NP	NEPAL
NQ	NICARAGUA
NR	NIGERIA
NU	NAURU
NZ	NEW ZEALAND
PE	PERU
PG	GUINEA-BISSAU
PH	PHILIPPINES
PK	PAKISTAN
PL	POLAND
PN	PANAMA
PO	PORTUGAL
PP	PAPUA NEW GUINEA
PR	PUERTO RICO
PY	PARAGUAY
QA	QATAR
RE	REUNION
RH	ZIMBABWE
RM	RUMANIA
RU	RUSSIA
RW	RWANDA
SA	SOUTH AFRICA
SE	SEYCHELLES
SF	SAO TOME PRINCIPE
SG	SENEGAL
SI	SINGAPORE
SJ	SUDAN
SL	SIERRA LEONE
SM	SAN MARINO
SO	SOMALIA
SP	SPAIN
SQ	SWAZILAND
SR	SURINAM
SU	SAUDI ARABIA
SW	SWEDEN
SX	NAMIBIA (FORMERLY SOUTH-WEST AFRICA)
SY	SYRIA
SZ	SWITZERLAND
TA	TAJIKISTAN
TC	TURKS AND CAICOS ISLANDS
TG	TOGO
TH	THAILAND
TI	TUNISIA
TK	TURKMENISTAN
TO	TONGA
TR	TRINIDAD & TOBAGO
TS	UNITED ARAB EMIRATES
TU	TURKEY
TZ	TANZANIA
UA	EGYPT (ARAB REPUBLIC OF EGYPT)
UG	UGANDA
UI	UNITED KINGDOM MISC. ISLANDS
UK	UNITED KINGDOM
UN	UNITED NATIONS
US	UNITED STATES
UV	BURKINA FASO
UY	URUGUAY
UZ	UZBEKISTAN
VB	BRITISH VIRGIN ISLANDS
VC	VATICAN CITY
VE	VENEZUELA
VI	U.S. VIRGIN ISLANDS
VN	VIETNAM
WS	WESTERN SAMOA
XC	MALDIVE ISLANDS
XE	MARSHALL ISLANDS
XI	ST. KITTS-NEVIS
XK	SAINT LUCIA
XM	SAINT VINCENT
XN	MACEDONIA
XV	SLOVENIA
YE	YEMEN, REPUBLIC OF
YU	YUGOSLAVIA
ZA	ZAMBIA
ZR	ZAIRE

Country Sequence

AFGHANISTAN - AF
ALBANIA - AA
ALGERIA - AE
AMERICAN SAMOA - AS
ANDORRA - AN
ANGOLA - AO
ANTARTICA - AY
ANTIGUA - AQ
ARGENTINA - AG
ARMENIA - AI
AUSTRALIA - AT
AUSTRIA - AU
AZERBAIJAN - AJ
BAHAMAS - BF
BAHRAIN - BA
BANGLADESH - BG
BARBADOS - BB
BELARUS - BW
BELGIUM - BE
BELIZE - BH
BENIN - DM
BERMUDA - BM
BHUTAN - BT
BOLIVIA - BO
BOSNIA HERCEGOVINA - BN
BOTSWANA - BS
BRAZIL - BL
BRITISH VIRGIN ISLANDS - VB
BRUNEI DARUSSALAM - BX
BULGARIA - BU
BURKINA FASO - UV
BURUNDI - BD
CAMBODIA - CB
CAMEROON - CM
CANADA - CN
CANAL ZONE - CZ
CAPE VERDE - CV
CAYMAN ISLANDS - CJ
CENTRAL AFRICAN REPUBLIC - CX
CHAD - CD
CHILE - CL
CHINA, PEOPLE'S REPUBLIC OF - CC
CHINA, REPUBLIC OF - CH
COLOMBIA - CK
CONGO (BRAZZAVILLE) - CF
COSTA RICA - CR
CROATIA - CI
CUBA - CU
CYPRUS - CY
CZECHOSLOVAKIA - CS
DENMARK - DK
DJIBOUTI - FT
DOMINICA - DQ
DOMINICAN REPUBLIC - DR
ECUADOR - EC
EGYPT (ARAB REPUBLIC OF EGYPT) - UA
EL SALVADOR - ES
EQUATORIAL GUINEA - EG
ESTONIA - ER
ETHIOPIA - ET
EUROPEAN COMMUNITIES - EI
FAEROE ISLANDS - FA
FALKLAND ISLANDS - FK
FEDERATED STATES OF MICRONESIA - FM
FIJI - FJ
FINLAND - FI
FRANCE - FR
FRENCH GUIANA - FG
FRENCH POLYNESIA - FP
GABON - GO
GAMBIA - GM
GEORGIA - GS

GERMANY - GW
GHANA - GH
GIBRALTAR - GI
GREECE - GR
GREENLAND - GL
GRENADA - GD
GUADELOUPE - GP
GUAM - GU
GUATEMALA - GT
GUINEA - GV
GUINEA - BISSAU - PG
GUYANA - GY
HAITI - HT
HONDURAS - HO
HONG KONG - HK
HUNGARY - HU
ICELAND - IC
INDIA - II
INDONESIA - IO
IRAN - IR
IRAQ - IQ
IRELAND - IE
ISRAEL - IS
ITALY - IT
IVORY COAST - IV
JAMAICA - JM
JAPAN - JA
JORDAN - JO
KAZAKHSTAN - KZ
KENYA - KE
KOREA, NORTH - KN
KOREA, SOUTH - KO
KUWAIT - KU
KYRGYZSTAN - KG
LAOS - LS
LATVIA - LV
LEBANON - LE
LESOTHO - LO
LIBERIA - LB
LIBYA - LY
LIECHTENSTEIN - LH
LITHUANIA - LI
LUXEMBOURG - LU
MACAO - MH
MACEDONIA - XN
MALAGASY REPUBLIC
 (MADAGASCAR) - MG
MALAWI - MW
MALAYSIA - MY
MALDIVE ISLANDS - XC
MALI - ML
MALTA - MM
MARSHALL ISLANDS - XE
MARTINIQUE - MQ
MAURITANIA - MU
MAURITIUS - MF
MEXICO - MX
MOLDOVA - MV
MONACO - MC
MONGOLIA - MP
MONTSERRAT - MJ
MOROCCO - MR
MOZAMBIQUE - MZ
NAMIBIA (FORMERLY SOUTH-WEST
 AFRICA) - SX
NAURU - NU
NEPAL - NP
NETHERLANDS - NE
NETHERLANDS ANTILLES - NA
NEW CALEDONIA - NL
NEW ZEALAND - NZ
NICARAGUA - NQ

NIGER - NG
NIGERIA - NR
NORWAY - NO
PAKISTAN - PK
PANAMA - PN
PAPUA NEW GUINEA - PP
PARAGUAY - PY
PERU - PE
PHILIPPINES - PH
POLAND - PL
PORTUGAL - PO
PUERTO RICO - PR
QATAR - QA
REUNION - RE
RUMANIA - RM
RUSSIA - RU
RWANDA - RW
SAINT KITTS-NEVIS-XI
SAINT LUCIA - XK
SAINT VINCENT - XM
SAN MARINO - SM
SAO TOME E PRINCIPE - SF
SAUDI ARABIA - SU
SENEGAL - SG
SEYCHELLES - SE
SIERRA LEONE - SL
SINGAPORE - SI
SLOVENIA - XV
SOLOMON ISLANDS - BP
SOMALIA - SO
SOUTH AFRICA - SA
SPAIN - SP
SRI LANKA - CE
SUDAN - SJ
SULTANATE OF OMAN - MK
SURINAM - SR
SWAZILAND - SQ
SWEDEN - SW
SWITZERLAND - SZ
SYRIA - SY
TAJIKISTAN - TA
TANZANIA - TZ
THAILAND - TH
TOGO - TH
TONGA - TO
TRINIDAD & TOBAGO - TR
TUNISIA - TI
TURKEY - TU
TURKMENISTAN - TK
TURKS AND CAICOS ISLANDS - TC
UGANDA - UG
UKRAINE - KR
UNION OF MYANMAR (FORMERLY BURMA) - BR
UNITED ARAB EMIRATES - TS
UNITED KINGDOM - UK
UNITED KINGDOM MISC. ISLANDS - UI
UNITED NATIONS - UN
UNITED STATES - US
URUGUAY - UY
U.S VIRGIN ISLANDS - VI
UZBEKISTAN - UZ
VANUATU (NEW HEBRIDES) - NN
VATICAN CITY - VC
VENEZUELA - VE
VIETNAM - VN
WESTERN SAMOA - WS
YEMEN, REPUBLIC OF - YE
YUGOSLAVIA - YU
ZAIRE - ZR
ZAMBIA - ZA
ZIMBABWE - RH

Abstracting and Indexing Services

This list contains the full names of all abstracting and indexing services whose abbreviations are used in entries in the Classified List of Serials. For all currently published abstracting and indexing services, entries containing full bibliographic information will be found in the Classified List of Serials. Consult the Title Index for page numbers. (Bibliographic information for ceased titles can be found in the Bowker International Serials Database online.)

A

A.A.P.P.Abstr.	Amino Acids, Peptides & Proteins Abstracts (Now: Cambridge Scientific Biochemistry Abstracts, Part 3: Amino Acids, Peptides & Proteins)
AAR	Accounting Articles
ABC	Abstracts in BioCommerce
A.B.C.Pol.Sci.	ABC Pol Sci; A Bibliography of Contents: Political Science and Government
ABI Inform.	A B I-INFORM
ABTICS	Abstracts and Book Title Index Card Services (Ceased)
A.D.& D.	Alcohol, Drugs and Driving: Abstracts and Reviews (Now: Alcohol, Drugs and Driving)
AESIS	A E S I S Quarterly (Australian Earth Sciences Information System)
A.I.Abstr.	Artificial Intelligence Abstracts (United States)
A.I.C.P.	Anthropological Index to Current Periodicals in the Library of the Museum of Mankind Library
A.I.D.Res.Dev. Abstr.	A.I.D. Research & Development Abstracts (Agency for International Development)
A.I.P.P.	Annual Index to Poetry in Periodicals (Now: Roth's American Poetry Annual)
AIT Reports	A I T Reports and Publications on Renewable Energy Resources. Abstracts (Asian Institute of Technology) (Now: A I T Reports and Publications on Energy. Abstracts)
API Abstr.	A P I Abstracts: Literature (American Petroleum Institute) (Now: Literature Abstracts)
ALISA	A L I S A (Australian Library and Information Science Abstracts)
API Catal.	A P I Abstracts: Catalysts & Catalysis (Now: Literature Abstracts: Catalysts & Catalysis)
API Hlth.& Environ.	A P I Abstracts: Health & Environment (Now: Literature Abstracts: Health & Environment)
API Oil.	A P I Abstracts: Oilfield Chemicals (Now: Literature and Patent Abstracts: Oilfield Chemicals)
API Pet.Ref.	A P I Abstracts: Petroleum Refining and Petrochemicals (Now: Literature Abstracts: Petroleum Refining and Petrochemicals)
API Pet.Subst.	A P I Abstracts: Petroleum Substitutes (Now: Literature Abstracts: Petroleum Substitutes)
API Transport.	A P I Abstracts: Transportation and Storage (Now: Literature Abstracts: Transportation and Storage)
A.S.& T.Ind.	Applied Science & Technology Index
ASCA	Automatic Subject Citation Alert (Now: Research Alert (Philadelphia))
ASEAN Manage. Abstr.	A S E A N Management Abstracts (Association of South East Asian Nations)
ASSIA	A S S I A (Applied Social Sciences Index & Abstracts)
ASTIS	A S T I S Bibliography (Arctic Science & Technology Information System)
Abr.R.G.	Abridged Readers' Guide to Periodical Literature
Abstr.Anthropol.	Abstracts in Anthropology
Abstr.Bk.Rev. Curr.Leg.Per.	Abstracts of Book Reviews in Current Legal Periodicals (Ceased)
Abstr.Bulg.Sci. Med.Lit.	Abstracts of Bulgarian Scientific Medical Literature
Abstr.Bull.Inst. Pap.Chem.	Institute of Paper Chemistry. Abstract Bulletin
Abstr.Crim.& Pen.	Abstracts on Criminology and Penology (Now: Criminology, Penology & Police Science Abstracts)
Abstr.Engl.Stud.	Abstracts of English Studies
Abstr.Folk.Stud.	Abstracts of Folklore Studies (Ceased)
Abstr.Health Care Manage. Stud.	Abstracts of Health Care Management Studies (Ceased)
Abstr.Health Eff. Environ. Pollut.	Abstracts on Health Effects of Environmental Pollutants (Ceased)

Abstr.Hosp.Manage.Stud.	Abstracts of Hospital Management Studies (Now: Abstracts of Health Care Management Studies)	Anbar	Anbar Publications Ltd. Accounting & Data Processing Abstracts Marketing & Distribution Abstracts Personnel & Training Abstracts Top Management Abstracts Work Study & O and M Abstracts (Now: Management Services & Production Abstracts)
Abstr.Hum.Comp.Inter.	Abstracts in Human-Computer Interaction		
Abstr.Hyg.	Abstracts on Hygiene and Communicable Diseases		
Abstr.Inter.Med.	Abstracts in Internal Medicine (Now: Abstracts in Medicine and Key Word Index)		
		Anim.Behav.Abstr.	Animal Behavior Abstracts
Abstr.J.Earthq.Eng.	Abstract Journal in Earthquake Engineering	Anim.Breed.Abstr.	Animal Breeding Abstracts
Abstr.Mil.Bibl.	Abstracts of Military Bibliography	Ap.Ind.	Apple Index
Abstr.Musl.Rel.	European Muslims and Christian-Muslim Relations. Abstracts. (Ceased)	Apic.Abstr.	Apicultural Abstracts
		Appl.Ecol.Abstr.	Applied Ecology Abstracts (Now: Ecology Abstracts)
Abstr.N.Amer.Geol.	Abstracts of North American Geology (Ceased)	Appl.Mech.Rev.	Applied Mechanics Reviews
		Aqua.Sci.& Fish.Abstr.	Aquatic Sciences & Fisheries Abstracts (Parts 1, 2)
Abstr.Pop.Cult.	Abstracts of Popular Culture (Ceased)	Aquacult.Abstr.	A S F A Aquaculture Abstracts
Abstr.Rural Dev.Trop.	Abstracts on Rural Development in the Tropics	Archit.Per.Ind.	Architectural Periodicals Index
		Arct.Bibl.	Arctic Bibliography (Ceased)
Abstr.Soc.Geront.	Abstracts in Social Gerontology: Current Literature on Aging	Art & Archaeol.Tech.Abstr.	Art and Archaeology Technical Abstracts
Abstr.Soc.Work.	Abstracts for Social Workers (Now: Social Work Research & Abstracts)	Art Ind.	Art Index
		Art.Int.Abstr.	Artificial Intelligence Abstracts (England) (Ceased)
Abstr.Trop.Agri.	Abstracts on Tropical Agriculture	Artbibl.	Artbibliographies Current Titles
Acad.Ind.	Academic Index	Artbibl.Mod.	Artbibliographies Modern
Access	Access: the Supplementary Index to Periodicals	Arts & Hum.Cit.Ind.	Arts & Humanities Citation Index
Account.& Data Proc.Abstr.	Accounting & Data Processing Abstracts (Now: Accounting & Finance Abstracts) (see: Anbar)	Ash.G.Bot.Per.	Asher's Guide to Botanical Periodicals (Now: Guide to Botanical Periodicals) (Ceased)
		Asian-Pac.Econ.Lit.	Asian-Pacific Economic Literature
Account.Ind.	Accountant's Index	Astron.& Astrophys.Abstr.	Astronomy and Astrophysics Abstracts
Acid Pre.Dig.	Acid Precipitation Digest		
Acid Rain Abstr.	Acid Rain Abstracts (Now: Environment Abstracts)	Astron.Jahresber.	Astronomischer Jahresbericht (Now: Astronomy and Astrophysics Abstracts)
Acid Rain Ind.	Acid Rain Annual Index (Now: Environment Abstracts Annual)		
Acoust.Abstr.	Acoustics Abstracts	Aus.Educ.Ind.	Australian Education Index
Adol.Ment.Hlth.Abstr.	Adolescent Mental Health Abstracts (Ceased)	Aus.Leg.Mon.Dig.	Australian Legal Monthly Digest
Agri.Eng.Abstr.	Agricultural Engineering Abstracts	Aus.P.A.I.S.	Australian Public Affairs Information Service (Now: A P A I S: Australian Public Affairs Information Service)
Agri.Ind.	Agriculture Index (Now: Biological & Agricultural Index)		
Agrindex	Agrindex		
Agroforest.Abstr.	Agroforestry Abstracts		
Air Un.Lib.Ind.	Air University Library Index to Military Periodicals	Aus.Rd.Ind.	Australian Road Index (Ceased)
		Aus.Sci.Ind.	Australian Science Index (Ceased)
Alloys Ind.	Alloys Index	Aus.Speleo Abstr.	Australian Speleo Abstracts
Alt.Press Ind.	Alternative Press Index	Avery Ind.Archit.Per.	Avery Index to Architectural Periodicals
Amer.Bibl.Slavic & E.Eur.Stud.	American Bibliography of Slavic and East European Studies		
		B	
Amer.Hist.& Life	America: History & Life (Parts A, B, C, D)	B.C.I.R.A.	B.C.I.R.A. Abstracts of International Foundry Literature (British Cast Iron Research Association) (Now: B C I R A Abstracts on International Literature on Metal Casting Production)
Amer.Hum.Ind.	American Humanities Index		
Amer.Stat.Ind.	American Statistics Index		
Anal.Abstr.	Analytical Abstracts		

BIM	Bibliography and Index of Micropaleontology	Biul.Inst.Hod. Aklim.Rosl.	Instytut Hodowli i Aklimatyzacji Roslin. Biuletyn
BMT	B M T Abstracts (British Maritime Technology)	Biwk.Pap.Rad. Chem.& Photochem.	Biweekly List of Papers on Radiation Chemistry and Photochemistry
B.P.I.	Business Periodicals Index	Bk.Rev.Dig.	Book Review Digest
BPIA	Business Publications Index and Abstracts (Ceased)	Bk.Rev.Ind.	Book Review Index
B.R.I.	BioResearch Index (Now: Biological Abstracts/R R M (Reports, Reviews, Meetings)	Bk.Rev.Mo.	Book Reviews of the Month (Ceased)
		Br.Archaeol. Abstr.	British Archaeological Abstracts (Now: British Archaeological Bibliography)
BSL Biol.	Abstracts of Bulgarian Scientific Literature. Biology	Br.Ceram.Abstr.	British Ceramic Abstracts (Now: World Ceramic Abstracts)
BSL Econ.	Abstracts of Bulgarian Scientific Literature. Economics and Law	Br.Educ.Ind.	British Education Index
BSL Geo.	Abstracts of Bulgarian Scientific Literature. Geosciences	Br.Geol.Lit.	British Geological Literature
		Br.Hum.Ind.	British Humanities Index
BSL Indus.	Abstracts of Bulgarian Scientific Literature. Industry, Building and Transport	Br.Rail.Bd.	British Railways Board. Monthly Review of Technical Literature (Ceased)
BSL Math.	Abstracts of Bulgarian Scientific Literature. Mathematical and Physical Sciences	Br.Tech.Ind.	British Technology Index (Now: Current Technology Index)
		Build.Manage. Abstr.	Building Management Abstracts (Now: Technical Information Service–TIS)
Bangladesh Agr. Sci.Abstr.	Bangladesh Agricultural Sciences Abstracts	Bull.Anal.Ent. Med.Vet.	Bulletin Analytique d'Entomologie Medicale et Veterinaire (Ceased)
Bank.Lit.Ind.	Banking Literature Index	Bull.Signal.	Bulletin Signaletique (Now: P A S C A L Explore, P A S C A L Folio, P A S C A L Thema) (Programme Applique a la Selection et la Compilation Automatique de la Literature)
Behav.Abstr.	Behavioural Abstracts (Ceased)		
Behav.Med.Abstr.	Behavioral Medicine Abstracts (Now: Annals of Behavioral Medicine)		
Ber.Biochem. Biol.	Berichte Biochemie und Biologie (Ceased)		
Bibl.Agri.	Bibliography of Agriculture	Bull.Thermodyn.& Thermochem.	Bulletin of Thermodynamics & Thermochemistry (Now: Bulletin of Chemical Thermodynamics) (Ceased)
Bibl.& Ind.Geol.	Bibliography & Index of Geology (see: GeoRef)		
Bibl.Cart.	Bibliographia Cartographica	Bus.Comput.Ind.	Business Computer Index
Bibl.Dev.Med.& Child Neur.	Bibliography of Developmental Medicine & Child Neurology. Books and Articles Received	Bus.Educ.Ind.	Business Education Index
		Bus.Ind.	Business Index
Bibl.Engl.Lang. & Lit.	Bibliography of English Language and Literature (Now: Annual Bibliography of English Language and Literature)	**C**	
		CAD CAM Abstr.	C A D/C A M Abstracts
Bibl.Ind.	Bibliographic Index	CALL	C A L L (Current Awareness—Library Literature)
Bibl.IULA	Bibliographia I U L A (International Union of Local Authorities) (Ceased)	C.C.L.P.	Contents of Current Legal Periodicals (Now: Legal Contents) (Ceased)
Bibl.Repro.	Bibliography of Reproduction	C.C.M.J.	Contents of Contemporary Mathematical Journals (Now: Current Mathematical Publications)
Bibliogr.Bras. Odontol.	Bibliografia Brasileira de Odontologia		
Bio-Contr.News & Info.	Bio-Control News and Information	CCR	Current Christian Abstracts (Now: Current Thoughts & Trends)
Biodet.Abstr.	Biodeterioration Abstracts	CERDIC	Universite de Strasbourg. Centre de Recherche et de Documentation des Institutions Chretiennes. Bulletin du CERDIC (Ceased)
Bioeng.Abstr.	Bioengineering Abstracts		
Biog.& Gen.Master Ind.	Biography and Genealogy Master Index		
Biog.Ind.	Biography Index		
Biol.Abstr.	Biological Abstracts	CHNI	Consumer Health & Nutrition Index
Biol.& Agr.Ind.	Biological & Agricultural Index	C.I.J.E.	Current Index to Journals in Education
Biol.Dig.	Biology Digest		
Biostat.	Biostatistica	CINAHL (also C.I.N.L.)	Cumulative Index to Nursing and Allied Health Literature
Biotech.Abstr.	Biotechnology Research Abstracts		

ABSTRACTING AND INDEXING xxxi

CIRF Abstr.	C I R F Abstracts (Now: T&D Abstracts) (Ceased)	Coll.Stud.Pers. Abstr.	College Student Personnel Abstracts (Now: Higher Education Abstracts)
C.I.S. Abstr.	C I S Abstracts (Centre International d'Information de Securite et Hygiene du Travail) (Now: Safety and Health at Work)	Commun.Abstr.	Communication Abstracts
		Community Ment.Health Rev.	Community Mental Health Review (Now: Prevention in Human Services)
C.I.S. Ind.	C I S Index (Congressional Information Service)	Compumath	Compumath Citation Index
CJPI	Criminal Justice Periodical Index	Comput.& Info. Sys.	Computer and Information Systems Abstracts Journal
C.L.I.	Current Law Index	Comput.Abstr.	Computer Abstracts
CLOA	Current Literature on Aging (Now: Abstracts in Social Gerontology: Current Literature on Aging)	Comput.& Contr. Abstr.	Computer & Control Abstracts (Also see: INSPEC; also see: Sci. Abstr.)
CMI	Canadian Magazine Index	Comput.Bus.	Computer Business
C.P.I.	Current Physics Index	Comput.Cont.	Computer Contents (Ceased)
C.R.E.J.	Contents of Recent Economics Journals	Comput.Dtbs.	Computer Database
		Comput.Indus.Up.	Computer Industry Update
C.R.I. Abstr.	C R I Abstracts (Cement Research Institute of India)	Comput.Lit.Ind.	Computer Literature Index
		Comput.Rev.	Computing Reviews
CS Ind.	Canadian Statistics Index	Concr.Abstr.	Concrete Abstracts
CSI Fed.Ind.	C S I Federal Index (Capitol Services, Inc.)	Consum.Ind.	Consumers Index
		Cont.Pg.Educ.	Contents Pages in Education
CWHM	Current Work in the History of Medicine	Cont.Pg.Manage.	Contents Pages in Management
Cab.Vid.Ind.	Cable-Video Index	Copper Abstr.	Copper Abstracts (Now: International Copper Information Bulletin)
Cadscan	Cadscan		
Cal.Per.Ind.	California Periodicals Index	Corros.Abstr.	Corrosion Abstracts
Cal.Tiss.Abstr.	Calcified Tissue Abstracts	Cott.& Trop.Fibr. Abstr.	Cotton and Tropical Fibres Abstracts (Now: Cotton and Tropical Fibres)
Can.B.P.I.	Canadian Business Periodicals Index (Now: Canadian Business Index)		
Can.Educ.Ind.	Canadian Education Index	Crim.Just.Abstr.	Criminal Justice Abstracts
Can.Lit.Ind.	Canadian Literature Index	Crime Delinq. Abstr.	Crime and Delinquency Abstracts (Ceased)
Can.Per.Ind.	Canadian Periodical Index		
Can.Rev.Comp. Lit.	Canadian Review of Comparative Literature	Crime Delinq.Lit.	Crime & Delinquency Literature (Now: Criminal Justice Abstracts)
Can.Wom.Per.Ind.	Canadian Women's Periodicals Index	Crop Physiol.Abstr.	Crop Physiology Abstracts
Canadiana	Canadiana	Curr.Adv.Biochem.	Current Advances in Biochemistry (Now: Current Advances in Protein Biochemistry)
Canon Law Abstr.	Canon Law Abstracts		
Carcinog.Abstr.	Carcinogenesis Abstracts (Now: Cancergram)		
		Curr.Adv.Cancer Res.	Current Advances in Cancer Research
Cath.Ind.	Catholic Periodical & Literature Index		
Ceram.Abstr.	Ceramic Abstracts	Curr.Adv.Cell & Devel.Biol.	Current Advances in Cell and Developmental Biology
Chem.Abstr.	Chemical Abstracts		
Chem.Eng.Abstr.	Chemical Engineering Abstracts	Curr.Adv.Clin. Chem.	Current Advances in Clinical Chemistry
Chem.Indus.Notes	Chemical Industry Notes		
Chem.Infd.	Chemischer Informationsdienst (Now: ChemInform)	Curr.Adv.Ecol.Sci.	Current Advances in Ecological Sciences (Now: Current Advances in Ecological and Environmental Sciences)
Chem.Titles	Chemical Titles		
Chemorec.Abstr.	Chemoreception Abstracts		
Chicago Psychoanal. Lit.Ind.	Chicago Psychoanalytic Literature Index (Ceased)	Curr.Adv.Genetics & Molec.Biol.	Current Advances in Genetics and Molecular Biology
		Curr.Adv.Immunol.	Current Advances in Immunology (Now: Current Advances in Immunology & Infectious Diseases)
Chic.Per.Ind.	Chicano Periodical Index (Now: Chicano Index)		
Child.Auth.& Illus.	Children's Authors and Illustrators	Curr.Adv.Microbiol.	Current Advances in Microbiology (Now: Current Advances in Applied Microbiology & Biotechnology)
Child.Bk.Rev.Ind.	Children's Book Review Index		
Child Devel.Abstr.	Child Development Abstracts and Bibliography		
		Curr.Adv.Neurosci.	Current Advances in Neuroscience
Child.Lit.Abstr.	Children's Literature Abstracts	Curr.Adv.Pharmacol. & Toxicol.	Current Advances in Pharmacology & Toxicology (Now: Current Advances in Toxicology)
Chr.Per.Ind.	Christian Periodical Index		
Clin-Alert	Clin-Alert		

Curr.Adv.Physiol.	Current Advances in Physiology (Now: Current Advances in Endocrinology & Metabolism)
Curr.Adv.Plant Sci.	Current Advances in Plant Science
Curr.Aus.N.Z.Leg.Lit.Ind.	Current Australian and New Zealand Legal Literature Index
Curr.Bibl.Aquatic Sci.& Fish	Current Bibliography for Aquatic Sciences & Fisheries (Now: Aquatic Sciences and Fisheries Abstracts. Parts 1,2,3)
Curr.Biotech.Abstr.	Current Biotechnology Abstracts
Curr.Bk.Rev.Cit.	Current Book Review Citations (Ceased)
Curr.Chem.React.	Current Chemical Reactions
Curr.Cont.	Current Contents
Curr.Cont.Africa	Current Contents Africa
Curr.Cont.M.E.	Current Contents of Periodicals on the Middle East
Curr.Dig.Sov.Press	Current Digest of Soviet Press (Now: Current Digest of the Post-Soviet Press)
Curr.Ind.Commonw.Leg.Per.	Current Index to Commonwealth Legal Periodicals (Now: Index to Commonwealth Legal Periodicals) (Ceased)
Curr.Ind.Stat.	Current Index to Statistics
Curr.Leather Lit.	Current Leather Literature (Now: Leather Science Abstracts)
Curr.Lit.Blood	Current Literature of Blood (Ceased)
Curr.Lit.Fam.Plan.	Current Literature in Family Planning
Curr.Pack.Abstr.	Current Packaging Abstracts
Curr.Pap.Phys.	Current Papers in Physics (Also see: INSPEC)
Curr.Tit.Dent.	Current Titles in Dentistry
Curr.Tit.Electrochem.	Current Titles in Electrochemistry
Curr.Tit.Ocean	Current Titles in Ocean, Coastal, Lake & Waterway Sciences (Ceased)
Cyb.Abstr.	Cybernetics Abstracts

D

DAAI	Design and Applied Arts Index
DM&T	Defense Markets and Technology (Now: Aerospace Defense Markets and Technology) (Ceased)
DNP	Digest of Neurology & Psychiatry
DSH Abstr.	D S H Abstracts (Deafness, Speech and Hearing) (Ceased)
Dairy Sci.Abstr.	Dairy Science Abstracts
Data Process.Dig.	Data Processing Digest
Deep Sea Res.& Oceanogr.Abstr.	Deep Sea Research & Oceanographic Abstracts (Now: Deep-Sea Research. Parts A, B)
Dent.Abstr.	Dental Abstracts
Dent.Ind.	Index to Dental Literature
Devindex	Devindex (Ceased)
Diab.Lit.Ind.	Diabetes Literature Index (Ceased)
Doc.Geogr.	Documentatio Geographica (Now: Dokumentation zur Raumentwicklung) (Ceased)
Dok.Arbeitsmed.	Dokumentation Arbeitsmedizin (Now: Arbeitsmedizin)
Dok.Raum.	Dokumentation zur Raumentwicklung (Ceased)
Dok.Str.	Dokumentation Strasse

E

EC Ind.	E C Index (European Communities)
E.I.	E I (Excerpta Indonesica)
ERIC	Eric Clearinghouse (See: C.I.J.E.)
Ecol.Abstr.	Ecological Abstracts
Econ.Abstr.	Economic Abstracts (Now: Key to Economic Science)
Educ.Admin.Abstr.	Educational Administration Abstracts
Educ.Ind.	Education Index
Educ.Tech.Abstr.	Educational Technology Abstracts
Ekist.Ind.	Ekistic Index
Elec.& Electron.Abstr.	Electrical & Electronics Abstracts (Also see: INSPEC; also see: Sci.Abstr.)
Electroanal.Abstr.	Electroanalytical Abstracts (Ceased)
Electron.& Communic.Abstr.J.	Electronics and Communications Abstracts Journal
Endocrin.Abstr.	Endocrinology Abstracts (Now: C S A Neurosciences Abstracts)
Endocrin.Ind.	Endocrinology Index (Ceased)
Energy Abstr.	Energy Abstracts
Energy Ind.	Energy Index (Now: Energy Information Abstracts Annual)
Energy Info.Abstr.	Energy Information Abstracts
Energy Res.Abstr.	Energy Research Abstracts
Energy Rev.	Energy Review (Santa Barbara)
Eng.Ind.	Engineering Index (Now: Engineering Index Monthly)
Eng.Mat.Abstr.	Engineered Materials Abstracts
Entomol.Abstr.	Entomology Abstracts
Environ.Abstr.	Environment Abstracts
Environ.Ind.	Environment Index (Now: Environment Abstracts Annual)
Environ.Per.Bibl.	Environmental Periodicals Bibliography
Ergon.Abstr.	Ergonomics Abstracts
Except.Child Educ.Abstr.	Exceptional Child Education Abstracts (Now: Exceptional Child Education Resources)
Excerp.Bot.	Excerpta Botanica (Sections A, B)
Excerp.Criminol.	Excerpta Criminologica (Now: Criminology and Penology Abstracts)
Excerp.Med.	Excerpta Medica

F

F.A.C.T.	Fuel Abstracts and Current Titles (Now: Fuel and Energy Abstracts)
FAMLI	F A M L I (Family Medicine Literature Index)
F.R.	Fanatic Reader
Fababean Abstr.	Fababean Abstracts
Farm & Garden Ind.	Farm & Garden Index (Ceased)
Fed Print	Fed in Print
Fert.Abstr.	Fertilizer Abstracts (Ceased)

Field Crop Abstr.	Field Crop Abstracts
Film Lit.Ind.	Film Literature Index
Fluidex	Fluidex
	Consists of:
	Civil Engineering Hydraulics Abstracts
	Current Fluid Engineering Titles (Ceased)
	Fluid Flow Measurement Abstracts
	Fluid Power Abstracts
	Fluid Sealing Abstracts
	Industrial Aerodynamics Abstracts
	Industrial Jetting Report
	Pipelines Abstracts
	Pumps and Other Fluids Machinery Abstracts
	Pumps and Turbines (Ceased)
	River and Flood Control Abstracts (Ceased)
	Solid-Liquid Flow Abstracts
	Tribos-Tribology Abstracts
	World Ports and Harbours Abstracts
	World Ports and Harbours News (Ceased)
Food Sci.&Tech. Abstr.	Food Science and Technology Abstracts
Foreign Leg.Per.	Index to Foreign Legal Periodicals
Forest.Abstr.	Forestry Abstracts
Forest Prod.Abstr.	Forest Products Abstracts
Foul.Prev.Res.Dig.	Fouling Prevention Research Digest (Now: Heat Transfer & Fluid Flow Service Digest)
Fuel & Energy Abstr.	Fuel & Energy Abstracts
Fut.Abstr.	Future - Abstracts
Fut.Surv.	Future Survey

G

G.Indian Per.Lit.	Guide to Indian Periodical Literature
G.Perf.Arts	Guide to the Performing Arts (Ceased)
G.Soc.Sci.& Rel. Per.Lit.	Guide to Social Science and Religion in Periodical Literature
Gard.Lit.	Garden Literature
Gas Abstr.	Gas Abstracts
Gastroenterol: Abstr.& Cit.	Gastroenterology: Abstracts & Citations (Ceased)
Gdlns.	Guidelines
Gen.Phys.Adv. Abstr.	General Physics Advance Abstracts
Gen.Sci.Ind.	General Science Index
Geneal.Per.Ind.	Genealogical Periodical Annual Index
Genet.Abstr.	Genetics Abstracts
Geo.Abstr.	Geographical Abstracts
Geophys.Abstr.	Geophysical Abstracts (Ceased)
GeoRef	Bibliography and Index of Geology (Also known as GeoRef)
Geosci.Doc.	Geoscience Documentation
Geotech.Abstr.	Geotechnical Abstracts
Ger.J.Psych.	German Journal of Psychology
Gleanings	Gleanings
Graph.Arts Abstr.	Graphic Arts Abstracts (Now: G A T F World)
Graph.Arts Lit. Abstr.	Graphic Arts Literature Abstracts (Now: Institute of Paper Science and Technology. Graphic Arts Bulletin)

H

HMA	Healthcare Marketing Abstracts
HR Rep.	Human Rights Internet Reporter
HRIS	H R I S Abstracts (Now: Highway Research Abstracts)
Helminthol.Abstr.	Helminthological Abstracts. Series A (Now: Helminthological Abstracts) Helminthological Abstracts. Series B (Now: Nematological Abstracts)
Herb.Abstr.	Herbage Abstracts
High.Educ.Abstr.	Higher Education Abstracts
High.Educ.Curr. Aware.Bull.	Higher Education Current Awareness Bulletin (Ceased)
Hisp.Amer.Per.Ind.	Hispanic American Periodicals Index
Hist.Abstr.	Historical Abstracts (Parts A, B)
Hlth.Dev.Alerts	Health Devices Alerts
Hlth.Ind.	Health Index
Hlth.Phys.Educ.& Rec.	Health, Physical Education and Recreation Microform Publication Bulletin
Hort.Abstr.	Horticultural Abstracts
Hosp.Abstr.	Hospital Abstracts (Now: Health Service Abstracts)
Hosp.Abstr.Serv.	Hospital Abstracts Service (Ceased)
Hosp.Lit.Ind.	Hospital Literature Index
Hospit.Ind.	Hospitality Index
Hum.Ind.	Humanities Index
Human Resour. Abstr.	Human Resources Abstracts
Hung.Build.Bull.	Hungarian Building Bulletin (Ceased)
Hung.Lib.& Info. Sci.Abstr.	Hungarian Library and Information Science Abstracts
Hwy.Res.Abstr.	Highway Research Abstracts (Now: Transportation Research Abstracts) (Ceased)

I

IBM PC Ind.	I B M PC Index (Personal Computer)
IBR	I B R (International Bibliography of Book Reviews of Scholarly Literature)
IBZ	Internationale Bibliographie der Zeitschriftenliteratur aus allen Gebieten des Wissens/International Bibliography of Periodicals from all Fields of Knowledge
I.C.U.I.S.Abstr.	I C U I S Abstracts Service (Institute on the Church in Urban Industrial Society) (Now: I C U I S Justice Ministries) (Ceased)
I D A	International Development Abstracts
IIS	Index to International Statistics

I.M.M.Abstr.	I M M Abstracts (Institute of Mining & Metallurgy) (Now: I M M Abstracts and Index)	I.P.A.	International Pharmaceutical Abstracts
I.N.E.P.	Index to New England Periodicals	I.R.A.	Information Resources Annual (Ceased)
INIS Atomind.	I N I S Atomindex (International Nuclear Information System)	ISMEC	I S M E C Bulletin (Information Service in Mechanical Engineering (Now: I S M E C: Mechanical Engineering Abstracts)
INSPEC	INSPEC (The Institution of Electrical Engineers):		
	Computers & Control Abstracts (Alternative title: INSPEC, Section C. Represents: Science Abstracts. Section C) (Also see: Comput. & Contr.Abstr.; also see: Sci.Abstr.)	Immun.Abstr.	Immunology Abstracts
		Ind.Agri.Am.Lat. Caribe	Indice Agricole de America Latina y el Caribe (Ceased)
		Ind.Amer.Per. Verse	Index of American Periodical Verse
		Ind.Artic.Jew.Stud.	Index of Articles on Jewish Studies
	Current Papers in Computers & Control	Ind.Bk.Rev.Hum.	Index to Book Reviews in the Humanities (Ceased)
		Ind.Bus.Rep.	Index to Business Reports
	Current Papers in Electrical & Electronics Engineering	Ind.Can.L.P.L.	Index to Canadian Legal Periodical Literature
	Current Papers in Physics (Also see: Curr.Pap.Phys.)	Ind.Chem.	Index Chemicus
		Ind.Child.Mag.	Subject Index to Children's Magazines (Now: Children's Magazine Guide)
	Electrical & Electronics Abstracts (Alternative title: INSPEC, Section B. Represents: Science Abstracts. Section B.) (Also see: Elec.&Electron.Abstr.; also see: Sci.Abstr.)	Ind.Curr.Urb.Doc.	Index to Current Urban Documents
		Ind.Develop.Abstr.	Industrial Development Abstracts
		Ind.Free Per.	Index to Free Periodicals
		Ind.Heb.Per.	Index to Hebrew Periodicals
	Key Abstracts Advanced Materials	Ind.How To Do It	Index to How to Do It Information
	Key Abstracts Antennas & Propagation	Ind.Hyg.Dig.	Industrial Hygiene Digest
		Ind.India	Index India
	Key Abstracts Artificial Intelligence	Ind.Islam.	Index Islamicus
	Key Abstracts Business Automation	Ind.Jew.Per.	Index to Jewish Periodicals
	Key Abstracts Computer Communication and Storage	Ind.Lit.Amer. Indian	Index to Literature on the American Indian (Ceased)
	Key Abstracts Computing in Electronics & Power	Ind.Lit.Dent.	Indice de la Literatura Dental Periodica en Castellano
	Key Abstracts Electronic Circuits	Ind.Little Mag.	Index to Little Magazines (Ceased)
	Key Abstracts Electronic Instrumentation	Ind.Med.	Index Medicus
		Ind.Med.Esp.	Indice Medico Espanol
	Key Abstracts Factory Automation	Ind.N.Z.Per.	Index to New Zealand Periodicals (Now: Index New Zealand)
	Key Abstracts High-Temperature Superconductors		
	Key Abstracts Human-Computer Interaction	Ind.Per.Art.Relat. Law	Index to Periodical Articles Related to Law
	Key Abstracts Machine Vision	Ind.Per.Blacks	Index to Periodical Articles by and about Blacks (Now: Index to Black Periodicals)
	Key Abstracts Measurements in Physics		
	Key Abstracts Microelectronics & Printed Circuits	Ind.Per.Lit.	Index to Indian Periodical Literature (Ceased)
	Key Abstracts Microwave Technology	Ind.Per.Negroes	Index to Periodical Articles by & about Negroes (Now: Index to Black Periodicals)
	Key Abstracts Neural Networks		
	Key Abstracts Optoelectronics	Ind.Phil.Per.	Index to Philippine Periodicals
	Key Abstracts Power Systems & Applications	Ind.Rheum.	Annual Index of Rheumatology (Ceased)
	Key Abstracts Robotics & Control	Ind.S.A.Per.	Index to South African Periodicals
	Key Abstracts Semiconductor Devices	Ind.Sci.Rev.	Index to Scientific Reviews
		Ind.Sel.Per.	Index to Selected Periodicals (Now: Index to Black Periodicals)
	Key Abstracts Software Engineering		
	Key Abstracts Telecommunications		
	Physics Abstracts (Alternative title: INSPEC, Section A. Represents: Science Abstracts. Section A) (Also see: Phys.Abstr.; also see: Sci.Abstr.)	Ind.SST.	Index to Spanish Science and Technology
		Ind.U.S.Gov.Per.	Index to U.S. Government Periodicals
		Ind.Vet.	Index Veterinarius
		Indian Educ.Abstr.	Indian Education Abstracts

Indian Lib.Sci. Abstr.	Indian Library Science Abstracts	JCT	Japan Computer Technology and Applications Abstracts (Ceased)
Indian Psychol. Abstr.	Indian Psychological Abstracts	JTA	Japanese Technical Abstracts (Now: Japan Technology Series) (Ceased)
Indian Sci.Abstr.	Indian Science Abstracts	J.Cont. Quant.Meth.	Journal Contents in Quantitative Methods
Indian Sci.Ind.	Indian Science Index (Ceased)		
Info.Media & Tech.	Information Media and Technology	J.Curr.Laser Abstr.	Journal of Current Laser Abstracts
Inform.Sci.Abstr.	Information Science Abstracts	J.of Abstr.Int. Educ.	Journal of Abstracts in International Education
Inpharma	InPharma		
Instrum.Abstr.	Instrument Abstracts (Now: Metron) (Ceased)	J.of Econ.Abstr.	Journal of Economic Abstracts (Now: Journal of Economic Literature)
Int.Abstr.Biol.Sci.	International Abstracts of Biological Sciences (Now: Current Awareness in Biological Sciences)	J.of Ferroc.	Journal of Ferrocement
		Jap.Per.Ind.	Japanese Periodicals Index (Humanities and Social Science Section; Medical Sciences and Pharmacology (Ceased); Science and Technology)
Int.Abstr.Oper.Res.	International Abstracts in Operations Research		
Int.Aerosp.Abstr.	International Aerospace Abstracts	Jazz Ind.	Jazz Index (Ceased)
Int.Bibl.Soc.Sci.	International Bibliography of the Social Sciences: Anthropology, Political Science, Economics, Sociology (Ceased)	Jun.High Mag. Abstr.	Junior High Magazine Abstracts
		K	
Int.Build.Serv. Abstr.	International Building Services Abstracts	Key to Econ.Sci.	Key to Economic Science
Int.Dredg.Abstr.	International Dredging Abstracts (Now: World Ports and Harbours Abstracts; see: Fluidex)	Key Word Ind.Ser. Titl.	Keyword Index to Serial Titles
		Key Word Ind. Wildl.Res.	Key Word Index of Wildlife Research
Int.G.Class.Stud.	International Guide to Classical Studies (Ceased)	**L**	
Int.Ind.Film Per.	International Index to Film Periodicals		
Int.Lab.Doc.	International Labor Documentation	LAMP	L A M P (Literature Analysis of Microcomputer Publications)
Int.Nurs.Ind.	International Nursing Index		
Int.Packag.Abstr.	International Packaging Abstracts	LCR	Literary Criticism Register
Int.Polit.Sci.Abstr.	International Political Science Abstracts	LHTN	Library Hi Tech News
Int.Sci.Rev.	International Science Review Series (Ceased)	L.I.I.	Life Insurance Index (Ceased)
		LISA	Library & Information Science Abstracts
Int.Z.Bibelwiss.	Internationale Zietschriften fuer Bibelwissenschaft und Grenzgebiete (Ceased)	L.R.I.	Legal Resource Index
Intl.Bibl.Burns	International Bibliography on Burns	Lab.Haz.Bull	Laboratory Hazards Bulletin
Intl.Bibl.S.S.Econ.	International Bibliography of the Social Sciences: Economics	Landwirt. Zentralbl.	Landwirtschaftliches Zentralblatt (Now: Agroselekt)
Intl.Bibl.S.S.Pol. Sci.	International Bibliography of the Social Sciences: Political Science	Lang.& Lang. Behav.Abstr.	Language and Language Behaviour Abstracts (Now: Linguistics and Language Behavior Abstracts)
Intl.Bibl.S.S. Soc.Cult.Anthro.	International Bibliography of the Social Sciences. Anthropology	Lang.Teach.& Ling.Abstr.	Language Teaching and Linguistics Abstracts (Now: Language Teaching)
Intl.Civil Eng. Abstr.	International Civil Engineering Abstracts	Lat.Lit.Fam.Plan.	Latest Literature in Family Planning (Ceased)
Intl.Ind.TV.	International Index to Television Periodicals	Law Ofc.Info.Svc.	Law Office Information Service
		Lead Abstr.	Lead Abstracts (Now: Leadscan)
Intl.Mgmt.Info.	International Management Information Business Digest (Ceased)	Left Ind.	Left Index
		Leg.Cont.	Legal Contents (Ceased)
Intl.Polym.Sci.& Tech.	International Polymer Science and Technology	Leg.Info.Manage. Ind.	Legal Information Management Index
Iron & Steel Indus. Pr.	Iron and Steel Industry Profiles (Ceased)	Leg.Per.	Index to Legal Periodicals
		Lib.Lit.	Library Literature
Irr.& Drain.Abstr.	Irrigation & Drainage Abstracts	Lib.Sci.Abstr.	Library Science Abstracts (Now: Library & Information Science Abstracts)
J			
JAMA	JAMA: The Journal of the American Medical Association	Lit.Automat.	Literature on Automation (Now: New Literature on Automation)

M

MEDOC	MEDOC: Index to U.S. Government Publications in the Medical and Health Sciences
MEDSOC	Medical Socioeconomic Research Sources (Ceased)
MELSA	MELSA Messenger (Metropolitan Library Service) (Ceased)
M.L.A.	M L A Abstracts of Articles in Scholarly Journals (Ceased)
M.M.R.I.	Multi-Media Reviews Index (Now: Media Review Digest)
Mag.Ind.	Magazine Index
Maize Abstr.	Maize Abstracts
Manage.Abstr.	Management Abstracts (India) (Now: Indian Management)
Manage.Cont.	Management Contents (Ceased)
Mar.Aff.Bibl.	Marine Affairs Bibliography
Mar.Sci.Cont.Tab.	Marine Science Contents Tables
Mark.Res.Abstr.	Market Research Abstracts
Mass Spectr.Bull.	Mass Spectrometry Bulletin
Math.R.	Mathematical Reviews
Med.Abstr.	Medical Abstract Service (Ceased)
Med.Care Rev.	Medical Care Review
Med.Res.Ind.	Medical Research Index (Now: Medical Research Centres)
Media Rev.Dig.	Media Review Digest
Ment.Retard.Abstr.	Mental Retardation Abstracts (Now: Developmental Disabilities Abstracts) (Ceased)
Met.Abstr.	Metallurgical Abstracts (Now: Metals Abstracts) see also: Cleaning/Finishing/Coating Digest Corrosion Prevention/Inhibition Digest Heat Processing Digest
Met.Finish.Abstr.	Metal Finishing Abstracts (Now: Surface Treatment Technology Abstracts)
Meteor.& Geo-astrophys. Abstr.	Meteorological & Geoastrophysical Abstracts
Meth.Per.Ind.	Methodist Periodical Index (Now: United Methodist Periodical Index) (Ceased)
Mgmt.Abstr.	Management Abstracts (Trinidad)
Mgmt.& Market. Abstr.	Management & Marketing Abstracts
Mich.Mag.Ind.	Michigan Magazine Index (Ceased)
Microbiol.Abstr.	Microbiological Abstracts (Sections A, B, C)
Microcomp.Ind.	Microcomputer Index
Microcomp.Indus. Up.	Microcomputer Industry Update
Mid.East: Abstr. & Ind.	Middle East: Abstracts and Index (Ceased)
Mineral.Abstr.	Mineralogical Abstracts
Mkt.Inform.Guide	Marketing Information Guide (Ceased)
Multi.Scler.Abstr.	Multiple Sclerosis Indicative Abstracts (Ceased)
Music Artic.Guide	Music Article Guide
Music Ind.	Music Index
Mycol.Abstr.	Abstracts of Mycology

N

NAA	N A A (Nordic Archaeological Abstracts)
NASA	N A S A Patent Abstracts Bibliography: A Continuing Bibliography. Section 2. Indexes (National Aeronautics and Space Administration)
NRN	Nutrition Research Newsletter
Nav.Abstr.	Naval Abstracts (Ceased)
Neurosci.Abstr.	Neurosciences Abstracts (Now: C S A Neurosciences Abstracts)
New Per.Ind.	New Periodicals Index (Ceased)
New Sil.Tech	New Silver Technology (Ceased)
New Test.Abstr.	New Testament Abstracts
Noise Pollut. Publ.Abstr.	Noise Pollution Publications Abstracts (Ceased)
Nucl.Sci.Abstr.	Nuclear Science Abstracts (Superseded by: I N I S Atomindex)
Numis.Lit.	Numismatic Literature
Nurs.Abstr.	Nursing Abstracts
Nurs.Res.Abstr.	Nursing Research Abstracts
Nutr.Abstr.	Nutrition Abstracts & Reviews (Now: Nutrition Abstracts and Reviews Series A: Human and Experimental; Nutrition Abstracts and Reviews Series B: Livestock Feeds and Feeding)
Nutr.Plan.	Nutrition Planning (Ceased)

O

Occup.Saf.& Health Abstr.	Occupational Safety & Health Abstracts (Now: Safety at Health at Work)
Ocean.Abstr.	Oceanic Abstracts
Ocean.Abstr.Bibl.	Oceanic Abstracts and Bibliography (Now: Deep Sea Research. Parts A, B)
Ocean.Ind.	Oceanic Index (Now: Oceanic Abstracts)
Old Test.Abstr.	Old Testament Abstracts
Oncol.Abstr.	Oncology Abstracts (Ceased)
Oper.Res.Manage. Sci.	Operations Research/Management Science
Ophthal.Lit.	Ophthalmic Literature
Oral Res.Abstr.	Oral Research Abstracts (Ceased)
Ornam.Hort.	Ornamental Horticulture

P

P.A.I.S.	P A I S Bulletin (Public Affairs Information Service) (Now: P A I S International in Print)
P.A.I.S.For. Lang.Ind.	Public Affairs Information Service Foreign Language Index (Now: P A I S International in Print)
PC Abstr.	P C Abstracts (Personal Computing) (Ceased)
PCR2	P C R2 (Personal Computer Review—Squared)
PHRA	Poverty & Human Resources Abstracts (Now: Human Resources Abstracts)
P.I.R.A.	P.I.R.A. Marketing Abstracts (Packaging Industry Research Association) (Now: Management and Marketing Abstracts)
P.L.I.I.	Property & Liability Insurance Index (Ceased)
P.M.I.	Photography Magazine Index (Ceased)
PMR	Popular Magazine Review (Now: Magazine Article Summaries)
P.N.I.	Pharmaceutical News Index
PROMT	Predicasts Overview of Markets and Technologies
PSI	Philanthropic Studies Index
Packag.Abstr.	Packaging Abstracts (Now: International Packaging Abstracts)
Packag.Sci.Tech.	Packaging Science and Technology Abstracts
Paper.& Bd.Abstr.	Paper and Board Abstracts
Past.Care & Couns. Abstr.	Pastoral Care & Counseling Abstracts (Now: Abstracts of Research in Pastoral Care and Counseling)
Peace Res.Abstr.	Peace Research Abstracts Journal
Peat Abstr.	Peat Abstracts
Perf.Arts Biog. Master Ind.	Performing Arts Biography Master Index
Periodex	Periodex (Now: Point de Repere)
Pers.Lit.	Personnel Literature
Pers.Manage. Abstr.	Personnel Management Abstracts
Petrol.Abstr.	Petroleum Abstracts
Petrol.Energy B.N.I.	Petroleum/Energy Business News Index
Pharmacog.Tit.	Pharmacognosy Titles (Ceased)
Phil.Ind.	Philosopher's Index
Philip.Abstr.	Philippine Abstracts (Now: Philippine Science & Technology Abstracts)
Photo.Abstr.	Photographic Abstracts (Now: Imaging Abstracts)
Photo.Ind.	Photography Index
Phys.Abstr.	Physics Abstracts (Also see: INSPEC; also see: Sci.Abstr.)
Phys.Ber.	Physikalische Berichte (Now: Physics Briefs)
Phys.Ed.Ind.	Physical Education Index
Pig News & Info.	Pig News and Information
Pinpointer	Pinpointer
Plant Breed.Abstr.	Plant Breeding Abstracts
Plant Grow.Reg. Abstr.	Plant Growth Regulator Abstracts
Plast.Abstr.	Plastics Abstracts (Ceased)
Pol.Tech.Abstr.	Polish Technical Abstracts (Now: Polish Technical and Economic Abstracts)
Polit.Sci.Abstr.	Political Science Abstracts
Pollut.Abstr.	Pollution Abstracts
Pop.Mus.Per.Ind.	Popular Music Periodicals Index (Ceased)
Pop.Per.Ind.	Popular Periodical Index
Popul.Ind.	Population Index
Potato Abstr.	Potato Abstracts
Poult.Abstr.	Poultry Abstracts
Pr.Briefs	Predi-Briefs
Predi.F & S Ind.Eur.	Predicasts F & S Index Europe
Predi.F & S Ind.Intl.	Predicasts F & S Index International
Predi.F & S Ind. U.S.	Predicasts F & S Index United States
Print.Abstr.	Printing Abstracts
Protozool.Abstr.	Protozoological Abstracts
Psychoanal.Abstr.	Psychoanalytic Abstracts (Now: PsychScan: Psychoanalysis)
Psychol.Abstr.	Psychological Abstracts
Psychol.R.G.	Psychological Reader's Guide (Ceased)
Psychopharmacol. Abstr.	Psychopharmacology Abstracts (Ceased)
Psycscan	Psycscan: Applied Psychology
Psycscan C.P.	Psycscan: Clinical Psychology
Psycscan D.P.	Psycscan: Development Psychology
Pt.de Rep.	Point de Repere (Formed by the merger of: Periodex and RADAR)
Pub.Admin.Abstr.	Public Administration Abstracts and Index of Articles (Now: Documentation in Public Administration & Sage Public Administration Abstracts)

Q

Qual.Contr. Appl.Stat.	Quality Control and Applied Statistics

R

RADAR	Repertoire Analytique d'Articles des Revues du Quebec (Now: Point de Repere)
RAPRA	R A P R A Abstracts (Rubber and Plastics Research Association of Great Britain)
R.G.	Readers' Guide to Periodical Literature
R.G.Abstr.	Readers' Guide Abstracts
RICS	R I C S Abstracts and Reviews (Now: R I C S Library Information Service Abstracts and Reviews) (Royal Institute of Chartered Surveyors)
RILA	R I L A (International Repertory of the Literature of Art) (Now: B H A (Bibliography of the History of Art))

Abbreviation	Full Title
RILM	R I L M Abstracts of Music Literature (International Repertory of Music Literature)
Reac.	Reactions
Ref.Pt.Food Indus.Abstr.	Reference Point: Food Industry Abstracts
Ref.Sour.	Reference Sources (Ceased)
Ref.Zh.	Referativnyi Zhurnal
Refug.Abstr.	Refugee Abstracts
Rehabil.Lit.	Rehabilitation Literature (Ceased)
Rel.& Theol.Abstr.	Religious & Theological Abstracts
Rel.Ind.One	Religion Index One: Periodicals
Rel.Ind.Two	Religion Index Two: Multi-Author Works
Rel.Per.	Index to Religious Periodical Literature (Now: Religion Index One: Periodicals)
Res.Educ.	Research in Education (Now: Resources in Education)
Res.High.Educ.Abstr.	Research into Higher Educaton Abstracts
Resour.Ctr.Ind.	Resource Center Index
Rev.Appl.Entomol.	Review of Applied Entomology (Series A, B) (Now: Review of Agricultural Entomology & Review of Medical and Veterinary Entomology)
Rev.Appl.Mycol.	Review of Applied Mycology (Now: Review of Plant Pathology)
Rev.Med.& Vet.Mycol.	Review of Medical and Veterinary Mycology
Rev.Plant Path.	Review of Plant Pathology
Rheol.Abstr.	Rheology Abstracts
Rice Abstr.	Rice Abstracts
Risk Abstr.	Risk Abstracts
Robomat.	Robomatix Reporter (Now: Robotics Abstracts)
Rom.Sci.Abstr.	Romanian Scientific Abstracts
Rural Devel.Abstr.	Rural Development Abstracts
Rural Ext.Educ.& Tr.Abstr.	Rural Extension, Education and Training Abstracts (Ceased)
Rural Recreat. Tour.Abstr.	Rural Recreation and Tourism Abstracts (Now: Leisure, Recreation and Tourism Abstracts)

S

Abbreviation	Full Title
S.A.Waterabstr.	S.A. Waterabstracts (South Africa) (Ceased)
SCIMP	S C I M P (Selective Cooperative Index of Management Periodicals)
SOPODA	Social Planning, Policy and Development Abstracts
SRI	Statistical Reference Index
SSCI	Social Science Citation Index
Saf.Sci.Abstr.	Safety Science Abstracts Journal (Now: Health and Safety Science Abstracts)
Sage Fam.Stud.Abstr.	Sage Family Studies Abstracts
Sage Pub.Admin.Abstr.	Sage Public Administration Abstracts
Sage Urb.Stud.Abstr.	Sage Urban Studies Abstracts
Sci.Abstr.	Science Abstracts A. Physics Abstracts (Also see INSPEC; also see: Phys.Abstr.) B. Electrical & Electronics Abstracts (Also see: Elec.&Electron.Abstr.; also see: INSPEC) C. Computer & Control Abstracts (Also see: Comput.&Cont.Abstr.; also see: INSPEC)
Sci.Cit.Ind.	Science Citation Index
Sci.Res.Abstr.	Science Research Abstracts (Now: Solid State and Superconductivity Abstracts)
Search	Search
Seed Abstr.	Seed Abstracts
Sel.Bibl.Homosex.	Selected Bibliography of Homosexuality
Sel.J.Water	Selected Journals on Water (Ceased)
Sel.Water Res. Abstr.	Selected Water Resources Abstracts
Ship Abstr.	Ship Abstracts
Sh.& Vib.Dig.	Shock and Vibration Digest
Sinop.Odontol.	Sinopse de Odontologia (Ceased)
Small Anim.Abstr.	Small Animal Abstracts (Now: Small Animals)
So.Pac.Per.Ind.	South Pacific Periodicals Index
Soc.Sci.Ind.	Social Sciences Index
Soc.Work Res.& Abstr.	Social Work Research & Abstracts
Sociol.Abstr.	Sociological Abstracts
Sociol.Educ.Abstr.	Sociology of Education Abstracts
Soft.Abstr.Eng.	Software Abstracts for Engineers
Soils & Fert.	Soils & Fertilizers
Solid St.Abstr.	Solid State Abstracts (Now: Solid State and Superconductivity Abstracts)
Sorghum & Millets Abstr.	Sorghum and Millets Abstracts
South.Bap.Per.Ind.	Southern Baptist Periodical Index (Ceased)
Soyabean Abstr.	Soyabean Abstracts
Sp.Ed.Needs Abstr.	Special Educational Needs Abstracts
Speleol.Abstr.	Speleological Abstracts
Sport Fish.Abstr.	Sport Fishery Abstracts (Now: Fisheries Review) (Ceased)
Sports Per.Ind.	Sports Periodicals Index
Sportsearch	Sportsearch
Sri Lanka Sci.Ind.	Sri Lanka Science Index
St.Educ.J.Ind.	State Education Journal Index
Stamp J.Ind.	Stamp Journals Index
Stat.Theor.Meth.Abstr.	Statistical Theory and Method Abstracts
Steel Cas.Abstr.	Steel Castings Abstracts (Ceased)
Stud.Wom.Abstr.	Studies on Women Abstracts
Sugar Ind.Abstr.	Sugar Industry Abstracts

T

Abbreviation	Full Title
TBRI	Technical Book Review Index (Ceased)

T.C.E.A.	Theoretical Chemical Engineering Abstracts	Vis.Ind.	Vision Index (Ceased)
TOM	T O M (Text on Microfilm)	VITIS	Vitis – Viticulture and Enology Abstracts
Tech.Educ.Abstr.	Technical Education Abstracts		
Tel.Abstr.	Telecommunications Abstracts (Ceased)		

W

Tel.Alert	Telecommunications Alert	W.R.C.Inf.	W.R.C. Information (Water Research Centre) (Now: Aqualine Abstracts)
Telegen	Telegen Reporter (Now: Telegen Abstracts) (Ceased)	Water Pollut.Abstr.	Water Pollution Abstracts (Now: Aqualine Abstracts)
Text.Dig.	Textile Digest (Ceased)		
Text.Tech.Dig.	Textile Technology Digest	Water Resour.Abstr.	Water Resources Abstracts (Now: Hydro-Abstracts)
Therm.Abstr.	Thermal Abstracts (Now: International Building Services Abstracts)	Weed Abstr.	Weed Abstracts
Tob.Abstr.	Tobacco Abstracts	Wild Life Rev.	Wildlife Review (Ceased)
Tob.Bibl.	Tobacco Bibliography (Ceased)	Wom.Stud.Abstr.	Women Studies Abstracts
Top Manage.Abstr.	Top Management Abstracts (See: Anbar)	Work Rel.Abstr.	Work Related Abstracts
Tox.Abstr.	Toxicology Abstracts	World Agri.Econ.& Rural Sociol. Abstr.	World Agricultural Economics & Rural Sociology Abstracts
Tr.& Indus.Ind.	Trade & Industry Index		
Trans.Res.Abstr.	Transportation Research Abstracts (Ceased)	World Alum.Abstr.	World Aluminum Abstracts
		World Bank.Abstr.	World Banking Abstracts
Triticale Abstr.	Wheat, Barley and Triticale Abstracts	World Bibl.Soc.Sec.	World Bibliography of Social Security
Trop.Abstr.	Tropical Abstracts (Now: Abstracts on Tropical Agriculture)	World Fish.Abstr.	World Fisheries Abstracts (Ceased)
		World Surf.Coat.	World Surface Coatings Abstracts
Trop.Dis.Bull.	Tropical Diseases Bulletin	World Text.Abstr.	World Textile Abstracts
Trop.Oil Seeds Abstr.	Tropical Oil Seeds Abstracts (Now: Tropical Oil Seeds)		

Y

		Yrbk.Assoc.Educ.& Rehab.Blind	Association for Education and Rehabilitation of the Blind and Visually Impaired. Yearbook (Ceased)

U

Urb.Aff.Abstr.	Urban Affairs Abstracts

V

Z

Va.Hist.Abstr.	Virginia Historical Abstracts (Ceased)	Zent.Math.	Zentralblatt fuer Mathematik und ihre Grenzgebiete
Vert.File Ind.	Vertical File Index		
Vet.Bull.	Veterinary Bulletin	Zinscan	Zinscan
Virol.Abstr.	Virology Abstracts (Now: Virology and A I D S Abstracts)	Zion.Lit.	Zionist Literature
		Zoo.Rec.	Zoological Record

Subject Guide to Abstracting and Indexing

The 124 subject headings listed below are major subjects which contain a sub-category headed "Abstracting, Bibliographies, Statistics." This sub-category, which follows the major subject headings in the Classified List of Serials, identifies publications which abstract and/or index publications in the relevant subject. Bibliographies and statistical publications pertaining to the subject are also included in this sub-category. This guide will enable users to quickly locate subject areas of interest for which abstracting and indexing publications have been identified and to build profiles by combination of relevant subject areas. Page numbers refer to the first page on which the sub-category appears.

SUBJECT CATEGORY	PAGE
A	
Advertising and Public Relations	40
Aeronautics and Space Flight	66
Agriculture	131
Anthropology	253
Archaeology	290
Architecture	309
Art	351
Arts and Handicrafts	357
Astronomy	371
B	
Beauty Culture	375
Beverages	388
Biography	424
Biology	461
Birth Control	598
Building and Construction	636
Business and Economics	701
C	
Ceramics, Glass and Pottery	1167
Chemistry	1191
Children and Youth	1247
Civil Defense	1274
Classical Studies	1281
Cleaning and Dyeing	1282
Clothing Trade	1288
Communications	1346
Computers	1402
Conservation	1501
Consumer Education and Protection	1509
Criminology and Law Enforcement	1524

SUBJECT CATEGORY	PAGE
D	
Dance	1532
Drug Abuse and Alcoholism	1540
E	
Earth Sciences	1549
Education	1673
Encyclopedias and General Almanacs	1782
Energy	1797
Engineering	1841
Environmental Studies	1972
Ethnic Interests	2030
F	
Fire Prevention	2035
Fish and Fisheries	2050
Folklore	2060
Food and Food Industries	2084
Forests and Forestry	2111
G	
Gardening and Horticulture	2141
Genealogy and Heraldry	2168
Geography	2267
Gerontology and Geriatrics	2280
H	
Handicapped	2285
Heating, Plumbing and Refrigeration	2304
History	2327
Hobbies	2444

SUBJECT CATEGORY	PAGE
Home Economics	2450
Homosexuality	2458
Hospitals	2470
Hotels and Restaurants	2482
Housing and Urban Planning	2499
Humanities: Comprehensive Works	2519

I

Instruments	2525
Insurance	2545
Interior Design and Decoration	2556

J

Jewelry, Clocks and Watches	2566
Journalism	2577

L

Labor Unions	2592
Law	2697
Leather and Fur Industries	2738
Library and Information Sciences	2792
Linguistics	2854
Literary and Political Reviews	2890
Literature	2980

M

Machinery	3025
Mathematics	3062
Medical Sciences	3165
Meetings and Congresses	3395
Metallurgy	3424
Meteorology	3444
Metrology and Standardization	3449
Military	3476
Mines and Mining Industry	3498
Motion Pictures	3519
Museums and Art Galleries	3536
Music	3588

N

Nutrition and Dietetics	3613

O

Occupational Health and Safety	3623
Occupations and Careers	3631
Oriental Studies	3646

P

Packaging	3652
Paints and Protective Coatings	3656

SUBJECT GUIDE TO ABSTRACTING AND INDEXING, CONTINUED

SUBJECT CATEGORY	PAGE
Paleontology	3661
Paper and Pulp	3667
Parapsychology and Occultism	3672
Patents, Trademarks and Copyrights	3679
Petroleum and Gas	3704
Pharmacy and Pharmacology	3747
Philosophy	3738
Photography	3798
Physical Fitness and Hygiene	3811
Physics	3836
Plastics	3868
Political Science	3936
Population Studies	3989
Printing	4006
Psychology	4051
Public Administration	4078
Public Health and Safety	4116
Publishing and Book Trade	4139

R

Real Estate	4159
Religions and Theology	4211
Rubber	4294

S

Sciences: Comprehensive Works	4354
Shoes and Boots	4362
Social Sciences: Comprehensive Works	4394
Social Services and Welfare	4425
Sociology	4457
Sound Recording and Reproduction	4462
Sports and Games	4498

T

Technology: Comprehensive Works	4613
Textile Industries and Fabrics	4628
Theater	4643
Tobacco	4646
Transportation	4661
Travel and Tourism	4798

V

Veterinary Science	4820

W

Water Resources	4834
Women's Interests	4858
Women's Studies	4861

Subjects

ENGLISH	FRENCH	GERMAN	SPANISH
Abstracting and Indexing Services	Services d'Analyse et Indexage	Referate- und Indexdienste	Servicios de Extractos e Indices
Advertising and Public Relations	Publicité et Relations Publiques	Reklamewesen und Public Relations	Publicidad y Relaciones Públicas
Aeronautics and Space Flight	Aéronautique et Astronautique	Luft- und Raumfahrt	Aeronáutica y Vuelo Espacial
Computer Applications	Applications des Ordinateurs	Computer Anwendung	Aplicaciones de los Ordenadores
Agriculture	Agriculture	Landwirtschaft	Agricultura
Agricultural Economics	Agriculture Economique	Agrarökonomie	Economía Agrícola
Agricultural Equipment	Outillage Agricole	Gerate	Aparatos Agrícolas
Computer Applications	Applications des Ordinateurs	Computer Anwendung	Aplicaciones de los Ordenadores
Crop Production and Soil	Récolte et Terre	Produkte und Boden	Producción de Cosecha, Tierra
Dairying and Dairy Products	Production Laitière	Milchwirtschaft	Lechería y Productos Lácteos
Feed, Flour and Grain	Pature, Farine et Grain	Futter, Mehl und Getreide	Forraje, Granos y Harina
Poultry and Livestock	Elevage	Geflügel- und Viehwirtschaft	Ganadería
Animal Welfare	Protection des Animaux	Tierschutz	Bienestar Animal
Anthropology	Anthropologie	Anthropologie	Antropología
Antiques	Antiquités	Antiquitäten	Antiguedades
Archaeology	Archeologie	Archaeologie	Arqueología
Computer Applications	Applications des Ordinateurs	Computer Anwendung	Aplicaciones de los Ordenadores
Architecture	Architecture	Architektur	Arquitectura
Computer Applications	Applications des Ordinateurs	Computer Anwendung	Aplicaciones de los Ordenadores
Art	Art	Kunst	Arte
Computer Applications	Applications des Ordinateurs	Computer Anwendung	Aplicaciones de los Ordenadores
Arts and Handicrafts	Arts et Metiers	Kunst und Handwerk	Artes y Obras de Mano
Astrology	Astrologie	Astrologie	Astrología
Astronomy	Astronomie	Astronomie	Astronomía
Computer Applications	Applications des Ordinateurs	Computer Anwendung	Aplicaciones de los Ordenadores
Beauty Culture	Soins de Beauté	Schönheitspflege	Belleza Personal
Perfumes and Cosmetics	Parfums et Cosmétiques	Kosmetik und Parfüme	Perfumes y Cosméticos
Beverages	Boissons	Getränke	Bebidas
Bibliographies	Bibliographies	Bibliographien	Bibliografías
Biography	Biographie	Biographie	Biografía
Biology	Biologie	Biologie	Biología
Bioengineering	Biogénie	Bioingenieurwesen	Bio-ingeniería
Biological Chemistry	Chimie Biologique	Biochemie	Química Biológica
Biophysics	Biophysique	Biophysik	Biofísica
Biotechnology	Biotecnologie	Biotechnologie	Biotecnología
Botany	Botanique	Botanik	Botánica
Cytology and Histology	Cytologie et Histologie	Zytologie und Histologie	Citología e Histología
Entomology	Entomologie	Entomologie	Entomología
Genetics	Génétique	Genetik	Genética
Microbiology	Microbiologie	Mikrobiologie	Microbiología
Microscopy	Microscopie	Mikroskopie	Microscopia
Ornithology	Ornithologie	Ornithologie	Ornitología
Physiology	Physiologie	Physiologie	Fisiología
Zoology	Zoologie	Zoologie	Zoología
Birth Control	Limitation des Naissances	Geburtenregelung	Reglamentación del Nacimiento
Building and Construction	Batiment et Construction	Bauwesen	Edificios y Construcción
Carpentry and Woodwork	Charpenterie et Menuiserie	Zimmerhandwerk und Holzbau	Carpintería y Ebanistería
Hardware	Quincaillerie	Metallbaustoffe	Quincalla

SUBJECTS

Business and Economics	Affaires et Economie	Wirtschaft und Handel	Negocios y Economía
Accounting	Comptabilité	Rechnungswesen	Contabilidad
Banking and Finance	Banque et Finance	Bank- und Finanzwesen	Bancos y Finanzas

Banking and Finance-
    Computer Applications
	Banque et Finance-
	    Applications des Ordinateurs
		Bank- und Finanzwesen-
		    Computer Anwendung
			Bancos y Finanzas-
			    Aplicaciones de los Ordenadores

Chamber of Commerce
    Publications
	Publications des Chambres
	    de Commerce
		Veröffentlichungen von Handel-
		    kammern
			Publicaciones de las Cámaras de
			    Comercio

Computer Applications	Applications des Ordinateurs	Computer Anwendung	Aplicaciones de los Ordenadores
Cooperatives	Coopératives	Genossenschaften	Cooperativos
Domestic Commerce	Commerce Interieur	Binnenhandel	Comercio Interior

Economic Situation and
    Conditions
	Situations et Conditions
	    Economiques
		Wirtschaftliche Situation und
		    Verhältnisse
			Situaciones y Condiciones
			    Económicas

Economic Systems and Theories,
    Economic History
	Systèmes et Theories Economiques,
	    Histoire Economique
		Ökonomische Systeme und
		    Theorien, Wirtschafts-
		    geschichte
			Sistemas y Teorías Económicos,
			    Historia Económica

International Commerce	Commerce International	Aussenhandel	Comercio Internacional

International Development and
    Assistance
	Développement et Assistance
	    Internationaux
		Internationale Entwicklungshilfe	Desarrollo y Asistencia Inter-
			    nacionales

Investments	Investissements	Investitionen	Inversiones
Labor and Industrial Relations	Travail et Relations Industrielles	Arbeits- und Industrielle Beziehungen	Trabajo y Relaciones Industriales
Macroeconomics	Macroeconomique	Makroökonomie	Macroeconomía
Management	Gestion	Betriebsführung	Gerencia
Marketing and Purchasing	Cours et Achats	Marketing und Kauf	Compra y Venta
Office Equipment and Services	Matériel et Entretien de Bureaux	Büroeinrichtung und Service	Equipo y Servicios de Oficinas
Personnel Management	Direction de Personnel	Personal Führung	Dirección de Empleados
Production of Goods and Services	Production	Produktion	Producción
Public Finance, Taxation	Finance Publique, Impots	Staatsfinanzen, Steuerwesen	Finanza Publica, Impuestos
Small Business	Petites et Moyennes Affaires	Kleinbetrieb	Negocios Pequeños

Trade and Industrial Directories	Directoires de Commerce et
	    Industrie
		Firmenverzeichnisse	Directorios de Comercio e
			    Industria

Ceramics, Glass and Pottery	Céramique, Verrerie et Poterie	Keramik, Glas und Töpferei	Cerámica, Vidrio y Porcelana
Chemistry	Chimie	Chemie	Química
Analytical Chemistry	Chimie Analytique	Analytische Chemie	Química Analítica
Computer Applications	Applications des Ordinateurs	Computer Anwendung	Aplicaciones de los Ordenadores
Crystallography	Cristallographie	Kristallographie	Cristalografía
Electrochemistry	Electrochimie	Elektrochemie	Electroquímica
Inorganic Chemistry	Chimie Inorganique	Anorganische Chemie	Química Inorgánica
Organic Chemistry	Chimie Organique	Organische Chemie	Química Orgánica
Physical Chemistry	Chimie Physique	Physikalische Chemie	Fisicoquímica
Children and Youth	Enfance et Adolescence	Kinder und Jugend	Niños y Jóvenes
About	Au Sujet de	Über	Acerca
For	Pour	Für	Para
Civil Defense	Defense Civile	Ziviler Bevölkerungsschutz	Defensa Civil
Classical Studies	Etudes Classiques	Klassische Studien	Estudios Clásicos
Cleaning and Dyeing	Nettoyage et Teinturerie	Reinigen und Farben	Limpieza y Tintura
Clothing Trade	Vêtement	Bekleidungsgewerbe	Industria de Vestidos
Fashions	Mode	Moden	Modas
Clubs	Clubs	Klubs	Clubes
College and Alumni	Université et Diplomés	Universitäten und Hochschul- Absolventen	Universidades y Exalumnos
Communications	Communications	Nachrichtentechnik	Comunicaciones
Computer Applications	Applications des Ordinateurs	Computer Anwendung	Aplicaciones de los Ordenadores
Postal Affairs	Postes	Postwesen	Correo
Radio	Radio	Rundfunk	Radio
Telephone and Telegraph	Téléphone et Télégraphe	Telephon und Telegraph	Teléfono y Telégrafo
Television and Cable	Télévision	Fernsehen und Bildfrequenzkanal	Televisión y Cable
Video	Vidéo	Video	Video
Computers	Ordinateurs	Computer	Ordenadores
Artificial Intelligence	Intelligence Artificielle	Künstliche-Intelligenz	Inteligencia Artificial
Automation	Automation	Automatisierung	Automación
Calculating Machines	Calculateurs	Rechenmaschine	Calculadoras
Circuits	Circuits	Kreisbewegung	Circuitos
Computer Architecture	Architecture de la Machine	Computer Architektur	Arquitectura de los Ordenadores

Computer-Assisted Instruction	Enseignement Assisté par
	    Ordinateur
		Computer Beistande Anweisung	Instrucción con la Ayuda de
			    Ordenador

Computer Engineering	Technique d'Ordinateur	Computer Bewerkstellingen	Ingeniería de Ordenador
Computer Games	Jeux des Ordinateurs	Computer Spiele	Juegos de Ordenadores

Computer Graphics	Conception Assistée par
	    Ordinateur
		Computergraphik	Diseño con la Ayuda de
			    Ordenador

Computer Industry	Industrie d'Ordinateur	Computer Fleiss	Industrias de los Ordenadores
Computer Industry Directories	Annuaire de la Industrie Ordinateur	Computer Fleiss Fernsprechbuch	Directorios de los Ordenadores

Computer Industry, Vocational
    Guidance
	Industrie d'Ordinateur,
	    Orientation Professionnelle
		Computer Fleiss Berufsberatung
		    Ratschlag
			Industria de los Ordenadores
			    Gobierno Práctico

Computer Music	Musique d'Ordinateur	Computer Musik	Música de Ordenadores
Computer Networks	Reseaux des Ordinateurs	Computer Netzwerk	Red para Transmición de Datos
Computer Programming	Programme Machine	Computer Programm	Programa de Ordenador
Computer Sales	Ventes des Ordinateurs	Computer Verkaufen	Ventas de Ordenadores
Computer Security	Protection des Ordinateurs	Computer Sicherheit	Protección de los Ordenadores
Computer Simulation	Simulation des Ordinateurs	Computer Verstellung	Simulación de los Ordenadores
Computer Systems	Systemes des Ordinateurs	Computer Systemen	Sistemas de los Ordenadores
Cybernetics	Cybernetiques	Kybernetik	Cibernéticas

Data Communications, Data
    Transmission Systems
	Données de Communication	Daten Bekanntmachung, Daten
		    Verschickung Systems
			Datos de Comunicación

SUBJECTS

Data Base Management	Gestion de Base de Données	Datenbank Verwaltung	Gestión de Banco de Datos
Electronic Data Processing	Traitement de l'Information Electronique	Elektrisiert-Daten Aufbereitung	Proceso de Datos Electronico
Hardware	Materiel	Eisenwaren	Equipo Físico
Information Science, Information Theory	Théorie de l'Information	Nachrichtenswissenschaft, Nachrichtenstheorie	Ciencia, Teoría de la Información
Machine Theory	Theorie de Machine	Maschinetheorie	Teoría de la Maquina
Microcomputers	Micro-Ordinateurs	Mikrocomputer	Microordenadores
Minicomputers	Mini-Ordinateurs	Minicomputer	Miniordenadores
Personal Computers	Ordinateurs Privé	Persoenlichecomputer	Ordenador Personal
Software	Logiciel	Weichwaren	Soporte Lógico
Theory of Computing	Théorie de Traitement	Computertheorie	Theoria de Cálculo
Word Processing	Traitement de Textes	Wortbehandlung	Proceso de la Palabras
Conservation	Conservation	Landschaftsschutz	Conservación
Consumer Education and Protection	Protection de Consommateur	Verbraucherswirtschaftsschutz	Protección del Consumidor
Criminology and Law Enforcement	Criminologie et Police	Kriminologie und Strafvollzug	Criminologia y Accion Policial
Computer Applications	Applications des Ordinateurs	Computer Anwendung	Aplicaciones de los Ordenadores
Security	Securité	Sicherheit	Seguridad
Dance	Danse	Tanz	Baile
Drug Abuse and Alcoholism	Toxicomanie et Alcoolisme	Rauschgiftsucht und Alkoholismus	Drogadismo y Alcoholismo
Earth Sciences	Sciences Géologiques	Wissenschaften der Erde	Ciencias Geológicas
Computer Applications	Applications des Ordinateurs	Computer Anwendung	Aplicaciones de los Ordenadores
Geology	Géologie	Geologie	Geología
Geophysics	Géophysique	Geophysik	Geofísica
Hydrology	Hydrologie	Hydrologie	Hidrología
Oceanography	Océanographie	Ozeanographie	Oceanografía
Education	Education	Bildungswesen	Educación
Adult Education	Enseignement des Adultes	Erwachsenenbildung	Enseñanza de Adultos
Computer Applications	Applications des Ordinateurs	Computer Anwendung	Aplicaciones de los Ordenadores
Guides to Schools and Colleges	Guides d'Ecoles et Colleges	Führer zur Schulen und Universitaten	Guías de Escuelas y Colegios
Higher Education	Enseignement Supérieur	Hochschulwesen	Enseñanza Superior
International Education Programs	Programmes de'Education Internationale	Internazionale Erziehungs-Programme	Programas de Enseñanza Internacional
School Organization and Administration	Organisation et Administration de l'Ecole	Organisation und Verwaltung von dem Schule	Administración y Dirección de la Escuela
Special Education and Rehabilitation	Enseignement Special et Réhabilitation	Fachunterricht und Rehabilitierung	Enseñanza Especial y Rehabilitación
Teaching Methods and Curriculum	Méthodes Pédagogiques et Programmes Scolaires	Lehrmethoden und Lehrplan	Métodos de Enseñanza y Planes de Estudios
Electronics	Electronique	Elektronik	Electrónicos
Computer Applications	Applications des Ordinateurs	Computer Anwendung	Aplicaciones de los Ordenadores
Encyclopedias and General Almanacs	Encyclopédies et Almanachs Générales	Enzyklopädien und Allgemeine Nachschlagewerke	Enciclopedias y Almanaques Generales
Energy	Energie	Energie	Energía
Computer Applications	Applications des Ordinateurs	Computer Anwendung	Aplicaciones de los Ordenadores
Electrical Energy	Energie Eléctrique	Elektrizitätsenergie	Energía Eléctrica
Geothermal Energy	Energie Géothermique	Thermalenergie	Energía Geotérmica
Hydroelectrical Energy	Energie Hydraulique	Hydroelektroenergie	Energía Hidroeléctrica
Nuclear Energy	Energie Nucléaire	Kernenergie	Energía Nuclear
Solar Energy	Energie Solaire	Sonnenenergie	Energía Solar
Wind Energy	Energie à Vent	Windenergie	Energía del Viento
Engineering	Génie	Ingenieurwesen	Ingeniería
Chemical Engineering	Génie Chimique	Chemieingenieurwesen	Ingeniería Química
Civil Engineering	Génie Civil	Bauingenierurwesen	Ingeniería Civil
Computer Applications	Applications des Ordinateurs	Computer Anwendung	Aplicaciones de los Ordenadores
Electrical Engineering	Génie Eléctrique	Elektrotechnik	Ingeniería Eléctrica
Engineering Mechanics and Materials	Mechánique de Génie et Materiels	Ingenieurwesen Mechanik und Materialien	Mecanica de Ingeniería y Materiales
Hydraulic Engineering	Génie Hydraulique	Wasserbau	Ingeniería Hidráulica
Industrial Engineering	Génie Industriel	Industrieingenieurwesen	Ingeniería Industrial
Mechanical Engineering	Génie Mécanique	Maschinenbau	Ingeniería Mecánica
Environmental Studies	Science de l'Environnement	Umweltschutz	Ciencias Ecológicas
Computer Applications	Applications des Ordinateurs	Computer Anwendung	Aplicaciones de los Ordenadores
Pollution	Pollution	Umweltverschmutzung	Contaminación
Toxicology and Environmental Safety	Toxicologie et Sécurité de l'Environnement	Toxokologie und Umweltsicherheit	Toxicología y Seguridad Ambiental
Waste Management	Gestion des Déchets	Abfallwirtschaft	Manejo de la Basura
Ethnic Interests	Publications de l'Orientation Ethnique	Veröffentlichungen von Minoritäten	Publicaciones de Temas Etnicos
Fire Prevention	Précaution contre l'Incendie	Brandbekaempfung	Prevención del Fuego
Fish and Fisheries	Poisson et Peche	Fische und Fischerei	Pesca y Pesquerías
Folklore	Folklore	Volkskunde	Folklore
Food and Food Industries	Alimentation et Industries Alimentaires	Nahrungsmittel und Lebensmittelindustrie	Alimentos e Industrias Alimenticias
Bakers and Confectioners	Boulangerie et Confiserie	Bäcker- und Konditorgewerbe	Panaderías y Dulcerías
Grocery Trade	Epicerie	Kolonialwarenhandel	Abacerías
Forest and Forestry	Forêts et Exploitation Forestiére	Forstwesen und Waldwirtschaft	Bosques y Selvicultura
Lumber and Wood	Bois	Holz	Maderas
Funerals	Funérailles	Beerdigungen	Funerales
Gardening and Horticulture	Jardinage et Horticulture	Gartenpflege und Gartenbau	Jardinería y Horticultura
Florist Trade	Commerce des Fleurs	Blumenhandel	Floristas
Genealogy and Heraldry	Généalogie et Science Héraldique	Genealogie und Wappenkunde	Genealogía y Heráldica
Computer Applications	Applications des Ordinateurs	Computer Anwendung	Aplicaciones de los Ordenadores

SUBJECTS xlv

General Interest Periodicals (Subdivided by country)	Publications d'Intérêt Général (Selon pays)	Allgemeine Zeitschriften (nach Land)	Periódicos de Interés General (por país)
Geography	Géographie	Geographie	Geografía
Computer Applications	Applications des Ordinateurs	Computer Anwendung	Aplicaciones de los Ordenadores
Gerontology and Geriatrics	Gérontologie	Gerontologie	Gerontología y Geriátrica
Giftware and Toys	Cadeaux et Jouets	Geschenkartikel und Spielwaren	Regalos y Juguetes
Handicapped	Handicapés	Behinderung	Desventajados
Computer Applications	Applications des Ordinateurs	Computer Anwendung	Aplicaciones de los Ordenadores
Hearing Impaired	Sourds	Schwerhörigkeit	Debilitado del Oído
Physically Impaired	Handicapés Physique	Körperbehinderung	Debilitado Físicamente
Visually Impaired	Aveugles	Blindheit	Debilitado Visualmente
Heating, Plumbing, and Refrigeration	Chauffage, Plomberie et Réfrigeration	Heizung, Kühlung und Installation	Calefaccion, Plomería y Refrigeración
History	Histoire	Geschichte	Historia
Computer Applications	Applications des Ordinateurs	Computer Anwendung	Aplicaciones de los Ordenadores
History of Africa	Histoire de l'Afrique	Geschichte-Afrika	Historia de Africa
History of Asia	Histoire de l'Asie	Geschichte-Asien	Historia de Asia
History of Australasia	Histoire de l'Australasie	Geschichte-Australasien	Historia de Australasia
History of Europe	Histoire de l'Europe	Geschichte-Europa	Historia de la Europa
History of North and South America	Histoire de l'Amérique du Nord et du Sud	Geschichte-Nord- und Südamerika	Historia de la América del Norte y de la del Sur
History of Near East	Histoire du Proche-Orient	Geschichte-Nahe Osten	Historia del Cercano Oriente
Hobbies	Passe-Temps	Hobbies	Pasatiempos
Home Economics	Enseignement Ménager	Hauswirtschaft	Economía Doméstica
Homosexuality	Homosexualisme	Homosexualität	Homosexualismo
Hospitals	Hôpitaux	Krankenhäuser	Hospitales
Computer Applications	Applications des Ordinateurs	Computer Anwendung	Aplicaciones de los Ordenadores
Hotels and Restaurants	Hôtels et Restaurants	Hotels und Restaurants	Hoteles y Restaurantes
Computer Applications	Applications des Ordinateurs	Computer Anwendung	Aplicaciones de los Ordenadores
Housing and Urban Planning	Lógement et Urbanisme	Wohnungswesen und Stadtplanung	Viviendas y Urbanismo
Computer Applications	Applications des Ordinateurs	Computer Anwendung	Aplicaciones de los Ordenadores
How-To and Do-It-Yourself	Bricolage	Selbstanfertigung	Cómo Hacerlo y Hágalo Si Mismo
Humanities: Comprehensive Works	Humanités: Oeuvres Comprehensives	Geisteswissenschaften	Humanidades: Obras Comprensivas
Computer Applications	Applications des Ordinateurs	Computer Anwendung	Aplicaciones de los Ordenadores
Instruments	Instruments	Instrumente	Instrumentos
Insurance	Assurances	Versicherungswesen	Seguros
Computer Applications	Applications des Ordinateurs	Computer Anwendung	Aplicaciones de los Ordenadores
Interior Design and Decoration	Agencements Intérieurs et Décoration	Innenarchitektur und Innenausstattung	Diseño del Interior y Ornamentación
Furniture and House Furnishing	Meubles et Articles pour la Maison	Möbel and Wohnungseinrichtung	Muebles y Articulos para el Hogar
Jewelry, Clocks und Watches	Bijouterie et Horlogerie	Schmuck und Uhren	Joyería y Relojería
Journalism	Journalisme	Journalismus	Periodismo
Labor Unions	Syndicalisme	Gewerkschaften	Sindicatos
Law	Droit	Recht	Derecho
Civil Law	Droit Civil	Zivilrecht	Derecho Civil
Computer Applications	Applications des Ordinateurs	Computer Anwendung	Aplicaciónes de los Ordenadores
Constitutional Law	Droit Constitutionel	Verfassungsrecht	Derecho Constitucional
Corporate Law	Droit Commercial	Handelsrecht	Derecho Corporativo
Criminal Law	Droit Penal	Strafrecht	Derecho Criminal
Estate Planning	Succession	Mobiliarvermögensrecht	Planificación de los Bienes
Family And Matrimonial Law	Droit Familial et Matrimonial	Ehegesetz und Familienrecht	Derecho Familial y Matrimonial
International Law	Droit International	Völkerrecht	Derecho Internacional
Judicial Systems	Système Judiciaire	Gerichtswesen	Sistemas Judiciales
Legal Aid	Assistance Judiciaire	Rechtshilfe	Ayuda Legal
Maritime Law	Droit Maritime	Seerecht	Derecho Marítimo
Military Law	Droit Militaire	Kriegsrecht	Derecho Militar
Leather and Fur Industries	Maroquinerie et Pelleterie	Leder und Pelz	Pieles y Cuero
Leisure and Recreation	Loisirs et Récréation	Freizeit und Unterhaltung	Ocio y Recreo
Library and Information Science	Bibliothéconomie et Informatique	Bibliothek- und Informationswissenschaft	Bibliotecologia y Ciencia de la Información
Computer Applications	Applications des Ordinateurs	Computer Anwendung	Aplicaciones de los Ordenadores
Linguistics	Linguistique	Sprachwissenschaft	Linguística
Computer Applications	Applications des Ordinateurs	Computer Anwendung	Aplicaciones de los Ordenadores
Literary and Political Reviews	Revues Littéraires et Politiques	Literarische und Politische Zeitschriften	Revistas Literarias y Politicas
Literature	Litterature	Literatur	Literatura
Adventure and Romance	Aventure et Romance	Abenteuer und Romantik	Aventura y Romance
Mystery and Detective	Mystere et Policier	Geheimnis und Detektivroman	Misterio y Detective
Poetry	Poésie	Poesie	Poesía
Science Fiction, Fantasy, Horror	Science-Fiction, Oeuvres Fantastiques, Oeuvre d'Epouvante	Zukunftsroman, Phantasiegebilde, Grausen	Ciencia Ficción, Fantasía, Horror
Machinery	Machines	Maschinenwesen	Maquinaria
Computer Applications	Applications des Ordinateurs	Computer Anwendung	Aplicaciones de los Ordenadores
Mathematics	Mathématiques	Mathematik	Matemática
Computer Applications	Applications des Ordinateurs	Computer Anwendung	Aplicaciones de los Ordenadores
Matrimony	Mariage	Ehestand	Matrimonio
Computer Applications	Applications des Ordinateurs	Computer Anwendung	Aplicaciones de los Ordenadores
Medical Sciences	Sciences Médicales	Medizinische Wissenschaften	Ciencias Médicas
Allergology and Immunology	Allergologie et Immunologie	Allergie und Immunologie	Alergología e Imunología
Anaesthesiology	Anesthésiologie	Anaesthesiologie	Anestesiología
Cancer	Cancer	Krebs	Cancer
Cardiovascular Diseases	Maladies Cardiovasculaires	Kreislauferkrankungen	Enfermedades Cardiovasculares

SUBJECTS

Chiropractic, Homeopathy, Osteopathy	Chiropraxie, Homépathie, Ostéopathie	Chiropraktik, Homöopathie, Osteopathie	Quiropractica, Homeopatia Osteopatía
Communicable Diseases	Maladies Contagieuses	Infektiöse Krankheiten	Enfermedades Contagiosas
Computer Applications	Applications des Ordinateurs	Computer Anwendung	Aplicaciónes de los Ordenadores
Dentistry	Dentisterie	Zahnmedizin	Dentistería
Dermatology and Venereology	Dermatologie et Maladies Vénériennes	Dermatologie und Geschlechtskrankheiten	Dermatología y Venereología
Endocrinology	Endocrinologie	Endokrinologie	Endocrinología
Experimental Medicine Laboratory Technique	Médicine Expérimentale, Techniques de Laboratoire	Versuchsmedizin, Laboratoriumstechnik	Medicina Experimental, Tecnicas del Laboratorio
Forensic Sciences	Médecine Légale	Gerichtliche Medizin	Ciencias Forenses
Gastroenterology	Gastroentérologie	Gastroenterologie	Gastroenterología
Hematology	Hématologie	Hämatologie	Hematología
Hypnosis	Hypnose	Hypnose	Hipnotismo
Nurses and Nursing	Personnel et Soins Infirmiers	Krankenpflege	Enfermeros y Enfermería
Obstetrics and Gynecology	Obstétrique et Gynécologie	Gynäkologie und Geburtshilfe	Obstetricia y Ginecología
Ophthalmology and Optometry	Ophtalmologie et Optométrie	Opthalmologie und Optometrie	Oftalmología y Optometría
Orthopedics and Traumatology	Orthopédie et Traumatologie	Orthopädie und Traumatologie	Ortopedia y Traumatologia
Otorhinolaryngology	Otorhinolaryngologie	Otorhinolaryngologie	Otorinolaringología
Pediatrics	Pédiatrie	Pädiatrie	Pediatría
Psychiatry and Neurology	Psychiatrie et Neurologie	Psychiatrie und Neurologie	Psiquiatría y Neurología
Radiology and Nuclear Medicine	Radiologie et Médecine Nucléaire	Radiologie und Nuklearmedizin	Radiología y Medicina Nuclear
Respiratory Diseases	Maladies Respiratoires	Atmungskrankheiten	Enfermedades Respiratorios
Rheumatology	Rhumatologie	Rheumatologie	Reumatología
Sports Medicine	Médecine du Sport	Sportmedizin	Medicina de Deportes
Surgery	Chirurgie	Chirurgie	Cirugía
Urology and Nephrology	Urologie et Néphrologie	Urologie und Nephrologie	Urología y Nefrología
Men's Health	Santé de l'Homme	Gesundheit von Mannern	Salud Masculina
Men's Interests	Publications d'Interêt Masculin	Männer Interessen	Intereses Masculinos
Men's Studies	Etudes de l'Homme	Männerstudien	Estudios de los Hombres
Meetings and Congresses	Réunions et Congrès	Tagungen und Kongresse	Conferencias y Congresos
Metallurgy	Métallurgie	Metallurgie	Metalurgia
Computer Applications	Applications des Ordinateurs	Computer Anwendung	Aplicaciones de los Ordenadores
Welding	Soudure	Schweissen	Soldadura
Meteorology	Météorologie	Meteorologie	Meteorología
Computer Applications	Applications des Ordinateurs	Computer Anwendung	Aplicaciones de los Ordenadores
Metrology and Standardization	Métrologie et Standardisation	Mass- und Gewichtskunde, Normung	Metrología y Normalización
Computer Applications	Applications des Ordinateurs	Computer Anwendung	Aplicaciones de los Ordenadores
Military	Militaires	Militärwesen	Militares
Mines and Mining Industry	Mines et Resources Minières	Bergwesen und Bergbauindustrie	Mines y Minerales
Computer Applications	Applications des Ordinateurs	Computer Anwendung	Aplicaciones de los Ordenadores
Motion Pictures	Cinéma	Film und Kino	Películas
Museums and Art Galleries	Musées et Galleries	Museen und Kunstgalerien	Museos y Galerías del Arte
Music	Musique	Musik	Música
Computer Applications	Applications des Ordinateurs	Computer Anwendung	Aplicaciones de los Ordenadores
Needlework	Travaux à l'Aiguille	Nedelarbeiten	Bordados
New Age	Nouvelle Ere	New Age	Nueva Epoca
Numismatics	Numismatique	Numismatik	Numismática
Nutrition and Dietetics	Nutrition et Diététique	Ernährung und Diätetik	Nutrición y Dietética
Occupational Health and Safety	Medicine du Travail et Prevention	Berufsgesundheitspflege und -Sicherheit	Sanidad y Seguridad de Oficio
Occupations and Careers	Occupations et Carrières	Berufe	Empleos y Ocupaciones
Oriental Studies	Etudes Orientales	Orientalistik	Estudios Orientales
Packaging	Emballage	Verpackung	Empaque
Computer Applications	Applications des Ordinateurs	Computer Anwendung	Aplicaciones de los Ordenadores
Paints and Protective Coatings	Couleurs et Peintures	Farben	Pinturas y Revestimientos Protectores
Paleontology	Paléontologie	Paleontologie	Paleontología
Computer Applications	Applications des Ordinateurs	Computer Anwendung	Aplicaciones de los Ordenadores
Paper and Pulp	Papier et Pulpe	Papier und Papierstoff	Papel y Pasta
Parapsychology and Occultism	Parapsychologie et Occultisme	Parapsychologie und Okkultismus	Parapsicología y Ocultismo
Patents, Trademarks and Copyrights	Brevets, Marques de Fabrique et Droits d'Auteur	Patente, Schutzmarken und Urheberrechte	Patentes, Marcas de Fabrica y Derechos de Autor
Petroleum and Gas	Pétrole et Gas Naturel	Petroleum und Gas	Petróleo y Gas Natural
Computer Applications	Applications des Ordinateurs	Computer Anwendung	Aplicaciones de los Ordenadores
Pets	Animaux Familiers	Haustiere	Animales Domésticos
Pharmacy and Pharmacology	Pharmacie et Pharmacologie	Pharmazie und Pharmakologie	Farmacia y Farmacología
Computer Applications	Applications des Ordinateurs	Computer Anwendung	Aplicaciones de los Ordenadores
Philately	Philatelie	Philatélie	Filatelia
Philosophy	Philosophie	Philosophie	Filosofía
Photography	Photographie	Photographie	Fotografía
Computer Applications	Applications des Ordinateurs	Computer Anwendung	Aplicaciones de los Ordenadores
Physical Fitness and Hygiene	Santé Physique et Hygiène	Gesundheitszustand und Hygiene	Salud Física e Higiene
Physics	Physique	Physik	Física
Computer Applications	Applications des Ordinateurs	Computer Anwendung	Aplicaciones de los Ordenadores
Electricity	Electricité	Elektrizität	Electricidad
Heat	Chaleur	Wärme	Calor
Mechanics	Mécanique	Mechanik	Mecánica
Nuclear Physics	Physique Nucléaire	Kernphysik	Física Nuclear
Optics	Optique	Optik	Optica
Sound	Son	Schall	Sonido
Plastics	Plastiques	Kunststoffe	Plásticos
Computer Applications	Applications des Ordinateurs	Computer Anwendung	Aplicaciones de los Ordenadores
Political Science	Sciences Politiques	Politische Wissenschafte	Ciencias Políticas
Civil Rights	Droits Civiques	Bürgerrechte	Derechos Civiles
International Relations	Relations Internationales	Internationale Beziehungen	Relaciones Internacionales
Population Studies	Démographie	Bevölkerungswissenschaft	Demografía

SUBJECTS xlvii

Printing	Imprimerie	Druck	Imprenta
Computer Applications	Applications des Ordinateurs	Computer Anwendung	Aplicaciónes de los Ordenadores
Psychology	Psychologie	Psychologie	Psicología
Public Administration	Administration Publique	Öffentliche Verwaltung	Administración Pública
Computer Applications	Applications des Ordinateurs	Computer Anwendung	Aplicaciónes de los Ordenadores
Municipal Government	Gouvernement Municipal	Kommunalverwaltung	Gobierno Municipal
Public Health and Safety	Santé Publique et Prevention	Öffentliche Gesundheitspflege	Salud Pública y Seguridad
Publishing and Book Trade	Edition et Commerce du Livre	Verlagswesen und Buchhandel	Editoriales y Librería
Computer Applications	Applications des Ordinateurs	Computer Anwendung	Aplicaciónes de los Ordenadores
Real Estate	Immobilières	Grundbesitz und Immobilien	Bienes Raíces
Computer Applications	Applications des Ordinateurs	Computer Anwendung	Aplicaciónes de los Ordenadores
Religions and Theology	Religions et Théologie	Religion und Theologie	Religión y Teología
Buddhist	Bouddhisme	Buddhist	Budista
Eastern Orthodox	Eglises Orthodoxes	Griechischkatolische Kirche	Ortodoxo Oriental
Hindu	Hindou	Hindu	Hindú
Islamic	Islamique	Islamische	Islámico
Judaic	Judaique	Jüdäistische	Judaico
Protestant	Protestant	Evangelische	Protestante
Roman Catholic	Catholique romain	Römisch-katholische	Católico Romano
Other Sects	Autres sectes	Andere Sekte	Otras Sectas
Rubber	Caoutchouc	Gummi	Caucho
Computer Applications	Applications des Ordinateurs	Computer Anwendung	Aplicaciones de los Ordenadores
Sciences: Comprehensive Works	Sciences: Oeuvres Comprehensives	Wissenschaften: Umfassende Werke	Ciencias: Obras Comprensivas
Computer Applications	Applications des Ordinateurs	Computer Anwendung	Aplicaciónes de los Ordenadores
Shoes and Boots	Chaussures et Bottes	Schuhe und Stiefel	Zapatos y Botas
Singles' Interests and Lifestyles	Intérêts et Style de Vie Célibataire	Ledigenstandinteressen	Intereses y Estilos de Vivir de los Solteros
Social Sciences: Comprehensive Works	Sciences Sociales: Oeuvres Comprehensives	Sozialwissenschaften: Umfassende Werke	Ciencias Sociales: Obras Comprensivas
Social Service and Welfare	Service Social et Protection Sociale	Sozialpflege und Fürsorge	Asistencia Social y Bienestar
Sociology	Sociologie	Soziologie	Sociología
Computer Applications	Applications des Ordinateurs	Computer Anwendung	Aplicaciónes de los Ordenadores
Sound Recording and Reproduction	Enregistrement et Reproduction du Son	Tonaufnahme und Tonwiedergabe	Grabaciones y Reproducciones Sonoras
Computer Applications	Applications des Ordinateurs	Computer Anwendung	Aplicaciones de los Ordenadores
Sports and Games	Sports et Jeux	Sport und Spiele	Deportes y Juegos
Ball Games	Jeux de Balle	Ballspiele	Juegos de Pelota
Bicycles and Motorcycles	Bicyclettes et Motorcyclettes	Fahrräder und Motorräder	Bicicletas y Motocicletas
Boats and Boating	Bateaux et Canotage	Boote und Bootssport	Botes y Bartelaje
Horses and Horsemanship	Equitation	Pferde und Reitsport	Caballos y Equitación
Outdoor Life	Vie en Plein Air	Im Freien	Vida de Campo
Statistics	Statistique	Statistik	Estadísticas
Technology: Comprehensive Works	Technologie: Oeuvres Comprehensives	Technologie: Umfassende Werke	Tecnologia: Obras Comprensivas
Textile Industries and Fabrics	Textiles	Textil	Textiles y Telas
Computer Applications	Applications des Ordinateurs	Computer Anwendung	Aplicaciones de los Ordenadores
Theater	Théâtre	Theater	Teatro
Tobacco	Tabac	Tabak	Tabaco
Transportation	Transports	Transport	Transportación
Air Transport	Transport Aérien	Luftverkehr	Transporte Aéreo
Automobiles	Automobiles	Kraftfahrzeugen	Automóviles
Computer Applications	Applications des Ordinateurs	Computer Anwendung	Aplicaciónes de los Ordenadores
Railroads	Chemins de Fer	Eisenbahnen	Ferrocarriles
Roads and Traffic	Routes et Circulation	Strassen und Strassenverkehr	Caminos y Tráfico
Ships and Shipping	Navires et Transport Maritimes	Schiffe und Schiffahrt	Barcos y Embarques
Trucks and Trucking	Transports Routiers	Lastkraftwagen	Camiones
Travel and Tourism	Voyages et Tourisme	Reisen und Tourismus	Viaje y Turismo
Airline Inflight and Hotel Inroom	Revues en Vol des Lignes Aérienne et en Chambre des Hôtels	Fluggesellschaft und Hotel Veröffentlichungen	Aerolínea En-Vuelo y Hotel En-Cuarto
Veterinary Sciences	Science Vétérinaire	Tierheilkunde	Veterinaria
Computer Applications	Applications des Ordinateurs	Computer Anwendung	Aplicaciones de los Ordenadores
Water Resources	Ressources de l'Eau	Wasserwirtschaft	Recursos de Aqua
Computer Applications	Applications des Ordinateurs	Computer Anwendung	Aplicaciones de los Ordenadores
Women's Health	Santé de la Femme	Gesundheit von Frauen	Salud Feminina
Women's Interests	Publications d'Intérêt Feminin	Veröffentlichungen für Frauen	Intereses Femininas
Women's Studies	Etudes de la Femme	Frauenstudien	Estudios de las Mujeres

Cross-Index to Subjects

A I D S see MEDICAL SCIENCES - Communicable Diseases 3216
Abortions see BIRTH CONTROL 595, see also MEDICAL SCIENCES - Obstetrics And Gynecology 3288
Abrasives see MACHINERY 3015, see also METALLURGY 3401
ABSTRACTING AND INDEXING SERVICES 1
Accident Prevention see OCCUPATIONAL HEALTH AND SAFETY 3614, see also TRANSPORTATION - Roads and Traffic 4717
ACCOUNTING 25
Acoustics see PHYSICS - Sound 3858, see also SOUND RECORDING AND REPRODUCTION 4459
Acquired Immunodeficiency Syndrome see MEDICAL SCIENCES - Communicable Diseases 3216
Activation Analysis see PHYSICS - Nuclear Physics 3846
Actuarial Science see INSURANCE 2525, see also MATHEMATICS 3025
Acupuncture see MEDICAL SCIENCES 3068
Addictions see DRUG ABUSE AND ALCOHOLISM 1532
Adhesives see ENGINEERING - Chemical Engineering 1847
ADULT EDUCATION 25
ADVENTURE AND ROMANCE 25
ADVERTISING AND PUBLIC RELATIONS 25
ADVERTISING AND PUBLIC RELATIONS — Abstracting, Bibliographies, Statistics 40
Advertising Art see ADVERTISING AND PUBLIC RELATIONS 25
Aerobics see PHYSICAL FITNESS AND HYGIENE 3798, see also SPORTS AND GAMES 4463
Aerodynamics see PHYSICS - Mechanics 3842
AERONAUTICS AND SPACE FLIGHT 42, see also ENGINEERING - Mechanical Engineering 1926, TRANSPORTATION - Air Transport 4669
AERONAUTICS AND SPACE FLIGHT — Abstracting, Bibliographies, Statistics 66
AERONAUTICS AND SPACE FLIGHT — Computer Applications 66
Aerophysics see PHYSICS - Mechanics 3842
Aerospace Medicine see MEDICAL SCIENCES 3068
Aesthetics see ART 309, see also PHILOSOPHY 3759
African History see HISTORY - History of Africa 2330
African Studies see HISTORY - History of Africa 2330
Agricultural Aviation see AERONAUTICS AND SPACE FLIGHT 42
Agricultural Chemistry see AGRICULTURE 67, see also CHEMISTRY 1168
AGRICULTURAL ECONOMICS 67
Agricultural Engineering see AGRICULTURE 67, see also ENGINEERING 1813
AGRICULTURAL EQUIPMENT 67
Agricultural Marketing see AGRICULTURE - Agricultural Economics 145, see also FOOD AND FOOD INDUSTRIES - Grocery Trade 2090
AGRICULTURE 67, see also FOOD AND FOOD INDUSTRIES 2060, FORESTS AND FORESTRY 2094, GARDENING AND HORTICULTURE 2120
AGRICULTURE — Abstracting, Bibliographies, Statistics 131
AGRICULTURE — Agricultural Economics 145
AGRICULTURE — Agricultural Equipment 161
AGRICULTURE — Computer Applications 165
AGRICULTURE — Crop Production And Soil 165
AGRICULTURE — Dairying And Dairy Products 197
AGRICULTURE — Feed, Flour And Grain 204
AGRICULTURE — Poultry And Livestock 209
Agronomy see AGRICULTURE 67
Air Conditioning see HEATING, PLUMBING AND REFRIGERATION 2297
Air Defense see MILITARY 3449
Air Force see MILITARY 3449
Air Law see AERONAUTICS AND SPACE FLIGHT 42, see also LAW 2592, TRANSPORTATION - Air Transport 4669
Air Navigation see AERONAUTICS AND SPACE FLIGHT 42
Air Pollution see ENVIRONMENTAL STUDIES - Pollution 1975

AIR TRANSPORT 229
AIRLINE INFLIGHT AND HOTEL INROOM 229
Airplanes see AERONAUTICS AND SPACE FLIGHT 42, see also TRANSPORTATION - Air Transport 4669
Airports see AERONAUTICS AND SPACE FLIGHT 42, see also TRANSPORTATION - Air Transport 4669
Alcoholic Beverages see BEVERAGES 377
Alcoholism see DRUG ABUSE AND ALCOHOLISM 1532
Algae see BIOLOGY - Botany 491
ALLERGOLOGY AND IMMUNOLOGY 229
Almanacs, General see ENCYCLOPEDIAS AND GENERAL ALMANACS 388
Alumni see COLLEGE AND ALUMNI 1302
Amateur Radio see COMMUNICATIONS - Radio 1354
Amusement Guides see COMMUNICATIONS - Television And Cable 1368, see also MUSIC 3536, THEATER 4629, TRAVEL AND TOURISM 4750
ANAESTHESIOLOGY 229
Analogue Computation see COMPUTERS - Hardware 1453, see also COMPUTERS - Theory of Computing 1481
ANALYTICAL CHEMISTRY 229
Anatomy see BIOLOGY 424, see also MEDICAL SCIENCES 3068
Ancient History see ARCHAEOLOGY 260, see also HISTORY 2305
Angiology see MEDICAL SCIENCES - Cardiovascular Diseases 3203
ANIMAL WELFARE 229
Animals see AGRICULTURE - Poultry and Livestock 209, see also ANIMAL WELFARE 229, BIOLOGY - Zoology 575, LEATHER AND FUR INDUSTRIES 2735, PETS 3707, SPORTS AND GAMES - Horses and Horsemanship 4531, VETERINARY SCIENCE 4804
ANTHROPOLOGY 232, see also ARCHAEOLOGY 260
ANTHROPOLOGY — Abstracting, Bibliographies, Statistics 253
Anti-Vivisection see ANIMAL WELFARE 229
Antibiotics see PHARMACY AND PHARMACOLOGY 3714
ANTIQUES 254
Antiquities see CLASSICAL STUDIES 1274
Apparel see CLOTHING TRADE 1282
Appliances see HEATING, PLUMBING AND REFRIGERATION 2297, see also INTERIOR DESIGN AND DECORATION - Furniture and House Furnishings 2556, PHYSICS - Electricity 3840
Applied Mechanics see ENGINEERING - Engineering Mechanics and Materials 1911
Apprenticeship see OCCUPATIONS AND CAREERS 3624
Aquariums see BIOLOGY - Zoology 575, see also FISH AND FISHERIES 2035, PETS 3707
ARCHAEOLOGY 260, see also ANTHROPOLOGY 232, ART 309, HISTORY 2305
ARCHAEOLOGY — Abstracting, Bibliographies, Statistics 290
ARCHAEOLOGY — Computer Applications 290
Archery see SPORTS AND GAMES 4463
ARCHITECTURE 291, see also BUILDING AND CONSTRUCTION 598, ENGINEERING - Civil Engineering 1861, HOUSING AND URBAN PLANNING 2482
ARCHITECTURE — Abstracting, Bibliographies, Statistics 309
ARCHITECTURE — Computer Applications 309
Archives see HISTORY 2305, see also LIBRARY AND INFORMATION SCIENCES 2739
Area Planning see HOUSING AND URBAN PLANNING 2482
Armed Forces see MILITARY 3449
ART 309
ART — Abstracting, Bibliographies, Statistics 351
ART — Computer Applications 352
Art Exhibitions see MUSEUMS AND ART GALLERIES 3520
Art History see ART 309
Arteriosclerosis see MEDICAL SCIENCES - Cardiovascular Diseases 3203
Arthritis see MEDICAL SCIENCES - Rheumatology 3368

ARTIFICIAL INTELLIGENCE 352
Arts see ART 309, see also DANCE 1528, LITERATURE 2890, MOTION PICTURES 3502, MUSIC 3536, THEATER 4629
ARTS AND HANDICRAFTS 352
ARTS AND HANDICRAFTS — Abstracting, Bibliographies, Statistics 357
Asbestos see BUILDING AND CONSTRUCTION 598
Asian History see HISTORY - History of Asia 2336
Asphalt see BUILDING AND CONSTRUCTION 598, see also ENGINEERING - Civil Engineering 1861, TRANSPORTATION - Roads and Traffic 4717
Asthma see MEDICAL SCIENCES - Respiratory Diseases 3364
ASTROLOGY 357
Astronautics see AERONAUTICS AND SPACE FLIGHT 42
ASTRONOMY 359
ASTRONOMY — Abstracting, Bibliographies, Statistics 371
Astrophysics see ASTRONOMY 359
Athletics see MEDICAL SCIENCES - Sports Medicine 3370, see also SPORTS AND GAMES 4463
Atmospheric Sciences see METEOROLOGY 3431
Atomic Energy see ENERGY - Nuclear Energy 1803
Audio Equipment see ELECTRONICS 1764, see also SOUND RECORDING AND REPRODUCTION 4459
Audio-Visual Education see EDUCATION - Teaching Methods and Curriculum 1742, see also MOTION PICTURES 3502
Audiology see MEDICAL SCIENCES - Otorhinolaryngology 3312
Auditing see BUSINESS AND ECONOMICS - Accounting 744
AUTOMATION 371
Automobile Racing see SPORTS AND GAMES 4463
AUTOMOBILES 371
Aviation see AERONAUTICS AND SPACE FLIGHT 42, see also TRANSPORTATION - Air Transport 4669
Aviculture see BIOLOGY - Ornithology 561
Bacteriology see BIOLOGY - Microbiology 548, see also MEDICAL SCIENCES - Communicable Diseases 3216
Badminton see SPORTS AND GAMES 4463
BAKERS AND CONFECTIONERS 371
BALL GAMES 371
Ballet see DANCE 1528
BANKING AND FINANCE 371
BANKING AND FINANCE - Computer Applications see also COMPUTERS - Electronic Data Processing 1448
Banking Law see BUSINESS AND ECONOMICS - Banking and Finance 757, see also LAW 2592
Barbering see BEAUTY CULTURE 371
Baseball see SPORTS AND GAMES - Ball Games 4499
Batteries see PHYSICS - Electricity 3840, see also TRANSPORTATION - Automobiles 4678
BEAUTY CULTURE 371
BEAUTY CULTURE — Abstracting, Bibliographies, Statistics 375
BEAUTY CULTURE — Perfumes And Cosmetics 375
Beekeeping see AGRICULTURE 67
Beer see BEVERAGES 377
Behavioral Sciences see PSYCHOLOGY 4007, see also SOCIOLOGY 4427
BEVERAGES 377, see also FOOD AND FOOD INDUSTRIES 2060
BEVERAGES — Abstracting, Bibliographies, Statistics 388
Biblical Studies see RELIGIONS AND THEOLOGY 4161
BIBLIOGRAPHIES 388, see also ABSTRACTING AND INDEXING SERVICES 1, LIBRARY AND INFORMATION SCIENCES 2739, PUBLISHING AND BOOK TRADE 4119
BICYCLES AND MOTORCYCLES 417
Billiards see SPORTS AND GAMES - Ball Games 4499
Biochemistry see BIOLOGY - Biological Chemistry 470
Biocybernetics see MEDICAL SCIENCES 3068
Bioenergetics see BIOLOGY 424, see also PHYSICAL FITNESS AND HYGIENE 3798
BIOENGINEERING 417
Biofeedback see MEDICAL SCIENCES 3068, see also PHYSICAL FITNESS AND HYGIENE 3798
BIOGRAPHY 417
BIOGRAPHY — Abstracting, Bibliographies, Statistics 424
BIOLOGICAL CHEMISTRY 424
BIOLOGY 424, see also MEDICAL SCIENCES 3068
BIOLOGY — Abstracting, Bibliographies, Statistics 461
BIOLOGY — Bioengineering 468
BIOLOGY — Biological Chemistry 470
BIOLOGY — Biophysics 484
BIOLOGY — Biotechnology 487
BIOLOGY — Botany 491
BIOLOGY — Cytology And Histology 522
BIOLOGY — Entomology 527
BIOLOGY — Genetics 539
BIOLOGY — Microbiology 548
BIOLOGY — Microscopy 559
BIOLOGY — Ornithology 561
BIOLOGY — Physiology 568
BIOLOGY — Zoology 575
Biometeorology see METEOROLOGY 3431
Biometry see BIOLOGY 424, see also STATISTICS 4560
Bionics see COMPUTERS - Cybernetics 1440
BIOPHYSICS 595
BIOTECHNOLOGY 595
Birds see BIOLOGY - Ornithology 561, see also CONSERVATION 1482, PETS 3707
BIRTH CONTROL 595
BIRTH CONTROL — Abstracting, Bibliographies, Statistics 598
Black Studies see ETHNIC INTERESTS 1988
Blind see EDUCATION - Special Education and Rehabilitation 1732, see also HANDICAPPED - Visually Impaired 2290, MEDICAL SCIENCES - Ophthalmology And Optometry 3297, SOCIAL SERVICES AND WELFARE 4396
Blood Transfusion see MEDICAL SCIENCES - Cardiovascular Diseases 3203, see also MEDICAL SCIENCES - Hematology 3270

BOATS AND BOATING 598
Bobsleighing see SPORTS AND GAMES - Outdoor Life 4539
Bodybuilding see PHYSICAL FITNESS AND HYGIENE 3798, see also SPORTS AND GAMES 4463
Bond Market see BUSINESS AND ECONOMICS - Investments 937
Book Collecting see PUBLISHING AND BOOK TRADE 4119
Book Illustrating see PUBLISHING AND BOOK TRADE 4119
Book Reviews see LITERATURE 2890, see also PUBLISHING AND BOOK TRADE 4119
Book Trade see BIBLIOGRAPHIES 388, see also PRINTING 3997, PUBLISHING AND BOOK TRADE 4119
Bookbinding see PUBLISHING AND BOOK TRADE 4119
Bookkeeping see BUSINESS AND ECONOMICS - Accounting 744
Booksellers see PUBLISHING AND BOOK TRADE 4119
Boots see SHOES AND BOOTS 4360
BOTANY 598
Bottling see BEVERAGES 377, see also PACKAGING 3647
Bowling see SPORTS AND GAMES - Ball Games 4499
Boxes see PACKAGING 3647
Boxing see SPORTS AND GAMES 4463
Braille see HANDICAPPED - Visually Impaired 2290
Brass Instruments see MUSIC 3536
Brewing see BEVERAGES 377
Bricks see BUILDING AND CONSTRUCTION 598, see also CERAMICS, GLASS AND POTTERY 1160
Brides And Bridal Apparel see CLOTHING TRADE - Fashions 1289, see also MATRIMONY 3066
Bridge see SPORTS AND GAMES 4463
Bridge Construction see ENGINEERING - Civil Engineering 1861
Broadcasting see COMMUNICATIONS - Radio 1354, see also COMMUNICATIONS - Television And Cable 1368
Bryology see BIOLOGY - Botany 491
BUDDHISM 598
BUILDING AND CONSTRUCTION 598, see also ARCHITECTURE 291, ENGINEERING - Civil Engineering 1861, HOUSING AND URBAN PLANNING 2482
BUILDING AND CONSTRUCTION — Abstracting, Bibliographies, Statistics 636
BUILDING AND CONSTRUCTION — Carpentry And Woodwork 639
BUILDING AND CONSTRUCTION — Hardware 641
Bullfighting see SPORTS AND GAMES 4463
Burns see MEDICAL SCIENCES - Orthopedics and Traumatology 3306
Buses see TRANSPORTATION - Automobiles 4678
Business Administration see BUSINESS AND ECONOMICS - Management 1000
BUSINESS AND ECONOMICS 643
BUSINESS AND ECONOMICS — Abstracting, Bibliographies, Statistics 701
BUSINESS AND ECONOMICS — Accounting 744
BUSINESS AND ECONOMICS — Banking And Finance 757
BUSINESS AND ECONOMICS — Banking and Finance - Computer Applications 804
BUSINESS AND ECONOMICS — Chamber Of Commerce Publications 806
BUSINESS AND ECONOMICS — Computer Applications 825
BUSINESS AND ECONOMICS — Cooperatives 828
BUSINESS AND ECONOMICS — Domestic Commerce 833
BUSINESS AND ECONOMICS — Economic Situation And Conditions 841
BUSINESS AND ECONOMICS — Economic Systems And Theories, Economic History 888
BUSINESS AND ECONOMICS — International Commerce 899
BUSINESS AND ECONOMICS — International Development And Assistance 925
BUSINESS AND ECONOMICS — Investments 937
BUSINESS AND ECONOMICS — Labor And Industrial Relations 970
BUSINESS AND ECONOMICS — Macroeconomics 998
BUSINESS AND ECONOMICS — Management 1000
BUSINESS AND ECONOMICS — Marketing And Purchasing 1032
BUSINESS AND ECONOMICS — Office Equipment And Services 1057
BUSINESS AND ECONOMICS — Personnel Management 1062
BUSINESS AND ECONOMICS — Production Of Goods And Services 1071
BUSINESS AND ECONOMICS — Public Finance, Taxation 1087
BUSINESS AND ECONOMICS — Small Business 1112
BUSINESS AND ECONOMICS — Trade And Industrial Directories 1119
Business Law see LAW - Corporate Law 2706
Butane see PETROLEUM AND GAS 3680
Cable Television see COMMUNICATIONS - Television And Cable 1368
Cables see COMMUNICATIONS - Telephone and Telegraph 1361, see also ENGINEERING - Electrical Engineering 1880
Cafeterias see HOTELS AND RESTAURANTS 2471
Calendars of Events see MEETINGS AND CONGRESSES 3390, see also TRAVEL AND TOURISM 4750
Calligraphy see ART 309
Camping see LEISURE AND RECREATION 2738, see also SPORTS AND GAMES - Outdoor Life 4539, TRAVEL AND TOURISM 4750
Canals see TRANSPORTATION - Ships and Shipping 4723
CANCER 1160
Candy see FOOD AND FOOD INDUSTRIES - Bakers and Confectioners 2086
Canning and Preserving see FOOD AND FOOD INDUSTRIES 2060, see also HOME ECONOMICS 2444
Canoeing see SPORTS AND GAMES - Boats and Boating 4521
Canon Law see RELIGIONS AND THEOLOGY 4161
Canvas see TEXTILE INDUSTRIES AND FABRICS 4615
Carboniferous Geology see EARTH SCIENCES - Geophysics 1586
Cardiology see MEDICAL SCIENCES - Cardiovascular Diseases 3203
CARDIOVASCULAR DISEASES 1160
Cardiovascular Surgery see MEDICAL SCIENCES - Surgery 3373
Careers see OCCUPATIONS AND CAREERS 3624
Cargo Handling see TRANSPORTATION - Ships and Shipping 4723
Caribbean History see HISTORY - History of North and South America 2397
CARPENTRY AND WOODWORK 1160
Carpets and Rugs see INTERIOR DESIGN AND DECORATION - Furniture and House Furnishings 2556
Cartography see GEOGRAPHY 2240
Cartoons see ART 309

Catering see HOTELS AND RESTAURANTS 2471
Cattle see AGRICULTURE - Poultry and Livestock 209
Caves see EARTH SCIENCES - Geology 1552
Cement see BUILDING AND CONSTRUCTION 598
Cemeteries see FUNERALS 2119
CERAMICS, GLASS AND POTTERY 1160, see also ART 309, ARTS AND HANDICRAFTS 352
CERAMICS, GLASS AND POTTERY — Abstracting, Bibliographies, Statistics 1167
Cereals see AGRICULTURE - Feed, Flour and Grain 204, see also FOOD AND FOOD INDUSTRIES 2060
Cerebral Palsy see MEDICAL SCIENCES - Psychiatry and Neurology 3327
CHAMBER OF COMMERCE PUBLICATIONS 1168
Chaplains see MILITARY 3449, see also RELIGIONS AND THEOLOGY 4161
Charities see SOCIAL SERVICES AND WELFARE 4396
CHEMICAL ENGINEERING 1168
Chemical Wastes see ENVIRONMENTAL STUDIES - Pollution 1975, see also ENVIRONMENTAL STUDIES - Waste Management 1984
CHEMISTRY 1168
CHEMISTRY — Abstracting, Bibliographies, Statistics 1191
CHEMISTRY — Analytical Chemistry 1203
CHEMISTRY — Crystallography 1210
CHEMISTRY — Electrochemistry 1211
CHEMISTRY — Inorganic Chemistry 1213
CHEMISTRY — Organic Chemistry 1215
CHEMISTRY — Physical Chemistry 1224
Chemotherapy see BIOLOGY - Biological Chemistry 470, see also MEDICAL SCIENCES 3068, PHARMACY AND PHARMACOLOGY 3714
Chess see SPORTS AND GAMES 4463
Chest Diseases see MEDICAL SCIENCES - Respiratory Diseases 3364
Child Psychology see PSYCHOLOGY 4007
Child Welfare see CHILDREN AND YOUTH - About 1231, see also SOCIAL SERVICES AND WELFARE 4396
CHILDREN AND YOUTH — About 1231
CHILDREN AND YOUTH — Abstracting, Bibliographies, Statistics 1247
CHILDREN AND YOUTH — For 1248
Chromatography see CHEMISTRY - Analytical Chemistry 1203
Church History see RELIGIONS AND THEOLOGY 4161
Cigarettes and Cigars see TOBACCO 4643
Cinematography see MOTION PICTURES 3502, see also PHOTOGRAPHY 3788
CIRCUITS 1273
Circulatory System see MEDICAL SCIENCES - Cardiovascular Diseases 3203
Circus see THEATER 4629
Cities and Towns see HOUSING AND URBAN PLANNING 2482, see also PUBLIC ADMINISTRATION - Municipal Government 4083
Citizenship see POLITICAL SCIENCE 3869
Citrus Fruits see AGRICULTURE - Crop Production and Soil 165, see also FOOD AND FOOD INDUSTRIES 2060, GARDENING AND HORTICULTURE 2120
City Planning see HOUSING AND URBAN PLANNING 2482
Civil Aeronautics see TRANSPORTATION - Air Transport 4669
CIVIL DEFENSE 1273, see also MILITARY 3449
CIVIL DEFENSE — Abstracting, Bibliographies, Statistics 1274
CIVIL ENGINEERING 1274
CIVIL LAW 1274
Civil Liberties see LAW - Constitutional Law 2705, see also POLITICAL SCIENCE - Civil Rights 3939
CIVIL RIGHTS 1274
Civil Service see OCCUPATIONS AND CAREERS 3624, see also PUBLIC ADMINISTRATION 4052
Clairvoyance see NEW AGE PUBLICATIONS 3593, see also PARAPSYCHOLOGY AND OCCULTISM 3668
CLASSICAL STUDIES 1274, see also ARCHAEOLOGY 260, HISTORY 2305, LINGUISTICS 2799, LITERATURE 2890
CLASSICAL STUDIES — Abstracting, Bibliographies, Statistics 1281
CLEANING AND DYEING 1281
CLEANING AND DYEING — Abstracting, Bibliographies, Statistics 1282
Climatology see METEOROLOGY 3431
Clinical Medicine see MEDICAL SCIENCES 3068
CLOTHING TRADE 1282
CLOTHING TRADE — Abstracting, Bibliographies, Statistics 1288
CLOTHING TRADE — Fashions 1289
CLUBS 1295
CLUBS — Abstracting, Bibliographies, Statistics 1302
Coaching see SPORTS AND GAMES 4463
Coastal Engineering see ENGINEERING - Hydraulic Engineering 1923
Coffee see BEVERAGES 377
Cognitive Studies see PSYCHOLOGY 4007
Coins see NUMISMATICS 3597
Collectibles see ANTIQUES 254
Collectors and Collecting see ANTIQUES 254, see also HOBBIES 2432
COLLEGE AND ALUMNI 1302, see also CLUBS 1295, EDUCATION - Higher Education 1698
College Management see EDUCATION - Higher Education 1698, see also EDUCATION - School Organization and Administration 1724
Colloids see CHEMISTRY - Physical Chemistry 1224, see also PHYSICS 3812
Combustion see CHEMISTRY - Physical Chemistry 1224, see also PHYSICS - Heat 3840
Commerce see BUSINESS AND ECONOMICS - Domestic Commerce 833, see also BUSINESS AND ECONOMICS - International Commerce 899
Commercial Art see ADVERTISING AND PUBLIC RELATIONS 25, see also ART 309
Commercial Education see EDUCATION - Teaching Methods and Curriculum 1742
Commercial Law see BUSINESS AND ECONOMICS 643, see also LAW 2592
COMMUNICABLE DISEASES 1331
COMMUNICATIONS 1331, see also JOURNALISM 2566
COMMUNICATIONS — Abstracting, Bibliographies, Statistics 1346
COMMUNICATIONS — Computer Applications 1349
COMMUNICATIONS — Postal Affairs 1352
COMMUNICATIONS — Radio 1354
COMMUNICATIONS — Telephone And Telegraph 1361
COMMUNICATIONS — Television And Cable 1368
COMMUNICATIONS — Video 1384
Communism see BUSINESS AND ECONOMICS - Economic Systems and Theories, Economic History 888, see also POLITICAL SCIENCE 3869
Community Affairs see PUBLIC ADMINISTRATION - Municipal Government 4083
Comparative Psychology see PSYCHOLOGY 4007
Compressed Air see ENGINEERING - Mechanical Engineering 1926
COMPUTERS 1388, see also COMPUTERS - Information Science and Information Theory 1455
COMPUTERS — Abstracting, Bibliographies, Statistics 1402
COMPUTERS — Artificial Intelligence 1406, see also COMPUTERS - Cybernetics 1440
COMPUTERS — Automation 1411
COMPUTERS — Circuits 1416, see also COMPUTERS - Computer Engineering 1417
COMPUTERS — Computer Architecture 1416, see also COMPUTERS - Computer Engineering 1417
COMPUTERS — Computer Assisted Instruction 1416, see also EDUCATION - Computer Applications 1688
COMPUTERS — Computer Engineering 1417, see also COMPUTERS - Computer Architecture 1416
COMPUTERS — Computer Games 1418
COMPUTERS — Computer Graphics 1420, see also PRINTING - Computer Applications 4007
COMPUTERS — Computer Industry 1423
COMPUTERS — Computer Industry Directories 1424
COMPUTERS — Computer Industry, Vocational Guidance 1425, see also EDUCATION 1612, OCCUPATIONS AND CAREERS 3624
COMPUTERS — Computer Music 1426, see also MUSIC - Computer Applications 3589
COMPUTERS — Computer Networks 1426
COMPUTERS — Computer Programming 1429, see also COMPUTERS - Software 1475
COMPUTERS — Computer Sales 1432, see also BUSINESS AND ECONOMICS - Marketing and Purchasing 1032
COMPUTERS — Computer Security 1433
COMPUTERS — Computer Simulation 1435
COMPUTERS — Computer Systems 1436, see also COMPUTERS - Computer Architecture 1416
COMPUTERS — Cybernetics 1440, see also COMPUTERS - Artificial Intelligence 1406
COMPUTERS — Data Base Management 1443
COMPUTERS — Data Communications And Data Transmission Systems 1445
COMPUTERS — Electronic Data Processing 1448, see also BUSINESS AND ECONOMICS - Banking and Finance - Computer Applications 804
COMPUTERS — Hardware 1453
COMPUTERS — Information Science And Information Theory 1455, see also COMPUTERS 1388
COMPUTERS — Machine Theory 1457
COMPUTERS — Microcomputers 1457, see also COMPUTERS - Personal Computers 1466
COMPUTERS — Minicomputers 1466
COMPUTERS — Personal Computers 1466, see also COMPUTERS - Microcomputers 1457
COMPUTERS — Software 1475, see also COMPUTERS - Computer Programming 1429
COMPUTERS — Theory Of Computing 1481
COMPUTERS — Word Processing 1482
Conchology see BIOLOGY - Zoology 575
Confectioners see FOOD AND FOOD INDUSTRIES - Bakers and Confectioners 2086
Congenital Abnormalities see BIOLOGY - Genetics 539, see also MEDICAL SCIENCES 3068
Congresses see MEETINGS AND CONGRESSES 3390
CONSERVATION 1482, see also ENVIRONMENTAL STUDIES 1941, FISH AND FISHERIES 2035, FORESTS AND FORESTRY 2094, WATER RESOURCES 4821
CONSERVATION — Abstracting, Bibliographies, Statistics 1501
CONSTITUTIONAL LAW 1502
Construction see BUILDING AND CONSTRUCTION 598, see also ENGINEERING - Civil Engineering 1861
Consumer Credit see BUSINESS AND ECONOMICS - Banking and Finance 757
CONSUMER EDUCATION AND PROTECTION 1502
CONSUMER EDUCATION AND PROTECTION — Abstracting, Bibliographies, Statistics 1509
Consumer Electronics see ELECTRONICS 1764
Contact Lenses see MEDICAL SCIENCES - Ophthalmology and Optometry 3297
Containers see PACKAGING 3647
Contraception see BIRTH CONTROL 595
Contractors see BUILDING AND CONSTRUCTION 598
Convention Dates see MEETINGS AND CONGRESSES 3390
Cookery see HOME ECONOMICS 2444, see also HOTELS AND RESTAURANTS 2471
COOPERATIVES 1509
Copying and Duplicating see PHOTOGRAPHY 3788, see also PRINTING 3997
Copyrights see PATENTS, TRADEMARKS AND COPYRIGHTS 3672
CORPORATE LAW 1509
Correspondence Education see EDUCATION - Adult Education 1681
Corrosion see METALLURGY 3401, see also PAINTS AND PROTECTIVE COATINGS 3652
Cosmetics see BEAUTY CULTURE - Perfumes and Cosmetics 375
Counseling see EDUCATION 1612, see also PSYCHOLOGY 4007, SOCIAL SERVICES AND WELFARE 4396
Crafts see ARTS AND HANDICRAFTS 352
Credit and Collections see BUSINESS AND ECONOMICS - Banking and Finance 757
Credit Unions see BUSINESS AND ECONOMICS - Banking and Finance 757
Cricket see SPORTS AND GAMES 4463
CRIMINAL LAW 1509
CRIMINOLOGY AND LAW ENFORCEMENT 1509
CRIMINOLOGY AND LAW ENFORCEMENT — Abstracting, Bibliographies, Statistics 1524

CRIMINOLOGY AND LAW ENFORCEMENT — Security 1525
CROP PRODUCTION AND SOIL 1528
Croquet see SPORTS AND GAMES - Ball Games 4499
Cryogenic Engineering see ENGINEERING - Mechanical Engineering 1926
Cryogenics see PHYSICS - Heat 3840
CRYSTALLOGRAPHY 1528
Currency see BUSINESS AND ECONOMICS - Banking and Finance 757
Curriculum and Teaching Methods see EDUCATION - Teaching Methods and Curriculum 1742
Customs and Excise see BUSINESS AND ECONOMICS - Public Finance, Taxation 1087
Cybernetic Medicine see MEDICAL SCIENCES 3068
CYBERNETICS 1528
Cystic Fibrosis see MEDICAL SCIENCES 3068
CYTOLOGY AND HISTOLOGY 1528
DAIRYING AND DAIRY PRODUCTS 1528
DANCE 1528, see also MUSIC 3536, THEATER 4629
DANCE — Abstracting, Bibliographies, Statistics 1532
DATA BASE MANAGEMENT 1532
DATA COMMUNICATIONS AND DATA TRANSMISSION SYSTEMS 1532
Data Processing see COMPUTERS - Electronic Data Processing 1448
Deaf see EDUCATION - Special Education and Rehabilitation 1732, see also HANDICAPPED - Hearing Impaired 2285, MEDICAL SCIENCES - Otorhinolaryngology 3312, SOCIAL SERVICES AND WELFARE 4396
Decoration see INTERIOR DESIGN AND DECORATION 2547
Defense see CIVIL DEFENSE 1273, see also MILITARY 3449
Delinquency see CHILDREN AND YOUTH - About 1231, see also CRIMINOLOGY AND LAW ENFORCEMENT 1509, SOCIAL SERVICES AND WELFARE 4396
Demography see POPULATION STUDIES 3979
DENTISTRY 1532
Department Stores see BUSINESS AND ECONOMICS - Marketing and Purchasing 1032
DERMATOLOGY AND VENEREOLOGY 1532
Desalination see ENVIRONMENTAL STUDIES 1941, see also WATER RESOURCES 4821
Design see ART 309
Detective Magazines see LITERATURE - Mystery And Detective 2985
Detectives see CRIMINOLOGY AND LAW ENFORCEMENT 1509
Diabetes see MEDICAL SCIENCES - Endocrinology 3250
Dialysis see MEDICAL SCIENCES - Urology and Nephrology 3386
Diecasting see ENGINEERING 1813
Diesel Engines see ENGINEERING - Mechanical Engineering 1926
Dietetics see NUTRITION AND DIETETICS 3602
Digestive System see MEDICAL SCIENCES - Gastroenterology 3266
Digital Computers see COMPUTERS - Hardware 1453
Diplomatic Service see POLITICAL SCIENCE - International Relations 3948
Disability, Disabled see HANDICAPPED 2283, see also INSURANCE 2525, OCCUPATIONAL HEALTH AND SAFETY 3614, SOCIAL SERVICES AND WELFARE 4396
Disarmament see MILITARY 3449, see also POLITICAL SCIENCE 3869
Disk Drives see COMPUTERS - Hardware 1453
Distilling see BEVERAGES 377
Divorce see MATRIMONY 3066
Documentation see COMPUTERS - Computer Programming 1429, see also COMPUTERS - Software 1475
Domestic Animals and Birds see ANIMAL WELFARE 229, see also PETS 3707, VETERINARY SCIENCE 4804
DOMESTIC COMMERCE 1532
Drafting see ENGINEERING 1813, see also TECHNOLOGY: COMPREHENSIVE WORKS 4592
Drama see LITERATURE 2890, see also THEATER 4629
Drawing and Sketching see ART 309
DRUG ABUSE AND ALCOHOLISM 1532
DRUG ABUSE AND ALCOHOLISM — Abstracting, Bibliographies, Statistics 1540
Drugs see PHARMACY AND PHARMACOLOGY 3714
Dry Goods see CLOTHING TRADE 1282, see also TEXTILE INDUSTRIES AND FABRICS 4615
Dyes and Dyeing see CLEANING AND DYEING 1281, see also TEXTILE INDUSTRIES AND FABRICS 4615
E C G see MEDICAL SCIENCES - Cardiovascular Diseases 3203
E E G see MEDICAL SCIENCES - Psychiatry and Neurology 3327
EARTH SCIENCES 1540
EARTH SCIENCES — Abstracting, Bibliographies, Statistics 1549
EARTH SCIENCES — Geology 1552
EARTH SCIENCES — Geophysics 1586
EARTH SCIENCES — Hydrology 1596
EARTH SCIENCES — Oceanography 1601
EASTERN ORTHODOX 1612
Ecclesiastical Art see ART 309, see also RELIGIONS AND THEOLOGY 4161
Ecclesiastical Law see RELIGIONS AND THEOLOGY 4161
Ecology see BIOLOGY 424, see also CONSERVATION 1482, ENVIRONMENTAL STUDIES 1941
Economic Geology see EARTH SCIENCES - Geology 1552
ECONOMIC SITUATION AND CONDITIONS 1612
ECONOMIC SYSTEMS AND THEORIES, ECONOMIC HISTORY 1612
ECONOMICS 1612
Editing see JOURNALISM 2566, see also PUBLISHING AND BOOK TRADE 4119
EDUCATION 1612, see also CHILDREN AND YOUTH - About 1231
EDUCATION — Abstracting, Bibliographies, Statistics 1673
EDUCATION — Adult Education 1681
EDUCATION — Computer Applications 1688, see also COMPUTERS - Computer Assisted Instruction 1416
EDUCATION — Guides To Schools And Colleges 1691
EDUCATION — Higher Education 1698
EDUCATION — International Education Programs 1721
EDUCATION — School Organization And Administration 1724
EDUCATION — Special Education And Rehabilitation 1732
EDUCATION — Teaching Methods And Curriculum 1742

Educational Films see EDUCATION - Teaching Methods and Curriculum 1742, see also MOTION PICTURES 3502
Educational Psychology see PSYCHOLOGY 4007
Egyptology see ARCHAEOLOGY 260, see also ART 309, HISTORY - History of Africa 2330
ELECTRICAL ENERGY 1764
ELECTRICAL ENGINEERING 1764
ELECTRICITY 1764
ELECTROCHEMISTRY 1764
ELECTRONIC DATA PROCESSING 1764
ELECTRONICS 1764
ELECTRONICS — Computer Applications 1779
Electroplating see ENGINEERING - Electrical Engineering 1880, see also METALLURGY 3401
Electrotherapy see MEDICAL SCIENCES - Psychiatry and Neurology 3327, see also MEDICAL SCIENCES - Radiology and Nuclear Medicine 3356
Embroidery and Needlework see NEEDLEWORK 3590
Embryology see BIOLOGY 424, see also MEDICAL SCIENCES 3068
Emigration see POPULATION STUDIES 3979
Emotionally Disturbed Children see CHILDREN AND YOUTH - About 1231, see also EDUCATION - Special Education and Rehabilitation 1732
Employment see BUSINESS AND ECONOMICS - Labor and Industrial Relations 970, see also OCCUPATIONS AND CAREERS 3624
Encephalitis see MEDICAL SCIENCES - Psychiatry and Neurology 3327
ENCYCLOPEDIAS AND GENERAL ALMANACS 1779
ENCYCLOPEDIAS AND GENERAL ALMANACS — Abstracting, Bibliographies, Statistics 1782
ENDOCRINOLOGY 1783
ENERGY 1783
ENERGY — Abstracting, Bibliographies, Statistics 1797
ENERGY — Electrical Energy 1801
ENERGY — Geothermal Energy 1802
ENERGY — Hydroelectrical Energy 1802
ENERGY — Nuclear Energy 1803
ENERGY — Solar Energy 1810
ENERGY — Wind Energy 1812
ENGINEERING 1813
ENGINEERING — Abstracting, Bibliographies, Statistics 1841
ENGINEERING — Chemical Engineering 1847
ENGINEERING — Civil Engineering 1861
ENGINEERING — Computer Applications 1877
ENGINEERING — Electrical Engineering 1880
ENGINEERING — Engineering Mechanics And Materials 1911
ENGINEERING — Hydraulic Engineering 1923
ENGINEERING — Industrial Engineering 1925
ENGINEERING — Mechanical Engineering 1926
Engines see ENGINEERING - Mechanical Engineering 1926, see also TRANSPORTATION 4646
English Language - Study and Teaching see LINGUISTICS 2799
Engraving see ART 309, see also PRINTING 3997
Entertainment see COMMUNICATIONS - Radio 1354, see also COMMUNICATIONS - Television And Cable 1368, COMMUNICATIONS - Video 1384, DANCE 1528, MOTION PICTURES 3502, MUSIC 3536, SPORTS AND GAMES 4463, THEATER 4629, TRAVEL AND TOURISM 4750
ENTOMOLOGY 1941
Environmental Health see ENVIRONMENTAL STUDIES 1941, see also PUBLIC HEALTH AND SAFETY 4096
ENVIRONMENTAL STUDIES 1941, see also CONSERVATION 1482
ENVIRONMENTAL STUDIES — Abstracting, Bibliographies, Statistics 1972
ENVIRONMENTAL STUDIES — Computer Applications 1975
ENVIRONMENTAL STUDIES — Pollution 1975
ENVIRONMENTAL STUDIES — Toxicology And Environmental Safety 1980
ENVIRONMENTAL STUDIES — Waste Management 1984
Enzymes see BIOLOGY - Biological Chemistry 470, see also MEDICAL SCIENCES 3068
Ephemerides see ASTRONOMY 359
Epidemiology see PUBLIC HEALTH AND SAFETY 4096
Epilepsy see MEDICAL SCIENCES - Psychiatry and Neurology 3327
Ergonomics see BUSINESS AND ECONOMICS - Labor and Industrial Relations 970, see also PSYCHOLOGY 4007
Erosion see AGRICULTURE - Crop Production and Soil 165, see also CONSERVATION 1482
Esperanto see LINGUISTICS 2799
ESTATE PLANNING LAW 1988
ETHNIC INTERESTS 1988
ETHNIC INTERESTS — Abstracting, Bibliographies, Statistics 2030
Ethnography see ANTHROPOLOGY 232, see also SOCIOLOGY 4427
Eugenics see BIOLOGY - Genetics 539
European History see HISTORY - History of Europe 2346
Exceptional Children, Education see EDUCATION - Special Education and Rehabilitation 1732
EXPERIMENTAL MEDICINE, LABORATORY TECHNIQUE 2030
Exports and Imports see BUSINESS AND ECONOMICS - International Commerce 899
Extrasensory Perception see PARAPSYCHOLOGY AND OCCULTISM 3668
Eye Care see MEDICAL SCIENCES - Ophthalmology and Optometry 3297
Fabrics see TEXTILE INDUSTRIES AND FABRICS 4615
FAMILY AND MATRIMONIAL LAW 2030
Family Planning see BIRTH CONTROL 595
Family Therapy see MATRIMONY 3066
Farm Equipment see AGRICULTURE - Agricultural Equipment 161, see also MACHINERY 3015
Farm Management see AGRICULTURE 67
FASHIONS 2030
FEED, FLOUR AND GRAIN 2030
Fellowships see EDUCATION - Higher Education 1698
Feminist Movement see POLITICAL SCIENCE - Civil Rights 3939, see also WOMEN'S INTERESTS 4836, WOMEN'S STUDIES 4858
Fencing see SPORTS AND GAMES 4463

Fertilizers see AGRICULTURE - Crop Production and Soil 165
Fiction see LITERATURE 2890
Filmmaking see MOTION PICTURES 3502
Finance see BUSINESS AND ECONOMICS - Banking and Finance 757, see also BUSINESS AND ECONOMICS - Investments 937
Finishing see PAINTS AND PROTECTIVE COATINGS 3652
FIRE PREVENTION 2030
FIRE PREVENTION — Abstracting, Bibliographies, Statistics 2035
Firearms see HOBBIES 2432, see also SPORTS AND GAMES 4463
First Aid see MEDICAL SCIENCES 3068, see also PUBLIC HEALTH AND SAFETY 4096
FISH AND FISHERIES 2035, see also BIOLOGY - Zoology 575
FISH AND FISHERIES — Abstracting, Bibliographies, Statistics 2050
Fishing, Sport see SPORTS AND GAMES - Outdoor Life 4539
Flax see AGRICULTURE - Crop Production and Soil 165, see also TEXTILE INDUSTRIES AND FABRICS 4615
Floor Coverings see INTERIOR DESIGN AND DECORATION - Furniture and House Furnishings 2556
Floral Decorations see ART 309, see also GARDENING AND HORTICULTURE 2120
FLORIST TRADE 2052
Flowers see BIOLOGY - Botany 491, see also GARDENING AND HORTICULTURE 2120
Fluid Power see ENGINEERING - Mechanical Engineering 1926
Flying see AERONAUTICS AND SPACE FLIGHT 42, see also TRANSPORTATION - Air Transport 4669
Flying Saucers see AERONAUTICS AND SPACE FLIGHT 42, see also LITERATURE - Science Fiction, Fantasy, Horror 3010
FOLKLORE 2052
FOLKLORE — Abstracting, Bibliographies, Statistics 2060
FOOD AND FOOD INDUSTRIES 2060
FOOD AND FOOD INDUSTRIES — Abstracting, Bibliographies, Statistics 2084
FOOD AND FOOD INDUSTRIES — Bakers And Confectioners 2086
FOOD AND FOOD INDUSTRIES — Grocery Trade 2090
Football see SPORTS AND GAMES - Ball Games 4499
Footwear see LEATHER AND FUR INDUSTRIES 2735, see also SHOES AND BOOTS 4360
Foreign Affairs see POLITICAL SCIENCE - International Relations 3948
Foreign Aid see BUSINESS AND ECONOMICS - International Development and Assistance 925
Foreign Commerce see BUSINESS AND ECONOMICS - International Commerce 899
Foreign Legion see MILITARY 3449
FORENSIC SCIENCES 2094
Forest Fires see FIRE PREVENTION 2030, see also FORESTS AND FORESTRY 2094
FORESTS AND FORESTRY 2094
FORESTS AND FORESTRY — Abstracting, Bibliographies, Statistics 2111
FORESTS AND FORESTRY — Lumber And Wood 2113
Foundry Practices see METALLURGY 3401
Fraternal Organizations see CLUBS 1295, see also COLLEGE AND ALUMNI 1302
Freight see TRANSPORTATION 4646
French Language - Study and Teaching see LINGUISTICS 2799
Frequency Modulation see COMMUNICATIONS - Radio 1354, see also COMMUNICATIONS - Television And Cable 1368, SOUND RECORDING AND REPRODUCTION 4459
Fretted Instruments see MUSIC 3536
Frozen Food see FOOD AND FOOD INDUSTRIES 2060
Fruit see AGRICULTURE - Crop Production and Soil 165, see also FOOD AND FOOD INDUSTRIES 2060, GARDENING AND HORTICULTURE 2120
Fuel see ENERGY 1783, see also HEATING, PLUMBING AND REFRIGERATION 2297, MINES AND MINING INDUSTRY 3477, PETROLEUM AND GAS 3680
Fundraising see SOCIAL SERVICES AND WELFARE 4396
FUNERALS 2119
Fur see LEATHER AND FUR INDUSTRIES 2735
Furnaces see HEATING, PLUMBING AND REFRIGERATION 2297, see also METALLURGY 3401
FURNITURE AND HOUSE FURNISHINGS 2120
Galleries see MUSEUMS AND ART GALLERIES 3520
Gambling see SPORTS AND GAMES 4463
Game Breeding see AGRICULTURE - Poultry and Livestock 209
Games see SPORTS AND GAMES 4463
Garages see TRANSPORTATION - Automobiles 4678
GARDENING AND HORTICULTURE 2120, see also AGRICULTURE 67, BIOLOGY - Botany 491
GARDENING AND HORTICULTURE — Abstracting, Bibliographies, Statistics 2141
GARDENING AND HORTICULTURE — Florist Trade 2141
Gas Chromatography see CHEMISTRY - Analytical Chemistry 1203
Gas Dynamics see PHYSICS - Mechanics 3842
Gas Turbines see ENGINEERING - Mechanical Engineering 1926
GASTROENTEROLOGY 2143
Gastronomy see HOME ECONOMICS 2444
Gemstones see JEWELRY, CLOCKS AND WATCHES 2562
Gender Studies see MEN'S STUDIES 3400, see also WOMEN'S STUDIES 4858
GENEALOGY AND HERALDRY 2143
GENEALOGY AND HERALDRY — Abstracting, Bibliographies, Statistics 2168
GENEALOGY AND HERALDRY — Computer Applications 2168
GENERAL INTEREST PERIODICALS — Africa 2168
GENERAL INTEREST PERIODICALS — Argentina 2170
GENERAL INTEREST PERIODICALS — Australasia 2171
GENERAL INTEREST PERIODICALS — Australia 2171
GENERAL INTEREST PERIODICALS — Austria 2173
GENERAL INTEREST PERIODICALS — Bahrain 2173
GENERAL INTEREST PERIODICALS — Bangladesh 2173
GENERAL INTEREST PERIODICALS — Belarus 2174
GENERAL INTEREST PERIODICALS — Belgium 2174
GENERAL INTEREST PERIODICALS — Bermuda 2175
GENERAL INTEREST PERIODICALS — Bolivia 2175
GENERAL INTEREST PERIODICALS — Brazil 2175
GENERAL INTEREST PERIODICALS — Bulgaria 2175
GENERAL INTEREST PERIODICALS — Canada 2175
GENERAL INTEREST PERIODICALS — Central America 2180
GENERAL INTEREST PERIODICALS — Chile 2180
GENERAL INTEREST PERIODICALS — China 2180
GENERAL INTEREST PERIODICALS — Colombia 2183
GENERAL INTEREST PERIODICALS — Cuba 2184
GENERAL INTEREST PERIODICALS — Cyprus 2184
GENERAL INTEREST PERIODICALS — Czechoslovakia 2184
GENERAL INTEREST PERIODICALS — Denmark 2185
GENERAL INTEREST PERIODICALS — Dominican Republic 2185
GENERAL INTEREST PERIODICALS — Ecuador 2185
GENERAL INTEREST PERIODICALS — Egypt 2185
GENERAL INTEREST PERIODICALS — Estonia 2186
GENERAL INTEREST PERIODICALS — Ethiopia 2186
GENERAL INTEREST PERIODICALS — Finland 2186
GENERAL INTEREST PERIODICALS — France 2186
GENERAL INTEREST PERIODICALS — Germany 2188
GENERAL INTEREST PERIODICALS — Ghana 2192
GENERAL INTEREST PERIODICALS — Great Britain 2193
GENERAL INTEREST PERIODICALS — Greece 2196
GENERAL INTEREST PERIODICALS — Greenland 2196
GENERAL INTEREST PERIODICALS — Guatemala 2196
GENERAL INTEREST PERIODICALS — Guyana 2196
GENERAL INTEREST PERIODICALS — Haiti 2197
GENERAL INTEREST PERIODICALS — Hong Kong 2197
GENERAL INTEREST PERIODICALS — Hungary 2197
GENERAL INTEREST PERIODICALS — Iceland 2198
GENERAL INTEREST PERIODICALS — India 2198
GENERAL INTEREST PERIODICALS — Indonesia 2202
GENERAL INTEREST PERIODICALS — Iran 2202
GENERAL INTEREST PERIODICALS — Iraq 2202
GENERAL INTEREST PERIODICALS — Ireland 2202
GENERAL INTEREST PERIODICALS — Israel 2203
GENERAL INTEREST PERIODICALS — Italy 2204
GENERAL INTEREST PERIODICALS — Japan 2207
GENERAL INTEREST PERIODICALS — Jordan 2208
GENERAL INTEREST PERIODICALS — Kenya 2208
GENERAL INTEREST PERIODICALS — Korea 2209
GENERAL INTEREST PERIODICALS — Kuwait 2209
GENERAL INTEREST PERIODICALS — Latvia 2209
GENERAL INTEREST PERIODICALS — Lebanon 2209
GENERAL INTEREST PERIODICALS — Libya 2209
GENERAL INTEREST PERIODICALS — Lithuania 2209
GENERAL INTEREST PERIODICALS — Malagasy Republic 2209
GENERAL INTEREST PERIODICALS — Malawi 2209
GENERAL INTEREST PERIODICALS — Malaysia 2209
GENERAL INTEREST PERIODICALS — Mexico 2210
GENERAL INTEREST PERIODICALS — Middle East 2210
GENERAL INTEREST PERIODICALS — Mozambique 2211
GENERAL INTEREST PERIODICALS — Nepal 2211
GENERAL INTEREST PERIODICALS — Netherlands 2211
GENERAL INTEREST PERIODICALS — New Zealand 2212
GENERAL INTEREST PERIODICALS — Nigeria 2212
GENERAL INTEREST PERIODICALS — Norway 2212
GENERAL INTEREST PERIODICALS — Oceania 2213
GENERAL INTEREST PERIODICALS — Pakistan 2213
GENERAL INTEREST PERIODICALS — Panama 2213
GENERAL INTEREST PERIODICALS — Paraguay 2213
GENERAL INTEREST PERIODICALS — Peru 2213
GENERAL INTEREST PERIODICALS — Philippines 2213
GENERAL INTEREST PERIODICALS — Poland 2214
GENERAL INTEREST PERIODICALS — Portugal 2214
GENERAL INTEREST PERIODICALS — Puerto Rico 2215
GENERAL INTEREST PERIODICALS — Rumania 2215
GENERAL INTEREST PERIODICALS — Russia 2215
GENERAL INTEREST PERIODICALS — Saudi Arabia 2216
GENERAL INTEREST PERIODICALS — Scandinavia 2216
GENERAL INTEREST PERIODICALS — Singapore 2216
GENERAL INTEREST PERIODICALS — South Africa 2216
GENERAL INTEREST PERIODICALS — South America 2217
GENERAL INTEREST PERIODICALS — Spain 2217
GENERAL INTEREST PERIODICALS — Sri Lanka 2218
GENERAL INTEREST PERIODICALS — Sudan 2218
GENERAL INTEREST PERIODICALS — Sweden 2218
GENERAL INTEREST PERIODICALS — Switzerland 2218
GENERAL INTEREST PERIODICALS — Syria 2219
GENERAL INTEREST PERIODICALS — Taiwan 2219
GENERAL INTEREST PERIODICALS — Tanzania 2219
GENERAL INTEREST PERIODICALS — Thailand 2219
GENERAL INTEREST PERIODICALS — Turkey 2220
GENERAL INTEREST PERIODICALS — Uganda 2220
GENERAL INTEREST PERIODICALS — Ukraine 2220
GENERAL INTEREST PERIODICALS — Union Of Myanmar 2220
GENERAL INTEREST PERIODICALS — United Arab Emirates 2220
GENERAL INTEREST PERIODICALS — United States 2220
GENERAL INTEREST PERIODICALS — Uruguay 2238
GENERAL INTEREST PERIODICALS — Venezuela 2238
GENERAL INTEREST PERIODICALS — Vietnam 2238
GENERAL INTEREST PERIODICALS — West Indies 2239
GENERAL INTEREST PERIODICALS — Yugoslavia 2239
GENERAL INTEREST PERIODICALS — Zambia 2239
GENERAL INTEREST PERIODICALS — Zimbabwe 2240
Generators see ENGINEERING - Electrical Engineering 1880, see also PHYSICS - Electricity 3840
GENETICS 2240
Geochemistry see EARTH SCIENCES - Geology 1552
Geodesy see EARTH SCIENCES - Geophysics 1586, see also GEOGRAPHY 2240
GEOGRAPHY 2240, see also TRAVEL AND TOURISM 4750
GEOGRAPHY — Abstracting, Bibliographies, Statistics 2267

GEOGRAPHY — Computer Applications 2268
GEOLOGY 2269
Geomagnetism see EARTH SCIENCES - Geophysics 1586
GEOPHYSICS 2269
GEOTHERMAL ENERGY 2269
German Language - Study and Teaching see LINGUISTICS 2799
GERONTOLOGY AND GERIATRICS 2269
GERONTOLOGY AND GERIATRICS — Abstracting, Bibliographies, Statistics 2280
GIFTWARE AND TOYS 2280
Glaciology see EARTH SCIENCES - Geology 1552
Glass see CERAMICS, GLASS AND POTTERY 1160
Glasses, Eye see MEDICAL SCIENCES - Ophthalmology and Optometry 3297
Glaucoma see MEDICAL SCIENCES - Ophthalmology and Optometry 3297
Gliders see AERONAUTICS AND SPACE FLIGHT 42
Golf see SPORTS AND GAMES - Ball Games 4463
Government see POLITICAL SCIENCE 3869, see also PUBLIC ADMINISTRATION 4052
Graphic Arts see ART 309, see also PRINTING 3997
Graphology see PSYCHOLOGY 4007
Greenhouses see GARDENING AND HORTICULTURE 2120
Greeting Cards see GIFTWARE AND TOYS 2280
GROCERY TRADE 2283
GUIDES TO SCHOOLS AND COLLEGES 2283
Guns see SPORTS AND GAMES 4463
Gymnastics see SPORTS AND GAMES 4463
Gynecology see MEDICAL SCIENCES - Obstetrics and Gynecology 3288
Hair Removal see BEAUTY CULTURE 371
Hairdressing see BEAUTY CULTURE 371
Handbags see CLOTHING TRADE 1282, see also LEATHER AND FUR INDUSTRIES 2735
HANDICAPPED 2283
HANDICAPPED — Abstracting, Bibliographies, Statistics 2285
HANDICAPPED — Computer Applications 2285
HANDICAPPED — Hearing Impaired 2285
HANDICAPPED — Physically Impaired 2290
HANDICAPPED — Visually Impaired 2290
Handicrafts see ARTS AND HANDICRAFTS 352
Harbors see TRANSPORTATION - Ships and Shipping 4723
HARDWARE 2297
HARDWARE (COMPUTER) 2297
Harnesses see LEATHER AND FUR INDUSTRIES 2735
Hazardous Substances see ENVIRONMENTAL STUDIES - Waste Management 1984
Health Foods see FOOD AND FOOD INDUSTRIES 2060, see also NUTRITION AND DIETETICS 3602, PHYSICAL FITNESS AND HYGIENE 3798
Health Insurance see INSURANCE 2525
Hearing see MEDICAL SCIENCES - Otorhinolaryngology 3312
HEARING IMPAIRED 2297
Heart Diseases see MEDICAL SCIENCES - Cardiovascular Diseases 3203
HEAT 2297
HEATING, PLUMBING AND REFRIGERATION 2297, see also BUILDING AND CONSTRUCTION 598, ENGINEERING - Mechanical Engineering 1926
HEATING, PLUMBING AND REFRIGERATION — Abstracting, Bibliographies, Statistics 2304
Helicopters see AERONAUTICS AND SPACE FLIGHT 42
HEMATOLOGY 2305
Heraldry see GENEALOGY AND HERALDRY 2143
Herbs see AGRICULTURE 67, see also GARDENING AND HORTICULTURE 2120
Heredity see BIOLOGY - Genetics 539
Hides see LEATHER AND FUR INDUSTRIES 2735
HIGHER EDUCATION 2305
Highways see ENGINEERING - Civil Engineering 1861, see also TRANSPORTATION - Roads and Traffic 4717
HINDUISM 2305
Histochemistry see BIOLOGY - Cytology and Histology 522
Histology see BIOLOGY - Cytology and Histology 522
Historic Sites see HISTORY 2305, see also TRAVEL AND TOURISM 4750
HISTORY 2305, see also ARCHAEOLOGY 260, BIOGRAPHY 417, CLASSICAL STUDIES 1274
HISTORY — Abstracting, Bibliographies, Statistics 2327
HISTORY — Computer Applications 2330
HISTORY — History Of Africa 2330
HISTORY — History Of Asia 2336
HISTORY — History Of Australasia And Other Areas 2343
HISTORY — History Of Europe 2346
HISTORY — History Of North And South America 2397
HISTORY — History Of The Near East 2427
HOBBIES 2432, see also SPORTS AND GAMES 4463
HOBBIES — Abstracting, Bibliographies, Statistics 2444
Hockey see SPORTS AND GAMES 4463
HOME ECONOMICS 2444
HOME ECONOMICS — Abstracting, Bibliographies, Statistics 2450
Home Improvement see HOW-TO AND DO-IT-YOURSELF 2500
Home Remodeling And Repairs see HOW-TO AND DO-IT-YOURSELF 2500
Homeopathy see MEDICAL SCIENCES - Chiropractic, Homeopathy, Osteopathy 3213
HOMOSEXUALITY 2450
HOMOSEXUALITY — Abstracting, Bibliographies, Statistics 2458
Hormones see MEDICAL SCIENCES - Endocrinology 3250
Horology see JEWELRY, CLOCKS AND WATCHES 2562
HORSES AND HORSEMANSHIP 2458
Horticulture see GARDENING AND HORTICULTURE 2120
Hosiery see CLOTHING TRADE 1282
Hospices see HOSPITALS 2458
Hospital Supplies see HOSPITALS 2458, see also PHARMACY AND PHARMACOLOGY 3714
HOSPITALS 2458, see also MEDICAL SCIENCES 3068
HOSPITALS — Abstracting, Bibliographies, Statistics 2470
HOTELS AND RESTAURANTS 2471
HOTELS AND RESTAURANTS — Abstracting, Bibliographies, Statistics 2482

House Furnishings see INTERIOR DESIGN AND DECORATION - Furniture and House Furnishings 2556
Household Management see HOME ECONOMICS 2444
HOUSING AND URBAN PLANNING 2482, see also BUILDING AND CONSTRUCTION 598, PUBLIC ADMINISTRATION 4052, REAL ESTATE 4144
HOUSING AND URBAN PLANNING — Abstracting, Bibliographies, Statistics 2499
HOW-TO AND DO-IT-YOURSELF 2500
Human Ecology see SOCIOLOGY 4427
Human Geography see GEOGRAPHY 2240, see also POPULATION STUDIES 3979
Human Rights see POLITICAL SCIENCE - Civil Rights 3939
Humanism see PHILOSOPHY 3759
HUMANITIES: COMPREHENSIVE WORKS 2501
HUMANITIES: COMPREHENSIVE WORKS — Abstracting, Bibliographies, Statistics 2519
HUMANITIES: COMPREHENSIVE WORKS — Computer Applications 2520
Hunting see SPORTS AND GAMES - Outdoor Life 4539
HYDRAULIC ENGINEERING 2520
Hydroelectric Engineering see ENGINEERING - Electrical Engineering 1880
HYDROELECTRICAL ENERGY 2520
Hydrography see WATER RESOURCES 4821
HYDROLOGY 2520
Hygiene see OCCUPATIONAL HEALTH AND SAFETY 3614, see also PHYSICAL FITNESS AND HYGIENE 3798, PUBLIC HEALTH AND SAFETY 4096
Hypertension see MEDICAL SCIENCES - Cardiovascular Diseases 3203
Illumination see ENGINEERING - Electrical Engineering 1880, see also PHYSICS - Electricity 3840
Immigration see POPULATION STUDIES 3979
Immunology see MEDICAL SCIENCES - Allergology and Immunology 3182
Imports see BUSINESS AND ECONOMICS - International Commerce 899
Indexing Services see ABSTRACTING AND INDEXING SERVICES 1
Indoor Games and Amusements see HOBBIES 2432, see also SPORTS AND GAMES 4463
Industrial Arts see TECHNOLOGY 4592
Industrial Chemistry see ENGINEERING - Chemical Engineering 1847
Industrial Design see ENGINEERING 1813, see also TECHNOLOGY: COMPREHENSIVE WORKS 4592
INDUSTRIAL ENGINEERING 2521
Industrial Relations see BUSINESS AND ECONOMICS - Labor and Industrial Relations 970, see also BUSINESS AND ECONOMICS - Personnel Management 1062
Industry see BUSINESS AND ECONOMICS - Production of Goods and Services 1071
Infectious Diseases see MEDICAL SCIENCES - Communicable Diseases 3216, see also PUBLIC HEALTH AND SAFETY 4096
INFORMATION SCIENCE AND INFORMATION THEORY 2521
INORGANIC CHEMISTRY 2521
Input-Output Systems see COMPUTERS - Hardware 1453
Insects see BIOLOGY - Entomology 527
INSTRUMENTS 2521
INSTRUMENTS — Abstracting, Bibliographies, Statistics 2525
Insulation see BUILDING AND CONSTRUCTION 598, see also HEATING, PLUMBING AND REFRIGERATION 2297
INSURANCE 2525
INSURANCE — Abstracting, Bibliographies, Statistics 2545
INSURANCE — Computer Applications 2547
Intensive Care Medicine see MEDICAL SCIENCES 3068
INTERIOR DESIGN AND DECORATION 2547, see also HOME ECONOMICS 2444
INTERIOR DESIGN AND DECORATION — Abstracting, Bibliographies, Statistics 2556
INTERIOR DESIGN AND DECORATION — Furniture And House Furnishings 2556
Internal Medicine see MEDICAL SCIENCES 3068
International Affairs see BUSINESS AND ECONOMICS - International Development and Assistance 925, see also LITERARY AND POLITICAL REVIEWS 2857, POLITICAL SCIENCE - International Relations 3948
INTERNATIONAL COMMERCE 2562
INTERNATIONAL DEVELOPMENT AND ASSISTANCE 2562
INTERNATIONAL EDUCATION PROGRAMS 2562
INTERNATIONAL LAW 2562
INTERNATIONAL RELATIONS 2562
Interplanetary Flight see AERONAUTICS AND SPACE FLIGHT 42
INVESTMENTS 2562
Ionization see CHEMISTRY - Electrochemistry 1211
Irrigation see AGRICULTURE 67, see also CONSERVATION 1482, ENGINEERING - Hydraulic Engineering 1923, WATER RESOURCES 4821
ISLAM 2562
Italian Language - Study and Teaching see LINGUISTICS 2799
JEWELRY, CLOCKS AND WATCHES 2562
JEWELRY, CLOCKS AND WATCHES — Abstracting, Bibliographies, Statistics 2566
Job Opportunities see BUSINESS AND ECONOMICS - Labor and Industrial Relations 970, see also OCCUPATIONS AND CAREERS 3624
Jogging see PHYSICAL FITNESS AND HYGIENE 3798
JOURNALISM 2566
JOURNALISM — Abstracting, Bibliographies, Statistics 2577
JUDAISM 2579
JUDICIAL SYSTEMS 2579
Judo see SPORTS AND GAMES 4463
Jury see LAW - Criminal Law 2712
Jute see TEXTILE INDUSTRIES AND FABRICS 4615
Juvenile Delinquency see CHILDREN AND YOUTH - About 1231, see also CRIMINOLOGY AND LAW ENFORCEMENT 1509
Juvenile Literature see CHILDREN AND YOUTH - For 1248, see also PUBLISHING AND BOOK TRADE 4119
Karate see SPORTS AND GAMES 4463
Kinetics see CHEMISTRY - Organic Chemistry 1215, see also CHEMISTRY - Physical Chemistry 1224, PHYSICS 3812
Knit Goods see CLOTHING TRADE 1282, see also TEXTILE INDUSTRIES AND FABRICS 4615
Knitting see NEEDLEWORK 3590
LABOR AND INDUSTRIAL RELATIONS 2579
Labor Law see BUSINESS AND ECONOMICS - Labor and Industrial Relations 970, see also LAW 2592

LABOR UNIONS 2579
LABOR UNIONS — Abstracting, Bibliographies, Statistics 2592
Laboratory Animals see MEDICAL SCIENCES - Experimental Medicine, Laboratory Technique 3256
LABORATORY TECHNIQUE 2592
Laboratory Techniques see INSTRUMENTS 2521, see also MEDICAL SCIENCES - Experimental Medicine, Laboratory Technique 3256
Land Management see CONSERVATION 1482
Land Reclamation see AGRICULTURE - Crop Production and Soil 165
Landscaping see ARCHITECTURE 291, see also GARDENING AND HORTICULTURE 2120
Language, Study and Teaching see LINGUISTICS 2799
Laryngology see MEDICAL SCIENCES - Otorhinolaryngology 3312
Lasers see PHYSICS - Optics 3851
Lathes see MACHINERY 3015
Latin American History see HISTORY - History of North and South America 2397
Latin Language and Literature see CLASSICAL STUDIES 1274, see also LINGUISTICS 2799
Laundries see CLEANING AND DYEING 1281
LAW 2592
LAW — Abstracting, Bibliographies, Statistics 2697
LAW — Civil Law 2701
LAW — Computer Applications 2705
LAW — Constitutional Law 2705
LAW — Corporate Law 2706
LAW — Criminal Law 2712
Law Enforcement see CRIMINOLOGY AND LAW ENFORCEMENT 1509
LAW — Estate Planning 2714
LAW — Family And Matrimonial Law 2716
LAW — International Law 2719
LAW — Judicial Systems 2731
LAW — Legal Aid 2734
LAW — Maritime Law 2734
LAW — Military Law 2735
Lawns see GARDENING AND HORTICULTURE 2120
LEATHER AND FUR INDUSTRIES 2735, see also SHOES AND BOOTS 4360
LEATHER AND FUR INDUSTRIES — Abstracting, Bibliographies, Statistics 2738
LEGAL AID 2738
Legislation see LAW 2592, see also POLITICAL SCIENCE 3869, PUBLIC ADMINISTRATION 4052
LEISURE AND RECREATION 2738
Leprosy see MEDICAL SCIENCES - Communicable Diseases 3216
Leukemia see MEDICAL SCIENCES - Hematology 3270
Lexicography see LINGUISTICS 2799
LIBRARY AND INFORMATION SCIENCES 2739, see also BIBLIOGRAPHIES 388, COMPUTERS - Information Science and Information Theory 1455, PUBLISHING AND BOOK TRADE 4119
LIBRARY AND INFORMATION SCIENCES — Abstracting, Bibliographies, Statistics 2792
LIBRARY AND INFORMATION SCIENCES — Computer Applications 2796
Library Bookbinding see LIBRARY AND INFORMATION SCIENCES 2739, see also PUBLISHING AND BOOK TRADE 4119
Lighting see INTERIOR DESIGN AND DECORATION - Furniture and House Furnishings 2556, see also PHYSICS - Electricity 3840
Limnology see EARTH SCIENCES - Hydrology 1596
LINGUISTICS 2799
LINGUISTICS — Abstracting, Bibliographies, Statistics 2854
LINGUISTICS — Computer Applications 2856
Liquor see BEVERAGES 377
LITERARY AND POLITICAL REVIEWS 2857, see also LITERATURE 2890
LITERARY AND POLITICAL REVIEWS — Abstracting, Bibliographies, Statistics 2890
Literary Criticism see LITERARY AND POLITICAL REVIEWS 2857, see also LITERATURE 2890
LITERATURE 2890, see also LINGUISTICS 2799, LITERARY AND POLITICAL REVIEWS 2857
LITERATURE — Abstracting, Bibliographies, Statistics 2980
LITERATURE — Adventure And Romance 2983
LITERATURE — Mystery And Detective 2985
LITERATURE — Poetry 2986, see also LITERARY AND POLITICAL REVIEWS 2857
LITERATURE — Science Fiction, Fantasy, Horror 3010
Lithography see PRINTING 3997
Little Magazines see LITERARY AND POLITICAL REVIEWS 2857
Livestock see AGRICULTURE - Poultry and Livestock 209, see also VETERINARY SCIENCE 4804
Locks see BUILDING AND CONSTRUCTION -Hardware 641
Lubrication and Lubricants see ENGINEERING - Mechanical Engineering 1926, see also PETROLEUM AND GAS 3680
Luggage see LEATHER AND FUR INDUSTRIES 2735
LUMBER AND WOOD 3015
MACHINE THEORY 3015
Machine Translating see COMPUTERS - Computer Programming 1429, see also LINGUISTICS 2799
MACHINERY 3015, see also AGRICULTURE - Agricultural Equipment 161, ENGINEERING - Mechanical Engineering 1926, TECHNOLOGY: COMPREHENSIVE WORKS 4592
MACHINERY — Abstracting, Bibliographies, Statistics 3025
MACHINERY — Computer Applications 3025
MACROECONOMICS 3025
Macromolecules see CHEMISTRY - Organic Chemistry 1215
Magazine Business see PUBLISHING AND BOOK TRADE 4119
Magic see HOBBIES 2432
Magnetism see PHYSICS 3812
Mail Order Business see BUSINESS AND ECONOMICS - Marketing and Purchasing 1032
Malacology see BIOLOGY - Zoology 575
Malpractice see LAW - Civil Law 2701, see also MEDICAL SCIENCES 3068
MANAGEMENT 3025

Manufacturing see BUSINESS AND ECONOMICS - Production of Goods and Services 1071
Marijuana see DRUG ABUSE AND ALCOHOLISM 1532
Marine Biology see BIOLOGY 424, see also EARTH SCIENCES - Oceanography 1601
Marine Engineering see ENGINEERING 1813, see also TRANSPORTATION - Ships and Shipping 4723
Marine Policy see LAW - Maritime Law 2734
MARITIME LAW 3025
MARKETING AND PURCHASING 3025
Marxism see BUSINESS AND ECONOMICS - Economic Systems and Theories, Economic History 888, see also POLITICAL SCIENCE 3869
Masonry see BUILDING AND CONSTRUCTION 598
Mass Transit see TRANSPORTATION 4646
Mathematical Geography see GEOGRAPHY 2240
Mathematical Physics see PHYSICS 3812
MATHEMATICS 3025
MATHEMATICS — Abstracting, Bibliographies, Statistics 3062
MATHEMATICS — Computer Applications 3063
MATRIMONY 3066
Mechanical Drawing see ENGINEERING 1813, see also TECHNOLOGY: COMPREHENSIVE WORKS 4592
MECHANICAL ENGINEERING 3068
Mechanical Handling see MACHINERY 3015, see also TECHNOLOGY: COMPREHENSIVE WORKS 4592, TRANSPORTATION 4646
Mechanical Translating see COMPUTERS - Computer Programming 1429, see also LINGUISTICS 2799
MECHANICS 3068
Medical Bacteriology see MEDICAL SCIENCES - Communicable Diseases 3216
Medical Engineering see MEDICAL SCIENCES 3068
Medical Jurisprudence see MEDICAL SCIENCES - Forensic Sciences 3263
Medical Parasitology see MEDICAL SCIENCES - Communicable Diseases 3216
MEDICAL SCIENCES 3068, see also BIOLOGY 424, DRUG ABUSE AND ALCOHOLISM 1532, GERONTOLOGY AND GERIATRICS 2269, HOSPITALS 2458, NUTRITION AND DIETETICS 3602, OCCUPATIONAL HEALTH AND SAFETY 3614, PHARMACY AND PHARMACOLOGY 3714, PHYSICAL FITNESS AND HYGIENE 3798, PUBLIC HEALTH AND SAFETY 4096
MEDICAL SCIENCES — Abstracting, Bibliographies, Statistics 3165
MEDICAL SCIENCES — Allergology And Immunology 3182
MEDICAL SCIENCES — Anaesthesiology 3189
MEDICAL SCIENCES — Cancer 3192
MEDICAL SCIENCES — Cardiovascular Diseases 3203
MEDICAL SCIENCES — Chiropractic, Homeopathy, Osteopathy 3213
MEDICAL SCIENCES — Communicable Diseases 3216
MEDICAL SCIENCES — Computer Applications 3224
MEDICAL SCIENCES — Dentistry 3226
MEDICAL SCIENCES — Dermatology And Venereology 3245
MEDICAL SCIENCES — Endocrinology 3250
MEDICAL SCIENCES — Experimental Medicine, Laboratory Technique 3256
MEDICAL SCIENCES — Forensic Sciences 3263
MEDICAL SCIENCES — Gastroenterology 3266
MEDICAL SCIENCES — Hematology 3270
MEDICAL SCIENCES — Hypnosis 3274
MEDICAL SCIENCES — Nurses And Nursing 3274
MEDICAL SCIENCES — Obstetrics And Gynecology 3288
MEDICAL SCIENCES — Ophthalmology And Optometry 3297
MEDICAL SCIENCES — Orthopedics And Traumatology 3306
MEDICAL SCIENCES — Otorhinolaryngology 3312
MEDICAL SCIENCES — Pediatrics 3317
MEDICAL SCIENCES — Psychiatry And Neurology 3327
MEDICAL SCIENCES — Radiology And Nuclear Medicine 3356
MEDICAL SCIENCES — Respiratory Diseases 3364
MEDICAL SCIENCES — Rheumatology 3368
MEDICAL SCIENCES — Sports Medicine 3370
MEDICAL SCIENCES — Surgery 3373
MEDICAL SCIENCES — Urology And Nephrology 3386
Medieval Studies see HISTORY - History of Europe 2346, see also LITERATURE 2890, PHILOSOPHY 3759
MEETINGS AND CONGRESSES 3390
MEETINGS AND CONGRESSES — Abstracting, Bibliographies, Statistics 3395
Memory Structures see COMPUTERS - Hardware 1453
MEN'S HEALTH 3395
MEN'S INTERESTS 3395
MEN'S STUDIES 3400
Menswear see CLOTHING TRADE 1282
Mental Health see PSYCHOLOGY 4007
Mental Hygiene see PUBLIC HEALTH AND SAFETY 4096
Mental Retardation see EDUCATION - Special Education and Rehabilitation 1732, see also MEDICAL SCIENCES - Psychiatry and Neurology 3327, PSYCHOLOGY 4007
Merchandising see BUSINESS AND ECONOMICS - Marketing and Purchasing 1032
Metabolism see BIOLOGY - Physiology 568, see also MEDICAL SCIENCES 3068
Metal Industries see METALLURGY 3401
METALLURGY 3401, see also MINES AND MINING INDUSTRY 3477
METALLURGY — Abstracting, Bibliographies, Statistics 3424
METALLURGY — Welding 3429
Metaphysics see PHILOSOPHY 3759
METEOROLOGY 3431
METEOROLOGY — Abstracting, Bibliographies, Statistics 3444
METROLOGY AND STANDARDIZATION 3444
METROLOGY AND STANDARDIZATION — Abstracting, Bibliographies, Statistics 3449
MICROBIOLOGY 3449
MICROCOMPUTERS 3449
Microfilming see PHOTOGRAPHY 3788
Microphotography see PHOTOGRAPHY 3788
MICROSCOPY 3449
Microwaves see ELECTRONICS 1764
Midwifery see MEDICAL SCIENCES - Obstetrics and Gynecology 3288
Migration see POPULATION STUDIES 3979
MILITARY 3449

MILITARY — Abstracting, Bibliographies, Statistics 3476
Military Engineering see ENGINEERING 1813
MILITARY LAW 3477
Military Medicine see MEDICAL SCIENCES 3068
Millinery see CLOTHING TRADE 1282
Milling see AGRICULTURE - Feed, Flour and Grain 204
Mineral Resources see EARTH SCIENCES - Geology 1552, see also MINES AND MINING INDUSTRY 3477
Mineralogy see MINES AND MINING INDUSTRY 1552
MINES AND MINING INDUSTRY 3477
MINES AND MINING INDUSTRY — Abstracting, Bibliographies, Statistics 3498
MINICOMPUTERS 3502
Missiles see AERONAUTICS AND SPACE FLIGHT 42
Mobile Homes see HOUSING AND URBAN PLANNING 2482, see also TRANSPORTATION 4646
Models and Model Building see HOBBIES 2432
Modems see COMPUTERS - Hardware 1453
Mollusca see BIOLOGY - Zoology 575
Monitors see COMPUTERS - Hardware 1453
Morphology see BIOLOGY 424, see also MEDICAL SCIENCES 3068
Mosses see BIOLOGY - Botany 491
Motels see HOTELS AND RESTAURANTS 2471
MOTION PICTURES 3502
MOTION PICTURES — Abstracting, Bibliographies, Statistics 3519
Motor Scooters see SPORTS AND GAMES - Bicycles and Motorcycles 4515
Motorcycles see SPORTS AND GAMES - Bicycles and Motorcycles 4515
Mountaineering see SPORTS AND GAMES - Outdoor Life 4539
Movies see MOTION PICTURES 3502
Multiple Sclerosis see MEDICAL SCIENCES - Psychiatry and Neurology 3327
MUNICIPAL GOVERNMENT 3520
Municipal Law see LAW 2592, see also PUBLIC ADMINISTRATION - Municipal Government 4083
Municipal Transportation see TRANSPORTATION 4646
MUSEUMS AND ART GALLERIES 3520
MUSEUMS AND ART GALLERIES — Abstracting, Bibliographies, Statistics 3536
MUSIC 3536
MUSIC — Abstracting, Bibliographies, Statistics 3588
MUSIC — Computer Applications 3589, see also COMPUTERS - Computer Music 1426
Music Therapy see EDUCATION - Special Education and Rehabilitation 1732, see also MUSIC 3536
Mutual Funds see BUSINESS AND ECONOMICS - Investments 937
Mycology see BIOLOGY - Botany 491
MYSTERY AND DETECTIVE 3590
Mysticism see NEW AGE PUBLICATIONS 3593, see also PARAPSYCHOLOGY AND OCCULTISM 3668
Mythology see FOLKLORE 2052
Narcotics see DRUG ABUSE AND ALCOHOLISM 1532, see also PHARMACY AND PHARMACOLOGY 3714
Natural Food see NUTRITION AND DIETETICS 3602
Natural Resources see CONSERVATION 1482, see also ENVIRONMENTAL STUDIES 1941
Naturalization see POLITICAL SCIENCE 3869
Nautical Arts and Sciences see TRANSPORTATION - Ships and Shipping 4723
Naval Architecture see TRANSPORTATION - Ships and Shipping 4723
Naval Engineering see TRANSPORTATION - Ships and Shipping 4723
Naval Medicine see MEDICAL SCIENCES 3068
NEEDLEWORK 3590
Nephrology see MEDICAL SCIENCES - Urology and Nephrology 3386
Neurology see MEDICAL SCIENCES - Psychiatry and Neurology 3327
Neurophysiology see MEDICAL SCIENCES - Psychiatry and Neurology 3327
Neuroradiology see MEDICAL SCIENCES - Radiology and Nuclear Medicine 3356
Neurosurgery see MEDICAL SCIENCES - Psychiatry and Neurology 3327, see also MEDICAL SCIENCES - Surgery 3373
NEW AGE PUBLICATIONS 3593, see also PARAPSYCHOLOGY AND OCCULTISM 3668
Newspaper Business see JOURNALISM 2566
Noise Control see ENGINEERING - Mechanical Engineering 1926
Noise Pollution see ENVIRONMENTAL STUDIES - Pollution 1975
North American History see HISTORY - History of North and South America 2397
NUCLEAR ENERGY 3597
Nuclear Medicine see MEDICAL SCIENCES - Radiology and Nuclear Medicine 3356
NUCLEAR PHYSICS 3597
Nudism see PHYSICAL FITNESS AND HYGIENE 3798
NUMISMATICS 3597
NUMISMATICS — Abstracting, Bibliographies, Statistics 3602
Nurseries see GARDENING AND HORTICULTURE - Florist Trade 2141
NURSES AND NURSING 3602
Nursing Homes see HOSPITALS 2458, see also SOCIAL SERVICES AND WELFARE 4396
NUTRITION AND DIETETICS 3602, see also FOOD AND FOOD INDUSTRIES 2060, HOSPITALS 2458, PHARMACY AND PHARMACOLOGY 3714, PHYSICAL FITNESS AND HYGIENE 3798
NUTRITION AND DIETETICS — Abstracting, Bibliographies, Statistics 3613
OBSTETRICS AND GYNECOLOGY 3614
Occultism see PARAPSYCHOLOGY AND OCCULTISM 3668
OCCUPATIONAL HEALTH AND SAFETY 3614
OCCUPATIONAL HEALTH AND SAFETY — Abstracting, Bibliographies, Statistics 3623
Occupational Therapy see EDUCATION - Special Education and Rehabilitation 1732, see also MEDICAL SCIENCES 3068
OCCUPATIONS AND CAREERS 3624, see also BUSINESS AND ECONOMICS - Labor and Industrial Relations 970
OCCUPATIONS AND CAREERS — Abstracting, Bibliographies, Statistics 3631
OCEANOGRAPHY 3632
OFFICE EQUIPMENT AND SERVICES 3632
Oils and Fats see CHEMISTRY - Organic Chemistry 1215
Old Age see GERONTOLOGY AND GERIATRICS 2269
OPHTHALMOLOGY AND OPTOMETRY 3632

OPTICS 3632
Optometry see MEDICAL SCIENCES - Ophthalmology and Optometry 3297
ORGANIC CHEMISTRY 3632
ORIENTAL STUDIES 3632, see also HISTORY - History of Asia 2336, LINGUISTICS 2799, LITERATURE 2890, PHILOSOPHY 3759
ORIENTAL STUDIES — Abstracting, Bibliographies, Statistics 3646
ORNITHOLOGY 3647
Orthodontics see MEDICAL SCIENCES - Dentistry 3226
ORTHOPEDICS AND TRAUMATOLOGY 3647
Osteopathy see MEDICAL SCIENCES - Chiropractic, Homeopathy, Osteopathy 3213
Otology see MEDICAL SCIENCES - Otorhinolaryngology 3312
OTORHINOLARYNGOLOGY 3647
OUTDOOR LIFE 3647
PACKAGING 3647
PACKAGING — Abstracting, Bibliographies, Statistics 3652
PAINTS AND PROTECTIVE COATINGS 3652
PAINTS AND PROTECTIVE COATINGS — Abstracting, Bibliographies, Statistics 3656
Paleobotany see BIOLOGY - Botany 491
PALEONTOLOGY 3656
PALEONTOLOGY — Abstracting, Bibliographies, Statistics 3661
PAPER AND PULP 3661, see also FORESTS AND FORESTRY - Lumber and Wood 2113
PAPER AND PULP — Abstracting, Bibliographies, Statistics 3667
Papyrus see PAPER AND PULP 3661
Parachuting see SPORTS AND GAMES 4463
Paraplegia see MEDICAL SCIENCES - Psychiatry and Neurology 3327
PARAPSYCHOLOGY AND OCCULTISM 3668, see also NEW AGE PUBLICATIONS 3593
PARAPSYCHOLOGY AND OCCULTISM — Abstracting, Bibliographies, Statistics 3672
Parasitology see BIOLOGY 424
Parent Teacher Associations see EDUCATION - School Organization and Administration 1724
Parenting see CHILDREN AND YOUTH - About 1231
Parks and Recreation Areas see CONSERVATION 1482, see also SPORTS AND GAMES - Outdoor Life 4539, TRAVEL AND TOURISM 4750
PATENTS, TRADEMARKS AND COPYRIGHTS 3672
PATENTS, TRADEMARKS AND COPYRIGHTS — Abstracting, Bibliographies, Statistics 3679
Paving see BUILDING AND CONSTRUCTION 598, see also TRANSPORTATION - Roads and Traffic 4717
Peat see HEATING, PLUMBING AND REFRIGERATION 2297
PEDIATRICS 3680
Penology see CRIMINOLOGY AND LAW ENFORCEMENT 1509
Pensions see BUSINESS AND ECONOMICS - Labor and Industrial Relations 970, see also INSURANCE 2525, SOCIAL SERVICES AND WELFARE 4396
Performing Arts see DANCE 1528, see also MOTION PICTURES 3502, MUSIC 3536, THEATER 4629
PERFUMES AND COSMETICS 3680
Peripherals see COMPUTERS - Hardware 1453
PERSONAL COMPUTERS 3680
PERSONNEL MANAGEMENT 3680
Pest Control see AGRICULTURE 67, see also BIOLOGY - Entomology 527, PUBLIC HEALTH AND SAFETY 4096
PETROLEUM AND GAS 3680
PETROLEUM AND GAS — Abstracting, Bibliographies, Statistics 3704
Petrology see EARTH SCIENCES - Geology 1552
PETS 3707
PHARMACY AND PHARMACOLOGY 3714, see also MEDICAL SCIENCES 3068
PHARMACY AND PHARMACOLOGY — Abstracting, Bibliographies, Statistics 3747
Philanthropy see SOCIAL SERVICES AND WELFARE 4396
PHILATELY 3748
PHILATELY — Abstracting, Bibliographies, Statistics 3759
Philology see LINGUISTICS 2799
PHILOSOPHY 3759
PHILOSOPHY — Abstracting, Bibliographies, Statistics 3787
Phonetics see LINGUISTICS 2799
Phonographs see MUSIC 3536, see also SOUND RECORDING AND REPRODUCTION 4459
Photogrammetry see GEOGRAPHY 2240, see also PHOTOGRAPHY 3788
Photographic Surveying see ENGINEERING - Civil Engineering 1861
PHOTOGRAPHY 3788, see also MOTION PICTURES 3502
PHOTOGRAPHY — Abstracting, Bibliographies, Statistics 3798
Photomechanical Processing see PRINTING 3997
PHYSICAL CHEMISTRY 3798
Physical Education see EDUCATION - Teaching Methods and Curriculum 1742, see also PHYSICAL FITNESS AND HYGIENE 3798, SPORTS AND GAMES 4463
PHYSICAL FITNESS AND HYGIENE 3798
PHYSICAL FITNESS AND HYGIENE — Abstracting, Bibliographies, Statistics 3811
Physical Therapy see MEDICAL SCIENCES 3068
PHYSICALLY IMPAIRED 3812
PHYSICS 3812
PHYSICS — Abstracting, Bibliographies, Statistics 3836
PHYSICS — Computer Applications 3840
PHYSICS — Electricity 3840
PHYSICS — Heat 3840
PHYSICS — Mechanics 3842
PHYSICS — Nuclear Physics 3846
PHYSICS — Optics 3851
PHYSICS — Sound 3858
PHYSIOLOGY 3860
Planned Parenthood see BIRTH CONTROL 595
Plant Breeding see AGRICULTURE - Crop Production and Soil 165, see also BIOLOGY - Botany 491, GARDENING AND HORTICULTURE 2120
Plasma Physics see PHYSICS 3812
Plastic Surgery see MEDICAL SCIENCES - Surgery 3373
PLASTICS 3860, see also CHEMISTRY - Physical Chemistry 1224, ENGINEERING - Chemical Engineering 1847
PLASTICS — Abstracting, Bibliographies, Statistics 3868

Plays see LITERATURE 2890, see also THEATER 4629
Plumbing see HEATING, PLUMBING AND REFRIGERATION 2297
POETRY 3869
Police see CRIMINOLOGY AND LAW ENFORCEMENT 1509
Poliomyelitis see MEDICAL SCIENCES - Psychiatry and Neurology 3327
Political Reviews see LITERARY AND POLITICAL REVIEWS 2857
POLITICAL SCIENCE 3869, see also LITERARY AND POLITICAL REVIEWS 2857, PUBLIC ADMINISTRATION 4052
POLITICAL SCIENCE — Abstracting, Bibliographies, Statistics 3936
POLITICAL SCIENCE — Civil Rights 3939
POLITICAL SCIENCE — International Relations 3948
POLLUTION 3979
Polymers see CHEMISTRY 1168, see also ENGINEERING - Chemical Engineering 1847
POPULATION STUDIES 3979
POPULATION STUDIES — Abstracting, Bibliographies, Statistics 3989
Ports see TRANSPORTATION - Ships and Shipping 4723
Portuguese LANGUAGE - Study and Teaching see LINGUISTICS 2799
POSTAL AFFAIRS 3997
Pottery see CERAMICS, GLASS AND POTTERY 1160
POULTRY AND LIVESTOCK 3997
Power Plants see ENERGY 1783
Pre-school Education see EDUCATION 1612
Precision Mechanics see INSTRUMENTS 2521
Prefabricated Houses see BUILDING AND CONSTRUCTION 598
Preventive Medicine see PUBLIC HEALTH AND SAFETY 4096
PRINTING 3997
PRINTING — Abstracting, Bibliographies, Statistics 4006
PRINTING — Computer Applications 4007, see also COMPUTERS - Computer Graphics 1420
Prisons see CRIMINOLOGY AND LAW ENFORCEMENT 1509
Private Schools see EDUCATION - Guides to Schools and Colleges 1691, see also EDUCATION - School Organization and Administration 1724
Produce see FOOD AND FOOD INDUSTRIES 2060
PRODUCTION OF GOODS AND SERVICES 4007
Programmed Instruction see EDUCATION - Teaching Methods and Curriculum 1742
Programming, Automatic see COMPUTERS - Computer Programming 1429
Proofreading see JOURNALISM 2566, see also PRINTING 3997
Prosthetics see MEDICAL SCIENCES - Orthopedics and Traumatology 3306
Protective Coatings see PAINTS AND PROTECTIVE COATINGS 3652
PROTESTANTISM 4007
Protozoology see BIOLOGY - Zoology 575
PSYCHIATRY AND NEUROLOGY 4007
Psychic Phenomena see PARAPSYCHOLOGY AND OCCULTISM 3668
Psychical Research see PARAPSYCHOLOGY AND OCCULTISM 3668
Psychoanalysis see PSYCHOLOGY 4007
Psychological Testing see PSYCHOLOGY 4007
PSYCHOLOGY 4007
PSYCHOLOGY — Abstracting, Bibliographies, Statistics 4051
Psychosomatic Medicine see MEDICAL SCIENCES 3068
Psychotherapy see MEDICAL SCIENCES - Psychiatry and Neurology 3327
PUBLIC ADMINISTRATION 4052, see also POLITICAL SCIENCE 3869
PUBLIC ADMINISTRATION — Abstracting, Bibliographies, Statistics 4078
PUBLIC ADMINISTRATION — Computer Applications 4083
PUBLIC ADMINISTRATION — Municipal Government 4083
Public Affairs see POLITICAL SCIENCE 3869, see also PUBLIC ADMINISTRATION 4052, SOCIAL SCIENCES 4364
PUBLIC FINANCE, TAXATION 4096
PUBLIC HEALTH AND SAFETY 4096, see also DRUG ABUSE AND ALCOHOLISM 1532, ENVIRONMENTAL STUDIES 1941, FIRE PREVENTION 2030, HOSPITALS 2458, MEDICAL SCIENCES 3068, OCCUPATIONAL HEALTH AND SAFETY 3614
PUBLIC HEALTH AND SAFETY — Abstracting, Bibliographies, Statistics 4116
Public Relations see ADVERTISING AND PUBLIC RELATIONS 25
Public Transportation see TRANSPORTATION 4646
Public Utilities see PETROLEUM AND GAS 3680, see also PUBLIC ADMINISTRATION 4052
Public Welfare see SOCIAL SERVICES AND WELFARE 4396
Public Works see BUILDING AND CONSTRUCTION 598, see also ENGINEERING - Civil Engineering 1861, HOUSING AND URBAN PLANNING 2482, PUBLIC ADMINISTRATION 4052
Publicity see ADVERTISING AND PUBLIC RELATIONS 25
PUBLISHING AND BOOK TRADE 4119, see also BIBLIOGRAPHIES 388, LIBRARY AND INFORMATION SCIENCES 2739, PATENTS, TRADEMARKS AND COPYRIGHTS 3672, PRINTING 3997
PUBLISHING AND BOOK TRADE — Abstracting, Bibliographies, Statistics 4139
PUBLISHING AND BOOK TRADE — Computer Applications 4143
Pulp see PAPER AND PULP 3661
Puppets see HOBBIES 2432, see also THEATER 4629
Puzzles see SPORTS AND GAMES 4463
Quality Control see BUSINESS AND ECONOMICS - Management 1000, see also METROLOGY AND STANDARDIZATION 3444
Quantum Chemistry see CHEMISTRY - Physical Chemistry 1224
Quarries see MINES AND MINING INDUSTRY 3477
Race Relations see POLITICAL SCIENCE - Civil Rights 3939, see also SOCIOLOGY 4427
Racing see SPORTS AND GAMES - Horses and Horsemanship 4531, see also TRANSPORTATION - Automobiles 4678
Radar see COMMUNICATIONS 1331
Radiation see ASTRONOMY 359, see also BIOLOGY - Biophysics 484, CHEMISTRY - Physical Chemistry 1224, MEDICAL SCIENCES - Radiology and Nuclear Medicine 3356, PHYSICS - Nuclear Physics 3846
RADIO 4144
Radio Advertising see ADVERTISING AND PUBLIC RELATIONS 25, see also COMMUNICATIONS - Radio 1354
Radiobiology see BIOLOGY 424
Radiocarbon see PHYSICS - Nuclear Physics 3846
RADIOLOGY AND NUCLEAR MEDICINE 4144
Railroad Engineering see TRANSPORTATION - Railroads 4707

RAILROADS 4144
Railway Ties see FORESTS AND FORESTRY - Lumber and Wood 2113, see also TRANSPORTATION - Railroads 4707
Rare Earths see CHEMISTRY - Inorganic Chemistry 1213
Reading Guides and Aids see ABSTRACTING AND INDEXING SERVICES 1, see also BIBLIOGRAPHIES 388, EDUCATION - Teaching Methods and Curriculum 1742, LIBRARY AND INFORMATION SCIENCES 2739
REAL ESTATE 4144, see also BUILDING AND CONSTRUCTION 598, BUSINESS AND ECONOMICS 643, HOUSING AND URBAN PLANNING 2482, LAW 2714
REAL ESTATE — Abstracting, Bibliographies, Statistics 4159
Recorded Music see MUSIC 3536, see also SOUND RECORDING AND REPRODUCTION 4459
Recreation see DANCE 1528, see also HOBBIES 2432, LEISURE AND RECREATION 2738, SPORTS AND GAMES 4463
Recreation Areas see CONSERVATION 1482, see also TRAVEL AND TOURISM 4750
Recreational Vehicles see TRANSPORTATION - Automobiles 4678
Red Cross see SOCIAL SERVICES AND WELFARE 4396
Refrigeration see HEATING, PLUMBING AND REFRIGERATION 2297, see also PHYSICS - Heat 3840
Regional Planning see HOUSING AND URBAN PLANNING 2482
Rehabilitation see EDUCATION - Special Education and Rehabilitation 1732, see also MEDICAL SCIENCES 3068, SOCIAL SERVICES AND WELFARE 4396
Reincarnation see NEW AGE PUBLICATIONS 3593, see also PARAPSYCHOLOGY AND OCCULTISM 3668, RELIGIONS AND THEOLOGY 4161
RELIGIONS AND THEOLOGY 4161
RELIGIONS AND THEOLOGY — Abstracting, Bibliographies, Statistics 4211
RELIGIONS AND THEOLOGY — Buddhist 4213
RELIGIONS AND THEOLOGY — Eastern Orthodox 4217
RELIGIONS AND THEOLOGY — Hindu 4217
RELIGIONS AND THEOLOGY — Islamic 4217
RELIGIONS AND THEOLOGY — Judaic 4221
RELIGIONS AND THEOLOGY — Other Denominations And Sects 4279
RELIGIONS AND THEOLOGY — Protestant 4227
RELIGIONS AND THEOLOGY — Roman Catholic 4254
Religious History see RELIGIONS AND THEOLOGY 4161
Repairs see HOW-TO AND DO-IT-YOURSELF 2500
Reproduction and Fertility see BIOLOGY 424, see also MEDICAL SCIENCES 3068
Research and Development see TECHNOLOGY: COMPREHENSIVE WORKS 4592
Resins see PLASTICS 3860
Resorts see HOTELS AND RESTAURANTS 2471, see also TRAVEL AND TOURISM 4750
RESPIRATORY DISEASES 4290
Restaurants see HOTELS AND RESTAURANTS 2471
Retailing see BUSINESS AND ECONOMICS - Marketing and Purchasing 1032
Rheology see PHYSICS - Mechanics 3842
RHEUMATOLOGY 4290
Rhinology see MEDICAL SCIENCES - Otorhinolaryngology 3312
ROADS AND TRAFFIC 4290
Robotics see COMPUTERS - Artificial Intelligence 1406
Rockets see AERONAUTICS AND SPACE FLIGHT 42
Rodeo see SPORTS AND GAMES - Horses and Horsemanship 4531
Roller Skating see SPORTS AND GAMES 4463
ROMAN CATHOLICISM 4290
RUBBER 4290, see also ENGINEERING - Chemical Engineering 1847, PLASTICS 3860
RUBBER — Abstracting, Bibliographies, Statistics 4294
Rugby see SPORTS AND GAMES - Ball Games 4499
Safety Education see BUSINESS AND ECONOMICS - Labor and Industrial Relations 970, see also INDUSTRIAL HEALTH AND SAFETY 3614, PUBLIC HEALTH AND SAFETY 4096, TRANSPORTATION - Roads and Traffic 4717
Sailing see SPORTS AND GAMES - Boats and Boating 4521
Salesmanship see BUSINESS AND ECONOMICS - Marketing and Purchasing 1032
Sanitary Engineering see PUBLIC HEALTH AND SAFETY 4096
Sanitation see ENGINEERING - Civil Engineering 1861, see also PHYSICAL FITNESS AND HYGIENE 3798, PUBLIC HEALTH AND SAFETY 4096
Savings and Loan see BUSINESS AND ECONOMICS - Banking and Finance 757
Scholarships see EDUCATION - Higher Education 1698
SCHOOL ORGANIZATION AND ADMINISTRATION 4295
SCIENCE FICTION, FANTASY, HORROR 4295
SCIENCES: COMPREHENSIVE WORKS 4295
SCIENCES: COMPREHENSIVE WORKS — Abstracting, Bibliographies, Statistics 4354
SCIENCES: COMPREHENSIVE WORKS — Computer Applications 4358
Scooters see SPORTS AND GAMES - Bicycles and Motorcycles 4515
Sculpture see ART 309
Seaweed see BIOLOGY - Botany 491, see also EARTH SCIENCES - Oceanography 1601
Securities see BUSINESS AND ECONOMICS - Investments 937
SECURITY 4360
Sediment Data see ENGINEERING - Hydraulic Engineering 1923
Sedimentology see EARTH SCIENCES - Geophysics 1586
Seeds see AGRICULTURE - Crop Production and Soil 165
Seismology see EARTH SCIENCES - Geophysics 1586
Selling see ADVERTISING AND PUBLIC RELATIONS 25, see also BUSINESS AND ECONOMICS - Marketing and Purchasing 1032
Semantics see LINGUISTICS 2799
Semiconductors see PHYSICS - ELECTRICITY 3840
Senior Citizens see GERONTOLOGY AND GERIATRICS 2269
Service Stations see PETROLEUM AND GAS 3680, see also TRANSPORTATION - Automobiles 4678
Sewage and Waste Treatment see PUBLIC ADMINISTRATION 4052, see also PUBLIC HEALTH AND SAFETY 4096
Sewing see CLOTHING TRADE - Fashions 1289, see also NEEDLEWORK 3590
Sex Education see PHYSICAL FITNESS AND HYGIENE 3798
Sheet Metal see METALLURGY 3401
Shipbuilding see TRANSPORTATION - Ships and Shipping 4723
SHIPS AND SHIPPING 4360
SHOES AND BOOTS 4360, see also LEATHER AND FUR INDUSTRIES 2735
SHOES AND BOOTS — Abstracting, Bibliographies, Statistics 4362

Shooting see SPORTS AND GAMES - Outdoor Life 4539
Short Wave see COMMUNICATIONS - Radio 1354
Shorthand see BUSINESS AND ECONOMICS - Office Equipment and Services 1057
Sign Manufacturing see ADVERTISING AND PUBLIC RELATIONS 25
Silicosis see MEDICAL SCIENCES 3068
SINGLES' INTERESTS AND LIFESTYLES 4362
Site Selection see HOUSING AND URBAN PLANNING 2482, see also REAL ESTATE 4144
Skating see SPORTS AND GAMES 4463
Skeet Shooting see SPORTS AND GAMES - Outdoor Life 4539
Skiing see SPORTS AND GAMES - Outdoor Life 4539
Slavonic Languages - Study and Teaching see LINGUISTICS 2799
SMALL BUSINESS 4364
Smoking see DRUG ABUSE AND ALCOHOLISM 1532, see also PHYSICAL FITNESS AND HYGIENE 3798, PUBLIC HEALTH AND SAFETY 4096, TOBACCO 4643
Snack Foods see FOOD AND FOOD INDUSTRIES - Bakers and Confectioners 2086
Soap see BEAUTY CULTURE - Perfumes and Cosmetics 375
Soccer see SPORTS AND GAMES - Ball Games 4499
Social Insurance see INSURANCE 2525, see also SOCIAL SERVICES AND WELFARE 4396
Social Psychology see PSYCHOLOGY 4007, see also SOCIOLOGY 4427
SOCIAL SCIENCES: COMPREHENSIVE WORKS 4364
SOCIAL SCIENCES: COMPREHENSIVE WORKS — Abstracting, Bibliographies, Statistics 4394
Social Security see INSURANCE 2525, see also SOCIAL SERVICES AND WELFARE 4396
SOCIAL SERVICES AND WELFARE 4396
SOCIAL SERVICES AND WELFARE — Abstracting, Bibliographies, Statistics 4425
Socialism see BUSINESS AND ECONOMICS - Economic Systems and Theories, Economic History 888, see also POLITICAL SCIENCE 3869
SOCIOLOGY 4427, see also POPULATION STUDIES 3979
SOCIOLOGY — Abstracting, Bibliographies, Statistics 4457
SOCIOLOGY — Computer Applications 4458
Soft Drinks see BEVERAGES 377
SOFTWARE 4459
Soil see AGRICULTURE - Crop Production and Soil 165, see also CONSERVATION 1482, ENGINEERING - Civil Engineering 1861
Soil Pollution see ENVIRONMENTAL STUDIES - Pollution 1975
SOLAR ENERGY 4459
Solid Waste see ENVIRONMENTAL STUDIES - Waste Management 1984
SOUND 4459
SOUND RECORDING AND REPRODUCTION 4459
SOUND RECORDING AND REPRODUCTION — Abstracting, Bibliographies, Statistics 4462
South American History see HISTORY - History of North and South America 2397
Space Flight see AERONAUTICS AND SPACE FLIGHT 42
Spanish Language - Study and Teaching see LINGUISTICS 2799
Spearfishing see SPORTS AND GAMES - Outdoor Life 4539
SPECIAL EDUCATION AND REHABILITATION 4463
Spectroscopy see PHYSICS - Optics 3851
Speech and Hearing Disorders see EDUCATION - Special Education and Rehabilitation 1732, see also HANDICAPPED - Hearing Impaired 2285, MEDICAL SCIENCES - Psychiatry and Neurology 3327
Speech - Study and Teaching see EDUCATION - Special Education and Rehabilitation 1732, see also LINGUISTICS 2799
Speleology see EARTH SCIENCES - Geophysics 1586
Spices see FOOD AND FOOD INDUSTRIES 2060
Spinning see NEEDLEWORK 3590
Spiritualism see NEW AGE PUBLICATIONS 3593, see also PARAPSYCHOLOGY AND OCCULTISM 3668
Sporting Goods see SPORTS AND GAMES 4463
SPORTS AND GAMES 4463
SPORTS AND GAMES — Abstracting, Bibliographies, Statistics 4498
SPORTS AND GAMES — Ball Games 4499
SPORTS AND GAMES — Bicycles And Motorcycles 4515
SPORTS AND GAMES — Boats And Boating 4521
SPORTS AND GAMES — Horses And Horsemanship 4531
SPORTS AND GAMES — Outdoor Life 4539
Sports Cars see TRANSPORTATION - Automobiles 4678
Sportswear see CLOTHING TRADE 1282
Stained Glass see ART 309, see also ARTS AND HANDICRAFTS 352, CERAMICS, GLASS AND POTTERY 1160
Standards see METROLOGY AND STANDARDIZATION 3444
Stationery and Office Equipment see BUSINESS AND ECONOMICS - Office Equipment and Services 1057
STATISTICS 4560, see also POPULATION STUDIES 3979
Stenography see BUSINESS AND ECONOMICS - Office Equipment and Services 1057
Sterilization see BIRTH CONTROL 595
Stock and Stock-Breeding see AGRICULTURE - Poultry and Livestock 209
Stocks and Bonds see BUSINESS AND ECONOMICS - Investments 937
Store Display and Promotion see ADVERTISING AND PUBLIC RELATIONS 25
Stress see PSYCHOLOGY 4007
Student Aid see EDUCATION 1612
Supermarkets see FOOD AND FOOD INDUSTRIES - Grocery Trade 2090
Surfing see SPORTS AND GAMES - Outdoor Life 4539
SURGERY 4592
Surgical Instruments see MEDICAL SCIENCES - Surgery 3373
Surveying see ENGINEERING - Civil Engineering 1861, see also GEOGRAPHY 2240
Swimming see SPORTS AND GAMES 4463
Synthetic Fabrics see TEXTILE INDUSTRIES AND FABRICS 4615
Table Tennis see SPORTS AND GAMES - Ball Games 4499
Tailoring see CLOTHING TRADE 1282
Talking Books see HANDICAPPED - Visually Impaired 2290
Tape Drives see COMPUTERS - Hardware 1453
Tape Recording see SOUND RECORDING AND REPRODUCTION 4459
Tariffs see BUSINESS AND ECONOMICS - International Commerce 899, see also BUSINESS AND ECONOMICS - Public Finance, Taxation 1087

TAXATION 4592, see also BUSINESS AND ECONOMICS - Public Finance, Taxation 1087
Taxicabs see TRANSPORTATION - Automobiles 4678
Tea see BEVERAGES 377
TEACHING METHODS AND CURRICULUM 4592
TECHNOLOGY: COMPREHENSIVE WORKS 4592
TECHNOLOGY: COMPREHENSIVE WORKS — Abstracting, Bibliographies, Statistics 4613
Telecommunications see COMMUNICATIONS 1331, see also ENGINEERING - Electrical Engineering 1880
Telepathy see NEW AGE PUBLICATIONS 3593, see also PARAPSYCHOLOGY AND OCCULTISM 3668
TELEPHONE AND TELEGRAPH 4615
TELEVISION AND CABLE 4615
Tennis see SPORTS AND GAMES - Ball Games 4499
Terminals see COMPUTERS - Hardware 1453
Textbooks see EDUCATION - Teaching Methods and Curriculum 1742, see also PUBLISHING AND BOOK TRADE 4119
TEXTILE INDUSTRIES AND FABRICS 4615
TEXTILE INDUSTRIES AND FABRICS — Abstracting, Bibliographies, Statistics 4628
Thanatology see MEDICAL SCIENCES 3068
THEATER 4629
THEATER — Abstracting, Bibliographies, Statistics 4643
Theology see RELIGIONS AND THEOLOGY 4161
THEORY OF COMPUTING 4643
Theosophy see PHILOSOPHY 3759, see also RELIGIONS AND THEOLOGY 4161
Thermodynamics see CHEMISTRY - Physical Chemistry 1224, see also PHYSICS - Heat 3840
Thoracic Surgery see MEDICAL SCIENCES - Surgery 3373
Thrombosis see MEDICAL SCIENCES - Cardiovascular Diseases 3203
Timber see FORESTS AND FORESTRY - Lumber and Wood 2113
Timetables see TRANSPORTATION 4646
Tires see RUBBER 4290, see also TRANSPORTATION - Automobiles 4678
TOBACCO 4643
TOBACCO — Abstracting, Bibliographies, Statistics 4646
Toiletries see BEAUTY CULTURE 371
Tools see MACHINERY 3015
Touring see TRAVEL AND TOURISM 4750
Tourist Camps see HOTELS AND RESTAURANTS 2471, see also TRAVEL AND TOURISM 4750
Town Planning see HOUSING AND URBAN PLANNING 2482
Toxicology see MEDICAL SCIENCES 3068, see also PHARMACY AND PHARMACOLOGY 3714
TOXICOLOGY AND ENVIRONMENTAL SAFETY 4646
Toys see GIFTWARE AND TOYS 2280
Track and Field see SPORTS AND GAMES 4463
Tractors see AGRICULTURE - Agricultural Equipment 161
Trade see BUSINESS AND ECONOMICS - Domestic Commerce 833, see also BUSINESS AND ECONOMICS - International Commerce 899
TRADE AND INDUSTRIAL DIRECTORIES 4646
Trade Shows see MEETINGS AND CONGRESSES 3390
Trade Unions see LABOR UNIONS 2579
Trademarks see PATENTS, TRADEMARKS AND COPYRIGHTS 3672
Traffic see TRANSPORTATION - Roads and Traffic 4717
Trailers see TRANSPORTATION 4646
Transistors see ELECTRONICS 1764
Translation Services see LINGUISTICS 2799
TRANSPORTATION 4646
TRANSPORTATION — Abstracting, Bibliographies, Statistics 4661
TRANSPORTATION — Air Transport 4669
TRANSPORTATION — Automobiles 4678
TRANSPORTATION — Computer Applications 4706
Transportation Law see LAW 2592
TRANSPORTATION — Railroads 4707
TRANSPORTATION — Roads And Traffic 4717
TRANSPORTATION — Ships And Shipping 4723
TRANSPORTATION — Trucks And Trucking 4742
Trapping see LEATHER AND FUR INDUSTRIES 2735
Trapshooting see SPORTS AND GAMES - Outdoor Life 4539
Traumatology see MEDICAL SCIENCES - Orthopedics and Traumatology 3306
TRAVEL AND TOURISM 4750, see also GEOGRAPHY 2240, HOTELS AND RESTAURANTS 2471
TRAVEL AND TOURISM — Abstracting, Bibliographies, Statistics 4798
TRAVEL AND TOURISM — Airline Inflight And Hotel Inroom 4801
Treaties see LAW - International Law 2719
Trees see FORESTS AND FORESTRY 2094, see also GARDENING AND HORTICULTURE 2120
Trial Law see LAW - Criminal Law 2712
Tropical Diseases see MEDICAL SCIENCES - Communicable Diseases 3216
Tuberculosis see MEDICAL SCIENCES - Respiratory Diseases 3364
Typewriters see BUSINESS AND ECONOMICS - Office Equipment and Services 1057
Typography see PRINTING 3997
Ultrasonics see PHYSICS - Sound 3858
Underground Periodicals see LITERARY AND POLITICAL REVIEWS 2857, see also POLITICAL SCIENCE 3869
Underwear see CLOTHING TRADE 1282
Unemployment see BUSINESS AND ECONOMICS - Labor and Industrial Relations 970
Unidentified Flying Objects see AERONAUTICS AND SPACE FLIGHT 42
Unions see LABOR UNIONS 2579
U. S. Armed Forces see MILITARY 3449
Universities and Colleges see EDUCATION - Higher Education 1698
Upholstery see INTERIOR DESIGN AND DECORATION - Furniture and House Furnishings 2556
Urban Renewal see HOUSING AND URBAN PLANNING 2482
UROLOGY AND NEPHROLOGY 4804
Utilities see ENGINEERING - Electrical Engineering 1880, see also PUBLIC ADMINISTRATION 4052
Vaccines see PHARMACY AND PHARMACOLOGY 3714

Vacuum Sciences see ENGINEERING - Mechanical Engineering 1926, see also PHYSICS - Mechanics 3842
Vegetarianism see NUTRITION AND DIETETICS 3602
Vending Machines see BUSINESS AND ECONOMICS - Marketing and Purchasing 1032
Venereology see MEDICAL SCIENCES - Dermatology and Venereology 3245
Ventilation see HEATING, PLUMBING AND REFRIGERATION 2297
Veterans see MILITARY 3449
VETERINARY SCIENCE 4804
VETERINARY SCIENCE — Abstracting, Bibliographies, Statistics 4820
VETERINARY SCIENCE — Computer Applications 4821
VIDEO 4821
Virology see BIOLOGY - Microbiology 548
VISUALLY IMPAIRED 4821
Vital Statistics see POPULATION STUDIES 3979
Vitamins see PHARMACY AND PHARMACOLOGY 3714
Viticulture see AGRICULTURE - Crop Production and Soil 165
Vocational Education see EDUCATION - Teaching Methods and Curriculum 1612, see also OCCUPATIONS AND CAREERS 3624
Volume Feeding see HOTELS AND RESTAURANTS 2471
Wages see BUSINESS AND ECONOMICS - Labor and Industrial Relations 970
WASTE MANAGEMENT 4821
Waste Reclamation see ENVIRONMENTAL STUDIES 1941
Watchmaking see JEWELRY, CLOCKS AND WATCHES 2562
Water Pollution see ENVIRONMENTAL STUDIES - Pollution 1975
WATER RESOURCES 4821, see also AGRICULTURE 67, CONSERVATION 1482, ENVIRONMENTAL STUDIES 1941, PUBLIC HEALTH AND SAFETY 4096
WATER RESOURCES — Abstracting, Bibliographies, Statistics 4834
Water Sports see SPORTS AND GAMES 4463
Weather see METEOROLOGY 3431
Weaving see NEEDLEWORK 3590, see also TEXTILE INDUSTRIES AND FABRICS 4615
Weddings see MATRIMONY 3066
Weightlifting see PHYSICAL FITNESS AND HYGIENE 3798, see also SPORTS AND GAMES 4463
WELDING 4835
Welfare see SOCIAL SERVICES AND WELFARE 4396
Wildlife see BIOLOGY 424, see also CONSERVATION 1482
WIND ENERGY 4835
Window Covering see INTERIOR DESIGN AND DECORATION - Furniture and House Furnishings 2556
Windows see BUILDING AND CONSTRUCTION 598, see also CERAMICS, GLASS AND POTTERY 1160
Wine see BEVERAGES 377
Wire see MACHINERY 3015, see also METALLURGY 3015
Wit and Humor see LITERARY AND POLITICAL REVIEWS 2857
WOMEN'S HEALTH 4835, see also MEDICAL SCIENCES - Obstetrics and Gynecology 4835
WOMEN'S INTERESTS 4836
WOMEN'S INTERESTS — Abstracting, Bibliographies, Statistics 4858
Women's Liberation Movement see POLITICAL SCIENCE - Civil Rights 3939, see also WOMEN'S INTERESTS 4836
WOMEN'S STUDIES 4858
WOMEN'S STUDIES — Abstracting, Bibliographies, Statistics 4861
Women's Wear see CLOTHING TRADE 1282
Wood see BUILDING AND CONSTRUCTION - Carpentry and Woodwork 639, see also FORESTS AND FORESTRY - Lumber and Wood 2113
Wood Pulp see PAPER AND PULP 3661
Woodwork see BUILDING AND CONSTRUCTION - Carpentry and Woodwork 639
WORD PROCESSING 4861
Wrestling see SPORTS AND GAMES 4463
Writers and Writing see JOURNALISM 2566, see also LITERATURE 2890, PUBLISHING AND BOOK TRADE 4119
Yachting see SPORTS AND GAMES - Boats and Boating 4521
Yoga see PHILOSOPHY 3759, see also PHYSICAL FITNESS AND HYGIENE 3798
Youth see CHILDREN AND YOUTH - About 1231
Zoning see HOUSING AND URBAN PLANNING 2482
ZOOLOGY 4861
Zootechniques see AGRICULTURE - Poultry and Livestock 209, see also VETERINARY SCIENCE 4804

Refereed Serials

A A P G BULLETIN.
American Association of Petroleum Geologists, Box 979, Tulsa, OK 74101. TEL 918-584-2555. *3680*

A A P G EXPLORER.
American Association of Petroleum Geologists, Box 979, Tulsa, OK 74101. TEL 918-584-2555. *3680*

A A P G STUDIES IN GEOLOGY SERIES.
American Association of Petroleum Geologists, Box 979, Tulsa, OK 74101. TEL 918-584-2555. *3680*

A A S HISTORY SERIES.
Univelt, Inc., (American Astronautical Society, Inc.) Box 28130, San Diego, CA 92198. TEL 619-746-4005. *42*

A A V S O BULLETIN: PREDICTED DATES OF MAXIMA AND MINIMA OF LONG PERIOD VARIABLE STARS.
American Association of Variable Star Observers, 25 Birch St., Cambridge, MA 02138. TEL 617-354-0484. *359*

A A V S O REPORTS AND MONOGRAPHS.
American Association of Variable Star Observers, 25 Birch St., Cambridge, MA 02138. TEL 617-354-0484. *360*

A C M MONOGRAPH SERIES.
Academic Press, Inc., (Association for Computing Machinery) 1250 Sixth Ave., San Diego, CA 92101. TEL 619-231-0926. FAX 619-699-6715. *1388*

A C O G CURRENT JOURNAL REVIEW.
Elsevier Science Publishing Co., Inc. (New York), (American College of Obstetricians and Gynecologists) 655 Ave. of the Americas, New York, NY 10010. TEL 212-989-5800. FAX 212-633-3965. *3165*

A C S SYMPOSIUM SERIES.
American Chemical Society, 1155 16th St. N.W., Washington, DC 20036. TEL 202-872-4363. FAX 202-872-4615. *1168*

A D R I D.
Paul De Haen International, 2750 S. Shoshone St., Englewood, CO 80110. TEL 800-438-0296. FAX 303-789-2534. *3715*

A F I P ATLAS OF RADIOLOGIC-PATHOLOGIC CORRELATION.
Hanley & Belfus, Inc., (Armed Forces Institute of Pathology) 210 S. 13th St., Philadelphia, PA 19107. TEL 215-546-7293. FAX 215-790-9330. *3068*

A I A A JOURNAL.
American Institute of Aeronautics and Astronautics, Inc., 370 L'Enfant Promenade, S.W., Washington, DC 20024. TEL 202-646-7400. *42*

A I CH E EQUIPMENT TESTING PROCEDURES.
American Institute of Chemical Engineers, 345 E. 47th St., New York, NY 10017. TEL 212-705-7657. FAX 212-752-3294. *1847*

A I CH E JOURNAL.
American Institute of Chemical Engineers, 345 E. 47th St., New York, NY 10017. TEL 212-705-7663. FAX 212-752-3294. *1847*

A I CH E M I MODULAR INSTRUCTION. SERIES A: PROCESS CONTROL.
American Institute of Chemical Engineers, 345 E. 47th St., New York, NY 10017. TEL 212-705-7657. FAX 212-752-3294. *1847*

A I CH E M I MODULAR INSTRUCTION. SERIES C: TRANSPORT.
American Institute of Chemical Engineers, 345 E. 47th St., New York, NY 10017. TEL 212-705-7657. FAX 212-752-3294. *1847*

A I CH E M I MODULAR INSTRUCTION. SERIES D: THERMODYNAMICS.
American Institute of Chemical Engineers, 345 E. 47th St., New York, NY 10017. TEL 212-705-7657. FAX 212-752-3294. *1847*

A I CH E M I MODULAR INSTRUCTION. SERIES E: KINETICS.
American Institute of Chemical Engineers, 345 E. 47th St., New York, NY 10017. TEL 212-705-7657. FAX 212-752-3294. *1847*

A I CH E M I MODULAR INSTRUCTION. SERIES F: MATERIAL AND ENERGY BALANCES.
American Institute of Chemical Engineers, 345 E. 47th St., New York, NY 10017. TEL 212-705-7657. FAX 212-752-3294. *1847*

A I CH E M I MODULAR INSTRUCTION. SERIES G: DESIGN OF EQUIPMENT.
American Institute of Chemical Engineers, 345 E. 47th St., New York, NY 10017. TEL 212-705-7657. FAX 212-752-3294. *1847*

A I D S ALERT.
American Health Consultants, Inc., Six Piedmont Center, Ste. 400, 3525 Piedmont Rd., N.E., Atlanta, GA 30305. TEL 404-262-7436. FAX 800-284-3291. *3216*

A I D S & PUBLIC POLICY JOURNAL.
University Publishing Group, Inc., 107 E. Church St., Frederick, MD 21701. TEL 800-654-8188. *3216*

A I D S EDUCATION AND PREVENTION.
Guilford Publications, Inc., (International Society of AIDS Education) 72 Spring St., 4th Fl., New York, NY 10012. TEL 212-431-9800. FAX 212-966-6708. *3216*

A I D S INFORMATION EXCHANGE.
U S Conference of Mayors, 1620 Eye St., N.W., Washington, DC 20006. TEL 202-293-7330. FAX 202-293-2352. *3216*

A I D S PATIENT CARE.
Mary Ann Liebert, Inc., 1651 Third Ave., New York, NY 10128. TEL 212-289-2300. FAX 212-289-4697. *3217*

A I D S RESEARCH AND HUMAN RETROVIRUSES.
Mary Ann Liebert, Inc., 1651 Third Ave., New York, NY 10128. TEL 212-289-2300. FAX 212-289-4697. *3217*

A J D C: AMERICAN JOURNAL OF DISEASES OF CHILDREN.
American Medical Association, 515 N. State St., Chicago, IL 60610. TEL 312-464-0183. FAX 312-464-5834. *3317*

A J N R.
Williams & Wilkins, (American Society of Neuroradiology) 428 E. Preston St., Baltimore, MD 21202. TEL 301-528-4000. FAX 301-528-4312. *3356*

A J R.
Williams & Wilkins, (American Roentgen Ray Society) 428 E. Preston St., Baltimore, MD 21202. TEL 301-528-4000. FAX 301-528-4312. *3356*

A M S STUDIES IN ANTHROPOLOGY.
A M S Press, Inc., (Abrahams Magazine Service) 56 E. 13th St., New York, NY 10003. TEL 212-777-4700. FAX 212-995-5413. *232*

A N Q: A QUARTERLY JOURNAL OF SHORT ARTICLES, NOTES AND REVIEWS.
University Press of Kentucky, 663 S. Limestone St., Lexington, KY 40508-4008. TEL 606-257-2951. *2891*

A N R E D ALERT.
Anorexia Nervosa & Related Eating Disorders, Inc., Box 5102, Eugene, OR 97405. TEL 503-344-1144. *4008*

REFEREED SERIALS

A O A C INTERNATIONAL JOURNAL.
A O A C International, 2200 Wilson Blvd., Ste. 400, Arlington, VA 22201-3301. TEL 703-522-3032. FAX 703-522-5468. *1203*

A O H A TODAY.
American Osteopathic Hospital Association, 5301 Wisconsin Ave., N.W., Ste. 630, Washington, DC 20015-2015. TEL 202-686-1700. FAX 202-686-7615. *2458*

A R S C JOURNAL.
Association for Recorded Sound Collections. Inc., c/o Phillip Rochlin, Exec. Dir., Box 10162, Silver Spring, MD 20914. TEL 301-593-6552. *4459*

ABRAHAM LINCOLN ASSOCIATION. JOURNAL.
University of Illinois Press, 54 E. Gregory Dr., Champaign, IL 61820. TEL 217-333-0950. FAX 217-244-8082. *2305*

ABSTRACTS IN ANTHROPOLOGY.
Baywood Publishing Co., Inc., 26 Austin Ave., Box 337, Amityville, NY 11701. TEL 516-691-1270. FAX 516-691-1770. *253*

ACADEMIC MEDICINE.
Association of American Medical Colleges, One Dupont Circle, N.W., Washington, DC 20036. TEL 202-828-0590. FAX 202-785-5027. *3069*

ACADEMIC PRESS GEOLOGY SERIES.
Academic Press, Inc., 1250 Sixth Ave., San Diego, CA 92101. TEL 619-231-0926. FAX 619-699-6715. *1553*

ACADEMIC PRESS SERIES IN COGNITION AND PERCEPTION.
Academic Press, Inc., 1250 Sixth Ave., San Diego, CA 92101. TEL 619-231-0926. FAX 619-699-6715. *4008*

ACADEMIC PSYCHIATRY.
American Psychiatric Press, Inc., Journals Division, (American Association of Directors of Psychiatric Residency Training) 1400 K St., N.W., Ste. 1101, Washington, DC 20005. TEL 202-682-6272. FAX 202-789-2648. *3327*

ACADEMY OF SCIENCE OF THE U S S R. LEBEDEV PHYSICS INSTITUTE. PROCEEDINGS.
Nova Science Publishers, Inc., (Academy of Sciences of the U S S R, Lebedev Physics Institute) 283 Commack Rd., Ste. 300, Commack, NY 11725. TEL 516-499-3103. *3851*

ACADEMY OF SCIENCES OF THE U S S R. BIOLOGY BULLETIN.
Plenum Publishing Corp., Consultants Bureau, (Akademiya Nauk S.S.S.R.) 233 Spring St., New York, NY 10013-1578. TEL 212-620-8468. FAX 212-463-0742. *425*

ACADEMY OF SCIENCES OF THE U S S R. DIVISION OF CHEMICAL SCIENCES. BULLETIN.
Plenum Publishing Corp., Consultants Bureau, (Akademiya Nauk S.S.S.R.) 233 Spring St., New York, NY 10013-1578. TEL 212-620-8468. FAX 212-463-0742. *1168*

ACADEMY OF SCIENCES OF THE U S S R. INSTITUTE OF GENERAL PHYSICS. PROCEEDINGS.
Nova Science Publishers, Inc., (Akademiya Nauk S.S.S.R., Institut Obshchei Fiziki) 283 Commack Rd., Ste. 300, Commack, NY 11725. TEL 516-499-3103. *3812*

ACADEMY OF SCIENCES OF THE U S S R. MATHEMATICAL NOTES.
Plenum Publishing Corp., Consultants Bureau, (Akademiya Nauk S.S.S.R.) 233 Spring St., New York, NY 10013-1578. TEL 212-620-8468. FAX 212-463-0742. *3026*

ACCELERATORS AND STORAGE RINGS SERIES.
Harwood Academic Publishers, 270 Eighth Ave., New York, NY 10011. TEL 212-206-8900. FAX 212-645-2459. *3846*

ACCIDENT ANALYSIS & PREVENTION.
Pergamon Press, Inc., Journals Division, 660 White Plains Rd., Tarrytown, NY 10591-5153. TEL 914-524-9200. FAX 914-333-2444. *4097*

ACCOUNTABILITY IN RESEARCH.
Gordon & Breach Science Publishers, 270 Eighth Ave., New York, NY 10011. TEL 212-206-8900. FAX 212-645-2459. *4296*

ACCOUNTING, MANAGEMENT AND INFORMATION TECHNOLOGIES.
Pergamon Press, Inc., Journals Division, 660 White Plains Rd., Tarrytown, NY 10591-5153. TEL 914-524-9200. FAX 914-333-2444. *746*

ACCOUNTING, ORGANIZATIONS AND SOCIETY.
Pergamon Press, Inc., Journals Division, 660 White Plains Rd., Tarrytown, NY 10591-5153. TEL 914-524-9200. FAX 914-333-2444. *746*

ACCOUNTS OF CHEMICAL RESEARCH.
American Chemical Society, 1155 16th St., N.W., Washington, DC 20036. TEL 800-227-5558. FAX 202-872-4615. *1168*

ACCREDITED PROFESSIONAL PROGRAMS OF COLLEGES AND SCHOOLS OF PHARMACY.
American Council on Pharmaceutical Education, 311 W. Superior St., Chicago, IL 60610. TEL 312-664-3575. FAX 312-664-4652. *3715*

ACID PRECIPITATION DIGEST.
Center for Environmental Information, (Acid Rain Information Clearinghouse) 46 Prince St., Rochester, NY 14607. *1941*

ACOUSTICAL IMAGING.
Plenum Publishing Corp., 233 Spring St., New York, NY 10013-1578. TEL 212-620-8000. FAX 212-463-0742. *3858*

ACOUSTICAL SOCIETY OF AMERICA. JOURNAL.
American Institute of Physics, 335 E. 45th St., New York, NY 10017. TEL 212-661-9404. FAX 516-349-9704. *3858*

ACQUISITIONS LIBRARIAN.
Haworth Press, Inc., 10 Alice St., Binghamton, NY 13904. TEL 607-722-1695. FAX 607-722-1424. *2741*

ACTA ASTRONAUTICA.
Pergamon Press, Inc., Journals Division, (International Academy of Austronautics) 660 White Plains Rd., Tarrytown, NY 10591-5153. TEL 914-524-9200. FAX 914-333-2444. *42*

ACTA ASTRONOMICA.
Copernicus Foundation for Polish Astronomy, Al. Ujazdowskie 4, 00-478 Warsaw, Poland. TEL 48-22-295346. *360*

ACTA BOTANICA MALACITANA.
Universidad de Malaga, Facultad de Ciencias, Apdo. 59, 29080 Malaga, Spain. TEL 131944. FAX 132000. *492*

ACTA CIENTIFICA VENEZOLANA.
Asociacion Venezolana para el Avance de la Ciencia, Av. Neveri-Colina de Bello Monte, Apdo. 47286, Caracas, Venezuela. TEL 751.1420. *4297*

ACTA CONCILIUM OPHTHALMOLOGICUM.
International Federation of Ophthalmological Societies, c/o Prof. A. Deutman, Sec., Dept. of Ophthalmology, Univ. of Nijmegen, P. van Leijdenlaan 15, 6525 EX Nijmegen, Netherlands. TEL 080-513138. FAX 080-540522. *3297*

ACTA CYTOLOGICA.
Science Printers and Publishers, Inc., (International Academy of Cytology) 8342 Olive Blvd., St. Louis, MO 63132. TEL 314-991-4440. FAX 314-991-4654. *522*

ACTA ENDOCRINOLOGICA.
Scandinavian University Press, P.O. Box 2959 Toeyen, N-0608 Oslo, Norway. TEL 47-2-677600. FAX 47-2-677575. *3250*

ACTA GEOLOGICA HISPANICA.
Universidad de Barcelona, Institut de Ciencies de la Terra Jaume Almera, c/o Marti i Franques s-n, 08028 Barcelona, Spain. TEL 3-402-1420. FAX 3-402-1340. *1553*

ACTA GEOLOGICA SINICA.
Pergamon Press, Inc., Journals Division, (Geological Society of China) 660 White Plains Rd., Tarrytown, NY 10591-5153. TEL 914-524-9200. FAX 914-333-2444. *1553*

ACTA HISTOCHEMICA ET CYTOCHEMICA.
Japan Society of Histochemistry and Cytochemistry, c/o Dept. of Anatomy, Faculty of Medicine, Kyoto University, Konoe-cho, Yoshida, Sakyo-ku, Kyoto 606-01, Japan. TEL 075-751-7727. FAX 075-751-7286. *522*

ACTA INFORMATION.
Springer-Verlag, 175 Fifth Ave., New York, NY 10010. *1455*

ACTA MATHEMATICA SINICA, NEW SERIES.
Kexue Chubanshe, 16 Donghuangchenggen Beijie, Beijing 100707, People's Republic of China. TEL 4010642. FAX 4012180. *3026*

ACTA MATHEMATICAE APPLICATAE SINICA.
Science Press, Marketing and Sales Department, (Chinese Mathematics Society) 16 Donghuangchenggen Beijie, Beijing 100707, People's Republic of China. *3026*

ACTA MECHANICA SINICA.
Science Press, Marketing and Sales Department, (Chinese Society of Theoretical and Applied Mechanics) 16 Donghuangchenggen Beijie, Beijing 100707, People's Republic of China. TEL 4010642. FAX 4012180. *3842*

ACTA MECHANICA SOLIDA SINICA.
Pergamon Press, Inc., Journals Division, (Chinese Society for Theoretical and Applied Mechanics) 660 White Plains Rd., Tarrytown, NY 10591-5153. TEL 914-524-9200. FAX 914-333-2444. *3842*

ACTA MEDICA IRANICA.
Medical Sciences University of Teheran, School of Medicine, Enghelab Ave., Teheran 14-174, Iran. TEL 021-6112743. FAX 0098-21-6404377. *3070*

ACTA METALLURGICA ET MATERIALIA.
Pergamon Press, Inc., Journals Division, 660 White Plains Rd., Tarrytown, NY 10591-5153. TEL 914-524-9200. FAX 914-333-2444. *3401*

ACTA METEOROLOGICA SINICA.
China Meteorological Press, (Zhongguo Qixiang Xuehui) 46 Baishiqiao Road, West Suburb, Beijing 100081, People's Republic of China. *3431*

ACTA OCEANOLOGICA SINICA.
China Ocean Press, International Cooperation Department, (Chinese Society of Oceanography) Haimao Dalou, 1 Fuxingmenwai Dajie, Beijing 100860, People's Republic of China. TEL 868941. FAX 862209. *1601*

ACTA PSYCHOLOGICA.
North-Holland P.O. Box 211, 1000 AE Amsterdam, Netherlands. TEL 020-5803911. FAX 020-5803598. *4008*

ACTA REPRODUCTIVA TURCICA.
Hacettepe University, Department of Gynecology and Obstetrics, Ankara, Turkey. *3288*

ACTA SEISMOLOGICA SINICA.
Pergamon Press, Inc., Journals Division, (Seismological Society of China) 660 White Plains Rd., Tarrytown, NY 10591-5153. TEL 914-524-9200. FAX 914-333-2444. *1586*

ACTA TROPICA.
Elsevier Science Publishers B.V., (Schweizerisches Tropeninstitut) P.O. Box 211, 1000 AE Amsterdam, Netherlands. TEL 020-5803911. FAX 020-5803598. *3217*

ACTA ZOOLOGICA.
Pergamon Press, Inc., Journals Division, 660 White Plains Rd., Tarrytown, NY 10591-5153. TEL 914-524-9200. FAX 914-333-2444. *576*

ACTIVE AND PASSIVE ELECTRONIC COMPONENTS.
Gordon & Breach Science Publishers, 270 Eighth Ave., New York, NY 10011. TEL 212-206-8900. FAX 212-645-2459. *1881*

ACTIVITIES, ADAPTATION & AGING.
Haworth Press, Inc., 10 Alice St., Binghamton, NY 13904. TEL 800-342-9678. FAX 607-722-1424. *2269*

ACUPUNCTURE AND ELECTRO-THERAPEUTICS RESEARCH.
Pergamon Press, Inc., Journals Division, (International College of Acupuncture and Electro-Therapeutics) 660 White Plains Rd., Tarrytown, NY 10591-5153. TEL 914-524-9200. FAX 914-333-2444. *3071*

ADAPTED PHYSICAL ACTIVITY QUARTERLY.
Human Kinetics Publishers, Inc., Box 5076, Champaign, IL 61825-5076. TEL 217-351-5076. FAX 217-351-2674. *1733*

ADDICTIVE BEHAVIORS.
Pergamon Press, Inc., Journals Division, 660 White Plains Rd., Tarrytown, NY 10591-5153. TEL 914-524-9200. FAX 914-333-2444. *1533*

ADHESION.
Elsevier Science Publishers Ltd., Books Division, Crown House, Linton Rd., Barking, Essex IG11 8JU, England, England. TEL 081-594-7272. FAX 081-594-5942. *3861*

ADMINISTRATION AND POLICY IN MENTAL HEALTH.
Human Sciences Press, Inc. 233 Spring St., New York, NY 10013-1578. TEL 212-620-8000. FAX 212-463-0742. *3071*

ADMINISTRATION IN SOCIAL WORK.
Haworth Press, Inc., 10 Alice St., Binghamton, NY 13904. TEL 800-342-9678. FAX 607-722-1424. *4397*

ADMINISTRATIVE RADIOLOGY.
Glendale Publishing Corp., 1305 Glenoaks Blvd., Glendale, CA 91201. TEL 818-500-1872. *3356*

ADOLESCENT AND PEDIATRIC GYNECOLOGY.
Springer-Verlag, Journals, (North American Society for Pediatric and Adolescent Gynecology) 175 Fifth Ave., New York, NY 10010. TEL 212-460-1612. *3318*

ADOLESCENT MEDICINE (PHILADELPHIA).
Hanley & Belfus, Inc., 210 S. 13th St., Philadelphia, PA 19107. TEL 215-546-7293. FAX 215-790-9330. *3318*

ADOLESCENT PSYCHIATRY.
University of Chicago Press, Journals Division, (American Society for Adolescent Psychiatry) 5720 S. Woodlawn Ave., Chicago, IL 60637. TEL 312-702-7600. FAX 312-702-0694. *3328*

ADVANCED CARDIAC LIFE SUPPORT.
American Health Consultants, Inc., Six Piedmont Center, Ste. 400, 3525 Piedmont Rd., N.E., Atlanta, GA 30305. TEL 800-688-2421. FAX 800-284-3291. *3203*

ADVANCED CERAMICS AND GLASS.
Gruppo Editoriale Faenza Editrice S.p.A., Via Pier. de Crescenzi, 44, 48018 Faenza RA, Italy. TEL 0546-663480. FAX 0546-660440. *1160*

ADVANCED COMPOSITE MATERIALS.
V S P, (Japan Society for Composite Materials) P.O. Box 346, 3700 AH Zeist, Netherlands. TEL 03404-25790. FAX 03404-32081. *1911*

ADVANCED COMPOSITES LETTERS.
Woodhead Publishing Ltd., Abington Hall, Abington, Cambridge CB1 6AH, England. TEL 0223-891358. FAX 0223-893694. *3861*

ADVANCED DRUG DELIVERY REVIEWS.
Elsevier Science Publishers B.V., P.O. Box 211, 1000 BM Amsterdam, Netherlands. TEL 002-5803911. FAX 020-5803598. *3715*

ADVANCED LABANOTATION.
Harwood Academic Publishers, 270 Eighth Ave., New York, NY 10011. TEL 212-206-8900. FAX 212-645-2459. *3256*

ADVANCED SERIES IN MANAGEMENT.
Elsevier Science Publishers B.V., Books Division, P.O. Box 211, 1000 AE Amsterdam, Netherlands. TEL 020-5803911. FAX 020-5803705. *1002*

ADVANCED STUDIES IN CONTEMPORARY MATHEMATICS.
Gordon & Breach Science Publishers, P.O. Box 90, Reading, Berkshire RG1 8JL, England. TEL 0734-560-080. FAX 0734-568-211. *3027*

ADVANCED TEXTBOOKS IN ECONOMICS.
Elsevier Science Publishers B.V., Books Division, P.O. Box 211, 1000 AE Amsterdam, Netherlands. TEL 020-5803911. FAX 020-5803705. *889*

ADVANCES IN AGRONOMY.
Academic Press, Inc., (American Society for Agronomy, Inc.) 1250 Sixth Ave., San Diego, CA 92101. TEL 619-231-0926. FAX 619-699-6715. *68*

ADVANCES IN ANATOMY, EMBRYOLOGY AND CELL BIOLOGY.
Springer-Verlag, 175 Fifth Ave., New York, NY 10010. TEL 212-460-1500. *426*

ADVANCES IN APPLIED MATHEMATICS.
Academic Press, Inc., Journal Division, 1250 Sixth Ave., San Diego, CA 92101. TEL 619-230-1840. FAX 619-699-6800. *3027*

ADVANCES IN APPLIED MECHANICS.
Academic Press, Inc., 1250 Sixth Ave., San Diego, CA 92101. TEL 619-231-0926. FAX 619-699-6715. *3842*

ADVANCES IN APPLIED MICROBIOLOGY.
Academic Press, Inc., 1250 Sixth Ave., San Diego, CA 92101. TEL 619-231-0926. FAX 619-699-6715. *548*

ADVANCES IN APPLIED SOCIAL PSYCHOLOGY.
Lawrence Erlbaum Associates, Inc., 365 Broadway, Hillsdale, NJ 07642. TEL 201-666-4110. FAX 201-666-2394. *4008*

ADVANCES IN ATMOSPHERIC SCIENCES.
China Ocean Press, International Cooperation Department, (Chinese Committee of Meteorology and Atmospheric Physics) Haimao Dalou, 1 Fuxingmenwai Dajie, Beijing 100860, People's Republic of China. TEL 868941. FAX 862209. *3432*

ADVANCES IN BEHAVIORAL BIOLOGY.
Plenum Publishing Corp., 233 Spring St., New York, NY 10013-1578. TEL 212-620-8000. FAX 212-463-0742. *4008*

ADVANCES IN BEHAVIOUR RESEARCH AND THERAPY.
Pergamon Press, Inc., Journals Division, 660 White Plains Rd., Tarrytown, NY 10591-5153. TEL 914-524-9200. FAX 914-333-2444. *4008*

ADVANCES IN BIOCHEMICAL PSYCHOPHARMACOLOGY.
Raven Press, 1185 Ave. of the Americas, New York, NY 10036. TEL 212-930-9500. FAX 212-869-3495. *3715*

ADVANCES IN BIOENGINEERING.
American Society of Mechanical Engineers, 345 E. 47th St., New York, NY 10017. TEL 212-705-7722. *468*

ADVANCES IN BIOMATERIALS.
Elsevier Science Publishers B.V., Books Division, P.O. Box 211, 1000 AE Amsterdam, Netherlands. TEL 020-5803911. FAX 020-5803705. *470*

ADVANCES IN BIOPHYSICS.
Elsevier Scientific Publishers Ireland Ltd., (Biophysical Society of Japan) P.O. Box 85, Limerick, Ireland. TEL 061-61944. FAX 061-62144. *484*

ADVANCES IN BOTANICAL RESEARCH.
Academic Press, Inc., 1250 Sixth Ave., San Diego, CA 92101. TEL 619-231-0926. FAX 619-699-6715. *493*

ADVANCES IN CANCER RESEARCH.
Academic Press, Inc., 1250 Sixth Ave., San Diego, CA 92101. TEL 619-231-0926. FAX 619-699-6715. *3192*

ADVANCES IN CARBOHYDRATE CHEMISTRY AND BIOCHEMISTRY.
Academic Press, Inc., 1250 Sixth Ave., San Diego, CA 92101. TEL 619-231-0926. FAX 619-699-6715. *1215*

ADVANCES IN CATALYSIS.
Academic Press, Inc., 1250 Sixth Ave., San Diego, CA 92101. TEL 619-231-0926. FAX 619-699-6715. *1224*

ADVANCES IN CELL CULTURE.
Academic Press, Inc., 1250 Sixth Ave., San Diego, CA 92101. TEL 619-231-0926. FAX 619-699-6715. *522*

ADVANCES IN CHEMICAL ENGINEERING.
Academic Press, Inc., 1250 Sixth Ave., San Diego, CA 92101. TEL 619-231-0923. FAX 619-699-6715. *1848*

ADVANCES IN CHEMICAL PHYSICS.
John Wiley & Sons, Inc., 605 Third Ave., New York, NY 10158-0012. TEL 212-850-6000. FAX 212-850-6099. *3813*

ADVANCES IN CHEMISTRY SERIES.
American Chemical Society, 1155 16th St., N.W., Washington, DC 20036. TEL 202-872-4363. FAX 202-872-4615. *1168*

ADVANCES IN CHILD DEVELOPMENT AND BEHAVIOR.
Academic Press, Inc., 1250 Sixth Ave., San Diego, CA 92101. TEL 619-231-0926. FAX 619-699-6715. *4008*

ADVANCES IN CHROMATOGRAPHY.
Marcel Dekker, Inc., 270 Madison Ave., New York, NY 10016. TEL 212-696-9000. FAX 212-685-4540. *1203*

ADVANCES IN CLINICAL CHEMISTRY.
Academic Press, Inc., 1250 Sixth Ave., San Diego, CA 92101. TEL 619-231-0926. FAX 619-699-6715. *470*

ADVANCES IN CLINICAL CHILD PSYCHOLOGY.
Plenum Publishing Corp., 233 Spring St., New York, NY 10013-1578. TEL 212-620-8000. FAX 212-463-0742. *4008*

ADVANCES IN COLLOID AND INTERFACE SCIENCE.
Elsevier Science Publishers B.V., P.O. Box 211, 1000 AE Amsterdam, Netherlands. TEL 020-5803911. FAX 020-5803598. *1224*

ADVANCES IN COMPUTERS.
Academic Press, Inc., 1250 Sixth Ave., San Diego, CA 92101. TEL 619-231-0926. FAX 619-699-6715. *1389*

ADVANCES IN CRYOGENIC ENGINEERING.
Plenum Publishing Corp., 233 Spring St., New York, NY 10013-1578. TEL 212-620-8000. FAX 212-463-0742. *3840*

ADVANCES IN DESCRIPTIVE PSYCHOLOGY.
J A I Press Inc., (Society for Descriptive Psychology) 55 Old Post Rd., No. 2, Box 1678, Greenwich, CT 06836-1678. TEL 203-661-7602. *4008*

ADVANCES IN DESERT AND ARID LAND TECHNOLOGY AND DEVELOPMENT SERIES.
Harwood Academic Publishers, 270 Eighth Ave., New York, NY 10011. TEL 212-206-8900. FAX 212-645-2459. *2241*

ADVANCES IN DEVELOPMENTAL AND BEHAVIORAL PEDIATRICS.
Jessica Kingsley Publishers, 118 Pentonville Rd., London N1 9JN, England. TEL 071-883-2307. FAX 071-837-2917. *3318*

ADVANCES IN DEVELOPMENTAL PSYCHOLOGY.
Lawrence Erlbaum Associates, Inc., 365 Broadway, Hillsdale, NJ 07642. TEL 201-666-4110. FAX 201-666-2394. *4008*

ADVANCES IN DRUG RESEARCH.
Academic Press, Inc., 1250 Sixth Ave., San Diego, CA 92101. TEL 619-231-0926. FAX 619-699-6715. *3715*

ADVANCES IN DRYING.
Hemisphere Publishing Corporation 1900 Frost Rd., Ste. 101, Bristol, PA 19007-1598. TEL 215-785-5800. FAX 215-785-5515. *1926*

ADVANCES IN ECOLOGICAL RESEARCH.
Academic Press, Inc., 1250 Sixth Ave., San Diego, CA 92101. TEL 619-231-0926. FAX 619-699-6715. *1941*

ADVANCES IN ECONOMIC BOTANY.
New York Botanical Garden, Scientific Publications Department, Bronx, NY 10458. TEL 212-220-8721. FAX 212-220-6504. *493*

REFEREED SERIALS

ADVANCES IN ELECTRONICS AND ELECTRON PHYSICS.
Academic Press, Inc., 1250 Sixth Ave., San Diego, CA 92101. TEL 619-231-0926. FAX 619-699-6715. *1881*

ADVANCES IN ENGINEERING.
Society of Automotive Engineers, 400 Commonwealth Dr., Warrendale, PA 15096-0001. TEL 412-776-4841. FAX 412-776-5760. *4679*

ADVANCES IN ENGINEERING SOFTWARE.
Elsevier Science Publishers Ltd., Crown House, Linton Rd., Barking, Essex IG11 8JU, England. TEL 081-594-7272. FAX 081-594-5942. *1877*

ADVANCES IN ENVIRONMENTAL PSYCHOLOGY.
Lawrence Erlbaum Associates, Inc., 365 Broadway, Hillsdale, NJ 07642. TEL 201-666-4110. FAX 201-666-2394. *4008*

ADVANCES IN ENVIRONMENTAL SCIENCE AND ENGINEERING.
Gordon & Breach Science Publishers, 270 Eighth Ave., New York, NY 10011. TEL 212-206-8900. FAX 212-645-2459. *1941*

ADVANCES IN ENZYME REGULATION.
Pergamon Press, Inc., Journals Division, 660 White Plains Rd., Tarrytown, NY 10591-5153. TEL 914-524-9200. FAX 914-333-2444. *3071*

ADVANCES IN ENZYMOLOGY AND RELATED AREAS OF MOLECULAR BIOLOGY.
John Wiley & Sons, Inc., Journals, 605 Third Ave., New York, NY 10158-0012. TEL 212-850-6418. *470*

ADVANCES IN EXPERIMENTAL MEDICINE AND BIOLOGY.
Plenum Publishing Corp., 233 Spring St., New York, NY 10013-1578. TEL 212-620-8000. FAX 212-463-0742. *426*

ADVANCES IN GENETICS.
Academic Press, Inc., 1250 Sixth Ave., San Diego, CA 92101. TEL 619-231-0926. FAX 619-699-6715. *539*

ADVANCES IN GEOPHYSICS.
Academic Press, Inc., 1250 Sixth Ave., San Diego, CA 92101. TEL 619-231-0926. FAX 619-699-6715. *1586*

ADVANCES IN HEALTH ECONOMICS AND HEALTH SERVICES RESEARCH.
J A I Press Inc., 55 Old Post Rd., No. 2, Box 1678, Greenwich, CT 06836-1678. TEL 203-661-7602. *3799*

ADVANCES IN HEALTH EDUCATION: CURRENT RESEARCH.
A M S Press, Inc., 56 E. 13th St., New York, NY 10003. TEL 212-777-4700. FAX 212-995-5413. *1743*

ADVANCES IN HEAT TRANSFER.
Academic Press, Inc., 1250 Sixth Ave., San Diego, CA 92101. TEL 619-231-0926. FAX 619-699-6715. *3840*

ADVANCES IN HETEROCYCLIC CHEMISTRY.
Academic Press, Inc., 1250 Sixth Ave., San Diego, CA 92101. TEL 619-231-0926. FAX 619-699-6715. *1215*

ADVANCES IN HUMAN - COMPUTER INTERACTION.
Ablex Publishing Corporation, 355 Chestnut St., Norwood, NJ 07648. TEL 201-767-8450. FAX 201-767-6717. *1411*

ADVANCES IN HUMAN FACTORS - ERGONOMICS.
Elsevier Science Publishers B.V., Books Division, P.O. Box 211, 1000 AE Amsterdam, Netherlands. TEL 020-5803911. FAX 020-5803705. *4009*

ADVANCES IN HUMAN GENETICS.
Plenum Publishing Corp., 233 Spring St., New York, NY 10013-1578. TEL 212-620-8000. FAX 212-463-0742. *539*

ADVANCES IN HUMAN PSYCHOPHARMACOLOGY.
Jessica Kingsley Publishers, 118 Pentonville Rd., London N1 9JN, England. TEL 071-833-2307. FAX 071-837-2917. *3715*

ADVANCES IN INDUSTRIAL ENGINEERING.
Elsevier Science Publishers B.V., Books Division, P.O. Box 211, 1000 AE Amsterdam, Netherlands. TEL 020-5803911. FAX 020-5803705. *1925*

ADVANCES IN INFANCY RESEARCH.
Ablex Publishing Corporation, 355 Chestnut St., Norwood, NJ 07648. TEL 201-767-8450. FAX 201-767-6717. *3318*

ADVANCES IN INFLAMMATION RESEARCH.
Raven Press, 1185 Ave. of the Americas, New York, NY 10036. TEL 212-930-9500. FAX 212-869-3495. *3071*

ADVANCES IN INORGANIC BIOCHEMISTRY.
Elsevier Science Publishers B.V., Books Division, P.O. Box 211, 1000 AE Amsterdam, Netherlands. TEL 020-5803911. FAX 020-5803705. *1213*

ADVANCES IN INORGANIC CHEMISTRY AND RADIOCHEMISTRY.
Academic Press, Inc., 1250 Sixth Ave., San Diego, CA 92101. TEL 619-231-0926. FAX 619-699-6715. *1213*

ADVANCES IN INSECT PHYSIOLOGY.
Academic Press, Inc., 1250 Sixth Ave., San Diego, CA 92101. TEL 619-231-0926. FAX 619-699-6715. *527*

ADVANCES IN INSTRUCTIONAL PSYCHOLOGY.
Lawrence Erlbaum Associates, Inc., 365 Broadway, Hillsdale, NJ 07642. TEL 201-666-4110. FAX 201-666-2394. *4009*

ADVANCES IN INSTRUMENTATION.
Instrument Society of America, 67 Alexander Dr., Box 12277, Research Triangle Park, NC 27709. TEL 919-549-8411. FAX 919-549-8288. *2521*

ADVANCES IN LEARNING AND BEHAVIORAL DISABILITIES.
J A I Press Inc., 55 Old Post Rd., No. 2, Box 1678, Greenwich, CT 06836-1678. TEL 203-661-7602. *1232*

ADVANCES IN LIPID RESEARCH.
Academic Press, Inc., 1250 Sixth Ave., San Diego, CA 92101. TEL 619-231-0926. FAX 619-699-6715. *470*

ADVANCES IN MAGNETIC RESONANCE.
Academic Press, Inc., 1250 Sixth Ave., San Diego, CA 92101. TEL 619-231-0926. FAX 619-699-6715. *3813*

ADVANCES IN MAGNETIC RESONANCE IMAGING.
Ablex Publishing Corporation, 355 Chestnut St., Norwood, NJ 07648. TEL 201-767-8450. FAX 201-767-6717. *1420*

ADVANCES IN MARINE BIOLOGY.
Academic Press, Inc., 1250 Sixth Ave., San Diego, CA 92101. TEL 619-231-0926. FAX 619-699-6715. *426*

ADVANCES IN MATHEMATICS.
Academic Press, Inc., Journal Division, 1250 Sixth Ave., San Diego, CA 92101. TEL 619-230-1840. FAX 619-699-6800. *3027*

ADVANCES IN MEDICAL SOCIAL SCIENCE.
Gordon & Breach Science Publishers, 270 Eighth Ave., New York, NY 10011. TEL 212-206-8900. FAX 212-645-2459. *4364*

ADVANCES IN METABOLIC DISORDERS.
Academic Press, Inc., 1250 Sixth Ave., San Diego, CA 92101. TEL 619-231-0926. FAX 619-699-6715. *3250*

ADVANCES IN MICROBIAL ECOLOGY.
Plenum Publishing Corp., 233 Spring St., New York, NY 10013-1578. TEL 212-620-8000. FAX 212-463-0742. *548*

ADVANCES IN MICROBIAL PHYSIOLOGY.
Academic Press, Inc., 1250 Sixth Ave., San Diego, CA 92101. TEL 619-231-0926. FAX 619-699-6715. *548*

ADVANCES IN MICROWAVES.
Academic Press, Inc., 1250 Sixth Ave., San Diego, CA 92101. TEL 619-231-0926. FAX 619-699-6715. *1881*

ADVANCES IN MODELLING & ANALYSIS.
A M S E Press, (International Association for the Advancement of Modelling and Simulation Techniques in Enterprises) 16 av. de Grange Blanche, 69160 Tassin-la-Demi-Lune, France. TEL 78-34-36-04. FAX 78-34-54-17. *3064*

ADVANCES IN MOLTEN SALT CHEMISTRY.
Plenum Publishing Corp., 233 Spring St., New York, NY 10013-1578. TEL 212-620-8000. FAX 212-463-0742. *1213*

ADVANCES IN MOTOR DEVELOPMENT RESEARCH.
A M S Press, Inc., 56 E. 13th St., New York, NY 10003. TEL 212-777-4700. FAX 212-995-5413. *3799*

ADVANCES IN NEURAL AND BEHAVIORAL DEVELOPMENT.
Ablex Publishing Corporation, 355 Chestnut St., Norwood, NJ 07648. TEL 201-767-8450. FAX 201-767-6717. *4009*

ADVANCES IN NEUROCHEMISTRY.
Plenum Publishing Corp., 233 Spring St., New York, NY 10013-1578. TEL 212-620-8000. FAX 212-463-0742. *470*

ADVANCES IN NEUROIMMUNOLOGY.
Pergamon Press plc, Headington Hill Hall, Oxford OX3 0BW, England. TEL 0865-794141. FAX 0865-743911. *3182*

ADVANCES IN NEUROLOGY.
Raven Press, 1185 Ave. of the Americas, New York, NY 10036. TEL 212-930-9500. FAX 212-869-3495. *3328*

ADVANCES IN NUCLEAR PHYSICS.
Plenum Publishing Corp., 233 Spring St., New York, NY 10013-1578. TEL 212-620-8000. FAX 212-463-0742. *3846*

ADVANCES IN NUCLEAR SCIENCE AND TECHNOLOGY.
Plenum Publishing Corp., 233 Spring St., New York, NY 10013-1578. TEL 212-620-8047. *3846*

ADVANCES IN NURSING SCIENCE.
Aspen Publishers, Inc., 200 Orchard Ridge Dr., Gaithersburg, MD 20878. TEL 301-417-7500. FAX 301-417-7550. *3275*

ADVANCES IN NUTRITIONAL RESEARCH.
Plenum Publishing Corp., 233 Spring St., New York, NY 10013-1578. TEL 212-620-8000. FAX 212-463-0742. *3602*

ADVANCES IN OPHTHALMIC PLASTIC & RECONSTRUCTIVE SURGERY.
Pergamon Press plc, Headington Hill Hall, Oxford OX3 0BW, England. TEL 0865-794141. FAX 0865-743911. *3297*

ADVANCES IN OPTICAL AND ELECTRON MICROSCOPY.
Academic Press, Inc., 1250 Sixth Ave., San Diego, CA 92101. TEL 619-699-6715. FAX 619-231-6616. *3851*

ADVANCES IN ORGANIC COATINGS SCIENCE AND TECHNOLOGY.
Technomic Publishing Co., Inc., 851 New Holland Ave., Box 3535, Lancaster, PA 17604. TEL 717-291-5609. FAX 717-295-4538. *1215*

ADVANCES IN ORGANOMETALLIC CHEMISTRY.
Academic Press, Inc., 1250 Sixth Ave., San Diego, CA 92101. TEL 619-231-0926. FAX 619-699-6715. *1215*

ADVANCES IN ORTHOPAEDIC SURGERY.
Data Trace Medical Publishers, Inc., 606 Baltimore Ave., Ste.322, Baltimore, MD 21204. TEL 301-494-4994. FAX 301-494-0515. *3306*

ADVANCES IN PAIN RESEARCH AND THERAPY.
Raven Press, 1185 Ave. of the Americas, New York, NY 10036. TEL 212-930-9500. FAX 212-869-3495. *3328*

ADVANCES IN PARASITOLOGY.
Academic Press, Inc., 1250 Sixth Ave., San Diego, CA 92101. TEL 619-231-0926. FAX 619-699-6715. *576*

ADVANCES IN PERSONALITY ASSESSMENT.
Lawrence Erlbaum Associates, Inc., 365 Broadway, Hillsdale, NJ 07642. TEL 201-666-4110. FAX 201-666-2394. *4009*

ADVANCES IN PETROLEUM GEOCHEMISTRY.
Academic Press, Inc., 2150 Sixth Ave., San Diego, CA 92101. TEL 619-231-6616. FAX 619-699-6715. *3681*

ADVANCES IN PHARMACEUTICAL SCIENCES.
Academic Press, Inc., 1250 Sixth Ave., San Diego, CA 92101. TEL 619-231-0926. FAX 619-699-6715. *3715*

ADVANCES IN PHARMACOLOGY.
Academic Press, Inc., 1250 Sixth Ave., San Diego, CA 92101. TEL 619-231-0926. FAX 619-699-6715. *3715*

ADVANCES IN PHOTOCHEMISTRY.
John Wiley & Sons, Inc., 605 Third Ave., New York, NY 10158-0012. TEL 212-850-6645. *1224*

ADVANCES IN PHYSICAL ORGANIC CHEMISTRY.
Academic Press, Inc., 1250 Sixth Ave., San Diego, CA 92101. TEL 619-231-0926. FAX 619-699-6715. *1224*

ADVANCES IN PHYSICS.
Taylor & Francis Ltd., Rankine Rd., Basingstoke, Hants. RG24 OPR, England. TEL 0256-840366. FAX 0256-479438. *3813*

ADVANCES IN PLANT PATHOLOGY.
Academic Press, Inc., 1250 Sixth Ave., San Diego, CA 92101. TEL 305-345-2000. FAX 619-699-6715. *493*

ADVANCES IN PROBABILITY AND RELATED TOPICS.
Marcel Dekker, Inc., 270 Madison Ave., New York, NY 10016. TEL 212-696-9000. FAX 212-685-4540. *3027*

ADVANCES IN PROSTAGLANDIN, THROMBOXANE, AND LEUKOTRIENE RESEARCH.
Raven Press, 1185 Ave. of the Americas, New York, NY 10036. TEL 212-930-9500. FAX 212-869-3495. *3250*

ADVANCES IN PROTEIN CHEMISTRY.
Academic Press, Inc., 1250 Sixth Ave., San Diego, CA 92101. TEL 619-231-0926. FAX 619-699-6715. *470*

ADVANCES IN PSYCHOLOGY.
Elsevier Science Publishers B.V., Books Division, P.O. Box 211, 1000 AE Amsterdam, Netherlands. TEL 020-5803911. FAX 020-5803705. *4009*

ADVANCES IN QUANTUM CHEMISTRY.
Academic Press, Inc., 1250 Sixth Ave., San Diego, CA 92101. TEL 619-231-0926. FAX 619-699-6715. *1169*

ADVANCES IN RADIATION BIOLOGY.
Academic Press, Inc., 1250 Sixth Ave., San Diego, CA 92101. TEL 619-231-0926. FAX 619-699-6715. *484*

ADVANCES IN RISK ANALYSIS.
Plenum Publishing Corp., (Society for Risk Analysis) 233 Spring St., New York, NY 10013-1578. TEL 212-620-8000. FAX 212-463-0742. *4116*

ADVANCES IN SCHOOL PSYCHOLOGY.
Lawrence Erlbaum Associates, Inc., 365 Broadway, Hillsdale, NJ 07642. TEL 201-666-4110. FAX 201-666-2394. *4009*

ADVANCES IN SECOND MESSENGER AND PHOSPHOPROTEIN RESEARCH.
Raven Press, 1185 Ave. of the Americas, New York, NY 10036. TEL 212-930-9500. FAX 212-869-3495. *470*

ADVANCES IN SMALL ANIMAL MEDICINE AND SURGERY.
John Colet Press, Inc., 31 St. James Ave., Boston, MA 02116-4101. TEL 617-426-2303. FAX 617-426-9767. *4804*

ADVANCES IN SOFTWARE ENGINEERING.
J A I Press Inc., 55 Old Post Rd., No. 2, Box 1678, Greenwich, CT 06836-1678. TEL 203-661-7602. *1475*

ADVANCES IN SOFTWARE SCIENCE AND TECHNOLOGY.
Academic Press, Inc., (Japanese Society for Software Science and Technology) 1250 Sixth Ave., San Diego, CA 92101. TEL 619-231-6616. FAX 619-699-6715. *1475*

ADVANCES IN SOLAR ENERGY: AN ANNUAL REVIEW OF RESEARCH AND DEVELOPMENT.
Plenum Publishing Corp., (American Solar Energy Society, Inc.) 233 Spring St., New York, NY 10013-1578. TEL 212-620-8000. FAX 212-463-0742. *1810*

ADVANCES IN SPACE RESEARCH.
Pergamon Press, Inc., Journals Division, (International Council of Scientific Unions, Committee on Space Research) 660 White Plains Rd., Tarrytown, NY 10591-5153. TEL 914-524-9200. FAX 914-333-2444. *43*

ADVANCES IN SPATIAL REASONING.
Ablex Publishing Corporation, 355 Chestnut St., Norwood, NJ 07648. TEL 201-767-8450. FAX 201-676-6717. *1406*

ADVANCES IN SUBSTANCE ABUSE: BEHAVIORAL AND BIOLOGICAL RESEARCH.
Jessica Kingsley Publishers, 118 Pentonville Rd., London N1 9JN, England. TEL 071-833-2307. FAX 071-837-2917. *1533*

ADVANCES IN THE ASTRONAUTICAL SCIENCES.
Univelt, Inc., (American Astronautical Society) Box 28130, San Diego, CA 92198. TEL 619-746-4005. *43*

ADVANCES IN THE BIOSCIENCES.
Pergamon Press, Inc., Journals Division, 660 White Plains Rd., Tarrytown, NY 10591-5153. TEL 914-524-9200. FAX 914-333-2444. *426*

ADVANCES IN THE MECHANICS AND PHYSICS OF SURFACES SERIES.
Harwood Academic Publishers, 270 Eighth Ave., New York, NY 10011. TEL 212-206-8900. FAX 212-645-2459. *3842*

ADVANCES IN THE PSYCHOLOGY OF HUMAN INTELLIGENCE.
Lawrence Erlbaum Associates, Inc., 365 Broadway, Hillsdale, NJ 07642. TEL 201-666-4110. FAX 201-666-2394. *4009*

ADVANCES IN THE STUDY OF AGGRESSION.
Academic Press, Inc., 1250 Sixth Ave., San Diego, CA 92101. TEL 619-231-6616. FAX 619-699-6715. *4009*

ADVANCES IN THE STUDY OF BEHAVIOR.
Academic Press, Inc., 1250 Sixth Ave., San Diego, CA 92101. TEL 619-231-0926. FAX 619-699-6715. *4009*

ADVANCES IN THE STUDY OF COMMUNICATION AND AFFECT.
Plenum Publishing Corp., 233 Spring St., New York, NY 10013-1578. TEL 212-620-8000. FAX 212-463-0742. *4009*

ADVANCES IN URETHANE SCIENCE AND TECHNOLOGY.
Technomic Publishing Co., Inc., 851 New Holland Ave., Box 3535, Lancaster, PA 17604. TEL 717-291-5609. FAX 717-295-4538. *1215*

ADVANCES IN VETERINARY SCIENCE AND COMPARATIVE MEDICINE.
Academic Press, Inc., 1250 Sixth Ave., San Diego, CA 92101. TEL 619-231-0926. FAX 619-699-6715. *4804*

ADVANCES IN VIRUS RESEARCH.
Academic Press, Inc., 1250 Sixth Ave., San Diego, CA 92101. TEL 619-231-0926. FAX 619-699-6715. *548*

ADVANCES IN WATER RESOURCES.
Elsevier Science Publishers Ltd., Crown House, Linton Rd., Barking, Essex IG11 8JU, England. TEL 081-594-7272. FAX 081-594-5942. *4821*

ADVANCES IN X-RAY ANALYSIS.
Plenum Publishing Corp., (University of Denver, Denver Research Institute) 233 Spring St., New York, NY 10013-1578. TEL 212-620-8000. FAX 212-463-0742. *4593*

AERONAUTICAL MANUFACTURING TECHNOLOGY.
Beijing Hangkong Gongyi Yanjiusuo, P.O. Box 863, Beijing 100024, People's Republic of China. TEL 5761731. FAX 5762306. *43*

AEROSOL SCIENCE AND TECHNOLOGY.
Elsevier Science Publishing Co., Inc. (New York), (American Association for Aerosol Research) 655 Ave. of the Americas, New York, NY 10010. TEL 212-989-5800. FAX 212-633-3965. *1169*

AGE.
American Aging Association, 600 S. 42nd St., Omaha, NE 68198-4635. TEL 402-559-4416. *2269*

AGGRESSIVE BEHAVIOR.
John Wiley & Sons, Inc., Journals, (International Society for Research on Agression) 605 Third Ave., New York, NY 10158. TEL 212-850-6000. FAX 212-850-6088. *4009*

AGING (NEW YORK).
Raven Press, 1185 Ave. of the Americas, New York, NY 10036. TEL 212-930-9500. FAX 212-869-3495. *2269*

AGING (WASHINGTON).
U.S. Administration on Aging, U.S Dept. of Health and Human Services, Washington, DC 20201. TEL 202-783-3238. FAX 202-275-0019. *2269*

AGING: IMMUNOLOGY & INFECTIOUS DISEASE.
Mary Ann Liebert, Inc., 1651 Third Ave., New York, NY 10128. TEL 212-289-2300. FAX 212-289-4697. *2269*

AGRI-PRACTICE.
Veterinary Practice Publishing Co., 7 Ashley Ave. S., Santa Barbara, CA 93103-9989. TEL 805-965-1028. FAX 805-965-0722. *4805*

AGRICULTURAL AND FOREST METEOROLOGY.
Elsevier Science Publishers B.V., P.O. Box 211, 1000 AE Amsterdam, Netherlands. TEL 020-5803911. FAX 020-5803598. *3432*

AGRICULTURAL ECONOMICS.
Elsevier Science Publishers B.V., P.O. Box 211, 1000 AE Amsterdam, Netherlands. TEL 020-5803911. FAX 020-5803598. *146*

AGRICULTURAL FINANCE REVIEW.
Cornell University, Department of Agricultural Economics, Ithaca, NY 14853. TEL 607-255-4534. FAX 607-255-9984. *146*

AGRICULTURAL HISTORY.
University of California Press, Journals Division, (Agricultural History Society) 2120 Berkeley Way, Berkeley, CA 94720. TEL 510-642-4191. FAX 510-643-7127. *71*

AGRICULTURAL SYSTEMS.
Elsevier Science Publishers Ltd., Crown House, Linton Rd., Barking, Essex IG11 8JU, England. TEL 081-594-7272. FAX 081-594-5942. *72*

AGRICULTURAL WATER MANAGEMENT.
Elsevier Science Publishers B.V., P.O. Box 211, 1000 AE Amsterdam, Netherlands. TEL 020-5803911. FAX 020-5803598. *167*

AGRICULTURE, ECOSYSTEMS AND ENVIRONMENT.
Elsevier Science Publishers B.V., P.O. Box 211, 1000 AE Amsterdam, Netherlands. TEL 020-5803911. FAX 020-5803598. *72*

AGROBOREALIS.
University of Alaska, Fairbanks, Agricultural and Forestry Experiment Station, Fairbanks, AK 99775. TEL 907-474-7653. *73*

AGRONOMIE.
Editions Scientifiques Elsevier, (Institut National de la Recherche Agronomique (INRA)) 29, rue Buffon, 75005 Paris, France. TEL 47-07-11-22. FAX 43-36-80-93. *167*

ALABAMA GEOLOGICAL SOCIETY. GUIDEBOOK FOR THE ANNUAL FIELD TRIP.
Alabama Geological Society, Box 6184, Tuscaloosa, AL 35486. TEL 205-349-2852. *1553*

REFEREED SERIALS

ALASKA. DIVISION OF GEOLOGICAL AND GEOPHYSICAL SURVEYS. GEOLOGIC - PROFESSIONAL REPORT.
Department of Natural Resources, Division of Geological and Geophysical Surveys, 794 University Ave., Ste.200, Fairbanks, AK 99709-3645. TEL 907-474-7147. FAX 907-479-4779. *1554*

ALASKA. DIVISION OF GEOLOGICAL AND GEOPHYSICAL SURVEYS. INFORMATION CIRCULAR.
Department of Natural Resources, Division of Geological and Geophysical Surveys, 794 University Ave. Ste. 200, Fairbanks, AK 99709-3645. TEL 907-474-7147. FAX 907-479-4779. *1554*

ALASKA. DIVISION OF GEOLOGICAL AND GEOPHYSICAL SURVEYS. REPORT OF INVESTIGATIONS.
Department of Natural Resources, Division of Geological and Geophysical Surveys, 794 Universtiy Ave. Ste. 200, Fairbanks, AK 99709-3645. TEL 907-474-7147. FAX 907-479-4779. *1554*

ALASKA. DIVISION OF GEOLOGICAL AND GEOPHYSICAL SURVEYS. SPECIAL REPORT.
Department of Natural Resources, Division of Geological and Geophysical Surveys, 794 University Ave. Ste. 200, Fairbanks, AK 99709-3645. TEL 907-474-7147. FAX 907-479-4779. *1554*

ALCOHOL.
Pergamon Press, Inc., Journals Division, 660 White Plains Rd., Tarrytown, NY 10591-5153. TEL 914-524-9200. FAX 914-333-2444. *1533*

ALCOHOL & ALCOHOLISM.
Pergamon Press, Inc., Journals Division, (Medical Council on Alcoholism) 660 White Plains Rd., Tarrytown, NY 10591-5153. TEL 914-524-9200. FAX 914-333-2444. *1533*

ALCOHOLISM: CLINICAL AND EXPERIMENTAL RESEARCH.
Williams & Wilkins, (Research Society on Alcoholism) 428 E. Preston St., Baltimore, MD 21202. TEL 301-528-4000. FAX 301-528-4312. *1534*

ALCOHOLISM TREATMENT QUARTERLY.
Haworth Press, Inc., 10 Alice St., Binghamton, NY 13904. TEL 800-342-9678. FAX 607-722-1424. *1534*

ALGEBRA AND LOGIC.
Plenum Publishing Corp., Consultants Bureau, (Russian Academy of Sciences) 233 Spring St., New York, NY 10013-1578. TEL 212-620-8468. FAX 212-463-0742. *3027*

ALGEBRA, LOGIC AND APPLICATIONS.
Gordon & Breach Science Publishers, P.O. Box 90, Reading, Berkshire RG1 8JL, England. TEL 0734-560-080. FAX 0734-568-211. *3027*

ALGORITHMICA.
Springer-Verlag, Journals, 175 Fifth Ave., New York, NY 10010. TEL 212-460-1500. *1389*

ALISO.
Rancho Santa Ana Botanic Garden, 1500 N. College Ave., Claremont, CA 91711. TEL 714-625-8767. FAX 714-626-7670. *493*

ALKALOIDS.
Academic Press, Inc., 1250 Sixth Ave., San Diego, CA 92101. TEL 619-231-0926. FAX 619-699-6715. *1216*

ALLERTONIA.
National Tropical Botanical Garden, Box 340, Lawai, Kauai, HI 96765. TEL 808-332-7324. FAX 808-332-9765. *493*

ALZHEIMER DISEASE AND ASSOCIATED DISORDERS.
1185 Ave. of the Americas, New York, NY 10036. TEL 212-930-9500. FAX 212-869-3495. *2270*

AMBIO.
Allen Press, Inc., (Royal Swedish Academy of Sciences) Box 1897, Lawrence, KS 66044. TEL 913-843-1234. *1942*

AMBIX.
Black Bear Press Ltd., (Society for the History of Alchemy and Chemistry) Kings Hedges Rd., Cambridge CB4 2PQ, England. *1169*

AMERICAN ACADEMY OF CHILD AND ADOLESCENT PSYCHIATRY. JOURNAL.
Williams & Wilkins, 428 E. Preston St., Baltimore, MD 21202. TEL 301-528-4000. FAX 301-528-4312. *3329*

AMERICAN ACADEMY OF DERMATOLOGY. JOURNAL.
Mosby - Year Book, Inc. (American Academy of Dermatology) 11830 Westline Industrial Dr., St. Louis, MO 63146. TEL 800-325-4117. FAX 314-432-1380. *3245*

AMERICAN ACADEMY OF NURSE PRACTITIONERS. JOURNAL.
J.B. Lippincott Co., E. Washington Sq., Philadelphia, PA 19105. TEL 215-238-4200. *3275*

AMERICAN ACADEMY OF PHYSICIAN ASSISTANTS. JOURNAL.
Mosby - Year Book, Inc. 11830 Westline Industrial Dr., St. Louis, MO 63146. TEL 800-325-4117. FAX 314-432-1380. *3073*

AMERICAN ACADEMY OF PSYCHOANALYSIS. JOURNAL.
Guilford Publications, Inc., (American Academy of Psychoanalysis) 72 Spring St., 4th Fl., New York, NY 10012. TEL 212-431-9800. FAX 212-966-6708. *4009*

AMERICAN ANIMAL HOSPITAL ASSOCIATION JOURNAL.
American Animal Hospital Association, Box 150899, Denver, CO 80215-0899. TEL 303-279-2500. FAX 303-729-1816. *4805*

AMERICAN ANNALS OF THE DEAF.
Convention of American Instructors of the Deaf, KDES, PAS-6, 800 Florida Ave., N.E., Washington, DC 20002. TEL 202-651-5340. FAX 202-651-5708. *2286*

AMERICAN ANTHROPOLOGIST.
American Anthropological Association, 1703 New Hampshire Ave., N.W., Washington, DC 20009. TEL 202-232-8800. *233*

AMERICAN ANTHROPOLOGIST. SPECIAL PUBLICATION.
American Anthropological Association, 1703 New Hampshire Ave., N.W., Washington, DC 20009. TEL 202-232-8800. *233*

AMERICAN ART.
Rizzoli International Publications, Inc., (Smithsonian Institution, National Museum of Art) 300 Park Ave. S., New York, NY 10010. TEL 212-387-3400. FAX 212-387-3535. *311*

AMERICAN ASSOCIATION OF OCCUPATIONAL HEALTH NURSES JOURNAL.
Slack, Inc., (American Association of Occupational Health Nurses, Inc.) 6900 Grove Rd., Thorofare, NJ 08086. TEL 609-848-1000. FAX 609-853-5991. *3275*

AMERICAN BIOLOGY TEACHER.
National Association of Biology Teachers, Inc., 11250 Roger Bacon Dr., Ste. 19, Reston, VA 22090. TEL 703-471-1134. *427*

AMERICAN BOTTOM ARCHAEOLOGY.
University of Illinois Press, 54 E. Gregory Dr., Champaign, IL 61820. TEL 217-333-0950. FAX 217-244-8082. *261*

AMERICAN BUSINESS LAW JOURNAL.
Academy of Legal Studies in Business, c/o Daniel J. Herron, School of Business, Western Carolina University, Cullowhee, NC 28723. TEL 704-586-1423. FAX 704-227-7414. *2597*

AMERICAN CERAMIC SOCIETY. JOURNAL.
American Ceramic Society, 735 Ceramic Pl., Westerville, OH 43081. TEL 614-890-4700. FAX 614-899-6109. *1161*

AMERICAN COLLEGE OF CARDIOLOGY. ABSTRACTS.
Elsevier Science Publishing Co., Inc. (New York), (American College of Cardiology) 655 Ave. of the Americas, New York, NY 10010. TEL 212-989-5800. FAX 212-633-3965. *3166*

AMERICAN COLLEGE OF CARDIOLOGY. JOURNAL.
Elsevier Science Publishing Co., Inc. (New York), (American College of Cardiology) 655 Ave. of the Americas, New York, NY 10010. TEL 212-989-5800. FAX 212-633-3965. *3203*

AMERICAN COLLEGE OF DENTISTS. JOURNAL.
American College of Dentists, 839-J Quince Orchard Blvd., Gaitersburg, MD 20878. TEL 301-986-0555. FAX 301-654-3275. *3227*

AMERICAN COLLEGE OF LABORATORY ANIMAL MEDICINE SERIES.
Academic Press, Inc., 1250 Sixth Ave., San Diego, CA 92101. TEL 619-231-6616. FAX 619-699-6715. *3257*

AMERICAN COLLEGE OF NUTRITION. JOURNAL.
John Wiley & Sons, Inc., Journals, 605 Third Ave., New York, NY 10158-0012. TEL 212-850-6000. FAX 212-850-6088. *3603*

AMERICAN COLLEGE OF TOXICOLOGY. JOURNAL. PART A.
Mary Ann Liebert, Inc., 1651 Third Ave., New York, NY 10128. TEL 212-289-2300. FAX 212-289-4697. *1980*

AMERICAN DENTAL ASSOCIATION. JOURNAL.
A D A Publishers, Inc., 211 E. Chicago Ave., Chicago, IL 60611. TEL 312-440-2500. *3227*

AMERICAN DIETETIC ASSOCIATION. JOURNAL.
American Dietetic Association, 216 W. Jackson Blvd., Ste. 800, Chicago, IL 60606-6995. TEL 312-899-0040. FAX 312-899-1757. *3603*

AMERICAN FAMILY PHYSICIAN.
American Academy of Family Physicians, 8880 Ward Pkwy., Kansas City, MO 64114. TEL 816-333-9700. FAX 816-822-0580. *3074*

AMERICAN FISHERIES SOCIETY. SPECIAL PUBLICATION.
American Fisheries Society, 5410 Grosvenor Ln., Ste. 110, Bethesda, MD 20814-2199. TEL 301-897-8616. FAX 301-897-8096. *2036*

AMERICAN FISHERIES SOCIETY. SYMPOSIUM.
American Fisheries Society, 5410 Grosvenor Ln., Ste. 110, Bethesda, MD 20814-2199. TEL 301-897-8616. FAX 301-897-8096. *2036*

AMERICAN FISHERIES SOCIETY. TRANSACTIONS.
American Fisheries Society, 5410 Grosvenor Ln., Ste. 110, Bethesda, MD 20814-2199. TEL 301-897-8616. FAX 301-897-8096. *2036*

AMERICAN FISHERIES SOCIETY MONOGRAPH.
American Fisheries Society, 5410 Grosvenor Ln., Ste. 110, Bethesda, MD 20814-2199. TEL 301-897-8616. FAX 301-897-8096. *2036*

AMERICAN FOREIGN POLICY LIBRARY.
Harvard University Press, 79 Garden St., Cambridge, MA 02138. TEL 617-495-2600. FAX 617-495-5898. *3949*

AMERICAN FRIENDS OF LAFAYETTE. GAZETTE.
American Friends of Lafayette, Skillman Library, Lafayette College, Easton, PA 18042. TEL 215-250-5161. FAX 215-252-0370. *2398*

AMERICAN GENEALOGIST.
Ruth Wilder Sherman, Ed.& Pub., 128 Massasoit Dr., Warwick, RI 02888. TEL 401-781-6759. *2143*

AMERICAN GEOPHYSICAL UNION. GEOPHYSICAL MONOGRAPH BOOK SERIES.
American Geophysical Union, 2000 Florida Ave., N.W., Washington, DC 20009. TEL 202-462-6900. *1587*

AMERICAN GERIATRICS SOCIETY. JOURNAL.
Williams & Wilkins, (American Geriatrics Society) 428 E. Preston St., Baltimore, MD 21202. TEL 301-528-4000. FAX 301-528-4321. *2270*

AMERICAN GROUP PSYCHOTHERAPY MONOGRAPH SERIES.
International Universities Press, Inc., 59 Boston Post Rd., Box 1524, Madison, CT 06443-1524. TEL 203-245-4000. *4009*

AMERICAN HEART ASSOCIATION. SUPPLEMENTS.
American Heart Association, 7272 Greenville Ave., Dallas, TX 75231-4596. TEL 214-706-1310. FAX 214-691-2704. *3203*

AMERICAN HEART JOURNAL.
Mosby - Year Book, Inc. 11830 Westline Industrial Dr., St. Louis, MO 63146. TEL 800-325-4117. FAX 314-432-1380. *3204*

AMERICAN HISTORICAL REVIEW.
American Historical Association, 400 A St., S.E., Washington, DC 20003. TEL 202-544-2422. *2305*

AMERICAN IMAGO.
Johns Hopkins University Press, Journals Publishing Division, (Association for Applied Psychoanalysis) 701 W. 40th St., Ste. 275, Baltimore, MD 21211. TEL 401-516-6980. FAX 410-516-6998. *3329*

AMERICAN INDUSTRIAL HYGIENE ASSOCIATION JOURNAL.
American Industrial Hygiene Association, 345 White Pond Dr., Box 8390, Akron, OH 44320-1155. TEL 216-873-2442. FAX 216-873-1642. *3614*

AMERICAN JOURNAL OF ALTERNATIVE AGRICULTURE.
Institute for Alternative Agriculture, Inc., 9200 Edmonston Rd., Ste. 117, Greenbelt, MD 20770. TEL 301-441-8777. *76*

AMERICAN JOURNAL OF ALZHEIMER'S CARE AND RELATED DISORDERS AND RESEARCH.
Prime National Publishing Corp., 470 Boston Post Rd., Weston, MA 02193. TEL 617-899-4311. FAX 617-899-4361. *3074*

AMERICAN JOURNAL OF ASTHMA & ALLERGY FOR PEDIATRICIANS.
Slack, Inc., 6900 Grove Rd., Thorofare, NJ 08086-9447. TEL 609-848-1000. FAX 609-853-5991. *3183*

AMERICAN JOURNAL OF CARDIAC IMAGING.
W.B. Saunders Co. Curtis Center, Independence Square W., Philadelphia, PA 19106. TEL 215-238-7800. *3204*

AMERICAN JOURNAL OF CARDIOLOGY.
Cahners Publishing Company (New York), Medical-Health Care Group, Yorke Medical Journals Division of Reed Publishing (USA) Inc., 249 W. 17th St., New York, NY 10011-5301. TEL 212-645-0067. FAX 212-242-6987. *3204*

AMERICAN JOURNAL OF CLINICAL ONCOLOGY.
Raven Press, 1185 Ave. of the Americas, New York, NY 10036. TEL 212-930-9500. FAX 212-869-3495. *3193*

AMERICAN JOURNAL OF CLINICAL PATHOLOGY.
J.B. Lippincott Co., (American Society of Clinical Pathologists) E. Washington Sq., Philadelphia, PA 19105. TEL 215-238-4200. *3074*

AMERICAN JOURNAL OF COMMUNITY PSYCHOLOGY.
Plenum Publishing Corp., 233 Spring St., New York, NY 10013-1578. TEL 212-620-8000. FAX 212-463-0742. *4428*

AMERICAN JOURNAL OF DANCE THERAPY.
Human Sciences Press, Inc. (American Dance Therapy Association, Inc.) 233 Spring St., New York, NY 10013-1578. TEL 212-620-8000. FAX 212-463-0742. *1528*

AMERICAN JOURNAL OF DERMATOPATHOLOGY.
Raven Press, (International Society of Dermatopathology) 1185 Ave. of the Americas, New York, NY 10036. TEL 212-930-9500. FAX 212-869-3495. *3245*

AMERICAN JOURNAL OF DRUG AND ALCOHOL ABUSE.
Marcel Dekker Journals, 270 Madison Ave., New York, NY 10016. TEL 212-696-9000. FAX 212-685-4540. *1534*

AMERICAN JOURNAL OF E E G TECHNOLOGY.
American Society of Electroneurodiagnostic Technologists, Inc., Executive Office, 204 W. Seventh, Carroll, IA 51401. TEL 712-792-2978. *3329*

AMERICAN JOURNAL OF EDUCATION.
University of Chicago Press, Journals Division, 5720 S. Woodlawn Ave., Chicago, IL 60637. TEL 312-753-3347. FAX 312-702-0694. *1615*

AMERICAN JOURNAL OF EMERGENCY MEDICINE.
W.B. Saunders Co., Curtis Center, Independence Square W., Philadelphia, PA 19106. TEL 215-238-7800. *3306*

AMERICAN JOURNAL OF ENOLOGY AND VITICULTURE.
American Society for Enology and Viticulture, Box 1855, Davis, CA 95617. TEL 916-753-3142. FAX 209-727-3439. *377*

AMERICAN JOURNAL OF EPIDEMIOLOGY.
Johns Hopkins University, School of Hygiene and Public Health, (Society for Epidemiologic Research) 2007 E. Monument St., Baltimore, MD 21205. TEL 301-955-3441. *3074*

AMERICAN JOURNAL OF FORENSIC MEDICINE AND PATHOLOGY.
Raven Press, (National Association of Medical Examiners) 1185 Ave. of the Americas, New York, NY 10036. TEL 212-930-9500. FAX 212-869-3495. *3264*

AMERICAN JOURNAL OF FORENSIC PSYCHIATRY.
Edward Miller, Ed. & Pub., (American College of Forensic Psychiatry) 26701 Quail Creek, No. 295, Laguna Hills, CA 92656. TEL 714-831-0236. *3264*

AMERICAN JOURNAL OF FORENSIC PSYCHOLOGY.
Edward Miller, Ed. & Pub., (American College of Forensic Psychology) 26701 Quail Creek, No. 295, Laguna Hills, CA 92656. TEL 714-831-0236. *4010*

AMERICAN JOURNAL OF GASTROENTEROLOGY.
Williams & Wilkins, (American College of Gastroenterology, Inc.) 428 E. Preston St., Baltimore, MD 21202. TEL 301-528-4000. FAX 301-528-4312. *3266*

AMERICAN JOURNAL OF GERIATRIC CARDIOLOGY.
Cardiovascular Reviews & Reports, Inc., 47 Arch St., Greenwich, CT 06830. TEL 203-625-0194. FAX 203-625-0393. *3204*

AMERICAN JOURNAL OF GERMANIC LINGUISTICS AND LITERATURES.
Society for Germanic Philology, Box 020225, Brooklyn, NY 11202-0005. TEL 718-997-5587. *2802*

AMERICAN JOURNAL OF HEALTH PROMOTION.
Michael P. O'Donnell, Ed. & Pub., 1812 S Rochester Rd., Ste. 200, Rochester Hills, MI 48307-3532. TEL 313-650-9600. *4097*

AMERICAN JOURNAL OF HEMATOLOGY.
John Wiley & Sons, Inc., Journals, 605 Third Ave., New York, NY 10158. TEL 212-850-6000. FAX 212-850-6-88. *3270*

AMERICAN JOURNAL OF HOSPICE CARE.
Prime National Publishing Corp., 470 Boston Post Rd., Weston, MA 02193. TEL 617-899-2702. *4398*

AMERICAN JOURNAL OF HOSPITAL PHARMACY.
American Society of Hospital Pharmacists, c/o Jean Rogers, Dir., Mkt. Svcs., 4630 Montgomery Ave., Bethesda, MD 20814. TEL 301-657-3000. *3716*

AMERICAN JOURNAL OF HUMAN GENETICS.
University of Chicago Press, Journals Division, (American Society of Human Genetics) 5720 S. Woodlawn Ave., Chicago, IL 60637. TEL 312-753-3347. FAX 312-702-0694. *539*

AMERICAN JOURNAL OF HYPERTENSION.
Elsevier Science Publishing Co., Inc. (New York), (American Society of Hypertension) 655 Ave. of the Americas, New York, NY 10010. TEL 212-989-5800. FAX 212-633-3965. *3204*

AMERICAN JOURNAL OF INDUSTRIAL MEDICINE.
John Wiley & Sons, Inc., Journals, 605 Third Ave., New York, NY 10158. TEL 212-850-6000. FAX 212-850-6088. *3614*

AMERICAN JOURNAL OF KIDNEY DISEASES.
W.B. Saunders Co. (National Kidney Foundation) Curtis Center, Independence Square W., Philadelphia, PA 19106. TEL 215-238-7800. *3387*

AMERICAN JOURNAL OF KNEE SURGERY.
Slack, Inc., 6900 Grove Rd., Thorofare, NJ 08086-9447. TEL 609-848-1000. FAX 609-853-5991. *3374*

AMERICAN JOURNAL OF LAW & MEDICINE.
American Society of Law & Medicine, Inc., 765 Commonwealth Ave., Ste. 1634, Boston, MA 02215. TEL 617-262-4990. FAX 617-437-7596. *2598*

AMERICAN JOURNAL OF MEDICAL GENETICS.
John Wiley & Sons, Inc., Journals, 605 Third Ave., New York, NY 10158. TEL 212-850-6000. FAX 212-850-6088. *539*

AMERICAN JOURNAL OF MEDICINE.
Cahners Publishing Company (New York), Medical-Health Care Group, Yorke Medical Journals Division of Reed Publishing (USA) Inc., 249 W. 17th St., New York, NY 10011-5301. TEL 212-463-6460. FAX 212-463-6470. *3074*

AMERICAN JOURNAL OF NURSING.
American Journal of Nursing Co., (American Nurses' Association) 555 W. 57th St., New York, NY 10019. TEL 212-582-8820. FAX 212-586-5462. *3275*

AMERICAN JOURNAL OF OBSTETRICS AND GYNECOLOGY.
Mosby - Year Book, Inc. (American Gynecological and Obstetrical Society) 11830 Westline Industrial Dr., St. Louis, MO 63146. TEL 800-325-4117. FAX 314-432-1380. *3289*

AMERICAN JOURNAL OF OCCUPATIONAL THERAPY.
American Occupational Therapy Association, Inc., 1383 Piccard Dr., Box 1725, Rockville, MD 20850-0882. TEL 301-948-9626. FAX 301-948-5512. *3074*

AMERICAN JOURNAL OF OPHTHALMOLOGY.
Ophthalmic Publishing Co., 435 N. Michigan Ave., Ste. 1415, Chicago, IL 60611. TEL 312-787-3853. FAX 312-787-5186. *3297*

AMERICAN JOURNAL OF ORTHODONTICS AND DENTOFACIAL ORTHOPEDICS.
Mosby - Year Book, Inc. (American Association of Orthodontists) 11830 Westline Industrial Dr., St. Louis, MO 63146. TEL 800-325-4117. FAX 314-432-1380. *3227*

AMERICAN JOURNAL OF ORTHOPSYCHIATRY.
American Orthopsychiatric Association, Inc., 19 W. 44th St., New York, NY 10036. TEL 212-354-5770. FAX 212-302-9463. *4010*

AMERICAN JOURNAL OF OTOLARYNGOLOGY.
W.B. Saunders Co., Curtis Center, Independence Square W., Philadelphia, PA 19106. TEL 215-574-4874. *3313*

AMERICAN JOURNAL OF PATHOLOGY.
J.B. Lippincott Co., (American Association of Pathologists) E. Washington Sq., Philadelphia, PA 19105. TEL 215-238-4200. *3074*

AMERICAN JOURNAL OF PEDIATRIC HEMATOLOGY - ONCOLOGY.
Raven Press, (American Society of Pediatric Hematology, Oncology) 1185 Ave. of the Americas, New York, NY 10036. TEL 212-930-9500. FAX 212-869-3495. *3318*

AMERICAN JOURNAL OF PERINATOLOGY.
Thieme Medical Publishers, Inc., 381 Park Ave., So., Ste. 1501, New York, NY 10016. TEL 212-683-5088. FAX 212-779-9020. *3289*

AMERICAN JOURNAL OF PHARMACEUTICAL EDUCATION.
American Association of Colleges of Pharmacy, 1426 Prince St., Alexandria, VA 22314-2815. TEL 703-739-2330. *3716*

AMERICAN JOURNAL OF PHARMACY (1981).
Philadelphia College of Pharmacy and Science, 43rd St. & Kingsessing Mall, Philadelphia, PA 19104. TEL 215-596-8800. *3716*

AMERICAN JOURNAL OF PHYSICAL ANTHROPOLOGY.
John Wiley & Sons, Inc., Journals, (American Association of Physical Anthropologists) 605 Third Ave., New York, NY 10158. TEL 212-850-6000. FAX 212-850-6088. *233*

AMERICAN JOURNAL OF PHYSICAL MEDICINE AND REHABILITATION.
Williams & Wilkins, (Association of Academic Physiatrists) 428 E. Preston St., Baltimore, MD 21202. TEL 301-528-4000. FAX 301-528-4312. *3075*

AMERICAN JOURNAL OF PHYSICS.
American Association of Physics Teachers, 5112 Berwyn Rd., College Park, MD 20740. TEL 301-345-4200. *3814*

AMERICAN JOURNAL OF PHYSIOLOGIC IMAGING.
Munksgaard International Publishers Ltd, P.O. Box 2148, DK-1016 Copenhagen K, Denmark. TEL 45-33-12-70-30. FAX 45-33-12-93-87. *427*

AMERICAN JOURNAL OF PHYSIOLOGY.
American Physiological Society, 9650 Rockville Pike, Bethesda, MD 20814. TEL 301-530-7071. FAX 301-571-1814. *569*

AMERICAN JOURNAL OF PHYSIOLOGY: CELL PHYSIOLOGY.
American Physiological Society, 9650 Rockville Pike, Bethesda, MD 20814. TEL 301-530-7071. FAX 301-571-1814. *569*

AMERICAN JOURNAL OF PHYSIOLOGY: ENDOCRINOLOGY AND METABOLISM.
American Physiological Society, 9650 Rockville Pike, Bethesda, MD 20814. TEL 301-530-7071. FAX 301-571-1814. *569*

AMERICAN JOURNAL OF PHYSIOLOGY: GASTROINTESTINAL AND LIVER PHYSIOLOGY.
American Physiological Society, 9650 Rockville Pike, Bethesda, MD 20814. TEL 301-530-7071. FAX 301-571-1814. *569*

AMERICAN JOURNAL OF PHYSIOLOGY: HEART AND CIRCULATORY PHYSIOLOGY.
American Physiological Society, 9650 Rockville Pike, Bethesda, MD 20814. TEL 301-530-7071. FAX 301-571-1814. *3204*

AMERICAN JOURNAL OF PHYSIOLOGY: LUNG CELLULAR AND MOLECULAR PHYSIOLOGY.
American Physiological Society, 9650 Rockville Pike, Bethesda, MD 20814. TEL 301-530-7071. FAX 301-571-1814. *569*

AMERICAN JOURNAL OF PHYSIOLOGY: REGULATORY, INTEGRATIVE AND COMPARATIVE PHYSIOLOGY.
American Physiological Society, 9650 Rockville Pike, Bethesda, MD 20814. TEL 301-530-7071. FAX 301-571-1814. *569*

AMERICAN JOURNAL OF PHYSIOLOGY: RENAL, FLUID AND ELECTROLYTE PHYSIOLOGY.
American Physiological Society, 9650 Rockville Pike, Bethesda, MD 20814. TEL 301-530-7071. FAX 301-571-1814. *569*

AMERICAN JOURNAL OF PREVENTIVE MEDICINE.
Oxford University Press, Journals, (American College of Preventive Medicine) 200 Madison Ave., New York, NY 10016. TEL 212-679-7300. FAX 212-725-2972. *3075*

AMERICAN JOURNAL OF PRIMATOLOGY.
John Wiley & Sons, Inc., Journals, 605 Third Ave., New York, NY 10108. TEL 212-850-6000. FAX 212-850-6088. *427*

AMERICAN JOURNAL OF PROCTOLOGY, GASTROENTEROLOGY & COLON & RECTAL SURGERY.
McMahon Publishing Co., (International Academy of Proctology) 83 Peaceable St., West Redding, CT 06896. TEL 203-544-9343. *3266*

AMERICAN JOURNAL OF PSYCHIATRY.
American Psychiatric Press, Inc., Journals Division, (American Psychiatric Association) 1400 K St., N.W., Washington, DC 20005. TEL 202-682-6020. FAX 202-682-6016. *3329*

AMERICAN JOURNAL OF PSYCHOANALYSIS.
Human Sciences Press, Inc. (Association for the Advancement of Psychoanalysis) 233 Spring St., New York, NY 10013. TEL 212-620-8000. FAX 212-463-0742. *4010*

AMERICAN JOURNAL OF PSYCHOLOGY.
University of Illinois Press, (University of Illinois at Urbana-Champaign) 54 E. Gregory Dr., Champaign, IL 61820. TEL 217-333-0950. FAX 217-244-8082. *4010*

AMERICAN JOURNAL OF PSYCHOTHERAPY.
Association for the Advancement of Psychotherapy, 114 E. 78th St., New York, NY 10021. TEL 212-529-1087. *3329*

AMERICAN JOURNAL OF PUBLIC HEALTH.
American Public Health Association, 1015 15th St., N.W., Washington, DC 20005. TEL 202-789-5600. *4097*

AMERICAN JOURNAL OF REPRODUCTIVE IMMUNOLOGY AND MICROBIOLOGY.
Munksgaard International Publishers Ltd., (American Society for the Immunology of Reproduction) P.O. Box 2148, DK-1016 Copenhagen K, Denmark. TEL 45-33-12-70-30. FAX 45-33-12-93-87. *3183*

AMERICAN JOURNAL OF SCIENCE.
American Journal of Science, (Yale University, Kline Geology Laboratory) Box 6666, Yale Sta., New Haven, CT 06511-8130. TEL 203-432-3131. FAX 203-432-5668. *1541*

AMERICAN JOURNAL OF SOCIOLOGY.
University of Chicago Press, Journals Division, 5720 S. Woodlawn Ave., Chicago, IL 60637. TEL 312-753-3347. FAX 312-702-0694. *4428*

AMERICAN JOURNAL OF SURGERY.
Cahners Publishing Company (New York), Medical-Health Care Group, Yorke Medical Journals Division of Reed Publishing (USA) Inc., 249 W. 17th St., New York, NY 10011-5301. TEL 212-463-6441. FAX 212-463-6470. *3374*

AMERICAN JOURNAL OF SURGICAL PATHOLOGY.
Raven Press, (Arthur Purdy Stout Society of Surgical Pathologists) 1185 Ave. of the Americas, New York, NY 10036. TEL 212-930-9500. FAX 212-869-3495. *3374*

AMERICAN JOURNAL OF THE MEDICAL SCIENCES.
J.B. Lippincott Co., E. Washington Sq., Philadelphia, PA 19105. TEL 215-238-4200. *3075*

AMERICAN JOURNAL OF THERAPY.
McMahon Publishing Co., 83 Peaceable St., West Redding, CT 06896. TEL 203-544-9343. *3075*

AMERICAN JOURNAL OF VETERINARY RESEARCH.
American Veterinary Medical Association, 1931 N. Meacham Rd., Ste. 100, Schaumburg, IL 60173-4360. TEL 708-605-8070. FAX 708-330-2862. *4805*

AMERICAN LEATHER CHEMISTS ASSOCIATION. JOURNAL.
American Leather Chemists Association, Campus Sta., Location 14, Cincinnati, OH 45221. TEL 513-556-1197. *2735*

AMERICAN LITERATURE.
Duke University Press, 6697 College Station, Durham, NC 27708. TEL 919-684-2173. FAX 919-684-8644. *2893*

AMERICAN MALACOLOGICAL BULLETIN.
American Malacological Union, Inc., c/o Dr. Robert Prezant, Biology Department, Indiana University of Pennsylvania, Indiana, PA 15705. *577*

AMERICAN MATHEMATICAL SOCIETY. ABSTRACTS OF PAPERS PRESENTED.
American Mathematical Society, Box 1571, Annex Sta., Providence, RI 02901-9930. TEL 401-455-4000. *3028*

AMERICAN MATHEMATICAL SOCIETY. BULLETIN. NEW SERIES.
American Mathematical Society, Box 1571, Annex Sta., Providence, RI 02901-9930. TEL 401-455-4000. *3028*

AMERICAN MATHEMATICAL SOCIETY. C B M S REGIONAL CONFERENCE SERIES IN MATHEMATICS.
American Mathematical Society, Box 1571, Annex Sta., Providence, RI 02901-9930. TEL 401-455-4000. *3028*

AMERICAN MATHEMATICAL SOCIETY. COLLOQUIUM PUBLICATIONS.
American Mathematical Society, Box 1571, Annex Sta., Providence, RI 02901-9930. TEL 401-455-4000. *3028*

AMERICAN MATHEMATICAL SOCIETY. JOURNAL.
American Mathematical Society, Box 1571, Annex Sta., Providence, RI 02901-9930. TEL 401-455-4000. *3028*

AMERICAN MATHEMATICAL SOCIETY. SYMPOSIA IN APPLIED MATHEMATICS. PROCEEDINGS.
American Mathematical Society, Box 1517, Annex Sta., Providence, RI 02901-9930. TEL 401-455-4000. *3028*

AMERICAN MATHEMATICAL SOCIETY. TRANSACTIONS.
American Mathematical Society, Box 1571, Annex Sta., Providence, RI 02901-9930. TEL 401-455-4000. *3028*

AMERICAN METEOROLOGICAL SOCIETY. BULLETIN.
American Meteorological Society, 45 Beacon St., Boston, MA 02108-3693. TEL 617-227-2425. FAX 618-742-8718. *3432*

AMERICAN METEOROLOGICAL SOCIETY. METEOROLOGICAL MONOGRAPHS.
American Meteorological Society, 45 Beacon St., Boston, MA 02108-3693. TEL 617-227-2425. FAX 617-742-8718. *3432*

AMERICAN METEOROLOGICAL SOCIETY HISTORICAL MONOGRAPH SERIES.
American Meteorological Society, 45 Beacon St., Boston, MA 02108-3693. TEL 617-227-2425. FAX 617-742-8718. *3432*

AMERICAN MIDLAND NATURALIST.
University of Notre Dame, American Midland Naturalist, Notre Dame, IN 46556. TEL 219-239-7481. *4298*

AMERICAN MIDLAND NATURALIST MONOGRAPH SERIES.
University of Notre Dame, American Midland Naturalist, Notre Dame, IN 46556. TEL 219-239-7481. *427*

AMERICAN MOSQUITO CONTROL ASSOCIATION. JOURNAL.
American Mosquito Control Association, Box 5416, Lake Charles, LA 70606. TEL 318-474-2723. FAX 318-478-9434. *528*

AMERICAN MUSEUM NOVITATES.
American Museum of Natural History, Central Park W. at 79th St., New York, NY 10024-5192. TEL 212-769-5412. FAX 212-769-5233. *577*

AMERICAN MUSEUM OF NATURAL HISTORY. ANTHROPOLOGICAL PAPERS.
American Museum of Natural History, Central Park W. at 79th St., New York, NY 10024-5192. TEL 212-769-5412. FAX 212-769-5233. *233*

AMERICAN MUSIC.
University of Illinois Press, (Sonneck Society) 54 E. Gregory Dr., Champaign, IL 61820. TEL 217-333-0950. FAX 217-244-8082. *3537*

AMERICAN NATURALIST.
University of Chicago Press, Journals Division, (American Society of Naturalists) 5720 S. Woodlawn Ave., Chicago, IL 60637. TEL 312-753-3347. *428*

AMERICAN OPTOMETRIC ASSOCIATION. JOURNAL.
American Optometric Association, 243 N. Lindbergh Blvd., St. Louis, MO 63141. TEL 314-991-4100. FAX 314-991-4101. *3298*

AMERICAN ORTHOPTIC JOURNAL.
University of Wisconsin Press, Journal Division, (American Association of Certified Othoptists) 114 N. Murray St., Madison, WI 53715. TEL 608-262-4952. FAX 608-262-7560. *3298*

AMERICAN PETROLEUM INSTITUTE. HEALTH AND ENVIRONMENTAL SCIENCES DEPARTMENT. REPORTS AND OTHER PUBLICATIONS, INDEX AND ABSTRACTS.
American Petroleum Institute, Central Abstracting & Information Services, 275 Seventh Ave., New York, NY 10001. *4116*

AMERICAN PHARMACY.
American Pharmaceutical Association, 2215 Constitution Ave., N.W., Washington, DC 20037. TEL 202-628-4410. *3716*

AMERICAN PODIATRIC MEDICAL ASSOCIATION. JOURNAL.
American Podiatric Medical Association, 9312 Old Georgetown Rd., Bethesda, MD 20814-1621. TEL 301-571-9200. FAX 301-530-2752. *3375*

AMERICAN PSYCHOANALYTIC ASSOCIATION. JOURNAL.
International Universities Press, Inc., Journal Department, 59 Boston Post Rd., Box 1524, Madison, CT 06443-1524. TEL 203-245-4000. FAX 203-245-0775. *4010*

AMERICAN PSYCHOANALYTIC ASSOCIATION. JOURNAL. MONOGRAPH.
International Universities Press, Inc., 59 Boston Post Rd., Box 1524, Madison, CT 06443-1524. TEL 203-245-4000. *4010*

AMERICAN PSYCHOANALYTIC ASSOCIATION. WORKSHOP SERIES.
International Universities Press, Inc., 59 Boston Post Rd., Box 1524, Madison, CT 06443-1524. TEL 203-245-4000. *4010*

AMERICAN PSYCHOLOGIST.
American Psychological Association, 750 First St., N.E., Washington, DC 20002-4242. TEL 202-336-5563. FAX 202-336-5568. *4010*

AMERICAN REVIEW OF RESPIRATORY DISEASE.
American Lung Association, (American Thoracic Society) 1740 Broadway, New York, NY 10019-4374. TEL 212-315-8700. *3364*

AMERICAN SOCIETY FOR GERIATRIC DENTISTRY. JOURNAL.
Academy of Geriatric Dentistry, 891 Pleasant Ave., Highland Park, IL 60035. TEL 312-432-2341. *3228*

AMERICAN SOCIETY FOR MASS SPECTROMETRY. JOURNAL.
Elsevier Science Publishing Co., Inc. (New York), 655 Ave. of the Americas, New York, NY 10010. TEL 212-989-5800. FAX 212-633-3965. *3851*

AMERICAN SOCIETY FOR TESTING AND MATERIALS. DATA SERIES PUBLICATIONS.
American Society for Testing and Materials, 1916 Race St., Philadelphia, PA 19103. TEL 215-299-5400. FAX 215-977-9679. *1911*

AMERICAN SOCIETY FOR TESTING AND MATERIALS. FIVE-YEAR INDEX TO A S T M TECHNICAL PAPERS AND REPORTS.
American Society for Testing and Materials, 1916 Race St., Philadelphia, PA 19103. TEL 215-299-5400. FAX 215-977-9679. *1911*

AMERICAN SOCIETY FOR TESTING AND MATERIALS. SPECIAL TECHNICAL PUBLICATIONS.
American Society for Testing and Materials, 1916 Race St., Philadelphia, PA 19103. TEL 215-299-5400. FAX 215-977-9679. *1911*

AMERICAN SOCIETY OF BREWING CHEMISTS. JOURNAL.
American Society of Brewing Chemists, 3340 Pilot Knob Rd., St. Paul, MN 55121-2097. TEL 612-454-7250. FAX 612-454-0766. *377*

AMERICAN SOCIETY OF MAMMALOGISTS. SPECIAL PUBLICATIONS.
American Society of Mammalogists, c/o Dr. H. Duane Smith, Sec.-Treas., Department of Zoology, Brigham Young University, Provo, UT 84602. TEL 801-378-2492. *577*

AMERICAN SOCIETY OF NEPHROLOGY. JOURNAL.
Williams & Wilkins, 428 E. Preston St., Baltimore, MD 21202. TEL 301-528-4000. FAX 301-528-4321. *3387*

AMERICAN SOCIOLOGIST.
Transaction Publishers, Transaction Periodicals Consortium, (American Sociological Association) Department 3092, Rutgers University, New Brunswick, NJ 08903. TEL 908-932-2280. FAX 908-932-3138. *4428*

AMERICAN SURGEON.
J.B. Lippincott Co., (Southeastern Surgical Congress) E. Washington Sq., Philadelphia, PA 19105. TEL 215-238-4273. *3375*

AMERICAN TAXATION ASSOCIATION. JOURNAL.
American Taxation Association, c/o American Accounting Assn., 5717 Bessie Dr., Sarasota, FL 34233. *1087*

AMERICAN UNIVERSITY STUDIES. SERIES 8. PSYCHOLOGY.
Peter Lang Publishing, Inc., 62 W. 45th St., 4th Fl., New York, NY 10036. TEL 212-302-6740. *4010*

AMERICAN VETERINARY MEDICAL ASSOCIATION. JOURNAL.
American Veterinary Medical Association, 1931 N. Meacham Rd., Ste. 100, Schaumburg, IL 60173-4360. TEL 708-605-8070. FAX 708-330-2862. *4805*

AMERICAN ZOOLOGIST.
American Society of Zoologists, c/o Milton Fingerman, Man.Ed., Department of Ecology, Evolution, and Organismal Biology, New Orleans, LA 70118. TEL 504-865-5546. FAX 504-865-6785. *577*

ANACRUSIS.
Association of Canadian Choral Conductors, 250 Heath St. W., Ste. 1504, Toronto, Ont. M5B 3L4, Canada. TEL 416-488-7842. *3538*

ANALOG INTEGRATED CIRCUITS AND SIGNAL PROCESSING.
Kluwer Academic Publishers, P.O. Box 17, 3300 AD Dordrecht, Netherlands. TEL 078-334911. FAX 078-0334254. *1881*

ANALUSIS.
Editions Scientifiques Elsevier, (Societe Francaise de Chimie) 29, rue Buffon, 75005 Paris, France. TEL 47-07-11-22. FAX 43-36-80-93. *1203*

ANALYSIS INSTRUMENTATION.
Instrument Society of America, 67 Alexander Dr., Box 12277, Research Triangle Park, NC 27709. TEL 919-549-8411. FAX 919-549-8288. *2521*

ANALYST.
Royal Society of Chemistry, Thomas Graham House, Science Park, Milton Rd., Cambridge CB4 4W, England. TEL 0462-672555. FAX 0462-480947. *1203*

ANALYTICA CHIMICA ACTA.
Elsevier Science Publishers B.V., P.O. Box 211, 1000 AE Amsterdam, Netherlands. TEL 020-5803911. FAX 020-5803598. *1203*

ANALYTICAL AND QUANTITATIVE CYTOLOGY AND HISTOLOGY.
Science Printers and Publishers, Inc., (International Academy of Cytology) 8342 Olive Blvd., St. Louis, MO 63132. TEL 314-991-4440. FAX 314-991-4654. *522*

ANALYTICAL BIOCHEMISTRY.
Academic Press, Inc., Journal Division, 1250 Sixth Ave., San Diego, CA 92101. TEL 619-230-1840. FAX 619-699-6800. *471*

ANALYTICAL CELLULAR PATHOLOGY.
Elsevier Science Publishers B.V., (European Society for Analytical Cellular Pathology) P.O. Box 211, 1000 AE Amsterdam, Netherlands. TEL 020-5803911. FAX 020-5803598. *522*

ANALYTICAL CHEMISTRY OF THE ELEMENTS SERIES.
Ellis Horwood Ltd., Market Cross House, Cooper St., Chichester, W. Sussex PO19 1EB, England. *1204*

ANALYTICAL CHEMISTRY SYMPOSIA SERIES.
Elsevier Science Publishers B.V., Books Division, P.O. Box 211, 1000 AE Amsterdam, Netherlands. TEL 020-5803911. FAX 020-5803705. *1204*

ANALYTICAL INSTRUMENTATION.
Marcel Dekker Journals, 270 Madison Ave., New York, NY 10016. TEL 212-696-9000. FAX 212-685-4540. *1204*

ANALYTICAL LETTERS: CHEMICAL ANALYSIS - CLINICAL AND BIOMEDICAL ANALYSIS.
Marcel Dekker Journals, 270 Madison Ave., New York, NY 10016. TEL 212-696-9000. FAX 212-685-4540. *1204*

ANALYTICAL PROFILES OF DRUG SUBSTANCES.
Academic Press, Inc., 1250 Sixth Ave., San Diego, CA 92101. TEL 619-231-0926. FAX 609-699-6715. *3716*

ANATOMICAL RECORD.
Wiley-Liss, Inc., (American Association of Anatomists) 41 E. 11th St., New York, NY 10003. TEL 212-475-7700. *428*

ANCIENT T L.
University of Durham, Department of Archaeology, Woodside Building, South Rd., Durham DH1 3LE, England. TEL 091-374-3624. FAX 091-374-3741. *262*

ANESTHESIA AND ANALGESIA.
Elsevier Science Publishing Co., Inc. (New York), (International Anesthesia Research Society) 655 Ave. of the Americas, New York, NY 10010. TEL 212-989-5800. FAX 212-633-3965. *3190*

ANESTHESIA PROGRESS.
Elsevier Science Publishing Co., Inc. (New York), (American Dental Society of Anesthesiology) 655 Ave. of the Americas, New York, NY 10010. TEL 212-989-5800. FAX 212-633-3965. *3228*

ANESTHESIOLOGY.
J.B. Lippincott Co., (American Society of Anesthesiologists) E. Washington Sq., Philadelphia, PA 19105. TEL 215-238-4200. *3190*

ANIMAL BIOTECHNOLOGY.
Marcel Dekker Journals, 270 Madison Ave., New York, NY 10016. TEL 212-696-9000. FAX 212-685-4540. *487*

ANIMAL FEED SCIENCE AND TECHNOLOGY.
Elsevier Science Publishers B.V., P.O. Box 211, 1000 AE Amsterdam, Netherlands. TEL 020-5803911. FAX 020-5803598. *204*

ANIMAL FEEDING AND NUTRITION.
Academic Press, Inc., 1250 Sixth Ave., San Diego, CA 92101. TEL 619-231-6616. FAX 619-699-6715. *4805*

ANIMAL REPRODUCTION SCIENCE.
Elsevier Science Publishers B.V., P.O. Box 211, 1000 AE Amsterdam, Netherlands. TEL 020-5803911. FAX 020-5803598. *210*

ANNALES DE BIOLOGIE CLINIQUE.
Editions Scientifiques Elsevier, (Societe Francaise de Chimie Clinique) 29, rue Buffon, 75005 Paris, France. TEL 47-07-11-22. FAX 43-36-80-93. *428*

ANNALES DE READAPTATION ET DE MEDECINE PHYSIQUE.
Editions Scientifiques Elsevier, (Societe Francaise de Reeducation Fonctionnelle de Readaptation et de Medecine Physique) 29, rue Buffon, 75005 Paris, France. TEL 47-07-11-22. FAX 43-36-80-93. *3076*

ANNALES DE ZOOTECHNIE.
Editions Scientifiques Elsevier, (Institut National de la Recherche Agronomique (INRA)) 29, rue Buffon, 75005 Paris, France. TEL 47-07-11-22. FAX 43-36-80-93. *577*

ANNALES DES SCIENCES FORESTIERES.
Editions Scientifique Elsevier, (Institut National de la Recherche Agronomique (INRA)) 29, rue Buffon, 75005 Paris, France. TEL 47-07-11-22. FAX 43-36-80-93. *2095*

ANNALES DES TELECOMMUNICATIONS.
Presses Polytechniques et Universitaires Romandes, EPFL - Ecublens, CH-1015 Lausanne, Switzerland. TEL 45-29-51-08. *1331*

REFEREED SERIALS

ANNALI DI CHIMICA.
Societa Chimica Italiana, Viale Liegi, 48, 00198 Rome, Italy. TEL 06-8549691. FAX 06-8548734. *1170*

ANNALS OF BIOMEDICAL ENGINEERING.
Pergamon Press, Inc., Journals Division, (Biomedical Engineering Society) 660 White Plains Rd., Tarrytown, NY 10591-5153. TEL 914-524-9200. FAX 914-333-2444. *468*

ANNALS OF CHILD DEVELOPMENT.
Jessica Kingsley Publishers, 118 Pentonville Rd., London N1 9JN, England. TEL 071-833-2307. FAX 071-837-2917. *4011*

ANNALS OF CLINICAL BIOCHEMISTRY.
Royal Society of Medicine Services Ltd., (Association of Clinical Biochemists) 1 Wimpole St., London W1M 8AE, England. TEL 071-408-2119. FAX 071-355-3198. *471*

ANNALS OF CLINICAL PSYCHIATRY.
Elsevier Science Publishing Co. Inc. (New York), (American Academy of Clinical Psychiatrists) 655 Ave. of the Americas, New York, NY 10010. TEL 212-989-5800. FAX 212-633-3965. *3330*

ANNALS OF DISCRETE MATHEMATICS.
Elsevier Science Publishers B.V., Books Division, P.O. Box 211, 1000 AE Amsterdam, Netherlands. TEL 020-5803911. FAX 020-5803705. *3029*

ANNALS OF DYSLEXIA.
Orton Dyslexia Society, 8600 LaSalle Rd., Ste. 382, Baltimore, MD 21204-6020. TEL 301-296-0232. *1733*

ANNALS OF EMERGENCY MEDICINE.
American College of Emergency Physicians, (Society for Academic Emergency Medicine) Box 619911, Dallas, TX 75261-9911. TEL 214-550-0911. FAX 214-580-2816. *3306*

ANNALS OF EPIDEMIOLOGY.
Elsevier Science Publishing Co., Inc. (New York), (American College of Epidemiology) 655 Ave. of the Americas, New York, NY 10010. TEL 212-989-5800. FAX 212-633-3965. *3076*

ANNALS OF HUMAN BIOLOGY.
Taylor & Francis Ltd., (Society for the Study of Human Biology) Rankine Rd., Basingstoke, Hants RG24 0PR, England. TEL 0256-840366. FAX 0256-479438. *428*

ANNALS OF INTERNAL MEDICINE.
American College of Physicians, Independence Mall W., Sixth St. at Race, Philadelphia, PA 19106-1572. TEL 215-351-2400. *3076*

ANNALS OF NEUROLOGY.
Little, Brown and Company, Medical Journals, (American Neurological Association) 34 Beacon St., Boston, MA 02108. TEL 617-859-5500. FAX 617-859-0629. *3330*

ANNALS OF NUCLEAR ENERGY.
Pergamon Press, Inc., Journals Division, 660 White Plains Rd., Tarrytown, NY 10591-5153. TEL 914-524-9200. FAX 914-333-2444. *1803*

ANNALS OF OCCUPATIONAL HYGIENE.
Pergamon Press, Inc., Journals Division, (British Occupational Hygiene Society) 660 White Plains Rd., Tarrytown, NY 10591-5153. TEL 914-524-9200. FAX 914-333-2444. *4097*

ANNALS OF OPHTHALMOLOGY.
Altier & Maynard Communications, Inc., (American Society of Contemporary Ophthalmology) 6 Farmingville Rd., Ridgefield, CT 06877. *3298*

ANNALS OF OTOLOGY, RHINOLOGY AND LARYNGOLOGY.
Annals Publishing Co., 4507 Laclede Ave., St. Louis, MO 63108. TEL 314-367-4987. FAX 314-367-4988. *3313*

ANNALS OF PHYSICS.
Academic Press, Inc., Journal Division, 1250 Sixth Ave., San Diego, CA 92101. TEL 619-230-1840. FAX 619-699-6800. *3814*

ANNALS OF PLASTIC SURGERY.
Little, Brown and Company, Medical Journals, 34 Beacon St., Boston, MA 02108. TEL 617-859-5500. FAX 617-859-0629. *3375*

ANNALS OF PROBABILITY.
Institute of Mathematical Statistics, Business Office, 3401 Investment Blvd., Ste. 7, Hayward, CA 94545. TEL 510-783-8141. *3029*

ANNALS OF PURE AND APPLIED LOGIC.
North-Holland (Association for Symbolic Logic) P.O. Box 211, 1000 AE Amsterdam, Netherlands. TEL 020-5803911. FAX 020-5803598. *3029*

ANNALS OF SURGERY.
J.B. Lippincott Co., E. Washington Sq., Philadelphia, PA 19105. TEL 215-238-4200. *3375*

ANNALS OF THEORETICAL PSYCHOLOGY.
Plenum Publishing Corp., 233 Spring St., New York, NY 10013-1578. TEL 212-670-8000. FAX 212-463-0742. *4011*

ANNALS OF THORACIC SURGERY.
Elsevier Science Publishing Co., Inc. (New York), (Society of Thoracic Surgeons) 655 Ave. of the Americas, New York, NY 10010. TEL 212-989-5800. FAX 212-633-3965. *3375*

ANNALS OF TOURISM RESEARCH.
Pergamon Press, Inc., Journals Division, 660 WHite Plains Rd., Tarrytown, NY 10591-5153. TEL 914-524-9200. FAX 914-333-2444. *4752*

ANNUAL ACCOUNTING REVIEW.
Harwood Academic Publishers, 270 Eighth Ave., New York, NY 10011. TEL 212-206-8900. FAX 212-645-2459. *747*

ANNUAL EDITIONS: AGING.
Dushkin Publishing Group, Inc., Sluice Dock, Guilford, CT 06437-9989. TEL 203-453-4351. FAX 203-453-6000. *2270*

ANNUAL EDITIONS: AMERICAN GOVERNMENT.
Dushkin Publishing Group, Inc., Sluice Dock, Guilford, CT 06437-9989. TEL 203-453-4351. FAX 203-453-6000. *3873*

ANNUAL EDITIONS: AMERICAN HISTORY.
Dushkin Publishing Group, Inc., Sluice Dock, Guilford, CT 06437-9989. TEL 203-453-4351. FAX 203-453-6000. *2398*

ANNUAL EDITIONS: ANTHROPOLOGY.
Dushkin Publishing Group, Inc., Sluice Dock, Guilford, CT 06437-9989. TEL 203-453-4351. FAX 203-453-6000. *233*

ANNUAL EDITIONS: BIOLOGY.
Dushkin Publishing Group, Inc., Sluice Dock, Guilford, CT 06437-9989. TEL 203-453-4351. FAX 203-453-6000. *428*

ANNUAL EDITIONS: BUSINESS ETHICS.
Dushkin Publishing Group, Inc., Sluice Dock, Guilford, CT 06437-9989. TEL 203-453-4351. FAX 203-543-6000. *645*

ANNUAL EDITIONS: CANADIAN POLITICS.
Dushkin Publishing Group, Inc., Sluice Dock, Guilford, CT 06437-9989. TEL 203-453-4351. FAX 203-453-6000. *3873*

ANNUAL EDITIONS: COMPARATIVE POLITICS.
Dushkin Publishing Group, Inc., Sluice Dock, Guilford, CT 06437-9989. TEL 203-453-4351. FAX 203-453-6000. *3873*

ANNUAL EDITIONS: CRIMINAL JUSTICE.
Dushkin Publishing Group, Inc., Sluice Dock, Guilford, CT 06437-9989. TEL 203-453-4351. FAX 203-453-6000. *1510*

ANNUAL EDITIONS: EARLY CHILDHOOD EDUCATION.
Dushkin Publishing Group, Inc., Sluice Duck, Guilford, CT 06437-9989. TEL 203-453-4351. FAX 203-453-6000. *1615*

ANNUAL EDITIONS: ECONOMICS.
Dushkin Publishing Group, Inc., Sluice Dock, Guilford, CT 06437-9989. TEL 203-453-4351. FAX 203-453-6000. *645*

ANNUAL EDITIONS: EDUCATING EXCEPTIONAL CHILDREN.
Dushkin Publishing Group, Inc., Sluice Dock, Guilford, CT 06437-9989. TEL 203-453-4351. FAX 203-453-6000. *1733*

ANNUAL EDITIONS: EDUCATION.
Dushkin Publishing Group, Inc., Sluice Dock, Guilford, CT 06437-9989. TEL 203-453-4351. FAX 203-453-6000. *1615*

ANNUAL EDITIONS: EDUCATIONAL PSYCHOLOGY.
Dushkin Publishing Group, Inc., Sluice Dock, Guilford, CT 06437-9989. TEL 203-453-4351. FAX 203-453-6000. *4011*

ANNUAL EDITIONS: ENVIRONMENT.
Dushkin Publishing Group, Inc., Sluice Dock, Guilford, CT 06437-9989. TEL 203-453-4351. FAX 203-453-6000. *1943*

ANNUAL EDITIONS: GEOGRAPHY.
Dushkin Publishing Group, Inc., Sluice Dock, Guilford, CT 06437-9989. TEL 203-453-4351. FAX 203-453-6000. *2241*

ANNUAL EDITIONS: GLOBAL ISSUES.
Dushkin Publishing Group, Inc., Sluice Dock, Guilford, CT 06437-9989. TEL 203-453-4351. FAX 203-453-6000. *2241*

ANNUAL EDITIONS: HEALTH.
Dushkin Publishing Group, Inc., Sluice Dock, Guilford, CT 06437-9989. TEL 203-453-4351. FAX 203-453-6000. *3799*

ANNUAL EDITIONS: HUMAN DEVELOPMENT.
Dushkin Publishing Group, Inc., Sluice Dock, Guilford, CT 06437-9989. TEL 203-453-4351. FAX 203-453-6000. *569*

ANNUAL EDITIONS: HUMAN RESOURCES.
Dushkin Publishing Group, Inc., Sluice Dock, Guilford, CT 06437-9989. TEL 203-453-4351. FAX 203-453-6000. *4429*

ANNUAL EDITIONS: HUMAN SEXUALITY.
Dushkin Publishing Group, Inc., Sluice Dock, Guilford, CT 06437-9989. TEL 203-453-4351. FAX 203-453-6000. *428*

ANNUAL EDITIONS: INTERNATIONAL BUSINESS.
Dushkin Publishing Group, Inc., Sluice Dock, Guilford, CT 06437-9989. TEL 203-453-4351. FAX 203-453-6000. *900*

ANNUAL EDITIONS: MACROECONOMICS.
Dushkin Publishing Group, Inc., Sluice Dock, Guilford, CT 06437-9989. TEL 203-453-4351. FAX 203-453-6000. *998*

ANNUAL EDITIONS: MANAGEMENT.
Dushkin Publishing Group, Inc., Sluice Dock, Guilford, CT 06437-9989. TEL 203-453-4351. FAX 203-453-6000. *1002*

ANNUAL EDITIONS: MARKETING.
Dushkin Publishing Group, Inc., Sluice Dock, Guilford, CT 06437-9989. TEL 203-453-4351. FAX 203-453-6000. *1033*

ANNUAL EDITIONS: MARRIAGE AND FAMILY.
Dushkin Publishing Group, Inc., Sluice Dock, Guilford, CT 06437-9989. TEL 203-453-4351. FAX 203-453-6000. *3066*

ANNUAL EDITIONS: MICROECONOMICS.
Dushkin Publishing Group, Inc., Sluice Dock, Guilford, CT 06437-9989. TEL 203-453-4351. FAX 203-453-6000. *889*

ANNUAL EDITIONS: MONEY AND BANKING.
Dushkin Publishing Group, Inc., Sluice Dock, Guilford, CT 06437-9989. TEL 203-453-4351. FAX 203-453-6000. *759*

ANNUAL EDITIONS: NUTRITION.
Dushkin Publishing Group, Inc., Sluice Dock, Guilford, CT 06437-9989. TEL 203-453-4351. FAX 203-453-6000. *3603*

ANNUAL EDITIONS: PERSONAL GROWTH AND BEHAVIOR.
Dushkin Publishing Group, Inc., Sluice Dock, Guilford, CT 06437-9989. TEL 203-453-4351. FAX 203-453-6000. *4011*

ANNUAL EDITIONS: PSYCHOLOGY.
Dushkin Publishing Group, Inc., Sluice Dock, Guilford, CT 06437-9989. TEL 203-453-4351. FAX 203-453-6000. *4011*

ANNUAL EDITIONS: PUBLIC ADMINISTRATION.
Dushkin Publishing Group, Inc., Sluice Dock, Guilford, CT 06437-9989. TEL 203-453-4351. FAX 203-453-6000. *4053*

ANNUAL EDITIONS: RACE & ETHNIC RELATIONS.
Dushkin Publishing Group, Inc., Sluice Dock, Guilford, CT 06437-9989. TEL 203-453-4351. FAX 203-453-6000. *4429*

ANNUAL EDITIONS: SOCIAL PROBLEMS.
Dushkin Publishing Group, Inc., Sluice Dock, Guilford, CT 06437-9989. TEL 203-453-4351. FAX 203-453-6000. *4398*

ANNUAL EDITIONS: SOCIOLOGY.
Dushkin Publishing Group, Inc., Sluice Dock, Guilford, CT 06437-9989. TEL 203-453-4351. FAX 203-453-6000. *4429*

ANNUAL EDITIONS: STATE & LOCAL GOVERNMENT.
Dushkin Publishing Group, Inc., Sluice Dock, Guilford, CT 06437-9989. TEL 203-453-4351. FAX 203-453-6000. *4053*

ANNUAL EDITIONS: THIRD WORLD.
Dushkin Publishing Group, Inc., Sluice Dock, Guilford, CT 06437-9989. TEL 203-453-4351. FAX 203-453-6000. *2241*

ANNUAL EDITIONS: URBAN SOCIETY.
Dushkin Publishing Group, Inc., Sluice Dock, Guilford, CT 06437-9989. TEL 203-453-4351. FAX 203-453-6000. *4429*

ANNUAL EDITIONS: VIOLENCE AND TERRORISM.
Dushkin Publishing Group, Inc., Sluice Dock, Guilford, CT 06437-9989. TEL 203-453-4351. FAX 203-453-6000. *1510*

ANNUAL EDITIONS: WESTERN CIVILIZATION.
Dushkin Publishing Group, Inc., Sluice Dock, Guilford, CT 06437-9989. TEL 203-453-4351. FAX 203-453-6000. *2306*

ANNUAL EDITIONS: WORLD HISTORY.
Dushkin Publishing Group, Inc., Sluice Dock, Guilford, CT 06437-9989. TEL 800-243-6532. FAX 203-453-6000. *2306*

ANNUAL EDITIONS: WORLD POLITICS.
Dushkin Publishing Group, Inc., Sluice Dock, Guilford, CT 06437-9989. TEL 203-453-4351. FAX 203-453-6000. *3950*

ANNUAL PROGRESS IN CHILD PSYCHIATRY AND CHILD DEVELOPMENT.
Brunner-Mazel Publishing Co., 19 Union Sq. W., New York, NY 10003. TEL 212-924-3344. *3330*

ANNUAL REPORTS IN MEDICINAL CHEMISTRY.
Academic Press, Inc., (American Chemical Society) 1250 Sixth Ave., San Diego, CA 92101. TEL 619-231-0926. FAX 619-699-6715. *3717*

ANNUAL REPORTS IN ORGANIC SYNTHESIS.
Academic Press, Inc., 1250 Sixth Ave., San Diego, CA 92101. TEL 619-231-0926. FAX 619-699-6715. *1224*

ANNUAL REPORTS ON N M R SPECTROSCOPY.
Academic Press, Inc., 1250 Sixth Ave., San Diego, CA 92101. TEL 619-231-0926. FAX 619-699-6715. *3851*

ANNUAL REVIEW IN AUTOMATIC PROGRAMMING.
Pergamon Press, Inc., Journals Division, 660 White Plains Rd., Tarrytown, NY 10591-5153. TEL 914-524-9200. FAX 914-333-2444. *1429*

ANNUAL REVIEW OF ADDICTIONS RESEARCH AND TREATMENT.
Pergamon Press, Inc., Journals Division, 660 White Plains Rd., Tarrytown, NY 10591-5153. TEL 914-524-9200. FAX 914-333-2444. *1534*

ANNUAL REVIEW OF BIOCHEMISTRY.
Annual Reviews Inc., 4139 El Camino Way, Box 10139, Palo Alto, CA 94303-0897. TEL 415-493-4400. FAX 415-855-9815. *471*

ANNUAL REVIEW OF BIOPHYSICS AND BIOMOLECULAR STRUCTURE.
Annual Reviews Inc., 4139 El Camino Way, Box 10139, Palo Alto, CA 94303-0897. TEL 415-493-4400. FAX 415-855-9815. *484*

ANNUAL REVIEW OF CELL BIOLOGY.
Annual Reviews Inc., 4139 El Camino Way, Box 10139, Palo Alto, CA 94303-0897. TEL 415-493-4400. FAX 415-855-9815. *522*

ANNUAL REVIEW OF CHRONOPHARMACOLOGY.
Raven Press, 1185 Ave. of the Americas, New York, NY 10036. TEL 212-930-9500. FAX 212-869-3495. *3717*

ANNUAL REVIEW OF FISH DISEASES.
Pergamon Press, Inc., Journals Division, 660 White Plains Rd., Tarrytown, NY 10591-5153. TEL 914-524-9200. FAX 914-333-2444. *578*

ANNUAL REVIEW OF GENETICS.
Annual Reviews Inc., 4139 El Camino Way, Box 10139, Palo Alto, CA 94303-0897. TEL 415-493-4400. FAX 415-855-9815. *539*

ANNUAL REVIEW OF IMMUNOLOGY.
Annual Reviews Inc., 4139 El Camino Way, Box 10139, Palo Alto, CA 94303-0897. TEL 415-493-4400. FAX 415-855-9815. *3183*

ANNUAL REVIEW OF INFORMATION SCIENCE AND TECHNOLOGY.
Elsevier Science Publishers B.V., Books Division, (American Society for Information Science, Information & Business Division) P.O. Box 211, 1000 AE Amsterdam, Netherlands. TEL 020-5803911. FAX 020-5803705. *2743*

ANNUAL REVIEW OF MEDICINE: SELECTED TOPICS IN THE CLINICAL SCIENCES.
Annual Reviews Inc., 4139 El Camino Way, Box 10139, Palo Alto, CA 94303-0897. TEL 415-493-4400. *3077*

ANNUAL REVIEW OF MICROBIOLOGY.
Annual Reviews Inc., 4139 El Camino Way, Box 10139, Palo Alto, CA 94303-0897. TEL 415-493-4400. FAX 415-855-9815. *549*

ANNUAL REVIEW OF NEUROSCIENCE.
Annual Reviews Inc., 4139 El Camino Way, Box 10139, Palo Alto, CA 94303-0897. TEL 415-493-4400. FAX 415-855-9815. *3330*

ANNUAL REVIEW OF NUTRITION.
Annual Reviews Inc., 4139 El Camino Way, Box 10139, Palo Alto, CA 94303-0897. TEL 800-523-8635. FAX 415-855-9815. *3603*

ANNUAL REVIEW OF PHARMACOLOGY AND TOXICOLOGY.
Annual Reviews Inc., 4139 El Camino Way, Box 10139, Palo Alto, CA 94303-0897. TEL 415-493-4400. FAX 415-855-9815. *3717*

ANNUAL REVIEW OF PHYSIOLOGY.
Annual Reviews Inc., 4139 El Camino Way, Box 10139, Palo Alto, CA 94303-0897. TEL 415-493-4400. FAX 415-855-9815. *569*

ANNUAL REVIEW OF PSYCHOLOGY.
Annual Reviews Inc., 4139 El Camino Way, Box 10139, Palo Alto, CA 94303-0897. TEL 415-493-4400. FAX 415-855-9815. *4011*

ANNUAL REVIEW OF PUBLIC HEALTH.
Annual Reviews Inc., 4139 El Camino Way, Box 10139, Palo Alto, CA 94303-0897. TEL 415-493-4400. FAX 415-855-9815. *4097*

ANTHROPOLOGICA.
Wilfrid Laurier University Press, (Wilfrid Laurier University) 75 University Ave. W., Waterloo, Ont. N2L 3C5, Canada. TEL 519-884-1970. FAX 519-886-8853. *233*

ANTHROPOLOGY AND ARCHEOLOGY OF EURASIA.
M.E. Sharpe, Inc., 80 Business Park Dr., Armonk, NY 10504. TEL 914-273-1800. FAX 914-273-2106. *234*

ANTHROPOLOGY OF CONSCIOUSNESS.
Society for the Anthropology of Consciousness, 2906 Ocean Ave., Venice, CA 90291. TEL 213-827-0937. FAX 603-536-1896. *234*

ANTHROPOLOGY U C L A.
University of California, Los Angeles, Department of Anthropology, 405 Hilgard Ave., Los Angeles, CA 90024. TEL 213-825-2055. *234*

ANTHROZOOS.
Delta Society, Box 1080, Renton, WA 98097-1080. TEL 206-226-7357. FAX 206-235-1076. *235*

ANTIBODY, IMMUNOCONJUGATES, AND RADIOPHARMACEUTICALS.
Mary Ann Liebert, Inc., 1651 Third Ave., New York, NY 10128. TEL 212-289-2300. FAX 212-289-4697. *3193*

ANTIMICROBIAL AGENTS AND CHEMOTHERAPY.
American Society for Microbiology, 1325 Massachusetts Ave., N.W., Washington, DC 20005. TEL 202-737-3600. *549*

ANTIMICROBIAL AGENTS ANNUAL.
Elsevier Science Publishers B.V., Books Division, P.O. Box 211, 1000 AE Amsterdam, Netherlands. TEL 020-5803911. FAX 020-5803705. *549*

ANTIMICROBIC NEWSLETTER.
Elsevier Science Publishing Co., Inc. (New York), 655 Ave. of the Americas, New York, NY 10010. TEL 212-989-5800. FAX 212-633-3965. *3218*

ANTIVIRAL RESEARCH.
Elsevier Science Publishers B.V., (International Society for Antiviral Research) P.O. Box 211, 1000 AE Amsterdam, Netherlands. TEL 020-5803911. FAX 020-5803598. *549*

ANXIETY RESEARCH.
Harwood Academic Publishers, 270 Eighth Ave., New York, NY 10011. TEL 212-206-8900. FAX 212-645-2459. *4011*

APERIODICITY AND ORDER.
Academic Press, Inc., 1250 Sixth Ave., San Diego, CA 92101. TEL 619-231-6616. FAX 619-699-6715. *3814*

APHASIOLOGY.
Taylor & Francis Ltd., Rankine Rd., Basingstoke, Hants RG24 0PR, England. TEL 0256-840366. FAX 0256-479438. *3330*

APIDOLOGIE.
Editions Scientifiques Elsevier, (Institut National de la Recherche Agronomique (INRA)) 29, rue Buffon, 75005 Paris, France. TEL 47-07-11-22. FAX 43-36-80-93. *528*

APOTHECARY.
Health Care Marketing Services, H C M S Inc., (Massachusetts College of Pharmacy and Allied Health Sciences) Box AP, Los Altos, CA 94023-0179. FAX 415-941-2303. *3717*

APPLICABLE ANALYSIS.
Gordon and Breach Science Publishers, 270 Eighth Ave., New York, NY 10011. TEL 212-206-8900. FAX 212-645-2459. *3029*

APPLIED ACOUSTICS.
Elsevier Science Publishers Ltd., Crown House, Linton Rd., Barking, Essex IG11 8JU, England. TEL 081-594-7272. FAX 081-594-5942. *3858*

APPLIED AND ENVIRONMENTAL MICROBIOLOGY.
American Society for Microbiology, 1325 Massachusetts Ave., N.W., Washington, DC 20005. TEL 202-737-3600. *549*

APPLIED ANIMAL BEHAVIOUR SCIENCE.
Elsevier Science Publishers B.V., P.O. Box 211, 1000 AE Amsterdam, Netherlands. TEL 020-5803911. FAX 020-5803598. *578*

APPLIED ARTIFICIAL INTELLIGENCE.
Hemisphere Publishing Corporation 1900 Frost Rd., Ste. 101, Bristol, PA 19007-1598. TEL 215-785-5800. FAX 215-785-5515. *1406*

APPLIED BIOCHEMISTRY AND BIOTECHNOLOGY.
Humana Press Inc., Crescent Manor, Box 2148, Clifton, NJ 07015. TEL 201-256-1699. FAX 201-256-8341. *471*

APPLIED BIOCHEMISTRY AND MICROBIOLOGY.
Plenum Publishing Corp., Consultants Bureau, (Russian Academy of Sciences) 233 Spring St., New York, NY 10013-1578. TEL 212-620-8468. FAX 212-463-0742. *471*

APPLIED CATALYSIS.
Elsevier Science Publishers B.V., P.O. Box 211, 1000 AE Amsterdam, Netherlands. TEL 020-5803911. FAX 020-5803598. *1848*

APPLIED CATALYSIS B: ENVIRONMENTAL.
Elsevier Science Publishers B.V., P.O. Box 211, 1000 AE Amsterdam, Netherlands. TEL 020-5803911. FAX 020-5803598. *1848*

APPLIED CLAY SCIENCE.
Elsevier Science Publishers B.V., P.O. Box 211, 1000 AE Amsterdam, Netherlands. TEL 020-5803911. FAX 020-5803598. *1554*

APPLIED ENERGY.
Elsevier Science Publishers Ltd., Crown House, Linton Rd., Barking, Essex IG11 8JU, England. TEL 081-594-7272. FAX 081-594-5942. *1783*

APPLIED ERGONOMICS.
Butterworth - Heinemann Ltd. Linacre House, Jordan Hill, Oxford OX2 8DP, England. TEL 0865-310366. FAX 0865-310898. *1814*

APPLIED FINANCIAL ECONOMICS.
Chapman & Hall, 2-6 Boundary Row, London SE1 8HN, England. TEL 071-865-0066. FAX 071-522-9623. *843*

APPLIED GEOCHEMISTRY.
Pergamon Press, Inc., Journals Division, (International Association of Geochemistry and Cosmochemistry) 660 White Plains Rd., Tarrytown, NY 10591-5153. TEL 914-524-9200. FAX 914-333-2444. *1554*

APPLIED GEOGRAPHY.
Butterworth - Heinemann Ltd. Linacre House, Jordan Hill, Oxford OX2 8DP, England. TEL 0865-310366. FAX 0865-310898. *2242*

APPLIED MATHEMATICAL MODELLING.
Butterworth - Heinemann Ltd. 80 Montvale Ave., Stoneham, MA 02180. TEL 617-438-8464. FAX 617-438-1479. *3064*

APPLIED MATHEMATICS.
Gordon & Breach Science Publishers, P.O. Box 90, Reading, Berkshire RG1 8JL, England. TEL 0734-560-080. FAX 0734-568-211. *3029*

APPLIED MATHEMATICS AND COMPUTATION.
Elsevier Science Publishing Co., Inc. (New York), 655 Ave. of the Americas, New York, NY 10010. TEL 212-989-5800. FAX 212-633-3965. *3029*

APPLIED MATHEMATICS AND MECHANICS.
Academic Press, Inc., 1250 Sixth Ave., San Diego, CA 92101. TEL 619-231-0926. FAX 619-699-6715. *3029*

APPLIED MATHEMATICS LETTERS.
Pergamon Press, Inc., Journals Division, 660 White Plains Rd., Tarrytown, NY 10591-5153. TEL 914-524-9200. FAX 914-333-2444. *3029*

APPLIED MEASUREMENT IN EDUCATION.
Lawrence Erlbaum Associates, Inc., (Buros Institute of Mental Measurements) 365 Broadway, Hillsdale, NJ 07642. TEL 201-666-4110. FAX 201-666-2394. *1616*

APPLIED MECHANICS REVIEWS.
American Society of Mechanical Engineers, 345 E. 47th St., New York, NY 10017. TEL 212-705-7703. *1841*

APPLIED NUMERICAL MATHEMATICS.
North-Holland (International Association for Mathematics and Computers in Simulation) P.O. Box 211, 1000 AE Amsterdam, Netherlands. TEL 020-5803911. FAX 020-5803598. *3064*

APPLIED OCEAN RESEARCH.
Elsevier Science Publishers Ltd., Crown House, Linton Rd., Barking, Essex IG11 8JU, England. TEL 081-594-7272. FAX 081-594-5942. *1601*

APPLIED OPTICS. SUPPLEMENT.
Optical Society of America, Inc., 2010 Massachusetts Ave., N.W., Washington, DC 20036-1023. TEL 202-223-8130. *3851*

APPLIED PSYCHOLINGUISTICS AND COMMUNICATION DISORDERS.
Plenum Publishing Corp., 233 Spring St., New York, NY 10013-1578. TEL 212-620-8000. FAX 212-463-0742. *2803*

APPLIED PSYCHOLOGY.
Lawrence Erlbaum Associates Ltd., (International Association of Applied Psychology) 27 Palmeira Mansions, Church Rd., Hove, East Sussex BN3 2FA, England. TEL 0273-207411. FAX 0273-205612. *4011*

APPLIED SOLAR ENERGY.
Allerton Press, Inc., (Uzbek Academy of Sciences) 150 Fifth Ave., New York, NY 10011. TEL 212-924-3950. *1810*

APPLIED SOLID STATE SCIENCE.
Academic Press, Inc., 1250 Sixth Ave., San Diego, CA 92101. TEL 619-231-0926. FAX 619-669-6715. *1882*

APPLIED SPECTROSCOPY.
Society for Applied Spectroscopy, Box 64008, Baltimore, MD 21264. TEL 301-694-8122. *3852*

APPLIED SPECTROSCOPY REVIEWS.
Marcel Dekker Journals, 270 Madison Ave., New York, NY 10016. TEL 212-696-9000. FAX 212-685-4540. *3852*

APPLIED SUPERCONDUCTIVITY.
Pergamon Press plc, Headington Hill Hall, Oxford OX3 0BW, England. TEL 0865-794141. FAX 0865-743911. *1882*

APPLIED SURFACE SCIENCE.
North-Holland P.O. Box 211, 1000 AE Amsterdam, Netherlands. TEL 020-5803911. FAX 020-5803598. *3402*

APPLIED VIROLOGY RESEARCH.
Plenum Publishing Corp., 233 Spring St., New York, NY 10013-1578. TEL 212-620-8000. FAX 212-463-0742. *550*

AQUACULTURAL ENGINEERING.
Elsevier Science Publishers Ltd., Crown House, Linton Rd., Barking, Essex IG11 8JU, England. TEL 081-594-7272. FAX 081-594-5942. *1814*

AQUACULTURE.
Elsevier Science Publishers B.V., P.O. Box 211, 1000 AE Amsterdam, Netherlands. TEL 020-5803911. FAX 020-5803598. *2036*

AQUARICULTURE AND AQUATIC SCIENCES. JOURNAL.
Written Word, 7601 E. Forest Lake Drive, Parkville, MO 64152. TEL 816-842-5936. FAX 816-474-5597. *429*

AQUATIC BOTANY.
Elsevier Science Publishers B.V., P.O. Box 211, 1000 AE Amsterdam, Netherlands. TEL 020-5803911. FAX 020-5803598. *494*

AQUATIC TOXICOLOGY.
Elsevier Science Publishers B.V., P.O. Box 211, 1000 AE Amsterdam, Netherlands. TEL 020-5803911. FAX 020-5803598. *1980*

ARABIAN JOURNAL FOR SCIENCE AND ENGINEERING.
King Fahd University of Petroleum and Minerals, P.O. Box 8, Dhahran 31231, Saudi Arabia. FAX 966-3-860-5458. *1815*

ARCHAEOASTRONOMY.
Center for Archaeoastronomy, Box X, College Park, MD 20740. TEL 301-864-6637. *262*

ARCHAEOLOGICAL EXPLORATION OF SARDIS. MONOGRAPHS.
Harvard University Press, 79 Garden St., Cambridge, MA 02138. TEL 617-495-2600. FAX 617-495-5898. *263*

ARCHIVES OF A I D S RESEARCH.
Reproductive Health Center, 78 Surfsong Rd., Kiawah Island, SC 29455. TEL 803-768-5556. *3218*

ARCHIVES OF ANDROLOGY.
Hemisphere Publishing Corporation 1900 Frost Rd., Ste. 101, Bristol, PA 19007-1598. TEL 215-785-5800. FAX 215-785-5515. *3077*

ARCHIVES OF BIOCHEMISTRY AND BIOPHYSICS.
Academic Press, Inc., Journal Division, 1250 Sixth Ave., San Diego, CA 92101. TEL 619-230-1840. FAX 619-699-6800. *471*

ARCHIVES OF CLINICAL NEUROPSYCHOLOGY.
Pergamon Press, Inc., Journals Division, 660 White Plains Rd., Tarrytown, NY 10591-5153. TEL 914-524-9200. FAX 914-333-2444. *3330*

ARCHIVES OF DERMATOLOGY.
American Medical Association, 515 N. State St., Chicago, IL 60610. TEL 312-464-0183. FAX 312-464-5834. *3246*

ARCHIVES OF ENVIRONMENTAL HEALTH.
Heldref Publications, (Helen Dwight Reid Educational Foundation) 1319 Eighteenth St., N.W., Washington, DC 20036-1802. TEL 202-296-6267. FAX 202-296-5149. *3077*

ARCHIVES OF GENERAL PSYCHIATRY.
American Medical Association, 515 N. State St., Chicago, IL 60610. TEL 312-464-0183. FAX 312-464-5834. *3330*

ARCHIVES OF GERONTOLOGY AND GERIATRICS.
Elsevier Science Publishers B.V., P.O. Box 211, 1000 AE Amsterdam, Netherlands. TEL 020-5803911. FAX 020-5803598. *2270*

ARCHIVES OF GYNECOLOGY AND OBSTETRICS.
Springer-Verlag, (Deutsche Gesellschaft fuer Gynaekologie) Heidelberger Platz 3, D-1000 Berlin 33, Germany. TEL 030-8207-1. *3289*

ARCHIVES OF INSECT BIOCHEMISTRY AND PHYSIOLOGY.
John Wiley & Sons, Inc., Journals, (Entomological Society of America) 605 Third Ave., New York, NY 10158. TEL 212-850-6000. FAX 212-850-6088. *528*

ARCHIVES OF INTERNAL MEDICINE.
American Medical Association, 515 N. State St., Chicago, IL 60610. TEL 312-464-0183. FAX 312-464-5834. *3077*

ARCHIVES OF NEUROLOGY.
American Medical Association, 515 N. State St., Chicago, IL 60610. TEL 312-464-0183. FAX 312-464-5834. *3330*

ARCHIVES OF OPHTHALMOLOGY.
American Medical Association, 515 N. State St., Chicago, IL 60610. TEL 312-464-0183. FAX 312-464-5834. *3298*

ARCHIVES OF ORAL BIOLOGY.
Pergamon Press, Inc., Journals Division, 660 White Plains Rd., Tarrytown, NY 10591-5153. TEL 914-524-9200. FAX 914-333-2444. *3228*

ARCHIVES OF OTOLARYNGOLOGY - HEAD & NECK SURGERY.
American Medical Association, 515 N. State St., Chicago, IL 60610. TEL 312-464-0183. FAX 312-464-5834. *3313*

ARCHIVES OF PATHOLOGY & LABORATORY MEDICINE.
American Medical Association, 515 N. State St., Chicago, IL 60610. TEL 312-464-0183. FAX 312-464-5834. *3077*

ARCHIVES OF PHYSICAL MEDICINE AND REHABILITATION.
W.B. Saunders Co., Journals Department, (American Congress of Rehabilitation Medicine) Independence Sq. W., Philadelphia, PA 19106. TEL 215-238-7824. FAX 215-238-7883. *3077*

ARCHIVES OF PSYCHIATRIC NURSING.
W.B. Saunders Co. Curtis Center, Independence Square W., Philadelphia, PA 19106. TEL 215-238-7800. *3275*

ARCHIVES OF SEXUAL BEHAVIOR.
Plenum Publishing Corp., 233 Spring St., New York, NY 10013-1578. TEL 212-620-8000. FAX 212-463-0742. *3077*

ARCHIVES OF SOVIET SCIENCE SERIES: PHYSICAL SCIENCES SECTION.
Harwood Academic Publishers, 270 Eighth Ave., New York, NY 10011. TEL 212-206-8900. FAX 212-645-2459. *3846*

ARCHIVES OF SURGERY.
American Medical Association, 515 N. State St., Chicago, IL 60610. TEL 312-464-0183. FAX 312-464-5834. *3376*

ARCHIVOS DE ZOOTECNIA.
Consejo Superior de Investigaciones Cientificas (C.S.I.C.), Instituto de Zootecnica, Avda. de Medina Azahara, 9, 14005 Cordoba, Spain. TEL 957-237589. FAX 957-413903. *211*

ARCTIC AND ALPINE RESEARCH.
University of Colorado, Institute of Arctic and Alpine Research, Campus Box 450, Boulder, CO 80309-6450. TEL 303-492-3765. FAX 303-492-6388. *4299*

ARCTIC ANTHROPOLOGY.
University of Wisconsin Press, Journal Division, 114 N. Murray St., Madison, WI 53715. TEL 608-262-4952. FAX 608-262-7560. *235*

ARID SOIL RESEARCH AND REHABILITATION.
Taylor & Francis Ltd., Rankine Rd., Basingstoke, Hants RG24 OPR, England. TEL 0256-840366. FAX 0256-479438. *168*

ARIZONA-NEVADA ACADEMY OF SCIENCE. JOURNAL.
Arizona-Nevada Academy of Science, Office of Climatology, Arizona State University, Tempe, AZ 85287-1508. TEL 602-965-6265. FAX 602-965-2012. *4300*

ARKANSAS FARM RESEARCH.
Agricultural Experiment Station, Agricultural Publications A-110, University of Arkansas, Division of Agriculture, Fayetteville, AR 72701. TEL 501-575-5647. *77*

ARNOLDIA.
Harvard University, Arnold Arboretum, 125 Arbor Way, Jamaica Plain, MA 02130-2795. TEL 617-524-1718. FAX 617-524-1418. *495*

ART DOCUMENTATION.
Art Libraries Society of North America, 3900 E. Timrod St., Tucson, AZ 85711. TEL 602-881-8479. FAX 602-322-6778. *2744*

ART REFERENCE SERVICES QUARTERLY.
Haworth Press, Inc., 10 Alice St., Binghamton, NY 13904-1580. TEL 607-722-1695. FAX 607-722-1424. *315*

ARTERIOSCLEROSIS AND THROMBOSIS.
American Heart Association, 7272 Greenville Ave., Dallas, TX 75231-4596. TEL 214-706-1310. FAX 214-691-6342. *3205*

ARTHRITIS AND RHEUMATISM.
J.B. Lippincott Co., (American College of Rheumatology) E. Washington Sq., Philadelphia, PA 19105. TEL 215-238-4200. FAX 215-238-4227. *3368*

ARTHRITIS CARE AND RESEARCH.
Elsevier Science Publishing Co., Inc. (New York), (Arthritis Foundation, Arthritis Health Professions Association) 655 Ave. of the Americas, New York, NY 10010. TEL 212-989-5800. FAX 212-633-3965. *3368*

ARTHROPODS OF FLORIDA AND NEIGHBORING LAND AREAS.
Department of Agriculture and Consumer Services, Division of Plant Industry, 1911 S.W. 34th St., Box 147100, Gainesville, FL 32614-7100. TEL 904-372-3505. FAX 904-374-6801. *529*

ARTHROSCOPY.
Raven Press, 1185 Ave. of the Americas, New York, NY 10036. TEL 212-930-9500. FAX 212-869-3495. *3307*

ARTIFICIAL INTELLIGENCE.
North-Holland P.O. Box 211, 1000 AE Amsterdam, Netherlands. TEL 020-5803911. FAX 020-5803598. *1407*

ARTIFICIAL INTELLIGENCE IN ENGINEERING.
Elsevier Science Publishers Ltd., Crown House, Linton Rd., Barking, Essex IG11 8JU, England. TEL 081-594-7272. FAX 081-594-5942. *1407*

ARTIFICIAL INTELLIGENCE IN MEDICINE.
Elsevier Science Publishers B.V., P.O. Box 211, 1000 AC Amsterdam, Netherlands. TEL 020-5803911. FAX 020-5803598. *3224*

ARTIFICIAL ORGANS.
Blackwell Scientific Publications Inc., (International Society for Artificial Organs) Three Cambridge Center, Ste. 208, Cambridge, MA 02142-1413. TEL 617-225-0401. FAX 617-225-0412. *3257*

THE ARTS IN PSYCHOTHERAPY.
Pergamon Press, Inc., Journals Division, 660 White Plains Rd., Tarrytown, NY 10591-5153. TEL 914-524-9200. FAX 914-333-2444. *4012*

ASIAN AFFAIRS: AN AMERICAN REVIEW.
Heldref Publications, (American-Asian Educational Exchange, Inc.) 1319 Eighteenth St., N.W., Washington, DC 20036-1802. TEL 202-296-6267. FAX 202-296-5149. *3950*

ASIAN AND PACIFIC DEVELOPMENT CENTRE NEWSLETTER.
Asian and Pacific Development Centre, P.O. Box 12224, 50770 Kuala Lumpur, Malaysia. TEL 03-2548088. FAX 03-2550316. *844*

ASIAN AND PACIFIC WOMEN'S RESOURCE AND ACTION SERIES.
Asian and Pacific Development Centre, P.O. Box 12224, 50770 Kuala Lumpur, Malaysia. TEL 03-2548088. FAX 03-2550316. *4837*

ASIAN LIBRARIES.
Library Marketing Services Ltd., 11th Fl., Hophing Centre, 8 Hennessy Road, Hong Kong. TEL 66-2-2471032. FAX 66-2-2471033. *2744*

ASIAN PERSPECTIVES.
University of Hawaii Press, Journals Department, (University of Hawaii) 2840 Kolowalu St., Honolulu, HI 96822. TEL 808-956-8833. FAX 808-988-6052. *266*

ASIAN SURVEY.
University of California Press, Journals Division, 2120 Berkeley Way, Berkeley, CA 94720. TEL 510-642-4191. FAX 510-643-7127. *3874*

ASIAN THEATRE JOURNAL.
University of Hawaii Press, Journals Department, (Association for Asian Performance) 2840 Kolowalu St., Honolulu, HI 96822. TEL 808-956-8833. FAX 808-988-6052. *4629*

ASSOCIATION FOR RESEARCH IN NERVOUS AND MENTAL DISEASE. RESEARCH PUBLICATIONS.
Raven Press, 1185 Ave. of the Americas, New York, NY 10036. TEL 212-930-9500. FAX 212-869-3495. *3331*

ASSOCIATION OF CHILDREN'S PROSTHETIC-ORTHOTIC CLINICS. JOURNAL.
Association of Children's Prosthetic-Orthotic Clinics, 222 S. Prospect Ave., Park Ridge, IL 60068. TEL 708-698-1694. FAX 708-823-0536. *3079*

ASSOCIATION OF NURSES IN A I D S CARE. JOURNAL.
Nursecom Inc., 1211 Locust St., Philadelphia, PA 19107. TEL 215-545-7222. *3218*

ASTERISQUE.
Societe Mathematique de France, Ecole Normale Superieure, Tour L, 1 rue Maurice Arnoux, 92120 Montrouge, France. TEL 1-40-84-80-54. FAX 1-40-84-80-52. *3030*

ASTRONOMICAL AND ASTROPHYSICAL TRANSACTIONS.
Gordon and Breach Science Publishers, (Soviet Astronomical Society) 270 Eighth Ave., New York, NY 10011. TEL 212-206-8900. FAX 212-645-2459. *361*

ASTRONOMICAL JOURNAL.
American Institute of Physics, (American Astronomical Society) 335 E. 45th St., New York, NY 10017. TEL 212-661-9404. *361*

ASTROPARTICLE PHYSICS.
North-Holland P.O. Box 211, 1000 AE Amsterdam, Netherlands. TEL 020-5803911. FAX 020-5803598. *362*

ASTROPHYSICAL JOURNAL.
University of Chicago Press, Journals Division, (American Astronomical Society) 5720 S. Woodlawn Ave., Chicago, IL 60637. TEL 312-753-3347. FAX 312-702-0694. *362*

ASTROPHYSICAL JOURNAL. SUPPLEMENT SERIES.
University of Chicago Press, Journals Division, (American Astronomical Society) 5720 S. Woodlawn Ave., Chicago, IL 60637. TEL 312-753-3347. FAX 312-702-0694. *362*

ASTROPHYSICAL LETTERS AND COMMUNICATIONS.
Gordon and Breach Science Publishers, 270 Eighth Ave., New York, NY 10011. TEL 212-206-8900. FAX 212-645-2459. *362*

ASTROPHYSICS.
Plenum Publishing Corp., Consultants Bureau, (Armenian Academy of Sciences) 233 Spring St., New York, NY 10013-1578. TEL 212-620-8468. FAX 212-463-0742. *362*

ASYMPTOTIC ANALYSIS.
North-Holland P.O. Box 211, 1000 AE Amsterdam, Netherlands. TEL 020-5803911. FAX 020-5803598. *3030*

ATHEROSCLEROSIS.
Elsevier Scientific Publishers Ireland Ltd., (International Atherosclerosis Society) P.O. Box 85, Limerick, Ireland. TEL 061-61944. FAX 061-62144. *3205*

ATHEROSCLEROSIS REVIEWS.
Raven Press, 1185 Ave. of the Americas, New York, NY 10036. TEL 212-930-9500. FAX 212-869-3495. *3205*

ATMOSPHERIC ENVIRONMENT. PART A: GENERAL TOPICS.
Pergamon Press, Inc., Journals Division, 660 White Plains Rd., Tarrytown, NY 10591-5153. TEL 914-524-9200. FAX 914-333-2444. *1976*

ATMOSPHERIC ENVIRONMENT. PART B: URBAN ATMOSPHERE.
Pergamon Press, Inc., Journals Division, 660 White Plains Rd., Tarrytown, NY 10591-5153. TEL 914-524-9200. FAX 914-333-2444. *1976*

ATMOSPHERIC RESEARCH.
Elsevier Science Publishers B.V., P.O. Box 211, 1000 AE Amsterdam, Netherlands. TEL 020-5803911. FAX 020-5803598. *3433*

ATOMIC DATA AND NUCLEAR DATA TABLES.
Academic Press, Inc., Journal Division, 1250 Sixth Ave., San Diego, CA 92101. TEL 619-230-1840. FAX 619-699-6800. *3846*

ATOMIC ENERGY LEVELS AND GROTRIAN DIAGRAMS.
Elsevier Science Publishers B.V., Books Division, P.O. Box 211, 1000 AE Amsterdam, Netherlands. TEL 020-5803911. FAX 020-5803705. *3846*

ATOMIC SPECTROSCOPY.
Perkin - Elmer Corp., 761 Main Ave., Norwalk, CT 06859-0105. TEL 203-762-6023. FAX 203-762-6037. *1204*

ATOMIZATION AND SPRAYS.
Hemisphere Publishing Corporation 1900 Frost Rd., Ste. 101, Bristol, PA 19007-1598. TEL 215-785-5800. FAX 215-785-5515. *1848*

AUDIO-DIGEST ANESTHESIOLOGY.
Audio-Digest Foundation 1577 E. Chevy Chase Dr., Glendale, CA 91206. TEL 213-245-8505. FAX 818-240-7379. *3190*

AUDIO-DIGEST EMERGENCY MEDICINE.
Audio-Digest Foundation 1577 E. Chevy Chase Dr., Glendale, CA 91206. TEL 213-245-8505. FAX 818-240-7379. *3079*

REFEREED SERIALS

AUDIO-DIGEST FAMILY PRACTICE.
Audio-Digest Foundation 1577 E. Chevy Chase Dr., Glendale, CA 91206. TEL 213-245-8505. FAX 818-240-7379. *3079*

AUDIO-DIGEST GASTROENTEROLOGY.
Audio-Digest Foundation 1577 E. Chevy Chase Dr., Glendale, CA 91206. TEL 213-245-8505. FAX 818-240-7379. *3266*

AUDIO-DIGEST GENERAL SURGERY.
Audio-Digest Foundation 1577 E. Chevy Chase Dr., Glendale, CA 91206. TEL 213-245-8505. FAX 818-240-7379. *3376*

AUDIO-DIGEST INTERNAL MEDICINE.
Audio-Digest Foundation 1577 E. Chevy Chase Dr., Glendale, CA 91206. TEL 213-245-8505. FAX 818-240-7379. *3079*

AUDIO-DIGEST OBSTETRICS - GYNECOLOGY.
Audio-Digest Foundation 1577 E. Chevy Chase Dr., Glendale, CA 91206. TEL 213-245-8505. FAX 818-240-7379. *3289*

AUDIO-DIGEST OPHTHALMOLOGY.
Audio-Digest Foundation 1577 E. Chevy Chase Dr., Glendale, CA 91206. TEL 213-245-8505. FAX 818-240-7379. *3298*

AUDIO-DIGEST ORTHOPAEDICS.
Audio-Digest Foundation 1577 E. Chevy Chase Dr., Glendale, CA 91206. TEL 213-245-8505. FAX 818-240-7379. *3307*

AUDIO-DIGEST OTOLARYNGOLOGY - HEAD AND NECK SURGERY.
Audio-Digest Foundation 1577 E. Chevy Chase Dr., Glendale, CA 91206. TEL 213-245-8505. FAX 818-240-7379. *3313*

AUDIO-DIGEST PEDIATRICS.
Audio-Digest Foundation 1577 E. Chevy Chase Dr., Glendale, CA 91206. TEL 213-245-8505. FAX 818-240-7379. *3319*

AUDIO-DIGEST PSYCHIATRY.
Audio-Digest Foundation 1577 E. Chevy Chase Dr., Glendale, CA 91206. TEL 213-245-8505. FAX 818-240-7379. *3331*

AUDIO-DIGEST UROLOGY.
Audio-Digest Foundation 1577 E. Chevy Chase Dr., Glendale, CA 91206. TEL 213-245-8505. FAX 818-240-7379. *3387*

AUDITING.
American Accounting Association, 5717 Bessie Dr., Sarasota, FL 34233. TEL 813-921-7747. *747*

AUK.
American Ornithologists' Union, c/o Marion Jenkinson, Treas., Museum of Natural History, University of Kansas, Lawrence, KS 66045. TEL 913-864-4540. *562*

AUSTRALIAN & NEW ZEALAND JOURNAL OF SERIALS LIBRARIANSHIP.
Haworth Press, Inc., 10 Alice St., Binghamton, NY 13904. TEL 800-342-8678. FAX 607-722-1424. *2745*

AUSTRALIAN ENTOMOLOGICAL MAGAZINE.
Entomological Society of Queensland, P.O. Box 537, Indooroopilly, Qld. 4068, Australia. FAX 07-365-1922. *529*

AUSTRALIAN JOURNAL OF PUBLIC HEALTH.
Public Health Association of Australia, G.P.O. Box 2204, Canberra, A.C.T. 2601, Australia. TEL 06-285-2373. FAX 06-282-5438. *4098*

AUSTRALIAN MAMMALOGY.
Australian Mammal Society Inc., c/o R. Rose, University of Tasmania, Zoology Dept., G.P.O. Box 252C, Hobart, Tas. 7001, Australia. TEL 062-421712. FAX 062-413343. *578*

AUSTRALIAN SCIENCE EDUCATION RESEARCH ASSOCIATION. RESEARCH IN SCIENCE EDUCATION.
Australian Science Education Research Association, c/o Richard T. White, Faculty of Education, Monash University, Melbourne, 3168, Australia. TEL 03-565-2862. FAX 61-3-565-2779. *1744*

AUSTRALIAN SOCIETY FOR HISTORICAL ARCHAEOLOGY. RESEARCH BULLETIN.
Australian Society for Historical Archaeology, Box 220 Holme Bldg., University of Sydney, Sydney, N.S.W. 2001, Australia. TEL 02-692-2763. FAX 02-692-4203. *266*

AUTOIMMUNITY.
Harwood Academic Publishers, 270 Eighth Ave., New York, NY 10011. TEL 212-206-8900. FAX 212-645-2459. *3080*

AUTOMATICA.
Pergamon Press, Inc., Journals Division, (International Federation for Automatic Control) 660 White Plains Rd., Tarrytown, NY 10591-5153. TEL 914-524-9200. FAX 914-333-2444. *1411*

AUTOMATION AND REMOTE CONTROL.
Plenum Publishing Corp., Consultants Bureau, (Russian Academy of Sciences) 233 Spring St., New York, NY 10013-1578. TEL 212-620-8468. FAX 212-463-0742. *1412*

AUTOMEDICA.
Gordon and Breach Science Publishers, 270 Eighth Ave., New York, NY 10011. TEL 212-206-8900. FAX 212-645-2459. *3225*

AUTONOMIC NERVOUS SYSTEM.
Harwood Academic Publishers, 270 Eighth Ave., New York, NY 10011. TEL 212-206-8900. FAX 212-645-2459. *570*

AVIAN DISEASES.
American Association of Avian Pathologists, Inc., University of Pennsylvania, New Bolton Center, Kennett Square, PA 19348-1692. TEL 215-444-4282. FAX 215-444-5387. *4807*

AVIATION, SPACE, AND ENVIRONMENTAL MEDICINE.
Aerospace Medical Association, 320 S. Henry St., Alexandria, VA 22314-3579. TEL 703-739-2240. *3080*

B B A - BIOENERGETICS.
Elsevier Science Publishers B.V., P.O. Box 211, 1000 AE Amsterdam, Netherlands. TEL 020-5803911. FAX 020-5803598. *484*

B B A - BIOMEMBRANES.
Elsevier Science Publishers B.V., P.O. Box 211, 1000 AE Amsterdam, Netherlands. TEL 020-5803911. FAX 020-5803598. *471*

B B A - GENE STRUCTURE AND EXPRESSION.
Elsevier Science Publishers B.V., P.O. Box 211, 1000 AE Amsterdam, Netherlands. TEL 020-5803911. FAX 020-5803598. *540*

B B A - GENERAL SUBJECTS.
Elsevier Science Publishers B.V., P.O. Box 211, 1000 AE Amsterdam, Netherlands. TEL 020-5803911. FAX 020-5803598. *471*

B B A - LIPIDS & LIPID METABOLISM.
Elsevier Science Publishers B.V., P.O. Box 211, 1000 AE Amsterdam, Netherlands. TEL 020-5803911. FAX 020-5803598. *471*

B B A - MOLECULAR BASIS OF DISEASE.
Elsevier Science Publishers B.V., P.O. Box 211, 1000 AE Amsterdam, Netherlands. TEL 020-5803911. FAX 020-5803598. *3080*

B B A - MOLECULAR CELL RESEARCH.
Elsevier Science Publishers B.V., P.O. Box 211, 1000 AE Amsterdam, Netherlands. TEL 020-5803911. FAX 020-5803598. *484*

B B A - PROTEIN STRUCTURE AND MOLECULAR ENZYMOLOGY.
Elsevier Science Publishers B.V., P.O. Box 211, 1000 AE Amsterdam, Netherlands. TEL 020-5803911. FAX 020-5803598. *472*

B B A - REVIEWS ON BIOMEMBRANES.
Elsevier Science Publishers B.V., P.O. Box 211, 1000 AE Amsterdam, Netherlands. TEL 020-5803911. FAX 020-5803598. *522*

B B A - REVIEWS ON CANCER.
Elsevier Science Publishers B.V., P.O. Box 211, 1000 AE Amsterdam, Netherlands. TEL 020-5803911. FAX 020-5803598. *3193*

BAILEYA.
L. H. Bailey Hortorium, Cornell University, Ithaca, NY 14853. TEL 607-255-7976. *495*

BAILLIERE'S CLINICAL RHEUMATOLOGY.
Grune & Stratton Ltd., Harcourt Brace Jovanovich, Publishers, 24-28 Oval Rd., London NW1, 7DX, England. *3368*

BANDAOTI XUEBAO.
Science Press, Marketing and Sales Department, (Chinese Academy of Sciences, Institute of Semiconductors) 16 Donghuangchenggen Beijie, Beijing 100707, People's Republic of China. TEL 4010642. FAX 4012180. *1764*

BANKING LAW JOURNAL.
Warren, Gorham and Lamont, One Penn Plaza, New York, NY 10119. TEL 800-950-1205. FAX 212-971-5240. *766*

BAO PO.
Wuhan Gongye Daxue, Bao Po Bianjibu, Luoshi Lu, Wuchang, Wuhan, Hubei 430070, People's Republic of China. *1848*

BARTONIA.
Philadelphia Botanical Club, c/o Academy of Natural Sciences of Philadelphia, 19th St. and The Parkway, Philadelphia, PA 19103. TEL 215-299-1000. *495*

BASIC AND APPLIED SOCIAL PSYCHOLOGY.
Lawrence Erlbaum Associates, Inc., 365 Broadway, Hillsdale, NJ 07642. TEL 201-666-4110. FAX 201-666-2394. *4012*

BASIC AND CLINICAL CARDIOLOGY SERIES.
Marcel Dekker, Inc., 270 Madison Ave., New York, NY 10016. TEL 212-696-9000. FAX 212-685-4540. *3205*

BASIC & CLINICAL ENDOCRINOLOGY.
Marcel Dekker, Inc., 270 Madison Ave., New York, NY 10016. TEL 212-696-9000. FAX 212-685-4540. *3250*

BASIC AND CLINICAL NUTRITION.
Marcel Dekker, Inc., 270 Madison Ave., New York, NY 10016. TEL 212-696-9000. FAX 212-685-4540. *3603*

BASIC LIFE SCIENCES.
Plenum Publishing Corp., 233 Spring St., New York, NY 10013-1578. TEL 212-620-8000. FAX 212-463-0742. *430*

BEADS.
Society of Bead Researchers, 1600 Liverpool Ct., Ottawa, Ont. K1A 0H3, Canada. TEL 613-990-4814. FAX 613-952-1756. *2563*

BEAM MODIFICATION OF MATERIALS.
Elsevier Science Publishers B.V., Books Division, P.O. Box 211, 1000 AE Amsterdam, Netherlands. TEL 020-5803911. FAX 020-5803705. *3852*

BEHAVIOR AND INFORMATION TECHNOLOGY.
Taylor & Francis Ltd., Rankine Rd., Basingstoke, Hants RG24 0PR, England. TEL 0256-840366. FAX 0256-479438. *4012*

BEHAVIOR AND PHILOSOPHY.
Cambridge Center for Behavioral Studies, 11 Waterhouse St., Cambridge, MA 02138. TEL 617-491-9020. FAX 617-491-1072. *4012*

BEHAVIOR GENETICS.
Plenum Publishing Corp., 233 Spring St., New York, NY 10013-1578. TEL 212-620-8000. FAX 212-463-0742. *540*

BEHAVIOR RESEARCH METHODS, INSTRUMENTS, AND COMPUTERS.
Psychonomic Society, Inc., 1710 Fortview Rd., Austin, TX 78704. TEL 512-462-2442. *4013*

BEHAVIOR THERAPY.
Association for Advancement of Behavior Therapy, 15 W. 36th St., New York, NY 10018. TEL 212-279-7970. *4013*

BEHAVIORAL AND NEURAL BIOLOGY.
Academic Press, Inc., Journal Division, 1250 Sixth Ave., San Diego, CA 92101. TEL 619-230-1840. FAX 619-699-6800. *430*

REFEREED SERIALS

BEHAVIORAL & SOCIAL SCIENCES LIBRARIAN.
Haworth Press, Inc., 10 Alice St., Binghamton, NY 13904. TEL 800-342-9678. FAX 607-722-1424. *2746*

BEHAVIORAL ASSESSMENT.
Pergamon Press, Inc., Journals Division, (Association for Advancement of Behavior Therapy) 660 White Plains Rd., Tarrytown, NY 10591-5153. TEL 914-524-9200. FAX 914-333-2444. *4013*

BEHAVIORAL BRAIN RESEARCH.
Elsevier Science Publishers B.V., P.O. Box 211, 1000 AE Amsterdam, Netherlands. TEL 020-5803911. FAX 020-5803598. *3331*

BEHAVIORAL ECOLOGY.
Oxford University Press, Journals, (International Society for Behavioral Ecology) 200 Madison Ave., New York, NY 10016. TEL 212-679-7300. FAX 212-725-2972. *430*

BEHAVIORAL MEDICINE.
Heldref Publications, (Helen Dwight Reid Educational Foundation) 1319 Eighteenth St., N.W., Washington, DC 20036-1802. TEL 202-396-6267. FAX 202-296-5149. *4013*

BEHAVIORAL NEUROPSYCHIATRY.
Behavioral Neuropsychiatry Medical Publishers, Inc., 61 East 86th St., New York, NY 10028. *3331*

BEHAVIORAL NEUROSCIENCE.
American Psychological Association, 750 First St., N.E., Washington, DC 20002-4242. TEL 202-336-5500. FAX 202-336-5568. *4013*

BEHAVIOUR RESEARCH AND THERAPY.
Pergamon Press, Inc., Journals Division, 660 White Plains Rd., Tarrytown, NY 10591-5153. TEL 914-524-9200. FAX 914-333-2444. *4013*

BEHAVIOURAL PROCESSES.
Elsevier Science Publishers B.V., P.O. Box 211, 1000 AE Amsterdam, Netherlands. TEL 020-5803911. FAX 020-5803598. *3331*

BEIJING YIKE DAXUE XUEBAO.
Beijing Yike Daxue, Xueyuan Lu, Beijing 100083, People's Republic of China. TEL 2017601. *3081*

BERGEY'S MANUAL OF DETERMINATIVE BACTERIOLOGY.
Williams and Wilkins, 428 E. Preston St., Baltimore, MD 21202. TEL 301-528-4000. FAX 301-528-4312. *550*

BERKELEY WOMEN'S LAW JOURNAL.
University of California Press, Journals Division, 2120 Berkeley Way, Berkeley, CA 94720. TEL 510-642-4191. FAX 510-643-7127. *2604*

BEST OF LONG RANGE PLANNING.
Pergamon Press, Inc., Journals Division, 660 White Plains Rd., Tarrytown, NY 10591-5153. TEL 914-524-9200. FAX 914-333-2444. *1003*

BINARY: COMPUTING IN MICROBIOLOGY.
Academic Press Ltd., (Society for General Microbiology) 24-28 Oval Rd., London NW1 7DX, England. TEL 071-267-4466. FAX 071-482-2293. *550*

BINGDUXUE ZAZHI.
Science Press, Marketing and Sales Department, (Chinese Academy of Sciences, Wuhan Institute of Virology) 16 Donghuangchenggen Beijie, Beijing 100707, People's Republic of China. TEL 4010642. FAX 4012180. *550*

BIO-MEDICAL MATERIALS AND ENGINEERING.
Pergamon Press, Inc., Journals Division, 660 White Plains Rd., Tarrytown, NY 10591-5153. TEL 914-524-9200. FAX 914-333-2444. *468*

BIO-TECHNOLOGY.
Nature Publishing Co. 65 Bleecker St., New York, NY 10012. TEL 212-477-9600. *487*

BIOCATALYSIS.
Harwood Academic Publishers, 270 Eighth Ave., New York, NY 10011. TEL 212-206-8900. FAX 212-645-2459. *472*

BIOCHEMICAL AND BIOPHYSICAL RESEARCH COMMUNICATIONS.
Academic Press, Inc., Journal Division, 1250 Sixth Ave., San Diego, CA 92101. TEL 619-230-1840. FAX 619-699-6800. *472*

BIOCHEMICAL EDUCATION.
Pergamon Press, Inc., Journals Division, (International Union of Biochemistry) 660 White Plains Rd., Tarrytown, NY 10591-5153. TEL 914-524-9200. FAX 914-333-2444. *472*

BIOCHEMICAL GENETICS.
Plenum Publishing Corp., 233 Spring St., New York, NY 10013-1578. TEL 212-620-8000. FAX 212-463-0742. *472*

BIOCHEMICAL MEDICINE AND METABOLIC BIOLOGY.
Academic Press, Inc., Journal Division, 1250 Sixth Ave., San Diego, CA 92101. TEL 619-230-1840. FAX 619-699-6800. *472*

BIOCHEMICAL PHARMACOLOGY.
Pergamon Press, Inc., Journals Division, 660 White Plains Rd., Tarrytown, NY 10591-5153. TEL 914-524-9200. FAX 914-333-2444. *3719*

BIOCHEMICAL SYSTEMATICS AND ECOLOGY.
Pergamon Press, Inc., Journals Division, 660 White Plains Rd., Tarrytown, NY 10591-5153. TEL 914-524-9200. FAX 914-333-2444. *472*

BIOCHEMISTRY.
Plenum Publishing Corp., Consultants Bureau, (Russian Academy of Sciences) 233 Spring St., New York, NY 10013-1578. TEL 212-620-8468. FAX 212-463-0742. *473*

BIOCHEMISTRY AND CELL BIOLOGY.
National Research Council of Canada, Research Journals, Ottawa, Ont. K1A 0R6, Canada. TEL 613-993-9084. FAX 613-952-7656. *473*

BIOCHEMISTRY OF DISEASE.
Marcel Dekker, Inc., 270 Madison Ave., New York, NY 10016. TEL 212-696-9000. FAX 212-685-4540. *473*

BIOCHEMISTRY OF THE ELEMENTS.
Plenum Publishing Corp., 233 Spring St., New York, NY 10013-1578. TEL 212-620-8000. FAX 212-463-0742. *473*

BIOCHEMISTRY: SERIES OF MONOGRAPHS.
John Wiley & Sons, Inc., Journals, 605 Third Ave., New York, NY 10158-0012. TEL 212-850-6000. *473*

BIOCHIMICA ET BIOPHYSICA ACTA.
Elsevier Science Publishers B.V., P.O. Box 211, 1000 AE Amsterdam, Netherlands. TEL 020-5803911. FAX 020-5803598. *473*

BIOCHIMIE.
Editions Scientifique Elsevier, (Societe Francaise de Biochimie et Biologie Moleculaire) 29, rue Buffon, 75005 Paris, France. TEL 47-07-11-22. FAX 43-36-80-93. *473*

BIOCYCLE.
J G Press, Inc., 419 State Ave., Emmaus, PA 18049. TEL 215-967-4135. *1984*

BIOELECTROCHEMISTRY AND BIOENERGETICS.
Elsevier Sequoia S.A., P.O. Box 564, CH-1001 Lausanne, Switzerland. TEL 021-207381. FAX 021-235444. *473*

BIOELECTROMAGNETICS.
John Wiley & Sons, Inc., Journals, (Bioelectromagnetics Society) 605 Third Ave., New York, NY 10158. TEL 212-850-6000. FAX 212-850-6088. *3082*

BIOFEEDBACK & SELF REGULATION.
Plenum Publishing Corp., 233 Spring St., New York, NY 10013-1578. TEL 212-620-8000. FAX 212-463-0742. *4014*

BIOFOULING.
Harwood Academic Publishers, 270 Eighth Ave., New York, NY 10011. TEL 212-206-8900. FAX 212-645-2459. *1980*

BIOGRAPHY (HONOLULU).
University of Hawaii Press, Journals Department, (Biographical Research Center) 2840 Kolowalu St., Honolulu, HI 96822. TEL 808-956-8833. FAX 808-988-6052. *417*

BIOLOGICAL BULLETIN.
Kexue Chubanshe, Qikan Bu, (Chinese Society of Zoology) 16 Donghuangchenggen Beijie, Beijing 100707, People's Republic of China. TEL 4010642. FAX 4012180. *431*

BIOLOGICAL CONSERVATION.
Elsevier Science Publishers Ltd., Crown House, Linton Rd., Barking, Essex IG11 8JU, England. TEL 081-594-7272. FAX 081-594-5942. *1484*

BIOLOGICAL MAGNETIC RESONANCE.
Plenum Publishing Corp., 233 Spring St., New York, NY 10013-1578. TEL 212-620-8000. FAX 212-463-0742. *3815*

BIOLOGICAL MEMBRANES.
Harwood Academic Publishers, 270 Eighth Ave., New York, NY 10011. TEL 212-206-8900. FAX 212-645-2459. *484*

BIOLOGICAL PSYCHIATRY.
Elsevier Science Publishing Co., Inc. (New York), (Society of Biological Psychiatry) 655 Ave. of the Americas, New York, NY 10010. TEL 212-989-5800. FAX 212-633-3965. *3332*

BIOLOGICAL PSYCHOLOGY.
North-Holland P.O. Box 211, 1000 AE Amsterdam, Netherlands. TEL 020-5803911. FAX 020-5803598. *4014*

BIOLOGICAL REGULATION & DEVELOPMENT.
Plenum Publishing Corp., 233 Spring St., New York, NY 10013-1578. TEL 212-620-8000. FAX 212-463-0742. *474*

BIOLOGICAL TRACE ELEMENT RESEARCH.
Humana Press Inc., (International Association of Bioinorganic Scientists) Crescent Manor, Box 2148, Clifton, NJ 07015. TEL 201-256-1699. FAX 201-256-8341. *474*

BIOLOGY OF REPRODUCTION.
Society for the Study of Reproduction, 309 W. Clark St., Champaign, IL 61820. FAX 904-392-7652. *540*

BIOLOGY OF THE CELL.
Editions Scientifiques Elsevier, (European Cell Biology Organization) 29, rue Buffon, 75005 Paris, France. TEL 47-07-11-22. FAX 43-36-80-93. *559*

BIOMASS & BIOENERGY.
Pergamon Press plc, Headington Hill Hall, Oxford OX3 0BW, England. TEL 0865-794141. FAX 0865-743911. *1784*

BIOMATERIALS.
Butterworth - Heinemann Ltd. Linacre House, Jordan Hill, Oxford OX2 8DP, England. TEL 0865-310366. FAX 0865-310898. *3082*

BIOMATERIALS, ARTIFICIAL CELLS AND IMMOBILIZATION BIOTECHNOLOGY.
Marcel Dekker Journals, 270 Madison Ave., New York, NY 10016. TEL 212-696-9000. FAX 212-685-4540. *3257*

BIOMEDICAL AND ENVIRONMENTAL SCIENCES.
Zhongguo Yufang Kexue Yanjiuyuan, 207 Ruijin 2 Lu, Shanghai 200025, People's Republic of China. TEL 4377008. FAX 619-699-6800. *3082*

BIOMEDICAL ENGINEERING.
Plenum Publishing Corp., Consultants Bureau, (Ministerstvo Zdravookhraneniya) 233 Spring St., New York, NY 10013-1578. TEL 212-620-8468. FAX 212-463-0742. *3082*

BIOMEDICAL ENGINEERING AND COMPUTATION SERIES.
Harwood Academic Publishers, 270 Eighth Ave., New York, NY 10011. TEL 212-206-8900. FAX 212-645-2459. *468*

BIOMEDICAL ENGINEERING AND INSTRUMENTATION SERIES.
Marcel Dekker, Inc., 270 Madison Ave., New York, NY 10016. TEL 212-696-9000. FAX 212-685-4540. *468*

BIOMEDICAL INSTRUMENTATION & TECHNOLOGY.
Hanley & Belfus, Inc., (Association for the Advancement of Medical Instrumentation) 210 S. 13th St., Philadelphia, PA 19107. TEL 215-546-7293. FAX 215-790-9330. *3082*

BIOMEDICAL SCIENCE.
Royal Society of Chemistry, Thomas Graham House, Science Park, Milton Rd., Cambridge CB4 4WF, England. *3082*

BIOMEDICAL SCIENCES INSTRUMENTATION.
Instrument Society of America, 67 Alexander Dr., Box 12277, Research Triangle Park, NC 27709. TEL 919-549-8411. FAX 919-549-8288. *3082*

BIOMEDICINE AND PHARMACOTHERAPY.
Editions Scientifiques Elsevier, 29, rue Buffon, 75005 Paris, France. TEL 47-07-11-22. FAX 43-36-80-93. *3082*

BIOMEMBRANES.
Plenum Publishing Corp., 233 Spring St., New York, NY 10013-1578. TEL 212-620-8000. FAX 212-463-0742. *522*

BIOMETRICS.
Biometric Society, 1429 Duke St., Ste. 401, Alexandria, VA 22314-3402. TEL 703-836-8311. *4565*

BIOMIMETICS.
Plenum Publishing Corp., 233 Spring St., New York, NY 10013-1578. TEL 212-620-8000. FAX 212-463-0742. *468*

BIOORGANIC & MEDICINAL CHEMISTRY LETTERS.
Pergamon Press plc, Headington Hill Hall, Oxford OX3 0BW, England. TEL 0865-794141. FAX 0865-60285. *1216*

BIOORGANIC CHEMISTRY.
Academic Press, Inc., Journal Division, 1250 Sixth Ave., San Diego, CA 92101. TEL 619-230-1840. FAX 619-699-6800. *1216*

BIOPHYSICAL CHEMISTRY.
Elsevier Science Publishers B.V., P.O. Box 211, 1000 AE Amsterdam, Netherlands. TEL 020-5803911. FAX 020-5803598. *484*

BIOPHYSICAL JOURNAL.
Rockefeller University Press, (Biophysical Society) 222 E. 70th St., New York, NY 10021. TEL 212-570-8572. FAX 212-570-7944. *484*

BIOPHYSICAL SOCIETY. ABSTRACTS.
Rockefeller University Press, 222 E. 70th St., New York, NY 10021. TEL 212-570-8572. FAX 212-579-7944. *462*

BIOPHYSICS.
Pergamon Press, Inc., Journals Division, 660 White Plains Rd., Tarrytown, NY 10591-5153. TEL 914-524-9200. FAX 914-333-2444. *484*

BIOPOLYMERS.
John Wiley & Sons, Inc., Journals, 605 Third Ave., New York, NY 10158-0012. TEL 212-692-6000. FAX 212-850-6088. *1216*

BIOPROCESS TECHNOLOGY SERIES.
Marcel Dekker, Inc., 270 Madison Ave., New York, NY 10016. TEL 212-696-9000. FAX 212-685-4540. *433*

BIOPSY INTERPRETATION SERIES.
Raven Press, 1185 Ave. of the Americas, New York, NY 10036. TEL 212-930-9500. FAX 212-869-3495. *3258*

BIORESOURCE TECHNOLOGY.
Elsevier Science Publishers Ltd., Crown House, Linton Rd., Barking, Essex IG11 8JU, England. TEL 081-594-7272. FAX 081-594-5942. *487*

BIORHEOLOGY.
Pergamon Press, Inc., Journals Division, 660 White Plains Rd., Tarrytown, NY 10591-5153. TEL 914-524-9200. FAX 914-333-2444. *485*

BIOSCIENCE.
American Institute of Biological Sciences, 730 11th St., N.W., Washington, DC 20001-4521. TEL 202-628-1500. FAX 202-628-1509. *433*

BIOSCIENCE REPORTS.
Plenum Publishing Corp., (Biochemical Society) 233 Spring St., New York, NY 10013-1578. TEL 212-620-8000. FAX 212-463-0742. *474*

BIOSENSORS AND BIOELECTRONICS.
Elsevier Science Publishers Ltd., Crown House, Linton Rd., Barking, Essex IG11 8JU, England. *485*

BIOSYNTHETIC PRODUCTS FOR CANCER CHEMOTHERAPY.
Elsevier Science Publishers B.V., Books Division, P.O. Box 211, 1000 AE Amsterdam, Netherlands. TEL 020-5803911. FAX 020-5803705. *3193*

BIOSYSTEMS.
Elsevier Scientific Publishers Ireland Ltd., P.O. Box 85, Limerick, Ireland. TEL 061-61944. FAX 061-62144. *433*

BIOTECHNIC AND HISTOCHEMISTRY.
Williams & Wilkins, (Biological Stain Commission) 428 E. Preston St., Baltimore, MD 21202. TEL 301-528-4000. FAX 301-528-4312. *559*

BIOTECHNOLOGY ADVANCES.
Pergamon Press, Inc., Journals Division, 660 White Plains Rd., Tarrytown, NY 10591-5153. TEL 914-524-9200. FAX 914-333-9200. *488*

BIOTECHNOLOGY AND APPLIED BIOCHEMISTRY.
Academic Press, Inc., Journal Division, (International Union of Biochemistry) 1250 Sixth Ave., San Diego, CA 92101. TEL 619-230-1840. FAX 619-699-6800. *488*

BIOTECHNOLOGY AND BIOENGINEERING.
John Wiley & Sons, Inc., Journals, 605 Third Ave., New York, NY 10158-0012. TEL 212-850-6000. FAX 212-850-6088. *488*

BIOTECHNOLOGY EDUCATION.
Pergamon Press, Inc., Journals Division, 660 White Plains Rd., Tarrytown, NY 10591-5153. TEL 914-524-9200. FAX 914-333-2444. *488*

BIOTECHNOLOGY PROGRESS.
American Chemical Society, 1155 16th St., N.W., Washington, DC 20036. TEL 202-872-4363. FAX 202-872-4615. *488*

BIOTECHNOLOGY THERAPEUTICS.
Marcel Dekker Journals, 270 Madison Ave., New York, NY 10016. TEL 212-969-9000. FAX 212-685-4540. *489*

BIOTROPICA.
Association for Tropical Biology, Inc., c/o Dr. Julie S. Denslow, Exec. Dir., Department of Ecology, Evolution & Organismal Biology, Tulane University, New Orleans, LA 70718. TEL 504-865-5546. FAX 504-865-6785. *433*

BIRTH DEFECTS INSTITUTE. SYMPOSIA.
Academic Press, Inc., 1250 Sixth Ave., San Diego, CA 92101. TEL 619-231-0926. FAX 619-699-6715. *3083*

BLACK SACRED MUSIC.
Duke University Press, 6697 College Station, Durham, NC 27708. TEL 919-684-2173. FAX 919-684-8644. *3541*

BLACKS IN THE NEW WORLD.
University of Illinois Press, 54 E. Gregory Dr., Champaign, IL 61820. TEL 217-333-0950. FAX 217-244-8082. *1994*

BLOOD.
W.B. Saunders Co. (American Society of Hematology) Curtis Center, Independence Square W., Philadelphia, PA 19106. TEL 215-238-7800. *3271*

BLUMEA.
Rijksherbarium - Hortus Botanicus, Publications Department, P.O. Box 9514, 2300 RA Leiden, Netherlands. *496*

BONE.
Pergamon Press, Inc., Journals Division, 660 White Plains Rd., Tarrytown, NY 10591-5153. TEL 914-524-9200. FAX 914-333-2444. *3229*

BONE AND MINERAL.
Elsevier Science Publishers B.V., (International Conferences on Calcium Regulating Hormones, Inc.) P.O. Box 211, 1000 AE Amsterdam, Netherlands. TEL 020-5803911. FAX 020-5803598. *3251*

BONE AND MINERAL RESEARCH ANNUAL.
Elsevier Science Publishers B.V., Books Division, P.O. Box 211, 1000 AE Amsterdam, Netherlands. TEL 020-5803911. FAX 020-5803705. *3307*

BOOKS IN LIBRARY AND INFORMATION SCIENCE SERIES.
Marcel Dekker, Inc., 270 Madison Ave., New York, NY 10016. TEL 212-696-9000. FAX 212-685-4540. *2792*

BOOKS IN SOILS AND THE ENVIRONMENT SERIES.
Marcel Dekker, Inc., 270 Madison Ave., New York, NY 10016. TEL 212-696-9000. FAX 212-685-4540. *171*

BOTANICAL REVIEW.
New York Botanical Garden, Scientific Publications Department, Bronx, NY 10458. TEL 212-220-8721. FAX 212-220-6504. *497*

BOUNDARY 2.
Duke University Press, 6697 College Station, Durham, NC 27708. TEL 919-684-2173. FAX 919-684-8644. *2900*

BRAIN AND COGNITION.
Academic Press, Inc., Journal Division, 1250 Sixth Ave., San Diego, CA 92101. TEL 619-230-1840. FAX 619-699-6800. *4014*

BRAIN AND LANGUAGE.
Academic Press, Inc., Journal Division, 1250 Sixth Ave., San Diego, CA 92101. TEL 619-230-1840. FAX 619-699-6800. *4014*

BRAIN, BEHAVIOR, AND IMMUNITY.
Academic Press, Inc., Journal Division, 1250 Sixth Ave., San Diego, CA 92101. TEL 619-230-1840. FAX 619-699-6800. *3184*

BRAIN INJURY.
Taylor & Francis Ltd., Rankine Rd., Basingstoke, Hants RG24 0PR, England. TEL 0256-840366. FAX 0256-479438. *3332*

BRAIN RESEARCH BULLETIN.
Pergamon Press, Inc., Journals Division, 660 White Plains Rd., Tarrytown, NY 10591-5153. TEL 914-524-9200. FAX 914-333-2444. *3332*

BRAIN TOPOGRAPHY.
Human Sciences Press, Inc. 233 Spring St., New York, NY 10013-1578. TEL 212-620-8000. FAX 212-463-0742. *3332*

BREAST DISEASES (NEW YORK).
Elsevier Science Publishing Co., Inc. (New York), 655 Ave. of the Americas, New York, NY 10010. TEL 212-989-5800. FAX 212-633-3965. *3083*

BRITISH ASSOCIATION OF TEACHERS OF THE DEAF. JOURNAL.
British Association of Teachers of the Deaf, Mottram Rd., Alderley Edge, Cheshire SK9 7JH, England. *2286*

BRITISH JOURNAL FOR THE HISTORY OF SCIENCE.
Cambridge University Press, (British Society for the History of Science) Edinburgh Bldg., Shaftesbury Rd., Cambridge CB2 2RU, England. TEL 0223-312393. FAX 0223-31505. *4302*

BRITISH JOURNAL OF CLINICAL PRACTICE.
Medicom UK Ltd., The Quandrant, 118 London Rd., Kingston-upon-Thames KT2 6QJ, England. TEL 081-541-5666. FAX 081-541-4746. *3084*

BRITISH JOURNAL OF SURGERY.
Butterworth - Heinemann Ltd. (Surgery Society Ltd.) Linacre House, Jordan Hill, Oxford OX2 8DP, England. TEL 0865-310366. FAX 0865-310898. *3376*

BRITTONIA.
New York Botanical Garden, Scientific Publications Department, Bronx, NY 10458. TEL 212-220-8721. FAX 212-220-6504. *498*

BROOKHAVEN SYMPOSIA IN BIOLOGY.
Plenum Publishing Corp., (Brookhaven National Laboratory) 233 Spring St., New York, NY 10013-1578. TEL 212-620-8000. FAX 212-463-0742. *433*

BROWN BOVERI SYMPOSIA. PROCEEDINGS.
Plenum Publishing Corp., 233 Spring St., New York, NY 10013-1578. TEL 212-620-8000. FAX 212-463-0742. *1883*

BUDDHIST - CHRISTIAN STUDIES.
University of Hawaii Press, Journals Department, (Society for Buddhist-Christian Studies, East-West Religions Project) 2840 Kolowalu St., Honolulu, HI 96822. TEL 808-956-8833. FAX 808-988-6052. *4214*

BUILDING AND ENVIRONMENT.
Pergamon Press, Inc., Journals Division, 660 White Plains Rd., Tarrytown, NY 10591-5153. TEL 914-524-9200. FAX 914-333-2444. *605*

BULLETIN DU CANCER.
Editions Scientifiques Elsevier, (Societe Francaise du Cancer) 29, rue Buffon, 75005 Paris, France. TEL 47-07-11-22. FAX 43-36-80-93. *3193*

BULLETIN DU CANCER - RADIOTHERAPIE.
Editions Scientifiques Elsevier, (Societe Francaise de Radiotherapie Oncologique) 29, rue Buffon, 75005 Paris, France. TEL 47-07-11-22. FAX 43-36-80-93. *3194*

BULLETIN OF CONCERNED ASIAN SCHOLARS.
Bulletin of Concerned Asian Scholars, Inc., 3239 9th St., Boulder, CO 80304-2112. TEL 303-449-7439. FAX 303-449-8870. *3952*

BULLETIN OF EXPERIMENTAL BIOLOGY AND MEDICINE.
Plenum Publishing Corp., Consultants Bureau, (Akademiya Meditsinskikh Nauk S.S.S.R.) 233 Spring St., New York, NY 10013-1578. TEL 212-620-8468. FAX 212-463-0742. *433*

BULLETIN OF HISTORICAL RESEARCH IN MUSICAL EDUCATION.
University of Kansas, A M E M T Department, 311 Baily Hall, Lawrence, KS 66045-2344. TEL 913-864-4784. *3543*

BULLETIN OF LATIN AMERICAN RESEARCH.
Pergamon Press plc, (Society for Latin American Studies) Headington Hill Hall, Oxford OX3 0BW, England. TEL 0865-794141. FAX 0865-743911. *4367*

BULLETIN OF MARINE SCIENCE.
Rosenstiel School of Marine and Atmospheric Science, 4600 Rickenbacker Causeway, Miami, FL 33149. TEL 305-361-4190. *1602*

BULLETIN OF MATHEMATICAL BIOLOGY.
Pergamon Press, Inc., Journals Division, 660 White Plains Rd., Tarrytown, NY 10591-5153. TEL 914-524-9200. FAX 914-333-2444. *433*

BULLETIN OF SCIENCE TECHNOLOGY AND SOCIETY.
102 Materials Research Laboratory, Pennsylvania State University, University Park, PA 16802. TEL 814-865-1137. *4303*

BULLETIN OF THE HISTORY OF DENTISTRY.
American Academy of the History of Dentistry, c/o Dr. Hannelore T. Loevy, Ed., 5524 S. Harper Ave., Chicago, IL 60037. *3229*

BURNS.
Butterworth - Heinemann Ltd. (International Society for Burn Injuries) Linacre House, Jordan Hill, Oxford OX2 8DP, England. TEL 0865-310366. FAX 0865-310898. *3307*

BUSINESS AND SOCIETY.
Roosevelt University, Walter E. Heller College of Business Administration, 430 S. Michigan Ave., Chicago, IL 60605. TEL 312-341-3820. *649*

BUSINESS COMPUTER DIGEST.
Association of Computer Users, Box 2189, Berkeley, CA 94702-0189. TEL 303-241-0125. *825*

BUSINESS LIBRARY REVIEW.
Gordon and Breach Science Publishers S.A., 270 Eighth Ave., New York, NY 10011. TEL 212-206-8900. FAX 212-645-2459. *769*

BUSINESS STUDIES ON THE U.S.S.R.
Gordon and Breach Scientific Publishers, (Worldwide Information Systems, Inc.) 270 Eighth Ave., New York, NY 10011. TEL 212-206-8900. FAX 212-645-2459. *902*

BYZANTINOSLAVICA.
John Benjamins Publishing Co, (Czechoslovak Academy of Sciences, Institute of Greek, Roman and Latin Studies) Amsteldijk 44, P.O. Box 75577, 1070 AN Amsterdam, Netherlands. TEL 020-6738156. FAX 020-6739773. *3635*

C A L I C O JOURNAL.
Computer Assisted Language & Instruction Consortium, 014 Language Bldg., Duke University, Durham, NC 27706. TEL 919-684-6455. FAX 919-681-6485. *1688*

C B M S. N S F. REGIONAL CONFERENCE SERIES IN APPLIED MATHEMATICS.
Society for Industrial and Applied Mathematics, Conference Board of the Mathematical Sciences, Attn: P. Manning, 3600 University City Science Center, Philadelphia, PA 19104-2688. TEL 215-382-9800. FAX 215-386-7999. *3062*

C I M BULLETIN.
Canadian Institute of Mining, Metallurgy & Petroleum, Xerox Tower, 3400 de Maisonneuve Blvd. W., Ste. 1210, Montreal, Que. H3Z 3B8, Canada. TEL 514-939-2710. FAX 514-939-2714. *3479*

C L A O JOURNAL.
Kellner-McCaffery Associates, Inc., (Contact Lens Association of Ophthalmologists) 150 Fifth Ave., New York, NY 10011. TEL 212-741-0280. FAX 212-929-2174. *3299*

C L R.
Medical Economics Company Inc., (Medical Laboratory Observer) Five Paragon Dr., Montvale, NJ 07645. TEL 201-358-7200. FAX 201-573-1045. *3258*

C O D A T A BULLETIN.
Hemisphere Publishing Corporation (International Council of Scientific Unions, Committee on Data for Science and Technology) 1900 Frost Rd., Ste. 101, Bristol, PA 19007-1598. TEL 215-785-5800. FAX 215-785-5515. *4303*

C O S P A R INFORMATION BULLETIN.
Pergamon Press, Inc., Journals Division, (Committee on Space Research) 660 White Plains Rd., Tarrytown, NY 10591-5153. TEL 914-524-9200. FAX 914-333-2444. *49*

C W I. MONOGRAPHS.
Stichting Mathematisch Centrum, Centrum voor Wiskunde en Informatica, P.O. Box 4079, 1009 AB Amsterdam, Netherlands. TEL 020-5924005. FAX 020-5924199. *3064*

CA - A CANCER JOURNAL FOR CLINICIANS.
J.B. Lippincott Co. (New York), (American Cancer Society, Inc.) 1180 Ave. of the Americas, 6th Fl., New York, NY 10036. TEL 212-840-7760. FAX 212-840-7813. *3194*

CAHIERS DE DROIT EUROPEEN.
Maison Ferdinand Larcier S.A., Rue des Minimes 39, 1000 Brussels, Belgium. TEL 02-5124712. FAX 02-5139009. *2608*

CALCIFIED TISSUE INTERNATIONAL.
Springer-Verlag, Journals, 175 Fifth Ave., New York, NY 10010. TEL 212-460-1500. *522*

CALIFORNIA ACADEMY OF SCIENCES. ACADEMY NEWSLETTER.
California Academy of Sciences, Golden Gate Park, San Francisco, CA 94118. TEL 415-750-7142. *4303*

CALIFORNIA ACADEMY OF SCIENCES. MEMOIRS.
California Academy of Sciences, Golden Gate Park, San Francisco, CA 94118. TEL 415-750-7243. *4303*

CALIFORNIA ACADEMY OF SCIENCES. OCCASIONAL PAPERS.
California Academy of Sciences, Golden Gate Park, San Francisco, CA 94118. TEL 415-750-7243. *4303*

CALIFORNIA ACADEMY OF SCIENCES. PROCEEDINGS.
California Academy of Sciences, Golden Gate Park, San Francisco, CA 94118. TEL 415-750-7243. *4303*

CALIFORNIA CHIROPRACTIC ASSOCIATION JOURNAL.
California Chiropractic Association, 7801 Folsom Blvd., Ste. 375, Sacramento, CA 95826. TEL 916-387-0177. FAX 916-325-4855. *3213*

CALIFORNIA COOPERATIVE OCEANIC FISHERIES INVESTIGATIONS REPORTS.
California Cooperative Oceanic Fisheries Investigations, Scripps Institution of Oceanography, University of California, La Jolla, CA 92093-0227. TEL 619-534-4236. FAX 619-534-5306. *580*

CALIFORNIA INSECT SURVEY. BULLETIN.
University of California Press, 2120 Berkeley Way, Berkeley, CA 94720. TEL 415-642-4247. FAX 415-643-7127. *529*

CALIFORNIA LAW REVIEW.
University of California Press, Journals Division, 2120 Berkeley Way, Berkeley, CA 94720. TEL 510-642-4191. FAX 510-643-7127. *2609*

CALIFORNIA NATURAL HISTORY GUIDES.
University of California Press, 2120 Berkeley Way, Berkeley, CA 94720. FAX 415-643-7127. *434*

CALIFORNIA READER.
California Reading Association, 2790 Harbor Blvd., Ste. 204, Costa Mesa, CA 92626-5156. *1746*

CALIFORNIA SCHOOL BOARDS JOURNAL.
California School Board Association, 3100 Beacon Blvd., Box 1660, W. Sacramento, CA 95819. TEL 916-371-4691. FAX 916-371-3407. *1619*

CALIFORNIA STUDIES IN THE HISTORY OF ART.
University of California Press, 2120 Berkeley Way, Berkeley, CA 94720. TEL 415-642-4247. FAX 415-643-7127. *320*

CALPHAD.
Pergamon Press, Inc., Journals Division, 660 White Plains Rd., Tarrytown, NY 10591-5153. TEL 914-524-9200. FAX 914-333-2444. *4359*

CANADIAN ADMINISTRATOR.
University of Alberta, Department of Educational Administration, Edmonton, Alta. T6G 2G5, Canada. TEL 403-492-5241. FAX 403-492-2024. *1726*

CANADIAN ASSOCIATION OF RADIOLOGISTS. JOURNAL.
Canadian Medical Association, P.O. Box 8650, Ottawa, Ont. K1G 0G8, Canada. TEL 613-731-9331. FAX 613-523-0937. *3357*

CANADIAN BULLETIN OF MEDICAL HISTORY.
Wilfrid Laurier University Press, (Canadain Society for the History of Medicine) Waterloo, Ont. N2L 3C5, Canada. TEL 519-884-1970. *3085*

CANADIAN DENTAL ASSOCIATION. JOURNAL.
Canadian Dental Association, 1815 Alta Vista Dr., Ottawa, Ont. K1G 3Y6, Canada. TEL 613-523-1770. FAX 613-523-7736. *3229*

CANADIAN DIETETIC ASSOCIATION. JOURNAL.
Canadian Dietetic Association, 480 University Ave., Ste. 601, Toronto, Ont. M5G 1V2, Canada. TEL 416-596-0857. FAX 416-596-0603. *3604*

CANADIAN GEMMOLOGIST.
Canadian Gemmological Association, 21 Dundas Square, Ste. 1209, Toronto, Ont. M5B 1B7, Canada. TEL 416-603-0451. *2563*

CANADIAN GEOTECHNICAL JOURNAL.
National Research Council of Canada, Research Journals, Ottawa, Ont. K1A 0R6, Canada. TEL 613-993-9084. FAX 613-952-7656. *1542*

CANADIAN JOURNAL OF BOTANY.
National Research Council of Canada, Research Journals, Ottawa, Ont. K1A 0R6, Canada. TEL 613-993-9084. FAX 613-952-7656. *499*

CANADIAN JOURNAL OF CARDIOLOGY.
Pulsus Group Inc., 2902 S. Sheridan Way, Oakville, Ont. L6J 7L6, Canada. TEL 416-829-4770. FAX 416-829-4799. *3205*

CANADIAN JOURNAL OF CARDIOVASCULAR NURSING.
Canadian Council of Cardiovascular Nurses, 160 George St., Ste. 200, Ottawa, Ont. K1N 9M2, Canada. TEL 613-237-4361. FAX 416-521-0048. *3276*

CANADIAN JOURNAL OF CHEMISTRY.
National Research Council of Canada, Research Journals, Ottawa, Ont. K1A 0R6, Canada. TEL 613-993-9084. FAX 613-952-7656. *1171*

CANADIAN JOURNAL OF CIVIL ENGINEERING.
National Research Council of Canada, Research Journals, Ottawa, Ont. K1A 0R6, Canada. TEL 613-993-9084. FAX 613-952-7656. *1863*

CANADIAN JOURNAL OF COMMUNICATION.
Wilfrid Laurier University Press, 75 University Ave. W., Waterloo, Ont. N2L 3C5, Canada. TEL 519-884-1970. FAX 519-884-8853. *1371*

CANADIAN JOURNAL OF DERMATOLOGY.
Rodar Publishing Inc., 19180 Trans Canada Hwy., Baie d'Urfe, Que. H9X 3T9, Canada. TEL 514-457-2673. FAX 514-457-2679. *3246*

CANADIAN JOURNAL OF DRAMA AND THEATRE.
University of Calgary Press, 816 MacKimmie Library Tower, 2500 University Dr. N.W., Calgary, Alta. T2N 1N4, Canada. TEL 403-220-7578. FAX 403-282-0085. *4631*

CANADIAN JOURNAL OF EARTH SCIENCES.
National Research Council of Canada, Research Journals, Ottawa, Ont. K1A 0R6, Canada. TEL 613-993-9084. FAX 613-952-7656. *1542*

CANADIAN JOURNAL OF FOREST RESEARCH.
National Research Council of Canada, Research Journals, Ottawa, Ont. K1A 0R6, Canada. TEL 613-993-9088. FAX 613-952-7656. *2097*

CANADIAN JOURNAL OF GASTROENTEROLOGY.
Pulsus Group Inc., 2902 S. Sheridan Way, Oakville, Ont. L6J 7L6, Canada. TEL 416-829-4770. FAX 416-829-4799. *3266*

CANADIAN JOURNAL OF INFECTIOUS DISEASES.
Pulsus Group Inc., 2902 S. Sheridan Way, Oakville, Ont. L6J 7L6, Canada. TEL 416-829-4770. FAX 416-829-4799. *3218*

CANADIAN JOURNAL OF INFECTIOUS DISEASES.
Pulsus Group Inc., 2902 S. Sheridan Way, Oakville, Ont. L6J 7L6, Canada. TEL 416-829-4770. FAX 416-829-4799. *3218*

CANADIAN JOURNAL OF IRISH STUDIES.
Canadian Association for Irish Studies, c/o Univ. of Saskatchewan, Dept. of English, Saskatoon, Sask. S7N 0W0. FAX 306-966-8839. *2504*

CANADIAN JOURNAL OF LAW AND SOCIETY.
University of Calgary Press, 2500 University Dr., N.W., Calgary, Alta. T2N 1N4, Canada. TEL 403-220-7578. FAX 403-282-0085. *2611*

CANADIAN JOURNAL OF MARKETING RESEARCH.
Professional Marketing Research Society, 2 Sheppard Ave., E., Ste. 1004, North York, Ont. M2N 5Y7, Canada. TEL 416-222-7030. *1035*

CANADIAN JOURNAL OF MICROBIOLOGY.
National Research Council of Canada, Research Journals, Ottawa, Ont. K1A 0R6, Canada. TEL 613-993-9084. FAX 613-952-7656. *550*

CANADIAN JOURNAL OF NURSING ADMINISTRATION.
Health Media Inc., 14453 29A Ave., White Rock, B.C. V4A 9K8, Canada. TEL 604-535-7933. *3276*

CANADIAN JOURNAL OF NURSING RESEARCH.
McGill University, School of Nursing, 3506 University St., Montreal, Que. H3A 2A7, Canada. TEL 514-392-4160. FAX 514-398-8455. *3276*

CANADIAN JOURNAL OF OPHTHALMOLOGY.
Canadian Ophthalmological Society, 1525 Carling Ave., No. 610, Ottawa, Ont. K1Z 8R9, Canada. TEL 613-729-6779. FAX 613-729-7209. *3299*

CANADIAN JOURNAL OF PEDIATRICS.
Rodar Publishing Inc., 19180 Trans Canada Hwy., Baie d'Urfe, Que. H9X 3T9, Canada. TEL 514-457-2673. FAX 514-457-2679. *3319*

CANADIAN JOURNAL OF PHYSICS.
National Research Council of Canada, Research Journals, Ottawa, Ont. K1A 0R6, Canada. TEL 613-993-9084. FAX 613-952-7656. *3815*

CANADIAN JOURNAL OF PHYSIOLOGY AND PHARMACOLOGY.
National Research Council of Canada, Research Journals, Ottawa, Ont. K1A 0R6, Canada. TEL 613-993-9084. FAX 613-952-7656. *570*

CANADIAN JOURNAL OF POLITICAL SCIENCE.
Canadian Political Science Association, No. 205 - 1 Stewart St., Ottawa, Ont. K1N 6H7, Canada. FAX 613-230-2746. *3878*

CANADIAN JOURNAL OF SPORT SCIENCES.
Human Kinetics Publishers, Inc., (Canadian Association of Sport Sciences) Box 5076, Champaign, IL 61825-5076. TEL 217-351-5076. FAX 217-351-2674. *4468*

CANADIAN JOURNAL OF UNIVERSITY CONTINUING EDUCATION.
Canadian Association for University Continuing Education, 151 Slater St., Suite 1001, Ottawa, Ont. K1P 5N1, Canada. TEL 613-563-1236. FAX 613-563-7739. *1702*

CANADIAN JOURNAL OF ZOOLOGY.
National Research Council of Canada, Research Journals, Ottawa, Ont. K1A 0R6, Canada. TEL 613-993-9084. FAX 613-952-7656. *580*

CANADIAN LIBRARY JOURNAL.
Canadian Library Association, 200 Elgin St., Ste. 602, Ottawa, Ont. K2P 1L5, Canada. TEL 613-232-9625. FAX 613-563-9895. *2751*

CANADIAN MARITIME BIBLIOGRAPHY.
Memorial University of Newfoundland, Maritime Studies Research Unit, St. John's, Nfld. A1C 5S7, Canada. TEL 709-737-8424. FAX 709-737-4569. *4663*

CANADIAN METALLURGICAL QUARTERLY.
Pergamon Press, Inc., Journals Division, (Canadian Institute of Mining & Metallurgy, Metallurgical Society) 660 White Plains Rd., Tarrytown, NY 10591-5153. TEL 914-524-9200. FAX 914-333-2444. *3403*

CANADIAN PHARMACEUTICAL JOURNAL.
Canadian Pharmaceutical Association, 1785 Alta Vista Dr., Ottawa, Ont. K1G 3Y6, Canada. TEL 613-523-7877. FAX 613-523-0445. *3720*

CANADIAN WATER RESOURCES JOURNAL.
Canadian Water Resources Association, c/o Faculty of Engineering, University of Saskatchewan, Saskatchewan, Sask. S7N 0W0, Canada. TEL 306-966-5335. FAX 306-966-5334. *4823*

CANCER.
J.B. Lippincott Co., (American Cancer Society, Inc.) E. Washington Sq., Philadelphia, PA 19105. TEL 215-238-4200. *3194*

CANCER BIOCHEMISTRY BIOPHYSICS.
Gordon and Breach Science Publishers, 270 Eighth Ave., New York, NY 10011. TEL 212-206-8900. FAX 212-645-2459. *3194*

CANCER CHEMOTHERAPY AND BIOLOGICAL RESPONSE MODIFIERS.
Elsevier Science Publishers B.V., Books Division, P.O. Box 211, 1000 AE Amsterdam, Netherlands. TEL 020-5803911. FAX 020-5803705. *3194*

CANCER GENETICS & CYTOGENETICS.
Elsevier Science Publishing Co., Inc. (New York), 655 Ave. of the Americas, New York, NY 10010. TEL 212-989-5800. FAX 212-633-3965. *3194*

CANCER INVESTIGATION.
Marcel Dekker Journals, (Inter-American Society for Chemotherapy, Cancer Section) 270 Madison Ave., New York, NY 10016. TEL 212-696-9000. FAX 212-685-4540. *3195*

CANCER LETTERS.
Elsevier Scientific Publishers Ireland Ltd., P.O. Box 85, Limerick, Ireland. TEL 061-61944. FAX 061-62144. *3195*

CANCER NURSING.
Raven Press, 1185 Ave. of the Americas, New York, NY 10036. TEL 212-930-9500. FAX 212-869-3495. *3277*

CANCER PREVENTION.
Williams & Wilkins, 428 E. Preston St., Baltimore, MD 21202. TEL 301-528-4000. FAX 301-528-4321. *3195*

CANCER RESEARCH.
Waverly Press, Inc. (American Association for Cancer Research) 428 E. Preston St., Baltimore, MD 21202. TEL 301-528-4000. *3195*

CARBOHYDRATE POLYMERS.
Elsevier Science Publishers Ltd., Crown House, Linton Rd., Barking, Essex IG11 8JU, England. TEL 081-594-7272. FAX 081-594-5942. *1216*

CARBOHYDRATE RESEARCH.
Elsevier Science Publishers B.V., P.O. Box 211, 1000 AE Amsterdam, Netherlands. TEL 020-5803911. FAX 020-5803598. *1217*

CARBON.
Pergamon Press, Inc., Journals Division, (American Carbon Society) 660 White Plains Rd., Tarrytown, NY 10591-5153. TEL 914-524-9200. FAX 914-333-2444. *1217*

CARBONATES AND EVAPORITES.
Northeastern Science Foundation, Inc., 15 Third St., Box 746, Troy, NY 12181-0746. TEL 518-273-3247. *1556*

CARCINOGENESIS.
Raven Press, 1185 Ave. of the Americas, New York, NY 10036. TEL 212-930-9500. FAX 212-869-3495. *3195*

CARDIAC SURGERY.
Hanley & Belfus, Inc., 210 S. 13th St., Philadelphia, PA 19107. TEL 215-546-7293. FAX 215-790-9330. *3205*

CARDIOLOGY BOARD REVIEW.
M R A Publications, Inc., 3 Greenwich Office Park, Greenwich, CT 06831-5154. TEL 203-629-3550. FAX 203-629-2536. *3206*

CARDIOLOGY UPDATE.
Elsevier Science Publishing Co., Inc. (New York), 655 Ave. of the Americas, New York, NY 10010. TEL 212-989-5800. FAX 212-633-3965. *3206*

CARDIOTHORACIC SURGERY SERIES.
Marcel Dekker, Inc., 270 Madison Ave., New York, NY 10016. TEL 212-696-9000. FAX 212-685-4540. *3206*

CARDIOVASCULAR DRUGS AND THERAPY.
Kluwer Academic Publishers, (International Society of Cardiovascular Pharmacotherapy) 101 Philip Dr., Norwell, MA 02061. TEL 617-871-6300. FAX 617-871-6528. *3206*

CARDIOVASCULAR NURSING.
American Heart Association, 7272 Greenville Ave., Dallas, TX 75231-4596. TEL 214-706-1310. FAX 214-691-6342. *3277*

CARDIOVASCULAR PATHOLOGY.
Elsevier Science Publishing Co., Inc. (New York), (Society for Cardiovascular Pathology) 655 Ave. of the Americas, New York, NY 10010. TEL 212-989-5800. FAX 212-633-3965. *3206*

CARDIOVASCULAR REVIEWS & REPORTS.
Cardiovascular Reviews & Reports, Inc., 47 Arch St., Greenwich, CT 06830. TEL 203-625-0194. FAX 203-625-0393. *3206*

CARDIOVASCULAR SURGERY.
American Heart Association, 7272 Greenville Ave., Dallas, TX 75231-4596. TEL 214-706-1310. FAX 214-691-6342. *3206*

CARIBBEAN GEOGRAPHY.
U W I Publishers Association, (University of the West Indies Publishers' Association) P.O. Box 139, Mona, Kingston 7, Jamaica, W.I. TEL 809-927-1201. FAX 809-927-2409. *2244*

CARIBBEAN STUDIES (NEW YORK).
Gordon & Breach Science Publishers, 270 Eighth Ave., New York, NY 10011. TEL 212-206-8900. FAX 212-645-2459. *2402*

CARL NEWELL JACKSON LECTURES.
Harvard University Press, 79 Garden St., Cambridge, MA 02138. TEL 617-495-2600. FAX 617-495-5898. *2053*

CARNEGIE-ROCHESTER CONFERENCE SERIES ON PUBLIC POLICY.
North-Holland P.O. Box 211, 1000 AE Amsterdam, Netherlands. TEL 020-5803911. FAX 020-5803598. *654*

CATALOGING & CLASSIFICATION QUARTERLY.
Haworth Press, Inc., 10 Alice St., Binghamton, NY 13904. TEL 800-342-9678. FAX 607-722-1424. *2751*

CATALOGUE OF PALAEARCTIC DIPTERA.
Elsevier Science Publishers B.V., Books Division, P.O. Box 211, 1000 AE Amsterdam, Netherlands. TEL 020-5803911. FAX 020-5803705. *529*

CATALYSIS REVIEWS: SCIENCE AND ENGINEERING.
Marcel Dekker Journals, 270 Madison Ave., New York, NY 10016. TEL 212-696-9000. FAX 212-685-4540. *1225*

CATALYSIS TODAY.
Elsevier Science Publishers B.V., P.O. Box 211, 1000 AH Amsterdam, Netherlands. TEL 020-5803911. FAX 020-5803598. *1849*

CATALYST FOR ENVIRONMENT - ENERGY.
Catalyst for Environment, Energy, 274 Madison Ave., New York, NY 10016. TEL 212-685-8310. *1945*

CATHETERIZATION AND CARDIOVASCULAR DIAGNOSIS.
John Wiley & Sons, Inc., Journals, 605 Third Ave., New York, NY 10158. TEL 212-850-6000. FAX 212-850-6088. *3206*

CELL.
Cell Press, 50 Church St., Cambridge, MA 02138. TEL 617-661-7060. *523*

CELL BIOLOGY AND TOXICOLOGY.
Princeton Scientific Publishing Co., Inc., (Genetic Toxicology Association) Box 2155, Princeton, NJ 08543. TEL 609-683-4750. FAX 609-683-0838. *1980*

CELL BIOPHYSICS.
Humana Press Inc., Crescent Manor, Box 2148, Clifton, NJ 07015. TEL 201-256-1699. FAX 201-256-8341. *474*

CELL MEMBRANES, METHODS AND REVIEWS.
Plenum Publishing Corp., 233 Spring St., New York, NY 10013-1578. TEL 212-620-8000. FAX 212-463-0742. *434*

CELL MOTILITY AND THE CYTOSKELETON.
John Wiley & Sons. Inc., Journals, 605 Third Ave., New York, NY 10158. TEL 212-850-6000. FAX 212-850-6088. *523*

CELL TRANSPLANTATION.
Pergamon Press plc, Headington Hill Hall, Oxford OX3 OBW, England. TEL 0865-794141. FAX 0865-743911. *474*

CELLS AND MATERIALS.
Scanning Microscopy International, Inc., Box 66507, AMF O'Hare, Chicago, IL 60666-0507. TEL 708-529-6677. FAX 708-980-6698. *3086*

CELLULAR & MOLECULAR BIOLOGY.
Pergamon Press, Inc., Journals Division, 660 White Plains Rd., Tarrytown, NY 10591-5153. TEL 914-524-9200. FAX 914-333-2444. *523*

CELLULAR & MOLECULAR NEUROBIOLOGY.
Plenum Publishing Corp., 233 Spring St., New York, NY 10013-1578. TEL 212-620-8000. FAX 212-463-0742. *3333*

CELLULAR IMMUNOLOGY.
Academic Press, Inc., Journal Division, 1250 Sixth Ave., San Diego, CA 92101. TEL 619-230-1840. FAX 619-699-6800. *3184*

CELLULAR NEUROBIOLOGY.
Academic Press, Inc., 1250 Sixth Ave., San Diego, CA 92101. TEL 619-231-0926. FAX 619-699-6715. *434*

CELLULAR SIGNALLING.
Pergamon Press plc, Headington Hill Hall, Oxford OX3 OBW, England. TEL 0865-794141. FAX 0865-743911. *524*

CEMENT AND CONCRETE COMPOSITES.
Elsevier Science Publishers Ltd., Crown House, Linton Rd., Barking, Essex IG11 8JU, England. TEL 081-594-7272. FAX 081-594-5942. *609*

CEMENT AND CONCRETE RESEARCH.
Pergamon Press, Inc., Journals Division, 660 White Plains Rd., Tarrytown, NY 10591-5153. TEL 914-524-9200. FAX 914-333-2444. *609*

CENTER FOR CHILDREN'S BOOKS. BULLETIN.
University of Chicago Press, Journals Division, (University of Chicago, Graduate Library School) 5720 S. Woodlawn Ave., Chicago, IL 60637. TEL 312-753-3347. *397*

CENTRAL ASIAN SURVEY.
Pergamon Press plc, (Society for Central Asian Studies) Headington Hill Hall, Oxford OX3 OBW, England. TEL 0865-794141. FAX 0865-743911. *3879*

CENTRE D'ETUDES DE L'ASIE DE L'EST. CAHIERS.
Universite de Montreal, Faculte des Arts et des Sciences, C.P. 6128, Succ. A, Montreal, Que. H3C 3J7, Canada. TEL 514-343-5970. FAX 514-343-7716. *3635*

CERAMICA PER L'ARCHITETTURA.
Gruppo Editoriale Faenza Editrice S.p.A., Via Pier. de Crescenzi, 44, Faenza, Italy. TEL 0546-663488. FAX 0546-660440. *1162*

CERAMICS INTERNATIONAL.
Elsevier Science Publishers Ltd., Crown House, Linton Rd., Barking, Essex IG11 8JU, England. TEL 081-594-7272. FAX 081-594-5942. *1162*

CEREBRAL CORTEX.
Oxford University Press, Journals, 200 Madison Ave., New York, NY 10016. TEL 212-679-7300. FAX 212-725-2972. *3086*

CEREBROVASCULAR AND BRAIN METABOLISM REVIEWS.
Raven Press, 1185 Ave. of the Americas, New York, NY 10036. TEL 212-930-9500. FAX 212-869-3495. *3333*

CHALLENGE (ARMONK).
M. E. Sharpe, Inc., 80 Business Park Dr., Armonk, NY 10504. TEL 914-273-1800. FAX 914-273-2106. *655*

CHANGE (WASHINGTON).
Heldref Publications, (American Association of Higher Education) 1319 Eighteenth St., N.W., Washington, DC 20036-1802. TEL 202-296-6267. FAX 202-296-5149. *1702*

CHANGES.
Lawrence Erlbaum Associates Ltd., (Psychology and Psychotherapy Association) 27 Palmeira Mansions, Church Rd., Hove, E. Sussex BN3 2FA, England. TEL 0273-207411. FAX 0273-205612. *4401*

CHAOS.
American Institute of Physics, 335 E. 45th St., New York, NY 10017-3483. TEL 212-661-9404. FAX 212-949-0473. *3815*

CHAOS, SOLITONS AND FRACTALS.
Pergamon Press, Inc., Journals Division, 660 White Plains Rd., Tarrytown, NY 10591-5153. TEL 914-524-9200. FAX 914-333-2444. *3032*

CHARLES ELIOT NORTON LECTURES.
Harvard University Press, 79 Garden St., Cambridge, MA 02138. TEL 617-495-2600. FAX 617-495-5898. *2505*

CHECK CLUB NEWSLETTER.
F I S I - Madison Financial Corporation Editor, Member Newsletters, Box 40726, Nashville, TN 37204. TEL 615-371-2775. *772*

CHEMICAL ANALYSIS.
John Wiley & Sons, Inc., 605 Third Ave., New York, NY 10158-0012. TEL 212-850-6000. FAX 212-850-6088. *1205*

CHEMICAL AND PETROLEUM ENGINEERING.
Plenum Publishing Corp, Consultants Bureau, 233 Spring St., New York, NY 10013-1578. TEL 212-620-8468. FAX 212-463-0742. *1849*

CHEMICAL ENGINEER.
Taylor & Francis Ltd., (Institution of Chemical Engineers) Rankine Rd., Basingstoke, Hants. RG24 OPR, England. TEL 0256-840366. FAX 0256-479438. *1849*

CHEMICAL ENGINEERING.
McGraw-Hill, Inc., 1221 Ave. of the Americas, New York, NY 10020. TEL 212-512-2000. *1849*

CHEMICAL ENGINEERING AND PROCESSING.
Elsevier Sequoia S.A., P.O. Box 564, CH-1001 Lausanne, Switzerland. TEL 021-207381. FAX 021-235444. *1849*

CHEMICAL ENGINEERING: CONCEPTS AND REVIEWS.
Gordon & Breach Science Publishers, P.O. Box 90, Reading, Berkshire RG1 8JL, England. TEL 0734-560080. FAX 0734-568211. *1850*

CHEMICAL ENGINEERING EDUCATION.
American Society for Engineering Education, Chemical Engineering Division, Dept. of Chemical Engineering, University of Florida, Gainesville, FL 32611. TEL 904-392-0857. FAX 904-392-0861. *1850*

CHEMICAL ENGINEERING JOURNAL AND BIOCHEMICAL ENGINEERING JOURNAL.
Elsevier Sequoia S.A., P.O. Box 564, CH-1001 Lausanne 1, Switzerland. TEL 021-207381. FAX 021-235444. *1850*

CHEMICAL ENGINEERING MONOGRAPHS.
Elsevier Science Publishers B.V., Books Division, P.O. Box 211, 1000 AE Amsterdam, Netherlands. TEL 020-5803911. FAX 020-5803705. *1850*

CHEMICAL ENGINEERING PROGRESS.
American Institute of Chemical Engineers, 345 E. 47th St., New York, NY 10017. TEL 212-705-7663. FAX 212-752-3294. *1850*

CHEMICAL ENGINEERING RESEARCH & DESIGN.
Taylor & Francis Ltd., (Institution of Chemical Engineers) Rankine Rd., Basingstoke, Hants. RG24 OPR, England. TEL 0256-840366. FAX 0256-479438. *1850*

CHEMICAL ENGINEERING SCIENCE.
Pergamon Press, Inc., Journals Division, 660 White Plains Rd., Tarrytown, NY 10591-5153. TEL 914-524-9200. FAX 914-333-2444. *1850*

CHEMICAL GEOLOGY.
Elsevier Science Publishers B.V., (European Association for Geochemistry) P.O. Box 211, 1000 AE Amsterdam, Netherlands. TEL 020-5803911. FAX 020-5803598. *1542*

CHEMICAL GEOLOGY. ISOTOPE GEOSCIENCE SECTION.
Elsevier Science Publishers B.V., P.O. Box 211, 1000 AE Amsterdam, Netherlands. TEL 020-5803911. FAX 020-5803598. *1557*

CHEMICAL PHYSICS.
North-Holland P.O. Box 211, 1000 AE Amsterdam, Netherlands. TEL 020-5803911. FAX 020-5803598. *1225*

CHEMICAL PHYSICS LETTERS.
North-Holland P.O. Box 211, 1000 AE Amsterdam, Netherlands. TEL 020-5803911. FAX 020-5803598. *1225*

CHEMICAL RESEARCH IN TOXICOLOGY.
American Chemical Society, 1155 16th St., N.W., Washington, DC 20036. TEL 800-333-9511. FAX 202-872-4615. *1980*

CHEMICAL SUBSTANCES CONTROL.
The Bureau of National Affairs, Inc., 1231 25th St., N.W., Washington, DC 20037. TEL 202-452-4200. FAX 202-822-8092. *1173*

CHEMICALLY MODIFIED SURFACES.
Gordon & Breach Science Publishers, 270 Eighth Ave., New York, NY 10011. TEL 212-206-8900. FAX 212-645-2459. *1225*

CHEMICO-BIOLOGICAL INTERACTIONS.
Elsevier Scientific Publishers Ireland Ltd., P.O. Box 85, Limerick, Ireland. TEL 061-61944. FAX 061-62144. *1980*

CHEMIST.
American Institute of Chemists, Inc., 7315 Wisconsin Ave., Bethesda, MD 20814-3202. TEL 301-652-2447. *1174*

CHEMISTRY AND BIOCHEMISTRY OF AMINO ACIDS, PEPTIDES, AND PROTEINS.
Marcel Dekker, Inc., 270 Madison Ave., New York, NY 10016. TEL 212-696-9000. FAX 212-685-4540. *474*

CHEMISTRY AND ECOLOGY.
Gordon and Breach Science Publishers, 270 Eighth Ave., New York, NY 10011. TEL 212-206-8900. FAX 212-645-2459. *1174*

CHEMISTRY AND PHYSICS OF CARBON: A SERIES OF ADVANCES.
Marcel Dekker, Inc., 270 Madison Ave., New York, NY 10016. TEL 212-696-9000. FAX 212-685-4540. *1217*

CHEMISTRY AND PHYSICS OF LIPIDS.
Elsevier Scientific Publishers Ireland Ltd., P.O. Box 85, Limerick, Ireland. TEL 061-61944. FAX 061-62144. *475*

CHEMISTRY AND TECHNOLOGY OF FUELS AND OILS.
Plenum Publishing Corp., Consultants Bureau, (Russian Academy of Sciences) 233 Spring St., New York, NY 10013-1578. TEL 212-762-8468. FAX 212-463-0742. *3684*

CHEMISTRY OF FUNCTIONAL GROUPS.
John Wiley & Sons, Inc., 605 Third Ave., New York, NY 10158-0012. TEL 212-850-6000. FAX 212-850-6088. *1174*

CHEMISTRY OF HETEROCYCLIC COMPOUNDS (NEW YORK, 1951).
John Wiley & Sons, Inc., 605 Third Ave., New York, NY 10158-0012. TEL 212-850-6000. FAX 212-850-6088. *1217*

CHEMISTRY OF HETEROCYCLIC COMPOUNDS (NEW YORK, 1965).
Plenum Publishing Corp., Consultants Bureau, (Latvian Academy of Sciences) 233 Spring St., New York, NY 10013-1578. TEL 212-620-8468. FAX 212-463-0742. *1217*

CHEMISTRY OF NATURAL COMPOUNDS.
Plenum Publishing Corp., Consultants Bureau, (Uzbek Academy of Sciences) 233 Spring St., New York, NY 10013-1578. TEL 212-620-8468. FAX 212-463-0742. *1217*

CHEMOMETRICS AND INTELLIGENT LABORATORY SYSTEMS.
Elsevier Science Publishers B.V., (Chemometrics Society) P.O. Box 211, 1000 AH Ansterdan, Netherlands. TEL 020-5803911. FAX 020-5803598. *1205*

CHEMOSPHERE.
Pergamon Press, Inc., Journals Division, 660 White Plains Rd., Tarrytown, NY 10591-5153. TEL 914-524-9200. FAX 914-333-2444. *1981*

CHENJI XUEBAO.
Science Press, Marketing and Sales Department, 16 Donghuangchenggen Beijie, Beijing 100707, People's Republic of China. TEL 4010642. FAX 4012180. *1557*

CHEST.
American College of Chest Physicians, 3300 Dundee Rd., Northbrook, IL 60062. FAX 708-498-5460. *3364*

CHICAGO GUIDES TO WRITING, EDITING, AND PUBLISHING.
University of Chicago Press, 5801 S. Ellis Ave., Chicago, IL 60637. TEL 312-702-7899. *4125*

CHICAGO HISTORY OF AMERICAN CIVILIZATION.
University of Chicago Press, 5801 S. Ellis Ave., Chicago, IL 60637. TEL 312-702-7899. *2402*

CHICAGO HISTORY OF AMERICAN RELIGION.
University of Chicago Press, 5801 S. Ellis Ave., Chicago, IL 60637. TEL 312-702-7899. *4168*

CHICAGO HISTORY OF SCIENCE AND MEDICINE.
University of Chicago Press, 5801 S. Ellis Ave., Chicago, IL 60637. TEL 312-702-7899. *2308*

CHICAGO LECTURES IN MATHEMATICS.
University of Chicago Press, 5801 S. Ellis Ave., Chicago, IL 60637. TEL 312-702-7899. *3032*

CHICAGO LECTURES IN PHYSICS.
University of Chicago Press, 5801 S. Ellis Ave., Chicago, IL 60637. TEL 312-702-7899. *3816*

CHICAGO STUDIES IN THE HISTORY OF JUDAISM.
University of Chicago Press, 5801 S. Ellis Ave., Chicago, IL 60637. TEL 312-702-7899. *4222*

CHILD ABUSE & NEGLECT.
Pergamon Press, Inc., Journals Division, (International Society for Prevention of Child Abuse and Neglect) 660 White Plains Rd., Tarrytown, NY 10591-5153. TEL 914-524-9200. FAX 914-333-2444. *1234*

CHILD AND ADOLESCENT SOCIAL WORK JOURNAL.
Human Sciences Press, Inc. 233 Spring St., New York, NY 10013-1578. TEL 212-620-8000. FAX 212-463-0742. *4431*

CHILD & FAMILY BEHAVIOR THERAPY.
Haworth Press, Inc., 10 Alice St., Binghamton, NY 13904. TEL 800-342-9678. FAX 607-722-1424. *4015*

CHILD AND YOUTH CARE FORUM.
Human Sciences Press, Inc. 233 Spring St., New York, NY 10013-1578. TEL 212-620-8000. FAX 212-463-0742. *1234*

CHILD & YOUTH SERVICES.
Haworth Press, Inc., 10 Alice St., Binghamton, NY 13904. TEL 800-342-9678. FAX 607-722-1424. *4401*

CHILD DEVELOPMENT.
University of Chicago Press, Journals Division, (Society for Research in Child Development, Inc.) 5720 S. Woodlawn Ave., Chicago, IL 60637. TEL 312-753-3347. *1234*

CHILD DEVELOPMENT ABSTRACTS AND BIBLIOGRAPHY.
University of Chicago Press, Journals Division, (Society for Research in Child Development, Inc.) 5720 S. Woodlawn Ave., Chicago, IL 60637. TEL 312-753-3347. *1247*

CHILD NURTURANCE.
Plenum Publishing Corp., 233 Spring St., New York, NY 10013-1578. TEL 212-620-8000. FAX 212-463-0742. *1234*

CHILD PSYCHIATRY AND HUMAN DEVELOPMENT.
Human Sciences Press, Inc. (American Association of Psychiatric Services for Children) 233 Spring St., New York, NY 10013-1578. TEL 212-620-8000. FAX 212-463-0742. *3333*

CHILD STUDY JOURNAL.
State University of New York at Buffalo, Behavioral and Humanistic Studies, Bacon Hall 312J, 1300 Elmwood Ave., Buffalo, NY 14222-1095. TEL 716-878-5302. *1621*

CHILDREN AND YOUTH SERVICES REVIEW.
Pergamon Press, Inc., Journals Division, 660 White Plains Rd., Tarrytown, NY 10591-5153. TEL 914-524-9200. FAX 914-333-2444. *1234*

CHILDREN'S HOSPITAL QUARTERLY.
Human Sciences Press, Inc. 233 Spring St., New York, NY 10013. TEL 212-620-8000. FAX 212-463-0742. *3319*

CHILDREN'S LANGUAGE.
Lawrence Erlbaum Associates, Inc., 365 Broadway, Hillsdale, NJ 07642. TEL 201-666-4110. FAX 201-666-2394. *2809*

CHILDREN'S LEGAL RIGHTS JOURNAL.
William S. Hein & Co., Inc., 1285 Main St., Buffalo, NY 14209. TEL 800-828-7571. FAX 716-883-8100. *2612*

CHILDREN'S LITERATURE IN EDUCATION.
Human Sciences Press, Inc. 233 Spring St., New York, NY 10013. TEL 212-620-8000. FAX 212-463-0742. *1235*

CHILD'S NERVOUS SYSTEM.
Springer-Verlag, (International Society for Paediatric Neurosurgery) Heidelberger Platz 3, D-1000 Berlin 33, Germany. TEL 030-8207-1. *3333*

CHILTON'S REVIEW OF OPTOMETRY.
Chilton Co., Chilton Way, Radnor, PA 19089. TEL 215-964-4370. *3299*

CHINA CENTER OF ADVANCED SCIENCE AND TECHNOLOGY SERIES.
Gordon & Breach Science Publishers, P.O. Box 90, Reading, Berkshire RG1 8JL, England. TEL 0734-560-080. FAX 0734-568-211. *4304*

CHINA OCEAN ENGINEERING.
Pergamon Press, Inc., Journals Division, (Chinese Ocean Engineering Society) 660 White Plains Rd., Tarrytown, NY 10591-5153. TEL 914-524-9200. FAX 914-333-2444. *1816*

CHINESE ANDROLOGY.
China Ocean Press, International Cooperation Department, Haimao Dalou, 1 Fuxingmenwai Dajie, Beijing 100860, People's Republic of China. TEL 868941. FAX 862209. *3087*

CHINESE ASTRONOMY AND ASTROPHYSICS.
Pergamon Press, Inc., Journals Division, 660 White Plains Rd., Tarrytown, NY 10591-5153. TEL 914-524-9200. FAX 914-333-2444. *363*

CHINESE CHEMICAL LETTERS.
Pergamon Press plc, Headington Hill Hall, Oxford OX3 0BW, England. TEL 0865-794141. FAX 0865-743911. *1175*

CHINESE ECONOMIC STUDIES.
M.E. Sharpe, Inc., 80 Business Park Dr., Armonk, NY 10504. TEL 914-273-1800. FAX 914-273-2106. *655*

CHINESE EDUCATION.
M. E. Sharpe, Inc., 80 Business Park Dr., Armonk, NY 10504. TEL 914-273-1800. FAX 914-273-2106. *1621*

CHINESE GEOGRAPHICAL SCIENCE.
Science Press, Marketing and Sales Department, (Zhongguo Kexueyuan, Changchun Dilisuo) 16 Donghuangchenggen Beijie, Beijing 100707, People's Republic of China. TEL 4010642. FAX 4012180. *1557*

CHINESE JOURNAL OF ACOUSTICS.
Science Press, Marketing and Sales Department, (Acoustical Society of China) 16 Donghuangchenggen Beijie, Beijing 100707, People's Republic of China. TEL 4010642. FAX 4012180. *3859*

CHINESE JOURNAL OF ATMOSPHERIC SCIENCES.
Allerton Press, Inc., (Academia Sinica (Chinese Academy of Sciences), Institute of Atmospheric Physics) 150 Fifth Ave., New York, NY 10011. TEL 212-924-3950. *3434*

CHINESE JOURNAL OF BIOTECHNOLOGY.
Allerton Press, Inc., 150 Fifth Ave., New York, NY 10011. TEL 212-924-3950. *489*

CHINESE JOURNAL OF BOTANY.
Science Press, Marketing and Sales Department, (Chinese Academy of Sciences, Institute of Botany) 16 Donghuangchenggen Beijie, Beijing 100707, People's Republic of China. TEL 4010642. FAX 4012180. *499*

CHINESE JOURNAL OF CANCER RESEARCH.
Beijing Institute for Cancer Research, Da-Hong-Luo-Chang Street, Western District, Beijing, People's Republic of China. *3196*

CHINESE JOURNAL OF CHEMISTRY.
Kexue Chubanshe, Qikan Bu, (Chinese Chemical Society) 16 Donghuangchenggen Beijie, Beijing 100707, People's Republic of China. TEL 4010642. FAX 4012180. *1175*

CHINESE JOURNAL OF COMPUTER SCIENCE AND TECHNOLOGY.
Science Press, Marketing and Sales Department, (Academia Sinica, Chinese Computer Federation) 16 Donghuangchenggen Beijie, Beijing 100707, People's Republic of China. TEL 4010642. FAX 4012180. *1482*

CHINESE JOURNAL OF ENGINEERING THERMOPHYSICS.
Allerton Press, Inc., (Chinese Society of Engineering Thermophysics) 150 Fifth Ave., New York, NY 10011. TEL 212-924-3950. *1927*

CHINESE JOURNAL OF GEOCHEMISTRY.
Science Press, Marketing and Sales Department, 16 Donghuangchenggen Beijie, Beijing 100707, People's Republic of China. TEL 4010642. FAX 4012180. *1557*

CHINESE JOURNAL OF GEOPHYSICS.
Allerton Press, Inc., (Chinese Geophysical Society) 150 Fifth Ave., New York, NY 10011. TEL 212-924-3950. *1587*

CHINESE JOURNAL OF MECHANICAL ENGINEERING.
China Machine Press, (Chinese Mechanical Engineering Society) 1 Nanjie, Baiwanzhuang, Beijing 100037, People's Republic of China. TEL 8317766. FAX 01-3211613. *1927*

CHINESE JOURNAL OF METAL SCIENCE & TECHNOLOGY.
Chinese Society of Metals, Dongsi Xidajie 46, Beijing 100711, People's Republic of China. *3404*

CHINESE JOURNAL OF NUCLEAR PHYSICS.
China Ocean Press, International Cooperation Department, (China Institute of Atomic Energy) Haimao Dalou, 1 Fuxingmenwai Dajie, Beijing 100860, People's Republic of China. TEL 868941. FAX 862209. *3847*

CHINESE JOURNAL OF OCEANOLOGY AND LIMNOLOGY.
Science Press, Marketing and Sales Department, 16 Donghuangchenggen Beijie, Beijing 100707, People's Republic of China. TEL 4010642. FAX 4012180. *1603*

CHINESE JOURNAL OF PHYSIOLOGICAL SCIENCES.
Science Press, Marketing and Sales Department, (Shanghai Institute of Physiology) 16 Donghuangchenggen Beijie, Beijing 100707, People's Republic of China. TEL 4010642. FAX 4012180. *570*

CHINESE LAW AND GOVERNMENT.
M.E. Sharpe, Inc., 80 Business Park Dr., Armonk, NY 10504. TEL 914-273-1800. FAX 914-273-2106. *2612*

CHINESE MEDICAL JOURNAL.
Chinese Medical Association, 42 Dongsi Xidajie, Beijing 100710, People's Republic of China. TEL 546231-292. *3087*

CHINESE PHYSICS.
American Institute of Physics, 335 E. 45th St., New York, NY 10017. TEL 212-661-9404. *3816*

CHINESE PHYSICS LETTERS.
Allerton Press, Inc., 150 Fifth Ave., New York, NY 10011. TEL 212-924-3950. *3816*

CHINESE SCIENCE BULLETIN.
Science Press, Marketing and Sales Department, 16 Donghuangchenggen Beijie, Beijing People's Republic of China. TEL 4010642. FAX 4012180. *4305*

CHINESE SOCIOLOGY AND ANTHROPOLOGY.
M. E. Sharpe, Inc., 80 Business Park Dr., Armonk, NY 10504. TEL 914-273-1800. FAX 914-273-2106. *4431*

CHINESE STUDIES IN HISTORY.
M. E. Sharpe, Inc., 80 Business Park Dr., Armonk, NY 10504. TEL 914-273-1800. FAX 914-273-2106. *2308*

CHINESE STUDIES IN PHILOSOPHY.
M.E. Sharpe, Inc., 80 Business Park Dr., Armonk, NY 10504. TEL 914-273-1800. FAX 914-273-2106. *3763*

CHIROPRACTIC JOURNAL OF AUSTRALIA.
Chiropractors' Association of Australia, P.O. Box 748, Wagga Wagga, N.S.W. 2650, Australia. TEL 61-69-21-3238. FAX 61-69-21-8869. *3213*

CHIROPRACTIC SPORTS MEDICINE.
Williams & Wilkins, 428 E. Preston St., Baltimore, MD 21202. TEL 301-528-4000. FAX 301-528-4312. *3213*

CHIROPRACTIC TECHNIQUE.
Williams & Wilkins, (National College of Chiropractic) 428 E. Preston St., Baltimore, MD 21202. TEL 301-528-4000. FAX 301-528-4312. *3213*

CHOREOGRAPHY AND DANCE.
Harwood Academic Publishers, 270 Eighth Ave., New York, NY 10011. TEL 212-206-8900. FAX 212-645-2459. *4631*

CHRISTIAN SCHOLAR'S REVIEW.
c/o Calvin College, Grand Rapids, MI 49546. *4170*

CHROMATOGRAPHIA.
Friedr. Vieweg und Sohn Verlagsgesellschaft mbH, Postfach 5829, 6200 Wiesbaden 1, Germany. TEL 0611-160230. FAX 0611-160229. *1205*

CHROMATOGRAPHIC SCIENCE SERIES.
Marcel Dekker, Inc., 270 Madison Ave., New York, NY 10016. TEL 212-696-9000. FAX 212-685-4540. *1205*

CHROMATOGRAPHY ABSTRACTS.
Elsevier Science Publishers Ltd., (Chromatography Society) Crown House, Linton Rd., Barking, Essex IG11 8JU, England. TEL 081-594-7272. FAX 081-594-5942. *1200*

CHRONOBIOLOGY INTERNATIONAL.
Raven Press, (International Society of Chronobiology) 1185 Ave. of the Americas, New York, NY 10036. TEL 212-930-9500. FAX 212-869-3495. *435*

CIENCIA DEL SUELO.
Asociacion Argentina de la Ciencia del Suelo, J. Ramirez de Velasco 847, 1414 Buenos Aires, Argentina. TEL 01-771-8968. *173*

CINEMA JOURNAL.
University of Illinois Press, (Society for Cinema Studies) 54 E. Gregory Dr., Champaign, IL 61820. TEL 217-333-0950. FAX 217-244-8082. *3506*

CIRCULATION.
American Heart Association, 7272 Greenville Ave., Dallas, TX 75231-4596. TEL 214-706-1310. FAX 214-691-6342. *3207*

CIRCULATION RESEARCH.
American Heart Association, 7272 Greenville Ave., Dallas, TX 75231-4596. TEL 214-706-1310. FAX 214-691-6342. *3207*

CIRCULATORY SHOCK.
John Wiley & Sons, Inc., Journals, (Shock Society) 605 Third Ave., New York, NY 10158. TEL 212-850-6000. FAX 212-850-6088. *3207*

CITIES.
Butterworth - Heinemann Ltd. Linacre House, Jordan Hill, Oxford OX2 8DP, England. TEL 0865-310366. FAX 0865-310898. *4085*

CIVIL ENGINEERING A S C E.
American Society of Civil Engineers, 345 E. 47th St., New York, NY 10017-2398. TEL 212-705-7288. FAX 212-980-4681. *1863*

CLASSICAL ANTIQUITY.
University of California Press, Journals Division, 2120 Berkeley Way, Berkeley, CA 94720. TEL 510-642-4191. FAX 510-643-7127. *1275*

CLASSICAL PHILOLOGY.
University of Chicago Press, Journals Division, 5702 S. Woodlawn Ave., Chicago, IL 60637. TEL 312-753-3347. FAX 312-702-0694. *1276*

CLASSICS IN THE HISTORY AND PHILOSOPHY OF SCIENCE.
Gordon and Breach Scientific Publishers, 279 Eighth Ave., New York, NY 10011. TEL 212-206-8900. FAX 212-645-2459. *4305*

CLASSICS OF BRITISH HISTORICAL LITERATURE.
University of Chicago Press, 5801 S. Ellis Ave., Chicago, IL 60637. TEL 312-702-7899. *2906*

CLASSICS OF SOVIET MATHEMATICS.
Gordon and Breach Scientific Publishers, 270 Eighth Ave., New York, NY 10011. TEL 212-206-8900. FAX 212-645-2459. *3032*

CLEARING HOUSE.
Heldref Publications, (Helen Dwight Reid Educational Foundation) 1319 Eighteenth St., N.W., Washington, DC 20036-1802. TEL 202-296-6267. FAX 202-296-5149. *1621*

CLEFT PALATE - CRANIOFACIAL JOURNAL.
Decker Periodicals, (American Cleft Palate-Craniofacial Association) One James St. S., P.O. Box 620, LCD 1, Hamilton, Ont. L8N 3K7, Canada. TEL 416-522-7017. FAX 416-522-7839. *3377*

CLEVELAND CLINIC JOURNAL OF MEDICINE.
Cleveland Clinic Educational Foundation, 9500 Euclid Ave., Cleveland, OH 44195-5058. TEL 216-444-2662. FAX 216-444-9385. *3088*

CLINICA CHIMICA ACTA.
Elsevier Science Publishers B.V., P.O. Box 211, 1000 AE Amsterdam, Netherlands. TEL 020-5803911. FAX 020-5803598. *3088*

CLINICAL ANATOMY.
John Wiley & Sons, Inc., Journals, (American Association of Clinical Anatomists) 605 Third Ave., New York, NY 10158. TEL 212-850-6000. FAX 212-850-6088. *435*

CLINICAL AND BIOCHEMICAL ANALYSIS.
Marcel Dekker, Inc., 270 Madison Ave., New York, NY 10016. TEL 212-696-9000. FAX 212-685-4540. *475*

CLINICAL AND EXPERIMENTAL HYPERTENSION. PART A: THEORY AND PRACTICE.
Marcel Dekker Journals, 270 Madison Ave., New York, NY 10016. TEL 212-696-9000. FAX 212-685-4540. *3088*

CLINICAL AND EXPERIMENTAL HYPERTENSION. PART B: HYPERTENSION IN PREGNANCY.
Marcel Dekker Journals, (International Society for the Study of Hypertension in Pregnancy) 270 Madison Ave., New York, NY 10016. TEL 212-696-9000. FAX 212-685-4540. *3088*

CLINICAL BIOCHEMISTRY (TARRYTOWN).
Pergamon Press, Inc., Journals Division, (Canadian Society of Clinical Chemists) 660 White Plains Rd., Tarrytown, NY 10591-5153. TEL 914-524-9200. FAX 914-333-2444. *475*

CLINICAL BIOMECHANICS.
Butterworth - Heinemann Ltd. (Osteopathic Association of Great Britain) Linacre House, Jordan Hill, Oxford OX2 8DP, England. TEL 0865-310366. FAX 0865-310898. *3214*

CLINICAL CARDIOLOGY.
Clinical Cardiology Publishing Company, Inc., Box 832, Mahwah, NJ 07430-0832. TEL 201-818-1010. FAX 201-818-0086. *3207*

CLINICAL CHEMISTRY.
American Association for Clinical Chemistry, Inc., 2029 K St. N.W., 7th fl., Washington, DC 20006. TEL 800-892-1400. FAX 202-887-5093. *3088*

CLINICAL CHEMISTRY AND ENZYMOLOGY COMMUNICATIONS.
Harwood Academic Publishers, 270 Eighth Ave., New York, NY 10011. TEL 212-206-8900. FAX 212-645-2459. *475*

CLINICAL CHEMISTRY LOOKOUT.
Elsevier Science Publishers B.V., (Swedish Society for Clinical Chemistry) P.O. Box 211, 1000 AE Amsterdam, Netherlands. TEL 020-5803911. FAX 020-5803598. *3168*

CLINICAL DIABETES.
American Diabetes Association, Inc., 1660 Duke St., Alexandria, VA 22314. TEL 703-549-1500. FAX 703-836-7439. *3251*

CLINICAL ELECTROENCEPHALOGRAPHY.
American Medical Electroencephalographic Association, 850 Elm Grove Rd., Ste. 11, Elm Grove, WI 53122. TEL 414-797-7800. *3333*

CLINICAL ENGINEERING INFORMATION SERVICE.
Scientific Enterprises, Inc., 5104 Randolph Rd., N. Little Rock, AR 72116-6836. TEL 501-771-1775. *3258*

CLINICAL ENGINEERING SERIES.
Academic Press, Inc., 1250 Sixth Ave., San Diego, CA 92101. TEL 619-231-0926. FAX 619-699-6715. *3089*

CLINICAL EYE AND VISION CARE.
Butterworth - Heinemann Ltd. 80 Montvale Ave., Stoneham, MA 02180. TEL 617-438-8464. FAX 617-438-1479. *3299*

CLINICAL GERONTOLOGIST.
Haworth Press, Inc., 10 Alice St., Binghamton, NY 13904. TEL 800-342-9678. FAX 607-722-1424. *2271*

CLINICAL HEMORHEOLOGY.
Pergamon Press, Inc., Journals Division, (International Society of Biorheology) 660 White Plains Rd., Tarrytown, NY 10591-5153. TEL 914-524-9200. FAX 914-333-2444. *3271*

CLINICAL IMAGING.
Elsevier Science Publishing Co., Inc. (New York), 655 Ave. of the Americas, New York, NY 10010. TEL 212-989-5800. FAX 212-633-3965. *3357*

CLINICAL IMMUNOLOGY NEWSLETTER.
Elsevier Science Publishing Co., Inc. (New York), 655 Ave. of the Americas, New York, NY 10010. TEL 212-989-5800. FAX 212-633-3965. *3184*

CLINICAL INFANT REPORTS. MONOGRAPH.
International Universities Press, Inc., (National Center for Clinical Infant Programs) 59 Boston Post Rd., Box 1524, Madison, CT 06443-1524. TEL 203-245-4000. *3319*

CLINICAL INFECTIOUS DISEASES.
University of Chicago Press, Journals Division, (Infectious Diseases Society of America) 5720 S. Woodlawn Ave., Chicago, IL 60637. TEL 312-753-3347. FAX 312-702-0694. *3218*

CLINICAL JOURNAL OF PAIN.
Raven Press, (American Academy of Pain Medicine) 1185 Ave. of the Americas, New York, NY 10036. TEL 212-930-9500. FAX 212-869-3495. *3334*

CLINICAL JOURNAL OF SPORT MEDICINE.
Raven Press, (Canadian Academy of Sport Medicine) 1185 Ave. of the Americas, New York, NY 10036. TEL 212-930-9500. FAX 212-869-3495. *3371*

CLINICAL JOURNAL OF SPORTS MEDICINE.
Raven Press, 1185 Ave. of the Americas, New York, NY 10036. TEL 212-930-9500. FAX 212-869-3495. *3371*

CLINICAL KINESIOLOGY.
American Kinesiotherapy Association, Box 890665, Houston, TX 77289-0665. *3371*

CLINICAL LABORATORY PRODUCT COMPARISON SYSTEM.
E C R I, (Emergency Care Research Institute) 5200 Butler Pike, Plymouth Meeting, PA 19462. TEL 215-825-6000. FAX 215-834-1275. *3258*

CLINICAL LINGUISTICS & PHONETICS.
Taylor & Francis Ltd., Rankine Rd., Basingstoke, Hants RG24 0PR, England. TEL 0256-840366. FAX 0256-479438. *3334*

CLINICAL MATERIALS.
Elsevier Science Publishers Ltd., Crown House, Linton Rd., Barking, Essex IG11 8JU, England. TEL 081-594-7272. FAX 081-594-5942. *3089*

CLINICAL NEUROPHARMACOLOGY.
Raven Press, 1185 Ave. of the Americas, New York, NY 10036. TEL 212-950-9500. FAX 212-869-3495. *3721*

CLINICAL NUCLEAR MEDICINE.
J.B. Lippincott Co., E. Washington Sq., Philadelphia, PA 19105. TEL 215-238-4200. *3357*

CLINICAL NURSE SPECIALIST.
Williams & Wilkins, 428 E. Preston St., Baltimore, MD 21202. TEL 301-528-4000. FAX 301-528-4312. *3277*

CLINICAL OBSTETRICS AND GYNECOLOGY.
J.B. Lippincott Co., E. Washington Sq., Philadelphia, PA 19105. TEL 215-238-4200. *3290*

CLINICAL ONCOLOGY ALERT.
American Health Consultants, Inc., Six Piedmont Center, Ste. 400, 3525 Piedmont Rd., N.E., Atlanta, GA 30305. TEL 404-262-7436. FAX 800-284-3291. *3196*

CLINICAL ORTHOPAEDICS AND RELATED RESEARCH.
J.B. Lippincott Co., E. Washington Sq., Philadelphia, PA 19105. TEL 215-238-4200. *3307*

CLINICAL PEDIATRICS.
Cortlandt Group, Inc., 500 Executive Blvd., Ste. 302, Ossining, NY 10562. TEL 914-762-0647. FAX 914-762-8820. *3319*

CLINICAL PEDIATRICS SERIES.
Marcel Dekker, Inc., 270 Madison Ave., New York, NY 10016. TEL 212-696-9000. FAX 212-685-4540. *3319*

CLINICAL PHARMACOLOGY & THERAPEUTICS.
Mosby - Year Book, Inc. (American Society for Pharmacology and Experimental Therapeutics) 11830 Westline Industrial Dr., St. Louis, MO 63146. TEL 800-325-4117. FAX 314-432-1380. *3721*

CLINICAL PHARMACY.
American Society of Hospital Pharmacists, c/o Jean Rogers, Dir., Mkt. Svcs., 4630 Montgomery Ave., Bethesda, MD 20814. TEL 301-657-3000. *3721*

CLINICAL PRACTICE OF GYNECOLOGY.
Elsevier Science Publishing Co., Inc. (New York), 655 Ave. of Americas, New York, NY 10010. *3290*

CLINICAL PREVENTIVE DENTISTRY.
Stevens Publishing Corporation, 225 N. New Rd., Waco, TX 76710. TEL 817-776-9000. FAX 817-775-9018. *3230*

CLINICAL PSYCHOLOGIST.
Pergamon Press, Inc., Journals Division, (American Psychological Association) 660 White Plains Rd., Tarrytown, NY 10591-5153. TEL 914-524-9200. FAX 914-333-2444. *4016*

CLINICAL PSYCHOLOGY REVIEW.
Pergamon Press, Inc., Journals Division, (American Psychological Association, Division of Clinical Psychology) 660 White Plains Rd., Tarrytown, NY 10591-5153. TEL 914-524-9200. FAX 914-333-2444. *4016*

CLINICAL RESEARCH.
Slack, Inc., (American Federation for Clinical Research) 6900 Grove Rd., Thorofare, NJ 08086. TEL 609-848-1000. FAX 609-853-5991. *3168*

CLINICAL RESEARCH AND REGULATORY AFFAIRS.
Marcel Dekker Journals, 270 Madison Ave., New York, NY 10016. TEL 212-696-9000. FAX 212-685-4540. *3721*

CLINICAL REVIEWS IN ALLERGY.
Humana Press Inc., Box 2148, Clifton, NJ 07015. TEL 201-256-1699. FAX 201-256-8341. *3184*

CLINICAL SOCIAL WORK JOURNAL.
Human Sciences Press, Inc. (National Federation of Societies for Clinical Social Work) 233 Spring St., New York, NY 10013-1578. TEL 212-620-8000. FAX 212-463-0742. *4402*

CLINICAL SUPERVISOR.
Haworth Press, Inc., 10 Alice St., Binghamton, NY 13904. TEL 800-342-9678. FAX 607-722-1424. *4402*

CLINICAL THERAPEUTICS.
Excerpta Medica, Inc., Core Publishing Division 105 Raider Blvd., Belle Mead, NJ 08502-1510. TEL 908-874-8550. FAX 908-874-5633. *3089*

CLINICAL TRIALS AND META-ANALYSIS.
Elsevier Science Publishers B.V., P.O. Box 211, 1000 AE Amsterdam, Netherlands. FAX 020-5803911. *3089*

CLINICAL VISION SCIENCES.
Pergamon Press PLC, Headington Hill Hall, Oxford OX3 0BW, England. TEL 0865-794141. FAX 0865-743911. *3299*

CLINICALLY IMPORTANT ADVERSE DRUG INTERACTIONS.
Elsevier Science Publishers B.V., Books Division, P.O. Box 211, 1000 AE Amsterdam, Netherlands. TEL 020-5803911. FAX 020-5803705. *3721*

CLINICS IN DERMATOLOGY.
Elsevier Science Publishing Co., Inc. (New York), 655 Ave. of the Americas, New York, NY 10010. TEL 212-989-5800. FAX 212-633-3965. *3246*

COAL PREPARATION.
Gordon & Breach Science Publishers, 270 Eighth Ave., New York, NY 10011. TEL 212-206-8900. FAX 212-645-2459. *3481*

COAL SCIENCE AND TECHNOLOGY.
Elsevier Science Publishers B.V., Books Division, P.O. Box 211, 1000 AE Amsterdam, Netherlands. TEL 020-5803911. FAX 020-5803705. *3481*

COASTAL ENGINEERING.
Elsevier Science Publishers B.V., P.O. Box 211, 1000 AE Amsterdam, Netherlands. TEL 020-5803911. FAX 020-5803598. *1863*

COASTAL MANAGEMENT.
Taylor & Francis, 1900 Frost Rd., Ste. 101, Bristol, PA 19007. TEL 215-785-5800. FAX 215-785-5515. *1603*

COASTAL RESEARCH.
Florida State University, Geology Department, Tallahassee, FL 32306. TEL 904-644-5860. *1603*

COCUK SAGLIGI VE HASTALIKLARI DERGISI.
Turkish and International Children's Center, P.O. Box 66, Samanpazari, 06240 Ankara, Turkey. TEL 4-324-2326. FAX 4-311-2253. *3320*

COGNITION.
Elsevier Science Publishers B.V., P.O. Box 211, 1000 AE Amsterdam, Netherlands. TEL 020-5803911. FAX 020-5803598. *4016*

COGNITION AND EMOTION.
Lawrence Erlbaum Associates Ltd., 27 Palmeira Mansions, Church Rd., Hove, E. Sussex BN3 2FA, England. 0273-207411. FAX 0273-205612. *4016*

COGNITION AND INSTRUCTION.
Lawrence Erlbaum Associates, Inc., 365 Broadway, Hillsdale, NJ 07642. TEL 201-666-4110. FAX 201-666-2394. *4016*

COGNITION AND LANGUAGE.
Plenum Publishing Corp., 233 Spring St., New York, NY 10013-1578. TEL 212-620-8000. FAX 212-463-0742. *2809*

COGNITIVE BRAIN RESEARCH.
Elsevier Science Publishers B.V., P.O. Box 211, 1000 AE Amsterdam, Netherlands. TEL 020-5803911. FAX 020-5803598. *3334*

COGNITIVE NEUROPSYCHOLOGY.
Lawrence Erlbaum Associates Ltd., 27 Palmeira Mansions, Church Rd., Hove, E. Sussex BN3 2FA, England. TEL 0273-207411. FAX 0273-205612. *4016*

COGNITIVE PSYCHOLOGY.
Academic Press, Inc., Journal Division, 1250 Sixth Ave., San Diego, CA 92101. TEL 619-230-1840. FAX 619-699-6800. *4016*

COGNITIVE SCIENCE SERIES (CAMBRIDGE).
Harvard University Press, 79 Garden St., Cambridge, MA 02138. TEL 617-495-2600. FAX 617-495-5898. *4016*

COGNITIVE SCIENCE SERIES: TECHNICAL MONOGRAPHS AND EDITED COLLECTIONS.
Lawrence Erlbaum Associates, Inc., 365 Broadway, Hillsdale, NJ 07642. TEL 201-666-4110. FAX 201-666-2394. *4016*

COGNITIVE THERAPY AND RESEARCH.
Plenum Publishing Corp., 233 Spring St., New York, NY 10013-1578. TEL 212-620-8000. FAX 212-463-0742. *4016*

COLD REGIONS SCIENCE AND TECHNOLOGY.
Elsevier Science Publishers B.V., P.O. Box 211, 1000 AE Amsterdam, Netherlands. TEL 020-5803911. FAX 020-5803598. *4595*

COLLECTION MANAGEMENT.
Haworth Press, Inc., 10 Alice St., Binghamton, NY 13904. TEL 800-342-9678. FAX 607-722-1424. *2752*

COLLEGE MATHEMATICS JOURNAL.
Mathematical Association of America, 1529 18th St. N.W., Washington, DC 20036. TEL 202-387-5200. *3032*

COLLEGE TEACHING.
Heldref Publications, (Helen Dwight Reid Educational Foundation) 1319 Eighteenth St., N.W., Washington, DC 20036-1802. TEL 202-296-6267. FAX 202-296-5149. *1703*

COLLOID JOURNAL OF THE U S S R.
Plenum Publishing Corp., Consultants Bureau, (Russian Academy of Sciences) 233 Spring St., New York, NY 10013-1578. TEL 212-620-8468. FAX 212-463-0742. *1225*

COLLOIDS AND SURFACES.
Elsevier Science Publishers B.V., P.O. Box 211, 1000 AE Amsterdam, Netherlands. TEL 020-5803911. FAX 020-5803598. *1225*

COLLOQUIA MATHEMATICA SOCIETATIS JANOS BOLYAI.
Elsevier Science Publishers B.V., Books Division, P.O. Box 211, 1000 AE Amsterdam, Netherlands. TEL 020-5803911. FAX 020-5803705. *3032*

COLOR RESEARCH AND APPLICATION.
John Wiley & Sons, Inc., Journals, 605 Third Ave., New York, NY 10158-0012. TEL 212-692-6000. FAX 212-850-6088. *1852*

COLORADO MEDICINE.
Colorado Medical Society, 7800 E. Dorado Pl., Englewood, CO 80111. TEL 303-779-5455. FAX 303-779-8775. *3090*

COLUMBIA BIOLOGICAL SERIES.
Columbia University Press, 562 W. 113th St., New York, NY 10025. TEL 212-678-6777. *435*

COLUMBIA SERIES IN MOLECULAR BIOLOGY.
Columbia University Press, 562 W. 113th St., New York, NY 10025. TEL 212-678-6777. *524*

COMBUSTION AND FLAME.
Elsevier Science Publishing Co., Inc. (New York), (Combustion Institute) 655 Ave. of the Americas, New York, NY 10010. TEL 212-989-5800. FAX 212-633-3965. *1817*

COMBUSTION, EXPLOSION, AND SHOCK WAVES.
Plenum Publishing Corp., Consultants Bureau, (Russian Academy of Sciences, Siberian Division) 233 Spring St., New York, NY 10013-1578. TEL 212-620-8468. FAX 212-463-0742. *1852*

COMBUSTION SCIENCE AND TECHNOLOGY.
Gordon & Breach Science Publishers, 270 Eighth Ave., New York, NY 10011. TEL 212-206-8900. FAX 212-645-2459. *1225*

COMMENTS ON ASTROPHYSICS.
Gordon & Breach Science Publishers, 270 Eighth Ave., New York, NY 10011. TEL 212-206-8900. FAX 212-645-2459. *363*

COMMUNICATION (LONDON, 1975).
Gordon and Breach Science Publishers, 270 Eighth Ave., New York, NY 10011. TEL 212-206-8900. FAX 212-645-2459. *1333*

COMMUNICATION AND COGNITION.
Communication and Cognition, (Rijksuniversiteit Gent) Blandijnberg 2, 9000 Ghent, Belgium. TEL 32-91-25-75-71. FAX 32-91-24-16-21. *1333*

COMMUNICATION AND THE HUMAN CONDITION.
Gordon & Breach Science Publishers, 270 Eighth Ave., New York, NY 10011. TEL 212-206-8900. FAX 212-645-2459. *2907*

COMMUNICATION THEORY.
Guilford Publications, Inc., (International Communication Association) 72 Spring St., 4th Fl., New York, NY 10012. TEL 212-431-9800. FAX 212-966-6708. *2809*

COMMUNICATIONS IN ALGEBRA.
Marcel Dekker Journals, 270 Madison Ave., New York, NY 10016. TEL 212-696-9000. FAX 212-685-4540. *3033*

COMMUNICATIONS IN APPLIED NUMERICAL METHODS.
John Wiley & Sons Ltd., Journals, Baffins Lane, Chichester, Sussex PO19 1UD, England. TEL 0243 779777. FAX 0243-775878. *3033*

COMMUNICATIONS IN PARTIAL DIFFERENTIAL EQUATIONS.
Marcel Dekker Journals, 270 Madison Ave., New York, NY 10016. TEL 212-696-9000. FAX 212-685-4540. *3033*

COMMUNICATIONS IN SOIL SCIENCE AND PLANT ANALYSIS.
Marcel Dekker Journals, 270 Madison Ave., New York, NY 10016. TEL 212-696-9000. FAX 212-685-4540. *174*

COMMUNICATIONS IN STATISTICS. PART A: THEORY AND METHODS.
Marcel Dekker Journals, 270 Madison Ave., New York, NY 10016. TEL 212-696-9000. FAX 212-685-4540. *4569*

COMMUNICATIONS IN STATISTICS. PART B: SIMULATION AND COMPUTATION.
Marcel Dekker Journals, 270 Madison Ave., New York, NY 10016. TEL 212-696-9000. FAX 212-685-4540. *4569*

COMMUNICATIONS IN THEORETICAL PHYSICS.
International Academic Publishers (IAP), (Academia Sinica, Institute of Theoretical Physics) Xizhimenwai Dajie, Beijing Exhibition Centre, Beijing 100044, People's Republic of China. TEL 8316677. FAX 4015664. *3816*

COMMUNICATIONS ON PURE AND APPLIED MATHEMATICS.
John Wiley & Sons, Inc., Journals, (Courant Institute of Mathematical Sciences) 605 Third Ave., New York, NY 10158-0012. TEL 212-850-6000. FAX 212-850-6088. *3033*

COMMUNITY & JUNIOR COLLEGE LIBRARIES.
Haworth Press, Inc., 10 Alice St., Binghamton, NY 13904. TEL 800-342-9678. FAX 607-722-1424. *2753*

COMMUNITY JUNIOR COLLEGE: QUARTERLY OF RESEARCH AND PRACTICE.
Hemisphere Publishing Corporation (Virginia Commonwealth University, Adult Education Program) 1900 Frost Rd., Ste. 101, Bristol, PA 19007-1598. TEL 215-785-5800. FAX 215-785-5515. *1683*

COMMUNITY LEADER BRIEFINGS.
City Leaders Institute, 3045 Thayen Pl., Boise, ID 83709. TEL 208-375-6337. FAX 208-375-6337. *4086*

COMMUNITY MENTAL HEALTH JOURNAL.
Human Sciences Press, Inc. (National Council of Community Mental Health Centers, Inc.) 233 Spring St., New York, NY 10013-1578. TEL 212-620-8000. FAX 212-463-0742. *4402*

COMPARATIVE BIOCHEMISTRY AND PHYSIOLOGY. PART A: COMPARATIVE PHYSIOLOGY.
Pergamon Press, Inc., Journals Division, 660 White Plains Rd., Tarrytown, NY 10591-5153. TEL 914-524-9200. FAX 914-333-2444. *571*

COMPARATIVE BIOCHEMISTRY AND PHYSIOLOGY. PART B: COMPARATIVE BIOCHEMISTRY.
Pergamon Press, Inc., Journals Division, 660 White Plains Rd., Tarrytown, NY 10591-5153. TEL 914-524-9200. FAX 914-333-2444. *475*

COMPARATIVE BIOCHEMISTRY AND PHYSIOLOGY. PART C: COMPARATIVE PHARMACOLOGY & TOXICOLOGY.
Pergamon Press, Inc., Journals Division, 660 White Plains Rd., Tarrytown, NY 10591-5153. TEL 914-524-9200. FAX 914-333-2444. *475*

COMPARATIVE EDUCATION REVIEW.
University of Chicago Press, Journals Division, (Comparative and International Education Society) 5720 S. Woodlawn Ave., Chicago, IL 60637. TEL 312-702-7600. FAX 312-753-3347. *1622*

COMPARATIVE IMMUNOLOGY, MICROBIOLOGY AND INFECTIOUS DISEASES.
Pergamon Press, Inc., Journals Division, 660 White Plains Rd., Tarrytown, NY 10591-5153. TEL 914-524-9200. FAX 914-333-2444. *550*

COMPARATIVE MEDICINE.
Academic Press, Inc., Journal Division, 1250 Sixth Ave., San Diego, CA 92101. TEL 619-230-1840. FAX 619-699-6800. *3258*

COMPARATIVE STRATEGY.
Taylor & Francis, 1900 Frost Rd., Ste. 101, Bristol, PA 19007. TEL 215-785-5800. FAX 215-785-5515. *3881*

COMPLEX VARIABLES: THEORY AND APPLICATION.
Gordon and Breach Science Publishers, 270 Eighth Ave., New York, NY 10011. TEL 212-206-8900. FAX 212-645-2459. *3033*

COMPLEXITY.
Pergamon Press plc, Headington Hill Hall, Oxford OX3 0BW, England. TEL 0865-794141. FAX 0865-743911. *1877*

COMPOSITE STRUCTURES.
Elsevier Science Publishers Ltd., Crown House, Linton Rd., Barking, Essex IG11 8JU, England. TEL 081-594-7272. FAX 081-594-5942. *1864*

COMPOSITES.
Butterworth - Heinemann Ltd. Linacre House, Jordan Hill, Oxford OX2 8DP, England. TEL 0865-310366. FAX 0865-310898. *1916*

COMPOSITES ENGINEERING.
Pergamon Press plc, Headington Hill Hall, Oxford OX3 0BW, England. TEL 0865-794141. FAX 0865-743911. *1817*

COMPOSITES MANUFACTURING.
Butterworth - Heinemann Ltd. Linacre House, Jordan Hill, Oxford OX2 8DP, England. TEL 0865-310366. FAX 0865-310898. *1928*

COMPOSITES SCIENCE AND TECHNOLOGY.
Elsevier Science Publishers Ltd., Crown House, Linton Rd., Barking, Essex IG11 8JU, England. TEL 081-594-7272. FAX 081-594-5942. *4595*

COMPREHENSIVE ANALYTICAL CHEMISTRY.
Elsevier Science Publishers B.V., Books Division, P.O. Box 211, 1000 AE Amsterdam, Netherlands. TEL 020-5803911. FAX 020-5803705. *1205*

COMPREHENSIVE CHEMICAL KINETICS.
Elsevier Science Publishers B.V., Books Division, P.O. Box 211, 1000 AE Amsterdam, Netherlands. TEL 020-5803911. FAX 020-5803705. *1225*

COMPREHENSIVE ENDOCRINOLOGY.
Raven Press, 1185 Ave. of the Americas, New York, NY 10036. TEL 212-930-9500. FAX 212-869-3495. *3251*

COMPREHENSIVE IMMUNOLOGY.
Plenum Publishing Corp., 233 Spring St., New York, NY 10013-1578. TEL 212-620-8000. FAX 212-463-0742. *3184*

COMPREHENSIVE PSYCHIATRY.
W.B. Saunders Co. (American Psychopathological Association) Curtis Center, Independence Square W., Philadelphia, PA 19106. TEL 215-238-7800. *3334*

COMPREHENSIVE PSYCHOTHERAPY.
Gordon & Breach Science Publishers, P.O. Box 90, Reading, Berkshire RG1 8JL, England. TEL 0734-560-080. FAX 0734-568-211. *4017*

COMPREHENSIVE THERAPY.
International Publishing Group, (American Society of Contemporary Medicine and Surgery) 4959 Commerce Pkwy., Cleveland, OH 44128. TEL 800-342-6237. FAX 216-464-1835. *3090*

COMPUTATIONAL GEOMETRY.
North-Holland P.O. Box 211, 1000 AE Amsterdam, Netherlands. TEL 020-5803911. FAX 020-5803598. *1390*

COMPUTATIONAL LINGUISTICS.
M I T Press, (Association for Computational Linguistics) 55 Hayward St., Cambridge, MA 02142. TEL 617-253-2889. FAX 617-258-6779. *2856*

COMPUTATIONAL MATERIALS SCIENCE.
Elsevier Science Publishers B.V., P.O. Box 211, 1000 AE Amsterdam, Netherlands. TEL 020-5803911. FAX 020-5803598. *1916*

COMPUTATIONAL MATHEMATICS AND APPLICATIONS.
Academic Press, Inc., 1250 Sixth Ave., San Diego, CA 92101. TEL 619-231-0926. FAX 619-699-6715. *1440*

COMPUTATIONAL MATHEMATICS AND MODELING.
Plenum Publishing Corp., Consultants Bureau, 233 Spring St., New York, NY 10013. TEL 212-620-8000. FAX 212-463-0742. *3064*

COMPUTATIONAL STATISTICS AND DATA ANALYSIS.
North-Holland P.O. Box 211, 1000 AE Amsterdam, Netherlands. TEL 020-5803911. FAX 020-5803598. *1403*

COMPUTER-AIDED CHEMICAL ENGINEERING.
Elsevier Science Publishers B.V., Books Division, P.O. Box 211, 1000 AE Amsterdam, Netherlands. TEL 020-5803911. FAX 020-5803705. *1877*

COMPUTER-AIDED DESIGN.
Butterworth - Heinemann Ltd. Linacre House, Jordan Hill, Oxford OX2 8DP, England. TEL 0865-310366. FAX 0865-310898. *1420*

COMPUTER-AIDED DESIGN OF ELECTRONIC CIRCUITS.
Elsevier Science Publishers B.V., Books Division, P.O. Box 211, 1000 AE Amsterdam, Netherlands. TEL 020-5803911. FAX 020-5803705. *1877*

COMPUTER-AIDED GEOMETRIC DESIGN.
North-Holland P.O. Box 211, 1000 AE Amsterdam, Netherlands. TEL 020-5803911. FAX 020-5803598. *1420*

COMPUTER AUDIT UPDATE.
Elsevier Science Publishers Ltd., Crown House, Linton Rd., Barking, Essex I611 8JU, England. TEL 081-594-7272. FAX 081-594-5942. *1433*

COMPUTER COMMUNICATIONS.
Butterworth - Heinemann Ltd. Linacre House, Jordan Hill, Oxford OX2 8DP, England. TEL 0865-310366. FAX 0865-310898. *1446*

COMPUTER DESIGN AND ARCHITECTURE SERIES.
Elsevier Science Publishing Co., Inc. (New York), 655 Ave. of the Americas, New York, NY 10010. TEL 212-989-5800. FAX 212-633-3965. *1416*

COMPUTER GRAPHICS FORUM.
Basil Blackwell Ltd., (European Association for Computer Graphics) 108 Cowley Rd., Oxford OX4 1JF, England. TEL 0865-791100. FAX 0865-791347. *1421*

COMPUTER-INTEGRATED MANUFACTURING SYSTEMS.
Butterworth - Heinemann Ltd. Linacre House, Jordan Hill, Oxford OX2 8DP, England. TEL 0865-310366. FAX 0865-310898. *1877*

COMPUTER LANGUAGES.
Pergamon Press, Inc., Journals Division, 660 White Plains Rd., Tarrytown, NY 10591-5153. TEL 914-524-9200. FAX 914-333-2444. *1429*

COMPUTER LAW AND SECURITY REPORT.
Elsevier Science Publishers Ltd., Crown House, Linton Rd., Barking, Essex IG11 8JU, England. TEL 081-594-7272. FAX 081-594-5942. *1434*

COMPUTER METHODS & PROGRAMS IN BIOMEDICINE.
Elsevier Science Publishers B.V., P.O. Box 211, 1000 AE Amsterdam, Netherlands. TEL 020-5803911. FAX 020-5803598. *3225*

COMPUTER METHODS IN APPLIED MECHANICS AND ENGINEERING.
Elsevier Sequoia S.A., P.O. Box 564, CH-1001 Lausanne, Switzerland. TEL 021-207381. FAX 021-235444. *1877*

COMPUTER NETWORKS AND I S D N SYSTEMS.
North-Holland (International Council for Computer Communications) P.O. Box 211, 1000 AE Amsterdam, Netherlands. TEL 020-5803911. FAX 020-5803598. *1426*

COMPUTER PHYSICS COMMUNICATIONS.
North-Holland P.O. Box 211, 1000 AE Amsterdam, Netherlands. TEL 020-5803911. FAX 020-5803598. *4359*

COMPUTER STANDARDS AND INTERFACES.
Elsevier Science Publishers B.V., P.O. Box 211, 1000 AE Amsterdam, Netherlands. TEL 020-5803911. FAX 020-5803598. *1392*

COMPUTER STUDIES: COMPUTERS IN EDUCATION.
Dushkin Publishing Group, Inc., Sluice Dock, Guilford, CT 06437-9989. TEL 203-453-4351. FAX 203-453-6000. *1689*

COMPUTER SYSTEMS SCIENCE AND ENGINEERING.
C R L Publishing Ltd., P.O. Box 140, Aldershot, Hants GU12 5QX, England. TEL 0252-519239. FAX 0252-517625. *1436*

COMPUTERIZED MEDICAL IMAGING AND GRAPHICS.
Pergamon Press, Inc., Journals Division, 660 White Plains Rd., Tarrytown, NY 10591-5153. TEL 914-524-9200. FAX 914-333-2444. *3225*

COMPUTERS AND BIOMEDICAL RESEARCH.
Academic Press, Inc., Journal Division, (American Medical Informatics Association) 1250 Sixth Ave., San Diego, CA 92101. TEL 619-230-1840. FAX 619-699-6800. *3225*

COMPUTERS & CHEMICAL ENGINEERING.
Pergamon Press, Inc., Journals Division, 660 White Plains Rd., Tarrytown, NY 10591-5153. TEL 914-524-9200. FAX 914-333-2444. *1878*

COMPUTERS & CHEMISTRY.
Pergamon Press, Inc., Journals Division, 660 White Plains Rd., Tarrytown, NY 10591-5153. TEL 914-524-9200. FAX 914-333-2444. *4359*

COMPUTERS & EDUCATION.
Pergamon Press, Inc., Journals Division, 660 White Plains Rd., Tarrytown, NY 10591-5153. TEL 914-524-9200. FAX 914-333-2444. *1689*

COMPUTERS & ELECTRICAL ENGINEERING.
Pergamon Press, Inc., Journals Division, 660 White Plains Rd., Tarrytown, NY 10591-5153. TEL 914-524-9200. FAX 914-333-2444. *1878*

COMPUTERS AND ELECTRONICS IN AGRICULTURE.
Elsevier Science Publishers B.V., P.O. Box 211, 1000 AE Amsterdam, Netherlands. TEL 020-5803911. FAX 020-5803598. *165*

COMPUTERS & FLUIDS.
Pergamon Press, Inc., Journals Division, 660 White Plains Rd., Tarrytown, NY 10591-5153. TEL 914-524-9200. FAX 914-333-2444. *1878*

COMPUTERS & GEOSCIENCES.
Pergamon Press, Inc., Journals Division, (International Association for Mathematical Geology) 660 White Plains Rd., Tarrytown, NY 10591-5153. TEL 914-524-9200. FAX 914-333-2444. *1878*

COMPUTERS AND GEOTECHNICS.
Elsevier Science Publishers Ltd., Crown House, Linton Rd., Barking, Essex IG11 8JU, England. TEL 081-594-7272. FAX 081-594-5942. *1878*

COMPUTERS & GRAPHICS.
Pergamon Press, Inc., Journals Division, 660 White Plains Rd., Tarrytown, NY 10591-5153. TEL 914-524-9200. FAX 914-333-2444. *1421*

COMPUTERS & INDUSTRIAL ENGINEERING.
Pergamon Press, Inc., Journals Division, 660 White Plains Rd., Tarrytown, NY 10591-5153. TEL 914-524-9200. FAX 914-333-2444. *1878*

COMPUTERS & MATHEMATICS WITH APPLICATIONS.
Pergamon Press, Inc., Journals Division, 660 White Plains Rd., Tarrytown, NY 10591-5153. TEL 914-524-9200. FAX 914-333-2444. *3064*

COMPUTERS & OPERATIONS RESEARCH.
Pergamon Press, Inc., Journals Division, 660 White Plains Rd., Tarrytown, NY 10591-5153. TEL 914-524-9200. FAX 914-333-2444. *1393*

COMPUTERS & SECURITY.
Elsevier Science Publishers Ltd., (International Federation for Information Processing, Technical Committee on Computer Security) Crown House, Linton Road, Barking, Essex IG11 8JU, England. TEL 081-594-7272. FAX 081-594-5942. *1434*

COMPUTERS & STRUCTURES.
Pergamon Press, Inc., Journals Division, 660 White Plains Rd., Tarrytown, NY 10591-5153. TEL 914-524-9200. FAX 914-333-2444. *1878*

COMPUTERS AND THE HISTORY OF ART.
Harwood Academic Publishers, 270 Eighth Ave., New York, NY 10011. TEL 212-206-8900. FAX 212-6452459. *352*

COMPUTERS, ENVIRONMENT AND URBAN SYSTEMS.
Pergamon Press, Inc., Journals Division, 660 White Plains Rd., Tarrytown, NY 10591-5153. TEL 914-524-9200. FAX 914-333-2444. *1975*

COMPUTERS IN BIOLOGY AND MEDICINE.
Pergamon Press, Inc., Journals Division, 660 White Plains Rd., Tarrytown, NY 10591-5153. TEL 914-524-9200. FAX 914-333-2444. *3225*

COMPUTERS IN EDUCATION JOURNAL.
American Society for Engineering Education, Computers in Education Division, Box 68, Port Royal Sq., Port Royal, VA 22535. TEL 804-742-5611. *1689*

COMPUTERS IN HUMAN BEHAVIOR.
Pergamon Press, Inc., Journals Division, 660 White Plains Rd., Tarrytown, NY 10591-5153. TEL 914-524-9200. FAX 914-333-2444. *4458*

COMPUTERS IN HUMAN SERVICES.
Haworth Press, Inc., 10 Alice St., Binghamton, NY 13904. TEL 800-342-8678. FAX 607-722-1424. *4458*

COMPUTERS IN INDUSTRY.
North-Holland P.O. Box 211, 1000 AE Amsterdam, Netherlands. TEL 020-5803911. FAX 020-5803598. *826*

COMPUTERS IN MUSIC RESEARCH.
Wisconsin Center for Music Technology, School of Music, University of Wisconsin, Madison, WI 53706. TEL 608-263-1900. *3589*

COMPUTERS IN THE SCHOOLS.
Haworth Press, Inc., 10 Alice St., Binghamton, NY 13904. TEL 800-342-9678. FAX 607-722-1424. *1689*

COMPUTERWORLD HONG KONG.
Asia Computerworld Communications Ltd., (International Data Group) 701-4 Kam Chung Bldg., 54 Jaffe Rd., Wanchai, Hong Kong. TEL 852-861-3228. FAX 852-861-0953. *1423*

COMPUTING SYSTEMS.
University of California Press, Journals Division, (Usenix Association) 2120 Berkeley Way, Berkeley, CA 94720. TEL 510-642-4191. FAX 510-643-7127. *1429*

COMPUTING SYSTEMS IN ENGINEERING.
Pergamon Press, Inc., Journals Division, 660 White Plains Rd., Tarrytown, NY 10591-5153. TEL 914-524-9200. FAX 914-333-2444. *1878*

CONDENSED MATTER NEWS.
Gordon & Breach Science Publishers, 270 Eighth Ave., New York, NY 10011. TEL 212-206-8900. FAX 212-645-2459. *1884*

CONDENSED MATTER THEORIES.
Plenum Publishing Corp., 233 Spring St., New York, NY 10013-1578. TEL 212-620-8000. FAX 212-463-0742. *3816*

CONNECTICUT ACADEMY OF ARTS AND SCIENCES. TRANSACTIONS.
Connecticut Academy of Arts and Sciences, Drawer 93A, Yale Sta., New Haven, CT 06520. TEL 203-432-3113. *2505*

CONNECTIVE TISSUE RESEARCH.
Gordon and Breach Science Publishers, 270 Eighth Ave., New York, NY 10011. TEL 212-206-8900. FAX 212-645-2459. *524*

CONSCIOUSNESS AND COGNITION.
Academic Press, Inc., Journal Division, 1250 Sixth Ave., San Diego, CA 92101. TEL 619-230-1840. FAX 619-699-6800. *4017*

CONSCIOUSNESS AND SELF-REGULATION: ADVANCES IN RESEARCH AND THEORY.
Plenum Publishing Corp., 233 Spring St., New York, NY 10013-1578. TEL 212-620-8000. FAX 212-463-0742. *4017*

CONTEMPORARY ACCOUNTING RESEARCH.
Canadian Academic Accounting Association, CAAA Secretariat, Faculty of Management Studies, Univ. of Toronto, 246 Bloor St. W., Toronto, Ont. M5S 1V4, Canada. FAX 416-978-5433. *749*

CONTEMPORARY ANALYSES IN EDUCATION.
Taylor & Francis Ltd., Rankine Rd., Basingstoke, Hants. RF24 0PR, England. *1623*

CONTEMPORARY CONCEPTS IN PHYSICS.
Harwood Academic Publishers, 270 Eighth Ave., New York, NY 10011. *3816*

CONTEMPORARY ENDOCRINOLOGY.
Plenum Publishing Corp., 233 Spring St., New York, NY 10013-1578. TEL 212-620-8000. FAX 212-463-0742. *3251*

CONTEMPORARY EUROPEAN AFFAIRS.
Pergamon Press, Inc., Journals Division, 660 White Plains Rd., Tarrytown, NY 10591-5153. TEL 914-524-9200. FAX 914-333-2444. *3882*

CONTEMPORARY FAMILY THERAPY.
Human Sciences Press, Inc. 233 Spring St., New York, NY 10013-1578. TEL 212-620-8000. FAX 212-463-0742. *4017*

CONTEMPORARY GASTROENTEROLOGY.
Medical Economics Publishing Co., Five Paragon Dr., Montvale, NJ 07645. TEL 800-526-4870. FAX 201-573-1045. *3267*

CONTEMPORARY GERIATRIC MEDICINE.
Plenum Publishing Corp., 233 Spring St., New York, NY 10013-1578. TEL 212-620-8000. FAX 212-463-0742. *2271*

CONTEMPORARY HEMATOLOGY - ONCOLOGY.
Plenum Publishing Corp., 233 Spring St., New York, NY 10013-1578. TEL 212-620-8000. FAX 212-463-0742611. *3271*

CONTEMPORARY METABOLISM.
Plenum Publishing Corp., 233 Spring St., New York, NY 10013-1578. TEL 212-620-8000. FAX 212-463-0742. *3251*

CONTEMPORARY MUSIC REVIEW.
Harwood Academic Publishers, 270 Eighth Ave., New York, NY 10011. TEL 212-206-8900. FAX 212-645-2459. *3547*

CONTEMPORARY MUSIC STUDIES.
Harwood Academic Publishers, 270 Eighth Ave., New York, NY 10011. TEL 212-206-8900. FAX 212-645-2459. *3547*

CONTEMPORARY NEPHROLOGY.
Plenum Publishing Corp., 233 Spring St., New York, NY 10013-1578. TEL 212-620-8000. FAX 212-463-0742. *3387*

CONTEMPORARY NEUROLOGY SERIES.
F.A. Davis Company, 1915 Arch St., Philadelphia, PA 19103. TEL 800-523-4049. *3334*

CONTEMPORARY OB-GYN.
Medical Economics Company Inc., 680 Kinderkamack Rd., Oradell, NJ 07649. TEL 800-526-4870. FAX 201-262-2760. *3291*

CONTEMPORARY ORTHOPAEDICS.
Bobit Publishing Company, 2512 Artesia Blvd., Redondo Beach, CA 90278. TEL 310-376-8788. FAX 310-376-9043. *3307*

CONTEMPORARY PACIFIC.
University of Hawaii Press, Journals Department, 2840 Kolowalu St., Honolulu, HI 96822. TEL 808-956-8833. FAX 808-988-6052. *2171*

CONTEMPORARY PEDIATRICS.
Medical Economics Publishing Co., Five Paragon Dr., Montvale, NJ 07645. TEL 201-358-7200. FAX 201-573-1045. *3320*

CONTEMPORARY PHYSICS.
Taylor & Francis Ltd., Rankine Rd., Basingstoke, Hants. RG24 0PR, England. TEL 0256-840366. FAX 0256-479438. *3816*

CONTEMPORARY PSYCHOANALYSIS.
William Alanson White Psychoanalytic Institute, 20 W. 74th St., New York, NY 10023. TEL 212-873-0725. FAX 212-362-6967. *4017*

CONTEMPORARY PSYCHOLOGY.
American Psychological Association, 750 First St., N.E., Washington, DC 20002-4646. TEL 202-336-5500. FAX 202-336-5568. *4017*

CONTEMPORARY REVIEWS IN OBSTETRICS AND GYNAECOLOGY.
Butterworth - Heinemann Ltd. Linacre House, Jordan Hill, Oxford OX2 8DP, England. TEL 0865-310366. FAX 0865-310898. *3291*

CONTEMPORARY SURGERY.
Bobit Publishing Company, 2512 Artesia Blvd., Redondo Beach, CA 90278. TEL 310-376-8788. FAX 310-376-9043. *3378*

CONTEMPORARY THEATRE REVIEW.
Harwood Academic Publishers, 270 Eighth Ave., New York, NY 10011. TEL 212-206-8900. FAX 212-645-2459. *4631*

CONTEMPORARY THEATRE STUDIES.
Harwood Academic Publishers, 270 Eighth Ave., New York, NY 10011. TEL 212-206-8900. FAX 212-645-2459. *4631*

CONTEMPORARY TOPICS IN IMMUNOBIOLOGY.
Plenum Publishing Corp., 233 Spring St., New York, NY 10013-1578. TEL 212-620-8000. FAX 212-463-0742. *3184*

CONTEMPORARY TOPICS IN INFORMATION TRANSFER.
Elsevier Science Publishers B.V., Books Division, P.O. Box 211, 1000 AE Amsterdam, Netherlands. TEL 020-5803911. FAX 020-5803705. *1455*

CONTEMPORARY TOPICS IN MOLECULAR IMMUNOLOGY.
Plenum Publishing Corp., 233 Spring St., New York, NY 10013-1578. TEL 212-620-8047. FAX 212-463-0742. *3184*

CONTEMPORARY TOPICS IN PURE AND APPLIED CONDENSED MATTER SCIENCE.
Gordon and Breach Scientific Publishers, 270 Eighth Ave., New York, NY 10011. TEL 212-206-8900. FAX 212-645-2459. *3816*

CONTEMPORARY UROLOGY.
Medical Economics Publishing Co., Five Paragon Dr., Montvale, NJ 07645. TEL 201-358-7200. FAX 201-573-1045. *3387*

CONTINENTAL SHELF RESEARCH.
Pergamon Press, Inc., Journals Division, 660 White Plains Rd., Tarrytown, NY 10591-5153. TEL 914-524-9200. FAX 914-333-2444. *1603*

CONTRACEPTION.
Butterworth - Heinemann Ltd. 80 Montvale Ave., Stoneham, MA 02180. TEL 617-438-8464. FAX 617-438-1479. *596*

CONTRACEPTIVE TECHNOLOGY UPDATE.
American Health Consultants, Inc., Six Piedmont Center, Ste. 400, 3525 Piedmont Rd., N.E., Atlanta, GA 30305. TEL 404-262-7436. FAX 800-284-3291. *596*

CONTRIBUTIONS FROM THE NEW YORK BOTANICAL GARDEN.
New York Botanical Garden, Scientific Publications Department, Bronx, NY 10458. TEL 212-220-8721. FAX 212-220-6504. *500*

CONTRIBUTIONS IN MARINE SCIENCE - MONOGRAPHIC SERIES.
University of Texas at Austin, Marine Science Institute, Box 1267, Port Aransas, TX 78373-1267. TEL 512-749-6723. FAX 512-749-6725. *435*

CONTRIBUTIONS IN SCIENCE.
Natural History Museum of Los Angeles County, 900 Exposition Blvd., Los Angeles, CA 90007. TEL 213-744-3330. FAX 213-742-0730. *4306*

CONTRIBUTIONS TO ECONOMIC ANALYSIS.
Elsevier Science Publishers B.V., Books Division, P.O. Box 211, 1000 AE Amsterdam, Netherlands. TEL 020-5803911. FAX 020-5803705. *890*

CONTRIBUTIONS TO MINERALOGY AND PETROLOGY.
Springer-Verlag, Heidelberger Platz 3, D-1000 Berlin 33, Germany. TEL 030-8207-1. *1558*

CONTROLLED CLINICAL TRIALS.
Elsevier Science Publishing Co., Inc. (New York), (Society for Clinical Trials) 655 Ave. of the Americas, New York, NY 10010. TEL 212-989-5800. FAX 212-633-3965. *3258*

CONVULSIVE THERAPY.
Raven Press, 1185 Ave. of the Americas, New York, NY 10036. TEL 212-930-9500. FAX 212-869-3495. *3334*

COOPERATIVES ET DEVELOPPEMENT.
Centre Interuniversitaire de Recherche d'Information et d'Ensiegnement sur les Cooperatives, 5255 av. Decelles, Montreal, Que. H3T 1V6, Canada. TEL 514-340-6016. FAX 514-340-5639. *830*

COORDINATION CHEMISTRY REVIEWS.
Elsevier Science Publishers B.V., P.O. Box 211, 1000 AE Amsterdam, Netherlands. TEL 020-5803911. FAX 020-5803598. *1175*

COPEIA.
American Society of Ichthyologists and Herpetologists, c/o Dr. Brooks M. Burr, Sec., Department of Zoology, Southern Illinois University, Carbondale, IL 62901-6501. TEL 618-453-4112. *580*

COPING WITH MEDICAL ISSUES.
Elsevier Science Publishers B.V., Books Division, P.O. Box 211, 1000 AE Amsterdam, Netherlands. TEL 020-5803911. FAX 020-5803705. *3091*

CORE JOURNALS IN CARDIOLOGY.
Elsevier Science Publishers B.V., P.O. Box 211, 1000 AE Amsterdam, Netherlands. TEL 020-5803911. FAX 020-5803598. *3168*

CORE JOURNALS IN CLINICAL NEUROLOGY.
Elsevier Science Publishers B.V., P.O. Box 211, 1000 AE Amsterdam, Netherlands. TEL 020-5803911. FAX 020-5803598. *3168*

CORE JOURNALS IN DERMATOLOGY.
Elsevier Science Publishers B.V., P.O. Box 211, 1000 AE Amsterdam, Netherlands. TEL 020-5803911. FAX 020-5803598. *3168*

CORE JOURNALS IN GASTROENTEROLOGY.
Elsevier Science Publishers B.V., P.O. Box 211, 1000 AE Amsterdam, Netherlands. TEL 020-5803911. FAX 020-5803598. *3168*

CORE JOURNALS IN OBSTETRICS - GYNECOLOGY.
Elsevier Science Publishers B.V., P.O. Box 211, 1000 AE Amsterdam, Netherlands. TEL 020-5803911. FAX 020-5803598. *3169*

CORE JOURNALS IN OPHTHALMOLOGY.
Elsevier Science Publishers B.V., P.O. Box 211, 1000 AE Amsterdam, Netherlands. TEL 020-5803911. FAX 020-5803598. *3169*

CORE JOURNALS IN PEDIATRICS.
Elsevier Science Publishers B.V., P.O. Box 211, 1000 AE Amsterdam, Netherlands. TEL 020-5803911. FAX 020-5803598. *3169*

CORNELL BIENNIAL ELECTRICAL ENGINEERING CONFERENCE.
Cornell University, School of Electrical Engineering, (Institute of Electrical and Electronics Engineers, Inc.) Phillips Hall, Ithaca, NY 14853. *1885*

CORNELL HOTEL & RESTAURANT ADMINISTRATION QUARTERLY.
Elsevier Science Publishing Co., Inc. (New York), (Cornell University, School of Hotel Administration) Box 882, Madison Sq. Sta., New York, NY 10159. TEL 212-989-5800. FAX 212-633-3965. *2473*

CORNELL VETERINARIAN.
Cornell Veterinarian, Inc., Ithaca, NY 14853. *4808*

CORPORATE MANAGEMENT.
Institute of Corporate Managers, Secretaries and Administrators Ltd., G.P.O. Box 1594, Sydney, N.S.W. 2001, Australia. TEL 61-2-223-5744. FAX 61-2-232-7174. *1006*

CORRECTIVE AND SOCIAL PSYCHIATRY AND JOURNAL OF BEHAVIORAL TECHNOLOGY METHODS AND THERAPY.
Martin Psychiatric Research Foundation, Box 3365, Fairfield, CA 94533-0587. FAX 7078640910. *4017*

CORROSION.
National Association of Corrosion Engineers (NACE), Box 218340, Houston, TX 77218. TEL 713-492-0535. FAX 713-492-8254. *1928*

CORROSION ABSTRACTS.
National Association of Corrosion Engineers (NACE), Box 218340, Houston, TX 77218. TEL 713-492-0535. FAX 713-492-8254. *1842*

CORROSION SCIENCE.
Pergamon Press, Inc., Journals Division, (Institute of Corrosion) 660 White Plains Rd., Tarrytown, NY 10591-5153. TEL 914-524-9200. FAX 914-333-2444. *3405*

CORRUGATED CONTAINERS CONFERENCE (YEAR).
Technical Association of the Pulp and Paper Industry, Inc., Technology Park-Atlanta, Box 105113, Atlanta, GA 30348. TEL 404-446-1400. FAX 404-446-6947. *3648*

COSMETIC SCIENCE AND TECHNOLOGY SERIES.
Marcel Dekker, Inc., 270 Madison Ave., New York, NY 10016. TEL 212-696-9000. FAX 212-685-4540. *3091*

COSMIC RESEARCH.
Plenum Publishing Corp., Consultants Bureau, (Russian Academy of Sciences) 233 Spring St., New York, NY 10013-1578. TEL 212-620-8468. FAX 212-463-0742. *1818*

CRANIO: JOURNAL OF CRANIOMANDIBULAR PRACTICE.
Williams & Wilkins, 428 E. Preston St., Baltimore, MD 21202. TEL 301-528-4000. FAX 301-528-4312. *3091*

CRIME AND JUSTICE.
University of Chicago Press, Journals Division, 5720 S. Woodlawn Ave., Chicago, IL 60637. TEL 312-702-7600. *1512*

CRIMINAL LAW BULLETIN.
Warren, Gorham and Lamont, One Penn Plaza, New York, NY 10119. TEL 800-950-1205. FAX 212-971-5240. *2712*

CRIMINAL LAW FORUM.
Rutgers University, School of Law - Camden, 5th & Penn Streets, Camden, NJ 08102. TEL 609-757-6352. FAX 609-757-6487. *1513*

CRITICAL CARE MEDICINE.
Williams & Wilkins, (Society of Critical Care Medicine) 428 E. Preston St., Baltimore, MD 21202. TEL 301-528-4000. FAX 301-528-4312. *3091*

CRITICAL CARE NURSE.
American Association of Critical Care Nurses, 101 Columbia, Aliso Viejo, CA 92656. TEL 714-362-2000. *3277*

CRITICAL INQUIRY.
University of Chicago Press, Journals Division, 5720 S. Woodlawn Ave., Chicago, IL 60637. TEL 312-753-3347. FAX 312-702-0694. *2863*

CRITICAL ISSUES IN DEVELOPMENTAL & BEHAVIORAL PEDIATRICS.
Plenum Publishing Corp., 233 Spring St., New York, NY 10013-1578. TEL 212-620-8000. FAX 212-463-0742. *4018*

CRITICAL REVIEWS IN BIOCHEMISTRY AND MOLECULAR BIOLOGY.
C R C Press, Inc., 2000 Corporate Blvd., N.W., Boca Raton, FL 33431. TEL 407-994-0555. FAX 407-998-9784. *475*

CRITICAL REVIEWS IN BIOMEDICAL ENGINEERING.
C R C Press, Inc., 2000 Corporate Blvd., N.W., Boca Raton, FL 33431. TEL 407-994-0555. FAX 407-998-9784. *469*

CRITICAL REVIEWS IN BIOTECHNOLOGY.
C R C Press, Inc., 2000 Corporate Blvd., N.W., Boca Raton, FL 33431. TEL 407-994-0555. FAX 407-998-9784. *489*

CRITICAL REVIEWS IN CLINICAL LABORATORY SCIENCES.
C R C Press, Inc., 2000 Corporate Blvd., N.W., Boca Raton, FL 33431. TEL 407-994-0555. FAX 407-998-9784. *3091*

CRITICAL REVIEWS IN DIAGNOSTIC IMAGING.
C R C Press, Inc., 2000 Corporate Blvd., N.W., Boca Raton, FL 33431. TEL 407-994-0555. FAX 407-998-9784. *3357*

CRITICAL REVIEWS IN IMMUNOLOGY.
C R C Press, Inc., 2000 Corporate Blvd., N.W., Boca Raton, FL 33431. TEL 407-994-0555. FAX 407-998-9784. *3184*

CRITICAL REVIEWS IN MICROBIOLOGY.
C R C Press, Inc., 2000 Corporate Blvd., N.W., Boca Raton, FL 33431. TEL 407-994-0555. FAX 407-998-9784. *550*

CRITICAL REVIEWS IN ONCOLOGY - HEMATOLOGY.
Elsevier Science Publishers B.V., P.O. Box 211, 1000 AE Amsterdam, Netherlands. TEL 020-5803911. FAX 020-5803598. *3196*

CRITICAL REVIEWS IN PLANT SCIENCES.
C R C Press, Inc., 2000 Corporate Blvd., N.W., Boca Raton, FL 33431. TEL 407-994-0555. FAX 407-998-9784. *174*

CRITICAL REVIEWS IN TOXICOLOGY.
C R C Press, Inc., 2000 Corporate Blvd., N.W., Boca Raton, FL 33431. TEL 407-994-0555. FAX 407-998-9784. *1981*

CRITIQUE: STUDIES IN MODERN FICTION.
Heldref Publications, (Helen Dwight Reid Educational Foundation) 1319 Eighteenth St., N.W., Washington, DC 20036-1802. TEL 202-296-6267. FAX 202-296-5149. *2909*

CROP PROTECTION.
Butterworth - Heinemann Ltd. Linacre House, Jordan Hill, Oxford OX2 8DP, England. TEL 0865-310366. FAX 0865-310898. *174*

CRYOBIOLOGY.
Academic Press, Inc., Journal Division, (Society for Cryobiology) 1250 Sixth Ave., San Diego, CA 92101. TEL 619-230-1840. FAX 619-699-6800. *485*

CRYOGENICS.
Butterworth - Heinemann Ltd. Linacre House, Jordan Hill, Oxford OX2 8 DP, England. TEL 0865-310366. FAX 0865-310898. *3840*

CRYSTALLOGRAPHY REVIEWS.
Gordon & Breach Science Publishers, 270 Eighth Ave., New York, NY 10011. TEL 212-206-8900. FAX 212-645-2459. *1210*

CUADERNOS DE ECONOMIA.
Pontificia Universidad Catolica de Chile, Instituto de Economia, Casilla 274-V, Correo 21, Santiago, Chile. FAX 56-2-5525692. *658*

CUIHUA XUEBAO.
Science Press, Marketing and Sales Department, (Chinese Academy of Sciences, Dalian Institute of Chemical Physics) 16 Donghuangchenggen Beijie, Beijing 100707, People's Republic of China. TEL 4010642. FAX 4012180. *1213*

CURRENT (WASHINGTON, 1960).
Heldref Publications, (Helen Dwight Reid Educational Foundation) 1319 Eighteenth St., N.W., Washington, DC 20036-1802. TEL 202-296-6267. FAX 202-296-5149. *1624*

CURRENT ADVANCES IN APPLIED MICROBIOLOGY & BIOTECHNOLOGY.
Pergamon Press, Inc., Journals Division, 660 White Plains Rd., Tarrytown, NY 10591-5153. TEL 914-524-9200. FAX 914-333-2444. *464*

CURRENT ADVANCES IN CANCER RESEARCH.
Pergamon Press, Inc., Journals Division, 660 White Plains Rd., Tarrytown, NY 10591-5153. TEL 914-524-9200. FAX 914-333-2444. *3169*

CURRENT ADVANCES IN CELL AND DEVELOPMENTAL BIOLOGY.
Pergamon Press, Inc., Journals Division, 660 White Plains Rd., Tarrytown, NY 10591-5153. TEL 914-524-9200. FAX 914-333-2444. *464*

CURRENT ADVANCES IN CLINICAL CHEMISTRY.
Pergamon Press, Inc., Journals Division, (Association of Clinical Biochemists) 660 White Plains Rd., Tarrytown, NY 10591-5153. TEL 914-524-9200. FAX 914-333-2444. *1200*

CURRENT ADVANCES IN ECOLOGICAL AND ENVIRONMENTAL SCIENCES.
Pergamon Press, Inc., Journals Division, 660 White Plains Rd., Tarrytown, NY 10591-5153. TEL 914-524-9200. FAX 914-333-2444. *1973*

CURRENT ADVANCES IN ENDOCRINOLOGY & METABOLISM.
Pergamon Press, Inc., Journals Division, 660 White Plains Rd., Tarrytown, NY 10591-5153. TEL 914-524-9200. FAX 914-333-2444. *3169*

CURRENT ADVANCES IN GENETICS AND MOLECULAR BIOLOGY.
Pergamon Press, Inc., Journals Division, 660 White Plains Rd., Tarrytown, NY 10591-5153. TEL 914-524-9200. FAX 914-333-2444. *464*

CURRENT ADVANCES IN IMMUNOLOGY & INFECTIOUS DISEASES.
Pergamon Press, Inc., Journals Division, 660 White Plains Rd., Tarrytown, NY 10591-5153. TEL 914-524-9200. FAX 914-333-2444. *3169*

CURRENT ADVANCES IN NEUROSCIENCE.
Pergamon Press, Inc., Journals Division, 660 White Plains Rd., Tarrytown, NY 10591-5153. TEL 914-524-9200. FAX 914-333-2444. *3169*

CURRENT ADVANCES IN PLANT SCIENCE.
Pergamon Press, Inc., Journals Division, 660 White Plains Rd., Tarrytown, NY 10591-5153. TEL 914-524-9200. FAX 914-333-2444. *464*

CURRENT ADVANCES IN PROTEIN BIOCHEMISTRY.
Pergamon Press, Inc., Journals Division, 660 White Plains Rd., Tarrytown, NY 10591-5153. TEL 914-524-9200. FAX 914-333-2444. *464*

CURRENT ADVANCES IN TOXICOLOGY.
Pergamon Press, Inc., Journals Division, 660 White Plains Rd., Tarrytown, NY 10591-5153. TEL 914-524-9200. FAX 914-333-2444. *3747*

CURRENT ANTHROPOLOGY.
University of Chicago Press, Journals Division, (Wenner-Gren Foundation for Anthropological Research) 5720 S. Woodlawn Ave., Chicago, IL 60637. TEL 312-753-3347. *238*

CURRENT AWARENESS ABSTRACTS.
Vibration Institute, 6262 S. Kingery Hwy., Ste. 212, Willowbrook, IL 60514. TEL 708-654-2254. FAX 708-654-2271. *1842*

CURRENT AWARENESS IN BIOLOGICAL SCIENCES.
Pergamon Press, Inc., Journals Division, 660 White Plains Rd., Tarrytown, NY 10591-5153. TEL 914-524-9200. FAX 914-333-2444. *464*

CURRENT AWARENESS PROFILE ON QUANTUM CHEMISTRY.
Indiana University, Department of Chemistry, Bloomington, IN 47405. TEL 812-335-4784. FAX 812-855-5678. *1175*

CURRENT CHEMICAL CONCEPTS.
Academic Press, Inc., 1250 Sixth Ave., San Diego, CA 92101. TEL 619-231-0926. FAX 619-669-6715. *1175*

CURRENT CLINICAL PRACTICE.
Elsevier Science Publishers B.V., Books Division, P.O. Box 211, 1000 AE Amsterdam, Netherlands. TEL 020-5803911. FAX 020-5803705. *3092*

CURRENT COMMUNICATIONS IN CELL AND MOLECULAR BIOLOGY SERIES.
Cold Spring Harbor Laboratory Press, Publications Department, Box 100, Cold Spring Harbor, NY 11724. TEL 800-843-4388. FAX 516-349-1946. *551*

CURRENT ENDOCRINOLOGY.
Elsevier Science Publishers B.V., Books Division, P.O. Box 211, 1000 AE Amsterdam, Netherlands. TEL 020-5803911. FAX 020-5803705. *3251*

CURRENT MAMMALOGY.
Plenum Publishing Corp., 233 Spring St., New York, NY 10013-1578. TEL 212-620-8000. FAX 212-463-0742. *581*

CURRENT ORNITHOLOGY.
Plenum Publishing Corp., 233 Spring St., New York, NY 10013-1578. TEL 212-620-8000. FAX 212-463-0742. *563*

CURRENT PSYCHOLOGY (NEW BRUNSWICK).
Transaction Publishers, Transaction Periodicals Consortium, Department 3092, Rutgers University, New Brunswick, NJ 08903. TEL 908-932-2280. FAX 908-932-3138. *4018*

CURRENT SURGERY.
J.B. Lippincott Co., (Association of Program Directors in Surgery) E. Washington Sq., Philadelphia, PA 19105. TEL 215-238-4200. *3378*

CURRENT THERAPEUTIC RESEARCH.
Excerpta Medica, Inc., Core Publishing Division 105 Raider Blvd., Belle Mead, NJ 08502-1510. TEL 908-874-8550. FAX 908-874-5633. *3092*

CURRENT TOPICS IN BIOENERGETICS.
Academic Press, Inc., 1250 Sixth Ave., San Diego, CA 92101. TEL 619-231-0926. FAX 619-669-6715. *485*

CURRENT TOPICS IN CELLULAR REGULATION.
Academic Press, Inc. 1250 Sixth Ave., San Diego, CA 92101. TEL 619-231-0926. FAX 619-669-6715. *436*

CURRENT TOPICS IN CHINESE SCIENCE. SECTION A: PHYSICS.
Gordon & Breach Science Publishers, P.O. Box 90, Reading, Berkshire RG1 8JL, England. TEL 0734-560-080. FAX 0734-568-211. *3816*

CURRENT TOPICS IN CHINESE SCIENCE. SECTION B: CHEMISTRY.
Gordon & Breach Science Publishers, P.O. Box 90, Reading, Berkshire RG1 8JL, England. TEL 0734-560-080. FAX 0734-568-211. *1175*

CURRENT TOPICS IN CHINESE SCIENCE. SECTION C: MATHEMATICS.
Gordon & Breach Science Publishers, P.O. Box 90, Reading, Berkshire RG1 8JL, England. TEL 0734-560-080. FAX 0734-568-211. *3033*

CURRENT TOPICS IN CHINESE SCIENCE. SECTION D: BIOLOGY.
Gordon & Breach Science Publishers, P.O. Box 90, Reading, Berkshire RG1 8JL, England. TEL 0734-560-080. FAX 0734-568-211. *436*

CURRENT TOPICS IN CHINESE SCIENCE. SECTION E: ASTRONOMY.
Gordon & Breach Science Publishers, P.O. Box 90, Reading, Berkshire RG1 8JL, England. TEL 0734-560-080. FAX 0734-568-211. *363*

CURRENT TOPICS IN CHINESE SCIENCE. SECTION F: EARTH SCIENCE.
Gordon & Breach Science Publishers, P.O. Box 90, Reading RG1 8JL, England. TEL 0734-560080. FAX 0734-568211. *1542*

CURRENT TOPICS IN CHINESE SCIENCE. SECTION G: MEDICAL SCIENCE.
Gordon & Breach Science Publishers, P.O. Box 90, Reading, Berkshire RG1 8JL, England. TEL 0734-560-080. FAX 0734-568-211. *3092*

CURRENT TOPICS IN DEVELOPMENTAL BIOLOGY.
Academic Press, Inc., 1250 Sixth Ave., San Diego, CA 92101. TEL 619-231-0926. FAX 619-699-6715. *436*

CURRENT TOPICS IN ENVIRONMENTAL AND TOXICOLOGICAL CHEMISTRY.
Gordon & Breach Science Publishers, P.O. Box 90, Reading, Berkshire RG1 8JL, England. TEL 0734-560-080. FAX 0734-568-211. *1981*

CURRENT TOPICS IN EXPERIMENTAL ENDOCRINOLOGY.
Academic Press, Inc., 1250 Sixth Ave., San Diego, CA 92101. TEL 619-231-0926. FAX 619-699-6715. *3251*

CURRENT TOPICS IN MATERIALS SCIENCE.
Elsevier Science Publishers B.V., Books Division, P.O. Box 211, 1006 AE Amsterdam, Netherlands. TEL 020-5803911. FAX 020-5803705. *3817*

CURRENT TOPICS IN MEMBRANES AND TRANSPORT.
Academic Press, Inc., 1250 Sixth Ave., San Diego, CA 92101. TEL 619-231-0926. FAX 619-699-6715. *524*

CURRENT TOPICS IN NUTRITION AND DISEASE.
Wiley-Liss, Inc., 41 E. 11th St., New York, NY 10003. TEL 212-475-7700. *3604*

CURRENT TOPICS IN REMOTE SENSING.
Gordon and Breach Scientific Publishers, 270 Eighth Ave., New York, NY 10011. TEL 212-206-8900. FAX 212-645-2459. *2245*

CURRENT TOPICS OF CONTEMPORARY THOUGHT.
Gordon & Breach Science Publishers, 270 Eighth Ave., New York, NY 10011. TEL 212-206-8900. FAX 212-645-2459. *4306*

CURRICULUM INQUIRY.
Basil Blackwell Inc., (University of Toronto, Ontario Institute for Studies in Education) 3 Cambridge Center, Cambridge, MA 02142. TEL 617-225-0430. *1747*

CUTIS.
Cahners Publishing Company (New York), Medical-Health Care Group Division of Reed Publishing (USA) Inc., 249 W. 17th St., New York, NY 10011. TEL 212-645-0067. FAX 212-242-6987. *3247*

CYBERNETICS AND SYSTEMS (BRISTOL).
Hemisphere Publishing Corporation (Austrian Society for Cybernetic Studies) 1900 Frost Rd., Ste. 101, Bristol, PA 19007-1598. TEL 215-785-5800. FAX 215-785-5515. *1440*

CYBERNETICS AND SYSTEMS (NEW YORK).
Gordon & Breach Science Publishers, 270 Eighth Ave., New York, NY 10011. TEL 212-206-8900. FAX 212-645-2459. *1441*

CYBERNETICS AND SYSTEMS ANALYSIS.
Plenum Publishing Corp., Consultants Bureau, (Ukrainian Academy of Sciences) 233 Spring St., New York, NY 10013-1578. TEL 212-620-8468. FAX 212-463-0742. *1441*

CZECHOSLOVAK JOURNAL OF PHYSICS.
Plenum Publishing Corp., (Czechoslovak Academy of Sciences, Institute of Physics) 233 Spring St., New York, NY 10013-1578. TEL 212-620-8000. FAX 212-463-0742. *3817*

CZECHOSLOVAK MATHEMATICAL JOURNAL.
Plenum Publishing Corp., (Czechoslovak Academy of Sciences, Mathematical Institute) 233 Spring St., New York, NY 10013-1578. TEL 212-620-8000. FAX 212-463-0742. *3033*

C1 MOLECULE CHEMISTRY.
Harwood Academic Publishers, 270 Eighth Ave., New York, NY 10011. TEL 212-206-8900. FAX 212-645-2459. *1176*

D I C P - THE ANNALS OF PHARMACOTHERAPY.
Harvey Whitney Books Company, Box 42696, Cincinnati, OH 45242. TEL 513-793-3555. FAX 513-793-3600. *3722*

D N A AND CELL BIOLOGY.
Mary Ann Liebert, Inc., 1651 Third Ave., New York, NY 10128. TEL 212-289-2300. FAX 212-289-4697. *476*

DADI GOUZAO YU CHENGKUANGXUE.
Science Press, Marketing and Sales Department, 16 Donghuangchenggen Beijie, Beijing 100707, People's Republic of China. TEL 4010642. FAX 4012180. *1558*

DALHOUSIE UNIVERSITY. SCHOOL OF LIBRARY AND INFORMATION STUDIES. OCCASIONAL PAPERS.
Dalhousie University, School of Library and Information Studies, Halifax, N.S. B3H 4H8, Canada. TEL 902-494-3656. FAX 902-494-2319. *2797*

DAQI KEXUE.
Science Press, Marketing and Sales Department, (Chinese Academy of Sciences, Institute of Atmospheric Physics) 16 Donghuangchenggen Beijie, Beijing 100707, People's Republic of China. TEL 4010642. FAX 4012180. *3434*

DATA & KNOWLEDGE ENGINEERING.
North-Holland P.O. Box 211, 1000 AE Amsterdam, Netherlands. TEL 020-5803911. FAX 020-5803598. *1394*

DATA HANDLING IN SCIENCE AND TECHNOLOGY.
Elsevier Science Publishers B.V., Books Division, P.O. Box 211, 1000 AE Amsterdam, Netherlands. TEL 020-5803911. FAX 020-5803705. *1444*

DATABASE TECHNOLOGY.
Pergamon Press, Inc., Journals Division, 660 White Plains Rd., Tarrytown, NY 10591-5153. TEL 914-524-9200. FAX 914-333-2444. *1444*

DAXUE HUAXUE.
Zhongguo Huaxue Xuehui, Daxue Huaxue Bianjibu, Beijing Daxue - Beijing University, Haidian-qu, Beijing 100871, People's Republic of China. TEL 282471. *1176*

DAY CARE AND EARLY EDUCATION.
Human Sciences Press, Inc. 233 Spring St., New York, NY 10013-1578. TEL 212-620-8000. FAX 212-463-0742. *4403*

DEATH STUDIES.
Hemisphere Publishing Corporation 1900 Frost Rd., Ste. 101, Bristol, PA 19007-1598. TEL 215-785-5800. FAX 215-785-5515. *4018*

DECISION SUPPORT SYSTEMS.
North-Holland P.O. Box 211, 1000 AE Amsterdam, Netherlands. TEL 020-5803911. FAX 020-5803598. *1007*

DECUBITUS.
S - N Publications, Inc., 103 N. Second St., Ste. 200, W. Dundee, IL 60118. TEL 708-426-6100. FAX 708-426-6146. *3247*

DEEP-SEA RESEARCH. PART A: OCEANOGRAPHIC RESEARCH PAPERS.
Pergamon Press, Inc., Journals Division, 660 White Plains Rd., Tarrytown, NY 10591-5153. TEL 914-524-9200. FAX 914-333-2444. *1603*

REFEREED SERIALS

DEEP-SEA RESEARCH. PART B: OCEANOGRAPHIC LITERATURE REVIEW.
Pergamon Press, Inc., Journals Division, 660 White Plains Rd., Tarrytown, NY 10591-5153. TEL 914-524-9200. FAX 914-333-2444. *1550*

DEFECTS IN SOLIDS.
Elsevier Science Publishers B.V., Books Division, P.O. Box 211, 1000 AE Amsterdam, Netherlands. TEL 020-5803911. FAX 020-5803705. *1210*

DEMOGRAPHIC MONOGRAPHS.
Gordon & Breach Science Publishers, 270 Eighth Ave., New York, NY 10011. TEL 212-206-8900. FAX 212-645-2459. *3981*

DENTO MAXILLO FACIAL RADIOLOGY.
Butterworth - Heinemann Ltd. (International Association of Dento Maxillo Facial Radiology) Linacre House, Jordan Hill, Oxford OX2 8DP, England. TEL 0865-310366. FAX 0865-310898. *3358*

THE DEPARTMENT CHAIR.
Anker Publishing Company, Inc., 176 Ballville Rd., Box 249, Bolton, MA 01740-0249. TEL 508-779-6190. FAX 508-779-6296. *1726*

DERMATOLOGY NURSING.
Anthony J. Jannetti, Inc., (Dermatology Nurses' Association) North Woodbury Road, Box 56, Pitman, NJ 08071. TEL 609-589-2319. *3247*

DERMATOLOGY SERIES.
Marcel Dekker, Inc., 270 Madison Ave., New York, NY 10016. TEL 212-696-9000. FAX 212-685-4540. *3247*

DESALINATION.
Elsevier Science Publishers B.V., P.O. Box 211, 1000 AE Amsterdam, Netherlands. TEL 020-5803911. FAX 020-5803598. *4823*

DESIGN FOR ARTS IN EDUCATION.
Heldref Publications, (Helen Dwight Reid Educational Foundation) 1319 Eighteenth St., N.W., Washington, DC 20036-1802. TEL 202-296-6267. FAX 202-296-5149. *324*

DESIGN NEWS.
Cahners Publishing Company (Newton) Division of Reed Publishing (USA) Inc., 275 Washington St., Newton, MA 02158-1630. TEL 617-964-3030. FAX 617-558-4402. *4596*

DESIGN STUDIES.
Butterworth - Heinemann Ltd. Linacre House, Jordan Hill, Oxford OX2 8DP, England. TEL 0865-310366. FAX 0865-310898. *298*

DEVELOPMENT COMMUNICATION REPORT.
Clearinghouse on Development Communication, (Institute for International Research) 1815 N. Ft. Myer Dr., Ste. 600, Arlington, VA 22209. TEL 703-527-5546. FAX 703-527-4661. *4596*

DEVELOPMENT, GROWTH AND DIFFERENTIATION.
Business Center for Academic Societies Japan, 16-9, Honkomagome 5-chome, Bunkyo-ku, Tokyo 113, Japan. TEL 81-3-5814-5811. FAX 81-3-5814-5822. *436*

DEVELOPMENT IN MAMMALS.
Elsevier Science Publishers B.V., Books Division, P.O. Box 211, 1000 AE Amsterdam, Netherlands. TEL 020-5803911. FAX 020-5803705. *581*

DEVELOPMENTAL AND COMPARATIVE IMMUNOLOGY.
Pergamon Press, Inc., Journals Division, (International Society of Developmental and Comparative Immunology) 660 White Plains Rd., Tarrytown, NY 10591-5153. TEL 914-524-9200. FAX 914-333-2444. *3184*

DEVELOPMENTAL BIOLOGY.
Academic Press, Inc., Journal Division, 1250 Sixth Ave., San Diego, CA 92101. TEL 619-230-1840. FAX 619-699-6800. *436*

DEVELOPMENTAL DYNAMICS.
John Wiley & Sons, Inc., Journals, 605 Third Ave., New York, NY 10158. TEL 212-850-6000. FAX 212-850-6088. *436*

DEVELOPMENTAL GENETICS.
John Wiley & Sons, Inc., Journals, 605 Third Ave., New York, NY 10158. TEL 212-850-6000. FAX 212-850-6088. *541*

DEVELOPMENTAL IMMUNOLOGY.
Harwood Academic Publishers, 270 Eighth Ave., New York, NY 10011. TEL 212-206-8900. FAX 212-645-2459. *3184*

DEVELOPMENTAL NEUROPSYCHOLOGY.
Lawrence Erlbaum Associates, Inc., 365 Broadway, Hillsdale, NJ 07642. TEL 201-666-4100. FAX 201-666-2394. *4019*

DEVELOPMENTAL PSYCHOBIOLOGY.
John Wiley & Sons, Inc., Journals, (International Society for Developmental Psychology) 605 Third Ave, New York, NY 10158-0012. TEL 212-692-6000. *436*

DEVELOPMENTAL PSYCHOLOGY.
American Psychological Association, 750 First St., N.E., Washington, DC 20002-4242. TEL 202-336-5500. FAX 202-336-5568. *4019*

DEVELOPMENTAL REVIEW.
Academic Press, Inc., Journal Division, 1250 Sixth Ave., San Diego, CA 92101. TEL 619-230-1840. FAX 619-699-6800. *4019*

DEVELOPMENTS IN AGRICULTURAL AND MANAGED FOREST ECOLOGY.
Elsevier Science Publishers B.V., Books Division, P.O. Box 211, 1000 AE Amsterdam, Netherlands. TEL 020-5803911. FAX 020-5803705. *2098*

DEVELOPMENTS IN AGRICULTURAL ECONOMICS.
Elsevier Science Publishers B.V., Books Division, P.O. Box 211, 1000 AE Amsterdam, Netherlands. TEL 020-5803911. FAX 020-5803705. *149*

DEVELOPMENTS IN AGRICULTURAL ENGINEERING.
Elsevier Science Publishers B.V., Books Division, P.O. Box 211, 1000 AE Amsterdam, Netherlands. TEL 020-5803911. FAX 020-5803705. *175*

DEVELOPMENTS IN ANIMAL AND VETERINARY SCIENCES.
Elsevier Science Publishers B.V., Books Division, P.O. Box 211, 1000 AE Amsterdam, Netherlands. TEL 020-5803911. FAX 020-5803705. *4808*

DEVELOPMENTS IN AQUACULTURE AND FISHERIES SCIENCE.
Elsevier Science Publishers B.V., Books Division, P.O. Box 211, 1000 AE Amsterdam, Netherlands. TEL 020-5803911. FAX 020-5803705. *581*

DEVELOPMENTS IN ATMOSPHERIC SCIENCE.
Elsevier Science Publishers B.V., Books Division, P.O. Box 211, 1000 AE Amsterdam, Netherlands. TEL 020-5803911. FAX 020-5803705. *3435*

DEVELOPMENTS IN BIOCHEMISTRY.
Elsevier Science Publishers B.V., Books Division, P.O. Box 211, 1000 AE Amsterdam, Netherlands. TEL 020-5803911. FAX 020-5803705. *476*

DEVELOPMENTS IN BIOENERGETICS AND BIOMEMBRANES.
Elsevier Science Publishers B.V., Books Division, P.O. Box 211, 1000 AE Amsterdam, Netherlands. TEL 020-5803911. FAX 020-5803705. *469*

DEVELOPMENTS IN CANCER RESEARCH.
Elsevier Science Publishers B.V., Books Division, P.O. Box 211, 1000 AE Amsterdam, Netherlands. TEL 020-5803911. FAX 020-5803705. *3196*

DEVELOPMENTS IN CIVIL ENGINEERING.
Elsevier Science Publishers B.V., Books Division, P.O. Box 211, 1000 AE Amsterdam, Netherlands. TEL 020-5803911. FAX 020-5803705. *1864*

DEVELOPMENTS IN CROP SCIENCE.
Elsevier Science Publishers B.V., Books Division, P.O. Box 211, 1000 AE Amsterdam, Netherlands. TEL 020-5803911. FAX 020-5803705. *175*

DEVELOPMENTS IN ECONOMIC GEOLOGY.
Elsevier Science Publishers B.V., Books Division, P.O. Box 211, 1000 AE Amsterdam, Netherlands. TEL 020-5803911. FAX 020-5803705. *1558*

DEVELOPMENTS IN ENDOCRINOLOGY.
Elsevier Science Publishers B.V., Books Division, P.O. Box 211, 1000 AE Amsterdam, Netherlands. TEL 020-5803911. FAX 020-5803705. *3251*

DEVELOPMENTS IN ENVIRONMENTAL MODELLING.
Elsevier Science Publishers B.V., Books Division, P.O. Box 211, 1000 AE Amsterdam, Netherlands. TEL 020-5803911. FAX 020-5803705. *1947*

DEVELOPMENTS IN FOOD PRESERVATION.
Elsevier Science Publishers Ltd., Books Division, Crown House, Linton Rd., Barking, Essex IG11 8JU, England. TEL 081-594-7272. FAX 081-594-5942. *2066*

DEVELOPMENTS IN FOOD PROTEINS.
Elsevier Science Publishers Ltd., Books Division, Crown House, Linton Rd., Barking, Essex IG11 8JU, England. TEL 081-594-7272. FAX 081-594-5942. *2066*

DEVELOPMENTS IN FOOD SCIENCE.
Elsevier Science Publishers B.V., Books Division, P.O. Box 211, 1000 AE Amsterdam, Netherlands. TEL 020-5803911. FAX 020-5803705. *1218*

DEVELOPMENTS IN GEOCHEMISTRY.
Elsevier Science Publishers B.V., Books Division, P.O. Box 211, 1000 AE Amsterdam, Netherlands. TEL 020-5803911. FAX 020-5803705. *1558*

DEVELOPMENTS IN GEOMATHEMATICS.
Elsevier Science Publishers B.V., Books Division, P.O. Box 211, 1000 AE Amsterdam, Netherlands. TEL 020-5803911. FAX 020-5803705. *1588*

DEVELOPMENTS IN GEOTECHNICAL ENGINEERING.
Elsevier Science Publishers B.V., Books Division, P.O. Box 211, 1000 AE Amsterdam, Netherlands. TEL 020-5803911. FAX 020-5803705. *1864*

DEVELOPMENTS IN GEOTECTONICS.
Elsevier Science Publishers B.V., Books Division, P.O. Box 211, 1000 AE Amsterdam, Netherlands. TEL 020-5803911. FAX 020-5803705. *1559*

DEVELOPMENTS IN IMMUNOLOGY.
Elsevier Science Publishers B.V., Books Division, P.O. Box 211, 1000 AE Amsterdam, Netherlands. TEL 020-5803911. FAX 020-5803705. *437*

DEVELOPMENTS IN INDUSTRIAL MICROBIOLOGY.
Elsevier Science Publishers B.V., Books Division, P.O. Box 211, 1000 AE Amsterdam, Netherlands. TEL 020-5803911. FAX 020-5803705. *551*

DEVELOPMENTS IN MARINE BIOLOGY.
Elsevier Science Publishers B.V., Books Division, P.O. Box 211, 1000 AE Amsterdam, Netherlands. TEL 020-5803911. FAX 020-5803705. *1604*

DEVELOPMENTS IN MINERAL PROCESSING.
Elsevier Science Publishers B.V., Books Division, P.O. Box 211, 1000 AE Amsterdam, Netherlands. TEL 020-5803911. FAX 020-5803705. *1559*

DEVELOPMENTS IN NANOTECHNOLOGY.
Gordon and Breach Scientific Publishers, 270 Eighth Ave., New York, NY 10011. TEL 212-206-8900. FAX 212-645-2459. *3817*

DEVELOPMENTS IN NEUROSCIENCE.
Elsevier Science Publishers B.V., Books Division, P.O. Box 211, 1000 AE Amsterdam, Netherlands. TEL 020-5803911. FAX 020-5803705. *3335*

DEVELOPMENTS IN PALAEONTOLOGY AND STRATIGRAPHY.
Elsevier Science Publishers B.V., Books Division, P.O. Box 211, 1000 AE Amsterdam, Netherlands. TEL 020-5803911. FAX 020-5803705. *3657*

DEVELOPMENTS IN PETROLEUM SCIENCE.
Elsevier Science Publishers B.V., Books Division, P.O. Box 211, 1000 AE Amsterdam, Netherlands. TEL 020-5803911. FAX 020-5803705. *3684*

DEVELOPMENTS IN PETROLOGY.
Elsevier Science Publishers B.V., Books Division, P.O. Box 211, 1000 AE Amsterdam, Netherlands. TEL 020-5803911. FAX 020-5803705. *1559*

DEVELOPMENTS IN PLANT BIOLOGY.
Elsevier Science Publishers B.V., Books Division, P.O. Box 211, 1000 AE Amsterdam, Netherlands. TEL 020-5803911. FAX 020-5803705. *500*

DEVELOPMENTS IN PRECAMBRIAN GEOLOGY.
Elsevier Science Publishers B.V., Books Division, P.O. Box 211, 1000 AE Amsterdam, Netherlands. TEL 020-5803911. FAX 020-5803705. *1559*

DEVELOPMENTS IN PSYCHIATRY.
Elsevier Science Publishers B.V., Books Division, P.O. Box 211, 1000 AE Amsterdam, Netherlands. TEL 020-5803911. FAX 020-5803705. *3335*

DEVELOPMENTS IN RUBBER TECHNOLOGY.
Elsevier Science Publishers Ltd., Books Division, Crown House, Linton Rd., Barking, Essex IG11 8JU, England. TEL 081-594-7272. FAX 081-594-5942. *4291*

DEVELOPMENTS IN SEDIMENTOLOGY.
Elsevier Science Publishers B.V., Books Division, P.O. Box 211, 1000 AE Amsterdam, Netherlands. TEL 020-5803911. FAX 020-5803705. *1559*

DEVELOPMENTS IN SOIL SCIENCE.
Elsevier Science Publishers B.V., Books Division, P.O. Box 211, 1000 AE Amsterdam, Netherlands. TEL 020-5803911. FAX 020-5803705. *176*

DEVELOPMENTS IN SOLID EARTH GEOPHYSICS.
Elsevier Science Publishers B.V., Books Division, P.O. Box 211, 1000 AE Amsterdam, Netherlands. TEL 020-5803911. FAX 020-5803705. *1588*

DEVELOPMENTS IN TOXICOLOGY AND ENVIRONMENTAL SCIENCE.
Elsevier Science Publishers B.V., Books Division, P.O. Box 211, 1000 AE Amsterdam, Netherlands. TEL 020-5803911. FAX 020-5803705. *1981*

DEVELOPMENTS IN WATER SCIENCE.
Elsevier Science Publishers B.V., Books Division, P.O. Box 211, 1000 AE Amsterdam, Netherlands. TEL 020-5803911. FAX 020-5803705. *1597*

DEVIANT BEHAVIOR.
Hemisphere Publishing Corporation 1900 Frost Rd., Ste. 101, Bristol, PA 19007-1598. TEL 215-785-5800. FAX 215-785-5515. *4433*

DIABETES.
American Diabetes Association, Inc., 1660 Duke St., Alexandria, VA 22314. TEL 703-549-1500. FAX 703-836-7439. *3251*

DIABETES ANNUAL.
Elsevier Science Publishers B.V., Books Division, P.O. Box 211, 1000 AE Amsterdam, Netherlands. TEL 020-5803911. FAX 020-5803705. *3251*

DIABETES CARE.
American Diabetes Association, Inc., 1660 Duke St., Alexandria, VA 22314. TEL 703-549-1500. FAX 703-836-7439. *3251*

DIABETES RESEARCH AND CLINICAL PRACTICE.
Elsevier Science Publishers B.V., (International Diabetes Federation) P.O. Box 211, 1000 AE Amsterdam, Netherlands. TEL 020-5803911. FAX 020-5803598. *3252*

DIABETES SPECTRUM.
American Diabetes Association, Inc., 1660 Duke St., Alexandria, VA 22314. TEL 703-549-1500. FAX 703-836-7439. *3252*

THE DIABETIC TRAVELER.
Box 8223 - RW, Stamford, CT 06905. TEL 203-327-5832. *3801*

DIAGNOSTIC IMAGING & RADIOLOGY PRODUCT COMPARISON SYSTEM.
E C R I, (Emergency Care Research Institute) 5200 Butler Pike, Plymouth Meeting, PA 19462. TEL 215-825-6000. FAX 215-834-1275. *3358*

DIAGNOSTIC MICROBIOLOGY AND INFECTIOUS DISEASE.
Elsevier Science Publishing Co., Inc. (New York), 655 Ave. of the Americas, New York, NY 10010. TEL 212-989-5800. FAX 212-633-3965. *551*

DIAGNOSTIC MOLECULAR PATHOLOGY.
Raven Press, 1185 Ave. of the Americas, New York, NY 10036. TEL 212-930-9500. FAX 212-869-3495. *3094*

DIAGNOSTIC RADIOLOGY SERIES.
Marcel Dekker, Inc., 270 Madison Ave., New York, NY 10016. TEL 212-696-9000. FAX 212-685-4540. *3358*

DIALECTICAL ANTHROPOLOGY.
Kluwer Academic Publishers, Postbus 17, 3300 AA Dordrecht, Netherlands. TEL 078-334911. FAX 078-334254. *238*

DIALOGUE: CANADIAN PHILOSOPHICAL REVIEW.
Wilfrid Laurier University Press, (Canadian Philosophical Association) 75 University Ave. W., Waterloo, Ont. N2L 3C5, Canada. TEL 519-884-1970. FAX 519-884-8853. *3765*

DIALYSIS & TRANSPLANTATION.
Creative Age Publications, 7628 Densmore Ave., Van Nuys, CA 91406-2088. TEL 818-782-7328. *3387*

DIAMOND AND RELATED MATERIALS.
Elsevier Science Publishers B.V., P.O. Box 211, 1000 AE Amsterdam, Netherlands. TEL 020-5803911. FAX 020-5803598. *1210*

DIANZI KEXUE XUEKAN.
Science Press, Marketing and Sales Department, (Chinese Academy of Sciences, Institute of Electronics) 16 Donghuangchenggen Beijie, Beijing 100707, People's Republic of China. TEL 4010642. FAX 4012180. *1765*

DICENGXUE ZAZHI.
Science Press, Marketing and Sales Department, (Zhongguo Kexueyuan, Nanjing Dizhi Gushengwu Yanjiusuo) 16 Donghuangchenggen Beijie, Beijing 100707, People's Republic of China. TEL 4010642. FAX 4012180. *1559*

DIFFERENTIAL EQUATIONS.
Plenum Publishing Corp., Consultants Bureau, (Akademiya Navuk Belarusskai S.S.R.) 233 Spring St., New York, NY 10013-1578. TEL 212-620-8468. FAX 212-463-0742. *3034*

DIFFERENTIAL GEOMETRY AND ITS APPLICATIONS.
North-Holland P.O. Box 211, 1000 AE Amsterdam, Netherlands. TEL 020-5803911. FAX 020-5803598. *3034*

DIGESTIVE DISEASES AND SCIENCES.
Plenum Publishing Corp., 233 Spring St., New York, NY 10013-1578. TEL 212-620-8000. FAX 212-463-0742. *3267*

DILI KEXUE.
Science Press, Marketing and Sales Department, (Chinese Academy of Sciences, Changchun Institute of Geography) 16 Donghuangchenggen Beijie, Beijing 100707, People's Republic of China. TEL 4010642. FAX 4012180. *2246*

DILI XUEBAO.
Science Press, Marketing and Sales Press, (Zhongguo Dili Xuehui) 16 Donghuangchenggen Beijie, Beijing 100707, People's Republic of China. TEL 4010642. FAX 4012180. *2246*

DILI YANJIU.
Science Press, Marketing and Sales Department, (Chinese Academy of Sciences, Institute of Geography) 16 Donghuangchenggen Beijie, Beijing 100707, People's Republic of China. TEL 4010642. FAX 4012180. *2246*

DIMENSIONS OF CRITICAL CARE NURSING.
Hall Johnson Communications, Inc., 9737 W. Ohio Ave., Lakewood, CO 80226. TEL 303-988-0056. *3277*

DIPLOMATIC HISTORY.
Scholarly Resources, Inc., (Society for Historians of American Foreign Relations) 104 Greenhill Ave., Wilmington, DE 19805. TEL 302-654-7713. FAX 302-654-3871. *2309*

DIQIU HUAXUE.
Science Press, Marketing and Sales Department, 16 Donghuangchenggen Beijie, Beijing 100707, People's Republic of China. TEL 4010642. FAX 4012180. *1559*

DIQIU WULI XUEBAO.
Science Press, Marketing and Sales Department, (Chinese Academy of Sciences, Institute of Geophysics and Meteorology) 16 Donghuangchenggen Beijie, Beijing 100707, People's Republic of China. TEL 4010642. FAX 4012180. *1588*

DIRASAT. SERIES A: HUMANITIES.
University of Jordan, Deanship of Academic Research, Amman, Jordan. FAX 962-6-832318. *2506*

DIRASAT. SERIES B: PURE AND APPLIED SCIENCES.
University of Jordan, Deanship of Academic Research, Amman, Jordan. FAX 962-6-832318. *4307*

DIRECTORY OF UNPUBLISHED EXPERIMENTAL MENTAL MEASURES.
Human Sciences Press, Inc. 233 Spring St., New York, NY 10013-1578. TEL 212-620-8000. FAX 212-463-0742. *4019*

DISABILITY AND REHABILITATION.
Taylor & Francis Ltd., Rankine Road, Basingstoke, Hants. RG24 0PR, England. TEL 0256-840366. FAX 0256-479438. *3094*

DISCOVERIES IN PHARMACOLOGY.
Elsevier Science Publishers B.V., Books Division, P.O. Box 211, 1000 AE Amsterdam, Netherlands. TEL 020-5803911. FAX 020-5803705. *3722*

DISCOVERY (NEW HAVEN).
Peabody Museum of Natural History, Yale University, 170 Whitney Ave., Box 6666, New Haven, CT 06511-8161. TEL 203-432-3786. *4308*

DISCRETE APPLIED MATHEMATICS.
North-Holland P.O. Box 211, 1000 AE Amsterdam, Netherlands. TEL 020-5803911. FAX 020-5803598. *3034*

DISCRETE EVENT DYNAMIC SYSTEMS: THEORY & APPLICATIONS.
Kluwer Academic Publishers, Postbus 17, 3300 AA Dordrecht, Netherlands. TEL 078-334911. FAX 078-334254. *1435*

DISCRETE MATHEMATICS.
North-Holland P.O. Box 211, 1000 AE Amsterdam, Netherlands. TEL 020-5803911. FAX 020-5803598. *3034*

DISCUSSIONS IN NEUROSCIENCE.
Elsevier Science Publishers B.V., (Fondation pour l'Etude du Systeme Nerveux Central et Peripherique) P.O. Box 211, 1000 AE Amsterdam, Netherlands. TEL 020-5803911. FAX 020-5803598. *3335*

DISEASES OF THE COLON AND RECTUM.
Williams & Wilkins, (American Society of Colon and Rectal Surgeons) 428 E. Preston St., Baltimore, MD 21202. TEL 301-528-4000. FAX 301-528-4321. *3378*

DISIJI YANJIU.
Science Press, Marketing and Sales Department, (China Quaternaria Research Committee) 16 Donghuangchenggen Beijie, Beijing 100707, People's Republic of China. TEL 4010642. FAX 4012180. *1559*

DISLOCATIONS IN SOLIDS.
Elsevier Science Publishers B.V., Books Division, P.O. Box 211, 1000 AE Amsterdam, Netherlands. TEL 020-5803911. FAX 020-5803705. *3817*

DISPLAYS.
Butterworth - Heinemann Ltd. Linacre House, Jordan Hill, Oxford OX2 8DP, England. TEL 0865-310366. FAX 0865-310898. *1421*

DIWEN WULI XUEBAO.
Science Press, Marketing and Sales Department, (Zhongguo Kexue Jishu Daxue) 16 Donghuangchenggen Beijie, Beijing 100707, People's Republic of China. TEL 4010642. FAX 4012180. *3840*

DIZHEN DIZHI.
Guojia Dizhenju, Dizhi Yanjiusuo 519, Qijia Huozi, Dewai, Beijing 100029, People's Republic of China. TEL 4016611. *1588*

DIZHEN GONGCHENG YU GONGCHENG ZHENDONG.
Science Press, Marketing and Sales Department, 16 Donghuangchenggen Beijie, Beijing 100707, People's Republic of China. TEL 4010642. FAX 4012180. *1588*

DIZHEN XUEBAO.
Science Press, Marketing and Sales Department, 16 Donghuangchenggen Beijie, Beijing 100707, People's Republic of China. TEL 4010642. FAX 4012180. *1588*

DIZHI KEXUE.
Science Press, Marketing and Sales Department, 16 Donghuangchenggen Beijie, Beijing 100707, People's Republic of China. TEL 4010642. FAX 4012180. *1559*

DIZHI XUEBAO.
Science Press, Marketing and Sales Department, (Institute of Scientific and Technological Information of China) 16 Donghuangchenggen Beijie, Beijing 100707, People's Republic of China. TEL 4010642. FAX 4012180. *1559*

DOKLADY BIOCHEMISTRY.
Plenum Publishing Corp., Consultants Bureau, (Russian Academy of Sciences, Biochemistry Section) 233 Spring St., New York, NY 10013-1578. TEL 212-620-8468. FAX 212-463-0742. *476*

DOKLADY BIOLOGICAL SCIENCES.
Plenum Publishing Corp., Consultants Bureau, (Russian Academy of Sciences, Biology Section) 233 Spring St., New York, NY 10013-1578. TEL 212-620-8468. FAX 212-463-0742. *437*

DOKLADY BIOPHYSICS.
Plenum Publishing Corp., Consultants Bureau, (Russian Academy of Sciences, Biophysics Section) 233 Spring St., New York, NY 10013-1578. TEL 212-620-8468. FAX 212-463-0742. *485*

DOKLADY BOTANICAL SCIENCES.
Plenum Publishing Corp., Consultants Bureau, (Russian Academy of Sciences, Botanical Section) 233 Spring St., New York, NY 10013-1578. TEL 212-620-8468. FAX 212-463-0742. *501*

DOKLADY CHEMICAL TECHNOLOGY.
Plenum Publishing Corp., Consultants Bureau, (Russian Academy of Sciences, Chemical Technology Section) 233 Spring St., New York, NY 10013-1578. TEL 212-620-8468. FAX 212-463-0742. *1852*

DOKLADY CHEMISTRY.
Plenum Publishing Corp., Consultants Bureau, (Russian Academy of Sciences, Chemical Section) 233 Spring St., New York, NY 10013-1578. TEL 212-620-8468. FAX 212-463-0742. *1176*

DOKLADY PHYSICAL CHEMISTRY.
Plenum Publishing Corp., Consultants Bureau, (Russian Academy of Sciences, Physical Chemistry Section) 233 Spring St., New York, NY 10013-1578. TEL 212-620-8468. FAX 212-463-0742. *1225*

DOMESTIC ANIMAL ENDOCRINOLOGY.
Butterworth - Heinemann Ltd. (Auburn University, College of Veterinary Medicine) 80 Montvale Ave., Stoneham, MA 02180. TEL 617-438-8464. FAX 617-279-4851. *3252*

DONGWU FENLEI XUEBAO.
Science Press, Marketing and Sales Department, (Chinese Academy of Sciences, Institute of Zoology) 16 Donghuangchenggen Beijie, Beijing 100707, People's Republic of China. TEL 4010642. FAX 4012180. *581*

DONGWU XUEBAO.
Science Press, Marketing and Sales Department, (Chinese Academy of Sciences, Institute of Zoology) 16 Donghuangchenggen Beijie, Beijing 100707, People's Republic of China. TEL 4010642. FAX 4012180. *581*

DONGWUXUE ZAZHI.
Science Press, Marketing and Sales Press, (Chinese Academy of Sciences, Institute of Zoology) 16 Donghuangchenggen Beijie, Beijing 100707, People's Republic of China. TEL 4010642. FAX 4012180. *581*

DREAM SWITCHBOARD.
Dream Switchboard, (Community Dreamsharing Network) Box 8032, Hicksville, NY 11802-8032. TEL 516-796-9455. FAX 516-731-2395. *4019*

DREAMING.
Human Sciences Press, Inc. (Association for the Study of Dreams) 233 Spring St., New York, NY 10013. TEL 212-620-8000. FAX 212-463-0742. *571*

DRUG AND ALCOHOL DEPENDENCE.
Elsevier Scientific Publishers Ireland Ltd., (International Council on Alcohol and Addictions) P.O. Box 85, Limerick, Ireland. TEL 061-61944. FAX 061-62144. *1535*

DRUG AND CHEMICAL TOXICOLOGY.
Marcel Dekker Journals, 270 Madison Ave., New York, NY 10016. TEL 212-696-9000. FAX 212-685-4540. *3723*

DRUG AND CHEMICAL TOXICOLOGY SERIES.
Marcel Dekker, Inc., 270 Madison Ave., New York, NY 10016. TEL 212-696-9000. FAX 212-685-4540. *3723*

DRUG DESIGN AND DISCOVERY.
Harwood Academic Publishers, 270 Eighth Ave., New York, NY 10011. TEL 212-206-8900. FAX 212-645-2459. *3723*

DRUG DEVELOPMENT AND INDUSTRIAL PHARMACY.
Marcel Dekker Journals, 270 Madison Ave., New York, NY 10016. TEL 212-696-9000. FAX 212-685-4540. *3723*

DRUG DEVELOPMENT RESEARCH.
John Wiley & Sons, Inc., Journals, 605 Third Ave., New York, NY 10158. TEL 212-475-7700. FAX 212-850-6088. *3723*

DRUG INDUCED DISORDERS.
Elsevier Science Publishers B.V., Books Division, P.O. Box 211, 1000 AE Amsterdam, Netherlands. TEL 020-5803911. FAX 020-5803705. *1535*

DRUG INFORMATION JOURNAL.
Pergamon Press, Inc., Journals Division, (Drug Information Association) 660 White Plains Rd., Tarrytown, NY 10591-5153. TEL 914-524-9200. FAX 914-333-2444. *3723*

DRUG METABOLISM AND DISPOSITION.
Williams & Wilkins, (American Society for Pharmacology and Experimental Therapeutics, Inc.) 428 E. Preston St., Baltimore, MD 21202. TEL 301-528-4000. FAX 301-528-4312. *3723*

DRUG METABOLISM REVIEWS.
Marcel Dekker Journals, 270 Madison Ave., New York, NY 10016. TEL 212-696-9000. FAX 212-685-4540. *3095*

DRUG TARGETING AND DELIVERY.
Academic Press, Inc., Journal Division, 1250 Sixth Ave., San Diego, CA 92101. TEL 619-230-1840. FAX 619-699-6800. *3724*

DRUGS & SOCIETY.
Haworth Press, Inc., 10 Alice St., Binghamton, NY 13904. TEL 800-342-9678. FAX 607-722-1424. *1536*

DRUGS AND THE PHARMACEUTICAL SCIENCES.
Marcel Dekker, Inc., 270 Madison Ave., New York, NY 10016. TEL 212-696-9000. FAX 212-685-4540. *3724*

DRUGS IN RESEARCH.
Paul De Haen International, 2750 S. Shoshone St., Englewood, CO 80110. TEL 800-438-0296. FAX 303-789-2534. *3724*

DRYING TECHNOLOGY.
Marcel Dekker Journals, 270 Madison Ave., New York, NY 10016. TEL 212-696-9000. FAX 212-685-4540. *1225*

DUKE MATHEMATICAL JOURNAL.
Duke University Press, 6697 College Station, Durham, NC 27708. TEL 919-684-2173. FAX 919-684-8644. *3034*

DUKENGINEER.
Duke University, School of Engineering, Durham, NC 27706. TEL 919-684-2214. *1819*

DUODECIMAL BULLETIN.
Dozenal Society of America, c/o Math Department, Nassau Community College, Garden City, NY 11530. TEL 516-669-0273. *3035*

DYES AND PIGMENTS.
Elsevier Science Publishers Ltd., Crown House, Linton Rd., Barking, Essex IG11 8JU, England. TEL 081-594-7272. FAX 081-594-5942. *1176*

DYNAMIC ECONOMICS: THEORY AND APPLICATIONS (SERIES).
Elsevier Science Publishers B.V., Books Division, P.O. Box 211, 1000 AE Amsterdam, Netherlands. TEL 020-5803911. FAX 020-5803705. *659*

DYNAMICAL PROPERTIES OF SOLIDS.
Elsevier Science Publishers B.V., Books Division, P.O. Box 211, 1000 AE Amsterdam, Netherlands. TEL 020-5803911. FAX 020-5803705. *3843*

DYNAMICS AND CONTROL.
Kluwer Academic Publishers, Postbus 17, 3300 AA Dordrecht, Netherlands. TEL 078-334911. FAX 078-334254. *1437*

DYNAMICS OF ATMOSPHERES AND OCEANS.
Elsevier Science Publishers B.V., P.O. Box 211, 1000 AE Amsterdam, Netherlands. TEL 020-5803911. FAX 020-5803705. *3435*

DYSMORPHOLOGY AND CLINICAL GENETICS.
Blackwell Scientific Publications Inc., (Center for Birth Defects Information Services, Inc.) Three Cambridge Center, Ste. 280, Cambridge, MA 02142-1413. TEL 617-225-0401. FAX 617-225-0412. *541*

E A A EXPERIMENTER.
Experimental Aircraft Association, EAA Aviation Center, 3000 Poberezny Rd., Box 3086, Oshkosh, WI 54903-3086. TEL 414-426-4800. FAX 414-426-4828. *51*

E E: EVALUATION ENGINEERING.
Nelson Publishing Co., 2504 N. Tamiami Trail, Nokomis, FL 34275-3476. TEL 813-966-9521. FAX 813-966-2590. *1766*

E H P.
U.S. Department of Health and Human Services, National Institute of Environmental Health Sciences, Box 12233, Research Triangle Park, NC 27709. TEL 919-541-3406. FAX 919-541-2260. *1947*

E S C W A POPULATION BULLETIN.
United Nations Publications, (Economic and Social Commission for Western Asia, Social Development and Population Division) Room DC2-853, New York, NY 10017. *3981*

EAR AND HEARING.
Williams & Wilkins, (American Auditory Society) 428 E. Preston St., Baltimore, MD 21202. TEL 301-528-4000. FAX 301-528-4312. *3314*

EAR, NOSE AND THROAT JOURNAL.
International Publishing Group, 4959 Commerce Pkwy., Cleveland, OH 44128. TEL 800-342-6237. FAX 216-464-1835. *3314*

EARLY AMERICAN LITERATURE.
University of North Carolina Press, (University of North Carolina at Chapel Hill, Department of English) Box 2288, Chapel Hill, NC 27515-2288. TEL 919-966-3561. FAX 919-966-3829. *2913*

EARLY CHILD DEVELOPMENT AND CARE.
Gordon and Breach Science Publishers, 270 Eighth Ave., New York, NY 10011. TEL 212-206-8900. FAX 212-645-2459. *1236*

EARLY HUMAN DEVELOPMENT.
Elsevier Scientific Publishers Ireland Ltd., P.O. Box 85, Limerick, Ireland. TEL 061-61944. FAX 061-62144. *3291*

EARLY KEYBOARD STUDIES NEWSLETTER.
Westfield Center for Early Keyboard Studies, One Cottage St., Easthampton, MA 01027. TEL 413-527-7664. *3550*

EARTH AND PLANETARY SCIENCE LETTERS.
Elsevier Science Publishers B.V., P.O. Box 211, 1000 AE Amsterdam, Netherlands. TEL 020-5803911. FAX 020-5803598. *1543*

EARTH SCIENCE REVIEWS.
Elsevier Science Publishers B.V., P.O. Box 211, 1000 AE Amsterdam, Netherlands. TEL 020-5803911. FAX 020-5803598. *1543*

EAST EUROPEAN POLITICS & SOCIETIES.
University of California Press, Journals Division, (Joint Committee on Eastern Europe) 2120 Berkeley Way, Berkeley, CA 94720. TEL 510-642-4191. FAX 510-643-7127. *3891*

EAST - WEST FILM JOURNAL.
University of Hawaii Press, Journal Department, (Institute of Culture & Communication, East-West Center) 2840 Kolowalu St., Honolulu, HI 96822. TEL 808-956-8833. FAX 808-988-6052. *3508*

EASTERN EUROPEAN ECONOMICS.
M.E. Sharpe, Inc., 80 Business Park Dr., Armonk, NY 10504. TEL 914-273-1800. FAX 914-273-2106. *659*

ECOL NEWS.
Minneapolis Public Library and Information Center, 300 Nicollet Mall, Minneapolis, MN 55401. TEL 612-372-6570. *1948*

ECOLOGICAL APPLICATIONS.
Ecological Society of America (Ithaca), c/o Center for Environmental Studies, Arizona State University, Tempe, AZ 85287. TEL 602-965-3000. FAX 602-965-8087. *1948*

ECOLOGICAL ECONOMICS.
Elsevier Science Publishers B.V., (International Society for Ecological Economics) P.O. Box 211, 1000 AH Amsterdam, Netherlands. TEL 020-5803911. FAX 020-5803598. *1948*

ECOLOGICAL ENGINEERING.
Elsevier Science Publishers B.V., P.O. Box 211, 1000 AE Amsterdam, Netherlands. TEL 020-5803911. FAX 020-5803705. *1948*

ECOLOGICAL MODELLING.
Elsevier Science Publishers B.V., P.O. Box 211, 1000 AE Amsterdam, Netherlands. TEL 020-5803911. FAX 020-5803598. *1975*

ECOLOGICAL MONOGRAPHS.
Ecological Society of America, c/o Center for Environmental Studies, Arizona State University, Tempe, AZ 85287. TEL 602-965-3000. FAX 602-965-8087. *1948*

ECOLOGICAL PSYCHOLOGY.
Lawrence Erlbaum Associates, Inc., (International Society for Ecological Psychology) 365 Broadway, Hillsdale, NJ 07642. TEL 201-666-4110. FAX 201-666-2394. *4019*

ECOLOGY.
Ecological Society of America, c/o Center for Environmental Studies, Arizona State University, Tempe, AZ 85287. TEL 602-965-3000. FAX 602-965-8087. *1948*

ECOLOGY LAW QUARTERLY.
University of California Press, Journals Division, 2120 Berkeley Way, Berkeley, CA 94720. TEL 510-642-4191. FAX 510-643-7127. *2621*

ECOLOGY OF FOOD AND NUTRITION.
Gordon and Breach Science Publishers, 270 Eighth Ave., New York, NY 10011. FAX 212-645-2459. *3605*

ECONOMIC BOTANY.
New York Botanical Garden, Scientific Publications Department, (Society for Economic Botany) Bronx, NY 10458. TEL 212-220-8721. FAX 212-220-6504. *501*

ECONOMIC DEVELOPMENT AND CULTURAL CHANGE.
University of Chicago Press, Journals Division, (University of Chicago, Research Center in Economic Development and Cultural Change) 5720 S. Woodlawn Ave., Chicago, IL 60637. TEL 312-753-3347. FAX 312-702-0694. *929*

ECONOMIC MICROBIOLOGY.
Academic Press, Inc., 1250 Sixth Ave., San Diego, CA 92101. TEL 619-231-0926. FAX 619-699-6715. *551*

ECONOMIC MODELLING.
Butterworth - Heinemann Ltd. Linacre House, Jordan Hill, Oxford OX2 8DP, England. TEL 0865-310366. FAX 0865-310898. *661*

ECONOMIC PERSPECTIVES: AN ANNUAL SURVEY OF ECONOMICS.
Harwood Academic Publishers, 270 Eighth Ave., New York, NY 10011. TEL 212-206-8900. FAX 212-645-2459. *893*

ECONOMICS LETTERS.
Elsevier Sequoia S.A., P.O. Box 564, CH-1001 Lausanne, Switzerland. TEL 021-207381. FAX 021-235444. *893*

ECONOMICS OF EDUCATION REVIEW.
Pergamon Press, Inc., Journals Division, 660 White Plains Rd., Tarrytown, NY 10591-5153. TEL 914-524-9200. FAX 914-333-2444. *1726*

ECONOMICS OF INNOVATION AND NEW TECHNOLOGY.
Harwood Academic Publishers, 270 Eighth Ave., New York, NY 10011. TEL 212-206-8900. FAX 212-645-2459. *4597*

ECONOMIE ET SOCIALISME.
Centre d'Etudes et de Recherches Aziz Belal, B.P. 6330, Rabat, Morocco. TEL 77-62-17. FAX 77-38-89. *863*

ECOSYSTEMS OF THE WORLD.
Elsevier Science Publishers B.V., Books Division, P.O. Box 211, 1000 AE Amsterdam, Netherlands. TEL 020-5803911. FAX 020-5803705. *1949*

ECOTASS (ENGLISH EDITION).
Pergamon Press plc, (Russian News Agency TASS) Headington Hill Hall, Oxford OX3 0BW, England. TEL 0865-794141. FAX 0865-743911. *863*

ECOTOXICOLOGY AND ENVIRONMENTAL SAFETY.
Academic Press, Inc., Journal Division, (International Society of Ecotoxicology and Environmental Safety) 1250 Sixth Ave., San Diego, CA 92101. TEL 619-250-1840. FAX 61-699-6800. *1981*

ECQUID NOVI.
Institute for Communication Research, Potchefstroom University, Potchefstroom 2520, South Africa. TEL 0148-99-1641. FAX 0148-992799. *2569*

EDUCATION & COMPUTING.
Elsevier Science Publishers B.V., P.O. Box 211, 1000 AE Amsterdam, Netherlands. TEL 020-5803911. FAX 020-5803598. *1689*

EDUCATION AND TREATMENT OF CHILDREN.
Pro-Ed Inc., 8700 Shoal Creek Blvd., Austin, TX 78758. TEL 512-451-3246. FAX 512-451-8542. *1748*

EDUCATION FOR LIBRARIANSHIP: AUSTRALIA.
Australian Library and Information Association, P.O. Box E441, Queen Victoria Terrace, A.C.T. 2600, Australia. TEL 06-285-1877. FAX 06-282-2249. *2756*

EDUCATIONAL ADMINISTRATION QUARTERLY.
Corwin Press, Inc. (University Council for Educational Administration) 2455 Teller Rd., Newbury Park, CA 91320. TEL 805-499-0721. FAX 805-499-0871. *1727*

EDUCATIONAL GERONTOLOGY.
Hemisphere Publishing Corporation 1900 Frost Rd., Ste. 101, Bristol, PA 19007-1598. TEL 215-785-5800. FAX 215-785-5515. *1683*

EDUCATIONAL POLICY.
Corwin Press, Inc. 2455 Teller Rd., Newbury Park, CA 91320. TEL 805-499-0721. FAX 805-499-0871. *1630*

EDUCATIONAL PSYCHOLOGIST.
Lawrence Erlbaum Associates, Inc., (American Psychological Association, Division of Educational Psychology) 365 Broadway, Hillsdale, NJ 07642. TEL 201-666-4110. FAX 201-666-2394. *4020*

EDUCATIONAL PSYCHOLOGY REVIEW.
Plenum Publishing Corp., 233 Spring St., New York, NY 10013-1578. TEL 212-620-8000. FAX 212-463-0742. *1630*

EDUCATIONAL TECHNOLOGY RESEARCH & DEVELOPMENT.
Association for Educational Communications and Technology, 1025 Vermont Ave. N.W., Ste. 820, Washington, DC 20005-3516. TEL 202-347-7834. FAX 202-347-7839. *1748*

EGYPTIAN JOURNAL OF DAIRY SCIENCE.
Egyptian Society of Dairy Science, National Research Centre, Sharia Tahrir, Dokki, Cairo, Egypt. FAX 02-700931. *199*

EIRENE.
John Benjamins Publishing Co., (Czechoslovak Academy of Sciences, Institute for Greek, Latin and Roman Studies) Amsteldijk 44, P.O. Box 75577, 1070 AN Amsterdam, Netherlands. TEL 020-6738156. FAX 020-6739773. *2360*

ELECTORAL STUDIES.
Butterworth - Heinemann Ltd. Linacre House, Jordan Hill, Oxford OX2 8DP, England. TEL 0865-310366. FAX 0865-310898. *3892*

ELECTRIC MACHINES AND POWER SYSTEMS.
Hemisphere Publishing Corporation 1900 Frost Rd., Ste. 101, Bristol, PA 19007-1598. TEL 215-785-5800. FAX 215-785-5515. *1887*

ELECTRIC POWER SYSTEMS RESEARCH.
Elsevier Sequoia S.A., P.O. Box 564, CH-1001 Lausanne, Switzerland. TEL 021-207381. FAX 021-235444. *1887*

ELECTRIC TECHNOLOGY U.S.S.R.
Pergamon Press, Inc., Journals Division, 660 White Plains Rd., Tarrytown, NY 10591-5153. TEL 914-524-9200. FAX 914-333-2444. *1887*

ELECTROANALYTICAL CHEMISTRY: A SERIES OF ADVANCES.
Marcel Dekker, Inc., 270 Madison Ave., New York, NY 10016. TEL 212-696-9000. FAX 212-685-4540. *1205*

ELECTROCHIMICA ACTA.
Pergamon Press, Inc., Journals Division, (International Society of Electrochemistry) 660 White Plains Rd., Tarrytown, NY 10591-5153. TEL 914-524-9200. FAX 914-333-2444. *1212*

ELECTROCOMPONENT SCIENCE MONOGRAPHS.
Gordon & Breach Science Publishers, 270 Eighth Ave., New York, NY 10011. TEL 212-206-8900. FAX 212-645-2459. *1889*

ELECTROENCEPHALOGRAPHY AND CLINICAL NEUROPHYSIOLOGY INCLUDING EVOKED POTENTIALS AND ELECTROMYOGRAPHY AND MOTOR CONTROL.
Elsevier Scientific Publishers Ireland Ltd., (International Federation of Societies for Electroencephalography and Clinical Neurophysiology) P.O. Box 85, Limerick, Ireland. TEL 061-61944. FAX 061-62144. *3335*

ELECTROMAGNETICS.
Hemisphere Publishing Corporation 1900 Frost Rd., Ste. 101, Bristol, PA 19007-1598. TEL 215-785-5800. FAX 215-758-5515. *1889*

ELECTROMECHANICAL BENCH REFERENCE.
Barks Publications, Inc., 400 N. Michigan Ave., Chicago, IL 60611-4198. TEL 312-321-9440. *1889*

ELECTROMYOGRAPHY AND MOTOR CONTROL.
Elsevier Scientific Publishers Ireland Ltd., (International Federation of Societies for Electroencephalography and Clinical Neurophysiology) P.O. Box 85, Limerick, Ireland. TEL 061-61944. FAX 061-62144. *3335*

ELECTRON MICROSCOPY REVIEWS.
Pergamon Press, Inc., Journals Division, 660 White Plains Rd., Tarrytown, NY 10591-5153. TEL 914-524-9200. FAX 914-333-2444. *559*

ELECTRONIC MODELING.
Gordon and Breach Science Publishers, 270 Eighth Ave., New York, NY 10011. TEL 212-206-8900. FAX 212-645-2459. *1768*

ELECTRONIC PUBLISHING.
John Wiley & Sons Ltd., Journals, Baffins Lane, Chichester, W. Sussex PO19 1UD, England. TEL 0243-779777. FAX 0243-775878. *4143*

ELECTROSOFT.
Elsevier Science Publishers Ltd., Crown House, Linton Rd., Barking, Essex IG11 8JU, England. TEL 081-594-5942. FAX 081-594-7272. *3064*

ELEMENTARY SCHOOL JOURNAL.
University of Chicago Press, Journals Division, 5720 S. Woodlawn Ave., Chicago, IL 60637. TEL 312-753-3347. *1631*

ELSEVIER OCEANOGRAPHY SERIES.
Elsevier Science Publishers B.V., Books Division, P.O. Box 211, 1000 AE Amsterdam, Netherlands. TEL 020-5803911. FAX 020-5803705. *1604*

ELSEVIER SERIES IN FORENSIC AND POLICE SCIENCE.
Elsevier Science Publishers B.V., Books Division, P.O. Box 211, 1000 AE Amsterdam, Netherlands. TEL 020-5803911. FAX 020-5803705. *3264*

ELSEVIER SERIES IN PRACTICAL ASPECTS OF CRIMINAL & FORENSIC INVESTIGATION.
Elsevier Science Publishers B.V., Books Division, P.O. Box 211, 1000 AE Amsterdam, Netherlands. TEL 020-5803911. FAX 020-5803705. *3264*

EMERGENCY LIBRARIAN.
Dyad Services, P.O. Box 46258, Station G, Vancouver, B.C. V6R 4G6, Canada. TEL 604-734-0255. FAX 604-734-0221. *2757*

EMERGENCY PREHOSPITAL MEDICINE.
C M E Communications, Inc., 20854 Dalton Rd., P.O. Box 507, Sutton West, Ont. L0E 1L0, Canada. TEL 416-722-9839. FAX 416-722-9687. *3378*

EMORY UNIVERSITY JOURNAL OF MEDICINE.
Emory University, 1462 Clifton Rd., N.E., Ste. 301, Atlanta, GA 30322. TEL 404-727-3530. FAX 404-727-3309. *3096*

EMOTION.
Academic Press, Inc., 1250 Sixth Ave., San Diego, CA 92101. TEL 619-231-0926. FAX 619-699-6715. *4020*

EMOTIONS AND BEHAVIOR. MONOGRAPH.
International Universities Press, Inc., (Chicago Institute for Psychoanalysis) 59 Boston Post Rd., Box 1524, Madison, CT 06443-1524. TEL 203-245-4000. *3335*

EMPLOYEE ASSISTANCE QUARTERLY.
Haworth Press, Inc., 10 Alice St., Binghamton, NY 13904. TEL 800-342-9678. FAX 607-722-1424. *1064*

EMPLOYEE RESPONSIBILITIES AND RIGHTS JOURNAL.
Plenum Publishing Corp., (Council on Employee Responsibilities and Rights) 233 Spring St., New York, NY 10013-1578. TEL 212-620-8000. FAX 212-463-0742. *978*

ENCYCLIA.
Utah Academy of Sciences, Arts, and Letters, c/o Thomas F. Rogers, Ed., 4089A JKHB, Brigham Young University, Provo, UT 84602. TEL 801-378-3385. FAX 802-378-4649. *4308*

ENDEAVOUR (TARRYTOWN).
Pergamon Press, Inc., Journals Division, 660 White Plains Rd., Tarrytown, NY 10591-5153. TEL 914-524-9200. FAX 914-333-2444. *4308*

ENDOCRINE RESEARCH.
Marcel Dekker Journals, 270 Madison Ave., New York, NY 10016. TEL 212-696-9000. FAX 212-685-4540. *3252*

THE ENDOCRINOLOGIST.
Williams & Wilkins, 428 E. Preston St., Baltimore, MD 21202. TEL 301-528-4000. FAX 301-528-4321. *3253*

ENDOCRINOLOGY.
Williams & Wilkins, (Endocrine Society) 428 E. Preston St., Baltimore, MD 21202. TEL 301-528-4000. FAX 301-528-4312. *3253*

ENERGY.
Pergamon Press, Inc., Journals Division, 660 White Plains Rd., Tarrytown, NY 10591-5153. TEL 914-524-9200. FAX 914-333-2444. *1786*

ENERGY AND BUILDINGS.
Elsevier Sequoia S.A., P.O. Box 564, CH-1001 Lausanne, Switzerland. TEL 021-207381. FAX 021-235444. *1787*

ENERGY AND ENGINEERING SCIENCE.
Gordon & Breach Science Publishers, 270 Eighth Ave., New York, NY 10011. TEL 212-206-8900. FAX 212-645-2459. *1787*

ENERGY CONVERSION AND MANAGEMENT.
Pergamon Press, Inc., Journals Division, 660 White Plains Rd., Tarrytown, NY 10591-5153. TEL 914-524-9200. FAX 914-333-2444. *1787*

ENERGY ECONOMICS.
Butterworth - Heinemann Ltd. Linacre House, Jordan Hill, Oxford OX2 8DP, England. TEL 0865-310366. FAX 0865-310898. *1787*

ENERGY JOURNAL.
Oelgeschlager, Gunn & Hain, Inc., (International Association of Energy Economists) 245 Merriam St., Weston, MA 02193. TEL 617-647-3609. *1788*

ENERGY POLICY.
Butterworth - Heinemann Ltd. Linacre House, Jordan Hill, Oxford OX2 8DP, England. TEL 0865-310366. FAX 0865-310898. *1788*

ENERGY RESEARCH.
Elsevier Science Publishers B.V., Books Division, P.O. Box 211, 1000 AE Amsterdam, Netherlands. TEL 020-5803911. FAX 020-5803705. *1789*

ENERGY SOURCES.
Taylor & Francis, 1900 Frost Rd., Ste. 101, Bristol, PA 19007-1598. TEL 215-785-5800. FAX 215-785-5515. *1789*

ENERGY SYSTEMS AND POLICY.
Taylor & Francis, 1900 Frost Rd., Ste. 101, Bristol, PA 19007-1598. TEL 215-785-5800. FAX 215-785-5515. *1789*

ENGINEERING ANALYSIS WITH BOUNDARY ELEMENTS.
Elsevier Science Publishers Ltd., Crown House, Linton Rd., Barking, Essex IG11 8JU, England. TEL 081-594-7272. FAX 081-594-5942. *1929*

ENGINEERING APPLICATIONS OF ARTIFICIAL INTELLIGENCE.
Pergamon Press plc, Headington Hill Hall, Oxford OX3 0BW, England. TEL 0865-794141. FAX 0865-743911. *1407*

ENGINEERING DESIGN GRAPHICS JOURNAL.
American Society for Engineering Education, Engineering Design Graphics Division, c/o John B. Crittenden, Ed., Division of Engineering Fundamentals, Virginia Polytechnic Institute and State University, Blacksburg, VA 24061-0218. TEL 703-231-6555. *4597*

ENGINEERING FRACTURE MECHANICS.
Pergamon Press, Inc., Journals Division, 660 White Plains Rd., Tarrytown, NY 10591-5153. TEL 914-524-9200. FAX 914-333-2444. *1916*

ENGINEERING GEOLOGY.
Elsevier Science Publishers B.V., P.O. Box 211, 1000 AE Amsterdam, Netherlands. TEL 020-5803911. FAX 020-5803598. *1865*

ENGINEERING OPTIMIZATION.
Gordon & Breach Science Publishers, 270 Eighth Ave., New York, NY 10011. TEL 212-206-8900. FAX 212-645-2459. *1820*

ENGINEERING STRUCTURES.
Butterworth - Heinemann Ltd. Linacre House, Jordan Hill, Oxford OX2 8DP, England. TEL 0865-310366. FAX 0865-310898. *1865*

ENGLISH FOR SPECIFIC PURPOSES.
Pergamon Press, Inc., Journals Division, 660 White Plains Rd., Tarrytown, NY 10591-5153. TEL 914-524-9200. FAX 914-333-2444. *1749*

ENGLISH MONARCH SERIES.
University of California Press, 2120 Berkeley Way, Berkeley, CA 94720. TEL 415-642-4247. FAX 415-643-7127. *2360*

ENGLISH QUARTERLY.
Canadian Council of Teachers of English, 1243 Wood Place, Oakville, Ont. L6L 2R4, Canada. *1749*

ENHANCED OIL-RECOVERY FIELD REPORTS.
Society of Petroleum Engineers, Inc., Box 833836, Richardson, TX 75083-3836. TEL 214-669-3377. FAX 214-669-0135. *3685*

ENRICO FERMI INTERNATIONAL SUMMER SCHOOL OF PHYSICS.
Elsevier Science Publishers B.V., Books Division, P.O. Box 211, 1000 AE Amsterdam, Netherlands. TEL 020-5803911. FAX 020-5803705. *3817*

ENTOMOLOGICAL NEWS.
American Entomological Society, Academy of Natural Sciences, 1900 Race St., Philadelphia, PA 19103. TEL 215-561-3978. *530*

ENTOMOLOGICAL REVIEW.
Scripta Technica, Inc. (Russian Academy of Sciences) 7961 Eastern Ave., Silver Spring, MD 20910. TEL 301-588-0484. FAX 301-588-5278. *530*

ENTOMOLOGICAL SOCIETY OF AMERICA. ANNALS.
Entomological Society of America, 9301 Annapolis Rd., Lanham, MD 20706. TEL 301-731-4535. FAX 301-731-4538. *531*

ENTOMOLOGICAL SOCIETY OF AMERICA. MISCELLANEOUS PUBLICATIONS.
Entomological Society of America, 9301 Annapolis Rd., Lanham, MD 20706. TEL 301-731-4535. FAX 301-731-4538. *531*

ENTOMOLOGICAL SOCIETY OF WASHINGTON. MEMOIRS.
Entomological Society of Washington, c/o Dept. of Entomology, Smithsonian Institution NHB 168, Washington, DC 20560. *531*

ENTREPRENEURSHIP & REGIONAL DEVELOPMENT.
Taylor & Francis Ltd., Rankine Rd., Basingstoke, Hampshire RG24 0PR, England. TEL 0256-840366. FAX 0256-479438. *664*

ENTREPRENEURSHIP, INNOVATION AND CHANGE.
Plenum Publishing Corp., 233 Spring St., New York, NY 10013-1578. TEL 212-620-8000. FAX 212-463-0742. *1114*

ENVIRONMENT (WASHINGTON).
Heldref Publications, (Scientists' Institute for Public Information) 1319 Eighteenth St., N.W., Washington, DC 20036-1802. TEL 202-296-6267. FAX 202-296-5149. *1949*

ENVIRONMENT INTERNATIONAL.
Pergamon Press, Inc., Journals Division, 660 White Plains Rd., Tarrytown, NY 10591-5153. TEL 914-524-9200. FAX 914-333-2444. *1950*

ENVIRONMENTAL AND EXPERIMENTAL BOTANY.
Pergamon Press, Inc., Journals Division, 660 White Plains Rd., Tarrytown, NY 10591-5153. TEL 914-524-9200. FAX 914-333-2444. *501*

ENVIRONMENTAL AND MOLECULAR MUTAGENESIS.
John Wiley & Sons, Inc., Journals, (Environmental Mutagen Society) 605 Third Ave., New York, NY 10158. TEL 212-850-6000. FAX 212-850-6088. *438*

ENVIRONMENTAL BIOLOGY.
Cornell University, Department of Entomology, 6126 Comstock Hall, Ithaca, NY 14853. TEL 607-255-2212. FAX 607-255-0939. *1950*

ENVIRONMENTAL CONSERVATION.
Elsevier Sequoia S.A., (Foundation for Environmental Conservation) P.O. Box 564, CH-1001 Lausanne, Switzerland. TEL 021-207381. FAX 021-235444. *1951*

ENVIRONMENTAL ENTOMOLOGY.
Entomological Society of America, 9301 Annapolis Rd., Lanham, MD 20706. TEL 301-731-4535. FAX 301-731-4538. *532*

ENVIRONMENTAL POLLUTION.
Elsevier Science Publishers Ltd., Crown House, Linton Rd., Barking, Essex IG11 8JU, England. TEL 081-594-7272. FAX 081-594-5942. *1977*

ENVIRONMENTAL PROTECTION.
Stevens Publishing Corporation, 225 N. New Rd., Waco, TX 76710. TEL 817-776-9000. *1953*

ENVIRONMENTAL RESEARCH.
Academic Press, Inc., Journal Division, 1250 Sixth Ave., San Diego, CA 92101. TEL 619-230-1840. FAX 619-699-6800. *1953*

ENVIRONMENTAL SOFTWARE.
Elsevier Science Publishers Ltd., Crown House, Linton Rd., Barking, Essex IG11 8JU, England. TEL 081-594-7272. FAX 081-594-5942. *1975*

ENVIRONMENTAL TOPICS.
Gordon and Breach Scientific Publishers, 270 Eighth Ave., New York, NY 10011. TEL 212-206-8900. FAX 212-645-2459. *1954*

ENVIRONMENTAL TOXICOLOGY AND CHEMISTRY.
Pergamon Press, Inc., Journals Division, (Society of Environmental Toxicology and Chemistry) 660 White Plains Rd., Tarrytown, NY 10591-5153. TEL 914-524-9200. FAX 914-333-2444. *1981*

ENVIRONMENTAL TOXICOLOGY AND WATER QUALITY.
John Wiley & Sons, Inc., Journals, 605 Third Ave., New York, NY 10158-0012. TEL 212-850-6000. FAX 212-850-6088. *1981*

ENZYME AND MICROBIAL TECHNOLOGY.
Butterworth - Heinemann Ltd. 80 Montvale Ave., Stoneham, MA 02180. TEL 617-438-8464. FAX 617-438-1479. *551*

ENZYME ENGINEERING.
New York Academy of Sciences, 2 E. 63rd St., New York, NY 10021. TEL 212-838-0230. *476*

EOS.
American Geophysical Union, 2000 Florida Ave., N.W., Washington, DC 20009. TEL 202-462-6900. FAX 202-328-0566. *1588*

EPILEPSIA.
Raven Press, (International League against Epilepsy) 1185 Ave. of the Americas, New York, NY 10036. TEL 212-930-9500. FAX 212-869-3495. *3336*

EPILEPSY RESEARCH.
Elsevier Science Publishers B.V., P.O. Box 211, 1000 AE Amsterdam, Netherlands. TEL 020-5803911. FAX 020-5803598. *3336*

EQUINE PRACTICE.
Veterinary Practice Publishing Co., 7 Ashley Ave. S., Santa Barbara, CA 93103-9989. TEL 805-965-1028. FAX 805-965-0722. *4809*

ERGONOMICS.
Taylor & Francis Ltd., (Ergonomics Society) Rankine Rd., Basingstoke, Hants. RG24 OPR, England. TEL 0256-840366. FAX 0256-479438. *1821*

ERGONOMICS ABSTRACTS.
Taylor & Francis Ltd., (Ergonomics Information Analysis Centre) Rankine Rd., Basingstoke, Hants RG24 OPR, England. TEL 0256-840366. FAX 0256-479438. *1843*

ERNEST BLOCH LECTURES.
University of California Press, 2120 Berkeley Way, Berkeley, CA 94720. TEL 415-642-4247. FAX 415-643-7127. *1706*

ESSAYS FOR THE THIRD CENTURY.
University Press of Kentucky, 663 S. Limestone St., Lexington, KY 40508-4008. TEL 606-257-2951. *3892*

ESSAYS IN BIOCHEMISTRY.
Academic Press, Inc., (Biochemical Society) 1250 Sixth Ave., San Diego, CA 92101. TEL 619-231-0926. FAX 619-699-6715. *476*

ESSAYS IN CHEMISTRY.
Academic Press, Inc., 1250 Sixth Ave., San Diego, CA 92101. TEL 619-231-0926. FAX 619-699-6715. *1177*

ESTATE PLANNING.
Warren, Gorham and Lamont, One Penn Plaza, New York, NY 10119. TEL 800-950-1205. FAX 212-971-5240. *945*

ESTUARIES.
Estuarine Research Federation, Box 544, Crownsville, MD 21032-0544. *438*

ETHICS: AN INTERNATIONAL JOURNAL OF SOCIAL, POLITICAL AND LEGAL PHILOSOPHY.
University of Chicago Press, Journals Division, 5720 S. Woodlawn Ave., Chicago, IL 60637. TEL 312-753-3347. FAX 312-702-0694. *3766*

ETHICS & BEHAVIOR.
Lawrence Erlbaum Associates, Inc., 365 Broadway, Hillsdale, NJ 07642. TEL 201-666-4110. FAX 201-666-2394. *4020*

ETHNIC GROUPS.
Gordon and Breach Science Publishers, 270 Eighth Ave., New York, NY 10011. TEL 212-206-8900. FAX 212-645-2459. *2001*

ETHNIC HISTORY OF CHICAGO.
University of Illinois Press, 54 E. Gregory Dr., Champaign, IL 61820. TEL 217-333-0950. FAX 217-244-8082. *2001*

ETHNOHISTORY.
Duke University Press, 6697 College Station, Durham, NC 27708. TEL 919-684-2173. FAX 919-684-8644. *238*

EUROPE IN THE MIDDLE AGES.
Elsevier Science Publishers B.V., Books Division, P.O. Box 211, 1000 AEAmsterdam, Netherlands. TEL 212-989-5800. FAX 020-5803705. *2360*

EUROPEAN ACADEMY OF DERMATOLOGY AND VENEREOLOGY. JOURNAL.
Elsevier Science Publishers B.V., P.O. Box 211, 1000 AE Amsterdam, Netherlands. TEL 020-5803911. FAX 020-5803598. *3247*

EUROPEAN APPLIED RESEARCH REPORTS: NUCLEAR SCIENCE AND TECHNOLOGY SECTION.
Harwood Academic Publishers, 270 Eighth Ave., New York, NY 10011. TEL 212-206-8900. FAX 212-645-2459. *3847*

EUROPEAN APPLIED RESEARCH REPORTS SPECIAL TOPICS SERIES.
Harwood Academic Publishers, 270 Eighth Ave., New York, NY 10011. TEL 212-206-8900. FAX 212-645-2459. *3847*

EUROPEAN CERAMIC SOCIETY. JOURNAL.
Elsevier Science Publishers Ltd., Crown House, Linton Rd., Barking, Essex IG11 8JU, England. TEL 081-594-7272. FAX 081-594-5942. *1163*

EUROPEAN ECONOMIC REVIEW.
North-Holland (European Economic Association) P.O. Box 211, 1000 AE Amsterdam, Netherlands. TEL 020-5803911. FAX 020-5803598. *664*

EUROPEAN EDUCATION.
M. E. Sharpe, Inc., 80 Business Park Dr., Armonk, NY 10504. TEL 914-273-1800. FAX 914-273-2106. *1632*

EUROPEAN JOURNAL OF CANCER PART A.
Pergamon Press, Inc., Journals Division, (Federation of European Cancer Societies) 660 White Plains Rd., Tarrytown, NY 10591-5153. TEL 914-524-9200. FAX 914-333-2444. *3197*

EUROPEAN JOURNAL OF CANCER PART B: ORAL ONCOLOGY.
Pergamon Press plc, Headington Hill Hall, Oxford OX3 0BW, England. TEL 0865-794141. FAX 0865-743911. *3197*

EUROPEAN JOURNAL OF CLINICAL MICROBIOLOGY & INFECTIOUS DISEASES.
Friedr. Vieweg und Sohn Verlagsgesellschaft mbH, Postfach 5829, 6200 Wiesbaden 1, Germany. TEL 0611-160320. FAX 0611-160229. *551*

EUROPEAN JOURNAL OF COGNITIVE PSYCHOLOGY.
Lawrence Erlbaum Associates Ltd., (European Society for Cognitive Psychology) 27 Palmeira Mansions, Church Rd., Hove, E. Sussex BN3 2FA, England. TEL 0273-207411. FAX 0273-205612. *4020*

EUROPEAN JOURNAL OF MECHANICAL ENGINEERING.
Elsevier Science Publishers B.V., (Societe Belge des Mecaniciens) P.O. Box 211, 1000 AE Amsterdam, Netherlands. TEL 020-5803911. FAX 020-5803598. *1929*

EUROPEAN JOURNAL OF MEDICINAL CHEMISTRY.
Editions Scientifiques Elsevier, (Societe Francaise de Chimie Therapeutique) 29, rue Buffon, 75005 Paris, France. TEL 47-07-11-22. *476*

EUROPEAN JOURNAL OF MINERALOGY.
E. Schweizerbart'sche Verlagsbuchhandlung, (Deutsche Mineralogische Gesellschaft) Johannesstr. 3A, 7000 Stuttgart 1, Germany. TEL 0711-625001. FAX 0711-625005. *3483*

EUROPEAN JOURNAL OF OBSTETRICS, GYNECOLOGY AND REPRODUCTIVE BIOLOGY.
Elsevier Science Publishers B.V., (European Association of Gynaecologists and Obstetricians) P.O. Box 211, 1000 AE Amsterdam, Netherlands. TEL 020-5803911. FAX 020-5803598. *3291*

EUROPEAN JOURNAL OF OPERATIONAL RESEARCH.
North-Holland (Association of European Operational Research Societies) P.O. Box 211, 1000 AE Amsterdam, Netherlands. TEL 020-5803911. FAX 020-5803598. *1009*

EUROPEAN JOURNAL OF PHARMACOLOGY.
Elsevier Science Publishers B.V., P.O. Box 211, 1000 AE Amsterdam, Netherlands. TEL 020-5803911. FAX 020-5803598. *3725*

EUROPEAN JOURNAL OF PHARMACOLOGY. ENVIRONMENTAL TOXICOLOGY AND PHARMACOLOGY SECTION.
Elsevier Science Publishers B.V., P.O. Box 211, 1000 AE Amsterdam, Netherlands. TEL 020-5803911. FAX 020-5803705. *1981*

EUROPEAN JOURNAL OF PHARMACOLOGY. MOLECULAR PHARMACOLOGY SECTION.
Elsevier Science Publishers B.V., P.O. Box 211, 1000 AE Amsterdam, Netherlands. TEL 020-5803911. FAX 020-5803598. *3725*

EUROPEAN JOURNAL OF POLITICAL ECONOMY.
North-Holland P.O. Box 211, 1000 AE Amsterdam, Netherlands. TEL 020-5803911. FAX 020-5803598. *998*

EUROPEAN JOURNAL OF POPULATION.
North-Holland (European Association for Population Studies) P.O. Box 211, 1000 AE Amsterdam, Netherlands. TEL 020-5803911. FAX 020-5803598. *3992*

EUROPEAN JOURNAL OF RADIOLOGY.
Elsevier Science Publishers B.V., (European Association of Radiology) P.O. Box 211, 1000 AE Amsterdam, Netherlands. TEL 020-5803911. FAX 020-5803598. *3358*

EUROPEAN JOURNAL OF SERIALS LIBRARIANSHIP.
Haworth Press, Inc., 10 Alice St., Binghamton, NY 13904. TEL 800-342-9678. FAX 607-722-1424. *2757*

EUROPEAN JUDAISM.
Pergamon Press plc, Headington Hill Hall, Oxford OX3 OBW, England. TEL 0865-794141. FAX 0865-743911. *4222*

EUROPEAN NEUROPSYCHOPHARMACOLOGY.
Elsevier Science Publishers B.V., (European College of Neuropsychopharmacology) P.O. Box 211, 1000 AE Amsterdam, Netherlands. TEL 020-5803911. FAX 020-5803598. *3336*

EUROPEAN ORGANIZATION FOR RESEARCH ON TREATMENT OF CANCER. MONOGRAPH SERIES.
Raven Press, 1185 Ave. of the Americas, New York, NY 10036. TEL 212-930-9500. FAX 212-869-3495. *3197*

EUROPEAN POLYMER JOURNAL.
Pergamon Press, Inc., Journals Division, 660 White Plains Rd., Tarrytown, NY 10591-5153. TEL 914-524-9200. FAX 914-333-2444. *1218*

EUROPEAN PSYCHIATRY.
Editions Scientifiques Elsevier, (Association of European Psychiatrists) 29, rue Buffon, 75005 Paris, France. TEL 47-07-11-22. *3336*

EUROPEAN STUDIES IN LAW.
Elsevier Science Publishers B.V., Books Division, P.O. Box 211, 1000 AE Amsterdam, Netherlands. TEL 020-5803911. FAX 020-5803705. *2624*

EUROPEAN WATER POLLUTION CONTROL.
Elsevier Science Publishers B.V., (European Water Pollution Control Association) P.O. Box 211, 1000 AE Amsterdam, Netherlands. TEL 020-5803911. FAX 020-5803598. *1977*

EVALUATION AND PROGRAM PLANNING.
Pergamon Press, Inc., Journals Division, 660 White Plains Rd., Tarrytown, NY 10591-5153. TEL 914-524-9200. FAX 914-333-2444. *4372*

EVOKED POTENTIALS.
Elsevier Scientific Publishers Ireland Ltd., (International Federation of Societies for Electroencephalography and Clinical Neurophysiology) P.O. Box 85, Limerick, Ireland. TEL 061-61944. FAX 061-62144. *3336*

EVOLUTION.
Allen Press, Inc., (Society for the Study of Evolution) 1041 New Hampshire Ave., Box 1897, Lawrence, KS 66044-8897. TEL 800-627-0629. FAX 913-843-1274. *541*

EVOLUTIONARY BIOLOGY.
Plenum Publishing Corp., 233 Spring St., New York, NY 10013-1578. TEL 212-620-8000. FAX 212-463-0742. *541*

EVOLUTIONARY MONOGRAPHS.
University of Chicago, Department of Ecology and Evolution, 1101 E. 57th St., Chicago, IL 60637. TEL 312-702-9475. *438*

EVOLUTIONARY THEORY AND REVIEW.
University of Chicago, Department of Ecology and Evolution, 1191 E. 57th St., Chicago, IL 60637. TEL 312-702-9475. *438*

EXEMPLARIA.
Medieval and Rennaissance Texts and Studies, LNG 99, State University of New York, Binghamton, NY 13902-6000. *2916*

EXPERIMENTAL & APPLIED ACAROLOGY.
Elsevier Science Publishers B.V., P.O. Box 211, 1000 AE Amsterdam, Netherlands. TEL 020-5803911. FAX 020-5803598. *438*

EXPERIMENTAL AND CLINICAL GASTROENTEROLOGY.
Pergamon Press plc, Headington Hill Hall, Oxford OX3 0BW, England. TEL 0865-794141. FAX 0865-743911. *3267*

EXPERIMENTAL AND CLINICAL PSYCHIATRY.
Marcel Dekker, Inc., 270 Madison Ave., New York, NY 10016. TEL 212-696-9000. FAX 212-685-4540. *3336*

EXPERIMENTAL AND MOLECULAR PATHOLOGY.
Academic Press, Inc., Journal Division, 1250 Sixth Ave., San Diego, CA 92101. TEL 619-230-1840. FAX 619-699-6800. *3097*

EXPERIMENTAL CELL RESEARCH.
Academic Press, Inc., Journal Division, (International Society for Cell Biology) 1250 Sixth Ave., San Diego, CA 92101. TEL 619-230-1840. FAX 619-699-6800. *524*

EXPERIMENTAL GERONTOLOGY.
Pergamon Press, Inc., Journals Division, 660 White Plains Rd., Tarrytown, NY 10591-5153. TEL 914-524-9200. FAX 914-333-2444. *2272*

EXPERIMENTAL HEAT TRANSFER.
Hemisphere Publishing Corporation 1900 Frost Rd., Ste. 101, Bristol, PA 19007-1598. TEL 215-785-5800. FAX 215-785-5515. *3840*

EXPERIMENTAL LUNG RESEARCH.
Hemisphere Publishing Corporation 1900 Frost Rd., Ste. 101, Bristol, PA 19007-1598. TEL 215-785-5800. FAX 215-785-5515. *3365*

EXPERIMENTAL MECHANICS.
Society for Experimental Mechanics, 7 School St., Bethel, CT 06801. TEL 203-790-6373. FAX 203-790-4472. *1916*

EXPERIMENTAL MYCOLOGY.
Academic Press, Inc., Journal Division, 1250 Sixth Ave., San Diego, CA 92101. TEL 619-230-1840. FAX 619-699-6800. *502*

EXPERIMENTAL NEUROLOGY.
Academic Press, Inc., Journal Division, 1250 Sixth Ave., San Diego, CA 92101. TEL 619-230-1840. FAX 619-699-6800. *3337*

EXPERIMENTAL PARASITOLOGY.
Academic Press, Inc., Journal Division, 1250 Sixth Ave., San Diego, CA 92101. TEL 619-230-1840. FAX 619-699-6800. *3219*

EXPERIMENTAL TECHNIQUES.
Society for Experimental Mechanics, 7 School St., Bethel, CT 06801. TEL 203-790-6373. FAX 203-790-4472. *1916*

EXPERIMENTAL THERMAL AND FLUID SCIENCE.
Elsevier Science Publishing Co., Inc. (New York), 655 Ave. of the Americas, New York, NY 10010. TEL 212-989-5800. FAX 212-633-3965. *1821*

EXPERIMENTAL VIROLOGY.
Academic Press, Inc., 1250 Sixth Ave., San Diego, CA 92101. TEL 619-231-0926. FAX 619-699-6715. *551*

EXPERT SYSTEMS WITH APPLICATIONS.
Pergamon Press, Inc., Journals Division, 660 White Plains Rd., Tarrytown, NY 10591-5153. TEL 914-524-9200. FAX 914-333-2444. *1437*

EXPLICATOR.
Heldref Publications, (Helen Dwight Reid Educational Foundation) 1319 Eighteenth St., N.W., Washington, DC 20036-1802. TEL 202-296-6267. FAX 202-296-5149. *2916*

EXPLORATION & MINING GEOLOGY.
Pergamon Press, Inc., Journals Division, (Canadian Institute of Metallurgy, Geological Society) 395 Saw Mill River Rd., Elmsford, NY 10523. TEL 914-592-7700. FAX 914-592-3625. *1560*

EXPLORATIONS IN ETHNIC STUDIES.
National Association for Ethnic Studies, Inc., Department of English, Arizona State University, Tempe, AZ 85287-0302. TEL 602-965-3168. FAX 602-965-1093. *2001*

EYE SCIENCE.
Sun Yat-sen University of Medical Sciences, Zhongshan Ophthalmic Center, Xianlie Road, Guangzhou, Guangdong 510060, People's Republic of China. *3300*

F A S E B JOURNAL.
Federation of American Societies for Experimental Biology, 9650 Rockville Pike, Bethesda, MD 20814. TEL 301-530-7100. FAX 301-571-1855. *439*

F E M S. MICROBIOLOGY.
Elsevier Science Publishers B.V., (Federation of European Microbiological Societies) P.O. Box 211, 1000 AE Amsterdam, Netherlands. TEL 020-5803911. FAX 020-5803598. *551*

F E M S. MICROBIOLOGY ECOLOGY.
Elsevier Science Publishers B.V., (Federation of European Microbiological Societies) P.O. Box 211, 1000 AE Amsterdam, Netherlands. TEL 020-5803911. FAX 020-5803598. *551*

F E M S. MICROBIOLOGY IMMUNOLOGY.
Elsevier Science Publishers B.V., (Federation of European Microbiological Societies) P.O. Box 211, 1000 AE Amsterdam, Netherlands. TEL 020-5803911. FAX 020-5803598. *551*

F E M S. MICROBIOLOGY LETTERS.
Elsevier Science Publishers B.V., (Federation of European Microbiological Societies) P.O. Box 211, 1000 AE Amsterdam, Netherlands. TEL 020-5803911. FAX 020-5803598. *551*

F E M S. MICROBIOLOGY REVIEWS.
Elsevier Science Publishers B.V., (Federation of European Microbiological Societies) P.O. Box 211, 1000 AE Amsterdam, Netherlands. TEL 020-5803911. FAX 020-5803598. *465*

FALMER.
University of Sussex Society c/o Alumni Office, Sussex House, Falmer, Brighton BN1 9RH, England. FAX 0273-678335. *1311*

FAMILY BUSINESS REVIEW.
Jossey-Bass Inc., Publishers, (Family Firm Institute) 350 Sansome St., 5th Fl., San Francisco, CA 94104. TEL 415-433-1767. FAX 415-433-0499. *1114*

FAMILY DYNAMICS OF ADDICTION QUARTERLY.
Aspen Publishers, Inc., 200 Orchard Ridge Dr., Gaithersburg, MD 20878. TEL 301-417-7500. FAX 301-417-7550. *4021*

FAMILY PHYSICIAN'S COMPENDIUM OF DRUG THERAPY.
Excerpta Medica, Inc., Core Publishing Division 105 Raider Blvd., Belle Mead, NJ 08052. TEL 908-874-8550. FAX 908-874-0700. *3725*

FAMILY PRACTICE RECERTIFICATION.
M R A Publications, Inc., (Medical Recertification Associates) 3 Greenwich Office Park, Greenwich, CT 06831-5154. TEL 203-629-3550. FAX 203-629-2536. *3098*

FAMILY PRACTICE RESEARCH JOURNAL.
Human Sciences Press, Inc. (American Academy of Family Physicians) 233 Spring St., New York, NY 10013-1578. TEL 212-620-8000. FAX 212-463-0742. *3098*

FARADAY DISCUSSIONS.
Royal Society of Chemistry, Thomas Graham House, Science Park, Milton Rd., Cambridge CB4 4WF, England. TEL 0462-672555. FAX 0462-480947. *1226*

FATIGUE & FRACTURE OF ENGINEERING MATERIALS AND STRUCTURES.
Pergamon Press, Inc., Journals Division, (European Structural Integrity Group) 660 White Plains Rd., Tarrytown, NY 10591-5153. TEL 914-524-9200. FAX 914-333-2444. *1822*

FEDERAL INFORMATION PROCESSING STANDARDS PUBLICATION.
U.S. National Institute of Standards and Technology, Gaithersburg, MD 20899. TEL 301-975-3058. *3446*

FEDERAL SENTENCING REPORTER.
University of California Press, Journals Division, (Vera Institute of Justice) 2120 Berkeley Way, Berkeley, CA 94720. TEL 510-642-4191. FAX 510-643-7127. *1514*

FELINE PRACTICE.
Veterinary Practice Publishing Co., 7 Ashley Ave. S., Santa Barbara, CA 93103-9989. TEL 805-965-1028. FAX 805-965-0722. *4809*

FERROELECTRICITY AND RELATED PHENOMENA.
Gordon & Breach Science Publishers, 270 Eighth Ave., New York, NY 10011. TEL 212-206-8900. FAX 212-645-2459. *1892*

FERROELECTRICS.
Gordon and Breach Science Publishers, 270 Eighth Ave., New York, NY 10011. TEL 212-206-8900. FAX 212-645-2459. *3818*

FERROELECTRICS LETTERS.
Gordon & Breach Science Publishers, 270 Eighth Ave., New York, NY 10011. TEL 212-206-8900. FAX 212-645-2459. *1892*

FERTILIZER SCIENCE AND TECHNOLOGY SERIES.
Marcel Dekker, Inc., 270 Madison Ave., New York, NY 10016. TEL 212-696-9000. FAX 212-658-4540. *177*

FIBER AND INTEGRATED OPTICS.
Taylor & Francis, 1900 Frost Rd., Ste. 101, Bristol, PA 19007. TEL 215-785-5800. FAX 215-785-5515. *3852*

FIBER SCIENCE SERIES.
Marcel Dekker, Inc., 270 Madison Ave., New York, NY 10016. TEL 212-696-9000. FAX 212-685-4540. *4618*

FIBRE CHEMISTRY.
Plenum Publishing Corp., Consultants Bureau, (Russian Academy of Sciences) 233 Spring St., New York, NY 10013-1578. TEL 212-620-8468. FAX 212-463-0742. *4618*

FIELD CROPS RESEARCH.
Elsevier Science Publishers B.V., P.O. Box 211, 1000 AE Amsterdam, Netherlands. TEL 020-5803911. FAX 020-5803598. *177*

FIELDIANA: ANTHROPOLOGY.
Field Museum Press, (Field Museum of Natural History, Library - Publications Division) Roosevelt Rd. at Lake Shore Dr., Chicago, IL 60605-2498. TEL 312-922-9410. FAX 312-427-7269. *239*

FIELDIANA: BOTANY.
Field Museum Press, (Field Museum of Natural History, Library - Publications Division) Roosevelt Rd. at Lake Shore Dr., Chicago, IL 60605-2498. TEL 312-922-9410. FAX 312-427-7269. *502*

FIELDIANA: GEOLOGY.
Field Museum Press, (Field Museum of Natural History, Library - Publications Division) Roosevelt Rd. at Lake Shore Dr., Chicago, IL 60605-2498. TEL 312-922-9410. FAX 312-427-7269. *1560*

FIELDIANA: ZOOLOGY.
Field Museum Press, (Field Museum of Natural History, Library - Publications Division) Roosevelt Rd. at Lake Shore Dr., Chicago, IL 60605-2498. TEL 312-922-9410. FAX 312-427-7269. *582*

FILM QUARTERLY.
University of California Press, Journals Division, Berkeley, CA 94720. TEL 510-642-4191. FAX 510-643-7127. *3509*

FILTRATION & SEPARATION.
Elsevier Science Publishers Ltd., (Filtration Society) Crown House, Linton Rd., Barking, Essex IG11 8JU, England. TEL 081-594-7272. FAX 081-594-5942. *1853*

FINITE ELEMENTS IN ANALYSIS AND DESIGN.
North-Holland P.O. Box 211, 1000 AE Amsterdam, Netherlands. TEL 020-5803911. FAX 020-5803598. *1879*

FIRE SAFETY JOURNAL.
Elsevier Science Publishers Ltd., Crown House, Linton Rd., Barking, Essex IG11 8JU, England. TEL 081-594-7272. FAX 081-594-5942. *2032*

FISH AND SHELLFISH IMMUNOLOGY.
Academic Press Ltd., 24-28 Oval Rd., London NW1 7DX, England. TEL 071-267-4466. *439*

FISHERIES.
American Fisheries Society, 5410 Grosvenor Ln., Ste. 110, Bethesda, MD 20814-2199. TEL 301-897-8616. FAX 301-897-8096. *2040*

FISHERIES RESEARCH.
Elsevier Science Publishers B.V., P.O. Box 211, 1000 AE Amsterdam, Netherlands. TEL 020-5803911. FAX 020-5803598. *2040*

FLORA MALESIANA BULLETIN.
Rijksherbarium - Hortus Botanicus, Publications Department, P.O. Box 9514, 2300 RA Leiden, Netherlands. *503*

FLORA NEOTROPICA.
New York Botanical Garden, Scientific Publications Department, (Organization for Flora Neotropica) Bronx, NY 10458. TEL 212-220-8721. FAX 212-220-6504. *503*

FLORIDA ENTOMOLOGIST.
Florida Entomological Society, Box 14565, Gainesville, FL 32604. TEL 813-324-5502. FAX 904-374-5852. *532*

FLORIDA JOURNAL OF ANTHROPOLOGY.
University of Florida, Florida Anthropology Student Association, Department of Anthropology, 1350 GPA, Gainesville, FL 32611. TEL 904-392-2031. FAX 904-392-6929. *239*

FLORIDA MEDICAL ASSOCIATION. JOURNAL.
Florida Medical Association, Inc., Box 2411, Jacksonville, FL 32203. TEL 904-356-1571. FAX 904-353-1247. *3098*

FLORIDA STATE UNIVERSITY RESEARCH IN REVIEW.
Florida State University, Office of Graduate Studies and Research, 109 HMB R-23, Tallahassee, FL 32306. TEL 904-644-8634. *4309*

FLOW MEASUREMENT AND INSTRUMENTATION.
Butterworth - Heinemann Ltd. Linacre House, Jordan Hill, Oxford OX2 8DP, England. TEL 0865-310366. FAX 0865-310898. *2522*

FLUID DYNAMICS.
Plenum Publishing Corp., Consultants Bureau, (Russian Academy of Sciences) 233 Spring St., New York, NY 10013-1578. TEL 212-620-8468. FAX 212-463-0742. *3843*

FLUID DYNAMICS RESEARCH.
North-Holland (Japan Society of Fluid Mechanics) P.O. Box 211, 1000 AE Amsterdam, Netherlands. TEL 020-5803911. FAX 020-5803598. *1923*

FLUID MECHANICS OF ASTROPHYSICS AND GEOPHYSICS.
Gordon & Breach Science Publishers, 270 Eighth Ave., New York, NY 10011. TEL 212-206-8900. FAX 212-645-2459. *3843*

FLUID PHASE EQUILIBRIA.
Elsevier Science Publishers B.V., P.O. Box 211, 1000 AE Amsterdam, Netherlands. TEL 020-5803911. FAX 020-5803598. *1226*

FOLIA OPHTHALMOLOGICA JAPONICA.
Osaka University Medical School, Department of Ophthalmology, 1-1-50 Fukushima, Fukushima-ku, Osaka 553, Japan. FAX 81-6-458-2669. *3300*

FOLKLORE & SOCIETY.
University of Illinois Press, 54 E. Gregory Dr., Champaign, IL 61820. TEL 217-333-0950. FAX 217-244-8082. *2054*

FOLKTALES OF THE WORLD.
University of Chicago Press, 5801 S. Ellis Ave., Chicago, IL 60637. TEL 312-702-7899. *2055*

FOOD ADDITIVES AND CONTAMINANTS.
Taylor & Francis Ltd., Rankine Rd., Basingstoke, Hants RG24 0PR, England. TEL 0256-840366. FAX 0256-479438. *3727*

FOOD AND BIOPRODUCTS PROCESSING.
Taylor & Francis Ltd., (Institution of Chemical Engineers) Rankine Rd., Basingstoke, Hants. RG24 0PR, England. TEL 0256-840366. FAX 0256-479438. *477*

FOOD AND CHEMICAL TOXICOLOGY.
Pergamon Press, Inc., Journals Division, (British Industrial Biological Research Association) 660 White Plains Rd., Tarrytown, NY 10591-5153. TEL 914-524-9200. FAX 914-333-2444. *1981*

FOOD AND FOODWAYS.
Harwood Academic Publishers, 270 Eighth Ave., New York, NY 10011. TEL 212-206-8900. FAX 212-645-2459. *3605*

FOOD AND NUTRITION IN HISTORY AND ANTHROPOLOGY.
Gordon & Breach Science Publishers, 270 Eighth Ave., New York, NY 10011. TEL 212-206-8900. FAX 212-645-2459. *240*

FOOD BIOTECHNOLOGY.
Marcel Dekker Journals, 270 Madison Ave., New York, NY 10016. TEL 212-969-9000. FAX 212-685-4540. *489*

FOOD CHEMISTRY.
Elsevier Science Publishers Ltd., Crown House, Linton Rd., Barking, Essex IG11 8JU, England. TEL 081-594-7272. FAX 081-594-5942. *1177*

FOOD POLICY.
Butterworth - Heinemann Ltd. Linacre House, Jordan Hill, Oxford OX2 8DP, England. TEL 0865-310366. FAX 0865-310898. *150*

FOOD QUALITY AND PREFERENCE.
Elsevier Science Publishers Ltd., Crown House, Linton Rd., Barking, Essex IG11 8JU, England. TEL 081-594-7272. FAX 081-594-5942. *2069*

FOOD RESEARCH INTERNATIONAL.
Elsevier Science Publishers Ltd., (Canadian Institute of Food Science and Technology) Crown House, Linton Rd., Barking, Essex IG11 8JU, England. TEL 081-594-7272. FAX 081-594-5942. *2070*

FOOD SCIENCE SERIES.
Marcel Dekker, Inc., 270 Madison Ave., New York, NY 10016. TEL 212-696-9000. FAX 212-685-4540. *2070*

FOOD STRUCTURE.
Scanning Microscopy International, Inc., Box 66507, AMF O'Hare, Chicago, IL 60666-0507. TEL 312-529-6677. FAX 312-980-6698. *3606*

THE FOOT.
Churchill Livingstone Medical Journals, (International College of Foot Medicine and Surgery (CIP)) Robert Stevenson House, 1-3 Baxter's Pl., Leith Walk, Edinburgh EH1 3AF, Scotland. TEL 031-556-2424. FAX 031-558-1278. *3308*

FOOT & ANKLE.
Williams & Wilkins, (American Orthopaedic Foot and Ankle Society Inc.) 428 E. Preston St., Baltimore, MD 21202. TEL 301-528-4000. FAX 301-528-4312. *3308*

FORENSIC REPORTS.
Hemisphere Publishing Corporation 1900 Frost Rd., Ste. 101, Bristol, PA 19007-1598. TEL 215-785-5800. FAX 215-785-5515. *3264*

FORENSIC SCIENCE INTERNATIONAL.
Elsevier Scientific Publishers Ireland Ltd., P.O. Box 85, Limerick, Ireland. TEL 061-61944. FAX 061-62144. *3264*

FOREST & CONSERVATION HISTORY.
Forest History Society, 701 Vickers Ave., Durham, NC 27701-3147. TEL 919-682-9319. *2099*

FOREST ECOLOGY AND MANAGEMENT.
Elsevier Science Publishers B.V., P.O. Box 211, 1000 AE Amsterdam, Netherlands. TEL 020-5803911. FAX 020-5803598. *2099*

FORUM FOR APPLIED RESEARCH AND PUBLIC POLICY.
University of Tennessee, Energy, Environment and Resources Center, Knoxville, TN 37996-0710. FAX 615-974-1838. *1955*

FORUM FOR READING.
Fitchburg State College, Department of Education, (International Reading Association, College Reading Improvement) 160 Pearl St., Fitchburg, MA 01420-2697. TEL 508-345-2151. *1750*

FOUNDATION.
Science Fiction Foundation, Polytechnic of East London, Longbridge Rd., Dagenham, Essex RM8 2AS, England. TEL 081-590-7722. FAX 081-590-7799. *3011*

FOUNDATIONS OF PHYSICS.
Plenum Publishing Corp., 233 Spring St., New York, NY 10013-1578. TEL 212-620-8000. FAX 212-463-0742. *3818*

FOUNDATIONS OF PHYSICS LETTERS.
Plenum Publishing Corp., 233 Spring St., New York, NY 10013-1578. TEL 212-620-8000. FAX 212-463-0742. *3818*

FRAMES ARCHITETTURA DEI SERRAMENTI.
Gruppo Editoriale Faenza Editrice S.p.A., Via Pier. de Crescenzi, 44, 48018 Faenza RA, Italy. TEL 0546-663488. FAX 0546-660440. *618*

FRANKLIN INSTITUTE. JOURNAL.
Pergamon Press, Inc., Journals Division, 660 White Plains Rd., Tarrytown, NY 10591-5153. TEL 914-524-9200. FAX 914-333-2444. *4310*

FREE RADICAL BIOLOGY & MEDICINE.
Pergamon Press, Inc., Journals Division, (Oxygen Society) 660 White Plains Rd., Tarrytown, NY 10591-5153. TEL 914-524-9200. FAX 914-333-2444. *485*

FREE RADICAL RESEARCH COMMUNICATIONS.
Harwood Academic Publishers, 270 Eighth Ave., New York, NY 10011. TEL 212-206-8900. FAX 212-645-2459. *1177*

FRONTIERS IN AGING SERIES.
Human Sciences Press, Inc. 233 Spring St., New York, NY 10013-1578. TEL 212-620-8000. FAX 212-463-0742. *2272*

FRONTIERS IN APPLIED MATHEMATICS.
Society for Industrial and Applied Mathematics, Customer Service, 3600 University City Science Ctr., Philadelphia, PA 19104-2688. TEL 215-382-9800. FAX 215-386-7999. *3036*

FRONTIERS IN NEUROENDOCRINOLOGY.
Raven Press, 1185 Ave. of the Americas, New York, NY 10036. TEL 212-930-9500. FAX 212-869-3495. *3253*

FUEL.
Butterworth - Heinemann Ltd. Linacre House, Jordan Hill, Oxford OX2 8DP, England. TEL 0865-310366. FAX 0865-310898. *3686*

FUEL AND ENERGY ABSTRACTS.
Butterworth - Heinemann Ltd. (Institute of Energy) Linacre House, Jordan Hill, Oxford OX2 8DP, England. TEL 0865-310366. FAX 0865-310898. *3705*

FUEL PROCESSING TECHNOLOGY.
Elsevier Science Publishers B.V., P.O. Box 211, 1000 AE Amsterdam, Netherlands. TEL 020-5803911. FAX 020-5803598. *3686*

FUEL SCIENCE AND TECHNOLOGY INTERNATIONAL.
Marcel Dekker Journals, 270 Madison Ave., New York, NY 10016. TEL 212-696-9000. FAX 212-685-4540. *1822*

FUNCTIONAL ANALYSIS AND ITS APPLICATIONS.
Plenum Publishing Corp., Consultants Bureau, (Russian Academy of Sciences) 233 Spring St., New York, NY 10013-1578. TEL 212-620-8468. FAX 212-463-0742. *3036*

FUNCTIONAL AND DEVELOPMENTAL MORPHOLOGY.
Plenum Publishing Corp., (Czechoslovak Academy of Sciences, Institute of Morphology) 233 Spring St., New York, NY 10013-1578. TEL 212-620-8000. FAX 212-463-0742. *439*

FUNCTIONS OF THE NERVOUS SYSTEM.
Elsevier Science Publishers B.V., Books Division, P.O. Box 211, 1000 AE Amsterdam, Netherlands. TEL 020-5803911. FAX 020-5803705. *3337*

FUNDAMENTA SCIENTIAE.
Association des Amis de Fundamentiae Scientiae, Universite Louis Pasteur, 4 Rue Blaise Pascal, 67070 Strasbourg Cedex, France. *4372*

FUNDAMENTAL AND APPLIED TOXICOLOGY.
Academic Press, Inc., Journal Division, (Society of Toxicology) 1250 Sixth Ave., San Diego, CA 92101. TEL 619-230-1840. FAX 619-699-6800. *1982*

FUNDAMENTAL AND CLINICAL PHARMACOLOGY.
Editions Scientifiques Elsevier, (Association des Pharmacologistes) 29, rue Buffon, 75005 Paris, France. *3727*

FUNDAMENTAL ASPECTS OF POLLUTION CONTROL AND ENVIRONMENTAL SCIENCE.
Elsevier Science Publishers B.V., Books Division, P.O. Box 211, 1000 AE Amsterdam, Netherlands. TEL 020-5803911. FAX 020-5803705. *1977*

FUNDAMENTAL STUDIES IN COMPUTER SCIENCE.
Elsevier Science Publishers B.V., Books Division, P.O. Box 211, 1000 AE Amsterdam, Netherlands. TEL 020-5803911. FAX 020-5803705. *1395*

FUNDAMENTAL STUDIES IN ENGINEERING.
Elsevier Science Publishers B.V., Books Division, P.O. Box 211, 1000 AE Amsterdam, Netherlands. TEL 020-5803911. FAX 020-5803705. *1822*

FUNDAMENTALS OF COSMIC PHYSICS.
Gordon and Breach Science Publishers, 270 Eighth Ave., New York, NY 10011. TEL 212-206-8900. FAX 212-645-2459. *364*

FUNDAMENTALS OF PURE AND APPLIED ECONOMICS SERIES.
Harwood Academic Publishers, 270 Eighth Ave., New York, NY 10011. TEL 212-206-8900. FAX 212-645-2459. *894*

FUSION ENGINEERING AND DESIGN.
North-Holland P.O. Box 211, 1000 AE Amsterdam, Netherlands. TEL 020-5803911. FAX 020-5803598. *1929*

FUSION TECHNOLOGY.
American Nuclear Society, 555 N. Kensington Ave., La Grange Park, IL 60525. TEL 708-352-6611. *1805*

FUTURES.
Butterworth - Heinemann Ltd. Linacre House, Jordan Hill, Oxford OX2 8DP, England. TEL 0865-310366. FAX 0865-310898. *4598*

FUZZY SETS AND SYSTEMS.
North-Holland (International Fuzzy Systems Association (IFSA)) P.O. Box 211, 1000 AE Amsterdam, Netherlands. TEL 020-5803911. FAX 020-5803598. *3036*

G W U M C. DEPARTMENT OF BIOCHEMISTRY. ANNUAL SPRING SYMPOSIA SERIES.
Plenum Publishing Corp., (George Washington University Medical Center) 233 Spring St., New York, NY 10013-1578. TEL 212-620-8000. FAX 212-463-0742. *477*

GANGUANG KEXUE YU GUANGHUAXUE.
Science Press, Marketing and Sales Department, (Chinese Academy of Sciences, Institute of Photographic Chemistry) 16 Donghuangchenggen Beijie, Beijing 100707, People's Republic of China. TEL 4010642. FAX 4012180. *3791*

GANN MONOGRAPHS ON CANCER RESEARCH.
Japan Scientific Societies Press, (Japanese Cancer Association) 6-2-10 Hongo, Bunkyo-ku, Tokyo 113, Japan. *3197*

GAOFENZI XUEBAO.
Science Press, Marketing and Sales Department, (Chinese Chemical Society) 16 Donghuangchenggen Beijie, Beijing 100707, People's Republic of China. TEL 4010642. FAX 4012180. *1226*

GAONENG WULI YU HE WULI.
Science Press, Marketing and Sales Department, (Chinese Society of High Energy Physics) 16 Donghuangchenggen Beijie, Beijing 100707, People's Republic of China. TEL 4010642. FAX 4102180. *3847*

GAS SEPARATION AND PURIFICATION.
Butterworth - Heinemann Ltd. Linacre House, Jordan Hill, Oxford OX2 8DP, England. TEL 0865-310366. FAX 0865-310898. *1853*

GASTROENTEROLOGY SERIES.
Marcel Dekker, Inc., 270 Madison Ave., New York, NY 10016. TEL 212-696-9000. FAX 212-685-4540. *3268*

GASTROINTESTINAL ENDOSCOPY.
Williams & Wilkins, 428 E. Preston St., Baltimore, MD 21202. TEL 301-528-4000. FAX 301-528-4312. *3268*

GAZZETTA CHIMICA ITALIANA.
Societa Chimica Italiana, Viale Liege 48, 00198 Rome, Italy. TEL 06-8549691. FAX 06-8548734. *1177*

GENE.
Elsevier Science Publishers B.V., P.O. Box 211, 1000 AE Amsterdam, Netherlands. TEL 020-5803911. FAX 020-5803598. *541*

GENE AMPLIFICATION AND ANALYSIS SERIES.
Elsevier Science Publishers B.V., Books Division, P.O. Box 211, 1000 AE Amsterdam, Netherlands. TEL 020-5803911. FAX 020-5803705. *541*

GENERAL AND COMPARATIVE ENDOCRINOLOGY.
Academic Press, Inc., Journal Division, 1250 Sixth Ave., San Diego, CA 92101. TEL 619-230-1840. FAX 619-699-6800. *3253*

GENERAL DENTISTRY.
Academy of General Dentistry, 211 E. Chicago Ave., Ste. 1200, Chicago, IL 60611. TEL 312-440-4300. FAX 312-440-0559. *3234*

GENERAL HOSPITAL PSYCHIATRY.
Elsevier Science Publishing Co., Inc. (New York), 655 Ave. of the Americas, New York, NY 10010. TEL 212-989-5800. FAX 212-633-3965. *3337*

GENERAL MOTORS SYMPOSIA SERIES.
Plenum Publishing Corp., 233 Spring St., New York, NY 10013-1578. TEL 212-620-8000. FAX 212-463-0742. *4691*

GENERAL PHARMACOLOGY.
Pergamon Press, Inc., Journals Division, 660 White Plains Rd., Tarrytown, NY 10591-5153. TEL 914-524-9200. FAX 914-333-2444. *3727*

GENERAL RELATIVITY AND GRAVITATION.
Plenum Publishing Corp., (International Committee on General Relativity and Gravitation) 233 Spring St., New York, NY 10013-1578. TEL 212-620-8000. FAX 212-463-0742. *3819*

GENESIS OF BEHAVIOR.
Plenum Publishing Corp., 233 Spring St., New York, NY 10013-1578. TEL 212-620-8000. FAX 212-463-0742. *3337*

GENETIC ANALYSIS: TECHNIQUES AND APPLICATIONS.
Elsevier Science Publishing Co., Inc. (New York), 655 Ave. of the Americas, New York, NY 10010. TEL 212-989-5800. FAX 212-633-3965. *542*

GENETIC ENGINEERING.
Plenum Publishing Corp., 233 Spring St., New York, NY 10013-1578. TEL 212-620-8000. FAX 212-463-0742. *542*

GENETIC ENGINEERING AND BIOTECHNOLOGY YEARBOOK.
Elsevier Science Publishers B.V., Books Division, P.O. Box 211, 1000 AE Amsterdam, Netherlands. TEL 020-5803911. FAX 020-5803705. *542*

GENETIC EPIDEMIOLOGY.
John Wiley & Sons, Inc., Journals, 605 Third Ave., New York, NY 10158. TEL 212-850-6000. FAX 212-850-6088. *542*

GENETIC, SOCIAL, AND GENERAL PSYCHOLOGY MONOGRAPHS.
Heldref Publications, (Helen Dwight Reid Educational Foundation) 1319 Eighteenth St., N.W., Washington, DC 20036-1802. TEL 202-296-6267. FAX 202-296-5149. *4022*

GENETICS.
Genetics Society of America, 9650 Rockville Pike, Bethesda, MD 20814. TEL 301-571-1825. *542*

GENETICS, SELECTION, EVOLUTION.
Editions Scientifiques Elsevier, (Institut National de la Recherche Agronomique (INRA)) 29, rue Buffon, 75005 Paris, France. TEL 47-07-11-22. FAX 43-36-80-93. *543*

GENEVA PAPERS ON RISK AND INSURANCE THEORY.
Kluwer Academic Publishers, (Geneva Association) P.O. Box 17, 3300 AA Dordrecht, Netherlands. TEL 078-334911. FAX 078-334254. *2532*

GENOME.
National Research Council of Canada, Research Journals, (Genetics Society of Canada) Ottawa, Ont. K1A 0R6, Canada. TEL 613-993-9084. FAX 613-952-7656. *543*

GENOMICS.
Academic Press, Inc., Journal Division, 1250 Sixth Ave., San Diego, CA 92101. TEL 619-230-1840. FAX 619-699-6800. *543*

GENTES HERBARUM.
L. H. Bailey Hortorium, Cornell University, Ithaca, NY 14853. TEL 607-255-7976. *504*

GEOCHIMICA ET COSMOCHIMICA ACTA.
Pergamon Press, Inc., Journals Division, (Geochemical Society) 660 White Plains Rd., Tarrytown, NY 10591-5153. TEL 914-524-9200. FAX 914-333-2444. *1561*

GEODERMA.
Elsevier Science Publishers B.V., P.O. Box 211, 1000 AE Amsterdam, Netherlands. TEL 020-5803911. FAX 020-5803598. *178*

GEOFORUM.
Pergamon Press, Inc., Journals Division, 660 White Plains Rd., Tarrytown, NY 10591-5153. TEL 914-524-9200. FAX 914-333-2444. *1544*

GEOLOGICAL SOCIETY OF AMERICA. BULLETIN.
Geological Society of America, 3300 Penrose Pl., Box 9140, Boulder, CO 80301. TEL 303-447-2020. FAX 303-447-1133. *1563*

GEOLOGICAL SOCIETY OF AMERICA. SPECIAL PAPERS.
Geological Society of America, 3300 Penrose Pl., Box 9140, Boulder, CO 80301. TEL 303-447-2020. FAX 303-447-1133. *1563*

GEOLOGY (BOULDER).
Geological Society of America, 3300 Penrose Pl., Box 9140, Boulder, CO 80301. TEL 303-447-2020. FAX 303-447-1133. *1565*

GEOLOGY OF THE PACIFIC OCEAN.
Harwood Academic Publishers, 270 Eighth Ave., New York, NY 10011. TEL 212-206-8900. FAX 212-645-2459. *1565*

GEOMICROBIOLOGY JOURNAL.
Taylor & Francis, 1900 Frost Rd., Ste. 101, Bristol, PA 19007. TEL 215-785-5800. FAX 215-785-5515. *552*

GEOMORPHOLOGY.
Elsevier Science Publishers B.V., P.O. Box 211, 1000 AE Amsterdam, Netherlands. TEL 20-5803911. FAX 20-5803598. *1565*

GEOPHYSICAL AND ASTROPHYSICAL FLUID DYNAMICS.
Gordon and Breach Science Publishers, 270 Eighth Ave., New York, NY 10011. TEL 212-206-8900. FAX 212-645-2459. *1589*

GEOPHYSICAL JOURNAL.
Gordon and Breach Science Publishers, 270 Eighth Ave., New York, NY 10011. TEL 212-206-8900. FAX 212-645-2459. *1589*

GEOPHYSICAL RESEARCH LETTERS.
American Geophysical Union, 2000 Florida Ave., N.W., Washington, DC 20009. TEL 202-462-6900. FAX 202-328-0566. *1589*

GEORGIA JOURNAL OF SCIENCE.
Georgia Academy of Science, c/o Andy C. Reese, Ed., Medical College of Georgia, Augusta, GA 30912. TEL 404-790-2056. FAX 404-721-6608. *4311*

GEOTECHNICAL TESTING JOURNAL.
American Society for Testing and Materials, 1916 Race St., Philadelphia, PA 19103. TEL 215-299-5400. FAX 215-977-9679. *1866*

GEOTEXTILES AND GEOMEMBRANES.
Elsevier Science Publishers Ltd., (International Geotextile Society) Crown House, Linton Rd., Barking, Essex IG11 8JU, England. TEL 081-594-7272. FAX 081-594-5942. *485*

GEOTHERMAL SCIENCE AND TECHNOLOGY.
Gordon & Breach Science Publishers, 270 Eighth Ave., New York, NY 10011. TEL 212-206-8900. FAX 212-645-2459. *1566*

GEOTHERMICS.
Pergamon Press, Inc., Journals Division, (International Institute for Geothermal Research, Pisa) 660 White Plains Rd., Tarrytown, NY 10591-5153. TEL 914-524-9200. FAX 914-333-2444. *1545*

GERIATRICS.
Avanstar Communications, Inc., 7500 Old Oak Blvd., Cleveland, OH 44130. TEL 216-826-2839. FAX 216-891-2726. *2273*

GERMANIC REVIEW.
Heldref Publications, (Helen Dwight Reid Educational Foundation) 1319 Eighteenth St., N.W., Washington, DC 20036-1802. TEL 202-296-6267. FAX 202-296-5149. *2816*

GERONTOLOGIST.
Gerontological Society of America, 1275 K St., N.W., Ste. 350, Washington, DC 20005-4006. TEL 202-842-1275. *2273*

GERONTOLOGY & GERIATRICS EDUCATION.
Haworth Press, Inc., 10 Alice St., Binghamton, NY 13904. TEL 800-342-9678. FAX 607-722-1424. *2273*

GLASS AND CERAMICS.
Plenum Publishing Corp., Consultants Bureau, (Russian Academy of Sciences) 233 Spring St., New York, NY 10013-1578. TEL 212-620-8468. FAX 212-463-0742. *1164*

GLASS SCIENCE AND TECHNOLOGY.
Elsevier Science Publishers B.V., Books Division, P.O. Box 211, 1000 AE Amsterdam, Netherlands. TEL 020-5803911. FAX 020-5803705. *1164*

GLOBAL AND PLANETARY CHANGE.
Elsevier Science Publishers B.V., P.O. Box 211, 1000 AE Amsterdam, Netherlands. TEL 020-5803911. FAX 020-5803598. *1566*

GLOBAL BIOGEOCHEMICAL CYCLES.
American Geophysical Union, 2000 Florida Ave., N.W., Washington, DC 20009. TEL 202-462-6900. FAX 202-328-0566. *4311*

GLOBAL CLIMATE CHANGE DIGEST.
Elsevier Science Publishing Co., Inc. (New York), 655 Ave. of the Americas, New York, NY 10010. TEL 212-989-5800. FAX 212-633-3965. *1955*

GNOSIS.
Concordia University, Philosophy Department, 1455 de Maisonneuve West, Montreal, Que. H3G 1M8, Canada. TEL 514-848-2500. *3767*

GONGCHENG LIXUE.
Science Press, Marketing and Sales Department, (Zhongguo Lixue Xuehui) 16 Donghuangchenggen Beijie, Beijing 100707, People's Republic of China. TEL 4010642. FAX 4012180. *1917*

GONGCHENG RE-WULI XUEBAO.
Kexue Chubanshe, Qikan Bu, (Chinese Society of Engineering Thermophysics) 16 Donghuangchenggen Beijie, Beijing 100707, People's Republic of China. TEL 4010642. FAX 4012180. *3840*

GOVERNMENT PUBLICATIONS REVIEW.
Pergamon Press, Inc., Journals Division, 660 White Plains Rd., Tarrytown, NY 10591-5153. TEL 914-524-9200. FAX 914-333-2444. *4062*

GREAT LAKES ENTOMOLOGIST.
Michigan Entomological Society, c/o Dept. of Entomology, Michigan State Univ., East Lansing, MI 48824. TEL 517-321-2192. *533*

GREAT PLAINS QUARTERLY.
University of Nebraska, Lincoln, Center for Great Plains Studies, 1214 Oldfather Hall, Lincoln, NE 68588-0313. TEL 402-472-6058. FAX 402-472-2410. *2407*

GROUND WATER.
Water Well Journal Publishing Co., (National Water Well Association) 6375 Riverside Dr., Dublin, OH 43017. TEL 614-846-4967. *1598*

GROUND WATER MONITORING REVIEW.
Water Well Journal Publishing Co., 6375 Riverside Dr., Dublin, OH 43017. TEL 614-846-4967. *1598*

GROWTH AND CHANGE.
University of Kentucky, College of Business and Economics, 301 Mathews Bldg., Lexington, KY 40506-0047. TEL 606-257-7675. FAX 606-257-8938. *1077*

GROWTH, DEVELOPMENT & AGING.
Growth Publishing Co., Inc., Box 42, Bar Harbor, ME 04609-0042. TEL 207-288-3533. FAX 207-288-5079. *3101*

GROWTH FACTORS.
Harwood Academic Publishers, 270 Eighth Ave., New York, NY 10011. TEL 212-206-8900. FAX 212-645-2459. *572*

GROWTH OF CRYSTALS.
Plenum Publishing Corp., Consultants Bureau, (Russian Academy of Sciences) 233 Spring St., New York, NY 10013-1578. TEL 212-620-8000. FAX 212-463-0742. *1210*

GROWTH REGULATION.
Churchill Livingstone Medical Journals, Robert Stevenson House, 1-3 Baxter's Pl., Leith Walk, Edinburgh EH1 3AF, Scotland. TEL 031-556-2424. FAX 031-558-1278. *3253*

GUANGPUXUE YU GUANGPU FENXI.
Zhongguo Guangxue Xuehui, 76 Xueyuan Nanlu, Haidian-qu, Beijing 100081, People's Republic of China. TEL 892179. *3852*

GUISUANYAN XUEBAO.
Chinese Silicate Society, Guojia Jiancaiju Nei (Inside National Bureau of Building Materials), Baiwanzhuang, Beijing 100831, People's Republic of China. TEL 8311144. *1213*

GUJIZHUI DONGWU XUEBAO.
Science Press, Marketing and Sales Department, (Zhongguo Kexueyuan, Gujizhui Dongwu yu Gurenlei Yanjiusuo) 16 Donghuangchenggen Beijie, Beijing 100707, People's Republic of China. TEL 4010642. FAX 4012180. *3657*

GUSHENGWU XUEBAO.
Science Press, Marketing and Sales Department, (Zhongguo Kexueyuan, Nanjing Dizhi Gushengwusuo) 16 Donghuangchenggen Beijie, Beijing 100707, People's Republic of China. TEL 4010642. FAX 4012180. *3657*

GYNECOLOGIC ONCOLOGY.
Academic Press, Inc., Journal Division, 1250 Sixth Ave., San Diego, CA 92101. TEL 619-230-1840. FAX 619-699-6800. *3292*

GYPSY LORE SOCIETY. JOURNAL.
Gypsy Lore Society, 5607 Greenleaf Rd., Cheverly, MD 20785. TEL 301-341-1261. *240*

GYPSY LORE SOCIETY. PUBLICATIONS.
Gypsy Lore Society, 5607 Greenleaf Rd., Cheverly, MD 20785. TEL 301-341-1261. *240*

H P B SURGERY.
Harwood Academic Publishers, 270 Eighth Ave., New York, NY 10011. TEL 212-206-8900. FAX 212-645-2459. *3379*

H P L C: ADVANCES AND PERSPECTIVES.
Academic Press, Inc., 1250 Sixth Ave., San Diego, CA 92101. TEL 619-231-0926. FAX 619-699-6715. *1205*

HABITAT INTERNATIONAL.
Pergamon Press, Inc., Journals Division, 660 White Plains Rd., Tarrytown, NY 10591-5153. TEL 914-524-9200. FAX 914-333-2444. *1957*

HAIYANG XUEBAO.
China Ocean Press, International Cooperation Department, (Chinese Society of Oceanography) Haimao Dalou, 1 Fuxingmenwai Dajie, Beijing 100860, People's Republic of China. TEL 868941. FAX 862209. *1604*

HAIYANG YU HUZHAO.
Science Press, Marketing and Sales Department, (Chinese Academy of Sciences) 16 Donghuangchenggen Beijie, Beijing 100707, People's Republic of China. TEL 4010642. FAX 4012180. *1605*

HALCYON.
Nevada Humanities Committee, 1101 N. Virginia St., P.O. Box 8029, Reno, NV 89507. TEL 702-784-6587. FAX 702-597-4097. *2507*

HANDBOOK OF COMPOSITES.
Elsevier Science Publishers B.V., Books Division, P.O. Box 211, 1000 AE Amsterdam, Netherlands. TEL 020-5803911. FAX 020-5803705. *1226*

HANDBOOK OF ENDOTOXIN.
Elsevier Science Publishers B.V., Books Division, P.O. Box 211, 1000 AE Amsterdam, Netherlands. TEL 020-5803911. FAX 020-5803705. *3727*

HANDBOOK OF EXPLORATION GEOCHEMISTRY.
Elsevier Science Publishers B.V., Books Division, P.O. Box 211, 1000 AE Amsterdam, Netherlands. TEL 020-5803911. FAX 020-5803705. *1567*

HANDBOOK OF INFLAMMATION.
Elsevier Science Publishers B.V., Books Division, P.O. Box 211, 1000 AE Amsterdam, Netherlands. TEL 020-5803911. FAX 020-5803705. *3102*

HANDBOOK OF NATURAL TOXINS.
Marcel Dekker, Inc., 270 Madison Ave., New York, NY 10016. TEL 212-696-9000. FAX 212-685-4540. *3102*

HANDBOOK OF PAPER SCIENCE.
Elsevier Science Publishers B.V., Books Division, P.O. Box 211, 1000 AE Amsterdam, Netherlands. TEL 020-5803911. FAX 020-5803705. *3663*

HANDBOOK OF PLASMA PHYSICS.
Elsevier Science Publishers B.V., Books Division, P.O. Box 211, 1000 AE Amsterdam, Netherlands. TEL 020-5803911. FAX 020-5803705. *3819*

HANDBOOK OF POWDER TECHNOLOGY.
Elsevier Science Publishers B.V., Books Division, P.O. Box 211, 1000 AE Amsterdam, Netherlands. TEL 020-5803911. FAX 020-5803705. *1866*

HANDBOOK OF PSYCHOLOGY AND HEALTH SERIES.
Lawrence Erlbaum Associates, Inc., 365 Broadway, Hillsdale, NJ 07642. TEL 201-666-4110. FAX 201-666-2394. *4023*

HANDBOOK OF STRATA-BOUND AND STRATIFORM ORE DEPOSITS.
Elsevier Science Publishers B.V., Books Division, P.O. Box 211, 1000 AE Amsterdam, Netherlands. TEL 020-5803911. FAX 020-5803705. *1567*

HANDBOOK OF THE SPINAL CORD.
Marcel Dekker, Inc., 270 Madison Ave., New York, NY 10016. TEL 212-696-9000. FAX 212-685-4540. *3102*

HANDBOOK ON FERROMAGNETIC MATERIALS.
Elsevier Science Publishers B.V., Books Division, P.O. Box 211, 1000 AE Amsterdam, Netherlands. TEL 020-5803911. FAX 020-5803705. *3407*

HANDBOOK ON SEMICONDUCTORS.
Elsevier Science Publishers B.V., Books Division, P.O. Box 211, 1000 AE Amsterdam, Netherlands. TEL 020-5803911. FAX 020-5803705. *1771*

HANDBOOK ON THE PHYSICS AND CHEMISTRY OF RARE EARTHS.
Elsevier Science Publishers B.V., Books Division, P.O. Box 211, 1000 AE Amsterdam, Netherlands. TEL 020-5803911. FAX 020-5803705. *3819*

HANDBOOK ON THE PHYSICS AND CHEMISTRY OF THE ACTINIDES.
Elsevier Science Publishers B.V., Books Division, P.O. Box 211, 1000 AE Amsterdam, Netherlands. TEL 020-5803911. FAX 020-5803705. *3819*

HANDBOOKS IN ECONOMICS.
Elsevier Science Publishers B.V., Books Division, P.O. Box 211, 1000 AE Amsterdam, Netherlands. TEL 020-5803911. FAX 020-5803705. *895*

HANDBOOKS OF PHYSIOLOGY.
Oxford University Press, (American Physiological Society) 200 Madison Ave., New York, NY 10016. TEL 212-679-7300. *572*

HARVARD ARMENIAN TEXTS AND STUDIES.
Harvard University Press, 79 Garden St., Cambridge, MA 02138. TEL 617-495-2600. FAX 617-495-5898. *2429*

HARVARD BOOKS IN BIOPHYSICS.
Harvard University Press, (Harvard University Medical School, Department of Biophysics) 79 Garden St., Cambridge, MA 02138. TEL 617-495-2600. FAX 617-495-5898. *485*

HARVARD EAST ASIAN SERIES.
Harvard University Press, (Harvard University, East Asian Research Center) 79 Garden St., Cambridge, MA 02138. TEL 617-495-2600. FAX 617-495-5898. *2338*

HARVARD ECONOMIC STUDIES.
Harvard University Press, 79 Garden St., Cambridge, MA 02138. TEL 617-495-2600. FAX 617-495-5898. *668*

HARVARD HISTORICAL MONOGRAPHS.
Harvard University Press, (Harvard University, Department of History) 79 Garden St., Cambridge, MA 02138. TEL 617-495-2600. FAX 617-495-5898. *2311*

HARVARD HISTORICAL STUDIES.
Harvard University Press, (Harvard University, Department of History) 79 Garden St., Cambridge, MA 02138. TEL 617-495-2600. FAX 617-495-5898. *2311*

HARVARD HUMAN RIGHTS YEARBOOK.
Harvard Law School, Cambridge, MA 02138. TEL 617-495-9362. *3942*

HARVARD PUBLICATIONS IN MUSIC.
Harvard University Press, 79 Garden St., Cambridge, MA 02138. TEL 617-495-2600. FAX 617-495-5898. *3554*

HARVARD STUDIES IN BUSINESS HISTORY.
Harvard University Press, (Harvard University Graduate School of Business Administration) 79 Garden St., Cambridge, MA 02138. TEL 617-495-2600. FAX 617-495-5898. *895*

HARVARD STUDIES IN CLASSICAL PHILOLOGY.
Harvard University Press, 79 Garden St., Cambridge, MA 02138. TEL 617-495-2600. FAX 617-495-5898. *2817*

HARVARD STUDIES IN COMPARATIVE LITERATURE.
Harvard University Press, 79 Garden St., Cambridge, MA 02138. TEL 617-495-2600. FAX 617-495-5898. *2921*

HARVARD STUDIES IN URBAN HISTORY.
Harvard University Press, 79 Garden St., Cambridge, MA 02138. TEL 617-495-2600. FAX 617-495-5898. *2488*

HARVARD UNIVERSITY. MUSEUM OF COMPARATIVE ZOOLOGY. DEPARTMENT OF MOLLUSKS. OCCASIONAL PAPERS ON MOLLUSKS.
Harvard University, Museum of Comparative Zoology, Cambridge, MA 02138. TEL 617-495-2468. *583*

HARVARD UNIVERSITY. RUSSIAN RESEARCH CENTER. STUDIES.
Harvard University Press, 79 Garden St., Cambridge, MA 02138. TEL 617-495-2600. FAX 617-495-5898. *2365*

HARVARD - YENCHING INSTITUTE. STUDIES.
Harvard University Press, 79 Garden St., Cambridge, MA 02138. TEL 617-495-2600. FAX 617-495-5898. *2338*

HARVEY LECTURES.
Academic Press, Inc., 1250 Sixth Ave., San Diego, CA 92101. TEL 619-231-0926. FAX 619-699-6715. *3102*

DER HAUTARZT.
Springer-Verlag, Heidelberger Platz 3, D-1000 Berlin 33, Germany. TEL 030-8207-1. *3248*

HAWAII INSTITUTE OF MARINE BIOLOGY. TECHNICAL REPORTS.
Hawaii Institute of Marine Biology, Box 1346, Kaneohe, HI 96744. TEL 808-237-7401. FAX 808-247-6634. *440*

HAWAIIAN ENTOMOLOGICAL SOCIETY. PROCEEDINGS.
Hawaiian Entomological Society, c/o Entomology Dept., University of Hawaii, 3050 Maile Way, Honolulu, HI 96822. TEL 808-956-7076. FAX 808-956-2428. *533*

HE JISHU.
Science Press, Marketing and Sale Department, 16 Donghuangchenggen Beijie, Beijing 100707, People's Republic of China. TEL 4010642. FAX 4012180. *1805*

HEAD & NECK.
John Wiley & Sons, Inc., Journals, 605 Third Ave., New York, NY 10158-0012. TEL 212-692-6000. *3379*

HEADACHE QUARTERLY.
International Universities Press, Inc., Journal Department, 59 Boston Post Rd., Box 1524, Madison, CT 06443-1524. TEL 203-245-4000. FAX 203-245-0775. *3102*

HEALTH COMMUNICATION.
Lawrence Erlbaum Associates, Inc., 365 Broadway, Hillsdale, NJ 07642. TEL 201-666-4110. FAX 201-666-2394. *4103*

HEALTH DEVICES.
E C R I, (Emergency Care Research Institute) 5200 Butler Pike, Plymouth Meeting, PA 19462. TEL 215-825-6000. FAX 215-834-1275. *3259*

HEALTH DEVICES ALERTS.
E C R I, (Emergency Care Research Institute) 5200 Butler Pike, Plymouth Meeting, PA 19462. TEL 215-825-6000. FAX 215-834-1275. *3175*

HEALTH DEVICES INSPECTION & PREVENTIVE MAINTENANCE SYSTEM.
E C R I, (Emergency Care Research Institute) 5200 Butler Pike, Plymouth Meeting, PA 19462. TEL 215-825-6000. FAX 215-834-1275. *3103*

HEALTH DEVICES SOURCEBOOK.
E C R I, (Emergency Care Research Institute) 5200 Butler Pike, Plymouth Meeting, PA 19462. TEL 215-825-6000. FAX 215-834-1275. *3103*

HEALTH EDUCATION QUARTERLY.
John Wiley & Sons, Inc., Journals, (Society for Public Health Education) 605 Third Ave., New York, NY 10158-0012. TEL 212-692-6000. *3103*

HEALTH EDUCATION RESEARCH.
I R L Press Ltd. Pinkhill House, Southfield Road, Eynsham, Oxford OX8 1JJ, England. TEL 0865-882283. FAX 0865-882890. *4407*

HEALTH MARKETING QUARTERLY.
Haworth Press, Inc., 10 Alice St., Binghamton, NY 13904. TEL 800-342-9678. FAX 607-722-1424. *4103*

HEALTH PHYSICS.
Williams & Wilkins, (Health Physics Society) 428 E. Preston St., Baltimore, MD 21202. TEL 301-528-4000. FAX 301-528-4321. *3104*

HEALTH POLICY.
Elsevier Science Publishers B.V., (European Health Policy Forum) P.O. Box 211, 1000 AE Amsterdam, Netherlands. TEL 020-5803911. FAX 020-5803598. *4103*

HEALTH PSYCHOLOGY.
Lawrence Erlbaum Associates, Inc., (American Psychological Association, Division of Health Psychology) 365 Broadway, Hillsdale, NJ 07642. TEL 201-666-4110. FAX 201-666-2394. *4023*

HEALTH SERVICES RESEARCH.
Health Administration Press, (Foundation of the American College of Healthcare Executives) 1021 E. Huron St., Ann Arbor, MI 48104-9990. TEL 312-943-0544. FAX 708-450-1618. *3104*

HEALTH, SOCIETY AND CULTURE.
Gordon & Breach Science Publishers, 270 Eighth Ave., New York, NY 10011. TEL 212-206-8900. FAX 212-645-2459. *4436*

HEALTH TECHNOLOGY MANAGEMENT.
E C R I, (Emergency Care Research Institute) 5200 Butler Pike, Plymouth Meeting, PA 19462. TEL 215-825-6000. FAX 215-834-1275. *3104*

HEALTH TECHNOLOGY TRENDS.
E C R I, (Emergency Care Research Institute) 5200 Butler Pike, Plymouth Meeting, PA 19462. TEL 215-825-6000. FAX 215-834-1275. *2462*

HEALTH VALUES.
P N G Publications, Box 4593, Star City, WV 26504-4593. TEL 304-293-4699. FAX 304-293-4693. *3803*

HEALTHCARE ENVIRONMENTAL MANAGEMENT SYSTEM.
E C R I, (Emergency Care Research Institute) 5200 Butler Pike, Plymouth Meeting, PA 19462. TEL 215-825-6000. FAX 215-834-1275. *3104*

HEALTHCARE HAZARDOUS MATERIALS MANAGEMENT.
E C R I, (Emergency Care Research Institute) 5200 Butler Pike, Plymouth Meeting, PA 19462. TEL 215-834-1275. FAX 215-834-1275. *2463*

HEARING RESEARCH.
Elsevier Science Publishers B.V., P.O. Box 211, 1000 AE Amsterdam, Netherlands. TEL 020-5803911. FAX 020-5803598. *3314*

HEART AND LUNG.
Mosby - Year Book, Inc. 11830 Westline Industrial Dr., St. Louis, MO 63146. TEL 800-325-4117. FAX 314-432-1380. *3278*

HEAT RECOVERY SYSTEMS & C H P.
Pergamon Press, Inc., Journals Division, 660 White Plains Rd., Tarrytown, NY 10591-5153. TEL 914-524-9200. FAX 914-333-2444. *3841*

HEAT TRANSFER ENGINEERING.
Hemisphere Publishing Corporation 1900 Frost Rd., Ste. 101, Bristol, PA 19007-1598. TEL 215-785-5800. FAX 215-785-5515. *1853*

HEBREW STUDIES.
National Association of Professors of Hebrew, 1346 Van Hise Hall, 1220 Linden Dr., University of Wisconsin-Madison, Madison, WI 53706. TEL 608-262-2089. *2817*

HECATE.
Hecate Press, c/o English Dept., Univ. Queensland, St. Lucia, Qld. 4067, Australia. TEL 07-377-4401. FAX 07-371-9578. *4859*

HEMATOLOGIC PATHOLOGY.
Marcel Dekker Journals, 270 Madison Ave., New York, NY 10016. TEL 212-696-9000. FAX 212-685-4540. *3272*

HEMATOLOGY - ONCOLOGY CLINICS OF NORTH AMERICA.
W.B. Saunders Co., Curtis Center, Independence Square W., Philadelphia, PA 19106. TEL 215-574-4700. *3197*

HEMATOLOGY REVIEWS AND COMMUNICATIONS.
Harwood Academic Publishers, 270 Eighth Ave., New York, NY 10011. TEL 212-206-8900. FAX 212-645-2459. *3272*

HEMATOLOGY SERIES.
Marcel Dekker, Inc., 270 Madison Ave., New York, NY 10016. TEL 212-696-9000. FAX 212-658-4540. *3272*

HEMOGLOBIN.
Marcel Dekker Journals, 270 Madison Ave., New York, NY 10016. TEL 212-696-9000. FAX 212-685-4540. *3272*

HEPATOLOGY (ST. LOUIS).
Mosby - Year Book, Inc. (American Association for the Study of Liver Diseases) 11830 Westline Industrial Dr., St. Louis, MO 63146. TEL 800-325-4117. FAX 314-432-1380. *3105*

HERPETOLOGICAL REVIEW.
Society for the Study of Amphibians and Reptiles, Department of Zoology, Miami University, Oxford, OH 45056. *583*

HETEROCYCLES.
Japan Institute of Heterocyclic Chemistry, 1-7-503, 1-chome, Motoakasaka, Minato-ku, Tokyo 107, Japan. TEL 03-3404-5019. FAX 03-3497-9370. *1218*

HIGH ENERGY CHEMISTRY.
Plenum Publishing Corp., Consultants Bureau, (Russian Academy of Sciences) 233 Spring St., New York, NY 10013-1578. TEL 212-620-8468. FAX 212-463-0742. *1226*

HIGH ENERGY PHYSICS AND NUCLEAR PHYSICS.
Allerton Press, Inc., (Chinese Society of High Energy Physics) 150 Fifth Ave., New York, NY 10011. TEL 212-924-3950. *3847*

HIGH PRESSURE RESEARCH.
Gordon & Breach Science Publishers, 270 Eighth Ave., New York, NY 10011. TEL 212-206-8900. FAX 212-645-2459. *3843*

HIGH-PURITY SUBSTANCES.
Plenum Publishing Corp., Consultants Bureau, (Russian Academy of Sciences) 233 Spring St., New York, NY 10013-1578. TEL 212-620-8468. FAX 212-463-0742. *1178*

HIGH SCHOOL JOURNAL.
University of North Carolina Press, (University of North Carolina at Chapel Hill, Department of English) Box 2288, Chapel Hill, NC 27515-2288. TEL 919-966-3561. FAX 919-966-3829. *1637*

HIGH TECHNOLOGY LAW JOURNAL.
University of California Press, Journals Division, 2120 Berkeley Way, Berkeley, CA 94720. TEL 510-642-4191. FAX 510-643-7127. *2632*

HIGH TEMPERATURE.
Plenum Publishing Corp., Consultants Bureau, (Russian Academy of Sciences) 233 Spring St., New York, NY 10013-1578. TEL 212-620-8468. FAX 212-463-0742. *3841*

HIGH TEMPERATURE SCIENCE.
Humana Press Inc., Crescent Manor, Box 2148, Clifton, NJ 07015. TEL 201-256-1699. FAX 201-256-8341. *1226*

HIGHLIGHTS OF AGRICULTURAL RESEARCH.
Alabama Agricultural Experiment Station, 110 Comer Hall, Auburn University, AL 36849. TEL 205-844-4000. *95*

HISPANIC AMERICAN HISTORICAL REVIEW.
Duke University Press, (American Historical Association, Conference on Latin American Studies) 6697 College Station, Durham, NC 27708. TEL 919-684-2173. FAX 919-684-8644. *2408*

HISTOIRE DES SCIENCES ET DES TECHNIQUES.
Gordon and Breach Scientific Publishers, 270 Eighth Ave., New York, NY 10011. TEL 212-206-8900. FAX 212-645-2459. *4312*

HISTORIA MATHEMATICA.
Academic Press, Inc., Journal Division, (International Commission on the History of Mathematics) 1250 Sixth Ave., San Diego, CA 92101. TEL 619-230-1840. FAX 619-699-6800. *3037*

HISTORIC BRASS SOCIETY JOURNAL.
Historic Brass Society, Inc., 148 W. 23rd St., No. 2A, New York, NY 10011. TEL 212-627-3820. *3554*

HISTORIC BRASS SOCIETY NEWSLETTER.
Historic Brass Society, Inc., 148 West 23rd St., No. 2A, New York, NY 10011. TEL 212-627-3820. *3554*

HISTORICAL BIOLOGY.
Harwood Academic Publishers, 270 Eighth Ave., New York, NY 10011. TEL 212-206-8900. FAX 212-645-2459. *3657*

HISTORICAL METHODS.
Heldref Publications, (University of Illinois at Chicago Circle, Department of History) 1319 Eighteenth St., N.W., Washington, DC 20036-1802. TEL 202-296-6267. FAX 202-296-5149. *2312*

HISTORICAL STUDIES IN THE PHYSICAL AND BIOLOGICAL SCIENCES.
University of California Press, Journals Division, 2120 Berkeley Way, Berkeley, CA 94720. TEL 510-642-4191. FAX 510-643-7127. *4313*

HISTORY AND ANTHROPOLOGY.
Harwood Academic Publishers, 270 Eighth Ave., New York, NY 10011. TEL 212-206-8900. FAX 212-645-2459. *240*

HISTORY AND PHILOSOPHY OF LOGIC.
Taylor & Francis Ltd., Rankine Rd., Basingstoke, Hants RG24 0PR, England. TEL 0256-840366. FAX 0256-479438. *3768*

HISTORY AND PHILOSOPHY OF THE LIFE SCIENCES.
Taylor & Francis Ltd., (Stazione Zoologica di Napoli) Rankine Rd., Basingstoke, Hants RG24 0PR, England. TEL 0256-840366. FAX 0256-479438. *440*

HISTORY AND TECHNOLOGY.
Harwood Academic Publishers, 270 Eighth Ave., New York, NY 10011. TEL 212-206-8900. FAX 212-645-2459. *2313*

HISTORY OF EDUCATION.
Taylor & Francis Ltd., (History of Education Society) Rankine Rd., Basingstoke, Hants RG24 0PR, England. TEL 0256-840366. FAX 0256-479438. *1637*

HISTORY OF EUROPEAN IDEAS.
Pergamon Press, Inc., Journals Division, (International Society for the Study of European Ideas) 660 White Plains Rd., Tarrytown, NY 10591-5153. TEL 914-524-9200. FAX 914-333-2444. *2367*

HISTORY OF HIGHER EDUCATION ANNUAL.
Northwestern University, School of Education & Social Policy, 2003 Sheridan Rd., Evanston, IL 60208-2610. FAX 708-491-8999. *1708*

HISTORY OF PHOTOGRAPHY.
Taylor and Francis Ltd., Rankine Rd., Basingstoke, Hants. RG24 0PR, England. TEL 0256-840366. FAX 0256-479438. *3792*

HISTORY OF POLITICAL ECONOMY.
Duke University Press, 6697 College Station, Durham, NC 27708. TEL 919-684-2173. FAX 919-684-8644. *895*

HISTORY OF RELIGIONS.
University of Chicago Press, Journals Division, 5720 S. Woodlawn Ave., Chicago, IL 60637. TEL 312-753-3347. FAX 312-753-3347. *4181*

HISTORY: REVIEWS OF NEW BOOKS.
Heldref Publications, (Helen Dwight Reid Educational Foundation) 1319 Eighteenth St., N.W., Washington, DC 20036-1802. TEL 202-296-6267. FAX 202-296-5149. *4129*

HOLOCAUST AND GENOCIDE STUDIES.
Oxford University Press, Journals, (Yad Vashem Holocaust Martyrs' and Heroes' Remembrance Authority) 200 Madison Ave., New York, NY 10016. TEL 212-679-7300. FAX 212-725-2972. *2367*

HOME HEALTH CARE SERVICES QUARTERLY.
Haworth Press, Inc., 10 Alice St., Binghamton, NY 13904. TEL 800-342-9678. FAX 607-722-1424. *2463*

HOME SCHOOL RESEARCHER.
National Home Education Research Institute, Western Baptist College, 5000 Deer Park Dr., Salem, OR 97301-9330. TEL 503-581-8600. FAX 503-585-4316. *1637*

HOMEOSTASIS IN HEALTH & DISEASE.
Pergamon Press, Inc., Journals Division, (International Association for Integrative Nervous Functions) 660 White Plains Rd., Tarrytown, NY 10591-5153. TEL 914-524-9200. FAX 914-333-2444. *3338*

HORIZONS.
Haifa University, Department of Geography, Mount Carmel, Haifa 31905, Israel. FAX 04-246814. *2252*

HORMONES AND BEHAVIOR.
Academic Press, Inc., Journal Division, 1250 Sixth Ave., San Diego, CA 92101. TEL 619-230-1840. FAX 619-699-6800. *3254*

HORN CALL ANNUAL.
International Horn Society, c/o Ellen Powley, Exc. Secretary, 2220 N. 140 E., Provo, UT 84604. TEL 801-377-3026. *3555*

HOSPICE JOURNAL.
Haworth Press, Inc., 10 Alice St., Binghamton, NY 13904. TEL 800-342-9678. FAX 607-722-1424. *2463*

EL HOSPITAL (CINCINNATI).
Gregory Loomis, Ed. & Pub., 5790 Eaglesridge Lane, Cincinnati, OH 45230. TEL 513-232-0511. FAX 513-232-0662. *3105*

HOSPITAL AND COMMUNITY PSYCHIATRY.
American Psychiatric Press, Inc., Journals Division, (American Psychiatric Association) 1400 K St., N.W., Washington, DC 20005. TEL 202-682-6240. FAX 202-789-2648. *3338*

HOSPITAL MEDICINE.
Cahners Publishing Company (New York), Health Care Group Division of Reed Publishing (USA) Inc., 249 W. 17th St., New York, NY 10011. TEL 212-645-0067. FAX 914-878-4158. *3105*

HOSPITAL PRACTICE.
H P Publishing Co. 55 Fifth Ave., New York, NY 10003-6903. TEL 212-989-2100. FAX 212-727-7316. *3106*

HOSPITAL PRODUCT COMPARISON SYSTEM.
E C R I, (Emergency Care Research Institute) 5200 Butler Pike, Plymouth Meeting, PA 19462. TEL 215-825-6000. FAX 215-834-1275. *2465*

HOSPITAL RISK CONTROL.
E C R I, (Emergency Care Research Institute) 5200 Butler Pike, Plymouth Meeting, PA 19462. TEL 215-825-6000. FAX 215-834-1275. *2465*

HOSPITAL TOPICS.
Heldref Publications, 1319 Eighteenth St., N.W., Washington, DC 20036. TEL 202-296-6267. FAX 202-296-5149. *2465*

LES HOUCHES SUMMER SCHOOL PROCEEDINGS.
Elsevier Science Publishers B.V., Books Division, (Ecole d'Ete de Physique Theorique, Les Houches) P.O. Box 211, 1000 AE Amsterdam, Netherlands. TEL 020-5803911. FAX 020-5803705. *3819*

HOUSING POLICY DEBATE.
Federal National Mortgage Association, (Fannie Mae, Office of Housing Policy Research) 3900 Wisconsin Ave., N.W., Washington, DC 20016-2899. TEL 202-752-4422. FAX 202-752-4933. *2488*

HUANJING HUAXUE.
Kexue Chubanshe, Qikan Bu, (Chinese Academy of Sciences, Ecology and Environment Research Centre) 16 Donghuangchenggen Beijie, Beijing 100707, People's Republic of China. TEL 4010642. FAX 4012180. *1178*

HUANJING KEXUE.
Science Press, Marketing and Sales Department, (Chinese Academy of Sciences, Environmental Science Committee) 16 Donghuangchenggen Beijie, Beijing 100707, People's Republic of China. TEL 4010642. FAX 4012180. *1957*

HUANJING KEXUE XUEBAO.
Science Press, Marketing and Sales Department, (Chinese Academy of Sciences, Ecology and Environment Research Centre) 16 Donghuangchenggen Beijie, Beijing 100707, People's Republic of China. TEL 4010642. FAX 4012180. *1957*

HUANJING YAOGAN.
Science Press, Marketing and Sales Department, (Chinese Geographic Society) 16 Donghuangchenggen Beijie, Beijing 100707, People's Republic of China. TEL 4010642. FAX 4012180. *2252*

HUAXUE XUEBAO.
Science Press, Marketing and Sales Press, (Chinese Chemical Society) 16 Donghuangchenggen Beijie, Beijing 100707, People's Republic of China. TEL 4010642. FAX 4012180. *1178*

HUISARTS EN WETENSCHAP.
Bohn Stafleu van Loghum B.V., (Nederlands Huisartsengenootschap) P.O. Box 246, 3990 GA Houten, Netherlands. TEL 03403-95711. *3106*

HUMAN ANTIBODIES AND HYBRIDOMAS.
Butterworth - Heinemann Ltd. 80 Montvale Ave., Stoneham, MA 02180. TEL 617-438-8464. FAX 617-438-1479. *3185*

HUMAN BEHAVIOR AND ENVIRONMENT.
Plenum Publishing Corp., 233 Spring St., New York, NY 10013-1578. TEL 212-620-8000. FAX 212-463-0742. *4023*

HUMAN BIOLOGY (DETROIT).
Wayne State University Press, 5959 Woodward Ave., Detroit, MI 48202. TEL 313-577-6120. FAX 313-577-6131. *440*

HUMAN - COMPUTER INTERACTION (HILLSDALE).
Lawrence Erlbaum Associates, Inc., 365 Broadway, Hillsdale, NJ 07642. TEL 201-666-4110. FAX 66-2394. *1395*

HUMAN DEVELOPMENT (NORWOOD).
Ablex Publishing Corporation, 355 Chestnut St., Norwood, NJ 07648. TEL 201-767-8450. FAX 201-767-6717. *4023*

HUMAN ECOLOGY (NEW YORK).
Plenum Publishing Corp., 233 Spring St., New York, NY 10013-1578. TEL 212-620-8000. FAX 212-463-0742. *241*

HUMAN IMMUNOLOGY.
Elsevier Science Publishing Co., Inc. (New York), (American Society for Histocompatibility and Immunogenetics) 655 Ave. of the Americas, New York, NY 10010. TEL 212-989-5800. FAX 212-633-3965. *3185*

HUMAN MOVEMENT SCIENCE.
North-Holland P.O. Box 211, 1000 AE Amsterdam, Netherlands. TEL 020-5803911. FAX 020-5803598. *3106*

HUMAN NUTRITION.
Plenum Publishing Corp., 233 Spring St., New York, NY 10013-1578. TEL 212-620-8468. FAX 212-463-0742. *3606*

HUMAN PARASITIC DISEASES.
Elsevier Science Publishers B.V., Books Division, P.O. Box 211, 1000 AE Amsterdam, Netherlands. TEL 020-5803911. FAX 020-5803705. *3219*

HUMAN PATHOLOGY.
W.B. Saunders Co., Curtis Center, Independence Square W., Philadelphia, PA 19106. TEL 215-238-7800. *3106*

HUMAN PERFORMANCE.
Lawrence Erlbaum Associates, Inc., 365 Broadway, Hillsdale, NJ 07642. TEL 201-666-4110. FAX 201-666-2394. *4023*

HUMAN PHYSIOLOGY.
Plenum Publishing Corp., Consultants Bureau, (Russian Academy of Sciences) 233 Spring St., New York, NY 10013-1578. TEL 212-620-8468. FAX 212-463-0742. *572*

HUMAN RELATIONS.
Plenum Publishing Corp., (Tavistock Institute of Human Relations) 233 Spring St., New York, NY 10013-1578. TEL 212-260-8000. FAX 212-463-0742. *4374*

HUMAN RESOURCE DEVELOPMENT QUARTERLY.
Jossey-Bass Inc., Publishers, (American Society for Training and Development) 350 Sansome St., 5th fl., San Francisco, CA 94104. TEL 415-433-1767. FAX 415-433-0499. *1066*

HUMANE MEDICINE.
Canadian Medical Association, P.O. Box 8650, Ottawa, Ont. K1G 0G8, Canada. TEL 613-731-9331. FAX 613-523-0937. *3106*

HYBRIDOMA.
Mary Ann Liebert, Inc., 1651 Third Ave., New York, NY 10128. TEL 212-289-2300. FAX 212-289-4697. *3185*

HYDROMETALLURGY.
Elsevier Science Publishers B.V., P.O. Box 211, 1000 AE Amsterdam, Netherlands. TEL 020-5803911. FAX 020-5803598. *3408*

HYDROTECHNICAL CONSTRUCTION.
Plenum Publishing Corp., Consultants Bureau, (Ministerstvo Energetiki i Elektrifikatsii S.S.S.R., Nauchno-Tekhnicheskoc Obshchcstvo Energetike i Elektrotekhnicheskoi Promyshlennosti) 233 Spring St., New York, NY 10013-1578. TEL 212-620-8000. FAX 212-463-0742. *1867*

HYMN SOCIETY OF GREAT BRITAIN AND IRELAND.
Hymn Society of Great Britain and Ireland, c/o Re. Michael Garland, St. Nicholas Rectory, Curdworth, Sutton Coldfield, West Midlands B76 9ES, England. TEL 0675-470-384. *3555*

HYPERTENSION.
American Heart Association, 7272 Greenville Ave., Dallas, TX 75231-4596. TEL 214-706-1310. FAX 214-691-6342. *3208*

I B M JOURNAL OF RESEARCH AND DEVELOPMENT.
International Business Machines Corp., 500 Columbus Ave., Thornwood, NY 10594. TEL 914-742-5850. *1395*

I B M SYSTEMS JOURNAL.
International Business Machines Corp., 500 Columbus Ave., Thornwood, NY 10594. TEL 914-742-5850. *1437*

I D N - INFECTIOUS DISEASES NEWSLETTER.
Elsevier Science Publishing Co., Inc. (New York), 655 Ave. of the Americas, New York, NY 10010. TEL 212-989-5800. FAX 212-633-3965. *3219*

I F A C SYMPOSIA SERIES.
Pergamon Press, Inc., Journals Division, (International Federation of Automatic Control) 660 White Plains Rd., Tarrytown, NY 10591-5153. TEL 914-524-9200. FAX 914-333-2444. *1930*

I I E TRANSACTIONS.
Industrial Engineering and Management Press, (Institute of Industrial Engineers) 25 Technology Park-Atlanta, Norcross, GA 30092. TEL 404-449-0460. FAX 404-263-8532. *1925*

I S A TRANSACTIONS.
Instrument Society of America, 67 Alexander Dr., Box 12277, Research Triangle Park, NC 27709. TEL 919-549-8411. FAX 919-549-8288. *1824*

I S L A: A JOURNAL OF MICRONESIAN STUDIES.
University of Guam Press, (University of Guam, Graduate School and Research) UOG Station, Mangilao, Guam 96923. TEL 671-734-9401. FAX 617-734-3676. *2344*

I S P R A COURSES ON NUCLEAR ENGINEERING AND TECHNOLOGY SERIES.
Harwood Academic Publishers, 270 Eighth Ave., New York, NY 10011. TEL 212-206-8900. FAX 212-645-2459. *1805*

I S P R S JOURNAL OF PHOTOGRAMMETRY AND REMOTE SENSING.
Elsevier Science Publishers B.V., (International Society for Photogrammetry and Remote Sensing) P.O. Box 211, 1000 AE Amsterdam, Netherlands. TEL 020-5803911. FAX 020-5803598. *2252*

I U P STRESS AND HEALTH SERIES.
International Universities Press, Inc., 59 Boston Post Rd., Box 1524, Madison, CT 06443-1524. TEL 203-245-4000. *3338*

ICHNOS.
Harwood Academic Publishers, 270 Eighth Ave., New York, NY 10011. TEL 212-206-8900. FAX 212-645-2459. *441*

IDAHO YESTERDAYS.
Idaho State Historical Society, 450 N. 4th St., Boise, ID 83702. TEL 208-334-3428. *2409*

ILLINOIS. NATURAL HISTORY SURVEY. BIOLOGICAL NOTES.
Department of Energy and Natural Resources, Natural History Survey, Natural Resources Bldg., 607 E. Peabody Dr., Champaign, IL 61820. TEL 217-244-0871. FAX 217-333-4949. *441*

ILLINOIS. NATURAL HISTORY SURVEY. BULLETIN.
Department of Energy and Natural Resources, Natural History Survey Division, Natural Resources Bldg., 607 E. Peabody Dr., Champaign, IL 61820. TEL 217-333-6880. FAX 217-333-4949. *441*

ILLINOIS. STATE MUSEUM. INVENTORY OF THE COLLECTIONS.
Illinois State Museum, Springfield, IL 62706. TEL 217-782-7386. FAX 217-782-1254. *3525*

ILLINOIS. STATE MUSEUM. POPULAR SCIENCE SERIES.
Illinois State Museum, Springfield, IL 62706. TEL 217-782-7386. FAX 217-782-1254. *4314*

ILLINOIS. STATE MUSEUM. RESEARCH SERIES. PAPERS IN ANTHROPOLOGY.
Illinois State Museum, Springfield, IL 62706. TEL 217-782-7386. FAX 217-782-1254. *241*

ILLINOIS. STATE MUSEUM. SCIENTIFIC PAPERS SERIES.
Illinois State Museum, Springfield, IL 62706. TEL 217-782-7386. FAX 217-782-1254. *4314*

ILLINOIS BIOLOGICAL MONOGRAPHS.
University of Illinois Press, 54 E. Gregory Dr., Champaign, IL 61820. TEL 217-333-0950. FAX 217-244-8082. *441*

ILLINOIS JOURNAL OF MATHEMATICS.
University of Illinois Press, (University of Illinois at Urbana-Champaign, Department of Mathematics) 54 E. Gregory Dr., Champaign, IL 61820. TEL 217-333-0950. FAX 217-244-8082. *3038*

ILLINOIS MEDIEVAL MONOGRAPH SERIES.
University of Illinois Press, 54 E. Gregory Dr., Champaign, IL 61820. TEL 217-333-0950. FAX 217-244-8082. *2368*

ILLINOIS RESEARCH.
University of Illinois at Urbana-Champaign, Agricultural Experiment Station, 47 Mumford Hall, 1301 W. Gregory Dr., IL 61801. TEL 217-333-4780. *96*

ILLINOIS SHORT FICTION.
University of Illinois Press, 54 E. Gregory Dr., Champaign, IL 61820. TEL 217-333-0950. *2924*

ILLINOIS STATE ACADEMY OF SCIENCE. TRANSACTIONS.
Illinois State Academy of Sciences, Illinois State Museum, Springfield, IL 62706. TEL 217-782-7386. *4314*

ILLINOIS STUDIES IN ANTHROPOLOGY.
University of Illinois Press, 54 E. Gregory Dr., Champaign, IL 61820. TEL 217-333-0950. FAX 217-244-8082. *241*

IMAGE AND VISION COMPUTING.
Butterworth - Heinemann Ltd. Linacre House, Jordan Hill, Oxford OX2 8DP, England. TEL 0865-310366. FAX 0865-310898. *1422*

IMAGING ABSTRACTS.
Pergamon Press plc, (Royal Photographic Society of Great Britain, Imaging Science and Technology Group) Headington Hill Hall, Oxford, OX3 0BW, England. TEL 0865-794141. FAX 0865-743911. *3798*

IMMIGRATION AND NATIONALITY LAW REVIEW.
William S. Hein & Co., Inc., 1285 Main St., Buffalo, NY 14209. TEL 716-882-2600. FAX 716-883-8100. *2702*

IMMUNODEFICIENCY REVIEWS.
Harwood Academic Publishers, 270 Eighth Ave., New York, NY 10011. TEL 212-206-8900. FAX 212-645-2459. *3185*

IMMUNOLOGICAL INVESTIGATIONS.
Marcel Dekker Journals, 270 Madison Ave., New York, NY 10016. TEL 212-696-9000. FAX 212-685-4540. *3185*

IMMUNOLOGY LETTERS.
Elsevier Science Publishers B.V., (European Federation of Immunological Societies (E.F.I.S.)) P.O. Box 211, 1000 AE Amsterdam, Netherlands. TEL 020-5803911. FAX 020-5803598. *3186*

IMMUNOLOGY SERIES.
Marcel Dekker, Inc., 270 Madison Ave., New York, NY 10016. TEL 212-696-9000. FAX 212-685-4540. *3186*

IMMUNOMETHODS.
Academic Press, Inc., Journal Division, 1250 Sixth Ave., San Diego, CA 92101. TEL 619-230-1840. FAX 619-699-6800. *3186*

IMMUNOPHARMACOLOGY.
Elsevier Science Publishers B.V., P.O. Box 211, 1000 AE Amsterdam, Netherlands. TEL 020-5803911. FAX 020-5803598. *3186*

IMMUNOPHARMACOLOGY AND IMMUNOTOXICOLOGY.
Marcel Dekker Journals, 270 Madison Ave., New York, NY 10016. TEL 212-696-9000. FAX 212-685-4540. *3728*

IMPACT OF SCIENCE ON SOCIETY.
Taylor & Francis Ltd., 4 John St., London WC1N 2ET, England. TEL 071-405-2237. *4314*

IMPLANT DENTISTRY.
Williams & Wilkins, 428 E. Preston St., Baltimore, MD 21202. TEL 410-528-4000. *3234*

IN SITU.
Marcel Dekker Journals, 270 Madison Ave., New York, NY 10016. TEL 212-696-9000. FAX 212-685-4540. *1824*

IN VITRO CELLULAR & DEVELOPMENTAL BIOLOGY - ANIMAL.
Tissue Culture Association, 8815 Centre Park Dr., Ste. 210, Columbia, MD 21045. TEL 301-992-0946. *552*

IN VITRO CELLULAR & DEVELOPMENTAL BIOLOGY - PLANT.
Tissue Culture Association, 8815 Centre Park Dr., Ste. 210, Columbia, MD 21045. TEL 301-992-0946. *552*

INCOGNITA.
E.J. Brill, P.O. Box 9000, 2300 PA Leiden, Netherlands. TEL 071-312-624. FAX 071-317-532. *2508*

INDAGATIONES MATHEMATICAE.
North-Holland (Koninklijke Nederlandse Akademie van Wetenschappen) P.O. Box 211, 1000 AE Amsterdam, Netherlands. TEL 020-5803911. FAX 020-5803598. *3038*

INDIAN JOURNAL OF NUTRITION AND DIETETICS.
Avinashilingam Institute for Home Science and Higher Education for Women, c/o Rajammal P. Devadas, Ed., Coimbatore 641 043, India. TEL 40241. *3607*

INDIANA UNIVERSITY MATHEMATICS JOURNAL.
Indiana University, Department of Mathematics, Swain Hall East 222, Bloomington, IN 47405. TEL 812-855-2252. FAX 812-855-0046. *3038*

INDO-PACIFIC FISHES.
Bishop Museum Press, (Bishop Museum, Division of Ichthyology) 1525 Bernice St., Box 19000-A, Honolulu, HI 96817. TEL 808-848-4135. *584*

INDUSTRIAL CRISIS QUARTERLY.
Elsevier Science Publishers B.V., Postbus 211, 1000 AE Amsterdam, Netherlands. TEL 020-5803911. FAX 020-5803598. *1013*

INDUSTRIAL CROPS AND PRODUCTS.
Elsevier Science Publishers B.V., (Association for the Advancement of Industrial Crops) P.O. Box 211, 1000 AE Amsterdam, Netherlands. TEL 020-5803911. FAX 020-5803598. *180*

INDUSTRIAL LABORATORY.
Plenum Publishing Corp., Consultants Bureau, (Ministerstvo Chernoi Metallurgii S.S.S.R., Tsentral'noe Upravlenie Nauchno-Tekhnicheskogo Obshchestvoi po Chernoi Metallurgii) 233 Spring St., New York, NY 10013-1578. TEL 212-620-8468. FAX 212-463-0742. *4600*

INDUSTRIAL MARKETING MANAGEMENT.
Elsevier Science Publishing Co., Inc. (New York), 655 Ave. of the Americas, New York, NY 10010. TEL 212-989-5800. FAX 212-633-3965. *1041*

INDUSTRIAL METROLOGY.
Elsevier Science Publishers B.V., P.O. Box 211, 1000 AE Amsterdam, Netherlands. TEL 020-5803911. FAX 020-5803598. *3446*

INDUSTRIAL RELATIONS LAW JOURNAL.
University of California Press, Journals Division, (University of California, Berkeley, Boalt Hall School of Law) 2120 Berkeley Way, Berkeley, CA 94720. TEL 510-642-4191. FAX 510-643-7127. *982*

INDUSTRY AND HIGHER EDUCATION.
In Print Publishing Ltd., c/o Mr. A. Dingwall, Dir., 9 Beaufort Terr., Brighton, BN2 2SU, England. TEL 0273-682-836. FAX 0273-620-958. *1709*

INFANT BEHAVIOR AND DEVELOPMENT.
Ablex Publishing Corporation, 355 Chestnut St., Norwood, NJ 07648. TEL 201-767-8450. FAX 201-767-6717. *4024*

INFANT MENTAL HEALTH JOURNAL.
Clinical Psychology Publishing Co., Inc., (Michigan Association for Infant Mental Health) 4 Conant Sq., Brandon, VT 05733. TEL 802-247-6871. FAX 802-247-6853. *3321*

INFECTION AND IMMUNITY.
American Society for Microbiology, 1325 Massachusetts Ave., N.W., Washington, DC 20005. TEL 202-737-3600. *3186*

INFECTION CONTROL & HOSPITAL EPIDEMIOLOGY.
Slack, Inc., 6900 Grove Rd., Thorofare, NJ 08086. TEL 609-848-1000. FAX 609-853-5991. *3219*

INFECTIOUS AGENTS AND DISEASE.
Raven Press, 1185 Ave. of the Americas, New York, NY 10036. TEL 212-930-9500. FAX 212-869-3495. *3220*

INFERTILITY.
Hemisphere Publishing Corporation 1900 Frost Rd., Ste. 101, Bristol, PA 19007-1598. TEL 215-785-5800. FAX 215-785-5515. *3293*

INFLAMMATION.
Plenum Publishing Corp., 233 Spring St., New York, NY 10013-1578. TEL 212-620-8000. FAX 212-463-0742. *3108*

INFLAMMOPHARMACOLOGY.
Kluwer Academic Publishers, Postbus 17, 3300 AA Dordrecht, Netherlands. TEL 078-334911. FAX 078-334254. *3729*

INFOMEDIARY.
I O S Press, Van Diemenstraat 94, 1013 CN Amsterdam, Netherlands. TEL 020-6382189. FAX 020-6203419. *2762*

INFORMATION & DECISION TECHNOLOGIES.
North-Holland P.O. Box 211, 1000 AE Amsterdam, Netherlands. TEL 020-5803911. FAX 020-5803598. *1437*

INFORMATION AND MANAGEMENT.
North-Holland (International Federation for Information Processing, Applied Information Processing Group) P.O. Box 211, 1000 AE Amsterdam, Netherlands. TEL 020-5803911. FAX 020-5803598. *1445*

INFORMATION AND SOFTWARE TECHNOLOGY.
Butterworth - Heinemann Ltd. Linacre House, Jordan Hill, Oxford OX2 8DP, England. TEL 0865-310366. FAX 0865-310898. *1451*

INFORMATION ECONOMICS AND POLICY.
North-Holland P.O. Box 211, 1000 AE Amsterdam, Netherlands. TEL 020-5803911. FAX 020-5803598. *671*

INFORMATION NORTH.
Arctic Institute of North America, University of Calgary, 2500 University Dr. N.W., Calgary, Alta. T2N 1N4, Canada. TEL 403-220-7515. FAX 403-282-4609. *4315*

INFORMATION PROCESSING & MANAGEMENT.
Pergamon Press, Inc., Journals Division, 660 White Plains Rd., Tarrytown, NY 10591-5153. TEL 914-524-9200. FAX 914-333-2444. *2762*

INFORMATION PROCESSING LETTERS.
North-Holland P.O. Box 211, 1000 AE Amsterdam, Netherlands. TEL 020-5803911. FAX 020-5803598. *1451*

INFORMATION RESOURCES MANAGEMENT JOURNAL.
Idea Group Publishing, (Information Resource Management Association) 4811 Jonestown Rd., Ste. 230, Harrisburg, PA 17109-1751. TEL 717-541-9150. FAX 717-541-9159. *1013*

INFORMATION SERVICES & USE.
Elsevier Science Publishers B.V., P.O. Box 211, 1000 AE Amsterdam, Netherlands. TEL 020-5803911. FAX 020-5803598. *2763*

INFORMATION SOCIETY.
Taylor & Francis, 1900 Frost Rd., Ste. 101, Bristol, PA 19007. TEL 215-785-5800. FAX 215-785-5515. *1456*

INFORMATION SYSTEMS (TARRYTOWN).
Pergamon Press, Inc., Journals Division, 660 WHite Plains Rd., Tarrytown, NY 10591-5153. TEL 914-524-9200. FAX 914-333-2444. *2798*

INFORMATION TECHNOLOGY AND LIBRARIES.
American Library Association, (Library and Information Technology Association) 50 E. Huron St, Chicago, IL 60611-2795. TEL 312-944-6780. FAX 312-440-9374. *2798*

INFORMATIZATION AND THE PUBLIC SECTOR.
Elsevier Science Publishers B.V., P.O. Box 211, 1000 AE Amsterdam, Netherlands. TEL 020-5803911. FAX 020-5803598. *1337*

INFRARED PHYSICS.
Pergamon Press, Inc., Journals Division, 660 White Plains Rd., Tarrytown, NY 10591-5153. TEL 914-524-9200. FAX 914-333-2444. *3853*

INHALATION TOXICOLOGY.
Hemisphere Publishing Corporation 1900 Frost Rd., Ste. 101, Bristol, PA 19007-1598. TEL 215-785-5800. FAX 215-785-5515. *1982*

INJURY.
Butterworth - Heinemann Ltd. (Institute of Accident Surgery) Linacre House, Jordan Hill, Oxford OX2 8DP, England. TEL 0865-310366. FAX 0865-310898. *3308*

INNOVATIVE HIGHER EDUCATION.
Human Sciences Press, Inc. 233 Spring St., New York, NY 10013-1578. TEL 212-620-8000. FAX 212-463-0742. *1709*

INORGANIC MATERIALS.
Plenum Publishing Corp., Consultants Bureau, (Russian Academy of Sciences) 233 Spring St., New York, NY 10013-1578. TEL 212-620-8468. FAX 212-463-0742. *1213*

INORGANIC SYNTHESES SERIES.
McGraw-Hill, Inc., (Inorganic Syntheses, Inc.) 1221 Ave. of the Americas, New York, NY 10020. TEL 212-997-1221. *1226*

INORGANICA CHIMICA ACTA.
Elsevier Sequoia S.A., P.O. Box 564, CH-1001 Lausanne, Switzerland. TEL 021-207381. FAX 021-235444. *1213*

INQUIRY (CHICAGO).
Blue Cross and Blue Shield Association, 676 N. St. Clair St., Chicago, IL 60611. TEL 312-440-5575. FAX 312-440-5705. *3109*

INSECT BIOCHEMISTRY AND MOLECULAR BIOLOGY.
Pergamon Press, Inc., Journals Division, 660 White Plains Rd., Tarrytown, NY 10591-5153. TEL 914-524-9200. FAX 914-333-2444. *533*

INSECTICIDE AND ACARICIDE TESTS.
Entomological Society of America, 9301 Annapolis Rd., Lanham, MD 20706. TEL 301-731-4535. FAX 301-731-4538. *533*

INSECTS OF VIRGINIA.
Virginia Polytechnic Institute and State University, Department of Entomology, Blacksburg, VA 24061-0319. TEL 703-231-6341. *534*

INSTITUT PASTEUR. ANNALES. ACTUALITES.
Editions Scientifiques Elsevier, 29, rue Buffon, 75005 Paris, France. *552*

INSTITUT PASTEUR. BULLETIN.
Editions Scientifiques Elsevier, 29, rue Buffon, 75005 Paris, France. *3220*

INSTITUTE OF ENVIRONMENTAL SCIENCES. JOURNAL.
Institute of Environmental Sciences, 940 E. Northwest Hwy., Mt. Prospect, IL 60056. TEL 708-255-1561. *1958*

INSTITUTE OF MATHEMATICAL GEOGRAPHY. MONOGRAPH SERIES.
Institute of Mathematical Geography, 2790 Briarcliff, Ann Arbor, MI 48105-1429. TEL 313-761-1231. *3038*

INSTITUTE OF STATISTICAL MATHEMATICS. ANNALS.
Kluwer Academic Publishers, Tokyo, (Institute of Statistical Mathematics) 303 Jiyugaoka Komatsu Bldg., 24-17, Midorigaoka 2-chome, Meguro-ku, Tokyo 152, Japan. TEL 03-718-4405. FAX 03-718-4406. *3038*

INSTITUTION OF CHEMISTS (INDIA). JOURNAL.
Institution of Chemists (India), 11-4, Dr. Biresh Guha Road, Calcutta 700 017, India. TEL 40-3832. *1179*

INSTITUTION OF ELECTRONICS AND TELECOMMUNICATION ENGINEERS. JOURNAL.
Institution of Electronics and Telecommunication Engineers, 2, Institutional Area, Lodi Rd., New Delhi 110 003, India. TEL 11-618529. *1337*

INSTRUMENTATION FOR THE PROCESS INDUSTRIES.
Instrument Society of America, 67 Alexander Dr., Box 12277, Research Triangle Park, NC 27709. TEL 919-549-8411. FAX 919-549-8288. *2523*

INSTRUMENTATION IN THE CHEMICAL AND PETROLEUM INDUSTRIES.
Instrument Society of America, 67 Alexander Dr., Box 12277, Research Triangle Park, NC 27709. TEL 919-549-8411. FAX 919-549-8288. *2523*

INSTRUMENTATION IN THE FOOD AND PHARMACEUTICAL INDUSTRIES.
Instrument Society of America, 67 Alexander Dr., Box 12277, Research Triangle Park, NC 27709. TEL 919-549-8411. FAX 919-832-0237. *2523*

INSTRUMENTATION IN THE MINING AND METALLURGY INDUSTRIES.
Instrument Society of America, 67 Alexander Dr., Box 12277, Research Triangle Park, NC 27709. TEL 919-549-8411. FAX 919-549-8288. *3409*

INSTRUMENTATION IN THE POWER INDUSTRY.
Instrument Society of America, 67 Alexander Dr., Box 12277, Research Triangle Park, NC 27709. TEL 919-549-8411. FAX 919-549-8288. *2523*

INSTRUMENTATION IN THE PULP AND PAPER INDUSTRY.
Instrument Society of America, 67 Alexander Dr., Box 12277, Research Triangle Park, NC 27709. TEL 919-549-8411. FAX 919-549-8288. *3663*

INSTRUMENTS AND EXPERIMENTAL TECHNIQUES.
Plenum Publishing Corp., Consultants Bureau, (Russian Academy of Sciences) 233 Spring St., New York, NY 10013-1578. TEL 212-620-8468. FAX 212-463-0742. *2523*

INSURANCE: MATHEMATICS & ECONOMICS.
North-Holland P.O. Box 211, 1000 AE Amsterdam, Netherlands. TEL 020-5803911. FAX 020-5803598. *2534*

INTEGRATED FERROELECTRICS.
Gordon and Breach Science Publishers, 270 Eighth Ave., New York, NY 10011. TEL 212-206-8900. FAX 212-645-2459. *1899*

INTEGRATION.
Elsevier Science Publishers B.V., P.O. Box 211, 1000 AE Amsterdam, Netherlands. TEL 020-5803911. FAX 020-5803598. *1454*

INTEGRATIVE PSYCHIATRY.
International Universities Press, Inc., (Academia Medicina Psychiatria) 59 Boston Post Rd., Box 1523, CT 06443-1524. TEL 203-245-4000. FAX 203-245-0775. *3339*

INTELLECTUAL PROPERTY LAW.
Harwood Academic Publishers, 270 Eighth Ave., New York, NY 10011. TEL 212-206-8900. FAX 212-645-2459. *2636*

INTELLIGENCE (NORWOOD).
Ablex Publishing Corporation, 355 Chestnut St., Norwood, NJ 07648. TEL 201-767-8450. FAX 201-767-6717. *4025*

INTELLIGENT INSTRUMENTS & COMPUTERS.
Elsevier Science Publishing Co., Inc. (New York), 655 Ave. of the Americas, New York, NY 10010. TEL 212-989-5800. FAX 212-633-3965. *4359*

INTERACTING WITH COMPUTERS.
Butterworth - Heinemann Ltd. (British Computer Society, HCI Specialist Group) Linacre House, Jordan Hill, Oxford OX2 8DP, England. TEL 0865-310366. FAX 0865-310898. *1396*

INTERCULTURAL COMMUNICATION STUDIES.
Trinity University, Trinitonian Office, 715 Stadium Dr., San Antonio, TX 78212. *4438*

INTERFACES: LINGUISTICS, PSYCHOLOGY AND HEALTH THERAPEUTICS.
Providence College Press, Providence, RI 02918. *2819*

INTERNATIONAL ADVANCES IN NONDESTRUCTIVE TESTING.
Gordon & Breach Science Publishers, 270 Eighth Ave., New York, NY 10011. TEL 212-206-8900. FAX 212-645-2459. *1917*

INTERNATIONAL ANNALS OF ADOLESCENT PSYCHIATRY.
University of Chicago Press, Journals Division, (International Society for Adolescent Psychiatry) 5720 S. Woodlawn Ave., Chicago, IL 60637. TEL 312-702-7600. *3339*

INTERNATIONAL BIODETERIORATION.
Elsevier Science Publishers Ltd., (Biodeterioration Society) Crown House, Linton Rd., Barking, Essex IG11 8JU, England. TEL 081-594-7272. FAX 081-594-5942. *490*

INTERNATIONAL COMMISSION ON RADIOLOGICAL PROTECTION. ANNALS.
Pergamon Press, Inc., Journals Division, 660 White Plains Rd., Tarrytown, NY 10591-5153. TEL 914-524-9200. FAX 914-333-2444. *3358*

INTERNATIONAL COMMUNICATIONS IN HEAT AND MASS TRANSFER.
Pergamon Press, Inc., Journals Division, (International Centre for Heat and Mass Transfer) 660 White Plains Rd., Tarrytown, NY 10591-5153. TEL 914-524-9200. FAX 914-333-2444. *1931*

INTERNATIONAL CONFERENCE ON COMPUTER COMMUNICATIONS. (PROCEEDINGS).
Elsevier Science Publishing Co., Inc. (New York), 655 Ave. of the Americas, New York, NY 10010. TEL 212-989-5800. FAX 212-633-3965. *1447*

INTERNATIONAL CONFERENCE ON VERY LARGE DATA BASES. PROCEEDINGS.
Morgan Kaufmann Publishers, Inc., 2929 Campus Dr., Ste. 260, San Mateo, CA 94403. TEL 415-578-9911. FAX 415-578-0672. *1445*

INTERNATIONAL CONGRESS SERIES.
Elsevier Science Publishers B.V., Books Division, P.O. Box 211, 1000 AE Amsterdam, Netherlands. TEL 020-5803911. FAX 020-5803705. *3393*

INTERNATIONAL CONTACT LENS CLINIC.
Butterworth - Heinemann Ltd. 80 Montvale Ave., Stoneham, MA 02180. TEL 617-438-8464. FAX 617-438-1479. *3301*

INTERNATIONAL CRYOGENICS MONOGRAPH SERIES.
Plenum Publishing Corp., 233 Spring St., New York, NY 10013-1578. TEL 212-620-8000. FAX 212-463-0742. *3841*

INTERNATIONAL DAIRY JOURNAL.
Elsevier Science Publishers Ltd., Crown House, Linton Rd., Barking, Essex IG11 8JU, England. TEL 081-594-7272. FAX 081-594-5942. *200*

INTERNATIONAL DENTAL JOURNAL.
Federation Dentaire Internationale, 64 Wimpole St., London W1M 8AL. FAX 0865-310898. *3234*

INTERNATIONAL ECONOMIC JOURNAL.
Department of International Economics, College of Social Sciences, Seoul University, Seoul 151-742, S. Korea. TEL 02-880-6394. FAX 02-888-4454. *870*

INTERNATIONAL EDUCATION.
University of Tennessee, College of Education, 212 Claxton, Knoxville, TN 37996-3400. TEL 615-974-2272. *1722*

INTERNATIONAL FEDERATION FOR INFORMATION AND DOCUMENTATION. PROCEEDINGS OF CONGRESS.
Elsevier Science Publishers B.V., Books Division, P.O. Box 211, 1000 AE Amsterdam, Netherlands. TEL 020-5803911. FAX 020-5803705. *2764*

INTERNATIONAL FIBER SCIENCE AND TECHNOLOGY SERIES.
Marcel Dekker, Inc., 270 Madison Ave., New York, NY 10016. TEL 212-696-9000. FAX 212-685-4540. *1218*

INTERNATIONAL INSTRUMENTATION SYMPOSIUM.
Instrument Society of America, 67 Alexander Dr., Box 12277, Research Triangle Park, NC 27709. TEL 919-549-8411. FAX 919-549-8288. *56*

INTERNATIONAL INTERACTIONS.
Gordon and Breach Science Publishers, 270 Eighth Ave., New York, NY 10011. TEL 212-206-8900. FAX 212-645-2459. *3961*

INTERNATIONAL JOURNAL.
Canadian Institute of International Affairs, 15 King's College Circle, Toronto, Ont. M5S 2V9, Canada. TEL 416-979-1851. FAX 416-979-8575. *3961*

INTERNATIONAL JOURNAL FOR PARASITOLOGY.
Pergamon Press, Inc., Journals Division, (Australian Society for Parasitology) 660 White Plains Rd., Tarrytown, NY 10591-5153. TEL 914-524-9200. FAX 914-333-2444. *3220*

INTERNATIONAL JOURNAL FOR THE PSYCHOLOGY OF RELIGION.
Lawrence Erlbaum Associates, Inc., 365 Broadway, Hillsdale, NJ 07642. TEL 201-666-4110. FAX 201-666-2394. *4182*

INTERNATIONAL JOURNAL OF ADHESION AND ADHESIVES.
Butterworth - Heinemann Ltd. Linacre House, Jordan Hill, Oxford OX2 8DP, England. TEL 0865-310366. FAX 0865-310898. *3862*

INTERNATIONAL JOURNAL OF ADULT ORTHODONTICS AND ORTHOGNATHIC SURGERY.
Quintessence Publishing Co., Inc., 551 Kimberly Dr., Carol Stream, IL 60188-1881. TEL 708-682-3223. FAX 708-682-3288. *3235*

INTERNATIONAL JOURNAL OF AGING & HUMAN DEVELOPMENT.
Baywood Publishing Co., Inc., 26 Austin Ave., Box 337, Amityville, NY 11701. TEL 516-691-1270. FAX 516-691-1770. *2274*

INTERNATIONAL JOURNAL OF AMERICAN LINGUISTICS.
University of Chicago Press, Journals Division, 5720 S. Woodlawn Ave., Chicago, IL 60637. TEL 312-753-3347. *2819*

INTERNATIONAL JOURNAL OF ANTIMICROBIAL AGENTS.
Elsevier Science Publishers B.V., P.O. Box 211, 1000 AE Amsterdam, Netherlands. TEL 020-5803911. FAX 020-5803598. *553*

INTERNATIONAL JOURNAL OF APPLIED ELECTROMAGNETICS IN MATERIALS.
Elsevier Science Publishers B.V., P.O. Box 211, 1000 AE Amsterdam, Netherlands. TEL 020-5803911. FAX 020-5803598. *1900*

INTERNATIONAL JOURNAL OF APPROXIMATE REASONING.
Elsevier Science Publishing Co., Inc. (New York), (North American Fuzzy Information Processing Society) 655 Ave. of the Americas, New York, NY 10010. TEL 212-989-5800. FAX 212-633-3965. *1408*

INTERNATIONAL JOURNAL OF ARTS MEDICINE.
I J A M, M M B Music, Inc., (International Arts Medicine Association) 10370 Page Industrial Blvd., St. Louis, MO 63132. *3110*

INTERNATIONAL JOURNAL OF AVIATION PSYCHOLOGY.
Lawrence Erlbaum Associates, Inc., 365 Broadway, Hillsdale, NJ 07642. TEL 201-666-4110. FAX 201-666-2394. *56*

INTERNATIONAL JOURNAL OF BEHAVIORAL DEVELOPMENT.
Lawrence Erlbaum Associates Ltd., (International Society for the Study of Behavioral Development) 27 Palmeira Mansions, Church Rd., Hove, E. Sussex BN3 2FA, England. TEL 0273-207411. FAX 0273-205612. *4025*

INTERNATIONAL JOURNAL OF BIO-MEDICAL COMPUTING.
Elsevier Scientific Publishers Ireland Ltd., P.O. Box 85, Limerick, Ireland. TEL 061-61944. FAX 061-62144. *3226*

INTERNATIONAL JOURNAL OF BIOCHEMISTRY.
Pergamon Press, Inc., Journals Division, 660 White Plains Rd., Tarrytown, NY 10591-5153. TEL 914-524-9200. FAX 914-333-2444. *477*

INTERNATIONAL JOURNAL OF BIOLOGICAL MACROMOLECULES.
Butterworth - Heinemann Ltd. Linacre House, Jordan Hill, Oxford OX2 8DP, England. TEL 0865-310366. FAX 0865-310898. *477*

INTERNATIONAL JOURNAL OF BIOSOCIAL AND MEDICAL RESEARCH.
Life Sciences Press, (Foundation for Biosocial Research) Box 1174, Tacoma, WA 98401-1174. TEL 206-922-0442. FAX 206-922-0479. *3607*

INTERNATIONAL JOURNAL OF CANCER.
John Wiley & Sons, Inc., (International Union Against Cancer) 605 Third Ave., New York, NY 10158. TEL 212-850-6000. FAX 212-850-6088. *3198*

INTERNATIONAL JOURNAL OF CARDIOLOGY.
Elsevier Science Publishers B.V., P.O. Box 211, 1000 AE Amsterdam, Netherlands. TEL 020-5803911. FAX 020-5803598. *3209*

INTERNATIONAL JOURNAL OF CELL CLONING.
AlphaMed Press, Inc., 4100 S. Kettering Blvd., Dayton, OH 45439-2092. TEL 513-293-8508. FAX 513-293-7652. *560*

INTERNATIONAL JOURNAL OF COAL GEOLOGY.
Elsevier Science Publishers B.V., P.O. Box 211, 1000 AE Amsterdam, Netherlands. TEL 020-5803911. FAX 020-5803598. *1569*

INTERNATIONAL JOURNAL OF COMPARATIVE PSYCHOLOGY.
Human Sciences Press, Inc. (International Society for Comparative Psychology) 233 Spring St., New York, NY 10013-1578. TEL 212-620-8000. FAX 212-463-0742. *4025*

INTERNATIONAL JOURNAL OF COMPUTER INTEGRATED MANUFACTURING.
Taylor & Francis Ltd., Rankine Rd., Basingstoke, Hants RG24 0PR, England. TEL 0256-840366. FAX 0256-479438. *827*

INTERNATIONAL JOURNAL OF COMPUTER MATHEMATICS.
Gordon and Breach Science Publishers, 270 Eighth Ave., New York, NY 10011. TEL 212-206-8900. FAX 212-645-2459. *3065*

INTERNATIONAL JOURNAL OF CONTROL.
Taylor & Francis Ltd., Rankine Rd., Basingstoke, Hants. RG24 0PR, England. TEL 0256-840366. FAX 0256-479438. *1826*

INTERNATIONAL JOURNAL OF DAMAGE MECHANICS.
Technomic Publishing Co., Inc., 851 New Holland Ave., Box 3535, Lancaster, PA 17604. TEL 717-291-5609. FAX 717-295-4538. *1931*

INTERNATIONAL JOURNAL OF DERMATOLOGY.
J.B. Lippincott Co., (International Society of Dermatology: Tropical, Geographic, and Ecologic) E. Washington Sq., Philadelphia, PA 19105. TEL 215-238-4200. *3248*

INTERNATIONAL JOURNAL OF DEVELOPMENTAL NEUROSCIENCE.
Pergamon Press, Inc., Journals Division, (International Society for Developmental Neuroscience) 660 White Plains Rd., Tarrytown, NY 10591-5153. TEL 914-524-9200. FAX 914-333-2444. *3339*

INTERNATIONAL JOURNAL OF DIGITAL & ANALOG COMMUNICATION SYSTEMS.
John Wiley & Sons Ltd., Journals, Baffins Ln., Chichester, W. Sussex PO19 1UD, England. TEL 0243-778777. FAX 0243-775878. *1900*

INTERNATIONAL JOURNAL OF EDUCATIONAL DEVELOPMENT.
Pergamon Press plc, Headington Hill Hall, Oxford OX3 0BW, England. TEL 0865-794141. FAX 0865-743911. *1640*

INTERNATIONAL JOURNAL OF EDUCATIONAL REFORM.
Technomic Publishing Co., Inc., 851 New Holland Ave., Box 3535, Lancaster, PA 17604. TEL 717-291-5609. FAX 717-295-4538. *1640*

INTERNATIONAL JOURNAL OF EDUCATIONAL RESEARCH.
Pergamon Press, Inc., Journals Division, 660 White Plains Rd., Tarrytown, NY 10591-5153. TEL 914-524-9200. FAX 914-333-2444. *1722*

INTERNATIONAL JOURNAL OF ELECTRONICS.
Taylor & Francis Ltd., Rankine Rd., Basingstoke, Hants RG24 0PR, England. TEL 0256-840366. FAX 0256-479438. *1774*

INTERNATIONAL JOURNAL OF ENGINEERING SCIENCE.
Pergamon Press, Inc., Journals Division, 660 White Plains Rd., Tarrytown, NY 10591-5153. TEL 914-524-9200. FAX 914-333-2444. *1826*

INTERNATIONAL JOURNAL OF ENVIRONMENTAL AND ANALYTICAL CHEMISTRY.
Gordon and Breach Science Publishers, 270 Eighth Ave., New York, NY 10011. FAX 212-645-2459. *1206*

INTERNATIONAL JOURNAL OF ENVIRONMENTAL STUDIES. SECTIONS A & B.
Gordon and Breach Science Publishers, 270 Eighth Ave., New York, NY 10011. TEL 212-206-8900. FAX 212-645-2459. *1959*

INTERNATIONAL JOURNAL OF FATIGUE.
Butterworth - Heinemann Ltd. Linacre House, Jordan Hill, Oxford OX2 8DP, England. TEL 0865-310366. FAX 0865-310898. *1917*

INTERNATIONAL JOURNAL OF FOOD MICROBIOLOGY.
Elsevier Science Publishers B.V., (International Union of Microbiological Societies) P.O. Box 211, 1000 AE Amsterdam, Netherlands. TEL 020-5803911. FAX 020-5803598. *466*

INTERNATIONAL JOURNAL OF FORECASTING.
North-Holland (International Institute of Forecasters) P.O. Box 211, 1000 AE Amsterdam, Netherlands. TEL 020-5803911. FAX 020-5803598. *672*

INTERNATIONAL JOURNAL OF GENERAL SYSTEMS.
Gordon and Breach Science Publishers, 270 Eighth Ave., New York, NY 10011. TEL 212-206-8900. FAX 212-645-2459. *1437*

INTERNATIONAL JOURNAL OF GEOGRAPHICAL INFORMATION SYSTEMS.
Taylor & Francis Ltd., Rankine Rd., Basingstoke, Hants RG24 0PR, England. TEL 0256-840366. FAX 0256-479438. *2268*

INTERNATIONAL JOURNAL OF GROUP PSYCHOTHERAPY.
Guilford Publications, Inc., (American Group Psychotherapy Association) 72 Spring St., 4th Fl., New York, NY 10012. TEL 212-431-9800. FAX 212-966-6708. *4025*

INTERNATIONAL JOURNAL OF GROUP TENSIONS.
Human Sciences Press, Inc. (International Organization for the Study of Group Tensions) 233 Spring St., New York, NY 10013-1578. TEL 212-620-8000. FAX 212-463-0742. *4025*

INTERNATIONAL JOURNAL OF GYNAECOLOGY AND OBSTETRICS.
Elsevier Scientific Publishers Ireland Ltd., (International Federation of Gynaecology and Obstetrics) P.O. Box 85, Limerick, Ireland. TEL 061-61944. FAX 061-62144. *3293*

INTERNATIONAL JOURNAL OF GYNECOLOGICAL PATHOLOGY.
Raven Press, (International Society of Gynecological Pathologists) 1185 Ave. of the Americas, New York, NY 10036. TEL 212-930-9500. FAX 212-869-3495. *3293*

INTERNATIONAL JOURNAL OF HEALTH SERVICES.
Baywood Publishing Co., Inc., 26 Austin Ave., Box 337, Amityville, NY 11701. TEL 516-691-1270. FAX 516-691-1770. *4105*

INTERNATIONAL JOURNAL OF HEAT AND FLUID FLOW.
Butterworth - Heinemann Ltd. 80 Montvale Ave., Stoneham, MA 02180. TEL 617-438-8464. FAX 617-438-1479. *3841*

INTERNATIONAL JOURNAL OF HEAT AND MASS TRANSFER.
Pergamon Press, Inc., Journals Division, (International Centre for Heat and Mass Transfer) 660 White Plains Rd., Tarrytown, NY 10591-5153. TEL 914-524-9200. FAX 914-333-2444. *1932*

INTERNATIONAL JOURNAL OF HEMATOLOGY.
Elsevier Science Publishers B.V., (Japanese Society of Hematology) P.O. Box 211, 1000 AE Amsterdam, Netherlands. TEL 020-5803911. FAX 020-5803598. *3272*

INTERNATIONAL JOURNAL OF HOSPITALITY MANAGEMENT.
Pergamon Press, Inc., Journals Division, (International Association of Hotel Management Schools) 660 White Plains Rd., Tarrytown, NY 10591-5153. TEL 914-524-9200. FAX 914-333-2444. *4772*

INTERNATIONAL JOURNAL OF HUMANITIES AND PEACE.
Vassant Merchant, Ed. & Pub., 1436 N. Evergreen Dr., Flagstaff, AZ 86001. TEL 602-774-4793. *2508*

INTERNATIONAL JOURNAL OF HYDROGEN ENERGY.
Pergamon Press, Inc., Journals Division, (International Association for Hydrogen Energy) 660 White Plains Rd., Tarrytown, NY 10591-5153. TEL 914-524-9200. FAX 914-333-2444. *1791*

INTERNATIONAL JOURNAL OF HYPERTHERMIA.
Taylor & Francis Ltd., (North American Hyperthermia Group) Rankine Rd., Basingstoke, Hants. RG24 0PR, England. TEL 0256-840366. FAX 0256-479438. *3198*

INTERNATIONAL JOURNAL OF IMMUNOPHARMACOLOGY.
Pergamon Press, Inc., Journals Division, 660 White Plains Rd., Tarrytown, NY 10591-5153. TEL 914-524-9200. FAX 914-333-2444. *3729*

INTERNATIONAL JOURNAL OF IMPACT ENGINEERING.
Pergamon Press, Inc., Journals Division, 660 White Plains Rd., Tarrytown, NY 10591-5153. TEL 914-524-9200. FAX 914-333-2444. *1826*

INTERNATIONAL JOURNAL OF INDUSTRIAL ERGONOMICS.
Elsevier Science Publishers B.V., P.O. Box 211, 1000 AE Amsterdam, Netherlands. TEL 020-5803911. FAX 020-5803598. *1827*

INTERNATIONAL JOURNAL OF INDUSTRIAL ORGANIZATION.
North-Holland P.O. Box 211, 1000 AE Amsterdam, Netherlands. TEL 020-5803911. FAX 020-5803598. *983*

INTERNATIONAL JOURNAL OF INFORMATION MANAGEMENT.
Butterworth - Heinemann Ltd. Linacre House, Jordan Hill, Oxford OX2 8DP, England. TEL 0865-310366. FAX 0865-301898. *1456*

INTERNATIONAL JOURNAL OF INFRARED AND MILLIMETER WAVES.
Plenum Publishing Corp., 233 Spring St., New York, NY 10013-1578. TEL 212-620-8000. FAX 212-463-0742. *3853*

INTERNATIONAL JOURNAL OF INSECT MORPHOLOGY AND EMBRYOLOGY.
Pergamon Press, Inc., Journals Division, 660 White Plains Rd., Tarrytown, NY 10591-5153. TEL 914-524-9200. FAX 914-333-2444. *534*

INTERNATIONAL JOURNAL OF INTELLIGENT SYSTEMS.
John Wiley & Sons, Inc., Journals, 605 Third Ave., New York, NY 10158. TEL 212-570-6000. FAX 212-850-6088. *1408*

INTERNATIONAL JOURNAL OF INTERCULTURAL RELATIONS.
Pergamon Press, Inc., Journals Division, (Society for International Education, Training and Research) 660 White Plains Rd., Tarrytown, NY 10591-5153. TEL 914-524-9200. FAX 914-333-2444. *4438*

INTERNATIONAL JOURNAL OF LAW AND PSYCHIATRY.
Pergamon Press, Inc., Journals Division, 660 White Plains Rd., Tarrytown, NY 10591-5153. TEL 914-524-9200. FAX 914-333-2444. *2636*

INTERNATIONAL JOURNAL OF LIFELONG EDUCATION.
Taylor & Francis Ltd., Rankine Rd., Basingstoke, Hants. RG24 0PR, England. TEL 0256-840366. FAX 0256-479438. *1684*

INTERNATIONAL JOURNAL OF MACHINE TOOLS & MANUFACTURE.
Pergamon Press, Inc., Journals Division, 660 White Plains Rd., Tarrytown, NY 10591-5153. TEL 914-524-9200. FAX 914-333-2444. *3018*

INTERNATIONAL JOURNAL OF MARITIME HISTORY.
Memorial University of Newfoundland, Maritime Studies Research Unit, St. John's, Nfld. A1C 5S7, Canada. TEL 709-737-8424. FAX 709-737-4569. *4729*

INTERNATIONAL JOURNAL OF MASS SPECTROMETRY AND ION PROCESSES.
Elsevier Science Publishers B.V., P.O. Box 211, 1000 AE Amsterdam, Netherlands. TEL 212-989-5800. FAX 020-5803598. *3853*

INTERNATIONAL JOURNAL OF MATHEMATICAL EDUCATION IN SCIENCE AND TECHNOLOGY.
Taylor & Francis Ltd., Rankine Rd., Basingstoke, Hants RG24 0PR, England. TEL 0256-840366. FAX 0256-479438. *3039*

INTERNATIONAL JOURNAL OF MECHANICAL SCIENCES.
Pergamon Press, Inc., Journals Division, 660 White Plains Rd., Tarrytown, NY 10591-5153. TEL 914-524-9200. FAX 914-333-2444. *1917*

INTERNATIONAL JOURNAL OF MENTAL HEALTH.
M.E. Sharpe, Inc., 80 Business Park Dr., Armonk, NY 10504. TEL 914-273-1800. FAX 913-273-2106. *4025*

INTERNATIONAL JOURNAL OF MICROCIRCULATION: CLINICAL & EXPERIMENTAL.
Kluwer Academic Publishers, 101 Philip Dr., Norwell, MA 02061. TEL 617-871-6600. FAX 617-871-6528. *3110*

INTERNATIONAL JOURNAL OF MICROGRAPHICS & OPTICAL TECHNOLOGY.
Pergamon Press, Inc., Journals Division, 660 White Plains Rd., Tarrytown, NY 10591-5153. TEL 914-524-9200. FAX 914-333-2444. *2798*

INTERNATIONAL JOURNAL OF MINERAL PROCESSING.
Elsevier Science Publishers B.V., P.O. Box 211, 1000 AE Amsterdam, Netherlands. TEL 020-5803911. FAX 020-5803598. *3486*

INTERNATIONAL JOURNAL OF MULTIPHASE FLOW.
Pergamon Press, Inc., Journals Division, 660 White Plains Rd., Tarrytown, NY 10591-5153. TEL 914-524-9200. FAX 914-333-2444. *1932*

INTERNATIONAL JOURNAL OF NEURAL NETWORK.
Learned Information, Inc., 143 Old Marlton Pike, Medford, NJ 08055. TEL 609-654-6266. FAX 609-654-4309. *1408*

INTERNATIONAL JOURNAL OF NEUROSCIENCE.
Gordon and Breach Science Publishers, 270 Eighth Ave., New York, NY 10011. TEL 212-206-8900. FAX 212-645-2459. *3339*

INTERNATIONAL JOURNAL OF NON-LINEAR MECHANICS.
Pergamon Press, Inc., Journals Division, 660 White Plains Rd., Tarrytown, NY 10591-5153. TEL 914-524-9200. FAX 914-333-2444. *1918*

INTERNATIONAL JOURNAL OF NURSING STUDIES.
Pergamon Press, Inc., Journals Division, 665 White Plains Rd., Tarrytown, NY 10591-5153. TEL 914-524-9200. FAX 914-333-2444. *3279*

INTERNATIONAL JOURNAL OF OBSTETRIC ANESTHESIA.
Churchill Livingstone Medical Journals, Robert Stevenson House, 1-3 Baxter's Pl., Leith Walk, Edinburgh EH1 3AF, Scotland. TEL 031-556-2424. FAX 031-558-1278. *3191*

INTERNATIONAL JOURNAL OF OFFENDER THERAPY AND COMPARATIVE CRIMINOLOGY.
Guilford Publications, Inc., 72 Spring St., 4th Fl., New York, NY 10012. TEL 212-431-9800. FAX 212-966-6708. *1515*

INTERNATIONAL JOURNAL OF OFFSHORE AND POLAR ENGINEERING.
International Society of Offshore and Polar Engineers, Box 1107, Golden, CO 80402-1107. TEL 303-273-3673. FAX 303-420-3760. *1932*

INTERNATIONAL JOURNAL OF OPTOELECTRONICS.
Taylor & Francis Ltd., Rankine Rd., Basingstoke, Hants RG24 0PR, London, England. TEL 0256-840366. FAX 0256-479438. *3853*

INTERNATIONAL JOURNAL OF ORAL & MAXILLOFACIAL IMPLANTS.
Quintessence Publishing Co., Inc., (Academy of Osseointegration) 551 Kimberly Dr., Carol Stream, IL 60188-1881. TEL 708-682-3223. FAX 708-682-3288. *3235*

INTERNATIONAL JOURNAL OF ORAL IMPLANTOLOGY.
International Congress of Oral Implantologists, Box 912, Upper Montclair, NJ 07043. TEL 201-783-6300. FAX 201-783-1175. *3235*

INTERNATIONAL JOURNAL OF PANCREATOLOGY.
Humana Press Inc., (International Association of Pancreatology) Box 2148, Clifton, NJ 07015. TEL 201-256-1699. FAX 201-256-8341. *3254*

INTERNATIONAL JOURNAL OF PARALLEL PROGRAMMING.
Plenum Publishing Corp., 233 Spring St., New York, NY 10013-1578. TEL 212-620-8000. FAX 212-463-0742. *1430*

INTERNATIONAL JOURNAL OF PARTIAL HOSPITALIZATION.
Plenum Publishing Corp., 233 Spring St., New York, NY 10013-1578. TEL 212-620-8000. FAX 212-463-0742. *4409*

INTERNATIONAL JOURNAL OF PATTERN RECOGNITION AND ARTIFICIAL INTELLIGENCE.
World Scientific Publishing Co. Pte. Ltd., Farrer Rd., P.O. Box 128, Singapore 9128, Singapore. TEL 3825663. FAX 3825919. *1422*

INTERNATIONAL JOURNAL OF PEDIATRIC OTORHINOLARYNGOLOGY.
Elsevier Science Publishers B.V., P.O. Box 211, 1000 AE Amsterdam, Netherlands. TEL 020-5803911. FAX 020-5803598. *3315*

INTERNATIONAL JOURNAL OF PERIODONTICS & RESTORATIVE DENTISTRY.
Quintessence Publishing Co., Inc., 551 Kimberly Dr., Carol Stream, IL 60188-1881. TEL 708-682-3223. FAX 708-682-3288. *3235*

INTERNATIONAL JOURNAL OF PERSONAL CONSTRUCT PSYCHOLOGY.
Hemisphere Publishing Corporation 1900 Frost Rd., Ste. 101, Bristol, PA 19007-1598. TEL 215-785-5800. FAX 215-785-5515. *4025*

INTERNATIONAL JOURNAL OF PHARMACEUTICS.
Elsevier Science Publishers B.V., P.O. Box 211, 1000 AE Amsterdam, Netherlands. TEL 020-5803911. FAX 020-5803598. *3729*

INTERNATIONAL JOURNAL OF PLANT SCIENCES.
University of Chicago Press, Journals Division, 5720 S. Woodlawn Ave., Chicago, IL 60637. TEL 312-753-3347. *506*

INTERNATIONAL JOURNAL OF PLASTICITY.
Pergamon Press, Inc., Journals Division, 660 White Plains Rd., Tarrytown, NY 10591-5153. TEL 914-524-9200. FAX 914-333-2444. *1918*

INTERNATIONAL JOURNAL OF POLITICAL ECONOMY.
M. E. Sharpe, Inc., 80 Business Park Dr., Armonk, NY 10504. TEL 914-273-1800. FAX 914-273-2106. *3899*

INTERNATIONAL JOURNAL OF POLITICS, CULTURE, AND SOCIETY.
Human Sciences Press, Inc. (Florida Atlantic University) 233 Spring St., New York, NY 10013. TEL 212-620-8000. FAX 212-463-0742. *3961*

INTERNATIONAL JOURNAL OF POLYMERIC MATERIALS.
Gordon and Breach Science Publishers, 270 Eighth Ave., New York, NY 10011. TEL 212-206-8900. FAX 212-645-2459. *1854*

INTERNATIONAL JOURNAL OF PRESSURE VESSELS AND PIPING.
Elsevier Science Publishers Ltd., Crown House, Linton Rd., Barking, Essex IG11 8JU, England. TEL 081-594-7272. FAX 081-594-5942. *1932*

INTERNATIONAL JOURNAL OF PRIMATOLOGY.
Plenum Publishing Corp., 233 Spring St., New York, NY 10013-1578. TEL 212-620-8000. FAX 212-463-0742. *584*

INTERNATIONAL JOURNAL OF PRODUCTION ECONOMICS.
Elsevier Science Publishers B.V., P.O. Box 211, 1000 AE Amsterdam, Netherlands. TEL 020-5803911. FAX 020-5803598. *1827*

INTERNATIONAL JOURNAL OF PROJECT MANAGEMENT.
Butterworth - Heinemann Ltd. (International Project Management Association (INTERNET)) Linacre House, Jordan Hill, Oxford OX2 8DP, England. TEL 0865-310366. FAX 0865-310898. *827*

INTERNATIONAL JOURNAL OF PROSTHODONTICS.
Quintessence Publishing Co., Inc., (International College of Prosthodontists) 551 Kimberly Dr., Carol Stream, IL 60188-1881. TEL 708-682-3223. FAX 708-682-3288. *3235*

INTERNATIONAL JOURNAL OF PSYCHIATRY IN MEDICINE.
Baywood Publishing Co., Inc., 26 Austin Ave., Box 337, Amityville, NY 11701. TEL 516-691-1270. FAX 516-691-1770. *3339*

INTERNATIONAL JOURNAL OF QUALITATIVE STUDIES IN EDUCATION.
Taylor & Francis Ltd., Rankine Rd., Basingstoke, Hants RG24 OPR, England. TEL 0256-840366. FAX 0256-479438. *1640*

INTERNATIONAL JOURNAL OF RADIATION APPLICATIONS AND INSTRUMENTATION. PART A: APPLIED RADIATION AND ISOTOPES.
Pergamon Press, Inc., Journals Division, 660 White Plains Rd., Tarrytown, NY 10591-5153. TEL 914-524-9200. FAX 914-333-2444. *3847*

INTERNATIONAL JOURNAL OF RADIATION APPLICATIONS AND INSTRUMENTATION. PART B: NUCLEAR MEDICINE AND BIOLOGY.
Pergamon Press, Inc., Journals Division, 660 White Plains Rd., Tarrytown, NY 10591-5153. TEL 914-524-9200. FAX 914-333-2444. *3359*

INTERNATIONAL JOURNAL OF RADIATION APPLICATIONS AND INSTRUMENTATION. PART C: RADIATION PHYSICS AND CHEMISTRY.
Pergamon Press, Inc., Journals Division, 660 White Plains Rd., Tarrytown, NY 10591. TEL 914-524-9200. FAX 914-333-2444. *3847*

INTERNATIONAL JOURNAL OF RADIATION APPLICATIONS AND INSTRUMENTATION. PART D: NUCLEAR TRACKS AND RADIATION MEASUREMENTS.
Pergamon Press, Inc., Journals Division, 395 Saw Mill River Rd., Elmsford, NY 10523. TEL 914-592-7700. FAX 914-592-3625. *3847*

INTERNATIONAL JOURNAL OF RADIATION APPLICATIONS AND INSTRUMENTATION. PART E: NUCLEAR GEOPHYSICS.
Pergamon Press plc, Headington Hill Hall, Oxford OX3 OBW, England. TEL 0865-794141. FAX 0865-743911. *1591*

INTERNATIONAL JOURNAL OF RADIATION BIOLOGY.
Taylor & Francis Ltd., Rankine Rd., Basingstoke, Hants RG24 OPR, England. TEL 0256-840366. FAX 0256-479438. *3198*

INTERNATIONAL JOURNAL OF RADIATION: ONCOLOGY - BIOLOGY - PHYSICS.
Pergamon Press, Inc., Journals Division, 660 White Plains Rd., Tarrytown, NY 10591-5153. TEL 914-524-9200. FAX 914-333-2444. *3848*

INTERNATIONAL JOURNAL OF REFRACTORY METALS & HARD MATERIALS.
Elsevier Science Publishers Ltd., (International Plansee Society for Powder Metallurgy) Crown House, Linton Rd., Barking, Essex IG11 8JU, England. TEL 081-594-7272. FAX 081-594-5942. *3409*

INTERNATIONAL JOURNAL OF REFRIGERATION.
Butterworth - Heinemann Ltd. (International Institute of Refrigeration) Linacre House, Jordan Hill, Oxford OX2 8DP, England. TEL 0865-310366. FAX 0865-310898. *2301*

INTERNATIONAL JOURNAL OF REHABILITATION RESEARCH.
Chapman & Hall, (Rehabilitation International) 2-6 Boundary Row, London SE1, England. TEL 071-865-0066. *3110*

INTERNATIONAL JOURNAL OF REMOTE SENSING.
Taylor & Francis Ltd., Rankine Rd., Basingstoke, Hants. RG24 OPR, England. TEL 0256-840366. FAX 0256-479438. *1545*

INTERNATIONAL JOURNAL OF RESEARCH IN MARKETING.
North-Holland (European Marketing Academy) P.O. Box 211, 1000 AE Amsterdam, Netherlands. TEL 020-5803911. FAX 020-5803598. *1042*

INTERNATIONAL JOURNAL OF RISK AND SAFETY IN MEDICINE.
Elsevier Science Publishers B.V., P.O. Box 211, 1000 AE Amsterdam, Netherlands. TEL 020-5803911. FAX 020-5803598. *3111*

INTERNATIONAL JOURNAL OF ROCK MECHANICS AND MINING SCIENCES & GEOMECHANICS ABSTRACTS.
Pergamon Press, Inc., Journals Division, 660 White Plains Rd., Tarrytown, NY 10591-5153. TEL 914-524-9200. FAX 914-333-2444. *3499*

INTERNATIONAL JOURNAL OF S T D & A I D S.
Royal Society of Medicine Services Ltd., 1 Wimpole St., London W1M 8AE, England. TEL 071-408-2119. FAX 071-355-3198. *3220*

INTERNATIONAL JOURNAL OF SCIENCE EDUCATION.
Taylor & Francis Ltd., Rankine Rd., Basingstoke, Hants RG24 OPR, England. TEL 0256-840366. FAX 0256-479438. *1640*

INTERNATIONAL JOURNAL OF SOCIOLOGY.
M. E. Sharpe, Inc., 80 Business Park Dr., Armonk, NY 10504. TEL 914-273-1800. FAX 914-273-2106. *4438*

INTERNATIONAL JOURNAL OF SOLAR ENERGY.
Harwood Academic Publishers, 270 Eighth Ave., New York, NY 10011. TEL 212-206-8900. FAX 212-645-2459. *1811*

INTERNATIONAL JOURNAL OF SOLIDS AND STRUCTURES.
Pergamon Press, Inc., Journals Division, 660 White Plains Rd., Tarrytown, NY 10591-5153. TEL 914-524-9200. FAX 914-333-2444. *3843*

INTERNATIONAL JOURNAL OF SPORT BIOMECHANICS.
Human Kinetics Publishers, Inc., (International Society of Biomechanics) Box 5076, Champaign, IL 61825-5076. TEL 217-351-5076. FAX 217-351-2674. *4476*

INTERNATIONAL JOURNAL OF SPORT NUTRITION.
Human Kinetics Publishers, Inc., Box 5076, Champaign, IL 61825-5076. TEL 217-351-5076. FAX 217-351-2674. *3607*

INTERNATIONAL JOURNAL OF STRUCTURES.
Nem Chand & Bros., Civil Lines, Roorkee 247667, India. TEL 01332-2258. *1868*

INTERNATIONAL JOURNAL OF SYSTEMATIC BACTERIOLOGY.
American Society for Microbiology, (International Union of Microbiological Societies, International Committee on Systematic Bacteriology) 1325 Massachusetts Ave. N.W., Washington, DC 20005. TEL 202-737-3600. *553*

INTERNATIONAL JOURNAL OF SYSTEMS SCIENCE.
Taylor & Francis Ltd., Rankine Rd., Basingstoke, Hants. RG24 OPR, England. TEL 0256-840366. FAX 0256-479438. *1827*

INTERNATIONAL JOURNAL OF TECHNOLOGY & AGING.
Human Sciences Press, Inc. 233 Spring St., New York, NY 10013-1578. TEL 212-620-8000. FAX 212-463-0742. *2274*

INTERNATIONAL JOURNAL OF THE ADDICTIONS.
Marcel Dekker Journals, 270 Madison Ave., New York, NY 10016. TEL 212-696-9000. FAX 212-685-4540. *1536*

INTERNATIONAL JOURNAL OF THEORETICAL PHYSICS.
Plenum Publishing Corp., 233 Spring St., New York, NY 10013-1578. TEL 212-620-8000. FAX 212-463-0742. *3820*

INTERNATIONAL JOURNAL OF THERMOPHYSICS.
Plenum Publishing Corp., 233 Spring St., New York, NY 10013-1578. TEL 212-620-8000. FAX 212-463-0742. *3841*

INTERNATIONAL JOURNAL OF VALUE-BASED MANAGEMENT.
Iona College, Hagan School of Business, c/o Dr. Samuel Natale, 715 North Ave., New Rochelle, NY 10801. TEL 914-633-2370. *1014*

INTERNATIONAL JOURNAL OF WATER RESOURCES DEVELOPMENT.
Butterworth - Heinemann Ltd. Linacre House, Jordan Hill, Oxford OX2 8DP, England. TEL 0865-310366. FAX 0865-310898. *4826*

INTERNATIONAL LABOR AND WORKING CLASS HISTORY.
University of Illinois Press, (Study Group on Labor and Working Class History) 54 E. Gregory Dr., Champaign, IL 61820. TEL 217-333-0950. FAX 217-244-8082. *983*

INTERNATIONAL LAW PRACTICUM.
New York State Bar Association, International Law and Practice Section, One Elk St., Albany, NY 12207-1096. TEL 518-463-3200. *2725*

INTERNATIONAL LECTURE SERIES IN COMPUTER SCIENCE.
Academic Press, Inc., 1250 Sixth Ave., San Diego, CA 92101. TEL 619-231-0926. FAX 619-699-6715. *1397*

INTERNATIONAL NEWSLETTER OF MARITIME HISTORY.
Memorial University of Newfoundland, Maritime Studies Research Unit, St. John's, Nfld. A1C 5S7, Canada. TEL 709-737-8424. FAX 709-737-4569. *4729*

INTERNATIONAL PHARMACY JOURNAL.
Medpharm GmbH Scientific Publishers, (International Pharmaceutical Federation) Birkenwaldstr. 44, Postfach 105339, 7000 Stuttgart 1, Germany. TEL 0711-25820. FAX 0711-2582290. *3730*

INTERNATIONAL PROGRESS IN URETHANES.
Technomic Publishing Co., Inc., 851 New Holland Ave., Box 3535, Lancaster, PA 17604. TEL 717-291-5609. FAX 717-295-4538. *3863*

INTERNATIONAL REGIONAL SCIENCE REVIEW.
Regional Research Institute, West Virginia Univ., Morgantown, WV 26506. TEL 304-293-2896. FAX 304-293-6699. *4376*

INTERNATIONAL REVIEW OF CYTOLOGY.
Academic Press, Inc., 1250 Sixth Ave., San Diego, CA 92101. TEL 619-231-0926. FAX 619-699-6715. *525*

INTERNATIONAL REVIEW OF EXPERIMENTAL PATHOLOGY.
Academic Press, Inc., 1250 Sixth Ave., San Diego, CA 92101. TEL 619-231-0926. FAX 619-699-6715. *3111*

INTERNATIONAL REVIEW OF LAW AND ECONOMICS.
Butterworth - Heinemann Ltd. 80 Montvale Ave., Stoneham, MA 02180. TEL 617-438-8464. FAX 617-438-1479. *2636*

INTERNATIONAL REVIEW OF NEUROBIOLOGY.
Academic Press, Inc., 1250 Sixth Ave., San Diego, CA 92101. TEL 619-231-0926. FAX 619-699-6715. *3339*

INTERNATIONAL REVIEW OF RESEARCH IN MENTAL RETARDATION.
Academic Press, Inc., 1250 Sixth Ave., San Diego, CA 92101. TEL 619-231-0926. FAX 619-699-6715. *3339*

INTERNATIONAL REVIEWS IN IMMUNOLOGY.
Harwood Academic Publishers, 270 Eighth Ave., New York, NY 10011. TEL 212-206-8900. FAX 212-645-2459. *3187*

INTERNATIONAL REVIEWS IN PHYSICAL CHEMISTRY.
Taylor & Francis Ltd., Rankine Rd., Basingstoke, Hants RG24 OPR, England. TEL 0256-840366. FAX 0256-479438. *1221*

INTERNATIONAL SCHOOL OF PHYSICS "ENRICO FERMI". ITALIAN PHYSICAL SOCIETY. PROCEEDINGS.
Academic Press, Inc., (Societa Italiana di Fisica) 1250 Sixth Ave., San Diego, CA 92101. TEL 619-231-0926. FAX 619-699-6715. *3820*

INTERNATIONAL SERIES OF MONOGRAPHS ON CHEMISTRY.
Oxford University Press, 200 Madison Ave., New York, NY 10016. TEL 212-679-7300. *1179*

INTERNATIONAL SERIES OF MONOGRAPHS ON PHYSICS.
Oxford University Press, 200 Madison Ave., New York, NY 10016. TEL 212-679-7300. *3820*

INTERNATIONAL SOCIETY OF CITRICULTURE. PROCEEDINGS.
International Society of Citriculture, c/o Prof. C.W. Coggins Jr., Department of Botany and Plant Sciences, University of California, Riverside, CA 92521. TEL 714-787-4412. FAX 714-787-4437. *99*

INTERNATIONAL STUDIES IN GLOBAL CHANGE.
Harwood Academic Publishers, 270 Eighth Ave., New York, NY 10011. TEL 212-206-8900. FAX 212-645-2459. *2509*

INTERNATIONAL STUDIES OF MANAGEMENT AND ORGANIZATION.
M. E. Sharpe, Inc., 80 Business Park Dr., Armonk, NY 10504. TEL 914-273-1800. FAX 914-273-2106. *1015*

INTERNATIONAL STUDIES QUARTERLY.
Basil Blackwell Inc., (International Studies Association) 3 Cambridge Center, Cambridge, MA 02142. TEL 617-225-0430. *3962*

INTERNATIONAL SYMPOSIUM ON ATOMIC, MOLECULAR AND SOLID-STATE THEORY, COLLISION PHENOMENA AND COMPUTATIONAL METHODS. PROCEEDINGS.
John Wiley & Sons, Inc., 605 Third Ave., New York, NY 10158-0012. TEL 212-850-6000. *1179*

INTERNATIONAL SYMPOSIUM ON COMPUTER HARDWARE DESCRIPTION LANGUAGES. PROCEEDINGS.
Elsevier Science Publishing Co., Inc. (New York), (I E E E Computer Society) 655 Ave. of the Americas, New York, NY 10010. TEL 212-989-5800. FAX 212-633-3965. *1454*

INTERNATIONAL SYMPOSIUM ON QUANTUM BIOLOGY AND QUANTUM PHARMACOLOGY. PROCEEDINGS.
John Wiley & Sons, Inc., 605 Third Ave., New York, NY 10158-0012. TEL 212-850-6000. FAX 212-850-6088. *442*

INTERNATIONAL TAX AND BUSINESS LAWYER.
University of California Press, Journals Division, 2120 Berkeley Way, Berkeley, CA 94720. TEL 510-642-6221. FAX 510-643-7127. *2725*

INTERNATIONAL TELEMETERING CONFERENCE.
Instrument Society of America, 67 Alexander Dr., Box 12277, Research Triangle Park, NC 27709. TEL 919-549-8411. FAX 919-549-8288. *1338*

INTERNATIONAL TRADE JOURNAL.
Taylor & Francis, 1900 Frost Rd., Bristol, PA 19007-1598. TEL 215-785-5800. FAX 215-785-5515. *913*

INTERNATIONAL YEARBOOK OF RURAL PLANNING.
Elsevier Science Publishers Ltd., Books Division, Crown House, Linton Rd., Barking, Essex IG11 8JU, England. TEL 081-594-7272. FAX 081-594-5942. *2489*

INTERNATIONAL YEARBOOK OF SERIALS LIBRARIANSHIP.
Haworth Press, Inc., 10 Alice St., Binghamton, NY 13904. TEL 800-342-9678. FAX 607-722-1424. *2764*

INTERNETWORKING: RESEARCH AND EXPERIENCE.
John Wiley & Sons Ltd., Journals, Baffins Lane, Chichester, Sussex PO19 1UD, England. TEL 0243-779777. FAX 0243-775878. *1427*

INVENTIONES MATHEMATICAE.
Springer-Verlag, Heidelberger Platz 3, D-1000 Berlin 33, Germany. TEL 030-8207-1. *3039*

INVESTIGATIONAL NEW DRUGS.
Kluwer Academic Publishers, 101 Philip Dr., Norwell, MA 02061. TEL 617-871-6600. FAX 617-871-6528. *3730*

INVESTIGATIVE OPHTHALMOLOGY & VISUAL SCIENCE.
J.B. Lippincott Co., (Association for Research in Vision and Ophthalmology) E. Washington Sq., Philadelphia, PA 19105. TEL 215-238-4200. *3301*

INVESTIGATIVE RADIOLOGY.
J.B. Lippincott Co., (Association of University Radiologists) E. Washington Sq., Philadelphia, PA 19105. TEL 215-238-4200. *3359*

ION EXCHANGE AND SOLVENT EXTRACTION.
Marcel Dekker, Inc., 270 Madison Ave., New York, NY 10016. TEL 212-696-9000. FAX 212-685-4540. *1227*

IOWA ACADEMY OF SCIENCE. JOURNAL.
Iowa Academy of Science, Sci. 3538, University of Northern Iowa, Cedar Falls, IA 50614. TEL 319-273-2021. *4316*

IOWA SCIENCE TEACHERS JOURNAL.
Iowa Academy of Science, Sci. 3538, University of Northern Iowa, Cedar Falls, IA 50614. TEL 319-273-2021. *4316*

IOWA STATE UNIVERSITY. ENGINEERING RESEARCH INSTITUTE. ENGINEERING RESEARCH REPORT.
Iowa State University, Engineering Research Institute, Ames, IA 50011. TEL 515-294-2336. FAX 515-294-9273. *1827*

IRISH BIRDS.
Irish Wildbird Conservancy, Ruttledge House, 8 Longford Pl., Monkstown, Co. Dublin, Ireland. TEL 01-2804322. FAX 01-2844407. *564*

IRISH JOURNAL OF PSYCHOLOGICAL MEDICINE.
Irish Institute of Psychological Medicine, c/o Dr. Mark Hartman, Ed., St. Brendan's Hospital, Rathdown Rd., Dublin 7, Ireland. TEL 35388-578406. FAX 3531-2800504. *3340*

ISELYA.
X Club, Department of Biological Science, Nicholls State University, Thibodaux, LA 70310. *506*

ISIS.
University of Chicago Press, Journals Division, (History of Science Society, Inc.) 5720 S. Woodlawn Ave., Chicago, IL 60637. TEL 312-702-7600. FAX 312-702-0694. *4316*

ISLAMIC ACADEMY OF SCIENCES. JOURNAL.
Anadolu Health and Research Foundation, (Islamic Academy of Sciences) Mithatpasha Caddesi 66-5, Yenishehir, Ankara, Turkey. TEL 1250319. FAX 3114777. *4316*

ISOTOPES IN ORGANIC CHEMISTRY.
Elsevier Science Publishers B.V., Books Division, P.O. Box 211, 1000 AE Amsterdam, Netherlands. TEL 020-5803911. FAX 020-5803705. *1218*

ISOZYMES: CURRENT TOPICS IN BIOLOGICAL AND MEDICAL RESEARCH.
Wiley-Liss, Inc., 41 E. 11th St., New York, NY 10003. TEL 212-475-7700. *442*

ISRAEL JOURNAL OF OBSTETRICS & GYNECOLOGY.
Menachem Horowitz Publishing, (Israel Society of Obstetrics & Gynecology) 22 Shlomzion Hamalca St., Tel Aviv 62276, Israel. TEL 03-448676. FAX 03-449422. *3293*

ISRAEL SOCIAL SCIENCE RESEARCH.
Hubert H. Humphrey Institute for Social Ecology, Ben-Gurion University of the Negev, P.O. Box 653, Beersheva 84105, Israel. TEL 057-461112. FAX 057-71536. *4376*

ISSUES IN ACCOUNTING EDUCATION.
American Accounting Association, 5717 Bessie Dr., Sarasota, FL 33583-2399. TEL 813-921-7747. FAX 813-923-4093. *752*

ISSUES IN COMPREHENSIVE PEDIATRIC NURSING.
Hemisphere Publishing Corporation 1900 Frost Rd., Ste. 101, Bristol, PA 19007-1598. TEL 215-785-5800. FAX 215-785-5515. *3279*

ISSUES IN MENTAL HEALTH NURSING.
Hemisphere Publishing Corporation 1900 Frost Rd., Ste. 101, Bristol, PA 19007-1598. TEL 215-785-5800. FAX 215-785-5515. *3279*

ISSUES IN REPRODUCTIVE AND GENETIC ENGINEERING.
Pergamon Press, Inc., Journals Division, 660 White Plains Rd., Tarrytown, NY 10591-5153. TEL 914-524-9200. FAX 914-333-2444. *544*

ISSUES IN WRITING.
University of Wisconsin at Stevens Point, Department of English, Stevens Point, WI 54481. TEL 715-346-3568. *2571*

J A M A: THE JOURNAL OF THE AMERICAN MEDICAL ASSOCIATION.
American Medical Association, 515 N. State St., Chicago, IL 60610. TEL 312-464-0183. FAX 312-464-5834. *3112*

J A O A: JOURNAL OF THE AMERICAN OSTEOPATHIC ASSOCIATION.
American Osteopathic Association, 142 E. Ontario St., Chicago, IL 60611. TEL 312-280-5800. FAX 312-280-5893. *3215*

J E G P: JOURNAL OF ENGLISH AND GERMANIC PHILOLOGY.
University of Illinois Press, (University of Illinois at Urbana-Champaign) 54 E. Gregory Dr., Champaign, IL 61820. TEL 217-333-0950. FAX 217-244-8082. *2819*

J E T: JOURNAL OF EDUCATIONAL THOUGHT.
University of Calgary, Faculty of Education, Rm. 502, Education Tower, Calgary, Alta. T2N 1N4, Canada. TEL 403-220-5629. FAX 403-282-7208. *1641*

J G R: JOURNAL OF GEOPHYSICAL RESEARCH.
American Geophysical Union, 2000 Florida Ave., N.W., Washington, DC 20009. TEL 202-462-6900. FAX 202-328-0566. *3437*

J G R: JOURNAL OF GEOPHYSICAL RESEARCH: OCEANS.
American Geophysical Union, 2000 Florida Ave., N.W., Washington, DC 20009. TEL 202-462-6900. FAX 202-328-0566. *1591*

J G R: JOURNAL OF GEOPHYSICAL RESEARCH: SOLID EARTH.
American Geophysical Union, 2000 Florida Ave., N.W., Washington, DC 20009. TEL 202-462-6900. FAX 202-328-0566. *1591*

J M P T: JOURNAL OF MANIPULATIVE AND PHYSIOLOGICAL THERAPEUTICS.
Williams & Wilkins, (National College of Chiropractic) 428 E. Preston St., Baltimore, MD 21202. TEL 301-528-4000. FAX 301-528-4312. *3215*

J P T: JOURNAL OF PETROLEUM TECHNOLOGY.
Society of Petroleum Engineers, Inc., Box 833836, Richardson, TX 75083-3836. TEL 214-669-3377. FAX 214-669-0135. *3690*

JAPAN AND THE WORLD ECONOMY.
North-Holland P.O. Box 211, 1000 AE Amsterdam, Netherlands. TEL 020-5803911. FAX 020-5803598. *914*

JAPANESE ECONOMIC STUDIES.
M.E. Sharpe, Inc., 80 Business Park Dr., Armonk, NY 10504. TEL 914-273-1800. FAX 914-273-2106. *672*

JAPANESE TECHNOLOGY REVIEWS: BIOTECHNOLOGY (SECTION E).
Gordon and Breach Science Publishers, 270 Eighth Ave., New York, NY 10011. TEL 212-206-8900. FAX 212-645-2459. *490*

JAPANESE TECHNOLOGY REVIEWS: COMPUTERS AND COMMUNICATION (SECTION B).
Gordon and Breach Science Publishers, 270 Eighth Ave., New York, NY 10011. TEL 212-206-8900. FAX 212-645-2459. *1351*

JAPANESE TECHNOLOGY REVIEWS: ELECTRONICS (SECTION A).
Gordon & Breach Science Publishers, 270 Eighth Ave., New York, NY 10011. TEL 212-206-8900. FAX 212-645-2459. *1774*

JAPANESE TECHNOLOGY REVIEWS: MANUFACTURING ENGINEERING (SECTION D).
Gordon and Breach Science Publishers, 270 Eighth Ave., New York, NY 10011. TEL 212-206-8900. FAX 212-645-2459. *1827*

JAPANESE TECHNOLOGY REVIEWS: NEW MATERIALS (SECTION C).
Gordon and Breach Science Publishers, 270 Eighth Ave., New York, NY 10011. TEL 212-206-8900. FAX 212-645-2459. *4602*

JAWETZ, MELNICK & ADELBERG'S MEDICAL MICROBIOLOGY.
Appleton & Lange 25 Van Zant St., Box 5630, Norwalk, CT 06856. TEL 203-838-4400. *553*

JEWISH JURISPRUDENCE SERIES.
Harwood Academic Publishers, 270 Eighth Ave., New York, NY 10011. TEL 212-206-8900. FAX 212-645-2459. *2638*

JEWISH LAW ANNUAL.
Harwood Academic Publishers, 270 Eighth Ave., New York, NY 10011. TEL 212-206-8900. FAX 212-645-2459. *2638*

JEWISH LAW IN CONTEXT.
Harwood Academic Publishers, 270 Eighth Ave., New York, NY 10011. TEL 212-206-8900. FAX 212-645-2459. *2638*

JIANGSU NONGYE XUEBAO.
Jiangsu Sheng Nongye Kexueyuan, Xiaolingwei, Nanjing, Jiangsu, People's Republic of China. *101*

JISUAN JIEGOU LIXUE JIQI YINGYONG.
Dalian Ligong Daxue, P.O. Box 320, Dalian, Liaoning 116023, People's Republic of China. TEL 471511. *1932*

JISUAN SHUXUE.
Science Press, Marketing and Sales Department, (Chinese Academy of Sciences, Computer Centre) 16 Donghuangchenggen Beijie, Beijing 100707, People's Republic of China. TEL 4010642. FAX 4012180. *3040*

JISUANJI XUEBAO.
Science Press, Marketing and Sales Department, (Chinese Academy of Sciences, Chinese Computer Federation) 16 Donghuangchenggen Beijie, Beijing 100707, People's Republic of China. TEL 4010642. FAX 4012180. *1482*

JISUANJI YANJIU YU FAZHAN.
Science Press, Marketing and Sales Department, (Chinese Academy of Sciences, Institute of Computer Science) 16 Donghuangchenggen Beijie, Beijing 100707, People's Republic of China. TEL 4010642. FAX 4012180. *1418*

JISUANJI YU YINGYONG HUAXUE.
Science Press, Marketing and Sales Department, (Chinese Academy of Sciences, East China Institute of Metallurgy) 16 Donghuangchenggen Beijie, Beijing 100707, People's Republic of China. TEL 4010642. FAX 4012180. *4359*

JOHNS HOPKINS A P L TECHNICAL DIGEST.
Johns Hopkins University, Applied Physics Laboratory, Johns Hopkins Rd., Laurel, MD 20723. TEL 301-953-5625. *3821*

JOHNS HOPKINS OCEANOGRAPHIC STUDIES.
Johns Hopkins University Press, 701 W. 40th St., Ste. 275, Baltimore, MD 21211. TEL 410-516-6900. FAX 410-516-6998. *1606*

JOHNS HOPKINS STUDIES IN THE HISTORY OF TECHNOLOGY.
Johns Hopkins University Press, 701 W. 40th St., Ste. 275, Baltimore, MD 21211. TEL 410-516-6900. FAX 410-516-6998. *4602*

JOHNS HOPKINS UNIVERSITY STUDIES IN GEOLOGY.
Johns Hopkins University Press, (Johns Hopkins University, Department of Earth and Planetary Sciences) 701 W. 40th St., Ste. 275, Baltimore, MD 21211. TEL 410-516-6900. FAX 410-516-6998. *1569*

JOHNSONIA.
Harvard University, Museum of Comparative Zoology, Cambridge, MA 02138. TEL 617-495-2468. *585*

JOINT CENTER FOR URBAN STUDIES. PUBLICATIONS.
Harvard University Press, 79 Garden St., Cambridge, MA 02138. TEL 617-495-2600. FAX 617-495-5898. *2490*

JOURNAL DE CHIMIE PHYSIQUE ET DE PHYSICO-CHIMIE BIOLOGIQUE.
Editions Scientifuques Elsevier, (Societe Francaise de Chimie, Division de Chimie Physique) 29, rue Buffon, 75005 Paris, France. *1227*

JOURNAL DES TRIBUNAUX.
Maison Ferdinand Larcier S.A., Rue des Minimes 39, 1000 Brussels, Belgium. TEL 02-5124712. *2638*

JOURNAL FOR ETHNOMUSICOLOGY.
Society for Ethnomusicology, Morrison Hall 005, Indiana University, Bloomington, IN 47405-2051. TEL 812-855-6672. *3559*

JOURNAL FOR THE EDUCATION OF THE GIFTED.
University of North Carolina Press, (Association for the Gifted) Box 2288, Chapel Hill, NC 27515-2288. TEL 919-966-3561. FAX 919-966-3829. *1737*

JOURNAL FOR THE STUDY OF RELIGION.
Association for the Study of Religion in Southern Africa, University of Natal, Department of Religious Studies, P.O. Box 375, Pietermaritzburg 3200, South Africa. TEL 0331-955571. *4184*

JOURNAL OF ABDOMINAL SURGERY.
American Society of Abdominal Surgeons, 675 Main St., Melrose, MA 02176. TEL 617-665-6102. *3379*

JOURNAL OF ABNORMAL CHILD PSYCHOLOGY.
Plenum Publishing Corp. 233 Spring St., New York, NY 10013-1578. TEL 212-620-8000. FAX 212-463-0742. *4026*

JOURNAL OF ABNORMAL PSYCHOLOGY.
American Psychological Association, 750 First St., N.E., Washington, DC 20002-4242. TEL 202-336-5500. FAX 202-336-5568. *4026*

JOURNAL OF ACADEMIC LIBRARIANSHIP.
Mountainside Publishing, Inc., 321 S. Main St., Box 8330, Ann Arbor, MI 48107. TEL 313-662-3925. FAX 313-662-4450. *2765*

JOURNAL OF ACCOUNTING AND ECONOMICS.
North-Holland P.O. Box 211, 1000 AE Amsterdam, Netherlands. TEL 020-5803911. FAX 020-5803598. *752*

JOURNAL OF ACCOUNTING AND PUBLIC POLICY.
Elsevier Science Publishing Co., Inc. (New York), 655 Ave. of the Americas, New York, NY 10010. TEL 212-989-5800. FAX 212-633-3965. *752*

JOURNAL OF ACCOUNTING EDUCATION.
Pergamon Press, Inc., Journals Division, (James Madison University, School of Accounting) 660 White Plains Rd., Tarrytown, NY 10591-5153. TEL 914-524-9200. FAX 914-333-2444. *752*

JOURNAL OF ACCOUNTING LITERATURE.
University of Florida, Accounting Research Center, Fisher School of Accounting-267 BUS, College of Business Administration, Gainsville, FL 32611. TEL 904-392-0155. *752*

JOURNAL OF ACQUIRED IMMUNE DEFICIENCY SYNDROMES.
Raven Press, 1185 Ave. of the Americas, New York, NY 10036. TEL 212-930-9500. FAX 212-869-3495. *3221*

JOURNAL OF ADDICTIVE DISEASES.
Haworth Press, Inc., 10 Alice St., Binghamton, NY 13904. TEL 800-342-9678. FAX 607-722-1424. *1537*

JOURNAL OF ADHESION.
Gordon and Breach Science Publishers, 270 Eighth Ave., New York, NY 10011. TEL 212-206-8900. FAX 212-645-2459. *3821*

JOURNAL OF ADOLESCENT CHEMICAL DEPENDENCY.
Haworth Press, Inc., 10 Alice St., Binghamton, NY 13904. TEL 800-342-9678. FAX 607-722-1424. *1537*

JOURNAL OF ADOLESCENT HEALTH.
Elsevier Science Publishing Co., Inc. (New York), (Society for Adolescent Medicine) 655 Ave. of the Americas, New York, NY 10010. TEL 212-989-5800. FAX 212-633-3965. *3114*

JOURNAL OF ADOLESCENT RESEARCH.
Sage Publications, Inc., 2455 Teller Rd., Newbury Park, CA 91320. TEL 805-499-0721. FAX 805-499-0871. *1239*

JOURNAL OF ADVANCEMENT IN MEDICINE.
Human Sciences Press, Inc. (American College of Advancement in Medicine) 233 Spring St., New York, NY 10013-1578. TEL 212-620-8000. FAX 212-463-0742. *3114*

JOURNAL OF AEROSOL SCIENCE.
Pergamon Press, Inc., Journals Division, (Gesellschaft fuer Aerosolforschung) 660 White Plains Rd., Tarrytown, NY 10591-5153. TEL 914-524-9200. FAX 914-333-2444. *3649*

JOURNAL OF AEROSPACE ENGINEERING.
American Society of Civil Engineers, 345 E. 47th St., New York, NY 10017-2398. TEL 212-705-7288. FAX 212-980-4681. *1869*

JOURNAL OF AESTHETIC EDUCATION.
University of Illinois Press, (University of Illinois at Urbana-Champaign) 54 E. Gregory Dr., Champaign, IL 61820. TEL 217-333-0950. FAX 217-244-8082. *1641*

JOURNAL OF AFFECTIVE DISORDERS.
Elsevier Science Publishers B.V., P.O. Box 211, 1000 AE Amsterdam, Netherlands. TEL 020-5803911. FAX 020-5803598. *3340*

JOURNAL OF AFRICAN EARTH SCIENCES (AND THE MIDDLE EAST).
Pergamon Press, Inc., Journals Division, 660 White Plains Rd., Tarrytown, NY 10591-5153. TEL 914-524-9200. FAX 914-333-2444. *1569*

JOURNAL OF AGING AND HEALTH.
Sage Publications, Inc., 2455 Teller Rd., Newbury Park, CA 91320. TEL 805-499-0721. FAX 805-499-0871. *2274*

JOURNAL OF AGING & SOCIAL POLICY.
Haworth Press, Inc., 10 Alice St., Binghamton, NY 13904. TEL 800-342-9678. FAX 607-722-1424. *2274*

JOURNAL OF AGRICULTURAL AND ENVIRONMENTAL ETHICS.
University of Guelph, MacKinnon Bldg., Rm 039, Guelph, Ont., Canada. TEL 519-824-4120. *3770*

JOURNAL OF AGRICULTURAL AND FOOD CHEMISTRY.
American Chemical Society, 1155 16th St., N.W., Washington, DC 20036. TEL 800-333-9511. FAX 202-872-4615. *182*

JOURNAL OF AGRICULTURAL & FOOD INFORMATION.
Haworth Press, Inc., 10 Alice St., Binghamton, NY 13904-1580. TEL 800-342-9678. FAX 607-722-1424. *101*

JOURNAL OF AGRONOMIC EDUCATION.
American Society of Agronomy, Inc., 677 S. Segoe Rd., Madison, WI 53711. TEL 608-273-8080. FAX 608-273-2021. *182*

JOURNAL OF AIRCRAFT.
American Institute of Aeronautics and Astronautics, Inc., 370 L'Enfant Promenade, S.W., Washington, DC 20024. TEL 202-646-7400. *57*

JOURNAL OF ALGEBRA.
Academic Press, Inc., Journal Division, 1250 Sixth Ave., San Diego, CA 92101. TEL 619-230-1840. FAX 619-699-6800. *3040*

JOURNAL OF ALGORITHMS.
Academic Press, Inc., Journal Division, 1250 Sixth Ave., San Diego, CA 92101. TEL 619-230-1840. FAX 619-699-6800. *3065*

JOURNAL OF ALLERGY AND CLINICAL IMMUNOLOGY.
Mosby - Year Book, Inc. (American Academy of Allergy and Immunology) 11830 Westline Industrial Dr., St. Louis, MO 63146. TEL 800-325-4117. FAX 314-432-1380. *3187*

JOURNAL OF ALLOYS AND COMPOUNDS.
Elsevier Sequoia S.A., P.O. Box 564, CH-1001 Lausanne, Switzerland. TEL 021-207381. FAX 021-235444. *3411*

JOURNAL OF AMBULATORY CARE MARKETING.
Haworth Press, Inc., 10 Alice St., Binghamton, NY 13904. TEL 800-342-9678. *3308*

JOURNAL OF AMBULATORY MONITORING.
Taylor & Francis Ltd., Rankine Rd., Basingstoke, Hants RG24 0PR, England. TEL 0256-840366. FAX 0256-479438. *3209*

JOURNAL OF AMERICAN COLLEGE HEALTH.
Heldref Publications, (American College Health Association) 1319 Eighteenth St., N.W., Washington, DC 20036-1802. TEL 202-296-6267. FAX 202-296-5149. *3805*

JOURNAL OF ANALYTIC SOCIAL WORK.
Haworth Press, Inc., 10 Alice St., Binghamton, NY 13904-1580. TEL 800-342-9678. FAX 607-722-1424. *4410*

JOURNAL OF ANALYTICAL AND APPLIED PYROLYSIS.
Elsevier Science Publishers B.V., P.O. Box 211, 1000 AE Amsterdam, Netherlands. TEL 020-5803911. FAX 020-5803598. *1180*

JOURNAL OF ANALYTICAL ATOMIC SPECTROMETRY.
Royal Society of Chemistry, Thomas Graham House, Science Park, Milton Rd., Cambridge CB4 4WF, England. TEL 0462-672555. FAX 0462-480947. *1206*

JOURNAL OF ANALYTICAL CHEMISTRY OF THE U S S R.
Plenum Publishing Corp., Consultants Bureau, (Russian Academy of Sciences) 233 Spring St., New York, NY 10013-1578. TEL 212-620-8468. FAX 212-463-0742. *1206*

JOURNAL OF ANALYTICAL TOXICOLOGY.
Preston Publications, Inc., 7800 Merrimac Ave., Box 48312, Niles, IL 60648. TEL 708-965-0566. FAX 708-965-7639. *1982*

JOURNAL OF ANDROLOGY.
J.B. Lippincott Co., (American Society of Andrology) E. Washington Sq., Philadelphia, PA 19105. TEL 215-238-4200. *3114*

JOURNAL OF ANIMAL SCIENCE.
American Society of Animal Science, 309 W. Clark St., Champaign, IL 61820. TEL 217-356-3182. FAX 217-398-4119. *219*

JOURNAL OF ANIMAL SCIENCE. SUPPLEMENT. BIENNIAL SYMPOSIUM ON ANIMAL REPRODUCTION.
American Society of Animal Science, 309 W. Clark St., Champaign, IL 61820. TEL 217-356-3192. FAX 217-398-4119. *220*

JOURNAL OF ANTHROPOLOGICAL ARCHAEOLOGY.
Academic Press, Inc., Journal Division, 1250 Sixth Ave., San Diego, CA 92101. TEL 619-230-1840. FAX 619-699-6859. *242*

JOURNAL OF ANXIETY DISORDERS.
Pergamon Press plc, Headington Hill Hall, Oxford OX3 0BW, England. TEL 0865-794141. FAX 0865-743911. *4026*

JOURNAL OF APPLIED AQUACULTURE.
Haworth Press, Inc., 10 Alice St., Binghamton, NY 13904. TEL 607-722-1695. FAX 607-722-1424. *2044*

JOURNAL OF APPLIED BEHAVIOR ANALYSIS.
Society for the Experimental Analysis of Behavior, Inc. (Lawrence), c/o Department of Human Development, University of Kansas, Lawrence, KS 66045. *4027*

JOURNAL OF APPLIED BUSINESS RESEARCH.
Box 620760, Littleton, CO 80162. TEL 303-972-6604. FAX 303-978-0413. *673*

JOURNAL OF APPLIED CHEMISTRY OF THE U S S R.
Plenum Publishing Corp., Consultants Bureau, (Russian Academy of Sciences) 233 Spring St., New York, NY 10013-1578. TEL 212-620-8468. FAX 212-463-0742. *1855*

JOURNAL OF APPLIED DEVELOPMENTAL PSYCHOLOGY.
Ablex Publishing Corporation, 355 Chestnut St., Norwood, NJ 07648. TEL 201-767-8450. FAX 201-767-6717. *4027*

JOURNAL OF APPLIED GEOPHYSICS.
Elsevier Science Publishers B.V., P.O. Box 211, 1000 AE Amsterdam, Netherlands. TEL 020-5803911. FAX 020-5803598. *1591*

JOURNAL OF APPLIED GERONTOLOGY.
Sage Publications, Inc., (Southern Gerontological Society) 2455 Teller Rd., Newbury Park, CA 91320. TEL 805-499-0721. FAX 805-499-0871. *2274*

JOURNAL OF APPLIED MATHEMATICS AND MECHANICS.
Pergamon Press, Inc., Journals Division, 660 White Plains Rd., Tarrytown, NY 10591-5153. TEL 914-524-9200. FAX 914-333-2444. *1918*

JOURNAL OF APPLIED MECHANICS AND TECHNICAL PHYSICS.
Plenum Publishing Corp., Consultants Bureau, (Russian Academy of Sciences, Siberian Division) 233 Spring St., New York, NY 10013-1578. TEL 212-620-8468. FAX 212-463-0742. *1918*

JOURNAL OF APPLIED METEOROLOGY.
American Meteorological Society, 45 Beacon St., Boston, MA 02108-3693. TEL 617-227-2425. FAX 617-742-8718. *3437*

JOURNAL OF APPLIED NUTRITION.
International Academy of Nutrition and Preventive Medicine, Box 18433, Asheville, NC 28814-0433. TEL 704-258-3243. *3608*

JOURNAL OF APPLIED PHYSIOLOGY.
American Physiological Society, 9650 Rockville Pike, Bethesda, MD 20814. TEL 301-530-7071. FAX 301-571-1814. *572*

JOURNAL OF APPLIED POLYMER SCIENCE. SYMPOSIA.
John Wiley & Sons, Inc., 605 Third Ave., New York, NY 10158-0012. TEL 212-692-6000. FAX 212-850-6088. *1855*

JOURNAL OF APPLIED PSYCHOLOGY.
American Psychological Association, 750 First St., N.E., Washington, DC 20002-4242. TEL 202-336-5500. FAX 202-336-5568. *4027*

JOURNAL OF APPLIED SOCIAL PSYCHOLOGY.
V.H. Winston & Son, Inc., 7961 Eastern Ave., Ste. 202A, Silver Spring, MD 20910. TEL 301-587-3356. *4027*

JOURNAL OF APPLIED SPECTROSCOPY.
Plenum Publishing Corp., Consultants Bureau, 233 Spring St., New York, NY 10013-1578. TEL 212-620-8468. FAX 212-463-0742. *3854*

JOURNAL OF APPLIED SPORT PSYCHOLOGY.
Association for the Advancement of Applied Sport Psychology, University of North Carolina, 203 Fetzer-8700, Chapel Hill, NC 27599. *3371*

JOURNAL OF APPROXIMATION THEORY.
Academic Press, Inc., Journal Division, 1250 Sixth Ave., San Diego, CA 92101. TEL 619-230-1840. FAX 619-699-6800. *3040*

JOURNAL OF AQUACULTURE IN THE TROPICS.
Oxford & I B H Publishing Co. Pvt. Ltd., 22 Park Mansion, Calcutta 700016, India. FAX 91-11-3325993. *2044*

JOURNAL OF AQUATIC ANIMAL HEALTH.
American Fisheries Society, 5410 Grosvenor Ln., Ste. 110, Bethesda, MD 20814-2199. TEL 301-897-8616. FAX 301-897-8096. *2044*

JOURNAL OF AQUATIC ECOSYSTEM HEALTH.
Kluwer Academic Publishers, Postbus 17, 3300 AA Dordrecht, Netherlands. TEL 078-334911. FAX 078-334254. *1960*

JOURNAL OF AQUATIC FOOD PRODUCT TECHNOLOGY.
Haworth Press, Inc., 10 Alice St., Binghamton, NY 13904-1580. TEL 800-342-9678. FAX 607-722-1424. *2074*

JOURNAL OF AQUATIC PLANT MANAGEMENT.
Aquatic Plant Management Society, Inc., Box 2695, Washington, DC 20013-2695. TEL 301-330-8831. FAX 301-977-4712. *507*

JOURNAL OF ARCHITECTURAL AND PLANNING RESEARCH.
Locke Science Publishing Company, Inc., Box 146413, Chicago, IL 60614. *302*

JOURNAL OF ARCHITECTURAL EDUCATION.
Butterworth - Heinemann Ltd. (Association of Collegiate Schools of Architecture, Inc.) 80 Montvale Ave., Stoneham, MA 02180. TEL 617-438-8464. FAX 617-438-1479. *302*

JOURNAL OF ARTHROPLASTY.
Churchill Livingstone Medical Journals, 650 Ave. of the America, New York, NY 10011. TEL 212-206-4050. FAX 212-727-7808. *3309*

JOURNAL OF ARTIFICIAL INTELLIGENCE IN EDUCATION.
Association for the Advancement of Computing in Education, Box 2966, Charlottesville, VA 22902-2966. TEL 804-973-3987. *1690*

JOURNAL OF ARTS MANAGEMENT AND LAW.
Heldref Publications, (Helen Dwight Reid Educational Foundation) 1319 Eighteenth St., N.W., Washington, DC 20036-1802. TEL 202-296-6267. FAX 202-296-5149. *2638*

JOURNAL OF ASIAN AND AFRICAN AFFAIRS.
Box 44843, Washington, DC 20026-4843. TEL 703-491-9231. *3639*

JOURNAL OF ASIAN PACIFIC COMMUNICATION.
Multilingual Matters Ltd., Bank House, 8a Hill Rd., Clevedon, Avon BS21 7HH, England. TEL 0272-876519. FAX 0272-343096. *1338*

JOURNAL OF ASSISTED REPRODUCTION AND GENETICS.
Plenum Publishing Corp., 233 Spring St., New York, NY 10013-1578. TEL 212-620-8000. FAX 212-463-0742. *3293*

JOURNAL OF ASTHMA (NEW YORK).
Marcel Dekker Journals, (Association for the Care of Asthma) 270 Madison Ave., New York, NY 10016. FAX 212-685-4540. *3365*

JOURNAL OF ATMOSPHERIC AND OCEANIC TECHNOLOGY.
American Meteorological Society, 45 Beacon St., Boston, MA 02108-3693. TEL 617-227-2425. FAX 617-742-8718. *3437*

JOURNAL OF ATMOSPHERIC AND TERRESTRIAL PHYSICS.
Pergamon Press, Inc., Journals Division, 660 White Plains Rd., Tarrytown, NY 10591-5153. TEL 914-524-9200. FAX 914-333-2444. *1591*

JOURNAL OF AUDIOVISUAL MEDIA IN MEDICINE.
Butterworth - Heinemann Ltd. (Institute of Medical & Biological Illustration) Linacre House, Jordan Hill, Oxford OX2 8DP, England. TEL 0865-310366. FAX 0865-310898. *3114*

JOURNAL OF AUTISM AND DEVELOPMENTAL DISORDERS.
Plenum Publishing Corp., 233 Spring St., New York, NY 10013-1578. TEL 212-620-8000. FAX 212-463-0742. *3340*

JOURNAL OF AUTOMATIC CHEMISTRY.
Taylor & Francis Ltd., Rankine Rd., Basingstoke, Hants RG24 0PR, England. TEL 0256-840366. FAX 0256-479438. *4359*

JOURNAL OF BACTERIOLOGY.
American Society for Microbiology, 1325 Massachusetts Ave. N.W., Washington, DC 20005. TEL 202-737-3600. *553*

JOURNAL OF BANKING AND FINANCE.
North-Holland (Universita degli Studi di Bergamo) P.O. Box 211, 1000 AE Amsterdam, Netherlands. TEL 020-5803911. FAX 020-5803598. *787*

JOURNAL OF BASIC WRITING.
City University of New York, Office of Academic Affairs, Instructional Resource Center, 535 E. 80th St., New York, NY 10021. TEL 212-794-5445. FAX 212-794-5706. *1752*

JOURNAL OF BEHAVIOR THERAPY AND EXPERIMENTAL PSYCHIATRY.
Pergamon Press, Inc., Journals Division, (Behavior Therapy and Research Society) 660 White Plains Rd., Tarrytown, NY 10591-5153. TEL 914-524-9200. FAX 914-333-2444. *3340*

JOURNAL OF BEHAVIORAL EDUCATION.
Human Sciences Press, Inc. 233 Spring St., New York, NY 10013. TEL 212-620-8000. FAX 212-463-0742. *4027*

JOURNAL OF BEHAVIORAL MEDICINE.
Plenum Publishing Corp., 233 Spring St., New York, NY 10013-1578. TEL 212-620-8000. FAX 212-463-0742. *3340*

JOURNAL OF BIOACTIVE AND COMPATIBLE POLYMERS.
Technomic Publishing Co., Inc., 851 New Holland Ave., Box 3535, Lancaster, PA 17604. TEL 717-291-5609. FAX 717-295-4538. *478*

JOURNAL OF BIOCHEMICAL AND BIOPHYSICAL METHODS.
Elsevier Science Publishers B.V., P.O. Box 211, 1000 AE Amsterdam, Netherlands. TEL 020-5803911. FAX 020-5803598. *478*

JOURNAL OF BIOELECTRICITY.
Marcel Dekker Journals, (International Society for Bioelectricity) 270 Madison Ave., New York, NY 10016. TEL 212-696-9000. FAX 212-685-4540. *485*

JOURNAL OF BIOENERGETICS AND BIOMEMBRANES.
Plenum Publishing Corp., 233 Spring St., New York, NY 10013-1578. TEL 212-620-8000. FAX 212-463-0742. *486*

JOURNAL OF BIOLOGICAL CHEMISTRY.
American Society for Biochemistry and Molecular Biology, Inc., 9650 Rockville Pike, Bethesda, MD 20814. TEL 301-530-7150. FAX 301-571-1824. *478*

JOURNAL OF BIOLOGICAL PHOTOGRAPHY.
Biological Photographic Association, Inc., 115 Stoneridge Dr., Chapel Hill, NC 27514-9772. FAX 919-967-8246. *443*

JOURNAL OF BIOLOGICAL RHYTHMS.
Guilford Publications, Inc., (Society for Research in Biological Rhythms) 72 Spring St., 4th Fl., New York, NY 10012. TEL 212-431-9800. FAX 212-966-6708. *3340*

JOURNAL OF BIOMATERIALS APPLICATIONS.
Technomic Publishing Co., Inc., 851 New Holland Ave., Box 3535, Lancaster, PA 17604. TEL 717-291-5609. FAX 717-295-4538. *3863*

JOURNAL OF BIOMECHANICAL ENGINEERING.
American Society of Mechanical Engineers, 345 E. 47th St., New York, NY 10017. TEL 212-705-7703. *469*

JOURNAL OF BIOMECHANICS.
Pergamon Press, Inc., Journals Division, (American Society of Biomechanics) 660 White Plains Rd., Tarrytown, NY 10591-5153. TEL 914-524-9200. FAX 914-333-2444. *4106*

JOURNAL OF BIOMEDICAL ENGINEERING.
Butterworth - Heinemann Ltd. (Biological Engineering Society) Linacre House, Jordan Hill, Oxford OX2 8DP, England. TEL 0865-310366. FAX 0865-310898. *469*

JOURNAL OF BIOMEDICAL MATERIALS RESEARCH.
John Wiley & Sons, Inc., Journals, (Society for Biomaterials) 605 Third Ave., New York, NY 10158-0012. TEL 212-850-6000. FAX 212-850-6088. *490*

JOURNAL OF BIOPHARMACEUTICAL STATISTICS.
Marcel Dekker Journals, 270 Madison Ave., New York, NY 10016. TEL 212-696-9000. FAX 212-685-4540. *478*

JOURNAL OF BIOTECHNOLOGY.
Elsevier Science Publishers B.V., P.O. Box 211, 1000 AE Amsterdam, Netherlands. TEL 020-5803911. FAX 020-5803598. *490*

JOURNAL OF BONE AND JOINT SURGERY: AMERICAN VOLUME.
Journal of Bone and Joint Surgery, Inc., 10 Shattuck St., Boston, MA 02115. TEL 617-734-2835. *3309*

JOURNAL OF BRITISH STUDIES.
University of Chicago Press, Journals Division, (North American Conference on British Studies) 5720 S. Woodlawn Ave., Chicago, IL 60637. TEL 312-753-3347. FAX 312-702-0694. *2370*

JOURNAL OF BURN CARE AND REHABILITATION.
Mosby - Year Book, Inc. (American Burn Association) 11830 Westline Industrial Dr., St. Louis, MO 63146. TEL 800-325-4117. FAX 314-432-1380. *3114*

JOURNAL OF BUSINESS (CHICAGO).
University of Chicago Press, Journals Division, 5720 S. Woodlawn Ave., Chicago, IL 60637. TEL 312-753-3347. *673*

JOURNAL OF BUSINESS AND ECONOMIC STUDIES.
Fairfield University, School of Business, Fairfield, CT 06430. TEL 203-254-4070. *673*

JOURNAL OF BUSINESS & FINANCE LIBRARIANSHIP.
Haworth Press, Inc., 10 Alice St., Binghamton, NY 13904. TEL 800-342-9678. FAX 607-722-1424. *2765*

JOURNAL OF BUSINESS & PSYCHOLOGY.
Human Sciences Press, Inc. (Business Psychology Research Institute) 233 Spring St., New York, NY 10013-1578. TEL 212-620-8000. FAX 212-463-0742. *4027*

JOURNAL OF BUSINESS RESEARCH.
Elsevier Science Publishing Co., Inc. (New York), 655 Ave. of the Americas, New York, NY 10010. TEL 212-989-5800. FAX 212-633-3965. *673*

JOURNAL OF BUSINESS-TO-BUSINESS MARKETING.
Haworth Press, Inc., 10 Alice St., Binghamton, NY 13904-1580. TEL 800-342-9678. FAX 607-722-1424. *1042*

JOURNAL OF BUSINESS VENTURING.
Elsevier Science Publishing Co., Inc. (New York), 655 Ave. of the Americas, New York, NY 10010. TEL 212-989-5800. FAX 212-633-3965. *673*

JOURNAL OF CANCER EDUCATION.
Pergamon Press plc, (American Association for Cancer Education) Headington Hill Hall, Oxford OX3 0BW, England. TEL 0865-794141. FAX 0865-743911. *3199*

JOURNAL OF CANCER RESEARCH AND CLINICAL ONCOLOGY.
Springer-Verlag, (Deutsche Krebsgesellschaft) Heidelberger Platz 3, D-1000 Berlin 33, Germany. TEL 030-8207-1. *3199*

JOURNAL OF CARBOHYDRATE CHEMISTRY.
Marcel Dekker Journals, 270 Madison Ave., New York, NY 10016. TEL 212-696-9000. FAX 212-685-4540. *1180*

JOURNAL OF CARDIAC SURGERY.
Futura Publishing Company, Inc., 2 Bedford Ridge Rd., Box 330, Mt. Kisco, NY 10549. TEL 800-877-8761. FAX 914-666-0993. *3209*

JOURNAL OF CARDIOPULMONARY REHABILITATION.
J.B. Lippincott Co., (American Association of Cardiovascular & Pulmonary Rehabilitation) E. Washington Sq., Philadelphia, PA 19105. TEL 215-238-4200. *3209*

JOURNAL OF CARDIOTHORACIC AND VASCULAR ANESTHESIA.
W.B. Saunders Co. Curtis Center, Independence Square W., Philadelphia, PA 19106. TEL 215-238-7800. *3191*

JOURNAL OF CARDIOVASCULAR PHARMACOLOGY.
Raven Press, 1185 Ave. of the Americas, New York, NY 10036. TEL 212-930-9500. FAX 212-869-3495. *3731*

JOURNAL OF CARDIOVASCULAR TECHNOLOGY.
Mary Ann Liebert, Inc., 1651 Third Ave., New York, NY 10128. TEL 212-289-2300. FAX 212-289-4697. *3210*

JOURNAL OF CAREER DEVELOPMENT.
Human Sciences Press, Inc. 233 Spring St., New York, NY 10013-1578. TEL 212-620-8000. FAX 212-463-0742. *3629*

JOURNAL OF CATALYSIS.
Academic Press, Inc., Journal Division, 1250 Sixth Ave., San Diego, CA 92101. TEL 619-230-1840. FAX 619-699-6800. *1227*

JOURNAL OF CATARACT AND REFRACTIVE SURGERY.
American Society of Cataract and Refractive Surgery, 3702 Pender Dr., No. 250, Fairfax, VA 22030-6039. TEL 703-591-2220. FAX 703-591-0614. *3301*

JOURNAL OF CELL BIOLOGY.
Rockefeller University Press, (American Society for Cell Biology) 222 E. 70th St., New York, NY 10021. TEL 212-570-8572. FAX 212-570-7944. *525*

JOURNAL OF CELLULAR BIOCHEMISTRY.
John Wiley & Sons, Inc., Journals, 605 Third Ave., New York, NY 10158. TEL 212-850-6000. FAX 212-850-6088. *525*

JOURNAL OF CELLULAR PHYSIOLOGY.
John Wiley & Sons, Inc., Journals, 605 Third Ave., New York, NY 10158. TEL 212-850-6000. FAX 212-850-6088. *572*

JOURNAL OF CELLULAR PLASTICS.
Technomic Publishing Co., Inc., 851 New Holland Ave., Box 3535, Lancaster, PA 17604. TEL 717-291-5609. FAX 717-295-4538. *3863*

REFEREED SERIALS

JOURNAL OF CEREBRAL BLOOD FLOW AND METABOLISM.
Raven Press, (International Society of Cerebral Blood Flow and Metabolism) 1185 Ave. of the Americas, New York, NY 10036. TEL 212-930-9500. FAX 212-869-3495. *3340*

JOURNAL OF CHEMICAL DEPENDENCY TREATMENT.
Haworth Press, Inc., 10 Alice St., Binghamton, NY 13904. TEL 800-342-9678. FAX 607-722-1424. *1537*

JOURNAL OF CHEMICAL ECOLOGY.
Plenum Publishing Corp., 233 Spring St., New York, NY 10013-1578. TEL 212-620-8000. FAX 212-463-0742. *1960*

JOURNAL OF CHEMICAL EDUCATION: SOFTWARE. SERIES A.
American Chemical Society, Division of Chemical Education, Inc., 238 Kent Rd., Springfield, PA 19064. TEL 215-542-7862. FAX 202-872-4615. *1690*

JOURNAL OF CHEMICAL EDUCATION: SOFTWARE. SERIES B.
American Chemical Society, Division of Chemical Education, Inc., 238 Kent Rd., Springfield, PA 19064. TEL 215-543-7862. FAX 202-872-4615. *1690*

JOURNAL OF CHEMICAL EDUCATION: SOFTWARE. SERIES C.
American Chemical Society, Division of Chemical Education, Inc., 238 Kent Rd., Springfield, PA 19064. TEL 215-543-7862. FAX 202-872-4615. *1690*

JOURNAL OF CHEMICAL EDUCATION: SOFTWARE. SPECIAL ISSUE SERIES.
American Chemical Society, Division of Chemical Education, Inc., 238 Kent Rd., Springfield, PA 19064. TEL 215-543-7862. FAX 202-872-4615. *1690*

JOURNAL OF CHEMICAL INFORMATION AND COMPUTER SCIENCES.
American Chemical Society, 1155 16th St. N.W., Washington, DC 20036. TEL 800-333-9511. FAX 202-872-4615. *4360*

JOURNAL OF CHEMICAL PHYSICS.
American Institute of Physics, 335 E. 45th St., New York, NY 10017. TEL 212-661-9404. *3821*

JOURNAL OF CHEMICAL RESEARCH.
Royal Society of Chemistry, Thomas Graham House, Science Park, Milton Rd., Cambridge CB4 4WF, England. TEL 0462-672555. FAX 0462-480947. *1180*

JOURNAL OF CHEMICAL TECHNOLOGY AND BIOTECHNOLOGY.
Elsevier Science Publishers Ltd., (Society of Chemical Industry) Crown House, Linton Rd., Barking, Essex IG11 8JU, England. TEL 081-594-7272. FAX 081-594-5942. *490*

JOURNAL OF CHEMICAL VAPOR DEPOSITION.
Technomic Publishing Co., Inc., 851 New Holland Ave., Box 3535, Lancaster, PA 17604. TEL 717-291-5609. FAX 717-295-4538. *1210*

JOURNAL OF CHILD AND ADOLESCENT GROUP THERAPY.
Human Sciences Press, Inc. 233 Spring St., New York, NY 10013. TEL 212-620-8000. FAX 212-463-0742. *3341*

JOURNAL OF CHILD AND FAMILY STUDIES.
Human Sciences Press, Inc. 233 Spring St., New York, NY 10013-1578. TEL 212-620-8000. FAX 212-463-0742. *4027*

JOURNAL OF CHILD NEUROLOGY.
Mosby - Year Book, Inc. 11830 Westline Industrial Dr., St. Louis, MO 63146. TEL 800-325-4177. *3341*

JOURNAL OF CHILD PSYCHOLOGY & PSYCHIATRY & ALLIED DISCIPLINES.
Pergamon Press, Inc., Journals Division, (Association of Child Psychology and Psychiatry) 660 White Plains Rd., Tarrytown, NY 10591-5153. TEL 914-524-9200. FAX 914-333-2444. *4027*

JOURNAL OF CHILD SEXUAL ABUSE.
Haworth Press, Inc., 10 Alice St., Binghamton, NY 13904-1580. TEL 800-342-9678. FAX 607-722-1424. *4410*

JOURNAL OF CHINESE LINGUISTICS.
Project on Linguistic Analysis, 2222 Piedmont Ave., Berkeley, CA 94720. TEL 510-642-5939. *2820*

JOURNAL OF CHINESE LINGUISTICS MONOGRAPH SERIES.
Project on Linguistic Analysis, 2222 Piedmont Ave., Berkeley, CA 94720. TEL 510-642-5939. *2820*

JOURNAL OF CHIROPRACTIC.
American Chiropractic Association, Inc., 8229 Maryland Ave., St. Louis, MO 63105. TEL 314-862-7800. FAX 314-721-5171. *3215*

JOURNAL OF CHROMATOGRAPHY.
Elsevier Science Publishers B.V., P.O. Box 211, 1000 AE Amsterdam, Netherlands. TEL 020-5803911. FAX 020-5803598. *1206*

JOURNAL OF CHROMATOGRAPHY - BIOMEDICAL APPLICATIONS.
Elsevier Science Publishers B.V., P.O. Box 211, 1000 AE Amsterdam, Netherlands. TEL 020-5803911. FAX 020-5803598. *1180*

JOURNAL OF CHROMATOGRAPHY LIBRARY.
Elsevier Science Publishers B.V., Books Division, P.O. Box 211, 1000 AE Amsterdam, Netherlands. TEL 020-5803911. FAX 020-5803598. *1206*

JOURNAL OF CLIMATE.
American Meteorological Society, 45 Beacon St., Boston, MA 02108-3693. TEL 617-227-2425. FAX 617-742-8718. *3437*

JOURNAL OF CLINICAL AND EXPERIMENTAL GERONTOLOGY.
Marcel Dekker Journals, 270 Madison Ave., New York, NY 10016. TEL 212-696-9000. FAX 212-685-4540. *2274*

JOURNAL OF CLINICAL ANESTHESIA.
Butterworth - Heinemann Ltd. 80 Montvale Ave., Stoneham, MA 02180. TEL 617-438-8464. FAX 617-438-1479. *3191*

JOURNAL OF CLINICAL APHERESIS.
John Wiley & Sons, Inc., Journals, (American Society for Apheresis) 605 Third Ave., New York, NY 10158. TEL 212-850-6000. FAX 212-850-6088. *3388*

JOURNAL OF CLINICAL CHILD PSYCHOLOGY.
Lawrence Erlbaum Associates, Inc., (American Psychological Association, Clinical Child Psychology) 365 Broadway, Hillsdale, NJ 07642. TEL 504-388-3202. FAX 201-666-2394. *4027*

JOURNAL OF CLINICAL ENDOCRINOLOGY AND METABOLISM.
Williams & Wilkins, (Endocrine Society) 428 E. Preston St., Baltimore, MD 21202. TEL 301-528-4000. FAX 301-528-4312. *3254*

JOURNAL OF CLINICAL ENGINEERING.
Quest Publishing Co., 1351 Titan Way, Brea, CA 92621. TEL 714-738-6400. *469*

JOURNAL OF CLINICAL EPIDEMIOLOGY.
Pergamon Press, Inc., Journals Division, 660 White Plains Rd., Tarrytown, NY 10591-5153. TEL 914-524-9200. FAX 914-333-2444. *3114*

JOURNAL OF CLINICAL ETHICS.
University Publishing Group, Inc., 107 E. Church St., Frederick, MD 21701. TEL 301-694-8531. *3114*

JOURNAL OF CLINICAL GASTROENTEROLOGY.
Raven Press, 1185 Ave. of the Americas, New York, NY 10036. TEL 212-930-9500. FAX 212-869-3495. *3269*

JOURNAL OF CLINICAL IMMUNOASSAY.
Kellner-McCaffery Associates, Inc., (Clinical Ligand Assay Society) 150 Fifth Ave., Ste. 322, New York, NY 10011. TEL 212-741-0280. *3187*

JOURNAL OF CLINICAL IMMUNOLOGY.
Plenum Publishing Corp., 233 Spring St., New York, NY 10013-1578. TEL 212-620-8000. FAX 212-463-0742. *3187*

JOURNAL OF CLINICAL INVESTIGATION.
Rockefeller University Press, (American Society for Clinical Investigation) 222 E. 70th St., New York, NY 10021. TEL 212-570-8572. FAX 212-570-7944. *3114*

JOURNAL OF CLINICAL MICROBIOLOGY.
American Society for Microbiology, 1325 Massachusetts Ave., N.W., Washington, DC 20005. TEL 202-737-3600. *554*

JOURNAL OF CLINICAL MONITORING.
Little, Brown and Company, Medical Journals, (Society for Technology in Anesthesia) 34 Beacon St., Boston, MA 02108. TEL 617-859-5500. FAX 617-859-0629. *3114*

JOURNAL OF CLINICAL NEURO-OPHTHALMOLOGY.
Raven Press, 1185 Ave. of the Americas, New York, NY 10036. TEL 212-930-9500. FAX 212-869-3495. *3301*

JOURNAL OF CLINICAL NEUROPHYSIOLOGY.
Raven Press, (American Electroencephalographic Society) 1185 Ave. of the Americas, New York, NY 10036. TEL 212-930-9500. FAX 212-869-3495. *3341*

JOURNAL OF CLINICAL ONCOLOGY.
W.B. Saunders Co. (American Society of Clinical Oncology) Curtis Center, Independence Square W., Philadelphia, PA 19106. TEL 215-238-7800. *3199*

JOURNAL OF CLINICAL ORTHODONTICS.
J C O Inc., 1828 Pearl St., Boulder, CO 80302. FAX 303-443-9356. *3235*

JOURNAL OF CLINICAL PHARMACOLOGY.
J.B. Lippincott Co., (American College of Clinical Pharmacology) E. Washington Sq., Philadelphia, PA 19105. TEL 215-238-4225. *3731*

JOURNAL OF CLINICAL PSYCHIATRY.
Physicians Postgraduate Press, Inc., Box 240008, Memphis, TN 38124. TEL 901-682-1001. FAX 901-682-6992. *3341*

JOURNAL OF CLINICAL PSYCHOANALYSIS.
International Universities Press, Inc., 59 Boston Post Rd., Box 1524, Madison, CT 06443-1524. TEL 203-245-4000. FAX 203-245-0775. *4027*

JOURNAL OF CLINICAL PSYCHOLOGY.
Clinical Psychology Publishing Co., Inc., 4 Conant Sq., Brandon, VT 05733. TEL 802-247-6871. FAX 802-247-6853. *4027*

JOURNAL OF CLINICAL PSYCHOPHARMACOLOGY.
Williams & Wilkins, 428 E. Preston St., Baltimore, MD 21202. TEL 301-528-4000. FAX 301-528-4312. *3731*

JOURNAL OF CLINICAL RESEARCH AND PHARMACOEPIDEMIOLOGY.
Elsevier Science Publishing Co., Inc. (New York), (Associates of Clinical Pharmacology) 655 Ave. of the Americas, New York, NY 10010. TEL 212-989-5800. FAX 212-633-3965. *3731*

JOURNAL OF CLINICAL ULTRASOUND.
John Wiley & Sons, Inc., Journals, 605 Third Ave., New York, NY 10158-0012. TEL 212-850-6000. FAX 212-850-6088. *3859*

JOURNAL OF CLUSTER SCIENCE.
Plenum Publishing Corp., 233 Spring St., New York, NY 10013-1578. TEL 212-620-8000. FAX 212-463-0742. *1180*

JOURNAL OF COATED FABRICS.
Technomic Publishing Co., Inc., 851 New Holland Ave., Box 3535, Lancaster, PA 17604. TEL 717-291-5609. FAX 717-295-4538. *4621*

JOURNAL OF COGNITIVE NEUROSCIENCE.
M I T Press, (Cognitive Neuroscience Institute) 55 Hayward St., Cambridge, MA 02142. TEL 617-253-2889. FAX 617-258-6779. *3341*

JOURNAL OF COGNITIVE PSYCHOTHERAPY.
Springer Publishing Company, 536 Broadway, New York, NY 10012. TEL 212-431-4370. FAX 212-941-7842. *4027*

JOURNAL OF COLD REGIONS ENGINEERING.
American Society of Civil Engineers, 345 E. 47th St., New York, NY 10017-2398. TEL 212-705-7288. FAX 212-980-4681. *1869*

JOURNAL OF COLLEGE AND ADULT READING.
North Central Reading Association, Simpson College, 701 North "C" St., Indianola, IA 50125. *1685*

JOURNAL OF COLLEGE & UNIVERSITY FOODSERVICE.
Haworth Press, Inc., Food Products Press, 10 Alice St., Binghamton, NY 13904-1580. TEL 800-342-9678. FAX 607-722-1424. *2074*

JOURNAL OF COLLEGE STUDENT PSYCHOTHERAPY.
Haworth Press, Inc., 10 Alice St., Binghamton, NY 13904. TEL 800-342-9678. FAX 607-722-1424. *4028*

JOURNAL OF COLLOID AND INTERFACE SCIENCE.
Academic Press, Inc., Journal Division, 1250 Sixth Ave., San Diego, CA 92101. TEL 619-230-1840. FAX 619-699-6800. *1227*

JOURNAL OF COMBINATORIAL THEORY. SERIES A.
Academic Press, Inc., Journal Division, 1250 Sixth Ave., San Diego, CA 92101. TEL 619-230-1840. FAX 619-699-6800. *3040*

JOURNAL OF COMBINATORIAL THEORY. SERIES B.
Academic Press, Inc., Journal Division, 1250 Sixth Ave., San Diego, CA 92101. TEL 619-230-1840. FAX 619-699-6800. *3040*

JOURNAL OF COMMUNICATION DISORDERS.
Elsevier Science Publishing Co., Inc. (New York), 655 Ave. of the Americas, New York, NY 10010. TEL 212-989-5800. FAX 212-633-3965. *4028*

JOURNAL OF COMMUNITY HEALTH.
Human Sciences Press, Inc. 233 Spring St., New York, NY 10013-1578. TEL 212-620-8000. FAX 212-463-0742. *3115*

JOURNAL OF COMMUNITY HEALTH NURSING.
Lawrence Erlbaum Associates, Inc., 365 Broadway, Hillsdale, NJ 07642. TEL 201-666-4110. FAX 201-666-2394. *3280*

JOURNAL OF COMMUNITY PSYCHOLOGY.
Clinical Psychology Publishing Co., Inc., 4 Conant Sq., Brandon, VT 05733. TEL 802-247-6871. FAX 802-247-6853. *4028*

THE JOURNAL OF COMPARATIVE NEUROLOGY.
John Wiley & Sons, Inc., Journals, 605 Third Ave., New York, NY 10158. TEL 212-850-6000. FAX 212-850-6088. *3341*

JOURNAL OF COMPARATIVE PHYSICAL AND EDUCATION SPORT.
Verlag Karl Hofmann, (International Society on Comparative Physical Education and Sport (ISCPES)) Steinwasenstr. 6-8, Postfach 1360, 7060 Schorndorf, Germany. TEL 07181-7811. *4477*

JOURNAL OF COMPARATIVE PSYCHOLOGY.
American Psychological Association, 750 First St., N.E., Washington, DC 20002-4242. TEL 202-336-5500. FAX 202-336-5568. *4028*

JOURNAL OF COMPLEXITY.
Academic Press, Inc., Journal Division, 1250 Sixth Ave., San Diego, CA 92101. TEL 619-230-1840. FAX 619-699-6800. *3065*

JOURNAL OF COMPOSITE MATERIALS.
Technomic Publishing Co., Inc., 851 New Holland Ave., Box 3535, Lancaster, PA 17604. TEL 717-291-5609. FAX 717-295-4538. *1918*

JOURNAL OF COMPOSITES TECHNOLOGY AND RESEARCH.
American Society for Testing and Materials, 1916 Race St., Philadelphia, PA 19103. TEL 215-299-5400. FAX 215-977-9679. *1933*

JOURNAL OF COMPUTATIONAL AND APPLIED MATHEMATICS.
North-Holland (Computational and Applied Mathematics Group) P.O. Box 211, 1000 AE Amsterdam, Netherlands. TEL 020-5803911. FAX 020-5803598. *3041*

JOURNAL OF COMPUTATIONAL CHEMISTRY.
John Wiley & Sons, Inc., Journals, 605 Third Ave., New York, NY 10158-0012. TEL 212-850-6000. FAX 212-850-6088. *1181*

JOURNAL OF COMPUTATIONAL MATHEMATICS.
Science Press, Marketing and Sales Department, 16 Donghuangchenggen Beijie, Beijing 100707, People's Republic of China. TEL 4010642. FAX 4012180. *3041*

JOURNAL OF COMPUTATIONAL PHYSICS.
Academic Press, Inc., Journal Division, 1250 Sixth Ave., San Diego, CA 92101. TEL 619-230-1840. FAX 619-699-6800. *3840*

JOURNAL OF COMPUTER AND SYSTEM SCIENCES.
Academic Press, Inc., Journal Division, 1250 Sixth Ave., San Diego, CA 92101. TEL 619-230-1840. FAX 619-699-6800. *1397*

JOURNAL OF COMPUTER-ASSISTED MICROSCOPY.
Plenum Publishing Corp., 233 Spring St., New York, NY 10013-1578. TEL 212-620-8000. FAX 212-463-0742. *1435*

JOURNAL OF COMPUTER ASSISTED TOMOGRAPHY.
Raven Press, 1185 Ave. of the Americas, New York, NY 10036. TEL 212-930-9500. FAX 212-869-3495. *3359*

JOURNAL OF COMPUTERS IN MATHEMATICS AND SCIENCE TEACHING.
Association for the Advancement of Computing in Education, Box 2966, Charlottesville, VA 22902-2966. TEL 804-973-3987. *3065*

JOURNAL OF COMPUTING IN CHILDHOOD EDUCATION.
Association for the Advancement of Computing in Education, Box 2966, Charlottesville, VA 22902-2966. TEL 804-973-3987. *1690*

JOURNAL OF CONSTRUCTIONAL STEEL RESEARCH.
Elsevier Science Publishers Ltd., Crown House, Linton Rd., Barking, Essex IG11 8JU, England. TEL 081-594-7272. FAX 081-594-5942. *1869*

JOURNAL OF CONSULTING AND CLINICAL PSYCHOLOGY.
American Psychological Association, 750 First St., N.E., Washington, DC 20002-4242. TEL 202-336-5500. FAX 202-336-5568. *4028*

JOURNAL OF CONSUMER PSYCHOLOGY.
Lawrence Erlbaum Associates, Inc., (Society for Consumer Psychology) 365 Broadway, Hillsdale, NJ 07642. TEL 201-666-4110. FAX 201-666-2394. *33*

JOURNAL OF CONSUMER RESEARCH.
University of Chicago Press, Journals Division, 5720 S. Woodlawn Ave., Chicago, IL 60637. TEL 312-702-7600. FAX 312-702-0694. *1042*

JOURNAL OF CONTAMINANT HYDROLOGY.
Elsevier Science Publishers B.V., P.O. Box 211, 1000 AH Amsterdam, Netherlands. TEL 020-5803911. FAX 020-5803598. *1599*

JOURNAL OF CONTEMPORARY HEALTH LAW AND POLICY.
Catholic University of America, Columbus School of Law, Washington, DC 20064. TEL 202-319-5732. *3115*

JOURNAL OF CONTEMPORARY PSYCHOTHERAPY.
Human Sciences Press, Inc. 233 Spring St., New York, NY 10013-1578. TEL 212-620-8000. FAX 212-463-0742. *4028*

JOURNAL OF CONTINUING HIGHER EDUCATION.
Association for Continuing Higher Education (University Park), 210 J. Orvis Keller Bldg., Pennsylvania State University, University Park, PA 16802. TEL 814-863-7752. FAX 814-865-3003. *1685*

JOURNAL OF CONTROLLED RELEASE.
Elsevier Science Publishers B.V., (Controlled Release Society) P.O. Box 211, 1000 AE Amsterdam, Netherlands. TEL 020-5803911. *478*

JOURNAL OF COORDINATION CHEMISTRY. SECTIONS A & B.
Gordon and Breach Science Publishers, 270 Eighth Ave., New York, NY 10011. TEL 212-206-8900. FAX 212-645-2459. *1181*

JOURNAL OF COUNSELING PSYCHOLOGY.
American Psychological Association, 750 First St., N.E., Washington, DC 20002-4242. TEL 202-336-5500. FAX 202-336-5568. *4028*

JOURNAL OF COUPLES THERAPY.
Haworth Press, Inc., 10 Alice St., Binghamton, NY 13904. TEL 800-342-9678. FAX 607-722-1424. *4028*

JOURNAL OF CRANIOFACIAL GENETICS AND DEVELOPMENTAL BIOLOGY.
Munksgaard International Publishers Ltd., (Society of Craniofacial Genetics) P.O. Box 2148, DK-1016 Copenhagen K, Denmark. TEL 45-33-12-70-30. FAX 45-33-12-93-87. *544*

JOURNAL OF CRANIOFACIAL SURGERY.
Little, Brown and Company, Medical Journals, (American Association of Pediatric Plastic Surgeons) 34 Beacon St., Boston, MA 02108. TEL 617-859-5500. FAX 617-859-0629. *3380*

JOURNAL OF CRANIOMANDIBULAR DISORDERS.
Quintessence Publishing Co., Inc., (American Academy of Craniomandibular Disorders) 551 Kimberly Dr., Carol Stream, IL 60188-1881. TEL 708-682-3223. FAX 708-682-3288. *3236*

JOURNAL OF CRIMINAL JUSTICE.
Pergamon Press, Inc., Journals Division, 660 White Plains Rd., Tarrytown, NY 10591-5153. TEL 914-524-9200. FAX 914-333-2444. *2639*

JOURNAL OF CRITICAL CARE.
W.B. Saunders Co. Curtis Center, Independence Square W., Philadelphia, PA 19106. TEL 215-238-7800. *3115*

JOURNAL OF CRUSTACEAN BIOLOGY.
Crustacean Society, c/o Denton Belk, 840 E. Mulberry, San Antonio, TX 78212-3194. TEL 512-732-8809. *585*

JOURNAL OF CRYSTAL GROWTH.
North-Holland P.O. Box 211, 1000 AE Amsterdam, Netherlands. TEL 020-5803911. FAX 020-5803598. *1211*

JOURNAL OF CRYSTALLOGRAPHIC AND SPECTROSCOPIC RESEARCH.
Plenum Publishing Corp., 233 Spring St., New York, NY 10013-1578. TEL 212-620-8000. FAX 212-463-0742. *1211*

JOURNAL OF CULINARY PRACTICE.
Haworth Press, Inc., 10 Alice St., Binghamton, NY 13904. TEL 800-342-9678. FAX 607-722-1424. *2074*

JOURNAL OF CURRICULUM STUDIES.
Taylor & Francis Ltd., Rankine Rd., Basingstoke, Hants RG24 0PR, England. TEL 0256-840366. FAX 0256-479438. *1752*

JOURNAL OF D N A SEQUENCING AND MAPPING.
Harwood Academic Publishers, 270 Eighth Ave., New York, NY 10011. TEL 212-206-8900. FAX 212-645-2459. *545*

JOURNAL OF DATABASE ADMINISTRATION.
Idea Group Publishing, 4811 Jonestown Rd., Ste. 230, Harrisburg, PA 17109-1751. TEL 717-541-9150. FAX 717-541-9159. *1445*

JOURNAL OF DENTAL HYGIENE.
American Dental Hygienists' Association, 444 N. Michigan Ave., Ste. 3400, Chicago, IL 60611. TEL 312-440-8900. FAX 312-440-8929. *3236*

JOURNAL OF DENTAL RESEARCH.
American Association for Dental Research, (International Association for Dental Research) 1111 14th St., N.W., Ste. 1000, Washington, DC 20005. TEL 202-898-1050. FAX 202-789-1033. *3236*

JOURNAL OF DENTISTRY.
Butterworth - Heinemann Ltd. Linacre House, Jordan Hill, Oxford OX2 8DP, England. TEL 0865-310366. FAX 0865-310898. *3236*

JOURNAL OF DENTISTRY FOR CHILDREN.
American Society of Dentistry for Children, 211 E. Chicago Ave., Ste. 1430, Chicago, IL 60611. TEL 312-943-1244. FAX 312-943-5341. *3236*

JOURNAL OF DERMATOLOGIC SURGERY AND ONCOLOGY.
Elsevier Science Publishing Co., Inc. (New York), (American Society for Dermatologic Surgery) 655 Ave. of the Americas, New York, NY 10010. TEL 212-989-5800. FAX 212-633-3965. *3380*

JOURNAL OF DERMATOLOGICAL SCIENCE.
Elsevier Science Publishers B.V., (Japanese Society for Investigative Dermatology) P.O. Box 211, 1000 AE Amsterdam, Netherlands. TEL 020-5803911. FAX 020-5803598. *3248*

JOURNAL OF DESIGN MANUFACTURING.
Chapman & Hall, 2-6 Boundary Row, London SE1 8HN, England. TEL 071-865-0066. FAX 071-522-9623. *1933*

JOURNAL OF DEVELOPMENT ECONOMICS.
North-Holland P.O. Box 211, 1000 AE Amsterdam, Netherlands. TEL 020-5803911. FAX 020-5803598. *932*

JOURNAL OF DEVELOPMENTAL AND BEHAVIORAL PEDIATRICS.
Williams & Wilkins, (Society for Behavioral Pediatrics) 428 E. Preston St., Baltimore, MD 21202. TEL 301-528-4000. FAX 301-528-4312. *3321*

JOURNAL OF DEVELOPMENTAL AND PHYSICAL DISABILITIES.
Plenum Publishing Corp., 233 Spring St., New York, NY 10013-1578. TEL 212-620-8000. FAX 212-463-0742. *2284*

JOURNAL OF DIABETES AND ITS COMPLICATIONS.
Elsevier Science Publishing Co., Inc. (New York), 655 Ave. of the Americas, New York, NY 10010. TEL 212-989-5800. FAX 212-633-3965. *3254*

JOURNAL OF DIAGNOSTIC MEDICAL SONOGRAPHY.
J.B. Lippincott Co., (Society of Diagnostic Medical Sonographers) E. Washington Sq., Philadelphia, PA 19105. TEL 215-238-4200. *3115*

JOURNAL OF DIFFERENTIAL EQUATIONS.
Academic Press, Inc., Journal Division, 1250 Sixth Ave., San Diego, CA 92101. TEL 619-230-1840. FAX 619-699-6800. *3041*

JOURNAL OF DISPERSION SCIENCE AND TECHNOLOGY.
Marcel Dekker Journals, 270 Madison Ave., New York, NY 10016. TEL 212-696-9000. FAX 212-685-4540. *1227*

JOURNAL OF DISTANCE EDUCATION.
Canadian Association for Distance Education, 151 Slater St., Ottawa, Ont. K1P 5N1, Canada. FAX 604-291-4964. *1685*

JOURNAL OF DIVORCE & REMARRIAGE.
Haworth Press, Inc., 10 Alice St., Binghamton, NY 13904. TEL 800-342-9678. FAX 607-722-1424. *3067*

JOURNAL OF DRUG DEVELOPMENT.
Gardiner - Caldwell Communications Ltd., Old Ribbon Mill, Pitt St., Macclesfield, Cheshire SK11 7PT, England. TEL 0625-618507. FAX 0625-610260. *3731*

JOURNAL OF DRUG ISSUES.
Journal of Drug Issues Inc., Box 4021, Leon Station, Tallahassee, FL 32303. *1537*

JOURNAL OF DYNAMIC SYSTEMS, MEASUREMENT AND CONTROL.
American Society of Mechanical Engineers, 345 E. 47th St., New York, NY 10017. TEL 212-705-7703. *1918*

JOURNAL OF DYNAMICS AND DIFFERENTIAL EQUATIONS.
Plenum Publishing Corp., 233 Spring St., New York, NY 10013-1578. TEL 212-620-8000. FAX 212-463-0742. *3041*

JOURNAL OF EARLY ADOLESCENCE.
Sage Publications, Inc., 2455 Teller Rd., Newbury Park, CA 91320. TEL 805-499-0721. FAX 805-499-0871. *1239*

JOURNAL OF ECOLOGY.
Blackwell Scientific Publications Ltd., (British Ecological Society) Osney Mead, Oxford OX2 OEL, England. TEL 0865-240201. FAX 0865-721205. *444*

JOURNAL OF ECONOMETRICS.
Elsevier Sequoia S.A., P.O. Box 564, CH-1001 Lausanne, Switzerland. FAX 021-235444. *674*

JOURNAL OF ECONOMIC BEHAVIOR & ORGANIZATION.
North-Holland P.O. Box 211, 1000 AE Amsterdam, Netherlands. TEL 020-5803911. FAX 020-5803598. *674*

JOURNAL OF ECONOMIC DYNAMICS AND CONTROL.
North-Holland P.O. Box 211, 1000 AE Amsterdam, Netherlands. TEL 020-5803911. FAX 020-5803598. *896*

JOURNAL OF ECONOMIC EDUCATION.
Heldref Publications, (Helen Dwight Reid Educational Foundation) 1319 Eighteenth St., N.W., Washington, DC 20036-1802. TEL 202-296-6267. FAX 202-296-5149. *674*

JOURNAL OF ECONOMIC ENTOMOLOGY.
Entomological Society of America, 9301 Annapolis Rd., Lanham, MD 20706. TEL 301-731-4535. FAX 301-731-4538. *535*

JOURNAL OF ECONOMIC PSYCHOLOGY.
North-Holland (Society "European Research in Economic Psychology") P.O. Box 211, 1000 AE Amsterdam, Netherlands. TEL 020-5803911. FAX 020-5803598. *1043*

JOURNAL OF EDUCATION FOR BUSINESS.
Heldref Publications, (Helen Dwight Reid Educational Foundation) 1319 Eighteenth St., N.W., Washington, DC 20036-1802. TEL 202-296-6267. FAX 202-296-5149. *674*

JOURNAL OF EDUCATION FOR LIBRARY AND INFORMATION SCIENCE.
Association for Library and Information Science Education, 5623 Palm Aire Dr., Sarasota, FL 34243-3702. TEL 813-355-1795. *2765*

JOURNAL OF EDUCATION POLICY.
Taylor & Francis Ltd., Rankine Rd., Basingstoke, Hants RG24 OPR, England. TEL 0256-840366. FAX 0256-479438. *1728*

JOURNAL OF EDUCATIONAL AND PSYCHOLOGICAL CONSULTATION.
Lawrence Erlbaum Associates, Inc., (Association for Educational and Psychological Consultants) 365 Broadway, Hillsdale, NJ 07642. TEL 201-666-4110. FAX 201-666-2394. *1642*

JOURNAL OF EDUCATIONAL COMPUTING RESEARCH.
Baywood Publishing Co., Inc., 26 Austin Ave., Box 337, Amityville, NY 11701. TEL 516-691-1270. FAX 516-691-1770. *1690*

JOURNAL OF EDUCATIONAL MULTIMEDIA AND HYPERMEDIA.
Association for the Advancement of Computing in Education, Box 2966, Charlottesville, VA 22902-2966. TEL 804-973-3987. *1690*

JOURNAL OF EDUCATIONAL PSYCHOLOGY.
American Psychological Association, 750 First St., N.E., Washington, DC 20002-4242. TEL 202-336-5500. FAX 202-336-5568. *4029*

JOURNAL OF EDUCATIONAL RESEARCH.
Heldref Publications, (Helen Dwight Reid Educational Foundation) 1319 Eighteenth St., N.W., Washington, DC 20036-1802. TEL 202-296-6267. FAX 202-296-5149. *1642*

JOURNAL OF ELASTOMERS AND PLASTICS.
Technomic Publishing Co. Inc., 851 New Holland Ave., Box 3535, Lancaster, PA 17604. TEL 717-291-5609. FAX 717-295-4538. *3863*

JOURNAL OF ELDER ABUSE & NEGLECT.
Haworth Press, Inc., 10 Alice St., Binghamton, NY 13904. TEL 800-342-9678. FAX 607-722-1424. *2275*

JOURNAL OF ELECTROANALYTICAL CHEMISTRY AND INTERFACIAL ELECTROCHEMISTRY.
Elsevier Sequoia S.A., P.O. Box 564, CH-1001 Lausanne, Switzerland. TEL 021-207381. FAX 021-235444. *1206*

JOURNAL OF ELECTROCARDIOLOGY.
Churchill Livingstone Medical Journals, 650 Ave. of the Americas, New York, NY 10011. TEL 212-819-5400. FAX 212-727-7808. *3210*

JOURNAL OF ELECTROMYOGRAPHY AND KINESIOLOGY.
Raven Press, 1185 Ave. of the Americas, New York, NY 10036. TEL 212-930-9500. FAX 212-869-3495. *444*

JOURNAL OF ELECTRON SPECTROSCOPY AND RELATED PHENOMENA.
Elsevier Science Publishers B.V., P.O. Box 211, 1000 AE Amsterdam, Netherlands. TEL 020-5803911. FAX 020-5803598. *3854*

JOURNAL OF ELECTRONICS.
Science Press, Marketing and Sales Department, (Chinese Academy of Sciences, Institute of Electronics) 16 Donghuangchenggen Beijie, Beijing 100707, People's Republic of China. TEL 4010642. FAX 4012180. *1774*

JOURNAL OF ELECTRONICS MANUFACTURING.
Chapman & Hall, 2-6 Boundary Row, London SE1 8HN, England. TEL 071-865-0066. FAX 071-522-9623. *1775*

JOURNAL OF ELECTROSTATICS.
Elsevier Science Publishers B.V., P.O. Box 211, 1000 AE Amsterdam, Netherlands. TEL 020-5803911. FAX 020-5803598. *1901*

JOURNAL OF ELECTROTOPOGRAPHY.
Electrotopograph Corporation, (Ensanian Physiochemical Institute) Box 98, Eldred, PA 16731. TEL 814-225-3296. *3821*

JOURNAL OF EMERGENCY MEDICINE.
Pergamon Press, Inc., Journals Division, 660 White Plains Rd., Tarrytown, NY 10591-5153. TEL 914-524-9200. FAX 914-333-2444. *3115*

JOURNAL OF ENDODONTICS.
Williams & Wilkins, (American Association of Endodontics) 428 E. Preston St., Baltimore, MD 21202. TEL 301-528-4000. FAX 301-528-4312. *3236*

JOURNAL OF ENDOUROLOGY.
Mary Ann Liebert, Inc., (Endourological Society) 1651 Third Ave., New York, NY 10128. TEL 212-289-2300. FAX 212-289-4697. *3388*

JOURNAL OF ENERGY RESOURCES TECHNOLOGY.
American Society of Mechanical Engineers, 345 E. 47th St., New York, NY 10017. TEL 212-705-7703. *1792*

JOURNAL OF ENGINEERING AND TECHNOLOGY MANAGEMENT.
Elsevier Science Publishers B.V., P.O. Box 211, 1000 AE Amsterdam, Netherlands. TEL 020-5803911. FAX 020-5803598. *1015*

JOURNAL OF ENGINEERING MATERIALS AND TECHNOLOGY.
American Society of Mechanical Engineers, 345 E. 47th St., New York, NY 10017. TEL 212-705-7703. *1918*

JOURNAL OF ENGINEERING MECHANICS.
American Society of Civil Engineers, 345 E. 47th St., New York, NY 10017-2398. TEL 212-705-7288. FAX 212-980-4681. *1869*

JOURNAL OF ENTEROSTOMAL THERAPY.
Mosby - Year Book, Inc. (International Association for Enterostomal Therapy) 11830 Westline Industrial Dr., St. Louis, MO 63146. TEL 800-325-4117. FAX 314-432-1380. *3380*

JOURNAL OF ENTOMOLOGICAL SCIENCE.
Georgia Entomological Society, Inc., c/o G. David Buntin, Department of Entomology, Georgia Experiment Station, Griffin, GA 30223-1797. TEL 404-228-7288. *535*

JOURNAL OF ENVIRONMENTAL EDUCATION.
Heldref Publications, (Helen Dwight Reid Educational Foundation) 1319 Eighteenth St., N.W., Washington, DC 20036-1802. TEL 202-296-6267. *1960*

JOURNAL OF ENVIRONMENTAL ENGINEERING.
American Society of Civil Engineers, 345 E. 47th St., New York, NY 10017-2398. TEL 212-705-7288. FAX 212-980-4681. *1960*

JOURNAL OF ENVIRONMENTAL HEALTH.
National Environmental Health Association, 720 S. Colorado Blvd., No. 970 S. Tower, Denver, CO 80222-1904. TEL 303-756-9090. FAX 303-691-9490. *1960*

JOURNAL OF ENVIRONMENTAL HORTICULTURE.
Horticultural Research Institute, 1250 I St., N.W., Ste. 500, Washington, DC 20005. FAX 202-789-1893. *102*

JOURNAL OF ENVIRONMENTAL PATHOLOGY, TOXICOLOGY AND ONCOLOGY.
Blackwell Scientific Publications Inc., (International Society for Environmental Toxicology and Cancer) Three Cambridge Center, Ste. 208, Cambridge, MA 02142-1413. TEL 617-225-0401. FAX 617-225-0412. *1982*

JOURNAL OF ENVIRONMENTAL PLANNING AND MANAGEMENT.
Carfax Publishing Co., (University of Newcastle-upon-Tyne, Department of Town and Country Planning) P.O. Box 25, Abingdon, Oxfordshire OX14 3UE, England. TEL 0235-55535. FAX 0235-22359. *2490*

JOURNAL OF ENVIRONMENTAL POLYMER DEGRADATION.
Plenum Publishing Corp., 233 Spring St., New York, NY 10013-1578. TEL 212-620-8000. FAX 212-463-0742. *478*

JOURNAL OF ENVIRONMENTAL QUALITY.
American Society of Agronomy, Inc., 677 S. Segoe Rd., Madison, WI 53711. TEL 608-273-8080. FAX 608-273-2021. *1960*

JOURNAL OF ENVIRONMENTAL RADIOACTIVITY.
Elsevier Science Publishers Ltd., (University of Glasgow, Department of Chemistry) Crown House, Linton Rd., Barking, Essex IG11 8JU, England. TEL 081-594-7272. FAX 081-594-5942. *1960*

JOURNAL OF ENVIRONMENTAL SCIENCE AND HEALTH. PART A: ENVIRONMENTAL SCIENCE AND ENGINEERING.
Marcel Dekker Journals, 270 Madison Ave., New York, NY 10016. TEL 212-696-9000. FAX 212-685-4540. *1961*

JOURNAL OF ENVIRONMENTAL SCIENCE AND HEALTH. PART B: PESTICIDES, FOOD CONTAMINANTS, AND AGRICULTURAL WASTES.
Marcel Dekker Journals, 270 Madison Ave., New York, NY 10016. TEL 212-696-9000. FAX 212-685-4540. *1961*

JOURNAL OF ENVIRONMENTAL SCIENCE AND HEALTH. PART C: ENVIRONMENTAL CARCINOGENESIS AND ECOTOXICOLOGY REVIEWS.
Marcel Dekker Journals, 270 Madison Ave., New York, NY 10016. TEL 212-696-9000. FAX 212-685-4540. *1982*

JOURNAL OF ENVIRONMENTAL SYSTEMS.
Baywood Publishing Co., Inc., 26 Austin Ave., Box 337, Amityville, NY 11701. TEL 516-691-1270. FAX 516-691-1770. *1961*

JOURNAL OF ENZYME INHIBITION.
Harwood Academic Publishers, 270 Eighth Ave., New York, NY 10011. TEL 212-206-8900. FAX 212-645-2459. *478*

JOURNAL OF ETHNOBIOLOGY.
Society of Ethnobiology, c/o Catherine S. Fowler, Department of Anthropology, University of Nevada, Reno, NV 89557. FAX 702-784-1300. *444*

JOURNAL OF ETHNOPHARMACOLOGY.
Elsevier Scientific Publishers Ireland Ltd., P.O. Box 85, Limerick, Ireland. TEL 061-61944. FAX 061-62144. *3731*

JOURNAL OF EUROMARKETING.
Haworth Press, Inc., 10 Alice St., Binghamton, NY 13904. TEL 800-342-9678. FAX 607-722-1424. *1043*

JOURNAL OF EVOLUTIONARY BIOCHEMISTRY AND PHYSIOLOGY.
Plenum Publishing Corp., Consultants Bureau, (Russian Academy of Sciences) 233 Spring St., New York, NY 10013-1578. TEL 212-620-8468. FAX 212-463-0742. *478*

JOURNAL OF EXPERIMENTAL & THEORETICAL ARTIFICIAL INTELLIGENCE.
Taylor & Francis Ltd., Rankine Rd., Basingstoke, Hants RG24 0PR, England. TEL 0256-840366. FAX 0256-479438. *1409*

JOURNAL OF EXPERIMENTAL CHILD PSYCHOLOGY.
Academic Press, Inc., Journal Division, 1250 Sixth Ave., San Diego, CA 92101. TEL 619-230-1840. FAX 619-699-6800. *4029*

JOURNAL OF EXPERIMENTAL EDUCATION.
Heldref Publications, (Helen Dwight Reid Educational Foundation) 1319 Eighteenth St., N.W., Washington, DC 20036-1802. TEL 202-296-6267. FAX 202-296-5149. *1753*

JOURNAL OF EXPERIMENTAL MARINE BIOLOGY AND ECOLOGY.
Elsevier Science Publishers B.V., P.O. Box 211, 1000 AE Amsterdam, Netherlands. TEL 020-5803911. FAX 020-5803598. *444*

JOURNAL OF EXPERIMENTAL MEDICINE.
Rockefeller University Press, 222 E. 70th St., New York, NY 10021. TEL 212-570-8572. FAX 212-570-7944. *3260*

JOURNAL OF EXPERIMENTAL PSYCHOLOGY: ANIMAL BEHAVIOR PROCESSES.
American Psychological Association, 750 First St., N.E., Washington, DC 20002-4242. TEL 202-336-5500. FAX 202-336-5568. *4029*

JOURNAL OF EXPERIMENTAL PSYCHOLOGY: GENERAL.
American Psychological Association, 750 First St., N.E., Washington, DC 20002-4242. TEL 202-336-5500. FAX 202-336-5568. *4029*

JOURNAL OF EXPERIMENTAL PSYCHOLOGY: HUMAN PERCEPTION AND PERFORMANCE.
American Psychological Association, 750 First St., N.E., Washington, DC 20002-4242. TEL 202-336-5500. FAX 202-336-5568. *4029*

JOURNAL OF EXPERIMENTAL PSYCHOLOGY: LEARNING, MEMORY, AND COGNITION.
American Psychological Association, 750 First St., N.E., Washington, DC 20002-4242. TEL 202-336-5500. FAX 202-336-5568. *4029*

JOURNAL OF EXPERIMENTAL SOCIAL PSYCHOLOGY.
Academic Press, Inc., Journal Division, 1250 Sixth Ave., San Diego, CA 92101. TEL 619-230-1840. FAX 619-699-6800. *4029*

JOURNAL OF EXPERIMENTAL ZOOLOGY.
John Wiley & Sons, Inc., Journals, 605 Third Ave., New York, NY 10158. TEL 212-850-6000. FAX 212-850-6000. *586*

JOURNAL OF FAMILY AND ECONOMIC ISSUES.
Human Sciences Press, Inc. 233 Spring St., New York, NY 10013-1578. TEL 212-620-8000. FAX 212-463-0742. *4029*

JOURNAL OF FAMILY PRACTICE.
Appleton & Lange, Journal Division 25 Van Zant St., Box 5630, Norwalk, CT 06855. TEL 203-838-4400. *3115*

JOURNAL OF FAMILY PSYCHOTHERAPY.
Haworth Press, Inc., 10 Alice St., Binghamton, NY 13904. TEL 800-342-9678. FAX 607-722-1424. *4029*

JOURNAL OF FAMILY VIOLENCE.
Plenum Publishing Corp., 233 Spring St., New York, NY 10013-1578. TEL 212-620-8000. FAX 212-463-0742. *1516*

JOURNAL OF FEMINIST FAMILY THERAPY.
Haworth Press, Inc., 10 Alice St., Binghamton, NY 13904. TEL 800-342-9678. FAX 607-722-1424. *4859*

JOURNAL OF FERMENTATION AND BIOENGINEERING.
Society of Fermentation Technology, c/o Osaka Daigaku Kogakubu, 2-1 Yamadaoka, Suita-shi, Osaka-fu 565, Japan. TEL 06-876-2731. FAX 06-876-2773. *469*

JOURNAL OF FINANCIAL ECONOMICS.
Elsevier Sequoia S.A., P.O. Box 564, CH-1001 Lausanne, Switzerland. TEL 021-207381. FAX 021-235444. *674*

JOURNAL OF FINANCIAL INTERMEDIATION.
Academic Press, Inc., Journal Division, 1250 Sixth Ave., San Diego, CA 92101. TEL 619-230-1840. FAX 619-699-6800. *870*

JOURNAL OF FIRE SCIENCES.
Technomic Publishing Co., Inc., 851 New Holland Ave., Box 3535, Lancaster, PA 17604. TEL 717-291-5609. FAX 717-295-4538. *2033*

JOURNAL OF FLUENCY DISORDERS.
Elsevier Science Publishing Co., Inc. (New York), 655 Ave. of the Americas, New York, NY 10010. TEL 212-989-5800. FAX 212-633-3965. *4030*

JOURNAL OF FLUID CONTROL.
Delbridge Publishing Co., Box 160817, Cupertino, CA 95016. TEL 408-446-3131. FAX 408-446-3131. *1933*

JOURNAL OF FLUIDS ENGINEERING.
American Society of Mechanical Engineers, 345 E. 47th St., New York, NY 10017. TEL 212-705-7703. *1924*

JOURNAL OF FLUORESCENCE.
Plenum Publishing Corp., 233 Spring St., New York, NY 10013-1578. TEL 212-620-8000. FAX 212-463-0742. *1214*

JOURNAL OF FLUORINE CHEMISTRY.
Elsevier Sequoia S.A., P.O. Box 564, CH-1001 Lausanne, Switzerland. TEL 021-207381. FAX 021-235444. *1214*

JOURNAL OF FOOD ENGINEERING.
Elsevier Science Publishers Ltd., Crown House, Linton Rd., Barking, Essex IG11 8JU, England. TEL 081-594-7272. FAX 081-594-5942. *2075*

JOURNAL OF FOOD PRODUCTS MARKETING.
Haworth Press, Inc., 10 Alice St., Binghamton, NY 13904. TEL 607-722-1695. FAX 607-722-1424. *2075*

JOURNAL OF FOOD PROTECTION.
International Association of Milk, Food and Environmental Sanitarians, Inc., 502 E. Lincoln Way, Ames, IA 50010-6666. TEL 515-232-6699. FAX 515-232-4736. *4106*

JOURNAL OF FOOT SURGERY.
Williams & Wilkins, 428 E. Preston St., Baltimore, MD 21202. TEL 301-528-4000. FAX 301-528-4312. *3380*

JOURNAL OF FORAMINIFERAL RESEARCH.
Cushman Foundation for Foraminiferal Research, Rm. E-206, MRC NHB 121, National Museum of Natural History, Washington, DC 20560. TEL 202-357-2405. *3658*

JOURNAL OF FORENSIC SCIENCES.
American Society for Testing and Materials, (American Academy of Forensic Sciences) 1916 Race St., Philadelphia, PA 19103. TEL 215-299-5400. FAX 215-977-9679. *3265*

JOURNAL OF FUNCTIONAL ANALYSIS.
Academic Press, Inc., Journal Division, 1250 Sixth Ave., San Diego, CA 92101. TEL 619-230-1840. FAX 619-699-6800. *3041*

REFEREED SERIALS

JOURNAL OF FUSION ENERGY.
Plenum Publishing Corp., 233 Spring St., New York, NY 10013-1578. TEL 212-620-8000. FAX 212-463-0742. *1806*

JOURNAL OF GAMBLING STUDIES.
Human Sciences Press, Inc. (National Council on Problem Gambling) 233 Spring St., New York, NY 10013-1578. TEL 212-620-8000. FAX 212-463-0742. *3341*

JOURNAL OF GARDEN HISTORY.
Taylor & Francis Ltd., Rankine Rd., Basingstoke, Hants RG24 OPR, England. TEL 0256-840366. FAX 0256-479438. *2132*

JOURNAL OF GAY & LESBIAN PSYCHOTHERAPY.
Haworth Press, Inc., 10 Alice St., Binghamton, NY 13904. TEL 800-342-9678. FAX 607-722-1424. *2454*

JOURNAL OF GAY & LESBIAN SOCIAL SERVICES.
Haworth Press, Inc., 10 Alice St., Binghamton, NY 13904-1580. TEL 800-342-9678. FAX 607-722-1424. *4410*

JOURNAL OF GENERAL CHEMISTRY OF THE U S S R.
Plenum Publishing Corp., Consultants Bureau, (Russian Academy of Sciences) 233 Spring St., New York, NY 10013-1578. TEL 212-620-8468. FAX 212-463-0742. *1181*

JOURNAL OF GENERAL INTERNAL MEDICINE.
Hanley & Belfus, Inc., (American College of Physicians, Society for General Internal Medicine) 210 S. 13th St., Philadelphia, PA 19107. TEL 215-546-4995. FAX 215-790-9330. *3115*

JOURNAL OF GENERAL PHYSIOLOGY.
Rockefeller University Press, (Society of General Physiologists) 222 E. 70th St., New York, NY 10021. TEL 212-570-8572. FAX 212-570-7944. *572*

JOURNAL OF GENERAL PSYCHOLOGY.
Heldref Publications, (Helen Dwight Reid Educational Foundation) 1319 Eighteenth St., N.W., Washington, DC 20036. TEL 202-296-6267. FAX 202-296-5149. *4030*

JOURNAL OF GENETIC COUNSELING.
Human Sciences Press, Inc. (National Society of Genetic Counselors, Inc.) 233 Spring St., New York, NY 10013-1578. TEL 212-620-8432. FAX 212-463-0742. *4030*

JOURNAL OF GENETIC PSYCHOLOGY.
Heldref Publications, (Helen Dwight Reid Educational Foundation) 1319 Eighteenth St., N.W., Washington, DC 20036-1802. TEL 202-296-6267. FAX 202-296-5149. *4030*

JOURNAL OF GEOCHEMICAL EXPLORATION.
Elsevier Science Publishers B.V., (Association of Exploration Geochemists) P.O. Box 211, 1000 AE Amsterdam, Netherlands. TEL 020-5803911. FAX 020-5803598. *1546*

JOURNAL OF GEODYNAMICS.
Pergamon Press plc, Headington Hill Hall, Oxford OX3 OBW, England. TEL 0865-794141. FAX 0865-743911. *1591*

JOURNAL OF GEOLOGY.
University of Chicago Press, Journals Division, 5720 S. Woodlawn Ave., Chicago, IL 60637. TEL 312-753-3347. *1569*

JOURNAL OF GEOMETRY AND PHYSICS.
North-Holland P.O. Box 211, 1000 AE Amsterdam, Netherlands. TEL 020-5803911. FAX 020-5803598. *3041*

JOURNAL OF GEOTECHNICAL ENGINEERING.
American Society of Civil Engineers, 345 E. 47th St., New York, NY 10017-2398. TEL 212-705-7288. FAX 212-980-4681. *1869*

JOURNAL OF GERIATRIC DRUG THERAPY.
Haworth Press, Inc., 10 Alice St., Binghamton, NY 13904. TEL 800-342-9678. FAX 607-722-1424. *3731*

JOURNAL OF GERIATRIC PSYCHIATRY.
International Universities Press, Inc., Journal Department, (Boston Society for Gerontologic Psychiatry, Inc.) 59 Boston Post Rd., Box 1524, Madison, CT 06443-1524. TEL 203-245-4000. FAX 203-245-0775. *3341*

JOURNAL OF GERONTOLOGICAL NURSING.
Slack, Inc., 6900 Grove Rd., Thorofare, NJ 08086. TEL 609-848-1000. FAX 609-853-5991. *2275*

JOURNAL OF GERONTOLOGICAL SOCIAL WORK.
Haworth Press, Inc., 10 Alice St., Binghamton, NY 13904. TEL 800-342-9678. FAX 607-722-1424. *2275*

JOURNAL OF GLOBAL BUSINESS.
Association for Global Business, Box 1381, Harrisonburg, VA 22801. TEL 703-568-3079. FAX 703-568-3299. *674*

JOURNAL OF GLOBAL MARKETING.
Haworth Press, Inc., 10 Alice St., Binghamton, NY 13904. TEL 800-342-9678. FAX 607-722-1424. *1043*

JOURNAL OF GLOBAL OPTIMIZATION.
Kluwer Academic Publishers, Postbus 17, 3300 AA Dordrecht, Netherlands. TEL 078-334911. FAX 078-334254. *4360*

JOURNAL OF GRAPH THEORY.
John Wiley & Sons, Inc., Journals, 605 Third Ave., New York, NY 10158-0012. TEL 212-850-6000. FAX 212-850-6088. *3041*

JOURNAL OF GROUP PSYCHOTHERAPY, PSYCHODRAMA & SOCIOMETRY.
Heldref Publications, (American Society of Group Psychotherapy and Psychodrama) 1319 Eighteenth St., N.W., Washington, DC 20036-1802. TEL 202-296-6267. FAX 202-296-5149. *4030*

JOURNAL OF GUIDANCE, CONTROL, AND DYNAMICS.
American Institute of Aeronautics and Astronautics, Inc., 370 L'Enfant Promenade, S.W., Washington, DC 20024. TEL 202-646-7400. *57*

JOURNAL OF GYNECOLOGIC SURGERY.
Mary Ann Liebert, Inc., (Gynecologic Laser Society) 1651 Third Ave., New York, NY 10128. TEL 212-289-2300. FAX 212-289-4697. *3294*

JOURNAL OF HAND SURGERY: AMERICAN VOLUME.
Mosby - Year Book, Inc. (American Society for Surgery of the Hand) 11830 Westline Industrial Dr., St. Louis, MO 63146. TEL 800-325-4117. FAX 314-432-1380. *3380*

JOURNAL OF HAND THERAPY.
Hanley & Belfus, Inc., (American Society of Hand Therapists) 210 S. 13th St., Philadelphia, PA 19107. TEL 215-546-7293. FAX 215-790-9330. *3115*

JOURNAL OF HAZARDOUS MATERIALS.
Elsevier Science Publishers B.V., P.O. Box 211, 1000 AE Amsterdam, Netherlands. TEL 020-5803911. FAX 020-5803598. *1855*

JOURNAL OF HEAD TRAUMA REHABILITATION.
Aspen Publishers, Inc., 200 Orchard Ridge Dr., Gaithersburg, MD 20878. TEL 301-417-7500. FAX 301-417-7550. *3309*

JOURNAL OF HEALTH AND SOCIAL BEHAVIOR.
American Sociological Association, 1722 N St., N.W., Washington, DC 20036. TEL 202-833-3410. FAX 202-785-0146. *4440*

JOURNAL OF HEALTH & SOCIAL POLICY.
Haworth Press, Inc., 10 Alice St., Binghamton, NY 13904. TEL 800-342-9678. FAX 607-722-1424. *4410*

JOURNAL OF HEALTH CARE CHAPLAINCY.
Haworth Press, Inc., 10 Alice St., Binghamton, NY 13904. TEL 800-342-9678. FAX 607-722-1424. *3805*

JOURNAL OF HEALTH CARE FOR THE POOR AND UNDERSERVED.
Institute on Health Care for the Poor and Underserved, Meharry Medical College, 1005 D B Todd Blvd., Nashville, TN 37208. *3116*

JOURNAL OF HEALTH ECONOMICS.
North-Holland P.O. Box 211, 1000 AE Amsterdam, Netherlands. TEL 020-5803911. FAX 020-5803598. *4106*

JOURNAL OF HEALTH POLITICS, POLICY AND LAW.
Duke University Press, (Duke University, Department of Health Administration) 6697 College Station, Durham, NC 27708. TEL 919-684-2173. FAX 919-684-8644. *3116*

JOURNAL OF HEART AND LUNG TRANSPLANTATION.
Mosby - Year Book, Inc. (International Society for Heart Transplantation) 11830 Westline Industrial Dr., St. Louis, MO 63146. TEL 800-325-4117. FAX 314-432-1380. *3380*

JOURNAL OF HEAT TRANSFER.
American Society of Mechanical Engineers, 345 E. 47th St., New York, NY 10017. TEL 212-705-7722. *1933*

JOURNAL OF HEAT TREATING.
Springer-Verlag, Journals, (A S M International) 175 Fifth Ave., New York, NY 10010. TEL 212-460-1583. *3411*

JOURNAL OF HERBS, SPICES & MEDICINAL PLANTS.
Haworth Press, Inc., 10 Alice St., Binghamton, NY 13904. TEL 800-342-9678. FAX 607-722-1424. *2132*

JOURNAL OF HERPETOLOGY.
Society for the Study of Amphibians and reptiles, Department of Zoology, Miami University, Oxford, OH 45056. *586*

JOURNAL OF HISTOCHEMISTRY AND CYTOCHEMISTRY.
Histochemical Society, P.O. Box 1023, Planetarium Station, NY 10024-1023. TEL 212-362-1801. FAX 212-874-8313. *525*

JOURNAL OF HISTOTECHNOLOGY.
Mayo Publications, Inc., (National Society for Histotechnology) 5900 Princess Garden Parkway, Ste. 805, Lanham, MD 20706. TEL 708-969-3828. *4602*

JOURNAL OF HOME & CONSUMER HORTICULTURE.
Haworth Press, Inc., 10 Alice St., Binghamton, NY 13904. TEL 800-342-9678. FAX 607-722-1424. *2132*

JOURNAL OF HOMOSEXUALITY.
Haworth Press, Inc., (San Francisco State University, Center for Research and Education in Sexuality) 10 Alice St., Binghamton, NY 13904. TEL 800-342-9678. FAX 607-722-1424. *2454*

JOURNAL OF HOSPITAL MARKETING.
Haworth Press, Inc., 10 Alice St., Binghamton, NY 13904. TEL 800-342-9678. FAX 607-722-1424. *1043*

JOURNAL OF HOSPITALITY & LEISURE MARKETING.
Haworth Press, Inc., 10 Alice St., Binghamton, NY 13904-1580. TEL 800-342-9678. FAX 607-722-1424. *2477*

JOURNAL OF HOUSING FOR THE ELDERLY.
Haworth Press, Inc., 10 Alice St., Binghamton, NY 13904. TEL 800-342-9678. FAX 607-722-1424. *2275*

JOURNAL OF HOUSING RESEARCH.
Federal National Mortgage Association, (Fannie Mae, Office of Housing Policy Research) 3900 Wisconsin Ave., N.W., Washington, DC 20016-2899. TEL 202-752-4422. FAX 202-752-4933. *2490*

JOURNAL OF HUMAN LACTATION.
Human Sciences Press, Inc. (International Lactation Consultants Association) 233 Spring St., New York, NY 10013. TEL 212-620-8000. FAX 212-463-0742. *3294*

JOURNAL OF HYDRAULIC ENGINEERING (NEW YORK).
American Society of Civil Engineers, 345 E. 47th St., New York, NY 10017-2398. TEL 212-705-7288. FAX 212-980-4681. *1869*

JOURNAL OF HYDRODYNAMICS.
China Ocean Press, International Cooperation Department, (Zhongguo Chuanbo Kexue Yanjiu Zhongxin, Shanghai Fenbu) Haimao Dalou, 1 Fuxingmenwai Dajie, Beijing 100860, People's Republic of China. TEL 868941. FAX 862209. *3822*

JOURNAL OF HYDROLOGY.
Elsevier Science Publishers B.V., P.O. Box 211, 1000 AE Amsterdam, Netherlands. TEL 020-5803911. FAX 020-5803598. *1599*

JOURNAL OF IDEAS.
Institute for Memetic Research, Box 16327, Panama City, FL 32406-1327. TEL 904-265-4378. *4317*

JOURNAL OF IMMUNOASSAY.
Marcel Dekker Journals, 270 Madison Ave., New York, NY 10016. TEL 212-696-9000. FAX 212-685-4540. *3731*

JOURNAL OF IMMUNOLOGICAL METHODS.
Elsevier Science Publishers B.V., P.O. Box 211, 1000 AE Amsterdam, Netherlands. TEL 020-5803911. FAX 020-5803598. *3187*

JOURNAL OF IMMUNOLOGY.
American Association of Immunologists, 428 E. Preston St., Baltimore, MD 21202. TEL 301-530-7178. FAX 301-571-1831. *3187*

JOURNAL OF IMMUNOTHERAPY.
Raven Press, (Society for Biological Therapy) 1185 Ave. of the Americas, New York, NY 10036. TEL 212-930-9500. FAX 212-869-3495. *3116*

JOURNAL OF INDEPENDENT SOCIAL WORK.
Haworth Press, Inc., 10 Alice St., Binghamton, NY 13904. TEL 800-342-9678. FAX 607-722-1424. *4410*

JOURNAL OF INDIGENOUS STUDIES.
Gabriel Dumont Institute of Native Studies and Applied Research, 121 Broadway Ave., E., Regina, Sask. S4N 0Z6, Canada. TEL 306-522-5691. FAX 306-565-0809. *243*

JOURNAL OF INDUSTRIAL MICROBIOLOGY.
Elsevier Science Publishers B.V., (Society for Industrial Microbiology) P.O. Box 211, 1000 AE Amsterdam, Netherlands. TEL 020-5803911. FAX 020-5803598. *490*

JOURNAL OF INFECTIOUS DISEASES.
University of Chicago Press, Journals Division, (Infectious Diseases Society of America) 5720 S. Woodlawn Ave., Chicago, IL 60637. TEL 312-753-3347. FAX 312-702-0694. *3221*

JOURNAL OF INFORMATION ETHICS.
St. Cloud State University, St. Cloud, MN 56301. TEL 612-255-4822. *2639*

JOURNAL OF INFORMATION SCIENCE.
Elsevier Science Publishers B.V., (Institute of Information Scientists) P.O. Box 211, 1000 AE Amsterdam, Netherlands. TEL 020-5803911. FAX 020-5803598. *2766*

JOURNAL OF INORGANIC AND ORGANOMETALLIC POLYMERS.
Plenum Publishing Corp., 233 Spring St., New York, NY 10013-1578. TEL 212-620-8000. FAX 212-463-0742. *1219*

JOURNAL OF INORGANIC BIOCHEMISTRY.
Elsevier Science Publishing Co., Inc. (New York), 655 Ave. of the Americas, New York, NY 10010. TEL 212-989-5800. FAX 212-633-3965. *479*

JOURNAL OF INSECT BEHAVIOR.
Plenum Publishing Corp., 233 Spring St., New York, NY 10013-1578. TEL 212-620-8000. FAX 212-463-0742. *535*

JOURNAL OF INSECT PHYSIOLOGY.
Pergamon Press, Inc., Journals Division, 660 White Plains Rd., Tarrytown, NY 10591-5153. TEL 914-524-9200. FAX 914-333-2444. *535*

JOURNAL OF INTELLIGENT MANUFACTURING.
Chapman & Hall, 2-6 Boundary Row, London SE1 8HN, England. TEL 071-865-0066. FAX 071-522-9623. *1414*

JOURNAL OF INTELLIGENT MATERIAL SYSTEMS AND STUCTURES.
Technomic Publishing Co., Inc., 851 New Holland Ave., Box 3535, Lancaster, PA 17604. TEL 717-291-5609. FAX 717-295-4538. *4317*

JOURNAL OF INTENSIVE CARE MEDICINE.
Blackwell Scientific Publications Inc., Three Cambridge Center, Ste. 208, Cambridge, MA 02142-1413. *3116*

JOURNAL OF INTERFERON RESEARCH.
Mary Ann Liebert, Inc., (International Society for Interferon Research) 1651 Third Ave., New York, NY 10128. TEL 212-289-2300. FAX 212-289-4697. *3116*

JOURNAL OF INTERLIBRARY LOAN & INFORMATION SUPPLY.
Haworth Press, Inc., 10 Alice St., Binghamton, NY 13904. TEL 800-342-9678. FAX 607-722-1424. *2766*

JOURNAL OF INTERNATIONAL CONSUMER MARKETING.
Haworth Press, Inc., 10 Alice St., Binghamton, NY 13904. TEL 800-342-9678. FAX 607-722-1424. *1506*

JOURNAL OF INTERNATIONAL ECONOMICS.
North-Holland P.O. Box 211, 1000 AE Amsterdam, Netherlands. TEL 020-5803911. FAX 020-5803598. *675*

JOURNAL OF INTERNATIONAL FINANCIAL MARKETS, INSTITUTIONS & MONEY.
Haworth Press, Inc., 10 Alice St., Binghamton, NY 13904. TEL 607-722-1695. FAX 607-722-1424. *788*

JOURNAL OF INTERNATIONAL FOOD & AGRIBUSINESS MARKETING.
Haworth Press, Inc., 10 Alice St., Binghamton, NY 13904. TEL 800-342-9678. FAX 607-722-1424. *153*

JOURNAL OF INTERNATIONAL MEDICAL RESEARCH.
Cambridge Medical Publications Ltd., 3 Liverpool Gardens, Worthing, West Sussex BN11 1TF, England. TEL 0903-205884. FAX 0903-34862. *3116*

JOURNAL OF INTERNATIONAL MONEY AND FINANCE.
Butterworth - Heinemann Ltd. Linacre House, Jordan Hill, Oxford OX2 8DP, England. TEL 0865-310366. FAX 0865-310898. *788*

JOURNAL OF INTERPROFESSIONAL CARE.
Carfax Publishing Co., (British Holistic Medical Association) P.O. Box 25, Abingdon, Oxfordshire OX14 3UE, England. TEL 0235-555335. FAX 0235-553559. *3215*

JOURNAL OF INTRAVENOUS NURSING.
J.B. Lippincott Co., (Intravenous Nurses Society) E. Washington Sq., Philadelphia, PA 19105. TEL 800-638-3030. *3280*

JOURNAL OF INVASIVE CARDIOLOGY.
Health Management Publications, Inc., 550 American Ave., King of Prussia, PA 19406-1441. TEL 215-337-4466. FAX 215-337-0890. *3210*

JOURNAL OF INVERTEBRATE PATHOLOGY.
Academic Press, Inc., Journal Division, 1250 Sixth Ave., San Diego, CA 92101. TEL 619-230-1840. FAX 619-699-6800. *535*

JOURNAL OF INVESTIGATIVE DERMATOLOGY.
Elsevier Science Publishing Co., Inc. (New York), (Society of Investigative Dermatology, Inc.) 655 Ave. of the Americas, New York, NY 10010. TEL 212-989-5800. FAX 212-633-3965. *3248*

JOURNAL OF INVESTIGATIVE SURGERY.
Taylor & Francis, 1900 Frost Rd., Ste. 101, Bristol, PA 19007. TEL 215-785-5800. FAX 215-785-5515. *3380*

JOURNAL OF IRRIGATION AND DRAINAGE.
American Society of Civil Engineers, 345 E. 47th St, New York, NY 10017-2398. TEL 212-705-7288. FAX 212-980-4681. *1870*

JOURNAL OF J A S T R O.
Pergamon Press, Inc., Journals Division, (Japanese Society for Therapeutic Radiation and Oncology) 660 White Plains Rd., Tarrytown, NY 10591-5153. TEL 914-524-9200. FAX 914-333-2444. *3359*

JOURNAL OF JAPANESE STUDIES.
Society for Japanese Studies, Thomson Hall, DR-05, University of Washington, Seattle, WA 98195. TEL 206-543-9302. FAX 206-685-0668. *3639*

JOURNAL OF JEWISH THOUGHT AND PHILOSOPHY.
Harwood Academic Publishers, 270 Eighth Ave., New York, NY 10011. TEL 212-206-8900. FAX 212-206-2459. *4224*

JOURNAL OF LABOR ECONOMICS.
University of Chicago Press, Journals Division, (National Opinion Research Center, Economics Research Center) 5720 S. Woodlawn Ave., Chicago, IL 60637. TEL 312-753-2247. FAX 312-702-0694. *753*

JOURNAL OF LABORATORY AND CLINICAL MEDICINE.
Mosby - Year Book, Inc. (Central Society for Clinical Research) 11830 Westline Industrial Dr., St. Louis, MO 63146. TEL 800-325-4117. FAX 314-432-1380. *3260*

JOURNAL OF LASER APPLICATIONS.
Laser Institute of America, 12424 Research Pkwy., Ste.130, Orlando, FL 32826-3274. TEL 800-345-2737. FAX 419-380-5588. *3854*

JOURNAL OF LAW AND ECONOMICS.
University of Chicago Press, Journals Division, (University of Chicago Law School) 5720 S. Woodlawn Ave., Chicago, IL 60637. TEL 312-753-3347. FAX 312-702-0694. *2639*

JOURNAL OF LEARNING DISABILITIES.
Donald D. Hammill Foundation, 8700 Shoal Creek Blvd., Austin, TX 78758. TEL 512-451-3246. FAX 512-451-8542. *1737*

JOURNAL OF LEGAL MEDICINE.
Hemisphere Publishing Corporation 1900 Frost Rd., Ste.101, Bristol, PA 19007-1598. TEL 215-785-5800. FAX 215-785-5515. *3116*

JOURNAL OF LEGAL STUDIES.
University of Chicago Press, Journals Division, (University of Chicago Law School) 5720 S. Woodlawn Ave., Chicago, IL 60637. TEL 312-753-3347. FAX 312-702-0694. *2640*

JOURNAL OF LIBRARY ADMINISTRATION.
Haworth Press, Inc., 10 Alice St., Binghamton, NY 13904. TEL 800-342-9678. FAX 607-722-1424. *2766*

JOURNAL OF LIGHTWAVE TECHNOLOGY.
Institute of Electrical and Electronics Engineers, Inc., 345 E. 47th St., New York, NY 10017-2394. TEL 212-705-7366. FAX 212-705-7682. *3854*

JOURNAL OF LIPID MEDIATORS.
Elsevier Science Publishers B.V., P.O. Box 211, 1000 AE Amsterdam, Netherlands. TEL 020-5803911. FAX 020-5803598. *3116*

JOURNAL OF LIPID RESEARCH.
Federation of American Societies for Experimental Biology, 9650 Rockville Pike, Bethesda, MD 20814. TEL 301-530-7100. FAX 301-571-1855. *479*

JOURNAL OF LIPOSOME RESEARCH.
Marcel Dekker Journals, 270 Madison Ave., New York, NY 10016. TEL 212-696-9000. FAX 212-685-4540. *3731*

JOURNAL OF LIQUID CHROMATOGRAPHY.
Marcel Dekker Journals, 270 Madison Ave., New York, NY 10016. TEL 212-696-9000. FAX 212-685-4540. *1181*

JOURNAL OF LOGIC PROGRAMMING.
Elsevier Science Publishing Co., Inc. (New York), 655 Ave. of the Americas, New York, NY 10010. TEL 212-989-5800. FAX 212-633-3965. *1431*

JOURNAL OF LOSS PREVENTION IN THE PROCESS INDUSTRIES.
Butterworth - Heinemann Ltd. Linacre House, Jordan Hill, Oxford OX2 8DP, England. TEL 0865-310366. FAX 0865-310898. *1855*

JOURNAL OF LOW TEMPERATURE PHYSICS.
Plenum Publishing Corp., 233 Spring St., New York, NY 10013-1578. TEL 212-620-8000. FAX 212-463-0742. *3841*

JOURNAL OF LUMINESCENCE.
North-Holland P.O. Box 211, 1000 AE Amsterdam, Netherlands. TEL 020-5803911. FAX 020-5803598. *3854*

JOURNAL OF MACROMOLECULAR SCIENCE: PART A - PURE AND APPLIED CHEMISTRY.
Marcel Dekker Journals, 270 Madison Ave., New York, NY 10016. TEL 212-696-9000. FAX 212-685-4540. *1219*

JOURNAL OF MACROMOLECULAR SCIENCE: PART B - PHYSICS.
Marcel Dekker Journals, 270 Madison Ave., New York, NY 10016. TEL 212-696-9000. FAX 212-685-4540. *3822*

JOURNAL OF MACROMOLECULAR SCIENCE: PART C - REVIEWS IN MACROMOLECULAR CHEMISTRY AND PHYSICS.
Marcel Dekker Journals, 270 Madison Ave., New York, NY 10016. TEL 212-696-9000. FAX 212-685-4540. *1219*

JOURNAL OF MAGNETIC RESONANCE.
Academic Press, Inc., Journal Division, 1250 Sixth Ave., San Diego, CA 92101. TEL 619-230-1840. FAX 619-699-6800. *3822*

JOURNAL OF MAGNETISM AND MAGNETIC MATERIALS.
North-Holland (European Physical Society) P.O. Box 211, 1000 AE Amsterdam, Netherlands. TEL 020-5803911. FAX 020-5803598. *3822*

JOURNAL OF MAMMALOGY.
American Society of Mammalogists, c/o Dr. H. Duane Smith, Sec.-Treas., Department of Zoology, Brigham Young University, Provo, UT 84602. TEL 801-378-2492. *586*

JOURNAL OF MANAGEMENT CONSULTING.
North-Holland P.O. Box 211, 1000 AE Amsterdam, Netherlands. TEL 020-5803911. FAX 020-5803598. *1016*

JOURNAL OF MANAGEMENT INFORMATION SYSTEMS.
M. E. Sharpe, Inc., 80 Business Park Dr., Armonk, NY 10504. TEL 914-273-1800. FAX 914-273-2106. *1016*

JOURNAL OF MANUFACTURING AND OPERATIONS MANAGEMENT.
Elsevier Science Publishing Co., Inc. (New York), 655 Ave. of the Americas, New York, NY 10010. TEL 212-989-5800. FAX 212-633-3965. *1016*

JOURNAL OF MANUFACTURING SYSTEMS.
Elsevier Science Publishers Ltd., (Society of Manufacturing Engineers, Computer and Automated Systems Association) Crown House, Linton Rd., Barking, Essex IG11 8JU, England. TEL 081-594-7272. FAX 081-594-5942. *1438*

JOURNAL OF MARINE SYSTEMS.
Elsevier Science Publishers B.V., (European Association of Marine Sciences and Techniques) P.O. Box 211, 1000 AE Amsterdam, Netherlands. TEL 020-5803911. FAX 020-5803598. *1607*

JOURNAL OF MARKETING CHANNELS.
Haworth Press, Inc., 10 Alice St., Binghamton, NY 13904. TEL 607-722-1695. FAX 607-722-1424. *1043*

JOURNAL OF MARKETING FOR HIGHER EDUCATION.
Haworth Press, Inc., 10 Alice St., Binghamton, NY 13904. TEL 800-342-9678. FAX 607-722-1424. *1043*

JOURNAL OF MASS MEDIA ETHICS.
Lawrence Erlbaum Associates, Inc., 365 Broadway, Hillsdale, NJ 07642. TEL 201-666-4110. FAX 201-666-2394. *1338*

JOURNAL OF MATERIALS ENGINEERING.
Springer-Verlag, Journals, (A S M International) 175 Fifth Ave., New York, NY 10010. TEL 212-460-1583. *3411*

JOURNAL OF MATERIALS IN CIVIL ENGINEERING: PROPERTIES, APPLICATIONS, DURABILITY.
American Society of Civil Engineers, 345 E. 47th St., New York, NY 10017-2398. TEL 212-705-7288. FAX 212-980-4681. *1870*

JOURNAL OF MATERIALS PROCESSING TECHNOLOGY.
Elsevier Science Publishers B.V., P.O. Box 211, 1000 AE Amsterdam, Netherlands. TEL 020-5803911. FAX 020-5803598. *1933*

JOURNAL OF MATERIALS SCIENCE: MATERIALS IN ELECTRONICS.
Chapman & Hall, 2-6 Boundary Row, London SE1 8HN, England. TEL 071-865-0066. FAX 071-522-9626. *1919*

JOURNAL OF MATERIALS SCIENCE: MATERIALS IN MEDICINE.
Chapman & Hall, (European Society for Biomaterials) 2-6 Boundary Row, London SE1 8HN, England. TEL 071-865-0066. FAX 071-522-9623. *1919*

JOURNAL OF MATERIALS SHAPING TECHNOLOGY.
Springer-Verlag, Journals, (A S M International) 175 Fifth Ave., New York, NY 10010. TEL 212-460-1583. *3411*

JOURNAL OF MATHEMATICAL ANALYSIS AND APPLICATIONS.
Academic Press, Inc., Journal Division, 1250 Sixth Ave., San Diego, CA 92101. TEL 619-230-1840. FAX 619-699-6800. *3041*

JOURNAL OF MATHEMATICAL BEHAVIOR.
Ablex Publishing Corporation, 355 Chestnut St., Norwood, NJ 07648. TEL 201-767-8450. FAX 201-767-6717. *3041*

JOURNAL OF MATHEMATICAL BIOLOGY.
Springer-Verlag, Heidelberger Platz 3, D-1000 Berlin 33, Germany. TEL 030-8207-1. *444*

JOURNAL OF MATHEMATICAL ECONOMICS.
North-Holland P.O. Box 211, 1000 AE Amsterdam, Netherlands. TEL 020-5803911. FAX 020-5803598. *896*

JOURNAL OF MATHEMATICAL PHYSICS.
American Institute of Physics, 335 E. 45th St., New York, NY 10017. TEL 212-661-9404. *3822*

JOURNAL OF MATHEMATICAL PSYCHOLOGY.
Academic Press, Inc., Journal Division, 1250 Sixth Ave., San Diego, CA 92101. TEL 619-230-1840. FAX 619-699-6800. *4030*

JOURNAL OF MATHEMATICAL SOCIOLOGY.
Gordon and Breach Science Publishers, 270 Eighth Ave., New York, NY 10011. TEL 212-206-8900. FAX 212-645-2459. *4440*

JOURNAL OF MECHANICAL DESIGN.
American Society of Mechanical Engineers, 22 Law Dr., Box 2300, Fairfield, NJ 07007-2300. TEL 800-321-2633. *1933*

JOURNAL OF MEDICAL ENGINEERING & TECHNOLOGY.
Taylor & Francis Ltd., Rankine Rd., Basingstoke, Hants RG24 OPR, England. TEL 0256-840366. FAX 0256-479438. *3117*

JOURNAL OF MEDICAL ENTOMOLOGY.
Entomological Society of America, 9301 Annapolis Rd., Lanham, MD 20706. TEL 301-731-4535. FAX 301-731-4538. *3221*

JOURNAL OF MEDICAL HUMANITIES.
Human Sciences Press, Inc. 233 Spring St., New York, NY 10013-1578. TEL 212-620-8000. FAX 212-463-0742. *3117*

JOURNAL OF MEDICAL SYSTEMS.
Plenum Publishing Corp., 233 Spring St., New York, NY 10013-1578. TEL 212-620-8000. FAX 212-463-0742. *3226*

JOURNAL OF MEDICAL VIROLOGY.
John Wiley & Sons, Inc., Journals, 605 Third Ave., New York, NY 10158. TEL 212-850-6000. FAX 212-850-6088. *3117*

JOURNAL OF MEDICINAL CHEMISTRY.
American Chemical Society, 1155 16th St., N.W., Washington, DC 20036. TEL 800-333-9511. FAX 202-872-4615. *3732*

JOURNAL OF MEDICINE (CLINICAL, EXPERIMENTAL AND THEORETICAL).
P J D Publications Ltd., Box 966, Westbury, NY 11590. TEL 516-626-0650. *3117*

JOURNAL OF MEDIEVAL AND RENAISSANCE STUDIES.
Duke University Press, 6697 College Station, Durham, NC 27708. TEL 919-684-2173. FAX 919-684-8644. *2509*

JOURNAL OF MEDIEVAL HISTORY.
Elsevier Science Publishers B.V., P.O. Box 211, 1000 AE Amsterdam, Netherlands. TEL 020-5803911. FAX 020-5803598. *2371*

JOURNAL OF MEMBRANE BIOLOGY.
Springer-Verlag, Heidelberger Platz 3, 1000 Berlin 33, Germany. TEL 030-8207-1. *525*

JOURNAL OF MEMBRANE SCIENCE.
Elsevier Science Publishers B.V., P.O. Box 211, 1000AE Amsterdam, Netherlands. TEL 020-5803911. FAX 020-5803598. *1227*

JOURNAL OF MICROBIOLOGICAL METHODS.
Elsevier Science Publishers B.V., P.O. Box 211, 1000 AE Amsterdam, Netherlands. TEL 020-5803911. FAX 020-5803598. *554*

JOURNAL OF MICROCOLUMN SEPARATIONS.
Brigham Young University, Chemistry Department, Rm. 112ESC, Provo, UT 84602-1211. TEL 801-378-2135. FAX 801-378-5474. *1206*

JOURNAL OF MICROCOMPUTER SYSTEMS MANAGEMENT.
Idea Group Publishing, (Information Resources Management Association) 4811 Jonestown Rd., Ste. 230, Harrisburg, PA 17109-1751. TEL 717-541-9150. FAX 717-541-9159. *1461*

JOURNAL OF MICROENCAPSULATION.
Taylor & Francis Ltd., Rankine Rd., Basingstoke, Hants. RG25 OPR, England. TEL 0256-840366. FAX 0256-479438. *3732*

JOURNAL OF MICROSCOPY RESEARCH AND TECHNIQUE.
John Wiley & Sons, Inc., Journals, 605 Third Ave., New York, NY 10158. TEL 212-850-6000. FAX 212-850-6088. *444*

JOURNAL OF MICROWAVE POWER.
International Microwave Power Institute, 13542 Union Village Cir., Clifton, VA 22024-2305. TEL 703-830-5588. *1901*

JOURNAL OF MODERN HISTORY.
University of Chicago Press, Journals Division, 5720 S. Woodlawn Ave., Chicago, IL 60637. TEL 312-753-3347. FAX 312-702-0694. *2315*

JOURNAL OF MODERN OPTICS.
Taylor & Francis Ltd., Rankine Rd., Basingstoke, Hants. RG24 OPR, England. TEL 0256-840366. FAX 0256-479438. *3854*

JOURNAL OF MOLECULAR CATALYSIS.
Elsevier Sequoia S.A., P.O. Box 564, CH-1001 Lausanne, Switzerland. TEL 021-207381. FAX 021-235444. *1228*

JOURNAL OF MOLECULAR EVOLUTION.
Springer-Verlag, Journals, 175 Fifth Ave., New York, NY 10010. TEL 212-460-1500. *545*

JOURNAL OF MOLECULAR GRAPHICS.
Butterworth - Heinemann Ltd. (Molecular Graphics Society) 80 Montvale Ave., Stoneham, MA 02180. TEL 617-438-8464. FAX 617-438-1479. *1422*

JOURNAL OF MOLECULAR LIQUIDS.
Elsevier Science Publishers B.V., P.O. Box 211, 1000 AE Amsterdam, Netherlands. TEL 020-5803911. FAX 020-5803598. *1228*

JOURNAL OF MOLECULAR SPECTROSCOPY.
Academic Press, Inc., Journal Division, 1250 Sixth Ave., San Diego, CA 92101. TEL 619-230-1840. FAX 619-699-6800. *3854*

JOURNAL OF MOLECULAR STRUCTURE.
Elsevier Science Publishers B.V., P.O. Box 211, 1000 AE Amsterdam, Netherlands. TEL 020-5803911. FAX 020-5803598. *1181*

JOURNAL OF MOLECULAR STRUCTURE: THEOCHEM.
Elsevier Science Publishers B.V., P.O Box 211, 1000 AE Amsterdam, Netherlands. TEL 020-5803911. FAX 020-5803598. *1181*

JOURNAL OF MONETARY ECONOMICS.
North-Holland P.O. Box 211, 1000 AE Amsterdam, Netherlands. TEL 020-5803911. FAX 020-5803598. *788*

JOURNAL OF MORPHOLOGY.
John Wiley & Sons, Inc., Journals, 605 Third Ave., New York, NY 10158. TEL 212-850-6000. FAX 212-850-6088. *444*

JOURNAL OF MOTOR BEHAVIOR.
Heldref Publications, (Helen Dwight Reid Educational Foundation) 1319 Eighteenth St., N.W., Washington, DC 20036-1802. TEL 202-296-5149. FAX 202-296-5149. *4031*

JOURNAL OF MULTICULTURAL SOCIAL WORK.
Haworth Press, Inc., 10 Alice St., Binghamton, NY 13904. TEL 607-722-1695. FAX 607-722-1424. *4440*

JOURNAL OF MULTINATIONAL FINANCIAL MANAGEMENT.
Haworth Press, Inc., 10 Alice St., Binghamton, NY 13904. TEL 607-722-1695. FAX 607-722-1424. *915*

JOURNAL OF MULTIVARIATE ANALYSIS.
Academic Press, Inc., Journal Division, 1250 Sixth Ave., San Diego, CA 92101. TEL 619-230-1840. FAX 619-699-6800. *3041*

JOURNAL OF MUSCULOSKELETAL MEDICINE.
Cliggott Publishing Co., 55 Holly Hill Lane, Box 4010, Greenwich, CT 06830. TEL 203-661-0600. *3309*

JOURNAL OF MUSCULOSKELETAL PAIN.
Haworth Press, Inc., 10 Alice St., Binghamton, NY 13904. TEL 800-342-9678. FAX 607-722-1424. *3309*

JOURNAL OF MUSIC THERAPY.
National Association for Music Therapy, Inc., 8455 Colesville Rd, K930, Silver Spring, MD 20910-3319. *3559*

JOURNAL OF MUSICOLOGICAL RESEARCH.
Gordon and Breach Science Publishers, 270 Eighth Ave., New York, NY 10011. TEL 212-206-8900. FAX 212-645-2459. *3559*

JOURNAL OF MUSICOLOGY.
University of California Press, Journals Division, 2120 Berkeley Way, Berkeley, CA 94720. TEL 510-642-6221. FAX 510-643-7127. *3559*

JOURNAL OF NARRATIVE AND LIFE HISTORY.
Lawrence Erlbaum Associates, Inc., 365 Broadway, Hillsdale, NJ 07642. TEL 201-444-4110. FAX 201-666-2394. *2928*

JOURNAL OF NATURAL HISTORY.
Taylor & Francis Ltd., Rankine Rd., Basingstoke, Hants RG24 0PR, England. TEL 0256-840366. FAX 0256-479438. *444*

JOURNAL OF NATURAL PRODUCTS.
American Society of Pharmacognosy, c/o David J. Slatkin, Treasurer, Chicago School of Pharmacy, 555 31st St., Downers Grove, IL 60515. TEL 708-971-6417. FAX 708-971-6097. *3732*

JOURNAL OF NEAR-DEATH STUDIES.
Human Sciences Press, Inc. (International Association for Near-Death Studies) 233 Spring St., New York, NY 10013-1578. TEL 212-620-8000. FAX 212-463-0742. *4031*

JOURNAL OF NEAR EASTERN STUDIES.
University of Chicago Press, Journals Division, 5720 S. Woodlawn Ave., Chicago, IL 60637. TEL 312-753-3347. FAX 312-702-0694. *276*

JOURNAL OF NEMATOLOGY.
Society of Nematologists, c/o L.W. Duncan, Treas., Univ. Florida, CREC, 700 Experimental Sta. Rd., Lake Alfred, FL 33850. TEL 813-956-1151. FAX 813-956-4631. *586*

JOURNAL OF NERVOUS AND MENTAL DISEASE.
Williams & Wilkins, 428 E. Preston St., Baltimore, MD 21202. TEL 301-528-4000. FAX 301-528-4312. *3342*

JOURNAL OF NEURO-ONCOLOGY.
Kluwer Academic Publishers, 101 Philip Dr., Norwell, MA 02061. TEL 617-871-6600. FAX 617-871-6528. *3199*

JOURNAL OF NEUROBIOLOGY.
John Wiley & Sons, Inc., Journals, 605 Third Ave., New York, NY 10158-0012. TEL 212-850-6000. FAX 212-850-6088. *573*

JOURNAL OF NEUROCHEMISTRY.
Raven Press, (International Society for Neurochemistry) 1185 Ave. of the Americas, New York, NY 10036. TEL 212-930-9500. FAX 212-869-3495. *479*

JOURNAL OF NEUROGENETICS.
Harwood Academic Publishers, 270 Eighth Ave., New York, NY 10011. TEL 212-206-8900. FAX 212-645-2459. *3342*

JOURNAL OF NEUROIMAGING.
Little, Brown and Company, Medical Journals, (American Society of Neuroimaging) 34 Beacon St., Boston, MA 02108. TEL 617-859-5500. FAX 617-859-0629. *3342*

JOURNAL OF NEUROIMMUNOLOGY.
Elsevier Science Publishers B.V., (International Society for Neuroimmunology) P.O. Box 211, 1000 AE Amsterdam, Netherlands. *3342*

JOURNAL OF NEUROLINGUISTICS.
Pergamon Press, Inc., Journals Division, 660 White Plains Rd., Tarrytown, NY 10591-5153. TEL 914-524-9200. FAX 914-333-2444. *3342*

JOURNAL OF NEUROPATHOLOGY AND EXPERIMENTAL NEUROLOGY.
American Association of Neuropathologists, Inc., c/o Dr. Michael N. Hart, Ed., Division of Neuropathology, University of Iowa, College of Medicine, Rm. 147A ML, Iowa City, IA 52242-1009. TEL 319-335-8273. FAX 319-335-6510. *3342*

JOURNAL OF NEUROPHYSIOLOGY.
American Physiological Society, 9650 Rockville Pike, Bethesda, MD 20814. TEL 301-530-7071. FAX 301-571-1814. *573*

JOURNAL OF NEUROPSYCHIATRY AND CLINICAL NEUROSCIENCES.
American Psychiatric Press, Inc., Journals Division, (American Psychiatric Association) 1400 K St. N.W., Ste., 1101, Washington, DC 20005. TEL 202-682-6272. FAX 202-789-2648. *3342*

JOURNAL OF NEUROSCIENCE.
Oxford University Press, Journals, (Society for Neuroscience) 200 Madison Ave., New York, NY 10016. TEL 212-679-7300. FAX 212-725-2972. *3342*

JOURNAL OF NEUROSCIENCE METHODS.
Elsevier Science Publishers B.V., P.O. Box 211, 1000 AE Amsterdam, Netherlands. TEL 020-5803911. FAX 020-5803598. *3343*

JOURNAL OF NEUROSCIENCE NURSING.
American Association of Neuroscience Nurses, 224 N. Des Plaines, Ste. 601, Chicago, IL 60661. TEL 312-993-0043. *3280*

JOURNAL OF NEUROSCIENCE RESEARCH.
John Wiley & Sons, Inc., Journals, 605 Third Ave., New York, NY 10158. TEL 212-850-6000. FAX 212-850-6088. *3343*

JOURNAL OF NEUROSURGERY.
American Association of Neurological Surgeons, Dartmouth Medical School, Hanover, NH 03756. TEL 603-643-4163. FAX 603-643-4166. *3343*

JOURNAL OF NEUROSURGICAL ANESTHESIOLOGY.
Raven Press, 1185 Ave. of the Americas, New York, NY 10036. TEL 212-930-9500. FAX 212-869-3495. *3191*

JOURNAL OF NON-CRYSTALLINE SOLIDS.
North-Holland P.O. Box 211, 1000 AE Amsterdam, Netherlands. TEL 020-5803911. FAX 020-5803598. *3822*

JOURNAL OF NON-NEWTONIAN FLUID MECHANICS.
Elsevier Science Publishers B.V., P.O. Box 211, 1000 AE Amsterdam, Netherlands. TEL 020-5803911. FAX 020-5803598. *3843*

JOURNAL OF NONDESTRUCTIVE EVALUATION.
Plenum Publishing Corp., 233 Spring St., New York, NY 10013-1578. TEL 212-620-8000. FAX 212-463-0742. *1919*

JOURNAL OF NONPROFIT & PUBLIC SECTOR MARKETING.
Haworth Press, Inc., 10 Alice St., Binghamton, NY 13904. TEL 800-342-9678. FAX 607-722-1424. *1043*

JOURNAL OF NONVERBAL BEHAVIOR.
Human Sciences Press, Inc. 233 Spring St., New York, NY 10013-1578. TEL 212-620-8000. FAX 212-463-0742. *4031*

JOURNAL OF NUCLEAR MATERIALS.
North-Holland P.O. Box 211, 1000 AE Amsterdam, Netherlands. TEL 020-5803911. FAX 020-5803598. *3848*

JOURNAL OF NUCLEAR MATERIALS MANAGEMENT.
Institute of Nuclear Materials Management, Inc., 60 Revere Dr., Ste. 500, Northbrook, IL 60062-1563. TEL 708-480-9573. FAX 708-480-9282. *1806*

JOURNAL OF NUCLEAR MEDICINE.
Society of Nuclear Medicine, 136 Madison Ave., New York, NY 10016. TEL 212-889-0717. FAX 212-545-0221. *3359*

JOURNAL OF NUCLEAR MEDICINE TECHNOLOGY.
Society of Nuclear Medicine, 136 Madison Ave., New York, NY 10016. TEL 212-889-0717. FAX 212-545-0221. *3360*

JOURNAL OF NUMBER THEORY.
Academic Press, Inc., Journal Division, 1250 Sixth Ave., San Diego, CA 92101. TEL 619-230-1840. FAX 619-699-6800. *3042*

JOURNAL OF NURSE-MIDWIFERY.
Elsevier Science Publishing Co., Inc. (New York), (American College of Nurse-Midwives) 655 Ave. of the Americas, New York, NY 10010. TEL 212-989-5800. FAX 212-633-3965. *3294*

JOURNAL OF NUTRITION.
American Institute of Nutrition, 9650 Rockville Pike, Bethesda, MD 20814. TEL 301-530-7027. FAX 301-571-1892. *3608*

JOURNAL OF NUTRITION FOR THE ELDERLY.
Haworth Press, Inc., 10 Alice St., Binghamton, NY 13904. TEL 800-342-9678. FAX 607-722-1424. *2275*

JOURNAL OF NUTRITION, GROWTH AND CANCER.
Food & Nutrition Press, Inc., (International Association for Vitamins and Nutritional Oncology) 2 Corporate Dr., Box 374, Trumbull, CT 06611. TEL 203-261-8587. *3608*

JOURNAL OF NUTRITION IN RECIPE & MENU DEVELOPMENT.
Haworth Press, Inc., Food Products Press, 10 Alice St., Binghamton, NY 13904-1580. TEL 800-342-9678. FAX 607-722-1424. *3608*

JOURNAL OF NUTRITIONAL IMMUNOLOGY.
Haworth Press, Inc., 10 Alice St., Binghamton, NY 13904. TEL 800-342-9678. FAX 607-722-1424. *3187*

REFEREED SERIALS

JOURNAL OF OCCUPATIONAL MEDICINE.
Williams & Wilkins, (American College of Occupational Medicine) 428 E. Preston St., Baltimore, MD 21202. TEL 301-528-4000. FAX 301-528-4312. *3117*

JOURNAL OF OCCUPATIONAL REHABILITATION.
Plenum Publishing Corp., 233 Spring St., New York, NY 10013-1578. TEL 212-620-8000. FAX 212-463-0742. *3118*

JOURNAL OF OFFENDER REHABILITATION.
Haworth Press, Inc., 10 Alice St., Binghamton, NY 13904. TEL 800-342-9678. FAX 607-722-1424. *1516*

JOURNAL OF OFFSHORE MECHANICS AND ARCTIC ENGINEERING.
American Society of Mechanical Engineers, 345 E. 47th St., New York, NY 10017. TEL 212-705-7722. *1933*

JOURNAL OF OPTIMIZATION THEORY AND APPLICATIONS.
Plenum Publishing Corp., 233 Spring St., New York, NY 10013-1578. TEL 212-620-8000. FAX 212-463-0742. *3062*

JOURNAL OF ORAL AND MAXILLOFACIAL SURGERY.
W.B. Saunders Co., (American Association of Oral and Maxillofacial Surgeons) Curtis Center, Independence Square W., Philadelphia, PA 19106. TEL 215-238-7800. *3236*

JOURNAL OF ORGANIC CHEMISTRY.
American Chemical Society, 1155 16th St., N.W., Washington, DC 20036. TEL 202-872-4363. FAX 202-872-4615. *1219*

JOURNAL OF ORGANIC CHEMISTRY OF THE U S S R.
Plenum Publishing Corp., Consultants Bureau, (Russian Academy of Sciences) 233 Spring St., New York, NY 10013-1578. TEL 212-620-8468. FAX 212-463-0742. *1219*

JOURNAL OF ORGANIZATIONAL BEHAVIOR MANAGEMENT.
Haworth Press, Inc., 10 Alice St., Binghamton, NY 13904. TEL 800-342-9678. FAX 607-722-1424. *4031*

JOURNAL OF ORGANOMETALLIC CHEMISTRY.
Elsevier Sequoia S.A., P.O. Box 564, CH-1001 Lausanne, Switzerland. TEL 021-207381. FAX 021-235444. *1219*

JOURNAL OF ORGANOMETALLIC CHEMISTRY LIBRARY.
Elsevier Science Publishers B.V., Books Division, P.O. Box 211, 1000 AE Amsterdam, Netherlands. TEL 020-5803911. FAX 020-5803705. *1181*

JOURNAL OF ORGONOMY.
American College of Orgonomy, Box 490, Princeton, NJ 08542. TEL 908-821-1144. FAX 908-821-0174. *3343*

JOURNAL OF ORTHOPAEDIC AND SPORTS PHYSICAL THERAPY.
Williams & Wilkins, (American Physical Therapy Association, Orthopaedic and Sports Physical Therapy Sections) 428 E. Preston St., Baltimore, MD 21202. TEL 301-528-4000. FAX 301-528-4312. *3372*

JOURNAL OF ORTHOPAEDIC RESEARCH.
Raven Press, (Orthopaedic Research Society) 1185 Ave. of the Americas, New York, NY 10036. TEL 212-930-9500. FAX 212-869-3495. *3309*

JOURNAL OF PAEDIATRICS AND CHILD HEALTH.
Blackwell Scientific Publications (Australia) Pty. Ltd., (Australian College of Paediatrics) P.O. Box 378, Carlton, Vic. 3053, Australia. TEL 03-347-0300. FAX 03-3475001. *3322*

JOURNAL OF PAIN AND SYMPTOM MANAGEMENT.
Elsevier Science Publishing Co., Inc. (New York), (University of Wisconsin-Madison, Department of Anesthesiology) 655 Ave. of the Americas, New York, NY 10010. TEL 212-989-5800. FAX 212-633-3965. *3191*

JOURNAL OF PALEONTOLOGY.
Paleontological Society, Business Office, 1261 Trumansburg Rd., Ithaca, NY 14850-1313. TEL 607-273-6623. *3658*

JOURNAL OF PALESTINE STUDIES.
University of California Press, Journals Division, (Institute for Palestine Studies) 2120 Berkeley Way, Berkeley, CA 94720. TEL 202-342-3990. FAX 202-342-3927. *2430*

JOURNAL OF PARALLEL AND DISTRIBUTED COMPUTING.
Academic Press, Inc., Journal Division, 1250 Sixth Ave., San Diego, CA 92101. TEL 619-230-1840. FAX 619-699-6800. *1397*

JOURNAL OF PEDIATRIC & PERINATAL NUTRITION.
Haworth Press, Inc., 10 Alice St., Binghamton, NY 13904. TEL 800-342-9678. FAX 607-722-1424. *3322*

JOURNAL OF PEDIATRIC GASTROENTEROLOGY AND NUTRITION.
Raven Press, 1185 Ave. of the Americas, New York, NY 10036. TEL 212-930-9500. FAX 212-869-3495. *3269*

JOURNAL OF PEDIATRIC HEALTH CARE (ST. LOUIS).
Mosby - Year Book, Inc. (National Association of Pediatric Nurse Associates and Practitioners) 11830 Westline Industrial Dr., St. Louis, MO 63146. TEL 800-325-4117. FAX 314-432-1380. *3322*

JOURNAL OF PEDIATRIC NURSING.
W.B. Saunders Co., Journals Department Curtis Center, Independence Sq. W., Philadelphia, PA 19106. TEL 215-238-7800. *3280*

JOURNAL OF PEDIATRIC OPHTHALMOLOGY AND STRABISMUS.
Slack, Inc., 6900 Grove Rd, Thorofare, NJ 08086. TEL 609-848-1000. FAX 609-853-5991. *3302*

JOURNAL OF PEDIATRIC ORTHOPEDICS.
Raven Press, 1185 Ave. of the Americas, New York, NY 10036. TEL 212-930-9500. FAX 212-869-3495. *3309*

JOURNAL OF PEDIATRIC PSYCHOLOGY.
Plenum Publishing Corp., (Society of Pediatric Psychology) 233 Spring St., New York, NY 10013-1578. TEL 212-620-8000. FAX 212-463-0742. *4031*

JOURNAL OF PEDIATRIC SURGERY.
W.B. Saunders Co. (American Academy of Pediatrics, Surgical Section) Curtis Center, Independence Square W., Philadelphia, PA 19106. TEL 215-238-7800. *3380*

JOURNAL OF PEDIATRICS.
Mosby - Year Book, Inc. 11830 Westline Industrial Dr., St. Louis, MO 63146. TEL 800-325-4117. FAX 314-432-1380. *3322*

JOURNAL OF PERINATOLOGY.
Appleton & Lange, Journal Division (National Perinatal Association) 25 Van Zant St., Box 5630, Norwalk, CT 06855. TEL 203-838-4400. *3294*

JOURNAL OF PERIODONTOLOGY.
American Academy of Periodontology, 737 N. Michigan, Ste. 800, Chicago, IL 60611. TEL 312-787-5518. FAX 312-787-3670. *3237*

JOURNAL OF PERSONALITY.
Duke University Press, 6697 College Station, Durham, NC 27708. TEL 919-684-2173. FAX 919-684-8644. *4031*

JOURNAL OF PERSONALITY AND SOCIAL PSYCHOLOGY.
American Psychological Association, 750 First St., N.E., Washington, DC 20002-4242. TEL 202-336-5500. FAX 202-336-5568. *4031*

JOURNAL OF PERSONALITY ASSESSMENT.
Lawrence Erlbaum Associates, Inc., (Society for Personality Assessment) 365 Broadway, Hillsdale, NJ 07642. TEL 201-666-4110. FAX 201-666-2394. *4031*

JOURNAL OF PERSONALITY DISORDERS.
Guilford Publications, Inc., (International Society for the Study of Personality Disorders) 72 Spring St., 4th Fl., New York, NY 10012. TEL 212-431-9800. FAX 212-966-6708. *4031*

JOURNAL OF PETROLEUM SCIENCE AND ENGINEERING.
Elsevier Science Publishers B.V., P.O. Box 211, 1000 AE Amsterdam, Netherlands. TEL 020-5803911. FAX 020-5803598. *3691*

JOURNAL OF PHARMACEUTICAL AND BIOMEDICAL ANALYSIS.
Pergamon Press, Inc., Journals Division, 660 White Plains Rd., Tarrytown, NY 10591-5153. TEL 914-524-9200. FAX 914-333-2444. *3732*

JOURNAL OF PHARMACEUTICAL CARE IN PAIN & SYMPTOM CONTROL.
Haworth Press, Inc., 10 Alice St., Binghamton, NY 13904. TEL 800-342-9678. FAX 607-722-1424. *3732*

JOURNAL OF PHARMACEUTICAL MARKETING AND MANAGEMENT.
Haworth Press, Inc., 10 Alice St., Binghamton, NY 13904. TEL 800-342-9678. FAX 607-722-1424. *3732*

JOURNAL OF PHARMACEUTICAL SCIENCES.
American Pharmaceutical Association, 2215 Constitution Ave., N.W., Washington, DC 20037. TEL 202-628-4410. FAX 202-783-2351. *3732*

JOURNAL OF PHARMACOEPIDEMIOLOGY.
Haworth Press, Inc., 10 Alice St., Binghamton, NY 13904. TEL 800-342-9678. FAX 607-722-1424. *3732*

JOURNAL OF PHARMACOKINETICS AND BIOPHARMACEUTICS.
Plenum Publishing Corp., 233 Spring St., New York, NY 10013-1578. TEL 212-620-8000. FAX 212-463-0742. *3732*

JOURNAL OF PHARMACOLOGICAL AND TOXICOLOGICAL METHODS.
Elsevier Science Publishing Co., Inc. (New York), 655 Ave. of the Americas, New York, NY 10010. TEL 212-989-5800. FAX 212-633-3965. *1982*

JOURNAL OF PHARMACOLOGY AND EXPERIMENTAL THERAPEUTICS.
Williams & Wilkins, (American Society of Pharmacology and Experimental Therapeutics) 428 Preston St., Baltimore, MD 21202. TEL 301-528-4000. FAX 301-528-4312. *3733*

JOURNAL OF PHARMACY TEACHING.
Haworth Press, Inc., 10 Alice St., Binghamton, NY 13904. TEL 800-342-9678. FAX 607-722-1424. *3733*

JOURNAL OF PHARMACY TECHNOLOGY.
Harvey Whitney Books Company, Box 42696, Cincinnati, OH 45242. TEL 513-793-3555. FAX 513-793-3600. *3733*

JOURNAL OF PHASE EQUILIBRIA.
A S M International, Materials Park, OH 44073-0002. TEL 216-338-5151. FAX 216-338-4634. *3411*

JOURNAL OF PHOTOCHEMISTRY AND PHOTOBIOLOGY, A: CHEMISTRY.
Elsevier Sequoia S.A., P.O. Box 564, 1001 Lausanne, Switzerland. TEL 021-207381. FAX 021-235444. *1228*

JOURNAL OF PHOTOCHEMISTRY AND PHOTOBIOLOGY, B: BIOLOGY.
Elsevier Sequoia S.A., (European Society for Photobiology) P.O. Box 564, CH-1001 Lausanne, Switzerland. TEL 021-207381. FAX 021-235444. *479*

JOURNAL OF PHOTOGRAPHIC SCIENCE.
The Barn, Whitehall, Near Middle Marwood, Barnstaple, N. Devon EX31 4EQ, England. TEL 0271-72482. FAX 0271-72482. *3792*

JOURNAL OF PHYCOLOGY.
Allen Press, Inc., (Phycological Society of America) 1041 New Hampshire St., Box 1897, Lawrence, KS 66044. TEL 913-843-1234. FAX 913-843-1274. *507*

JOURNAL OF PHYSICAL AND CHEMICAL REFERENCE DATA.
American Institute of Physics, 335 E. 45th St., New York, NY 10017. TEL 212-661-9404. FAX 202-872-4615. *1181*

JOURNAL OF PHYSICAL CHEMISTRY.
American Chemical Society, 1155 16th St., N.W., Washington, DC 20036. TEL 202-872-4363. FAX 202-872-4615. *1228*

JOURNAL OF PHYSICAL OCEANOGRAPHY.
American Meteorological Society, 45 Beacon St., Boston, MA 02108-3693. TEL 617-227-2425. FAX 617-742-8718. *1607*

JOURNAL OF PHYSICS AND CHEMISTRY OF SOLIDS.
Pergamon Press, Inc., Journals Division, 660 White Plains Rd., Tarrytown, NY 10591-5153. TEL 914-524-9200. FAX 914-333-2444. *3823*

JOURNAL OF PINEAL RESEARCH.
Munksgaard International Publishers Ltd., P.O. Box 2148, DK-1016 Copenhagen K, Denmark. TEL 45-33-12-70-30. FAX 45-33-12-70-30. *3343*

JOURNAL OF PLANNING LITERATURE.
Sage Publications, Inc., (Ohio State University, Department of City and Regional Planning) 2455 Teller Rd., Newbury Park, CA 91320. TEL 805-499-0721. FAX 805-499-0871. *2490*

JOURNAL OF PLANT GROWTH REGULATION.
Springer-Verlag, Journals, (International Plant Growth Substance Association) 175 Fifth Ave., New York, NY 10010. TEL 212-460-1500. *507*

JOURNAL OF PLANT NUTRITION.
Marcel Dekker Journals, 270 Madison Ave., New York, NY 10016. TEL 212-696-9000. FAX 212-685-4540. *507*

JOURNAL OF PLASTIC FILM AND SHEETING.
Technomic Publishing Co., Inc., 851 New Holland Ave., Box 3535, Lancaster, PA 07604. TEL 717-295-4538. *3863*

JOURNAL OF POETRY THERAPY.
Human Sciences Press, Inc. (National Association for Poetry Therapy) 233 Spring St., New York, NY 10013-1578. TEL 212-620-8000. FAX 212-463-0742. *2996*

JOURNAL OF POLICY MODELING.
Elsevier Science Publishing Co., Inc. (New York), (Society for Policy Modeling) 655 Ave. of the Americas, New York, NY 10010. TEL 212-989-5800. FAX 212-633-3965. *3902*

JOURNAL OF POLITICAL ECONOMY.
University of Chicago Press, Journals Division, 5720 S. Woodlawn Ave., Chicago, IL 60637. TEL 312-753-3347. FAX 312-702-0694. *675*

JOURNAL OF POLYMER MATERIALS.
Oxford & I.B.H. Publishing Co. Pvt. Ltd., 22 Park Mansion, Calcutta 700016, India. FAX 31-10-4135947. *1219*

JOURNAL OF POLYMER SCIENCE. PART A: POLYMER CHEMISTRY.
John Wiley & Sons, Inc., Journals, 605 Third Ave., New York, NY 10158-0012. TEL 212-850-6000. FAX 212-850-6088. *1219*

JOURNAL OF POLYMER SCIENCE. PART B: POLYMER PHYSICS.
John Wiley & Sons, Inc., Journals, 605 Third Ave., New York, NY 10158-0012. TEL 212-850-6000. FAX 212-850-6088. *1219*

JOURNAL OF POLYMER SCIENCE. POLYMER SYMPOSIA EDITION.
John Wiley & Sons, Inc., Journals, 605 Third Ave., New York, NY 10158-0012. TEL 212-850-6000. FAX 212-850-6088. *1219*

JOURNAL OF POPULAR FILM AND TELEVISION.
Heldref Publications, (Helen Dwight Reid Educational Foundation) 1319 Eighteenth St., N.W., Washington, DC 20036-1802. TEL 202-296-6267. FAX 202-296-5149. *3512*

JOURNAL OF POST ANESTHESIA NURSING.
W.B. Saunders Co. (American Society of Post Anesthesia Nurses) Curtis Center, Independence Square W., Philadelphia, PA 19106. TEL 215-238-7800. *3280*

JOURNAL OF POST KEYNESIAN ECONOMICS.
M. E. Sharpe, Inc., 80 Business Park Dr., Armonk, NY 10504. TEL 914-273-1800. FAX 914-273-2106. *871*

JOURNAL OF POTASSIUM RESEARCH.
Rotash Research Institute of India, Sector 19, Dundabera, Gurgaon 122 001 (Haryana), India. *3411*

JOURNAL OF POWER SOURCES.
Elsevier Sequoia S.A., P.O. Box 564, CH-1001 Lausanne, Switzerland. TEL 021-207381. FAX 021-235444. *1901*

JOURNAL OF PRACTICAL NURSING.
National Association for Practical Nurse Education and Service, Inc., 1400 Spring St., Ste. 310, Silver Spring, MD 20910. FAX 301-588-2839. *3280*

JOURNAL OF PRAGMATICS.
North-Holland P.O. Box 211, 1000 AE Amsterdam, Netherlands. TEL 020-5803911. FAX 020-5803598. *2821*

JOURNAL OF PRIMARY PREVENTION.
Human Sciences Press, Inc. (Vermont Conference on Primary Prevention of Psychopathology) 233 Spring St., New York, NY 10013-1578. TEL 212-620-8000. FAX 212-463-0742. *4032*

JOURNAL OF PRISON AND JAIL HEALTH.
Human Sciences Press, Inc. (National Commission on Correctional Health Care) 233 Spring St., New York, NY 10013-1578. TEL 212-620-8000. FAX 212-463-0742. *3118*

JOURNAL OF PRODUCT INNOVATION MANAGEMENT.
Elsevier Science Publishing Co., Inc. (New York), (Product Development & Management Association) 655 Ave. of the Americas, New York, NY 10010. TEL 212-989-5800. FAX 212-633-3965. *1079*

JOURNAL OF PRODUCTS LIABILITY.
Pergamon Press, Inc., Journals Division, 660 White Plains Rd., Tarrytown, NY 10591-5153. TEL 914-524-9200. FAX 914-333-2444. *2640*

JOURNAL OF PROFESSIONAL ISSUES IN ENGINEERING AND PRACTICE.
American Society of Civil Engineers, 345 E. 47th St., New York, NY 10017-2398. TEL 212-705-7288. FAX 212-980-4681. *1870*

JOURNAL OF PROFESSIONAL SERVICES MARKETING.
Haworth Press, Inc., 10 Alice St., Binghamton, NY 13904. TEL 800-342-9678. FAX 607-722-1424. *1043*

JOURNAL OF PROGRESSIVE HUMAN SERVICES.
Haworth Press, Inc., (Institute for Social Services Alternatives, Inc.) 10 Alice St., Binghamton, New York, NY 13904. TEL 800-342-9678. FAX 607-722-1424. *4410*

JOURNAL OF PROMOTION MANAGEMENT.
Haworth Press, Inc., 10 Alice St., Binghamton, NY 13904-1580. TEL 800-342-9678. FAX 607-722-1424. *33*

JOURNAL OF PROPULSION AND POWER.
American Institute of Aeronautics and Astronautics, Inc., 370 L'Enfant Promenade, S.W., Washington, DC 20024. TEL 202-646-7400. *57*

JOURNAL OF PROSTHETIC DENTISTRY.
Mosby - Year Book, Inc. (Academy of Denture Prosthetics) 11830 Westline Industrial Dr., St. Louis, MO 63146. TEL 800-325-4117. FAX 314-432-1380. *3237*

JOURNAL OF PROSTHETICS AND ORTHOTICS.
American Academy of Orthotists and Prosthetists, 1650 King St., Ste. 500, Alexandria, VA 22314. TEL 703-836-7116. FAX 703-836-0838. *3118*

JOURNAL OF PROTEIN CHEMISTRY.
Plenum Publishing Corp., 233 Spring St., New York, NY 10013-1578. TEL 212-620-8000. FAX 212-463-0742. *1219*

JOURNAL OF PROTOZOOLOGY.
Allen Press, Inc., (Society of Protozoologists) 1041 New Hampshire Ave., Box 1897, Lawrence, KS 66044. TEL 800-627-0629. *586*

JOURNAL OF PSYCHIATRIC RESEARCH.
Pergamon Press, Inc., Journals Division, 660 White Plains Rd., Tarrytown, NY 10591-5153. TEL 914-524-9200. FAX 914-333-2444. *3343*

JOURNAL OF PSYCHOACTIVE DRUGS.
Haight-Ashbury Publications, 409 Clayton St., 2nd Fl., San Francisco, CA 94117. TEL 415-565-1904. FAX 415-621-7354. *1537*

JOURNAL OF PSYCHOEDUCATIONAL ASSESSMENT.
Clinical Psychology Publishing Co., Inc., 4 Conant Sq., Brandon, VT 05733. TEL 802-247-6871. FAX 802-247-6853. *4032*

JOURNAL OF PSYCHOLINGUISTIC RESEARCH.
Plenum Publishing Corp., 233 Spring St., New York, NY 10013-1578. TEL 212-620-8000. FAX 212-463-0742. *2821*

JOURNAL OF PSYCHOLOGY.
Heldref Publications, (Helen Dwight Reid Educational Foundation) 1319 Eighteenth St., N.W., Washington, DC 20036-1802. TEL 202-296-6267. FAX 202-296-5149. *4032*

JOURNAL OF PSYCHOLOGY & HUMAN SEXUALITY.
Haworth Press, Inc., 10 Alice St., Binghamton, NY 13904. TEL 800-342-8678. FAX 607-722-1424. *4032*

JOURNAL OF PSYCHOLOGY AND JUDAISM.
Human Sciences Press, Inc. 233 Spring St., New York, NY 10013-1578. TEL 212-620-8000. FAX 212-463-0742. *4032*

JOURNAL OF PSYCHOPATHOLOGY AND BEHAVIORAL ASSESSMENT.
Plenum Publishing Corp., 233 Spring St., New York, NY 10013-1578. TEL 212-620-8000. FAX 212-463-0742. *4032*

JOURNAL OF PSYCHOSOCIAL ONCOLOGY.
Haworth Press, Inc., 10 Alice St., Binghamton, NY 13904. TEL 800-342-9678. FAX 607-722-1424. *3199*

JOURNAL OF PSYCHOSOMATIC RESEARCH.
Pergamon Press, Inc., Journals Division, 660 White Plains Rd., Tarrytown, NY 10591-5153. TEL 914-524-9200. FAX 914-333-2444. *3343*

JOURNAL OF PSYCHOTHERAPY INTEGRATION.
Plenum Publishing Corp., 233 Spring St., New York, NY 10013-1578. TEL 212-620-8000. FAX 212-463-0742. *3343*

JOURNAL OF PUBLIC HEALTH POLICY.
Journal of Public Health Policy, Inc., 208 Meadowood Dr., South Burlington, VT 05403. TEL 802-658-0136. FAX 802-862-4011. *4106*

JOURNAL OF PUBLIC RELATIONS RESEARCH.
Lawrence Erlbaum Associates, Inc., 365 Broadway, Hillsdale, NJ 07642. TEL 201-666-4110. FAX 201-666-2394. *33*

JOURNAL OF PURE AND APPLIED ALGEBRA.
North-Holland P.O. Box 211, 1000 AE Amsterdam, Netherlands. TEL 020-5803911. FAX 020-5803598. *3042*

JOURNAL OF QUANTITATIVE CRIMINOLOGY.
Plenum Publishing Corp., 233 Spring St., New York, NY 10013-1578. TEL 212-620-8000. FAX 212-463-0742. *1516*

JOURNAL OF QUANTITATIVE SPECTROSCOPY AND RADIATIVE TRANSFER.
Pergamon Press, Inc., Journals Division, 660 White Plains Rd., Tarrytown, NY 10591-5153. TEL 914-524-9200. FAX 914-333-2444. *3854*

JOURNAL OF RADIOANALYTICAL AND NUCLEAR CHEMISTRY. ARTICLES.
Elsevier Sequoia S.A., P.O. Box 564, CH-1001 Lausanne, Switzerland. TEL 021-207381. FAX 021-235444. *1207*

JOURNAL OF RADIOANALYTICAL AND NUCLEAR CHEMISTRY. LETTERS.
Elsevier Sequoia S.A., P.O. Box 564, CH-1001 Lausanne, Switzerland. TEL 021-207381. FAX 021-235444. *1207*

JOURNAL OF RANGE MANAGEMENT.
Society for Range Management, 1839 York St., Denver, CO 80206-1213. *445*

JOURNAL OF RARE EARTHS.
International Academic Publishers, (Zhongguo Xitu Xuehui) Beijing Zhanlanguan, Xizhimenwai Dajie, Beijing 100044, People's Republic of China. TEL 8316677. FAX 0086-1-4015664. *3411*

JOURNAL OF RATIONAL-EMOTIVE AND COGNITIVE-BEHAVIOR THERAPY.
Human Sciences Press, Inc. (Institute for Rational-Emotive Therapy) 233 Spring St., New York, NY 10013-1578. TEL 212-620-8000. FAX 212-463-0742. *4032*

JOURNAL OF READING, WRITING, AND LEARNING DISABILITIES INTERNATIONAL.
Hemisphere Publishing Corporation 1900 Frost Rd., Ste. 101, Bristol, PA 19007-1598. TEL 215-785-5800. FAX 215-785-5515. *1737*

JOURNAL OF RECEPTOR RESEARCH.
Marcel Dekker Journals, 270 Madison Ave., New York, NY 10016. TEL 212-696-9000. FAX 212-685-4540. *3118*

JOURNAL OF REINFORCED PLASTICS & COMPOSITES.
Technomic Publishing Co., Inc., 851 New Holland Ave., Box 3535, Lancaster, PA 17604. TEL 717-291-5609. FAX 717-295-4538. *1919*

JOURNAL OF RELIGION.
University of Chicago Press, Journals Division, 5720 S. Woodlawn Ave., Chicago, IL 60637. TEL 312-753-3347. FAX 312-702-0694. *4185*

JOURNAL OF RELIGION AND HEALTH.
Human Sciences Press, Inc. (Institute of Religion) 233 Spring St., New York, NY 10013-1578. TEL 212-620-8000. FAX 212-463-0742. *4185*

JOURNAL OF RELIGION IN PSYCHOTHERAPY.
Haworth Press, Inc., (Princeton Theological Seminary) 10 Alice St., Binghamton, NY 13904. TEL 607-722-1695. FAX 607-722-1424. *4185*

JOURNAL OF RELIGIOUS & THEOLOGICAL INFORMATION.
Haworth Press, Inc., 10 Alice St., Binghamton, NY 13904-1580. TEL 800-342-9678. FAX 607-722-1424. *4185*

JOURNAL OF RELIGIOUS GERONTOLOGY.
Haworth Press, Inc., 10 Alice St., Binghamton, NY 13904. TEL 800-342-9678. FAX 607-722-1424. *2275*

JOURNAL OF REPRODUCTIVE IMMUNOLOGY.
Elsevier Scientific Publishers Ireland Ltd., (International Society for Immunology of Reproduction) P.O. Box 85, Limerick, Ireland. TEL 061-61944. FAX 061-62144. *3187*

JOURNAL OF REPRODUCTIVE MEDICINE.
Journal of Reproductive Medicine, Inc., 8342 Olive Blvd., St. Louis, MO 63132. TEL 314-991-4440. FAX 314-991-4654. *3294*

JOURNAL OF RESEARCH AND DEVELOPMENT IN EDUCATION.
University of Georgia, College of Education, 427 Tucker Hall, Athens, GA 30602. TEL 404-542-1154. *1643*

JOURNAL OF RESEARCH IN MUSIC EDUCATION.
Music Educators National Conference, (Society for Research in Music Education) 1902 Association Dr., Reston, VA 22091-1597. TEL 703-860-4000. FAX 703-860-1531. *3559*

JOURNAL OF RESEARCH IN PERSONALITY.
Academic Press, Inc., Journal Division, 1250 Sixth Ave., San Diego, CA 92101. TEL 619-230-1840. FAX 619-699-6800. *4033*

JOURNAL OF RESEARCH IN PHARMACEUTICAL ECONOMICS.
Haworth Press, Inc., 10 Alice St., Binghamton, NY 13904. TEL 800-342-9678. FAX 067-722-1424. *3733*

JOURNAL OF RESEARCH IN SCIENCE TEACHING.
John Wiley & Sons, Inc., Journals, (National Association for Research in Science Teaching) 605 Third Ave., New York, NY 10158-0012. TEL 212-850-6000. FAX 212-850-6088. *4318*

JOURNAL OF RESEARCH ON ADOLESCENCE.
Lawrence Erlbaum Associates, Inc., (Society for Research on Adolescence) 365 Broadway, Hillsdale, NJ 07642. TEL 201-666-4110. FAX 201-666-2394. *1239*

JOURNAL OF RESPIRATORY DISEASES.
Cliggott Publishing Co., 55 Holly Hill Ln., Box 4010, Greenwich, CT 06830. TEL 203-661-0600. *3365*

JOURNAL OF RESTAURANT & FOODSERVICE MARKETING.
Haworth Press, Inc., 10 Alice St., Binghamton, NY 13904. TEL 800-342-9678. FAX 607-722-1424. *2477*

JOURNAL OF RHEOLOGY.
John Wiley & Sons, Inc., Journals, (Society of Rheology) 605 Third Ave., New York, NY 10158-0012. TEL 212-692-6000. *3844*

JOURNAL OF RISK AND UNCERTAINTY.
Kluwer Academic Publishers, 101 Philip Dr., Norwell, MA 02061. TEL 617-871-6600. FAX 617-871-6528. *675*

JOURNAL OF RURAL STUDIES.
Pergamon Press, Inc., Journals Division, 660 White Plains Rd., Tarrytown, NY 10591-5153. TEL 914-524-9200. FAX 914-333-2444. *4441*

JOURNAL OF RUSSIAN AND EAST EUROPEAN PSYCHIATRY.
M.E. Sharpe, Inc., 80 Business Park Dr., Armonk, NY 10504. TEL 914-273-1800. FAX 914-273-2106. *3343*

JOURNAL OF RUSSIAN AND EAST EUROPEAN PSYCHOLOGY.
M.E. Sharpe, Inc., 80 Business Park Dr., Armonk, NY 10504. TEL 914-273-1800. FAX 914-273-2106. *4033*

JOURNAL OF SAFETY RESEARCH.
Pergamon Press, Inc., Journals Division, (National Safety Council) 660 White Plains Rd., Tarrytown, NY 10591-5153. TEL 914-524-9200. FAX 914-333-2444. *4652*

JOURNAL OF SCHOOL LEADERSHIP.
Technomic Publishing Co., Inc., 851 New Holland Ave., Box 3535, Lancaster, PA 17604. TEL 717-291-5609. FAX 717-295-4538. *1729*

JOURNAL OF SCHOOL PSYCHOLOGY.
Pergamon Press, Inc., Journals Division, 660 White Plains Rd., Tarrytown, NY 10591-5153. TEL 914-524-9200. FAX 914-333-2444. *4033*

JOURNAL OF SCIENCE EDUCATION AND TECHNOLOGY.
Plenum Publishing Corp., 233 Spring St., New York, NY 10013-1578. TEL 212-620-8000. FAX 212-463-0742. *1643*

JOURNAL OF SCIENTIFIC COMPUTING.
Plenum Publishing Corp., 233 Spring St., New York, NY 10013-1578. TEL 212-620-8000. FAX 212-463-0742. *4360*

JOURNAL OF SCIENTIFIC EXPLORATION.
Society for Scientific Exploration, c/o Rm. ERL 306, Stanford University, Stanford, CA 94305-4055. TEL 415-723-1438. *4318*

JOURNAL OF SEDIMENTARY PETROLOGY.
S E P M, Box 4756, Tulsa, OK 74159-0756. TEL 918-743-9765. *1546*

JOURNAL OF SEED TECHNOLOGY.
Association of Official Seed Analysts, Inc., 268 Plant Science, Lincoln, NE 68583-0911. TEL 402-472-1444. *102*

JOURNAL OF SEX EDUCATION AND THERAPY.
Guilford Publications, Inc., (American Association of Sex Educators, Counselors and Therapists) 72 Spring St., 4th Fl., New York, NY 10012. TEL 212-431-9800. FAX 212-966-6708. *1643*

JOURNAL OF SHELLFISH RESEARCH.
National Shellfisheries Association, Inc., c/o Sandra E. Shumway, Ed., Dept. of Marine Resources & Bigelow Laboratory for Ocean Sciences, W. Boothbay Harbor, ME 04575. TEL 207-633-5572. FAX 207-633-7109. *586*

JOURNAL OF SHOULDER AND ELBOW SURGERY.
Mosby - Year Book, Inc. 11830 Westline Industrial Dr., St. Louis, MO 63146. TEL 314-872-8370. FAX 314-432-1380. *3381*

JOURNAL OF SMALL FRUIT & VITICULTURE.
Haworth Press, Inc., 10 Alice St., Binghamton, NY 13904. TEL 800-342-8678. FAX 607-722-1424. *183*

JOURNAL OF SOCIAL AND CLINICAL PSYCHOLOGY.
Guilford Publications, Inc., 72 Spring St., 4th Fl., New York, NY 10012. TEL 212-431-9800. FAX 212-966-6708. *4033*

JOURNAL OF SOCIAL DEVELOPMENT IN AFRICA.
School of Social Work, Private Bag 66022, Kopje, Harare, Zimbabwe. TEL 707414. *4410*

JOURNAL OF SOCIAL DISTRESS AND THE HOMELESS.
Human Sciences Press, Inc. 233 Spring St., New York, NY 10013. TEL 212-620-8000. FAX 212-463-0742. *4411*

JOURNAL OF SOCIAL ISSUES.
Plenum Publishing Corp., (Society for the Psychological Study of Social Issues) 233 Spring St., New York, NY 10013-1578. TEL 212-620-8000. FAX 212-463-0742. *4033*

JOURNAL OF SOCIAL PSYCHOLOGY.
Heldref Publications, (Helen Dwight Reid Educational Foundation) 1319 Eighteenth St., N.W., Washington, DC 20036-1802. TEL 202-296-6267. FAX 202-296-5149. *4033*

JOURNAL OF SOCIAL SERVICE RESEARCH.
Haworth Press, Inc., 10 Alice St., Binghamton, NY 13904. TEL 800-342-9678. FAX 607-722-1424. *4411*

JOURNAL OF SOCIAL WORK AND HUMAN SEXUALITY.
Haworth Press, Inc., 10 Alice St., Binghamton, NY 13904. TEL 800-342-9678. FAX 607-722-1424. *4411*

JOURNAL OF SOFTWARE MAINTENANCE.
John Wiley & Sons Ltd., Journals, Baffins Lane, Chichester, Sussex PO19 1UD, England. TEL 0243-779777. FAX 0243-775878. *1478*

JOURNAL OF SOIL AND WATER CONSERVATION.
Soil and Water Conservation Society, 7515 Northeast Ankeny Rd., Ankeny, IA 50021. TEL 515-289-2331. FAX 515-289-1227. *183*

JOURNAL OF SOLAR ENERGY ENGINEERING.
American Society of Mechanical Engineers, 345 E. 47th St., New York, NY 10017. TEL 212-705-7722. *1811*

JOURNAL OF SOLID STATE CHEMISTRY.
Academic Press, Inc., Journal Division, 1250 Sixth Ave., San Diego, CA 92101. TEL 619-230-1840. FAX 619-699-6800. *1228*

JOURNAL OF SOLUTION CHEMISTRY.
Plenum Publishing Corp., 233 Spring St, New York, NY 10013-1578. TEL 212-620-8000. FAX 212-463-0742. *1228*

JOURNAL OF SOUTH AMERICAN EARTH SCIENCES.
Pergamon Press plc, Headington Hill Hall, Oxford OX3 0BW, England. TEL 0865-794141. FAX 0865-743911. *1546*

JOURNAL OF SOUTH-EAST ASIAN EARTH SCIENCES.
Pergamon Press, Inc., Journals Division, 660 White Plains Rd., Tarrytown, NY 10591-5153. TEL 914-524-9200. FAX 914-333-2444. *1570*

JOURNAL OF SOVIET LASER RESEARCH.
Plenum Publishing Corp., Consultants Bureau, 233 Spring St., New York, NY 10013-1578. TEL 212-620-8468. FAX 212-463-0742. *1828*

JOURNAL OF SOVIET MATHEMATICS.
Plenum Publishing Corp., Consultants Bureau, (Russian Academy of Sciences, Mathematical Institute - V.A. Steklova) 233 Spring St., New York, NY 10013-1578. TEL 212-620-8468. FAX 212-463-0742. *3042*

JOURNAL OF SPACECRAFT AND ROCKETS.
American Institute of Aeronautics and Astronautics, Inc., 370 L'Enfant Promenade, S.W., Washington, DC 20024. TEL 202-646-7400. *57*

JOURNAL OF SPECIAL EDUCATION TECHNOLOGY.
Association of Special Education Technology, c/o Managing Editor, Box 328, Peabody College, Nashville, TN 37203. *1737*

JOURNAL OF SPINAL DISORDERS.
Raven Press, 1185 Ave. of the Americas, New York, NY 10036. TEL 212-930-9500. FAX 212-869-3495. *3309*

JOURNAL OF SPORT AND EXERCISE PSYCHOLOGY.
Human Kinetics Publishers, Inc., Box 5076, Champaign, IL 61825-5076. TEL 217-351-5076. FAX 217-351-2674. *4033*

JOURNAL OF SPORT MANAGEMENT.
Human Kinetics Publishers, Inc., (North American Society for Sport Management) Box 5076, Champaign, IL 61825-5076. TEL 217-351-5076. FAX 217-351-2674. *4477*

JOURNAL OF SPORT REHABILITATION.
Human Kinetics Publishers, Inc., Box 5076, Champaign, IL 61825. TEL 217-351-5076. FAX 217-351-2674. *3372*

JOURNAL OF STATISTICAL COMPUTATION AND SIMULATION.
Gordon & Breach Science Publishers, 270 Eighth Ave., New York, NY 10011. TEL 212-206-8900. FAX 212-645-2459. *1435*

JOURNAL OF STATISTICAL PHYSICS.
Plenum Publishing Corp., 233 Spring St., New York, NY 10013-1578. TEL 212-620-8000. FAX 212-463-0742. *3823*

JOURNAL OF STATISTICAL PLANNING AND INFERENCE.
North-Holland P.O. Box 211, 1000 AE Amsterdam, Netherlands. TEL 020-5803911. FAX 020-5803598. *4576*

JOURNAL OF STEROID BIOCHEMISTRY AND MOLECULAR BIOLOGY.
Pergamon Press, Inc., Journals Division, 660 White Plains Rd., Tarrytown, NY 10591-5153. TEL 914-524-9200. FAX 914-333-2444. *479*

JOURNAL OF STORED PRODUCTS RESEARCH.
Pergamon Press, Inc., Journals Division, 660 White Plains Rd., Tarrytown, NY 10591-5153. TEL 914-524-9200. FAX 914-333-2444. *183*

JOURNAL OF STRATEGIC I T.
Butterworth - Heinemann Ltd. Linacre House, Jordan Hill, Oxford OX2 8DP, England. TEL 0865-310366. FAX 0865-310898. *1434*

JOURNAL OF STRUCTURAL BIOLOGY.
Academic Press, Inc., Journal Division, 1250 Sixth Ave., San Diego, CA 92101. TEL 619-230-1840. FAX 619-699-6859. *445*

JOURNAL OF STRUCTURAL CHEMISTRY.
Plenum Publishing Corp., Consultants Bureau, (Russian Academy of Sciences) 233 Spring St., New York, NY 10013-1578. TEL 212-620-8468. FAX 212-463-0742. *1181*

JOURNAL OF STRUCTURAL GEOLOGY.
Pergamon Press, Inc., Journals Division, 660 White Plains Rd., Tarrytown, NY 10591-5153. TEL 914-524-9200. FAX 914-333-2444. *1570*

JOURNAL OF STRUCTURAL LEARNING.
Gordon & Breach Science Publishers, (International Study Group for Mathematics Learning) 270 Eighth Ave., New York, NY 10011. TEL 212-206-8900. FAX 212-645-2459. *4033*

JOURNAL OF SUBSTANCE ABUSE TREATMENT.
Pergamon Press, Inc., Journals Division, (North Shore University Hospital) 660 White Plains Rd., Tarrytown, NY 10591-5153. TEL 914-524-9200. FAX 914-333-2444. *1537*

JOURNAL OF SUPERCOMPUTING.
Kluwer Academic Publishers, 101 Philip Dr., Norwell, MA 02061. TEL 617-871-6300. FAX 617-871-6528. *1397*

JOURNAL OF SUPERCONDUCTIVITY.
Plenum Publishing Corp., 233 Spring St., New York, NY 10013-1578. TEL 212-620-8000. FAX 212-463-0742. *3844*

JOURNAL OF SURGICAL ONCOLOGY.
John Wiley & Sons, Inc., Journals, 605 Third Ave., New York, NY 10158. TEL 212-850-6000. FAX 212-850-6088. *3381*

JOURNAL OF SURGICAL RESEARCH.
Academic Press, Inc., Journal Division, (Association for Academic Surgery) 1250 Sixth Ave., San Diego, CA 92101. TEL 619-230-1840. FAX 619-699-6800. *3381*

JOURNAL OF SURVEYING ENGINEERING.
American Society of Civil Engineers, 345 E. 47th St., New York, NY 10017-2398. TEL 212-705-7288. FAX 212-980-4681. *1870*

JOURNAL OF SUSTAINABLE AGRICULTURE.
Haworth Press, Inc., 10 Alice St., Binghamton, NY 13904-1580. TEL 800-342-9678. FAX 607-722-1424. *1490*

JOURNAL OF SUSTAINABLE FORESTRY.
Haworth Press, Inc., 10 Alice St., Binghamton, NY 13904. TEL 800-342-9678. FAX 607-722-1424. *2103*

JOURNAL OF SWIMMING RESEARCH.
American Swimming Coaches Association, 304 S.E. 20th St., Fort Lauderdale, FL 33316. FAX 305-462-6280. *4477*

JOURNAL OF SYNTHETIC LUBRICATION.
Leaf Coppin Publishing Co., P.O. Box 111, Deal, Kent CT14 6SX, England. TEL 33-2187-2521. FAX 33-2187-0511. *3691*

JOURNAL OF SYSTEMS AND SOFTWARE.
Elsevier Science Publishing Co., Inc. (New York), 655 Ave. of the Americas, New York, NY 10010. TEL 212-989-5800. FAX 212-633-3965. *1478*

JOURNAL OF SYSTEMS ENGINEERING AND ELECTRONICS.
Science Press, Marketing and Sales Department, (Ministry of Aero-Space Industry, The Second Academy) 16 Donghuangchenggen Beijie, Beijing 100707, People's Republic of China. TEL 4010642. FAX 4012180. *57*

JOURNAL OF SYSTEMS INTEGRATION.
Kluwer Academic Publishers, Postbus 17, 3300 AA Dordrecht, Netherlands. TEL 078-334911. FAX 078-334254. *1438*

JOURNAL OF TAXATION.
Warren, Gorham and Lamont, One Penn Plaza, New York, NY 10119. TEL 800-950-1205. FAX 212-971-5240. *1099*

JOURNAL OF TEACHING IN INTERNATIONAL BUSINESS.
Haworth Press, Inc., 10 Alice St., Binghamton, NY 13904. TEL 800-342-9678. FAX 607-722-1424. *1643*

JOURNAL OF TEACHING IN PHYSICAL EDUCATION.
Human Kinetics Publishers, Inc., Box 5076, Champaign, IL 61825-5076. TEL 217-351-5076. FAX 217-351-2674. *3805*

JOURNAL OF TEACHING IN SOCIAL WORK.
Haworth Press, Inc., 10 Alice St., Binghamton, NY 13904. TEL 800-342-9678. FAX 607-722-1424. *1753*

JOURNAL OF TECHNICAL WRITING AND COMMUNICATION.
Baywood Publishing Co., Inc., 26 Austin Ave., Box 337, Amityville, NY 11701. TEL 516-691-1270. FAX 516-691-1770. *1643*

JOURNAL OF TECHNOLOGY AND TEACHER EDUCATION.
Association for the Advancement of Computing in Education, Box 2966, Charlottesville, VA 22901-2966. TEL 804-973-3987. *1691*

JOURNAL OF TECHNOLOGY IN MATHEMATICS.
Academic Press, Inc., Journal Division, 1250 Sixth Ave., San Diego, CA 92101. TEL 619-230-1840. FAX 619-699-6800. *3042*

JOURNAL OF TECHNOLOGY TRANSFER.
Technology Transfer Society, 611 N. Capitol Ave., Indianapolis, IN 46204. *4602*

JOURNAL OF TERRAMECHANICS.
Pergamon Press, Inc., Journals Division, (International Society for Terrain Vehicle Systems) 660 White Plains Rd., Tarrytown, NY 10591-5153. TEL 914-524-9200. FAX 914-333-2444. *3019*

JOURNAL OF TESTING AND EVALUATION.
American Society for Testing and Materials, 1916 Race St., Philadelphia, PA 19103. TEL 215-299-5400. FAX 215-977-9679. *1919*

JOURNAL OF THE ATMOSPHERIC SCIENCES.
American Meteorological Society, 45 Beacon St., Boston, MA 02108-3693. TEL 617-227-2425. FAX 617-742-8718. *3438*

JOURNAL OF THE AUTONOMIC NERVOUS SYSTEM.
Elsevier Science Publishers B.V., P.O. Box 211, 1000 AE Amsterdam, Netherlands. TEL 020-5803911. FAX 020-5803598. *3343*

JOURNAL OF THE CHEMICAL SOCIETY. CHEMICAL COMMUNICATIONS.
Royal Society of Chemistry, Thomas Graham House, Science Park, Milton Rd., Cambridge CB4 4WF, England. TEL 0462-672555. FAX 0462-480947. *1181*

JOURNAL OF THE FRESHMAN YEAR EXPERIENCE.
University of South Carolina, National Center for the Study of the Freshman Year Experience, 1728 College St., Columbia, SC 29208. TEL 803-777-6029. FAX 803-777-4699. *1710*

JOURNAL OF THE HISTORY OF SEXUALITY.
University of Chicago Press, 5720 S. Woodlawn Ave., Chicago, IL 60637. TEL 312-753-3347. FAX 312-702-0694. *4441*

JOURNAL OF THE HISTORY OF THE BEHAVIORAL SCIENCES.
Clinical Psychology Publishing Co., Inc., 4 Conant Sq., Brandon, VT 05733. TEL 802-247-6871. FAX 802-247-6853. *4034*

JOURNAL OF THE LEARNING SCIENCES.
Lawrence Erlbaum Associates, Inc., 365 Broadway, Hillsdale, NY 07642. TEL 201-666-4110. FAX 201-666-2394. *1643*

JOURNAL OF THE MECHANICS AND PHYSICS OF SOLIDS.
Pergamon Press, Inc., Journals Division, 660 White Plains Rd., Tarrytown, NY 10591-5153. TEL 914-524-9200. FAX 914-333-2444. *3844*

JOURNAL OF THE NEUROLOGICAL SCIENCES.
Elsevier Science Publishers B.V., (World Federation of Neurology) P.O. Box 211, 1000 AE Amsterdam, Netherlands. TEL 020-5803911. FAX 020-5803598. *3344*

JOURNAL OF THE PHILOSOPHY OF SPORT.
Human Kinetics Publishers, Inc., (Philosophic Society for the Study of Sport) Box 5076, Champaign, IL 61825-5076. TEL 217-351-5076. FAX 217-351-2674. *4477*

JOURNAL OF THE SCIENCE OF FOOD AND AGRICULTURE.
Elsevier Science Publishers Ltd., (Society of Chemical Industry) Crown House, Linton Rd., Barking, Essex IG11 8JU, England. TEL 081-594-7272. FAX 081-594-5942. *102*

JOURNAL OF THEORETICAL PROBABILITY.
Plenum Publishing Corp., 233 Spring St., New York, NY 10013-1578. TEL 212-620-8000. FAX 212-463-0742. *3042*

JOURNAL OF THERMAL ANALYSIS.
John Wiley & Sons Ltd., Journals, Baffins Lane, Chichester, West Sussex PO19 1UD, England. TEL 0243-779777. FAX 0243-775878. *1207*

JOURNAL OF THERMAL INSULATION.
Technomic Publishing Co., Inc., 851 New Holland Ave., Box 3535, Lancaster, PA 17604. TEL 717-291-5609. FAX 717-295-4538. *1828*

JOURNAL OF THERMAL SCIENCE.
Science Press, Marketing and Sales Department, (Chinese Academy of Sciences, Institute of Engineering Thermophysics) 16 Donghuangchenggen Beijie, Beijing 100707, People's Republic of China. TEL 4010642. FAX 4012180. *3841*

JOURNAL OF THERMAL STRESSES.
Hemisphere Publishing Corporation 1900 Frost Rd., Ste. 101, Bristol, PA 19007-1598. TEL 215-785-5800. FAX 215-785-5515. *1933*

JOURNAL OF THERMOPHYSICS AND HEAT TRANSFER.
American Institute of Aeronautics and Astronautics, Inc., 370 L'Enfant Promenade, S.W., Washington, DC 20024. TEL 202-646-7400. *3823*

JOURNAL OF THERMOPLASTIC COMPOSITE MATERIALS.
Technomic Publishing Co., Inc., 851 New Holland Ave., Box 3535, Lancaster, PA 17604. TEL 717-291-5609. FAX 717-295-4538. *3863*

JOURNAL OF THORACIC AND CARDIOVASCULAR SURGERY.
Mosby - Year Book, Inc. (American Association for Thoracic Surgery) 11830 Westline Industrial Dr., St. Louis, MO 63146. TEL 800-325-4117. FAX 314-432-1380. *3381*

JOURNAL OF TISSUE CULTURE METHODS.
Tissue Culture Association, 8815 Centre Park Dr., Ste. 210, Columbia, MD 21045. TEL 301-992-0946. *554*

JOURNAL OF TOXICOLOGY AND ENVIRONMENTAL HEALTH.
Hemisphere Publishing Corporation 1900 Frost Rd., Ste. 101, Bristol, PA 19007-1598. TEL 215-785-5800. FAX 215-785-5515. *1982*

JOURNAL OF TOXICOLOGY: CLINICAL TOXICOLOGY.
Marcel Dekker Journals, (American Academy of Clinical Toxicology) 270 Madison Ave., New York, NY 10016. TEL 212-696-9000. FAX 212-685-4540. *1982*

JOURNAL OF TOXICOLOGY: CUTANEOUS AND OCULAR TOXICOLOGY.
Marcel Dekker Journals, 270 Madison Ave., New York, NY 10016. TEL 212-696-9000. FAX 212-685-4540. *3733*

JOURNAL OF TOXICOLOGY: TOXIN REVIEWS.
Marcel Dekker Journals, 270 Madison Ave., New York, NY 10016. TEL 212-696-9000. FAX 212-685-4540. *3733*

JOURNAL OF TRACE AND MICROPROBE TECHNIQUES.
Marcel Dekker Journals, 270 Madison Ave., New York, NY 10016. TEL 212-696-9000. FAX 212-685-4540. *1207*

THE JOURNAL OF TRACE ELEMENTS IN EXPERIMENTAL MEDICINE.
John Wiley & Sons, Inc., Journals, (International Society for Trace Element Research in Humans) 605 Third Ave., New York, NY 10158. TEL 212-850-6000. FAX 212-850-6088. *3260*

JOURNAL OF TRANSPORTATION ENGINEERING.
American Society of Civil Engineers, 345 E. 47th St., New York, NY 10017-2398. TEL 212-705-7288. FAX 212-980-4681. *4652*

JOURNAL OF TRAUMA.
Williams & Wilkins, (American Association for the Surgery of Trauma) 428 E. Preston St., Baltimore, MD 21202. TEL 301-528-4000. FAX 301-528-4312. *3310*

JOURNAL OF TRAUMATIC STRESS.
Plenum Publishing Corp., 233 Spring St., New York, NY 10013-1578. TEL 212-620-8000. FAX 212-463-0742. *4034*

JOURNAL OF TRAVEL & TOURISM MARKETING.
Haworth Press, Inc., 10 Alice St., Binghamton, NY 13904-1580. TEL 800-342-9678. FAX 607-722-1424. *4773*

JOURNAL OF TRIBOLOGY.
American Society of Mechanical Engineers, 345 E. 47th St., New York, NY 10017. TEL 212-705-7722. *3691*

JOURNAL OF TROPICAL FOREST SCIENCE.
Forest Research Institute Malaysia, P.O. Box 201, Kepong, 52109 Kuala Lumpur, Malaysia. *2103*

JOURNAL OF TURBOMACHINERY.
American Society of Mechanical Engineers, 345 E. 47th St., New York, NY 10017. TEL 212-705-7722. *1934*

JOURNAL OF ULTRASOUND IN MEDICINE.
American Institute for Ultrasound in Medicine, 4405 East-West Hwy, Ste. 504, Bethesda, MD 20814. *3119*

JOURNAL OF UNDERGRADUATE MATHEMATICS.
Guilford College, Department of Mathematics, Greensboro, NC 27410. *3042*

JOURNAL OF UNDERGRADUATE RESEARCH IN PHYSICS.
Guilford College, Department of Physics, (American Institute of Physics) Guilford, NC 27410. FAX 919-854-3606. *3823*

JOURNAL OF URBAN ANALYSIS AND PUBLIC MANAGEMENT.
Gordon and Breach Science Publishers, 270 Eighth Ave., New York, NY 10011. TEL 212-206-8900. FAX 212-645-2459. *2490*

JOURNAL OF UROLOGY.
Williams & Wilkins, (American Urological Association) 428 E. Preston St., Baltimore, MD 21202. TEL 301-528-4000. FAX 301-528-4312. *3388*

JOURNAL OF VACUUM SCIENCE AND TECHNOLOGY. PART A. VACUUM, SURFACES AND FILMS.
American Institute of Physics, (American Vacuum Society) 335 E. 45th St., New York, NY 10017. TEL 212-661-9404. *3823*

JOURNAL OF VACUUM SCIENCE AND TECHNOLOGY. PART B. MICROELECTRONICS PROCESSING AND PHENOMENA.
American Institute of Physics, (American Vacuum Society) 335 E. 45th St., New York, NY 10017. TEL 212-661-9404. *3823*

JOURNAL OF VASCULAR AND INTERVENTIONAL RADIOLOGY.
Radiological Society of North America, Inc., 2021 Spring Rd., Ste. 600, Oak Brook, IL 60521. TEL 708-571-7819. FAX 708-571-7837. *3360*

JOURNAL OF VASCULAR SURGERY.
Mosby - Year Book, Inc. (Society for Vascular Surgery) 11830 Westline Industrial Dr., St. Louis, MO 63146. TEL 800-325-4117. FAX 314-432-1380. *3381*

JOURNAL OF VERTEBRATE PALEONTOLOGY.
Society of Vertebrate Paleontology, W. 436 Nebraska Hall, University of Nebraska, Lincoln, NE 68588-0542. TEL 402-472-4604. *3658*

JOURNAL OF VESTIBULAR RESEARCH: EQUILIBRIUM AND ORIENTATION.
Pergamon Press, Inc., Journals Division, 660 White Plains Rd., Tarrytown, NY 10591-5153. TEL 914-524-9200. FAX 914-333-2444. *573*

JOURNAL OF VETERINARY INTERNAL MEDICINE.
J.B. Lippincott Co., (American College of Veterinary Internal Medicine) E. Washington Sq., Philadelphia, PA 19105. TEL 215-238-4200. *4812*

JOURNAL OF VIBRATION AND ACOUSTICS.
American Society of Mechanical Engineers, 22 Law Dr., Box 2300, Fairfield, NJ 07007-2300. TEL 800-321-2633. *1934*

JOURNAL OF VINYL TECHNOLOGY.
Society of Plastics Engineers, Inc., 14 Fairfield Dr., Brookfield, CT 06804-0403. TEL 203-775-0471. FAX 203-775-8490. *3863*

JOURNAL OF VIROLOGICAL METHODS.
Elsevier Science Publishers B.V., P.O. Box 211, 1000 AE Amsterdam, Netherlands. TEL 020-5803911. FAX 020-5803598. *554*

JOURNAL OF VISUAL COMMUNICATION AND IMAGE REPRESENTATION.
Academic Press, Inc., Journal Division, 1250 Sixth Ave., San Diego, CA 92101. TEL 619-230-1840. FAX 619-699-6800. *1422*

JOURNAL OF VISUAL IMPAIRMENT & BLINDNESS.
American Foundation for the Blind, Inc., 15 W. 16th St., New York, NY 10011. TEL 212-620-2000. FAX 212-620-2105. *2293*

JOURNAL OF VOICE.
Raven Press, (Voice Foundation) 1185 Ave. of the Americas, New York, NY 10036. TEL 212-930-9500. FAX 212-869-3495. *3315*

JOURNAL OF VOLCANOLOGY AND GEOTHERMAL RESEARCH.
Elsevier Science Publishers B.V., P.O. Box 211, 1000 AE Amsterdam, Netherlands. TEL 020-5803911. FAX 020-5803598. *1592*

JOURNAL OF WATER RESOURCES PLANNING AND MANAGEMENT.
American Society of Civil Engineers, 345 E. 47th St., New York, NY 10017-2398. TEL 212-705-7288. FAX 212-980-4681. *1870*

JOURNAL OF WILDERNESS MEDICINE.
Chapman & Hall, (Wilderness Medical Society) 2-6 Boundary Row, London SE1 8HN, England. TEL 071-865-0066. FAX 071-522-9623. *3372*

JOURNAL OF WILDLIFE DISEASES.
Wildlife Disease Association, Inc., 224 S.E. 16th St., Box 886, Ames, IA 50010. TEL 515-233-1931. *4812*

JOURNAL OF WIND ENERGY TECHNOLOGY.
Windbooks, Inc., Box 4008, St. Johnsbury, VT 05819. TEL 802-748-2425. *1812*

JOURNAL OF WIND ENGINEERING AND INDUSTRIAL AERODYNAMICS.
Elsevier Science Publishers B.V., (International Association for Wind Engineering) P.O. Box 211, 1000 AE Amsterdam, Netherlands. TEL 020-5803911. FAX 020-5803598. *1934*

JOURNAL OF WOMEN AND AGING.
Haworth Press, Inc., 10 Alice St., Binghamton, NY 13904. TEL 800-342-9678. FAX 607-722-1424. *4860*

JOURNAL OF WOOD CHEMISTRY AND TECHNOLOGY.
Marcel Dekker Journals, 270 Madison Ave., New York, NY 10016. TEL 212-696-9000. FAX 212-685-4540. *1181*

JOURNAL OF WORLD HISTORY.
University of Hawaii Press, Journals Department, (World History Association) 2840 Kolowalu St., Honolulu, HI 96822. TEL 808-956-8833. FAX 808-988-6052. *2316*

JOURNAL OF WORLD PREHISTORY.
Plenum Publishing Corp., 233 Spring St., New York, NY 10013-1578. TEL 212-620-8000. FAX 212-463-0742. *276*

JOURNAL OF X-RAY SCIENCE AND TECHNOLOGY.
Academic Press, Inc., Journal Division, 1250 Sixth Ave., San Diego, CA 92101. TEL 619-230-1840. FAX 619-699-6800. *3823*

JOURNAL OF YOUTH AND ADOLESCENCE.
Plenum Publishing Corp., 233 Spring St., New York, NY 10013-1578. TEL 212-620-8000. FAX 212-463-0742. *1239*

JOURNAL OF ZOO AND WILDLIFE MEDICINE.
American Association of Zoo Veterinarians, 3400 Girard Ave., Philadelphia, PA 19104-1196. TEL 215-387-9094. FAX 215-387-8733. *4812*

JUDICATURE.
American Judicature Society, 25 E. Washington, Ste. 1600, Chicago, IL 60602-1805. *2732*

KANSAS ENTOMOLOGICAL SOCIETY. JOURNAL.
Kansas Entomological Society, Box 1897, Lawrence, KS 66044-8897. TEL 913-843-1221. FAX 913-843-1274. *535*

KANSAS WORKS.
Ellsworth Reporter, Box 7, 220 Court St., Ellsworth, KS 67439. TEL 913-472-4835. FAX 913-472-3268. *675*

KAOGU.
Science Press, Marketing and Sales Department, (Chinese Academy of Sciences, Institute of Archaeolgoy) 16 Donghuangchenggen Beijie, Beijing 100707, People's Republic of China. TEL 4010642. FAX 4012180. *276*

KAOGU XUEBAO.
Science Press, Marketing and Sales Department, (Chinese Academy of Sciences, Institute of Archaeology) 16 Donghuangchenggen Beijie, Beijing 100707, People's Republic of China. TEL 4010642. FAX 4012180. *276*

KENTUCKY ACADEMY OF SCIENCE. TRANSACTIONS.
Kentucky Academy of Science, c/o Vardley Wiedeman, University of Louisville, Louisville, KY 40292. TEL 502-588-5943. *4320*

KENTUCKY MEDICAL ASSOCIATION. JOURNAL.
Kentucky Medical Association, 301 N. Hurstbourne Ln., Ste. 200, Louisville, KY 40222-5142. TEL 502-459-9790. FAX 502-459-9796. *3119*

KEXUE TONGBAO.
Science Press, Marketing and Sales Department, (Chinese Academy of Sciences) 16 Donghuangchenggen Beijie, Beijing 100707, People's Republic of China. TEL 4010642. FAX 4012180. *4320*

KIDNEY.
National Kidney Foundation, 30 East 33rd St., New York, NY 10016. TEL 212-889-2210. *3388*

KIDNEY DISEASES.
Marcel Dekker, Inc., 270 Madison Ave., New York, NY 10016. TEL 212-696-9000. FAX 212-685-4540. *3388*

KIMIKA.
Kapisanan ng mga Kimiko sa Pilipinas, P.O. Box CM70, Murphy District Rd., Santolan Rd., Quezon City, Philippines. TEL 2-996868. *1182*

KINETICS AND CATALYSIS.
Plenum Publishing Corp., Consultants Bureau, (Russian Academy of Sciences) 233 Spring St., New York, NY 10013-1578. TEL 212-620-8468. FAX 212-463-0742. *1228*

KING SAUD UNIVERSITY. JOURNAL. ADMINISTRATIVE SCIENCES.
King Saud University, University Libraries, P.O. Box 22480, Riyadh 11495, Saudi Arabia. TEL 4676148. FAX 4676162. *676*

KING SAUD UNIVERSITY. JOURNAL. AGRICULTURAL SCIENCES.
King Saud University, University Libraries, P.O. Box 22480, Riyadh 11495, Saudi Arabia. TEL 4676148. FAX 4676162. *103*

KING SAUD UNIVERSITY. JOURNAL. ARCHITECTURE AND PLANNING.
King Saud University, University Libraries, P.O. Box 22480, Riyadh 11495, Saudi Arabia. TEL 4676148. FAX 4676162. *2491*

KING SAUD UNIVERSITY. JOURNAL. ARTS.
King Saud University, University Libraries, P.O. Box 22480, Riyadh 11495, Saudi Arabia. TEL 4676148. FAX 4676162. *332*

KING SAUD UNIVERSITY. JOURNAL. EDUCATIONAL SCIENCES.
King Saud University, University Libraries, P.O. Box 22480, Riyadh 11495, Saudi Arabia. TEL 4676148. FAX 4676162. *1644*

KING SAUD UNIVERSITY. JOURNAL. ENGINEERING SCIENCES.
King Saud University, University Libraries, P.O. Box 22480, Riyadh 11495, Saudi Arabia. TEL 4676148. FAX 4676162. *1829*

KING SAUD UNIVERSITY. JOURNAL. SCIENCES.
King Saud University, University Libraries, P.O Box 22480, Riyadh 11495, Saudi Arabia. TEL 4676148. FAX 4676162. *4320*

KNOWLEDGE-BASED SYSTEMS.
Butterworth - Heinemann Ltd. Linacre House, Jordan Hill, Oxford OX2 8DP, England. TEL 0865-310366. FAX 0865-310898. *1409*

KODO RYOHO KENKYU.
Kodo Ryoho Gakkai, c/o Yuji Sakano, Sec.-Gen., Dept. of Health Sciences, School of Human Sciences, Waseda University, Mikajima 2-579-15, Tokorozawa, Saitama 359, Japan. TEL 03-3203-4141. FAX 03-3203-4141-764413. *4034*

KONGJIAN KEXUE XUEBAO.
Science Press, Marketing and Sales Department, 16 Donghuangchenggen Beijie, Beijing 100707, People's Republic of China. TEL 4010642. FAX 4012180. *58*

KONGQI DONGLIXUE XUEBAO.
Zhongguo Kongqi Dongli Yanjiu yu Fazhan Zhongxin, P.O. Box 211, Mianyang, Sichuan 621000, People's Republic of China. TEL 24012. *3844*

KONINKLIJKE NEDERLANDSE AKADEMIE VAN WETENSCHAPPEN. AFDELING LETTERKUNDE. VERHANDELINGEN. NIEUWE REEKS.
Elsevier Science Publishers B.V., Books Division, P.O. Box 211, 1000 AE Amsterdam, Netherlands. TEL 020-5803911. FAX 020-5803705. *2510*

KONINKLIJKE NEDERLANDSE AKADEMIE VAN WETENSCHAPPEN. AFDELING NATUURKUNDE. VERHANDELINGEN. TWEEDE REEKS.
Elsevier Science Publishers B.V., Books Division, P.O. Box 211, 1000 AE Amsterdam, Netherlands. TEL 020-5803911. FAX 020-5803705. *4321*

KOREAN STUDIES.
University of Hawaii Press, Journals Department, (University of Hawaii, Center for Korean Studies) 2840 Kolowalu St., Honolulu, HI 96822. TEL 808-956-8833. FAX 808-988-6052. *3640*

KRONOS.
University of the Western Cape, Institute for Historical Research, Private Bag X17, Bellville 7530, South Africa. FAX 021-959-2616. *2333*

KUNCHONG XUEBAO.
Science Press, Marketing and Sales Department, (Chinese Academy of Sciences, Institute of Zoology) 16 Donghuangchenggen Beijie, Beijing 100707, People's Republic of China. TEL 4010642. FAX 4012180. *535*

L I T: LITERATURE INTERPRETATION THEORY.
Gordon and Breach Science Publishers, 270 Eighth Ave., New York, NY 10011. TEL 212-206-8900. FAX 212-645-2459. *2931*

LAB ANIMAL.
Nature Publishing Co. 65 Bleecker St., New York, NY 10012. TEL 212-477-9600. *3261*

LABMEDICA.
Globetech Publishing, 30 Cannon Rd., Wilton, CT 06897. TEL 203-762-3432. FAX 203-762-8640. *3261*

LABORATORY ANIMAL SCIENCE.
American Association for Laboratory Animal Science, 70 Timber Creek Dr., Ste. 5, Cordova, TN 38018. *3261*

LABORATORY INFORMATION MANAGEMENT.
Elsevier Science Publishers B.V., P.O. Box 211, 1000 AE Amsterdam, Netherlands. TEL 020-5803911. FAX 020-5803598. *3261*

LABORATORY INVESTIGATION.
Williams & Wilkins, (United States and Canadian Academy of Pathology) 428 E. Preston St., Baltimore, MD 21202. TEL 301-528-4000. FAX 301-528-4312. *3261*

LABORATORY MEDICINE.
American Society of Clinical Pathologists, 2100 W. Harrison St., Chicago, IL 60612. TEL 312-738-4890. FAX 312-738-1619. *3121*

LABORATORY ROBOTICS AND AUTOMATION.
V C H Verlagsgesellschaft mbH, Postfach 101161, 6940 Weinheim, Germany. TEL 06201-602-0. FAX 06201-602-328. *1414*

LABORATORY TECHNIQUES IN BIOCHEMISTRY AND MOLECULAR BIOLOGY.
Elsevier Science Publishers B.V., Books Division, P.O. Box 211, 1000 AE Amsterdam, Netherlands. TEL 020-5803911. FAX 020-5803705. *479*

LABOUR HISTORY.
Australian Society for the Study of Labour History, Faculty of Economics, Sydney University, N.S.W. 2006, Australia. FAX 61-2-552-3015. *986*

LE LAIT.
Editions Scientifiques Elsevier, (Institut National de la Recherche Agronomique (INRA)) 29, rue Buffon, 75005 Paris, France. TEL 47-07-11-22. FAX 43-36-80-93. *201*

LANCET (EDITION FRANCAISE).
Editions Scientifiques Elsevier, 29, rue Buffon, 75005 Paris, France. *3121*

LANCET (NORTH AMERICAN EDITION).
Williams & Wilkins, 428 E. Preston St., Baltimore, MD 21202. TEL 301-528-4000. FAX 301-528-4312. *3121*

LAND USE POLICY.
Butterworth - Heinemann Ltd. Linacre House, Jordan Hill, Oxford OX2 8DP, England. TEL 0865-310366. FAX 0865-310898. *2491*

LANDSCAPE ECOLOGY.
S P B Academic Publishing b.v., P.O. Box 97747, 2509 GC The Hague, Netherlands. *1962*

LANE STUDIES IN REGIONAL GOVERNMENT.
University of California Press, 2120 Berkeley Way, Berkeley, CA 94720. TEL 415-642-4247. FAX 415-643-7127. *4066*

LANGUAGE ACQUISITION.
Lawrence Erlbaum Associates, Inc., 365 Broadway, Hillsdale, NJ 07642. TEL 201-666-4110. FAX 201-666-2394. *2823*

LANGUAGE AND COGNITIVE PROCESSES.
Lawrence Erlbaum Associates Ltd., 27 Palmeira Mansions, Church Rd., Hove, E. Sussex BN3 2FA, England. TEL 0273-207411. FAX 0273-205612. *2823*

LANGUAGE & COMMUNICATION.
Pergamon Press, Inc., Journals Division, 660 White Plains Rd., Tarrytown, NY 10591-5153. TEL 914-524-9200. FAX 914-333-2444. *2823*

LANGUAGE, CULTURE AND CURRICULUM.
Multilingual Matters Ltd., (Linguistic Institute of Ireland) Bank House, 8a Hill Rd., Clevedon, Avon BS21 7HH, England. TEL 0272-876519. FAX 0272-343096. *2823*

LANGUAGE INTERNATIONAL.
John Benjamins Publishing Co., Amsteldijk 44, P.O. Box 75577, 1070 AN Amsterdam, Netherlands. TEL 020-6738156. FAX 020-6739773. *2823*

LANGUAGE OF DANCE.
Gordon & Breach Science Publishers, 270 Eighth Ave., New York, NY 10011. TEL 212-206-8900. FAX 212-645-2459. *1531*

LANGUAGE SCIENCES.
Pergamon Press plc, Headington Hill Hall, Oxford OX3 0BW, England. TEL 0865-794141. FAX 0865-743911. *2824*

LANGUAGES OF DESIGN.
Elsevier Science Publishers B.V., P.O. Box 211, 1000 AE Amsterdam, Netherlands. TEL 020-5803911. FAX 020-5803598. *2856*

REFEREED SERIALS

LARGE ANIMAL VETERINARIAN.
Watt Publishing Co., Sandstone Bldg., 122 S. Wesley Ave., Mt. Morris, IL 61054-1497. TEL 815-734-4171. *220*

LARYNGOSCOPE.
Triological Foundation, Inc., (American Laryngological, Rhinological and Otological Society) 10 S. Broadway, Ste. 1401, St. Louis, MO 63102-1714. TEL 314-621-6550. FAX 314-621-6688. *3315*

LASER CHEMISTRY.
Harwood Academic Publishers, 270 Eighth Ave., New York, NY 10011. TEL 212-206-8900. FAX 212-645-2459. *3854*

LASER SCIENCE AND TECHNOLOGY.
Harwood Academic Publishers, 270 Eighth Ave., New York, NY 10011. TEL 212-206-8900. FAX 212-645-2459. *3855*

LASERS & OPTRONICS.
Gordon Publications, Inc., 301 Gibraltar Dr., Morris Plains, NJ 07950-0650. TEL 201-292-5100. FAX 201-898-9281. *3855*

LASERS IN ENGINEERING.
Gordon and Breach Scientific Publishers, 270 Eighth Ave., New York, NY 10011. TEL 212-206-8900. FAX 212-645-2459. *3855*

LASERS IN MEDICINE.
Excerpta Medica P.O. Box 548, 1000 AM Amsterdam, Netherlands. TEL 020-5803911. FAX 020-5803222. *3177*

LASERS IN SURGERY AND MEDICINE.
John Wiley & Sons, Inc., Journals, 605 Third Ave., New York, NY 10158. TEL 212-850-6000. FAX 212-850-6088. *3381*

LASERS IN THE LIFE SCIENCES.
Harwood Academic Publishers, 270 Eighth Ave., New York, NY 10011. TEL 212-206-8900. FAX 212-645-2459. *3855*

LATIN AMERICAN ANTIQUITY.
Society for American Archaeology, 808 17th St., N.W., Washington, DC 20006. *277*

LAW AND HISTORY REVIEW.
University of Illinois Press, (American Society for Legal History) 54 E. Gregory Dr., Champaign, IL 61820. TEL 217-244-0626. FAX 217-244-8082. *2644*

LAW AND HUMAN BEHAVIOR.
Plenum Publishing Corp., 233 Spring St., New York, NY 10013-1578. TEL 212-620-8000. FAX 212-463-0742. *2644*

LAW AND SOCIAL INQUIRY.
University of Chicago Press, Journals Division, (American Bar Foundation) 5720 S. Woodlawn Ave., Chicago, IL 60637. TEL 312-753-3347. FAX 312-702-0694. *2644*

LAW, SOCIETY, AND POLICY.
Plenum Publishing Corp., 233 Spring St., New York, NY 10013-1578. TEL 212-620-8000. FAX 212-463-0742. *2646*

LAWRENCE BERKELEY LABORATORY. MATERIALS AND CHEMICAL SCIENCES DIVISION. ANNUAL REPORT.
University of California, Berkeley, Materials and Chemical Sciences Division, Berkeley, CA 94720. TEL 415-422-1100. *1919*

LAWRENCE REVIEW OF NATURAL PRODUCTS NEWSLETTER.
Facts and Comparisons, 111 West Port Plaza, Ste. 423, St. Louis, MO 63146-3098. FAX 314-878-5563. *3734*

LEARNING AND INSTRUCTION.
Pergamon Press, Inc., Journals Division, (European Association for Research on Learning and Instruction) 660 White Plains Rd., Tarrytown, NY 10591-5153. TEL 914-524-9200. FAX 914-333-2444. *1645*

LECTURES IN ECONOMICS: THEORY, INSTITUTIONS, POLICY.
Elsevier Science Publishers B.V., Books Division, P.O. Box 211, 1000 AE Amsterdam, Netherlands. TEL 020-5803911. FAX 020-5803705. *896*

THE LEECH.
University of the Witwatersrand Medical School, 7 York Rd., Parktown 2193, South Africa. TEL 011-643-4318. FAX 011-647-2451. *3122*

LEGAL REFERENCE SERVICES QUARTERLY.
Haworth Press, Inc., 10 Alice St., Binghamton, NY 13904. TEL 800-342-9678. FAX 607-722-1424. *2768*

LEIDEN BOTANICAL SERIES.
Rijksherbarium - Hortus Botanicus, Publications Department, P.O. Box 9514, 2300 RA Leiden, Netherlands. *508*

LEISURE SCIENCES.
Taylor & Francis, 1900 Frost Rd., Ste. 101, Bristol, PA 19007. TEL 215-785-5800. FAX 215-785-5515. *2739*

LENS AND EYE TOXICITY RESEARCH.
Marcel Dekker Journals, (International Society of Ocular Toxicology) 270 Madison Ave., New York, NY 10016. TEL 212-696-9000. FAX 212-685-4540. *3302*

LEONARDO: ART SCIENCE AND TECHNOLOGY.
Pergamon Press, Inc., Journals Division, (International Society for the Arts, Sciences and Technology) 660 White Plains Rd., Tarrytown, NY 10591-5153. TEL 914-524-9200. FAX 914-333-2444. *334*

LEONARDO MUSIC JOURNAL.
Pergamon Press, Inc., Journals Division, 660 White Plains Rd., Tarrytown, NY 10591-5153. TEL 914-524-9200. FAX 914-333-2444. *3561*

LEUKEMIA.
Macmillan Publishing Company, Macmillan Research, (Leukemia Society of America) 866 Third Ave., New York, NY 10022. TEL 212-319-1216. *3177*

LEUKEMIA AND LYMPHOMA.
Harwood Academic Publishers, 270 Eighth Ave., New York, NY 10011. TEL 212-206-8900. FAX 212-645-2459. *3273*

LEUKEMIA RESEARCH.
Pergamon Press, Inc., Journals Division, 660 White Plains Rd., Tarrytown, NY 10591-5153. TEL 914-524-9200. FAX 914-333-2444. *3273*

LIBRARY ACQUISITIONS: PRACTICE AND THEORY.
Pergamon Press, Inc., Journals Division, 660 White Plains Rd., Tarrytown, NY 10591-5153. TEL 914-524-9200. FAX 914-333-2444. *2769*

LIBRARY & ARCHIVAL SECURITY.
Haworth Press, Inc., 10 Alice St., Binghamton, NY 13904. TEL 800-342-9678. FAX 607-722-1424. *2769*

LIBRARY HI TECH JOURNAL.
Pierian Press, Box 1808, Ann Arbor, MI 48106. TEL 313-434-5530. FAX 313-434-6409. *2798*

LIBRARY OF ANALYTICAL PSYCHOLOGY SERIES.
Brunner-Mazel Publishing Co., (Society of Analytical Psychology) 19 Union Sq. W., New York, NY 10003. TEL 212-924-3344. *4034*

LIBRARY OF ANTHROPOLOGY.
Gordon & Breach Science Publishers, 270 Eighth Ave., New York, NY 10011. TEL 212-206-8900. FAX 212-645-2459. *244*

LIBRARY QUARTERLY.
University of Chicago Press, Journals Division, (University of Chicago Graduate Library School) 5720 S. Woodlawn Ave., Chicago, IL 60637. TEL 312-753-3347. FAX 712-702-0694. *2771*

LIFE CHEMISTRY REPORTS.
Harwood Academic Publishers, 270 Eighth Ave., New York, NY 10011. TEL 212-206-8900. FAX 212-245-2459. *1183*

LIFE SCIENCES (1973).
Pergamon Press, Inc., Journals Division, 660 White Plains Rd., Tarrytown, NY 10591-5153. TEL 914-524-9200. FAX 914-333-2444. *4323*

LIMNETICA.
Asociacion Espanola de Limnologia, Museo Nacional de Ciencias Naturales, C. Jose Gutierrez Abascal, 2, 28006 Madrid, Spain. TEL 91-4649881. FAX 91-3974168. *1599*

LIMNOLOGY AND OCEANOGRAPHY.
American Society of Limnology and Oceanography, Inc., School of Oceanography, WB-10, University of Washington, Seattle, WA 98195. FAX 206-543-6073. *1599*

LINEAR ALGEBRA AND ITS APPLICATIONS.
Elsevier Science Publishing Co., Inc. (New York), 655 Ave. of the Americas, New York, NY 10010. TEL 212-989-5800. FAX 212-633-3965. *3043*

LINEAR AND MULTILINEAR ALGEBRA.
Gordon and Breach Science Publishers, 270 Eighth Ave., New York, NY 10011. TEL 212-206-8900. FAX 212-645-2459. *3043*

LINGUA.
North-Holland P.O. Box 211, 1000 AE Amsterdam, Netherlands. TEL 020-5803911. FAX 020-5803598. *2825*

LINGUISTIC INQUIRY.
M I T Press, 55 Hayward St., Cambridge, MA 02142. TEL 617-253-2889. FAX 617-258-6779. *2826*

LINYE KEXUE.
Science Press, Marketing and Sales Department, (Chinese Institute of Forestry) 16 Donghuangchenggen Beijie, Beijing 100707, People's Republic of China. TEL 4010642. FAX 4012180. *2104*

LIPID TECHNOLOGY.
Elsevier Science Publishers Ltd., Crown House, Linton Rd., Barking, Essex IG11 8JU, England. TEL 081-594-7272. FAX 081-594-5942. *479*

LIQUID CRYSTALS.
Taylor & Francis Ltd., Rankine Rd., Basingstoke, Hants RG24 0PR, England. TEL 0256-840366. FAX 0256-479438. *1211*

LITHIUM.
Churchill Livingstone Medical Journals, Robert Stevenson House, 1-3 Baxter's Pl., Leith Walk, Edinburgh EH1 3AF, Scotland. TEL 031-556-2424. FAX 031-558-1278. *3344*

LITHOLOGY AND MINERAL RESOURCES.
Plenum Publishing Corp., Consultants Bureau, (Russian Academy of Sciences) 233 Spring St., New York, NY 10013-1578. TEL 212-620-8468. FAX 212-463-0742. *1571*

LITHOS.
Elsevier Science Publishers B.V., P.O. Box 211, 1000 AH Amsterdam, Netherlands. TEL 020-5803911. FAX 020-5803598. *1571*

LITHUANIAN MATHEMATICAL JOURNAL.
Plenum Publishing Corp., Consultants Bureau, 233 Spring St., New York, NY 10013-1578. TEL 212-620-8468. FAX 212-463-0742. *3043*

LIVESTOCK PRODUCTION SCIENCE.
Elsevier Science Publishers B.V., (European Association for Animal Production) P.O. Box 211, 1000 AE Amsterdam, Netherlands. TEL 020-5803911. FAX 020-5803598. *220*

LIXUE JINZHAN.
Zhongguo Kexueyuan, Lixue Yanjiusuo, 15 Zhongguancun Lu, Beijing 100080, People's Republic of China. TEL 2554108. FAX 86-1-2561284. *3844*

LIXUE XUEBAO.
Science Press, Marketing and Sales Department, (Chinese Society of Theoretical and Applied Mechanics) 16 Donghuangchenggen Beijie, Beijing 100707, People's Republic of China. TEL 4010642. FAX 4012180. *3844*

LIXUE YU SHIJIAN.
Science Press, Marketing and Sales Department, 16 Donghuangchenggen Beijie, Beijing 100707, People's Republic of China. TEL 4010642. FAX 4012180. *1934*

LOEB CLASSICAL LIBRARY.
Harvard University Press, 79 Garden St., Cambridge, MA 02138. TEL 617-495-2600. FAX 617-495-5898. *2935*

LONDON MATHEMATICAL SOCIETY. MONOGRAPHS.
Academic Press, Inc., 1250 Sixth Ave., San Diego, CA 92101. TEL 619-231-0926. FAX 619-699-6715. *3044*

LONG RANGE PLANNING.
Pergamon Press, Inc., Journals Division, (Strategic Planning Society) 660 White Plains Rd., Tarrytown, NY 10591-5153. TEL 914-524-9200. FAX 914-333-2444. *1018*

LORIS.
Wildlife & Nature Protection Society of Sri Lanka, Chaitiya Rd., Fort, Colombo 1, Sri Lanka. TEL 25248. FAX 941-580721. *1491*

LOSS, GRIEF & CARE.
Haworth Press, Inc., 10 Alice St., Binghamton, NY 13904. TEL 800-342-8678. FAX 607-722-1424. *4034*

LUBRICATION SCIENCE.
Leaf Coppin Publishing Co., P.O. Box 111, Deal, Kent CT14 6SX, England. TEL 0304-360241. *3841*

LUNG BIOLOGY IN HEALTH AND DISEASE.
Marcel Dekker, Inc., 270 Madison Ave., New York, NY 10016. TEL 212-696-9000. FAX 212-685-4540. *3365*

LUNG CANCER.
Elsevier Science Publishers B.V., (International Association for the Study of Lung Cancer) P.O. Box 211, 1000 AE Amsterdam, Netherlands. TEL 020-5803911. FAX 020-5803598. *3199*

LYMPHOKINE AND CYTOKINE RESEARCH.
Mary Ann Liebert, Inc., 1651 Third Ave., New York, NY 10128. TEL 212-289-2300. FAX 212-289-4697. *3273*

LYSOSOMES IN BIOLOGY AND PATHOLOGY.
Elsevier Science Publishers B.V., Books Division, P.O. Box 211, 1000 AE Amsterdam, Netherlands. TEL 020-5803911. FAX 020-5803705. *446*

M C L C LETTERS.
Gordon & Breach Science Publishers, 270 Eighth Ave., New York, NY 10011. TEL 212-206-8900, 0734-560080. FAX 0734-568211. *1211*

M M I PRESS POLYMER MONOGRAPH SERIES.
Harwood Academic Publishers, 270 Eighth Ave., New York, NY 10011. TEL 212-206-8900. FAX 212-645-2459. *3044*

M M I PRESS SYMPOSIUM SERIES.
Harwood Academic Publishers, 270 Eighth Ave., New York, NY 10011. TEL 212-206-8900. FAX 212-645-2459. *3044*

MACHINE INTELLIGENCE AND PATTERN RECOGNITION.
Elsevier Science Publishers B.V., Books Division, P.O. Box 211, 1000 AE Amsterdam, Netherlands. TEL 020-5803911. FAX 020-5803705. *1409*

MACHINE LEARNING.
Kluwer Academic Publishers, 101 Philip Dr., Norwell, MA 02061. TEL 617-871-6300. FAX 617-871-6528. *1398*

MACHINE - MEDIATED LEARNING.
Taylor & Francis, 1900 Frost Rd., Ste. 101, Bristol, PA 19007. TEL 215-785-5800. FAX 215-785-5515. *1417*

MACROMOLECULES.
American Chemical Society, 1155 16th St., N.W., Washington, DC 20036. TEL 202-872-4363. FAX 202-872-4615. *1220*

MADRAS AGRICULTURAL JOURNAL.
Madras Agricultural Students' Union, Tamil Nadu Agricultural University Campus, Coimbatore 641 003, India. *106*

MAGNETIC AND ELECTRICAL SEPARATION.
Gordon & Breach Science Publishers, 270 Eighth Ave., New York, NY 10011. TEL 212-206-8900. FAX 212-645-2459. *3824*

MAGNETIC RESONANCE IMAGING.
Pergamon Press, Inc., Journals Division, (Society for Magnetic Resonance Imaging) 660 White Plains Rd., Tarrytown, NY 10591-5153. TEL 914-524-9200. FAX 914-333-2444. *3360*

MAGNETIC RESONANCE IN MEDICINE.
Academic Press, Inc., Journal Division, 1250 Sixth Ave., San Diego, CA 92101. TEL 619-230-1840. FAX 619-699-6800. *3360*

MAGNETIC RESONANCE REVIEW.
Gordon and Breach Science Publishers, 270 Eighth Ave., New York, NY 10011. TEL 212-206-8900. FAX 212-645-2459. *3824*

MAGNETOHYDRODYNAMICS.
Plenum Publishing Corp., Consultants Bureau, (Latvian Academy of Sciences) 233 Spring St., New York, NY 10013-1578. TEL 212-620-8468. FAX 212-463-0742. *1902*

MAGNETS IN YOUR FUTURE.
L H Publishing Agency, (A Z Industries, Inc.) Box 250, Ash Flat, AR 72513. TEL 501-856-3877. FAX 501-856-3590. *1902*

MAGYAR EGYHAZTORTENETI VAZLATOK.
International Society of Toronto for Hungarian Church History, Regis College, 15 St. Mary St., Toronto, Ont. M4Y 2R5, Canada. TEL 416-922-2476. FAX 416-922-2898. *2374*

AL-MAJALLAH AL-ARABIYYAH LIL-IDARAH.
Arab Administrative Development Organization, P.O. Box 17159, Amman, Jordan. TEL 814118. FAX 816972. *4066*

MAJALLAT AL-WAHDAH AL-IQTISADIYYAH AL-ARABIYYAH.
Majlis al-Wahdah al-Iqtisadiyyah al-Arabiyyah, Al-Amanah al-Aamah, P.O. Box 925100, Amman, Jordan. TEL 664329. *896*

MALAYSIAN JOURNAL OF SCIENCE.
University of Malaya Co-operative Bookshop Ltd., (University of Malaya, Faculty of Science) P.O. Box 1127, Jalan Pantai Baru, Kuala Lumpur, Malaysia. TEL 565000. *4323*

MAMMALIAN SPECIES.
American Society of Mammalogists, c/o Dr. H. Duane Smith, Sec.-Treas., Department of Zoology, Brigham Young University, Provo, UT 84602. TEL 801-378-2492. *587*

MANOA.
University of Hawaii Press, Journals Department, 2840 Kolowalu St., Honolulu, HI 96822. TEL 808-948-8833. FAX 808-988-6052. *2936*

MANUFACTURING RESEARCH AND TECHNOLOGY.
Elsevier Science Publishers B.V., Books Division, P.O. Box 211, 1000 AE Amsterdam, Netherlands. TEL 020-5803911. FAX 020-5803705. *1080*

MARINE AND PETROLEUM GEOLOGY.
Butterworth - Heinemann Ltd. (Geological Society) Linacre House, Jordan Hill, Oxford OX2 8DP, England. TEL 0865-310366. FAX 0865-310898. *1572*

MARINE BEHAVIOUR AND PHYSIOLOGY. SECTIONS A & B.
Gordon and Breach Science Publishers, 270 Eighth Ave., New York, NY 10011. TEL 212-206-8900. FAX 212-645-2459. *446*

MARINE CHEMISTRY.
Elsevier Science Publishers B.V., P.O. Box 211, 1000 AE Amsterdam, Netherlands. TEL 020-5803911. FAX 020-5803598. *1547*

MARINE ENVIRONMENTAL RESEARCH.
Elsevier Science Publishers Ltd., Crown House, Linton Rd., Barking, Essex IG11 8JU, England. TEL 081-594-7272. FAX 081-594-5942. *1977*

MARINE GEODESY.
Taylor & Francis, 1900 Frost Rd., Ste. 101, Bristol, PA 19007. TEL 215-785-5800. FAX 215-785-5515. *2256*

MARINE GEOLOGY.
Elsevier Science Publishers B.V., P.O. Box 211, 1000 AE Amsterdam, Netherlands. TEL 020-5803911. FAX 020-5803598. *1607*

MARINE GEOTECHNOLOGY.
Taylor & Francis, 1900 Frost Rd., Ste. 101, Bristol, PA 19007. TEL 215-785-5800. FAX 215-785-5515. *1607*

MARINE MICROPALEONTOLOGY.
Elsevier Science Publishers B.V., P.O. Box 211, 1000 AE Amsterdam, Netherlands. TEL 020-5803911. FAX 020-5803598. *3658*

MARINE MINING.
Taylor & Francis, 1900 Frost Rd., Ste. 101, Bristol, PA 19007. TEL 215-785-5800. FAX 215-785-5515. *3487*

MARINE POLICY.
Butterworth - Heinemann Ltd. Linacre House, Jordan Hill, OX2 8DP, England. TEL 0865-310366. FAX 0865-310898. *1608*

MARINE POLLUTION BULLETIN.
Pergamon Press, Inc., Journals Division, 660 White Plains Rd., Tarrytown, NY 10591-5153. TEL 914-524-9200. FAX 914-333-2444. *1978*

MARINE STRUCTURES, DESIGN, CONSTRUCTION AND SAFETY.
Elsevier Science Publishers Ltd., (International Ship and Offshore Structures Congress) Crown House, Linton Rd., Barking, Essex IG11 8JU, England. TEL 081-594-7272. FAX 081-594-5942. *1935*

MARINE TECHNOLOGY.
Society of Naval Architects and Marine Engineers, 601 Pavonia Ave., Jersey City, NJ 07306-2907. *4732*

MARINE TECHNOLOGY SOCIETY JOURNAL.
Marine Technology Society, Inc., 1828 L St., N.W., 9th Fl., Washington, DC 20036. TEL 202-775-5966. FAX 202-429-9417. *1608*

MARITIME POLICY AND MANAGEMENT.
Taylor & Francis Ltd., Rankine Rd., Basingstoke, Hants RG24 0PR, England. TEL 0256-840366. FAX 0256-479438. *4733*

MARKETING AND RESEARCH TODAY.
North-Holland (European Society for Opinion and Marketing Research) P.O. Box 211, 1000 AE Amsterdam, Netherlands. TEL 020-5803911. FAX 020-5803598. *1046*

MARKETING RESEARCH.
American Marketing Association, 250 S. Wacker Dr., Ste. 200, Chicago, IL 60606. TEL 312-648-0536. FAX 312-993-7542. *1046*

MARRIAGE & FAMILY REVIEW.
Haworth Press, Inc., 10 Alice St., Binghamton, NY 13904. TEL 800-342-9678. FAX 607-722-1424. *4442*

MARTIN CLASSICAL LECTURES.
Princeton University Press, (Oberlin College) 3175 Princeton Pike, Lawrenceville, NJ 08648. *1278*

MARYLAND HISTORIAN.
University of Maryland, Department of History, College Park, MD 20742. TEL 301-405-4331. *2317*

MASONRY SOCIETY JOURNAL.
Masonry Society, 2619 Spruce St., Boulder, CO 80302. TEL 303-939-9700. FAX 303-444-3239. *623*

MASS SPECTROMETRY REVIEWS.
John Wiley & Sons, Inc., Journals, 605 Third Ave., New York, NY 10158-0012. TEL 212-850-6000. FAX 212-850-6088. *3855*

REFEREED SERIALS

MASSACHUSETTS INSTITUTE OF TECHNOLOGY. FLIGHT TRANSPORTATION LABORATORY. F T L REPORTS AND MEMORANDA.
Massachusetts Institute of Technology, Department of Aeronautics and Astronautics, Rm. 33-412, Cambridge, MA 02139. TEL 617-253-2424. *58*

MASSACHUSETTS INSTITUTE OF TECHNOLOGY. RESEARCH LABORATORY OF ELECTRONICS. R L E PROGRESS REPORT.
Massachusetts Institute of Technology, Research Laboratory of Electronics, Cambridge, MA 02139. TEL 617-253-2566. FAX 617-258-7864. *1903*

MASTER'S THESES IN THE PURE AND APPLIED SCIENCES.
Plenum Publishing Corp., 233 Spring St., New York, NY 10013-1578. TEL 212-620-8000. FAX 212-463-0742. *4357*

MATEKON.
M. E. Sharpe, Inc., 80 Business Park Dr., Armonk, NY 10504. TEL 914-273-1800. FAX 914-273-2106. *679*

MATEMATICA APLICADA E COMPUTACIONAL.
Editora Campus Ltda. (Sociedade Brasileira de Matematica Aplicada e Computacional) Rua Barao de Itapagipe, 55 Rio Comprido, 20261 Rio de Janeiro-RJ, Brazil. TEL 021-293-6443. FAX 021-293-5683. *3065*

MATERIALS & MANUFACTURING PROCESSES.
Marcel Dekker Journals, 270 Madison Ave., New York, NY 10016. TEL 212-696-9000. FAX 212-685-4540. *1935*

MATERIALS AND PROCESSING REPORT.
Elsevier Science Publishing Co., Inc. (New York), 655 Ave. of the Americas, New York, NY 10010. TEL 212-989-5800. FAX 212-633-3965. *3412*

MATERIALS CHARACTERIZATION.
Elsevier Science Publishing Co., Inc. (New York), (International Metallographic Society Inc.) 655 Ave. of the Americas, New York, NY 10010. TEL 212-989-5800. FAX 212-633-3965. *3412*

MATERIALS CHEMISTRY AND PHYSICS.
Elsevier Sequoia S.A., P.O. Box 564, CH-1001 Lausanne, Switzerland. TEL 021-207381. FAX 021-235444. *1920*

MATERIALS EVALUATION.
American Society for Nondestructive Testing, 1711 Arlingate Lane, Box 28518, Columbus, OH 43228-0158. TEL 614-274-6003. FAX 614-274-6899. *1920*

MATERIALS LETTERS.
North-Holland (Materials Research Society) P.O. Box 211, 1000 AE Amsterdam, Netherlands. TEL 020-5803911. FAX 020-5803598. *3824*

MATERIALS PROCESSING: THEORY AND PRACTICES.
Elsevier Science Publishers B.V., Books Division, P.O. Box 211, 1000 AE Amsterdam, Netherlands. TEL 020-5803911. FAX 020-5803705. *3824*

MATERIALS RESEARCH BULLETIN.
Pergamon Press, Inc., Journals Division, 660 White Plains Rd, Tarrytown, NY 10591-5153. TEL 914-524-9200. FAX 914-333-2444. *1211*

MATERIALS SCIENCE AND ENGINEERING A: STRUCTURAL MATERIALS: PROPERTIES, MICROSTRUCTURES AND PROCESSING.
Elsevier Sequoia S.A., P.O. Box 564, CH-1001 Lausanne, Switzerland. TEL 021-207381. FAX 021-235444. *1920*

MATERIALS SCIENCE & ENGINEERING B: SOLID-STATE MATERIALS FOR ADVANCED TECHNOLOGY.
Elsevier Sequoia S.A., P.O. Box 564, CH-1001 Lausanne, Switzerland. TEL 021-207381. FAX 021-235444. *1920*

MATERIALS SCIENCE MONOGRAPHS.
Elsevier Science Publishers B.V., Books Division, P.O. Box 211, 1000 AE Amsterdam, Netherlands. TEL 020-5803911. FAX 020-5803705. *1830*

MATERIALS SCIENCE REPORTS.
North-Holland P.O. Box 211, 1000 AC Amsterdam, Netherlands. TEL 020-5803911. FAX 020-5803598. *3824*

MATERIALS SCIENCE RESEARCH.
Plenum Publishing Corp., 233 Spring St., New York, NY 10013-1578. TEL 212-620-8000. FAX 212-463-0742. *1920*

MATHEMATICAL AND COMPUTER MODELLING.
Pergamon Press, Inc., Journals Division, (International Association for Mathematical and Computer Modelling) 660 White Plains Rd., Tarrytown, NY 10591-5153. TEL 914-524-9200. FAX 914-333-2444. *3045*

MATHEMATICAL BIOSCIENCES.
Elsevier Science Publishing Co., Inc. (New York), 655 Ave. of the Americas, New York, NY 10010. TEL 212-989-5800. FAX 212-633-3965. *3045*

MATHEMATICAL CHEMISTRY.
Harwood Academic Publishers, 270 Eighth Ave., New York, NY 10011. TEL 212-206-8900. FAX 212-645-2459. *1183*

MATHEMATICAL GEOLOGY.
Plenum Publishing Corp., 233 Spring St., New York, NY 10013-1578. TEL 212-620-8000. FAX 212-463-0742. *1572*

MATHEMATICAL POPULATION STUDIES.
Gordon & Breach Science Publishers, 270 Eighth Ave., New York, NY 10011. TEL 212-206-8900. FAX 212-645-2459. *3984*

MATHEMATICAL PROGRAMMING.
North-Holland (Mathematical Programming Society) P.O. Box 211, 1000 AE Amsterdam, Netherlands. TEL 020-5803911. FAX 020-5803598. *3065*

MATHEMATICAL REPORTS.
Harwood Academic Publishers, 270 Eighth Ave., New York, NY 10011. TEL 212-206-8900. FAX 212-645-2459. *3046*

MATHEMATICAL REVIEWS.
American Mathematical Society, Box 1571, Annex Sta., Providence, RI 02901-9930. TEL 401-455-4000. *3063*

MATHEMATICAL SOCIAL SCIENCES.
North-Holland P.O. Box 211, 1000 AE Amsterdam, Netherlands. TEL 020-5803911. FAX 020-5803598. *3046*

MATHEMATICS AND COMPUTERS IN SIMULATION.
North-Holland (International Association for Mathematics and Computers in Simulation) P.O. Box 211, 1000 AE Amsterdam, Netherlands. TEL 020-5803911. FAX 020-5803598. *1435*

MATHEMATICS AND ITS APPLICATIONS.
Gordon & Breach Science Publishers, P.O. Box 90, Reading, Berkshire RG1 8JL, England. TEL 0734-560-080. FAX 0734-568-211. *3046*

MATHEMATICS EDUCATION RESEARCH JOURNAL.
Mathematics Education Research Group of Australasia, c/o P. Clarkson, Marcy Campus, Australian Catholic University, 251 Mt. Alexander Rd., Ascot Vale, Vic. 3032, Australia. TEL 03-373-3549. FAX 03-373-3405. *1754*

MATHEMATICS IN SCIENCE AND ENGINEERING.
Academic Press, Inc., 1250 Sixth Ave., San Diego, CA 92101. TEL 619-231-0926. FAX 619-699-6715. *3047*

MATHEMATICS OF COMPUTATION.
American Mathematical Society, Box 1571, Annex Sta., Providence, RI 02940-9930. TEL 401-455-4000. *3047*

MATHEMATICS OF OPERATIONS RESEARCH.
Institute of Management Sciences, 290 Westminister St., Providence, RI 02903. TEL 401-274-2525. *1398*

MATHEMATICS OF THE U S S R - IZVESTIYA.
American Mathematical Society, Box 1571, Annex Sta., Providence, RI 02901-9930. TEL 401-455-4000. *3047*

MATURITAS.
Elsevier Scientific Publishers Ireland Ltd., (International Menopause Society) P.O. Box 85, Limerick, Ireland. TEL 061-61944. FAX 061-62144. *2276*

MEASUREMENT TECHNIQUES.
Plenum Publishing Corp., Consultants Bureau, (Komitet po Delam Standartov Mer i Izmeritel'noy Tekhniki Soveta Ministrov S.S.S.R.) 233 Spring St., New York, NY 10013-1578. TEL 212-620-8468. FAX 212-463-0742. *3447*

MEASUREMENTS AND CONTROL.
Measurements & Data Corp., 2994 W. Liberty Ave., Pittsburgh, PA 15216. TEL 412-343-9666. *2524*

MEAT SCIENCE.
Elsevier Science Publishers Ltd., Crown House, Linton Rd., Barking, Essex IG11 8JU, England. TEL 081-594-7272. FAX 081-594-5942. *2077*

MECHANICAL ENGINEERING.
American Society of Mechanical Engineers, 345 E. 47th St., New York, NY 10017. TEL 212-705-7722. *1935*

MECHANICAL ENGINEERING SERIES.
Marcel Dekker, Inc., 270 Madison Ave., New York, NY 10016. TEL 212-696-9000. FAX 212-658-4540. *1935*

MECHANICS AND MATHEMATICAL METHODS - SERIES OF HANDBOOKS.
Elsevier Science Publishers B.V., Books Division, P.O. Box 211, 1000 AE Amsterdam, Netherlands. TEL 020-5803911. FAX 020-5803705. *3048*

MECHANICS OF COMPOSITE MATERIALS.
Plenum Publishing Corp., Consultants Bureau, (Latvian Academy of Sciences) 233 Spring St., New York, NY 10013. TEL 212-620-8468. FAX 212-463-0742. *1856*

MECHANICS OF MATERIALS.
North-Holland P.O. Box 211, 1000 AE Amsterdam, Netherlands. TEL 020-5803911. FAX 020-5803598. *1921*

MECHANICS OF STRUCTURES AND MACHINES.
Marcel Dekker Journals, 270 Madison Ave., New York, NY 10016. TEL 212-696-9000. FAX 212-685-4540. *1935*

MECHANICS RESEARCH COMMUNICATIONS.
Pergamon Press, Inc., Journals Division, (International Centre for Mechanical Sciences) 660 White Plains Rd., Tarrytown, NY 10591-5153. TEL 914-524-9200. FAX 914-333-2444. *1921*

MECHANISM AND MACHINE THEORY.
Pergamon Press, Inc., Journals Division, (International Federation for the Theory of Machines and Mechanisms) 660 White Plains Rd., Tarrytown, NY 10591-5153. TEL 914-524-9200. FAX 914-333-2444. *1935*

MECHANISMS OF AGEING AND DEVELOPMENT.
Elsevier Scientific Publishers Ireland Ltd., P.O. Box 85, Limerick, Ireland. TEL 061-61944. FAX 061-62144. *2276*

MECHANISMS OF DEVELOPMENT.
Elsevier Scientific Publishers Ireland Ltd., P.O. Box 85, Limerick, Ireland. TEL 061-61944. FAX 061-62144. *525*

MECHANISMS OF INORGANIC AND ORGANOMETALLIC REACTIONS.
Plenum Publishing Corp., 233 Spring St., New York, NY 10013-1578. TEL 212-620-8000. FAX 212-463-0742. *1214*

MECHATRONICS.
Pergamon Press, Inc., Journals Division, 660 White Plains Rd., Tarrytown, NY 10591-5153. TEL 914-524-9200. FAX 914-333-2444. *1935*

MEDIA.
Media & Marketing, Ltd., 1002 McDonald's Bldg., 46-54 Yee Wo Street, Causeway Bay, Hong Kong. TEL 852-577-2628. FAX 852-576-9171. *34*

MEDIATION QUARTERLY.
Jossey-Bass Inc., Publishers, (Academy of Family Mediators) 350 Sansome St., 5th Fl., San Francisco, CA 94104. TEL 415-433-1767. FAX 415-433-0499. *4035*

MEDICAL AND PEDIATRIC ONCOLOGY.
John Wiley & Sons, Inc., Journals, (International Society of Pediatric Oncology) 605 Third Ave., New York, NY 10158. TEL 212-850-6000. FAX 212-850-6088. *3200*

MEDICAL ANTHROPOLOGY.
Gordon & Breach Science Publishers, 270 Eighth Ave., New York, NY 10011. TEL 212-206-8900. FAX 212-645-2459. *244*

MEDICAL CARE.
J.B. Lippincott Co., (American Public Health Association, Medical Care Section) E. Washington Sq., Philadelphia, PA 19105. TEL 215-238-4200. *3125*

MEDICAL CARE REVIEW.
Health Administration Press, (Foundation of the American College of Healthcare Executives) 1021 E. Huron St., Ann Arbor, MI 48104-9990. TEL 312-943-0544. FAX 708-450-1618. *4118*

MEDICAL DECISION MAKING.
Hanley & Belfus, Inc., (Society for Medical Decision Making, Inc.) 210 S. 13th St., Philadelphia, PA 19107. TEL 215-546-7293. FAX 215-790-9330. *3125*

MEDICAL DOSIMETRY.
Pergamon Press, Inc., Journals Division, (American Association of Medical Dosimetrists) 660 White Plains Rd., Tarrytown, NY 10591-5153. TEL 914-524-9200. FAX 914-333-2444. *3360*

MEDICAL INFORMATICS.
Taylor and Francis Ltd., Rankine Rd., Basingstoke, Hants RG24 0PR, England. TEL 0256-840366. FAX 0256-479438. *3226*

MEDICAL PHYSICS.
American Institute of Physics, (American Association of Physicists in Medicine) 335 E. 45th St., New York, NY 10017. TEL 212-661-9404. *3127*

MEDICAL PHYSICS SERIES.
Academic Press, Inc., 1250 Sixth Ave., San Diego, CA 92101. TEL 619-231-0926. FAX 619-699-6715. *3127*

MEDICAL PROBLEMS OF PERFORMING ARTISTS.
Hanley & Belfus, Inc., 210 S. 13th St., Philadelphia, PA 19107. TEL 215-546-7293. FAX 215-790-9330. *3127*

MEDICAL PSYCHOTHERAPY.
Hogrefe & Huber Publishers, (American Board of Medical Psychotherapists) 14 Bruce Park Ave., Toronto, Ont. M4P 2S3, Canada. TEL 416-482-6339. FAX 416-484-4200. *4035*

MEDICAL REFERENCE SERVICES QUARTERLY.
Haworth Press, Inc., 10 Alice St., Binghamton, NY 13904. TEL 800-342-9678. FAX 607-722-1424. *2773*

MEDICAL TECHNOLOGY S A.
Medical Technology News, (Society of Medical Laboratory Technologists of South Africa) P.O. Box 253, Rondebosch 7700, South Africa. TEL 021-4610054. *3262*

MEDICINA TORACICA.
Masson Italia Periodici, (Societa Italiana di Fisiopatologia Respiratoria) Via Statuto 2-4, 20121 Milan, Italy. TEL 02-6367-1. FAX 02-6367211. *3366*

MEDICINAL CHEMISTRY RESEARCH.
Birkhaeuser Boston, Inc., 675 Massachusetts Ave., Cambridge, MA 02139-3309. FAX 201-348-4505. *3129*

MEDICINAL RESEARCH SERIES.
Marcel Dekker, Inc., 270 Madison Ave., New York, NY 10016. TEL 212-696-9000. FAX 212-658-4540. *3129*

MEDICINE (BALTIMORE).
Williams & Wilkins, 428 E. Preston St., Baltimore, MD 21202. TEL 301-528-4000. FAX 301-528-4312. *3129*

MEDICINE AND SCIENCE IN SPORTS AND EXERCISE.
Williams & Wilkins, (American College of Sports Medicine) 428 E. Preston St., Baltimore, MD 21202. TEL 301-528-4000. FAX 301-528-4312. *3372*

MEDITERRANEAN QUARTERLY.
Duke University Press, 6697 College Station, Durham, NC 27708. TEL 919-684-2173. FAX 919-684-8644. *3965*

MELANDERIA.
Washington State Entomological Society, Department of Entomology, Washington State University, Pullman, WA 99164-6382. TEL 509-335-3681. *536*

MELBOURNE JOURNAL OF POLITICS.
University of Melbourne, Political Science Society, Parkville, Vic. 3052, Australia. TEL 03-344-4000. *3906*

MELSHEIMER ENTOMOLOGICAL SERIES.
Entomological Society of Pennsylvania, 103 Patterson Bldg., University Park, PA 16802. TEL 814-863-4640. *536*

MELTS.
Plenum Publishing Corp., Consultants Bureau, (Russian Academy of Sciences) 233 Spring St., New York, NY 10013-1578. TEL 212-620-8468. FAX 212-463-0742. *1183*

MEMBRANE BIOCHEMISTRY.
Taylor & Francis, 1900 Frost Rd., Ste. 101, Bristol, PA 19007. TEL 215-785-5800. FAX 215-785-5515. *480*

MEMBRANE SCIENCE AND TECHNOLOGY SERIES.
Elsevier Science Publishers B.V., Books Division, P.O. Box 211, 1000 AE Amsterdam, Netherlands. TEL 020-5803911. FAX 020-5803705. *480*

MENNINGER CLINIC. BULLETIN.
Menninger Foundation, Box 829, Topeka, KS 66601-0829. TEL 913-273-7500. FAX 913-273-8625. *3344*

MENTAL RETARDATION AND DEVELOPMENTAL DISABILITIES.
Plenum Publishing Corp., 233 Spring St., New York, NY 10013-1578. TEL 212-620-8000. FAX 212-463-0742. *3345*

MERIDIAN.
Map and Geography Round Table, American Library Association, Dept. of Geography, University of Kansas, KS 66045-2121. TEL 602-621-4312. *2256*

METABOLIC ASPECTS OF CARDIOVASCULAR DISEASE.
Elsevier Science Publishers B.V., Books Division, P.O. Box 211, 1000 AE Amsterdam, Netherlands. TEL 020-5803911. FAX 020-5803705. *3210*

METABOLIC BRAIN DISEASE.
Plenum Publishing Corp., 233 Spring St., New York, NY 10013-1578. TEL 212-620-8000. FAX 212-463-0742. *3131*

METABOLISM: CLINICAL AND EXPERIMENTAL.
W.B. Saunders Co. Curtis Center, Independence Square W., Philadelphia, PA 19106. TEL 215-238-7800. *3255*

METAL FINISHING.
Elsevier Science Publishing Co., Inc. (New York), 655 Ave of the Americas, New York, NY 10010. TEL 212-989-5800. FAX 212-633-3965. *3413*

METAL IONS IN BIOLOGICAL SYSTEMS.
Marcel Dekker, Inc., 270 Madison Ave., New York, NY 10016. TEL 212-696-9000. FAX 212-658-4540. *1214*

METAL SCIENCE AND HEAT TREATMENT.
Plenum Publishing Corp., Consultants Bureau, (Ministerstvo Moshinostroeniya i Aiborostroeniya S.S.S.R., Tsentral'nyi Sovet Nauchno-Tekhnicheskogo Obshchestva po Mashinostroeniyi) 233 Spring St., New York, NY 10013-1578. TEL 212-620-8468. FAX 212-463-0742. *3414*

METALLURGICAL TRANSACTIONS A - PHYSICAL METALLURGY AND MATERIALS SCIENCE.
A S M International, Materials Park, OH 44073-0002. TEL 216-338-5151. FAX 216-338-4634. *3414*

METALLURGICAL TRANSACTIONS B - PROCESS METALLURGY.
A S M International, Materials Park, OH 44073-0002. TEL 216-338-5151. FAX 216-338-4634. *3414*

METALLURGIST.
Plenum Publishing Corp., Consultants Bureau, (Ministerstvo Chernoi Metallurgii S.S.S.R.) 233 Spring St., New York, NY 10013-1578. TEL 212-620-8468. FAX 212-463-0742. *3415*

METAPHOR AND SYMBOLIC ACTIVITY.
Lawrence Erlbaum Associates, Inc., 365 Broadway, Hillside, NJ 07642. TEL 201-666-4110. FAX 201-666-2394. *2829*

METEORITICS.
Dept. of Chemistry, University of Arkansas, Fayetteville, AR 72701. FAX 501-575-4049. *367*

METEOROLOGICAL AND GEOASTROPHYSICAL ABSTRACTS.
American Meteorological Society, c/o Inforonics, Inc., 550 Newtown Rd., Box 458, Littleton, MA 01460. TEL 508-486-8976. FAX 508-486-0027. *3444*

METHODS: A COMPANION TO METHODS IN ENZYMOLOGY.
Academic Press, Inc., Journal Division, 1250 Sixth Ave., San Diego, CA 92101. TEL 619-230-1840. FAX 619-699-6800. *480*

METHODS AND PHENOMENA.
Elsevier Science Publishers B.V., Books Division, P.O. Box 211, 1000 AE Amsterdam, Netherlands. TEL 020-5803911. FAX 020-5803705. *4324*

METHODS IN CELL BIOLOGY.
Academic Press, Inc., 1250 Sixth Ave., San Diego, CA 92101. TEL 619-231-0926. FAX 619-699-6715. *525*

METHODS IN ENZYMOLOGY.
Academic Press, Inc., 1250 Sixth Ave., San Diego, CA 92101. TEL 619-231-0926. FAX 619-699-6715. *480*

METHODS IN GEOCHEMISTRY AND GEOPHYSICS.
Elsevier Science Publishers B.V., Books Division, P.O. Box 211, 1000 AE Amsterdam, Netherlands. TEL 020-5803911. FAX 020-5803705. *1547*

METHODS IN MICROANALYSIS.
Gordon and Breach Scientific Publishers, 270 Eighth Ave., New York, NY 10011. TEL 212-206-8900. FAX 212-645-2459. *560*

METHODS OF BIOCHEMICAL ANALYSIS.
John Wiley and Sons, Inc., 605 Third Ave., New York, NY 10158-0012. TEL 212-850-6000. *480*

METHODS OF COMPUTATIONAL CHEMISTRY.
Plenum Publishing Corp., 233 Spring St., New York, NY 10013. TEL 212-620-8000. FAX 212-463-0742. *1184*

METHODS OF EXPERIMENTAL PHYSICS.
Academic Press, Inc., 1250 Sixth Ave., San Diego, CA 92101. TEL 619-231-0926. FAX 619-699-6715. *3825*

METRIKA.
Physica-Verlag GmbH und Co., Tiergarten 17, Postfach 105280, 6900 Heidelberg 1, Germany. TEL 030-8207-424. FAX 030-8207-448. *4579*

MEXICAN STUDIES.
University of California Press, Journals Division, 2120 Berkeley Way, Berkeley, CA 94720. TEL 510-642-4191. FAX 510-643-7127. *2511*

MICHIGAN ACADEMICIAN.
Michigan Academy of Science, Arts and Letters, 400 Fourth St., Ann Arbor, MI 48109-4816. TEL 313-936-2938. *4324*

MICHIGAN STATE UNIVERSITY. MUSEUM PUBLICATIONS. ANTHROPOLOGICAL SERIES.
Michigan State University, Museum, East Lansing, MI 48824. TEL 517-355-2370. *244*

REFEREED SERIALS

MICROBIAL ECOLOGY IN HEALTH & DISEASE.
John Wiley & Sons Ltd., Journals, Baffins Ln., Chichester, W. Sussex PO19 1UD, England. TEL 0240-779777. FAX 0243-775878. *3188*

MICROBIOLOGICAL REVIEWS.
American Society for Microbiology, 1325 Massachusetts Ave. N.W., Washington, DC 20005. TEL 202-737-3600. *555*

MICROBIOLOGY.
Plenum Publishing Corp., Consultants Bureau, (Russian Academy of Sciences) 233 Spring St., New York, NY 10013-1578. TEL 212-620-8468. FAX 212-463-0742. *555*

MICROBIOLOGY SERIES.
Marcel Dekker, Inc., 270 Madison Ave., New York, NY 10016. TEL 212-889-9595. FAX 212-658-4540. *555*

MICROCHEMICAL JOURNAL.
Academic Press, Inc., Journal Division, 1250 Sixth Ave., San Diego, CA 92101. TEL 619-230-1840. FAX 619-699-6800. *560*

MICROCIRCULATION, ENDOTHELIUM AND LYMPHATICS.
c/o B.M. Altura, Ed., Department of Physiology, Box 31, State University of New York, Downstate Medical Center, 450 Clarkson Ave., Brooklyn, NY 11203. *3273*

MICROCOMPUTERS IN CIVIL ENGINEERING.
Elsevier Science Publishers Ltd., Crown House, Linton Rd., Barking, Essex IG11 8JU, England. TEL 081-594-7272. FAX 081-594-5942. *1880*

MICROELECTRONIC ENGINEERING.
North-Holland P.O. Box 211, 1000 AE Amsterdam, Netherlands. TEL 020-5803911. FAX 020-5803598. *1775*

MICROELECTRONICS AND RELIABILITY.
Pergamon Press, Inc., Journals Division, 660 White Plains Rd., Tarrytown, NY 10591-5153. TEL 914-524-9200. FAX 914-333-2444. *1775*

MICROELECTRONICS JOURNAL.
Elsevier Science Publishers Ltd., Crown House, Linton Rd., Barking, Essex IG11 8JU, England. TEL 081-594-7272. FAX 081-594-5942. *1775*

MICROGRAVITY QUARTERLY.
Pergamon Press, Inc., Journals Division, (Microgravity Advanced Research and Support Center) 660 White Plains Rd., Tarrytown, NY 10591-5153. TEL 914-524-9200. FAX 914-333-2444. *58*

MICRON AND MICROSCOPICA ACTA.
Pergamon Press, Inc., Journals Division, 660 White Plains Rd., Tarrytown, NY 10591-5153. TEL 914-524-9200. FAX 914-333-2444. *560*

MICROPALEONTOLOGY.
American Museum of Natural History, Central Park W. at 79th St., New York, NY 10024-5192. TEL 212-769-5656. FAX 212-769-5233. *3658*

MICROPROCESSING AND MICROPROGRAMMING.
North-Holland (European Association for Micro-Processing and Micro-Programming) P.O. Box 211, 1000 AE Amsterdam, Netherlands. TEL 020-5803911. FAX 020-5803598. *1462*

MICROPROCESSORS & MICROSYSTEMS.
Butterworth - Heinemann Ltd. Linacre House, Jordan Hill, Oxford OX2 8DP, England. TEL 0865-310366. FAX 0865-310898. *1462*

MICROSCOPE.
McCrone Research Institute, 2820 S. Michigan Ave., Chicago, IL 60616-3292. TEL 312-842-7100. FAX 312-842-1078. *560*

MICROSCOPICAL SOCIETY OF CANADA. BULLETIN.
Microscopical Society of Canada, 1712 Avenue Rd., P.O. Box 54560, Toronto, Ont. M5M 4N5, Canada. TEL 416-483-3712. FAX 416-483-3712. *560*

MICROSOFT WORKS IN EDUCATION.
International Society for Technology in Education, 1787 Agate St., Eugene, OR 97403-1923. TEL 503-346-4414. FAX 503-346-5890. *1417*

MICROSURGERY.
John Wiley & Sons, Inc., Journals, 605 Third Ave., New York, NY 10158. TEL 212-850-6000. FAX 212-850-6088. *3381*

MICROVASCULAR RESEARCH.
Academic Press, Inc., Journal Division, 1250 Sixth Ave., San Diego, CA 92101. TEL 619-230-1840. FAX 619-699-6800. *3210*

MICROWAVE JOURNAL (INTERNATIONAL EDITION).
Horizon - House - Publications, Inc., 685 Canton St., Norwood, MA 02062. TEL 617-769-9750. FAX 617-762-9230. *1903*

MID-AMERICAN JOURNAL OF BUSINESS.
Ball State University, Bureau of Business Research, Muncie, IN 47306. TEL 317-285-5926. FAX 317-285-8024. *679*

MILITARY OPERATIONS RESEARCH.
Gordon & Breach Science Publishers, 270 Eighth Ave., New York, NY 10011. TEL 212-206-8900. FAX 212-645-2459. *3465*

MILITARY PSYCHOLOGY.
Lawrence Erlbaum Associates, Inc., (American Psychological Association, Division 19) 365 Broadway, Hillsdale, NJ 07642. TEL 201-666-4110. FAX 201-666-2394. *4035*

MINERAL PROCESSING AND EXTRACTIVE METALLURGY REVIEW.
Gordon and Breach Science Publishers, 270 Eighth Ave., New York, NY 10011. TEL 212-206-8900. FAX 212-645-2459. *3415*

MINERALS ENGINEERING.
Pergamon Press, Inc., Journals Division, 660 White Plains Rd., Tarrytown, NY 10591-5153. TEL 914-524-9200. FAX 914-333-2444. *3489*

MINERALS RESEARCH LABORATORY NEWSLETTER.
North Carolina State University, Minerals Research Laboratory, 180 Coxe Ave., Asheville, NC 28801. TEL 704-251-6155. *3489*

MINNESOTA ACADEMY OF SCIENCE. JOURNAL.
Minnesota Academy of Science, 350 Robert St. N., Ste. 583, St. Paul, MN 55101-1502. TEL 612-227-6361. *4324*

MINNESOTA SCIENCE.
University of Minnesota, Agricultural Experiment Station, 405 Coffey Hall, St. Paul, MN 55108. TEL 612-625-7290. *4324*

MINNESOTA STUDIES IN THE PHILOSOPHY OF SCIENCE.
University of Minnesota Press, (Minnesota Center for Philosophy of Science) 2037 University Ave., S.E., Minneapolis, MN 55414. TEL 612-624-2516. FAX 612-626-7313. *3773*

MISSOURI. DIVISION OF GEOLOGICAL SURVEY AND WATER RESOURCES. ENGINEERING GEOLOGY SERIES.
Department of Natural Resources, Division of Geology and Land Survey, Box 250, Rolla, MO 65401. TEL 314-364-1752. *1871*

MODELLING, MEASUREMENT AND CONTROL.
A M S E Press, (International Association for the Advancement of Modelling and Simulation Techniques in Enterprises) 16 av. de Grange Blanche, 69160 Tassin-la-Demi-Lune, France. TEL 78-34-36-04. FAX 78-34-54-17. *3065*

MODELS OF SCIENTIFIC THOUGHT.
Harwood Academic Publishers, 270 Eighth Ave., New York, NY 10011. TEL 212-206-8900. FAX 212-645-2459. *2829*

MODERN AGING RESEARCH.
Wiley-Liss, Inc., 41 E. 11th St., New York, NY 10003. TEL 212-475-7700. *2276*

MODERN ANALYTICAL CHEMISTRY.
Plenum Publishing Corp., 233 Spring St., New York, NY 10013-1578. TEL 212-620-8000. FAX 212-463-0742. *1207*

MODERN ASPECTS OF ELECTROCHEMISTRY.
Plenum Publishing Corp., 233 Spring St., New York, NY 10013-1578. TEL 212-620-8000. FAX 212-463-0742. *1212*

MODERN BIOLOGY SERIES.
Holt, Rinehart and Winston, Inc., c/o Harcourt Brace Jovanovich, 6277 Cea Harbor Dr., Orlando, FL 32887. TEL 407-345-2500. *447*

MODERN GEOLOGY.
Gordon and Breach Science Publishers, 270 Eighth Ave., New York, NY 10011. TEL 212-206-8900. FAX 212-645-2459. *1573*

MODERN MEDICINE.
Avanstar Communications, Inc., 7500 Old Oak Blvd., Cleveland, OH 44130. TEL 216-826-2839. FAX 216-891-2726. *3132*

MODERN METHODS IN PHARMACOLOGY.
Wiley-Liss, Inc., 41 E. 11th St., New York, NY 10003. TEL 212-475-7700. *3735*

MODERN MONOGRAPHS IN ANALYTICAL CHEMISTRY.
Marcel Dekker, Inc., 270 Madison Ave., New York, NY 10016. TEL 212-696-9000. FAX 212-658-4540. *1207*

MODERN PATHOLOGY.
Williams & Wilkins, (U S and Canadian Academy of Pathology) 428 E. Preston St., Baltimore, MD 21202. TEL 301-528-4000. FAX 301-528-4312. *3132*

MODERN PHARMACOLOGY - TOXICOLOGY SERIES.
Marcel Dekker, Inc., 270 Madison Ave., New York, NY 10016. TEL 212-696-9000. FAX 212-658-4540. *3735*

MODERN PHILOLOGY.
University of Chicago Press, Journals Division, 5720 S. Woodlawn Ave., Chicago, IL 60637. TEL 312-753-3347. FAX 312-702-0694. *2829*

MODERN PSYCHOANALYSIS.
Center for Modern Psychoanalytic Studies, 16 W. 10th St., New York, NY 10011. TEL 212-260-7050. *4036*

MODERN TECHNICS IN SURGERY. NEUROSURGERY.
Futura Publishing Company, Inc., 2 Bedford Ridge Rd., Box 330, Mount Kisco, NY 10549. TEL 800-877-8761. FAX 914-666-0993. *3381*

MODERN TECHNICS IN SURGERY. UROLOGIC SURGERY.
Futura Publishing Company, Inc., 2 Bedford Ridge Rd., Box 330, Mount Kisco, NY 10549. TEL 914-666-7528. FAX 914-666-0993. *3382*

MOLECULAR AND BIOCHEMICAL PARASITOLOGY.
Elsevier Science Publishers B.V., P.O. Box 211, 1000 AE Amsterdam, Netherlands. TEL 020-5803911. FAX 020-5803598. *556*

MOLECULAR AND CELLULAR BIOLOGY.
American Society for Microbiology, 1325 Massachusetts Ave., N.W., Washington, DC 20005. TEL 202-737-3600. *556*

MOLECULAR AND CELLULAR ENDOCRINOLOGY.
Elsevier Scientific Publishers Ireland Ltd., P.O. Box 85, Limerick, Ireland. TEL 061-61944. FAX 061-62144. *3255*

MOLECULAR AND CELLULAR NEUROSCIENCES.
Academic Press, Inc., Journal Division, 1250 Sixth Ave., San Diego, CA 92101. TEL 619-230-1840. FAX 619-699-6800. *3345*

MOLECULAR AND CHEMICAL NEUROPATHOLOGY.
Humana Press Inc., Box 2148, Clifton, NJ 07015. TEL 201-256-1699. FAX 201-256-8341. *3345*

MOLECULAR ASPECTS OF MEDICINE.
Pergamon Press, Inc., Journals Division, 660 White Plains Rd., Tarrytown, NY 10591-5153. TEL 914-524-9200. FAX 914-333-2444. *3360*

MOLECULAR BIOLOGY (NEW YORK).
Plenum Publishing Corp., Consultants Bureau, (Russian Academy of Sciences) 233 Spring St., New York, NY 10013-1578. TEL 212-620-8468. FAX 212-463-0742. *526*

MOLECULAR BIOLOGY AND EVOLUTION.
University of Chicago Press, Journals Division, 5702 S. Woodlawn Ave., Chicago, IL 60637. TEL 312-753-3347. FAX 312-702-0694. *447*

MOLECULAR BIOTHERAPY.
Butterworth - Heinemann Ltd. 80 Montvale Ave., Stoneham, MA 02180. TEL 617-438-8464. FAX 617-438-1479. *3200*

MOLECULAR CRYSTALS AND LIQUID CRYSTALS SCIENCE AND TECHNOLOGY. SECTION A: MOLECULAR CRYSTALS AND LIQUID CRYSTALS.
Gordon & Breach Science Publishers, 270 Eighth Ave., New York, NY 10011. TEL 212-206-8900. FAX 212-645-2459. *1211*

MOLECULAR CRYSTALS AND LIQUID CRYSTALS SCIENCE AND TECHNOLOGY. SECTION B: NONLINEAR OPTICS.
Gordon and Breach Science Publishers, 270 Eighth Ave., New York, NY 10011. TEL 212-206-8900. FAX 212-645-2459. *3855*

MOLECULAR CRYSTALS AND LIQUID CRYSTALS SCIENCE AND TECHNOLOGY. SECTION C: MOLECULAR MATERIALS.
Gordon and Breach Science Publishers, 270 Eighth Ave., New York, NY 10011. TEL 212-206-8900. FAX 212-645-2459. *1211*

MOLECULAR CRYSTALS AND LIQUID CRYSTALS SCIENCE AND TECHNOLOGY. SECTION D: DISPLAY AND IMAGING.
Gordon & Breach Science Publishers, 270 Eighth Ave., New York, NY 10011. TEL 212-206-8900. FAX 212-645-2459. *3855*

MOLECULAR ENDOCRINOLOGY.
Williams & Wilkins, 428 E. Preston St., Baltimore, MD 21202. TEL 301-528-4000. FAX 301-528-4312. *3255*

MOLECULAR GENETICS, MICROBIOLOGY AND VIROLOGY.
Allerton Press, Inc., (U.S.S.R. Ministry of Health) 150 Fifth Ave., New York, NY 10011. TEL 212-924-3950. *448*

MOLECULAR IMMUNOLOGY.
Pergamon Press, Inc., Journals Division, 660 WHite Plains Rd., Tarrytown, NY 10591-5153. TEL 914-524-9200. FAX 914-333-2444. *480*

MOLECULAR NEUROBIOLOGY.
Humana Press Inc., Crescent Manor, Box 2148, Clifton, NJ 07015. TEL 201-256-1699. FAX 201-256-8341. *3345*

MOLECULAR PHARMACOLOGY.
Williams & Wilkins, (American Society for Pharmacology & Experimental Therapeutics) 428 E. Preston St., Baltimore, MD 21202. TEL 301-528-4000. FAX 301-528-4312. *3735*

MOLECULAR PHYLOGENETICS AND EVOLUTION.
Academic Press, Inc., Journal Division, 1250 Sixth Ave., San Diego, CA 92101. TEL 619-230-1840. FAX 619-699-6800. *545*

MOLECULAR PHYSICS.
Taylor & Francis Ltd., Rankine Rd., Basingstoke, Hants. RG24 0PR, England. TEL 0256-840366. FAX 0256-479438. *1229*

MOLECULAR SIMULATION.
Gordon & Breach Science Publishers, 270 Eighth Ave., New York, NY 10011. TEL 212-206-8900. FAX 212-645-2459. *1184*

MON-KHMER STUDIES.
University of Hawaii Press, Journals Department, 2840 Kolowalu St., Honolulu, HI 96822. TEL 808-956-8833. FAX 808-988-6052. *2829*

MONO GEO GRAPHY.
Haifa University, Department of Geography, Mount Carmel, Haifa 31905, Israel. FAX 04-246814. *2256*

MONOGRAPH SERIES ON SCHIZOPHRENIA.
International Universities Press, Inc., 59 Boston Post Rd., Box 1524, Madison, CT 06443-1524. TEL 203-245-4000. *3345*

MONOGRAPHS IN ANAESTHESIOLOGY.
Elsevier Science Publishers B.V., Books Division, P.O. Box 211, 1000 AE Amsterdam, Netherlands. TEL 020-5803911. FAX 020-5803705. *3191*

MONOGRAPHS IN ELECTROANALYTICAL CHEMISTRY AND ELECTROCHEMISTRY SERIES.
Marcel Dekker, Inc., 270 Madison Ave., New York, NY 10016. TEL 212-696-9000. FAX 212-658-4540. *1212*

MONOGRAPHS IN EPIDEMIOLOGY AND BIOSTATISTICS.
Oxford University Press, 200 Madison Ave., New York, NY 10016. TEL 212-679-7300. *448*

MONOGRAPHS IN NEUROSCIENCE.
Gordon & Breach Science Publishers, 270 Eighth Ave., New York, NY 10011. TEL 212-206-8900. FAX 212-645-2459. *3345*

MONOGRAPHS IN PHYSICAL MEASUREMENT.
Academic Press, Inc., 1250 Sixth Ave., San Diego, CA 92101. TEL 619-231-0926. FAX 619-699-6715. *1830*

MONOGRAPHS IN PRIMATOLOGY.
Wiley-Liss, Inc., 41 E. 11th St., New York, NY 10003. *448*

MONOGRAPHS IN PSYCHOBIOLOGY.
Gordon & Breach Science Publishers, 270 Eighth Ave., New York, NY 10011. TEL 212-206-8900. FAX 212-645-2459. *4036*

MONOGRAPHS ON ASTRONOMICAL SUBJECTS.
Oxford University Press, 200 Madison Ave., New York, NY 10016. TEL 212-679-7300. *367*

MONOGRAPHS ON CRYOGENICS.
Oxford University Press, 200 Madison Ave., New York, NY 10016. TEL 212-679-7300. *1831*

MONOGRAPHS ON MUSICOLOGY.
Gordon & Breach Science Publishers, 270 Eighth Ave., New York, NY 10011. TEL 212-206-8900. FAX 212-645-2459. *3563*

MONOGRAPHS ON NUMERICAL ANALYSIS.
Oxford University Press, 200 Madison Ave., New York, NY 10016. TEL 212-679-7300. *3048*

MONOGRAPHS ON PHYSICAL BIOCHEMISTRY.
Oxford University Press, 200 Madison Ave., New York, NY 10016. TEL 212-679-7300. *1229*

MONOGRAPHS ON SCIENCE, TECHNOLOGY, AND SOCIETY.
Oxford University Press, 200 Madison Ave., New York, NY 10016. TEL 212-679-7300. *4604*

MONOGRAPHS ON SOIL AND RESOURCES SURVEY.
Oxford University Press, 200 Madison Ave., New York, NY 10016. TEL 212-679-7300. *185*

MONOGRAPHS ON THE PHYSICS AND CHEMISTRY OF MATERIALS.
Oxford University Press, 200 Madison Ave., New York, NY 10016. TEL 212-679-7300. *3825*

MONUMENTS OF RENAISSANCE MUSIC.
University of Chicago Press, 5801 S. Ellis Ave., Chicago, IL 60637. TEL 312-702-7899. *3563*

MORTON ARBORETUM QUARTERLY.
Morton Arboretum, Lisle, IL 60532. TEL 708-968-0074. FAX 708-719-2433. *509*

MOSCOW PHYSICAL SOCIETY. JOURNAL.
I O P Publishing, Techno House, Redcliffe Way, Bristol BS1 6NX, England. TEL 0272-297481. FAX 0272-294318. *3825*

MOTIVATION AND EMOTION.
Plenum Publishing Corp., 233 Spring St., New York, NY 10013-1578. TEL 212-620-8000. FAX 212-463-0742. *4036*

MOUNTAIN PLAINS JOURNAL OF ADULT EDUCATION.
Mountain Plains Adult Education Association, Journal, College of Education, University of Wyoming, Box 3374, Laramie, WY 82071. TEL 307-766-3042. FAX 307-766-6668. *1685*

MOUNTAIN RESEARCH AND DEVELOPMENT.
University of California Press, Journals Division, (International Mountain Society) 2120 Berkeley Way, Berkeley, CA 94720. TEL 510-642-4191. FAX 510-643-7127. *1547*

REFEREED SERIALS 4931

MOVEMENT DISORDERS.
Raven Press, 1185 Ave. of the Americas, New York, NY 10036. TEL 212-930-9500. FAX 212-869-3495. *3345*

MULTIPHASE SCIENCE AND TECHNOLOGY.
Hemisphere Publishing Corporation 1900 Frost Rd., Ste. 101, Bristol, PA 19007-1598. TEL 215-785-5800. FAX 215-785-5515. *1831*

MULTIVARIATE BEHAVIORAL RESEARCH.
Lawrence Erlbaum Associates, Inc., 365 Broadway, Hillsdale, NJ 07642. TEL 201-666-4110. FAX 201-666-2394. *4036*

MUSEUM MANAGEMENT AND CURATORSHIP.
Butterworth - Heinemann Ltd. Linacre House, Jordan Hill, Oxford OX2 8DP, England. TEL 0865-310366. FAX 0865-310898. *3529*

MUSIC IN AMERICAN LIFE.
University of Illinois Press, 54 E. Gregory Dr., Champaign, IL 61820. TEL 217-333-0950. FAX 217-244-8082. *3564*

MUSIC PERCEPTION.
University of California Press, Journals Division, 2120 Berkeley Way, Berkeley, CA 94720. TEL 510-642-4191. FAX 510-643-7127. *3565*

MUSIC REFERENCE SERVICES QUARTERLY.
Haworth Press, Inc., 10 Alice St., Binghamton, NY 13904. TEL 800-342-9678. FAX 607-722-1424. *2774*

MUTATION RESEARCH.
Elsevier Science Publishers B.V., P.O. Box 211, 1000 AE Amsterdam, Netherlands. TEL 020-5803911. FAX 020-5803598. *546*

MUTATION RESEARCH - D N A REPAIR.
Elsevier Science Publishers B.V., P.O. Box 211, 1000 AE Amsterdam, Netherlands. TEL 020-5803911. FAX 020-5803598. *546*

MUTATION RESEARCH - D N AGING.
Elsevier Science Publishers B.V., P.O. Box 211, 1000 AE Amsterdam, Netherlands. TEL 020-5803911. FAX 020-5803598. *546*

MUTATION RESEARCH - GENETIC TOXICOLOGY TESTING.
Elsevier Science Publishers B.V., P.O. Box 211, 1000 AE Amsterdam, Netherlands. TEL 020-5803911. FAX 020-5803598. *546*

MUTATION RESEARCH LETTERS.
Elsevier Science Publishers B.V., P.O. Box 211, 1000 AE Amsterdam, Netherlands. TEL 020-5803911. FAX 020-5803598. *546*

MUTATION RESEARCH - REVIEWS IN GENETIC TOXICOLOGY.
Elsevier Science Publishers B.V., P.O. Box 211, 1000 AE Amsterdam, Netherlands. TEL 020-5803911. FAX 020-5803598. *546*

MYCOLOGIA.
New York Botanical Garden, Scientific Publications Department, (Mycological Society of America) Bronx, NY 10458. TEL 212-220-8721. FAX 212-220-6504. *510*

MYCOLOGY SERIES.
Marcel Dekker, Inc., 270 Madison Ave., New York, NY 10016. TEL 212-696-9000. FAX 212-658-4540. *510*

N A T O ADVANCED SCIENCE INSTITUTES SERIES A: LIFE SCIENCES.
Plenum Publishing Corp., (North Atlantic Treaty Organization, Scientific Affairs Division) 233 Spring St., New York, NY 10013-1578. TEL 212-620-8000. FAX 212-463-0742. *448*

N A T O ADVANCED SCIENCE INSTITUTES SERIES B: PHYSICS.
Plenum Publishing Corp., (North Atlantic Treaty Organization, Scientific Affairs Division) 233 Spring St., New York, NY 10013. TEL 212-620-8000. FAX 212-463-0742. *3825*

N D T INTERNATIONAL.
Butterworth - Heinemann Ltd. Linacre House, Jordan Hill, Oxford OX2 8DP, England. TEL 0865-310366. FAX 0865-310898. *1921*

N I S T BUILDING SCIENCE SERIES.
U.S. National Institute of Standards and Technology, Gaithersburg, MD 20899. TEL 301-975-3058. *625*

N I S T HANDBOOK.
U.S. National Institute of Standards and Technology, Gaithersburg, MD 20899. TEL 301-975-3058. *3447*

N I S T MONOGRAPH.
U.S. National Institute of Standards and Technology, Gaithersburg, MD 20899. TEL 301-975-3058. *3447*

N I S T SPECIAL PUBLICATION.
U.S. National Institute of Standards and Technology, Gaithersburg, MD 20899. TEL 301-975-3058. *3447*

N I S T TECHNICAL NOTE.
U.S. National Institute of Standards and Technology, Gaithersburg, MD 20899. TEL 301-975-3058. *3447*

N S R D S - N B S: NATIONAL STANDARD REFERENCE DATA SERIES.
U.S. National Institute of Standards and Technology, Gaithersburg, MD 20899. TEL 301-975-3058. *3447*

NANOSTRUCTURED MATERIALS.
Pergamon Press plc, (Acta Metallurgica, Inc.) Headington Hill Hall, Oxford OX3 0BW, England. TEL 0865-794141. FAX 0865-743911. *1921*

NANOTECHNOLOGY.
I O P Publishing, (Institute of Physics) Techno House, Redcliffe Way, Bristol BS1 6NX, England. TEL 0272-297481. FAX 0272-294318. *3825*

NATAL MUSEUM. ANNALS.
Natal Museum, Private Bag 9070, Pietermaritzburg 3200, South Africa. TEL 0331-451404. *589*

NATAL MUSEUM JOURNAL OF HUMANITIES.
Natal Museum, Private Bag 9070, Pietermaritzburg 3200, South Africa. TEL 0331-451404. *279*

NATIONAL CANCER INSTITUTE. JOURNAL.
U.S. National Cancer Institute, 9030 Old Georgetown Rd., Rm. 213, Bethesda, MD 20814. TEL 301-496-4907. *3200*

NATIONAL CONFERENCE ON WEIGHTS AND MEASURES. REPORT.
U.S. National Institute of Standards and Technology, Gaithersburg, MD 20899. TEL 301-975-3058. *3447*

NATIONAL FORUM OF APPLIED EDUCATIONAL RESEARCH JOURNAL.
National Forum Journals, (Wright State University) 1930 Nicholas St., Lake Charles, LA 70605. TEL 318-474-6976. *1649*

NATIONAL FORUM OF EDUCATION ADMINISTRATION AND SUPERVISION JOURNAL.
National Forum Journals, 1930 Nicholas St., Lake Charles, LA 70605. TEL 318-474-6976. *1730*

NATIONAL FORUM OF INSTRUCTIONAL TECHNOLOGY JOURNAL.
National Forum Journals, 1930 Nicholas St., Lake Charles, LA 70605. TEL 318-474-6976. *1691*

NATIONAL FORUM OF SPECIAL EDUCATION JOURNAL.
National Forum Journals, (University of Mississippi) 1930 Nicholas St., Lake Charles, LA 70605. TEL 318-474-6976. *1739*

NATIONAL FORUM TEACHER EDUCATION JOURNAL.
National Forum Journals, (McNeese State University) 1930 Nicholas St., Lake Charles, LA 70605. TEL 318-474-6976. *1649*

NATIONAL INSTITUTE OF STANDARDS AND TECHNOLOGY. JOURNAL OF RESEARCH.
U.S. National Institute of Standards and Technology, U.S. Dept. of Commerce, Gaithersburg, MD 20899. TEL 301-975-3069. *3448*

NATURAL AREAS JOURNAL.
Natural Areas Association, 320 S. Third St., Rockford, IL 61104. TEL 815-964-6666. FAX 815-964-6661. *1963*

NATURAL HISTORY.
American Museum of Natural History, Central Park W. at 79th St., New York, NY 10024-5192. TEL 212-769-5500. FAX 212-769-5511. *4327*

NATURAL HISTORY MISCELLANEA.
Chicago Academy of Sciences, 2001 N. Clark St., Chicago, IL 60614. TEL 312-549-0606. *449*

NATURAL HISTORY MUSEUM OF LOS ANGELES COUNTY. SCIENCE SERIES.
Natural History Museum of Los Angeles County, 900 Exposition Blvd., Los Angeles, CA 90007. TEL 213-744-3330. FAX 213-742-0730. *4327*

NATURAL HISTORY RESEARCH.
Natural History Museum and Institute, Chiba, 955-2 Aoba-cho, Chiba 280, Japan. *2340*

NATURAL HISTORY SOCIETY OF NORTHUMBRIA. TRANSACTIONS.
Natural History Society of Northumbria, Hancock Museum, Newcastle Upon Tyne NE2 4PT, England. *4327*

NATURAL RESOURCES FORUM.
Butterworth - Heinemann Ltd. (United Nations Centre for Natural Resources, Energy and Transport) Linacre House, Jordan Hill, Oxford OX2 8DP, England. TEL 0865-310366. FAX 0865-310898. *2257*

NATURE.
Macmillan Magazines Ltd. 4 Little Essex St., London WC2R 3LF, England. TEL 071-836-6633. FAX 0256-842084. *4327*

NEBRASKA ACADEMY OF SCIENCES. TRANSACTIONS.
Nebraska Academy of Sciences, 302 Morrill Hall, 14th & U Sts., Lincoln, NE 68588-0339. *4329*

NEGOTIATION JOURNAL.
Plenum Publishing Corp., (Program on Negotiation) 233 Spring St., New York, NY 10013-1578. TEL 212-620-8000. FAX 212-463-0742. *3966*

NEONATAL INTENSIVE CARE.
Goldstein and Associates, 1150 Yale St., Ste. 12, Santa Monica, CA 90403-4738. TEL 213-828-1309. *3295*

NETHERLANDS JOURNAL OF MEDICINE.
Elsevier Science Publishers B.V., (Nederlandse Internisten Vereniging) P.O. Box 211, 1000 AE Amsterdam, Netherlands. TEL 020-5803911. FAX 020-5803598. *3134*

NEURAL COMPUTATION.
M I T Press, 55 Hayward St., Cambridge, MA 02142. TEL 617-253-2889. FAX 617-258-6779. *1409*

NEURAL NETWORKS.
Pergamon Press, Inc., Journals Division, (International Neural Networks Society) 660 White Plains Rd., Tarrytown, NY 10591-5153. TEL 914-524-9200. FAX 914-333-2444. *1409*

NEUROBIOLOGY OF AGING.
Pergamon Press, Inc., Journals Division, 660 White Plains Rd., Tarrytown, NY 10591-5153. TEL 914-524-9200. FAX 914-333-2444. *573*

NEUROCHEMICAL RESEARCH.
Plenum Publishing Corp., 233 Spring St., New York, NY 10013-1578. TEL 212-620-8000. FAX 212-463-0742. *3346*

NEUROCHEMISTRY.
Harwood Academic Publishers, 270 Eighth Ave., New York, NY 10011. TEL 212-206-8900. FAX 212-645-2459. *480*

NEUROCHEMISTRY INTERNATIONAL.
Pergamon Press, Inc., Journals Division, 660 White Plains Rd., Tarrytown, NY 10591-5153. TEL 914-524-9200. FAX 914-333-2444. *3346*

NEUROCOMPUTING.
North-Holland P.O. Box 211, 1000 AE Amsterdam, Netherlands. TEL 020-5803911. FAX 020-5803598. *1409*

NEUROENDOCRINE PERSPECTIVES.
Springer-Verlag, 175 Fifth Ave., New York, NY 10010. TEL 212-460-1500. *3346*

NEUROIMAGE.
Academic Press, Inc., Journal Division, 1250 Sixth Ave., San Diego, CA 92101. TEL 619-230-1840. FAX 619-699-6800. *3346*

NEUROLOGICAL RESEARCH.
Forefront Publishing Group, c/o Dr. G. Austin, 2320 Bath St., Ste. 301, Santa Barbara, CA 93105. FAX 508-443-0221. *3347*

NEUROLOGY.
Avanstar Communications, Inc., 7500 Old Oak Blvd., Cleveland, OH 44130. TEL 216-826-2839. FAX 216-891-2726. *3347*

NEUROMUSCULAR DISORDERS.
Pergamon Press plc, Headington Hill Hall, Oxford OX3 0BW, England. TEL 0865-794141. FAX 0865-60285. *3347*

NEUROPHARMACOLOGY.
Pergamon Press, Inc., Journals Division, 660 White Plains Rd., Tarrytown, NY 10591-5153. TEL 914-524-9200. FAX 914-333-2444. *3736*

NEUROPHYSIOLOGIE CLINIQUE.
Editions Scientifiques Elsevier, (Societe d'E E G et de Neurophysiologie Clinique de Langue Francaise) 29, rue Buffon, 75005 Paris, France. TEL 47-07-11-22. FAX 43-36-80-93. *3347*

NEUROPHYSIOLOGY.
Plenum Publishing Corp., Consultants Bureau, 233 Spring St., New York, NY 10013-1578. TEL 212-620-8468. FAX 212-463-0742. *3347*

NEUROPROTOCOLS.
Academic Press, Inc., Journal Division, 1250 Sixth Ave., San Diego, CA 92101. TEL 619-230-1840. FAX 619-699-6800. *3347*

NEUROPSYCHIATRY, NEUROPSYCHOLOGY AND BEHAVIORAL NEUROLOGY.
Raven Press, 1185 Ave. of the Americas, New York, NY 10036. TEL 212-930-9500. FAX 212-869-3495. *3347*

NEUROPSYCHOLOGIA.
Pergamon Press, Inc., Journals Division, 660 White Plains Rd., Tarrytown, NY 10591-5153. TEL 914-524-9200. FAX 914-333-2444. *3348*

NEUROPSYCHOLOGY.
Taylor & Francis, 1900 Frost Rd., Ste. 101, Bristol, PA 19007-1598. TEL 215-785-5800. FAX 215-785-5515. *3348*

NEUROPSYCHOLOGY REVIEW.
Plenum Publishing Corp., 233 Spring St., New York, NY 10013-1578. TEL 212-620-8000. FAX 212-463-0742. *3348*

NEUROPSYCHOPHARMACOLOGY.
Elsevier Science Publishing Co., Inc. (New York), (American College of Neuropsychopharmacology) 655 Ave. of the Americas, New York, NY 10010. TEL 212-989-5800. FAX 212-633-3965. *3348*

NEUROSCIENCE.
Pergamon Press, Inc., Journals Division, (International Brain Research Organization) 660 White Plains Rd., Tarrytown, NY 10591-5153. TEL 914-524-9200. FAX 914-333-2444. *3348*

NEUROSCIENCE AND BEHAVIORAL PHYSIOLOGY.
Plenum Publishing Corp., Consultants Bureau, (Federation of American Societies for Experimental Biology) 233 Spring St., New York, NY 10013-1578. TEL 212-620-8468. FAX 212-463-0742. *3348*

NEUROSCIENCE AND BIOBEHAVIORAL REVIEWS.
Pergamon Press, Inc., Journals Division, 660 White Plains Rd., Tarrytown, NY 10591-5153. TEL 914-524-9200. FAX 914-333-2444. *3348*

NEUROSCIENCE LETTERS.
Elsevier Scientific Publishers Ireland Ltd., P.O. Box 85, Limerick, Ireland. TEL 061-69144. FAX 061-62144. *3348*

NEUROSCIENCE RESEARCH.
Elsevier Scientific Publishers Ireland Ltd., (Japan Neuroscience Society) P.O. Box 85, Limerick, Ireland. TEL 061-61944. FAX 016-62144. *3348*

NEUROSURGERY (BALTIMORE).
Williams & Wilkins, (Congress of Neurological Surgeons) 428 E. Preston St., Baltimore, MD 21202. TEL 301-528-4000. FAX 301-528-4312. *3349*

NEUROSURGERY QUARTERLY.
Raven Press, 1185 Ave. of the Americas, New York, NY 10036. TEL 212-930-9500. FAX 212-869-3495. *3382*

NEUROTOXICOLOGY AND TERATOLOGY.
Pergamon Press, Inc., Journals Division, (Behavioral Toxicology Society) 660 White Plains Rd., Tarrytown, NY 10591-5153. TEL 914-524-9200. FAX 914-333-2444. *3349*

NEUROUROLOGY AND URODYNAMICS.
Journals, New York, NY 10158. TEL 212-850-6000. FAX 212-850-6088. *3389*

NEUTRON NEWS.
Gordon and Breach Science Publishers, 270 Eighth Ave., New York, NY 10011. TEL 212-206-8900. FAX 212-645-2459. *3848*

NEVADA REVIEW OF BUSINESS AND ECONOMICS.
University of Nevada, Bureau of Business and Economic Research, College of Business Administration, Reno, NV 89557-0016. TEL 702-784-6877. *681*

NEW COMPREHENSIVE BIOCHEMISTRY.
Elsevier Science Publishers B.V., Books Division, P.O. Box 211, 1000 AE Amsterdam, Netherlands. TEL 020-5803911. FAX 020-5803705. *480*

NEW ENGLAND JOURNAL OF MEDICINE.
Massachusetts Medical Society, 1440 Main St., Waltham, MA 02254. TEL 617-734-9800. *3135*

NEW ENGLAND JOURNAL OF OPTOMETRY.
New England Council of Optometrists, 101 Tremont St., Boston, MA 02108. TEL 617-542-1233. *3302*

NEW HAMPSHIRE. AGRICULTURAL EXPERIMENT STATION, DURHAM. RESEARCH REPORTS.
University of New Hampshire, Agricultural Experiment Station, Durham, NH 03824. TEL 603-862-1234. *109*

NEW HORIZONS IN THERAPEUTICS: SMITH, KLINE & FRENCH LABORATORIES RESEARCH SYMPOSIA SERIES.
Plenum Publishing Corp., 233 Spring St., New York, NY 10013-1578. TEL 212-620-8000. FAX 212-463-0742. *3135*

NEW IDEAS IN PSYCHOLOGY.
Pergamon Press, Inc., Journals Division, 660 White Plains Rd., Tarrytown, NY 10591-5153. TEL 914-524-9200. FAX 914-333-2444. *4036*

NEW YORK ACADEMY OF SCIENCES. ANNALS.
New York Academy of Sciences, 2 E. 63rd St., New York, NY 10021. TEL 212-838-0230. *4329*

NEW YORK ACADEMY OF SCIENCES. TRANSACTIONS.
New York Academy of Sciences, 2 E. 63rd St., New York, NY 10021. *4329*

NEW YORK BOTANICAL GARDEN. MEMOIRS.
New York Botanical Garden, Scientific Publications Department, Bronx, NY 10458. TEL 212-220-8721. FAX 212-220-6504. *511*

NEW YORK ENTOMOLOGICAL SOCIETY. JOURNAL.
New York Entomological Society, c/o American Museum of Natural History, Central Park West at 79th St., New York, NY 10024-5192. TEL 212-769-5613. FAX 212-769-5233. *536*

NEW YORK INTERNATIONAL LAW REVIEW.
New York State Bar Association, International Law and Practice Section, One Elk St., Albany, NY 12207-1096. TEL 518-463-3200. *2727*

NEW YORK PSYCHOANALYTIC INSTITUTE. KRIS STUDY GROUP. MONOGRAPHS.
International Universities Press, Inc., 59 Boston Post Rd., Box 1524, Madison, CT 06443-1524. TEL 203-245-4000. *4037*

NEW YORK STATE NURSES ASSOCIATION. JOURNAL.
New York State Nurses Association, 2113 Western Ave., Guilderland, NY 12084. TEL 518-456-5371. FAX 518-456-0697. *3282*

NEW YORK TAX UPDATE.
William S. Hein & Co., Inc., 1285 Main St., Buffalo, NY 14209-1987. TEL 800-828-7571. FAX 716-883-8100. *1102*

NEW ZEALAND VETERINARY JOURNAL.
New Zealand Veterinary Association, P.O. Box 27-499, Wellington, New Zealand. TEL 64-4-384-3632. FAX 64-4-384-3631. *4813*

NIELS BOHR - COLLECTED WORKS.
Elsevier Science Publishers B.V., Books Division, P.O. Box 211, 1000 AE Amsterdam, Netherlands. TEL 020-5803911. FAX 020-5803598. *3825*

NIHON CONTACT LENS GAKKAISHI.
Nihon Kontakuto Renzu Gakkaishi Henshubu, (Japan Contact Lens Society) Osaka University Medical School, Department of Ophthamology, 1-1-50 Fukushima, Fukushima-ku, Osaka 553, Japan. FAX 81-6-458-2669. *3302*

NINETEENTH-CENTURY LITERATURE (BERKELEY).
University of California Press, Journals Division, 2120 Berkeley Way, Berkeley, CA 94720. TEL 510-642-4191. FAX 510-643-7127. *2943*

NINETEENTH-CENTURY STUDIES.
The Citadel - The Military College of South Carolina, Department of English, (Southeastern Nineteenth-Century Studies Association) Charleston, SC 29409. *2943*

NOISE CONTROL ENGINEERING JOURNAL.
Institute of Noise Control Engineering, Department of Mechanical Engineering, Auburn University, Auburn, AL 36849-3501. TEL 205-844-3306. FAX 205-844-3307. *1936*

NON-FERROUS METAL DATA.
American Bureau of Metal Statistics Inc., Box 1405, Plaza Sta., 400 Plaza Dr., Secaucus, NJ 07094-0405. TEL 201-863-6900. FAX 201-863-6050. *3416*

NONDESTRUCTIVE TESTING AND EVALUATION.
Gordon and Breach Science Publishers, 270 Eighth Ave., New York, NY 10011. TEL 212-206-8900. FAX 212-645-2459. *1921*

NONDESTRUCTIVE TESTING MONOGRAMS AND TRACTS.
Gordon & Breach Science Publishers, 270 Eighth Ave., New York, NY 10011. TEL 212-206-8900. FAX 212-645-2459. *1921*

NONGYE HUANJING BAOHU.
Zhongguo Nongye Shengtai Huanjing Baohu Xiehui, 31 Kangfu Lu, Nankai Qu, Tianjin 300191, People's Republic of China. TEL 361247. *1964*

NONLINEAR ANALYSIS.
Pergamon Press, Inc., Journals Division, 660 White Plains Rd., Tarrytown, NY 10591-5153. TEL 914-524-9200. FAX 914-333-2444. *1832*

NONPARAMETRIC STATISTICS.
Gordon and Breach Science Publishers, 270 Eighth Ave., New York, NY 10011. TEL 212-206-8900. FAX 212-645-2459. *4581*

NONPROFIT AND VOLUNTARY SECTOR QUARTERLY.
Jossey-Bass Inc., Publishers, (Association of Voluntary Action Scholars) 350 Sansome St., 5th Fl., San Francisco, CA 94104. TEL 415-433-1767. FAX 415-433-0499. *4415*

NONPROFIT MANAGEMENT AND LEADERSHIP.
Jossey-Bass Inc., Publishers, 350 Sansome St., 5th Fl., San Francisco, CA 94104. TEL 415-433-1767. FAX 415-433-0499. *1022*

NORSK POLARINSTITUTT. SKRIFTER.
Norsk Polarinstitutt, Postboks 158, 1330 Oslo Lufthavn, Norway. FAX 02-123854. *1576*

NORTH AMERICAN FLORA.
New York Botanical Garden, Scientific Publications Department, Bronx, NY 10458. TEL 212-220-8721. FAX 212-220-6504. *511*

NORTH AMERICAN JOURNAL OF FISHERIES MANAGEMENT.
American Fisheries Society, 5410 Grosvenor Ln., Ste. 110, Bethesda, MD 20814-2199. TEL 301-897-8616. FAX 301-897-8096. *2047*

NORTH-HOLLAND LINGUISTIC SERIES.
Elsevier Science Publishers B.V., Books Division, P.O. Box 211, 1000 AE Amsterdam, Netherlands. TEL 020-5803911. FAX 020-5803705. *2831*

NORTH-HOLLAND MATHEMATICAL LIBRARY.
Elsevier Science Publishers B.V., Books Division, P.O. Box 211, 1000 AE Amsterdam, Netherlands. TEL 020-5803911. FAX 020-5803705. *3049*

NORTH-HOLLAND MATHEMATICS STUDIES.
Elsevier Science Publishers B.V., Books Division, P.O. Box 211, 1000 AE Amsterdam, Netherlands. TEL 020-5803911. FAX 020-5803705. *3049*

NORTH-HOLLAND SERIES IN APPLIED MATHEMATICS AND MECHANICS.
Elsevier Science Publishers B.V., Books Division, P.O. Box 211, 1000 AE Amsterdam, Netherlands. TEL 020-5803911. FAX 020-5803705. *3049*

NORTH-HOLLAND SERIES IN SYSTEM SCIENCE AND ENGINEERING.
Elsevier Science Publishers B.V., Books Division, P.O. Box 211, 1000 AE Amsterdam, Netherlands. TEL 020-5803911. FAX 020-5803705. *1880*

NORTH-HOLLAND STUDIES IN TELECOMMUNICATION.
Elsevier Science Publishers B.V., Books Division, P.O. Box 211, 1000 AE Amsterdam, Netherlands. TEL 020-5803911. FAX 020-5803705. *1341*

NORTH-HOLLAND SYSTEMS AND CONTROL SERIES.
Elsevier Science Publishers B.V., Books Division, P.O. Box 211, 1000 AE Amsterdam, Netherlands. TEL 020-5803911. FAX 020-5803705. *1438*

NORTH EASTERN DOCTORS CALLING.
Indian Medical Association, Chaiduar Branch, c/o Dr. Ranjib Baruah, Secr., Hoogrijan 786 601, Assam, India. *3136*

NORTHWEST ANTHROPOLOGICAL RESEARCH NOTES.
University of Idaho, Alfred W. Bowers Laboratory of Anthropology, Moscow, ID 83843. TEL 208-885-6123. *246*

NORTHWEST SCIENCE.
Washington State University Press, (Northwest Scientific Association) Pullman, WA 99164-5910. TEL 509-335-3518. *4330*

NORTHWESTERN UNIVERSITY. ROBERT H. LURIE CANCER CENTER. JOURNAL.
Northwestern University, Robert H. Lurie Cancer Center, Olson Pavilion 8250, 303 E. Chicago Ave., Chicago, IL 60611. TEL 312-908-5250. *3200*

NOTRE DAME TECHNICAL REVIEW.
University of Notre Dame, Engineering Department, Engineering Bldg., Notre Dame, IN 46556. TEL 219-283-3524. FAX 219-239-8007. *1832*

NOUVELLE REVUE D'ONOMASTIQUE.
Societe Francaise d'Onomastique, 87 rue Vielle-du-Temple, 75003 Paris, France. *2832*

NUCLEAR ENGINEERING AND DESIGN.
North-Holland P.O. Box 211, 1000 AE Amsterdam, Netherlands. TEL 020-5803911. FAX 020-5803598. *1921*

NUCLEAR INSTRUMENTS & METHODS IN PHYSICS RESEARCH. SECTION A. ACCELERATORS, SPECTROMETERS, DETECTORS, AND ASSOCIATED EQUIPMENT.
North-Holland P.O. Box 211, 1000 AE Amsterdam, Netherlands. TEL 020-5803911. FAX 020-5803598. *3848*

NUCLEAR INSTRUMENTS & METHODS IN PHYSICS RESEARCH. SECTION B. BEAM INTERACTIONS WITH MATERIALS AND ATOMS.
North-Holland P.O. Box 211, 1000 AE Amsterdam, Netherlands. TEL 020-5803911. FAX 020-5803598. *3849*

NUCLEAR MEDICINE.
Gordon & Breach Science Publishers, 270 Eighth Ave., New York, NY 10011. TEL 212-206-8900. FAX 212-645-2459. *3361*

NUCLEAR MEDICINE ANNUAL.
Raven Press, 1185 Ave. of the Americas, New York, NY 10036. TEL 212-930-9500. FAX 212-869-3495. *3361*

NUCLEAR MEDICINE COMMUNICATIONS.
Chapman & Hall, 2-6 Boundary Row, London SE1 8HN, England. TEL 071-865-0066. FAX 071-522-9623. *3361*

NUCLEAR PHYSICS NEWS.
Gordon and Breach Science Publishers, (Nuclear Physics European Collaboration Committee) 270 Eighth Ave., New York, NY 10011. TEL 212-206-8900. FAX 212-645-2459. *3849*

NUCLEAR PHYSICS, SECTION A.
North-Holland P.O. Box 211, 1000 AE Amsterdam, Netherlands. TEL 020-5803911. FAX 020-5803598. *3849*

NUCLEAR PHYSICS, SECTION B.
North-Holland P.O. Box 211, 1000 AE Amsterdam, Netherlands. TEL 020-5803911. FAX 020-5803598. *3849*

NUCLEAR PHYSICS, SECTION B, PROCEEDINGS SUPPLEMENTS.
North-Holland P.O. Box 211, 1000 AE Amsterdam, Netherlands. TEL 020-5803911. FAX 020-5803598. *3849*

NUCLEAR SCIENCE AND ENGINEERING.
American Nuclear Society, 555 N. Kensington Ave., La Grange Park, IL 60525. TEL 708-352-6611. *1808*

NUCLEAR SCIENCE AND TECHNIQUES.
Science Press, (Chinese Aacademy of Sciences) 16 Donghuangchenggen Beijie, Beijing 100707, People's Republic of China. TEL 4010642. FAX 4012180. *3849*

NUCLEAR SCIENCE APPLICATIONS - SECTION A: SHORT REVIEWS, RESEARCH PAPERS, AND COMMENTS.
Harwood Academic Publishers, 270 Eighth Ave., New York, NY 10011. TEL 212-206-8900. FAX 212-645-2459. *3849*

NUCLEAR SCIENCE APPLICATIONS - SECTION B: IN DEPTH REVIEWS.
Harwood Academic Publishers, 270 Eighth Ave., New York, NY 10011. TEL 212-206-8900. FAX 212-645-2459. *3849*

NUCLEAR SCIENCE RESEARCH CONFERENCE SERIES.
Harwood Academic Publishers, 270 Eighth Ave., New York, NY 10011. TEL 212-260-8900. FAX 212-645-2459. *3849*

NUMERICAL FUNCTIONAL ANALYSIS AND OPTIMIZATION.
Marcel Dekker Journals, 270 Madison Ave., New York, NY 10016. TEL 212-696-9000. FAX 212-685-4540. *3049*

NUMERICAL HEAT TRANSFER PART A: APPLICATIONS.
Hemisphere Publishing Corporation 1900 Frost Rd., Ste. 101, Bristol, PA 19007-1598. TEL 215-785-5800. FAX 215-785-5515. *1936*

NUMERICAL HEAT TRANSFER PART B: FUNDAMENTALS.
Hemisphere Publishing Corporation 1900 Frost Rd., Ste. 101, Bristol, PA 19007-1598. TEL 215-785-5800. FAX 215-785-5515. *1936*

NUMERICAL METHODS FOR PARTIAL DIFFERENTIAL EQUATIONS: AN INTERNATIONAL JOURNAL.
John Wiley & Sons, Inc., Journals, 605 Third Ave., New York, NY 10158-0012. TEL 212-850-6000. FAX 212-850-6088. *3049*

NURSE ANESTHESIA.
Appleton & Lange, Journal Division 25 Van Zant St., Box 5630, Norwalk, CT 06856. TEL 203-838-4400. *3283*

NURSING MANAGEMENT.
S - N Publications, Inc., 103 N. Second St., Ste. 200, W. Dundee, IL 60118. TEL 708-426-6100. FAX 708-426-6146. *3284*

NUTRITION.
Nutrition, Inc., Box 3748, 3001 N. San Fernando Blvd., Burbank, CA 91510. TEL 818-845-3748. FAX 315-464-6238. *3610*

NUTRITION AND CANCER.
Lawrence Erlbaum Associates, Inc., 365 Broadway, Hillsdale, NJ 07642. TEL 201-666-4110. FAX 201-666-2394. *3200*

NUTRITION RESEARCH.
Pergamon Press, Inc., Journals Division, 660 White Plains Rd., Tarrytown, NY 10591-5153. TEL 914-524-9200. FAX 914-333-2444. *3610*

O P E C REVIEW.
Pergamon Press plc, (Organization of the Petroleum Exporting Countries, Public Information Department) Headington Hill Hall, Oxford OX3 0BW, England. TEL 0865-794141. FAX 0865-743911. *3694*

O R L - HEAD AND NECK NURSING.
Health Information Publications, Inc., (Society of Otorhinolaryngology and Head - Neck Nurses) 92 S. Highland Ave., Ossining, NY 10562. TEL 914-762-6498. FAX 914-762-0239. *3316*

OBSTETRIC ANESTHESIA DIGEST.
Obstetric Anesthesia Digest, Inc., Box 20057, Wichita, KS 67208-1057. TEL 316-733-5952. FAX 316-733-5952. *3192*

OBSTETRICS AND GYNECOLOGY.
Elsevier Science Publishing Co., Inc. (New York), (American College of Obstetricians and Gynecologists) 655 Ave. of the Americas, New York, NY 10010. TEL 212-989-5800. FAX 212-633-3965. *3295*

OBSTETRICS AND GYNECOLOGY CLINICS.
W.B. Saunders Co., Curtis Center, Independence Sq. W., Philadelphia, PA 19106. TEL 215-238-7800. *3295*

OCCASIONAL PAPERS IN ANTHROPOLOGY.
Pennsylvania State University, Department of Anthropology, 409 Carpenter Bldg., University Park, PA 16802. TEL 814-865-2509. *246*

OCCASIONAL PAPERS IN ENTOMOLOGY.
Department of Food and Agriculture, Division of Plant Industry, 1220 N St., Sacramento, CA 95814. TEL 916-445-5421. *536*

OCCUPATIONAL HEALTH & SAFETY.
Stevens Publishing Corporation, 225 N. New Rd., Waco, TX 76710. TEL 817-776-9000. FAX 817-776-9018. *3619*

OCCUPATIONAL MEDICINE.
Butterworth - Heinemann Ltd. (Society of Occupational Medicine) Linacre House, Jordan Hill, Oxford OX2 8DP, England. TEL 0865-310366. FAX 0865-310898. *3137*

OCCUPATIONAL MEDICINE.
Hanley & Belfus, Inc., 210 S. 13th St., Philadelphia, PA 19107. TEL 215-546-7293. FAX 215-790-9330. *3620*

OCCUPATIONAL SAFETY AND HEALTH SERIES (NEW YORK).
Marcel Dekker, Inc., 270 Madison Ave., New York, NY 10016. TEL 212-696-9000. FAX 212-658-4540. *4109*

OCCUPATIONAL THERAPY IN HEALTH CARE.
Haworth Press, Inc., 10 Alice St., Binghamton, NY 13904. TEL 800-342-9678. FAX 607-722-1424. *3137*

OCCUPATIONAL THERAPY IN MENTAL HEALTH.
Haworth Press, Inc., 10 Alice St., Binghamton, NY 13904. TEL 800-342-9678. FAX 607-722-1424. *3349*

OCCUPATIONAL THERAPY JOURNAL OF RESEARCH.
Slack, Inc., (American Occupational Therapy Foundation, Inc.) 6900 Grove Rd., Thorofare, NJ 08086-9447. TEL 609-848-1000. FAX 609-853-5991. *3137*

OCEAN-AIR INTERACTIONS.
Gordon and Breach Science Publishers, 270 Eighth Ave., New York, NY 10011. TEL 212-206-8900. FAX 212-645-2459. *1609*

OCEAN AND COASTAL MANAGEMENT.
Elsevier Science Publishers Ltd., Crown House, Linton Rd., Barking, Essex IG11 8JU, England. TEL 081-594-7272. FAX 081-594-5942. *1609*

OCEAN DEVELOPMENT AND INTERNATIONAL LAW.
Taylor & Francis, 1900 Frost Rd., Ste. 101, Bristol, PA 19007-1598. TEL 215-785-5800. FAX 215-785-5515. *1609*

OCEAN ENGINEERING.
Pergamon Press, Inc., Journals Division, 660 White Plains Rd., Tarrytown, NY 10591-5153. TEL 914-524-9200. FAX 914-333-2444. *1609*

OCEAN YEARBOOK.
University of Chicago Press, (International Ocean Institute) 5801 S. Ellis Ave., Chicago, IL 60637. TEL 312-702-7899. *1609*

OCEANIC LINGUISTICS.
University of Hawaii Press, Journals Department, 2840 Kolowalu St., Honolulu, HI 96822. TEL 808-956-8833. FAX 808-988-6052. *2832*

OCEANS. CONFERENCE RECORD.
Institute of Electrical and Electronics Engineers, Inc., (I E E E, Oceanic Engineering Society) 345 E. 47th St., New York, NY 10017-2394. TEL 212-705-7900. FAX 212-705-7682. *1832*

OFFICE SYSTEMS RESEARCH JOURNAL.
Office Systems Research Association, Washington University, Campus Box 1141, 1 Brookings Dr., St. Louis, MO 63130. TEL 314-935-4487. FAX 314-935-4479. *1060*

OHIO BIOLOGICAL SURVEY. BIOLOGICAL NOTES.
Ohio Biological Survey, 1315 Kinnear Rd., Columbus, OH 43212. TEL 614-292-9645. *450*

OHIO STATE UNIVERSITY. BYRD POLAR RESEARCH CENTER. CONTRIBUTION SERIES.
Ohio State University, Byrd Polar Research Center, 125 S. Oval Mall, Columbus, OH 43210-1308. TEL 614-292-6531. *4331*

OILFIELD REVIEW.
Elsevier Science Publishers B.V., (Schlumberger-Doll Research) P.O. Box 211, 1000 AE Amsterdam, Netherlands. TEL 020-5803911. FAX 020-5803598. *3696*

OKLAHOMA GEOLOGICAL SURVEY. CIRCULAR.
Oklahoma Geological Survey, University of Oklahoma, 100 E. Boyd, Rm. N-131, Norman, OK 73019. TEL 405-325-3031. *1576*

OKLAHOMA GEOLOGICAL SURVEY. SPECIAL PUBLICATION SERIES.
Oklahoma Geological Survey, University of Oklahoma, 100 E. Boyd, Rm. N-131, Norman, OK 73019. TEL 405-325-3031. *1577*

OKLAHOMA GEOLOGY NOTES.
Oklahoma Geological Survey, University of Oklahoma, 100 E. Boyd, Rm. N-131, Norman, OK 73019. TEL 405-325-3031. *1577*

OLD TESTAMENT ESSAYS.
Serva Publishers, (Old Testament Society of South Africa) P.O. Box 30043, Sunnyside 0132, Transvaal, South Africa. *4193*

OLIFANT.
University of Virginia, Dept. of French, Charlottesville, VA 22903. TEL 804-924-4627. *2999*

OMEGA (TARRYTOWN).
Pergamon Press, Inc., Journals Division, 660 White Plains Rd., Tarrytown, NY 10591-5153. TEL 914-524-9200. FAX 914-333-2444. *1023*

OMNI.
Omni Publications International, Ltd., 1965 Broadway, New York, NY 10023-5965. TEL 212-496-6100. *4331*

ONCOGENE RESEARCH.
Harwood Academic Publishers, 270 Eighth Ave., New York, NY 10011. TEL 212-206-8900. FAX 212-645-2459. *3201*

ONCOLOGY RESEARCH.
Pergamon Press, Inc., Journals Division, 660 White Plains Rd., Tarrytown, NY 10591-5153. TEL 914-524-9200. FAX 914-333-2444. *3201*

ONOMASTICA CANADIANA.
Canadian Society for the Study of Names, Dept. of Languages, Literatures and Linguistics, York Univesity, 4700 Keele St., North York, Ont. M3J 1P3, Canada. TEL 416-736-5016. *2833*

OPERA QUARTERLY.
Duke University Press, Box 6697, College Station, Durham, NC 27708. TEL 919-684-2173. FAX 919-684-8644. *3572*

OPERATING ROOM RISK MANAGEMENT.
E C R I, (Emergency Care Research Institute) 5200 Butler Pike, Plymouth Meeting, PA 19462. TEL 215-825-6000. FAX 215-834-1275. *3382*

OPERATIONS RESEARCH.
Operations Research Society of America, Mount Royal and Guilford Aves., Baltimore, MD 21202. TEL 301-528-4146. *1399*

OPERATIONS RESEARCH LETTERS.
North-Holland (Operations Research Society of America) P.O. Box 211, 1000 AE Amsterdam, Netherlands. TEL 020-5803911. FAX 020-5803598. *4332*

OPHTHALMIC AND PHYSIOLOGICAL OPTICS.
Butterworth - Heinemann Ltd. (British College of Optometrists) Linacre House, Jordan Hill, Oxford OX2 8DP, England. TEL 0865-310366. FAX 0865-310898. *3303*

OPHTHALMOLOGY.
J.B. Lippincott Co., (American Academy of Ophthalmology) E. Washington Sq., Philadelphia, PA 19105. TEL 215-238-4200. *3303*

OPTICAL COMPUTING AND PROCESSING.
Taylor & Francis Ltd., Rankine Rd., Basingstoke, Hants. RG24 0PR, England. TEL 0256-840366. FAX 0256-479438. *1454*

OPTICAL MATERIALS.
North-Holland P.O. Box 211, 1000 AE Amsterdam, Netherlands. TEL 020-5803911. FAX 020-5803705. *3856*

OPTICAL MEMORY REPORT.
Rothchild Consultants Inc., 2140 Shattuck Ave., Berkeley, CA 94704-1210. *3856*

OPTICAL PHYSICS AND ENGINEERING.
Plenum Publishing Corp., 233 Spring St., New York, NY 10013-1578. TEL 212-620-8000. FAX 212-463-0742. *3856*

OPTICAL SOCIETY OF AMERICA. JOURNAL PART A.
Optical Society of America, Inc, 2010 Massachusetts Ave., N.W., Washington, DC 20036-1023. TEL 202-223-8130. *3856*

OPTICAL SOCIETY OF AMERICA. JOURNAL PART B.
Optical Society of America, Inc., 2010 Massachusetts Ave., N.W., Washington, DC 20036-1023. TEL 202-223-8130. *3856*

OPTICS AND LASER TECHNOLOGY.
Butterworth - Heinemann Ltd. Linacre House, Jordan Hill, Oxford OX2 8DP, England. TEL 0865-310366. FAX 0865-310898. *3856*

OPTICS AND LASERS IN ENGINEERING.
Elsevier Science Publishers Ltd., Crown House, Linton Rd., Barking, Essex IG11 8JU, England. TEL 081-594-7272. FAX 081-594-5942. *3856*

OPTICS AND SPECTROSCOPY.
American Institute of Physics, (Optical Society of America, Inc.) 335 E. 45th St., New York, NY 10017. TEL 212-661-9404. *3856*

OPTICS COMMUNICATIONS.
North-Holland P.O. Box 211, 1000 AE Amsterdam, Netherlands. TEL 020-5803911. FAX 020-5803598. *3857*

OPTOMETRY AND VISION SCIENCE.
Williams & Wilkins, (American Academy of Optometry) 428 E. Preston St., Baltimore, MD 21202. TEL 301-528-4000. FAX 301-528-4312. *3304*

OPTOMETRY CLINICS.
Appleton & Lange, Journal Division (Prentice Society) 25 Van Zant St., Box 5630, Norwalk, CT 06856. TEL 203-838-4400. *3304*

ORAL SURGERY, ORAL MEDICINE AND ORAL PATHOLOGY.
Mosby - Year Book, Inc. (American Academy of Oral Pathology) 11830 Westline Industrial Dr., St. Louis, MO 63146. TEL 800-325-4117. FAX 314-432-1380. *3239*

ORE GEOLOGY REVIEWS.
Elsevier Science Publishers B.V., P.O. Box 211, 1000 AE Amsterdam, Netherlands. TEL 020-5803911. FAX 020-5803598. *1577*

OREGON GEOLOGY.
Department of Geology and Mineral Industries, 800 N.E. Oregon St., Portland, OR 97232-2109. TEL 503-229-5580. FAX 503-229-5639. *1577*

ORGANIC CHEMISTRY.
Academic Press, Inc., 1250 Sixth Ave., San Diego, CA 92101. TEL 619-231-0926. FAX 619-699-6715. *1221*

ORGANIC ELECTRONIC SPECTRAL DATA.
John Wiley & Sons, Inc., (Organic Electronic Spectral Data, Inc.) 605 Third Ave., New York, NY 10158-0012. TEL 212-850-6000. FAX 212-850-6088. *1207*

ORGANIC GEOCHEMISTRY.
Pergamon Press, Inc., Journals Division, (European Association of Organic Geochemists) 660 White Plains Rd., Tarrytown, NY 10591-5153. TEL 914-524-9200. FAX 914-333-2444. *1221*

ORGANIC PHOTOCHEMISTRY: A SERIES OF ADVANCES.
Marcel Dekker, Inc., 270 Madison Ave., New York, NY 10016. TEL 212-696-9000. FAX 212-685-4540. *1221*

ORGANIC PREPARATIONS AND PROCEDURES INTERNATIONAL.
Organic Preparations and Procedures, Inc., Box 9, Newton Highlands, MA 02161. *1221*

ORGANIC REACTION MECHANISMS. ANNUAL SURVEY.
John Wiley & Sons, Inc., 605 Third Ave., New York, NY 10158-0012. TEL 212-850-6000. FAX 212-860-6088. *1221*

ORGANIC REACTIONS.
John Wiley & Sons, Inc., 605 Third Ave., New York, NY 10158-0012. TEL 212-850-6000. FAX 212-850-6088. *1221*

ORGANIC SYNTHESES.
John Wiley & Sons, Inc., 605 Third Ave., New York, NY 10158-0012. TEL 212-850-6000. FAX 212-850-6088. *1221*

ORGANOMETALLIC SYNTHESES.
Academic Press, Inc., 1250 Sixth Ave., San Diego, CA 92101. TEL 619-231-0926. FAX 619-699-6715. *3417*

ORGANOMETALLICS.
American Chemical Society, 1155 16th St., N.W., Washington, DC 20036. TEL 800-333-9511. FAX 202-872-4615. *1221*

ORIENTAL INSECTS.
Associated Publishers, Box 140103, Gainesville, FL 32614-0103. TEL 904-371-4071. *536*

ORIGINS (LOMA LINDA).
Loma Linda University, (Geoscience Research Institute) Loma Linda, CA 92350. TEL 714-824-4548. *4332*

ORION.
Operations Research Society of South Africa, P.O. Box 3982, Johannesburg 2000, South Africa. *3050*

ORTHOPAEDIC REVIEW.
Excerpta Medica, Inc., Core Publishing Division 105 Raider Blvd., Belle Mead, NJ 08052. TEL 908-874-8550. FAX 908-874-0700. *3310*

ORTHOPEDIC CLINICS OF NORTH AMERICA.
W.B. Saunders Co., Curtis Center, Independence Square W., Philadelphia, PA 19106. TEL 215-238-7800. *3310*

ORTHOPEDICS (THOROFARE).
Slack, Inc., 6900 Grove Rd., Thorofare, NJ 08086. TEL 609-848-1000. FAX 609-853-5991. *3310*

OSIRIS (CHICAGO).
University of Chicago Press, Journals Division, (History of Science Society) 5720 S. Woodlawn Ave., Chicago, IL 60637. TEL 312-702-7600. FAX 312-702-0694. *4332*

OSTEOPATHIC MEDICAL EDUCATION: A HANDBOOK FOR MINORITY APPLICANTS.
American Association of Colleges of Osteopathic Medicine, 6110 Executive Blvd., Ste. 405, Rockville, MD 20852. TEL 301-468-0990. *1714*

OTHER REALITIES.
Undena Publications, (University of California, Los Angeles, Department of Anthropology) Box 97, Malibu, CA 90265. TEL 805-746-5870. FAX 805-746-2728. *246*

OTOLARYNGOLOGY - HEAD AND NECK SURGERY.
Mosby - Year Book, Inc., (American Academy of Otolaryngology, Head and Neck Surgery Foundation) 11830 Westline Industrial Dr., St. Louis, MO 63146. TEL 800-325-4117. FAX 314-432-1380. *3316*

OUTLOOK ON AGRICULTURE.
C.A.B. International, Wallingford, Oxon OX10 8DE, England. TEL 0491-32111. FAX 0491-33508. *113*

OXFORD MATHEMATICAL MONOGRAPHS.
Oxford University Press, 200 Madison Ave., New York, NY 10016. TEL 212-679-7300. *3050*

OXFORD MONOGRAPHS ON BIOGEOGRAPHY.
Oxford University Press, 200 Madison Ave., New York, NY 10016. TEL 212-679-7300. *450*

OXFORD MONOGRAPHS ON MEDICAL GENETICS.
Oxford University Press, 200 Madison Ave., New York, NY 10016. TEL 212-679-7300. *3138*

OXFORD MONOGRAPHS ON METEOROLOGY AND PHYSICAL OCEANOGRAPHY.
Oxford University Press, 200 Madison Ave., New York, NY 10016. TEL 212-679-7300. *3440*

OXFORD NEUROLOGICAL MONOGRAPHS.
Oxford University Press, 200 Madison Ave., New York, NY 10016. TEL 212-679-7300. *3349*

OXFORD REVIEWS OF REPRODUCTIVE BIOLOGY.
Oxford University Press, 200 Madison Ave., New York, NY 10016. TEL 212-679-7300. *590*

OXIDATION OF METALS.
Plenum Publishing Corp., 233 Spring St., New York, NY 10013-1578. TEL 212-620-8000. FAX 212-463-0742. *1229*

OZONE.
Lewis Publishers, Inc., Journals Department, (International Ozone Association, Inc.) 2000 Corporate Blvd., N.W. Boca Raton, FL 33431. TEL 313-475-8619. FAX 313-475-8650. *1857*

P & T.
Excerpta Medica, Inc., Core Publishing Division 105 Raider Blvd., Belle Mead, NJ 08052. TEL 908-874-8550. FAX 908-874-0700. *3737*

P C R METHODS AND APPLICATIONS.
Cold Spring Harbor Laboratory Press, Publications Department, Box 100, Cold Spring Harbour, NY 11724. TEL 800-843-4388. FAX 516-349-1946. *556*

P S R QUARTERLY.
Williams & Wilkins, (Physicians for Social Responsibility) 428 Preston St., Baltimore, MD 21202. TEL 301-528-4000. FAX 301-528-4321. *4109*

REFEREED SERIALS

PACIFIC HISTORICAL REVIEW.
University of California Press, Journals Division, (American Historical Association, Pacific Coast Branch) 2120 Berkeley Way, Berkeley, CA 94720. TEL 510-642-4191. FAX 510-643-7127. *2418*

PACIFIC ISLANDS MONOGRAPH SERIES.
University of Hawaii Press, (University of Hawaii, Center for Pacific Islands Studies) 2840 Kolowalu St., Honolulu, HI 96822. TEL 808-956-8255. FAX 808-988-6052. *2418*

PACIFIC JOURNAL OF MATHEMATICS.
American Mathematical Society, Pacific Journal of Mathematics, c/o V.S. Varadarajan, Ed., Mathematics Department, University of California, Los Angeles, CA 90024-1555. FAX 213-206-6673. *3050*

PACIFIC SCIENCE.
University of Hawaii Press, Journals Department, 2840 Kolowalu St., Honolulu, HI 96822. TEL 808-956-8833. FAX 808-988-6052. *4332*

PAEDIATRIC NURSING.
Scutari Projects Ltd., Viking House, 17-19 Peterborough Rd., Harrow-on-the-Hill, Middlesex HA1 2AX, England. TEL 081-423-1066. FAX 081-423-3867. *3285*

PAIDEUSIS.
Canadian Philosophy of Education Society, c/o Prof. Don Cochrane, Manag.Ed., University of Saskatchewan, Dept. of Educational Foundations, Saskatoon, Sask. S7N 0W0, Canada. FAX 306-966-8719. *3775*

PAIN.
Elsevier Science Publishers B.V., (International Association for the Study of Pain) P.O. Box 211, 1000 AE Amsterdam, Netherlands. TEL 020-5803911. FAX 020-5803598. *3349*

PAINT TITLES.
Pergamon Press plc, (Paint Research Association) Headington Hill Hall, Oxford OX3 0BW, England. TEL 0865-794141. FAX 0865-743911. *3656*

PAKISTAN JOURNAL OF APPLIED ECONOMICS.
University of Karachi, Applied Economics Research Centre, P.O. Box 8403, Karachi 75270, Pakistan. TEL 474749. *878*

PAKISTAN JOURNAL OF PHARMACEUTICAL SCIENCES.
University of Karachi, Faculty of Pharmacy, Karachi 75270, Pakistan. *3737*

PALAEOGEOGRAPHY, PALAEOCLIMATOLOGY, PALAEOECOLOGY.
Elsevier Science Publishers B.V., P.O. Box 211, 1000 AE Amsterdam, Netherlands. TEL 020-5803911. FAX 020-5803598. *3659*

PALAEONTOGRAPHICA AMERICANA.
Paleontological Research Institution, 1259 Trumansburg Road, Ithaca, NY 14850. TEL 607-273-6623. *3659*

PALAEONTOLOGIA CATHAYANA.
Kexue Chubanshe, Qikan Bu, 16 Donghuangchenggen Beijie, Beijing 100707, People's Republic of China. TEL 4010642. FAX 4012180. *3659*

PALEOBIOLOGY.
Paleontological Society, Business Office, 1261 Trumansburg Rd., Ithaca, NY 14850-1313. TEL 607-273-6623. *3659*

PALEOCEANOGRAPHY.
American Geophysical Union, 2000 Florida Ave., N.W., Washington, DC 20009. TEL 202-462-6900. FAX 202-328-0566. *4333*

PALEONTOLOGICAL JOURNAL.
Scripta Technica, Inc. (Akademii Nauk S.S.S.R.) 7961 Eastern Ave., Silver Spring, MD 20910. TEL 301-588-0484. FAX 301-588-5278. *3660*

PALYNOLOGY.
American Association of Stratigraphic Palynologists Foundation, c/o Robert T. Clarke, Mobil R & D Corp.-D R L, Box 819047, Dallas, TX 75381. TEL 214-851-8481. FAX 214-851-8185. *3660*

PAN-PACIFIC ENTOMOLOGIST.
Pacific Coast Entomological Society, c/o California Academy of Sciences, Golden Gate Park, San Francisco, CA 94118-4599. TEL 415-750-7227. FAX 415-750-7106. *537*

PANCREAS.
Raven Press, 1185 Ave. of the Americas, New York, NY 10036. TEL 212-930-9500. FAX 212-869-3495. *3255*

PAPERS IN REGIONAL SCIENCE.
Regional Science Association International, 1 Observatory, 901 S. Mathews, Univ. of Illinois, Urbana, IL 61801-3682. TEL 217-333-8904. FAX 217-244-1785. *4382*

PARALLEL COMPUTING.
North-Holland P.O. Box 211, 1000 AE Amsterdam, Netherlands. TEL 020-5803911. FAX 020-5803598. *1438*

PARASITOLOGY TODAY.
Elsevier Science Publishers Ltd., Crown House, Linton Rd, Barking, Essex IG11 8JU, England. TEL 081-594-7272. FAX 081-594-5942. *3139*

PARERGON.
Australian and New Zealand Association for Medieval and Renaissance Studies, University of Sydney, Department of English, Sydney, N.S.W. 2006, Australia. FAX 02-692-2434. *2947*

PARTICLE ACCELERATORS.
Gordon and Breach Science Publishers, 270 Eighth Ave., New York, NY 10011. TEL 212-206-8900. FAX 212-645-2459. *3849*

PARTICLE WORLD.
Gordon and Breach Science Publishers, 270 Eighth Ave., New York, NY 10011. TEL 212-206-8900. FAX 212-645-2459. *3826*

PARTICULATE SCIENCE AND TECHNOLOGY.
Hemisphere Publishing Corporation (Fine Particle Society) 1900 Frost Rd., Ste. 101, Bristol, PA 19007-1598. TEL 215-785-5800. FAX 215-785-5515. *1857*

PASTORAL PSYCHOLOGY.
Human Sciences Press, Inc., 233 Spring St., New York, NY 10013-1578. TEL 212-620-8000. FAX 212-463-0742. *4037*

PATHOLOGY.
Hanley & Belfus, Inc., 210 S. 13th St., Philadelphia, PA 19107. TEL 215-546-7293. FAX 215-790-9330. *3139*

PATHOLOGY ANNUAL.
Appleton & Lange, Journal Division 25 Van Zant St., Box 5630, Norwalk, CT 06856. TEL 203-838-4400. *3139*

PATIENT EDUCATION AND COUNSELING.
Elsevier Scientific Publishers Ireland Ltd., (International Patient Education Council) P.O. Box 85, Limerick, Ireland. TEL 061-61944. FAX 061-62144. *4109*

PATTERN RECOGNITION.
Pergamon Press, Inc., Journals Division, (Pattern Recognition Society) 660 White Plains Rd., Tarrytown, NY 10591-5153. TEL 914-524-9200. FAX 914-333-2444. *4333*

PATTERN RECOGNITION AND IMAGE ANALYSIS.
New Soviet Sciences Press (USA), c/o Allen Press, Inc., Dist., Box 1897, Lawrence, KS 66044-8897. TEL 913-843-1235. FAX 913-843-1274. *3050*

PATTERN RECOGNITION LETTERS.
North-Holland (International Association for Pattern Recognition) P.O. Box 211, 1000 AE Amsterdam, Netherlands. TEL 020-5803911. FAX 020-5803598. *1422*

PEDIATRIC DENTISTRY.
American Academy of Pediatric Dentistry, 211 E. Chicago Ave., Ste. 1036, Chicago, IL 60611-2616. TEL 312-337-2169. FAX 312-337-6329. *3240*

PEDIATRIC DERMATOLOGY.
Blackwell Scientific Publications Inc., (Society for Pediatric Dermatology) Three Cambridge Center, Ste. 208, Cambridge, MA 02142-1413. TEL 617-225-0401. FAX 617-225-0412. *3249*

PEDIATRIC EMERGENCY CARE.
Williams & Wilkins, 428 E. Preston St., Baltimore, MD 21202. TEL 301-528-4000. FAX 301-528-4312. *3324*

PEDIATRIC EXERCISE SCIENCE.
Human Kinetics Publishers, Inc., Box 5076, Champaign, IL 61825-5076. TEL 217-351-5076. FAX 217-351-2674. *3324*

PEDIATRIC HABILITATION SERIES.
Marcel Dekker, Inc., 270 Madison Ave., New York, NY 10016. TEL 212-696-9000. FAX 212-685-4540. *3324*

PEDIATRIC HEMATOLOGY & ONCOLOGY.
Hemisphere Publishing Corporation 1900 Frost Rd., Ste. 101, Bristol, PA 19007-1598. TEL 215-785-5800. FAX 215-785-5515. *3324*

THE PEDIATRIC INFECTIOUS DISEASE JOURNAL.
Williams & Wilkins, 428 E. Preston St., Baltimore, MD 21202. TEL 301-528-4000. FAX 301-528-4312. *3324*

PEDIATRIC PATHOLOGY.
Hemisphere Publishing Corporation (International Paediatric Pathology Association) 1900 Frost Rd., Ste. 101, Bristol, PA 19007-1598. TEL 215-785-5800. FAX 215-785-5515. *3324*

PEDIATRIC PHYSICAL THERAPY.
Williams & Wilkins, (American Physical Therapy Association, Section on Pediatrics) 428 Preston St., Baltimore, MD 21202. TEL 301-528-4000. FAX 301-528-4312. *3324*

PEDIATRIC PULMONOLOGY.
John Wiley & Sons, Inc., Journals, 605 Third Ave., New York, NY 10158. TEL 212-850-6000. FAX 212-850-6088. *3324*

PEDIATRIC RESEARCH.
Williams & Wilkins, (International Pediatric Research Foundation Inc.) 428 E. Preston St., Baltimore, MD 21202. TEL 301-528-4000. FAX 301-528-4312. *3325*

PEDIATRIC REVIEWS AND COMMUNICATIONS.
Harwood Academic Publishers, 270 Eighth Ave., New York, NY 10011. TEL 212-206-8900. FAX 212-645-2459. *3325*

PEDIATRIC THERAPEUTICS & TOXICOLOGY.
Riverpress, Inc., Box 23, Jersey City, NJ 07303-0023. TEL 201-434-5073. FAX 201-434-7230. *3180*

PEDIATRICS IN REVIEW.
American Academy of Pediatrics, 141 Northwest Point Blvd., Box 927, Elk Grove Village, IL 60009-0927. TEL 708-228-5005. *3325*

PEDOSPHERE.
Science Press, Marketing and Sales Department, (Zhongguo Kexueyuan, Turangsuo) 16 Donghuangchenggen Beijie, Beijing 100707, People's Republic of China. TEL 4010642. FAX 4012180. *1547*

PENNSYLVANIA ACADEMY OF SCIENCE. JOURNAL.
Pennsylvania Academy of Science, c/o Dr. S.K. Majumdar, Ed., Dept. of Biology, Lafayette College, Easton, PA 18042. TEL 215-250-5464. FAX 215-250-6557. *451*

PEPTIDES.
Pergamon Press, Inc., Journals Division, 660 White Plains Rd., Tarrytown, NY 10591-5153. TEL 914-524-9200. FAX 914-333-2444. *481*

PERCEPTION & PSYCHOPHYSICS.
Psychonomic Society, Inc., 1710 Fortview Rd., Austin, TX 78704. TEL 512-462-2442. *4038*

PERFORMANCE EVALUATION.
North-Holland P.O. Box 211, 1000 AE Amsterdam, Netherlands. TEL 020-5803911. FAX 020-5803598. *1399*

PERSONALITY AND INDIVIDUAL DIFFERENCES.
Pergamon Press, Inc., Journals Division, (International Society for the Study of Individual Differences) 660 White Plains Rd., Tarrytown, NY 10591-5153. TEL 914-524-9200. FAX 914-333-2444. *4038*

PERSONALITY, PSYCHOPATHOLOGY AND PSYCHOTHERAPY.
Academic Press, Inc., 1250 Sixth Ave., San Diego, CA 92101. TEL 619-231-0926. FAX 619-699-6715. *4038*

PERSONNEL PSYCHOLOGY.
Personnel Psychology, Inc., 745 Haskins Rd., Ste. A, Bowling Green, OH 43402-1600. TEL 419-352-1562. FAX 419-352-2645. *4038*

PERSOONIA.
Rijksherbarium - Hortus Botanicus, Publications Department, P.O. Box 9514, 2300 RA Leiden, Netherlands. *512*

PERSPECTIVE OF PHYSICS (NEW YORK).
Gordon & Breach Science Publishers, 270 Eighth Ave., New York, NY 10011. TEL 212-206-8900. FAX 212-645-2459. *3826*

PERSPECTIVES.
University of Durban-Westville, Faculty of Commerce and Administration, Private Bag X54001, Durban 4000, South Africa. TEL 031-820-9111. FAX 031-820-2383. *879*

PERSPECTIVES IN ARTIFICIAL INTELLIGENCE.
Academic Press, Inc., 1250 Sixth Ave., San Diego, CA 92101. TEL 619-231-6616. FAX 619-699-6715. *1410*

PERSPECTIVES IN BIOLOGY AND MEDICINE.
University of Chicago Press, Journals Division, 5720 S. Woodlawn Ave., Chicago, IL 60637. TEL 312-753-3347. FAX 312-702-0694. *3140*

PERSPECTIVES IN BIOMECHANICS.
Harwood Academic Publishers, 270 Eighth Ave., New York, NY 10011. TEL 212-206-8900. FAX 212-645-2459. *451*

PERSPECTIVES IN CARDIOVASCULAR RESEARCH.
Raven Press, 1185 Ave. of the Americas, New York, NY 10036. TEL 212-930-9500. FAX 212-869-3495. *3211*

PERSPECTIVES IN COMPUTING (SAN DIEGO).
Academic Press, Inc., 1250 Sixth Ave., San Diego, CA 92101. TEL 619-231-6616. FAX 619-699-6715. *1399*

PERSPECTIVES IN ETHOLOGY.
Plenum Publishing Corp., 233 Spring St., New York, NY 10013-1578. TEL 212-620-8000. FAX 212-463-0742. *4814*

PERSPECTIVES IN IMMUNOLOGY.
Academic Press, Inc., 1250 Sixth Ave., San Diego, CA 92101. TEL 619-231-0926. FAX 619-699-6715. *3188*

PERSPECTIVES IN LAW AND PSYCHOLOGY.
Plenum Publishing Corp., 233 Spring St., New York, NY 10013. TEL 212-620-8000. FAX 212-463-0742. *2666*

PERSPECTIVES IN MATHEMATICS.
Academic Press, Inc., 1250 Sixth Ave., San Diego, CA 92101. TEL 619-231-6616. FAX 619-699-6715. *3050*

PERSPECTIVES IN NEUROLINGUISTICS, NEUROPSYCHOLOGY, AND PSYCHOLINGUISTICS.
Academic Press, Inc., 1250 Sixth Ave., San Diego, CA 92101. TEL 619-231-6616. FAX 619-699-6715. *3350*

PERSPECTIVES IN PHYSICS (SAN DIEGO).
Academic Press, Inc., 1250 Sixth Ave., San Diego, CA 92101. TEL 619-231-6616. FAX 619-699-6715. *3826*

PERSPECTIVES IN PSYCHOTHERAPY.
Gordon & Breach Science Publishers, 270 Eighth Ave., New York, NY 10011. TEL 212-206-8900. FAX 212-645-2459. *4038*

PERSPECTIVES ON POLITICAL SCIENCE.
Heldref Publications, (Helen Dwight Reid Educational Foundation) 1319 Eighteenth St., N.W., Washington, DC 20036-1802. TEL 202-296-6267. FAX 202-296-5149. *3915*

PERSPECTIVES ON SOUTHERN AFRICA.
University of California Press, 2120 Berkeley Way, Berkeley, CA 94720. TEL 415-642-4247. FAX 415-643-7127. *3915*

PERSPECTIVES ON THE AMERICAN SOUTH.
Gordon & Breach Science Publishers, 270 Eighth Ave., New York, NY 10011. TEL 212-206-8900. FAX 212-645-2459. *2419*

PEST CONTROL.
Avanstar Communications, Inc., 7500 Old Oak Blvd., Cleveland, OH 44130. TEL 216-826-2839. FAX 216-891-2726. *187*

PESTICIDE BIOCHEMISTRY AND PHYSIOLOGY.
Academic Press, Inc., Journal Division, 1250 Sixth Ave., San Diego, CA 92101. TEL 619-230-1840. FAX 619-699-6800. *187*

PESTICIDE SCIENCE.
Elsevier Science Publishers Ltd., (Society of Chemical Industry) Crown House, Linton Rd., Barking, Essex IG11 8JU, England. TEL 081-594-7272. FAX 081-594-5942. *188*

PETROLEUM CHEMISTRY U.S.S.R.
Pergamon Press, Inc., Journals Division, 660 White Plains Rd., Tarrytown, NY 10591-5153. TEL 914-524-9200. FAX 914-333-2444. *3697*

PHARMACEUTICAL CHEMISTRY JOURNAL.
Plenum Publishing Corp., Consultants Bureau, (Ministerstvo Zdravookhraneniya S.S.S.R.) 233 Spring St., New York, NY 10013-1578. TEL 212-620-8468. FAX 212-463-0742. *3738*

PHARMACEUTICAL RESEARCH.
Plenum Publishing Corp., (American Association of Pharmaceutical Scientists) 233 Spring St., New York, NY 10013-1578. TEL 212-620-8000. FAX 212-463-0742. *3738*

PHARMACEUTICAL TECHNOLOGY.
Aster Publishing Corporation, 859 Willamette St., Box 10955, Eugene, OR 97440. TEL 503-343-1200. FAX 503-343-3641. *3738*

PHARMACOCHEMISTRY LIBRARY.
Elsevier Science Publishers B.V., Books Division, P.O. Box 211, 1000 AE Amsterdam, Netherlands. TEL 020-5803911. FAX 020-5803705. *1185*

PHARMACOLOGICAL REVIEWS.
Williams & Wilkins, (American Society for Pharmacology and Experimental Therapeutics) 428 E. Preston St., Baltimore, MD 21202. TEL 301-528-4000. FAX 301-528-4312. *3739*

PHARMACOLOGY AND THERAPEUTICS.
Pergamon Press, Inc., Journals Division, (International Union of Pharmacology) 660 White Plains Rd., Tarrytown, NY 10591-5153. TEL 914-524-9200. FAX 914-333-2444. *3739*

PHARMACOLOGY, BIOCHEMISTRY AND BEHAVIOR.
Pergamon Press, Inc., Journals Division, 660 White Plains Rd., Tarrytown, NY 10591-5153. TEL 914-524-9200. FAX 914-333-2444. *590*

PHARMACOTHERAPY.
Pharmacotherapy Publications, Inc., New England Medical Center, 171 Harrison Ave., Box 806, Boston, MA 02111. TEL 617-956-5390. FAX 617-956-5318. *3739*

PHASE TRANSITIONS. SECTIONS A & B.
Gordon and Breach Science Publishers, 270 Eighth Ave., New York, NY 10011. TEL 212-206-8900. FAX 212-645-2459. *3826*

PHILIPS JOURNAL OF RESEARCH.
Elsevier Science Publishers Ltd., (Philips Corporate Research Laboratories) Crown House, Linton Rd., Barking, Essex IG11 8JU, England. TEL 081-594-7272. FAX 081-594-5942. *3050*

PHILOSOPHICAL MAGAZINE.
Taylor & Francis Ltd., Rankine Rd., Basingstoke, Hants. RG24 0PR, England. TEL 0256-840366. FAX 0256-479438. *3826*

PHILOSOPHICAL MAGAZINE LETTERS.
Taylor & Francis Ltd., Rankine Rd., Basingstoke, Hants RG24 0PR, England. TEL 0256-840366. FAX 0256-479438. *3826*

PHILOSOPHY AND RELIGION: A COMPARATIVE YEARBOOK.
E.J. Brill, P.O. Box 9000, 2300 PA Leiden, Netherlands. TEL 071-312624. FAX 071-317352. *3777*

PHILOSOPHY EAST AND WEST.
University of Hawaii Press, Journals Department, 2840 Kolowalu St., Honolulu, HI 96822. TEL 808-956-8833. FAX 808-988-6052. *3777*

PHILOSOPHY OF SCIENCE.
Philosophy of Science Association, 503 S. Kedzie Hall, Dept. of Philosophy, Michigan State Univ., East Lansing, MI 48824-1032. TEL 517-353-9392. *4333*

PHOENIX LITERATURE.
University of Chicago Press, 5801 S. Ellis Ave., Chicago, IL 60637. TEL 312-702-7899. *2948*

PHOENIX POETS.
University of Chicago Press, 5801 S. Ellis Ave., Chicago, IL 60637. TEL 708-702-7899. *3001*

PHOSPHORUS, SULPHUR AND SILICON AND THE RELATED ELEMENTS.
Gordon and Breach Science Publishers, 270 Eighth Ave., New York, NY 10011. TEL 212-206-8900. FAX 212-645-2459. *1214*

PHOTOCHEMICAL & PHOTOBIOLOGICAL REVIEWS.
Plenum Publishing Corp., 233 Spring St., New York, NY 10013-1578. TEL 212-620-8000. FAX 212-463-0742. *1185*

PHOTOCHEMISTRY AND PHOTOBIOLOGY.
Pergamon Press, Inc., Journals Division, (American Society for Photobiology) 660 White Plains Rd., Tarrytown, NY 10591-5153. TEL 914-524-9200. FAX 914-333-2444. *1185*

PHYSICA A - STATISTICAL AND THEORETICAL PHYSICS.
North-Holland (European Physical Society) P.O. Box 211, 1000 AE Amsterdam, Netherlands. TEL 020-5803911. FAX 020-5803598. *3826*

PHYSICA B - PHYSICS OF CONDENSED MATTER.
North-Holland (European Physical Society) P.O. Box 211, 1000 AE Amsterdam, Netherlands. TEL 020-5803911. FAX 020-5803598. *3826*

PHYSICA C - SUPERCONDUCTIVITY.
North-Holland (European Physical Society) P.O. Box 211, 1000 AE Amsterdam, Netherlands. TEL 020-5803911. FAX 020-5803598. *3826*

PHYSICA D - NONLINEAR PHENOMENA.
North-Holland (European Physical Society) P.O. Box 211, 1000 AE Amsterdam, Netherlands. TEL 020-5803911. FAX 020-5803598. *3826*

PHYSICAL ACOUSTICS: PRINCIPLES AND METHODS.
Academic Press, Inc., 1250 Sixth Ave., San Diego, CA 92101. TEL 619-231-0926. FAX 619-699-6715. *3860*

PHYSICAL & OCCUPATIONAL THERAPY IN GERIATRICS.
Haworth Press, Inc., 10 Alice St., Binghamton, NY 13904. TEL 800-342-9678. FAX 607-722-1424. *2277*

PHYSICAL & OCCUPATIONAL THERAPY IN PEDIATRICS.
Haworth Press, Inc., 10 Alice St., Binghamton, NY 13904. TEL 800-342-9678. FAX 607-722-1424. *3325*

PHYSICAL GEOGRAPHY.
V.H. Winston & Son, Inc., 7961 Eastern Ave., Ste. 202A, Silver Spring, MD 20910. TEL 301-587-3356. *1547*

PHYSICAL MEDICINE & REHABILITATION.
Hanley & Belfus, Inc., 210 S. 13th St., Philadelphia, PA 19107. TEL 215-546-7293. FAX 215-790-9330. *3141*

PHYSICAL REVIEW A (GENERAL PHYSICS).
American Institute of Physics, (American Physical Society) 335 E. 45th St., New York, NY 10017. TEL 212-661-9404. *3827*

REFEREED SERIALS

PHYSICAL REVIEW B (CONDENSED MATTER).
American Institute of Physics, (American Physical Society) 335 E. 45th St., New York, NY 10017. TEL 212-661-9404. *3827*

PHYSICAL REVIEW C (NUCLEAR PHYSICS).
American Institute of Physics, (American Physical Society) 335 E. 45th St., New York, NY 10017. TEL 212-661-9404. *3849*

PHYSICAL REVIEW ABSTRACTS.
American Institute of Physics, (American Physical Society) 335 E. 45th St., New York, NY 10017. TEL 212-661-9404. *3838*

PHYSICAL REVIEW LETTERS.
American Institute of Physics, (American Physical Society) 335 E. 45th St., New York, NY 10017. TEL 212-661-9404. *3827*

PHYSICAL SCIENCES DATA.
Elsevier Science Publishers B.V., Books Division, P.O. Box 211, 1000 AE Amsterdam, Netherlands. TEL 020-5803911. FAX 020-5803705. *1229*

PHYSICAL THERAPY IN HEALTH CARE.
Haworth Press, Inc., 10 Alice St., Binghamton, NY 13904. TEL 800-342-9678. FAX 607-722-1424. *3141*

PHYSICS: A SERIES OF MONOGRAPHS & TRACTS.
Harwood Academic Publishers, 270 Eighth Ave., New York, NY 10011. TEL 212-206-8900. FAX 212-645-2459. *3827*

PHYSICS AND CHEMISTRY OF LIQUIDS.
Gordon and Breach Science Publishers, 270 Eighth Ave., New York, NY 10011. TEL 212-206-8900. FAX 212-645-2459. *3844*

PHYSICS AND CHEMISTRY OF THE EARTH.
Pergamon Press, Inc., Journals Division, 660 White Plains Rd., Tarrytown, NY 10591-5153. TEL 914-524-9200. FAX 914-333-2444. *1548*

PHYSICS AND EVOLUTION OF THE EARTH'S INTERIOR.
Elsevier Science Publishers B.V., Books Division, P.O. Box 211, 1000 AE Amsterdam, Netherlands. TEL 020-5803911. FAX 020-5803705. *1577*

PHYSICS, CHEMISTRY AND MECHANICS OF SURFACES.
Gordon & Breach Science Publishers, 270 Eighth Ave., New York, NY 10011. TEL 212-206-8900. FAX 212-645-2459. *1937*

PHYSICS EDUCATION.
Wiley Eastern Ltd., Journal Division, (University of Poona, Department of Physics) 4835-24 Ansari Road, New Delhi 110 002, India. *3827*

PHYSICS LETTERS. SECTION A: GENERAL, ATOMIC AND SOLID STATE PHYSICS.
North-Holland P.O. Box 211, 1000 AE Amsterdam, Netherlands. TEL 020-5803911. FAX 020-5803598. *3850*

PHYSICS LETTERS. SECTION B: NUCLEAR, ELEMENTARY PARTICLE AND HIGH-ENERGY PHYSICS.
North-Holland P.O. Box 211, 1000 AE Amsterdam, Netherlands. TEL 020-5803911. FAX 020-5803598. *3850*

PHYSICS - MATHEMATICS INFORMATION REVIEW.
Nova Science Publishers, Inc., 283 Commack Rd., Ste. 300, Commack, NY 11725-3401. *3827*

PHYSICS OF FLUIDS A: FLUID DYNAMICS.
American Institute of Physics, 335 E. 45th St., New York, NY 10017-3483. TEL 212-661-9404. *3828*

PHYSICS OF FLUIDS B: PLASMA PHYSICS.
American Institute of Physics, 335 E. 45th St., New York, NY 10017-3483. TEL 212-661-9404. *3828*

PHYSICS OF METALS.
Gordon and Breach Science Publishers, 270 Eighth Ave., New York, NY 10011. TEL 212-206-8900. FAX 212-645-2459. *3417*

PHYSICS OF METALS AND METALLOGRAPHY.
Pergamon Press, Inc., Journals Division, 660 White Plains Rd., Tarrytown, NY 10591-5153. TEL 914-524-9200. FAX 914-333-2444. *3417*

PHYSICS OF THE EARTH AND PLANETARY INTERIORS.
Elsevier Science Publishers B.V., P.O. Box 211, 1000 AE Amsterdam, Netherlands. TEL 020-5803911. FAX 020-5803598. *1593*

PHYSICS OF THIN FILMS; ADVANCES IN RESEARCH AND DEVELOPMENT.
Academic Press, Inc., 1250 Sixth Ave., San Diego, CA 92101. TEL 619-231-0926. FAX 619-699-6715. *3828*

PHYSICS REPORTS.
North-Holland P.O. Box 211, 1000 AE Amsterdam, Netherlands. TEL 020-5803911. FAX 020-5803598. *3828*

PHYSICS REPORTS REPRINTS BOOK SERIES.
Elsevier Science Publishers B.V., Books Division, P.O. Box 211, 1000 AE Amsterdam, Netherlands. TEL 020-5803911. FAX 020-5803705. *3828*

PHYSICS TODAY.
American Institute of Physics, 335 E. 45th St., New York, NY 10017. TEL 212-661-9404. *3828*

PHYSIOLOGICAL CHEMISTRY AND PHYSICS AND MEDICAL N M R.
Pacific Press, Box 1452 Melville, NY 11747. TEL 516-694-2929. FAX 516-249-3734. *486*

PHYSIOLOGICAL REVIEWS.
American Physiological Society, 9650 Rockville Pike, Bethesda, MD 20814. TEL 301-530-7071. FAX 301-571-1814. *574*

PHYSIOLOGICAL ZOOLOGY.
University of Chicago Press, Journals Division, (American Society of Zoologists, Division of Comparative Physiology and Biochemistry) 5720 S. Woodlawn Ave., Chicago, IL 60637. TEL 312-753-3347. FAX 312-702-0694. *590*

PHYSIOLOGIST.
American Physiological Society, 9650 Rockville Pike, Bethesda, MD 20814. TEL 301-530-7164. FAX 301-571-1814. *574*

PHYSIOLOGY AND BEHAVIOR.
Pergamon Press, Inc., Journals Division, 660 White Plains Rd., Tarrytown, NY 10591-5153. TEL 914-524-9200. FAX 914-333-2444. *574*

PHYSIOTHERAPY THEORY AND PRACTICE.
Lawrence Erlbaum Associates Ltd., 27 Palmeira Masions, Church Rd., Hove, E. Sussex BN3 2FA, England. TEL 0273-207411. FAX 0273-205612. *3142*

PHYTOCHEMISTRY.
Pergamon Press, Inc., Journals Division, (Phytochemical Society of Europe) 660 White Plains Rd., Tarrytown, NY 10591-5153. TEL 914-524-9200. FAX 914-333-2444. *513*

PHYTOLOGIA.
c/o Michael J. Warnock, Ed., 185 Westridge Dr., Huntsville, TX 77340. TEL 409-295-5410. FAX 409-291-0009. *513*

PHYTOPATHOLOGY.
A P S Press, (American Phytopathological Society) 3340 Pilot Knob Rd., St. Paul, MN 55121-2097. TEL 800-328-7560. FAX 612-454-0766. *513*

PLAINS ANTHROPOLOGIST.
Plains Anthropological society, c/o Lawrence Tomsyck, 410 Wedgewood Dr., Lincoln, NE 68510. TEL 402-488-3813. *247*

PLANETARY AND SPACE SCIENCE.
Pergamon Press, Inc., Journals Division, 660 White Plains Rd., Tarrytown, NY 10591-5153. TEL 914-524-9200. FAX 914-333-2444. *368*

PLANT DISEASE.
A P S Press, (American Phytopathological Society) 3340 Pilot Knob Rd., St. Paul, MN 55121-2097. TEL 800-328-7560. FAX 612-454-0766. *188*

PLANT PHYSIOLOGY.
American Society of Plant Physiologists, 15501 Monona Dr., Rockville, MD 20855. TEL 301-251-0560. FAX 301-279-2996. *514*

PLANT PROTECTION QUARTERLY.
R.G. Richardson, Ed. & Pub., 18 Koornalla Cres., Mt. Eliza, Vic. 3930, Australia. TEL 03-787-3804. FAX 03-785-2007. *189*

PLANT SCIENCE.
Elsevier Scientific Publishers Ireland Ltd., P.O. Box 85, Limerick, Ireland. TEL 061-61944. FAX 061-62144. *515*

PLASMA CHEMISTRY & PLASMA PROCESSING.
Plenum Publishing Corp., 233 Spring St., New York, NY 10013-1578. TEL 212-620-8000. FAX 212-463-0742. *1857*

PLASMA DEVICES AND OPERATIONS.
Gordon and Breach Science Publishers, 270 Eighth Ave., New York, NY 10011. TEL 212-206-8900. FAX 212-645-2459. *3828*

PLASMA PHYSICS AND CONTROLLED FUSION.
Pergamon Press, Inc., Journals Division, (Institute of Physics) 660 White Plains Rd., Tarrytown, NY 10591-5153. TEL 914-524-9200. FAX 914-333-2444. *3828*

PLASMID.
Academic Press, Inc., Journal Division, 1250 Sixth Ave., San Diego, CA 92101. TEL 619-230-1840. FAX 619-699-6800. *451*

PLASTIC AND RECONSTRUCTIVE SURGERY.
Williams & Wilkins, (American Society of Plastic & Reconstructive Surgeons) 428 E. Preston St., Baltimore, MD 21202. TEL 301-528-4000. FAX 301-528-4312. *3382*

PLASTICS DESIGN FORUM.
Avanstar Communications, Inc., 7500 Old Oak Blvd., Cleveland, OH 44130. TEL 216-243-8100. FAX 216-826-2726. *3866*

PLASTICS ENGINEERING SERIES.
Marcel Dekker, Inc., 270 Madison Ave., New York, NY 10016. TEL 212-696-9000. FAX 212-685-4540. *3866*

PLASTICS IN BUILDING CONSTRUCTION.
Technomic Publishing Co., Inc., 851 New Holland Ave., Box 3535, Lancaster, PA 17604. TEL 717-291-5609. FAX 717-295-45388. *628*

PLASTICS, RUBBER AND COMPOSITES PROCESSING AND APPLICATIONS.
Elsevier Science Publishers Ltd., (Plastics and Rubber Institute) Crown House, Linton Rd., Barking, Essex IG11 8JU, England. TEL 081-594-7272. FAX 081-594-5942. *3866*

PLAY & CULTURE.
Human Kinetics Publishers, Inc., (Association for the Study of Play) Box 5076, Champaign, IL 61825-5076. TEL 217-351-5076. FAX 217-351-2674. *4444*

POETICS.
North-Holland P.O. Box 211, 1000 AE Amsterdam, Netherlands. TEL 020-5803911. FAX 020-5803598. *2949*

POETICS TODAY.
Duke University Press, (Porter Institute for Poetics and Semiotics) 6697 College Station, Durham, NC 27708. TEL 919-684-2173. FAX 919-684-8644. *2879*

POLAR RESEARCH.
Norwegian Polar Research Institute, P.O. Box 158, 1330 Oslo Lufthavn, Norway. *4334*

POLICING AND SOCIETY.
Harwood Academic Publishers, 270 Eighth Ave., New York, NY 10011. TEL 212-206-8900. FAX 212-645-2459. *1520*

POLISH JOURNAL OF OCCUPATIONAL MEDICINE AND ENVIRONMENTAL HEALTH.
Institute of Occupational Medicine, P.O. Box 199, Ul. Teresy 8, 90-950 Lodz, Poland. TEL 42-569632. FAX 42-348331. *3620*

POLITICAL BEHAVIOR.
Plenum Publishing Corp., 233 Spring St., New York, NY 10013-1578. TEL 212-620-8000. FAX 212-463-0742. *3916*

POLITICAL COMMUNICATION AND PERSUASION.
Taylor & Francis, 1900 Frost Rd., Ste. 101, Bristol, PA 19007. TEL 215-785-5800. FAX 215-785-5515. *3916*

POLITICAL GEOGRAPHY QUARTERLY.
Butterworth - Heinemann Ltd. Linacre House, Jordan Hill, Oxford OX2 8DP, England. TEL 0865-310366. FAX 0865-310898. *2259*

POLITICAL PSYCHOLOGY.
Plenum Publishing Corp., (International Society of Political Psychology) 233 Spring St., New York, NY 10013-1578. TEL 212-620-8000. FAX 212-463-0742. *3917*

POLITICS AND SOCIETY.
Sage Publications, Inc., 2455 Teller Rd., Newbury Park, CA 91320. TEL 805-499-0721. FAX 805-499-0871. *3917*

POLITIKON.
Staatkundige Vereniging van Suid Afrika, P.O. Box 1041, Florida 1710, South Africa. *3918*

POLYCYCLIC AROMATIC COMPOUNDS.
Gordon and Breach Science Publishers, 270 Eighth Ave., New York, NY 10011. TEL 212-206-8900. FAX 212-645-2459. *1222*

POLYHEDRON.
Pergamon Press, Inc., Journals Division, 660 White Plains Rd., Tarrytown, NY 10591-5153. TEL 914-524-9200. FAX 914-333-2444. *1214*

POLYMER.
Butterworth - Heinemann Ltd. Linacre House, Jordan Hill, Oxford OX2 8DP, England. TEL 0865-31-366. FAX 0865-310898. *1222*

POLYMER BLENDS, ALLOYS AND INTERPENETRATING POLYMER NETWORKS ABSTRACTS.
Technomic Publishing Co., Inc., 851 New Holland Ave., Box 3535, Lancaster, PA 17604. TEL 717-291-5609. FAX 717-295-4538. *1202*

POLYMER CONTENTS.
Elsevier Science Publishers Ltd., Crown House, Linton Rd., Barking, Essex IG11 8JU, England. TEL 081-594-7272. FAX 081-594-5942. *1845*

POLYMER DEGRADATION AND STABILITY.
Elsevier Science Publishers Ltd., Crown House, Linton Rd., Barking, Essex IG11 8JU, England. TEL 081-594-7272. FAX 081-594-5942. *1222*

POLYMER ENGINEERING AND SCIENCE.
Society of Plastics Engineers, Inc., 14 Fairfield Dr., Brookfield Center, CT 06805. TEL 203-775-0471. FAX 203-775-8490. *1858*

POLYMER INTERNATIONAL.
Elsevier Science Publishers Ltd, Crown House, Linton Rd., Barking, Essex IG11 8JU, England. TEL 081-594-7272. FAX 081-594-5942. *3867*

POLYMER MONOGRAPHS.
Gordon & Breach Science Publishers, 270 Eighth Ave., New York, NY 10011. TEL 212-206-8900. FAX 212-645-2459. *1222*

POLYMER NEWS.
Gordon and Breach, Science Publishers, 270 Eighth Ave., New York, NY 10011. TEL 212-206-8900. FAX 212-645-2459. *1222*

POLYMER-PLASTICS TECHNOLOGY AND ENGINEERING.
Marcel Dekker Journals, 270 Madison Ave., New York, NY 10016. TEL 212-696-9000. FAX 212-685-4540. *1222*

POLYMER PREPRINTS.
American Chemical Society, Division of Polymer Chemistry, Inc., c/o Bill M. Culbertson, Ed., College of Dentistry, Ohio State University, 305 W. 12th Ave., Columbus, OH 43210. FAX 614-292-7619. *1222*

POLYMER SCIENCE AND TECHNOLOGY.
Plenum Publishing Corp., 233 Spring St., New York, NY 10013-1578. TEL 212-620-8000. FAX 212-463-0742. *1222*

POLYMER SCIENCE LIBRARY.
Elsevier Science Publishers B.V., Books Division, P.O. Box 211, 1000 AE Amsterdam, Netherlands. TEL 020-5803911. FAX 020-5803705. *1186*

POLYMER SCIENCE U.S.S.R.
Pergamon Press, Inc., Journals Division, 660 White Plains Rd., Tarrytown, NY 10591-5153. TEL 914-524-9200. FAX 914-333-2444. *1222*

POLYMER SCIENCE YEARBOOK.
Harwood Academic Publishers, 270 Eighth Ave., New York, NY 10011. TEL 212-206-8900. FAX 212-645-2459. *1186*

POLYMER TESTING.
Elsevier Science Publishers Ltd., Crown House, Linton Rd., Barking, Essex IG11 8JU, England. TEL 081-594-7272. FAX 081-594-5942. *3867*

POLYMERIC MATERIALS SCIENCE AND ENGINEERING.
American Chemical Society, Division of Polymeric Materials Science & Engineering, Distribution Office, 1155 16th St., N.W., Washington, DC 20036. *1222*

POPULAR CULTURE IN LIBRARIES.
Haworth Press, Inc., 10 Alice St., Binghamton, NY 13904-1580. TEL 800-342-9678. FAX 607-722-1424. *2779*

POPULATION AND ENVIRONMENT.
Human Sciences Press, Inc. (American Psychological Association, Division of Population and Environmental Psychology) 233 Spring St., New York, NY 10013-1578. TEL 212-620-8000. FAX 212-463-0742. *4038*

POST MARKETING SURVEILLANCE.
Elsevier Science Publishers B.V., P.O. Box 211, 1000 AE Amsterdam, Netherlands. TEL 020-5803911. FAX 020-5803598. *3740*

POSTGRADUATE MEDICINE.
McGraw-Hill, Inc., 1221 Ave. of the Americas, New York, NY 10020. TEL 212-512-2000. *3143*

POSTHARVEST BIOLOGY AND TECHNOLOGY.
Elsevier Science Publishers B.V., P.O. Box 211, 1000 AE Amsterdam, Netherlands. TEL 020-5803911. FAX 020-5803598. *491*

POULTRY SCIENCE REVIEWS.
Elsevier Science Publishers Ltd., Crown House, Linton Rd., Barking, Essex IG11 8JU, England. TEL 081-594-7272. FAX 081-594-5942. *224*

POVIJESNI PRILOZI.
Institut za Suvremenu Povijest, Opaticka 10, 41000 Zagreb, Croatia. *2319*

POWDER TECHNOLOGY.
Elsevier Sequoia S.A., P.O. Box 564, CH-1001 Lausanne, Switzerland. TEL 021-207381. FAX 021-235444. *1858*

POWER (NEW YORK).
McGraw-Hill, Inc., 1221 Ave. of the Americas, New York, NY 10020. TEL 212-512-2000. *1938*

PRACTICAL DIABETES.
Home & Law Publishing Ltd., (Newbourne Group) Greater London House, Hampstead Rd., London NW1 7QQ, England. TEL 01-388-3171. FAX 01-387-9518. *3255*

PRACTICAL METHODS IN ELECTRON MICROSCOPY.
Elsevier Science Publishers B.V., Books Division, P.O. Box 211, 1000 AE Amsterdam, Netherlands. TEL 020-5803911. FAX 020-5803705. *561*

PRACTICAL SPECTROSCOPY SERIES.
Marcel Dekker, Inc., 270 Madison Ave., New York, NY 10016. TEL 212-696-9000. FAX 212-685-4540. *1208*

PRAGMATICS & COGNITION.
John Benjamins Publishing Co., Amsteldijk 44, P.O. Box 75577, 1070 AN Amsterdam, Netherlands. TEL 020-6738156. FAX 020-6739773. *2857*

PRAIRIE FORUM.
Canadian Plains Research Center, University of Regina, Regina, Sask. S4S 0A2, Canada. TEL 306-585-4795. FAX 306-586-9862. *1966*

PRE- AND PERI-NATAL PSYCHOLOGY JOURNAL.
Human Sciences Press, Inc. (Pre- and Peri-Natal Psychology Association of North America) 233 Spring St., New York, NY 10013-1578. TEL 212-620-8000. FAX 212-463-0742. *3295*

PRECAMBRIAN RESEARCH.
Elsevier Science Publishers B.V., (International Union of Geological Sciences, Subcommission on Precambrian Stratigraphy) P.O. Box 211, 1000 AE Amsterdam, Netherlands. TEL 020-5803911. FAX 020-5803598. *1578*

PRECISION ENGINEERING.
Butterworth - Heinemann Ltd. (American Society for Precision Engineering) 80 Montvale Ave., Stoneham, MA 02180. TEL 617-438-8464. FAX 617-279-4851. *1834*

PRECISION MACHINERY.
Gordon and Breach Science Publishers, 270 Eighth Ave., New York, NY 10011. TEL 212-206-8900. FAX 212-645-2459. *1410*

PREHISTORIC ARCHAEOLOGY AND ECOLOGY.
University of Chicago Press, 5801 S. Ellis Ave., Chicago, IL 60637. TEL 312-702-7899. *282*

PREHOSPITAL AND DISASTER MEDICINE.
Jems Publishing Co., Inc., (World Association for Emergency and Disaster Medicine) Box 2789, Carlsbad, CA 92018. TEL 619-431-9797. FAX 619-431-8176. *3143*

PREPARATIVE BIOCHEMISTRY.
Marcel Dekker Journals, 270 Madison Ave., New York, NY 10016. TEL 212-696-9000. FAX 212-685-4540. *481*

PREPARATIVE CHROMATOGRAPHY.
Gordon & Breach Science Publishers, 270 Eighth Ave., New York, NY 10011. TEL 212-206-8900. FAX 212-645-2459. *1208*

PRESIDENTIAL STUDIES QUARTERLY.
Center for the Study of the Presidency, 208 E. 75th St., New York, NY 10021. TEL 212-249-1200. FAX 212-628-9503. *3919*

PRESIDENT'S REPORT.
F I S I - Madison Financial Corporation Box 40726, Nashville, TN 37204. TEL 615-371-2775. *796*

PREVENTING SCHOOL FAILURE.
Heldref Publications, (Helen Dwight Reid Educational Foundation) 1319 Eighteenth St., N.W., Washington, DC 20036-1802. TEL 202-296-6267. FAX 202-296-5149. *1740*

PREVENTION IN HUMAN SERVICES.
Haworth Press, Inc., 10 Alice St., Binghamton, NY 13904. TEL 800-342-9678. FAX 607-722-1424. *4051*

PREVENTIVE MEDICINE.
Academic Press, Inc., Journal Division, (American Society of Preventive Oncology) 1250 Sixth Ave., San Diego, CA 92101. TEL 619-230-1840. FAX 619-699-6800. *3144*

PREVENTIVE VETERINARY MEDICINE.
Elsevier Science Publishers B.V., P.O. Box 211, 1000 AE Amsterdam, Netherlands. TEL 020-5803911. FAX 020-5803598. *4814*

PREVIEWS OF HEAT AND MASS TRANSFER.
Pergamon Press, Inc., Journals Division, (International Centre for Heat and Mass Transfer) 660 White Plains Rd., Tarrytown, NY 10591-5153. TEL 914-524-9200. FAX 914-333-2444. *1846*

PRIMARY CARDIOLOGY.
P W Communications, Inc., 400 Plaza Dr., Secaucus, NJ 07094. TEL 201-865-7500. *3211*

PRIMARY CARE RHEUMATOLOGY.
American College of Rheumatology, 60 Executive Park S., Ste. 150, Atlanta, GA 30329. TEL 404-633-3777. FAX 404-633-1870. *3369*

REFEREED SERIALS

PRIMARY SOURCES & ORIGINAL WORKS.
Haworth Press, Inc., 10 Alice St., Binghamton, NY 13904. TEL 800-342-9678. FAX 607-722-1424. *2779*

PRIMUS.
Rose-Hulman Institute of Technology, Department of Mathematics, Terre Haute, IN 47803. TEL 812-877-8412. *3051*

PRINCETON ENGINEER.
Princeton University, School of Engineering and Applied Science, ACE 23 E-Quad, Princeton, NJ 08544. TEL 609-452-4554. *1834*

PRINCETON MATHEMATICAL SERIES.
Princeton University Press, 3175 Princeton Pike, Lawrenceville, NJ 08648. TEL 609-896-1344. FAX 609-895-1081. *3051*

PRINCETON SERIES IN PHYSICS.
Princeton University Press, 3175 Princeton Pike, Lawrenceville, NJ 08648. TEL 609-896-1344. FAX 609-895-1081. *3829*

PROBABILISTIC ENGINEERING MECHANICS.
Elsevier Science Publishers Ltd., Crown House, Linton Rd., Barking, Essex IG11 8JU, England. TEL 081-594-7272. FAX 081-594-5942. *1938*

PROBABILITY AND MATHEMATICAL STATISTICS.
Academic Press, Inc., 1250 Sixth Ave., San Diego, CA 92101. TEL 619-231-0926. FAX 619-699-6715. *3051*

PROBLEMS IN ECONOMIC TRANSITION.
M.E. Sharpe, Inc., 80 Business Park Dr., Armonk, NY 10504. TEL 914-273-1800. FAX 914-273-2106. *686*

PROBLEMS IN PLASTIC AND RECONSTRUCTIVE SURGERY.
J.J. Lippincott Co., 227 E. Washington Sq., Philadelphia, PA 19106. TEL 215-238-4200. FAX 215-238-4493. *3383*

PROBLEMS IN PRIVATE INTERNATIONAL LAW.
Elsevier Science Publishers B.V., Books Division, P.O. Box 211, 1000 AE Amsterdam, Netherlands. TEL 020-5803911. FAX 020-5803705. *2728*

PROBLEMS IN UROLOGY.
J.B. Lippincott Co., E. Washington Sq., Philadelphia, PA 19105. TEL 215-238-4200. *3389*

PROBLEMS OF DESERT DEVELOPMENT.
Allerton Press, Inc., 150 Fifth Ave., New York, NY 10011. TEL 212-924-3950. *1966*

PROBLEMS OF INDUSTRIAL PSYCHIATRIC MEDICINE SERIES.
Human Sciences Press, Inc. 233 Spring St., New York, NY 10013-1578. TEL 212-620-8000. FAX 212-463-0742. *4039*

PROBLEMS OF INFORMATION TRANSMISSION.
Plenum Publishing Corp., Consultants Bureau, (Russian Academy of Sciences) 233 Spring St., New York, NY 10013-1578. TEL 212-620-8468. FAX 212-463-0742. *1447*

PROCESS BIOCHEMISTRY.
Elsevier Science Publishers Ltd., Crown House, Linton Rd., Barking, Essex IG11 8JU, England. TEL 081-594-7272. FAX 081-594-5942. *491*

PROCESS CONTROL AND QUALITY.
Elsevier Science Publishers B.V., P.O. Box 211, Amsterdam, Netherlands. TEL 020-5803911. FAX 020-5803598. *3448*

PROCESS EQUIPMENT SERIES.
Technomic Publishing Co., Inc., 851 New Holland Ave., Box 3535, Lancaster, PA 17604. TEL 717-291-5609. FAX 717-295-4538. *1859*

PROCESS METALLURGY.
Elsevier Science Publishers B.V., Books Division, P.O. Box 211, 1000 AE Amsterdam, Netherlands. TEL 020-5803911. FAX 020-5803705. *3418*

PROCESS SAFETY AND ENVIRONMENTAL PROTECTION.
Taylor & Francis Ltd., (Institution of Chemical Engineers) Rankine Rd., Basingstoke, Hants. RG24 0PR, England. TEL 0256-840366. FAX 0256-479438. *1186*

PROCESS TECHNOLOGY PROCEEDINGS.
Elsevier Science Publishers B.V., Books Division, P.O. Box 211, 1000 AE Amsterdam, Netherlands. TEL 020-5803911. FAX 020-5803705. *1400*

PROCESSING OF ADVANCED MATERIALS.
Chapman & Hall, 2-6 Boundary Row, London SE1 8HN, England. TEL 071-865-0066. FAX 071-522-9623. *1922*

PRODUCTION PLANNING & CONTROL.
Taylor & Francis Ltd., Rankine Rd., Basingstoke, Hants. RG24 0PR, England. TEL 0256-840366. FAX 0256-479438. *1880*

PROFESSIONAL PSYCHOLOGY: RESEARCH AND PRACTICE.
American Psychological Association, 750 First St., N.E., Washington, DC 20002-4242. TEL 202-336-7500. FAX 202-336-5568. *4039*

PROGRAMMING AND COMPUTER SOFTWARE.
Plenum Publishing Corp., Consultants Bureau, (Russian Academy of Sciences) 233 Spring St., New York, NY 10013-1578. TEL 212-620-8468. FAX 212-463-0742. *1431*

PROGRESS AND TOPICS IN CYTOGENETICS.
Wiley-Liss, Inc., 41 E. 11th St., New York, NY 10003. TEL 212-475-7700. *546*

PROGRESS IN AEROSPACE SCIENCES.
Pergamon Press, Inc., Journals Division, 660 White Plains Rd., Tarrytown, NY 10591-5153. TEL 914-524-9200. FAX 914-333-2444. *60*

PROGRESS IN ANESTHESIOLOGY.
Raven Press, 1185 Ave. of the Americas, New York, NY 10036. TEL 212-930-9500. FAX 212-869-3495. *3192*

PROGRESS IN BIOPHYSICS & MOLECULAR BIOLOGY.
Pergamon Press, Inc., Journals Division, 660 White Plains Rd., Tarrytown, NY 10591-5153. TEL 914-524-9200. FAX 914-333-2444. *486*

PROGRESS IN BRAIN RESEARCH.
Elsevier Science Publishers B.V., Books Division, P.O. Box 211, 1000 AE Amsterdam, Netherlands. TEL 020-5803911. FAX 020-5803705. *3350*

PROGRESS IN CANCER RESEARCH AND THERAPY.
Raven Press, 1185 Ave. of the Americas, New York, NY 10036. TEL 212-930-9500. FAX 212-869-3495. *3201*

PROGRESS IN CARDIOLOGY.
Lea & Febiger, 200 Chester Field Parkway, Malvern, PA 19355. TEL 800-444-1785. FAX 215-251-2229. *3211*

PROGRESS IN CARDIOVASCULAR DISEASES.
W.B. Saunders Co. Curtis Center, Independence Square W., Philadelphia, PA 19106. TEL 215-238-7800. *3211*

PROGRESS IN CLINICAL AND BIOLOGICAL RESEARCH.
Wiley-Liss, Inc., 41 E. 11th St., New York, NY 10003. TEL 212-475-7700. *3144*

PROGRESS IN CRYSTAL GROWTH AND CHARACTERIZATION OF MATERIALS.
Pergamon Press, Inc., Journals Division, 660 White Plains Rd., Tarrytown, NY 10591-5153. TEL 914-524-9200. FAX 914-333-2444. *1211*

PROGRESS IN ENERGY AND COMBUSTION SCIENCE.
Pergamon Press, Inc., Journals Division, 660 White Plains Rd., Tarrytown, NY 10591-5153. TEL 914-524-9200. FAX 914-333-2444. *1859*

PROGRESS IN FILTRATION AND SEPARATION.
Elsevier Science Publishers B.V., Books Division, P.O. Box 211, 1000 AE Amsterdam, Netherlands. TEL 020-5803911. FAX 020-5803705. *1186*

PROGRESS IN FOOD & NUTRITION SCIENCE.
Pergamon Press, Inc., Journals Division, 660 White Plains Rd., Tarrytown, NY 10591-5153. TEL 914-524-9200. FAX 914-333-2444. *3611*

PROGRESS IN GROWTH FACTOR RESEARCH.
Pergamon Press, Inc., Journals Division, 660 White Plains Rd., Tarrytown, NY 10591-5153. TEL 914-524-9200. FAX 914-333-2444. *561*

PROGRESS IN HEMATOLOGY.
W.B. Saunders Co. Curtis Center, Independence Square W., Philadelphia, PA 19106. TEL 215-238-7800. *3273*

PROGRESS IN HEMOSTASIS AND THROMBOSIS.
W.B. Saunders Co. Curtis Center, Independence Square W., Philadelphia, PA 19106. TEL 215-238-7800. *3211*

PROGRESS IN INDUSTRIAL MICROBIOLOGY.
Elsevier Science Publishers B.V., Books Division, P.O. Box 211, 1000 AE Amsterdam, Netherlands. TEL 020-5803911. FAX 020-5803705. *556*

PROGRESS IN INORGANIC CHEMISTRY.
John Wiley & Sons, Inc., 605 Third Ave., New York, NY 10158-0012. TEL 212-850-6000. FAX 212-850-6088. *1214*

PROGRESS IN LIPID RESEARCH.
Pergamon Press, Inc., Journals Division, 660 White Plains Rd., Tarrytown, NY 10591-5153. TEL 914-524-9200. FAX 914-333-2444. *1222*

PROGRESS IN LOW TEMPERATURE PHYSICS.
Elsevier Science Publishers B.V., Books Division, P.O. Box 211, 1000 AE Amsterdam, Netherlands. TEL 020-5803911. FAX 020-5803705. *3841*

PROGRESS IN MATERIALS SCIENCE.
Pergamon Press, Inc., Journals Division, 660 White Plains Rd., Tarrytown, NY 10591-5153. TEL 914-524-9200. FAX 914-333-2444. *1922*

PROGRESS IN MEDICINAL CHEMISTRY.
Elsevier Science Publishers B.V., Books Division, P.O. Box 211, 1000 AE Amsterdam, Netherlands. TEL 020-5803911. FAX 020-5803705. *1186*

PROGRESS IN MOLECULAR AND SUBCELLULAR BIOLOGY.
Springer-Verlag, 175 Fifth Ave., New York, NY 10010. TEL 212-460-1500. *526*

PROGRESS IN MUTATION RESEARCH.
Elsevier Science Publishers B.V., Books Division, P.O. Box 211, 1000 AE Amsterdam, Netherlands. TEL 020-5803911. FAX 020-5803705. *546*

PROGRESS IN NEURO-PSYCHOPHARMACOLOGY AND BIOLOGICAL PSYCHIATRY.
Pergamon Press plc, Headington Hill Hall, Oxford OX3 0BW, England. TEL 0865-794141. FAX 0865-743911. *3741*

PROGRESS IN NEUROBIOLOGY.
Pergamon Press, Inc., Journals Division, 660 White Plains Rd., Tarrytown, NY 10591-5153. TEL 914-524-9200. FAX 914-333-2444. *452*

PROGRESS IN NEUROENDOCRIN IMMUNOLOGY.
Thieme Medical Publishers, Inc., 381 Park Ave. S., New York, NY 10016. TEL 212-683-5088. FAX 212-779-9020. *3188*

PROGRESS IN NEUROPATHOLOGY.
Raven Press, 1185 Ave. of the Americas, New York, NY 10036. TEL 212-930-9500. FAX 212-869-3495. *3350*

PROGRESS IN NUCLEAR ENERGY.
Pergamon Press, Inc., Journals Division, 660 White Plains Rd., Tarrytown, NY 10591-5153. TEL 914-524-9200. FAX 914-333-2444. *1208*

PROGRESS IN NUCLEAR MAGNETIC RESONANCE SPECTROSCOPY.
Pergamon Press, Inc., Journals Division, 660 White Plains Rd., Tarrytown, NY 10591-5153. TEL 914-524-9200. FAX 914-333-2444. *3850*

PROGRESS IN NUCLEIC ACID RESEARCH AND MOLECULAR BIOLOGY.
Academic Press, Inc., 1250 Sixth Ave., San Diego, CA 92101. TEL 619-231-0926. FAX 619-699-6715. *452*

PROGRESS IN OCEANOGRAPHY.
Pergamon Press, Inc., Journals Division, 660 White Plains Rd., Tarrytown, NY 10591-5153. TEL 914-524-9200. FAX 914-333-2444. *1610*

PROGRESS IN OPTICS.
Elsevier Science Publishers B.V., Books Division, P.O. Box 211, 1000 AE Amsterdam, Netherlands. TEL 020-5803911. FAX 020-5803705. *3857*

PROGRESS IN ORGANIC COATINGS.
Elsevier Sequoia S.A., P.O. Box 564, CH-1001 Lausanne, Switzerland. TEL 021-207381. FAX 021-235444. *3655*

PROGRESS IN PARTICLE AND NUCLEAR PHYSICS.
Pergamon Press, Inc., Journals Division, 660 White Plains Rd., Tarrytown, NY 10591-5153. TEL 914-524-9200. FAX 914-333-2444. *3850*

PROGRESS IN PHYCOLOGICAL RESEARCH.
Elsevier Science Publishers B.V., Books Division, P.O. Box 211, 1000 AE Amsterdam, Netherlands. TEL 020-5803911. FAX 020-5803705. *515*

PROGRESS IN PHYSICAL ORGANIC CHEMISTRY.
John Wiley & Sons, Inc., 605 Third Ave., New York, NY 10158-0012. TEL 212-850-6000. FAX 212-850-6088. *1229*

PROGRESS IN PLANNING.
Pergamon Press, Inc., Journals Division, 660 White Plains Rd., Tarrytown, NY 10591-5153. TEL 914-524-9200. FAX 914-333-2444. *2494*

PROGRESS IN POLYMER SCIENCE.
Pergamon Press, Inc., Journals Division, 660 White Plains Rd., Tarrytown, NY 10591-5153. TEL 914-524-9200. FAX 914-333-2444. *1222*

PROGRESS IN PSYCHOBIOLOGY AND PHYSIOLOGICAL PSYCHOLOGY.
Academic Press, Inc., 1250 Sixth Ave., San Diego, CA 92101. TEL 619-231-0926. FAX 619-699-6715. *4039*

PROGRESS IN QUANTUM ELECTRONICS.
Pergamon Press, Inc., Journals Division, 660 White Plains Rd., Tarrytown, NY 10591-5153. TEL 914-524-9200. FAX 914-333-2444. *1777*

PROGRESS IN REACTION KINETICS.
Pergamon Press, Inc., Journals Division, 660 White Plains Rd., Tarrytown, NY 10591-5153. TEL 914-524-9200. FAX 914-333-2444. *1229*

PROGRESS IN RETINAL RESEARCH.
Pergamon Press, Inc., Journals Division, 660 White Plains Rd., Tarrytown, NY 10591-5153. TEL 914-524-9200. FAX 914-333-2444. *3304*

PROGRESS IN SELF PSYCHOLOGY.
Guilford Publications, Inc., 72 Spring St., 4th Fl., New York, NY 10012. TEL 212-431-9800. FAX 212-966-6708. *4039*

PROGRESS IN SOLID STATE CHEMISTRY.
Pergamon Press, Inc., Journals Division, 660 White Plains Rd., Tarrytown, NY 10591-5153. TEL 914-524-9200. FAX 914-333-2444. *1229*

PROGRESS IN SURFACE AND MEMBRANE SCIENCE.
Academic Press, Inc., 1250 Sixth Ave., San Diego, CA 92101. TEL 619-231-0926. FAX 619-699-6715. *1229*

PROGRESS IN SURFACE SCIENCE.
Pergamon Press, Inc., Journals Division, 660 White Plains Rd., Tarrytown, NY 10591-5153. TEL 914-524-9200. FAX 914-333-2444. *3829*

PROGRESS IN THEORETICAL ORGANIC CHEMISTRY.
Elsevier Science Publishers B.V., Books Division, P.O. Box 211, 1000 AE Amsterdam, Netherlands. TEL 020-5803911. FAX 020-5803911. *1222*

PROGRESS IN VETERINARY & COMPARATIVE OPHTHALMOLOGY.
Veterinary Practice Publishing Co., 7 Ashley Ave. S., Santa Barbara, CA 93103-9989. TEL 805-965-1028. FAX 805-965-0722. *4814*

PROGRESS IN VETERINARY NEUROLOGY.
Veterinary Practice Publishing Co., 7 Ashley Ave., S., Santa Barbara, CA 93103-9989. TEL 805-965-1028. FAX 805-965-0722. *4814*

PROGRESSIVE FISH-CULTURIST.
American Fisheries Society, (U.S. Fish and Wildlife Service) 5410 Grosvenor Lane, Ste. 110, Bethesda, MD 20814-2199. TEL 301-897-8616. FAX 301-897-8096. *2047*

PROSTAGLANDINS.
Butterworth - Heinemann Ltd. 80 Montvale Ave., Stoneham, MA 02180. TEL 617-438-8464. FAX 617-438-1479. *3255*

PROTECTION OF METALS.
Plenum Publishing Corp., Consultants Bureau, (Russian Academy of Sciences) 233 Spring St., New York, NY 10013-1578. TEL 212-620-8468. FAX 212-463-0742. *3418*

PROTEIN ENGINEERING.
I R L Press Ltd. Pinkhill House, Southfield Road, Eynsham, Oxford OX8 1JJ, England. TEL 0865-882283. FAX 0865-882890. *482*

PROTEIN EXPRESSION AND PURIFICATION.
Academic Press, Inc., Journal Division, 1250 Sixth Ave., San Diego, CA 92101. TEL 619-230-1840. FAX 619-699-6800. *482*

PROTIDES OF THE BIOLOGICAL FLUIDS.
Pergamon Press, Inc., Journals Division, (William Beaumont Hospital) 660 White Plains Rd., Tarrytown, NY 10591-5153. TEL 914-524-9200. FAX 914-333-2444. *452*

PSYCHE.
Cambridge Entomological Club, 26 Oxford St., Cambridge, MA 02138. FAX 617-495-5667. *537*

PSYCHIATRIC GENETICS.
Rapid Communications of Oxford Ltd., The Old Malthouse, Paradise St., Oxford OX1 1LD, England. TEL 071-515-7322. FAX 071-537-3559. *546*

PSYCHIATRIC QUARTERLY.
Human Sciences Press, Inc. (New York School of Psychiatry) 233 Spring St., New York, NY 10013-1578. TEL 212-620-8000. FAX 212-463-0742. *3351*

PSYCHIATRY.
Guilford Publications, Inc., (Washington School of Psychiatry) 72 Spring St., 4th Fl., New York, NY 10012. TEL 212-431-9800. FAX 212-966-6708. *3351*

PSYCHIATRY RESEARCH.
Elsevier Scientific Publishers Ireland Ltd., P.O. Box 85, Limerick, Ireland. TEL 061-61944. FAX 061-62144. *3351*

PSYCHIATRY RESEARCH: NEUROIMAGING SECTION.
Elsevier Science Publishers Ireland Ltd., P.O. Box 85, Limerick, Ireland. TEL 061-61944. FAX 061-62144. *3351*

PSYCHIC STUDIES.
Gordon & Breach Science Publishers, 270 Eighth Ave., New York, NY 10011. TEL 212-206-8900. FAX 212-645-2459. *3670*

PSYCHOANALYSIS AND CONTEMPORARY THOUGHT.
International Universities Press, Inc., Journal Department, (Psychoanalysis and Contemporary Science, Inc.) 59 Boston Post Rd., Box 1524, Madison, CT 06443-1524. TEL 203-245-4000. FAX 203-245-0775. *3352*

PSYCHOANALYTIC PSYCHOLOGY.
Lawrence Erlbaum Associates, Inc., (American Psychological Association, Division of Psychoanalysis) 365 Broadway, Hillsdale, NJ 07642. TEL 201-666-4110. FAX 201-666-2394. *4040*

PSYCHOANALYTIC REVIEW.
Guilford Publications, Inc., (National Psychological Association for Psychoanalysis, Inc.) 72 Spring St., 4th Fl., New York, NY 10012. TEL 212-431-9800. FAX 212-966-6708. *4040*

PSYCHOBIOLOGY.
Psychonomic Society, Inc., 1710 Fortview Rd., Austin, TX 78704. TEL 512-462-2442. *4040*

PSYCHOLOGICAL ASSESSMENT: A JOURNAL OF CONSULTING AND CLINICAL PSYCHOLOGY.
American Psychological Association, 750 First St., N.E., Washington, DC 20002-4242. TEL 202-336-5500. FAX 202-336-5568. *4040*

PSYCHOLOGICAL BULLETIN.
American Psychological Association, 750 First St., N.E., Washington, DC 20002-4242. TEL 202-336-5568. FAX 202-336-5568. *4041*

PSYCHOLOGICAL INQUIRY.
Lawrence Erlbaum Associates, Inc., 365 Broadway, Hillsdale, NJ 07642. TEL 201-666-4110. FAX 201-666-2394. *4041*

PSYCHOLOGICAL ISSUES.
International Universities Press, Inc., 59 Boston Post Rd., Box 1524, Madison, CT 06443-1524. TEL 203-245-4000. *4041*

PSYCHOLOGICAL REVIEW.
American Psychological Association, 750 First St., N.E., Washington, DC 20002-4242. TEL 202-336-5500. FAX 202-336-5568. *4041*

PSYCHOLOGY & HEALTH.
Harwood Academic Publishers, 270 Eighth Ave., New York, NY 10011. TEL 212-206-8900. FAX 212-645-2459. *4042*

PSYCHOLOGY IN THE SCHOOLS.
Clinical Psychology Publishing Co., Inc., 4 Conant Sq., Brandon, VT 05733. TEL 802-247-6871. FAX 802-247-6853. *4042*

PSYCHOLOGY TODAY.
Sussex Publishers Inc., 24 E. 23rd St., 5th Fl., New York, NY 10010. TEL 212-260-7210. FAX 212-260-7445. *4042*

PSYCHONEUROENDOCRINOLOGY.
Pergamon Press, Inc., Journals Division, (International Society of Psychoneuroendocrinology) 660 White Plains Rd., Tarrytown, NY 10591-5153. TEL 914-524-9200. FAX 914-333-2444. *3352*

PSYCHOPHARMACOLOGY.
Elsevier Science Publishers B.V., Books Division, P.O. Box 211, 1000 AE Amsterdam, Netherlands. TEL 020-5803911. FAX 020-5803705. *3741*

PSYCHOPHYSIOLOGY.
Society for Psychophysiological Research, 2101 Winchester Dr., Champaign, IL 61821. TEL 217-398-6969. FAX 217-244-5876. *3145*

PSYCHOSOCIAL REHABILITATION JOURNAL.
Boston University, Sargent College of Allied Health Professions, 730 Commonwealth Ave., Boston, MA 02215. TEL 617-353-3549. FAX 617-353-7700. *4043*

PSYCHOSOMATIC MEDICINE.
Williams & Wilkins, (American Psychosomatic Society) 428 E. Preston St., Baltimore, MD 21202. TEL 301-528-4000. FAX 301-528-4312. *3352*

PSYCHOSOMATICS.
American Psychiatric Press, Inc., Journals Division, (Academy of Psychosomatic Medicine) 1400 K St., N.W., Ste. 1101, Washington, DC 20005. TEL 202-682-6130. FAX 202-789-2648. *3352*

PSYCHOTHERAPY IN PRIVATE PRACTICE.
Haworth Press, Inc., 10 Alice St., Binghamton, NY 13904. TEL 800-342-9678. FAX 607-722-1424. *4043*

PSYCHOTHERAPY PATIENT.
Haworth Press, Inc., 10 Alice St., Binghamton, NY 13904. TEL 800-342-9678. FAX 607-722-1424. *4043*

PSYCHOTHERAPY RESEARCH.
Guilford Publications, Inc., (Society for Psychotherapy Research) 72 Spring St., 4th Fl., New York, NY 10012. TEL 212-431-9800. FAX 212-966-6708. *4043*

PUBLIC CULTURE.
University of Pennsylvania, Center for Transnational Cultural Studies, University Museum, University of Pennsylvania, 33rd & Spruce Sts., Philadelphia, PA 19104-6324. TEL 215-898-4054. FAX 215-898-0657. *2880*

PUBLIC HEALTH REVIEWS.
Technosdar Ltd., P.O. Box 31684, Tel Aviv 61316, Israel. TEL 3-622418. FAX 3-614932. *4110*

THE PUBLIC HISTORIAN.
University of California Press, Journals Division, (National Council on Public History) 2120 Berkeley Way, Berkeley, CA 94720. TEL 510-642-4191. FAX 510-643-7127. *2320*

PUBLIC LIBRARY QUARTERLY.
Haworth Press, Inc., 10 Alice St., Binghamton, NY 13904. TEL 800-342-9678. FAX 607-722-1424. *2780*

REFEREED SERIALS

PUBLIC OPINION QUARTERLY.
University of Chicago Press, Journals Division, (American Association for Public Opinion Research) 5720 S. Woodlawn Ave., Chicago, IL 60637. TEL 312-753-3347. FAX 312-702-0694. *3920*

PUBLIC POLICY ISSUES IN RESOURCE MANAGEMENT.
University of Washington Press, (University of Washington, Graduate School of Public Affairs) Box 50096, Seattle, WA 98105. TEL 206-543-4050. *1083*

PUBLIC PRODUCTIVITY AND MANAGEMENT REVIEW.
Jossey-Bass Inc., Publishers, (American Society for Public Administration and the National Center for Public Productivity, Section on Management Science) 350 Sansome St., 5th Fl., San Francisco, CA 94104. TEL 415-433-1767. FAX 415-433-0499. *4071*

PULMONARY AND CRITICAL CARE MEDICINE.
Hanley & Belfus, Inc., 210 S. 13th St., Philadelphia, PA 19107. TEL 215-546-7293. FAX 215-790-9330. *3211*

PURE AND APPLIED MATHEMATICS.
Academic Press, Inc., 1250 Sixth Ave., San Diego, CA 92101. TEL 619-231-0926. FAX 619-699-6715. *3051*

PURE AND APPLIED MATHEMATICS: A WILEY INTERSCIENCE SERIES OF TEXTS, MONOGRAPHS AND TRACTS.
John Wiley & Sons, Inc., Wiley Interscience Journals, 605 Third Ave., New York, NY 10158-0012. TEL 212-850-6418. *3051*

PURE AND APPLIED MATHEMATICS SERIES.
Marcel Dekker, Inc., 270 Madison Ave., New York, NY 10016. TEL 212-696-9000. FAX 212-685-4540. *3051*

QIANGJIGUANG YU LIZISU.
Ke Gongye Bu, 9 Yuan, P.O. Box 501-5, Chengdu, Sichuan 610003, People's Republic of China. TEL 667333. *1809*

QIDONG SHIYAN YU CELIANG KONGZHI.
Zhongguo Kongqi Dongli Yanjiu yu Fazhan Zhongxin, P.O. Box 211, Mianyang, Sichuan 621000, People's Republic of China. TEL 24012. *3845*

QIXIANG XUEBAO.
China Meteorological Press, (Zhongguo Qixiang Xuehui) 46 Baishiqiao Road, Xijiao (West Suburb), Beijing 100081, People's Republic of China. TEL 8312277. *3440*

QUALITATIVE SOCIOLOGY.
Human Sciences Press, Inc. 233 Spring St., New York, NY 10013-1578. TEL 212-620-8000. FAX 212-463-0742. *4445*

QUALITY ASSURANCE AND UTILIZATION REVIEW.
Williams & Wilkins, (American College of Medical Quality) 428 E. Preston St., Baltimore, MD 21202. TEL 301-528-4000. FAX 301-528-4312. *1026*

QUALITY ASSURANCE IN HEALTH CARE.
Pergamon Press, Inc., Journals Division, (International Society for Quality Assurance in Health Care) 660 White Plains Rd., Tarrytown, NY 10591-5153. TEL 914-524-9200. FAX 914-333-2444. *3145*

QUALITY ENGINEERING.
Marcel Dekker Journals, (American Society for Quality Control) 270 Madison Ave., New York, NY 10016. TEL 212-696-9000. FAX 212-685-4540. *1835*

QUARTERLY JOURNAL OF EXPERIMENTAL PSYCHOLOGY. SECTION A: HUMAN EXPERIMENTAL PSYCHOLOGY.
Lawrence Erlbaum Associates, Ltd., (Experimental Psychology Society) 27 Palmeira Mansions, Church Rd., Hove, E. Sussex BN3 2FA, England. TEL 0273-207411. FAX 0273-205612. *4043*

QUARTERLY JOURNAL OF EXPERIMENTAL PSYCHOLOGY. SECTION B: COMPARATIVE AND PHYSIOLOGICAL PSYCHOLOGY.
Lawrence Erlbaum Associates, Ltd., (Experimental Psychology Society) 27 Palmeira Mansions, Church Rd., Hove, E. Sussex BN3 2FA, England. TEL 0273-207411. FAX 0273-205612. *4044*

QUARTERLY OF APPLIED MATHEMATICS.
Brown University, Providence, RI 02912. TEL 401-831-5037. *3052*

QUARTERLY REVIEW OF BIOLOGY.
University of Chicago Press, Journals Division, 5720 S. Woodlawn Ave., Chicago, IL 60637. TEL 312-702-7600, 312-702-0694. *452*

QUARTERLY REVIEW OF FILM AND VIDEO.
Harwood Academic Publishers, 270 Eighth Ave., New York, NY 10011. TEL 212-206-8900. FAX 212-645-2459. *3516*

QUATERNARY INTERNATIONAL.
Pergamon Press, Inc., Journals Division, (International Union for Quaternary Research) 660 White Plains Rd., Tarrytown, NY 10591-5153. TEL 914-524-9200. FAX 914-333-2444. *1578*

QUATERNARY RESEARCH.
Academic Press, Inc., Journal Division, 1250 Sixth Ave., San Diego, CA 92101. TEL 619-230-1840. FAX 619-699-6800. *3660*

QUATERNARY SCIENCE REVIEWS.
Pergamon Press, Inc., Journals Division, 660 White Plains Rd., Tarrytown, NY 10591-5153. TEL 914-524-9200. FAX 914-333-2444. *4335*

QUEEN'S QUARTERLY.
Queen's Quarterly, Queen's University, Kingston, Ont. K7L 3N6, Canada. TEL 613-545-2667. FAX 613-545-6822. *2178*

QUEST (CHAMPAIGN).
Human Kinetics Publishers, Inc., (National Association for Physical Education in Higher Education) Box 5076, Champaign, IL 61825-5076. TEL 217-351-5076. FAX 217-351-2674. *1758*

QUINTESSENCE INTERNATIONAL.
Quintessence Publishing Co., Inc., 551 Kimberly Dr., Carol Stream, IL 60188-1881. TEL 708-682-3223. FAX 708-682-3288. *3241*

R A I R O RECHERCHE OPERATIONNELLE.
Dunod, (Association Francaise des Sciences et Technologies de l'Information et des Systemes) 15 rue Gossin, 92543 Montrouge Cedex, France. TEL 33-1-40-92-65-00. FAX 33-1-40-92-65-97. *1442*

R A P R A ABSTRACTS.
Pergamon Press plc, (Rubber and Plastics Research Association of Great Britain) Headington Hill Hall, Oxford OX3 0BW, England. TEL 0865-794141. FAX 0865-743911. *4295*

R A P R A REVIEW REPORTS.
Pergamon Press, Inc., Journals Division, (Rubber and Plastics Research Association of Great Britain) 660 White Plains Rd., Tarrytown, NY 10591-5153. TEL 914-524-9200. FAX 914-333-2444. *3869*

R Q.
American Library Association, 50 E. Huron St., Chicago, IL 60611-2795. TEL 800-545-2433. FAX 312-440-9374. *2780*

R R T: THE CANADIAN JOURNAL OF RESPIRATORY THERAPY.
Canadian Medical Association, P.O. Box 8650, Ottawa, Ont. K1G 0G8, Canada. TEL 613-731-9331. FAX 613-523-0937. *3366*

R S R.
Pierian Press, Box 1808, Ann Arbor, MI 48106. TEL 313-434-5530. FAX 313-434-6409. *4142*

RADIATION CURING - JOURNAL OF RADIATION CURING.
Technology Marketing Corporation, One Technology Plaza, Norwalk, CT 06854. TEL 203-852-6800. FAX 203-853-2845. *1186*

RADIATION EFFECTS AND DEFECTS IN SOLIDS.
Gordon & Breach Science Publishers, 270 Eighth Ave., New York, NY 10011. TEL 212-206-8900. FAX 212-645-2459. *3850*

RADIATION RESEARCH.
Academic Press, Inc., Journal Division, 1250 Sixth Ave., San Diego, CA 92101. TEL 619-230-1840. FAX 619-699-6800. *3850*

RADIO SCIENCE.
American Geophysical Union, 2000 Florida Ave., N.W., Washington, DC 20009. TEL 202-462-6900. FAX 202-328-0566. *1593*

RADIOACTIVE WASTE MANAGEMENT AND THE NUCLEAR FUEL CYCLE.
Harwood Academic Publishers, 270 Eighth Ave., New York, NY 10011. TEL 212-206-8900. FAX 212-645-2459. *1986*

RADIOACTIVE WASTE MANAGEMENT HANDBOOK.
Harwood Academic Publishers, 270 Eighth Ave., New York, NY 10011. TEL 212-206-8900. FAX 212-645-2459. *1986*

RADIOACTIVE WASTE MANAGEMENT SERIES.
Harwood Academic Publishers, 270 Eighth Ave., New York, NY 10011. TEL 212-206-8900. FAX 212-645-2459. *1986*

RADIOCARBON.
University Arizona, Department of Geosciences, 4717 E. Ft. Lowell Rd., Tucson, AZ 85721. TEL 602-621-8888. FAX 602-881-0554. *4335*

RADIOPHARMACY AND RADIOPHARMACOLOGY YEARBOOK SERIES.
Gordon & Breach Science Publishers, P.O. Box 90, Reading, Berkshire RG1 8JL, England. TEL 0734-560-080. FAX 0734-568-211. *3741*

RADIOPHYSICS AND QUANTUM ELECTRONICS.
Plenum Publishing Corp., Consultants Bureau, (Vysshie Uchebnye Zavedeniya S.S.S.R.) 233 Spring St., New York, NY 10013-1578. TEL 212-620-8468. FAX 212-463-0742. *1777*

RADIOTHERAPY & ONCOLOGY.
Elsevier Science Publishers B.V., (European Society for Therapeutic Radiology and Oncology) P.O. Box 211, 1000 AE Amsterdam, Netherlands. TEL 020-5803911. FAX 020-5803598. *3362*

RAND JOURNAL OF ECONOMICS.
Rand Corporation, Publications Department, 1700 Main St., Box 2138, Santa Monica, CA 90407-2138. TEL 310-393-0411. FAX 310-393-4818. *687*

RANLIAO HUAXUE XUEBAO.
Science Press, Marketing and Sales Department, (Chinese Academy of Sciences, Shanxi Institute of Coal Chemistry) 16 Donghuangchenggen Beijie, Beijing 100707, People's Republic of China. TEL 4010642. FAX 4012180. *1859*

RAVEN PRESS SERIES IN PHYSIOLOGY.
Raven Press, 1185 Ave. of the Americas, New York, NY 10036. TEL 212-930-9500. FAX 212-869-3495. *574*

LA RAZA LAW JOURNAL.
University of California Press, Journals Division, 2120 Berkeley Way, Berkeley, CA 94720. TEL 510-642-4191. FAX 510-643-7127. *2670*

REACTION KINETICS AND CATALYSIS LETTERS.
Akademiai Kiado, Publishing House of the Hungarian Academy of Sciences, P.O. Box 24, H-1363 Budapest, Hungary. *1229*

REACTIVE POLYMERS.
Elsevier Science Publishers B.V., P.O. Box 211, 1000 AE Amsterdam, Netherlands. TEL 020-5803911. FAX 020-5803598. *1859*

REACTIVITY AND STRUCTURE: CONCEPTS OF ORGANIC CHEMISTRY.
Springer-Verlag, 175 Fifth Ave., New York, NY 10010. TEL 212-460-1500. *1223*

READING PSYCHOLOGY.
Hemisphere Publishing Corporation (North Texas State University, College of Education) 1900 Frost Rd., Ste. 101, Bristol, PA 19007-1598. TEL 215-785-5800. FAX 215-785-5515. *1758*

READINGS IN WESTERN CIVILIZATION.
University of Chicago Press, 5801 S. Ellis Ave., Chicago, IL 60637. TEL 312-702-7899. *2320*

REAL ESTATE LAW JOURNAL.
Warren, Gorham and Lamont, One Penn Plaza, New York, NY 10119. TEL 800-950-1205. FAX 212-971-5240. *2716*

REAL ESTATE REVIEW.
Warren, Gorham and Lamont, One Penn Plaza, New York, NY 10119. TEL 800-950-1201. FAX 212-971-5240. *4156*

RECENT ADVANCES IN NUCLEAR MEDICINE.
W.B. Saunders Co. Curtis Center, Independence Square W., Philadelphia, PA 19106. TEL 215-238-7800. *3362*

RECENT ADVANCES IN OBESITY RESEARCH.
Technomic Publishing Co., Inc., 851 New Holland Ave., Box 3535, Lancaster, PA 17604. TEL 717-291-5609. FAX 717-295-4538. *3146*

RECENT DEVELOPMENTS IN ALCOHOLISM.
Plenum Publishing Corp., (American Medical Society on Alcoholism) 233 Spring St., New York, NY 10013-1578. TEL 212-620-8000. FAX 212-463-0742. *1538*

RECENT PROGRESS IN HORMONE RESEARCH. PROCEEDINGS OF THE LAURENTIAN HORMONE CONFERENCE.
Academic Press, Inc., 1250 Sixth Ave., San Diego, CA 92101. TEL 619-231-0926. FAX 619-699-6715. *3256*

RECENT PROGRESS IN SURFACE MEMBRANE SCIENCE.
Academic Press, Inc., 1250 Sixth Ave., San Diego, CA 92101. TEL 619-231-0926. FAX 619-699-6715. *1230*

RECEPTOR.
Humana Press Inc., Crescent Manor, Box 2148, Clifton, NJ 07015. TEL 201-256-1699. FAX 201-256-8341. *482*

RECEPTORS AND LIGANDS IN INTERCELLULAR COMMUNICATION SERIES.
Marcel Dekker, Inc., 270 Madison Ave., New York, NY 10016. TEL 212-696-9000. FAX 212-685-4540. *526*

RECHERCHES FEMINISTES.
Universite Laval, Groupe de Recherche Multidisciplinaire Feministe, 3e etage, 2336 Chemin Ste-Foy, Quebec, Que. G1K 7P4, Canada. TEL 418-656-5421. FAX 418-656-3266. *4851*

RECUEIL DES TRAVAUX CHIMIQUES DES PAYS-BAS.
Elsevier Science Publishers B.V., (Koninklijke Nederlandse Chemische Vereniging) P.O. Box 211, 1000 AH Amsterdam, Netherlands. TEL 020-5803911. FAX 020-5803598. *1186*

REDAI HAIYANG.
Science Press, Marketing and Sales Department, (Chinese Academy of Sciences, Institute of South China Sea) 16 Donghuangchengen Beijie, Beijing 100707, People's Republic of China. TEL 4010642. FAX 4012180. *1610*

REFERENCE LIBRARIAN.
Haworth Press, Inc., 10 Alice St., Binghamton, NY 13904. TEL 800-342-9678. FAX 607-722-1424. *2781*

REFRACTIVE & CORNEAL SURGERY.
SLACK, Inc., (International Society of Refractive Keratoplasty) 6900 Grove Rd., Thorofare, NJ 08068. TEL 609-848-1000. FAX 609-853-5991. *3383*

REFRACTORIES.
Plenum Publishing Corp., Consultants Bureau, (Ministerstvo Chernoi Metallurgii S.S.S.R., Tsentralnyi Sovet Nauchno-Tekhnicheskogo Obshchestvo po Chernoi Metallurgii) 233 Spring St., New York, NY 10013-1578. TEL 212-620-8468. FAX 212-463-0742. *1165*

REGIONAL SCIENCE & URBAN ECONOMICS.
North-Holland P.O. Box 211, 1000 AE Amsterdam, Netherlands. TEL 020-5803911. FAX 020-5803598. *2495*

REGULATORY PEPTIDES.
Elsevier Science Publishers B.V., P.O. Box 211, 1000 AE Amsterdam, Netherlands. TEL 020-5803911. FAX 020-5803598. *1223*

REGULATORY TOXICOLOGY AND PHARMACOLOGY.
Academic Press, Inc., Journal Division, 1250 Sixth Ave., San Diego, CA 92101. TEL 619-230-1840. FAX 619-699-6800. *3265*

REHABILITATION EDUCATION.
Elliot & Fitzpatrick Inc., Box 1945, Athens, GA 30603. TEL 404-548-8161. *1740*

REIMPRESSION.
Gordon & Breach Science Publishers, P.O. Box 90, Reading, Berkshire RG1 8JL, England. TEL 0734-560-080. FAX 0734-568-211. *2953*

RELIABILITY ASSESSMENT.
North American Electric Reliability Council, 101 College Rd., E., Princeton, NJ 08540-6601. TEL 609-452-8060. *1802*

RELIABILITY ENGINEERING AND SYSTEM SAFETY.
Elsevier Science Publishers Ltd., Crown House, Linton Rd., Barking, Essex IG11 8JU, England. TEL 081-594-7272. FAX 081-594-5942. *1835*

RELIABILITY PHYSICS.
Institute of Electrical and Electronics Engineers, Inc., (I E E E, Electron Devices Society and Reliability Society) 345 E. 47th St., New York, NY 10017-2394. TEL 212-705-7900. FAX 212-705-7682. *3838*

REMOTE SENSING OF EARTH RESOURCES: A QUARTERLY BIBLIOGRAPHY.
University of New Mexico, Technology Application Center, 2808 Central Ave., S.E., Albuquerque, NM 87131-6031. TEL 505-277-3622. FAX 505-277-3614. *1552*

REMOTE SENSING OF ENVIRONMENT.
Elsevier Science Publishing Co., Inc. (New York), 655 Ave. of the Americas, New York, NY 10010. TEL 212-989-5800. FAX 212-633-3965. *2260*

REMOTE SENSING REVIEWS.
Harwood Academic Publishers, 270 Eighth Ave., New York, NY 10011. TEL 212-206-8900. FAX 212-645-2459. *1835*

RENAL FAILURE.
Marcel Dekker Journals, 270 Madison Ave., New York, NY 10016. TEL 212-696-9000. FAX 212-685-4540. *3389*

RENEWABLE ENERGY (TARRYTOWN).
Pergamon Press, Inc., Journals Division, 660 White Plains Rd., Tarrytown, NY 10591-5153. TEL 914-524-9200. FAX 914-333-2444. *1795*

RENLEIXUE XUEBAO.
Science Press, Marketing and Sales Department, (Chinese Academy of Sciences, Institute of Vertebrata Palasiatica) 16 Donghuangchengen Beijie, Beijing 100707, People's Republic of China. TEL 4010642. FAX 4012180. *247*

REPORTS ON MATHEMATICAL PHYSICS.
Pergamon Press, Inc., Journals Division, (Nicoulas Copernicus University, Institute of Physics) 660 White Plains Rd., Tarrytown, NY 10591-5153. TEL 914-524-9200. FAX 914-333-2444. *3829*

REPORTS ON RESEARCH ASSISTED BY THE PETROLEUM RESEARCH FUND.
American Chemical Society, 1155 16th St., N.W., Washington, DC 20036. TEL 202-872-4600. FAX 202-872-4615. *3700*

REPRESENTATIONS.
University of California Press, Journals Division, 2120 Berkeley Way, Berkeley, CA 94720. TEL 510-642-4191. FAX 510-643-7127. *2513*

REPRODUCTION, NUTRITION, DEVELOPMENT.
Editions Scientifiques Elsevier, (Institut National de la Recherche Agronomique (INRA)) 29, rue Buffon, 75005 Paris, France. TEL 47-07-11-22. FAX 43-36-80-93. *453*

REPRODUCTIVE TOXICOLOGY.
Pergamon Press, Inc., Journals Division, (Reproductive Toxicology Center) 660 White Plains Rd., Tarrytown, NY 10591-5153. TEL 914-524-9200. FAX 914-333-2444. *1983*

REQUIREMENTS FOR CERTIFICATION OF TEACHERS, COUNSELORS, LIBRARIANS, ADMINISTRATORS FOR ELEMENTARY SCHOOLS, SECONDARY SCHOOLS, JUNIOR COLLEGES.
University of Chicago Press, 5801 S. Ellis Ave., Chicago, IL 60637. TEL 312-702-7899. *1731*

RESEARCH ADVANCES IN ALCOHOL & DRUG PROBLEMS.
Plenum Publishing Corp., 233 Spring St., New York, NY 10013-1578. TEL 212-620-8000. FAX 212-463-0742. *1538*

RESEARCH & DEVELOPMENT.
Cahners Publishing Company (Des Plaines) Division Reed Publishing (USA) Inc., 1350 E. Touhy Ave., Box 5080, Des Plaines, IL 60017-5080. TEL 708-635-8800. FAX 908-390-2618. *4607*

RESEARCH AND TEACHING IN DEVELOPMENTAL EDUCATION.
New York College Learning Skills Association, University Learning Center, Niagara University, NY 14109. *1658*

RESEARCH COMMUNICATIONS IN CHEMICAL PATHOLOGY AND PHARMACOLOGY.
P J D Publications Ltd., Box 966, Westbury, NY 11590. TEL 516-626-0650. *3147*

RESEARCH COMMUNICATIONS IN PSYCHOLOGY, PSYCHIATRY AND BEHAVIOR.
P J D Publications Ltd., Box 966, Westbury, NY 11590. TEL 516-626-0650. *4044*

RESEARCH COMMUNICATIONS IN SUBSTANCES OF ABUSE.
P J D Publications Ltd., Box 966, Westbury, NY 11590. TEL 516-626-0650. *3742*

RESEARCH EVALUATION.
Beech Tree Publishing, 10 Watford Close, Guildford, Surrey GU1 2EP, England. TEL 0483-67497. FAX 0483-67497. *4336*

RESEARCH IN DEVELOPMENTAL DISABILITIES.
Pergamon Press, Inc., Journals Division, 660 White Plains Rd., Tarrytown, NY 10591-5153. TEL 914-524-9200. FAX 914-333-2444. *3147*

RESEARCH IN EXPERIMENTAL MEDICINE.
Springer-Verlag, Heidelberger Platz 3, D-1000 Berlin 33, Germany. TEL 030-8207-1. *3263*

RESEARCH IN HIGHER EDUCATION.
Human Sciences Press, Inc. 233 Spring St., New York, NY 10013. TEL 212-620-8000. FAX 212-463-0742. *1731*

RESEARCH IN IMMUNOLOGY.
Editions Scientifiques Elsevier, (Institut Pasteur) 29, rue Buffon, 75005 Paris, France. TEL 47-07-11-22. FAX 43-36-80-93. *3188*

RESEARCH IN MICROBIOLOGY.
Editions Scientifiques Elsevier, 29, rue Buffon, 75005 Paris, France. *557*

RESEARCH IN NURSING & HEALTH.
John Wiley & Sons, Inc., Journals, 605 Third Ave., New York, NY 10158-0012. TEL 212-850-6000. FAX 212-850-6088. *3286*

RESEARCH IN PHILOSOPHY AND TECHNOLOGY.
J A I Press Inc., (Society for Philosophy and Technology) 55 Old Post Rd., No. 2, Box 1678, Greenwich, CT 06836-1678. TEL 203-661-7602. *3779*

RESEARCH IN THE SOCIAL SCIENTIFIC STUDY OF RELIGION.
J A I Press Inc., (Abilene Christian University) 55 Old Post Rd., No. 2, Box 1678, Greenwich, CT 06836-1678. TEL 203-661-7602. *4198*

RESEARCH IN VIROLOGY.
Editions Scientifiques Elsevier, 29, rue Buffon, 75005 Paris, France. *3223*

RESEARCH METHODS IN NEUROCHEMISTRY.
Plenum Publishing Corp., 233 Spring St., New York, NY 10013-1578. TEL 212-620-8000. FAX 212-463-0742. *482*

RESEARCH MONOGRAPHS IN CELL AND TISSUE PHYSIOLOGY.
Elsevier Science Publishers B.V., Books Division, P.O. Box 211, 1000 AE Amsterdam, Netherlands. TEL 020-5803911. FAX 020-5803705. *3147*

RESEARCH MONOGRAPHS IN IMMUNOLOGY.
Elsevier Science Publishers B.V., Books Division, P.O. Box 211, 1000 AE Amsterdam, Netherlands. TEL 020-5803911. FAX 020-5803705. *3188*

RESEARCH NOTES IN MATHEMATICS.
John Wiley & Sons, Inc., Journals, 605 Third Ave., New York, NY 10158-0012. TEL 212-850-6000. FAX 212-850-6088. *3052*

RESEARCH ON CHEMICAL INTERMEDIATES.
Elsevier Science Publishers B.V., P.O. Box 211, 1000 AE Amsterdam, Netherlands. TEL 020-5803911. FAX 020-5803598. *1186*

RESEARCH ON TECHNOLOGICAL INNOVATION, MANAGEMENT AND POLICY.
J A I Press Inc., 55 Old Post Rd., No. 2, Box 1678, Greenwich, CT 06836-1678. TEL 203-661-7602. *4607*

RESEARCH POLICY.
North-Holland P.O. Box 211, 1000 AE Amsterdam, Netherlands. TEL 020-5803911. FAX 020-5803598. *1026*

RESEARCH: VIRGINIA TECH.
Virginia Polytechnic Institute and State University, Research Division, 309 Burruss Hall, Blacksburg, VA 24061-0244. TEL 703-231-9356. *1715*

RESIDENTIAL TREATMENT FOR CHILDREN & YOUTH.
Haworth Press, Inc., 10 Alice St., Binghamton, NY 13904. TEL 800-342-9678. FAX 607-722-1424. *1243*

RESOURCE MANAGEMENT AND OPTIMIZATION.
Harwood Academic Publishers, 270 Eighth Ave., New York, NY 10011. TEL 212-206-8900. FAX 212-645-2459. *1496*

RESOURCE SHARING & INFORMATION NETWORKS.
Haworth Press, Inc., 10 Alice St., Binghamton, NY 13904. TEL 800-342-9678. FAX 607-722-1424. *2781*

RESOURCES (NASHVILLE).
F I S I - Madison Financial Corporation Box 40726, Nashville, TN 37204. TEL 615-371-2775. *961*

RESOURCES AND ENERGY.
North-Holland P.O. Box 211, 1000 AE Amsterdam, Netherlands. TEL 020-5803911. FAX 020-5803598. *1795*

RESOURCES, CONSERVATION AND RECYCLING.
Elsevier Science Publishers B.V., P.O. Box 211, 100 AE Amsterdam, Netherlands. TEL 020-5803911. FAX 020-5803598. *1987*

RESOURCES POLICY.
Butterworth - Heinemann Ltd. Linacre House, Jordan Hill, Oxford OX2 8DP, England. TEL 0865-310366. FAX 0865-310898. *1795*

RESPIRATION PHYSIOLOGY.
Elsevier Science Publishers B.V., P.O. Box 211, 1000 AE Amsterdam, Netherlands. TEL 020-5803911. FAX 020-5803598. *574*

RESPONSE TO THE VICTIMIZATION OF WOMEN AND CHILDREN.
Guilford Publications, Inc., (Response, Inc.) 72 Spring St., 4th Fl., New York, NY 10012. TEL 212-431-9800. FAX 212-966-6708. *4851*

RESTORATIVE NEUROLOGY AND NEUROSCIENCE.
Elsevier Science Publishers B.V., P.O. Box 1527, 1000 BM Amsterdam, Netherlands. TEL 020-5803911. FAX 020-5803598. *3353*

RESUSCITATION.
Elsevier Scientific Publishers Ireland Ltd., P.O. Box 85, Limerick, Ireland. TEL 061-61944. FAX 061-62144. *3367*

RETINA.
J.B. Lippincott Co., E. Washington Sq., Philadelphia, PA 19105. TEL 215-238-4200. *3304*

REUSE - RECYCLE.
Technomic Publishing Co. Inc., 851 New Holland Ave., Box 3535, Lancaster, PA 17604. TEL 717-291-5609. FAX 717-295-4538. *1987*

REVIEW (WASHINGTON).
Heldref Publications, (Helen Dwight Reid Educational Foundation) 1319 Eighteenth St., N.W., Washington, DC 20036-1802. TEL 202-296-6267. FAX 202-296-5149. *2295*

REVIEW OF CHILD DEVELOPMENT RESEARCH.
University of Chicago Press, (Society for Research in Child Development, Inc.) 5720 S. Woodlawn Ave., Chicago, IL 60637. TEL 312-702-7600. FAX 312-702-0694. *1243*

REVIEW OF ECONOMICS AND STATISTICS.
North-Holland (Harvard University, Economics Department) P.O. Box 211, 1000 AE Amsterdam, Netherlands. TEL 020-5803911. FAX 020-5803598. *736*

REVIEW OF EDUCATION.
Gordon and Breach Science Publishers, 270 Eighth Ave., New York, NY 10011. TEL 212-206-8900. FAX 212-645-2459. *1679*

REVIEW OF EXISTENTIAL PSYCHOLOGY AND PSYCHIATRY.
Box 23220, Seattle, WA 98102. TEL 206-524-3880. *4044*

REVIEW OF PALAEOBOTANY AND PALYNOLOGY.
Elsevier Science Publishers B.V., P.O. Box 211, 1000 AE Amsterdam, Netherlands. TEL 020-5803911. FAX 020-5803598. *3660*

REVIEW OF SCIENTIFIC INSTRUMENTS.
American Institute of Physics, 335 E. 45th St., New York, NY 10017. TEL 212-661-9404. *2524*

REVIEWS IN ANTHROPOLOGY.
Gordon and Breach Science Publishers, 270 Eighth Ave., New York, NY 10011. TEL 212-206-8900. FAX 212-245-2459. *248*

REVIEWS IN BIOCHEMICAL TOXICOLOGY.
Elsevier Science Publishing Co., Inc. (New York), 655 Ave. of the Americas, New York, NY 10010. TEL 212-989-5800. FAX 212-633-3965. *482*

REVIEWS IN CANCER EPIDEMIOLOGY.
Elsevier Science Publishers B.V., Books Division, P.O. Box 211, 1000 AE Amsterdam, Netherlands. TEL 020-5803911. FAX 020-5803705. *3201*

REVIEWS IN ENGINEERING GEOLOGY.
Geological Society of America, 3300 Penrose Pl., Box 9140, Boulder, CO 80301. TEL 303-447-2020. FAX 303-447-1133. *1873*

REVIEWS IN PERINATAL MEDICINE.
Raven Press, 1185 Ave. of the Americas, New York, NY 10036. TEL 212-930-9500. FAX 212-869-3495. *3296*

REVIEWS OF GEOPHYSICS.
American Geophysical Union, 2000 Florida Ave., N.W., Washington, DC 20009. TEL 202-462-6900. FAX 202-328-0566. *1593*

REVIEWS OF HEMATOLOGY.
P J D Publications Ltd., Box 966, Westbury, NY 11590. TEL 516-626-0650. *3273*

REVIEWS OF MAGNETIC RESONANCE IN MEDICINE.
Pergamon Press, Inc., Journals Division, 660 White Plains Rd., Tarrytown, NY 10591-5153. TEL 914-524-9200. FAX 914-333-2444. *3362*

REVIEWS OF MODERN PHYSICS.
American Institute of Physics, (American Physical Society) 335 E. 45th St., New York, NY 10017-3483. TEL 212-661-9404. *3830*

REVIEWS OF PHYSIOLOGY, BIOCHEMISTRY AND EXPERIMENTAL PHARMACOLOGY.
Springer-Verlag, 175 Fifth Ave., New York, NY 10010. TEL 212-460-1500. *574*

REVIEWS OF PLASMA PHYSICS.
Plenum Publishing Corp., Consultants Bureau, 233 Spring St., New York, NY 10013-1578. TEL 212-620-8000. FAX 212-463-0742. *3830*

REVIEWS ON POWDER METALLURGY & PHYSICAL CERAMICS.
Elsevier Science Publishers Ltd., Crown House, Linton Rd., Barking, Essex IG11 8JU, England. TEL 081-594-7272. FAX 081-594-5942. *3418*

REVISION.
Heldref Publications, (Helen Dwight Reid Education Foundation) 1319 Eighteenth St., N.W., Washington, DC 20036-1802. TEL 202-296-6267. FAX 202-296-5149. *3596*

REVISTA BRASILEIRA DE FISICA.
Sociedade Brasileira de Fisica, Universidade de Sao Paulo, Instituto de Fisica, Caixa Postal 20553, 01000 Sao Paulo, Brazil. FAX 081-2710359. *3830*

REVISTA COLOMBIANA DE MATEMATICAS.
Sociedad Colombiana de Matematicas, Apdo. Aereo No. 25-21, Bogota, Colombia. FAX 2686465. *3052*

REVISTA DE SAUDE PUBLICA.
Universidade de Sao Paulo, Faculdade de Saude Publica, Av. Dr. Arnaldo 715, Sao Paulo, Brazil. FAX 011-852-9630. *4111*

REVUE DE DROIT COMMERCIAL BELGE.
Palais de Justice, Place Poelaert, B-1000 Brussels, Belgium. TEL 02-508-62-45. FAX 02-358-4597. *2674*

REVUE DES ETUDES GEORGIENNES ET CAUCASIENNES.
Editions Peeters s.p.r.l., Bondgenotenlaan 153, B-3000 Louvain, Belgium. TEL 016-235170. FAX 016-228500. *2383*

REVUE FRANCOPHONE DE LOUISIANE.
University of Southwestern Louisiana, Conseil International d'Etudes Francophones, Box 43331, Lafayette, LA 70504. TEL 318-231-6811. *2021*

REVUE MEDICALE DE LIEGE.
Institut de Medecine, (Universite de Liege) 13 rue Alex Bouvy, 4020 Liege, Belgium. TEL 041-437572. *3149*

RHEOLOGY ABSTRACTS.
Pergamon Press, Inc., Journals Division, (British Society of Rheology) 660 White Plains Rd., Tarrytown, NY 10591-5153. TEL 914-524-9200. FAX 914-333-2444. *3839*

RHETORICA.
University of California Press, Journals Division, (International Society for the History of Rhetoric) 2120 Berkeley Way, Berkeley, CA 94720. TEL 510-642-4191. FAX 510-643-7127. *2838*

RISK ANALYSIS.
Plenum Publishing Corp., (Society for Risk Analysis) 233 Spring St., New York, NY 10013-1578. TEL 212-620-8000. FAX 212-463-0742. *3053*

ROBOTICS AND AUTONOMOUS SYSTEMS.
North-Holland P.O. Box 211, 1000 AE Amsterdam, Netherlands. TEL 020-5803911. FAX 020-5803598. *1410*

ROBOTICS AND COMPUTER-INTEGRATED MANUFACTURING.
Pergamon Press, Inc., Journals Division, 660 White Plains Rd., Tarrytown, NY 10591-5153. TEL 914-524-9200. FAX 914-333-2444. *1410*

ROBOTICS AND EXPERT SYSTEMS.
Instrument Society of America, 67 Alexander Dr., Box 12277, Research Triangle Park, NC 27709. TEL 919-549-8411. FAX 919-549-8288. *1410*

ROCKS AND MINERALS.
Heldref Publications, (Helen Dwight Reid Educational Foundation) 1319 Eighteenth St., N.W., Washington, DC 20036-1802. TEL 202-296-6267. FAX 202-296-5149. *3495*

ROCKY MOUNTAIN JOURNAL OF MATHEMATICS.
Rocky Mountain Mathematics Consortium, Arizona State University, Department of Mathematics, Tempe, AZ 85287. TEL 602-965-3788. *3053*

RODD'S CHEMISTRY OF CARBON COMPOUNDS.
Elsevier Science Publishers B.V., Books Division, P.O. Box 211, 1000 AE Amsterdam, Netherlands. TEL 020-5803911. FAX 020-5803705. *1223*

ROMANCE PHILOLOGY.
University of California Press, Journals Division, Berkeley, CA 94720. TEL 510-642-4191. FAX 510-643-7127. *2838*

THE ROUND TABLE.
Carfax Publishing Co., P.O. Box 25, Abingdon, Oxfordshire OX14 3UE, England. TEL 0235-555335. FAX 0235-553559. *3971*

ROUX'S ARCHIVES OF DEVELOPMENTAL BIOLOGY.
Springer-Verlag, (European Developmental Biology Organization, Executive Board) Heidelberger Platz 3, D-1000 Berlin 33, Germany. TEL 030-2807-1. *454*

ROYAL COLLEGE OF PHYSICIANS AND SURGEONS OF CANADA. ANNALS.
Royal College of Physicians & Surgeons of Canada, 74 Stanley Ave., Ottawa, Ont. K1M 1P4, Canada. TEL 613-746-8177. FAX 613-746-8833. *3150*

ROYAL COLLEGE OF SURGEONS OF EDINBURGH. JOURNAL.
Butterworth - Heinemann Ltd. (Royal College of Surgeons of Edinburgh) Linacre House, Jordan Hill, Oxford OX2 8DP, England. TEL 0865-310366. FAX 0865-310898. *3383*

ROYAL NETHERLANDS ACADEMY OF SCIENCES. PROCEEDINGS.
North-Holland (Royal Netherlands Academy of Sciences) P.O. Box 211, 1000 AE Amsterdam, Netherlands. TEL 020-5803911. FAX 020-5803598. *4336*

ROYAL SOCIETY OF CHEMISTRY. JOURNAL: DALTON TRANSACTIONS.
Royal Society of Chemistry, Thomas Graham House, Science Park, Milton Rd., Cambridge CB4 4WF, England. TEL 0462-672555. FAX 0462-480947. *1214*

ROYAL SOCIETY OF CHEMISTRY. JOURNAL: FARADAY TRANSACTIONS.
Royal Society of Chemistry, Thomas Graham House, Science Park, Milton Rd., Cambridge CB4 4WF, England. TEL 0462-672555. FAX 0462-480947. *1230*

ROYAL SOCIETY OF CHEMISTRY. JOURNAL: PERKIN TRANSACTIONS 1.
Royal Society of Chemistry, Thomas Graham House, Science Park, Milton Rd., Cambridge CB4 4WF, England. TEL 0462-672555. FAX 0462-480947. *1223*

ROYAL SOCIETY OF CHEMISTRY. JOURNAL: PERKIN TRANSACTIONS 2.
Royal Society of Chemistry, Thomas Graham House, Science Park, Milton Rd., Cambridge CB4 4WF, England. TEL 0462-672555. FAX 0462-480947. *1230*

ROYAL SOCIETY OF LONDON. NOTES AND RECORDS.
Royal Society of London, 6 Carlton House Terr., London SW1Y 5AG, England. TEL 071-839-5561. FAX 071-976-1837. *4337*

ROYAL SOCIETY OF LONDON. PHILOSOPHICAL TRANSACTIONS. SERIES A. PHYSICAL SCIENCES AND ENGINEERING.
Royal Society of London, 6 Carlton House Terrace, London SW1Y 5AG, England. TEL 071-839-5561. FAX 071-976-1837. *3830*

ROYAL SOCIETY OF LONDON. PHILOSOPHICAL TRANSACTIONS. SERIES B. BIOLOGICAL SCIENCES.
Royal Society of London, 6 Carlton House Terrace, London SW1Y 5AG, England. TEL 071-839-5561. FAX 071-976-1837. *454*

ROYAL SOCIETY OF LONDON. PROCEEDINGS. SERIES A. MATHEMATICAL AND PHYSICAL SCIENCES.
Royal Society of London, 6 Carlton Terrace, London SW1Y 5AG, England. TEL 071-839-5561. FAX 071-976-1837. *3053*

RUANJIAN XUEBAO.
Science Press - Kexue Chubanshe, Qikan Bu, 16 Donghuangchenggen Beijie, Beijing 100707, People's Republic of China. TEL 4010642. FAX 4012180. *1479*

RUSSIAN AND EAST EUROPEAN FINANCE AND TRADE.
M.E. Sharpe, Inc., 80 Business Park Dr., Armonk, NY 10504. TEL 914-273-1800. FAX 914-273-2106. *920*

RUSSIAN EDUCATION AND SOCIETY.
M.E. Sharpe, Inc., 80 Business Park Dr., Armonk, NY 10504. TEL 914-273-1800. FAX 914-273-2106. *1660*

RUSSIAN JOURNAL OF ENGINEERING THERMOPHYSICS.
Elsevier Science Publishing Co., Inc. (New York), 655 Ave. of Americas, New York, NY 10010. TEL 212-989-5800. FAX 212-633-3965. *3830*

RUSSIAN JOURNAL OF THEORETICAL AND APPLIED MECHANICS.
Elsevier Science Publishing Co., Inc. (New York), 655 Ave. of Americas, New York, NY 10010. TEL 212-989-5800. FAX 212-633-3965. *3830*

RUSSIAN LITERATURE.
North-Holland P.O. Box 211, 1000 AE Amsterdam, Netherlands. TEL 020-5803911. FAX 020-5803598. *2956*

RUSSIAN POLITICS.
M.E. Sharpe, Inc., 80 Business Park Dr., Armonk, NY 10504. TEL 914-273-1800. FAX 914-273-2106. *2676*

RUSSIAN SOCIAL SCIENCE REVIEW.
M.E. Sharpe, Inc., 80 Business Park Dr., Armonk, NY 10504. TEL 914-273-1800. FAX 914-273-2106. *3923*

RUSSIAN STUDIES IN HISTORY.
M.E. Sharpe, Inc., 80 Business Park Dr., Armonk, NY 10504. TEL 914-273-1800. FAX 914-273-2106. *2321*

RUSSIAN STUDIES IN LITERATURE.
M.E. Sharpe, Inc., 80 Business Park Dr., Armonk, NY 10504. FAX 914-273-2106. *2956*

S A Q: THE SOUTH ATLANTIC QUARTERLY.
Duke University Press, 6697 College Station, Durham, NC 27708. TEL 919-684-2173. FAX 919-684-8644. *2882*

S E R I. ETHANOL ANNUAL REPORT.
Solar Energy Research Institute, (U.S. Department of Energy, Conservation and Renewable Energy Office) Technical Inquiry Service, 1617 Cole Blvd., Golden, CO 80401-3393. TEL 303-231-1000. *1795*

S I A M - A M S PROCEEDINGS.
American Mathematical Society, (Society for Industrial and Applied Mathematics) Box 1571, Annex Sta., Providence, RI 02901-9930. TEL 401-455-4000. *3053*

S I A M JOURNAL ON APPLIED MATHEMATICS.
Society for Industrial and Applied Mathematics, Attn: M. Lafferty, 3600 University City Science Center, Philadelphia, PA 19104-2688. TEL 215-382-9800. FAX 215-386-7999. *3053*

S I A M JOURNAL ON COMPUTING.
Society for Industrial and Applied Mathematics, Attn: P. Clifford, 3600 University City Science Center, Philadelphia, PA 19104-2688. TEL 215-382-9800. FAX 215-386-7999. *3066*

S I A M JOURNAL ON CONTROL AND OPTIMIZATION.
Society for Industrial and Applied Mathematics, Attn: M. Lafferty, 3600 University City Science Center, Philadelphia, PA 19104-2688. TEL 215-382-9800. FAX 215-386-7999. *3053*

S I A M JOURNAL ON DISCRETE MATHEMATICS.
Society for Industrial and Applied Mathematics, Attn: P. Clifford, 3600 University City Science Center, Philadelphia, PA 19104-2688. TEL 215-382-9800. FAX 215-386-7998. *3053*

S I A M JOURNAL ON MATHEMATICAL ANALYSIS.
Society for Industrial and Applied Mathematics, Attn: M. Lafferty, 3600 University City Science Center, Philadelphia, PA 19104-2688. TEL 215-382-9800. FAX 215-386-7999. *3053*

S I A M JOURNAL ON MATRIX ANALYSIS AND APPLICATIONS.
Society for Industrial and Applied Mathematics, Attn: P. Clifford, 3600 University City Science Ctr., Philadelphia, PA 19104-2688. TEL 215-382-9800. FAX 215-386-7999. *3053*

S I A M JOURNAL ON NUMERICAL ANALYSIS.
Society for Industrial and Applied Mathematics, Attn.: M. Lafferty, 3600 University City Science Center, Philadelphia, PA 19104-2688. TEL 215-382-9800. FAX 215-386-7999. *3053*

S I A M JOURNAL ON OPTIMIZATION.
Society for Industrial and Applied Mathematics, Attn: P. Clifford, 3600 University City Science Ctr., Philadelphia, PA 19104. TEL 215-382-9800. FAX 215-386-7999. *3054*

S I A M JOURNAL ON SCIENTIFIC AND STATISTICAL COMPUTING.
Society for Industrial and Applied Mathematics, Attn: P. Clifford, 3600 University City Science Center, Philadelphia, PA 19104-2688. TEL 215-382-9800. FAX 215-386-7999. *4585*

S I A M NEWS.
Society for Industrial and Applied Mathematics, Attn: M. Lafferty, 3600 University City Science Center, Philadelphia, PA 19104-2688. TEL 215-382-9800. FAX 215-386-7999. *3054*

S I A M REVIEW.
Society for Industrial and Applied Mathematics, Attn: M. Lafferty, 3600 University City Science Center, Philadelphia, PA 19104-2688. TEL 215-382-9800. FAX 215-386-7999. *3054*

S I D INTERNATIONAL SYMPOSIUM. DIGEST OF TECHNICAL PAPERS.
Palisades Institute for Research Services, (Society for Information Display) Attn: Jay Morreale, 201 Varick St., 11th Fl., New York, NY 10014. *1836*

S M P T E JOURNAL.
Society of Motion Picture and Television Engineers, 595 W. Hartsdale Ave., White Plains, NY 10607-1824. TEL 914-761-1100. FAX 914-761-3115. *3517*

S P E DRILLING ENGINEERING.
Society of Petroleum Engineers, Inc., Box 833836, Richardson, TX 75083-3836. TEL 214-669-3377. FAX 214-669-0135. *3700*

S P E FORMATION EVALUATION.
Society of Petroleum Engineers, Inc., Box 833836, Richardson, TX 75083-3836. TEL 214-669-3377. FAX 214-669-0135. *3700*

S P E PRODUCTION ENGINEERING.
Society of Petroleum Engineers, Inc., Box 833836, Richardson, TX 75083-3836. TEL 214-669-3377. FAX 214-669-0135. *3700*

S P E RESERVOIR ENGINEERING.
Society of Petroleum Engineers, Inc., Box 833836, Richardson, TX 75083-3836. TEL 214-952-9393. FAX 214-952-9435. *3700*

SAFETY SCIENCE.
Elsevier Science Publishers B.V., P.O. Box 211, 1000 AE Amsterdam, Netherlands. TEL 020-5803911. FAX 020-5803598. *3621*

SAGAMORE ARMY MATERIALS RESEARCH CONFERENCE. PROCEEDINGS.
Plenum Publishing Corp., 233 Spring St., New York, NY 10013-1578. TEL 212-620-8000. FAX 212-463-0742. *3470*

SAGGI.
Edizioni La Nostra Famiglia, (Scientific Institute "Eugenio Medea" - Bosisio Parini) Via Don Luigi Monza, 1, 22037 Ponte Lambro, Italy. TEL 031-625111. FAX 031-625275. *3353*

ST. JOHN'S JOURNAL OF MEDICINE.
St. John's Medical College, Alumni Association, c/o Dr. S.V. Srikishna, Gen. Sec., Robert Koch Bhavan, 1st Fl., St. John's Medical College, Bangalore 560 034, India. TEL 565435. *3151*

SASKATCHEWAN LAW REVIEW.
University of Saskatchewan, College of Law, Law Building, Saskatoon, Sask. S7N 0W0, Canada. TEL 306-966-5872. FAX 306-966-5900. *2677*

SATHER CLASSICAL LECTURES.
University of California Press, 2120 Berkeley Way, Berkeley, CA 94720. TEL 415-642-4247. FAX 415-643-7127. *1279*

SAURIA.
Terrariengemeinschaft Berlin e.V., c/o Peter Grossmann, Lepsiusstr. 53, 1000 Berlin 41, Germany. TEL 030-7924736. *591*

SCANDINAVIAN JOURNAL OF MANAGEMENT.
Pergamon Press, Inc., Journals Division, 660 White Plains Rd., Tarrytown, NY 10591-5153. TEL 914-524-9200. FAX 914-333-2444. *1027*

SCANDINAVIAN JOURNAL OF MEDICINE & SCIENCE IN SPORTS.
Munksgaard International Publishers Ltd., P.O. Box 2148, DK-1016 Copenhagen K, Denmark. *3373*

SCANNING MICROSCOPY.
Scanning Microscopy International, Inc., Box 66507, AMF O'Hare, Chicago, IL 60666. TEL 708-529-6677. FAX 708-980-6698. *561*

SCHIZOPHRENIA RESEARCH.
Elsevier Science Publishers B.V., P.O. Box 211, 1000 AE Amsterdam, Netherlands. TEL 020-5803911. FAX 020-5803598. *3354*

SCHOOL EFFECTIVENESS AND SCHOOL IMPROVEMENT.
Swets Publishing Service Heereweg 347, 2161 CA Lisse, Netherlands. TEL 31-2521-35111. FAX 31-2521-15888. *1661*

SCHOOL OF INTERNATIONAL STUDIES. PUBLICATIONS ON ASIA.
University of Washington Press, (University of Washington, School of International Studies) Box 50096, Seattle, WA 98105. TEL 206-543-4050. *2341*

SCHOOL OF INTERNATIONAL STUDIES. PUBLICATIONS ON RUSSIA AND EASTERN EUROPE.
University of Washington Press, (University of Washington, School of International Studies) Box 50096, Seattle, WA 98105. TEL 206-543-4050. *3924*

SCHOOL PSYCHOLOGY QUARTERLY.
Guilford Publications, Inc., (American Psychological Association, Division of School Psychology) 72 Spring St., 4th Fl., New York, NY 10012. TEL 212-431-9800. FAX 212-966-6708. *4046*

SCIENCE.
American Association for the Advancement of Science, 1333 H St., N.W., Washington, DC 20005. TEL 202-326-6500. *4338*

SCIENCE ACTIVITIES.
Heldref Publications, (Helen Dwight Reid Educational Foundation) 1319 Eighteenth St., N.W., Washington, DC 20036-1802. TEL 202-296-6267. FAX 202-296-5149. *1662*

SCIENCE AND GLOBAL SECURITY.
Gordon & Breach Science Publishers, 270 Eighth Ave., New York, NY 10011. TEL 212-206-8900. FAX 212-645-2459. *4339*

SCIENCE AND GLOBAL SECURITY MONOGRAPH SERIES.
Gordon and Breach Scientific Publishers, 270 Eighth Ave., New York, NY 10011. TEL 212-206-8900. FAX 212-645-2459. *3971*

SCIENCE AND ITS CONCEPTUAL FOUNDATIONS.
University of Chicago Press, 5801 S. Ellis Ave., Chicago, IL 60637. TEL 312-702-7899. *4339*

SCIENCE AND PRACTICE OF SURGERY SERIES.
Marcel Dekker, Inc., 270 Madison Ave., New York, NY 10016. TEL 212-696-9000. FAX 212-685-4540. *3384*

SCIENCE AND SOCIETY.
Guilford Publications, Inc., 72 Spring St., 4th Fl., New York, NY 10012. TEL 212-431-9800. FAX 212-966-6708. *3924*

SCIENCE AND TECHNOLOGY (SAN DIEGO, 1987).
Greenhaven Press, Inc., Box 289009, San Diego, CA 92198-0009. TEL 619-485-7424. FAX 619-485-9549. *455*

SCIENCE & TECHNOLOGY LIBRARIES.
Haworth Press, Inc., 10 Alice St., Binghamton, NY 13904. TEL 800-342-9678. FAX 607-722-1424. *2783*

SCIENCE AND TECHNOLOGY SERIES.
Univelt, Inc., (American Astronautical Society, Inc.) Box 28130, San Diego, CA 92198. TEL 619-746-4005. *61*

SCIENCE EDUCATION.
John Wiley & Sons, Inc., Journals, 605 Third Ave., New York, NY 10158-0012. TEL 212-692-6000. *4339*

SCIENCE ET SPORTS.
Editions Scientifiques Elsevier, (Societe Francaise de Medecine du Sport) 29, rue Buffon, 75005 Paris, France. *3373*

SCIENCE IN CHINA. SERIES A: MATHEMATICS, PHYSICS, ASTRONOMY & TECHNOLOGICAL SCIENCES.
Science Press, Marketing and Sales Department, 16 Donghuangchenggen Beijie, Beijing 100707, People's Republic of China. TEL 4010642. FAX 4012180. *4340*

SCIENCE IN CHINA. SERIES B: CHEMISTRY, LIFE SCIENCES & EARTH SCIENCES.
Science Press, Marketing and Sales Department, 16 Donghuangchenggen Beijie, Beijing 100707, People's Republic of China. TEL 4010642. FAX 4012180. *4340*

SCIENCE OF ADVANCED MATERIAL AND PROCESS ENGINEERING SERIES.
Society for the Advancement of Material and Process Engineering, Box 2459, Covina, CA 91722. TEL 818-331-0616. FAX 818-332-8929. *1922*

SCIENCE OF COMPUTER PROGRAMMING.
North-Holland P.O. Box 211, 1000 AE Amsterdam, Netherlands. TEL 020-5803911. FAX 020-5803598. *1431*

SCIENCE OF FOOD AND AGRICULTURE.
Council for Agricultural Science and Technology, 137 Lynn Ave., Ames, IA 50010-7197. TEL 515-292-2125. FAX 515-292-4512. *2081*

SCIENCE OF THE TOTAL ENVIRONMENT.
Elsevier Science Publishers B.V., P.O. Box 211, 1000 AE Amsterdam, Netherlands. TEL 020-5803911. FAX 020-5803598. *1968*

SCIENCES.
New York Academy of Sciences, 2 E. 63rd St., New York, NY 10021. *4341*

SCIENTIA HORTICULTURAE.
Elsevier Science Publishers B.V., (International Society for Horticultural Science) P.O. Box 211, 1000 AE Amsterdam, Netherlands. TEL 020-5803911. FAX 020-5803598. *2138*

SCIENTIA PAEDAGOGICA EXPERIMENTALIS.
State University Ghent, Labo Pedagogiek, Blandijnberg 2, B-9000 Gent, Belgium. TEL 91-643952. FAX 91-646498. *1662*

SCIENTIFIC AMERICAN.
Scientific American, Inc., 415 Madison Ave., New York, NY 10017. TEL 212-754-0550. *4341*

SCIENTIFIC AND APPLIED PHOTOGRAPHY AND CINEMATOGRAPHY.
Gordon & Breach Science Publishers, 270 Eighth Ave., New York, NY 10011. TEL 212-206-8900. FAX 212-645-2459. *3797*

SCIENTOMETRICS.
Elsevier Science Publishers B.V., P.O. Box 211, 1000 AE Amsterdam, Netherlands. TEL 020-5803911. FAX 020-5803598. *4342*

SCREENING.
Elsevier Science Publishers B.V., (International Society of Neonatal Screening) P.O. Box 211, 1000 AE Amsterdam, Netherlands. TEL 020-5803911. FAX 020-5803598. *3326*

SCRIPPS INSTITUTION OF OCEANOGRAPHY. BULLETIN.
University of California Press, 2120 Berkeley Way, Berkeley, CA 94720. TEL 415-642-4247. FAX 415-643-7127. *1610*

SCRIPTA METALLURGICA ET MATERIALIA.
Pergamon Press, Inc., Journals Division, 660 White Plains Rd., Tarrytown, NY 10591-5153. TEL 914-524-9200. FAX 914-333-2444. *3419*

SCRIPTURA.
University of Stellenbosch, Department of Biblical Studies, 7600 Stellenbosch, South Africa. TEL 02231-772029. FAX 02231-772031. *4248*

SEA TECHNOLOGY.
Compass Publications, Inc. (Arlington), Ste. 1000, 1117 N. 19th St., Arlington, VA 22209. TEL 703-524-3136. FAX 703-841-0852. *1836*

SECOND MESSENGERS AND PHOSPHOPROTEINS.
Marcel Dekker Journals, 270 Madison Ave., New York, NY 10016. TEL 212-696-9000. *455*

SECURITIES REGULATION LAW JOURNAL.
Warren, Gorham and Lamont, One Penn Plaza, New York, NY 10119. TEL 800-950-1205. FAX 212-971-5240. *963*

SECURITY JOURNAL.
Butterworth - Heinemann Ltd. (A S I S Foundation) 80 Montvale Ave., Stoneham, MA 02180. TEL 617-438-8464. FAX 617-438-1479. *1527*

SEDIMENTARY GEOLOGY.
Elsevier Science Publishers B.V., P.O. Box 211, 1000 AE Amsterdam, Netherlands. TEL 020-5803911. FAX 020-5803598. *1580*

SEISMOLOGICAL RESEARCH LETTERS.
Seismological Society of America, 201 Plaza Professional Bldg., El Cerrito. TEL 415-525-5474. FAX 415-525-7204. *1594*

SELECTED TABLES IN MATHEMATICAL STATISTICS.
American Mathematical Society, Box 1571, Annex Sta., Providence, RI 02901-9930. TEL 401-455-4000. *3054*

SELECTED TOPICS IN SOLID STATE PHYSICS.
Elsevier Science Publishers B.V., Books Division, P.O. Box 211, 1000 AE Amsterdam, Netherlands. TEL 020-5803911. FAX 020-5803705. *3830*

SELECTIVE CANCER THERAPEUTICS.
Mary Ann Liebert, Inc., 1651 Third Ave., New York, NY 10128. TEL 212-289-2300. FAX 212-289-4697. *3202*

SELECTIVE ELECTRODE REVIEWS.
Pergamon Press, Inc., Journals Division, 660 White Plains Rd., Tarrytown, NY 10591-5153. TEL 914-524-9200. FAX 914-333-2444. *3830*

SEMICONDUCTORS AND INSULATORS.
Gordon and Breach Science Publishers, 270 Eighth Ave., New York, NY 10011. TEL 212-206-8900. FAX 212-645-2459. *1778*

SEMINARS IN ARTHRITIS & RHEUMATISM.
W.B. Saunders Co. Curtis Center, Independence Square W., Philadelphia, PA 19106. TEL 215-238-7800. *3370*

SEMINARS IN VETERINARY MEDICINE AND SURGERY: SMALL ANIMAL.
W.B. Saunders Co. Curtis Center, Independence Square W., Philadelphia, PA 19106. TEL 215-238-7800. *4815*

SENIOR NURSE (W. SUSSEX).
Scutari Projects Ltd., Viking House, 17-19 Peterborough Rd., Harrow-on-the-Hill, Middlesex HA1 2AX, England. TEL 081-423-1066. FAX 081-423-3867. *3287*

SENSOR TECHNOLOGY.
Technical Insights, Inc., 32 N. Dean St., Englewood, NJ 07631. TEL 201-568-4744. FAX 201-568-8247. *1443*

SENSORS.
Helmers Publishing, Inc., 174 Concord St., Box 874, Peterborough, NH 03458-0874. TEL 603-924-9631. FAX 603-924-7408. *2525*

SENSORS AND ACTUATORS: A PHYSICAL.
Elsevier Sequoia S.A., P.O. Box 564, CH-1001 Lausanne, Switzerland. TEL 021-207381. FAX 021-235444. *3840*

SENSORS AND ACTUATORS: B CHEMICAL.
Elsevier Sequoia S.A., P.O. Box 564, CH-1001 Lausanne, Switzerland. TEL 021-207381. FAX 021-235444. *1212*

SENSORY SYSTEMS.
Plenum Publishing Corp., Consultants Bureau, (Russian Academy of Sciences) 233 Spring St., New York, NY 10013-1578. TEL 212-620-8468. FAX 212-463-0742. *4046*

SEPARATION AND PURIFICATION METHODS.
Marcel Dekker Journals, 270 Madison Ave., New York, NY 10016. TEL 212-696-9000. FAX 212-685-4540. *1208*

SEPARATION SCIENCE AND TECHNOLOGY.
Marcel Dekker Journals, 270 Madison Ave., New York, NY 10016. TEL 212-696-9000. FAX 212-685-4540. *1208*

SEPARATIONS TECHNOLOGY.
Butterworth - Heinemann Ltd. 80 Montvale Ave., Stoneham, MA 02180. TEL 617-438-8464. FAX 617-438-1479. *1860*

SERIALS LIBRARIAN.
Haworth Press, Inc., 10 Alice St., Binghamton, NY 13904. TEL 800-342-9678. FAX 607-722-1424. *2784*

SERIALS REVIEW.
Pierian Press, Box 1808, Ann Arbor, MI 48106. TEL 313-434-5530. FAX 313-434-6409. *2784*

SERIE MEMORIA VIVA DA EDUCACAO BRASILEIRA.
Instituto Nacional de Estudos e Pesquisa Educacionais, Campus da UNB, Acesso Sul - Asa Norte, 70910 Brasilia, Brazil. TEL 061-347-8970. FAX 061-347-8270. *1662*

SERIES IN DEATH EDUCATION, AGING, AND HEALTH CARE.
Hemisphere Publishing Corporation 1900 Frost Rd., Ste. 101, Bristol, PA 19007-1598. TEL 215-785-5800. FAX 215-785-5515. *4046*

SEX ROLES.
Plenum Publishing Corp., 233 Spring St., New York, NY 10013-1578. TEL 212-620-8000. FAX 212-463-0742. *4046*

SEXUALITY AND DISABILITY.
Human Sciences Press, Inc. 233 Spring St., New York, NY 10013-1578. TEL 212-620-8000. FAX 212-463-0742. *3152*

SEXUALLY TRANSMITTED DISEASES.
J.B. Lippincott Co., (American Venereal Disease Association) E. Washington Sq., Philadelphia, PA 19105. TEL 215-238-4200. *3249*

SHANDI YANJIU.
Science Press, Marketing and Sales Department, (Chinese Academy of Sciences, Chengdu Institute of Geography) 16 Donghuangchenggen Beijie, Beijing 100707, People's Republic of China. TEL 4010642. FAX 4012180. *1580*

SHENGLI KEXUE JINZHAN.
Zhongguo Shengli Xuehui, 42 Dongsi Xidajie, Beijing 100710, People's Republic of China. TEL 556970. FAX 00861-201-5681. *574*

SHENGLI XUEBAO.
Science Press, Marketing and Sales Department, (Shanghai Institute of Physiology) 16 Donghuangchenggen Beijie, Beijing 100707, People's Republic of China. TEL 4010642. FAX 4012180. *574*

SHENGTAI XUEBAO.
Science Press, Marketing and Sales Department, (Zhongguo Shengtaixue Xuehui) 16 Donghuangchenggen Beijie, Beijing 100707, People's Republic of China. TEL 4010642. FAX 4012180. *1968*

SHENGWU FANGZHI TONGBAO.
Zhongguo Nongye Kexueyuan, Shengwu Fangzhi Yanjiushi, 30 Baishiqiao Lu, Beijing 100081, People's Republic of China. TEL 8314433. *455*

SHENGWU GONGCHENG XUEBAO.
Science Press, Marketing and Sales Department, (Chinese Academy of Sciences, Institute of Microbiology) 16 Donghuangchenggen Beijie, Beijing 100707, People's Republic of China. TEL 4010642. FAX 4012180. *491*

SHENGWU HUAXUE YU SHENGWU WULI JINZHAN.
Science Press, Marketing and Sales Department, (Chinese Academy of Sciences, Institute of Biophysics) 16 Donghuangchenggen Beijie, Beijing 100707, People's Republic of China. TEL 4010642. FAX 4012180. *482*

SHENGWU HUAXUE ZAZHI.
Beijing Yike Daxue, Shengwu Huaxue Xi, No. 38, Xueyuan Lu, Beijing 100083, People's Republic of China. TEL 2017601. FAX 00861-2015681. *483*

SHENGXUE XUEBAO.
Science Press, Marketing and Sales Department, (Acoustical Society of China) 16 Donghuangchenggen Beijie, Beijing 100707, People's Republic of China. TEL 4010642. FAX 4012180. *3860*

SHIYONG ZHONGLIU ZAZHI.
Zhejiang Yike Daxue, 157 Yan'an Lu, Hangzhou, Zhejiang 310006, People's Republic of China. TEL 722700. *3202*

SHOUDU YIXUEYUAN XUEBAO.
Shoudu Yixueyuan, You'anmenwai, Beijing 100054, People's Republic of China. TEL 3014433. *3153*

SHOULEI XUEBAO.
Science Press, Marketing and Sales Department, 16 Donghuangchenggen Beijie, Beijing 100707, People's Republic of China. TEL 4010642. FAX 4012180. *591*

SHUISHENG SHENGWU XUEBAO.
Science Press, Marketing and Sales Department, (Chinese Academy of Sciences, Institute of Hydrobiology) 16 Donghuangchenggen Beijie, Beijing 100707, People's Republic of China. TEL 4010642. FAX 4012180. *455*

SHUXUE DE SHIJIAN YU RENSHI.
Science Press, Marketing and Sales Department, (Chinese Academy of Sciences, Institute of Systems Science) 16 Donghuangchenggen Beijie, Beijing 100707, People's Republic of China. TEL 4010642. FAX 4012180. *3055*

SHUXUE XUEBAO.
Science Press, Marketing and Sales Department, (Chinese Academy of Science, Institute of Mathematics) 16 Donghuangchenggen Beijie, Beijing 100707, People's Republic of China. TEL 4010642. FAX 4012180. *3055*

SHUZHI JISUAN YU JISUANJI YINGYONG.
Science Press, Marketing and Sales Department, (Chinese Academy of Sciences, Computer Centre) 16 Donghuangchenggen Beijie, Beijing 100707, People's Republic of China. TEL 4010642. FAX 4012180. *4360*

SIBERIAN MATHEMATICAL JOURNAL.
Plenum Publishing Corp., Consultants Bureau, (Russian Academy of Sciences, Siberian Division) 233 Spring St., New York, NY 10013-1578. TEL 212-620-8468. FAX 212-463-0742. *3055*

SIDA; CONTRIBUTIONS TO BOTANY.
Botanical Research Institute of Texas, Inc., 509 Pecan St., Fort Worth, TX 76102-4060. TEL 817-332-4441. *517*

SIDE EFFECTS OF DRUGS ANNUAL.
Elsevier Science Publishers B.V., Books Division, P.O. Box 211, 1000 AE Amsterdam, Netherlands. TEL 020-5803911. FAX 020-5803705. *3743*

SIGNAL PROCESSING.
Elsevier Science Publishers B.V., (European Association for Signal Processing) P.O. Box 211, Amsterdam, Netherlands. TEL 020-5803911. FAX 020-5803598. *1431*

SIGNAL PROCESSING: IMAGE COMMUNICATION.
Elsevier Science Publishers B.V., (European Association for Signal Processing) P.O. Box 211, 1000 AE Amsterdam, Netherlands. TEL 020-5803911. FAX 020-5803598. *1380*

SIGNS: JOURNAL OF WOMEN IN CULTURE AND SOCIETY.
University of Chicago Press, Journals Division, 5720 S. Woodlawn Ave., Chicago, IL 60637. TEL 312-753-3347. FAX 312-702-0694. *4852*

SMALL RUMINANT RESEARCH.
Elsevier Science Publishers B.V., (International Goat Association) P.O. Box 211, 1000 AE Amsterdam, Netherlands. TEL 020-5803911. FAX 020-5803598. *226*

SOCIAL AND ECONOMIC STUDIES.
University of the West Indies, Institute of Social and Economic Research, Mona Campus, Kingston 7, Jamaica, W.I. TEL 809-927-1020. FAX 809-927-2409. *4386*

SOCIAL BIOLOGY.
Society for the Study of Social Biology, Box 2349, Port Angeles, WA 98362. TEL 608-233-1487. *547*

SOCIAL COGNITION.
Guilford Publications, Inc., 72 Spring St., 4th Fl., New York, NY 10012. TEL 212-431-9800. FAX 212-966-6708. *4047*

SOCIAL EPISTEMOLOGY.
Taylor & Francis Ltd., Rankine Rd., Basingstoke, Hants RG24 OPR, England. TEL 0256-840366. FAX 0256-479438. *3781*

SOCIAL FORCES.
University of North Carolina Press, (University of North Carolina at Chapel Hill, Departmnet of English) Box 2288, Chapel Hill, NC 27515-2288. TEL 919-966-3561. FAX 919-966-3829. *4449*

SOCIAL JUSTICE RESEARCH.
Plenum Publishing Corp., 233 Spring St., New York, NY 10013-1578. TEL 212-620-8000. FAX 212-463-0742. *4449*

SOCIAL NETWORKS.
North-Holland (International Network for Social Network Analysis) P.O. Box 211, 1000 AE Amsterdam, Netherlands. TEL 020-5803911. FAX 020-5803598. *4387*

SOCIAL ORDERS SERIES.
Harwood Academic Publishers, 270 Eighth Ave., New York, NY 10011. TEL 212-206-8900. FAX 212-645-2459. *4449*

SOCIAL PROBLEMS.
University of California Press, Journals Division, (Society for the Study of Social Problems, Inc.) 2120 Berkeley Way, Berkeley, CA 94720. TEL 510-642-4191. FAX 510-643-7127. *4449*

SOCIAL PSYCHOLOGICAL APPLICATIONS TO SOCIAL ISSUES.
Plenum Publishing Corp., (Society for the Psychological Study of Social Issues) 233 Spring St., New York, NY 10013-1578. TEL 212-620-8000. FAX 212-463-0742. *4047*

SOCIAL SCIENCE & MEDICINE.
Pergamon Press, Inc., Journals Division, 660 White Plains Rd., Tarrytown, NY 10591-5153. TEL 914-524-9200. FAX 914-333-2444. *3153*

SOCIAL SCIENCE COMPUTER REVIEW.
Duke University Press, (North Carolina State University, Social Science Research and Instructional Computing Lab) 6697 College Station, Durham, NC 27708. TEL 919-684-2173. FAX 919-684-8644. *1691*

SOCIAL SCIENCE HISTORY.
Duke University Press, (Social Science History Association) 6697 College Station, Durham, NC 27708. TEL 919-684-2173. FAX 919-684-8644. *4387*

REFEREED SERIALS

SOCIAL SERVICE REVIEW.
University of Chicago Press, Journals Division, 5720 S. Woodlawn Ave., Chicago, IL 60637. TEL 312-753-3347. FAX 312-702-0694. *4420*

SOCIAL STUDIES.
Heldref Publications, (Helen Dwight Reid Educational Foundation) 1319 Eighteenth St., N.W., Washington, DC 20036-1802. TEL 202-296-6267. FAX 202-296-5149. *1664*

SOCIAL WORK IN HEALTH CARE.
Haworth Press, Inc., 10 Alice St., Binghamton, NY 13904. TEL 800-342-9678. FAX 607-722-1424. *4420*

SOCIAL WORK WITH GROUPS.
Haworth Press, Inc., 10 Alice St., Binghamton, NY 13904. TEL 800-342-9678. FAX 607-722-1424. *4420*

SOCIEDAD ESPANOLA DE QUIMICA CLINICA. REVISTA.
Ediciones Mayo, S.A., Muntaner, 374-376, 4o, 08006 Barcelona, Spain. TEL 343-209-02-55. FAX 343-202-06-43. *1188*

SOCIETE BELGE DE PHOTOGRAMMETRIE - TELEDETECTION ET CARTOGRAPHIE. BULLETIN TRIMESTRIEL.
Societe Belge de Photogrammetrie-Teledetection et Cartographie, C.A.E.-Tour Finances, Bte. 38, 50 Bd. du Jardin Botanique, B-1010 Brussels, Belgium. TEL 02-210-35-75. *2262*

SOCIETE CHIMIQUE DE FRANCE. BULLETIN.
Editions Scientifiques Elsevier, 29, rue Buffon, 75005 Paris, France. *1188*

SOCIETE FRANCAISE DE CHIMIE. ANNUAIRE.
Societe Francaise de Chimie, 250 rue St. Jacques, 75005 Paris, France. *1188*

SOCIETE MATHEMATIQUE DE FRANCE. BULLETIN ET MEMOIRES.
Societe Mathematique de France, Ecole Normale Superieure, Tour L, 1 rue Maurice Arnoux, France. TEL 33-40-84-80-54. FAX 33-40-84-80-52. *3055*

SOCIETE ZOOLOGIQUE DE FRANCE. BULLETIN.
Societe Zoologique de France, 195 rue Saint-Jacques, 75005 Paris, France. *591*

SOCIETE ZOOLOGIQUE DE FRANCE. MEMOIRES.
Societe Zoologique de France, 195 rue Saint Jacques, 75005 Paris, France. TEL 40-79-37-10. *591*

SOCIETY AND ANIMALS.
Psychologists for the Ethical Treatment of Animals, Box 1297, Washington Grove, MD 20880-1297. FAX 301-963-4751. *231*

SOCIETY AND NATURAL RESOURCES.
Taylor & Francis Ltd., Rankine Rd., Basingstoke, Hants RG24 OPR, England. TEL 0256-840366. FAX 0256-479438. *1968*

SOCIETY FOR APPLIED BACTERIOLOGY. SYMPOSIUM SERIES.
Academic Press, Inc., 1250 Sixth Ave., San Diego, CA 92101. TEL 619-231-0926. FAX 619-699-6719. *557*

SOCIETY FOR APPLIED BACTERIOLOGY. TECHNICAL SERIES.
Academic Press, Inc., 1250 Sixth Ave., San Diego, CA 92101. TEL 619-231-0926. FAX 619-699-6715. *557*

SOCIETY FOR EXPERIMENTAL BIOLOGY AND MEDICINE. PROCEEDINGS.
Williams & Wilkins, (Society for Experimental Biology and Medicine) 428 E. Preston St., Baltimore, MD 21202. TEL 301-528-4000. FAX 301-528-4312. *456*

SOCIETY FOR RESEARCH IN CHILD DEVELOPMENT. MONOGRAPHS.
University of Chicago Press, 5720 S. Woodlawn Ave., Chicago, IL 60637. TEL 312-702-7600. FAX 312-753-3347. *1244*

SOCIETY OF ACTUARIES. TRANSACTIONS (GENERAL).
Society of Actuaries, 475 N. Martingale, Ste. 800, Schaumburg, IL 60173-2226. TEL 708-706-3500. FAX 708-706-3599. *2543*

SOCIETY OF EXPLORATION GEOPHYSICISTS. SPECIAL PUBLICATIONS (SYMPOSIA) SERIES.
Society of Exploration Geophysicists, Box 702740, Tulsa, OK 74170-2740. TEL 918-493-3516. *1594*

SOCIETY OF PETROLEUM ENGINEERS. REPRINT SERIES.
Society of Petroleum Engineers, Inc., Box 833836, Richardson, TX 75083-3836. TEL 214-659-3377. FAX 214-669-0135. *3701*

SOCIETY OF PETROLEUM ENGINEERS. TRANSACTIONS.
Society of Petroleum Engineers, Inc., Box 833836, Richardson, TX 75083-3836. TEL 214-669-3377. *3701*

SOCIETY OF THE PLASTICS INDUSTRY. URETHANE DIVISION. CONFERENCE PROCEEDINGS.
Technomic Publishing Co., Inc., 851 New Holland Ave., Box 3535, Lancaster, PA 17604. TEL 717-291-5609. FAX 717-295-4538. *3868*

SOCIO-ECONOMIC PLANNING SCIENCES.
Pergamon Press, Inc., Journals Division, 660 White Plains Rd., Tarrytown, NY 10591-5153. TEL 914-524-9200. FAX 914-333-2444. *4073*

SOCIOBIOLOGY.
California State University, Chico, Department of Biological Sciences, Chico, CA 95926. TEL 916-859-5116. FAX 916-898-6804. *456*

SOCIOLOGICAL FORUM.
Plenum Publishing Corp., (Eastern Sociological Society) 233 Spring St., New York, NY 10013-1578. TEL 212-620-8000. FAX 212-463-0742. *4451*

SOCIOLOGICAL RECORD.
M.E. Sharpe, Inc., 80 Business Park Dr., Armonk, NY 10504. TEL 914-273-1800. FAX 914-273-2106. *4451*

SOCIOLOGICAL SPECTRUM.
Hemisphere Publishing Corporation (Mid-South Sociological Association) 1900 Frost Rd., Ste. 101, Bristol, PA 19007-1598. TEL 215-785-5800. FAX 215-785-5515. *4451*

SOCIOLOGICAL VIEWPOINTS.
Pennsylvania Sociological Society, c/o M.Y. Rynn, Man. Ed., University of Scranton, Scranton, PA 18510-4605. TEL 717-941-6137. FAX 717-941-6369. *4451*

SOCIOLOGY OF SPORT JOURNAL.
Human Kinetics Publishers, Inc., (North American Society for the Sociology of Sport) Box 5076, Champaign, IL 61825-5076. TEL 217-351-5076. FAX 217-351-2674. *4452*

SOFTWARE DEVELOPMENT MONITOR.
Elsevier Science Publishers Ltd., Crown House, Linton Rd., Barking, Essex IG11 8JU, England. TEL 081-594-7272. FAX 081-594-5942. *1480*

SOIL AND TILLAGE RESEARCH.
Elsevier Science Publishers B.V., (International Soil Tillage Research Organisation) P.O. Box 211, 1000 AE Amsterdam, Netherlands. TEL 020-5803911. FAX 020-5803911. *120*

SOIL BIOLOGY & BIOCHEMISTRY.
Pergamon Press, Inc., Journals Division, (Council of Biological and Medical Abstracts) 660 White Plains Rd., Tarrytown, NY 10591-5153. TEL 914-524-9200. FAX 914-333-2444. *457*

SOIL DYNAMICS AND EARTHQUAKE ENGINEERING.
Elsevier Science Publishers Ltd., Crown House, Linton Rd., Barking, Essex IG11 8JU, England. TEL 081-594-7272. FAX 081-594-5942. *1594*

SOIL MECHANICS AND FOUNDATION ENGINEERING.
Plenum Publishing Corp., Consultants Bureau, (Gosudarstvennyi Komitet po Delam Stroitel'stva S.S.S.R.) 233 Spring St., New York, NY 10013-1578. TEL 212-620-8468. FAX 212-463-0742. *1874*

SOIL SCIENCE.
Williams & Wilkins, (Rutgers University) 428 E. Preston St., Baltimore, MD 21202. TEL 301-528-4000. FAX 301-528-4312. *192*

SOIL SCIENCE SOCIETY OF AMERICA. JOURNAL.
Soil Science Society of America, 677 S. Segoe Rd., Madison, WI 53711. TEL 608-273-8080. FAX 608-273-2021. *192*

SOLAR ENERGY.
Pergamon Press, Inc., Journals Division, (International Solar Energy Society) 660 White Plains Rd., Tarrytown, NY 10591. TEL 914-524-9200. FAX 914-333-2444. *1811*

SOLAR ENERGY MATERIALS AND SOLAR CELLS.
Elsevier Science Publishers B.V., P.O. Box 211, 1000 AE Amsterdam, Netherlands. TEL 020-5803911. FAX 020-5803598. *1811*

SOLAR SYSTEM RESEARCH.
Plenum Publishing Corp., Consultants Bureau, (Russian Academy of Sciences) 233 Spring St., New York, NY 10013-1578. TEL 212-620-8468. FAX 212-463-0742. *369*

SOLID FUEL CHEMISTRY.
Allerton Press, Inc., (Russian Academy of Sciences) 150 Fifth Ave., New York, NY 10011. TEL 212-924-3950. *1860*

SOLID STATE COMMUNICATIONS.
Pergamon Press, Inc., Journals Division, 660 White Plains Rd., Tarrytown, NY 10591-5153. TEL 914-524-9200. FAX 914-333-2444. *3831*

SOLID-STATE ELECTRONICS.
Pergamon Press, Inc., Journals Division, 660 White Plains Rd., Tarrytown, NY 10591-5153. TEL 914-524-9200. FAX 914-333-2444. *1778*

SOLID STATE IONICS.
North-Holland P.O. Box 211, 1000 AE Amsterdam, Netherlands. TEL 020-5803911. FAX 020-5803598. *3831*

SOLID STATE PHYSICS: ADVANCES IN RESEARCH AND APPLICATIONS.
Academic Press, Inc., 1250 Sixth Ave., San Diego, CA 92101. TEL 619-231-0926. FAX 619-699-6715. *3831*

SOLID STATE TECHNOLOGY.
PennWell Publishing Co. (Port Washington), 14 Vanderventer Ave., Port Washington, NY 11050. TEL 516-883-6200. *1778*

SOLOS E ROCHAS.
Associacao Brasiliera de Mecanica dos Solos, I P T, Predio Geotecnica, Cidade Universitaria, Caixa Postal 7141, 01051 Sao Paulo, Brazil. TEL 011-268-7325. *1836*

SOLSTICE: AN ELECTRONIC JOURNAL OF GEOGRAPHY AND MATHEMATICS.
Institute of Mathematical Geography, 2790 Briarcliff, Ann Arbor, MI 48105-1429. TEL 313-761-1231. *3056*

SOLUBILITY DATA SERIES.
Pergamon Press, Inc., Journals Division, (International Union of Pure and Applied Chemistry) 660 White Plains Rd., Tarrytown, NY 10591-5153. TEL 914-524-9200. FAX 914-333-2444. *1188*

SOLVENT EXTRACTION AND ION EXCHANGE.
Marcel Dekker Journals, 270 Madison Ave., New York, NY 10016. TEL 212-696-9000. FAX 212-685-4540. *1208*

SOMATIC CELL AND MOLECULAR GENETICS.
Plenum Publishing Corp., 233 Spring St., New York, NY 10013-1578. TEL 212-620-8000. FAX 212-463-0742. *547*

SOMATOSENSORY AND MOTOR RESEARCH.
Guilford Publications, Inc., 72 Spring St., 4th Fl., New York, NY 10012. TEL 212-431-9800. FAX 212-966-6708. *575*

SOUTH AFRICAN INSTITUTE OF MINING AND METALLURGY. JOURNAL.
South African Institute of Mining and Metallurgy, P.O. Box 61127, Marshalltown 2107, South Africa. TEL 011-834-1273. FAX 011-838-5923. *3420*

SOUTH AFRICAN MUSEUM. ANNALS.
South African Museum, Box 61, Cape Town 8000, South Africa. TEL 021-243-330. FAX 021-246716. *457*

SOUTH ASIAN SOCIAL SCIENTIST.
South Asian Social Scientists Association, Department of Anthropology, University of Madras, Tamil Nadu, Madras 600 005, India. TEL 568778. *3644*

SOUTHEASTERN GEOLOGY.
Duke University, Geology Department, Durham, NC 27706. TEL 919-684-5321. FAX 919-684-5833. *1581*

SOUTHERN FOLKLORE.
University Press of Kentucky, 663 S. Limestone St., Lexington, KY 40508-4008. TEL 606-257-8439. FAX 606-257-2984. *2058*

SOUTHERN LITERARY JOURNAL.
University of North Carolina Press, (University of North Carolina at Chapel Hill, Department of English) Box 2288, Chapel Hill, NC 27515-2288. TEL 919-966-3561. FAX 919-966-3829. *2962*

SOUTHERN MEDICAL JOURNAL.
Southern Medical Association, 35 Lakeshore Dr., Box 190088, Birmingham, AL 35219-0088. TEL 205-945-1840. FAX 205-945-1548. *3154*

SOUTHERN STUDIES: AN INTERDISCIPLINARY JOURNAL OF THE SOUTH.
Northwestern State University of Louisiana, Southern Studies Institute, Natchitoches, LA 71497. TEL 318-357-6195. FAX 318-357-6125. *4388*

SOVIET APPLIED MECHANICS.
Plenum Publishing Corp., Consultants Bureau, (Ukrainian Academy of Sciences) 233 Spring St., New York, NY 10013-1578. TEL 212-620-8468. FAX 212-463-0742. *1922*

SOVIET ATOMIC ENERGY.
Plenum Publishing Corp., Consultants Bureau, (Russian Academy of Sciences) 233 Spring St., New York, NY 10013-1578. TEL 212-620-8468. FAX 212-463-0742. *1809*

SOVIET ELECTROCHEMISTRY.
Plenum Publishing Corp., Consultants Bureau, (Russian Academy of Sciences) 233 Spring St., New York, NY 10013-1578. TEL 212-620-8468. FAX 212-463-0742. *1213*

SOVIET GENETICS.
Plenum Publishing Corp., Consultants Bureau, (Russian Academy of Sciences) 233 Spring St., New York, NY 10013-1578. TEL 212-620-8468. FAX 212-463-0742. *547*

SOVIET JOURNAL OF BIOORGANIC CHEMISTRY.
Plenum Publishing Corp., Consultants Bureau, (Russian Academy of Sciences) 233 Spring St., New York, NY 10013-1578. TEL 212-620-8468. FAX 212-463-0742. *1223*

SOVIET JOURNAL OF CHEMICAL PHYSICS.
Gordon & Breach Science Publishers, 270 Eighth Ave., New York, NY 10011. TEL 212-206-8900. FAX 212-645-2459. *3831*

SOVIET JOURNAL OF COORDINATION CHEMISTRY.
Plenum Publishing Corp., Consultants Bureau, (Russian Academy of Sciences) 233 Spring St., New York, NY 10013-1578. TEL 212-620-8468. FAX 212-463-0742. *1188*

SOVIET JOURNAL OF DEVELOPMENTAL BIOLOGY.
Plenum Publishing Corp., Consultants Bureau, (Russian Academy of Sciences) 233 Spring St., New York, NY 10013-1578. TEL 212-620-8468. FAX 212-463-0742. *547*

SOVIET JOURNAL OF ECOLOGY.
Plenum Publishing Corp., Consultants Bureau, 233 Spring St., New York, NY 10013-1578. TEL 212-620-8468. FAX 212-463-0742. *1969*

SOVIET JOURNAL OF GLASS PHYSICS AND CHEMISTRY.
Plenum Publishing Corp., Consultants Bureau, (Rusian Academy of Sciences) 233 Spring St., New York, NY 10013-1578. TEL 212-620-8468. FAX 212-463-0742. *1166*

SOVIET JOURNAL OF MARINE BIOLOGY.
Plenum Publishing Corp., Consultants Bureau, (Russian Academy of Sciences) 233 Spring St., New York, NY 10013-1578. TEL 212-620-8468. FAX 212-463-0742. *457*

SOVIET JOURNAL OF NONDESTRUCTIVE TESTING.
Plenum Publishing Corp., Consultants Bureau, (Russian Academy of Sciences) 233 Spring St., New York, NY 10013-1578. TEL 212-620-8468. FAX 212-463-0742. *1188*

SOVIET JOURNAL OF PSYCHOLOGY.
International Universities Press, Inc., Journal Department, 59 Boston Post Rd., Box 1524, Madison, CT 06443-1524. TEL 203-245-4000. FAX 203-245-0775. *4047*

SOVIET JOURNAL OF REMOTE SENSING.
Harwood Academic Publishers, 270 Eighth Ave., New York, NY 10011. TEL 212-206-8900. FAX 212-645-2459. *1837*

SOVIET MATERIALS SCIENCE.
Plenum Publishing Corp., Consultants Bureau, (Ukrainian Academy of Sciences) 233 Spring St., New York, NY 10013-1578. TEL 212-620-8468. FAX 212-463-0742. *1922*

SOVIET MEDICAL REVIEWS. SECTION A: CARDIOLOGY REVIEWS.
Harwood Academic Publishers, 270 Eighth Ave., New York, NY 10011. TEL 212-206-8900. FAX 212-645-2459. *3212*

SOVIET MEDICAL REVIEWS. SECTION B: PHYSICOCHEMICAL ASPECTS OF MEDICINE REVIEWS.
Harwood Academic Publishers, 270 Eighth Ave., New York, NY 10011. TEL 212-206-8900. FAX 212-645-2459. *575*

SOVIET MEDICAL REVIEWS. SECTION C: HEMATOLOGY REVIEWS.
Harwood Academic Publishers, 270 Eighth Ave., New York, NY 10011. TEL 212-206-8900. FAX 212-645-2459. *3274*

SOVIET MEDICAL REVIEWS. SECTION D: IMMUNOLOGY REVIEWS.
Harwood Academic Publishers, 270 Eighth Ave., New York, NY 10011. TEL 212-206-8900. FAX 212-645-2459. *3188*

SOVIET MEDICAL REVIEWS. SECTION E: VIROLOGY REVIEWS.
Harwood Academic Publishers, 270 Eighth Ave., New York, NY 10011. TEL 212-206-8900. FAX 212-645-2459. *557*

SOVIET MEDICAL REVIEWS. SECTION F: ONCOLOGY REVIEWS.
Harwood Academic Publishers, 270 Eighth Ave., New York, NY 10011. TEL 212-645-2459. FAX 212-645-2459. *3202*

SOVIET MICROELECTRONICS.
Plenum Publishing Corp., Consultants Bureau, (Russian Academy of Sciences) 233 Spring St., New York, NY 10013-1578. TEL 212-620-8468. FAX 212-463-0742. *1778*

SOVIET MINING SCIENCE.
Plenum Publishing Corp., Consultants Bureau, (Russian Academy of Sciences, Siberian Division) 233 Spring St., New York, NY 10013-1578. TEL 212-620-8468. FAX 212-463-0742. *3496*

SOVIET PHYSICS JOURNAL.
Plenum Publishing Corp., Consultants Bureau, (Vysshie Uchebnye Zavedeniya S.S.S.R.) 233 Spring St., New York, NY 10013-1578. TEL 212-620-8468. FAX 212-463-0742. *3832*

SOVIET PLANT PHYSIOLOGY.
Plenum Publishing Corp., Consultants Bureau, (Russian Academy of Sciences) 233 Spring St., New York, NY 10013-1578. TEL 212-620-8468. FAX 212-463-0742. *518*

SOVIET RADIOCHEMISTRY.
Plenum Publishing Corp., Consultants Bureau, (Russian Academy of Sciences) 233 Spring St., New York, NY 10013-1578. TEL 212-620-8468. FAX 212-463-0742. *1230*

SOVIET SCIENTIFIC REVIEWS. SECTION A: PHYSICS REVIEWS.
Harwood Academic Publishers, 270 Eighth Ave., New York, NY 10011. TEL 212-206-8900. FAX 212-645-2459. *3832*

SOVIET SCIENTIFIC REVIEWS. SECTION B: CHEMISTRY REVIEWS.
Harwood Academic Publishers, 270 Eighth Ave., New York, NY 10011. TEL 212-206-8900. FAX 212-645-2459. *1188*

SOVIET SCIENTIFIC REVIEWS. SECTION C: MATHEMATICAL PHYSICS REVIEWS.
Harwood Academic Publishers, 270 Eighth Ave., New York, NY 10011. TEL 212-206-8900. FAX 212-645-2459. *3832*

SOVIET SCIENTIFIC REVIEWS. SECTION D: PHYSIOCHEMICAL BIOLOGY REVIEWS.
Harwood Academic Publishers, 270 Eighth Ave., New York, NY 10011. TEL 212-206-8900. FAX 212-645-2459. *483*

SOVIET SCIENTIFIC REVIEWS. SECTION E: ASTROPHYSICS & SPACE PHYSICS REVIEWS.
Harwood Academic Publishers, 270 Eighth Ave., New York, NY 10011. TEL 212-206-8900. FAX 212-645-2459. *369*

SOVIET SCIENTIFIC REVIEWS. SECTION F: PHYSIOLOGY AND GENERAL BIOLOGY REVIEWS.
Harwood Academic Publishers, 270 Eighth Ave., New York, NY 10011. TEL 212-206-8900. FAX 212-645-2459. *575*

SOVIET SCIENTIFIC REVIEWS. SECTION G: GEOLOGY REVIEWS.
Harwood Academic Publishers, 270 Eighth Ave., New York, NY 10011. TEL 212-206-8900. FAX 212-645-2459. *1581*

SOVIET SCIENTIFIC REVIEWS SUPPLEMENT SERIES. SECTION C: PHYSICOCHEMICAL BIOLOGY.
Harwood Academic Publishers, 270 Eighth Ave., New York, NY 10011. TEL 212-260-8900. FAX 212-645-2459. *483*

SOVIET STUDIES.
Harwood Academic Publishers, 270 Eighth Ave., New York, NY 10011. TEL 212-206-8900. FAX 212-645-2459. *4453*

SOVIET TECHNOLOGY REVIEWS. SECTION A: ENERGY REVIEWS.
Harwood Academic Publishers, 270 Eighth Ave., New York, NY 10011. TEL 212-206-8900. FAX 212-645-2459. *1796*

SOVIET TECHNOLOGY REVIEWS. SECTION B: THERMAL PHYSICS REVIEWS.
Harwood Academic Publishers, 270 Eighth Ave., New York, NY 10011. TEL 212-206-8900. FAX 212-645-2459. *3842*

SOVIET TECHNOLOGY REVIEWS. SECTION C: WELDING AND SURFACING REVIEWS.
Harwood Academic Publishers, 270 Eighth Ave., New York, NY 10011. TEL 212-206-8900. FAX 212-645-2459. *3430*

SPACE COMMERCE.
Harwood Academic Publishers, 270 Eighth Ave., New York, NY 10011. TEL 212-206-8900. FAX 212-645-2459. *62*

SPACE POLICY.
Butterworth - Heinemann Ltd. Linacre House, Jordan Hill, Oxford OX2 8DP, England. TEL 0865-310366. FAX 0865-310898. *62*

SPACE TECHNOLOGY.
Pergamon Press, Inc., Journals Division, 660 White Plains Rd., Tarrytown, NY 10591-5153. TEL 914-524-9200. FAX 914-333-2444. *4609*

SPECIAL ASPECTS OF EDUCATION.
Gordon & Breach Science Publishers, 270 Eighth Ave., New York, NY 10011. TEL 212-206-8900. FAX 212-645-2459. *1664*

SPECIAL SERVICES IN THE SCHOOLS.
Haworth Press, Inc., 10 Alice St., Binghamton, NY 13904. TEL 800-342-9678. FAX 607-722-1424. *1741*

SPECTROCHIMICA ACTA. PART A: MOLECULAR SPECTROSCOPY.
Pergamon Press, Inc., Journals Division, 660 White Plains Rd., Tarrytown, NY 10591-5153. TEL 914-524-9200. FAX 914-333-2444. *1208*

SPECTROCHIMICA ACTA. PART B: ATOMIC SPECTROSCOPY.
Pergamon Press, Inc., Journals Division, 660 White Plains Rd., Tarrytown, NY 10591-5153. TEL 914-524-9200. FAX 914-333-2444. *1208*

SPECTROCHIMICA ACTA REVIEWS.
Pergamon Press, Inc., Journals Division, 660 White Plains Rd., Tarrytown, NY 10591-5153. TEL 914-524-9200. FAX 914-333-2444. *1208*

SPECTROSCOPY: AN INTERNATIONAL JOURNAL.
Elsevier Science Publishers B.V., P.O. Box 211, 1000 A E Amsterdam, Netherlands. TEL 020-5803911. FAX 020-5803598. *1188*

SPECTROSCOPY LETTERS.
Marcel Dekker Journals, 270 Madison Ave., New York, NY 10016. TEL 212-696-9000. FAX 212-685-4540. *3857*

SPEECH COMMUNICATION.
North-Holland (European Association for Signal Processing) P.O. Box 211, 1000 AE Amsterdam, Netherlands. TEL 020-5803911. FAX 020-5803598. *2857*

SPINE (PHILADELPHIA, 1986).
Hanley & Belfus, Inc., 210 S. 13th St., Philadelphia, PA 19107. TEL 215-546-7293. FAX 215-790-9330. *3311*

THE SPORT PSYCHOLOGIST.
Human Kinetics Publishers, Inc., (International Society of Sport Psychology) Box 5076, Champaign, IL 61825-5076. TEL 217-351-5076. FAX 217-351-2674. *4047*

SPORT SCIENCE REVIEW.
Human Kinetics Publishers, Inc., Box 5076, Champaign, IL 61825-5076. TEL 217-351-5076. FAX 217-351-3674. *3373*

SPORTS MEDICINE, TRAINING AND REHABILITATION.
Harwood Academic Publishers, 270 Eighth Ave., New York, NY 10011. TEL 212-206-8900. FAX 212-645-2459. *3373*

STADLER GENETICS SYMPOSIUM. PROCEEDINGS.
Plenum Publishing Corp., 233 Spring St., New York, NY 10013-1578. TEL 212-620-8000. FAX 212-463-0742. *547*

STANDARDS ACTIVITIES OF ORGANIZATIONS IN THE U S.
U.S. National Institute of Standards and Technology, Gaithersburg, MD 20899. TEL 301-975-3058. *3449*

STATE GEOLOGISTS JOURNAL.
Virginia Division of Mineral Resources, (Association of American State Geologists) c/o Robert C. Milici, Box 3667, Charlottesville, VA 22903. TEL 804-293-5121. FAX 804-293-2239. *1581*

STATISTICAL SCIENCE.
Institute of Mathematical Statistics, 3401 Investment Blvd., Ste. 7, Hayward, CA 94545. TEL 510-783-8141. *4588*

STATISTICS AND COMPUTING.
Chapman & Hall, 2-6 Boundary Row, London SE1 8HN, England. TEL 071-865-0066. FAX 071-522-9623. *4588*

STATISTICS & PROBABILITY LETTERS.
North-Holland P.O. Box 211, 1000 AE Amsterdam, Netherlands. TEL 020-5803911. FAX 020-5803598. *4588*

STATUTES AND DECISIONS.
M.E. Sharpe, Inc., 80 Business Park Dr., Armonk, NY 10504. TEL 914-273-1800. FAX 914-273-2106. *2682*

STEEL INDIA.
Steel Authority of India Ltd., R & D Centre for Iron & Steel, Ranchi 834 002, India. FAX 0651-300023. *3420*

STEROIDS: STRUCTURE, FUNCTION AND REGULATION.
Butterworth - Heinemann Ltd. 80 Montvale Ave., Stoneham, MA 02180. TEL 617-438-8464. FAX 617-438-1479. *483*

STOCHASTIC ANALYSIS AND APPLICATIONS.
Marcel Dekker Journals, 270 Madison Ave., New York, NY 10016. TEL 212-696-9000. FAX 212-685-4540. *3056*

STOCHASTIC PROCESSES AND THEIR APPLICATIONS.
North-Holland (Bernoulli Society for Mathematical Statistics and Probability) P.O. Box 211, 1000 AE Amsterdam, Netherlands. TEL 020-5803911. FAX 020-5803598. *4346*

STOCHASTICS AND STOCHASTICS REPORTS.
Gordon and Breach Science Publishers, 270 Eighth Ave., New York, NY 10011. TEL 212-206-8900. FAX 212-645-2459. *3056*

STOCHASTICS MONOGRAPHS.
Gordon & Breach Science Publishers, 270 Eighth Ave., New York, NY 10011. TEL 212-206-8900. FAX 212-645-2459. *3056*

STOCHASTIK IN DER SCHULE.
Verein zur Foerderung des Schulischen Statistikunterrichts e.V., Kammannstr. 13, 5800 Hagen 1, Germany. *4589*

STRATEGIC MANAGEMENT JOURNAL.
John Wiley & Sons Ltd., Baffins Lane, Chichester, Sussex PO19 1UD, England. TEL 0243-779777. FAX 0243-775878. *1028*

STRENGTH AND FRACTURE.
Hemisphere Publishing Corporation 1900 Frost Rd., Ste. 101, Bristol, PA 19007-1598. TEL 215-785-5800. FAX 215-785-5515. *1837*

STRENGTH OF MATERIALS.
Plenum Publishing Corp., Consultants Bureau, (Ukrainian Academy of Sciences) 233 Spring St., New York, NY 10013-1578. TEL 212-620-8468. FAX 212-463-0742. *1922*

STRESS AND EMOTION.
Hemisphere Publishing Corporation 1900 Frost Rd., Ste. 101, Bristol, PA 19007-1598. TEL 215-785-5800. FAX 215-785-5515. *4047*

STROKE.
American Heart Association, 7272 Greenville Ave., Dallas, TX 75231-4596. TEL 214-706-1310. FAX 214-691-6342. *3212*

STRUCTURAL ENGINEER.
Institution of Structural Engineers, 11 Upper Belgrave St., London SW1X 8BH, England. TEL 071-235-4535. FAX 071-235-4535. *1874*

STRUCTURAL FOAM CONFERENCE. PROCEEDINGS.
Technomic Publishing Co. Inc., (Society of the Plastics Industry) 851 New Holland Ave., Box 3535, Lancaster, PA 17604. TEL 717-291-5609. FAX 717-295-4538. *3868*

STRUCTURAL SAFETY.
Elsevier Science Publishers B.V., P.O. Box 211, 1000 AE Amsterdam, Netherlands. TEL 020-5803911. FAX 020-5803598. *1874*

STUDIA GEOPHYSICA ET GEODAETICA.
Plenum Publishing Corp., (Czechoslovak Academy of Sciences, Geophysical Institute) 233 Spring St., New York, NY 10013-1578. TEL 212-620-8000. FAX 212-463-0742. *1595*

STUDIES IN ANALYTICAL CHEMISTRY.
Elsevier Science Publishers B.V., Books Division, P.O. Box 211, 1000 AE Amsterdam, Netherlands. TEL 020-5803911. FAX 020-5803705. *1208*

STUDIES IN ANTHROPOLOGY AND HISTORY.
Harwood Academic Publishers, 270 Eighth Ave., New York, NY 10011. TEL 212-206-8900. FAX 212-645-2459. *2323*

STUDIES IN APPLIED MATHEMATICS.
Elsevier Science Publishing Co., Inc. (New York), (Massachusetts Institute of Technology, Applied Mathematics Group) 655 Ave. of the Americas, New York, NY 10010. TEL 212-989-5800. FAX 212-633-3965. *3056*

STUDIES IN APPLIED MECHANICS.
Elsevier Science Publishers B.V., Books Division, P.O. Box 211, 1000 AE Amsterdam, Netherlands. TEL 020-5803911. FAX 020-5803705. *3845*

STUDIES IN ASTRONAUTICS.
Elsevier Science Publishers B.V., Books Division, P.O. Box 211, 1000 AE Amsterdam, Netherlands. TEL 020-5803911. FAX 020-5803705. *63*

STUDIES IN AUTOMATION AND CONTROL.
Elsevier Science Publishers B.V., Books Division, P.O. Box 211, 1000 AE Amsterdam, Netherlands. TEL 020-5803911. FAX 020-5803705. *1416*

STUDIES IN BAYESIAN ECONOMETRICS AND STATISTICS.
Elsevier Science Publishers B.V., Books Division, P.O. Box 211, 1000 AE Amsterdam, Netherlands. TEL 020-5803911. FAX 020-5803705. *898*

STUDIES IN BUSINESS AND SOCIETY.
University of Chicago Press, (University of Chicago, Graduate School of Business) 5801 S. Ellis Ave., Chicago, IL 60637. TEL 312-702-7899. *693*

STUDIES IN COMPARATIVE COMMUNISM.
Butterworth - Heinemann Ltd. Linacre House, Jordan Hill, Oxford OX2 8DP, England. TEL 0865-310366. FAX 0865-310898. *3928*

STUDIES IN COMPARATIVE LITERATURE (CHAPEL HILL).
University of North Carolina Press, (University of North Carolina at Chapel Hill, Department of English) Box 2288, Chapel Hill, NC 27515-2288; TEL 919-966-3561. FAX 919-966-3829. *2965*

STUDIES IN CONFLICT AND TERRORISM.
Taylor & Francis, 1900 Frost Rd., Ste. 101, Bristol, PA 19007. TEL 215-785-5800. FAX 215-785-5515. *3973*

STUDIES IN CYBERNETICS.
Gordon & Breach Science Publishers, 270 Eighth Ave., New York, NY 10011. TEL 212-206-8900. FAX 212-645-2459. *1443*

STUDIES IN EDUCATIONAL EVALUATION.
Pergamon Press, Inc., Journals Division, (University of California, Los Angeles, Center for the Study of Evaluation) 660 White Plains Rd., Tarrytown, NY 10591-5153. TEL 914-524-9200. FAX 914-333-2444. *1666*

STUDIES IN ELECTRICAL AND ELECTRONIC ENGINEERING.
Elsevier Science Publishers B.V., Books Division, P.O. Box 211, 1000 AE Amsterdam, Netherlands. TEL 020-5803911. FAX 020-5803705. *1908*

STUDIES IN ENVIRONMENTAL SCIENCE.
Elsevier Science Publishers B.V., Books Division, P.O. Box 211, 1000 AE Amsterdam, Netherlands. TEL 020-5803911. FAX 020-5803705. *1969*

STUDIES IN GENDER AND CULTURE.
Gordon & Breach Science Publishers, 270 Eighth Ave., New York, NY 10011. TEL 212-206-8900. FAX 212-645-2459. *4453*

STUDIES IN HIGH ENERGY PHYSICS SERIES.
Harwood Academic Publishers, 270 Eighth Ave., New York, NY 10011. TEL 212-206-8900. FAX 212-645-2459. *3833*

STUDIES IN HISTORY AND PHILOSOPHY OF SCIENCE.
Pergamon Press, Inc., Journals Division, 660 White Plains Rd., Tarrytown, NY 10591-5153. TEL 914-524-9200. FAX 914-333-2444. *4346*

STUDIES IN HISTORY OF BIOLOGY.
Johns Hopkins University Press, 701 W. 40th St., Ste. 275, Baltimore, MD 21211. TEL 410-516-6900. FAX 410-516-6998. *457*

STUDIES IN INFECTIOUS DISEASES RESEARCH.
University of Chicago Press, 5801 S. Ellis Ave., Chicago, IL 60637. TEL 312-702-7899. *3224*

STUDIES IN INORGANIC CHEMISTRY.
Elsevier Science Publishers B.V., Books Division, P.O. Box 211, 1000 AE Amsterdam, Netherlands. TEL 020-5803911. FAX 020-5803705. *1215*

STUDIES IN INTERNATIONAL ECONOMICS.
Elsevier Science Publishers B.V., P.O. Box 211, 1000 AE Amsterdam, Netherlands. TEL 020-5803911. FAX 020-5803705. *693*

STUDIES IN LEGAL HISTORY.
University of North Carolina Press, (University of North Carolina at Chapel Hill, Department of English) Box 2288, Chapel Hill, NC 27515-2288. TEL 919-966-3561. FAX 919-966-3829. *2683*

STUDIES IN LOGIC AND THE FOUNDATIONS OF MATHEMATICS.
Elsevier Science Publishers B.V., Books Division, P.O. Box 211, 1000 AE Amsterdam, Netherlands. TEL 020-5803911. FAX 020-5803705. *3057*

STUDIES IN MANAGEMENT SCIENCE AND SYSTEMS.
Elsevier Science Publishers B.V., Books Division, P.O. Box 211, 1000 AE Amsterdam, Netherlands. TEL 020-5803911. FAX 020-5803705. *1028*

STUDIES IN MATHEMATICAL AND MANAGERIAL ECONOMICS.
Elsevier Science Publishers B.V., Books Division, P.O. Box 211, 1000 AE Amsterdam, Netherlands. TEL 020-5803911. FAX 020-5803705. *1028*

STUDIES IN MATHEMATICS (WASHINGTON).
Mathematical Association of America, 1529 Eighteenth St., N.W., Washington, DC 20036. TEL 202-387-5200. *3057*

STUDIES IN MATHEMATICS AND ITS APPLICATIONS.
Elsevier Science Publishers B.V., Books Division, P.O. Box 211, Amsterdam, Netherlands. TEL 020-5803911. FAX 020-5803705. *3057*

STUDIES IN MECHANICAL ENGINEERING.
Elsevier Science Publishers B.V., Books Division, P.O. Box 211, 1000 AE Amsterdam, Netherlands. TEL 020-5803911. FAX 020-5803705. *1939*

STUDIES IN MODERN THERMODYNAMICS.
Elsevier Science Publishers B.V., Books Division, P.O. Box 211, 1000 AE Amsterdam, Netherlands. TEL 020-5803911. FAX 020-5803705. *1230*

STUDIES IN MONETARY ECONOMICS.
Elsevier Science Publishers B.V., Books Division, P.O. Box 211, 1000 AE Amsterdam, Netherlands. TEL 020-5803911. FAX 020-5803705. *800*

STUDIES IN OPERATIONS RESEARCH.
Gordon & Breach Science Publishers, 270 Eighth Ave., New York, NY 10011. TEL 212-206-8900. FAX 212-645-2459. *1400*

STUDIES IN ORGANIC CHEMISTRY SERIES.
Marcel Dekker, Inc., 270 Madison Ave., New York, NY 10016. TEL 212-696-9000. FAX 212-685-4540. *1223*

STUDIES IN PHILOLOGY.
University of North Carolina Press, (University of North Carolina at Chapel Hill, Department of English) Box 2288, Chapel Hill, NC 27515-2288. TEL 919-966-3561. FAX 919-966-3829. *2846*

STUDIES IN PHYSICAL AND THEORETICAL CHEMISTRY.
Elsevier Science Publishers B.V., Books Division, P.O. Box 211, 1000 AE Amsterdam, Netherlands. TEL 020-5803911. FAX 020-5803705. *1230*

STUDIES IN PLANT SCIENCE.
Elsevier Science Publishers B.V., Books Division, P.O. Box 211, 1000 AE Amsterdam, Netherlands. TEL 020-5803911. FAX 020-5803705. *518*

STUDIES IN POLITICAL ECONOMY. SOCIALIST REVIEW.
Politecon, (Social Sciences and Humanities Research Council of Canada) Box 4729, Station E, Ottawa, Ont. K1S 5H9, Canada. TEL 613-788-6625. *3928*

STUDIES IN POPULAR CULTURE.
Popular Culture Association in the South, c/o Dennis Hall, Ed., University of Louisville, Department of English, Louisville, KY 40292. *4453*

STUDIES IN PRODUCTION AND ENGINEERING ECONOMICS.
Elsevier Science Publishers B.V., Books Division, P.O. Box 211, 1000 AE Amsterdam, Netherlands. TEL 020-5803911. FAX 020-5803705. *693*

STUDIES IN REGIONAL SCIENCE AND URBAN ECONOMICS.
Elsevier Science Publishers B.V., Books Division, P.O. Box 211, Amsterdam, Netherlands. TEL 020-5803911. FAX 020-5803705. *885*

STUDIES IN STATISTICAL MECHANICS.
Elsevier Science Publishers B.V., Books Division, P.O. Box 211, 1000 AE Amsterdam, Netherlands. TEL 020-5803911. FAX 020-5803705. *3845*

STUDIES IN SURFACE SCIENCE AND CATALYSIS.
Elsevier Science Publishers B.V., Books Division, P.O. Box 211, 1000 AE Amsterdam, Netherlands. TEL 020-5803911. FAX 020-5803705. *3845*

STUDIES IN THE DEVELOPMENT OF MODERN MATHEMATICS.
Gordon and Breach Scientific Publishers, 270 Eighth Ave., New York, NY 10011. TEL 212-206-8900. FAX 212-645-2459. *3057*

STUDIES IN THE GERMANIC LANGUAGES AND LITERATURES.
University of North Carolina Press, (University of North Carolina at Chapel Hill, Department of English) Box 2288, Chapel Hill, NC 27515-2288. TEL 919-966-3561. FAX 919-966-3829. *2966*

STUDIES IN THE HISTORY OF MATHEMATICS AND PHYSICAL SCIENCES.
Springer-Verlag, 175 Fifth Ave., New York, NY 10010. TEL 212-460-1500. *3057*

STUDIES ON THE MORPHOLOGY AND SYSTEMATICS OF SCALE INSECTS.
Virginia Polytechnic Institute and State University, Department of Entomology, Blacksburg, VA 24061-0319. TEL 703-231-6341. *538*

SUB-CELLULAR BIOCHEMISTRY.
Plenum Publishing Corp., 233 Spring St., New York, NY 10013-1578. TEL 212-620-8000. FAX 212-463-0742. *483*

SUGAR SERIES.
Elsevier Science Publishers B.V., Books Division, P.O. Box 211, 1000 AE Amsterdam, Netherlands. TEL 020-5803911. FAX 020-5803705. *2082*

SUICIDE AND LIFE-THREATENING BEHAVIOR.
Guilford Publications, Inc., (American Association of Suicidology) 72 Spring St., 4th Fl., New York, NY 10012. TEL 212-431-9800. FAX 212-966-6708. *4048*

SULFUR LETTERS.
Harwood Academic Publishers, 270 Eighth Ave., New York, NY 10011. TEL 212-206-8900. FAX 212-645-2459. *1189*

SULFUR REPORTS.
Harwood Academic Publishers, 270 Eighth Ave., New York, NY 10011. TEL 212-206-8900. FAX 212-645-2459. *1189*

SUMMARIES OF B F R L FIRE RESEARCH IN-HOUSE AND GRANTS (YEAR).
U.S. National Institute of Standards and Technology, Fire Research Information Services, Bldg. 224, Rm. A252, Gaithersburg, MD 20899. TEL 301-975-6862. *2035*

SUOMEN LAAKARILEHTI.
Suomen Laakariliitto, Makelankatu 2, 00500 Helsinki, Finland. TEL 90-393-091. *3155*

SUPREME COURT REVIEW.
University of Chicago Press, Journals Division, 5720 S. Woodlawn Ave., Chicago, IL 60637. TEL 312-702-7600. FAX 312-702-0694. *2733*

SURFACE AND COATINGS TECHNOLOGY.
Elsevier Sequoia S.A., P.O. Box 564, CH-1001 Lausanne, Switzerland. TEL 021-207381. FAX 021-235444. *1209*

SURFACE SCIENCE.
North-Holland P.O. Box 211, 1000 AE Amsterdam, Netherlands. TEL 020-5803911. FAX 020-5803598. *3833*

SURFACE SCIENCE REPORTS.
North-Holland P.O. Box 211, 1000 AE Amsterdam, Netherlands. TEL 020-5803911. FAX 020-5803598. *3833*

SURFACTANT SCIENCE SERIES.
Marcel Dekker, Inc., 270 Madison Ave., New York, NY 10016. TEL 212-696-9000. FAX 212-685-4540. *1189*

SURGERY.
Mosby - Year Book, Inc., (Society of University Surgeons) 11830 Westline Industrial Dr., St. Louis, MO 63146. TEL 800-325-4117. FAX 314-432-1380. *3384*

SURGICAL LAPAROSCOPY AND ENDOSCOPY.
Raven Press, 1185 Ave. of the Americas, New York, NY 10036. TEL 212-930-9500. FAX 212-869-3495. *3385*

SURGICAL NEUROLOGY.
Elsevier Science Publishing Co., Inc. (New York), 655 Ave. of the Americas, New York, NY 10010. TEL 212-989-5800. FAX 212-633-3965. *3385*

SURGICAL PRACTICE NEWS.
McMahon Publishing Co., 83 Peaceable St., West Redding, CT 06896. TEL 203-944-9343. *3385*

SURGICAL RESEARCH COMMUNICATIONS.
Harwood Academic Publishers, 270 Eighth Ave., New York, NY 10011. TEL 212-206-8900. FAX 212-645-2459. *3385*

SURGICAL UPDATE.
American Association of Oral and Maxillofacial Surgeons, 9700 W. Bryn Mawr Ave., Rosemont, IL 60018. TEL 708-678-6200. FAX 708-678-6286. *3243*

SURVEYS & REFERENCE WORKS IN MATHEMATICS.
John Wiley and Sons, Inc., 605 Third Avenue, New York, NY 10158-0012. TEL 212-850-6000. FAX 212-850-6088. *3057*

SURVEYS IN HIGH ENERGY PHYSICS.
Harwood Academic Publishers, 270 Eighth Ave., New York, NY 10011. TEL 212-206-8900. FAX 212-645-2459. *3833*

SYMPOSIA FOUNDATION MERIEUX.
Elsevier Science Publishers B.V., Books Division, P.O. Box 211, 1000 AE Amsterdam, Netherlands. TEL 020-5803911. FAX 020-5803705. *3155*

SYMPOSIA MATHEMATICA.
Academic Press, Inc., (Istituto Nazionale di Alta Matematica Francesco Severi) 1250 Sixth Ave., San Diego, CA 92101. TEL 619-231-0926. FAX 619-699-6715. *3057*

SYMPOSIUM.
Heldref Publications, (Syracuse University, Department of Romance Languages) 1319 Eighteenth St., N.W., Washington, DC 20036-1802. TEL 202-296-6267. FAX 202-296-5149. *2967*

SYMPOSIUM (INTERNATIONAL) ON COMBUSTION.
Combustion Institute, 5001 Baum Blvd., Pittsburgh, PA 15213. TEL 412-387-1366. FAX 412-687-0340. *1230*

SYMPOSIUM ON COMPUTER APPLICATIONS IN MEDICAL CARE. PROCEEDINGS.
S C A M C, Inc., c/o American Medical Informatics Association, 4915 St. Elmo Ave., Ste. 302, Bethesda, MD 20814. TEL 301-657-1291. FAX 301-657-1296. *3226*

SYMPOSIUM ON COMPUTER ARITHMETIC. PROCEEDINGS.
I E E E Computer Society Press, (Institute of Electrical and Electronics Engineers, Inc.) 10662 Los Vaqueros Circle, Los Alamitos, CA 90720-1264. TEL 714-821-8380. FAX 714-821-4010. *1443*

SYMPOSIUM ON FUSION ENGINEERING. PROCEEDINGS.
Institute of Electrical and Electronics Engineers, Inc., 345 E. 47th St., New York, NY 10017-2394. TEL 212-705-7900. FAX 212-705-7682. *1809*

SYNCHROTRON RADIATION NEWS.
Gordon & Breach Science Publishers, 270 Eighth Ave., New York, NY 10011. TEL 212-206-8900. FAX 212-645-2459. *3851*

SYNTHESIS AND REACTIVITY IN INORGANIC AND METALORGANIC CHEMISTRY.
Marcel Dekker Journals, 270 Madison Ave., New York, NY 10016. TEL 212-696-9000. FAX 212-685-4540. *1230*

SYNTHETIC COMMUNICATIONS.
Marcel Dekker Journals, 270 Madison Ave., New York, NY 10016. TEL 212-696-9000. FAX 212-685-4540. *1223*

SYNTHETIC METALS.
Elsevier Sequoia S.A., P.O. Box 564, CH-1001 Lausanne, Switzerland. TEL 021-207381. FAX 021-235444. *1189*

SYRACUSE CHEMIST.
American Chemical Society, Syracuse Section, c/o David Orser, Ed., General Electric Co., Electronics Park, Bldg. 6, Rm. 305, Syracuse, NY 13221. *1189*

SYSTEM.
Pergamon Press, Inc., Journals Division, 660 White Plains Rd., Tarrytown, NY 10591-5153. TEL 914-524-9200. FAX 914-333-2444. *1760*

SYSTEMATIC BIOLOGY.
Society of Systematic Biologists, 1041 New Hampshire St., Box 1897, Lawrence, KS 66044. TEL 913-843-1234. FAX 205-460-7357. *592*

SYSTEMATIC BOTANY.
American Society of Plant Taxonomists, Department of Biology, Saint Mary's College, Notre Dame, IN 46556. TEL 219-284-4674. FAX 219-284-4716. *518*

SYSTEMS AND CONTROL LETTERS.
North-Holland P.O. Box 211, 1000 AE Amsterdam, Netherlands. TEL 020-5803911. FAX 020-5803598. *1439*

SYSTEMS PRACTICE.
Plenum Publishing Corp., 233 Spring St., New York, NY 10013-1578. TEL 212-620-8000. FAX 212-463-0742. *1029*

SYSTEMS RESEARCH AND INFORMATION SCIENCE.
Gordon & Breach Science Publishers, 270 Eighth Ave., New York, NY 10011. TEL 212-206-8900. FAX 212-645-2459. *1439*

SYSTEMS RESEARCH IN PSYCHOLOGY.
Gordon & Breach Science Publishers, 270 Eighth Ave., New York, NY 10011. TEL 212-206-8900. FAX 212-645-2459. *4048*

SYSTEMS SCIENCE AND MATHEMATICAL SCIENCES.
Allerton Press, Inc., (Chinese Academy of Sciences, Institute of Systems Science) 150 Fifth Ave., New York, NY 10011. TEL 212-924-3950. *3057*

T A P P I JOURNAL.
Technical Association of the Pulp and Paper Industry, Inc., Technology Park-Atlanta, Box 105113, Atlanta, GA 30348. TEL 404-446-1400. FAX 404-446-6947. *3666*

T A P P I PROCEEDINGS.
Technical Association of the Pulp and Paper Industry, Inc., Technology Park-Atlanta, Box 105113, Atlanta, GA 30348. TEL 404-446-1400. FAX 404-446-6947. *3666*

T A P P I TEST METHODS.
Technical Association of the Pulp and Paper Industry, Inc., Technology Park-Atlanta, Box 105113, Atlanta, GA 30348. TEL 404-446-1400. FAX 404-446-6947. *3666*

T E S O L MATTERS.
Teachers of English to Speakers of Other Languages, 1600 Cameron St., Ste. 300, Alexandria, VA 22314-2751. TEL 703-836-0774. FAX 703-836-7864. *2847*

T I M S STUDIES IN THE MANAGEMENT SCIENCES.
Elsevier Science Publishers B.V., Books Division, P.O. Box 211, 1000 AE Amsterdam, Netherlands. TEL 020-5803911. FAX 020-5803705. *828*

T R C SPECTRAL DATA - INFARED.
Thermodynamics Research Center, Texas Engineering Experiment Station, Texas A & M University System, College Station, TX 77843-3111. TEL 409-845-4940. FAX 409-847-8590. *1209*

T R C SPECTRAL DATA - ULTRAVIOLET.
Thermodynamics Research Center, Texas Engineering Experiment Station, Texas A & M University System, College Station, TX 77843-3111. TEL 409-845-4940. FAX 409-847-8590. *1209*

T R C SPECTRAL DATA - 13 C NUCLEAR MAGNETIC RESONANCE.
Thermodynamics Research Center, Texas Engineering Experiment Station, Texas A & M University System, College Station, TX 77843-3111. TEL 409-845-4940. FAX 409-847-8590. *1209*

T R C THERMODYNAMIC TABLES - HYDROCARBONS.
Thermodynamics Research Center, Texas Engineering Experiment Station, Texas A & M University System, College Station, TX 77843-3111. TEL 409-845-4940. FAX 409-847-8590. *1230*

T R C THERMODYNAMIC TABLES - NON-HYDROCARBONS.
Thermodynamics Research Center, Texas Engineering Experiment Station, Texas A & M University System, College Station, TX 77843-3111. TEL 409-845-4940. FAX 409-847-8590. *1209*

TALANTA.
Pergamon Press, Inc., Journals Division, 660 White Plains Rd., Tarrytown, NY 10591-5153. TEL 914-524-9200. FAX 914-333-2444. *1209*

TANMIAT AL-RAFIDAIN.
Majallat Tanmiat al-Rafidain, (Mosul University, Faculty of Administration and Economics) P.O. Box 78, Mosul, Iraq. TEL 814433. *4075*

TARGET ORGAN TOXICOLOGY SERIES.
Raven Press, 1185 Ave. of the Americas, New York, NY 10036. TEL 212-930-9500. FAX 212-869-3495. *1983*

TAXATION FOR LAWYERS.
Warren, Gorham and Lamont, (Tax Research Group, Ltd.) One Penn Plaza, New York, NY 10119. TEL 800-950-1205. FAX 212-971-5240. *1110*

TE REO.
Linguistic Society of New Zealand, c/o Romance Languages, University, Private Bag 92019, Auckland 1, New Zealand. TEL 64-9-737917. FAX 64-9-733429. *2847*

TEACHING AND LEARNING IN MEDICINE.
Lawrence Erlbaum Associates, Inc., 365 Broadway, Hillsdale, NJ 07642. TEL 201-666-4110. FAX 201-666-2394. *3156*

TEACHING AND LEARNING: THE JOURNAL OF NATURAL INQUIRY.
University of North Dakota, Center for Teaching and Learning, Box 8158, Grand Fork, ND 58202. TEL 701-777-2674. *1761*

TEACHING & TEACHER EDUCATION.
Pergamon Press, Inc., Journals Division, 660 White Plains Rd., Tarrytown, NY 10591-5153. TEL 914-524-9200. FAX 914-333-2444. *1761*

TEACHING ELEMENTARY PHYSICAL EDUCATION.
Human Kinetics Publishers, Inc., Box 5076, Champaign, IL 61825-5076. TEL 217-351-5076. FAX 217-351-2674. *1761*

TEACHING OF PSYCHOLOGY.
Lawrence Erlbaum Associates, Inc., (American Psychological Association, Division Two) 365 Broadway, Hillside, NJ 07642. TEL 201-666-4110. FAX 201-666-2394. *4048*

TEACHING PROFESSOR.
Magna Publications, 2718 Dryden Dr., Madison, WI 53704. TEL 608-246-3580. FAX 608-249-0355. *1717*

TEACHING THINKING & PROBLEM SOLVING NEWSLETTER.
Lawrence Erlbaum Associates, Inc., (American Psychological Association, Clinical Psychology) 365 Broadway, Hillsdale, NJ 07642. TEL 201-666-4110. FAX 201-666-2394. *4048*

TECHNICAL ASSOCIATION OF THE PULP AND PAPER INDUSTRY. COATING CONFERENCE. PROCEEDINGS (YEAR).
Technical Association of the Pulp and Paper Industry, Inc., Technology Park-Atlanta, Box 105113, Atlanta, GA 30348. TEL 404-446-1400. FAX 404-446-6947. *3666*

TECHNICAL ASSOCIATION OF THE PULP AND PAPER INDUSTRY. ENGINEERING CONFERENCE PROCEEDINGS (YEAR).
Technical Association of the Pulp and Paper Industry, Inc., Technology Park-Atlanta, Box 105113, Atlanta, GA 30348. TEL 404-446-1400. FAX 404-446-6947. *3667*

TECHNICAL ASSOCIATION OF THE PULP AND PAPER INDUSTRY. ENVIRONMENTAL CONFERENCE PROCEEDINGS (YEAR).
Technical Association of the Pulp and Paper Industry, Inc., Technology Park-Atlanta, Box 105113, Atlanta, GA 30348. TEL 404-446-1400. FAX 404-446-6947. *1969*

TECHNICAL ASSOCIATION OF THE PULP AND PAPER INDUSTRY. FINISHING AND CONVERTING CONFERENCE. PROCEEDINGS (YEAR).
Technical Association of the Pulp and Paper Industry, Inc., Technology Park-Atlanta, Box 105113, Atlanta, GA 30348. TEL 404-446-1400. FAX 404-446-6947. *3667*

TECHNICAL ASSOCIATION OF THE PULP AND PAPER INDUSTRY. INTERNATIONAL PROCESS & PRODUCT QUALITY CONFERENCE PROCEEDINGS (YEAR).
Technical Association of the Pulp and Paper Industry, Inc., Technology Park-Atlanta, Box 105113, Atlanta, GA 30348. TEL 404-446-1400. FAX 404-446-6947. *3667*

TECHNICAL ASSOCIATION OF THE PULP AND PAPER INDUSTRY. NONWOOD PLANT FIBER PULPING PROGRESS REPORT.
Technical Association of the Pulp and Paper Industry, Inc., Technology Park-Atlanta, Box 105113, Atlanta, GA 30348. TEL 404-446-1400. FAX 404-446-6947. *3667*

TECHNICAL ASSOCIATION OF THE PULP AND PAPER INDUSTRY. NONWOVENS CONFERENCE. PROCEEDINGS (YEAR).
Technical Association of the Pulp and Paper Industry, Inc., Box 105113, Atlanta, GA 30348. TEL 404-446-1400. FAX 404-446-6947. *3667*

TECHNICAL ASSOCIATION OF THE PULP AND PAPER INDUSTRY. PAPERMAKERS CONFERENCE PROCEEDINGS (YEAR).
Technical Association of the Pulp and Paper Industry, Inc., Technology Park-Atlanta, Box 105113, Atlanta, GA 30348. TEL 404-446-1400. FAX 404-446-6947. *3667*

TECHNICAL ASSOCIATION OF THE PULP AND PAPER INDUSTRY. POLYMERS, LAMINATIONS & COATINGS CONFERENCE. PROCEEDINGS (YEAR).
Technical Association of the Pulp and Paper Industry, Inc., Box 105113, Atlanta, GA 30348. TEL 404-446-1400. FAX 404-446-6947. *3667*

TECHNICAL ASSOCIATION OF THE PULP AND PAPER INDUSTRY. PROCESS CONTROL CONFERENCE. PROCEEDINGS (YEAR).
Technical Association of the Pulp and Paper Industry, Inc., Box 105113, Atlanta, GA 30348. TEL 404-446-1400. FAX 404-446-6947. *3667*

TECHNICAL ASSOCIATION OF THE PULP AND PAPER INDUSTRY. PULPING CONFERENCE PROCEEDINGS (YEAR).
Technical Association of the Pulp and Paper Industry, Inc., Technology Park-Atlanta, Box 105113, Atlanta, GA 30348. TEL 404-446-1400. *3667*

TECHNICAL SERVICES QUARTERLY.
Haworth Press, Inc., 10 Alice St., Binghamton, NY 13904. TEL 800-342-9678. FAX 607-722-1424. *2787*

REFEREED SERIALS

TECHNIQUES AND APPLICATIONS IN ORGANIC SYNTHESIS SERIES.
Marcel Dekker, Inc., 270 Madison Ave., New York, NY 10016. TEL 212-696-9000. FAX 212-685-4540. *1223*

TECHNIQUES AND INSTRUMENTATION IN ANALYTICAL CHEMISTRY.
Elsevier Science Publishers B.V., Books Division, P.O. Box 211, 1000 AE Amsterdam, Netherlands. TEL 020-5803911. FAX 020-5803705. *1209*

TECHNIQUES OF CHEMISTRY.
John Wiley & Sons, Inc., 605 Third Ave., New York, NY 10158-0012. TEL 212-850-6000. FAX 212-850-6088. *1189*

TECHNIQUES OF PHYSICS.
Academic Press, Inc., 1250 Sixth Ave., San Diego, CA 92101. TEL 619-231-0926. FAX 619-699-6715. *3833*

TECHNOLOGICAL FORECASTING AND SOCIAL CHANGE.
Elsevier Science Publishing Co., Inc. (New York), 655 Ave. of the Americas, New York, NY 10010. TEL 212-989-5800. FAX 212-633-3965. *4610*

TECHNOLOGY AND CULTURE.
University of Chicago Press, Journals Division, (Society for the History of Technology) c/o Alex Roland, Secretary, Department of History, Duke University, Durham, NC 27706. TEL 312-753-3347. FAX 312-702-0694. *4611*

TECHNOLOGY FOR ANESTHESIA.
E C R I, (Emergency Care Research Institute) 5200 Butler Pike, Plymouth Meeting, PA 19462. TEL 215-825-6000. FAX 215-834-1275. *3192*

TECHNOLOGY FOR CARDIOLOGY.
E C R I, (Emergency Care Research Institute) 5200 Butler Pike, Plymouth Meeting, PA 19462. TEL 215-825-6000. FAX 215-834-1275. *3212*

TECHNOLOGY FOR CRITICAL CARE NURSES.
E C R I, (Emergency Care Research Institute) 5200 Butler Pike, Plymouth Meeting, PA 19462. TEL 215-825-6000. FAX 215-834-1274. *3287*

TECHNOLOGY FOR EMERGENCY CARE NURSES.
E C R I, (Emergency Care Research Institute) 5200 Butler Pike, Plymouth Meeting, PA 19462. TEL 215-825-6000. FAX 215-834-1275. *3287*

TECHNOLOGY FOR IMAGING & RADIOLOGY.
E C R I, (Emergency Care Research Institute) 5200 Butler Pike, Plymouth Meeting, PA 19462. TEL 215-825-6000. FAX 215-834-1275. *3363*

TECHNOLOGY FOR LABORATORY MEDICINE.
E C R I, (Emergency Care Research Institute) 5200 Butler Pike, Plymouth Meeting, PA 19462. TEL 215-825-6000. FAX 215-834-1275. *3156*

TECHNOLOGY FOR MATERIALS MANAGEMENT.
E C R I, (Emergency Care Research Institute) 5200 Butler Pike, Plymouth Meeting, PA 19462. TEL 215-825-6000. FAX 215-834-1275. *3156*

TECHNOLOGY FOR RESPIRATORY THERAPY.
E C R I, (Emergency Care Research Institute) 5200 Butler Pike, Plymouth Meeting, PA 19462. TEL 215-825-6000. FAX 215-834-1275. *3367*

TECHNOLOGY FOR SURGERY.
E C R I, (Emergency Care Research Institute) 5200 Butler Pike, Plymouth Meeting, PA 19462. TEL 215-825-6000. FAX 215-834-1275. *3385*

TECHNOLOGY IN SOCIETY.
Pergamon Press, Inc., Journals Division, 660 White Plains Rd., Tarrytown, NY 10591-5153. TEL 914-524-9200. FAX 914-333-2444. *4454*

TECHNOMETRICS.
American Statistical Association, 1429 Duke St., Alexandria, VA 22314-3402. TEL 703-684-1221. FAX 703-684-2037. *1838*

TECHNOVATION.
Elsevier Science Publishers Ltd., Crown House, Linton Rd., Barking, Essex IG11 8JU, England. TEL 081-594-7272. FAX 081-594-5942. *4611*

TECHTRENDS.
Association for Educational Communications and Technology, 1025 Vermont Ave., N.W., Ste. 820, Washington, DC 20005-3516. TEL 202-347-7834. FAX 202-347-7839. *1762*

TECTONOPHYSICS.
Elsevier Science Publishers B.V., P.O. Box 211, 1000 AE Amsterdam, Netherlands. TEL 020-5803911. FAX 020-5803598. *1595*

TEKNIK DERGI.
Turkish Chamber of Civil Engineers, Selanik Caddesi 19-1, Kizilay 06650 Ankara, Turkey. TEL 4-1337626. FAX 4-1170632. *1875*

TELECOMMUNICATIONS POLICY.
Butterworth - Heinemann Ltd. Linacre House, Jordan Hill, Oxford OX2 8DP, England. TEL 0865-310366. FAX 0865-310898. *1344*

TELEMATICS AND INFORMATICS.
Pergamon Press, Inc., Journals Division, 660 White Plains Rd., Tarrytown, NY 10591-5153. TEL 914-524-9200. FAX 914-333-2444. *1344*

TEMPORARY CULTURE.
Box 43072, Upper Montclair, NJ 07043. *2886*

TENNESSEE ACADEMY OF SCIENCE. JOURNAL.
Tennessee Academy of Science, 2001 Craven Ln., Prairie Peninsula, Hixson, TN 37343. TEL 615-251-1573. *4347*

TERATOGENESIS, CARCINOGENESIS, AND MUTAGENESIS.
John Wiley & Sons, Inc., Journals, 605 Third Ave., New York, NY 10158. TEL 212-850-6000. FAX 212-850-6088. *3156*

TERATOLOGY.
John Wiley & Sons, Inc., Journals, (Teratology Society) 605 Third Ave., New York, NY 10158. TEL 212-850-6000. FAX 212-850-6088. *457*

TETRAHEDRON.
Pergamon Press, Inc., Journals Division, 660 WHite Plains Rd., Tarrytown, NY 10591-5153. TEL 914-524-9200. FAX 914-333-2444. *1224*

TETRAHEDRON: ASYMMETRY.
Pergamon Press, Inc., Journals Division, 660 White Plains Rd., Tarrytown, NY 10591-5153. TEL 914-524-9200. FAX 914-333-2444. *1224*

TETRAHEDRON LETTERS.
Pergamon Press, Inc., Journals Division, 660 White Plains Rd., Tarrytown, NY 10591-5153. TEL 914-524-9200. FAX 914-333-2444. *1224*

TEXAS JOURNAL OF SCIENCE.
Texas Academy of Science, c/o Texas Tech University, The Museum, Box 4499, Lubbock, TX 79409. TEL 806-742-2487. *4347*

TEXTILE RESEARCH JOURNAL.
Textile Research Institute, 601 Prospect Ave., Box 625, Princeton, NJ 08542. TEL 609-924-3150. FAX 609-683-7836. *4626*

TEXTILE SCIENCE AND TECHNOLOGY.
Elsevier Science Publishers B.V., Books Division, P.O. Box 211, 1000 AE Amsterdam, Netherlands. TEL 020-5803911. FAX 020-5803705. *4626*

TEXTURES AND MICROSTRUCTURES.
Gordon & Breach Science Publishers, 270 Eighth Ave., New York, NY 10011. TEL 212-206-8900. FAX 212-645-2459. *1582*

THEATRE TOPICS.
Johns Hopkins University Press, Journals Publishing Division, (Association for Theatre in Higher Education) 701 W. 40th St., Ste. 275, Baltimore, MD 21211. TEL 410-516-6980. FAX 410-516-6998. *4641*

THEORETICAL AND APPLIED FRACTURE MECHANICS.
Elsevier Science Publishers B.V., P.O. Box 211, 1000 AE Amsterdam, Netherlands. TEL 020-5803911. FAX 020-5803598. *3846*

THEORETICAL AND EXPERIMENTAL BIOLOGY.
Academic Press, Inc., 1250 Sixth Ave., San Diego, CA 92101. TEL 619-231-0962. FAX 619-699-6715. *457*

THEORETICAL AND EXPERIMENTAL CHEMISTRY.
Plenum Publishing Corp., Consultants Bureau, (Ukrainian Academy of Sciences) 233 Spring St., New York, NY 10013-1578. TEL 212-620-8468. FAX 212-463-0742. *1189*

THEORETICAL AND MATHEMATICAL PHYSICS.
Plenum Publishing Corp., Consultants Bureau, (Russian Academy of Sciences) 233 Spring St., New York, NY 10013-1578. TEL 212-620-8468. FAX 212-463-0742. *3834*

THEORETICAL CHEMISTRY.
Academic Press, Inc., 1250 Sixth Ave., San Diego, CA 92101. TEL 619-231-0926. FAX 619-699-6715. *1189*

THEORETICAL COMPUTER SCIENCE.
North-Holland P.O. Box 211, 1000 AE Amsterdam, Netherlands. TEL 020-5803911. FAX 020-5803598. *1482*

THEORETICAL FOUNDATIONS OF CHEMICAL ENGINEERING.
Plenum Publishing Corp., Consultants Bureau, (Russian Academy of Sciences) 233 Spring St., New York, NY 10013-1578. TEL 212-620-8468. FAX 212-463-0742. *1860*

THEORETICAL PARAPSYCHOLOGY.
Gordon and Breach Science Publishers, 270 Eighth Ave., New York, NY 10011. TEL 212-206-8900. FAX 212-645-2459. *4048*

THEORETICAL POPULATION BIOLOGY.
Academic Press, Inc., Journal Division, 1250 Sixth Ave., San Diego, CA 92101. TEL 619-230-1840. FAX 619-699-6800. *458*

THEORY AND RESEARCH IN BEHAVIORAL PEDIATRICS.
Plenum Publishing Corp., 233 Spring St., New York, NY 10013-1578. TEL 202-620-8000. FAX 212-463-0742. *4048*

THEORY INTO PRACTICE.
Ohio State University, College of Education, 174 Arps Hall, 1945 N. High St., Columbus, OH 43210-1172. TEL 614-292-2801. *1667*

THEORY OF PROBABILITY AND ITS APPLICATIONS.
Society for Industrial and Applied Mathematics, Attn: P. Clifford, 3600 University City Science Center, Philadelphia, PA 19104-2688. TEL 215-382-9800. FAX 215-386-7999. *3058*

THERIOGENOLOGY.
Butterworth - Heinemann Ltd. 80 Montvale Ave., Stoneham, MA 02180. TEL 617-438-8464. FAX 617-438-1479. *4816*

THERMOCHIMICA ACTA.
Elsevier Science Publishers B.V., P.O. Box 211, 1000 AE Amsterdam, Netherlands. TEL 020-5803911. FAX 020-5803598. *1231*

THERMODYNAMICS AT TEXAS A & M.
Thermodynamics Research Center, Texas Engineering Experiment Station, Texas A & M University System, College Station, TX 77843. TEL 409-845-4940. FAX 409-847-8590. *1231*

THERMOLOGY.
American Academy of Thermology, Vienna Professional Bldg., 138 Church St., N.E., Vienna, VA 22180. TEL 703-938-6140. FAX 703-938-1482. *575*

THIN FILMS SCIENCE AND TECHNOLOGY.
Elsevier Science Publishers B.V., Books Division, P.O. Box 211, 1000 AE Amsterdam, Netherlands. TEL 020-5803911. FAX 020-5803705. *3834*

THIN SOLID FILMS.
Elsevier Sequoia S.A., P.O. Box 564, CH-1001 Lausanne, Switzerland. TEL 021-207381. FAX 021-235444. *3834*

THIN-WALLED STRUCTURES.
Elsevier Science Publishers Ltd., Crown House, Linton Rd., Barking, Essex IG11 8JU, England. TEL 081-594-7272. FAX 081-594-5942. *1940*

THOMAS SAY FOUNDATION MONOGRAPHS.
Entomological Society of America, 9301 Annapolis Rd., Lanham, MD 20706. TEL 301-731-4535. FAX 301-731-4538. *538*

THROMBOSIS RESEARCH.
Pergamon Press, Inc., Journals Division, 660 White Plains Rd., Tarrytown, NY 10591-5153. TEL 914-524-9200. FAX 914-333-2444. *3212*

THYMUS UPDATE.
Harwood Academic Publishers, 270 Eighth Ave., New York, NY 10011. TEL 212-260-8900. FAX 212-645-2459. *3189*

TIANTI WULI XUEBAO.
Science Press, Marketing and Sales Department, 16 Donghuangchenggen Beijie, Beijing 100707, People's Republic of China. TEL 4010642. FAX 4012180. *370*

TIANWEN XUEBAO.
Science Press, Marketing and Sales Department, 16 Donghuangchenggen Beijie, Beijing 100707, People's Republic of China. TEL 4010642. FAX 4012180. *370*

TIANWENXUE JINZHAN.
Science Press, Marketing and Sales Department, (Chinese Academy of Sciences, Shanghai Astronomical Observatory) 16 Donghuangchenggen Beijie, Beijing 100707, People's Republic of China. TEL 4010642. FAX 4012180. *370*

TISSUE & CELL.
Churchill Livingstone Medical Journals, Robert Stevenson House, 1-3 Baxter's Pl., Leith Walk, Edinburgh EH1 3AF, Scotland. TEL 031-556-2424. *527*

TISSUE CULTURE ASSOCIATION. MONOGRAPH SERIES.
Tissue Culture Association, 8815 Centre Park Dr., Columbia, MD 21045. TEL 301-992-0946. *558*

TISSUE CULTURE ASSOCIATION. PROCEEDINGS.
Tissue Culture Association, 8815 Centre Park Dr., Ste. 210, Columbia, MD 21045. TEL 301-992-0946. *558*

TODAY'S C P A.
Texas Society of C P A's, 1421 W. Mockingbird Ln., Ste. 100, Dallas, TX 75247-4957. TEL 214-689-6000. FAX 214-689-6046. *757*

TOPICS IN CHEMICAL ENGINEERING.
Gordon & Breach Science Publishers, P.O. Box 90, Reading, Berkshire RG1 8JL, England. TEL 0734-560-080. FAX 0734-568-211. *1860*

TOPICS IN COMPUTER MATHEMATICS.
Gordon & Breach Science Publishers, P.O. Box 90, Reading, Berkshire RG1 8JL, England. TEL 0734-560-080. FAX 0734-568-211. *3066*

TOPICS IN ENVIRONMENTAL HEALTH.
Elsevier Science Publishers B.V., Books Division, P.O. Box 211, 1000 AE Amsterdam, Netherlands. TEL 020-5803911. FAX 020-5803705. *458*

TOPICS IN GASTROENTEROLOGY.
Plenum Publishing Corp., 233 Spring St., New York, NY 10013-1578. TEL 212-620-8000. FAX 212-463-0742. *3270*

TOPICS IN GEOBIOLOGY.
Plenum Publishing Corp., 233 Spring St., New York, NY 10013-1578. TEL 212-620-8000. FAX 212-463-0742. *1583*

TOPICS IN INORGANIC AND GENERAL CHEMISTRY.
Elsevier Science Publishers B.V., Books Division, P.O. Box 211, 1000 AE Amsterdam, Netherlands. TEL 020-5803911. FAX 020-5803705. *1215*

TOPICS IN MOLECULAR PHARMACOLOGY.
Elsevier Science Publishers B.V., Books Division, P.O. Box 211, 1000 AE Amsterdam, Netherlands. TEL 020-5803911. FAX 020-5803705. *3744*

TOPICS IN PHILOSOPHY.
University of California Press, 2120 Berkeley Way, Berkeley, CA 94720. TEL 415-642-4247. FAX 415-643-7127. *3784*

TOPICS IN PHOTOSYNTHESIS.
Elsevier Science Publishers B.V., Books Division, P.O. Box 211, 1000 AE Amsterdam, Netherlands. TEL 020-5803911. FAX 020-5803705. *458*

TOPICS IN STEREOCHEMISTRY.
John Wiley & Sons, Inc., 605 Third Ave., New York, NY 10158-0012. TEL 212-850-6000. FAX 212-850-6088. *1190*

TOPOLOGY.
Pergamon Press, Inc., Journals Division, 660 White Plains Rd., Tarrytown, NY 10591-5153. TEL 914-524-9200. FAX 914-333-2444. *3058*

TOPOLOGY AND ITS APPLICATIONS.
North-Holland P.O. Box 211, 1000 AE Amsterdam, Netherlands. TEL 020-5803911. FAX 020-5803598. *3058*

TOPOLOGY PROCEEDINGS.
Auburn University, Mathematics Department, Auburn, AL 36830. TEL 205-844-6566. FAX 205-887-3799. *3058*

TOURISM MANAGEMENT.
Butterworth - Heinemann Ltd. Linacre House, Jordan Hill, Oxford OX2 8DP, England. TEL 0865-310366. FAX 0865-310898. *4790*

TOXIC SUBSTANCES JOURNAL.
Hemisphere Publishing Corporation 1900 Frost Rd., Ste. 101, Bristol, PA 19007-1598. TEL 215-785-5800. FAX 215-785-5515. *1987*

TOXICOLOGIC PATHOLOGY.
Society of Toxicologic Pathologists, c/o Dr. Benjamin F. Trump, Ed., Dept. of Pathology, School of Medicine, Univ. of Maryland, Baltimore, MD 21201. FAX 301-328-3743. *1983*

TOXICOLOGICAL AND ENVIRONMENTAL CHEMISTRY.
Gordon and Breach Science Publishers, 270 Eighth Ave., New York, NY 10011. TEL 212-206-8900. FAX 212-645-2459. *1983*

TOXICOLOGY AND APPLIED PHARMACOLOGY.
Academic Press, Inc., Journal Division, 1250 Sixth Ave., San Diego, CA 92101. TEL 619-230-1840. FAX 619-699-6800. *1983*

TOXICOLOGY IN VITRO.
Pergamon Press, Inc., Journals Division, (British Industrial Biological Research Association) 660 White Plains Rd., Tarrytown, NY 10591-5153. TEL 914-524-9200. FAX 914-333-2444. *1983*

TOXICOLOGY LETTERS.
Elsevier Science Publishers B.V., P.O. Box 211, 1000 AE Amsterdam, Netherlands. TEL 020-5803911. FAX 020-5803598. *1983*

TOXICOLOGY METHODS.
Raven Press, 1185 Ave. of the Americas, New York, NY 10036. TEL 212-930-9500. FAX 212-869-3495. *1983*

TOXICON.
Pergamon Press, Inc., Journals Division, (International Society on Toxinology) 660 White Plains Rd., Tarrytown, NY 10591-5153. TEL 914-524-9200. FAX 914-333-2444. *3744*

TRACE ANALYSIS.
Academic Press, Inc., 1250 Sixth Ave., San Diego, CA 92101. TEL 619-231-0926. FAX 619-699-6715. *4113*

TRACE SUBSTANCES IN ENVIRONMENTAL HEALTH.
Science Reviews Ltd., 40 The Fairway, Northwood, Middlesex HA6 3DY, England. *1984*

TRADITIONAL DWELLINGS AND SETTLEMENTS REVIEW.
International Association for the Study of Traditional Environments, Center for Environmental Design Research, 390 Wurster Hall, Department of Architecture, University of California, Berkeley, CA 94720. TEL 415-642-2896. FAX 415-643-5571. *307*

TRAJECTA.
Uitgeverij Kerckebosch B.V., Postbus 122, 3700 AC Zeist, Netherlands. TEL 03404-21444. FAX 3404-12174. *4277*

TRANSFUSION SCIENCE.
Pergamon Press, Inc., Journals Division, (European Society for Haemapheresis) 660 White Plains Rd., Tarrytown, NY 10591-5153. TEL 914-524-9200. FAX 914-333-2444. *3274*

TRANSNATIONAL CORPORATIONS AND TRANSBORDER DATA FLOWS.
Elsevier Science Publishers B.V., Books Division, (United Nations Centre on Transnational Corporations) P.O. Box 211, 1000 AE Amsterdam, Netherlands. TEL 020-5803911. FAX 020-5803705. *828*

TRANSPLANTATION.
Williams & Wilkins, (Transplantation Society) 428 E. Preston St., Baltimore, MD 21202. TEL 301-528-4000. FAX 301-528-4312. *3385*

TRANSPLANTATION PROCEEDINGS.
Appleton & Lange, Journal Division (Transplantation Society) 25 Van Zant St., Box 5630, Norwalk, CT 06856. TEL 203-838-4400. *3385*

TRANSPORT REVIEWS.
Taylor & Francis Ltd., Rankine Rd., Basingstoke, Hants RG24 0PR, England. TEL 0256-840366. FAX 0256-479438. *4658*

TRANSPORT THEORY AND STATISTICAL PHYSICS.
Marcel Dekker Journals, 270 Madison Ave., New York, NY 10016. TEL 212-696-9000. FAX 212-685-4540. *3834*

TRANSPORTATION PLANNING AND TECHNOLOGY.
Gordon and Breach Science Publishers, 270 Eighth Ave., New York, NY 10011. TEL 212-206-8900. FAX 212-645-2459. *4659*

TRANSPORTATION RESEARCH. PART A: GENERAL.
Pergamon Press, Inc., Journals Division, 660 White Plains Rd., Tarrytown, NY 10591-5153. TEL 914-524-9200. FAX 914-333-2444. *4659*

TRANSPORTATION RESEARCH. PART B: METHODOLOGICAL.
Pergamon Press, Inc., Journals Division, 660 White Plains Rd., Tarrytown, NY 10591-5153. TEL 914-524-9200. FAX 914-333-2444. *4659*

TRANSPORTATION RESEARCH RECORD.
National Research Council, Transportation Research Board, 2101 Constitution Ave., N.W., Washington, DC 20418. TEL 202-334-3218. FAX 202-334-2519. *4722*

TRANSPORTATION STUDIES.
Gordon & Breach Science Publishers, P.O. Box 90, Reading, Berkshire RG1 8JL, England. TEL 0734-560-080. FAX 0734-568-211. *4659*

TREATISE ON MATERIALS SCIENCE & TECHNOLOGY.
Academic Press, Inc., 1250 Sixth Ave., San Diego, CA 92101. TEL 619-231-0926. FAX 619-699-6715. *1922*

TREE PHYSIOLOGY.
Heron Publishing, Box 5579, Station "B", Victoria, B.C. V8R 6S4, Canada. TEL 604-592-5173. FAX 604-721-8855. *519*

TRENDS IN ANALYTICAL CHEMISTRY.
Elsevier Science Publishers B.V., P.O. Box 211, 1000 AE Amsterdam, Netherlands. TEL 020-5803911. FAX 020-5803598. *1209*

TRENDS IN BIOCHEMICAL SCIENCES.
Elsevier Science Publishers Ltd., (International Union of Biochemistry) Crown House, Linton Rd., Barking, Essex IG11 8JU, England. TEL 081-594-7272. FAX 081-594-5942. *483*

TRENDS IN CARDIOVASCULAR MEDICINE.
Elsevier Science Publishing Co., Inc. (New York), 655 Ave. of Americas, New York, NY 10010. TEL 212-989-5800. FAX 212-633-3965. *3212*

TRENDS IN CELL BIOLOGY.
Elsevier Science Publishers Ltd., Crown House, Linton Rd., Barking, Essex IG11 8JU, England. TEL 081-594-7272. FAX 081-594-5942. *527*

TRENDS IN ENDOCRINOLOGY AND METABOLISM.
Elsevier Science Publishing Co., Inc. (New York), 655 Ave. of the Americas, New York, NY 10010. TEL 212-989-5800. FAX 212-633-3965. *3256*

TRENDS IN FOOD SCIENCE AND TECHNOLOGY.
Elsevier Science Publishers Ltd., Crown House, Linton Rd., Barking, Essex IG11 8JU, England. TEL 081-594-7272. FAX 081-594-5942. *2083*

TRENDS IN GLYCOSCIENCE AND GLYCOTECHNOLOGY.
F C C A, 3-10-1 Koufudai, Fujishiro-cho, Kitasoma-gun, Ibaraki-ken 300-15, Japan. TEL 81-297-837635. FAX 81-297-837645. *1224*

TRENDS IN NEUROSCIENCES.
Elsevier Science Publishers Ltd., Crown House, Linton Rd., Barking, Essex IG11 8JU, England. TEL 081-594-7272. FAX 081-594-5942. *3355*

TRENDS IN PHARMACOLOGICAL SCIENCES.
Elsevier Science Publishers Ltd., Crown House, Linton Rd., Barking, Essex IG11 8JU,.England. TEL 081-594-7272. FAX 081-594-5942. *3744*

TRIBOLOGY INTERNATIONAL.
Butterworth - Heinemann Ltd. Linacre House, Jordan Hill, Oxford OX2 8DP, England. TEL 0865-310366. FAX 0865-310898. *1940*

TRIBOLOGY SERIES.
Elsevier Science Publishers B.V., Books Division, P.O. Box 211, 1000 AE Amsterdam, Netherlands. TEL 020-5803911. FAX 020-5803705. *1940*

TRIESTE NOTES IN PHYSICS.
Springer-Verlag, 175 Fifth Ave., New York, NY 10010. TEL 212-460-1500. *3834*

TRISOMY 21.
Eterna International, Inc., 27 W. 560 Warrenville Rd., Warrenville, IL 60555. TEL 708-393-2930. *3327*

TROPHOBLAST RESEARCH.
Plenum Publishing Corp., 233 Spring St., New York, NY 10013-1578. TEL 212-620-8000. FAX 212-463-0742. *3297*

TROPICAL AGRICULTURE.
Butterworth - Heinemann Ltd. (University of the West Indies, Imperial College of Tropical Agriculture) Linacre House, Jordan Hill, Oxford OX2 8DP, England. TEL 0865-310366. FAX 0865-310898. *125*

TROPICAL PEST MANAGEMENT.
Taylor & Francis Ltd., Rankine Rd., Basingstoke, Hants RG24 OPR, England. TEL 0256-840366. FAX 0256-479438. *195*

TUIJIN JISHU.
Hangkong Hangtian Gongye-bu, Di 3 Yanjiuyuan, 31 Suo, P.O. Box 7208-26, Beijing 100074, People's Republic of China. TEL 8376141. *63*

TULANE STUDIES IN GEOLOGY AND PALEONTOLOGY.
Tulane University, Department of Geology, New Orleans, LA 70118. TEL 504-865-5198. *1583*

TULANE STUDIES IN ZOOLOGY AND BOTANY.
Tulane University, Department of Biology, New Orleans, LA 70118. TEL 504-865-5191. *592*

LA TUNISIE MEDICALE.
Societe Tunisienne des Sciences Medicales, 16 Rue Touraine, 1002 Tunis - Belvedere, Tunisia. TEL 284-895. *3158*

TUNNELLING AND UNDERGROUND SPACE TECHNOLOGY.
Pergamon Press, Inc., Journals Division, (International Tunnelling Association) 660 White Plains Rd., Tarrytown, NY 10591-5153. TEL 914-524-9200. FAX 914-333-2444. *1839*

TURANG XUEBAO.
Science Press, Marketing and Sales Department, 16 Donghuangchenggen Beijie, Beijing 100707, People's Republic of China. TEL 4010642. FAX 4012180. *1549*

TURKISH JOURNAL OF PEDIATRICS.
Turkish and International Children's Center, P.O. Box 66, Samanpazari, 06240 Ankara, Turkey. FAX 4-311-2253. *3327*

U C L A FORUM IN MEDICAL SCIENCES.
Academic Press, Inc., (University of California, Los Angeles) 1250 Sixth Ave., San Diego, CA 92101. TEL 619-231-0926. FAX 619-699-6715. *3158*

U C L A SYMPOSIUM ON MOLECULAR BIOLOGY PROCEEDINGS.
Academic Press, Inc., (International Chemical and Nuclear Corp.) 1250 Sixth Ave., San Diego, CA 92101. TEL 619-231-0926. FAX 619-699-6715. *527*

U C L A SYMPOSIUM SERIES ON MOLECULAR AND CELLULAR BIOLOGY.
Wiley-Liss, Inc., (University of California, Los Angeles) 41 E. 11th St., New York, NY 10003. TEL 212-475-7700. *458*

U S S R COMPUTATIONAL MATHEMATICS AND MATHEMATICAL PHYSICS.
Pergamon Press, Inc., Journals Division, 660 White Plains Rd., Tarrytown, NY 10591-5153. TEL 914-524-9200. FAX 914-333-2444. *3059*

UKRAINIAN MATHEMATICAL JOURNAL.
Plenum Publishing Corp., Consultants Bureau, (Ukrainian Academy of Sciences, Mathematical Institute) 233 Spring St., New York, NY 10013-1578. TEL 212-620-8468. FAX 212-463-0742. *3059*

ULTRAMICROSCOPY.
North-Holland P.O. Box 211, 1000 AE Amsterdam, Netherlands. TEL 020-5803911. FAX 020-5803598. *561*

ULTRASONICS.
Butterworth - Heinemann Ltd. Linacre House, Jordan Hill, OX2 8DP St., England. TEL 0865-310366. FAX 0865-310898. *3860*

ULTRASOUND ANNUAL.
Raven Press, 1185 Ave. of the Americas, New York, NY 10036. TEL 212-930-9500. FAX 212-869-3495. *3363*

ULTRASOUND IN MEDICINE & BIOLOGY.
Pergamon Press, Inc., Journals Division, (World Federation for Ultrasound in Medicine and Biology) 660 White Plains Rd., Tarrytown, NY 10591-5153. TEL 914-524-9200. FAX 914-333-2444. *458*

ULTRASOUND QUARTERLY.
Raven Press, 1185 Ave. of the Americas, New York, NY 10036. TEL 212-930-9500. FAX 212-869-3495. *3363*

ULTRASTRUCTURAL PATHOLOGY.
Hemisphere Publishing Corporation 1900 Frost Rd., Ste. 101, Bristol, PA 19007-1598. TEL 215-785-5800. FAX 215-785-5515. *527*

UNDERSEA BIOMEDICAL RESEARCH.
Undersea and Hyperbaric Medical Society, Inc., 9650 Rockville Pike, Bethesda, MD 20814. TEL 301-571-1818. FAX 301-571-1815. *3159*

UNITED STATES IN THE WORLD: FOREIGN PERSPECTIVES.
University of Chicago Press, 5801 S. Ellis Ave., Chicago, IL 60637. TEL 312-702-7899. *3976*

UNIVERSIDAD CENTRAL DE VENEZUELA. FACULTAD DE AGRONOMIA. REVISTA.
Universidad Central de Venezuela, Facultad de Agronomia, Apdo. 4579, Maracay, Edo. Aragua 2101, Venezuela. TEL 043-22212. FAX 43-453242. *126*

UNIVERSITY OF ALASKA. ANTHROPOLOGICAL PAPERS.
University of Alaska, Fairbanks, Department of Anthropology, 310 Eielson Bldg., Fairbanks, AK 99775. TEL 907-474-7288. *251*

UNIVERSITY OF ALASKA. BIOLOGICAL PAPERS.
University of Alaska, Institute of Arctic Biology, 308 Irving, Fairbanks, AK 99775-0180. TEL 907-474-6676. FAX 907-474-6967. *459*

UNIVERSITY OF ALASKA. INSTITUTE OF MARINE SCIENCE. OCCASIONAL PUBLICATION.
University of Alaska, Institute of Marine Science, Fairbanks, AK 99775-1080. TEL 907-474-7843. *459*

UNIVERSITY OF ALASKA. INSTITUTE OF MARINE SCIENCE. TECHNICAL REPORT.
University of Alaska, Institute of Marine Science, Fairbanks, AK 99775-1080. TEL 907-474-7843. *459*

UNIVERSITY OF ARKANSAS. LECTURE NOTES IN THE MATHEMATICAL SCIENCES.
John Wiley & Sons, Inc., 605 Third Ave., New York, NY 10158-0012. TEL 212-850-6000. FAX 212-850-6088. *3060*

UNIVERSITY OF CAIRO. FACULTY OF MEDICINE. MEDICAL JOURNAL.
University of Cairo, Faculty of Medicine, Manyal University Hospital, Kasr El-Aini Post, Cairo, Egypt. TEL 726-0595. *3160*

UNIVERSITY OF CALIFORNIA, LOS ANGELES. CENTER FOR MEDIEVAL AND RENAISSANCE STUDIES. CONTRIBUTIONS.
University of California Press, 2120 Berkeley Way, Berkeley, CA 94720. TEL 415-642-4247. FAX 415-643-7127. *2325*

UNIVERSITY OF CALIFORNIA, LOS ANGELES. CENTER FOR MEDIEVAL AND RENAISSANCE STUDIES. PUBLICATIONS.
University of California Press, 2120 Berkeley Way, Berkeley, CA 94720. TEL 415-642-4247. FAX 415-643-7127. *2325*

UNIVERSITY OF CALIFORNIA, LOS ANGELES. CENTER FOR THE STUDY OF COMPARATIVE FOLKLORE AND MYTHOLOGY. PUBLICATIONS.
University of California Press, 2120 Berkeley Way, Berkeley, CA 94720. TEL 415-642-4247. FAX 415-643-7127. *2059*

UNIVERSITY OF CALIFORNIA PUBLICATIONS. ANTHROPOLOGICAL RECORDS.
University of California Press, 2120 Berkeley Way, Berkeley, CA 94720. TEL 415-642-4247. FAX 415-643-7127. *251*

UNIVERSITY OF CALIFORNIA PUBLICATIONS. CLASSICAL STUDIES.
University of California Press, 2120 Berkeley Way, Berkeley, CA 94720. TEL 415-642-4247. FAX 415-643-7127. *1280*

UNIVERSITY OF CALIFORNIA PUBLICATIONS. FOLKLORE & MYTHOLOGY STUDIES.
University of California Press, 2120 Berkeley Way, Berkeley, CA 94720. TEL 415-642-4247. FAX 415-643-7127. *2059*

UNIVERSITY OF CALIFORNIA PUBLICATIONS. NEAR EASTERN STUDIES.
University of California Press, 2120 Berkeley Way, Berkeley, CA 94720. TEL 415-642-4247. FAX 415-643-7127. *2343*

UNIVERSITY OF CALIFORNIA PUBLICATIONS IN ANTHROPOLOGY.
University of California Press, 2120 Berkeley Way, Berkeley, CA 94720. TEL 415-642-4247. FAX 415-643-7127. *251*

UNIVERSITY OF CALIFORNIA PUBLICATIONS IN BOTANY.
University of California Press, 2120 Berkeley Way, Berkeley, CA 94720. TEL 415-642-4247. FAX 415-643-7127. *520*

UNIVERSITY OF CALIFORNIA PUBLICATIONS IN ENTOMOLOGY.
University of California Press, 2120 Berkeley Way, Berkeley, CA 94720. TEL 415-642-4247. FAX 415-643-7127. *538*

UNIVERSITY OF CALIFORNIA PUBLICATIONS IN GEOGRAPHY.
University of California Press, 2120 Berkeley Way, Berkeley, CA 94720. TEL 415-642-4247. FAX 415-643-7127. *2265*

UNIVERSITY OF CALIFORNIA PUBLICATIONS IN GEOLOGICAL SCIENCES.
University of California Press, 2120 Berkeley Way, Berkeley, CA 94720. TEL 415-642-4247. FAX 415-643-7127. *1549*

UNIVERSITY OF CALIFORNIA PUBLICATIONS IN LINGUISTICS.
University of California Press, 2120 Berkeley Way, Berkeley, CA 94720. FAX 415-643-7127. *2849*

UNIVERSITY OF CALIFORNIA PUBLICATIONS IN MODERN PHILOLOGY.
University of California Press, 2120 Berkeley Way, Berkeley, CA 94720. TEL 415-642-4247. FAX 415-643-7127. *2849*

REFEREED SERIALS

UNIVERSITY OF CALIFORNIA PUBLICATIONS IN ZOOLOGY.
University of California Press, 2120 Berkeley Way, Berkeley, CA 94720. TEL 510-642-4247. FAX 510-643-7127. *593*

UNIVERSITY OF CHICAGO. GEOGRAPHY RESEARCH PAPERS.
University of Chicago Press, 5801 S. Ellis Ave., Chicago, IL 60637. TEL 800-621-2736. FAX 312-660-2235. *2265*

UNIVERSITY OF CHICAGO STUDIES IN LIBRARY SCIENCE.
University of Chicago Press, 5801 S. Ellis Ave., Chicago, IL 60637. TEL 312-702-7899. *2788*

UNIVERSITY OF COLORADO. INSTITUTE OF ARCTIC AND ALPINE RESEARCH. OCCASIONAL PAPERS.
University of Colorado, Institute of Arctic and Alpine Research, Campus Box 450, Boulder, CO 80309-6450. TEL 303-492-3765. FAX 803-492-6388. *4350*

UNIVERSITY OF CONNECTICUT. INSTITUTE OF WATER RESOURCES. REPORT SERIES.
University of Connecticut, Institute of Water Resources, Storrs, CT 06269-4018. TEL 203-486-0335. *4829*

UNIVERSITY OF DELAWARE. DISASTER RESEARCH CENTER. REPORT SERIES.
University of Delaware, Disaster Research Center, Newark, DE 19716. TEL 302-451-6618. FAX 302-451-2828. *4114*

UNIVERSITY OF FLORIDA. SCHOOL OF FOREST RESOURCES & CONSERVATION. COOPERATIVE FOREST GENETICS RESEARCH PROGRAM. PROGRESS REPORT.
University of Florida, School of Forest Resources & Conservation, Gainesville, FL 32601. TEL 904-392-1792. *2110*

UNIVERSITY OF HAWAII. WATER RESOURCES RESEARCH CENTER. COLLECTED REPRINTS.
University of Hawaii, Water Resources Research Center, 2540 Dole St., Honolulu, HI 96822. TEL 808-948-7847. *4829*

UNIVERSITY OF HAWAII. WATER RESOURCES RESEARCH CENTER. TECHNICAL REPORT.
University of Hawaii, Water Resources Research Center, 2540 Dole St., Honolulu, HI 96822. TEL 808-948-7847. *4829*

UNIVERSITY OF IDAHO ANTHROPOLOGICAL MONOGRAPHS.
University of Idaho, Alfred W. Bowers Laboratory of Anthropology, Moscow, ID 83843. TEL 208-885-6123. *251*

UNIVERSITY OF ILLINOIS AT URBANA-CHAMPAIGN. ENGINEERING EXPERIMENT STATION. SUMMARY OF ENGINEERING RESEARCH.
University of Illinois at Urbana-Champaign, College of Engineering, 112 Engineering Hall, 1308 W. Green St., Urbana, IL 61801. TEL 217-333-1510. *1839*

UNIVERSITY OF ILLINOIS AT URBANA-CHAMPAIGN. WATER RESOURCES CENTER. RESEARCH REPORT.
University of Illinois at Urbana-Champaign, Water Resources Center, 205 N. Mathews, Urbana, IL 61801. TEL 217-333-0536. FAX 217-244-6633. *4829*

UNIVERSITY OF KANSAS. DEPARTMENT OF ANTHROPOLOGY. PUBLICATIONS IN ANTHROPOLOGY.
University of Kansas, Department of Anthropology, c/o Exchange and Gifts Dept., Lawrence, KS 66045. TEL 913-864-2700. *252*

UNIVERSITY OF KANSAS. MUSEUM OF NATURAL HISTORY. MISCELLANEOUS PUBLICATIONS.
University of Kansas, Museum of Natural History, 602 Dyche Hall, Lawrence, KS 66045-2454. TEL 913-864-4540. FAX 913-864-5335. *459*

UNIVERSITY OF KANSAS. MUSEUM OF NATURAL HISTORY. MONOGRAPHS.
University of Kansas, Museum of Natural History, 602 Dyche Hall, Lawrence, KS 66044-2454. TEL 913-864-4540. FAX 913-864-5335. *459*

UNIVERSITY OF KANSAS. MUSEUM OF NATURAL HISTORY. OCCASIONAL PAPERS.
University of Kansas, Museum of Natural History, 602 Dyche Hall, Lawrence, KS 66045-2454. *4350*

UNIVERSITY OF KANSAS. MUSEUM OF NATURAL HISTORY. SPECIAL PUBLICATIONS.
University of Kansas, Museum of Natural History, 602 Dyche Hall, Lawrence, KS 66045-2454. *459*

UNIVERSITY OF KANSAS. PALEONTOLOGICAL CONTRIBUTIONS. NEW SERIES.
University of Kansas, Paleontological Institute, 121 Lindley Hall, Lawrence, KS 66045. TEL 913-864-3338. *3661*

UNIVERSITY OF MICHIGAN. DIVISION OF RESEARCH DEVELOPMENT AND ADMINISTRATION. RESEARCH NEWS.
University of Michigan, Division of Research Development and Administration, 475 E. Jefferson, Ann Arbor, MI 48109-1248. TEL 313-763-5587. FAX 313-763-4053. *1720*

UNIVERSITY OF MICHIGAN. HERBARIUM. CONTRIBUTIONS.
University of Michigan, Herbarium, North University Building, Ann Arbor, MI 48109-1057. TEL 313-764-2407. FAX 313-763-0369. *520*

UNIVERSITY OF MICHIGAN. MUSEUM OF ANTHROPOLOGY. TECHNICAL REPORTS.
University of Michigan, Museum of Anthropology, University Museums Bldg., Rm. 4009, Ann Arbor, MI 48109. TEL 313-764-0485. *252*

UNIVERSITY OF MICHIGAN. MUSEUM OF PALEONTOLOGY. CONTRIBUTIONS.
University of Michigan, Museum of Paleontology, Museums Bldg., Ann Arbor, MI 48109. TEL 313-764-0489. *3661*

UNIVERSITY OF MICHIGAN. MUSEUM OF PALEONTOLOGY. PAPERS ON PALEONTOLOGY.
University of Michigan, Museum of Paleontology, Ann Arbor, MI 48109. TEL 313-764-0489. *3661*

UNIVERSITY OF MICHIGAN. MUSEUM OF ZOOLOGY. MISCELLANEOUS PUBLICATIONS.
University of Michigan, Museum of Zoology, Ann Arbor, MI 48109-1079. TEL 313-764-0476. FAX 313-763-4080. *593*

UNIVERSITY OF MICHIGAN. MUSEUM OF ZOOLOGY. OCCASIONAL PAPERS.
University of Michigan, Museum of Zoology, Ann Arbor, MI 48109-1079. TEL 313-764-0476. FAX 313-763-4080. *593*

UNIVERSITY OF MISSOURI, COLUMBIA. MUSEUM OF ANTHROPOLOGY. MISCELLANEOUS PUBLICATIONS IN ANTHROPOLOGY.
University of Missouri, Columbia, Museum of Anthropology, 104 Swallow Hall, Columbia, MO 65211. TEL 314-882-3573. *252*

UNIVERSITY OF MISSOURI MONOGRAPHS IN ANTHROPOLOGY.
University of Missouri, Columbia, Museum of Anthropology, 104 Swallow Hall, Columbia, MO 65211. TEL 314-882-3573. *252*

UNIVERSITY OF NEVADA. DESERT RESEARCH INSTITUTE. TECHNICAL REPORT.
University of Nevada, Desert Research Institute, Social Sciences Center, Box 60220, Reno, NV 89506. TEL 702-673-7303. *4350*

UNIVERSITY OF NEW MEXICO. INSTITUTE OF METEORITICS. SPECIAL PUBLICATION.
University of New Mexico, Institute of Meteoritics, Albuquerque, NM 87131. TEL 505-277-2747. FAX 505-277-3577. *370*

UNIVERSITY OF NORTH DAKOTA. INSTITUTE FOR ECOLOGICAL STUDIES. RESEARCH REPORT.
Institute for Ecological Studies, University of North Dakota, Box 8278, University Sta., Grand Forks, ND 58202. TEL 701-777-2851. *1970*

UNIVERSITY OF NORTHERN COLORADO. MUSEUM OF ANTHROPOLOGY. OCCASIONAL PUBLICATIONS IN ANTHROPOLOGY. MISCELLANEOUS SERIES.
University of Northern Colorado, Museum of Anthropology, Attn. George E. Fay, Ed., Greeley, CO 80639. TEL 303-352-1890. *252*

UNIVERSITY OF OREGON ANTHROPOLOGICAL PAPERS.
University of Oregon, Department of Anthropology, Eugene, OR 97403. TEL 503-346-5102. FAX 503-346-3660. *252*

UNIVERSITY OF SOUTH CAROLINA. BELLE W. BARUCH LIBRARY IN MARINE SCIENCE AND COASTAL RESEARCH. COLLECTED PAPERS.
University of South Carolina Press, c/o Ribin Sumner, Rights & Permissions, Columbia, SC 29208. TEL 803-777-5243. *1612*

UNIVERSITY OF SOUTH FLORIDA. INTERNATIONAL BIOMEDICAL SYMPOSIA SERIES.
Plenum Publishing Corp., 233 Spring St., New York, NY 10013-1578. TEL 212-620-8000. FAX 212-463-0742. *459*

UNIVERSITY OF TEXAS AT AUSTIN. BUREAU OF ECONOMIC GEOLOGY. SPECIAL PUBLICATIONS.
University of Texas at Austin, Bureau of Economic Geology, Box X, Univeristy Sta., Austin, TX 78713. TEL 512-471-7721. FAX 512-471-0140. *1584*

UNIVERSITY OF TEXAS AT AUSTIN. CENTER FOR RESEARCH IN WATER RESOURCES. TECHNICAL REPORT SERIES.
University of Texas at Austin, Center for Research in Water Resources, Balcones Research Center, Austin, TX 78712. TEL 512-471-3131. FAX 512-471-0072. *4830*

UNIVERSITY OF UTAH ANTHROPOLOGICAL PAPERS.
University of Utah Press, Salt Lake City, UT 84112. TEL 801-581-6771. *252*

UNIVERSITY OF WISCONSIN, MADISON. ENGINEERING EXPERIMENT STATION. ANNUAL REPORT.
University of Wisconsin-Madison, Engineering Experiment Station, Informational Resources Office, 1500 Johnson Dr., Madison, WI 53706. TEL 605-263-1610. *3441*

UNIVERSITY OF WYOMING. CONTRIBUTIONS TO GEOLOGY.
University of Wyoming, Department of Geology and Geophysics, Box 3006, University Sta., Laramie, WY 82071. TEL 307-766-3386. FAX 307-766-6679. *1584*

UNIVERSITY SERIES IN MODERN ENGINEERING.
Springer-Verlag, (Optimization Software Inc., New York) 175 Fifth Ave., New York, NY 10010. TEL 212-460-1500. *1839*

UPDATE.
George Warman Publications (Pty.) Ltd., 77 Hout St., P.O. Box 704, Cape Town 8000, South Africa. TEL 021-245320. FAX 021-261332. *3160*

URBAN ANTHROPOLOGY AND STUDIES OF CULTURAL SYSTEMS AND WORLD ECONOMIC DEVELOPMENT.
Institute Incorporated, 56 Centennial Ave., Brockport, NY 14420. TEL 716-637-6531. *252*

URBAN DESIGN AND PRESERVATION QUARTERLY.
American Planning Association, Urban Design and Preservation, Univ. of Colorado, School of Architecture, 1200 Larimer St., Denver, CO 80204-5300. *2498*

URBAN EDUCATION.
Corwin Press, Inc. 2455 Teller Rd., Newbury Park, CA 91320. TEL 805-499-0721. FAX 805-499-0871. *1670*

URBAN POLICY & RESEARCH.
Urban Policy and Research, P.O. Box 2620W, Melbourne, Vic. 3001, Australia. TEL 03-660-2226. *2498*

THE URBAN REVIEW.
Human Sciences Press, Inc. 233 Spring St., New York, NY 10013. TEL 212-620-8000. FAX 212-463-0742. *1670*

URETHANE ABSTRACTS.
Technomic Publishing Co., Inc., 851 New Holland Ave., Box 3535, Lancaster, PA 17604. TEL 717-291-5609. FAX 717-295-4538. *3868*

UROLOGY.
Cahners Publishing Company (New York), Medical-Health Care Group Division of Reed Publishing (USA) Inc., 249 W. 17th St., New York, NY 10011. TEL 212-645-0067. FAX 212-463-6700. *3390*

VAARD I NORDEN.
Sygeplegerskernes Samarbejde i Norden, P.O. Box 2681, St. Hanshaugen, N-131 Oslo 1, Norway. TEL 47-2 38 20 00. FAX 47-2-38-54-47. *3287*

VACCINE.
Butterworth - Heinemann Ltd. Linacre House, Jordan Hill, Oxford OX2 8DP, England. TEL 0865-310366. FAX 0865-310898. *3189*

VACUUM.
Pergamon Press, Inc., Journals Division, (British Vacuum Council) 660 White Plains Rd., Tarrytown, NY 10591-5153. TEL 914-524-9200. FAX 914-333-2444. *3839*

VANDERBILT UNIVERSITY. DEPARTMENT OF ENVIRONMENTAL AND WATER RESOURCES ENGINEERING. TECHNICAL REPORTS.
Vanderbilt University, Department of Civil & Environmental Engineering, Box 6304, Sta. B, Nashville, TN 37235. TEL 615-322-2720. *1971*

VANDERBILT UNIVERSITY PUBLICATIONS IN ANTHROPOLOGY.
Vanderbilt University Publications in Anthropology, (Vanderbilt University, Department of Anthropology) Box 1532, Sta. B, Nashville, TN 37235. TEL 615-322-7522. *252*

VERA LEX.
Pace University, Buchsbaum House, Pleasantville, NY 10570. TEL 914-773-3309. FAX 914-773-3541. *3786*

VETERINARIA E ZOOTECNIA.
Universidade Estadual Paulista, Av. Vicente Ferreira 1278, Caixa Postal 603, 17500 Marilia SP, Brazil. TEL 0144-33-1844. FAX 0144-22-2504. *4817*

VETERINARY AND COMPARATIVE ORTHOPAEDICS AND TRAUMATOLOGY.
F.K. Schattauer Verlagsgesellschaft mbH, Postfach 104545, 7000 Stuttgart 10, Germany. TEL 0711-22987-0. FAX 0711-22987-50. *4817*

VETERINARY AND HUMAN TOXICOLOGY.
Comparative Toxicology Laboratories, Publication Office, (American Academy of Veterinary and Comparative Toxicology) Kansas State University, Manhattan, KS 66506-5606. TEL 913-532-4334. FAX 913-532-4481. *1984*

VETERINARY DERMATOLOGY.
Pergamon Press, Inc., Journals Division, (European Society of Veterinary Dermatology) 660 White Plains Rd., Tarrytown, NY 10591-5153. TEL 914-524-9200. FAX 914-333-2444. *4818*

VETERINARY FOCUS.
Arthurs Publications Ltd., 5200 Dixie Rd., Ste. 204, Mississauga, Ontario L4W 1E4, Canada. *4818*

VETERINARY IMMUNOLOGY AND IMMUNOPATHOLOGY.
Elsevier Science Publishers B.V., P.O. Box 211, 1000 AE Amsterdam, Netherlands. TEL 020-5803911. FAX 020-5803598. *4818*

VETERINARY MEDICINE.
Veterinary Medicine Publishing Co., 9073 Lenexa Dr., Lenexa, KS 66215. TEL 913-492-4300. *4818*

VETERINARY MICROBIOLOGY.
Elsevier Science Publishers B.V., P.O. Box 211, 1000 AE Amsterdam, Netherlands. TEL 020-5803911. FAX 020-5803598. *4818*

VETERINARY PARASITOLOGY.
Elsevier Science Publishers B.V., P.O. Box 211, 1000 AE Amsterdam, Netherlands. TEL 020-5803911. FAX 020-5803598. *4818*

VETERINARY PATHOLOGY.
Waverly Press, Inc. (American College of Veterinary Pathologists) 428 E. Preston St., Box 64025, Baltimore, MD 21202. TEL 301-528-4000. *4818*

VETERINARY RADIOLOGY & ULTRASOUND.
American College of Veterinary Radiology, c/o Lucinda Ayres, 2520 Beechridge Rd., Raleigh, NC 27608. TEL 919-881-4165. FAX 919-821-9578. *4819*

VETERINARY SURGERY.
J.B. Lippincott Co., (American College of Veterinary Surgeons, Inc.) East Washington Sq., Philadelphia, PA 19105. TEL 215-238-4200. *4819*

VIATOR.
University of California Press, Journals Division, (University of California, Los Angeles, Center for Medieval and Renaissance Studies) 2120 Berkeley Way, Berkeley, CA 94720. TEL 510-642-4191. FAX 510-643-7127. *2325*

VIBRATIONAL SPECTRA AND STRUCTURE.
Elsevier Science Publishers B.V., Books Division, P.O. Box 211, 1000 AE Amsterdam, Netherlands. TEL 020-5803911. FAX 020-5803705. *1231*

VIBRATIONAL SPECTROSCOPY.
Elsevier Science Publishers B.V., P.O. Box 211, 1000 AE Amsterdam, Netherlands. TEL 020-5803911. FAX 020-5803598. *1190*

VIDEO INDUSTRY STATISTICAL REPORT.
Corbell Publishing, 2554 Lincoln Blvd., Ste. 1015, Marina Del Rey, CA 90291. TEL 310-821-6675. FAX 310-641-9769. *1349*

VIDEO JOURNAL OF COLOR FLOW IMAGING.
Dynamedia, Inc., 2 Fulham Court, Silver Spring, MD 20902-3016. TEL 301-649-6886. FAX 301-579-3447. *3363*

VIDEO JOURNAL OF ECHOCARDIOGRAPHY.
Dynamedia, Inc., 2 Fulham Court, Silver Spring, MD 20902-3016. TEL 301-649-6886. FAX 301-649-3447. *3212*

VIRAL IMMUNOLOGY.
Mary Ann Liebert, Inc., 1651 Third Ave., New York, NY 10128. TEL 212-289-2300. FAX 212-289-4697. *3189*

VIRGINIA POLYTECHNIC INSTITUTE AND STATE UNIVERSITY. DEPARTMENT OF ENTOMOLOGY. OCCASIONAL PAPERS.
Virginia Polytechnic Institute and State University, Department of Entomology, Blacksburg, VA 24061-0319. TEL 703-231-6341. *538*

VIROLOGY.
Academic Press, Inc., Journal Division, 1250 Sixth Ave., San Diego, CA 92101. TEL 619-230-1840. FAX 619-688-6800. *558*

VIRUS GENES.
Kluwer Academic Publishers, 101 Philip Dr., Norwell, MA 02061. TEL 617-871-6600. FAX 617-871-6528. *558*

VIRUS RESEARCH.
Elsevier Science Publishers B.V., P.O. Box 211, 1000 AE Amsterdam, Netherlands. TEL 020-5803911. FAX 020-5803598. *558*

VISION RESEARCH.
Pergamon Press, Inc., Journals Division, (Association for Research in Vision and Ophthalmology) 660 White Plains Rd., Tarrytown, NY 10591-5153. TEL 914-524-9200. FAX 914-333-2444. *3305*

VISTAS IN ASTRONOMY.
Pergamon Press, Inc., Journals Division, 660 White Plains Rd., Tarrytown, NY 10591-5153. TEL 914-524-9200. FAX 914-333-2444. *371*

VISUAL ANTHROPOLOGY.
Harwood Academic Publishers, (Commission on Visual Anthropology) 270 Eighth Ave., New York, NY 10011. TEL 212-206-8900. FAX 212-645-2459. *252*

VISUAL RESOURCES.
Gordon & Breach Science Publishers, 270 Eighth Ave., New York, NY 10011. TEL 212-206-8900. FAX 212-645-2459. *349*

VITAMINS AND HORMONES: ADVANCES IN RESEARCH AND APPLICATIONS.
Academic Press, Inc. 1250 Sixth Ave., San Diego, CA 92101. TEL 619-231-0926. FAX 619-699-6715. *3745*

VOLCANOLOGY & SEISMOLOGY.
Gordon & Breach Science Publishers, 270 Eighth Ave., New York, NY 10011. TEL 212-206-8900. FAX 212-645-2459. *1596*

VYAPAR (HINDI EDITION).
Suarashtra Trust, Janmabhoomi Bhavan, Janmabhoomi Marg, Fort, Bombay 400 001, India. TEL 2870831. *698*

WASHINGTON HISTORY.
Historical Society of Washington, D.C., 1307 New Hampshire N.W., Washington, DC 20036-1507. TEL 202-785-2478. FAX 202-331-1979. *2426*

WASMANN JOURNAL OF BIOLOGY.
University of San Francisco, Biology Department, San Francisco, CA 94117. TEL 415-666-6381. *460*

WASTE MANAGEMENT: NUCLEAR, CHEMICAL, BIOLOGICAL, MUNICIPAL.
Pergamon Press, Inc., Journals Division, 660 White Plains Rd., Tarrytown, NY 10591-5153. TEL 914-524-9200. FAX 914-333-2444. *1988*

WATER INTERNATIONAL.
International Water Resources Association, University of Illinois, 205 N. Mathews Ave., Urbana, IL 61801. TEL 217-333-0536. FAX 217-244-6633. *4832*

WATER POLLUTION: A SERIES OF MONOGRAPHS.
Academic Press, Inc., 1250 Sixth Ave., San Diego, CA 92101. TEL 619-231-0926. FAX 619-699-6715. *4832*

WATER POLLUTION CONTROL FEDERATION. RESEARCH JOURNAL.
Water Pollution Control Federation, 601 Wythe St., Alexandria, VA 22314-1994. TEL 703-684-2400. FAX 703-684-2492. *1979*

WATER RESEARCH.
Pergamon Press, Inc., Journals Division, (International Association on Water Pollution Research and Control) 660 White Plains Rd., Tarrytown, NY 10591-5153. TEL 914-524-9200. FAX 914-333-2444. *4832*

WATER RESOURCES.
Plenum Publishing Corp., Consultants Bureau, (Russian Academy of Sciences) 233 Spring St., New York, NY 10013-1578. TEL 212-620-8468. FAX 212-463-0742. *4832*

WATER RESOURCES BULLETIN.
American Water Resources Association, 5410 Grosvenor Lane, Ste. 220, Bethesda, MD 20814. TEL 301-493-8600. FAX 301-493-5844. *4832*

WATER SCIENCE AND TECHNOLOGY.
Pergamon Press, Inc., Journals Division, (International Association on Water Pollution Research and Control) 660 White Plains Rd., Tarrytown, NY 10591-5153. TEL 914-524-9200. FAX 914-333-2444. *4833*

WATER TREATMENT.
China Ocean Press, International Cooperation Department, (Guojia Haiyang-ju, Hangzhou Shui Chuli Jishu Kaifa Zhongxin) Haimao Dalou, 1 Fuxingmenwai Dajie, Beijing 100860, People's Republic of China. TEL 868941. FAX 862209. *4833*

WAVE MOTION.
North-Holland P.O. Box 211, 1000 AE Amsterdam, Netherlands. TEL 020-5803911. FAX 020-5803598. *3835*

WEAR.
Elsevier Sequoia S.A., P.O. Box 564, CH-1001 Lausanne, Switzerland. TEL 021-207381. FAX 021-235444. *1941*

WEATHERWISE.
Heldref Publications, (Helen Dwight Reid Educational Foundation) 1319 Eighteenth St., N.W., Washington, DC 20036-1802. TEL 202-296-6267. FAX 202-296-5149. *3442*

WEED SCIENCE.
Weed Science Society of America, 309 W. Clark St., Champaign, IL 61820. TEL 217-356-3182. FAX 217-398-4119. *196*

WEEKLY BULLETIN.
Magyar Tavirati Iroda, Kiado Hivatal, Pl. Naphegy No. 7-8, 1016 Budapest, Hungary. TEL 1756-722. FAX 1188-297. *2198*

WEISHENGWU XUEBAO.
Science Press, Marketing and Sales Department, (Chinese Academy of Sciences, Institute of Microbiology) 16 Donghuangchenggen Beijie, Beijing 100707, People's Republic of China. TEL 4010642. FAX 4012180. *558*

WEITI GUSHENGWU XUEBAO.
Science Press, Marketing and Sales Department, (Zhongguo Kexueyuan, Nanjing Dizhi Gushengwu-suo) 16 Donghuangchenggen Beijie, Beijing 100707, People's Republic of China. TEL 4010642. FAX 4012180. *559*

WELDING IN THE WORLD.
Pergamon Press plc, (International Institute of Welding) Headington Hill Hall, Oxford OX3 0BW, England. TEL 0865-794141. FAX 0865-743911. *3431*

WERTHEIM PUBLICATIONS IN INDUSTRIAL RELATIONS.
Harvard University Press, 79 Garden St., Cambridge, MA 02138. TEL 617-495-2600. FAX 617-495-5898. *997*

WEST INDIAN MEDICAL JOURNAL.
University of the West Indies, Faculty of Medical Sciences, Mona Campus, Kingston 7, Jamaica, W.I. TEL 809-92-71214. FAX 809-92-72556. *3162*

WEST VIRGINIA MEDICAL JOURNAL.
West Virginia State Medical Association, 4307 MacCorkle Ave., Box 4106, Charleston, WV 25364. TEL 304-925-0342. FAX 304-925-0345. *3162*

WESTERN CANADIAN ANTHROPOLOGIST.
University of Saskatchewan, Department of Anthropology and Archaeology, Saskatoon, Sask., S7N 0W0, Canada. TEL 306-966-4175. *253*

WESTERN JOURNAL OF MEDICINE.
California Medical Association, 221 Main St., San Francisco, CA 94105. TEL 415-882-5179. FAX 415-882-5116. *3162*

WETLANDS.
Society of Wetlands Scientists, Box 296, Wilmington, NC 28402. *4834*

WETLANDS ECOLOGY AND MANAGEMENT.
S P B Academic Publishing b.v., P.O. Box 97747, 2509 GC The Hague, Netherlands. *4834*

WILDFLOWER, JOURNAL OF THE NATIONAL WILDFLOWER RESEARCH CENTER.
National Wildflower Research Center, 2600 FM 973 N, Austin, TX 78725. TEL 512-929-3600. *520*

WILDLIFE BEHAVIOR AND ECOLOGY.
University of Chicago Press, 5801 S. Ellis Ave., Chicago, IL 60637. TEL 312-702-7899. *460*

WILEY SERIES IN GEOTECHNICAL ENGINEERING.
John Wiley & Sons, Inc., 605 Third Ave., New York, NY 10158-0012. TEL 212-850-6000. FAX 212-850-6088. *196*

WIND ENGINEERING.
Multi-Science Publishing Co. Ltd., 107 High St., Brentwood, Essex CM14 4RX, England. TEL 0277-224632. FAX 0277-224632. *1813*

WINTERTHUR PORTFOLIO: A JOURNAL OF AMERICAN MATERIAL CULTURE.
University of Chicago Press, Journals Division, (Henry Francis Du Pont Winterthur Museum) 5801 S. Woodlawn Ave., Chicago, IL 60637. TEL 312-753-3347. FAX 312-702-0694. *3535*

WOMEN & CRIMINAL JUSTICE.
Haworth Press, Inc., 10 Alice St., Binghamton, NY 13904. TEL 800-342-9678. FAX 607-722-1424. *2714*

WOMEN & HEALTH.
Haworth Press, Inc., 10 Alice St., Binghamton, NY 13904. TEL 800-342-9678. FAX 607-722-1424. *4836*

WOMEN & POLITICS.
Haworth Press, Inc., 10 Alice St., Binghamton, NY 13904. TEL 800-342-9678. FAX 607-722-1424. *3934*

WOMEN & THERAPY.
Haworth Press, Inc., 10 Alice St., Binghamton, NY 13904. TEL 800-342-9678. FAX 607-722-1424. *4050*

WOMEN IN CONTEXT.
Plenum Publishing Corp., 233 Spring St., New York, NY 10013-1578. TEL 212-620-8000. FAX 212-463-0742. *4836*

WOMEN IN CULTURE AND SOCIETY.
University of Chicago Press, 5801 S. Ellis Ave., Chicago, IL 60637. TEL 312-702-7899. *4856*

WOMEN'S HEALTH ISSUES.
Elsevier Academy Science Publishing Co., Inc. (New York), (Jacobs Institute of Women's Health) 655 Ave. of Americas, New York, NY 10010. TEL 212-989-5800. FAX 212-633-3965. *4836*

WOMEN'S STUDIES (CHAMPAIGN).
University of Illinois Press, 54 E. Gregory Dr., Champaign, IL 61820. TEL 217-333-0950. FAX 217-244-8082. *4860*

WOMEN'S STUDIES (NEW YORK).
Gordon and Breach Science Publishers, 270 Eighth Ave., New York, NY 10011. TEL 212-206-8900. FAX 212-645-2459. *4861*

WOMEN'S STUDIES INTERNATIONAL FORUM.
Pergamon Press, Inc., Journals Division, 660 White Plains Rd., Tarrytown, NY 10591-5153. TEL 914-524-9200. FAX 914-333-2444. *4861*

WOOL TECHNOLOGY AND SHEEP BREEDING.
Wool Technology Press, (University of New South Wales, Department of Wool Science) P.O. Box 1, Kensington, N.S.W. 2033, Australia. TEL 61-2-697-4495. FAX 61-2-313-6404. *228*

WORD & IMAGE.
Taylor & Francis Ltd., Rankine Rd., Basingstoke, Hants RG24 0PR, England. TEL 0256-840366. FAX 0256-479438. *2889*

WORK AND STRESS.
Taylor & Francis Ltd., Rankine Rd., Basingstoke, Hants RG24 0PR, England. TEL 0256-840366. FAX 0256-479438. *4050*

WORLD AFFAIRS.
Heldref Publications, (American Peace Society) 1319 Eighteenth St., N.W., Washington, DC 20036-1802. TEL 202-296-6267. FAX 202-296-5149. *3977*

WORLD ANIMAL SCIENCE.
Elsevier Science Publishers B.V., Books Division, P.O. Box 211, 1000 AE Amsterdam, Netherlands. TEL 020-5803911. FAX 020-5803705. *593*

WORLD CERAMIC ABSTRACTS.
Pergamon Press plc, (British Ceramic Research Limited) Headington Hill Hall, Oxford OX3 0BW, England. TEL 0865-794141. FAX 0865-743911. *1167*

WORLD DEVELOPMENT.
Pergamon Press, Inc., Journals Division, 660 White Plains Rd., Tarrytown, NY 10591-5153. TEL 914-524-9200. FAX 914-333-2444. *937*

WORLD ENGLISHES.
Pergamon Press, Inc.. Journals Division, 660 White Plains Rd., Tarrytown, NY 10591-5153. TEL 914-524-9200. FAX 914-333-2444. *2852*

WORLD FUTURES.
Gordon and Breach Science Publishers, 270 Eighth Ave., New York, NY 10011. TEL 212-206-8900. FAX 212-645-2459. *3786*

WORLD JOURNAL OF PSYCHOSYNTHESIS.
World Journal Press, (Michigan Institute of Psychosynthesis) Box 859, E. Lansing, MI 48823. TEL 517-372-4660. FAX 517-372-9959. *3356*

THE WORLD OF A S P.
American Self-Protection Association, 825 Greengate Oval, Sagamore Hills, OH 44067. TEL 216-467-1750. *4497*

WORLD PATENT INFORMATION.
Pergamon Press, Inc., Journals Division, (Commission of the European Communities) 660 White Plains Rd., Tarrytown, NY 10591-5153. TEL 914-524-9200. FAX 914-333-2444. *3679*

WORLD SURFACE COATING ABSTRACTS.
Pergamon Press plc, (Paint Research Association) Headington Hill Hall, Oxford OX3 0BW, England. TEL 0865-794141. FAX 0865-743911. *3656*

WORLD'S POULTRY SCIENCE JOURNAL.
Butterworth - Heinemann Ltd. (World's Poultry Science Association) Linacre House, Jordan Hill, Oxford OX2 8DP, England. TEL 0865-310366. FAX 0865-310898. *229*

WUJI CAILIAO XUEBAO.
Science Press, Marketing and Sales Department, (Chinese Academy of Sciences, Shanghai Institute of Silica) 16 Donghuangchenggen Beijie, Beijing 100707, People's Republic of China. TEL 4010642. FAX 4012180. *1215*

WULI.
Science Press, Marketing and Sales Department, (Zhongguo Wuli Xuehui) 16 Donghuangchenggen Beijie, Beijing 100707, People's Republic of China. TEL 4010642. FAX 4012180. *3835*

WULI XUEBAO.
Science Press, Marketing and Sales Department, (Zhongguo Wuli Xuehui) Donghuangchenggen Beijie, Beijing 100707, People's Republic of China. TEL 4010642. FAX 4012180. *3835*

XENOBIOTICA.
Taylor & Francis Ltd., Rankine Rd., Basingstoke, Hants RG24 0PR, England. TEL 0256-840366. FAX 0256-479438. *483*

XINLI XUEBAO.
Science Press, Marketing and Sales Department, 16 Donghuangchenggen Beijie, Beijing 100707, People's Republic of China. TEL 4010642. FAX 4012180. *4050*

XITONG KEXUE YU SHUXUE.
Science Press, Marketing and Sales Department, (Chinese Academy of Sciences, Institute of Systems Science) 16 Donghuangchenggen Beijie, Beijing 100707, People's Republic of China. TEL 4010642. FAX 4012180. *1440*

YAD VASHEM STUDIES.
Pergamon Press, Inc., Journals Division, (Yad Vashem Martyrs' and Heroes' Remembrance Authority) 660 White Plains Rd., Tarrytown, NY 10591-5153. TEL 914-524-9200. FAX 914-333-2444. *4227*

YALE JOURNAL OF BIOLOGY AND MEDICINE.
Yale Journal of Biology and Medicine, Inc., 333 Cedar St., New Haven, CT 06510. TEL 203-785-4251. *3163*

YALE SCIENTIFIC.
Yale Scientific Publications, Inc., (Yale University) 244-A Yale Sta., New Haven, CT 06520. TEL 203-432-2374. *4352*

YALE UNIVERSITY. DEPARTMENT OF ANTHROPOLOGY. PUBLICATIONS IN ANTHROPOLOGY.
Yale University, Department of Anthropology, 2114 Yale Station, New Haven, CT 06520. TEL 203-432-3670. FAX 203-432-3669. *253*

YANDI BING.
West China University of Medical Sciences, 1st Teaching Hospital, No. 37, Guo-Xie-Xiong, Chengdu, Sichuan 610041, People's Republic of China. TEL 551255. FAX 028-582-944. *3305*

YANSHI LIXUE YU GONGCHENG XUEBAO.
Zhongguo Yanshi Lixue yu Gongcheng Xuehui, No. A-11, Datun Lu, Dewai, Beijing 100101, People's Republic of China. *3846*

YANSHI XUEBAO.
Science Press, Marketing and Sales Department, 16 Donghuangchenggen Beijie, Beijing 100707, People's Republic of China. TEL 4010642. FAX 4012180. *1586*

YANTU LIXUE.
Zhongguo Kexueyuan, Wuhan Yantu Lixue Yanjiusuo, Xiaohongshan, Wuhan, Hubei 430071, People's Republic of China. TEL 813712. *3846*

YAOWU FENXI ZAZHI.
Zhongguo Yaoxuehui, Tiantan Xili, Beijing 100050, People's Republic of China. TEL 757351. *3746*

YEARBOOK OF SUBSTANCE USE AND ABUSE.
Human Sciences Press, Inc. 233 Spring St., New York, NY 10013-1578. TEL 212-620-8000. FAX 212-463-0742. *1540*

YICHUAN XUEBAO.
Science Press, Marketing and Sales Department, (Chinese Academy of Sciences, Institute of Genetics) 16 Donghuangchenggen Beijie, Beijing 100707, People's Republic of China. TEL 4010642. FAX 4012180. *548*

YINGYONG SHENGXUE.
Science Press, Marketing and Sales Department, (Zhongguo Shengxue Xuehui) 16 Donghuangchenggen Beijie, Beijing 100707, People's Republic of China. TEL 4010642. FAX 4012180. *3860*

YINGYONG SHUXUE XUEBAO.
Science Press, Marketing and Sales Department, (Chinese Mathematics Society) 16 Donghuangchenggen Beijie, Beijing 100707, People's Republic of China. TEL 4010642. FAX 4012180. *3061*

YINGYONG SHUXUE YU LIXUE.
Chongqing Jiaotong Xueyuan, 107, Dahuang Lu, Daping, Chongqing, Sichuan 630042, People's Republic of China. TEL 813708. *3061*

YOUJI HUAXUE.
Science Press, Marketing and Sales Department, (Shanghai Institute of Organic Chemistry) 16 Donghuangchenggen Beijie, Beijing 100707, People's Republic of China. TEL 4010642. FAX 4012180. *1224*

YUGOSLAV JOURNAL OF OPERATIONS RESEARCH.
University of Belgrade, Faculty of Organizational Sciences, Jove Ilica 154, 11000 Belgrade, Yugoslavia. TEL 3811-465-855. FAX 3811-461-221. *1402*

Z O R - METHODS AND MODELS OF OPERATIONS RESEARCH.
Physica-Verlag GmbH und Co., Tiergartenstr. 17, Postfach 105280, 6900 Heidelberg 1, Germany. TEL 030-8207-448. FAX 030-8207-424. *1402*

ZEOLITES.
Butterworth - Heinemann Ltd. 80 Montvale Ave., Stoneham, MA 02180. TEL 617-438-8464. FAX 617-438-1479. *1209*

ZHENJUN XUEBAO.
Science Press, Marketing and Sales Department, (Chinese Academy of Sciences, Institute of Microbiology) 16 Donghuangchenggen Beijie, Beijing 100707, People's Republic of China. TEL 4010642. FAX 4102180. *521*

ZHIWU BINGLI XUEBAO.
Zhongguo Zhiwu Bingli Xuehui, Department of Plant Protection, Beijing University of Agriculture, Beijing 100094, People's Republic of China. TEL 2582244. *521*

ZHIWU FENLEI XUEBAO.
Science Press, Marketing and Sales Department, (Chinese Academy of Sciences, Institute of Botany) 16 Donghuangchenggen Beijie, Beijing 100707, People's Republic of China. TEL 4010642. FAX 4012180. *521*

ZHIWU SHENGLI XUEBAO.
Science Press, Marketing and Sales Department, (Chinese Society of Plant Physiology) 16 Donghuangchenggen Beijie, Beijing 100707, People's Republic of China. TEL 4010642. FAX 4012180. *521*

ZHIWU SHENGTAIXUE YU DIZHIWUXUE XUEBAO.
Science Press, Marketing and Sales Department, 16 Donghuangchenggen Beijie, Beijing 100707, People's Republic of China. TEL 4010642. FAX 4012180. *521*

ZHIWU XUEBAO.
Science Press, Marketing and Sales Department, (Chinese Academy of Sciences, Institute of Botany) 16 Donghuangchenggen Beijie, Beijing 100707, People's Republic of China. TEL 4010642. FAX 4012180. *521*

ZHIWUXUE TONGBAO.
Zhongguo Kexueyuan, Zhiwu Yanjiusuo, 141 Xizhimenwai Dajie, Beijing 100044, People's Republic of China. TEL 893831. *521*

ZHONGGUO BINGLI SHENGLI ZAZHI.
Zhongguo Bingli Shengli Xuehui, Jinan Daxue, Shipai, Guangzhou, Guangdong 510632, People's Republic of China. TEL 516511. *3164*

ZHONGGUO HANGTIAN.
Aerospace China Press, (Hangkong Hangtian Gongye-bu, Keji Qingbao-suo) P.O. Box 1408, Beijing 100013, People's Republic of China. TEL 8373440. FAX 4227606. *66*

ZHONGGUO KEXUE A.
Science Press, Marketing and Sales Department, (Zhongguo Kexueyuan) 16 Donghuangchenggen Beijie, Beijing 100707, People's Republic of China. TEL 4010642. FAX 4102180. *4353*

ZHONGGUO KEXUE B.
Science Press, Marketing and Sales Department, (Chinese Academy of Sciences) 16 Donghuangchenggen Beijie, Beijing 100707, People's Republic of China. TEL 4010642. FAX 4012180. *4353*

ZHONGGUO MIANYIXUE ZAZHI.
Jilin Sheng Weisheng Ting, Fu 2, Dong Minzhu Dajie, Changchun, Jilin 130061, People's Republic of China. TEL 825027. *3189*

ZHONGGUO NONGYE QIXIANG.
Zhongguo Nongye Kexueyuan, 30 Baishiqiao Lu, Beijing 100081, People's Republic of China. TEL 8314433. *3444*

ZHONGGUO XIAODUXUE ZAZHI.
Zhonghua Yufang Yixuehui, A-23 Qilizhuang Lu, Fengtai, Beijing 100071, People's Republic of China. TEL 6888229. FAX 861-8213044. *3164*

ZHONGGUO XINLI WEISHENG ZAZHI.
Beijing Yike Daxue, Jingshen Weisheng Yanjiusuo, Huayuan Beilu, Beijing 100083, People's Republic of China. TEL 2010890. *4051*

ZHONGGUO YAOLI XUEBAO.
Science Press, Marketing and Sales Department, (Chinese Society of Pharmacology) 16 Donghuangchenggen Beijie, Beijing 100707, People's Republic of China. TEL 4010642. FAX 4012180. *3746*

ZHONGGUO YINGYONG SHENGLIXUE ZAZHI.
Zhongguo Shengli Xuehui, 27 Taiping Rd., Beijing 100850, People's Republic of China. FAX 861-8213044. *575*

ZHONGGUO YIXUE KEXUEYUAN XUEBAO.
Chinese Academy of Medical Sciences (CAMS), 9 Dong Dan San Tiao, Beijing 100730, People's Republic of China. TEL 5127733. *3165*

ZIDONGHUA XUEBAO.
Science Press, Marketing and Sales Department, (Chinese Association of Automation) 16 Donghuangchenggen Beijie, Beijing 100707, People's Republic of China. TEL 4010642. FAX 4012180. *1416*

ZIRAN ZIYUAN XUEBAO.
Science Press, Marketing and Sales Department, (Zhongguo Kexueyuan, Ziran Ziyuan Zonghe Kaocha Weiyuanhui) 16 Donghuangchenggen Beijie, Beijing 100707, People's Republic of China. TEL 4010642. FAX 4012180. *1549*

ZOO BIOLOGY.
John Wiley & Sons, Inc., Journals, 605 Third Ave., New York, NY 10158. TEL 212-850-6000. FAX 212-850-6088. *594*

ZOOLOGICA SCRIPTA.
Pergamon Press plc, (Kungliga Svenska Vetenskapsakademien) Headington Hill Hall, Oxford OX3 0BW, England. TEL 0865-794141. FAX 0865-743911. *594*

ZUOWU XUEBAO.
Science Press, Marketing and Sales Department, (Zhongguo Zuowu Xuehui) 16 Donghuangchenggen Beijie, Beijing 100707, People's Republic of China. TEL 4010642. FAX 4012180. *197*

ZUOWU ZAZHI.
Zhongguo Zuowu Xuehui, Zhongguo Nongye Kexueyuan, 30 Baishiqiao Lu, Beijing 100081, People's Republic of China. TEL 891731. *131*

19TH CENTURY MUSIC.
University of California Press, Journals Division, 2120 Berkeley Way, Berkeley, CA 94720. TEL 510-642-4191. FAX 510-643-7127. *3588*

Controlled Circulation Serials

A A A TODAY MAGAZINE.
Automobile Club Publications, 1380 Dublin Rd., Ste. 109, Columbus, OH 43215-1025. TEL 614-481-8088.
circ. 1,900,000. *4678*

A A B BULLETIN.
American Association of Bioanalysts, 818 Olive St., Ste. 918, St. Louis, MO 63101. TEL 314-241-1445.
circ. 1,700. *3256*

A.A.R.N. NEWSLETTER.
Alberta Association of Registered Nurses, 11620-168 St., Edmonton, Alta. T5M 4A6, Canada. TEL 403-451-0043. FAX 403-452-3276.
circ. 24,400. *3274*

A B C CAR FERRY GUIDE.
Reed Travel Group Church St., Dustable, Bedfordshire LU5 4HB, England. TEL 0582-600111.
circ. 5,000. *4723*

A B E S P BOLETIM.
Associacao Brasileira de Endodontia, Seccao Sao Paulo, Praca Amadeu Amaral 47-8, Sao Paulo, SP, Brazil.
circ. 2,500. *3226*

A B F BY-LINES.
A B F Freight System, Inc., 301 S. 11th St., Ft. Smith, AR 72901.
circ. 10,000. *4646*

A C M S I G P L A N NOTICES.
Association for Computing Machinery, Special Interest Group on Programming Languages, 1515 Broadway, 17th Fl., New York, NY 10036. TEL 212-869-7440. FAX 212-302-5826.
circ. 11,600. *1429*

A C O G NEWSLETTER.
American College of Obstetricians and Gynecologists, 409 12th St., S.W., Washington, DC 20024. TEL 202-638-5577. FAX 202-484-5107.
circ. 31,000. *3288*

A C S A NEWS.
Association of Collegiate Schools of Architecture, Inc., 1735 New York Ave., N.W., Washington, DC 20006. TEL 202-785-2324. FAX 202-626-7421.
circ. 3,800. *291*

A C U BULLETIN OF CURRENT DOCUMENTATION (ABCD).
Association of Commonwealth Universities, John Foster House, 36 Gordon Square, London WC1H OPF, England. TEL 071-387-8572. FAX 071-387-2655. *1698*

A D L LAW REPORT.
Anti-Defamation League of B'nai B'rith, 823 United Nations Plaza, New York, NY 10017. TEL 212-490-2525.
circ. 5,000. *2593*

A D N O C NEWS.
Abu Dhabi National Oil Company, Public Relations Department, P.O. Box 898, Abu Dhabi, United Arab Emirates. TEL 666000. FAX 655745.
circ. 3,500. *3680*

A E A M NEWSLETTER JOURNAL.
Adult Education Association in Massachusetts, Inc., 32 Whites Ave., No. 34, Watertown, MA 02172.
circ. 1,200. *1681*

A E R REPORT.
Association for Education and Rehabilitation of the Blind and Visually Impaired (AER), 206 N. Washington St., Alexandria, VA 22314. TEL 703-548-1884. *2290*

A F F I LETTER.
American Frozen Food Institute, 1764 Old Meadow Lane, Ste. 350, McLean, VA 22102. TEL 703-821-0770. FAX 703-821-1350.
circ. 1,300. *2060*

A F T M A TRADE SHOW DIRECTORY AND BUYERS' GUIDE.
American Fishing and Tackle Manufacturing Association, 1250 Grove Ave., Ste. 300, Barrington, IL 60010. TEL 312-381-9490. FAX 708-381-9518.
circ. 10,000. *2035*

A G E REFDEX.
Asian Geotechnical Engineering Information Center, c/o Asian Institute of Technology, Box 2754, Bangkok, Thailand. TEL 66-2-524-5862. FAX 66-2-516-2126.
circ. 300. *1549*

A G NEWS.
Associated Grocers of Colorado Inc., 707 17th St., Ste. 2800, Denver, CO 80202-3428.
circ. 2,000. *2090*

A I A NEWSLETTER.
Alberta Institute of Agrologists, 8506 - 104 St., Edmonton, Alb. T6E 4G4, Canada. TEL 403-432-0663. *67*

A I D RESEARCH AND DEVELOPMENT ABSTRACTS.
U.S. Agency for International Development, Policy Directorate, POL-CDIE-DI, Dept. of State, Washington, DC 20523-1802. TEL 202-875-4818. FAX 703-351-4039.
circ. 5,000. *701*

A I M C FORUM.
Association of International Management Consultants, Box 304, E. Bloomfield, NY 14443. TEL 716-657-7878. FAX 716-924-4946.
circ. 500. *1000*

A L E B C I; BOLETIN INFORMATIVO.
Asociacion Latinoamericana de Escuelas de Bibliotecologia y Ciencias de la Informacion, Escuela de Bibliotecologia, Centro Regional de Veraguas, Santiago de Veraguas, Panama. FAX 984056.
circ. 500. *2740*

A L S A R.
Ediciones Anel, San Vicente Ferrer 13, Granada, Spain.
circ. 25,000. *67*

A M.
Editora Ave Maria Ltda, Rua Martins Francisco 646, Caixa Postal, 615, 01000 Sao Paulo, Brazil.
circ. 50,000. *4254*

A M A - AGRICULTURAL MECHANIZATION IN ASIA, AFRICA AND LATIN AMERICA.
Farm Machinery Industrial Research Corp., 7, 2chome, Kanda Nishikicho, Chiyoda-ku, Tokyo 101, Japan. TEL 03-3291-3674. FAX 03-3291-5717.
circ. 15,000. *161*

A M A MANAGEMENT BRIEFINGS.
American Management Association, 135 W. 50th St., New York, NY 10020-1201. TEL 212-586-8100. *1001*

A M A VICTORIA BRANCH NEWS.
Australian Medical Association, Victoria Branch, 293 Royal Parade, Parkville, Vic. 3052, Australia. FAX 03-347-9871. *3068*

A M MAGAZINE.
Aston Martin Owners' Club Ltd., 22 Bank St., Braintree, Essex, England. FAX 0376-551431.
circ. 4,000. *4678*

A N S UTILITY QUARTERLY.
American Nuclear Society, 555 N. Kensington Ave., La Grange Park, IL 60523. TEL 708-352-6611. FAX 708-352-0499.
circ. 4,000. *1803*

A O.
Stichting IVIO, Postbus 37, 8200 AA Lelystad, Netherlands. TEL 03200-76411. FAX 03200-33756.
circ. 11,000. *2211*

A P A C INFORM.
Associazione Professionale Autonoma Cineoperatori, Via P.S. Mancini, 20148 Milan, Italy. *3502*

A P A MAGAZINE.
Advertising Photographers of America, 27 W. 20th St., Rm. 601, New York, NY 10011. TEL 212-807-0399. FAX 212-727-8120.
circ. 7,500. *3788*

A P F NEWSLETTER.
Association of Professional Foresters, 4 West Point, Marine Parade West, Lee on the Solent, Hampshire PO13 9LW, England. TEL 0705-551998. FAX 0705-552272. *2095*

A P F REPORTER.
Alicia Patterson Foundation, 1001 Pennsylvania Ave., N.W., Ste. 1250, Washington, DC 20004. TEL 202-393-5995. FAX 301-951-8512.
circ. 3,200. *2566*

A R D R I NEWS.
University of Fort Hare, Agricultural and Rural Development Research Institute, Private Bag X1314, Alice, Ciskei, South Africa. TEL 0404-31154. FAX 0404-31730. *67*

A R: THE COMPLETE ANNUAL REPORT AND COMPLETE IMAGE PLANNING BOOK.
Alexander Communications, Inc., 212 W. Superior, Ste. 203, Chicago, IL 60610. TEL 312-944-5115. FAX 312-944-7865.
circ. 15,000. *1001*

A S A E ASSOCIATION LAW AND POLICY.
American Society of Association Executives, 1575 I St., N.W., Washington, DC 20005. TEL 202-626-2723. FAX 202-408-9635.
circ. 600. *1001*

A S A E INTERNATIONAL NEWS.
American Society of Association Executives, 1575 I St., N.W., Washington, DC 20005. TEL 202-626-2723. FAX 202-408-9635.
circ. 500. *1001*

A S A MAGAZINE.
Leon Maister (Pty) Ltd., Langham House, 59 Long St, P.O. Box 4385, Cape Town, South Africa.
circ. 21,500. *4707*

A S A NEWS.
American Supply Association, 222 Merchandise Mart Pl., Ste. 1360, Chicago, IL 60654. TEL 312-464-0090. FAX 312-464-0091.
circ. 7,500. *2297*

A S I C & E D A.
Vercom Group, 480 San Antonio Rd., Ste. 425, Mountain View, CA 94040. TEL 415-949-2742. FAX 415-949-3635.
circ. 51,000. *1411*

A S I D REPORT.
American Society of Interior Designers, 608 Massachusetts Ave., N.E., Washington, DC 20002-6006. TEL 202-546-3480. FAX 202-546-3240.
circ. 35,000. *2547*

A S T R NEWSLETTER.
American Society for Theatre Research, c/o P.T. Dircks, Ed., C.W. Post College, Dept. of English, Greenvale, NY 11548. TEL 516-299-2391.
circ. 600. *4629*

A S W LOG.
Lockheed Aeronautical Systems Company, 86 S. Cobb Dr., Marietta, GA 30063-0237. TEL 404-494-2406. FAX 404-494-0145.
circ. 30,000. *42*

A T.
Svenska Arkitekters Riksfoerbund, Norrlandsgatan 18, 111 43 Stockholm, Sweden. FAX 08-6114930.
circ. 5,700. *291*

A T F ANNUAL REPORT.
Australian Teachers Union, P.O. Box 415, Carlton South, Vic. 3053, Australia. TEL 03-348-1700. FAX 03-347-6330. *1613*

DE AANDRIJFKRANT.
Hofstad Vakpers B.V., Postbus 119, 2700 AC Zoetermeer, Netherlands. TEL 079-711811. FAX 079-711803.
circ. 7,500. *1861*

ABBEY.
White Urp Press, 5360 Fallriver Row Ct., Columbia, MD 21044.
circ. 200. *2986*

ABSTRACT OF STATISTICS FOR TAMIL NADU.
Director of Statistics, Madras 600006, India. *4561*

ABU DHABI. DA'IRAT AL-TAKHTIT. AL-NASHRAH AL-SANAWIYYAH LI-AS'AR AL-TAJZI'AH.
Planning Administration, Statistical Department, P.O. Box 12, Abu Dhabi, United Arab Emirates. TEL 727200.
circ. 500. *702*

ABU DHABI. DA'IRAT AL-TAKHTIT. AL-NASHRAH AL-SHAHRIYYAH LI-AS'AR AL-TAJZI'AH.
Planning Administration, Statistical Department, P.O. Box 12, Abu Dhabi, United Arab Emirates. TEL 727200. *702*

ABU DHABI. FOREIGN TRADE STATISTICS.
Government of Abu Dhabi, P.O. Box 255, Abu Dhabi, United Arab Emirates. TEL 720700. *702*

ABU DHABI CHAMBER OF COMMERCE AND INDUSTRY. ANNUAL REPORT.
Abu Dhabi Chamber of Commerce and Industry, P.O. Box 662, Abu Dhabi, United Arab Emirates. TEL 2-214000. FAX 2-215867.
circ. 500. *806*

ACADEMIA.
Oesterreichischer Cartell-Verband, Lerchenfelderstr. 14, A-1080 Vienna, Austria. FAX 0222-42162233.
circ. 20,000. *2857*

ACADEMIA CAMPINENSE DE LETRAS. PUBLICACOES.
Academia Campinense de Letras, Rua Marechal Deodoro, 525, 13020 Campinas SP, Brazil.
circ. 200. *2891*

ACADEMIA DE CIENCIAS DE CUBA. INSTITUTO DE GEOLOGIA. SERIE GEOLOGICA.
Academia de Ciencias de Cuba, Instituto de Geologia, Calzada no. 851, Esq. a Calle 4, Havana 4, Cuba. *1553*

ACADEMY OF MANAGEMENT NEWSLETTER.
Academy of Management (Waco), c/o D. Ray Bagby, Ed., Hankamer School of Business, Baylor University, Waco, TX 76798-8011. TEL 817-755-2265. FAX 817-755-2421.
circ. 8,500. *1001*

ACCESSOIREX.
Societe d'Editions Medico-Pharmaceutiques (SEMP), 26 rue le Brun, 75013 Paris, France. TEL 1-43-37-83-50. FAX 43-31-94-11.
circ. 11,000. *3715*

ACCOMMODATOR.
Motels Ontario, 347 Pido Rd., Unit 2, R.R. 6, Peterborough, Ont. K9J 6X7, Canada. TEL 705-745-4482. FAX 705-745-4483.
circ. 5,000. *2471*

ACCOUNTANCY AGE.
V N U Business Publications BV, 32-34 Broadwick St., London W1A 2HG, England.
circ. 62,202. *745*

ACERVO.
Arquivo Nacional, Rua Azeredo Coutinho 77, CEP 20230 Rio de Janeiro, Brazil.
circ. 2,000. *2397*

ACHETEURS.
Edipresse, 16 rue Guillaume Tell, 75017 Paris, France. TEL 1-47 66 00 05.
circ. 4,478. *1032*

ACHIEVEMENT.
World Trade Magazines Ltd., World Trade House, 49 Dartford Rd., Sevenoaks, Kent TN13 3TE, England. TEL 0732-458144. FAX 0732-456295.
circ. 10,760. *899*

ACQUA ARIA.
Editrice Arti Poligrafiche Europee, Via Casella 16, 20156 Milan, Italy. TEL 02-330221. FAX 02-39214341.
circ. 5,000. *1941*

ACQUISITION COLUMBUS.
Acquisition Columbus, 1445 Worthington Woods Blvd., Worthington, OH 43085-6707. TEL 614-841-0085. *4144*

ACTA ACADEMIAE AGRICULTURAE AC TECHNICAE OLSTENENSIS. AEDIFICATIO ET MECHANICA.
Wydawnictwo A R T Olsztyn, Blok 21, 10-957 Olsztyn-Kortowo, Poland. TEL 48-89-273310.
circ. 190. *1926*

ACTA ACADEMIAE AGRICULTURAE AC TECHNICAE OLSTENENSIS. AGRICULTURA - AGRICULTURE.
Wydawnictwo A R T Olsztyn, Blok 21, 10-957 Olsztyn-Kortowo, Poland. TEL 48 89 273310.
circ. 300. *166*

ACTA ACADEMIAE AGRICULTURAE AC TECHNICAE OLSTENENSIS. GEODAESIA ET RURIS REGULATIO - GEODESY AND AGRICULTURAL ARRANGEMENT.
Wydawnictwo A R T Olsztyn, Blok 21, 10-957 Olsztyn-Kortowo, Poland. TEL 48-89-273310.
circ. 210. *68*

ACTA ACADEMIAE AGRICULTURAE AC TECHNICAE OLSTENENSIS. OECONOMICA - ECONOMICS.
Wydawnictwo A R T Olsztyn, Blok 21, 10-957 Olsztyn-Kortowo, Poland. TEL 48-89-273310.
circ. 250. *145*

ACTA ACADEMIAE AGRICULTURAE AC TECHNICAE OLSTENENSIS. PROTECTIO AQUARUM ET PISCATORIA - WATER CONSERVATION AND INLAND FISHERIES.
Wydawnictwo A R T Olsztyn, Blok 21, 10-957 Olsztyn-Kortowo, Poland. TEL 48-89-273310.
circ. 280. *4821*

ACTA ACADEMIAE AGRICULTURAE AC TECHNICAE OLSTENENSIS. TECHNOLOGIA ALIMENTORUM - FOOD TECHNOLOGY.
Wydawnictwo A R T Olsztyn, Blok 21, 10-957 Olsztyn-Kortowo, Poland. TEL 48-89-273310.
circ. 250. *2060*

ACTA ACADEMIAE AGRICULTURAE AC TECHNICAE OLSTENENSIS. VETERINARIA - VETERINARY MEDICINE.
Wydawnictwo A R T Olsztyn, Blok 21, 10-957 Olsztyn-Kortowo, Poland. TEL 48-89-273310.
circ. 210. *4804*

ACTA BIOQUIMICA CLINICA LATINOAMERICANA.
Federacion Bioquimica de la Provincia de Buenos Aires, Calle 6, No. 1344, 1900 La Plata, Buenos Aires, Argentina. TEL 021-38821-42797. FAX 54-21-254224.
circ. 3,000. *470*

ACTA CONCILIUM OPHTHALMOLOGICUM.
International Federation of Ophthalmological Societies, c/o Prof. A. Deutman, Sec., Dept. of Ophthalmology, Univ. of Nijmegen, P. van Leijdenlaan 15, 6525 EX Nijmegen, Netherlands. TEL 080-513138. FAX 080-540522.
circ. 8,500. *3297*

ACTA MEDICA OKAYAMA.
Okayama Daigaku, Igakubu, 2-5-1 Shikata-cho, Okayama 700, Japan. *3070*

ACTA ORDINIS FRATRUM MINORUM.
Ordo Fratrum Minorum, Curia Generalis, Via S. Maria Mediatrice, 25, I-00165 Rome, Italy. TEL (06) 632241. *4254*

ACTIVITY.
Ranks Hovis McDougall PLC., King Edward House, P.O. Box 527, King Edward Court, Windsor, Berks SL4 1TJ, England. FAX 0753-840401.
circ. 35,000. *2086*

ACTUALITE CHIMIQUE.
Societe Francaise de Chimie, 250 rue Saint Jacques, 75005 Paris, France. FAX 43-25-87-63.
circ. 2,378. *1168*

AD MARGINEM.
Universitaet zu Koeln, Institut fuer Musikalische Volkskunde, Gronewaldstr. 2, 5000 Cologne 41, Germany. TEL 0221-470-5269. *3536*

AD VERBUM.
Confederacion Argentina de Sordomudos, Av. Pedro Medrano 1352, Buenos Aires, Argentina.
circ. 5,000. *2285*

ADDICTION RESEARCH FOUNDATION OF ONTARIO. ANNUAL REPORT.
Addiction Research Foundation of Ontario, Subscription - Distribution Centre, 33 Russell St., Toronto, Ontario M5S 2S1, Canada. TEL 416-595-6102. FAX 416-593-4694.
circ. 4,000. *1533*

ADHESIVE TRENDS.
Adhesive Manufacturers Association, 401 N. Michigan Ave., Chicago, IL 60611-4267. TEL 312-644-6610. FAX 312-321-6869.
circ. 300. *4291*

ADLINE.
Adline Publishing Ltd., 361-363 Moseley Rd., Birmingham B12 9DE, England. TEL 021-446-4466. FAX 021-446-4462.
circ. 14,000. *26*

ADMARINE.
Nigel Gearing Ltd., No.4 Red Barn Mews, High St., Battle, E. Sussex TN33 0AG, England. TEL 04246-4982. FAX 04246-4321.
circ. 20,000. *4521*

ADULT STUDENTS.
Iowa State University, Adult Students on Campus Organization, Dean of Students Office, 2nd Fl., Student Services Bldg., Ames, IA 50011. TEL 515-294-1020.
circ. 3,500. *1681*

ADVANCE (LIBERTY).
Target Marketing, Inc., 115 Blue Jay Dr., Box 217, Liberty, MO 64068. TEL 800-331-2496. FAX 816-792-3892.
circ. 250,000. *3624*

ADVANCED COMPOSITES MANUFACTURING CENTRE NEWSLETTER.
Advanced Composites Manufacturing Centre, c/o Polytechnic South West, School of Manufacturing, Materials and Mechanical Engineering, Drake Circus, Plymouth, Devon PL4 8AA, England. TEL 0752-232650. FAX 0752-232638.
circ. 4,600. *3861*

ADVENTURE ROAD.
Amoco Enterprises, Inc., Amoco Motor Club, 200 E. Randolph Dr., Chicago, IL 60601-0607. TEL 312-856-2583. FAX 312-856-2379.
circ. 1,500,000. *4751*

ADVERTENTIEBLAD.
B. V. Rotadruk, Postbus 16, Axel, Netherlands. *26*

ADVERTISING AND PUBLICITY RESOURCES FOR SCHOLARLY BOOKS.
Association of American University Presses, Inc., 584 Broadway, Ste. 410, New York, NY 10012. TEL 212-941-6610. *27*

ADVOCATE (SAINT PAUL).
Minnesota Education Association, 41 Sherburne Ave., St. Paul, MN 55103. TEL 612-227-9541. FAX 612-227-9788.
circ. 46,000. *1614*

ADVOKATEN.
Danske Advokatsamfund, Kronprinsessegade 28, 1306 Copenhagen K, Denmark. FAX 33-321831.
circ. 5,500. *2595*

AEROGRAM.
College of Aeronautics, Cranfield Institute of Technology, Cranfield, Beds. MK43 0AL, England. FAX 0234-750780.
circ. 3,500. *43*

AEROLOGICAL DATA OF JAPAN.
Japan Weather Association, c/o Japan Meteorological Agency, 1-3-4 Otemachi, Chiyoda-ku, Tokyo 101, Japan. *3432*

AERONAUTICA AND AIR LABEL COLLECTOR.
Aeronautica & Air Label Collectors Club, Box 1239, Elgin, IL 60121-1239. TEL 708-742-3328. *3749*

AEROSPACE.
Asian Business Press Pte. Ltd. 100 Beach Rd., 26-00 Shaw Towers, Singapore 0718, Singapore. TEL 294-3366. FAX 298-5534.
circ. 14,669. *43*

AEROSPACE & DEFENCE REVIEW.
Smiths Industries Aerospace & Defence Systems Co., 765 Finchley Rd., Childs Hill, London NW11 8DS, England. TEL 081-458-4380. FAX 081-458-3232.
circ. 5,000. *44*

AEROSPACE NEWS.
Aerospace Industries Association of Canada, 60 Queen St., Ste. 1200, Ottawa, Ont. K1P 5Y7, Canada. TEL 613-232-4297. FAX 613-232-1142.
circ. 1,500. *44*

AEROVISAO.
Ministerio da Aeronautica, Centro de Relacoes Publicas da Aeronautica, Av. Mal. Camara 233, 20000 Rio de Janeiro, Brazil. *44*

AERSCEALA.
Aer Lingus, Communications Department, Dublin Airport PA6, Dublin, Ireland. TEL 01-7052326.
circ. 9,000. *44*

AERZTLICHER RATGEBER FUER WERDENDE UND JUNGE MUETTER.
Wort und Bild Verlag Konradshoehe GmbH, Konradshoehe, 8021 Baierbrunn, Germany. TEL 089-7270-0. FAX 089-7934393.
circ. 240,000. *3288*

AETNAIZER.
Aetna Life and Casualty, 151 Farmington Ave., TS4N, Hartford, CT 06156. TEL 203-273-6245.
circ. 15,000. *2526*

AFFIRMATIVE ACTION REGISTER.
Warren H. Green, Ed.& Pub., 8356 Olive Blvd., St. Louis, MO 63132. TEL 314-991-1335. FAX 314-997-1788.
circ. 60,000. *3624*

AFRICA PRODUCT DIGEST.
South African Foreign Trade Organisation, Publishing Division, P.O. Box 782706, Sandton 2146, South Africa. TEL 011-883-3737. FAX 011-883-6569.
circ. 6,000. *899*

AFRICAN BOOK PUBLISHING RECORD.
Hans Zell Publishers P.O. Box 56, Oxford OX1 2SJ, England. TEL 0865-511428. FAX 0865-311534.
circ. 800. *4139*

AFRICANA LIBRARIES NEWSLETTER.
c/o Joseph J. Lauer, Ed., Africana Bibliographer, Michigan State University Libraries, E. Lansing, MI 48824-1048. TEL 517-355-2366. FAX 517-336-1445.
circ. 600. *2741*

AG ENGINEERS NOTEBOOK.
Cornell University, Agriculture Engineering Extension, Riley-Robb Hall, Ithaca, NY 14853. TEL 607-255-2280. FAX 607-255-4080. *166*

AGENDA (NEW YORK, 1991).
Scholastic Inc., 730 Broadway, New York, NY 10003. TEL 212-505-3121.
circ. 250,000. *1614*

AGENT ORANGE REVIEW.
U.S. Department of Veterans Affairs, Environmental Agents Service (116A), 810 Vermont Ave., N.W., Washington, DC 20420. TEL 202-535-7183. *2595*

AGIMPACT.
Cornell Cooperative Extension of Genesee County, 420 E. Main St., Batavia, NY 14020. TEL 716-343-3040. FAX 716-439-8455.
circ. 2,000. *68*

AGORA.
Lakehead University, Oliver Rd., Thunder Bay, Ont. P7B 5E1, Canada. TEL 807-343-8631. FAX 807-343-8023.
circ. 1,700. *1302*

AGRARTECHNIK (WUERZBURG).
Vogel-Verlag und Druck KG, Postfach 6740, 8700 Wuerzburg 1, Germany. TEL 0931-418-0.
circ. 14,421. *69*

AGRIBUSINESS WORLDWIDE.
Sosland Publishing Company, 4800 Main St., Ste. 100, Kansas City, MO 64112. TEL 816-756-1000. FAX 816-756-0494.
circ. 25,000. *146*

AGRICULTURA EM SAO PAULO.
Instituto de Economia Agricola, Servico de Biblioteca e Documentacao, Av. Miguel Estefano, 3900, Caixa Postal 8114, 04301 Sao Paulo, Brazil. *146*

AGRICULTURA TECNICA EN MEXICO.
Instituto Nacional de Investigaciones Forestales y Agropecuarias, Subdireccion de Difusion Cientifica y Tecnologica, Apdo. Postal 6-882, 06600 Mexico, D.F., Mexico.
circ. 7,000. *70*

AGRICULTURAL EDUCATORS DIRECTORY.
Charles M. Henry Printing Co., Box 68, Greensburg, PA 15601. TEL 412-834-7600. FAX 412-836-7759.
circ. 13,118. *71*

AGRICULTURAL FINANCE REVIEW.
Cornell University, Department of Agricultural Economics, Ithaca, NY 14853. TEL 607-255-4534. FAX 607-255-9984.
circ. 2,000. *146*

AGRICULTURAL STATISTICS OF SABAH.
Department of Agriculture, Statistics Unit, 88632 Kota Kinabalu, Sabah, Malaysia. TEL 088-55155. FAX 088-239046.
circ. 500. *132*

AGROBOREALIS.
University of Alaska, Fairbanks, Agricultural and Forestry Experiment Station, Fairbanks, AK 99775. TEL 907-474-7653.
circ. 7,500. *73*

AGROCIENCIA.
Colegio de Postgraduados, Comite Editorial, Montecillos, Tezcoco, Mexico.
circ. 1,500. *73*

AGROFORESTRY TODAY.
International Council for Research in Agroforestry, Box 30677, Nairobi, Kenya. TEL 254-2-521450. FAX 254-2-521001.
circ. 8,700. *74*

AIR CADET REVIEW.
Headquarters Air Cadets, R.A.F. Newton, Nottingham NG13 8HR, England. TEL 0949-20771-441. FAX 0949-20771-455.
circ. 38,100. *1248*

AIR POLLUTION CONTROL (NOVI).
Eagle Publications, Inc., 42400 Nine Mile Rd., Ste. B, Novi, MI 48375. TEL 800-783-3491. FAX 313-347-3492.
circ. 18,000. *1942*

AIR QUALITY DATA FOR ARIZONA.
Department of Health Services, Bureau of Air Quality Control, 1740 W. Adams St., Phoenix, AZ 85007. TEL 602-255-1142. *1942*

AIRCRAFT TECHNICIAN.
Johnson Hill Press, Inc., 1233 Janesville Ave., Fort Atkinson, WI 53538. TEL 414-563-6388. FAX 414-563-1701.
circ. 25,000. *4670*

AIRPORT REPORT.
American Association of Airport Executives, 4224 King St., Alexandria, VA 22302. FAX 703-820-1395. *4670*

AITIA MAGAZINE.
State University of New York at Farmingdale, Center for Philosophy, Law, Citizenship, Knapp Hall 15, Farmingdale, NY 11735. TEL 516-420-2050. FAX 516-420-2698.
circ. 3,000. *2502*

AJMAN.
Ajman Chamber of Commerce and Industry, P.O. Box 662, Ajman, United Arab Emirates. TEL 422177.
circ. 1,000. *806*

4964 CONTROLLED CIRCULATION SERIALS

AKHBAR AL-BUTRUL WAL-SINA'A.
Ministry of Petroleum and Mineral Wealth, P.O. Box 59, Abu Dhabi, United Arab Emirates. TEL 651810. FAX 663414.
circ. 2,000. *3681*

AKRON.
University of Akron, Department for Akron Magazine, Akron, OH 44325-0604. TEL 216-972-7820. FAX 216-972-6168.
circ. 70,000. *1303*

AKTUELLT MAALERI.
L M P Foerlagsgruppen, Box 630, 10128 Stockholm, Sweden.
circ. 2,681. *3652*

ALABAMA FOOD MERCHANTS JOURNAL.
Southeast Publishers, 1631 Pinevale, Jackson, MS 39211.
circ. 875. *2090*

ALASKA. STATE HOUSING AUTHORITY. ANNUAL REPORT.
State Housing Authority, Box 230329, Anchorage, AK 99523. TEL 907-562-2813. FAX 907-786-6248.
circ. 1,000. *2482*

ALASKA AIRLINES MAGAZINE.
Paradigm Press, 2701 1st Ave., Ste. 250, Seattle, WA 98121. TEL 206-441-5871. FAX 206-448-6939.
circ. 40,000. *4801*

ALASKA LIBRARY DIRECTORY.
Alaska Library Association (Fairbanks), c/o Isabelle Mudd, Exec.Sec., Box 81084, Fairbanks, AK 99708. TEL 907-479-4522. *2742*

ALBERTA AGRICULTURE. ANNUAL REPORT.
Department of Agriculture, Print Media Branch, 7000 113th St., Edmonton, Alta. T6H 5T6, Canada. TEL 403-427-2121. FAX 403-427-2861. *75*

ALBERTA ASSOCIATION OF COLLEGE LIBRARIANS. NEWSLETTER.
Alberta Association of College Librarians, Canadian Union College Library, Box 460, College Heights, Alta. TOC 0Z0, Canada.
circ. 100. *2742*

ALDRICHIMICA ACTA.
Aldrich Chemical Company, Inc., 1001 W. St. Paul Ave., Milwaukee, WI 53233. FAX 414-273-4979.
circ. 200,000. *1216*

ALDUS MAGAZINE.
Aldus Corporation, 411 First Ave., S., Seattle, WA 98104. TEL 206-622-5500. FAX 206-343-3273.
circ. 23,000. *1475*

ALERE FLAMMAM.
Comando Scuola di Guerra, 00053 Civitavecchia, Italy.
circ. 900. *3450*

ALLEGHENY COUNTY MEDICAL SOCIETY. BULLETIN.
Allegheny County Medical Society, 713 Ridge Ave., Pittsburgh, PA 15212. TEL 412-321-5030. FAX 412-321-5323.
circ. 3,400. *3073*

ALLEGRO.
Associated Musicians of Greater New York, Local 802, A F M, 330 W. 42nd St., New York, NY 10036. TEL 212-239-4802. FAX 212-268-8696.
circ. 20,000. *2580*

ALLT OM HUSVAGN OCH CAMPING.
Caravan Press AB, P.O. Box 1263, 171 24 Solna, Sweden. TEL 08-7305485. FAX 08-7355710.
circ. 30,242. *4540*

ALLT OM M C.
Albinsson & Sjoeberg Foerlags AB, Box 529, S-371 23 Karlskrona, Sweden. TEL 45-455-196-85. FAX 46-455-117-15.
circ. 22,065. *4515*

ALPHA PSI OMEGA: PLAYBILL.
Alpha Psi Omega National Theatre Honorary, c/o Wabash College, Crawfordsville, IN 47933. TEL 217-581-2021.
circ. 7,000. *4629*

ALPINO.
Associazione Nazionale Alpini, Via Marsala 9, 20121 Milan, Italy. TEL 02-6552692. FAX 02-6592364. *2204*

ALUMNI COMPANION.
University of New Hampshire, Office of University Publications, 8 Garrison Ave., Durham, NH 03824. TEL 603-862-1463. FAX 603-862-1188.
circ. 42,000. *1303*

AMATEUR ATHLETE.
Eliot Wineberg, Ed. & Pub., 7842 N. Lincoln Ave., Skokie, IL 60077. TEL 708-676-1900. FAX 708-676-0063.
circ. 35,000. *4463*

AMBULATORY PEDIATRIC ASSOCIATION NEWSLETTER.
Ambulatory Pediatric Association, Department of Pediatrics, c/o Dr. John P. Pascoe, 600 Highland Ave., Madison, WI 53792. TEL 608-263-9405. FAX 608-263-0440.
circ. 1,500. *3318*

AMERICA COOPERATIVA.
Organization of the Cooperatives of America, Carrera 11 No. 86, 32 Ofc. 101, Apdo. Postal 241263, Bogota, D.E., Colombia. TEL 2181295-6103296.
circ. 5,000. *829*

AMERICAN.
American University, Office of University Publications, Washington, DC 20016-8121. TEL 202-885-5970. FAX 202-885-5949.
circ. 65,000. *1303*

AMERICAN ACADEMY OF OSTEOPATHY YEARBOOK.
American Academy of Osteopathy, 1127 Mt. Vernon Rd., Box 750, Newark, OH 43058-0750. TEL 614-366-7911.
circ. 1,100. *3213*

AMERICAN ASSOCIATION FOR DENTAL AESTHETICS NEWSLETTER.
American Association for Dental Aesthetics, 635 Madison Ave., New York, NY 10022. TEL 212-371-4575.
circ. 3,000. *3227*

AMERICAN ASSOCIATION OF BIOANALYSTS. PROFICIENCY TESTING SERVICE. TEST OF THE MONTH.
American Association of Bioanalysts, 205 W. Levee, Brownsville, TX 78520. TEL 512-546-5313.
circ. 4,500. *3257*

AMERICAN ASSOCIATION OF DENTAL EXAMINERS. BOARD BULLETIN.
American Association of Dental Examiners, 211 E. Chicago Ave., Ste. 844, Chicago, IL 60611. TEL 312-440-7464. FAX 312-440-7494.
circ. 1,100. *3227*

AMERICAN ASSOCIATION OF STATE HIGHWAY AND TRANSPORTATION OFFICIALS. SUB-COMMITTEE ON COMPUTER TECHNOLOGY. NATIONAL CONFERENCE. PROCEEDINGS.
American Association of State Highway and Transportation Officials, 444 N. Capitol St. N.W., Ste. 225, Washington, DC 20001. TEL 202-624-5800. *4706*

AMERICAN ASSOCIATION OF TISSUE BANKS NEWSLETTER.
American Association of Tissue Banks, 1350 Beverly Rd., Ste. 220A, McLean, VA 22101. TEL 703-827-9582. FAX 703-356-2198.
circ. 1,000. *3073*

AMERICAN ASSOCIATION OF WOMEN DENTISTS. CHRONICLE.
American Association of Women Dentists, 401 N. Michigan Ave., Chicago, IL 60611-4267. TEL 312-644-6610.
circ. 2,200. *3227*

AMERICAN BIOTECHNOLOGY LABORATORY.
International Scientific Communications, Inc., 30 Controls Dr., Box 870, Shelton, CT 06484-0870. TEL 203-926-9300. FAX 203-926-9310.
circ. 77,299. *487*

AMERICAN CHEMICAL SOCIETY. ABSTRACTS OF PAPERS (AT THE REGIONAL MEETINGS).
American Chemical Society, 1155 16th St., N.W., Washington, DC 20036. TEL 202-872-4600. FAX 202-872-4615. *1191*

AMERICAN CLINICAL LABORATORY.
International Scientific Communications, Inc., 30 Controls Dr., Box 870, Shelton, CT 06484-0870. TEL 203-926-9300. FAX 203-926-9310.
circ. 70,436. *3257*

AMERICAN COLLEGE OF CARDIOLOGY ANNUAL SCIENTIFIC SESSION NEWS.
American College of Cardiology, 9111 Old Georgetown Rd., Bethesda, MD 20814. TEL 301-897-2627. FAX 301-897-9745.
circ. 55,000. *3203*

AMERICAN COLLEGE OF FOOT ORTHOPEDISTS NEWSLETTER.
American College of Foot Orthopedists, 108 Orange St., Ste. 6, Redlands, CA 92373. TEL 714-798-8910.
circ. 400. *3306*

AMERICAN COLLEGE OF PHYSICIANS OBSERVER.
American College of Physicians, Independence Mall W., Sixth St. at Race, Philadelphia, PA 19106. TEL 215-351-2400.
circ. 53,000. *3073*

AMERICAN COLLEGE OF SURGEONS. BULLETIN.
American College of Surgeons, 55 E. Erie St., Chicago, IL 60611-2797. TEL 312-664-4050. FAX 312-440-7014.
circ. 65,000. *3374*

THE AMERICAN DREAM.
Yorktown Publishing, 2454 Ridge St., Yorktown Heights, NY 10598. TEL 914-962-2565.
circ. 11,350. *2556*

AMERICAN FEDERATION OF ASTROLOGERS BULLETIN.
American Federation of Astrologers, Inc., 6535 S. Rural Rd., Box 22040, Tempe, AZ 85285. TEL 602-838-1751. FAX 602-838-8293.
circ. 4,200. *358*

AMERICAN FOREIGN LAW ASSOCIATION NEWSLETTER.
American Foreign Law Association, c/o Richard Lutringer, 200 Park Ave., 28th Fl., New York, NY 10017. TEL 212-836-8000. FAX 212-351-3131. *2597*

AMERICAN FROZEN FOOD INSTITUTE. MEMBERSHIP DIRECTORY AND BUYER'S GUIDE.
American Frozen Food Institute, 1764 Old Meadow Lane, Ste.350, McLean, VA 22102. TEL 703-821-0770. FAX 703-821-1350.
circ. 3,500. *2061*

AMERICAN HEALTH SYSTEMS REVIEW.
F A H S Review, Inc., 1405 N. Pierce St., Ste. 308, Little Rock, AR 72207. TEL 501-661-9555. FAX 501-663-4903.
circ. 25,000. *2458*

AMERICAN HOCKEY MAGAZINE.
Publishing Group (Bloomington), 1022 W. 80th St., Bloomington, MN 55420. TEL 612-881-3183. FAX 612-881-2172.
circ. 253,241. *4464*

AMERICAN INSTITUTE FOR CANCER RESEARCH NEWSLETTER.
American Institute for Cancer Research (AICR), 1759 R St., N.W., Washington, DC 20009. TEL 202-328-7744. FAX 202-328-7226.
circ. 1,000,000. *3192*

AMERICAN INTERNATIONAL JOURNAL OF ARTS, SCIENCES, ENGINEERING AND MEDICINE.
Siveast Consultants, Inc., USA, P.O. Box 1755, Kathmandu, Nepal.
circ. 10. *311*

AMERICAN JOURNAL OF LAW & MEDICINE.
American Society of Law & Medicine, Inc., 765 Commonwealth Ave., Ste. 1634, Boston, MA 02215. TEL 617-262-4990. FAX 617-437-7596.
circ. 6,500. *2598*

AMERICAN LABORATORY.
International Scientific Communications, Inc., 30 Controls Dr., Box 870, Shelton, CT 06484-0870. TEL 203-926-9300. FAX 203-926-9310.
circ. 135,116. *1203*

AMERICAN MACHINIST (1988).
Penton Publishing 1100 Superior Ave., Cleveland, OH 44114-2543. TEL 216-696-7000. FAX 216-696-8765.
circ. 80,000. *1071*

AMERICAN NEWSPAPER CARRIER.
W.H. Lowry, Ed. & Pub., Box 2225, Kernersville, NC 27285. TEL 919-788-4336.
circ. 35,000. *1248*

AMERICAN PRINTER (CHICAGO, 1982).
Maclean Hunter Publishing Company, 29 N. Wacker Dr., Chicago, IL 60606. TEL 312-726-2802. FAX 312-726-2574.
circ. 94,839. *3997*

AMERICAN RED ANGUS.
Red Angus Association of America, 4201 I-35 North, Denton, TX 76201. FAX 817-383-4036.
circ. 6,000. *210*

AMERICAN TRUST FOR THE BRITISH LIBRARY. NEWSLETTER.
British Library, Humanities and Social Sciences, Great Russell St., London WC1B 3DG, England. TEL 071-323-7704. FAX 071-323-7736. *2743*

AMERON NEWS.
Ameron, 4700 Ramona Blvd., Monterey Park, CA 91754. FAX 213-263-7690.
circ. 10,000. *4593*

AMI DES JARDINS ET DE LA MAISON.
Ami des Jardins, S.A., 8-10 rue Pierre Brossolette, 92300 Levallois Perret, France.
circ. 200,000. *2121*

AMITYVILLE HISTORICAL SOCIETY DISPATCH.
Amityville Historical Society, Box 764, Amityville, NY 11701.
circ. 525. *2398*

AMOCO TRAVELER.
Amoco Enterprises, Inc., 200 E. Randolph Dr., Chicago, IL 60601. TEL 212-303-6987. FAX 312-856-2379.
circ. 75,000. *4752*

AMPHIBIOUS WARFARE REVIEW.
Marine Corps League, Capital Marines, 25 S. Quaker Ln., No. 20, Alexandria, VA 22314. TEL 703-823-5208. FAX 703-823-2813.
circ. 25,000. *3450*

AMPURIAS.
Diputacion Provincial de Barcelona, Instituto de Prehistoria y Arqueologia, Palacio del Museo Arqueologico, Parque de Montjuich, Barcelona 4, Spain. *261*

AMTRAK EXPRESS.
Pace Communications Inc., 1301 Carolina St., Greensboro, NC 27401. TEL 919-378-6065. FAX 919-275-2864.
circ. 253,000. *4801*

ANAIS HIDROGRAFICOS.
Ministerio da Marinha, Diretoria de Hidrografia e Navegacao, Rio de Janeiro, Brazil. *4821*

ANALECTA VATICANO-BELGICA. DEUXIEME SERIE. SECTION A: NONCIATURE DE FLANDRE.
N.V. Brepols I.G.P., Steenweg op Tielem 68, 2300 Turnhout, Belgium. TEL 014-41-54-63. FAX 014-42-89-19. *4255*

ANALECTA VATICANO-BELGICA. DEUXIEME SERIE. SECTION B: NONCIATURE DE COLOGNE.
N.V. Brepols I.G.P., Steenweg op Tielen 68, 2300 Turnhout, Belgium. TEL 014-41-54-63. FAX 014-42-89-19. *4255*

ANALECTA VATICANO-BELGICA. DEUXIEME SERIE. SECTION C: NONCIATURE DE BRUXELLES.
N.V. Brepols I.G.P., Steenweg op Tielen 68, 2300 Turnhout, Belgium. TEL 014-41-54-63. FAX 014-42-89-19. *4255*

ANALECTA VATICANO-BELGICA. PREMIERE SERIE: DOCUMENTS RELATIFS AUX ANCIENS DIOCESES DE CAMBRAI, LIEGE, THEROUANNE ET TOURNAI.
N.V. Brepols I.G.P., Steenweg op Tielen 68, 2300 Turnhout, Belgium. TEL 014-41-54-63. FAX 014-42-89-19. *4255*

ANALES DE LEGISLACION ARGENTINA.
Ediciones la Ley S.A., 1471 Tucuman, Buenos Aires, Argentina.
circ. 11,000. *2598*

ANALOG DIALOGUE.
Analog Devices, Inc., 1 Technology Way, Box 9106, Norwood, MA 02062-9106. TEL 617-461-3392. FAX 617-326-8703.
circ. 50,000. *1417*

ANDAR PER CERAMICHE.
Via C. Cavour 24, 42013 Casalgrande, Reggio Emilia, Italy.
circ. 8,000. *1161*

ANESTHESIOLOGY REVIEW.
Excerpta Medica, Inc., Core Publishing Division 105 Raider Blvd., Belle Mead, NJ 08520. TEL 908-874-8550. FAX 908-874-0700.
circ. 18,045. *3190*

ANGLIA FARMER AND CONTRACTOR.
B C Publications, 16C Market Pl., Diss, Norfolk IP22 3AB, England. TEL 0379-644200. FAX 0379-650480.
circ. 7,500. *76*

ANGLO-AMERICAN FORUM.
Verlag Peter Lang GmbH, Eschborner Landstr. 42-50, 6000 Frankfurt a.M. 90, Germany. TEL 069-7807050. FAX 069-785893.
circ. 400. *2895*

ANGLO - NORDIC TIMES.
41 Stone Bridge Crt., Lings, Northhampton, Northants NN3 4LY, England. TEL 0604-403282. FAX 0604-404041.
circ. 4,000. *900*

ANGOLA. SECRETARIA PROVINCIAL DE SAUDE, TRABALHO. PREVIDENCIA E ASSISTENCIA. SINTESE DA ACTIVIDADE DOS SERVICOS E ORGANISMOS.
Secretaria Provincial de Saude, Trabalho, Previdencia e Assistencia, Luanda, Angola. *4097*

ANGOLA PEACE MONITOR.
International Freedom Foundation, 200 G St., N.E., Ste. 300, Washington, DC 20002. TEL 202-546-5788. FAX 202-546-5488.
circ. 1,000. *3950*

ANNALI ITALIANI DI DERMATOLOGIA CLINICA E SPERIMENTALE.
Pensiero Scientifico Editore s.r.l., Via Panama, 48, I-00198 Rome, Italy. TEL 06-8549506. FAX 06-8841741.
circ. 1,000. *3245*

ANNALS OF OPHTHALMOLOGY.
Altier & Maynard Communications, Inc., 6 Farmingville Rd., Ridgefield, CT 06877. *3298*

ANNALS OF SAUDI MEDICINE.
King Faisal Specialist Hospital and Research Centre, P.O. Box 3354, Riyadh 11211, Saudi Arabia. FAX 442-7237.
circ. 14,000. *3076*

ANNUAIRE DE L'AFRIQUE DU NORD.
Editions du C N R S, 1 Place Aristide Briand, 92195 Meudon Cedex, France. TEL 1-45-34-75-50. FAX 1-46-26-28-49.
circ. 1,500. *4365*

ANNUAIRE DE LEGISLATION FRANCAISE ET ETRANGERE.
Editions du C N R S, 1 Place Aristide Briand, 92195 Meudon Cedex, France. TEL 1-45-34-75-50. FAX 1-46-36-38-49.
circ. 1,250. *2598*

ANNUAIRE FRANCAIS DE DROIT INTERNATIONAL.
Editions du C N R S, 1 Place Aristide Briand, 92195 Meudon Cedex, France. TEL 1-45-34-75-50. FAX 1-42-26-28-49.
circ. 1,500. *2719*

ANNUAL EDUCATIONAL SUMMARY, NEW YORK STATE.
Education Department, Information Center on Education, Education Bldg. Annex, Rm. 385, Albany, NY 12234. TEL 518-474-8716. *1615*

ANNUAL NEW MEXICO WATER CONFERENCE. PROCEEDINGS.
New Mexico Water Resources Research Institute, Box 30001, Dept. 3167, New Mexico State University, Las Cruces, NM 88003-0001. TEL 505-646-4337. FAX 505-646-6418.
circ. 500. *4821*

ANNUAL SUMMARY OF PROGRESS IN GRAVITATION SCIENCES.
Minas Ensanian Corporation, Box 98, Eldred, PA 16731. TEL 814-225-3296.
circ. 100. *3814*

ANRITSU TECHNICAL BULLETIN.
Anritsu Corporation, 1800 Atsugi-shi, Kanagawa 243, Japan.
circ. 5,000. *1882*

ANTARKTIESE BULLETIN.
South African Antarctic Association, 32 Park Ave., Bordeaux, Randburg, South Africa.
circ. 7,000. *1541*

ANTIK & AUKTION.
Aller Specialtidninger AB, P.O. Box 63, 262 31 Simrishamn, Sweden. TEL 0414-13770. FAX 0414-13455.
circ. 57,412. *254*

ANUARIO INDIGENISTA.
Instituto Indigenista Interamericano, Insurgentes Sur 1690, Colonia Florida, Mexico 01030, D.F., Mexico. TEL 660-00-07. FAX 534-8090. *235*

AOMORI-KEN NOGYO KISHO JUNPO.
Aomori Local Meteorological Observatory, 155-4 Tsukuda, Matsumori, Aomori 030, Japan.
circ. 180. *3432*

AOMORI PREFECTURE. MONTHLY REPORT OF METEOROLOGY.
Aomori Local Meteorological Observatory, 155-4 Tsukuda, Matsumori, Aomori 030, Japan.
circ. 340. *3432*

APARTMENT OWNER.
Apartment Association, 14550 Archwood St., Van Nuys, CA 91405. TEL 818-787-3455. FAX 818-374-3240.
circ. 4,000. *4144*

L'APICOLTORE MODERNO.
Universita di Torino, Osservatorio di Apicoltura, Via Leonardo da Vinci 44, 10095 Grugliasco TO, Italy. TEL 011-4033893. FAX 011-687016.
circ. 2,500. *76*

APOTHECARY.
Health Care Marketing Services, H C M S Inc., Box AP, Los Altos, CA 94023-0179. FAX 415-941-2303.
circ. 67,335. *3717*

APPAREL INDUSTRY MAGAZINE.
Shore Communications, Inc., 180 Allen Rd., N.E., Ste. 300 N., Atlanta, GA 30328. TEL 404-252-8831. FAX 404-252-4436.
circ. 18,600. *1283*

APPLICATOR.
Sealant, Waterproofing and Restoration Institute, 3101 Broadway, Ste. 585, Kansas City, MO 64111. TEL 816-561-8230. FAX 816-561-7765.
circ. 800. *600*

APPROACH.
Takenaka Corporation, 1-13, 4-chome, Hon-machi, Chuo-ku, Osaka 541, Japan. *292*

AQUARIAN VOICES.
Kathleen Blake, Ed. & Pub., Box 2070, Arnold Hollow Rd., Brandon, VT 05733. TEL 802-247-8087.
circ. 1,000. *358*

AQUASPHERE.
New England Aquarium, Central Wharf, Boston, MA 02110. TEL 617-742-8830.
circ. 13,000. *1943*

AQUATICS INTERNATIONAL.
Communication Channels, Inc., 6255 Barfield Rd., Atlanta, GA 30328-4369. TEL 404-256-9800. FAX 404-256-3116.
circ. 30,000. *4464*

AQUI (PHOENIX).
Wilcox Graphics, c/o Impact Communications, 2800 N. Central Ave. K Ste. 1500, Phoenix, AZ 85004-1046. TEL 602-230-2424. FAX 602-274-5130.
circ. 10,000. *1991*

ARBEIDERVERN.
Direktoratet for Arbeidstilsynet, Fr. Nansens vei 14, Box 8103 Dep., 0032 Oslo 1, Norway. TEL 02-957000.
circ. 36,427. *3614*

ARBEIT UND SICHERHEIT.
Verlag Glueckauf GmbH, Franz-Fischer-Weg 61, Postfach 103945, 4300 Essen 1, Germany. FAX 0201-293630. *3478*

ARBITRO.
Federazione Italiana Giuoco Calcio, Via Gregorio Allegri 14, 00198 Rome, Italy.
circ. 20,000. *4499*

ARCHAEOLOGICAL REVIEW FROM CAMBRIDGE.
c/o Department of Archaeology, Downing St., Cambridge CB2 3D2, England.
circ. 200. *263*

ARCHAEONAUTICA.
Editions du C N R S, 1 Place Aristide Briand, 92195 Meudon Cedex, France. TEL 1-45-34-75-50. FAX 1-46-26-28-49.
circ. 1,250. *264*

ARCHITECT & CONTRACTOR.
William A. Ullner Company, Box 119, Yountville, CA 94599.
circ. 5,000. *600*

ARCHITECTURAL RECORD REVIEW.
McGraw-Hill, Inc., 1221 Ave. of the Americas, New York, NY 10020. TEL 212-512-2000. *293*

ARCHIV FUER OEFFENTLICHE UND FREIGEMEINNUETZIGE UNTERNEHMEN.
Verlag Otto Schwartz und Co., Annastr. 7, 3400 Goettingen, Germany. TEL 0551-31051. FAX 0551-372812.
circ. 800. *1072*

ARCHIVES OF HISTOLOGY AND CYTOLOGY.
Japan Society of Histological Documentation (Societatis Histochemicae Japonicae), c/o Department of Anatomy, Niigata University School of Medicine, Asahimachi, Niigata, Japan. FAX 025-224-1767.
circ. 700. *522*

ARCHIVES PARLEMENTAIRES DE 1787 A 1860.
Editions du C N R S, 1 Place Aristide Briand, 92195 Meudon Cedex, France. TEL 1-45-34-75-50. FAX 1-46-26-28-49.
circ. 1,500. *3873*

ARCHIVOS ARGENTINOS DE DERMATOLOGIA.
Paraguay 1307, 4 38, 1057 Buenos Aires, Argentina.
circ. 1,600. *3246*

ARCTIC MEDICAL RESEARCH.
Nordic Council for Arctic Medical Research, Aapistie 3, SF-90220 Oulu, Finland. FAX 358-81-334765.
circ. 1,400. *3078*

ARENA (EDINBURGH).
Scottish Sports Council, Caledonia House, South Gyle, Edinburgh EH12 9DQ, Scotland. TEL 031-317-7200. FAX 031-317-7202.
circ. 2,000. *4464*

ARIZONA. DEPARTMENT OF HEALTH SERVICES. ANNUAL REPORT.
Department of Health Services, 1740 W. Adams St., Phoenix, AZ 85007. TEL 602-542-1000. FAX 602-542-1235.
circ. 500. *4098*

ARKANSAS. DEPARTMENT OF LABOR. EMPLOYMENT SECURITY DIVISION. ANNUAL REPORT.
Department of Labor, Employment Security Division, Box 2981, Little Rock, AR 72203. TEL 501-682-3119. *3624*

ARKANSAS EPISCOPALIAN.
Episcopal Diocese of Arkansas, Box 164668, Little Rock, AR 72216-4668. TEL 501-372-2168.
circ. 8,000. *4229*

ARKANSAS GROCER.
Arkansas Grocer Publishing Co., Box 7806, Pine Bluff, AR 71601. TEL 501-534-8803.
circ. 3,000. *2090*

ARKANSAS HIGHWAYS.
State Highway and Transportation Department, Public Affairs Office, Box 2261, Little Rock, AR 72203. TEL 501-569-2000. *4717*

ARKANSAS OIL AND GAS STATISTICAL BULLETIN.
Oil and Gas Commission, Box 1472, El Dorado, AR 71731-1472. TEL 501-862-4965. *3704*

ARMENIAN REPORTER.
A.R. Publishing Co., Inc., Box 600, Fresh Meadows, NY 11365. TEL 718-380-3636. FAX 718-380-8057. *1992*

ARMSTRONG LOGIC.
Armstrong World Industries, Inc., Floor Division, Box 3001, Lancaster, PA 17604. TEL 717-397-0611.
circ. 80,000. *2556*

ARMY LOGISTICIAN.
U.S. Army Logistics Management College, Ft. Lee, VA 23801-6044. TEL 804-734-4342. FAX 804-734-3576.
circ. 72,000. *3452*

ARMY RESERVE MAGAZINE.
U.S. Army Reserve, Support Center, 1815 N. Ft. Myer Dr., Rm. 501, Arlington, VA 22209-1005. TEL 703-696-3962. FAX 703-696-5300.
circ. 600,000. *3452*

AROGYA.
Kasturba Medical College Trust, Manipal, Department of Clinical Biochemistry, Editor - Arogyal, Manipal - 576 119, India. TEL 20060.
circ. 1,000. *3799*

ARRIVED.
Russ Moore & Associates Inc., 4151 Knob Dr., Ste. 200, Eagan, MN 55122. TEL 612-452-0571.
circ. 200,000. *4802*

ARROWHEAD.
Society of Archer-Antiquaries, c/o Alf Webb, 5 Park Court, Bathhurst Park Rd., Lydney, Glos. GL15 5HG, England. TEL 0594-843548. *4464*

ARS DECORATIVA.
Iparmuveszeti Muzeum, Hopp Ferenc Keletazsiai Muveszeti Muzeum, Ulloi ut 33-37, 1091 Budapest 9, Hungary. FAX 1-117-5880.
circ. 1,000. *3521*

ARS LYRICA: JOURNAL OF LYRICA.
Society for Word-Music Relations, 90 Church St., Guilford, CT 06437.
circ. 250. *3539*

ART AND DESIGN NEWS.
Boyd Publishing Co., Inc., Box 50110, Indianapolis, IN 46250-6100. TEL 317-849-6110. FAX 317-576-5859.
circ. 52,500. *313*

ART WORKERS GUILD. ANNUAL REPORT.
Art Workers Guild, 6 Queen Sq., London WC1N 3AR, England.
circ. 400. *315*

ARTS ALIVE!
Admar Associates - Theatrical Faces Inc., 548 N. New St., Bethlehem, PA 18018. TEL 215-758-8211. FAX 215-691-0234.
circ. 12,000. *4629*

ARTS & CRAFTS SHOWGUIDE.
A C N Publications, Box 104628, Jefferson City, MO 65110-4628. TEL 314-636-0491.
circ. 12,000. *353*

ARTS EN AUTO.
Wegener Tijl Tijdschriften Groep B.V., P.B. 9943, 1006 AP Amsterdam, Netherlands. TEL 020-5182828. FAX 020-5182843.
circ. 46,000. *4679*

ARZTRECHT.
Verlag fuer Arztrecht, Schinnrainstr. 15, 7500 Karlsruhe 41, Germany. TEL 0721-402904. *3078*

ASBESTOS WORKER.
International Association of Asbestos Workers, Machinists Bldg., 1300 Connecticut Ave., N.W., Washington, DC 20036. TEL 202-785-2388. *2580*

ASEGURADORES.
Colegios de Agentes y Corredores de Seguros, Consejo General, Nunez de Balboa 116, 28006 Madrid, Spain. FAX 2622702.
circ. 29,000. *2526*

ASHEVILLE REPORT.
Asheville Area Chamber of Commerce, Box 1010, Asheville, NC 28802. TEL 704-258-3858. FAX 704-251-0926. *807*

ASIA PACIFIC CHEMICALS.
Reed Business Publishing Group Quadrant House, The Quadrant, Sutton, Surrey SM2 5AS, England. TEL 081-652-3187. FAX 081-652-3375.
circ. 7,000. *1170*

ASIA PACIFIC FOODSERVICE PRODUCT NEWS.
Young - Conway Publications, 104 Fifth Ave., New York, NY 10011. TEL 212-206-7440. FAX 212-727-0919.
circ. 29,921. *2471*

ASIA TRAVEL TRADE.
Interasia Publications, Ltd., 190 Middle Rd., No.11-01 Fortune Centre, Singapore 0718, Singapore. TEL 339-7622. FAX 339-8521.
circ. 14,300. *4752*

ASIAN ADVERTISING AND MARKETING.
Travel & Trade Publishing (Asia) Ltd., 16-F, Capitol Centre, 5-19 Jardine's Bazaar, Causeway Bay, Hong Kong. TEL 890-30677. FAX 895-2378. *28*

ASIAN AND PACIFIC COUNCIL. FOOD AND FERTILIZER TECHNOLOGY CENTER. EXTENSION - TECHNICAL BULLETIN.
Asian and Pacific Council, Food and Fertilizer Technology Center, 14 Wenchow St., 5th Fl., Taipei, Taiwan, Republic of China. FAX 02-362-0478.
circ. 4,300. *77*

ASIAN ELECTRICITY.
Reed Business Publishing Group Quadrant House, The Quadrant, Sutton, Surrey SM2 5AS, England. TEL 081-652-8742. FAX 081-652-8986.
circ. 6,525. *1882*

ASIAN MEETINGS AND INCENTIVES.
Travel & Trade Publishing (Asia) Ltd., 16-F, Capitol Centre, 5-19 Jardine's Bazaar, Causeway Bay, Hong Kong. TEL 890-3067. FAX 895-2378.
circ. 12,000. *3390*

ASIAN PLASTICS NEWS.
Reed Business Publishing Group Quadrant House, The Quadrant, Sutton, Surrey SM2 5AS, England. TEL 081-652-8039. FAX 081-652-8986.
circ. 9,877. *3861*

ASPHALT.
Asphalt Institute, Box 14052, Lexington, KY 40512-4052. FAX 606-288-4999.
circ. 16,000. *4717*

ASSISTANT LIBRARIAN.
Association of Assistant Librarians, Sherwood Library, Spondon Street, Mansfield Road, Nottingham NG5 4AB, England. TEL 0602-606680. FAX 0602-504207.
circ. 10,500. *2745*

ASSOCIACAO PAULISTA DE CIRURGIOES DENTISTAS. JOURNAL.
Associacao Paulista de Cirurgioes Dentistas, Rua Humaita 389, 01321 Sao Paulo (SP), Brazil.
circ. 23,500. *3228*

ASSOCIATED ACCOUNTING FIRMS INTERNATIONAL NEWSLETTER.
Associated Accounting Firms International, 1612 K St., N.W., Ste. 900, Washington, DC 20006. TEL 202-463-7900. FAX 202-296-0741.
circ. 3,500. *747*

ASSOCIATED SCIENTIFIC AND TECHNICAL SOCIETIES OF SOUTH AFRICA. ANNUAL PROCEEDINGS.
Associated Scientific and Technical Societies of South Africa, P.O. Box 93480, Yeoville 2143, South Africa. TEL 011-487-1512. FAX 011-648-1876. *4300*

ASSOCIATED SOCIETY OF LOCOMOTIVE ENGINEERS AND FIREMEN. ANNUAL REPORT AND BALANCE SHEET.
Associated Society of Locomotive Engineers and Firemen, 9 Arkwright Rd., Hampstead, London NW3 6AB, England. *4707*

ASSOCIATION EDUCATION DIRECTOR.
American Society of Association Executives, 1575 I St., N.W., Washington, DC 20005. TEL 202-626-2723. FAX 202-408-9635.
circ. 900. *1003*

ASSOCIATION FOR PSYCHOANALYTIC MEDICINE. BULLETIN.
Association for Psychoanalytic Medicine, 4560 Delafield Ave., Bronx, NY 10471. TEL 212-874-0070.
circ. 1,500. *4012*

ASSOCIATION FRANCAISE POUR L'ETUDE DU SOL. SCIENCE DU SOL. BULLETIN.
Association Francaise pour l'Etude du Sol, 4 rue Redon, 78370 Plaisir, France.
circ. 1,300. *169*

ASSOCIATION OF AMERICAN LAW SCHOOLS. NEWSLETTER.
Association of American Law Schools, 1201 Connecticut Ave., N.W., Ste. 800, Washington, DC 20036. TEL 202-296-8851. *2601*

ASSOCIATION OF AMERICAN UNIVERSITY PRESSES DIRECTORY.
Association of American University Presses, Inc., 584 Broadway, Ste. 410, New York, NY 10012. TEL 212-941-6610. *4121*

ASSOCIATION OF CARIBBEAN UNIVERSITY RESEARCH AND INSTITUTIONAL LIBRARIES. CARTA INFORMATIVA DE A C U R I L.
Association of Caribbean University Research and Institutional Libraries, Box S, Estacion de la Universidad, San Juan, PR 00931. *2745*

ASSOCIATION OF LIFE INSURANCE MEDICAL DIRECTORS OF AMERICA. TRANSACTIONS.
Association of Life Insurance Medical Directors of America, Southeastern Head Office, Metropolitan Plaza, Tampa, FL 33607.
circ. 1,000. *2527*

ASSOCIATION OF MENTAL HEALTH ADMINISTRATORS. NEWSLETTER.
Association of Mental Health Administrators, 60 Revere Dr., Ste. 500, Northbrook, IL 60062. TEL 708-480-9626.
circ. 1,800. *4098*

ASSOCIATION OF NEW BRUNSWICK LAND SURVEYORS. ANNUAL REPORT.
Association of New Brunswick Land Surveyors, P.O. Box 22, Fredericton, N.B. E3B 4Y2, Canada. TEL 506-458-8266. FAX 506-458-8267.
circ. 250. *4145*

ASSOCOM REVIEW.
Association of Chambers of Commerce of South Africa, Box 91267, Auckland Park 2006, South Africa.
circ. 25,000. *807*

ASSURANTIE MAGAZINE.
Samsom BedrijfsInformatie, Postbus 4, Prinses Margrietlaan 3, 2404 MA Alphen aan den Rijn, Netherlands. TEL 01720-66571. FAX 01720-22892.
circ. 30,000. *2527*

ASSYRIAN STAR.
Assyrian-American National Federation, c/o Executive Secretary, 2935 Jessie Ct., San Jose, CA 95124. TEL 408-723-1646.
circ. 1,500. *1992*

ASU HYVIN.
Kauppiaitten Kustannus Oy, Rauhankatu 15, 00170 Helsinki 17, Finland.
circ. 123,431. *641*

AT THE CENTRE.
Canadian Centre for Occupational Health and Safety (CCOHS), 250 Main St., E., Hamilton, Ont. L8N 1H6, Canada. TEL 416-572-2981. FAX 416-572-2206.
circ. 7,000. *3615*

ATENEA.
Universidad de Puerto Rico, Faculty of Arts and Sciences, Mayaguez Campus, Mayaguez, PR 00681. FAX 809-834-3031.
circ. 800. *2859*

ATHLETIC DIRECTOR.
National Council of Secondary School Athletic Directors, 1900 Association Dr., Reston, VA 22091. TEL 703-476-3400. FAX 703-476-9527. *1744*

ATLANTA INQUIRER.
Atlanta Inquirer, Inc., 947 Martin Luther King Jr. Dr. N.W., Box 92367, Morris Brown Sta., Atlanta, GA 30314. TEL 404-523-6086.
circ. 50,000. *2221*

ATLANTA N O W NEWS.
National Organization for Women, Atlanta Chapter, Box 8556, Atlanta, GA 30306-0556. TEL 404-523-1227. FAX 404-688-0869.
circ. 700. *4837*

ATLANTA SMALL BUSINESS MONTHLY.
Media 3 Publications, Inc., 2342 Perimeter Park Dr., No. 100, Atlanta, GA 30341-1304. TEL 404-986-0545. FAX 404-986-0650.
circ. 25,000. *1113*

ATLANTIC PROVINCES BOOK REVIEW.
St. Mary's University, Halifax, N.S. B3H 3C3, Canada. TEL 902-420-5716.
circ. 50,000. *4121*

ATLAS HISTORIQUE DES VILLES DE FRANCE.
Editions du C N R S, 1 Place Aristide Briand, 92195 Meudon Cedex, France. TEL 1-45-34-75-50. FAX 1-46-26-28-49.
circ. 1,500. *2350*

ATMA JAYA RESEARCH CENTRE. SOCIO-RELIGIOUS RESEARCH REPORT.
Atma Jaya Research Centre, Jalan Jenderal Sudirman 57, P.O. Box 2639, Jakarta 10001, Indonesia. *4214*

ATOMIC DATA AND NUCLEAR DATA TABLES.
Academic Press, Inc., Journal Division, 1250 Sixth Ave., San Diego, CA 92101. TEL 619-230-1840. FAX 619-699-6800. *3846*

AU FIL DU RAIL.
Canadian National Railways, P.O. Box 8100, Montreal, Que. H3C 3N4, Canada. TEL 514-399-8041. FAX 514-399-5344.
circ. 16,700. *4707*

AUCTUS.
Medical University of South Carolina, Office of Development, 171 Ashley Ave., Charleston, SC 29425. TEL 803-792-4275. *1304*

AUDIO-DIGEST GASTROENTEROLOGY.
Audio-Digest Foundation 1577 E. Chevy Chase Dr., Glendale, CA 91206. TEL 213-245-8505. FAX 818-240-7379. *3266*

AUDIO-DIGEST INTERNAL MEDICINE.
Audio-Digest Foundation 1577 E. Chevy Chase Dr., Glendale, CA 91206. TEL 213-245-8505. FAX 818-240-7379. *3079*

AUDIO-DIGEST OBSTETRICS - GYNECOLOGY.
Audio-Digest Foundation 1577 E. Chevy Chase Dr., Glendale, CA 91206. TEL 213-245-8505. FAX 818-240-7379. *3289*

AUDIO-DIGEST OPHTHALMOLOGY.
Audio-Digest Foundation 1577 E. Chevy Chase Dr., Glendale, CA 91206. TEL 213-245-8505. FAX 818-240-7379. *3298*

AUDIO-DIGEST ORTHOPAEDICS.
Audio-Digest Foundation 1577 E. Chevy Chase Dr., Glendale, CA 91206. TEL 213-245-8505. FAX 818-240-7379. *3307*

AUDIO-DIGEST UROLOGY.
Audio-Digest Foundation 1577 E. Chevy Chase Dr., Glendale, CA 91206. TEL 213-245-8505. FAX 818-240-7379. *3387*

DIE AUSLESE.
Dr. Krueger Verlag, Am Schiessberg 19, 6348 Herborn, Germany. TEL 02772-2427.
circ. 21,000. *4164*

AUSTIN GREENSHEET.
Gordon Publications (Austin), Box 140721, Austin, TX 78714-0721. TEL 512-454-1003. *1502*

AUSTIN HEALTH & FITNESS.
D D J & L Publishing Inc., Box 1343, Round Rock, TX 78680. TEL 512-255-1512.
circ. 50,000. *3799*

AUSTRALIAN ABORIGINAL STUDIES.
Australian Institute of Aboriginal and Torres Strait Islander Studies, P.O. Box 553, Canberra, A.C.T. 2601, Australia. FAX 062-497310. *235*

AUSTRALIAN APPAREL MANUFACTURER.
Yaffa Publishing Group, 17-21 Bellevue St., Surry Hills, N.S.W. 2010, Australia. TEL 02-281-2333. FAX 02-281-2750.
circ. 2,939. *4616*

AUSTRALIAN BEAUTY COUNTER.
Reed Business Publishing Pty. Ltd., 1-5 Railway St., Chatswood, N.S.W 20672010, Australia. TEL 02-372-5222. FAX 02-419-7533.
circ. 8,145. *375*

AUSTRALIAN BUILDING NEWS.
Sydney Building Information Centre Ltd., 525 Elizabeth St., Surry Hills, N.S.W. 2010, Australia. TEL 02-318-2988. FAX 02-319-1890.
circ. 17,505. *601*

AUSTRALIAN DEFENCE FORCE JOURNAL.
Department of Defence, Board of Management, Canberra A.C.T. 2600, Australia. FAX 06-2510991.
circ. 17,500. *3452*

AUSTRALIAN FOREST RESOURCES.
Australian Bureau of Agricultural and Resource Economics, G.P.O. Box 1563, Canberra, A.C.T. 2601, Australia. TEL 06-2469111.
circ. 700. *2096*

AUSTRALIAN HARDWARE JOURNAL.
Glenvale Publications Pty. Ltd., 4 Palmer Court, Mount Waverley, Vic. 3149, Australia. TEL 03-544-2233. FAX 03-543-1150.
circ. 5,173. *641*

AUSTRALIAN JAYCEE.
Australian Jaycees, 6 Thesiger Court, Deakin, A.C.T. 2600, Australia. TEL 062-81-1066.
circ. 3,000. *1296*

AUSTRALIAN JEWISH NEWS (DARLINGHURST).
Australian Jewish Press Pty. Limited, c/o Susan Bures, Ed., 146 Darlinghurst Rd., Darlinghurst, N.S.W. 2010, Australia. TEL 02-360-5100. FAX 02-332-4207. *1992*

AUSTRALIAN JOURNAL OF PHYSIOTHERAPY.
Australian Physiotherapy Association, 141 St. Georges Rd., N. Fitzroy, Vic. 3068, Australia. TEL 03-482-1044. FAX 03-482-2348.
circ. 8,300. *3080*

AUSTRALIAN PAINT AND PANEL.
Yaffa Publishing Group, 17-21 Bellevue St., Surry Hills, N.S.W. 2010, Australia. TEL 02-281-2333. FAX 02-281-2750.
circ. 4,644. *3652*

AUSTRALIAN PRESCRIBER.
Commonwealth Department of Community Health, Housing and Services, P.O. Box 100, Woden, A.C.T. 2606, Australia. TEL 06-289-7038.
circ. 68,000. *3718*

AUSTRALIAN TRADER.
Exportad Pty. Ltd., 115-117 Cooper St, Surry Hills, N.S.W. 2010, Australia.
circ. 5,500. *900*

AUTO AGE.
M H West, Inc. 6633 Odessa Ave., Van Nuys, CA 91406. TEL 818-997-0644. FAX 818-997-1058.
circ. 33,501. *4679*

AUTO C A D WORLD.
12416 Hymeadow Dr., Austin, TX 78750-1896. TEL 512-250-9023. FAX 512-331-3900.
circ. 29,000. *1426*

AUTO-JOURNAL.
Societe EDP, 8-10, rue Pierre Brossolette, 92300 Levallois Perret, France. FAX 40-87-42-37.
circ. 267,000. *4680*

AUTO MERCHANDISING NEWS.
Mortimer Communications, Inc., Box 1185, Fairfield, CT 06430. TEL 203-384-9323. FAX 203-375-1463.
circ. 23,224. *4680*

AUTO RENTAL FLEET.
Bobit Publishing Company, 2512 Artesia Blvd., Redondo Beach, CA 90278. TEL 310-376-8788. FAX 310-376-9043.
circ. 15,000. *1033*

AUTOFACHMANN.
Vogel-Verlag und Druck KG, Max-Planck-Str. 7-9, Postfach 6740, 8700 Wuerzburg 1, Germany. TEL 0931-418-0.
circ. 76,812. *4681*

AUTOMATISERING GIDS.
Stam Tijdschriften B.V., Postbus 235, 2280 AE Rijswjk, Netherlands. TEL 070-3988100. FAX 070-988276.
circ. 80,000. *1448*

AUTOMOTIVE BODY REPAIR NEWS.
Chilton Co., Chilton Way, Radnor, PA 19089. TEL 215-964-4000. FAX 215-964-4981.
circ. 60,503. *4682*

AUTOMOTIVE ENGINEER.
Institute of Automotive Mechanical Engineers (Inc.), 227 Great North Rd., Fivedock, N.S.W. 2046, Australia. TEL 02-713-4711. FAX 02-713-2671.
circ. 24,800. *4683*

AUTOMOTIVE FLEET.
Bobit Publishing Company, 2512 Artesia Blvd., Redondo Beach, CA 90278. TEL 310-376-8788. FAX 310-376-9043.
circ. 24,000. *4683*

AUTOMOTIVE REBUILDER.
Babcox Publications, 11 S. Forge St., Box 1810, Akron, OH 44309-1810. TEL 216-535-6117. FAX 216-535-0874.
circ. 22,402. *4683*

AUTOMOVIL DE VENEZUELA.
Ortiz & Asociados s.r.l., Calle Sorbona, Edif. Marta, Piso 1, Ofic. 18, Colinas de Bello Monte, Caracas, Venezuela. TEL 58-2-751-1355. FAX 58-2-751-11-22.
circ. 7,500. *4684*

AUTONEWS.
News Publishers Ltd., 4th Fl., Norwich Union Bldg., Mama Ngina St., Nairobi, Kenya.
circ. 15,000. *4684*

AUTOPISTA.
Luike - Motorpress, Ancora 40, 28045 Madrid, Spain. TEL 91-3470100. FAX 91-3470135.
circ. 90,000. *4684*

AVENTURA LIFESTYLES.
G S & J Publishing, Inc., 5212 N.W. 54th Ave., Pompano Beach, FL 33073-3755. TEL 305-977-5901.
circ. 15,000. *2221*

AVIATION EQUIPMENT MAINTENANCE.
Delta Communications, Inc. (Chicago) 400 N. Michigan Ave., Ste. 1200, Chicago, IL 60611. TEL 312-222-2000. FAX 312-222-2026.
circ. 37,488. *47*

AVIONICS.
Phillips Publishing, Inc., 7811 Montrose Rd., Potomac, MD 20854. TEL 301-340-2100. FAX 301-309-3847. *48*

AXIAL.
Editorial Axial, Apartado Postal 62, Merida, Venezuela.
circ. 1,000. *2988*

AYIN L'TZION.
Zionist Organization of America, Masada Youth Movement, Jacob and Libby Goodman Z.O.A. House, 4 E. 34th St., New York, NY 10016. TEL 212-481-1500.
circ. 2,500. *1992*

AZ.
Trend Magazines, Inc., P.O. Box 611, St. Petersburg, FL 33731-0611. TEL 602-230-1117.
circ. 60,000. *2221*

AZALEA CITY NEWS & REVIEW.
Box 369, Bayou La Batre, AL 36509-0369.
circ. 10,000. *2221*

AZIONE COOPERATIVA.
Comitato Regionale Lombardo delle Cooperative, Via Palmanova 22, 20132 Milan, Italy. *4399*

B C DAIRY DIRECTORY.
DoMac Publications Ltd., 207 W. Hastings St., Ste.810, Vancouver, B.C. V6B 1J8, Canada. TEL 604-684-8255. FAX 604-684-1928.
circ. 1,600. *1122*

B C T C - C A M R A S O - IN-SITE.
British Carpet Technical Centre, Cleaning & Maintenance Research & Services Organization, Wira House, West Park, Ring Rd., Leeds LS16 6QL, England. TEL 0532-781381. FAX 0532-780386. *1281*

B G F BULLETIN.
Banana Growers Federation Co-operative Ltd., P.O. Box 31, Murwillumbah, N.S.W. 2484, Australia. TEL 066-722488. FAX 066-724868.
circ. 2,000. *170*

B.G. RUDOLPH LECTURES IN JUDAIC STUDIES.
Syracuse University, Jewish Studies Program, Syracuse, NY 13244-1170. TEL 315-443-3861. FAX 315-443-5390.
circ. 500. *4221*

B I F U REPORT.
Banking Insurance & Finance Union, Sheffield House, 1B Amity Grove, Raynes Park, London SW20 OLG, England. TEL 01-946-9151. FAX 01-879-3728.
circ. 112,000. *760*

B L E S M A G.
M & B (Felstead) Ltd., 185-187 High Rd., Chadwell Heath, Essex RM6 6NA, England. TEL 01-590-1124.
circ. 10,000. *4399*

B M MAGAZINE.
British Museum Society, Great Russell St., London WC1B 3DG, England. TEL 071-637 9983.
circ. 7,000. *3522*

B N A C COMMUNICATOR.
B N A Communications, Inc. 9439 Key West Ave., Rockville, MD 20850-3396. TEL 301-948-0540. FAX 301-948-2085.
circ. 150,000. *647*

B N NEWS.
Burlington Northern Railroad, 2900 Continental Plaza, 777 Main St., Fort Worth, TX 76102. TEL 817-878-3046. FAX 817-878-7997.
circ. 55,000. *4708*

B 70.
Bibliotekarforbundet, Lindevangs Alle 2, 2000 Frederiksberg, Denmark. TEL 38-881770. FAX 38-883201.
circ. 6,067. *2746*

BABSON BULLETIN.
Babson College, Babson Park, MA 02157-0310. TEL 617-239-4269. FAX 617-239-5231.
circ. 29,000. *1304*

BACKGROUND.
Ministry of Municipal Affairs, 777 Bay St., 13th Fl., Toronto, Ont. M5G 2E5, Canada. TEL 416-585-6255. *4084*

BADMINTON SPORTING DIARY.
Frank Smythson Ltd., 44 New Bond St., London W1Y ODE, England. TEL 01-629-8558. FAX 01-495-6111.
circ. 3,000. *4465*

BAECKER - WERK.
Baecker - Innung Nuerenberg, Ostendstr. 149-151, D-8500 Nuerenberg 50, Germany.
circ. 3,000. *2086*

BAENDER, BLECHE, ROHRE.
Vogel-Verlag und Druck KG, Max-Planck-Str. 7-9, Postfach 67 40, 8700 Wuerzburg 1, Germany. TEL 0931-418-0.
circ. 8,536. *3402*

BAHAMAS. CHAMBER OF COMMERCE. ANNUAL DIRECTORY.
Chamber of Commerce, Attn: Executive Dir., P.O. Box N665, Nassau, Bahamas. TEL 809-322-2145. FAX 809-322-4649.
circ. 10,000. *808*

BAHNENGOLFER.
Deutscher Bahnengolf-Verband, Postfach 1213, 2000 Schenefeld, Germany. TEL 04101-41861.
circ. 1,300. *4500*

BAKING BUYER.
Sosland Publishing Company, 4800 Main St., Ste. 100, Kansas City, MO 64112. TEL 816-756-1000. FAX 816-756-0494.
circ. 30,000. *2087*

BALDE BRANCO.
Cooperativa Central de Laticinios do Estado de Sao Paulo, Rua Gomes Cardim 532, 03050 Sao Paulo, SP, Brazil.
circ. 30,000. *198*

BALLET-HOO.
Royal Winnipeg Ballet, 380 Graham Ave., Winnipeg, Man. R3C 4K2, Canada. TEL 204-956-0183. FAX 204-943-1994.
circ. 12,000. *1528*

BALTIMORE COUNTY MUSTER.
Sons of the American Revolution, Maryland Society, 10605 Lakespring Way, Hunt Valley, MD 21030. TEL 301-628-2490.
circ. 200. *2400*

BALTIMORE SPORTS FOCUS.
Capital Sports Focus, Inc., 1432 Fenwick Ln., Silver Spring, MD 20910-3323. TEL 301-587-9351. FAX 301-587-6347.
circ. 30,000. *4466*

BANCA Y COMERCIO.
Escuela Bancaria y Comercial, Paseo de la Reforma 202, Mexico 06600 D.F., Mexico. FAX 905-546-0326.
circ. 6,500. *760*

BANCO DO BRASIL. BOLETIM DE INFORMACAO AO PESSOAL.
Banco do Brasil S.A., Departamento Geral de Selecao e Desenvolvimento do Pessoal, Setor Bancario Sul Lote 32, Quadra 4, CP 562, Brazil, DF.
circ. 100,000. *762*

BANDARI.
Kenya Ports Authority, P.O. Box 95009, Mombasa, Kenya.
circ. 12,000. *4647*

BANDERSNATCH.
Lewis Carroll Society, 69 Ashby Rd., Woodville, Burton-on-Trent, Staffs, England.
circ. 350. *2898*

BANK DIRECTORY OF NEW ENGLAND.
Shawmut Bank, N.A., Correspondent Banking Group, One Federal St., Boston, MA 02211. TEL 617-292-3823. FAX 617-292-4417. *763*

BANK FOR INTERNATIONAL SETTLEMENTS. ANNUAL REPORT.
Bank for International Settlements, 7 Centralbahnstr., Case Postale 262, CH-4002 Basel, Switzerland. *763*

BANK MELLI IRAN. BULLETIN.
Bank Melli Iran, Ferdowsi Ave., P.O. Box 11365-171, Teheran, Iran. TEL 021-3231. *763*

BANK NEGARA MALAYSIA. ANNUAL REPORT.
Bank Negara Malaysia, P.O. Box 10922, Jalan Lumpur, Malaysia. TEL 2988044. FAX 2912990. *845*

BANK NEGARA MALAYSIA. BULLETIN EKONOMI SUKU TAHUNAN - QUARTERLY ECONOMIC BULLETIN.
Bank Negara Malaysia, P.O. Box 10922, Jalan Kuching, 50929 Kuala Lumpur, Malaysia. TEL 03-2988044. FAX 03-2912990. *845*

BANK NEGARA MALAYSIA. STATISTICAL BULLETIN.
Bank Negara Malaysia, P.O. Box 10922, Jalan Kuching, 50929 Kuala Jumpur, Malaysia. TEL 2988044. FAX 2912990. *845*

BANK SYSTEMS & TECHNOLOGY.
Miller Freeman Inc. (New York) 1515 Broadway, New York, NY 10036. TEL 212-869-1300. FAX 212-302-6273.
circ. 25,000. *765*

BANKING SOFTWARE REVIEW.
I C P, Inc., Box 40946, Indianapolis, IN 46240-0946. TEL 317-844-7461. FAX 317-574-0571.
circ. 15,000. *805*

BAPTIST PROGRESS.
Baptist Missionary Association of Texas, Box 2085, Waxahachie, TX 75165. TEL 214-923-0756. FAX 214-923-2679.
circ. 15,000. *4230*

BAPTIST PUBLIC RELATIONS ASSOCIATION NEWSLETTER.
Baptist Public Relations Association, Box 347, Brentwood, TN 37027. TEL 615-373-2255. *4230*

BAPTIST UNION OF WESTERN CANADA. YEARBOOK.
Baptist Union of Western Canada, 838 11th Ave., S.W., Ste. 202, Calgary, Alta. T2R 0E5, Canada. TEL 403-234-9044. FAX 403-269-6755.
circ. 700. *4230*

BAR GIORNALE.
Pubblistampa Edizioni Periodici S.r.l., C E P Communication, Via Aurispa 7, 20122 Milan, Italy. TEL 02-58310026. FAX 02-58310008.
circ. 273,000. *2472*

BARCHE E CATALOGO.
Gruppo Editoriale Commerciale, Via G. Galilei, 6, 20124 Milan, Italy. TEL 02-29002410. FAX 02-6552271.
circ. 35,000. *4522*

BARLEY GENETICS NEWSLETTER.
American Malting Barley Association, Inc., 735 N. Water St., Ste. 908, Milwaukee, WI 53202.
circ. 600. *495*

BARS AND STRIPES.
Detroit Police Lieutenants & Sergeants Association, 28 W. Adams St., No. 1308, Detroit, MI 48226.
circ. 2,900. *1510*

BASEBALL HOBBY NEWS.
4540 Kearny Villa Rd., Ste. 215, San Diego, CA 92123. TEL 619-565-2848. FAX 619-565-6608.
circ. 91,000. *4500*

BASILICATA.
Basilicata Editrice, Via Ridola 20, Casella Postale 70, Matera 75100, Italy.
circ. 10,000. *3875*

BASSE NORMANDIE AUTOMOBILE.
Chambre Syndicale Nationale du Commerce et de la Reparation Automobile, Secteur Regional Basse-Normandie, 4 rue Pasteur, B.P. No. 7, 14011 Caen Cedex, France.
circ. 1,000. *4685*

BATTELLE TODAY.
Battelle Memorial Institute, Communications Office, Attn: Harry R. Templeton, Ed., 505 King Ave., Columbus, OH 43201. TEL 614-424-7818.
circ. 36,000. *4594*

BATTLER COLUMNS.
Alderson-Broaddus College, Philippi, WV 26416. TEL 304-457-1700. FAX 304-457-1700.
circ. 1,200. *1304*

BAUEN.
Fachschriften Verlag GmbH, Hoehenstr. 17, Postfach 1329, 7012 Fellbach, Germany. TEL 0711-5206-1. FAX 0711-5281424.
circ. 110,000. *602*

BAUEN UND FERTIGHAUS.
Fachschriften Verlag GmbH, Hoehenstr. 17, Postfach 1329, 7012 Fellbach-Stuttgart, Germany. TEL 0711-5206-1. FAX 0711-5281424.
circ. 125,000. *602*

BAUMARKT.
Bertelsmann Fachzeitschriften GmbH, Postfach 6666, 4830 Guetersloh 100, Germany. TEL 05241-80-2179. FAX 05241-73055. *602*

BAUMASCHINE - BAUGERAET - BAUSTELLE.
Technopress Fachzeitschriften Verlagsgesellschaft m.b.H., Felix-Mottl-Str. 12, A-1190 Vienna, Austria.
circ. 15,000. *602*

DAS BAUZENTRUM.
Verlag das Beispiel GmbH, Spreestr. 9, 6100 Darmstadt 1, Germany. TEL 06151-33557. FAX 06151-313089.
circ. 35,000. *295*

BAY AREA REPORTER.
Benro Enterprises, Inc., 395 Ninth St., San Francisco, CA 94103-3831. TEL 415-861-5019. FAX 415-861-6534.
circ. 35,000. *2451*

BAYERISCH-SCHWAEBISCHE WIRTSCHAFT.
Industrie- und Handelskammer fuer Augsburg und Schwaben, Stettenstr. 1-3, 8900 Augsburg, Germany. FAX 0821-3162-323.
circ. 19,000. *808*

BAYLOR DENTAL JOURNAL.
Baylor College of Dentistry, Office of Alumni and Public Relations, 3302 Gaston Ave., Dallas, TX 75246. TEL 214-828-8214. FAX 214-828-8346.
circ. 5,000. *3229*

DE BAZUIN.
Stichting De Bazuin, P.O. Box 2456, 3500 GL Utrecht, Netherlands.
circ. 5,000. *4164*

BEACH CONSERVATION.
Queensland Beach Protection Authority, P.O. Box 155, North Quay, Bris Bane, Qld. 4002, Australia. FAX 07-221-0768.
circ. 2,500. *1484*

BEACON (GEORGIA).
Georgia Southern University, Department of Foreign Languages, Statesboro, GA 30460. TEL 912-681-5278.
circ. 1,000. *1618*

THE BEACON REVIEW.
Century Publications, Inc., 1805 S. Bellaire, Ste. 235, Denver, CO 80222. TEL 303-692-8940.
circ. 30,000. *2270*

BEALE'S LETTER.
Colin Beale, Ed. & Pub., 3 Bentall Centre, P.O. Box 48651, Vancouver, B.C. V7X 1A3, Canada.
circ. 300. *1072*

BEAN PROGRAM ANNUAL REPORT.
Centro Internacional de Agricultura Tropical, Bean Program, Apdo. Aereo 6713, Cali, Colombia. TEL 57-23-675050. FAX 57-23-647243.
circ. 900. *78*

BEDFORD INSTITUTE OF OCEANOGRAPHY. SCIENCE REVIEW.
Department of Fisheries and Oceans, Bedford Institute of Oceanography, Dartmouth, N.S. B2Y 4A2, Canada. TEL 902-426-4093. FAX 902-426-2256.
circ. 5,000. *1602*

BEDRIJFSDOCUMENTAIRE.
Koggeschip Vakbladen B.V., P.O. Box 1198, 1000 BD Amsterdam, Netherlands. TEL 020-916666. FAX 020-960396.
circ. 110,000. *1003*

BEDROOM.
Bobit Publishing Company, 2512 Artesia Blvd., Redondo Beach, CA 90278. TEL 310-376-8788. FAX 310-376-9043.
circ. 21,000. *2557*

BEEF.
Intertec Publishing Corp., Webb Division, 7900 Int'l Dr., Minneapolis, MN 55425. TEL 612-851-4710. FAX 612-851-4601.
circ. 105,446. *212*

BEER CAN COLLECTORS NEWS REPORT.
Beer Can Collectors of America, 747 Merus Ct., Fenton, MO 63026-2092. TEL 314-343-6486.
circ. 400. *2434*

BEERMAT MAGAZINE.
British Beer-mat Collectors Society (BBCS), c/o B.W. West, 10 Coombe Hill Crescent, Thame, Oxfordshire OX9 2EH, England.
circ. 600. *2434*

BEGONIAN.
American Begonia Society, Box 231129, Encinitas, CA 92023-1129. TEL 707-764-5407.
circ. 2,000. *2122*

BEHAVIORAL NEUROPSYCHIATRY.
Behavioral Neuropsychiatry Medical Publishers, Inc., 61 East 86th St., New York, NY 10028.
circ. 25,000. *3331*

BEIERSDORF JOURNAL.
Beiersdorf AG, Unnastr. 48, 2000 Hamburg 20, Germany. FAX 040-5693434. *1072*

BEKLAEDNADSFOLKET.
Beklaednadsarbetarnes Foerbund, P.O. Box 1120, 111 81 Stockholm, Sweden. FAX 08-242354.
circ. 31,000. *2580*

BELGIAN BUSINESS MAGAZINE.
Diligentia Business Press, Hulstlaan 42, B-1170 Brussels, Belgium. TEL 02-673-81-70. FAX 02-660-36-00.
circ. 31,500. *1072*

BELGIUM. RIJKSSTATION VOOR LANDBOUWTECHNIEK. MEDEDELINGEN.
Rijksstation voor Landbouwtechniek, Van Gansberghelaan 115, B-9820 Merelbeke, Belgium. FAX 091-52-15-83. *79*

BELOIT MAGAZINE.
Beloit College, 700 College St., Beloit, WI 53511. TEL 608-363-2828. FAX 608-363-2870.
circ. 22,000. *1304*

BELSER KUNSTQUARTAL.
Chr. Belser Verlag, Falkertstr. 73, 7000 Stuttgart, Germany.
circ. 33,000. *3522*

BERGEN COUNTY DENTAL SOCIETY. NEWSLETTER.
Bergen County Dental Society, 1060 Main St., River Edge, NJ 07661.
circ. 700. *3229*

BERLINER AERZTEBLATT.
CB Verlag Carl Boldt, Baseler Str. 80, 1000 Berlin 45, Germany. FAX 030-8339125.
circ. 18,500. *3081*

BEST WISHES.
Family Communications, Inc., 37 Hanna Ave., Toronto, Ont. M6K 1X1, Canada.
circ. 158,000. *1233*

BETON.
FeBe - Federation de l'Industrie du Beton, Bd. Aug. Reyers 207-209, B-1040 Brussels, Belgium. TEL 02-735-80-15. FAX 02-734-77-94.
circ. 8,500. *603*

BETRIEBLICHE AUSBILDUNGSPRAXIS.
Verlag und Vertriebsgesellschaft mbH, Breite Str. 69, Postfach 8232, 4000 Duesseldorf 1, Germany.
circ. 1,800. *3403*

DER BETRIEBSLEITER.
Verlag fuer Technik und Wirtschaft GmbH & Co., Lise-Meitner-Str. 2, Postfach 4029, 6500 Mainz, Germany.
circ. 17,000. *1003*

BETTER MANAGEMENT.
Genus, Westmere Dr., Crewe, Cheshire CW1 12D. TEL 0270-536585. FAX 0270-536601.
circ. 40,000. *198*

BETTER ROADS.
William O. Dannhausen, Pub., Box 558, Park Ridge, IL 60068. TEL 708-693-7710. FAX 708-696-3445. *1862*

BETWEEN THE LEAVES.
Queensland Forest Service, G.P.O. Box 944, Brisbane, Qld. 4001, Australia. TEL 07-234-0157.
circ. 5,000. *2096*

BEVERAGE DIGEST.
Tomac & Company, Inc., Box 238, Old Greenwich, CT 06870. TEL 203-358-8198. FAX 203-327-9761. *378*

BEVERAGE WORLD EN ESPANOL.
Keller International Publishing Corporation, 150 Great Neck Rd., Great Neck, NY 11021. TEL 516-829-9210.
circ. 7,100. *379*

BHABHA ATOMIC RESEARCH CENTRE. NUCLEAR PHYSICS DIVISION. ANNUAL REPORT.
Bhabha Atomic Research Centre, Trombay, Bombay 400085, India. *3846*

BIBEL UND GEMEINDE.
Bibelbund e.V., Breite Str. 16, 5300 Bonn, Germany.
circ. 3,500. *4165*

BIBLIOGRAPHIA SCIENTIAE NATURALIS HELVETICA.
Bibliotheque Nationale Suisse, Hallwylstr. 15, CH-3003 Berne, Switzerland.
circ. 700. *4354*

BIBLIOGRAPHICAL SOCIETY OF CANADA. BULLETIN.
Bibliographical Society of Canada, P.O. Box 575, Station "P", Toronto, Ont. M5S 2T1, Canada.
circ. 400. *392*

BIBLIOGRAPHIE ANNUELLE DE L'HISTOIRE DE FRANCE.
Editions du C N R S, 1 Place Aristide Briand, 92195 Meudon Cedex, France. TEL 1-45-34-75-50. FAX 1-46-26-28-49.
circ. 1,500. *2327*

BIBLIOGRAPHY ON SMOKING AND HEALTH.
U.S. Office on Smoking and Health, National Center for Chronic Disease Prevention and Health Promotion, Centers for Disease Control, MS K-12, 1600 Clifton Rd., N.E., Atlanta, GA 30333. *3811*

BIBLIOTECA "JOSE ARTIGAS". BOLETIN.
Biblioteca "Jose Artigas", 25 de Mayo 609, Montevideo, Uruguay.
circ. 300. *393*

BIBLIOTEKSBLADET.
Sveriges Allmaenna Biblioteksfoerening, Box 3127, 103 62 Stockholm, Sweden. TEL 08-7230082. FAX 08-7230038.
circ. 5,206. *2747*

BIENVENIDOS A MIAMI.
Welcome Publications, Inc., Box 630-518, 1751 NE 162nd St., Miami, FL 33163. TEL 305-944-9444.
circ. 13,000. *4802*

BINDEN EN BOUWEN.
Sint-Bernardinuscollege, Akerstraat 95, Heerlen, Netherlands.
circ. 2,000. *1305*

BINGO NEWS & GAMING HI-LITES.
Bingo Hi-Lites Ltd., Box 3364, Leduc, Alta. T9E 6M2, Canada. TEL 403-986-5088. FAX 403-986-5089.
circ. 24,300. *1502*

BIOLOGIA PESQUERA.
Universidad Catolica de Chile, Sede Regional Talcahuano, Casilla 127, Talcahuano, Chile. FAX 056-041-542134. *2037*

BIOTECH BUYER'S GUIDE.
American Chemical Society, 1155 16th St., N.W., Washington, DC 20036. TEL 202-872-4363. FAX 202-872-4615.
circ. 65,000. *488*

BIOWORLD ONLINE.
Io Publishing, 217 South B St., San Mateo, CA 94401. TEL 800-879-8790. FAX 415-696-6590. *433*

BIRMINGHAM & WARWICKSHIRE ARCHAEOLOGICAL SOCIETY. TRANSACTIONS.
Birmingham & Warwickshire Archaeological Society, Birmingham & Midland Institute, Margaret Street, Birmingham B3 3BS, England.
circ. 450. *267*

BIRMINGHAM BAR ASSOCIATION. BULLETIN.
Birmingham Bar Association, 109 N. 20th St., Birmingham, AL 35203. TEL 205-251-8006.
circ. 1,600. *2605*

BIRTH NOTES.
Association for Childbirth at Home, International (A C H I), 166 S. Louise, Glendale, CA 91205. TEL 213-667-0839.
circ. 10,000. *3290*

BLACK BAG.
Galenicals Society, Bristol University Medical School, Dolphin House, Bristol Royal Infirmary, Bristol 2, England.
circ. 1,000. *3083*

BLACK EMPLOYMENT AND EDUCATION.
Hamdani, Inc., 2625 Piedmont Rd., Ste. 56-282, Atlanta, GA 30324. TEL 404-469-5891.
circ. 150,000. *1994*

BLACKJACK FORUM.
R G E Publishing, 414 Santa Clara Ave., Oakland, CA 94610. TEL 510-465-6452. FAX 510-652-4330. *4466*

BLACKPOOL HOTEL & GUEST HOUSE ASSOCIATION. JOURNAL.
Blackpool Hotel and Guest House Association Ltd., 87a Coronation St., Blackpool FY1 4PD, Lancastershire, England. *2472*

BLOMSTER-BRANSCHEN.
Swedish Florist's Association, Box 808, S-161 24 Bromma, Sweden. FAX 08-269606.
circ. 3,000. *2141*

BLUE PITCHER.
Unicorn Press, Inc., 200 E. Bessemer Ave, Greensboro, NC 27401-1416. TEL 919-852-0281.
circ. 1,000. *2989*

BLUEPRINT.
Dorset Police, Force Headquarters, Winfrith, Nr. Dorchester DT2 8DZ, England. FAX 0305-253987. *1511*

BLUES AT THE FOUNDATION.
Blues Foundation, 174 Beale St., Memphis, TN 38103. TEL 901-527-2583. FAX 901-529-4030.
circ. 3,000. *3542*

BOATING BUSINESS AND MARINE TRADE NEWS.
Rushton Marine Press Ltd., Woodside, Burnhams Rd., Leatherhead, Surrey KT23 3BA, England. TEL 0372-453316. FAX 0372-459974.
circ. 7,000. *4523*

LA BOBINA - NOTIVEST.
Bobbin Blenheim Media Corp., 1110 Shop Rd., Box 1986, Columbia, SC 29202. TEL 803-771-7500. FAX 803-799-1461.
circ. 20,329. *1283*

BODYSHOP BUSINESS.
Babcox Publications, 11 S. Forge St., Box 1810, Akron, OH 44309-1810. TEL 216-535-6117. FAX 216-535-0874.
circ. 54,386. *4685*

BOERN & UNGE.
Fagbladet Boern og Unge, Blegdamsvej 124, 4, DK-2100 Copenhagen Oe, Denmark. TEL 35-43-10-00. FAX 35-43-22-99.
circ. 32,697. *1618*

BOERNETEATERAVISEN.
Teatercentrum i Danmark, Frederiksborggade 20, DK-1360 Copenhagen K, Denmark. TEL 33-156900. FAX 33-13-14-39.
circ. 14,000. *4630*

BOGG.
Bogg Publications, 422 N. Cleveland St., Arlington, VA 22201. TEL 703-243-6019.
circ. 750. *2989*

BOLETIM U E R J.
Universidade do Estado do Rio de Janeiro, R. Sao Francisco Xavier, 524 sala T-01, CEP 20550 Maracana, Rio de Janeiro, Brazil.
circ. 2,000. *1618*

BOLETIN DE ARQUEOLOGIA MEDIEVAL.
Asociacion Espanola de Arqueologia Medieval, Apdo. Postal 50449, Breton de los Herreros 59, 30 Izq., 28080 Madrid, Spain.
circ. 558. *267*

BOLETIN HIDROLOGICO.
Instituto Costarricense de Electricidad (ICE), Apto. 10032, San Jose, Costa Rica. *1597*

BOLETIN I I E.
Instituto de Investigaciones Electricas, Division de Informacion Tecnologica y Desarrollo Profesional, Liebnitz 14, 3 piso, Col. Anzures, Del. M. Hidalgo, 11590, Mexico, D.F., Mexico. FAX 73-189-854.
circ. 5,500. *1883*

BOLETIN OFICIAL ECLESIASTICO DEL ARZOBISPADO CASTRENSE DE ESPANA.
Arrolispado Castrense de Orpana, Nuncio 13, 28005 Madrid, Spain. *4166*

BOMBUS.
Verein fuer Naturwissenschaftliche Heimatforschung zu Hamburg e.V., Zoologisches Institut und Museum, Martin-Luther-King-Platz 3, 2000 Hamburg 13, Germany.
circ. 300. *529*

BOND.
Lutheran Brotherhood, 625 Fourth Ave. S., Minneapolis, MN 55415. TEL 612-340-7000.
circ. 540,000. *4231*

BONDINGS.
New Ways Ministry, 4012 29th St., Mt. Rainier, MD 20712. TEL 301-277-5674.
circ. 2,000. *2451*

BOOK ALERT (BRIDGEWATER).
Baker and Taylor Books, 652 E. Main St., Box 6920, Bridgewater, NJ 08807-0920. TEL 908-218-0400. FAX 908-218-3980.
circ. 20,000. *4122*

BOOKENDS.
Friends of the Reading-Berks Public Libraries, Box 227, Wernersville, PA 19565. TEL 215-678-6480.
circ. 2,000. *2749*

BOOKER FOOD MAGAZINE.
C P R Publishing, Northern Rock House, 20 Market Place, Guisborough, Cleveland TS14 6HF, England. TEL 0287-639111. FAX 0287-637201.
circ. 80,000. *2062*

BOOKMARK (MOSCOW).
University of Idaho Library, Moscow, ID 83843. TEL 208-885-6584. FAX 208-885-6817.
circ. 1,100. *2749*

BOOKS AND LIBRARIES AT THE UNIVERSITY OF KANSAS.
University of Kansas Libraries, Lawrence, KS 66045. TEL 913-864-4334. *2749*

BOOTS NEWS.
Boots Co. PLC, 1 Thane Rd. W., Nottingham NG2 3AA, England. TEL 0602-592365. FAX 0602-592727.
circ. 56,000. *3719*

BORD IASCAIGH MHARA. TUARASCAIL AGUS CUNTAISI.
Irish Sea Fisheries Board, P.O. Box 12, Crofton Rd., Dun Laoghaire, Co. Dublin, Ireland. TEL 01-2841544. FAX 01-2841123.
circ. 3,500. *2037*

BOSCH TECHNISCHE BERICHTE.
Robert Bosch GmbH, Abteilung FSD, Postfach 106050, 7000 Stuttgart 10, Germany. *1883*

BOTANICA.
Delhi University Botanical Society, Department of Botany, University of Delhi, Delhi 110007, India.
circ. 500. *496*

BOTANICAL SURVEY OF INDIA. BULLETIN.
Botanical Survey of India, P-8, Brabourne Road, Howrah 700 001, India. TEL 26-1635.
circ. 250. *497*

BOTANISCHE STAATSSAMMLUNG MUENCHEN. MITTEILUNGEN.
Botanische Staatssammlung Muenchen, Menzinger Str. 67, 8000 Munich 19, Germany. *497*

BOUWADVISEUR.
Hofstad Vakpers B.V., Postbus 119, 2700 AC Zoetermeer, Netherlands. TEL 079-711811. FAX 079-711803.
circ. 10,350. *604*

BOUWREVUE.
Uitgeversmaatschappij C. Misset B.V., Hanzestr. 1, 7006 RH Doetinchem, Netherlands. TEL 08340-49911. FAX 08340-43839.
circ. 14,000. *604*

BOWLING PROPRIETOR.
Bowling Proprietors' Association of America, Box 5802, Arlington, TX 76005. TEL 817-649-5105. FAX 817-633-2940.
circ. 4,500. *4501*

BRADEA.
Herbarium Bradeanum, C.P. 15005, CEP 20031 Rio de Janeiro, RJ, Brazil.
circ. 400. *497*

BRAILLE TECHNICAL TABLES BANK CATALOG.
National Braille Association, Inc., 1290 University Ave., Rochester, NY 14607. TEL 716-473-0900. *2291*

BRANCHING OUT.
Baltimore County Public Library, 320 York Rd., Towson, MD 21204. TEL 301-296-8500. FAX 301-296-3139.
circ. 1,000. *2749*

BRAZIL. DEPARTAMENTO NACIONAL DA PRODUCAO MINERAL. PROGRAMACAO.
Departmento Nacional da Producao Mineral, Setor Autarcuia Norte, Quadra 1, Bloco B, Brasilia, D.F., Brazil. TEL (061)224-2670.
circ. 150. *3479*

BRAZIL. FUNDACAO INSTITUTO BRASILEIRO DE GEOGRAFIA E ESTATISTICA. BOLETIM BIBLIOGRAFICO.
Fundacao Instituto Brasileiro de Geografia e Estatistica, Rua General Canabarro, 666 Bloco B, Rio de Janeiro, RJ 20271, Brazil. FAX 021-234-6189.
circ. 250. *2267*

BREEDER & FEEDER.
Ontario Cattlemen's Association, 50 Dovercliffe Rd., Unit 6, Guelph, Ont. N1G 3A6, Canada. TEL 519-824-0334. FAX 519-824-9101.
circ. 21,006. *212*

BRETHREN MISSIONARY HERALD.
Brethren Missionary Herald, Inc., Box 544, Winona Lake, IN 46590. TEL 219-267-7158. FAX 219-267-4745.
circ. 5,000. *4280*

BREWING AND MALTING BARLEY RESEARCH INSTITUTE. ANNUAL REPORT.
Brewing and Malting Barley Research Institute, 206-167 Lombard Ave., Winnipeg, Man. R3B 0T6, Canada. TEL 204-942-1407. *379*

BREWING RESEARCH CONVENTION. CURRENT AWARENESS MONTHLY.
European Brewery Convention, Box 510, NL-2380 BB Zoeterwoude, Netherlands. TEL 31-71-456047. FAX 31-71-410013.
circ. 400. *388*

BRICKBATS & BOUQUETS.
Employers Insurance of Texas, Box 2759, Dallas, TX 75221. TEL 214-760-6282. FAX 214-760-3751.
circ. 2,100. *2528*

BRIDGE S A.
South African Bridge Federation, P.O. Box 890347, Lyndhurst 2106, South Africa. FAX 011-4406435.
circ. 2,500. *4467*

BRIERCREST ECHO.
Briercrest Schools, 510 College Dr., Caronport, Sask. S0H 0S0, Canada. TEL 306-756-3200. FAX 306-756-3366.
circ. 24,000. *1305*

BRILLIANT IDEAS FOR PUBLISHERS.
Creative Brilliance Associates, Box 44237, Madison, WI 53744-4237. TEL 608-233-2669.
circ. 15,000. *2567*

BRITISH AIRWAYS EXECUTIVE.
British Airways PLC., Box 10, Heathrow Airport, Middlesex TW6 2JA, England.
circ. 110,000. *4671*

BRITISH ARACHNOLOGICAL SOCIETY. BULLETIN.
British Arachnological Society, c/o Dr. P. Merrett, Ed., 6 Hillcrest, Durlston Rd., Swanage, Dorset BH19 2HS, England.
circ. 700. *579*

BRITISH CACTUS & SUCCULENT JOURNAL.
British Cactus & Succulent Society, 8 Stonehouse Close, Cubbington, Leamington Spa, CV32 7LP, England. TEL 0926-429702.
circ. 5,600. *2123*

BRITISH COLUMBIA. LAW REFORM COMMISSION. ANNUAL REPORT.
Law Reform Commission, 601-865 Hornby St., Vancouver, B.C. V6Z 2G3, Canada. TEL 604-660-2366. FAX 604-660-2378.
circ. 2,000. *2605*

BRITISH COLUMBIA AGRI DIGEST: DAIRY ISSUE.
DoMac Publications Ltd., 207 W. Hastings St., Ste. 810, Vancouver, B.C. V6B 1J8, Canada. TEL 604-684-8255. FAX 604-684-1928.
circ. 1,390. *198*

BRITISH COLUMBIA AGRI DIGEST: FARM BUSINESS ISSUE.
DoMac Publications Ltd., 207 W. Hastings St., Ste. 810, Vancouver, B.C. V6B 1J8, Canada. TEL 604-684-8255. FAX 604-684-1924.
circ. 3,300. *148*

BRITISH COLUMBIA AGRI DIGEST: HORSE ISSUE.
DoMac Publications Ltd., 207 W. Hastings St., Ste. 810, Vancouver, B.C. V6B 1J8, Canada. TEL 604-684-8255. FAX 604-684-1928.
circ. 3,800. *4532*

BRITISH COLUMBIA AGRI DIGEST: HORTICULTURE.
DoMac Publications Ltd., 207 W. Hastings St., Ste. 810, Vancouver, B.C. V6B 1J8, Canada. TEL 604-684-8255. FAX 604-684-1928.
circ. 1,590. *2123*

BRITISH COLUMBIA AGRI DIGEST: POULTRY & SWINE ISSUE.
DoMac Publications Ltd., 207 W. Hastings St., Ste. 810, Vancouver, B.C. V6B 1J8, Canada. TEL 604-684-8255. FAX 604-684-1928.
circ. 990. *213*

BRITISH COLUMBIA ORCHARDIST.
557 Groves Ave., Kelowna, B.C. V1Y 4Y8, Canada. TEL 604-763-1116. FAX 604-860-5002.
circ. 2,728. *2123*

BRITISH ELECTROTECHNICAL APPROVALS BOARD. ANNUAL LIST OF APPROVED ELECTROTECHNICAL EQUIPMENT.
B E A B, Mark House, the Green, 9-11 Queen's Rd., Hersham, Walton-on-Thames, Surrey KT12 5NA, England.
circ. 10,000. *4594*

BRITISH EXPORTS.
Kompass Windsor Court, East Grinstead House, East Grinstead, West Sussex RH19 1XD, England. TEL 0342-326972. FAX 0342-317241.
circ. 12,000. *1124*

BRITISH EXPORTS TO EUROPE.
Kompass Windsor Court, E. Grinstead House, E. Grinstead, W. Sussex RH19 1XA, England. TEL 0342-326972.
circ. *1124*

BRITISH EXPORTS TO NORTH AMERICA.
Kompass Windsor Court, East Grinstead House, East Grinstead, W. Sussex RH19 1XA, England. TEL 0342-326972.
circ. 20,000. *1124*

BRITISH INDUSTRY AND ENGINEERING.
British Industrial Publicity Overseas Ltd., 90 Moorsom St., Birmingham B6 4NT, England. TEL 021-359-0030. FAX 021-359-7441. *4594*

BRITISH-ISRAEL TRADE.
British-Israel Chamber of Commerce, 14-15 Rodmarton St., London W1H 3FW, England. TEL 071-486-2371. FAX 071-224-1783.
circ. 2,800. *809*

BRITISH JOURNAL OF RUSSIAN PHILATELY.
Postbus 16636, 1001 RC Amsterdam, Netherlands.
circ. 250. *3750*

BRITISH NATURISM.
Central Council for British Naturism, Assurance House, 35-41 Hazelwood Rd., Northampton NN1 1LL, England. FAX 0604-230176.
circ. 11,000. *3800*

BRITISH RACING NEWS.
British Racing & Sports Car Club, Brands Hatch Circuit, Fawkham, Dartford, Kent DA3 8NH, England.
circ. 4,000. *4467*

BRITISH SOCIETY OF RHEOLOGY. BULLETIN.
British Society of Rheology, c/o Mrs. C.A. Moules, Krus UK Ltd., 5-6 Carrington House, 37 Upper King St., Royston, Herts SG8 9AZ, England. TEL 0763-244280. FAX 0763-244298. *3842*

BROADCAST TECHNOLOGY.
Diversified Publications Ltd., Box 420, Bolton, Ont. L7E 5T3, Canada. TEL 416-857-6076. FAX 416-857-6045.
circ. 10,600. *1332*

BROADCASTING ABROAD.
Cahners Publishing Company (Washington), Division of Reed Publishing (USA) Inc. 1705 DeSales St., N.W., Washington, DC 20036. TEL 202-659-2340. FAX 202-429-0651.
circ. 7,500. *1369*

BROKEN SPOKE.
Calgary Sports Car Club, P.O. Box 61143 Kensington Postal Stn., Calgary, Alta. T2N 4S6, Canada. TEL 403-285-1177. FAX 403-270-3525.
circ. 200. *4685*

BROTHERHOOD.
National Federation of Temple Brotherhoods, 838 Fifth Ave., New York, NY 10021. TEL 212-570-0707.
circ. 75,000. *4222*

BROTS DE COLLCEROLA.
Delegacion Vallvidrera del C. E. A., Mont d'Orsa 17, Barcelona 17, Spain.
circ. 150. *1296*

BRUCE TRAIL NEWS.
Trail News Inc., 17 Marlborough Avenue, Toronto, Ont. M5R 1X5, Canada. TEL 416-964-7281.
circ. 10,000. *4542*

BRUG.
Publicarto N.V., Langestraat 170, B-1150 Brussels, Belgium. TEL 02-782-00-00. FAX 02-782-16-16.
circ. 41,236. *1619*

BRUNSWICK MONTHLY.
Georgia - Pacific, Brunswick Operations, Box 1438, Brunswick, GA 31521. FAX 912-265-8060.
circ. 1,000. *3662*

BRUNSWICKAN.
University of New Brunswick, Student Union, P.O. Box 4400, Fredericton, N.B. E3B 5A3, Canada. TEL 506-453-4983.
circ. 10,000. *1305*

BUDAPESTI KOZGAZDASAGTUDOMANYI EGYETEM OKTATOINAK SZAKIRODALMI MUNKASSAGA.
Budapesti Kozgazdasagtudomanyi Egyetem, Fovam Ter 8, 1093 Budapest, Hungary. TEL 1179-377. FAX 1174-910.
circ. 300. *707*

BUEHNE.
O R A C Zeitschriftenverlag GmbH, Schoenbrunnerstr. 59, A-1050 Vienna, Austria. TEL 0222-551621-0. FAX 0222-551621-78.
circ. 126,000. *4630*

BUGLE (MISSOULA).
Rocky Mountain Elk Foundation, Box 8249, Missoula, MT 59807-8249. TEL 406-721-0010. FAX 406-549-4325.
circ. 200,000. *4542*

CONTROLLED CIRCULATION SERIALS

BUILD.
Belenos Publications Ltd., 50 Fitzwilliam Square West, Dublin 2, Ireland. TEL 766192. FAX 619781.
circ. 4,560. *604*

BUILDER (COLUMBUS).
Midland Mutual Life Insurance Company, 250 E. Broad St., Columbus, OH 43215. TEL 614-228-2001.
circ. 1,300. *2528*

BUILDERS' MERCHANT NEWS.
B & M Publications (London) Ltd., P.O. Box 13, Hereford House, Bridle Path, Croydon, Surrey CR9 4NL, England. TEL 081-680-4200. FAX 081-681-5049.
circ. 7,500. *605*

BUILDING CONSTRUCTION NEWS.
Builders Exchange, Inc., 981 Keynote Circle, Cleveland, OH 44131-1842. *606*

BUILDING HOMES & RENOVATION.
Southam Business Communications Inc., 1450 Don Mills Rd., Don Mills, Ont. M3B 2X7, Canada. TEL 416-445-6641. FAX 416-442-2077.
circ. 17,188. *606*

BUILDING INDUSTRIES FEDERATION. ANNUAL REPORT.
Building Industries Federation, 14 Alexandra Ave., Halfway House 1685, South Africa. TEL 011-8051985. FAX 011-315-1644.
circ. 6,000. *606*

BUILDING INSPECTORS' ASSOCIATION OF NOVA SCOTIA. REPORTER.
Building Inspectors' Association of Nova Scotia, P.O. Box 9001, Halifax, N.S. B3K 5M6, Canada.
circ. 200. *606*

BUILDING PRODUCTS.
Hanley-Wood Inc., 655 15th St., N.W., Ste. 475, Washington, DC 20005-5710. TEL 202-737-0717. FAX 202-737-2439.
circ. 80,000. *606*

BUILDINGS.
Stamats Communications, Inc., c/o Wayne Bayliss, 427 Sixth Ave., S.E., Box 1888, Cedar Rapids, IA 52406. TEL 319-364-6167. FAX 319-364-4278.
circ. 42,000. *607*

BULLETIN OF ZOO MANAGEMENT.
Royal Zoological Society of South Australia, Inc., Zoological Gardens, Frome Road, Adelaide, S.A. 5000, Australia.
circ. 250. *580*

BULLPEN.
Babe Ruth League, 1770 Brunswick Ave., Box 5000, Trenton, NJ 09638. TEL 609-695-1434. FAX 609-695-2505.
circ. 32,000. *4501*

BUR.
Loyola University Chicago, School of Dentistry, 820 N Michigan Ave., Chicago, IL 60611. TEL 708-216-6700. FAX 708-216-8199.
circ. 7,200. *3229*

BURRELLE'S CLIPPING ANALYST.
Burrelle's Press Clipping Service, 75 E. Northfield Rd., Livingston, NJ 07039. TEL 201-992-6600. FAX 201-992-5122.
circ. 5,000. *29*

BUSINESS COMPUTERNEWS.
Moorshead Publications Ltd., 1300 Don Mills Rd., Toronto, Ont. M3B 3M8, Canada. TEL 416-445-5600. FAX 416-445-8149.
circ. 15,415. *825*

BUSINESS DIGEST OF CENTRAL MASSACHUSETTS.
40 Southbridge St., Worcester, MA 01609. TEL 508-755-4500. FAX 508-799-0256.
circ. 12,500. *1113*

BUSINESS DIGEST OF GREATER WATERBURY.
Four Stars Publishing Co., Inc., Box 9018, 94 Benedict St., Waterbury, CT 06724. TEL 203-754-9922. FAX 203-754-5192.
circ. 6,300. *649*

BUSINESS DIRECTORY.
Mt. Diablo Peace Center, 65 Eckley Lane, Walnut Creek, CA 94596. TEL 415-933-7850. FAX 284-5357.
circ. 5,000. *834*

BUSINESS EDUCATION INTERNATIONAL.
L C C I Examinations Board, Marlow House, Staitons Rd., Sidcup, Kent DA15 7BJ, England. TEL 081-302-0261. FAX 081-302-4169.
circ. 12,000. *834*

BUSINESS JOURNAL (PORTLAND).
American City Business Journals, Inc. (Portland), Box 14490, Portland, OR 97214. TEL 503-274-8733. FAX 503-227-2650.
circ. 4,100. *848*

BUSINESS JOURNAL (SAN JOSE).
City Business - U S A Publications, Inc., 152 N. 3rd St., Ste. 100, San Jose, CA 95112. TEL 408-295-3800. FAX 408-295-5028.
circ. 2,800. *651*

BUSINESS MARKETING.
Crain Communications, Inc. (Chicago), 740 Rush St., Chicago, IL 60611-2590. TEL 312-649-5260. FAX 312-649-5228.
circ. 47,853. *1034*

BUSINESS MEMO FROM BELGIUM.
Embassy of Belgium, Investments Office, 3330 Garfield St. N.W., Washington, DC 20008. TEL 202-625-5888. FAX 202-625-7567.
circ. 3,200. *809*

BUSINESS NEWS. SOUTH WALES EDITION.
Euro Publications Ltd., Euro House, 14 Pearl St., Cardiff CF2 1HD, Wales.
circ. 5,000. *848*

BUSINESS NEWS. WEST OF ENGLAND EDITION.
Euro Publications Ltd., Euro House, 14 Pearl St., Cardiff CF2 1HD, Wales.
circ. 5,000. *848*

BUSINESS OF SPORTS.
722 Ounwoodie Dr., Cincinnati, OH 45230-3905. TEL 513-241-3741.
circ. 50,000. *4467*

BUSINESS TO BUSINESS.
Bracebridge Examiner Ltd., 16 Manitoba St., Box 1049, Bracebridge, Ont. P0B 1C0, Canada. TEL 705-645-8771. FAX 705-645-1718.
circ. 6,034. *652*

BUSINESS TRAVEL MANAGEMENT.
Coastal Communications Corporation, 488 Madison Ave., New York, NY 10022. TEL 212-888-1500. FAX 212-888-8008.
circ. 42,000. *1004*

BUSINESS TRENDS ASIA REPORT: INDONESIA.
M P R C (Asia) Sdn. Berhad, 132-B Jalan Kasah, Damansara Heights, 50490 Kuala Lumpur, Malaysia. TEL 03-2548139. *848*

BUSINESS WORLD.
Business World, P.O. Box 2718, Sta. F, Scarborough, Ont. M1W 3P3, Canada. TEL 416-492-0130. FAX 416-492-6408.
circ. 7,000. *769*

BUTLER ALUMNI QUARTERLY.
Butler University, 4600 Sunset Ave., Indianapolis, IN 46208. TEL 317-283-9426.
circ. 24,000. *1306*

BUTLER AVIATION'S ECHELON.
Halsey Publishing Co., 12955 Biscayne Blvd., No. 202, North Miami, FL 33181. TEL 305-893-1520. *2222*

BYGG & TRAEVARUHANDELN.
Sveriges Bygg- och Traevaruhandelsfoerbund, Box 14019, 104 40 Stockholm 14, Sweden.
circ. 2,300. *607*

BYWAYS (FAIRFAX).
National Motorcoach Network, Inc., Patriot Sq., 10527-C Braddock Rd., Fairfax, VA 22032. TEL 703-250-7897. FAX 703-250-1477.
circ. 37,000. *4755*

C A D - C A M REPORT.
Dressler Verlag GmbH, Hauptstr. 29, 6900 Heidelberg, Germany. TEL 6221-91130. FAX 6221-911321.
circ. 19,700. *1420*

C A - D E NEWS.
Council for Alcohol - Drug Education of N.J., 526 Route 206, Trenton, NJ 08610. TEL 609-291-0500.
circ. 16,000. *1535*

C A E NEWS.
C A E Industries Ltd., P.O. Box 30, Royal Bank Plaza, Toronto, Ont. M5J 2J1, Canada. TEL 416-865-0070. FAX 416-865-0337.
circ. 14,000. *49*

C A S NEWSLETTER.
Catholic Archives Society, c/o M.A. Kuhn-Regnier, Flat 7, Dawes House, High St., Burwash, Etchingham, Sussex TN19 7HD, England.
circ. 260. *4257*

C B REPORT.
Texas Higher Education Coordinating Board, Box 12788, Capitol Sta., Austin, TX 78711. TEL 512-483-6111.
circ. 2,000. *1701*

C B T DIRECTIONS.
Weingarten Publications, Inc., 38 Chauncy St., Boston, MA 02111. TEL 617-542-0146.
circ. 10,000. *1389*

C. BREWER TODAY.
C. Brewer & Co. Ltd., Box 1826, Honolulu, HI 96805. TEL 808-536-4461.
circ. 2,000. *1073*

C E I P FUND. CONNECTIONS.
C E I P Fund, Inc., 68 Harrison Ave., Boston, MA 02111-1919. TEL 617-426-4375. *1944*

C E O - INTERNATIONAL STRATEGIES.
C E O Institutes of International Media Partners, 611 Broadway, Ste. 322, New York, NY 10012. TEL 212-995-9595.
circ. 30,000. *902*

C F A DIGEST.
Association for Investment Management and Research, Box 3668, Charlottesville, VA 22903. TEL 804-977-6600. FAX 804-977-1103.
circ. 11,500. *769*

C F P TODAY.
Institute of Certified Financial Planners, 7600 E. Eastman Ave., Ste. 301, Denver, CO 80231. TEL 303-751-7600. FAX 303-751-1037.
circ. 47,000. *1004*

C H I L D NEWSLETTER.
C H I L D, Inc., Box 2604, Sioux City, IA 51106. TEL 712-948-3500.
circ. 450. *1233*

C I D A ANNUAL REPORT.
Canadian International Development Agency, Communications Branch, 200 Promenade du Portage, Hull, Que. K1A 0G4, Canada. TEL 819-953-6060. FAX 819-953-4433. *927*

C-I-G WORLD.
Colorado Interstate Gas Co., Box 1087, Colorado Springs, CO 80944. TEL 719-520-4451. FAX 719-520-4318.
circ. 1,500. *3683*

C I I - E S R I BUSINESS FORECAST.
Confederation of Irish Industry, Confederation House, Kildare St., Dublin 2, Ireland. *1073*

C.I.I. NEWSLETTER.
Confederation of Irish Industry, Confederation House, Kildare St., Dublin 2, Ireland. *1073*

C I L E C T NEWSLETTER.
Centre International de Liaison des Ecoles de Cinema et de Television, c/o Australian Film Television and Radio School, P.O. Box 126, N. Ryde, N.S.W. 2113, Australia. TEL 28056611. FAX 28871030. *1370*

C I R I A REPORT.
Construction Industry Research and Information Association, 6 Storey's Gate, Westminster, London SW1P 3AU, England. TEL 071-222-8891. FAX 071-222-1708.
circ. 500. *1862*

C L R.
Medical Economics Company Inc., Five Paragon Dr., Montvale, NJ 07645. TEL 201-358-7200. FAX 201-573-1045.
circ. 59,000. *3258*

C M D S.
Christian Medical & Dental Society, 1616 Gateway Blvd., Box 830689, Richardson, TX 75083-0689. TEL 214-783-8384.
circ. 7,900. *3085*

C O P A CONVERSATION.
Canadian Office Products Association, 1243 Islington Ave., Ste. 911, Toronto, Ont. M8X 1Y9, Canada. TEL 416-239-2737. FAX 416-239-1553.
circ. 5,000. *1057*

C P D A NEWS.
Council for Periodical Distributors Associations, 60 E. 42nd St., New York, NY 10165. FAX 212-983-4699.
circ. 4,000. *4124*

C P I PURCHASING.
Cahners Publishing Company (Newton) Division of Reed Publishing (USA) Inc., 275 Washington St., Newton, MA 02158-1630. TEL 617-558-4651. FAX 617-558-4327.
circ. 40,000. *1035*

C Q RADIO AMATEUR.
Boixareu Editores, S.A., Gran Via de les Corts Catalanes, 594, 08007 Barcelona, Spain.
circ. 10,700. *1883*

C R R I ROAD ABSTRACTS.
Central Road Research Institute, P.O. Central Road Research Institute, New Delhi 110020, India. TEL 6832274. *1842*

C S A FRATERNAL LIFE.
Cicero Berwyn Press, 2701 S. Harlem Ave., Berwyn, IL 60402.
circ. 10,385. *1995*

C S A NEWS.
Council of Supervisors and Administrators of the City of New York, Local 1, American Federation of School Administrators, AFL-CIO, 16 Court St., 4th Fl., Brooklyn, NY 11241. TEL 718-852-3000. FAX 718-403-0278.
circ. 10,500. *1725*

C T A ACTION.
California Teachers Association, 1705 Murchison Dr., Burlingame, CA 94010. TEL 415-697-1400. FAX 415-697-0786.
circ. 245,000. *1701*

C W R U: THE MAGAZINE OF CASE WESTERN RESERVE UNIVERSITY.
Case Western Reserve University, 10900 Euclid Ave., Cleveland, OH 44106. TEL 216-368-6265. FAX 216-368-4835.
circ. 90,000. *1306*

CABLE WORLD.
Cable World Associates, 1905 Sherman St., Denver, CO 80203. TEL 303-837-0900. FAX 303-837-0915.
circ. 11,000. *1371*

CACHE CITIZEN.
Utah State University, Department of Communications, Box 703, Logan, UT 84321. TEL 801-750-3292.
circ. 18,000. *2222*

CAHIERS DE L'UNIVERSITE DE PERPIGNAN.
Universite de Perpignan, 36, Chemin de la Passio Vella, 66025 Perpignan Cedex, France. TEL 68-66-20-00. FAX 68-66-20-19.
circ. 300. *2902*

CAHIERS DE NUTRITION ET DE DIETETIQUE.
S.P.P.I.F. 7 rue Laromiguiere, 75005 Paris, France. TEL 33-1-46-34-21-60. FAX 33-1-45-87-29-99.
circ. 3,000. *3604*

CAHIERS DE PALEOANTHROPOLOGIE.
Editions du C N R S, 1 Place Aristide Briand, 92195 Meudon Cedex, France. TEL 1-45-34-75-50. FAX 1-46-26-28-49.
circ. 1,250. *3656*

CAHIERS DE PALEONTOLOGIE.
Editions du C N R S, 1 Place Aristide Briand, 92195 Meudon Cedex, France. TEL 1-45-34-75-50. FAX 1-46-26-28-49.
circ. 1,500. *3656*

CAHIERS DE PALEONTOLOGIE EST-AFRICAINE.
Editions du C N R S, 1 Place Aristide Briand, 92195 Meudon Cedex, France. TEL 1-45-34-75-50. FAX 1-46-26-28-49.
circ. 1,500. *3656*

CAHIERS NEPALAIS.
Editions du C N R S, 1 Place Aristide Briand, 92195 Meudon Cedex, France. TEL 1-45-34-75-50. FAX 1-46-26-28-49.
circ. 1,500. *3877*

CALENDAR OF CONFERENCES, MEETINGS AND EXHIBITIONS TO BE HELD IN SOUTH AFRICA.
Council for Scientific and Industrial Research, Division of Information Services, P.O. Box 395, Pretoria 0001, South Africa.
circ. 3,200. *3391*

CALIFORNIA. DEPARTMENT OF WATER RESOURCES. BULLETIN.
Department of Water Resources, Box 924836, Sacramento, CA 94236-0001. TEL 916-445-9248. *4822*

CALIFORNIA. TEACHERS RETIREMENT BOARD. STATE TEACHER'S RETIREMENT SYSTEM; ANNUAL REPORT TO THE GOVERNOR AND THE LEGISLATURE.
Teachers Retirement Board, Box 15275-C, Sacramento, CA 95851. TEL 916-386-3700.
circ. 1,500. *1725*

CALIFORNIA COOPERATIVE OCEANIC FISHERIES INVESTIGATIONS REPORTS.
California Cooperative Oceanic Fisheries Investigations, Scripps Institution of Oceanography, University of California, La Jolla, CA 92093-0227. TEL 619-534-4236. FAX 619-534-5306.
circ. 1,500. *580*

CALIFORNIA F P.
California Academy of Family Physicians, 114 Sansome St. K No.1305, San Francisco, CA 94104-3824. FAX 415-394-9119.
circ. 6,900. *3085*

CALIFORNIA FRUIT GROWER.
Blue Anchor, Inc., 730 Howe Ave., Box 15498, Sacramento, CA 95813. TEL 916-929-3050. FAX 916-921-9362.
circ. 9,500. *2063*

CALIFORNIA PARKS & RECREATION.
California Park & Recreation Society Inc., 3031 F St., Ste. 202, Box 161118, Sacramento, CA 95816. TEL 916-446-2777. *1485*

CALIFORNIA RIVIERA MAGAZINE.
Greater Laguna Company, Box 536, Laguna, CA 92651. TEL 714-494-2659. FAX 714-497-6911.
circ. 50,000. *2222*

CALIFORNIA SCHOOL EMPLOYEE.
California School Employees Association, Box 640, San Jose, CA 95106. TEL 408-263-8000. FAX 408-954-0948.
circ. 106,000. *1725*

CALIFORNIA WATER POLLUTION CONTROL ASSOCIATION. BULLETIN.
California Water Pollution Control Association, Inc., 3050 Citrus Cir., Ste. 225, Walnut Creek, CA 94598-2628. FAX 510-938-0182.
circ. 7,000. *4822*

CALL TO ACTION.
Board of Education, 5057 Woodward, Detroit, MI 48202. TEL 313-494-1000.
circ. 22,000. *1619*

CAMARA ARGENTINA DE PRODUCTOS QUIMICOS. BOLETIN INFORMATIVO.
Camara Argentina del Libro, Ave. Belgrano 1580, 6 Piso, 1093 Buenos Aires, Argentina.
circ. 250. *1171*

CAMARA DE COMERCIO HISPANO-SUECA DE MADRID. INFO.
Camara de Comercio Hispano-Sueca de Madrid, Caracas, 23, 28010 Madrid, Spain.
circ. 500. *810*

CAMARA NACIONAL DE LA INDUSTRIA DE TRANSFORMACION. BOLETIN INFORMATIVO.
Camara Nacional de la Industria de Transformacion, Apdo Postal 60-468, Av. San Antonio 256, C.P. 03849, Mexico, D.F., Mexico. *1073*

CAMERA DI COMMERCIO ITALIANA PER LA GRAN BRETAGNA E IL COMMONWEALTH. SEGNALAZIONI.
Camera di Commercio Italiana per la Gran Bretagna e il Commonwealth, Via B. Cerretti 27, 00167 Rome, Italy.
circ. 5,000. *811*

CAMOUFLAGE AIR JOURNAL.
Paul Camelio, Ed. & Pub., Marine Blanche K, 13014 Marseille, France.
circ. 500. *49*

CAMPESINO.
Editora Dosmil, Carrera 39 A No 15-11, Bogota D.E., Colombia.
circ. 70,000. *2183*

CAMPGROUND MANAGEMENT.
Woodall Publishing Co., 28167 N. Keith Dr., Lake Forest, IL 60045. TEL 708-362-6700. FAX 708-362-8776.
circ. 16,900. *4542*

CAMPING & OUTDOOR LEISURE TRADER.
97 Front St., Whickham, Newcastle-upon-Tyne NE16 4JL, England. *4543*

CAMPUS LEADER.
University of Manila, 546 Dr. M.V. de los Santos St., Manila D-403, Philippines.
circ. 8,000. *1620*

CAMPUS VOICE.
Whittle Communications L.P., 333 Main Ave., Knoxville, TN 37902. TEL 615-595-5000. FAX 615-595-5390.
circ. 1,200,000. *1306*

CANADA. AGRICULTURE CANADA. ENGINEERING & STATISTICAL RESEARCH INSTITUTE, OTTAWA. RESEARCH REPORT.
Agriculture Canada, Engineering & Statistical Research Institute, Ottawa, Ont. K1A 0C6, Canada. TEL 613-995-5222.
circ. 300. *172*

CANADA. AGRICULTURE CANADA. FORAGE NOTES.
Agriculture Canada, Plant Research Centre, Forage Bldg. No.12, Ottawa, Ont. K1A 0C6, Canada. TEL 613-995-3700.
circ. 600. *205*

CANADA. GRAIN COMMISSION. ECONOMICS AND STATISTICS DIVISION. EXPORTS OF CANADIAN GRAIN AND WHEAT FLOUR.
Grain Commission, Economics and Statistics Division, 747-303 Main St., Winnipeg, Man. R3C 3G8, Canada. TEL 204-983-2759.
circ. 300. *205*

CANADA. LAW REFORM COMMISSION. WORKING PAPER.
Law Reform Commission, 130 Albert St., Ottawa, Ont. K1A 0L6, Canada. TEL 613-996-7844. FAX 613-996-8599.
circ. 10,000. *2610*

CANADA GRAINS COUNCIL. ANNUAL REPORT.
Canada Grains Council, 760-360 Main St., Winnipeg, Man. R3C 3Z3, Canada. TEL 204-942-2254. *205*

CANADIAN ASSOCIATION FOR LABORATORY ANIMAL SCIENCE NEWSLETTER.
Canadian Association for Laboratory Animal Science (CALAS), c/o Dr. Donald G. McKay, Biosciences Animal Service, University of Alberta, Edmonton, Alta. T6G 2E9, Canada.
circ. 1,000. *3258*

CONTROLLED CIRCULATION SERIALS

CANADIAN ASSOCIATION OF ANATOMISTS. BULLETIN.
Canadian Association of Anatomists, c/o Dept. of Anatomy, University of Western Ontario, London, Ont. N6A 5C1, Canada. TEL 519-679-2111. *434*

CANADIAN ASSOCIATION OF SLAVISTS NEWSLETTER.
Canadian Association of Slavists, c/o Gust Olson, Slavic Department, University of Alberta, Edmonton, Alta. T6G 2E6, Canada. TEL 403-492-3537. *2504*

CANADIAN CAMPER.
Canadian Family Camping Federation, P.O. Box 397, Rexdale, Ont. M9W 5L4, Canada. circ. 300. *4543*

CANADIAN DIRECT MARKETING NEWS.
C D M N Publishing, 3160 Steeles Ave., Ste. 210, Markham, Ont. L3R 4G9, Canada. TEL 416-479-7436. FAX 416-479-7432. circ. 7,000. *1035*

CANADIAN ENVIRONMENTAL PROTECTION.
Baum Publications, 831 Helmcken St., Vancouver, B.C. V6Z 1B1, Canada. TEL 604-689-2804. FAX 604-682-8347. circ. 27,211. *1945*

CANADIAN FARM ECONOMICS.
Agriculture Canada, Communications Branch, 930 Carling Ave., Ottawa, Ont. K1A 0C7, Canada. TEL 613-995-8963. circ. 63,900. *148*

CANADIAN FREEMASON.
270 Thornway Ave., Thornhill, Ont. L4J 7X8, Canada. TEL 416-660-1532. circ. 12,000. *1296*

CANADIAN FRUITGROWER.
N C C Publishing, 222 Argyle Ave., Delhi, Ont. N4B 2Y2, Canada. TEL 519-582-2510. FAX 519-582-4040. circ. 4,000. *2123*

CANADIAN HOME ECONOMICS JOURNAL.
Canadian Home Economics Association, Burnside Bldg. Suite 901, 151 Slater St., Ottawa, Ont. K1P 5H3, Canada. TEL 613-238-8817. FAX 613-238-1677. circ. 3,400. *2445*

CANADIAN INDEPENDENT ADJUSTER.
Journal Management, 216 Market Square, Newmarket, Ont. L3Y 4A8, Canada. circ. 3,400. *2529*

CANADIAN JOURNAL OF DERMATOLOGY.
Rodar Publishing Inc., 19180 Trans Canada Hwy., Baie d'Urfe, Que. H9X 3T9, Canada. TEL 514-457-2673. FAX 514-457-2679. circ. 9,640. *3246*

CANADIAN JOURNAL OF GASTROENTEROLOGY.
Pulsus Group Inc., 2902 S. Sheridan Way, Oakville, Ont. L6J 7L6, Canada. TEL 416-829-4770. FAX 416-829-4799. circ. 18,000. *3266*

CANADIAN JOURNAL OF OB-GYN & WOMEN'S HEALTH CARE.
Rodar Publishing Inc., 19180 Trans Canada Hwy., Baie d'Urfe, Que. H9X 3T9, Canada. TEL 514-457-2673. FAX 514-457-2679. circ. 17,000. *3290*

CANADIAN JOURNAL OF PEDIATRICS.
Rodar Publishing Inc., 19180 Trans Canada Hwy., Baie d'Urfe, Que. H9X 3T9, Canada. TEL 514-457-2673. FAX 514-457-2679. circ. 14,500. *3319*

CANADIAN LEATHERCRAFT.
Canadian Society of Creative Leathercraft, c/o Betsy Rennie, 1357 Baldwin St., Burlington, Ont. L7S 1K1, Canada. circ. 150. *353*

CANADIAN METEOROLOGICAL AND OCEANOGRAPHIC SOCIETY. ANNUAL CONGRESS.
Canadian Meteorological and Oceanographic Society, P.O. Box 334, Newmarket, Ont. L3Y 4X7, Canada. TEL 416-898-1040. FAX 416-898-7937. circ. 1,000. *3434*

CANADIAN MUSIC TRADE.
Norris Publications, 3284 Yonge St., Toronto, Ont. M4N 3M7, Canada. TEL 416-485-8284. FAX 416-485-8924. circ. 3,000. *3544*

CANADIAN MUSLIM.
Ottawa Muslim Association, P.O. Box 2952, Sta. D, Ottawa, Ont. 51P 5W9, Canada. TEL 613-725-0004. circ. 2,000. *4218*

CANADIAN PROCESS EQUIPMENT & CONTROL NEWS.
Canadian Process Equipment & Control News Ltd., 343 Eglinton Ave.E., Toronto, Ont. M4P 1L7, Canada. TEL 416-481-6483. FAX 416-481-6436. circ. 25,567. *654*

CANADIAN RAIL.
Canadian Railroad Historical Association, Box 22, Sta. B, Montreal, Que. H3B 3J5, Canada. circ. 1,600. *4708*

CANADIAN REAL ESTATE.
Canadian Real Estate Association, Place de Ville, Tower A, 320 Queen St., 21st Fl., Ottawa, Ont. K1R 5A3, Canada. TEL 613-234-3372. FAX 613-234-2567. circ. 89,000. *4146*

CANADIAN SAILOR.
Seafarers International Union of Canada, 1333 rue St-Jacques, Montreal, Que. H3C 4K2, Canada. FAX 514-931-3667. circ. 5,000. *3453*

CANADIAN SPORTSCARD COLLECTOR.
Trajan Publishing Corp., 103 Lakeshore Rd., Ste. 202, St. Catharines, Ont. L2N 2T6, Canada. TEL 416-646-7744. FAX 416-646-0995. circ. 13,503. *2434*

CANCER RESEARCH CAMPAIGN. ANNUAL REPORT.
Cancer Research Campaign, 2 Carlton House Terrace, London SW1Y 5AR, England. *3195*

CANOE FOCUS.
British Canoe Union, Adbolton Lane, West Bridgford, Nottingham NG2 5AS, England. TEL 0602-821100. FAX 0602-821797. circ. 16,000. *4524*

CANOMA.
Canadian Permanent Committee on Geographical Names, Secretariat CPCGN - Geographical Names, Room 650-615, Booth St., Ottawa, Ont. K1A 0E9, Canada. TEL 613-992-3892. FAX 613-992-4961. circ. 500. *2244*

CANTERAS Y EXPLOTACIONES.
Pedeca Sociedad Cooperativa, Ltda., Maria Auxiliadora 5, 28040 Madrid, Spain. TEL 459 60 00. circ. 10,000. *3480*

CAPE COD LIFE.
Cape Cod Life, Inc., Box 767, Cataumet, MA 02534-0767. TEL 508-564-4466. FAX 508-564-4470. circ. 4,500. *2222*

CAPITAL GAY.
Stonewall Press Ltd., 38 Mount Pleasant, London WC1X 0AP, England. TEL 071-278-3764. FAX 071-278-3250. circ. 17,776. *2451*

CAPITAL MAGAZINE.
Cappub, Inc., 300 Mill St., Vienna, VA 22180-4524. FAX 703-938-4562. circ. 70,000. *4756*

CAPITAL SPORTS FOCUS.
Capital Sports Focus, Inc., 1432 Fenwick Ln., Silver Spring, MD 20910-3328. TEL 301-587-9351. FAX 301-587-6347. circ. 100,000. *4468*

CAPTION.
National Captioning Institute, Inc., 5203 Leesburg Pike, Falls Church, VA 22041. FAX 703-998-2450. circ. 100,000. *1371*

CARAVANNER.
Airstream, Inc., 419 W. Pike St., Jackson Center, OH 45334. TEL 513-596-6111. FAX 614-596-6092. circ. 350,000. *4756*

CARDIOLOGY BOARD REVIEW.
M R A Publications, Inc., 3 Greenwich Office Park, Greenwich, CT 06831-5154. TEL 203-629-3550. FAX 203-629-2536. circ. 65,000. *3206*

CAREERS & MAJORS.
Oxendine Publishing, Inc., Box 14081, Gainesville, FL 32604-2081. TEL 904-373-6907. circ. 18,000. *3625*

CARGO CLAN.
Emphasis HK Ltd., 10-F, Wilson House, 19-27 Wyndham St., Central, Hong Kong. TEL 521-5392. FAX 810-6738. circ. 10,000. *4725*

CARGOVISION.
Multi Media International, P.O. Box 469, 1180 AL Amstelveen, Netherlands. TEL 20-5473550. FAX 20-6438581. circ. 40,000. *4672*

CARIBBEAN UPDATE.
Kal Wagenheim, Ed. & Pub., 52 Maple Ave., Maplewood, NJ 07040. TEL 800-647-9990. FAX 201-762-9585. *903*

CARNEGIE MUSEUM OF NATURAL HISTORY. BULLETIN.
Carnegie Museum of Natural History, Office of Scientific Publications, 4400 Forbes Ave., Pittsburgh, PA 15213-4080. TEL 412-622-3287. FAX 412-622-8837. *4304*

CAROLINA GOLFER.
Wing Publications, Inc., Box 11268, Columbia, SC 29211. *4502*

CAROLINA SPORTSMAN.
Wing Publications, Inc., Box 11268, Columbia, SC 29211. *4543*

CARPETS.
Siveast Consultants, Inc., USA, c/o P.O. Box 1755, Kathmandu, Nepal. *654*

CARROSSERIE.
Nederlandse Vereniging van Ondernemers in het Carrosseriebedrijf, Postbus 299, 2170 AG Sassenheim, Netherlands. FAX 02522-65255. circ. 2,700. *4687*

CARSON - NEWMAN COLLEGE, JEFFERSON CITY, TENNESSEE. FACULTY STUDIES.
Carson - Newman College, Jefferson City, TN 37760. TEL 615-475-9061. *1702*

CARTOLOGICA.
Universite Laval, Bibliotheque Generale, Quebec, Que. G1K 7P4, Canada. TEL 418-656-2002. *2267*

CASA STILE.
Agenzia Gestione Periodici, Via D. Trentacoste 9, 20134 Milan, Italy. TEL 02-2640009. circ. 19,000. *2549*

CASE AND COMMENT MAGAZINE (ROCHESTER).
Robert E. Weber, 50 Broad St. E., Rochester, NY 14694. TEL 716-546-5530. FAX 716-262-4075. circ. 110,000. *2612*

CASHEW BULLETIN.
Cashew Export Promotion Council, Chittoor Rd., Cochin 682 016, India. circ. 700. *2063*

CASSIOPEIA.
Canadian Astronomical Society, c/o David Dunlap Observatory, Box 360, Richmond Hill, Ont. L4C 4Y6, Canada. TEL 416-884-9562. circ. 400. *363*

CASTING DESIGN & APPLICATION.
Penton Publishing 1100 Superior Ave., Cleveland, OH 44114. TEL 216-696-7000. circ. 22,000. *3404*

CASTLE DRACULA.
Gothick Gateway, c/o Gordon R. Guy, Ed., Box 423, Glastonbury, E. Hartford, CT 06033. *3010*

CATALOGO MOTORISTICO.
Azienda Cataloghi Italiani s.a.s., Piazzale Lugano 9, 20158 Milan, Italy. TEL 02-39322181. FAX 02-6454786.
circ. 35,000. *4687*

CATERING WORLD.
C P R Publishing, Northern Rock House, 20 Market Place, Guisborough, Cleveland TS14 6HF, England. TEL 0287-639111.
circ. 150,000. *2472*

THE CATHOLIC.
Incorporated Catholic Truth Society, 38-40 Eccleston Square, London SW1V 1PD, England. TEL 071-834 4392.
circ. 25,000. *4258*

CATHOLIC FORESTER.
Catholic Order of Foresters, 425 W. Shuman Blvd., Box 3012, Naperville, IL 60566-7012. TEL 708-983-4900. FAX 708-983-4057.
circ. 170,000. *2223*

CATHOLIC NEAR EAST MAGAZINE.
Catholic Near East Welfare Association, 1011 First Ave., New York, NY 10022-4195. TEL 212-826-1480. FAX 212-838-1344.
circ. 170,000. *3940*

CATHOLIC UNIVERSITY MEDICAL COLLEGE JOURNAL.
Catholic University, Graduate School, Bampo-dong, Kannam-ku, Seoul 137, S. Korea. TEL 02-593-5141. FAX 02-532-3112.
circ. 1,000. *3086*

CATHOLIC WORKMAN.
Box 47, New Prague, MN 56071. TEL 612-758-2229. FAX 612-758-5041.
circ. 8,300. *4260*

CATPLAN REPORT.
Research Press Inc., 4500 W. 72nd Terrace, Prairie Village, KS 66208. TEL 913-362-9667. *1090*

CATS.
Our Dogs Publishing Co. Ltd., 5 James Leigh St., Manchester M1 6EX, England. TEL 061-236-0577. FAX 061-236-5534.
circ. 7,000. *3709*

CAVALLO MAGAZINE.
Solitaire s.r.l., Viale Milanofiori, Strada 3a, Palazzo B 11, 20094 Accago (Milan), Italy. TEL 02 824711-226. FAX 02-8241477.
circ. 55,000. *230*

CEMENTO PORTLAND.
Instituto del Cemento Portland Argentino, Calle San Martin 1137, Buenos Aires, Argentina. *609*

CENTRAL BANK OF BARBADOS. BALANCE OF PAYMENTS.
Central Bank of Barbados, Research Department, P.O. Box 1016, Church Village, Bridgetown, Barbados, W.I. TEL 809-436-6870. FAX 809-427-1431.
circ. 2,000. *710*

CENTRAL BUSINESS REVIEW.
University of Central Oklahoma, College of Business Administration, 100 N. University Dr., Edmond, OK 73034. TEL 405-341-2980. FAX 405-341-4964.
circ. 2,500. *655*

CENTRAL COUNCIL FOR EDUCATION AND TRAINING IN SOCIAL WORK. REPORT OF COUNCIL MEETING.
Central Council for Education and Training in Social Work, Derbyshire House, St. Chad's St., London WC1H 8AD, England. FAX 071-278-2934. *4401*

CENTRAL PENN BUSINESS JOURNAL.
C P N C Inc., 1500 N. Second St., Harrisburg, PA 17102-2527. TEL 717-236-4300. FAX 717-236-6803.
circ. 16,000. *655*

CENTRAL ROAD RESEARCH INSTITUTE, NEW DELHI. ROAD RESEARCH PAPER.
Central Road Research Institute, P.O. Central Road Research Institute, New Delhi 110020, India. TEL 6832274. *4718*

CENTRAL SERICULTURAL RESEARCH AND TRAINING INSTITUTE. ANNUAL REPORT.
Central Sericultural Research and Training Institute, Manandavadi Rd., Sriramapura, Mysore 570008, India. FAX 0091-0821-28545.
circ. 300. *83*

CENTRE FOR INTERGROUP STUDIES. ANNUAL REPORT.
Centre for Intergroup Studies, 37 Grotto Rd., Rondebosch, South Africa. TEL 021-6502503. FAX 021-6852142.
circ. 2,200. *4431*

CENTRE NATIONAL DE DOCUMENTATION SCIENTIFIQUE ET TECHNIQUE. RAPPORT D'ACTIVITE.
Centre National de Documentation Scientifique et Technique, 4, Bd. de l'Empereur, B-1000 Brussels, Belgium.
circ. 1,000. *4595*

CENTRE NATIONAL DE LA RECHERCHE SCIENTIFIQUE. ANNUAIRE EUROPEEN D'ADMINISTRATION PUBLIQUE.
Editions du C N R S, 1 Place Aristide Briand, 92195 Meudon Cedex, France. TEL 1-45-34-75-50. FAX 1-46-26-28-49.
circ. 1,500. *4056*

CENTREPOINT.
Christian Centre Party, 157 Vicarage Rd., London E10 5DU, England. TEL 081-539-3876. *3879*

CERVEZA Y MALTA.
Asociacion Espanola de Tecnicos de Maquinaria para la Construccion Obras Publicas y Mineria, c/o Cruz del Sur, No. 3 bajo, 28007 Madrid, Spain.
circ. 1,000. *380*

CESKOSLOVENSKA AKADEMIE VED. GEOGRAFICKY USTAV, BRNO. ZPRAVY.
Ceskoslovenska Akademie Ved, Geograficky Ustav, Brno, Mendlovo nam. 1, 662 82 Brno, Czechoslovakia. TEL 425-3160. *2245*

CHAMBRE DE COMMERCE, D'AGRICULTURE, D'INDUSTRIE ET D'ARTISANAT DU NIGER. WEEKLY BULLETIN.
Chambre de Commerce, d'Agriculture, d'Industrie et d'Artisanat du Niger, B.P. 209, Niamey, Niger.
circ. 170. *812*

CHANGING MEDICAL MARKETS.
Theta Corporation, Theta Bldg., Middlefield, CT 06455. TEL 203-349-1054. FAX 203-349-1227. *3087*

CHANNEL D L S.
Department of Public Instruction, Division for Library Services, 125 S. Webster St., 5th Fl., Box 7841, Madison, WI 53707. TEL 608-266-9679. FAX 608-267-1052.
circ. 3,450. *2752*

THE CHANTICLEER.
Jacksonville State University, Communications Board, Jacksonville, AL 36265. TEL 205-782-5701. FAX 205-782-5291.
circ. 7,000. *1307*

CHAPLIN.
Svenska Filminstitutet, P.O. Box 27126, S-102 52 Stockholm, Sweden. TEL 08-665-1203. FAX 08-663-8009.
circ. 5,700. *3505*

CHARTERED INSTITUTE OF PUBLIC FINANCE AND ACCOUNTANCY. CONFERENCE HANDBOOK.
Chartered Institute of Public Finance and Accountancy, 3 Robert St., London WC2N 6BH, England. TEL 01-895-8823. FAX 01-895-8825. *749*

CHATELAINE'S NEW MOTHER.
Maclean Hunter Ltd., Maclean Hunter Bldg., 777 Bay St., Toronto, Ont. M5W 1A7, Canada. TEL 416-596-5230. FAX 416-593-3197.
circ. 430,000. *1233*

CHECK CLUB NEWSLETTER.
F I S I - Madison Financial Corporation Editor, Member Newsletters, Box 40726, Nashville, TN 37204. TEL 615-371-2775.
circ. 237,040. *772*

CHECKLIST OF PUBLICATIONS OF THE STATE OF ARIZONA.
Department of Library, Archives and Public Records, 1700 W. Washington St., Rm. 142, Phoenix, AZ 85007. TEL 602-542-4343. FAX 602-542-4500.
circ. 132. *397*

CHEMICAL BUSINESS.
Schnell Publishing Co., Inc., 80 Broad St., New York, NY 10004. TEL 212-248-4177. FAX 212-248-4901.
circ. 38,500. *1172*

CHEMICAL DISTILLATIONS.
Cyrus J. Lawrence, Inc., 1290 Ave. of the Americas, New York, NY 10104. TEL 212-468-5000. *1172*

CHEMICAL INDUSTRY MONITOR.
Cyrus J. Lawrence, Inc., 1290 Ave. of the Americas, New York, NY 10104. TEL 212-468-5000. *1172*

CHEMICAL PROCESSING.
Putman Publishing Co., 301 E. Erie St., Chicago, IL 60611. TEL 312-644-2020.
circ. 80,042. *1851*

CHEMICAL SAFETY.
Goldstein and Associates, 1150 Yale St., Ste. 12, Santa Monica, CA 90403-1309. TEL 213-828-1309.
circ. 11,000. *1851*

CHEMICALS, ADHESIVES AND PHARMACEUTICALS (YEAR).
South African Foreign Trade Organisation, Publishing Division, P.O. Box 782706, Sandton 2146, South Africa. TEL 011-883-3737. FAX 011-883-6569. *1851*

CHEMIE-ANLAGEN UND VERFAHREN.
Konradin-Verlag Robert Kohlhammer GmbH, Postfach 100252, 7022 Leinfelden-Echterdingen, Germany. TEL 0711-7594-0.
circ. 25,000. *1851*

CHEMISCHE RUNDSCHAU.
Vogt-Schild AG, Zuchwilerstr. 21, CH-4501 Solothurn 1, Switzerland. TEL 065-247247. FAX 065-247335.
circ. 18,300. *1174*

CHEMIST & DRUGSTORE NEWS.
India Publications Co., Denabank House, 2nd Fl., 31 Hamam St., Bombay 1, India. *3720*

CHENGSHI GONGYONG SHIYE.
Shanghai Gongyong Shiye Yanjiusuo, 706 Hengshan Road, Shanghai 200030, People's Republic of China. TEL 4314037. FAX 0086-21-3217616.
circ. 4,000. *4056*

CHESHIRE SMILE.
Leonard Cheshire Foundation, Arnold House, 66 The Ridgeway, Enfield, Middx EN2 8JA, England. TEL 081-367-3544.
circ. 7,050. *2290*

CHIANG MAI MEDICAL BULLETIN.
Chiang Mai University, Faculty of Medicine, 110 Intavaroros Street, Chiang Mai 50002, Thailand. TEL 52-221122. FAX 53-217144.
circ. 1,000. *3087*

CHIBA UNIVERSITY. FACULTY OF ENGINEERING. JOURNAL.
Chiba University, Faculty of Engineering, 1-33 Yayoicho, Chiba 280, Japan. TEL 0472-51-1111. FAX 0472-51-7337.
circ. 550. *1816*

CHICAGO GENEALOGIST.
Chicago Genealogical Society, Box 1160, Chicago, IL 60690.
circ. 900. *2147*

CHICAGO MARKET.
Bolger Publications Inc., 3301 Como Ave., S.E., Minneapolis, MN 55414. TEL 612-645-6311. FAX 612-645-1750.
circ. 26,000. *2281*

CHICAGO PURCHASOR.
Purchasing Management Association of Chicago, 201 N. Wells, Chicago, IL 60606. TEL 312-782-1940. *1035*

CHICAGO TALENT SOURCEBOOK (NO.).
Alexander Communications, Inc., 212 W. Superior, Ste. 203, Chicago, IL 60610. TEL 312-944-5115. FAX 312-944-7865.
circ. 12,000. *3998*

CHILD MAGAZINE'S GUIDE TO HAVING A BABY.
New York Times Company, Magazine Group, 110 Fifth Ave., New York, NY 10011. TEL 212-463-1600. FAX 212-463-1553.
circ. 1,200,000. *1234*

CHILD SAFETY REVIEW.
Child Accident Prevention Trust, 28 Portland Place, London W1N 4DE, England. TEL 071-636-2545.
circ. 5,500. *1234*

CHILDCARE.
Cara Communications Ltd., 100 Court Ave., Ste. 206, Des Moines, IA 50309-2200. TEL 515-282-2888.
circ. 125,000. *1234*

CHILDREN'S HEALTH CARE JOURNAL.
Waverly Press, Inc. 428 E. Preston St., Box 64025, Baltimore, MD 21202. TEL 301-528-4000.
circ. 4,000. *4402*

CHILE. DIRECCION DE PRESUPUESTOS. DEPARTAMENTO DE ESTUDIOS FINANCIEROS. FINANZAS PUBLICAS.
Direccion de Presupuestos, Teatinos 120, Piso 12, Of. 27, Santiago, Chile. *1090*

CHILE. SERVICIO NACIONAL DE PESCA. ANUARIO ESTADISTICO DE PESCA.
Servicio Nacional de Pesca, Departamento de Recursos Naturales, Yungay 1731 4o piso, Valparaiso, Chile. FAX 259564. *2038*

CHILEAN NEWS.
Anglo Chilean Society, 12 Devonshire St., London W1N 2DS, England. TEL 01-580-1271.
circ. 600. *3953*

THE CHIMES (LA MIRADA).
Biola University, 13800 Biola Ave., La Mirada, CA 90639. TEL 213-944-0351.
circ. 3,000. *1307*

CHINA EXCHANGE NEWS.
National Academy of Sciences, Committee on Scholarly Communication with the People's Republic of China, 2101 Constitution Ave. N.W., Washington, DC 20418. TEL 202-334-2718. FAX 202-334-1774.
circ. 4,000. *4304*

CHINESE AGRICULTURAL CHEMICAL SOCIETY. JOURNAL.
Chinese Agricultural Chemical Society, Department of Agricultural Chemistry, National Taiwan University, Taipei, Taiwan, Republic of China. TEL 02-363-3123. FAX 886-2-363-3123. *173*

CHIROPRACTIC PRODUCTS.
Novicom, Inc., 3510 Torrance Blvd., No.315, Torrance, CA 90503. TEL 310-316-8112. FAX 310-316-8422.
circ. 35,059. *3213*

CHIZU NO TOMO.
Japan Map Association, Shinsen Bldg., 8-2 Shinsen-cho, Shibuya, Tokyo 150, Japan. FAX 03-3461-0244. *2245*

CHLODNICTWO.
Wydawnictwo Czasopism i Ksiazek Technicznych SIGMA - NOT, Ul. Biala 4, P.O. Box 1004, 00-950 Warsaw, Poland.
circ. 1,050. *2298*

CHRISTIAN MEDICAL COLLEGE VELLORE ALUMNI JOURNAL.
Christian Medical College, Alumni Association, Vellore 632 002, Tamil Nadu, India. TEL 22603.
circ. 1,700. *3087*

CHRISTIANS IN CRISIS.
Christian Forum Research Foundation, 1111 Fairgrounds Rd., Grand Rapids, MN 55744. TEL 218-326-2688.
circ. 1,000. *4170*

CHROMATOGRAM.
Beckman Instruments, Inc., Altex Division, Box 3100, Fullerton, CA 92634-3100. TEL 415-866-0511. FAX 415-866-3018.
circ. 30,000. *1205*

CHRONICA DERMATOLOGICA.
Istituto Dermopatico dell'Immacolata, Via Monti di Creta, 106, 00167 Rome, Italy. FAX 06-6211746.
circ. 7,000. *3246*

CHRONICLE (GRAYSLAKE).
College of Lake County, 19351 W. Washington, Grayslake, IL 60030. TEL 708-223-3634. FAX 708-223-9371.
circ. 4,000. *1307*

CHRONICLE (HEMPSTEAD).
Hofstra University, Student Government Association, 203 Student Center, Hempstead, NY 11550. TEL 516-560-6965. FAX 516-564-0119.
circ. 10,000. *1307*

CHUGOKU ELECTRIC POWER CO. TECHNICAL LABORATORY REPORT.
Chugoku Electric Power Co., Inc., 4-32 Osu 4-chome, Hiroshima 730, Japan. *1884*

CHUKI KEIZAI YOSOKU.
Japan Center for Economic Research, Economic Analysis Division, Nikkei Kayabacho Bldg., 6-1 Nihonbashi Kayaba-cho 2-chome, Chuo-ku, Tokyo 103, Japan. TEL 03-3639-2801. *851*

CHURCH MUSIC QUARTERLY.
Royal School of Church Music, Addington Palace, Croydon CR9 5AD, England. FAX 081-340-0021.
circ. 14,500. *3545*

CIAO.
Ciao Publishing Co., 1081 Bas l'Assomption Nord, Ville de l'Assomption, Que. JOK 1GO, Canada. FAX 514-589-4485.
circ. 40,000. *1997*

CIENCIA BIOLOGICA: BIOLOGIA MOLECULAR E CELULAR.
Universidade de Coimbra, Instituto de Zoologia, Coimbra, Portugal. FAX 351-3935812.
circ. 800. *580*

CINDERELLA PHILATELIST.
Cinderella Stamp Club, c/o L.N. Williams, 44 The Ridgeway, London NW11 8QS, England.
circ. 800. *3751*

CINE-OJA.
Sociedad Civil Cine al Dia, Apdo. 50446, Sabana Grande, Caracas, Venezuela.
circ. 2,500. *3505*

CIRCLE (PORTLAND).
Circle Forum, Box 176, Portland, OR 97207. *2990*

CIRCUIT RIDER (NASHVILLE).
United Methodist Publishing House, 201 Eighth Ave. S., Box 801, Nashville, TN 37202. TEL 615-749-6731.
circ. 40,000. *4234*

CIRCUITS ASSEMBLY.
Miller Freeman, Inc. 600 Harrison St., San Francisco, CA 94107. TEL 415-905-2200. FAX 415-905-2232.
circ. 40,000. *1765*

CIRCULATION MANAGEMENT.
Ganesa Corporation, 611 Broadway, Ste. 401, New York, NY 10012-2608. TEL 212-989-2133. FAX 212-620-0396.
circ. 10,000. *4125*

CIRUGIA DEL URUGUAY.
Sociedad de Cirugia del Uruguay, Hospital de Clinicas "Dr. Manuel Quintela", C.C. 10.972, Piso 4, Montevideo, Uruguay.
circ. 1,000. *3377*

CITY & COUNTRY CLUB LIFE.
Club Publications, 665 La Villa Dr., Miami Springs, FL 33166. TEL 305-887-1701. FAX 305-885-1923.
circ. 26,000. *2223*

CITY & STATE.
Crain Communications, Inc. (Chicago), 740 N. Rush St., Chicago, IL 60611-2590. TEL 312-649-5260. FAX 312-649-5228.
circ. 45,777. *4056*

CITY CLUB GADFLY.
City Club of New York, 33 W. 42nd St., New York, NY 10036. TEL 212-921-9870.
circ. 2,500. *4085*

CIUDADANO.
Atocha 26, 3o Izqda., 28012 Madrid, Spain. TEL 3691285. FAX 3691272.
circ. 70,000. *1503*

CIVIL AVIATION TRAINING.
Monch UK Ltd., 84 Alexandra Rd., Farnborough, Hants GU14 6DD, England. TEL 0252-517974. FAX 0252-512714.
circ. 12,000. *4672*

CIVIL ENGINEERING CONTRACTOR.
Brooke Pattrick (Pty) Ltd:, P.O. Box 422, Bedfordview 2008, South Africa. TEL 011-6224666. FAX 011-6167196.
circ. 4,500. *1863*

CIVIL LIBERTIES REPORTER.
American Civil Liberties Union of New Jersey, 2 Washington Place, Newark, NJ 07102. TEL 201-642-2084.
circ. 6,600. *2701*

CIVITAN MAGAZINE.
Civitan International, Box 130744, Birmingham, AL 35213-0744. TEL 205-591-8910. FAX 205-592-6307.
circ. 37,000. *1297*

CLAMAVI.
Stichting Mensen in Nood - Caritas Neerlandica, Hekellaan 6, 5211 LX 's-Hertogenbosch, Netherlands. TEL 073-144544. FAX 073-132115.
circ. 250,000. *4402*

CLAN MACTAVISH ASSOCIATION NEWSLETTER.
Clan MacTavish Association, 222 Katherine Ave., Salinas, CA 93901-3136. TEL 408-422-4212.
circ. 30. *2147*

CLAN MCLAREN SOCIETY, U S A. QUARTERLY.
Clan McLaren Society, U S A, 5843 Royalcrest, Dallas, TX 75230.
circ. 145. *2147*

CLAN ROSS NEWSLETTER.
Clan Ross Association of the United States, Inc., Rt. 2, Box 424, Richmond Hill, GA 31324. TEL 912-727-2560.
circ. 400. *1997*

CLARIN INTERNACIONAL.
Arte Grafico Editorial Argentino S.A., Piedras 1743, Buenos Aires, Argentina. *2170*

CLARION MAGAZINE.
Clarion University, 974 E. Wood St., Clarion, PA 16214. TEL 814-226-2334.
circ. 22,000. *1307*

CLARK UNIVERSITY NEWS.
Clark University, 950 Main St., Worcester, MA 01610. TEL 508-793-7441. FAX 508-794-7565.
circ. 25,000. *1307*

CLASS.
Class Editori, Corso Italia 22, 20122 Milan, Italy. TEL 02-8029-241. FAX 02-8052832.
circ. 90,000. *1063*

CLASSICUM.
Classical Association of New South Wales, c/o Department of Classics, Sydney University, Sydney, N.S.W. 2006, Australia. FAX 02-692-4203.
circ. 300. *1276*

CLEANROOMS INTERNATIONAL.
Witter Publishing Co., Inc., 84 Park Ave., Flemington, NJ 08822. TEL 908-788-0343. FAX 908-788-3782.
circ. 25,000. *3616*

CLEAR TRACK.
National Railroad Construction and Maintenance Association, Inc., 10765 Woodwater Cir., Eden Prairie, MN 55347. FAX 612-942-8947.
circ. 1,500. *4708*

CLEMATIS.
Bairnsdale Field Naturalists' Club, P.O. Box 563, Bairnsdale, Vic. 3875, Australia. *1945*

CLEMSON UNIVERSITY. DEPARTMENT OF FOREST RESOURCES. FORESTRY BULLETIN.
Clemson University, Department of Forest Resources, Clemson, SC 29634-1003. TEL 803-656-3302.
circ. 500. *2097*

CLEMSON UNIVERSITY. WATER RESOURCES RESEARCH INSTITUTE. REPORT.
Clemson University, Water Resources Research Institute, Clemson, SC 29634-2900. TEL 803-656-2698. FAX 803-656-4780. *4823*

CLEVELAND CLINIC JOURNAL OF MEDICINE.
Cleveland Clinic Educational Foundation, 9500 Euclid Ave., Cleveland, OH 44195-5058. TEL 216-444-2662. FAX 216-444-9385.
circ. 88,000. *3088*

CLIK.
Clik, 20 Lower Spadina Ave., Toronto, Ont. M5V 2Z1, Canada. TEL 416-367-2545. FAX 416-367-0382.
circ. 2,500. *1252*

CLINICAL LABORATORY INTERNATIONAL.
Pan European Publishing Co., Rue Verte 216, B-1210 Brussels, Belgium. TEL 02-242-29-92. FAX 02-242-71-11.
circ. 30,012. *3258*

CLUB LIVING.
Club Living, Inc., 16 Copper Beech Cir., White Plains, NY 10605-4702.
circ. 51,000. *4469*

COAL.
Maclean Hunter Publishing Company, 29 N. Wacker Dr., Chicago, IL 60606. TEL 312-726-2802. FAX 312-726-2574.
circ. 22,307. *3481*

COASTGUARD.
Department of Transport, H.M. Coastguard, Rm. S13-19 2, Marsham St., London SW1P 3EB, England. TEL 01-276-5082. FAX 01-276-5179.
circ. 15,000. *4726*

COCOA GROWERS BULLETIN.
Cadbury Ltd., Bournville, Birmingham B30 2LU, England.
circ. 1,500. *173*

COCOCASSETTE.
T & D Software, Box 1256, Holland, MI 49423-1256. TEL 616-396-7577.
circ. 2,000. *1468*

COFFEE MAZDOOR SAHAKARI.
All India Coffee Workers Cooperative Societies Federation Ltd., 10 U.B. Bungalow Rd., Jawahar Nagar, Delhi 7, India. *2064*

COIFFURE.
Hofstad Vakpers B. V., Postbus 119, 2700 AC Zoetermeer, Netherlands. TEL 079-711811. FAX 079-711803.
circ. 6,345. *372*

COLD SPRING HARBOR LABORATORY. ABSTRACTS OF PAPERS PRESENTED AT MEETINGS.
Cold Spring Harbor Laboratory Press, Publications Department, Box 100, Cold Spring Harbor, NY 11724. TEL 800-843-4388. FAX 516-349-1946. *435*

COLD SPRING HARBOR LABORATORY. ANNUAL REPORT.
Cold Spring Harbor Laboratory Press, Publications Department, Box 100, Cold Spring Harbor, NY 11724. TEL 800-843-4388. FAX 516-349-1946. *435*

COLEGIO DE INGENIEROS ARQUITECTOS Y AGRIMENSORES DE PUERTO RICO. REVISTA.
Insular Publishers Corp, Box GA, Caparra Heights, Puerto Rico, PR 00936.
circ. 5,500. *1863*

COLLEGE AND UNIVERSITY ADMISSIONS AND ENROLLMENT, NEW YORK STATE.
Education Department, Post-Secondary Policy Analysis, Cultural Education Bldg., Rm. 5B44, Albany, NY 12230. TEL 518-474-3874. *1702*

COLLEGE AND UNIVERSITY DEGREES CONFERRED, NEW YORK STATE.
Education Department, Post Secondary Policy Analysis, Cultural Education Bldg., Rm. 5B44, Albany, NY 12230. TEL 518-474-3874. *1702*

COLLEGE AND UNIVERSITY EMPLOYEES, NEW YORK STATE.
Education Department, Office of Post-Secondary Policy Analysis, c/o James J. Brady, Chief, Bureau of Post-Secondary Statistical Service, Rm. 5B44 CEC, Albany, NY 12230. TEL 518-474-3874. *1703*

COLLEGE OF ANAESTHETISTS. NEWSLETTER.
College of Anaesthetists, 35-43 Lincoln's Inn Fields, London WC2A 3PN, England. TEL 071-405-3474. FAX 071-831-9019.
circ. 6,000. *3191*

COLLEGE SWIMMING COACHES ASSOCIATION OF AMERICA NEWSLETTER.
College Swimming Coaches Association of America, c/o Penny Lee Dean, Ed., 698 Birch Ave., Upland, CA 91786.
circ. 650. *4469*

COLLEGE UNION & ON-CAMPUS HOSPITALITY.
Executive Business Media, Inc., Box 1500, 825 Old Country Rd., Westbury, NY 11590. TEL 516-334-3030.
circ. 11,000. *1308*

COLLEGE VOICE (TRENTON).
Mercer County Community College, Box B, Trenton, NJ 08690. TEL 609-586-4800. FAX 609-890-6338. *1308*

COLLEGIAN (ELYRIA).
Lorain County Community College, Student Activities Office, 1005 N. Abbe Rd., Elyria, OH 44035.
TEL 216-365-4191. *1308*

COLOMBO PLAN NEWSLETTER.
Colombo Plan Bureau, 12 Melbourne Ave., P.O. Box 596, Colombo 4, Sri Lanka. TEL 1-581813. FAX 1-580721.
circ. 2,500. *927*

COLOR PUBLISHING.
PennWell Publishing Co. (Westford), One Technology Park Dr., Westford, MA 01886. TEL 508-392-2157. FAX 508-692-0525.
circ. 24,000. *4125*

COLORADO NORTH REVIEW.
University of Northern Colorado, Student Media Corporation, University Center, Greeley, CO 80639. TEL 303-351-1350.
circ. 2,500. *2907*

COLOUR.
Ulick Publishing Co., Box 8551, Bartlett, IL 60103. TEL 708-213-1300.
circ. 80,000. *4125*

COLUMBAN MISSION.
Columban Fathers, St. Columbans, NE 68056.
FAX 402-291-8693.
circ. 180,000. *4261*

COLUMBIA COLLEGE TODAY.
Columbia University, Columbia College, Office of Alumni Affairs, 100 Hamilton Hall, New York, NY 10027. TEL 212-854-5538. FAX 212-854-1211.
circ. 44,000. *1308*

COLUMBIA ENGINEERING RESEARCH.
Columbia University, School of Engineering & Applied Science, 164 Engineering Terr., New York, NY 10027. TEL 212-854-2997.
circ. 12,000. *1817*

COLUMBUS MARKET.
Bolger Publications Inc., 3301 Como Ave. S.E., Minneapolis, MN 55414. TEL 612-645-6311. FAX 612-645-1750.
circ. 16,000. *2281*

COLUMNS (SEATTLE).
University of Washington Alumni Association, 1415 N.E. 45 St., Seattle, WA 98105. TEL 206-543-0540. FAX 206-685-0611.
circ. 160,000. *1308*

COMBAT CREW.
U.S. Air Force Strategic Air Command, c/o Superintendant of Documents, U.S. Govt. Printing Office, Washington, DC 20402. TEL 202-275-0186. FAX 202-512-2233. *3454*

COMBONI MISSIONS.
Comboni Missionaries of the Heart of Jesus, 8108 Beechmont Ave., Cincinnati, OH 45255. TEL 513-474-4997. FAX 513-474-0382.
circ. 25,000. *4261*

COMERCIO EXTERIOR.
Fundacao Visconde de Cabo Frio, SIA Trecho 6, lote 140, 71200 Brasilia DF, Brazil.
circ. 6,000. *904*

COMERCIO HISPANO BRITANICO.
Spanish Chamber of Commerce in Great Britain, 5 Cavendish Square, London WIM ODP, England.
TEL 071-637-9061. FAX 071-436-7188.
circ. 2,500. *813*

COMERCIO Y PRODUCCION.
Chamber of Commerce of Puerto Rico, Box 3789, San Juan, PR 00904.
circ. 1,500. *813*

COMICS RETAILER.
Krause Publications, Inc., 700 E. State St., Iola, WI 54990. TEL 715-445-2214. FAX 715-445-4087.
circ. 6,000. *1114*

COMMERCIAL NEWS U S A.
U.S. Department of Commerce, International Trade Administration, Rm. 2106, Washington, DC 20230. TEL 202-377-4918. FAX 202-377-0178.
circ. 200,000. *904*

COMMISSION OF THE EUROPEAN COMMUNITIES. ANNUAL REPORTS ON THE PROGRESS OF RESEARCH WORK PROMOTED BY THE ECSC.
Commission of the European Communities, 200 rue de la Loi, B-1049 Brussels, Belgium, Belgium. *4099*

COMMISSION OF THE EUROPEAN COMMUNITIES. FINANCIAL REPORT.
Commission of the European Communities, 200 rue de la Loi, B-1049 Brussels, Belgium. *1091*

COMMISSION OF THE EUROPEAN COMMUNITIES. MARCHES AGRICOLES: SERIE "PRIX". PRODUITS ANIMAUX.
Commission of the European Communities, 200 rue de la Loi, B-1049 Brussels, Belgium. *149*

COMMISSION OF THE EUROPEAN COMMUNITIES. MARCHES AGRICOLES: SERIE "PRIX". PRODUITS VEGETAUX.
Commission of the European Communities, 200 rue de la Loi, B-1049 Brussels, Belgium. *149*

COMMON CARRIER WEEK.
Warren Publishing, Inc., 2115 Ward Ct., N.W., Washington, DC 20037. TEL 202-872-9200. FAX 202-293-3435. *1362*

COMMONWEALTH INSTITUTE, LONDON. ANNUAL REPORT.
Commonwealth Institute, Kensington High St., London W8 6NQ, England. *2245*

COMMONWEALTH SCIENTIFIC AND INDUSTRIAL RESEARCH ORGANIZATION. DIVISION OF ANIMAL HEALTH. REPORT.
C.S.I.R.O., Division of Animal Health, Private Bag No. 1, Parkville, Vic. 3052, Australia. TEL 03-342-9700. FAX 03-347-4042.
circ. 1,000. *4808*

COMMONWEALTH SCIENTIFIC AND INDUSTRIAL RESEARCH ORGANIZATION. INSTITUTE OF ENERGY AND EARTH RESOURCES. ANNUAL REPORT.
C.S.I.R.O., Institute of Energy and Earth Resources, Box 225, Dickson, A.C.T. 2602, Australia.
circ. 2,000. *3482*

CONTROLLED CIRCULATION SERIALS

COMMONWEALTH SCIENTIFIC AND INDUSTRIAL RESEARCH ORGANIZATION. INSTITUTE OF ENERGY AND EARTH RESOURCES. INVESTIGATION REPORT.
C.S.I.R.O., Institute of Energy and Earth Resources, P.O. Box 136, North Ryde, N.S.W. 2113, Australia.
circ. 825. *3482*

COMMONWEALTH SCIENTIFIC AND INDUSTRIAL RESEARCH ORGANIZATION. INSTITUTE OF ENERGY AND EARTH RESOURCES. MINERALS & ENERGY BULLETIN.
C.S.I.R.O., Institute of Energy and Earth Resources, P.O. Box 225, Dickson, A.C.T. 2602, Australia.
circ. 2,300. *3482*

COMMONWEALTH SCIENTIFIC AND INDUSTRIAL RESEARCH ORGANIZATION. INSTITUTE OF ENERGY AND EARTH RESOURCES. TECHNICAL COMMUNICATION.
C.S.I.R.O., Institute of Energy and Earth Resources, Box 136, North Ryde, N.S.W. 2113, Australia.
3482

COMMUNICATE.
Spotlight Publications Ltd., 245 Blackfriars Rd., London SE1 9UR. FAX 01-760-0973.
circ. 20,206. *1362*

COMMUNICATION INDUSTRIES.
Communications Industry Association of Japan, Sankei Bldg. Annex, 1-7-2, Ohte-machi, Chiyoda-ku, Tokyo 100, Japan. TEL 03-3231-3156. FAX 03-3246-0495. *1362*

COMMUNICATION NEWS.
American Society of Association Executives, 1575 I St., N.W., Washington, DC 20005. TEL 202-626-2723. FAX 202-408-9635.
circ. 2,200. *1005*

COMMUNICATOR (WASHINGTON, 1953).
Associated Credit Bureaus, Inc., 1090 Vermont Ave., N.W., Ste. 200, Washington, DC 20005-4905. TEL 202-371-0910. FAX 202-371-0134. *772*

COMMUNICATOR COMMUNITY NEWS.
Gloria Greco, Ed. & Pub., Box 9090, Reno, NV 89507-9090. TEL 702-747-4400.
circ. 24,000. *2223*

COMMUNITY TRANSPORTATION REPORTER.
Community Transportation Association of America, 725 15th St., N.W., Ste. 900, Washington, DC 20005. TEL 202-628-1480. FAX 202-737-9197.
circ. 10,000. *4648*

COMPANY.
3441 N. Ashland Ave., Chicago, IL 60657. TEL 312-281-1534. FAX 312-281-2667.
circ. 150,000. *4262*

COMPASS (JACKSONVILLE).
Jacksonville University, 2800 University Blvd. N., Jacksonville, FL 32211. TEL 904-744-3950. FAX 904-774-0101.
circ. 12,000. *1308*

COMPASSION MAGAZINE (COLORADO SPRINGS).
Compassion International, Box 700, Colorado Springs, CO 80933. TEL 719-594-9900. FAX 719-594-6271.
circ. 128,000. *4234*

COMPETITION ANGLER.
2160 Renwick Dr., Poland, OH 44514. TEL 216-757-8171. FAX 216-533-3865.
circ. 500. *4544*

COMPRESSED AIR.
Compressed Air Magazine Co., 253 E. Washington Ave., Washington, NJ 07882. TEL 908-850-7818.
circ. 150,000. *1928*

COMPUTECH.
Technews (Pty) Ltd., P.O. Box 626, Kloof 3640, South Africa. TEL 031-764-0593. FAX 031-864-0386.
circ. 12,500. *4595*

COMPUTER-AIDED ENGINEERING.
Penton Publishing 1100 Superior Ave., Cleveland, OH 44114-2543. TEL 216-696-7000. FAX 216-696-8765.
circ. 60,000. *1877*

COMPUTEREPORT.
Virginia Commonwealth University, Academic Computing, 1015 Floyd Ave, Box 174, Richmond, VA 23284. TEL 804-786-4719. *1392*

COMPUTERS IN H R MANAGEMENT.
Warren, Gorham and Lamont Inc., One Penn Plaza, New York, NY 10119. TEL 212-971-5202.
circ. 35,000. *825*

COMPUTERWORLD.
I D G Danmark A-S, Krumtappen 4, 2500 Valby, Denmark. TEL 36-44-28-00. FAX 36-44-20-33.
circ. 24,300. *1393*

COMPUTERWORLD HONG KONG.
Asia Computerworld Communications Ltd., 701-4 Kam Chung Bldg., 54 Jaffe Rd., Wanchai, Hong Kong. TEL 852-861-3228. FAX 852-861-0953.
circ. 10,800. *1423*

CONCRETE PRODUCTS.
Maclean Hunter Publishing Company, 29 N. Wacker Dr., Chicago, IL 60606. TEL 312-726-2802. FAX 312-726-2574.
circ. 23,126. *611*

CONCRETE TRADER.
Aberdeen Group, 426 S. Westgate, Addison, IL 60101. TEL 708-543-0870. FAX 708-543-3112. *611*

CONFISERIE.
Editions de la Confiserie, 103 rue La Fayette, 75481 Paris Cedex 10, France. FAX 40-16-01-45.
circ. 4,000. *2087*

CONGRESSO.
Cura Enterprises Ltd., 10865 96th St., No. 11, Edmonton, Alta. T5H 2K2, Canada. TEL 403-424-3010.
circ. 5,000. *1997*

CONNECTICUT FAMILY.
New York Family Publications, Inc., 141 Halstead Ave., Ste. 3D, Mamaroneck, NY 10543-2652. TEL 914-381-7474.
circ. 30,000. *1235*

CONNECTICUT GOVERNMENT.
University of Connecticut, Institute of Public Service, Storrs, CT 06269-4014. TEL 203-486-2828. *4057*

CONNECTICUT REAL ESTATE JOURNAL.
Brian P. Heneghan, 57 Washington St., Norwell, MA 02061. TEL 800-654-4993. FAX 617-871-1853. *4147*

CONNSTRUCTION MAGAZINE.
McHugh Design, 62 LaSallle Rd., Ste. 211, W. Hartford, CT 06107. TEL 203-236-5505. FAX 203-231-8808.
circ. 4,800. *611*

CONSCIOUS CONSUMER.
New Consumer Institute, Inc., Box 51, Wauconda, IL 60084. TEL 708-526-0522. FAX 708-526-1174. *1946*

CONSERVATION AND RENEWABLE ENERGY TECHNOLOGIES FOR BUILDING TECHNOLOGIES.
Solar Energy Research Institute, Technical Inquiry Service, 1617 Cole Blvd., Golden, CO 80401-3393. TEL 303-231-1000. *1810*

CONSERVATION AND RENEWABLE ENERGY TECHNOLOGIES FOR INDUSTRIAL TECHNOLOGIES.
Solar Energy Research Institute, Technical Inquiry Service, 1617 Cole Blvd., Golden, CO 80401-3393. TEL 303-231-1000. *1785*

CONSERVATION AND RENEWABLE ENERGY TECHNOLOGIES FOR TRANSPORTATION TECHNOLOGIES.
Solar Energy Research Institute, Technical Inquiry Service, 1617 Cole Blvd., Golden, CO 80401-3393. TEL 303-231-1000. *1785*

CONSERVATION AND RENEWABLE ENERGY TECHNOLOGIES FOR UTILITY TECHNOLOGIES.
Solar Energy Research Institute, Technical Inquiry Service, 1617 Cole Blvd., Golden, CO 80401-3393. TEL 303-231-1000. *1785*

CONSTITUTION CHRONICLE.
U S S Constitution Museum Foundation, Box 1812, Boston, MA 02129. TEL 617-426-1812. FAX 617-242-0496.
circ. 2,500. *3454*

CONSTRUCTION MARKETING TODAY.
Aberdeen Group, 426 S. Westgate, Addison, IL 60101. TEL 708-543-0870. FAX 708-543-3112.
circ. 5,000. *613*

CONSUMER CHOICE.
Consumers Association of Ireland Ltd., 45 Upper Mount St., Dublin 2, Ireland. TEL 01-686836. FAX 01-612464.
circ. 10,000. *1503*

CONSUMERS' WATCH.
Pick 'n Pay Stores, P.O. Box 23087, Claremont 7735, South Africa. TEL 021-683-2140. FAX 021-6832514.
circ. 200,000. *1504*

CONTACT (CRAWLEY, 1947).
Bowthorpe Holdings PLC, Gatwick Road, Crawley, W. Sussex RH10 2RZ, England. TEL 0293-528888. FAX 0293-541905.
circ. 7,000. *2193*

CONTACT (QUEBEC).
Public Relations Services, Pavillon Felix A. Savard, Local 214, Laval University, Quebec, Que. G1K 7P4, Canada. TEL 418-656-2571. FAX 418-656-2809.
circ. 92,000. *2176*

CONTEMPORARY GASTROENTEROLOGY.
Medical Economics Publishing Co., Five Paragon Dr., Montvale, NJ 07645. TEL 800-526-4870. FAX 201-573-1045.
circ. 40,000. *3267*

CONTEMPORARY ORTHOPAEDICS.
Bobit Publishing Company, 2512 Artesia Blvd., Redondo Beach, CA 90278. TEL 310-376-8788. FAX 310-376-9043.
circ. 30,000. *3307*

CONTEMPORARY SURGERY.
Bobit Publishing Company, 2512 Artesia Blvd., Redondo Beach, CA 90278. TEL 310-376-8788. FAX 310-376-9043.
circ. 51,000. *3378*

CONTINGENCIES.
American Academy of Actuaries, 1720 I St., N.W., Washington, DC 20006. TEL 202-223-8196. FAX 202-872-1948.
circ. 22,000. *2530*

CONTRACT BRIDGE BULLETIN.
American Contract Bridge League, 2990 Airways Blvd., Memphis, TN 38116-3847. TEL 901-332-5586. FAX 901-398-7754.
circ. 175,000. *4470*

CONTRACTING BUSINESS.
Penton Publishing 1100 Superior Ave., Cleveland, OH 44114-2543. TEL 216-696-7000. FAX 216-696-8765.
circ. 52,600. *2298*

CONTROLS AND SYSTEMS.
Penton Publishing 1100 Superior Ave., Cleveland, OH 44114-2543. TEL 216-696-7000. FAX 216-696-8765.
circ. 91,000. *1818*

CONVENIENT AUTOMOTIVE SERVICES RETAILER.
Graphic Concepts, Inc., 1801 Rockville Pike, Ste. 330, Rockville, MD 20852. TEL 301-984-4000. FAX 301-984-7340.
circ. 9,000. *4688*

CONVENTIONS AND EXPOSITIONS.
American Society of Association Executives, 1575 I St., N.W., Washington, DC 20005. TEL 202-626-2723. FAX 202-408-9635.
circ. 3,000. *1006*

CONVENTIONS & MEETINGS CANADA.
Effective Communications Ltd., 5762 Highway 7, Ste. 207, Markham, Ont. L3P 1A8, Canada. TEL 416-471-1550. FAX 416-471-1552.
circ. 10,688. *3391*

CONVENTIONSOUTH.
Covey Communications Corp., Box 2267, Gulf Shores, AL 36547. TEL 205-968-5300. FAX 205-968-4532.
circ. 7,500. *3392*

COOKSON MONTHLY BULLETIN FOR THE CERAMIC INDUSTRY.
Cookson Ceramics & Plastics Division, Stoke-on-Trent ST3 7PX, England. FAX 0782-337127.
circ. 400. *1163*

COOP - ZEITUNG.
Coop Schweiz, Thiersteineralle 12, Postfach 2550, CH-4002 Basel, Switzerland. TEL 061-3366666. FAX 061-3367072.
circ. 930,000. *829*

COOPER HELLER RESEARCH. NEWSLETTER.
Cooper Heller Research, Inc., 622 S. 42nd St., Philadelphia, PA 19104. TEL 215-823-5490. *8*

COOPERATIVE FARMER.
Southern States Cooperative, Inc., Box 26234, Richmond, VA 23260. TEL 804-281-1317. FAX 804-281-1141.
circ. 180,000. *85*

COPPER TOPICS.
Copper Development Association Inc., Box 1840, Greenwich, CT 06836. TEL 203-625-8210. FAX 203-625-0174.
circ. 25,000. *3404*

CORDIALITY.
234 Fifth Ave., Ste. 301, New York, NY 10001. TEL 212-677-2200. FAX 212-213-6737.
circ. 100,000. *2223*

CORN FARMER.
Meredith Corporation, 1716 Locust St., Des Moines, IA 50336. TEL 515-284-2700.
circ. 68,000. *85*

CORNELL UNIVERSITY. NEW YORK STATE COLLEGE OF AGRICULTURE AND LIFE SCIENCES. BIOMETRICS UNIT. ANNUAL REPORT.
New York State College of Agriculture and Life Sciences, Department of Plant Breeding and Biometry, Cornell University, 337 Warren Hall, Ithaca, NY 14853. *464*

CORPORATE CLEVELAND.
Business Journal Publishing Co. (Cleveland), 1720 Euclid Ave., Cleveland, OH 44115. TEL 216-621-1644. FAX 216-621-5918.
circ. 30,500. *657*

CORPORATE COMPUTING.
Ziff-Davis Publishing Co. (Foster City), 950 Tower Ln., 19th Fl., Foster City, CA 94404. TEL 415-578-7600.
circ. 155,000. *826*

CORPORATE DETROIT MAGAZINE.
Business Journal Publishing Co. (Southfield), 26111 Evergreen Rd., Ste. 303, Southfield, MI 48076-4499. TEL 313-357-8300. FAX 313-357-8308.
circ. 41,000. *657*

CORPORATE RISK MANAGEMENT.
Oster Communications, Inc., 219 Main St., Cedar Falls, IA 50613. TEL 319-277-1271. FAX 312-977-1042.
circ. 25,000. *943*

CORPUS DES LUTHISTES FRANCAIS.
Editions du C N R S, 1 Place Aristide Briand, 92195 Meudon Cedex, France. TEL 1-45-34-75-50. FAX 1-46-26-28-49.
circ. 1,500. *2357*

CORPUS VITREARUM.
Editions du C N R S, 1 Place Aristide Briand, 92195 Meudon Cedex, France. TEL 1-45-34-75-50. FAX 1-46-26-28-49.
circ. 1,500. *2357*

CORREIO AGRICOLA (PORTUGAL).
Bayer Portugal S A R L, Apdo. 3306, 1308 Lisbon, Portugal. TEL 417-21-21. FAX 417-20-64. *174*

COTTAGE CONNECTIONS.
Cottage Connections, 11113 Radisson Ct., Burnsville, MN 55337.
circ. 1,000. *4840*

COUNTERMAN.
Babcox Publications, 11 S. Forge St., Box 1810, Akron, OH 44309-1810. TEL 216-535-6617. FAX 216-535-0874.
circ. 52,500. *4688*

CREATIVE DELAWARE VALLEY.
Calsun Publications, Box 327, Ramsey, NJ 07446. TEL 215-546-9001.
circ. 10,000. *323*

CRESCENDO.
Toronto Musicians' Association, 101 Thorncliffe Park Dr., Toronto, Ont. M4H 1M2, Canada. TEL 416-421-1020. FAX 416-421-7011.
circ. 5,600. *3548*

CRESCENDO (INTERLOCHEN).
Interlochen Arts Academy, Interlochen Arts Camp, Interlochen, MI 49643. TEL 616-276-9221. FAX 616-276-6321.
circ. 48,000. *323*

CRITERION.
Riverside County Publishing Co., 7190 Jurupa Ave., Riverside, CA 92504-1016.
circ. 2,000. *1309*

CRITICA.
Universidad Nacional Autonoma de Mexico, Instituto de Investigaciones Filosoficas, Apdo. Postal 70-447, Mexico, D.F., Mexico.
circ. 1,000. *3764*

CROP PROTECTION COURIER (INTERNATIONAL).
Bayer AG, 5090 Leverkusen, Germany.
circ. 33,500. *174*

CROWN JOURNAL.
Higgs and Hill PLC, Crown House, Kingston Rd., New Malden, Surrey KT3 3ST, England. TEL 01-942-8921. FAX 01-949-9280.
circ. 7,000. *614*

CUISINE ET VINS DE FRANCE.
Groupe Marie Claire, 11 bis., rue Boissy d'Anglas, 75008 Paris, France. TEL 1-42-66-88-88. FAX 47-42-89-16.
circ. 85,000. *2065*

CULTURED MARBLE NEWS.
Cultured Marble Institute, 435 N. Michigan Ave., Chicago, IL 60611. TEL 312-644-0828. FAX 312-644-8557.
circ. 2,200. *1114*

CURRENT CANADIAN BOOKS.
John Coutts Library Services Ltd., 6900 Kinsmen, P.O. Box 1000, Niagara Falls, Ont. L2E 7E7, Canada. TEL 416-364-9919. FAX 416-356-5064.
circ. 100. *4126*

THE CURRENT OF KAPPA DELTA EPSILON.
Kappa Delta Epsilon, Oconee County Public Schools, Box 146, School St., Watkinsville, GA 30677. TEL 205-822-4106.
circ. 1,500. *1309*

CUSTOM BUILDER.
Willows Publishing Group, Inc., 38 Laffayette St., Box 998, Yarmouth, ME 04096-0470. TEL 207-846-0970. FAX 207-846-1561.
circ. 30,000. *615*

CUSTOM WOODWORKING BUSINESS.
Vance Publishing Corporation, 400 Knightsbridge Pkwy., Lincolnshire, IL 60069. TEL 708-634-2600.
circ. 60,000. *639*

CYCLOPEDIA.
Student Enterprises & Assistance League, Box 250, Station P., Toronto, Ont. M5S 2T9, Canada.
circ. 25,000. *1624*

D B P BULLETIN.
Development Bank of the Philippines, P.O. Box 800, Makati Central Post Office 1299, Makati, Metro Manila, Philippines.
circ. 2,000. *944*

D F W PEOPLE - THE AIRPORT NEWSPAPER.
Wood Publications, Inc., 400 Fuller-Wiser, Ste. 125, Euless, TX 76039. TEL 817-540-4666. FAX 817-685-7562.
circ. 12,000. *4672*

D G A A E NACHRICHTEN.
Deutsche Gesellschaft fuer Allgemeine und Angewandte Entomologie, Albert-Einstein-Allee 11, 7900 Ulm, Germany. TEL 0731-5022661. FAX 0731-5022038.
circ. 800. *530*

D H LAWRENCE REVIEW.
University of Delaware, English Department, 204 Memorial Hall, Newark, DE 19716. TEL 302-454-1480.
circ. 750. *2910*

D J K - AKTIV.
Deutsche Jugendkraft e.V., Deutschhoeferstr. 17, 8720 Schweinfurt, Germany. TEL 09721-24163.
circ. 2,500. *4470*

D M NEWS.
D M News Corp. 19 W. 21st St., New York, NY 10010. TEL 212-741-2095. FAX 212-633-9367.
circ. 31,000. *1037*

D S S NEWSLETTER.
Department of Social Services, Public Information Office, 1510 Guilford Ave., Baltimore, MD 21202. TEL 301-361-2002. FAX 301-361-3150.
circ. 4,000. *4403*

DAILY FREE PRESS.
Back Bay Publishing Co., 842 Commonwealth Ave., Boston, MA 02215. TEL 617-232-6841. FAX 617-232-0592.
circ. 18,500. *1309*

DAIRY RESEARCH REVIEW.
Dairy Research Foundation, 6300 N. River Rd., Rosemont, IL 60018. TEL 312-696-1870.
circ. 600. *199*

DAIRY WORLD.
Independent Buyers Association Inc., 27 Providence Rd., Millbury, MA 01527. TEL 508-865-2507.
circ. 41,250. *199*

DALLAS - FORT WORTH HOME BUYER'S GUIDE.
Home Buyer's Guide (Dallas), 5501 LBJ Frwy., Ste. 300, Dallas, TX 75240-6202. TEL 214-239-2399.
circ. 75,000. *4147*

DANCE RESEARCH.
Oxford University Press, Oxford Journals, Pinkhill House, Southfield Road, Eynsham, Oxford OX8 1JJ, England. TEL 0865-882283. FAX 0865-882890.
circ. 700. *1530*

DANSK INDUSTRI.
Industriraadet, H.C. Andersens Blvd. 18, DK-1596 Copenhagen V, Denmark. TEL 33-15-22-33. FAX 33-93-22-61.
circ. 9,000. *1074*

DANSK LANDBRUG.
Vest Media A-S, Storegade 28, Skansen, 6800 Varde, Denmark. TEL 75 22 44 00. FAX 75-22-44-77.
circ. 126,495. *86*

DANSKE MALERMESTRE.
Bygeriets Arbejdsgivere, Kejsergade 2, 1155 Copenhagen K, Denmark. FAX 45-33-15-31-11.
circ. 3,200. *3653*

DANSKE PIONEER.
Bertelsen Publishing Co., 1582 Glen Lake Rd., Hoffman Estates, IL 60195. TEL 708-882-2552. FAX 708-882-7082.
circ. 3,400. *1998*

DANSKE VOGNMAEND.
Danske Vognmaend Hovedorganisationen, Gammeltorv 18, 1457 Copenhagen K, Denmark.
circ. 6,750. *4744*

DATA-BOY - NIGHTLIFE.
Data-Boy Enterprises, Inc., 7626 Santa Monica Blvd., Los Angeles, CA 90046. TEL 213-656-2960.
circ. 38,000. *2452*

DATA NEWS.
Diligentia Business Press, Hulstlaan 42, B-1170 Brussels, Belgium. TEL 2-673-81-70. FAX 2-660-36-00.
circ. 22,000. *1350*

DATAWEEK.
Technews (Pty) Ltd., P.O. Box 626, Kloof 3640, South Africa. TEL 031-764-0593. FAX 031-764-0386.
circ. 7,800. *4596*

DE VERE HOTELS MAGAZINE.
C P R Publishing, Northern Rock House, 20 Market Place, Guisborough, Cleveland TS14 6HF, England. TEL 0287-639111. FAX 0287-637201.
circ. 30,000. *2473*

DEALERS' CHOICE.
Texas Automobile Dealers Association, 1108 Lavaca St., Box 1028, Austin, TX 78767-1028. TEL 512-476-2686. FAX 512-476-2179.
circ. 1,800. *4689*

DEEP FOUNDATIONS NEWS.
Deep Foundations Institute, 49 Woodport Rd., Sparta, NJ 07871. TEL 201-729-9679. FAX 201-729-0732.
circ. 1,000. *1864*

DEFENSE TRANSPORTATION JOURNAL.
National Defense Transportation Association, 50 S. Pickett St., No. 220, Alexandria, VA 22304-3008. TEL 703-751-5011. FAX 703-823-8761.
circ. 8,100. *4649*

DEHI RAZAKAR.
National Farm Guide Council of Pakistan, 5-C, 24 Jail Road, Lahore 54000, Pakistan. TEL 42-486437. *86*

DEKE QUARTERLY.
Delta Kappa Epsilon Fraternity, Inc., 35 McKinley Place, Grosse Pte Farms, MI 48236. TEL 313-886-2400. FAX 313-8862227.
circ. 25,000. *1297*

DEL CONDOMINIUM LIFE.
Del Property Management Inc., 4800 Dufferin St., Downsview, Ont. M3H 5S9, Canada. TEL 416-661-3640. FAX 416-661-8923.
circ. 25,000. *2550*

DELAWARE AGENDA.
Department of Agriculture, 2320 S. DuPont Hwy., Dover, DE 19901. TEL 302-739-4811. FAX 302-697-6287.
circ. 5,000. *86*

DELUXE.
Maxwell Custom Publishing, 1999 Shepard Rd., St. Paul, MN 55116. TEL 612-690-7200. FAX 612-690-7357. *775*

DENKMALPFLEGE INFORMATIONEN.
Bayerisches Landesamt fuer Denkmalpflege, Hofgraben 4, 8000 Munich 22, Germany. TEL 089-2114-213. FAX 089-2114-300.
circ. 3,000. *4058*

DENTAL LAB MANAGEMENT TODAY.
Dental Lab Publications, Inc., 205 Liberty Square., E. Norwalk, CT 06855. TEL 203-866-3302. FAX 203-838-3454.
circ. 18,500. *3231*

DENTAL PRODUCTS REPORT.
Medical Economics Company Inc., 680 Kinderkamack Rd., Oradell, NJ 07649. TEL 201-262-3030. FAX 201-262-5461.
circ. 147,801. *3232*

DENVER HOUSING GUIDE.
Baker Publications, 2323 S. Troy, Ste. 103, Aurora, CO 80014. TEL 303-695-8440. FAX 303-695-8449.
circ. 70,000. *4147*

DES MOINES. PUBLIC LIBRARY. MONTHLY MEMO.
Public Library of Des Moines, 100 Locust St., Des Moines, IA 50308. TEL 515-283-4152. FAX 515-283-4503.
circ. 1,000. *2754*

DESARROLLO NACIONAL.
Intercontinental Publications, Inc., 25 Sylvan Rd. S., Box 5017, Westport, CT 06880. TEL 203-226-7463. FAX 203-222-8793.
circ. 22,000. *4058*

DESIGN NEWS O E M - SUPPLIERS SPECIAL ISSUE.
Cahners Publishing Company (Newton) Division of Reed Publishing (USA) Inc., 275 Washington St., Newton, MA 02158-1630. TEL 617-964-3030. FAX 617-558-4470. *3017*

DESIGNS.
Association Communication Innovation Designs 4, C.P. 692, succ. Place D'Armes, Montreal, Que. H2Y 3H8, Canada. TEL 514-842-4436. FAX 514-848-9730.
circ. 13,900. *2551*

DESKTOP PUBLISHING TODAY.
Industrial Medial Ltd., Blair House, 184-190 High St., Tonbridge, Kent TN9 1BQ, England. TEL 0732-359990. FAX 0732-770049.
circ. 10,500. *4143*

DESTINATION CALGARY.
Calgary Convention and Visitors Bureau, 237 8th Ave., S.E., Calgary, Alta. T2E OK8, Canada. TEL 403-263-8510. FAX 403-262-3809.
circ. 1,050. *4759*

DETAIL-BLADET.
Erhvervs-Bladet A-S, Vesterbrogade 12, 1620 Copenhagen V, Denmark.
circ. 63,508. *1037*

DEUTSCHE MILCHWIRTSCHAFT.
Verlag Th. Mann, Nordring 10, Postfach 200254, 4650 Gelsenkirchen-Buer, Germany. TEL 0209-37431.
circ. 3,600. *199*

DEUTSCHES SOLDATENJAHRBUCH.
Schild-Verlag GmbH, Federseestr. 1, 8000 Munich 60, Germany. TEL 089-8641189.
circ. 7,000. *3457*

DEVELOPMENT COMMUNICATION REPORT.
Clearinghouse on Development Communication, 1815 N. Ft. Myer Dr., Ste. 600, Arlington, VA 22209. TEL 703-527-5546. FAX 703-527-4661.
circ. 7,000. *4596*

DIA CUATRO QUE FUERA...
Junta Central de Fiestas de Moros y Cristianos, Palacio Municipal, Villena, Alicante, Spain. *4470*

DIABETES SELF-MANAGEMENT.
R.A. Rapaport Publishing, Inc., 150 W. 22nd St., New York, NY 10011. TEL 212-989-0200. FAX 212-989-4786.
circ. 50,000. *3252*

DIABLO.
Diablo Country Magazine Inc., 2520 Camino Diablo, Walnut Creek, CA 94596-3939. TEL 415-943-1111. FAX 415-943-1045.
circ. 50,000. *2224*

DIAKONIESCHWESTER.
Ev. Diakonieverein e.V., Glockenstr. 8, 1000 Berlin 37, Germany. TEL 030-8018091. FAX 030-8022452.
circ. 4,000. *4174*

DIAL ELECTRICAL - ELECTRONICS.
Dial Industry Publications Windsor Court, Grinstead House, E. Grinstead, W. Sussex RH19 1XA, England. TEL 0342-326972. FAX 0342-315130.
circ. 25,000. *1765*

DIAL ENGINEERING.
Dial Industry Publications Windsor Court, E. Grinstead House, E. Grinstead, W. Sussex RH19 1XA, England. TEL 0342-326972. FAX 0342-315130.
circ. 28,000. *1916*

DIANGONG JISHU XUEBAO.
China Machine Press, 1 Nanli, Baiwanzhuang, Beijing 100037, People's Republic of China. TEL 8317766-415. FAX 00861-8311613.
circ. 1,000. *1885*

DIBEVO VAKBLAD.
Landelijke Organisatie DIBEVO, Postbus 94, 3800 AB Amersfoort, Netherlands. TEL 033-550433. FAX 033-552835.
circ. 6,500. *3710*

AL-DIBLOMASI.
Ministry of Foreign Affairs, Department of Legal Affairs and Studies, P.O. Box 1, Abu Dhabi, United Arab Emirates. TEL 652200. FAX 668015.
circ. 500. *3955*

DICKINSON COUNTY HERITAGE CENTER. GAZETTE.
Dickinson County Heritage Center, Box 506, Abilene, KS 67410. TEL 913-263-2681.
circ. 650. *2404*

DIENST LANDBOUWKUNDIG ONDERZOEK. STARING CENTRUM, INSTITUUT VOOR ONDERZOEK VAN HET LANDELIJKE GEBIED. JAARVERSLAG.
Dienst Landbouwkundig Onderzoek, Staring Centrum, Instituut voor Onderzoek van het Landelijke Gebied, P.O. Box 125, 6700 AC Wageningen, Netherlands. TEL 75230 VISI NL. FAX 08370-24812.
circ. 2,500. *176*

DIESEL & GAS TURBINE WORLDWIDE.
Diesel & Gas Turbine Publications, 13555 Bishop's Ct., Brookfield, WI 53005-6286. TEL 414-784-9177. FAX 414-784-8133.
circ. 22,040. *1928*

A DIFFERENT LIGHT REVIEW.
A Different Light Bookstores, 548 Hudson St., New York, NY 10014. TEL 212-989-4850. FAX 212-989-2158.
circ. 30,000. *2452*

DIGEST OF LABOUR CASES.
V. Subramanian, Ed. & Pub., 337 Thambu Chetty St., Madras 600001, India.
circ. 280. *2619*

DIGITAL DESKTOP.
Publications & Communications, Inc., 12416 Hymeadow Dr., Austin, TX 78750-1896. TEL 512-250-9023. FAX 512-331-3900.
circ. 20,000. *1469*

DIGITAL REVIEW.
Cahners Publishing Company (Newton) Division of Reed Publishing (USA) Inc., 275 Washington St., Newton, MA 02158-1630. TEL 617-964-3030. FAX 617-558-4506.
circ. 84,000. *1460*

DIN FASTIGHET.
Tjaellden-Gruppen AB, Drottningg 55, S-111 21 Stockholm, Sweden. TEL 08-105730. FAX 46-8-108215.
circ. 110,000. *616*

DIPLOMAT.
Diplomatist Associates, 58 Theobalds Rd., London WC1X 8SF, England. TEL 44-1-405-4874. FAX 071-831-0667.
circ. 3,000. *3955*

DIRASAT. SERIES A: HUMANITIES.
University of Jordan, Deanship of Academic Research, Amman, Jordan. FAX 962-6-832318.
circ. 1,000. *2506*

DIRASAT. SERIES B: PURE AND APPLIED SCIENCES.
University of Jordan, Deanship of Academic Research, Amman, Jordan. FAX 962-6-832318.
circ. 1,000. *4307*

DIRECTIONS (BRIDGEWATER).
Baker & Taylor Books, 652 E. Main St., Box 6920, Bridgewater, NJ 08807-0920. TEL 908-218-0400. FAX 908-218-3980.
circ. 8,000. *4126*

DIRECTIONS FOR UTAH LIBRARIES.
Department of Community and Economic Development, State Library Division, 2150 S. 300 W., Ste. 16, Salt Lake City, UT 84115. TEL 801-466-5888. FAX 801-533-4657.
circ. 2,000. *2754*

DIRECTORIO INDUSTRIAL DE COLOMBIA.
Legis S.A., Av. Eldorado 81-10, Bogota, Colombia. TEL 263-4100.
circ. 35,000. *1128*

DIRECTORY OF FLORIDA INDUSTRIES.
Florida Chamber of Commerce Management Corp., Inc., Box 11309, Tallahassee, FL 32302-3309. TEL 904-425-1230. FAX 904-425-1260.
circ. 5,000. *1130*

DIRECTORY OF FULBRIGHT ALUMNI.
United States Educational Foundation in India, Fulbright House, 12 Hailey Rd., New Delhi 110001, India. *1704*

DIREKT-KONTAKT BETRIEBSBEDARF.
Konradin-Verlag Robert Kohlhammer GmbH, Postfach 100252, 7022 Leinfelden-Echterdingen, Germany. TEL 0711-7594-0.
circ. 22,350. *1037*

DISCOVERY Y M C A.
Y M C A of the U S A, 101 N. Wacker Dr., Chicago, IL 60606. TEL 312-977-0031. FAX 312-977-9063.
circ. 88,000. *4404*

DISPATCH (SPRINGFIELD).
Illinois State Historical Society, Old State Capitol, Springfield, IL 62701. TEL 217-782-2635.
circ. 3,800. *2404*

DISPATCHER (COLUMBUS).
Nebraska Public Power District, Box 499, Columbus, NE 68602-0499. TEL 402-563-5811. FAX 402-563-5511.
circ. 3,000. *1885*

DISPLAY & DESIGN IDEAS.
Shore Communications, Inc., 180 Allen Rd., N.E., Ste. 300 N., Atlanta, GA 30328. TEL 404-252-8831. FAX 404-252-4436.
circ. 18,039. *2551*

DISTINCTIONS.
F I S I - Madison Financial Corporation Box 40726, Nashville, TN 37204. TEL 615-371-2775.
circ. 294,333. *776*

DIVERSION (NEW YORK).
Hearst Professional Magazines, Inc., 60 E. 42nd St., Ste. 2424, New York, NY 10065. TEL 212-297-9600. FAX 212-808-9079.
circ. 176,000. *4471*

DIVINE SLAVE GITA.
Hohm Press, Box 2501, Prescott, AZ 86302. TEL 602-778-9189.
circ. 100. *4282*

DOCTOR JAZZ MAGAZINE.
Vijverweg 4, 5461 AL Veghel, Netherlands. TEL 04130-63542.
circ. 850. *3549*

DOCTOR'S SHOPPER.
Marketing Communications, Inc., 1086 Remsen Ave., Brooklyn, NY 11236. TEL 718-257-8484. FAX 718-257-8845.
circ. 208,000. *3094*

DOCUMENTATIE REVUE.
C. Misset B.V., Hanzestr. 1, 70006 RH Doetinchem, Netherlands. TEL 08340-49911. FAX 08340-43839.
circ. 15,000. *1038*

DOCUMENTATION EUROPEENNE - SERIE AGRICOLE.
Commission of the European Communities, 200 rue de la Loi 200, B-1049 Brussels, Belgium. *87*

DOCUMENTATION EUROPEENNE - SERIE SYNDICALE ET OUVRIERE.
Commission of the European Communities, Direction Generale de la Presse et Information, Rue de la Loi 200, 1049 Brussels, Belgium. *977*

DOG WATCH.
B & E Publications, Inc., 11331 Ventura Blvd., Ste. 301, Studio City, CA 91604. TEL 818-761-3647. FAX 818-761-7586.
circ. 5,000. *3710*

DOLLARS & CENTS.
American Society of Association Executives, 1575 I St., N.W., Washington, DC 20005. TEL 202-626-2723. FAX 202-408-9635.
circ. 3,000. *1008*

DOLLARSENSE.
E.F. Baumer & Company, 401 Shatto Pl., Ste. 105, Los Angeles, CA 90020. TEL 213-386-2111. FAX 213-386-6470.
circ. 800,000. *776*

DOMINICAN REPUBLIC. CENTRO NACIONAL DE INVESTIGACIONES AGROPECUARIAS. LABORATORIO DE SANIDAD VEGETAL. SANIDAD VEGETAL.
Centro Nacional de Investigaciones Agropecuarias, Laboratorio de Sanidad Vegetal, San Cristobal, Dominican Republic. *437*

DON & ADONIS.
Foerster-Verlag GmbH, Riedstr. 8, 6100 Darmstadt, Germany. TEL 06151-33469. FAX 06151-317513.
circ. 35,000. *2452*

DOORKIJK.
Katholiek Vrouwengilde Nederland, Bisonspoor 1204, 3605 KZ Maarssen, Netherlands. TEL 03465-73670.
circ. 500. *1819*

DOORS AND HARDWARE.
Door and Hardware Institute, 14170 Newbrook Dr., Chantilly, VA 22023. TEL 703-222-2010. FAX 703-222-2410.
circ. 10,500. *642*

DOSSIER EUROPA.
Commissione delle Comunita Europee, Ufficio per l'Italia, Via Poli 29, 00187 Rome, Italy. TEL 06-699-1160. FAX 06-472-2163.
circ. 5,000. *3891*

DOTS AND TAPS.
Canadian National Institute for the Blind, Ontario Division, 1929 Bayview Ave., Toronto, Ont. M4G 3E8, Canada. TEL 416-480-7417. FAX 416-480-7699.
circ. 355. *2292*

DOUGLAS PROPERTIES INTERNATIONAL.
Jon Douglas Company, 11900 Olympic Blvd., Los Angeles, CA 90064. TEL 310-442-8002. FAX 310-271-1530.
circ. 20,000. *4148*

DRAHTWELT.
Vogel-Verlag und Druck KG, Max-Planck-Str. 7-9, Postfach 6740, 8700 Wuerzburg 1, Germany. TEL 0931-418-0.
circ. 7,216. *3405*

DREAM HOME MAGAZINE.
Bob Gervasi, Ed. & Pub., Box 32057, Cincinnati, OH 45232. TEL 513-541-5588.
circ. 13,000. *616*

DREAMIN'
Hood County News, Box 879, Granbury, TX 76408. TEL 817-573-7066.
circ. 10,000. *2224*

DREW.
Drew University, Office of University Relations, Rt. 24, Madison, NJ 07940. TEL 201-408-3150. FAX 201-408-3940.
circ. 20,000. *1310*

DRILLING CONTRACTOR.
Drilling Contractor Publications, Inc., Box 4287, Houston, TX 77210. TEL 713-578-7171. FAX 713-578-0589.
circ. 17,000. *3685*

DROIT INTERNATIONAL PRIVE.
Editions du C N R S, 1 Place Aristide Briand, 92195 Meudon Cedex, France. TEL 1-45-34-75-50. FAX 1-46-26-28-49.
circ. 1,500. *2722*

DROVERS JOURNAL.
Vance Publishing Corporation, Vance Livestock Publications, 7950 College Blvd., Shawnee Mission, KS 66210. TEL 913-451-2200. FAX 913-451-5821.
circ. 56,547. *216*

DRUM!
12 S. First St., Ste. 417, San Jose, CA 95113. TEL 408-971-9794. FAX 408-971-0382.
circ. 30,000. *3549*

DRURY MIRROR.
Drury College, 900 N. Benton, Springfield, MO 65802. TEL 417-865-8731. FAX 416-865-3138.
circ. 1,000. *1310*

DUBAI EXTERNAL TRADE STATISTICS.
Central Accounting Administration, Statistics Section, P.O. Box 516, Dubai, United Arab Emirates. TEL 531074. FAX 531959.
circ. 500. *713*

DUCA POST.
Duca Community Credit Union Ltd., Box 1100, Willowdale, Ont. M2N 5W5, Canada. TEL 416-223-8502. FAX 416-223-2575.
circ. 18,000. *776*

DUCTILE IRON NEWS.
Charnas, Inc., 76 Eastern Blvd., Glastonbury, CT 06033-1201. TEL 203-657-8600. FAX 203-657-8753.
circ. 2,800. *3405*

DUESSELDORF MAGAZIN.
Landeshauptstadt Duesseldorf, Postfach 1120, 4000 Duesseldorf 1, Germany.
circ. 5,500. *4087*

DURBAN MUSEUM NOVITATES.
Durban Natural Science Museum, P.O. Box 4085, Durban 4000, South Africa. FAX 300-6302.
circ. 280. *581*

DYNA.
Universidad Nacional de Colombia, Facultad Nacional de Minas, Apdo. Aereo 1027, Medellin, Colombia. FAX 2345704.
circ. 1,500. *1819*

DYNAMICA.
University of South Africa, Department of Business Economics, P.O. Box 392, Pretoria 0001, South Africa. FAX 012-429-4573.
circ. 8,000. *659*

DYNAMO NEWSLETTER.
Pugh-Roberts Associates, Inc., 41 William Linskey Way, Cambridge, MA 02142. TEL 617-864-8880. FAX 617-864-8884. *1460*

E A A REVIEW.
Edinburgh Architectural Association, 15 Rutland Sq., Edinburgh EH1 2BE, Scotland. FAX 031-228-2188.
circ. 1,200. *299*

E O NEWS SETTIMANALE.
Gruppo Editoriale Jackson S.p.A., Via Pola 9, 20124 Milan, Italy. TEL 39-2-6948247. FAX 39-2-6948238.
circ. 18,594. *1766*

E O S - E S D TECHNOLOGY EUROPE.
Brinton Group Inc., 49 Eaton Road, Framingham, MA 01701. TEL 508-877-7958. FAX 508-877-3457. *4597*

E T S NEWS.
Electric Power Research Institute, Inc., 236 Crim Street, Bowling Green, OH 43402. TEL 419-354-7677. FAX 419-354-7756.
circ. 2,800. *1886*

THE EAGLE (PHOENIX).
Valley National Corporation, Communication Services (B-646), Box 71, Phoenix, AZ 85001. TEL 602-221-4840. FAX 602-221-4899.
circ. 9,500. *776*

EARLY CHILDHOOD TEACHER.
Scholastic Inc., 730 Broadway, New York, NY 10003. TEL 212-505-3000.
circ. 60,000. *1626*

EARLY CHINA.
University of California, Berkeley, Institute of East Asian Studies, 2223 Fulton St., Berkeley, CA 94720. TEL 415-643-6325. FAX 415-643-7062.
circ. 250. *2337*

EARLY INTERVENTION.
Illinois Public Health Association, 428 W. Jefferson, Springfield, IL 62702. TEL 217-522-5687.
circ. 3,500. *1735*

EASTBOURNIAN.
Eastbourne College, Eastbourne, Sussex, England.
circ. 1,200. *1310*

EASTERN AFTERMARKET JOURNAL.
Stan Hubsher, Ed. & Pub., Box 373, Cedarhurst, NY 11516. TEL 516-295-3680. FAX 516-569-5296.
circ. 8,570. *4689*

CONTROLLED CIRCULATION SERIALS

EASTERN MASSACHUSETTS REGIONAL LIBRARY SYSTEM. EASTERN REGION NEWS.
Eastern Massachusetts Regional Library System, Boston Public Library, Copley Square, Boston, MA 02117. TEL 617-536-4010.
circ. 2,400. *2756*

ECOLOGY CENTER TERRAIN.
Ecology Center, 2530 San Pablo Ave., Berkeley, CA 94702. TEL 510-548-2220.
circ. 7,500. *1948*

ECONOMIA.
Yokohama Kokuritsu Daigaku, Society for Economics and Business Administration, 156 Tokiwadai, Hodogaya-ku, Yokohama 240, Japan.
circ. 1,800. *660*

ECONOMIA GUIPUZCOANA.
Camara Oficial de Comercio, Industria y Navegacion de Guipuzcoa, Ramon Maria Lili, 6, San Sebastian, Spain. FAX 43293105.
circ. 12,000. *814*

ECOS.
Editorial Sucre, Monzon a Barcenas No. 135, Caracas, Venezuela.
circ. 18,000. *4404*

ECOTROPICA. ECOSISTEMAS TROPICALES. BOLETIN.
Universidad de Bogota Jorge Tadeo Lozano, Museo del Mar, Calle 23 No. 4-47, Bogota, Colombia.
circ. 1,200. *1604*

L'ECRIT-VOIR.
Collectif pour l'Histoire de l'Art, 3 rue Michelet, 75006 Paris, France. *325*

EDINBURGH ACADEMY CHRONICLE.
Edinburgh Academy, Henderson Row, Edinburgh EH3 5BL, Scotland.
circ. 4,100. *1626*

EDISI CHUSUS BULLETIN KOPERASI.
Department of Cooperatives, Directorate General of the Institutional Promotion for Cooperatives - Direktorat Bina Penyuluhan Koperasi, Jalan H.R. Rasuna Said Kav. 3-5, Jakarta 12940, Indonesia. TEL 5204382.
circ. 7,500. *863*

EDMONTON CHAMBER OF COMMERCE. COMMERCE NEWS.
Edmonton Chamber of Commerce, Suite 600, 10123-99 St., Edmonton, Alta. T5J 3G9, Canada. FAX 403-424-7946.
circ. 14,000. *815*

EDNEWS.
Department of Education, Office of Communication Services, 1933 Capital Plaza Tower, Frankfort, KY 40601. TEL 502-564-3421. FAX 502-564-6771.
circ. 50,000. *1626*

EDUCATION.
S. Kumar and Associates, Mass Communications Division, 32 Sarojini Debi Lane, Maqboolganj, Lucknow 226078, Uttar Pradesh, India.
circ. 2,000. *1627*

EDUCATION AND HEALTH.
Schools Health Education Unit, University of Exeter, School of Education, St. Luke's, Exeter EX1 2LU, England. FAX 0392-264736.
circ. 12,000. *1726*

EDUCATION EQUIPMENT.
Bouverie Publishing Company Ltd., 4th fl., 58 Fleet St., Entrance 3 Pleydell St., London EC4Y 1JU, England. TEL 071-583-6463. FAX 071-583-6069.
circ. 13,394. *1748*

EDUCATION EQUIPMENT SELECTOR.
A G B Publications Ltd., Audit House, Field End Rd., Ruislip, Middx. HA4 9LT, England. TEL 01-868-4499. FAX 01-429-3117. *1726*

EDUCATION MANITOBA.
Manitoba Education and Training, Communications Services Branch, 210 Osborne St., N., 3rd Fl., Winnipeg, Man. R3C 1V4, Canada. TEL 204-945-6183. FAX 204-948-2147.
circ. 16,000. *1629*

EDUCATION QUARTERLY.
University of the Philippines, College of Education, Diliman, Quezon City, Philippines. *1629*

EDUCATION REPORTER.
Education Writers Association, 1001 Connecticut Ave. N.W., Ste. 310, Washington, DC 20036-5541. TEL 202-429-9680. FAX 202-872-4050.
circ. 700. *1629*

EDUCATION SAN DIEGO COUNTY.
Department of Education, Superintendent of Schools, 6401 Linda Vista Rd., San Diego, CA 92111. TEL 619-292-3500.
circ. 13,000. *1629*

EDUCATION STATISTICS, NEW YORK STATE.
Education Department, Information Center on Education, Education Bldg. Annex, Rm. 385, Albany, NY 12234. TEL 518-474-8716. *1676*

EDUCATIONAL DEALER.
Fahy - Williams Publishing, Inc., Box 1080, Geneva, NY 14456-8080. FAX 315-789-0458.
circ. 13,092. *1748*

EDUCATIONAL FACILITY PLANNER.
Council of Educational Facility Planners, 941 Chatham Lane, Ste. 217, Columbus, OH 43221. TEL 614-442-1811. *1630*

EDUCATIONAL I R M QUARTERLY.
International Society for Technology in Education, University of Oregon, 1787 Agate St., Eugene, OR 97403-1923. TEL 503-346-4414.
circ. 10,000. *1748*

EIGEN AARD.
Publicarto N.V., Langestraat 170, B-1150 Brussels 15, Belgium.
circ. 156,273. *4840*

EIKONOS.
Editorial ECO, S.A., Calle de la Cruz 44, Barcelona 17, Spain.
circ. 12,000. *3508*

EILBOTE.
Eilbote Boomgaarden Verlag GmbH, Postfach 1263, Winsener Landstr. 45, OT Luhdorf, 2090 Winsen-Luhe, Germany. TEL 04171-71058. FAX 04171-74984.
circ. 9,500. *161*

EISEI KAGAKU.
Pharmaceutical Society of Japan, 12-15, Shibuya 2-chome, Shibuya-ku, Tokyo 150, Japan.
circ. 1,700. *1981*

EISENBAHN MODELLBAHN MAGAZIN.
Alba Publikationen Alf Teloeken, Roemerstrasse 9, Postfach 320109, 4000 Duesseldorf 30, Germany. TEL 0211-469010. FAX 0211-484382.
circ. 85,000. *4709*

ELAN.
174775 Canada Inc., 1620 Pine Ave. W., Montreal, Que. H3G 1B4, Canada. TEL 514-931-7322. FAX 514-931-0254.
circ. 9,640. *1290*

ELECTRIC CONSUMER.
Indiana Statewide Rural Electric Cooperative Inc., 720 N. High School Rd., Indianapolis, IN 46214. TEL 317-248-9453. FAX 317-247-5220.
circ. 186. *1801*

ELECTRICAL EQUIPMENT REPRESENTATIVES ASSOCIATION. DIRECTORY.
Electrical Equipment Representatives Association, c/o John S. McDermott, Ed., 406 W. 34th St., Kansas City, MO 64111-2736. FAX 816-753-1954.
circ. 1,000. *1888*

ELECTRICAL WORLD DIRECTORY OF ELECTRIC UTILITIES.
McGraw-Hill, Inc., 1221 Ave. of the Americas, New York, NY 10020. *1888*

ELECTRICITE DE FRANCE. STATISTIQUES DE LA PRODUCTION ET DE LA CONSOMMATION.
Electricite de France, Direction de la Production et du Transport, Departement Statistiques, 6 rue de Messine, 75008 Paris, France. *1843*

ELECTRONIC BUSINESS.
Cahners Publishing Company (Newton) Division of Reed Publishing (USA) Inc., 275 Washington St., Newton, MA 02158-1630. TEL 617-558-4250. FAX 617-558-4470.
circ. 77,331. *1767*

ELECTRONIC BUSINESS ASIA.
Cahners Publishing Company (Newton) Division of Reed Publishing (USA) Inc., 275 Washington St., Newton, MA 02158-1630. TEL 617-964-3030. FAX 617-558-4506.
circ. 41,087. *1767*

ELECTRONIC DISTRIBUTION TODAY.
Custom Media, Inc., 7912 Country Ln., Chagrin Falls, OH 44022. TEL 216-543-9451. FAX 216-543-9764.
circ. 7,125. *1767*

ELECTRONIC ENGINEERING TIMES.
C M P Publications, Inc., 600 Community Dr., Manhasset, NY 11030. TEL 516-562-5000. FAX 516-562-5325.
circ. 125,000. *1767*

ELECTRONIC EQUIPMENT MONITOR.
Thompsons International, 100 Avenue Rd., London NW3 3TP, England. TEL 935 6611.
circ. 27,200. *1767*

ELECTRONIC PRODUCT DESIGN.
I M L Techpress, Blair House, 184-186 High St., Tonbridge, Kent TN9 1BQ, England. TEL 0732-359990. FAX 0732-77049.
circ. 24,270. *1889*

ELECTRONIC PRODUCT NEWS.
Pan European Publishing Co., Rue Verte 216, B-1210 Brussels, Belgium. TEL 02-242-29-92. FAX 02-242-71-11.
circ. 52,501. *1768*

ELECTRONIC PRODUCTS.
Hearst Business Communications, Inc., 645 Stewart Ave., Garden City, NY 11530. TEL 516-227-1300. FAX 516-227-1444.
circ. 124,126. *1768*

ELECTRONIC WORLD NEWS.
C M P Publications, Inc., 600 Community Dr., Manhasset, NY 11030. TEL 516-562-5000.
circ. 32,000. *1768*

ELEKTRO RADIO HANDEL.
Erb-Verlag GmbH & Co. KG, Mariahilferstr. 71, Postfach 101, A-1061 Vienna, Austria.
circ. 9,000. *1356*

ELEKTRONICA REVUE.
C. Misset B.V., Hanzestr. 1, 7006 RH Doetinchem, Netherlands. TEL 08340-49911. FAX 08340-43839. *1770*

ELEKTRONIK ENTWICKLUNG.
Verlag fuer Technik und Wirtschaft GmbH & Co., Lise-Meitner-Str. 2, Postfach 4029, 6500 Mainz, Germany.
circ. 16,000. *1770*

ELEKTRONIK NYT.
Thomson Communications (Scandinavia) A-S, Struenseegade 7-9, DK-2200 Copenhagen, Denmark. TEL 455-37 80 55. *1770*

ELEKTRONIKA UMACHSHAVIM.
Tzavta Publishing, P.O. Box 18287, Tel Aviv 61181, Israel. TEL 03-5622076. FAX 3-5618549.
circ. 8,500. *1394*

ELEKTRONIKPRAXIS.
Vogel-Verlag und Druck KG, Max-Planck-Str. 7-9, Postfach 6740, 8700 Wuerzburg 1, Germany. TEL 0931-418-0.
circ. 39,742. *1770*

ELEKTRONIKSCHAU.
Erb-Verlag GmbH & Co. KG, Eichenstr. 38, A-1120 Vienna, Austria.
circ. 16,000. *1373*

ELEKTROTECHNIK.
Vogel-Verlag und Druck KG, Max-Planck-Str. 7-9, Postfach 6740, 8700 Wuerzburg 1, Germany. TEL 0931-418-0.
circ. 16,653. *1890*

ELETTRONICA OGGI.
Gruppo Editoriale Jackson S.p.A., Via Pola 9, 20124 Milan, Italy. TEL 39-2-69481. FAX 39-2-6948238.
circ. 11,223. *1770*

CONTROLLED CIRCULATION SERIALS 4983

ELLIS COUSINS NEWSLETTER.
Ellis Publishers Inc., 1201 Maple St., Friona, TX 68935. TEL 806-247-3053.
circ. 600. *2149*

EMAJL-KERAMIKA-STAKLO.
Udruzenje Emajliraca Jugoslavije, Srebrnjak 169, 41000 Zagreb, Croatia.
circ. 1,000. *1163*

EMBASSY OF SWITZERLAND BULLETIN.
Embassy of Switzerland, Science and Technology Section, 2900 Cathedral Ave., N.W., Washington, DC 20008. TEL 202-745-7900. FAX 202-387-2564.
circ. 3,000. *4308*

EMERGENCY PREPAREDNESS DIGEST.
Emergency Preparedness Canada, Second Floor, Jackson Bldg., 122 Bank St.W., Ottawa, Ont. K1A 0W6, Canada. TEL 613-991-7077. FAX 613-996-0995.
circ. 16,000. *1273*

EMPLO REVIEW/TYDSKRIF.
South African Railways and Harbours Employees' Union, Boston House, Rm. 335, Waterkant St., Cape Town 8001, South Africa.
circ. 10,000. *2582*

EMPLOYMENT LAW REPORTS.
The Round Hall Press, Kill Lane, Blackrock, Co. Dublin, Ireland. TEL 2892922. FAX 2893072.
circ. 400. *2622*

EMPLOYMENT OUTLOOK SURVEY.
Manpower Temporary Services, International Headquarters, 5301 N. Ironwood Rd., Milwaukee, WI 53201. TEL 414-961-1000. FAX 414-332-0796.
circ. 40,000. *978*

EN VILLE.
Les Publications En Ville Ltee., 8270 Mountain Sights, Ste. 201, Montreal, Que. H4P 2B7, Canada. TEL 514-731-9471. FAX 514-731-7459.
circ. 300,000. *4761*

ENCINITAS.
Jim Baumann, Ed. & Pub., 345 First St., Ste. M, Encinitas, CA 92024. TEL 619-632-7447.
circ. 4,000. *2225*

ENDUSTRI MUHENDISLIGI.
Chamber of Mechanical Engineers, Sumer Sokak, 36-1-A Demirtepe, 06440 Ankara, Turkey. TEL 4-2313164. FAX 4-2313165.
circ. 5,000. *1928*

ENERGIEONDERZOEK CENTRUM NEDERLAND. JAARVERSLAG.
Energieonderzoek Centrum Nederland, Postbus 1, 1755 ZG Petten, Netherlands. TEL 02246-4413. FAX 02246-3053.
circ. 4,000. *1786*

ENFORCEMENT JOURNAL.
National Police Association, 4119 Bardstown Rd, No. 6A, Louisville, KY 40218-3229. TEL 502-451-7550.
circ. 22,500. *1514*

ENGINEERING & MINING JOURNAL.
Maclean Hunter Publishing Company, 29 N. Wacker Dr., Chicago, IL 60606. TEL 312-726-2802. FAX 312-726-2574.
circ. 32,076. *3483*

ENGINEERING CAPACITY.
International Thomson Business Publishing, 100 Avenue Road, London NW3 3TP, England. TEL 01-935-6611.
circ. 10,136. *1820*

ENGINEERING COMPUTERS.
Findlay Publications Ltd., Franks Hall, Horton Kirby, Kent DA4 9LL, England.
circ. 51,000. *1418*

ENGINEER'S DIGEST (OVERLAND PARK).
Intertec Publishing Corp., 9221 Quivira Rd., Overland Park, KS 66215. TEL 913-888-4664. FAX 913-541-6697.
circ. 125,000. *1821*

ENJINIASU.
Union of Japanese Scientists and Engineers, 5-10-11 Sendagaya, Shibuya-ku, Tokyo 151, Japan. TEL 03-5379-1227. FAX 03-3225-1813.
circ. 11,000. *1821*

ENJOY.
Travel Publications, Inc., Box 610, Alta Loma, CA 91701.
circ. 125,000. *1504*

ENSIGN.
Canadian Forces Base Cornwallis, CFB Cornwallis, Cornwallis, N.S. B0S 1H0, Canada. TEL 902-638-8536.
circ. 800. *3457*

ENTRETIEN DES TEXTILES.
Centre Technique de la Teinture et du Nettoyage (CTTN), Chemin des Mouilles, B.P. 41, 69131 Ecully Cedex, France. FAX 78-43-34-12. *4618*

ENVIRONMENTAL AND URBAN ISSUES.
Florida Atlantic University - Florida International University, Joint Center for Environmental and Urban Problems, 220 S.E. Second Ave., Ste. 709, Ft. Lauderdale, FL 33301. TEL 305-355-5255. FAX 305-760-5666.
circ. 5,000. *1950*

ENVIRONMENTAL CAREERS.
P H Publishing, Inc., 760 Whalers Way, Ste. 100-A, Fort Collins, CO 80525. TEL 303-229-0029.
circ. 60,000. *3627*

ENVIRONMENTAL ENGINEERING.
American Academy of Environmental Engineers, 130 Holiday Ct., Ste. 100, Annapolis, MD 21401. TEL 410-266-3311. FAX 410-266-7653. *1951*

ENVIRONMENTAL MANAGEMENT.
Environmental Management Association, 12835 E. Arapahoe Rd., 5th Fl., Englewood, CO 80112-3940. TEL 303-320-7855. FAX 303-393-0770.
circ. 6,500. *4100*

EQUINE BUSINESS JOURNAL.
Rich Publications, Box 72001, San Clemente, CA 92672-9201. TEL 714-361-1955. FAX 714-361-0333.
circ. 13,000. *4534*

EQUIPE DE ODONTOLOGIA SANITARIA. BOLETIM.
Departamento da Saude, Esplanada dos Ministerios, Bloco 11, 70058 Brasilia, D.F., Brazil.
circ. 1,000. *3233*

EQUIPMENT TODAY.
Johnson Hill Press, Inc., 1233 Janesville Ave., Ft. Atkinson, WI 53538. TEL 414-563-6388. FAX 414-563-1701.
circ. 83,000. *617*

ERHVERVS-BLADET.
Erhvervs-Bladet A-S, Vesterbrogade 12, DK-1620 Copenhagen V, Denmark.
circ. 110,448. *1075*

ESCALPELO.
Universidad de Puerto Rico, School of Medicine, Office of the Dean of Students, San Juan, PR 00905.
circ. 500. *1311*

ESPACES TROPICAUX.
Centre d'Etudes de Geographie Tropicale, Domaine Universitaire, Esplanade des Antilles, 33405 Talence Cedex, France. TEL 56-84-68-30. FAX 56-84-68-55.
circ. 400. *2247*

ESSAYS IN ARTS AND SCIENCES.
University of New Haven, Library, Serials Dept., West Haven, CT 06516. TEL 203-932-7364. FAX 203-932-1469.
circ. 600. *4309*

ESSENTIAL NEWS FOR KIDS.
Garrett Communications, Inc., 209 E. Baseline Rd., Tempe, AZ 85283. TEL 602-345-7323. FAX 602-345-8801.
circ. 400,000. *1254*

ESSOBRON.
Esso Nederland B.V., Jan van Nassaustraat 129-131, The Hague, Netherlands. FAX 070-324-3319.
circ. 10,000. *3685*

ESTACION EXPERIMENTAL REGION AGROPECUARIA PERGAMINO. INFORME TECNICO.
Instituto Nacional de Tecnologia Agropecuaria, Estacion Experimental Regional Agropecuaria Pergamino, C.C.31, 2700 Pergamino, Argentina.
circ. 2,000. *88*

ESTATISTICA BRASILEIRA DE ENERGIA.
Conselho Mundial da Energia, Comite Nacional Brasileiro, Rua Real Grandeza, 219 - 6o C, 22283 Rio de Janeiro RJ, Brazil. TEL 5521-246-8593. FAX 5521-226-0508.
circ. 1,000. *1799*

ESTUDIOS OCEANOLOGICOS.
Universidad de Antofagasta, Facultad de Recursos del Mar, Casilla 170, Antofagasta, Chile. FAX 083-247786.
circ. 600. *1604*

ESTUDOS LEOPOLDENSES.
Unisinos, Av. Unisinos, 950, 93010 Sao Leopoldo RS, Brazil. TEL 0512-92-6333. FAX 0512-921035.
circ. 1,400. *1954*

ETHOS (AMES).
Iowa Scientist, Inc., Student Publications, Ames, IA 50011. TEL 515-294-2464.
circ. 3,200. *2506*

ETUDES CELTIQUES.
Editions du C N R S, 1 Place Aristide Briand, 92195 Meudon Cedex, France. TEL 1-45-34-75-50. FAX 1-46-26-28-49.
circ. 1,250. *2813*

ETUDES D'HISTOIRE DE L'ART.
N.V. Brepols I.G.P., Steenweg op Tielen 68, 2300 Turnhout, Belgium. TEL 014-41-54-63. FAX 014-42-89-19. *325*

ETUDES D'HISTOIRE ECONOMIQUE ET SOCIALE.
N.V. Brepols I.G.P., Steenwegop Tielen 68, 2300 Turnhout, Belgium. TEL 014-41-54-63. FAX 014-42-89-19. *894*

ETUDES DE PHILOLOGIE, D'ARCHEOLOGIE ET D'HISTOIRE ANCIENNE.
N.V. Brepols I.G.P., Steenweg op Tielen 68, 2300 Turnhout, Belgium. TEL 014-41-54-63. FAX 014-42-89-19. *2813*

EUROPE SUD-EST.
Editions Europe Sud-Est, 18 Anagnostopoulou, Athens 136, Greece.
circ. 3,000. *3893*

EUROPEAN CLINICAL LABORATORY.
International Scientific Communications, Inc., 30 Controls Dr., Box 870, Shelton, CT 06484-0870. TEL 203-926-9300. FAX 203-926-9310.
circ. 39,300. *3259*

EUROPEAN COAL AND STEEL COMMUNITY. CONSULTATIVE COMMITTEE. HANDBOOK.
European Coal and Steel Community, Consultative Committee, Secretariat, B.P. 1907, Luxembourg, Luxembourg. TEL 4301-2843. FAX 4301-4455. *929*

EUROPEAN COAL AND STEEL COMMUNITY. CONSULTATIVE COMMITTEE. YEARBOOK.
European Coal and Steel Community, Consultative Committee, Secretariat, B.P. 1907, Luxembourg. TEL 4301-2843. FAX 4301-4455. *929*

EUROPEAN FEDERATION OF FINANCE HOUSE ASSOCIATIONS. ANNUAL REPORT.
European Federation of Finance House Associations, 267 av. de Tervuren, B-1150 Brussels, Belgium. FAX 02-770-7596. *778*

EUROPEAN FEDERATION OF FINANCE HOUSE ASSOCIATIONS. NEWSLETTER.
European Federation of Finance House Associations, 267 av. de Tervuren, B-1150 Brussels, Belgium. FAX 02-770-7596. *778*

EUROPEAN PLASTICS NEWS.
Reed Business Publishing Group Quadrant House, The Quadrant, Sutton, Surrey SM2 5AS, England. TEL 081-652-8986. FAX 081-652-8986.
circ. 24,051. *3862*

EUROPETROLEUM.
Aberdeen Petroleum Publishing Ltd., 37 Huntly St., Aberdeen AB1 1TJ, Scotland. TEL 0224-644725. FAX 0224-647574. *3685*

EUROSUD.
Centro Studi Comunita Europee, c/o Eurocampus, Strata Prov. Bitonto, Km. 2.200, S. Spirito, 70032 Bitonto, Italy.
circ. 1,800. *3957*

L'EVENEMENT.
Groupe R. Dupuis, Rue de Stalle 70-82, B-1180 Brussels, Belgium. TEL 32-2-332-04-05. FAX 32-2-332-05-98.
circ. 30,000. *2174*

EVERY WEDNESDAY.
Afro-American Co. of Baltimore City, 628 N. Eutaw St., Baltimore, MD 21201. TEL 410-728-8200. FAX 410-383-3213.
circ. 15,000. *2001*

EXCALIBUR.
Excalibur Publications Inc., 4700 Keele St., Downsview, Ont. M3J 1P3, Canada. TEL 416-736-5238.
circ. 16,000. *1311*

EXCEPTIONAL PARENT.
Psy-Ed Corp., 1170 Commonwealth Ave., Boston, MA 02134. TEL 800-247-8080. FAX 617-730-8742.
circ. 7,000. *1237*

EXCURSIONS EN AUTOCAR.
Publicom Inc., 1055 Beaver Hall, Ste. 400, Montreal, Que. H2Z 1S5, Canada. TEL 514-874-0874. FAX 514-878-9779.
circ. 5,729. *4762*

EXECUTIVE NORTH EAST.
Executive North East Magazine, 30 Queen St., Redcar, Cleveland TS10 1BD, England. TEL 0287-39261.
circ. 10,000. *864*

EXECUTIVE SEARCH SERVICE NEWS.
National Society of Fund Raising Executives, 1101 King St., Ste. 3000, Alexandria, VA 22314. TEL 703-684-0410. FAX 703-684-0540.
circ. 12,000. *4405*

EXECUTIVE TRAVEL.
Reed Travel Group (London) Francis House, 11 Francis St., London SW1P 1BZ, England. TEL 071-828-8989. FAX 071-798-9710.
circ. 40,000. *4762*

EXPANSION MANAGEMENT.
New Hope Communications, Inc., 1301 Spruce St., Boulder, CO 80302-4832. TEL 303-939-8440. FAX 303-939-8640.
circ. 30,000. *864*

EXPECTATIONS.
Braille Institute of America, Inc., 741 N. Vermont Ave., Los Angeles, CA 90029. TEL 213-663-1111.
circ. 3,000. *2292*

EXPECTING.
Gruner & Jahr U.S.A. Publishing, 685 Third Ave., New York, NY 10017. TEL 212-878-8700.
circ. 1,300,000. *3291*

EXPO (KANSAS CITY).
Sanford Publishing Co., 8016 Pennsylvania, Kansas City, MO 64114. TEL 816-523-5693. FAX 816-523-5693.
circ. 7,500. *1010*

EXPORT COURIER.
Stokes & Lindley-Jones Ltd, 36 Stonehills House, Welwyn Garden City, Herts AL8 6NA, England. FAX 0707-323447.
circ. 8,000. *907*

EXPORT FINANCE & INSURANCE REVIEW.
Export Finance and Insurance Corporation, AIDC Tower, Maritime Centre, 201 Kent St., Sydney, N.S.W 2000, Australia. FAX 02-3902137.
circ. 3,000. *907*

EXPORT - IMPORT NEWS.
India - International News Service, 12 India Exchange Place, Calcutta 700 001, India. *907*

EXPORT MAGAZINE.
Exportbevorderings- en Voorlichtingsdienst (EVD), Bezuidenhoutsweg 151, 2594 AG The Hague, Netherlands. TEL 070-3797468.
circ. 5,500. *907*

EXPORT MARKETING HANDBOOK.
South African Foreign Trade Organisation, Publishing Division, P.O. Box 782706, Sandton 2146, South Africa. TEL 011-883-3737. FAX 011-883-6569. *1039*

EXPORT PRACTICE HANDBOOK.
South African Foreign Trade Organisation, Publishing Division, P.O. Box 782706, Sandton 2146, South Africa. TEL 011-883-3737. FAX 011-883-6569. *907*

EXTENSAO EM MINAS GERAIS.
Emater-MG, Assessoria de Relacoes Publicas 3 Impresa, Av. Raja Gabaglia 1626, 6 andar, Minas Gerais, Brazil.
circ. 4,500. *89*

EYES.
Ten-Fifty Publications, W. Tower, Ste. 1050, 11845 W. Olympic Blvd., Los Angeles, CA 90064. TEL 213-312-8245.
circ. 100,000. *3957*

F A P I G.
First Atomic Power Industry Group, Nissho-Iwai Bldg. 3rd Fl., 2-4-5 Akasaka, Minato-ku, Tokyo, Japan. TEL 03-3588-4171.
circ. 2,000. *1805*

F B O.
Johnson Hill Press, Inc., 1233 Janesville Ave., Ft. Atkinson, WI 53538. TEL 414-563-6388. FAX 414-563-1701.
circ. 17,500. *4673*

F E B S LETTERS.
Elsevier Science Publishers B.V., P.O. Box 211, 1000 AE Amsterdam, Netherlands. TEL 020-5803911. FAX 020-5803598. *476*

F L I C C NEWSLETTER.
U.S. Library of Congress, Federal Library and Information Center Committee, Washington, DC 20540. TEL 202-707-4828. FAX 202-707-4818. *2757*

F M T.
Verlag fuer Technik und Handwerk, Fremerbergstr. 1, 7570 Baden-Baden, Germany.
circ. 43,000. *2436*

F N V MAGAZINE (AMSTERDAM).
Box 9354, 1006 AJ Amsterdam, Netherlands. TEL 020-6143105. FAX 020-6151091.
circ. 48,500. *3999*

F-5 TECHNICAL DIGEST.
Northrop Corporation, Northrop Aircraft Group, One Northrop Ave., Hawthorne, CA 90250. TEL 213-970-2000.
circ. 50,000. *52*

FABRICATION & GLAZING INDUSTRIES.
T B B Publications Ltd., 4 Simon Campion Court, High St., Epping, Essex CM16 4AU, England. TEL 0992-560215. FAX 0992-560216.
circ. 9,500. *1163*

FABRICNEWS.
Arthur J. Imparato Associates, 80 Park Ave., New York, NY 10016. TEL 213-274-6752.
circ. 9,500. *4618*

FABRIK 2000.
Vogel Verlag und Druck KG, Max-Planck-Str. 7-9, Postfach 6740, 8700 Wuerzburg 1, Germany. TEL 0931-418-0.
circ. 29,913. *3406*

FACETS OF FRESHWATER.
Freshwater Foundation, 725 County Rd. 6, Waynata, MN 55391. TEL 612-449-0092. FAX 617-449-0592. *4824*

FACTS & FIGURES.
Organization of the Petroleum Exporting Countries, Obere Donaustr. 93, A-1020 Vienna, Austria. FAX 222-264320.
circ. 10,000. *1789*

FAGTIDSSKRIFTET SYKEPLEIEN.
Norsk Sykepleierforbund, Postboks 2633, St. Hanshaugen, 0131 Oslo 1, Norway. FAX 02-353663.
circ. 45,000. *3278*

FAHRSCHULE.
Heinrich Vogel Fachzeitschriften GmbH, Neumarkter Str. 18, Postfach 802020, 8000 Munich 80, Germany. TEL 089-43180-0.
circ. 16,500. *4690*

FAITH AND MISSION.
Southeastern Baptist Theological Seminary, Inc., Wake Forest, NC 27587. TEL 919-556-3101.
circ. 1,000. *4238*

FAITH FOR DAILY LIVING.
Faith for Daily Living Foundation, P.O. Box 3737, Durban, Natal, South Africa.
circ. 120,000. *4282*

FAMILY PRACTICE RECERTIFICATION.
M R A Publications, Inc., 3 Greenwich Office Park, Greenwich, CT 06831-5154. TEL 203-629-3550. FAX 203-629-2536.
circ. 83,365. *3098*

FARM EQUIPMENT.
Johnson Hill Press, Inc., 1233 Janesville Ave., Ft. Atkinson, WI 53538. TEL 414-563-6388. FAX 414-563-1701.
circ. 16,500. *162*

FARM INDUSTRY NEWS.
Intertec Publishing Corp., Webb Division, 7900 Int'l Dr., Minneapolis, MN 55425. TEL 612-851-4684. FAX 612-851-4601.
circ. 300,866. *90*

FARM STORE.
Miller Publishing Co., 12400 Whitewater Dr., Ste. 160, Box 2400, Minnetonka, MN 55343-2524. TEL 612-931-0211. FAX 612-931-0910.
circ. 35,744. *90*

FARMING.
Farming Magazine, 43 So. Water St. E., Fort Atkinson, WI 53508. TEL 414-563-9500.
circ. 600,000. *150*

FARMIS - REPTILEN.
Farmaceutiska Studentkaaren, Box 8036, S-750 08 Uppsala, Sweden.
circ. 1,200. *3726*

EL FARO.
Associated Collectors of El Salvador, c/o Robert A. Fisher, Ed., 28 Edgewood Dr., Granville, OH 43023-1076.
circ. 100. *3752*

FARUMASHIA.
Pharmaceutical Society of Japan, 12-15, Shibuya 2-chome, Shibuya-ku, Tokyo 150, Japan.
circ. 21,000. *3726*

FASTENER TECHNOLOGY INTERNATIONAL.
Initial Publications Inc., 3869 Darrow Rd., Ste. 101, Stow, OH 44224. TEL 216-686-9544. FAX 216-686-9563.
circ. 13,000. *642*

FATIMA FINDINGS.
Reparation Society of the Immaculate Heart of Mary, Inc., Fatima House, 100 E. 20th St., Baltimore, MD 21218-6091. TEL 410-685-7403.
circ. 4,000. *4282*

FAX PLUS.
Montreal Children's Hospital, 2300 Tupper St., Ste. E-203, Montreal, Que. H3H 1P3, Canada. TEL 514-934-4307.
circ. 1,500. *2461*

FEDERAL CIVILIAN WORK FORCE STATISTICS. PAY STRUCTURE OF THE FEDERAL CIVIL SERVICE.
U.S. Office of Personnel Management, Personnel Systems and Oversight Group, Office of Workforce Information, Washington, DC 20415. TEL 703-487-4650. FAX 202-606-1719.
circ. 900. *715*

FEDERAL CIVILIAN WORK FORCE STATISTICS. WORK YEARS AND PERSONNEL COSTS. EXECUTIVE BRANCH, UNITED STATES GOVERNMENT.
U.S. Office of Personnel Management, Personnel Systems and Oversight Group, Office of Workforce Information, 1900 E St., N.W., Washington, DC 20415. TEL 703-487-4650.
circ. 400. *715*

FEDERAL CIVILIAN WORKFORCE STATISTICS. EMPLOYMENT AND TRENDS.
U.S. Office of Personnel Management, Personnel Systems and Oversight Group, Office of Workforce Information, 1900 E St., N.W., Washington, DC 20415. TEL 202-606-1178.
circ. 950. *715*

FEDERAL INVESTIGATOR.
Dale Corporation, 84 Executive Dr., Troy, MI 48083-4504. TEL 313-597-9040. FAX 313-597-9043.
circ. 4,000. *1514*

FEDERATION INTERNATIONALE DE RUGBY AMATEUR. ANNUAIRE.
International Amateur Rugby Federation, 7 Cite d'Antin, 75009 Paris, France. FAX 45-26-19-19.
circ. 700. *4503*

FEDERATION JAZZ.
Federation of Jazz Societies, 2787 Del Monte St., W. Sacramento, CA 95691. TEL 916-372-5277.
circ. 300. *3551*

FEED AND GRAIN.
Johnson Hill Press, Inc., 1233 Janesville Ave., Ft. Atkinson, WI 53538. TEL 414-563-6388. FAX 414-563-1701.
circ. 19,500. *205*

FELIX LETTER.
Clara Felix, Ed. & Pub., Box 7094, Berkeley, CA 94707.
circ. 2,000. *3605*

FERRETECNIC - F Y T.
Publitecnic S.A., Calle 4, no. 188, Apdo. Postal 74-290, C.P. 09070, Mexico 13, D.F., Mexico. TEL 685-28-19. FAX 6706318.
circ. 10,000. *3406*

FILIPINO TEACHER.
373 Quezon Avenue, Quezon City, Philippines.
circ. 42,000. *1633*

FILM BILL.
Film Bill, Inc., 250 W. 54 St., New York, NY 10019. TEL 212-977-4140. FAX 212-977-4404.
circ. 500,000. *3508*

FILTRATION NEWS.
Eagle Publications, Inc., 42400 Nine Mile Rd., Ste. B, Novi, MI 48375. TEL 800-783-3491. FAX 313-347-3492.
circ. 30,000. *1954*

FINANCIAL PLANNING ON WALL STREET.
S D C Publishing, 40 W. 57th St., Ste. 802, New York, NY 10019. TEL 212-765-5311.
circ. 50,000. *946*

FINDING.
L D A Publishers, 42-36 209 St., Bayside, NY 11361. TEL 718-224-9484. FAX 718-224-9487.
circ. 3,500. *2758*

FINE FOODS.
Griffin Publishing Company, Inc., 1099 Hingham St., Rockland, MA 02370. TEL 617-878-5300. FAX 617-871-4721.
circ. 12,000. *2067*

FIRE MARSHALS ASSOCIATION OF NORTH AMERICA. DIRECTORY.
Fire Marshals Association of North America, NFPA, Baterymarch Park, Quincy, MA 02269-9101. TEL 617-770-3000.
circ. 1,400. *2032*

FIRST-TIME PARENTS.
Cahners Publishing Company (New York), Consumer and Entertainment Division Division of Reed Publising (USA) Inc., 475 Park Ave. S., New York, NY 10016-6901. TEL 212-779-1999. FAX 212-545-5400.
circ. 500,000. *1237*

FISH AND GAME FINDER.
Fish and Game Finder Magazines, 1233 W. Jackson St., Orlando, FL 32805. TEL 407-425-0045. FAX 407-425-1529.
circ. 300,000. *4546*

FISHERMAN.
Fisherman Publishing Society, 111 Victoria Dr., No. 160, Vancouver, B.C. V5L 4C4, Canada. TEL 604-255-1366. FAX 604-255-3162.
circ. 10,500. *2040*

FISHING TACKLE TRADE NEWS.
Fishing Tackle Trade News, Inc., Div. Vickers Communications, Box 2669, Vancouver, WA 98668-2669. TEL 206-693-4721. FAX 206-693-3997.
circ. 21,500. *4546*

FISKERITIDSKRIFT FOER FINLAND.
Kalatalouden Keskusliitto, Koydenpunojankatu 7 B 23, 00180 Helsinki 18, Finland. TEL 358-0-640126. FAX 358-0-608309.
circ. 4,863. *2041*

FITECH INTERNATIONAL.
F M J International Publications Ltd., Queensway House, 2 Queensway, Redhill, Surrey RH1 1QS, England. TEL 0737-768611. FAX 0737-761685.
2033

FITOTERAPIA.
Inverni della Beffa Holding, Via Ripamonti 99, 20141 Milan, Italy. FAX 02-57404620.
circ. 5,000. *502*

FLEET OPERATORS HANDBOOK.
Emap Response Ltd., Wentworth House, Wentworth St., Peterborough PE1 1DS, England. TEL 0733-63100. FAX 0733-67367.
circ. 10,000. *4690*

FLEET OWNER.
F M Business Publications, Inc., 707 Westchester Ave., Ste. 101, White Plains, NY 10604. TEL 914-949-8500.
circ. 100,000. *4744*

DIE FLEISCHEREI.
Hans Holzmann Verlag GmbH, Gewerbestr. 2, Postfach 1342, 8939 Bad Woerishofen, Germany. TEL 08247-35401. FAX 08247-354170.
circ. 8,052. *2067*

FLIPPING FLIPPINS.
Flippin Family Association, 12206 Brisbane Ave., Dallas, TX 75234-6528.
circ. 65. *2151*

FLORA-LINE.
Berry Hill Press, 7336 Berry Hill, Palos Verdes, CA 90274-4404. TEL 310-377-7040.
circ. 2,000. *2125*

FLORACULTURE INTERNATIONAL.
International Horticulture Publications, 122 S. Wesley Ave., Mt. Morris, IL 61054. TEL 815-734-4171. FAX 815-734-4201.
circ. 10,000. *2125*

FLORIDA AND THE OTHER FORTY-NINE.
Department of Commerce, Bureau of Economic Analysis, 107 W. Gaines St., Tallahassee, FL 32399-2000. TEL 904-487-2971. *717*

FLORIDA CONSTRUCTOR.
Associated Publications Corporation, 495 E. Summerlin St., Box 89, Bartow, FL 33830. TEL 813-533-4835.
circ. 21,000. *618*

FLORIDA COUNTY COMPARISONS.
Department of Commerce, Bureau of Economic Analysis, 107 W. Gaines St., Tallahassee, FL 32399-2000. TEL 904-487-2971. *717*

FLORIDA COUNTY PROFILES.
Department of Commerce, Bureau of Economic Analysis, 107 W. Gaines St., Tallahassee, FL 32399-2000. TEL 904-487-2971. *815*

FLORIDA CREATIVE DIRECTORY.
Alexander Communications, Inc., 212 W. Superior, Ste. 203, Chicago, IL 60610. TEL 312-944-5115. FAX 312-944-7865.
circ. 6,000. *3999*

FLORIDA FORUM.
F R S A, Drawer 4850, Winter Park, FL 32793. TEL 407-671-3772. FAX 407-679-0010.
circ. 9,200. *618*

FLORIDA GOLF REPORTER.
Golf Reporter Enterprises Inc., Box 951422, Lake Mary, FL 32795-1422. FAX 407-767-5748.
circ. 20,000. *4503*

FLORIDA GULF COAST HOMEBUYER'S GUIDE.
Real Estate Magazines, Inc. (Tampa), 1715 N. Westshore Blvd., Ste. 244, Tampa, FL 33607-3926. TEL 813-879-1197. FAX 813-874-3077.
circ. 60,000. *4149*

FLORIDA INDEPENDENT ACCOUNTANT.
Florida Association of Independent Accountants, Box 13089, Tallahassee, FL 32317. TEL 904-878-3134. FAX 904-878-1291.
circ. 900. *751*

FLORIDA PUBLIC DOCUMENTS.
State Library, Documents Section, Tallahassee, FL 32399. TEL 904-487-2651. *4060*

FLORIDA THOROUGHBRED.
Thoroughbred Publications Inc., 801 Corporate Dr., Ste. 101, Box 8237, Lexington, KY 40503. TEL 606-223-9800. FAX 800-231-5210.
circ. 6,700. *4534*

FLUE CURED TOBACCO FARMER.
Specialized Agricultural Publications, Inc., Box 95075, Raleigh, NC 27625. TEL 919-872-5040. FAX 919-872-6531.
circ. 25,000. *4643*

FLUID POWER HANDBOOK & DIRECTORY.
Penton Publishing 1100 Superior Ave., Cleveland, OH 44114-2543. TEL 216-696-7000. FAX 216-696-8765.
circ. 36,000. *1917*

FLYDOSCOPE.
Luxair, B.P. 2203, L-2987 Luxembourg, Luxembourg. TEL 4798-2221. FAX 43-63-44.
circ. 40,000. *4802*

FLYING DUTCHMAN DIRECTIONS.
Multi Media International, P.O. Box 469, 1180 AL Amstelveen, Netherlands. TEL 020-5473550. FAX 020-6438581.
circ. 100,000. *4802*

FOCUS (NEW YORK, 1978).
State University of New York, Health Science Center at Brooklyn, 450 Clarkson Ave., Brooklyn, NY 11203. *3098*

FOCUS ON PAKISTAN.
Pakistan Tourism Development Corporation, House No. 2, Street 61, F-7-4, P.O. Box 1465, Islambad 44000, Pakistan. TEL 811001.
circ. 5,000. *4763*

FOCUS ON WOMEN.
Campbell Communications Inc., 1218 Langley St., 3rd Fl., Victoria, B.C. V8W 1W2, Canada. TEL 604-388-7231. FAX 604-383-1140.
circ. 29,800. *4843*

FOERDERUNGSDIENST.
Bundesministerium fuer Land- und Forstwirtschaft, Stubenring 1, A-1010 Vienna, Austria.
circ. 3,500. *92*

FOERSVARSFORSKNINGSREFERAT.
Foersvarets Forskningsanstalt, S-172 90 Sundbyberg, Sweden.
circ. 950. *1274*

FOLK OG FRITID.
Folkeligt Oplysnings Forbund, Moellevej 9, DK-5683 Haarby, Denmark.
circ. 7,500. *1634*

FOLKEVIRKE.
Folkevirke, Solsortvej 1, 2000 Frederiksberg, Denmark. FAX 4553510151.
circ. 2,500. *2866*

FOLKLIVSSTUDIER.
Svenska Litteratursaellskapet i Finland, Marieg. 8, 00170 Helsinki 17, Finland. FAX 0-632820. *240*

FOOD AND AGRICULTURE ORGANIZATION OF THE UNITED NATIONS. ASIA AND PACIFIC PLANT PROTECTION COMMISSION. TECHNICAL DOCUMENT.
Food and Agriculture Organization of the United Nations, Regional Office for Asia and the Pacific, Maliwan Mansion, Phra Atit Rd., Bangkok 10200, Thailand.
circ. 500. *178*

FOOD & BEVERAGE MONITOR.
Donaldson, Lufkin & Jenrette, 140 Broadway, New York, NY 10005. TEL 212-504-4209. *946*

FOOD & BEVERAGE SPOTLIGHT.
Donaldson, Lufkin & Jenrette, 140 Broadway, New York, NY 10005. TEL 212-504-4209. *946*

FOOD MANUFACTURING NEWS.
Yaffa Publishing Group, 17-21 Bellevue St., Surry Hills, N.S.W. 2010, Australia. TEL 02-281-2333. FAX 02-281-2750.
circ. 4,283. *2069*

FOOD PROCESSING (CHICAGO).
Putman Publishing Co., 301 E. Erie St., Chicago, IL 60611. TEL 312-644-2020.
circ. 66,000. *2069*

FOOD SCIENCE.
Macmillan Press Ltd., Houndmills, Basingstoke, Hampshire RG2 2XS, England.
circ. 1,000. *3606*

FOODMAGAZINE - INTERNATIONAL.
Audet Tijdschriften bv, Postbus 16, 6500 AA Nijmegen, Netherlands. TEL 080-228316. FAX 080-239561. *2092*

THE FOODSERVICE DISTRIBUTOR.
Penton Publishing 1100 Superior Ave., Cleveland, OH 44114-2543. TEL 216-696-7000. FAX 216-696-8765.
circ. 38,946. *1135*

FOODSERVICE PRODUCT NEWS.
Young - Conway Publications, 104 Fifth Ave., New York, NY 10011. TEL 212-206-7440. FAX 212-727-0919.
circ. 132,000. *2474*

FOOTBALL REFEREE.
Referees' Association, Westhill Rd., Coundon, Coventry, West Midlands CV6 2AD, England. TEL 0203-601701. FAX 0203-601556.
circ. 8,000. *4504*

FOOTPRINTS (PLAINVIEW).
Wayland Baptist University, 1900 W. 7th St., Plainview, TX 79072. TEL 806-296-5521.
circ. 11,000. *1311*

FOOTWEAR BUSINESS INTERNATIONAL.
S A T R A Footwear Technology Centre, SATRA House, Rockingham Road, Kettering, Northants NN16 9JH, England. TEL 0536-410000. FAX 0536-410626.
circ. 1,500. *4360*

FOOTWEAR PLUS.
Earnshaw Publications, Inc., 225 W. 34th St., Ste. 1212, New York, NY 10001. TEL 212-563-2742.
circ. 18,000. *4361*

FORCES.
Societe d'Edition de la Revue Forces, 500 rue Sherbrooke Oeust, Bur. 430, Montreal, Que. H3A 3C6, Canada. TEL 514-286-7600. *2177*

FORD NEW HOLLAND NEWS.
Ford New Holland, Inc., 500 Diller Ave., New Holland, PA 17557. TEL 717-354-1121.
circ. 420,000. *92*

FORECAST (BRIDGEWATER).
Baker & Taylor Books, 652 E. Main St., Box 6920, Bridgewater, NJ 08807-0920. TEL 908-218-0400. FAX 908-218-3980.
circ. 22,000. *4128*

FOREST INDUSTRIES.
Miller Freeman, Inc. 600 Harrison St., San Francisco, CA 94107. TEL 415-905-2200. FAX 415-905-2232.
circ. 29,000. *2114*

FORGING.
Penton Publishing 1100 Superior Ave., Cleveland, OH 44114-2534. TEL 216-696-7000. FAX 216-696-7658.
circ. 5,000. *3406*

FORM & FUNCTION.
U S G Corporation, 101 S. Wacker Dr., Chicago, IL 60606. TEL 312-606-4181. FAX 312-606-5566.
circ. 140,000. *299*

FORMAT.
Stilt Press, c/o Alan & Joan Tucker, The Bookshop, Stroud, Gloucestershire, England. FAX 0453-766899.
circ. 150. *2993*

FORMGHI QUARTERLY.
Fellowship of the Makers and Researchers of Historical Instruments, Faculty of Music, St. Aldate's, Oxford OX1 1DB, England. FAX 0365-276128.
circ. 700. *3552*

FORSIKRING.
Forlaget Forsikring, Amaliegade 10, DK-1256 Copenhagen K, Denmark. TEL 45-33-13 75 55. FAX 45-33-33-02-71.
circ. 3,300. *2532*

FORTSCHRITTE DER MEDIZIN.
Verlag Urban und Vogel, Postfach 15 22 09, 8000 Munich 15, Germany. TEL 089-53292-0. FAX 089-53292-100.
circ. 48,500. *3099*

FORUM.
Energieonderzoek Centrum Nederland, Postbus 1, 1755 ZG Petten, Netherlands. TEL 02246-4413. FAX 02246-3053.
circ. 1,500. *1790*

FORUM.
Office of Court Administration, Vela St., Stop 35 1-2, Hato Rey Station, Call Box 917 A, Hato Rey, PR 00919.
circ. 600. *2628*

FORUM (SYRACUSE).
Independent Insurance Agents Association of New York State, Inc., Box 9001, Mt. Vernon, NY 10552. TEL 914-699-2020. FAX 914-664-1503.
circ. 3,000. *2532*

FORUM LINGUISTICUM.
Verlag Peter Lang GmbH, Eschborner Landstr. 42-50, 6000 Frankfurt a.M. 90, Germany. TEL 069-7807050. FAX 069-785893.
circ. 400. *2814*

FORVM.
Gerhard Oberschlick Ed. & Pub., Museumstr. 5, A-1070 Vienna, Austria. FAX 938368.
circ. 25,000. *2866*

FOTEC FIBER OPTIC TESTING NEWS.
Fotec Inc., 529 Main St., Box 246, Boston, MA 02129. TEL 617-241-7810. FAX 617-241-8616.
circ. 15,000. *1336*

FOUNDRY DATABOOK & CATALOG FILE.
Penton Publishing 1100 Superior Ave., Cleveland, OH 44114-2543. TEL 216-696-7000. FAX 216-696-8765.
circ. 24,000. *3406*

FOUNDRY MANAGEMENT & TECHNOLOGY.
Penton Publishing 1100 Superior Ave., Cleveland, OH 44114-2543. TEL 216-696-7000. FAX 216-696-8765.
circ. 22,000. *3406*

FOURTH ESTATE.
Fourth Estate Partnership, P.O. Box 971, Cornwall, P.E.I. COA 1HO, Canada.
circ. 1,500. *2569*

FRACHT MANAGEMENT.
Konradin-Verlag Robert Kohlhammer GmbH, Postfach 100252, 7022 Leinfelden-Echterdingen KG, Germany. TEL 0711-7594-0.
circ. 15,051. *4650*

FRANCE. CONSEIL NATIONAL DU CREDIT. STATISTIQUES MENSUELLES.
Banque de France, Service de l'Information, 48, rue Croix des Petits Champs, 75001 Paris, France. TEL 1-42-92-39-08. FAX 1-42-92-39-40. *717*

FRANCE. CONSEIL NATIONAL DU CREDIT. STATISTIQUES TRIMESTRIELLES.
Banque de France, Service de l'Information, 48, Croix des Petits Champs, 75001 Paris, France. TEL 1-42-92-39-08. FAX 1-42-92-39-40. *717*

FRANCE AVIATION.
25 Bd. de Vaugirard, 75757 Paris Cedex 15, France. TEL 1-43-20-05-02. FAX 1-43-23-94-02.
circ. 50,000. *53*

FRANCE MAGAZINE.
Maison Francaise, 4101 Reservoir Rd., N.W., Washington, DC 20007. TEL 202-944-6069. FAX 202-944-6072.
circ. 67,000. *2187*

FRANCHISING INVESTMENTS AROUND THE WORLD.
Sutton Place Publications, 221 S.W. 64th Ter., Hollywood, FL 33023-1238.
circ. 38,500. *947*

FRANKLIN MINT ALMANAC.
Franklin Mint, Franklin Center, PA 19091. TEL 215-459-6000. FAX 215-459-6880.
circ. 1,020. *3599*

FREE STATE EDUCATIONAL NEWS.
Ficksburg Press (Pty) Ltd., P.O. Box 380, Ficksburg, Orange Free State, South Africa.
circ. 1,000. *1634*

FREEDOM TO READ FOUNDATION NEWS.
Freedom to Read Foundation, 50 E. Huron St., Chicago, IL 60611. TEL 312-280-4223. FAX 312-440-9374. *2758*

FREEDOM WRITER.
Institute for First Amendment Studies, Inc., Box 589, Great Barrington, MA 01230. TEL 413-274-3786. FAX 413-274-3786.
circ. 7,000. *3942*

FREIGHT.
Freight Transport Association, Hermes House, St. John's Rd., Tunbridge Wells, Kent TN4 9UZ, England. TEL 0892-26171. FAX 0892-34989.
circ. 14,989. *4650*

FREIGHT & CONTAINER WEEKLY.
Travel and Trade Publishing (Pty) Ltd., 12 Loveday St., P.O. Box 6202, Johannesburg 2000, South Africa. TEL 011-833-1030. FAX 011-834-6889.
circ. 3,800. *666*

FREIGHT HANDLER.
K.A.V. Publicity (Glasgow) Ltd., 113 West Regent St., Glasgow G2, Scotland. TEL 041 226 3861.
circ. 9,500. *4650*

FREMANTLE PORT NEWS.
Fremantle Port Authority, P.O. Box 95, Fremantle, W.A. 6160, Australia. TEL 09-430-4911. FAX 09-430-4112.
circ. 4,200. *4727*

FRENCH - AMERICAN NEWS.
French - American Chamber of Commerce in the United States, Inc., 509 Madison Ave., Ste. 1900, New York, NY 10022-5501. TEL 212-371-4466. FAX 212-371-5623.
circ. 650. *816*

FRIDAY FLASH.
National Association of Insurance Brokers, Inc., 1401 New York Ave., N.W., No. 720, Washington, DC 20005. TEL 202-628-6700. *2532*

FRIENDLY EXCHANGE.
Meredith Publishing Services 1912 Grand Ave., Des Moines, IA 50309. TEL 515-284-2008.
circ. 5,400,000. *2225*

FRIENDS OF YOUTH NEWSLETTER.
Friends of Youth, 2500 Lake Washington Blvd. N., Renton, WA 98056. TEL 206-228-5775. FAX 206-228-5777.
circ. 5,000. *1237*

FRIVAKT.
Soelberg Trykk A-S, c/o Arne Christiansen, P.O. Box 27, 1335 Smaraya, Norway.
circ. 14,700. *4406*

FROBBER.
FROBCO, c/o Embarcadero Venture, Box 2600, Menlo Park, CA 94026-2600.
circ. 200. *1460*

FRONTIERES.
Universite de Quebec a Montreal, Service des Publications, Centre d'Etudes sur la Mort, Box 8888, Succ. A, Montreal, Que H3C 3P8, Canada. TEL 514-987-4581. FAX 514-987-7856.
circ. 1,500. *4022*

FRONTIERS OF PLANT SCIENCE.
Agricultural Experiment Station, Box 1106, New Haven, CT 06504-1106. TEL 203-789-7223.
circ. 6,000. *503*

FULCRUM.
University of the Witwatersrand, Johannesburg, Student Engineers Council, CM 1124-1125, P.O. Box WITS, Johannesburg 2050, South Africa. FAX 27-11-716-5467.
circ. 3,000. *1822*

FUNBOARD.
Verlag Delius Klasing und Co., Siekerwall 21, Postfach 48 09, 4800 Bielefeld 1, Germany. TEL 0521-559280. FAX 0521-559113.
circ. 800. *4472*

FUNDACION JIMENEZ DIAZ. BOLETIN.
Fundacion Jimenez Diaz, Av. de los Reyes Catolicos 2, Madrid 3, Spain.
circ. 43,251. *3099*

FUTURES (CEDAR FALLS).
Oster Communications, Inc., 219 Parkade, Cedar Falls, IA 50613. TEL 319-277-1271. FAX 319-277-5803.
circ. 60,000. *947*

FUTURES (EAST LANSING).
Michigan State University, Agricultural Experiment Station, 310 Agriculture Hall, East Lansing, MI 48824-1039. TEL 517-336-1555. FAX 517-355-1804.
circ. 5,000. *93*

FUTURES MAGAZINE REFERENCE GUIDE TO FUTURES MARKETS.
Oster Communications, Inc., 219 Main St., Cedar Falls, IA 50613. TEL 319-277-1271. FAX 319-277-5803.
circ. 60,000. *947*

G A T F SECOND SIGHT.
Graphic Arts Technical Foundation, 4615 Forbes Ave., Pittsburgh, PA 15213-3796. TEL 412-621-6941. FAX 412-621-3049. *4598*

G E I C O DIRECT.
Maxwell Custom Publishing, 1999 Shepard Rd., St. Paul, MN 55666. TEL 612-690-7200. FAX 612-690-7357. *2532*

G E S. BOLETIN DE INFORMACION.
General Espanola de Seguros, S.A., Plaza de las Cortes, 2, Madrid 28014, Spain.
circ. 1,500. *2532*

G I S NEWSLETTER.
Geoscience Information Society, c/o American Geological Institute, 4220 King St., Alexandria, VA 22302.
circ. 270. *1544*

G M I ALUMNI NEWS.
G M I Engineering & Management Institute, 1700 W. Third Ave., Flint, MI 48504-4898. TEL 313-762-9752. FAX 313-762-9837.
circ. 18,500. *1312*

G R.
G L M Publications 2 Park Ave., Ste. 1100, New York, NY 10016. TEL 212-686-6070. *2281*

G R I D.
Gas Research Institute, Technical Communications Department, 8600 W. Bryn Mawr Ave., Chicago, IL 60631. TEL 312-399-8100. FAX 312-399-8170.
circ. 14,000. *3686*

GALAXIA 71.
Grupo Escritores de Venezuela, Apdo. 4023, Carmelitas 101, Caracas, Venezuela.
circ. 5,000. *2867*

GALLIA. SUPPLEMENT.
Editions du C N R S, 1 Place Aristide Briand, 92195 Meudon Cedex, France. TEL 1-45-34-75-50. FAX 1-46-26-28-49.
circ. 1,500. *272*

GALLIA PREHISTOIRE. SUPPLEMENT.
Editions du C N R S, 1 Place Aristide Briand, 92195 Meudon Cedex, France. TEL 1-45-34-75-50. FAX 1-46-26-28-49.
circ. 1,500. *273*

GARAGE & SERVICE STATION NEWS.
Garage & Service Station News Publishing Co., No. 204, 260 Raymur Ave., Vancouver 6, B.C., Canada. *4691*

GARDEN SUPPLY RETAILER GREEN BOOK.
Chilton Co., 201 King of Prussia Rd., Radnor, PA 19089. TEL 215-964-4269.
circ. 41,500. *2127*

GARDEN TRADE NEWS.
Frontline Ltd. Park House, 117 Park Rd., Peterborough PE1 2TR, England. TEL 0733-555161. FAX 62788. *2127*

GARUDA MAGAZINE.
P.T. Travia Duta, 3rd Fl., Hotel Borobudur Inter-Continental, Jalan Lapangan Bateng Selatan, Jakarta 10220, Indonesia. TEL 21-3809595. FAX 21-359-741.
circ. 150,000. *4802*

GASTRONOMIE-RUNDSCHAU.
Verlag K. Hoerning GmbH, Weberstr. 1, 6900 Heidelberg, Germany. *2071*

GATEWAY.
University of Alberta, Students Union, Students' Union Bldg., Edmonton, Alta. T6G 2J7, Canada. TEL 403-432-5168.
circ. 13,000. *1312*

GATEWAY ENGINEER.
Association Publishers Box 13066, St. Louis, MO 63119. TEL 314-533-9333. *1822*

GAZETTE DES COMMUNES, DES DEPARTEMENTS, DES REGIONS.
Publications du Moniteur, 17, Rue d'Uzes, 75002 Paris, France. TEL 1-40-13-30-30. FAX 1-40-26-20-94.
circ. 18,550. *1011*

GAZETTE DES FEMMES.
Conseil du Statut de la Femme, 8 rue Cook, 3e Etage, Bur. 300, Quebec, Que. G1R 5J7, Canada. TEL 418-643-4326. FAX 418-643-8926.
circ. 100,000. *4843*

GAZZETTINO AGRICOLO (PARMA).
Unione Provinciale Agricoltori di Parma, Piazzale A. Barezzi 3, 43100 Parma, Italy.
circ. 6,500. *93*

GEGENSCHEIN.
Gegenschein Press, 421 Hudson St., Ste. 220, New York, NY 10014. TEL 212-989-7845.
circ. 750. *2919*

GENEALOGY BULLETIN.
Dollarhide Systems, 203 W. Holly St., Ste. M4, Bellingham, WA 98225. TEL 206-671-3808. FAX 206-676-5805.
circ. 5,000. *2152*

GENERAL COMMISSION ON SAFETY AND HEALTH IN THE IRON AND STEEL INDUSTRY. REPORT.
General Commission on Safety and Health in the Iron and Steel Industry, Rue de la Loi 200, 1040 Brussels, Belgium. *3617*

GENETICS NEWSLETTER.
South African Genetic Society, c/o Department of Genetics, University of Stellenbosch, Stellenbosch, South Africa. *542*

GENIE INDUSTRIEL; CATALOGUE DE L'INGENIERIE.
Documentations Industrielles et Techniques, 11 rue de Madrid, 75008 Paris, France. *1822*

GENRE (NEW YORK).
Don Tuthill, Ed.& Pub, 60 E. 42nd St., Ste. 1166, New York, NY 10017. TEL 212-714-8160.
circ. 100,000. *3397*

GEO INFO SYSTEMS.
Aster Publishing Corporation, 859 Willamette St., Box 10955, Eugene, OR 97440. TEL 503-343-1200. FAX 503-343-3641.
circ. 30,000. *2268*

GEOLOGIA COLOMBIANA.
Universidad Nacional de Colombia, Departamento de Geociencias, Apdo. Aereo 14490, Bogota, D.E., Colombia. TEL 2682289. FAX 2682289.
circ. 5,000. *1562*

GEOMINAS.
Universidad de Oriente, Escuela de Geologia y Minas, c/o Comision de Publicaciones, La Sabanita, Ciudad Bolivar, 8001, Venezuela. *1544*

GEORGESON REPORT.
Georgeson & Company Inc., 88 Pine St., New York, NY 10005. FAX 212-440-9014.
circ. 8,000. *947*

GEORGIA ADVOCATE.
University of Georgia School of Law, Athens, GA 30602. TEL 404-542-7959.
circ. 6,000. *1312*

GEORGIA ALUMNI RECORD.
University of Georgia Alumni Society, Alumni House, Athens, GA 30602. TEL 404-542-3354. FAX 404-542-9492.
circ. 18,000. *1312*

GEORGIA FORESTRY.
Forestry Commission, Forest Education Department, Box 819, Macon, GA 31298. TEL 912-744-3363. FAX 912-744-3270.
circ. 6,000. *2101*

GEORGIA HUMANITIES.
Georgia Humanities Council, Emory University, 1556 Clifton Rd., N.E., Atlanta, GA 30322. TEL 404-727-7500. FAX 404-727-0206.
circ. 5,000. *2507*

GEORGIA MAGAZIN (ATLANTA, 1990).
Pacific Gateway Publications, Inc., 2310 Parklake Dr., Ste. 300, Atlanta, GA 30345. TEL 404-270-2854.
circ. 30,000. *2226*

GEORGIA STATE UNIVERSITY SIGNAL.
Georgia State University, Box 1862, University Plaza, Atlanta, GA 30303. TEL 404-651-2242. FAX 404-651-1045.
circ. 8,000. *1312*

GEORGIA TREND.
Grimes Publications, Inc. (Atlanta), Box 56447, Atlanta, GA 30343. TEL 404-522-7200.
circ. 39,400. *783*

GEORGIA VITAL STATISTICS REPORT.
Department of Human Resources, Division of Public Health, 878 Peachtree St., N.E., Ste. 200, Atlanta, GA 30309. TEL 404-894-6482.
circ. 600. *3992*

GEOSCOPE.
University of Ottawa, Department of Geography, Ottawa, Ont. K1N 6N5, Canada. TEL 613-564-2395. FAX 613-564-3304. *2251*

GESAMTSTATISTIK DER KRAFTFAHRTVERSICHERUNG.
Verband der Haftpflicht-, Unfall- und Kraftverkehrsversicherer e.V., Glockengiesserwall 1, 2000 Hamburg 1, Germany. *2546*

GESELLSCHAFT FUER BIBLIOTHEKSWESEN UND DOKUMENTATION DES LANDBAUES. MITTEILUNGEN.
Gesellschaft fuer Bibliothekswesen und Dokumentation des Landbaues, Engesserstr. 20, 7500 Karlsruhe 1, Germany. TEL 0721-66250. FAX 0721-6625111.
circ. 150. *138*

GETTING ABOUT BRITAIN.
Drumport Ltd., 21 Church Walk, Thames Ditton, Surrey KT7 0NP, England. TEL 4481-398-8332.
circ. 40,000. *4768*

GEZINSBLAD.
Uitgeversmaatschappij Born B.V., Esstraat 10, Box 22, Assen, Netherlands.
circ. 47,000. *2211*

GHANA. NATIONAL COUNCIL ON WOMEN AND DEVELOPMENT. ANNUAL REPORT.
National Council on Women and Development, Box M.53, Accra, Ghana. TEL 229119.
circ. 3,000. *4843*

CONTROLLED CIRCULATION SERIALS

GHAQDA BIBLJOTEKARJI.
Library Association, c/o Public Library, Beltissebh, Malta.
circ. 170. *2759*

GIFTWARE NEWS.
Giftware News, Box 5398, Deptford, NJ 08096.
TEL 609-227-0798.
circ. 42,400. *2281*

GINTONG BUTIL.
National Food Authority, E. Rodriguez Ave., Quezon City, Philippines. FAX 7121701.
circ. 20,000. *206*

GIORNALE DELLO SPETTACOLO.
Gestioni Editoriali A G I S, Via di Villa Patrizi 10, Rome 00161, Italy. FAX 06-8848079.
circ. 13,000. *1530*

GIRARD HOME NEWS.
Girard Home News, Inc., 106 S. 7th St., Ste. 600, Philadelphia, PA 19106.
circ. 13,500. *2226*

GLASGOW & WEST OF SCOTLAND FAMILY HISTORY SOCIETY. NEWSLETTER.
Glasgow & West of Scotland Family History Society, c/o Hon.Sec., 3 Fleming Rd., Bishopton PA7 5HW, Scotland.
circ. 800. *2153*

GLASGOW UNIVERSITY STUDENTS' HANDBOOK.
Students Representative Council, John McIntyre Bldg., The University, Glasgow G12 8QQ, Scotland.
TEL 041-339-8541. FAX 041-330-4808.
circ. 8,000. *1635*

GLASS & PORSELEN.
A-S Ursus Forlag og Pressbyraa, Odins gt. 26, 0266 Oslo, Norway. TEL 02-434060. FAX 02-43-61-43.
circ. 3,000. *1164*

GLOBAL.
Bull H N Information Systems Inc., Technology Park, Mail Stop 314N, Billerica, MA 01821-4199.
TEL 508-294-6000.
circ. 50,000. *909*

GLOBAL STAMP NEWS.
Brandewie Inc., 715 Johnston Dr., Box 97, Sidney, OH 45365. TEL 513-492-3183. FAX 513-492-6514.
circ. 20,000. *3753*

GO!
Shell South Africa (Pty) Ltd., P.O. Box 2231, Cape Town 8000, South Africa. TEL 021-408-4911. FAX 021-253807.
circ. 1,500. *4691*

GO WEST.
Motor Transport Management Group, 1251 Beacon Blvd., West Sacramento, CA 95691. TEL 916-373-3510. FAX 916-373-3631.
circ. 46,238. *4744*

GOLD BULLETIN.
World Gold Council, 1 rue de la Rotisserie, CH-1204 Geneva, Switzerland. TEL 022-219666. FAX 022-288160.
circ. 5,500. *3425*

GOLDA MEIR LIBRARY NEWSLETTER.
University of Wisconsin-Milwaukee, Golda Meir Library, 2311 E. Hartford Ave., Box 604, Milwaukee, WI 53201. TEL 414-229-4786. FAX 414-229-4380.
circ. 4,000. *2759*

GOLDEN STATE.
Golden State Publishing, 80 S. Lake Ave., No. 818, Pasadena, CA 91101. TEL 818-584-9703. FAX 818-584-9719.
circ. 3,125,000. *4768*

GOLF INDUSTRY.
Sterling Southeast Inc., 3230 W. Commercial Blvd., No. 250, Fort Lauderdale, FL 33309-3451.
TEL 305-893-8771. FAX 305-893-8783.
circ. 16,692. *4505*

GONGYE JIANZHU.
Yejin-bu, Jianzhu Yanjiu Zongyuan, 33 Xitucheng Lu, Haidian-qu, Beijing 100088, People's Republic of China. TEL 2015599.
circ. 8,000. *618*

GOOD NEWS (BIRMINGHAM).
Additional Curates Society for England and Wales, 246a Washwood Heath Rd., Birmingham B8 2XS, England. TEL 021-3280749. FAX 021-327-7951.
circ. 20,000. *4179*

THE GOOD NEWS LETTER (WASHINGTON).
National Institute for the Word of God, 487 Michigan Ave., N.E., Washington, DC 20017.
circ. 5,000. *4265*

GOPHER OVERSEA'R.
Veterans of Foreign Wars of the United States, Department of Minnesota, Veterans Service Bldg., St. Paul, MN 55155. TEL 612-291-1757.
FAX 612-291-2753.
circ. 85,000. *3459*

GOURMET RETAILER.
Sterling Southeast Inc., 3230 W. Commercial Blvd., No. 250, Fort Lauderdale, FL 33309-3451.
TEL 305-893-8771.
circ. 17,389. *2071*

GOVERNMENT BUSINESS.
Momentum Magazines, 4040 Credit View Rd., Unit 11, Box 6900, Mississauga, Ont. L5C 3A8, Canada. TEL 416-569-6900. FAX 416-569-6915.
circ. 27,000. *1040*

GOVERNMENT GREEN GUIDE.
Momentum Magazines, 4040 Credit View Dr., Unit 11, Box 6900, Mississauga, Ont. L5C 3A8, Canada. TEL 416-569-6900. FAX 416-569-6915.
circ. 17,000. *4062*

GOVERNMENT PRODUCT NEWS.
Penton Publishing 1100 Superior Ave., Cleveland, OH 44114-2543. TEL 216-696-7000. FAX 216-696-8765.
circ. 85,000. *4062*

GOVERNMENT PURCHASING GUIDE.
Moorshead Publications Ltd., 1300 Don Mills Rd., North York, Ont. M3B 3M8, Canada. TEL 416-445-5600. FAX 416-445-8149.
circ. 20,000. *4062*

GOVERNMENT RELATIONS.
American Society of Association Executives, 1575 I St., N.W., Washington, DC 20005. TEL 202-626-2723. FAX 202-408-9635.
circ. 900. *1011*

GOVERNMENT TECHNOLOGY.
G T Publications, Inc., 9719 Lincoln Village Dr., No. 500, Sacramento, CA 95827-3303. TEL 916-363-5000. FAX 916-363-5197.
circ. 56,000. *4083*

GRANDS NOTABLES DU PREMIER EMPIRE.
Editions du C N R S, 1 Place Aristide Briand, 92195 Meudon Cedex, France. TEL 1-45-34-75-50. FAX 1-46-26-28-49.
circ. 1,500. *419*

GRANITE STATE LIBRARIES.
State Library, Department of Cultural Affairs, 20 Park St., Concord, NH 03301. TEL 603-271-2425. FAX 603-271-2205.
circ. 2,500. *2759*

GRAPHIC ARTS MONTHLY.
Cahners Publishing Company (New York) Division of Reed Publishing (USA) Inc., 249 W. 17th St., New York, NY 10011. TEL 212-463-6834. FAX 212-463-6733.
circ. 94,015. *4000*

GRAPHIC ARTS PRODUCT NEWS (CHICAGO).
Maclean Hunter Publishing Company, 29 N. Wacker Dr., Chicago, IL 60606. TEL 312-726-2802. FAX 312-726-2574.
circ. 94,524. *4000*

GRAPHIC DESIGN: U S A.
Kaye Publishing Corporation, 120 E. 56th St., New York, NY 10022. TEL 212-759-8813. FAX 212-753-5990.
circ. 28,091. *32*

GRAPHICUS.
Associazione Culturale Progresso Grafico, Via Morgari 36/B, Castello del Valentino, 10125 Turin, Italy. TEL 39-650-96-59.
circ. 5,500. *4000*

GRASSO CONTACT.
Grasso's Koninklijke Machinefabrieken N.V., Parallelweg 27, S-Hertogenbosch, Netherlands.
TEL 073-283111. FAX 073-210310.
circ. 1,600. *3017*

GRAVURE ENVIRONMENTAL NEWSLETTER.
Gravure Association of America, Inc., 1200A Scottsville Rd., Rochester, NY 14624-5703.
TEL 716-436-2150. FAX 716-436-7689.
circ. 1,000. *4000*

GRAYBAR OUTLOOK.
Graybar Electric Co., Box 7231, St. Louis, MO 63177. TEL 314-727-3900. *1893*

GREAT BRITAIN. OVERSEAS DEVELOPMENT ADMINISTRATION. REPORT ON RESEARCH AND DEVELOPMENT.
Overseas Development Administration, Eland House, Stag Place, London SW1E 5DH, England. TEL 01-273 3000. *930*

GREAT LAKES GETAWAY.
Farmers' Advance News, Inc., 130 S. Main St., Box 8, Camden, MI 49232-0008. TEL 517-368-5201. FAX 517-368-5131.
circ. 130,000. *4769*

GREAT LAKES SCIENCE ADVISORY BOARD. REPORT.
International Joint Commission, Great Lakes Regional Commission, 100 Ouellette Ave., 8th Fl., Windsor, Ont. N9A 6T3, Canada. TEL 519-256-7821. FAX 519-256-7791.
circ. 8,000. *4824*

GREATER SEATTLE.
Pacific Northwest Media, Inc. 701 Dexter Ave. N., Ste. 101, Seattle, WA 98109. TEL 206-284-1750. FAX 206-284-2550.
circ. 34,000. *2226*

GREATER WASHINGTON BOARD OF TRADE NEWS.
Greater Washington Board of Trade, 1129 20th St., N.W., Washington, DC 20036. TEL 202-857-5900. FAX 202-223-2648. *835*

GREEN PAGES.
Murdoch, Mockler & Associates, 1130 K St., Ste. 210, Sacramento, CA 95814. TEL 916-441-3883.
circ. 10,000. *1137*

GREENHOUSE PRODUCT NEWS.
Scranton Gillette Communications, Inc., 380 E. Northwest Hwy., Des Plaines, IL 60016. TEL 708-298-6622. FAX 708-390-0408.
circ. 20,000. *2142*

GRIEVANCE BULLETIN.
United Nurses of Alberta, Park Plaza, 9th Fl., 10611 98 Ave., Edmonton, Alta. T5K 2P7, Canada. TEL 403-425-1025. FAX 403-426-2093.
circ. 325. *980*

GROCERS REPORT.
Supermarket Productions, Box 6124, San Rafael, CA 94903-0124. TEL 415-479-0211. FAX 415-479-0211.
circ. 15,000. *2092*

GROUNDS MAINTENANCE.
Intertec Publishing Corp., 9221 Quivira Rd., Box 12901, Overland Park, KS 66212-9981. TEL 913-888-4664. FAX 913-541-6697.
circ. 45,521. *2129*

GROUNDSMAN.
Adam Publishing Ltd., 42 West End Avenue, Pinner, Middlesex HA5 1BJ, England. TEL 081-868-3600. FAX 081-429-2374.
circ. 6,000. *4547*

GROUP TRAVEL LEADER.
Group Travel Leader, Inc., 340 S. Broadway, Lexington, KY 40508. TEL 606-253-0455. FAX 606-253-0499.
circ. 30,000. *4769*

GRUMMAN HORIZONS.
Grumman Corporation, 1111 Stewart Ave., Bethpage, NY 11714. TEL 516-575-7345. FAX 516-575-1400.
circ. 18,500. *53*

GUIA AUTOMOTRIZ DE VENEZUELA.
Promotrix, S.R.L., Calle Sorbona, Edif. Marta, Piso 1, Ofic. 18, Colinas de Bello Monte, Caracas, Venezuela. TEL 7511355. FAX 582-7511122. circ. 8,000. *4692*

GUIDE DES FUTURS EPOUX.
11 bis rue du Docteur Baudin, 28004 Chartres Cedex 92, France.
circ. 400,000. *4436*

GUILD OF AIR PILOTS AND AIR NAVIGATORS. JOURNAL.
Guild of Air Pilots and Air Navigators, Cobham House, 291 Gray's Inn Rd., London WC1X 8QF, England. TEL 071-837 3323. FAX 071-833-3190. circ. 2,000. *53*

GULF COAST GOLFER.
Golfer Magazines, Inc., 9182 Old Katy Rd., Ste. 212, Houston, TX 77055-7432. TEL 713-464-0308. FAX 713-464-0129.
circ. 30,000. *4506*

GULF COAST PLUMBING - HEATING - COOLING NEWS.
Box 430434, Houston, TX 77243-0434.
circ. 2,000. *2299*

GUNNERIA.
Universitetet i Trondheim, Vitenskapmuseet, Erling Skakkes gt. 47, N-7013 Trondheim, Norway. TEL 7-592145. FAX 7-592223. *273*

H I V FUNDING WATCH.
Department of Health, H I V Division, 1100 West 49th St., Austin, TX 78756-3199. TEL 512-458-7684. *3219*

H M A T.
National Asphalt Pavement Association, N.A.P.A. Bldg. 5100 Forbes Blvd., Lanham, MD 20706-4413. TEL 301-731-4748. FAX 301-731-4621. circ. 25,000. *4719*

H P A C TECHLIT SELECTOR.
Penton Publishing 1100 Superior Ave., Cleveland, OH 44114-2543. TEL 216-696-7000. FAX 216-696-8765.
circ. 52,000. *1930*

H R D I ADVISORY.
Human Resources Development Institute, 815 16th St., N.W., Washington, DC 20006. TEL 202-638-3912.
circ. 2,700. *980*

HAAGSE JAZZ CLUB.
Haagse Jazz Club, Laan van Heldenburg 7, Voorburg, Netherlands.
circ. 250. *3553*

HABIT.
Foerlags AB FackMedia, Sandhamnsgatan 71, Box 27817, S-115 93 Stockholm, Sweden. TEL 08-6704100. FAX 08-6616455.
circ. 8,049. *1291*

HAIYANG YUYE.
Zhongguo Shuichan Kexue Yuanjiuyuan, Donghai Shuichan Yanjiusuo, 300 Jungong Lu, Shanghai 200090, People's Republic of China.
TEL 5434590.
circ. 500. *2042*

HAMILTON ALUMNI REVIEW.
Hamilton College, Trustees of Hamilton College, Connell Alumni Center, Clinton, NY 13323.
TEL 315-859-4680. FAX 315-859-4648.
circ. 19,000. *1313*

HANDELSBESTYREREN.
Handelsbestyrerforbundet, Arbeidersamfundets Plass 1, 0181 Oslo, Norway. TEL 02-20-52-40. FAX 47-2-113194.
circ. 1,450. *1011*

HANDY SHIPPING GUIDE.
Wilkinson Bros. Ltd., 230-234 Long Lane, London SE1 4QE, England. FAX 071-403-0233. *4728*

HARDHAT (OKLAHOMA CITY).
National Marketing Center, Inc., Box 60150, Oklahoma City, OK 73146. TEL 405-840-2135. *619*

HARDWARE AGE "WHO MAKES IT" BUYERS' GUIDE.
Chilton Co., Chilton Way, Radnor, PA 19089.
TEL 215-964-4269. *1137*

HARDWARE AND GARDEN REVIEW.
Faversham House Group Ltd., Faversham House, 111 St. James's Rd., Croydon, Surrey CR9 2TH, England. TEL 081-684-4082. FAX 081-684-9729. *642*

HARDWOOD FLOORS.
Athletic Business Publications, Inc., 1842 Hoffman St., Ste. 201, Madison, WI 53704. TEL 608-249-0186. FAX 608-249-1153.
circ. 24,000. *639*

HARROWSMITH COUNTRY LIFE.
Camden House Publishing, Ferry Rd., Charlotte, VT 05445. TEL 802-425-3961. FAX 802-425-3307. circ. 250,000. *2129*

THE HARTFORD AGENT.
I T T Hartford Insurance Group, Hartford Plaza, Hartford, CT 06115. TEL 203-547-4976. FAX 203-547-3799.
circ. 30,000. *2533*

HARVARD UNIVERSITY. GRADUATE SCHOOL OF EDUCATION. BULLETIN.
Harvard University, Graduate School of Education, Appian Way, Cambridge, MA 02138. TEL 617-495-3615.
circ. 17,750. *1636*

HARYANA HEALTH JOURNAL.
State Health Education Bureau, Directorate of Health Services, 36 Madhaya Marg, Sector 7C, Chandigarh, Haryana, India. *4102*

HASSADEH.
Hassadeh Hoza'at Hamekaz Hahaklai Ltd., 8 Shaul Hamelech St., P.O. Box 40044, 61400 Tel Aviv, Israel. FAX 03-5429979.
circ. 6,500. *95*

HAVEN.
Det Danske Haveselskab, Rolighedsvej 26, DK-1958 Frederiksberg C, Denmark. TEL 31-35-11-35. FAX 45-31-35-71-44.
circ. 80,000. *2129*

HAWAII. OFFICE OF THE OMBUDSMAN. REPORT.
Office of the Ombudsman, Kekuanaoa Bldg., 4th Fl., 465 S. King St., Honolulu, HI 96813. TEL 808-587-0770. *4088*

HAWAII BEVERAGE GUIDE.
Service Publications, Inc. (Honolulu), Box 853, Honolulu, HI 96808. TEL 808-923-7084.
circ. 1,850. *381*

HAWAII DENTAL JOURNAL.
Hawaii Dental Association, 1000 Bishop St., Ste. 805, Honolulu, HI 96813. TEL 808-536-2135.
FAX 808-536-2137.
circ. 950. *3234*

HAWAII HEALTH MESSENGER.
Department of Health, Communication Office, Box 3378, Honolulu, HI 96801. TEL 808-586-4442.
FAX 808-586-4444.
circ. 5,500. *4102*

HAWAII HEALTH PLANNING NEWS.
State Health Planning and Development Agency, Box 3378, Honolulu, HI 96801. TEL 808-548-4050. *4102*

HAWAIIAN ACQUISITION LIST.
University of Hawaii Library, Hawaiian and Pacific Collection, 2550 the Mall, Honolulu, HI 96822.
TEL 808-948-7203.
circ. 400. *402*

HAWAIIAN JOURNAL OF HISTORY.
Hawaiian Historical Society, 560 Kawaiahao St., Honolulu, HI 96813. TEL 808-537-6271.
circ. 1,000. *2344*

HAZELDEN NEWS AND PROFESSIONAL UPDATE.
Hazelden Foundation, 1400 Park Ave. S., Minneapolis, MN 55404. TEL 612-349-4290.
FAX 612-339-5195.
circ. 88,000. *1536*

HEADLINES (LONDON).
Newspaper Society, Bloomsbury House, Bloomsbury Sq., 74-77 Gt. Russell St., London WC1B 3DA, England. TEL 071-636-7014. FAX 071-631-5119. circ. 9,000. *2570*

HEALTH AND PHYSICAL EDUCATION.
Taishukan Publishing Co. Ltd., 3-24 Kanda Nishikicho, Chiyoda-ku, Tokyo 101, Japan. FAX 03-3295-4107.
circ. 5,000. *1637*

HEALTH CONSEQUENCES OF SMOKING.
U.S. Office on Smoking and Health, National Center for Chronic Disease Prevention and Health Promotion, Centers for Disease Control, MS K-12, 1600 Clifton Rd., N.E., Atlanta, GA 30333. *1536*

HEALTH JOURNAL.
Madison Publishing, 347 Congress St., Boston, MA 02210. TEL 617-451-1155. FAX 617-451-3320. circ. 1,108,229. *3803*

HEALTH MANAGEMENT QUARTERLY.
Baxter Foundation, One Baxter Parkway, Deerfield, IL 60015. TEL 708-948-2000. FAX 708-948-2887. circ. 23,000. *2462*

HEALTH PROMOTION.
Department of National Health and Welfare, Ottawa, Ont. K1A 1B4, Canada. TEL 613-954-8842.
FAX 613-990-7097.
circ. 14,000. *4103*

HEALTHCARE INFORMATICS.
Health Data Analysis, Inc., Box 2830, Evergreen, CO 80439-2830. TEL 303-674-2774.
circ. 28,000. *3225*

HEARING JOURNAL.
Laux Company, Inc., 63 Great Rd., Maynard, MA 01754. TEL 617-897-5552. FAX 508-897-6824.
circ. 20,000. *2287*

HEARTBEAT (NASHVILLE).
Free Will Baptist Foreign Missions, Box 5002, Antioch, TN 37011-5002. TEL 615-361-1010.
FAX 615-731-0049.
circ. 45,000. *4239*

HEARTH & HOME.
Village West Publishing, Box 2008, Laconia, NH 03247-2008. TEL 603-528-4285. FAX 603-524-0643.
circ. 21,000. *1790*

HEAT TREATING.
Hitchcock Publishing, Heat Treating 191 S. Gary Ave., Carol Stream, IL 60188. TEL 708-462-2286. FAX 708-462-2225.
circ. 21,426. *3407*

HEATING - PIPING - AIR CONDITIONING.
Penton Publishing 1100 Superior Ave., Cleveland, OH 44114-2543. TEL 216-969-7000. FAX 216-696-8765.
circ. 52,000. *2300*

HEBREW UNIVERSITY OF JERUSALEM. AUTHORITY FOR RESEARCH AND DEVELOPMENT. CURRENT RESEARCH.
Hebrew University of Jerusalem, Jerusalem, Israel.
TEL 02-630241. FAX 02-664740. *4373*

HELICE.
Mexican Air Line Pilots Association, c/o Capt. J.J. Castillo A., Av. Palomas 110, Lomas de Sotelo, Mexico 10, D.F., Mexico. FAX 52-5-202-25-73. circ. 2,000. *54*

HER MAJESTY'S CONSULS LIST.
Southern Magazines Ltd., Jewson Complex, Eccelson Rd., Tovil, Maidstone, Kent ME15 6ST, England. TEL 0622-677014. FAX 0622-759818.
circ. 3,500. *3897*

HERE AND NOW.
Institute of Psychological Research, Inc., 34 Fleury St. W., Montreal, Que. H3L 1S9, Canada. TEL 514-382-3000. FAX 514-382-3007.
circ. 2,000. *4023*

HERON.
Technische Universitiet Delft, Faculty of Civil Engineering, c/o J.G.M van Mier, P.O. Box 5048, 2600 GA Delft, Netherlands. FAX 31-15-611465. circ. 2,000. *1866*

HI CLASS LIVING.
M N R Promotions, Inc., 111 Charlotte Pl., Englewood Cliffs, NJ 07632. TEL 201-871-2221. FAX 201-871-2223.
circ. 15,000. *2226*

HIFI & VIDEO MARKT.
S Z V KG, Schellingstr. 39-43, 8000 Munich 40, Germany. TEL 089-23726-0. FAX 089-23726-125.
circ. 8,900. *4460*

HIGH SCHOOL RAGE.
High School Publications Inc., 18923 98 Ave., Edmonton, Alta. T5T 5T3, Canada. TEL 403-448-7314. FAX 403-484-1008.
circ. 38,000. *1256*

HIGHLIGHTS (EDWARDSVILLE).
Southern Illinois University, Edwardsville, Regional Research and Development Services, Campus Box 1456, Edwardsville, IL 62026-1456. TEL 618-692-3500. FAX 618-692-2886.
circ. 1,000. *2488*

HILLTOP.
Howard University, 2251 Sherman Ave., N.W., Washington, DC 20059. TEL 202-806-6866.
circ. 10,000. *1314*

HINDUSTAN CHAMBER REVIEW.
Hindustan Chamber of Commerce, 8 Kondi Chetty St., Madras 1, India. *816*

HINE'S DIRECTORY OF INSURANCE ADJUSTERS.
Hine's Legal Directory, Inc., Box 280, Glen Ellyn, IL 60138. TEL 708-462-9670.
circ. 7,000. *2533*

HINE'S INSURANCE COUNSEL.
Hine's Legal Directory, Inc., Box 280, Glen Ellyn, IL 60138. TEL 708-462-9670.
circ. 7,000. *2632*

HIPPOCRATES.
Hippocrates Partners, 301 Howard St., 18th Fl., San Francisco, CA 94105-2252. TEL 415-512-9100. *3105*

HIROSHIMA MEDICAL ASSOCIATION. JOURNAL.
Hiroshima Medical Association, 1-1-1 Kannonhon-machi, Hiroshima 733, Japan. FAX 082-293-3363.
circ. 5,700. *3105*

HIROSHIMA UNIVERSITY. RESEARCH INSTITUTE FOR NUCLEAR MEDICINE AND BIOLOGY. PROCEEDINGS.
Hiroshima University, Research Institute for Nuclear Medicine and Biology, Kasumi, Hiroshima 734, Japan.
circ. 450. *3358*

HISTORICAL GEOGRAPHY RESEARCH SERIES.
Historical Geography Research Group, Department of Geography, Cheltenham & Gloucester College of Higher Education, Park, Cheltenham, Glos. GL50 2RH, England. FAX 0242-532997.
circ. 450. *2252*

HISTORICAL STUDIES.
Irish Historical Society, 195 Pearse St., Trinity College, Dublin 2, Ireland.
circ. 1,000. *2366*

HITACHI ZOSEN TECHNICAL REVIEW.
Hitachi Zosen Corporation, Technical Research Institute, 1-3-22 Sakurajima, Konohana-ku, Osaka 554, Japan. FAX 03-3213-0914.
circ. 2,800. *1823*

HITSAUSTEKNIIKKA - SVETSTEKNIK.
Suomen Hitsausteknillinen Yhdistys, Makelankatu 36A, 00510 Helsinki, Finland. FAX 0-715093.
circ. 5,500. *3429*

HJELPEPLEIEREN.
Norsk Hjelpepleierforbund, P.O. Box 151, Brun, 0611 Oslo 1, Norway. FAX 645602.
circ. 38,000. *3278*

HOG FARM MANAGEMENT.
Miller Publishing Co., 12400 Whitewater Dr., Ste. 160, Box 2400, Minnetonka, MN 55343-2524. TEL 612-931-0211. FAX 612-931-0910.
circ. 44,500. *217*

HOGAR.
Editores Nacionales, Aguirre 724 y Boyaca, Apdo. 1239, Guayaquil, Ecuador. TEL 4-327-200.
circ. 35,000. *4844*

HOJA DEL LUNES DE ORENSE.
Region, Cardenal Quiroga 11 y 15, Orense, Spain. *2217*

HOLD PUSTEN.
Norsk Radiografforbund, FAX 2-175204.
circ. 1,200. *3358*

HOLLAND HERALD.
Multi Media International, P.O. Box 469, 1180 AL Amstelveen, Netherlands. TEL 20-5473550. FAX 20-6438581.
circ. 250,000. *2211*

HOME BUILDER MAGAZINE.
Work-4 Projects Ltd., 4920 de Maisonneuve W. Ste. 102, Westmount, Que. H3Z 1N1, Canada. TEL 514-489-4941. FAX 514-489-5505.
circ. 16,391. *619*

HOME FINDERS GUIDEBOOK.
Southeast Publishing, 12015 Park 35 Circle, Ste. 207.6, Austin, TX 78753. TEL 512-339-6281. FAX 512-832-0221.
circ. 25,000. *4149*

HOMEBUYER'S GUIDE - DALLAS - FORT WORTH.
Living Partners, Ltd., Regency Center II, 5501 LBJ Frwy., Ste. 300, Dallas, TX 75240. TEL 214-239-2399. FAX 214-239-7850.
circ. 70,000. *4149*

HOMEBUYER'S GUIDE - FLORIDA GULF COAST.
HomeBuyer's Guide (Tampa) 1715 N. Westshore Blvd., Ste. 244, Tampa, FL 33607-3926. TEL 813-879-1177. FAX 813-874-3077.
circ. 50,000. *4149*

HOMEFINDERS GUIDE.
Travel Publications, Inc., Alta Loma, CA 91701.
circ. 35,000. *4150*

HOMEMAKERS'S MAGAZINE.
Telemedia Procom Inc., 50 Holly St., 2nd fl., Toronto, Ont. M4S 3B3, Canada. TEL 416-482-9399. FAX 416-482-3975.
circ. 1,600,000. *2447*

HOMEWORLD BUSINESS.
I C D Publications, Box 14307, Hauppauge, NY 11788-0477. TEL 516-979-7878. FAX 516-979-8182.
circ. 12,800. *2560*

HONG KONG APPAREL.
Hong Kong Trade Development Council, 38th Fl., Office Tower, Convention Plaza, 1 Harbour Rd., Wanchai, Hong Kong. TEL 584-4333. FAX 824-0249.
circ. 27,500. *1285*

HONG KONG EXTERNAL TRADE.
Census and Statistics Department, Wanchai Tower 1, 12 Harbour Rd., Wanchai, Hong Kong. TEL 582-4915. FAX 8024000.
circ. 700. *720*

HONG KONG TOYS.
Hong Kong Trade Development Council, 36-39th Fl., Office Tower, Convention Plaza, 1 Harbour Rd., Wanchai, Hong Kong. TEL 584-4333. FAX 824-0249.
circ. 35,000. *2281*

HONG KONG VISITOR.
South China Morning Post Publishers Ltd., 6-F, South China Morning Post Bldg., Tong Chong Street 57, Quarry Bay, Hong Kong. TEL 5652430. FAX 5658961.
circ. 50,000. *4771*

HONOURABLE ARTILLERY COMPANY JOURNAL.
Honourable Artillery Company, Armoury House, London, EC1Y 2BQ, England.
circ. 2,800. *3459*

HOOSIER INDEPENDENT.
Indiana Oil Marketers Association, Inc., 8780 Purdue Rd., Ste. 4, Indianapolis, IN 46268. FAX 317-875-6721.
circ. 1,400. *3688*

HOOSIER PURCHASOR.
National Purchasing Management Association - Indianapolis, 37 E. Ninth St., Indianapolis, IN 46204. TEL 317-635-3818. FAX 317-635-3931.
circ. 4,500. *1040*

HORIZON AIR MAGAZINE.
Paradigm Press, 2701 First Ave., Ste. 250, Seattle, WA 98121. TEL 206-441-5871.
circ. 20,000. *4802*

HORSE BRASS.
National Horse Brass Society, 69 West Chiltern, Woodcote, Reading RG8 0SG, England, England.
circ. 500. *2437*

HOSIERY STATISTICS.
National Association of Hosiery Manufacturers, 447 S. Sharon Amity Rd., Charlotte, NC 28211. TEL 704-365-0913. FAX 704-362-2056.
circ. 1,000. *1288*

HOSPICE TODAY.
Hospice of the Florida Suncoast, 300 E. Bay Dr., Largo, FL 34640. TEL 813-586-4432.
circ. 36,000. *4407*

HOSPITAL AND HEALTHCARE AUSTRALIA.
Yaffa Publishing Group, 17-21 Bellevue St., Surry Hills, N.S.W. 2010, Australia. TEL 02-281-2333. FAX 02-281-2750.
circ. 3,948. *2464*

HOSPITAL BLUE BOOK (OFFICIAL SOUTHERN EDITION).
Billian Publishing, Inc., 2100 Powers Ferry Rd., Ste. 300, Atlanta, GA 30339. TEL 404-955-5656. FAX 404-952-0669.
circ. 10,654. *2464*

HOSPITAL DEVELOPMENT.
United Trade Press Ltd., U.T.P. House, 33-35 Bowling Green Ln., London EC1R 0DA, England. TEL 01-837 1212.
circ. 8,635. *2464*

HOSPITALIS.
Hospitalis Verlag AG, Hermetschloostr. 75, Postfach 1632, CH-8048 Zuerich, Switzerland. TEL 01-4330242. FAX 01-4330242.
circ. 9,150. *2466*

HOSPITALITY & TOURISM EDUCATOR.
Council on Hotel, Restaurant and Institutional Education, 1200 17th St., 7th Fl., Washington, DC 20036-3047. TEL 202-331-5990. FAX 202-331-2429.
circ. 2,000. *1684*

HOT PICKS.
Baker & Taylor Books, 652 E. Main St., Box 6920, Bridgewater, NJ 08807-0920. TEL 908-218-0400. FAX 908-218-3980.
circ. 33,000. *4129*

HOTEL & RESORT INDUSTRY.
Coastal Communications Corporation, 488 Madison Ave., New York, NY 10022. TEL 212-888-1500. FAX 212-888-8008.
circ. 49,074. *2475*

HOTEL BUSINESS.
I C D Publications, 1393 Veterans Hwy., Ste. 214 N., Hauppauge, NY 11788. TEL 516-979-7878.
circ. 45,000. *2475*

HOTEL UND GASTGEWERBE.
S H Z Fachverlag AG, Alte Landstr. 43, CH-8700 Kuesnacht-Zurich, Switzerland. TEL 01-9108022. FAX 01-9105155.
circ. 10,000. *2476*

HOTLINE (KANSAS CITY).
National Office Machine Dealers Association, 12411 Wornall Rd., Kansas City, MO 64145. TEL 816-941-3100.
circ. 5,000. *1058*

HOUSE BUILDER.
Housebuilder Publications Ltd., 82 New Cavendish St., London W1M 8AD, England. TEL 071-580-5588. FAX 071-323-0890.
circ. 24,437. *619*

HOUSE, HOME & GARDEN.
Berkeley House Enterprises, Inc., 809 Virginia Ave., Martinsburg, WV 25401. TEL 304-267-2673.
circ. 10,000. *2226*

CONTROLLED CIRCULATION SERIALS

HOUSING POLICY DEBATE.
Federal National Mortgage Association, 3900 Wisconsin Ave., N.W., Washington, DC 20016-2899. TEL 202-752-4422. FAX 202-752-4933.
circ. 2,300. *2488*

HOUSTON LIVING HOUSING GUIDE.
Lash Publications, Inc. (Bellaire), 6700 W. Loop S., 100, Bellaire, TX 77401-4107. TEL 713-777-4636.
circ. 80,000. *4150*

HET HOUTBLAD.
Het Houtblad B.V., Postbus 401, 1400 AK Bussem, Netherlands. TEL 02159-50488. FAX 02159-50487.
circ. 18,000. *639*

HOW TO START YOUR OWN BUSINESS WITH 2000 TO 5000 DOLLARS.
Siveast Consultants, Inc., USA, c/o P.O. Box 1755, Kathmandu, Nepal.
circ. 20. *1115*

HUMANA HOSPITAL - MICHAEL REESE NEWS.
Humana Hospital - Michael Reese, Corporate Communications Department, 2816 S. Ellis Ave., Chicago, IL 60616. TEL 312-791-4462.
circ. 16,000. *2466*

HUNTER EDUCATION INSTRUCTOR.
Outdoor Empire Publishing, Inc., 511 Eastlake Ave. E., Box C 19000, Seattle, WA 98109. TEL 206-624-3845.
circ. 10,000. *4548*

HUNTER'S HILL TRUST JOURNAL.
Hunter's Hill Trust, P.O. Box 85, Hunter Hill, N.S.W. 2110, Australia. FAX 33-99506.
circ. 1,000. *1489*

HYDRAULICS & PNEUMATICS.
Penton Publishing 1100 Superior Ave., Cleveland, OH 44114-2543. TEL 216-696-7000. FAX 216-696-8765.
circ. 52,000. *1924*

I A T A ANNUAL REPORT.
International Air Transport Association, 2000 Peel St., Montreal, Que. H3A 2R4, Canada. TEL 514-844-6311. *4674*

I A T A REVIEW.
International Air Transport Association, 2000 Peel St., Montreal, Que. H3A 2R4, Canada. TEL 514-844-6311. *4674*

I B M UK NEWS.
I B M United Kingdom Ltd., P.O. Box 41, North Harbour, Portsmouth PO6 3AU, England.
circ. 19,000. *1396*

I B W A NEWS.
International Bottled Water Association, 113 N. Henry St., Alexandria, VA 22314. TEL 703-683-5213. FAX 703-683-4074.
circ. 2,500. *381*

I B W A TECHNICAL BULLETIN.
International Bottled Water Association, 113 N. Henry St., Alexandria, VA 22314. TEL 703-683-5213. FAX 703-683-4074.
circ. 2,500. *381*

I C A NEWSLETTER.
International Communication Association, 8140 Burnet Rd., Box 9589, Austin, TX 78766. TEL 512-454-8299. FAX 512-454-4221. *1336*

I C A S A L S NEWSLETTER.
International Center for Arid and Semiarid Land Studies, Texas Tech Univ., Box 41036, Lubbock, TX 79409-1036. TEL 806-742-2218.
circ. 3,000. *96*

I C M R BULLETIN.
Shri J.N. Mathur, P.O. Box 4508, Ansari Nagar, New Delhi 110 029, India.
circ. 6,200. *3107*

I C-WISSEN BUEROKOMMUNIKATION.
Vogel-Verlag und Druck KG, Max-Planck-Str. 7-9, Postfach 67 40, 8700 Wuerzburg 1, Germany. TEL 0931-418-0.
circ. 167,800. *1058*

I E N - EUROPE.
Pan European Publishing Co. Rue Verte 216, B-1210 Brussels, Belgium. TEL 02-2422992. FAX 02-2427111.
circ. 50,000. *1925*

I F M A WORLD.
International Foodservice Manufacturers Association, 321 N. Clark, Chicago, IL 60610. TEL 312-644-8989. *2072*

I L A REPORTER.
Illinois Library Association, 33 W. Grand Ave No. 301, Chicago, IL 60610. TEL 312-644-1896. FAX 312-644-1899.
circ. 4,400. *2761*

I L C A PROGRAMME AND BUDGET.
International Livestock Centre for Africa, P.O. Box 5689, Addis Ababa, Ethiopia. *218*

I LAISVE.
Friends of the Lithuanian Front, 1634-49th Ave., Cicero, IL 60650. *2005*

IN D A C.
Indianapolis Athletic Club, 350 North Meridian St, Indianapolis, IN 46204. TEL 317-634-4331.
circ. 3,500. *1298*

I N F O.
Tulsa City-County Library System, Business and Technology Dept., 400 Civic Center, Tulsa, OK 74103. TEL 918-596-7988. FAX 918-596-7895.
circ. 1,400. *2793*

I O M MONTHLY DISPATCH.
International Organization for Migration, 17 route des Morillons, Case Postale 71, CH-1211 Geneva 19, Switzerland. TEL 022-717-9111. *3982*

I P A AKTUELL.
A. Bernecker Verlag, Unter dem Schoeneberg 1, 3508 Melsungen, Germany. TEL 05661-731-0. FAX 05661-73189.
circ. 54,500. *1515*

I P A S E BIBLIOTECA INFORMA.
Instituto de Previdencia e Assistencia dos Servidores do Estado, Divisao de Relacoes Publicas, Biblioteca, Rua Pedro Lessa 36, 13 Andar, Rio de Janeiro, G B, Brazil.
circ. 400. *2793*

I P P F MEDICAL BULLETIN.
International Planned Parenthood Federation, Regent's College, Inner Circle, Regent's Park, London NW1 4NS, England. TEL 071-486-0741. FAX 071-487-7950.
circ. 30,000. *597*

I-PUNKT.
Echter Wuerzburg, Fraenkische Gesellschaftsdruckerei und Verlag GmbH, Postfach 5560, Juliuspromenade 64, 8700 Wuerzburg 1, Germany. *981*

I.Q.S.
Institut Quimic de Sarria, Barcelona 17, Spain. FAX 2056266. *1178*

I S P NEWS.
M I S Training Institute Press, Inc., 498 Concord St., Framingham, MA 01701. TEL 508-879-7999.
circ. 25,000. *1526*

I S S A TODAY.
International Sanitary Supply Association, Inc., 7373 N. Lincoln Ave., Lincolnwood, IL 60646. TEL 312-982-0800.
circ. 3,200. *4104*

I T A A MEMBERSHIP DIRECTORY.
Information Technology Association of America, Publications Dept., 1616 N. Fort Myer Dr., Ste. 1300, Arlington, VA 22209-9998. TEL 703-522-5055. FAX 703-525-2279.
circ. 10,000. *1451*

I T E M.
R & B Enterprises (West Conshohocken) 20 Clipper Rd., West Conshohocken, PA 19428. TEL 215-825-1960. FAX 215-825-1684.
circ. 25,000. *1898*

I T R.
Technopress Fachzeitschriften Verlagsgesellschaft mbH, Felix-Mottl-Str. 12, 1190 Vienna, Austria. TEL 0222-322551.
circ. 14,000. *4745*

ICE CREAM & FROZEN CONFECTIONERY.
Ice Cream Alliance, 90-94 Gray's Inn Rd., London WC1X 8AH, England. TEL 071-405-0712. FAX 071-404-5879.
circ. 1,250. *2088*

IDAHO. DEPARTMENT OF FISH AND GAME. FEDERAL AID INVESTIGATION PROJECTS. PROGRESS REPORTS AND PUBLICATIONS.
Department of Fish and Game, Box 25, Boise, ID 83707. TEL 208-334-4697. *1489*

IDAHO CITIES.
Association of Idaho Cities, 3314 Grace St., Boise, ID 83703. TEL 208-344-8594. FAX 208-344-8677.
circ. 2,250. *4088*

IDEA TODAY.
Idea, Inc., 6190 Cornerstone Ct. E., Ste. 204, San Diego, CA 92121-3773. TEL 619-535-8979. FAX 619-535-8234.
circ. 20,000. *3804*

IDEAS FOR BETTER LIVING.
Boulevard Publications, 1755 Northwest Blvd., Columbus, OH 43212. TEL 614-488-8252. FAX 614-488-9124.
circ. 350,000. *2552*

IEVANHEL'S'KYI HOLOS.
Evangelical Voice, RR 1, Wilsonville, Ont. NOE 1Z0, Canada. TEL 519-443-7742.
circ. 1,200. *4284*

ILLINOIS DENTAL JOURNAL.
Illinois State Dental Society, 524 S. Fifth St., Box 376, Springfield, IL 62705. TEL 217-525-1406. FAX 217-525-8872.
circ. 6,000. *3234*

ILLINOIS NOTES.
State Library, 300 S. Second St., Springfield, IL 62701. TEL 217-782-7846.
circ. 3,900. *2761*

ILLINOIS POLICE ASSOCIATION. OFFICIAL JOURNAL.
Illinois Police Association, 6009 Wayzata Blvd., Ste. 228, Minneapolis, MN 55416.
circ. 17,000. *1515*

ILLINOIS QUARTERLY.
University of Illinois at Urbana-Champaign, Alumni Association, University of Illinois, 227 Illini Union, Urbana, IL 61801. TEL 217-337-1471. FAX 217-333-7803.
circ. 117,000. *1314*

ILLINOIS STATE AND REGIONAL ECONOMIC DATA BOOK.
Department of Commerce and Community Affairs, 620 E. Adams, Springfield, IL 62701. TEL 217-782-1438.
circ. 2,000. *868*

ILLINOIS STATE GENEALOGICAL SOCIETY QUARTERLY.
Illinois State Genealogical Society, Box 10195, Springfield, IL 62791.
circ. 2,500. *2155*

ILLINOIS TRUCK NEWS.
Illinois Trucking Association, 2000 N. 5th Ave., River Grove, IL 60171-1907. FAX 708-452-3508.
circ. 5,326. *4745*

ILMAILU.
Suomen Ilmailuliitto, Malmi Airport, 00700 Helsinki 70, Finland. TEL 0-378-055. FAX 0-374-1551.
circ. 9,600. *55*

IMAGES OF NASHVILLE.
Journal Communications, 5123 Paddock Village Ct., Ste. C-23, Brentwood, TN 37027. TEL 615-371-0010.
circ. 50,000. *2227*

IMBAT.
International Association of Jazz Appreciation, Box 48146, Los Angeles, CA 90048. TEL 213-673-7541. FAX 213-673-0757.
circ. 5,000. *3555*

IMPERIAL CANCER RESEARCH FUND. SCIENTIFIC REPORT.
Imperial Cancer Research Fund, Lincoln's Inn Fields, London WC2A 3PX, England. TEL 071-242-0200. FAX 071-404-4182.
circ. 1,900. *3198*

IMPORT AUTOMOTIVE PARTS & ACCESORIES.
Meyers Publishing Corp., 6211 Van Nuys Blvd., Ste. 200, Van Nuys, CA 91401. TEL 818-785-3900. FAX 818-785-4397.
circ. 35,000. *4692*

IN THE DRIVER'S SEAT.
Ontario Safety League, 21 Four Seasons Place, Etobicoke, Ont. M9B 6J8, Canada. TEL 416-593-2670. *4693*

INDEPENDENT BUSINESS.
First Sierra Publishing Co., 875 S. Westlake Blvd., Ste. 211, Westlake Village, CA 91361. TEL 805-496-6156. FAX 805-496-5469.
circ. 560,000. *670*

INDEPENDENT GASOLINE MARKETING.
Society of Independent Gasoline Marketers of America, 11911 Freedom Dr., No. 590, Reston, VA 22090-5602. TEL 703-709-7007. FAX 703-379-4561.
circ. 4,000. *3688*

INDEX NEW ZEALAND.
National Library of New Zealand, Collection Management, P.O. Box 1467, Wellington, New Zealand. TEL 4743-098. FAX 04-4743-035.
circ. 300. *14*

INDIA. CENTRAL VIGILANCE COMMISSION. REPORT.
Central Vigilance Commission, No.3, Dr. Rajendra Prasad Road, New Delhi, India. *4063*

INDIA. DEPARTMENT OF SPACE. ANNUAL REPORT.
Department of Space, Cauvery Bhavan, F-Block, Kempegowda Rd., Bangalore 560009, India.
circ. 5,000. *55*

INDIA. MINISTRY OF EDUCATION AND SOCIAL WELFARE. DEPARTMENT OF SOCIAL WELFARE. DOCUMENTATION SERVICE BULLETIN.
Ministry of Education and Social Welfare, Department of Social Welfare, Shastri Bhavan, New Delhi 110001, India. *4395*

INDIA. MINISTRY OF EDUCATION AND SOCIAL WELFARE. PROVISIONAL STATISTICS OF EDUCATION IN THE STATES.
Ministry of Education and Social Welfare, Department of Education, Shastri Bhavan, New Delhi 110001, India. *1677*

INDIA. MINISTRY OF FINANCE. FINANCE LIBRARY. WEEKLY BULLETIN.
Ministry of Finance, Finance Library, North Block, New Delhi 110001, India. TEL 3013852. *784*

INDIAN CHEMICALS AND PHARMACEUTICALS STATISTICS.
Ministry of Chemicals and Fertilizers, Economics and Statistics Division, New Delhi, India. *3748*

INDIAN CRUSADER.
American Indian Liberation Crusade, Inc., 4009 Halldale Ave., Los Angeles, CA 90062. TEL 213-299-1810.
circ. 8,000. *2006*

INDIAN EDUCATION ABSTRACTS.
Ministry of Education and Social Welfare, Department of Education, Shastri Bhavan, New Dehli 110001, India. *1677*

INDIAN FERTILISER STATISTICS.
Ministry of Chemicals and Fertilisers, Economics and Statistics Division, New Delhi, India. *138*

INDIAN INSTITUTE OF TROPICAL METEOROLOGY. ANNUAL REPORT.
Indian Institute of Tropical Meteorology, Ramdurg House, University Rd., Poona 411 005, India. *3436*

INDIAN JOURNAL OF MEDICAL RESEARCH.
Indian Council of Medical Research, PO Box 4508, Ansari Nagar, New Delhi 110029, India.
circ. 1,000. *3108*

INDIAN PETROLEUM AND NATURAL GAS STATISTICS.
Ministry of Petroleum & Chemicals, Department of Petroleum & Natural Gas, Economics and Statistics Division, Shastri Bhawan, New Delhi 110 001, India. FAX 66235. *3705*

INDIAN VACUUM SOCIETY. BULLETIN.
Indian Vacuum Society, c/o Technical Physics & Prototype Engineering Division, Bhabha Atomic Research Centre, Bombay 400 085, India. TEL (022)5516910.
circ. 500. *3820*

INDIANA CONTRACTOR.
Indiana Association of Plumbing - Heating - Cooling Contractors, Inc., Box 40963, Indianapolis, IN 46240. TEL 317-575-9292. FAX 317-575-9378.
circ. 5,100. *2300*

INDIANA HISTORICAL SOCIETY NEWS.
Indiana Historical Society, 315 W. Ohio St., Indianapolis, IN 46202. TEL 317-232-1882. FAX 317-233-3109.
circ. 9,500. *2410*

INDIANA PUBLISHER.
Hoosier State Press Association, Inc., 300 Consolidated Building, 115 N. Pennsylvania St., Indianapolis, IN 46204. TEL 317-637-3966. FAX 317-631-1199. *2571*

INDO - U S BUSINESS.
Indo-American Chamber of Commerce, Vulcan Insurance Bldg., Veer Nariman Rd., Churchgate, Bombay 400 020, India.
circ. 1,800. *817*

INDONESIA. DIREKTORAT PERUMAHAN RAKJAT. LAPORAN KERDJA.
Direktorat Perumahan Rakjat, Jalan Wijaya I-68, Kebayoran Baru, Jakarta, Indonesia. *2489*

INDUSTRI-NOTICIAS.
Publi-News Latinoamericana, S.A.C.V., Colima 436, Mexico 7, D.F., Mexico. *670*

INDUSTRIA INTERNACIONAL.
Publicaciones Internacionales S.A., Castellana 210, 28046 Madrid, Spain.
circ. 6,000. *1077*

INDUSTRIA TURISTICA.
Charles Francis Publications, Inc., Box 52-1898, Miami, FL 33152-1898. TEL 305-592-3168.
circ. 6,000. *4772*

INDUSTRIAL COMPUTING.
E M A P Business & Computer Publications Ltd., Priory Court, 30-32 Farringdon Ln., London EC1R 3AU, England.
circ. 15,002. *1396*

INDUSTRIAL COMPUTING.
I S A Services, Inc., 67 Alexander Dr., Box 12277, Research Triangle Park, NC 27709. TEL 919-549-8411. FAX 919-549-8288.
circ. 45,000. *1424*

INDUSTRIAL HEATING.
Business News Publishing Co., Box 2600, Troy, MI 48007. TEL 313-362-3700. FAX 313-362-0317.
circ. 22,516. *3841*

INDUSTRIAL LOCOMOTIVE.
Industrial Locomotive Society, Gilfachddu, Llanberis, Gwynedd, Wales LL55 4TY, England. *4710*

INDUSTRIAL NOTTINGHAMSHIRE.
Nottinghamshire Chamber of Commerce and Industry, 395 Mansfield Rd., Nottingham NG5 2DL, England. TEL 0602-624624. FAX 0602-605981.
circ. 2,500. *817*

INDUSTRIAL PROGRESS.
Donnelly Marketing 1901 S. Meyers Rd., Ste. 700, Oakbrook Terrace, IL 60181.
circ. 60,000. *4600*

INDUSTRIAL PUERTO RICO.
Antilles Publishing, 721 Hernandez St., Miramar Towers, Apt. 12B, Santurce 00908, PR 00901.
circ. 7,500. *1078*

INDUSTRIAL WORLD.
Johnston International Publishing 950 Lee St., Des Plaines, IL 60016. TEL 708-296-0770. FAX 708-803-3328.
circ. 80,000. *4600*

INDUSTRIE-AUSRUESTUNGS-MAGAZIN.
Konradin-Verlag Robert Kohlhammer GmbH, Ernst-Mey-Str. 8, Postfach 100252, 7022 Leinfelden-Echterdingen 1, Germany. TEL 0711-7594-0.
circ. 25,226. *3018*

INDUSTRIE MEISTER.
Vogel-Verlag und Druck KG, Max-Planck-Str. 7-9, 8700 Wuerzburg 1, Germany.
circ. 18,000. *1078*

INDUSTRY WEEK.
Penton Publishing 1100 Superior Ave., Cleveland, OH 44114-2543. TEL 216-696-7000. FAX 216-696-8765.
circ. 288,000. *1013*

INFECTIONS IN MEDICINE.
S C P Communications, Inc., 134 W. 29th St., New York, NY 10001-5304. TEL 212-714-1740.
circ. 61,693. *3219*

INFO MAGAZINE.
Union Pacific Railroad, Employee Communications Department, 1416 Dodge St., Omaha, NE 68179.
circ. 78,000. *4710*

INFORM-ACTION.
Manitoba Teachers Society, 191 Harcourt St., Winnipeg, Man. R3J 3H2, Canada. TEL 204-888-7961. FAX 204-831-0877.
circ. 1,800. *2818*

INFORMACION ARQUEOLOGICA.
Diputacion Provincial de Barcelona, Instituto de Prehistoria y Arqueologia, Parque de Montjuich, Barcelona 4, Spain. *274*

INFORMACOES ECONOMICAS.
Instituto de Economia Agricola, Servico de Biblioteca e Documentacao, Av. Miguel Stefano, 3900, Caixa Postal 8114, 04301 Sao Paulo, SP, Brazil. FAX 01122484. *152*

INFORMAL LOGIC.
Department of Philosophy, University of Windsor, Windsor, Ont. N9B 3P4, Canada. TEL 519-253-4232. FAX 519-973-7050.
circ. 300. *3769*

INFORMATICA OGGI SETTIMANALE.
Gruppo Editoriale Jackson S.p.A., Via Pola 9, 20124 Milan, Italy. TEL 39-2-69481. FAX 39-2-6948290.
circ. 35,523. *1451*

INFORMATION FUER DIE TRUPPE.
Bundesministerium der Verteidigung, Fue SI 3, Postfach 1328, 5300 Bonn 1, Germany. *3460*

INFORMATION OM REHABILITERING.
Handikappinstitutet, Box 510, S-162 15 Vaellingby, Sweden. TEL 08-620-1700. FAX 08-739-2152. *2284*

INFORMATION RESOURCES MANAGEMENT JOURNAL.
Idea Group Publishing, 4811 Jonestown Rd., Ste. 230, Harrisburg, PA 17109-1751. TEL 717-541-9150. FAX 717-541-9159.
circ. 500. *1013*

INFORMATORE DI URIO.
Edizioni Ares, Via Stradivari 7, 20131 Milan, Italy. TEL 02-29526156. FAX 02-29514202.
circ. 4,760. *4266*

INFORME ANUAL DEL PROGRAMA DE PASTOS TROPICALES.
Centro Internacional de Agricultura Tropical, Tropical Pastures Program, Apdo. Aereo 6713, Cali, Colombia. TEL 2-3675050. FAX 2-3647243.
circ. 650. *97*

INFORME DE OPERACION DE LAS PRINCIPALES EMPRESAS PRODUCTORAS Y DISTRIBUIDORAS DE ENERGIA ELECTRICA DE COSTA RICA.
Instituto Costarricense de Electricidad (ICE), P.O. Box 10032, San Jose, Costa Rica. *1899*

INGENIERIA DE COSTOS.
D. Pastrana Editores, S.A., Kepler 147-A, Mexico 5, D.F., Mexico.
circ. 5,000. *1013*

INGENIEUR ET INDUSTRIE.
Association pour la Promotion des Publications Scientifiques (APPS), 26 av. de l'Amarante, B-1020 Brussels, Belgium. TEL 02-268-29-33. FAX 02-268-25-14.
circ. 20,000. *1825*

INLAND.
Inland Steel Flat Product Co., 30 W. Monroe St., Chicago, IL 60603. TEL 312-346-0300.
circ. 12,000. *2227*

INLINE.
InLine, Inc., 1919 14th St., Boulder, CO 80302. TEL 303-440-5111.
circ. 26,000. *4548*

INNER CIRCLE LETTER.
Nelson Newsletter Publishing Corp., Box 41630, Tucson, AZ 85717-1630. TEL 602-629-0868. FAX 602-629-0387. *2437*

INNOMINATE.
Sydney University Medical Society, Council of the Sydney University Medical Society, Blackburn Bldg. D06, University of Sydney, Sydney, N.S.W. 2006, Australia. *1314*

INSIDE DINING.
Yaffa Publishing Group, 17-21 Bellevue St., Surry Hills, N.S.W. 2010, Australia. TEL 02-281-2333. FAX 02-281-2750.
circ. 15,490. *2073*

INSIDE TRACKS.
93 Goulding Ave., N. York, Ont. M2M 1L3, Canada. TEL 416-229-9213.
circ. 5,000. *3556*

INSIDE WAU.
University of Washington Libraries, M171 Suzzallo Library, Seattle, WA 98195. TEL 206-543-1760. FAX 206-685-8049. *2763*

INSIEME.
Publications Ensemble Inc., 4358 rue Charleroi, Montreal-Nord, Que. H1H 1T3, Canada. TEL 514-328-2062. FAX 514-328-6562.
circ. 2,000. *2006*

INSIGHT (AKRON).
Akron-Summit County Public Library, 55 S. Main St., Akron, OH 44326. TEL 216-762-7621.
circ. 2,000. *2763*

INSIGHTS (WASHINGTON, 1988).
Library of Congress Professional Association, Library of Congress, Washington, DC 20540. TEL 202-707-3635.
circ. 2,000. *2763*

INSPAIN.
InSpain Magazine, Dr. Esquerdo 35, 1F, 28028 Madrid, Spain. TEL 256-1779. FAX 256-1779.
circ. 15,000. *4772*

INSTALLATEUR.
E S I Publications 5 et 7, rue Laromiguiere, 75005 Paris, France. TEL 1-46-34-21-60. FAX 1-45-87-29-99.
circ. 10,000. *2300*

INSTALLATION NEWS.
Bobit Publishing Company, 2512 Artesia Blvd., Redondo Beach, CA 90278-3210. TEL 213-376-8788. FAX 213-376-9043.
circ. 27,000. *1337*

INSTALLATIONS NYT.
Thomson Communications(Scandinavia) A-S, Struenseegade 7-9, DK-2200 Copenhagen, Denmark. TEL 45-35-37-80-55.
circ. 8,894. *1899*

INSTITUT FUER WISSENSCHAFT UND KUNST. MITTEILUNGEN.
Institut fuer Wissenschaft und Kunst, Berggasse 17-1, 1090 Vienna, Austria.
circ. 2,000. *1709*

INSTITUT GEOGRAPHIQUE NATIONAL. BULLETIN D'INFORMATION.
Institut Geographique National, Service de la Documentation Geographique, 136 bis, rue de Grenelle, 75700 Paris, France. TEL 43-98-80-00. *2268*

INSTITUT HISTORIQUE BELGE DE ROME. BULLETIN.
N.V. Brepols I.G.P., Steenweg op Tielen 68, 2300 Turnhout, Belgium. TEL 014-41-54-63. FAX 014-42-89-19. *2368*

INSTITUTA ET MONUMENTA. SERIE II: INSTITUTA.
Fondazione "Claudio Monteverdi", Via Ugolani Dati 4, 26100 Cremona, Italy. TEL 0372-26580.
circ. 500. *3556*

INSTITUTE OF ENERGY. JOURNAL.
Institute of Energy, 18 Devonshire St., London W1N 2AU, England. TEL 071-580-0008. FAX 071-580-4420.
circ. 2,500. *1791*

INSTITUTE OF ENGINEERS & TECHNICIANS JOURNAL.
Deeson Editorial Services Ltd., Ewell House, Graveney Rd., Faversham, Kent ME13 8UP, England. FAX 01-795-535469.
circ. 6,500. *1930*

INSTITUTE OF HEALTH EDUCATION. JOURNAL.
Institute of Health Education, 9 Elm Ridge Dr., Hale Barns, Altrincham, Cheshire WA15 0JE, England. TEL 0742-660790. FAX 061-980-7446. *3109*

INSTITUTE OF MUSLIM MINORITY AFFAIRS. JOURNAL.
Institute of Muslim Minority Affairs, 46 Goodge St., London W1P 1FJ, England. TEL 636-6740. FAX 632-4194.
circ. 5,000. *2429*

INSTITUTO BUTANTAN. MEMORIAS.
Instituto Butantan, Caixa Postal 65, 01051 Sao Paulo, Brazil. FAX 011-8151505.
circ. 800. *584*

INSTITUTO INDIGENISTA INTERAMERICANO SERIE DE EDICIONES ESPECIALES.
Instituto Indigenista Interamericano, Insurgentes Sur 1690, Colonia Florida, Mexico 01030, D.F., Mexico. TEL 660-00-07. FAX 534-8090. *242*

INSTYTUT TRANSPORTU SAMOCHODOWEGO. ZESZYTY NAUKOWE.
Instytut Transportu Samochodowego, Stalingradzka 40, Warsaw, Poland. TEL 48 22 11-29-33. *4651*

INSURANCE FIELD.
Insurance Field Company, 1812 Production Ct., Louisville, KY 40299. TEL 502-491-5857. FAX 502-491-5905.
circ. 3,000. *2534*

INTENSIVE CARING UNLIMITED.
Intensive Caring Unlimited (ICU), 910 Bent Lane, Philadelphia, PA 19118. TEL 215-233-6994.
circ. 3,000. *1239*

INTER-AMERICAN DEVELOPMENT BANK. INSTITUTE FOR LATIN AMERICAN INTEGRATION. ANNUAL REPORT.
Banco Interamericano de Desarrollo, Instituto para la Integracion de America Latina, Esmeralda 130, Buenos Aires, Argentina. TEL 394-2059. FAX 394-2293. *931*

INTERAVIA AIR LETTER.
Jane's Information Group, Sentinel House, 163 Brighton Rd., Coulsdon, Surrey CR5 2NH, England. TEL 081-763-1030. FAX 081-763-1005. *55*

INTERCHANGE (PORTLAND).
Oregon Educational Media Association, 16695 S.W. Rosa Rd., Beaverton, OR 97007. TEL 503-649-5764. *1639*

INTERCHANGE CUSTOMER NEWSLETTER.
Nebraska Public Power District, Box 499, Columbus, NE 68601-0499. TEL 402-563-5811. FAX 402-563-5511.
circ. 5,000. *2227*

INTERCON.
Intercontinental Church Society, 175 Tower Bridge Rd., London SE1 2AQ, England. TEL 071-407-4588. FAX 071-407-6038.
circ. 5,000. *4182*

INTERIEUR.
Forlaget Cahier, Box 244, Langebjergvej 139, DK-3050 Humlebaek, Denmark. TEL 45-42-19-08-55. FAX 45-42-19-01-25.
circ. 6,781. *2552*

INTERIOR DECORATORS' HANDBOOK.
Columbia Communications, Inc., 370 Lexington Ave., New York, NY 10017. TEL 212-532-9290. FAX 212-779-8345.
circ. 20,000. *2552*

INTERIORSCAPE.
Brantwood Publications, Inc., 3023 Eastland Blvd., Ste. 103, Clearwater, FL 34621-4106. TEL 813-796-3877.
circ. 7,500. *2553*

INTERNATIONAL ARTHURIAN SOCIETY. NEWSLETTER.
Dalhousie University, Department of French, Halifax, N.S. B3H 3J5, Canada. TEL 902-494-2430. *2925*

INTERNATIONAL ASSOCIATION OF METEOROLOGY AND ATMOSPHERIC PHYSICS. REPORT OF PROCEEDINGS OF GENERAL ASSEMBLY.
International Association of Meteorology and Atmospheric Physics, c/o Prof. M. Kuhn, Institut fuer Met. und Geophys., Univ. Innsbruck, Innrain 52, A-6020 Innsbruck, Austria. TEL 512-5072183. FAX 512-5072170. *3436*

INTERNATIONAL ASSOCIATION OF MILK CONTROL AGENCIES. PROCEEDINGS OF ANNUAL MEETINGS.
International Association of Milk Control Agencies, c/o R.C. Pearce, New York Dept. of Agriculture and Markets, 1 Winners Circle, Albany, NY 12235. TEL 518-457-6773. *200*

INTERNATIONAL ASSOCIATION OF MUSEUMS OF ARMS AND MILITARY HISTORY. CONGRESS REPORTS.
International Association of Museums of Arms and Military History, c/o Ernst Aichner, Bayerisches Armeemuseum, D-8070 Ingolstadt, Neues Schloss, Paradeplatz 4, Germany. *3525*

INTERNATIONAL ASSOCIATION OF PHYSICAL EDUCATION AND SPORTS FOR GIRLS AND WOMEN. PROCEEDINGS OF THE INTERNATIONAL CONGRESS.
Japan Association of Physical Education for Women and Girls, 6-102 O.M.Y.C., 3-1 Jinen-cho Yoyogi, Shibuya-ku, Tokyo, Japan. *4475*

INTERNATIONAL BASKETBALL FEDERATION. OFFICIAL REPORT OF THE WORLD CONGRESS.
International Basketball Federation, Postfach 700607, 8000 Munich 70, Germany. FAX 089-785-3596.
circ. 300. *4507*

INTERNATIONAL BIODETERIORATION.
Elsevier Science Publishers Ltd., Crown House, Linton Rd., Barking, Essex IG11 8JU, England. TEL 081-594-7272. FAX 081-594-5942. *490*

INTERNATIONAL BIOTECHNOLOGY LABORATORY.
International Scientific Communications, Inc., 30 Controls Dr., Box 870, Shelton, CT 06484-0870. TEL 203-926-9300. FAX 203-926-9310.
circ. 37,000. *490*

INTERNATIONAL CABLE.
Transmedia Partners, 50 South Steele, Ste. 500, Denver, CO 80209. TEL 303-355-2101. FAX 303-355-2144. *1375*

INTERNATIONAL COMMISSION FOR THE CONSERVATION OF ATLANTIC TUNAS. COLLECTIVE VOLUME OF SCIENTIFIC PAPERS.
International Commission for the Conservation of Atlantic Tunas, Principe de Vergara 17, 28001 Madrid, Spain. *2043*

INTERNATIONAL COMMISSION FOR THE CONSERVATION OF ATLANTIC TUNAS. DATA RECORD.
International Commission for the Conservation of Atlantic Tunas, Principe de Vergara 17, 28001 Madrid, Spain. *2043*

INTERNATIONAL COMMISSION FOR THE CONSERVATION OF ATLANTIC TUNAS. STATISTICAL BULLETIN.
International Commission for the Conservation of Atlantic Tunas, Principe de Vergara 17, 28001 Madrid, Spain. *2051*

INTERNATIONAL CONFERENCE ON LASERS. PROCEEDINGS.
S T S Press, Box 245, McLean, VA 22101. TEL 703-642-5835. FAX 703-642-5838. circ. 400. *3853*

INTERNATIONAL FEDERATION FOR HOUSING AND PLANNING. DIRECTORY.
International Federation for Housing and Planning, Wassenaarseweg 43, 2596 CG The Hague, Netherlands. circ. 1,500. *2489*

INTERNATIONAL FIBER JOURNAL.
McMickle Publications, Inc., 2919 Spalding Dr., Atlanta, GA 30350-4628. TEL 404-394-6098. FAX 404-393-0161. circ. 8,000. *4620*

INTERNATIONAL FINANCIER.
International Society of Financiers, Box 18508, Asheville, NC 28814. TEL 800-777-5907. FAX 704-251-5061. circ. 500. *785*

INTERNATIONAL GRAVIMETRIQUE BUREAU. BULLETIN D'INFORMATION.
Bureau Gravimetric International, 18 av. Edouard Belin, 31055 Toulouse Cedex, France. FAX 33-61-25-30-98. circ. 350. *1590*

INTERNATIONAL HOSPITAL EQUIPMENT.
Pan European Publishing Co., Rue Verte 216, B-1210 Brussels, Belgium. TEL 02-242-29-92. FAX 02-242-71-11. circ. 30,010. *3110*

INTERNATIONAL INSTITUTE OF SEISMOLOGY AND EARTHQUAKE ENGINEERING. YEAR BOOK.
International Institute of Seismology and Earthquake Engineering, Building Research Institute-Ministry of Construction, 1 Tatehare, Oho-machi, Tsukuba-gun, Ibaraki Prefecture 305, Japan. *1591*

INTERNATIONAL JOURNAL OF THE SOCIOLOGY OF LANGUAGE.
Mouton de Gruyter, Postfach 110240, 1000 Berlin 11, Germany. circ. 900. *2819*

INTERNATIONAL LABORATORY.
International Scientific Communications, Inc., 30 Controls Dr., Box 870, Shelton, CT 06484-0870. TEL 203-926-9300. FAX 203-926-9310. circ. 63,500. *1206*

INTERNATIONAL LEADS.
American Library Association, International Relations Round Table, 50 E. Huron St., Chicago, IL 60611. TEL 312-944-6780. FAX 312-440-9374. circ. 800. *2764*

INTERNATIONAL LEAGUE FOR HUMAN RIGHTS. ANNUAL REPORT.
International League for Human Rights, 432 Park Ave. S., Ste. 1103, New York, NY 10016-8013. TEL 212-972-9554. *3944*

INTERNATIONAL RELATIONS.
David Davies Memorial Institute of International Studies, 2 Chadwick St., London SW1P 2EP, England. *3961*

INTERNATIONAL SADDLERY AND APPAREL JOURNAL.
Equine Excellence Management Group, Inc., Box 3039, Berea, KY 40403-3039. FAX 606-986-1770. circ. 14,000. *4535*

INTERNATIONAL SKYLINE.
I.S.P. of Canada, 3738 - 39th Ave. West, Vancouver, B.C. V6N 3A7, Canada. circ. 18,000. *1338*

INTERNATIONAL SOCIETY OF TORONTO FOR HUNGARIAN CHURCH HISTORY. NEWSLETTER.
International Society of Toronto for Hungarian Church History, Regis College, 15 St. Mary St., Toronto, Ont. M4Y 2R5, Canada. TEL 416-922-2476. FAX 416-922-2898. *2369*

INTERNATIONAL THEATRE INSTITUTE OF THE UNITED STATES. NEWSLETTER.
International Theatre Institute of the United States, Inc., 220 W. 42nd St., Ste. 1710, New York, NY 10036. TEL 212-944-1490. FAX 212-944-1506. circ. 1,500. *4634*

INTERNATIONAL TRANSPORT WORKERS' FEDERATION REPORT ON ACTIVITIES.
International Transport Workers' Federation, 133-135 Great Suffolk St., London SE1 1PD, England. circ. 500. *2585*

INTERPLANETARY NEWS.
Interplanetary Space Travel Research Association (United Kingdom), 21 Hargwyne St., Stockwell, London SW9 9RQ, England. *56*

INTERVUE.
Intergraph Corporation, LR24C2, Huntsville, AL 35894. TEL 205-730-8172. FAX 205-730-8300. circ. 60,000. *1424*

INTRODUCTION TO GRAVITATION CHEMISTRY.
Ensanian Physicochemical Institute, Box 98, Eldred, PA 16731. TEL 814-225-3296. circ. 100. *1179*

INVESTIGACION BIBLIOTECOLOGICA.
Universidad Nacional Autonoma de Mexico, Centro Universitario de Investigaciones Bibliotecologicas, Torre II de Humanidades, pisos 12 y 13, Ciudad Universitaria, 04510 Mexico, D.F., Mexico. TEL 550-5931. FAX 550-74-61. circ. 1,000. *2764*

INVESTIGACION Y EDUCACION EN ENFERMERIA.
Universidad de Antioquia, Facultad de Enfermeria, Apdo. Aereo 1226, Carrera 53, no. 62-65, Medellin, Colombia. TEL 5742-110058. FAX 5742-638282. circ. 1,000. *3279*

INVESTMENT MANAGEMENT.
Mitre House Publishing, Mascot House, 36 Greville St., London EC1N 8AR, England. TEL 01-831-9093. circ. 6,400. *787*

IOWA. DEPARTMENT OF JOB SERVICE. ANNUAL REPORT.
Department of Job Service, 1000 E. Grand Ave., Des Moines, IA 50319. TEL 515-281-3201. circ. 2,000. *984*

IOWA ACADEMY OF SCIENCE. JOURNAL.
Iowa Academy of Science, Sci. 3538, University of Northern Iowa, Cedar Falls, IA 50614. TEL 319-273-2021. circ. 2,100. *4316*

IOWA AGRICULTURE AND HOME ECONOMICS EXPERIMENT STATION. RESEARCH BULLETIN.
Iowa State University of Science and Technology, 304 Curtiss Hall, Ames, IA 50011. TEL 515-294-5616. FAX 515-294-8716. *99*

IOWA AGRICULTURIST.
Iowa Agriculturist, Inc., Student Publications, Ames, IA 50011. TEL 515-294-2037. circ. 3,500. *100*

IOWA CITY MAGAZINE.
Gazette Company, Box 2672, Iowa City, IA 52244-2672. TEL 319-351-0466. FAX 319-351-0466. circ. 15,000. *2227*

IOWA ENGINEER.
Iowa Engineer, Inc., Student Publications, Iowa State University, IA 50011-0001. TEL 515-294-0476. circ. 4,000. *1827*

IOWA TRUCKING LIFELINER.
Iowa Motor Truck Association, Capital Center One, 600 E. Court, Ste. D, Des Moines, IA 50309-2020. TEL 515-244-5193. FAX 515-244-2204. circ. 3,187. *4745*

IRAN. MINISTRY OF ECONOMY. INTERNAL WHOLESALE TRADE STATISTICS.
Ministry of Finance and Economic Affairs, Teheran, Iran. *723*

IRAN. MINISTRY OF ECONOMY. INTERNATIONAL TRADE STATISTICS.
Ministry of Finance and Economic Affairs, Teheran, Iran. *723*

IRISH BACON NEWS.
Tara Publishing Co. Ltd., Poolbeg House, Poolbeg St., Dublin 2, Ireland. circ. 7,000. *2074*

IRISH COOPERATIVE ORGANIZATION SOCIETY. ANNUAL REPORT.
Irish Cooperative Organization Society Ltd., Plunkett House, 84 Merrion Square, Dublin 2, Ireland. TEL 353-1-681784. FAX 353-1-764783. *100*

IRISH CRIMINAL LAW JOURNAL.
Round Hall Press, Kill Lane, Blackrock, Co. Dublin, Ireland. TEL 2892922. FAX 2893072. circ. 350. *2713*

IRISH EUROPEAN LAW JOURNAL.
The Round Hall Press, Kill Lane, Blackrock, Co. Dublin, Ireland. TEL 2892922. FAX 2893072. circ. 300. *2637*

IRISH MEDICAL TIMES.
Medical Publications Ltd., 30 Lancaster Gate, London W2 3LP, England. *3111*

IRISH MOTOR INDUSTRY.
Jude Publications Ltd., 4 Tara St., Dublin 2, Ireland. TEL 713500. FAX 713074. circ. 2,500. *4693*

IRON AGE.
Hitchcock Publishing 191 S. Gary Ave., Carol Stream, IL 60188. TEL 708-462-2286. FAX 708-462-2225. circ. 24,000. *3409*

AL-ISLAM.
c/o Jamiat Ahl-e-Hadith, 106 Ravi Rd., Lahore, Pakistan. FAX 042-54072. circ. 4,000. *4219*

ISLAM INTERNATIONAL.
Siveast Consultants, Inc., USA, c/o P.O. Box 1755, Kathmandu, Nepal. circ. 20. *3900*

ISRAEL. GOVERNMENT PRESS OFFICE. DAILY NEWS AND EDITORIAL SURVEY.
Government Press Office, Agron House, 37 Hillel St., Jerusalem 94581, Israel. *2203*

ISRAEL. KNESSET. HA-VA'ADA LE-INYANEI BIKORET HA-MEDINA. SIKUMEHA VE-HATSA'OTEHA SHEL HA-VA'ADA LE-INYANEI BIKORET HA-MEDINA LE-DIN VE-KHESHBON SHEL MEVAKER HA-MEDINA.
Knesset, Jerusalem, Israel. *4089*

ISRAEL. KNESSET. VA'ADAT HA-KESAFIM MISPARIM AL VA'ADAT HA-KESAFIM.
Knesset, Jerusalem, Israel. *1099*

ISRAELI MAP COLLECTORS SOCIETY. JOURNAL.
Israeli Map Collectors Society, 4 Brenner St., Jerusalem 92103, Israel. TEL 02-639711. FAX 02-820992. circ. 100. *2437*

ISTITUTO STORICO ARTISTICO ORVIETANO. BOLLETTINO.
Istituto Storico Artistico Orvietano, Piazza Febei N.1, 05018 Orvieto, Italy. *2369*

IVY LEAF.
Alpha Kappa Alpha Sorority, Inc., 5656 S. Stony Island Ave., Chicago, IL 60637. *1315*

J A M A EN ESPANOL.
Editorial ECO, S.A., Calle de la Cruz 44, Barcelona 17, Spain. circ. 35,000. *3112*

J A M I F.
Association des Medecins Israelites de France, 11 ave. de la Republique, 94260 Fresnes, France. circ. 8,500. *3112*

J L B SMITH INSTITUTE OF ICHTHYOLOGY. ICHTHYOLOGICAL BULLETIN.
J L B Smith Institute of Ichthyology, Private Bag 1015, Grahamstown 6140, South Africa. TEL 0461-27124. FAX 0461-25049.
circ. 1,000. *585*

J L B SMITH INSTITUTE OF ICHTHYOLOGY. SPECIAL PUBLICATION.
J L B Smith Institute of Ichthyology, Private Bag 1015, Grahamstown 6140, South Africa. TEL 0461-27124. FAX 0461-25049.
circ. 1,500. *585*

J P C NEWSLETTER.
Joint Planning Commission, Lehigh - Northampton Counties, ABE Airport, Lehigh Valley, PA 18103. TEL 215-264-4544.
circ. 1,600. *2490*

J W PLUS.
Jewellery World Ltd., 20 Eglinton Ave. W., Ste. 1203, Toronto, Ont. M4R 1K8, Canada. TEL 416-480-1450. FAX 416-480-2342.
circ. 9,015. *2564*

JAEGER.
Danmarks Jaegerforbund, Einer-Jensens Vaenge 1, 2000 Frederiksberg, Denmark. TEL 38 33 29 11. FAX 31-19-02-41. *4549*

JAMA'AT AL-TA'RIKH AL-TABI'I. NASHRAT.
Cultural Foundation, Natural History Group, P.O. Box 2380, Abu Dhabi, United Arab Emirates. TEL 215300. FAX 336059.
circ. 500. *4316*

JAMI'AT AL-AZHAR. KULLIYYAT AL-LUGHAH AL-ARABIYYAH BIL-ZAGAZIG. MAJALLAH.
Jami'at al-Azhar, Kulliyyat al-Lughah al-Arabiyyah bil-Zagazig, Zagazig, Egypt. TEL 02-055-3302040. *2820*

JANA SANGH PATRIKA.
Bharatiya Janasangh Kerala Pradesh, M.G. Road, Cochin 11, India. *3901*

JANUS.
Foundation Janus, Joh. Verhulststraat 185, 1075 GZ Amsterdam, Netherlands. *4317*

JAPAN SOCIETY OF CIVIL ENGINEERS. JOURNAL.
Japan Society of Civil Engineers, 1-chome, Yotsuya, Shinjuku-ku, Tokyo 160, Japan. *1868*

JAPANESE BULLETIN OF ART THERAPY.
Societe Japonaise de Psychopathologie de l'Expression, c/o Neuropsychiatric Research Institute, 91 Bentencho, Shinjuku-ku, Tokyo 162, Japan.
circ. 4,500. *331*

JAPANESE JOURNAL OF EDUCATIONAL PSYCHOLOGY.
Japanese Association of Educational Psychology, c/o Faculty of Education, University of Tokyo, 7-3-1 Hongo, Bunkyo-ku, Tokyo 113, Japan. *4026*

JAZZ.
Hochuli AG, Box 4132, Mutteuz, Switzerland.
circ. 10,000. *3557*

JERSEY.
Jersey Cattle Society of the U.K., Jersey House, 154 Castle Hill, Reading, Berks. RG1 7RP, England. *219*

JERSEY AT HOME.
Royal Jersey Agricultural and Horticultural Society, Springfield, St. Helier, Jersey, Channel Islands. *200*

JERSEY JAZZ.
New Jersey Jazz Society, 836 W. Inman Ave., Rahway, NJ 07065.
circ. 1,500. *3558*

JEWELRY FASHION GUIDE.
Miller Freeman Inc. (New York) 1515 Broadway, New York, NY 10036. TEL 212-869-1300. FAX 212-302-6273.
circ. 37,000. *2565*

JEWISH CIVIC PRESS.
Box 15500, New Orleans, LA 70175. TEL 504-895-8784.
circ. 3,285. *2008*

JEWISH QUARTERLY.
Jewish Literary Trust Ltd., P.O. Box 1148, London NW5 2AZ, England. TEL 071-485-4062. FAX 908-932-3138.
circ. 5,000. *2009*

JEWISH STAR (SAN FRANCISCO).
Fraternal Media, 109 Minna St., Ste. 323, San Francisco, CA 94105-3701. TEL 415-421-4874. FAX 415-398-7983.
circ. 3,000. *2009*

JEWISH WESTERN BULLETIN.
Anglo-Jewish Publishers, 3268 Heather St., Vancouver, B.C. V5Z 3K5, Canada. TEL 604-879-6575. FAX 604-879-6573.
circ. 2,402. *2009*

JOBSON'S CHEERS.
Jobson Publishing Corp., 352 Park Ave. S., New York, NY 10010. TEL 212-685-4848. FAX 212-696-5318.
circ. 60,000. *382*

JOHN & MABLE RINGLING MUSEUM OF ART.
John and Mable Ringling Museum of Art Foundation, Box 1838, Sarasota, FL 34230. TEL 813-355-5101. FAX 813-351-7959.
circ. 5,000. *3525*

JOINT GOVERNMENTAL SALARY AND BENEFITS SURVEY: ARIZONA.
Department of Administration, Personnel Division, 1831 W. Jefferson, Phoenix, AZ 85007. TEL 602-542-5250. *725*

JOURNAL DE L'ILE DE LA REUNION.
Cazal S.A., 42 rue Alexis-de-Villeneuve, B.P. 98, 97463 Saint-Denis, Reunion. TEL 21-32-64. FAX 262-410977.
circ. 26,000. *2169*

JOURNAL HOLDINGS IN THE NATIONAL CAPITAL AREA.
Interlibrary Users Association, c/o Macron Systems, Inc., 212 Elmhurst Circle, Evans City, PA 16033.
circ. 250. *2765*

JOURNAL INDUSTRIEL DU QUEBEC.
Info-Industriel Inc., 2370 E. Boul. Henri-Bourassa, Montreal, Que. H2B 1T6, Canada. TEL 514-388-8801. FAX 514-388-7871.
circ. 25,000. *622*

JOURNAL OF ATHLETIC TRAINING.
National Athletic Trainers Association, Inc., 2952 N. Stemmons Fwy., Dallas, TX 75247-6117. TEL 800-879-6282. FAX 214-637-2206.
circ. 15,000. *3371*

JOURNAL OF COLLEGE AND UNIVERSITY STUDENT HOUSING.
Association of College and University Housing Officers' International, 101 Curl Dr., Ste. 140, Columbus, OH 43210-1195. TEL 609-292-0099. FAX 609-292-3205.
circ. 2,600. *1710*

JOURNAL OF COMPUTER INFORMATION SYSTEMS.
International Association for Computer Information Systems, College of Business, Oklahoma State University, Stillwater, OK 74078. TEL 405-744-5090.
circ. 1,000. *1417*

JOURNAL OF COOPERATIVE EDUCATION.
Cooperative Education Association, 3311 Toledo Terr., Ste. A101, Hyattsville, MD 20782. TEL 301-559-8850.
circ. 3,000. *1642*

JOURNAL OF CYTOLOGY AND GENETICS.
Society of Cytologists and Geneticists, Department of Botany, Bangalore University, Bangalore 560 056, India.
circ. 425. *545*

JOURNAL OF DATABASE ADMINISTRATION.
Idea Group Publishing, 4811 Jonestown Rd., Ste. 230, Harrisburg, PA 17109-1751. TEL 717-541-9150. FAX 717-541-9159.
circ. 200. *1445*

JOURNAL OF ELECTROTOPOGRAPHY.
Electrotopograph Corporation, Box 98, Eldred, PA 16731. TEL 814-225-3296.
circ. 1,000. *3821*

JOURNAL OF HOUSING RESEARCH.
Federal National Mortgage Association, 3900 Wisconsin Ave., N.W., Washington, DC 20016-2899. TEL 202-752-4422. FAX 202-752-4933.
circ. 2,300. *2490*

JOURNAL OF INTERNATIONAL MARKETING & MARKETING RESEARCH.
European Marketing Association, 18 St. Peters Steps, Brixham, Devon, England. *1043*

JOURNAL OF KANSAS PHARMACY.
Kansas Pharmacists Association, 1308 W. 10th, Topeka, KS 66604. TEL 913-232-0439.
circ. 1,200. *3731*

JOURNAL OF MEDICINAL AND AROMATIC PLANTS.
Gyogynoveny Kutato Intezet, P.O.B. 11, 2011 Budakalasz, Hungary. TEL 16-88-042.
circ. 450. *507*

JOURNAL OF MICROCOMPUTER SYSTEMS MANAGEMENT.
Idea Group Publishing, 4811 Jonestown Rd., Ste. 230, Harrisburg, PA 17109-1751. TEL 717-541-9150. FAX 717-541-9159.
circ. 300. *1461*

JOURNAL OF MICROWAVE POWER.
International Microwave Power Institute, 13542 Union Village Cir., Clifton, VA 22024-2305. TEL 703-830-5588.
circ. 1,000. *1901*

JOURNAL OF MIND AND BEHAVIOR.
Institute of Mind & Behavior, Box 522, Village Sta., New York, NY 10014. TEL 212-595-4853.
circ. 1,089. *4030*

JOURNAL OF N I H RESEARCH.
William M. Miller, 2101 L Steet, N.W., Ste. 207, Washington, DC 20037. TEL 202-785-5333. FAX 202-872-7738.
circ. 28,000. *3117*

JOURNAL OF NON-CRYSTALLINE SOLIDS.
North-Holland P.O. Box 211, 1000 AE Amsterdam, Netherlands. TEL 020-5803911. FAX 020-5803598. *3822*

JOURNAL OF NUCLEAR AGRICULTURE AND BIOLOGY.
Indian Society for Nuclear Techniques in Agriculture and Biology, Nuclear Research Laboratory, Indian Agricultural Research Institute, New Delhi 110012, India.
circ. 400. *183*

JOURNAL OF OSTEOPATHIC MEDICINE.
Professional Marketing Systems, Inc., 10 E. 21st St., New York, NY 10010. TEL 212-505-2423.
circ. 33,000. *3309*

JOURNAL OF PAN AFRICAN STUDIES.
California Institute of Pan African Studies, Box 13063, Fresno, CA 93794-3063. TEL 209-266-2550.
circ. 1,000. *4378*

JOURNAL OF POPULATION AND HEALTH STUDIES.
Korea Institute for Population and Health, SAN 42-14 Bulgwang-Dong, Eunpyung-Ku, Seoul 122, S. Korea. *597*

JOURNAL OF PROTECTIVE COATINGS AND LININGS.
Technology Publishing Co., 2100 Wharton St., Ste. 31, Pittsburgh, PA 15203. TEL 412-431-8300. FAX 412-431-5428.
circ. 13,000. *3654*

JOURNAL OF RESEARCH ON COMPUTING IN TEACHER EDUCATION.
International Society for Technology in Education, 1787 Agate St., Eugene, OR 97403-1923. TEL 503-346-4414. FAX 503-346-5890.
circ. 2,500. *1691*

JOURNAL OF SPORTS PHILATELY.
Sports Philatelists International, c/o Reiss, 322 Riverside Dr., Huron, OH 44839.
circ. 500. *3753*

JOURNAL OF TOSOH RESEARCH.
Tosoh Corporation, 4560 Tonda, Shinnanyo-shi, Yamaguchi-ken 746, Japan.
circ. 750. *1856*

JOURNAL OF TRAINING & PRACTICE IN PROFESSIONAL PSYCHOLOGY.
Forest Institute of Professional Psychology, 2611 Leeman Fery Rd., Huntsville, AL 35801-5611. TEL 205-536-9088. FAX 205-533-7405.
circ. 1,600. *4034*

JOURNAL OF TRANSPORTATION MEDICINE.
Japanese Association of Transportation Medicine, c/o Nihon Gakkai Jimu Center, Yayoi 2-4-16, Bunkyo-ku, Tokyo 112, Japan. TEL 03-3817-5801. FAX 03-3817-5815.
circ. 600. *3310*

JOURNAL S O G C.
Ribosome Communications, 55 Charles St., W., Ste. 3104, Toronto, Ont. M5S 2W9, Canada. TEL 416-925-7715. FAX 416-323-3064.
circ. 30,000. *3294*

JOURNALEN SYKEPLEIEN.
Norsk Sykepleierforbund, Postboks 2633, St. Hanshaugen, 0131 Oslo 1, Norway. FAX 02-353663.
circ. 45,000. *3281*

JOURNALIST'S HANDBOOK.
Carrick Publishing, 28 Miller Rd., Ayr KA7 2AY, Scotland. FAX 0292-266679.
circ. 2,600. *2572*

JOURNALS OF DISSENT AND SOCIAL CHANGE.
California State University, Sacramento, Library, 2000 Jed Smith Dr., Sacramento, CA 95819. TEL 916-278-6634. *4458*

JOURNEE VINICOLE.
La Journee Vinicole, s.a.r.l., B.P. 1064, 34007 Montpellier Cedex 1, France. TEL 67-47-93-63. FAX 67-27-82-99.
circ. 20,000. *382*

AL-JUNDI.
Ministry of Defence, P.O. Box 2838, Dubai, United Arab Emirates. TEL 04-451515. FAX 04-45503.
circ. 4,000. *3462*

K E M - EUROPEAN DESIGN ENGINEERING.
Konradin-Verlag Robert Kohlhammer GmbH, Ernst-Mey-Str. 8, Postfach 100252, 7022 Leinfelden-Echterdingen 1, Germany. TEL 0711-7594-0.
circ. 30,096. *1828*

K F Z BETRIEB AKTUELLE WOCHENZEITUNG.
Vogel Verlag und Druck KG, Max-Planck-Str. 7-9, Postfach 6740, 8700 Wuerzburg 1, Germany. TEL 0931-418-0.
circ. 29,570. *4694*

K F Z BETRIEB UNTERNEHMERMAGAZIN.
Vogel-Verlag und Druck KG, Max-Planck-Str. 7-9, Postfach 6740, 8700 Wuerzburg 1, Germany. TEL 0931-418-0.
circ. 29,589. *4694*

K MITTEILUNGEN.
Gesamtverband Kunststoffverarbeitende Industrie e.V., Froschpfort 16, 5430 Montabaur, Germany. FAX 02602-4308. *3863*

K O A DIRECTORY ROAD ATLAS AND CAMPING GUIDE.
Meredith Corporation, 1716 Locust St., Des Moines, IA 50336. TEL 515-284-3412. FAX 515-284-2700.
circ. 1,900,000. *1141*

K: REVISTA DE POESIA.
Lubio Cardozo y Juan Pinto, Eds. & Pubs., Apartado 410, Herida, Venezuela. *2996*

KAERNTER BAUER.
Kammer fuer Land- und Forstwirtschaft Kaernten, Museumgasse 5, A-9020 Klagenfurt, Austria. TEL 0463-5850. FAX 0463-5850251.
circ. 30,000. *102*

KAGAKU GIJUTSU BUNKEN SABISU.
National Diet Library, 1-10-1 Nagata-cho, Chiyoda-ku, Tokyo 100, Japan. TEL 03-3581-2331.
circ. 1,300. *4318*

KAGAKU GIJUTSU BUNKEN TOYAMA.
Kagaku Gijutsu Bunken Riyo Shikokai, c/o Toyama Prefectural Library, 206-3 Chayamachi, Toyama 930-01, Japan.
circ. 500. *4614*

KALAMAZOO COLLEGE QUARTERLY.
Kalamazoo College, 1200 Academy St., Kalamazoo, MI 49007-3295. TEL 616-383-8595. FAX 616-383-8503.
circ. 15,000. *1315*

KALASTAJA.
Kalatalouden Keskusliitto, Koydenpunojankatu 7 B 23, 00180 Helsinki 18, Finland. TEL 358-0-640-126. FAX 358-0-608-309.
circ. 9,636. *2045*

KALEIDOSCOPE (BIRMINGHAM).
University of Alabama at Birmingham, Box 76, University Center, Birmingham, AL 35294-1150. TEL 205-934-3354.
circ. 7,050. *1315*

KANSAS. LEGISLATIVE RESEARCH DEPARTMENT. REPORT ON KANSAS LEGISLATIVE INTERIM STUDIES.
Legislative Research Department, Topeka, KS 66612. TEL 913-296-3181. *3902*

KANSAS RESTAURANT.
Kansas Restaurant Association, 359 S. Hydraulic, Wichita, KS 67211. TEL 316-267-8383.
circ. 1,500. *2477*

KANSAS WILDFLOWER SOCIETY NEWSLETTER.
Hall Publishing Co., Mulvane Arts Center, Washburn University, Topeka, KS 66621.
circ. 600. *2133*

KANTINEN.
Kantineledernes Landsklub, Kollerup lund 63, 2665 Vallensbaek Strand, Denmark. FAX 45-43-54-34-52.
circ. 4,347. *1299*

KAPPA TAU ALPHA. NEWSLETTER.
Kappa Tau Alpha, U M School of Journalism, Box 838, Columbia, MO 65205. TEL 314-882-7685. FAX 314-882-4823.
circ. 1,700. *2572*

KARAYOLLARI TEKNIK BULTENI.
General Directorate of Highways, Ankara, Turkey.
circ. 3,000. *1870*

DER KARTOFFELBAU.
Verlag Th. Mann, Nordring 10, Postfach 200254, 4650 Gelsenkirchen-Buer, Germany. TEL 0209-37431. FAX 0209-395398.
circ. 5,200. *183*

KARTOFLEXMARKT.
Barneveldse Drukkerij & Uitgeverij B.V., Postbus 67, 3770 AB Barneveld, Netherlands. TEL 03420-94911. FAX 03420-13141.
circ. 4,000. *3649*

KASHRUT GUIDE.
Union of Orthodox Synagogues of South Africa, P.O. Box 4110, Johannesburg 2000, South Africa. TEL 011-648-9136. FAX 011-648-4014.
circ. 13,000. *4224*

KASVATUS.
Jyvaskylan Yliopisto, Kasvatustieteiden Tutkimuslaitos, P.O. Box 35, SF-40351 Jyvaskyla, Finland. TEL 358-41-603213. FAX 358-41-603201.
circ. 200. *1644*

KATES KIN.
29 W. Main St., Box 8, Rarden, OH 45671. TEL 614-372-6705.
circ. 800. *2156*

KATORIKKU KENKYU.
Sophia University, Theological Society, Kamishakujii 4-32-11, Nerima-ku, Tokyo 177, Japan. TEL 03-5991-0343.
circ. 1,000. *4267*

KEADILAN.
Islamic University of Indonesia, Faculty of Law, Jalan Taman Siswa 158, Yogyakarta 55151, Indonesia. TEL 2978.
circ. 2,500. *2642*

KEHITTYVAE KAUPPA.
Kauppiaitten Kustannus Oy, Rauhankatu 15, 00170 Helsinki 17, Finland.
circ. 30,219. *1044*

KEIZAIGAKU KENKYU.
Keizai Riron Gakkai, c/o Rikkyo Daigaku Keizaigakubu, 3 Ikebukuro, Toshima-ku, Tokyo 171, Japan. *676*

KEIZAIGAKU RONSHU.
Tokyo Daigaku Shuppankai - University of Tokyo Press, 3-1 Hongo 7-chome, Bunkyo-ku, Tokyo 113, Japan. *676*

KELLY'S BUSINESS LINK.
Kelly's Directories Windsor Court, East Grinstead House, East Grinstead, W. Sussex RH19 1XB, England. TEL 0342-326972.
circ. 60,000. *1141*

KELLY'S EXPORT SERVICES.
Kelly's Directories Windsor Court, East Grinstead House, East Grinstead, W. Sussex RH19 1XB, England. TEL 0342-326972.
circ. 5,000. *1141*

KELLY'S LONDON BUSINESS LINK.
Kelly's Directories Windsor Court, East Grinstead House, East Grinstead, W. Sussex RH19 1XA, England. TEL 0342-326972.
circ. 80,000. *1141*

KELLY'S OIL & GAS INDUSTRY DIRECTORY.
Kelly's Directories Windsor Court, East Grinstead House, East Grinstead, W. Sussex RH19 1XA, England. TEL 0342-326972.
circ. 8,000. *1141*

KELLY'S UNITED KINGDOM EXPORTS DIRECTORY.
Kelly's Directories Windsor Court, East Grinstead House, East Grinstead, West Sussex RH19 1XA, England. TEL 0342-326972. FAX 0342-315130.
circ. 30,000. *1141*

KELVIN NEWS.
Associated Scientific and Technical Societies of South Africa, P.O. Box 93480, Yeoville 2143, South Africa. TEL 011-487-1512. FAX 011-648-1876. *4320*

KENNEL REVIEW.
B & E Publications, Inc., 11331 Ventura Blvd., Ste. 301, Studio City, CA 91604. TEL 818-761-3647. FAX 818-761-7586.
circ. 8,500. *3711*

KENTUCKIANA PURCHASOR.
Purchasing Management Association of Louisville, 3415 Bardstown Rd., Box 35428, Louisville, KY 40232. TEL 502-454-4636. FAX 502-454-4637.
circ. 2,900. *1044*

KENTUCKY PRAIRIE FARMER.
Farm Progress Publications 191 S. Gary Ave., Carol Stream, IL 60188. TEL 708-690-5600. FAX 708-462-2869.
circ. 14,500. *183*

KENTUCKY SCHOOL DIRECTORY.
Department of Education, Office of Communication Services, 1912 Capital Plaza Tower, 1500 Mero Street, 19th fl., Frankfort, KY 40601. TEL 502-564-3421. *1695*

KERALA SABHA.
Better Life Movement, Better Life Center, Aloor, Kallettumkara, Kerala 680 683, India.
circ. 2,000. *4284*

KESHEV.
Bar-Ilan University, Institute of Holocaust Research, Ramat Gan 52100, Israel.
circ. 1,000. *2371*

KEYNOTES (NEW ORLEANS).
New Orleans Public Library, 219 Loyola Ave., New Orleans, LA 70140. TEL 504-596-2619.
circ. 200. *2767*

KHADYA VIGYAN.
Central Food Technological Research Institute, Mysore 570 013, India.
circ. 1,500. *2075*

KINDAI EIGA.
Kindai-Eiga Corp., Owaricho Bldg., 2F, 6-8-3 Ginza, Chuo-ku, Tokyo 104, Japan. TEL 03-5568-2811. FAX 03-5568-2818. *3512*

KIR - OU - KIRK.
Armenian Literary Society - New York, Inc., 77 Everett Rd., Demarest, NJ 07627. TEL 201-767-1494.
circ. 900. *2930*

KIRJAPAINOTAITO - GRAAFIKKO.
Osuuskunta Kirjapainotaito, Loennrotinkatu 11 A, 00120 Helsinki, Finland. FAX 358-0-603914.
circ. 4,313. *4002*

KIRJASTOLEHTI.
Suomen Kirjastoseura, Museokatu 18 A 5, 00100 Helsinki 10, Finland. FAX 358-0-441345.
circ. 7,015. *2767*

KIROLAK.
c/o Jose Acosta Montoro, Ed., Villa Cord, Miraconcha, San Sebastian, Spain.
circ. 18,500. *4478*

KITCHENS.
Maclean Hunter Ltd., Maclean Hunter House, Chalk Lane, Cockfosters Rd., Barnet, Herts EN4 OBU, England. TEL 081-975-9759. FAX 081-440-1796.
circ. 11,604. *622*

KOBE UNIVERSITY. SCHOOL OF BUSINESS ADMINISTRATION. ANNALS.
Kobe Daigaku, School of Business Administration, Rokkodai-cho, Nada-ku, Kobe-shi, Hyogo-ken 657, Japan. FAX 078-881-8100. *1017*

KOEBENHAVNS HAVNEBLAD.
Faellesrepraesentationen for Funktionaerer ved Koebenhavns Havnevaesen, Nordre Toldbod 7, Postboks 2083, 1013 Copenhagen K, Denmark. TEL 33 14 43 40, local 310. FAX 33-93-23-40.
circ. 4,400. *4730*

KOEBENHAVNS UNIVERSITET. GEOLOGISK CENTRALINSTITUT. AARSBERETNING.
Koebenhavns Universitet, Geologisk Centralinstitut, Oester Voldgade 10, DK-1350 Copenhagen K, Denmark. TEL 33-11-22-32.
circ. 525. *1571*

KOKURITSU KAGAKU HAKUBUTSUKAN SENPO.
Monbu-sho, Kokuritsu Kagaku Hakubutsukan, 7-20 Ueno Koen, Taito-ku, Tokyo 110, Japan.
circ. 1,000. *4321*

KOKUSAIHO GAIKO ZASSHI.
Kokusaiho Gakkai, c/o Faculty of Law, University of Tokyo, 3-1, Hongo 7-chome, Bunkyo-ku, Tokyo, Japan.
circ. 800. *2726*

KOLDFAX.
Air-Conditioning and Refrigeration Institute, 1501 Wilson Blvd., 6th Fl., Arlington, VA 22209-2403. TEL 703-524-8800. FAX 703-528-3816. *2301*

KONCAR STRUCNE INFORMACIJE.
S O U R Rade Koncar, O O U R Elektrotehnicki Institut, Bastijanova ul. bb, 41001 Zagreb, Croatia. TEL 041 312-222. FAX 38--41-334170.
circ. 2,500. *1902*

KONEVIESTI.
Viestilehdet Oy, Revontulentie 8b, 02100 Espoo 10, Finland. TEL 90-131151. FAX 0-131-15209.
circ. 53,500. *3019*

KONJUNKTURNI BAROMETAR.
Zavod za Trzisna Istrazivanja, Mose Pijade 8-I, 11001 Belgrade, Yugoslavia. *1080*

KONSTRUKTIONSPRAXIS.
Vogel Verlag und Druck KG, Max-Planck-Str. 7-9, Postfach 6740, 8700 Wuerzburg 1, Germany. TEL 0931-418-0.
circ. 29,827. *1919*

KONTROLLE.
Konradin-Verlag Robert Kohlhammer GmbH, Ernst-May-Str. 8, Postfach 100252, 7022 Leinfelden-Echterdingen 1, Germany. TEL 0711-7594-0.
circ. 21,000. *1829*

KOOKS MAGAZINE.
Out-of-Kontrol Data Institute, Box 953, Allston, MA 02134. TEL 617-782-5602.
circ. 750. *3595*

KOOTENAY BUSINESS JOURNAL.
Catalyst Communications Inc., P.O. Box 784, Nelson, B.C. V1L 5P5, Canada. TEL 604-352-6397. FAX 604-352-2588.
circ. 6,500. *676*

KOREAN OTOLARYNGOLOGICAL SOCIETY. JOURNAL.
Korean Otolaryngological Society, c/o Seoul National University Hospital, Chongno-gu, Seoul, S. Korea.
circ. 600. *3315*

KOSMOS.
Deutsche Verlags-Anstalt GmbH, Neckarstr. 121, Postfach 106012, 7000 Stuttgart 10, Germany. TEL 0711-7200591. FAX 0711-2631292.
circ. 60,000. *4321*

KRISTDEMOKRATEN.
Samhaellsgemenskaps Foerlags AB, P.O. Box 19098, S-10432 Stockholm, Sweden. FAX 08-6127953.
circ. 10,000. *3903*

KUKHOEBO.
National Assembly, c/o Secretary-General, 1-1 Yeoidodong, Yeongdungpo-ku, Seoul, S. Korea. TEL 788-2058. FAX 788-3348.
circ. 5,500. *3903*

KULDE.
Skarland Press A-S, P.O. Box 5042 Maj., 0301 Oslo 3, Norway. TEL 47-2-60-13-90. FAX 47-2-69-36-50.
circ. 6,946. *2301*

KUNSTHISTORISCHES INSTITUT IN FLORENZ. MITTEILUNGEN.
Kunsthistorisches Institut in Florenz, Via Giusti 44, I-50121 Florence, Italy. FAX 39-55-2479161.
circ. 1,000. *333*

KUSPI.
Turun Hammaslaaketieteenkandidaattiseura, Lemminkaisenkatu 2, 20520 Turku 52, Finland.
circ. 2,600. *3237*

KYOIKU HYORON.
Japan Teachers' Union, Kyoiku-Kaikan, 2-6-2 Hitotsubashi, Kanda, Chiyoda-ku, Tokyo, Japan.
circ. 20,000. *1645*

KYOTO PREFECTURAL UNIVERSITY OF MEDICINE. MEDICAL SOCIETY. JOURNAL.
Kyoto Prefectural University of Medicine, Kyoto Foundations for the Promotion of Medical Science, Hirokoji, Kawara-machi, Kamigyo-ku, Kyoto 602, Japan. FAX 075-211-7093.
circ. 1,350. *3121*

KYOTO UNIVERSITY. FACULTY OF ENGINEERING. MEMOIRS.
Kyoto University, Faculty of Engineering, Yoshida Hon-machi, Sakyo-ku, Kyoto 606, Japan. *1829*

KYOTO UNIVERSITY. INSTITUTE FOR VIRUS RESEARCH. ANNUAL REPORT.
Kyoto University, Institute for Virus Research, Shogoin Kawahara-cho, Kyoto 606, Japan. *554*

KYRKOFOERFATTNINGAR.
Verbum Forlag AB, Box 151 69, S-104 65 Stockholm, Sweden. FAX 08-6414585.
circ. 2,500. *4187*

KYUSHU NEURO-PSYCHIATRY.
Kyushu Association of Neuro-Psychiatry, c/o Department of Neuro-Psychiatry, Faculty of Medicine, Kyushu University 60, Maidashi, Higashi-ku, Fukuoka 812, Japan. FAX 092-632-3558.
circ. 690. *3344*

L A N A NYT.
Lokalhistoriske Arkiver i Nordjyllands Amt, c/o Historisk Arkiv, Museumsgade 2, DK-9800 Hjoerring, Denmark.
circ. 800. *2372*

L A N COMPUTING.
Professional Press, Inc., 101 Witmer Rd., Horsham, PA 19044. TEL 215-957-1500. FAX 215-957-1050.
circ. 40,000. *1427*

L M S - LABORATORY MARKETING SPECTRUM.
George Warman Publications (Pty.) Ltd., 77 Hout St., P.O. Box 704, 8000 Cape Town, South Africa. TEL 021-24-5320. FAX 021-26-1332.
circ. 5,700. *3261*

LAB PRODUCTS INTERNATIONAL.
Pan European Publishing Co. Rue Verte 216, B-1210 Brussels, Belgium. TEL 02-242-29-92. FAX 02-242-71-11.
circ. 50,000. *3261*

LABO.
Verlag Hoppenstedt und Co., Havelstr. 9, Postfach 4006, 6100 Darmstadt, Germany. TEL 06151-380-0. FAX 06151-380-360.
circ. 16,000. *3261*

LABOR FORCE AND NONAGRICULTURAL EMPLOYMENT ESTIMATES.
Department of Employment Security, 500 James Robertson Pkwy., 11th Fl., Nashville, TN 37245-1000. TEL 615-741-1729. *726*

LABOR LEADER.
San Diego-Imperial Counties Labor Council, 4265 Fairmount Ave., San Diego, CA 92105-1265.
circ. 33,000. *2585*

LABOR VOICE.
Australian Labor Party, Western Australia Branch, 2nd Fl., Labor Centre, 82 Beaufort St., Perth, W.A. 6000, Australia. FAX 09-2279585.
circ. 10,000. *3903*

LABORATORY PRODUCT NEWS.
Southam Business Communications Inc. 1450 Don Mills Rd., Don Mills, Ont. M3B 2X7, Canada. TEL 416-445-6641. FAX 416-442-2261.
circ. 18,677. *3261*

LABORPRAXIS.
Vogel-Verlag und Druck KG, Max-Planck-Str. 7-9, Postfach 67 40, 8700 Wuerzburg 1, Germany.
circ. 16,000. *3262*

LACE & CRAFTS.
Laces and Lace Making, 3201 E. Lakeshore Dr., Tallahassee, FL 32312. TEL 904-385-5093. FAX 904-422-3646.
circ. 30,000. *3591*

LADUE PUBLIC SCHOOLS BULLETIN.
Ladue Board of Education, 9703 Conway Rd., St. Louis, MO 63124. TEL 314-994-7080.
circ. 9,500. *1645*

LAGOS EDUCATION REVIEW.
Joja Educational Research and Publishers Limited, 13 B Ikorodu Rd., Maryland, P.M.B. 21526, Ikeja, Lagos, Nigeria. TEL 01-933866.
circ. 3,000. *1645*

LAKE BIWA STUDY MONOGRAPHS.
Otsushigyo Co., Ltd., 1-10, Uchide-hama, Otsu, Shiga 520, Japan. TEL 0775-26-4800. FAX 0775-26-4803.
circ. 400. *1599*

LAMAZE PARENTS' MAGAZINE.
Lamaze Publishing Co., 30 Old Kings Highway, Darien, CT 06820. TEL 203-656-1127. FAX 203-655-8960.
circ. 2,000,000. *3294*

LAMBTON LEADER.
Lambton College, Box 969, Sarnia, Ont. N7U 7K4, Canada. TEL 519-542-7751. FAX 519-542-6667.
circ. 2,000. *1316*

LAMP (NEW YORK).
Exxon Corporation, 225 E. John W. Carpenter Freeway, Irving, TX 75062-2298. TEL 214-444-1116. FAX 214-444-1139.
circ. 650,000. *3691*

LANCASHIRE CONSTABULARY JOURNAL.
Lancashire Constabulary, County Police Headquarters, P.O. Box 77, Hutton, Preston PR4 5SB, England. FAX 0772-616715.
circ. 5,000. *1517*

LAND LINE MAGAZINE.
Owner-Operator Independent Drivers Association of America, Box L, Grain Valley, MO 64029. FAX 816-229-0518.
circ. 82,500. *4745*

LANDESVERSICHERUNGSANSTALT WUERTTEMBERG. MITTEILUNGEN.
W. Kohlhammer GmbH, Hessbruehlstr. 69, Postfach 800430, 7000 Stuttgart 80, Germany. TEL 0711-8363-1. *4412*

LANDSCAPE CONTRACTOR.
Maury Boyd and Associates, Inc., 5783 Park Plaza Court, Indianapolis, IN 46220-3995. TEL 708-790-4844.
circ. 2,200. *2133*

LANTERN'S CORE.
Northwestern University Library, Staff Association, 1935 Sheridan Rd., Evanston, IL 60208. TEL 312-491-7633. FAX 312-491-5685.
circ. 650. *2768*

LASER APPLICAZIONI INDUSTRIALI, TECNOLOGIE, MERCATI.
Gruppo Editoriale Jackson S.p.A., Via Pola 9, 20124 Milan, Italy. TEL 39-2-69481. FAX 39-2-6948238.
circ. 6,000. *3854*

LAUREL OF PHI KAPPA TAU.
Phi Kappa Tau Fraternity, 15 N. Campus Ave., Oxford, OH 45056-0030. TEL 513-523-4193. FAX 513-523-9325. *1316*

LAW, MEDICINE & HEALTH CARE.
American Society of Law & Medicine, Inc., 765 Commonwealth Ave., Ste. 1634, Boston, MA 02215. TEL 617-262-4990. FAX 617-437-7596.
circ. 7,500. *3265*

THE LAWYERS WEEKLY.
Butterworths Canada Ltd., 75 Clegg Rd., Markham, Ont. L6G 1A1, Canada. TEL 416-479-2665. FAX 416-479-2826.
circ. 29,000. *2647*

LEATHER TODAY.
Fur Publishing Plus, Inc., 19 W. 21st St., Ste. 403, New York, NY 10010. TEL 212-727-1210.
circ. 13,500. *2737*

LEBENSMITTEL PRAXIS.
Lebensmittel Praxis Verlag GmbH, Hermannstr. 40, Postfach 1920, 5450 Neuwied, Germany. *2093*

DER LEBENSMITTELKAUFMANN.
Oesterreichischer Wirtschaftsverlag, Nikolsdorfer Gasse 7-11, A-1051 Vienna, Austria. TEL 0222-555585.
circ. 21,200. *2093*

LEDER ECHO.
Gewerkschaft Leder, Will-Bleicher-Str. 20, 7000 Stuttgart 1, Germany. FAX 0711-293345.
circ. 42,000. *2737*

LEE HOWARD NEWSLETTER.
Selective Books, Inc., Box 1140, Clearwater, FL 34617. TEL 813-447-0100.
circ. 5,500. *4131*

LEGAL EXECUTIVE.
Institute of Legal Executives, Kempston Manor, Kempston, Bedford, England. TEL 0234-840-022. FAX 0234-841-999.
circ. 19,997. *2647*

LEGAL PUBLISHING PREVIEW.
R.R. Bowker, A Reed Reference Publishing Company, Division of Reed Publishing (USA) Inc., 121 Chanlon Rd., New Providence, NJ 07974. TEL 800-521-8110. FAX 908-665-6688.
circ. 5,000. *2648*

LEHRMITTEL AKTUELL - LEHRMITTEL COMPUTER.
Westermann Schulbuchverlag GmbH, Georg-Westermann-Allee 66, Postfach 4938, 3300 Braunschweig, Germany. TEL 0531-708240. FAX 0531-708248.
circ. 40,310. *1729*

LEISUREWAYS.
Canada Wide Magazines Ltd. (Toronto), 2 Carlton St., Ste. 1707, Toronto, Ont. M5B 1J3, Canada. TEL 416-595-5007. FAX 416-924-6308.
circ. 600,000. *2178*

LENNOX NEWS.
Lennox International Inc., Office of Government and Public Relations, Box 799900, Dallas, TX 75379-9900. TEL 214-497-5258. FAX 214-497-5292.
circ. 15,000. *2301*

LESBIAN NEWS.
Deborah Bergman, Ed. & Pub., 7985 Santa Monica Blvd., Ste. 109-13, W. Hollywood, CA 90046. TEL 213-658-0258.
circ. 20,000. *2455*

LET'S PLAY HOCKEY.
Let's Play, Inc., 2721 E. 42nd St., Minneapolis, MN 55406. TEL 612-729-0023. FAX 612-729-0259.
circ. 18,000. *4478*

LEUKEMIA SOCIETY OF AMERICA. SOCIETY NEWS.
Leukemia Society of America, Inc., 733 Third Ave., 14th Fl., New York, NY 10017. TEL 212-573-8484. FAX 212-972-5776.
circ. 18,000. *3199*

LEVERANSTIDNINGEN ENTREPRENAD.
Svensk Leveranstidning AB, Siktgatan 10, 162 83 Vaellingby, Sweden.
circ. 19,832. *622*

LEVNEDSMIDDELBLADET - SUPERMARKEDET.
Forlaget Beilin og Johansen ApS, 1, Rosenborggade, 1130 Copenhagen K, Denmark. TEL 33 15 22 77. FAX 33-15-93-43.
circ. 7,063. *2093*

LEY.
Ediciones la Ley S.A., 1471 Tucuman, Buenos Aires (R.34), Argentina.
circ. 12,000. *2649*

LIBERAL REVIEW.
Liberal Party, 88-1 Rosmead Place, Colombo 7, Sri Lanka. TEL 582779. FAX 588875.
circ. 1,000. *3904*

LIBRA.
Chartered Accountant Students' Society of London (CASSL), 18 Bedford Square, London WC1, England. FAX 071-631-3002.
circ. 9,000. *753*

LIBRARY DEVELOPMENTS.
Texas State Library, Library Development Division, Box 12927, Austin, TX 78711. TEL 512-463-5465. FAX 512-463-5436.
circ. 1,000. *2769*

LICENSEE.
National Licensed Victuallers' Association, Boardman House, 2 Downing St., Farnham, Surrey GU9 7NX, England. TEL 0252-714448. FAX 0252-723742.
circ. 15,000. *383*

LIFE LINES.
Monumental Life Insurance Company, 2 E. Chase St., Baltimore, MD 21202. TEL 301-685-2900. FAX 301-347-8666.
circ. 850. *2537*

LIFELINE (KINGSTON).
Empire Life Insurance Co., Head Office, 259 King St. E., Kingston, Ont. K7L 3A8, Canada. TEL 613-548-1881. FAX 613-541-4104.
circ. 1,800. *2537*

LIGHT.
A F L - C I O, Utility Workers Union of America, 815 Sixteenth St., N.W., Washington, DC 20006. TEL 202-347-8105. FAX 202-347-4872.
circ. 62,000. *987*

LIGHT (WHEATON).
Christian Blind Mission International Inc., Box 19000, Greenville, SC 29602-9000. TEL 803-239-0065. FAX 803-239-0069.
circ. 38,000. *2294*

LIGHT DESIGN AND TECHNOLOGY.
Gruppo Editoriale Jackson S.p.A., Via Pola 9, 20124 Milan, Italy. TEL 39-2-69481. FAX 39-2-6948238.
circ. 14,500. *3855*

LINGUISTIC CIRCLE OF MANITOBA AND NORTH DAKOTA. PROCEEDINGS.
University of North Dakota, Department of Philosophy and Religion, Box 8258, Grand Forks, ND 58202. FAX 701-777-3650.
circ. 500. *2826*

LINK (TROY).
Yellow Pages Publishers Association, 340 E. Big Beaver, Troy, MI 48083. TEL 313-680-8880. *34*

LINKAGE.
National Diet Library, Information Processing Division, 1-10-1 Nagata-cho, Chiyoda-ku, Tokyo 100, Japan. TEL 03-3581-2331. FAX 03-3597-9104.
circ. 1,000. *1398*

LINKING LIBRARIES.
Rochester Regional Library Council, 302 N. Goodman St. at Village Gate, Rochester, NY 14607.
circ. 1,050. *2771*

LINKING RING.
International Brotherhood of Magicians, c/o Howard Bamman, Ed., 42 Fiddlers Green Dr., Huntington, NY 11743.
circ. 13,000. *2438*

LIQUOR REPORTER.
Smithwrite Communications, Inc., 101 Milwaukee Blvd. S., Pacific, WA 98047. TEL 206-833-9642.
circ. 10,500. *383*

LITERARY ONOMASTICS STUDIES.
University of Georgia, Department of English, Athens, GA 30602. *2933*

LITHO WEEK.
Haymarket Magazines Ltd., 38-42 Hampton Rd., Teddington, Middx. TW11 0JE, England. TEL 081-943-5000.
circ. 12,832. *4002*

LIVE RAIL.
Southern Electric Group, 32 Crowthorne Rd., Sandhurst, Camberley, Surrey GU17 8EP, England. *4711*

LIVING LIGHT.
United States Catholic Conference, Office for Publishing and Promotion Services, 3211 Fourth St., N.E., Washington, DC 20017-1194. TEL 202-541-3089. FAX 202-541-3091.
circ. 1,200. *4268*

LIVINGSTON COUNTY AGRICULTURAL NEWS.
Cooperative Extension Association of Livingston County, Agricultural Division, 158 S. Main St., Mount Morris, NY 14510. TEL 716-658-4110. FAX 716-658-4707.
circ. 500. *105*

LIVSMEDELSTEKNIK.
Svenska Livsmedelstekniska Foereningen, Katarinavaegen 20, 116 45 Stockholm, Sweden. FAX 08-6408045.
circ. 2,981. *2076*

LLOYDS BANK ANNUAL REVIEW.
Pinter Publishers Ltd., 25 Floral St., London WC2E 9DS, England. *789*

LOCAL GOVERNMENT FINANCES IN MARYLAND.
Department of Fiscal Services, Division of Fiscal Research, 90 State Circle, Annapolis, MD 21401. TEL 301-841-3710. FAX 301-841-3722. *1100*

LOCAL GOVERNMENT MANAGEMENT.
Institute of Municipal Management, P.O. Box 409, S. Melbourne, Vic. 3205, Australia. TEL 03-696-5799. FAX 03-690-4217.
circ. 5,000. *4090*

LOCO-REVUE.
Editions Loco-Revue s.a.r.l., B.P. 104, Le Sablen, 56401 Auray (Morbihan), France. FAX 33-97-56-55-89.
circ. 31,000. *2438*

LODGING HOSPITALITY.
Penton Publishing 1100 Superior Ave., Cleveland, OH 44114-2543. TEL 216-696-7000. FAX 216-696-8765.
circ. 49,000. *2477*

LONDON COLLEGE OF MUSIC MAGAZINE.
London College of Music, Polytechnic of West London, St. Mary's Rd., Ealingi London W5 5RF, England. TEL 081-579-5000. FAX 081-566-1353. *3561*

LONG ISLAND PARENTING NEWS.
R D M Publishing Corporation, Box 214, Island Park, NY 11558. TEL 516-889-5510. FAX 516-889-5513.
circ. 40,000. *1241*

LONGWOOD GRADUATE PROGRAM SEMINARS.
University of Delaware, College of Agricultural Sciences, 153 Townsend Hall, Newark, DE 19717-1303. TEL 302-451-2517. FAX 302-292-3651.
circ. 800. *509*

LOS PERROS DEL MUNDO.
Publitecnic S.A., Calle 4, no. 188, Box 74-290, C.P. 09070, Mexico 13, D.F., Mexico. TEL 685-28-19. FAX 67-06318.
circ. 10,000. *3712*

LOUISIANA AGRICULTURE.
Louisiana State University, Agricultural Experiment Station, Baton Rouge, LA 70803. TEL 504-388-2263. FAX 504-388-2478.
circ. 4,500. *105*

LOUISIANA STATE UNIVERSITY. LIBRARY LECTURES.
Louisiana State University, Library, Baton Rouge, LA 70803-7507. TEL 504-388-2217. *2771*

LOUISIANA WATER RESOURCES RESEARCH INSTITUTE. ANNUAL REPORT.
Louisiana Water Resources Research Institute, 3418 Ceba Bldg., Louisiana State University, Baton Rouge, LA 70803. FAX 504-388-5990. *4826*

LOURDES - ROSEN.
Deutscher Lourdes-Verein, Schwalbengasse 10, 5000 Cologne 1, Germany.
circ. 25,000. *4268*

LOYOLA MAGAZINE.
Loyola University of Chicago, Office of Public Relations, 820 N. Michigan Ave., Chicago, IL 60611. TEL 312-915-6157. FAX 312-915-6215.
circ. 93,000. *1316*

LUCKY MEE FAMILY ASSOCIATION. YEARBOOK.
Lucky Mee Family Association, Drawer 4487, El Paso, TX 79914. TEL 915-751-7233.
circ. 180. *2157*

LUREN.
Scandinavian Philatelic Library of Southern California, Box 741639, Los Angeles, CA 90004-9639. TEL 714-626-1764.
circ. 250. *3754*

LUXEMBOURG. MINISTERE DES FINANCES. BUDGET DE L'ETAT.
Ministere des Finances, 3 rue de la Congregation, L-1352 Luxembourg, Luxembourg. *1100*

LYCOMING COUNTY HISTORICAL SOCIETY JOURNAL.
Lycoming County Historical Society, 858 W. Fourth St., Williamsport, PA 17701. TEL 717-326-3326. FAX 717-326-3326.
circ. 1,200. *2413*

M & T - METALLHANDWERK & TECHNIK.
Charles Coleman Verlag GmbH, Wahmstr. 56, Postfach 2134, 2400 Luebeck 1, Germany. TEL 0451-71505. FAX 0451-71507. *623*

M B.
Bitaon Publishing Co. Ltd., 15 Rambam St., P.O. Box 1480, Tel Aviv, Israel. FAX 03-664435.
circ. 4,000. *2204*

M E A T.
M E A T Communications, Inc., P.O. Box 35, Sta. O, Toronto, Ont. M4A 2M8, Canada. TEL 416-699-8486. FAX 416-690-6697.
circ. 35,000. *3562*

M E M C O NEWS.
Miller Electric Manufacturing Co., 1635 W. Spencer, Box 1079, Appleton, WI 54911. TEL 414-734-9821. FAX 414-735-4135.
circ. 54,000. *3429*

M E R P MEMO.
Indiana University, School of Medicine, 1100 W. Michigan St., Indianapolis, IN 46202. TEL 317-264-8157.
circ. 1,000. *3123*

M F D REGISTER.
Milwaukee Fire Department Athletic Association, 711 W. Wells St., Milwaukee, WI 53233. TEL 414-276-5656. *4107*

M H L S NEWS.
Mid-Hudson Library System, 103 Market St., Poughkeepsie, NY 12601. TEL 914-471-6060. FAX 914-454-5940.
circ. 1,100. *2772*

M H - R V BUILDERS NEWS.
Dan Kamrow & Associates, Inc., Box 72367, Roselle, IL 60172. TEL 708-893-8872.
circ. 10,022. *623*

M L T A NEWS.
Modern Language Teachers' Association of New South Wales, c/o School of Modern Languages, Macquarie University, N. Ryde, NSW 2113, Australia.
circ. 650. *2828*

M P R C REPORT ON FINANCE, COMMERCE, INDUSTRY: INDONESIA.
M P R C (Asia) Sdn. Berhad, 132-B Jalan Kasah, Damansara Heights, 50490 Kuala Lumpur, Malaysia. TEL 03-2548139. *873*

M P R C REPORT ON FINANCE, COMMERCE, INDUSTRY: SINGAPORE.
M P R C (Asia) Sdn. Berhad, 132-B Jalan Kasah, Damansara Heights, 50490 Kuala Lumpur, Malaysia. TEL 03-2548139. *873*

M P R C REPORT ON FINANCE, COMMERCE, INDUSTRY: SOUTH EAST ASIA.
M P R C (Asia) Sdn. Berhad, 132-B Jalan Kasah, Damansara Heights, 50490 Kuala Lumpur, Malaysia. TEL 03-2548139. *873*

M P R C REPORT ON FINANCE, COMMERCE, INDUSTRY: THAILAND.
M P R C (Asia) Sdn. Berhad, 132-B Jalan Kasah, Damansara Heights, 50490 Kuala Lumpur, Malaysia. TEL 03-2548139. *873*

M P R C SOUTH EAST ASIA.
M P R C (Asia) Sdn. Berhad, 132-B Jalan Kasah, Damansara Heights, 50490 Kuala Lumpur, Malaysia. TEL 03-2548139. *873*

M P S A NEWSLETTER.
Missouri Political Science Association, c/o George Connor, Sect.-Treas., Dept. of Political Science, Southwest Missouri State University, Springfield, MO 65804. TEL 417-836-6956.
circ. 200. *3905*

M S L A V A JOURNAL.
Manitoba School Library Audio Visual Association, c/o Manitoba Teachers' Society, 191 Harcourt St., Winnipeg, Man. R3J 3H2, Canada. TEL 204-888-7961.
circ. 400. *2772*

M S U ALUMNI MAGAZINE.
Michigan State University, Alumni Association, Rm. 108, Student Union, E. Lansing, MI 48824-1029. TEL 517-355-8314. FAX 517-355-5265.
circ. 44,000. *1316*

M S U MATHEMATICS NEWSLETTER.
Montana State University, Mathematical Sciences Department, Bozeman, MT 59717. TEL 406-994-3601. *3044*

M S U U NEWSLETTER: GLEANINGS.
Ministerial Sisterhood Unitarian Universalist, c/o Universalist Unitarian Church, 740 E. Main St., Santa Paula, CA 93060. TEL 805-525-8859.
circ. 300. *4243*

M S W MANAGEMENT.
Forester Communications, Inc., 1640 Fifth St., Ste. 108, Santa Monica, CA 90401. TEL 213-576-6180. FAX 213-570-6182.
circ. 24,000. *4107*

M T I REPORTER.
Madison Teachers, Inc., 821 Williamson St., Madison, WI 53703. TEL 608-257-0491. *1646*

M T S ECHO.
Manitoba Telephone System, 489 Empress St., Winnipeg, Man. R3C 3V6, Canada. TEL 204-947-4111.
circ. 6,000. *1364*

M T S UPDATE.
Manitoba Teachers' Society, 191 Harcourt St., Winnipeg, Man. R3J 3H2, Canada. TEL 204-888-7961. FAX 204-831-0877.
circ. 17,000. *1646*

M T TODAY.
Valley Forge Press, 1288 Valley Forge Rd., Box 1135, Valley Forge, PA 19481. TEL 215-935-1296. FAX 215-935-3072.
circ. 60,000. *3262*

MAANEDSMAGASINET ERHVERV - NORDJYLLAND.
Sct. Thoegersvej 8, P.O. Box 30, 7770 Vestervig, Denmark. FAX 97-94-14-10.
circ. 16,600. *1018*

MACCABI WORLD UNION. NEWSLETTER.
Maccabi World Union, Kfar Hamaccabiah, Israel.
circ. 500. *4479*

MACHINE DESIGN.
Penton Publishing 1100 Superior Ave., Cleveland, OH 44114-2543. TEL 216-696-7000. FAX 216-696-8765.
circ. 180,500. *1934*

MACHINE TOOL SELECTOR.
A.G.B. Hulton Ltd., Warwick House, Azalea Dr., Swanley, Kent BR8 8JE, England.
circ. 18,634. *3019*

MACHINERY & EQUIPMENT M R O.
Southam Business Communications Inc., 1450 Don Mills Rd., Don Mills, Ont. M3B 2X7, Canada. TEL 416-445-6641. FAX 416-442-2077.
circ. 25,000. *3019*

MCKINSEY QUARTERLY.
McKinsey & Co. Inc., 55 E. 52nd St., New York, NY 10022. TEL 212-909-8400. *1018*

MACTECH JOURNAL.
Tech Alliance, 290 S.W. 43rd St., Renton, WA 98055. TEL 206-251-5222.
circ. 20,000. *1470*

MACUSER.
Ziff-Davis Publishing Co. (Foster City), 950 Tower Ln., 18th Fl., Foster City, CA 94404. TEL 415-378-5600.
circ. 311,253. *1470*

MADENCILIK.
Turk Muhendis ve Mimar Odalari Birligi, Maden Muhendisleri Odasi, Selanik Cad. 19-3, 06650 Ankara, Turkey. TEL 4-1251080. FAX 4-1175290.
circ. 5,000. *3487*

MAERKISCHE ZEITUNG.
Landsmannschaft Berlin-Mark Brandenburg, Landesverband Berlin, Stresemannstr. 90, 1000 Berlin 61, Germany. TEL 2611046.
circ. 8,500. *3905*

"MAGISCHE" WELT.
Verlag W. Geissler-Werry, In den Benden 13, 5160 Dueren, Germany. TEL (02421)51667.
circ. 13,000. *2438*

MAGNET MARKETING.
Graham Communications, 40 Oval Rd., Quincy, MA 02170. TEL 617-328-0069. FAX 617-471-1504.
circ. 3,500. *1045*

MAGNIFICAT.
Apostles of Infinite Love, Monastery of the Magnificat of the Mother of God, Box 308, St. Jovite, Que. JOT 2H0, Canada. FAX 819-688-5225.
circ. 4,000. *4268*

MAGYAR KOZGAZDASAGI IRODALOM.
Budapesti Kozgazdasagtudomanyi Egyetem, Fovam Ter 8, 1093 Budapest, Hungary. TEL 1179-377. FAX 1174-910.
circ. 350. *728*

MAHARASHTRA STATE BUDGET IN BRIEF.
Directorate of Economics and Statistics, D.D. Bldg., Old Custom House, Bombay 400023, India. *1100*

MAIL TRADE.
George O. Dillon, Ed. & Pub., 1904 Jeanette Ln., Springfield, IL 62702. TEL 217-787-1968.
circ. 20,000. *1045*

MAINE POTATO NEWS.
Northeast Publishing Company, Box 510, Presque Isle, ME 04769. TEL 207-764-7033. FAX 207-764-4499.
circ. 6,000. *184*

MAINE PRINCIPAL.
Maine Secondary School Principals' Association, Box 2468, Augusta, ME 04338-2468. FAX 207-622-1513.
circ. 480. *1729*

MAINE TRAILS.
Maine Better Transportation Association, 146 State St., Augusta, ME 04330. TEL 207-622-0526. FAX 207-623-2928.
circ. 1,200. *1871*

MAINTENANCE TECHNOLOGY.
Applied Technology Publications, Inc., 1300 S. Grove Ave., Barrington, IL 60010. TEL 708-382-8100. FAX 708-304-8603.
circ. 80,000. *4603*

MAKEDONSKI JAZIK.
Institut za Makedonski Jazik, Skopje, P.O. Box 434, 91000 Skopje, Macedonia.
circ. 1,000. *2828*

MAKERERE UNIVERSITY. ALBERT COOK LIBRARY. LIBRARY BULLETIN AND ACCESSION LIST.
Makerere University, Albert Cook Library, Makerere Medical School, Box 7072, Kampala, Uganda.
2794

MALAWI. NATIONAL LIBRARY SERVICE BOARD. ANNUAL REPORT.
National Library Service Board, Box 30314, Lilongwe 3, Malawi. FAX 730626. *2772*

MALAWI NATIONAL LIBRARY SERVICE BOARD. STAFF NEWSLETTER.
National Library Service Board, P.O. Box 30314, Lilongwe 3, Milawi. FAX 365-730626. *2772*

MALAYSIAN AGRICULTURAL JOURNAL.
Ministry of Agriculture, Publications Officer, Wisma Tani, Jalan Mahameru, 50624 Kuala Lumpur, Malaysia.
circ. 1,500. *106*

MALAYSIAN JOURNAL OF ECONOMIC STUDIES.
Malaysian Economic Association, Faculty of Economics and Administration, University of Malaya, Kuala Lumpur, Malaysia. TEL 03-7560075. FAX 03-7563139.
circ. 1,250. *678*

MAMMALIA.
Museum National d'Histoire Naturelle, Mammiferes et Oiseaux, 55 rue Buffon, 75005 Paris, France. TEL 40-79-30-62.
circ. 670. *587*

MANAGEMENT.
Jemma Publications Ltd. (Sandycove), Marino House, 53 Glasthule Rd., Sandycove, Co. Dublin, Ireland. TEL 01-800000. FAX 01-844041.
circ. 8,000. *1018*

MANAGEMENT ACCOUNTER.
Society of Management Accountants of Alberta, 1800-125 Ninth Ave., S.E., Calgary, Alt. T2G 0P6, Canada. TEL 403-269-5341. FAX 403-262-5477.
circ. 7,000. *753*

MANAGEMENT BRIEFS.
Clinical Laboratory Management Association, 193-195 W. Lancaster Ave., Paoli, PA 19301. TEL 215-647-8970. FAX 215-889-9731.
circ. 6,800. *2467*

MANAGEMENT OF THE CALIFORNIA STATE WATER PROJECT.
Department of Water Resources, Box 942836, Sacramento, CA 94236-0001. TEL 916-445-9248.
4826

MANIPULACION DE MATERIALES EN LA INDUSTRIA.
Publicaciones Internacionales S.A., P. Castellana, 210, 28046 Madrid, Spain.
circ. 2,000. *623*

MANITOBA. ECONOMIC DEVELOPMENT NETWORK. COMMUNITY PROFILE INFORMATION SYSTEM.
Economic Development Network, 20 3rd St. N.E., Portage la Prairie, Man. R1N 1N4, Canada. TEL 204-857-8736. FAX 204-239-6519. *873*

MANITOBA MUSEUM OF MAN AND NATURE. ANNUAL REPORT.
Manitoba Museum of Man and Nature, 190 Rupert Ave., Winnipeg, Man. R3B ON2, Canada. TEL 204-956-2830. FAX 204-942-3679.
circ. 3,000. *3527*

MANUFACTURING SYSTEMS.
Hitchcock Publishing 191 S. Gary Ave., Carol Stream, IL 60188-2292. TEL 708-665-1000. FAX 708-462-2225.
circ. 115,000. *1080*

MAPLE LEAVES.
Canadian Philatelic Society of Great Britain, c/o D.F. Sessions, Ed., 36 The Chimes, Nailsea, Bristol BS19 2NH, England.
circ. 560. *3754*

MAQUINAS & METAIS.
Aranda Editora Ltda., Rua D. Elisa no. 167, Perdizes, 01155 Sao Paulo, SP, Brazil. TEL 011-826-4511. FAX 011-669585.
circ. 19,000. *3020*

MAR.
Liga Maritima de Chile, Errazurriz 471, Casilla 117-V, Valparaiso, Chile. TEL 255179.
circ. 2,000. *4732*

MARINE INDUSTRY NEWS.
Yaffa Publishing Group, 17-21 Bellevue St., Surry Hills, N.S.W. 2010, Australia. TEL 02-271-2333. FAX 02-281-2750.
circ. 3,510. *4732*

MARITIME REPORT.
Laurentian Business Publishing, 140 Baig Blvd., Moncton, N.B. E1E 1C8, Canada. TEL 506-857-9696. FAX 506-859-7395.
circ. 17,000. *4733*

MARKETEER.
c/o J. Cook, Ed., 1602 E. Glen Ave., Peoria, IL 61614.
circ. 2,000. *1045*

MARKETPLACE MAGAZINE.
A D D Inc., 211 N. Lyndale Dr., Ste. 6, Appleton, WI 54914-3943. TEL 414-735-5969. FAX 414-733-6470.
circ. 16,000. *678*

MARQUETTE TRIBUNE.
Marquette University, 1131 W. Wisconsin Ave., Milwaukee, WI 53233. TEL 414-288-7057.
circ. 7,500. *1317*

MARTLET.
Martlet Publishing Society, Box 3035, Victoria, B.C. V8W 3P3, Canada. TEL 604-721-8358. FAX 604-721-8728.
circ. 10,000. *1317*

MARYLAND CRIME CONTROL DIRECTORY.
Crime Investigating Commission, Inc., Box 3208, Baltimore, MD 21228. TEL 301-747-1121.
circ. 15,000. *1518*

MARYLAND MUSIC EDUCATOR.
Maryland Music Educators Association, c/o Thomas W. Fugate, Ed., 27 Meadow Ln., Thurmont, MD 21788. *3562*

MARYLAND P T A BULLETIN.
Maryland Congress of Parents and Teachers, 13 S. Carrollton Ave., Baltimore, MD 21223. TEL 301-685-0865. *1647*

MAS.
Univision Publications, 605 Third Ave., 12th Fl., New York, NY 10158. TEL 212-455-5200. FAX 212-867-6710.
circ. 630,000. *2013*

MASSACHUSETTS STATE LABOR COUNCIL A F L - C I O NEWSLETTER.
Massachusetts State Labor Council, A F L - C I O, 8 Beacon St., Boston, MA 02108. TEL 617-227-8260. FAX 617-227-2010.
circ. 8,000. *2586*

MAST.
R B Publishing Company, 6000 Gisholt Dr., Ste. 201, Madison, WI 57313-4816. FAX 608-221-0263.
circ. 36,000. *1353*

MASTER LOCK NEWS TODAY.
Master Lock Co., 2600 N. 32nd St., Milwaukee, WI 53210. TEL 414-444-2800. FAX 414-449-3193.
circ. 1,900. *642*

MASTER PLUMBER.
Master Plumbers and Mechanical Contractors Association of New South Wales, P.O. Box 65, Haberfield, N.S.W. 2045, Australia. FAX 02-799-5841. *2301*

MASTER PLUMBER OF SOUTH AUSTRALIA.
Master Plumbers & Mechanical Services Association, 219 Henley Rd., Torrensville, S.A. 5031, Australia.
circ. 550. *2301*

MASTHEAD.
North Island Sound Ltd., 1606 Sedlescomb Dr., Unit 8, Mississauga, Ont. L4X 1M6, Canada. TEL 416-625-7070. FAX 416-625-4856.
circ. 4,504. *4132*

MATERIAL HANDLING ENGINEERING.
Penton Publishing 1100 Superior Ave., Cleveland, OH 44114-2543. TEL 216-696-7000. FAX 216-696-8765.
circ. 105,600. *3020*

MATERIAL HANDLING ENGINEERING HANDBOOK AND DIRECTORY.
Penton Publishing 1100 Superior Ave., Cleveland, OH 44114-2543. TEL 216-696-7000. FAX 216-696-8765.
circ. 113,000. *3020*

MATERIALS ENGINEERING.
Penton Publishing 1100 Superior Ave., Cleveland, OH 44114-2543. TEL 216-696-7000. FAX 216-696-8765.
circ. 56,000. *1920*

MATERIALS HANDLING NEWS.
Reed Business Publishing Group, Enterprise Division, Quadrant House, The Quadrant, Sutton, Surrey SM2 5AS, England. TEL 081-652-3227. FAX 081-652-8991.
circ. 36,724. *3021*

MATERIALS ON ASIA - ACCESSION LIST AND REVIEW.
National Diet Library, 1-10-1 Nagata-cho, Chiyoda-ku, Tokyo 100, Japan. TEL 03-3581-2331.
circ. 540. *406*

MATERNAL & CHILD HEALTH.
Barker Publications Ltd., Barker House, 539 London Rd., Isleworth, Middlesex TW7 4DA, England. TEL 081-847-1774.
circ. 17,000. *3322*

MATHEMATICAL LOG.
Mu Alpha Theta, 601 Elm St., Rm. 423, Norman, OK 73019. TEL 405-325-4489.
circ. 25,000. *3045*

MATHEMATICS TEACHING.
Association of Teachers of Mathematics, 7 Shaftesbury St., Derby DE3 8YB, England. TEL 0332 46599.
circ. 6,000. *3047*

MATHILDA AND TERENCE KENNEDY INSTITUTE OF RHEUMATOLOGY. ANNUAL REPORT.
Mathilda and Terence Kennedy Institute of Rheumatology, 6 Bute Gardens, Hammersmith, London W6 7DW, England. TEL 01-748-9966. FAX 01-748-5090.
circ. 1,000. *3369*

MATHITIKI ESTIA.
Ministry of Education, Nicosia School Committee, Nicosia, Cyprus. *1260*

MATTER.
G L M Publications 2 Park Ave., Ste. 1100, New York, NY 10016. TEL 212-686-6070. *356*

MATURE GROUP TRAVELER.
Meetings Info-Resources, Inc., 1 Atlantic St., No.413, Stamford, CT 06901. TEL 203-975-1416. FAX 203-975-1418.
circ. 13,600. *4775*

MAY DAY PICTORIAL NEWS.
Wion Publications, 201 Astrid Dr., Pleasant Hill, CA 94523-4305. TEL 415-947-2138.
circ. 5,298. *4733*

CONTROLLED CIRCULATION SERIALS 5001

MAYO AGRICOLA.
Distrito de Riego No. 38, Rio Mayo, Pesqueira y Jimenez, Navojoa, Sonora, Mexico. *107*

MAYO ALUMNUS.
Mayo Foundation, Mayo Alumnus, Rochester, MN 55905.
circ. 14,000. *3124*

ME.
Viestintaerengas Oy, c/o Eka Co-op, P.O. Box 72, 00501 Helsinki, Finland. FAX 0-733-3264.
circ. 310,000. *831*

MECCANICA OGGI.
Gruppo Editoriale Jackson S.p.A., Via Pola 9, 20124 Milan, Italy. TEL 39-2-6948289. FAX 39-2-6948238.
circ. 10,329. *3844*

MEDECIN DU QUEBEC.
Federation des Medecins Omnipraticiens du Quebec, 1440 W. St. Catherine St., Ste. 1100, Montreal, Que. H3G 1R8, Canada. TEL 514-878-1911. FAX 514-878-4455.
circ. 18,500. *3124*

MEDICAL DEVICE TECHNOLOGY.
Aster Publishing Corporation, 859 Willamette St., Box 10955, Eugene, OR 97440. TEL 503-343-1200. FAX 503-343-3641.
circ. 20,000. *3125*

MEDICAL FOCUS.
Beta Publishing, Postfach 140121, 5300 Bonn 1, Germany. TEL 0228-252061. FAX 0228-252067.
circ. 24,714. *4107*

MEDICAL INDUSTRY EXECUTIVE.
Medical Industry Publications, Inc., 1190 Hightower Trail, Atlanta, GA 30350. TEL 404-998-9797. FAX 404-594-6998.
circ. 40,000. *3126*

MEDICAL MARKETING & MEDIA.
C P S Communications, Inc., 7200 W. Camino Real, Ste. 215, Boca Raton, FL 33433. TEL 407-368-9301. FAX 407-368-7870.
circ. 11,800. *3734*

MEDICAL PROTECTION SOCIETY. ANNUAL REPORT.
Medical Protection Society Ltd., 50 Hallam Street, London W1N 6DE, England. TEL 44 71 637-0541. FAX 44-71-636-0690.
circ. 120,000. *3127*

MEDICAL REHABILITATION REVIEW.
National Association of Rehabilitation Review, Box 17675, Washington, DC 20041. TEL 703-648-9300. FAX 703-648-8646.
circ. 1,000. *3127*

MEDICAL RESEARCH COUNCIL NEWSLETTER.
Medical Research Council of Canada, Tunney's Pasture, Ottawa, Ont. K1A 0W9, Canada. TEL 613-954-1806.
circ. 4,500. *3127*

MEDICAL RESEARCH COUNCIL OF CANADA. REPORT OF THE PRESIDENT.
Medical Research Council of Canada, Tunney's Pasture, Ottawa, Ont. K1A 0W9, Canada. TEL 613-954-1806.
circ. 2,300. *3127*

MEDICAL RESEARCH FUNDING BULLETIN.
Science Support Center, Box 7507, New York, NY 10150.
circ. 2,000. *4412*

MEDICAL TRIBUNE (1980).
Medical Tribune, Inc., 257 Park Ave. South, New York, NY 10010. TEL 212-674-8500. FAX 212-529-8490.
circ. 136,000. *3128*

MEDICAMUNDI.
Philips Medical Systems International, P.O. Box 10000, 5680 DA Best, Netherlands. FAX 40-762317.
circ. 14,000. *3360*

MEDICINA DE EMPRESA.
Sociedad Catalana de Seguridad y Medicina del Trabajo, Tapineria, 10, 2, Barcelona 2, Spain. *3619*

MEDICINA DO ESPORTE.
Federacao Brasileira de Medicina Desportiva, Centro de Documentacao e Informacao Em Ciencias do Esporte, Av. Sen. Salgado Filho, 135 - 6, 90000 Porto Alegre, R.S., Brazil.
circ. 1,000. *3372*

MEDICO-LEGAL SOCIETY OF VICTORIA. PROCEEDINGS.
Medico-Legal Society of Victoria, 205 William St., Melbourne, Vic. 3000, Australia.
circ. 600. *2703*

MEDIUM.
Saskatchewan Teachers' Federation, Box 1108, Saskatoon, Sask. S7K 3N3, Canada. TEL 306-525-0368.
circ. 400. *2773*

MEDIZINISCHE KLINIK.
Urban und Vogel, Lindwurmstr. 95, Postfach 152209, 8000 Munich 15, Germany. TEL 089-53292-0. FAX 089-53292-100.
circ. 10,500. *3130*

MEETING NEWS.
Miller Freeman Inc. (New York) 1515 Broadway, New York, NY 10036. TEL 212-869-1300. FAX 212-302-6273.
circ. 75,000. *3393*

MEETINGS MONTHLY.
Publicom Inc., 1055 Beaver Hall Hill, Ste. 200, Montreal, Que. H2Z 1S5, Canada. TEL 514-874-0874. FAX 514-878-9779.
circ. 12,168. *3393*

MEGAPHONE (CANTON).
Culver-Stockton College, Attn.: Cathy Johnson, Canton, MO 63435. TEL 314-288-5221. *1317*

MEMBERSHIP MARKETER.
American Society of Association Executives, 1575 I St., N.W., Washington, DC 20005. TEL 202-626-2723. FAX 202-408-9635.
circ. 900. *1021*

MEMISA NIEUWS.
Memisa, Eendrachtsweg 48, 3012 LD Rotterdam, Netherlands. FAX 010-4047319.
circ. 5,000. *3131*

MEMO (WASHINGTON, 1947).
American Institute of Architects Press, 1735 New York Ave., N.W., Washington, DC 20006. TEL 202-626-7465.
circ. 56,000. *303*

MEMO: TO THE PRESIDENT.
American Association of State Colleges and Universities, One Dupont Circle, N.W., Ste. 700, Washington, DC 20036. TEL 202-293-7070. FAX 202-296-5819. *1711*

MEMOIRES ET DOCUMENTS GEOGRAPHIE.
Editions du C N R S, 1 Place Aristide Briand, 92195 Meudon Cedex, France. TEL 1-45-34-75-50. FAX 1-46-26-28-49.
circ. 1,500. *2256*

MENSA BULLETIN.
American Mensa Ltd. (Brooklyn), 2626 E. 14th St., Brooklyn, NY 11235-3992. *1299*

MENTAL HEALTH MATTERS.
Northern Ireland Association for Mental Health, 80 University St., Belfast BT7 1HE, N. Ireland. FAX 0232-234940. *4035*

LA MER.
Societe Franco-Japonaise d'Oceanographie, c/o Maison Franco-Japonaise, Kanda Surugadai 2-3, Chiyoda-ku, Tokyo 101, Japan.
circ. 600. *447*

MESSENGER.
Southeast Asia Union Mission of Seventh-Day Adventists, 251 Upper Serangoon Rd., Singapore, Singapore.
circ. 2,000. *4285*

METAL CENTER NEWS.
Hitchcock Publishing 191 S. Gary Ave., Carol Stream, IL 60188. TEL 708-665-1000. FAX 708-462-2225.
circ. 12,600. *3413*

METAL FORMING.
Precision Metal Forming Association, 27027 Chardon Rd., Richmond Hts., OH 44143. TEL 216-585-8800.
circ. 52,000. *3413*

METALES Y METALURGIA.
Tecnipublicaciones, S.A., Fernando VI, 27, 28004 Madrid, Spain. TEL 91-419 90 66.
circ. 5,000. *3414*

METRO (REDONDO BEACH).
Bobit Publishing Company, 2512 Artesia Blvd., Redondo Beach, CA 90278. TEL 310-376-8788. FAX 310-376-9043.
circ. 18,000. *4653*

METROPOLITAN NASHVILLE BOARD OF EDUCATION. NEWS AND VIEWS.
Metropolitan Nashville Board of Education, 2601 Bransford Ave., Nashville, TN 37204. TEL 615-259-8400.
circ. 7,500. *1647*

METROSPORTS MAGAZINE.
Tate House Enterprises, Inc., 695 Washington St., New York, NY 10014. TEL 212-627-7040. FAX 212-242-3293.
circ. 185,000. *4479*

MEXICO BUSINESS MONTHLY.
Kal Wagenheim, Ed. & Pub., 52 Maple Ave., Maplewood, NJ 07040. TEL 800-647-9990. FAX 201-762-9585. *917*

MICHIGAN. DEPARTMENT OF STATE POLICE. ANNUAL REPORT.
Department of State Police, 714 S. Harrison Rd., East Lansing, MI 48823. TEL 517-332-2521. *1518*

MICHIGAN. STATE COURT ADMINISTRATOR. ANNUAL REPORT.
State Court Administrative Office, Box 30048, Lansing, MI 48909. TEL 517-373-0130. FAX 517-373-8922.
circ. 1,500. *2700*

MICHIGAN ASSOCIATION OF SECONDARY SCHOOL PRINCIPALS' BULLETIN.
Michigan Association of Secondary School Principals, 418 Erickson Hall, Michigan State University, E. Lansing, MI 48823. *1648*

MICHIGAN AVIATION.
Aeronautics Commission, Capital City Airport, Lansing, MI 48906. TEL 517-373-1834. FAX 517-886-0366.
circ. 17,000. *58*

MICHIGAN CORRECTIONS ASSOCIATION REPORT.
Dale Corporation, 84 Executive Dr., Troy, MI 48083-4504. TEL 313-597-9040. FAX 313-597-9043.
circ. 1,500. *1518*

MICHIGAN FARM NEWS - RURAL LIVING.
Michigan Farm Bureau, 7373 W. Saginaw Hwy., Box 30690, Lansing, MI 48909. TEL 517-323-7000.
circ. 98,000. *107*

MICHIGAN FOOD NEWS.
Michigan Grocers Association, 221 N. Walnut St., Lansing, MI 48933. TEL 517-372-6800. FAX 517-372-3002.
circ. 6,000. *2077*

MICHIGAN JOURNAL OF POLITICAL SCIENCE.
University of Michigan, Michigan Journal of Political Science, 5620 Haven Hall, Ann Arbor, MI 48109-1045. TEL 313-764-6386.
circ. 1,000. *3907*

MICHIGAN LUTHERAN.
Lutheran Church - Missouri Synod, Michigan District, 3773 Geddes Road, Ann Arbor, MI 48105. TEL 313-665-3791. FAX 313-665-0255.
circ. 76,000. *4243*

MICHIGAN STATE UNIVERSITY. AGRICULTURAL ECONOMICS REPORT.
Michigan State University, Department of Agricultural Economics, Reference Rm., E. Lansing, MI 48824-1039. TEL 517-355-6650. FAX 517-366-1800.
circ. 90. *154*

MICHIGAN STATE UNIVERSITY. LIBRARY. AFRICANA: SELECT RECENT ACQUISITIONS.
Michigan State University Libraries, East Lansing, MI 48824-1048. TEL 517-355-2366. FAX 517-336-1445.
circ. 500. *406*

MICRO MARKETWORLD.
C W Communications, Inc., 375 Cochituate Rd., Box 9171, Framingham, MA 01701-9171. TEL 617-879-0700.
circ. 45,000. *1433*

MICROSCOPIA ELECTRONICA Y BIOLOGIA CELULAR.
Centro Regional de Investigaciones Cientificas y Tecnologicas, Casilla de Correo 131, 5500 Mendoza, Argentina. TEL 061-254400-441. FAX 061-25330. *560*

MICROWAVES & R F PRODUCT EXTRA.
Penton Publishing (Hasbrouck Heights) 611 Rt. 46 W., Hasbrouck Heights, NJ 07604. TEL 201-393-6060.
circ. 40,000. *1903*

MID-AM REPORTER.
Mid-America Dairymen, Inc., 3253 E. Chestnut Expy., Springfield, MO 65802-2584. TEL 417-865-7100. FAX 417-865-9176.
circ. 18,000. *201*

MID-AMERICA BANNER.
Mid-America Machine Dealers Association, 40625 N. Sunset Dr., Antioch, IL 60002. TEL 708-395-4660. FAX 708-395-6922.
circ. 1,400. *1081*

MID-AMERICAN REVIEW.
Bowling Green State University, Department of English, c/o George Looney, Ed., Bowling Green University, Bowling Green, OH 43403. TEL 419-372-2725.
circ. 1,000. *2874*

MIDDLE ATLANTIC PERSPECTIVE.
Middle Atlantic Regional Medical Library Program, New York Academy of Medicine, 2 E. 103rd St., New York, NY 10029. TEL 212-876-8763.
circ. 2,100. *3131*

MIDDLE EAST POLICY.
Middle East Policy Council, 1730 M St., N.W., Ste. 512, Washington, DC 20036. TEL 202-296-6767. FAX 202-296-5791.
circ. 15,000. *3965*

MIDDLE EAST TRADE.
Middle East Trade Publications Ltd., 11 Gower St., London WC1E GHB, England. TEL 071-636-2911.
circ. 15,320. *917*

MIDWEST AUTOMOTIVE & AUTOBODY NEWS.
Automotive Publishing Co., 2900 W. Peterson Ave., Chicago, IL 60659. TEL 312-764-1640.
circ. 11,562. *4695*

MIE UNIVERSITY. FACULTY OF FISHERIES. JOURNAL.
Mie Daigaku, Suisan Gakubu, 2-80 Edobashi, Tsu-shi, Mie-ken 514, Japan. *2045*

DIE MILCHPRAXIS UND RINDERMAST.
Verlag Th. Mann, Nordring 10, Postfach 200254, 4650 Gelsenkirchen-Buer, Germany. TEL 0209-37431.
circ. 88,000. *201*

MILES ALKALIZER.
Miles Inc. Box 40, Elkhart, IN 46515. TEL 219-262-7584.
circ. 6,500. *447*

MILITARY & AEROSPACE ELECTRONICS.
Sentry Publishing Company, Inc., 346 Commerce St., Alexandria, VA 22314. TEL 703-739-0007.
circ. 45,000. *59*

MILITARY CLUB & HOSPITALITY.
Executive Business Media, Inc., 825 Old Country Rd., Box 1500, Westbury, NY 11590. TEL 516-334-3030.
circ. 11,000. *2077*

MILITARY LIFESTYLE.
Downey Communications, Inc., 4800 Montgomery Ln., 7th Fl., Bethesda, MD 20814-5341. TEL 301-718-7600. FAX 301-718-7652.
circ. 520,000. *3465*

MILK BULLETIN.
Scottish Milk Marketing Board, Underwood Rd., Paisley, Renfrewshire PA3 1TJ, Scotland. FAX 041-889-1225.
circ. 3,200. *201*

MILK NEWS.
Aberdeen and District Milk Marketing Board, Twin Spires Creamery, Bucksburn, Aberdeen, Scotland. *201*

MILK TOPICS.
North of Scotland Milk Marketing Board, Claymore House, 29 Ardconnel Terrace, Inverness, Scotland. FAX 0463-710923.
circ. 650. *202*

MILL NECK MANOR BULLETIN.
Mill Neck Foundation, Frost Mill Rd., Box 100, Mill Neck, NY 11765. TEL 516-922-4100. FAX 516-922-3759.
circ. 76,000. *2288*

MINBAR AL-TAMRID.
Ministry of Health, School of Nursing, P.O. Box 3798, Abu Dhabi, United Arab Emirates. TEL 665472.
circ. 1,000. *3282*

MINI DATA REPORT.
Siemens, S.A., Calle Orense No. 2, Madrid 20, Spain. *1466*

MINING IN ZIMBABWE.
Thomson Publications Zimbabwe (Pvt) Ltd., Thomson House, P.O. Box 1683, Harare, Zimbabwe. TEL 736835. *3490*

MINING NEWS.
Chamber of Mines of South Africa, P.O. Box 809, Johannesburg 2000, South Africa. *3490*

MINISTERIALTIDENDE FOR KONGERIGET DANMARK.
Justisministeriet, Sekretariatet for Retsinformation, Axeltorv 6, 5. sal, DK-1609 Copenhagen V, Denmark. TEL 33-32-52-22. FAX 33-91-28-01.
circ. 2,007. *4067*

MINNESOTA AGRICULTURAL ECONOMIST.
University of Minnesota, Department of Agricultural & Applied Economics, 1994 Buford Ave., St. Paul, MN 55108. TEL 612-625-1705. FAX 612-625-6245.
circ. 4,000. *154*

MINNESOTA CLUBWOMAN.
General Federation of Women's Clubs of Minnesota, Inc., 5701 Normandale Rd., Ste. 315, Minneapolis, MN 55424. TEL 612-920-2057.
circ. 4,800. *1299*

MINNESOTA SCIENCE.
University of Minnesota, Agricultural Experiment Station, 405 Coffey Hall, St. Paul, MN 55108. TEL 612-625-7290.
circ. 21,000. *4324*

MINORITY M B A.
Peterson's - C O G Publishing, 16030 Ventura Blvd., Ste. 560, Encino, CA 91436. TEL 818-789-5293. FAX 818-789-5488.
circ. 13,381. *3629*

MINOTAUR.
Minotaur Press, Box 4039, Felton, CA 95018.
circ. 150. *2998*

MINZU YANJIU.
Zhongguo Shehui Kexueyuan, Minzu Yanjiusuo, 27 Baishiqiao Lu, Beijing 100081, People's Republic of China. TEL 8022288.
circ. 5,000. *3641*

MIRROR AND PROBE.
Dental Students' Association, University of Sri Lanka, University Park, Peradeniya, Sri Lanka. *3238*

MISSIONHURST.
Missionhurst, Inc., 4651 N. 25th St., Arlington, VA 22207-3500. TEL 703-528-3800. FAX 703-528-3804.
circ. 90,000. *4269*

MISSISSIPPI CONGRESS OF PARENTS AND TEACHERS. PROCEEDINGS.
Mississippi Congress of Parents and Teachers, Box 1937, Jackson, MS 39215-1937. TEL 601-352-7383. *1729*

MISSISSIPPI CONGRESS OF PARENTS AND TEACHERS. YEARBOOK.
Mississippi Congress of Parents and Teachers, Box 1937, Jackson, MS 39215-1937. TEL 601-352-7383. *1729*

MISSISSIPPI GROCERS' GUIDE.
Mississippi Retail Grocers Association, 1631 Pinevale, Jackson, MS 39211.
circ. 1,075. *2093*

MISSOURI. DIVISION OF HIGHWAY SAFETY. HIGHWAY SAFETY PLAN.
Division of Highway Safety, Box 104808, Jefferson City, MO 65110-4808. TEL 314-751-4161. FAX 314-634-5977. *4720*

MISSOURI ARCHAEOLOGICAL SOCIETY. SPECIAL PUBLICATIONS.
Missouri Archaeological Society, 908 Woodson Way, University of Missouri, Columbia, MO 65211. TEL 314-882-3544.
circ. 1,500. *278*

MISSOURI LIBRARIES.
State Library, Box 387, Jefferson City, MO 65102-0387. TEL 314-751-2680. FAX 314-751-3612.
circ. 4,250. *2774*

MISSOURI PIPELINE.
Missouri Petroleum Marketers Association, 238 E. High St., Jefferson City, MO 65101. TEL 314-635-7117. FAX 314-635-3575.
circ. 1,400. *3692*

MITRE.
Bishop's University, Student's Representative Council, Lennoxville, Que. J1M 1Z7, Canada. TEL 819-569-9551. *2874*

HA-MIZRAH HEHADASH.
Israel Oriental Society, Hebrew University, Jerusalem, Israel.
circ. 2,500. *3641*

MOBILE PRODUCT NEWS.
Phillips Publishing, Inc., 7811 Montrose Rd., Potomac, MD 20854. TEL 301-340-2100. FAX 301-309-3847. *1364*

MODEL ROCKET NEWS.
Estes Industries, Penrose, CO 81240. TEL 719-372-6565. *2439*

MODERN AFRICA.
Wideworld Communications, 57-59 Whitechapel Rd., London E1 1DU, England. TEL 071-377-8413. FAX 071-247-5407.
circ. 14,050. *917*

MODERN BAKING.
Donohue - Meehan Publishing Company, 2700 River Rd., Des Plaines, IL 60018. TEL 708-299-4430. FAX 708-296-1968.
circ. 27,000. *2089*

MODERN FARMING.
Massey-Ferguson, Stareton, Near Kenilworth, Warwickshire CV8 2LJ, England. TEL 0203-531221. FAX 0203-531229.
circ. 14,500. *108*

MODERN HEALTHCARE (YEAR).
Crain Communications, Inc. (Chicago), 740 N. Rush St., Chicago, IL 60611-2590. TEL 312-649-5341. FAX 312-280-3189.
circ. 80,966. *2467*

MODERN JEWELER NATIONAL.
Vance Publishing Corporation, 7950 College Blvd., Shawnee Mission, KS 66210. TEL 913-451-2200.
circ. 38,000. *2565*

MODERN MEDIA.
Eiken Chemical Co. Ltd., 1-33-8 Hongo, Bunkyo-ku, Tokyo 113, Japan. *555*

MODERN OFFICE TECHNOLOGY.
Penton Publishing 1100 Superior Ave., Cleveland, OH 44114-2543. TEL 216-696-7000. FAX 609-696-8765.
circ. 159,000. *1059*

MODERN TIRE DEALER: TIRE, TOOLS & EQUIPMENT MERCHANDISING GUIDE.
Bill Communications, Inc. (Akron), 341 White Pond Dr., Box 3599, Akron, OH 44309-3599. TEL 216-867-4401. FAX 216-867-0019.
circ. 33,000. *4653*

MOEBEL-KULTUR.
Ferdinand Holzmann Verlag, P.O.B. 60 10 49, 2000 Hamburg 60, Germany. TEL 040-632018-0. *2561*

MOEBELMARKT.
Verlag Matthias Ritthammer GmbH, Burgschmietstr. 25, Postfach 3850, 8500 Nuernberg 90, Germany. FAX 0911-334400.
circ. 13,500. *2561*

MONDO ECONOMICO.
Societa Editoriale Media Economici Seme S.p.A., Via P. Lomazzo, 52, 20154 Milan, Italy. TEL 02-331211. FAX 02-316905.
circ. 36,000. *874*

MONEYPLUS NEWS.
First Estate Financial Services, 2222 Kansas St., Bldg. J, Box 5879, Riverside, CA 92517. TEL 714-787-7770.
circ. 7,500. *1116*

MONITEUR DES TRAVAUX PUBLICS ET DU BATIMENT.
Publications du Moniteur, 17 rue d'Uzes, 75002 Paris Cedex, France. TEL 1-40-13-30-30. FAX 1-40-41-94-95.
circ. 76,950. *1871*

MONKEY.
Japan Monkey Centre, Kanrin Inuyama 26, Aichi 484, Japan.
circ. 2,000. *588*

THE MONOCACY VALLEY REVIEW.
Mount Saint Mary's College, Emmitsburg, MD 21727. TEL 301-447-6122.
circ. 500. *2940*

MONTANA.
Montana Historical Society, 225 N. Roberts St., Helena, MT 59620. TEL 406-444-4708.
circ. 10,000. *2415*

MONTANA FARM BUREAU SPOKESMAN.
Montana Farm Bureau Federation, 502 S. 19th, Bozeman, MT 59715.
circ. 4,100. *108*

MONTANA NEWSLETTER.
State Library, 1515 E. 6th Ave., Helena, MT 59620. TEL 406-444-3115. FAX 406-444-5612. *2774*

MONTANA STATE LIBRARY NEWS UPDATE.
Montana State Library, 1515 E. 6th Ave., Helena, MT 59620. TEL 406-444-3115. FAX 406-444-5612.
circ. 1,200. *2774*

MONTHLY BREWING INDUSTRY COMMENTARY.
Cyrus J. Lawrence, Inc., 1290 Ave. of the Americas, New York, NY 10104. TEL 212-468-5000. *874*

MONTREAL BUSINESS FORUM.
Ancor Press, 1080 Beaver Hall Hill, Ste. 710, Montreal, Que. H2Z 1S9, Canada. TEL 514-878-4651. FAX 514-878-2262.
circ. 10,000. *820*

MONTREAL SCOPE.
Metro Plaza Ltd., Rm. 232, 1253 McGill College, Montreal, Que. H3B 2Y5, Canada. TEL 514-933-3333. FAX 514-931-9581.
circ. 40,000. *2178*

MOOREA.
Irish Garden Plant Society, c/o National Botanical Gardens, Glasnevin, Dublin 9, Ireland. FAX 337329.
circ. 600. *2134*

MOTOR CARAVANNER.
Motor Caravanners' Club, 71 Cricklewood Broadway, London NW2 3JR, England. *4550*

MOTOR CLUB NEWS.
Motor Club of America, c/o Marlene Timm, Ed., 484 Central Ave., Newark, NJ 07107.
circ. 130,000. *4778*

MOTOR IMPORTED CAR CRASH ESTIMATING GUIDE.
Motor Publications, Crash Books Department, 5600 Crooks Rd., Ste. 102, Troy, MI 48098. *4696*

MOTOR TRADER.
Reed Business Publishing Group, Enterprise Division Quadrant House, The Quadrant, Sutton, Surrey SM2 5AS, England. TEL 081-652-3276. FAX 081-652-8986.
circ. 37,059. *4696*

MOTOR TRANSPORT.
Reed Business Publishing Group, Enterprise Division Quadrant House, The Quadrant, Sutton, Surrey SM2 5AS, England. TEL 081-652-3284. FAX 081-652-3925.
circ. 44,697. *4746*

MOTORCYCLE INDUSTRY MAGAZINE.
Industry Shopper Publishing, Inc., 31194 La Baya Dr., Ste. 200, Westlake Village, CA 91362. TEL 818-991-2070. FAX 818-991-9427.
circ. 12,000. *4519*

MOTORCYCLE PRODUCT NEWS.
M H West, Inc. 6633 Odessa Ave., Van Nuys, CA 91406. TEL 818-997-0664. FAX 818-997-1058.
circ. 12,951. *4519*

MOTORING.
Western India Automobile Association, 76 Veer Nariman Rd., Churchgate, Bombay 20, India.
circ. 30,000. *4697*

MOTORING & LEISURE.
Civil Service Motoring Association Ltd., Britannia House, 95 Queens Rd., Brighton BN1 3WY, England. TEL 0273-21921. FAX 0273-23990.
circ. 270,000. *4697*

MOUNTAIN CONSTRUCTOR & RECLAMATIONIST.
Phoenix Publishing Corporation, Box 6048, Denver, CO 80206-0048. TEL 303-988-2784.
circ. 11,201. *625*

MOUNTAIN RIDERS.
South By Southwest Ranch, 15190 Tierra Rejada, Moor Park, CA 93021. TEL 805-523-9334.
circ. 5,000. *4536*

MOUNTAIN TIMES (KILLINGTON).
B R D Corp., Box 183, Killington, VT 05751. TEL 802-773-6970. FAX 802-773-4482.
circ. 11,350. *4778*

MUENCHNER MEDIZINISCHE WOCHENSCHRIFT EN ESPANOL.
Editorial ECO, S.A., Calle de la Cruz 44, Barcelona 34, Spain.
circ. 25,000. *3132*

MUHENDIS VE MAKINA.
Chamber of Mechanical Engineers, Sumer Sokak, 36-1-A Demirtepe, 06440 Ankara, Turkey. TEL 4-2313164. FAX 4-2313165.
circ. 30,000. *1936*

MULTINATIONAL EXECUTIVE TRAVEL COMPANION.
Guides to Multinational Business, Inc., Harvard Sq., Box 92, Cambridge, MA 02238. TEL 617-868-2288.
circ. 250,000. *917*

MUNDO NEGRO.
Misioneros Combonianos, Congregacion Misionera, Arturo Soria, 101, 28043 Madrid, Spain. FAX 91-5192550.
circ. 80,000. *4191*

MUNICIPAL ASSOCIATION OF TASMANIA. SESSION. MINUTES OF PROCEEDINGS.
Municipal Association of Tasmania, 34 Patrick St., Hobart, Tas. 7000, Australia. TEL 002-310666. FAX 002-240086.
circ. 200. *4091*

MUNICIPAL ATTORNEY.
National Institute of Municipal Law Officers, 1000 Connecticut Ave., N.W., Ste. 902, Washington, DC 20036. TEL 202-466-5424. FAX 202-785-0152.
circ. 2,500. *2655*

MUNRO EAGLE.
Clan Munro Association U S A, Inc., 11 Las Huertas Ridge Rd., Placitas, NM 87043.
circ. 650. *2159*

MUSEUM OF THE CITY OF NEW YORK QUARTERLY.
Museum of the City of New York, 5th Ave. at 103rd St., New York, NY 10029. TEL 212-534-1672. FAX 212-534-5974.
circ. 3,000. *3529*

MUSEUM OF THE FUR TRADE QUARTERLY.
Museum of the Fur Trade, HC-74, Box 18, Chadron, NE 69337. TEL 308-432-3843.
circ. 2,000. *2415*

MUSEUM QUARTERLY.
Ontario Museum Association, 50 Baldwin St., George Brown House, Toronto, Ont. M5T 1L4, Canada. TEL 416-348-8672. FAX 416-348-8689.
circ. 2,400. *3529*

MUSHROOM JOURNAL.
Mushroom Growers' Association, 2 St. Pauls St., Stamford, Lincs. PE9 2BE, England. TEL 01-235 5077.
circ. 1,000. *2134*

MUSIC & COMPUTER EDUCATOR.
T A M E E Publications, 16 N. Broadway, Hicksville, NY 11801-2913. TEL 516-549-3200. FAX 516-385-7104.
circ. 20,000. *3590*

MUSIC RETAILING.
Out to Launch Communications Inc. Forest Rd., Hancock, NH 03449. TEL 603-525-4201.
circ. 12,000. *3565*

MUSICAL HERITAGE REVIEW MAGAZINE.
Musical Heritage Society, 1710 Highway 35, Ocean, NJ 07712. TEL 201-531-7000. *3566*

MUSICAL MERCHANDISE REVIEW.
Larkin-Pluznick-Larkin, Inc., 100 Wells Ave., Box 9103, Newton, MA 02159-9103. TEL 617-964-5100.
circ. 12,000. *3566*

MUTUALITE.
Association Internationale des Societes d'Assurance Mutuelle, 114 rue la Boetie, 75008 Paris, France. FAX 1-42-56-04-49.
circ. 2,500. *2538*

MUZIEKHANDEL.
Nederlandse Muziek Federatie, Eikbosserweg 181, 1213 RX Hilversum, Netherlands. TEL 035-48104. FAX 02159-46173.
circ. 700. *3569*

MYCOPHILE.
North American Mycological Association, 3556 Oakwood, Ann Arbor, MI 48104-5213.
circ. 1,700. *510*

MYCOTAXON.
Mycotaxon, Ltd., Box 264, Ithaca, NY 14851. TEL 607-273-4357. FAX 607-255-4471.
circ. 650. *510*

N A A F I NEWS.
Navy, Army & Air Force Institutes, Kennington, London SE11, England.
circ. 11,000. *3466*

N A B P NEWSLETTER.
National Association of Boards of Pharmacy, 1300 Higgins Rd., No. 103, Park Ridge, IL 60068-5743. TEL 708-698-6227.
circ. 1,800. *3735*

N A C L O NEWS.
National Association of Canoe Liveries and Outfitters, R.R. 2, Box 249, Butler, KY 41006-9674. TEL 606-472-2205. FAX 606-472-2030.
circ. 350. *4526*

N A C W P I JOURNAL.
Simpson Publishing Co., c/o Dr. R. Weerts, Ed., Division of Fine Arts, Northeast Missouri State University, Kirksville, MO 63501. TEL 816-785-4442.
circ. 6,000. *3569*

N A E B BULLETIN.
National Association of Educational Buyers, 450 Wireless Blvd., Hauppauge, NY 11788-3934. TEL 516-273-2600. FAX 516-273-2305. *1755*

N A E I R ADVANTAGE.
National Association for the Exchange of Industrial Resources, 560 McClure St., Box 8076, Galesburg, IL 61402. TEL 309-343-0704. FAX 309-343-0862.
circ. 40,000. *4413*

N A F O LIST OF FISHING VESSELS.
Northwest Atlantic Fisheries Organization, P.O. Box 638, Dartmouth, N.S. B2Y 3Y9, Canada. TEL 902-469-9105. *2046*

N A M A JOURNAL.
National Account Marketing Association, 38 E. 23rd St., 3rd Fl., New York, NY 10010-4490. TEL 212-983-5140.
circ. 300. *1048*

N A M M MUSIC RETAILER NEWS.
National Association of Music Merchants Inc., 5140 Avenida Encinas, Carlsbad, CA 92008. TEL 619-438-8001.
circ. 10,500. *3569*

N A R D ALMANAC AND HEALTH GUIDE.
National Association of Retail Druggists, 205 Daingerfield Rd., Alexandria, VA 22314. TEL 703-683-8200. FAX 703-683-3619.
circ. 1,125,250. *1048*

N A T NEWS.
Newton Mann Ltd., Sherwood House, Matlock, Derbyshire DE4 3LY, England. TEL 0629 583941. FAX 0629-580479.
circ. 5,500. *3282*

N C - C I M GUIDEBOOK.
Gardner Publications, Inc., 6600 Clough Pike, Cincinnati, OH 45244-4090. TEL 513-231-8020. FAX 513-231-2818.
circ. 70,000. *3025*

N D R E PUBLICATIONS.
Norwegian Defence Research Establishment, Box 25, N-2007 Kjeller, Norway. FAX 06-807159. *4325*

N E C RESEARCH AND DEVELOPMENT.
Nippon Electric Co. Ltd., NEC Bldg., 5-33-1 Shiba, Minato-ku, Tokyo 108, Japan.
circ. 5,000. *1904*

N I W O MEDEDELINGEN.
Nederlandsche Internationale Wegvervoer Organisatie, Postbus 3004, 2280 MB Rijswijk, Netherlands. TEL 070-3992011.
circ. 3,500. *4653*

N N F A MONITOR.
National Nutritional Foods Association, 150 E. Paulerino, Ste. 285, Costa Mesa, CA 92626. TEL 714-966-6632. *3609*

N N O MAGAZINE.
Noord - Nederlands Orkest, Emmaplein 2, P.O. Box 818, 9700 AV Groningen, Netherlands. TEL 31-50-126200. FAX 31-50-138164.
circ. 3,500. *3569*

N R A G PAPERS.
Northern Rockies Action Group, Inc., 9 Placer St., Helena, MT 59601.
circ. 400. *4413*

N S G A RETAIL FOCUS.
National Sporting Goods Association, 1699 Wall St., Mt. Prospect, IL 60056-5780. TEL 708-439-4000. FAX 708-439-0111. *1048*

N S R A NEWS.
Nuclear Safety Research Association, 1-2-2 Uchisaiwai-cho, Chiyoda-ku, Tokyo 100, Japan. TEL 03-3503-5785.
circ. 1,500. *1807*

N Y HABITAT.
Carol Group Ltd., 928 Broadway, New York, NY 10010. TEL 212-505-2030. FAX 212-254-6795.
circ. 10,000. *4153*

N Y S S A SPHERE.
New York State Society of Anesthesiologists, Inc., 41 E. 42nd St., No. 1605, New York, NY 10017. FAX 716-845-8518.
circ. 2,500. *3191*

N Y: THE CITY JOURNAL.
Manhattan Institute, 42 E. 71st St., New York, NY 10021. TEL 212-988-7300.
circ. 5,000. *3908*

NACION.
Estudios y Publicaciones Economicas y Sociales, S.A., Cerrada de Eugenia, 25, Col. del Valle, Delegacion Benito Juarez, Apartado Postal 32-470, CP 03100 Mexico DF, Mexico. TEL 536-18-31. FAX 525-687-2922.
circ. 15,000. *3908*

NADI ABU DHABI AL-SIYAHI.
Nadi Abu Dhabi al-Siyahi, P.O. Box 28, Abu Dhabi, United Arab Emirates. TEL 724954.
circ. 1,000. *1300*

NADI AL-WASL.
Nadi al-Wasl, P.O. Box 3888, Dubai, United Arab Emirates. TEL 374487.
circ. 500. *1300*

NAERINGSFORSKNING.
Swedish Nutrition Foundation, Ideon, S-22370 Lund, Sweden. TEL 46-46-182280. FAX 46-46-182281.
circ. 2,500. *3609*

NAGOYA MATHEMATICAL JOURNAL.
Nagoya Daigaku Rigakubu, Sugaku Kyoshitsu, Chikusa-ku, Nagoya 464-01, Japan. FAX 52-781-4437.
circ. 1,250. *3048*

NAGOYA UNIVERSITY. FACULTY OF ENGINEERING. AUTOMATIC CONTROL LABORATORY. RESEARCH REPORTS.
Nagoya Daigaku, Kogakubu, Furo-cho, Chikusa-ku, Nagoya 464-01, Japan. *1415*

NAILPRO.
Creative Age Publications, 7628 Densmore Ave., Van Nuys, CA 91406. TEL 818-782-7328.
circ. 32,300. *376*

NAME GLEANER.
York University, S. 561 Ross Bldg., 4700 Keele St., N. York, Ont. M3J 1P3, Canada.
circ. 120. *2830*

NARA IGAKU ZASSHI.
Nara Igakkai, Nara Medical University, Kashihara 634, Nara, Japan. TEL 07442-2-3051. *3133*

NAROD POLSKI.
Polish Roman Catholic Union of America, 984 Milwaukee Ave., Chicago, IL 60622. TEL 312-278-3210. FAX 312-278-4595.
circ. 30,000. *2015*

NASHRAT A D M A.
Abu Dhabi Marine Operating Company, P.O. Box 303, Abu Dhabi, United Arab Emirates. TEL 776600. FAX 720028.
circ. 2,400. *3692*

NASSAU COUNTY HISTORICAL SOCIETY JOURNAL.
Nassau County Historical Society, Box 207, Garden City, NY 11530.
circ. 600. *2415*

NATCHEZ TRACE TRAVELER.
Natchez Trace Genealogical Society, Box 420, Florence, AL 35631.
circ. 150. *2159*

NATIONAL ASSOCIATION OF WOMEN ARTISTS. ANNUAL EXHIBITION CATALOG.
National Association of Women Artists, 41 Union Sq., W., Rm. 906, New York, NY 10003. TEL 212-675-1616.
circ. 1,000. *337*

NATIONAL BOTANIC RESEARCH INSTITUTE, LUCKNOW. PROGRESS REPORT.
National Botanical Research Institute, Lucknow. Progress Report, Lucknow 226001, India. *510*

NATIONAL BRAILLE ASSOCIATION. GENERAL INTEREST CATALOG.
National Braille Association, Inc., 1290 University Ave., Rochester, NY 14607. TEL 716-473-0900. *2294*

NATIONAL BRAILLE ASSOCIATION. MUSIC CATALOG.
National Braille Association, Inc., 1290 University Ave., Rochester, NY 14607. TEL 716-473-0900. *2295*

NATIONAL BRAILLE ASSOCIATION. TEXTBOOK CATALOG.
National Braille Association, Inc., 1290 University Ave., Rochester, NY 14607. TEL 716-473-0900. *2295*

NATIONAL CENTRE FOR OCCUPATIONAL HEALTH. ANNUAL REPORT.
Department of National Health and Population Development, National Centre for Occupational Health, Box 4788, Johannesburg 2000, South Africa. FAX 011-720-6608.
circ. 400. *3619*

NATIONAL CLOTHESLINE.
B P S Communications, 717 E. Chelten Ave., Philadelphia, PA 19144. TEL 215-843-9795. FAX 215-843-8511.
circ. 46,000. *1282*

NATIONAL CONFERENCE OF STATE SOCIAL SECURITY ADMINISTRATORS. PROCEEDINGS.
National Conference of State Social Security Administrators, c/o Social Security Division, c/o Jim Larche, Deputy Dir., Employee Retirement System of Georgia, Two Northside 75, Ste. 300, Atlanta, GA 30318. TEL 404-352-6400. *4413*

NATIONAL COUNCIL OF TEACHERS OF MATHEMATICS. YEARBOOK.
National Council of Teachers of Mathematics, 1906 Association Dr., Reston, VA 22091. TEL 703-620-9840. FAX 703-476-2970. *3048*

NATIONAL COUNCIL OF UNITED STATES MAGISTRATES. BULLETIN.
National Council of United States Magistrates, c/o Ralph J. Geffen, Ed., U.S. Courthouse, Los Angeles, CA 90012. TEL 213-688-3698.
circ. 400. *2657*

NATIONAL DAIRY COUNCIL OF CANADA. DIRECTION.
National Dairy Council of Canada, 221 Laurier Ave., E., Ottawa, Ont. K1N 6P1, Canada. TEL 613-238-4116. FAX 613-238-6247.
circ. 1,000. *202*

NATIONAL DEVELOPMENT.
Intercontinental Publications, Inc., 25 Sylvan Rd. S., Box 5017, Westport, CT 06880. TEL 203-226-7463. FAX 203-222-8793.
circ. 22,000. *4068*

NATIONAL DEVELOPMENT FINANCE CORPORATION. QUARTERLY REVIEW.
National Development Finance Corporation, Finance and Trade Center, 2nd Fl., Shahrah-e Faisal, Karachi, Pakistan. FAX 525310.
circ. 1,200. *875*

NATIONAL DIET LIBRARY. NEWSLETTER.
National Diet Library, 10-1 Nagata-cho 1-chome, Chiyoda-ku, Tokyo 100, Japan. TEL 03-3581-2331.
circ. 1,000. *2775*

NATIONAL FEDERATION OF FRUIT & POTATO TRADES. FEDERATION NEWS.
National Federation of Fruit and Potato Trades, Ltd., 103-107 Market Towers, 1 Nine Elms Ln., London SW8 5NQ, England. *108*

NATIONAL FEDERATION OF PLAYGOERS SOCIETIES. NEWSLETTER.
National Federation of Playgoers Societies, 3 Gwenfo Dr., Wenvoe, Cardiff CF5 6ER, England.
circ. 50. *4635*

NATIONAL FORUM (AUBURN).
Honor Society of Phi Kappa Phi (Auburn), c/o Stephen W. White, Ed., 129 Quad Center, Mell St., Auburn, AL 36849-5306. TEL 205-844-5200. FAX 205-844-5994.
circ. 126,000. *1318*

NATIONAL FOUNDATION FOR ADVANCEMENT IN THE ARTS. ANNUAL REPORT.
National Foundation for Advancement in the Arts, 3915 Biscayne Blvd., 1st Fl., Miami, FL 33137. TEL 305-573-0490. FAX 305-573-4870.
circ. 2,500. *337*

CONTROLLED CIRCULATION SERIALS

NATIONAL HOG FARMER.
Intertec Publishing Corp., Webb Division, 7900 Int'l Dr., Minneapolis, MN 55425. TEL 612-851-4710. FAX 612-851-4601.
circ. 100,150. *221*

NATIONAL HOUSING REGISTER.
William D. Diemer, Ed. & Pub., 27239 Meadowbrook Dr., Davis, CA 95616-5049. TEL 916-757-6403.
circ. 30. *2492*

NATIONAL INSTITUTE FOR EDUCATIONAL RESEARCH. RESEARCH BULLETIN.
National Institute for Educational Research, 6-5-22 Shimo-Meguro, Meguro-ku, Tokyo 153, Japan.
1650

NATIONAL INVESTMENT BANK, GHANA. ANNUAL REPORT.
National Investment Bank, 37 Liberty Ave., P.O. Box 3726, Accra, Ghana. *792*

NATIONAL MISSING PERSONS REPORT.
Search Reports, Inc., 345 Boulevard, Hasbrouck Heights, NJ 07604. TEL 201-288-4445. *1519*

NATIONAL MUSEUM OF THE PHILIPPINES. ANNUAL REPORT.
National Museum of the Philippines, Padre Burgos Street, Manila, Philippines. TEL 48-14-27. FAX 632-46-19-69. *3530*

NATIONAL PIG NEWS.
B C Publications, 16C Market Place, Diss, Norfolk IP22 3AB, England. TEL 0379-644200. FAX 0379-650480.
circ. 7,000. *108*

NATIONAL SAFETY.
Safety First Association, 7 Pitcairn Rd., Blairgowrie, Johannesburg 2194, South Africa. TEL 011-782-7698.
circ. 2,567. *4108*

NATUN THIKANA.
71-4 Dr. Nilmani Sarkar St., Calcutta 50, India.
2875

NATURAL FOOD TRADER.
I B T M Ltd., Queensway House, 2 Queensway, Redhill, Surrey RH1 1QS, England. TEL 0737-768611. FAX 0737-760425.
circ. 4,500. *3609*

NATURAL FOODS MERCHANDISER.
New Hope Communications, Inc., 1301 Spruce St., Boulder, CO 80302-4832. TEL 303-939-8440. FAX 303-939-9559.
circ. 13,000. *1048*

NATURAL WORLD.
R S N C - The Wildlife Trusts Partnership, 20 Upper Ground, London SE1 9PF, England. TEL 071-9282111. FAX 071-6201594.
circ. 190,000. *1493*

NAVAL AVIATION NEWS.
U.S. Department of the Navy, Asst. C N O (Air Warfare), c/o LCdr. Richard R. Burgess, Bldg. 159 E., WNY Annex, Washington, DC 20374-1595. TEL 202-783-3238. FAX 202-475-2104.
circ. 33,000. *59*

NAVAL WAR COLLEGE REVIEW.
U.S. Naval War College, Naval War College Press, Newport, RI 02841. TEL 401-841-4552. *3466*

NAVY SUPPLY CORPS NEWSLETTER.
U.S. Department of the Navy, Supply Systems Command, Washington, DC 20374. TEL 703-607-1301. FAX 703-607-2221.
circ. 15,000. *3467*

NAWPA PACHA.
Institute of Andean Studies, Box 9307, Berkeley, CA 94709.
circ. 550. *279*

NAZARETH.
Via Filitteria 10, 06049 Spoleto, Italy.
circ. 2,000. *4191*

NEBRASKA. DEPARTMENT OF ROADS. TRAFFIC ANALYSIS UNIT. CONTINUOUS TRAFFIC COUNT DATA AND TRAFFIC CHARACTERISTICS ON NEBRASKA STREETS AND HIGHWAYS.
Department of Roads, Transportation Planning Division, 1500 Nebraska Hwy. 2, Box 94759, Lincoln, NE 68509-4759. TEL 402-471-4567. FAX 402-479-4325. *4720*

NEBRASKA. DEPARTMENT OF SOCIAL SERVICES. ANNUAL REPORT.
Department of Social Services, Research and Finance Division, Box 95026, 301 Centennial Mall So., Lincoln, NE 68509. FAX 402-471-9455.
circ. 500. *4414*

NEBRASKA HIGHWAY PROGRAM.
Department of Roads, 1500 N.E. Hwy. 2, Box 94759, Lincoln, NE 68509-4759. TEL 402-479-4316. FAX 402-479-4325. *4720*

NEBRASKA MUSIC EDUCATOR.
Nebraska Music Educators Association, 2325 S. 24th St., Lincoln, NE 68502-4099.
circ. 1,950. *3570*

NEDERDUITSE GEREFORMEERDE KERK VAN NATAL GEMEENTE VRYHEID. MAANDBRIEF.
Nederduitse Gereformeerde Kerk van Natal Gemeentevryheid, Smalstraat 82, Vryheid, Natal, South Africa.
circ. 600. *4245*

NEERLANDIA.
Algemeen Nederlands Verbond, J. van Nassaustraat 109, 2596 BS The Hague, Netherlands. TEL 070-3245514. FAX 070-3246186.
circ. 3,000. *4443*

NETWORK (ARLINGTON).
National School Public Relations Association, 1501 Lee Highway, Ste. 201, Arlington, VA 22209. TEL 703-528-5840. *35*

NETWORK COMPUTING (MANHASSET).
C M P Publications, Inc., 600 Community Dr., Manhasset, NY 11030. TEL 516-562-5000. FAX 516-365-4601.
circ. 175,000. *1428*

NETWORKING MANAGEMENT.
PennWell Publishing Co. (Westford), Advanced Technology Group, One Technology Park Dr., Westford, MA 01886-0989. TEL 508-692-0700. FAX 508-692-7831.
circ. 90,018. *1447*

NEW AGE RETAILER.
Continuity Publishing, Inc., Box 224, Greenbank, WA 98253. TEL 206-678-7772. FAX 206-678-8803.
circ. 5,800. *3595*

NEW ALASKAN.
New Alaskan Publishing Co., 8339 Snug Harbor Ln., Ketchikan, AK 99901. TEL 907-247-2490.
circ. 6,000. *2229*

NEW BOOKS ON FAMILY PLANNING.
National Institute of Health and Family Welfare, New Mehrauli Rd., Munirka, New Delhi 110067, India.
circ. 1,250. *598*

NEW BRUNSWICK. DEPARTMENT OF AGRICULTURE. APPLE NEWSLETTER.
Department of Agriculture, Plant Industry Branch, P.O. Box 6000, Fredericton, N.B. E3B 5H1, Canada. TEL 506-453-2666. FAX 506-453-7978.
circ. 300. *186*

NEW BRUNSWICK. DEPARTMENT OF LABOUR. ANNUAL REPORT.
Department of Labour, P.O. Box 6000, Fredericton, N.B. E3B 5H1, Canada. TEL 506-453-2303. FAX 506-453-3806.
circ. 700. *989*

NEW CANTERBURY LITERARY SOCIETY NEWSLETTER.
Norman T. Gates, Ed. & Pub., 520 Woodland Ave., Haddonfield, NJ 08033.
circ. 100. *2941*

NEW CITY.
New City Press, Box 332, Manila, Philippines. FAX 02-623956.
circ. 10,000. *4191*

NEW DOMINION.
Dominion Publishing, Inc., 2000 N. 14th St., Ste. 730, Arlington, VA 22201-2500. TEL 703-527-1199.
circ. 40,000. *2230*

NEW ELECTRONICS.
International Thomson Business Publishing Ltd., 100 Avenue Rd., London NW3 3TP, England.
1904

NEW ENGLAND ECONOMIC INDICATORS.
Federal Reserve Bank of Boston, Research Department, 600 Atlantic Ave., Boston, MA 02106. TEL 617-973-3542. FAX 617-973-3957. *875*

NEW ENGLAND REAL ESTATE JOURNAL - SHOPPING CENTERS.
Brian P. Heneghan, 57 Washington St., Norwell, MA 02061. TEL 800-654-4993. FAX 617-871-1853. *4153*

NEW ENGLAND SKIERS' GUIDE.
Ski Racing International, Box 1125, Waitsfield, VT 05673-1125. TEL 802-496-7700. FAX 802-496-7704.
circ. 90,000. *4551*

NEW ENGLAND SNOWBOARDER.
North Shore Weeklies, Box 468, Marblehead, MA 01945-0468. TEL 617-639-2838.
circ. 15,000. *4551*

NEW EQUIPMENT DIGEST.
Penton Publishing 1100 Superior Ave., Cleveland, OH 44114-2543. TEL 216-696-7000. FAX 216-696-8765.
circ. 213,000. *4605*

NEW ERA LAUNDRY & CLEANING LINES.
New Era Magazine, 22031 Bushard, Huntington Beach, CA 92646. TEL 714-962-1351. FAX 714-962-1354.
circ. 23,606. *1282*

NEW HAMPSHIRE QUARTER NOTES.
New Hampshire Music Educators Association, Rt. 5, Box 240, Penacook, NH 03303.
circ. 750. *3570*

NEW HOMES MAGAZINE.
New Homes, Inc., 5500 Lincoln Dr., Ste. 195, Minneapolis, MN 55436. FAX 612-933-6310.
circ. 60,000. *4153*

NEW JERSEY AVIATION.
Department of Transportation, Division of Aeronautics, 1035 Parkway Ave., CN 600, Trenton, NJ 08625. TEL 609-530-2914. FAX 609-530-5719.
circ. 1,000. *59*

NEW JERSEY SAVINGS LEAGUE NEWS.
New Jersey Savings League, 411 North Ave. E., Cranford, NJ 07016. FAX 908-272-6626. *793*

NEW JERSEY SPEECH AND HEARING ASSOCIATION. JOURNAL.
New Jersey Speech and Hearing Association, c/o Auriemma, 6 Crest Ln., Warren, NJ 07059-5110.
circ. 1,100. *3135*

NEW METHODS.
New Methods Co., Box 22605, San Francisco, CA 94122-0605. TEL 415-664-3469.
circ. 6,000. *4813*

NEW MEXICO. STATE RECORDS CENTER & ARCHIVES. ANNUAL PUBLICATIONS LIST.
State Records Center and Archives, State Rules and Publications Division, 404 Montezuma, Santa Fe, NM 87503. TEL 505-827-8860.
circ. 30. *2329*

NEW ON THE CHARTS.
Music Business Reference, Inc., 70 Laurel Pl., New Rochelle, NY 10801. TEL 914-632-3349. FAX 914-633-7690.
circ. 2,500. *3570*

NEW PAGES.
New Pages Press, Box 438, Grand Blanc, MI 48439. TEL 313-743-8055. FAX 313-743-2730.
circ. 5,000. *4133*

Contr Circ

CONTROLLED CIRCULATION SERIALS

NEW RESOURCES.
South Carolina State Library, 1500 Senate St., Box 11469, Columbia, SC 29211. TEL 803-734-8666. FAX 803-734-8676.
circ. 600. *407*

NEW SOUTH WALES OFFICIAL PUBLICATIONS RECEIVED IN THE STATE LIBRARY OF NEW SOUTH WALES.
State Library of New South Wales, Macquarie St., Sydney, N.S.W. 2000, Australia. TEL 02-230-1425. FAX 02-233-2003.
circ. 280. *407*

NEW TECH TIMES.
New York City Technical College, 300 Jay St, Rm. A310, Brooklyn, NY 11201. *1319*

NEW YORK (STATE). CRIME VICTIMS BOARD. REPORT.
Crime Victims Board, 845 Central Ave., Albany, NY 12206-1588.
circ. 500. *1519*

NEW YORK (STATE) DEPARTMENT OF LABOR. OPERATIONS - EMPLOYMENT SERVICE AND UNEMPLOYMENT INSURANCE.
Department of Labor, Division of Research and Statistics, One Main St., 9th Fl., Brooklyn, NY 11201. TEL 718-797-7703. *989*

NEW YORK (STATE). INSURANCE DEPARTMENT. BULLETIN.
Insurance Department, Research Bureau, 160 W. Broadway, 21st Fl., New York, NY 10013. TEL 212-602-0473. FAX 212-602-0437.
circ. 4,100. *2539*

NEW YORK AUTO REPAIR NEWS.
Van Allen Publishing Co., Box 354, Hicksville, NY 11802. TEL 516-422-5521.
circ. 11,300. *4698*

NEW YORK BODIES.
New York Bodies, 105 Lexington Ave., No. 8B, New York, NY 10016. TEL 212-447-5312.
circ. 50,000. *3807*

NEW YORK BUSINESS SPEAKS.
New York Board of Trade, 1328 Broadway, No.1031-1035, New York, NY 10001. TEL 212-661-6300.
circ. 45,000. *681*

NEW YORK DOCTOR.
Chase Communications Group, Ltd., 25-35 Beechwood Ave., Box 9001, Mt. Vernon, NY 10552-9001. TEL 914-699-2020. FAX 914-664-1503.
circ. 15,000. *3135*

NEW YORK HOLSTEIN NEWS.
Holstein-Friesian World, Inc., 8036 Lake St., Box 299, Sandy Creek, NY 13145. TEL 315-387-3441. FAX 315-387-3655.
circ. 5,900. *202*

NEW YORK STATE BAR JOURNAL.
New York State Bar Association, One Marine Midland Plaza, Binghamton, NY 13902. FAX 607-772-6093.
circ. 59,000. *2660*

NEW YORK STATE URBAN DEVELOPMENT CORPORATION. ANNUAL REPORT.
Urban Development Corporation, 1515 Broadway, New York, NY 10036. TEL 212-930-0305. FAX 212-930-0444. *4068*

NEW ZEALAND. CENTRAL ADVISORY COMMITTEE ON THE APPOINTMENTS AND PROMOTION OF PRIMARY TEACHERS. REPORT TO THE MINISTER OF EDUCATION.
Government Printing Office, c/o Department of Education, Private Bag, Government Buildings, Wellington, New Zealand. *1651*

NEW ZEALAND. HEALTH STATISTICAL SERVICES. CANCER DATA: NEW REGISTRATIONS AND DEATHS.
Health Statistical Services, c/o Josephine Ryan, 133 Molesworth St., P.O. Box 5013, Wellington, New Zealand. TEL 04-496-2000. FAX 04-496-2050. *3178*

NEW ZEALAND. HEALTH STATISTICAL SERVICES. FETAL AND INFANT DEATHS.
Health Statistical Services, c/o Josephine Ryan, 133 Molesworth St., P.O. Box 5013, Wellington, New Zealand. TEL 04-496-2000. FAX 04-496-2050. *3178*

NEW ZEALAND. HEALTH STATISTICAL SERVICES. MENTAL HEALTH DATA.
Health Statistical Services, c/o Josephine Ryan, 133 Molesworth St., P.O. Box 5013, Wellington, New Zealand. TEL 04-496-2000. FAX 04-496-2050. *3178*

NEW ZEALAND. HEALTH STATISTICAL SERVICES. MORTALITY AND DEMOGRAPHIC DATA.
Health Statistical Services, c/o Josephine Ryan, 133 Molesworth St., P.O. Box 5013, Wellington, New Zealand. TEL 04-469-2000. FAX 04-496-2050. *3994*

NEW ZEALAND JOURNAL OF PHYSIOTHERAPY.
New Zealand Society of Physiotherapists (Inc.), P.O. Box 27386, Wellington, New Zealand. FAX 801-5571.
circ. 1,500. *3135*

NEW ZEALAND MARINE SCIENCES SOCIETY NEWSLETTER.
New Zealand Marine Sciences Society, Fisheries Research Centre, P.O. Box 297, Wellington, New Zealand. FAX 04-3861-299.
circ. 300. *449*

NEW ZEALAND PLUMBING REVIEW.
Akron Consolidated Ltd., Box 51-182, Auckland 6, New Zealand.
circ. 1,250. *2301*

NEW ZEALAND R S A REVIEW.
181-183 Willis St., P.O. Box 27-248, Wellington, New Zealand. TEL 04-384-7994. FAX 04-384-7994.
circ. 86,005. *4415*

NEWMEDIA AGE.
HyperMedia Communications, Inc., 901 Mariners Island, Ste. 365, San Mateo, CA 94404. TEL 415-573-5170. FAX 408-773-8309.
circ. 40,000. *1377*

NEWPORT NAVALOG.
Edward A. Sherman Publishing Co., 101 Malbone Rd., Box 420, Newport, RI 02840. FAX 401-849-3300.
circ. 7,200. *3467*

NEWS ABOUT LIBRARY SERVICES FOR THE BLIND AND PHYSICALLY HANDICAPPED.
South Carolina State Library, 1500 Senate St., Box 11469, Columbia, SC 29211. TEL 803-737-9970.
circ. 7,200. *2284*

NEWS ABOUT THE A - V SCENE.
South Carolina State Library, 1500 Senate St., Box 11469, Columbia, SC 29211. TEL 803-734-8666. FAX 803-734-8676.
circ. 125. *3514*

NEWS & VIEWS OF INDEPENDENT EDUCATION.
Society of Assistants Teaching in Preparatory Schools, 7 Fairholme Close, Ashstead, Surrey KT21 2HP, England.
circ. 1,400. *1651*

NEWS CIRCLE.
News Circle Publishing House, Box 3684, Glendale, CA 91201. TEL 818-545-0333. FAX 818-242-5039.
circ. 5,000. *2017*

NEWS FOR SOUTH CAROLINA LIBRARIES.
South Carolina State Library, 1500 Senate St., Box 11469, Columbia, SC 29211. TEL 803-734-8666. FAX 803-734-8676.
circ. 1,800. *2776*

NEWS FROM HOPE COLLEGE.
Hope College, 137 E. 12th St., Holland, MI 49423. TEL 616-394-7860. FAX 616-394-7922.
circ. 55,000. *1319*

NEWSINC.
A S M Communications, Inc. (New York), 49 E. 21st St., New York, NY 10010. TEL 212-529-5500.
circ. 15,000. *4133*

NIEDERSAECHSISCHE GEMEINDE.
Niedersaechsischer Staedte-und Gemeindebund, Seelhorststr. 18, 3000 Hannover, Germany. TEL 0511-280720. FAX 0511-854107.
circ. 12,700. *4092*

NIET ZO BENAUWD.
Stichting Familieclub Johannes van der Linden, Salomeschouw 61, 2726 JP Zoetermeer, Netherlands.
circ. 150. *2159*

NIGERIA INDUSTRIAL DIRECTORY.
Malthouse press ltd., 8 Amore St. (off Toyin St.), P.O. Box 8917, Ikeja, Lagos, Nigeria.
circ. 5,000. *1148*

NIHON DAIGAKU RIKOGAKU KENKYUJO SHOHO.
Nihon Daigaku, Rikogaku Kenkyujo, 1-8 Kanda Surugadai, Chiyoda-ku, Tokyo 101, Japan. *4605*

NIHON SHINSEIJI GAKKAI ZASSHI.
Nihon Shinseiji Gakkai, c/o Nihon University, School of Medicine, Department of Pediatrics, 30-1 Oyaguchi-Kami-machi, Itabashi-ku, Tokyo 173, Japan.
circ. 4,000. *3323*

NIKKEI MEDICAL.
Nikkei Business Publications, Inc., 3-3-23, Misakicho, Chiyoda-ku, Tokyo 101, Japan. TEL 03-5210-8502. FAX 03-5210-8119.
circ. 108,000. *3136*

NIPPON JUI CHIKUSAN DAIGAKU KENKYU HOKOKU.
Nippon Jui Chikusan Daigaku, 1-7-1 Kyonan-cho, Musashino-shi, Tokyo 180, Japan. TEL 422-31-4151. FAX 422-33-2035.
circ. 500. *4813*

NIPPON MEDICAL SCHOOL. JOURNAL.
Nippon Medical School, Medical Association, 1-1-5 Sendagi, Bunkyo-ku, Tokyo 113, Japan. FAX 03-3822-8575.
circ. 2,600. *3136*

NOBEL HEFTE.
Sprengtechnischer Dienst der Dynamit Nobel AG und der Wasagchemie Sythen GmbH, Maerkische Str. 56-58, 4600 Dortmund 1, Germany. FAX 0231-579997. *1857*

THE NOISE.
Wingate Enterprises, Ltd., 443 E. Irving Dr., Box 3204, Burbank, CA 91504. TEL 818-846-0400. FAX 818-841-4380.
circ. 40,000. *1261*

NONPUBLIC SCHOOL ENROLLMENT AND STAFF, NEW YORK STATE.
Education Department, Information Center on Education, Education Bldg. Annex, Rm. 385, Albany, NY 12234. TEL 518-474-8716. *1651*

NORDIC CONTRACT.
N O V A Kommunikation A-S, Solvang 23, P.O. Box 146, DK-3450 Alleroed, Denmark. TEL 42-27-00-78. FAX 42-27-13-05.
circ. 22,000. *2554*

NORDISK TIDSSKRIFT FOR RENSNING OG VASK.
Forlaget Beilin og Johansen ApS, 1, Rosenborggade, DK-1130 Copenhagen, Denmark. TEL 33 15 22 77. FAX 33-15-93-43.
circ. 3,479. *1282*

NORSK FARMACEUTISK TIDSSKRIFT.
Norges Farmaceutiske Forening, Stenersgt. 4, 0184 Oslo 1, Norway. FAX 02-170960.
circ. 2,415. *3736*

NORSK FISKEINDUSTRI.
Fiskerinaeringens Landsforening, P.O. Box 267, 9001 Tromsoe, Norway. FAX 47-8355497.
circ. 1,011. *2046*

NORSK SKIBSFOERERTIDENDE. MASKIN-TIDENDE STYRMANSBLAD.
Norsk Styrmandsforening, P.B. 1936, Vika, 0125 Oslo 1, Norway.
circ. 16,000. *4735*

NORSK SKOLEBLAD.
Norsk Laererlag, Rosenkrantzgt. 15, Oslo 1, Norway. TEL 02-41-58-75. FAX 02-425137.
circ. 58,600. *1651*

NORTH AMERICAN ASSOCIATION OF SUMMER SESSIONS. NEWSLETTER.
North American Association of Summer Sessions, 11728 Summerhaven Dr., St. Louis, MO 63146.
1319

NORTH CAROLINA DENTAL REVIEW.
University of North Carolina, School of Dentistry, Brauer Hall, Rm. 410, CB 7450, Chapel Hill, NC 27599-7450. TEL 919-966-4563. FAX 919-839-8672.
circ. 6,000. *3239*

NORTH CAROLINA MANUAL.
Secretary of State, 300 N. Salisbury St., Raleigh, NC 27603-5909. TEL 919-733-7355.
circ. 5,000. *4069*

NORTH CAROLINA PLUMBING - HEATING - COOLING FORUM.
North Carolina Association of Plumbing - Heating - Cooling Contractors, Inc., 413 Glenwood Ave., Raleigh, NC 27603. TEL 919-833-0372. FAX 919-832-1776.
circ. 4,000. *2302*

NORTH CAROLINA SEED LAW.
Department of Agriculture, Box 27647, Raleigh, NC 27611. TEL 919-733-7125. *111*

NORTH CAROLINA STATE UNIVERSITY. COLLEGE OF FOREST RESOURCES. TECHNICAL REPORT.
North Carolina State University, College of Forest Resources, Raleigh, NC 27695.
circ. 160. *2105*

NORTH CENTRAL JOURNAL OF AGRICULTURAL ECONOMICS.
N C A-12 (North Central Administrative Committee), Department Heads in Agricultural Economics at Land Grant Universities, c/o Department of Agricultural Economics, Michigan State University, East Lansing, MI 48824-1039. TEL 517-353-9172. FAX 517-336-1800.
circ. 600. *155*

NORTH COUNTRY FARM NEWS.
Clinton County Cooperative Extension, RFD 6, Box 1613, Plattsburgh, NY 12901-9601.
circ. 900. *111*

NORTH DAKOTA. JUDICIAL SYSTEM. ANNUAL REPORT.
Judicial System, Office of State Court Administrator, State Capitol, Bismarck, ND 58505. TEL 701-224-4216.
circ. 1,000. *2700*

NORTH DAKOTA FARM RESEARCH.
North Dakota State University, North Dakota Agricultural Experiment Station, State University Sta., Fargo, ND 58102. TEL 701-237-7654. FAX 701-237-7044.
circ. 8,600. *111*

NORTH DAKOTA HUMAN SERVICES.
Department of Human Services, State Capitol, 600 East Blvd., Bismarck, ND 58505. FAX 701-224-2359. *4415*

NORTH DAKOTA'S HIGHWAY SAFETY PLAN.
Department of Transportation, Driver's License and Traffic Safety, Traffic Safety Programs Section, 608 E. Blvd. Ave., Bismarck, ND 58505-0700. TEL 701-224-2600. FAX 701-224-4545.
circ. 150. *4720*

NORTH LOOP NEWS.
North Loop News Corp., 1332 N. Halsted St., No. 204, Chicago, IL 60622-2632. TEL 312-787-5396. FAX 312-787-1616.
circ. 24,700. *2231*

NORTH TEXAS GOLFER.
Golfer Magazines, Inc., 9182 Old Katy Rd., Ste. 212, Houston, TX 77055. TEL 713-464-0308. FAX 713-464-0129.
circ. 28,000. *4509*

NORTH WIND.
Northern Michigan University, Marquette, MI 49855. TEL 906-227-2545. *1319*

NORTH YORK BUSINESS AGE.
Toronto Business Age Inc., 146 Laird Dr., Ste. 106, Toronto, Ont. M4G 3V7, Canada. TEL 416-467-4778. FAX 416-467-4778.
circ. 7,000. *682*

NORTHERN LIGHTS MAGAZINE.
Northern Lights Magazine, 106 Vernon St., Box 728, Angus, Ont. LOM 1B0, Canada. TEL 705-737-3128. FAX 705-721-0933.
circ. 67,800. *2178*

NORTHERN NEW ENGLAND REAL ESTATE JOURNAL.
Brian P. Heneghan, 57 Washington St., Norwell, MA 02061. TEL 800-654-4993. FAX 617-871-1853.
4154

NORTHERN NEW ENGLAND REVIEW.
Franklin Pierce College, Box 825, Rindge, NH 03461. TEL 603-899-5111.
circ. 600. *2943*

NORTHWEST ASSOCIATION OF SCHOOLS AND COLLEGES. CONVENTION PROCEEDINGS.
Northwest Association of Schools and Colleges, Boise State University, Ed.528, Boise, ID 83725. TEL 208-385-1596. *1713*

NORTHWEST ASSOCIATION OF SCHOOLS AND COLLEGES. NEWSLETTER.
Northwest Association of Schools and Colleges, Boise State University, Boise, ID 83725. TEL 208-385-1596. *1651*

NORTHWEST PASSAGES.
Northwest Airlines, Inc., 5101 Northwest Dr., St. Paul, MN 55111-3034. TEL 612-726-7357.
circ. 58,000. *4676*

NORTHWESTERN UNIVERSITY. MATERIALS RESEARCH CENTER. ANNUAL TECHNICAL REPORT.
Northwestern University, Materials Research Center, 2145 Sheridan Rd., Evanston, IL 60208-3116. TEL 708-491-3116. FAX 312-491-4133. *1921*

NORWEGIAN OFFSHORE INDEX.
Selvig Publishing A-S, Box 9070 Vaterland, 0134 Oslo 1, Norway. TEL 02-364440. FAX 02-360550.
3706

NOS MAISONS FAMILIALES DE VACANCES.
Federation des Maisons Familiales de Vacances, 28 place St-Georges, 75442 Paris 9, France. *4780*

NOTI S A I.
Sociedad Antioquena de Ingenieros y Arquitectos, Calle 71, No. 65-100, Apdo. Aereo 4754, Medellin, Colombia. TEL 257-3900. FAX 255-4584.
circ. 2,500. *1832*

NOTICIAS (NEW YORK).
National Foreign Trade Council, Inc., 1270 Ave. of the Americas, New York, NY 10020. TEL 212-399-7128. FAX 212-399-7144. *918*

NOUVEAU COMMERCE.
A C N C Nouveau Commerce, Librarie Anima, 3 rue Ravignan, 75018 Paris, France. TEL 1-42-64-05-25.
circ. 1,000. *2944*

NOUVEAU GLOSSAIRE NAUTIQUE D'AUGUSTIN JAL.
Editions du C N R S, 1 Place Aristide Briand, 92195 Meudon Cedex, France. TEL 1-45-34-75-50. FAX 1-46-26-28-49.
circ. 1,250. *1609*

NOVA SCOTIA. DEPARTMENT OF ECONOMIC DEVELOPMENT. ANNUAL REPORT.
Department of Industry, Trade and Technology, P.O. Box 519, Halifax, N.S. B3J 2R7, Canada. TEL 902-424-8920. FAX 902-424-5739.
circ. 300. *4069*

NOVAS DE ALEGRIA.
Casa Publicadora das Assembleias de Deus, Av. Alm. Gago Coutinho 158, 1700 Lisbon, Portugal.
circ. 20,000. *4286*

NUCLEAR INDIA.
Department of Atomic Energy, Publications Officer, Chhatrapati Shivaji Maharaj Marg, Bombay 400039, India.
circ. 5,000. *1807*

NUCLEAR INDUSTRY.
U.S. Council for Energy Awareness, 1776 Eye St., N.W., Ste. 400, Washington, DC 20006-3708.
circ. 10,000. *1807*

NUEVA LENTE.
Miguel J. Goni Fernandez, Ed. & Pub., Ardemans 64, Madrid, Spain.
circ. 10,000. *3793*

NUEVO TIEMPO HISPANO.
Impacto Publications Inc., 933 Crandon Blvd., Miami, FL 33149-2753. TEL 305-371-7309.
circ. 100,000. *2018*

NUMAGA.
Vereniging Numaga, P.O. Box 1359, 6501 BJ Nijmegen, Netherlands.
circ. 1,300. *2378*

NUMBER ONE.
Volunteer State Community College, Humanities Division, Nashville Pike, Gallatin, TN 37066. TEL 615-452-8600.
circ. 1,000. *2999*

NUORTEN SARKA.
Suomen·4H-Liitto, Bulevardi 28, 00120 Helsinki 12, Finland. TEL 0-645133.
circ. 30,500. *111*

NURSCENE.
Manitoba Association of Registered Nurses, 647 Broadway, Winnipeg, Man. R3C 0X2, Canada. TEL 204-774-3477. FAX 204-775-6052.
circ. 11,000. *3283*

NURSERY BUSINESS.
Brantwood Publications, Inc., 3023 Eastland Blvd., Ste. 103, Clearwater, FL 34621-4106. TEL 813-796-3877.
circ. 18,000. *2135*

NURSING (YEAR) CAREER DIRECTORY.
Springhouse Corporation, 1111 Bethlehem Pike, Springhouse, PA 19477. TEL 215-646-8700.
circ. 125,000. *1148*

NURSING MANAGEMENT.
S - N Publications, Inc., 103 N. Second St., Ste. 200, W. Dundee, IL 60118. TEL 708-426-6100. FAX 708-426-6146.
circ. 135,000. *3284*

NURSING QUEBEC.
Order of Nurses of Quebec, 4200 Dorchester Blvd. W., Montreal, Que. H3Z 1V4, Canada. TEL 514-935-2501. FAX 514-935-1799.
circ. 61,803. *3284*

NUSLECA.
Nusleca Publications, Shripney Works, Bognor Regis, W. Sussex PO22 9NQ, England. FAX 0243-868052.
circ. 5,000. *2302*

NUTRITION FORUM.
Canadian Society for Nutritional Sciences, Department of Foods and Nutrition, University of Manitoba, Winnipeg, Man. R3T 2N2, Canada. TEL 613-993-4484. *3610*

NUTRITION NEWS IN ZAMBIA.
National Food and Nutrition Commission, P.O. Box 32669, Lusaka, Zambia.
circ. 5,000. *2078*

NUTSHELL.
Shell South Africa (Pty) Ltd., P.O. Box 2231, Cape Town 8000, South Africa. TEL 021-408-4911. FAX 021-253807.
circ. 7,500. *3694*

NUTZFAHRZEUG.
Heinrich Vogel Fachzeitschriften GmbH, Neumarkter Str. 18, Postfach 802020, 8000 Munich 80, Germany. TEL 089-43180-0.
circ. 5,371. *4747*

NUX.
University of Natal, Students Representative Council, Box 375, Pietermaritzburg, Natal, South Africa.
circ. 2,500. *1319*

NWY NEWS.
British Gas Wales, Public Relations Dept., Helmont House, Churchill Way, Cardiff CF1 4NB, Wales. TEL 0222-239290. FAX 0222-290738.
circ. 6,300. *3694*

O.A.N. DIGGER.
Oregon Association of Nurserymen, 2780 S.E. Harrison, Ste. 102, Milwaukie, OR 97222. TEL 503-653-8723. FAX 503-653-1528.
circ. 4,000. *2136*

O C D DIAMOND.
American Cyanamid Co., Organic Chemical Division, Bound Brook, NJ 08805. TEL 201-831-2000.
circ. 6,500. *4605*

O E M DESIGN.
A G B Publications Ltd., Audit House, Field End Rd., Ruislip, Middx. HA4 9LT, England. TEL 01-868-4499.
circ. 30,500. *1832*

O P M A OVERSEAS MEDIA GUIDE.
Overseas Press and Media Association, c/o Sinclairs, 32 Queen Anne St., London W1M 9LB, England.
circ. 5,000. *1149*

O P T I M A NEWSLETTER.
Organization for the Phyto-Taxonomic Investigation of the Mediterranean Area, Koenigin-Luise-Str. 6-8, 1000 Berlin 33, Germany. FAX 030-83006218.
circ. 740. *512*

O S L A NEWSLETTER.
Ontario Association of Speech - Language Pathologists and Audiologists, 410 Jarvis St., Toronto, Ont. M4Y 2G6, Canada. TEL 416-920-3676. FAX 416-920-6214.
circ. 1,500. *2288*

O S M T UPDATE.
Ontario Society of Medical Technologists, 234 Eglinton Ave. E., Ste. 600, Toronto, Ont. M4P 1K5, Canada.
circ. 5,180. *3262*

O W N.
B U S Publications, 99 Jericho Tpke., Jericho, NY 11753. TEL 516-997-7740.
circ. 30,000. *1060*

OAKLAND UNIVERSITY MAGAZINE.
Oakland University, Publications Department, 109 N. Foundation Hall, Rochester, MI 48309-4401. TEL 313-370-3184. FAX 313-370-4249.
circ. 32,000. *1319*

OB G MANAGEMENT.
Dowden Publishing Company, 110 Summit Ave., Montvale, NJ 07645. TEL 201-391-9100. FAX 201-391-2778.
circ. 31,000. *3295*

OB-GYN NEWS.
International Medical News Group, 12230 Wilkins Ave., Rockville, MD 20852. TEL 301-770-6170.
circ. 30,450. *3295*

OBLATES.
Missionary Association of Mary Immaculate, 15 S. 59th St., Belleville, IL 62223-4694. TEL 618-233-2238.
circ. 600,000. *4193*

OCCASIONAL PAPERS IN ENTOMOLOGY.
Department of Food and Agriculture, Division of Plant Industry, 1220 N St., Sacramento, CA 95814. TEL 916-445-5421.
circ. 200. *536*

OCCUPATIONAL HAZARDS.
Penton Publishing 1100 Superior Ave., Cleveland, OH 44114-2543. TEL 216-696-7000. FAX 216-696-8765.
circ. 60,000. *3619*

OCEAN VOICE.
International Maritime Satellite Organization, 40 Melton St., London NW1 2EQ, England. TEL 01-387-9089. FAX 01-387-6703.
circ. 18,684. *4735*

OCEANOGRAPHIC RESEARCH INSTITUTE. INVESTIGATIONAL REPORT.
Oceanographic Research Institute, P.O. Box 10712, Marine Parade, Durban 4056, South Africa. TEL 031-373536. FAX 031-372132.
circ. 400. *590*

OESTERREICHISCHE BAUERNZEITUNG.
Baeuerlicher Presseverein, Castellezgasse 20-1, A-1020 Vienna, Austria.
circ. 16,000. *112*

OESTERREICHISCHE INSTALLATEURZEITUNG.
Verlag Piletzky, Nikolsdorfer Gasse 7, 1050 Vienna, Austria.
circ. 4,600. *2302*

OESTERREICHISCHES JUGENDROTKREUZ. ARBEITSBLAETTER.
Oesterreichisches Jugendrotkreuz, Wiedner Hauptstr. 32, A-1041 Vienna 4, Austria. FAX 0222-58900179.
circ. 10,000. *4415*

OESTERREICHISCHES STAATSARCHIV. MITTEILUNGEN.
Verlag Ferdinand Berger und Soehne GmbH, Wienerstr. 21-23, A-3580 Horn, Austria. TEL 02982-2317-0.
circ. 500. *2379*

OFFICE EQUIPMENT NEWS.
A G B Publications Ltd., Audit House, Field End Rd., Ruislip, Middx. HA4 9LT, England. TEL 01-868-4499. FAX 01-429-3117.
circ. 55,236. *1060*

OFFICE MAGAZINE.
Patey Doyle (Publishing) Ltd., Wilmington House, Church Hill, Wilmington, Dartford DA2 7EF, England.
circ. 55,000. *1060*

OFFICE PRODUCT NEWS.
Southam Business Communications Inc. 1450 Don Mills Rd., Don Mills, Ont. M3B 2X7, Canada. TEL 416-445-6641.
circ. 44,000. *1022*

OFFICIAL VISITORS GUIDE TO CENTRAL FLORIDA.
Orlando - Orange County Convention and Visitors Bureau, Inc., 7208 Sandlake Rd., Ste. 300, Orlando, FL 32819. TEL 407-363-5800.
circ. 1,000,000. *4781*

OFFICIAL WISCONSIN PASTORAL HANDBOOK.
Milwaukee Catholic Press Apostolate, 3501 S. Lake Dr., Box 07913, Milwaukee, WI 53207-7913. TEL 414-769-3472.
circ. 2,300. *4271*

OFFROAD AMERICA.
R A V Publishing Group, 7140 Beneva Rd. No. D, Sarasota, FL 34238-2804. TEL 813-921-5687. *4482*

OHIO BEVERAGE JOURNAL.
Midwest Beverage Publications, Inc., 3 12th St., Wheeling, WV 26003. TEL 304-232-7620. FAX 304-233-1236.
circ. 7,125. *384*

OHIO CONTRACTOR.
Triad, Inc., 6525 Busch Blvd., Columbus, OH 43229. TEL 614-846-8761. FAX 614-846-8763.
circ. 5,500. *627*

OHIO DENTAL JOURNAL.
Ohio Dental Association, 1370 Dublin Rd., Columbus, OH 43215-1098. TEL 614-486-2700.
circ. 5,300. *3239*

OHIO ENGINEERING.
Ohio Society of Professional Engineers, 445 King Ave., Columbus, OH 43201. TEL 614-424-6640.
circ. 4,000. *1832*

OHIO GRANGER.
Ohio State Grange, 1031 E. Broad St., Columbus, OH 43205. TEL 614-258-9569.
circ. 20,000. *112*

OHIO NURSES REVIEW.
Ohio Nurses Association, 4000 E. Main St., Columbus, OH 43213-2950. TEL 614-237-5414.
circ. 8,500. *3285*

OHIO SOURCEBOOK (YEAR).
Alexander Communications, Inc., 212 W. Superior, Ste. 203, Chicago, IL 60610. TEL 312-944-5115. FAX 312-944-7865.
circ. 6,200. *4003*

OHIO STATE UNIVERSITY. COLLEGE OF MEDICINE. JOURNAL.
Ohio State University, College of Medicine, 941 Chatham Ln., Columbus, OH 43221. TEL 614-459-3909. FAX 614-293-3666.
circ. 13,700. *3137*

OHIO STATE UNIVERSITY. SCHOOL OF PUBLIC ADMINISTRATION. WORKING PAPER SERIES.
Ohio State University, Administrative Science Research, 1775 College Rd., Columbus, OH 42310. TEL 614-422-8696. *4069*

OIL, GAS & PETROCHEM EQUIPMENT.
PennWell Publishing Co., Box 1260, Tulsa, OK 74101. TEL 918-835-3161.
circ. 36,000. *3696*

OIL MARKETER.
Oklahoma Oil Marketers Association, 5115 N. Western, Oklahoma City, OK 73118. TEL 405-842-6625. FAX 405-842-9564.
circ. 1,300. *3696*

OKANAGAN BUSINESS MAGAZINE.
Okanagan Life Publishing, Box 1479, Sta. A, Kelowna, B.C. V1Y 7V8, Canada. TEL 604-768-4442. FAX 604-764-8255.
circ. 10,170. *683*

OKLAHOMA. CONSERVATION COMMISSION. BIENNIAL REPORT.
Conservation Commission, 2800 Lincoln, Ste. 160, Oklahoma City, OK 73105. TEL 405-521-2384.
circ. 175. *1494*

OKLAHOMA DAILY.
University of Oklahoma, Student Publication Board, 860 Van Vleet, Norman, OK 73019. TEL 405-325-2521. FAX 405-325-7565.
circ. 14,500. *1320*

OKLAHOMA FARM BUREAU JOURNAL.
Shawnee News-Star, 2501 N. Stiles, Oklahoma City, OK 73105. TEL 405-273-4200. FAX 405-523-2439.
circ. 82,000. *112*

OKLAHOMA SCHOOL BOARD JOURNAL.
Oklahoma State School Boards Association, 2801 N. Lincoln Blvd., Oklahoma City, OK 73105. TEL 405-528-3571. FAX 405-528-5695.
circ. 4,600. *1652*

OLD BEN NEWS.
Newsvendors' Benevolent Institution, P.O. Box 306, Dunmow, Essex CM6 1HY, England.
circ. 46,000. *838*

OLD COURTHOUSE NEWS.
Northern Indiana Historical Society, 808 W. Washington, S. Bend, IN 46601. TEL 219-284-9664. *2417*

OLD OREGON.
University of Oregon, 101 Chapman Hall, Eugene, OR 97403. FAX 503-346-2537.
circ. 90,000. *1320*

OLD YORK ROAD HISTORICAL SOCIETY BULLETIN.
Old York Road Historical Society, c/o Jenkintown Library, York and Vista Rds., Jenkintown, PA 19046. TEL 215-884-0593.
circ. 265. *2417*

OMNIBUS (PISCATAWAY).
Publishing Management Group, Inc., 1711 S. Second St., Piscataway, NJ 08854. TEL 908-753-6100.
circ. 50,000. *2231*

OMNIBUS-REVUE UND BUS AKTUELL.
Heinrich Vogel Fachzeitschriften GmbH, Neumarkter Str. 18, Postfach 802020, 8000 Munich 80, Germany. TEL 089-43180-0.
circ. 6,300. *4699*

ON COURT.
Fourhand II, Inc., 1200 Sheppard Ave. E., Ste. 400, Willowdale, Ont. M2K 2S5, Canada. TEL 416-497-1370. FAX 416-494-5343.
circ. 50,000. *4509*

ONLINE KONTAKT.
Ustredi Vedeckych, Technickych a Ekonomickych Informaci (UVTEI), Konviktska 5, 113 57 Prague 1, Czechoslovakia. TEL 42-2-235-69. FAX 42-2-264775. *1399*

ONSEI GENGO IGAKU.
Nihon Onsei Gengo Igakkai, c/o Research Institute of Logopedics and Phoniatrics, Faculty of Medicine, University of Tokyo, 7-3-1 Hongo, Bunkyo-ku, Tokyo 113, Japan. FAX 03-813-2739.
circ. 1,507. *3316*

ONTARIO. MINISTRY OF THE ENVIRONMENT. INDUSTRIAL WASTE CONFERENCE. PROCEEDINGS.
Ministry of the Environment, Water Resources Branch, 1 St. Clair Ave., 4th Fl., Toronto, Ont. M4V 1K6, Canada. TEL 416-965-6141. *1986*

ONTARIO GOLF NEWS.
Ontario Golf News Inc., 2 Billingham Rd., Ste. 400, Toronto, Ont. M9B 6E1, Canada. TEL 416-232-2380.
circ. 40,000. *4509*

ONTARIO'S COMMON GROUND MAGAZINE.
320 Danforth Ave., Ste.204, Toronto, Ont. M4K 1P3, Canada. TEL 416-463-6677.
circ. 39,000. *3596*

OPEN DEUR.
Boekencentrum B.V., Box 84176, The Hague, Netherlands. *4245*

OPERATIONS EXCHANGE.
Credit Union Executives Society, Box 14167, Madison, WI 53714-0167. TEL 608-271-2664. FAX 608-271-2303.
circ. 500. *794*

OPERNWELT.
Orell Fuessli & Friedrich Verlag, Dietzingerstr. 3, CH-8036 Zurich, Switzerland. TEL 041-4667711. FAX 041-4667457.
circ. 10,000. *3572*

OPINION.
Opinion Publications, Box 254, E. Machias, ME 04630.
circ. 3,700. *3774*

OPPORTUNITIES BRIEFING.
International Freedom Foundation, 200 G St., N.E., Ste. 300, Washington, DC 20002. TEL 202-546-5788. FAX 202-546-5488.
circ. 400. *918*

OPPORTUNITIES IN OPTIONS.
Box 2126, Malibu, CA 90265. TEL 213-457-3199. FAX 213-457-5621.
circ. 2,500. *959*

OPPORTUNITY MAGAZINE.
Opportunity Associates, 73 Spring St., New York, NY 10012. *1049*

OPTICAL PRISM.
VezCom Inc., 31 Hastings Dr., Unionville, Ont. L3R 4Y5, Canada. FAX 416-477-2821.
circ. 7,964. *3303*

OPTIMUM.
Canada Communication Group, Publishing Division, Ottawa, Ont. K1A 0S9, Canada. TEL 819-956-4802.
circ. 1,200. *1023*

OPTIONS (WASHINGTON).
Center for Population Options, 1025 Vermont Ave., N.W., Ste. 210, Washington, DC 20005. TEL 202-347-5700. FAX 202-347-2263.
circ. 5,000. *3985*

OPUS DEI AWARENESS NETWORK.
Opus Dei Awareness Network, Box 4333, Pittsfield, MA 01202. TEL 413-499-7168. *4271*

ORAL HISTORY ASSOCIATION. NEWSLETTER.
Oral History Association, 1093 Broxton Ave., No. 720, Los Angeles, CA 90024. TEL 213-825-0597.
circ. 1,400. *2319*

ORANGE FREE STATE. DIRECTOR OF HOSPITAL SERVICES. REPORT.
Director of Hospital Services, PO Box 517, Bloemfontein 9300, South Africa. *2468*

ORANGE SEED TECHNICAL BULLETIN.
Department of State, Division of Library and Information Services, R.A. Gray Bldg., Tallahassee, FL 32399-0250. TEL 904-487-2651.
circ. 500. *2778*

OREGON PSYCHOLOGY.
Oregon Psychological Association, 1750 S.W. Skyline Blvd., No. 12, Portland, OR 97221.
circ. 700. *4037*

OREGON PURCHASOR.
Purchasing Management Association of Oregon, c/o Decorators West, Box 25191, Portland, OR 97225-0191. TEL 503-245-2296.
circ. 2,200. *1049*

ORGAN CLUB JOURNAL.
Organ Club, c/o Philip Weston, Gen. Sec., 36 Fortismere Ave., London N10 3BL, England. *3572*

ORGANIC CONSUMER REPORT.
Eden Ranch, Box 370, Topanga, CA 90290. TEL 213-455-2065. *3611*

ORIENTAL RUG.
Oriental Rug Importers Association of America, 15 E. 30th St., No.4-W, New York, NY 10016. *2561*

THE ORIGINAL AIRPORT NEWS.
Airport News, 7040 Torbram Rd., Unit 4, Mississauga, Ont. L4T 3Z4, Canada. TEL 416-672-0206. FAX 416-672-0244.
circ. 20,000. *4676*

ORITA.
University of Ibadan, Department of Religious Studies, Ibadan, Nigeria.
circ. 500. *4194*

ORLEANS PARISH MEDICAL SOCIETY. BULLETIN.
Orleans Parish Medical Society, 1800 Canal St., New Orleans, LA 70112. TEL 504-523-2474.
circ. 2,019. *3138*

ORNIS FENNICA.
Finnish Ornithological Society, University of Helsinki, Department of Zoology, P. Rautatiekatu 13, SF-00100 Helsinki, Finland. TEL 358-0-1917405. FAX 358-0-1917443.
circ. 1,260. *566*

OSMANIA UNIVERSITY. DEPARTMENT OF PSYCHOLOGY. RESEARCH BULLETIN.
Osmania University, Department of Psychology, Hyderabad 500007, Andhra Pradesh, India. *4037*

THE OSWEGONIAN.
State University of New York, Oswego, 216 Hewitt Union, Oswego, NY 13126. TEL 315-341-3600.
circ. 7,500. *1320*

OTTERBEIN MISCELLANY.
Otterbein College, Westerville, OH 43081. TEL 614-890-3000.
circ. 300. *2878*

OUR HERITAGE.
Genealogical Society of Van Zandt County, Box 716, Canton, TX 75103-0716.
circ. 300. *2161*

OUR VOICE.
American Mutual Life Association, 19424 S. Waterloo Rd., Cleveland, OH 44119-3250.
circ. 8,500. *2539*

OUT AND ABOUT SMITH MOUNTAIN LAKE.
Rte. 1, Box 437, Moneta, VA 24121. TEL 703-297-6444.
circ. 40,000. *4781*

OUTERWEAR.
Fur Publishing Plus, Inc., 19 W. 21st St., Ste. 403, New York, NY 10010. TEL 212-727-1210.
circ. 13,500. *1287*

OUTLOOK (WAKE FOREST).
Southeastern Baptist Theological Seminary, Inc., Wake Forest, NC 27587. TEL 919-556-3101. FAX 919-556-3101.
circ. 10,000. *4246*

OVERSEAS BUSINESS.
Cara Communications Ltd., 100 Court Ave., Ste. 206, Des Moines, IA 50309-2200. TEL 515-282-2888.
circ. 20,000. *919*

OXFORDSHIRE LOCAL HISTORY.
Oxfordshire Local History Association, The Registry, Oxford Polytechnic, Headington, Oxford OX3 0BP, England. FAX 0865-819073.
circ. 300. *2379*

P & S A NEWS.
Sema Publications, Box 4910, Diamond Bar, CA 91765-0910. TEL 714-860-2961. FAX 714-860-1709.
circ. 35,000. *4699*

P C DISTRIBUTOR.
Empresar Editores Ltda., Carrera 11, No. 94-02, L-123, Bogota, Colombia. TEL 2182730. FAX 610-1958.
circ. 5,000. *1472*

P C MAGAZINE (ITALY).
Gruppo Editoriale Jackson S.p.A., Via Pola 9, 20124 Milan, Italy. TEL 39-2-6948309. FAX 39-2-6948290.
circ. 35,105. *1472*

P C REPORT.
Boston Computer Society, IBM PC Users Group, 188 Needham St., Newton, MA 02164. TEL 617-332-5584.
circ. 16,000. *1472*

P C SPECIAL MONTHLY.
Interface Electronic Publisher, Flat 8, 13th Fl., Yeung Yiu Chung no.8, Ind. Bldg., 20 Wang Hoi Rd., Kowloon Bay, Kowloon, Hong Kong. TEL 3-7955582. FAX 3-7952962. *1472*

P C WEEK.
Ziff-Davis Publishing Co., 10 Presidents Landing, Medford, MA 02155-5146. TEL 617-393-3000.
circ. 128,277. *1473*

P.E.I. COMMUNITY STUDIES.
University of Prince Edward Island, Department of Sociology and Anthropology, Charlottetown, P.E.I. C1A 4P3, Canada. *4444*

P G W NEWSLINE.
Philadelphia Gas Works, 800 W. Montgomery Ave., Philadelphia, PA 19122. TEL 215-684-6564.
circ. 4,500. *3697*

P I M A MAGAZINE.
Paper Industry Management Association, 2400 E. Oakton St., Arlington Heights, IL 60005. TEL 708-956-0250. FAX 708-956-0520.
circ. 19,357. *3663*

P O B - POINT OF BEGINNING.
P O B Publishing Co., 5820 Lilley Rd., No.5, Canton, MI 48187. TEL 313-981-4600. FAX 313-981-0048.
circ. 60,000. *1872*

P P O UPDATE.
J.B. Lippincott Co., E. Washington Sq., Philadelphia, PA 19105. TEL 215-238-4200. FAX 215-238-4228.
circ. 25,000. *3201*

P S.
Editorial Perpetuo Socorro, Covarrubias, 19, Madrid-10, Spain.
circ. 14,000. *4194*

P T DISTRIBUTOR.
Penton Publishing 1100 Superior Ave., Cleveland, OH 44114-2543. TEL 216-696-7000. FAX 216-696-8765.
circ. 10,000. *1937*

P T I C BULLETIN.
Patent and Trademark Institute of Canada, Box 1298, Sta. B, Ottawa, Ont. K1P 5R3, Canada. TEL 613-234-0516. *3677*

P T N MASTER BUYING GUIDE & DIRECTORY.
P T N Publishing Corp., 445 Broad Hollow Rd., Ste. 21, Melville, NY 11747-4722. TEL 516-845-2700. FAX 516-845-7109.
circ. 10,000. *3794*

P T S NEWS.
Philatelic Traders Society Ltd., British Philatelic Centre, 107, Charterhouse St., London EC1M 6PT, England. TEL 071-490-1005. FAX 071-253-0414. *3755*

PACIFIC FORESTS.
Pacific Logging Congress, 2300 S.W. Sixth Ave., Ste. 200, Portland, OR 97201. TEL 503-224-8406. FAX 502-224-8406.
circ. 8,500. *2106*

PACIFIC HOSTELLER.
Canadian Hostelling Association, B.C. Region, 1515 Discovery St., Vancouver, B.C. V6R 4K5, Canada. TEL 604-224-7177. FAX 604-224-4852.
circ. 10,000. *4781*

PACKAGING NEWS.
Yaffa Publishing Group, 17-21 Bellevue St., Surry Hills, N.S.W. 2010, Australia. TEL 02-281-2333. FAX 02-281-2750.
circ. 5,524. *3650*

PADOVA ECONOMICA.
Camera di Commercio, Industria, Artigianato e Agricoltura di Padova, Via E. Filiberto 34, Padua, Italy.
circ. 2,000. *821*

PAGINAS DE CONTENIDO. ECONOMIA AGRICOLA Y DESARROLLO RURAL.
Centro Internacional de Agricultura Tropical, Publications Unit, Apdo. Aereo 6713, Cali, Colombia.
circ. 384. *141*

PAGINAS DE CONTENIDO. FISIOLOGIA VEGETAL.
Centro Internacional de Agricultura Tropical, Publications Unit, Apdo. Aereo 6713, Cali, Colombia.
circ. 333. *141*

PAGINAS DE CONTENIDO. PASTOS, PRODUCCION ANIMAL Y NUTRICION.
Centro Internacional de Agricultura Tropical, Publications Unit, Apdo. Aereo. 6713, Cali, Colombia.
circ. 363. *141*

PAGINAS DE CONTENIDO. PROTECCION DE PLANTAS.
Centro Internacional de Agricultura Tropical, Publications Unit, Apdo. Aereo 6713, Cali, Colombia.
circ. 474. *141*

PAGINAS DE CONTENIDO. SUELOS Y NUTRICION DE PLANTAS.
Centro Internacional de Agricultura Tropical, Information Unit, Apdo. Aereo 6713, Cali, Colombia.
circ. 215. *141*

PAINT & COATINGS INDUSTRY.
Business News Publishing, Co., Box 2600, Troy, MI 48007. TEL 313-362-3700. FAX 313-362-0317.
circ. 17,050. *3654*

PAKISTAN. FINANCE DIVISION. SUPPLEMENTARY DEMANDS FOR GRANTS AND APPROPRIATIONS.
Finance Division, Islamabad, Pakistan. *1103*

PAKISTAN. OFFICE OF THE ECONOMIC ADVISER. GOVERNMENT SPONSORED CORPORATIONS AND OTHER INSTITUTIONS.
Office of the Economic Adviser, Islamabad, Pakistan. *1082*

PAKISTAN. SURVEY OF PAKISTAN. GENERAL REPORT.
Survey of Pakistan, Office of the Director Map Publication, P.O. Box 10, Rawalpindi, Pakistan. *2341*

PAKISTAN JOURNAL OF BOTANY.
Pakistan Botanical Society, Dept. of Botany, University of Karachi, Karachi 75270, Pakistan. FAX 21-466896. *512*

PAKISTAN MANAGEMENT REVIEW.
Pakistan Institute of Management, Shahrah-Iran, Clifton, Karachi 6, Pakistan.
circ. 2,000. *1024*

PALAESTRA.
Via Tiglio S. Biagio, Maddaloni 81024, Italy.
circ. 1,000. *2946*

PALEORIENT.
Editions du C N R S, 1 Place Aristide Briand, 92195 Meudon Cedex, France. TEL 1-45-34-75-50. FAX 1-46-26-28-49.
circ. 1,500. *3660*

PALMER VIDEO MAGAZINE.
Palmer Video Corp., 1767 Morris Ave., Union, NJ 07083. TEL 908-686-3030. FAX 908-686-2151.
circ. 203,915. *1386*

PALMETTO.
Florida Native Plant Society, Box 680008, Orlando, FL 32868. TEL 407-229-1472.
circ. 2,000. *2136*

PAPER AGE.
Global Publications, 400 Old Hook Rd., Ste. G6, Westwood, NJ 07675. TEL 201-666-2262. FAX 201-666-9046.
circ. 31,400. *3664*

PAPER, FILM AND FOIL CONVERTER.
Maclean Hunter Publishing Company, 29 N. Wacker Dr., Chicago, IL 60606. TEL 312-726-2802. FAX 312-726-2574.
circ. 40,220. *3651*

PAPERWORLD.
6 Piedmont Center, Ste. 300, Atlanta, GA 30305. TEL 404-841-3333. FAX 404-841-3332.
circ. 40,000. *3664*

PAPUA NEW GUINEA NATIONAL BIBLIOGRAPHY.
Papua New Guinea National Library Service, P.O. Box 5770, Boroko, N.C.D., Papua New Guinea. FAX 675-254648.
circ. 280. *409*

PARABAS.
21-B, Quarter-6D, Chittaranjan, West Bengal, India. *2878*

PARAPHARMEX.
Societe d'Editions Medico-Pharmaceutiques (SEMP), 26 rue le Brun, 75013 Paris, France. TEL 1-43-37-83-50. FAX 43-31-94-11.
circ. 9,000. *3737*

PARISH AND COMMUNITY LIBRARIES NEWS.
Catholic Library Association, Parish Section, Box 16321, St. Paul, MN 55116. FAX 612-690-2131.
circ. 350. *2778*

PAROISSES ET COMMUNES DE FRANCE.
Editions du C N R S, 1 Place Aristide Briand, 92195 Meudon Cedex, France. TEL 1-45-34-75-50. FAX 1-46-26-28-49.
circ. 1,500. *2380*

PARTICIPATION.
International Political Science Association, c/o University of Oslo, Institute of Political Science, Box 1097 Blindern, 0317 Oslo 3, Norway. TEL 02-455168. *3914*

PASTE-UP.
Cedar Rapids Stamp Club, Box 2554, Cedar Rapids, IA 52406.
circ. 50. *3755*

PATENT AND TRADEMARK INSTITUTE OF CANADA. ANNUAL PROCEEDINGS.
Patent and Trademark Institute of Canada, Box 1298, Sta. B, Ottawa, Ont. K1P 5R3, Canada. TEL 613-234-0516. *3677*

PATHWAYS TO HEALTH.
A.R.E. Medical Clinic, 4018 N. 40th St., Phoenix, AZ 85018. TEL 602-955-0551.
circ. 3,500. *3775*

PATNA JOURNAL OF MEDICINE.
Indian Medical Association, Bihar State Branch, Medical Association Bldg., Patna 800004, India. TEL 55295.
circ. 6,500. *3140*

PATRIOT.
Runaway Publications, Box 1172, Ashland, OR 97520-0040. TEL 503-482-2578.
circ. 100. *3000*

PAVEMENT MAINTENANCE.
Aberdeen Group, 426 S. Westgate, Addison, IL 60101. TEL 708-543-0870. FAX 708-543-3112. *1872*

PEABODY NEWS.
Johns Hopkins University, Peabody Institute, 1 E. Mt. Vernon Place, Baltimore, MD 21202. TEL 301-659-8163. FAX 301-659-8168.
circ. 35,000. *1321*

PEACE & SECURITY.
Canadian Institute for International Peace and Security, 360 Albert St., Ste. 900, Ottawa, Ont. K1R 7X7, Canada. TEL 613-990-1593. FAX 613-563-0894.
circ. 9,000. *3968*

PEACE CORPS TIMES.
U.S. Peace Corps, 1990 K St., N.W., Washington, DC 20526. TEL 202-254-3371. FAX 202-606-3110.
circ. 19,000. *934*

PEACE GAZETTE.
Mount Diablo Peace Center, 65 Eckley Lane, Walnut Creek, CA 94596.
circ. 2,500. *3914*

PEANUT FARMER.
Specialized Agricultural Publications, Inc., 3000 Highwoods Blvd., Ste. 300, Box 95075, Raleigh, NC 27625. TEL 919-872-5040. FAX 919-872-6531.
circ. 20,000. *187*

PEANUT GROWER.
Vance Publishing Corp., Box 83, Tifton, GA 31793. TEL 912-386-8591. FAX 912-386-9772.
circ. 28,000. *187*

PEARLS OF WISDOM.
Summit Lighthouse, Box A, Livingston, MT 59047-1390. TEL 406-222-8300. FAX 406-222-8307. *3775*

PEAT ABSTRACTS.
Bord na Mona, Peat Research Centre, Droichead Nua, Co. Kildare, Ireland. FAX 045-33240. *3502*

PEDIATRIA MODERNA.
Grupo Editorial Moreira Jr., Rua Henrique Martins 493, Sao Paulo, Brazil. FAX 884-9993.
circ. 12,000. *3323*

PEDIATRIC MANAGEMENT.
Dowden Publishing Company, 110 Summit Ave., Montvale, NJ 07645. TEL 201-391-9100. FAX 201-391-2778.
circ. 33,000. *3324*

PEDOLOGIST.
Group of Japanese Pedologists, c/o National Institute of Agro-Environmental Sciences, 3-1-1 Kannondai, Yatabe, Tsukuba, Ibaraki 305, Japan.
circ. 1,000. *187*

PEGASUS JOURNAL.
Royal British Legion, Parachute Regiment and Airborne Forces, Browning Barracks, Aldershot, Hampshire GU11 2BU, England. TEL 0252-349624. FAX 0252-349203.
circ. 6,000. *3468*

PENMEN'S NEWS LETTER.
Eileen Richardson, Ed. & Pub., 34 Broadway Ave., Ottawa, Ont. K1S 2V6, Canada. TEL 613-232-3014.
circ. 300. *1654*

PENNSYLVANIA LAWYER.
Pennsylvania Bar Association, 100 South St., Harrisburg, PA 17108. TEL 717-238-6715.
circ. 30,000. *2666*

PENNSYLVANIA MESSAGE.
Pennsylvania Association for Retarded Citizens, Inc., 123 Forster St., Harrisburg, PA 17102-3498. FAX 717-234-7615.
circ. 8,500. *1739*

PENNSYLVANIA SCHOOLMASTER.
Pennsylvania Association of Secondary School Principals, Box 953, Easton, PA 18044.
circ. 3,000. *1654*

PENNTRUX.
Pennsylvania Motor Truck Association, Linda Lane, Box 128, Camp Hill, PA 17001-0128. TEL 717-761-7122. FAX 717-761-8434.
circ. 2,500. *4747*

PEPPER 'N SALT.
Standard Schnauzer Club of America, Rt. 2, Box 208, Galesburg, IL 61401.
circ. 500. *3712*

PERSONAL ENGINEERING & INSTRUMENTATION NEWS.
P E C Inc., Box 430, Rye, NH 03870-0430. TEL 603-427-1377. FAX 603-427-1388.
circ. 50,000. *1473*

PERSONENVERVOER.
Autotrend B.V., P.O. Box 55, 2235 ZH Valkenburg, Netherlands. FAX 070-559413.
circ. 3,000. *4654*

PERSONNEL CONSULTANT.
National Association of Personnel Consultants, 3133 Mt. Vernon Ave., Alexandria, VA 22305. TEL 703-684-0180. FAX 703-684-0071.
circ. 2,500. *3630*

PERSPECTIVE (INDIANAPOLIS).
Resort Condominiums International, Inc., Box 80229, Indianapolis, IN 46280-0229. TEL 317-871-9567. FAX 317-871-9699.
circ. 7,000. *4154*

PESQUISA AGROPECUARIA BRASILEIRA.
Empresa Brasileira de Pesquisa Agropecuaria, Servico de Producao e Informacao, Caixa Postal 040315, 70333 Brasilia, Brazil. TEL 062-3484236.
circ. 1,600. *114*

PESQUISA MEDICA.
Fundacao Faculdade Federal de Ciencias Medicas de Porto Alegre, Centro Academico XXII de Marco, Rua Sarmento Leite, 245, 90050 Porto Alegre RS, Brazil. TEL 0512-24-8822. FAX 0512-26-7913.
circ. 1,000. *3140*

PEST MANAGEMENT.
National Pest Control Association, 8100 Oak St., Dunn Loring, VA 22027. TEL 703-573-8330. FAX 703-573-4116.
circ. 6,000. *537*

PETROLEUM MARKETER.
McKeand Publications, Inc., 636 First Ave., Box 507, West Haven, CT 06516. TEL 203-934-5288.
circ. 17,000. *3698*

PFLANZENSCHUTZ KURIER.
Bayer AG, Geschaftsbereich Pflanzenschutz, 5090 Leverkusen, Germany.
circ. 168,000. *188*

PHARMACY COUNSELOR.
HealthTeam Interactive Communications, Inc., 274 Madison Ave., No. PH, New York, NY 10016-0701.
3739

PHARMACY NEWS.
Rajesh Publications, 1 Ansari Rd., Daryaganj, Dew Delhi 110 002, India.
circ. 12,000. *3739*

PHARMACY TODAY.
American Pharmaceutical Association, 2215 Constitution Ave., N.W., Washington, DC 20037. TEL 202-628-4410. FAX 202-783-2351.
circ. 40,000. *3740*

PHARMACY UPDATE.
Valley Forge Press, 1288 Valley Forge Rd., Box 1135, Valley Forge, PA 19481. TEL 215-935-1296. FAX 215-935-3072.
circ. 60,000. *3740*

PHILIPPINE ECONOMICS AND BUSINESS INDEX.
Robert S. Belano Management Company, Ltd., P.O. Box 4156, Manila, Philippines. TEL 818-09-39. FAX 632-521-7225.
circ. 4,500. *734*

PHILIPPINES. FOOD AND NUTRITION RESEARCH INSTITUTE. ANNUAL REPORT.
Food and Nutrition Research Institute, 727 Pedro Gil St., P.O. Box EA-467, Ermita, Manila, Philippines. TEL 595113. FAX 632-59-22-75.
3611

PHOTOGRAMMETRIC COYOTE.
E. Coyote Enterprises, Inc., Rt. 3, Bldg. 228, Box 1119, Mineral Wells, TX 76067. TEL 817-325-0757.
circ. 10,000. *2259*

PHOTOGRAPHIC JOURNAL.
Royal Photographic Society of Great Britain, Acorn House, 74-94 Cherry Orchard Dr., Croydon CR0 6BA, England. TEL 081-681-8339. FAX 081-681-1880.
circ. 10,000. *3795*

PHYSICIANS' DESK REFERENCE.
Medical Economics Publishing Co., Five Paragon Dr., Montvale, NJ 07645. TEL 201-357-7200. FAX 201-573-1045.
circ. 485,000. *3141*

PHYSICIANS' DESK REFERENCE FOR NONPRESCRIPTION DRUGS.
Medical Economics Publishing Co., Five Paragon Dr., Montvale, NJ 07645. TEL 201-358-7200. FAX 201-573-1045.
circ. 315,000. *3141*

PHYSICIANS FINANCIAL NEWS.
McGraw-Hill, Inc., 1221 Ave. of the Americas, New York, NY 10020. TEL 212-512-2000.
circ. 127,000. *795*

PHYSICIANS FOOD ADVISOR.
Cahners Publishing Company (New York) Division of Reed Publishing (USA) Inc., 249 W. 17th St., New York, NY 10011-5301. TEL 212-463-6441. FAX 212-463-6470.
circ. 83,600. *2079*

PHYSIOTHERAPY TODAY.
Ontario Physiotherapy Association, 29 Gervais Drive, Ste. 303, Don Mills, Ont. M3C 1Y9, Canada. TEL 416-391-4700. FAX 416-391-4702.
circ. 3,000. *3142*

PHYSIS.
Urban und Vogel, Lindwurmstr. 95, Postfach 152209, 8000 Munich 2, Germany. TEL 089-53292-0. FAX 089-53292-100.
circ. 48,500. *3142*

PHYTON.
Fundacion Romulo Raggio, Gaspar Campos 861, 1638 Vicente Lopez, Argentina.
circ. 750. *513*

THE PICK USER DIGEST.
Thurman Marketing Services Inc., 23181 Verdugo, Laguna Hills, CA 92653. TEL 714-855-4442. FAX 714-380-3942.
circ. 7,500. *1473*

PILGRIM JOURNAL.
Pilgrim Society, 75 Court St., Plymouth, MA 02360. TEL 508-746-1620.
circ. 900. *2419*

PINKER MODA.
Ediciones Tecnicas Doria, Avda. Puerta del Angel 7, Sobreat. A y B, 08002 Barcelona, Spain. FAX 3-3011105.
circ. 12,000. *4622*

THE PIONEER.
Church Army in Australia, P.O. Box 107, Frenchs Forest, N.S.W. 2086, Australia. TEL 02-451-8395. FAX 02-451-8877.
circ. 6,000. *4246*

PIPE SMOKER'S EPHEMERIS.
Tom Dunn, Ed.& Pub., 20-37 120th St., College Point, NY 11356.
circ. 7,500. *4644*

PIPELINE (ROY).
Doberman Pinscher Club of America, 29604 24th Ave. S., Roy, WA 98580.
circ. 2,000. *3713*

PIRKKA.
Kauppiaitten Kustannus Oy, Rauhankatu 15, 00170 Helsinki, Finland. TEL 90-175566.
circ. 1,717,803. *1050*

PITT MAGAZINE.
University of Pittsburgh, Department of University Relations, 400 Craig Hall, University of Pittsburgh, Pittsburgh, PA 15260. TEL 412-624-4147.
circ. 170,000. *1321*

PITTSBURGH MUSICIAN.
Pittsburgh Musical Society, Local No.60-471, A.F.M., 709 Forbes Ave., Pittsburgh, PA 15219. TEL 412-281-1822.
circ. 1,500. *3574*

PLACE OF GRADUATION FOR SELECTED HEALTH OCCUPATIONS.
University of British Columbia, Centre for Health Services and Policy Research, No. 429 - 2194 Health Sciences Mall, Vancouver, B.C. V6T 1Z3, Canada. TEL 604-822-4810. FAX 604-822-5690.
circ. 100. *3142*

PLAN AND ACTION.
Stichting Mensen in Nood - Caritas Neerlandica, Postbus 1041, 5200 BA 's-Hertogenbosch, Netherlands. TEL 073-144544. FAX 073-132115.
circ. 2,000. *4416*

PLAN & PRINT.
International Reprographic Association, 2000 York Rd., Ste. 125, Oak Brook, IL 60521-8820. TEL 708-571-4685. FAX 708-571-4731.
circ. 30,000. *4003*

PLANNING IN NORTHEASTERN ILLINOIS.
Northeastern Illinois Planning Commission, 400 W. Madison St., Chicago, IL 60606. TEL 312-454-0400.
circ. 9,500. *2494*

PLANT ENGINEERING PRODUCT SUPPLIER GUIDE.
Cahners Publishing Company (Des Plaines) Division of Reed Publishing (USA) Inc., 1350 E. Touhy Ave., Box 5080, Des Plaines, IL 60017-5080. TEL 708-635-8800. FAX 708-390-2636. *1833*

PLANT GENETIC RESOURCES NEWSLETTER.
Food and Agriculture Organization of the United Nations, International Board for Plant Genetic Resources, Via delle Sette Chiese 142, 00145 Rome, Italy. TEL 39-6-5744719. FAX 39-6-5750309.
circ. 5,000. *1495*

PLASTI-NOTICIAS.
Publi-News Latinoamericana, S.A.C.V., Colima 436, piso 2, Mexico 7 D.F., Mexico. *3865*

PLASTICHEM.
Singapore Polytechnic Polymer Society, Dover Rd., Singapore 5, Singapore.
circ. 1,000. *1857*

PLASTICS AND RUBBER WEEKLY.
E M A P Vision Ltd., 19 Scarbrook Rd., Croydon, Surrey CR9 1QH, England. TEL 081-760-9690. FAX 081-681-1672.
circ. 20,584. *3865*

PLAY SCHOOLS NEWSLETTER.
Play Schools Association, 9 E. 38th St., 8th Fl., New York, NY 10016. TEL 212-725-6540.
circ. 2,500. *1655*

PLAYBACK.
Brunico Communications Inc., 366 Adelaide St. W., Ste. 500, Toronto, Ont. M5V 1R9, Canada. TEL 416-408-2300. FAX 416-408-0870.
circ. 13,555. *1378*

PLEIN CHANT.
Editions Plein Chant, Bassac, 16120 Chateauneuf-sur-Charente, France.
circ. 1,000. *2948*

PLUG.
Culturele Raad Noordholland, Postbus 163, 1970 AD Ijmuiden, Netherlands.
circ. 62,500. *4637*

PLUMBERS FRIEND.
Utah Plumbing, Heating, Cooling Contractors, 669 So. 2nd East, Salt Lake City, UT 84111. TEL 801-364-7768. FAX 801-531-7725. *2302*

PLYMOTHIAN.
Plymouth College, Ford Park, Plymouth, Devonshire, England.
circ. 1,000. *1321*

PLYMOUTH COUNTY BUSINESS REVIEW.
Plymouth County Development Council, Box 1620, Pembroke, MA 02359. TEL 617-826-3136. FAX 617-826-0444.
circ. 5,000. *838*

POET.
Fine Arts Society, 2314 W. Sixth St., Mishawaka, IN 46544.
circ. 1,000. *3001*

POETS' ROUNDTABLE.
826 South Center St., Terre Haute, IN 47807. TEL 812-234-0819.
circ. 2,000. *3003*

POINT OF VIEW.
Holt Renfrew & Co., Limited, 50 Bloor St., W., Toronto, Ont. M4W 1A1, Canada. TEL 416-922-2333. FAX 416-922-3240.
circ. 150,000. *1294*

POINTS NORTH.
North Country Reference & Research Resources Council, Box 568, Canton, NY 13617. TEL 315-386-4569. FAX 315-379-9553.
circ. 200. *2779*

POLLUTION ATMOSPHERIQUE.
Association pour la Prevention de la Pollution Atmospheriques, 58 rue du Rocher, 75008 Paris, France. TEL 42-93-69-30. FAX 42-93-41-99.
circ. 2,000. *1978*

POLLUTION ENGINEERING.
Cahners Publishing Company (Des Plaines) Division of Reed Publishing (USA) Inc., 1350 E. Touhy Ave., Box 5080, Des Plaines, IL 60017-5080. TEL 708-635-8800. FAX 708-390-2636.
circ. 60,000. *1978*

POLYTECHNISCH WEEKBLAD.
Stam Tijdschriften B.V., Postbus 235, 2280 AE Rijswijk, Netherlands. TEL 070-3988100. FAX 070-3988276.
circ. 78,000. *1834*

PONDICHERRY INDUSTRIAL PROMOTION, DEVELOPMENT AND INVESTMENT CORPORATION. ANNUAL REPORTS AND ACCOUNTS.
Pondicherry Industrial Promotion, Development and Investment Corporation Ltd., 38 Romain Rolland St, Pondicherry 605001, India. *838*

POPULAR ASTRONOMY.
Junior Astronomical Society, c/o Ian Ridpath, Ed., 48 Otho Court, Brentford, Middlesex TW8 8PY, England. *368*

PORT OF NEW ORLEANS ANNUAL DIRECTORY.
Port of New Orleans, 2 Canal St., Box 60046, New Orleans, LA 70160. TEL 504-528-3249. FAX 504-524-4156.
circ. 20,000. *4655*

PORT OF ROTTERDAM MAGAZINE.
Wyt Publishers, Postbus 268, 3000 AG Rotterdam, Netherlands. TEL 010-4762566. FAX 010-4762315.
circ. 12,500. *4736*

PORTLAND ART MUSEUM NEWSLETTER.
Oregon Art Institute, 1219 S.W. Park Ave., Portland, OR 97205. TEL 503-226-2811. FAX 503-226-2842.
circ. 20,000. *3531*

PORTUGAL. INSTITUTO NACIONAL DE ESTATISTICA. SERIE ESTATISTICAS REGIONAIS.
Instituto Nacional de Estatistica, Av. Antonio Jose de Almeida, 1078 Lisbon Codex, Portugal. *4583*

POST EAGLE.
Post Publishing Co. Inc., 800 Van Houten Ave., Clifton, NJ 07013.
circ. 11,000. *2020*

POST GUTENBERG.
Lee Publications, Inc., Box 121, Grand St. W., Palatine Bridge, NY 13428. TEL 518-673-3237. FAX 518-673-2699.
circ. 21,000. *4003*

POSTAL HISTORY JOURNAL.
Postal History Society, Inc., Box 334, Woodside, NY 11377.
circ. 600. *1353*

POSTHORN.
Scandinavian Collectors Club, 1214 Lakeview Dr., Fergus Falls, MN 56537-3853. TEL 901-452-8701.
circ. 1,400. *3757*

POTATO NEWSLETTER.
Department of Agriculture, Plant Industry Branch, Box 6000, Fredericton, N.B. E3B 5H1, Canada. TEL 506-457-7244. FAX 506-457-7267.
circ. 1,000. *189*

POTOMAC LIFE.
C E R Publications, Box 59508, Potomac, MD 20859. TEL 301-299-5183.
circ. 32,000. *2232*

POWDER RIVER BREAKS.
Powder River Basin Resource Council, Box 1178, Douglas, WY 82633. TEL 307-358-5002.
circ. 975. *1966*

POWER TRANSMISSION DESIGN.
Penton Publishing 1100 Superior Ave., Cleveland, OH 44114-2543. TEL 216-696-7000. FAX 216-696-8765.
circ. 52,000. *1938*

POWER TRANSMISSION DESIGN HANDBOOK.
Penton Publishing 1100 Superior Ave., Cleveland, OH 44114-2543. TEL 216-696-7000. FAX 216-696-8765.
circ. 52,000. *1938*

PRACTICAL DIABETOLOGY.
R.A. Rapaport Publishing, Inc., 150 W. 22nd St., New York, NY 10011. TEL 212-989-0200. FAX 212-989-4786.
circ. 65,200. *3255*

PRACTICAL GASTROENTEROLOGY.
Shugar Publishing, 32 Mill Rd., Westhampton Beach, NY 11978. TEL 516-288-4404. FAX 516-288-4435.
circ. 65,000. *3269*

PRAIRIE HARVESTER.
Prairie Bible Institute, Prairie Alumni Fellowship, Three Hills, Alta. T0M 2A0, Canada. TEL 403-443-5540. FAX 403-443-5511.
circ. 15,000. *1321*

PRAXIS COMPUTER.
Deutscher Aertzte-Verlag GmbH, Dieselstr. 2, Postfach 400265, 5000 Cologne 40, Germany. TEL 02234-7011-0. FAX 02234-7011-444.
circ. 40,000. *1399*

PRESBYTERIAN.
Synod of the Sun, 920 Stemmons Frwy., Denton, TX 76205.
circ. 117,000. *4247*

PRESENTATION PRODUCTS MAGAZINE.
Full Circle Communications, 23410 Civic Center Way, Ste. E-10, Malibu, CA 90265. TEL 310-456-2283. FAX 310-456-8686.
circ. 56,000. *37*

PRESERVATION PERSPECTIVE.
Preservation New Jersey, Inc., 170 Township Line Rd., Belle Mead, NJ 08502. TEL 908-359-4557. FAX 908-874-6044.
circ. 3,000. *305*

PRESHIPMENT TESTING.
National Safe Transit Association, Box 10744, Chicago, IL 60610-0744. TEL 312-645-0083. FAX 312-645-1078.
circ. 3,200. *3651*

PRESIDENT'S REPORT.
F I S I - Madison Financial Corporation Box 40726, Nashville, TN 37204. TEL 615-371-2775.
circ. 1,010,400. *796*

PREVIEW THEATER BROCHURE.
American Film Institute, John F. Kennedy Center for the Performing Arts, Washington, DC 20566. TEL 202-828-4000. *3515*

PREVISOES IONOSFERICAS M U F.
Ministerio da Marinha, Directoria de Armamento e Comunicacoes, Rua 1 de Marco, 118, Rio de Janeiro, RJ, Brazil. *1378*

PRICE WATERHOUSE REVIEW.
Price Waterhouse, 1251 Ave. of the Americas, New York, NY 10020. TEL 212-489-8900. *755*

PRIESTERJAHRHEFT.
Bonifatiuswerk der Deutschen Katholiken e.V., Kamp 22, 4790 Paderborn, Germany. TEL 05251-29960. FAX 05251-299688.
circ. 20,000. *4273*

PRIMARY CARE & CANCER.
Dominus Publishing Company, Inc., 331 Willis Ave., Box 86, Williston Park, NY 11596. TEL 516-294-1880.
circ. 91,000. *3201*

PRIMARY CARE RHEUMATOLOGY.
American College of Rheumatology, 60 Executive Park S., Ste. 150, Atlanta, GA 30329. TEL 404-633-3777. FAX 404-633-1870.
circ. 30,000. *3369*

PRIMETIME LIVING.
PrimeTime Association, 1530K Jamacho Rd., No. 278, El Cajon, CA 92019-3754. TEL 619-278-7115.
circ. 110,000. *2277*

PRINCETON ALUMNI WEEKLY.
Princeton Alumni Publications, 194 Nassau St., Princeton, NJ 08542. TEL 609-258-4885. FAX 609-258-6305.
circ. 55,000. *1322*

PRINCETON UNIVERSITY CUTANEOUS RESEARCH PROJECT REPORTS.
Princeton University, Department of Psychology, Green Hall, Princeton, NJ 08544. TEL 609-258-5277. FAX 609-258-1113.
circ. 120. *4039*

PRINT & GRAPHICS.
East-West Communications, 911 N. Fillmore St., Arlington, VA 22201-2127. TEL 703-525-4800. FAX 703-525-4805.
circ. 20,000. *4004*

PRINTING JOURNAL.
East-West Communications, 911 N. Fillmore St., Arlington, VA 22201-2127. TEL 703-525-4800. FAX 703-525-4805.
circ. 19,000. *4004*

PRIVATE CARRIER.
National Private Truck Council, 1320 Braddock Pl., Ste. 720, Alexandria, VA 22314. TEL 703-683-1300. FAX 703-683-1217.
circ. 20,000. *4747*

PRIVATE LINE.
National Private Truck Council, 1320 Braddock Pl., Ste. 720, Alexandria, VA 22314. TEL 703-683-1300. FAX 703-683-1217.
circ. 12,500. *4747*

PRO.
Johnson Hill Press, Inc., 1233 Janesville Ave., Ft. Atkinson, WI 53538. TEL 414-563-6388. FAX 414-563-1701.
circ. 40,000. *2137*

PRO MOTION.
Beyond the Byte, c/o Emily Laisy, Ed., 2501 Laurel Brook Rd., No. 388, Fallston, MD 21047-0388. TEL 410-877-3524. FAX 410-877-7064.
circ. 175. *1341*

PRO RE NATA.
Art Davis Associates, Box 216, Cedar Falls, IA 50613. TEL 801-322-3439.
circ. 15,000. *3285*

PROBABLE LEVELS OF R & D EXPENDITURES: FORECAST AND ANALYSIS.
Battelle Memorial Institute, Columbus Operations, 505 King Ave., Columbus, OH 43201. TEL 614-424-6424. *4606*

PROBATUM EST.
Wissenschaft und Werbung, Freiburger Str. 23, 7844 Nuernberg, Germany. *3144*

PROBLEMI DI GESTIONE.
Centro di Formazione e Studi (Formez), Mostra d'Oltremare, Palazzo dei Congressi, 80125 Naples, Italy. FAX 081-615467.
circ. 6,700. *1025*

PROBLEMY RODZINY.
Panstwowy Zaklad Wydawnictw Lekarskich, Dluga 38-40, Warsaw, Poland. TEL 31-42-81.
circ. 4,000. *3986*

PROCESS INDUSTRIES CANADA.
Zanny Publications Ltd., 190 Main St., Unionville, Ont. L3R 2G9, Canada. TEL 416-477-2922. FAX 416-479-4834.
circ. 24,000. *1859*

PRODUCE MERCHANDISING.
Vance Publishing, 7950 College Blvd., Overland Park, KS 66210. TEL 913-451-2200. FAX 913-451-5821.
circ. 12,200. *2080*

PRODUCTEUR DE LAIT.
Zentralverband der Schweizerischen Milchproduzenten, Weststr. 10, 3000 Berne 6, Switzerland. *203*

PRODUCTION.
University of British Columbia, Centre for Health Services and Policy Research, No. 429 - 2194 Health Sciences Mall, Vancouver, B.C. V6T 1Z3, Canada. TEL 604-822-4810. FAX 604-822-5690.
circ. 250. *3144*

PRODUCTION JOURNAL.
Newspaper Society, Bloomsbury House, Bloomsbury Sq., 74-77 Great Russell St., London WC1B 3DA, England. TEL 071-636-7014.
circ. 3,000. *4005*

PRODUCTRONIC.
Dr. Alfred Huethig Verlag GmbH, Im Weiher 10, Postfach 102869, 6900 Heidelberg 1, Germany. TEL 06221-489-281. FAX 06221-489-279.
circ. 14,636. *1777*

PRODUKTIONS NYT.
Christtreu, Strandlodsvei 48, DK-2300 Copenhagen S, Denmark. TEL 32-844848. FAX 31-582055.
circ. 12,816. *3022*

PROFESSIONAL BOATBUILDER.
WoodenBoat Publications, Inc., Box 78, Brooklin, ME 04616. TEL 207-359-4651. FAX 207-359-8920.
circ. 20,000. *4528*

PROFESSIONAL FORESTER.
Ontario Professional Foresters Association, 27 West Beaver Creek Rd., Richmond Hill, Ont. L4B 1M8, Canada. TEL 416-764-2921. FAX 416-764-2921.
circ. 1,300. *2106*

PROFESSIONAL SURVEYOR.
American Surveyors Publishing Co., 901 S. Highland, Ste. 105, Arlington, VA 22204. TEL 703-892-0733. FAX 703-920-3652.
circ. 64,000. *1872*

PROGNOSTICO.
Instituto de Economia Agricola, Servico de Biblioteca e Documentacao, Av. Miguel Stefano 3900, Caixa Postal 8114, 04301 Sao Paulo S.P., Brazil. FAX 011-22484. *190*

PROGRESS IN DERMATOLOGY.
Dermatology Foundation, 1560 Sherman Ave., Ste. 302, Evanston, IL 60201-4802.
circ. 3,000. *3249*

PROGRESSIVE GROCER'S ANNUAL REPORT OF THE GROCERY INDUSTRY.
Maclean Hunter Publishing Company, 4 Stamford Forum, Stamford, CT 06901. TEL 203-325-3500. FAX 203-325-4377.
circ. 70,049. *2093*

PROPERTY REGISTER.
Tophill Press, 49 High St., Sevenoaks, Kent TN13 1L8, England. TEL 0732-743300. FAX 0732-743006. *4155*

PROPRIETE AGRICOLE.
Federation Nationale de la Propriete Agricole, 39 rue St. Dominique, 75007 Paris, France.
circ. 19,000. *115*

PROSPECT.
A E C I Ltd., Box 1122, Johannesburg 2000, South Africa. TEL 223-9111. FAX 011-223-1456.
circ. 12,000. *1859*

PROSPEROUS TIMES.
Howard Publications, 417 Fayette St., Hammond, IN 46320. TEL 219-933-3253.
circ. 42,000. *2232*

PROSTHETICS AND ORTHOTICS INTERNATIONAL.
International Society for Prosthetics and Orthotics, Borgervaenget 5, DK-2100 Copenhagen OE, Denmark. TEL 31-20-72-60.
circ. 2,800. *3145*

PROTEIN IDENTIFICATION RESOURCE NEWSLETTER.
National Biomedical Research Foundation, 3900 Reservoir Rd., N.W., Washington, DC 20007. TEL 202-687-2121. FAX 202-687-1662.
circ. 1,000. *452*

PROTOKOLLE ZUR FISCHEREITECHNIK.
Bundesforschungsanstalt fuer Fischerei, Institut fuer Fangtechnik, Palmaille 9, 2000 Hamburg 50, Germany. FAX 040-38905129.
circ. 400. *2047*

PROVENCE GENEALOGIE.
Centre Genealogique de Midi-Provence, 13110 Port-De-Bouc, France.
circ. 500. *2162*

PROVINCIAL NEWSLETTER.
British Columbia Registered Music Teachers' Association, 1 - 8560 162nd St., Surrey, B.C. V3S 3V4, Canada. TEL 604-492-8944.
circ. 779. *3575*

PROYECTOS QUIMICOS.
Tecnipublicaciones, S.A., Fernando VI, 27-1, 28004 Madrid, Spain. TEL 91-319-7889. FAX 91-319-7089.
circ. 3,000. *1186*

PRZEMYSLOWY INSTYTUT ELEKTRONIKI. PRACE.
Przemyslowy Instytut Elektroniki, Ul. Dluga 44-50, 00-241 Warsaw, Poland. FAX 31-30-14.
circ. 350. *1777*

PSIONIC MEDICINE.
Psionic Medical Society, Hindhead, Surrey, England.
circ. 500. *3145*

PSYCHIATRIC FORUM.
Department of Mental Health, William S. Hall Psychiatric Institute, Box 202, Columbia, SC 29202. TEL 803-734-7154. FAX 803-734-0791.
circ. 4,000. *3351*

PSYCHIATRIC TIMES.
C M E Inc., 1924 E. Deere Ave., Santa Ana, CA 92705-5723. TEL 800-447-4474. FAX 714-250-0445.
circ. 39,545. *3351*

PUBLIC SCHOOL ENROLLMENT AND STAFF, NEW YORK STATE.
Education Department, Information Center on Education, Education Bldg. Annex, Rm. 385, Albany, NY 12234. TEL 518-474-8716. *1657*

PUBLIC SCHOOL PROFESSIONAL PERSONNEL REPORT, NEW YORK STATE.
Education Department, Information Center on Education, Education Bldg. Annex, Rm. 385, Albany, NY 12234. TEL 518-474-8716. *1657*

PUBLIC SECTOR.
Auburn University, Center for Governmental Services, 2232 Haley Center, Auburn University, Auburn, AL 36849. TEL 205-844-1913. FAX 205-844-1919.
circ. 3,000. *4071*

PUBLIC SERVANT.
Public Servants Association of South Africa, P.S.A. Bldg., 563 Belvedere St., P.O. Box 40404, Arcadia 0007, South Africa. TEL 012-323-4481. FAX 012-325-7434.
circ. 78,000. *4071*

PUERTO RICO. DEPARTMENT OF LABOR. BUREAU OF LABOR STATISTICS. EMPLOYMENT HOURS AND EARNINGS IN THE MANUFACTURING ESTABLISHMENTS PROMOTED BY THE ECONOMIC DEVELOPMENT ADMINISTRATION OF THE PUERTO RICAN INDUSTRIAL DEVELOPMENT COMPANY.
Department of Labor, Bureau of Labor Statistics, 505 Munoz Rivera Ave., Hato Rey, PR 00918.
circ. 775. *736*

PUERTO RICO. OFICINA DE PRESUPUESTO Y GERENCIA. RESOLUCIONES CONJUNTAS DEL PRESUPUESTO GENERAL Y DE PRESUPUESTOS ESPECIALES.
Oficina de Presupuesto, Box 3228, San Juan, PR 00902. *1104*

PUGET SOUND COMPUTER USER.
K F H Publications, Inc., 3530 Bagley Ave. N., Seattle, WA 98103. TEL 206-547-4950. FAX 206-547-5355.
circ. 85,000. *1473*

PULP AND PAPER.
Miller Freeman, Inc., 600 Harrison St., San Francisco, CA 94107. TEL 415-905-2200. FAX 415-905-2232.
circ. 34,000. *3665*

PUNCH DIGEST FOR CANADIAN DOCTORS.
Punch Digest for Canadian Doctors Inc., 14845 Yonge St., Ste. 300, Aurora, Ont. L4G 6H8, Canada. TEL 416-841-5607. FAX 416-841-5688.
circ. 36,000. *3145*

PUNJABI SAHITYA.
c/o H. S. Kalra, Ed., 254 Rowley Gardens, Woodberry Grove, London N4 1HW, England.
circ. 4,000. *2880*

PUPPETRY JOURNAL.
Puppeteers of America, 8005 Swallow Dr., Macedonia, OH 44056.
circ. 2,500. *4637*

PURDUE UNIVERSITY. OFFICE OF MANPOWER STUDIES. MANPOWER & TECHNICAL EDUCATION REQUIREMENTS REPORTS.
Purdue University, Office of Manpower Studies, Knoy Hall, W. Lafayette, IN 47907. TEL 317-494-2559. FAX 317-494-0486. *992*

PURJEHTIJA.
Finnish Yachting Association, Radiokatu 20, SF-00240 Helsinki, Finland. TEL 358-0-1582350. FAX 358-0-1582369.
circ. 31,000. *4528*

Q U A.
Zimbabwe Amateur Radio Society, P.O. Box 2377, Harare, Zimbabwe. *1358*

QUADERNI SARDI DI ECONOMIA.
Banco di Sardegna, Viale Umberto, 36, 07100 Sassari, Italy.
circ. 2,000. *882*

QUADRANT.
C.G. Jung Foundation for Analytical Psychology, Inc., 28 E. 39th St., New York, NY 10016. TEL 212-697-6430. FAX 201-707-6717.
circ. 2,000. *4043*

QUAKER CAMPUS.
Whittier College, Quaker Campus, Box 8613, Whittier, CA 90608. TEL 310-907-4354. FAX 310-945-5301.
circ. 2,000. *1322*

QUALITY PAPERBACK BOOK CLUB REVIEW.
Quality Paperback Book Club, 485 Lexington Ave., New York, NY 10017. *4135*

QUALITY SOURCE.
American Group Practice Association, 1422 Duke St., Alexandria, VA 22314. TEL 703-838-0033. FAX 703-548-1890. *3145*

QUANTUM (WASHINGTON).
National Science Teachers Association, 1742 Connecticut Ave., N.W., Washington, DC 20009-1171. TEL 202-328-5800.
circ. 40,000. *4335*

QUARTERLY FORECAST OF JAPANESE ECONOMY.
Japan Center for Economic Research, Economic Analysis Division, Nikkei Kayabacho Bldg., 6-1 Nihonbashi Kayabacgi 2-chome, Chuo-ku, Tokyo 103, Japan. TEL 03-3639-2801. *1083*

QUARTERLY JOURNAL OF TAIWAN LAND CREDIT.
Land Bank of Taiwan, Research Department, Taipei, Taiwan, Republic of China.
circ. 500. *156*

QUARTERNOTE.
American Musicians Union, Inc., 8 Tobin Ct., Dumont, NJ 07628. TEL 201-384-5378.
circ. 350. *3575*

QUEEN'S AWARD MAGAZINE.
Merchant's Press Limited, Merchant House, 1 Micheldever Rd., London SE12 8LX, England. TEL 081-463-9449. FAX 081-463-9426.
circ. 20,000. *919*

QUEENSLAND FOREST SERVICE. RESEARCH NOTE.
Queensland Forest Service, G.P.O. Box 944, Brisbane, Qld. 4001, Australia. TEL 07-877-9727. FAX 07-371-2217.
circ. 400. *2106*

QUEENSLAND FOREST SERVICE. RESEARCH PAPER.
Queensland Forest Service, G.P.O. Box 944, Brisbane, Qld. 4001, Australia. TEL 07-877 9727. FAX 07-371-2217.
circ. 400. *2106*

QUERCE.
Collegio Alla Querce, Via della Piazzola 44, Florence 50133, Italy.
circ. 4,000. *1263*

QUEST: MANHATTAN PROPERTIES & COUNTRY ESTATES.
Quest Magazines, Inc., 1046 Madison Ave., New York, NY 10021-0137. FAX 212-288-4536.
circ. 102,000. *4155*

QUICK TOPICS NEWSLETTER.
National Candy Wholesalers Association, Inc., 1128 16th St., N.W., Washington, DC 20036. FAX 202-467-0559.
circ. 4,200. *2089*

QUIMERA.
Montesinos Editor, S.A., Maignon, 26, 3, 08024 Barcelona, Spain. TEL 210-69-06.
circ. 21,500. *2951*

QUINCY BUSINESS NEWS.
John R. Graham, Inc., 40 Oval Rd., Quincy, MA 02170-3813. TEL 617-328-0069. FAX 617-471-1504.
circ. 2,850. *687*

QUIRK'S MARKETING RESEARCH REVIEW.
Quirk Enterprises, Box 23536, Minneapolis, MN 55423. TEL 612-861-8051. FAX 612-861-8051.
circ. 13,000. *1051*

R A C B ROYAL AUTO.
Koninklijke Automobiel Club van Belgie, 53 rue d'Arlon, B-1040 Brussels, Belgium.
circ. 33,000. *4700*

R A NEWS.
Recreation Association of the Public Service of Canada, 2451 Riverside Dr., Ottawa, Ont. K1H 7X7, Canada. TEL 613-733-5100. FAX 613-733-3310.
circ. 26,000. *1300*

R B ELEKTRONICA MAGAZINE.
Uitgeverij de Muiderkring B.v., Hogeweyselaan 227, 1382 JL Weesp, Netherlands. TEL 02940-15210. FAX 02940-12782.
circ. 20,000. *1777*

R E I D QUARTERLY.
Prudential Insurance Co. of America, Public Relations & Advertising Dept., 5 Plaza, Newark, NJ 07101. TEL 201-877-6000.
circ. 3,000. *2540*

R E S.
Tecnipublicaciones S.A., Fernando VI 27-1, 28004 Madrid, Spain. TEL 91-319-7889. FAX 91-410-1069.
circ. 5,000. *796*

R I L M ABSTRACTS OF MUSIC LITERATURE.
R I L M Abstracts, City University of New York, 33 W. 42nd St., New York, NY 10036. TEL 212-642-2709. FAX 212-642-2642.
circ. 1,500. *3589*

R I P A REPORT.
Royal Institute of Public Administration, 3 Birdcage Walk, London SW1H 9JH, England. TEL 071-222-2248. FAX 071-222-2249. *4072*

R P M WEEKLY.
R P M Music Publications Ltd., 6 Brentcliffe Rd., Toronto, Ont. M4G 3Y2, Canada. TEL 416-425-0257.
circ. 5,000. *3576*

R S - MAGAZINE.
Computer Publishing Group, 1330 Beacon St., Ste. 220, Brookline, MA 02146-3202. TEL 617-739-7001. FAX 617-739-7003.
circ. 40,000. *1464*

R S WAVELENGTH.
American Society of Radiologic Technologists, 15000 Central Ave. S.E., Albuquerque, NM 87123. TEL 508-298-4500. FAX 508-298-5063.
circ. 50,000. *3361*

R T IMAGE.
Valley Forge Press, 1288 Valley Forge Rd., Box 1135, Valley Forge, PA 19481. TEL 215-935-1296. FAX 215-935-3072.
circ. 144,000. *3361*

R V BUSINESS.
T L Enterprises, Inc., 29901 Agoura Rd., Agoura, CA 91301. TEL 818-991-4980.
circ. 17,000. *4498*

RACIAL - ETHNIC DISTRIBUTION OF PUBLIC SCHOOL STUDENTS AND STAFF, NEW YORK STATE.
Education Department, Information Center on Education, Education Bldg. Annex, Rm. 385, Albany, NY 12234. TEL 518-474-8716. *1657*

RACQUETTE.
State University of New York, College at Potsdam, 119 Borrington Student Union, Potsdam, NY 13676. TEL 315-267-8451. FAX 315-267-2170.
circ. 3,500. *1322*

RADAR SYSTEMS INTERNATIONAL.
Marconi Radar Systems Ltd., Writtle Rd., Chelmsford CM1 3BN, England. *1342*

RADCLIFFE NEWS.
Radcliffe College, 10 Garden St., Cambridge, MA 02138. TEL 617-495-8608. FAX 617-495-8422.
circ. 43,000. *1322*

RADIOBOTE.
F.O. Rothy, Ed. & Pub., A-4360 Grein, Austria.
circ. 150,000. *1359*

RAIL WHISPERS.
Whisper Publications, Inc., 1865 Palmer Ave., Ste. 202, Larchmont, NY 10538. TEL 914-833-3634. FAX 914-834-7651.
circ. 30,000. *2233*

RAILWAYS IN SOUTHERN AFRICA.
Target Communications - Kommunikasies CC, P.O. Box 3445, 2125 Randburg, Transvaal, South Africa. TEL 011-787-3115. FAX 011-787-3112.
circ. 2,200. *4714*

RAINEY TIMES.
Rt. 4, Box 56, Sulphur Springs, TX 75482. TEL 214-885-3523.
circ. 300. *2162*

RANDSE AFRIKAANSE UNIVERSITEIT. JAARBOEK.
Rand Afrikaans University, Box 524, Johannesburg 2000, South Africa. FAX 011-489-2632. *1715*

RANSOMER.
Guild of Our Lady of Ransom, 31 Southdown Rd., Wimbledon, London SW20 8QJ, England. TEL 081-947-2598. FAX 081-944-6208.
circ. 2,000. *4273*

RAPPORT ANNUEL SUR LA COOPERATION AU DEVELOPPEMENT - BURUNDI.
United Nations Development Program, Programme des Nations Unies pour le Developpement au Burundi, c/o Ms. Linda Schrieber, Chief, Documentation and Statistics Office, BPPE, UNDP, New York, NY 10017. *934*

RAPPORT OM KONTROLLEN MED KONSUMMAELKPRODUKTER.
Veterinaerdirektoratet, Roligshedvej 25, DK-1958 Frederiksberg C, Denmark. FAX 45-31-35-85-44.
circ. 250. *1084*

RARE COIN REVIEW.
Bowers and Merena Galleries, Inc., Box 1224, Wolfeboro, NH 03894. TEL 603-596-5095. FAX 603-569-5319. *3601*

RASSEGNA DELL'ARBITRATO.
Associazione Italiana per l'Arbitrato, Via XX Settembre 5, 00187 Rome, Italy. FAX 06-462677.
circ. 1,500. *992*

RASSEGNA DELL'IMBALLAGGIO.
Editrice Arti Poligrafiche Europee, Via Casella 16, 20156 Milan, Italy. TEL 02-330221. FAX 02-39214341.
circ. 10,000. *3651*

RASSEGNA ECONOMICA (NAPLES).
Banco di Napoli, Direzione Generale, Ufficio Studi, Via Roma 177-178, 80132 Naples, Italy.
circ. 5,350. *882*

RASSEGNA GRAFICA.
Editrice Arti Poligrafiche Europee, Via Casella, 16, 20156 Milan, Italy. TEL 02-330221. FAX 02-39214341.
circ. 13,000. *4005*

RAZZA BOVINA PIEMONTESE.
Associazione Nazionale Allevatori Bovini di Razza Piemontese, Via Valeggio 22, 10128 Turin, Italy. *224*

READER (SAN DIEGO).
Box 85803, San Diego, CA 92138. TEL 619-235-3000. FAX 619-231-0489.
circ. 131,000. *2881*

READER'S DIGEST - DET BAESTA.
Reader's Digest AB, PO Box 25, 164 93 Kista, Sweden. TEL 08-752-0360. FAX 752-87-01.
circ. 157,479. *2218*

REAL SOCIEDAD ARQUEOLOGICA. BOLETIN ARQUEOLOGICO.
Real Sociedad Arqueologica Tarraconense, Museo Nacional Arqueologic, Tarragona, Spain.
circ. 1,000. *282*

RECHERCHE SUR LE XVIIE SIECLE.
Editions du C N R S, 1 Place Aristide Briand, 92195 Meudon Cedex, France. TEL 1-45-34-75-50. FAX 1-46-26-28-49.
circ. 1,250. *2382*

RECORDER (SEARCY).
Alpha Chi National Honor Society, Box 773, Harding University, Searcy, AR 72143. TEL 501-268-6161.
circ. 7,500. *1715*

RECUEIL DES INSTRUCTIONS DONNEES AUX AMBASSADEURS ET MINISTRES DE FRANCE.
Editions du C N R S, 1 Place Aristide Briand, 92195 Meudon Cedex, France. TEL 1-45-34-75-50. FAX 1-46-26-28-49.
circ. 1,500. *3970*

RECYCLE & SAVE.
Recycleneur Institute, 1717 N. Bayshore Dr., Execenter, Miami, FL 33132. TEL 305-539-0701. *1117*

RED AND BLACK (WASHINGTON).
Washington & Jefferson College, Washington, PA 15301. TEL 412-222-4400.
circ. 1,200. *1322*

REDWOOD NEWS.
California Redwood Association, 405 Enfrente Dr., Ste. 200, Novato, CA 94949. TEL 415-382-0662. FAX 415-382-8531. *306*

REFLECTIONS.
Springer-Verlag Hong Kong, Ltd., 701 Mirror Tower, 61 Mody Rd., Tsim Sha Tsui, Kowloon, Hong Kong. TEL 852-723-9698. FAX 852-724-2366.
circ. 5,000. *4136*

REFLEX MAGAZINE.
Xelfer, 105 S. Main, Ste. 204, Seattle, WA 98104. TEL 206-682-7688.
circ. 7,000. *342*

REGARDS SUR LE COMITE D'ETABLISSEMENT D'ORLY SUD.
Comite d'Etablissement Air France-Orly Sud, Extension Est, Batiment CRP, Aerogare d'Orly Sud, France.
circ. 8,000. *61*

REGENCY INTERNATIONAL DIRECTORY.
Regency International Publications Ltd., 325 Canterbury Road, Densole, Folkestone, Kent CT18 7BB, England. TEL 0303-893488. FAX 0303-893488. *1151*

REGIONAL AIRLINE ASSOCIATION. ANNUAL REPORT.
Regional Airline Association, 1101 Connecticut Ave., N.W., Ste. 700, Washington, DC 20036. TEL 202-857-7170. FAX 202-223-4579.
circ. 2,700. *4677*

REGIONAL DEVELOPMENT CORPORATION. ANNUAL REPORT.
Regional Development Corporation, P.O. Box 428, Fredericton, N.B. E3B 5R4, Canada. TEL 506-453-2277.
circ. 1,000. *882*

REINSURANCE DIRECTORY.
Robert W. Strain Publishing & Seminars, Box 1520, Athens, TX 75751. TEL 914-677-5974.
circ. 1,000. *2541*

REMOTE SENSING OF EARTH RESOURCES: A QUARTERLY BIBLIOGRAPHY.
University of New Mexico, Technology Application Center, 2808 Central Ave., S.E., Albuquerque, NM 87131-6031. TEL 505-277-3622. FAX 505-277-3614.
circ. 130. *1552*

REMOVALS AND STORAGE.
Quarrington-Curtis Ltd., 15 Canute Rd., Southampton SO1 1FJ, England. TEL 0703 63438. FAX 0703-632198.
circ. 1,800. *4655*

RENDER.
Editors West, 10961 Desert Lawn Dr., Ste. 57, Calimesa, CA 92320. TEL 714-795-4240. FAX 714-795-6440.
circ. 7,500. *116*

RENOVATIO.
Gianni Baget Bozzo, Ed. & Pub., Via 12 Ottobre 14, Genoa, Italy.
circ. 1,200. *4198*

RENTAL.
Johnson Hill Press, Inc., 1233 Janesville Ave., Ft. Atkinson, WI 53538. TEL 414-563-6388. FAX 414-563-1701.
circ. 20,000. *1084*

REPERTOIRE DES MANUSCRIPTS MEDIEVAUX (CORBIN).
Editions du C N R S, 1 Place Aristide Briand, 92195 Meudon Cedex, France. TEL 1-45-34-75-50. FAX 1-46-26-28-49.
circ. 1,500. *3577*

REPORT TO BUSINESS.
Better Business Bureau of Metropolitan New York Inc., 257 Park Ave. S., New York, NY 10010. TEL 212-533-7500. *1507*

REPORTERO INDUSTRIAL.
Keller International Publishing Corporation, 150 Great Neck Rd., Great Neck, NY 11021. TEL 516-829-9210. FAX 516-829-5414.
circ. 40,302. *3022*

RESEARCH.
Research Services, Inc., 2201 Third St., San Francisco, CA 94107. TEL 415-621-0220. FAX 415-621-0735.
circ. 61,500. *961*

RESEARCH & DEVELOPMENT.
Cahners Publishing Company (Des Plaines) Division Reed Publishing (USA) Inc., 1350 E. Touhy Ave., Box 5080, Des Plaines, IL 60017-5080. TEL 708-635-8800. FAX 908-390-2618.
circ. 120,107. *4607*

RESEARCH & DEVELOPMENT PRODUCT SOURCE TELEPHONE DIRECTORY.
Cahners Publishing Company (Des Plaines) Division of Reed Publishing (USA) Inc., 1350 E. Touhy Ave., Box 5080, Des Plaines, IL 60017-5080. TEL 708-635-8800. FAX 708-390-2618.
circ. 100,000. *4607*

RESELLER MANAGEMENT.
Gordon Publications, Inc., 301 Gibraltar Dr., Morris Plains, NJ 07950. TEL 201-292-5100. FAX 201-898-9281.
circ. 60,000. *1433*

RESERVE.
Case Western Reserve University, Office of Alumni and Parent Relations, 114 Baker Bldg., Cleveland, OH 44106. TEL 216-368-2416. *1323*

RESOURCE.
Pentecostal Assemblies of Canada, Church Ministries Department, 6745 Century Ave., Mississauga, Ont. L5N 6P7, Canada. TEL 416-542-7400. FAX 416-542-1624.
circ. 14,000. *4248*

RESOURCE MAGAZINE (BRIDGEPORT).
Bridgeport Hospital, 267 Grant St., Box 5000, Bridgeport, CT 06610. TEL 203-384-3000. FAX 203-384-3943.
circ. 90,000. *2469*

RESOURCES (NASHVILLE).
F I S I - Madison Financial Corporation Box 40726, Nashville, TN 37204. TEL 615-371-2775.
circ. 1,000,000. *961*

RESTAURANT HOSPITALITY.
Penton Publishing 1100 Superior Ave., Cleveland, OH 44114-2543. TEL 216-696-7000. FAX 216-696-8765.
circ. 138,000. *2479*

RESTAURANT TRENDS.
World Publications, Inc., 330 W. Canton, Box 2456, Winter Park, FL 32790. TEL 407-628-4802. FAX 407-628-4802.
circ. 20,000. *2479*

RESTYLING AND ACCESSORIES MARKETING.
Shore Communications, Inc., 180 Allen Rd., Ste. 300N, Atlanta, GA 30328-4893. TEL 404-252-8831. FAX 404-252-4436.
circ. 11,000. *4700*

RETAIL OBSERVER.
1442 Sierra Creek Way, San Jose, CA 95132. TEL 408-272-8974. FAX 408-251-6511.
circ. 3,888. *2561*

RETAIL PACKAGING.
Turret-Wheatland Ltd., 12 Greycaine Rd., Watford, Herts. WD2 4JP, England. *3651*

RETAILER NEWS: SOUTHERN CALIFORNIA - WESTERN STATES EDITION.
Target Publishing, Inc., PO Box 92317, Pasadena, CA 91109-3217. TEL 213-375-8786. FAX 213-375-0215.
circ. 25,000. *1052*

THE RETIRED OFFICER.
Retired Officers' Association, 201 N. Washington St., Alexandria, VA 22314-2529. TEL 703-549-2311. FAX 703-838-8173.
circ. 380,000. *3469*

REVIEW OF LATIN AMERICAN STUDIES.
San Diego State University Press, San Diego State University, San Diego, CA 92182. TEL 619-594-6220.
circ. 600. *2420*

REVISTA A T E M C O P.
Asociacion Espanola de Tecnicos de Maquinaria para la Construccion, Obras Publicas y Mineria, c/o Cruz del Sur, No. 3 bajo, 28007 Madrid, Spain. *1873*

REVISTA AEREA.
Strato Publishing Co., Inc., 310 E. 44th St., Ste. 1601, New York, NY 10017. TEL 212-370-1740. FAX 212-949-6756.
circ. 9,000. *61*

REVISTA ALENTEJANA.
Casa do Alentejo, Rua das Portas de Santo Antao 58, Lisbon 2, Portugal.
circ. 3,000. *2881*

REVISTA BRASILEIRA DE XADREZ POSTAL.
Clube de Xadrez Epistolar Brasileiro, Caixa Postal 317, 40001 Salvador (BA), Brazil. *4485*

CONTROLLED CIRCULATION SERIALS 5015

REVISTA CUBANA DE INVESTIGACIONES PESQUERAS. BOLETINES BIBLIOGRAFICOS.
Direccion de Ciencia y Tecnica, Ministerio de la Industria Pesquera, 5ta Avda. y 248 Barlovento, Santa Fe, Playa, Havana, Cuba. FAX 0511345.
circ. 900. *2048*

REVISTA DA CONSTRUCAO CIVIL.
Sindicato da Industria da Construcao Civil no Municipio do Rio de Janeiro, Rua do Senado 213, andar 1, 20231 Rio de Janeiro, RJ, Brazil.
circ. 5,000. *630*

REVISTA DE ARQUITECTURA.
Sociedad Central de Arquitectos, Montevideo 938, 1019 Buenos Aires, Argentina. TEL 54-1-812-3644. FAX 54-1-953-5508.
circ. 8,000. *306*

REVISTA DE CIENCIAS FARMACEUTICAS.
Universidade Estadual Paulista, Av. Vicente Ferreira 1278, Caixa Postal 603, 17.500 Marilia SP, Brazil. TEL 0144-331844. FAX 0144-22-2504. *3742*

REVISTA DE ESTUDIOS SOCIALES.
Centro de Estudios Sociales de la Santa Cruz del Valle de los Caidos, Palacio Real, Bailen s-n, Apdo. de Correas 14158, Madrid 15, Spain.
circ. 2,000. *4447*

REVISTA DE HISTORIA.
Comite Provincial del Partido Comunista de Cuba, Seccion de Investigaciones Historicas, Ave. 20 Aniversario y Plaza de la Revolucion, Holguin, Cuba. TEL 462013.
circ. 3,000. *2320*

REVISTA ECONOMICA.
Universidad Nacional de la Plata, Instituto de Investigaciones Economicas, Calle 48 No. 555, Piso 5, Ofic. 523, 1900 La Plata, Argentina.
circ. 1,000. *688*

REVISTA ELECTROTECNICA.
Asociacion Electrotecnia Argentina, Posadas 1659, C.P. 1112 Buenos Aires, Argentina. TEL 804-3454-1532.
circ. 1,600. *1907*

REVISTA TRIMESTRAL DE JURISPRUDENCIA.
Supremo Tribunal Federal, SIG-Quadra 6-Lote 800, 70604 Brasilia, D.F., Brazil.
circ. 2,000. *2673*

REVUE ARCHEOLOGIQUE DE L'EST ET DU CENTRE-EST.
Editions du C N R S, 1 Place Aristide Briand, 92195 Meudon Cedex, France. TEL 1-45-34-75-50. FAX 1-46-26-28-49.
circ. 1,500. *283*

REVUE ARCHEOLOGIQUE NARBONNAISE.
Editions du C N R S, 1 Place Aristide Briand, 92195 Meudon Cedex, France. TEL 1-45-34-75-50. FAX 1-46-26-28-49.
circ. 1,500. *283*

REVUE D'ELEVAGE ET DE MEDECINE VETERINAIRE DES PAYS TROPICAUX.
Expansion Scientifique, 15 rue Saint Benoit, 75278 Paris Cedex 06, France. *4815*

REVUE D'HISTOIRE DES TEXTES.
Editions du C N R S, 1 Place Aristide Briand, 92195 Meudon Cedex, France. TEL 1-45-34-75-50. FAX 1-46-26-28-49.
circ. 1,250. *2955*

REVUE FRANCAISE DE SERVICE SOCIAL.
Association Nationale des Assistants de Service Social, 15 rue de Bruxelles, 75009 Paris, France. TEL 45-26-33-79.
circ. 2,700. *4418*

REVUE MEDICALE DE BRUXELLES.
Universite Libre de Bruxelles, Association des Medecins Anciens Etudiants, Route de Lennik 808, Bte. 612, B-1070 Brussels, Belgium. TEL 02-555-6062. FAX 02-555-6117.
circ. 3,000. *3149*

REVUE MILITAIRE SUISSE.
Association de la Revue Militaire Suisse, 39 av. de la Gare, Ch-1000 Lausanne, Switzerland.
circ. 3,105. *3470*

Contr Circ

CONTROLLED CIRCULATION SERIALS

REVUE PRATIQUE DU FROID ET DU CONDITIONNEMENT DE L'AIR.
5 ave de Verdun, B.P. 105, 94208 Ivry-sur-Seine Cedex, France. TEL 1-49-60-86-36. FAX 1-46-72-41-85.
circ. 4,948. *2303*

RHODE ISLAND. DEPARTMENT OF EDUCATION. (YEAR) STATISTICAL TABLES.
Department of Education, 22 Hayes St., Providence, RI 02908. TEL 401-277-2842. *1679*

RHODE ISLAND. DEPARTMENT OF STATE LIBRARY SERVICES. NEWSLETTER.
Department of State Library Services, 300 Richmond St., Providence, RI 02903-4222. TEL 401-277-2726. FAX 401-831-1311.
circ. 800. *2782*

LE RICHELIEU DIMANCHE.
Promotion G. & P., 84, Richelieu Street, Saint-Jean-sur-Richelieu, Que. J3B 6X3, Canada. TEL 514-347-5371. FAX 514-347-4539.
circ. 34,400. *117*

RIGHT CHOICES.
Tinsley Communications, Inc., 100 Bridge St., Hampton, VA 23669. TEL 804-723-4499. FAX 804-723-4499.
circ. 300,410. *2021*

RIJKSUNIVERSITEIT UTRECHT. DE UNIVERSITEIT MEDIA BULLETIN.
Rijksuniversiteit te Utrecht, Afdeling Voorlichting, Heidelberglaan 8, 3584 CS Utrecht, Netherlands. TEL 030-533550. FAX 030-521818.
circ. 1,700. *1715*

RIO GRANDE DO SUL, BRAZIL. PROCURADORIA GERAL DO ESTADO. REVISTA.
Procuradoria Geral do Estado, Av. Borges Medeiros 1501, 13th, Porto Alegre 90060, Brazil. FAX 0512-255496.
circ. 1,500. *2675*

RISTORAZIONE PIU.
Editrice Arti Poligrafiche Europee, Via Casella 16, 20156 Milan, Italy. TEL 02-330221. FAX 02-39214341.
circ. 30,000. *2480*

RIVER'S EDGE.
Profit by Design, Inc., RR4, Box 118, Fredricksburg, VA 22405-9310. TEL 703-373-9203.
circ. 10,000. *2233*

ROAD AHEAD.
Road Ahead Publishing Co. Pty Ltd., G.P.O. Box 1403, Brisbane, Qld. 4001, Australia. FAX 257-1863.
circ. 580,000. *4700*

ROCAS Y MINERALES.
Editorial Rocas y Minerales, Arturo Baldasano, 15, 28043 Madrid, Spain. TEL 415 1804. FAX 415-1661.
circ. 6,000. *3494*

ROCK MAGNETISM AND PALEOGEOPHYSICS.
Rock Magnetism and Paleogeophysics Research Group in Japan, c/o Department of Geology and Mineralogy, Kyoto University, Kyoto 606-01, Japan. FAX 81-75-7534189.
circ. 500. *1594*

ROCKY MOUNTAIN FOOD DEALER.
Rocky Mountain Food Dealers Association, 800 Grant St., Ste.100, Denver, CO 80203-2344. TEL 303-830-7001.
circ. 1,400. *2093*

ROEH HACHESHBON.
Institute of Certified Public Accountants in Israel, Box 29281, 1 Montefiore St., Tel Aviv, Israel.
circ. 2,700. *756*

ROESSLERIA.
Instituto de Pesquisas de Recursos Naturais Renovaveis "Ataliba Paz", Rua Goncalves Dias 570, 90060 Porto Alegre, Brazil.
circ. 500. *1496*

ROHWEDDER.
Rough Weather Press, Box 29490, Los Angeles, CA 90029. TEL 213-256-5083.
circ. 1,500. *2955*

ROMA E PROVINCIA ATTRAVERSO LA STATISTICA.
Camera di Commercio Industria Artigianato e Agricoltura di Roma, Via De'Burro 147, 00186 Rome, Italy. *4584*

THE ROMANTIST.
F. Marion Crawford Memorial Society, Saracinesca House, 3610 Meadowbrook Ave., Nashville, TN 37205. TEL 615-292-9695.
circ. 300. *2984*

ROSACRUZ.
Supreme Grand Lodge of AMORC, Inc., Rosicrucian Park, San Jose, CA 95191. TEL 408-287-9171. *3780*

ROSSING MAGAZINE.
Rossing Uranium Ltd., P.O. Box 22391, Windhoek 9000, Namibia. FAX 061-228147.
circ. 4,000. *1496*

ROTOR AND WING INTERNATIONAL.
Phillips Publishing, Inc., 7811 Montrose Rd., Potomac, MD 20854. TEL 301-340-2100. FAX 301-309-3847. *61*

ROUNDUP (CLARKSVILLE).
Acme Boot Co., Inc., 1002 Stafford St., Box 749, Clarksville, TN 37040. TEL 615-552-2000.
circ. 2,500. *4361*

ROYAL AIR FORCE EDUCATION BULLETIN.
Royal Air Force School of Education & Training Support, Educational and Training Technology Development Unit, RAF Newton, Nottingham NG13 8HL, England.
circ. 1,500. *3470*

ROYAL BANK LETTER.
Royal Bank of Canada, Public Affairs Department, One Place Ville Marie, 7th Fl. W., Box 6001, Montreal, Que. H3C 3A9, Canada. TEL 514-874-2110.
circ. 400,000. *798*

ROYAL BOTANICAL GARDENS, HAMILTON, ONT. TECHNICAL BULLETIN.
Royal Botanical Gardens, Box 399, Hamilton, Ont. L8N 3H8, Canada. TEL 416-527-1158. FAX 416-577-0375.
circ. 1,000. *516*

ROYAL COLLEGE OF PHYSICIANS OF EDINBURGH. DIRECTORY.
Royal College of Physicians of Edinburgh, 9 Queen Street, Edinburgh EH2 1JQ, Scotland. TEL 031-225-7324. FAX 031-220-3939. *3150*

ROYAL INSTITUTION OF GREAT BRITAIN. RECORD.
Royal Institution of Great Britain, 21 Albemarle St., London W1X 4BS, England.
circ. 3,000. *4336*

ROYAL INSTITUTION OF GREAT BRITAIN. ROYAL INSTITUTION LECTURES.
Royal Institution of Great Britain, 21 Albemarle St., London, W1X 4BS, England.
circ. 4,000. *4336*

ROYAL SOCIETY NEWS.
Royal Society of London, 6 Carlton House Terrace, London SW1Y 5AG, England. TEL 071-839-5561. FAX 071-976-1837.
circ. 3,500. *4336*

RUBBER & PLASTICS NEWS.
Crain Communications Inc. (Akron), 1725 Merriman Rd., Ste. 300, Akron, OH 44313-3185. TEL 216-836-9180. FAX 216-836-1005.
circ. 15,867. *4293*

RUNAWAY.
Travel Publications, Inc., Box 610, Alta Loma, CA 91701.
circ. 356,000. *4785*

RURAL ELECTRIC NEBRASKAN.
Nebraska Rural Electric Association, 800 S. 13th St., Lincoln, NE 68501. TEL 402-475-4988.
circ. 58,000. *1907*

RUSSIAN BUYERS' GUIDE.
British Industrial Publicity Overseas Ltd., 90 Moorsom St., Birmingham B6 4NT, England. TEL 021-359-0030. FAX 021-359-7441. *920*

RUTGERS MAGAZINE.
Rutgers University, Department of University Communications, Alexander Johnston Hall, New Brunswick, NJ 08903. TEL 908-932-7315. FAX 908-932-8412.
circ. 134,000. *1323*

RUTLAND AREA SHOPPER.
Robert W. Maguire, Jr. Ltd., 98 Allen St., Rutland, VT 05701. TEL 802-775-4221. FAX 802-775-9535.
circ. 17,000. *38*

S A CLEANING REVIEW.
George Warman Publications (Pty.) Ltd., 77 Hout St., P.O. Box 704, 8000 Cape Town, South Africa. TEL 021-24-5320. FAX 021-26-1332.
circ. 1,800. *1282*

S A F T O EXPORTER.
South African Foreign Trade Organisation, Publishing Division, P.O. Box 782706, Sandton 2146, South Africa. TEL 011-883-3737. FAX 011-883-6569.
circ. 10,000. *920*

S A L S IN BRIEF.
Southern Adirondack Library System, 22 Whitney Place, Saratoga Springs, NY 12866. TEL 518-584-7300.
circ. 425. *2782*

S.A. MARKSMAN.
South African Pistol Association, MacKay Chambers, 11 Mackay Ave., Blairgowrie, Randburg 2194, South Africa. TEL 011-787-6915. FAX 0171-32427.
circ. 2,000. *4486*

S C A N.
U.S. National Aeronautics and Space Administration, Center for Aerospace Information, Box 8757, Baltimore - Washington International Airport, MD 21240. TEL 301-621-0153. *61*

S E C DOCKET.
U.S. Securities and Exchange Commission, 450 Fifth St., N.W., MISC-11, Washington, DC 20549. TEL 202-272-7460. FAX 202-272-7050.
circ. 12,500. *962*

S E C NEWS DIGEST.
U.S. Securities and Exchange Commission, 450 Fifth St., N.W., MISC-11, Washington, DC 20549. TEL 202-272-7460. FAX 202-272-7050. *962*

S E I U UPDATE.
Service Employees International Union, AFL-CIO, CLC, 1313 L St., N.W., Washington, DC 20005. TEL 202-898-3200. FAX 202-898-3438.
circ. 50,000. *2588*

S E R I. ETHANOL ANNUAL REPORT.
Solar Energy Research Institute, Technical Inquiry Service, 1617 Cole Blvd., Golden, CO 80401-3393. TEL 303-231-1000. *1795*

S E R I SCIENCE AND TECHNOLOGY IN REVIEW.
Solar Energy Research Institute, Technical Inquiry Service, 1617 Cole Blvd., Golden, CO 80401-3393. TEL 303-231-1000.
circ. 7,000. *1811*

S G V GROUP JOURNAL.
SyCip, Gorres, Velayo & Co., Information Center, P.O. Box 256, MCC Makati 1299, Metro Manila, Philippines. FAX 632-819-0872. *1084*

S I G A C T NEWS.
Association for Computing Machinery, Special Interest Group on Automata and Computability Theory, 1515 Broadway, 17th Fl., New York, NY 10036.
circ. 1,588. *1415*

S I G N U M NEWSLETTER.
Association for Computing Machinery, Special Interest Group on Numerical Mathematics, 1515 Broadway, 17th Fl., New York, NY 10036. TEL 212-869-7440.
circ. 1,800. *3066*

S K A V - FACHBLATT.
Schweizerischer Verband Christlicher Institutionen, Zaehringerstr. 19, 6000 Lucerne 7, Switzerland.
circ. 1,500. *4418*

CONTROLLED CIRCULATION SERIALS

S N E S U P BULLETIN.
Syndicat National de l'Enseignement Superieur, 78 rue du Faubourg Saint-Denis, 75010 Paris, France. *1716*

S O R T BULLETIN.
American Library Association, Staff Organizations Round Table, 8905 Chatwood Dr., Houston, TX 77078.
circ. 550. *2782*

S P E E A SPOTLITE.
Seattle Professional Engineering Employees Association, 15205 52nd Ave. S., Seattle, WA 98188. TEL 800-325-0811. FAX 206-248-3990.
circ. 15,500. *1836*

SAAGVERKEN.
AB Svensk Traevarutidning, Midskogsgraend 5, S-115 43 Stockholm, Sweden. TEL 46-8-664-34-00. FAX 46-8-664-21-24.
circ. 3,319. *2117*

SAASTOPANKKI.
Saastopankkiliitto, Postilokero 47, SF-00101 Helsinki 10, Finland. FAX 0-1334935.
circ. 30,942. *798*

SABAH. FOREST DEPARTMENT. ANNUAL REPORT.
Forest Department, P.O. Box 311, 90007 Sandakan, Malaysia. TEL 089-660811. FAX 089-669170. *2107*

SADELMAGER-OG TAPETSERER TIDENDE.
Saddlers and Upholsterer's Guild, Fortunstraede 5, 1065 Copenhagen K, Denmark.
circ. 3,200. *2561*

SADO MARINE BIOLOGICAL STATION. REPORT.
Niigata Daigaku, Rigakubu Fuzoku Sado Rinkai Jikkenjo, 2-8050 Igarashi, Niigata 950-21, Japan. TEL 025-262-6264. FAX 025-262-6116. *454*

SAFE CYCLING.
Motorcycle Safety Foundation, 2 Jenner St., Ste. 150, Irvine, CA 92718-3812. TEL 714-727-3227. FAX 714-727-4217.
circ. 6,500. *4520*

SAFE DRIVER.
Order of the Road, 14 Churchfields, Nutley, Uckfield, E. Sussex TN22 3NA, England. TEL 0825-71-2271.
circ. 1,800. *4701*

SAFECO AGENT.
Safeco Corporation, Safeco Plaza, Seattle, WA 98185. TEL 206-545-5000.
circ. 14,000. *2542*

SAGGI.
Edizioni La Nostra Famiglia, Via Don Luigi Monza, 1, 22037 Ponte Lambro, Italy. TEL 031-625111. FAX 031-625275.
circ. 800. *3353*

SAHKO - TELE.
Elektroingenjoersfoerbundet, Merikasarmink. 7J53, SF-00160 Helsinki, Finland. TEL 0-171050. FAX 358-0-657562.
circ. 3,928. *1907*

SAILBOARD RETAILER.
Gorge Publishing, Inc., 500 Morton Rd., Box 918, Hood River, OR 97031. TEL 503-386-7440. FAX 503-386-7480.
circ. 4,500. *4528*

ST. DUNSTAN'S ANNUAL REPORT.
St. Dunstan's for Men and Women Blinded on War Service, P.O. Box 4XB, 12-14 Harcourt St., London W1A 4XB, England. TEL 071-723-5021. *2295*

ST. GALLEN.
Verkehrsbuero St. Gallen, Postfach 476, Bahnhofplatz 1a, CH-9001 St. Gallen, Switzerland. FAX 071-234304.
circ. 5,500. *4785*

SAINT LOUIS UNIVERSITY RESEARCH JOURNAL.
Saint Louis University, Graduate School of Arts and Sciences, Box 71, Baguio City 2600, Philippines.
circ. 1,000. *2514*

SALES AND MARKETING STRATEGIES & NEWS.
Hughes Communications, Inc., 211 W. State St., Box 197, Rockford, IL 61105. TEL 800-435-2937. FAX 815-963-7773.
circ. 82,000. *1053*

SALMANTICENSIS.
Universidad Pontificia, Departamento de Ediciones y Publicaciones, Apdo. de Correos 541, 37080 Salamanca, Spain. TEL 923-21-51-40. FAX 923-21-34-50.
circ. 2,000. *4275*

SALUS MILITIAE.
Hospital Central de las Fuerzas Armadas, San Martin, Caracas-1060, Venezuela.
circ. 1,000. *3151*

SALUTE.
Military Forces Features, Inc., 169 Lexington Ave., New York, NY 10157-0014. TEL 212-532-0660. FAX 212-779-3080.
circ. 250,482. *2234*

SALVO.
Fort Point and Presidio Historical Association, Box 29163, Presidio of San Francisco, CA 94129. TEL 415-921-8193.
circ. 900. *2421*

SAMVADADHVAM.
Indian Statistical Institute, 203 Barrackpore Trunk Rd., Calcutta 700035, India.
circ. 2,500. *4585*

SAN ANTONIO LIVING.
Lash Publications, Inc. (San Antonio), 12451 Starcrest, San Antonio, TX 78216-2957. TEL 512-545-4663.
circ. 40,000. *4158*

SAN DIEGO EXECUTIVE MAGAZINE.
Executive North, Inc., 9449 Balboa Ave., Ste. 111, San Diego, CA 92111. TEL 619-467-1050. FAX 619-467-1154.
circ. 23,000. *690*

SAN FRANCISCO GIFTCENTER AND JEWELRYMART BUYER'S GUIDE.
Bolger Publications Inc., 3301 Como Ave., S.E., Minneapolis, MN 55414. TEL 612-645-6311. FAX 612-645-1750.
circ. 20,000. *2282*

SAN FRANCISCO PENINSULA PARENT.
Peninsula Parent Newspaper Inc., 1131 Vancouver, Burlingame, CA 94010. TEL 415-342-9203. FAX 415-342-9276.
circ. 60,000. *1243*

SANATORIO SAO LUCAS. BOLETIM.
Fundacao para o Progresso da Cirurgia, Rua Pirapitingui 80, Sao Paulo, Brazil.
circ. 2,000. *3383*

SANDUQ ABU DHABI LIL-INMA' AL-IQTISADI AL-ARABI. AL-TAQRIR AL-SANAWI.
Abu Dhabi Fund for Arab Economic Development, P.O. Box 814, Abu Dhabi, United Arab Emirates. TEL 725800.
circ. 1,000. *935*

SANDWICH ISLANDS MAGAZINE.
Resort Publications, Inc., Box 748, Kilauea, Kauai, HI 96754. TEL 808-828-1125. FAX 808-828-1266.
circ. 20,000. *4785*

SANEAMENTO.
Departamento Nacional de Obras de Saneamenento, Av. Pres. Vargas 62-11 andar, 20091 Rio de Janeiro R.J., Brazil.
circ. 16,000. *4112*

SANGYO GIJUTSU JOHO YOKKAICHI.
Yokkaichi-shiritsu Toshokan, 2-42 Kubota 1-chome, Yokkaichi-shi, Mie-ken 510, Japan. *4608*

SANKYO KENKYUSHO NEMPO.
Sankyo Co., Ltd., Research Institute, 1-2-58 Hiromachi, Shinagawa-ku, Tokyo 140, Japan. TEL 03-492-3131. FAX 03-495-6734. *3742*

SANYO KASEI NEWS.
Sanyo Chemical Industries Ltd., 11-1 Ikkyo Nomotocho, Higashiyama-ku, Kyoto 605, Japan.
circ. 6,000. *1187*

SAO PAULO (CITY) ARQUIVO MUNICIPAL. REVISTA.
Arquivo Municipal, Divisao de Arquivo Historico, Rua da Consolacao 1024, Sao Paulo, Brazil.
circ. 1,000. *2421*

SARAH LAWRENCE REVIEW.
Sarah Lawrence College, Writing Department, c/o Thomas Lux, Bronxville, NY 10708. TEL 914-337-0700.
circ. 1,500. *2883*

SARAWAK ELECTRICITY SUPPLY CORPORATION. ANNUAL REPORT.
Sarawak Electricity Supply Corporation, P.O. Box 149, 93700 Kuching, Sarawak, Malaysia. TEL 082-441188. FAX 082-444082.
circ. 2,000. *1907*

SASKATCHEWAN. DEPARTMENT OF INDUSTRY AND COMMERCE. INDUSTRIAL BENEFITS FROM RESOURCE DEVELOPMENT.
Government Printing Co., 2005 8th St., Regina, Sask. S4P 3V7, Canada. TEL 306-566-9393. *690*

SASKATCHEWAN BULLETIN.
Saskatchewan Teachers' Federation, 2317 Arlington Ave., Box 1108, Saskatoon, Sask. S7K 3N3, Canada. TEL 306-373-1160. FAX 306-374-1122.
circ. 22,300. *1661*

SASKATCHEWAN MANUFACTURERS GUIDE.
Government Printing Co., 2005 8th St., Regina, Sask. S4P 3V7, Canada. TEL 306-566-9393. *1152*

SATVISION MAGAZINE.
Satellite Broadcasting and Communications Association of America, 225 Reinekers Lane, Ste. 600, Alexandria, VA 22314-2322. TEL 703-549-6990. FAX 703-549-7640.
circ. 10,000. *1379*

SCAN.
Dienst Landbouwkundig Onderzoek, Staring Centrum, Instituut voor Onderzoek van het Landelijke Gebied, P.O. Box 125, 6700 AC Wageningen, Netherlands. TEL 0837-74200. FAX 0837-24812.
circ. 2,000. *191*

SCANDINAVIAN SHIPPING GAZETTE.
Nautisk Forlag, Bentzonsvej 54, P.B. 1462, 2000 Copenhagen K, Denmark.
circ. 4,000. *4737*

SCENE.
Scene, Inc., 930 Fifth Ave., New York, NY 10021. TEL 212-737-8100.
circ. 75,000. *3517*

SCHIFF UND HAFEN.
Seehafen Verlag GmbH, Wandalenweg 1, Postfach 105605, 2000 Hamburg 1, Germany. TEL 040-23714-02. FAX 040-23714-154.
circ. 2,500. *4737*

SCHOOL ADMINISTRATOR.
American Association of School Administrators, 1801 North Moore St., Arlington, VA 22209. TEL 703-528-0700. FAX 703-528-2146. *1731*

SCHOOL AND COLLEGE.
Penton Publishing 1100 Superior Ave., Cleveland, OH 44114-2543. TEL 216-696-7000. FAX 216-696-8765.
circ. 50,000. *1661*

SCHOOL BUS BRIEFS.
Department of Public Instruction, Pupil Transportation Service, 125 S. Webster St., Box 7841, Madison, WI 53707-7841. *4656*

SCHOOL BUS FLEET.
Bobit Publishing Company, 2512 Artesia Blvd., Redondo Beach, CA 90278. TEL 310-376-8788. FAX 310-376-9043.
circ. 19,000. *4656*

SCHOOL LIBRARIES BULLETIN.
Anambra State School Libraries Association, c/o Enugu Campus Library, University of Nigeria, Enugu, Nigeria.
circ. 250. *2783*

SCHOOL SHOP - TECH DIRECTIONS.
Prakken Publications, Inc., 416 Longshore Dr., Box 8623, Ann Arbor, MI 48107. TEL 313-769-1211. FAX 313-769-8383.
circ. 45,000. *1759*

CONTROLLED CIRCULATION SERIALS

SCHWEIZERISCHE FEUERWEHR-ZEITUNG.
Schweizerischer Feuerwehrverband, Ensingerstr. 37, CH-3000 Berne, Switzerland. *2034*

SCHWEIZERISCHE LEHRERZEITUNG.
Zuerichsee Zeitschriftenverlag, Seestrasse 86, CH-8712 Staefa, Switzerland. TEL 01-9285611.
circ. 16,500. *1662*

SCHWEIZERISCHE METZGER-ZEITUNG.
Verband Schweizer Metzgermeister, Postfach, CH-8028 Zurich, Switzerland. TEL 01-2527766. FAX 01-262874.
circ. 5,498. *2081*

SCHWIMMBAD UND SAUNA.
Fachschriften Verlag GmbH, Hoehenstr. 17, Postfach 1329, 7012 Fellbach, Germany. TEL 0711-5206-1. FAX 0711-5281424.
circ. 65,000. *631*

SCIENCE MUSEUM NEWS.
Association of Science Museum Directors, c/o The Carnegie Museum of Natural History, 4400 Forbes Ave., Pittsburgh, PA 15213. TEL 412-622-3377.
circ. 200. *3532*

SCOPE.
Verlag Hoppenstedt und Co., Havelstr. 9, Postfach 4006, 6100 Darmstadt, Germany. TEL 06151-380-0. FAX 06151-380-360.
circ. 25,000. *1084*

SCOTTISH LICENSED TRADE NEWS.
Peebles Publishing Group, Ltd., 2 Bergius House, Clifton St., Glasgow G3 7LA, Scotland. TEL 041-331-1022. FAX 041-331-1395.
circ. 12,223. *385*

SCOTTISH LITERARY JOURNAL.
Association for Scottish Literary Studies, Dept. of English, University of Aberdeen, Old Aberdeen AB9 2UB, Scotland. TEL 0224-272634.
circ. 820. *2957*

SCOTTISH MEDICINE.
Hermiston Publications Ltd., 2 Hill Sq., Edinburgh EH8 9DR, Scotland.
circ. 5,000. *3152*

SCOTTISH MUSEUM NEWS.
Scottish Museums Council, County House, 20-22 Tophichen St., Edinburgh EH3 8JB, Scotland. TEL 031-229-7465.
circ. 1,500. *3532*

SCOTTISH OPTOMETRIST.
Scottish Committee of Optometrist, c/o 24 Tweed Crescent, Pean Park, Renfred, Scotland. *3305*

SCREEN PRINTING.
S T Publications Inc., 407 Gilbert Ave., Cincinnati, OH 45202. TEL 513-421-2050. FAX 513-421-5144.
circ. 3,000. *4005*

SCRINIUM.
Verband Oesterreichischer Archivare, Postfach 164, A-1014 Vienna, Austria. *2783*

SCRIPPS RESEARCH INSTITUTE. SCIENTIFIC REPORT.
Scripps Research Institute, 10666 N. Torrey Pines Rd., La Jolla, CA 92037. TEL 619-455-8263. FAX 619-554-6357.
circ. 5,000. *3152*

SCRIPTA GEOLOGICA.
Nationaal Natuurhistorisch Museum, Postbus 9517, 2300 RA Leiden, Netherlands. TEL 071-143844. FAX 071-133344.
circ. 575. *1579*

SCROLL OF PHI DELTA THETA.
Phi Delta Theta Fraternity, 2 So. Campus, Oxford, OH 45056. TEL 513-523-6345. FAX 513-523-9200. *1324*

SEA BREEZE.
Wachters' Organic Sea Products Corporation, 360 Shaw Rd., South San Francisco, CA 94080. FAX 415-875-1626.
circ. 50,000. *4786*

SEA RESCUE.
Yachting News (Pty) Ltd., P.O. Box 3473, Cape Town 8000, South Africa. TEL 021-4617472. FAX 021-4613758.
circ. 10,000. *4738*

SEARCH (LONDON, 1957).
Muscular Dystrophy Group of Great Britain and Northern Ireland, 35 Macaulay Rd., London SW4 0QP, England. TEL 071-720-8055. FAX 071-498-0670. *3152*

SEARCH (YORK).
Joseph Rowntree Foundation, The Homestead, 40 Water End, York YO3 6LP, England. TEL 0904-629241. FAX 0904-620072.
circ. 6,000. *4419*

SECRETARIES AND MANAGERS JOURNAL OF AUSTRALIA.
Secretaries and Managers Association, Labor Council Bldg., 377-83 Sussex St., Sydney, N.S.W. 2000, Australia. TEL 02-264-6691. FAX 02-261-2407. *1027*

SECURITY NEWS (SALAMANCA).
Terra Publishing, Inc., RD 1, Box 142, Center St. Ext., Salamanca, NY 14779. TEL 716-945-3488. FAX 716-945-5238.
circ. 19,000. *1528*

SECURITY SALES.
Bobit Publishing Company, 2512 Artesia Blvd., Redondo Beach, CA 90278. TEL 310-376-8788. FAX 310-376-9043.
circ. 22,000. *643*

DER SELBSTAENDIGE.
Bund der Selbstaendigen Deutscher Gewerbeverband e.V., Hochkreuzallee 89, 5300 Bonn 2, Germany. TEL 0228-311046. FAX 0228-316966.
circ. 100,000. *1117*

SELECTA.
Selecta-Verlag, Pasinger Str. 8, 8033 Planegg, Germany. TEL 857030. *3152*

SELECTED READINGS IN PLASTIC SURGERY.
Baylor Universtiy Medical Center, 411 N. Washington Ave., Ste. 6900, Dallas, TX 75246. TEL 214-824-0154. FAX 214-824-0463.
circ. 1,800. *3384*

SEMBRADOR.
Parroquia Santisima Trinidad Rufino, La Misma del Punto (8), Italia 62, Rufino, Argentina. *2170*

SEMPEX.
Societe d'Editions Medico-Pharmaceutiques (SEMP), 26 rue le Brun, 75013 Paris, France. TEL 1-43-37-83-50. FAX 43-31-94-11.
circ. 11,000. *3743*

SENIOR CITIZENS POST.
Coordinating Council for Senior Citizens, 807 S. Duke St., Durham, NC 27701. TEL 919-688-8247. FAX 919-683-3406.
circ. 1,500. *2278*

SENIOR WORLD OF LOS ANGELES COUNTY.
Californian Publishing Co., Box 1565, El Cajon, CA 92022. TEL 619-593-2900.
circ. 150,000. *2279*

SENSOR REPORT.
P. Keppler GmbH und Co. KG, Industrie. 2, Postfach, 6056 Heusenstamm, Germany. TEL 06104-6060. FAX 06104-606333.
circ. 10,000. *2525*

SEOUL JOURNAL OF MEDICINE.
Seoul National University, College of Medicine, 28 Yunkeon-dong, Chongro-gu, Seoul, S. Korea. *3152*

SER PADRES.
Gruner & Jahr U.S.A. Publishing, 685 Third Ave., New York, NY 10017. TEL 212-878-8700.
circ. 225,000. *4852*

SERIALS HOLDINGS IN NEWFOUNDLAND LIBRARIES.
Memorial University of Newfoundland Library, Periodicals Division, St. John's, Nfld. A1C 5S7, Canada. TEL 709-737-7438. FAX 709-737-4569. *411*

SERICA.
Silk Association of Great Britain, c/o Rheinbergs Ltd., Morley Rd., Tonbridge TN9 1RN, England. TEL 0732-351357. FAX 0732-770217.
circ. 150. *4623*

SERPENTINE MUSE.
Adventuresses of Sherlock Holmes, c/o Evelyn Herzog, 360 W. 21st St., New York, NY 10011. TEL 212-527-7789. *2986*

SERVICE EMPLOYEES UNION.
Service Employees International Union, AFL-CIO, CLC, 1313 L St., N.W., Washington, DC 20005. TEL 202-898-3200. FAX 202-898-3438.
circ. 950,000. *2589*

SERVICING DEALER.
Communications Group, Inc., 3703 N. Main St., Ste. 108, Rockford, IL 61103-1677. TEL 815-633-2680. FAX 815-633-6880.
circ. 23,000. *3023*

SERVICIOS ELECTRICOS DEL GRAN BUENOS AIRES S.A. BOLETIN BIBLIOGRAFICO.
Servicios Electricos del Gran Buenos Aires S.A., Biblioteca y Hemeroteca, Balcare 184, Buenos Aires, Argentina. *4615*

SEVENTY SIX.
Unocal Corporation, Box 7600, Los Angeles, CA 90051. TEL 213-977-7600.
circ. 42,000. *3701*

SHALOM.
Jewish Peace Fellowship, Box 271, Nyack, NY 10960. TEL 914-358-4601. FAX 914-358-4924.
circ. 3,000. *3947*

SHELL-VENSTER.
Shell Nederland B.V., Dept. PAC/1, Hofplein 20, Rotterdam, Netherlands.
circ. 51,000. *3701*

THE SHEPHERD COLLEGE PICKET.
Shepherd College, Shepherdstown, WV 25443. TEL 304-876-2511. FAX 304-876-3262.
circ. 4,000. *1324*

SHICHOKAKU KYOIKU.
Japan Audio-Visual Education Association, 1-17-1 Toranomon, Minato-ku, Tokyo 105, Japan. FAX 03-3597-0564.
circ. 5,000. *1663*

SHIELD & DIAMOND.
Pi Kappa Alpha Fraternity, 8347 W. Range Cove, Memphis, TN 38125. TEL 901-748-1868.
circ. 90,000. *1324*

SHIPYARD BULLETIN.
Newport News Shipbuilding, Newport News, VA 23607. TEL 804-380-2342. FAX 804-380-3867.
circ. 30,000. *4739*

SHIPYARD LOG.
Pearl Harbor Naval Shipyard, Box 400, Pearl Harbor, HI 96860-5350. TEL 808-474-7108. FAX 808-471-1514.
circ. 6,300. *3471*

SHOOTING COMMERCIALS (MELVILLE).
P T N Publishing Corp., 445 Broad Hollow Rd., Ste. 21, Melville, NY 11747-4722. TEL 516-845-2700. FAX 516-845-7109.
circ. 17,086. *38*

SHOP.
Southam Business Communications Inc. 1450 Don Mills Rd., Don Mills, Ont. M3B 2X7, Canada. TEL 416-445-6641. FAX 416-442-2077.
circ. 11,671. *3023*

SHOPTALK (ENGLEWOOD).
American Humane Association, Animal Protection Division, 63 Inverness Dr. E., Englewood, CO 80112-5117. TEL 303-792-9900. FAX 303-792-5333.
circ. 3,600. *231*

SHOW MEETING.
Gruppo Editoriale G. Reina S.r.l., Via Filippo Carcano, 6, 20149 Milan, Italy. TEL 02-48193542. FAX 02-48012300.
circ. 15,000. *1342*

SHOWBOAT CENTENNIALS NEWSLETTER.
Showboat Centennials, 76 Glen Dr., Worthington, OH 43085. TEL 614-431-9422.
circ. 150. *4529*

SHOWCASE U S A.
Bobit Publishing Company, 2512 Artesia Blvd., Redondo Beach, CA 90278. TEL 310-376-8788. FAX 310-376-9043.
circ. 26,000. *920*

AL-SHURTA.
Ministry of the Interior, Department of Public Relations, P.O. Box 398, Abu Dhabi, United Arab Emirates. TEL 447666.
circ. 1,000. *1522*

SIGNATURE.
Griffin Printing and Lithograph, Co., Inc., 544 W. Colorado St., Glendale, CA 91204-1102. TEL 818-953-9025. FAX 818-242-1172.
circ. 6,500. *4137*

SIGNS OF THE TIMES (CINCINNATI).
S T Publications Inc., 407 Gilbert Ave., Cincinnati, OH 45202. TEL 513-421-2050. FAX 513-421-5144.
circ. 1,500. *38*

AL-SIJIL AL-SHAHRI LI-AHDATH AL-ALAM.
Ministry of Information and Culture, Information Department, P.O. Box 17, Abu Dhabi, United Arab Emirates. TEL 453000.
circ. 1,000. *3972*

AL-SIJIL AL-SHAHRI LI-AHDATH DAWLAT AL-IMARAT AL-ARABIYYAH AL-MUTTAHIDAH.
Ministry of Information and Culture, Information Department, P.O. Box 17, Abu Dhabi, United Arab Emirates. TEL 453000.
circ. 1,000. *4073*

SILENT ADVOCATE.
St. Rita School for the Deaf, 1720 Glendale-Milford Rd., Cincinnati, OH 45215. TEL 513-771-7600. FAX 513-771-7607.
circ. 25,000. *2289*

THE SILVER BARON - STOCKS U S A.
S B Stocks U S A, 5025 S. Eastern Ave., Las Vegas, NV 89119. TEL 702-597-9980. FAX 702-597-9510.
circ. 1,900. *963*

SIMMENTALER JOURNAL.
Simmentaler Cattle Breeders' Society, P.O. Box 3868, Bloemfontein 9800, South Africa. TEL 051-477696. FAX 051-471529.
circ. 1,500. *226*

SINGAPORE. HOUSING AND DEVELOPMENT BOARD. ANNUAL REPORT.
Housing and Development Board, 3451 Jalan Bukit Merah, Singapore 0315, Singapore. TEL 2739090. *2496*

SINGAPORE. MINISTRY OF THE ENVIRONMENT. ANNUAL REPORT.
Ministry of the Environment, Environment Building, 40 Scotts Road, Singapore 0922, Singapore. FAX 065-7319866. *1968*

SINGAPORE COMPUTER SOCIETY. BULLETIN.
Singapore Computer Society, P.O. Box 2570, Singapore, Singapore.
circ. 2,000. *1400*

SINGAPORE CONTRACTORS' EQUIPMENT CATALOGUE.
Times Trade Directories Pte. Ltd., Times Centre, 1 New Industrial Road, Singapore 1953, Singapore. TEL 2848844. FAX 2881186.
circ. 20,000. *1153*

SINGAPORE SOURCE BOOK ARCHITECTS & DESIGNERS.
Times Trade Directories Pte. Ltd., Times Centre, 1 New Industrial Road, Singapore 1953, Singapore. TEL 2848844. FAX 2881186.
circ. 15,000. *1153*

SINGLE FILE MAGAZINE.
Single Association, Inc., Box 6706, Grand Rapids, MI 49516. TEL 616-774-8100.
circ. 15,000. *4363*

SINGLE GENTLEMEN & WOMEN.
Mail Sort, Inc., 3880 Best Mill Rd., Winston-Salem, NC 27103. TEL 919-659-1100.
circ. 40,000. *4363*

SINGLE PARENT.
Parents Without Partners Inc., 8807 Colesville Rd., Silver Spring, MD 20910-4346. TEL 301-588-9354. FAX 301-588-9216.
circ. 110,000. *4419*

SINGLES CHOICE.
113 McHenry Rd., Buffalo Grove, IL 60089-1796. TEL 708-255-9940.
circ. 40,000. *4363*

SIREN MAGAZINE.
Box 66099, Houston, TX 77266-6099. TEL 713-526-1262. FAX 713-771-6849.
circ. 15,000. *2883*

SIXTH DISTRICT FOCUS.
Federal Home Loan Bank of Indianapolis, Library, Box 60, Indianapolis, IN 46206-0060. *799*

SJOESPORT.
Sjoesport A-S, P.O. Box 576, 5001 Bergen, Norway.
circ. 21,000. *4529*

SJONVARPSVISIR.
Frodi Ltd., Armuli 18, 108 Reykjavik, Iceland. TEL 354-1-812300. FAX 1-812946.
circ. 50,000. *1380*

SKETCH BOOK.
Kappa Pi International Honorary Art Fraternity, 9321 Paul Adrian Dr., Crestwood, MO 63126.
circ. 2,000. *344*

SKI - SCHWEIZER SKISPORT.
Habegger AG Druck und Verlag, Gutenbergstr. 1, CH-4552 Derendingen, Switzerland. TEL 065-411151. FAX 065-422632.
circ. 114,000. *4555*

SKIER'S POCKET GUIDE.
Pocket Guide Publications, Inc., 8630 Delmar, Ste., 215, St. Louis, MO 63124. TEL 314-991-5222. FAX 314-991-8911.
circ. 1,000,000. *4556*

SKOGSINDUSTRIARBETAREN.
Samverkande Traefacken, Box 1138, S-111 81 Stockholm, Sweden. TEL 08-230-425. FAX 08-112742.
circ. 125,000. *640*

SKOHANDLAREN.
Sveriges Skohandlarfoerbund, Kungsgatan 19, 111 43 Stockholm, Sweden. TEL 8-791-5300. FAX 8-213690.
circ. 2,100. *4362*

SKOLEFORUM.
Norsk Undervisningforbund - NUFO, Wergelandsveien 15, 0167 Oslo 1, Norway. TEL 47-2-20-94-94. FAX 47-2-42-65-87.
circ. 21,000. *1716*

SKOVEN.
Dansk Skovforening, Amalievej 20, 1875 Frederiksberg C, Denmark. TEL 31-244266. FAX 31-240242.
circ. 3,932. *2108*

SKUPNOST.
Slovenska Skupnost - Unione Slovena, Via Machiavelli 22, 34132 Trieste, Italy. TEL 040-639126.
circ. 5,000. *2023*

SLATE.
Slate, P.O. Box 1175, Kingston, Ont. K7L 4Y8, Canada. TEL 613-542-3717. FAX 613-542-1447.
circ. 12,100. *344*

SMALL BUSINESS ADVOCATE (WASHINGTON).
U.S. Small Business Administration, Office of Advocacy, Mail Code 3114, 409 Third St., N.W., Washington, DC 20416. TEL 202-205-6531. FAX 202-205-6928.
circ. 9,800. *1118*

SMALL BUSINESS BULLETIN (WORCESTER).
Small Business Service Bureau, Inc., Box 1441, 554 Main St., Worcester, MA 01601. TEL 508-756-3513. FAX 508-791-4709.
circ. 35,000. *1118*

SMALLHOLDER TEA AUTHORITY. ANNUAL REPORT.
Smallholder Tea Authority, Box 80, Thyolo, Malawi. *192*

SMOKING AND HEALTH BULLETIN.
U.S. Office on Smoking and Health, National Center for Chronic Disease Prevention and Health Promotion, Centers for Disease Control, MS K-12, 1600 Clifton Rd., N.E., Atlanta, GA 30333.
circ. 7,800. *1540*

SNOW GOER.
Camar Publications Ltd., 130 Spy Court, Markham, Ont. L3R 5H6, Canada. TEL 416-485-8440. FAX 416-475-9246.
circ. 170,000. *4556*

SOBEK'S EXCEPTIONAL ADVENTURES.
Mountain Travel - Sobek, 6420 Fairmount Ave., El Cerrito, CA 94530.
circ. 160,000. *4786*

SOBRE LOS DERIVADOS DE LA CANA DE AZUCAR.
Ediciones Cubana, Obispo No. 527, Apdo. 605, Havana, Cuba.
circ. 1,500. *192*

SOCIALFOERFATTNINGAR.
Foerlagshuset Gothia AB, P.O. Box 15169, S-104 65 Stockholm, Sweden. FAX 08-641-4585.
circ. 2,000. *4420*

SOCIALIST PERSPECTIVE.
Council for Political Studies, 140-20E, South Sinthee Rd., 1st Fl., Calcutta 700 050, India.
circ. 1,000. *3926*

SOCIALPAEDAGOGERNES LANDSFORBUND. T R INFORMATION.
Socialpaedagogernes Landsforbund, Brolaeggerstraede g-st., 1211 Copenhagen K, Denmark. *1664*

SOCIEDAD ARGENTINA DE ESTUDIOS GEOGRAFICOS BOLETIN.
Sociedad Argentina de Estudios Geograficos - GAEA, Rodriquez Pena 158, 4, 1020 Buenos Aires, Argentina. TEL 393-5682. *2262*

SOCIEDADE BRASILEIRA DE MEDICINA TROPICAL. REVISTA.
Sociedade Brasileira de Medicina Tropical, Rua Laura de Araujo 36, P.O. Box 1859, Rio de Janeiro, Brazil. *3223*

SOCIEDADE DE MEDICINA E CIRURGIA DE SAO JOSE DO RIO PRETO. REVISTA.
Sociedade de Medicina e Cirurgia de Sao Jose do Rio Preto, Rua Spinola s-n, Sao Jose da Rio Preto 15100, Brazil. *3384*

SOCIETE D'EDITION DE PERIODIQUES SPORTIFS.
Sopusi, 10 rue du Faubourg Montmartre, 75009 Paris, France.
circ. 175,000. *4488*

SOCIETE HISTORIQUE NICOLAS DENYS. REVUE D'HISTOIRE.
Societe Historique Nicolas Denys, Centre Universitaire, Shippagan, N.B. EOB 2P0, Canada.
circ. 800. *2422*

SOCIETE J.K. HUYSMANS. BULLETIN.
Societe J.K. Huysmans, 22 rue Guynemer, 75006 Paris, France.
circ. 600. *2884*

SOCIETE NATIONALE DES CHEMINS DE FER BELGES. RAPPORT ANNUEL.
Societe Nationale des Chemins de Fer Belges, Fonsnylaan 47B, Bureau 40-231, B-1060 Brussels, Belgium. *4715*

SOCIETY OF ARCHER-ANTIQUARIES. JOURNAL.
Society of Archer-Antiquaries, c/o Alf Webb, 5 Park Court, Bathurst Park Rd., Lydney, Glos. Gl15 5HG, England. TEL 0594-843548. *4488*

SOCIETY OF FEDERAL LINGUISTS. NEWSLETTER.
Society of Federal Linguists, Inc., Box 7765, Washington, DC 20044.
circ. 150. *2842*

SOCIETY OF PROFESSORS OF EDUCATION. OCCASIONAL PAPERS.
Society of Professors of Education, c/o Richard Wisniewski, College of Education, Univ. of Tennessee, Knoxville, TN 37996-3400. TEL 615-974-2201. FAX 615-974-8718. *1664*

SOCIOECONOMIC NEWSLETTER.
Institute for Socioeconomic Studies, Airport Rd., White Plains, NY 10604. TEL 914-428-7400.
circ. 17,500. *4450*

SOIL AND WATER CONSERVATION NEWS.
U.S. Soil Conservation Service, c/o Dept. of Agriculture, Box 2890, Washington, DC 20013. TEL 202-720-7547. FAX 202-690-1221.
circ. 25,000. *192*

SOKOL POLSKI.
Polish Falcons of America, 615 Iron City Dr., Pittsburgh, PA 15205-4397. FAX 412-922-5029.
circ. 16,600. *1301*

SOLDIERS.
U.S. Department of the Army, Cameron Sta., Alexandria, VA 22304-5050. TEL 703-274-6671. FAX 703-274-1896.
circ. 250,000. *3472*

SOLUTIONS.
Solutions Magazine, Inc., 339 Consort Dr., Manchester, MO 63011. FAX 314-256-4901.
circ. 27,111. *193*

SONG OF ZION.
Jackman Music Corp., Box 1900, Orem, UT 84059-5900. TEL 801-225-0859. FAX 801-225-0851.
circ. 13,000. *3581*

SONNTAGSPOST.
Oesterreichischer Verlag, Giselastrasse 3, A-6300, Wirgl, Tirol, Austria.
circ. 28,300. *2173*

SONS OF ITALY NEWS.
Order of the Sons of Italy in America, Grand Lodge of Massachusetts, 93 Concord Ave., Belmont, MA 02178-4042.
circ. 17,500. *1301*

SOUND AND VIBRATION.
Acoustical Publications, Inc., Box 40416, Bay Village, OH 44140. TEL 216-835-0101. FAX 216-835-9303.
circ. 20,000. *1939*

SOUNDINGS FROM AROUND THE WORLD.
World Neighbors, Inc., 4127 N.W. 122nd St., Oklahoma City, OK 73120-8869. TEL 405-752-9700. FAX 405-752-9393.
circ. 1,700. *3972*

SOURCES D'HISTOIRE MEDIEVALE.
Editions du C N R S, 1 Place Aristide Briand, 92195 Meudon Cedex, France. TEL 1-45-34-75-50. FAX 1-46-26-28-49.
circ. 1,250. *2388*

SOUTH AFRICA. DEPARTMENT OF AGRICULTURE AND FISHERIES. DIVISION OF ECONOMIC SERVICES. ABSTRACT OF AGRICULTURAL STATISTICS.
Department of Agriculture and Fisheries, Division of Economic Services, Private Bag X246, Pretoria 0001, South Africa. *143*

SOUTH AFRICA. DEPARTMENT OF AGRICULTURE AND FISHERIES. DIVISION OF ECONOMIC SERVICES. TRENDS IN THE AGRICULTURAL SECTOR.
Department of Agriculture and Fisheries, Division of Economic Services, Private Bag X246, Pretoria 0001, South Africa. *157*

SOUTH AFRICA. DEPARTMENT OF AGRICULTURE. OFFICIAL LIST OF PROFESSIONAL RESEARCH WORKERS, LECTURING STAFF AND EXTENSION WORKERS IN THE AGRICULTURAL FIELD.
Department of Agricultural Development, Private Bag X144, Pretoria 0001, South Africa. TEL 012-2062181. FAX 012-3232516. *121*

SOUTH AFRICA. DEPARTMENT OF REGIONAL AND LAND AFFAIRS. DIRECTORATE OF SURVEYS AND LAND INFORMATION. ANNUAL REPORT OF THE CHIEF SURVEYOR-GENERAL.
Department of Regional and Land Affairs, Directorate of Surveys and Land Information, Rhodes Ave., Mowbray 7705, South Africa. TEL 021-685-4070. FAX 021-6891351.
circ. 400. *1874*

SOUTH AFRICA. NATIONAL PARKS BOARD. ANNUAL REPORT.
National Parks Board, P.O. Box 787, Pretoria 0001, South Africa. TEL 012-343-9770. FAX 012-343-9958. *1497*

SOUTH AFRICAN DRAUGHTSMAN.
South African Institute of Draughtsmen, P.O. Box 30, Bergvliet 7864, South Africa. TEL 021-72-3938. FAX 021-72-3938.
circ. 3,000. *4609*

SOUTH AFRICAN FIRE SERVICES INSTITUTE. QUARTERLY.
South African Fire Services Institute, Fire Department, Nigel, South Africa.
circ. 1,200. *2034*

SOUTH AFRICAN JOURNAL OF OCCUPATIONAL THERAPY.
South African Association of Occupational Therapists, Box 145, Rondebosch 7700, South Africa. TEL 790-1009. FAX 790507.
circ. 900. *3154*

SOUTH AFRICAN MUSEUM. ANNALS.
South African Museum, Box 61, Cape Town 8000, South Africa. TEL 021-243-330. FAX 021-246716.
circ. 450. *457*

SOUTH CAROLINA LAWYER.
South Carolina Bar, c/o Beth Littlejohn, Man. Ed., Box 608, Columbia, SC 29202. TEL 803-799-6653. FAX 803-799-4118.
circ. 8,000. *2680*

SOUTH CAROLINA MEDICAL ASSOCIATION. JOURNAL.
South Carolina Medical Association, Box 11188, Columbia, SC 29211. TEL 803-798-6207. FAX 803-772-6783.
circ. 4,200. *3154*

SOUTH CAROLINA STATE LIBRARY. ANNUAL REPORT.
South Carolina State Library, 1500 Senate St., Box 11469, Columbia, SC 29211. TEL 803-734-8666. FAX 803-734-8676.
circ. 500. *2785*

SOUTH CAROLINA YOUNG FARMER AND FUTURE FARMER.
South Carolina Young Farmers and Future Farmers, 922 Rutledge Bldg., Columbia, SC 29201.
circ. 6,000. *121*

SOUTH DAKOTA ACADEMY OF SCIENCE. PROCEEDINGS.
South Dakota Academy of Science, HCR 531, Box 97, Pierre, SD 57501. TEL 605-224-7136.
circ. 350. *4345*

SOUTH DAKOTA DENTAL ASSOCIATION. NEWSLETTER.
South Dakota Dental Association, 108 W. Dakota Ave., Box 1194, Pierre, SD 57501. TEL 605-224-9133.
circ. 500. *3242*

SOUTH DAKOTA GEOLOGICAL SURVEY. BULLETIN.
Geological Survey, Science Center University, Vermillion, SD 57069. TEL 605-677-5227. FAX 605-677-5895. *1581*

SOUTH DAKOTA GEOLOGICAL SURVEY. CIRCULAR.
Geological Survey, Science Center University, Vermillion, SD 57069. TEL 605-677-5227. FAX 605-677-5895. *1581*

SOUTH DAKOTA GEOLOGICAL SURVEY. REPORTS OF INVESTIGATION.
Geological Survey, Science Center University, Vermillion, SD 57069. TEL 605-677-5227. FAX 605-677-5895. *1581*

SOUTH FLORIDA HOME BUYER'S GUIDE.
Home Buyer's Guide (Deerfield Beach), 2151 W. Hillsboro Blvd., Ste. 300, Deerfield Beach, FL 33442. TEL 305-428-5602.
circ. 70,000. *4158*

SOUTH FLORIDA PARENTING.
Ken Roberts, Ed. & Pub., 4200 Aurora St., Ste. R, Coral Gables, FL 33146. TEL 305-448-6003.
circ. 45,000. *1244*

SOUTH TEXAS AGRINEWS.
Big River Press, Inc., 1217 N. Conway, Mission, TX 78572. TEL 512-585-4893.
circ. 6,000. *121*

SOUTH TEXAS BUSINESS JOURNAL.
Box 2826, McAllen, TX 78501. TEL 512-783-0036.
circ. 3,500. *692*

SOUTHAMPTON CITY NEWS.
Southampton City Council, Civic Centre, Southampton SO9 4XR, England. TEL 0703-223855. FAX 0703-234537.
circ. 92,000. *4074*

SOUTHEASTERNER.
University of Kentucky, Southeast Community College, Cumberland, KY 40823. TEL 606-589-2145.
circ. 3,500. *2575*

SOUTHERN AFRICA'S TRAVEL NEWS WEEKLY.
Travel and Trade Publishing (Pty) Ltd., 12 Loveday Street, P.O. Box 6202, Johannesburg 2000, South Africa. TEL 011-833-1030. FAX 011-834-6889.
circ. 8,500. *4787*

SOUTHERN CALIFORNIA GUIDE.
Westworld Publishing Corp., 11385 Exposition Bl., No. 102, Los Angeles, CA 90064. TEL 213-391-8255.
circ. 28,000. *4787*

SOUTHERN EXPOSURE (CARBONDALE).
Southern Illinois University at Carbondale, Library, Carbondale, IL 62901. TEL 618-453-2818.
circ. 275. *2785*

SOUTHERN GARDENS.
Wing Publications, Inc., Box 11268, Columbia, SC 29211. *2139*

SOUTHERN ILLINOIS UNIVERSITY, EDWARDSVILLE. REGIONAL RESEARCH AND DEVELOPMENT SERVICES. REPORT: PRIVATE SECTOR INVESTMENTS.
Southern Illinois University, Edwardsville, Regional Research and Development Services, Campus Box 1456, Edwardsville, IL 62026-1456. TEL 618-692-3500. FAX 618-692-2886.
circ. 100. *2496*

SOUTHERN JEWISH WEEKLY.
Isadore Moscovitz, Ed. & Pub., P.O. Box 7966, Jacksonville, FL 32238-0966. TEL 904-634-1812.
circ. 28,500. *2024*

SOUTHERN SUPERMARKETING.
Southern Living, Inc., 2100 Lakeshore Dr., Birmingham, AL 35201. TEL 205-877-6320.
circ. 6,500. *2094*

SOUTHWEST PHILOSOPHY REVIEW. JOURNAL.
c/o James Swindler, 2160 Texas St., Salt Lake City, UT 84109.
circ. 250. *3782*

SOUTHWESTERN BELL CORPORATION. UPDATE.
Southwestern Bell Corporation, One Bell Center, Rm. 38-H-4, St. Louis, MO 63101. TEL 314-235-7130. FAX 314-331-9564.
circ. 85,000. *1366*

SOUTHWESTERN SPORTSMAN MAGAZINE.
Hetrick Publishing, Box H, Winkelman, AZ 85292. TEL 602-356-6049. *4557*

SOU'WESTER (EDWARDSVILLE).
Southern Illinois University, Edwardsville, Edwardsville, IL 62026-1438. TEL 618-692-3190.
circ. 300. *2962*

THE SOWER.
Bible Society of South Africa, P.O. Box 6215, Roggebaai, Cape Town 8012, South Africa. FAX 021-419-4846.
circ. 68,000. *4202*

SOYA INTERNATIONAL.
Soyatech, Inc., Box 84, Bar Harbour, ME 04609. FAX 207-288-5264.
circ. 1,500. *3612*

SPACE COMMERCE WEEK.
Warren Publishing, Inc., 2115 Ward Ct., N.W., Washington, DC 20037. TEL 202-872-9200. FAX 202-293-3435. *62*

SPARE TIME.
Kipen Publishing Corporation, 5810 W. Oklahoma Ave., Milwaukee, WI 53219. TEL 414-543-8110. FAX 414-543-9767.
circ. 300,000. *963*

SPAREBANKBLADET.
Sparebankforeningens Publikasjoner AS, P.O. Box 6772, St. Olavs Plass, O-130 Oslo, Norway. FAX 02-36-25-33.
circ. 10,000. *800*

SPECIAL LIBRARIES ASSOCIATION. EASTERN CANADA CHAPTER. BULLETIN.
Special Libraries Association, Eastern Canada Chapter, Box 1538, Sta. B, Montreal, Que. H3B 3L2, Canada.
circ. 375. *2785*

SPECTRUM.
Tzavta Publishing, P.O. Box 18287, Tel Aviv 61181, Israel. TEL 3-5622076. FAX 3-5618549.
circ. 4,000. *3857*

SPHINCTER.
University of Liverpool, Medical School, Royal Liverpool Hospital, Box 147, Liverpool L69 3BX, England.
circ. 900. *3154*

SPICAE.
Editions du C N R S, 1 Place Aristide Briand, 92195 Meudon Cedex, France. TEL 1-45-34-75-50. FAX 1-46-26-28-49.
circ. 1,500. *2842*

SPIEL UND THEATER.
Deutscher Theaterverlag GmbH, Koenigsberger Str. 18-22, Postfach 100261, 6940 Weinheim, Germany. FAX 06201-14988. *4638*

SPORTFISKAREN.
Sveriges Sportfiske och Fiskevaardsfoerbund, Box 11501, 100 61 Stockholm, Sweden.
circ. 60,000. *4557*

SPORTING SCENE.
Sporting Scene, 22 Maberley Cres., West Hill, Ont. M1C 3K8, Canada. TEL 416-284-0304. FAX 416-284-1299.
circ. 19,800. *4491*

SPORTS & LEISURE RETAILER.
Yaffa Publishing Group, 17-21 Bellevue St., Surry Hills, N.S.W. 2010, Australia. FAX 02-281-2750.
circ. 4,018. *4491*

SPORTS TREND.
Shore Communications, Inc., 180 Allen Rd., N.E., Ste. 300 N, Atlanta, GA 30328. TEL 404-252-8831. FAX 404-252-4436.
circ. 29,102. *4492*

SPORTS TURF BULLETIN.
Sports Turf Research Institute, Bingley, West Yorkshire BD16 1AU, England. TEL 0274-565131. FAX 0274-561891.
circ. 4,500. *193*

SPORTSFISKEREN.
Harlang & Toksvig Bladforlag A-S, Dronnigs Tvaergade 30, 1302 Copenhagen K, Denmark.
circ. 20,637. *2049*

SPORTSVISION QUARTERLY.
Miller Freeman Inc. (New York) 1515 Broadway, New York, NY 10036. TEL 212-869-1300. FAX 212-302-6273.
circ. 57,000. *3305*

SPOTLIGHT.
Icon Press, P.O. Box 144, Opotiki, New Zealand. TEL 03-315-4886. FAX 07-315-4621.
circ. 3,500. *4137*

SPRINGFIELD PUBLIC SCHOOLS. NEWS AND VIEWS.
Springfield Public Schools, Board of Education, 940 N. Jefferson, Springfield, MO 65802.
circ. 50,000. *1665*

SPRINKLER AGE.
American Fire Sprinkler Association, Inc., 11325 Pegasus, S-220, Dallas, TX 75238. TEL 214-349-5965. FAX 214-343-8898.
circ. 3,900. *2035*

SPRINKLER BULLETIN.
Mather and Platt Ltd., Park Works, Manchester M10 6BA, England.
circ. 10,000. *2543*

SQUILLA.
Fratini Missionari di Recco, Collegio Serafico, Via S. Francesco 4, 16036 Recco, Genoa, Italy.
circ. 4,000. *4202*

STADT UND GEMEINDE.
Verlag Otto Schwartz und Co., Annastr. 7, 3400 Goettingen, Germany. TEL 0551-31051. FAX 0551-372812.
circ. 7,000. *4074*

STAGE.
Lusaka Theatre Club (Co-Op) Ltd., P.O. Box 30615, Lusaka, Zambia.
circ. 300. *4638*

STAINLESS STEEL.
Southern Africa Stainless Steel Development Association, P.O. Box 4479, Rivonia 2128, South Africa. TEL 011-803-5610. FAX 011-803-2011.
circ. 9,500. *3420*

STAINLESS STEEL BUYER'S GUIDE (YEAR).
Southern Africa Stainless Steel Development Association, P.O. Box 4479, Rivonia 2128, South Africa. TEL 011-803-5610. FAX 011-803-2011.
circ. 4,000. *3420*

STAINLESS STEEL SCOPE.
Dickson and Johnson Pty. Ltd., 327-341 Chisholm Rd., Auburn, N.S.W. 2144, Australia.
circ. 2,000. *3420*

STAMP LOVER.
National Philatelic Society, 107 Charterhouse St., London EC1M 6PT, England. TEL 071-251-5040.
circ. 3,000. *3758*

STANDARD & POOR'S CORPORATION RECORDS.
Standard & Poor's Corporation, 25 Broadway, New York, NY 10004. TEL 212-208-8000. *964*

STAR CARRIER.
National Star Route Mail Contractors Association, 324 E. Capitol St., Washington, DC 20003. TEL 202-543-1661. FAX 202-543-8863.
circ. 5,000. *1354*

STATE OF THE UNION.
Union League Club of Chicago, 65 W. Jackson Blvd., Chicago, IL 60604. TEL 312-427-7800.
circ. 4,500. *1301*

STATE UNIVERSITY OF NEW YORK. RESEARCH.
State University of New York at Albany, Research Foundation, State University Plaza, Albany, NY 12246. TEL 518-434-7180. FAX 518-434-7290.
circ. 16,500. *1665*

STATISTICAL NOTES OF JAPAN.
International Statistical Affairs Division, Statistical Standards Department, Statistics Bureau, Management and Coordination Agency, 19-1 Wakamatsu-cho, Shinjuku-ku, Tokyo, Japan. FAX 81-3-5273-1181.
circ. 550. *4587*

STATISTICAL REPORT ON VISITOR ARRIVALS TO INDONESIA.
Department of Tourism, Post, and Telecommunications, Jalan Kebon Sirih, No.36, Jakarta, Indonesia. TEL 021-347611. FAX 021-375409.
circ. 500. *4800*

STATISTICS OF SOUTHERN COLLEGE AND UNIVERSITY LIBRARIES.
Louisiana State University, Baton Rouge, LA 70803. TEL 504-388-2217. *2795*

STATISTIK FOR HOVEDSTADSREGIONEN.
Hovedstadsregionens Statistikkontor, Gl. Koegelandevej 3, DK-2500 Valby, Denmark. TEL 45-36-44-29-29. FAX 45-36-44-11-44.
circ. 2,500. *4589*

STEEL SPIEL.
Dickson and Johnson Pty. Ltd., 327-341 Chisholm Rd., Auburn, N.S.W. 2144, Australia.
circ. 200. *3421*

STEERING WHEEL.
Texas Motor Transportation Association, Box 1669, 700 E. 11th, Austin, TX 78767. TEL 512-478-2541.
circ. 3,500. *4748*

STEN.
Sveriges Steninindustri Foerbund, Box 106, S-121 22 Johanneshov, Sweden. TEL 46-08-81-86-00. FAX 46-08-81-86-02.
circ. 8,200. *633*

STENOGRAFISK TIDSSKRIFT.
Dansk Stenografisk Forening, Grumstrupsalle 4, DK-86680 Skanderborg, Denmark. TEL 75-571350. *1062*

STEVENS INDICATOR.
Stevens Alumni Association, Castle Point, Hoboken, NJ 07030. TEL 201-216-5161. FAX 201-216-5374. *1325*

STILL WATERS NEWSLETTER.
Still Waters Foundation, Inc., 615 Stafford Lane, Pensacola, FL 32506. TEL 904-455-9511.
circ. 2,000. *3782*

STIMME DER MAERTYRER.
Hilfsaktion Maertyrerkirche e.V., Tuefingerstr. 3-5, Postfach 1160, 7772 Uhldingen 1, Germany. TEL 07556-6508. FAX 07556-8002.
circ. 38,000. *4203*

STIRPES.
Texas State Genealogical Society, Rt. 4, Box 56, Sulphur Springs, TX 75482. TEL 214-885-3523.
circ. 500. *2165*

STRITCH M.D.
Loyola University of Chicago, Stritch School of Medicine, 820 N. Michigan, Chicago, IL 60611. TEL 708-216-6700. FAX 708-216-8199.
circ. 6,500. *1325*

STROUT WORLD.
Strout Realty, Inc., 2951 S. Campbell Ave., Apt.A, Springfield, MO 65807-3632.
circ. 1,200. *4158*

STUD. MED.
Danish Medical Students Association, Blegdamsvej 3, 2200 Copenhagen N, Denmark.
circ. 5,000. *3155*

STUDIA PHONOLOGICA.
Kyoto University, Institution for Phonetic Sciences, Yoshida, Sakyo-ku, Kyoto 606, Japan. FAX 81-75-753-5977.
circ. 1,000. *2844*

STUDIES IN AVIAN BIOLOGY.
Cooper Ornithological Society, Inc. (San Diego), c/o Joseph R. Jehl, Jr., Sea World Research Institute, Hubbs Marine Research Center, 1700 S. Shore Rd., San Diego, CA 92109.
circ. 1,000. *567*

SUB-POSTMASTER.
National Federation of Sub-Postmasters, Evelyn House, 22 Windlesham Gardens, Shoreham-By-Sea, Sussex, England.
circ. 21,000. *1354*

SUBTERRANEAN SOCIOLOGY NEWSLETTER.
Subterranean Sociological Association, Dept. of Sociology, Eastern Michigan University, Ypsilanti, MI 48197. TEL 313-487-1849.
circ. 600. *4454*

5022 CONTROLLED CIRCULATION SERIALS

SUFFOLK UNIVERSITY MAGAZINE.
Suffolk University, Development Office, 8 Ashburton Pl., Boston, MA 02108-2770. TEL 617-573-8428. FAX 617-573-8711.
circ. 30,500. *1325*

SUGAR MILLING RESEARCH INSTITUTE. ANNUAL REPORT.
Sugar Milling Research Institute, University of Natal, King George V Ave., 4001 Durban, South Africa. TEL 031-2616882. FAX 031-2616886.
circ. 400. *2082*

SUGAR TECHNOLOGISTS' ASSOCIATION OF TRINIDAD AND TOBAGO. PROCEEDINGS.
Sugar Manufacturers' Association of Trinidad & Tobago, Suite 402, 4th Level, Mecalfab's Building, 92 Queen St., Port-of-Spain, Trinidad & Tobago, W.I. *2082*

SUMMARY OF STATE LAWS AND REGULATIONS RELATING TO DISTILLED SPIRITS.
Distilled Spirits Council of the United States, Inc., Legal Division, 1250 Eye St., N.W., Ste. 900, Washington, DC 20005. TEL 202-682-8825. FAX 202-682-8888. *385*

SUNTECH JOURNAL.
I D G Communications (Peterborough), 80 Elm St., Peterborough, NH 03458. TEL 603-924-0100. FAX 603-924-8779.
circ. 50,000. *1400*

SUOMEN KALASTUSLEHTI.
Kalatalouden Keskusliitto, Koydenpunojankatu 7 B 23, 00180 Helsinki 18, Finland. TEL 358-0-640-126. FAX 358-0-608-309.
circ. 4,392. *2049*

SUOMEN LAAKARILEHTI.
Suomen Laakariliitto, Makelankatu 2, 00500 Helsinki, Finland. TEL 90-393-091.
circ. 21,000. *3155*

SUOMEN LEHDISTO.
Sanomalehtien Liitto, Kalevankatu 4, 00100 Helsinki 10, Finland. TEL 358-0-607786. FAX 358-0-607989.
circ. 4,047. *2575*

SUOMI - FINLAND U S A.
Suomi-Amerikka Yhdistysten Liitto, Mechelininkatu 10A, 00100 Helsinki, Finland. FAX 0-408974.
circ. 40,000. *2025*

SURGICAL UPDATE.
American Association of Oral and Maxillofacial Surgeons, 9700 W. Bryn Mawr Ave., Rosemont, IL 60018. TEL 708-678-6200. FAX 708-678-6286.
circ. 150,000. *3243*

SURPLUS RECORD.
Surplus Record, Inc., 20 N. Wacker Dr., Chicago, IL 60606. TEL 312-372-9077. FAX 312-372-6537.
circ. 70,000. *3025*

SVENSK JAKT.
Svenska Jaegarefoerbundet, Box 26091, 10041 Stockholm, Sweden. FAX 08-7912303.
circ. 146,000. *4557*

SVENSK LEKSAKSREVY.
Sveriges Leksakshandlares Riksfoerbund, S-105 61 Stockholm, Sweden. FAX 08-102423.
circ. 1,450. *2282*

SVENSK PAPPERSTIDNING - NORDISK CELLULOSA.
Arbor Publishing AB, Midskogsgraend 5, S-115 43 Stockholm, Sweden. TEL 08-6643400. FAX 08-6642124.
circ. 7,687. *3666*

SVENSK VAEGTIDNING.
Svenska Vaegfoereningens Foerlags AB, Wallingatan 33, S-111 24 Stockholm, Sweden. FAX 46-8-7918158.
circ. 3,500. *1875*

SVENSK VETERINAERTIDNING.
Sveriges Veterinaerfoerbund, Kungsholms Hamnplan 7, S-112 20 Stockholm, Sweden. TEL 08-654-2480. FAX 08-6517082.
circ. 2,429. *4816*

SWAMP GAS JOURNAL.
Ufology Research of Manitoba, Box 1918, Winnipeg General Post Office, Winnipeg, Man. R3C 3R2, Canada.
circ. 250. *63*

SWATCHES.
National Association of Decorative Fabric Distributors, 3008 Millwood Ave., Columbia, SC 29205. TEL 803-252-5646.
circ. 17,000. *4623*

SWEET'S CANADIAN CONSTRUCTION CATALOGUE FILE.
McGraw-Hill Information Systems Company of Canada Ltd., 270 Yorkland Blvd., North York, Ont. M2J 1R8, Canada. TEL 416-496-3100.
circ. 7,000. *634*

SWINGERS UPDATE.
Contact Advertising, 2010 St. Lucie Blvd., Ft. Pierce, FL 34946.
circ. 9,000. *3400*

SYMANTEC.
Symantec Corporation, 10201 Torre Ave., Cupertino, CA 95014-2132. TEL 408-253-9600. FAX 408-253-3968.
circ. 650,000. *1481*

SYNDICAT NATIONAL DES ARCHITECTES D'INTERIEUR. BULLETIN.
Syndicat National des Architectes d'Interieur, 57, Bd. Richard Lenoir, 75011 Paris, France.
circ. 650. *307*

SYRACUSE NEW TIMES.
A. Zimmer Ltd., 1415 W. Genesee St., Syracuse, NY 13204. TEL 315-422-7011. FAX 315-422-1721.
circ. 45,000. *2886*

SYSTEMS INTEGRATION BUSINESS.
Cahners Publishing Company (Newton) Division of Reed Publishing (USA) Inc., 275 Washington St., Newton, MA 02158-1630. TEL 617-964-3030. FAX 617-558-4506.
circ. 110,485. *1439*

T A S P O GARTENKURIER.
Verlag Bernhard Thalacker, Hamburgerstr. 277, 3300 Braunschweig, Germany. TEL 0531-38004-0. FAX 0531-3800425.
circ. 120,000. *2139*

T & A M REPORT.
University of Illinois at Urbana-Champaign, Department of Theoretical and Applied Mechanics, 216 Talbot Laboratory, Urbana, IL 61801. TEL 217-333-1000.
circ. 120. *1922*

T E & M'S TELECOM ASIA.
Avanstar Communications, Inc. (Chicago), 2 Illinois Center, 233 North Michigan St., 24th Fl., Chicago, IL 60601. TEL 312-938-2300. FAX 312-938-4854.
circ. 12,000. *1366*

T G.
Ediciones Sohail, Velazques 21, Madrid 1, Spain.
circ. 10,000. *346*

T.H.E. JOURNAL.
Ed Warnshius Ltd., 150 El Camino Real, Ste. 112, Tustin, CA 92680-3670. TEL 714-730-4011. FAX 714-730-3739.
circ. 126,000. *1691*

T M A GUIDE TO TOBACCO TAXES.
Tobacco Merchants Association of the United States, Inc., 231 Clarksville Rd., Ste. 6, Box 8019, Princeton, NJ 08543-8019. TEL 609-275-4900. FAX 609-275-8379. *4644*

T M A LEAF BULLETIN.
Tobacco Merchants Association of the United States, Inc., 231 Clarksville Rd., Ste. 6, Box 8019, Princeton, NJ 08543-8019. TEL 609-275-4900. FAX 609-275-8379. *4644*

T M A TOBACCO BAROMETER.
Tobacco Merchants Association of the United States, Inc., 231 Clarksville Rd., Ste. 6, Box 8019, Princeton, NJ 08543-8019. TEL 609-275-4900. FAX 609-275-8379. *4644*

T M A TOBACCO BAROMETER: SMOKING, CHEWING, SNUFF.
Tobacco Merchants Association of the United States, Inc., 231 Clarksville Rd., Ste. 6, Box 8019, Princeton, NJ 08543-8019. TEL 609-275-4900. FAX 609-275-8379. *4644*

T M A TOBACCO TRADE BAROMETER.
Tobacco Merchants Association of the United States, Inc., 231 Clarksville Rd., Ste. 6, Box 8019, Princeton, NJ 08543-8019. TEL 609-275-4900. FAX 609-275-8379. *4644*

T.P.L. NEWS.
Toronto Public Library, 281 Front St.E., Toronto, Ont. M5A 4L2, Canada. TEL 416-393-7565. FAX 416-393-7782.
circ. 900. *2786*

T S S A REPORT.
Tackle & Shooting Sports Agents Association, 1250 Grove Ave., Ste. 300, Barrington, IL 60010. TEL 312-381-3032. FAX 708-381-9518.
circ. 400. *694*

T T R A NEWSLETTER.
University of Utah, Bureau of Economic & Business Research, Box 58066, Salt Lake City, UT 84158. TEL 801-581-3363. FAX 801-581-3354.
circ. 1,100. *4788*

T U C NEWS.
Trades Union Congress of Ghana, Hall of Trade Unions, P.O. Box 701, Accra, Ghana.
circ. 10,000. *2590*

T V TODAY.
National Association of Broadcasters, 1771 N St., N.W., Washington, DC 20036. TEL 202-429-5486. *1381*

T W I C E.
Cahners Publishing Company (New York) Division of Reed Publishing (USA) Inc., 249 W. 17th St., New York, NY 10011. TEL 212-645-0067. FAX 212-337-7066.
circ. 31,385. *1779*

TACKLE TIMES (BARRINGTON).
American Fishing Tackle Manufacturers Association, 1250 Grove Ave., Barrington, IL 60010. TEL 708-381-9490. FAX 708-381-9518.
circ. 2,000. *4558*

TACOMA - PIERCE COUNTY CHAMBER OF COMMERCE UPDATE.
Tacoma-Pierce County Chamber of Commerce, 950 Pacific Ave., Ste. 300, Box 1933, Tacoma, WA 98401. TEL 206-627-2175. FAX 206-597-7305.
circ. 3,500. *823*

TAITO.
Kasi- ja Taideteollisuusliitto, P.O. Box 186, 00181 Helsinki, Finland.
circ. 12,000. *357*

TAKE OFF.
Skandinavisk Bladforlag A-S, Frederiksberg Alle 3, DK-1621 Copenhagen V, Denmark. TEL 45-31-238099. FAX 45-31237042.
circ. 6,000. *4788*

TALKING MACHINE REVIEW, INTERNATIONAL.
International Talking Machine Review, 105 Sturdee Ave., Gillingham, Kent ME7 2HG, England. TEL 0634-851-823.
circ. 1,000. *4462*

TALLYBOARD.
Forest Products Accident Prevention Association, 128 McIntyre St. W., North Bay, Ont. P1B 8H2, Canada. TEL 705-472-4120. FAX 705-472-0207.
circ. 3,200. *2109*

TANNING TRENDS.
Tanning Trends Inc., 3101 Page Ave., Jackson, MI 49203. TEL 517-784-1772. FAX 517-787-3940. *3809*

TANZANIA. BUREAU OF STANDARDS. DIRECTOR'S ANNUAL REPORT.
Bureau of Standards, P.O. Box 9524, Dar es Salaam, Tanzania. TEL 255-51-48051. *3449*

TAR HEEL LIBRARIES.
Department of Cultural Resources, Division of State Library, 109 E. Jones St., Raleigh, NC 27611. TEL 919-733-2570. FAX 919-733-8748.
circ. 5,000. *2786*

TAREX.
Societe d'Editions Medico-Pharmaceutiques (SEMP), 26 rue Lebrun, 75013 Paris, France. TEL 1-43-37-83-50. FAX 43-31-94-11.
circ. 17,000. *3744*

TATER NEWS.
National Potato Promotion Board, 1385 S. Colorado Blvd., Ste. 512, Denver, CO 80222. TEL 303-758-7783. FAX 303-756-9256.
circ. 17,000. *194*

TAXI TALK.
Thomson Publications P.O. Box 56182, Pinegowrie 2123, South Africa. TEL 011-789-2144. FAX 011-789-3196.
circ. 36,702. *4703*

TAYLOR.
Taylor University, 500 W. Reade Ave., Upland, IN 46989. TEL 317-998-2751. FAX 317-998-4910.
1717

TEACHERS' MONEY MATTERS.
Teachers' Money Matters Ltd., 70 Scriven Rd., Bailieboro, Ont. K0L 1B0, Canada. TEL 705-939-1203. FAX 705-939-1179.
circ. 33,000. *801*

TEAM REHAB REPORT.
Miramar Publishing Co., Box 3640, Culver City, CA 90231-3640. TEL 213-337-9717. FAX 213-337-1041.
circ. 12,000. *3156*

TECHNION - ISRAEL INSTITUTE OF TECHNOLOGY. FACULTY OF AGRICULTURAL ENGINEERING. PUBLICATIONS.
Technion - Israel Institute of Technology, Lowdermilk Department of Agricultural Engineering, Technion City, Haifa 32000, Israel. FAX 221-529. *123*

TECHNION - ISRAEL INSTITUTE OF TECHNOLOGY. PRESIDENT'S REPORT.
Technion - Israel Institute of Technology, Division of Public Affairs, Haifa 3200, Israel.
circ. 30,000. *4610*

TECHNISCHE REVUE.
Uitgeversmaatschappij C. Misset B.V., Hanzestr. 1, 7006 RH Doetinchem, Netherlands. TEL 08340-49911. FAX 08340-43839.
circ. 15,230. *4610*

TECNICA E INVENCION.
Princesa 14, Madrid-8, Spain.
circ. 3,000. *3678*

EL TECOLOTE.
Accion Latina, 2017 Mission St., Ste. 200, San Francisco, CA 94110. TEL 415-252-5957. FAX 415-883-9318.
circ. 10,000. *2026*

TEESWATER SHEEP BREEDERS' ASSOCIATION. ANNUAL FLOCK BOOK.
Teeswater Sheep Breeders' Association, Mutton Hall, Old Hutton, Kendal, Cumbria LA8 0NW, England. TEL 05396-20471.
circ. 200. *227*

TEKNISK NYT.
Thomson Communications (Scandinavia) A-S, Struenseegade 7-9, DK-2200 Copenhagen, Denmark. TEL 45-35-37-80-55.
circ. 18,956. *1838*

TEKSTIILIOPETTAJA.
Tekstiiliopettajaliitto, Mannerheimintie 132 B 31, SF-00270 Helsinki, Finland.
circ. 1,500. *2449*

TELECOMMUNICATION AUTHORITY OF SINGAPORE. SINGAPORE TELECOM ANNUAL REPORT.
Telecommunication Authority of Singapore, Comcentre, 31 Exeter Rd., Singapore 0923, Singapore. FAX 733-1350. *1366*

TELECOMMUNICATIONS SOURCEBOOK.
North American Telecommunications Association, 2000 M St., N.W., Ste. 550, Washington, DC 20036. FAX 202-296-4993.
circ. 5,000. *1366*

TELEVISION & FAMILIES.
National Council for Families and Television, 3801 Barham Blvd., Ste. 300, Los Angeles, CA 90068-1007. TEL 213-876-5959. FAX 213-851-6180.
circ. 900. *1382*

TELEVISION BROADCAST.
P S N Publications 2 Park Ave., 18th Fl., New York, NY 10016. TEL 212-213-3444. FAX 212-213-3484.
circ. 29,581. *1383*

TELOCATOR.
Telocator, 1019 19th St., N.W., Ste. 1100, Washington, DC 20036. TEL 202-467-4770.
circ. 3,500. *1383*

TEMPORARY CULTURE.
Box 43072, Upper Montclair, NJ 07043. *2886*

TENNESSEE LAW ENFORCEMENT JOURNAL.
Tennessee Law Enforcement Officers Association, c/o Capt. B.D. Johnson, Box 731, Dyersburg, TN 38024-0731. FAX 612-541-0435.
circ. 3,000. *1523*

TENNESSEE PARENT - TEACHER BULLETIN.
Tennessee Congress of Parents and Teachers, 1905 Acklen Ave., Nashville, TN 37212. TEL 615-383-9740.
circ. 1,400. *1667*

TENNESSEE SCHOOL BOARD BULLETIN.
Tennessee School Boards Association, 500 13th Ave. North, Nashville, TN 37203-2830. FAX 615-741-2824.
circ. 1,800. *1732*

TENNESSEE TRUCKING NEWS.
Tennessee Trucking Association, Box 2847, Nashville, TN 37219. TEL 615-255-0558. FAX 615-244-0495.
circ. 1,000. *4748*

TENNIS INDUSTRY.
Sterling Southeast Inc., 1450 N.E. 123rd St., N. Miami, FL 33161-6051. TEL 305-893-8771. FAX 305-893-8783.
circ. 20,707. *4513*

TENNIS U S T A.
New York Times Magazine Group, Sports - Leisure Division, 5520 Park Ave., Box 395, Trumbull, CT 06611. TEL 203-373-7155. FAX 203-371-2199.
circ. 450,000. *4513*

TENTH TIMES.
Texas Dental Association, Tenth District Dental Society, 3303 Northland, No. 313, Austin, TX 78731. TEL 512-452-9296.
circ. 450. *3243*

TEVA VA-ARETZ.
Society for the Protection of Nature in Israel, 4 Hashfela St., Tel Aviv 66183, Israel. TEL 03-375063. *1498*

TEXAS AGGIE.
Texas A & M University, Association of Former Students, Box 7368, College Station, TX 77844. TEL 409-845-7514.
circ. 50,000. *1326*

TEXAS BICYCLIST.
Yellow Jersey Enterprises, 3600 Jeanetta Dr., Ste. 1604, Houston, TX 77063. TEL 713-782-1661. FAX 713-782-7666.
circ. 50,000. *4521*

TEXAS CIVIL ENGINEER.
American Society of Civil Engineers, Texas Section, Box 2161, Austin, TX 78768. TEL 806-742-3477. FAX 512-472-2934.
circ. 6,500. *1875*

TEXAS DIRECTOR.
Rector - Duncan & Associates, Box 14667, Austin, TX 78761. TEL 512-458-8256. FAX 512-451-9556.
circ. 1,000. *2120*

TEXAS HIGHER EDUCATION COORDINATING BOARD. C B POLICY PAPER.
Texas Higher Education Coordinating Board, Box 12788, Capitol Sta., Austin, TX 78711. TEL 512-483-6111.
circ. 2,000. *1717*

TEXAS HIGHER EDUCATION COORDINATING BOARD. C B STUDY PAPER.
Texas Higher Education Coordinating Board, Capitol Sta., Box 12788, Austin, TX 78711. TEL 512-483-6111.
circ. 2,000. *1717*

TEXAS INSTRUMENTS TECHNICAL JOURNAL.
Texas Instruments, Box 650311, Mail Sta. 3940, Dallas, TX 75265. TEL 214-917-3906.
circ. 16,500. *1838*

TEXAS L P - GAS NEWS.
Texas L P - Gas Association, Box 140735, Austin, TX 78714-0735. TEL 512-836-8620. FAX 512-834-0758.
circ. 1,259. *3702*

TEXAS LEGION TIMES.
Adcraft Agency, 101 N. Main, Ste. 200, Jacksboro, TX 76458. TEL 817-567-6622. FAX 817-567-6372.
circ. 100,500. *1301*

TEXAS LIBRARIES.
Texas State Library and Archives Commission, Box 12927, Austin, TX 78711. TEL 512-463-5492. FAX 512-463-5436.
circ. 1,400. *2787*

TEXAS SOURCEBOOK (NO.).
Alexander Communications, Inc., 212 W. Superior, Ste. 203, Chicago, IL 60610. TEL 312-944-5115. FAX 312-944-7865.
circ. 7,000. *4006*

TEXTIELVERZORGING.
Uitgeverij Noordervliet, Postbus 268, 3700 AG Zeist, Netherlands. FAX 03404-16616.
circ. 1,400. *1282*

TEXTILE WORLD.
MacLean Hunter Publishing Company, Textile Publications, 4170 Ashford-Dunwoody Rd., Ste. 420, Atlanta, GA 30319. TEL 404-847-2770. FAX 404-252-6150.
circ. 28,142. *4626*

THAQAFA WA FANN.
Cultural Foundation, Culture and Arts Department, P.O. Box 2380, Abu Dhabi, United Arab Emirates. TEL 215300. FAX 336059.
circ. 500. *346*

THAT'S MY BABY.
That's My Baby, Inc., Box 1156, Lake Oswego, OR 97035. TEL 503-635-1697. FAX 503-620-9132.
circ. 50,000. *1245*

THEATER HEUTE.
Orell Fuessli & Friedrich Verlag, Dietzingerstr. 3, CH-8036 Zurich, Switzerland. TEL 041-4667711. FAX 041-4667457.
circ. 20,000. *4640*

THEOLOGIA REFORMATA.
Drukkerij Oosterbaan en Le Cointre B.V., Postbus 25, 4460 AA Goes, Netherlands. TEL 08380-17091.
circ. 750. *4250*

THEOLOGICA XAVERIANA.
Pontificia Universidad Javeriana, Facultad de Teologia, Carrera 10, No. 65-48, Bogota 2 D.E., Colombia. *4277*

THIRD DEGREE (REGINA).
University of Regina, Communications Office, Regina, Sask. S4S 0A2, Canada. TEL 306-585-4403. FAX 306-585-4780.
circ. 26,000. *1326*

THOMIST.
Thomist Press, 487 Michigan Ave., N.E., Washington, DC 20017. TEL 202-529-5300.
circ. 1,000. *4277*

CONTROLLED CIRCULATION SERIALS

THOROUGHBRED RACING ASSOCIATIONS. DIRECTORY AND RECORD BOOK.
Thoroughbred Racing Associations, 420 Fair Hill Dr., No.1, Elkton, MD 21921-2573. FAX 516-328-8137.
circ. 3,000. *4538*

TIEMPO LATINO.
Tiempo Latino Publishing Co., 965 Mission St., Ste. 450, San Fransisco, CA 94103-2921. TEL 415-512-1820.
circ. 40,00. *2026*

TIETOVERKKO.
Oy Talentum Ab, P.O. Box 920, SF-00101 Helsinki, Finland. TEL 358-0-148-801. FAX 358-0-141-382.
circ. 8,000. *1428*

TIILI.
Suomen Tiiliteollisuusliitto r.y., Laturinkuja 2, 02600 Espoo, Finland. *634*

TIJDSCHRIFT VOOR CRIMINOLOGIE.
Gouda Quint B.V., P.O. Box 1148, 6801 MK Arnhem, Netherlands. TEL 085-454762. FAX 085-514509.
circ. 600. *1523*

TIMES BUSINESS DIRECTORY OF SINGAPORE.
Times Trade Directories Pte.Ltd., Times Centre, 1 New Industrial Rd., Singapore 1953, Singapore. TEL 2848844. FAX 2881186.
circ. 25,000. *1155*

TIMES GUIDE TO COMPUTERS.
Times Trade Directories Pte. Ltd., Times Centre, 1 New Industrial Road, Singapore 1953, Singapore. TEL 2848844. FAX 2881186.
circ. 25,000. *1155*

TIPSICO BULLETIN.
Tipsico Coin Co., Box 1128, 2141 Broadway, N. Bend, OR 97459. TEL 503-756-7111.
circ. 1,000. *3602*

TITLES.
Larkspur Publishing, Inc., 200 Gate Five Rd., Ste. 214, Sausalito, CA 94965. TEL 415-331-1211.
circ. 60,000. *4138*

TODAY'S DISTRIBUTOR.
Johnson Hill Press, Inc., 1233 Janesville Ave., Ft. Atkinson, WI 53538. TEL 414-563-6388. FAX 414-563-1701.
circ. 42,000. *1055*

TODAY'S REFINERY.
Percy Publishing Company, Inc., 170 King St, Box 287, Chappaqua, NY 10514. TEL 914-238-0205. FAX 914-238-0210.
circ. 7,000. *3702*

TOELEVEREN EN UITBESTEDEN.
Uitgeversmaatschappij C. Misset B.V., Hanzestr. 1, 7006 RH Doetinchem, Netherlands. TEL 08340-49911. FAX 08340-43839.
circ. 6,000. *3024*

TOHOKU DAIGAKU SENKO SEIREN KENKYUJO IHO.
Tohoku Daigaku, Senko Seiren Kenkyujo, 1-1 Katahira 2-chome, Aoba-ku, Sendai 980, Japan. FAX 022-261-0938. *3422*

TOHOKU KOGYO DAIGAKU KIYO, 1. RIKOGAKU HEN.
Tohoku Kogyo Daigaku, 35-1 Kasumi-cho, Yagiyama, Taihaku-ku, Sendai-shi, Miyagi-ken 982, Japan.
circ. 730. *1838*

TOLSTOY FOUNDATION NEWS.
Tolstoy Foundation, Inc., 200 Park Ave. S., Rm. 1612, New York, NY 10003-1522. TEL 212-677-7770. FAX 212-674-0519. *4422*

THE TOMBSTONE.
Cochise Genealogical Society, Box 68, Pirtleville, AZ 85626.
circ. 75. *2166*

TOP BUSINESS.
Verlag Moderne Industrie AG, Ingolstaedter Str. 20-22, 8000 Munich 45, Germany. TEL 089-35093-0. FAX 089-352286. *1029*

TOPICS IN PEDIATRICS.
Minneapolis Children's Medical Center, 2525 Chicago Ave., S., Minneapolis, MN 55404. TEL 612-863-6222. FAX 612-863-6674.
circ. 10,000. *3327*

TORCH (CHICAGO).
International Association of Torch Clubs, Tribune Tower, 435 N. Michigan Ave., Ste. 1717, Chicago, IL 60611-4067. TEL 312-644-0828. FAX 312-644-8557.
circ. 3,600. *1301*

TORONTO BUSINESS AGE.
Toronto Business Age Inc., 146 Laird Dr., Ste. 106, Toronto, Ont. M4G 3V7, Canada. TEL 416-467-4778. FAX 416-467-4778.
circ. 21,000. *695*

TORONTO STOCK EXCHANGE REVIEW.
Toronto Stock Exchange, 2 First Canadian Place, Toronto, Ont. M5X 1J2, Canada. TEL 416-947-4222. FAX 416-947-4585.
circ. 1,150. *966*

TOUCHSTONE MAGAZINE.
University of Wisconsin-Madison, University-Industry Research Program, 1215 WARF Bldg., 610 Walnut St., Madison, WI 53705. TEL 608-263-2840. FAX 608-263-2841.
circ. 6,000. *4348*

TOURS ON MOTORCOACH.
Publicom Inc., 1055 Beaver Hall, Ste. 200, Montreal, Que. H2Z 1S5, Canada. TEL 514-874-0874. FAX 514-878-9779.
circ. 12,127. *4791*

TOW TIMES.
T T Publications, Inc., 398 N. Freeman St., Longwood, FL 32750. TEL 407-260-0712. FAX 407-260-1486.
circ. 30,000. *4748*

TOWN AND COUNTRY FARMER.
Town and Country Farmer Publications Pty. Ltd., P.O. Box 798, Benalla, Vic. 3672, Australia. TEL 057-64-1348. FAX 057-64-1349.
circ. 20,000. *124*

TOXICOLOGIC PATHOLOGY.
Society of Toxicologic Pathologists, c/o Dr. Benjamin F. Trump, Ed., Dept. of Pathology, School of Medicine, Univ. of Maryland, Baltimore, MD 21201. FAX 301-328-3743.
circ. 810. *1983*

TOY & HOBBY RETAILER.
Yaffa Publishing Group, 17-21 Bellevue St., Surry Hills, N.S.W. 2010, Australia. TEL 02-281-2333. FAX 020-281-2750.
circ. 3,552. *2282*

TRACES OF INDIANA AND MIDWESTERN HISTORY.
Indiana Historical Society, 315 W. Ohio, Indianapolis, IN 46202. TEL 317-232-1882. FAX 317-233-3109.
circ. 9,500. *2424*

TRADE CHRONICLE.
Chronicle Publications, P.O. Box 5257, Iftikhar Chambers, Altaf Hussain Rd., Karachi 74000, Pakistan. TEL 92-21-218129. FAX 92-21-7735276.
circ. 5,500. *1086*

TRADERS MAGAZINE.
Trader's Magazine, Inc., 888 Seventh Ave., Ste. 250, New York, NY 10106. TEL 212-265-4610. FAX 212-265-5924.
circ. 4,000. *801*

TRADESHOW AND EXHIBIT MANAGER.
Goldstein and Associates, 1150 Yale St., Ste. 12, Santa Monica, CA 90403-4738. TEL 213-828-1309.
circ. 12,000. *1029*

TRADEWIND MAGAZINE.
Caribbean Travel and Life, Inc., 8403 Colesville Rd., Ste. 830, Silver Spring, MD 20910. TEL 301-588-2300. FAX 301-588-2256.
circ. 250,000. *4791*

TRAILER-BODY BUILDERS.
Tunnell Publications, Inc., Box 66010, Houston, TX 77266. TEL 713-523-8124. FAX 713-523-8384.
circ. 14,000. *4748*

TRAIN COLLECTORS QUARTERLY.
Train Collectors Association, 213 Fannie Ave., Lancaster, PA 17602. TEL 717-687-8623.
circ. 25,000. *2443*

TRANSATLANTIC PERSPECTIVES.
German Marshall Fund of the United States, 11 Dupont Circle, N.W., Washington, DC 20036. TEL 202-745-3950. FAX 202-265-1662.
circ. 9,000. *3974*

TRANSCEND.
Transcend Publications, 4 Daniels Farm Rd., Ste. 134, Trumbull, CT 06611.
circ. 15,000. *2026*

TRANSMISSION AND DISTRIBUTION.
Intertec Publishing Corp. (Edgemont), 5072 W. Chester Pike, Box 556, Edgemont, PA 19028. TEL 215-359-1249. FAX 215-359-9379.
circ. 34,600. *1909*

TRANSMISSION & DISTRIBUTION INTERNATIONAL.
Intertec Publishing (Edgemont), 5072 W. Chester Pike, Box 556, Edgemont, PA 19028. TEL 215-359-1249. FAX 215-359-9379.
circ. 25,000. *1909*

TRANSPONDER.
Terra Publishing, Inc., RD 1, Box 142, Center St. Ext., Salamanca, NY 14779. TEL 716-945-3488.
circ. 14,500. *1383*

TRANSPORT 2000 AND INTERMODAL WORLD.
BuenaVentura Publishing Co., 965 Mission St., San Francisco, CA 94103-2921.
circ. 11,000. *4658*

TRANSPORT 2000 CANADA. NEWS BULLETIN.
Box 3594, Regina, Sask. S4P 3L7, Canada. TEL 306-565-6291.
circ. 400. *4716*

TRANSPORTATION. CURRENT LITERATURE.
U.S. Department of Transportation, 400 Seventh St., S.W., Washington, DC 20590. TEL 202-655-4000.
circ. 950. *4667*

TRANSPORTATION & DISTRIBUTION.
Penton Publishing 1100 Superior Ave., Cleveland, OH 44114-2543. TEL 216-696-7000. FAX 216-696-8765.
circ. 74,138. *4658*

TRAVEL DIRECTORY (YEAR).
Interasia Publications Ltd., Fortune Centre 11-01, 190 Middle Rd., Singapore 0718, Singapore. TEL 3397622. FAX 3398521.
circ. 3,700. *4792*

TRAVEL TRADE REPORTER - ASIA.
Orient Pacific Enterprises Ltd., Asia Bldg., 6th Fl., 294-1 Phya Thai Rd., Bangkok 10400, Thailand. TEL 2-215-4685. FAX 2-216-6599.
circ. 8,500. *4793*

TRAVELAGE EAST.
Official Airline Guides, Inc. (New York), 1775 Broadway, 19th Fl., New York, NY 10019. TEL 212-237-3000. FAX 212-237-3007. *4793*

TRAVELAGE WEST.
Official Airline Guides, Inc. (San Francisco), 49 Stevenson, No. 460, San Francisco, CA 94105-2909. TEL 415-905-1155. FAX 415-905-1145.
circ. 34,277. *4794*

TRAVELLERS GUIDE TO MEXICO.
Promociones de Mercados Turisticos, S.A., Gen. Juan Cano 68, Col. San Miguel Chapultepec, Apdo. 6-1007, 11850 Mexico D.F. TEL 525-5150925. FAX 525-272-5942.
circ. 3,500,000. *4794*

TREASURY.
Economist Group, 235 Summer St., Boston, MA 02210. TEL 617-345-9700.
circ. 45,000. *801*

TRI-STATE NEIGHBOR.
2701 S. Minnesota, Sioux Falls, SD 57105. TEL 605-335-7300. FAX 605-335-7300.
circ. 29,000. *124*

TRI-STATE REAL ESTATE JOURNAL.
Lionmark Publications, Inc., 236 W. Route 38, Box 1008, Moorestown, NJ 08057-0908. TEL 609-866-1300. FAX 609-866-1912.
circ. 7,000. *4158*

TRIBUS.
Linden-Museum Stuttgart-Staatliches Museum fuer Voelkerkunde, Hegelplatz 1, 7000 Stuttgart 1, Germany.
circ. 800. *251*

TRIBUTE GOES TO THE MOVIES.
Tribute Publishing, Inc., 95 Barber Greene Rd., Ste. 201, Don Mills, Ontario M3C 3E9, Canada. TEL 416-445-0544.
circ. 300,000. *3518*

TRINITY REVIEW.
Trinity Foundation, Box 700, Jefferson, MD 21755. TEL 301-371-7155.
circ. 2,000. *3784*

TRUXPRESS.
Alberta Trucking Association, Box 5520, Station "A", Calgary, Alta. T2H 1X9, Canada. TEL 403-253-8401.
circ. 800. *4749*

TRZISTE STOKE I STOCIHH PROIZODA.
Zavod za Trzisna Istrazivanja, Mose Pijade 8-I, 11001 Belgrade, Yugoslavia. *144*

TUG WORLD NEWSLETTER.
Thomas Reed Publications Ltd., Weir House, Hurst RD., E. Molesey, Surrey KT8 9AQ, England. TEL 081-941-8090. FAX 081-941-8046.
circ. 2,500. *4741*

TUIJIN JISHU.
Hangkong Hangtian Gongye-bu, Di 3 Yanjiuyuan, 31 Suo, P.O. Box 7208-26, Beijing 100074, People's Republic of China. TEL 8376141.
circ. 1,000. *63*

TULANIAN.
Tulane University, University Relations, Hebert Hall, Rm. 300, New Orleans, LA 70118. TEL 504-865-5000. FAX 504-865-5621.
circ. 65,000. *1327*

TURNBERRY.
G S & J Publishing, Inc., 5212 N.W. 54th Ave., Pompano Beach, FL 33073-3755. TEL 305-977-5901.
circ. 5,000. *347*

TUTTI AL BAR.
Tuttopress Editrice s.r.l., Via Cagliero, 21, 20125 Milan, Italy. TEL 02-6882228. FAX 02-6072185.
circ. 150,000. *2481*

TYDSKRIF VIR VOLKSKUNDE EN VOLKSTAAL.
Genootskap vir Afrikaanse Volkskunde, Box 4585, Johannesburg 2000, South Africa.
circ. 210. *2059*

TYLER JUNIOR COLLEGE NEWS.
Tyler Junior College, Box 9020, Tyler, TX 75711. TEL 214-510-2335. FAX 903-510-2634.
circ. 3,000. *1327*

U F M G. ESCOLA DE BIBLIOTECONOMIA. REVISTA.
Universidade Federal de Minas Gerais, Escola de Biblioteconomia, Caixa Postal 1906, 30161 Belo Horizonte MG, Brazil. TEL 441-1131. FAX 031-441-9354.
circ. 800. *2788*

U N I D O NEWSLETTER.
United Nations Industrial Development Organization, Box 300, A-1400 Vienna, Austria.
circ. 38,500. *936*

U OF L.
University of Louisville, Alumni Association, 19 Development and University Relations Bldg., University of Louisville, Louisville, KY 40292. FAX 502-588-7658.
circ. 71,000. *1327*

U P E N.
University of Port Elizabeth, Box 1600, Port Elizabeth 6000, South Africa.
circ. 2,800. *1327*

U S A AMATEUR BOXING FEDERATION. MEDIA GUIDE.
U S A Amateur Boxing Federation, 1750 E. Boulder St., Colorado Springs, CO 80909. TEL 719-578-4506. *4495*

U S A TRADE OPPORTUNITIES.
United States and Foreign Commercial Service, American Embassy, Dag Hammarskjolds Alle 24, DK-2100 Copenhagen O, Denmark. TEL 31-423144. FAX 31-420175.
circ. 2,000. *923*

UITGELEZEN.
Ministerie van Sociale Zaken, Library and Documentation Service, P.O. Box 90801, 2509 LV The Hague, Netherlands.
circ. 1,500. *4396*

UMWELTMAGAZIN.
Vogel-Verlag und Druck KG, Max-Planck-Str. 7-9, 8700 Wuerzburg 1, Germany. TEL 0931-418-0.
circ. 18,000. *1970*

UNDERGROUND FOREST - SELVA SUBTERRANEA.
1701 Bluebell Ave., Boulder, CO 80302.
circ. 5,000. *2887*

UNDERPASS.
Underpass Press, 574-21, 10405 Jasper Ave., Edmonton, Alta., Canada.
circ. 200. *3007*

UNDZER VEG.
Achdut Ha-Avoda-Poale Zion of Canada, 272 Codsell Ave., Downsview, Ont. M3H 3X2, Canada.
circ. 4,000. *2027*

THE UNEXPLAINED.
Krastman Productions, Box 16790, Encino, CA 91416. TEL 818-705-8865.
circ. 20,000. *3597*

DIE UNIE.
Suid-Afrikaanse Onderwysersunie, P.O. Box 196, Cape Town 8000, South Africa. TEL 021-461-6340. FAX 021-461-9238.
circ. 8,500. *1669*

UNIFICATION.
Unification Printers & Publishers Pty. Ltd., 132 Regent St., Redfern, N.S.W. 2016, Australia. TEL 02 698-2392.
circ. 4,300. *2027*

UNIFORMS AND ACCESSORIES REVIEW.
A F G Enterprises, Inc., 15 W. 44th St., New York, NY 10036. TEL 212-840-3045. FAX 212-575-9391.
circ. 3,000. *1295*

UNION MATTERS.
Saskatchewan Government Employees' Union, 1440 Broadway Ave., Regina, Sask. S4P 1E2, Canada. TEL 306-522-8571. FAX 306-352-1969.
circ. 17,500. *2591*

UNION MEDICALE BALKANIQUE. ARCHIVES.
Union Medicale Balkanique, Str. Gabriel Peri Nr. 1, Bucharest, Rumania.
circ. 2,000. *3159*

UNION SIGNAL.
National Woman's Christian Temperance Union, 1730 Chicago Ave., Evanston, IL 60201. TEL 708-864-1396. *1539*

UNITA.
Unita S.p.A., Via d'Aracoeli 13, 20162 Milan, Italy.
circ. 400,000. *3931*

UNITED ARAB EMIRATES. AL-MASRAF AL-MARKAZI. AL-MULHIQ AL-IHSA'I.
Central Bank, P.O. Box 854, Abu Dhabi, United Arab Emirates. TEL 652220. FAX 668483.
circ. 500. *741*

UNITED ARAB EMIRATES. AL-MASRAF AL-MARKAZI. AL-NASHRAH AL-IQTISADIYYAH.
Central Bank, P.O. Box 854, Abu Dhabi, United Arab Emirates. TEL 652220. FAX 668483. *802*

UNITED ARAB EMIRATES. AL-MASRAF AL-MARKAZI. AL-TAQRIR AL-SANAWI.
Central Bank, P.O. Box 854, Abu Dhabi, Abu Dhabi, United Arab Emirates. TEL 652220. FAX 668483. *1111*

UNITED ARAB EMIRATES. DA'IRAT AL-MUSHTARIAT. AL-KITAB AL-IHSA'I AL-SANAWI.
Purchasing Department, Information Office, P.O. Box 838, Abu Dhabi, United Arab Emirates. TEL 212700. *4082*

UNITED ARAB EMIRATES. WIZARAT AL-SIHHAH. AL-KITAB AL-IHSA'I AL-SANAWI.
Wizarat al-Sihhah, Idarat al-Takhtit, P.O. Box 838, Abu Dhabi, United Arab Emirates. TEL 214100.
circ. 1,000. *3181*

UNITED ARAB EMIRATES. WIZARAT AL-SIHHAH. IDARAT AL-TIBB AL-WAQA'I. AL-TAQRIR AL-SANAWI.
Wizarat al-Sihhah, Idarat al-Tibb al-Waqa'i, P.O. Box 344, Abu Dhabi, United Arab Emirates. TEL 333485.
circ. 1,000. *4114*

UNITED ARAB EMIRATES. WIZARAT AL-TARBIYYAH WAL-TA'LIM. AL-TAQRIR AL-SANAWI.
Wizarat al-Tarbiyyah wal-Ta'lim, Idarat al-I'lam al-Tarbawi, P.O. Box 259, Abu Dhabi, United Arab Emirates. TEL 213800.
circ. 1,000. *1732*

UNITED KINGDOM FREEDOM BULLETIN.
International Freedom Foundation, 200 G St., N.E., Ste. 300, Washington, DC 20002. TEL 202-546-5788. FAX 202-546-5488.
circ. 1,500. *3975*

U.S. CENTERS FOR DISEASE CONTROL. ABORTION SURVEILLANCE REPORT.
U.S. Centers for Disease Control, 1600 Clifton Rd., Atlanta, GA 30333. TEL 404-329-3311. *598*

U.S. COAST GUARD. ENVIRONMENTAL PROTECTION NEWSLETTER.
U.S. Coast Guard, 2100 Second St., S.W., Washington, DC 20593. TEL 202-267-2823. *1970*

U.S. DIRECTOR OF SELECTIVE SERVICE. SEMIANNUAL REPORT.
U.S. Selective Service System, Washington, DC 20435. TEL 202-724-0424. *3474*

U.S. EARTH SCIENCE INFORMATION CENTER. NEWSLETTER.
U.S. Geological Survey, U.S. Earth Science Information Office, 12201 Sunrise Valley Dr., MS 509, Reston, VA 22092. TEL 703-648-5912. FAX 703-648-5939.
circ. 3,000. *2264*

U.S. FOREIGN AGRICULTURAL SERVICE. FOOD AND AGRICULTURAL EXPORT DIRECTORY.
U.S. Department of Agriculture, Foreign Agricultural Service, Export Programs Division, Rm. 4944-S, Washington, DC 20250-1001. TEL 202-447-3031.
circ. 5,000. *159*

U.S. FOREST SERVICE. GENERAL TECHNICAL REPORT N C.
U.S. Forest Service, North Central Forest Experiment Sta., 1992 Folwell Ave., St. Paul, MN 55108. TEL 612-649-5276.
circ. 1,000. *2109*

U.S. FOREST SERVICE. NORTH CENTRAL FOREST EXPERIMENT STATION. LIST OF PUBLICATIONS.
U.S. Forest Service, North Central Forest Experiment Sta., 1992 Folwell Ave., St. Paul, MN 55108. TEL 612-649-5276.
circ. 1,500. *2113*

U.S. FOREST SERVICE. RESEARCH NOTE N C.
U.S. Forest Service, North Central Forest Experiment Sta., 1992 Folwell Ave., St. Paul, MN 55108. TEL 612-649-5276.
circ. 2,000. *2109*

U.S. FOREST SERVICE. RESEARCH PAPER N C.
U.S. Forest Service, North Central Forest Experiment Sta., 1992 Folwell Ave., St. Paul, MN 55108. TEL 612-649-5276.
circ. 2,000. *2110*

U.S. FOREST SERVICE. RESOURCE BULLETIN N C.
U.S. Forest Service, North Central Forest Experiment Sta., 1992 Folwell Ave., MN 55108. TEL 612-649-5276.
circ. 4,000. *2110*

U.S. LIBRARY OF CONGRESS. ACCESSIONS LIST: BRAZIL AND URUGUAY. ANNUAL LIST OF SERIALS.
U.S. Library of Congress, Overseas Operation Division, Washington, DC 20540. TEL 202-707-5273.
circ. 625. *414*

U.S. NATIONAL AERONAUTICS AND SPACE ADMINISTRATION. RESEARCH AND TECHNOLOGY OPERATING PLAN (RTOP) SUMMARY.
U.S. National Aeronautics and Space Administration, Center for Aerospace Information, Box 8757, Baltimore-Washington International Airport, MD 21240. TEL 301-621-0153. *64*

UNITED STATES PILOTS ASSOCIATION NEWSLETTER.
United States Pilots Association, 483 S. Kirkwood Rd., Ste. 10, St. Louis, MO 63122. *64*

UNITED WAY OF AMERICA. INFORMATION CENTER. DIGEST OF SELECTED REPORTS.
United Way of America, 701 N. Fairfax St., Alexandria, VA 22314. TEL 703-836-7100. *4427*

UNIVERSAL MESSAGE.
Islamic Research Academy, D-35, Block 5, Federal 'B' Area, Karachi 75950, Pakistan. TEL 681157. FAX 422827.
circ. 1,000. *4221*

UNIVERSIDAD AUTONOMA DE SANTO DOMINGO. BIBLIOTECA CENTRAL. BOLETIN DE ADQUISICIONES.
Universidad Autonoma de Santo Domingo, Biblioteca Central, Santo Domingo, Dominican Republic. *415*

UNIVERSIDAD DE ORIENTE. INSTITUTO OCEANOGRAFICO BIBLIOTECA. BOLETIN BIBLIOGRAFICO.
Universidad de Oriente, Instituto Oceanografico, Apdo. Postal 94, Cumana, Sucre, Venezuela.
circ. 1,000. *1552*

UNIVERSIDAD DE ORIENTE. INSTITUTO OCEANOGRAFICO. CUADERNOS OCEANOGRAFICOS.
Universidad de Oriente, Instituto Oceanografico, Apdo. Postal 94, Cumana Sucre, Venezuela.
circ. 1,500. *1611*

UNIVERSIDAD NACIONAL AUTONOMA DE MEXICO. SEMINARIO DE INVESTIGACIONES BIBLIOTECOLOGICA. PUBLICACIONES. SERIE B. BIBLIOGRAFIA.
Universidad Nacional Autonoma de Mexico, Seminario de Investigaciones Bibliotecologicas, Cuidad Universitaria, 04510 Mexico D.F., Mexico. *415*

UNIVERSIDADE DE SAO PAULO. ESCOLA DE ENFERMAGEM. REVISTA.
Universidade de Sao Paulo, Escola de Enfermagem, Av. Dr. Eneas de Carvalho Aguiar, 419, SP, Caixa Postal 5751, 05403 Sao Paolo, Brazil. FAX 011-280-8213.
circ. 1,000. *3287*

UNIVERSIDADE ESTADUAL PAULISTA. REVISTA DE ODONTOLOGIA.
Universidade Estadual Paulista, Faculdade de Odontologia, Av. Vicente Ferreira, 1278, Caixa Postal 603, 17.500 Marilia SP, Brazil. TEL 0144 33-1844. FAX 0144-22-2504.
circ. 1,000. *3244*

UNIVERSIDADE FEDERAL DE SANTA MARIA. CENTRO DE CIENCIAS RURAIS. REVISTA.
Universidade Federal de Santa Maria, Centro de Ciencias Rurais, Campus Universitario, 97119 Santa Maria, Rio Grande do Sul, Brazil. FAX 055-226-19-75.
circ. 500. *126*

UNIVERSIDADE FEDERAL DO CEARA. CENTRO DE CIENCIAS DA SAUDE. REVISTA DE MEDICINA.
Universidade Federal do Ceara, Centro de Ciencias da Saude, Rua Alexandre Barauna 1019, Caixa Postal 688, Porangabucu, 60000 Fortaleza-Ceara, Brazil. FAX 085-243-95-13. *3160*

UNIVERSIDADE FEDERAL DO RIO DE JANEIRO. FACULDADE DE ODONTOLOGIA. ANAIS.
Universidade Federal do Rio de Janeiro, Faculdade de Odontologia, Ilha da Cidade Universitaria, Rio de Janeiro, Brazil. *3244*

UNIVERSIDADE FEDERAL DO RIO DE JANEIRO. INSTITUTO DE MATEMATICA. ESTUDOS E COMUNICACOES.
Universidade Federal do Rio de Janeiro, Instituto de Matematica, C.P. 68530, 21944 Rio de Janeiro, RJ, Brazil. *3059*

UNIVERSIDADE FEDERAL DO RIO DE JANEIRO. INSTITUTO DE MATEMATICA. MEMORIAS DE MATEMATICA.
Universidade Federal do Rio de Janeiro, Instituto de Matematica, C.P. 68530, 21944 Rio de Janeiro, RJ, Brazil. *3063*

UNIVERSITAS.
Universidade Federal da Bahia, Centro Editorial e Didatico, Rua Barao de Geremoabo s-no., Ondina, Salvador, Bahia 40000, Brazil.
circ. 500. *2517*

UNIVERSITAT DE BARCELONA. BIBLIOTECA. MEMORIA ANUAL.
Universitat de Barcelona, Biblioteca, Gran via de les Corts Catalanes, 585, 08007 Barcelona, Spain. *2788*

UNIVERSITE DE BRETAGNE OCCIDENTALE. GUIDE DE L'ETUDIANT.
Universite de Bretagne Occidentale, Rue de Archives, 29269 Brest, France. TEL 98-31-60-20. FAX 98-31-60-01. *1669*

UNIVERSITE DE MONCTON. REVUE.
Universite de Moncton, Moncton, N.B. E1A 3E9, Canada. TEL 506-858-4062.
circ. 600. *2179*

UNIVERSITY OF ALASKA MUSEUM. ANNUAL REPORT.
University of Alaska Museum, 907 Yukon Dr., Fairbanks, AK 99775-1200. TEL 907-474-7505. FAX 907-474-5469. *3534*

UNIVERSITY OF ALBERTA. CENTRE FOR CRIMINOLOGICAL RESEARCH. DISCUSSION PAPERS.
University of Alberta, Department of Sociology, Centre for Criminological Research, Edmonton, Alta. T6G 2H4, Canada. TEL 403-492-4659. FAX 403-432-7219.
circ. 150. *1524*

UNIVERSITY OF ALLAHABAD. EDUCATION DEPARTMENT. RESEARCHES AND STUDIES.
University of Allahabad, Education Department, Allahabad 211002, Uttar Pradesh, India. *1669*

UNIVERSITY OF CALIFORNIA. SEISMOGRAPHIC STATIONS. BULLETIN.
University of California, Berkeley, Seismographic Station, 475 Earth Sciences Bldg., Berkeley, CA 94720. TEL 415-642-3977. FAX 643-5811.
circ. 450. *1596*

UNIVERSITY OF CALIFORNIA, SANTA CRUZ. INSTITUTE FOR MARINE SCIENCES. SPECIAL PUBLICATION.
University of California, Santa Cruz, Institute of Marine Sciences, Santa Cruz, CA 95064. TEL 408-429-2464. FAX 408-429-0146.
circ. 500. *1612*

UNIVERSITY OF CHICAGO. PRITZKER SCHOOL OF MEDICINE. ALUMNI ASSOCIATION. MAGAZINE.
University of Chicago Hospitals, Office of Public Affairs, 5841 S. Maryland Ave., Mail Code 6063, Chicago, IL 60637. TEL 312-702-6241. FAX 312-702-3171.
circ. 12,000. *1328*

UNIVERSITY OF DENVER NEWS.
University of Denver, Office of Communications, Denver, CO 80208. TEL 303-871-2777. FAX 303-871-3827.
circ. 65,000. *1328*

UNIVERSITY OF GEORGIA. COLLEGE OF AGRICULTURE EXPERIMENT STATIONS. BULLETIN.
University of Georgia, College of Agriculture Experiment Stations, Connor Hall, Athens, GA 30602. TEL 404-542-3621. *127*

UNIVERSITY OF GEORGIA. COLLEGE OF AGRICULTURE EXPERIMENT STATIONS. RESEARCH REPORTS.
University of Georgia, College of Agriculture Experiment Stations, Connor Hall, Athens, GA 30602. TEL 404-542-3621.
circ. 1,500. *127*

UNIVERSITY OF HARTFORD STUDIES IN LITERATURE.
University of Hartford, English Department, 200 Bloomfield Ave., W. Hartford, CT 06117. TEL 203-243-4574.
circ. 500. *2972*

UNIVERSITY OF ILLINOIS AT URBANA-CHAMPAIGN. DEPARTMENT OF AGRICULTURAL ECONOMICS. LEASE SHARES AND FARM RETURNS.
University of Illinois at Urbana-Champaign, Department of Agricultural Economics, Urbana, IL 61801. TEL 217-333-2638. *159*

UNIVERSITY OF LONDON. ROYAL POSTGRADUATE MEDICAL SCHOOL. ANNUAL REPORT.
University of London, Royal Postgraduate Medical School, Hammersmith Hospital, Du Cane Rd., London W12 0NN, England. TEL 081-740-3200. FAX 081-740-3203.
circ. 1,000. *3160*

UNIVERSITY OF MANILA LAW GAZETTE.
University of Manila, 546 Dr. M. V. de los Santos St., Sampaloc, Manila D-403, Philippines.
circ. 500. *2690*

UNIVERSITY OF NEVADA. BASQUE STUDIES PROGRAM NEWSLETTER.
University of Nevada, Basque Studies Program, Getchell Library, Reno, NV 89557. TEL 702-784-4854. FAX 702-784-6010.
circ. 8,500. *2027*

UNIVERSITY OF NEWCASTLE. DEPARTMENT OF ELECTRICAL AND COMPUTER ENGINEERING. TECHNICAL REPORT EE.
University of Newcastle, Department of Electrical and Computer Engineering, Shortland, N.S.W. 2308, Australia. FAX 61-49-216024.
circ. 800. *1910*

UNIVERSITY OF OCCUPATIONAL AND ENVIRONMENTAL HEALTH. JOURNAL.
University of Occupational and Environmental Health, Japan, Iseigaoka 1-1, Yahatanishi-ku, Kita-Kyushu 807, Japan. FAX 093-692-4876.
circ. 900. *3622*

UNIVERSITY OF PORT ELIZABETH. INSTITUTE FOR PLANNING RESEARCH. ANNUAL REPORT.
University of Port Elizabeth, Institute for Planning Research, Box 1600, Port Elizabeth 6000, South Africa.
circ. 400. *1000*

UNIVERSITY OF RHODE ISLAND. LIBRARY. LIBRARY LETTER.
University of Rhode Island, Association of Friends of the Library, Kingston, RI 02881. *2789*

UNIVERSITY OF SINGAPORE. HISTORY SOCIETY. JOURNAL.
National University of Singapore, History Department, Kent Ridge, Singapore 0511, Singapore. TEL 772-3839. *2343*

UNIVERSITY OF THE PHILIPPINES. INSTITUTE OF LIBRARY SCIENCE. NEWSLETTER.
University of the Philippines, Institute of Library Science, Diliman, Quezon City 1101, Philippines. TEL 98-24-71-6249.
circ. 900. *2789*

UNIVERSITY OF THE PUNJAB. INSTITUTE OF GEOLOGY. GEOLOGICAL BULLETIN.
University of the Punjab, Institute of Geology, Qaid-E-Azam Campus, Lahore, Pakistan. *1584*

UNIVERSITY OF TOKYO. INSTITUTE OF APPLIED MICROBIOLOGY. REPORTS.
University of Tokyo, Institute of Applied Microbiology, 1-1-1 Yayoi, Bunkyo-ku, Tokyo 113, Japan. *468*

UNIVERSITY OF WATERLOO. GAZETTE.
University of Waterloo, Internal Communications Department, Waterloo, Ont. N2L 3G1, Canada. TEL 519-885-1211. FAX 519-888-4638.
circ. 11,000. *1669*

UNIVERSITY OF WATERLOO COURIER.
University of Waterloo, Waterloo, Ont. N2L 3G1, Canada. TEL 519-885-1211.
circ. 50,000. *1329*

UNIX REVIEW.
Miller Freeman, Inc. 600 Harrison St., San Francisco, CA 94107. TEL 415-905-2200. FAX 415-905-2232.
circ. 50,000. *1432*

UNMUZZLED OX.
Unmuzzled Ox Foundation, Ltd., 105 Hudson St., New York, NY 10013. TEL 212-226-7170.
circ. 20,000. *3008*

UP WITH PEOPLE NEWS.
Up with People, Inc., 3103 N. Campbell Ave., Tucson, AZ 85719. TEL 602-327-7351.
circ. 100,000. *4208*

UPDATE.
George Warman Publications (Pty.) Ltd., 77 Hout St., P.O. Box 704, Cape Town 8000, South Africa. TEL 021-245320. FAX 021-261332.
circ. 7,700. *3160*

UPPER CASE.
National Life Insurance Company of Vermont, Montpelier, VT 05604. TEL 802-229-3333.
circ. 3,000. *2544*

URBAN FOREST.
Ontario Shade Tree Council, 5 Shoreham Dr., North York, Ont. M3N 1S4, Canada. TEL 416-699-1213. FAX 416-851-9610.
circ. 300. *2110*

USED EQUIPMENT DIRECTORY.
Penton Publishing (Hasbrouck Heights) 611 Rte. 46 W., Hasbrouck Heights, NJ 07604-3120. TEL 800-526-6052. FAX 201-393-9553.
circ. 75,000. *3024*

UTAH CATTLEMAN.
Utah Cattlemen's Association, 150 S. Sixth E., Ste. 10B, Salt Lake City, UT 84102. TEL 801-355-5748.
circ. 4,550. *227*

UTILITY CONSTRUCTION AND MAINTENANCE.
Practical Communications, Inc., Box 183, Cary, IL 60013-0183. TEL 708-639-2200. FAX 708-639-9542.
circ. 25,500. *635*

UTTAR BHARAT BHOOGOL PATRIKA.
Uttar Bharat Parishad, c/o V.K. Shrivastava, Secy., 236, Daudpur, Gorakhpur 273 001, India. TEL 335221. *2266*

UTTAR PRADESH. STATE PLANNING INSTITUTE. QUARTERLY BULLETIN OF STATISTICS.
State Planning Institute, Economic and Statistics Division, Uttar Pradesh, India. *4591*

V.C.F. NEWSLETTER.
Veterinary Christian Fellowship, 2 Saxon Close, Godmanchester, Cambs PG18 8JL, England. TEL 0480-52601.
circ. 420. *4817*

V D E W DIE OEFFENTLICHE ELEKTRIZITAETSVERSORGUNG.
Vereinigung Deutscher Elektrizitaetswerke e.V., Stresemannallee 23, 6000 Frankfurt a.M., Germany. FAX 069-6304339. *1910*

V F A PROFIL.
Profil Verlag, Bloherfelderstr. 213, 2900 Oldenburg, Germany. TEL 0441-54747. FAX 0441-55570.
circ. 34,000. *308*

V S T A NEWS.
Victorian Secondary Teachers' Association, 112 Trenerry Crescent, Abbotsford, Vic. 3067, Australia. TEL 03-417-2822. FAX 03-417-6198.
circ. 17,000. *1762*

VAART BLAD.
Norges Kooperative Landsforening. Kirkegt. 4, 0107 Oslo 1, Norway.
circ. 250,000. *832*

VAART VERN.
Krigsskoleutdannede Offiserers Landsforening, P.O. Box 7207, Ho, N-0307 Oslo 3, Norway. TEL 02-52-15-46. FAX 02-69-56-08.
circ. 2,000. *3474*

VAEXTSKYDDS - KURIREN.
Bayer (Sverige) AB, Agro-Kemi, Hemsoegatan 10 A, S-211 24 Malmoe, Sweden.
circ. 40,000. *195*

VANCOUVER CHILD.
Vancouver Child Publications, 757 Union St., Vancouver, B.C. V6A 2C3, Canada. TEL 604-251-1760.
circ. 20,000. *1245*

VANCOUVER ISLAND REGIONAL LIBRARY NEWSLETTER.
Vancouver Island Regional Library, Box 3333, 6250 Hammond Bay Road, Namaimo, B.C. V9R 5N3, Canada. TEL 604-758-4697. FAX 604-758-2482.
circ. 389. *2790*

VANDTEKNIK.
Dansk Vandteknisk Forening, Vilh. Becks Vej 60, 8260 Viby J, Denmark. TEL 86112333609.
circ. 1,525. *4830*

VANGUARD (LA HABRA).
Alpha Beta Company, 777 S. Harbor Blvd., La Habra, CA 90631. TEL 714-738-2000.
circ. 34,000. *2083*

EL VAQUERO.
Glendale Community College, 1500 N. Verdugo Rd., Glendale, CA 91208-2894. TEL 818-240-1000. FAX 818-549-9436.
circ. 3,500. *1329*

VARME OG SANITETS NYT.
Christtreu, Strandlodsvei 48, DK-2300 Copenhagen S, Denmark. TEL 32-844848. FAX 31-582055.
circ. 14,305. *2304*

VARSITY.
S R C Press, University of Cape Town, Rondesbosch 7700, South Africa. TEL 021 698531.
circ. 7,500. *1329*

VEHICULE DES CONDUCTEURS PROPRIETAIRES.
Editions Bomart Ltee., 7493 TransCanada Hwy., Ste. 103, St. Laurent, Que. H4T 1T3, Canada. TEL 514-337-9043. FAX 514-337-1862.
circ. 14,580. *4749*

VEILIG VLIEGEN.
Koninklijke Luchtmacht, Afdeling Bedrijfsveiligheid Koninklijke Luchtmachtstaf, Binckhorstlaan 135, Postbus 20703, 2500 ES The Hague, Netherlands. TEL 70-3492358. FAX 70-3492500.
circ. 5,000. *64*

VENEZUELA. OFICINA CENTRAL DE ESTADISTICA E INFORMATICA. ENCUESTA CUALITATIVA.
Oficina Central de Estadistica e Informatica, Apdo. de Correos 4593, Carmelitas, Caracas 1010A, Venezuela. TEL 782-11-33. FAX 781-13-80. *743*

VENTURI.
University of Pretoria Student Publishers, Student Council Office, 84 Tindall Rd., Box 3194, Pretoria, South Africa.
circ. 1,000. *1329*

VEREIN ZUM SCHUTZ DER BERGWELT. JAHRBUCH.
Verein zum Schutz der Bergwelt e.V., Praterinsel 5, 8000 Munich 22, Germany. TEL 089-235090-0. FAX 089-4706168. *1499*

VERITAS FORUM.
Veritas Corporate Communications, Det novske Veritas, N-1322 Hovik, Norway.
circ. 15,000. *1876*

VERKEHRSBLATT.
Verkehrsblattverlag, Hohe Str. 39, Postfach 100555, 4600 Dortmund 1, Germany. FAX 0231-125640.
circ. 10,000. *4722*

VERMONT. COMMISSIONER OF BANKING INSURANCE AND SECURITIES. ANNUAL REPORT OF THE BANK COMMISSIONER.
Department of Banking Insurance and Securities, Division of Banking, 120 State St., Montpelier, VT 05620-3101. TEL 802-828-3301.
circ. 1,700. *803*

VERMONT EDUCATION DIRECTORY.
Department of Education, State Office Building, Montpelier, VT 05602. TEL 802-828-3151.
circ. 8,000. *1670*

VERMONT PHILATELIST.
Vermont Philatelic Society, 18 Fuller St., Montpelier, VT 05602. *3759*

VERWARMING EN VENTILATIE.
Vereniging van Nederlandse Installatiebedrijven (VNI), Postbus 7272, 2701 AG Zoetermeer, Netherlands.
circ. 4,000. *2304*

VERZEICHNIS DER KONSULARISCHEN VERTRETUNGEN IN OESTERREICH.
Bundesministerium fuer Auswaertige Angelegenheiten, Ballhausplatz 2, A-1014 Vienna, Austria. *3976*

VETERANTICS.
Veteran Car Club of South Africa, Box 1204, Durban, Natal, South Africa. *259*

VETERINARY FORUM.
Forum Publications, Inc., 1610-A Frederica Rd., St. Simons Island, GA 31522-2509. TEL 912-638-4848. FAX 912-634-0768.
circ. 42,000. *4818*

VIA SATELLITE.
Phillips Publishing, Inc., 7811 Montrose Rd., Potomac, MD 20854. TEL 301-340-2100. FAX 301-340-0542. *1345*

VIBRATIONS.
Indiana University, Alumni Association, Bloomington, IN 47402-4822. TEL 812-855-4822.
circ. 3,800. *2790*

VICTORIAN REAL ESTATE JOURNAL.
Real Estate Institute of Victoria Ltd., P.O. Box 443, Camberwell, Vic. 3124, Australia. TEL 03-882-9188. FAX 03-882-8112.
circ. 2,500. *4159*

VIDA RELIGIOSA.
Misioneros Hijos del Inmaculado Corazon de Maria (Claretianos), Buen Suceso, 22, 28008 Madrid, Spain. TEL 91-2482101.
circ. 10,000. *4278*

VIDEO INNOVATIONS.
Brunico Communications Inc., 366 Adelaide St. W., Ste. 500, Toronto, Ont. M5V 1R9, Canada. TEL 416-408-2300. FAX 416-408-0870. *1386*

VIDEO RETAILER SHOWCASE.
Tel-Aire Publications, Inc., 3105 E. Carpenter Frwy., Irving, TX 75062. TEL 214-438-4111. FAX 214-579-7483.
circ. 19,500. *1387*

VIDEO STORE MAGAZINE.
Avanstar Communications, Inc., 7500 Old Oak Blvd., Cleveland, OH 44130. TEL 216-243-8100. FAX 216-891-2726.
circ. 44,300. *1387*

VIE ET SANTE.
Editions Vie et Sante, 60 av. Emile Zola, 77192 Dammarie les Lys Cedex, France. FAX 64-87-00-66.
circ. 40,000. *3810*

VIE SOCIALE.
Centre d'Etudes, de Documentation, d'Information et d'Action Sociales (CEDIAS), 5 rue Las-Cases, 75007 Paris, France. TEL 45-51-66-10.
circ. 1,750. *4456*

VIEWPOINT (LONDON, 1965).
Delane Press, 157 Vicarage Rd., London E10 5DU, England. TEL 081-539-3876. *3932*

VIKING SOCIETY FOR NORTHERN RESEARCH. SAGA BOOK.
Viking Society for Northern Research, c/o Dept. of Scandinavian Studies, University College, London WC1E 6BT, England.
circ. 600. *2394*

VIM & VIGOR.
Vim & Vigor, Inc., 8805 N. 23rd Ave., No. 11, Phoenix, AZ 85021. FAX 602-395-5853.
circ. 550,000. *3810*

VINTNERS WORLD.
Jemma Publications Ltd., Marino House, 52-53 Glasthule Rd., Sandycove, Dun Laoghaire, Co. Dublin, Ireland. TEL 01-800000. FAX 01-844041.
circ. 6,912. *386*

VIRGINIA MARITIMER.
Port Authority, 600 World Trade Center, Norfolk, VA 23510. TEL 804-683-8000. FAX 804-683-8500.
circ. 8,000. *4741*

VIRGINIA P H C IMAGE.
Virginia Association of Plumbing - Heating - Cooling Contractors, 2103 Lake Ave., Richmond, VA 23230. TEL 804-288-2080. FAX 804-282-1620.
circ. 4,420. *2304*

VIRGINIA POLYTECHNIC INSTITUTE AND STATE UNIVERSITY. DEPARTMENT OF GEOLOGICAL SCIENCES. GEOLOGICAL GUIDEBOOKS.
Virginia Polytechnic Institute and State University, Department of Geological Sciences, 4044 Derring Hall, Blacksburg, VA 24061. TEL 703-961-6521.
1585

VIRGINIA SCHOOL BOARDS ASSOCIATION NEWSLETTER.
Virginia School Boards Association, 2250 Old Ivy Road, Ste. 1, Charlottesville, VA 22901. TEL 804-295-8722. FAX 804-295-8785.
circ. 2,000. *1732*

VIRKSOMHEDS NYT.
Christtreu, Strandlodsvei 48, DK-2300 Copenhagen S, Denmark. TEL 32-844848. FAX 31-582055.
circ. 19,691. *4660*

VITA TRENTINA.
Vita Trentina Editrice - Coop.r.l., Via S. Giovanni Bosco, 5, 38100 Trento, Italy. TEL 0461-982143. FAX 0461-233446.
circ. 15,000. *2207*

VITAL SIGNS (OKLAHOMA).
University of Oklahoma, O.U. Health Sciences Center, Library Rm. 162, Box 26901, Oklahoma City, OK 73190. TEL 405-271-2323.
circ. 6,500. *3810*

VITALITY.
Vitality, Inc., 8080 N. Central, LB 78, Dallas, TX 75206. TEL 214-691-1480.
circ. 750,000. *3810*

VITALITY MAGAZINE.
320 Danforth Ave., Ste. 204, Toronto, Ont. M4K 1P3, Canada. TEL 416-463-6677.
circ. 24,500. *3810*

VOETBAL TOTAAL.
Koninklijke Nederlandsche Voetbalbond, P.O. Box 515, 3700 AM Zeist, Netherlands. TEL 03439-9211. FAX 03439-1397.
circ. 30,500. *4514*

VOICE OF SILENCE NEWSLETTER.
World Federation of the Deaf, 120 via Gregoria VII, Rome 00165, Italy.
circ. 500. *2289*

VOICE OF WALDEN.
Walden Forever, Inc., Box 275, Concord, MA 01742. TEL 508-371-2421. *1499*

VOIES DE LA CREATION THEATRALE.
Editions du C N R S, 1 Place Aristide Briand, 92195 Meudon Cedex, France. TEL 1-45-34-75-50. FAX 1-46-26-28-49.
circ. 1,500. *4642*

VOLKSDANS.
Landelijk Centrum Volksdans, P.O. Box 452, 3500 AL Utrecht, Netherlands. FAX 030-332721.
circ. 3,300. *2059*

THE VOLUNTEER LIBRARIAN.
Association of Private Libraries, c/o Sophie Mitrisin, 66 Frankfort St., Apt. 2G, New York, NY 10038-1622. *2790*

VOLUNTEERS.
United Church of Christ, Board for Homeland Ministries, 700 Prospect Ave., Cleveland, OH 44115. TEL 216-736-3266. FAX 216-736-3263.
circ. 8,000. *4252*

VORSCHAU.
Forschungsgesellschaft fuer Wohnene, Bauen und Planen, Loewengasse 47, A-1030 Vienna, Austria.
635

VORTEX.
American Chemical Society, California Section, 2140 Shattuck Ave., Rm. 1101, Berkeley, CA 94704. TEL 415-848-0512.
circ. 4,000. *1190*

VYZIVA.
Spolecnost pro Racionalni Vyzivu, Narodni tr. 24, Nove Mesto, 110 00 Prague, Czechoslovakia. TEL 29-01-91.
circ. 5,500. *3613*

VYZOV.
Permskii Gorispolkom, Upravlenie Vnutrennikh Del, Ul. Druzhby 34, 614600 Perm, Russia. TEL 48-39-24. FAX 32-52-19.
circ. 50,000. *3948*

W A NEWS.
American Diabetes Association, Washington Affiliate, Inc., 557 Roy St., Seattle, WA 98109. TEL 206-282-4616. FAX 206-282-4729.
circ. 6,500. *3161*

W N C BUSINESS JOURNAL.
Nason & Associates, Box 8204, Asheville, NC 28804. TEL 704-258-1322.
circ. 19,000. *698*

W R R I NEWS.
North Carolina State University, Water Resources Research Institute, Box 7912, Raleigh, NC 27695-7912. TEL 919-515-2815. FAX 919-515-7802.
circ. 150. *4830*

DIE WAAGE.
Gruenenthal GmbH, Steinfeldstr. 2, 5190 Stolberg, Germany.
circ. 35,000. *2192*

WAGES AND BENEFITS.
Employee Futures Research, Box 385, Pt. Richey, FL 34673-0385.
circ. 700. *1732*

WAKE FOREST LAW REVIEW.
Wake Forest Law Review Association, Inc., Wake Forest University, Winston-Salem, NC 27109. TEL 919-761-5439. FAX 919-759-6077.
circ. 1,500. *2693*

WALKING-STICK NOTES.
Placebo Press, 4051 East Olive Rd., Ste. 231, Pensacola, FL 32514. TEL 904-477-3995. *357*

WALLACES FARMER.
1501 42nd St., Ste. 501, West Des Moines, IA 50265. TEL 515-224-6000.
circ. 140,500. *129*

WANASAN.
Royal Forest Department, Vanasarn Forest Journal Office, Bangkok, Thailand.
circ. 5,400. *2110*

WASHINGTON (STATE). DEPARTMENT OF REVENUE. RESEARCH SECTION. COMPARATIVE STATE - LOCAL TAXES.
Department of Revenue, Research Section, General Administration Bldg. AX-02, Olympia, WA 98504. TEL 206-753-2087. FAX 206-586-5543. *1112*

WASHINGTON (STATE). DEPARTMENT OF REVENUE. RESEARCH SECTION. PROPERTY TAX STATISTICS.
Department of Revenue, Research Section, General Administration Bldg. AX-02, Olympia, WA 98504. TEL 206-753-2087. FAX 206-586-5543. *1112*

WASHINGTON INDUSTRY AND ASSOCIATION NEWS.
Acropolis Books Ltd., 13950 Park Center Rd., Herndon, VA 22071-3222.
circ. 3,500. *4006*

WASHINGTON REAL ESTATE NEWS.
Department of Licensing, Real Estate Division, Box 9015, Olympia, WA 98504. TEL 206-586-4602.
circ. 60,000. *4159*

WASHINGTON RESEARCH COUNCIL. NOTEBOOK.
Washington Research Council, 906 S. Columbia, Ste. 350, Olympia, WA 98501. TEL 206-357-6643.
circ. 2,500. *4077*

WAT KAN ONS OPVOER'
Dramatic Artistic & Literary Rights Organisation (Pty) Ltd., SAMRO House, Cor. de Beer & Juta Streets, Braamfontein, South Africa.
circ. 2,000. *4642*

WATER CONDITIONING AND PURIFICATION.
Publicom Inc., 4651 N. First Ave., Ste. 101, Tucson, AZ 85718. FAX 602-887-2383.
circ. 14,000. *4831*

WATER SCOOTER BUSINESS.
Ehlert Publishing Group, Inc., 319 Barry Ave. S., Ste. 101, Wayzata, MN 55391-1603. TEL 612-962-0598.
circ. 5,000. *4530*

AL-WATHA'IQ AL-FILASTINIYYAH.
Cultural Foundation, Centre for Documentation and Research, P.O. Box 2380, Abu Dhabi, United Arab Emirates. TEL 212900. FAX 541595.
circ. 1,000. *2432*

WATT.
Gruppo Editoriale Jackson S.p.A., Via Pola 9, 20124 Milan, Italy. TEL 39-2-6948228. FAX 39-2-6948290.
circ. 15,853. *1910*

WAYNE STATE MAGAZINE.
Wayne State University, Alumni Association, Office of Alumni Relations, Detroit, MI 48202. TEL 313-577-2300. FAX 313-577-2302.
circ. 29,000. *1330*

WE PROCEEDED ON.
Lewis and Clark Trail Heritage Foundation, Inc., Box 3434, Great Falls, MT 59403. TEL 406-453-2826.
circ. 1,500. *2426*

WEEKLY PETROLEUM ARGUS.
Petroleum Argus Ltd., 93 Shepperton Rd., London N1 3DF, England. TEL 071-359-8792. FAX 071-226-0695. *3703*

WELDER.
Boc-Murex, Hertford Rd., Waltham Cross, Herts., England.
circ. 15,500. *3430*

WELDING DESIGN AND FABRICATION.
Penton Publishing 1100 Superior Ave., Cleveland, OH 44114-2543. TEL 216-696-7000. FAX 216-696-8765.
circ. 40,000. *3431*

WELDING DISTRIBUTOR.
Penton Publishing 1100 Superior Ave., Cleveland, OH 44114-2543. TEL 216-696-7000. FAX 216-696-8765.
circ. 8,000. *3431*

WELDING RESEARCH ABROAD.
Welding Research Council, 345 E. 47th St., New York, NY 10017. TEL 212-705-7956.
circ. 800. *3431*

WELDING RESEARCH COUNCIL BULLETIN.
Welding Research Council, 345 E. 47th St., New York, NY 10017. TEL 212-705-7956.
circ. 900. *3431*

WELL SERVICING.
Workover-Well Servicing Publications, Inc., 6060 N. Central Expy., Ste. 428, Dallas, TX 75206. TEL 214-692-0771.
circ. 12,000. *3703*

WELLINGTON REGIONAL EMPLOYERS ASSOCIATION NEWSLETTER.
Wellington Regional Employers Association (Inc.), Federation House, 6th Floor, Box 1087, 95-99 Molesworth St., Wellington, New Zealand. TEL (04) 737-224. FAX 374501. *997*

WELSH FARMER.
Farmers' Union of Wales, Llys Amaeth, Queens Square, Aberystwyth, Dyfed, Wales. FAX 0970-624369.
circ. 16,000. *129*

WERBEARTIKEL - BERATER.
Vogel Verlag und Druck KG, Max-Planck-Str. 7-9, Postfach 6740, 8700 Wuerzburg 1, Germany. TEL 0931-418-0.
circ. 17,752. *2283*

WERBUNG.
Schweizerischer Reklameverband, Kappelergasse 14, CH-8022 Zurich, Switzerland. FAX 01-2118018.
circ. 2,468. *39*

WE'RE NEXT.
Box GG, Jal, NM 88252. TEL 505-395-2053.
circ. 200,000. *1270*

WERTPAPIER.
Deutsche Schutzvereinigung fuer Wertpapierbesitz e.V., Humboldtstr. 9, D-4000 Dusseldorf, Germany.
circ. 34,000. *969*

DIE WESER.
Weserbund e.V., Erste Schlachtpforte 1, 2800 Bremen 1, Germany. TEL 0421-325868. FAX 0421-323289.
circ. 1,200. *1971*

WEST VIRGINIA. COMMISSION ON AGING. ANNUAL PROGRESS REPORT.
Commission on Aging, State Capitol, Charleston, WV 25305. TEL 304-348-3317.
circ. 500. *2280*

WESTCHESTER FAMILY.
New York Family Publications, Inc., 141 Halstead Ave., Ste. 3D, Mamaroneck, NY 10543-2652. TEL 914-381-7474.
circ. 35,000. *1246*

WESTERN AUSTRALIA. DEPARTMENT FOR COMMUNITY SERVICES. ANNUAL REPORT.
Department for Community Services, 189 Royal St., E. Perth, W.A. 6004, Australia. FAX 09-2222861.
circ. 600. *4424*

WESTERN AUSTRALIA. DEPARTMENT OF TRANSPORT. ANNUAL REPORT.
Department of Transport, 136-138 Stirling Highway, Nedlands, W.A. 6009, Australia. FAX 09-386-5119.
circ. 200. *4660*

WESTERN AUSTRALIA. GEOLOGICAL SURVEY. MINERAL RESOURCES BULLETIN.
Geological Survey of Western Australia, 100 Plain St., E. Perth, W.A. 6004, Australia. TEL 09 222-3333. *3498*

WESTERN AUSTRALIAN COASTAL SHIPPING COMMISSION. ANNUAL REPORT.
Coastal Shipping Commission, P.O. Box 394, Fremantle, Australia. *4742*

WESTERN GROCERY NEWS.
Sunset Publishing Corp., 3055 Wilshire Blvd., Los Angeles, CA 90010. TEL 213-380-9680. FAX 213-380-4217.
circ. 9,000. *2094*

WESTERN HOG JOURNAL.
Alberta Pork Producers Development Corp., 10319 Princess Elizabeth Ave., Edmonton, Alta. T5G 0Y5, Canada. TEL 403-474-8065. FAX 403-471-8065.
circ. 16,310. *228*

WESTERN LINKS.
Southern Links Magazine Publishing Associates, Box 76289, Hilton Head Island, SC 29938. TEL 803-842-6200. FAX 803-842-6233.
circ. 60,000. *4514*

WESTERN PACIFIC ORTHOPAEDIC ASSOCIATION. JOURNAL.
Hong Kong University Press, 139 Pokfulam Rd., Hong Kong. TEL 8170018. FAX 8557350.
circ. 2,000. *3312*

WESTERN POLICIES.
Siveast Consultants, Inc., USA, c/o P.O. Box 1755, Kathmandu, Nepal.
circ. 10. *3934*

WESTERN SHOW NEWS.
Bolger Publications Inc., 3301 Como Ave., S.E., Minneapolis, MN 55414. TEL 612-645-6311. FAX 612-645-1750.
circ. 24,000. *2283*

WHAT'S NEW IN COMPUTING.
Westwick-Farrow Pty. Ltd., Cnr. Fox Valley Rd. and Kiogle Sts., Wahroonga, N.S.W. 2076, Australia. TEL 02-487-2700. FAX 02-489-1265.
circ. 10,200. *1402*

WHAT'S NEW IN ELECTRONICS.
Westwick-Farrow Pty. Ltd., Cnr. Fox Valley Rd. and Kiogle St., Wahroonga, N.S.W. 2076, Australia.
circ. 8,200. *1779*

WHAT'S NEW IN PROCESS ENGINEERING.
Westwick-Farrow Pty. Ltd., Cnr. Fox Valley Rd. and Kiogle St., Wahroonga, N.S.W. 2076, Australia. TEL 02-487-2700. FAX 02-489-1265.
circ. 10,200. *1840*

WHAT'S NEW IN RADIO COMMUNICATIONS.
Westwick-Farrow Pty. Ltd., Cnr. Fox Valley Rd. and Kiogle St., Wahroonga, N.S.W. 2076, Australia. TEL 02-487-2700. FAX 02-489-1265.
circ. 8,200. *1360*

WHAT'S NEW IN SCIENTIFIC & LABORATORY TECHNOLOGY.
Westwick-Farrow Pty. Ltd., Cnr. Fox Valley Rd. and Kiogle St., Wahroonga, N.S.W. 2076, Australia.
circ. 8,200. *4613*

WHEAT GROWER.
National Association of Wheat Growers Foundation, 415 Second St., N.E., Ste. 300, Washington, DC 20002-4993. TEL 202-547-7800.
circ. 67,000. *208*

WHERE (NEW YORK).
600 Third Ave., 15th Fl., New York, NY 10016. TEL 212-687-4646.
circ. 128,000. *4797*

WHERE HALIFAX - DARTMOUTH.
Metro-Guide Publishing, 1496 Lower Water St., Halifax. N.S. B3J 1R9, Canada. TEL 902-420-9943. FAX 902-429-9058.
circ. 27,900. *2179*

WHERE OTTAWA - HULL.
Capital Guide Publishers, 400 Cumberland St., Ottawa, Ont. K1N 8X3, Canada. TEL 613-238-4736. FAX 613-238-3281.
circ. 35,000. *2179*

WHERE ROCKY MOUNTAINS.
R M V Publications Ltd., Ste. 250, One Palliser Sq., 125 Ninth Ave. S.E., Calgary, Alta. T2G 0P6, Canada. TEL 403-266-5085. FAX 403-290-0573.
circ. 360,000. *4797*

WHERE TORONTO.
Key Publishers Co. Ltd., 6 Church St., 2nd fl., Toronto, Ont. M5E 1M1, Canada. TEL 416-364-3333.
circ. 90,000. *4797*

WILDLIFE RESCUE NEWS.
Wildlife Rescue Association of British Columbia, 5216 Glencarin Dr., Burnaby, B.C. V5B 3C1, Canada. TEL 604-526-7275.
circ. 10,000. *232*

WINGED HEAD.
Pittsburgh Athletic Association, 4215 Fifth Ave., Pittsburgh, PA 15213. TEL 412-621-2400. FAX 412-321-4541.
circ. 3,500. *1302*

WINGSPAN: JOURNAL OF THE MALE SPIRIT.
Box 23550, Brightmoor Sta., Detroit, MI 48223. TEL 617-876-1999.
circ. 150,000. *3400*

WIRTSCHAFT NORDHESSEN.
Industrie- und Handelskammer Kassel, Kurfuerstenstr. 9, Postfach 101949, 3500 Kassel, Germany. TEL 0561-78910. FAX 0561-7891290.
circ. 20,600. *824*

WISCONSIN DENTAL ASSOCIATION. JOURNAL.
Wisconsin Dental Association, St. 507, Clark Bldg., 633 W. Wisconsin Ave., Milwaukee, WI 53203. TEL 414-276-4520.
circ. 3,400. *3244*

WISCONSIN P-H-C CONTRACTOR.
Target Communications Corp., 7626 W. Donges Bay Rd., Box 188, Meguon, WI 53092. TEL 414-242-3990.
circ. 6,000. *2304*

WISCONSIN SCHOOL NEWS.
Wisconsin Association of School Boards, 122 W. Washington Ave., Madison, WI 53703. TEL 608-257-2622. FAX 608-257-8386.
circ. 5,500. *1732*

WITNESS (FARMINGTON HILLS).
Oakland Community College, 27055 Orchard Lake Rd., Farmington Hills, MI 48334. TEL 313-471-7740.
circ. 2,500. *3009*

WOMEN IN THE ARTS.
National Museum of Women in the Arts, 1250 New York Ave. N.W., Washington, DC 20005-3920. TEL 202-783-5000. FAX 202-393-3235.
circ. 65,000. *350*

WOMEN'S STUDIES QUARTERLY.
Feminist Press at the City University of New York, 311 E. 94th St., New York, NY 10128-5603. TEL 212-360-5790. FAX 212-348-1241.
circ. 3,000. *4861*

WOMEN'S VIEW.
Smith Family, 16 Larkin St., Camperdown, N.S.W. 2050, Australia. TEL 02-550-4422. FAX 02-550-4235.
circ. 26,000. *4857*

WOOD DIGEST.
Johnson Hill Press, Inc., 1233 Janesville Ave., Ft. Atkinson, WI 53538. TEL 414-563-6388. FAX 414-563-1701.
circ. 52,000. *2562*

WOODMEN OF THE WORLD MAGAZINE.
Woodmen of the World Life Insurance Society, 1700 Farnam St., Omaha, NE 68102. TEL 402-342-1890. FAX 402-271-7269.
circ. 480,000. *2545*

WOODWORKING REVIEW.
Vogel-Verlag und Druck KG, Max-Planck-Str. 7-9, Postfach 67 40, 8700 Wuerzburg 1, Germany. TEL 0931-418-0. FAX 0931-418-2025.
circ. 11,756. *2111*

WOOL NEWS.
Wool & Woollens Export Promotion Council, 612-714 Ashoka Estate, 24 Barakhamba Rd., New Delhi 110001, India. TEL 011-3315512. FAX 91-011-3314626.
circ. 1,000. *4627*

WORKBOAT INTERNATIONAL.
Rushton Marine Press Ltd., Woodside, Burnhams Rd., Little Bookham, Leatherhead, Surrey KT23 3BA, England. TEL 0372-453316. FAX 0372-459974.
circ. 6,000. *4742*

WORKERS EDUCATION JOURNAL.
Central Board for Workers Education, 1400 West High Court, Gokulpeth, Nagpur 440010, India.
circ. 2,000. *1688*

WORKMEN'S CIRCLE CALL.
Workmen's Circle, 45 E. 33 St., New York, NY 10016. TEL 212-898-6800.
circ. 40,000. *2029*

WORLD AEROSPACE TECHNOLOGY.
Sterling Publications Ltd., 86-88 Edgware Rd., London W2 2YW, England. TEL 01-258-0066. *65*

WORLD BROADCAST NEWS.
Intertec Publishing Corp., 9221 Quivira Rd., Box 12901, Overland Park, KS 66212-9981. TEL 212-332-0600, 913-341-1300. FAX 913-967-1898.
circ. 11,212. *1384*

WORLD MUSIC CONNECTIONS.
White Cliffs Media Company, Box 561, Crown Point, IN 46307. TEL 219-322-5537. FAX 219-322-5537.
circ. 3,000. *3586*

WORLD OUTLOOK.
Baptist Men's Movement, Kingsley, Pontesbury, Shrewsbury, Shrops. SY5 0QH, England. TEL 0743-790377.
circ. 1,200. *4253*

WORLD PEACEMAKERS QUARTERLY.
World Peacemakers Inc., 2025 Massachussetts Ave., N.W., Washington, DC 20036. TEL 202-265-7582.
circ. 1,000. *3935*

WORLD'S CHILDREN.
Save the Children Fund, Mary Datchelor House, 17 Grove Ln., London SE5 8RD, England. TEL 071-703-5400. FAX 071-703-2278.
circ. 200,000. *1246*

WRITERS GUILD OF AMERICA, EAST. NEWSLETTER.
Writers Guild of America, East, Inc., 555 W. 57th St., New York, NY 10019. TEL 212-767-7800.
circ. 3,500. *2976*

WRITER'S N W.
Media Weavers 24450 N.W Hansen Rd., Hillsboro, OR 97124. TEL 503-621-3911.
circ. 75,000. *4139*

WYOMING. STATE OF WYOMING ANNUAL REPORT.
Department of Administration and Information, State Library, Supreme Court Bldg., Cheyenne, WY 82002. TEL 307-777-7504. *4078*

WYOMING ANNUAL PLANNING REPORT.
Wyoming Department of Employment, Research & Planning Division, Box 2760, Casper, WY 82602. TEL 307-235-3646.
circ. 650. *997*

WYOMING LABOR FORCE TRENDS.
Wyoming Department of Employment, Research & Planning Division, Box 2760, Casper, WY 82602. TEL 307-235-3646.
circ. 650. *997*

XEROX DISCLOSURE JOURNAL.
Xerox Corporation (Rochester), Xerox Sq. 021, Rochester, NY 14644. TEL 716-423-3255.
circ. 500. *3679*

XIANDAI FAXUE.
Xiandai Faxue Zazhishe, Chongqing, Sichuan 630031, People's Republic of China. TEL 661671.
circ. 50,000. *2695*

Y A B A FRAMEWORK.
Young American Bowling Alliance, 5301 S. 76th St., Greendale, WI 53129. TEL 414-421-4700. FAX 414-421-1194.
circ. 25,000. *4515*

Y TRIANGLE.
Young Men's Christian Association of Canada, 2160 Yonge St., Toronto, Ont. M4S 2A9, Canada. TEL 416-485-9447. FAX 416-485-8228.
circ. 4,000. *1302*

YAMAGUCHI UNIVERSITY. SCHOOL OF MEDICINE. BULLETIN.
Yamaguchi Daigaku, Igakubu, Kogushi, Ube-shi 755, Japan. *3163*

YARD AND GARDEN.
Johnson Hill Press, Inc., 1233 Janesville Ave., Ft. Atkinson, WI 53538. TEL 414-563-6388. FAX 414-563-1701.
circ. 35,000. *2140*

(YEAR) ANNUAL INDEX: PHOTOFACT, COMPUTERFACT, V C R FACT, RADIO, T V & SELECTED ORIGINAL MANUFACTURER'S SERVICE DATA.
Howard W. Sams & Co., 2647 Waterfront Parkway East Dr., Indianapolis, IN 46214-2012. TEL 317-298-5400. *1384*

YEON-GU WEOLBO.
Jeon la Bug-do Gyo Yug Yeon Gu Won, Jeon Ju, S. Korea.
circ. 2,500. *1672*

YES YOU CAN.
Glenn Griffin and Friends Inc., 534 Richmond St. W., Toronto, Ont. M5V 1Y4, Canada. TEL 416-366-0973. FAX 416-366-9231.
circ. 541,000. *636*

YORK JOURNAL OF CONVOCATION.
Convocation of York, c/o Synodal Secretary, Church House, West Walls, Carlishe CA3 8UE, England.
circ. 400. *4210*

YOU AND YOUR BUSINESS.
Thomas J. Martin, Ed. & Pub., 383 S. Broadway, Hicksville, NY 11801. TEL 516-681-2111. *1119*

YOUNG ISRAEL VIEWPOINT.
National Council of Young Israel, 3 West 16th St, New York, NY 10011. TEL 212-929-1525. FAX 212-727-9526.
circ. 40,000. *4227*

YOUNG MEN'S INSTITUTE. INSTITUTE JOURNAL.
Young Men's Institute, 50 Oak St., San Francisco, CA 94102. TEL 415-621-4948.
circ. 4,500. *4210*

Z B S REVIEW.
Bureau of Standards, P.O. Box 50259, Lusaka, Zambia. TEL 286918.
circ. 500. *1086*

Z M P D. KWARTALNY BIULETYN INFORMACYJNY.
Zrzeszenie Miedzynarodowych Przewoznikow Drogowych, Grojecka 17, 02-021 Warsaw, Poland. *4750*

ZAJEDNICAR.
Croatian Fraternal Union of America, 100 Delaney Dr., Pittsburgh, PA 15235.
circ. 40,000. *2029*

ZAKENAUTO.
Uitgeversmaatschappij C. Misset B.V., P.O. Box 4, 7000 BA Doetinchem, Netherlands. TEL 08340-49911. FAX 08340-43839.
circ. 174,000. *4706*

ZAMBIA. MINISTRY OF AGRICULTURE AND WATER DEVELOPMENT. LAND USE BRANCH. SOIL SURVEY REPORT.
Ministry of Agriculture and Water Development, Land Use Branch, c/o Soil Survey Unit, Mount Makulu Research Station, Bag 7, Chilanga, Zambia. TEL 278087. *197*

ZAMBIA LAW JOURNAL.
University of Zambia, School of Law, P.O. Box 32379, Lusaka, Zambia. FAX 260-1-253952.
circ. 300. *2696*

ZEITSCHRIFT FUER VERKEHRSERZIEHUNG.
Rot-Gelb-Gruen Lehrmittel GmbH, Theodor-Heuss-Str. 3, 3300 Braunschweig, Germany. TEL 0531-809070. FAX 0531-8090721.
circ. 5,000. *4723*

ZERO ONE.
Zero One Publications, 39 Minford Gardens, W. Kensington, London W14 0AP, England.
circ. 600. *2196*

ZGODA.
Polish National Alliance of North America, 6100 N. Cicero Ave., Chicago, IL 60646-4385. TEL 312-286-0500. FAX 312-286-9148.
circ. 72,200. *2030*

ZHIYE YU JIANKANG.
Tianjin Institute of Labor Hygiene and Occupational diseases, 221, Machangdao Street, Tianjin 300204, People's Republic of China. TEL 317375.
circ. 100,000. *4116*

ZIMBABWE. COTTON RESEARCH INSTITUTE. ANNUAL REPORT.
Ministry of Lands, Agriculture and Rural Resettlement, Research and Specialist Services, P.O. Box 8108, Causeway, Zimbabwe.
circ. 300. *197*

ZIMBABWE: A FIELD FOR INVESTMENT.
Thomson Publications Zimbabwe (Pvt) Ltd., Thomson House, P.O. Box 1683, Harare, Zimbabwe. TEL 736835.
circ. 14,000. *888*

ZIMBABWE RESEARCH INDEX.
Scientific Liaison Office, P.O. Box 8510, Causeway, Harare, Zimbabwe. TEL 700573.
circ. 500. *4358*

ZINBVN.
Kyoto University, Institute for Research in Humanities, Ushinomiya-cho, Yoshida, Sakyo-ku, Kyoto 606, Japan. *2519*

2 X 4.
Editions C.R. Inc., P.O. Box 1010, Victoriaville, Que. G6P 8Y1, Canada. TEL 819-752-4243. FAX 819-758-8812.
circ. 9,000. *2119*

27STRALIAN SCIENCE TEACHERS' JOURNAL.
Australian Science Teachers Association, University of South Australia (Salisbury Campus), Smith Rd., Salisbury East, S.A. 5109, Australia. TEL 08-302-5137. FAX 08-302-5101.
circ. 5,500. *1764*

33 METAL PRODUCING.
Penton Publishing 1100 Superior Ave., Cleveland, OH 44114. TEL 216-696-7000. FAX 216-696-8765.
circ. 22,000. *3424*

100 LIVELIHOOD OCCUPATIONS.
Siveast Consultants, Inc., USA, c/o P.O. Box 1755, Kathmandu, Nepal.
circ. 50. *3631*

Serials Available On CD-ROM

A B C DER DEUTSCHEN WIRTSCHAFT.
A B C Publishing Group, P.O. Box 4034, D-6100 Darmstadt 1, Germany. TEL 6151-33411. FAX 6151-33164. *1119*

A B I - INFORM.
University Microfilms International, Data Courier, 620 S. Third St., Louisville, KY 40202-2475. TEL 800-626-2823. FAX 502-589-5572. Producer(s): University Microfilms International. *701*

A I D S.
Current Science, 20 N. Third St., Philadelphia, PA 19106. TEL 800-552-5866. FAX 215-574-2270. *3068*

A L I S A.
Australian Clearing House for Library & Information Science, Library, S.A.C.A.E., Lorne Ave., Magill, S. Aust. 5072, Australia. TEL 08 3339457. FAX 61-8-3326122. *2792*

A S F A AQUACULTURE ABSTRACTS.
Cambridge Scientific Abstracts, 7200 Wisconsin Ave., 6th Fl., Bethesda, MD 20814. TEL 301-961-6750. FAX 301-961-6720. Producer(s): Cambridge Scientific Abstracts (Compact Cambridge ASFA). *2050*

A S F A MARINE BIOTECHNOLOGY ABSTRACTS.
Cambridge Scientific Abstracts, 7200 Wisconsin Ave., 6th Fl., Bethesda, MD 20814. TEL 301-961-6750. FAX 301-961-6720. Producer(s): Cambridge Scientific Abstracts (Compact Cambridge Life Sciences Collection and Compact Cambridge ASFA). *1549*

A S S I A.
Bowker-Saur Ltd., 59-60 Grosvenor St., London W1X 9DA, England. TEL 071-493-5841. FAX 071-499-1590. Producer(s): R.R. Bowker. *4394*

A S T I S BIBLIOGRAPHY.
Arctic Science & Technology Information System, Arctic Institute of North America, University of Calgary, 2500 University Dr. N.W., Calgary, Alta. T2N 1N4, Canada. TEL 403-220-4036. *1549*

A S T I S CURRENT AWARENESS BULLETIN.
Arctic Science & Technology Information System, Arctic Institute of North America, University of Calgary, 2500 University Dr. N.W., Calgary, Alta. T2N 1N4, Canada. TEL 403-284-7515. *4613*

A S T I S OCCASIONAL PUBLICATIONS.
Arctic Science & Technology Information System, Arctic Institute of North America, University of Calgary, Calgary, Alta. T2N 1N4, Canada. TEL 403-220-4036. FAX 403-282-4609. *388*

ABSTRACTS ON RURAL DEVELOPMENT IN THE TROPICS.
Koninklijk Instituut voor de Tropen, Mauritskade 63, 1092 AD Amsterdam, Netherlands. TEL 20-5688711. FAX 20-5688444. *701*

ABSTRACTS ON TROPICAL AGRICULTURE.
Koninklijk Instituut voor de Tropen, Mauritskade 63, 1092 AD Amsterdam, Netherlands. TEL 020-5688290. FAX 020-5688444. *132*

ACADEMIA SINICA. BOTANICAL BULLETIN.
Academia Sinica, Institute of Botany, Nankang, Taipei, Taiwan 11529, Republic of China. TEL 886-2-782-1605. FAX 886-2-7827954. *491*

ACADEMIC INDEX.
Information Access Company, 362 Lakeside Dr., Foster City, CA 94404. TEL 800-227-8431. FAX 415-378-5499. *2519*

ACKNOWLEDGE THE WINDOW LETTER.
Mendham Technology Group, 144 Talmadge Rd., Box 11, Mendham, NJ 07945. TEL 201-543-2273. FAX 201-543-6033. *1458*

ACTA PSIQUIATRICA Y PSICOLOGICA DE AMERICA LATINA.
Fundacion Acta Fondo para la Salud Mental, Malabia 2274 13 A, 1425 Buenos Aires, Argentina. FAX 541-7856935. *3328*

ADVANCE LOCATOR FOR CAPITOL HILL.
Staff Directories Ltd., Box 62, Mt. Vernon, VA 22121. TEL 703-765-3400. FAX 703-765-1300. *3870*

AGROFORESTRY ABSTRACTS.
C.A.B. International, Wallingford, Oxon OX10 8DE, England. TEL 0491-32111. FAX 0491-33508. *2111*

AIR CONDITIONING & HEATING SERVICE & REPAIR - DOMESTIC CARS, LIGHT TRUCKS & VANS.
Mitchell International, Inc., 9889 Willow Creek Rd., Box 26260, San Diego, CA 92196-0260. TEL 800-648-8010. FAX 619-578-4752. *4679*

AIR CONDITIONING & HEATING SERVICE & REPAIR - IMPORTED CARS & TRUCKS.
Mitchell International, Inc., 9889 Willow Creek Rd., Box 26260, San Diego, CA 92196-0260. TEL 800-878-6550. FAX 619-578-4752. *4679*

ALLOYS INDEX.
A S M International, Materials Information, Materials Park, OH 44073. TEL 216-338-5151. FAX 216-338-4634. Producer(s): Dialog Information Services. *3424*

AMERICA.
America Press Inc., 106 W. 56th St., New York, NY 10019. TEL 212-581-4640. FAX 212-399-3596. *4254*

AMERICA: HISTORY AND LIFE. ARTICLES ABSTRACT AND CITATIONS OF REVIEWS AND DISSERTATIONS COVERING THE UNITED STATES AND CANADA.
A B C-Clio, 130 Cremona, Box 1911, Santa Barbara, CA 93116-1911. TEL 805-968-1911. FAX 805-685-9685. *2327*

AMERICAN ACADEMY OF PEDIATRICS. COMMITTEE ON INFECTIOUS DISEASES. REPORT (YEAR).
American Academy of Pediatrics, 141 Northwest Point Blvd., Box 927, Elk Grove Village, IL 60009-0927. TEL 708-228-5005. *3318*

AMERICAN BOOK TRADE DIRECTORY.
R.R. Bowker, A Reed Reference Publishing Company, Division of Reed Publishing (USA) Inc., 121 Chanlon Rd., New Providence, NJ 07974. TEL 800-521-8110. FAX 908-665-6688. Producer(s): R.R. Bowker. *4120*

AMERICAN DOCTORAL DISSERTATIONS.
University Microfilms International, Dissertation Publishing, c/o Dorie Mickelson, Mgr., 300 N. Zeeb Rd., Ann Arbor, MI 48106. TEL 313-761-4700. Producer(s): University Microfilms International. *1699*

AMERICAN FAMILY PHYSICIAN.
American Academy of Family Physicians, 8880 Ward Pkwy., Kansas City, MO 64114. TEL 816-333-9700. FAX 816-822-0580. *3074*

AMERICAN HOSPITAL FORMULARY SERVICE DRUG INFORMATION.
American Society of Hospital Pharmacists, c/o Jean Rogers, Dir., Mkt. Svcs., 4630 Montgomery Ave., Bethesda, MD 20814. TEL 301-657-3000. Producer(s): University Microfilms International. *3716*

SERIALS AVAILABLE ON CD-ROM

AMERICAN JOURNAL OF INTERNATIONAL LAW.
American Society of International Law, 2223 Massachusetts Ave., N.W., Washington, DC 20008-2864. TEL 202-265-4313. FAX 202-797-7133.
Producer(s): University Microfilms International. *2719*

AMERICAN LIBRARY DIRECTORY.
R.R. Bowker, A Reed Reference Publishing Company, Division of Reed Publishing (USA) Inc., 121 Chanlon Rd., New Providence, NJ 07974. TEL 800-521-8110. FAX 908-665-6688.
Producer(s): R.R. Bowker. *2742*

AMERICAN MANUFACTURERS DIRECTORY.
American Business Information, Inc., American Business Directories, 5711 S. 86th Circle, Box 27347, Omaha, NE 68127. TEL 402-593-4600. FAX 402-331-1505. *1121*

AMERICAN MEN AND WOMEN OF SCIENCE.
R.R. Bowker, A Reed Reference Publishing Company, Division of Reed Publishing (USA) Inc., 121 Chanlon Rd., New Providence, NJ 07974. TEL 800-521-8110. FAX 908-665-6688.
Producer(s): R.R. Bowker. *417*

AMERICAN SPECTATOR.
2020 N. 14th St., Ste. 750, Box 549, Arlington, VA 22216. TEL 703-243-3733. FAX 703-243-6814. *2858*

AMERICAN STATISTICS INDEX.
Congressional Information Service, 4520 East-West Hwy., Bethesda, MD 20814-3389. TEL 301-654-1550. FAX 301-654-4033. *4561*

AMTLICHES TELEFAX- UND TELEBRIEFVERZEICHNIS DER DEUTSCHEN BUNDESPOST TELECOM.
Deutsche Postreklame GmbH, Wiesenhuettenstr. 18, Postfach 160211, 6000 Frankfurt a.M. 1, Germany. TEL 069-2682-0. FAX 069-2682-218. *1352*

ANIMAL BEHAVIOR ABSTRACTS.
Cambridge Scientific Abstracts, 7200 Wisconsin Ave., 6th Fl., Bethesda, MD 20814. TEL 301-961-6750. FAX 301-961-6720.
Producer(s): Cambridge Scientific Abstracts (Compact Cambridge Life Sciences Collection). *461*

ANNUAIRE TELEXPORT.
Chambre de Commerce et d'Industrie de Paris (CEDIP), 2 place de la Bourse, 75002 Paris, France. *807*

ANNUARIO GENERALE ITALIANO.
Guida Monaci S.p.A., Via Vitorchiano 107, 00189 Rome, Italy. TEL 06-3288805. FAX 06-3275693. *833*

ANTARCTIC BIBLIOGRAPHY.
Library of Congress, Washington, DC 20540. *2242*

ANTIMICROBIAL AGENTS AND CHEMOTHERAPY.
American Society for Microbiology, 1325 Massachusetts Ave., N.W., Washington, DC 20005. TEL 202-737-3600. *549*

APPLIED AND ENVIRONMENTAL MICROBIOLOGY.
American Society for Microbiology, 1325 Massachusetts Ave., N.W., Washington, DC 20005. TEL 202-737-3600. *549*

APPLIED SCIENCE AND TECHNOLOGY INDEX.
H.W. Wilson Co., 950 University Ave., Bronx, NY 10452. TEL 800-367-6770.
Producer(s): H.W. Wilson. *1841*

AQUATIC SCIENCES & FISHERIES ABSTRACTS. PART 1: BIOLOGICAL SCIENCES AND LIVING RESOURCES.
Cambridge Scientific Abstracts, 7200 Wisconsin Ave., 6th Fl., Bethesda, MD 20814. TEL 301-961-6750. FAX 301-961-6720.
Producer(s): Cambridge Scientific Abstracts (Compact Cambridge ASFA). *4834*

AQUATIC SCIENCES & FISHERIES ABSTRACTS. PART 2: OCEAN TECHNOLOGY, POLICY AND NON-LIVING RESOURCES.
Cambridge Scientific Abstracts, 7200 Wisconsin Ave., 6th Fl., Bethesda, MD 20814. TEL 301-961-6750. FAX 301-961-6720.
Producer(s): Cambridge Scientific Abstracts (Compact Cambridge ASFA). *4834*

AQUATIC SCIENCES & FISHERIES ABSTRACTS. PART 3: AQUATIC POLLUTION AND ENVIRONMENTAL QUALITY.
Cambridge Scientific Abstracts, 7200 Wisconsin Ave., 6th Fl., Bethesda, MD 20814. TEL 301-961-6700. FAX 301-961-6720.
Producer(s): Cambridge Scientific Abstracts. *2051*

ARCTIC & ANTARCTIC REGIONS (COLD REGIONS 1800 - PRESENT).
National Information Services Corporation, Ste. 6, Wyman Towers, 3100 St. Paul St., Baltimore, MD 21218. TEL 301-243-0797. FAX 301-243-0982.
Available only on CD-ROM. *1550*

ARQUIVOS DE NEURO-PSIQUIATRIA.
Associacao Arquivos Neuro-Psiquiatria Dr. Oswaldo Lange, Caixa Postal 8877, Sao Paulo 01065, SP, Brazil. TEL 5511-2879726. FAX 5511-2898879. *3331*

ART INDEX.
H.W. Wilson Co., 950 University Ave., Bronx, NY 10452. TEL 800-367-6770. FAX 212-538-2716.
Producer(s): H.W. Wilson (WILSONDISC). *351*

ARTS & HUMANITIES CITATION INDEX.
Institute for Scientific Information, 3501 Market St., Philadelphia, PA 19104. TEL 215-386-0100. FAX 215-386-2991.
Producer(s): Institute for Scientific Information (A&HCI/CDE). *351*

ASSIA.
Shaare Zedek Medical Center, Falk Schlesinger Institute for Medical Halachic Research, P.O. Box 3235, Jerusalem 91031, Israel. TEL 555266. *3079*

AUSTRALIAN FAMILY AND SOCIETY ABSTRACTS.
Australian Institute of Family Studies, 300 Queen St., Melbourne, Vic. 3000, Australia. TEL 03-608-6888. FAX 03-600-0886. *4457*

B C S PROFESSIONAL.
Boston Computer Society, Consultants and Entrepreneurs Group, One Kendall Sq., Cambridge, MA 02139-1562. TEL 617-252-0600. FAX 617-572-9365. *825*

B D I DEUTSCHLAND LIEFERT.
Verlag W. Sachon, Schloss Mindelburg, Postfach 1463, 8948 Mindelheim, Germany. *901*

B I R D.
Centre International de l'Enfance, Chateau de Longchamp, Bois de Boulogne, 75016 Paris, France. TEL 1-45-20-79-92. FAX 1-45-25-73-67. *1247*

B S I CATALOGUE.
British Standards Institution, Linford Wood, Milton Keynes MK14 6LE, England. *3445*

BANK LETTER.
Institutional Investor, Inc., 488 Madison Ave., New York, NY 10022-5782. TEL 212-303-3233. FAX 212-303-3353. *763*

BEST BOOKS FOR CHILDREN.
R.R. Bowker, A Reed Reference Publishing Company, Division of Reed Publishing (USA) Inc., 121 Chanlon Rd., New Providence, NJ 07974. TEL 800-521-8110. FAX 908-665-6688. *1233*

BIBLIOGRAFIA LATINOAMERICANA: PART I.
Universidad Nacional Autonoma de Mexico, Centro de Informacion Cientifica y Humanistica, Apdo. Postal 70-392, C.P. 04510 Mexico, D.F., Mexico. *3*

BIBLIOGRAFIA LATINOAMERICANA: PART II.
Universidad Nacional Autonoma de Mexico, Centro de Informacion Cientifica y Humanistica, Apdo. Postal 70-392, C.P. 04510 Mexico, D.F., Mexico. *3*

BIBLIOGRAPHIE DE LA FRANCE. PUBLICATIONS OFFICIELLES.
Bibliotheque Nationale, 58 rue de Richelieu, 75002 Paris, France. TEL 42-74-22-22. FAX 42-96-84-47. *392*

BIBLIOGRAPHY AND INDEX OF GEOLOGY.
American Geological Institute, 4220 King St., Alexandria, VA 22302-1507. TEL 703-379-2480. FAX 703-379-7563.
Producer(s): SilverPlatter (GeoRef). *1550*

BIBLIOGRAPHY OF AGRICULTURE.
Oryx Press, 4041 N. Central at Indian School Rd., Phoenix, AZ 85012-3397. TEL 602-265-2651. FAX 602-265-6250.
Producer(s): SilverPlatter. *134*

BIBLIOGRAPHY OF ECONOMIC GEOLOGY.
Geosystems, Box 40, Didcot, Oxon Ox11 9BX, England. *3479*

BIBLIOGRAPHY OF EDUCATION THESES IN AUSTRALIA.
Australian Council for Educational Research, Radford House, P.O. Box 210, Hawthorn, Vic. 3122, Australia. TEL 61-3-819-1400. FAX 61-3-819-5502. *1674*

BIBLIOGRAPHY ON COLD REGIONS SCIENCE & TECHNOLOGY.
U.S. Army, Cold Regions Research and Engineering Laboratory, 72 Lyme Rd., Hanover, NH 03755-1290. TEL 603-646-4221. FAX 603-646-4695. *1841*

BIG BUSINESSES DIRECTORY.
American Business Information, Inc. 5711 S. 86th Circle, Box 27347, Omaha, NE 68127. TEL 402-593-4600. FAX 402-331-5481. *1123*

BILLBOARD HISTORY OF ROCK 'N ROLL.
B P I Information & Research Group, 1515 Broadway, New York, NY 10010.
Available only on CD-ROM. *3541*

BIOGRAPHY INDEX.
H.W. Wilson Co., 950 University Ave., Bronx, NY 10452. TEL 800-367-6770. FAX 212-538-2716.
Producer(s): H.W. Wilson (WILSONDISC). *424*

BIOLOGICAL ABSTRACTS.
BIOSIS, 2100 Arch St., Philadelphia, PA 19103-1399. TEL 215-587-4800. FAX 215-587-2016.
Producer(s): SilverPlatter. *462*

BIOLOGICAL & AGRICULTURAL INDEX.
H.W. Wilson Co., 950 University Ave., Bronx, NY 10452. TEL 800-367-6770. FAX 212-538-2716.
Producer(s): H.W. Wilson (WILSONDISC). *462*

BIOTECHNOLOGY RESEARCH ABSTRACTS.
Cambridge Scientific Abstracts, 7200 Wisconsin Ave., 6th Fl., Bethesda, MD 20814. TEL 301-961-6750. FAX 301-961-6720.
Producer(s): Cambridge Scientific Abstracts (Compact Cambridge Life Sciences Collection). *462*

BOLETIN DE TRADUCCIONES.
Instituto de Informacion y Documentacion en Ciencia y Tecnologia, Joaquin Costa 22, 28002 Madrid, Spain. *4354*

BOND INFORMATION DATABASE SERVICE.
Moody's Investors Service 99 Church St., New York, NY 10007. TEL 212-553-0300. FAX 212-553-4700. *1448*

BOOK REVIEW DIGEST.
H.W. Wilson Co., 950 University Ave., Bronx, NY 10452. TEL 800-367-6770. FAX 212-538-2716.
Producer(s): H.W. Wilson (WILSONDISC). *4140*

BOOKS IN PRINT.
R.R. Bowker, A Reed Reference Publishing Company, Division of Reed Publishing (USA) Inc., 121 Chanlon Rd., New Providence, NJ 07974. TEL 800-521-8110. FAX 908-665-6688.
Producer(s): R.R. Bowker (Books in Print PLUS). *394*

BOOKS IN PRINT PLUS.
R.R. Bowker, A Reed Reference Publishing Company, Division of Reed Publishing (USA) Inc., 121 Chanlon Rd., New Providence, NJ 07974. TEL 908-665-2867. FAX 908-665-6688.
Available only on CD-ROM. Producer(s): R.R. Bowker (Books in Print PLUS). *394*

BOOKS IN PRINT SUPPLEMENT.
R.R. Bowker, A Reed Reference Publishing Company, Division of Reed Publishing (USA) Inc., 121 Chanlon Rd., New Providence, NJ 07974. TEL 800-521-8110. FAX 908-665-6688.
Producer(s): R.R. Bowker (Books in Print PLUS). *394*

BOOKS IN SERIES.
R.R. Bowker, A Reed Reference Publishing Company, Division of Reed Publishing (USA) Inc., 121 Chanlon Rd., New Providence, NJ 07974. TEL 800-521-8110. FAX 908-665-6688. *394*

BOOKS OUT-OF-PRINT.
R.R. Bowker, A Reed Reference Publishing Company, Division of Reed Publishing (USA) Inc., 121 Chanlon Rd., New Providence, NJ 07974. TEL 800-521-8110. FAX 908-665-6688. Producer(s): R.R. Bowker (Books Out-of-Print PLUS). *395*

BOOKS OUT-OF-PRINT PLUS.
R.R. Bowker, A Reed Reference Publishing Company, Division of Reed Publishing (USA) Inc., 121 Chanlon Rd., New Providence, NJ 07974. TEL 908-665-2867. FAX 908-665-6688. Available only on CD-ROM. Producer(s): R.R. Bowker (Books Out-of-Print PLUS). *395*

BOSTON SPA CONFERENCES ON C D - R O M.
British Library, Document Supply Centre, Boston Spa, Wetherby, W. Yorkshire LS23 7BQ, England. TEL 0937-843434. FAX 0937-546333. Available only on CD-ROM. *395*

BOSTON SPA SERIALS ON C D - R O M.
British Library, Document Supply Centre, Boston Spa, Wetherby, W. Yorkshire LS23 7BQ, England. TEL 0937-546077. FAX 0937-546333. Available only on CD-ROM. *395*

THE BOWKER ANNUAL LIBRARY AND BOOK TRADE ALMANAC.
R.R. Bowker, A Reed Reference Publishing Company, Division of Reed Publishing (USA) Inc., 121 Chanlon Rd., New Providence, NJ 07974. TEL 800-521-8110. FAX 908-665-6688. *2749*

BOWKER'S COMPLETE VIDEO DIRECTORY.
R.R. Bowker, A Reed Reference Publishing Company, Division of Reed Publishing (USA) Inc., 121 Chanlon Rd., New Providence, NJ 07974. TEL 800-521-8110. FAX 908-665-6688. *1384*

BRITISH HUMANITIES INDEX.
Bowker-Saur Ltd., 59-60 Grosvenor St., London W1X 9DA, England. TEL 071-493-5841. FAX 071-499-1590. Producer(s): R.R. Bowker. *2519*

BRITISH INSTITUTE OF MANAGEMENT DATABASES ON C D - R O M.
Bowker-Saur Ltd. 59-60 Grosvenor St., London W1X 9DA, England. TEL 071-493-5841. FAX 071-499-1590. Available only on CD-ROM. *1004*

BRITISH MEDICAL JOURNAL.
B M J Publishing Group, B.M.A. House, Tavistock Sq., London WC1H 9JR, England. TEL 071-387-4499. *3084*

BRITISH NATIONAL BIBLIOGRAPHY.
British Library, National Bibliographic Service, Boston Spa, Wetherby, W. Yorkshire LS23 7BQ, England. TEL 0937-546613. FAX 0937-546586. *4140*

BULLETIN OF THE ATOMIC SCIENTISTS.
Educational Foundation for Nuclear Science, 6042 S. Kimbark Ave., Chicago, IL 60637. TEL 312-702-2555. FAX 312-702-0725. *3952*

BUSINESS ECONOMICS.
National Association of Business Economists, 28790 Chagrin Blvd., Ste. 300, Cleveland, OH 44122. TEL 216-464-7986. FAX 216-464-6352. *650*

BUSINESS HISTORY.
Frank Cass & Co. Ltd., Gainsborough House, 11 Gainsborough Rd., London E11 1RS, England. TEL 081-530-4226. FAX 081-530-7795. *650*

BUSINESS PERIODICALS INDEX.
H.W. Wilson Co., 950 University Ave., Bronx, NY 10452. TEL 800-367-6770. FAX 212-538-2716. Producer(s): H.W. Wilson (WILSONDISC). *707*

C D - R O M SOURCEBOOK.
Disc Company, 6609 Rosecroft Pl., Falls Church, VA 22043-1828. TEL 703-237-0682. FAX 703-532-5447. *2796*

C I S INDEX.
Congressional Information Service, 4520 East-West Hwy., Ste. 800, Bethesda, MD 20814. TEL 301-654-1550. FAX 301-654-4033. *4079*

C L A S E.
Universidad Nacional Autonoma de Mexico, Centro de Informacion Cientifica y Humanistica, Ciudad Universitaria, Apdo. Postal 70-392, C.P. 04510 Mexico, D.F., Mexico. *2519*

C S A NEUROSCIENCES ABSTRACTS.
Cambridge Scientific Abstracts, 7200 Wisconsin Ave., 6th Fl., Bethesda, MD 20814. TEL 301-961-6750. FAX 301-961-6720. Producer(s): Cambridge Scientific Abstracts (Compact Cambridge Life Sciences Collection). *3168*

C U S I P CORPORATE DIRECTORY.
Standard & Poor's Corporation, 25 Broadway, New York, NY 10004. TEL 212-208-8000. *941*

C U S I P MASTER DIRECTORY.
Standard & Poor's Corporation, 25 Broadway, New York, NY 10004. TEL 212-208-8000. *941*

C USERS JOURNAL.
R & D Publications, Inc., 1601 W. 23rd St., Ste. 200, Lawrence, KS 66046. TEL 913-841-1631. FAX 913-841-2624. *1429*

CALCIFIED TISSUE ABSTRACTS.
Cambridge Scientific Abstracts, 7200 Wisconsin Ave., 6th Fl., Bethesda, MD 20814. TEL 301-961-6750. FAX 301-961-6720. Producer(s): Cambridge Scientific Abstracts (Compact Cambridge Life Sciences Collection). *463*

CAMBRIDGE SCIENTIFIC BIOCHEMISTRY ABSTRACTS: PART 1. BIOLOGICAL MEMBRANES.
Cambridge Scientific Abstracts, 7200 Wisconsin Ave., 6th Fl., Bethesda, MD 20814. TEL 301-961-6750. FAX 301-961-6720. Producer(s): Cambridge Scientific Abstracts (Compact Cambridge Life Sciences Collection). *463*

CAMBRIDGE SCIENTIFIC BIOCHEMISTRY ABSTRACTS: PART 2. NUCLEIC ACIDS.
Cambridge Scientific Abstracts, 7200 Wisconsin Ave., 6th Fl., Bethesda, MD 20814. TEL 301-961-6750. FAX 301-961-6720. Producer(s): Cambridge Scientific Abstracts (Compact Cambridge Life Sciences Collection). *463*

CAMBRIDGE SCIENTIFIC BIOCHEMISTRY ABSTRACTS: PART 3. AMINO-ACIDS, PEPTIDES & PROTEINS.
Cambridge Scientific Abstracts, 7200 Wisconsin Ave., 6th Fl., Bethesda, MD 20814. TEL 301-961-6700. FAX 301-961-6720. Producer(s): Cambridge Scientific Abstracts (Compact Cambridge Life Science Collection). *464*

CANADIAN BUSINESS INDEX.
Micromedia Ltd., 20 Victoria St., Toronto, Ont. M5C 2N8, Canada. TEL 416-362-5211. FAX 416-362-6161. Producer(s): Dialog Information Services. *709*

CANADIAN EDUCATION INDEX.
Micromedia Ltd., 20 Victoria St., Toronto, Ont. M5C 2N8, Canada. TEL 416-362-5211. FAX 416-362-6161. *1675*

CANADIAN MAGAZINE INDEX.
Micromedia Ltd., 20 Victoria St., Toronto, Ont. M5C 2N8, Canada. TEL 416-362-5211. FAX 416-362-6161. Producer(s): Dialog Information Services. *396*

CANADIAN NEWS INDEX.
Micromedia Ltd., 20 Victoria St., Toronto, Ont. M5C 2N8, Canada. TEL 416-362-5211. FAX 416-362-6161. Producer(s): Dialog Information Services. *2577*

CANADIAN PERIODICAL INDEX.
Info Globe, 444 Front St. W., Toronto, Ontario M5V 2S9, Canada. TEL 416-585-5250. FAX 416-585-5249. *7*

CANADIANA.
National Library of Canada, 395 Wellington St., Ottawa, Ont. K1A 0N4, Canada. TEL 819-994-6912. FAX 819-953-0291. *396*

CANCER.
J.B. Lippincott Co., E. Washington Sq., Philadelphia, PA 19105. TEL 215-238-4200. *3194*

CATALOGO DEI LIBRI IN COMMERCIO.
Editrice Bibliografica s.r.l., Viale Vittorio Veneto 24, 20124 Milan, Italy. TEL 02-6597950. FAX 02-654624. *397*

CATALOGUE AFNOR (NORMES FRANCAISES).
Association Francaise de Normalisation, Tour Europe - Cedex 7, 92049 Paris La Defense, France. TEL 42-91-55-33. FAX 42-91-56-56. *3445*

CATALOGUE OF BRITISH OFFICIAL PUBLICATIONS NOT PUBLISHED BY H.M.S.O.
Chadwyck-Healey Ltd., Cambridge Place, Cambridge CB2 1NR, England. TEL 0223-311479. FAX 0223-66440. *397*

CERAMIC ABSTRACTS.
American Ceramic Society, 735 Ceramic Pl., Westerville, OH 43081. TEL 614-890-6136. FAX 614-899-6109. *1167*

CHEMORECEPTION ABSTRACTS.
Cambridge Scientific Abstracts, 7200 Wisconsin Ave., 6th Fl., Bethesda, MD 20814. TEL 301-961-6750. FAX 301-961-6720. Producer(s): Cambridge Scientific Abstracts (Compact Cambridge Life Sciences Collection). *1200*

CHICAGO - KENT LAW REVIEW.
Chicago - Kent College of Law, 77 S. Wacker Dr., Chicago, IL 60606. TEL 312-567-5013. FAX 312-567-5880. *2612*

CHICANO INDEX.
Chicano Studies Library, Publication Unit, University of California, Berkeley, 3404 Dwinelle Hall, Berkeley, CA 94702. TEL 510-642-3859. *2030*

CHILDREN'S BOOKS IN PRINT.
R.R. Bowker, A Reed Reference Publishing Company, Division of Reed Publishing (USA) Inc., 121 Chanlon Rd., New Providence, NJ 07974. TEL 800-521-8110. FAX 908-665-6688. Producer(s): R.R. Bowker (Books in Print PLUS). *397*

CINCH. AUSTRALIAN CRIMINOLOGY DATABASE.
Australian Institute of Criminology, G.P.O. Box 2944, Canberra, A.C.T. 2601, Australia. FAX 06-274-0260. *1511*

CLINMED - C D.
SilverPlatter Information, Inc., 100 River Ridge Dr., Norwood, MA 02062. TEL 617-239-0306. FAX 617-235-1715. Available only on CD-ROM. *3168*

CLOTHING AND TEXTILE ARTS INDEX.
Box 1300, Monument, CO 80132. TEL 719-488-3716. *1288*

COMPLETE DIRECTORY OF LARGE PRINT BOOKS AND SERIALS.
R.R. Bowker, A Reed Reference Publishing Company, Division of Reed Publishing (USA) Inc., 121 Chanlon Rd., New Providence, NJ 07974. TEL 800-521-8110. FAX 908-655-6688. Producer(s): R.R. Bowker. *2285*

COMPUTER LIBRARY'S COMPUTER PERIODICALS DATABASE.
Ziff Communications, One Park Ave., New York, NY 10016. TEL 212-503-4400. FAX 212-503-4414. *2793*

COMPUTER REVIEW.
G M L Corporation, 594 Marrett Rd., Lexington, MA 02173. TEL 617-861-0515. *1453*

CONGRESSIONAL STAFF DIRECTORY.
Staff Directories Ltd., Box 62, Mount Vernon, VA 22121. TEL 703-739-0900. FAX 703-739-0234. *3881*

CONSOLIDATED TREATIES & INTERNATIONAL AGREEMENTS: EUROPEAN COMMUNITY DOCUMENT SERVICE.
Oceana Publications, Inc., 75 Main St., Dobbs Ferry, NY 10522. TEL 914-693-8100. FAX 914-693-0402. *2721*

5034　SERIALS AVAILABLE ON CD-ROM

CONSOLIDATED TREATIES & INTERNATIONAL AGREEMENTS: UNITED STATES CURRENT DOCUMENT SERVICE.
Oceana Publications, Inc., 75 Main St., Dobbs Ferry, NY 10522. TEL 914-693-8100. FAX 914-693-0402. *2722*

CONSUMER HEALTH AND NUTRITION INDEX.
Oryx Press, 4041 N. Central at Indian School Rd., Phoenix, AZ 85012-3397. TEL 602-265-2651. FAX 602-265-6250. *3614*

CONSUMER REPORTS.
Consumers Union of United States, Inc., 101 Truman Ave., Yonkers, NY 10703-1057. TEL 914-378-2000. *1503*

CONSUMERS INDEX.
Pierian Press, Box 1808, Ann Arbor, MI 48106. TEL 313-434-5530. FAX 313-434-6409. *1509*

CORPORATE FINANCING WEEK.
Institutional Investor, Inc., 488 Madison Ave., New York, NY 10022. TEL 212-303-3233. FAX 212-303-3353. *773*

CORPORATE TECHNOLOGY DIRECTORY.
Corporate Technology Information Services, Inc., 12 Alfred St., Ste. 200, Woburn, MA 01801. TEL 617-932-3939. FAX 617-932-6335.
Producer(s): R.R. Bowker. *4595*

CORROSION ABSTRACTS.
National Association of Corrosion Engineers (NACE), Box 218340, Houston, TX 77218. TEL 713-492-0535. FAX 713-492-8254. *1842*

CRITICAL CARE MEDICINE.
Williams & Wilkins, 428 E. Preston St., Baltimore, MD 21202. TEL 301-528-4000. FAX 301-528-4312. *3091*

CULTIVOS TROPICALES.
Instituto Nacional de Ciencias Agricolas, Gaveta Postal No. 1, San Jose de las Lajas, Havana 22700, Cuba. TEL 30-07-75. FAX 30-35-82. *175*

CUMULATIVE BOOK INDEX.
H.W. Wilson Co., 950 University Ave, Bronx, NY 10452. TEL 800-367-6770. FAX 212-538-2716.
Producer(s): H.W. Wilson. *398*

CUMULATIVE INDEX TO NURSING & ALLIED HEALTH LITERATURE.
C I N A H L Information Systems, Box 871, Glendale, CA 91209-0871. TEL 818-409-8005. FAX 818-546-5679.
Producer(s): C I N A H L, SilverPlatter. *3169*

CURRENT INDEX TO JOURNALS IN EDUCATION.
Oryx Press, 4041 N. Central at Indian School Rd., Phoenix, AZ 85012-3397. TEL 602-265-2651. FAX 602-265-6250.
Producer(s): O C L C, SilverPlatter (ERIC). *1675*

CURRENT MATHEMATICAL PUBLICATIONS.
American Mathematical Society, Box 1571, Annex Sta., Providence, RI 02901-9930. TEL 401-455-4000.
Producer(s): SilverPlatter (MathDisc). *3062*

CURRENT TECHNOLOGY INDEX.
Bowker-Saur Ltd. 59-60 Grosvenor St., London W1X 9DA, England. TEL 071-493-5841. FAX 071-499-1590.
Producer(s): R.R. Bowker. *4614*

CYMBIOSIS.
Cymbiosis, Inc., 6201 W. Sunset Blvd., Ste. 80, Hollywood, CA 90028-8704. TEL 213-463-3808. FAX 213-463-5426. *3548*

C2C ABSTRACTS: JAPAN - ANALYTICAL CHEMISTRY.
Scan C2C, 500 E St. S.W., Ste. 800, Washington, DC 20024. TEL 800-525-3865. FAX 202-863-3855.
Producer(s): Dialog Information Services. *1200*

C2C ABSTRACTS: JAPAN - CERAMICS.
Scan C2C, 500 E St. S.W., Ste. 800, Washington, DC 20024. TEL 800-525-3865. FAX 202-863-3855.
Producer(s): Dialog Information Services. *1167*

C2C ABSTRACTS: JAPAN - CHEMICAL ENGINEERING.
Scan C2C, 500 E St. S.W., Ste. 800, Washington, DC 20024. TEL 800-525-3865. FAX 202-863-3855.
Producer(s): Dialog Information Services. *1843*

C2C ABSTRACTS: JAPAN - CRYSTALLOGRAPHY.
Scan C2C, 500 E St. S.W., Ste. 800, Washington, DC 20024. TEL 800-525-3865. FAX 202-863-3855.
Producer(s): Dialog Information Services. *1201*

C2C ABSTRACTS: JAPAN - HYDROCARBONS.
Scan C2C, 500 E St. S.W., Ste. 800, Washington, DC 20024. TEL 800-525-3865. FAX 202-863-3855.
Producer(s): Dialog Information Services. *1201*

C2C ABSTRACTS: JAPAN - INORGANIC CHEMISTRY.
Scan C2C, 500 E St. S.W., Ste. 800, Washington, DC 20024. TEL 800-525-3865. FAX 202-863-3855.
Producer(s): Dialog Information Services. *1201*

C2C ABSTRACTS: JAPAN - MATERIALS SCIENCE.
Scan C2C, 500 E St. S.W., Ste. 800, Washington, DC 20024. TEL 800-525-3865. FAX 202-863-3855.
Producer(s): Dialog Information Services. *1843*

C2C ABSTRACTS: JAPAN - METALS.
Scan C2C, 500 E St. S.W., Ste. 800, Washington, DC 20024. TEL 800-525-3865. FAX 202-863-3855.
Producer(s): Dialog Information Services. *3425*

C2C ABSTRACTS: JAPAN - ORGANIC CHEMISTRY.
Scan C2C, 500 E St. S.W., Ste. 800, Washington, DC 20024. TEL 800-525-3865. FAX 202-863-3855.
Producer(s): Dialog Information Services. *1201*

C2C ABSTRACTS: JAPAN - PHYSICAL CHEMISTRY.
Scan C2C, 500 E St. S.W., Ste. 800, Washington, DC 20024. TEL 800-525-3865. FAX 202-863-3855.
Producer(s): Dialog Information Services. *1201*

C2C ABSTRACTS: JAPAN - PLASTICS.
Scan C2C, 500 E St. S.W., Ste. 800, Washington, DC 20024. TEL 800-525-3865. FAX 202-863-3855.
Producer(s): Dialog Information Services. *3868*

C2C ABSTRACTS: JAPAN - POLYMER CHEMISTRY.
Scan C2C, 500 E St., Ste. 800, Washington, DC 20024. TEL 800-525-3865. FAX 202-863-3855.
Producer(s): Dialog Information Services. *1201*

C2C ABSTRACTS: JAPAN - SURFACE CHEMISTRY.
Scan C2C, 500 E St. S.W., Ste. 800, Washington, DC 20024. TEL 800-525-3865. FAX 202-863-3855.
Producer(s): Dialog Information Services. *1201*

C2C ABSTRACTS: JAPAN - TEXTILES.
Scan C2C, 500 E St. S.W., Ste. 800, Washington, DC 20024. TEL 800-525-3865. FAX 202-863-3855.
Producer(s): Dialog Information Services. *4628*

C2C CURRENTS: JAPAN - CHEMISTRY.
Scan C2C, 500 E St. S.W., Ste. 800, Washington, DC 20024. TEL 800-525-3865. FAX 202-863-3855.
Producer(s): Dialog Information Services. *1201*

C2C CURRENTS: JAPAN - COMPUTERS.
Scan C2C, 500 E St. S.W., Ste. 800, Washington, DC 20024. TEL 800-525-3865. FAX 202-863-3855.
Producer(s): Dialog Information Services. *1404*

C2C CURRENTS: JAPAN - ELECTRONICS.
Scan C2C, 500 E St. S.W., Ste. 800, Washington, DC 20024. TEL 800-525-3865. FAX 202-863-3855.
Producer(s): Dialog Information Services. *1765*

C2C CURRENTS: JAPAN - MATERIALS.
Scan C2C, 500 E St. S.W., Ste. 800, Washington, DC 20024. TEL 800-525-3865. FAX 202-863-3855.
Producer(s): Dialog Information Services. *1843*

DATA COMMUNICATIONS REPORTS.
Faulkner Information Services, Inc., 114 Cooper Center, 7905 Browning Rd., Pennsauken, NJ 08109-4319. TEL 609-662-2070. FAX 609-662-3380. *1446*

DATAWORLD.
Faulkner Information Services, Inc., 114 Cooper Center, 7905 Browning Rd., Pennsauken, NJ 08109-4319. TEL 609-662-2070. FAX 609-662-3380. *1450*

DEUTSCHE NATIONALBIBLIOGRAPHIE. C D - R O M EDITION.
Buchhaendler-Vereinigung GmbH, Grosser Hirschgraben 17-21, 6000 Frankfurt a.M. 1, Germany. TEL 069-1306-243.
Available only on CD-ROM. *4141*

DICTIONNAIRE VIDAL.
O.V.P. - Editions du Vidal, 11 rue Quentin Bauchart, 75008 Paris, France. TEL 33-1-47-23-90-91. FAX 47-20-72-89. *3722*

DIGITAL REVIEW.
Cahners Publishing Company (Newton) Division of Reed Publishing (USA) Inc., 275 Washington St., Newton, MA 02158-1630. TEL 617-964-3030. FAX 617-558-4506. *1460*

DIRECTORY OF AMERICAN RESEARCH AND TECHNOLOGY.
R.R. Bowker, A Reed Reference Publishing Company, Division of Reed Publishing (USA) Inc., 121 Chanlon Rd., New Providence, NJ 07974. TEL 800-521-8110. FAX 908-665-6688.
Producer(s): R.R. Bowker. *4596*

DIRECTORY OF LEADING PRIVATE COMPANIES, INCLUDING CORPORATE AFFILIATIONS.
National Register Publishing Co., A Reed Reference Publishing Company, Division of Reed Publishing (USA) Inc., 121 Chanlon Rd., New Providence, NJ 07974. TEL 800-521-8110. FAX 908-665-6688. *1131*

DIRECTORY OF RESEARCH GRANTS.
Oryx Press, 4041 N. Central at Indian School Rd., Phoenix, AZ 85012-3397. TEL 602-265-2651. FAX 602-265-6250.
Producer(s): Dialog Information Services. *1705*

DISC MAGAZINE.
Disc Company, 6609 Rosecroft Pl., Falls Church, VA 22043-1828. TEL 702-237-5447. FAX 703-532-5447. *2797*

DISSERTATION ABSTRACTS.
University Microfilms International, 300 N. Zeeb Rd., Ann Arbor, MI 48016-1304. TEL 800-521-0600. FAX 313-973-1540.
Producer(s): University Microfilms International. *2519*

DISSERTATION ABSTRACTS INTERNATIONAL. SECTION A: HUMANITIES AND SOCIAL SCIENCES.
University Microfilms International, Dissertation Publishing, c/o Dorie Mickelson, Mgr., 300 N. Zeeb Rd., Ann Arbor, MI 48106. TEL 313-761-4700.
Producer(s): University Microfilms International. *2520*

DISSERTATION ABSTRACTS INTERNATIONAL. SECTION B: PHYSICAL SCIENCES AND ENGINEERING.
University Microfilms International, Dissertation Publishing, c/o Dorie Mickelson, Mgr., 300 N. Zeeb Rd., Ann Arbor, MI 48106. TEL 313-761-4700.
Producer(s): University Microfilms International. *4355*

DISSERTATION ABSTRACTS INTERNATIONAL. SECTION C: WORLDWIDE.
University Microfilms International, Dissertation Publishing, c/o Dorie Mickelson, Mgr., 300 N. Zeeb Rd., Ann Arbor, MI 48106. TEL 313-761-4700.
Producer(s): University Microfilms International. *399*

DOMESTIC CARS SERVICE & REPAIR.
Mitchell International, Inc., 9889 Willow Creek Rd., Box 26260, San Diego, CA 92196-0260. TEL 800-648-8010. FAX 619-578-4752. *4689*

SERIALS AVAILABLE ON CD-ROM 5035

DOMESTIC LIGHT TRUCKS & VANS SERVICE & REPAIR.
Mitchell International, Inc., 9889 Willow Creek Rd., Box 26260, San Diego, CA 92196-0260. TEL 800-648-8010. FAX 619-578-4752. *4689*

E U D I S E D - R & D BULLETIN.
K.G. Saur Verlag KG, Ortlerstr. 8, Postfach 701620, 8000 Munich 70, Germany. TEL 089-76902-0. FAX 089-76902150. *1676*

EARTHQUAKE HISTORY OF THE UNITED STATES.
National Oceanic and Atmospheric Administration, National Geophysical Data Center, 325 Broadway, Boulder, CO 80303-3328. TEL 303-497-6419. *1588*

ECOLOGY ABSTRACTS.
Cambridge Scientific Abstracts, 7200 Wisconsin Ave., 6th Fl., Bethesda, MD 20814. TEL 301-961-6750. FAX 301-961-6720.
Producer(s): Cambridge Scientific Abstracts (Compact Cambridge Life Sciences Collection). *1973*

EDUCATION AUTHORITIES' DIRECTORY AND ANNUAL.
School Government Publishing Co. Ltd., Darby House, Bletchingley Rd., Merstham, Redhill, Surrey RH1 3DN, England. TEL 0737-642223. FAX 0737-644283. *1628*

EDUCATION DIGEST.
Prakken Publications, Inc., 416 Longshore Dr., Box 8623, Ann Arbor, MI 48107. TEL 313-769-1211. FAX 313-769-8383. *1628*

EDUCATION INDEX.
H.W. Wilson Co., 950 University Ave., Bronx, NY 10452. TEL 800-367-6770. FAX 212-538-2716.
Producer(s): H.W. Wilson (WILSONDISC). *1676*

ELECTRICAL COMPONENT LOCATOR - DOMESTIC CARS, LIGHT TRUCKS & VANS.
Mitchell International, Inc., 9889 Willow Creek Rd., Box 26260, San Diego, CA 92196-0260. TEL 800-648-8010. FAX 619-578-4752. *4690*

ELECTRICAL COMPONENT LOCATOR - IMPORTED CARS, LIGHT TRUCKS & VANS.
Mitchell International, Inc., 9889 Willow Creek Rd., Box 26260, San Diego, CA 92196-0260. TEL 800-648-8010. FAX 619-578-4752. *4690*

EL-HI TEXTBOOKS AND SERIALS IN PRINT.
R.R. Bowker, A Reed Reference Publishing Company, Division of Reed Publishing (USA) Inc., 121 Chanlon Rd., New Providence, NJ 07974. TEL 800-521-8110. FAX 908-665-6688. *1676*

EMPLOYMENT AND EARNINGS: UNITED STATES.
U.S. Bureau of Labor Statistics, Dept. of Labor, 441 G St. N.W., Washington, DC 20212. TEL 202-655-4000. *714*

ENCYCLOPEDIA OF ASSOCIATIONS.
Gale Research Inc., 835 Penobscot Bldg., Detroit, MI 48226. TEL 313-961-2242. FAX 313-961-6083. *1780*

ENERGY INFORMATION ABSTRACTS.
R.R. Bowker, Bowker A & I Publishing, A Reed Reference Publishing Company, Division of Reed Publishing (USA) Inc., 121 Chanlon Rd., New Providence, NJ 07974. TEL 800-521-8110. FAX 908-665-6688.
Producer(s): R.R. Bowker (Enviro/Energyline Abstracts PLUS). *1799*

ENERGY INFORMATION ABSTRACTS ANNUAL.
R.R. Bowker, Bowker A & I Publishing, A Reed Reference Publishing Company, Division of Reed Publishing (USA) Inc., 121 Chanlon Rd., New Providence, NJ 07974. TEL 800-521-8110. FAX 908-665-6688.
Producer(s): R.R. Bowker (Enviro/Energyline Abstracts PLUS). *1799*

ENGINEERED MATERIALS ABSTRACTS.
A S M International, Materials Information, Materials Park, OH 44073. TEL 216-338-5151. FAX 216-338-4634.
Producer(s): Dialog Information Services. *1843*

ENGINEERING INDEX ANNUAL.
Engineering Information, Inc., Castle Point on the Hudson, Hoboken, NJ 07030. TEL 800-221-1044. FAX 201-216-8532.
Producer(s): Dialog Information Services (COMPENDEX PLUS CD-ROM). *1843*

ENGINEERING INDEX MONTHLY.
Engineering Information, Inc., Castle Point on the Hudson, Hoboken, NJ 07030. TEL 800-221-1044. FAX 201-216-8532.
Producer(s): Dialog Information Services (COMPENDEX PLUS CD-ROM). *1843*

ENTOMOLOGY ABSTRACTS.
Cambridge Scientific Abstracts, 7200 Wisconsin Ave., 6th Fl., Bethesda, MD 20814. TEL 301-961-6750. FAX 301-961-6720.
Producer(s): Cambridge Scientific Abstracts (Compact Cambridge Life Sciences Collection). *465*

ENVIRONMENT ABSTRACTS.
R.R. Bowker, Bowker A & I Publishing, A Reed Reference Publishing Company, Division of Reed Publishing (USA) Inc., 121 Chanlon Rd., New Providence, NJ 07974. TEL 800-521-8110. FAX 908-665-6688.
Producer(s): R.R. Bowker (Enviro/Energyline Abstracts PLUS). *1973*

ENVIRONMENT ABSTRACTS ANNUAL.
R.R. Bowker, Bowker A & I Publishing, A Reed Reference Publishing Company, Division of Reed Publishing (USA) Inc., 121 Chanlon Rd., New Providence, NJ 07974. TEL 800-521-8110. FAX 908-665-6688.
Producer(s): R.R. Bowker (Enviro/Energyline Abstracts PLUS). *1973*

ENVIRONMENT AND ECOLOGY.
M K K Publications, 91A Ananda Palit Rd., Calcutta, West Bengal 700 014, India. *1949*

ENVIRONMENTAL NUTRITION.
Environmental Nutrition, Inc., 2112 Broadway, Ste. 200, New York, NY 10023. TEL 212-362-0424. *3605*

ENVIRONMENTAL PERIODICALS BIBLIOGRAPHY.
International Academy at Santa Barbara, 800 Garden St., Ste. D, Santa Barbara, CA 93101-1552. TEL 805-965-5010. FAX 805-965-6071. *1974*

ESSAY AND GENERAL LITERATURE INDEX.
H.W. Wilson Co., 950 University Ave., Bronx, NY 10452. TEL 800-367-6770. FAX 212-538-2716.
Producer(s): H.W. Wilson (WILSONDISC). *2981*

EUROPEAN DIRECTORY OF AGROCHEMICAL PRODUCTS.
Royal Society of Chemistry, Thomas Graham House, Science Park, Milton Rd., Cambridge CB4 4WF, England. TEL 0462-672555. FAX 0462-480947. *88*

EXCERPTA MEDICA ABSTRACT JOURNALS.
Excerpta Medica, P.O. Box 548, 1000 AM Amsterdam, Netherlands. TEL 020-5803911. FAX 020-5803222.
Producer(s): SilverPlatter (Excerpta Medica Library Service). *3171*

EXCERPTA MEDICA. SECTION 1: ANATOMY, ANTHROPOLOGY, EMBRYOLOGY & HISTOLOGY.
Excerpta Medica, P.O. Box 548, 1000 AM Amsterdam, Netherlands. TEL 020-5803911. FAX 020-5803222.
Producer(s): SilverPlatter. *3171*

EXCERPTA MEDICA. SECTION 2: PHYSIOLOGY.
Excerpta Medica, P.O. Box 548, 1000 AM Amsterdam, Netherlands. TEL 020-5803911. FAX 020-5803222.
Producer(s): SilverPlatter. *3171*

EXCERPTA MEDICA. SECTION 3: ENDOCRINOLOGY.
Excerpta Medica, P.O. Box 548, 1000 BM Amsterdam, Netherlands. TEL 020-5803911. FAX 020-5803222.
Producer(s): SilverPlatter. *3171*

EXCERPTA MEDICA. SECTION 4: MICROBIOLOGY: BACTERIOLOGY, MYCOLOGY, PARASITOLOGY AND VIROLOGY.
Excerpta Medica, P.O. Box 548, 1000 AM Amsterdam, Netherlands. TEL 020-5803911. FAX 020-5803222.
Producer(s): SilverPlatter. *3171*

EXCERPTA MEDICA. SECTION 5: GENERAL PATHOLOGY AND PATHOLOGICAL ANATOMY.
Excerpta Medica, P.O. Box 548, 1000 AM Amsterdam, Netherlands. TEL 020-5803911. FAX 020-5803222.
Producer(s): SilverPlatter. *3171*

EXCERPTA MEDICA. SECTION 6: INTERNAL MEDICINE.
Excerpta Medica, P.O. Box 548, 1000 AM Amsterdam, Netherlands. TEL 020-5803911. FAX 020-5803222.
Producer(s): SilverPlatter. *3171*

EXCERPTA MEDICA. SECTION 7: PEDIATRICS AND PEDIATRIC SURGERY.
Excerpta Medica, P.O. Box 548, 1000 AM Amsterdam, Netherlands. TEL 020-5803911. FAX 020-5803222.
Producer(s): SilverPlatter. *3172*

EXCERPTA MEDICA. SECTION 8: NEUROLOGY AND NEUROSURGERY.
Excerpta Medica, P.O. Box 548, 1000 AM Amsterdam, Netherlands. TEL 020-5803911. FAX 020-5803222.
Producer(s): SilverPlatter. *3172*

EXCERPTA MEDICA. SECTION 9: SURGERY.
Excerpta Medica, P.O. Box 548, 1000 AM Amsterdam, Netherlands. TEL 020-5803911. FAX 020-5803222.
Producer(s): SilverPlatter. *3172*

EXCERPTA MEDICA. SECTION 10: OBSTETRICS AND GYNECOLOGY.
Excerpta Medica, P.O. Box 548, 1000 AM Amsterdam, Netherlands. TEL 020-5803911. FAX 020-5803222.
Producer(s): SilverPlatter. *3172*

EXCERPTA MEDICA. SECTION 11: OTORHINOLARYNGOLOGY.
Excerpta Medica, P.O. Box 548, 1000 AM Amsterdam, Netherlands. TEL 020-5803911. FAX 020-5803222.
Producer(s): SilverPlatter. *3172*

EXCERPTA MEDICA. SECTION 12: OPHTHALMOLOGY.
Excerpta Medica, P.O. Box 548, 1000 AM Amsterdam, Netherlands. TEL 020-5803911. FAX 020-5803222.
Producer(s): SilverPlatter. *3172*

EXCERPTA MEDICA. SECTION 13: DERMATOLOGY AND VENEREOLOGY.
Excerpta Medica, P.O. Box 548, 1000 AM Amsterdam, Netherlands. TEL 020-5803911. FAX 020-5803222.
Producer(s): SilverPlatter. *3172*

EXCERPTA MEDICA. SECTION 14: RADIOLOGY.
Excerpta Medica, P.O. Box 548, 1000 AM Amsterdam, Netherlands. TEL 020-5803911. FAX 020-5803222.
Producer(s): SilverPlatter. *3172*

EXCERPTA MEDICA. SECTION 15: CHEST DISEASES, THORACIC SURGERY AND TUBERCULOSIS.
Excerpta Medica, P.O. Box 548, 1000 AM Amsterdam, Netherlands. TEL 020-5803911. FAX 020-5803222.
Producer(s): SilverPlatter. *3172*

EXCERPTA MEDICA. SECTION 16: CANCER.
Excerpta Medica, P.O. Box 548, 1000 AM Amsterdam, Netherlands. TEL 020-5803911. FAX 020-5803222.
Producer(s): SilverPlatter. *3172*

EXCERPTA MEDICA. SECTION 17: PUBLIC HEALTH, SOCIAL MEDICINE & EPIDEMIOLOGY.
Excerpta Medica, P.O. Box 548, 1000 AM Amsterdam, Netherlands. TEL 020-5803911. FAX 020-5803222.
Producer(s): SilverPlatter. *4117*

EXCERPTA MEDICA. SECTION 18: CARDIOVASCULAR DISEASES AND CARDIOVASCULAR SURGERY.
Excerpta Medica, P.O. Box 548, 1000 AM Amsterdam, Netherlands. TEL 020-5803911. FAX 020-5803222.
Producer(s): SilverPlatter. *3172*

EXCERPTA MEDICA. SECTION 19: REHABILITATION AND PHYSICAL MEDICINE.
Excerpta Medica, P.O. Box 548, 1000 AM Amsterdam, Netherlands. TEL 020-5803911. FAX 020-5803222.
Producer(s): SilverPlatter. *3173*

EXCERPTA MEDICA. SECTION 20: GERONTOLOGY AND GERIATRICS.
Excerpta Medica, P.O. Box 548, 1000 AM Amsterdam, Netherlands. TEL 020-5803911. FAX 020-5803222.
Producer(s): SilverPlatter. *2280*

EXCERPTA MEDICA. SECTION 21: DEVELOPMENTAL BIOLOGY AND TERATOLOGY.
Excerpta Medica, P.O. Box 548, 1000 AM Amsterdam, Netherlands. TEL 020-5803911. FAX 020-5803222.
Producer(s): SilverPlatter. *3173*

EXCERPTA MEDICA. SECTION 22: HUMAN GENETICS.
Excerpta Medica, P.O. Box 548, 1000 AM Amsterdam, Netherlands. TEL 020-5803911. FAX 020-5803222.
Producer(s): SilverPlatter. *465*

EXCERPTA MEDICA. SECTION 23: NUCLEAR MEDICINE.
Excerpta Medica, P.O. Box 548, 1000 AM Amsterdam, Netherlands. TEL 020-5803911. FAX 020-5803222.
Producer(s): SilverPlatter. *3173*

EXCERPTA MEDICA. SECTION 24: ANESTHESIOLOGY.
Excerpta Medica, P.O. Box 548, 1000 AM Amsterdam, Netherlands. TEL 020-5803911. FAX 020-5803222.
Producer(s): SilverPlatter. *3173*

EXCERPTA MEDICA. SECTION 25: HEMATOLOGY.
Excerpta Medica, P.O. Box 548, 1000 AM Amsterdam, Netherlands. TEL 020-5803911. FAX 020-5803222.
Producer(s): SilverPlatter. *3173*

EXCERPTA MEDICA. SECTION 26: IMMUNOLOGY, SEROLOGY AND TRANSPLANTATION.
Excerpta Medica, P.O. Box 548, 1000 AM Amsterdam, Netherlands. TEL 020-5803911. FAX 020-5803222.
Producer(s): SilverPlatter. *3173*

EXCERPTA MEDICA. SECTION 27: BIOPHYSICS, BIO-ENGINEERING AND MEDICAL INSTRUMENTATION.
Excerpta Medica, P.O. Box 548, 1000 AM Amsterdam, Netherlands. TEL 020-5803439. FAX 020-5803222.
Producer(s): SilverPlatter. *3173*

EXCERPTA MEDICA. SECTION 28: UROLOGY AND NEPHROLOGY.
Excerpta Medica, P.O. Box 548, 1000 AM Amsterdam, Netherlands. TEL 020-5803911. FAX 020-5803222.
Producer(s): SilverPlatter. *3173*

EXCERPTA MEDICA. SECTION 29: CLINICAL AND EXPERIMENTAL BIOCHEMISTRY.
Excerpta Medica, P.O. Box 548, 1000 AM Amsterdam, Netherlands. TEL 020-5803911. FAX 020-5803222.
Producer(s): SilverPlatter. *3173*

EXCERPTA MEDICA. SECTION 30: CLINICAL AND EXPERIMENTAL PHARMACOLOGY.
Excerpta Medica, P.O. Box 548, 1000 AM Amsterdam, Netherlands. TEL 020-5803911. FAX 020-5803222.
Producer(s): SilverPlatter. *3747*

EXCERPTA MEDICA. SECTION 31: ARTHRITIS AND RHEUMATISM.
Excerpta Medica, P.O. Box 548, 1000 AM Amsterdam, Netherlands. TEL 020-5803911. FAX 020-5803222.
Producer(s): SilverPlatter. *3173*

EXCERPTA MEDICA. SECTION 32: PSYCHIATRY.
Excerpta Medica, P.O. Box 548, 1000 AM Amsterdam, Netherlands. TEL 020-5803911. FAX 020-5803222.
Producer(s): SilverPlatter. *3174*

EXCERPTA MEDICA. SECTION 33: ORTHOPEDIC SURGERY.
Excerpta Medica, P.O. Box 548, 1000 AM Amsterdam, Netherlands. TEL 020-5803911. FAX 020-5803222.
Producer(s): SilverPlatter. *3174*

EXCERPTA MEDICA. SECTION 35: OCCUPATIONAL HEALTH AND INDUSTRIAL MEDICINE.
Excerpta Medica, P.O. Box 548, 1000 AM Amsterdam, Netherlands. TEL 020-5803911. FAX 020-5803222.
Producer(s): SilverPlatter. *3174*

EXCERPTA MEDICA. SECTION 36: HEALTH POLICY, ECONOMICS AND MANAGEMENT.
Excerpta Medica, P.O. Box 548, 1000 AM Amsterdam, Netherlands. TEL 020-5803911. FAX 020-5803222.
Producer(s): SilverPlatter. *2470*

EXCERPTA MEDICA. SECTION 38: ADVERSE REACTIONS TITLES.
Excerpta Medica, P.O. Box 548, 1000 AM Amsterdam, Netherlands. TEL 020-5803911. FAX 020-5803222.
Producer(s): SilverPlatter. *3174*

EXCERPTA MEDICA. SECTION 40: DRUG DEPENDENCE, ALCOHOL ABUSE AND ALCOHOLISM.
Excerpta Medica, P.O. Box 548, 1000 AM Amsterdam, Netherlands. TEL 020-5803911. FAX 020-5803222.
Producer(s): SilverPlatter. *3174*

EXCERPTA MEDICA. SECTION 46: ENVIRONMENTAL HEALTH AND POLLUTION CONTROL.
Excerpta Medica, P.O. Box 548, 1000 AM Amsterdam, Netherlands. TEL 020-5803911. FAX 020-5803222.
Producer(s): SilverPlatter. *1974*

EXCERPTA MEDICA. SECTION 48: GASTROENTEROLOGY.
Excerpta Medica, P.O. Box 548, 1000 AM Amsterdam, Netherlands. TEL 020-5803911. FAX 020-5803222.
Producer(s): SilverPlatter. *3174*

EXCERPTA MEDICA. SECTION 49: FORENSIC SCIENCE ABSTRACTS.
Excerpta Medica, P.O. Box 548, 1000 AM Amsterdam, Netherlands. TEL 020-5803911. FAX 020-5803222.
Producer(s): SilverPlatter. *3174*

EXCERPTA MEDICA. SECTION 50: EPILEPSY ABSTRACTS.
Excerpta Medica, P.O. Box 548, 1000 AM Amsterdam, Netherlands. TEL 020-5803911. FAX 020-5803222.
Producer(s): SilverPlatter. *3174*

EXCERPTA MEDICA. SECTION 52: TOXICOLOGY.
Excerpta Medica, P.O. Box 548, 1000 AM Amsterdam, Netherlands. TEL 020-5803911. FAX 020-5803222.
Producer(s): SilverPlatter. *3747*

EXECUTIVE SPEECHES.
Executive Speaker Co., Box 292437, Dayton, OH 45429. TEL 513-294-8493. FAX 513-294-6044. *665*

FACTS ON FILE WORLD NEWS DIGEST WITH INDEX.
Facts on File, Inc., 460 Park Ave. S., New York, NY 10016. TEL 212-683-2244. *2310*

FAULKNER REPORT ON MICROCOMPUTERS AND SOFTWARE.
Faulkner Information Services, Inc., 114 Cooper Center, 7905 Browning Rd., Pennsauken, NJ 08109-4319. TEL 609-662-2070. FAX 609-662-3380. *1460*

FEDERAL STAFF DIRECTORY.
Staff Directories Ltd., Box 62, Mount Vernon, VA 22121. TEL 703-739-0900. FAX 703-739-0234. *4060*

FILM & VIDEO FINDER.
Plexus Publishing, Inc., 143 Old Marlton Pike, Medford, NJ 08055-8750. TEL 609-654-4888.
Producer(s): SilverPlatter. *1676*

FILMSTRIP AND SLIDE SET FINDER.
Access Innovations, Inc., Box 40130, Albuquerque, NM 87196. TEL 505-265-3591. *1676*

FINANCIEEL EKONOMISCHE TIJD.
Uitgeversbedrijf Tijd n.v., Brouwersvliet 5, Bus 3, B-2000 Antwerp, Belgium. TEL 03-231-57-56. FAX 03-225-22-09. *665*

FOOD SCIENCE AND TECHNOLOGY ABSTRACTS.
International Food Information Service (IFIS Publishing), Lane End House, Shinfield, Reading RG2 9B, England. TEL 734-883895. FAX 734-805065.
Producer(s): SilverPlatter (COMPU-INFO). *2085*

FOREIGN POLICY (WASHINGTON).
Carnegie Endowment for International Peace, 2400 N St., N.W., Ste. 700, Washington, DC 20037. TEL 202-862-7900. *3957*

FORTHCOMING BOOKS.
R.R. Bowker, A Reed Reference Publishing Company, Division of Reed Publishing (USA) Inc., 121 Chanlon Rd., New Providence, NJ 07974. TEL 800-521-8110. FAX 908-665-6688.
Producer(s): R.R. Bowker (Books in Print PLUS). *400*

FRANCE. MINISTERE DE L'ENVIRONNEMENT ET DU CADRE DE VIE. INSPECTION GENERALE DE L'EQUIPEMENT.
Direction des Journaux Officiels, 26 rue Desaix, 75727 Paris Cedex 15, France. TEL 1-45-78-61-44. *4060*

GAS CHROMATOGRAPHY LITERATURE - ABSTRACTS & INDEX.
Preston Publications, Inc., 7800 Merrimac Ave., Box 48312, Niles, IL 60648. TEL 708-965-0566. FAX 708-965-7639. *1201*

GENERAL SCIENCE INDEX.
H.W. Wilson Co., 950 University Ave., Bronx, NY 10452. TEL 800-367-6770. FAX 212-538-2716.
Producer(s): H.W. Wilson (WILSONDISC). *4356*

GENETICS ABSTRACTS.
Cambridge Scientific Abstracts, 7200 Wisconsin Ave., 6th Fl., Bethesda, MD 20814. TEL 301-961-6750. FAX 301-961-6720.
Producer(s): Cambridge Scientific Abstracts (Compact Cambridge Life Sciences Collection). *465*

GEOSCIENCE DOCUMENTATION.
Geosystems, Box 40, Didcot, Oxon OX11 9BX, England. *1551*

GEOSOURCES.
Geosystems, P.O. Box 40, Didcot, Oxon OX11 9BX, England. *1545*

GOVERNMENT COMPUTER NEWS.
Cahners Publishing Company (Silver Spring) Division of Reed Publishing (USA) Inc., 8601 Georgia Ave., Ste. 300, Silver Spring, MD 20910. FAX 301-650-2111. *4083*

GUIDA DELLE REGIONI D'ITALIA.
SISPR - Societa Italiana per lo Studio dei Problemi Regionali, Via della Scrofa 14, 00186 Rome, Italy. TEL 06-6879852. FAX 06-6867637. *1137*

HANDBOOK ON INJECTABLE DRUGS.
American Society of Hospital Pharmacists, c/o Jean Rogers, Dir., Mkt. Svcs., 4630 Montgomery Ave., Bethesda, MD 20814. TEL 301-657-3000. *3727*

HASTINGS COMMUNICATIONS AND ENTERTAINMENT LAW JOURNAL (COMM - ENT).
University of California, San Francisco, Hastings College of the Law, 200 McAllister St., San Francisco, CA 94102-4978. TEL 415-565-4731. FAX 415-565-4814. *2631*

HASTINGS CONSTITUTIONAL LAW QUARTERLY.
University of California, San Francisco, Hastings College of the Law, 200 McAllister St., San Francisco, CA 94102-4978. TEL 415-565-4726. FAX 415-565-4814. *2706*

HEALTH AND SAFETY SCIENCE ABSTRACTS.
Cambridge Scientific Abstracts, 7200 Wisconsin Ave., 6th Fl., Bethesda, MD 20814. TEL 301-961-6750. FAX 301-961-6720.
Producer(s): Cambridge Scientific Abstracts. *4117*

HEALTH DEVICES ALERTS.
E C R I, 5200 Butler Pike, Plymouth Meeting, PA 19462. TEL 215-825-6000. FAX 215-834-1275. *3175*

HEALTH INDEX.
Information Access Company, 362 Lakeside Dr., Foster City, CA 94404. TEL 800-227-8431. FAX 415-378-5499. *3175*

HEWLETT-PACKARD JOURNAL.
Hewlett Packard Co. (Palo Alto), 3200 Hillview Ave., Palo Alto, CA 94304. TEL 415-857-2004. FAX 415-857-3880. *1460*

HISTORICAL ABSTRACTS. PART A: MODERN HISTORY ABSTRACTS, 1450-1914.
A B C-Clio, 130 Cremona, Box 1911, Santa Barbara, CA 93116-1911. TEL 805-968-1911. FAX 805-685-9685. *2329*

HORIZONTES (SAN FRANCISCO).
Horizontes, 2601 Mission St., Ste. 900, San Francisco, CA 94110. TEL 415-641-6051. FAX 415-282-3320. *2005*

HOSPITAL PRODUCT COMPARISON SYSTEM.
E C R I, 5200 Butler Pike, Plymouth Meeting, PA 19462. TEL 215-825-6000. FAX 215-834-1275.
Producer(s): Dialog Information Services. *2465*

HOSPITALITY INDEX.
American Hotel and Motel Association, H L T R F, 1201 New York Ave., N.W., Washington, DC 20005-3917. TEL 202-289-3196. FAX 202-289-3199. *2482*

HUMAN GENOME ABSTRACTS.
Cambridge Scientific Abstracts, 7200 Wisconsin Ave., 6th Fl., Bethesda, MD 20814. TEL 301-961-6700. FAX 301-961-6720.
Producer(s): Cambridge Scientific Abstracts (Compact Cambridge Life Sciences Collection). *465*

HUMANITIES INDEX.
H.W. Wilson Co., 950 University Ave., Bronx, NY 10452. TEL 800-367-6770. FAX 212-538-2716.
Producer(s): H.W. Wilson (WILSONDISC). *2520*

I N I S ATOMINDEX.
International Atomic Energy Agency, Lane End House, Sheenfield, Reading RG2 9BB, England. TEL 734-883-895.
Producer(s): SilverPlatter (INIS). *3837*

I S D S REGISTER (MICROFICHE EDITION).
International Serials Data System, International Centre, 20 rue Bachaumont, 75002 Paris, France. FAX 40-26-32-43. *402*

I S D S REGISTER (TAPE EDITION).
International Serials Data System, International Centre, 20 rue Bachaumont, 75002 Paris, France. TEL 42-36-73-81. FAX 40-26-32-43. *402*

I S S N COMPACT.
International Serials Data System, International Centre, 20 rue Bachaumont, 75002 Paris, France. TEL 33-1-42-36-73-81. FAX 33-1-40-26-32-43. *402*

I T A SERIES.
C C H Canadian Ltd., 6 Garamond Ct., Don Mills, Ont. M3C 1Z5, Canada. TEL 416-441-2992. FAX 416-444-9011. *1097*

IDAHO MANUFACTURING DIRECTORY.
University of Idaho, Center for Business Development and Research, College of Business and Economics, Moscow, ID 83843. TEL 208-885-6611. FAX 708-322-1100. *1138*

IMMUNOLOGY ABSTRACTS.
Cambridge Scientific Abstracts, 7200 Wisconsin Ave., 6th Fl., Bethesda, MD 20814. TEL 301-961-6750. FAX 301-961-6720.
Producer(s): Cambridge Scientific Abstracts (Compact Cambridge Life Sciences Collection). *3176*

IMPORTED CARS, LIGHT TRUCKS & VANS SERVICE & REPAIR.
Mitchell International, Inc., 9889 Willow Creek Rd., Box 26260, San Diego, CA 92196-0260. TEL 800-648-8010. FAX 619-578-4752. *4693*

INDEX: FOREIGN BROADCAST INFORMATION SERVICE DAILY REPORTS: AFRICA SUB-SAHARA.
NewsBank, Inc., 58 Pine St., New Canaan, CT 06840-5426. TEL 203-966-1100. FAX 203-966-6254. *3937*

INDEX: FOREIGN BROADCAST INFORMATION SERVICE DAILY REPORTS: CHINA.
NewsBank, Inc., 58 Pine St., New Canaan, CT 06840-5426. TEL 203-966-1100. FAX 203-966-6254. *3937*

INDEX: FOREIGN BROADCAST INFORMATION SERVICE DAILY REPORTS: EAST ASIA.
NewsBank, Inc., 58 Pine St., New Canaan, CT 06840-5426. TEL 203-966-1100. FAX 203-966-6254. *3937*

INDEX: FOREIGN BROADCAST INFORMATION SERVICE DAILY REPORTS: EASTERN EUROPE.
NewsBank, Inc., 58 Pine St., New Canaan, CT 06840-5426. TEL 203-966-1100. FAX 203-966-6254. *3937*

INDEX: FOREIGN BROADCAST INFORMATION SERVICE DAILY REPORTS: LATIN AMERICA.
NewsBank, Inc., 58 Pine St., New Canaan, CT 06840-5426. TEL 203-966-1100. FAX 203-966-6254. *3937*

INDEX: FOREIGN BROADCAST INFORMATION SERVICE DAILY REPORTS: NEAR EAST AND SOUTH ASIA.
NewsBank, Inc., 58 Pine St., New Canaan, CT 06840-5426. TEL 203-966-1100. FAX 203-966-6254. *3937*

INDEX: FOREIGN BROADCAST INFORMATION SERVICE DAILY REPORTS: SOVIET UNION.
NewsBank, Inc., 58 Pine St., New Canaan, CT 06840-5426. TEL 203-966-1100. FAX 203-966-6254. *3937*

INDEX: FOREIGN BROADCAST INFORMATION SERVICE DAILY REPORTS: WESTERN EUROPE.
NewsBank, Inc., 58 Pine St., New Canaan, CT 06840-5426. TEL 203-966-1100. FAX 203-966-6254. *3937*

INDEX MEDICUS.
U.S. National Library of Medicine, 8600 Rockville Pike, Bethesda, MD 20894. TEL 301-496-6308. FAX 301-496-4450.
Producer(s): Cambridge Scientific Abstracts (Compact Cambridge MEDLINE), Dialog Information Services (DIALOG OnDisc MEDLINE), SilverPlatter (MEDLINE). *3176*

INDEX MEDICUS LATINOAMERICANO.
Latin American and Caribbean Center on Health Sciences Information (BIREME), Rua Botucatu, 862, Caixa Postal 20.381, V. Clementino, 04023 Sao Paulo, Brazil. TEL (011) 5492611. FAX 5511-5711919. *3176*

INDEX TO BOOK REVIEWS IN RELIGION.
American Theological Library Association, Religion Indexes, 820 Church St., 3rd Fl., Evanston, IL 60201-3707. TEL 708-869-7788. *4213*

INDEX TO DENTAL LITERATURE.
American Dental Association, 211 E. Chicago Ave., Chicago, IL 60611. TEL 312-440-2500.
Producer(s): Cambridge Scientific Abstracts (Compact Cambridge MEDLINE), Dialog Information Services (DIALOG OnDisc MEDLINE), SilverPlatter (MEDLINE). *3176*

INDEX TO INTERNATIONAL STATISTICS.
Congressional Information Service, 4520 East-West Hwy., Bethesda, MD 20814-3389. TEL 301-654-1550. FAX 301-654-4033. *4574*

INDEX TO LEGAL PERIODICALS.
H.W. Wilson Co., 950 University Ave., Bronx, NY 10452. TEL 800-367-6770. FAX 212-538-2716.
Producer(s): H.W. Wilson (WILSONDISC). *2699*

INDEX TO U.S. GOVERNMENT PERIODICALS.
InforData International Inc., 4927 N. Bernard, Chicago, IL 60625-5109.
Producer(s): H.W. Wilson. *15*

INDICE DE LA LITERATURA DENTAL EN CASTELLANO.
Asociacion Odontologica Argentina, Junin 959, Buenos Aires, Argentina. *3176*

INDICE ESPANOL DE CIENCIA Y TECNOLOGIA.
Instituto de Informacion y Documentacion en Ciencia y Tecnologia, Joaquin Costa 22, 28002 Madrid, Spain. TEL 91-5635482. FAX 91-5642644. *4356*

INDICE ESPANOL DE CIENCIAS SOCIALES. SERIES A: PSYCHOLOGY AND EDUCATIONAL SCIENCES.
Instituto de Informacion y Documentacion en Ciencias Sociales y Humanidades, Pinar, 25, 28006 Madrid, Spain. *4051*

INDICE ESPANOL DE CIENCIAS SOCIALES. SERIES B: ECONOMICS, SOCIOLOGY AND POLITICAL SCIENCE.
Instituto de Informacion y Documentacion en Ciencias Sociales y Humanidades, Pinar, 25, 3, 28006 Madrid, Spain. *721*

INDICE ESPANOL DE CIENCIAS SOCIALES. SERIES C: LAW.
Instituto de Informacion y Documentacion en Ciencias Sociales y Humanidades, Pinar, 25, 3, 28006 Madrid, Spain. *2699*

INDICE ESPANOL DE CIENCIAS SOCIALES. SERIES D: SCIENCE AND SCIENTIFIC INFORMATION.
Instituto de Informacion y Documentacion en Ciencias Sociales y Humanidades, Pinar, 25, 3, 28006 Madrid, Spain. *4356*

INDICE ESPANOL DE CIENCIAS SOCIALES. SERIES E: URBAN PLANNING.
Instituto de Informacion y Documentacion en Ciencias Sociales y Humanidades, Pinar, 25, 3, 28006 Madrid, Spain. *2500*

INDICE ESPANOL DE HUMANIDADES. SERIES A: ART.
Instituto de Informacion y Documentacion en Ciencias Sociales y Humanidades, Pinar, 25, 3, 28006 Madrid, Spain. *352*

INDICE ESPANOL DE HUMANIDADES. SERIES B: HISTORICAL SCIENCES.
Instituto de Informacion y Documentacion en Ciencias Sociales y Humanidades, Pinar 25, 3, 28006 Madrid, Spain. *2329*

INDICE ESPANOL DE HUMANIDADES. SERIES C: LINGUISTICS AND LITERATURE.
Instituto de Informacion y Documentacion en Ciencias Sociales y Humanidades, Pinar 25, 3, 28006 Madrid, Spain. *2855*

INDICE ESPANOL DE HUMANIDADES. SERIES D: PHILOSOPHY.
Instituto de Informacion y Documentacion en Ciencias Sociales y Humanidades, Pinar 25, 3, 28006 Madrid, Spain. *3787*

INDICE MEDICO ESPANOL.
Universidad de Valencia, Facultad de Medicina, Avda. Blasco Ibanez - 17, 46010 Valencia, Spain. FAX 3613975. *3176*

INDUSTRIAL NEWS (IAEGER).
Box 180, Iaeger, WV 24844. TEL 304-938-2142. *670*

INFECTION AND IMMUNITY.
American Society for Microbiology, 1325 Massachusetts Ave., N.W., Washington, DC 20005. TEL 202-737-3600. *3186*

INSIGHT (WASHINGTON).
Washington Times Corporation, 3600 New York Ave., N.E., Washington, DC 20002. TEL 800-356-3588. FAX 202-529-2484. *2227*

INSTITUTIONAL INVESTOR.
Institutional Investor, Inc., Circulation Department, 488 Madison Ave., New York, NY 10022. TEL 212-303-3570. FAX 212-303-3592. *950*

SERIALS AVAILABLE ON CD-ROM

INSTITUTIONAL INVESTOR INTERNATIONAL EDITION.
Institutional Investor, Inc., Circulation Department, 488 Madison Ave., New York, NY 10022. TEL 212-303-3570. FAX 212-303-3592. *950*

INSTYTUT ZOOTECHNIKI. ROCZNIKI NAUKOWE ZOOTECHNIKI.
Instytut Zootechniki, 32-083 Balice near Krakow, Poland. TEL 048-12-113211. FAX 48-12-228065. *219*

INTERNAL AUDITOR.
Institute of Internal Auditors, Inc., 249 Maitland Ave., Altamonte Springs, FL 32701-4201. TEL 407-830-7600. FAX 407-831-5171. *752*

INTERNATIONAL AEROSPACE ABSTRACTS.
American Institute of Aeronautics and Astronautics, Technical Information Service, 555 W. 57th St., New York, NY 10019. TEL 212-247-6500. FAX 212-582-4861. *66*

INTERNATIONAL BOOKS IN PRINT.
K.G. Saur Verlag KG, Ortlerstr. 8, Postfach 701620, 8000 Munich 70, Germany. TEL 089-76902-0. FAX 089-76902150. *403*

INTERNATIONAL BUILDING SCIENCE & CONSTRUCTION ABSTRACTS.
C I T I S Ltd., 2 Rosemount Terrace, Blackrock, Dublin, Ireland. TEL 353-1-2886227. FAX 353-1-2885971. *638*

INTERNATIONAL CIVIL ENGINEERING ABSTRACTS.
C I T I S Ltd., 2 Rosemount Terrace, Blackrock, Dublin, Ireland. TEL 353-1-2886227. FAX 353-1-885.971. *1845*

INTERNATIONAL FINANCIAL STATISTICS.
International Monetary Fund, Publications Unit, 700 19th St., N.W., Washington, DC 20431. TEL 202-623-7430. FAX 202-623-7201. *722*

INTERNATIONAL FREQUENCY LIST.
International Telecommunication Union, International Frequency Registration Board, Place des Nations, CH-1211 Geneva 20, Switzerland. TEL 41-22995111. FAX 41-22337256. *1375*

INTERNATIONAL LITERARY MARKET PLACE.
R.R. Bowker, A Reed Reference Publishing Company, Division of Reed Publishing (USA) Inc., 121 Chanlon Rd., New Providence, NJ 07974. TEL 800-521-8110. FAX 908-665-6688. *4130*

INTERNATIONAL NURSING INDEX.
American Journal of Nursing Co., 555 W. 57th St., New York, NY 10019. TEL 212-582-8820. Producer(s): Cambridge Scientific Abstracts (Compact Cambridge MEDLINE), Dialog Information Services (DIALOG OnDisc MEDLINE), SilverPlatter (MEDLINE). *3176*

INTERNATIONAL PHARMACEUTICAL ABSTRACTS.
American Society of Hospital Pharmacists, c/o Jean Rogers, Dir., Mkt. Svcs., 4630 Montgomery Ave., Bethesda, MD 20814. TEL 301-657-3000. Producer(s): SilverPlatter. *3748*

J & W TELEX INTERNATIONAL. INTERNATIONAL TELEX AND TELETEX DIRECTORY.
Telex - Verlag Jaeger & Waldmann GmbH, Birkenweg 8-10, Postfach 111060, 6100 Darmstadt 11, Germany. TEL 6151-3302-0. FAX 6151-3302-50. *1363*

J & W TRAVEL INTERNATIONAL.
Telex - Verlag Jaeger & Waldmann GmbH, Birkenweg 8-10, Postfach 111060, 6100 Darmstadt 11, Germany. TEL 6151-3302-0. FAX 6151-3302-50. *1363*

JANE'S A F V RETROFIT SYSTEMS.
Jane's Information Group, Sentinel House, 163 Brighton Rd., Coulsdon, Surrey CR5 2NH, England. TEL 081-763-1030. FAX 081-763-1005. *3460*

JANE'S ALL THE WORLD AIRCRAFT.
Jane's Information Group, Sentinel House, 163 Brighton Rd., Coulsdon, Surrey CR5 2NH, England. TEL 081-763-1030. FAX 081-763-1005. *57*

JANE'S ARMOUR AND ARTILLERY.
Jane's Information Group, Sentinel House, 163 Brighton Rd., Coulsdon, Surrey CR5 2NH, England. TEL 081-763-1030. FAX 081-763-1005. *3460*

JANE'S AVIONICS.
Jane's Information Group, Sentinel House, 163 Brighton Rd., Coulsdon, Surrey CR5 2NH, England. TEL 081-763-1030. FAX 081-763-1005. *57*

JANE'S BATTLEFIELD SURVEILLANCE.
Jane's Information Group, Sentinel House, 163 Brighton Rd., Coulsdon, Surrey CR5 2NH, England. TEL 081-763-1030. FAX 081-763-1005. *3461*

JANE'S C 3 I SYSTEMS.
Jane's Information Group, Sentinel House, 163 Brighton Rd., Coulsdon, Surrey CR5 2NH, England. TEL 081-763-1030. FAX 081-763-1005. *3461*

JANE'S FIGHTING SHIPS.
Jane's Information Group, Sentinel House, 163 Brighton Rd., Coulsdon, Surrey CR5 2NH, England. TEL 081-763-1030. FAX 081-763-1005. *3461*

JANE'S INFANTRY WEAPONS.
Jane's Information Group, Sentinel House, 163 Brighton Rd., Coulsdon, Surrey CR5 2NH, England. TEL 081-763-1030. FAX 081-763-1005. *3461*

JANE'S LAND-BASED AIR DEFENCE.
Jane's Information Group, Sentinel House, 163 Brighton Rd., Coulsdon, Surrey CR5 2NH, England. TEL 081-763-1030. FAX 081-763-1005. *3461*

JANE'S MILITARY COMMUNICATIONS.
Jane's Information Group, Sentinel House, 163 Brighton Rd., Coulsdon, Surrey CR5 2NH, England. TEL 081-763-1030. FAX 081-763-1005. *3461*

JANE'S MILITARY TRAINING SYSTEMS.
Jane's Information Group, Sentinel House, 163 Brighton Rd., Coulsdon, Surrey CR5 2NH, England. TEL 081-763-1030. FAX 081-763-1005. *3461*

JANE'S MILITARY VEHICLES AND LOGISTICS.
Jane's Information Group, Sentinel House, 163 Brighton Rd., Coulsdon, Surrey CR5 2NH, England. TEL 081-763-1030. FAX 081-763-1005. *3461*

JANE'S NAVAL WEAPON SYSTEM.
Jane's Information Group, Sentinel House, 163 Brighton Rd., Coulsdon, Surrey CR5 2NH, England. TEL 081-763-1030. FAX 081-763-1005. *3461*

JANE'S RADAR AND E-W SYSTEMS.
Jane's Information Group, Sentinel House, 163 Brighton Rd., Coulsdon, Surrey CR5 2NH, England. TEL 081-763-1030. FAX 081-763-1005. *3461*

JANE'S UNDERWATER WARFARE SYSTEMS.
Jane's Information Group, Sentinel House, 163 Brighton Rd., Coulsdon, Surrey CR5 2NH, England. TEL 081-736-1030. FAX 081-763-1005. *3461*

JANE'S WORLD AIRLINES.
Jane's Information Group, Sentinel House, 163 Brighton Rd., Coulsdon, Surrey CR5 2NH, England. TEL 081-763-1030. FAX 081-763-1005. *4675*

JARDIN BOTANICO DE MADRID. ANALES.
Real Jardin Botanico de Madrid, Plaza de Murillo, 2, 28014 Madrid, Spain. TEL 1-585-5959. FAX 1-420-0157. *506*

JOURNAL OF ADVERTISING.
American Academy of Advertising, University of Houston, Department of Marketing, College of Business Administration, Houston, TX 77204-6283. TEL 713-749-6671. FAX 713-749-6895. *33*

JOURNAL OF BACTERIOLOGY.
American Society for Microbiology, 1325 Massachusetts Ave. N.W., Washington, DC 20005. TEL 202-737-3600. *553*

JOURNAL OF BIOLOGICAL CHEMISTRY.
American Society for Biochemistry and Molecular Biology, Inc., 9650 Rockville Pike, Bethesda, MD 20814. TEL 301-530-7150. FAX 301-571-1824. *478*

JOURNAL OF CLINICAL MICROBIOLOGY.
American Society for Microbiology, 1325 Massachusetts Ave., N.W., Washington, DC 20005. TEL 202-737-3600. *554*

JOURNAL OF COMMONWEALTH LITERATURE.
Bowker-Saur Ltd. 59-60 Grosvenor St., London W1X 9DA, England. TEL 071-493-5841. FAX 071-499-1590. *2928*

JOURNAL OF CONSUMER RESEARCH.
University of Chicago Press, Journals Division, 5720 S. Woodlawn Ave., Chicago, IL 60637. TEL 312-702-7600. FAX 312-702-0694. *1042*

JOURNAL OF DEVELOPMENT STUDIES.
Frank Cass & Co. Ltd., Gainsborough House, 11 Gainsborough Rd., London E11 1RS, England. TEL 081-530-4226. FAX 081-530-7795. *932*

JOURNAL OF ECONOMIC LITERATURE.
American Economic Association, 2014 Broadway, Ste. 305, Nashville, TN 37203. TEL 615-322-2595.
Producer(s): SilverPlatter. *725*

JOURNAL OF EVOLUTIONARY PSYCHOLOGY.
Institute for Evolutionary Psychology, 5117 Forbes Ave., Pittsburgh, PA 15213. TEL 412-621-7057. *4029*

JOURNAL OF HIGHER EDUCATION.
Ohio State University Press, 1070 Carmack Rd., Columbus, OH 43210. TEL 614-292-6930.
Producer(s): University Microfilms International. *1710*

JOURNAL OF MONEY, CREDIT & BANKING.
Ohio State University Press, 1070 Carmack Rd., Columbus, OH 43210. TEL 614-292-6930.
Producer(s): University Microfilms International. *788*

JOURNAL OF PORTFOLIO MANAGEMENT.
Institutional Investor, Inc., Circulation Department, 488 Madison Ave., 15th Fl., New York, NY 10022. TEL 212-303-3570. FAX 212-421-3592. *953*

JOURNAL OF SHELLFISH RESEARCH.
National Shellfisheries Association, Inc., c/o Sandra E. Shumway, Ed., Dept. of Marine Resources & Bigelow Laboratory for Ocean Sciences, W. Boothbay Harbor, ME 04575. TEL 207-633-5572. FAX 207-633-7109. *586*

JOURNAL OF TECHNOLOGY TRANSFER.
Technology Transfer Society, 611 N. Capitol Ave., Indianapolis, IN 46204. *4602*

JOURNAL OF TRAUMA.
Williams & Wilkins, 428 E. Preston St., Baltimore, MD 21202. TEL 301-528-4000. FAX 301-528-4312. *3310*

JUDICIAL STAFF DIRECTORY.
Staff Directories Ltd., Box 62, Mount Vernon, VA 22121. TEL 703-739-0900. FAX 703-739-0234. *2640*

KANSAS CITY BUSINESS JOURNAL.
American City Business Journals, Inc. (Kansas City), 324 E. 11th St., Ste. 800, Kansas City, MO 64106-2417. TEL 816-561-5900. FAX 816-753-2012. *871*

KNJIZNICA.
Zveza Bibliotekarskih Drustev Slovenije, Turjaska 1, Ljubljana, Slovenia. TEL 061-150-131. *2767*

KOMPASS BELGIUM.
Kompass Belgium S.A., Av. Moliere 256, 1060 Brussels, Belgium. TEL 02-3451983. FAX 02-3473340. *1142*

KOMPASS ITALIA.
Kompass Italia S.p.A., Via Seruais, 125, 10146 Turin, Italy.
Producer(s): SilverPlatter. *1142*

KOMPASS SVERIGE.
Kompass Sweden, Saltmaetargatan 8, Box 3223, 10364 Stockholm, Sweden. FAX 08-311898. *1142*

KOMPASS UNITED KINGDOM.
Kompass Windsor Court, E. Grinstead House, E. Grinstead, W. Sussex RH19 1XD, England. TEL 0342-326972. FAX 0342-317241. *1142*

LANCET.
Lancet Ltd., 46 Bedford Square, London WC1B 3SL, England. TEL 01-436-4981. FAX 01-436-7550. *3121*

LEGAL RESOURCE INDEX.
Information Access Company, 362 Lakeside Dr., Foster City, CA 94404. TEL 800-227-8431. FAX 415-378-5499. *2700*

LIBRARY & INFORMATION SCIENCE ABSTRACTS.
Bowker-Saur Ltd., 59-60 Grosvenor St., London W1X 9DA, England. TEL 071-493-5841. FAX 071-499-1590. *2794*

LIBRARY LITERATURE.
H.W. Wilson Co., 950 University Ave., Bronx, NY 10452. TEL 800-367-6770. FAX 212-538-2716. Producer(s): H.W. Wilson (WILSONDISC). *2794*

LIBROS ESPANOLES EN VENTA.
Ministerio de Cultura, Centro del Libro y de la Lectura, Santiago Rusinol, 8, 28040 Madrid, Spain. TEL 553-93-29. FAX 553-99-90. *405*

LIEFERN UND LEISTEN.
Deutscher Adressbuch-Verlag, Holzhofallee 38, Postfach 110452, 6100 Darmstadt, Germany. TEL 06151-391-0. FAX 06151-391200. *1143*

LINKAGE.
National Diet Library, Information Processing Division, 1-10-1 Nagata-cho, Chiyoda-ku, Tokyo 100, Japan. TEL 03-3581-2331. FAX 03-3597-9104. *1398*

LIQUID CHROMATOGRAPHY LITERATURE - ABSTRACTS AND INDEX.
Preston Publications, Inc., 7800 Merrimac Ave., Box 48312, Niles, IL 60648. TEL 708-965-0566. FAX 708-965-7639. *1202*

LITERARY MARKET PLACE.
R.R. Bowker, A Reed Reference Publishing Company, Division of Reed Publishing (USA) Inc., 121 Chanlon Rd., New Providence, NJ 07974. TEL 800-521-8110. FAX 908-665-6688. *4132*

LOTUS.
Lotus Publishing Corporation, Box 9123, Cambridge, MA 02139-9123. TEL 800-678-1278. *1478*

LUCKNOW LIBRARIAN.
Uttar Pradesh Library Association, Lucknow Branch, U.P. Library Association, P.O. Box 446, Lucknow 226 001, India. *2772*

M L A INTERNATIONAL BIBLIOGRAPHY OF BOOKS AND ARTICLES ON THE MODERN LANGUAGES AND LITERATURES.
Modern Language Association of America, 10 Astor Place, New York, NY 10003. TEL 212-475-9500. FAX 212-477-9863.
Producer(s): H.W. Wilson. *405*

MACGUIDE REPORT.
MacGuide Magazine Inc., 444 17th St., Ste. 200, P.O. Box 480927, Denver, CO 80248-0927. TEL 303-893-1454. FAX 303-893-9340. *1470*

MACINTOSH PRODUCT REGISTRY.
Redgate Communications Corp., 660 Beachland Blvd., Vero Beach, FL 32963. TEL 407-231-6904. FAX 407-231-7872. *1470*

MACTUTOR.
MacTutor, Xplain Corporation, Box 250055, Los Angeles, CA 90025. TEL 310-575-4343. FAX 310-575-0925. *1470*

MACWORLD.
MacWorld Communications, 501 Second St., San Francisco, CA 94107. TEL 415-243-0505. *1470*

MAGAZINE ARTICLE SUMMARIES.
EBSCO Publishing, Box 325, Topsfield, MA 01983. TEL 800-221-1826. FAX 508-887-3923. *16*

MAGAZINE INDEX.
Information Access Company, 362 Lakeside Dr., Foster City, CA 94404. TEL 800-227-8431. FAX 415-378-5499. *4142*

MARINE TECHNOLOGY SOCIETY JOURNAL.
Marine Technology Society, Inc., 1828 L St., N.W., 9th Fl., Washington, DC 20036. TEL 202-775-5966. FAX 202-429-9417. *1608*

MARTINDALE-HUBBELL LAW DIRECTORY.
R.R. Bowker, A Reed Reference Publishing Company, Division of Reed Publishing (USA) Inc., Box 1001, Summit, NJ 07902-1001. TEL 800-526-4902. FAX 201-464-3553. *2653*

MASTERS ABSTRACTS INTERNATIONAL.
University Microfilms International, Dissertation Publishing, c/o Dorie Mickelson, Mgr., 300 N. Zeeb Rd., Ann Arbor, MI 48106. TEL 313-761-4700. Producer(s): University Microfilms International. *1678*

MATHEMATICAL REVIEWS.
American Mathematical Society, Box 1571, Annex Sta., Providence, RI 02901-9930. TEL 401-455-4000.
Producer(s): SilverPlatter (MathDisc). *3063*

MEDICAL AND HEALTH CARE BOOKS AND SERIALS IN PRINT.
R.R. Bowker, A Reed Reference Publishing Company, Division of Reed Publishing (USA) Inc., 121 Chanlon Rd., New Providence, NJ 07974. TEL 800-521-8110. FAX 908-665-7974. *3177*

METALS ABSTRACTS.
A S M International, Materials Information, Materials Park, OH 44073. TEL 216-338-5151. FAX 216-338-4634.
Producer(s): Dialog Information Services. *3427*

METALS ABSTRACTS INDEX.
A S M International, Materials Information, Materials Park, OH 44073. TEL 216-338-5151. FAX 216-338-4634.
Producer(s): Dialog Information Services. *3427*

MICROBIOLOGY ABSTRACTS: SECTION A. INDUSTRIAL & APPLIED MICROBIOLOGY.
Cambridge Scientific Abstracts, 7200 Wisconsin Ave., 6th Fl., Bethesda, MD 20814. TEL 301-961-6750. FAX 301-961-6720.
Producer(s): Cambridge Scientific Abstracts (Compact Cambridge Life Sciences Collection). *466*

MICROBIOLOGY ABSTRACTS: SECTION B. BACTERIOLOGY.
Cambridge Scientific Abstracts, 7200 Wisconsin Ave., 6th Fl., Bethesda, MD 20814. TEL 301-961-6750. FAX 301-961-6720.
Producer(s): Cambridge Scientific Abstracts (Compact Cambridge Life Sciences Collection). *466*

MICROBIOLOGY ABSTRACTS: SECTION C. ALGOLOGY, MYCOLOGY AND PROTOZOOLOGY.
Cambridge Scientific Abstracts, 7200 Wisconsin Ave., 6th Fl., Bethesda, MD 20814. TEL 301-961-6750. FAX 301-961-6720.
Producer(s): Cambridge Scientific Abstracts (Compact Cambridge Life Sciences Collection). *466*

MICROLOG: CANADIAN RESEARCH INDEX.
Micromedia Ltd., 20 Victoria St., Toronto, Ont. M5C 2N8, Canada. TEL 416-362-5211. FAX 416-362-6161. *17*

MIDDLE SCHOOLS DIRECTORY.
School Government Publishing Co. Ltd., Darby House, Bletchingley Rd., Merstham, Redhill, Surrey RH1 3DN, England. TEL 0737-642223. FAX 0737-644283. *1695*

MILITARY SPECIFICATIONS AND STANDARDS SERVICES NUMERIC INDEX.
Information Handling Services, 15 Inverness Way East, Englewood, CO 80150. TEL 303-790-0600. FAX 303-799-4085. *3465*

MILLION DOLLAR DIRECTORY SERIES.
Dun and Bradstreet Information Services 3 Sylvan Way, Parsippany, NJ 07054-3896. TEL 201-605-6000.
Producer(s): Dun's Marketing Services. *1048*

MINNESOTA STATUTES ON C D - R O M.
Office of Revisor of Statutes, 700 State Office Bldg., St. Paul, MN 55155. TEL 612-296-2868. Available only on CD-ROM. *2655*

MISSOURI UNION LIST OF SERIAL PUBLICATIONS.
St. Louis Public Library, Board of Directors, 1301 Olive St., St. Louis, MO 63103. FAX 314-241-3840. *2794*

MOLECULAR AND CELLULAR BIOLOGY.
American Society for Microbiology, 1325 Massachusetts Ave., N.W., Washington, DC 20005. TEL 202-737-3600. *556*

MONEY MANAGEMENT LETTER.
Institutional Investor, Inc., Circulation Department, 488 Madison Ave., 15th Fl., New York, NY 10022. TEL 212-303-3233. FAX 212-303-3353. *955*

MONTHLY CATALOG OF UNITED STATES GOVERNMENT PUBLICATIONS.
U.S. Government Printing Office, Superintendent of Documents, Washington, DC 20402-9341. TEL 202-783-3238. FAX 202-2512-2250.
Producer(s): SilverPlatter, H.W. Wilson. *4081*

MOODY'S COMPANY DATA.
Moody's Investors Service 99 Church St., New York, NY 10007-0300. TEL 212-553-0300. FAX 212-553-4700.
Available only on CD-ROM. *1431*

MOODY'S INTERNATIONAL PLUS.
Moody's Investors Service 99 Church St., New York, NY 10007. TEL 212-553-0300. FAX 212-553-4700.
Available only on CD-ROM. *956*

MULTIMEDIA COMPUTING & PRESENTATIONS.
Multimedia Computing Corporation, 3501 Ryder St., Santa Clara, CA 95051. TEL 408-737-7575. FAX 408-739-8019. *1482*

N A B E INDUSTRY SURVEY.
National Association of Business Economists, 28790 Chagrin Blvd., Ste. 300, Cleveland, OH 44122. TEL 216-464-7986. FAX 216-464-6352. *874*

N A B E OUTLOOK.
National Association of Business Economists, 28790 Chagrin Blvd., Ste. 300, Cleveland, OH 44122. TEL 216-464-7986. FAX 216-464-6352. *874*

N A B E POLICY SURVEY.
National Association of Business Economists, 28790 Chagrin Blvd., Ste. 300, Cleveland, OH 44122. TEL 216-464-7986. FAX 216-464-6352. *874*

N I O S H T I C DATABASE.
U.S. National Technical Information Service, 5285 Port Royal Rd., Springfield, VA 22161. TEL 703-487-4630. *3619*

N T I S BIBLIOGRAPHIC DATA BASE.
U.S. National Technical Information Service, 5285 Port Royal Rd., Springfield, VA 22161. TEL 703-487-4630.
Producer(s): Dialog Information Services, O C L C, SilverPlatter. *4143*

NATIONAL NEWSPAPER INDEX.
Information Access Company, 362 Lakeside Dr., Foster City, CA 94404. TEL 800-227-8431. FAX 415-378-5499. *730*

NATIONAL REVIEW.
National Review, Inc., 150 E. 35th St., New York, NY 10016. TEL 212-679-7330. FAX 212-696-0309. *3909*

NATURAL RESOURCES METABASE.
National Information Services Corporation, Ste. 6, Wyman Towers, 3100 St. Paul St., Baltimore, MD 21218. TEL 301-243-0797. FAX 301-243-0982. Available only on CD-ROM. *1974*

NETWORK WORLD.
Network World Inc., 161 Worcester Rd., 5th Fl., Framingham, MA 01701. TEL 508-875-6400. *1351*

NEW ENGLAND WATER WORKS ASSOCIATION. JOURNAL.
New England Water Works Association, 42A Dilla St., Milford, MA 01757. TEL 508-478-6996. FAX 508-634-8643.
Producer(s): Dialog Information Services. *4827*

NEW YORK TIMES INDEX.
University Microfilms International, Serials Data Management, 300 N. Zeeb Rd., Ann Arbor, MI 48106. TEL 313-761-4700. *2578*

SERIALS AVAILABLE ON CD-ROM

NEWSBANK REVIEW OF THE ARTS: FILM AND TELEVISION.
NewsBank, Inc., 58 Pine St., New Canaan, CT 06840-5426. TEL 203-966-1100. FAX 203-966-6254. *3515*

NONFERROUS METALS ALERT.
A S M International, Materials Information, Materials Park, OH 44073. TEL 216-338-5151. FAX 216-338-4634.
Producer(s): Dialog Information Services. *3427*

NORSK SKATTELOVSAMLING.
Jacob Jaroey, Vraasgt. 18, N-3701 Skien, Norway. *1102*

OFFICIAL JOURNAL OF THE EUROPEAN COMMUNITIES. L & C: LEGISLATION AND COMPETITION.
Office for Official Publications of the European Communities, L-2985 Luxembourg, Luxembourg. *3967*

OHIO STATE LAW JOURNAL.
Ohio State University, College of Law, 1659 North High St., Columbus, OH 43210-1391. TEL 614-292-6829. *2663*

ONCOGENES AND GROWTH FACTORS ABSTRACTS.
Cambridge Scientific Abstracts, 7200 Wisconsin Ave., 6th Fl., Bethesda, MD 20814. TEL 301-961-6750. FAX 301-961-6720.
Producer(s): Cambridge Scientific Abstracts (Compact Cambridge Life Sciences Collection). *3178*

ONLINE HOTLINE NEWS SERVICE.
Information Intelligence, Inc., Box 31098, Phoenix, AZ 85046. TEL 800-228-9982. *1428*

ONLINE LIBRARIES AND MICROCOMPUTERS.
Information Intelligence, Inc., Box 31098, Phoenix, AZ 85046. TEL 800-228-9982. *2799*

ONLINE NEWSLETTER.
Information Intelligence Inc., Box 31098, Phoenix, AZ 85046. TEL 800-228-9982. *1428*

P A I S INTERNATIONAL IN PRINT.
Public Affairs Information Service, Inc., 521 W. 43rd St., 5th Fl., New York, NY 10036-4396. TEL 212-736-6629. FAX 212-643-2848.
Producer(s): Public Affairs Information Service (PAIS), SilverPlatter. *733*

P C LETTER.
301 Island Pkwy., No. 201, Belmont, CA 94002-4109. TEL 415-592-8880. FAX 415-592-9192. *1433*

PAPERBOUND BOOKS IN PRINT.
R.R. Bowker, A Reed Reference Publishing Company, Division of Reed Publishing (USA) Inc., 121 Chanlon Rd., New Providence, NJ 07974. TEL 800-521-8110. FAX 908-665-6688. *409*

PATENT OFFICE RECORD (CANADA).
Department of Consumer and Corporate Affairs, Patent Office, 50 Victoria St., Hull, Que. K1A 0C9, Canada. TEL 819-997-2525. *3677*

PEACE CORPS TIMES.
U.S. Peace Corps, 1990 K St., N.W., Washington, DC 20526. TEL 202-254-3371. FAX 202-606-3110. *934*

PEDIATRICS.
American Academy of Pediatrics, 141 Northwest Point Blvd., Box 927, Elk Grove Village, IL 60009-0927. TEL 708-228-5005. *3325*

PERIODICA. INDICE DE REVISTAS LATINOAMERICANAS EN CIENCIAS.
Universidad Nacional Autonoma de Mexico, Centro de Informacion Cientifica y Humanistica, Apdo. Postal 70-392, C.P. 04510 Mexico, D.F., Mexico. *4357*

PETERSON'S GUIDE TO GRADUATE AND PROFESSIONAL PROGRAMS: AN OVERVIEW (YEAR) (BOOK 1).
Peterson's Guides, Inc., 202 Carnegie Center, Box 2123, Princeton, NJ 08543-2123. TEL 609-243-9111. FAX 609-243-9150.
Producer(s): SilverPlatter (PETERSON'S GRADLINE). *1696*

PETERSON'S GUIDE TO GRADUATE PROGRAMS IN BUSINESS, EDUCATION, HEALTH, AND LAW (YEAR) (BOOK 6).
Peterson's Guides, Inc., 202 Carnegie Center, Box 2123, Princeton, NJ 08543-2123. TEL 609-243-9111. FAX 609-243-9150.
Producer(s): SilverPlatter (PETERSON'S GRADLINE). *1696*

PETERSON'S GUIDE TO GRADUATE PROGRAMS IN ENGINEERING AND APPLIED SCIENCES (YEAR) (BOOK 5).
Peterson's Guides, Inc., 202 Carnegie Center, Box 2123, Princeton, NJ 08543-2123. TEL 609-243-9111. FAX 609-243-9150.
Producer(s): SilverPlatter (PETERSON'S GRADLINE). *1696*

PETERSON'S GUIDE TO GRADUATE PROGRAMS IN THE BIOLOGICAL AND AGRICULTURAL SCIENCES (YEAR) (BOOK 3).
Peterson's Guides, Inc., 202 Carnegie Center, Box 2123, Princeton, NJ 08543-2123. TEL 609-243-9111. FAX 609-243-9150.
Producer(s): SilverPlatter (PETERSON'S GRADLINE). *1696*

PETERSON'S GUIDE TO GRADUATE PROGRAMS IN THE HUMANITIES AND SOCIAL SCIENCES (YEAR) (BOOK 2).
Peterson's Guides, Inc., 202 Carnegie Center, Box 2123, Princeton, NJ 08543-2123. TEL 609-243-9111. FAX 609-243-9150.
Producer(s): SilverPlatter (PETERSON'S GRADLINE). *1696*

PETERSON'S GUIDE TO GRADUATE PROGRAMS IN THE PHYSICAL SCIENCES AND MATHEMATICS (YEAR) (BOOK 4).
Peterson's Guides, Inc., 202 Carnegie Center, Box 2123, NJ 08543-2123. TEL 609-243-9111. FAX 609-243-9150.
Producer(s): SilverPlatter (PETERSON'S GRADLINE). *1696*

PHILOSOPHER'S INDEX.
Bowling Green State University, Philosophy Documentation Center, Bowling Green, OH 43403-0189. TEL 419-372-2419. FAX 419-372-6987. *3787*

PHYSICIANS' DESK REFERENCE.
Medical Economics Publishing Co., Five Paragon Dr., Montvale, NJ 07645. TEL 201-357-7200. FAX 201-573-1045. *3141*

PHYSICIANS' DESK REFERENCE FOR NONPRESCRIPTION DRUGS.
Medical Economics Publishing Co., Five Paragon Dr., Montvale, NJ 07645. TEL 201-358-7200. FAX 201-573-1045. *3141*

PINKERTON EYE ON TRAVEL.
Pinkerton Risk Assessment Services, 1600 Wilson Blvd., Ste. 901, Arlington, VA 22209-2507. TEL 703-525-6111. FAX 703-525-2454. *4782*

PINPOINTER.
Libraries Board of South Australia, G.P.O. Box 419, Adelaide, S.A. 5001, Australia. *1509*

PLASTICS AND RUBBERS MATERIALS DISC.
Pergamon Press plc, Headington Hill Hall, Oxford OX3 0BW, England. TEL 0865-794141. FAX 0865-743911.
Available only on CD-ROM. *4295*

POLAR AND GLACIOLOGICAL ABSTRACTS.
Cambridge University Press, Journals Publicity Department, Edinburgh Bldg., Shaftesbury Rd., Cambridge CB2 2RU, England. TEL 0223-312393. FAX 0223-315052. *1552*

POLLUTION ABSTRACTS.
Cambridge Scientific Abstracts, 7200 Wisconsin Ave., 6th Fl., Bethesda, MD 20814. TEL 301-961-6750. FAX 301-961-6720.
Producer(s): Cambridge Scientific Abstracts (Compact Cambridge Pol/Tox). *1974*

POLYMERS, CERAMICS, COMPOSITE ALERT.
A S M International, Materials Information, Materials Park, OH 44073. TEL 216-338-5151. FAX 216-338-4634.
Producer(s): Dialog Information Services. *3869*

POPULATION INDEX.
Princeton University, Office of Population Research, 21 Prospect Ave., Princeton, NJ 08544-2091. TEL 609-258-4949. FAX 609-258-1039.
Producer(s): SilverPlatter. *3994*

PORTFOLIO LETTER.
Institutional Investor, Inc., Circulation Department, 488 Madison Ave., New York, NY 10022. TEL 212-303-3233. FAX 212-303-3353. *960*

POSTMODERN CULTURE.
Box 8105, Raleigh, NC 27695. TEL 919-832-7808. *2949*

POWDER DIFFRACTION FILE SEARCH MANUAL. ALPHABETICAL LISTING. INORGANIC.
Joint Committee on Powder Diffraction Standards, International Centre for Diffraction Data, 1601 Park Lane, Swarthmore, PA 19081. TEL 215-328-9400. FAX 215-328-2503. *1207*

POWDER DIFFRACTION FILE SEARCH MANUAL. HANAWALT METHOD. INORGANIC.
Joint Committee on Powder Diffraction Standards, International Centre for Diffraction Data, 1601 Park Lane, Swarthmore, PA 19081. TEL 215-328-9400. FAX 215-328-2503. *1208*

POWDER DIFFRACTION FILE SEARCH MANUAL. ORGANIC.
Joint Committee on Powder Diffraction Standards, International Centre for Diffraction Data, 1601 Park Lane, Swarthmore, PA 19081. TEL 215-328-9400. FAX 215-328-2503. *1222*

PRIMARY EDUCATION DIRECTORY.
School Government Publishing Co. Ltd., Darby House, Bletchingley Rd., Merstham, Redhill, Surrey RH1 3DN, England. TEL 0737-642223. FAX 0737-644283. *1697*

PRODIRECT.
American Business Information, Inc., Optical Products Division, 5711 S. 86th Circle, Box 27347, Omaha, NE 68127. TEL 402-593-4564. FAX 402-339-0265.
Available only on CD-ROM. *1150*

PRODUCER PRICE INDEXES.
U.S. Bureau of Labor Statistics, 441 G St., N.W., Washington, DC 20212. TEL 202-655-4000. *736*

PSYCHOLOGICAL ABSTRACTS.
American Psychological Association, 750 First St., N.E., Washington, DC 20002-4242. TEL 202-336-5500. FAX 202-336-5568.
Producer(s): American Psychological Association, SilverPlatter (PsycLIT). *4051*

PUBLISHERS, DISTRIBUTORS & WHOLESALERS OF THE UNITED STATES.
R.R. Bowker, A Reed Reference Publishing Company, Division of Reed Publishing (USA) Inc., 121 Chanlon Rd., New Providence, NJ 07974. TEL 800-521-8110. FAX 908-665-6688.
Producer(s): R.R. Bowker. *1151*

PUBLISHERS' INTERNATIONAL I S B N DIRECTORY.
K.G. Saur Verlag KG, Ortlerstr. 8, Postfach 701620, 8000 Munich 70, Germany. TEL 089-76902-0. FAX 089-76902150.
Producer(s): K.G. Saur. *4142*

PUERTO RICO HEALTH SCIENCES JOURNAL.
University of Puerto Rico, Office of the Dean for Academic Affairs, Medical Sciences Campus, Box 365067, San Juan, PR 00936-5067. TEL 809-758-2525. FAX 809-764-2470. *3145*

PUNCH IN INTERNATIONAL TRAVEL AND ENTERTAINMENT MAGAZINE.
Enterprises Publishing, 400 E. 59th St., Ste. 9F, New York, NY 10022. TEL 212-755-4563. *4783*

R A P R A ABSTRACTS.
Pergamon Press plc, Headington Hill Hall, Oxford OX3 0BW, England. TEL 0865-794141. FAX 0865-743911. *4295*

R I L M ABSTRACTS OF MUSIC LITERATURE.
R I L M Abstracts, City University of New York, 33 W. 42nd St., New York, NY 10036. TEL 212-642-2709. FAX 212-642-2642. *3589*

READERS' GUIDE ABSTRACTS. MICROFICHE EDITION.
H.W. Wilson Co., 950 University Ave., Bronx, NY 10452-9978. TEL 800-367-6770. FAX 212-538-2716.
Producer(s): H.W. Wilson. *4142*

READERS' GUIDE TO PERIODICAL LITERATURE.
H.W. Wilson Co., 950 University Ave., Bronx, NY 10452-9978. TEL 800-367-6770. FAX 212-538-2716.
Producer(s): H.W. Wilson (WILSONDISC). *20*

REFERENCE AND RESEARCH BOOK NEWS.
Book News, Inc. (Portland), 5606 N.E. Hassalo St., Portland, OR 97213. TEL 503-281-9230. FAX 503-284-8859. *410*

REGISTRY OF TOXIC EFFECTS OF CHEMICAL SUBSTANCES.
Department of Health and Human Services, National Institute of Occupational Safety and Health, Attn.: Doris Sweet, Ed. (C-28), 4676 Columbia Pkwy., Cincinnati, OH 45226. TEL 513-533-8317.
Producer(s): SilverPlatter. *3621*

RELIGION INDEX ONE: PERIODICALS.
American Theological Library Association, Religion Indexes, 820 Church St., 3rd Fl., Evanston, IL 60201-3707. TEL 708-869-7788. *4213*

RELIGION INDEX TWO: MULTI-AUTHOR WORKS.
American Theological Library Association, Religion Indexes, 820 Church St., 3rd Fl., Evanston, IL 60201-3707. TEL 708-869-7788. *4213*

RELIGION INDEXES: THESAURUS.
American Theological Library Association, Religion Indexes, 820 Church St., 3rd Fl., Evanston, IL 60201-3707. TEL 708-869-7788. *4197*

RELIGIOUS & THEOLOGICAL ABSTRACTS.
Religious & Theological Abstracts Inc., 121 S. College St., Box 215, Myerstown, PA 17067. TEL 717-866-6734. *4213*

REPERTORIO CRONOLOGICO DE LEGISLACION.
Editorial Aranzadi, S.A., Avda. Carlos III, 34, Apdo. 111, 31080 Pamplona, Spain. TEL 948-331212. FAX 948-330919. *2671*

REPERTORIO DE JURISPRUDENCIA.
Editorial Aranzadi, S.A., Avda. Carlos III, 34, Apdo. 111, 31080 Pamplona, Spain. TEL 948-331212. FAX 948-330919. *2672*

REPERTORIO DEL FORO ITALIANO.
Zanichelli Editore, Via Irnerio 34, 40126 Bologna, Italy. TEL 051-293111. FAX 051-249782.
Available only on CD-ROM. *2672*

RESEARCH IN MINISTRY.
American Theological Library Association, Religion Indexes, 820 Church St., 3rd Fl., Evanston, IL 60201-3707. TEL 708-869-7788. *4213*

RESOURCES IN EDUCATION.
Educational Resources Information Center, Processing and Reference Facility, 2440 Research Blvd., Ste. 400, Rockville, MD 20850. TEL 301-590-1420.
Producer(s): Dialog Information Services, O C L C, SilverPlatter (ERIC). *1679*

REVISTA BRASILEIRA DE PATOLOGIA CLINICA.
Sociedade Brasileira de Patologia Clinica, Rua Sampaio Viana, 92, Rio de Janeiro, RJ 20261, Brazil. TEL 021-293-3848. FAX 021-2932041. *3147*

REVISTA COSTARRICENSE DE CIENCIAS MEDICAS.
Caja Costarricense de Seguro Social, Centro de Docencia e Investigacion en Salud y Seguridad Social, Apdo. 10105, San Jose, Costa Rica. FAX 506-338359. *3147*

REVISTA DE INVESTIGACION CONTABLE (TEUKEN).
Universidad Nacional de la Patagonia San Juan Bosca, Facultad de Ciencias Economicas, Sarmiento 553 Casilla de Correo 172, 9000 C. Rivadavia, Argentina. TEL 0967-24463. FAX 54-96724463. *755*

REVISTA ESPANOLA DE DOCUMENTACION CIENTIFICA.
Instituto de Informacion y Documentacion en Ciencia y Tecnologia, Joaquin Costa 22, 28002 Madrid, Spain. TEL 91-5635482. FAX 91-5642644. *2782*

RISK MANAGEMENT.
Risk Management Society Publishing, Inc., 205 E. 42nd St., New York, NY 10017. TEL 212-286-9364. FAX 212-986-9716. *2541*

S C I M P.
European Business School Librarians Group, c/o Helsinki School of Economics Library, Runeberginkatu 22-24, 00100 Helsinki, Finland. TEL 0-4313-413. FAX 0-4313-539. *737*

SAFETY AND HEALTH AT WORK.
International Labour Office, International Occupational Safety and Health Information Centre, CH-1211 Geneva 22, Switzerland. TEL 799-65-40.
Producer(s): SilverPlatter. *3623*

SCHWEIZERISCHE ZEITSCHRIFT FUER VOLKSWIRTSCHAFT UND STATISTIK.
Helbing & Lichtenhahn Verlag AG, Freiestr. 82, CH-4051 Basel, Switzerland. TEL 064-268626. FAX 064-245780.
Producer(s): SilverPlatter. *737*

SCIENCE CITATION INDEX.
Institute for Scientific Information, 3501 Market St., Philadelphia, PA 19104. TEL 215-386-0100. FAX 215-386-2991.
Producer(s): Institute for Scientific Information (SCI CDE). *4357*

SCIENTIFIC AND TECHNICAL BOOKS AND SERIALS IN PRINT.
R.R. Bowker, A Reed Reference Publishing Company, Division of Reed Publishing (USA) Inc., 121 Chanlon Rd., New Providence, NJ 07974. TEL 800-521-8110. FAX 908-665-6688. *4358*

SCITECH BOOK NEWS.
Book News, Inc. (Portland), 5600 N.E. Hassalo St., Portland, OR 97213. TEL 503-281-9230. FAX 503-284-8859. *411*

SCITECH REFERENCE PLUS.
R.R. Bowker, A Reed Reference Publishing Company, Division of Reed Publishing (USA) Inc., 121 Chanlon Rd., New Providence, NJ 07974. TEL 908-665-2867. FAX 908-665-6688.
Available only on CD-ROM. *4358*

SECURITE ET SANTE AU TRAVAIL.
International Labour Office, International Occupational Safety and Health Information Centre, CH-1211 Geneva 22, Switzerland. TEL 22-799-6740. FAX 41-22-798-8685.
Producer(s): SilverPlatter. *3623*

SEDIMENT DATA FOR SELECTED CANADIAN RIVERS.
Environment Canada, Inland Waters Directorate, Ottawa, Ont. K1A OH3, Canada. TEL 613-953-3680. FAX 613-997-8701. *1579*

SELECTED WATER RESOURCES ABSTRACTS.
U.S. Geological Survey, Water Resources Scientific Information Center, 425 National Center, Reston, VA 22092. TEL 703-648-6820.
Producer(s): O C L C. *1552*

SERIALS DIRECTORY.
EBSCO Publishing Box 1943, Birmingham, AL 35201. TEL 800-826-3024. FAX 205-995-1582. *411*

SEYBOLD REPORT ON DESKTOP PUBLISHING.
Seybold Publications, Inc., Box 644, Media, PA 19063. TEL 215-565-2480. *1465*

SHAREDEBATE INTERNATIONAL.
Applied Foresight, Inc., Box 20607, Bloomington, MN 55420. *4385*

SIDE EFFECTS OF DRUGS ANNUAL.
Elsevier Science Publishers B.V., Books Division, P.O. Box 211, 1000 AE Amsterdam, Netherlands. TEL 020-5803911. FAX 020-5803705.
Producer(s): SilverPlatter (SEDBASE). *3743*

SOCIAL PLANNING - POLICY & DEVELOPMENT ABSTRACTS.
Sociological Abstracts, Inc., Box 22206, San Diego, CA 92192. TEL 619-695-8803. FAX 619-695-0416.
Producer(s): SilverPlatter, Sociological Abstracts, Inc. (SocioFile). *4426*

SOCIAL SCIENCES CITATION INDEX.
Institute for Scientific Information, 3501 Market St., Philadelphia, PA 19104. TEL 215-386-0100. FAX 215-386-2991.
Producer(s): Institute for Scientific Information (SSCI). *4396*

SOCIAL SCIENCES INDEX.
H.W. Wilson Co., 950 University Ave., Bronx, NY 10452. TEL 800-367-6770. FAX 212-538-2716.
Producer(s): H.W. Wilson. *4396*

SOCIOLOGICAL ABSTRACTS.
Sociological Abstracts, Inc., Box 22206, San Diego, CA 92192. TEL 619-695-8803. FAX 619-695-0416.
Producer(s): SilverPlatter, Sociological Abstracts, Inc. (SocioFile). *4458*

SOFT.LETTER.
Mercury Group, Inc., 17 Main St., Watertown, MA 02272-9154. TEL 617-924-3944. FAX 617-924-7288. *1480*

SOFTWARE ABSTRACTS FOR ENGINEERS.
C I T I S Ltd., 2 Rosemount Terrace, Blackrock, Dublin, Ireland. TEL 353-1-2886227. FAX 353-1-885971. *1480*

SOLAR-GEOPHYSICAL DATA. PART 1 - PROMPT REPORTS.
National Oceanic and Atmospheric Administration, National Geophysical Data Center, 325 Broadway, Boulder, CO 80303-3328. TEL 303-497-6223. *369*

SOLAR-GEOPHYSICAL DATA: PART 2 - COMPREHENSIVE REPORTS.
National Oceanic and Atmospheric Administration, National Geophysical Data Center, 325 Broadway, Boulder, CO 80303-3328. TEL 303-497-6223. *369*

SPORTSEARCH.
Sport Information Resource Centre (SIRC), 1600 James Naismith Drive, Gloucester, Ont. K1B 5N4, Canada. TEL 613-748-5658. FAX 613-748-5701.
Producer(s): SilverPlatter. *4499*

STANDARD & POOR'S CORPORATE REGISTERED BOND INTEREST RECORD.
Standard & Poor's Corporation, 25 Broadway, New York, NY 10004. TEL 212-208-8000. *964*

STANDARD & POOR'S CORPORATION RECORDS.
Standard & Poor's Corporation, 25 Broadway, New York, NY 10004. TEL 212-208-8000. *964*

STANDARD & POOR'S REGISTER OF CORPORATIONS, DIRECTORS AND EXECUTIVES.
Standard & Poor's Corporation, 25 Broadway, New York, NY 10004. TEL 212-208-8000. *1028*

STATISTICAL ABSTRACT OF LOUISIANA.
University of New Orleans, Division of Business and Economic Research, New Orleans, LA 70148. FAX 504-286-6094. *739*

STATISTICAL REFERENCE INDEX.
Congressional Information Service, 4520 East-West Hwy., Bethesda, MD 20814-3389. TEL 301-654-1550. FAX 301-654-4033. *4588*

STEELS ALERT.
A S M International, Materials Information, Materials Park, OH 44073. TEL 216-338-5151. FAX 216-338-4634.
Producer(s): Dialog Information Services. *3428*

SUBJECT GUIDE TO BOOKS IN PRINT.
R.R. Bowker, A Reed Reference Publishing Company, Division of Reed Publishing (USA) Inc., 121 Chanlon Rd., New Providence, NJ 07974. TEL 800-521-8110. FAX 908-665-6688. *412*

SERIALS AVAILABLE ON CD-ROM

SUBJECT GUIDE TO CHILDREN'S BOOKS IN PRINT.
R.R. Bowker, A Reed Reference Publishing Company, Division of Reed Publishing (USA) Inc., 121 Chanlon Rd., New Providence, NJ 07974. TEL 800-521-8110. FAX 908-665-6688. *413*

SUOMEN KIRJALLISUUS.
Helsingin Yliopiston Kirjasto, Box 312, 00171 Helsinki, Finland. FAX 358-0-7084441. *413*

T O M.
Information Access Company, 357 Lakeside Dr., Foster City, CA 94404. TEL 800-227-8431. FAX 415-378-5499. *24*

TAX TREATIES DATA BASE ON C D - R O M.
International Bureau of Fiscal Documentation, P.O. Box 20237, 1000 HE Amsterdam, Netherlands. TEL 020-267726. FAX 020-228658. Available only on CD-ROM. *1109*

TEXAS ECONOMIC FORECAST.
Texas Economic Publishers, Inc., Box 6028, Waco, TX 76706-0028. TEL 817-755-8705. FAX 817-755-0381. *886*

TEXTILE TECHNOLOGY DIGEST.
Institute of Textile Technology, Charlottesville, VA 22902. TEL 804-296-5511. FAX 804-977-5400. *4628*

THOMAS REGISTER OF AMERICAN MANUFACTURERS AND THOMAS REGISTER CATALOG FILE.
Thomas Publishing Company, Five Penn Plaza, 250 W. 34th St., New York, NY 10001. TEL 212-695-0500.
Producer(s): Dialog Information Services. *1055*

TOXICOLOGY ABSTRACTS.
Cambridge Scientific Abstracts, 7200 Wisconsin Ave., 6th Fl., Bethesda, MD 20814. TEL 301-961-6750. FAX 301-961-6720.
Producer(s): Cambridge Scientific Abstracts (Compact Cambridge Life Sciences Collection and Compact Cambridge Pol/Tox). *3748*

TRADE & INDUSTRY INDEX.
Information Access Company, 362 Lakeside Dr., Foster City, CA 94404. TEL 800-227-8431. FAX 415-378-5499. *741*

TRADEMARK REGISTER OF THE UNITED STATES.
Trademark Register, National Press Bldg., 1297, Washington, DC 20045. TEL 202-662-1233. *3678*

TRENDS - TENDANCES.
Lexico Belgium S.A., Research Park Zellik, De Haak, B-1731 Zellik, Belgium. FAX 02-467-57-58. *695*

U C DAVIS LAW REVIEW.
University of California, Davis, School of Law, Martin Luther King, Jr. Hall, Davis, CA 95616. TEL 916-752-2551. FAX 916-752-4704. *2687*

U K SPECIAL EDUCATION DIRECTORY.
School Government Publishing Co. Ltd., Darby House, Bletchingley Rd., Merstham, Redhill, Surrey RH1 3DN, England. TEL 0737-642223. FAX 0737-644283. *1742*

ULRICH'S INTERNATIONAL PERIODICALS DIRECTORY.
R.R. Bowker, A Reed Reference Publishing Company, Division of Reed Publishing (USA) Inc., 121 Chanlon Rd., New Providence, NJ 07974. TEL 908-665-2847. FAX 908-771-7725.
Producer(s): R.R. Bowker (Ulrich's PLUS). *414*

ULRICH'S PLUS.
R.R. Bowker, A Reed Reference Publishing Company, Division of Reed Publishing (USA) Inc., 121 Chanlon Rd., New Providence, NJ 07974. TEL 908-665-2867. FAX 908-665-6688. Available only on CD-ROM. Producer(s): R.R. Bowker (Ulrich's PLUS). *414*

ULRICH'S UPDATE.
R.R. Bowker, A Reed Reference Publishing Company, Division of Reed Publishing (USA) Inc., 121 Chanlon Rd., New Providence, NJ 07974. TEL 800-521-8110. FAX 908-665-6688. *414*

ULSTER MEDICAL JOURNAL.
Ulster Medical Society, c/o Queens University Medical Library, Institute of Clinical Science, Grosvenor Rd., Belfast BT12 6BJ, N. Ireland. TEL 0232-322043. FAX 0232-247068.
Producer(s): SilverPlatter (MEDLINE). *3159*

UNION LIST OF SCIENTIFIC SERIALS IN CANADIAN LIBRARIES.
C.I.S.T.I. Cataloguing Section, Ottawa, Ont. K1A 0S2, Canada. TEL 613-993-3449. *4358*

UNITED NATIONS DOCUMENTS AND PUBLICATIONS.
NewsBank, Inc., 58 Pine St., New Canaan, CT 06840-5426. TEL 800-752-4650. FAX 203-966-6254. *414*

U.S. BUREAU OF LABOR STATISTICS. C P I DETAILED REPORT.
U.S. Bureau of Labor Statistics, 441 G St., N.W., Washington, DC 20212. TEL 202-655-4000. *1000*

U.S. BUREAU OF LABOR STATISTICS. CURRENT WAGE DEVELOPMENTS.
U.S. Bureau of Labor Statistics, 441 G St., N.W., Washington, DC 20212. TEL 202-655-4000. *742*

U.S. BUREAU OF LABOR STATISTICS. HANDBOOK OF LABOR STATISTICS.
U.S. Bureau of Labor Statistics, 441 G St., N.W., Washington, DC 20212. TEL 202-655-4000. *742*

U.S. BUREAU OF LABOR STATISTICS. MONTHLY LABOR REVIEW.
U.S. Bureau of Labor Statistics, 441 G St., N.W., Washington, DC 20212. TEL 202-523-1327. *742*

U.S. BUREAU OF LABOR STATISTICS. PRODUCTIVITY MEASURES FOR SELECTED INDUSTRIES.
U.S. Bureau of Labor Statistics, 441 G St., N.W., Washington, DC 20212. TEL 202-523-9244. *742*

U.S. BUREAU OF THE CENSUS. COUNTY BUSINESS PATTERNS.
U.S. Bureau of the Census, Data User Services Division, Washington, DC 20233. TEL 301-763-4100. *742*

U.S. CONGRESS. CONGRESSIONAL RECORD.
U.S. Congress, Washington, DC 20515. TEL 202-275-2051. FAX 202-275-0019. *3931*

UNIVERSITY PRESS BOOK NEWS.
Book News, Inc. (Portland), 5600 N.E. Hassalo St., Portland, OR 97213. TEL 503-281-9230. FAX 503-284-8859. *415*

URBAN ABSTRACTS.
London Research Centre, Parliament House, 81 Black Prince Rd., London SE1 7SZ, England. *4083*

VAARD I NORDEN.
Sygeplegerskernes Samarbejde i Norden, P.O. Box 2681, St. Hanshaugen, N-131 Oslo 1, Norway. TEL 47-2 38 20 00. FAX 47-2-38-54-47.
Producer(s): SilverPlatter. *3287*

VARIETY'S VIDEO DIRECTORY PLUS.
R.R. Bowker, A Reed Reference Publishing Company, Division of Reed Publishing (USA) Inc., 121 Chanlon Rd., New Providence, NJ 07974. TEL 908-665-2867. FAX 908-665-6688. Available only on CD-ROM. *3519*

VENDOR CATALOG SERVICES INDEX.
Information Handling Services, 15 Inverness Way E., Englewood, CO 80150. TEL 303-790-0600. FAX 303-799-4085. *1158*

VERBUM.
Verbum, Inc., Box 12564, San Diego, CA 92112-3564. FAX 619-233-9976. *352*

VERZEICHNIS LIEFERBARER BUECHER.
K.G. Saur Verlag KG, Ortlerstr. 8, Postfach 701620, 8000 Munich 70, Germany. TEL 089-76902-0. FAX 089-76902150. *415*

VIGILE URBANO.
Maggioli Editore, Via Crimera, 1, Casella Postale 290, 47037 Rimini, Italy. TEL 0541-626777. FAX 0541-622020. *1524*

VINTAGE JAZZ MART.
c/o M. Berresford, R. Sher, 1 Station Cottages, Moor Rd., Bestwood Village, Nottingham NG6 8SZ, England. TEL 0602-264465. *3585*

VIROLOGY AND A I D S ABSTRACTS.
Cambridge Scientific Abstracts, 7200 Wisconsin Ave., 6th Fl., Bethesda, MD 20814. TEL 301-961-6750. FAX 301-961-6720.
Producer(s): Cambridge Scientific Abstracts (Compact Cambridge Life Sciences Collection). *3181*

WALL STREET LETTER.
Institutional Investor, Inc., Circulation Department, 488 Madison Ave., New York, NY 10022. TEL 212-303-3233. FAX 212-303-3353. *968*

WER LIEFERT WAS?
Wer Liefert Was? GmbH Bezugsquellennachweis fuer den Einkauf, Normannenweg 18-20, 2000 Hamburg 26, Germany. TEL 040-251508-0. FAX 040-25150838. *1158*

WHITAKER'S BOOKS IN PRINT.
J. Whitaker & Sons Ltd., 12 Dyott St., London WC1A 1DF, England. TEL 071-836-8911. FAX 071-836-2909. *416*

WHOLE EARTH REVIEW.
Point Foundation, 27 Gate Five Rd., Sausalito, CA 94965. TEL 415-332-1716. FAX 415-332-2416. *3597*

WILDLIFE REVIEW (FORT COLLINS).
U.S. Fish and Wildlife Service (Fort Collins), 1025 Pennock Pl., Fort Collins, CO 80524. TEL 303-493-8401. FAX 303-226-9455. *1502*

WINE ON LINE.
Enterprises Publishing, 400 E. 59th St., Ste. 9F, New York, NY 10022. TEL 212-755-4563. *387*

WIRTSCHAFTS UND STEUER HEFTE.
D I E Verlag H. Schaefer GmbH, Postfach 2243, 6380 Bad Homburg, Germany. FAX 06172-71288. *699*

WORLD ENERGY AND NUCLEAR DIRECTORY (YEAR).
Longman Group UK Ltd., Westgate House, The High, Harlow, Essex CM20 1YR, England. *1797*

WORLD FACTBOOK.
U.S. Central Intelligence Agency, Washington, DC 20505. *3977*

YEAR BOOK OF CARDIOLOGY.
Mosby - Year Book, Inc., Continuity Division, 200 N. LaSalle, Chicago, IL 60601. TEL 312-726-9733. FAX 312-726-6075.
Producer(s): SilverPlatter (ClinMED-CD). *3212*

YEAR BOOK OF CRITICAL CARE MEDICINE.
Mosby - Year Book, Inc., Continuity Division, 200 N. LaSalle, Chicago, IL 60601. TEL 312-726-9733.
Producer(s): SilverPlatter (ClinMED-CD). *3163*

YEAR BOOK OF ONCOLOGY.
Mosby - Year Book, Inc., Continuity Division, 200 N. LaSalle, Chicago, IL 60601. TEL 312-726-9733. FAX 312-726-6075.
Producer(s): SilverPlatter. *3203*

ZEITUNGS - INDEX.
K.G. Saur Verlag KG, Ortlerstr. 8, Postfach 701620, 8000 Munich 70, Germany. TEL 089-76902-0. FAX 089-76902150. *2579*

Producer Listing/Serials On CD-ROM

AMERICAN PSYCHOLOGICAL ASSN.
750 First St., NE, Washington, DC 20002-4242.
Tel: 202-336-5769
Fax: 703-525-5081.
Psychological Abstracts.

BOWKER, R. R. (Subsidiary of: A Reed Reference Publishing Company)
121 Chanlon Rd., New Providence, NJ 07974.
Tel: 908-464-6800 Telex: 12-7703
Fax: 908-464-3553.
A S S I A.
American Book Trade Directory.
American Library Directory.
American Men and Women of Science.
Books in Print. (Books in Print PLUS)
Books in Print Plus. (Books in Print PLUS)
Books in Print Supplement. (Books in Print PLUS)
Books Out-of-Print. (Books Out-of-Print PLUS)
Books Out-of-Print Plus. (Books Out-of-Print PLUS)
British Humanities Index.
Children's Books in Print. (Books in Print PLUS)
Complete Directory of Large Print Books and Serials.
Corporate Technology Directory.
Current Technology Index.
Directory of American Research and Technology.
Energy Information Abstracts. (Enviro/Energyline Abstracts PLUS)
Energy Information Abstracts Annual. (Enviro/Energyline Abstracts PLUS)
Environment Abstracts. (Enviro/Energyline Abstracts PLUS)
Environment Abstracts Annual. (Enviro/Energyline Abstracts PLUS)
Forthcoming Books. (Books in Print PLUS)
Publishers, Distributors & Wholesalers of the United States.
Ulrich's International Periodicals Directory. (Ulrich's PLUS)
Ulrich's Plus. (Ulrich's PLUS)

CINAHL
Box 871, Glendale, CA 91209-0871.
1509 Wilson Terr., Glendale, CA 91209.
Tel: 818-409-8005   Fax: 818-546-5679.
Cumulative Index to Nursing & Allied Health Literature.

CAMBRIDGE SCIENTIFIC ABSTRACTS (Subsidiary of: Cambridge Information Group)
7200 Wisconsin Ave., Suite 601, Bethesda, MD 20814. Tel: 301-961-6750 Telex: 89-8452
Fax: 301-961-6720.
A S F A Aquaculture Abstracts. (Compact Cambridge ASFA)
A S F A Marine Biotechnology Abstracts. (Compact Cambridge Life Sciences Collection and Compact Cambridge ASFA)
Animal Behavior Abstracts. (Compact Cambridge Life Sciences Collection)
Aquatic Sciences & Fisheries Abstracts. Part 1: Biological Sciences and Living Resources. (Compact Cambridge ASFA)
Aquatic Sciences & Fisheries Abstracts. Part 2: Ocean Technology, Policy and Non-Living Resources. (Compact Cambridge ASFA)
Aquatic Sciences & Fisheries Abstracts. Part 3: Aquatic Pollution and Environmental Quality.
Biotechnology Research Abstracts. (Compact Cambridge Life Sciences Collection)
C S A Neurosciences Abstracts. (Compact Cambridge Life Sciences Collection)
Calcified Tissue Abstracts. (Compact Cambridge Life Sciences Collection)
Cambridge Scientific Biochemistry Abstracts: Part 1. Biological Membranes. (Compact Cambridge Life Sciences Collection)
Cambridge Scientific Biochemistry Abstracts: Part 2. Nucleic Acids. (Compact Cambridge Life Sciences Collection)
Cambridge Scientific Biochemistry Abstracts: Part 3. Amino-Acids, Peptides & Proteins. (Compact Cambridge Life Science Collection)
Chemoreception Abstracts. (Compact Cambridge Life Sciences Collection)
Ecology Abstracts. (Compact Cambridge Life Sciences Collection)
Entomology Abstracts. (Compact Cambridge Life Sciences Collection)
Genetics Abstracts. (Compact Cambridge Life Sciences Collection)
Health and Safety Science Abstracts.
Human Genome Abstracts. (Compact Cambridge Life Sciences Collection)
Immunology Abstracts. (Compact Cambridge Life Sciences Collection)
Index Medicus. (Compact Cambridge MEDLINE)
Index to Dental Literature. (Compact Cambridge MEDLINE)
International Nursing Index. (Compact Cambridge MEDLINE)
Microbiology Abstracts: Section A. Industrial & Applied Microbiology. (Compact Cambridge Life Sciences Collection)
Microbiology Abstracts: Section B. Bacteriology. (Compact Cambridge Life Sciences Collection)
Microbiology Abstracts: Section C. Algology, Mycology and Protozoology. (Compact Cambridge Life Sciences Collection)
Oncogenes and Growth Factors Abstracts. (Compact Cambridge Life Sciences Collection)
Pollution Abstracts. (Compact Cambridge Pol/Tox)
Toxicology Abstracts. (Compact Cambridge Life Sciences Collection and Compact Cambridge Pol/Tox)
Virology and A I D S Abstracts. (Compact Cambridge Life Sciences Collection)

DIALOG INFORMATION SERVICES, INC. (Subsidiary of: Knight-Ridder, Inc.)
3460 Hillview Ave., Palo Alto, CA 94304. Tel: 415-858-2700 Telex: 334499 DIALOG
Fax: 415-858-7069.
Alloys Index.
Canadian Business Index.
Canadian Magazine Index.
Canadian News Index.
C2C Abstracts: Japan - Analytical Chemistry.
C2C Abstracts: Japan - Ceramics.
C2C Abstracts: Japan - Chemical Engineering.
C2C Abstracts: Japan - Crystallography.
C2C Abstracts: Japan - Hydrocarbons.
C2C Abstracts: Japan - Inorganic Chemistry.
C2C Abstracts: Japan - Materials Science.
C2C Abstracts: Japan - Metals.
C2C Abstracts: Japan - Organic Chemistry.
C2C Abstracts: Japan - Physical Chemistry.
C2C Abstracts: Japan - Plastics.
C2C Abstracts: Japan - Polymer Chemistry.
C2C Abstracts: Japan - Surface Chemistry.
C2C Abstracts: Japan - Textiles.
C2C Currents: Japan - Chemistry.
C2C Currents: Japan - Computers.
C2C Currents: Japan - Electronics.
C2C Currents: Japan - Materials.
Directory of Research Grants.
Engineered Materials Abstracts.
Engineering Index Annual. (COMPENDEX PLUS CD-ROM)
Engineering Index Monthly. (COMPENDEX PLUS CD-ROM)
Hospital Product Comparison System.
Index Medicus. (DIALOG OnDisc MEDLINE)
Index to Dental Literature. (DIALOG OnDisc MEDLINE)
International Nursing Index. (DIALOG OnDisc MEDLINE)
Metals Abstracts.
Metals Abstracts Index.
N T I S Bibliographic Data Base.
New England Water Works Association. Journal.
Nonferrous Metals Alert.
Polymers, Ceramics, Composite Alert.
Resources in Education.
Steels Alert.

Thomas Register of American Manufacturers and Thomas Register Catalog File.
Environmental Nutrition.
National Review.
Excerpta Medica Abstract Journals. (Excerpta Medica Library Service)
Excerpta Medica. Section 1: Anatomy, Anthropology, Embryology & Histology.
Excerpta Medica. Section 2: Physiology.
Excerpta Medica. Section 3: Endocrinology.
Excerpta Medica. Section 4: Microbiology: Bacteriology, Mycology, Parasitology and Virology.
Excerpta Medica. Section 5: General Pathology and Pathological Anatomy.
Excerpta Medica. Section 6: Internal Medicine.
Excerpta Medica. Section 7: Pediatrics and Pediatric Surgery.
Excerpta Medica. Section 8: Neurology and Neurosurgery.
Excerpta Medica. Section 9: Surgery.
Excerpta Medica. Section 10: Obstetrics and Gynecology.
Excerpta Medica. Section 11: Otorhinolaryngology.
Excerpta Medica. Section 12: Ophthalmology.
Excerpta Medica. Section 13: Dermatology and Venereology.
Excerpta Medica. Section 14: Radiology.
Excerpta Medica. Section 15: Chest Diseases, Thoracic Surgery and Tuberculosis.
Excerpta Medica. Section 16: Cancer.
Excerpta Medica. Section 17: Public Health, Social Medicine & Epidemiology.
Excerpta Medica. Section 18: Cardiovascular Diseases and Cardiovascular Surgery.
Excerpta Medica. Section 19: Rehabilitation and Physical Medicine.
Excerpta Medica. Section 20: Gerontology and Geriatrics.
Excerpta Medica. Section 21: Developmental Biology and Teratology.
Excerpta Medica. Section 22: Human Genetics.
Excerpta Medica. Section 23: Nuclear Medicine.
Excerpta Medica. Section 24: Anesthesiology.
Excerpta Medica. Section 25: Hematology.
Excerpta Medica. Section 26: Immunology, Serology and Transplantation.
Excerpta Medica. Section 27: Biophysics, Bio-Engineering and Medical Instrumentation.
Excerpta Medica. Section 28: Urology and Nephrology.
Excerpta Medica. Section 29: Clinical and Experimental Biochemistry.
Excerpta Medica. Section 30: Clinical and Experimental Pharmacology.
Excerpta Medica. Section 31: Arthritis and Rheumatism.
Excerpta Medica. Section 32: Psychiatry.
Excerpta Medica. Section 33: Orthopedic Surgery.
Excerpta Medica. Section 35: Occupational Health and Industrial Medicine.
Excerpta Medica. Section 36: Health Policy, Economics and Management.
Excerpta Medica. Section 38: Adverse Reactions Titles.
Excerpta Medica. Section 40: Drug Dependence, Alcohol Abuse and Alcoholism.
Excerpta Medica. Section 46: Environmental Health and Pollution Control.
Excerpta Medica. Section 48: Gastroenterology.
Excerpta Medica. Section 49: Forensic Science Abstracts.
Excerpta Medica. Section 50: Epilepsy Abstracts.
Excerpta Medica. Section 52: Toxicology.
Film & Video Finder.
Food Science and Technology Abstracts. (COMPU-INFO)

I N I S Atomindex. (INIS)
Index Medicus. (MEDLINE)
Index to Dental Literature. (MEDLINE)
International Nursing Index. (MEDLINE)
International Pharmaceutical Abstracts.
Journal of Economic Literature.
Kompass Italia.
Mathematical Reviews. (MathDisc)
Monthly Catalog of United States Government Publications.
N T I S Bibliographic Data Base.
P A I S International in Print.
Peterson's Guide to Graduate and Professional Programs: An Overview (Year) (Book 1). (PETERSON'S GRADLINE)
Peterson's Guide to Graduate Programs in Business, Education, Health, and Law (Year) (Book 6). (PETERSON'S GRADLINE)
Peterson's Guide to Graduate Programs in Engineering and Applied Sciences (Year) (Book 5). (PETERSON'S GRADLINE)
Peterson's Guide to Graduate Programs in the Biological and Agricultural Sciences (Year) (Book 3). (PETERSON'S GRADLINE)
Peterson's Guide to Graduate Programs in the Humanities and Social Sciences (Year) (Book 2). (PETERSON'S GRADLINE)
Peterson's Guide to Graduate Programs in the Physical Sciences and Mathematics (Year) (Book 4). (PETERSON'S GRADLINE)
Population Index.
Psychological Abstracts. (PsycLIT)
Registry of Toxic Effects of Chemical Substances.
Resources in Education. (ERIC)
Safety and Health at Work.
Schweizerische Zeitschrift fuer Volkswirtschaft und Statistik.
Securite et Sante au Travail.
Side Effects of Drugs Annual. (SEDBASE)
Social Planning - Policy & Development Abstracts.
Sociological Abstracts.
SportSearch.
Ulster Medical Journal. (MEDLINE)
Vaard i Norden.
Year Book of Cardiology. (ClinMED-CD)
Year Book of Critical Care Medicine. (ClinMED-CD)
Year Book of Oncology.

DUN & BRADSTREET INFORMATION SERVICES
(Subsidiary of: Dun & Bradstreet Corp.)
899 Eaton Ave., Bethlehem, PA 18025.
Tel: 215- 882-7000
Fax: 201-605-6911.
Million Dollar Directory Series.
Current Index to Journals in Education.
N T I S Bibliographic Data Base.
Resources in Education.
Selected Water Resources Abstracts.

INSTITUTE FOR SCIENTIFIC INFORMATION
3501 Market St., Philadelphia, PA 19104.
Tel: 215-386-0100 Telex: 845305
Fax: 215-386-6362.
Arts & Humanities Citation Index. (A&HCI/CDE)
Science Citation Index. (SCI CDE)
Social Sciences Citation Index. (SSCI)

PUBLIC AFFAIRS INFORMATION SERVICE, INC.
521 W. 43rd St., New York, NY 10036-4396.
Tel: 212-736-6629 Telex: 4909991777
Fax: 212-643-2848.
P A I S International in Print. (PAIS)

SAUR K. G. (Subsidiary of: R. R. Bowker)
121 Chanlon Rd., New Providence, NJ 07974.
Tel: 908-665-2828
Fax: 908-665-6707.
Publishers' International I S B N Directory.

SILVERPLATTER INFORMATION, INC.
1 Newton Executive Pk., Newton Lower Falls, MA 02162. Tel: 617-969-2332
Fax: 617-969-5554.
Bibliography and Index of Geology. (GeoRef)
Bibliography of Agriculture.
Biological Abstracts.
Cumulative Index to Nursing & Allied Health Literature.
Current Index to Journals in Education. (ERIC)
Current Mathematical Publications. (MathDisc)

SOCIOLOGICAL ABSTRACTS, INC.
Box 22206, San Diego, CA 92122-0206.
Tel: 619-695-8803
Fax: 619-695-0416.
Social Planning - Policy & Development Abstracts. (SocioFile)
Sociological Abstracts. (SocioFile)

UNIVERSITY MICROFILMS INTERNATIONAL
300 N. Zeeb Rd., Ann Arbor, MI 48106.
Tel: 313-761-4700
Fax: 313-761-1203.
A B I - INFORM.
American Doctoral Dissertations.
American Hospital Formulary Service Drug Information.
American Journal of International Law.
Dissertation Abstracts.
Dissertation Abstracts International. Section A: Humanities and Social Sciences.
Dissertation Abstracts International. Section B: Physical Sciences and Engineering.
Dissertation Abstracts International. Section C: Worldwide.
Journal of Higher Education.
Journal of Money, Credit & Banking.
Masters Abstracts International.

WILSON, H. W.
950 University Ave., Bronx, NY 10452.
Tel: 718- 588-8400 Cable: WILSONDEX
Fax: 212-590-1617.
Applied Science and Technology Index.
Art Index. (WILSONDISC)
Biography Index. (WILSONDISC)
Biological & Agricultural Index. (WILSONDISC)
Book Review Digest. (WILSONDISC)
Business Periodicals Index. (WILSONDISC)
Cumulative Book Index.
Education Index. (WILSONDISC)
Essay and General Literature Index. (WILSONDISC)
General Science Index. (WILSONDISC)
Humanities Index. (WILSONDISC)
Index to Legal Periodicals. (WILSONDISC)
Index to U.S. Government Periodicals.
Library Literature. (WILSONDISC)
M L A International Bibliography of Books and Articles on the Modern Languages and Literatures.
Monthly Catalog of United States Government Publications.
Readers' Guide Abstracts. Microfiche Edition.
Readers' Guide to Periodical Literature. (WILSONDISC)
Social Sciences Index.

Serials Available Online

This index contains abbreviated entries for all serials known to be available online. Vendor names are given if known, plus file names or numbers in parentheses. For full bibliographic information on these titles, please refer to the complete entry on the page indicated in italics.

A B A BANKING JOURNAL.
Simmons-Boardman Publishing Corporation, 345 Hudson St., New York, NY 10014-4502. TEL 212-620-7200. FAX 212-633-1165.
Vendor(s): BRS (TSAP), DIALOG (File no.648), Dow Jones/News Retrieval, Mead Data Central. *757*

A B A JOURNAL.
American Bar Association, 750 N. Lake Shore Dr., Chicago, IL 60611. TEL 312-988-5000. FAX 312-988-6014.
Vendor(s): Mead Data Central, WESTLAW. *2592*

A B A WASHINGTON LETTER.
American Bar Association, Governmental Affairs Office, 1800 M St., N.W., Washington, DC 20036. TEL 202-331-2609. *2592*

A B B REVIEW.
A B B Marketing Services Ltd., Ruetistr. 6, CH-5401 Baden, Switzerland. TEL 04156-751111. FAX 04156-212274.
Vendor(s): Data-Star, DIALOG. *1880*

A B C DER DEUTSCHEN WIRTSCHAFT.
A B C Publishing Group, P.O. Box 4034, D-6100 Darmstadt 1, Germany. TEL 6151-33411. FAX 6151-33164.
Vendor(s): Data-Star, FIZ Technik. *1119*

A B C EUROP PRODUCTION - EUROPEX.
A B C Publishing Group, P.O. Box 4034, D-6100 Darmstadt 1, Germany. TEL 6151-33411. FAX 6151-33164.
Vendor(s): Data-Star, FIZ Technik. *899*

A B I - INFORM.
University Microfilms International, Data Courier, 620 S. Third St., Louisville, KY 40202-2475. TEL 800-626-2823. FAX 502-589-5572.
Vendor(s): BRS (INFO), BRS/Saunders Colleague, Data-Star (INFO), DIALOG (File no.15), European Space Agency (File no.30), Human Resources Information Network (ETSI-HRIN), Mead Data Central (ABI), Orbit Information Technologies (INFORM). *701*

A C M GUIDE TO COMPUTING LITERATURE.
Association for Computing Machinery, 1515 Broadway, 17th Fl., New York, NY 10036. TEL 212-869-7440. FAX 212-869-0481.
Vendor(s): DIALOG. *1402*

A D R I D.
Paul De Haen International, 2750 S. Shoshone St., Englewood, CO 80110. TEL 800-438-0296. FAX 303-789-2534.
Vendor(s): DIALOG. *3715*

A E S I S QUARTERLY.
Australian Mineral Foundation, 63 Conyngham St., Glenside, S.A. 5065, Australia. TEL 08 379 0444. FAX 08-3794634. *1549*

A F L - C I O NEWS.
American Federation of Labor - Congress of Industrial Organizations, 815 16th St., N.W., Washington, DC 20006. TEL 202-637-5032. FAX 202-637-5058.
Vendor(s): DIALOG. *2579*

A I D S NEWSLETTER.
Bureau of Hygiene and Tropical Diseases, Keppel St., London WC1E 7HT, England. TEL 071-636-8636. FAX 071-580-6756.
Vendor(s): DIMDI. *3217*

A I D S POLICY AND LAW.
Buraff Publications 1350 Connecticut Ave. N.W., Ste. 1000, Washington, DC 20036. TEL 202-862-0990. FAX 202-822-8092.
Vendor(s): Human Resources Information Network (Files CDD, HDD). *3217*

A I EXPERT.
Miller Freeman, Inc. 600 Harrison St., San Francisco, CA 94107. TEL 415-905-2200. FAX 415-905-2232.
Vendor(s): DIALOG (File no.675), Mead Data Central (AIEXPT). *1406*

A I M REPORT.
Accuracy in Media, Inc., 1275 K St., N.W., Ste. 1150, Washington, DC 20005. TEL 202-371-6710. FAX 202-371-9054. *2566*

A J D C: AMERICAN JOURNAL OF DISEASES OF CHILDREN.
American Medical Association, 515 N. State St., Chicago, IL 60610. TEL 312-464-0183. FAX 312-464-5834.
Vendor(s): Mead Data Central. *3317*

A J R.
Williams & Wilkins, 428 E. Preston St., Baltimore, MD 21202. TEL 301-528-4000. FAX 301-528-4312. *3356*

A L C T S NETWORK NEWS.
American Library Association, Association for Library Collections & Technical Services, 50 E. Huron St., Chicago, IL 60611-2759. TEL 312-280-5035. FAX 312-280-3257.
Available only online. *2796*

A L I S A.
Australian Clearing House for Library & Information Science, Library, S.A.C.A.E., Lorne Ave., Magill, S. Aust. 5072, Australia. TEL 08 3339457. FAX 61-8-3326122.
Vendor(s): AUSINET. *2792*

A M P S BLACK RADIO AND TELEVISION DIARY.
S A Advertising Research Foundation, P.O. Box 78335, 2146 Sandton, South Africa. TEL 27-11-783-7560. FAX 27-11-783-7579. *40*

A M P S METER WEEKLY REPORTS.
S A Advertising Research Foundation, P.O. Box 78335, 2146 Sandton, South Africa. TEL 27-11-783-7560. FAX 27-11-783-7579. *40*

A M P S WHITE - COLOURED - ASIAN RADIO DIARY.
S A Advertising Research Foundation, P.O. Box 78335, 2146 Sandton, South Africa. TEL 011-783-7560. FAX 783-7579. *1346*

A M R E P DATABASE BULLETIN.
Australian Mineral Resource Politics Pty. Ltd., 10 Hampstead Hill Rd., Aldgate, S.A. 5154, Australia. TEL 8 339 2960. *3477*

A O A C INTERNATIONAL JOURNAL.
A O A C International, 2200 Wilson Blvd., Ste. 400, Arlington, VA 22201-3301. TEL 703-522-3032. FAX 703-522-5468.
Vendor(s): STN International (CJAOAC). *1203*

A P A I S: AUSTRALIAN PUBLIC AFFAIRS INFORMATION SERVICE.
National Library of Australia, Publications Section, Public Programs, Parkes Place, Canberra, A.C.T. 2600, Australia. TEL 06-262-1365. FAX 06-273-4493. *4078*

A P F REPORTER.
Alicia Patterson Foundation, 1001 Pennsylvania Ave., N.W., Ste. 1250, Washington, DC 20004. TEL 202-393-5995. FAX 301-951-8512.
Vendor(s): DIALOG. *2566*

A S F A AQUACULTURE ABSTRACTS.
Cambridge Scientific Abstracts, 7200 Wisconsin Ave., 6th Fl., Bethesda, MD 20814. TEL 301-961-6750. FAX 301-961-6720.
Vendor(s): BRS (CSAL), CISTI, DIMDI, DIALOG (File no.44), European Space Agency. *2050*

A S F A MARINE BIOTECHNOLOGY ABSTRACTS.
Cambridge Scientific Abstracts, 7200 Wisconsin Ave., 6th Fl., Bethesda, MD 20814. TEL 301-961-6750. FAX 301-961-6720.
Vendor(s): BRS (CSAL), DIALOG (File no. 44 and 76), European Space Agency. *1549*

5046 SERIALS AVAILABLE ONLINE

A S S I A.
Bowker-Saur Ltd., 59-60 Grosvenor St., London W1X 9DA, England. TEL 071-493-5841. FAX 071-499-1590.
Vendor(s): Data-Star (ASSI). *4394*

A S T I S BIBLIOGRAPHY.
Arctic Science & Technology Information System, Arctic Institute of North America, University of Calgary, 2500 University Dr. N.W., Calgary, Alta. T2N 1N4, Canada. TEL 403-220-4036.
Vendor(s): QL Systems Ltd.. *1549*

A S T I S CURRENT AWARENESS BULLETIN.
Arctic Science & Technology Information System, Arctic Institute of North America, University of Calgary, 2500 University Dr. N.W., Calgary, Alta. T2N 1N4, Canada. TEL 403-284-7515.
Vendor(s): QL Systems Ltd.. *4613*

A S T I S OCCASIONAL PUBLICATIONS.
Arctic Science & Technology Information System, Arctic Institute of North America, University of Calgary, Calgary, Alta. T2N 1N4, Canada. TEL 403-220-4036. FAX 403-282-4609.
Vendor(s): QL Systems Ltd.. *388*

ABRIDGED READERS' GUIDE TO PERIODICAL LITERATURE.
H.W. Wilson Co., 950 University Ave., Bronx, NY 10452. TEL 800-367-6770.
Vendor(s): BRS, BRS/Saunders Colleague, Wilsonline. *1*

ABSATZWIRTSCHAFT.
Handelsblatt GmbH, Kasernenstr. 67, Postfach 102717, 4000 Duesseldorf 1, Germany. TEL 0211-8870. *1032*

ABSTRACTS AND REVIEWS FROM ZENTRALBLATT FUER MATHEMATIK.
Fachinformationszentrum Karlsruhe, D-7514 Eggenstein-Leopoldshafen, Germany. TEL 030-2611585. *3062*

ABSTRACTS IN BIOCOMMERCE.
BioCommerce Data Ltd., Prudential Bldg., 95 High St., Slough, Berks. SL1 1DH, England. TEL 0753-511777. FAX 0753-512239.
Vendor(s): Data-Star (CELL), DIALOG (File no.286). *701*

ABSTRACTS IN MEDICINE AND KEY WORD INDEX.
Medical Information Systems, Reference & Index Services, Inc., 3951 N. Meridian St., Ste. 100, Indianapolis, IN 46208-4011. TEL 317-923-1575.
Vendor(s): DIALOG (File 219). *3165*

ABSTRACTS ON HYGIENE AND COMMUNICABLE DISEASES.
Bureau of Hygiene and Tropical Diseases, Keppel St., London WC1E 7HT, England. TEL 071-636-8636. FAX 071-580-6756.
Vendor(s): DIMDI. *3165*

ABSTRACTS ON TROPICAL AGRICULTURE.
Koninklijk Instituut voor de Tropen, Mauritskade 63, 1092 AD Amsterdam, Netherlands. TEL 020-5688290. FAX 020-5688444.
Vendor(s): Orbit Information Technologies (TROPAG). *132*

ACADEMIC ABSTRACTS C D - R O M.
EBSCO Publishing, Box 325, Topsfield, MA 01983. TEL 800-221-1826. FAX 508-887-3923.
Vendor(s): BRS. *2*

ACADEMIC INDEX.
Information Access Company, 362 Lakeside Dr., Foster City, CA 94404. TEL 800-227-8431. FAX 415-378-5499.
Vendor(s): BRS (ACAD), DIALOG (File no.88), Information Access Company. *2519*

ACADEMY OF MARKETING SCIENCE. JOURNAL.
J A I Press Inc., 55 Old Post Rd., No. 2, Box 1678, Greenwich, CT 06836-1678. TEL 305-284-6673.
Vendor(s): DIALOG. *1032*

ACADEMY OF MEDICINE, SINGAPORE. ANNALS.
Academy of Medicine, Singapore, 16 College Road, 01-01 College of Medicine Bldg., Singapore 0316, Singapore. TEL 2245166. FAX 2255155.
Vendor(s): National Library of Medicine. *3069*

ACCENT ON LIVING.
Cheever Publishing, Inc., Box 700, Bloomington, IL 61702. TEL 309-378-2961. FAX 309-378-4420.
Vendor(s): DIALOG (File no.149). *1733*

ACCESS: THE SUPPLEMENTARY INDEX TO PERIODICALS.
John Gordon Burke Publisher, Inc., Box 1492, Evanston, IL 60204-1492. TEL 708-866-8625. *2*

ACCOUNTANCY.
Institute of Chartered Accountants in England and Wales, P.O. Box 433, Moorgate Place, London EC2P 2BJ, England. *745*

ACCOUNTANCY AGE.
V N U Business Publications BV, 32-34 Broadwick St., London W1A 2HG, England. *745*

ACCOUNTANTS' INDEX.
American Institute of Certified Public Accountants, 1211 Ave. of the Americas, New York, NY 10036-8775. TEL 212-575-5515.
Vendor(s): Orbit Information Technologies (ACCOUNTANTS). *702*

ACCOUNTS OF CHEMICAL RESEARCH.
American Chemical Society, 1155 16th St., N.W., Washington, DC 20036. TEL 800-227-5558. FAX 202-872-4615.
Vendor(s): STN International (CJACS). *1168*

ACKNOWLEDGE THE WINDOW LETTER.
Mendham Technology Group, 144 Talmadge Rd., Box 11, Mendham, NJ 07945. TEL 201-543-2273. FAX 201-543-6033.
Vendor(s): Information Access Company. *1458*

ACROSS THE BOARD.
Conference Board, Inc., 845 Third Ave., New York, NY 10022. TEL 212-759-0900. FAX 212-980-7014. *1001*

ACTA PHARMACEUTICA HUNGARICA.
Magyar Gyogyszereszeti Tarsasag, Hogyes E. U. 4, 1092 Budapest, Hungary. FAX 1-1473-973. *3715*

ACTA PHARMACEUTICA JUGOSLAVICA.
Savez Farmaceutskih Drustava Jugoslavije, Masary Kova 2, 41000 Zagreb, Croatia. FAX 041-431-301. *3715*

ACTUALIDAD ECONOMICA.
Punto Editorial, S.A., Recoletos 1, 7o, 28001 Madrid, Spain. TEL 91-4310917. *842*

ACTUALITES PHARMACEUTIQUES.
S.U.T.I.P., 175 rue du Faubourg Poissonniere, 75009 Paris, France. FAX 42-82-98-00. *3715*

ADHESIVES ABSTRACTS.
R A P R A Technology Ltd., Shawbury, Shrewsbury, Shropshire SY4 4NR, England. TEL 0938-250383. FAX 0939-251118.
Vendor(s): Orbit Information Technologies. *1191*

ADHESIVES AGE.
Communication Channels, Inc., 6255 Barfield Rd., Atlanta, GA 30328-4369. TEL 404-256-9800. FAX 404-256-3116. *1847*

ADMAP.
Reed Business Publishing Group, 7-11 St. John's Hill, London SW11 1TE, England. TEL 071-228-3344. FAX 071-978-4393. *26*

ADMINISTRATIVE MANAGEMENT (NEW YORK).
Dalton Communications, Inc., 1123 Broadway, Ste. 1100, New York, NY 10010.
Vendor(s): DIALOG. *1001*

ADMINISTRATIVE SCIENCE QUARTERLY.
Cornell University, Johnson Graduate School of Management, 425 Caldwell Hall, Ithaca, NY 14853-2602. TEL 607-255-5581. FAX 607-255-7524.
Vendor(s): BRS, DIALOG, Dow Jones/News Retrieval, Information Access Company. *4052*

ADVANCED CERAMICS REPORT.
Elsevier Science Publishers Ltd., Crown House, Linton Rd., Barking, Essex IG11 8JU, England. TEL 081-594-7272. FAX 081-594-5942.
Vendor(s): Data-Star (PTBN), DIALOG (File no.636). *1160*

ADVANCED COATINGS & SURFACE TECHNOLOGY.
Technical Insights, Inc., 32 N. Dean St., Englewood, NJ 07631. TEL 201-568-4744. FAX 201-568-8247.
Vendor(s): Data-Star (PTBN), DIALOG (File no.636), NewsNet (RD26). *1203*

ADVANCED COMPOSITES BULLETIN.
Elsevier Science Publishers Ltd., Crown House, Linton Rd., Barking, Essex IG11 8JU, England. TEL 081-594-7272. FAX 081-594-5942.
Vendor(s): Data-Star (PTBN), DIALOG (File no.636). *3861*

ADVANCED MANUFACTURING TECHNOLOGY.
Technical Insights, Inc., 32 N. Dean St., Englewood, NJ 07631. TEL 201-568-4744. FAX 201-568-8247.
Vendor(s): Data-Star, DIALOG, Mead Data Central, NewsNet. *1411*

ADVANCED RECOVERY WEEK.
Pasha Publications Inc., 1401 Wilson Blvd., Ste. 900, Arlington, VA 22209-9970. TEL 703-528-1244. FAX 703-528-1253.
Vendor(s): Data-Star, DIALOG, Mead Data Central. *1783*

ADVANCED WIRELESS COMMUNICATION.
Capitol Publications Inc., Telecom Publishing Group, 1101 King St., Ste. 444, Box 1455, Alexandria, VA 22313-2055. TEL 800-327-7205. FAX 703-739-6490.
Vendor(s): Information Access Company, NewsNet. *1361*

ADVANCES IN PHARMACEUTICAL SCIENCES.
Academic Press, Inc., 1250 Sixth Ave., San Diego, CA 92101. TEL 619-231-0926. FAX 619-699-6715. *3715*

ADVERTISING AGE.
Crain Communications, Inc. (New York), 220 E. 42nd St., New York, NY 10017-5806. TEL 212-210-0100. FAX 212-210-0200.
Vendor(s): Mead Data Central (ADAGE). *27*

ADWEEK (LOS ANGELES).
A S M Communications, Inc. (Los Angeles), 5757 Wilshire Blvd., Ste. M110, Los Angeles, CA 90036. TEL 213-937-4330. FAX 213-938-4160.
Vendor(s): BRS (TSAP), DIALOG (File no.648). *27*

ADWEEK (NEW YORK).
B P I Communications, Inc. (New York), 49 E. 21st St., New York, NY 10010. TEL 212-529-5500.
Vendor(s): BRS (TSAP), DIALOG (File no.648), Mead Data Central. *27*

ADWEEK: SOUTHEAST.
A S M Communications, Inc. (Atlanta), 6 Piedmont Center, Ste. 300, Atlanta, GA 30305. TEL 404-841-3333.
Vendor(s): Mead Data Central. *27*

ADWEEK'S MARKETING WEEK.
B P I Communications, Inc. (New York), 49 E. 21st St., New York, NY 10010. TEL 212-529-5500. FAX 212-260-7919.
Vendor(s): BRS (TSAP), DIALOG (File no.648). *27*

AERA.
Asahi Shimbunsha - Asahi Shimbun Publishing Co., 3-2 Tsukiji 5-chome, Chuo-ku, Tokyo 104-11, Japan. *2207*

AEROSPACE AMERICA.
American Institute of Aeronautics and Astronautics, Inc., 370 L'Enfant Promenade, S.W., Washington, DC 20024. TEL 202-646-7471. FAX 202-646-7508.
Vendor(s): Mead Data Central (AEROAM). *44*

AEROSPACE DAILY.
McGraw-Hill, Inc., Aviation Week Group, 1156 15th St., N.W., Washington, DC 20005. TEL 202-822-4600.
Vendor(s): BRS (TSAP), DIALOG (File nos.624,648), Dow Jones/News Retrieval, European Space Agency (File no.72/AEROSPACE DAILY), Mead Data Central (AIRDLY). *44*

AEROSPACE FINANCIAL NEWS.
Phillips Publishing, Inc., Defense - Aviation Group, 1925 N. Lynn St., Ste. 1000, Arlington, VA 22209. TEL 703-522-8333. FAX 703-522-8334.
Vendor(s): Data-Star, DIALOG, NewsNet. *3449*

AEROSPACE PROPULSION.
McGraw-Hill, Inc., Aviation Week Group, 1156 15th St., N.W., Washington, DC 20005. TEL 202-822-4600. *44*

LES AFFAIRES.
Publications Transcontinental Inc., 465 St. Jean St., 9th Fl., Montreal, Que. H2Y 3S4, Canada. TEL 514-842-3131. FAX 514-842-6910. *758*

AFFLUENT MARKETS ALERT.
Alert Publishing, Inc., 37-06 30th Ave., Long Island City, NY 11103-3808. TEL 718-626-3356.
Vendor(s): Data-Star, DIALOG, NewsNet. *1502*

AFRICA ECONOMIC DIGEST.
Concord Press of Nigeria, 26-32 Whistler St., London N5 1NJ, England. TEL 071-359-5335. FAX 071-359-9173. *842*

AFRICA NEWS.
Africa News Service, Inc., Box 3851, Durham, NC 27702. TEL 919-286-0747. FAX 919-286-2614.
Vendor(s): NewsNet (IT15). *3870*

AFRICAN BUSINESS.
I.C. Publications Ltd., Box 261, Carlton House, 69 Gt. Queen St., London WC2B 5BN, England. TEL 071-404-4333. FAX 071-404-5336. *925*

AFTERMARKET BUSINESS.
Avanstar Communications, Inc., 7500 Old Oak Blvd., Cleveland, OH 44130. TEL 216-826-2839. FAX 216-891-2726.
Vendor(s): DIALOG. *4679*

AGE AND AGEING.
Oxford University Press, Oxford Journals, Pinkhill House, Southfield Road, Eynsham, Oxford OX8 1JJ, England. TEL 0865-882283. FAX 0865-882890.
Vendor(s): BRS. *2269*

AGGRESSIVE BEHAVIOR.
John Wiley & Sons, Inc., Journals, 605 Third Ave., New York, NY 10158. TEL 212-850-6000. FAX 212-850-6088. *4009*

AGING RESEARCH & TRAINING NEWS.
Business Publishers, Inc., 951 Pershing Dr., Silver Spring, MD 20910-4464. TEL 301-587-6300. FAX 301-585-9075.
Vendor(s): NewsNet. *2270*

AGRA EUROPE.
Agra Europe (London) Ltd., 25 Frant Rd., Tunbridge Wells, Kent TN2 5JT, England. TEL 44-892-533813. FAX 44-892-544895. *145*

AGRIBUSINESS WORLDWIDE.
Sosland Publishing Company, 4800 Main St., Ste. 100, Kansas City, MO 64112. TEL 816-756-1000. FAX 816-756-0494.
Vendor(s): BRS (TSAP), DIALOG (File no.648). *146*

AGRICULTURAL ENGINEERING ABSTRACTS.
C.A.B. International, Walingford, Oxon OX10 8DE, England. TEL 0491 32111.
Vendor(s): BRS (CABA), CISTI, DIMDI, DIALOG, European Space Agency (File nos.16 & 124/CAB). *132*

AGRICULTURAL RESEARCH DEPARTMENT. WINAND STARING CENTRE FOR INTEGRATED LAND, SOIL AND WATER RESEARCH. REPORTS.
Dienst Landbouwkundig Onderzoek, P.O. Box 125, 6700 AC Wageningen, Netherlands. TEL 08370-74200. FAX 08370-24812. *166*

AGRICULTURAL STATISTICS SERIES NO.2: ANIMAL PRODUCTION.
Statistical Office of the European Communities, L-2985 Luxembourg, Luxembourg. TEL 43011. *132*

AGRICULTURAL SUPPLY INDUSTRY.
Veratbrite Ltd., Chatham House, 115 Widmore Rd., Bromley, Kent BR1 3AH, England. TEL 081-3133134. FAX 081-4665045.
Vendor(s): BRS (TSAP), DIALOG (File no.648). *72*

AGRINDEX.
Food and Agriculture Organization of the United Nations, c/o UNIPUB, 4611-F Assembly Dr., Lanham, MD 20706-4391. FAX 301-459-0056.
Vendor(s): DIMDI, DIALOG (File no.203), European Space Agency (File no.29/AGRIS). *73*

AGROCHEMICALS HANDBOOK.
Royal Society of Chemistry, Thomas Graham House, Science Park, Milton Rd., Cambridge CB4 4WF, England. TEL 0462-672555. FAX 0462-480947.
Vendor(s): Data-Star, DIALOG (File no.306). *73*

AGROFORESTRY ABSTRACTS.
C.A.B. International, Wallingford, Oxon OX10 8DE, England. TEL 0491-32111. FAX 0491-33508.
Vendor(s): BRS, DIMDI, Data-Star, DIALOG, European Space Agency, STN International. *2111*

AGROINDEX - AUTOMATED INFORMATION SYSTEM.
Ustav Vedeckotechnickych Informaci pro Zemedelstvi, Slezska 7, 120 56 Prague 2, Czechoslovakia. TEL 257541. FAX 257090.
Vendor(s): DIALOG. *132*

AGROW.
P J B Publications Ltd., 18-20 Hill Rise, Richmond, Surrey TW10 6UA, England. TEL 081-948-3262. FAX 081-948-6866.
Vendor(s): BRS, Data-Star, DIALOG. *75*

AIR CARGO WORLD.
Communication Channels, Inc., 6255 Barfield Rd., Atlanta, GA 30328-4369. TEL 404-256-9800. FAX 404-256-3116. *4669*

AIR CONDITIONING, HEATING & REFRIGERATION NEWS.
Business News Publishing Co., Box 2600, Troy, MI 48007. TEL 313-362-3700. FAX 313-362-0317.
Vendor(s): BRS (TSAP), DIALOG (File no.648), Dow Jones/News Retrieval. *2297*

AIR SAFETY WEEK.
Phillips Publishing, Inc., Defense - Aviation Group, 1925 N. Lynn St., Ste. 1000, Arlington, VA 22209. TEL 703-522-8333. FAX 703-522-8334.
Vendor(s): Data-Star, DIALOG, NewsNet. *45*

AIR TOXICS REPORTS.
Business Publishers, Inc., 951 Pershing Dr., Silver Spring, MD 20910-4464. TEL 301-587-6300. FAX 301-585-9075.
Vendor(s): NewsNet. *1942*

AIR TRANSPORT WORLD.
Penton Publishing (Stamford) 600 Summer St., Box 1361, Stamford, CT 06904. TEL 203-348-7531. FAX 203-348-4023.
Vendor(s): DIALOG. *45*

AIR - WATER POLLUTION REPORT.
Business Publishers, Inc., 951 Pershing Dr., Silver Spring, MD 20910-4464. TEL 301-587-6300. FAX 301-585-9075.
Vendor(s): Data-Star, DIALOG, NewsNet. *1942*

AIRLINE BUSINESS.
Reed Business Publishing Group (London) 151 Wardour St., London W1V 4BN, England. TEL 081-661-3500.
Vendor(s): Data-Star, Mead Data Central. *4670*

AIRLINE EXECUTIVE INTERNATIONAL.
Communication Channels, Inc., 6255 Barfield Rd., Atlanta, GA 30328-4369. TEL 404-256-9800. FAX 404-256-3116. *4670*

AIRLINE FINANCIAL NEWS.
Phillips Publishing, Inc., Defense - Aviation Group, 1925 N. Lynn St., Ste. 1000, Arlington, VA 22209. TEL 703-522-8333. FAX 703-522-8334.
Vendor(s): Data-Star, DIALOG, NewsNet. *4670*

AIRPORTS.
McGraw-Hill, Inc., Aviation Week Group, 1156 15th St., N.W., Washington, DC 20005. TEL 202-822-4600.
Vendor(s): DIALOG (File no.624/McGRAW-HILL PULICATIONS ONLINE), Dow Jones/News Retrieval, Mead Data Central, NewsNet. *4671*

ALABAMA LAW REVIEW.
University of Alabama, School of Law, Box 870382, University, AL 35487-0382. TEL 205-348-7191.
Vendor(s): WESTLAW. *2596*

ALABAMA LAWYER.
State Bar of Alabama, Lock Box 4156, Montgomery, AL 36101. TEL 205-269-1515.
Vendor(s): WESTLAW. *2596*

SERIALS AVAILABLE ONLINE 5047

ALASKA BUSINESS MONTHLY.
Alaska Business Publishing Co., Box 241288, Anchorage, AK 99524-1288. TEL 907-276-4373. FAX 907-279-2900.
Vendor(s): DIALOG. *644*

ALASKA JOURNAL OF COMMERCE & PACIFIC RIM REPORTER.
Pacific Rim Publishing Co., Box 201894, Anchorage, AK 99520-1894. TEL 907-272-7500. FAX 907-279-1037.
Vendor(s): DIALOG. *833*

ALASKA SNOW SURVEYS - BASIN OUTLOOK REPORTS.
U.S. Soil Conservation Service (Anchorage), 201 E. 9th Ave., No. 300, Anchorage, AK 99501-3687. TEL 907-271-2424. FAX 907-868-2424. *4821*

ALBERTA DECISIONS, CIVIL AND CRIMINAL CASES.
Western Legal Publications, 301-1 Alexander St., Vancouver, B.C. V6A 1B2, Canada. TEL 604-687-5671. FAX 604-687-2796. *2596*

ALBERTA REPORTS.
Maritime Law Book Ltd., Box 302, Fredericton, N.B. E3B 4Y9, Canada. TEL 506-454-9921.
Vendor(s): QL Systems Ltd.. *2596*

ALL CANADA WEEKLY SUMMARIES - NATIONAL.
Canada Law Book Inc., 240 Edward St., Aurora, Ont. L4G 3S9, Canada. TEL 416-841-6472. *2596*

ALL ENGLAND LAW REPORTS.
Butterworth & Co. (Publishers) Ltd. 88 Kingsway, London WC2B 6AB, England. TEL 71-405-6900. FAX 71-405-1332.
Vendor(s): Mead Data Central. *2597*

ALL MEDIA & PRODUCT SURVEY.
S A Advertising Research Foundation, P.O. Box 78335, 2146 Sandton, South Africa. TEL 11-783-7560. FAX 11-783-7579. *40*

ALLIANCE ALERT.
Venture Economics, Inc., 11 Farnsworth St., Boston, MA 02210-1223. TEL 617-449-2100. FAX 617-449-7660.
Vendor(s): Data-Star, DIALOG. *938*

ALLOYS INDEX.
A S M International, Materials Information, Materials Park, OH 44073. TEL 216-338-5151. FAX 216-338-4634.
Vendor(s): CEDOCAR, CISTI, Data-Star (META), DIALOG (File no.32/METADEX), European Space Agency (File no.3), FIZ Technik (META), Orbit Information Technologies (METADEX), STN International. *3424*

ALMANAC OF FAMOUS PEOPLE.
Gale Research Inc., 835 Penobscot Bldg., Detroit, MI 48226. TEL 313-961-2242. FAX 313 961 6083.
Vendor(s): Mead Data Central. *417*

ALTERNATIVE ENERGY DIGESTS.
International Academy at Santa Barbara, 800 Garden St., Ste. D, Santa Barbara, CA 93101. TEL 805-965-5010.
Vendor(s): Data-Star, DIALOG. *1783*

AMERICA: HISTORY AND LIFE. ARTICLES ABSTRACT AND CITATIONS OF REVIEWS AND DISSERTATIONS COVERING THE UNITED STATES AND CANADA.
A B C-Clio, 130 Cremona, Box 1911, Santa Barbara, CA 93116-1911. TEL 805-968-1911. FAX 805-685-9685.
Vendor(s): DIALOG (File no.38). *2327*

AMERICAN BANKER.
American Banker, Bond Buyer, One State St. Plaza, New York, NY 10004. TEL 212-943-9589.
Vendor(s): BRS, Data-Star (BANK), DIALOG (File no.625), Mead Data Central, NewsNet. *758*

AMERICAN CHEMICAL SOCIETY. DIRECTORY OF GRADUATE RESEARCH.
American Chemical Society, 1155 16th St., N.W., Washington, DC 20036. TEL 202-872-4363. FAX 202-872-4615. *1692*

AMERICAN CHEMICAL SOCIETY. JOURNAL.
American Chemical Society, 1155 16th St., N.W., Washington, DC 20036. TEL 202-872-4363. FAX 202-872-4615.
Vendor(s): STN International (CJACS). *1169*

AMERICAN CITY & COUNTY.
Communication Channels, Inc., 6255 Barfield Rd., Atlanta, GA 30328-4369. TEL 404-256-9800. FAX 404-256-3116. *4084*

AMERICAN COLLEGE OF CARDIOLOGY. JOURNAL.
Elsevier Science Publishing Co., Inc. (New York), 655 Ave. of the Americas, New York, NY 10010. TEL 212-989-5800. FAX 212-633-3965.
Vendor(s): BRS. *3203*

AMERICAN CRIMINAL LAW REVIEW.
Georgetown University Law Center, 600 New Jersey Ave., N.W., Washington, DC 20001. TEL 202-662-9468.
Vendor(s): WESTLAW (ACRIMLREV). *1509*

AMERICAN DEMOGRAPHICS.
American Demographics, Inc., Box 68, Ithaca, NY 14851-0068. TEL 607-273-6343. FAX 607-273-3196.
Vendor(s): DIALOG, Dow Jones/News Retrieval, Mead Data Central. *3979*

AMERICAN DOCTORAL DISSERTATIONS.
University Microfilms International, Dissertation Publishing, c/o Dorie Mickelson, Mgr., 300 N. Zeeb Rd., Ann Arbor, MI 48106. TEL 313-761-4700.
Vendor(s): BRS, BRS/Saunders Colleague, DIALOG (File no.35). *1699*

AMERICAN DRUGGIST.
Hearst Corp., American Druggist, 60 E. 42nd St., No. 449, New York, NY 10165-0449. TEL 212-297-9680. FAX 212-286-9886. *3716*

AMERICAN FAMILY PHYSICIAN.
American Academy of Family Physicians, 8880 Ward Pkwy., Kansas City, MO 64114. TEL 816-333-9700. FAX 816-822-0580.
Vendor(s): BRS, Mead Data Central. *3074*

AMERICAN FITNESS.
Aerobics and Fitness Association of America, 15250 Ventura Blvd., Ste. 310, Sherman Oaks, CA 91403. TEL 818-905-0040.
Vendor(s): DIALOG (File no.149). *3799*

AMERICAN GERIATRICS SOCIETY. JOURNAL.
Williams & Wilkins, 428 E. Preston St., Baltimore, MD 21202. TEL 301-528-4000. FAX 301-528-4321. *2270*

AMERICAN HEALTH CARE ASSOCIATION. PROVIDER.
American Health Care Association, 1201 L St., N.W., Washington, DC 20005. TEL 202-842-4444. FAX 202-842-3860. *4398*

AMERICAN HEART JOURNAL.
Mosby - Year Book, Inc. 11830 Westline Industrial Dr., St. Louis, MO 63146. TEL 800-325-4117. FAX 314-432-1380.
Vendor(s): BRS, BRS/Saunders Colleague. *3204*

AMERICAN HERITAGE.
American Heritage 60 Fifth Ave., New York, NY 10011. TEL 212-206-5500. FAX 212-620-2332.
Vendor(s): DIALOG. *2398*

AMERICAN HOSPITAL FORMULARY SERVICE DRUG INFORMATION.
American Society of Hospital Pharmacists, c/o Jean Rogers, Dir., Mkt. Svcs., 4630 Montgomery Ave., Bethesda, MD 20814. TEL 301-657-3000.
Vendor(s): BRS (DIFT), BRS/Saunders Colleague, DIALOG (File no.229), Mead Data Central. *3716*

AMERICAN INDIAN LAW REVIEW.
University of Oklahoma, College of Law, 300 Timberdell Rd., Norman, OK 73019. TEL 405-325-2840.
Vendor(s): WESTLAW. *2597*

AMERICAN JOURNAL OF CARDIOLOGY.
Cahners Publishing Company (New York), Medical-Health Care Group, Yorke Medical Journals Division of Reed Publishing (USA) Inc., 249 W. 17th St., New York, NY 10011-5301. TEL 212-645-0067. FAX 212-242-6987.
Vendor(s): BRS, Mead Data Central. *3204*

AMERICAN JOURNAL OF DRUG AND ALCOHOL ABUSE.
Marcel Dekker Journals, 270 Madison Ave., New York, NY 10016. TEL 212-696-9000. FAX 212-685-4540. *1534*

AMERICAN JOURNAL OF HOSPITAL PHARMACY.
American Society of Hospital Pharmacists, c/o Jean Rogers, Dir., Mkt. Svcs., 4630 Montgomery Ave., Bethesda, MD 20814. TEL 301-657-3000. *3716*

AMERICAN JOURNAL OF INDUSTRIAL MEDICINE.
John Wiley & Sons, Inc., Journals, 605 Third Ave., New York, NY 10158. TEL 212-850-6000. FAX 212-850-6088. *3614*

AMERICAN JOURNAL OF INTERNATIONAL LAW.
American Society of International Law, 2223 Massachusetts Ave., N.W., Washington, DC 20008-2864. TEL 202-265-4313. FAX 202-797-7133.
Vendor(s): Mead Data Central. *2719*

AMERICAN JOURNAL OF KIDNEY DISEASES.
W.B. Saunders Co. Curtis Center, Independence Square W., Philadelphia, PA 19106. TEL 215-238-7800. *3387*

AMERICAN JOURNAL OF LEGAL HISTORY.
Temple University School of Law, Philadelphia, PA 19122. TEL 215-787-1256. FAX 215-787-1785.
Vendor(s): WESTLAW. *2598*

AMERICAN JOURNAL OF MEDICAL GENETICS.
John Wiley & Sons, Inc., Journals, 605 Third Ave., New York, NY 10158. TEL 212-850-6000. FAX 212-850-6088. *539*

AMERICAN JOURNAL OF MEDICINE.
Cahners Publishing Company (New York), Medical-Health Care Group, Yorke Medical Journals Division of Reed Publishing (USA) Inc., 249 W. 17th St., New York, NY 10011-5301. TEL 212-463-6460. FAX 212-463-6470.
Vendor(s): BRS, Mead Data Central. *3074*

AMERICAN JOURNAL OF NURSING.
American Journal of Nursing Co., 555 W. 57th St., New York, NY 10019. TEL 212-582-8820. FAX 212-586-5462. *3275*

AMERICAN JOURNAL OF OBSTETRICS AND GYNECOLOGY.
Mosby - Year Book, Inc. 11830 Westline Industrial Dr., St. Louis, MO 63146. TEL 800-325-4117. FAX 314-432-1380.
Vendor(s): BRS. *3289*

AMERICAN JOURNAL OF PHARMACEUTICAL EDUCATION.
American Association of Colleges of Pharmacy, 1426 Prince St., Alexandria, VA 22314-2815. TEL 703-739-2330. *3716*

AMERICAN JOURNAL OF PHARMACY (1981).
Philadelphia College of Pharmacy and Science, 43rd St. & Kingsessing Mall, Philadelphia, PA 19104. TEL 215-596-8800. *3716*

AMERICAN JOURNAL OF PHYSICAL MEDICINE AND REHABILITATION.
Williams & Wilkins, 428 E. Preston St., Baltimore, MD 21202. TEL 301-528-4000. FAX 301-528-4312.
Vendor(s): Mead Data Central. *3075*

AMERICAN JOURNAL OF PRIMATOLOGY.
John Wiley & Sons, Inc., Journals, 605 Third Ave., New York, NY 10108. TEL 212-850-6000. FAX 212-850-6088. *427*

AMERICAN JOURNAL OF PSYCHIATRY.
American Psychiatric Press, Inc., Journals Division, 1400 K St. N.W., Washington, DC 20005. TEL 202-682-6020. FAX 202-682-6016.
Vendor(s): BRS, BRS/Saunders Colleague. *3329*

AMERICAN JOURNAL OF PUBLIC HEALTH.
American Public Health Association, 1015 15th St., N.W., Washington, DC 20005. TEL 202-789-5600.
Vendor(s): BRS, BRS/Saunders Colleague. *4097*

AMERICAN JOURNAL OF REPRODUCTIVE IMMUNOLOGY AND MICROBIOLOGY.
Munksgaard International Publishers Ltd., P.O. Box 2148, DK-1016 Copenhagen K, Denmark. TEL 45-33-12-70-30. FAX 45-33-12-93-87. *3183*

AMERICAN JOURNAL OF SURGERY.
Cahners Publishing Company (New York), Medical-Health Care Group, Yorke Medical Journals Division of Reed Publishing (USA) Inc., 249 W. 17th St., New York, NY 10011-5301. TEL 212-463-6441. FAX 212-463-6470.
Vendor(s): BRS, Mead Data Central. *3374*

AMERICAN LIBRARIES.
American Library Association, 50 E. Huron St., Chicago, IL 60611-2795. TEL 800-545-2433. FAX 312-440-9374.
Vendor(s): DIALOG. *2742*

AMERICAN LIBRARY DIRECTORY.
R.R. Bowker, A Reed Reference Publishing Company, Division of Reed Publishing (USA) Inc., 121 Chanlon Rd., New Providence, NJ 07974. TEL 800-521-8110. FAX 908-665-6688.
Vendor(s): DIALOG (File no.460). *2742*

AMERICAN MANUFACTURERS DIRECTORY.
American Business Information, Inc., American Business Directories, 5711 S. 86th Circle, Box 27347, Omaha, NE 68127. TEL 402-593-4600. FAX 402-331-1505. *1121*

AMERICAN MARITIME CASES.
American Maritime Cases, Inc., 28 E. 21st St., Baltimore, MD 21218. TEL 410-752-2939. FAX 410-625-1174.
Vendor(s): Mead Data Central. *2598*

AMERICAN MARKETPLACE.
Business Publishers, Inc., 951 Pershing Dr., Silver Spring, MD 20910-4464. TEL 301-587-6300. FAX 301-585-9075.
Vendor(s): NewsNet. *3979*

AMERICAN MEN AND WOMEN OF SCIENCE.
R.R. Bowker, A Reed Reference Publishing Company, Division of Reed Publishing (USA) Inc., 121 Chanlon Rd., New Providence, NJ 07974. TEL 800-521-8110. FAX 908-665-6688.
Vendor(s): DIALOG (File no.236), Orbit Information Technologies (AMWS). *417*

AMERICAN METAL MARKET.
Capital Cities - A B C, Inc., 825 Seventh Ave., New York, NY 10019. TEL 212-887-8532. FAX 212-887-8358.
Vendor(s): DIALOG. *3402*

AMERICAN PETROLEUM INSTITUTE. DIVISION OF STATISTICS. WEEKLY STATISTICAL BULLETIN.
American Petroleum Institute, Publications Department, 1220 L St., N.W., Washington, DC 20005. TEL 202-682-8378. *3704*

AMERICAN PHARMACY.
American Pharmaceutical Association, 2215 Constitution Ave., N.W., Washington, DC 20037. TEL 202-628-4410. *3716*

AMERICAN PODIATRIC MEDICAL ASSOCIATION. JOURNAL.
American Podiatric Medical Association, 9312 Old Georgetown Rd., Bethesda, MD 20814-1621. TEL 301-571-9200. FAX 301-530-2752.
Vendor(s): National Library of Medicine. *3375*

AMERICAN REVIEW OF PUBLIC ADMINISTRATION.
University of Missouri, Kansas City, Henry W. Bloch School of Business and Public Administration, L.P. Cookingham Institute of Public Affairs, Kansas City, MO 64110. FAX 816-235-2312.
Vendor(s): DIALOG. *4053*

AMERICAN SALESMAN.
National Research Bureau, Inc. (Burlington), 424 N. Third St., Box 1, Burlington, IA 52601-0001. TEL 319-752-5415. FAX 319-752-3421.
Vendor(s): DIALOG. *1033*

AMERICAN SPECTATOR.
2020 N. 14th St., Ste. 750, Box 549, Arlington, VA 22216. TEL 703-243-3733. FAX 703-243-6814.
Vendor(s): Information Access Company. *2858*

AMERICAN STATISTICS INDEX.
Congressional Information Service, 4520 East-West Hwy., Bethesda, MD 20814-3389. TEL 301-654-1550. FAX 301-654-4033.
Vendor(s): DIALOG (File no.102). *4561*

AMERICAN UNIVERSITY LAW REVIEW.
American University, Washington College of Law, 4400 Massachusetts Ave., N.W., Washington, DC 20016. TEL 202-885-2652.
Vendor(s): WESTLAW. *2598*

SERIALS AVAILABLE ONLINE

AMTLICHES TELEFAX- UND TELEBRIEFVERZEICHNIS DER DEUTSCHEN BUNDESPOST TELECOM.
Deutsche Postreklame GmbH, Wiesenhuettenstr. 18, Postfach 160211, 6000 Frankfurt a.M. 1, Germany. TEL 069-2682-0. FAX 069-2682-218. *1352*

AMUSEMENT BUSINESS.
B P I Communications, Inc., Amusement Business Division, Box 24970, Nashville, TN 37202. TEL 615-321-4250. FAX 615-327-1575.
Vendor(s): DIALOG. *4629*

ANAIS DE FARMACIA E QUIMICA DE SAO PAULO.
Sociedade de Farmacia e Quimica de Sao Paulo, Avda. Brigadeiro Luis Antonio 393, 7 andar, CEP 01317, Sao Paulo, Brazil. *3716*

ANALYST.
Royal Society of Chemistry, Thomas Graham House, Science Park, Milton Rd., Cambridge CB4 4W, England. TEL 0462-672555. FAX 0462-480947.
Vendor(s): STN International (CJRSC). *1203*

ANALYTICA CHIMICA ACTA.
Elsevier Science Publishers B.V., P.O. Box 211, 1000 AE Amsterdam, Netherlands. TEL 020-5803911. FAX 020-5803598.
Vendor(s): STN International. *1203*

ANALYTICAL ABSTRACTS.
Royal Society of Chemistry, Thomas Graham House, Science Park, Milton Rd., Cambridge CB4 4WF, England. TEL 0462-672555. FAX 0462-480947.
Vendor(s): Data-Star (ANAB), DIALOG (File no.305), Orbit Information Technologies (ANALYTICA), STN International (ANABSTR). *1191*

ANALYTICAL CHEMISTRY.
American Chemical Society, 1155 16th St., N.W., Washington, DC 20036. TEL 202-872-4600. FAX 202-872-4615.
Vendor(s): STN International (CJACS). *1204*

ANATOLIAN STUDIES.
British Institute of Archaeology at Ankara, c/o British Academy, 20-21 Cornwall Terrace, London NW1 4QP, England. *261*

ANATOMICAL RECORD.
Wiley-Liss, Inc., 41 E. 11th St., New York, NY 10003. TEL 212-475-7700. *428*

ANESTHESIA AND ANALGESIA.
Elsevier Science Publishing Co., Inc. (New York), 655 Ave. of the Americas, New York, NY 10010. TEL 212-989-5800. FAX 212-633-3965.
Vendor(s): BRS. *3190*

ANESTHESIOLOGY.
J.B. Lippincott Co., E. Washington Sq., Philadelphia, PA 19105. TEL 215-238-4200.
Vendor(s): BRS. *3190*

ANGEWANDTE CHEMIE.
V C H Verlagsgesellschaft mbH, Postfach 101161, 6940 Weinheim, Germany. TEL 06201-602-0. FAX 06201-602328.
Vendor(s): STN International (CJVCH). *1170*

ANGEWANDTE CHEMIE: INTERNATIONAL EDITION.
V C H Verlagsgesellschaft mbH, Postfach 101161, 6940 Weinheim, Germany. TEL 06201-602-0. FAX 06201-602-328. *1170*

ANGOLA PEACE MONITOR.
International Freedom Foundation, 200 G St., N.E., Ste. 300, Washington, DC 20002. TEL 202-546-5788. FAX 202-546-5488.
Vendor(s): NewsNet. *3950*

ANIMAL BEHAVIOR ABSTRACTS.
Cambridge Scientific Abstracts, 7200 Wisconsin Ave., 6th Fl., Bethesda, MD 20814. TEL 301-961-6750. FAX 301-961-6720.
Vendor(s): BRS (CSAL), DIALOG (File no.76/LIFE SCIENCES COLLECTION). *461*

ANIMAL BREEDING ABSTRACTS.
C.A.B. International, Wallingford, Oxon OX10 8DE, England. TEL 0491-32111. FAX 0491-33508.
Vendor(s): BRS (CABA), CISTI, DIMDI, DIALOG, European Space Agency (File nos.16 & 124/CAB). *461*

ANIMAL DISEASE OCCURRENCE.
C.A.B. International, Wallingford, Oxon OX10 8DE, England. TEL 800-528-4841, 0491 32111. FAX 0491-33508.
Vendor(s): BRS (VETR), CISTI, DIMDI, DIALOG, European Space Agency (File nos.16 & 124/CAB). *4805*

ANIMAL PHARM.
P J B Publications Ltd., 18-20 Hill Rise, Richmond, Surrey TW10 6UA, England. TEL 081-948-3262. FAX 081-948-6866.
Vendor(s): BRS, Data-Star, DIALOG. *4806*

ANNALES PHARMACEUTIQUES FRANCAISES.
Masson, 120 bd. Saint-Germain, 75280 Paris Cedex 06, France. TEL 1-46-34-21-60. FAX 1-45-87-29-99. *3716*

ANNALS OF INTERNAL MEDICINE.
American College of Physicians, Independence Mall W., Sixth St. at Race, Philadelphia, PA 19106-1572. TEL 215-351-2400.
Vendor(s): BRS, BRS/Saunders Colleague. *3076*

ANNALS OF NEUROLOGY.
Little, Brown and Company, Medical Journals, 34 Beacon St., Boston, MA 02108. TEL 617-859-5500. FAX 617-859-0629.
Vendor(s): BRS, Mead Data Central. *3330*

ANNALS OF PLASTIC SURGERY.
Little, Brown and Company, Medical Journals, 34 Beacon St., Boston, MA 02108. TEL 617-859-5500. FAX 617-859-0629.
Vendor(s): Mead Data Central. *3375*

ANNALS OF SURGERY.
J.B. Lippincott Co., E. Washington Sq., Philadelphia, PA 19105. TEL 215-238-4200.
Vendor(s): BRS, BRS/Saunders Colleague, Mead Data Central. *3375*

ANNALS OF THE RHEUMATIC DISEASES.
B M J Publishing Group, B.M.A. House, Tavistock Sq., London WC1H 9JR, England. TEL 071-387-4499. FAX 071-383-6402.
Vendor(s): BRS. *3368*

ANNALS OF THORACIC SURGERY.
Elsevier Science Publishing Co., Inc. (New York), 655 Ave. of the Americas, New York, NY 10010. TEL 212-989-5800. FAX 212-633-3965.
Vendor(s): Mead Data Central. *3375*

ANNUAIRE TELEXPORT.
Chambre de Commerce et d'Industrie de Paris (CEDIP), 2 place de la Bourse, 75002 Paris, France.
Vendor(s): Data-Star. *807*

ANTARCTIC BIBLIOGRAPHY.
Library of Congress, Washington, DC 20540.
Vendor(s): Orbit Information Technologies (COLD). *2242*

ANTI-CENSORSHIP NEWSLETTER.
The Parent S I G, 1640 Via Pacifica, Ste.F-105, Corona, CA 91720. *4429*

ANTITRUST.
American Bar Association, Antitrust Law Section, 750 N. Lake Shore Dr., Chicago, IL 60611. TEL 312-988-5555.
Vendor(s): WESTLAW (ANTITR). *2599*

ANTITRUST & TRADE REGULATION REPORT.
The Bureau of National Affairs, Inc., 1231 25th St., N.W., Washington, DC 20037. TEL 202-452-4200. FAX 202-822-8092.
Vendor(s): Mead Data Central (TRADRG), WESTLAW (BNA-ATRR). *1072*

ANTITRUST FREEDOM OF INFORMATION LOG.
Washington Regulatory Reporting Associates, Box 2220, Springfield, VA 22152. TEL 703-690-8240.
Vendor(s): NewsNet. *900*

ANTITRUST LAW JOURNAL.
American Bar Association, Antitrust Law Section, 750 N. Lake Shore Dr., Chicago, IL 60611. TEL 312-988-5555.
Vendor(s): Mead Data Central, WESTLAW (ANTITRLJ). *2599*

APICULTURAL ABSTRACTS.
International Bee Research Association, 18 North Rd., Cardiff CF1 3DY, Wales. TEL 0222-372409.
Vendor(s): DIALOG, European Space Agency (File nos.16 & 124/CAB). *133*

APOTHECARY.
Health Care Marketing Services, H C M S Inc., Box AP, Los Altos, CA 94023-0179. FAX 415-941-2303. *3717*

APPAREL INDUSTRY MAGAZINE.
Shore Communications, Inc., 180 Allen Rd., N.E., Ste. 300 N., Atlanta, GA 30328. TEL 404-252-8831. FAX 404-252-4436.
Vendor(s): BRS, DIALOG, Information Access Company. *1283*

APPLIANCE MANUFACTURER.
Corcoran Communications, Inc., 29100 Aurora Rd., Ste. 200, Solon, OH 44139. TEL 216-349-3060. FAX 216-248-0187.
Vendor(s): DIALOG. *1882*

APPLIED CATALYSIS.
Elsevier Science Publishers B.V., P.O. Box 211, 1000 AE Amsterdam, Netherlands. TEL 020-5803911. FAX 020-5803598.
Vendor(s): STN International. *1848*

APPLIED GENETICS NEWS.
Business Communications Co., Inc. (Norwalk), 25 Van Zant St., Ste. 13, Norwalk, CT 06855. TEL 203-853-4266. FAX 203-853-0348.
Vendor(s): Data-Star, DIALOG, NewsNet. *539*

APPLIED NETWORKS REPORT.
International Data Corporation, Five Speen St., Box 9015, Framingham, MA 01701. TEL 508-872-8200. FAX 508-935-4015.
Vendor(s): NewsNet. *1426*

APPLIED SCIENCE AND TECHNOLOGY INDEX.
H.W. Wilson Co., 950 University Ave., Bronx, NY 10452. TEL 800-367-6770.
Vendor(s): Wilsonline (File AST). *1841*

AQUALINE ABSTRACTS.
Pergamon Press plc, Headington Hill Hall, Oxford OX3 0BW, England. TEL 0865-794141. FAX 0865-743911.
Vendor(s): DIALOG, European Space Agency, Orbit Information Technologies (AQUALINE), Pergamon Infoline (AQUALINE). *4834*

AQUARICULTURE AND AQUATIC SCIENCES. JOURNAL.
Written Word, 7601 E. Forest Lake Drive, Parkville, MO 64152. TEL 816-842-5936. FAX 816-474-5597.
Vendor(s): CompuServe Consumer Information Service. *429*

AQUATIC SCIENCES & FISHERIES ABSTRACTS. PART 1: BIOLOGICAL SCIENCES AND LIVING RESOURCES.
Cambridge Scientific Abstracts, 7200 Wisconsin Ave., 6th Fl., Bethesda, MD 20814. TEL 301-961-6750. FAX 301-961-6720.
Vendor(s): BRS (CSAL), CISTI, DIMDI, DIALOG (File no.44), European Space Agency. *4834*

AQUATIC SCIENCES & FISHERIES ABSTRACTS. PART 2: OCEAN TECHNOLOGY, POLICY AND NON-LIVING RESOURCES.
Cambridge Scientific Abstracts, 7200 Wisconsin Ave., 6th Fl., Bethesda, MD 20814. TEL 301-961-6750. FAX 301-961-6720.
Vendor(s): BRS (CSAL), CISTI, DIMDI, DIALOG (File no.44), European Space Agency. *4834*

AQUATIC SCIENCES & FISHERIES ABSTRACTS. PART 3: AQUATIC POLLUTION AND ENVIRONMENTAL QUALITY.
Cambridge Scientific Abstracts, 7200 Wisconsin Ave., 6th Fl., Bethesda, MD 20814. TEL 301-961-6700. FAX 301-961-6720.
Vendor(s): BRS (CSAL), DIMDI, DIALOG (File no.44), European Space Agency. *2051*

ARCHITECTURAL PERIODICALS INDEX.
R I B A Publications Ltd., Finsbury Mission, 39 Moreland St., London EC1V 8BB, England. TEL 071-251 0791. FAX 071-608-2375.
Vendor(s): DIALOG (File no.179). *309*

ARCHIVES OF DERMATOLOGY.
American Medical Association, 515 N. State St., Chicago, IL 60610. TEL 312-464-0183. FAX 312-464-5834.
Vendor(s): Mead Data Central. *3246*

ARCHIVES OF DISEASES IN CHILDHOOD.
B M J Publishing Group, B.M.A. House, Tavistock Sq., London WC1H 9JR, England.
Vendor(s): BRS, BRS/Saunders Colleague. *3318*

ARCHIVES OF GENERAL PSYCHIATRY.
American Medical Association, 515 N. State St., Chicago, IL 60610. TEL 312-464-0183. FAX 312-464-5834.
Vendor(s): Mead Data Central. *3330*

ARCHIVES OF INTERNAL MEDICINE.
American Medical Association, 515 N. State St., Chicago, IL 60610. TEL 312-464-0183. FAX 312-464-5834.
Vendor(s): Mead Data Central. *3077*

ARCHIVES OF NEUROLOGY.
American Medical Association, 515 N. State St., Chicago, IL 60610. TEL 312-464-0183. FAX 312-464-5834.
Vendor(s): Mead Data Central. *3330*

ARCHIVES OF OPHTHALMOLOGY.
American Medical Association, 515 N. State St., Chicago, IL 60610. TEL 312-464-0183. FAX 312-464-5834.
Vendor(s): Mead Data Central. *3298*

ARCHIVES OF OTOLARYNGOLOGY - HEAD & NECK SURGERY.
American Medical Association, 515 N. State St., Chicago, IL 60610. TEL 312-464-0183. FAX 312-464-5834.
Vendor(s): Mead Data Central. *3313*

ARCHIVES OF PATHOLOGY & LABORATORY MEDICINE.
American Medical Association, 515 N. State St., Chicago, IL 60610. TEL 312-464-0183. FAX 312-464-5834.
Vendor(s): Mead Data Central. *3077*

ARCHIVES OF SURGERY.
American Medical Association, 515 N. State St., Chicago, IL 60610. TEL 312-464-0183. FAX 312-464-5834.
Vendor(s): Mead Data Central. *3376*

THE ARCHWAY (SMITHFIELD).
Bryant College, Box 7, 1150 Douglas Pike, Smithfield, RI 02917-1284. TEL 401-232-6028. FAX 401-232-6319. *1303*

ARHIV ZA FARMACIJU.
Farmaceutsko Drustvo Srbije, Terazije 12, Box 664, Belgrade, Yugoslavia. *3718*

ARIZONA BUSINESS GAZETTE.
Phoenix Newspapers, Inc., Box 1950, Phoenix, AZ 85001. TEL 602-271-7373. FAX 602-271-7363.
Vendor(s): DIALOG, Dow Jones/News Retrieval, Mead Data Central, VU/TEXT Information Services, Inc.. *645*

ARIZONA STATE LAW JOURNAL.
Arizona State University, College of Law, Tempe, AZ 85287. TEL 602-965-6287.
Vendor(s): WESTLAW. *2600*

ARKANSAS BUSINESS AND ECONOMIC REVIEW.
University of Arkansas, College of Business Administration, Fayetteville, AR 72701. TEL 501-575-4151.
Vendor(s): DIALOG. *645*

ARS PHARMACEUTICA.
Universidad de Granada, Servicio de Publicaciones, Antiguo Colegio Maximo, Campus de Cartuja, 18071 Granada, Spain. TEL 281356. *3718*

ART COM: CONTEMPORARY ART COMMUNICATIONS.
Contemporary Arts Press, Box 3123, Rincon Annex, San Francisco, CA 94119. TEL 415-431-7524. FAX 415-431-7841. *314*

ART INDEX.
H.W. Wilson Co., 950 University Ave., Bronx, NY 10452. TEL 800-367-6770. FAX 212-538-2716.
Vendor(s): BRS, Wilsonline (File ART). *351*

ART SALES INDEX: OIL PAINTINGS, DRAWINGS, WATER COLOURS AND SCULPTURE.
Apollo Book (Distributor), Box 3839, Poughkeepsie, NY 12603-0839. TEL 914-462-0040. *315*

ARTBIBLIOGRAPHIES MODERN.
Clio Press Ltd., 55 St. Thomas' St., Oxford OX1 1JG, England. TEL 0865-250333.
Vendor(s): DIALOG (File no.56). *351*

ARTHRITIS AND RHEUMATISM.
J.B. Lippincott Co., E. Washington Sq., Philadelphia, PA 19105. TEL 215-238-4200. FAX 215-238-4227.
Vendor(s): BRS, Mead Data Central. *3368*

ARTS & HUMANITIES CITATION INDEX.
Institute for Scientific Information, 3501 Market St., Philadelphia, PA 19104. TEL 215-386-0100. FAX 215-386-2991.
Vendor(s): BRS (AHCI), DIALOG (File no.439). *351*

ARZNEIMITTEL-FORSCHUNG.
Editio Cantor, Postfach 1255, 7960 Aulendorf, Germany. TEL 07525-2060. FAX 07525-20680. *3718*

ASAHI SHIMBUN SHUKUSATUBAN.
Asahi Shimbunsha - Asahi Shimbun Publishing Co., 3-2 Tsukiji 5-chome, Chuo-ku, Tokyo 104-11, Japan. *2207*

ASBESTOS ABATEMENT REPORT.
Buraff Publications 1350 Connecticut Ave. N.W., Ste. 1000, Washington, DC 20036. TEL 202-862-0990. FAX 202-822-8092.
Vendor(s): Human Resources Information Network. *4098*

ASBESTOS CONTROL REPORT.
Business Publishers, Inc., 951 Pershing Dr., Silver Spring, MD 20910-4464. TEL 301-587-6300. FAX 301-587-1081.
Vendor(s): Data-Star, DIALOG, NewsNet. *1943*

ASIA - PACIFIC FORECASTING SERVICE.
Business International Asia-Pacific Ltd, 11-F Mount Parker House, Cityplaza, Taikoo Shing, Hong Kong. TEL 5-670491. FAX 5-8853279.
Vendor(s): DIALOG. *646*

ASIAN STUDIES CENTER BACKGROUNDER.
Heritage Foundation, 214 Massachusetts Ave., N.E., Washington, DC 20002. TEL 202-546-4400. FAX 202-546-8328.
Vendor(s): Mead Data Central. *3950*

ASSET INTERNATIONAL.
Asset International, Inc., 125 Greenwich Ave., Greenwich, CT 06830. TEL 203-629-5014. FAX 203-629-5024. *938*

ATLANTA BUSINESS CHRONICLE.
Scripps Howard Business Publications (Atlanta), 1801 Peachtree St., No.150, Atlanta, GA 30339-1859.
Vendor(s): DIALOG. *844*

ATLANTIC.
American Chamber of Commerce (UK), 75 Brook St., London W1Y 2EB, England. TEL 071-493 0381. FAX 071-493-2394.
Vendor(s): DIALOG. *807*

ATLANTIC ECONOMIC JOURNAL.
Atlantic Economic Society, c/o John M. Virgo, Ed., Box 1101, Southern Illinois University, Edwardsville, IL 62026-1101. TEL 618-692-2291. FAX 618-692-3400.
Vendor(s): DIALOG. *646*

ATLANTIC TRADE REPORT & GLOBAL DEFENSE INDUSTRY.
Bergerac International Ltd., Rt. One, Box 309, Gainesville, VA 20065. TEL 703-349-2922. FAX 703-349-2922. *900*

ATTENDERINGSBULLETIN STARING-GEBOUW: LAND, BODEM, WATER.
Dienst Landbouwkundig Onderzoek, Staring Centrum, Instituut voor Onderzoek van het Landelijk Gebied, P.O. Box 125, 6700 AC Wageningen, Netherlands. TEL 08370-74200. FAX 08370-24812. *1972*

AUDIO WEEK.
Warren Publishing, Inc., 475 5th Ave., No. 1202, New York, NY 10017-6223. TEL 212-686-5410. FAX 212-889-5097.
Vendor(s): Data-Star, DIALOG, NewsNet. *4459*

AUDIOCASSETTE FINDER.
Plexus Publishing, Inc., 143 Old Marlton Pike, Medford, NJ 08055-8750. TEL 609-654-4888. FAX 609-654-4309.
Vendor(s): DIALOG (File no.46). *1674*

AUDIOLOGY JAPAN.
Japan Audiological Society, c/o Chateau Takanawa 703, 3-23-14 Takanawa, Minato-ku, Tokyo 108, Japan. FAX 03-3445-5834.
Vendor(s): JICST. *3314*

AUDIOTEX UPDATE.
Worldwide Videotex, Box 138, Babson Park, Boston, MA 02157. TEL 617-449-1603.
Vendor(s): Data-Star, DIALOG, NewsNet. *1349*

AUSTIN BUSINESS JOURNAL.
Austin Business Journal Inc., 1301 Capital of Texas Hwy., Ste. C-200, Austin, TX 78746. TEL 512-328-0180. FAX 512-328-7304.
Vendor(s): DIALOG. *646*

AUSTRALIAN AND NEW ZEALAND JOURNAL OF MEDICINE.
Adis Press Australasia Pty. Ltd., 404 Sydney Rd., Balgowlah, N.S.W. 2093, Australia. FAX 02-949-5007. *3080*

AUSTRALIAN BOOKS IN PRINT.
D.W. Thorpe 18 Salmon St., Port Melbourne, Vic. 3207, Australia. TEL 03-645-1511. FAX 03-645-3981.
Vendor(s): AUSINET. *389*

AUSTRALIAN BUSINESS INDEX.
421 Riversdale Rd., E. Hawthorn, Vic. 3123, Australia. TEL 03-822-7344. FAX 03-822-6837. *704*

AUSTRALIAN BUSINESS MONTHLY.
Australian Consolidated Press, 54-58 Park St., Sydney, N.S.W. 2000, Australia. TEL 02-267-2150. FAX 02-267-2150. *646*

AUSTRALIAN COMMUNICATIONS.
Computer Publications Pty. Ltd., Level 6, 54 Park St., Sydney, N.S.W. 2000, Australia. TEL 64-2-2889111. FAX 64-2-2674909. *1361*

AUSTRALIAN CRIMINAL REPORTS.
Law Book Co. Ltd., 44-50 Waterloo Rd., North Ryde, N.S.W. 2113, Australia. TEL 02-887-0177. FAX 02-888-9706. *1510*

AUSTRALIAN EDUCATION INDEX.
Australian Council for Educational Research, P.O. Box 210, Hawthorn, Vic. 3122, Australia. TEL 03-819-1400. FAX 03-819-5502.
Vendor(s): AUSINET. *1674*

AUSTRALIAN FAMILY AND SOCIETY ABSTRACTS.
Australian Institute of Family Studies, 300 Queen St., Melbourne, Vic. 3000, Australia. TEL 03-608-6888. FAX 03-600-0886. *4457*

AUSTRALIAN GOVERNMENT PUBLICATIONS.
National Library of Australia, Publications Section, Public Programs, Parkes Place, Canberra, A.C.T. 2600, Australia. *389*

AUSTRALIAN JOURNAL OF DAIRY TECHNOLOGY.
Dairy Industry Association of Australia, Publications Committee, P.O. Box 20, Highett, Vic. 3190, Australia. FAX 0353-20003.
Vendor(s): DIALOG (File nos.50 & 53). *197*

AUSTRALIAN ROAD RESEARCH IN PROGRESS.
Australian Road Research Board, 500 Burwood Hwy., Vermont S., Vic. 3133, Australia. TEL 03-881-1555. FAX 03-887-8104.
Available only online. *1841*

AUSTRALIAN TAX FORUM.
Monash University, Australian Tax Forum, Wellington Rd., Clayton, Vic. 3168, Australia. TEL 61-3562416. FAX 61-35652426. *1088*

AUSZUEGE AUS DEN EUROPAEISCHEN PATENTANMELDUNGEN. TEIL 1. GRUND- UND ROHSTOFFINDUSTRIE, CHEMIE UND HUETTENWESEN, BAUWESEN, BERGBAU.
Wila Verlag Wilhelm Lampl GmbH, Landsberger Str. 191A, 8000 Munich 21, Germany. TEL 089-5795-0. FAX 089-5706693. *3672*

AUSZUEGE AUS DEN EUROPAEISCHEN PATENTANMELDUNGEN. TEIL 2. ELEKTROTECHNIK, PHYSIK, FEINMECHANIK UND OPTIK, AKUSTIK.
Wila Verlag Wilhelm Lampl GmbH, Landsberger Str. 191A, 8000 Munich 21, Germany. TEL 089-5795-0. FAX 089-5706693. *3672*

AUSZUEGE AUS DEN EUROPAEISCHEN PATENTANMELDUNGEN. TEIL 3. UEBRIGE VERARBEITUNGSINDUSTRIE UND ARBEITSVERFAHREN, MASCHINEN- UND FAHRZEUGBAU, ERNAEHRUNG, LANDWIRTSCHAFT.
Wila Verlag Wilhelm Lampl GmbH, Landsberger Str. 191A, 8000 Munich 21, Germany. TEL 089-5795-0. FAX 089-5706693. *3672*

AUSZUEGE AUS DEN EUROPAEISCHEN PATENTSCHRIFTEN. TEIL 1. GRUND- UND ROHSTOFFINDUSTRIE, CHEMIE UND HUETTEN-WESEN, BAUWESEN UND BERGBAU.
Wila Verlag Wilhelm Lampl GmbH, Landsberger Str. 191A, 8000 Munich 21, Germany. TEL 089-5795-0. FAX 089-5706693. *3672*

AUSZUEGE AUS DEN GEBRAUCHSMUSTERN.
Wila Verlag Wilhelm Lampl GmbH, Landsberger Str. 191A, 8000 Munich 21, Germany. TEL 089-5795-0. FAX 089-5706693. *3673*

AUSZUEGE AUS DEN OFFENLEGUNGSSCHRIFTEN. TEIL 1. GRUND- UND ROHSTOFFINDUSTRIE, CHEMIE UND HUETTEN-WESEN, BAUWESEN UND BERGBAU.
Wila Verlag Wilhelm Lampl GmbH, Landsberger Str. 191a, 8000 Munich 21, Germany. TEL 089-5795-0. FAX 089-5706693. *3673*

AUSZUEGE AUS DEN OFFENLEGUNGSSCHRIFTEN. TEIL 2. ELEKTROTECHNIK, PHYSIK, FEINMECHANIK UND OPTIK, AKUSTIK.
Wila Verlag Wilhelm Lampl GmbH, Landsberger Str. 191A, 8000 Munich 21, Germany. TEL 089-5795-0. FAX 089-5706693. *3673*

AUSZUEGE AUS DEN OFFENLEGUNGSSCHRIFTEN. TEIL 3. UEBRIGE VERARBEITUNGSINDUSTRIE UND ARBEITSVERFAHREN, MASCHINEN- UND FAHRZEUGBAU, ERNAEHRUNG, LANDWIRTSCHAFT.
Wila Verlag Wilhelm Lampl GmbH, Landsberger Str. 191A, 8000 Munich 21, Germany. TEL 089-5795-0. FAX 089-5706693. *3673*

AUSZUEGE AUS DEN PATENTSCHRIFTEN.
Wila Verlag Wilhelm Lampl GmbH, Landsberger Str. 191A, 8000 Munich 21, Germany. TEL 089-5795-0. FAX 089-5706693. *3673*

AUTOMOTIVE INDUSTRIES.
Chilton Co., Chilton Way, Radnor, PA 19089. TEL 215-964-4255.
Vendor(s): DIALOG, Mead Data Central. *4683*

AUTOMOTIVE PARTS INTERNATIONAL.
International Trade Services, Box 5950, Bethesda, MD 20824-5950. TEL 202-857-8454. FAX 301-229-2077. *4683*

AUTOPARTS REPORT.
Cutter Information Corp., 37 Broadway, Arlington, MA 02174. TEL 617-648-8700. FAX 617-648-8707.
Vendor(s): Data-Star, DIALOG, NewsNet. *4684*

AUTOWEEK.
Crain Communications, Inc. (Detroit), 1400 Woodridge Ave., Detroit, MI 48207-3187. TEL 313-446-6000. FAX 313-446-1650.
Vendor(s): Mead Data Central. *4684*

AVERY INDEX TO ARCHITECTURAL PERIODICALS.
G.K. Hall & Co., 70 Lincoln St., Boston, MA 02111. TEL 617-423-3990. FAX 617-423-3999.
Vendor(s): DIALOG, Research Libraries Information Network. *309*

AVIATION DAILY.
McGraw-Hill, Inc., Aviation Week Group, 1156 15th St., N.W., Washington, DC 20005. TEL 202-822-4600.
Vendor(s): DIALOG (File no.624/McGRAW-HILL PUBLICATIONS ONLINE), Dow Jones/News Retrieval, Mead Data Central (AVDLY). *47*

AVIATION GROUND EQUIPMENT MARKET.
Aviation Ground Equipment Market, Inc., 1340 Braddock Pl, Ste. 300, Alexandria, VA 22314-1561. TEL 800-422-6685. FAX 703-836-0029. *47*

AVIATION WEEK & SPACE TECHNOLOGY.
McGraw-Hill, Inc., Aviation Week Group, 1221 Ave. of the Americas, New York, NY 10020. TEL 609-426-5526. FAX 609-426-6068.
Vendor(s): DIALOG (File no.624/McGRAW-HILL PUBLICATIONS ONLINE), Dow Jones/News Retrieval, Mead Data Central. *48*

THE B B I NEWSLETTER.
Biomedical Business International 1524 Brookhollow Dr., Santa Ana, CA 92705-5426. TEL 714-755-5757. FAX 714-755-5704.
Vendor(s): Data-Star, DIALOG. *3080*

B C BUSINESS.
Canada Wide Magazines Ltd., 1701-2 Carlton St., Toronto, Ont. M5B 1J3, Canada. TEL 416-595-5007. FAX 416-924-6308.
Vendor(s): DIALOG. *647*

B C I S QUARTERLY REVIEW OF BUILDING PRICES.
Royal Institution of Chartered Surveyors, Building Cost Information Service, 85-87 Clarence St., Kingston upon Thames, Surrey KT1 1RB, England. FAX 081-547-1238. *601*

B D I DEUTSCHLAND LIEFERT.
Verlag W. Sachon, Schloss Mindelburg, Postfach 1463, 8948 Mindelheim, Germany.
Vendor(s): Data-Star, FIZ Technik. *901*

B H A.
J. Paul Getty Trust, Art History Information Program, Flo Sterling and Francine Clark Art Institute, Williamstown, MA 01267. TEL 413-458-8260. FAX 413-458-8503.
Vendor(s): DIALOG (File no.191, Art Literature International). *351*

B I R D.
Centre International de l'Enfance, Chateau de Longchamp, Bois de Boulogne, 75016 Paris, France. TEL 1-45-20-79-92. FAX 1-45-25-73-67. *1247*

B M T ABSTRACTS.
B M T Cortec Ltd., Wallsend Research Stn., Wallsend, Tyne and Wear NE28 6UY, England. FAX 091-263-8754. *4662*

B N A LABOR RELATIONS REPORTER.
The Bureau of National Affairs, Inc., 1231 25th St., N.W., Washington, DC 20037. TEL 202-452-4200. FAX 202-822-8092.
Vendor(s): DIALOG (Laborlaw, File 244). *972*

B N A LABOR RELATIONS REPORTER. LABOR ARBITRATION.
The Bureau of National Affairs, Inc., 1231 25th St., N.W., Washington, DC 20037. TEL 202-452-4200. FAX 202-822-8092.
Vendor(s): DIALOG, Human Resources Information Network, Mead Data Central, WESTLAW. *972*

B N A PENSION REPORTER.
The Bureau of National Affairs, Inc., 1231 25th St., N.W., Washington, DC 20037. TEL 202-452-4200. FAX 202-822-8092.
Vendor(s): Human Resources Information Network (CDD, HDD), Mead Data Central (PENSN), WESTLAW (BNA-PEN). *973*

B N A POLICY AND PRACTICE SERIES. FAIR EMPLOYMENT PRACTICES.
The Bureau of National Affairs, Inc., 1231 25th St., N.W., Washington, DC 20037. TEL 202-452-4200. FAX 202-822-8092.
Vendor(s): DIALOG, Human Resources Information Network. *973*

B N A SPECIAL REPORT SERIES ON WORK & FAMILY.
The Bureau of National Affairs, Inc., 1231 25th St., N.W., Washington, DC 20037. TEL 202-452-4200. FAX 202-822-8092.
Vendor(s): Human Resources Information Network. *4399*

B N A'S BANKING REPORT.
The Bureau of National Affairs, Inc., 1231 25th St., N.W., Washington, DC 20037. TEL 202-452-4200. FAX 202-822-8092.
Vendor(s): Bureau of National Affairs, Human Resources Information Network (CDD,HDD), Mead Data Central (BNABNK), WESTLAW (BNA-BNK). *2603*

B N A'S EMPLOYEE RELATIONS WEEKLY.
The Bureau of National Affairs, Inc., 1231 25th St., N.W., Washington, DC 20037. TEL 202-452-4200. FAX 202-822-8092.
Vendor(s): Human Resources Information Network (CDD,HDD). *973*

B N A'S PATENT, TRADEMARK & COPYRIGHT JOURNAL.
Bureau of National Affairs, 1231 25th St., N.W., Washington, DC 20037. TEL 202-452-4200. FAX 202-833-8092.
Vendor(s): Mead Data Central, WESTLAW (BNA-PTCJ). *3673*

B O C WEEK.
Capitol Publications Inc., Telecom Publishing Group, 1101 King St., Ste. 444, Box 1455, Alexandria, VA 22313-2055. TEL 800-327-7205. FAX 703-739-6490.
Vendor(s): DIALOG, NewsNet. *1361*

B P REPORT.
Simba Information, Inc., Box 7430, Wilton, CT 06897. TEL 203-834-0033. FAX 203-834-1771.
Vendor(s): DIALOG, NewsNet. *4121*

BAALMAN & WELL'S LAND TITLES OFFICE PRACTICE.
Law Book Co. Ltd., 44-50 Waterloo Rd., N. Ryde, N.S.W. 2113, Australia. TEL 02-887-0177. FAX 02-888-9706. *2603*

BACK PAIN MONITOR.
American Health Consultants, Inc., Six Piedmont Center, Ste. 400, 3525 Piedmont Rd., N.E., Atlanta, GA 30305. TEL 404-262-7436. FAX 800-284-3291.
Vendor(s): Mead Data Central. *3081*

BACKGROUNDER.
Heritage Foundation, 214 Massachusetts Ave., N.E., Washington, DC 20002. TEL 202-546-4400. FAX 202-546-8328.
Vendor(s): Mead Data Central. *3951*

BACKGROUNDER UPDATE.
Heritage Foundation, 214 Massachusetts Ave., N.E., Washington, DC 20002. TEL 202-546-4400. FAX 202-546-8328.
Vendor(s): Mead Data Central. *4054*

BACKPACKER.
Rodale Press, Inc., 33 E. Minor St., Emmaus, PA 18098. TEL 215-967-5171.
Vendor(s): DIALOG. *4541*

BAKERY PRODUCTION AND MARKETING.
Delta Communications, Inc. (Chicago) 400 N. Michigan Ave., Ste. 1200, Chicago, IL 60611. TEL 312-693-3200. FAX 312-222-2026.
Vendor(s): DIALOG. *2086*

BALTIMORE BUSINESS JOURNAL.
American City Business Journals, Inc. (Baltimore), 117 Water St., Baltimore, MD 21202. TEL 301-576-1161.
Vendor(s): DIALOG. *647*

BANGLADESH JOURNAL OF PUBLIC ADMINISTRATION.
Bangladesh Public Administration Training Centre, Attn: Asst. Publication Officer, Molla Mosharraf Hossain, Savar, Dhaka 1343, Bangladesh. TEL 831971-20-251. *4054*

BANGLADESH PHARMACEUTICAL JOURNAL.
Bangladesh Pharmaceutical Society, University of Dhaka, Ramna, Dhaka 2, Bangladesh. *3719*

BANK MANAGEMENT.
Faulkner & Gray, Inc. (New York), 11 Penn Plaza, 17th Fl., New York, NY 10001. TEL 212-967-7000. FAX 212-967-7155.
Vendor(s): Mead Data Central. *763*

BANKING EXPANSION REPORTER.
Law and Business, Inc. 270 Sylvan Ave., Englewood Cliffs, NJ 07632. TEL 201-894-8484.
Vendor(s): Mead Data Central. *766*

BANXQUOTE ONLINE.
Masterfund Inc., 2001 Fairfield Dr., Wilmington, DE 19810-4309.
Available only online. *939*

BARRON'S NATIONAL BUSINESS AND FINANCIAL WEEKLY.
Dow Jones & Co., Inc., 200 Liberty St., New York, NY 10281. TEL 212-416-2700. FAX 212-416-2829.
Vendor(s): Dow Jones/News Retrieval. *939*

BASIC EDUCATION.
Council for Basic Education, 725 15th St., N.W., Washington, DC 20005. TEL 202-347-4171. *1618*

BATTERY & E V TECHNOLOGY NEWS.
Business Communications Co., Inc. (Norwalk), 25 Van Zant St., Ste. 13, Norwalk, CT 06855.
TEL 203-853-4266. FAX 203-853-0348.
Vendor(s): Data-Star, DIALOG, NewsNet. *1883*

BEILSTEINS HANDBUCH DER ORGANISCHEN CHEMIE. SUPPLEMENT.
Springer-Verlag, 175 Fifth Ave., New York, NY 10010. TEL 212-460-1500.
Vendor(s): DIALOG (File no.390). *1216*

BENEFITS TODAY.
The Bureau of National Affairs, Inc., 1231 25th St., N.W., Washington, DC 20037. TEL 202-452-4200. FAX 202-822-8092.
Vendor(s): Human Resources Information Network, WESTLAW. *973*

BEST'S REVIEW. LIFE - HEALTH INSURANCE EDITION.
A.M. Best Co., Ambest Rd., Oldwick, NJ 08858. TEL 908-439-2200. FAX 908-439-3363.
Vendor(s): DIALOG. *2528*

BEST'S REVIEW. PROPERTY - CASUALTY INSURANCE EDITION.
A.M. Best Co., Ambest Rd., Oldwick, NJ 08858. TEL 908-439-2200. FAX 908-439-3363.
Vendor(s): DIALOG. *2528*

BETTER NUTRITION FOR TODAY'S LIVING.
Communication Channels, Inc., 6255 Barfield Rd., Atlanta, GA 30328-4369. TEL 404-256-9800. FAX 404-256-3116. *3603*

BEVERAGE WORLD (ENGLISH EDITION).
Keller International Publishing Corporation, 150 Great Neck Rd., Great Neck, NY 11021. TEL 516-829-9210. FAX 516-829-5414.
Vendor(s): DIALOG, Mead Data Central. *378*

BIBLIOGRAFIA BRASILEIRA.
Biblioteca Nacional de Brasil, Av. Rio Branco, 219, 20042 Rio de Janeiro, Brazil. TEL 021-240-8429. FAX 021-220-4173. *2792*

BIBLIOGRAFIA BRASILEIRA DE ENERGIA NUCLEAR.
Comissao Nacional de Energia Nuclear, Centro de Informacoes Nucleares, Rio de Janeiro, Brazil. TEL 021-5462440. FAX 021-5462447.
Available only online. *1797*

BIBLIOGRAFIA LATINOAMERICANA: PART I.
Universidad Nacional Autonoma de Mexico, Centro de Informacion Cientifica y Humanistica, Apdo. Postal 70-392, C.P. 04510 Mexico, D.F., Mexico. *3*

BIBLIOGRAFIA LATINOAMERICANA: PART II.
Universidad Nacional Autonoma de Mexico, Centro de Informacion Cientifica y Humanistica, Apdo. Postal 70-392, C.P. 04510 Mexico, D.F., Mexico. *3*

BIBLIOGRAFIA NAZIONALE ITALIANA.
Istituto Centrale per il Catalogo Unico delle Biblioteche Italiane e per le Informazioni Bibliografiche, Viale del Castro Pretorio, 105, Rome, Italy. *391*

BIBLIOGRAFIA VENEZOLANA.
Instituto Autonomo Biblioteca Nacional y de Servicios de Bibliotecas, Oficina de Information, Apdo. 6525, Caracas 1010A, Venezuela.
TEL 5723623. *2747*

BIBLIOGRAFIE VAN DE NEDERLANDSE TAAL- EN LITERATUUR WETENSCHAP.
Koninklijke Nederlandse Akademie van Wetenschappen, Bureau voor de Bibliografie van de Neerlandistiek, Keizersgracht 569-571, 1017 DR Amsterdam, Netherlands. *2855*

BIBLIOGRAFIJA JUGOSLAVIJE. CLANCI I PRILOZI U SERIJSKIM PUBLIKACIJAMA. SERIJA A: DRUSTVENE NAUKE.
Jugoslovenski Bibliografsko-Informacijski Institut (YUBIN), Terazije 26, Belgrade, Yugoslavia. FAX 11-687-760. *4394*

BIBLIOGRAFIJA JUGOSLAVIJE. CLANCI I PRILOZI U SERIJSKIM PUBLIKACIJAMA. SERIJA B: PRIRODNE, PRIMENJENE, MEDICINSKE I TEHNICKE NAUKE.
Jugoslovenski Bibliografsko-Informacijski Institut (YUBIN), Terazije 26, Belgrade, Yugoslavia. FAX 11-687-760. *4354*

BIBLIOGRAFIJA JUGOSLAVIJE. CLANCI I PRILOZI U SERIJSKIM PUBLIKACIJAMA. SERIJA C: UMETNOST, SPORT, FILOLOGIJA, KNJIZEVNOST.
Jugoslovenski Bibliografsko-Informacijski Institut (YUBIN), Terazije 26, Belgrade, Yugoslavia. FAX 11-687-760. *391*

BIBLIOGRAFIJA JUGOSLAVIJE. KNJIGE, BROSURE I MUZIKALIJE.
Jugoslovenski Bibliografsko-Informacijski Institut (YUBIN), Terazije 26, Belgrade, Yugoslavia. FAX 11-687-760. *391*

BIBLIOGRAFIJA PREVODA U S F R J.
Jugoslovenski Bibliografsko-Informacijski Institut (YUBIN), Terazije 26, Belgrade, Yugoslavia. FAX 11-687-760. *391*

BIBLIOGRAPHIA MEDICA CECHOSLOVACA.
Ustav Vedeckych Lekarskych Informaci, Sokolska 31, 121 32 Prague 2, Czechoslovakia. *3166*

BIBLIOGRAPHIC INDEX.
H.W. Wilson Co., 950 University Ave., Bronx, NY 10452. TEL 800-367-6770. FAX 212-538-2716.
Vendor(s): Wilsonline (File BIB). *392*

BIBLIOGRAPHIE DER PFLANZENSCHUTZLITERATUR.
Verlag Paul Parey (Berlin), Seelbuschring 9-17, 1000 Berlin 42, Germany. TEL 030-70784-0. FAX 030-70784199.
Vendor(s): DIMDI. *134*

BIBLIOGRAPHIE GEOGRAPHIQUE INTERNATIONALE.
Centre National de la Recherche Scientifique, Institut de l'Information Scientifique et Technique, 2 allee du Parc de Brabois, B.P. 54, 54514 Vandoeuvre-les-Nancy Cedex, France. FAX 1-43-29-65-29.
Vendor(s): Telesystemes - Questel. *2267*

BIBLIOGRAPHIE INTERNATIONALE DES INDUSTRIES AGRO-ALIMENTAIRES.
Association pour la Promotion Industrie-Agriculture, 35, rue du General Foy, 75008 Paris, France. FAX 60-11-75-85. *134*

BIBLIOGRAPHY AND INDEX OF GEOLOGY.
American Geological Institute, 4220 King St., Alexandria, VA 22302-1507. TEL 703-379-2480. FAX 703-379-7563.
Vendor(s): CISTI, DIALOG, Orbit Information Technologies, STN International (GeoRef). *1550*

BIBLIOGRAPHY OF AGRICULTURE.
Oryx Press, 4041 N. Central at Indian School Rd., Phoenix, AZ 85012-3397. TEL 602-265-2651. FAX 602-265-6250.
Vendor(s): CISTI. *134*

BIBLIOGRAPHY OF BIOETHICS.
Kennedy Institute of Ethics, National Reference Center for Bioethics Literature, Georgetown University, Washington, DC 20057. TEL 202-687-6738. FAX 202-687-6770.
Vendor(s): National Library of Medicine, Telesystemes - Questel (BIOETHICS). *3166*

BIBLIOGRAPHY OF ECONOMIC GEOLOGY.
Geosystems, Box 40, Didcot, Oxon Ox11 9BX, England.
Vendor(s): DIALOG. *3479*

BIBLIOGRAPHY OF EDUCATION THESES IN AUSTRALIA.
Australian Council for Educational Research, Radford House, P.O. Box 210, Hawthorn, Vic. 3122, Australia. TEL 61-3-819-1400. FAX 61-3-819-5502.
Vendor(s): AUSINET. *1674*

BIBLIOGRAPHY OF THE HISTORY OF MEDICINE.
U.S. National Library of Medicine, 8600 Rockville Pike, Bethesda, MD 20894. TEL 301-496-6308. FAX 301-496-4450.
Vendor(s): National Library of Medicine. *3166*

BIBLIOGRAPHY ON COLD REGIONS SCIENCE & TECHNOLOGY.
U.S. Army, Cold Regions Research and Engineering Laboratory, 72 Lyme Rd., Hanover, NH 03755-1290. TEL 603-646-4221. FAX 603-646-4695.
Vendor(s): Orbit Information Technologies (COLD). *1841*

BIBLIOTECA NACIONAL DE BRASIL. ANAIS.
Biblioteca Nacional de Brasil, Av. Rio Branco 219, 20042 Rio de Janeiro, Brazil. TEL 021-240-8429. FAX 021-220-4173. *2747*

BIBLIOTHEQUE AFRICAINE. LISTE DES ACQUISITIONS.
Bibliotheque Africaine, 65 rue Belleaid, B-1040 Brussels, Belgium. FAX 02-5143067.
Vendor(s): BELINDIS (AFLI). *394*

BIG BUSINESSES DIRECTORY.
American Business Information, Inc. 5711 S. 86th Circle, Box 27347, Omaha, NE 68127. TEL 402-593-4600. FAX 402-331-5481. *1123*

BILLBOARD (NEW YORK).
B P I Communications, Inc. (New York) 1515 Broadway, 39th Fl., New York, NY 10036.
TEL 212-764-7300. FAX 212-944-1719.
Vendor(s): DIALOG. *3541*

BIOCHEMISTRY.
American Chemical Society, 1155 16th St., N.W., Washington, DC 20036. TEL 202-872-4363. FAX 202-872-4615.
Vendor(s): STN International (CJACS). *472*

BIOCONTROL NEWS AND INFORMATION.
C.A.B. International, Wallingford, Oxon OX10 8DE, England. TEL 0491 32111. FAX 0491-33508.
Vendor(s): BRS, CISTI, DIMDI, DIALOG, European Space Agency. *430*

BIODETERIORATION ABSTRACTS.
C.A.B. International, Wallingford, Oxon OX10 3DE, England. TEL 0491-32111. FAX 0491-33508.
Vendor(s): BRS, DIMDI, Data-Star, DIALOG, European Space Agency, STN International. *461*

BIOELECTROMAGNETICS.
John Wiley & Sons, Inc., Journals, 605 Third Ave., New York, NY 10158. TEL 212-850-6000. FAX 212-850-6088. *3082*

BIOGRAPHY AND GENEALOGY MASTER INDEX.
Gale Research Inc., 835 Penobscot Bldg., Detroit, MI 48226. TEL 313-961-2242. FAX 313-961-6083.
Vendor(s): DIALOG (File nos.287,288). *424*

BIOGRAPHY INDEX.
H.W. Wilson Co., 950 University Ave., Bronx, NY 10452. TEL 800-367-6770. FAX 212-538-2716.
Vendor(s): Wilsonline (File BIO). *424*

BIOLOGICAL ABSTRACTS.
BIOSIS, 2100 Arch St., Philadelphia, PA 19103-1399. TEL 215-587-4800. FAX 215-587-2016.
Vendor(s): BRS (BIOL), CISTI, Central Institute for Scientific & Technical Information, DIMDI, Data-Star, DIALOG (File nos.5 & 55), European Space Agency, STN International (BIOSIS). *462*

SERIALS AVAILABLE ONLINE 5053

BIOLOGICAL ABSTRACTS - R R M.
BIOSIS, 2100 Arch St., Philadelphia, PA 19103-1399. TEL 215-587-4800. FAX 215-587-2016. Vendor(s): BRS (BIOL), CISTI, Central Institute for Scientific & Technical Information, DIMDI, Data-Star, DIALOG (File nos.5 & 55), European Space Agency (File no.7/BIOSIS), STN International (BIOSIS). *462*

BIOLOGICAL & AGRICULTURAL INDEX.
H.W. Wilson Co., 950 University Ave., Bronx, NY 10452. TEL 800-367-6770. FAX 212-538-2716. Vendor(s): Wilsonline. *462*

BIOLOGY DIGEST.
Plexus Publishing, Inc., 143 Old Marlton Pike, Medford, NJ 08055. TEL 609-654-6500. FAX 609-654-4309. *462*

BIOMEDICAL MATERIALS.
Elsevier Science Publishers Ltd., Crown House, Linton Rd., Barking, Essex IG11 8JU, England. TEL 081-594-7272. FAX 081-594-5942. Vendor(s): Data-Star, DIALOG. *3082*

BIOPOLYMERS.
John Wiley & Sons, Inc., Journals, 605 Third Ave., New York, NY 10158-0012. TEL 212-692-6000. FAX 212-850-6088. Vendor(s): STN International (CJWILEY). *1216*

BIOS.
Beta Beta Beta National Biological Society, Box 670, Madison, NJ 07940-0670. TEL 201-377-8407. *433*

BIOSCAN.
Oryx Press, 4041 N. Central at Indian School Rd., Phoenix, AR 85012-3397. TEL 602-265-2651. FAX 602-265-6250. *1123*

BIOTECH BUSINESS.
Worldwide Videotex, Box 138, Babson Park, Boston, MA 02157. TEL 617-449-1603. Vendor(s): Data-Star, DIALOG, NewsNet. *540*

BIOTECHNOLOGY INVESTMENT OPPORTUNITIES.
High Tech Publishing Company, Box 1923, Brattleboro, VT 05301. TEL 802-254-3539. Vendor(s): Data-Star, NewsNet. *939*

BIOTECHNOLOGY RESEARCH ABSTRACTS.
Cambridge Scientific Abstracts, 7200 Wisconsin Ave., 6th Fl., Bethesda, MD 20814. TEL 301-961-6750. FAX 301-961-6720. Vendor(s): BRS (CSAL), DIALOG (File no.76/LIFE SCIENCES COLLECTION). *462*

BIWEEKLY LIST OF PAPERS ON RADIATION CHEMISTRY AND PHOTOCHEMISTRY.
University of Notre Dame, Radiation Chemistry Data Center, Radiation Laboratory, Notre Dame, IN 46556. TEL 219-239-6527. FAX 219-239-8068. *1191*

BLOOD.
W.B. Saunders Co. Curtis Center, Independence Square W., Philadelphia, PA 19106. TEL 215-238-7800. Vendor(s): BRS, Mead Data Central. *3271*

BOARDWATCH MAGAZINE.
5970 South Vivian St., Littleton, CO 80127. TEL 303-973-6038. FAX 303-973-3731. *1443*

BOATING.
Hachette Magazines, Inc., 1633 Broadway, 45th Fl., New York, NY 10009. TEL 212-767-6000. Vendor(s): DIALOG. *4523*

BOATING INDUSTRY.
Communication Channels, Inc., 6255 Barfield Rd., Atlanta, GA 30328-4369. TEL 404-256-9800. FAX 404-256-3116. Vendor(s): DIALOG. *4523*

BOCOEX INDEX.
Boston Computer Exchange Index, 55 Temple Pl., Boston, MA 02111. TEL 617-542-4414. FAX 617-542-8849. *1423*

BOERNEBIBLIOTEKSKATALOG. BOEGER & TIDSSKRIFTER. FORFATTERKATALOG.
Bibliotekscentralen, Tempovej 7-11, DK-2750 Ballerup, Denmark. TEL 2-974000. FAX 2-655310. *394*

BOERNEBIBLIOTEKSKATALOG. BOEGER & TIDSSKRIFTER. TITELKATALOG.
Bibliotekscentralen, Tempovej 7-11, DK-2750 Ballerup, Denmark. TEL 2-974000. FAX 2-655310. *394*

BOERNEBIBLIOTEKSKATALOG. GRAMMOFONPLADER, KASSETTEBAAND.
Bibliotekscentralen, Tempovej 7-11, DK-2750 Ballerup, Denmark. TEL 2-974000. FAX 2-655310. *3588*

BOERNEBIBLIOTEKSKATALOG. LYDBOEGER, BOG & BAAND.
Bibliotekscentralen, Tempovej 7-11, DK-2750 Ballerup, Denmark. TEL 2-974000. FAX 2-655310. *1247*

BOLETIN DE TRADUCCIONES.
Instituto de Informacion y Documentacion en Ciencia y Tecnologia, Joaquin Costa 22, 28002 Madrid, Spain. *4354*

BOND BUYER.
American Banker, Bond Buyer, One State St. Plaza, New York, NY 10004. TEL 212-943-9589. FAX 212-943-6256. Vendor(s): DIALOG (File no.626), Mead Data Central. *940*

BOOK REVIEW DIGEST.
H.W. Wilson Co., 950 University Ave., Bronx, NY 10452. TEL 800-367-6770. FAX 212-538-2716. Vendor(s): Wilsonline (File BRD). *4140*

BOOK REVIEW INDEX.
Gale Research Inc., 835 Penobscot Bldg., Detroit, MI 48226. TEL 313-961-2242. FAX 313-961-6083. Vendor(s): DIALOG (File no.137). *4140*

BOOK WORLD.
Washington Post Co., 1150 15th St., N.W., Washington, DC 20071. TEL 202-334-6000. FAX 202-334-5547. Vendor(s): CompuServe Consumer Information Service, DIALOG, Dow Jones/News Retrieval, Mead Data Central, VU/TEXT Information Services, Inc.. *4122*

BOOKS IN PRINT.
R.R. Bowker, A Reed Reference Publishing Company, Division of Reed Publishing (USA) Inc., 121 Chanlon Rd., New Providence, NJ 07974. TEL 800-521-8110. FAX 908-665-6688. Vendor(s): BRS (BBIP), BRS/Saunders Colleague, DIALOG (File no.470). *394*

BOOKS IN PRINT SUPPLEMENT.
R.R. Bowker, A Reed Reference Publishing Company, Division of Reed Publishing (USA) Inc., 121 Chanlon Rd., New Providence, NJ 07974. TEL 800-521-8110. FAX 908-665-6688. Vendor(s): BRS (BBIP), BRS/Saunders Colleague, DIALOG (File no.470). *394*

BOOKS IN SERIES.
R.R. Bowker, A Reed Reference Publishing Company, Division of Reed Publishing (USA) Inc., 121 Chanlon Rd., New Providence, NJ 07974. TEL 800-521-8110. FAX 908-665-6688. *394*

BOOKS OUT-OF-PRINT.
R.R. Bowker, A Reed Reference Publishing Company, Division of Reed Publishing (USA) Inc., 121 Chanlon Rd., New Providence, NJ 07974. TEL 800-521-8110. FAX 908-665-6688. Vendor(s): BRS (BBIP), BRS/Saunders Colleague, DIALOG (File no.470). *395*

BOOT COVE ECONOMIC FORECAST.
Voight Industries, Inc., Box 200, Lubec, ME 04652. TEL 207-733-5593. Vendor(s): NewsNet. *847*

BORDER CROSSINGS.
Arts Manitoba Publications Inc., Y300-393 Portage Ave., Winnipeg, Man. R3B 3H6, Canada. TEL 204-942-5778. FAX 204-949-0793. *319*

BOSTON BUSINESS JOURNAL.
P & L Publications, 451 D St., Boston, MA 02210. TEL 617-330-1000. FAX 617-330-1015. Vendor(s): DIALOG. *847*

BOSTON COLLEGE ENVIRONMENTAL AFFAIRS LAW REVIEW.
Boston College, School of Law, 885 Centre St., Newton, MA 02159. TEL 617-552-4354. *1944*

BOSTON COLLEGE LAW REVIEW.
Boston College, School of Law, 885 Centre St., Newton, MA 02159. TEL 617-969-0100. Vendor(s): WESTLAW. *2605*

BOSTON UNIVERSITY LAW REVIEW.
Boston University, School of Law, 765 Commonwealth Ave., Boston, MA 02215. TEL 617-353-3118. Vendor(s): WESTLAW. *2605*

BOTTIN ENTREPRISES.
Societe Bottin, 31 Cours de Juilliottes, 94706 Maisons-Alfort Cedex, France. TEL 1-49-81-56-56. FAX 1-49-77-85-28. *1123*

THE BOWKER ANNUAL LIBRARY AND BOOK TRADE ALMANAC.
R.R. Bowker, A Reed Reference Publishing Company, Division of Reed Publishing (USA) Inc., 121 Chanlon Rd., New Providence, NJ 07974. TEL 800-521-8110. FAX 908-665-6688. Vendor(s): BRS, DIALOG, European Space Agency, Orbit Information Technologies. *2749*

BOYS' LIFE (INKPRINT EDITION).
Boy Scouts of America, Box 152079, Irving, TX 75015-2079. TEL 214-580-2000. Vendor(s): DIALOG. *1250*

BRAIN AND NERVE.
Igaku-Shoin Ltd., 5-24-3 Hongo, Bunkyo-ku, Tokyo 113-91, Japan. TEL 03-817-5701. Vendor(s): JICST. *3332*

BRANCH AUTOMATION NEWS.
Phillips Publishing, Inc., 7811 Montrose Rd., Potomac, MD 20854. TEL 301-340-2100. FAX 301-309-3847. Vendor(s): Data-Star, DIALOG, NewsNet. *805*

BRANDS AND THEIR COMPANIES.
Gale Research Inc., 835 Penobscot Bldg., Detroit, MI 48226. TEL 313-961-2242. FAX 313-961-6083. Vendor(s): DIALOG. *3673*

BRAZIL SERVICE.
Eurostudy Publishing Co. Ltd., Ludgate House, 107 Fleet St., London EC4A 2AB, England. TEL 44-71-583-1025. FAX 44-71-583-5958. Vendor(s): Data-Star (FSRI), DIALOG. *648*

BREWING RESEARCH CONVENTION. CURRENT AWARENESS MONTHLY.
European Brewery Convention, Box 510, NL-2380 BB Zoeterwoude, Netherlands. TEL 31-71-456047. FAX 31-71-410013. *388*

BRIEF (CHICAGO).
American Bar Association, Tort and Insurance Practice Section, 750 N. Lake Shore Dr., Chicago, IL 60611. TEL 312-988-5555. Vendor(s): WESTLAW (BRIEF). *2605*

BRIGHAM YOUNG UNIVERSITY LAW REVIEW.
Brigham Young University, J. Reuben Clark Law School, 453 JRCB, Provo, UT 84602. TEL 801-378-5678. FAX 801-378-3595. Vendor(s): WESTLAW. *2605*

BRISBANE CITYSCOPE.
Cityscope Publications Pty. Ltd., P.O. Box 807, Manly, N.S.W. 2095, Australia. TEL 02-976-2233. FAX 02-976-2263. *4160*

BRITISH CATALOGUE OF AUDIO-VISUAL MATERIALS.
British Library, Bibliographic Services, 2 Sheraton St., London W1V 4BH, England. TEL 01-323 7077. *4462*

BRITISH CATALOGUE OF MUSIC.
Bowker-Saur Ltd, 59-60 Grosvenor St., London W1X 9DA, England. TEL 071-493-5841. FAX 071-499-1590. *3542*

BRITISH COLUMBIA DECISIONS - CIVIL CASES.
Western Legal Publications, 301-1 Alexander St., Vancouver, B.C. V6A 1B2, Canada. TEL 604-681-5671. FAX 604-687-2796. *2701*

BRITISH COLUMBIA DECISIONS - CRIMINAL CONVICTION AND SENTENCE CASES.
Western Legal Publications, 301-1 Alexander St., Vancouver, B.C. V6A 1B2, Canada. TEL 604-687-5671. FAX 604-687-2796. *2712*

BRITISH COLUMBIA DECISIONS - FAMILY LAW CASES.
Western Legal Publications, 301-1 Alexander St., Vancouver, B.C. V6A 1B2, Canada. TEL 604-687-5671. FAX 604-687-2796. *2716*

BRITISH COLUMBIA DECISIONS - INDUSTRIAL RELATIONS COUNCIL.
Western Legal Publications, 301-1 Alexander St., Vancouver, B.C. V6A 1B2, Canada. TEL 604-687-5671. FAX 604-687-2796. *2707*

BRITISH COLUMBIA DECISIONS - INSURANCE LAW CASES.
Western Legal Publications, 301-1 Alexander St., Vancouver, B.C. V6A 1B2, Canada. TEL 604-687-5671. FAX 604-687-2796. *2606*

BRITISH COLUMBIA DECISIONS, LABOUR ARBITRATION.
Western Legal Publications, 301 One Alexander St., Vancouver, B.C. V6A 1B2, Canada. TEL 604-687-5671. FAX 604-687-2796. *974*

BRITISH COLUMBIA DECISIONS - MUNICIPAL LAW CASES.
Western Legal Publications, 301-1 Alexander St., Vancouver, B.C. V6A 1B2, Canada. TEL 604-687-5671. FAX 604-687-2796. *2606*

BRITISH EDUCATION INDEX.
British Education Index, Brotherton Library, University of Leeds, Leeds LS2 9JT, England. TEL 0532-335524. FAX 0532-336017.
Vendor(s): DIALOG (File no.121). *1675*

BRITISH EXPORTS.
Kompass Windsor Court, East Grinstead House, East Grinstead, West Sussex RH19 1XD, England. TEL 0342-326972. FAX 0342-317241. *1124*

BRITISH HEART JOURNAL.
B M J Publishing Group, B.M.A. House, Tavistock Sq., London WC1H 9JR, England. TEL 071-387-4499.
Vendor(s): BRS, BRS/Saunders Colleague. *3205*

BRITISH JOURNAL OF CLINICAL PHARMACOLOGY.
Blackwell Scientific Publications Ltd., Osney Mead, Oxford OX2 0EL, England. TEL 0865-240201. FAX 0865-721205. *3719*

BRITISH JOURNAL OF CLINICAL PRACTICE.
Medicom UK Ltd., The Quandrant, 118 London Rd., Kingston-upon-Thames KT2 6QJ, England. TEL 081-541-5666. FAX 081-541-4746. *3084*

BRITISH JOURNAL OF DERMATOLOGY.
Blackwell Scientific Publications Ltd., Osney Mead, Oxford OX2 0EL, England. TEL 0865-240201. FAX 0865-721205. *3246*

BRITISH JOURNAL OF OBSTETRICS & GYNAECOLOGY.
Blackwell Scientific Publications Ltd., Osney Mead, Oxford OX2 0EL, England. TEL 0865-240201. FAX 0865-721205.
Vendor(s): BRS. *3290*

BRITISH JOURNAL OF PHARMACOLOGY.
Macmillan Press Ltd., Scientific & Medical Division, Houndmills, Basingstoke, Hampshire RG21 2XS, England. TEL 0256-29242. FAX 0256-810526. *3719*

BRITISH JOURNAL OF RHEUMATOLOGY.
Bailliere Tindall, 24-28 Oval Rd., London NW1 7DX, England.
Vendor(s): BRS. *3084*

BRITISH JOURNAL OF SURGERY.
Butterworth - Heinemann Ltd. Linacre House, Jordan Hill, Oxford OX2 8DP, England. TEL 0865-310366. FAX 0865-310898.
Vendor(s): BRS, Mead Data Central. *3376*

BRITISH JOURNAL OF UROLOGY.
Churchill Livingstone Medical Journals, Robert Stevenson House, 1-3 Baxter's Pl., Leith Walk, Edinburgh EH1 3AF, Scotland. TEL 031-556-2424. FAX 031-558-1278.
Vendor(s): BRS. *3387*

BRITISH LIBRARY. DOCUMENT SUPPLY CENTRE. INDEX OF CONFERENCE PROCEEDINGS.
British Library, Document Supply Centre, Boston Spa, Wetherby, W. Yorkshire LS23 7BQ, England. TEL 0937-843434. FAX 0937-546333. *3395*

BRITISH MEDICAL BULLETIN.
Churchill Livingstone Medical Journals, Robert Stevenson House, 1-3 Baxter's Pl., Leith Walk, Edinburgh EH1 3AF, Scotland. TEL 031-556-2424. FAX 031-558-1278. *3084*

BRITISH MEDICAL JOURNAL.
B M J Publishing Group, B.M.A. House, Tavistock Sq., London WC1H 9JR, England. TEL 071-387-4499.
Vendor(s): BRS, BRS/Saunders Colleague. *3084*

BRITISH NATIONAL BIBLIOGRAPHY.
British Library, National Bibliographic Service, Boston Spa, Wetherby, W. Yorkshire LS23 7BQ, England. TEL 0937-546613. FAX 0937-546586. *4140*

BRITISH RATE AND DATA.
Maclean Hunter Ltd., Maclean Hunter House, Chalk Lane, Cockfosters Rd., Barnet, Herts EN4 0BU, England. TEL 081-975-9759. FAX 081-440-1796. *395*

BROADCAST WEEK.
Globe and Mail Ltd., 444 Front St. W., Toronto, Ont. M5V 2S9, Canada. TEL 416-585-5045. *1332*

BROADCASTING (WASHINGTON).
Cahners Publishing Company (Washington), Division of Reed Publishing (USA) Inc. 1705 DeSales St., N.W., Washington, DC 20036. TEL 202-659-2340. FAX 202-429-0651.
Vendor(s): DIALOG. *1369*

BROKER REPORT INDEX.
MappMail Publications, 575 Bourke St., Level 3, Melbourne, Vic. 3000, Australia. FAX 03-614-6587. *941*

BROOKLYN JOURNAL OF INTERNATIONAL LAW.
Brooklyn Law School, 250 Joralemon, Brooklyn, NY 11201. TEL 718-780-7971.
Vendor(s): WESTLAW. *2720*

BROOKLYN LAW REVIEW.
Brooklyn Law School, 250 Joralemon St., Brooklyn, NY 11201. TEL 718-780-7968.
Vendor(s): Mead Data Central. *2606*

BUFFALO LAW REVIEW.
State University of New York at Buffalo, Buffalo Law Review, 605 John Lord O'Brian Hall, Amherst Campus, Amherst, NY 14260. TEL 716-626-2059. FAX 716-636-2064.
Vendor(s): WESTLAW. *2606*

BUILDING DESIGN & CONSTRUCTION.
Cahners Publishing Company (Des Plaines) Division of Reed Publishing (USA) Inc., 1350 E. Touhy Ave., Box 5080, Des Plaines, IL 60017-5080. TEL 708-635-8800. FAX 708-635-9950.
Vendor(s): DIALOG. *606*

BUILDING SUPPLY HOME CENTERS.
Cahners Publishing Company (Des Plaines) Division of Reed Publishing (USA) Inc., 1350 E. Touhy Ave., Box 5080, Des Plaines, IL 60017-5080. TEL 708-635-8800. FAX 708-635-9950.
Vendor(s): DIALOG, Dow Jones/News Retrieval. *607*

BUILDINGS.
Stamats Communications, Inc., c/o Wayne Bayliss, 427 Sixth Ave., S.E., Box 1888, Cedar Rapids, IA 52406. TEL 319-364-6167. FAX 319-364-4278.
Vendor(s): DIALOG. *607*

THE BULLETIN (AUSTIN).
Publications & Communications, Inc., 12416 Hymeadow Dr., Austin, TX 78750-1896. TEL 512-250-9023. FAX 512-331-3900. *1458*

BULLETIN OF ENTOMOLOGICAL RESEARCH.
C.A.B. International, Wallingford, Oxon OX10 8DE, England. TEL 0491-32111. FAX 0491-33508.
Vendor(s): BRS, CISTI, DIMDI, DIALOG, European Space Agency. *529*

BULLETIN ON NARCOTICS.
United Nations Publications, Room DC2-853, New York, NY 10017. TEL 212-963-8300. FAX 212-963-3489. *1535*

BULLETIN ON THE RHEUMATIC DISEASES.
Arthritis Foundation, 1314 Spring St., N.W., Atlanta, GA 30309. TEL 404-872-7100. FAX 404-872-0457.
Vendor(s): Mead Data Central. *3368*

BULLETIN ON TRAINING.
The Bureau of National Affairs, Inc., 1231 25th St., N.W., Washington, DC 20037. TEL 202-452-4200. FAX 202-822-8092.
Vendor(s): Human Resources Information Network (CDD, HDD). *1063*

BULLETIN SIGNALETIQUE. PART 519: PHILOSOPHIE.
Centre National de la Recherche Scientifique, Institut del'Information Scientifique et Technique, 54 bd. Raspail, 75270 Paris Cedex 06, France. FAX 45-48-70-15.
Vendor(s): Telesystemes - Questel. *3787*

BULLETIN SIGNALETIQUE. PART 520: SCIENCES DE L'EDUCATION.
Centre National de la Recherche Scientifique, Institut de l'Information Scientifique et Technique, 54 bd. Raspail, 75270 Paris cedex 06, France. FAX 45487015.
Vendor(s): Telesystemes - Questel. *1675*

BULLETIN SIGNALETIQUE. PART 522: HISTOIRE DES SCIENCES ET DES TECHNIQUES.
Centre National de la Recherche Scientifique, Institut de l'Information Scientifique et Technique, 54 bd. Raspail, 75270 Paris cedex 06, France. FAX 45487015.
Vendor(s): European Space Agency, Telesystemes - Questel. *2328*

BULLETIN SIGNALETIQUE. PART 523: HISTOIRE ET SCIENCES DE LA LITTERATURE.
Centre National de la Recherche Scientifique, Institut de l'Information Scientifique et Technique, 54 bd. Raspail, 75270 Paris Cedex 06, France. FAX 45487015.
Vendor(s): Telesystemes - Questel. *2981*

BULLETIN SIGNALETIQUE. PART 524: SCIENCES DU LANGAGE.
Centre National de la Recherche Scientifique, Institut de l'Information Scientifique et Technique, 54 bd. Raspail, 75270 Paris cedex 06, France. FAX 45487015.
Vendor(s): Telesystemes - Questel. *2855*

BULLETIN SIGNALETIQUE. PART 525: PREHISTOIRE ET PROTOHISTOIRE.
Centre National de la Recherche Scientifique, Institut de l'Information Scientifique et Technique, 54 bd. Raspail, 75270 Paris cedex 06, France. FAX 45487015.
Vendor(s): Telesystemes - Questel. *2328*

BULLETIN SIGNALETIQUE. PART 526: ART ET ARCHEOLOGIE.
Centre National de la Recherche Scientifique, Institut de l'Information Scientifique et Technique, 54 bd. Raspail, 75270 Paris cedex 06, France. FAX 45487015.
Vendor(s): Telesystemes - Questel. *352*

BULLETIN SIGNALETIQUE. PART 527: HISTOIRE ET SCIENCES DES RELIGIONS.
Centre National de la Recherche Scientifique, Institut de l'Information Scientifique et Technique, 54 bd. Raspail, 75270 Paris cedex 06, France. FAX 45487015.
Vendor(s): Telesystemes - Questel. *4212*

BULLETIN SIGNALETIQUE. PART 528: BIBLIOGRAPHIE INTERNATIONALE DE SCIENCE ADMINISTRATIVE.
Centre National de la Recherche Scientifique, Institut de l'Information Scientifique et Technique, 54 bd. Raspail, 75270 Paris cedex 06, France. FAX 45487015.
Vendor(s): Telesystemes - Questel. *707*

BULLETIN SIGNALETIQUE. PART 529: ETHNOLOGIE.
Centre National de la Recherche Scientifique, Institut de l'Information Scientifique et Technique, 54 bd. Raspail, 75270 Paris cedex 06, France. FAX 45487015.
Vendor(s): Telesystemes - Questel. *254*

BULLETIN SIGNALETIQUE. PART 529: SOCIOLOGIE.
Centre National de la Recherche Scientifique, Institut de l'Information Scientifique et Technique, 54 bd. Raspail, 75270 Paris cedex 06, France. FAX 45487015.
Vendor(s): Telesystemes - Questel. *4457*

BULLETIN SIGNALETIQUE D'INFORMATION ADMINISTRATIVE.
Documentation Francaise, 29-31 quai Voltaire, 75340 Paris cedex 07, France. TEL 1-4015-7000.
Vendor(s): European Space Agency. *4079*

BULLETIN SIGNALETIQUE DES TELECOMMUNICATIONS.
Centre National d'Etudes des Telecommunications, Service des Abonnements, 38-40 rue du General Leclerc, 92131 Issy-les-Moulineaux Cedex, France. TEL 45-29-51-08.
Vendor(s): Telesystemes - Questel. *1332*

BULLETIN TO MANAGEMENT.
The Bureau of National Affairs, Inc., 1231 25th St., N.W., Washington, DC 20037. TEL 202-452-4200. FAX 202-822-8092.
Vendor(s): Human Resources Information Network (CDD, HDD). *1063*

BULLETIN WITH NEWSWEEK.
Australian Consolidated Press, 54-58 Park St., Sydney, N.S.W. 2000, Australia. TEL 02-282-8200. FAX 02-267-2150. *2171*

BUSINESS AMERICA.
U.S. Department of Commerce, 14th St. Between Constitution Ave. and Pennsylvania Ave., N.W., Washington, DC 20230. TEL 202-377-3251. FAX 202-377-5819.
Vendor(s): DIALOG, Dow Jones/News Retrieval. *833*

BUSINESS AND COMMERCIAL AVIATION.
McGraw-Hill, Inc., 1221 Ave. of the Americas, New York, NY 10020. TEL 212-512-2000.
Vendor(s): DIALOG. *49*

BUSINESS AND THE ENVIRONMENT.
Cutter Information Corp., 37 Broadway, Arlington, MA 02174-5539. TEL 617-648-8700. FAX 617-648-8708.
Vendor(s): Data-Star, DIALOG, NewsNet. *1944*

BUSINESS ASIA.
Business International Corp., 215 Park Ave. S., New York, NY 10003. TEL 212-460-0600. FAX 212-995-8837.
Vendor(s): DIALOG. *649*

BUSINESS ATLANTA.
Communication Channels, Inc., 6255 Barfield Rd., Atlanta, GA 30328-4369. TEL 404-256-9800. FAX 404-256-3116.
Vendor(s): DIALOG. *649*

BUSINESS AVIATION WEEKLY.
McGraw-Hill, Inc., Aviation Week Group, 1156 15th St., N.W., Washington, DC 20005. TEL 202-822-4600.
Vendor(s): DIALOG (File no.624/McGRAW-HILL PUBLICATIONS ONLINE), Dow Jones/News Retrieval, Mead Data Central (WBA). *4671*

BUSINESS COMPUTER DIGEST.
Association of Computer Users, Box 2189, Berkeley, CA 94702-0189. TEL 303-241-0125.
Vendor(s): NewsNet. *825*

BUSINESS DIGEST OF DELAWARE VALLEY.
Business Digest of Philadelphia Inc., 2449 Golf Rd., Philadelphia, PA 19131. TEL 215-477-8620.
Vendor(s): DIALOG. *1113*

BUSINESS DIGEST OF LEHIGH VALLEY.
Business Digest, Inc., Box 324, Bala Cynwyd, PA 19004. TEL 215-477-8620. FAX 215-477-7054.
Vendor(s): DIALOG. *650*

BUSINESS EAST MIDLANDS.
Business Magazine Group, Briarwood House, St. John St., Mansfield, Notts NG18 1QH, England. TEL 0623-422522. FAX 0623-27479. *650*

BUSINESS EASTERN EUROPE.
Business International Corp., 215 Park Ave. S., New York, NY 10003. TEL 212-460-0600. FAX 212-995-8837.
Vendor(s): DIALOG. *848*

BUSINESS EUROPE.
Business International Corp., 215 Park Ave. S., New York, NY 10003. TEL 212-460-0600. FAX 212-995-8837.
Vendor(s): DIALOG. *902*

BUSINESS FIRST.
Business First of New York, Inc., 472 Delaware Ave., Buffalo, NY 14202. TEL 716-822-6200. FAX 716-822-3020.
Vendor(s): DIALOG. *650*

BUSINESS HISTORY.
Frank Cass & Co. Ltd., Gainsborough House, 11 Gainsborough Rd., London E11 1RS, England. TEL 081-530-4226. FAX 081-530-7795.
Vendor(s): Information Access Company. *650*

BUSINESS HISTORY REVIEW.
Harvard Business School, Soldiers Field, Boston, MA 02163. TEL 617-495-6154. FAX 617-495-6001.
Vendor(s): DIALOG. *650*

BUSINESS HORIZONS.
Indiana University, School of Business, Bloomington, IN 47405. TEL 812-855-6342.
Vendor(s): DIALOG. *650*

BUSINESS INDEX.
Information Access Company, 362 Lakeside Dr., Foster City, CA 94404. TEL 800-227-8431. FAX 415-378-5499.
Vendor(s): BRS, DIALOG (File no.148), Mead Data Central. *707*

BUSINESS INSURANCE.
Crain Communications, Inc. (Chicago), 740 Rush St., Chicago, IL 60611. TEL 312-649-5286. FAX 312-280-3174.
Vendor(s): Mead Data Central. *2529*

BUSINESS INTERNATIONAL.
Business International Corp., 215 Park Ave. S., New York, NY 10003. TEL 212-460-0600. FAX 212-995-8837.
Vendor(s): DIALOG. *902*

BUSINESS INTERNATIONAL MONEY REPORT.
Business International Corp., 215 Park Ave. S., New York, NY 10003. TEL 212-460-0600. FAX 212-995-8837.
Vendor(s): DIALOG. *769*

BUSINESS JOURNAL (PHOENIX).
Phoenix Business Journal, Inc., 3737 N. 7th St., Ste. 200, Phoenix, AZ 85014-5017. TEL 602-230-8400.
Vendor(s): DIALOG. *651*

BUSINESS JOURNAL SERVING GREATER MILWAUKEE.
Business Journal of Milwaukee Inc., 2025 N. Summit Ave., Milwaukee, WI 53202. TEL 414-278-7788.
Vendor(s): DIALOG. *651*

BUSINESS LATIN AMERICA.
Business International Corp., 215 Park Ave. S., New York, NY 10003. TEL 212-460-0600. FAX 212-995-8837.
Vendor(s): DIALOG. *848*

BUSINESS LAW BRIEF.
Financial Times Business Information Ltd., Tower House, Southampton St., London WC2E 7HA, England. TEL 071-240 9391. FAX 071-240-7946.
Vendor(s): Data-Star, Mead Data Central. *2707*

BUSINESS LAWYER.
American Bar Association, Business Law Section, 750 N. Lake Shore Dr., Chicago, IL 60611. TEL 312-988-5588.
Vendor(s): Mead Data Central (BUSLAW), WESTLAW (BUSLAW). *2707*

BUSINESS NEW HAMPSHIRE MAGAZINE.
Laurentian Business Publishing Inc., 404 Chestnut St., Ste. 201, Manchester, NH 03101. TEL 603-626-6354.
Vendor(s): DIALOG. *834*

BUSINESS: NORTH CAROLINA.
News and Observer Publishing Co., 5435 77 Center Dr., Ste. 50, Charlotte, NC 28217-0711. TEL 704-523-6987. FAX 704-523-4211.
Vendor(s): DIALOG. *1113*

SERIALS AVAILABLE ONLINE 5055

BUSINESS NORTH EAST.
Business Magazine Group, Briarwood House, St. John St., Mansfield, Notts NG18 1QH, England. TEL 0642-232882. FAX 0623-232899. *651*

BUSINESS ORGANIZATIONS, AGENCIES, AND PUBLICATIONS DIRECTORY.
Gale Research Inc., 835 Penobscot Bldg., Detroit, MI 48226. TEL 313-961-2242. FAX 313-961-6083. *1125*

BUSINESS PERIODICALS INDEX.
H.W. Wilson Co., 950 University Ave., Bronx, NY 10452. TEL 800-367-6770. FAX 212-538-2716.
Vendor(s): Wilsonline (File BPI). *707*

BUSINESS QUARTERLY.
University of Western Ontario, School of Business Administration, c/o Andrew Grindlay, Ed., London, Ont. N6A 3K7, Canada. TEL 519-661-3309. FAX 519-661-3838.
Vendor(s): DIALOG. *652*

BUSINESS RECORD.
Business Publications Corporation, The Depot at Fourth, 100 4th St., Des Moines, IA 50309. TEL 515-288-3336. FAX 515-288-0309.
Vendor(s): DIALOG. *652*

BUSINESS TIMES.
Business Times, Inc., Box 580, New Haven, CT 06513-0580. *848*

BUSINESS TRAVEL NEWS.
C M P Publications, Inc., 600 Community Dr., Manhasset, NY 11030. TEL 516-562-5000. FAX 516-365-4601.
Vendor(s): Data-Star, DIALOG. *4755*

BUSINESS WEEK.
McGraw-Hill, Inc., 1221 Ave. of the Americas, New York, NY 10020. TEL 212-512-2000.
Vendor(s): DIALOG (File no.624/McGRAW-HILL PUBLICATIONS ONLINE), Dow Jones/News Retrieval, Mead Data Central. *652*

BUSINESS WEST MIDLANDS.
Business Magazine Group, Briarwood House, St. John St., Mansfield, Notts NG18 1QH, England. TEL 021-308-0077. FAX 021-308-0385. *653*

THE BUSINESS WHO'S WHO OF AUSTRALIA.
Riddell Informetion Services Pty. Ltd., 100 Alexander St., Crowns Nest, N.S.W. 2065, Australia.
Vendor(s): AUSINET. *1125*

BUYOUTS.
Venture Economics, Inc., 11 Farnsworth St., Boston, MA 02210-1223. TEL 617-449-2100.
Vendor(s): Data-Star, DIALOG. *941*

BYTE.
McGraw-Hill, Inc., Byte Publications, One Phoenix Mill Lane, Peterborough, NH 03458. TEL 603-924-9281.
Vendor(s): DIALOG (File no.624/McGRAW-HILL PUBLICATIONS ONLINE), Dow Jones/News Retrieval, Mead Data Central. *1436*

C.A.B. INTERNATIONAL BUREAU OF AGRICULTURAL ECONOMICS. ANNOTATED BIBLIOGRAPHIES SERIES A.
C.A.B. International, Wallingford, Oxon OX10 8DE, England. TEL 0491-32111. FAX 0491-33508.
Vendor(s): BRS, CISTI, DIMDI, DIALOG, European Space Agency. *134*

C.A.B. INTERNATIONAL BUREAU OF AGRICULTURAL ECONOMICS. ANNOTATED BIBLIOGRAPHIES. SERIES B: AGRICULTURAL POLICY AND RURAL DEVELOPMENT IN AFRICA.
C.A.B. International, Wallingford, Oxon OX10 8DE, England. TEL 0491-32111. FAX 0491-33508.
Vendor(s): BRS, CISTI, DIMDI, DIALOG, European Space Agency. *134*

C.A.B. INTERNATIONAL. BUREAU OF NUTRITION. ANNOTATED BIBLIOGRAPHIES.
C.A.B. International, Wallingford, Oxon OX10 8DE, England. TEL 0491-32111. FAX 0491-33508.
Vendor(s): BRS, CISTI, DIMDI, DIALOG, European Space Agency. *3613*

5056 SERIALS AVAILABLE ONLINE

C.A.B. INTERNATIONAL. BUREAU OF SOILS. ANNOTATED BIBLIOGRAPHIES.
C.A.B. International, Wallingford, Oxon OX10 8DE, England. TEL 0491-32111. FAX 0491-33508.
Vendor(s): BRS, CISTI, DIMDI, DIALOG, European Space Agency. *134*

C A D - C A M UPDATE.
Worldwide Videotex, Box 138, Babson Park, Boston, MA 02157. TEL 617-449-1603.
Vendor(s): NewsNet. *1420*

C A S E STRATEGIES.
Cutter Information Corp., 37 Broadway, Arlington, MA 02174. TEL 617-648-8700. FAX 617-648-8707.
Vendor(s): Data-Star, DIALOG, NewsNet. *1877*

C A S E TRENDS.
Software Productivity Group, Inc., Box 294, Shrewsbury, MA 01545-0294. TEL 508-842-4500. FAX 508-842-7119. *1443*

C B A RECORD.
Chicago Bar Association, 321 S. Plymouth Ct., Chicago, IL 60604-3907.
Vendor(s): WESTLAW. *2607*

C D C - A I D S WEEKLY.
Charles W. Henderson, Ed. & Pub., Box 5528, Atlanta, GA 30307-0528. TEL 404-377-8895. FAX 205-991-1479.
Vendor(s): Data-Star (PTS NEWSLETTER DATABASE), DIALOG (file no.636), NewsNet. *3218*

C D COMPUTING NEWS.
Worldwide Videotex, Box 138, Babson Park, Boston, MA 02157. TEL 617-449-1603.
Vendor(s): DIALOG, NewsNet. *1423*

C D - R O M DATABASES.
Worldwide Videotex, Box 138, Babson Park, Boston, MA 02157. TEL 617-449-1603.
Vendor(s): DIALOG, NewsNet. *2796*

C D - R O M LIBRARIAN.
Meckler Publishing Corporation, 11 Ferry Lane W., Westport, CT 06880-5808. TEL 203-226-6967.
Vendor(s): DIALOG, NewsNet. *2750*

C D - R O M PROFESSIONAL.
Pemberton Press Inc., 11 Tannery Ln., Weston, CT 06883. TEL 800-248-8466. FAX 203-222-0122.
Vendor(s): DIALOG (File no.170). *2796*

C E R F NET NEWS.
California Education and Research Federation Network, c/o San Diego Supercomputer Center, Box 85608, San Diego, CA 92186-9784. TEL 619-534-5087. *1426*

C I C'S STATE SCHOOL DIRECTORIES.
Market Data Retrieval, Inc., 16 Progress Dr., Shelton, CT 06484. TEL 203-926-4800. FAX 203-926-0721.
Vendor(s): DIALOG. *1692*

C I M STRATEGIES.
Cutter Information Corp., 37 Broadway, Arlington, MA 02174. TEL 617-648-8700. FAX 617-648-8707.
Vendor(s): NewsNet. *1412*

C I S INDEX.
Congressional Information Service, 4520 East-West Hwy., Ste. 800, Bethesda, MD 20814. TEL 301-654-1550. FAX 301-654-4033.
Vendor(s): DIALOG (File no.101). *4079*

C L A S E.
Universidad Nacional Autonoma de Mexico, Centro de Informacion Cientifica y Humanistica, Ciudad Universitaria, Apdo. Postal 70-392, C.P. 04510 Mexico, D.F., Mexico. *2519*

C L E JOURNAL AND REGISTER.
American Law Institute, Committee on Continuing Professional Education, 4025 Chestnut St., Philadelphia, PA 19104. TEL 215-243-1604. FAX 215-243-1664. *2608*

C M I DESCRIPTIONS OF FUNGI AND BACTERIA.
C.A.B. International, Wallingford, Oxon OX10 8DE, England. TEL 0491-32111. FAX 0491-33508.
Vendor(s): BRS, CISTI, DIMDI, DIALOG, European Space Agency. *434*

C O N S E R MICROFICHE.
National Library of Canada, Canadiana Editorial Division, 395 Wellington St., Ottawa, Ont. K1A 0N4, Canada. TEL 819-994-6918. *396*

THE C P A JOURNAL.
New York State Society of Certified Public Accountants, 200 Park Ave., New York, NY 10166-0010. TEL 212-973-8300. FAX 212-972-5710.
Vendor(s): DIALOG. *748*

C P T.
American Medical Association, 515 N. State St., Chicago, IL 60610. TEL 312-464-0183. FAX 312-464-5834. *3085*

C Q'S WASHINGTON ALERT.
Congressional Quarterly Inc., 1414 22nd St., N.W., Washington, DC 20037. TEL 202-887-8500. FAX 202-728-1863. *4085*

C S A NEUROSCIENCES ABSTRACTS.
Cambridge Scientific Abstracts, 7200 Wisconsin Ave., 6th Fl., Bethesda, MD 20814. TEL 301-961-6750. FAX 301-961-6720.
Vendor(s): BRS (CSAL), DIALOG (File no.76/LIFE SCIENCES COLLECTION). *3168*

C S E L T INFOTEL.
C S E L T - Centro Studi e Laboratori Telecomunicazioni S.p.A., Via Reiss Romoli, 274, 10148 Turin, Italy. TEL 39-11-2285111. FAX 39-11-2285095.
Vendor(s): European Space Agency. *1346*

C S E MONOGRAPH SERIES IN EVALUATION.
University of California, Los Angeles, Center for the Study of Evaluation, 405 Hilgard Ave., 145 Moore Hall, Los Angeles, CA 90024-1522. TEL 213-206-1512. *1745*

C S I CONGRESSIONAL RECORD ABSTRACTS: MASTER EDITION.
National Standards, 1200 Quince Orchard Blvd., Gaithersburg, MD 20878.
Vendor(s): BRS, DIALOG. *4080*

C S I FEDERAL INDEX.
National Standards, 1200 Quince Orchard Blvd., Gaithersburg, MD 20878.
Vendor(s): DIALOG (File no.20). *4080*

C S I FEDERAL REGISTER ABSTRACTS: MASTER EDITION.
National Standards, 1200 Quince Orchard Blvd., Gaithersburg, MD 20878.
Vendor(s): BRS (FREG), BRS/Saunders Colleague, DIALOG, Orbit Information Technologies. *4080*

C U P NEWS EXCHANGE.
Canadian University Press, 126 York St., Ste. 408, Ottawa, Ont. K1N 5T5, Canada. TEL 613-562-1799. FAX 613-562-1809. *1306*

CADENCE UNIVERSE PERFORMANCE REPORT.
C D A Investment Technologies, Inc., 1355 Piccard Dr., Rockville, MD 20850. TEL 301-975-9600. FAX 301-590-1350. *941*

CALCIFIED TISSUE ABSTRACTS.
Cambridge Scientific Abstracts, 7200 Wisconsin Ave., 6th Fl., Bethesda, MD 20814. TEL 301-961-6750. FAX 301-961-6720.
Vendor(s): BRS (CSAL), DIALOG (File no.76/LIFE SCIENCES COLLECTION). *463*

CALIFORNIA BUSINESS.
221 Main St., Ste. 700, San Francisco, CA 94105. TEL 415-543-8290.
Vendor(s): DIALOG. *849*

CALIFORNIA CONNECTIONS.
California Connections Publications, Box 90396, Long Beach, CA 90809-3096. TEL 213-434-7843. FAX 213-434-4202. *1125*

CALIFORNIA PLANNING AND DEVELOPMENT REPORT.
Torf Fulton Associates, 1275 Sunny Crest Ave., Ventura, CA 93003-1212. TEL 805-642-7838.
Vendor(s): Information Access Company, NewsNet. *4055*

CAMBRIDGE SCIENTIFIC BIOCHEMISTRY ABSTRACTS: PART 1. BIOLOGICAL MEMBRANES.
Cambridge Scientific Abstracts, 7200 Wisconsin Ave., 6th Fl., Bethesda, MD 20814. TEL 301-961-6750. FAX 301-961-6720.
Vendor(s): BRS (CSAL), DIALOG (File no.76/LIFE SCIENCES COLLECTION). *463*

CAMBRIDGE SCIENTIFIC BIOCHEMISTRY ABSTRACTS: PART 2. NUCLEIC ACIDS.
Cambridge Scientific Abstracts, 7200 Wisconsin Ave., 6th Fl., Bethesda, MD 20814. TEL 301-961-6750. FAX 301-961-6720.
Vendor(s): BRS (CSAL), DIALOG (File no.76/LIFE SCIENCES COLLECTION). *463*

CAMBRIDGE SCIENTIFIC BIOCHEMISTRY ABSTRACTS: PART 3. AMINO-ACIDS, PEPTIDES & PROTEINS.
Cambridge Scientific Abstracts, 7200 Wisconsin Ave., 6th Fl., Bethesda, MD 20814. TEL 301-961-6700. FAX 301-961-6720.
Vendor(s): BRS (CSAL), DIALOG (File no.76/LIFE SCIENCES COLLECTION). *464*

CAMPAIGN.
Marketing Publications Ltd., 22 Lancaster Gate, London W2 3LY, England.
Vendor(s): VU/TEXT Information Services, Inc.. *29*

CANADA. PETAWAWA NATIONAL FORESTRY INSTITUTE. INFORMATION REPORTS.
Petawawa National Forestry Institute, Chalk River, Ont. K0J 1J0, Canada. TEL 613-993-1210.
Vendor(s): CISTI (MICROLOG). *2097*

CANADIAN BUSINESS INDEX.
Micromedia Ltd., 20 Victoria St., Toronto, Ont. M5C 2N8, Canada. TEL 416-362-5211. FAX 416-362-6161.
Vendor(s): CISTI, DIALOG (File no.262), IST-INFORMATHEQUE, QL Systems Ltd.. *709*

CANADIAN BUSINESS REVIEW.
Conference Board of Canada, 255 Smyth Road, Ottawa, Ont. K1H 8M7, Canada. TEL 613-526-3280. FAX 613-526-4857.
Vendor(s): DIALOG. *654*

CANADIAN CRIMINAL CASES.
Canada Law Book Inc., 240 Edward St., Aurora, Ont. L4G 3S9, Canada. TEL 416-841-6472. *2712*

CANADIAN EDUCATION INDEX.
Micromedia Ltd., 20 Victoria St., Toronto, Ont. M5C 2N8, Canada. TEL 416-362-5211. FAX 416-362-6161. *1675*

CANADIAN FOREIGN RELATIONS.
Canadian Institute of International Affairs, 15 King's College Circle, Toronto, Ont. M5S 2V9, Canada. TEL 613-996-9134.
Vendor(s): QL Systems Ltd.. *3952*

CANADIAN FOREST INDUSTRIES.
Southam Business Communications Inc. 1450 Don Mills Rd., Don Mills, Ont. M3B 2X7, Canada. TEL 416-445-6641. FAX 416-442-2077. *2113*

CANADIAN JOURNAL OF HOSPITAL PHARMACY.
Canadian Society of Hospital Pharmacists, 1145 Hunt Club Rd., Ste. 350, Ottawa, Ont. K1V 0Y3, Canada. TEL 613-736-9733. FAX 613-736-5660. *3720*

CANADIAN MAGAZINE INDEX.
Micromedia Ltd., 20 Victoria St., Toronto, Ont. M5C 2N8, Canada. TEL 416-362-5211. FAX 416-362-6161.
Vendor(s): CISTI (Canadian Business and Current Affairs), DIALOG (File no.262). *396*

CANADIAN MEDICAL ASSOCIATION JOURNAL.
Canadian Medical Association, 1867 Alta Vista Dr., Box 8650, Ottawa, Ont. K1G 0G8, Canada. TEL 613-731-9331. FAX 613-731-0937.
Vendor(s): BRS. *3086*

CANADIAN MINING JOURNAL.
Southam North American Magazine Group, 1450 Don Mills Rd., Don Mills, Ont. M3B 2X7, Canada. TEL 416-445-6641. FAX 416-442-2272. *3480*

SERIALS AVAILABLE ONLINE 5057

CANADIAN NEWS INDEX.
Micromedia Ltd., 20 Victoria St., Toronto, Ont. M5C 2N8, Canada. TEL 416-362-5211. FAX 416-362-6161.
Vendor(s): CISTI, DIALOG (File no.262), IST-INFORMATHEQUE, QL Systems Ltd.. *2577*

CANADIAN OUTLOOK.
Conference Board of Canada, 255 Smyth Rd., Ottawa, Ont. K1H 8M7, Canada. TEL 613-526-3280. FAX 613-526-4857. *849*

CANADIAN PATENT REPORTER.
Canada Law Book Inc., 240 Edward St., Aurora, Ont. L4G 3S9, Canada. TEL 416-841-6472. *2611*

CANADIAN PERIODICAL INDEX.
Info Globe, 444 Front St. W., Toronto, Ontario M5V 2S9, Canada. TEL 416-585-5250. FAX 416-585-5249. *7*

CANADIAN PHARMACEUTICAL JOURNAL.
Canadian Pharmaceutical Association, 1785 Alta Vista Dr., Ottawa, Ont. K1G 3Y6, Canada. TEL 613-523-7877. FAX 613-523-0445. *3720*

CANADIAN SALES TAX REPORTER.
C C H Canadian Ltd., 6 Garamond Ct., Don Mills, Ont. M3C 1Z5, Canada. TEL 416-441-2992. FAX 416-444-9011.
Vendor(s): QL Systems Ltd.. *1090*

CANADIAN THESES.
National Library of Canada, 395 Wellington St., Ottawa, Ont. K1A 0N4, Canada. TEL 819-994-6912. FAX 819-953-0291.
Vendor(s): CISTI. *396*

CANADIAN WHO'S WHO.
University of Toronto Press, 5201 Dufferin St., Downsview, Ont. M3H 5T8, Canada. TEL 416-667-7791. FAX 416-667-7832. *418*

CANADIANA.
National Library of Canada, 395 Wellington St., Ottawa, Ont. K1A 0N4, Canada. TEL 819-994-6912. FAX 819-953-0291.
Vendor(s): CISTI. *396*

CANADIANA ON MICROFICHE.
National Library of Canada, 395 Wellington St., Ottawa, Ont. K1A 0N4, Canada. TEL 819-994-6912. FAX 819-953-0291.
Vendor(s): CISTI. *396*

CANADIANA PRE-1901.
National Library of Canada, 395 Wellington St., Ottawa, Ont. K1A 0N4, Canada. TEL 819-994-6912. FAX 819-996-0291.
Vendor(s): CISTI. *396*

CAPITAL DISTRICT BUSINESS REVIEW.
Albany Business Journal, Inc., Box 6609, Albany, NY 12206. TEL 518-432-1091.
Vendor(s): DIALOG. *849*

CAR AND DRIVER.
Hachette Magazines, Inc., 1633 Broadway, New York, NY 10009. TEL 212-767-6000.
Vendor(s): DIALOG. *4686*

CARBOHYDRATE RESEARCH.
Elsevier Science Publishers B.V., P.O. Box 211, 1000 AE Amsterdam, Netherlands. TEL 020-5803911. FAX 020-5803598.
Vendor(s): STN International. *1217*

CARD NEWS.
Phillips Publishing, Inc., 7811 Montrose Rd., Potomac, MD 20854. TEL 301-340-2100. FAX 301-309-3847.
Vendor(s): Data-Star, DIALOG, NewsNet. *770*

CARDIOLOGY CLINICS.
W.B. Saunders Co., Curtis Center, Independence Square W., Philadelphia, PA 19106. TEL 215-238-7800.
Vendor(s): BRS, BRS/Saunders Colleague. *3206*

CASE WESTERN RESERVE LAW REVIEW.
Case Western Reserve University, School of Law, Cleveland, OH 44106. TEL 216-368-3313.
Vendor(s): WESTLAW. *2612*

CATALOGO DEGLI EDITORI ITALIANI.
Editrice Bibliografica s.r.l., Viale Vittorio Veneto 24, 20124 Milan, Italy. TEL 02-6597950. *4125*

CATALOGO DEI LIBRI IN COMMERCIO.
Editrice Bibliografica s.r.l., Viale Vittorio Veneto 24, 20124 Milan, Italy. TEL 02-6597950. FAX 02-654624. *397*

CATALOGO DEI PERIODICI ITALIANI.
Editrice Bibliografica s.r.l., Viale Vittorio Veneto 24, 20124 Milan, Italy. TEL 02-6597950. *397*

CATALOGUE AFNOR (NORMES FRANCAISES).
Association Francaise de Normalisation, Tour Europe - Cedex 7, 92049 Paris La Defense, France. TEL 42-91-55-33. FAX 42-91-56-56.
Vendor(s): Telesystemes - Questel. *3445*

CATHOLIC UNIVERSITY LAW REVIEW.
Catholic University of America, Law School, Washington, DC 20064. TEL 202-319-5159.
Vendor(s): Mead Data Central. *2612*

CELL MOTILITY AND THE CYTOSKELETON.
John Wiley & Sons. Inc., Journals, 605 Third Ave., New York, NY 10158. TEL 212-850-6000. FAX 212-850-6088. *523*

CELLULAR SALES & MARKETING.
Creative Communications Inc. (Herndon), Box 1519-BKC, Herndon, VA 22070-1519. TEL 703-742-9696.
Vendor(s): NewsNet. *1362*

CENTRAL AMERICA UPDATE.
University of New Mexico, Latin American Institute, 801 Yale N.E., Albuquerque, NM 87131-1016. TEL 505-277-6839. FAX 505-277-5989.
Vendor(s): DIALOG, Mead Data Central, NewsNet. *3878*

CENTRAL AMERICA UPDATE.
Latin American Working Group, P.O. Box 2207, Sta. P, Toronto, Ont. M5S 2T2, Canada. TEL 416-533-4221. FAX 416-533-4579.
Vendor(s): DIALOG, NewsNet. *3953*

CENTRAL NEW YORK BUSINESS JOURNAL.
4317 E. Genesee St., Ste. 201, DeWitt, NY 13214-2121. TEL 315-446-3510. FAX 315-446-3537.
Vendor(s): DIALOG. *850*

CERAMIC ABSTRACTS.
American Ceramic Society, 735 Ceramic Pl., Westerville, OH 43081. TEL 614-890-6136. FAX 614-899-6109.
Vendor(s): DIALOG (File no.335), Orbit Information Technologies (CERAB), Pergamon Infoline (CERAB), STN International. *1167*

CESKOSLOVENSKA FARMACIE.
Avicenum, Czechoslovak Medical Press, Malostranske nam. 28, Mala Strana, 118 02 Prague 1, Czechoslovakia. *3720*

CHEM-FACTS: AMMONIA.
Chemical Intelligence Services, 39A Bowling Green Lane, London EC1R 0BJ, England. TEL 071-833-3812. FAX 071-833-1563.
Vendor(s): Data-Star, DIALOG, Pergamon Infoline. *1171*

CHEM-FACTS: BELGIUM.
Chemical Intelligence Services, 39A Bowling Green Lane, London EC1R 0BJ, England. TEL 071-833-3812. FAX 071-833-1563.
Vendor(s): Data-Star, DIALOG, Pergamon Infoline. *1171*

CHEM-FACTS: ETHYLENE & PROPYLENE.
Chemical Intelligence Services, 39A Bowling Green Lane, London EC1R 0BJ, England. TEL 071-833-3812. FAX 071-833-1563.
Vendor(s): Data-Star, DIALOG, Pergamon Infoline. *1171*

CHEM-FACTS: FEDERAL REPUBLIC OF GERMANY.
Chemical Intelligence Services, 39A Bowling Green Lane, London EC1R 0BJ, England. TEL 071-833-3812. FAX 071-833-1563.
Vendor(s): Data-Star, DIALOG, Pergamon Infoline. *1171*

CHEM-FACTS: METHANOL.
Chemical Intelligence Services, 39A Bowling Green Lane, London EC1R 0BJ, England. TEL 071-833-3812. FAX 071-833-1563.
Vendor(s): Data-Star, DIALOG, Pergamon Infoline. *1171*

CHEM-FACTS: NETHERLANDS.
Chemical Intelligence Services, 39A Bowling Green Lane, London EC1R 0BJ, England. TEL 071-833-3812. FAX 071-833-1563.
Vendor(s): Data-Star, DIALOG, Pergamon Infoline. *1171*

CHEM-FACTS: POLYETHYLENE.
Chemical Intelligence Services, 39A Bowling Green Lane, London EC1R 0BJ, England. TEL 071-833-3812. FAX 071-833-1563.
Vendor(s): Data-Star, Pergamon Infoline. *1217*

CHEM-FACTS: POLYPROPYLENE.
Chemical Intelligence Services, 39A Bowling Green Lane, London EC1R 0BJ, England. TEL 071-833-3812. FAX 071-833-1563.
Vendor(s): Data-Star, DIALOG, Pergamon Infoline. *1217*

CHEM-FACTS: UNITED KINGDOM.
Chemical Intelligence Services, 39A Bowling Green Lane, London EC1R 0BJ, England. TEL 071-833-3812. FAX 071-833-1563.
Vendor(s): Data-Star, Pergamon Infoline. *1171*

CHEM SOURCES INTERNATIONAL.
Chemical Sources International, Inc., Box 6190, Fernandina Beach, FL 32034-6190. TEL 803-646-7840. FAX 803-646-9938.
Vendor(s): STN International. *1126*

CHEM SOURCES U S A.
Chemical Sources International, Inc., Box 6190, Fernandina Beach, FL 32034-6190. TEL 803-646-7840. FAX 803-646-9938.
Vendor(s): STN International. *1126*

CHEMICAL ABSTRACTS - APPLIED CHEMISTRY AND CHEMICAL ENGINEERING SECTIONS.
Chemical Abstracts Service, 2540 Olentangy River Rd., Box 3012, Columbus, OH 43210. TEL 614-447-3663. FAX 614-447-3713.
Vendor(s): STN International (CA). *1199*

CHEMICAL ABSTRACTS - BIOCHEMISTRY SECTIONS.
Chemical Abstracts Service, 2540 Olentangy River Rd., Box 3012, Columbus, OH 43210. TEL 614-447-3600. FAX 614-447-3713.
Vendor(s): STN International (CA). *1199*

CHEMICAL ABSTRACTS - MACROMOLECULAR SECTIONS.
Chemical Abstracts Service, 2540 Olentangy River Rd., Box 3012, Columbus, OH 43210. TEL 614-447-3600. FAX 614-447-3713.
Vendor(s): STN International (CA). *1199*

CHEMICAL ABSTRACTS - ORGANIC CHEMISTRY SECTIONS.
Chemical Abstracts Service, 2540 Olentangy River Rd., Box 3012, Columbus, OH 43210. TEL 614-447-3600. FAX 614-447-3713.
Vendor(s): STN International (CA). *1199*

CHEMICAL ABSTRACTS - PHYSICAL, INORGANIC AND ANALYTICAL CHEMISTRY SECTIONS.
Chemical Abstracts Service, 2540 Olentangy River Rd., Box 3012, Columbus, OH 43210. TEL 614-447-3600. FAX 614-447-3713.
Vendor(s): STN International (CA). *1199*

CHEMICAL ABSTRACTS - SECTION GROUPINGS.
Chemical Abstracts Service, 2540 Olentangy River Rd., Box 3012, Columbus, OH 43210. TEL 614-447-3600. FAX 614-447-3713.
Vendor(s): BRS (CHEM), CISTI, Data-Star, DIALOG (CA SEARCH), European Space Agency (File no.2/CHEMABS), Orbit Information Technologies (CAS82), STN International (CA), Telesystemes - Questel (CAS). *1199*

CHEMICAL ABSTRACTS SERVICE SOURCE INDEX.
Chemical Abstracts Service, 2540 Olentangy River Rd., Columbus, OH 43210. TEL 614-447-3600. FAX 614-447-3713.
Vendor(s): Orbit Information Technologies (CASSI), STN International (CA). *1199*

CHEMICAL AGE PROJECT FILE.
Chemical Intelligence Services, 39A Bowling Green Lane, London EC1R 0BJ, England. TEL 071-833-3812. FAX 071-833-1563.
Vendor(s): Pergamon Infoline (CAPF). *1172*

CHEMICAL & PHARMACEUTICAL BULLETIN.
Pharmaceutical Society of Japan, 12-15, Shibuya 2-chome, Shibuya-ku, Tokyo 150, Japan. *1172*

CHEMICAL BUSINESS.
Schnell Publishing Co., Inc., 80 Broad St., New York, NY 10004. TEL 212-248-4177. FAX 212-248-4901.
Vendor(s): Data-Star. *1172*

CHEMICAL BUSINESS BULLETINS (SERIES): FERTILIZERS.
Royal Society of Chemistry, Thomas Graham House, Science Park, Milton Road, Cambridge CB4 4WF, England. TEL 0223-420066. FAX 0223-423623.
Vendor(s): Data-Star, DIALOG. *710*

CHEMICAL ENGINEERING.
McGraw-Hill, Inc., 1221 Ave. of the Americas, New York, NY 10020. TEL 212-512-2000.
Vendor(s): DIALOG (File no.624/McGRAW-HILL PUBLICATIONS ONLINE), Dow Jones/News Retrieval (CE), Mead Data Central (CHEMEN). *1849*

CHEMICAL ENGINEERING ABSTRACTS.
Royal Society of Chemistry, Thomas Graha House, Science Park, Milton Rd., Cambridge CB4 4WF, England. TEL 0462-672555. FAX 0462-480947.
Vendor(s): Data-Star (CEAB), DIALOG (File no.315), European Space Agency (File no.85/CHEMICAL ENGINEERING ABSTRACTS), Orbit Information Technologies (CEA). *1842*

CHEMICAL HAZARDS IN INDUSTRY.
Royal Society of Chemistry, Thomas Graham House, Science Park, Milton Rd., Cambridge CB4 4WF, England. TEL 0462-672555. FAX 0462-480947.
Vendor(s): Data-Star (CHIN), DIALOG (File no.317), STN International. *3615*

CHEMICAL INDUSTRY NOTES.
Chemical Abstracts Service, 2540 Olentangy River Rd., Box 3012, Columbus, OH 43210. TEL 614-447-3600. FAX 614-447-3713.
Vendor(s): Data-Star (CIND), DIALOG (File no.19), Orbit Information Technologies (CIN), STN International (CIN). *1199*

CHEMICAL MARKETING REPORTER.
Schnell Publishing Co., Inc., 80 Broad St., New York, NY 10004-2203. TEL 212-248-4177. FAX 212-248-4903.
Vendor(s): DIALOG. *1172*

CHEMICAL MONITOR.
Individual Publishing Co., Box 314, Lindenhurst, NY 11757-0314. TEL 516-669-8147. *1205*

CHEMICAL REGULATION REPORTER.
The Bureau of National Affairs, Inc., 1231 25th St., N.W., Washington, DC 20037. TEL 202-452-4200. FAX 202-822-8092.
Vendor(s): Human Resources Information Network, Mead Data Central (CHEMRG), WESTLAW. *1945*

CHEMICAL RESEARCH IN TOXICOLOGY.
American Chemical Society, 1155 16th St., N.W., Washington, DC 20036. TEL 800-333-9511. FAX 202-872-4615.
Vendor(s): STN International. *1980*

CHEMICAL REVIEWS.
American Chemical Society, 1155 16th St., N.W., Washington, DC 20036. TEL 800-333-9511. FAX 202-872-4615.
Vendor(s): STN International (CJACS). *1173*

CHEMICAL SUBSTANCES CONTROL.
The Bureau of National Affairs, Inc., 1231 25th St., N.W., Washington, DC 20037. TEL 202-452-4200. FAX 202-822-8092.
Vendor(s): Human Resources Information Network (CDD, HDD). *1173*

CHEMICAL TITLES.
Chemical Abstracts Service, 2540 Olentangy River Rd., Columbus, OH 43210. TEL 614-447-3600. FAX 614-447-3713.
Vendor(s): CISTI. *1200*

CHEMICAL WEEK.
Chemical Week Associates, 888 Seventh Ave., New York, NY 10106. TEL 212-621-4900. FAX 212-621-4949.
Vendor(s): Mead Data Central. *1851*

CHEMISCHE INDUSTRIE.
Handelsblatt GmbH, Kasernenstr. 67, Postfach 102717, 4000 Duesseldorf 1, Germany.
TEL 0211-8870. *1851*

CHEMIST & DRUGGIST.
Benn Publications Ltd., Sovereign Way, Tonbridge, Kent TN9 1RW, England. TEL 0732-364422. *3720*

CHEMORECEPTION ABSTRACTS.
Cambridge Scientific Abstracts, 7200 Wisconsin Ave., 6th Fl., Bethesda, MD 20814. TEL 301-961-6750. FAX 301-961-6720.
Vendor(s): BRS (CSAL), DIALOG (File no.76/LIFE SCIENCES COLLECTION). *1200*

CHEST.
American College of Chest Physicians, 3300 Dundee Rd., Northbrook, IL 60062. FAX 708-498-5460. *3364*

CHICAGO - KENT LAW REVIEW.
Chicago - Kent College of Law, 77 S. Wacker Dr., Chicago, IL 60606. TEL 312-567-5013. FAX 312-567-5880.
Vendor(s): WESTLAW. *2612*

CHICANO - LATINO LAW REVIEW.
University of California, Los Angeles, School of Law, 405 Hilgard Ave., Los Angeles, CA 90024.
TEL 213-825-2894.
Vendor(s): WESTLAW. *2612*

CHILD ABUSE & NEGLECT.
Pergamon Press, Inc., Journals Division, 660 White Plains Rd., Tarrytown, NY 10591-5153. TEL 914-524-9200. FAX 914-333-2444. *1234*

CHILD PROTECTION REPORT.
Business Publishers, Inc., 951 Pershing Dr., Silver Spring, MD 20910-4432. TEL 301-587-6300. FAX 301-585-9075.
Vendor(s): NewsNet. *1234*

CHILDREN TODAY.
U.S. Department of Health and Human Services, Office of Human Development Services, 200 Independence Ave., S.W., Rm. 348-F, Washington, DC 20201. TEL 202-245-2866.
Vendor(s): DIALOG. *1235*

CHILDREN'S BOOKS IN PRINT.
R.R. Bowker, A Reed Reference Publishing Company, Division of Reed Publishing (USA) Inc., 121 Chanlon Rd., New Providence, NJ 07974.
TEL 800-521-8110. FAX 908-665-6688.
Vendor(s): BRS (BBIP), BRS/Saunders Colleague, DIALOG (File no.470). *397*

CHILTON'S AUTOMOTIVE MARKETING.
Chilton Co. Chilton Way, Radnor, PA 19089. TEL 215-964-4395.
Vendor(s): DIALOG, Mead Data Central. *4687*

CHILTON'S DISTRIBUTION MAGAZINE.
Chilton Co., Chilton Way, Radnor, PA 19089. TEL 215-964-4379.
Vendor(s): DIALOG, Mead Data Central. *4648*

CHILTON'S FOOD ENGINEERING.
Chilton Co., Chilton Way, Box 2035, Radnor, PA 19089. TEL 215-964-4455.
Vendor(s): DIALOG, Mead Data Central. *2064*

CHILTON'S FOOD ENGINEERING INTERNATIONAL.
Chilton Co., Chilton Way, Box 2035, Radnor, PA 19089. TEL 215-964-4440.
Vendor(s): DIALOG. *2064*

CHILTON'S HARDWARE AGE.
Chilton Co., Chilton Way, Radnor, PA 19089. TEL 215-964-4275.
Vendor(s): DIALOG. *641*

CHILTON'S JEWELERS' CIRCULAR-KEYSTONE.
Chilton Co., Chilton Way, Radnor, PA 19089. TEL 215-964-4474.
Vendor(s): DIALOG. *2563*

CHILTON'S MOTOR AGE.
Chilton Co., Chilton Way, Radnor, PA 19089. TEL 215-964-4390.
Vendor(s): DIALOG, Mead Data Central. *4688*

CHINA BUSINESS REVIEW.
China Business Forum, 1818 N St., N.W., Ste. 500, Washington, DC 20036. TEL 202-429-0340.
FAX 202-775-2476.
Vendor(s): DIALOG, Wilsonline. *903*

CHINA TODAY.
Jinri Zhongguo Zazhishe, 24 Baiwanzhuang Lu, Beijing 100037, People's Republic of China.
TEL 892190. FAX 8328338.
Vendor(s): DIALOG. *2181*

CHINESE MEDICAL JOURNAL.
Chinese Medical Association, 42 Dongsi Xidajie, Beijing 100710, People's Republic of China.
TEL 546231-292. *3087*

CHING FENG.
Christian Study Centre on Chinese Religion & Culture, 6-F Kiu Kin Mansion, 566 Nathan Rd., Kowloon, Hong Kong. TEL 7703310.
FAX 7826869.
Vendor(s): BRS, DIALOG. *4168*

CHIROPRACTIC HISTORY.
Association for the History of Chiropractic, 207 Grandview Dr., S., Pittsburgh, PA 15215. FAX 412-237-4512.
Vendor(s): National Library of Medicine. *3213*

CHIRURGIA MAXILLOFACIALIS ET PLASTICA.
Zbor Lijecnika Hrvatske, Sekcija za Maksilofacijalnu i Plasticnu Kirurgiju, Subiceva 9, Zagreb. TEL 041-276 313. FAX 041-420-470. *3377*

CHOICES (NEW YORK).
Scholastic Inc., 730 Broadway, New York, NY 10003. TEL 212-505-3000.
Vendor(s): DIALOG. *2445*

CHRISTIAN SCIENCE MONITOR INDEX.
University Microfilms International, Data Courier, c/o Bonnie Maxwell, VP, 620 S. Third St., Louisville, KY 40202. TEL 800-626-2823. FAX 502-589-5572.
Vendor(s): DIALOG. *2577*

CHRONICLE OF LATIN AMERICAN ECONOMIC AFFAIRS.
University of Latin America, Latin American Institute, 801 Yale N.E., Albuquerque, NM 87131-1016.
TEL 505-277-6839. FAX 505-277-5989.
Vendor(s): DIALOG, Mead Data Central, NewsNet. *851*

CIENCIA E INDUSTRIA FARMACEUTICA.
Universidad de Barcelona, Departamento Farmacia Galenica, Nucleo Universitario Pedralbes, Barcelona (14), Spain. *3720*

CINCH. AUSTRALIAN CRIMINOLOGY DATABASE.
Australian Institute of Criminology, G.P.O. Box 2944, Canberra, A.C.T. 2601, Australia. FAX 06-274-0260. *1511*

CINCINNATI LAW REVIEW.
University of Cincinnati, College of Law, Rm. 300, Cincinnati, OH 45221-0040. TEL 513-556-5101.
Vendor(s): WESTLAW. *2612*

CIRCULATION.
American Heart Association, 7272 Greenville Ave., Dallas, TX 75231-4596. TEL 214-706-1310.
FAX 214-691-6342.
Vendor(s): BRS (JWAT). *3207*

CIRCULATION RESEARCH.
American Heart Association, 7272 Greenville Ave., Dallas, TX 75231-4596. TEL 214-706-1310.
FAX 214-691-6342.
Vendor(s): BRS. *3207*

CIRCULATORY SHOCK.
John Wiley & Sons, Inc., Journals, 605 Third Ave., New York, NY 10158. TEL 212-850-6000.
FAX 212-850-6088. *3207*

CIVICA SCUOLA DI MUSICA. QUADERNI.
Civica Scuola di Musica, Via Stilicone 36, 20142 Milan, Italy. TEL 02-313334. FAX 02-29400457. *3546*

CIVIL ENGINEERING HYDRAULICS ABSTRACTS.
S T I Ltd., 4 Kings Meadow, Ferry Hinksey Rd., Oxford OX2 0DU, England. TEL 0865-798898.
FAX 0865-798788.
Vendor(s): DIALOG (File no.96/FLUIDEX), European Space Agency (File no.48/FLUIDEX). *1842*

CLEAN COAL - SYNFUELS LETTER.
McGraw-Hill, Inc., Energy & Business Newsletters, 1221 Ave. of the Americas, 36th fl., New York, NY 10020.
Vendor(s): DIALOG (File no.624/McGRAW-HILL PUBLICATIONS ONLINE), Dow Jones/News Retrieval (CSL), Mead Data Central (SYNFLS). *1784*

CLEVELAND STATE LAW REVIEW.
Cleveland State University, Cleveland-Marshall College of Law, 1983 E. 24th St., Cleveland, OH 44115. TEL 216-687-2236.
Vendor(s): WESTLAW. *2613*

CLINICA.
P J B Publications Ltd., 18-20 Hill Rise, Richmond, Surrey TW10 6UA, England. TEL 081-948-3262. FAX 081-948-6866.
Vendor(s): BRS, Data-Star, DIALOG. *3088*

CLINICAL DIABETES.
American Diabetes Association, Inc., 1660 Duke St., Alexandria, VA 22314. TEL 703-549-1500. FAX 703-836-7439.
Vendor(s): BRS. *3251*

CLINICAL LASER MONTHLY.
American Health Consultants, Inc., Six Piedmont Center, Ste. 400, 3525 Piedmont Rd., N.E., Atlanta, GA 30305. TEL 404-262-7436. FAX 800-284-3291.
Vendor(s): Mead Data Central. *3377*

CLINICAL ORTHOPAEDICS AND RELATED RESEARCH.
J.B. Lippincott Co., E. Washington Sq., Philadelphia, PA 19105. TEL 215-238-4200.
Vendor(s): BRS, BRS/Saunders Colleague, Mead Data Central. *3307*

CLINICAL PEDIATRICS.
Cortlandt Group, Inc., 500 Executive Blvd., Ste. 302, Ossining, NY 10562. TEL 914-762-0647. FAX 914-762-8820.
Vendor(s): BRS, BRS/Saunders Colleague, Mead Data Central. *3319*

CLINICAL PHARMACOLOGY & THERAPEUTICS.
Mosby - Year Book, Inc., 11830 Westline Industrial Dr., St. Louis, MO 63146. TEL 800-325-4117. FAX 314-432-1380.
Vendor(s): BRS, BRS/Saunders Colleague. *3721*

COAL.
Maclean Hunter Publishing Company, 29 N. Wacker Dr., Chicago, IL 60606. TEL 312-726-2802. FAX 312-726-2574.
Vendor(s): Mead Data Central. *3481*

COAL ABSTRACTS.
I.E.A. Coal Research, Gemini House, 10-18 Putney Hill, London SW15 6AA, England. TEL 081-780-2111. FAX 081-780-1746.
Vendor(s): BELINDIS, CISTI, FIZ Technik (COAL), INKA, JICST, QL Systems Ltd., STN International. *3499*

COAL & SYNFUELS TECHNOLOGY.
Pasha Publications Inc., 1401 Wilson Blvd., Ste. 900, Arlington, VA 22209-9970. TEL 703-528-1244. FAX 703-528-1253.
Vendor(s): Data-Star, DIALOG, NewsNet. *1784*

COAL OUTLOOK.
Pasha Publications Inc., 1401 Wilson Blvd., Ste. 900, Arlington, VA 22209-9970. TEL 703-528-1244. FAX 703-528-1253.
Vendor(s): DIALOG, Mead Data Central. *3481*

COAL RESEARCH PROJECTS.
I.E.A. Coal Research, Gemini House, 10-18 Putney Hill, London SW1S 6AA, England. TEL 081-780-2111. FAX 081-780-1746.
Vendor(s): FIZ Technik (COALRIP), STN International. *3481*

COAL WEEK.
McGraw-Hill, Inc., Energy & Business Newsletters, 1221 Ave. of the Americas, 36th Fl., New York, NY 10020. TEL 212-512-6410.
Vendor(s): DIALOG (File no.624/McGRAW-HILL PUBLICATIONS ONLINE), Dow Jones/News Retrieval (COW), Mead Data Central (COALWK). *3481*

COAL WEEK INTERNATIONAL.
McGraw-Hill, Inc., Energy & Business Newsletters, 1221 Ave. of the Americas, 36th Fl., New York, NY 10020. TEL 212-512-6410.
Vendor(s): DIALOG (File no.624/McGRAW-HILL PUBLICATIONS ONLINE), Dow Jones/News Retrieval (CWI), Mead Data Central (COALIN). *3481*

CODE OF MARYLAND REGULATIONS.
Division of State Documents, Box 802, Annapolis, MD 21404. TEL 301-974-2486. FAX 301-974-2546. *4057*

COLECAO RODOLFO GARCIA.
Biblioteca Nacional de Brasil, Av. Rio Branco, 219, 20042 Rio de Janeiro, Brazil. TEL 021-240-8429. FAX 021-220-4173. *397*

COLEGIO OFICIAL DE FARMACEUTICO. CIRCULAR FARMACEUTICA.
Colegio Oficial de Farmaceuticos de la Provincia de Barcelona, Pau Claris, Barcelona 10, Spain. *3721*

COLLECTIVE BARGAINING NEGOTIATIONS & CONTRACTS.
The Bureau of National Affairs, Inc., 1231 25th St., N.W., Washington, DC 20037. TEL 202-452-4200. FAX 202-822-8092.
Vendor(s): Human Resources Information Network, WESTLAW. *975*

COLLEGAMENTO.
Unione Tecnica Italiana Farmacisti, Via Giuseppe Casaregis 52-8, 16129 Genova, Italy. *3721*

COLLEGE PRESS SERVICE.
Interrobang, Inc., 2505 W. Second Ave., Ste. 7, Denver, CO 80219. TEL 303-936-9630. FAX 303-936-0569. *1703*

COLORADO BUSINESS.
Wiesner Publishing, Inc., 7009 S. Potomac St., Englewood, CO 80112. TEL 303-397-7600. FAX 303-397-7619.
Vendor(s): DIALOG. *851*

COLUMBIA JOURNAL OF TRANSNATIONAL LAW.
Columbia Journal of Transnational Law Association, 435 W. 116th St., New York, NY 10027. TEL 212-854-3742.
Vendor(s): WESTLAW. *2721*

COLUMBIA LAW REVIEW.
Columbia Law Review Association, 435 W. 116th St., New York, NY 10027. TEL 212-854-4398.
Vendor(s): Mead Data Central. *2614*

COLUMBUS BUSINESS JOURNAL.
148 N. High St., Gahanna, OH 43230. TEL 614-476-1108.
Vendor(s): DIALOG. *656*

COMMENTS ON MONEY AND CREDIT.
D R I - McGraw-Hill, 24 Hartwell Ave., Lexington, MA 02173. TEL 617-863-5100. FAX 617-860-6332. *772*

COMMERCE BUSINESS DAILY.
U.S. International Trade Administration, U.S. Dept. of Commerce, Washington, DC 20230. TEL 202-783-3238.
Vendor(s): DIALOG (File nos.194 & 195), NewsNet, United Communications Group (CBD OnLine). *1036*

COMMON CARRIER WEEK.
Warren Publishing, Inc., 2115 Ward Ct., N.W., Washington, DC 20037. TEL 202-872-9200. FAX 202-293-3435.
Vendor(s): DIALOG, NewsNet. *1362*

COMMONWEALTH LAW REPORTS.
Law Book Co. Ltd., 44-50 Waterloo Rd., North Ryde, N.S.W. 2112, Australia. TEL 02-887-0177. FAX 02-888-9706. *2734*

COMMUNICATION WORLD.
International Association of Business Communicators, One Hallidie Plaza, Ste. 600, San Francisco, CA 94102. TEL 415-433-3400. FAX 415-362-8762.
Vendor(s): DIALOG. *1005*

COMMUNICATIONS DAILY.
Warren Publishing, Inc., 2115 Ward Ct., N.W., Washington, DC 20037. TEL 202-872-9200. FAX 202-293-3435.
Vendor(s): Data-Star, DIALOG, Mead Data Central, NewsNet. *1371*

COMMUNICATIONS NEWS.
Nelson Publishing Co., 2504 N. Tamiami Trail, Nokomis, FL 34275. TEL 813-966-9521. FAX 813-966-2590.
Vendor(s): DIALOG. *1334*

COMMUNICATIONS WEEK INTERNATIONAL.
C M P Publications, Inc., 600 Community Dr., Manhasset, NY 11030. TEL 516-562-5000. FAX 516-562-5474.
Vendor(s): Data-Star, DIALOG, Mead Data Central, NewsNet. *1334*

COMMUNITY SERVICES CATALYST.
National Council on Community Services & Continuing Education, c/o Darrel A. Clowes, Ed., Virginia Polytechnic Institute & State University, Blacksburg, VA 24061-0313. TEL 703-961-6136. FAX 703-231-3717. *1683*

COMMUTER AIR INTERNATIONAL.
Communication Channels, Inc., 6255 Barfield Rd., Atlanta, GA 30328-4369. TEL 404-256-9800. FAX 404-253-3116. *4672*

COMMUTER - REGIONAL AIRLINE NEWS.
Phillips Publishing, Inc., Defense - Aviation Group, 1925 N. Lynn St., Ste. 1000, Arlington, VA 22209. TEL 703-522-8333. FAX 703-522-8334.
Vendor(s): Data-Star, DIALOG, NewsNet. *4672*

COMPANIES AND THEIR BRANDS.
Gale Research Inc., 835 Penobscot Bldg., Detroit, MI 48226. TEL 313-961-2242. FAX 313-961-6083.
Vendor(s): DIALOG. *1127*

COMPENSATION AND BENEFITS REVIEW.
American Management Association, 135 W. 50th St., New York, NY 10020. TEL 212-903-8069. FAX 212-903-8168.
Vendor(s): DIALOG. *1006*

COMPLEMENTARY MEDICINE INDEX.
Medical Information Service, The British Library, Boston Spa, Wetherby, W. Yorkshire LS237BQ, England. TEL 0937-546039. FAX 0937-546236. *3168*

COMPLETE DIRECTORY OF LARGE PRINT BOOKS AND SERIALS.
R.R. Bowker, A Reed Reference Publishing Company, Division of Reed Publishing (USA) Inc., 121 Chanlon Rd., New Providence, NJ 07974. TEL 800-521-8110. FAX 908-655-6688. *2285*

COMPOSITES & ADHESIVES NEWSLETTER.
T C Press Box 36006, Los Angeles, CA 90036. TEL 213-938-6923.
Vendor(s): Data-Star, DIALOG. *3862*

COMPREHENSIVE PSYCHIATRY.
W.B. Saunders Co. Curtis Center, Independence Square W., Philadelphia, PA 19106. TEL 215-238-7800. *3334*

COMPUMATH CITATION INDEX.
Institute for Scientific Information, 3501 Market St., Philadelphia, PA 19104. TEL 215-386-0100. FAX 215-386-2991.
Vendor(s): BRS. *3062*

COMPUSERVE.
CompuServe Inc., 5000 Arlington Centre Blvd., Columbus, OH 43220. TEL 614-457-8600. FAX 614-457-0348.
Vendor(s): CompuServe Consumer Information Service. *1468*

COMPUTER-AIDED ENGINEERING.
Penton Publishing, 1100 Superior Ave., Cleveland, OH 44114-2543. TEL 216-696-7000. FAX 216-696-8765.
Vendor(s): DIALOG. *1877*

COMPUTER-AIDED PROCESS CONTROL ABSTRACTS.
S T I Ltd., 4 Kings Meadow, Ferry Hinksey Rd., Oxford OX2 0DU, England. TEL 0865-798898. FAX 0865-798788.
Vendor(s): DIALOG (File no. 96), European Space Agency (File no. 48). *1403*

COMPUTER & CONTROL ABSTRACTS.
INSPEC, I.E.E., Michael Faraday House, Six Hills Way, Stevenage, Herts. SG1 2AY, England. TEL 0438-313311. FAX 0438-742840. Vendor(s): BRS (INSP), CEDOCAR, CISTI, Data-Star, DIALOG (File nos.2,3 & 4/INSPEC), European Space Agency (File no.8/INSPEC), Orbit Information Technologies (INSPEC, STN International (INSPEC), University of Tsukuba. *1403*

COMPUTER AND INFORMATION SYSTEMS ABSTRACTS JOURNAL.
Cambridge Scientific Abstracts, 7200 Wisconsin Ave., 6th Fl., Bethesda, MD 20814. TEL 301-961-6750. FAX 301-961-6720. Vendor(s): BRS (CSEN). *1403*

COMPUTER BOOK REVIEW.
Computer Book Review, 735 Ekekela Place, Honolulu, HI 96817. Vendor(s): DIALOG. *1391*

COMPUTER DATABASE.
Information Access Company, 362 Lakeside Dr., Foster City, CA 94404. TEL 800-227-8431. FAX 415-378-5499. Available only online. Vendor(s): BRS (CMPT), Data-Star (CMPT), DIALOG (File no.275). *1403*

COMPUTER DEALER NEWS.
Plesman Publications Ltd., 2005 Sheppard Ave. E., Ste. 400, Willowdale, Ont. M2J 5B1, Canada. TEL 416-497-9562. FAX 416-497-9427. *1432*

COMPUTER DESIGN.
PennWell Publishing Co. (Westford), Advanced Technology Group, One Technology Park Dr., Westford, MA 01886-0989. TEL 508-692-0700. FAX 508-692-7780. Vendor(s): DIALOG. *1420*

COMPUTER FRAUD AND SECURITY BULLETIN.
Elsevier Science Publishers Ltd., Crown House, Linton Rd., Barking, Essex IG11 8JU, England. TEL 081-594-7272. FAX 081-594-5942. Vendor(s): Data-Star, DIALOG. *1434*

COMPUTER GAMING WORLD.
Golden Empire Publications, Inc., 130 S. Chaparral Ct., Ste. 260, Anaheim, CA 92808-2238. TEL 714-283-3000. FAX 714-283-3444. Vendor(s): Information Access Company. *1419*

COMPUTER GRAPHICS WORLD.
PennWell Publishing Co. (Westford), Advanced Technology Group, One Technology Park Dr., Westford, MA 01886-0989. TEL 508-692-0700. FAX 508-692-0525. Vendor(s): DIALOG. *1421*

COMPUTER LANGUAGE.
Miller Freeman, Inc. 600 Harrison St., San Francisco, CA 94107. TEL 415-905-2200. FAX 415-905-2232. Vendor(s): DIALOG. *1413*

COMPUTER LIBRARY'S COMPUTER PERIODICALS DATABASE.
Ziff Communications, One Park Ave., New York, NY 10016. TEL 212-503-4400. FAX 212-503-4414. *2793*

COMPUTER MUSIC JOURNAL.
M I T Press, 55 Hayward St., Cambridge, MA 02142. TEL 617-253-2889. FAX 617-258-6779. *3589*

COMPUTER PICTURES.
Montage Publishing, Inc. 701 Westchester Ave., White Plains, NY 10604. TEL 914-329-9157. FAX 914-328-9093. Vendor(s): DIALOG. *1421*

COMPUTER PROTOCOLS.
Worldwide Videotex, P.O. Box 138, Babson Park, Boston, MA 02157. Vendor(s): Data-Star, DIALOG, NewsNet. *1392*

COMPUTER - READABLE DATABASES.
Gale Research Inc., 835 Penobscot Bldg., Detroit, MI 48226. TEL 313-961-2242. FAX 313-961-6083. Vendor(s): DIALOG (File no.230). *1403*

COMPUTER USER'S SURVIVAL MAGAZINE.
Enterprises Publishing, 400 E. 59th St., Ste 9F, New York, NY 10022. TEL 212-755-4563. *1468*

COMPUTERS IN BANKING.
Investment Dealers' Digest, 2 World Trade Ctr., 18th Fl., New York, NY 10048. TEL 212-227-1200. Vendor(s): DIALOG. *805*

COMPUTERS IN HEALTHCARE.
Cardiff Publishing Co., 6300 S. Syracuse Way, Ste. 650, Englewood, CO 80111. TEL 303-220-0600. Vendor(s): DIALOG. *3225*

COMPUTERS IN LIBRARIES.
Meckler Publishing Corporation, 11 Ferry Lane W., Westport, CT 06880-5808. TEL 203-226-6967. Vendor(s): NewsNet. *1459*

COMPUTERWORLD.
Computerworld, Inc. 375 Cochituate Rd., Box 9171, Framingham, MA 01701-9171. TEL 508-879-0700. Vendor(s): DIALOG (File no.674), Mead Data Central. *1393*

COMPUTERWORLD HONG KONG.
Asia Computerworld Communications Ltd., 701-4 Kam Chung Bldg., 54 Jaffe Rd., Wanchai, Hong Kong. TEL 852-861-3228. FAX 852-861-0953. *1423*

COMPUTING CANADA.
Plesman Publications Ltd., 2005 Sheppard Ave. E., Ste. 400, Willowdale, Ont. M2J 5B1, Canada. TEL 416-497-9562. FAX 416-497-9427. *1476*

COMPUTING REVIEWS.
Association for Computing Machinery, 1515 Broadway, 17th Fl., New York, NY 10036. TEL 212-869-7440. FAX 212-869-0481. Vendor(s): DIALOG. *1404*

CONFERENCE PAPERS ANNUAL INDEX.
Cambridge Scientific Abstracts, 7200 Wisconsin Ave., 6th Fl., Bethesda, MD 20814. TEL 301-961-6750. FAX 301-961-6720. Vendor(s): DIALOG (File no. 77), European Space Agency (File no. 36). *3395*

CONFERENCE PAPERS INDEX.
Cambridge Scientific Abstracts, 7200 Wisconsin Ave., 6th Fl., Bethesda, MD 20814. TEL 301-961-6750. FAX 301-961-6720. Vendor(s): DIALOG (File no.77), European Space Agency (File no.36/CONFERENCE PAPERS INDEX). *3395*

CONFLICT RESOLUTION NOTES.
Conflict Resolution Center International, Inc., 7101 Hamilton Ave., Pittsburgh, PA 15208-1828. TEL 412-371-9884. FAX 412-371-9885. *2615*

CONGRESS IN PRINT.
Congressional Quarterly Inc., 1414 22 St., N.W., Washington, DC 20037. TEL 800-432-2250. FAX 202-728-1863. *3881*

CONGRESSIONAL INSIGHT.
Congressional Quarterly Inc., 1414 22nd St., N.W., Washington, DC 20037. TEL 800-432-2250. FAX 202-728-1863. *3881*

CONGRESSIONAL MONITOR.
Congressional Quarterly Inc., 1414 22nd St., N.W., Washington, DC 20037. TEL 800-432-2250. FAX 202-728-1863. *3881*

CONGRESSIONAL QUARTERLY SERVICE. WEEKLY REPORT.
Congressional Quarterly Inc., 1414 22nd St., N.W., Washington, DC 20037. TEL 800-432-2250. FAX 202-728-1863. *3881*

CONGRESSIONAL RECORD SCANNER.
Congressional Quarterly Inc., 1414 22nd St., N.W., Washington, DC 20037. TEL 800-432-2250. FAX 202-728-1863. *3936*

CONNECTICUT LAW REVIEW.
Connecticut Law Review Association, 65 Elizabeth St., Hartford, CT 06105-2290. TEL 203-241-4607. FAX 203-241-7666. Vendor(s): WESTLAW. *2615*

CONSTITUTIONAL COMMENTARY.
Constitutional Commentary, 229 19th Ave. S., Minneapolis, MN 55455. TEL 612-376-7235. FAX 612-625-2011. Vendor(s): WESTLAW. *3941*

CONSTRUCTION ALERT.
Council for Scientific and Industrial Research, Division of Information Services, P.O. Box 395, Pretoria 0001, South Africa. TEL 012-841-4062. *611*

CONSTRUCTION CLAIMS MONTHLY.
Business Publishers, Inc., 951 Pershing Dr., Silver Spring, MD 20910-4464. TEL 301-587-6300. FAX 301-585-9075. Vendor(s): NewsNet. *612*

CONSTRUCTION CLAIMS TRAINING GUIDE.
Business Publishers, Inc., 951 Pershing Dr., Silver Spring, MD 20910-4464. TEL 301-587-6300. FAX 301-585-9075. Vendor(s): NewsNet. *612*

CONSTRUCTION EQUIPMENT.
Cahners Publishing Company (Des Plaines) Division of Reed Publishing (USA) Inc., 1350 E. Touhy Ave., Box 5080, Des Plaines, IL 60017-5080. TEL 708-635-8800. FAX 708-390-2690. Vendor(s): DIALOG. *612*

CONSTRUCTION LABOR REPORT.
The Bureau of National Affairs, Inc., 1231 25th St., N.W., Washington, DC 20037. TEL 202-452-4200. FAX 202-822-8092. *976*

CONSTRUCTION REVIEW.
U.S. Department of Commerce, I T A - Basic Industries Division, Washington, DC 20230. TEL 202-377-0132. FAX 202-377-8836. Vendor(s): DIALOG. *613*

CONSULTANTS AND CONSULTING ORGANIZATIONS DIRECTORY.
Gale Research Inc., 835 Penobscot Bldg., Detroit, MI 48226. TEL 313-961-2242. FAX 313-961-6083. Vendor(s): Human Resources Information Network (CCOD). *1006*

CONSUMER INFORMATION APPLIANCE.
Jupiter Communications, 594 Broadway, Ste. 1003, New York, NY 10012-3233. TEL 212-941-9252. FAX 212-941-7376. Vendor(s): NewsNet. *1362*

CONSUMER REPORTS.
Consumers Union of United States, Inc., 101 Truman Ave., Yonkers, NY 10703-1057. TEL 914-378-2000. Vendor(s): DIALOG (File no.646). *1503*

CONSUMER REPORTS ON HEALTH.
Consumers Union of United States, Inc., 101 Truman Ave., Yonkers, NY 10703-1057. TEL 914-378-2000. FAX 914-378-2906. Vendor(s): DIALOG (File no.646). *3800*

CONSUMER REPORTS TRAVEL LETTER.
Consumers Union of United States, Inc., 101 Truman Ave., Yonkers, NY 10703-1057. TEL 914-378-2000. FAX 914-378-2906. Vendor(s): DIALOG (File no.646). *4758*

CONTAINER NEWS.
Communication Channels, Inc., 6255 Barfield Rd., Atlanta, GA 30328-4369. TEL 404-256-9800. FAX 404-256-3116. *4648*

CONTEMPORARY MUSICIANS.
Gale Research Inc., 835 Penobscot Bldg., Detroit, MI 48226. TEL 313-961-2242. FAX 313-961-6083. Vendor(s): Mead Data Central. *3547*

CONTRACEPTIVE TECHNOLOGY UPDATE.
American Health Consultants, Inc., Six Piedmont Center, Ste. 400, 3525 Piedmont Rd., N.E., Atlanta, GA 30305. TEL 404-262-7436. FAX 800-284-3291. Vendor(s): Mead Data Central. *596*

CONTRACTOR PROFIT NEWS.
Construction Industry Press, Box 9383, San Rafael, CA 94912. TEL 415-927-2155. Vendor(s): NewsNet. *614*

CONTROLS AND SYSTEMS.
Penton Publishing 1100 Superior Ave., Cleveland, OH 44114-2543. TEL 216-696-7000. FAX 216-696-8765. Vendor(s): DIALOG. *1818*

CONVERGENCE: INTERNATIONAL CONGRESS ON TRANSPORTATION ELECTRONICS. PROCEEDINGS.
Society of Automotive Engineers, 400 Commonwealth Dr., Warrendale, PA 15096-0001. TEL 412-776-4841. FAX 412-776-5760.
Vendor(s): European Space Agency, FIZ Technik, Orbit Information Technologies. *4688*

COOK POLITICAL REPORT.
Cook and Company, 900 Second St., N.E., Ste. 107, Washington, DC 20002. TEL 202-289-1625. FAX 202-289-0454. *3882*

COOK'S INDEX.
John Gordon Burke Publisher, Inc., Box 1492, Evanston, IL 60204-1492. TEL 708-866-8625. *2450*

CORNELL ENGINEER.
Cornell Engineer, Inc., Cornell University, B-48 Olin Hall, Ithaca, NY 14853. TEL 607-255-3312. *1818*

CORNELL INTERNATIONAL LAW JOURNAL.
Cornell University, Law School, Myron Taylor Hall, Ithaca, NY 14853. TEL 607-255-9666.
Vendor(s): WESTLAW. *2722*

CORNELL LAW REVIEW.
Cornell University, Law School, Myron Taylor Hall, Ithaca, NY 14853. TEL 607-255-3387.
Vendor(s): Mead Data Central, WESTLAW. *2616*

CORPORATE CAPITAL TRANSACTIONS COORDINATOR.
Research Institute of America, Inc., 90 Fifth Ave., New York, NY 10011. TEL 212-645-4800.
Vendor(s): Mead Data Central. *750*

CORPORATE CASHFLOW.
Communication Channels, Inc., 6255 Barfield Rd., Atlanta, GA 30328-4369. TEL 404-256-9800. FAX 404-256-3116. *773*

CORPORATE CASHFLOW DIRECTORY.
Communication Channels, Inc., 6255 Barfield Rd., Atlanta, GA 30328-4369. TEL 404-256-9800. FAX 404-256-3116. *773*

CORPORATE CLEVELAND.
Business Journal Publishing Co. (Cleveland), 1720 Euclid Ave., Cleveland, OH 44115. TEL 216-621-1644. FAX 216-621-5918.
Vendor(s): DIALOG. *657*

CORPORATE DETROIT MAGAZINE.
Business Journal Publishing Co. (Southfield), 26111 Evergreen Rd., Ste. 303, Southfield, MI 48076-4499. TEL 313-357-8300. FAX 313-357-8308.
Vendor(s): DIALOG. *657*

CORPORATE E F T REPORT.
Phillips Publishing, Inc., 7811 Montrose Rd., Potomac, MD 20854. TEL 301-340-2100. FAX 301-424-4297.
Vendor(s): DIALOG, Mead Data Central, NewsNet (Fl12). *773*

CORPORATE GIVING WATCH.
Taft Group, 12300 Twinbrook Pkwy., Ste. 450, Rockville, MD 20852. TEL 301-816-0210.
Vendor(s): NewsNet. *4403*

CORPORATE JOBS OUTLOOK!
Corporate Jobs Outlook!, Drawer 100, Boerne, TX 78006-0100. TEL 512-755-8810. FAX 512-755-2410.
Vendor(s): NewsNet (File no.GB.41). *3626*

CORPORATE REPORT MINNESOTA.
M C P, Inc., 5500 Wayzata Blvd., Ste. 800, Minneapolis, MN 55416. TEL 612-591-2500. FAX 612-591-2639.
Vendor(s): DIALOG. *1006*

CORPORATE TECHNOLOGY DIRECTORY.
Corporate Technology Information Services, Inc., 12 Alfred St., Ste. 200, Woburn, MA 01801. TEL 617-932-3939. FAX 617-932-6335.
Vendor(s): Orbit Information Technologies (CORP). *4595*

CORPORATE VENTURING NEWS.
Venture Economics, Inc., 11 Farnsworth St., Boston, MA 02210-1223. TEL 617-431-8100.
Vendor(s): Data-Star, DIALOG. *943*

COSMETIC INSIDER'S REPORT.
Advanstar Communications, 270 Madison Ave., New York, NY 10016. TEL 212-951-6600.
Vendor(s): Data-Star, DIALOG. *375*

COSMETICS AND TOILETRIES.
Allured Publishing, Bldg. C, Ste. 1600, 2100 Manchester Rd., Box 318, Wheaton, IL 60189-0318. TEL 708-653-2155. FAX 708-653-2192. *375*

COTTON AND TROPICAL FIBRES.
C.A.B. International, Wallingford, Oxon OX10 8DE, England. TEL 800-528-4841, 0491 32111. FAX 0491-33508.
Vendor(s): BRS (CABA), CISTI, DIMDI, DIALOG, European Space Agency (File nos.16 & 124/CAB). *136*

COUNTRY FORECASTS.
Political Risk Services Box 6482, Syracuse, NY 13217-6482. TEL 315-472-1224. FAX 315-472-1235.
Vendor(s): Data-Star, DIALOG, NewsNet. *3883*

COUNTRY PROFILES.
Business International Ltd., 40 Duke St., London W1A 1DW, England. TEL 71-493-6711. FAX 71-449-9767.
Vendor(s): DIALOG. *3887*

COUNTRY REPORTS.
Business International Ltd., 40 Duke St., London W1M 1DW, England. TEL 71-493-6711. FAX 71-499-9767.
Vendor(s): DIALOG. *858*

COURIER (PARIS).
Unesco, 7-9 Place de Fontenoy, 75700 Paris, France. TEL 577-16-10.
Vendor(s): DIALOG. *3954*

CRAIN'S CHICAGO BUSINESS.
Crain Communications, Inc. (Chicago), 740 N. Rush St., Chicago, IL 60611-2525. TEL 312-649-5270. FAX 312-649-5228.
Vendor(s): DIALOG, Mead Data Central (CHIBUS). *657*

CRAIN'S CLEVELAND BUSINESS.
Crain Communications, Inc. (Detroit), 1400 Woodbridge Ave., Detroit, MI 48207-3187. TEL 800-678-9595. FAX 216-694-4264.
Vendor(s): DIALOG. *858*

CRAIN'S DETROIT BUSINESS.
Crain Communications, Inc. (Detroit), 1400 Woodbridge Ave., Detroit, MI 48207-3187. TEL 313-446-0426. FAX 313-446-1650.
Vendor(s): DIALOG. *657*

CRAIN'S NEW YORK BUSINESS.
Crain Communications, Inc. (New York), 220 E. 42nd St., New York, NY 10017. TEL 212-210-0100. FAX 212-210-0799.
Vendor(s): DIALOG, Mead Data Central (NYBUS). *657*

CRANBERRIES.
Box 858, S. Carver, MA 02366.
Vendor(s): DIALOG. *2065*

CREDIT UNION WAY.
Credit Union of Central Saskatchewan, P.O. Box 3030, 2055 Albert St., Regina, Sask. S4P 3G8, Canada. TEL 306-566-1360. FAX 306-566-1372. *774*

CREIGHTON LAW REVIEW.
Creighton University, Creighton Law School, 2133 California St., Omaha, NE 68178. TEL 402-280-2980.
Vendor(s): WESTLAW. *2617*

CRIMINAL APPEAL REPORTS.
Sweet & Maxwell, S. Quay Plaza, 8th Fl., 183 Marsh Wall, London E14 9FT, England. TEL 071-538-8686. FAX 071-538-9508.
Vendor(s): Mead Data Central. *1512*

CRIMINAL JUSTICE ABSTRACTS.
Willow Tree Press, Inc., 124 Willow Tree Rd., Monsey, NY 10952. TEL 914-354-9139.
Vendor(s): WESTLAW. *1524*

CRIMINAL JUSTICE PERIODICAL INDEX.
University Microfilms International, Serials Data Management, 300 N. Zeeb Rd., Ann Arbor, MI 48106. TEL 313-761-4700.
Vendor(s): DIALOG (File no.171). *1525*

CRITICAL CARE MEDICINE.
Williams & Wilkins, 428 E. Preston St., Baltimore, MD 21202. TEL 301-528-4000. FAX 301-528-4312.
Vendor(s): Mead Data Central. *3091*

CRITICAL ISSUES.
Heritage Foundation, 214 Massachusetts Ave., N.E., Washington, DC 20002. TEL 202-546-4400. FAX 202-546-8328.
Vendor(s): Mead Data Central. *3889*

CRONACHE FARMACEUTICHE.
Societa Italiana di Scienze Farmaceutiche, Via Giorgio Jan. 18, 20129 Milan, Italy. *3722*

CROP PHYSIOLOGY ABSTRACTS.
C.A.B. International, Wallingford, Oxon OX10 8DE, England. TEL 0491 32111. FAX 0491-33508.
Vendor(s): BRS (CABA), CISTI, DIMDI, DIALOG, European Space Agency (File nos.16 & 124/CAB). *136*

CULTIVOS TROPICALES.
Instituto Nacional de Ciencias Agricolas, Gaveta Postal No. 1, San Jose de las Lajas, Havana 22700, Cuba. TEL 30-07-75. FAX 30-35-82. *175*

CUMBERLAND LAW REVIEW.
Samford University, Cumberland School of Law, 800 Lakeshore Dr., Birmingham, AL 35229. TEL 205-870-2757.
Vendor(s): WESTLAW. *2617*

CUMULATIVE BOOK INDEX.
H.W. Wilson Co., 950 University Ave, Bronx, NY 10452. TEL 800-367-6770. FAX 212-538-2716.
Vendor(s): Wilsonline (File CBI). *398*

CUMULATIVE CHANGES 1986 CODE AND REGULATIONS.
Maxwell Macmillan, Professional and Business Reference Publishing, 910 Sylvan Ave., Englewood Cliffs, NJ 07632-3310. TEL 800-562-0245.
Vendor(s): Prentice-Hall Information Network. *1091*

CUMULATIVE INDEX TO NURSING & ALLIED HEALTH LITERATURE.
C I N H A L Information Systems, Box 871, Glendale, CA 91209-0871. TEL 818-409-8005. FAX 818-546-5679.
Vendor(s): BRS (NAHL), Data-Star, DIALOG (File no. 218). *3169*

CURRENCY CONFIDENTIAL.
Eurostudy Publishing Co. Ltd., Ludgate House, 107 Fleet St., London EC4A 2AB, England. TEL 44-71-583-1025. FAX 44-71-583-5958.
Vendor(s): Data-Star, DIALOG. *775*

CURRENT ADVANCES IN APPLIED MICROBIOLOGY & BIOTECHNOLOGY.
Pergamon Press, Inc., Journals Division, 660 White Plains Rd., Tarrytown, NY 10591-5153. TEL 914-524-9200. FAX 914-333-2444.
Vendor(s): BRS (CABS). *464*

CURRENT ADVANCES IN CANCER RESEARCH.
Pergamon Press, Inc., Journals Division, 660 White Plains Rd., Tarrytown, NY 10591-5153. TEL 914-524-9200. FAX 914-333-2444.
Vendor(s): BRS (CABS). *3169*

CURRENT ADVANCES IN CELL AND DEVELOPMENTAL BIOLOGY.
Pergamon Press, Inc., Journals Division, 660 White Plains Rd., Tarrytown, NY 10591-5153. TEL 914-524-9200. FAX 914-333-2444.
Vendor(s): BRS (CABS). *464*

CURRENT ADVANCES IN CLINICAL CHEMISTRY.
Pergamon Press, Inc., Journals Division, 660 White Plains Rd., Tarrytown, NY 10591-5153. TEL 914-524-9200. FAX 914-333-2444.
Vendor(s): BRS (CABS). *1200*

SERIALS AVAILABLE ONLINE

CURRENT ADVANCES IN ECOLOGICAL AND ENVIRONMENTAL SCIENCES.
Pergamon Press, Inc., Journals Division, 660 White Plains Rd., Tarrytown, NY 10591-5153. TEL 914-524-9200. FAX 914-333-2444.
Vendor(s): BRS (CABS). *1973*

CURRENT ADVANCES IN ENDOCRINOLOGY & METABOLISM.
Pergamon Press, Inc., Journals Division, 660 White Plains Rd., Tarrytown, NY 10591-5153. TEL 914-524-9200. FAX 914-333-2444.
Vendor(s): BRS (CABS). *3169*

CURRENT ADVANCES IN GENETICS AND MOLECULAR BIOLOGY.
Pergamon Press, Inc., Journals Division, 660 White Plains Rd., Tarrytown, NY 10591-5153. TEL 914-524-9200. FAX 914-333-2444.
Vendor(s): BRS (CABS). *464*

CURRENT ADVANCES IN IMMUNOLOGY & INFECTIOUS DISEASES.
Pergamon Press, Inc., Journals Division, 660 White Plains Rd., Tarrytown, NY 10591-5153. TEL 914-524-9200. FAX 914-333-2444.
Vendor(s): BRS (CABS). *3169*

CURRENT ADVANCES IN NEUROSCIENCE.
Pergamon Press, Inc., Journals Division, 660 White Plains Rd., Tarrytown, NY 10591-5153. TEL 914-524-9200. FAX 914-333-2444.
Vendor(s): BRS (CABS). *3169*

CURRENT ADVANCES IN PLANT SCIENCE.
Pergamon Press, Inc., Journals Division, 660 White Plains Rd., Tarrytown, NY 10591-5153. TEL 914-524-9200. FAX 914-333-2444.
Vendor(s): BRS (CABS). *464*

CURRENT ADVANCES IN PROTEIN BIOCHEMISTRY.
Pergamon Press, Inc., Journals Division, 660 White Plains Rd., Tarrytown, NY 10591-5153. TEL 914-524-9200. FAX 914-333-2444.
Vendor(s): BRS (CABS). *464*

CURRENT ADVANCES IN TOXICOLOGY.
Pergamon Press, Inc., Journals Division, 660 White Plains Rd., Tarrytown, NY 10591-5153. TEL 914-524-9200. FAX 914-333-2444.
Vendor(s): BRS (CABS). *3747*

CURRENT AWARENESS IN BIOLOGICAL SCIENCES.
Pergamon Press, Inc., Journals Division, 660 White Plains Rd., Tarrytown, NY 10591-5153. TEL 914-524-9200. FAX 914-333-2444.
Vendor(s): BRS (CABS). *464*

CURRENT AWARENESS IN HEALTH EDUCATION.
U.S. Bureau of Health Education, Department of Health and Human Services, Washington, DC 20201. TEL 202-655-4000.
Vendor(s): BRS, BRS/Saunders Colleague. *3800*

CURRENT BIBLIOGRAPHY OF PLASTIC & RECONSTRUCTIVE SURGERY.
Plastic Surgery Education Foundation, c/o American Society of Plastic Surgeons, 444 E. Algonquin Rd., Arlington Heights, IL 60005. TEL 301-252-4022.
Vendor(s): National Library of Medicine. *3169*

CURRENT BIBLIOGRAPHY ON SCIENCE AND TECHNOLOGY: CHEMISTRY AND CHEMICAL ENGINEERING (FOREIGN).
Japan Information Center of Science and Technology, 5-2 Nagato-cho, 2-chome, Chiyoda-ku, Tokyo 100, Japan. TEL 03-3581-6411. FAX 03-3581-6446.
Vendor(s): JICST. *1200*

CURRENT BIBLIOGRAPHY ON SCIENCE AND TECHNOLOGY: CHEMISTRY AND CHEMICAL ENGINEERING (JAPANESE).
Japan Information Center of Science and Technology, 5-2 Nagato-cho, 2-chome, Chiyoda-ku, Tokyo 100, Japan. TEL 03-3581-6441. FAX 03-3581-6446.
Vendor(s): JICST. *1200*

CURRENT BIBLIOGRAPHY ON SCIENCE AND TECHNOLOGY: EARTH SCIENCE, MINING AND METALLURGY.
Japan Information Center of Science and Technology, 5-2 Nagato-cho, 2-chome, Chiyoda-ku, Tokyo 100, Japan. TEL 03-381-6411. FAX 03-3581-6446.
Vendor(s): JICST. *1550*

CURRENT BIBLIOGRAPHY ON SCIENCE AND TECHNOLOGY: ELECTRONICS AND ELECTRICAL ENGINEERING.
Japan Information Center of Science and Technology, 5-2 Nagata-cho, 2-chome, Chiyoda-ku, Tokyo 100, Japan. TEL 03-3581-6411. FAX 03-3581-6446.
Vendor(s): JICST. *1842*

CURRENT BIBLIOGRAPHY ON SCIENCE AND TECHNOLOGY: ENERGY.
Japan Information Center of Science and Technology, 5-2 Nagata-cho, 2-chome, Chiyoda-ku, Tokyo 100, Japan. TEL 03-3581-6411. FAX 03-3581-6446.
Vendor(s): JICST. *1798*

CURRENT BIBLIOGRAPHY ON SCIENCE AND TECHNOLOGY: ENVIRONMENTAL POLLUTION.
Japan Information Center of Science and Technology, 5-2 Nagata-cho, 2-chome, Chiyoda-ku, Tokyo 100, Japan. TEL 03-3581-6411. FAX 03-3581-6446.
Vendor(s): JICST. *1973*

CURRENT BIBLIOGRAPHY ON SCIENCE AND TECHNOLOGY: LIFE SCIENCES.
Japan Information Center of Science and Technology, 5-2, Nagata-cho 2-chome, Chiyoda-ku, Tokyo 100, Japan. TEL 03-3581-6411. FAX 03-3581-6446.
Vendor(s): JICST. *464*

CURRENT BIBLIOGRAPHY ON SCIENCE AND TECHNOLOGY: MANAGEMENT SCIENCE AND SYSTEMS ENGINEERING.
Japan Information Center of Science and Technology, 5-2 Nagata-cho, 2-chome, Chiyoda-ku, Tokyo 100, Japan. TEL 03-3581-6411. FAX 03-3581-6446.
Vendor(s): JICST. *712*

CURRENT BIBLIOGRAPHY ON SCIENCE AND TECHNOLOGY: MECHANICAL ENGINEERING.
Japan Information Center of Science and Technology, 5-2 Nagata-cho, 2-chome, Chiyoda-ku, Tokyo 100, Japan. TEL 03-3581-6411. FAX 03-3581-6446.
Vendor(s): JICST. *1842*

CURRENT BIBLIOGRAPHY ON SCIENCE AND TECHNOLOGY: NUCLEAR ENGINEERING.
Japan Information Center of Science and Technology, 5-2 Nagata-cho, 2-chome, Chiyoda-ku, Tokyo 100, Japan. TEL 03-3581-6411. FAX 03-3581-6446.
Vendor(s): JICST. *1842*

CURRENT BIBLIOGRAPHY ON SCIENCE AND TECHNOLOGY: PURE AND APPLIED PHYSICS.
Japan Information Center of Science and Technology, 5-2 Nagata-cho, 2-chome, Chiyoda-ku, Tokyo 100, Japan. TEL 03-3581-6411. FAX 03-3581-6446.
Vendor(s): JICST. *3837*

CURRENT BIOTECHNOLOGY ABSTRACTS.
Royal Society of Chemistry, Thomas Graham House, Science Park, Milton Rd., Cambridge CB4 4WF, England. TEL 0462-672555. FAX 0462-480947.
Vendor(s): Data-Star (CUBI), DIALOG (File no.358), European Space Agency (File no.95/CURRENT BIOTECHNOLOGY ABSTRACTS). *464*

CURRENT BUSINESS REPORTS: MONTHLY RETAIL TRADE, SALES AND INVENTORIES.
U.S. Bureau of the Census, Data User Services Division, Washington, DC 20233. TEL 301-763-4100.
Vendor(s): CompuServe Consumer Information Service, DIALOG. *712*

CURRENT BUSINESS REPORTS: MONTHLY WHOLESALE TRADE: SALES AND INVENTORIES.
U.S. Bureau of the Census, Data User Services Division, Washington, DC 20233. TEL 301-763-4100.
Vendor(s): CompuServe Consumer Information Service, DIALOG. *835*

CURRENT CONSTRUCTION REPORTS.
U.S. Bureau of the Census, Data User Services Division, Washington, DC 20233. TEL 301-763-4100.
Vendor(s): CompuServe Consumer Information Service, DIALOG. *614*

CURRENT CONSTRUCTION REPORTS: HOUSING STARTS.
U.S. Bureau of the Census, Data User Services Division, Washington, DC 20233. TEL 301-763-4100.
Vendor(s): CompuServe Consumer Information Service, DIALOG. *2486*

CURRENT CONSTRUCTION REPORTS: HOUSING UNITS AUTHORIZED BY BUILDING PERMITS.
U.S. Bureau of the Census, Data User Services Division, Washington, DC 20233. TEL 301-763-4100.
Vendor(s): CompuServe Consumer Information Service, DIALOG. *2486*

CURRENT CONSTRUCTION REPORTS: NEW ONE-FAMILY HOUSES SOLD AND FOR SALE.
U.S. Bureau of the Census, Data User Services Division, Washington, DC 20233. TEL 301-763-4100.
Vendor(s): CompuServe Consumer Information Service, DIALOG. *2486*

CURRENT CONSTRUCTION REPORTS: VALUE OF NEW CONSTRUCTION PUT IN PLACE.
U.S. Bureau of the Census, Data User Services Division, Washington, DC 20233. TEL 301-763-4100.
Vendor(s): CompuServe Consumer Information Service, DIALOG. *615*

CURRENT CONTENTS: AGRICULTURE, BIOLOGY & ENVIRONMENTAL SCIENCES.
Institute for Scientific Information, 3501 Market St., Philadelphia, PA 19104. TEL 215-386-0100. FAX 215-386-2991.
Vendor(s): BRS (CCON,AGRI), DIALOG (File no.440). *136*

CURRENT CONTENTS: ARTS & HUMANITIES.
Institute for Scientific Information, 3501 Market St., Philadelphia, PA 19104. TEL 215-386-0100. FAX 215-386-2991.
Vendor(s): BRS (CCON,ARTS), DIALOG (File no.440). *2519*

CURRENT CONTENTS: CLINICAL MEDICINE.
Institute for Scientific Information, 3501 Market St., Philadelphia, PA 19104. TEL 215-386-0100. FAX 215-386-2991.
Vendor(s): BRS (CCON,CLIN), DIALOG (File no.440). *3169*

CURRENT CONTENTS: ENGINEERING, TECHNOLOGY & APPLIED SCIENCES.
Institute for Scientific Information, 3501 Market St., Philadelphia, PA 19104. TEL 215-386-0100. FAX 215-386-2991.
Vendor(s): BRS (CCON,ENGI), DIALOG (File no.440). *1842*

CURRENT CONTENTS: LIFE SCIENCES.
Institute for Scientific Information, 3501 Market St., Philadelphia, PA 19104. TEL 215-386-0100. FAX 215-386-2991.
Vendor(s): BRS (CCON,LIFE), DIALOG (File no.440). *464*

CURRENT CONTENTS: PHYSICAL, CHEMICAL & EARTH SCIENCES.
Institute for Scientific Information, 3501 Market St., Philadelphia, PA 19104. TEL 215-386-0100. FAX 215-386-2991.
Vendor(s): BRS (CCON,PHYS), DIALOG (File no.440). *1200*

CURRENT CONTENTS: SOCIAL & BEHAVIORAL SCIENCES.
Institute for Scientific Information, 3501 Market St., Philadelphia, PA 19104. TEL 215-386-0100. FAX 215-386-2991.
Vendor(s): BRS (CCON,BEHA), DIALOG (File no.440). *4457*

CURRENT DIGEST OF THE POST-SOVIET PRESS.
Current Digest of the Soviet Press, 3857 N. High St., Columbus, OH 43214-3747. TEL 614-292-4234. FAX 614-267-6310.
Vendor(s): DIALOG (File no.645), Mead Data Central. *3937*

CURRENT GOVERNMENTS REPORTS: CITY EMPLOYMENT.
U.S. Bureau of the Census, Data User Services Division, Washington, DC 20233. TEL 301-763-4100.
Vendor(s): CompuServe Consumer Information Service, DIALOG. *712*

CURRENT GOVERNMENTS REPORTS: COUNTY GOVERNMENT EMPLOYMENT.
U.S. Bureau of the Census, Data User Services Division, Washington, DC 20233. TEL 301-763-4100.
Vendor(s): CompuServe Consumer Information Service, DIALOG. *4058*

CURRENT GOVERNMENTS REPORTS: GOVERNMENT FINANCES.
U.S. Bureau of the Census, Data User Services Division, Washington, DC 20233. TEL 301-763-4100.
Vendor(s): CompuServe Consumer Information Service, DIALOG. *1092*

CURRENT GOVERNMENTS REPORTS: PUBLIC EMPLOYMENT.
U.S. Bureau of the Census, Data User Services Division, Washington, DC 20233. TEL 301-763-4100.
Vendor(s): CompuServe Consumer Information Service, DIALOG. *976*

CURRENT GOVERNMENTS REPORTS: STATE GOVERNMENT TAX COLLECTIONS.
U.S. Bureau of the Census, Data User Services Division, Washington, DC 20233. TEL 301-763-4100.
Vendor(s): CompuServe Consumer Information Service, DIALOG. *1092*

CURRENT HISTORY.
Current History, Inc., 4225 Main St., Philadelphia, PA 19127. TEL 215-482-4464. FAX 215-482-9197.
Vendor(s): BRS, DIALOG. *3889*

CURRENT HOUSING REPORTS.
U.S. Bureau of the Census, Data User Services Division, Washington, DC 20233. TEL 301-763-4100.
Vendor(s): CompuServe Consumer Information Service, DIALOG. *2486*

CURRENT HOUSING REPORTS: HOUSING CHARACTERISTICS.
U.S. Bureau of the Census, Data User Services Division, Washington, DC 20233. TEL 301-763-4100.
Vendor(s): CompuServe Consumer Information Service, DIALOG. *2486*

CURRENT HOUSING REPORTS: HOUSING VACANCIES.
U.S. Bureau of the Census, Data User Services Division, Washington, DC 20233. TEL 301-763-4100.
Vendor(s): CompuServe Consumer Information Service, DIALOG. *2486*

CURRENT INDEX TO JOURNALS IN EDUCATION.
Oryx Press, 4041 N. Central at Indian School Rd., Phoenix, AZ 85012-3397. TEL 602-265-2651. FAX 602-265-6250.
Vendor(s): BRS, BRS/Saunders Colleague, CISTI, DIALOG (File no.1/ERIC), Orbit Information Technologies (ERIC). *1675*

CURRENT INDEX TO STATISTICS.
American Statistical Association, 1429 Duke St., Alexandria, VA 22314-3402. TEL 703-684-1221. FAX 703-684-2037.
Vendor(s): BRS (MATH), DIALOG, European Space Agency. *3062*

CURRENT INDUSTRIAL REPORTS: BROADWOVEN FABRICS (GRAY).
U.S. Bureau of the Census, Data User Services Division (DAUS), Washington, DC 20233. TEL 301-763-4100.
Vendor(s): CompuServe Consumer Information Service, DIALOG. *4628*

CURRENT INDUSTRIAL REPORTS: FATS AND OILS. OILSEED CRUSHINGS.
U.S. Bureau of the Census, Data User Services Division, Washington, DC 20233. TEL 301-763-4100.
Vendor(s): CompuServe Consumer Information Service, DIALOG. *2084*

CURRENT INDUSTRIAL REPORTS: FATS AND OILS. PRODUCTION, CONSUMPTION, AND STOCKS.
U.S. Bureau of the Census, Data User Services Division, Washington, DC 20233. TEL 301-763-4100.
Vendor(s): CompuServe Consumer Information Service, DIALOG. *2085*

CURRENT INFORMATION IN THE CONSTRUCTION INDUSTRY.
Property Services Agency, Projects Library & Information Services, Rm. C003, Whitgift Services Centre, Wellesley Rd., Croydon CR9 3LY, England. TEL 081-760-4525.
Vendor(s): Pergamon Infoline. *615*

CURRENT LAW INDEX.
Information Access Company, 362 Lakeside Dr., Foster City, CA 94404. TEL 800-227-8431. FAX 415-378-5499.
Vendor(s): BRS, DIALOG, Mead Data Central, WESTLAW. *2698*

CURRENT MATHEMATICAL PUBLICATIONS.
American Mathematical Society, Box 1571, Annex Sta., Providence, RI 02901-9930. TEL 401-455-4000.
Vendor(s): BRS, DIALOG, European Space Agency. *3062*

CURRENT PHYSICS INDEX.
American Institute of Physics, 335 E. 45th St., New York, NY 10017. TEL 212-661-9404.
Vendor(s): DIALOG. *3837*

CURRENT POPULATION REPORTS: CONSUMER INCOME. MONEY INCOME OF HOUSEHOLDS, FAMILIES AND PERSONS IN THE UNITED STATES (YEAR).
U.S. Bureau of the Census, Data User Services Division, Washington, DC 20233. TEL 301-763-4100.
Vendor(s): CompuServe Consumer Information Service, DIALOG. *998*

CURRENT POPULATION REPORTS: LOCAL POPULATION ESTIMATES.
U.S. Bureau of the Census, Data User Services Division, Washington, DC 20233. TEL 301-763-4100.
Vendor(s): CompuServe Consumer Information Service, DIALOG. *3980*

CURRENT POPULATION REPORTS: POPULATION CHARACTERISTICS. GEOGRAPHICAL MOBILITY.
U.S. Bureau of the Census, Data User Services Division, Washington, DC 20233. TEL 301-763-4100.
Vendor(s): CompuServe Consumer Information Service, DIALOG. *3980*

CURRENT POPULATION REPORTS: POPULATION CHARACTERISTICS. MARITAL STATUS AND LIVING ARRANGEMENTS.
U.S. Bureau of the Census, Data User Services Division, Washington, DC 20233. TEL 301-763-4100.
Vendor(s): CompuServe Consumer Information Service, DIALOG. *3980*

CURRENT POPULATION REPORTS: POPULATION CHARACTERISTICS. SCHOOL ENROLLMENT: SOCIAL AND ECONOMIC CHARACTERISTICS OF STUDENTS.
U.S. Bureau of the Census, Data User Services Division, Washington, DC 20233. TEL 301-763-4100.
Vendor(s): CompuServe Consumer Information Service, DIALOG. *3981*

CURRENT POPULATION REPORTS: POPULATION ESTIMATES AND PROJECTIONS.
U.S. Bureau of the Census, Data User Services Division, Washington, DC 20233. TEL 301-763-4100.
Vendor(s): CompuServe Consumer Information Service, DIALOG. *3981*

CURRENT POPULATION REPORTS: POPULATION ESTIMATES AND PROJECTIONS. UNITED STATES POPULATION ESTIMATES BY AGE, SEX, RACE AND HISPANIC ORIGIN.
U.S. Bureau of the Census, Data User Services Division, Washington, DC 20233. TEL 301-763-4100.
Vendor(s): CompuServe Consumer Information Service, DIALOG. *3981*

CURRENT RESEARCH IN BRITAIN. BIOLOGICAL SCIENCES.
British Library, Document Supply Centre, Boston Spa, Wetherby, W. Yorkshire LS23 7BQ, England. TEL 0937-843434. FAX 0937-546333.
Vendor(s): Pergamon Infoline (CRIB). *465*

CURRENT RESEARCH IN BRITAIN. HUMANITIES.
British Library, Document Supply Centre, Boston Spa, Wetherby, W. Yorkshire LS23 7BQ, England. TEL 0937-843434. FAX 0937-546333.
Vendor(s): Pergamon Infoline (CRIB). *2519*

CURRENT RESEARCH IN BRITAIN. PHYSICAL SCIENCES.
British Library, Document Supply Centre, Boston Spa, Wetherby, W. Yorkshire LS23 7BQ, England. TEL 0937-843434. FAX 0937-546333.
Vendor(s): Pergamon Infoline (CRIB). *4355*

CURRENT RESEARCH IN LIBRARY & INFORMATION SCIENCE.
Bowker-Saur Abstracts & Indexes, 59-60 Grosvenor St., London WX1 9DA, England. TEL 071-493-5841. FAX 071-499-1590.
Vendor(s): DIALOG (File no.61), Orbit Information Technologies. *2753*

CURRENT SCIENCE AND TECHNOLOGY RESEARCH IN JAPAN.
Japan Information Center of Science and Technology, 5-2 Nagata-cho, 2-chome, Chiyoda-ku, Tokyo 100, Japan. TEL 03-3581-6411. FAX 03-3581-6446.
Vendor(s): JICST. *4355*

CURRENT SURGICAL DIAGNOSIS & TREATMENT.
Appleton & Lange 25 Van Zant St., Box 5630, Norwalk, CT 06856. TEL 203-838-4400.
Vendor(s): Mead Data Central. *3378*

CURRENT TECHNOLOGY INDEX.
Bowker-Saur Ltd. 59-60 Grosvenor St., London W1X 9DA, England. TEL 071-493-5841. FAX 071-499-1590.
Vendor(s): DIALOG (File no.142). *4614*

CURRENT THOUGHTS & TRENDS.
Box 35004, Colorado Springs, CO 80935-3504. TEL 719-531-3585. FAX 719-598-7128. *4212*

THE CYPRUS REVIEW.
Intercollege, P.O. Box 4005, Nicosia, Cyprus. TEL 02-456892. FAX 02-456704.
Vendor(s): BRS, Data-Star, DIALOG. *4370*

C2C ABSTRACTS: JAPAN - ANALYTICAL CHEMISTRY.
Scan C2C, 500 E St. S.W., Ste. 800, Washington, DC 20024. TEL 800-525-3865. FAX 202-863-3855.
Vendor(s): Data-Star (JPTC), DIALOG (File no.582), European Space Agency (File no.241), Orbit Information Technologies (JTEC). *1200*

C2C ABSTRACTS: JAPAN - CERAMICS.
Scan C2C, 500 E St. S.W., Ste. 800, Washington, DC 20024. TEL 800-525-3865. FAX 202-863-3855.
Vendor(s): Data-Star (JPTC), DIALOG (File no.582), European Space Agency (File no.241), Orbit Information Technologies (JTEC). *1167*

C2C ABSTRACTS: JAPAN - CHEMICAL ENGINEERING.
Scan C2C, 500 E St. S.W., Ste. 800, Washington, DC 20024. TEL 800-525-3865. FAX 202-863-3855.
Vendor(s): Data-Star (JPTC), DIALOG (File no.582), European Space Agency (File no.2410), Orbit Information Technologies (JTEC). *1843*

C2C ABSTRACTS: JAPAN - CRYSTALLOGRAPHY.
Scan C2C, 500 E St. S.W., Ste. 800, Washington, DC 20024. TEL 800-525-3865. FAX 202-863-3855.
Vendor(s): Data-Star (JPTC), DIALOG (File no.582), European Space Agency (File no.241), Orbit Information Technologies (JTEC). *1201*

C2C ABSTRACTS: JAPAN - HYDROCARBONS.
Scan C2C, 500 E St. S.W., Ste. 800, Washington, DC 20024. TEL 800-525-3865. FAX 202-863-3855.
Vendor(s): Data-Star (JPTC), DIALOG (File no.582), European Space Agency (File no.241), Orbit Information Technologies (JTEC). *1201*

C2C ABSTRACTS: JAPAN - INORGANIC CHEMISTRY.
Scan C2C, 500 E St. S.W., Ste. 800, Washington, DC 20024. TEL 800-525-3865. FAX 202-863-3855.
Vendor(s): Data-Star (JPTC), DIALOG (File no.582), European Space Agency (File no.241), Orbit Information Technologies (JTEC). *1201*

C2C ABSTRACTS: JAPAN - MATERIALS SCIENCE.
Scan C2C, 500 E St. S.W., Ste. 800, Washington, DC 20024. TEL 800-525-3865. FAX 202-863-3855.
Vendor(s): Data-Star (JPTC), DIALOG (File no.582), European Space Agency (File no.241), Orbit Information Technologies (JTEC). *1843*

C2C ABSTRACTS: JAPAN - METALS.
Scan C2C, 500 E St. S.W., Ste. 800, Washington, DC 20024. TEL 800-525-3865. FAX 202-863-3855.
Vendor(s): Data-Star (JPTC), DIALOG (File no.582), European Space Agency (File no.241), Orbit Information Technologies (JTEC). *3425*

C2C ABSTRACTS: JAPAN - ORGANIC CHEMISTRY.
Scan C2C, 500 E St. S.W., Ste. 800, Washington, DC 20024. TEL 800-525-3865. FAX 202-863-3855.
Vendor(s): Data-Star (JPTC), DIALOG (File no.582), European Space Agency (File no.241), Orbit Information Technologies (JTEC). *1201*

C2C ABSTRACTS: JAPAN - PHYSICAL CHEMISTRY.
Scan C2C, 500 E St. S.W., Ste. 800, Washington, DC 20024. TEL 800-525-3865. FAX 202-863-3855.
Vendor(s): Data-Star (JPTC), DIALOG (File no.582), European Space Agency (File no.241), Orbit Information Technologies (JTEC). *1201*

C2C ABSTRACTS: JAPAN - PLASTICS.
Scan C2C, 500 E St. S.W., Ste. 800, Washington, DC 20024. TEL 800-525-3865. FAX 202-863-3855.
Vendor(s): Data-Star (JPTC), DIALOG (File no.582), European Space Agency (File no.241), Orbit Information Technologies (JTEC). *3868*

C2C ABSTRACTS: JAPAN - POLYMER CHEMISTRY.
Scan C2C, 500 E St. S.W., Ste. 800, Washington, DC 20024. TEL 800-525-3865. FAX 202-863-3855.
Vendor(s): Data-Star (JPTC), DIALOG (File no.582), European Space Agency (File no.241), Orbit Information Technologies (JTEC). *1201*

C2C ABSTRACTS: JAPAN - SURFACE CHEMISTRY.
Scan C2C, 500 E St. S.W., Ste. 800, Washington, DC 20024. TEL 800-525-3865. FAX 202-863-3855.
Vendor(s): Data-Star (JPTC), DIALOG (File no.582), European Space Agency (File no.241), Orbit Information Technologies (JTEC). *1201*

C2C ABSTRACTS: JAPAN - TEXTILES.
Scan C2C, 500 E St. S.W., Ste. 800, Washington, DC 20024. TEL 800-525-3865. FAX 202-863-3855.
Vendor(s): Data-Star (JPTC), DIALOG (File no.582), European Space Agency (File no.241), Orbit Information Technologies (JTEC). *4628*

C2C CURRENTS: JAPAN - CHEMISTRY.
Scan C2C, 500 E St. S.W., Ste. 800, Washington, DC 20024. TEL 800-525-3865. FAX 202-863-3855.
Vendor(s): Data-Star (JPTC), DIALOG (File no.582), European Space Agency (File no.241), Orbit Information Technologies (JTEC). *1201*

C2C CURRENTS: JAPAN - COMPUTERS.
Scan C2C, 500 E St. S.W., Ste. 800, Washington, DC 20024. TEL 800-525-3865. FAX 202-863-3855.
Vendor(s): Data-Star (JPTC), DIALOG (File no.582), European Space Agency (File no.241), Orbit Information Technologies (JTEC). *1404*

C2C CURRENTS: JAPAN - ELECTRONICS.
Scan C2C, 500 E St. S.W., Ste. 800, Washington, DC 20024. TEL 800-525-3865. FAX 202-863-3855.
Vendor(s): Data-Star (JPTC), DIALOG (File no.582), European Space Agency (File no.241), Orbit Information Technologies (JTEC). *1765*

C2C CURRENTS: JAPAN - MATERIALS.
Scan C2C, 500 E St. S.W., Ste. 800, Washington, DC 20024. TEL 800-525-3865. FAX 202-863-3855.
Vendor(s): Data-Star (JPTC), DIALOG (File no.582), European Space Agency (File no.241), Orbit Information Technologies (JTEC). *1843*

D G REVIEW.
Data Base Publications, 9390 Research Blvd., 2-300, Austin, TX 78759-6544. TEL 512-343-9066. FAX 512-345-1935.
Vendor(s): DIALOG. *1459*

D I C P - THE ANNALS OF PHARMACOTHERAPY.
Harvey Whitney Books Company, Box 42696, Cincinnati, OH 45242. TEL 513-793-3555. FAX 513-793-3600. *3722*

D K I LITERATUR-SCHNELLDIENST KUNSTSTOFFE KAUTSCHUK FASERN.
Deutsches Kunststoff-Institut, Schlossgartenstr. 6, 6100 Darmstadt, Germany. TEL 06151-162105. FAX 06151-292855.
Vendor(s): FIZ Technik, STN International. *3868*

D L A BULLETIN.
University of California, Division of Library Automation, 300 Lakeside Dr., 8th Fl., Oakland, CA 94612-3550. TEL 415-987-0564. *2796*

D M NEWS.
D M News Corp. 19 W. 21st St., New York, NY 10010. TEL 212-741-2095. FAX 212-633-9367.
Vendor(s): Mead Data Central. *1037*

D R I - MCGRAW-HILL U S FORECAST SUMMARY.
D R I - McGraw-Hill, 24 Hartwell Ave., Lexington, MA 02173. TEL 617-863-5100. FAX 617-860-6332. *859*

DAILY LABOR REPORT.
The Bureau of National Affairs, Inc., 1231 25th St., N.W., Washington, DC 20037. TEL 202-452-4200. FAX 202-822-8092.
Vendor(s): Bureau of National Affairs, Human Resources Information Network (CDD, HDD), Mead Data Central (DLABRT), WESTLAW (BNA-DLR). *976*

DAILY NEWS RECORD.
Fairchild Publications, Inc., Daily News Record 7 W. 34th St., New York, NY 10001. TEL 212-630-4000.
Vendor(s): DIALOG. *4618*

DAILY REPORT FOR EXECUTIVES.
The Bureau of National Affairs, Inc., 1231 25th St., N.W., Washington, DC 20037. TEL 202-452-4200. FAX 202-822-8092.
Vendor(s): Human Resources Information Network (CDD, HDD), Mead Data Central (DREXEC), NewsNet, WESTLAW (BNA-DER). *1007*

DAILY TAX REPORT.
The Bureau of National Affairs, Inc., 1231 25th St., N.W., Washington, DC 20037. TEL 202-452-4200. FAX 202-822-8092.
Vendor(s): Bureau of National Affairs, Mead Data Central (BNADTR), NewsNet, WESTLAW (BNA-DTR). *1092*

DAILY TEXAN.
Texas Student Publications, Box D, Austin, TX 78713-9804. TEL 512-471-4591. FAX 512-471-1576. *1309*

DAIRY FOODS.
Delta Communications, Inc. (Chicago) 400 N. Michigan Ave., Ste. 1200, Chicago, IL 60611. TEL 312-222-2000. FAX 312-222-2026.
Vendor(s): DIALOG. *2065*

DAIRY SCIENCE ABSTRACTS.
C.A.B. International, Wallingford, Oxon OX10 8DE, England. TEL 800-528-4841, 0491 32111. FAX 0491-33508.
Vendor(s): BRS (CABA), CISTI, DIMDI, DIALOG, European Space Agency (File nos.16 & 124/CAB). *136*

DALLAS - FORT WORTH BUSINESS JOURNAL.
American City Business Journals, Inc. (Houston), One W. Loop S., Ste. 650, Houston, TX 77027. TEL 713-688-8811.
Vendor(s): DIALOG. *658*

DANMARKS TEKNISKE BIBLIOTEK. KATALOG.
Danmarks Tekniske Bibliotek, Anker Engelunds Vej 1, DK-2800 Lungby, Denmark.
Available only online. *2754*

DANSK ANMELDELSESINDEKS.
Bibliotekscentralen, Tempovej 7-11, DK-2750 Ballerup, Denmark. TEL 2-974000. FAX 2-655310. *4140*

DANSK ARTIKELINDEKS: AVISER OG TIDSSKRIFTER.
Bibliotekscentralen, Tempovej 7-11, DK-2750 Ballerup, Denmark. TEL 2-974000. FAX 2-655310. *2578*

DANSK LYDFORTEGNELSE.
Bibliotekscentralen, Tempovej 7-11, DK-2750 Ballerup, Denmark. TEL 2-974000. FAX 2-655310. *3588*

DANSK MEDIA INDEX.
Dansk Media Komite, Egetoften 8, 2900 Hellerup, Denmark. FAX 45-01-610590. *1347*

DATA BASE REPORTS.
Insurance Information Institute, 110 William St., New York, NY 10038. TEL 212-699-9200. FAX 212-732-1916.
Vendor(s): Mead Data Central. *2530*

DATA BASED ADVISOR.
Data Based Solutions, Inc., 4010 Morena Blvd., Ste. 200, San Diego, CA 92117-4547. TEL 619-483-6400. FAX 619-483-9851.
Vendor(s): DIALOG. *1476*

DATA BROADCASTING REPORT.
Waters Information Services, Inc., Box 2248, Binghamton, NY 13902-2248. TEL 607-770-8535. FAX 607-798-1692.
Vendor(s): NewsNet. *1334*

DATA CHANNELS.
Phillips Publishing, Inc., 7811 Montrose Rd., Potomac, MD 20854. TEL 301-340-2100. FAX 301-309-3847.
Vendor(s): DIALOG, NewsNet (TE22). *1449*

DATA COMMUNICATIONS.
McGraw-Hill, Inc., 1221 Ave. of the Americas, New York, NY 10020. TEL 212-512-2000.
Vendor(s): DIALOG (File no.624/McGRAW-HILL PUBLICATIONS ONLINE), Dow Jones/News Retrieval, Mead Data Central. *1446*

DATABASE (WESTON).
Online, Inc., 11 Tannery Ln., Weston, CT 06883. TEL 203-227-8466. FAX 203-222-0122.
Vendor(s): DIALOG (File no.170). *1444*

DATABASE ALERT.
Knowledge Industry Publications, Inc., 701 Westchester Ave., White Plains, NY 10604. TEL 914-328-9157. FAX 914-328-9093.
Vendor(s): BRS (KIPD). *1425*

DATABASE DIRECTORY.
Knowledge Industry Publications, Inc., 701 Westchester Ave., White Plains, NY 10604. TEL 914-328-9157. FAX 914-328-9093.
Vendor(s): BRS (KIPD). *1425*

DATABASE SEARCHER.
Meckler Publishing Corporation, 11 Ferry Lane W., Westport, CT 06880-5808. TEL 203-226-6967.
Vendor(s): DIALOG, Mead Data Central. *1459*

DATAMATION.
Cahners Publishing Company (Newton) Division of Reed Publishing (USA) Inc., 275 Washington St., Newton, MA 02158-1630. TEL 617-964-3030. FAX 617-558-4506.
Vendor(s): DIALOG. *1449*

DEALERSCOPE MERCHANDISING.
North American Publishing Co., 401 N. Broad St., Philadelphia, PA 19108. TEL 215-238-5300. FAX 215-238-5457.
Vendor(s): DIALOG. *1765*

SERIALS AVAILABLE ONLINE 5065

DEALING WITH TECHNOLOGY.
Waters Information Services, Inc., Box 2248, Binghamton, NY 13902. TEL 607-770-8535. FAX 607-798-1692.
Vendor(s): Data-Star, DIALOG, NewsNet. *805*

DEFENSE & AEROSPACE ELECTRONICS.
Pasha Publications Inc., 1401 Wilson Blvd., Ste. 900, Arlington, VA 22209-9970. TEL 703-528-1244. FAX 703-528-1253.
Vendor(s): BRS (TSAP), Data-Star (PTBN), DIALOG (File nos.636,648), NewsNet (DE03). *3456*

DEFENSE & FOREIGN AFFAIRS.
International Media Corporation, 110 N. Royal St., Ste. 307, Alexandria, VA 22314. TEL 703-684-8455. FAX 703-684-2207.
Vendor(s): Mead Data Central. *3890*

DEFENSE AND FOREIGN AFFAIRS STRATEGIC POLICY.
International Media Corp., 110 N. Royal St., Ste. 307, VA 22314. TEL 703-684-8455. FAX 703-684-2207.
Vendor(s): Mead Data Central. *3456*

DEFENSE AND FOREIGN AFFAIRS WEEKLY.
International Media Corporation, 110 N. Royal St., Ste. 307, Alexandria, VA 22314. TEL 703-684-8455. FAX 703-684-2207.
Vendor(s): Mead Data Central. *3456*

DEFENSE CLEANUP.
Pasha Publications Inc., 1401 Wilson Blvd., Ste. 900, Arlington, VA 22209-9970. TEL 703-528-1244. FAX 703-528-1253.
Vendor(s): Data-Star, DIALOG. *1984*

DEFENSE DAILY.
Phillips Publishing, Inc., Defense - Aviation Group, 1925 N. Lynn St., Ste. 1000, Arlington, VA 22209. TEL 703-522-8333. FAX 703-522-6448.
Vendor(s): DIALOG, NewsNet (DE01). *51*

DEFENSE ELECTRONICS.
Cardiff Publishing Co., 6300 S. Syracuse Way, Englewood, CO 80111. TEL 303-220-0600.
Vendor(s): DIALOG, Mead Data Central. *1765*

DEFENSE MARKETING INTERNATIONAL.
Phillips Publishing, Inc., Defense - Aviation Group, 1925 N. Lynn St., Ste. 1000, Arlington, VA 22209. TEL 703-522-8333. FAX 703-522-6448.
Vendor(s): Data-Star, DIALOG, NewsNet. *3456*

DEFENSE TECHNOLOGY BUSINESS.
Phillips Publishing, Inc., Defense - Aviation Group, 1925 N. Lynn St., Ste. 1000, Arlington, VA 22209. TEL 703-522-8333. FAX 703-522-6448.
Vendor(s): Data-Star, DIALOG, NewsNet. *3457*

DEFENSE WEEK.
King Publishing Group, Inc., 627 National Press Bldg., Washington, DC 20045. TEL 202-638-4260. FAX 202-662-9744. *3457*

DELAWARE JOURNAL OF CORPORATE LAW.
Widener University, School of Law, Box 7286, Wilmington, DE 19803. TEL 302-477-2145.
Vendor(s): Mead Data Central, WESTLAW. *2709*

DELTA'S NEW PRODUCT NEWS.
Delta Communications, Inc. (Chicago) 400 N. Michigan Ave., Ste. 1200, Chicago, IL 60611. TEL 312-222-2000. FAX 312-222-2026.
Vendor(s): Mead Data Central. *2065*

DENMARK. STATENS BIBLIOTEKSTJENESTE. ALBA - ACCESSIONSKATALOGEN.
Statens Bibliotekstjeneste, Nyhavn 31E, DK-1051 Copenhagen K, Denmark. TEL 45 33 93 46 33. FAX 45-33-93-60-93.
Available only online. *398*

DENVER BUSINESS.
Tall Oaks Publishing Inc., 10394 W. Chatfield Ave., Ste. 108, Littleton, CO 80127. TEL 303-979-6660.
Vendor(s): DIALOG. *658*

DENVER JOURNAL OF INTERNATIONAL LAW AND POLICY.
University of Denver, College of Law, 7039 E. 18th Ave., Ste. 235, Denver, CO 80220. TEL 303-871-6170.
Vendor(s): WESTLAW. *2722*

DENVER POST INDEX.
University Microfilms International, Data Courier, c/o Bonnie Maxwell, VP, 620 S. Third St., Louisville, KY 40202. TEL 800-626-2823. FAX 502-589-5572.
Vendor(s): DIALOG. *2578*

DENVER UNIVERSITY LAW REVIEW.
University of Denver, College of Law, Porter Adm. Bldg., 7039 E. 18th Ave., Denver, CO 80220-1826. TEL 303-871-6171.
Vendor(s): WESTLAW. *2618*

DETROIT NEWS INDEX.
University Microfilms International, Data Courier, c/o Bonnie Maxwell, VP, 620 S. Third St., Louisville, KY 40202. TEL 800-626-2823. FAX 502-589-5572.
Vendor(s): DIALOG. *2578*

DER DEUTSCHE APOTHEKER.
Verlag "Der Deutsche Apotheker", Hans-Thoma-Str. 1, Postfach 1650, 6370 Oberursel-Taunus, Germany. TEL 06171-55012. FAX 06171-55142. *3722*

DEUTSCHE APOTHEKER ZEITUNG.
Deutscher Apotheker Verlag, Postfach 101061, 7000 Stuttgart 10, Germany. TEL 0711-2582-0. FAX 0711-2582290. *3722*

DEVELOPMENTAL DYNAMICS.
John Wiley & Sons, Inc., Journals, 605 Third Ave., New York, NY 10158. TEL 212-850-6000. FAX 212-850-6088. *436*

DEVELOPNET NEWS.
Volunteers in Technical Assistance, Inc., 1815 N. Lynn St., Ste.200, Arlington, VA 22209-2079. TEL 703-276-1800. FAX 703-243-1865.
Available only online. *4596*

DEVICES & DIAGNOSTICS LETTER.
Washington Business Information, Inc., c/o Karen Harrington, 1117 N. 19th St., Ste. 200, Arlington, VA 22209. TEL 703-247-3434. FAX 703-247-3421.
Vendor(s): BRS (DIOG), Data-Star, DIALOG. *3093*

DIABETES.
American Diabetes Association, Inc., 1660 Duke St., Alexandria, VA 22314. TEL 703-549-1500. FAX 703-836-7439.
Vendor(s): BRS. *3251*

DIABETES CARE.
American Diabetes Association, Inc., 1660 Duke St., Alexandria, VA 22314. TEL 703-549-1500. FAX 703-836-7439.
Vendor(s): BRS. *3251*

DICKINSON LAW REVIEW.
Dickinson School of Law, 150 S. College St., Carlisle, PA 17013. TEL 717-243-4611. FAX 717-243-4443.
Vendor(s): WESTLAW. *2618*

DICTIONARY OF CONTEMPORARY QUOTATIONS.
John Gordon Burke Publisher, Inc., Box 1492, Evanston, IL 60204-1492. TEL 708-866-8625. *2911*

DIENST LANDBOUWKUNDIG ONDERZOEK. STARING CENTRUM, INSTITUUT VOOR ONDERZOEK VAN HET LANDELIJKE GEBIED. JAARVERSLAG.
Dienst Landbouwkundig Onderzoek, Staring Centrum, Instituut voor Onderzoek van het Landelijke Gebied, P.O. Box 125, 6700 AC Wageningen, Netherlands. TEL 75230 VISI NL. FAX 08370-24812. *176*

DIENST LANDBOUWKUNDIG ONDERZOEK. STARING CENTRUM, INSTITUUT VOOR ONDERZOEK VAN HET LANDELIJK GEBIED. RAPPORTEN.
Dienst Landbouwkundig Onderzoek, Staring Centrum, Instituut voor Onderzoek van het Landelijk Gebied, P.O. Box 125, 6700 AC Wageningen, Netherlands. TEL 08370-74200. FAX 08370-24812. *176*

DIER - EN - ARTS.
Transmondial, Baron van Nagellstr. 27, 3781 AP Voorthuizen, Netherlands. TEL 03429-3135. FAX 03429-3154. *4809*

DIFFUSION EXPRESS.
Electricite de France, Direction des Etudes et Recherches, Departement Systemes d'Information et de Documentation, 1, av. du General de Gaulle, 92141 Clamart, France. TEL 47-65-41-58. FAX 47-65-31-24.
Vendor(s): European Space Agency (File no.27), Telesystemes - Questel (Base EDF.DOC). *1843*

DIGEST OF ACTIVITIES OF CONGRESS.
Oliphant Washington Service, Box 9808, Friendship Sta., Washington, DC 20016. TEL 202-338-3616.
Vendor(s): NewsNet. *4058*

DIGITAL REVIEW.
Cahners Publishing Company (Newton) Division of Reed Publishing (USA) Inc., 275 Washington St., Newton, MA 02158-1630. TEL 617-964-3030. FAX 617-558-4506.
Vendor(s): DIALOG. *1460*

DIRECTION OF TRADE STATISTICS.
International Monetary Fund, Publication Services, 700 19th St., N.W., Ste. C-100, Washington, DC 20431. TEL 202-623-7430. FAX 202-623-7201. *713*

DIRECTORIES IN PRINT.
Gale Research Inc., 835 Penobscot Bldg., Detroit, MI 48226. TEL 313-961-2242. FAX 313-961-6083.
Vendor(s): DIALOG. *399*

DIRECTORY OF AMERICAN RESEARCH AND TECHNOLOGY.
R.R. Bowker, A Reed Reference Publishing Company, Division of Reed Publishing (USA) Inc., 121 Chanlon Rd., New Providence, NJ 07974. TEL 800-521-8110. FAX 908-665-6688.
Vendor(s): Orbit Information Technologies (DART). *4596*

DIRECTORY OF ASSOCIATIONS IN CANADA.
Micromedia Ltd., 20 Victoria St., Toronto, Ont. M5C 2N8, Canada. TEL 416-362-5211. FAX 416-362-6161.
Vendor(s): CISTI. *1128*

DIRECTORY OF CORPORATE AFFILIATIONS.
National Register Publishing Co., A Reed Reference Publishing Company, Division of Reed Publishing (USA) Inc., 121 Chanlon Rd., New Providence, NJ 07974. TEL 800-521-8110. FAX 908-665-6688.
Vendor(s): DIALOG (File no.513), Pergamon Infoline. *1129*

DIRECTORY OF FEDERAL LABORATORIES.
High Tech Publishing Company, Box 1923, Brattleboro, VT 05301. TEL 802-254-3539.
Vendor(s): Data-Star, NewsNet. *1130*

DIRECTORY OF HISTORICAL ORGANIZATIONS IN THE UNITED STATES AND CANADA.
American Association for State and Local History, 172 Second Ave. N., Ste. 202, Nashville, TN 37201. TEL 615-255-2971. *2404*

DIRECTORY OF LEADING PRIVATE COMPANIES, INCLUDING CORPORATE AFFILIATIONS.
National Register Publishing Co., A Reed Reference Publishing Company, Division of Reed Publishing (USA) Inc., 121 Chanlon Rd., New Providence, NJ 07974. TEL 800-521-8110. FAX 908-665-6688.
Vendor(s): DIALOG (File no. 513). *1131*

DIRECTORY OF ONLINE DATABASES.
Gale Research Inc., 835 Penobscot Bldg., Detroit, MI 48226. TEL 313-961-2242. FAX 313-961-6038.
Vendor(s): Data-Star (CUAD), Orbit Information Technologies (CUADRA), Telesystemes - Questel (CUADRA). *1444*

DIRECTORY OF PORTABLE DATABASES.
Gale Research Inc., 835 Penobscot Bldg., Detroit, MI 48226. TEL 313-961-2242. FAX 313-961-6038.
Vendor(s): Data-Star, Orbit Information Technologies, Telesystemes - Questel. *1444*

DIRECTORY OF RESEARCH GRANTS.
Oryx Press, 4041 N. Central at Indian School Rd., Phoenix, AZ 85012-3397. TEL 602-265-2651. FAX 602-265-6250.
Vendor(s): DIALOG. *1705*

Online

DISCOUNT STORE NEWS.
Lebhar-Friedman, Inc., 425 Park Ave., New York, NY 10022. TEL 212-756-5000.
Vendor(s): DIALOG. *1038*

DISCOVER (BURBANK).
Walt Disney Magazine Publishing Group, 500 S. Buena Vista, Burbank, CA 91521-6012. TEL 818-973-4320.
Vendor(s): DIALOG, Mead Data Central, VU/TEXT Information Services, Inc.. *4308*

DISEASES OF THE COLON AND RECTUM.
Williams & Wilkins, 428 E. Preston St., Baltimore, MD 21202. TEL 301-528-4000. FAX 301-528-4321.
Vendor(s): Mead Data Central. *3378*

DISPLAY.
Dansk D I A N E Center, Sigurdsgade 41, DK-2200 Copenhagen N, Denmark. TEL 31-81-66-66. FAX 35-821655. *1426*

DISSERTATION ABSTRACTS.
University Microfilms International, 300 N. Zeeb Rd., Ann Arbor, MI 48016-1304. TEL 800-521-0600. FAX 313-973-1540.
Vendor(s): BRS (DISS), DIALOG. *2519*

DISSERTATION ABSTRACTS INTERNATIONAL. SECTION A: HUMANITIES AND SOCIAL SCIENCES.
University Microfilms International, Dissertation Publishing, c/o Dorie Mickelson, Mgr., 300 N. Zeeb Rd., Ann Arbor, MI 48106. TEL 313-761-4700.
Vendor(s): BRS (DISS), BRS/Saunders Colleague, DIALOG (File no.35). *2520*

DISSERTATION ABSTRACTS INTERNATIONAL. SECTION B: PHYSICAL SCIENCES AND ENGINEERING.
University Microfilms International, Dissertation Publishing, c/o Dorie Mickelson, Mgr., 300 N. Zeeb Rd., Ann Arbor, MI 48106. TEL 313-761-4700.
Vendor(s): BRS (DISS), BRS/Saunders Colleague, DIALOG (File no.35). *4355*

DISSERTATION ABSTRACTS INTERNATIONAL. SECTION C: WORLDWIDE.
University Microfilms International, Dissertation Publishing, c/o Dorie Mickelson, Mgr., 300 N. Zeeb Rd., Ann Arbor, MI 48106. TEL 313-761-4700.
Vendor(s): BRS (DISS), BRS/Saunders Colleague, DIALOG (File no.35). *399*

DISTRIBUTION.
Vereinigte Fachverlage GmbH, Lise-Meitner-Str. 2, Postfach 2760, 6500 Mainz, Germany.
TEL 06131-992-01. FAX 06131-992-100.
Vendor(s): DIALOG. *1038*

DO-IT-YOURSELF REPORT.
Euromonitor, 87-88 Turnmill St., London EC1M 5QU, England. TEL 071-251 8024. FAX 071-608-3149. *2501*

DOCUMENT IMAGE AUTOMATION UPDATE.
Meckler Publishing Corporation, 11 Ferry Lane W., Westport, CT 06880-5808. TEL 203-226-6967.
Vendor(s): NewsNet (EC51). *1372*

DOING BUSINESS WITH EASTERN EUROPE.
Business International Corp., 215 Park Ave. S., New York, NY 10003. TEL 212-460-0600. FAX 212-955-8837.
Vendor(s): DIALOG. *905*

DOMINION LAW REPORTS.
Canada Law Book Inc., 240 Edward St., Aurora, Ont. L4G 3S9, Canada. TEL 416-841-6472. *2620*

DR. DOBB'S JOURNAL.
M & T Publishing, Inc., 501 Galveston Dr., Redwood City, CA 94063-4728. TEL 415-366-3600. FAX 415-366-1685. *1460*

DRAGOCO REPORT.
Dragoco Gerberding & Co. GmbH, Dragocostr., 3450 Holzminden, Germany. TEL 05531-7040. FAX 05531-704391. *375*

DRAKE LAW REVIEW.
Drake University, Law School, Cartwright Hall, Des Moines, IA 50311. TEL 515-271-2930.
Vendor(s): WESTLAW. *2620*

DRUG AND CHEMICAL TOXICOLOGY.
Marcel Dekker Journals, 270 Madison Ave., New York, NY 10016. TEL 212-696-9000. FAX 212-685-4540. *3723*

DRUG AND COSMETIC INDUSTRY.
Avanstar Communications, Inc., 7500 Old Oak Blvd., Cleveland, OH 44130. TEL 216-826-2839. FAX 216-891-2726.
Vendor(s): DIALOG. *3723*

DRUG AND THERAPEUTICS BULLETIN.
Consumers' Association, 2 Marylebone Rd., London NW1 4DF, England. TEL 071-486-5544. *3723*

DRUG DEVELOPMENT AND INDUSTRIAL PHARMACY.
Marcel Dekker Journals, 270 Madison Ave., New York, NY 10016. TEL 212-696-9000. FAX 212-685-4540. *3723*

DRUG INFORMATION JOURNAL.
Pergamon Press, Inc., Journals Division, 660 White Plains Rd., Tarrytown, NY 10591-5153. TEL 914-524-9200. FAX 914-333-2444. *3723*

DRUG LICENSE OPPORTUNITIES.
IMSWORLD Publications Ltd., 11-13 Melton St., London NW1 2EH, England. *3723*

DRUG MERCHANDISING.
Maclean-Hunter Ltd., Business Publication Division, Maclean-Hunter Bldg., 777 Bay St., Toronto, Ont. M5W 1A7, Canada. TEL 416-596-5950. *3723*

DRUG THERAPY.
Excerpta Medica, Inc., Core Publishing Division 105 Raider Blvd., Belle Mead, NJ 08052. TEL 908-874-8550. FAX 908-874-0700. *3724*

DRUG TOPICS.
Medical Economics Publishing Co., Five Paragon Dr., Montvale, NJ 07645. TEL 201-358-7200. FAX 201-573-1045.
Vendor(s): DIALOG. *3724*

DRUGS IN PROSPECT.
Paul De Haen International, 2750 S. Shoshone St., Englewood, CO 80110. TEL 800-438-0296. FAX 303-789-2534.
Vendor(s): DIALOG. *3724*

DRUGS IN RESEARCH.
Paul De Haen International, 2750 S. Shoshone St., Englewood, CO 80110. TEL 800-438-0296. FAX 303-789-2534.
Vendor(s): DIALOG. *3724*

DRUGS IN USE.
Paul De Haen International, 2750 S. Shoshone St., Englewood, CO 80110. TEL 800-438-0296. FAX 303-789-2534.
Vendor(s): DIALOG. *3724*

DRUGS MADE IN GERMANY.
Editio Cantor, Postfach 1255, 7960 Aulendorf, Germany. TEL 07525-2060. FAX 07525-20680. *3724*

DUKE LAW JOURNAL.
Duke University, School of Law, Rm. 006, Durham, NC 27706-2580. TEL 919-684-5966. FAX 919-684-3417.
Vendor(s): Mead Data Central, WESTLAW. *2621*

DUTCHESS COUNTY HISTORICAL SOCIETY. YEARBOOK.
Dutchess County Historical Society, Box 88, Poughkeepsie, NY 12602.
Vendor(s): DIALOG. *2404*

E & M J MINING ACTIVITY DIGEST.
Maclean Hunter Publishing Company, 29 N. Wacker Dr., Chicago, IL 60606. TEL 312-726-2802. FAX 312-726-2574.
Vendor(s): Mead Data Central. *3405*

E B R I ISSUE BRIEF.
Employee Benefit Research Institute, 2121 K St., N.W., Ste. 600, Washington, DC 20037-1896. TEL 202-659-0670. FAX 202-775-6312. *1064*

E C ENERGY MONTHLY.
Financial Times Business Information Ltd., Tower House, Southampton St., London WC2E 7HA, England. TEL 071-240-9391. FAX 071-240-7946.
Vendor(s): Data-Star, Mead Data Central. *1785*

E C O D O C.
Centre National de la Recherche Scientifique, Institut de l'Information Scientifique et Technique, Sciences Humaines et Sociales, 54 bd. Raspail, B.P. 140, 75270 Paris Cedex 06, France. *713*

E D N MAGAZINE.
Cahners Publishing Company (Newton) Division of Reed Publishing (USA) Inc., 275 Washington St., Newton, MA 02158-1630. TEL 617-964-3030. FAX 617-558-4470.
Vendor(s): DIALOG. *1766*

E D U C O M REVIEW.
Educom, 1112 16th St., N.W., Ste 600, Washington, DC 20036-4823. TEL 202-872-4200. FAX 202-872-4318. *1689*

E F T REPORT.
Phillips Publishing, Inc., 7811 Montrose Rd., Potomac, MD 20854. TEL 301-340-2100.
Vendor(s): DIALOG, Mead Data Central, NewsNet (FI11). *805*

E M A JOURNAL.
Employment Management Association, 4101 Lake Boone Trail, Ste. 201, Raleigh, NC 27607.
TEL 919-787-6010. FAX 919-787-5302. *1064*

E M A REPORTER.
Employment Management Association, 4101 Lake Boone Trail, Ste. 201, Raleigh, NC 27607.
TEL 919-787-6010. FAX 919-787-5302. *977*

E N R.
McGraw-Hill, Inc., 1221 Ave. of the Americas, New York, NY 10020. TEL 212-512-2000.
Vendor(s): DIALOG (File no.624/McGRAW-HILL PUBLICATIONS ONLINE), Dow Jones/News Retrieval (ENR), Mead Data Central (ENR). *1865*

E R I C CLEARINGHOUSE ON URBAN EDUCATION. DIGEST.
E R I C Clearinghouse on Urban Education, Box 40, Teachers College, Columbia University, New York, NY 10027. TEL 212-678-3433.
Vendor(s): The Source. *1626*

E U D I S E D - R & D BULLETIN.
K.G. Saur Verlag KG, Ortlerstr. 8, Postfach 701620, 8000 Munich 70, Germany. TEL 089-76902-0. FAX 089-76902150.
Vendor(s): European Space Agency (File no.24/ EUDISED R&D). *1676*

EAST EUROPEAN INDUSTRIAL MONITOR.
Business International Corp., 215 Park Ave. S., New York, NY 10003. TEL 212-460-0600. FAX 212-995-8837.
Vendor(s): DIALOG. *906*

EAST EUROPEAN MARKETS.
Financial Times Business Information Ltd., Tower House, Southampton St., London WC2E 7HA, England. TEL 071-240 9391. FAX 071-240-7946.
Vendor(s): Data-Star, Mead Data Central. *659*

EASTERN EUROPEAN AND SOVIET TELECOM REPORT.
International Technology Consultants, 2940 28th St., N.W., Washington, DC 20008. TEL 202-234-2138. FAX 202-483-7922.
Vendor(s): NewsNet. *1335*

EASTERN PHARMACIST.
507 Ashok Bhawan, 93, Nehru Place, New Delhi 110019, India. *3724*

ECOLOGICAL ABSTRACTS.
Elsevier - Geo Abstracts, Regency House, 34 Duke St., Norwich NR3 3AP, England. TEL 0603-626327. FAX 0603-667934.
Vendor(s): DIALOG (File no.292), Orbit Information Technologies. *1973*

ECOLOGY ABSTRACTS.
Cambridge Scientific Abstracts, 7200 Wisconsin Ave., 6th Fl., Bethesda, MD 20814. TEL 301-961-6750. FAX 301-961-6720.
Vendor(s): BRS (CSAL), DIALOG (File no.76/LIFE SCIENCES COLLECTION). *1973*

ECONOMIC BULLETIN BOARD.
U.S. National Technical Information Service, 5825 Port Royal Rd., Springfield, VA 22161. TEL 703-487-4630.
Available only online. *861*

SERIALS AVAILABLE ONLINE 5067

ECONOMIC INDICATORS (WASHINGTON).
U.S. Executive Office of the President, Council of Economic Advisers, Executive Office Bldg., Washington, DC 20500. TEL 202-395-5062.
Vendor(s): DIALOG. *861*

ECONOMIC INQUIRY.
Western Economic Association International, 7400 Center Ave., Ste. 109, Huntington Beach, CA 92647. TEL 714-898-3222.
Vendor(s): DIALOG. *661*

ECONOMIC OPPORTUNITY REPORT.
Business Publishers, Inc., 951 Pershing Dr., Silver Spring, MD 20910-4464. TEL 301-587-6300. FAX 301-585-9075.
Vendor(s): NewsNet. *4404*

ECONOMIC TITLES - ABSTRACTS.
Kluwer Academic Publishers, Postbus 17, 3300 AA Dordrecht, Netherlands. TEL 078-334911. FAX 078-334254.
Vendor(s): BELINDIS, Data-Star, DIALOG. *714*

ECONOMIC WEEK.
Citicorp N A I B Economics, 55 Water St., 42nd Fl., New York, NY 10043. TEL 212-825-5026.
Vendor(s): Mead Data Central. *777*

ECONOMIST.
Economist Newspaper Ltd., 25 St. James's St., London SW1A 1HG, England. TEL 01-839-7000. FAX 01-839-2968.
Vendor(s): Mead Data Central, VU/TEXT Information Services, Inc.. *863*

ECONOMIST.
Economist Newspaper, 10 Rockefeller Plaza, 10th Fl., New York, NY 10020. TEL 212-541-5730. FAX 212-541-9378.
Vendor(s): DIALOG, Dow Jones/News Retrieval. *863*

ECQUID NOVI.
Institute for Communication Research, Potchefstroom University, Potchefstroom 2520, South Africa. TEL 0148-99-1641. FAX 0148-992799. *2569*

EDITORS ONLY.
Editors Only Publications, P.O. Box 17108, Fountain Hills, AZ 85269. TEL 602-837-6492. FAX 602-837-6872.
Vendor(s): NewsNet (PB13). *2569*

EDUCATION AUTHORITIES' DIRECTORY AND ANNUAL.
School Government Publishing Co. Ltd., Darby House, Bletchingley Rd., Merstham, Redhill, Surrey RH1 3DN, England. TEL 0737-642223. FAX 0737-644283. *1628*

EDUCATION DAILY.
Capitol Publications Inc., 1101 King St., Ste. 444, Box 1455, Alexandria, VA 22314. TEL 703-683-4100. FAX 703-739-6517.
Vendor(s): NewsNet. *1628*

EDUCATION FOR THE HANDICAPPED LAW REPORT.
L R P Publications, 747 Dresher Rd., Box 980, Horsham, PA 19044-0980. FAX 215-784-9639. *1735*

EDUCATION INDEX.
H.W. Wilson Co., 950 University Ave., Bronx, NY 10452. TEL 800-367-6770. FAX 212-538-2716.
Vendor(s): Wilsonline (File EDI). *1676*

EDUCATION OF THE HANDICAPPED.
Capitol Publications Inc., 1101 King St., Ste. 444, Alexandria, VA 22314. TEL 703-683-4100. FAX 703-739-6517.
Vendor(s): NewsNet. *1735*

EDUCATION TECHNOLOGY NEWS.
Business Publishers, Inc., 951 Pershing Dr., Silver Spring, MD 20910-4464. TEL 301-587-6300. FAX 301-585-9075.
Vendor(s): NewsNet. *1417*

EDUCATION WEEK.
Editorial Projects in Education, Inc., 4301 Connecticut Ave., N.W., Ste. 432, Washington, DC 20008. TEL 202-364-4114. *1629*

EDUCATIONAL MARKETER.
Simba Information, Inc., Box 7430, Wilton, CT 06897. TEL 203-834-0033. FAX 203-834-1771.
Vendor(s): DIALOG, NewsNet. *4127*

EGYPTIAN JOURNAL OF PHARMACEUTICAL SCIENCES.
National Information and Documentation Centre (NIDOC), Tahrir St., Dokki, Awqaf P.O., Cairo, Egypt. *3725*

EINKAUFS 1X1 DER DEUTSCHEN INDUSTRIE.
Deutscher Adressbuch-Verlag, Holzhofallee 38, Postfach 110452, 6100 Darmstadt, Germany. TEL 06151-391-0. FAX 06151-391200.
Vendor(s): Data-Star, FIZ Technik. *1134*

ELECTRIC UTILITY WEEK.
McGraw-Hill, Inc., 1221 Ave. of the Americas, New York, NY 10020.
Vendor(s): DIALOG (File no.624/McGRAW-HILL PUBLICATIONS ONLINE), Dow Jones/News Retrieval (EUW), Mead Data Central (ELUTL). *1887*

ELECTRICAL & ELECTRONICS ABSTRACTS.
INSPEC, I.E.E., Michael Faraday House, Six Hill Way, Stevenage, Herts. SG1 2AY, England. TEL 0438-313311. FAX 0438-742840.
Vendor(s): BRS (INSP), CEDOCAR, CISTI, Data-Star, DIALOG (File nos.2,3 & 4/INSPEC), European Space Agency (File no.8/INSPEC), JICST, Orbit Information Technologies (INSPEC), STN International (INSPEC), University of Tsukuba. *1843*

ELECTRO MANUFACTURING.
Worldwide Videotex, Box 138, Babson Park, Boston, MA 02157.
Vendor(s): NewsNet. *1878*

ELECTRONIC BOOKSTORE FOR EXECUTIVES.
High Tech Publishing Company, Box 1923, Brattleboro, VT 05301. TEL 802-254-3539.
Vendor(s): Data-Star, NewsNet. *4127*

ELECTRONIC BUSINESS.
Cahners Publishing Company (Newton) Division of Reed Publishing (USA) Inc., 275 Washington St., Newton, MA 02158-1630. TEL 617-558-4250. FAX 617-558-4470.
Vendor(s): DIALOG. *1767*

ELECTRONIC BUYERS' NEWS.
C M P Publications, Inc., 600 Community Dr., Manhasset, NY 11030. TEL 516-562-5000. FAX 516-562-5123.
Vendor(s): NewsNet. *1767*

ELECTRONIC DESIGN.
Penton Publishing (San Jose) San Jose Gateway, Ste. 354, 2025 Gateway Pl., San Jose, CA 95110. TEL 408-441-0550.
Vendor(s): DIALOG, Mead Data Central. *1767*

ELECTRONIC ENGINEERING TIMES.
C M P Publications, Inc., 600 Community Dr., Manhasset, NY 11030. TEL 516-562-5000. FAX 516-562-5325.
Vendor(s): NewsNet. *1767*

ELECTRONIC LEARNING.
Scholastic Inc., 730 Broadway, New York, NY 10003-9538. TEL 212-505-3000.
Vendor(s): DIALOG. *1689*

ELECTRONIC MEDIA.
Crain Communications, Inc. (Chicago), 740 Rush St., Chicago, IL 60611-2590. TEL 312-649-5200. FAX 312-649-5465.
Vendor(s): Mead Data Central. *1373*

ELECTRONIC MESSAGING NEWS.
Phillips Publishing, Inc., 7811 Montrose Rd., Potomac, MD 20854. TEL 301-340-2100. FAX 301-309-3847.
Vendor(s): NewsNet. *1350*

ELECTRONIC NEWS.
I D G Communications (Peterborough), 80 Elm St., Peterborough, NH 03458. TEL 603-924-0100. FAX 603-924-9384.
Vendor(s): DIALOG. *1768*

ELECTRONIC OFFICE.
Financial Times Business Information Ltd., Tower House, Southampton St., London WC2E 7HA, England. TEL 071-240 9391. FAX 071-240-7946.
Vendor(s): Data-Star, Mead Data Central. *1768*

ELECTRONIC TRADE & TRANSPORT NEWS.
Phillips Publishing, Inc., 7811 Montrose Rd., Potomac, MD 20854. TEL 301-340-2100. FAX 301-309-3847.
Vendor(s): NewsNet. *1447*

ELECTRONIC WORLD NEWS.
C M P Publications, Inc., 600 Community Dr., Manhasset, NY 11030. TEL 516-562-5000.
Vendor(s): NewsNet. *1768*

ELECTRONICS.
Penton Publishing (San Jose), San Jose Gateway, Ste. 354, 2025 Gateway Pl., San Jose, CA 95110. TEL 408-441-0550.
Vendor(s): DIALOG (File no.624/McGRAW-HILL PUBLICATIONS ONLINE), Mead Data Central. *1768*

ELECTRONICS AND COMMUNICATIONS ABSTRACTS JOURNAL.
Cambridge Scientific Abstracts, 7200 Wisconsin Ave., 6th Fl., Bethesda, MD 20814. TEL 301-961-6750. FAX 301-961-6720.
Vendor(s): BRS (CSEN). *1348*

ELEKTRON.
Smena Publishing House, Prazska 11, 812 84 Bratislava, Czechoslovakia. TEL 406-06. *4308*

EMERGENCY MEDICINE CLINICS OF NORTH AMERICA.
W.B. Saunders Co., Curtis Center, Independence Sq. W., Philadelphia, PA 19106. TEL 215-238-7800.
Vendor(s): BRS, BRS/Saunders Colleague. *3308*

EMERGENCY MEDICINE REPORTS.
American Health Consultants, Inc., Six Piedmont Center, Ste. 400, 3525 Piedmont Rd., N.E., Atlanta, GA 30305. TEL 404-262-7436. FAX 404-262-7837.
Vendor(s): BRS. *3096*

EMERGENCY PREPAREDNESS NEWS.
Business Publishers, Inc., 951 Pershing Dr., Silver Spring, MD 20910-4464. TEL 301-587-6300. FAX 301-585-9075.
Vendor(s): NewsNet (GT34). *1273*

EMORY LAW JOURNAL.
Emory University, School of Law, Gambrell Hall, Atlanta, GA 30322. TEL 404-727-6830. FAX 404-727-6820.
Vendor(s): WESTLAW. *2621*

EMPLOYEE BENEFIT CASES.
The Bureau of National Affairs, Inc., 1231 25th St., N.W., Washington, DC 20037. TEL 202-452-4200. FAX 202-822-8092. *977*

EMPLOYEE BENEFIT NOTES.
Employee Benefit Research Institute, 2121 K St., N.W., Ste. 600, Washington, DC 20037-1896. TEL 202-659-0670. FAX 202-775-6312. *977*

EMPLOYEE HEALTH AND FITNESS.
American Health Consultants, Inc., Six Piedmont Center, Ste. 400, 3525 Piedmont Rd., N.E., Atlanta, GA 30305. TEL 404-262-7436. FAX 800-284-3291.
Vendor(s): Mead Data Central. *3801*

EMPLOYEE RELATIONS LAW JOURNAL.
Executive Enterprises Publications Co., Inc., 22 W. 21st St., New York, NY 10010-6904. TEL 212-645-7880. FAX 212-645-1160.
Vendor(s): DIALOG. *2622*

EMPLOYMENT GUIDE.
The Bureau of National Affairs, Inc., 1231 25th St., N.W., Washington, DC 20037. TEL 202-452-4200. FAX 202-822-8092.
Vendor(s): Human Resources Information Network (EMPG, CDD, HDD). *1065*

EMPLOYMENT INFORMATION IN THE MATHEMATICAL SCIENCES.
American Mathematical Society, Box 1571, Annex Sta., Providence, RI 02901-9930. TEL 401-455-4000.
Vendor(s): Human Resources Information Network. *3035*

EMPLOYMENT OPPORTUNITIES (ENGLEWOOD).
National Guild of Community Schools of the Arts, Box 8018, Englewood, NJ 07631. TEL 201-871-3337.
Vendor(s): NewsNet. *3627*

SERIALS AVAILABLE ONLINE

ENCYCLOPEDIA OF ASSOCIATIONS.
Gale Research Inc., 835 Penobscot Bldg., Detroit, MI 48226. TEL 313-961-2242. FAX 313-961-6083.
Vendor(s): DIALOG (File no.114). *1780*

ENERGIA: BIBLIOGRAFIA SELETIVA.
Comissao Nacional de Energia Nuclear, Centro de Informacoes Nucleares, R. General Severiano, 90, Botafogo, Rio de Janeiro, Brazil. TEL 021-5462440. FAX 021-5462447.
Available only online. *1798*

ENERGY & FUELS.
American Chemical Society, 1155 16th St., N.W., Washington, DC 20036. TEL 800-333-9511. FAX 202-872-4615.
Vendor(s): STN International (CJACS). *1787*

ENERGY BOOKS QUARTERLY.
International Academy at Santa Barbara, 800 Garden St., Ste. D, Santa Barbara, CA 93101. TEL 805-965-5010.
Vendor(s): Data-Star, DIALOG. *1798*

ENERGY CONSERVATION NEWS.
Business Communications Co., Inc. (Norwalk), 25 Van Zant St., Ste. 13, Norwalk, CT 06855. TEL 203-853-4266. FAX 203-853-0348.
Vendor(s): Data-Star, DIALOG, NewsNet. *1787*

ENERGY DAILY.
King Publishing Group, Inc., 627 National Press Bldg., Washington, DC 20045. TEL 202-638-4260. FAX 202-662-9744.
Vendor(s): Data-Star, DIALOG, NewsNet. *1787*

ENERGY DATA BASE.
U.S. National Technical Information Service, 5285 Port Royal Rd., Springfield, VA 22161. TEL 703-487-4630.
Available only online. Vendor(s): DIALOG, STN International. *1787*

ENERGY DESIGN UPDATE.
Cutter Information Corp., 37 Broadway, Arlington, MA 02174. TEL 617-648-8700. FAX 617-648-8707.
Vendor(s): NewsNet. *617*

ENERGY ECONOMIST.
Financial Times Business Information Ltd., Tower House, Southampton St., London WC2E 7HA, England. TEL 071-240-9391. FAX 071-240-7946. *1787*

ENERGY INFORMATION ABSTRACTS.
R.R. Bowker, Bowker A & I Publishing, A Reed Reference Publishing Company, Division of Reed Publishing (USA) Inc., 121 Chanlon Rd., New Providence, NJ 07974. TEL 800-521-8110. FAX 908-665-6688.
Vendor(s): Data-Star (ENER), DIALOG (File no.69), European Space Agency (File no.19/ENERGYLINE), Orbit Information Technologies (Energyline). *1799*

ENERGY INFORMATION ABSTRACTS ANNUAL.
R.R. Bowker, Bowker A & I Publishing, A Reed Reference Publishing Company, Division of Reed Publishing (USA) Inc., 121 Chanlon Rd., New Providence, NJ 07974. TEL 800-521-8110. FAX 908-665-6688.
Vendor(s): Data-Star (ENER), DIALOG (File no.69), European Space Agency (File no.19/ENERGYLINE), Orbit Information Technologies (Energyline). *1799*

ENERGY REPORT.
Pasha Publications Inc., 1401 Wilson Blvd., Ste. 900, Arlington, VA 22209-9970. TEL 703-528-1244. FAX 703-528-1253.
Vendor(s): Data-Star, DIALOG, Mead Data Central, NewsNet. *1788*

ENERGY RESEARCH ABSTRACTS.
U.S. Department of Energy, Office of Scientific and Technical Information, Box 62, Oak Ridge, TN 37831. TEL 615-576-1155.
Vendor(s): STN International (ENERGY). *1799*

ENERGY STATISTICS.
Institute of Gas Technology, 3424 S. State St., Chicago, IL 60616. TEL 312-567-3650. *3705*

ENERGY USER NEWS.
Chilton Co. Chilton Way, Radnor, PA 19089. TEL 215-964-4278.
Vendor(s): DIALOG, Mead Data Central. *1789*

ENGINEERED MATERIALS ABSTRACTS.
A S M International, Materials Information, Materials Park, OH 44073. TEL 216-338-5151. FAX 216-338-4634.
Vendor(s): DIALOG (File no.293), European Space Agency (File no.134), Orbit Information Technologies (EMAB), STN International (EMA). *1843*

ENGINEERING & MINING JOURNAL.
Maclean Hunter Publishing Company, 29 N. Wacker Dr., Chicago, IL 60606. TEL 312-726-2802. FAX 312-726-2574.
Vendor(s): Mead Data Central. *3483*

ENGINEERING DIMENSIONS.
Association of Professional Engineers of Ontario, 1155 Yonge St., Toronto, Ont. M4T 2Y5, Canada. FAX 416-961-1499. *1820*

ENGINEERING INDEX ANNUAL.
Engineering Information, Inc., Castle Point on the Hudson, Hoboken, NJ 07030. TEL 800-221-1044. FAX 201-216-8532.
Vendor(s): BRS (COMP), CEDOCAR, Data-Star, DIALOG (File no.8), European Space Agency, Orbit Information Technologies, STN International. *1843*

ENGINEERING INDEX MONTHLY.
Engineering Information, Inc., Castle Point on the Hudson, Hoboken, NJ 07030. TEL 800-221-1044. FAX 201-216-8532.
Vendor(s): BRS (COMP), CEDOCAR, CISTI, Data-Star, DIALOG (File no.8), European Space Agency, Orbit Information Technologies, STN International (COMPENDEX). *1843*

ENHANCED SERVICES OUTLOOK.
Capitol Publications Inc., Telecom Publishing Group, 1101 King St., Ste. 444, Box 1455, Alexandria, VA 22313-2055. TEL 800-327-7205. FAX 703-739-6490.
Vendor(s): DIALOG, NewsNet. *1362*

ENTERTAINMENT WEEKLY.
Entertainment Weekly Inc. 1675 Broadway, New York, NY 10019. TEL 212-522-5600. FAX 212-522-0017.
Vendor(s): VU/TEXT Information Services, Inc.. *2225*

ENTOMOLOGY ABSTRACTS.
Cambridge Scientific Abstracts, 7200 Wisconsin Ave., 6th Fl., Bethesda, MD 20814. TEL 301-961-6750. FAX 301-961-6720.
Vendor(s): BRS (CSAL), DIALOG (File no.76/LIFE SCIENCES COLLECTION). *465*

ENTREPRENEURIAL MANAGER'S NEWSLETTER.
Center for Entrepreneurial Management, Inc., 180 Varick St., Penthouse, New York, NY 10014. TEL 212-633-0060. FAX 212-633-0063.
Vendor(s): NewsNet. *1009*

ENVIRONMENT ABSTRACTS.
R.R. Bowker, Bowker A & I Publishing, A Reed Reference Publishing Company, Division of Reed Publishing (USA) Inc., 121 Chanlon Rd., New Providence, NJ 07974. TEL 800-521-8110. FAX 908-665-6688.
Vendor(s): DIMDI, Data-Star (NVER; Acid Rain Abstracts NVAR), DIALOG (File no.40), European Space Agency (File no.11/ENVIROLINE and File no.109/Acid Rain Abstracts), Orbit Information Technologies (ENVIROLINE). *1973*

ENVIRONMENT ABSTRACTS ANNUAL.
R.R. Bowker, Bowker A & I Publishing, A Reed Reference Publishing Company, Division of Reed Publishing (USA) Inc., 121 Chanlon Rd., New Providence, NJ 07974. TEL 800-521-8110. FAX 908-665-6688.
Vendor(s): DIMDI, Data-Star (NVER/Acid Rain Abstracts NVAR), DIALOG (File no.40), European Space Agency (File no.11/File no.109 Acid Rain Abstracts), Orbit Information Technologies (Enviroline). *1973*

ENVIRONMENT REPORTER.
The Bureau of National Affairs, Inc., 1231 25th St., N.W., Washington, DC 20037. TEL 202-452-4200. FAX 202-822-8092.
Vendor(s): Human Resources Information Network, Mead Data Central (ENVREP), WESTLAW (BNA-ER). *1950*

ENVIRONMENT WEEK.
King Communications Group, Inc., 627 National Press Bldg., Washington, DC 20045. TEL 202-638-4260. FAX 202-662-9744.
Vendor(s): Data-Star, DIALOG, NewsNet. *1950*

ENVIRONMENTAL AND MOLECULAR MUTAGENESIS.
John Wiley & Sons, Inc., Journals, 605 Third Ave., New York, NY 10158. TEL 212-850-6000. FAX 212-850-6088. *438*

ENVIRONMENTAL COMPLIANCE UPDATE.
High Tech Publishing Company, Box 1923, Brattleboro, VT 05301. TEL 802-254-3539.
Vendor(s): Data-Star, NewsNet. *1951*

ENVIRONMENTAL DIRECTORY OF U.S. POWER PLANTS.
Utility Data Institute, Inc. 1700 K St., N.W., Ste. 400, Washington, DC 20006. TEL 202-466-3660. FAX 202-466-3667. *1891*

ENVIRONMENTAL HEALTH LETTER.
Business Publishers, Inc., 951 Pershing Dr., Silver Spring, MD 20910-4464. TEL 301-587-6300. FAX 301-585-9075.
Vendor(s): NewsNet. *3096*

ENVIRONMENTAL LAW (PORTLAND).
Northwestern School of Law, Lewis and Clark College, 10015 S.W. Terwilliger Blvd., Portland, OR 97219. TEL 503-244-1181.
Vendor(s): Mead Data Central, WESTLAW. *1952*

ENVIRONMENTAL LAW REPORTER.
Environmental Law Institute, 1616 P St. N.W., Ste. 200, Washington, DC 20036. TEL 202-328-5150.
Vendor(s): Mead Data Central, WESTLAW. *1952*

ENVIRONMENTAL PERIODICALS BIBLIOGRAPHY.
International Academy at Santa Barbara, 800 Garden St., Ste. D, Santa Barbara, CA 93101-1552. TEL 805-965-5010. FAX 805-965-6071.
Vendor(s): DIALOG. *1974*

ENVIRONMENTAL SANITATION ABSTRACTS - LOW COST OPTIONS.
Asian Institute of Technology, Environmental Sanitation Information Center, P.O. Box 2754, Bangkok 10501, Thailand. FAX 66-2-516-2126. *1953*

ENVIRONMENTAL SCIENCE & TECHNOLOGY.
American Chemical Society, 1155 16th St., N.W., Washington, DC 20036. TEL 800-333-9511. FAX 202-872-4615.
Vendor(s): STN International (CJACS). *1953*

EPIPHANY JOURNAL.
Epiphany Press, P.O. Box 2250, So. Portland, ME 04116-2250.
Vendor(s): BRS, DIALOG. *4176*

ESPIAL CANADIAN DATA BASE DIRECTORY.
Espial Publications Ltd., Box 624, Station "K", Toronto, Ont. M4P 2H1, Canada. TEL 416-485-8063. FAX 416-781-6929. *1404*

ESSAY AND GENERAL LITERATURE INDEX.
H.W. Wilson Co., 950 University Ave., Bronx, NY 10452. TEL 800-367-6770. FAX 212-538-2716.
Vendor(s): Wilsonline (File EGL). *2981*

ESSOR.
Union Francaise d'Annuaires Professionnels, 13 av. Hennequin, B.P. 36, 78192 Trappes Cedex, France. TEL 1-30-50-61-48. FAX 1-30-50-48-27. *906*

ESTATE AND FINANCIAL PLANNERS ALERT.
Research Institute of America, Inc., 90 Fifth Ave., New York, NY 10011. TEL 212-645-4800. FAX 212-337-4279.
Vendor(s): Mead Data Central. *945*

ESTATES GAZETTE.
Estates Gazette Ltd., 151 Wardour St., London W1V 4BN, England.
Vendor(s): Mead Data Central. *4148*

ESTUDIOS PUBLICOS.
Centro de Estudios Publicos, Monsenor Sotero Sanz No. 175, Providencia, Santiago - 9, Chile. TEL 2315324. FAX 562-231-0853. *864*

EUROBIOLOGISTE.
Centre National des Biologistes, 80 Av. du Maine, 75014 Paris, France. TEL 43-22-97-70. FAX 43-21-73-12. *476*

EUROMONEY.
Euromoney Publications PLC, Nestor House, Playhouse Yard, London EC4V 5EX, England. FAX 01-236-6970.
Vendor(s): DIALOG. *778*

THE EUROMONITOR BOOK REPORT (YEAR).
Euromonitor, 87-88 Turnmill St., London EC1M 5QU, England. TEL 071-251 8024. FAX 071-608-3149. *4127*

EUROPA CHEMIE.
Handelsblatt GmbH, Kasernenstr. 67, Postfach 102717, 4000 Duesseldorf 1, Germany. TEL 0211-8870. *1852*

EUROPEAN CHEMICAL NEWS.
Reed Business Publishing Group, Enterprise Division Quadrant House, The Quadrant, Sutton, Surrey SM2 5AS, England. TEL 081-652-8147. FAX 081-652-3375. *1853*

THE EUROPEAN COMMUNITY.
Political Risk Services, Box 6482, Syracuse, NY 13217-6482. TEL 315-472-1224. FAX 315-472-1235.
Vendor(s): Data-Star, NewsNet. *906*

EUROPEAN DIRECTORY OF AGROCHEMICAL PRODUCTS.
Royal Society of Chemistry, Thomas Graham House, Science Park, Milton Rd., Cambridge CB4 4WF, England. TEL 0462-672555. FAX 0462-480947.
Vendor(s): Data-Star, DIALOG (File no.316). *88*

EUROPEAN ENERGY REPORT.
Financial Times Business Information Ltd., Tower House, Southampton St., London WC2E 7HA, England. TEL 071-240 9391. FAX 071-240-7946. *1789*

EUROPEAN JOURNAL OF DRUG METABOLISM AND PHARMACOKINETICS.
Editions Medecine et Hygiene, Case Postale 456, CH-1211 Geneva 4, Switzerland. TEL 022-469355. FAX 022-475610. *3725*

EUROPEAN JOURNAL OF PHARMACEUTICS AND BIOPHARMACEUTICS.
Wissenschaftliche Verlagsgesellschaft mbH, Postfach 105339, 7000 Stuttgart 10, Germany. TEL 0711-2582-0. FAX 0711-2582-290. *3725*

EVALUATION COMMENT.
University of California, Los Angeles, Center for the Study of Evaluation, 145 Moore Hall, Graduate School of Education, 405 Hilgard Ave., Los Angeles, CA 90024-1522. TEL 213-206-1512. *1633*

EVENTLINE.
Elsevier Science Publishers B.V., P.O. Box 521, 1000 AM Amsterdam, Netherlands. TEL 020-5803260. FAX 020-5803270.
Vendor(s): Data-Star, DIALOG, European Space Agency. *1134*

EXCEPTIONAL CHILD EDUCATION RESOURCES.
Council for Exceptional Children, 1920 Association Dr., Reston, VA 22091-1589. TEL 703-620-3660. FAX 703-264-9494.
Vendor(s): BRS (ECER), BRS/Saunders Colleague, DIALOG (File no.54). *1676*

EXCEPTIONAL HUMAN EXPERIENCE.
Parapsychology Sources of Information Center, 2 Plane Tree Ln., Dix Hills, NY 11746. TEL 516-271-1243. *3672*

EXCERPTA MEDICA ABSTRACT JOURNALS.
Excerpta Medica, P.O. Box 548, 1000 AM Amsterdam, Netherlands. TEL 020-5803911. FAX 020-5803222.
Vendor(s): BRS, DIMDI, Data-Star, DIALOG, JICST. *3171*

EXCERPTA MEDICA. SECTION 1: ANATOMY, ANTHROPOLOGY, EMBRYOLOGY & HISTOLOGY.
Excerpta Medica, P.O. Box 548, 1000 AM Amsterdam, Netherlands. TEL 020-5803911. FAX 020-5803222.
Vendor(s): BRS, DIMDI, Data-Star, DIALOG, JICST. *3171*

EXCERPTA MEDICA. SECTION 2: PHYSIOLOGY.
Excerpta Medica, P.O. Box 548, 1000 AM Amsterdam, Netherlands. TEL 020-5803911. FAX 020-5803222.
Vendor(s): BRS, DIMDI, Data-Star, DIALOG, JICST. *3171*

EXCERPTA MEDICA. SECTION 3: ENDOCRINOLOGY.
Excerpta Medica, P.O. Box 548, 1000 BM Amsterdam, Netherlands. TEL 020-5803911. FAX 020-5803222.
Vendor(s): BRS, DIMDI, Data-Star, DIALOG, JICST. *3171*

EXCERPTA MEDICA. SECTION 4: MICROBIOLOGY: BACTERIOLOGY, MYCOLOGY, PARASITOLOGY AND VIROLOGY.
Excerpta Medica, P.O. Box 548, 1000 AM Amsterdam, Netherlands. TEL 020-5803911. FAX 020-5803222.
Vendor(s): BRS, DIMDI, Data-Star, DIALOG, JICST. *3171*

EXCERPTA MEDICA. SECTION 5: GENERAL PATHOLOGY AND PATHOLOGICAL ANATOMY.
Excerpta Medica, P.O. Box 548, 1000 AM Amsterdam, Netherlands. TEL 020-5803911. FAX 020-5803222.
Vendor(s): BRS, DIMDI, Data-Star, DIALOG, JICST. *3171*

EXCERPTA MEDICA. SECTION 6: INTERNAL MEDICINE.
Excerpta Medica, P.O. Box 548, 1000 AM Amsterdam, Netherlands. TEL 020-5803911. FAX 020-5803222.
Vendor(s): BRS, DIMDI, Data-Star, DIALOG, JICST. *3171*

EXCERPTA MEDICA. SECTION 7: PEDIATRICS AND PEDIATRIC SURGERY.
Excerpta Medica, P.O. Box 548, 1000 AM Amsterdam, Netherlands. TEL 020-5803911. FAX 020-5803222.
Vendor(s): BRS, DIMDI, Data-Star, DIALOG, JICST. *3172*

EXCERPTA MEDICA. SECTION 8: NEUROLOGY AND NEUROSURGERY.
Excerpta Medica, P.O. Box 548, 1000 AM Amsterdam, Netherlands. TEL 020-5803911. FAX 020-5803222.
Vendor(s): BRS, DIMDI, Data-Star, DIALOG, JICST. *3172*

EXCERPTA MEDICA. SECTION 9: SURGERY.
Excerpta Medica, P.O. Box 548, 1000 AM Amsterdam, Netherlands. TEL 020-5803911. FAX 020-5803222.
Vendor(s): BRS, DIMDI, Data-Star, DIALOG, JICST. *3172*

EXCERPTA MEDICA. SECTION 10: OBSTETRICS AND GYNECOLOGY.
Excerpta Medica, P.O. Box 548, 1000 AM Amsterdam, Netherlands. TEL 020-5803911. FAX 020-5803222.
Vendor(s): BRS, DIMDI, Data-Star, DIALOG, JICST. *3172*

EXCERPTA MEDICA. SECTION 11: OTORHINOLARYNGOLOGY.
Excerpta Medica, P.O. Box 548, 1000 AM Amsterdam, Netherlands. TEL 020-5803911. FAX 020-5803222.
Vendor(s): BRS, DIMDI, Data-Star, DIALOG, JICST. *3172*

EXCERPTA MEDICA. SECTION 12: OPHTHALMOLOGY.
Excerpta Medica, P.O. Box 548, 1000 AM Amsterdam, Netherlands. TEL 020-5803911. FAX 020-5803222.
Vendor(s): BRS, DIMDI, Data-Star, DIALOG, JICST. *3172*

EXCERPTA MEDICA. SECTION 13: DERMATOLOGY AND VENEREOLOGY.
Excerpta Medica, P.O. Box 548, 1000 AM Amsterdam, Netherlands. TEL 020-5803911. FAX 020-5803222.
Vendor(s): BRS, DIMDI, Data-Star, DIALOG, JICST. *3172*

EXCERPTA MEDICA. SECTION 14: RADIOLOGY.
Excerpta Medica, P.O. Box 548, 1000 AM Amsterdam, Netherlands. TEL 020-5803911. FAX 020-5803222.
Vendor(s): BRS, DIMDI, Data-Star, DIALOG, JICST. *3172*

EXCERPTA MEDICA. SECTION 15: CHEST DISEASES, THORACIC SURGERY AND TUBERCULOSIS.
Excerpta Medica, P.O. Box 548, 1000 AM Amsterdam, Netherlands. TEL 020-5803911. FAX 020-5803222.
Vendor(s): BRS, DIMDI, Data-Star, DIALOG, JICST. *3172*

EXCERPTA MEDICA. SECTION 16: CANCER.
Excerpta Medica, P.O. Box 548, 1000 AM Amsterdam, Netherlands. TEL 020-5803911. FAX 020-5803222.
Vendor(s): BRS, DIMDI, Data-Star, DIALOG, JICST. *3172*

EXCERPTA MEDICA. SECTION 17: PUBLIC HEALTH, SOCIAL MEDICINE & EPIDEMIOLOGY.
Excerpta Medica, P.O. Box 548, 1000 AM Amsterdam, Netherlands. TEL 020-5803911. FAX 020-5803222.
Vendor(s): BRS, DIMDI, Data-Star, DIALOG, JICST. *4117*

EXCERPTA MEDICA. SECTION 18: CARDIOVASCULAR DISEASES AND CARDIOVASCULAR SURGERY.
Excerpta Medica, P.O. Box 548, 1000 AM Amsterdam, Netherlands. TEL 020-5803911. FAX 020-5803222.
Vendor(s): BRS, DIMDI, Data-Star, DIALOG, JICST. *3172*

EXCERPTA MEDICA. SECTION 19: REHABILITATION AND PHYSICAL MEDICINE.
Excerpta Medica, P.O. Box 548, 1000 AM Amsterdam, Netherlands. TEL 020-5803911. FAX 020-5803222.
Vendor(s): BRS, DIMDI, Data-Star, DIALOG, JICST. *3173*

EXCERPTA MEDICA. SECTION 20: GERONTOLOGY AND GERIATRICS.
Excerpta Medica, P.O. Box 548, 1000 AM Amsterdam, Netherlands. TEL 020-5803911. FAX 020-5803222.
Vendor(s): BRS, DIMDI, Data-Star, DIALOG, JICST. *2280*

EXCERPTA MEDICA. SECTION 21: DEVELOPMENTAL BIOLOGY AND TERATOLOGY.
Excerpta Medica, P.O. Box 548, 1000 AM Amsterdam, Netherlands. TEL 020-5803911. FAX 020-5803222.
Vendor(s): BRS, DIMDI, Data-Star, DIALOG, JICST. *3173*

EXCERPTA MEDICA. SECTION 22: HUMAN GENETICS.
Excerpta Medica, P.O. Box 548, 1000 AM Amsterdam, Netherlands. TEL 020-5803911. FAX 020-5803222.
Vendor(s): BRS, DIMDI, Data-Star, DIALOG, JICST. *465*

EXCERPTA MEDICA. SECTION 23: NUCLEAR MEDICINE.
Excerpta Medica, P.O. Box 548, 1000 AM Amsterdam, Netherlands. TEL 020-5803911. FAX 020-5803222.
Vendor(s): BRS, DIMDI, Data-Star, DIALOG, JICST. *3173*

EXCERPTA MEDICA. SECTION 24: ANESTHESIOLOGY.
Excerpta Medica, P.O. Box 548, 1000 AM Amsterdam, Netherlands. TEL 020-5803911. FAX 020-5803222.
Vendor(s): BRS, DIMDI, Data-Star, DIALOG, JICST. *3173*

EXCERPTA MEDICA. SECTION 25: HEMATOLOGY.
Excerpta Medica, P.O. Box 548, 1000 AM Amsterdam, Netherlands. TEL 020-5803911. FAX 020-5803222.
Vendor(s): BRS, DIMDI, Data-Star, DIALOG, JICST. *3173*

5070 SERIALS AVAILABLE ONLINE

EXCERPTA MEDICA. SECTION 26: IMMUNOLOGY, SEROLOGY AND TRANSPLANTATION.
Excerpta Medica, P.O. Box 548, 1000 AM Amsterdam, Netherlands. TEL 020-5803911. FAX 020-5803222.
Vendor(s): BRS, DIMDI, Data-Star, DIALOG, JICST. *3173*

EXCERPTA MEDICA. SECTION 27: BIOPHYSICS, BIO-ENGINEERING AND MEDICAL INSTRUMENTATION.
Excerpta Medica, P.O. Box 548, 1000 AM Amsterdam, Netherlands. TEL 020-5803439. FAX 020-5803222.
Vendor(s): BRS, DIMDI, Data-Star, DIALOG, JICST. *3173*

EXCERPTA MEDICA. SECTION 28: UROLOGY AND NEPHROLOGY.
Excerpta Medica, P.O. Box 548, 1000 AM Amsterdam, Netherlands. TEL 020-5803911. FAX 020-5803222.
Vendor(s): BRS, DIMDI, Data-Star, DIALOG, JICST. *3173*

EXCERPTA MEDICA. SECTION 29: CLINICAL AND EXPERIMENTAL BIOCHEMISTRY.
Excerpta Medica, P.O. Box 548, 1000 AM Amsterdam, Netherlands. TEL 020-5803911. FAX 020-5803222.
Vendor(s): BRS, DIMDI, Data-Star, DIALOG, JICST. *3173*

EXCERPTA MEDICA. SECTION 30: CLINICAL AND EXPERIMENTAL PHARMACOLOGY.
Excerpta Medica, P.O. Box 548, 1000 AM Amsterdam, Netherlands. TEL 020-5803911. FAX 020-5803222.
Vendor(s): BRS, DIMDI, Data-Star, DIALOG, JICST. *3747*

EXCERPTA MEDICA. SECTION 31: ARTHRITIS AND RHEUMATISM.
Excerpta Medica, P.O. Box 548, 1000 AM Amsterdam, Netherlands. TEL 020-5803911. FAX 020-5803222.
Vendor(s): BRS, DIMDI, Data-Star, DIALOG, JICST. *3173*

EXCERPTA MEDICA. SECTION 32: PSYCHIATRY.
Excerpta Medica, P.O. Box 548, 1000 AM Amsterdam, Netherlands. TEL 020-5803911. FAX 020-5803222.
Vendor(s): BRS, DIMDI, Data-Star, DIALOG, JICST. *3174*

EXCERPTA MEDICA. SECTION 33: ORTHOPEDIC SURGERY.
Excerpta Medica, P.O. Box 548, 1000 AM Amsterdam, Netherlands. TEL 020-5803911. FAX 020-5803222.
Vendor(s): BRS, DIMDI, Data-Star, DIALOG, JICST. *3174*

EXCERPTA MEDICA. SECTION 35: OCCUPATIONAL HEALTH AND INDUSTRIAL MEDICINE.
Excerpta Medica, P.O. Box 548, 1000 AM Amsterdam, Netherlands. TEL 020-5803911. FAX 020-5803222.
Vendor(s): BRS, DIMDI, Data-Star, DIALOG, JICST. *3174*

EXCERPTA MEDICA. SECTION 36: HEALTH POLICY, ECONOMICS AND MANAGEMENT.
Excerpta Medica, P.O. Box 548, 1000 AM Amsterdam, Netherlands. TEL 020-5803911. FAX 020-5803222.
Vendor(s): BRS, DIMDI, Data-Star, DIALOG, JICST. *2470*

EXCERPTA MEDICA. SECTION 38: ADVERSE REACTIONS TITLES.
Excerpta Medica, P.O. Box 548, 1000 AM Amsterdam, Netherlands. TEL 020-5803911. FAX 020-5803222.
Vendor(s): BRS, DIMDI, Data-Star, DIALOG, JICST. *3174*

EXCERPTA MEDICA. SECTION 40: DRUG DEPENDENCE, ALCOHOL ABUSE AND ALCOHOLISM.
Excerpta Medica, P.O. Box 548, 1000 AM Amsterdam, Netherlands. TEL 020-5803911. FAX 020-5803222.
Vendor(s): BRS, DIMDI, Data-Star, DIALOG, JICST. *3174*

EXCERPTA MEDICA. SECTION 46: ENVIRONMENTAL HEALTH AND POLLUTION CONTROL.
Excerpta Medica, P.O. Box 548, 1000 AM Amsterdam, Netherlands. TEL 020-5803911. FAX 020-5803222.
Vendor(s): BRS, DIMDI, Data-Star, DIALOG, JICST. *1974*

EXCERPTA MEDICA. SECTION 48: GASTROENTEROLOGY.
Excerpta Medica, P.O. Box 548, 1000 AM Amsterdam, Netherlands. TEL 020-5803911. FAX 020-5803222.
Vendor(s): BRS, DIMDI, Data-Star, DIALOG, JICST. *3174*

EXCERPTA MEDICA. SECTION 49: FORENSIC SCIENCE ABSTRACTS.
Excerpta Medica, P.O. Box 548, 1000 AM Amsterdam, Netherlands. TEL 020-5803911. FAX 020-5803222.
Vendor(s): BRS, DIMDI, Data-Star, DIALOG, JICST. *3174*

EXCERPTA MEDICA. SECTION 50: EPILEPSY ABSTRACTS.
Excerpta Medica, P.O. Box 548, 1000 AM Amsterdam, Netherlands. TEL 020-5803911. FAX 020-5803222.
Vendor(s): BRS, DIMDI, Data-Star, DIALOG, JICST. *3174*

EXCERPTA MEDICA. SECTION 52: TOXICOLOGY.
Excerpta Medica, P.O. Box 548, 1000 AM Amsterdam, Netherlands. TEL 020-5803911. FAX 020-5803222.
Vendor(s): BRS, DIMDI, Data-Star, DIALOG, JICST. *3747*

EXECUTIVE FEMALE.
National Association for Female Executives, 127 W. 24th St., New York, NY 10011. TEL 212-645-0770. FAX 212-633-6489. *4841*

EXECUTIVE MEMORANDUM.
Heritage Foundation, 214 Massachusetts Ave., N.E., Washington, DC 20002. TEL 202-546-4400. FAX 202-546-8328.
Vendor(s): Mead Data Central. *3957*

EXECUTIVE REPORT.
Riverview Publications, Inc., Bigelow Sq., Pittsburgh, PA 15219-3028. TEL 412-471-4585.
Vendor(s): DIALOG. *1114*

EXECUTIVE SPEAKER.
Executive Speaker Co., Box 292437, Dayton, OH 45429. TEL 513-294-8493. FAX 513-294-6044.
Vendor(s): Mead Data Central. *31*

EXPERT AND THE LAW.
National Forensic Center, Box 3161, Princeton, NJ 08540. TEL 609-883-0550.
Vendor(s): Mead Data Central. *2624*

THE EXPORTER.
Trade Data Reports, Inc., 34 W. 37th St., New York, NY 10018. TEL 212-563-2772. FAX 212-563-2798.
Vendor(s): NewsNet. *908*

EXTRA!
Fairness & Accuracy In Reporting (F.A.I.R.), 130 W. 25th St., New York, NY 10001. TEL 212-633-6700. FAX 212-727-7668. *2225*

F A M L I.
College of Family Physicians of Canada, 4000 Leslie St., Willowdale, Ont. M2K 2R9, Canada. TEL 416-493-7513.
Vendor(s): National Library of Medicine. *3174*

F A S REPORT: WEEKLY ROUNDUP OF WORLD PRODUCTION AND TRADE.
U.S. Department of Agriculture, Foreign Agricultural Service, South Bldg., Rm. 4939, Washington, DC 20250-1000. TEL 202-720-7937. FAX 202-690-4374.
Vendor(s): DIALOG. *864*

F C C WEEK.
Capitol Publications Inc., Telecom Publishing Group, 1101 King St., Ste. 444, Box 1455, Alexandria, VA 22313-2055. TEL 800-327-7205. FAX 703-739-6490.
Vendor(s): DIALOG, NewsNet (TE52). *1335*

F D A CONSUMER.
U.S. Food and Drug Administration, Office of Public Affairs, 5600 Fishers Lane, Rockville, MD 20857. TEL 301-443-3220.
Vendor(s): DIALOG. *1504*

F D A ENFORCEMENT REPORT.
U.S. Food and Drug Administration, Rm. 1261, Parklawn Bldg., 5600 Fishers Lane, Rockville, MD 20857. TEL 301-443-1544.
Vendor(s): BRS (DIOG). *1514*

F D A MEDICAL BULLETIN.
U.S. Food and Drug Administration, 5600 Fisher's Ln., Rockville, MD 20857. TEL 301-443-3220.
Vendor(s): BRS (DIOG), Data-Star, DIALOG. *3725*

F O I A UPDATE.
U.S. Department of Justice, Office of Information and Privacy, Constitution Ave. & 10th Sts., N.W., Washington, DC 20530. TEL 202-514-3642. *2569*

F T C FREEDOM OF INFORMATION LOG.
Washington Regulatory Reporting Associates, Box 2220, Springfield, VA 22152.
Vendor(s): Data-Star, DIALOG, NewsNet. *908*

F T C: WATCH.
Washington Regulatory Reporting Associates, Box 2220, Springfield, VA 22152. TEL 703-690-8240.
Vendor(s): DIALOG, NewsNet. *908*

F X WEEK.
Waters Information Services, Inc., Box 2248, Binghamton, NY 13902-2248. TEL 607-770-8535. FAX 607-798-1692.
Vendor(s): Data-Star, DIALOG, NewsNet. *908*

FABA BEAN ABSTRACTS.
C.A.B. International, Wallingford, Oxon OX10 8DE, England. TEL 0491 32111. FAX 0491-33508.
Vendor(s): BRS (CABA), CISTI, DIMDI, DIALOG, European Space Agency (File nos.16 & 124/CAB). *137*

FACTS ON FILE WORLD NEWS DIGEST WITH INDEX.
Facts on File, Inc., 460 Park Ave. S., New York, NY 10016. TEL 212-683-2244.
Vendor(s): DIALOG (File no.264), Mead Data Central. *2310*

FAIR EMPLOYMENT PRACTICES SUMMARY OF LATEST DEVELOPMENTS.
The Bureau of National Affairs, Inc., 1231 25th St., N.W., Washington, DC 20037. TEL 202-452-4200. FAX 202-822-8092.
Vendor(s): Human Resources Information Network (CDD, HDD). *979*

FAIR EMPLOYMENT REPORT.
Business Publishers, Inc., 951 Pershing Dr., Silver Spring, MD 20910-4464. TEL 301-587-6300. FAX 301-585-9075.
Vendor(s): NewsNet. *979*

FAMILY ADVOCATE.
American Bar Association, Family Law Section, 750 N. Lake Shore Dr., Chicago, IL 60611. TEL 312-988-6069.
Vendor(s): WESTLAW (FAMADVO). *2717*

FAMILY LAW QUARTERLY.
American Bar Association, Family Law Section, 750 N. Lake Shore Dr., Chicago, IL 60611. TEL 312-988-6068.
Vendor(s): WESTLAW (FAMLQ). *2717*

FAMILY LAW REPORTS.
Jordan & Sons Ltd., 21 St. Thomas St., Bristol BS1 6JS, England. TEL 0272-230600. FAX 0272-230063.
Vendor(s): Mead Data Central. *2717*

FAMILY PUZZLERS.
Heritage Papers, Rt. 3, Box 3120, Danielsville, GA 30633-9611. TEL 404-789-3226. *2150*

FAMILY RELATIONS.
National Council on Family Relations, 3989 Central Ave., N.E., Ste. 550, Minneapolis, MN 55421-3921. TEL 612-781-9331. FAX 612-781-9348.
Vendor(s): BRS, DIALOG. *4435*

SERIALS AVAILABLE ONLINE

FARADAY DISCUSSIONS.
Royal Society of Chemistry, Thomas Graham House, Science Park, Milton Rd., Cambridge CB4 4WF, England. TEL 0462-672555. FAX 0462-480947.
Vendor(s): STN International (CJRSC). *1226*

FARM AND FOOD.
T.E.A.G.A.S.C., 19 Sandymount Ave., Dublin 4, Ireland. TEL 01-688188. FAX 01-688023. *89*

FARMACEUTICKY OBZOR.
Obzor, Ceskoslovenskej Armady 35, 815 85 Bratislava, Czechoslovakia. *3725*

FARMACEUTISK TIDENDE.
Dansk Farmaceutforening, Toldbbodgade 36, 1253 Copenhagen K, Denmark. *3725*

FARMACEUTSKI GLASNIK.
Hrvatsko Farmaceutsko Drustvo, Masarykova 2, 41000 Zagreb, Croatia. TEL 427-944. FAX 431-301. *3725*

FARMACEVTISK REVY.
Sveriges Farmacevtfoerbund, Bryggavgatan 10, Box 750, S-10135 Stockholm, Sweden. *3726*

FARMACEVTSKI VESTNIK.
Slovensko Farmacevtsko Drustvo, P.O. Box 311, Masera Spasica 10, 61001 Ljubljana, Slovenia. TEL 061-221-078. *3726*

FARMACI.
Danmarks Apotekerforening, Bredgade 54, 1260 Copenhagen K, Denmark. *3726*

FARMACIA.
Uniunea Societatilor De Stiinte Medicale Din Republica Socialista Rumania, Str. Progresului No. 8, Bucharest, Rumania. *3726*

FARMACJA POLSKA.
Wydawnictwo Polskiego Towarzystwa Farmaceutycznego, Dluga 16, 00-238 Warsaw, Poland. TEL 48-22-31-02-41. *3726*

FARMACO.
Societa Chimica Italiana, Viale Liegi, 48, 00198 Rome, Italy. TEL 06-8549691. FAX 06-8548734. *3726*

FEDERAL APPLIED TECHNOLOGY DATABASE.
U.S. National Technical Information Service, 5285 Port Royal Rd., Springfield, VA 22161. TEL 703-487-4630.
Available only online. Vendor(s): BRS. *4598*

FEDERAL BAR NEWS & JOURNAL.
Federal Bar Association, 1815 H St., N.W., Ste. 408, Washington, DC 20006-3697. TEL 202-638-0252. FAX 202-775-0295.
Vendor(s): WESTLAW. *2625*

FEDERAL CONTRACT DISPUTES.
Business Publishers, Inc., 951 Pershing Dr., Silver Spring, MD 20910-4464. TEL 301-587-6300. FAX 301-585-9075.
Vendor(s): NewsNet. *2625*

FEDERAL CONTRACTS REPORT.
The Bureau of National Affairs, Inc., 1231 25th St., N.W., Washington, DC 20037. TEL 202-452-4200. FAX 202-822-8092.
Vendor(s): Mead Data Central (FDCONT), WESTLAW. *1075*

FEDERAL COURT OF APPEAL DECISIONS.
Western Legal Publications, 301-1 Alexander St., Vancouver, BC V6A 1B2, Canada. TEL 604-687-5671. FAX 604-687-2796. *2731*

FEDERAL ESTATE AND GIFT TAXES.
Maxwell Macmillan, Professional and Business Reference Publishing, 910 Sylvan Ave., Englewood Cliffs, NJ 07632-3310. TEL 800-562-0245.
Vendor(s): Prentice-Hall Information Network. *1093*

FEDERAL EXCISE TAX.
Maxwell Macmillan, Professional and Business Reference Publishing, 910 Sylvan Ave., Englewood Cliffs, NJ 07632-3310. TEL 800-562-0245.
Vendor(s): Prentice-Hall Information Network. *1093*

FEDERAL GRANTS & CONTRACTS WEEKLY.
Capitol Publications Inc., 1101 King St., Ste. 444, Alexandria, VA 22314. TEL 703-683-4100. FAX 703-739-6517.
Vendor(s): NewsNet. *4060*

FEDERAL REGISTER.
U.S. Office of the Federal Register, National Archives and Records Administration, Washington, DC 20408. TEL 202-523-5240.
Vendor(s): BRS (DIOG), DIALOG (File no.669), Mead Data Central, WESTLAW. *2625*

FEDERAL RESEARCH IN PROGRESS DATABASE.
U.S. National Technical Information Service, 5285 Port Royal Rd., Springfield, VA 22161. TEL 703-487-4630.
Available only online. Vendor(s): DIALOG (File nos.265,266). *1822*

FEDERAL RESEARCH REPORT.
Business Publishers, Inc., 951 Pershing Dr., Silver Spring, MD 20910-4464. TEL 301-587-6300. FAX 301-585-9075.
Vendor(s): NewsNet (RD10). *1633*

FEDERAL RESERVE BANK OF NEW YORK. QUARTERLY REVIEW.
Federal Reserve Bank of New York, Public Information, 33 Liberty St., New York, NY 10045-0001. TEL 212-720-6150.
Vendor(s): DIALOG. *865*

FEDERAL RESERVE BULLETIN.
U.S. Federal Reserve System, Board of Governors, Publications Services, Rm. MS-138, Washington, DC 20551. TEL 202-452-3244.
Vendor(s): DIALOG, Mead Data Central. *779*

FEDERAL RULES OF EVIDENCE NEWS.
Callaghan & Co., 155 Pfingsten Rd., Deerfield, IL 60015. TEL 800-323-1336.
Vendor(s): WESTLAW. *2625*

FEDERAL TAX COORDINATOR 2D.
Research Institute of America, Inc., 90 Fifth Ave., New York, NY 10011. TEL 212-645-4800. FAX 212-337-4279.
Vendor(s): Mead Data Central. *1094*

FEDERAL TAX GUIDE.
Maxwell Macmillan, Professional and Business Reference Publishing, 910 Sylvan Ave., Englewood Cliffs, NJ 07632-3310. TEL 800-562-0245.
Vendor(s): Prentice-Hall Information Network. *1094*

FEDERAL TAX REGULATIONS.
Research Institute of America, Inc., 90 Fifth Ave., New York, NY 10011. TEL 212-645-4800.
Vendor(s): Prentice-Hall Information Network. *1094*

FEDERAL TAXES CITATOR.
Maxwell Macmillan, Professional and Business Reference Publishing, 910 Sylvan Ave., Englewood Cliffs, NJ 07632-3310. TEL 800-562-0245.
Vendor(s): Prentice-Hall Information Network. *1094*

FEDERAL TAXES 2ND.
Maxwell Macmillan, Professional and Business Reference Publishing, 910 Sylvan Ave., Englewood Cliffs, NJ 07632-3310. TEL 800-562-0245.
Vendor(s): Prentice-Hall Information Network. *1094*

FEDWATCH.
M M S International, 1301 Shoreway Rd., Ste.300, Belmont, CA 94002. TEL 415-595-0610. FAX 415-637-4303.
Vendor(s): CompuServe Consumer Information Service, Dow Jones/News Retrieval. *946*

FIBER OPTICS NEWS.
Phillips Publishing, Inc., 7811 Montrose Rd., Potomac, MD 20854. TEL 301-340-2100. FAX 301-424-4297.
Vendor(s): DIALOG, NewsNet (TE29). *1336*

FIBER OPTICS WEEKLY UPDATE.
Information Gatekeepers, Inc., 214 Harvard Ave., Boston, MA 02134. TEL 617-232-3111. FAX 617-734-8562.
Vendor(s): NewsNet. *1336*

FIELD CROP ABSTRACTS.
C.A.B. International, Wallingford, Oxon OX10 8DE, England. TEL 0491 32111. FAX 0491-33508.
Vendor(s): BRS (CABA), CISTI, DIMDI, DIALOG, European Space Agency (File nos.16 & 124/CAB). *137*

FILM & VIDEO FINDER.
Plexus Publishing, Inc., 143 Old Marlton Pike, Medford, NJ 08055-8750. TEL 609-654-4888.
Vendor(s): DIALOG (File no.46). *1676*

FILM - VIDEO CANADIANA.
National Film Board of Canada, Box 6100, Sta.A, Montreal, Que. H3C 3H5, Canada. TEL 514-283-9427. FAX 514-283-7564.
Vendor(s): QL Systems Ltd. (FVC,FVPD), VU/TEXT Information Services, Inc.. *3510*

FILMSTRIP AND SLIDE SET FINDER.
Access Innovations, Inc., Box 40130, Albuquerque, NM 87196. TEL 505-265-3591. *1676*

FINANCIAL EXECUTIVE.
Financial Executives Institute, 10 Madison Ave., Box 1938, Morristown, NJ 07961-1938. TEL 201-898-4600. FAX 201-898-4649.
Vendor(s): DIALOG. *1010*

FINANCIAL POST.
Financial Post Co., Ltd., 333 King St., Toronto, Ont. M5A 4N2, Canada. TEL 416-350-6300. FAX 416-350-6301. *780*

FINANCIAL POST MAGAZINE.
Financial Post Co., Ltd., 333 King St., E., Toronto, Ont. M5A 4N2, Canada. TEL 416-350-6516. FAX 416-350-6501. *780*

FINANCIAL REGULATION REPORT.
Financial Times Business Information Ltd., Tower House, Southampton St., London WC2E 7HA, England. TEL 071-240 9391. FAX 071-240-7946.
Vendor(s): Data-Star, Mead Data Central. *781*

FINANCIAL STOCK GUIDE SERVICE. DIRECTORY OF ACTIVE STOCKS.
Financial Information Incorporated, 30 Montgomery St., Jersey City, NJ 07302. FAX 201-332-8378. *946*

FINANCIAL TECHNOLOGY INSIGHT.
Elsevier Science Publishers Ltd., Crown House, Linton Rd., Barking, Essex IG11 8JU, England. TEL 081-594-7272. FAX 081-594-5942.
Vendor(s): Data-Star, DIALOG. *826*

FINANCIAL TIMES OF CANADA.
Financial Times of Canada, 440 Front St. W., Toronto, Ont. M5V 3E6, Canada. TEL 416-585-5000. FAX 416-585-5547. *781*

FINANCIAL TIMES WORLD SHIPPING YEARBOOK.
Financial Times Business Information Ltd., Tower House, Southampton St., London WC2E 7HA, England. TEL 01-240-9391. FAX 071-240-7946.
Vendor(s): DIALOG. *4727*

FINANCIAL TIMES WORLD TAX REPORT.
Financial Times Business Information Ltd., Tower House, Southampton St., London WC2E 7HA, England. TEL 071-240 9391. FAX 071-240-7946.
Vendor(s): DIALOG, Mead Data Central. *1094*

FINANCIAL WORLD.
Financial World Partners, 1328 Broadway, New York, NY 10001. TEL 212-594-5030. FAX 212-629-0021.
Vendor(s): Data-Star, DIALOG, Mead Data Central. *781*

FINANCING FOREIGN OPERATIONS: GLOBAL EDITION.
Business International Corp., 215 Park Ave. S., New York, NY 10003. TEL 212-460-0600. FAX 212-995-8837.
Vendor(s): DIALOG. *946*

FINDEX.
Cambridge Information Group Directories, Inc., 7200 Wisconsin Ave., Bethesda, MD 20814. TEL 301-961-6750. FAX 302-961-6720.
Vendor(s): DIALOG (File no.196), STN International. *716*

FIRMEN DER NEUEN BUNDESLAENDER.
Verlag Hoppenstedt und Co., Havelstr. 9, Postfach 4006, 6100 Darmstadt, Germany. TEL 06151-380-0. FAX 06151-380-360.
Vendor(s): Data-Star, DIALOG. *1076*

FIRST FACTS ON THE CURRENCY MARKET.
M M S International, 1301 Shoreway Rd., Ste. 300, Belmont, CA 94002. TEL 415-595-0610. FAX 415-637-4303.
Vendor(s): CompuServe Consumer Information Service. *782*

FIRST THINGS.
Institute on Religion & Public Life, 156 Fifth Ave., Ste. 400, New York, NY 10010. TEL 212-627-2288. FAX 212-627-2184. *4178*

FITOTERAPIA.
Inverni della Beffa Holding, Via Ripamonti 99, 20141 Milan, Italy. FAX 02-57404620. *502*

FLAME RETARDANCY NEWS.
Business Communications Co., Inc. (Norwalk), 25 Van Zant St., Ste. 13, Norwalk, CT 06855. TEL 203-853-4266. FAX 203-853-0348.
Vendor(s): NewsNet. *4598*

FLETCHER FORUM OF WORLD AFFAIRS.
Fletcher School of Law and Diplomacy, Tufts University, Medford, MA 02155. TEL 617-628-7010. FAX 617-381-3508.
Vendor(s): WESTLAW. *3957*

FLIGHT INTERNATIONAL.
Reed Business Publishing Group, Enterprise Division Quadrant House, The Quadrant, Sutton, Surrey SM2 5AS, England. TEL 081-652-3842. FAX 081-652-3840.
Vendor(s): Data-Star, Mead Data Central. *52*

FLORIDA BAR JOURNAL.
Florida Bar, 650 Apalachee Pkwy., Tallahassee, FL 32399-2300. TEL 904-561-5600. FAX 904-681-3859.
Vendor(s): WESTLAW. *2626*

FLORIDA BUSINESS - SOUTHWEST.
Business Journal Publishing Co., Box 9859, Naples, FL 33941. TEL 813-263-7525. FAX 813-263-1046.
Vendor(s): DIALOG. *866*

FLORIDA LAW REVIEW.
University of Florida, College of Law, Gainesville, FL 32611. TEL 904-392-0421.
Vendor(s): WESTLAW. *2627*

FLORIDA STATE UNIVERSITY LAW REVIEW.
Florida State University, College of Law, Tallahassee, FL 32306. TEL 904-644-2045.
Vendor(s): WESTLAW. *2627*

FLORIDA TREND.
Florida Trend Inc., Box 611, St. Petersburg, FL 33731. TEL 813-821-5800. FAX 813-822-5083.
Vendor(s): DIALOG. *866*

FLOWER AND GARDEN.
K C Publishing Inc., 4251 Pennsylvania Ave., Kansas City, MO 64111-9990. TEL 816-531-5730. FAX 816-531-3873.
Vendor(s): DIALOG. *2126*

FLUID FLOW MEASUREMENT ABSTRACTS.
S T I Ltd., 4 Kings Meadow, Ferry Hinksey Rd., Oxford OX2 ODU, England. TEL 0865-798898. FAX 0865-798788.
Vendor(s): DIALOG (File no.96/FLUIDEX), European Space Agency (File no.48/FLUIDEX). *1844*

FLUID SEALING ABSTRACTS.
S T I Ltd., 4 Kings Meadow, Ferry Hinksey Rd., Oxford OX2 ODU, England. TEL 0865-798898. FAX 0865-798788.
Vendor(s): DIALOG (File no.96/FLUIDEX), European Space Agency (File no.48/FLUIDEX). *1844*

FLYING.
Hachette Magazines, Inc., 1633 Broadway, New York, NY 10009. TEL 203-622-2706. FAX 203-622-2725.
Vendor(s): DIALOG. *53*

FOCUS (SAN FRANCISCO).
AIDS Health Project, University of California, San Francisco, Box 0884, San Francisco, CA 94143-0884. TEL 415-476-6430. FAX 415-476-7996. *3219*

FOCUS JAPAN.
Japan External Trade Organization, 2-5 Toranomon 2-chome, Minato-ku, Tokyo 105, Japan. FAX 03-582-3518. *908*

FOLIO (STAMFORD).
Cowles Business Media Six River Bend Center, 911 Hope St., Box 4949, Stamford, CT 06907-0949. TEL 203-358-9900. FAX 203-357-9014.
Vendor(s): DIALOG. *4128*

FOOD AND DRUG LETTER.
Washington Business Information, Inc., c/o Karen Harrington, 1117 N. 19th St., Ste.200, Arlington, VA 22209. TEL 703-247-3434. FAX 703-247-3421.
Vendor(s): BRS (DIOG), Data-Star, DIALOG. *1076*

FOOD CHEMICAL NEWS.
Food Chemical News, Inc., 1101 Pennsylvania Ave., S.E, Washington, DC 20003. TEL 202-544-1980. FAX 202-546-3890.
Vendor(s): Data-Star, DIALOG. *2068*

FOOD, COSMETICS AND DRUGS PACKAGING.
Elsevier Science Publishers Ltd., Crown House, Linton Rd., Barking, Essex IG11 8JU, England. TEL 081-594-7272. FAX 081-594-5942.
Vendor(s): DIALOG. *3648*

FOOD SCIENCE AND TECHNOLOGY ABSTRACTS.
International Food Information Service (IFIS Publishing), Lane End House, Shinfield, Reading RG2 9B, England. TEL 734-883895. FAX 734-805065.
Vendor(s): BRS (CABA), CISTI, DIMDI, Data-Star (FSTA), DIALOG (File no.51), European Space Agency (File no.20/FSTA), JICST, Orbit Information Technologies (FSTA). *2085*

FOODS ADLIBRA.
Foods Adlibra Publications, 9000 Plymouth Ave. N., Minneapolis, MN 55427. FAX 612-540-3166.
Vendor(s): DIALOG (File no.79). *2085*

FOOTWEAR NEWS.
Fairchild Publications, Inc., Footwear News, 7 W. 34th St., New York, NY 10001. TEL 212-630-4000.
Vendor(s): DIALOG. *4360*

FOR YOUR EYES ONLY.
Tiger Publications, Box 8759, Amarillo, TX 79114-8759. TEL 806-655-2009.
Vendor(s): NewsNet. *3458*

FORBES.
Forbes, Inc., 60 Fifth Ave., New York, NY 10011. TEL 212-620-2200.
Vendor(s): DIALOG, Mead Data Central. *1010*

FORD INVESTMENT MANAGEMENT REPORT.
Ford Investor Services, 11722 Sorrento Valley Rd., Ste. 11, San Diego, CA 92121. TEL 619-755-1327. *946*

FORD VALUE REPORT.
Ford Investor Services, 11722 Sorrento Valley Rd., Ste. 1, San Diego, CA 92121. TEL 619-755-1327. *946*

FORDHAM INTERNATIONAL LAW JOURNAL.
Fordham University, School of Law, 140 W. 62 St., New York, NY 10023. TEL 212-841-5175.
Vendor(s): WESTLAW. *2628*

FORDHAM LAW REVIEW.
Fordham University, School of Law, Lincoln Center, 140 W. 62nd St., New York, NY 10023. TEL 212-841-5243.
Vendor(s): Mead Data Central, WESTLAW. *2628*

FORDHAM URBAN LAW JOURNAL.
Fordham University, School of Law, Lincoln Center, 140 W. 62nd St., New York, NY 10023. TEL 212-841-5243.
Vendor(s): WESTLAW. *2628*

FORECAST (NEW YORK).
Scholastic Inc., 730 Broadway, New York, NY 10003. TEL 212-353-1094.
Vendor(s): DIALOG. *2446*

FOREIGN AFFAIRS.
Council on Foreign Relations, Inc., 58 E. 68th St., New York, NY 10021. TEL 212-734-0400.
Vendor(s): Mead Data Central. *3957*

FOREIGN TRADE REPORTS. U.S. EXPORT AND IMPORT MERCHANDISE TRADE AND SUPPLEMENT.
U.S. Bureau of the Census, Foreign Trade Division, Washington, DC 20233. TEL 301-763-5140.
Vendor(s): CompuServe Consumer Information Service, DIALOG. *909*

FORENSIC SERVICES DIRECTORY.
National Forensic Center, Box 3161, Princeton, NJ 08540. TEL 609-883-0550.
Vendor(s): Mead Data Central, WESTLAW. *2628*

FOREST INDUSTRIES.
Miller Freeman, Inc. 600 Harrison St., San Francisco, CA 94107. TEL 415-905-2200. FAX 415-905-2232.
Vendor(s): DIALOG. *2114*

FOREST PRODUCTS ABSTRACTS.
C.A.B. International, Wallingford, Oxon OX10 8DE, England. TEL 0491 32111. FAX 0491-33509.
Vendor(s): BRS (CABA), CISTI, DIMDI, DIALOG, European Space Agency (File nos.16 & 124/CAB). *2112*

FORESTRY.
Oxford University Press, Oxford Journals, Pinkhill House, Southfield Road, Eynsham, Oxford OX8 1JJ, England. TEL 0865-882283. FAX 0865-882890.
Vendor(s): European Space Agency (File nos.16 & 124/CAB). *2100*

FORESTRY ABSTRACTS.
C.A.B. International, Wallingford, Oxon OX10 8DE, England. TEL 0491-32111. FAX 0491-33508.
Vendor(s): BRS (CABA), CISTI, DIMDI, DIALOG, European Space Agency. *2112*

FORESTRY ABSTRACTS. LEADING ARTICLE REPRINT SERIES.
C.A.B. International, Wallingford, Oxon OX10 8DE, England. TEL 0491 32111. FAX 0491-33508.
Vendor(s): BRS, CISTI, DIMDI, DIALOG, European Space Agency. *2112*

FORLAGSSERIEKATALOG FOR BOERNE- OG SKOLEBIBLIOTEKER.
Bibliotekscentralen, Tempovej 7-11, DK-2750 Ballerup, Denmark. TEL 2-974000. FAX 2-655310. *1677*

FORTHCOMING BOOKS.
R.R. Bowker, A Reed Reference Publishing Company, Division of Reed Publishing (USA) Inc., 121 Chanlon Rd., New Providence, NJ 07974. TEL 800-521-8110. FAX 908-665-6688.
Vendor(s): BRS (BBIP), BRS/Saunders Colleague, DIALOG (File no.470). *400*

FORTSCHRITTE DER ARZNEIMITTELFORSCHUNG.
Birkhaeuser Verlag, P.O. Box 133, CH-4010 Basel, Switzerland. TEL 061-737740. FAX 061-737950. *3727*

FORTUNE MAGAZINE.
The Time Inc. Magazine Company, Time & Life Bldg., Rockefeller Center, 1271 Ave. of the Americas, New York, NY 10020-1393. TEL 212-522-1212.
Vendor(s): VU/TEXT Information Services, Inc.. *1010*

FOSTER NATURAL GAS REPORT.
Foster Associates, 1015 15th St., N.W., Washington, DC 20005-2605. TEL 202-408-7710. FAX 202-408-7723.
Vendor(s): Mead Data Central. *3686*

FOUNDATION DIRECTORY.
Foundation Center, 79 Fifth Ave., New York, NY 10003. TEL 212-620-4230.
Vendor(s): DIALOG. *4425*

FOUNDATION GRANTS INDEX.
Foundation Center, 79 Fifth Ave., New York, NY 10003. TEL 212-620-4230.
Vendor(s): DIALOG. *4426*

FOUNDRY MANAGEMENT & TECHNOLOGY.
Penton Publishing, 1100 Superior Ave., Cleveland, OH 44114-2543. TEL 216-696-7000. FAX 216-696-8765.
Vendor(s): DIALOG. *3406*

FOURTH ESTATE.
Fourth Estate Partnership, P.O. Box 971, Cornwall, P.E.I. C0A 1H0, Canada. *2569*

FRIDAY MEMO.
Information Industry Association, 555 New Jersey Ave., N.W., Ste. 800, Washington, DC 20001. TEL 202-639-8262. FAX 202-638-4403.
Vendor(s): NewsNet (PB15). *1395*

FROM THE STATE CAPITALS. CIVIL RIGHTS.
Wakeman-Walworth, Inc., 300 N. Washington St., Alexandria, VA 22314. TEL 703-549-8606. FAX 703-549-1372.
Vendor(s): WESTLAW. *3942*

FROM THE STATE CAPITALS. INSURANCE REGULATION.
Wakeman-Walworth, Inc., 300 N. Washington St., Alexandria, VA 22314. TEL 703-549-8606. FAX 703-549-1372.
Vendor(s): WESTLAW. *2532*

FROM THE STATE CAPITALS. JUSTICE POLICIES.
Wakeman-Walworth, Inc., 300 N. Washington St., Alexandria, VA 22314. TEL 703-549-8606. FAX 703-549-1372.
Vendor(s): WESTLAW. *2629*

FROM THE STATE CAPITALS. LABOR RELATIONS.
Wakeman-Walworth, Inc., 300 N. Washington St., Alexandria, VA 22314. TEL 703-549-8606. FAX 703-549-1372.
Vendor(s): DIALOG, Human Resources Information Network, WESTLAW. *980*

FROM THE STATE CAPITALS. PUBLIC UTILITIES.
Wakeman-Walworth, Inc., 300 N. Washington St., Alexandria, VA 22314. TEL 703-549-8606. FAX 703-549-1372.
Vendor(s): WESTLAW. *4061*

FROM THE STATE CAPITALS. TAXATION AND REVENUE POLICIES.
Wakeman-Walworth, Inc., 300 N. Washington St., Alexandria, VA 22314. TEL 703-549-8606. FAX 703-549-1372.
Vendor(s): WESTLAW. *1095*

FROM THE STATE CAPITALS. TAXES - PROPERTY.
Wakeman-Walworth, Inc., 300 N. Washington St., Alexandria, VA 22314. TEL 703-549-8606. FAX 703-549-1372.
Vendor(s): WESTLAW. *1095*

FROM THE STATE CAPITALS. WASTE DISPOSAL AND POLLUTION CONTROL.
Wakeman-Walworth, Inc., 300 N. Washington St., Alexandria, VA 22314. TEL 703-549-8606. FAX 703-549-1372.
Vendor(s): WESTLAW. *1984*

FROM THE STATE CAPITALS. WOMEN AND THE LAW.
Wakeman-Walworth, Inc., 300 N. Washington St., Alexandria, VA 22314. TEL 703-549-8606. FAX 703-549-1372.
Vendor(s): WESTLAW. *2629*

FUND RAISING MANAGEMENT.
Hoke Communications, Inc., 224 Seventh St., Garden City, NY 11530. TEL 516-746-6700.
Vendor(s): DIALOG. *782*

FUSION POWER REPORT.
Business Publishers, Inc., 951 Pershing Dr., Silver Spring, MD 20910-4464. TEL 301-587-6300. FAX 301-585-9075.
Vendor(s): DIALOG, NewsNet (EY46). *1805*

FUTURE HOME TECHNOLOGY NEWS.
Phillips Publishing, Inc., 7811 Montrose Rd., Potomac, MD 20854. TEL 301-340-2100. FAX 301-424-4297.
Vendor(s): Data-Star, DIALOG, NewsNet. *1879*

FUTURES WORLD NEWS.
Oster Communications, Inc., 219 Parkade, Cedar Falls, IA 50613. TEL 319-277-1271. FAX 319-277-5803.
Available only online. *947*

FUTURETECH.
Technical Insights, Inc., 32 N. Dean St., Englewood, NJ 07631. TEL 201-568-4744. FAX 201-568-8247.
Vendor(s): NewsNet. *4598*

THE FUTURIST.
World Future Society, 4916 St. Elmo Ave., Bethesda, MD 20814. TEL 301-656-8274.
Vendor(s): DIALOG. *4310*

G A P H Y O R. BASE DE DONNEES.
Centre National de la Recherche Scientifique, Institut de l'Information Scientifique et Technique, B.P. 54, 54514 Vandoeuvre-Les-Nancy Cedex, France. TEL 83-50-46-00. *3819*

G I S WORLD.
G I S World Inc., 2629 Redwing Rd., Ste. 280, Box 8090, Fort Collins, CO 80526. TEL 303-223-4848. FAX 303-223-5700. *2268*

G M P LETTER.
Washington Business Information, Inc., c/o Karen Harrington, 1117 N. 19th St., Ste. 200, Arlington, VA 22209. TEL 703-247-3434. FAX 703-247-3421.
Vendor(s): BRS (DIOG), Data-Star, DIALOG. *2522*

GAEA.
Association of Women Geoscientists, Geology Department, Macalester College, 1600 Grand Ave., St. Paul, MN 55105-1899. TEL 612-696-6448. FAX 612-696-6122. *1544*

GALE DIRECTORY OF PUBLICATIONS AND BROADCAST MEDIA.
Gale Research Inc., 835 Penobscot Bldg., Detroit, MI 48226. TEL 313-961-2242. FAX 313-961-6083.
Vendor(s): DIALOG. *400*

GALLUP POLL MONTHLY.
Gallup Poll News Service, 100 Palmer Sq., Box 628, Princeton, NJ 08542. TEL 609-924-9600. FAX 609-924-2584. *3896*

GAS ABSTRACTS.
Institute of Gas Technology, 3424 S. State St., Chicago, IL 60616. TEL 312-567-3650. *3705*

GAS DAILY.
Pasha Publications Inc., 1401 Wilson Blvd., Ste. 900, Arlington, VA 22209-9970. TEL 703-528-1244.
Vendor(s): Data-Star, DIALOG. *3686*

GASTROENTEROLOGY JOURNAL.
W.B. Saunders Company, 200 First St., S.W., Rochester, MN 02215-5491. TEL 507-284-9155.
Vendor(s): BRS. *3268*

GAY SCOTLAND.
58A Broughton St., Edinburgh EH1 3SA, Scotland. TEL 031-557-2625. *2453*

GEBORENER DEUTSCHER.
William L. Gage, Ed. & Pub., 2300 Ocean Ave., Brooklyn, NY 11229. TEL 718-627-0811. *2152*

GEKKAN MEDIA DATA.
Media Research Center, Inc., c/o Irimaziri Bldg., 6-40 Shin Ogawa-Machi, Shinjuku-ku, Tokyo 162, Japan. *32*

GENERAL ACCOUNTING OFFICE REPORTS AND TECHNOLOGY.
High Tech Publishing Company, Box 1923, Brattleboro, VT 05301. TEL 802-254-3539.
Vendor(s): Data-Star, NewsNet. *751*

GENERAL PRACTITIONER.
Haymarket Medical Publications Ltd., 30 Lancaster Gate, London W2 3LP, England.
Vendor(s): Data-Star (GPGP). *3100*

GENERAL SCIENCE INDEX.
H.W. Wilson Co., 950 University Ave., Bronx, NY 10452. TEL 800-367-6770. FAX 212-538-2716.
Vendor(s): Wilsonline (File GSI). *4356*

GENETIC EPIDEMIOLOGY.
John Wiley & Sons, Inc., Journals, 605 Third Ave., New York, NY 10158. TEL 212-850-6000. FAX 212-850-6088. *542*

GENETIC TECHNOLOGY NEWS.
Technical Insights, Inc., 32 N. Dean St., Englewood, NJ 07631. TEL 201-568-4744. FAX 201-568-8247.
Vendor(s): Data-Star, DIALOG, Mead Data Central, NewsNet. *542*

SERIALS AVAILABLE ONLINE

GENETICS ABSTRACTS.
Cambridge Scientific Abstracts, 7200 Wisconsin Ave., 6th Fl., Bethesda, MD 20814. TEL 301-961-6750. FAX 301-961-6720.
Vendor(s): BRS (CSAL), DIALOG (File no.76/LIFE SCIENCES COLLECTION). *465*

GENITOURINARY MEDICINE: THE JOURNAL OF SEXUAL HEALTH, STDS AND HIV.
B M J Publishing Group, B.M.A. House, Tavistock Sq., London WC1H 9JR, England. TEL 071-387-4499.
Vendor(s): BRS. *3247*

GEOGRAPHICAL ABSTRACTS: HUMAN GEOGRAPHY.
Elsevier - Geo Abstracts, Regency House, 34 Duke St., Norwich NR3 3AP, England. TEL 0603-626327. FAX 0603-667934.
Vendor(s): DIALOG (File no.292), Orbit Information Technologies. *2268*

GEOGRAPHICAL ABSTRACTS: PHYSICAL GEOGRAPHY.
Elsevier - Geo Abstracts, Regency House, 34 Duke St., Norwich NR3 3AP, England. TEL 0603-626327. FAX 0603-667934.
Vendor(s): DIALOG (File no.292), Orbit Information Technologies. *2268*

GEOLOGICAL ABSTRACTS.
Elsevier - Geo Abstracts, Regency House, 34 Duke St., Norwich NR3 3AP, England. TEL 0603-626327. FAX 0603-667934.
Vendor(s): DIALOG (File no.292), Orbit Information Technologies. *1551*

GEOLOGICAL SOCIETY OF INDIA. JOURNAL.
Geological Society of India, Post Box 1922, Gavipuran, Bangalore 560 019, India.
Vendor(s): DIALOG (File no.89). *1563*

GEORGE WASHINGTON JOURNAL OF INTERNATIONAL LAW AND ECONOMICS.
George Washington University, National Law Center, Burns Library, Rm. B433, 716 20th St., N.W., Washington, DC 20052. TEL 202-994-7164.
Vendor(s): WESTLAW. *2723*

GEORGE WASHINGTON LAW REVIEW.
George Washington University, G W Law Review, 716 20th St. N.W., Burns 4th Fl., Washington, DC 20052. TEL 202-994-6835. FAX 202-994-3090.
Vendor(s): Mead Data Central, WESTLAW. *2629*

GEORGETOWN LAW JOURNAL.
Georgetown University Law Center, 600 New Jersey Ave., N.W., Washington, DC 20001. TEL 202-662-9468.
Vendor(s): Mead Data Central, WESTLAW. *2629*

GEORGIA LAW REVIEW.
University of Georgia School of Law, Athens, GA 30602. TEL 404-542-7286.
Vendor(s): WESTLAW. *2629*

GEORGIA TREND.
Grimes Publications, Inc. (Atlanta), Box 56447, Atlanta, GA 30343. TEL 404-522-7200.
Vendor(s): DIALOG. *783*

GEOSCIENCE DOCUMENTATION.
Geosystems, Box 40, Didcot, Oxon OX11 9BX, England.
Vendor(s): DIALOG. *1551*

GEOTITLES.
Geosystems, P.O. Box 40, Didcot, Oxon OX11 9BX, England.
Vendor(s): DIALOG. *1551*

GERIATRIC NURSING.
Mosby Year - Book, Inc. (Littleton) 545 Great Rd., Littleton, MA 01460. TEL 800-225-5020. FAX 508-486-9423. *2272*

GERMANY (FEDERAL REPUBLIC, 1949-). BUNDESMINISTERIUM FUER FORSCHUNG UND TECHNOLOGIE. B M F T FOERDERUNGSKATALOG.
Bundesministerium fuer Forschung und Technologie, Referat Hausinterne Datenverarbeitung und Dokumentation, Postfach 200240, 5300 Bonn 2, Germany. TEL 0228-593334. FAX 0228-593601. *4311*

GERONTOLOGIST.
Gerontological Society of America, 1275 K St., N.W., Ste. 350, Washington, DC 20005-4006. TEL 202-842-1275. *2273*

GESTUS.
Brecht Society of America, Inc., 59 S. New St., Dover, DE 19901. TEL 302-734-3740. FAX 302-734-9354. *2919*

GIFTS & DECORATIVE ACCESSORIES.
Geyer-McAllister Publications, Inc., 51 Madison Ave., New York, NY 10010. TEL 212-689-4411. Vendor(s): DIALOG. *2281*

GIORNALE DI MEDICINA MILITARE.
Comando del Corpo di Sanita dell' Esercito, Via S. Stefano Rotondo, n.4, 00184 Rome, Italy. *3101*

GLOBAL ENVIRONMENTAL CHANGE.
Butterworth - Heinemann Ltd. Linacre House, Jordan Hill, Oxford OX2 8DP, England. TEL 0865-310366. FAX 0865-310898.
Vendor(s): Data-Star, DIALOG, NewsNet. *1956*

GLOBAL LINKS.
Overseas Development Network (San Francisco), 333 Valencia St., Ste. 330, San Francisco, CA 94103. TEL 415-431-4204. FAX 415-431-4481. *930*

GLOBE AND MAIL REPORT ON BUSINESS.
Globe and Mail Ltd., 444 Front St. W., Toronto, Ont. M5V 2S9, Canada. TEL 416-585-5000. *867*

GOING PUBLIC - THE I P O REPORTER.
Investment Dealers' Digest, 2 World Trade Ctr., 18th Fl., New York, NY 10048. TEL 212-227-1200.
Vendor(s): Data-Star, DIALOG. *783*

GOLDEN GATE UNIVERSITY LAW REVIEW.
Golden Gate University, School of Law, 536 Mission St., San Francisco, CA 94105. TEL 415-442-7250.
Vendor(s): WESTLAW. *2630*

GOVERNMENT COMPUTER NEWS.
Cahners Publishing Company (Silver Spring), Division of Reed Publishing (USA) Inc., 8601 Georgia Ave., Ste. 300, Silver Spring, MD 20910. FAX 301-650-2111.
Vendor(s): DIALOG. *4083*

GOVERNMENT EMPLOYEE RELATIONS REPORT.
The Bureau of National Affairs, Inc., 1231 25th St., N.W., Washington, DC 20037. TEL 202-452-4200. FAX 202-822-8092.
Vendor(s): Human Resources Information Network (CDD, HDD), Mead Data Central (GOVEMP), WESTLAW. *980*

GOVERNMENT FUNDING FOR UNITED KINGDOM BUSINESS: A COMPLETE GUIDE TO SOURCES, GRANTS AND APPLICABLE PROCEDURES.
Kogan Page, 120 Pentonville Rd., London N1 9JN, England. TEL 071-278-0433. FAX 071-837-6348. *867*

GOVERNMENT MANAGER.
The Bureau of National Affairs, Inc., 1231 25th St., N.W., Washington, DC 20037. TEL 202-452-4200. FAX 202-822-8092.
Vendor(s): Human Resources Information Network (CDD, HDD). *980*

GOVERNMENT PRODUCT NEWS.
Penton Publishing, 1100 Superior Ave., Cleveland, OH 44114-2543. TEL 216-696-7000. FAX 216-696-8765.
Vendor(s): DIALOG. *4062*

GOVERNMENT REPORTS ANNOUNCEMENTS AND INDEX JOURNAL.
U.S. National Technical Information Service, 5285 Port Royal Rd., Springfield, VA 22161. TEL 703-487-4630. FAX 703-321-8547.
Vendor(s): BRS, CEDOCAR, CISTI, Data-Star, DIALOG (File no.6), European Space Agency, JICST, Orbit Information Technologies (NTIS), STN International (NTIS). *4080*

GOVERNMENT RESEARCH DIRECTORY.
Gale Research Inc., 835 Penobscot Bldg., Detroit, MI 48226. TEL 313-961-2242. FAX 313-961-6083.
Vendor(s): DIALOG. *4599*

GOWER FEDERAL SERVICE - MINING.
Rocky Mountain Mineral Law Foundation, Porter Administration Bldg., 7039 E. 18th Ave., Denver, CO 80220. TEL 303-321-8100. FAX 303-321-7657.
Vendor(s): WESTLAW. *3484*

GOWER FEDERAL SERVICE - OUTER CONTINENTAL SHELF.
Rocky Mountain Mineral Law Foundation, Porter Administration Bldg., 7039 E. 18th Ave., Denver, CO 80220. TEL 303-321-8100. FAX 303-321-7657.
Vendor(s): WESTLAW. *3484*

GRAND RAPIDS BUSINESS JOURNAL.
Gemini Publications, 549 Ottawa Ave. N.W., Grand Rapids, MI 49503-1444. TEL 616-459-4545. FAX 616-459-4800.
Vendor(s): DIALOG. *835*

GRAPHIC ARTS MONTHLY.
Cahners Publishing Company (New York), Division of Reed Publishing (USA) Inc., 249 W. 17th St., New York, NY 10011. TEL 212-463-6834. FAX 212-463-6733.
Vendor(s): DIALOG. *4000*

GREEN MARKETS.
Pike & Fischer, Inc., 4600 East-West Hwy., Ste. 200, Bethesda, MD 20814.
Vendor(s): DIALOG (File no.624/McGRAW-HILL PUBLICATIONS ONLINE), Dow Jones/News Retrieval (GM), Mead Data Central (GRNMKT). *2128*

GREENHOUSE EFFECT REPORT.
Business Publishers, Inc., 951 Pershing Dr., Silver Spring, MD 20910-4464. TEL 301-587-6300. FAX 609-585-9075.
Vendor(s): NewsNet (EV01). *1956*

GROCER.
William Reed Ltd., Broadfield Park, Crawley, W. Sussex RH11 9RT, England. TEL 0293-613400. FAX 0293-515174. *2092*

GROUND WATER MONITOR.
Business Publishers, Inc., 951 Pershing Dr., Silver Spring, MD 20910-4464. TEL 301-587-6300. FAX 301-585-9075.
Vendor(s): Data-Star (PTBN), DIALOG, NewsNet (EV18). *4824*

GUNS & AMMO.
Petersen Publishing Co., 8490 Sunset Blvd., Los Angeles, CA 90069. TEL 213-854-2222.
Vendor(s): DIALOG. *4548*

GUT.
B M J Publishing Group, B.M.A. House, Tavistock Sq., London WC1H 9JR, England. TEL 071-387-4499.
Vendor(s): BRS. *3268*

GYOGYSZERESZET.
Ifjusagi Lap-es Konyvkiado Vallalat, Revay u. 16, 1374 Budapest 6, Hungary. *3727*

H F D - RETAILING HOME FURNISHINGS.
Fairchild Publications, Inc., H F D-Retailing Home Furnishings, 7 W. 34th St., New York, NY 10001. TEL 212-630-4000.
Vendor(s): DIALOG. *2559*

H R MAGAZINE.
Society for Human Resource Management, 606 N. Washington St., Alexandria, VA 22314-1914. TEL 703-548-3440. FAX 703-836-0367.
Vendor(s): Human Resources Information Network. *1065*

H T F S DIGEST.
Harwell Laboratory, Oxon OX11 ORA, England. FAX 0235-831981.
Vendor(s): European Space Agency (File no.138/HEATFLO). *1853*

HAMLINE LAW REVIEW.
Hamline University School of Law, Hamline Law Review, 1536 Hewitt Ave., St. Paul, MN 55104-1284. TEL 612-641-2350. FAX 612-641-2435.
Vendor(s): WESTLAW. *2631*

HANDBOOK ON INJECTABLE DRUGS.
American Society of Hospital Pharmacists, c/o Jean Rogers, Dir., Mkt. Svcs., 4630 Montgomery Ave., Bethesda, MD 20814. TEL 301-657-3000.
Vendor(s): BRS (DIFT), DIALOG (File no.229). *3727*

HANDBUCH DER GROSSUNTERNEHMEN.
Verlag Hoppenstedt und Co., Havelstr. 9, Postfach 4006, 6100 Darmstadt, Germany. TEL 06151-380-0. FAX 06151-380-360.
Vendor(s): Data-Star, DIALOG. *1077*

HANDELSBLATT.
Handelsblatt GmbH, Postfach 102717, 4000 Duesseldorf 1, Germany. TEL 0211-8870. *836*

HANGZHOU DAXUE XUEBAO (ZIRAN KEXUE BAN).
Hangzhou Daxue, 34 Tianmushan Lu, Hangzhou, Zhejiang 310028, People's Republic of China.
Vendor(s): DIALOG. *4312*

HARVARD BUSINESS REVIEW.
Harvard University, Graduate School of Business Administration, Soldiers Field Rd., Boston, MA 02163-1099. TEL 617-495-6182. FAX 617-495-9933.
Vendor(s): BRS (HBRO), Data-Star (HBRO), DIALOG (File no.122), Human Resources Information Network, Mead Data Central. *668*

HARVARD CIVIL RIGHTS - CIVIL LIBERTIES LAW REVIEW.
Harvard University, Law School, Publications Center, Hastings Hall, Cambridge, MA 02138. TEL 617-495-3694.
Vendor(s): WESTLAW. *2702*

HARVARD ENVIRONMENTAL LAW REVIEW.
Harvard University, Law School, Publications Center, Hastings Hall, Cambridge, MA 02138. TEL 617-495-3694.
Vendor(s): WESTLAW. *2631*

HARVARD HEALTH LETTER.
Harvard Medical School, HMS Health Publications Group, 164 Longwood Ave., 4th Fl., Boston, MA 02115. TEL 800-333-3438. FAX 617-432-1506.
Vendor(s): BRS, Information Access Company. *3802*

HARVARD INTERNATIONAL LAW JOURNAL.
Harvard University, Law School, Publications Center, Hastings Hall, Cambridge, MA 02138. TEL 617-495-3694.
Vendor(s): WESTLAW. *2723*

HARVARD JOURNAL OF LAW AND PUBLIC POLICY.
Harvard Society for Law and Public Policy, Inc., Harvard Law School, Cambridge, MA 02138. TEL 617-495-3105.
Vendor(s): WESTLAW. *2631*

HARVARD JOURNAL ON LEGISLATION.
Harvard University, Law School, Publications Center, Hastings Hall, Cambridge, MA 02138. TEL 617-495-3694.
Vendor(s): WESTLAW. *2631*

HARVARD LAW REVIEW.
Harvard Law Review Association, Gannett House, Cambridge, MA 02138. TEL 617-495-4650.
Vendor(s): Mead Data Central (Lexis), WESTLAW. *2631*

HARVARD WOMEN'S LAW JOURNAL.
Harvard University, Law School (Women's Law Journal), Publications Center, Hastings Hall, Cambridge, MA 02138. TEL 617-495-3726. FAX 617-495-1110.
Vendor(s): WESTLAW. *2631*

HASTINGS COMMUNICATIONS AND ENTERTAINMENT LAW JOURNAL (COMM - ENT).
University of California, San Francisco, Hastings College of the Law, 200 McAllister St., San Francisco, CA 94102-4978. TEL 415-565-4731. FAX 415-565-4814.
Vendor(s): WESTLAW. *2631*

HASTINGS CONSTITUTIONAL LAW QUARTERLY.
University of California, San Francisco, Hastings College of the Law, 200 McAllister St., San Francisco, CA 94102-4978. TEL 415-565-4726. FAX 415-565-4814.
Vendor(s): WESTLAW. *2706*

HASTINGS INTERNATIONAL AND COMPARATIVE LAW REVIEW.
University of California, San Francisco, Hastings College of the Law, 200 McAllister St., San Francisco, CA 94102-4978. TEL 415-565-4730. FAX 415-565-4825.
Vendor(s): WESTLAW. *2723*

HASTINGS LAW JOURNAL.
University of California, San Francisco, Hastings College of the Law, 200 McAllister St., San Francisco, CA 94102-4978. TEL 415-565-4727. FAX 415-565-4814.
Vendor(s): Mead Data Central, WESTLAW. *2632*

HAWAII BUSINESS.
Hawaii Business Publishing Corp., Box 913, Honolulu, HI 96814. TEL 808-946-3978.
Vendor(s): DIALOG. *867*

HAZARDOUS WASTE NEWS.
Business Publishers, Inc., 951 Pershing Dr., Silver Spring, MD 20910-4464. TEL 301-587-6300. FAX 301-585-9075.
Vendor(s): DIALOG, NewsNet (CH10). *1985*

HAZMAT TRANSPORT.
Business Publishers, Inc., 951 Pershing Dr., Silver Spring, MD 20910-4464. TEL 301-587-6300. FAX 301-585-9075.
Vendor(s): NewsNet (CH14). *1985*

HEALTH AND SAFETY SCIENCE ABSTRACTS.
Cambridge Scientific Abstracts, 7200 Wisconsin Ave., 6th Fl., Bethesda, MD 20814. TEL 301-961-6750. FAX 301-961-6720.
Vendor(s): BRS (CSEN), Orbit Information Technologies (ORBIT). *4117*

HEALTH CARE COMPETITION WEEK.
Capitol Publications Inc., 1101 King St., Ste. 444, Alexandria, VA 22314. TEL 703-683-4100. FAX 703-739-6517.
Vendor(s): NewsNet. *2462*

HEALTH CARE MANAGEMENT REVIEW.
Aspen Publishers, Inc., 200 Orchard Ridge Dr., Gaithersburg, MD 20878. TEL 301-417-7500. FAX 301-417-7550. *2462*

HEALTH DEVICES ALERTS.
E C R I, 5200 Butler Pike, Plymouth Meeting, PA 19462. TEL 215-825-6000. FAX 215-834-1275.
Vendor(s): DIALOG (File no.198). *3175*

HEALTH DEVICES SOURCEBOOK.
E C R I, 5200 Butler Pike, Plymouth Meeting, PA 19462. TEL 215-825-6000. FAX 215-834-1275.
Vendor(s): DIALOG (File no.188). *3103*

HEALTH GRANTS & CONTRACTS WEEKLY.
Capitol Publications Inc., 1101 King St., Ste. 444, Alexandria, VA 22314. TEL 703-683-4100. FAX 703-739-6517.
Vendor(s): NewsNet. *4062*

HEALTH INDEX.
Information Access Company, 362 Lakeside Dr., Foster City, CA 94404. TEL 800-227-8431. FAX 415-378-5499.
Vendor(s): BRS (HEAL), Data-Star (HLTH), DIALOG (File no.149). *3175*

HEALTH NEWS (TORONTO).
University of Toronto, Faculty of Medicine, Medical Sciences Bldg., Toronto, Ont. M5S 1A8, Canada. TEL 416-978-5411. FAX 416-978-7552.
Vendor(s): Information Access Company. *3103*

HEALTH NEWS DAILY.
F-D-C Reports, Inc., 5550 Friendship Blvd., Ste. One, Chevy Chase, MD 20815. TEL 301-657-9830. FAX 301-656-3094.
Vendor(s): BRS (HNDY), Data-Star, DIALOG, NewsNet. *3103*

HEALTH POLICY & BIOMEDICAL RESEARCH: THE BLUE SHEET.
F-D-C Reports, Inc., 5550 Friendship Blvd., Ste. One, Chevy Chase, MD 20815. TEL 301-657-9830. FAX 301-656-3094.
Vendor(s): Mead Data Central. *3104*

HEALTH PROGRESS.
Catholic Health Association of the United States, 4455 Woodson Rd., St. Louis, MO 63134-3797. TEL 314-427-2500. FAX 314-427-0029. *2462*

HEALTH SCIENCES SERIALS.
U.S. National Library of Medicine, 8600 Rockville Pike, Bethesda, MD 20894. TEL 301-496-6308. FAX 301-496-4450.
Vendor(s): National Library of Medicine. *3175*

HEALTHCARE FINANCIAL MANAGEMENT.
Healthcare Financial Management Association, Two Westbrook Corporate Center, Ste. 700, Westchester, IL 60154. TEL 708-531-9600. FAX 708-531-0032.
Vendor(s): DIALOG. *2463*

HEART AND LUNG.
Mosby - Year Book, Inc., 11830 Westline Industrial Dr., St. Louis, MO 63146. TEL 800-325-4117. FAX 314-432-1380.
Vendor(s): BRS, BRS/Saunders Colleague. *3278*

HEAT TRANSFER & FLUID FLOW SERVICE DIGEST.
Harwell Laboratory, Oxon OX11 ORA, England. FAX 0235-831981.
Vendor(s): European Space Agency (File no.138/ HEATFLO). *1853*

HELICOPTER NEWS.
Phillips Publishing, Inc., Defense - Aviation Group, 1925 N. Lynn St., Ste. 1000, Arlington, VA 22209. TEL 703-522-8333. FAX 703-522-6448.
Vendor(s): Data-Star, DIALOG, NewsNet (AE12). *54*

HELLER REPORT ON EDUCATION TECHNOLOGY AND TELECOMMUNICATIONS MARKETS.
Nelson B. Heller & Associates, 600 Central Ave., Ste. 312, Box 18, Highland Park, IL 60035-3255. TEL 708-831-6604. FAX 708-926-0202.
Vendor(s): NewsNet. *1728*

HELMINTHOLOGICAL ABSTRACTS.
C.A.B. International, Wallingford, Oxon OX10 8DE, England. TEL 0491 32111. FAX 0491-33508.
Vendor(s): BRS (VETR), CISTI, DIMDI, DIALOG, European Space Agency (File nos.16 & 124/CAB). *138*

HERBA POLONICA.
Instytut Przemyslu Zielarskiego, Libelta 27, 61-707 Poznan, Poland. TEL 52-56-16. *504*

HERBAGE ABSTRACTS.
C.A.B. International, Wallingford, Oxon OX10 8DE, England. TEL 0491 32111. FAX 0491-33508.
Vendor(s): BRS (CABA), CISTI, DIMDI, DIALOG, European Space Agency (File nos.16 & 124/CAB). *138*

HERITAGE FOUNDATION. ISSUE BULLETINS.
Heritage Foundation, 214 Massachusetts Ave., N.E., Washington, DC 20002. TEL 202-546-4400. FAX 202-546-8328.
Vendor(s): Mead Data Central. *3897*

HERITAGE LECTURES.
Heritage Foundation, 214 Massachusetts Ave., N.E., Washington, DC 20002. TEL 202-546-4400. FAX 202-546-8328.
Vendor(s): Mead Data Central. *4062*

HESSISCHE BIBLIOGRAPHIE.
K.G. Saur Verlag KG, Ortlerstr. 8, Postfach 701620, 8000 Munich 70, Germany. TEL 089-76902-0. FAX 089-76902150. *402*

HEWLETT-PACKARD JOURNAL.
Hewlett Packard Co. (Palo Alto), 3200 Hillview Ave., Palo Alto, CA 94304. TEL 415-857-2004. FAX 415-857-3880.
Vendor(s): DIALOG. *1460*

HIGH PERFORMANCE PLASTICS.
Elsevier Science Publishers Ltd., Crown House, Linton Rd., Barking, Essex IG11 8JU, England. TEL 081-594-7272. FAX 081-594-5942.
Vendor(s): Data-Star, DIALOG. *3862*

HIGH PERFORMANCE TEXTILES.
Elsevier Science Publishers Ltd., Crown House, Linton Rd., Barking, Essex IG11 8JU, England. TEL 081-594-7272. FAX 081-594-5942.
Vendor(s): DIALOG. *4619*

HIGH TECH CERAMICS NEWS.
Business Communications Co., Inc. (Norwalk), 25 Van Zant St., Ste. 13, Norwalk, CT 06855. TEL 203-853-4266. FAX 203-853-0348.
Vendor(s): Data-Star, DIALOG, NewsNet. *1164*

HIGH-TECH MATERIALS ALERT.
Technical Insights, Inc., 32 N. Dean St., Englewood, NJ 07631. TEL 201-568-4744. FAX 201-568-8247.
Vendor(s): Mead Data Central. *4599*

HIGH TECH SEPARATIONS NEWS.
Business Communications Co., Inc. (Norwalk), 25 Van Zant St., Ste. 13, Norwalk, CT 06855. TEL 203-853-4266. FAX 203-853-0348.
Vendor(s): Data-Star, DIALOG, NewsNet. *1205*

HIGHWAY & HEAVY CONSTRUCTION PRODUCTS.
Cahners Publishing Company (Des Plaines) Division Reed Publishing (USA) Inc., 1350 E. Touhy Ave., Box 5080, Des Plaines, IL 60017-5080. TEL 708-635-8800. FAX 708-299-8622.
Vendor(s): DIALOG. *1866*

HIGHWAY RESEARCH ABSTRACTS.
National Research Council, Transportation Research Board, 2101 Constitution Ave., N.W., Washington, DC 20418. TEL 202-334-3218. FAX 202-334-2519. *4664*

HIPPOCRATES.
Hippocrates Partners, 301 Howard St., 18th Fl., San Francisco, CA 94105-2252. TEL 415-512-9100. *3105*

HISTORICAL ABSTRACTS. PART A: MODERN HISTORY ABSTRACTS, 1450-1914.
A B C-Clio, 130 Cremona, Box 1911, Santa Barbara, CA 93116-1911. TEL 805-968-1911. FAX 805-685-9685.
Vendor(s): DIALOG (File no.39). *2329*

HISTORICAL ABSTRACTS. PART B: TWENTIETH CENTURY ABSTRACTS, 1914 TO THE PRESENT.
A B C-Clio, 130 Cremona, Box 1911, Santa Barbara, CA 93116-1911. TEL 805-968-1911. FAX 805-685-9685.
Vendor(s): DIALOG (File no.39). *2329*

HOFSTRA LAW REVIEW.
Hofstra University, School of Law, Hempstead, NY 11550. TEL 516-463-5910. FAX 516-560-7676.
Vendor(s): Mead Data Central, WESTLAW. *2633*

HOLLAND EXPORTS.
A B C voor Handel en Industrie C.V., Koningin Wilhelminalaan 16, P.O. Box 190, 2000 AD Haarlem, Netherlands. TEL 023-319031. FAX 023-327033.
Vendor(s): Data-Star. *911*

HOLT ADVISORY.
T.J. Holt & Co., Inc., Box 2923, W. Palm Beach, FL 33402. TEL 407-684-8100. FAX 407-684-9039.
Vendor(s): NewsNet. *669*

HORTICULTURAL ABSTRACTS.
C.A.B. International, Wallingford, Oxon OX10 8DE, England. TEL 0491 32111. FAX 0491-33508.
Vendor(s): BRS (CABA), CISTI, DIMDI, DIALOG, European Space Agency (File nos.16 & 124/CAB). *2141*

HOSPITAL ADMITTING MONTHLY.
American Health Consultants, Inc., Six Piedmont Center, Ste. 400, 3525 Piedmont Rd., N.E., Atlanta, GA 30305. TEL 404-262-7436. FAX 800-284-3291.
Vendor(s): Mead Data Central. *2463*

HOSPITAL EMPLOYEE HEALTH.
American Health Consultants, Inc., Six Piedmont Center, Ste. 400, 3525 Piedmont Rd., N.E., Atlanta, GA 30305. TEL 404-262-7436. FAX 800-284-3291.
Vendor(s): Mead Data Central. *2464*

HOSPITAL FORMULARY.
Avanstar Communications, Inc., 7500 Old Oak Blvd., Cleveland, OH 44130. TEL 216-826-2839. FAX 216-891-2726. *3728*

HOSPITAL INFECTION CONTROL.
American Health Consultants, Inc., Six Piedmont Center, Ste. 400, 3525 Piedmont Rd., N.E., Atlanta, GA 30305. TEL 404-262-7436. FAX 800-284-3291.
Vendor(s): Mead Data Central. *2464*

HOSPITAL LITERATURE INDEX.
American Hospital Publishing, Inc. 737 N. Michigan Ave., Chicago, IL 60611. TEL 312-440-6258. FAX 312-280-5979.
Vendor(s): DIMDI, National Library of Medicine. *2470*

HOSPITAL PATIENT RELATIONS REPORT.
Business Publishers, Inc., 951 Pershing Dr., Silver Spring, MD 20910-4464. TEL 301-587-6300. FAX 301-585-9075.
Vendor(s): NewsNet. *2465*

HOSPITAL PEER REVIEW.
American Health Consultants, Inc., Six Piedmont Center, Ste. 400, 3525 Piedmont Rd., N.E., Atlanta, GA 30305. TEL 404-262-7436. FAX 800-284-3291.
Vendor(s): Mead Data Central. *2465*

HOSPITAL PRACTICE.
H P Publishing Co. 55 Fifth Ave., New York, NY 10003-6903. TEL 212-989-2100. FAX 212-727-7316. *3106*

HOSPITAL RISK MANAGEMENT.
American Health Consultants, Six Piedmont Center, Ste. 400, 3525 Piedmont Rd., N.E., Atlanta, GA 30305. TEL 404-262-7436. FAX 800-284-3291.
Vendor(s): Mead Data Central. *2465*

HOSPITAL TOPICS.
Heldref Publications, 1319 Eighteenth St., N.W., Washington, DC 20036. TEL 202-296-6267. FAX 202-296-5149. *2465*

HOSPITALIS.
Hospitalis Verlag AG, Hermetschloostr. 75, Postfach 1632, CH-8048 Zuerich, Switzerland. TEL 01-4330242. FAX 01-4330242.
Vendor(s): DIALOG. *2466*

HOSPITALS.
American Hospital Publishing, Inc. 737 N. Michigan Ave., Chicago, IL 60611. TEL 312-440-6817. FAX 312-951-8491.
Vendor(s): DIALOG, Mead Data Central. *2466*

HOT ROD.
Petersen Publishing Co., 8490 Sunset Blvd., Los Angeles, CA 90069. TEL 213-854-2718. FAX 213-854-2865.
Vendor(s): DIALOG. *4692*

HOUSTON BUSINESS JOURNAL.
American Business City Journals, John Beddow Corp., One W. Loop S., Ste. 650, Houston, TX 77027. TEL 713-688-8811.
Vendor(s): DIALOG. *868*

HOUSTON JOURNAL OF INTERNATIONAL LAW.
University of Houston, Law Center, 4800 Calhoun Rd., BLB, Ste. 29, Houston, TX 77004-6370. TEL 713-749-3774.
Vendor(s): WESTLAW. *2633*

HOUSTON LAW REVIEW.
Houston Law Review Inc., University of Houston Law Center-University Park, Houston, TX 77004. TEL 713-749-3195. FAX 713-749-4661.
Vendor(s): WESTLAW. *2633*

HOUSTON POST INDEX.
University Microfilms International, Data Courier, c/o Bonnie Maxwell, VP, 620 S. Third St., Louisville, KY 40202. TEL 800-626-2823. FAX 502-589-5672.
Vendor(s): DIALOG. *2578*

HOWARD LAW JOURNAL.
Howard University, School of Law, 2900 Van Ness St., N.W., Washington, DC 20008. TEL 202-686-6570.
Vendor(s): WESTLAW. *2633*

HUMAN GENOME ABSTRACTS.
Cambridge Scientific Abstracts, 7200 Wisconsin Ave., 6th Fl., Bethesda, MD 20814. TEL 301-961-6700. FAX 301-961-6720.
Vendor(s): BRS (CSAL), DIALOG (File no.76). *465*

HUMAN RESOURCE EXECUTIVE.
Axon Group, 747 Dresher Rd., Ste. 500, Box 980, Horsham, PA 19044. TEL 215-784-0860. FAX 215-784-0870.
Vendor(s): Human Resources Information Network. *1066*

HUMAN RIGHTS.
American Bar Association, Individual Rights and Responsibilities Section, 750 N. Lake Shore Dr., Chicago, IL 60611. TEL 312-988-6047. FAX 312-988-6281.
Vendor(s): WESTLAW (HUMRT). *3943*

HUMANITIES INDEX.
H.W. Wilson Co., 950 University Ave., Bronx, NY 10452. TEL 800-367-6770. FAX 212-538-2716.
Vendor(s): Wilsonline (File HUM). *2520*

HYDRAULICS & PNEUMATICS.
Penton Publishing, 1100 Superior Ave., Cleveland, OH 44114-2543. TEL 216-696-7000. FAX 216-696-8765.
Vendor(s): DIALOG. *1924*

HYDROWIRE.
H C I Publications, 410 Archibald St., Kansas City, MO 64111-3046. TEL 816-931-1311. FAX 816-931-2015.
Vendor(s): NewsNet. *1803*

HYPATIA.
Indiana University Press, Journals Division, 601 N. Morton St., Bloomington, IN 47404. TEL 812-855-9449. FAX 812-855-7931.
Vendor(s): DIALOG (File no. 57), Information Access Company. *4859*

I B C - DONOGHUE'S MONEY FUND REPORT.
I B C - U S A (Publications) Inc., 290 Eliot St., Ashland, MA 01721. TEL 508-881-2800. FAX 508-881-0987. *949*

I B C'S MONEY MARKET INSIGHT.
I B C - U S A (Publications) Inc., 290 Eliot St., Ashland, MA 01721. TEL 508-881-2800. FAX 508-881-0982. *949*

I B J MONTHLY REPORT.
Industrial Bank of Japan, 1-3-3 Marunouchi, Chiyoda-ku, Tokyo, Japan. *868*

I B R.
Felix Dietrich Verlag, Jahnstr. 15, Postfach 1949, 4500 Osnabrueck, Germany. FAX 0541-41255. *4356*

I C O LIBRARY MONTHLY ENTRIES - COFFEELINE.
International Coffee Organization, 22 Berners St., London W1P 4DD, England. FAX 071-580-6129.
Vendor(s): DIALOG (File no.164). *2072*

I D P REPORT.
Simba Information, Inc., Box 7430, Wilton, CT 06897. TEL 203-834-0033. FAX 203-834-1771.
Vendor(s): DIALOG, NewsNet. *1444*

I M M ABSTRACTS AND INDEX.
Institution of Mining and Metallurgy, 44 Portland Place, London W1N 4BR, England. TEL 01-580 3802. FAX 01-436-5388.
Vendor(s): Pergamon Infoline (IMMAGE). *3499*

I N I S ATOMINDEX.
International Atomic Energy Agency, Lane End House, Sheenfield, Reading RG2 9BB, England. TEL 734-883-895.
Vendor(s): BELINDIS, CISTI, European Space Agency (File no.28/INIS), STN International (ENERGY). *3837*

I N I S NEWSLETTER.
International Atomic Energy Agency, Wagramer Str. 5, Box 100, A-1400 Vienna, Austria.
Vendor(s): STN International. *2761*

I R S MEMORANDA AND LETTER RULINGS.
Maxwell Macmillan, Professional and Business Reference Publishing, 910 Sylvan Ave., Englewood Cliffs, NJ 07632-3310. TEL 800-562-0245.
Vendor(s): Prentice-Hall Information Network. *1097*

I R S PUBLICATIONS.
Commerce Clearing House, Inc., 4025 W. Peterson Ave., Chicago, IL 60646. TEL 312-583-8500.
Vendor(s): Wilsonline. *1097*

I S D N NEWS.
Phillips Publishing, Inc., 7811 Montrose Rd., Potomac, MD 20854. TEL 301-340-2100. FAX 301-424-4297.
Vendor(s): Data-Star, DIALOG, NewsNet. *1351*

I S M E C: MECHANICAL ENGINEERING ABSTRACTS.
Cambridge Scientific Abstracts, 7200 Wisconsin Ave., 6th Fl., Bethesda, MD 20814. TEL 301-961-6700. FAX 301-961-6720.
Vendor(s): BRS (CSEN), DIALOG (File no.14), European Space Agency (File no.10/ISMEC). *1844*

I S T E UPDATE.
International Society for Technology in Education, 1787 Agate St., Eugene, OR 97403-1923. TEL 503-346-4414. FAX 503-346-5890. *1638*

I TO CHO.
Igaku-Shoin Ltd., 5-24-3 Hongo, Bunkyo-ku, Tokyo 113-91, Japan. TEL 03-817-5714.
Vendor(s): JICST. *3268*

ICE CREAM REPORTER.
Find-Svp Information Network, 625 Avenue of the Americas, New York, NY 10011-2002. TEL 212-645-4500. FAX 212-645-7681.
Vendor(s): NewsNet. *2088*

IDAHO LAW REVIEW.
University of Idaho, College of Law, Moscow, ID 83843. TEL 208-885-7241.
Vendor(s): WESTLAW. *2633*

ILLINOIS BUSINESS REVIEW.
University of Illinois at Urbana-Champaign, Bureau of Economic and Business Research, 428 Commerce Bldg., West, 1206 S. Sixth St., Champaign, IL 61820. TEL 217-333-2330. FAX 217-244-3118.
Vendor(s): DIALOG. *670*

ILLINOIS LEGAL TIMES.
Giant Steps Publishing Corporation, 420 W. Grand Ave., Chicago, IL 60610. TEL 312-644-4378. FAX 312-644-0765.
Vendor(s): WESTLAW. *2634*

IMAGING ABSTRACTS.
Pergamon Press plc, Headington Hill Hall, Oxford, OX3 0BW, England. TEL 0865-794141. FAX 0865-743911.
Vendor(s): Orbit Information Technologies (IMABS). *3798*

IMAGING UPDATE.
Worldwide Videotex, Box 138, Babson Park, Boston, MA 02157. TEL 617-449-1603.
Vendor(s): Data-Star, DIALOG, NewsNet. *1422*

IMMIGRATION POLICY & LAW.
Buraff Publications, 1350 Connecticut Ave., N.W., Ste. 1000, Washington, DC 20036. TEL 202-862-0990. FAX 202-822-8092.
Vendor(s): Human Resources Information Network (CDD, HDD). *3983*

IMMUNOLOGY ABSTRACTS.
Cambridge Scientific Abstracts, 7200 Wisconsin Ave., 6th Fl., Bethesda, MD 20814. TEL 301-961-6750. FAX 301-961-6720.
Vendor(s): BRS (CSAL), DIALOG (File no.76/LIFE SCIENCES COLLECTION). *3176*

IMPLEMENT & TRACTOR.
Farm Press Publications, Box 1420, Clarksdale, MS 38614. TEL 601-624-8503. FAX 601-627-1977.
Vendor(s): DIALOG. *162*

INC.
Goldhirsh Group, Inc., 38 Commercial Wharf, Boston, MA 02110. TEL 617-248-8000. FAX 617-248-8040.
Vendor(s): DIALOG, Mead Data Central. *1115*

INDEPENDENT POWER REPORT.
McGraw-Hill, Inc., Energy & Business Newsletters, 1221 Ave. of the Americas, 36th Fl., New York, NY 10020. TEL 212-512-6410.
Vendor(s): DIALOG (File no.624/McGRAW-HILL PUBLICATIONS ONLINE), Dow Jones/News Retrieval (COG), Mead Data Central (IPR). *1791*

INDEPENDENT SMALL PRESS REVIEW.
Independent Small Press Review (I.S.P.R.), No. 91336 Victoria Court, Santa Barbara, CA 93190-1336. TEL 805-687-4087. FAX 805-964-3337. *4129*

SERIALS AVAILABLE ONLINE 5077

INDEPENDENT TELCO NEWS.
Capitol Publications, Inc., Telecom Publishing Group, 1101 King St., Ste. 444, Box 1455, Alexandria, VA 22313-2055. TEL 800-327-7205. FAX 703-739-6490.
Vendor(s): Data-Star, DIALOG, NewsNet. *1363*

INDEX DOCUMENTATION - ECONOMIE - SCIENCE - TECHNIQUE.
Ministere du Plan, Centre National de Documentation, Charia Maa Al Ainain - Haut Agdal, B.P. 826, Rabat, Morocco. TEL 749-44. FAX 212-7731-34. *721*

INDEX MEDICUS.
U.S. National Library of Medicine, 8600 Rockville Pike, Bethesda, MD 20894. TEL 301-496-6308. FAX 301-496-4450.
Vendor(s): BRS (MESH, MESZ), DIALOG (File nos.154 & 155/MEDLINE), National Library of Medicine, STN International (MEDLINE). *3176*

INDEX NEW ZEALAND.
National Library of New Zealand, Collection Management, P.O. Box 1467, Wellington, New Zealand. TEL 4743-098. FAX 04-4743-035. *14*

INDEX OF CURRENT RESEARCH ON PIGS.
C.A.B. International, Wallingford, Oxon OX10 8DE, England. TEL 0491-32111. FAX 0491-33508.
Vendor(s): BRS, CISTI, DIMDI, DIALOG, European Space Agency. *138*

INDEX OF ECONOMIC ARTICLES IN JOURNALS AND COLLECTIVE VOLUMES.
American Economic Association, 2014 Broadway, Ste. 305, Nashville, TN 37203. TEL 615-322-2595.
Vendor(s): DIALOG (File no.139). *721*

INDEX OF FUNGI.
C.A.B. International, Wallingford, Oxon OX10 8DE, England. TEL 0491-32111. FAX 0491-33508.
Vendor(s): BRS, CISTI, DIMDI, DIALOG, European Space Agency. *466*

INDEX TO BOOK REVIEWS IN RELIGION.
American Theological Library Association, Religion Indexes, 820 Church St., 3rd Fl., Evanston, IL 60201-3707. TEL 708-869-7788.
Vendor(s): BRS, DIALOG (File no.190), Wilsonline. *4213*

INDEX TO CURRENT URBAN DOCUMENTS.
Greenwood Press, Inc. 88 Post Rd. W., Box 5007, Westport, CT 06881-5007. TEL 203-226-3571. FAX 203-222-1502. *2500*

INDEX TO DENTAL LITERATURE.
American Dental Association, 211 E. Chicago Ave., Chicago, IL 60611. TEL 312-440-2500.
Vendor(s): BRS (MESH, MESZ), DIALOG (File nos.154 & 155/MEDLINE), National Library of Medicine, STN International (MEDLINE). *3176*

INDEX TO LEGAL PERIODICALS.
H.W. Wilson Co., 950 University Ave., Bronx, NY 10452. TEL 800-367-6770. FAX 212-538-2716.
Vendor(s): Mead Data Central, WESTLAW, Wilsonline (File ILP). *2699*

INDEX TO SCIENTIFIC & TECHNICAL PROCEEDINGS.
Institute for Scientific Information, 3501 Market St., Philadelphia, PA 19104. TEL 215-386-0100. FAX 215-386-2991.
Vendor(s): Orbit Information Technologies. *4356*

INDEX TO SCIENTIFIC BOOK CONTENTS.
Institute for Scientific Information, 3501 Market St., Philadelphia, PA 19104. TEL 215-386-0100. FAX 215-386-2291.
Vendor(s): DIMDI (ISTP&B Search). *4356*

INDEX TO SOUTH AFRICAN PERIODICALS.
State Library, P.O. Box 397, Pretoria 0001, South Africa. TEL 012-21-8931. FAX 012-325-5984. *4141*

INDEX TO THE AMERICAN BANKER.
University Microfilms International, Serials Data Management, 300 N. Zeeb Rd., Ann Arbor, MI 48106. TEL 313-761-4700.
Vendor(s): Orbit Information Technologies. *721*

INDEX TO THE SPORTING NEWS.
John Gordon Burke Publisher, Inc., Box 1492, Evanston, IL 60204-1492. TEL 708-866-8625. *4498*

INDEX TO U.S. GOVERNMENT PERIODICALS.
Infordata International Inc., 4927 N. Bernard, Chicago, IL 60625-5109.
Vendor(s): BRS, Wilsonline. *15*

INDEX VETERINARIUS.
C.A.B. International, Wallingford, Oxon OX10 8DE, England. TEL 0491 32111. FAX 0491-33508.
Vendor(s): BRS (VETR), CISTI, DIMDI, DIALOG, European Space Agency (File nos.16 & 124/CAB). *4820*

INDIAN JOURNAL OF HOSPITAL PHARMACY.
Indian Hospital Pharmacists' Association, R-566 New Rajinder Nagar, New Delhi 110 060, India. *3728*

INDIAN JOURNAL OF PHARMACEUTICAL SCIENCES.
Indian Pharmaceutical Association, Kalina Santacruz East, Bombay 400098, India. *3728*

INDIANA BUSINESS.
Indiana Business Magazine, 6502 Westfield Blvd., Indianapolis, IN 46220. TEL 317-252-2737.
Vendor(s): DIALOG. *868*

INDIANA LAW JOURNAL.
Indiana University, School of Law, Law Building, Bloomington, IN 47405. TEL 812-855-5175. FAX 812-855-7099.
Vendor(s): Mead Data Central, WESTLAW. *2634*

INDIANA LAW REVIEW.
West Publishing Co., Box 64526, St. Paul, MN 55164-0526. TEL 800-328-9352.
Vendor(s): WESTLAW. *2634*

INDIANAPOLIS BUSINESS JOURNAL.
I B J Corp., 431 N. Pennsylvania, Indianapolis, IN 46204-1806. TEL 317-634-6200. FAX 317-263-5060.
Vendor(s): DIALOG. *836*

INDICE ESPANOL DE CIENCIA Y TECNOLOGIA.
Instituto de Informacion y Documentacion en Ciencia y Tecnologia, Joaquin Costa 22, 28002 Madrid, Spain. TEL 91-5635482. FAX 91-5642644. *4356*

INDICE ESPANOL DE CIENCIAS SOCIALES. SERIES A: PSYCHOLOGY AND EDUCATIONAL SCIENCES.
Instituto de Informacion y Documentacion en Ciencias Sociales y Humanidades, Pinar, 25, 28006 Madrid, Spain. *4051*

INDICE ESPANOL DE CIENCIAS SOCIALES. SERIES B: ECONOMICS, SOCIOLOGY AND POLITICAL SCIENCE.
Instituto de Informacion y Documentacion en Ciencias Sociales y Humanidades, Pinar, 25, 3, 28006 Madrid, Spain. *721*

INDICE ESPANOL DE CIENCIAS SOCIALES. SERIES C: LAW.
Instituto de Informacion y Documentacion en Ciencias Sociales y Humanidades, Pinar, 25, 3, 28006 Madrid, Spain. *2699*

INDICE ESPANOL DE CIENCIAS SOCIALES. SERIES D: SCIENCE AND SCIENTIFIC INFORMATION.
Instituto de Informacion y Documentacion en Ciencias Sociales y Humanidades, Pinar, 25, 3, 28006 Madrid, Spain. *4356*

INDICE ESPANOL DE CIENCIAS SOCIALES. SERIES E: URBAN PLANNING.
Instituto de Informacion y Documentacion en Ciencias Sociales y Humanidades, Pinar, 25, 3, 28006 Madrid, Spain. *2500*

INDICE ESPANOL DE HUMANIDADES. SERIES A: ART.
Instituto de Informacion y Documentacion en Ciencias Sociales y Humanidades, Pinar, 25, 3, 28006 Madrid, Spain. *352*

INDICE ESPANOL DE HUMANIDADES. SERIES B: HISTORICAL SCIENCES.
Instituto de Informacion y Documentacion en Ciencias Sociales y Humanidades, Pinar 25, 3, 28006 Madrid, Spain. *2329*

INDICE ESPANOL DE HUMANIDADES. SERIES C: LINGUISTICS AND LITERATURE.
Instituto de Informacion y Documentacion en Ciencias Sociales y Humanidades, Pinar 25, 3, 28006 Madrid, Spain. *2855*

INDICE ESPANOL DE HUMANIDADES. SERIES D: PHILOSOPHY.
Instituto de Informacion y Documentacion en Ciencias Sociales y Humanidades, Pinar 25, 3, 28006 Madrid, Spain. *3787*

INDICE MEDICO ESPANOL.
Universidad de Valencia, Facultad de Medicina, Avda. Blasco Ibanez - 17, 46010 Valencia, Spain. FAX 3613975. *3176*

INDIVIDUAL EMPLOYMENT RIGHTS.
The Bureau of National Affairs, Inc., 1231 25th St., N.W., Washington, DC 20037. TEL 202-452-4200. FAX 202-822-8092.
Vendor(s): Human Resources Information Network (CDD, HDD). *982*

INDOOR AIR QUALITY UPDATE.
Cutter Information Corp., 37 Broadway, Arlington, MA 02174. TEL 617-648-8700. FAX 617-648-8707.
Vendor(s): NewsNet. *301*

INDUSTRIAL AERODYNAMICS ABSTRACTS.
S T I Ltd., 4 Kings Meadow, Ferry Hinksey Rd., Oxford OX2 0DU, England. TEL 0865-798898. FAX 0865-7987881.
Vendor(s): DIALOG (File no.96/FLUIDEX), European Space Agency (File no.48/FLUIDEX). *1844*

INDUSTRIAL & ENGINEERING CHEMISTRY RESEARCH.
American Chemical Society, 1155 16th St. N.W., Washington, DC 20036. TEL 800-333-9511. FAX 202-872-4615.
Vendor(s): STN International (CJACS). *1854*

INDUSTRIAL AND LABOR RELATIONS REVIEW.
Cornell University, New York State School of Industrial and Labor Relations, Ithaca, NY 14853-3901. TEL 607-255-2732. FAX 607-255-2763.
Vendor(s): DIALOG. *982*

INDUSTRIAL BIOPROCESSING.
Technical Insights, Inc., 32 N. Dean St., Englewood, NJ 07631. TEL 201-568-4744. FAX 201-568-8247.
Vendor(s): Data-Star, DIALOG, Mead Data Central, NewsNet. *1218*

INDUSTRIAL CASES REPORTS.
Incorporated Council of Law Reporting for England and Wales, 3 Stone Bldgs., Lincoln's Inn, London WC2A 3XN, England. TEL 071-242 6471. FAX 071-831-5247.
Vendor(s): Mead Data Central. *2710*

INDUSTRIAL COMMUNICATIONS.
Phillips Publishing, Inc., 7811 Montrose Rd., Potomac, MD 20854. TEL 301-340-2100. FAX 301-424-4297.
Vendor(s): DIALOG, NewsNet (TE13). *1363*

INDUSTRIAL CORROSION ABSTRACTS.
S T I Ltd., 4 Kings Meadow, Ferry Hinksey Rd., Oxford OX2 0DU, England. TEL 0865-798898. FAX 0865-798788.
Vendor(s): DIALOG (File no. 96), European Space Agency (File no. 48). *3425*

INDUSTRIAL DISTRIBUTION.
Cahners Publishing Company (Newton), Division of Reed Publishing (USA) Inc., 275 Washington St., Newton, MA 02158-1630. TEL 617-964-3030. FAX 617-558-4506.
Vendor(s): DIALOG. *1041*

INDUSTRIAL ENERGY BULLETIN.
McGraw-Hill, Inc., Energy & Business Newsletters, 1221 Ave. of the Americas, 36th Fl., New York, NY 10020. TEL 212-512-2000.
Vendor(s): DIALOG (File no.624/McGRAW HIL-PUBLICATIONS ONLINE), Dow Jones/News Retrieval, Mead Data Central. *1791*

INDUSTRIAL ENGINEERING.
Institute of Industrial Engineers, 25 Technology Park-Atlanta, Norcross, GA 30092. TEL 404-449-0460.
Vendor(s): DIALOG. *1926*

INDUSTRIAL FINISHING.
Hitchcock Publishing 191 S. Gary Ave., Carol Stream, IL 60188. TEL 708-665-1000. FAX 708-462-2225.
Vendor(s): DIALOG. *3654*

INDUSTRIAL HEALTH.
National Institute of Industrial Health, 21-1 Nagao 6-chome, Tama-ku, Kawasaki-shi, Kanagawa-ken 214, Japan. TEL 81-044-865-6111. FAX 81-044-865-6116.
Vendor(s): DIALOG, JICST. *3617*

INDUSTRIAL HEALTH & HAZARDS UPDATE.
Merton Allen Associates, InfoTeam Inc., Box 15640, Plantation, FL 33318-5640. TEL 305-473-9560. FAX 305-473-0544.
Vendor(s): Data-Star, DIALOG, Human Resources Information Network, NewsNet (LA04). *4104*

INDUSTRIAL RELATIONS LAW REPORTS.
Eclipse Publications Ltd., 18-20 Highbury Place, London N5 1QP, England. TEL 071-354-5858. FAX 071-359-4000.
Vendor(s): Mead Data Central. *982*

INDUSTRIAL RESEARCHER.
Pranava Industrial Services Pvt. Ltd., 18, Sagar Tarang, Bhulabhai Desai Road, Bombay 400 036, India. TEL 822-1564.
Vendor(s): DIALOG. *670*

INDUSTRIAL SPECIALTIES NEWS.
Blendon Information Services, 126 Willowdale Ave., Ste. 1, Willowdale, Ont. M2N 2Y2, Canada. TEL 416-223-5397. FAX 416-225-9297.
Vendor(s): Data-Star, DIALOG. *1179*

INDUSTRIES IN TRANSITION.
Business Communications Co., Inc. (Norwalk), 25 Van Zant St., Norwalk, CT 06855. TEL 203-853-4266. FAX 203-853-0348.
Vendor(s): Data-Star, DIALOG, NewsNet. *1078*

INDUSTRY WEEK.
Penton Publishing 1100 Superior Ave., Cleveland, OH 44114-2543. TEL 216-696-7000. FAX 216-696-8765.
Vendor(s): DIALOG, Mead Data Central. *1013*

INFERTILITY.
Hemisphere Publishing Corporation 1900 Frost Rd., Ste. 101, Bristol, PA 19007-1598. TEL 215-785-5800. FAX 215-785-5515. *3293*

INFORMATION & INTERACTIVE SERVICES REPORT.
Telecommunications Reports 1333 H St., N.W., Ste. 1100-W., Washington, DC 20005. TEL 202-842-3006. FAX 202-842-30047.
Vendor(s): NewsNet (TE41). *4143*

INFORMATION EAUX.
Office International de l'Eau, Direction de la Documentation et des Donnees, Rue Edouard Chamberland, 87065 Limoges Cedex, France.
Vendor(s): European Space Agency (File no.73/AFEE). *4825*

INFORMATION MANAGEMENT REPORT.
Elsevier Science Publishers Ltd., Crown House, Linton Rd., Barking, Essex IG11 8JU, England. TEL 081-594-7272. FAX 081-594-5942.
Vendor(s): Data-Star (PTBN), DIALOG (File no.636). *2797*

INFORMATION REPORT.
Washington Researchers Publishing, 2612 P St., N.W., Washington, DC 20007. TEL 202-333-3533.
Vendor(s): NewsNet. *403*

INFORMATION SCIENCE ABSTRACTS.
I F I - Plenum 233 Spring St., New York, NY 10013. TEL 212-620-8000. FAX 212-463-0742.
Vendor(s): DIALOG (File no.202). *2793*

INFORMATION TECHNOLOGY DIGEST.
University of Michigan, Information Technology Division, 611 Church Street, 2nd Fl., Ann Arbor, MI 48104. TEL 313-998-7669. FAX 313-998-7718. *1396*

INFORMATION TODAY.
Learned Information, Inc., 143 Old Marlton Pike, Medford, NJ 08055. TEL 609-654-6266. FAX 609-654-4309.
Vendor(s): Mead Data Central. *2798*

INFORMATION WEEK.
C M P Publications, Inc., 600 Community Dr., Manhasset, NY 11030. TEL 516-562-5000. FAX 516-365-4601.
Vendor(s): NewsNet. *1445*

INFORMATIONS RECENTES SUR LES COMPTES NATIONAUX DES PAYS EN DEVELOPPEMENT.
Organization for Economic Cooperation and Development, 2 rue Andre-Pascal, 75775 Paris Cedex 16, France. TEL 45-24-82-00. FAX 45-24-85-00. *931*

INFORMATIONSDIENST KRANKENHAUSWESEN.
Technische Universitaet Berlin, Institut fuer Krankenhausbau, Strasse des 17. Juni 135, 1000 Berlin 12, Germany. TEL 030-31423905.
Vendor(s): DIMDI. *2466*

INFORMATIQUE ET SCIENCES JURIDIQUES.
Institut de l'Information Scientifique et Technique, INIST - CNRS, 2 allee du Parc de Brabois, 54514 Vandoeuvre-les-Nancy Cedex, France. TEL 33-83-50-46-00. FAX 33-83-50-46-50.
Vendor(s): DIALOG, Telesystemes - Questel. *2705*

INFOWORLD.
InfoWorld Publishing 155 Bovet Rd., Ste. 800, San Meteo, CA 94402. TEL 415-572-7341. FAX 415-358-1269.
Vendor(s): Mead Data Central. *1461*

INFUSION.
Shugar Publishing, 32 Mill Rd., Westhampton Beach, NY 11978. TEL 516-288-4404. FAX 516-288-4435. *3109*

INGRAM'S MAGAZINE.
Ingram Investment Co., 306 E. Twelfth St., Ste. 1014, Kansas City, MO 64106. TEL 816-842-9994. FAX 816-474-1111.
Vendor(s): DIALOG. *671*

INNOVATION.
A G Publications Ltd., P.O. Box 7422, Haifa 31070, Israel.
Vendor(s): Data-Star, DIALOG. *1078*

INNOVATOR'S DIGEST.
InfoTeam Inc., Box 15640, Plantation, FL 33318-5640. TEL 305-473-9560. FAX 305-473-0544.
Vendor(s): NewsNet (RD09). *4315*

INORGANIC CHEMISTRY.
American Chemical Society, 1155 16th St., N.W., Washington, DC 20036. TEL 800-333-9511. FAX 202-872-4615.
Vendor(s): STN International (CJACS). *1213*

INPHARMA.
Adis International Ltd., 41 Centorian Dr., Private Bag, Mairangi Bay, Auckland 10, New Zealand. TEL 479-8100.
Vendor(s): BRS. *3729*

INSIDE ENERGY WITH FEDERAL LANDS.
McGraw-Hill, Inc., Energy & Business Newsletters, 1221 Ave. of the Americas, 36th Fl., New York, NY 10020. TEL 212-512-6410.
Vendor(s): DIALOG (File no.624/McGRAW-HILL PUBLICATIONS ONLINE), Dow Jones/News Retrieval (IE), Mead Data Central (INERGY). *1791*

INSIDE F.E.R.C.
McGraw-Hill, Inc., 1221 Ave. of the Americas, New York, NY 10020.
Vendor(s): DIALOG (File no.624/McGRAW-HILL PUBLICATIONS ONLINE), Dow Jones/News Retrieval (FERC), Mead Data Central (INFERC). *1791*

INSIDE F E R C'S GAS MARKET REPORT.
McGraw-Hill, Inc., Energy & Business Newsletters, 1221 Ave. of the Americas, 36th Fl., New York, NY 10020. TEL 212-512-6410.
Vendor(s): DIALOG (File no.624/McGRAW-HILL PUBLICATIONS ONLINE), Dow Jones/News Retrieval (GSMR), Mead Data Central (GASMKT). *3689*

INSIDE MARKET DATA.
Waters Information Services, Inc., Box 2248, Binghamton, NY 13902-2248. TEL 607-770-8535. FAX 607-789-1692.
Vendor(s): Data-Star, DIALOG, NewsNet. *805*

INSIDE N R C.
McGraw-Hill, Inc., Energy and Business Newsletters, 1221 Ave. of the Americas, New York, NY 10020.
Vendor(s): DIALOG (File no.624/McGRAW-HILL PUBLICATIONS ONLINE), Dow Jones/News Retrieval (NRC), Mead Data Central (INNRC). *1805*

INSIDE R & D.
Technical Insights, Inc., 32 N. Dean St., Englewood, NJ 07631. TEL 201-568-4744. FAX 201-568-8247.
Vendor(s): DIALOG, Mead Data Central. *4601*

INSIGHT (WASHINGTON).
Washington Times Corporation, 3600 New York Ave., N.E., Washington, DC 20002. TEL 800-356-3588. FAX 202-529-2484. *2227*

INSTITUTE OF MUSLIM MINORITY AFFAIRS. JOURNAL.
Institute of Muslim Minority Affairs, 46 Goodge St., London W1P 1FJ, England. TEL 636-6740. FAX 632-4194.
Vendor(s): BRS, DIALOG. *2429*

INSTITUTE OF PAPER SCIENCE AND TECHNOLOGY. ABSTRACT BULLETIN.
Institute of Paper Science and Technology, 575 14th St., N.W., Atlanta, GA 30318. TEL 404-853-9500.
Vendor(s): DIALOG (File nos.240 & 840/PAPERCHEM). *3668*

INSTITUTION ANALYSIS.
Heritage Foundation, 214 Massachusetts Ave., N.E., Washington, DC 20002. TEL 202-546-4400. FAX 202-546-8328.
Vendor(s): Mead Data Central. *3899*

INSTITUTIONAL DISTRIBUTION.
Bill Communications, Inc., 633 Third Ave., New York, NY 10017. TEL 212-986-4800.
Vendor(s): DIALOG. *2073*

INSTRUMENTATION AND CONTROL SYSTEMS.
Chilton Co., Chilton Way, Radnor, PA 19089. TEL 215-964-4417. FAX 215-964-4947.
Vendor(s): DIALOG. *2523*

INSTYTUT ZOOTECHNIKI. ROCZNIKI NAUKOWE ZOOTECHNIKI.
Instytut Zootechniki, 32-083 Balice near Krakow, Poland. TEL 048-12-113211. FAX 48-12-228065. *219*

INSURANCE PERIODICALS INDEX.
N I L S Publishing Company, 21625 Prairie St., Box 2507, Chatsworth, CA 91311. TEL 818-998-8830. FAX 818-718-8482.
Vendor(s): DIALOG (File no.169), Mead Data Central (NEXIS/LEXIS), WESTLAW. *2546*

INTEGRATED CIRCUITS INTERNATIONAL.
Elsevier Science Publishers Ltd., Crown House, Linton Rd., Barking, Essex IG11 8JU, England. TEL 081-594-7272. FAX 081-594-5942.
Vendor(s): Data-Star, DIALOG. *1416*

INTEGRATED WASTE MANAGEMENT.
McGraw-Hill, Inc., Energy & Business Newsletters, 1221 Avenue of the Americas, 36th Fl., New York, NY 10020. TEL 212-512-6410.
Vendor(s): DIALOG (File no. 624/McGRAW-HILL PUBLICATIONS ONLINE), Dow Jones/News Retrieval, Mead Data Central. *1985*

INTELLIGENT NETWORK NEWS.
Capitol Publications Inc., Telecom Publishing Group, 1101 King St., Ste. 444, Box 1455, Alexandria, VA 22313-2055. TEL 800-327-7205. FAX 703-739-6490.
Vendor(s): Data-Star, DIALOG, NewsNet. *1338*

INTER-AMERICAN LAW REVIEW.
University of Miami, School of Law, Box 248087, Coral Gables, FL 33124. TEL 305-284-2523.
Vendor(s): WESTLAW. *2724*

INTERAMERICAN OPPORTUNITIES BRIEFING.
International Freedom Foundation, 200 G St., N.E., Ste. 300, Washington, DC 20002. TEL 202-546-5788. FAX 202-546-5488.
Vendor(s): NewsNet (File no. IT03). *931*

INTERAVIA: AEROSPACE REVIEW.
Jane's Information Group, Sentinel House, 163 Brighton Rd., Coulsdon, Surrey CR5 2NH, England. TEL 081-763-1030. FAX 081-763-1005.
Vendor(s): DIALOG, Mead Data Central. *55*

INTERAVIA AIR LETTER.
Jane's Information Group, Sentinel House, 163 Brighton Rd., Coulsdon, Surrey CR5 2NH, England. TEL 081-763-1030. FAX 081-763-1005.
Vendor(s): Mead Data Central. *55*

INTERIOR DESIGN.
A G B Publications Ltd., Audit House, Field End Rd., Ruislip, Middx HA4 9LT, England. TEL 01-868-4499. FAX 01-429-3117.
Vendor(s): DIALOG. *2552*

INTERNAL AUDITOR.
Institute of Internal Auditors, Inc., 249 Maitland Ave., Altamonte Springs, FL 32701-4201. TEL 407-830-7600. FAX 407-831-5171.
Vendor(s): Information Access Company. *752*

INTERNAL REVENUE CODE OF 1986 AS AMENDED.
Research Institute of America, Inc., 90 Fifth Ave., New York, NY 10011. TEL 212-645-4800.
Vendor(s): Prentice-Hall Information Network. *1098*

INTERNATIONAL AEROSPACE ABSTRACTS.
American Institute of Aeronautics and Astronautics, Technical Information Service, 555 W. 57th St., New York, NY 10019. TEL 212-247-6500. FAX 212-582-4861.
Vendor(s): DIALOG (File no.108), European Space Agency (File no.1/NASA). *66*

INTERNATIONAL ASTRONOMICAL UNION. CENTRAL BUREAU FOR ASTRONOMICAL TELEGRAMS. CIRCULAR.
Smithsonian Institution Astrophysical Observatory, 60 Garden St., Cambridge, MA 02138. TEL 617-495-7244. *365*

INTERNATIONAL ASTRONOMICAL UNION. MINOR PLANET CENTER. MINOR PLANET CIRCULARS - MINOR PLANETS AND COMETS.
Smithsonian Institution Astrophysical Observatory, 60 Garden St., Cambridge, MA 02138. TEL 617-495-7244. *365*

INTERNATIONAL BIBLIOGRAPHY OF THE SOCIAL SCIENCES. ECONOMICS.
British Library of Political and Economic Science, Lionel Robbins Building, 10 Portugal St., London WC2A 2HD, England. TEL 071-955-7144.
Vendor(s): QL Systems Ltd.. *722*

INTERNATIONAL BIBLIOGRAPHY OF THE SOCIAL SCIENCES. SOCIAL AND CULTURAL ANTHROPOLOGY.
British Library of Political and Economic Science, Lionel Robbins Building, 10 Portugal St., London WC2A 2HD, England WC2A 2HD. TEL 071-955-7144.
Vendor(s): QL Systems Ltd.. *254*

INTERNATIONAL BIBLIOGRAPHY OF THE SOCIAL SCIENCES. SOCIOLOGY.
British Library of Poltical and Economic Science, Lionel Robbins Building, 10 Portugal St., London WC2A 2HD, England. TEL 071-955-7144.
Vendor(s): QL Systems Ltd.. *4457*

INTERNATIONAL BIODETERIORATION.
Elsevier Science Publishers Ltd., Crown House, Linton Rd., Barking, Essex IG11 8JU, England. TEL 081-594-7272. FAX 081-594-5942.
Vendor(s): BRS, CISTI, DIMDI, DIALOG, European Space Agency (File nos.16 & 124/CAB). *490*

INTERNATIONAL BUILDING SERVICES ABSTRACTS.
Building Services Research and Information Association, Old Bracknell Lane West, Bracknell, Berks RG12 7AH, England. TEL 0344-426511. FAX 0344-487575.
Vendor(s): European Space Agency, Pergamon Infoline. *2304*

INTERNATIONAL BUSINESS.
American International Publishing Co., 500 Mamaroneck Ave., Ste. 314, Harrison, NY 10528-1600. TEL 800-274-8187. FAX 914-381-7713. *912*

INTERNATIONAL COAL REPORT.
Financial Times Business Information Ltd., Tower House, Southampton St., London WC2E 7HA, England. TEL 071-240 9391. FAX 071-240-7946.
Vendor(s): Data-Star, Mead Data Central. *3486*

INTERNATIONAL COUNTRY RISK GUIDE.
Eurostudy Publishing Co. Ltd., Ludgate House, 107 Fleet St., London EC4A 2AB, England. TEL 44-71-583-1025. FAX 44-71-583-5958.
Vendor(s): Data-Star, DIALOG. *785*

INTERNATIONAL DEFENSE REVIEW.
Jane's Information Group, Sentinel House, 163 Brighton Rd., Coulsdon, Surrey CR3 2NX, England. TEL 081-763-1030. FAX 081-763-1005.
Vendor(s): DIALOG, Mead Data Central. *3460*

INTERNATIONAL DEVELOPMENT ABSTRACTS.
Elsevier - Geo Abstracts, Regency House, 34 Duke St., Norwich NR3 3AP, England. TEL 0603-626327. FAX 0603-667934.
Vendor(s): DIALOG (File no.292), Orbit Information Technologies. *2268*

INTERNATIONAL DIRECTORY OF BRANDS AND THEIR COMPANIES.
Gale Research Inc., 835 Penobscot Bldg., Detroit, MI 48226-4094. TEL 800-877-GALE. FAX 313-961-6083.
Vendor(s): DIALOG. *3675*

INTERNATIONAL DIRECTORY OF CORPORATE AFFILIATIONS.
National Register Publishing Co., A Reed Reference Publishing Company, Division of Reed Publishing (USA) Inc., 121 Chanlon Rd., New Providence, NJ 07974. TEL 800-521-8110. FAX 908-665-6688.
Vendor(s): DIALOG (File no. 513), Pergamon Infoline. *1139*

INTERNATIONAL ENERGY ANNUAL.
U.S. Department of Energy, Energy Information Administration, National Energy Information Center, EI-231, Rm. 1F-048, Forrestal Bldg., 1000 Independence Ave., S.W., Washington, DC 20585. TEL 202-586-8800. *1791*

INTERNATIONAL ENVIRONMENT REPORTER.
The Bureau of National Affairs, Inc., 1231 25th St., N.W., Washington, DC 20037. TEL 202-452-4200. FAX 202-822-8092.
Vendor(s): Mead Data Central. *1959*

INTERNATIONAL FINANCIAL STATISTICS.
International Monetary Fund, Publications Unit, 700 19th St., N.W., Washington, DC 20431. TEL 202-623-7430. FAX 202-623-7201.
Vendor(s): National Data Corporation. *722*

INTERNATIONAL INDUSTRIAL OPPORTUNITIES.
High Tech Publishing Company, Box 1923, Brattleboro, VT 05301. TEL 802-254-3539.
Vendor(s): Data-Star, NewsNet. *913*

INTERNATIONAL JOURNAL OF COSMETIC SCIENCE.
Chapman & Hall, 2-6 Boundary Row, London SE1 8HN, England. TEL 071-865-0066. FAX 071-522-9623. *375*

INTERNATIONAL JOURNAL OF HEALTH SERVICES.
Baywood Publishing Co., Inc., 26 Austin Ave., Box 337, Amityville, NY 11701. TEL 516-691-1270. FAX 516-691-1770. *4105*

INTERNATIONAL JOURNAL OF PHARMACEUTICS.
Elsevier Science Publishers B.V., P.O. Box 211, 1000 AE Amsterdam, Netherlands. TEL 020-5803911. FAX 020-5803598. *3729*

INTERNATIONAL JOURNAL OF PURCHASING & MATERIALS MANAGEMENT.
National Association of Purchasing Management, 2055 E. Centennial Circle, Box 22160, Tempe, AZ 85285-2160. FAX 602-752-7890.
Vendor(s): DIALOG. *1042*

INTERNATIONAL JOURNAL OF ROCK MECHANICS AND MINING SCIENCES & GEOMECHANICS ABSTRACTS.
Pergamon Press, Inc., Journals Division, 660 White Plains Rd., Tarrytown, NY 10591-5153. TEL 914-524-9200. FAX 914-333-2444.
Vendor(s): Pergamon Infoline. *3499*

INTERNATIONAL JOURNAL OF SUPERCOMPUTER APPLICATIONS.
M I T Press, 55 Hayward St., Cambridge, MA 02142. TEL 617-253-2889. FAX 617-258-6779.
Vendor(s): DIALOG. *1478*

INTERNATIONAL LABOUR DOCUMENTATION.
I L O Publications, CH-1211 Geneva 22, Switzerland. TEL 022-7996111. FAX 022-7986358.
Vendor(s): European Space Agency (File no.53/LABORDOC), Human Resources Information Network, Orbit Information Technologies (LABORDOC). *722*

INTERNATIONAL LAWYER.
American Bar Association, International Law and Practice Section, 750 N. Lake Shore Dr., Chicago, IL 60611. TEL 312-988-6067.
Vendor(s): Mead Data Central, WESTLAW. *2725*

INTERNATIONAL LEGAL MATERIALS.
American Society of International Law, 2223 Massachusetts Ave., N.W., Washington, DC 20008-2864. TEL 202-265-4313. FAX 202-797-7133.
Vendor(s): Mead Data Central. *2725*

INTERNATIONAL MERGER LAW: EVENTS AND COMMENTARY.
Washington Regulatory Reporting Associates, Box 2220, Springfield, VA 22152. TEL 703-690-8240.
Vendor(s): NewsNet. *2725*

INTERNATIONAL MONETARY FUND. BALANCE OF PAYMENTS STATISTICS.
International Monetary Fund, Publication Services, 700 19th St., N.W., Washington, DC 20431. TEL 202-623-7430. FAX 020-623-7201. *723*

INTERNATIONAL NURSING INDEX.
American Journal of Nursing Co., 555 W. 57th St., New York, NY 10019. TEL 212-582-8820.
Vendor(s): BRS, DIALOG (File nos.154 & 155/MEDLINE), National Library of Medicine, STN International (MEDLINE). *3176*

INTERNATIONAL PACKAGING ABSTRACTS.
Pira International, Randalls Rd., Leatherhead, Surrey KT22 7RU, England. TEL 0372-376161.
Vendor(s): Data-Star, European Space Agency, FIZ Technik, Orbit Information Technologies (PIRA). *3652*

INTERNATIONAL PETROLEUM ABSTRACTS.
John Wiley & Sons Ltd., Baffins Lane, Chichester, Sussex PO19 1UD, England. TEL 0243-779777. FAX 0243-775878.
Vendor(s): Pergamon Infoline (IPA). *3705*

INTERNATIONAL PHARMACEUTICAL ABSTRACTS.
American Society of Hospital Pharmacists, c/o Jean Rogers, Dir., Mkt. Svcs., 4630 Montgomery Ave., Bethesda, MD 20814. TEL 301-657-3000.
Vendor(s): BRS (IPAB), DIMDI, DIALOG (File no.74), European Space Agency (File no.102/IPA), Mead Data Central, National Library of Medicine, University of Tsukuba. *3748*

INTERNATIONAL POPULATION DATA.
U.S. Bureau of the Census, Data User Services Division, Washington, DC 20233. TEL 301-763-4100.
Vendor(s): CompuServe Consumer Information Service, DIALOG. *3984*

INTERNATIONAL PRODUCT ALERT.
Marketing Intelligence Service Ltd., 33 Academy St., Naples, NY 14512. TEL 716-374-6326. FAX 716-374-5217.
Vendor(s): Data-Star, DIALOG. *2074*

INTERNATIONAL REPORTS.
Eurostudy Publishing Co. Ltd., Ludgate House, 107 Fleet St., London EC4A 2AB, England. TEL 44-71-583-1025. FAX 44-71-583-5958.
Vendor(s): Data-Star (FSRI). *786*

INTERNATIONAL RESEARCH CENTERS DIRECTORY.
Gale Research Inc., 835 Penobscot Bldg., Detroit, MI 48226. TEL 313-961-2242. FAX 313-961-6083.
Vendor(s): DIALOG. *1640*

INTERNATIONAL ROAD HAULAGE BY UNITED KINGDOM REGISTERED VEHICLES.
H.M.S.O., St. Crispin's, Duke St., Norwich NR3 1PD, England. *4745*

SERIALS AVAILABLE ONLINE

INTERNATIONAL SOLAR ENERGY INTELLIGENCE REPORT.
Business Publishers, Inc., 951 Pershing Dr., Silver Spring, MD 20910-4464. TEL 301-587-6300. FAX 301-585-9075.
Vendor(s): Data-Star, DIALOG, NewsNet. *1811*

INTERNATIONAL TAX REPORT.
Eurostudy Publishing Co. Ltd., Ludgate House, 107 Fleet St., London EC4A 2AB, England. TEL 44-71-583-1025. FAX 44-71-583-5958.
Vendor(s): Data-Star, Mead Data Central. *1098*

INTERNATIONAL TRADE FINANCE.
Financial Times Business Information Ltd., Tower House, Southampton St., London WC2E 7HA, England. TEL 071-240 9391. FAX 071-240-7946. *786*

INTERNATIONAL TRADE REPORTER CURRENT REPORTS.
The Bureau of National Affairs, Inc., 1231 25th St., N.W., Washington, DC 20037. TEL 202-452-4200. FAX 202-822-8092.
Vendor(s): Mead Data Central (INTRAD), WESTLAW (BNA-ITR). *913*

INTERNATIONAL VENTURE CAPITAL NETWORK.
High Tech Publishing Company, Box 1923, Brattleboro, VT 05301. TEL 802-254-3539.
Vendor(s): Data-Star, NewsNet. *786*

INTERNATIONALE BIBLIOGRAPHIE DER ZEITSCHRIFTENLITERATUR AUS ALLEN GEBIETEN DES WISSENS.
Felix Dietrich Verlag, Jahnstr. 15, Postfach 1949, 4500 Osnabrueck, Germany. *403*

INTERNATIONALES HANDBUCH - LAENDER AKTUELL.
Munzinger-Archiv GmbH, Hans-Zuericher-Weg 7, 7980 Ravensburg, Germany. TEL 0751-31916. FAX 0751-17261. *3962*

INTER-UNIVERSITY CONSORTIUM FOR POLITICAL AND SOCIAL RESEARCH. GUIDE TO RESOURCES AND SERVICES.
Inter-University Consortium for Political and Social Research, Box 1248, Ann Arbor, MI 48106. TEL 313-764-2570. FAX 313-764-8041. *4376*

INTRAVENOUS THERAPY NEWS.
McMahon Publishing Co., 83 Peaceable St., W. Redding, CT 06896. TEL 203-544-9343. *3209*

INVENTORY OF MARRIAGE AND FAMILY LITERATURE.
National Council on Family Relations, 3989 Central Ave., N.E., Ste. 550, Minneapolis, MN 55421-3921. TEL 612-781-9331. FAX 612-781-9331.
Vendor(s): BRS. *4458*

INVESTING, LICENSING & TRADING CONDITIONS ABROAD: GLOBAL EDITION.
Business International Corp., 215 Park Ave. S., New York, NY 10003. TEL 212-460-0600. FAX 212-995-8837. *914*

INVESTMENT ADVISORS EQUITY CHARACTERISTICS.
C D A Investment Technologies, Inc., 1355 Piccard Dr., Rockville, MD 20850. TEL 301-975-9600. FAX 301-590-1350. *951*

INVESTOR'S DAILY.
Box 25970, Los Angeles, CA 90025.
Vendor(s): Mead Data Central. *952*

INVESTOR'S DIGEST OF CANADA.
M P L Communications Inc., 133 Richmond St. W., Ste. 700, Toronto, Ont. M5H 3M8, Canada. TEL 416-869-1177. FAX 416-869-0456.
Vendor(s): Orbit Information Technologies, QL Systems Ltd.. *952*

IOWA LAW REVIEW.
University of Iowa, College of Law, Iowa City, IA 52242. TEL 319-335-9061.
Vendor(s): WESTLAW. *2637*

IOWA LEGISLATIVE NEWS SERVICE BULLETIN.
Iowa Legislative News Service, Box 8370, Des Moines, IA 50301. TEL 515-288-4676. *4064*

IRISH GEOGRAPHY.
Geographical Society of Ireland, Department of Geography, St. Patrick's College, Maynooth, County Kildare, Ireland. TEL 01-6285222. FAX 01-6289063. *2254*

IRISH JOURNAL OF AGRICULTURAL AND FOOD RESEARCH.
T.E.A.G.A.S.C., 19 Sandymount Ave., Dublin 4, Ireland. TEL 01-688188. FAX 01-688023. *100*

IRISH JOURNAL OF FOOD SCIENCE AND TECHNOLOGY.
T.E.A.G.A.S.C., 19 Sandymount Av., Dublin 4, Ireland. TEL 01-688188. FAX 01-688023. *2074*

IRON AGE.
Hitchcock Publishing 191 S. Gary Ave., Carol Stream, IL 60188. TEL 708-462-2286. FAX 708-462-2225.
Vendor(s): DIALOG. *3409*

IRRIGATION AND DRAINAGE ABSTRACTS.
C.A.B. International, Wallingford, Oxon OX10 8DE, England. TEL 0491 32111. FAX 0491-33508.
Vendor(s): BRS (CABA), CISTI, DIMDI, DIALOG, European Space Agency. *139*

ISRAEL PHARMACEUTICAL JOURNAL.
Pharmaceutical Association of Israel, P.O. Box 566, Tel Aviv 65 112, Israel. *3730*

ISSUES IN BANK REGULATION.
Bank Administration Institute, 1 N. Franklin St., Chicago, IL 60606-3401. TEL 708-228-6200.
Vendor(s): Mead Data Central. *787*

ISSUES IN LAW AND MEDICINE.
National Legal Center for the Medically Dependent and Disabled, Inc., Box 1586, Terre Haute, IN 47808-1586. TEL 812-232-0103.
Vendor(s): National Library of Medicine, WESTLAW. *2637*

ITEM PROCESSING REPORT.
Phillips Publishing, Inc., 7811 Montrose Rd., Potomac, MD 20854. TEL 301-340-2100. FAX 301-309-3847.
Vendor(s): Data-Star, DIALOG, NewsNet. *1452*

IWATE MEDICAL UNIVERSITY SCHOOL OF LIBERAL ARTS & SCIENCES. ANNUAL REPORT.
Iwate Ika Daigaku Kyoyobu, 16-1, 3-chome, Honcho-dori, Morioka-shi, Iwate-ken, Japan.
Vendor(s): JICST (JOIS-III). *4316*

J A M A: THE JOURNAL OF THE AMERICAN MEDICAL ASSOCIATION.
American Medical Association, 515 N. State St., Chicago, IL 60610. TEL 312-464-0183. FAX 312-464-5834.
Vendor(s): BRS (JWAT), Mead Data Central. *3112*

J I C S T ONLINE INFORMATION SYSTEM.
U.S. National Technical Information Service, 5285 Port Royal Rd., Springfield, VA 22161. TEL 703-487-4630.
Available only online. Vendor(s): JICST. *4359*

J P E N: JOURNAL OF PARENTERAL AND ENTERAL NUTRITION.
American Society of Parenteral and Enteral Nutrition, 8630 Fenton St., Ste. 412, Silver Spring, MD 20910-3805. TEL 301-587-6315. FAX 301-587-3323. *3607*

JACK O'DWYER'S NEWSLETTER.
J.R. O'Dwyer Co., Inc., 271 Madison Ave., New York, NY 10016. TEL 212-679-2471. FAX 212-683-2750.
Vendor(s): Mead Data Central. *33*

JANE'S AIRPORT REVIEW.
Jane's Information Group, Sentinel House, 163 Brighton Rd., Coulsdon, Surrey CR5 2NH, England. TEL 081-763-1030. FAX 081-763-1005.
Vendor(s): DIALOG. *4675*

JANE'S DEFENCE WEEKLY.
Jane's Information Group, Sentinel House, 163 Brighton Rd., Coulsdon, Surrey CR5 2NH, England. TEL 081-763-1030. FAX 081-763-1005.
Vendor(s): DIALOG. *3461*

JANE'S INTELLIGENCE REVIEW.
Jane's Information Group, Sentinel House, 163 Brighton Road, Couldsdon, Surrey CR3 2NH, England. TEL 081-763-1030. FAX 081-763-1007.
Vendor(s): DIALOG. *3461*

JAPAN ECONOMIC ALMANAC.
Japan Economic Journal, 1-9-5 Otemachi, Chiyoda-ku, Tokyo 100, Japan. TEL 03-5255-2310. *1079*

JAPAN ECONOMIC DAILY.
Kyodo News International, Inc., 50 Rockefeller Plaza, Ste. 832, New York, NY 10020. TEL 212-586-0152.
Available only online. Vendor(s): Dow Jones/News Retrieval. *870*

JAPAN FREE PRESS.
C T Whipple Co., Riverside E. 4, 1-9-11 Saga, Koto-ku, Tokyo 135, Japan. FAX 03-3643-3091.
Vendor(s): NewsNet. *2207*

JAPAN SOCIETY FOR SIMULATION TECHNOLOGY. JOURNAL.
Japan Technical Information Service, Sogo Kojimachi No. 2 Bldg., 4th Fl., 1-6 Koji-machi, Chiyoda-ku, Tokyo 102, Japan. TEL 03-239-4711. FAX 03-239-4714.
Vendor(s): JICST (JOIS). *1435*

JAPANESE INVESTMENT IN U S REAL ESTATE REVIEW.
Mead Ventures, Inc., Box 44952, Phoenix, AZ 85064. TEL 602-234-0044. FAX 602-234-0076.
Vendor(s): Data-Star, DIALOG, NewsNet. *952*

JAPANESE JOURNAL OF CLINICAL ONCOLOGY.
Foundation for Promotion of Cancer Research, c/o National Cancer Center Hospital, 1-1, Tsukiji 5-chome, Chuo-ku, Tokyo 104, Japan. TEL 03-3542-2511. FAX 03-3542-2511.
Vendor(s): JICST. *3199*

JARDIN BOTANICO DE MADRID. ANALES.
Real Jardin Botanico de Madrid, Plaza de Murillo, 2, 28014 Madrid, Spain. TEL 1-585-5959. FAX 1-420-0157. *506*

JIBI INKOKA, TOKEIBU GEKA.
Igaku-Shoin Ltd., 5-24-3 Hongo, Bunkyo-ku, Tokyo 113-91, Japan. TEL 03-817-5710.
Vendor(s): JICST. *3315*

JOB SAFETY & HEALTH (WASHINGTON).
The Bureau of National Affairs, Inc., 1231 25th St., N.W., Washington, DC 20037. TEL 202-452-4200. FAX 202-822-8092.
Vendor(s): Human Resources Information Network (CDD, HDD). *3618*

JOHN MARSHALL LAW REVIEW.
Christensen Inc. (Chicago), 315 S. Plymouth Ct., Chicago, IL 60604. TEL 312-987-1415. FAX 312-427-8307.
Vendor(s): WESTLAW. *2638*

JOURNAL DE MEDECINE LEGALE DROIT MEDICAL.
Masson, 120 bd. Saint-Germain, 75280 Paris Cedex 06, France. TEL 1-46-34-21-60. FAX 1-45-87-29-99. *3265*

JOURNAL DE PHARMACIE DE BELGIQUE.
Masson, 120 bd. Saint-Germain, 75280 Paris Cedex 06, France. TEL 1-46-34-21-60. FAX 1-45-87-29-99. *3730*

JOURNAL OF AGRICULTURAL AND FOOD CHEMISTRY.
American Chemical Society, 1155 16th St., N.W., Washington, DC 20036. TEL 800-333-9511. FAX 202-872-4615.
Vendor(s): STN International (CJACS). *182*

JOURNAL OF AIR LAW AND COMMERCE.
Southern Methodist University, School of Law, Dallas, TX 75275. TEL 214-692-2570. FAX 214-692-4330.
Vendor(s): WESTLAW. *2638*

JOURNAL OF ALLERGY AND CLINICAL IMMUNOLOGY.
Mosby - Year Book, Inc. 11830 Westline Industrial Dr., St. Louis, MO 63146. TEL 800-325-4117. FAX 314-432-1380.
Vendor(s): BRS. *3187*

JOURNAL OF ANALYTICAL ATOMIC SPECTROMETRY.
Royal Society of Chemistry, Thomas Graham House, Science Park, Milton Rd., Cambridge CB4 4WF, England. TEL 0462-672555. FAX 0462-480947.
Vendor(s): STN International (CJRSC). *1206*

JOURNAL OF APPLIED POLYMER SCIENCE.
John Wiley & Sons, Inc., Journals, 605 Third Ave., New York, NY 10158-0012. TEL 212-692-6000.
Vendor(s): STN International (CJWILEY). *1855*

JOURNAL OF BONE AND JOINT SURGERY: AMERICAN VOLUME.
Journal of Bone and Joint Surgery, Inc., 10 Shattuck St., Boston, MA 02115. TEL 617-734-2835.
Vendor(s): BRS, BRS/Saunders Colleague. *3309*

JOURNAL OF CELLULAR BIOCHEMISTRY.
John Wiley & Sons, Inc., Journals, 605 Third Ave., New York, NY 10158. TEL 212-850-6000.
FAX 212-850-6088. *525*

JOURNAL OF CELLULAR PHYSIOLOGY.
John Wiley & Sons, Inc., Journals, 605 Third Ave., New York, NY 10158. TEL 212-850-6000.
FAX 212-850-6088. *572*

JOURNAL OF CHEMICAL AND ENGINEERING DATA.
American Chemical Society, 1155 16th St. N.W., Washington, DC 20036. TEL 800-333-9511.
FAX 202-872-4615.
Vendor(s): STN International (CJACS). *1180*

JOURNAL OF CHEMICAL INFORMATION AND COMPUTER SCIENCES.
American Chemical Society, 1155 16th St. N.W., Washington, DC 20036. TEL 800-333-9511.
FAX 202-872-4615.
Vendor(s): STN International (CJACS). *4360*

JOURNAL OF CHEMICAL RESEARCH.
Royal Society of Chemistry, Thomas Graham House, Science Park, Milton Rd., Cambridge CB4 4WF, England. TEL 0462-672555. FAX 0462-480947.
Vendor(s): STN International (CJRSC). *1180*

JOURNAL OF CLINICAL EPIDEMIOLOGY.
Pergamon Press, Inc., Journals Division, 660 White Plains Rd., Tarrytown, NY 10591-5153. TEL 914-524-9200. FAX 914-333-2444. *3114*

JOURNAL OF CLINICAL INVESTIGATION.
Rockefeller University Press, 222 E. 70th St., New York, NY 10021. TEL 212-570-8572. FAX 212-570-7944.
Vendor(s): BRS. *3114*

JOURNAL OF CLINICAL ONCOLOGY.
W.B. Saunders Co. Curtis Center, Independence Square W., Philadelphia, PA 19106. TEL 215-238-7800. *3199*

JOURNAL OF CLINICAL PATHOLOGY.
British Medical Association, B.M.A. House, Tavistock Sq., London WC1H 9JR, England. TEL 071-387-4499.
Vendor(s): BRS, BRS/Saunders Colleague. *3115*

JOURNAL OF CLINICAL PHARMACOLOGY.
J.B. Lippincott Co., E. Washington Sq., Philadelphia, PA 19105. TEL 215-238-4225. *3731*

JOURNAL OF CLINICAL PHARMACY AND THERAPEUTICS.
Blackwell Scientific Publications Ltd., Osney Mead, Oxford OX2 0EL, England. TEL 0865-240201.
FAX 0865-721205. *3731*

JOURNAL OF COLD REGIONS ENGINEERING.
American Society of Civil Engineers, 345 E. 47th St., New York, NY 10017-2398. TEL 212-705-7288. FAX 212-980-4681. *1869*

JOURNAL OF COMMERCE AND COMMERCIAL.
Journal of Commerce, Inc., 2 World Trade Center, 27th Fl., New York, NY 10048-0203. TEL 212-837-7000. FAX 212-837-7035.
Vendor(s): DIALOG, VU/TEXT Information Services, Inc.. *837*

JOURNAL OF CONSUMER AFFAIRS.
American Council on Consumer Interests, 240 Stanley Hall, University of Missouri, Columbia, MO 65211. TEL 314-882-3817.
Vendor(s): DIALOG. *1505*

JOURNAL OF CONSUMER RESEARCH.
University of Chicago Press, Journals Division, 5720 S. Woodlawn Ave., Chicago, IL 60637. TEL 312-702-7600. FAX 312-702-0694.
Vendor(s): DIALOG. *1042*

JOURNAL OF CORPORATION LAW.
University of Iowa, College of Law, Iowa City, IA 52242. TEL 319-335-9061.
Vendor(s): WESTLAW. *2710*

JOURNAL OF CRANIOFACIAL GENETICS AND DEVELOPMENTAL BIOLOGY.
Munksgaard International Publishers Ltd., P.O. Box 2148, DK-1016 Copenhagen K, Denmark. TEL 45-33-12-70-30. FAX 45-33-12-93-87. *544*

JOURNAL OF CRIMINAL LAW & CRIMINOLOGY.
Northwestern University, School of Law, 357 E. Chicago Ave., Chicago, IL 60611. TEL 312-503-8467.
Vendor(s): WESTLAW. *1516*

JOURNAL OF DEVELOPMENT STUDIES.
Frank Cass & Co. Ltd., Gainsborough House, 11 Gainsborough Rd., London E11 1RS, England.
TEL 081-530-4226. FAX 081-530-7795.
Vendor(s): Information Access Company. *932*

JOURNAL OF DRUG EDUCATION.
Baywood Publishing Co., Inc., 26 Austin Ave., Box 337, Amityville, NY 11701. TEL 516-691-1270.
FAX 516-691-1770. *1537*

JOURNAL OF DRUG ISSUES.
Journal of Drug Issues Inc., Box 4021, Leon Station, Tallahassee, FL 32303. *1537*

JOURNAL OF DRUG RESEARCH OF EGYPT.
National Organisation for Drug Control and Research, Drug Research and Control Center, 6, Abou-Hazem St., Pyramids Ave., Box 29, Cairo, Egypt. *3731*

JOURNAL OF ECONOMIC LITERATURE.
American Economic Association, 2014 Broadway, Ste. 305, Nashville, TN 37203. TEL 615-322-2595.
Vendor(s): DIALOG (Economic Literature Index File no. 139). *725*

JOURNAL OF EXPERIMENTAL ZOOLOGY.
John Wiley & Sons, Inc., Journals, 605 Third Ave., New York, NY 10158. TEL 212-850-6000.
FAX 212-850-6000. *586*

JOURNAL OF FAMILY HISTORY.
J A I Press Inc., 55 Old Post Rd., No. 2, Box 1678, Greenwich, CT 06836-1678. TEL 203-661-7602.
FAX 612-781-9348.
Vendor(s): BRS. *4440*

JOURNAL OF FAMILY ISSUES.
Sage Publications, Inc., 2455 Teller Rd., Newbury Park, CA 91320. TEL 805-499-0721. FAX 805-499-0871.
Vendor(s): BRS. *4440*

JOURNAL OF FAMILY PRACTICE.
Appleton & Lange, Journal Division, 25 Van Zant St., Box 5630, Norwalk, CT 06855. TEL 203-838-4400. *3115*

JOURNAL OF FINANCIAL MANAGEMENT AND ANALYSIS.
Om Sai Ram Centre for Financial Management Research and Training, 15 Prakash Co-operative Housing Society, Relief Rd., Juhu, Santacruz (W.), Bombay 400 054, India. TEL 91-22-6121715. *788*

JOURNAL OF GERONTOLOGICAL NURSING.
Slack, Inc., 6900 Grove Rd., Thorofare, NJ 08086. TEL 609-848-1000. FAX 609-853-5991. *2275*

JOURNAL OF INDIGENOUS STUDIES.
Gabriel Dumont Institute of Native Studies and Applied Research, 121 Broadway Ave., E., Regina, Sask. S4N 0Z6, Canada. TEL 306-522-5691.
FAX 306-565-0809. *243*

JOURNAL OF INFECTION.
Academic Press Ltd., 24-28 Oval Rd., London, NW1 7DX, England. TEL 071-267-4466. FAX 071-482-2293. *3221*

JOURNAL OF INFECTIOUS DISEASES.
University of Chicago Press, Journals Division, 5720 S. Woodlawn Ave., Chicago, IL 60637. TEL 312-753-3347. FAX 312-702-0694.
Vendor(s): BRS (JWAT). *3221*

JOURNAL OF INVESTIGATIVE DERMATOLOGY.
Elsevier Science Publishing Co., Inc. (New York), 655 Ave. of the Americas, New York, NY 10010.
TEL 212-989-5800. FAX 212-633-3965. *3248*

JOURNAL OF LABORATORY AND CLINICAL MEDICINE.
Mosby - Year Book, Inc. 11830 Westline Industrial Dr., St. Louis, MO 63146. TEL 800-325-4117.
FAX 314-432-1380.
Vendor(s): BRS. *3260*

JOURNAL OF LAW & COMMERCE.
University of Pittsburgh, School of Law, 3900 Forbes Ave., Pittsburgh, PA 15260. TEL 412-648-1361. FAX 412-648-2649.
Vendor(s): WESTLAW. *2710*

JOURNAL OF LEUKOCYTE BIOLOGY.
John Wiley & Sons, Inc., Journals, 605 Third Ave., New York, NY 10158. TEL 212-850-6000.
FAX 212-850-6088. *3116*

JOURNAL OF MARRIAGE AND THE FAMILY.
National Council on Family Relations, 3989 Central Ave., N.E., Ste. 550, Minneapolis, MN 55421-3921. TEL 612-781-9331. FAX 612-781-9348.
Vendor(s): BRS. *4440*

JOURNAL OF MEDICAL AND PHARMACEUTICAL MARKETING.
Fred Atoki Publishing Co. Ltd., Plot 25 Kekere-Ekun St., Orile Iganmu, Box 7313, Lagos, Nigeria. *1043*

JOURNAL OF MEDICAL VIROLOGY.
John Wiley & Sons, Inc., Journals, 605 Third Ave., New York, NY 10158. TEL 212-850-6000.
FAX 212-850-6088. *3117*

JOURNAL OF MEDICINAL CHEMISTRY.
American Chemical Society, 1155 16th St., N.W., Washington, DC 20036. TEL 800-333-9511.
FAX 202-872-4615.
Vendor(s): STN International (CJACS). *3732*

JOURNAL OF MONEY, CREDIT & BANKING.
Ohio State University Press, 1070 Carmack Rd., Columbus, OH 43210. TEL 614-292-6930.
Vendor(s): Information Access Company. *788*

JOURNAL OF MORMON HISTORY.
Mormon History Association, Box 7010, University Sta., Provo, UT 84602. FAX 801-378-4048.
Vendor(s): DIALOG (File nos.38,39). *4284*

JOURNAL OF NATURAL PRODUCTS.
American Society of Pharmacognosy, c/o David J. Slatkin, Treasurer, Chicago School of Pharmacy, 555 31st St., Downers Grove, IL 60515. TEL 708-971-6417. FAX 708-971-6097. *3732*

JOURNAL OF NERVOUS AND MENTAL DISEASE.
Williams & Wilkins, 428 E. Preston St., Baltimore, MD 21202. TEL 301-528-4000. FAX 301-528-4312.
Vendor(s): Mead Data Central. *3342*

JOURNAL OF NEUROLOGY, NEUROSURGERY AND PSYCHIATRY.
B M J Publishing Group, B.M.A. House, Tavistock Sq., London WC1H 9JR, England. TEL 071-387-4499.
Vendor(s): BRS. *3342*

JOURNAL OF NUCLEAR MEDICINE.
Society of Nuclear Medicine, 136 Madison Ave., New York, NY 10016. TEL 212-889-0717.
FAX 212-545-0221. *3359*

JOURNAL OF NUCLEAR MEDICINE TECHNOLOGY.
Society of Nuclear Medicine, 136 Madison Ave., New York, NY 10016. TEL 212-889-0717.
FAX 212-545-0221. *3360*

JOURNAL OF ORGANIC CHEMISTRY.
American Chemical Society, 1155 16th St., N.W., Washington, DC 20036. TEL 202-872-4363.
FAX 202-872-4615.
Vendor(s): STN International (CJACS). *1219*

JOURNAL OF ORGANOMETALLIC CHEMISTRY.
Elsevier Sequoia S.A., P.O. Box 564, CH-1001 Lausanne, Switzerland. TEL 021-207381. FAX 021-235444.
Vendor(s): STN International. *1219*

JOURNAL OF PARENTERAL SCIENCE AND TECHNOLOGY.
Parenteral Drug Association, Inc., One Penn Center, 1617 JFK Blvd., Philadelphia, PA 19103. TEL 215-564-6466. FAX 215-564-6472. *3732*

JOURNAL OF PEDIATRIC SURGERY.
W.B. Saunders Co, Curtis Center, Independence Square W., Philadelphia, PA 19106. TEL 215-238-7800.
Vendor(s): Mead Data Central. *3380*

JOURNAL OF PEDIATRICS.
Mosby - Year Book, Inc. 11830 Westline Industrial Dr., St. Louis, MO 63146. TEL 800-325-4117. FAX 314-432-1380.
Vendor(s): BRS. *3322*

JOURNAL OF PHARMACEUTICAL SCIENCES.
American Pharmaceutical Association, 2215 Constitution Ave., N.W., Washington, DC 20037. TEL 202-628-4410. FAX 202-783-2351. *3732*

JOURNAL OF PHARMACOLOGY AND EXPERIMENTAL THERAPEUTICS.
Williams & Wilkins, 428 Preston St., Baltimore, MD 21202. TEL 301-528-4000. FAX 301-528-4312. *3733*

JOURNAL OF PHYSICAL CHEMISTRY.
American Chemical Society, 1155 16th St., N.W., Washington, DC 20036. TEL 202-872-4363. FAX 202-872-4615.
Vendor(s): STN International (CJACS). *1228*

JOURNAL OF PINEAL RESEARCH.
Munksgaard International Publishers Ltd., P.O. Box 2148, DK-1016 Copenhagen K, Denmark. TEL 45-33-12-70-30. FAX 45-33-12-70-30. *3343*

JOURNAL OF PLANNING AND ENVIRONMENT LAW.
Sweet & Maxwell, South Quay Plaza, 8th Floor, 183 Marsh Wall, London E14 9FT, England. TEL 071-538-8686. FAX 071-538-9508. *2640*

JOURNAL OF POLYMER SCIENCE. PART A: POLYMER CHEMISTRY.
John Wiley & Sons, Inc., Journals, 605 Third Ave., New York, NY 10158-0012. TEL 212-850-6000. FAX 212-850-6088.
Vendor(s): STN International (CJWILEY). *1219*

JOURNAL OF POLYMER SCIENCE. PART B: POLYMER PHYSICS.
John Wiley & Sons, Inc., Journals, 605 Third Ave., New York, NY 10158-0012. TEL 212-850-6000. FAX 212-850-6088.
Vendor(s): STN International (CJWILEY). *1219*

JOURNAL OF POLYMER SCIENCE. POLYMER SYMPOSIA EDITION.
John Wiley & Sons, Inc., Journals, 605 Third Ave., New York, NY 10158-0012. TEL 212-850-6000. FAX 212-850-6088.
Vendor(s): STN International. *1219*

JOURNAL OF PORTFOLIO MANAGEMENT.
Institutional Investor, Inc., Circulation Department, 488 Madison Ave., 15th Fl., New York, NY 10022. TEL 212-303-3570. FAX 212-421-3592.
Vendor(s): Mead Data Central. *953*

JOURNAL OF PSYCHOLOGY AND THEOLOGY.
Biola University, Rosemead School of Psychology, 13800 Biola Ave., La Mirada, CA 90639. TEL 213-903-6000.
Vendor(s): BRS, DIALOG. *4032*

JOURNAL OF RETAILING.
New York University, 202 Tisch Bldg., Washington Sq., New York, NY 10003. TEL 212-998-4153.
Vendor(s): DIALOG. *1044*

JOURNAL OF RISK AND INSURANCE.
American Risk and Insurance Association, c/o Dr. Patricia Cheshier, Executive Director, Clifornia State University, Sacramento, School of Business, BUS-3059, 6000 J Street, Sacramento, CA 95819-6088.
Vendor(s): DIALOG. *2536*

JOURNAL OF SMALL BUSINESS MANAGEMENT.
West Virginia University, Bureau of Business Research, Box 6025, Morgantown, WV 26506-6025. TEL 304-293-7534.
Vendor(s): Information Access Company. *1116*

JOURNAL OF SURGICAL ONCOLOGY.
John Wiley & Sons, Inc., Journals, 605 Third Ave., New York, NY 10158. TEL 212-850-6000. FAX 212-850-6088. *3381*

JOURNAL OF TECHNOLOGY TRANSFER.
Technology Transfer Society, 611 N. Capitol Ave., Indianapolis, IN 46204.
Vendor(s): BRS, DIALOG. *4602*

JOURNAL OF THE CHEMICAL SOCIETY. CHEMICAL COMMUNICATIONS.
Royal Society of Chemistry, Thomas Graham House, Science Park, Milton Rd., Cambridge CB4 4WF, England. TEL 0462-672555. FAX 0462-480947.
Vendor(s): STN International (CJRSC). *1181*

JOURNAL OF TOXICOLOGY: CLINICAL TOXICOLOGY.
Marcel Dekker Journals, 270 Madison Ave., New York, NY 10016. TEL 212-696-9000. FAX 212-685-4540. *1982*

JOURNAL RECORD.
Journal Record Publishing Co., 621 N. Robinson Ave., Box 26370, Oklahoma City, OK 73126-0370. TEL 405-235-3100. FAX 405-278-6907. *675*

JUDICATURE.
American Judicature Society, 25 E. Washington, Ste. 1600, Chicago, IL 60602-1805.
Vendor(s): WESTLAW. *2732*

JUDICIAL CONDUCT REPORTER.
American Judicature Society, Center for Judicial Conduct Organizations, 25 E. Washington, Ste. 1600, Chicago, IL 60602. TEL 312-558-6900. FAX 312-558-9175.
Vendor(s): WESTLAW. *2732*

KAGAKU GIJUTSU BUNKEN SOKUHO. DOBOKU, KENCHIKU KOGAKU HEN.
Japan Information Center of Science and Technology, 5-2 Nagata-cho, 2-chome, Chiyoda-ku, Tokyo 100, Japan. TEL 03-3581-6411. FAX 03-3581-6446.
Vendor(s): JICST. *1845*

KALEIDOSCOPE: CURRENT WORLD DATA.
A B C-Clio, 130 Cremona, Box 1911, Santa Barbara, CA 93116-1911. TEL 805-968-1911. FAX 805-685-9685.
Vendor(s): DIALOG, Mead Data Central. *3963*

KANSAS BUSINESS NEWS.
Chuck Henry Publications, Inc., RR 1 Box 149A, Augusta, KS 67010-9745. TEL 316-733-0088.
Vendor(s): DIALOG. *871*

KANSAS CITY BUSINESS JOURNAL.
American City Business Journals, Inc. (Kansas City), 324 E. 11th St., Ste. 800, Kansas City, MO 64106-2417. TEL 816-561-5900. FAX 816-753-2012.
Vendor(s): Mead Data Central, VU/TEXT Information Services, Inc.. *871*

KATALOG FOR SKOLEBIBLIOTEKER. SKOLEBIBLIOTEKARENS.
Bibliotekscentralen, Tempovej 7-11, DK-2750 Ballerup, Denmark. *404*

KATALOG FOR SKOLEBIBLIOTEKER. TITELKATALOG.
Bibliotekscentralen, Tempovej 7-11, DK-2750 Ballerup, Denmark. TEL 2-974000. FAX 2-655310. *404*

KEESING'S RECORD OF WORLD EVENTS.
Longman Group UK Ltd., Westgate House, The High, Harlow, Essex CM20 1YR, England. TEL 0279 442601. *3938*

KELLY'S BUSINESS DIRECTORY.
Kelly's Directories Windsor Court, East Grinstead House, East Grinstead, W. Sussex RH19 1XB, England. TEL 0342-326972. FAX 0342-315130. *1141*

KELLY'S UNITED KINGDOM EXPORTS DIRECTORY.
Kelly's Directories, Windsor Court, East Grinstead House, East Grinstead, West Sussex RH19 1XA, England. TEL 0342-326972. FAX 0342-315130. *1141*

KENTUCKY BUSINESS LEDGER.
Kentucky Communications, Inc., Box 470867, Charlotte, NC 28247.
Vendor(s): DIALOG. *676*

KENTUCKY LAW JOURNAL.
University of Kentucky, College of Law, Lexington, KY 40506. TEL 606-257-4747. FAX 606-258-1061.
Vendor(s): WESTLAW. *2642*

KERTGAZDASAG.
Agroinform, Atilla ut 93, 1012 Budapest 1, Hungary. TEL 156-8211. FAX 156-886. *2133*

KEXUE.
Shanghai Scientific and Technical Publishers, Journal Department, 450 Ruijin 2 Lu, Shanghai 200020, People's Republic of China. *4320*

KEY ABSTRACTS - BUSINESS AUTOMATION.
INSPEC, I.E.E., Michael Faraday House, Six Hill Way, Stevenage, Herts. SG1 2AY, England. TEL 0438-313311. FAX 0438-742840.
Vendor(s): BRS, CEDOCAR, CISTI, Data-Star, DIALOG (File nos.12 & 13/INSPEC), European Space Agency (File no.8/INSPEC), JICST, Orbit Information Technologies (INSPEC), STN International (INSPEC), University of Tsukuba. *1404*

KEY BRITISH ENTERPRISES.
Dun & Bradstreet Ltd., Holmers Farm Way, High Wycombe, Bucks HP12 4UL, England. *676*

KEY TO ECONOMIC SCIENCE.
Kluwer Academic Publishers, P.O. Box 17, 3300 AA Dordrecht, Netherlands. TEL 078-334911. FAX 078-334254.
Vendor(s): BELINDIS, Data-Star, DIALOG. *726*

KHIMIKO-FARMATSEVTICHESKII ZHURNAL.
Izdatel'stvo Meditsina, Petroverigskii pereulok 6-8, 101838 Moscow, Russia. *3733*

KIPLINGER'S PERSONAL FINANCE.
Kiplinger Washington Editors, Inc., 1729 H St., N.W., Washington, DC 20006. TEL 202-887-6400. FAX 202-331-1206.
Vendor(s): DIALOG. *1506*

KOKYO TO JUNKAN.
Igaku-Shoin Ltd., 5-24-3 Hongo, Bunkyo-ku, Tokyo 113-91, Japan. TEL 03-817-5703.
Vendor(s): JICST. *3365*

KOMPASS BELGIUM.
Kompass Belgium S.A., Av. Moliere 256, 1060 Brussels, Belgium. TEL 02-3451983. FAX 02-3473340. *1142*

KOMPASS SVERIGE.
Kompass Sweden, Saltmaetargatan 8, Box 3223, 10364 Stockholm, Sweden. FAX 08-311898. *1142*

KOMPASS UNITED KINGDOM.
Kompass Windsor Court, E. Grinstead House, E. Grinstead, W. Sussex RH19 1XD, England. TEL 0342-326972. FAX 0342-317241. *1142*

KONSUMENTRAETT OCH EKONOMI.
Konsumentverket, Sorterargatan 26, P.O. Box 503, S-162 15 Vaellingby, Sweden. TEL 08-759-8300. FAX 08-7598529. *1506*

KOREA AUTOMOTIVE REVIEW.
Mead Ventures, Inc., Box 44952, Phoenix, AZ 85064. TEL 602-234-0044. FAX 602-234-0076.
Vendor(s): Data-Star, DIALOG, NewsNet. *4694*

KUKA KUKIN ON.
Kustannusosakeyhtio Otava, Uudenmaankatu 10, SF-00120 Helsinki, Finland. FAX 358-0-643086. *419*

L A N PRODUCT NEWS.
Worldwide Videotex, Box 138, Babson Park, Boston, MA 02157.
Vendor(s): Data-Star, DIALOG, NewsNet. *1427*

L A N TIMES.
McGraw-Hill, Inc., 1221 Ave. of the Americas, New York, NY 10020. TEL 212-512-2000. FAX 801-565-5837.
Vendor(s): DIALOG, Dow Jones/News Retrieval, Mead Data Central. *1470*

L I N K LINE.
Planned Parenthood Federation of America, Inc., 810 Seventh Ave., New York, NY 10019. TEL 212-261-4638. FAX 212-247-6269. *597*

LABOR ARBITRATION AND DISPUTE SETTLEMENTS.
The Bureau of National Affairs, Inc., 1231 25th St., N.W., Washington, DC 20037. TEL 201-452-4200. FAX 202-822-8092.
Vendor(s): DIALOG (File no.244). *2643*

LABOR - MANAGEMENT RELATIONS ANALYSIS.
The Bureau of National Affairs, Inc., 1231 25th St., N.W., Washington, DC 20037. TEL 202-452-4200. FAX 202-822-8092.
Vendor(s): WESTLAW (File LLR-NEWS). *985*

LABOR RELATIONS WEEK.
The Bureau of National Affairs, Inc., 1231 25th St., N.W., Washington, DC 20037. TEL 202-452-4200. FAX 202-822-8092.
Vendor(s): Human Resources Information Network (CDD, HDD). *986*

LABORATORY HAZARDS BULLETIN.
Royal Society of Chemistry, Thomas Graham House, Science Park, Milton Rd., Cambridge CB4 4WF, England. TEL 0462-672555. FAX 0462-480947.
Vendor(s): Data-Star (CSNB), DIALOG (File no.317), European Space Agency (File no.90/LABORATORY HAZARDS BULLETIN), STN International (LHB). *3618*

LABOUR ARBITRATION CASES.
Canada Law Book Inc., 240 Edward St., Aurora, Ont. L4G 3S9, Canada. TEL 416-841-6472. *986*

LACROSSETALK.
All England Women's Lacrosse Association, 4 Western Ct., Bromley St., Digbeth, Birmingham 9, England. TEL 021-7734422. *4507*

LADIES HOME JOURNAL (INKPRINT EDITION).
Meredith Corporation, Special Interest Publications, 1716 Locust St., Des Moines, IA 50336. TEL 515-284-3000.
Vendor(s): DIALOG. *4846*

LANCET.
Lancet Ltd., 46 Bedford Square, London WC1B 3SL, England. TEL 01-436-4981. FAX 01-436-7550.
Vendor(s): BRS, BRS/Saunders Colleague. *3121*

LAND USE LAW REPORT.
Business Publishers, Inc., 951 Pershing Dr., Silver Spring, MD 20910-4464. TEL 301-587-6300. FAX 301-585-9075.
Vendor(s): NewsNet (EV02). *2491*

LANDBRUGETS MASKINOVERSIGT.
Landsudvalget for Bygninger og Maskiner, Udkaersvej 15, Skejby, DK-8200 Aarhus N., Denmark. TEL 45-86-10-90-88. FAX 45-86-10-97-00. *163*

LANGMUIR.
American Chemical Society, 1155 16th St., N.W., Washington, DC 20036. TEL 800-333-9511. FAX 202-872-4615.
Vendor(s): STN International (CJACS). *1228*

LASERS IN MEDICINE.
Excerpta Medica, P.O. Box 548, 1000 AM Amsterdam, Netherlands. TEL 020-5803911. FAX 020-5803222.
Vendor(s): BRS, DIMDI, Data-Star, DIALOG. *3177*

LATIN AMERICA REGIONAL REPORTS - BRAZIL.
Lettres (UK) Ltd., 61 Old St., London EC1V 9HX, England. TEL 071-251-0012. FAX 071-253-8193.
Vendor(s): Mead Data Central. *872*

LATIN AMERICA REGIONAL REPORTS - CARIBBEAN.
Lettres (UK) Ltd., 61 Old St., London EC1V 9HX, England. TEL 071-251-0012. FAX 071-253-8193.
Vendor(s): Mead Data Central. *872*

LATIN AMERICA REGIONAL REPORTS - MEXICO & CENTRAL AMERICA.
Lettres (UK) Ltd., 61 Old St., London EC1V 9HX, England. TEL 071-251-0012. FAX 071-253-8193.
Vendor(s): Mead Data Central. *872*

LATIN AMERICA WEEKLY REPORT.
Lettres (UK) Ltd., 61 Old St., London EC1V 9HX, England. TEL 071-251-0012. FAX 071-253-8193.
Vendor(s): Mead Data Central. *872*

LATIN AMERICAN REGIONAL REPORTS - ANDEAN GROUP.
Lettres (UK) Ltd., 61 Old St., London EC1V 9HX, England. TEL 071-251-0012. FAX 071-253-8193.
Vendor(s): Mead Data Central. *872*

LATIN AMERICAN REGIONAL REPORTS - SOUTHERN CONE.
Letter (UK) Ltd., 61 Old St., London EC1V 9HX, England. TEL 251-0012. FAX 253-8193.
Vendor(s): Mead Data Central. *872*

LAW & BUSINESS DIRECTORY OF CORPORATE COUNSEL.
Law & Business, Inc. 270 Sylvan Ave., Englewood Cliffs, NJ 07632. TEL 201-894-8484.
Vendor(s): WESTLAW. *2711*

LAW AND POLICY IN INTERNATIONAL BUSINESS.
Georgetown University Law Center, 600 New Jersey Ave., N.W., Washington, DC 20001. TEL 202-662-9468.
Vendor(s): WESTLAW. *2726*

LAW OFFICE TECHNOLOGY REVIEW.
2640 W. 183 St., Box 2577, Homewood, IL 60430. TEL 708-957-3322. FAX 708-957-3337.
Vendor(s): NewsNet. *2705*

LAW PRACTICE MANAGEMENT.
American Bar Association, Law Practice Management Section, 750 N. Lake Shore Dr., Chicago, IL 60611. TEL 312-988-5000.
Vendor(s): Mead Data Central, WESTLAW. *2645*

LEAD AND ZINC STATISTICS.
International Lead and Zinc Study Group, 58 St. James's St., London SW1A 1LD, England. TEL 071-499-9373. FAX 071-493-3725. *3427*

LEADERSHIP IN HEALTH SERVICES.
Canadian Hospital Association, 17 York St., Suite 100, Ottawa, Ont. K1N 9J6, Canada. TEL 613-238-8005. FAX 613-238-6924. *2467*

LEFT BUSINESS OBSERVER.
Doug Henwood, Ed. & Pub., 250 W. 85th St., New York, NY 10024. TEL 212-874-4020. *677*

LEGAL RESOURCE INDEX.
Information Access Company, 362 Lakeside Dr., Foster City, CA 94404. TEL 800-227-8431. FAX 415-378-5499.
Vendor(s): BRS (LAWS), DIALOG (File no.150), Mead Data Central (LGLIND), WESTLAW (LRI). *2700*

LEGAL SERVICE BULLETIN.
Legal Service Bulletin Co., Ltd., c/o Monash University, Faculty of Law, Wellington Rd., Clayton, Vic. 3168, Australia. TEL 64-3-544-0974. FAX 64-3-565-5305. *2648*

LEGAL TIMES.
American Lawyer Newspapers Group, Inc. (Washington), 1730 M St., N.W., Ste. 802, Washington, DC 20036. TEL 202-457-0686. FAX 202-457-0718.
Vendor(s): Mead Data Central. *2648*

LEGISLATIVE NETWORK FOR NURSES.
Business Publishers, Inc., 951 Pershing Dr., Silver Spring, MD 20910-4464. TEL 301-587-6300. FAX 301-585-9075.
Vendor(s): NewsNet. *3281*

LEISURE FUTURES.
Henley Centre for Forecasting Ltd., 2 Tudor St., Blackfriars, London EC4Y 0AA, England. TEL 071-3535-9961. *2739*

LEISURE INTELLIGENCE.
Mintel International Group Ltd., 18-19 Long Lane, London EC1A 9HE, England. TEL 071-606-4533. FAX 071-606-5159. *2739*

LEISURE, RECREATION AND TOURISM ABSTRACTS.
C.A.B. International, Wallingford, Oxon OX10 8DE, England. TEL 0491-32111. FAX 0491-33508.
Vendor(s): BRS (TOUR), CISTI, DIMDI, DIALOG, European Space Agency (File nos.16 & 124/CAB). *4799*

LENTILS.
C.A.B. International, Wallingford, Oxon OX10 8DE, England. TEL 800-528-4841, 0491-32111. FAX 0491-33508.
Vendor(s): BRS (CABA), CISTI, DIMDI, DIALOG, European Space Agency (File nos. 16 & 124/CAB). *140*

LETTER TO LIBRARIES ONLINE.
Oregon State Library, Salem, OR 97310-0640. TEL 503-378-2112. FAX 503-588-7119.
Available only online. *2798*

LIBRARY & INFORMATION SCIENCE ABSTRACTS.
Bowker-Saur Ltd., 59-60 Grosvenor St., London W1X 9DA, England. TEL 071-493-5841. FAX 071-499-1590.
Vendor(s): BRS (LISA), DIALOG (File no.61/LISA), Orbit Information Technologies (LISA). *2794*

LIBRARY LITERATURE.
H.W. Wilson Co., 950 University Ave., Bronx, NY 10452. TEL 800-367-6770. FAX 212-538-2716.
Vendor(s): BRS, BRS/Saunders Colleague, Wilsonline (File LIB). *2794*

LIBROS ESPANOLES EN VENTA.
Ministerio de Cultura, Centro del Libro y de la Lectura, Santiago Rusinol, 8, 28040 Madrid, Spain. TEL 553-93-29. FAX 553-99-90. *405*

LICENSED PRACTICAL NURSE.
McClain Publishing Co., Box 10619, Charlotte, NC 28212-5677. *3281*

LIFE (NEW YORK).
The Time Inc. Magazine Company Time & Life Bldg., Rockefeller Center, 1271 Ave. of the Americas, New York, NY 10020. TEL 212-522-1212. FAX 212-522-0379.
Vendor(s): DIALOG, Mead Data Central, VU/TEXT Information Services, Inc.. *2228*

LIMITED PARTNERSHIP INVESTMENT REVIEW.
Limited Partnership Investment Review, Inc., 55 Morris Ave., Springfield, NJ 07081. TEL 201-467-8700. FAX 201-467-0368.
Vendor(s): NewsNet. *1100*

LINGUISTIC INQUIRY.
M I T Press, 55 Hayward St., Cambridge, MA 02142. TEL 617-253-2889. FAX 617-258-6779. *2826*

LINGUISTICS AND LANGUAGE BEHAVIOR ABSTRACTS.
Sociological Abstracts, Inc., Box 22206, San Diego, CA 92192. TEL 619-695-8803. FAX 619-695-0416.
Vendor(s): BRS (LLBA), DIALOG (File no.36/LLBA). *2855*

LINK-UP.
Learned Information, Inc., 143 Old Marlton Pike, Medford, NJ 08055. TEL 609-654-6266. FAX 609-654-4309.
Vendor(s): Mead Data Central. *1447*

LIST OF SCIENTIFIC AND TECHNICAL LITERATURE RELATING TO THAILAND.
Thailand Institute of Scientific and Technological Research, 196 Phahonyothin Rd., Chatuchak, Bangkok 10900, Thailand. TEL 579-4929. FAX 662-579-8594. *4356*

LIST OF SERIALS INDEXED FOR ONLINE USERS.
U.S. National Library of Medicine, 8600 Rockville Pike, Bethesda, MD 20894. TEL 301-496-6308. FAX 301-496-4450.
Vendor(s): National Library of Medicine. *3177*

LITERATURE ABSTRACTS.
American Petroleum Institute, Central Abstracting & Information Services, 275 Seventh Ave., New York, NY 10001-6708. TEL 212-366-4040. FAX 212-366-4298.
Vendor(s): DIALOG, STN International. *3706*

LITERATURE ABSTRACTS: CATALYSTS & CATALYSIS.
American Petroleum Institute, Central Abstracting & Information Services, 275 Seventh Ave., New York, NY 10001. TEL 212-366-4040. FAX 212-366-4298.
Vendor(s): DIALOG, Orbit Information Technologies (APILIT). *1202*

LITERATURE AND PATENT ABSTRACTS: OILFIELD CHEMICALS.
American Petroleum Institute, Central Abstracting & Information Services, 275 Seventh Ave., New York, NY 10001-6708. TEL 212-366-4040. FAX 212-366-4298.
Vendor(s): Orbit Information Technologies, STN International. *3706*

LITIGATION.
American Bar Association, Litigation Section, 750 N. Lake Shore Dr., Chicago, IL 60611. TEL 312-988-5555.
Vendor(s): WESTLAW. *2650*

LITTERATUR PAA INDVANDRERSPROG I DANSKE FOLKEBIBLIOTEKER.
Bibliotekscentralen, Tempovej 7-11, 2750 Ballerup, Denmark. TEL 2-974000. FAX 2-655310. *2982*

LOCAL GOVERNMENT REPORTS OF AUSTRALIA.
Law Book Co. Ltd., 44-50 Waterloo Rd., North Ryde, N.S.W. 2112, Australia. TEL 02-887-0177. FAX 02-888-9706. *4066*

LODGING HOSPITALITY.
Penton Publishing 1100 Superior Ave., Cleveland, OH 44114-2543. TEL 216-696-7000. FAX 216-696-8765.
Vendor(s): DIALOG. *2477*

LOGIBASE.
Services Documentaires Multimedia Inc., 1685, rue Fleury Est, Montreal, Que. H2C 1T1, Canada. TEL 514-382-0895. FAX 514-384-9139. *1143*

LONDON BUSINESS MONTHLY MAGAZINE.
Bowes Publishers Ltd., Box 7400, Sta. E, London, Ont. N5Y 4X3, Canada. TEL 519-472-7601. FAX 519-473-2256.
Vendor(s): DIALOG. *677*

LONDON MAGAZINE (LONDON).
Blackburn Group, 540 York St., 2nd fl., London, Ont. N6B 1R5, Canada. TEL 519-679-4901. FAX 519-434-7842. *2178*

LONG-DISTANCE LETTER.
Phillips Publishing, Inc., 7811 Montrose Rd., Potomac, MD 20854. TEL 301-340-2100. FAX 301-424-4297.
Vendor(s): NewsNet. *1364*

LOOKOUT - FOODS.
Marketing Intelligence Service Ltd., 33 Academy St., Naples, NY 14512. TEL 716-374-6326. FAX 716-374-5217.
Vendor(s): Data-Star, DIALOG. *2076*

LOS ANGELES TIMES INDEX.
University Microfilms International, Data Courier, c/o Bonnie Maxwell, VP, 620 S. Third St., Louisville, KY 40202. TEL 800-626-2823. FAX 502-589-5572.
Vendor(s): DIALOG. *2578*

LOTERIA.
Loteria Nacional de Beneficencia, Departamento de Beneficencia Cultural, Apdo. 21, Panama 1, Panama. TEL 27-2202. *2213*

LOUISIANA LAW REVIEW.
Louisiana State University, Law School, Baton Rouge, LA 70803. TEL 504-388-1681. FAX 504-388-8202.
Vendor(s): Mead Data Central, WESTLAW. *2650*

LOUISVILLE MAGAZINE.
Louisville Chamber of Commerce, One Riverfront Plaza, Ste. 604, Louisville, KY 40202. TEL 502-526-0100. FAX 502-625-0010.
Vendor(s): DIALOG. *819*

LOVTIDENDE A FOR KONGERIGET DANMARK.
Justisministeriet, Sekretariatet for Retsinformation, Axeltorv 6, 5. sal, D-1609 Copenhagen V, Denmark. TEL 33-32-52-22. FAX 33-91-28-01. *2651*

LOVTIDENDE C FOR KONGERIGET DANMARK.
Justisministeriet, Sekretariatet for Retsinformation, Axeltorv 6, 5. sal, D-1609 Copenhagen V, Denmark. TEL 33-32-52-22. FAX 33-91-28-01. *2727*

LOYOLA LAW REVIEW.
Loyola University, School of Law, 7214 St. Charles, New Orleans, LA 70118. TEL 504-861-5558.
Vendor(s): WESTLAW. *2651*

LOYOLA OF LOS ANGELES INTERNATIONAL AND COMPARATIVE LAW JOURNAL.
Loyola of Los Angeles Law School, 1441 W. Olympic Blvd., Los Angeles, CA 90015-3980. TEL 213-736-1405. FAX 213-380-3769.
Vendor(s): WESTLAW. *2651*

M C N: AMERICAN JOURNAL OF MATERNAL CHILD NURSING.
American Journal of Nursing Co., 555 W. 57th St., New York, NY 10019. TEL 212-582-8820. *3282*

M E A L TRI-MEDIA DIGEST FOR BRANDS ADVERTISERS.
Media Expenditure Analysis Ltd., 63 St. Martins Lane, London WC2N 4JT, England.
Vendor(s): Reuters Ltd. *34*

M I R A AUTOMOBILE ABSTRACTS.
Motor Industry Research Association, Watling St., Nuneaton, Warwickshire CV10 0TU, England. FAX 0203-343772.
Vendor(s): European Space Agency. *4665*

M I R A AUTOMOTIVE BUSINESS INDEX.
Motor Industry Research Association, Watling St., Nuneaton, Warwickshire CV10 0TU, England. FAX 0203-343772.
Vendor(s): European Space Agency. *727*

M L A INTERNATIONAL BIBLIOGRAPHY OF BOOKS AND ARTICLES ON THE MODERN LANGUAGES AND LITERATURES.
Modern Language Association of America, 10 Astor Place, New York, NY 10003. TEL 212-475-9500. FAX 212-477-9863.
Vendor(s): DIALOG, Wilsonline. *405*

M UND A - MESSEPLANER INTERNATIONAL.
M und A Verlag fuer Messen, Ausstellungen und Kongresse GmbH Postfach 101528, 6000 Frankfurt a.M. 1, Germany. TEL 069-759502. FAX 069-75951640. *1144*

MCGRAW-HILL'S BIOTECHNOLOGY NEWSWATCH.
McGraw-Hill, Inc., Energy & Business Newsletters, 1221 Ave. of the Americas, 36th Fl., New York, NY 10020. TEL 212-512-6410.
Vendor(s): DIALOG (File no.624/McGRAW-HILL PUBLICATIONS ONLINE), Dow Jones/News Retrieval (BIO), Mead Data Central (BIOTEC). *490*

MACGUIDE REPORT.
MacGuide Magazine Inc., 444 17th St., Ste. 200, P.O. Box 480927, Denver, CO 80248-0927. TEL 303-893-1454. FAX 303-893-9340. *1470*

MACHINE DESIGN.
Penton Publishing 1100 Superior Ave., Cleveland, OH 44114-2543. TEL 216-696-7000. FAX 216-696-8765.
Vendor(s): DIALOG. *1934*

MACINTOSH PRODUCT REGISTRY.
Redgate Communications Corp., 660 Beachland Blvd., Vero Beach, FL 32963. TEL 407-231-6904. FAX 407-231-7872. *1470*

MACLEAN'S.
Maclean Hunter Ltd., Maclean Hunter Bldg., 777 Bay St., Toronto, Ont. M5W 1A7, Canada. TEL 416-596-5000. FAX 416-596-6001.
Vendor(s): Mead Data Central. *2178*

MACROMOLECULES.
American Chemical Society, 1155 16th St., N.W., Washington, DC 20036. TEL 202-872-4363. FAX 202-872-4615.
Vendor(s): STN International (CJACS). *1220*

MACWEEK.
Coastal Associates Publishing, L.P., Computer Publications Division, One Park Ave., New York, NY 10016. TEL 800-999-7467. FAX 212-503-3999.
Vendor(s): Mead Data Central. *1470*

MACWORLD.
MacWorld Communications, 501 Second St., San Francisco, CA 94107. TEL 415-243-0505. *1470*

MAGAZINE ARTICLE SUMMARIES.
EBSCO Publishing, Box 325, Topsfield, MA 01983. TEL 800-221-1826. FAX 508-887-3923.
Vendor(s): BRS (PMRO). *16*

MAGAZINE INDEX.
Information Access Company, 362 Lakeside Dr., Foster City, CA 94404. TEL 800-227-8431. FAX 415-378-5499.
Vendor(s): BRS (MAGS), DIALOG (File no.47), Mead Data Central. *4142*

MAGILL'S CINEMA ANNUAL.
Salem Press, Box 1097, Englewood Cliffs, NJ 07632. TEL 201-871-3700. FAX 201-871-8668.
Vendor(s): DIALOG. *3513*

MAINE LAW REVIEW.
University of Maine, School of Law, 246 Deering Ave., Portland, ME 04102. TEL 207-780-4357.
Vendor(s): WESTLAW. *2652*

MAINFRAME COMPUTING.
Worldwide Videotex, Box 138, Babson Park, Boston, MA 02157. TEL 617-449-1603.
Vendor(s): Data-Star, DIALOG, NewsNet. *1454*

MAIZE ABSTRACTS.
C.A.B. International, Wallingford, Oxon OX10 8DE, England. TEL 0491-32111. FAX 0491-33508.
Vendor(s): BRS (CABA), CISTI, DIMDI, DIALOG, European Space Agency (File nos.16 & 124/CAB). *140*

MANAGED CARE LAW OUTLOOK.
Capitol Publications Inc., 1101 King St., Ste. 444, Alexandria, VA 22314. TEL 703-683-4100. FAX 703-739-6517.
Vendor(s): NewsNet. *3124*

MANAGED CARE OUTLOOK.
Capitol Publications Inc., 1101 King St., Ste. 444, Alexandria, VA 22314. TEL 703-683-4100. FAX 703-739-6517.
Vendor(s): NewsNet. *3124*

MANAGEMENT AND MARKETING ABSTRACTS.
Pira International, Randalls Rd., Leatherhead, Surrey KT22 7RU, England. TEL 0372-376161.
Vendor(s): Data-Star, DIALOG, European Space Agency, Orbit Information Technologies (MMA). *728*

MANAGEMENT CONTENTS.
Information Access Company, 362 Lakeside Dr., Foster City, CA 94409. TEL 800-227-8431. Available only online. Vendor(s): BRS (MGMT), Data-Star (MGMT), DIALOG (File no.75). *728*

MANAGEMENT MATTERS.
Marton Allen Associates, InfoTeam Inc., Box 15640, Plantation, FL 33318-5640. TEL 305-473-9560. FAX 305-473-0544.
Vendor(s): Data-Star, DIALOG, Human Resources Information Network, NewsNet. *1019*

MANAGEMENT OF WORLD WASTES.
Communication Channels, Inc., 6255 Barfield Rd., Atlanta, GA 30328-4369. TEL 404-256-9800. FAX 404-256-3116. *1985*

MANAGERIAL LAW.
Barmarick Publications, Enholmes Hall, Patrington, Hull HU12 0PR, England. TEL 0964-630033.
Vendor(s): Mead Data Central. *988*

MANCHESTER GUARDIAN WEEKLY.
Guardian Publications Ltd., P.O. Box 19, Cheadle, Cheshire SK8 1DD, England. FAX 061-428-2108.
Vendor(s): Mead Data Central. *2194*

MANITOBA DECISIONS - CIVIL AND CRIMINAL CASES.
Western Legal Publications, 301-1 Alexander St., Vancouver, B.C. V6A 1B2, Canada. TEL 604-687-5671. FAX 604-687-2796. *2652*

MANITOBA REPORTS.
Maritime Law Book Ltd., Box 302, Fredericton, N.B. E3B 4Y9, Canada. TEL 506-454-9921.
Vendor(s): QL Systems Ltd.. *2652*

MANUFACTURING CHEMIST AND AEROSOL NEWS.
Morgan-Grampian (Process Press) Ltd., Calderwood St., London SE18 6QH, England. TEL 01-855-7777. FAX 01-854-7476. *1183*

MAPLE ORCHARD.
Loyal Ontario Group Interested in Computers Inc. (LOGIC), P.O. Box 696, Station "B", Willowdale, Ont. M2K 2P9, Canada. TEL 416-323-0828. *1470*

MARINE LOG.
Simmons-Boardman Publishing Corporation, 345 Hudson St., New York, NY 10014. TEL 212-620-7200.
Vendor(s): Mead Data Central. *4732*

MARINE TECHNOLOGY SOCIETY JOURNAL.
Marine Technology Society, Inc., 1828 L St., N.W., 9th Fl., Washington, DC 20036. TEL 202-775-5966. FAX 202-429-9417. *1608*

MARITIME INFORMATION REVIEW.
Netherlands Maritime Information Centre, P.O. Box 21873, 3001 AW Rotterdam, Netherlands. TEL 010-4130960. FAX 010-4112857. *4733*

MARKET INTELLIGENCE.
Mintel International Group Ltd., 18-19 Long Lane, London EC1A 9HE, England. TEL 071-606-4533. FAX 071-606-5159. *1045*

MARKET RESEARCH ABSTRACTS.
Market Research Society, 15 Northburgh St., London EC1V 0AH, England. *729*

MARKET SCREEN.
Market Guide Inc., 49 Glen Head Rd., Glen Head, NY 11545. TEL 516-759-1253. FAX 516-676-9240. *955*

MARKETING.
Marketing Publications Ltd., 22 Lancaster Gate, London W2 3LY, England.
Vendor(s): VU/TEXT Information Services, Inc.. *1045*

MARKETING RESEARCH REVIEW.
High Tech Publishing Company, Box 1923, Brattleboro, VT 05301. TEL 802-254-3539.
Vendor(s): Data-Star, NewsNet (AD06). *1046*

MARKETLETTER.
IMSWORLD Publications Ltd., 11-13 Melton St., London NW1 2EH, England.
Vendor(s): Data-Star. *3734*

MARQUETTE LAW REVIEW.
Marquette University, Law School, 1103 W. Wisconsin Ave., Milwaukee, WI 53233. TEL 414-224-5143.
Vendor(s): WESTLAW. *2653*

MARTINDALE-HUBBELL LAW DIRECTORY.
R.R. Bowker, A Reed Reference Publishing Company, Division of Reed Publishing (USA) Inc., Box 1001, Summit, NJ 07902-1001. TEL 800-526-4902. FAX 201-464-3553. *2653*

MARTINDALE: THE EXTRA PHARMACOPOEIA.
Royal Pharmaceutical Society of Great Britain, 1 Lambeth High St., London SE1 7JN, England. TEL 071-735-9141.
Vendor(s): Data-Star, DIALOG (File no.141). *3734*

MARYLAND. POLICE AND CORRECTIONAL TRAINING COMMISSIONS. REPORT TO THE GOVERNOR, THE SECRETARY OF PUBLIC SAFETY AND CORRECTIONAL SERVICES, AND MEMBERS OF THE GENERAL ASSEMBLY.
Correctional Training Commission, 3085 Hernwood Rd., Rm. 16, Woodstock, MD 21163. TEL 301-442-2700. FAX 301-442-5852.
Vendor(s): DIALOG. *1518*

MARYLAND BUSINESS & LIVING JOURNAL.
Philos Publications Inc., c/o D.N. Kuryk, 5 Light St., Ste. 950, Baltimore, MD 21202.
Vendor(s): DIALOG. *678*

MARYLAND LAW REVIEW.
University of Maryland School of Law, 500 W. Baltimore St., Baltimore, MD 21201. TEL 301-328-7214.
Vendor(s): WESTLAW. *2653*

MASS HIGH TECH.
Mass Tech Times, Inc., 500 W. Cummings Pk., Ste. 3500, Woburn, MA 01801. TEL 617-935-1100. FAX 617-935-0308. *4603*

MASS SPECTROMETRY BULLETIN.
Royal Society of Chemistry, Thomas Graham House, Science Park, Milton Rd., Cambridge CB4 4WF, England. TEL 0462-672555. FAX 0462-480947.
Vendor(s): European Space Agency (File no.86/MASS SPECTROMETRY BULLETIN), Pergamon Infoline. *1202*

MASTERS ABSTRACTS INTERNATIONAL.
University Microfilms International, Dissertation Publishing, c/o Dorie Mickelson, Mgr., 300 N. Zeeb Rd., Ann Arbor, MI 48106. TEL 313-761-4700.
Vendor(s): BRS, BRS/Saunders Colleague, DIALOG (File no.35). *1678*

MATERIALS BUSINESS INFORMATION.
Institute of Materials, 1 Carlton House Terrace, London SW1Y 5DB, England. TEL 071-839-4071. FAX 071-839-2078.
Vendor(s): DIALOG (File no.269). *3427*

MATERIALS INFORMATION TRANSLATIONS SERVICE.
Institute of Materials, 1 Carlton House Terrace, London SW1Y 5DB, England. TEL 071-839-4071. FAX 071-839-2289.
Vendor(s): DIALOG. *3413*

MATHEMATICAL REVIEWS.
American Mathematical Society, Box 1571, Annex Sta., Providence, RI 02901-9930. TEL 401-455-4000.
Vendor(s): BRS (MATH), DIALOG, European Space Agency (File no.80/MATHSCI). *3063*

MECHANICAL ENGINEERING.
American Society of Mechanical Engineers, 345 E. 47th St., New York, NY 10017. TEL 212-705-7722.
Vendor(s): Mead Data Central. *1935*

MEDECONOMICS.
Haymarket Medical Publications Ltd., 30 Lancaster Gate, London W2 3LP, England.
Vendor(s): Data-Star. *3125*

MEDIA MONITOR.
Financial Times Business Information Ltd., Tower House, Southampton St., London WC2E 7HA, England. TEL 071-240 9391. FAX 071-240-7946.
Vendor(s): Data-Star. *1339*

MEDIA WEEK.
B P I Communications, Inc. (New York), 49 E. 21st St., New York, NY 10010. TEL 212-529-5500.
Vendor(s): DIALOG. *35*

MEDICAL AND HEALTH CARE BOOKS AND SERIALS IN PRINT.
R.R. Bowker, A Reed Reference Publishing Company, Division of Reed Publishing (USA) Inc., 121 Chanlon Rd., New Providence, NJ 07974. TEL 800-521-8110. FAX 908-665-7974.
Vendor(s): BRS, DIALOG. *3177*

MEDICAL AND PEDIATRIC ONCOLOGY.
John Wiley & Sons, Inc., Journals, 605 Third Ave., New York, NY 10158. TEL 212-850-6000. FAX 212-850-6088. *3200*

MEDICAL CLINICS OF NORTH AMERICA.
W.B. Saunders Co., Curtis Center, Independence Square W., Philadelphia, PA 19106. TEL 215-238-7800.
Vendor(s): BRS, BRS/Saunders Colleague. *3125*

MEDICAL DEVICES, DIAGNOSTICS & INSTRUMENTATION REPORTS: THE GRAY SHEET.
F-D-C Reports, Inc., 5550 Friendship Blvd., Ste. One, Chevy Chase, MD 20815. TEL 301-657-9830. FAX 301-656-3094.
Vendor(s): Data-Star, DIALOG (File no.187), Mead Data Central. *3126*

MEDICAL ECONOMICS.
Medical Economics Publishing Co., Five Paragon Dr., Montvale, NJ 07645. TEL 201-358-7200. FAX 201-573-1045.
Vendor(s): DIALOG. *3126*

SERIALS AVAILABLE ONLINE 5085

MEDICAL JOURNAL OF AUSTRALIA.
Australasian Medical Publishing Co., P.O. Box 410, Kingsgrove, N.S.W. 2208, Australia. FAX 02-502-3626. *3126*

MEDICAL LETTER ON DRUGS AND THERAPEUTICS.
Medical Letter, Inc., 1000 Main St., New Rochelle, NY 10801. TEL 914-235-0500. FAX 914-576-3377.
Vendor(s): BRS. *3734*

MEDICAL SCIENCE RESEARCH.
Science and Technology Letters, P.O. Box 81, Northwood, Middlesex HA6 3DN, England. TEL 09274-23586. FAX 09274-25066.
Vendor(s): BRS, BRS/Saunders Colleague, DIMDI, Data-Star. *3128*

MEDICAL TEXTILES.
Elsevier Science Publishers Ltd., Crown House, Linton Rd., Barking, Essex IG11 8JU, England. TEL 081-594-7272. FAX 081-594-5942.
Vendor(s): Data-Star, DIALOG. *3128*

MEDICAL WASTE NEWS.
Business Publishers, Inc., 951 Pershing Dr., Silver Spring, MD 20910-4432. TEL 301-587-6300. FAX 301-585-9075.
Vendor(s): Data-Star, DIALOG, NewsNet. *1985*

MEDICAL WORLD.
Association of Scientific, Technical and Managerial Staffs, 10-26 Jamestown Rd., London NW1 7DT, England. *3128*

MEDICAL WORLD NEWS.
Medical Tribune, Inc., 257 Park Ave. S., New York, NY 10010. TEL 212-674-8500. FAX 212-529-8490. *3128*

MEDICINE (BALTIMORE).
Williams & Wilkins, 428 E. Preston St., Baltimore, MD 21202. TEL 301-528-4000. FAX 301-528-4312.
Vendor(s): BRS, BRS/Saunders Colleague, Mead Data Central. *3129*

MEDIO AMBIENTE.
Universidad Austral de Chile, Instituto de Ecologia y Evolucion, Facultad de Ciencias, Casilla 567, Valdivia, Chile. FAX 063-215012. *1962*

MEETINGS AND CONVENTIONS.
Reed Travel Group 500 Plaza Dr., Secaucus, NJ 07096. TEL 201-902-2000. FAX 201-319-1796.
Vendor(s): DIALOG. *3393*

MELBOURNE CITYSCOPE.
Cityscope Publications Pty. Ltd., P.O. Box 807, Manly, N.S.W. 2095, Australia. TEL 02-976-2233. FAX 02-976-2263. *4160*

MEMBRANE & SEPARATION TECHNOLOGY NEWS.
Business Communications Co., Inc. (Norwalk), 25 Van Zant St., Norwalk, CT 06855. TEL 203-853-4266. FAX 203-853-0348.
Vendor(s): Data-Star, DIALOG, NewsNet. *490*

MEMPHIS BUSINESS JOURNAL.
Mid-South Communications, Inc., 88 Union, Ste. 102, Memphis, TN 38103-5195. TEL 901-523-1000. FAX 901-526-5240.
Vendor(s): DIALOG. *679*

MENTAL HEALTH LAW REPORTER.
Business Publishers, Inc., 951 Pershing Dr., Silver Spring, MD 20910-4464. TEL 301-587-6300. FAX 301-585-9075.
Vendor(s): NewsNet. *2704*

MENTAL HEALTH REPORT.
Business Publishers, Inc., 951 Pershing Dr., Silver Spring, MD 20910-4464. TEL 301-587-6300. FAX 301-585-9075.
Vendor(s): NewsNet. *4413*

MENTAL MEASUREMENTS YEARBOOK.
Buros Institute of Mental Measurements, 135 Bancroft, University of Nebraska-Lincoln, Lincoln, NE 68588-0348. TEL 402-472-6203. FAX 402-472-6207.
Vendor(s): BRS (MMYD). *4035*

MERCER BUSINESS MAGAZINE.
Mercer County Chamber of Commerce, 2550 Kuser Rd., Box 8307, Trenton, NJ 08650. TEL 609-586-2056. FAX 609-586-8052.
Vendor(s): DIALOG. *819*

MERCER LAW REVIEW.
Mercer University, Walter F. George School of Law, Macon, GA 31207. TEL 912-752-2622.
Vendor(s): WESTLAW. *2654*

MERCK INDEX: AN ENCYCLOPEDIA OF CHEMICALS AND DRUGS.
Merck and Co., Inc., Attn: Michele Stotz, FTA-230, Box 2000, Rahway, NJ 07065. TEL 201-855-4558.
Vendor(s): BRS (MRCK), BRS/Saunders Colleague, CISTI, DIALOG, Telesystemes - Questel. *3748*

MERGERS & ACQUISITIONS.
M L R Publishing Company 229 S. 18th St., Philadelphia, PA 19103. TEL 215-790-7000. FAX 215-790-7005. *679*

MERGERS AND CORPORATE POLICY.
S D C Publishing, 40 W. 57th St., 8th Fl., New York, NY 10019. TEL 212-765-5311.
Vendor(s): NewsNet. *679*

METABOLISM: CLINICAL AND EXPERIMENTAL.
W.B. Saunders Co. Curtis Center, Independence Square W., Philadelphia, PA 19106. TEL 215-238-7800. *3255*

METALS ABSTRACTS.
A S M International, Materials Information, Materials Park, OH 44073. TEL 216-338-5151. FAX 216-338-4634.
Vendor(s): CEDOCAR, CISTI, Data-Star (META), DIALOG (File no.32/METADEX), European Space Agency (File no.3/METADEX), FIZ Technik (META), Orbit Information Technologies (METADEX), STN International (METADEX). *3427*

METALS ABSTRACTS INDEX.
A S M International, Materials Information, Materials Park, OH 44073. TEL 216-338-5151. FAX 216-338-4634.
Vendor(s): CEDOCAR, CISTI, Data-Star (META), DIALOG (File no.32/METADEX), European Space Agency (File no.3/METADEX), FIZ Technik (META), Orbit Information Technologies (METADEX), STN International (METADEX). *3427*

METALS WEEK.
McGraw-Hill, Inc., Commodity Services Group, 1221 Avenue of the Americas, 42nd Fl., New York, NY 10020. TEL 212-512-2000.
Vendor(s): DIALOG (File no.624/McGRAW-HILL PUBLICATIONS ONLINE), Dow Jones/News Retrieval (MW), Mead Data Central (METLWK). *3488*

METEOROLOGICAL AND GEOASTROPHYSICAL ABSTRACTS.
American Meteorological Society, c/o Inforonics, Inc., 550 Newtown Rd., Box 458, Littleton, MA 01460. TEL 508-486-8976. FAX 508-486-0027.
Vendor(s): DIALOG (File no.29). *3444*

METEOROLOGY AND HYDROLOGY.
Institutul de Meteorologie si Hidrologie, Soseaua Bucuresti-Ploiesti 97, Bucharest, Rumania. TEL 793240.
Available only online. *3439*

METROPOLITAN TORONTO BUSINESS JOURNAL.
Board of Trade of Metropolitan Toronto, P.O. Box 60, 1 First Canadian Place, Toronto, Ont. M5X 1C1, Canada. TEL 416-366-6811.
Vendor(s): DIALOG. *837*

MEXICO SERVICE.
International Reports 114 E. 32nd St., New York, NY 10016. TEL 212-685-6900. FAX 212-685-856658.
Vendor(s): Data-Star (FSRI), DIALOG. *955*

MICHIGAN BAR JOURNAL.
State Bar of Michigan, 306 Townsend, Lansing, MI 48933. TEL 517-372-9030.
Vendor(s): WESTLAW. *2654*

MICHIGAN LAW REVIEW.
Michigan Law Review Association, Ann Arbor, MI 48109-1215.
Vendor(s): Mead Data Central, WESTLAW. *2654*

MICHNET NEWS.
Merit Network, Inc., c/o Pat McGregor, 1075 Beal Ave., Ann Arbor, MI 48109-2112. TEL 313-764-9430. FAX 313-747-3185. *1427*

MICRO M D NEWSLETTER.
Micro M D Publishing, 170 University Ave. W, Waterloo, Ontario, Canada N2L 3E9.
Vendor(s): CompuServe Consumer Information Service, NewsNet. *3226*

MICROBIOLOGY ABSTRACTS: SECTION A. INDUSTRIAL & APPLIED MICROBIOLOGY.
Cambridge Scientific Abstracts, 7200 Wisconsin Ave., 6th Fl., Bethesda, MD 20814. TEL 301-961-6750. FAX 301-961-6720.
Vendor(s): BRS (CSAL), DIALOG (File no.76/LIFE SCIENCES COLLECTION). *466*

MICROBIOLOGY ABSTRACTS: SECTION B. BACTERIOLOGY.
Cambridge Scientific Abstracts, 7200 Wisconsin Ave., 6th Fl., Bethesda, MD 20814. TEL 301-961-6750. FAX 301-961-6720.
Vendor(s): BRS (CSAL), DIALOG (File no.76/LIFE SCIENCES COLLECTION). *466*

MICROBIOLOGY ABSTRACTS: SECTION C. ALGOLOGY, MYCOLOGY AND PROTOZOOLOGY.
Cambridge Scientific Abstracts, 7200 Wisconsin Ave., 6th Fl., Bethesda, MD 20814. TEL 301-961-6750. FAX 301-961-6720.
Vendor(s): BRS (CSAL), DIALOG (File no.76/LIFE SCIENCES COLLECTION). *466*

MICROCELL REPORT.
Microcell Strategies, Inc., 170 Broadway, Ste. 1515, New York, NY 10038. TEL 212-385-0280. FAX 212-571-7475.
Vendor(s): Data-Star, DIALOG, NewsNet. *1364*

MICROCOMPUTER INDEX.
Learned Information, Inc., 143 Old Marlton Pike, Medford, NJ 08055. TEL 609-654-6266. FAX 609-654-4309.
Vendor(s): DIALOG (File no. 233). *1405*

MICROCOMPUTERS IN EDUCATION.
John Mongillo, Ed. & Pub., Two Sequan Rd., Watch Hill, RI 02891. TEL 203-655-3798.
Vendor(s): NewsNet (EC59). *1691*

MICROLOG: CANADIAN RESEARCH INDEX.
Micromedia Ltd., 20 Victoria St., Toronto, Ont. M5C 2N8, Canada. TEL 416-362-5211. FAX 416-362-6161.
Vendor(s): CISTI. *17*

THE MIDDLE EAST.
I.C. Publications Ltd., Box 261, Carlton House, 69 Gt. Queen St., London WC2B 5BN, England.
TEL 071-404-4333. FAX 071-404-5336. *2874*

MIDDLE EAST BUSINESS INTELLIGENCE.
Eurostudy Publishing Co. Ltd., Ludgate House, 107 Fleet St., London EC4A 2AB, England. TEL 44-71-583-1025. FAX 44-71-583-5958.
Vendor(s): Mead Data Central, NewsNet (IT50). *917*

MIDDLE EAST EXECUTIVE REPORTS.
Eurostudy Publishing Co. Ltd., Ludgate House, 107 Fleet St., London EC4A 2AB, England. TEL 071-583-1025. FAX 071-583-5958.
Vendor(s): Mead Data Central. *874*

MIDWEST REAL ESTATE NEWS.
Communication Channels, Inc., 6255 Barfield Rd., Atlanta, GA 30324-4369. TEL 404-256-9800. FAX 404-256-3116. *4152*

MILITARY & COMMERCIAL FIBER BUSINESS.
Phillips Publishing, Inc., Defense - Aviation Group, 1925 N. Lynn St., Ste. 1000, Arlington, VA 22209. TEL 703-522-8333. FAX 703-522-6448.
Vendor(s): Data-Star, DIALOG, NewsNet. *3464*

MILITARY LAW REVIEW.
U.S. Army, Judge Advocate Generals School, Charlottesville, VA 22903-1781. TEL 804-293-4382.
Vendor(s): Mead Data Central. *2735*

MILITARY ROBOTICS NEWSLETTER.
L & B Limited, 19 Rock Creek Church Rd. NW, Washington, DC 20011-6005. TEL 202-723-5031. FAX 202-726-2979.
Vendor(s): DIALOG (NL0650), NewsNet (DE14). *1409*

MILITARY ROBOTICS SOURCEBOOK.
L & B Limited, 19 Rock Creek Church Rd. NW, Washington, DC 20011-6005. TEL 202-723-5031. FAX 202-726-2979.
Vendor(s): NewsNet. *1409*

MILITARY SPACE.
Pasha Publications Inc., 1401 Wilson Blvd., Ste. 900, Arlington, VA 22209-9970. TEL 703-528-1244. FAX 703-528-1253.
Vendor(s): NewsNet (DE04). *3465*

MILITARY SPECIFICATIONS AND STANDARDS SERVICES NUMERIC INDEX.
Information Handling Services, 15 Inverness Way East, Englewood, CO 80150. TEL 303-790-0600. FAX 303-799-4085.
Vendor(s): DIALOG. *3465*

MILLION DOLLAR DIRECTORY SERIES.
Dun and Bradstreet Information Services, 3 Sylvan Way, Parsippany, NJ 07054-3896. TEL 201-605-6000.
Vendor(s): DIALOG (File no.517), Pergamon Infoline. *1048*

MIMS MAGAZINE.
Haymarket Medical Publications, Ltd, 30 Lancaster Gate, London W2 3LP, England.
Vendor(s): Data-Star. *3132*

MINERALOGICAL ABSTRACTS.
Mineralogical Society, 41 Queen's Gate, London SW7 5HR, England. TEL 01-584 7516.
Vendor(s): DIALOG (File no.292). *3502*

MINING ANNUAL REVIEW.
Mining Journal Ltd., 60 Worship St., London EC2A 2HD, England. TEL 071-377-2020. FAX 071-247-4100.
Vendor(s): Mead Data Central. *3490*

MINING MAGAZINE.
Mining Journal Ltd., 60 Worship St., London EC2A 2HD, England. TEL 071-377-2020. FAX 071-247-4100.
Vendor(s): Mead Data Central. *3490*

MINISTERIALTIDENDE FOR KONGERIGET DANMARK.
Justisministeriet, Sekretariatet for Retsinformation, Axeltorv 6, 5. sal, DK-1609 Copenhagen V, Denmark. TEL 33-32-52-22. FAX 33-91-28-01. *4067*

MINNESOTA LAW REVIEW.
University of Minnesota, Law School, 229 19th Ave. S., Minneapolis, MN 55455. TEL 612-625-8034.
Vendor(s): Mead Data Central, WESTLAW. *2654*

MINORITY MARKETS ALERT.
Alert Publishing, Inc., 37-06 30th Ave., Long Island City, NY 11103-3808. TEL 718-626-3356.
Vendor(s): Data-Star, DIALOG, NewsNet. *1506*

MISSISSIPPI COLLEGE LAW REVIEW.
Mississippi College Law Review, 151 E. Griffith St., Jackson, MS 39201. TEL 601-944-1950.
Vendor(s): WESTLAW. *2655*

MISSISSIPPI LAW JOURNAL.
Mississippi Law Journal, Box 849, University, MS 38677. TEL 601-232-7361. FAX 601-232-7731.
Vendor(s): WESTLAW. *2655*

MISSOURI LAW REVIEW.
University of Missouri, Columbia, School of Law, Columbia, MO 65211. TEL 314-882-7055. FAX 314-882-7055.
Vendor(s): WESTLAW. *2655*

MITTELSTAENDISCHE UNTERNEHMEN.
Verlag Hoppenstedt und Co., Havelstr. 9, 6100 Darmstadt, Germany. TEL 06151-380-0. FAX 06151-380-360.
Vendor(s): Data-Star, DIALOG. *1081*

MIXING AND SEPARATION TECHNOLOGY ABSTRACTS.
S T I Ltd., 4 Kings Meadow, Ferry Hinksey Rd., Oxford OX2 0DU, England. TEL 0865-798898. FAX 0865-798788.
Vendor(s): DIALOG (File no. 96), European Space Agency (File no. 48). *1845*

MOBILE COMMUNICATIONS.
Financial Times Business Information Ltd., Tower House, Southampton St., London WC2E 7HA, England. TEL 071-240 9391. FAX 071-240-7946.
Vendor(s): Data-Star, Mead Data Central. *1340*

MOBILE DATA REPORT: BUSINESS INTELLIGENCE ON RADIO-BASED INFORMATION NETWORKS.
Waters Information Services, Inc., Box 2248, Binghamton, NY 13902-2248. TEL 607-770-8535. FAX 607-798-1692.
Vendor(s): Data-Star, DIALOG, NewsNet. *1340*

MOBILE PHONE NEWS.
Phillips Publishing, Inc., 7811 Montrose Rd., Potomac, MD 20854. TEL 301-340-2100. FAX 301-309-3847.
Vendor(s): NewsNet (TE25). *1364*

MOBILE SATELLITE REPORTS.
Warren Publishing, Inc., 2115 Ward Court, N.W., Washington, DC 20037. TEL 202-872-9200. FAX 202-293-3435.
Vendor(s): Data-Star, DIALOG, NewsNet. *1340*

MODEM USER NEWS.
Worldwide Videotex, Box 138, Babson Park, Boston, MA 02157. TEL 617-449-1603.
Vendor(s): Data-Star, DIALOG, NewsNet. *1454*

MODERN AGING RESEARCH.
Wiley-Liss, Inc., 41 E. 11th St., New York, NY 10003. TEL 212-475-7700. *2276*

MODERN BRIDE.
Cahners Publishing Company (New York), Consumer and Entertainment Division, Division of Reed Publishing (USA) Inc., 249 W. 17th St., New York, NY 10011. TEL 212-337-7000. FAX 212-545-5400.
Vendor(s): DIALOG. *3067*

MODERN HEALTHCARE (YEAR).
Crain Communications, Inc. (Chicago), 740 N. Rush St., Chicago, IL 60611-2590. TEL 312-649-5341. FAX 312-280-3189. *2467*

MODERN OFFICE TECHNOLOGY.
Penton Publishing 1100 Superior Ave., Cleveland, OH 44114-2543. TEL 216-696-7000. FAX 609-696-8765.
Vendor(s): DIALOG. *1059*

MODERN PAINT AND COATINGS.
Communication Channels, Inc., 6255 Barfield Rd., Atlanta, GA 30328-4369. TEL 404-256-9800. FAX 404-256-3116. *3654*

MODERN TIRE DEALER.
Bill Communications, Inc. (Akron), 341 White Pond Dr., Box 3599, Akron, OH 44309-3599. TEL 216-867-4401. FAX 216-867-0019.
Vendor(s): DIALOG. *4292*

MONEY.
The Time Inc. Magazine Company, Time & Life Bldg., Rockefeller Center, 1271 Ave. of the Americas, New York, NY 10020. TEL 212-522-1212.
Vendor(s): DIALOG, Mead Data Central, VU/TEXT Information Services, Inc.. *1506*

MONITOR DE LA FARMACIA Y DE LA TERAPEUTICA.
Centros Farmaceuticos Nacional S.A., Julian Camarillo, 37, 28037 Madrid, Spain. *3735*

MONTHLY CATALOG OF UNITED STATES GOVERNMENT PUBLICATIONS.
U.S. Government Printing Office, Superintendent of Documents, Washington, DC 20402-9341. TEL 202-783-3238. FAX 202-2512-2250.
Vendor(s): BRS, BRS/Saunders Colleague, DIALOG (File no.66). *4081*

MONTHLY INDEX TO THE FINANCIAL TIMES.
Financial Times Business Information Ltd., Tower House, Southampton St., London WC2E 7HA, England. TEL 071-240-9391. FAX 071-240-7946.
Vendor(s): DIALOG. *729*

MONTHLY PLANET.
Nuclear Weapons Freeze of Santa Cruz County, Box 8463, Santa Cruz, CA 95061-8463. TEL 408-429-8755. *3966*

MORE LIGHT UPDATE.
Presbyterians for Lesbian & Gay Concerns, Inc., Box 38, New Brunswick, NJ 08903-0038. TEL 201-846-1510. *2455*

MORGAN REPORT ON DIRECTORY PUBLISHING.
Morgan-Rand Publishing Co., 2200 Sansom St., Philadelphia, PA 19103. TEL 215-557-8200. FAX 215-557-8414.
Vendor(s): Data-Star (PTBN), DIALOG (File no.636), NewsNet (PB30). *1146*

MOTOR TREND.
Petersen Publishing Co., 8490 Sunset Blvd., Los Angeles, CA 90069. TEL 213-854-2222.
Vendor(s): DIALOG. *4696*

MOUNT SINAI JOURNAL OF MEDICINE.
Mount Sinai Hospital, Committee on Medical Education and Publications, 19 E. 98th St., Box 1094, New York, NY 10029. TEL 212-241-6108. FAX 212-722-6386.
Vendor(s): DIALOG. *3132*

MULTIMEDIA AND VIDEODISC MONITOR.
Future Systems, Inc., Box 26, Falls Church, VA 22040. TEL 703-241-1799. FAX 703-532-0529.
Vendor(s): DIALOG, NewsNet. *1438*

MULTIMEDIA COMPUTING & PRESENTATIONS.
Multimedia Computing Corporation, 3501 Ryder St., Santa Clara, CA 95051. TEL 408-737-7575. FAX 408-739-8019. *1482*

MUNIWEEK.
American Banker, Inc., Bond Buyer, One State St. Plaza, New York, NY 10004. TEL 212-943-9589. FAX 212-943-6256.
Vendor(s): DIALOG (File no.626), NewsNet. *957*

MUSIKALIER I DANSKE BIBLIOTEKER (ANNUAL).
Biblioteksentralen, Tempovej 7-11, DK-2750 Ballerup, Denmark. *3589*

MUSIKALIER I DANSKE BIBLIOTEKER (QUARTERLY).
Biblioteksentralen, Tempovej 7-11, 2750 Ballerup, Denmark. TEL 2-974000. FAX 2-655310. *2774*

N A B P NEWSLETTER.
National Association of Boards of Pharmacy, 1300 Higgins Rd., No. 103, Park Ridge, IL 60068-5743. TEL 708-698-6227. *3735*

N A S A SOFTWARE DIRECTORY.
High Tech Publishing Company, Box 1923, Brattleboro, VT 05301. TEL 802-254-3539.
Vendor(s): Data-Star, NewsNet. *1479*

N A T O ADVANCED SCIENCE INSTITUTES SERIES A: LIFE SCIENCES.
Plenum Publishing Corp., 233 Spring St., New York, NY 10013-1578. TEL 212-620-8000. FAX 212-463-0742.
Vendor(s): European Space Agency (File no.128). *448*

N A T Q ADVANCED SCIENCE INSTITUTES SERIES B: PHYSICS.
Plenum Publishing Corp., 233 Spring St., New York, NY 10013. TEL 212-620-8000. FAX 212-463-0742.
Vendor(s): European Space Agency (File no.128). *3825*

N A T O ADVANCED SCIENCE INSTITUTES SERIES C: MATHEMATICAL AND PHYSICAL SCIENCES.
Kluwer Academic Publishers, Postbus 17, 3300 AA Dordrecht, Netherlands. TEL 078-334911. FAX 078-334254.
Vendor(s): European Space Agency (File no.128). *3048*

N A T O ADVANCED SCIENCE INSTITUTES SERIES D: BEHAVIOURAL AND SOCIAL SCIENCES.
Kluwer Academic Publishers, Postbus 17, 3300 AA Dordrecht, Netherlands. TEL 078-334911. FAX 078-334254.
Vendor(s): European Space Agency (File no.128). *4380*

N A T O ADVANCED SCIENCE INSTITUTES SERIES E: APPLIED SCIENCES.
Kluwer Academic Publishers, Postbus 17, 3300 AA Dordrecht, Netherlands. TEL 078-334911. FAX 078-334254.
Vendor(s): European Space Agency (File no.128). *4604*

N A T O ADVANCED SCIENCE INSTITUTES SERIES F: COMPUTER AND SYSTEMS SCIENCES.
Kluwer Academic Publishers, P.O. Box 17, 3300 AA Dordrecht, Netherlands. TEL 078-334911. FAX 078-334254.
Vendor(s): European Space Agency (File no.128). *1438*

N A T O ADVANCED SCIENCE INSTITUTES SERIES G: ECOLOGICAL SCIENCES.
Kluwer Academic Publishers, P.O. Box 17, 330 AA Dordrecht, Netherlands. TEL 078-334911. FAX 078-334254.
Vendor(s): European Space Agency (File no.128). *1963*

N A T O ADVANCED SCIENCE INSTITUTES SERIES H: CELL BIOLOGY.
Kluwer Academic Publishers, P.O. Box 17, 3300 AA Dordrecht, Netherlands. TEL 078-334911. FAX 078-334254.
Vendor(s): European Space Agency (File no.128). *526*

N C I CANCER WEEKLY.
Charles W. Henderson, Ed. & Pub., Box 5528, Atlanta, GA 30307-0528. TEL 404-377-8895. FAX 205-991-1479.
Vendor(s): Data-Star, DIALOG, NewsNet. *3200*

N C J R S DOCUMENT RETRIEVAL INDEX.
U.S. National Institute of Justice, National Criminal Justice Reference Service, Box 6000, Department F, MD 20850. TEL 301-251-5500. FAX 301-251-5212.
Vendor(s): DIALOG. *1518*

N C R CONNECTION.
Publications & Communications, Inc., 12416 Hymeadow Dr., Austin, TX 78750-1896. TEL 512-250-9023. FAX 512-331-3900. *1471*

N I O S H T I C DATABASE.
U.S. National Technical Information Service, 5285 Port Royal Rd., Springfield, VA 22161. TEL 703-487-4630.
Vendor(s): DIALOG, Orbit Information Technologies. *3619*

N I S T UPDATE.
High Tech Publishing Company, Box 1923, Brattleboro, VT 05301. TEL 802-254-3539.
Vendor(s): Data-Star, NewsNet (GT32). *680*

N M F S FISHERIES MARKET NEWS REPORT.
Urner Barry Publications, Inc., Box 389, Toms River, NJ 08754. TEL 908-240-5330. FAX 908-341-0891. *2051*

N T I S BIBLIOGRAPHIC DATA BASE.
U.S. National Technical Information Service, 5285 Port Royal Rd., Springfield, VA 22161. TEL 703-487-4630.
Vendor(s): BRS, Data-Star, DIALOG, Orbit Information Technologies, STN International. *4143*

N T T TOPICS.
Ruder, Finn & Rotman, N T T Information Desk, 301 E. 57th St., New York, NY 10022.
Vendor(s): NewsNet (TE31). *1364*

NASHVILLE BUSINESS AND LIFESTYLES.
Southeast Magazines, Inc., 545 Mainstream Dr., Ste. 101, Nashville, TN 37228. TEL 615-242-6992. FAX 615-242-2248.
Vendor(s): BRS (BDLN), DIALOG (File no.635), Dow Jones/News Retrieval, Mead Data Central (ADV), VU/TEXT Information Services, Inc. (BDL,ADV). *681*

NATIONAL ASSOCIATION OF BOARDS OF PHARMACY. PROCEEDINGS.
National Association of Boards of Pharmacy, 1300 Higgins Rd., No. 103, Park Ridge, IL 60068-5743. TEL 708-698-6227. *3735*

NATIONAL ASSOCIATION OF INSURANCE COMMISSIONERS. PROCEEDINGS.
National Association of Insurance Commissioners, 120 W. 12th St., Kansas City, MO 64105. TEL 816-842-3600.
Vendor(s): Mead Data Central. *2538*

NATIONAL ASSOCIATION OF REALTORS. HOME SALES.
National Association of Realtors, Economics and Research Division, 777 14th St., N.W., Washington, DC 20005. TEL 202-383-1110. FAX 202-383-7568. *4153*

NATIONAL CANCER INSTITUTE. JOURNAL.
U.S. National Cancer Institute, 9030 Old Georgetown Rd., Rm. 213, Bethesda, MD 20814. TEL 301-496-4907.
Vendor(s): BRS, BRS/Saunders Colleague, Mead Data Central. *3200*

NATIONAL COUNCIL ON FAMILY RELATIONS. REPORT.
National Council on Family Relations, 3989 Central Ave., N.E., Ste. 550, Minneapolis, MN 55421-3921. TEL 612-781-9331. FAX 612-781-9348.
Vendor(s): BRS. *4443*

NATIONAL DATA BOOK OF FOUNDATIONS.
Foundation Center, 79 Fifth Ave., New York, NY 10003. TEL 212-620-4230.
Vendor(s): DIALOG. *4426*

NATIONAL JEWELER.
Miller Freeman Inc. (New York) 1515 Broadway, New York, NY 10036. TEL 212-869-1300. FAX 212-302-6273. *2565*

NATIONAL JOURNAL.
National Journal, Inc. 1730 M St., N.W., Ste. 1100, Washington, DC 20036. TEL 202-857-1400. FAX 202-833-8069.
Vendor(s): Mead Data Central. *3908*

NATIONAL LAW JOURNAL.
New York Law Publishing Co., 111 Eighth Ave., New York, NY 10011. TEL 212-741-8300.
Vendor(s): Mead Data Central. *2657*

NATIONAL LIBRARY NEWS.
National Library of Canada, Publication and Marketing Services, 395 Wellington St., Ottawa, Ont. K1A 0N4, Canada. TEL 613-995-7969. FAX 613-996-7941. *2775*

NATIONAL MEDICAL ASSOCIATION. JOURNAL.
Slack, Inc., 6900 Grove Rd., Thorofare, NJ 08086. TEL 609-848-1000. FAX 609-853-5991. *3134*

NATIONAL NEWSPAPER INDEX.
Information Access Company, 362 Lakeside Dr., Foster City, CA 94404. TEL 800-227-8431. FAX 415-378-5499.
Vendor(s): BRS (NOOZ), DIALOG (File no.111), Mead Data Central. *730*

NATIONAL PETROLEUM NEWS.
Hunter Publishing Limited Partnership, 950 Lee St., Des Plaines, IL 60016. TEL 708-296-0770. FAX 708-803-3328.
Vendor(s): DIALOG. *3693*

NATIONAL PHARMACEUTICAL ASSOCIATION. JOURNAL.
National Pharmaceutical Association, Inc., c/o Texas Southern University, College of Pharmacy, 3100 Cleburne, Houston, TX 77004. TEL 202-806-6530. *3735*

NATIONAL REAL ESTATE INVESTOR.
Communication Channels, Inc., 6255 Barfield Rd., Atlanta, GA 30328-4369. TEL 404-256-9800. FAX 404-256-3116. *4153*

NATIONAL REPORT ON COMPUTERS AND HEALTH.
United Communications Group, 11300 Rockville Pike, Ste. 1100, Rockville, MD 20852-3030. TEL 301-816-8950.
Vendor(s): Data-Star, DIALOG. *3226*

NATIONAL REPORT ON SUBSTANCE ABUSE.
Buraff Publications 1350 Connecticut Ave. N.W., Ste. 1000, Washington, DC 20036. TEL 202-862-0992. FAX 202-822-8092.
Vendor(s): Human Resources Information Network (CDD, HDD). *1538*

NATIONAL REPORT ON WORK & FAMILY.
Buraff Publications 1350 Connecticut Ave. N.W., Ste. 1000, Washington, DC 20036. TEL 202-862-0992. FAX 202-862-0999.
Vendor(s): Human Resources Information Network. *3629*

NATIONAL REPORTER.
Maritime Law Book Ltd., Box 302, Fredericton, N.B. E3B 4Y9, Canada. TEL 506-454-9921.
Vendor(s): QL Systems Ltd.. *2657*

NATIONAL RESEARCH COUNCIL, CANADA. ASSOCIATE COMMITTEE ON GEOTECHNICAL RESEARCH. TECHNICAL MEMORANDUM.
National Research Council of Canada, Associate Committee on Geotechnical Research, Ottawa, Ont. K1A OS2, Canada. TEL 613-993-9546. *1831*

NATIONAL REVIEW.
National Review, Inc., 150 E. 35th St., New York, NY 10016. TEL 212-679-7330. FAX 212-696-0309.
Vendor(s): DIALOG. *3909*

NATIONAL WRITING PROJECT. CENTER FOR THE STUDY OF WRITING QUARTERLY.
National Writing Project, Center for the Study of Writing, Tolman Hall, University of California, Berkeley, CA 94720. TEL 510-642-0976. *1756*

NATION'S BUSINESS.
Chamber of Commerce of the U.S., 1615 H St., N.W., Washington, DC 20062. TEL 202-463-5650. FAX 202-887-3437.
Vendor(s): DIALOG. *820*

NATION'S RESTAURANT NEWS.
Lebhar-Friedman, Inc., 425 Park Ave., New York, NY 10022. TEL 212-756-5000.
Vendor(s): DIALOG. *2478*

NATURAL HISTORY.
American Museum of Natural History, Central Park W. at 79th St., New York, NY 10024-5192. TEL 212-769-5500. FAX 212-769-5511.
Vendor(s): DIALOG. *4327*

NATURAL RESOURCES & ENVIRONMENT.
American Bar Association, Natural Resources, Energy, and Environmental Law Section, 750 N. Lake Shore Dr., Chicago, IL 60611. TEL 312-988-5000.
Vendor(s): WESTLAW. *1493*

NAVAL LAW REVIEW.
Naval Justice School, Naval Education and Training Center, Newport, RI 02841. FAX 401-841-3985.
Vendor(s): WESTLAW. *2657*

NAVY NEWS & UNDERSEA TECHNOLOGY.
Pasha Publications Inc., 1401 Wilson Blvd., Ste. 900, Arlington, VA 22209-9970. TEL 703-528-1244. FAX 703-528-1253.
Vendor(s): Data-Star, DIALOG, NewsNet. *3467*

NEBRASKA LAW REVIEW.
University of Nebraska, Lincoln, College of Law, Lincoln, NE 68583-0903. TEL 402-472-1267.
Vendor(s): WESTLAW. *2657*

NEMATOLOGICAL ABSTRACTS.
C.A.B. International, Wallingford, Oxon OX10 8DE, England. TEL 0491 32111. FAX 0491-33508.
Vendor(s): BRS (CABA), CISTI, DIMDI, DIALOG, European Space Agency (File nos.16 & 124/CAB). *140*

NETLINE.
DataTrends Publications, Inc., 8130 Boone Blvd., Ste. 210, Vienna, VA 22182. TEL 703-760-0660. FAX 703-760-9365.
Vendor(s): Data-Star, DIALOG, NewsNet. *1427*

NETWORK COMPUTING NEWS.
Publications & Communications, Inc., 12416 Hymeadow Dr., Austin, TX 78750-1896. TEL 512-250-9023. FAX 512-331-3900. *1463*

NETWORK MANAGEMENT SYSTEMS & STRATEGIES.
DataTrends Publications, Inc., 8130 Boone Blvd., Ste. 210, Vienna, VA 22182. TEL 703-760-0660. FAX 703-760-9365.
Vendor(s): Data-Star, DIALOG, NewsNet. *1428*

NETWORK WORLD.
Network World Inc., 161 Worcester Rd., 5th Fl., Framingham, MA 01701. TEL 508-875-6400.
Vendor(s): DIALOG (File no.674). *1351*

NETWORKING DIRECTORY.
Phillips Publishing, Inc., 7811 Montrose Rd., Potomac, MD 20854. TEL 800-777-5006. FAX 301-309-3847.
Vendor(s): NewsNet. *1428*

NETWORKS UPDATE.
Worldwide Videotex, Box 138, Babson Park, Boston, MA 02157. TEL 617-449-1603.
Vendor(s): Data-Star, DIALOG, NewsNet. *1428*

NEUROLOGICAL SURGERY.
Igaku-Shoin Ltd., 5-24-3 Hongo, Bunkyo-ku, Tokyo 113-91, Japan. TEL 03-817-5702.
Vendor(s): JICST. *3347*

NEUROLOGY.
Avanstar Communications, Inc., 7500 Old Oak Blvd., Cleveland, OH 44130. TEL 216-826-2839. FAX 216-891-2726.
Vendor(s): BRS. *3347*

NEW AFRICAN.
I.C. Publications Ltd., Box 261, Carlton House, 69 Gt. Queen St., London WC2B 5BN, England. TEL 071-404-4333. FAX 071-404-5336. *933*

NEW BRUNSWICK REPORTS.
Maritime Law Book Ltd., Box 302, Fredericton, N.B. E3B 4Y9, Canada. TEL 506-454-9921.
Vendor(s): QL Systems Ltd.. *2658*

NEW ENGLAND ECONOMIC INDICATORS.
Federal Reserve Bank of Boston, Research Department, 600 Atlantic Ave., Boston, MA 02106. TEL 617-973-3542. FAX 617-973-3957. *875*

NEW ENGLAND JOURNAL OF MEDICINE.
Massachusetts Medical Society, 1440 Main St., Waltham, MA 02254. TEL 617-734-9800.
Vendor(s): BRS (NEJM), BRS/Saunders Colleague. *3135*

NEW HAMPSHIRE BUSINESS REVIEW.
Business Publications, Inc. (Manchester), 150 Dow St., Manchester, NH 03101-1227. TEL 603-624-1442.
Vendor(s): DIALOG. *838*

NEW JERSEY LAWYER.
New Jersey Lawyer, Inc. 2825 Woodbridge Ave., Edison, NJ 08817. TEL 908-549-4800.
Vendor(s): WESTLAW. *2659*

NEW LAW JOURNAL.
Butterworth & Co. (Publishers) Ltd. 88 Kingsway, London WC2B 6AB, England. TEL 71-405-6900. FAX 71-405-1332.
Vendor(s): Mead Data Central. *2659*

NEW LEADER.
American Labor Conference on International Affairs, Inc., 275 Seventh Ave., New York, NY 10001. TEL 212-807-8240. FAX 212-727-2229.
Vendor(s): DIALOG. *2230*

NEW MARITIMES.
New Maritimes Editorial Council Society, 6106 Lawrence St., Halifax, N.S. B3L 1J6, Canada. TEL 902-425-6622. *2876*

NEW MATERIALS - JAPAN.
Elsevier Science Publishers Ltd., Crown House, Linton Rd., Barking, Essex IG11 8JU, England. TEL 081-594-7272. FAX 081-594-5942.
Vendor(s): Data-Star, DIALOG. *4605*

NEW MEDIA MARKETS.
Financial Times Business Information Ltd., Tower House, Southampton St., London WC2E 7HA, England. TEL 071-240 9391. FAX 071-240-7946.
Vendor(s): Data-Star, Mead Data Central. *1341*

NEW MEXICO BUSINESS JOURNAL.
Southwest Publications, Inc. (Albuquerque), Box 30550, Albuquerque, NM 87190-0550. TEL 505-243-5581.
Vendor(s): DIALOG. *681*

NEW ORLEANS CITYBUSINESS.
CityBusiness-New Orleans Inc., Heritage Plaza, Box 19308, New Orleans, LA 70179. TEL 504-834-9292.
Vendor(s): DIALOG. *1116*

NEW PRODUCT LAUNCH LETTER.
IMSWORLD Publications, Ltd., 11-13 Melton St., London NW1 2EH, England. *3736*

NEW REPUBLIC.
1220 19th St., N.W., Washington, DC 20036. TEL 202-331-7494. FAX 202-331-0275. Vendor(s): DIALOG. *2876*

NEW SCIENTIST.
I P C Magazines Ltd., Holborn Group Commonwealth House, 1-19 New Oxford St., London WC1 1NG, England. TEL 071-404-0700. Vendor(s): VU/TEXT Information Services, Inc.. *4329*

NEW SOUTH WALES LAW REPORTS.
Law Book Co. Ltd., 44-50 Waterloo Rd., North Ryde, N.S.W. 2113, Australia. TEL 02-887-0177. FAX 02-888-9706. *2659*

NEW TECHNOLOGY WEEK.
King Publishing Group, Inc., 627 National Press Bldg., Washington, DC 20045. TEL 202-638-4260. FAX 202-662-9744.
Vendor(s): Data-Star, DIALOG. *4605*

NEW YORK LAW JOURNAL.
New York Law Publishing Co., 111 Eighth Ave., New York, NY 10011. TEL 212-741-8300. Vendor(s): Mead Data Central, Wilsonline. *2660*

NEW YORK STATE BAR JOURNAL.
New York State Bar Association, One Marine Midland Plaza, Binghamton, NY 13902. FAX 607-772-6093.
Vendor(s): WESTLAW (NYSTBJ). *2660*

NEW YORK TIMES INDEX.
University Microfilms International, Serials Data Management, 300 N. Zeeb Rd., Ann Arbor, MI 48106. TEL 313-761-4700. *2578*

NEW YORK UNIVERSITY LAW REVIEW.
New York University, Law Review, 110 W. Third St., New York, NY 10012. TEL 212-998-6350. FAX 212-995-4032.
Vendor(s): Mead Data Central, WESTLAW. *2660*

NEW ZEALAND NATIONAL BIBLIOGRAPHY.
National Library of New Zealand, Private Bag, Wellington, New Zealand. TEL 04-743099. FAX 04-7433035. *407*

NEWFOUNDLAND & PRINCE EDWARD ISLAND REPORTS.
Maritime Law Book Ltd., Box 302, Fredericton, N.B. E3B 4Y9, Canada. TEL 506-454-9921.
Vendor(s): QL Systems Ltd.. *2660*

NEWSLETTER ON SERIALS PRICING ISSUES.
Marcia Tuttle, Ed. & Pub., Serials Department, C.B. 3938, Davis Library, University of North Carolina, Chapel Hill, NC 27599-3938. TEL 919-962-1067. FAX 919-962-0484. *2776*

NEWSLETTERS IN PRINT.
Gale Research Inc., 835 Penobscot Bldg., Detroit, MI 48226. TEL 313-961-2242. FAX 313-961-6083.
Vendor(s): DIALOG, Human Resources Information Network (NIP). *4133*

NEWSMAKERS.
Gale Research Inc., 835 Penobscot Bldg., Detroit, MI 48226. TEL 800-877-4253. FAX 313-221-7086.
Vendor(s): Mead Data Central. *420*

NEWSNET ACTION LETTER.
NewsNet, Inc., 945 Haverford Rd., Bryn Mawr, PA 19010. TEL 215-527-8030. FAX 215-527-0338. Vendor(s): NewsNet (PB99). *1351*

NEWSWEEK.
Newsweek, Inc., 444 Madison Ave., New York, NY 10022. TEL 212-350-4000.
Vendor(s): Mead Data Central. *2230*

THE NIKKEI WEEKLY.
Nihon Keizai Shimbun, Inc., 1-9-5 Ote-machi, Chiyoda-ku, Tokyo 100, Japan. TEL 03-5255-2310. FAX 03-5255-2631.
Vendor(s): Mead Data Central. *682*

NIPPON MEDICAL SCHOOL. JOURNAL.
Nippon Medical School, Medical Association, 1-1-5 Sendagi, Bunkyo-ku, Tokyo 113, Japan. FAX 03-3822-8575.
Vendor(s): JICST. *3136*

NOISE REGULATION REPORT.
Business Publishers, Inc., 951 Pershing Dr., Silver Spring, MD 20910-4464. TEL 301-587-6300. FAX 301-585-9075.
Vendor(s): NewsNet (EV19). *1978*

NONFERROUS METALS ALERT.
A S M International, Materials Information, Materials Park, OH 44073. TEL 216-338-5151. FAX 216-338-4634.
Vendor(s): CEDOCAR, CISTI, Data-Star (MBUS), DIALOG (File no.269), European Space Agency (File no.111), Orbit Information Technologies (MATERIALS/B), STN International (MATBUS). *3427*

NONWOVENS ABSTRACTS.
Pira International, Randalls Rd., Leatherhead, Surrey KT22 7RU, England. TEL 0372-376161. Vendor(s): Data-Star, DIALOG, European Space Agency, Orbit Information Technologies. *3869*

NORDICOM.
Nordic Documentation Center for Mass Communication Research, Statsbiblioteket, Universitetsparken, DK-8000 Aarhus C, Denmark. *1349*

NORTH CAROLINA JOURNAL OF INTERNATIONAL LAW AND COMMERCIAL REGULATION.
University of North Carolina at Chapel Hill, School of Law, Chapel Hill, NC 27599-3380. TEL 919-962-4402. FAX 914-962-1277.
Vendor(s): Wilsonline. *2727*

NORTH CAROLINA LAW REVIEW.
University of North Carolina at Chapel Hill, School of Law, Chapel Hill, NC 27514. TEL 919-962-3926. Vendor(s): Mead Data Central, WESTLAW. *2661*

NORTH DAKOTA LAW REVIEW.
University of North Dakota, School of Law, Grand Forks, ND 58201. TEL 701-777-2941. FAX 701-777-2217.
Vendor(s): WESTLAW. *2661*

NORTH SEA LETTER.
Financial Times Business Information Ltd., Tower House, Southampton St., London WC2E 7HA, England. TEL 071-240 9391. FAX 071-240-7946. Vendor(s): Data-Star, Mead Data Central. *3694*

NORTH SYDNEY CITYSCOPE.
Cityscope Publications Pty. Ltd., P.O. Box 807, Manly, N.S.W. 2095, Australia. TEL 02-976-2233. FAX 02-976-2263. *4160*

NORTHERN HOUSE PAMPHLET POETS.
Northern House, 19 Haldane Terrace, Newcastle-upon-Tyne NE2 3AN, England. *2999*

NORTHERN IRELAND NEWS SERVICE.
Box 57, Albany, NY 12211-0057. TEL 518-329-3003.
Vendor(s): NewsNet. *3911*

NORTHERN KENTUCKY LAW REVIEW.
Northern Kentucky University, Salmon P. Chase College of Law, Highland Heights, KY 41076. TEL 606-572-5444.
Vendor(s): WESTLAW. *2661*

THE NORTHERN MINER.
Southam North American Magazine Group, 1450 Don Mills Rd., Don Mills, Ont. M3B 2X7, Canada. TEL 416-445-6641. FAX 416-442-2272. *3492*

NORTHWESTERN JOURNAL OF INTERNATIONAL LAW & BUSINESS.
Northwestern University, School of Law, 357 E. Chicago Ave., Chicago, IL 60611. TEL 312-503-8467.
Vendor(s): WESTLAW. *2727*

NORTHWESTERN UNIVERSITY LAW REVIEW.
Northwestern University, School of Law, 357 E. Chicago Ave., Chicago, IL 60611. TEL 312-503-8467.
Vendor(s): Mead Data Central, WESTLAW. *2661*

NOTIZIARIO CHIMICO E FARMACEUTICO.
Societa Editoriale Farmaceutica s.r.l., Via Ausonio, 12, 20123 Milan, Italy. TEL 02-89404545. FAX 02-89401168. *3736*

NOTORNIS.
Ornithological Society of New Zealand Inc., P.O. Box 12-397, Wellington, New Zealand. *566*

NOTRE DAME LAW REVIEW.
University of Notre Dame, School of Law, Box 988, Notre Dame, IN 46556. TEL 219-239-7097. FAX 219-239-6371.
Vendor(s): WESTLAW. *2662*

NOVA LAW REVIEW.
Nova Law Review, 3100 S.W. 9th Ave., Fort Lauderdale, FL 33315. TEL 305-522-2300. Vendor(s): WESTLAW. *2662*

NOVA SCOTIA REPORTS.
Maritime Law Book Ltd., Box 302, Fredericton, N.B. E3B 4Y9, Canada. TEL 902-667-3889. Vendor(s): QL Systems Ltd.. *2662*

NOW AND THEN.
East Tennessee State University, Center for Appalachian Studies and Services, Box 70556, Johnson City, TN 37614-0556. TEL 615-929-5348. FAX 615-929-5770. *2944*

NUCLEAR AWARENESS NEWS.
Nuclear Awareness Project, Box 2331, Oshawa, Ont. L1H 7V4, Canada. TEL 416-725-1565. *1807*

NUCLEAR DATA SHEETS.
Academic Press, Inc., Journal Division, 1250 Sixth Ave., San Diego, CA 92101. TEL 619-230-1840. FAX 619-699-6800. *1807*

NUCLEAR NEWS.
American Nuclear Society, 555 N. Kensington Ave., La Grange Park, IL 60525. TEL 708-352-6611. Vendor(s): Mead Data Central. *1808*

NUCLEAR WASTE NEWS.
Business Publishers, Inc., 951 Pershing Dr., Silver Spring, MD 20910-4464. TEL 301-587-6300. FAX 301-585-9075.
Vendor(s): NewsNet (EV03). *1986*

NUCLEARFUEL.
McGraw-Hill, Inc., 1221 Ave. of the Americas, New York, NY 10020.
Vendor(s): DIALOG (File no.624/McGRAW-HILL PUBLICATIONS ONLINE), Dow Jones/News Retrieval (NUF), Mead Data Central (NUFUEL). *1808*

NUCLEONICS WEEK.
McGraw-Hill, Inc., Energy & Business Newsletters, 1221 Ave. of the Americas, 36th Fl., New York, NY 10020. TEL 212-512-6410.
Vendor(s): DIALOG (File no.624/McGRAW-HILL PUBLICATIONS ONLINE), Dow Jones/News Retrieval (NUC), Mead Data Central (NUWEEK). *1793*

NUCLEOTECNICA.
Comision Chilena de Energia Nuclear, Amunategui 95, Casilla 188-D, Santiago, Chile. TEL 56-2-699-0070. FAX 56-2-721703. *1808*

NURSE ANESTHESIA.
Appleton & Lange, Journal Division 25 Van Zant St., Box 5630, Norwalk, CT 06856. TEL 203-838-4400. *3283*

THE NURSE PRACTITIONER: THE AMERICAN JOURNAL OF PRIMARY HEALTH CARE.
Vernon Publications Inc., 3000 Northup Way, Ste. 200, Bellevue, WA 98004. TEL 206-827-9900. FAX 206-822-9372. *3283*

NURSING HOMES AND SENIOR CITIZEN CARE.
International Publishing Group, 4959 Commerce Pkwy., Cleveland, OH 44128. TEL 216-464-1210. FAX 216-464-1835.
Vendor(s): DIALOG. *3284*

NURSING OUTLOOK.
Mosby Year - Book, Inc. (Littleton) 545 Great Rd., Littleton, MA 01460. TEL 800-225-5020. FAX 508-486-9423. *3284*

NURSING RESEARCH.
American Journal of Nursing Co., 555 W. 57th St., New York, NY 10019. TEL 212-582-8820. *3284*

SERIALS AVAILABLE ONLINE

NUTRITION ABSTRACTS AND REVIEWS. SERIES A: HUMAN AND EXPERIMENTAL.
C.A.B. International, Wallingford, Oxon OX10 8DE, England. TEL 0491-32111. FAX 0491-33508.
Vendor(s): BRS (NUTR), CISTI, DIMDI, DIALOG, European Space Agency (File nos.16 & 124/CAB). *3614*

NUTRITION ABSTRACTS AND REVIEWS. SERIES B: LIVESTOCK FEEDS AND FEEDING.
C.A.B. International, Wallingford, Oxon OX10 8DE, England. TEL 0491-32111. FAX 0491-33508.
Vendor(s): BRS (VETR), CISTI, DIMDI, DIALOG, European Space Agency (File nos.16 & 124/CAB). *141*

NY LITTERATUR OM KVINNOR: EN BIBLIOGRAFI.
Goeteborgs Universitet, Universitetsbibliotek, Centralbiblioteket, Box 5096, S-402 22 Goeteborg, Sweden. *4861*

NYERE DANSK FAGLITTERATUR.
Bibliotekscentralen, Tempovej 7-11, DK-2750 Ballerup, Denmark. TEL 2-974000. FAX 2-655310. *408*

O A G FREQUENT FLYER.
Official Airline Guides, Inc. (New York), 1775 Broadway, 19th Fl., New York, NY 10019. TEL 800-323-3537. *4676*

O & M INTELLIGENCE.
Forecast International Inc. - D M S, 22 Commerce Rd., Newtown, CT 06470. TEL 203-426-0800. FAX 203-426-1964.
Vendor(s): DIALOG (File no.587/DMS DEFENSE NEWSLETTERS). *3467*

O E C D. QUARTERLY OIL STATISTICS AND ENERGY BALANCES.
Organization for Economic Cooperation and Development, 2 rue Andre-Pascal, 75775 Paris Cedex 16, France. TEL 45-24-82-00. FAX 45-24-85-00. *3706*

OAKLAND BUSINESS MONTHLY.
Spinal Column Publications, 7196 Cooley Lake Rd., Union Lake, MI 48085.
Vendor(s): DIALOG. *683*

OBSTETRICAL & GYNECOLOGICAL SURVEY.
Williams & Wilkins, 428 E. Preston St., Baltimore, MD 21202. TEL 301-528-4000. FAX 301-528-4312.
Vendor(s): BRS. *3295*

OBSTETRICS AND GYNECOLOGY.
Elsevier Science Publishing Co., Inc. (New York), 655 Ave. of the Americas, New York, NY 10010. TEL 212-989-5800. FAX 212-633-3965.
Vendor(s): BRS. *3295*

OCCASIONAL PAPERS ON RELIGION IN EASTERN EUROPE.
Christian Association for Relationships with Eastern Europe, c/o Rosemont College, Rosemont, PA 19010. TEL 215-527-0200. FAX 215-525-2930.
Vendor(s): BRS, DIALOG. *4193*

OCCUPATIONAL HEALTH & SAFETY LETTER.
Business Publishers, Inc., 951 Pershing Dr., Silver Spring, MD 20910-4464. TEL 301-587-6300. FAX 301-585-9075.
Vendor(s): NewsNet. *3619*

OCCUPATIONAL SAFETY & HEALTH REPORTER.
The Bureau of National Affairs, Inc., 1231 25th St., N.W., Washington, DC 20037. TEL 202-452-4200. FAX 202-822-8092.
Vendor(s): DIALOG (Laborlaw, File 244), Human Resources Information Network (CDD, HDD). *3620*

OCCUPATIONAL THERAPY INDEX.
Medical Information Service, The British Library, Boston Spa, Wetherby, W. Yorkshire LS23 7BQ, England. TEL 0937-546039. FAX 0937-546236. *3178*

OCEAN OIL WEEKLY REPORT.
PennWell Publishing Co. (Houston), Box 1941, Houston, TX 77251. TEL 713-621-9720. FAX 713-963-6285. *3694*

OCEANIC ABSTRACTS.
Cambridge Scientific Abstracts, 7200 Wisconsin Ave., 6th Fl., Bethesda, MD 20814. TEL 301-961-6750. FAX 301-961-6720.
Vendor(s): BRS (CSAL), DIALOG (File no.28), European Space Agency (File no.17/OCEANIC). *1551*

OCTANE WEEK.
Information Resources, Inc., 499 S. Capitol St., S.W., No. 406, Washington, DC 20003. TEL 800-USA-FUEL. FAX 202-554-0613.
Vendor(s): Data-Star, DIALOG. *3694*

OCTOBER.
M I T Press, 55 Hayward St., Cambridge, MA 02142. TEL 617-253-2889. FAX 617-258-6779. *339*

O'DWYER'S P R SERVICES REPORT.
J.R. O'Dwyer Co., Inc., 271 Madison Ave., New York, NY 10016. TEL 212-679-2471. FAX 212-683-2750.
Vendor(s): Mead Data Central. *36*

OFFICE COMPUTING REPORT.
Patricia Seybold's Office Computing Group, 148 State St., 7th Fl., Boston, MA 02109. TEL 617-742-5200. FAX 617-742-1028.
Vendor(s): NewsNet. *1452*

OFFSHORE ENGINEERING ABSTRACTS.
S T I Ltd., 4 Kings Meadow, Ferry Hinksey Rd., Oxford OX2 0DU, England. TEL 0865-798898. FAX 0865-798788.
Vendor(s): DIALOG (File no.96/FLUIDEX), European Space Agency (File no.48/FLUIDEX). *1845*

OFFSHORE INCORPORATING THE OILMAN.
PennWell Publishing Co., Box 1260, Tulsa, OK 74101. TEL 918-835-3161.
Vendor(s): Mead Data Central. *3694*

OHIO STATE JOURNAL ON DISPUTE RESOLUTION.
Ohio State University, College of Law, 1659 N. High St., Columbus, OH 43210-1391. TEL 614-292-7170.
Vendor(s): WESTLAW, Wilsonline. *2663*

OHIO STATE LAW JOURNAL.
Ohio State University, College of Law, 1659 North High St., Columbus, OH 43210-1391. TEL 614-292-6829.
Vendor(s): Mead Data Central, WESTLAW, Wilsonline. *2663*

OIL & GAS JOURNAL.
PennWell Publishing Co., Box 1260, Tulsa, OK 74101. TEL 918-835-3161.
Vendor(s): Mead Data Central. *3695*

OIL DAILY.
Oil Daily Co., 1401 New York Ave., N.W., Ste. 500, Washington, DC 20005. TEL 202-662-0700. FAX 202-783-8320.
Vendor(s): DIALOG. *3695*

OIL PRICE INFORMATION SERVICE.
United Communications Group, 11300 Rockville Pike, Ste. 1100, Rockville, MD 20852-3030. TEL 301-816-8950.
Vendor(s): United Communications Group (PETROSCAN). *3696*

OIL SPILL INTELLIGENCE REPORT.
Cutter Information Corp., 37 Broadway, Arlington, MA 02174. TEL 617-648-8700. FAX 617-648-8707.
Vendor(s): Data-Star, DIALOG, NewsNet. *3696*

OKLAHOMA CITY UNIVERSITY LAW REVIEW.
Oklahoma City University, School of Law, 2501 N. Blackwelder, Oklahoma City, OK 73106. TEL 405-521-5280.
Vendor(s): WESTLAW. *2663*

OKLAHOMA LAW REVIEW.
University of Oklahoma, College of Law, 300 Timberdell Rd., Norman, OK 73019. TEL 405-325-5191.
Vendor(s): WESTLAW. *2663*

OLDER AMERICANS REPORT.
Business Publishers, Inc., 951 Pershing Dr., Silver Spring, MD 20910-4464. TEL 301-587-6300. FAX 301-585-9075.
Vendor(s): NewsNet. *4415*

ONCOGENES AND GROWTH FACTORS ABSTRACTS.
Cambridge Scientific Abstracts, 7200 Wisconsin Ave., 6th Fl., Bethesda, MD 20814. TEL 301-961-6750. FAX 301-961-6720.
Vendor(s): BRS (CSAL), DIALOG (File no.76). *3178*

ONE TO ONE (FRESNO).
Creeyadio Services, Box 9787, Fresno, CA 93794. TEL 209-226-0558. FAX 209-226-7481.
Vendor(s): CompuServe Consumer Information Service. *1357*

ONLINE (WESTON).
Online, Inc., 11 Tannery Ln., Weston, CT 06883. TEL 203-227-8466. FAX 203-222-0122.
Vendor(s): DIALOG (File no 170). *1428*

ONLINE LIBRARIES AND MICROCOMPUTERS.
Information Intelligence, Inc., Box 31098, Phoenix, AZ 85046. TEL 800-228-9982.
Vendor(s): Data-Star, DIALOG, NewsNet. *2799*

ONLINE NEWSLETTER.
Information Intelligence Inc., Box 31098, Phoenix, AZ 85046. TEL 800-228-9982.
Vendor(s): Data-Star, DIALOG, NewsNet. *1428*

ONLINE PRODUCT NEWS.
Worldwide Videotex, Box 138, Babson Park, Boston, MA 02157. TEL 617-449-1603.
Vendor(s): NewsNet. *1445*

ONTARIO APPEAL CASES.
Maritime Law Book Ltd., Box 302, Fredericton, N.B. E3B 4Y9, Canada. TEL 506-454-9921.
Vendor(s): QL Systems Ltd.. *2664*

ONTARIO REPORTS.
Butterworths Canada Ltd., 75 Clegg Rd., Markham, Ont. L6G 1A1, Canada. TEL 416-479-2665. FAX 416-479-2826.
Vendor(s): QL Systems Ltd.. *2664*

OPEN: O S I PRODUCT AND EQUIPMENT NEWS.
DataTrends Publications, Inc., 8130 Boone Blvd., Ste. 210, Vienna, VA 22182. TEL 703-760-0660. FAX 703-760-9365.
Vendor(s): Data-Star, DIALOG, NewsNet. *1479*

OPEN SYSTEMS REPORT.
Phillips Publishing, Inc., 7811 Montrose Rd., Potomac, MD 20854. TEL 301-340-2100. FAX 301-309-3847.
Vendor(s): NewsNet. *1428*

OPPORTUNITIES BRIEFING.
International Freedom Foundation, 200 G St., N.E., Ste. 300, Washington, DC 20002. TEL 202-546-5788. FAX 202-546-5488.
Vendor(s): DIALOG, NewsNet (File no.IT33). *918*

OPTICAL & MAGNETIC REPORT.
Phillips Publishing, Inc., 7811 Montrose Rd., Potomac, MD 20854. TEL 301-340-2100. FAX 301-424-4297.
Vendor(s): Data-Star, DIALOG, NewsNet. *1454*

OPTICAL MATERIALS AND ENGINEERING NEWS.
Business Communications Co., Inc. (Norwalk), 25 Van Zant St., Norwalk, CT 06855. TEL 203-853-4266. FAX 203-853-0348.
Vendor(s): Data-Star, DIALOG, NewsNet. *3856*

OPTOMETRY CLINICS.
Appleton & Lange, Journal Division 25 Van Zant St., Box 5630, Norwalk, CT 06856. TEL 203-838-4400. *3304*

ORANGE COUNTY BUSINESS JOURNAL.
Orange County Business Journal, 4590 MacArthur Blvd., Ste. 100, Newport Beach, CA 92660. TEL 714-833-8373. FAX 714-833-8751.
Vendor(s): DIALOG. *878*

OREGON LAW REVIEW.
Christensen Inc. (Eugene), University of Oregon, School of Law, Eugene, OR 97403-1221. TEL 503-346-3844. FAX 503-346-3985.
Vendor(s): WESTLAW. *2664*

ORGANOMETALLICS.
American Chemical Society, 1155 16th St., N.W., Washington, DC 20036. TEL 800-333-9511. FAX 202-872-4615.
Vendor(s): STN International (CJACS). *1221*

ORIGINS, C N S DOCUMENTARY SERVICE.
Catholic News Service, 3211 4th St., N.E., Washington, DC 20017. TEL 202-541-3290. FAX 202-541-3255.
Vendor(s): NewsNet. *4272*

ORNAMENTAL HORTICULTURE.
C.A.B. International, Wallingford, Oxon OX10 8DE, England. TEL 0491-32111. FAX 0491-33508.
Vendor(s): BRS, CISTI, DIMDI, DIALOG, European Space Agency (File nos.16 & 124/CAB). *2141*

ORPHAN DISEASE UPDATE.
National Organization for Rare Disorders, Inc., Box 8923, New Fairfield, CT 06812. TEL 203-746-6518. FAX 203-746-6481.
Vendor(s): CompuServe Consumer Information Service (GO NORD). *3138*

ORTHOPEDICS TODAY.
Slack, Inc., 6900 Grove Rd., Thorofare, NJ 08086. TEL 609-848-1000. FAX 609-853-5991. *3310*

OUTDOOR LIFE.
Times Mirror Magazines, Inc., 2 Park Ave., New York, NY 10016. TEL 212-779-5000.
Vendor(s): DIALOG. *4552*

OUTLOOK (YEAR) PROCEEDINGS.
U.S. Department of Agriculture, World Agricultural Outlook Board, Rm. 5143 S. Bldg., Washington, DC 20250-3900. TEL 202-447-5447.
Vendor(s): BRS, DIALOG. *156*

OXY-FUEL NEWS.
Information Resources, Inc., 499 S. Capitol St., S.W., Ste. 406, Washington, DC 20003. TEL 202-554-0614. FAX 202-554-0613.
Vendor(s): Data-Star, DIALOG. *1793*

P A CS & LOBBIES.
Amward Publications, Inc., 2000 National Press Bldg., Washington, DC 20045. TEL 202-488-7227. FAX 301-251-9058.
Vendor(s): NewsNet (PO02). *3913*

P A I S INTERNATIONAL IN PRINT.
Public Affairs Information Service, Inc., 521 W. 43rd St., 5th Fl., New York, NY 10036-4396. TEL 212-736-6629. FAX 212-643-2848.
Vendor(s): BRS (PAIS), BRS/Saunders Colleague, Data-Star (PAIS), DIALOG (File no.49/PAIS). *733*

P A S C A L EXPLORE. E 30: MICROSCOPIE ELECTRONIQUE ET DIFFRACTION ELECTRONIQUE.
Centre National de la Recherche Scientifique, Institut de l'Information Scientifique et Technique, B.P. 54, 54514 Vandoevre-Les-Nancy Cedex, France. TEL 83-50-46-00.
Vendor(s): DIALOG. *466*

P A S C A L THEMA. T 215: BIOTECHNOLOGIES (EDITIONS FRANCAISE).
Centre National de la Recherche Scientifique, Institut de l'Information Scientifique et Technique, Chateau du Montet, 54514 Vandoeuvre-Les-Nancy Cedex, France.
Vendor(s): European Space Agency, Telesystemes - Questel. *3179*

P A S C A L THEMA. T 230: ENERGIE.
Centre National de la Recherche Scientifique, Institut de l'Information Scientifique et Technique, B.P. 54, 54514 Vandoeuvre-Les-Nancy Cedex, France. TEL 83-50-46-00.
Vendor(s): European Space Agency, Telesystemes - Questel. *3838*

P A S C A L THEMA. T 235: MEDECINE TROPICALE.
Centre National de la Recherche Scientifique, Institut de l'Information Scientifique et Technique, B.P. 54, 54514 Vandoeuvre-Les-Nancy Cedex, France. TEL 83-50-46-00.
Vendor(s): European Space Agency, Telesystemes - Questel. *3180*

P A S C A L THEMA. T 240: METAUX, METALLURGIE.
Centre National de la Recherche Scientifique, Institut de l'Information Scientifique et Technique, B.P. 54, 54514 Vandoeuvre-Les-Nancy Cedex, France. TEL 83-50-46-00.
Vendor(s): European Space Agency, Telesystemes - Questel. *3427*

P A S C A L THEMA. T 260: ZOOLOGIE FONDAMENTALE ET APPLIQUEE DES INVERTEBRES (MILIEU TERRESTRE, EAUX DOUCES).
Centre National de la Recherche Scientifique, Institut de l'Information Scientifique et Technique, B.P. 54, 54514 Vandoeuvre-Les-Nancy Cedex, France. TEL 83-50-46-00.
Vendor(s): European Space Agency, Telesystemes - Questel. *467*

P & T.
Excerpta Medica, Inc., Core Publishing Division 105 Raider Blvd., Belle Mead, NJ 08052. TEL 908-874-8550. FAX 908-874-0700. *3737*

P C BUSINESS PRODUCTS.
Worldwide Videotex, Box 138, Babson Park, Boston, MA 02157. TEL 617-449-1603.
Vendor(s): Data-Star, DIALOG, NewsNet. *805*

P C MAGAZIN.
Markt und Technik Verlag AG, Hans-Pinsel-str. 2, 8013 Haar, Germany. TEL 089-4613-0. FAX 089-4613-775.
Vendor(s): DIALOG. *1472*

P C T GAZETTE.
World Intellectual Property Organization (WIPO), Publications and Public Information Section, 34 Chemin des Colombettes, 1211 Geneva 20, Switzerland. TEL 022-730-9111. FAX 022-733-5428. *3680*

P C WEEK.
Ziff-Davis Publishing Co., 10 Presidents Landing, Medford, MA 02155-5146. TEL 617-393-3000.
Vendor(s): DIALOG. *1473*

P - D NEWS.
Publications & Communications, Inc., 12416 Hymeadow Dr., Austin, TX 78750-1896. TEL 512-331-3918. FAX 512-331-3900. *4606*

P N I.
University Microfilms International, Data Courier, 620 S. Third St., Louisville, KY 40202-2475. TEL 800-626-2823. FAX 502-589-5572.
Available only online. Vendor(s): BRS, DIALOG, Orbit Information Technologies. *3748*

PACIFIC BUSINESS NEWS.
Crossroads Press, Inc., Box 833, Honolulu, HI 96808. TEL 808-521-0021. FAX 808-528-2325.
Vendor(s): DIALOG. *684*

PACIFIC LAW JOURNAL.
Western Newspaper Publishing, Co., 3200 Fifth Ave., Sacramento, CA 95817. TEL 916-739-7171.
Vendor(s): WESTLAW. *2665*

PACKAGING.
Cahners Publishing Company (Des Plaines) Division of Reed Publishing (USA) Inc., 1350 E. Touhy Ave., Box 5080, Des Plaines, IL 60017-5080. TEL 708-635-8800. FAX 708-635-6856. *3650*

PACKAGING SCIENCE AND TECHNOLOGY ABSTRACTS.
International Food Information Service GmbH, Melibocusstr. 52, 6000 Frankfurt a.M. 71, Germany. TEL 069-6690070. FAX 069-66900710.
Vendor(s): CISTI, DIMDI, DIALOG (File no.252), European Space Agency (File no.55/PACKABS), FIZ Technik, Orbit Information Technologies. *3652*

PAKISTAN JOURNAL OF PHARMACY.
Trade and Industry Publications Limited, Trade and Industry House, West Wharf Rd., Box 4611, Karachi 2, Pakistan. *3737*

PAPER AND BOARD ABSTRACTS.
Pira International, Randalls Rd., Leatherhead, Surrey KT22 7RU, England.
Vendor(s): Orbit Information Technologies (PIRA), Pergamon Infoline. *3668*

PAPER SALES.
Avanstar Communications, Inc., 7500 Old Oak Blvd., Cleveland, OH 44130. TEL 216-826-2839. FAX 216-891-2726.
Vendor(s): Data-Star, DIALOG. *3664*

PAPERBOUND BOOKS IN PRINT.
R.R. Bowker, A Reed Reference Publishing Company, Division of Reed Publishing (USA) Inc., 121 Chanlon Rd., New Providence, NJ 07974. TEL 800-521-8110. FAX 908-665-6688.
Vendor(s): BRS (BBIP), BRS/Saunders Colleague, DIALOG (File no.470). *409*

PAPETIERES DU QUEBEC.
Guy Fortin, 3300 Cote Vertu, Ste. 410, St. Laurent, Que. H4R 2B7, Canada. TEL 514-339-1399. FAX 514-339-1396. *3664*

PATENT OFFICE RECORD (CANADA).
Department of Consumer and Corporate Affairs, Patent Office, 50 Victoria St., Hull, Que. K1A 0C9, Canada. TEL 819-997-2525. *3677*

PATENTS ABSTRACTS.
American Petroleum Institute, Central Abstracting & Information Services, 275 Seventh Ave., New York, NY 10001-6708. TEL 212-366-4040. FAX 212-366-4298.
Vendor(s): Orbit Information Technologies, STN International. *3706*

PATIENT CARE.
Medical Economics Publishing Co., Five Paragon Dr., Montvale, NJ 07645. TEL 201-358-7200. FAX 201-573-1045.
Vendor(s): DIALOG. *3140*

PATIENT EDUCATION AND COUNSELING.
Elsevier Scientific Publishers Ireland Ltd., P.O. Box 85, Limerick, Ireland. TEL 061-61944. FAX 061-62144. *4109*

PEACE NEWS.
Peace News Ltd., 55 Dawes St., London SE17 1EL, England. TEL 071-703-7189. FAX 071-708-2545. *3914*

PEDIATRIC CLINICS OF NORTH AMERICA.
W.B. Saunders Co., Curtis Center, Independence Square W., Philadelphia, PA 19106. TEL 215-238-7800.
Vendor(s): BRS, BRS/Saunders Colleague. *3324*

PEDIATRICS.
American Academy of Pediatrics, 141 Northwest Point Blvd., Box 927, Elk Grove Village, IL 60009-0927. TEL 708-228-5005.
Vendor(s): BRS, BRS/Saunders Colleague, Mead Data Central. *3325*

PENNSYLVANIA ACADEMY OF SCIENCE. JOURNAL.
Pennsylvania Academy of Science, c/o Dr. S.K. Majumdar, Ed., Dept. of Biology, Lafayette College, Easton, PA 18042. TEL 215-250-5464. FAX 215-250-6557. *451*

PENSION WORLD.
Communication Channels, Inc., 6255 Barfield Rd., Atlanta, GA 30328-4369. TEL 404-256-9800. FAX 404-256-3116. *795*

PENSIONS & INVESTMENTS.
Crain Communications, Inc. (New York), 220 E. 42nd St., New York, NY 10017-5806. TEL 212-210-0100. FAX 212-210-0799.
Vendor(s): Mead Data Central (PENINV). *959*

PEOPLE WEEKLY.
The Time Inc. Magazine Company Time & Life Bldg., Rockefeller Center, 1271 Ave. of the Americas, New York, NY 10020-1393. TEL 212-522-1212.
Vendor(s): Mead Data Central, VU/TEXT Information Services, Inc.. *2232*

PEPPERDINE LAW REVIEW.
Pepperdine University, School of Law, Malibu, CA 90265. TEL 213-456-4694. FAX 213-456-4266.
Vendor(s): WESTLAW. *2666*

PERFORMANCE MATERIALS.
McGraw-Hill, Inc., Aviation Week Group, 1156 15th St., N.W., Ste. 600, Washington, DC 20005. TEL 202-822-4600. FAX 202-293-2682.
Vendor(s): DIALOG (File no.624/McGRAW-HILL PUBLICATIONS ONLINE). *60*

PERFUMER & FLAVORIST.
Allured Publishing, Bldg. C, Ste. 1600, 2100 Manchester Rd., Box 318, Wheaton, IL 60189-0318. TEL 708-653-2155. FAX 708-653-2192. *376*

SERIALS AVAILABLE ONLINE

PERIODICA. INDICE DE REVISTAS LATINOAMERICANAS EN CIENCIAS.
Universidad Nacional Autonoma de Mexico, Centro de Informacion Cientifica y Humanistica, Apdo. Postal 70-392, C.P. 04510 Mexico, D.F., Mexico. *4357*

PERIODICALS IN SOUTHERN AFRICAN LIBRARIES.
State Library, P.O. Box 397, Pretoria 0001, South Africa. TEL 012-21-8931. FAX 012-325-5984. *409*

PERSONAL COMPUTER.
Vogel-Verlag und Druck KG, Max-Planck-Str. 7-9, Postfach 6740, 8700 Wuerzburg, Germany. TEL 0931-418-0.
Vendor(s): DIALOG. *1464*

PERSONAL COMPUTER MARKETS.
Basil Blackwell Ltd., 108 Cowley Rd., Oxford OX4 1JF, England. TEL 0865-791100. FAX 0865-791347.
Vendor(s): Data-Star. *1050*

PERSONAL FINANCE INTELLIGENCE.
Mintel International Group Ltd., 18-19 Long Lane, London EC1A 9HE, England. TEL 071-606-4533. FAX 071-606-5159. *795*

PERSONALIST FORUM.
Furman University, Department of Philosophy, Poinsett Hwy., Greenville, SC 29613. TEL 803-294-3139. FAX 803-294-3001.
Vendor(s): DIALOG. *3775*

PERSONNEL PSYCHOLOGY.
Personnel Psychology, Inc., 745 Haskins Rd., Ste. A, Bowling Green, OH 43402-1600. TEL 419-352-1562. FAX 419-352-2645.
Vendor(s): BRS, Information Access Company. *4038*

PERSPECTIVES (TORONTO).
Gerontological Nursing Association, P.O. Box 368, Station "K", Toronto, Ont. M4P 2G7, Canada. TEL 416-884-1951.
Vendor(s): National Library of Medicine (Perspectives - Toronto SR0051880, W1PE8705F). *2277*

PESTICIDE & TOXIC CHEMICAL NEWS.
Food Chemical News, Inc., 1101 Pennsylvania Ave., S.E., Washington, DC 20003. TEL 202-544-1980. FAX 202-546-3890.
Vendor(s): Data-Star, DIALOG. *2079*

PETERSEN'S PHOTOGRAPHIC.
Petersen Publishing Co., 8490 Sunset Blvd., Los Angeles, CA 90069. TEL 213-854-2222.
Vendor(s): DIALOG. *3794*

PETERSON'S GUIDE TO FOUR-YEAR COLLEGES (YEAR).
Peterson's Guides, Inc., 202 Carnegie Center, Box 2123, Princeton, NJ 08543-2123. TEL 609-243-9111. FAX 609-243-9150.
Vendor(s): BRS (PETE), CompuServe Consumer Information Service (PCG), DIALOG (File no.214), Dow Jones/News Retrieval (SCHOOL). *1696*

PETERSON'S GUIDE TO GRADUATE AND PROFESSIONAL PROGRAMS: AN OVERVIEW (YEAR) (BOOK 1).
Peterson's Guides, Inc., 202 Carnegie Center, Box 2123, Princeton, NJ 08543-2123. TEL 609-243-9111. FAX 609-243-9150.
Vendor(s): DIALOG (File no.273). *1696*

PETERSON'S GUIDE TO GRADUATE PROGRAMS IN BUSINESS, EDUCATION, HEALTH, AND LAW (YEAR) (BOOK 6).
Peterson's Guides, Inc., 202 Carnegie Center, Box 2123, Princeton, NJ 08543-2123. TEL 609-243-9111. FAX 609-243-9150.
Vendor(s): DIALOG (File no.273). *1696*

PETERSON'S GUIDE TO GRADUATE PROGRAMS IN ENGINEERING AND APPLIED SCIENCES (YEAR) (BOOK 5).
Peterson's Guides, Inc., 202 Carnegie Center, Box 2123, Princeton, NJ 08543-2123. TEL 609-243-9111. FAX 609-243-9150.
Vendor(s): DIALOG (File no.273). *1696*

PETERSON'S GUIDE TO GRADUATE PROGRAMS IN THE BIOLOGICAL AND AGRICULTURAL SCIENCES (YEAR) (BOOK 3).
Peterson's Guides, Inc., 202 Carnegie Center, Box 2123, Princeton, NJ 08543-2123. TEL 609-243-9111. FAX 609-243-9150.
Vendor(s): DIALOG (File no.273). *1696*

PETERSON'S GUIDE TO GRADUATE PROGRAMS IN THE HUMANITIES AND SOCIAL SCIENCES (YEAR) (BOOK 2).
Peterson's Guides, Inc., 202 Carnegie Center, Box 2123, Princeton, NJ 08543-2123. TEL 609-243-9111. FAX 609-243-9150.
Vendor(s): DIALOG (File no.273). *1696*

PETERSON'S GUIDE TO GRADUATE PROGRAMS IN THE PHYSICAL SCIENCES AND MATHEMATICS (YEAR) (BOOK 4).
Peterson's Guides, Inc., 202 Carnegie Center, Box 2123, NJ 08543-2123. TEL 609-243-9111. FAX 609-243-9150.
Vendor(s): DIALOG (File no.273). *1696*

PETERSON'S GUIDE TO TWO-YEAR COLLEGES (YEAR).
Peterson's Guides, Inc., 202 Carnegie Center, Box 2123, Princeton, NJ 08543-2123. TEL 609-243-9111. FAX 609-243-9150.
Vendor(s): BRS (PETE), CompuServe Consumer Information Service (PCG), DIALOG (File no.214), Dow Jones/News Retrieval (SCHOOL). *1697*

PETROFLASH.
Bloomberg Financial Markets, 100 Business Park Dr., Box 888, Princeton, NJ 08542-0888. TEL 609-497-3500. FAX 609-683-7523.
Available only online. *3697*

PETROLEUM ABSTRACTS.
University of Tulsa, Information Services Division, 600 South College, Tulsa, OK 74104. TEL 800-247-8678. FAX 918-599-9361.
Vendor(s): Orbit Information Technologies (TULSA). *3707*

PETROLEUM-ENERGY BUSINESS NEWS INDEX.
American Petroleum Institute, Central Abstracting & Information Services, 275 Seventh Ave., New York, NY 10001. TEL 212-366-4040. FAX 212-366-4298.
Vendor(s): Data-Star (PEAB), DIALOG, Orbit Information Technologies. *3707*

PHARMA TIMES.
Indian Pharmaceutical Association, Kalina Santacruz East, Bombay 400098, India. *3737*

PHARMACEUTICA ACTA HELVETIAE.
Societe Suisse de Pharmacie, Stationsstr. 12, CH-3097 Berne-Liebefeld, Switzerland. TEL 031-535858. *3737*

PHARMACEUTICAL BUSINESS NEWS.
Financial Times Business Information, 102 Clerkenwell Rd., London EC1M 5SA, England. TEL 071-240-9391. FAX 071-240-7946.
Vendor(s): Data-Star, DIALOG. *3737*

PHARMACEUTICAL SOCIETY OF JAPAN. JOURNAL.
Pharmaceutical Society of Japan, 12-15, Shibuya 2-chome, Shibuya-ku, Tokyo 150, Japan. *3738*

PHARMACEUTICALS MONTHLY.
Yakugyo Jiho Co. Ltd., 2-36 Kanda Jimbo-cho, Chiyoda-ku, Tokyo 101, Japan. *3738*

PHARMACIEN DE FRANCE.
Federation des Syndicats Pharmaceutiques de France, 13 rue Ballu, 75009 Paris, France. *3738*

PHARMACY IN HISTORY.
American Institute of the History of Pharmacy, Pharmacy Bldg., Madison, WI 53706. TEL 608-262-5635. *3739*

PHARMACY TIMES.
Romaine Pierson Publishers, Inc., 80 Shore Rd., Port Washington, NY 11050. TEL 516-883-6350. FAX 516-883-6609. *3740*

PHARMACY WEST.
Western Communications, Ltd., 333 W. Hampden Ave., Ste. 1050, Englewood, CO 80110-2340. TEL 303-761-8818. FAX 303-761-2440. *3740*

DIE PHARMAZEUTISCHE INDUSTRIE.
Editio Cantor, Postfach 1255, 7960 Aulendorf, Germany. TEL 07525-2060. FAX 07525-20680. *3740*

PHARMAZEUTISCHE ZEITUNG.
Govi-Verlag GmbH, Beethovenplatz 1-3, Postfach 970108, 6000 Frankfurt a.M. 97, Germany. *3740*

PHILOSOPHER'S INDEX.
Bowling Green State University, Philosophy Documentation Center, Bowling Green, OH 43403-0189. TEL 419-372-2419. FAX 419-372-6987.
Vendor(s): DIALOG (File no.57). *3787*

PHILOSOPHICAL FORUM.
Philosophical Forum, Inc., c/o Baruch College, Box 239, 17 Lexington Ave., NY 10010. TEL 212-387-1682.
Vendor(s): BRS. *3776*

PHILOTELIA.
Hellenic Philotelic Society, 57 Akademias St., GR-106 79 Athens, Greece. TEL 3621-125. *3756*

PHOTOBULLETIN.
PhotoSource International, Pine Lake Farm, Osceola, WI 54020. TEL 715-248-3800. FAX 715-248-7394.
Vendor(s): NewsNet (PB26). *3795*

PHOTOFILE.
Australian Centre for Photography, 257 Oxford St., Paddington, N.S.W. 2021, Australia. TEL 02-331-6253. FAX 02-331-6887. *3795*

PHOTOLETTER.
PhotoSource International, Pine Lake Farm, Osceola, WI 54020. TEL 715-248-3800. FAX 715-248-7394.
Vendor(s): NewsNet. *3796*

PHOTOMARKET.
PhotoSource International, Pine Lake Farm, Osceola, WI 54020. TEL 715-248-3800. FAX 715-248-7394.
Vendor(s): NewsNet (PB17). *3796*

PHYSICAL FITNESS - SPORTS MEDICINE.
U.S. Department of Health and Human Services, President's Council on Physical Fitness & Sports, 450 5th St., N.W., Ste. 7130, Washington, DC 20001. TEL 202-272-3421.
Vendor(s): National Library of Medicine. *3180*

PHYSICAL THERAPY.
American Physical Therapy Association, 1111 N. Fairfax St., Fairfax, VA 22314. TEL 703-684-2782.
Vendor(s): BRS, BRS/Saunders Colleague, Central Institute for Scientific & Technical Information, Information Access Company. *3141*

PHYSICIAN AND SPORTSMEDICINE.
McGraw-Hill, Inc., 1221 Avenue of the Americas, New York, NY 10020. TEL 212-512-2000.
Vendor(s): DIALOG, Dow Jones/News Retrieval, Mead Data Central. *3372*

PHYSICIANS' DESK REFERENCE.
Medical Economics Publishing Co., Five Paragon Dr., Montvale, NJ 07645. TEL 201-357-7200. FAX 201-573-1045. *3141*

PHYSICIANS' DESK REFERENCE FOR NONPRESCRIPTION DRUGS.
Medical Economics Publishing Co., Five Paragon Dr., Montvale, NJ 07645. TEL 201-358-7200. FAX 201-573-1045. *3141*

PHYSICIANS' DESK REFERENCE FOR OPHTHALMOLOGY.
Medical Economics Company Inc., 680 Kinderkamack Rd., Oradell, NJ 07649. TEL 201-262-3030. FAX 201-262-5461. *3304*

PHYSICS ABSTRACTS.
INSPEC, I.E.E., Michael Faraday House, Six Hills Way, Stevenage, Herts. SG1 2AY, England. TEL 0438-313311. FAX 0438-742840.
Vendor(s): BRS (INSP), CEDOCAR, CISTI, Data-Star, DIALOG (File nos.2,3 & 4/INSPEC), European Space Agency (File no.8/INSPEC), JICST, Orbit Information Technologies (INSPEC), STN International (INSPEC), University of Tsukuba. *3838*

SERIALS AVAILABLE ONLINE 5093

PHYSICS BRIEFS - PHYSIKALISCHE BERICHTE.
V C H Verlagsgesellschaft mbH, Postfach 101161, 6940 Weinheim, Germany. TEL 06201-602-0. FAX 06201-602328.
Vendor(s): STN International (PHYS). *3838*

PHYSIOTHERAPY INDEX.
Medical Information Service, The British Library, Boston Spa, Wetherby, W. Yorkshire LS23 7BQ, England. TEL 0937-546039. FAX 0937-546236. *3180*

PIG NEWS & INFORMATION.
C.A.B. International, Wallingford, Oxon OX10 8DE, England. TEL 0491 32111. FAX 0491-33508.
Vendor(s): BRS, CISTI, DIMDI, DIALOG, European Space Agency (File nos.16 & 124/CAB). *223*

PIPELINES ABSTRACTS.
S T I Ltd., 4 Kings Meadow, Ferry Hinksey Rd., Oxford OX2 0DU, England. TEL 0865-798898. FAX 0865-798788.
Vendor(s): DIALOG (File no.96/FLUIDEX), European Space Agency (File no.48/FLUIDEX). *3707*

PLANNING CONSUMER MARKETS.
Henley Centre for Forecasting Ltd., 2 Tudor St., Blackfriars, London EC4Y 0AA, England. TEL 071-353-9961. *795*

PLANT BREEDING ABSTRACTS.
C.A.B. International, Wallingford, Oxon OX10 8DE, England. TEL 0491 32111. FAX 0491-33508.
Vendor(s): BRS (CABA), CISTI, DIMDI, DIALOG, European Space Agency (File nos.16 & 124/CAB). *2141*

PLANT ENGINEERING.
Cahners Publishing Company (Des Plaines) Division of Reed Publishing (USA) Inc., 1350 E. Touhy Ave., Box 5080, IL 60017-5080. TEL 708-635-8800. FAX 708-390-2636.
Vendor(s): DIALOG. *1833*

PLANT GROWTH REGULATOR ABSTRACTS.
C.A.B. International, Wallingford, Oxon OX10 8DE, England. TEL 0491 32111. FAX 0491-33508.
Vendor(s): BRS (CABA), CISTI, DIMDI, DIALOG, European Space Agency. *142*

PLANTA MEDICA.
Georg Thieme Verlag, Ruedigerstr. 14, Postfach 104853, 7000 Stuttgart 10, Germany. TEL 0711-8931-0. FAX 0711-8931298. *3740*

PLASTICS BUSINESS NEWS.
Washington Business Information, Inc., c/o Karen Harrington, 1117 N. 19th St., Ste. 200, Arlington, VA 22209. TEL 703-247-3422. FAX 703-247-3421.
Vendor(s): NewsNet. *3865*

PLATT'S INTERNATIONAL PETROCHEMICAL REPORT.
McGraw-Hill, Inc., 1221 Avenue of the Americas, New York, NY 10020.
Vendor(s): DIALOG (File no.624/McGRAW-HILL PUBLICATIONS ONLINE), Dow Jones/News Retrieval, Mead Data Central. *3699*

PLATT'S OIL MARKETING BULLETIN.
McGraw-Hill, Inc., 1221 Ave. of the Americas, New York, NY 10020.
Vendor(s): Mead Data Central. *3699*

PLATT'S OILGRAM NEWS.
McGraw-Hill, Inc., Commodity Services Group, 1221 Ave. of the Americas, 42nd Fl., New York, NY 10020. TEL 212-512-2000.
Vendor(s): DIALOG (File no.624/McGRAW-HILL PUBLICATIONS ONLINE), Dow Jones/News Retrieval (PON), Mead Data Central (PONEWS). *3699*

PLATT'S OILGRAM PRICE REPORT.
McGraw-Hill, Inc., 1221 Ave. of the Americas, New York, NY 10020.
Vendor(s): DIALOG (File no.624/McGRAW-HILL PUBLICATIONS ONLINE), Dow Jones/News Retrieval (POP), Mead Data Central (PPRICE). *3699*

PLAYTHINGS.
Geyer-McAllister Publications, Inc., 51 Madison Ave., New York, NY 10010. TEL 212-689-4411.
Vendor(s): DIALOG. *2282*

PLUIMVEE DOCUMENTATIE.
Centrum voor Onderzoek en Voorlichting voor de Pluimveehouderij "Het Spelderholt", Spelderholt 9, 7361 DA Beekbergen, Netherlands. TEL 057-666230. FAX 057-663250. *142*

POINT DE REPERE.
Services Documentaires Multimedia Inc. (SDM), 1685 rue Fleury Est, Montreal, Que. H2C 1T1, Canada. TEL 514-382-0895. FAX 514-384-9139.
Vendor(s): IST-INFORMATHEQUE. *20*

POLAR AND GLACIOLOGICAL ABSTRACTS.
Cambridge University Press, Journals Publicity Department, Edinburgh Bldg., Shaftesbury Rd., Cambridge CB2 2RU, England. TEL 0223-312393. FAX 0223-315052.
Vendor(s): QL Systems Ltd.. *1552*

POLICY REVIEW.
Heritage Foundation, 214 Massachusetts Ave., N.E., Washington, DC 20002. TEL 202-546-4400. FAX 202-546-8328.
Vendor(s): Mead Data Central. *3915*

POLISH AMERICAN JOURNAL.
Panagraphics Corporation, 1275 Harlem Rd., Buffalo, NY 14206-1960. TEL 716-893-5771. FAX 716-893-5783. *2019*

POLISH JOURNAL OF PHARMACOLOGY AND PHARMACY.
Ossolineum, Publishing House of the Polish Academy of Sciences, Rynek 1-9, 106 Wroclaw, Poland. *3740*

POLISH MUSIC.
Agencja Autorska, Hipoteczna 2, P.O. Box 133, 00-950 Warsaw, Poland. TEL 22-27-83-96. FAX 22-27-58-82.
Available only online. *3574*

POLITICAL RISK LETTER.
Political Risk Services Box 6482, Syracuse, NY 13217-6482. TEL 315-472-1224. FAX 315-472-1235.
Vendor(s): Information Access Company, NewsNet. *919*

POLITICAL RISK YEARBOOK.
Political Risk Services Box 6482, Syracuse, NY 13217-6482. TEL 315-472-1224. FAX 315-472-1235.
Vendor(s): Data-Star (FSRI), Mead Data Central (COUNTRY REPORTS SERVICE). *795*

POLITICAL RISK YEARBOOK. VOLUME 1: NORTH & CENTRAL AMERICA.
Political Risk Services Box 6482, Syracuse, NY 13217-6482. TEL 315-472-1224. FAX 315-472-1235.
Vendor(s): Data-Star (FSRI), Mead Data Central (COUNTRY REPORTS SERVICE). *795*

POLITICAL RISK YEARBOOK. VOLUME 2: MIDDLE EAST & NORTH AFRICA.
Political Risk Services Box 6482, Syracuse, NY 13217-6482. TEL 315-472-1224. FAX 315-472-1235.
Vendor(s): Data-Star (FSRI), Mead Data Central (COUNTRY REPORTS SERVICE). *795*

POLITICAL RISK YEARBOOK. VOLUME 3: SOUTH AMERICA.
Political Risk Services Box 6482, Syracuse, NY 13217-6482. TEL 315-472-1224. FAX 315-472-1235.
Vendor(s): Data-Star (FSRI), Mead Data Central (COUNTRY REPORTS SERVICE). *795*

POLITICAL RISK YEARBOOK. VOLUME 4: SUB-SAHARAN AFRICA.
Political Risk Services Box 6482, Syracuse, NY 13217-6482. TEL 315-472-1224. FAX 315-472-1235.
Vendor(s): Data-Star (FSRI), Mead Data Central (COUNTRY REPORTS SERVICE). *795*

POLITICAL RISK YEARBOOK. VOLUME 5: ASIA & THE PACIFIC.
Political Risk Services Box 6482, Syracuse, NY 13217-6482. TEL 315-472-1224. FAX 315-472-1235.
Vendor(s): Data-Star (FSRI), Mead Data Central (COUNTRY REPORTS SERVICE). *795*

POLITICAL RISK YEARBOOK. VOLUME 6: EUROPE - COUNTRIES OF THE E C.
Political Risk Services Box 6482, Syracuse, NY 13217-6482. TEL 315-472-1224. FAX 315-472-1235.
Vendor(s): Data-Star (FSRI), Mead Data Central (COUNTRY REPORTS SERVICE). *795*

POLITICAL RISK YEARBOOK. VOLUME 7: EUROPE - OUTSIDE THE E C.
Political Risk Services Box 6482, Syracuse, NY 13217-6482. TEL 315-472-1224. FAX 315-472-1235.
Vendor(s): Data-Star (FSRI), Mead Data Central (COUNTRY REPORTS SERVICE). *795*

POLITICS IN AMERICA.
Congressional Quarterly Inc., 1414 22nd St., N.W., Washington, DC 20037. TEL 202-887-8500. FAX 202-728-1863. *3918*

POLLUTION ABSTRACTS.
Cambridge Scientific Abstracts, 7200 Wisconsin Ave., 6th Fl., Bethesda, MD 20814. TEL 301-961-6750. FAX 301-961-6720.
Vendor(s): BRS (CSAL), Data-Star (POLL), DIALOG (File no.41), European Space Agency (File no.18/POLLUTION). *1974*

POLYMERS, CERAMICS, COMPOSITE ALERT.
A S M International, Materials Information, Materials Park, OH 44073. TEL 216-338-5151. FAX 216-338-4634.
Vendor(s): CEDOCAR, CISTI, Data-Star (MBUS), DIALOG (File no.269), European Space Agency (File no.111), Orbit Information Technologies (MATERIALS/B), STN International (MATBUS). *3869*

POPULAR PHOTOGRAPHY.
Hachette Magazines, Inc., 1633 Broadway, New York, NY 10009. TEL 212-767-6000.
Vendor(s): DIALOG. *3796*

POPULAR SCIENCE.
Times Mirror Magazines, Inc., 2 Park Ave., New York, NY 10016. TEL 212-779-5000.
Vendor(s): DIALOG. *4606*

POPULATION INDEX.
Princeton University, Office of Population Research, 21 Prospect Ave., Princeton, NJ 08544-2091. TEL 609-258-4949. FAX 609-258-1039.
Vendor(s): National Library of Medicine. *3994*

POSTGRADUATE MEDICAL JOURNAL.
Macmillan Press Ltd., Scientific & Medical Division, Houndmills, Basingstoke, Hampshire RG2 2XS, England. TEL 0256-29242. FAX 0256-810526. *3143*

POTATO ABSTRACTS.
C.A.B. International, Wallingford, Oxon OX10 8DE, England. TEL 0491-32111. FAX 0491-33508.
Vendor(s): BRS (CABA), CISTI, DIMDI, DIALOG, European Space Agency (File nos.16 & 124/CAB). *142*

POULTRY ABSTRACTS.
C.A.B. International, Wallingford, Oxon OX10 8DE, England. TEL 0491-32111. FAX 0491-33508.
Vendor(s): BRS (CABA), CISTI, DIMDI, DIALOG, European Space Agency (File nos.16 & 124/CAB). *142*

POWER IN ASIA.
Financial Times Business Information Ltd., Tower House, Southampton, London WC2E 7HA, England. TEL 071-240-9391. FAX 071-240-7946.
Vendor(s): Data-Star, Mead Data Central. *1906*

POWER IN EUROPE.
Financial Times Business Information Ltd., Tower House, Southampton St., London WC2E 7HA, England. TEL 071-240-9391. FAX 071-240-7946.
Vendor(s): Data-Star, Mead Data Central. *1906*

POWER LETTER.
Forecast International Inc. - D M S, 22 Commerce Rd., Newtown, CT 06470-1643. TEL 203-426-0800. FAX 203-426-4262.
Vendor(s): DIALOG. *1794*

PRACTICAL PHARMACY.
Nanzando Co., Ltd., 4-1-11 Yushima, Bunkyoku, Tokyo 113-91, Japan. *3740*

PREDICASTS BASEBOOK.
Predicasts, A Ziff Communications Company, 11001 Cedar Ave., Cleveland, OH 44106. TEL 800-321-6388. FAX 216-229-9944.
Vendor(s): Data-Star, DIALOG. *735*

PREDICASTS F & S INDEX EUROPE.
Predicasts, A Ziff Communications Company, 11001 Cedar Ave., Cleveland, OH 44106-3088. TEL 800-321-6388. FAX 216-229-9944.
Vendor(s): BRS (PTSI), BRS/Saunders Colleague, Data-Star, DIALOG. *735*

PREDICASTS F & S INDEX INTERNATIONAL.
Predicasts, A Ziff Communications Company, 11001 Cedar Ave., Cleveland, OH 44106. TEL 800-321-6388. FAX 216-229-9944.
Vendor(s): BRS (PTSI), Data-Star, DIALOG. *735*

PREDICASTS F & S INDEX OF CORPORATE CHANGE.
Predicasts, A Ziff Communications Company, 11001 Cedar Ave., Cleveland, OH 44106. TEL 800-321-6388. FAX 216-229-9944.
Vendor(s): BRS (PTSI), DIALOG. *735*

PREDICASTS F & S INDEX UNITED STATES.
Predicasts, A Ziff Communications Company, 11001 Cedar Ave., Cleveland, OH 44106. TEL 800-321-6388. FAX 216-229-9944.
Vendor(s): BRS (PTSI), BRS/Saunders Colleague, Data-Star, DIALOG. *735*

PREDICASTS FORECASTS.
Predicasts, A Ziff Communications Company, 11001 Cedar Ave., Cleveland, OH 44106. TEL 800-321-6388. FAX 216-229-9944.
Vendor(s): Data-Star (PTFC), DIALOG. *736*

PREDICASTS OVERVIEW OF MARKETS AND TECHNOLOGY.
Predicasts, A Ziff Communications Company, 11001 Cedar Ave., Cleveland, OH 44106. TEL 800-321-6388. FAX 216-229-9944.
Vendor(s): BRS (PTSP), Data-Star, DIALOG. *1846*

PREPARED FOODS.
Delta Communications, Inc. (Chicago) 400 N. Michigan Ave., Ste. 1200, Chicago, IL 60611. TEL 312-222-2000. FAX 312-222-2026.
Vendor(s): Mead Data Central. *2079*

PRESCRIBERS' JOURNAL.
Departments of Health and Social Security, Hannibal House, Elephant and Castle, London SE1 6TE, England. *3740*

PRESCRIPTION AND O T C PHARMACEUTICALS: THE PINK SHEET.
F-D-C Reports, Inc., 5550 Friendship Blvd., Ste. One, Chevy Chase, MD 20815. TEL 301-657-9830. FAX 301-656-3094.
Vendor(s): Data-Star, DIALOG (File no.187), Mead Data Central. *3741*

PRESENCE.
Institut de Pastorale, 2715 Chemin de la Cote Sainte-Catherine, Montreal, Que. H3T 1B6, Canada. TEL 514-739-9797. FAX 514-739-1664. *4195*

PREVIEW OF UNITED STATES SUPREME COURT CASES.
American Bar Association, Public Education Division, 750 N. Lake Shore Dr., Chicago, IL 60611. TEL 312-988-5728. FAX 312-988-5494.
Vendor(s): WESTLAW. *2668*

PRIMARY EDUCATION DIRECTORY.
School Government Publishing Co. Ltd., Darby House, Bletchingley Rd., Merstham, Redhill, Surrey RH1 3DN, England. TEL 0737-642223. FAX 0737-644283. *1697*

PRINCETON ALUMNI WEEKLY.
Princeton Alumni Publications, 194 Nassau St., Princeton, NJ 08542. TEL 609-258-4885. FAX 609-258-6305. *1322*

PRINTING ABSTRACTS.
Pira International, Randalls Rd., Leatherhead, Surrey KT22 7RU, England.
Vendor(s): Orbit Information Technologies (PIRA). *4007*

PRIVATE LETTER RULINGS.
Maxwell Macmillan, Professional and Business Reference Publishing, 910 Sylvan Ave., Englewood Cliffs, NJ 07632-3310. TEL 800-562-0245.
Vendor(s): Prentice-Hall Information Network. *1104*

PRIVREDNA IZGRADNJA.
Savez Ekonomista Vojvodine, Zmaj Jovine 26, 21000 Novi Sad, Yugoslavia. TEL 021 24-971. *686*

PROBATE & PROPERTY.
American Bar Association, Real Property, Probate and Trust Law Section, 750 N. Lake Shore Dr., Chicago, IL 60611. TEL 312-988-5591.
Vendor(s): WESTLAW. *2668*

PRODUCER PRICE INDEXES.
U.S. Bureau of Labor Statistics, 441 G St., N.W., Washington, DC 20212. TEL 202-655-4000. *736*

PRODUCT ALERT.
Marketing Intelligence Service Ltd., 33 Academy St., Naples, NY 14512. TEL 716-374-6326. FAX 716-374-5217.
Vendor(s): Data-Star, DIALOG. *2080*

PRODUCT SAFETY LETTER.
Washington Business Information, Inc., c/o Karen Harrington, 1117 N. 19th St., Ste. 200, Arlington, VA 22209. TEL 703-247-3434. FAX 703-247-3421.
Vendor(s): NewsNet. *4110*

PRODUCTIVITY SOFTWARE.
Worldwide Videotex, Box 138, Babson Park, Boston, MA 02157. TEL 617-449-1603.
Vendor(s): Data-Star, DIALOG, NewsNet. *1479*

PRODUCTS LIABILITY REPORTER.
Commerce Clearing House, Inc., 4025 W. Peterson Ave., Chicago, IL 60646. TEL 312-583-8500. *2668*

PROFESSIONAL ENGINEER.
Association of Professional Engineers, Australia, G.P.O. Box 1272L, Melbourne, Vic. 3001, Australia. FAX 03-329-1028.
Vendor(s): DIALOG, Orbit Information Technologies. *1834*

PROGRES TECHNIQUE.
Association Nationale de la Recherche Technique, 101 av. Raymond Poincare, 75016 Paris, France. FAX 1-45-01-85-29. *4607*

PROGRESS IN CARDIOVASCULAR DISEASES.
W.B. Saunders Co. Curtis Center, Independence Square W., Philadelphia, PA 19106. TEL 215-238-7800.
Vendor(s): Mead Data Central. *3211*

PROGRESSIVE ARCHITECTURE.
Penton Publishing (Stamford) 600 Summer St., Box 1361, Stamford, CT 06904. TEL 203-348-7531. FAX 203-348-4023.
Vendor(s): DIALOG. *305*

PROGRESSIVE FARMER.
Southern Progress Corp. c/o H. Johnson, V.P. Circulation, 2100 Lakeshore Dr., Birmingham, AL 35209. TEL 205-877-6263. *115*

PROGRESSIVE GROCER.
Progressive Grocer Co. 4 Stamford Forum, Stamford, CT 06901. TEL 203-325-3500.
Vendor(s): DIALOG. *2093*

PROPERTY, PLANNING AND COMPENSATION REPORTS.
Sweet & Maxwell, South Quay Plaza, 8th Floor, 183 Marsh Wall, London E14 9FT, England. TEL 071-538-8686. FAX 071-538-9508.
Vendor(s): Mead Data Central. *2669*

PROSPECTIVE PAYMENT SURVIVAL.
American Health Consultants, Inc., 3525 Piedmont Rd., N.E., Six Piedmont Center, Ste. 400, Atlanta, GA 30305. TEL 404-262-7436. FAX 800-284-3291.
Vendor(s): Mead Data Central, NewsNet. *2468*

THE PROSTATE.
John Wiley & Sons, Inc., Journals, 605 Third Ave., New York, NY 10158. TEL 212-850-6000. FAX 212-850-6088. *3145*

PROTOZOOLOGICAL ABSTRACTS.
C.A.B. International, Wallingford, Oxon OX10 8DE, England. TEL 0491-32111. FAX 0491-33508.
Vendor(s): BRS (VETR), CISTI, DIMDI, DIALOG, European Space Agency (File nos.16 & 124/CAB). *467*

PROVINCIAL OUTLOOK.
Conference Board of Canada, 255 Smyth Road, Ottawa, Ont. K1H 8M7, Canada. TEL 613-526-3280. FAX 613-526-4857. *882*

PSYCHOLOGICAL ABSTRACTS.
American Psychological Association, 750 First St., N.E., Washington, DC 20002-4242. TEL 202-336-5500. FAX 202-336-5568.
Vendor(s): BRS, DIMDI, Data-Star (PSYC), DIALOG (File no.11/PsycINFO), Orbit Information Technologies. *4051*

PSYCHOLOGY TODAY.
Sussex Publishers Inc., 24 E. 23rd St., 5th Fl., New York, NY 10010. TEL 212-260-7210. FAX 212-260-7445.
Vendor(s): DIALOG. *4042*

PSYCHOPHARMACOLOGY BULLETIN.
U.S. Public Health Service, 5600 Fishers Lane, Rockville, MD 20857. TEL 301-496-4000.
Vendor(s): National Library of Medicine. *3741*

PSYCSCAN: APPLIED EXPERIMENTAL AND ENGINEERING PSYCHOLOGY.
American Psychological Association, 750 First St., N.E., Washington, DC 20002-4242. TEL 202-336-5500. FAX 202-336-5568. *4051*

PUBLIC BROADCASTING REPORT.
Warren Publishing, Inc., 2115 Ward Ct., N.W., Washington, DC 20037. TEL 202-872-9200. FAX 202-293-3435.
Vendor(s): NewsNet (PB04). *1378*

PUBLIC CONTRACT LAW JOURNAL.
American Bar Association, Public Contract Law Section, 750 N. Lake Shore Dr., Chicago, IL 60611. TEL 312-988-5000.
Vendor(s): WESTLAW. *2669*

PUBLIC FINANCE - WASHINGTON WATCH.
Thomas Publishing Corp., 1325 G St. N.W., Ste. 900, Washington, DC 20005. TEL 202-393-1277.
Vendor(s): NewsNet. *796*

PUBLIC HEALTH REPORTS.
U.S. Public Health Service, Parklawn Bldg., Rm. 13C-26, 5600 Fishers Ln., Rockville, MD 20857. TEL 301-443-0762. FAX 301-443-1719.
Vendor(s): Mead Data Central. *4110*

PUBLIC UTILITIES FORTNIGHTLY.
Public Utilities Reports, Inc., 2111 Wilson Blvd., Ste. 200, Arlington, VA 22201. TEL 703-243-7000. FAX 703-527-5829.
Vendor(s): WESTLAW. *1906*

PUBLISHERS DIRECTORY.
Gale Research Inc., 835 Penobscot Bldg., Detroit, MI 48226. TEL 313-961-2242. FAX 313-961-6083.
Vendor(s): DIALOG. *4135*

PUBLISHERS, DISTRIBUTORS & WHOLESALERS OF THE UNITED STATES.
R.R. Bowker, A Reed Reference Publishing Company, Division of Reed Publishing (USA) Inc., 121 Chanlon Rd., New Providence, NJ 07974. TEL 800-521-8110. FAX 908-665-6688.
Vendor(s): DIALOG (File no.450). *1151*

PUGET SOUND BUSINESS JOURNAL.
Scripps Howard Business Publications (Seattle), 101 Yesler Way, Ste. 200, Seattle, WA 98104-2525.
Vendor(s): DIALOG. *686*

PULP & PAPER CANADA.
Guy Tortolano, 3300 Cote Vertu, Suite 410, St. Laurent, Que. H4R 2B7, Canada. TEL 514-339-1399. FAX 514-399-1396. *3665*

PULP & PAPER CANADA GRADE DIRECTORY.
Guy Tortolano, 3300 Cote Vertu, Ste. 410, St. Laurent, Que. H4R 2B7, Canada. TEL 514-339-1399. FAX 514-399-1396. *3665*

PULP & PAPER CANADA'S ANNUAL & DIRECTORY.
Guy Tortolano, 3300 Cote Vertu, Ste. 410, St. Laurent, Que. H4R 2B7, Canada. TEL 514-339-1399. FAX 514-339-1396. *3665*

PUMPS AND OTHER FLUIDS MACHINERY ABSTRACTS.
S T I Ltd., 4 Kings Meadow, Ferry Hinksey Rd., Oxford OX2 0DU, England. TEL 0865-798898. FAX 0865-798788.
Vendor(s): DIALOG (File no.96/FLUIDEX), European Space Agency (File no.48/FLUIDEX). *3025*

PUNCH IN INTERNATIONAL TRAVEL AND ENTERTAINMENT MAGAZINE.
Enterprises Publishing, 400 E. 59th St., Ste. 9F, New York, NY 10022. TEL 212-755-4563. *4783*

PURPA LINES.
H C I Publications, 410 Archibald St., Kansas City, MO 64111-3046. TEL 816-931-1311. FAX 816-931-2015.
Vendor(s): NewsNet. *1794*

QUARTERLY COAL REPORT.
U.S. Department of Energy, Coal Division, 1000 Independence Ave., S.W., Washington, DC 20585. TEL 202-586-8800. FAX 202-586-0727.
Vendor(s): DIALOG. *1794*

QUARTERLY JOURNAL OF ECONOMICS.
M I T Press, 55 Hayward St., Cambridge, MA 02142. TEL 617-253-2889. FAX 617-258-6779. *897*

QUARTERLY JOURNAL OF MEDICINE.
Oxford University Press, Oxford Journals, Pinkhill Road, Southfield Road, Eynsham, Oxford OX2 1JJ, England. TEL 0865-882283. FAX 0865-882890.
Vendor(s): BRS. *3145*

QUICK RESPONSE NEWS.
Phillips Publishing, Inc., 7811 Montrose Rd., Potomac, MD 20854. TEL 301-340-2100. FAX 301-309-3847.
Vendor(s): Data-Star, DIALOG, NewsNet. *805*

R A P R A ABSTRACTS.
Pergamon Press plc, Headington Hill Hall, Oxford OX3 0BW, England. TEL 0865-794141. FAX 0865-743911.
Vendor(s): Orbit Information Technologies (RAPRA). *4295*

R A P R A NEW TRADE NAMES IN THE RUBBER AND PLASTICS INDUSTRIES.
Pergamon Press plc, Headington Hill Hall, Oxford OX3 0BW, England. TEL 0865-794141. FAX 0865-743911.
Vendor(s): Orbit Information Technologies (RAPRA). *4293*

R I C NEWS.
Rare-earth Information Center, Institute for Physical Research and Technology, Iowa State University, 255 Spedding Hall, Ames, IA 50011-3020. TEL 515-294-2272. FAX 515-294-3709. *3418*

R I L M ABSTRACTS OF MUSIC LITERATURE.
R I L M Abstracts, City University of New York, 33 W. 42nd St., New York, NY 10036. TEL 212-642-2709. FAX 212-642-2642.
Vendor(s): DIALOG (File no.97). *3589*

R I S C MANAGEMENT.
Elk Horn Publishing Company, 27360 Natoma Rd., Los Altos Hills, CA 94022-4307. TEL 415-941-6065.
Vendor(s): Data-Star, DIALOG. *1400*

R N.
Medical Economics Publishing Co., Five Paragon Dr., Montvale, NJ 07645. TEL 201-358-7200. FAX 201-573-1045.
Vendor(s): DIALOG. *3286*

RADIOLOGIC CLINICS OF NORTH AMERICA.
W.B. Saunders Co., Curtis Center, Independence Square W., Philadelphia, PA 19106. TEL 215-238-7800.
Vendor(s): BRS. *3362*

RADIOLOGY.
Radiological Society of North America, Inc., 2021 Spring Rd., Ste. 600, Oak Brook, IL 60521-1860. TEL 708-571-2670. FAX 708-574-3037. *3362*

RAFT.
c/o John A.C. Greppin, Ed., Cleveland State University, Cleveland, OH 44115. TEL 216-687-3967. FAX 216-687-9366. *3004*

RATEGRAM.
Bradshaw Group, Limited, Box 3517, San Rafael, CA 94912-3517. TEL 415-479-3815.
Vendor(s): NewsNet. *796*

REACTIONS.
Adis International Ltd., 41 Centorian Dr., Private Bag, Mairangi Bay, Auckland 10, New Zealand. TEL 479-8100.
Vendor(s): BRS. *3741*

READERS' GUIDE ABSTRACTS. MICROFICHE EDITION.
H.W. Wilson Co., 950 University Ave., Bronx, NY 10452-9978. TEL 800-367-6770. FAX 212-538-2716.
Vendor(s): Wilsonline (File RGA). *4142*

READERS' GUIDE TO PERIODICAL LITERATURE.
H.W. Wilson Co., 950 University Ave., Bronx, NY 10452-9978. TEL 800-367-6770. FAX 212-538-2716.
Vendor(s): Wilsonline (File RDG). *20*

REAL ESTATE INVESTMENT SITUATIONS.
High Tech Publishing Company, Box 1923, Brattleboro, VT 05301. TEL 802-254-3539.
Vendor(s): Data-Star, NewsNet. *4156*

REAL PROPERTY, PROBATE AND TRUST JOURNAL.
American Bar Association, Real Property, Probate and Trust Law Section, 750 N. Lake Shore Dr., Chicago, IL 60611. TEL 312-988-6083.
Vendor(s): WESTLAW. *2716*

REAL TIMES.
Michael Redman, Ed. & Pub., Box 1686, Bloomington, IN 47402. TEL 812-332-3498. *2233*

RECENT AWARDS IN ENGINEERING.
National Science Foundation, Directorate for Engineering, 1800 G St., N.W., Washington, DC 20550. TEL 202-357-9571. *1835*

RECHERCHE EN MATIERE D'ECONOMIE DES TRANSPORTS.
Organization for Economic Cooperation and Development, European Conference of Ministers of Transport, 19 rue de Franqueville, 75775 Paris Cedex 16, France. FAX 45-24-97-42.
Vendor(s): European Space Agency (File no.74/TRANSDOC Subfile: RESEARCH). *4655*

RECUEIL DES BREVETS D'INVENTION.
Ministry of Economic Affairs, Office de la Propriete Industrielle, 24-26 rue de Mot, B-1040 Brussels, Belgium. FAX 02-2310256.
Vendor(s): BELINDIS. *3678*

REFERATE: SCHWEISSEN UND VERWANDTE VERFAHREN.
Bundesanstalt fuer Materialforschung und -pruefung, Unter den Eichen 87, 1000 Berlin 45, Germany. TEL 030-8104-6401. FAX 030-8112029. *3428*

REFERATEORGAN: MESSEN MECHANISCHER GROESSEN.
Bundesanstalt fuer Materialforschung und -pruefung, Unter den Eichen 87, 1000 Berlin 45, Germany. TEL 030-8104-6101. FAX 030-811-2029. *1846*

REFERATEORGAN: ZERSTOERUNGSFREIE PRUEFUNG.
Bundesanstalt fuer Materialforschung und -pruefung, Unter den Eichen 87, 1000 Berlin 45, Germany. TEL 030-8104-6202. FAX 030-8112029.
Vendor(s): INKA. *1846*

REFERENCE BOOK OF CORPORATE MANAGEMENTS.
Dun's Marketing Services 3 Sylvan Way, Parsippany, NJ 07054-3896. TEL 201-455-0900.
Vendor(s): Pergamon Infoline (RBCM). *1026*

REGIONAL AVIATION WEEKLY.
McGraw-Hill, Inc., Aviation Week Group, 1156 15th St., N.W., Washington, DC 20005. TEL 202-822-4600.
Vendor(s): DIALOG (File no.624/McGRAW-HILL PUBLICATIONS ONLINE), Dow Jones/News Retrieval, Mead Data Central (RAWKY). *4677*

SERIALS AVAILABLE ONLINE 5095

REGISTRY OF TOXIC EFFECTS OF CHEMICAL SUBSTANCES.
Department of Health and Human Services, National Institute of Occupational Safety and Health, Attn.: Doris Sweet, Ed. (C-28), 4676 Columbia Pkwy., Cincinnati, OH 45226. TEL 513-533-8317.
Vendor(s): Chemical Information Systems, DIALOG (File no.336). *3621*

REHABILITATION INDEX.
Medical Information Service, The British Library, Document Supply Centre, Boston Spa, Wetherby, W. Yorkshire LS23 7BQ, England. TEL 0937-546039. FAX 0937-546236. *3181*

REINSURANCE DIRECTORY.
Robert W. Strain Publishing & Seminars, Box 1520, Athens, TX 75751. TEL 914-677-5974. *2541*

RELIGION INDEX ONE: PERIODICALS.
American Theological Library Association, Religion Indexes, 820 Church St., 3rd Fl., Evanston, IL 60201-3707. TEL 708-869-7788.
Vendor(s): BRS (RELI), BRS/Saunders Colleague, DIALOG (File no.190), Wilsonline. *4213*

RELIGION INDEX TWO: MULTI-AUTHOR WORKS.
American Theological Library Association, Religion Indexes, 820 Church St., 3rd Fl., Evanston, IL 60201-3707. TEL 708-869-7788.
Vendor(s): BRS, BRS/Saunders Colleague, DIALOG (File no.190), Wilsonline. *4213*

RELIGIOUS AND INSPIRATIONAL BOOKS AND SERIALS IN PRINT.
R.R. Bowker, A Reed Reference Publishing Company, Division of Reed Publishing (USA) Inc., 121 Chanlon Rd., New Providence, NJ 07974. TEL 800-521-8110. FAX 908-665-6688.
Vendor(s): BRS, DIALOG. *410*

RELIGIOUS LEADERS OF AMERICA.
Gale Research Inc., 835 Penobscot Bldg., Detroit, MI 48226. TEL 800-877-4253. FAX 313-961-6083.
Vendor(s): Mead Data Central. *4198*

REPERTOIRE DES BANQUES DE DONNEES TELETEL POUR L'ENTREPRISE.
Editions F L A Consultants, 27 rue de la Vistule, 75013 Paris, France. TEL 1-45-82-75-75. FAX 1-45-82-46-04.
Vendor(s): Telesystemes - Questel. *1351*

REPERTORIUM.
Dutch Association of the Pharmaceutical Industry (NEFARMA), Postbus 9193, 3506 GD Utrecht, Netherlands. FAX 30-614554. *3147*

REPORT ON A T & T.
Capitol Publications Inc., Telecom Publishing Group, 1101 King St., Ste. 444, Box 1455, Alexandria, VA 22313-2055. TEL 800-327-7205. FAX 703-739-6490.
Vendor(s): NewsNet (TE50). *1351*

REPORT ON DISABILITY PROGRAMS.
Business Publishers, Inc., 951 Pershing Dr., Silver Spring, MD 20910-4464. TEL 301-587-6300. FAX 301-585-9075.
Vendor(s): NewsNet. *4417*

REPORT ON EDUCATION OF THE DISADVANTAGED.
Business Publishers, Inc., 951 Pershing Dr., Silver Spring, MD 20910-4464. TEL 301-587-6300. FAX 301-585-9075.
Vendor(s): NewsNet. *1740*

REPORT ON EDUCATION RESEARCH.
Capitol Publications Inc., 1101 King St., Ste. 444, Alexandria, VA 22314. TEL 703-683-4100. FAX 703-739-6517.
Vendor(s): NewsNet. *1658*

REPORT ON I B M.
DataTrends Publications, Inc., 8130 Boone Blvd., Ste. 210, Vienna, VA 22182. TEL 703-760-0660. FAX 703-760-9365.
Vendor(s): NewsNet. *1455*

REPORT ON PRESCHOOL PROGRAMS.
Business Publishers, Inc., 951 Pershing Dr., Silver Spring, MD 20910-4464. TEL 301-587-6300. FAX 301-585-9075.
Vendor(s): NewsNet. *1658*

REPORT ON SCHOOL-AGED CHILD CARE.
Business Publishers, Inc., 951 Pershing Dr., Silver Spring, MD 20910-4464. TEL 301-587-6300. FAX 301-585-9075.
Vendor(s): NewsNet. *1243*

RESEARCH ALERT (NEW YORK).
Alert Publishing, Inc., 37-06 30th Ave., Long Island City, NY 11103-3808. TEL 718-626-3356.
Vendor(s): Data-Star, DIALOG, NewsNet. *1507*

RESEARCH & DEVELOPMENT.
Cahners Publishing Company (Des Plaines), Division Reed Publishing (USA) Inc., 1350 E. Touhy Ave., Box 5080, Des Plaines, IL 60017-5080. TEL 708-635-8800. FAX 908-390-2618.
Vendor(s): DIALOG. *4607*

RESEARCH CENTERS DIRECTORY.
Gale Research Inc., 835 Penobscot Bldg., Detroit, MI 48226. TEL 313-961-2242. FAX 313-961-6083.
Vendor(s): DIALOG. *4336*

RESEARCH IN MINISTRY.
American Theological Library Association, Religion Indexes, 820 Church St., 3rd Fl., Evanston, IL 60201-3707. TEL 708-869-7788.
Vendor(s): Data-Star, DIALOG, Wilsonline. *4213*

RESEARCH SERVICES DIRECTORY.
Gale Research Inc., 835 Penobscot Bldg., Detroit, MI 48226. TEL 313-961-2242. FAX 313-961-6083.
Vendor(s): DIALOG. *1152*

RESOURCES IN EDUCATION.
Educational Resources Information Center, Processing and Reference Facility, 2440 Research Blvd., Ste. 400, Rockville, MD 20850. TEL 301-590-1420.
Vendor(s): BRS, BRS/Saunders Colleague, CISTI, DIALOG (File no.1/ERIC). *1679*

RESPIRATORY MEDICINE.
Bailliere Tindall, 24-28 Oval Rd., London NW1 7DX, England. TEL 071-267-4466. FAX 071-482-2293.
Vendor(s): BRS. *3367*

RESTAURANT BUSINESS.
Bill Communications, Inc., 633 Third Ave., New York, NY 10017. TEL 212-986-4800.
Vendor(s): DIALOG. *2479*

RETAIL TRADE INTERNATIONAL.
Euromonitor, 87-88 Turnmill St., London EC1M 5QU, England. TEL 071-251-8024. FAX 071-608-3149. *1052*

REVIEW OF AGRICULTURAL ENTOMOLOGY.
C.A.B. International, Wallingford, Oxon OX10 8DE, England. TEL 0491-32111. FAX 0491-33508.
Vendor(s): BRS, CISTI, DIMDI, DIALOG, European Space Agency (File nos.16 & 124/CAB). *143*

REVIEW OF MEDICAL AND VETERINARY ENTOMOLOGY.
C.A.B. International, Wallingford, Oxon OX10 8DE, England. TEL 0491-32111. FAX 0491-33508.
Vendor(s): BRS (VETR), CISTI, DIMDI, DIALOG, European Space Agency (File nos.16 & 124/CAB). *4820*

REVIEW OF MEDICAL AND VETERINARY MYCOLOGY.
C.A.B. International, Wallingford, Oxon OX10 8DE, England. TEL 0491 32111. FAX 0491-33508.
Vendor(s): BRS (VETR), CISTI, DIMDI, DIALOG, European Space Agency (File nos.16 & 124/CAB). *467*

REVIEW OF PLANT PATHOLOGY.
C.A.B. International, Wallingford, Oxon OX10 8DE, England. TEL 0491 32111. FAX 0491-33508.
Vendor(s): BRS, CISTI, DIMDI, DIALOG, European Space Agency (File nos.16 & 124/CAB). *467*

REVISTA CANARIA DE ESTUDIOS INGLESES.
Universidad de La Laguna, Secretariado de Publicaciones, San Agustin, 30, 38201 La Laguna-Tenerife, Islas Canarias, Spain. TEL 922-25-81-27. *2837*

REVISTA COLOMBIANA DE CIENCIAS QUIMICO FARMACEUTICAS.
Universidad Nacional de Colombia, Departamento de Farmacia, Apdo. Aereo 14 490, Bogota, Colombia. *3742*

REVISTA CUBANA DE FARMACIA.
Ministerio de Salud Publica, Centro Nacional de Informacion de Ciencias Medicas, Calle E No. 452, e-19 y 21, Plaza de la Revolucion, Apdo. 6520, Havana, Cuba. TEL 809-32-5338. *3742*

REVISTA CUBANA DE MEDICINA GENERAL INTEGRAL.
Ministerio de Salud Publica, Centro Nacional de Informacion de Ciencias Medicas, Calle E No. 452, e-19 y 21, Plaza de la Revolucion, Apdo. 6520, Havana, Cuba. TEL 809-32-5338. *3148*

REVISTA DE ESTUDIOS EXTREMENOS.
Centro de Estudios Extremenos, Servicio de Publicaciones, Felipe Checa 15, 06071 Badajoz, Spain. *2218*

REVISTA ESPANOLA DE DOCUMENTACION CIENTIFICA.
Instituto de Informacion y Documentacion en Ciencia y Tecnologia, Joaquin Costa 22, 28002 Madrid, Spain. TEL 91-5635482. FAX 91-5642644. *2782*

REVISTA FARMACEUTICA.
Academia Argentina de Farmacia y Bioquimica, Junin 956, Buenos Aires 1113, Argentina. *3742*

REVISTA PORTUGUESA DE FARMACIA.
Sociedade Farmaceutica Lusitana, Rua da Sociedade Farmaceutica, No. 18, 1199 Lisbon Codex, Portugal. *3742*

RICE ABSTRACTS.
C.A.B. International, Wallingford, Oxon OX10 8DE, England. TEL 0491-32111. FAX 0491-33508.
Vendor(s): BRS (CABA), CISTI, DIMDI, DIALOG, European Space Agency (File nos.16 & 124/CAB). *143*

RIG MARKET FORECAST.
Financial Times Business Information Ltd., Tower House, Southampton St., London WC2E 7HA, England. TEL 071-240-9391. FAX 071-240-7946.
Vendor(s): Data-Star, Mead Data Central. *3700*

RIGAKU RYOHO JANARU.
Igaku-Shoin Ltd., 5-24-3 Hongo, Bunkyo-ku, Tokyo 113-91, Japan. TEL 03-3817-5703.
Vendor(s): JICST. *3216*

RIHABIRITESHON IGAKU.
Japanese Association of Rehabilitation Medicine, 1-39-11-502 Higashi-Ikebukuro, Toshima-ku, Tokyo 170, Japan. TEL 03-3981-6153. FAX 03-5396-0477.
Vendor(s): JICST. *3149*

ROAD TRAFFIC REPORTS.
Kenneth Mason Publications Ltd., 12 North St., Emsworth, Hants. PO10 7DQ, England. TEL 0243-377977. FAX 0243-379136.
Vendor(s): Mead Data Central. *4720*

ROBOTICS WORLD.
Communication Channels, Inc., 6255 Barfield Rd., Atlanta, GA 30328-4369. TEL 404-256-9800. FAX 404-256-3116. *1410*

ROBOTRONICS AGE NEWSLETTER.
Twenty-First Century Media Communications, Inc., 548 Cardero St., Vancouver, B.C. V6N 2K3, Canada. TEL 604-261-5712.
Vendor(s): NewsNet (EC16). *1410*

ROUNDSMANSHIP (YEAR).
Mosby - Year Book, Inc. (Chicago) 200 N. LaSalle St., Chicago, IL 60601-1080. TEL 312-726-9733. FAX 312-726-6075.
Vendor(s): BRS. *3150*

ROYAL SOCIETY OF CHEMISTRY. JOURNAL: DALTON TRANSACTIONS.
Royal Society of Chemistry, Thomas Graham House, Science Park, Milton Rd., Cambridge CB4 4WF, England. TEL 0462-672555. FAX 0462-480947.
Vendor(s): STN International (CJRSC). *1214*

ROYAL SOCIETY OF CHEMISTRY. JOURNAL: FARADAY TRANSACTIONS.
Royal Society of Chemistry, Thomas Graham House, Science Park, Milton Rd., Cambridge CB4 4WF, England. TEL 0462-672555. FAX 0462-480947.
Vendor(s): STN International (CJRSC). *1230*

ROYAL SOCIETY OF CHEMISTRY. JOURNAL: PERKIN TRANSACTIONS 1.
Royal Society of Chemistry, Thomas Graham House, Science Park, Milton Rd., Cambridge CB4 4WF, England. TEL 0462-672555. FAX 0462-480947.
Vendor(s): STN International (CJRSC). *1223*

ROYAL SOCIETY OF CHEMISTRY. JOURNAL: PERKIN TRANSACTIONS 2.
Royal Society of Chemistry, Thomas Graham House, Science Park, Milton Rd., Cambridge CB4 4WF, England. TEL 0462-672555. FAX 0462-480947.
Vendor(s): STN International (CJRSC). *1230*

ROYAL SOCIETY OF MEDICINE. JOURNAL.
Royal Society of Medicine Services Ltd., 1 Wimpole St., London W1M 8AE, England. TEL 071-408 2119. FAX 071-355-3198. *3150*

RURAL DEVELOPMENT ABSTRACTS.
C.A.B. International, Wallingford, Oxon OX10 8DE, England. TEL 0491-32111. FAX 0491-33508.
Vendor(s): BRS (ECON), CISTI, DIMDI, DIALOG, European Space Agency. *4082*

S A E HANDBOOK.
Society of Automotive Engineers, 400 Commonwealth Dr., Warrendale, PA 15096-0001. TEL 412-776-4841. FAX 412-776-5760.
Vendor(s): Orbit Information Technologies. *4701*

S A E TECHNICAL LITERATURE ABSTRACTS.
Society of Automotive Engineers, 400 Commonwealth Dr., Warrendale, PA 15096-0001. TEL 412-776-4841. FAX 412-776-5760.
Vendor(s): Orbit Information Technologies. *4666*

S A E TECHNICAL PAPERS.
Society of Automotive Engineers, 400 Commonwealth Dr., Warrendale, PA 15096-0001. TEL 412-776-4841. FAX 412-776-5760.
Vendor(s): European Space Agency, FIZ Technik, Orbit Information Technologies. *4701*

S A E TRANSACTIONS.
Society of Automotive Engineers, 400 Commonwealth Dr., Warrendale, PA 15096. TEL 412-776-4970.
Vendor(s): Orbit Information Technologies. *4701*

S C A D BULLETIN.
Commission of the European Communities, 200 rue de la Loi, B-1049 Brussels, Belgium. TEL 02-351111. *411*

S C I M P.
European Business School Librarians Group, c/o Helsinki School of Economics Library, Runeberginkatu 22-24, 00100 Helsinki, Finland. TEL 0-4313-413. FAX 0-4313-539. *737*

S CORPORATIONS (ENGLEWOOD CLIFFS).
Warren Gorham & Lamont, Inc., 210 South Street, Boston, MA 02111. TEL 617-423-2020. FAX 617-423-2026.
Vendor(s): Prentice-Hall Information Network. *1105*

S D I INTELLIGENCE REPORT.
Business Publishers, Inc., 951 Pershing Dr., Silver Spring, MD 20910-4464. TEL 301-587-6300. FAX 301-587-1081.
Vendor(s): NewsNet (DE09). *3470*

S D I MONITOR.
Pasha Publications Inc., 1401 Wilson Blvd., Ste. 900, Arlington, VA 22209-9970. TEL 703-528-1244. FAX 703-528-1253.
Vendor(s): NewsNet (DE05). *3470*

S E C DOCKET.
U.S. Securities and Exchange Commission, 450 Fifth St., N.W., MISC-11, Washington, DC 20549. TEL 202-272-7460. FAX 202-272-7050.
Vendor(s): WESTLAW. *962*

S E C NEWS DIGEST.
U.S. Securities and Exchange Commission, 450 Fifth St., N.W., MISC-11, Washington, DC 20549. TEL 202-272-7460. FAX 202-272-7050.
Vendor(s): Bureau of National Affairs, NewsNet (EV96), WESTLAW. *962*

S. KLEIN NEWSLETTER ON COMPUTER GRAPHICS.
BIS Strategic Decisions Box 68, Newtonville, MA 02160. TEL 617-893-9130. FAX 617-894-5093.
Vendor(s): NewsNet (EC02). *1423*

S M T TRENDS.
Market Intelligence Research Company, 2525 Charleston Rd., Mountain View, CA 94043. TEL 415-389-8671. FAX 415-389-8671.
Vendor(s): Data-Star, DIALOG, NewsNet. *3651*

S S D A NEWSLETTER.
Hebrew University, Faculty of Social Sciences, Mount Scopus, Jerusalem 91905, Israel. TEL 02-883007. FAX 02-322545. *4385*

S T A R.
U.S. National Aeronautics and Space Administration, Scientific and Technical Information Facility, Box 8757, Baltimore-Washington International Airport, MD 21240. TEL 301-621-0153.
Vendor(s): DIALOG (File no.108), European Space Agency. *66*

S T P PHARMA SCIENCES.
Editions de Sante, 19 rue Louis le Grand, 75002 Paris, France. TEL 47-42-84-30. FAX 42-65-09-66. *3742*

SAFETY AND HEALTH AT WORK.
International Labour Office, International Occupational Safety and Health Information Centre, CH-1211 Geneva 22, Switzerland. TEL 799-65-40.
Vendor(s): European Space Agency (File no.40/CISDOC), IST-INFORMATHEQUE, Orbit Information Technologies, Telesystemes - Questel. *3623*

ST. KILDA ROAD CITYSCOPE.
Cityscope Publications Pty. Ltd., P.O. Box 870, Manly, N.S.W. 2095, Australia. TEL 02-976-2263. FAX 02-976-2263. *4160*

ST. LOUIS BUSINESS JOURNAL.
St. Louis Business Journal Corp., 612 N. Second St., St. Louis, MO 63102. TEL 314-421-6200.
Vendor(s): DIALOG. *690*

ST. LOUIS COMMERCE.
Commerce Magazine, Inc., 100 S. Fourth St., Ste. 500, St. Louis, MO 63102. TEL 314-231-5555. FAX 314-444-1122. *822*

SAINT LOUIS UNIVERSITY LAW JOURNAL.
St. Louis University School of Law, 3700 Lindell Blvd., St. Louis, MO 63108. TEL 314-658-3933.
Vendor(s): WESTLAW. *2676*

SALES AND MARKETING MANAGEMENT.
I.S.E. Publications Ltd., Nat West House, 31 Upper George St., Luton, Beds. LU1 2RD, England. FAX 0582-453640.
Vendor(s): DIALOG. *1053*

SALES PRO.
Marketing Intelligence Service Ltd., 33 Academy St., Naples, NY 14512. TEL 716-374-6326. FAX 716-374-5217.
Vendor(s): Data-Star, DIALOG. *1053*

SALES PROSPECTOR.
Prospector Research Services, Inc., 751 Main St., Waltham, MA 02154. TEL 617-899-1271.
Vendor(s): NewsNet. *1084*

SAME-DAY SURGERY.
American Health Consultants, Inc., Six Piedmont Center, Ste. 400, 3525 Piedmont Rd., N.E., Atlanta, GA 30305. TEL 404-262-7436. FAX 800-284-3291.
Vendor(s): Mead Data Central. *3383*

SAN ANTONIO BUSINESS JOURNAL.
American City Business Journals, Inc. (San Antonio), 3201 Cherry Ridge St., Ste. D-400, San Antonio, TX 78230-4806. TEL 512-341-3202. FAX 512-341-3031.
Vendor(s): Information Access Company. *690*

SAN DIEGO BUSINESS JOURNAL.
San Diego Business Journal, Inc., 4909 Murphy Canyon Rd., No. 200, San Diego, CA 92123.
Vendor(s): DIALOG. *690*

SANTA CLARA COUNTY BUSINESS MAGAZINE.
Directory Publications San Jose, 450 E. Trimble Rd., San Jose, CA 95131. TEL 408-435-1170.
Vendor(s): DIALOG. *690*

SANTA CLARA LAW REVIEW.
Santa Clara University, School of Law, Santa Clara, CA 95053. TEL 408-554-4074.
Vendor(s): WESTLAW. *2677*

SASKATCHEWAN DECISIONS, CIVIL AND CRIMINAL CASES.
Western Legal Publications, 301-1 Alexander St., Vancouver, B.C. V6A 1B2, Canada. TEL 604-687-5671. FAX 604-687-2796. *2677*

SASKATCHEWAN REPORTS.
Maritime Law Book Ltd., Box 302, Fredericton, N.B. E3B 4Y9, Canada. TEL 506-454-9921.
Vendor(s): QL Systems Ltd.. *2677*

SATELLITE NEWS.
Phillips Publishing, Inc., 7811 Montrose Rd., Potomac, MD 20854. TEL 301-340-2100.
Vendor(s): NewsNet (TE03). *1342*

SATELLITE WEEK.
Warren Publishing, Inc., 2115 Ward Ct., N.W., Washington, DC 20037. TEL 202-872-9200. FAX 202-293-3435.
Vendor(s): NewsNet (AE01). *1379*

SATURDAY EVENING POST.
Benjamin Franklin Literary & Medical Society, Box 567, 1100 Waterway Blvd., Indianapolis, IN 46202. TEL 317-636-8881.
Vendor(s): DIALOG. *2234*

SCAN.
Dienst Landbouwkundig Onderzoek, Staring Centrum, Instituut voor Onderzoek van het Landeljke Gebied, P.O. Box 125, 6700 AC Wageningen, Netherlands. TEL 0837-74200. FAX 0837-24812. *191*

SCANP.
Helsinki School of Economics, Runeberginkatu 22-24, 00100 Helsinki 10, Finland. *737*

SCHOLASTIC UPDATE.
Scholastic Inc., 730 Broadway, New York, NY 10003. TEL 212-505-3000.
Vendor(s): DIALOG. *1264*

SCHOOL AND COLLEGE.
Penton Publishing 1100 Superior Ave., Cleveland, OH 44114-2543. TEL 216-696-7000. FAX 216-696-8765.
Vendor(s): DIALOG. *1661*

SCHOOL LAW NEWS.
Capitol Publications Inc., 1101 King St., Ste. 444, Alexandria, VA 22314. TEL 703-683-4100. FAX 703-739-6517.
Vendor(s): NewsNet. *1731*

SCHWEIZERISCHE ZEITSCHRIFT FUER VOLKSWIRTSCHAFT UND STATISTIK.
Helbing & Lichtenhahn Verlag AG, Freiestr. 82, CH-4051 Basel, Switzerland. TEL 064-268626. FAX 064-245780.
Vendor(s): DIALOG. *737*

SCIENCE.
American Association for the Advancement of Science, 1333 H St., N.W., Washington, DC 20005. TEL 202-326-6500.
Vendor(s): BRS (SCIE). *4338*

SCIENCE CITATION INDEX.
Institute for Scientific Information, 3501 Market St., Philadelphia, PA 19104. TEL 215-386-0100. FAX 215-386-2991.
Vendor(s): DIMDI, Data-Star, DIALOG (Files nos.34, 432,433,434/SCISEARCH), Orbit Information Technologies. *4357*

SCIENCE OF FOOD AND AGRICULTURE.
Council for Agricultural Science and Technology, 137 Lynn Ave., Ames, IA 50010-7197. TEL 515-292-2125. FAX 515-292-4512. *2081*

SCIENTIA PHARMACEUTICA.
Oesterreichische Apotheker-Verlagsgesellschaft, Spitalgasse 31, A-1094 Vienna, Austria. *3742*

SCIENTIFIC AMERICAN.
Scientific American, Inc., 415 Madison Ave., New York, NY 10017. TEL 212-754-0550.
Vendor(s): BRS (SAMM). *4341*

SCIENTIFIC AND TECHNICAL BOOKS AND SERIALS IN PRINT.
R.R. Bowker, A Reed Reference Publishing Company, Division of Reed Publishing (USA) Inc., 121 Chanlon Rd., New Providence, NJ 07974. TEL 800-521-8110. FAX 908-665-6688.
Vendor(s): Orbit Information Technologies (File name BIPS). *4358*

SCIENTIFIC SERIALS IN THAI LIBRARIES.
Thailand Institute of Scientific and Technological Research, 196 Phahonyothin Rd., Chatuchak, Bangkok 10900, Thailand. TEL 579-4929. FAX 662-579-8594. *4358*

SCOOP.
Dienst Landbouwkundig Onderzoek, Staring Centrum, Instituut voor Onderzoek van het Landelijk Gebied, P.O. Box 125, 6700 AC Wageningen, Netherlands. TEL 08370-74200. FAX 08370-24812. *1975*

SCOUTING.
Scout Association, Baden-Powell House, Queen's Gate, London SW7 5JS, England. FAX 071-581-9953.
Vendor(s): DIALOG. *1265*

SCREEN DIGEST.
Screen Digest Ltd., 37 Gower St., London WC1E 6HH, England. TEL 071-580-2842. FAX 071-580-0060.
Vendor(s): Data-Star, DIALOG. *1379*

SCRIP - WORLD PHARMACEUTICAL NEWS.
P J B Publications Ltd., 18-20 Hill Rise, Richmond, Surrey TW10 6UA, England. TEL 081-948-3262. FAX 081-948-6866.
Vendor(s): BRS, Data-Star (PHIND), DIALOG. *3743*

SEARCHABLE PHYSICS INFORMATION NOTICES.
American Institute of Physics, 335 E. 45th St., New York, NY 10017. TEL 212-661-9404.
Vendor(s): DIALOG (File no.62/SPIN). *3839*

SECOND OPINION (CHICAGO).
Park Ridge Center, 676 N. St. Clair, Ste. 450, Chicago, IL 60611. TEL 312-266-2222. FAX 312-266-6086.
Vendor(s): Information Access Company. *3152*

SECURITE ET SANTE AU TRAVAIL.
International Labour Office, International Occupational Safety and Health Information Centre, CH-1211 Geneva 22, Switzerland. TEL 22-799-6740. FAX 41-22-798-8685.
Vendor(s): European Space Agency, IST-INFORMATHEQUE, Orbit Information Technologies, Telesystemes - Questel. *3623*

SECURITIES REGULATION & LAW REPORT.
The Bureau of National Affairs, Inc., 1231 25th St., N.W., Washington, DC 20037. TEL 202-452-4200. FAX 202-822-8092.
Vendor(s): Bureau of National Affairs, Mead Data Central (SECREG), WESTLAW (BNA-SRLR). *2678*

SECURITIES WEEK.
McGraw-Hill, Inc., Business Week Management Information Center, 1221 Ave. of the Americas, 36th Fl., New York, NY 10020. TEL 212-512-4214.
Vendor(s): DIALOG (File no.624/McGRAW-HILL PUBLICATIONS ONLINE), Dow Jones/News Retrieval (SW), Mead Data Central (SECWK). *963*

SECURITY INTELLIGENCE REPORT.
Interests, Ltd., 8512 Cedar St., Silver Spring, MD 20910. TEL 301-588-7916. FAX 301-588-2085.
Vendor(s): NewsNet. *3924*

SEDIMENT DATA FOR SELECTED CANADIAN RIVERS.
Environment Canada, Inland Waters Directorate, Ottawa, Ont. K1A OH3, Canada. TEL 613-953-3680. FAX 613-997-8701. *1579*

SEED ABSTRACTS.
C.A.B. International, Wallingford, Oxon OX10 8DE, England. TEL 0491-32111. FAX 0491-33508.
Vendor(s): BRS (CABA), CISTI, DIMDI, DIALOG, European Space Agency. *143*

SEICHO.
Aichi-Gakuin University, Department of Anatomy, 1-100 Kusumoto-cho, Chikusaku-ku, Nagoya 464, Japan.
Vendor(s): JICST. *248*

SERIALS AVAILABLE ONLINE

SEIFEN, OELE, FETTE, WACHSE.
Verlag fuer Chemische Industrie H. Ziolkowsky KG, Beethovenstr. 16, 8900 Augsburg 1, Germany. TEL 0821-519345. FAX 0821-517953. *376*

SEISHIN IGAKU.
Igaku-Shoin Ltd., 5-24-3 Hongo, Bunkyo-ku, Tokyo 113-91, Japan. TEL 03-817-5711.
Vendor(s): JICST. *3354*

SELECTED WATER RESOURCES ABSTRACTS.
U.S. Geological Survey, Water Resources Scientific Information Center, 425 National Center, Reston, VA 22092. TEL 703-648-6820.
Vendor(s): DIALOG (File no.117). *1552*

SEMICONDUCTOR INDUSTRY & BUSINESS SURVEY NEWSLETTER.
H T E Research, Inc., 400 Oyster Point Blvd., Ste. 220, S. San Francisco, CA 94080. TEL 415-871-4377. FAX 415-871-0513.
Vendor(s): NewsNet (EC35). *1778*

SEMINARS IN ANESTHESIA.
W.B. Saunders Co. Curtis Center, Independence Square W., Philadelphia, PA 19106. TEL 215-238-7800. *3192*

SEMINARS IN ARTHRITIS & RHEUMATISM.
W.B. Saunders Co. Curtis Center, Independence Square W., Philadelphia, PA 19106. TEL 215-238-7800.
Vendor(s): Mead Data Central. *3370*

SEMINARS IN DERMATOLOGY.
W.B. Saunders Co. Curtis Center, Independence Square W., Philadelphia, PA 19106. TEL 215-238-7800. *3249*

SEMINARS IN DIAGNOSTIC PATHOLOGY.
W.B. Saunders Co. Curtis Center, Independence Square W., Philadelphia, PA 19106. TEL 215-238-7800. *3152*

SEMINARS IN HEMATOLOGY.
W.B. Saunders Co. Curtis Center, Independence Square W., Philadelphia, PA 19106. TEL 215-238-7800.
Vendor(s): Mead Data Central. *3273*

SEMINARS IN NEPHROLOGY.
W.B. Saunders Co. Curtis Center, Independence Square W., Philadelphia, PA 19106. TEL 215-238-7800. *3389*

SEMINARS IN NEUROLOGY.
Thieme Medical Publishers, Inc., 381 Park Ave. So., Ste. 1501, New York, NY 10016. TEL 212-683-5088.
Vendor(s): BRS. *3354*

SEMINARS IN NUCLEAR MEDICINE.
W.B. Saunders Co. Curtis Center, Independence Square W., Philadelphia, PA 19106. TEL 215-238-7800. *3363*

SEMINARS IN ONCOLOGY.
W.B. Saunders Co. Curtis Center, Independence Square W., Philadelphia, PA 19106. TEL 215-238-7800.
Vendor(s): Mead Data Central. *3202*

SEMINARS IN PERINATOLOGY.
W.B. Saunders Co. Curtis Center, Independence Square W., Philadelphia, PA 19106. TEL 215-238-7800. *3326*

SEMINARS IN RESPIRATORY MEDICINE.
Thieme Medical Publishers, Inc., 381 Park Avenue South, New York, NY 10016.
Vendor(s): BRS, BRS/Saunders Colleague. *3367*

SEMINARS IN ROENTGENOLOGY.
W.B. Saunders Co., Journals Department Curtis Center, Independence Square W., Philadelphia, PA 19106. TEL 215-238-7800. *3363*

SEMINARS IN ULTRASOUND, C T AND M R.
W.B. Saunders Co., Journals Department Curtis Center, Independence Square W., Philadelphia, PA 19106. TEL 215-238-7800. *3363*

SENSOR BUSINESS DIGEST.
Vital Information Publications, 321 Carrera Dr., Mill Valley, CA 94941-3995. TEL 415-961-9000. FAX 415-961-5042.
Vendor(s): Mead Data Central. *1053*

SENSOR REVIEW.
M C B University Press Ltd., 62 Toller Ln., Bradford, W. York BD8 9BY, England. TEL 0274-499821. FAX 0274-547143.
Vendor(s): Data-Star, DIALOG. *3023*

SENSOR TECHNOLOGY.
Technical Insights, Inc., 32 N. Dean St., Englewood, NJ 07631. TEL 201-568-4744. FAX 201-568-8247.
Vendor(s): Data-Star, DIALOG. *1443*

SEXUALLY TRANSMITTED DISEASES.
J.B. Lippincott Co., E. Washington Sq., Philadelphia, PA 19105. TEL 215-238-4200.
Vendor(s): BRS, Mead Data Central. *3249*

SEYBOLD OUTLOOK ON PROFESSIONAL COMPUTING.
Seybold Group, Inc., P.O. Box 4087, Santa Clara, CA 95056-4987. TEL 408-746-2448.
Vendor(s): NewsNet (EC20). *1424*

SHAREDEBATE INTERNATIONAL.
Applied Foresight, Inc., Box 20607, Bloomington, MN 55420. *4385*

SHINSHIN-IGAKU.
Igaku-Shoin Ltd., 5-24-3 Hongo, Bunkyo-ku, Tokyo 113-91, Japan. TEL 03-817-5711.
Vendor(s): JICST. *3354*

SHONIKA.
Kanehara & Co., Ltd., 31-14 Yushima 2-chome, Bunkyo-ku, Tokyo 113, Japan.
Vendor(s): BRS. *3326*

SHOPPER REPORT.
Consumer Network, Inc, 3624 Science Center, Philadelphia, PA 19104. TEL 215-386-5890. FAX 215-557-7692.
Vendor(s): Data-Star, DIALOG. *1053*

SHORT STORY INDEX.
H.W. Wilson Co., 950 University Ave., Bronx, NY 10452. TEL 800-267-6770. FAX 212-538-2716.
Vendor(s): Wilsonline. *2983*

SICKNESS AND WELLNESS PUBLICATIONS.
John Gordon Burke Publishers, Inc., Box 1492, Evanston, IL 60204-1492. TEL 708-866-8625. *3181*

SIDE EFFECTS OF DRUGS ANNUAL.
Elsevier Science Publishers B.V., Books Division, P.O. Box 211, 1000 AE Amsterdam, Netherlands. TEL 020-5803911. FAX 020-5803705.
Vendor(s): Data-Star (SEDB), DIALOG (File 70/SEDBASE). *3743*

SKIING TRADE NEWS.
C B S Magazines, Skiing Magazine Department Two Park Ave., New York, NY 10016. TEL 212-719-6600.
Vendor(s): DIALOG. *4556*

SKIN DIVER MAGAZINE.
Petersen Publishing Co., 8490 Sunset Blvd., Los Angeles, CA 90069. TEL 213-854-2222.
Vendor(s): DIALOG. *4488*

SLUDGE NEWSLETTER.
Business Publishers, Inc., 951 Pershing Dr., Silver Spring, MD 20910-4464. TEL 301-587-6300. FAX 301-585-9075.
Vendor(s): NewsNet (CH13). *1987*

SMALL ANIMALS.
C.A.B. International, Wallingford, Oxon OX10 8DE, England. TEL 0491 32111. FAX 0491-33508.
Vendor(s): BRS (VETR), CISTI, DIMDI, DIALOG, European Space Agency (File nos.16 & 124/CAB). *4820*

SMALL BUSINESS TAX REVIEW.
A - N Group, Inc., Box 895, Melville, NY 11747-0895. TEL 516-549-4090.
Vendor(s): NewsNet. *1106*

SMITHSONIAN.
Smithsonian Institution, Arts & Industries Bldg., 900 Jefferson Dr., Washington, DC 20560. TEL 202-357-2888. FAX 202-786-2564.
Vendor(s): DIALOG. *4386*

SMOKING AND HEALTH BULLETIN.
U.S. Office on Smoking and Health, National Center for Chronic Disease Prevention and Health Promotion, Centers for Disease Control, MS K-12, 1600 Clifton Rd., N.E., Atlanta, GA 30333.
Vendor(s): DIALOG (File no.160). *1540*

SOCIAL AND LABOUR BULLETIN.
I L O Publications, CH-1211 Geneva 22, Switzerland. TEL 022-7996111. FAX 022-798-6358.
Vendor(s): European Space Agency, Human Resources Information Network, Telesystemes - Questel. *993*

SOCIAL PLANNING - POLICY & DEVELOPMENT ABSTRACTS.
Sociological Abstracts, Inc., Box 22206, San Diego, CA 92192. TEL 619-695-8803. FAX 619-695-0416.
Vendor(s): BRS (SOCA), DIMDI (SA63), Data-Star (SOCA), DIALOG (File No.37). *4426*

SOCIAL SCIENCE & MEDICINE.
Pergamon Press, Inc., Journals Division, 660 White Plains Rd., Tarrytown, NY 10591-5153. TEL 914-524-9200. FAX 914-333-2444. *3153*

SOCIAL SCIENCES CITATION INDEX.
Institute for Scientific Information, 3501 Market St., Philadelphia, PA 19104. TEL 215-386-0100. FAX 215-386-2991.
Vendor(s): BRS (SSCI), DIMDI, Data-Star, DIALOG (File no.7/SOCIAL SCISEARCH). *4396*

SOCIAL SCIENCES INDEX.
H.W. Wilson Co., 950 University Ave., Bronx, NY 10452. TEL 800-367-6770. FAX 212-538-2716.
Vendor(s): Wilsonline (File SSI). *4396*

SOCIAL SECURITY BULLETIN.
U.S. Social Security Administration, Office of Research and Statistics, Van Ness Centre Bldg., Rm. 209, 4301 Connecticut Ave., N.W., Washington, DC 20008. TEL 202-282-7138. FAX 202-282-7219.
Vendor(s): DIALOG. *2542*

SOCIAL WORK RESEARCH AND ABSTRACTS.
National Association of Social Workers, Publications Department, 7981 Eastern Ave., Silver Spring, MD 20910. TEL 301-565-0333. FAX 301-587-1321.
Vendor(s): BRS (SWAB). *4427*

SOCIETE FRANCAISE DE CARDIOLOGIE. BULLETIN D'INFORMATIONS.
Grou-Radenez-Joly, 19 rue des Saints Peres, 75006 Paris, France. *3212*

SOCIOLOGICAL ABSTRACTS.
Sociological Abstracts, Inc., Box 22206, San Diego, CA 92192. TEL 619-695-8803. FAX 619-695-0416.
Vendor(s): BRS (SOCA), DIMDI (SA63), Data-Star (SOCA), DIALOG (File no.37). *4458*

SOCIOLOGY OF HEALTH AND ILLNESS.
Basil Blackwell Ltd., 108 Cowley Rd., Oxford OX4 1JF, England. TEL 0865-791100. FAX 0865-791347. *4452*

SOFTWARE CATALOG: MICROCOMPUTERS.
Elsevier Science Publishing Co., Inc. (New York), 655 Ave. of the Americas, New York, NY 10010. TEL 212-989-5800. FAX 212-633-3995.
Vendor(s): CompuServe Consumer Information Service, DIALOG. *1465*

SOFTWARE ENCYCLOPEDIA.
R.R. Bowker, A Reed Reference Publishing Company, Division of Reed Publishing (USA) Inc., 121 Chanlon Rd., New Providence, NJ 07974. TEL 800-521-8110. FAX 908-665-6688.
Vendor(s): DIALOG (File no.278). *1480*

SOFTWARE MAINTENANCE NEWS.
Software Maintenance News, Inc., 141 Saint Marks Pl., Ste.5F, Staten Island, NY 10301. TEL 718-816-5522. FAX 718-816-9038.
Vendor(s): Information Access Company. *1480*

SOFTWARE MARKETS.
Basil Blackwell Ltd., 108 Cowley Rd., Oxford OX4 1JF, England. TEL 0865-791100. FAX 0865-791347.
Vendor(s): Data-Star, DIALOG. *1480*

SOIL AND WATER CONSERVATION NEWS.
U.S. Soil Conservation Service, c/o Dept. of Agriculture, Box 2890, Washington, DC 20013. TEL 202-720-7547. FAX 202-690-1221. *192*

SOILS AND FERTILIZERS.
C.A.B. International, Wallingford, Oxon OX10 8DE, England. TEL 0491-32111. FAX 0491-33508. Vendor(s): BRS, CISTI, DIMDI, DIALOG, European Space Agency (File nos.16 & 124/CAB). *143*

SOLICITORS' AND BARRISTERS' DIRECTORY.
M B C Information Services, Paulton House, 8 Shepherdess Walk, London N1 7LB, England. TEL 071-490-0049. FAX 071-490-2979. *2679*

SOLID-LIQUID FLOW ABSTRACTS.
S T I Ltd., 4 Kings Meadow, Ferry Hinksey Rd., Oxford OX2 0DU, England. TEL 0865-798898. FAX 0865-798788.
Vendor(s): DIALOG (File no.96/FLUIDEX), European Space Agency (File no.48/FLUIDEX). *1846*

SOLID STATE AND SUPERCONDUCTIVITY ABSTRACTS.
Cambridge Scientific Abstracts, 7200 Wisconsin Ave., 6th Fl., Bethesda, MD 20814. TEL 301-961-6750. FAX 301-961-6720.
Vendor(s): BRS (CSEN). *3839*

SOLID WASTE REPORT.
Business Publishers, Inc., 951 Pershing Dr., Silver Spring, MD 20910-4464. TEL 301-587-6300. FAX 301-585-9075.
Vendor(s): NewsNet (EV20). *1968*

SOLSTICE: AN ELECTRONIC JOURNAL OF GEOGRAPHY AND MATHEMATICS.
Institute of Mathematical Geography, 2790 Briarcliff, Ann Arbor, MI 48105-1429. TEL 313-761-1231. *3056*

SORGHUM AND MILLETS ABSTRACTS.
C.A.B. International, Wallingford, Oxon OX10 8DE, England. TEL 0419-32111. FAX 0491-33508. Vendor(s): BRS (CABA), CISTI, DIMDI, DIALOG, European Space Agency (File nos.16 & 124/CAB). *143*

SOUND & VISION.
Sound & Vision, 99 Atlantic Ave., Ste.302, Toronto, Ont. M6K 3J8, Canada. TEL 416-535-7611. FAX 416-535-6325. *1343*

SOURCEMEX.
University of New Mexico, Latin American Institute, 801 Yale NE, Albuquerque, NM 87131-1016. TEL 505-277-6839. FAX 505-277-5989.
Vendor(s): DIALOG, Mead Data Central, NewsNet. *884*

SOUTH AFRICAN PHARMACEUTICAL JOURNAL.
Pharmaceutical Society of South Africa, P.O. Box 31360, Braamfontein, Johannesburg 2017, South Africa. FAX 011-403-1309. *3743*

SOUTH CAROLINA LAW REVIEW.
University of South Carolina, School of Law, Columbia, SC 29208. TEL 803-777-5874. FAX 803-777-9405.
Vendor(s): WESTLAW. *2680*

SOUTH DAKOTA LAW REVIEW.
University of South Dakota, School of Law, Vermilion, SD 57069. TEL 605-677-5646. FAX 605-677-5417.
Vendor(s): WESTLAW. *2680*

SOUTH TEXAS LAW REVIEW.
South Texas Law Review, Inc., c/o Kibun, Kibun Products International, 5609 Departure Dr., Raleigh, NC 27604-1642.
Vendor(s): WESTLAW. *2680*

SOUTHEAST REAL ESTATE NEWS.
Communication Channels, Inc., 6255 Barfield Rd., Atlanta, GA 30328-4369. TEL 404-256-9800. FAX 404-256-3116. *4158*

SOUTHERN AFRICA FREEDOM BULLETIN.
International Freedom Foundation, 200 G St., N.E., Ste. 300, Washington, DC 20002. TEL 202-546-5788. FAX 202-546-5488. *3972*

SOUTHERN LIVING.
Southern Progress Corp. c/o H. Jahnson, V.P. Circulation, 2100 Lakeshore Dr., Birmingham, AL 35209. TEL 205-877-6000. *2235*

SOUTHERN SOCIAL STUDIES JOURNAL.
Kentucky Council for the Social Studies, Morehead State University, 114 Rader Hall, Morehead, KY 40351. TEL 606-783-2347. FAX 606-783-2678. Vendor(s): BRS, DIALOG. *4388*

SOUTHSCAN.
P.O. Box 724, London N16 5RZ, England. TEL 071-359-2328. FAX 071-359-2443.
Vendor(s): NewsNet. *3927*

SOUTHWEST REAL ESTATE NEWS.
Communication Channels, Inc., 6255 Barfield Rd., Atlanta, GA 30328-4369. TEL 404-256-9800. FAX 404-256-3116. *4158*

SOUTHWESTERN LAW JOURNAL.
Southern Methodist University School of Law, Dallas, TX 75275. TEL 214-692-2594. FAX 214-692-4330.
Vendor(s): WESTLAW. *2680*

SOVIET AEROSPACE & TECHNOLOGY.
Phillips Publishing, Inc., Defense - Aerospace Group, 1925 N. Lynn St., Ste. 1000, Arlington, VA 22209. TEL 703-522-8333. FAX 703-522-6448. Vendor(s): Data-Star, DIALOG, NewsNet (DE02). *62*

SOVIET PERSPECTIVES.
International Freedom Foundation, 200 G St., N.E., Ste. 300, Washington, DC 20003. TEL 202-546-5788. FAX 202-546-5488.
Vendor(s): DIALOG, NewsNet (File no.IT17). *921*

SOYABEAN ABSTRACTS.
C.A.B. International, Wallingford, Oxon OX10 8DE, England. TEL 0491 32111. FAX 0491-33508. Vendor(s): BRS (CABA), CISTI, DIMDI, DIALOG, European Space Agency (File nos.16 & 124/CAB). *143*

SPACE BUSINESS NEWS.
Pasha Publications Inc., 1401 Wilson Blvd., Ste. 900, Arlington, VA 22209-9970. TEL 703-528-1244. FAX 703-528-1253.
Vendor(s): NewsNet (AE11). *62*

SPACE CALENDAR.
Space Age Publishing Company, 75-5751 Kuakini Highway, Ste. 209, Kaulua-Kona, HI 96740. TEL 808-326-2014. FAX 808-326-1825.
Vendor(s): NewsNet. *62*

SPACE COMMERCE WEEK.
Warren Publishing, Inc., 2115 Ward Ct., N.W., Washington, DC 20037. TEL 202-872-9200. FAX 202-293-3435.
Vendor(s): Data-Star, DIALOG, NewsNet (AE05). *62*

SPACE EXPLORATION TECHNOLOGY.
Phillips Publishing, Inc., Defense - Aerospace Group, 1925 N. Lynn St., Ste. 1000, Arlington, VA 22209. TEL 703-522-8333. FAX 703-522-6448. Vendor(s): Data-Star, DIALOG, NewsNet. *62*

SPACE FAX DAILY.
Space Age Publishing Company, 20431 Stevens Creek Blvd., Ste. 210, Cupertino, CA 95014. TEL 408-996-9210. FAX 408-996-2125.
Vendor(s): NewsNet. *62*

SPACE R & D ALERT.
Aerospace Communications, 5902 Mount Eagle Dr., No. 417, Alexandria, VA 22303-2516.
Vendor(s): NewsNet. *63*

SPAIN. BOLETIN OFICIAL DEL ESTADO.
Boletin Oficial del Estado, Trafalgar, 29, 28071 Madrid, Spain. TEL 5382100. FAX 5382348. *4074*

SPANG ROBINSON REPORT.
Louis G. Robinson & Associates, c/o Spang Robinson Wiley, 1819 Doris Dr., Menlo Park, CA 94025-6101.
Vendor(s): NewsNet. *1410*

SPECIALNA PEDAGOGIKA.
Univerzita Komenskeho, Pedagogicka Fakulta, Moskovska ul. 3, 813 34 Bratislava, Czechoslovakia. TEL 542-36. *1741*

SPECTRUM CONVERTIBLES.
C D A Investment Technologies, Inc., 1355 Piccard Dr., Rockville, MD 20850. TEL 800-232-6362. FAX 301-590-1329. *964*

SPECTRUM INTERNATIONAL.
C D A Investment Technologies, Inc., 1355 Piccard Dr., Rockville, MD 20850. TEL 800-232-6362. FAX 301-590-1329. *964*

SPECTRUM 1: U S AND EUROPEAN INVESTMENT COMPANY STOCK HOLDINGS SURVEY.
C D A Investment Technologies, Inc., 1355 Piccard Dr., Rockville, MD 20850. TEL 800-232-6362. FAX 301-590-1329. *964*

SPECTRUM 2: U S AND EUROPEAN INVESTMENT COMPANY PORTFOLIOS.
C D A Investment Technologies, Inc., 1355 Piccard Dr., Rockville, MD 20850. TEL 800-232-6362. FAX 301-590-1329. *964*

SPECTRUM 3: 13(F) INSTITUTIONAL STOCK HOLDINGS SURVEY.
C D A Investment Technologies, Inc., 1355 Piccard Dr., Rockville, MD 20850. TEL 800-232-6362. FAX 301-590-1329. *964*

SPECTRUM 4: 13(F) INSTITUTIONAL PORTFOLIOS.
C D A Investment Technologies, Inc., 1355 Piccard Dr., Rockville, MD 20850. TEL 800-232-6362. FAX 301-590-1329. *964*

SPECTRUM 5: FIVE PERCENT OWNERSHIP BASED ON 13D, 13G, & 14D-1 FILINGS.
C D A Investment Technologies, Inc., 1355 Piccard Dr., Rockville, MD 20850. TEL 800-232-6362. FAX 301-590-1350. *964*

SPECTRUM 6: INSIDER OWNERSHIP.
C D A Investment Technologies, Inc., 1355 Piccard Dr., Rockville, MD 20850. TEL 800-232-6362. FAX 301-590-1329. *964*

SPEEDNEWS.
Gil Speed & Associates, 1801 Ave. of the Stars, Ste. 210, Los Angeles, CA 90067-5904. TEL 213-203-9603. FAX 213-203-9352.
Vendor(s): NewsNet. *4677*

SPORTING NEWS.
Sporting News Publishing Co. 1212 N. Lindbergh Blvd., St. Louis, MO 63132. TEL 800-669-5700. Vendor(s): Mead Data Central. *4491*

SPORTS ILLUSTRATED.
The Time Inc. Magazine Company Time & Life Bldg., Rockefeller Center, 1271 Ave. of the Americas, New York, NY 10020-1393. TEL 212-522-1212. Vendor(s): DIALOG, Mead Data Central, VU/TEXT Information Services, Inc.. *4491*

SPORTSEARCH.
Sport Information Resource Centre (SIRC), 1600 James Naismith Drive, Gloucester, Ont. K1B 5N4, Canada. TEL 613-748-5658. FAX 613-748-5701. Vendor(s): BRS (SFDB), BRS/Saunders Colleague, Data-Star, DIALOG. *4499*

SPORTSTYLE.
Fairchild Publications, Inc., SportStyle, 7 W. 34th St., New York, NY 10001. TEL 212-630-4000. FAX 212-337-3247.
Vendor(s): DIALOG. *4492*

SPRAY TECHNOLOGY & MARKETING.
Industry Publications, Inc. (Fairfield), 389 Passaic Ave., Fairfield, NJ 07006. TEL 201-227-5151. FAX 201-227-9219. *3652*

STAND MAGAZINE.
Stand Magazine, 179 Wingrove Rd., Newcastle Upon Tyne NE4 9DA, England. TEL 091-273-328. *2963*

STANDARD & POOR'S CORPORATION RECORDS.
Standard & Poor's Corporation, 25 Broadway, New York, NY 10004. TEL 212-208-8000.
Vendor(s): DIALOG (File no.133/Corporate Descriptions). *964*

STANDARD & POOR'S DIVIDEND RECORD (DAILY).
Standard & Poor's Corporation, 25 Broadway, New York, NY 10004. TEL 212-208-8000. *964*

STANDARD & POOR'S REGISTER OF CORPORATIONS, DIRECTORS AND EXECUTIVES.
Standard & Poor's Corporation, 25 Broadway, New York, NY 10004. TEL 212-208-8000. *1028*

STANDARD CORPORATION RECORDS CURRENT NEWS EDITION.
Standard & Poor's Corporation, 25 Broadway, New York, NY 10004. TEL 212-208-8377. FAX 212-509-8994.
Vendor(s): DIALOG (File no.133). *692*

STANFORD JOURNAL OF INTERNATIONAL LAW.
Stanford University, Stanford Law School, Stanford, CA 94305-8610. TEL 415-723-1375.
Vendor(s): WESTLAW. *2729*

STANFORD LAW REVIEW.
Stanford University, Stanford Law School, Crown Quadrangle, Stanford, CA 94305-8610. TEL 415-723-3210.
Vendor(s): Mead Data Central, WESTLAW. *2681*

STAPP CAR CRASH CONFERENCE PROCEEDINGS.
Society of Automotive Engineers, 400 Commonwealth Dr., Warrendale, PA 15096-0001. TEL 412-776-4841. FAX 412-776-5760.
Vendor(s): European Space Agency, FIZ Technik, Orbit Information Technologies. *4702*

STATE AND LOCAL TAXES.
Maxwell Macmillan, Professional and Business Reference Publishing, 910 Sylvan Ave., Englewood Cliffs, NJ 07632-3310. TEL 800-562-0245.
Vendor(s): Prentice-Hall Information Network. *1106*

STATE AND LOCAL TAXES: PROPERTY TAXES.
Maxwell Macmillan, Professional and Business Reference Publishing, 910 Sylvan Ave., Englewood Cliffs, NJ 07632-3310. TEL 800-562-0245.
Vendor(s): Prentice-Hall Information Network. *1106*

STATE AND LOCAL TAXES: SALES AND USE TAXES.
Maxwell Macmillan, Professional and Business Reference Publishing, 910 Sylvan Ave., Englewood Cliffs, NJ 07632-3310. TEL 800-562-0245. FAX 609-201-3569.
Vendor(s): Prentice-Hall Information Network. *1106*

STATE INHERITANCE TAXES.
Maxwell Macmillan, Professional and Business Reference Publishing, 910 Sylvan Ave., Englewood Cliffs, NJ 07632-3310. TEL 800-562-0245.
Vendor(s): Prentice-Hall Information Network. *1106*

STATE REGULATION REPORT.
Business Publishers, Inc., 951 Pershing Dr., Silver Spring, MD 20910-4464. TEL 301-587-6300. FAX 301-587-1081.
Vendor(s): NewsNet (CH11). *1987*

STATE TAX REVIEW.
Commerce Clearing House, Inc., 4025 W. Peterson Ave., Chicago, IL 60646. TEL 312-583-8500.
Vendor(s): NewsNet. *1106*

STATE TELEPHONE REGULATION REPORT.
Capitol Publications Inc., Telecom Publishing Group, 1101 King St., Ste. 444, Box 1455, Alexandria, VA 22313-2055. TEL 800-327-7205. FAX 703-739-6490.
Vendor(s): NewsNet (TE47). *1366*

STATISTICAL ABSTRACT OF THE UNITED STATES.
U.S. Bureau of the Census, Data User Services Division, Washington, DC 20233. TEL 301-763-4100.
Vendor(s): CompuServe Consumer Information Service, DIALOG. *4587*

STEELS ALERT.
A S M International, Materials Information, Materials Park, OH 44073. TEL 216-338-5151. FAX 216-338-4634.
Vendor(s): CISTI, CREDO, Data-Star (MBUS), DIALOG (File no.269), European Space Agency (File no.111), Orbit Information Technologies (MATERIALS/B), STN International (MATBUS). *3428*

STEREO REVIEW.
Hachette Magazines, Inc., 1633 Broadway, New York, NY 10009. TEL 212-767-6000.
Vendor(s): DIALOG. *4462*

STETSON LAW REVIEW.
Stetson University, College of Law, 1401 61 St. So., St. Petersburg, FL 33707. TEL 813-345-1300. FAX 813-345-8973.
Vendor(s): WESTLAW. *2682*

STOCKS, BONDS, BILLS AND INFLATION (YEAR) YEARBOOK.
Ibbotson Associates, 8 S. Michigan Ave., Ste. 700, Chicago, IL 60603. TEL 312-263-3435. FAX 312-263-1398. *965*

STRATEGIC INFORMATION ON U S AIR TRAVEL.
Nationwide Intelligence, Box 1922, Saginaw, MI 48605. TEL 517-752-6123. *4677*

STROKE.
American Heart Association, 7272 Greenville Ave., Dallas, TX 75231-4596. TEL 214-706-1310. FAX 214-691-6342.
Vendor(s): BRS. *3212*

STUDENT AID NEWS.
Capitol Publications Inc., 1101 King St., Ste. 444, Alexandria, VA 22314. TEL 703-683-4100. FAX 703-739-6517.
Vendor(s): NewsNet. *1716*

STUDIES IN DEVELOPMENT.
Middle East Technical University, Faculty of Economic and Administrative Sciences, Ismet Inonu Bulvari, Ankara, Turkey. TEL 236943. FAX 90-4-223-6943. *1028*

SUB-SAHARAN MONITOR.
International Freedom Foundation, 200 G St., N.E., Ste. 300, Washington, DC 20002. TEL 202-546-5788. FAX 202-546-5488. *3973*

SUBJECT GUIDE TO BOOKS IN PRINT.
R.R. Bowker, A Reed Reference Publishing Company, Division of Reed Publishing (USA) Inc., 121 Chanlon Rd., New Providence, NJ 07974. TEL 800-521-8110. FAX 908-665-6688.
Vendor(s): BRS (BBIP), BRS/Saunders Colleague, DIALOG (File no.470). *412*

SUBJECT GUIDE TO CHILDREN'S BOOKS IN PRINT.
R.R. Bowker, A Reed Reference Publishing Company, Division of Reed Publishing (USA) Inc., 121 Chanlon Rd., New Providence, NJ 07974. TEL 800-521-8110. FAX 908-665-6688. *413*

SUFFOLK TRANSNATIONAL LAW JOURNAL.
Suffolk University Law School, Suffolk Transnational Law Journal, 41 Temple St., Boston, MA 02114-4280. TEL 617-573-8610.
Vendor(s): WESTLAW. *2683*

SUFFOLK UNIVERSITY LAW REVIEW.
Suffolk University Law School, Suffolk University Law Review, Beacon Hill, Boston, MA 02114. TEL 617-227-2854.
Vendor(s): WESTLAW. *2683*

SUNDAY MAIL.
Queensland Newspapers Pty. Ltd., Campbell St., Bowen Hills, Brisbane, Australia. FAX 07-252-6696. *2172*

SUNSET.
Sunset Publishing Corp., 80 Willow Rd., Menlo Park, CA 94025-3691. TEL 415-321-3600. FAX 415-321-0551.
Vendor(s): DIALOG. *2235*

SUPER MARKETING.
Reed Business Publishing Group, Carew Division, Quadrant House, The Quadrant, Sutton, Surrey SM2 5AS, England. TEL 081-661-3500. *2094*

SUPERCONDUCTOR WEEK.
Atlantic Information Services, Inc., 1050 17th St., N.W., Ste. 480, Washington, DC 20036. FAX 202-331-9542.
Vendor(s): Data-Star, DIALOG, NewsNet. *3842*

SUPERFUND.
Pasha Publications Inc., 1401 Wilson Blvd., Ste. 900, Arlington, VA 22209-9970. TEL 703-528-1244. FAX 703-528-1253.
Vendor(s): Data-Star, DIALOG, NewsNet. *1497*

SUPERMARKET NEWS.
Fairchild Publications, Inc., Supermarket News, 7 W. 34th St., New York, NY 10001. TEL 212-630-3770. FAX 212-630-3768.
Vendor(s): DIALOG. *2094*

SUPREME COURT OF CANADA DECISIONS.
Western Legal Publications, 301-1 Alexander St., Vancouver, B.C. V6A 1B2, Canada. TEL 604-687-5671. FAX 604-687-2796. *2733*

SURFACE MODIFICATION TECHNOLOGY NEWS.
Business Communications Co., Inc. (Norwalk), 25 Van Zant St., Ste. 13, Norwalk, CT 06855. TEL 203-426-3905. FAX 203-853-0348.
Vendor(s): NewsNet. *3833*

SURGERY, GYNECOLOGY & OBSTETRICS.
Franklin H. Martin Memorial Foundation, 54 E. Erie St., Chicago, IL 60611. TEL 312-787-9282. FAX 312-440-7026.
Vendor(s): Mead Data Central. *3385*

SURGICAL CLINICS OF NORTH AMERICA.
W.B. Saunders Co., Curtis Center, Independence Square W., Philadelphia, PA 19106. TEL 215-238-7800.
Vendor(s): BRS. *3385*

SURPLUS RECORD.
Surplus Record, Inc., 20 N. Wacker Dr., Chicago, IL 60606. TEL 312-372-9077. FAX 312-372-6537. *3025*

SURVEY OF CURRENT BUSINESS.
U.S. Bureau of Economic Analysis, U.S. Dept. of Commerce, Washington, DC 20230. TEL 202-523-0777.
Vendor(s): DIALOG. *885*

SVENSK FARMACEUTISK TIDSKRIFT.
Swedish Pharmaceutical Press, P.O. Box 1136, S-11181 Stockholm, Sweden. TEL 46-8-24 50 80. FAX 46-8-14-95-80. *3744*

SYDNEY CITYSCOPE.
Cityscope Publications Pty. Ltd., P.O. Box 807, Manly, N.S.W. 2095, Australia. TEL 02-976-2233. *4160*

SYNTHETIC METHODS OF ORGANIC CHEMISTRY.
S. Karger AG, Allschwilerstr. 10, P.O. Box, CH-4009 Basel, Switzerland. TEL 061-3061111. FAX 061-3061234.
Vendor(s): Orbit Information Technologies. *1223*

SYRACUSE JOURNAL OF INTERNATIONAL LAW & COMMERCE.
Joe Christensen, Inc. (Syracuse), E I White Hall, Ste. 0041, Syracuse, NY 13244-1030. TEL 315-443-2056.
Vendor(s): WESTLAW. *2729*

SYSTEMS AND NETWORKS INTEGRATION.
C M P Publications, Inc., 600 Community Dr., Manhassett, NY 11030. TEL 516-562-5000. FAX 516-562-5409.
Vendor(s): NewsNet. *1439*

T A M BULLETIN.
Travelling Art Mail, c/o T A M, Postbus 10388, 5000 JJ Tilburg, Netherlands. TEL 013-366103. *346*

T D R.
M I T Press, 55 Hayward St., Cambridge, MA 02142. TEL 617-253-2889. FAX 617-258-6779. *4639*

T M A EXECUTIVE SUMMARY.
Tobacco Merchants Association of the United States, Inc., 231 Clarksville Rd., Ste. 6, Box 8019, Princeton, NJ 08543-8019. TEL 609-275-4900. FAX 609-275-8379. *4644*

T M A LEGISLATIVE BULLETIN.
Tobacco Merchants Association of the United States, Inc., 231 Clarksville Rd., Ste. 6, Box 8019, Princeton, NJ 08543-8019. TEL 609-275-4900. FAX 609-275-8379. *4644*

T M A TOBACCO BAROMETER: SMOKING, CHEWING, SNUFF.
Tobacco Merchants Association of the United States, Inc., 231 Clarksville Rd., Ste. 6, Box 8019, Princeton, NJ 08543-8019. TEL 609-275-4900. FAX 609-275-8379. *4644*

T M A TRADEMARK REPORT.
Tobacco Merchants Association of the United States, Inc., 231 Clarksville Rd., Ste. 6, Box 8019, Princeton, NJ 08543-8019. TEL 609-275-4900. FAX 609-275-8379. *4645*

T M A WORLD ALERT.
Tobacco Merchants Association of the United States, Inc., 231 Clarksville Rd., Ste. 6, Box 8019, Princeton, NJ 08543-8019. TEL 609-275-4900. FAX 609-275-8379. *4645*

TAKEOVER TARGETS.
High Tech Publishing Company, Box 1923, Brattleboro, VT 05301. TEL 802-254-3539. Vendor(s): Data-Star, NewsNet. *694*

TASMANIAN REPORTS.
Law Book Co. Ltd., 44-50 Waterloo Rd., North Ryde, N.S.W. 2112, Australia. TEL 02-887-0177. FAX 02-888-9706. *2684*

TAX LAWYER.
American Bar Association, Taxation Section, 1800 M St., N.W., Washington, DC 20036. TEL 202-331-2231. FAX 202-331-2220. Vendor(s): Mead Data Central, WESTLAW. *2684*

TAX MANAGEMENT COMPENSATION PLANNING.
Tax Management, Inc. 1231 25th St., N.W., Washington, DC 20037. TEL 202-452-4200. FAX 202-822-8092. Vendor(s): WESTLAW (File TM-CP, TM-CP-OLD, TM-CPJ). *1108*

TAX MANAGEMENT COMPENSATION PLANNING JOURNAL.
Tax Management, Inc. 1231 25th St., N.W., Washington, DC 20037. TEL 202-452-4200. FAX 202-822-8092. Vendor(s): WESTLAW (File TM-CPJ). *1029*

TAX MANAGEMENT ESTATES, GIFTS AND TRUSTS.
Tax Management, Inc. 1231 25th St., N.W., Washington, DC 20037. TEL 202-452-4200. FAX 202-822-8092. Vendor(s): WESTLAW (File TM-EGT, TM-EGT-OLD, TM-EGTJ). *1108*

TAX MANAGEMENT ESTATES, GIFTS AND TRUSTS JOURNAL.
Tax Management, Inc. 1231 25th St., N.W., Washington, DC 20037. TEL 202-452-4200. FAX 202-822-8092. Vendor(s): WESTLAW (File TM-EGTJ). *966*

TAX MANAGEMENT FOREIGN INCOME PORTFOLIOS.
Tax Management, Inc. 1231 25th St., N.W., Washington, DC 20037. TEL 202-452-4200. FAX 202-822-8092. Vendor(s): WESTLAW (File TM-FOR). *1108*

TAX MANAGEMENT MEMORANDUM.
Tax Management, Inc. 1231 25th St., N.W., Washington, DC 20037. TEL 202-452-4200. FAX 202-822-8092. Vendor(s): WESTLAW (File TM-TMM). *1109*

TAX MANAGEMENT REAL ESTATE.
Tax Management, Inc. 1231 25th St., N.W., Washington, DC 20037. TEL 202-452-4556. FAX 202-452-4096. Vendor(s): WESTLAW (File TM-RE, TM-RE-OLD, TM-REJ). *4158*

TAX MANAGEMENT REAL ESTATE JOURNAL.
Tax Management, Inc. 1231 25th St., N.W., Washington, DC 20037. TEL 202-452-4200. FAX 202-822-8092. Vendor(s): WESTLAW (File TM-REJ). *4158*

TAX MANAGEMENT U S INCOME.
Tax Management, Inc. 1231 25th St., N.W., Washington, DC 20037. TEL 202-452-4200. FAX 202-822-8092. Vendor(s): WESTLAW (File TM-US, TM-US-OLD, TMWR). *1109*

TAX MANAGEMENT WEEKLY REPORT.
Tax Management, Inc. 1231 25th St., N.W., Washington, DC 20037. TEL 202-452-4200. FAX 202-822-8092. Vendor(s): Human Resources Information Network, NewsNet. *1109*

TAX NEWS SERVICE.
International Bureau of Fiscal Documentation, P.O. Box 20237, 1000 HE Amsterdam, Netherlands. TEL 020-267726. FAX 020-228658. *1109*

TAX NOTES.
Tax Analysts, 6830 N. Fairfax Dr., Arlington, VA 22213. TEL 703-533-4400. FAX 703-533-4444. Vendor(s): Mead Data Central, WESTLAW. *1109*

TAX PROFILE.
C C H Canadian Ltd., 6 Garamond Ct., Don Mills, Ont. M3C 1Z5, Canada. TEL 416-441-2992. FAX 416-444-9011. Vendor(s): QL Systems Ltd.. *1109*

TECHNICAL COMPUTING.
Stics, Inc., 9714 S. Rice Ave., Houston, TX 77096-4138. TEL 713-723-6658. Vendor(s): NewsNet. *1401*

TECHNOLOGY AND LEARNING.
Peter Li, Inc., 2451 East River Rd., Dayton, OH 45439. TEL 513-294-5785. FAX 513-294-7840. Vendor(s): DIALOG. *1691*

TECHNOLOGY MANAGEMENT ACTION.
Technology News Center, 975 Alkire Ave., Morgan Hill, CA 95037-4722. TEL 408-778-0889. FAX 408-778-9976. *922*

TECHNOLOGY REVIEW.
Massachusetts Institute of Technology, Association of Alumni and Alumnae, W59-200, Cambridge, MA 02139. TEL 617-253-8250. Vendor(s): DIALOG. *4347*

TECHNOLOGY WATCH.
Technology Watch, Inc., Box 2206, Springfield, VA 22152. *1423*

TEEN.
Petersen Publishing Co., 8490 Sunset Blvd., Los Angeles, CA 90069. TEL 213-854-2222. Vendor(s): DIALOG. *1267*

TEKSTILEC.
Urednistvo Tekstilec, Snezniska 5, p.p. 311, 61000 Ljubljana, Slovenia. TEL 61 224-417. Vendor(s): DIALOG. *4624*

TELE-SERVICE NEWS.
Worldwide Videotex, Box 138, Babson Park, Boston, MA 02157. TEL 617-449-1603. Vendor(s): Data-Star, DIALOG, NewsNet. *1366*

TELECOM MARKETS.
Financial Times Business Information Ltd., Tower House, Southampton St., London WC2E 7HA, England. TEL 071-240 9301. FAX 071-240-7946. Vendor(s): Data-Star, Mead Data Central. *1085*

TELECOM TODAY.
British Telecommunications plc, 81 Newgate St., London EC14 7AJ, England. TEL 01-356-5307. FAX 01-356-6540. Vendor(s): Data-Star, DIALOG, NewsNet. *1366*

TELECOMMUNICATIONS ALERT.
United Communications Group, 11300 Rockville Pike, Ste. 1100, Rockville, MD 20852-3030. TEL 301-816-8950. Vendor(s): NewsNet (TE75). *1349*

TELECOMMUNICATIONS REPORTS.
Telecommunications Reports 1333 H St., N.W., Ste. 1100-W., Washington, DC 20005. TEL 202-842-3006. FAX 202-842-3047. Vendor(s): NewsNet (TE11). *1344*

TELECOMMUNICATIONS WEEK.
Business Research Publications, Inc., 817 Broadway, New York, NY 10003. TEL 212-673-4700. FAX 212-475-1790. Vendor(s): NewsNet (TE59). *1344*

TELEPHONE ENGINEER AND MANAGEMENT.
Avanstar Communications, Inc. (Chicago), 2 Illinois Center, 233 North Michigan St., 24th Fl., Chicago, IL 60601. TEL 312-938-2300. FAX 312-938-4854. Vendor(s): DIALOG. *1367*

TELEPHONE ENGINEER & MANAGEMENT DIRECTORY.
Avanstar Communications, Inc., 7500 Old Oak Blvd., Cleveland, OH 44130. TEL 216-243-8100. FAX 216-891-2726. Vendor(s): DIALOG. *1367*

TELEPHONE NEWS.
Phillips Publishing, Inc., 7811 Montrose Rd., Potomac, MD 20854. TEL 301-340-2100. FAX 301-309-3847. Vendor(s): NewsNet (TE04). *1367*

SERIALS AVAILABLE ONLINE 5101

TELEVISION DIGEST WITH CONSUMER ELECTRONICS.
Warren Publishing, Inc., 2115 Ward Ct., N.W., Washington, DC 20037. TEL 202-872-9200. FAX 202-293-3435. Vendor(s): NewsNet (PB01). *1383*

TEMPLE LAW REVIEW.
Temple University School of Law, Philadelphia, PA 19122. TEL 215-787-7868. Vendor(s): WESTLAW. *2684*

TENNESSEE BAR JOURNAL.
Tennessee Bar Association, 3622 West End Ave., Nashville, TN 37205-2403. Vendor(s): WESTLAW. *2684*

TENNESSEE LAW REVIEW.
Tennessee Law Review Association, Inc., 1505 W. Cumberland Ave., Knoxville, TN 37996-1800. Vendor(s): WESTLAW. *2684*

TERATOGENESIS, CARCINOGENESIS, AND MUTAGENESIS.
John Wiley & Sons, Inc., Journals, 605 Third Ave., New York, NY 10158. TEL 212-850-6000. FAX 212-850-6088. *3156*

TERATOLOGY.
John Wiley & Sons, Inc., Journals, 605 Third Ave., New York, NY 10158. TEL 212-850-6000. FAX 212-850-6088. *457*

TERRY FAMILY HISTORIAN.
c/o Robert M. Terry, Ed., 1518 Skyline Cir., Sapulpa, OK 74066. *2165*

TEXAS LAW REVIEW.
University of Texas at Austin, School of Law Publications, 727 E. 26th St., Ste. 3.102A, Austin, TX 78705-1106. TEL 512-471-3164. FAX 512-471-6988. Vendor(s): Mead Data Central. *2685*

TEXAS LAWYER.
American Lawyer Media, L.P. (New York), 600 Third Ave., 3rd Fl., New York, NY 10016. TEL 212-973-2800. FAX 214-741-2325. *2685*

TEXAS TECH LAW REVIEW.
Texas Tech University, School of Law, Lubbock, TX 79409. TEL 806-742-3791. FAX 806-742-1629. Vendor(s): WESTLAW. *2685*

TEXTILE TECHNOLOGY DIGEST.
Institute of Textile Technology, Charlottesville, VA 22902. TEL 804-296-5511. FAX 804-977-5400. Vendor(s): DIALOG (File no.119). *4628*

THAI ABSTRACTS, SERIES A. SCIENCE AND TECHNOLOGY.
Thailand Institute of Scientific and Technological Research, 196 Phahonyothin Road, Bang Khen, Bangkok 10900, Thailand. TEL 579-4929. FAX 662-579-8594. *4358*

THEORETICAL CHEMICAL ENGINEERING ABSTRACTS.
Royal Society of Chemistry, Thomas Graham House, Science Park, Milton Rd., Cambridge CB4 4WF, England. TEL 0462-672555. FAX 0462-480947. Vendor(s): Data-Star, DIALOG, European Space Agency, Orbit Information Technologies. *1846*

THIRD WORLD RESOURCES.
Third World Resources, 464 19th St., Oakland, CA 94612-2297. TEL 510-835-4692. FAX 510-835-3017. *935*

THOMAS REGISTER OF AMERICAN MANUFACTURERS AND THOMAS REGISTER CATALOG FILE.
Thomas Publishing Company, Five Penn Plaza, 250 W. 34th St., New York, NY 10001. TEL 212-695-0500. Vendor(s): DIALOG (File no.535). *1055*

THORAX.
B M J Publishing Group, B.M.A. House, Tavistock Sq., London WC1H 9JR, England. TEL 071-387-4499. Vendor(s): BRS. *3157*

THURGOOD MARSHALL LAW REVIEW.
Texas Southern University, Thurgood Marshall School of Law, 3100 Cleburne, Houston, TX 77004. TEL 713-527-7246. FAX 713-639-1049. Vendor(s): WESTLAW. *2685*

Online

TIME.
The Time Inc. Magazine Company, Time & Life Bldg., Rockefeller Center, 1271 Ave. of the Americas, New York, NY 10020-1393. TEL 800-541-1000. Vendor(s): Dow Jones/News Retrieval, Mead Data Central, VU/TEXT Information Services, Inc.. *2236*

TIN INTERNATIONAL.
M I I D A Ltd., P.O. Box 2137, London NW10 6TN, England. TEL 081-961-7487. FAX 081-961-2137. Vendor(s): DIALOG. *3422*

TOHO UNIVERSITY MEDICAL SOCIETY. JOURNAL.
Toho University Medical Society, c/o Library, School of Medicine, 5-21-16 Omori Nishi, Ota-ku, Tokyo 143, Japan. FAX 764-1642. *3157*

TOILETRIES, FRAGRANCES AND SKIN CARE: THE ROSE SHEET.
F-D-C Reports, Inc., 5550 Friendship Blvd., Ste. One, Chevy Chase, MD 20815. TEL 301-657-9830. FAX 301-657-9830. Vendor(s): Data-Star (FDCR), DIALOG (File no.187), Mead Data Central. *377*

TOKYO FINANCIAL REVIEW.
Bank of Tokyo, Ltd., 3-26 Kanda Nishikicho, Chiyoda-ku, Toyko 101, Japan. *801*

TOOLING & PRODUCTION.
Huebcore Communications, Inc., 29100 Aurora Rd., Ste. 200, Solon, OH 44139. TEL 216-248-1125. FAX 612-686-0214. Vendor(s): DIALOG. *3024*

TORONTO STOCKWATCH.
Canjex Publishing Limited, 700 W. Georgia St., P.O. Box 10371, Vancouver, B.C. V7Y 1J6, Canada. TEL 604-687-1500. *966*

TORT & INSURANCE LAW JOURNAL.
American Bar Association, Tort and Insurance Practice Section, 750 N. Lake Shore Dr., Chicago, IL 60611. TEL 312-988-5000. Vendor(s): Mead Data Central, WESTLAW. *2686*

TOUR AND TRAVEL NEWS.
C M P Publications, Inc., 600 Community Dr., Manhasset, NY 11030. TEL 516-562-5000. FAX 516-365-4601. Vendor(s): Data-Star, DIALOG, NewsNet. *4789*

TOXIC MATERIALS NEWS.
Business Publishers, Inc., 951 Pershing Dr., Silver Spring, MD 20910-4464. TEL 301-587-6300. FAX 301-585-9075. Vendor(s): NewsNet (CH12). *1987*

TOXICOLOGY ABSTRACTS.
Cambridge Scientific Abstracts, 7200 Wisconsin Ave., 6th Fl., Bethesda, MD 20814. TEL 301-961-6750. FAX 301-961-6720. Vendor(s): BRS (CSAL), DIALOG (File no.76/LIFE SCIENCES COLLECTION). *3748*

TOXICOLOGY AND APPLIED PHARMACOLOGY.
Academic Press, Inc., Journal Division, 1250 Sixth Ave., San Diego, CA 92101. TEL 619-230-1840. FAX 619-699-6800. *1983*

TOXICOLOGY LETTERS.
Elsevier Science Publishers B.V., P.O. Box 211, 1000 AE Amsterdam, Netherlands. TEL 020-5803911. FAX 020-5803598. *1983*

TOXICS LAW REPORTER.
The Bureau of National Affairs, Inc., 1231 25th St. N.W., Washington, DC 20037. TEL 202-452-4200. FAX 202-822-8092. Vendor(s): Human Resources Information Network (CDD, HDD). *1987*

TRADE & INDUSTRY INDEX.
Information Access Company, 362 Lakeside Dr., Foster City, CA 94404. TEL 800-227-8431. FAX 415-378-5499. Vendor(s): BRS (TSAP), DIALOG (File no.148). *741*

TRADESCOPE.
Japan External Trade Organization, 2-5 Toranomon 2-chome, Minato-ku, Tokyo 105, Japan. FAX 03-582-3518. *1156*

TRADING SYSTEMS TECHNOLOGY.
Waters Information Services, Inc., Box 2248, Binghamton, NY 13902-2248. TEL 607-772-8086. FAX 607-798-1692. Vendor(s): Data-Star, DIALOG, NewsNet. *805*

TRAINING.
Lakewood Publications, Inc., 50 S. Ninth, Minneapolis, MN 55402. TEL 612-333-0471. Vendor(s): Human Resources Information Network. *1030*

TRAINING AND DEVELOPMENT ALERT.
Advanced Personnel Systems, Box 1438, Roseville, CA 95661. TEL 916-781-2900. FAX 916-781-2901. Vendor(s): Human Resources Information Network. *741*

TRAINING AND DEVELOPMENT ORGANIZATIONS DIRECTORY.
Gale Research Inc., 835 Penobscot Bldg., Detroit, MI 48226. TEL 313-961-2242. FAX 313-961-6083. Vendor(s): Human Resources Information Network (TDOD). *1030*

TRANSPLANTATION PROCEEDINGS.
Appleton & Lange, Journal Division 25 Van Zant St., Box 5630, Norwalk, CT 06856. TEL 203-838-4400. *3385*

TRANSPORTATION & DISTRIBUTION.
Penton Publishing 1100 Superior Ave., Cleveland, OH 44114-2543. TEL 216-696-7000. FAX 216-696-8765. Vendor(s): DIALOG. *4658*

TRAVAIL ET EMPLOI.
Masson, 120 bd. St. Germain, 75006 Paris Cedex 06, France. TEL 1-46-34-21-60. FAX 1-45-87-29-99. Vendor(s): Telesystemes - Questel. *995*

TRAVEL WEEKLY.
Reed Travel Group 500 Plaza Dr., Secaucus, NJ 07096. TEL 201-902-2000. Vendor(s): DIALOG. *4793*

TREE PHYSIOLOGY.
Heron Publishing, Box 5579, Station "B", Victoria, B.C. V8R 6S4, Canada. TEL 604-592-5173. FAX 604-721-8855. Vendor(s): DIALOG. *519*

TRIBOS - TRIBOLOGY ABSTRACTS.
S T I Ltd., 4 Kings Meadow, Ferry Hinksey Rd., Oxford OX2 ODU, England. TEL 0865-798898. FAX 0865-798788. Vendor(s): DIALOG (File no.96/FLUIDEX), European Space Agency (File no.48/FLUIDEX). *1846*

TRIBUNA FARMACEUTICA.
Universidade Federal do Parana, Faculdade de Farmacia, Rua Coronel Dulcidio 638, Caixa Postal 888, 80000 Curitiba, Parana, Brazil. FAX 041-2642243. *3744*

TROPICAL DISEASES BULLETIN.
Bureau of Hygiene and Tropical Diseases, Keppel St., London WC1E 7HT, England. TEL 071-636-8636. FAX 071-580-6756. Vendor(s): DIMDI. *3181*

TROPICAL OIL SEEDS.
C.A.B. International, Wallingford, Oxon OX10 8DE, England. TEL 0491-32111. FAX 0491-33508. Vendor(s): BRS (CABA), CISTI, DIMDI, DIALOG, European Space Agency (File nos.16 & 124/CAB). *144*

TRUSTS AND ESTATES.
Communication Channels, Inc., 6255 Barfield Rd., Atlanta, GA 30328-4369. TEL 404-256-9800. FAX 404-256-3116. *967*

TUIJIN JISHU.
Hangkong Hangtian Gongye-bu, Di 3 Yanjiuyuan, 31 Suo, P.O. Box 7208-26, Beijing 100074, People's Republic of China. TEL 8376141. *63*

TULANE LAW REVIEW.
Tulane Law Review Association, Tulane University Sta., New Orleans, LA 70118. TEL 504-865-5969. Vendor(s): Mead Data Central, WESTLAW. *2687*

TULANE MARITIME LAW JOURNAL.
Tulane University, School of Law, New Orleans, LA 70118. TEL 504-865-5959. FAX 504-865-6748. Vendor(s): Mead Data Central, WESTLAW. *2735*

TULSA LAW JOURNAL.
University of Tulsa, College of Law, 3120 E. Fourth Pl., Tulsa, OK 74104. TEL 918-631-2408. FAX 918-631-3556. Vendor(s): WESTLAW. *2687*

TURING INSTITUTE ABSTRACTS IN ARTIFICIAL INTELLIGENCE.
Springer-Verlag, Springer House, 8 Alexandra Rd., London SW19 7JZ, England. TEL 081-947-1280. FAX 081-947-1274. Vendor(s): Data-Star. *1405*

U C DAVIS LAW REVIEW.
University of California, Davis, School of Law, Martin Luther King, Jr. Hall, Davis, CA 95616. TEL 916-752-2551. FAX 916-752-4704. Vendor(s): Wilsonline. *2687*

U C L A LAW REVIEW.
University of California, Los Angeles, School of Law, 405 Hilgard Ave., Los Angeles, CA 90024. TEL 213-825-4841. Vendor(s): Mead Data Central. *2687*

U K INDUSTRIAL TRADE NAMES.
Kompass Windsor Court, E. Grinstead House, E. Grinstead, W. Sussex RH19 1XD, England. TEL 0342-326972. FAX 0342-317241. *1156*

U K UPSTREAM PETROLEUM DATABASE.
Arthur Andersen & Co., Petroleum Services Group, 1 Surrey St., London WC2R 2PS, England. TEL 071-438-3888. FAX 071-438-3881. Available only online. *3702*

U S A TODAY.
Society for the Advancement of Education, 99 W. Hawthorne Ave., Ste. 518, Valley Stream, NY 11580-6101. Vendor(s): DIALOG, Mead Data Central, VU/TEXT Information Services, Inc.. *3930*

U S NEWS & WORLD REPORT.
U S News & World Report, Inc., 599 Lexington Ave., New York, NY 10022. TEL 212-326-5300. Vendor(s): DIALOG, Mead Data Central. *2236*

U S OIL WEEK.
Capitol Publications Inc., 1101 King St., Ste. 444, Alexandria, VA 22314. TEL 703-683-4100. FAX 703-739-6517. Vendor(s): DIALOG. *3703*

U S PHARMACIST.
Jobson Publishing Corp., 352 Park Ave. S., New York, NY 10010. TEL 212-685-4848. FAX 212-696-5318. *3744*

U S RAIL NEWS.
Business Publishers, Inc., 951 Pershing Dr., Silver Spring, MD 20910-4464. TEL 301-587-6300. FAX 301-585-9075. Vendor(s): NewsNet (TS11). *4716*

U S STATISTICS.
U S Statistics, Inc., 1101 King St., Ste. 601, Alexandria, VA 22314. TEL 703-979-9699. *4591*

UDENLANDSK LITTERATUR I DANSKE FOLKEBIBLIOTEKER.
Bibliotekscentralen, Tempovej 7-11, DK-2750 Ballerup, Denmark. TEL 2-974000. FAX 2-655310. *2983*

UITGELEZEN.
Ministerie van Sociale Zaken, Library and Documentation Service, P.O. Box 90801, 2509 LV The Hague, Netherlands. *4396*

ULRICH'S INTERNATIONAL PERIODICALS DIRECTORY.
R.R. Bowker, A Reed Reference Publishing Company, Division of Reed Publishing (USA) Inc., 121 Chanlon Rd., New Providence, NJ 07974. TEL 908-665-2847. FAX 908-771-7725. Vendor(s): BRS (ULRI), DIALOG (File no.480), European Space Agency (File no.103/ULRICH'S PERIODICALS). *414*

ULRICH'S UPDATE.
R.R. Bowker, A Reed Reference Publishing Company, Division of Reed Publishing (USA) Inc., 121 Chanlon Rd., New Providence, NJ 07974. TEL 800-521-8110. FAX 908-665-6688. Vendor(s): BRS (ULRI), DIALOG (File no.480), European Space Agency (File no.103/ULRICH'S PERIODICALS). *414*

UNIGRAM.X.
G-2 Computer Intelligence Inc., 3 Maple Place, Glen Head, NY 11545-9845. TEL 516-759-7025. FAX 516-759-7028. *1481*

UNION LABOR REPORT.
The Bureau of National Affairs, Inc., 1231 25th St., N.W., Washington, DC 20037. TEL 202-452-4200. FAX 202-822-8092.
Vendor(s): Human Resources Information Network. *995*

UNION LABOR REPORT WEEKLY NEWSLETTER.
The Bureau of National Affairs, Inc., 1231 25th St., N.W., Washington, DC 20037. TEL 202-452-4200. FAX 202-822-8092.
Vendor(s): Human Resources Information Network (CDD, HDD). *995*

UNION LIST OF SCIENTIFIC SERIALS IN CANADIAN LIBRARIES.
C.I.S.T.I. Cataloguing Section, Ottawa, Ont. K1A 0S2, Canada. TEL 613-993-3449.
Vendor(s): CISTI. *4358*

UNIQUE (DENVILLE).
2601 Iowa St., Lawrence, KS 66047. TEL 913-841-1631. FAX 913-841-2624.
Vendor(s): NewsNet. *1465*

UNISYS WORLD.
Publications & Communications, Inc., 12416 Hymeadow Dr., Austin, TX 78750-1896. TEL 512-250-9023. FAX 512-331-3900. *1465*

UNITED NATIONS. NATIONAL ACCOUNTS STATISTICS. MAIN AGGREGATES AND DETAILED TABLES.
United Nations Publications, Room DC2-0853, New York, NY 10017. TEL 212-963-8300. FAX 212-963-3489. *742*

U.S. BUREAU OF LABOR STATISTICS. C P I DETAILED REPORT.
U.S. Bureau of Labor Statistics, 441 G St., N.W., Washington, DC 20212. TEL 202-655-4000. *1000*

U.S. BUREAU OF LABOR STATISTICS. MONTHLY LABOR REVIEW.
U.S. Bureau of Labor Statistics, 441 G St., N.W., Washington, DC 20212. TEL 202-523-1327.
Vendor(s): DIALOG. *742*

U.S. BUREAU OF THE CENSUS. ANNUAL SURVEY OF MANUFACTURES.
U.S. Bureau of the Census, Data User Services Division, Washington, DC 20233. TEL 301-763-4100.
Vendor(s): CompuServe Consumer Information Service, DIALOG. *742*

U.S. BUREAU OF THE CENSUS. CENSUS AND YOU.
U.S. Bureau of the Census, Data User Services Division, Washington, DC 20233. TEL 301-763-4100.
Vendor(s): CompuServe Consumer Information Service, DIALOG. *4591*

U.S. BUREAU OF THE CENSUS. CENSUS OF AGRICULTURE.
U.S. Bureau of the Census, Data User Services Division, Washington, DC 20233. TEL 301-763-4100.
Vendor(s): CompuServe Consumer Information Service, DIALOG. *126*

U.S. BUREAU OF THE CENSUS. CENSUS OF CONSTRUCTION INDUSTRIES.
U.S. Bureau of the Census, Data User Services Division, Washington, DC 20233. TEL 301-763-4100.
Vendor(s): CompuServe Consumer Information Service, DIALOG. *635*

U.S. BUREAU OF THE CENSUS. CENSUS OF GOVERNMENTS.
U.S. Bureau of the Census, Data User Services Division, Washington, DC 20233. TEL 301-763-4100.
Vendor(s): CompuServe Consumer Information Service, DIALOG. *4083*

U.S. BUREAU OF THE CENSUS. CENSUS OF MANUFACTURES.
U.S. Bureau of the Census, Data User Services Division, Washington, DC 20233. TEL 301-763-4100.
Vendor(s): CompuServe Consumer Information Service, DIALOG. *742*

U.S. BUREAU OF THE CENSUS. CENSUS OF RETAIL TRADE.
U.S. Bureau of the Census, Data User Services Division, Washington, DC 20233. TEL 301-763-4100.
Vendor(s): CompuServe Consumer Information Service, DIALOG. *742*

U.S. BUREAU OF THE CENSUS. CENSUS OF SERVICE INDUSTRIES.
U.S. Bureau of the Census, Data User Services Division, Washington, DC 20233. TEL 301-763-4100.
Vendor(s): CompuServe Consumer Information Service, DIALOG. *742*

U.S. BUREAU OF THE CENSUS. CENSUS OF WHOLESALE TRADE.
U.S. Bureau of the Census, Data User Services Division, Washington, DC 20233. TEL 301-763-4100.
Vendor(s): CompuServe Consumer Information Service, DIALOG. *742*

U.S. BUREAU OF THE CENSUS. COUNTY AND CITY DATA BOOK.
U.S. Bureau of the Census, Data User Services Division, Washington, DC 20233. TEL 301-763-4100.
Vendor(s): CompuServe Consumer Information Service, DIALOG. *4591*

U.S. BUREAU OF THE CENSUS. COUNTY BUSINESS PATTERNS.
U.S. Bureau of the Census, Data User Services Division, Washington, DC 20233. TEL 301-763-4100.
Vendor(s): CompuServe Consumer Information Service, DIALOG. *742*

U.S. BUREAU OF THE CENSUS. STATE AND METROPOLITAN AREA DATA BOOK.
U.S. Bureau of the Census, Data User Services Division, Washington, DC 20233. TEL 301-763-4100.
Vendor(s): CompuServe Consumer Information Service, DIALOG. *4591*

U.S. CENTERS FOR DISEASE CONTROL. MORBIDITY AND MORTALITY WEEKLY REPORT.
U.S. Department of Health and Human Services, Centers for Disease Control (MS: A28), Epidemiology Program Office, 1600 Clifton Road N.E., Atlanta, GA 30333. TEL 800-843-6356.
Vendor(s): BRS, NewsNet. *4114*

U.S. CONGRESS. CONGRESSIONAL RECORD.
U.S. Congress, Washington, DC 20515. TEL 202-275-2051. FAX 202-275-0019. *3931*

U.S. CROP REPORTING BOARD. AGRICULTURAL PRICES.
U.S. Crop Reporting Board, South Bldg., Rm. 5829, Washington, DC 20250. TEL 202-655-4000.
Vendor(s): DIALOG. *158*

U.S. CROP REPORTING BOARD. CATTLE ON FEED.
U.S. Crop Reporting Board, Washington, DC 20250. TEL 202-655-4000.
Vendor(s): DIALOG. *227*

U.S. CROP REPORTING BOARD. CROP PRODUCTION.
U.S. Crop Reporting Board, Washington, DC 20250. TEL 202-655-4000.
Vendor(s): DIALOG. *195*

U.S. DEPARTMENT OF AGRICULTURE. AGRICULTURAL INCOME AND FINANCE SITUATION AND OUTLOOK.
U.S. Department of Agriculture, Economics Management Staff, Information Division, 1301 New York Ave., N.W., Washington, DC 20005. TEL 202-783-3238.
Vendor(s): DIALOG. *158*

U.S. DEPARTMENT OF AGRICULTURE. AGRICULTURAL OUTLOOK.
U.S. Department of Agriculture, Economics Management Staff, Information Division, 1301 New York Ave., N.W., Washington, DC 20005. TEL 202-786-1767.
Vendor(s): DIALOG. *158*

U.S. DEPARTMENT OF AGRICULTURE. COTTON AND WOOL SITUATION AND OUTLOOK.
U.S. Department of Agriculture, Economic Research Service, Information Division, 1301 New York Ave., N.W., Ste. 228, Washington, DC 20005-4789. TEL 202-786-1494.
Vendor(s): DIALOG. *158*

U.S. DEPARTMENT OF AGRICULTURE. DAIRY SITUATION AND OUTLOOK.
U.S. Department of Agriculture, Economics Management Staff, Information Division, 1301 New York Ave., N.W., Washington, DC 20005. TEL 800-999-6779.
Vendor(s): DIALOG. *204*

U.S. DEPARTMENT OF AGRICULTURE. FEED SITUATION AND OUTLOOK.
U.S. Department of Agriculture, Economics Management Staff, Information Division, 1301 New York Ave., N.W., Washington, DC 20005-4788. TEL 800-999-6779.
Vendor(s): DIALOG. *208*

U.S. DEPARTMENT OF AGRICULTURE. FRUIT AND TREE NUTS SITUATION AND OUTLOOK REPORT.
U.S. Department of Agriculture, Economic Research Service, 1301 New York Ave., N.W., Washington, DC 20005-4788. TEL 202-786-1767.
Vendor(s): DIALOG. *195*

U.S. DEPARTMENT OF AGRICULTURE. LIVESTOCK AND POULTRY SITUATION AND OUTLOOK.
U.S. Department of Agriculture, Economics Management Staff, Information Division, 1301 New York Ave., N.W., Washington, DC 20005. TEL 800-999-6779.
Vendor(s): DIALOG. *227*

U.S. DEPARTMENT OF AGRICULTURE. OIL CROPS SITUATION AND OUTLOOK REPORT.
U.S. Department of Agriculture, Economics Management Staff, Information Division, 1301 New York Ave., N.W., Washington, DC 20005. TEL 800-999-6779.
Vendor(s): DIALOG. *158*

U.S. DEPARTMENT OF AGRICULTURE. RICE SITUATION AND OUTLOOK REPORT.
U.S. Department of Agriculture, Economic Research Service, 1301 New York Ave., N.W., Washington, DC 20005-4788. TEL 202-783-3238.
Vendor(s): DIALOG. *208*

U.S. DEPARTMENT OF AGRICULTURE. SUGAR AND SWEETENER SITUATION AND OUTLOOK.
U.S. Department of Agriculture, Economics Management Staff, Information Division, 1301 New York Ave., N.W., Washington, DC 20005. TEL 800-999-6779.
Vendor(s): DIALOG. *159*

U.S. DEPARTMENT OF AGRICULTURE. TOBACCO SITUATION AND OUTLOOK REPORT.
U.S. Department of Agriculture, Economic Research Service, Information Division, GHI Bldg., Rm. 292, 500 12th S.W., Washington, DC 20005-4789. TEL 202-786-1494.
Vendor(s): DIALOG. *159*

U.S. DEPARTMENT OF AGRICULTURE. VEGETABLE AND SPECIALTY CROP SITUATION AND OUTLOOK.
U.S. Department of Agriculture, Economics Management Staff, Information Division, 1301 New York Ave., N.W., Washington, DC 20005. TEL 202-783-3238.
Vendor(s): DIALOG. *159*

U.S. DEPARTMENT OF AGRICULTURE. WHEAT SITUATION AND OUTLOOK.
U.S. Department of Agriculture, Economic Research Service, Information Division, 1301 New York Ave., N.W., Ste. 228, Washington, DC 20005-4789. TEL 202-786-1494.
Vendor(s): DIALOG. *159*

U.S. DEPARTMENT OF STATE. KEY OFFICERS OF FOREIGN SERVICE POSTS.
U.S. Department of State, Office of Information Services, Washington, DC 20520. TEL 202-655-4000.
Vendor(s): DIALOG. *3976*

U.S. ENERGY INFORMATION ADMINISTRATION. WEEKLY PETROLEUM STATUS REPORT.
U.S. Department of Energy, Energy Information Administration, National Energy Information Center, El-231, Rm. 1F-048, Forrestal bldg., 1000 Independence Ave., S.W., Washington, DC 20585. TEL 202-586-8800. *3703*

U.S. GENERAL SERVICES ADMINISTRATION. CATALOG OF FEDERAL DOMESTIC ASSISTANCE.
U.S. General Services Administration, 300 Seventh St., S.W., Reporters Bldg., Rm. 101, Washington, DC 20407. TEL 202-708-5126. FAX 202-401-8233. *4076*

UNITED STATES BANKER.
Kalo Communications, Inc., 10 Valley Dr., Greenwich, CT 06831. TEL 203-869-8200. FAX 203-869-9235.
Vendor(s): Mead Data Central. *967*

UNITED STATES LAW WEEK.
The Bureau of National Affairs, Inc., 1231 25th St., N.W., Washington, DC 20037. TEL 202-452-4200. FAX 202-822-8092.
Vendor(s): Mead Data Central (USLW), WESTLAW. *2688*

UNITED STATES PATENTS QUARTERLY.
The Bureau of National Affairs, Inc., 1231 25th St., N.W., Washington, DC 20037. TEL 202-452-4200. FAX 202-822-8092.
Vendor(s): DIALOG (Patlaw, File 243), Pergamon Infoline. *3679*

UNITED STATES POLITICAL SCIENCE DOCUMENTS.
University of Pittsburgh, Mid-Atlantic Technology Applications Center (MTAC), 823 William Pitt Union, Pittsburgh, PA 15260. TEL 412-648-7000. FAX 412-648-7003.
Vendor(s): DIALOG (File no.93). *3932*

UNITED STATES TAX COURT REPORTS.
U.S. Tax Court, 400 Second St. N.W., Washington, DC 20217. TEL 202-512-2353.
Vendor(s): WESTLAW. *1111*

UNIVERSIDAD DE ZULIA. FACULTADAD DE INGENIERIA. REVISTA TECNICA.
Universidad de Zulia, Facultad de Ingenieria, Division Posgrado, Apdo. 98, Maracaibo, Venezuela. TEL 58-61-520730. FAX 58-61-520717. *1839*

UNIVERSIDADE DE SAO PAULO. REVISTA DE FARMACIA E BIOQUIMICA.
Universidade de Sao Paulo, Faculdade de Ciencias Farmaceuticas, C.P. 66355, Sao Paulo, Brazil. FAX 8153575. *3745*

UNIVERSITAET DES SAARLANDES. JAHRESBIBLIOGRAPHIE.
Universitaet des Saarlandes, Universitaetsbibliothek, 6600 Saarbruecken 11, Germany. TEL 0681-3022797. FAX 0681-3022796. *415*

UNIVERSITE DE BORDEAUX III. CENTRE DE RECHERCHES SUR L'AMERIQUE ANGLOPHONE. ANNALES.
Maison des Sciences de l'Homme d'Aquitaine, Esplanade des Antilles, Domaine Universitaire, 33405 Talence Cedex, France. TEL 56-84-68-00. FAX 56-84-68-10. *2972*

UNIVERSITY OF BALTIMORE LAW REVIEW.
University of Baltimore School of Law, Business Editor, 1420 N. Charles St., Baltimore, MD 21201. TEL 301-625-3440.
Vendor(s): WESTLAW. *2689*

UNIVERSITY OF CHICAGO LAW REVIEW.
University of Chicago Law School, 1111 E. 60th St., Chicago, IL 60637. TEL 312-702-9832. FAX 312-702-0730.
Vendor(s): Mead Data Central. *2689*

UNIVERSITY OF CHICAGO LEGAL FORUM.
University of Chicago Law School, 1111 E. 60th St., Chicago, IL 60637. TEL 312-702-9832. FAX 312-702-0730.
Vendor(s): WESTLAW. *2689*

UNIVERSITY OF ILLINOIS LAW REVIEW.
University of Illinois at Urbana-Champaign, College of Law, Champaign, IL 61820. TEL 217-333-1000.
Vendor(s): WESTLAW. *2690*

UNIVERSITY OF KANSAS LAW REVIEW.
University of Kansas, School of Law, Rm. 510, Green Hall, Lawrence, KS 66045. TEL 913-864-3463. FAX 913-864-3680.
Vendor(s): WESTLAW. *2690*

UNIVERSITY OF PENNSYLVANIA LAW REVIEW.
University of Pennsylvania Law Review, 3400 Chestnut St., Philadelphia, PA 19104. TEL 215-898-7060. FAX 215-573-2005.
Vendor(s): Mead Data Central. *2690*

UNIVERSITY OF PITTSBURGH LAW REVIEW.
University of Pittsburgh, School of Law, Pittsburgh, PA 15260. TEL 412-648-1354.
Vendor(s): Mead Data Central, WESTLAW. *2690*

UNIVERSITY OF RICHMOND LAW REVIEW.
University of Richmond, T. C. Williams School of Law, Richmond, VA 23173. TEL 804-289-8216. FAX 804-289-8683.
Vendor(s): WESTLAW. *2690*

UNIVERSITY OF SAN FRANCISCO LAW REVIEW.
University of San Francisco, School of Law, Kendrick Hall, 2130 Fulton St., San Francisco, CA 94117. TEL 415-666-6154. FAX 415-666-6433.
Vendor(s): WESTLAW. *2690*

UNIX TODAY.
C M P Publications, Inc., 600 Community Dr., Manhasset, NY 11030. TEL 516-562-5000. FAX 516-365-4601.
Vendor(s): Data-Star, DIALOG, NewsNet. *1440*

URBAN ABSTRACTS.
London Research Centre, Parliament House, 81 Black Prince Rd., London SE1 7SZ, England.
Vendor(s): European Space Agency. *4083*

URBAN TRANSPORT NEWS.
Business Publishers, Inc., 951 Pershing Dr., Silver Spring, MD 20910-4464. TEL 301-587-6300. FAX 301-585-9075.
Vendor(s): NewsNet (TS10). *4660*

USED EQUIPMENT DIRECTORY.
Penton Publishing (Hasbrouck Heights) 611 Rte. 46 W., Hasbrouck Heights, NJ 07604-3120. TEL 800-526-6052. FAX 201-393-9553. *3024*

UTAH LAW REVIEW.
University of Utah College of Law, Salt Lake City, UT 84112. TEL 801-581-6833.
Vendor(s): WESTLAW. *2691*

UTAH STATE DIGEST.
Department of Administrative Services, Division of Administrative Rules, Salt Lake City, UT 84114. *4096*

UTILITY REPORTER: FUELS ENERGY & POWER.
Merton Allen Associates, InfoTeam Inc., Box 15640, Plantation, FL 33318-5640. TEL 305-473-9560. FAX 305-473-0544.
Vendor(s): Data-Star, DIALOG, NewsNet (EY12). *1797*

V A X PROFESSIONAL.
Professional Press, Inc., 101 Witmer Rd., Horsham, PA 19044. TEL 215-957-1500. FAX 215-957-1050. *1402*

VAARD I NORDEN.
Sygeplegerskernes Samarbejde i Norden, P.O. Box 2681, St. Hanshaugen, N-131 Oslo 1, Norway. TEL 47-2 38 20 00. FAX 47-2-38-54-47.
Vendor(s): BRS, Data-Star, DIALOG. *3287*

VADEMECUM DEUTSCHER LEHR- UND FORSCHUNGSSTAETTEN. STAETTEN DER FORSCHUNG.
Dr. Josef Raabe Verlag GmbH, Rotebuehlstr. 77, 7000 Stuttgart 1, Germany. TEL 0711-629000. FAX 0711-6290010.
Vendor(s): STN International. *4350*

VANCOUVER STOCKWATCH.
Canjex Publishing Limited, 700 W. Georgia St., P.O. Box 10371, Vancouver, B.C. V7Y 1J6, Canada. TEL 604-687-1500. *968*

VANDERBILT JOURNAL OF TRANSNATIONAL LAW.
Vanderbilt University School of Law, Nashville, TN 37240. TEL 615-322-2284.
Vendor(s): WESTLAW. *2730*

VANDERBILT LAW REVIEW.
Vanderbilt University School of Law, Nashville, TN 37240. TEL 615-322-4766.
Vendor(s): Mead Data Central, WESTLAW. *2691*

VERMONT BUSINESS.
Manning Publications, Inc., Box 6120, Brattleboro, VT 05302-6120. TEL 802-257-4100.
Vendor(s): DIALOG. *698*

VERSICHERUNGSRECHT.
Verlag Versicherungswirtschaft e.V., Klosestr. 20-24, 7500 Karlsruhe 1, Germany. TEL 0721-3509126. FAX 0721-31833. *2544*

VERTICAL FILE INDEX.
H.W. Wilson Co., 950 University Ave., Bronx, NY 10452. TEL 800-367-6770. FAX 212-538-2716.
Vendor(s): Wilsonline (File VFI). *24*

VETERINARY BULLETIN.
C.A.B. International, Wallingford, Oxon OX10 8DE, England. TEL 0491-32111. FAX 0491-33508.
Vendor(s): BRS (VETR), CISTI, DIMDI, DIALOG, European Space Agency (File nos.16 & 124/CAB). *4820*

VICTORIAN PUBLIC LIBRARIES. ANNUAL SURVEY.
Victorian Ministry for the Arts, Library Services, Level 3, 176 Wellingotn Parade, E. Melbourne, Vic. 3005, Australia. TEL 03-649-8888. FAX 03-614-6186. *2796*

VICTORIAN REPORTS.
Butterworths Pty. Ltd., 271-273 Lane Cove Rd., North Ryde, N.S.W. 2113, Australia. TEL 02-335-4444. FAX 02-335-4655. *2692*

VIDEO MARKETING NEWS.
Phillips Publishing, Inc., 7811 Montrose Rd., Potomac, MD 20854. TEL 301-340-2100. FAX 301-424-4297.
Vendor(s): NewsNet. *1056*

VIDEO NEWS INTERNATIONAL.
Phillips Publishing, Inc., 7811 Montrose Rd., Potomac, MD 20854. TEL 301-340-2100. FAX 301-424-4297.
Vendor(s): Data-Star, DIALOG, NewsNet. *1387*

VIDEO TECHNOLOGY NEWS.
Phillips Publishing, Inc., 7811 Montrose Rd., Potomac, MD 20854. TEL 301-340-2100. FAX 301-309-3847.
Vendor(s): Data-Star, DIALOG, NewsNet. *1387*

VIDEO WEEK.
Warren Publishing, Inc., 2115 Ward Ct., N.W., Washington, DC 20037. TEL 202-872-9200. FAX 202-293-3435.
Vendor(s): NewsNet (EL01). *1387*

VIDEOLOG.
Trade Service Corporation, 10996 Torreyana Rd., San Diego, CA 92121. TEL 619-457-5920. FAX 619-457-1320. *1388*

VIDEOS FOR BUSINESS AND TRAINING.
Gale Research Inc., 835 Penobscot Bldg., Detroit, MI 48226-4094. TEL 313-961-2242. FAX 313-961-6083.
Vendor(s): Human Resources Information Network (Video). *1388*

VILLANOVA LAW REVIEW.
Villanova University Law School, Villanova, PA 19085. TEL 215-645-7053.
Vendor(s): WESTLAW. *2692*

VIRGINIA ENVIRONMENTAL LAW JOURNAL.
Virginia Environmental Law Journal, University of Virginia, School of Law, Charlottesville, VA 22901. TEL 804-924-3683.-FAX 804-924-7536.
Vendor(s): WESTLAW. *2693*

VIRGINIA JOURNAL OF INTERNATIONAL LAW.
University of Virginia, School of Law, Charlottesville, VA 22901. TEL 804-924-3415.
Vendor(s): WESTLAW. *2730*

SERIALS AVAILABLE ONLINE 5105

VIRGINIA TAX REVIEW.
Virginia Tax Review Association, University of Virginia, School of Law, Charlottesville, VA 22901. TEL 804-924-4726. FAX 804-924-7536.
Vendor(s): WESTLAW. *1111*

VIROLOGY AND A I D S ABSTRACTS.
Cambridge Scientific Abstracts, 7200 Wisconsin Ave., 6th Fl., Bethesda, MD 20814. TEL 301-961-6750. FAX 301-961-6720.
Vendor(s): BRS (CSAL), DIALOG (File no.76/LIFE SCIENCES COLLECTION). *3181*

VITIS - VITICULTURE AND ENOLOGY ABSTRACTS.
International Food Information Service GmbH, Melibocusstr. 52, 6000 Frankfurt a.M. 71, Germany. TEL 069-6690070. FAX 069-66900710.
Vendor(s): DIMDI, DIALOG, European Space Agency, Orbit Information Technologies. *144*

VOCATIONAL TRAINING NEWS.
Capitol Publications Inc., 1101 King St., Ste. 444, Box 1455, Alexandria, VA 22314. TEL 703-683-4100. FAX 703-739-6517.
Vendor(s): NewsNet. *3631*

VOICE TECHNOLOGY NEWS.
Phillips Publishing, Inc., 7811 Montrose Rd., Potomac, MD 20854. TEL 301-340-2100. FAX 301-309-3847.
Vendor(s): Data-Star, DIALOG, NewsNet. *1367*

W R R I NEWS.
North Carolina State University, Water Resources Research Institute, Box 7912, Raleigh, NC 27695-7912. TEL 919-515-2815. FAX 919-515-7802. *4830*

WALL STREET JOURNAL (EASTERN EDITION).
Dow Jones & Co., Inc., 200 Liberty St., New York, NY 10281. TEL 212-416-2000.
Vendor(s): Dow Jones/News Retrieval. *803*

WALL STREET JOURNAL INDEX.
University Microfilms International, 300 N. Zeeb Rd., Ann Arbor, MI 48106. *803*

WALL STREET TRANSCRIPT.
Wall Street Transcript Corp., 99 Wall St., New York, NY 10005. TEL 212-747-9500.
Vendor(s): VU/TEXT Information Services, Inc. *968*

WALT DISNEY WORLD (YEAR).
Hearst Corporation, Walt Disney World, 250 W. 55th St., 11th Fl., New York, NY 10019. TEL 212-903-5190. *4796*

WASHINGTON & LEE LAW REVIEW.
Washington and Lee University, School of Law, Lewis Hall, Lexington, VA 24450-1799. TEL 703-463-8566. FAX 703-463-8567.
Vendor(s): WESTLAW. *2693*

WASHINGTON BUSINESS JOURNAL.
American City Business Journals, Inc. (Arlington), 2000 14th St., N. Ste. 500, Arlington, VA 22201. TEL 703-875-2200. FAX 703-875-2231. *699*

WASHINGTON DRUG LETTER (WASHINGTON, 1979).
Washington Business Information, Inc., c/o Karen Harrington, 1117 N. 19th St., Arlington, VA 22209. TEL 703-247-3434. FAX 703-247-3421.
Vendor(s): BRS (DIOG), Data-Star. *3745*

WASHINGTON INTERNATIONAL BUSINESS REPORT.
International Business-Government Counsellors Inc., 818 Connecticut Ave. N.W., 12th Fl., Washington, DC 20006-2702. TEL 202-872-8181. FAX 202-872-8696. *924*

WASHINGTON LAW REVIEW.
Washington Law Review Association, Condon Hall, JB-20, 1100 N.E. Campus Pkwy., School of Law, University of Washington, WA 98105. TEL 206-543-6335. FAX 206-543-5671.
Vendor(s): Mead Data Central, WESTLAW. *2693*

WASHINGTON MONTHLY.
Washington Monthly Co., 1611 Connecticut Ave., N.W., Washington, DC 20009. TEL 202-462-0128.
Vendor(s): DIALOG. *3933*

WASHINGTON QUARTERLY.
M I T Press, 55 Hayward St., Cambridge, MA 02142. TEL 617-253-2889. FAX 617-258-6779.
Vendor(s): Mead Data Central. *3976*

WASTE INFORMATION DIGESTS.
International Academy at Santa Barbara, 800 Garden St., Ste. D, Santa Barbara, CA 93101. TEL 805-965-5010.
Vendor(s): Data-Star, DIALOG. *1988*

WASTE MANAGEMENT TODAY.
Waste Management Information Bureau, Building 7-12, Harwell Laboratory, Didcot, Oxon. OX11 0RA, England. TEL 0235-821111. FAX 0235-432854.
Vendor(s): Orbit Information Technologies. *1975*

WATER QUALITY INTERNATIONAL.
Pergamon Press plc, Headington Hill Hall, Oxford OX3 0BW, England. TEL 0865-794141. FAX 0865-743911. *1980*

WATER RESEARCH IN AUSTRALIA: CURRENT PROJECTS.
Department of Primary Industries and Energy, G.P.O. Box 858, Canberra, A.C.T. 2601, Australia. FAX 062-724526. *4832*

WEED ABSTRACTS.
C.A.B. International, Wallingford, Oxon OX10 8DE, England. TEL 0491 32111. FAX 0491-33508.
Vendor(s): BRS (CABA), CISTI, DIMDI, DIALOG, European Space Agency (File nos.16 & 124/CAB). *144*

WEEKLY CONGRESSIONAL MONITOR.
Congressional Quarterly Inc., 1414 22nd St., N.W., Washington, DC 20037. TEL 800-432-2250. FAX 728-1863. *3934*

WEEKLY CRIMINAL BULLETIN.
Canada Law Book Inc., 240 Edward St., Aurora, Ont. L4G 3S9, Canada. TEL 416-841-6472. *2714*

WEEKLY LAW REPORTS.
Incorporated Council of Law Reporting for England and Wales, 3 Stone Bldgs., Lincoln's Inn, London WC2A 3XN, England. TEL 071-242-6471. FAX 071-831-5247.
Vendor(s): Mead Data Central. *2694*

WELDING ABSTRACTS.
Pergamon Press, Inc., Journals Division, 660 White Plains Rd., Tarrytown, NY 10591-5153. TEL 914-524-9200. FAX 914-333-2444.
Vendor(s): Orbit Information Technologies. *3428*

WER BAUT MASCHINEN UND ANLAGEN.
Verlag Hoppenstedt und Co., Havelstr. 9, Postfach 4006, 6100 Darmstadt, Germany. TEL 06151-380-0. FAX 06151-380-360.
Vendor(s): Data-Star, FIZ Technik. *1941*

WER LIEFERT WAS?
Wer Liefert Was? GmbH Bezugsquellennachweis fuer den Einkauf, Normannenweg 18-20, 2000 Hamburg 26, Germany. TEL 040-251508-0. FAX 040-25150838.
Vendor(s): Data-Star. *1158*

WERBEARTIKEL NACHRICHTEN FUER INSIDER.
W A Verlag GmbH, Am Ringofen 3, 4054 Nettetal 2, Germany. TEL 02157-2072. FAX 02157-3729. *39*

WESTERN AUSTRALIA REPORTS.
Law Book Co. Ltd., 44-50 Waterloo Rd., North Ryde, N.S.W. 2113, Australia. TEL 02-887-0177. FAX 02-888-9706. *2694*

WESTERN BUSINESS.
Unicorn Communications, Box 36300, Billings, MT 59107-6300. TEL 406-252-4788.
Vendor(s): DIALOG. *699*

WESTERN GROWER AND SHIPPER.
Western Grower and Shipper Publishing Co., Box 2130, Newport Beach, CA 92658. TEL 714-863-1000. FAX 714-863-9028.
Vendor(s): DIALOG. *196*

WESTERN WEEKLY REPORTS.
Carswell Publications Corporate Plaza, 2075 Kennedy Rd., Scarborough, Ont. M1T 3V4, Canada. TEL 416-609-8000. FAX 416-298-5094.
Vendor(s): QL Systems Ltd.. *2694*

WESTPREUSSEN - JAHRBUCH.
Westpreussen-Verlag Muenster, Norbertstr. 29, 4400 Muenster, Germany. TEL 0251-523424. FAX 0251-533830. *2395*

WHEAT, BARLEY AND TRITICALE ABSTRACTS.
C.A.B. International, Wallingford, Oxon OX10 8DE, England. TEL 0491-32111. FAX 0491-33508.
Vendor(s): BRS (CABA), CISTI, DIMDI, DIALOG, European Space Agency (File nos.16 & 124/CAB). *145*

WHICH? WAY TO HEALTH.
Consumers' Association Ltd., 2 Marylebone Rd., London NW1 4DX, England. TEL 071-486 5544. FAX 071-935-1606. *3810*

WHITAKER'S BOOKS IN PRINT.
J. Whitaker & Sons Ltd., 12 Dyott St., London WC1A 1DF, England. TEL 071-836-8911. FAX 071-836-2909.
Vendor(s): DIALOG (File no.430). *416*

WHITE COUNTY HERITAGE.
White County Historical Society, Box 537, Searcy, AR 72143. TEL 501-268-8726. *2426*

WHO OWNS WHOM. AUSTRALASIA AND FAR EAST.
Dun & Bradstreet Ltd., Holmers Farm Way, High Wycombe, Bucks HP12 4UL, England. *1159*

WHO OWNS WHOM. CONTINENTAL EUROPE.
Dun & Bradstreet Ltd., Holmers Farm Way, High Wycombe, Bucks HP12 4UL, England. *1031*

WHO OWNS WHOM. UNITED KINGDOM AND REPUBLIC OF IRELAND.
Dun & Bradstreet Ltd., Holmers Farm Way, High Wycombe, Bucks HP12 4UL, England. *1159*

WHO OWNS WHOM, NORTH AMERICA.
Dun & Bradstreet Ltd., Holmers Fram Way, High Wycombe, Bucks HP12 4UL, England. *1056*

WHOLE EARTH REVIEW.
Point Foundation, 27 Gate Five Rd., Sausalito, CA 94965. TEL 415-332-1716. FAX 415-332-2416.
Vendor(s): DIALOG. *3597*

WHO'S WHO AMONG BLACK AMERICANS.
Gale Research Inc., 835 Penobscot Bldg., Detroit, MI 48226. TEL 313-961-2242. FAX 313-961-6083.
Vendor(s): Mead Data Central. *421*

WHO'S WHO AMONG HISPANIC AMERICANS.
Gale Research Inc., 835 Penobscot Bldg., Detroit, MI 48226. TEL 800-877-4253. FAX 313-961-6083.
Vendor(s): Mead Data Central. *421*

WHO'S WHO IN AMERICA.
Marquis Who's Who, A Reed Reference Publishing Company, Division of Reed Publishing (USA) Inc., 121 Chanlon Rd., New Providence, NJ 07974. TEL 800-521-8110. FAX 908-665-6688.
Vendor(s): DIALOG (File no.234). *421*

WHO'S WHO IN AMERICAN ART.
R.R. Bowker, A Reed Reference Publishing Company, Division of Reed Publishing (USA) Inc., 121 Chanlon Rd., New Providence, NJ 07974. TEL 800-521-8110. FAX 908-665-6688. *421*

WHO'S WHO IN TECHNOLOGY.
Gale Research Inc., Dept. 77748, Detroit, MI 48226. TEL 313-961-2242. FAX 313-961-6083. Vendor(s): Mead Data Central, Pergamon Infoline (WHOTECH). *4352*

WILDERNESS NEWS.
Wilderness Society, 130 Davey St., Hobart, Tas. 7000, Australia. TEL 04-349-366. FAX 002-233-651. *1971*

WILDERNESS RECORD.
California Wilderness Coalition, 2655 Portage Bay E., Ste. 5, Davis, CA 95616. TEL 916-758-0380. *1500*

WILLIAM MITCHELL LAW REVIEW.
William Mitchell College of Law, 875 Summit Ave., St. Paul, MN 55105. TEL 612-227-6305.
Vendor(s): WESTLAW. *2694*

WINDOWS JOURNAL.
Wugnet Publications, Inc., Box 1967, Media, PA 19063. TEL 215-565-1861. FAX 215-565-7106.
Vendor(s): CompuServe Consumer Information Service. *1402*

SERIALS AVAILABLE ONLINE

WINE INVESTOR: BUYERS' GUIDE.
Wine Investor, 3284 Barham Blvd., Ste. 201, Los Angeles, CA 90068. TEL 213-876-8400.
Vendor(s): CompuServe Consumer Information Service. *387*

WINE ON LINE.
Enterprises Publishing, 400 E. 59th St., Ste. 9F, New York, NY 10022. TEL 212-755-4563. *387*

WING.
Koku Shinbun Sha - Wing Aviation Press, Kanda Kitamura Bldg., 30 Kanda Higashi-Konya-cho, Chiyoda-ku, Tokyo 101, Japan. TEL 03-3258-0880. FAX 03-3258-5004.
Vendor(s): NewsNet. *65*

WING NEWSLETTER.
Koku Shinbun Sha - Wing Aviation Press, Kanda Kitamura Bldg., 30 Kanda Higashi-Konya-cho, Chiyoda-ku, Tokyo 101, Japan. TEL 03-3258-0880. FAX 03-3258-5004.
Vendor(s): Data-Star, DIALOG, NewsNet. *65*

WISCONSIN LAW REVIEW.
University of Wisconsin Law School, 975 Bascom Mall, Madison, WI 53706-1399. TEL 608-262-5815.
Vendor(s): Mead Data Central, WESTLAW. *2695*

WOMEN'S WEAR DAILY.
Fairchild Publications, Inc., Women's Wear Daily, 7 W. 34th St., New York, NY 10001. TEL 212-630-4000. FAX 212-620-4201.
Vendor(s): DIALOG. *1288*

WORKBASKET.
K C Publishing Inc., 4251 Pennsylvania Ave., Kansas City, MO 64111-9990. TEL 816-531-5730. FAX 816-531-3873.
Vendor(s): DIALOG. *3593*

WORKBENCH.
K C Publishing Inc., 4251 Pennsylvania Ave., Kansas City, MO 64111. TEL 816-531-5730. FAX 816-531-3873.
Vendor(s): DIALOG. *2501*

WORKING PAPERS IN BUSINESS.
High Tech Publishing Company, Box 1923, Brattleboro, VT 05301. TEL 802-254-3539.
Vendor(s): Data-Star, NewsNet. *744*

WORKING WOMAN.
Lang Communications, 230 Park Ave., New York, NY 10169. TEL 212-309-9800.
Vendor(s): DIALOG. *4858*

WORKSTATION MAGAZINE.
Publications & Communications, Inc., 12416 Hymeadow Dr., Austin, TX 78750-1896. TEL 512-250-5518. FAX 512-331-6778. *1402*

WORLD ACCOUNTING REPORT.
Financial Times Business Information Ltd., Tower House, Southampton St., London WC2E 7HA, England. TEL 071-240 9391. FAX 071-240-7946.
Vendor(s): Data-Star, Mead Data Central (WAR). *757*

WORLD AFFAIRS REPORT.
California Institute of International Studies, 766 Santa Ynez, Stanford, CA 94305. TEL 415-322-2026.
Available only online. Vendor(s): DIALOG (File no. 167). *3977*

WORLD AGRICULTURAL ECONOMICS AND RURAL SOCIOLOGY ABSTRACTS.
C.A.B. International, Wallingford, Oxon OX10 8DE, England. TEL 0491-32111. FAX 0491-33508.
Vendor(s): BRS (ECON), CISTI, DIMDI, DIALOG, European Space Agency (File nos.16 & 124/CAB). *145*

WORLD AGRICULTURAL SUPPLY AND DEMAND ESTIMATES.
U.S. Department of Agriculture, World Agricultural Outlook Board, 14th St. and Independence Ave. S.W., Rm. 5143-S, Washington, DC 20250-3800. TEL 202-250-3800.
Vendor(s): DIALOG. *160*

WORLD ALUMINUM ABSTRACTS.
Aluminum Association, Inc., 900 19th St., N.W., Ste. 300, Washington, DC 20006. TEL 202-862-5100.
Vendor(s): DIALOG (File no.33), European Space Agency (File no.9/ALUMINUM). *3429*

WORLD CERAMIC ABSTRACTS.
Pergamon Press plc, Headington Hill Hall, Oxford OX3 0BW, England. TEL 0865-794141. FAX 0865-743911.
Vendor(s): Orbit Information Technologies. *1167*

WORLD DRUG MARKET MANUAL.
IMSWORLD Publications Ltd., 11-13 Melton St., London NW1 2EH, England. *3746*

WORLD FOOD & DRINK REPORT.
King Publishing Group, Inc., 627 National Press Bldg., Washington, DC 20045. TEL 202-638-4260. FAX 202-662-9744. *2084*

WORLD HEALTH.
World Health Organization, Distribution and Sales, CH-1211 Geneva 27, Switzerland. TEL 022-791-2111.
Vendor(s): DIALOG. *4115*

WORLD HOSPITALS.
International Hospital Federation, 4 Abbots Pl., London NW6 4NP, England. TEL 071-372-7181. FAX 071-328-7433. *2470*

WORLD NUCLEAR PERFORMANCE.
McGraw-Hill, Inc., Energy & Business Newsletters, 1221 Ave. of the Americas, 36th Fl., New York, NY 10020. TEL 212-512-6410. *1810*

WORLD POLICY GUIDE.
Financial Times Business Information Ltd., Tower House, Southampton St., London WC2E 7HA, England. TEL 071-240-9391. FAX 071-240-7946. *2545*

WORLD PORTS AND HARBOURS ABSTRACTS.
S T I Ltd., 4 Kings Meadow, Ferry Hinksey Rd., Oxford OX2 0DU, England. TEL 0865-798898. FAX 0865-798788.
Vendor(s): DIALOG (File no.96/FLUIDEX), European Space Agency (File no.48/FLUIDEX). *4668*

WORLD PUBLISHING MONITOR.
Pira International, Randalls Rd., Leatherhead, Surrey KT22 7RU, England.
Vendor(s): Orbit Information Technologies (EPA). *1406*

WORLD SATELLITE DIRECTORY.
Phillips Publishing, Inc., 7811 Montrose Rd., Potomac, MD 20854. TEL 800-777-5006. FAX 301-309-3847.
Vendor(s): NewsNet. *1160*

WORLD SURFACE COATING ABSTRACTS.
Pergamon Press plc, Headington Hill Hall, Oxford OX3 0BW, England. TEL 0865-794141. FAX 0865-743911.
Vendor(s): Orbit Information Technologies (WSCA), Pergamon Infoline (WSCA). *3656*

WORLD TEXTILE ABSTRACTS.
Elsevier Science Publishers Ltd., Crown House, Linton Rd., Barking, Essex IG11 8JU, England. TEL 081-594-7272. FAX 081-594-5942.
Vendor(s): DIALOG (File no.67), Orbit Information Technologies (WTA), Pergamon Infoline (WTA). *4628*

WORLD TRANSLATION INDEX.
International Translations Centre (ITC), Schuttersveld 2, 2611 WE Delft, Netherlands. TEL 015-142242. FAX 015-158535.
Vendor(s): DIALOG (File no.295), European Space Agency (File no.33/WTI). *4358*

WORLDCASTS: PRODUCT EDITION.
Predicasts, A Ziff Communications Company, 11001 Cedar Ave., Cleveland, OH 44106. TEL 800-321-6388. FAX 216-229-9944.
Vendor(s): Data-Star, DIALOG. *744*

WORLDCASTS: REGIONAL EDITION.
Predicasts, A Ziff Communications Company, 11001 Cedar Ave., Cleveland, OH 44106. TEL 800-321-6388. FAX 216-229-9944.
Vendor(s): Data-Star, DIALOG. *744*

THE WORLDPAPER.
World Times, Inc., 210 World Trade Center, Boston, MA 02210. TEL 617-439-5400. FAX 617-439-5415.
Vendor(s): Mead Data Central. *3978*

WORLDWIDE BIOTECH.
Worldwide Videotex, Box 138, Babson Park, Boston, MA 02157. TEL 617-449-1603.
Vendor(s): Data-Star, DIALOG. *491*

WORLDWIDE DATABASES.
Worldwide Videotex, Box 138, Babson Park, Boston, MA 02157. TEL 617-449-1603.
Vendor(s): Data-Star, DIALOG, NewsNet. *1445*

WORLDWIDE FINANCIAL REGULATIONS.
Business International Corp., 215 Park Ave. S., New York, NY 10003. TEL 212-460-0600. FAX 212-995-8837.
Vendor(s): DIALOG. *925*

WORLDWIDE TELECOM.
Worldwide Videotex, Box 138, Babson Park, Boston, MA 02157. TEL 617-449-1603.
Vendor(s): Data-Star, DIALOG, NewsNet. *1368*

WORLDWIDE VIDEOTEX UPDATE.
Worldwide Videotex, Box 138, Babson Park, Boston, MA 02157. TEL 617-449-1603.
Vendor(s): Data-Star, DIALOG, NewsNet (PB08). *1402*

YALE JOURNAL ON REGULATION.
Yale University, School of Law, 401A Yale Sta., New Haven, CT 06520. TEL 203-432-4861. FAX 203-432-2592.
Vendor(s): WESTLAW. *2695*

YALE LAW JOURNAL.
Yale Law Journal Co., Inc., 401-A Yale Sta., New Haven, CT 06520. TEL 203-432-1666. FAX 203-432-2592.
Vendor(s): Mead Data Central. *2696*

YEAR BOOK OF ANESTHESIA.
Mosby - Year Book, Inc., Continuity Division, 200 N. LaSalle, Chicago, IL 60601. TEL 312-726-9733. FAX 312-726-6075.
Vendor(s): BRS. *3192*

YEAR BOOK OF CARDIOLOGY.
Mosby - Year Book, Inc., Continuity Division, 200 N. LaSalle, Chicago, IL 60601. TEL 312-726-9733. FAX 312-726-6075.
Vendor(s): BRS. *3212*

YEAR BOOK OF DENTISTRY.
Mosby - Year Book, Inc., Continuity Division, 200 N. LaSalle, Chicago, IL 60601. TEL 312-726-9733. FAX 312-726-6075.
Vendor(s): BRS. *3244*

YEAR BOOK OF DERMATOLOGIC SURGERY.
Mosby - Year Book, Inc. (Chicago) 200 N. LaSalle St., Chicago, IL 60601. TEL 312-726-9733.
Vendor(s): BRS. *3250*

YEAR BOOK OF DERMATOLOGY.
Mosby - Year Book, Inc., Continuity Division, 200 N. LaSalle, Chicago, IL 60601. TEL 312-726-9733. FAX 312-726-6075.
Vendor(s): BRS. *3250*

YEAR BOOK OF DIAGNOSTIC RADIOLOGY.
Mosby - Year Book, Inc., Continuity Division, 200 N. LaSalle, Chicago, IL 60601. TEL 312-726-9733. FAX 312-726-6075.
Vendor(s): BRS. *3363*

YEAR BOOK OF DIGESTIVE DISEASES.
Mosby - Year Book, Inc., Continuity Division, 200 N. LaSalle, Chicago, IL 60601. TEL 312-726-9746. FAX 312-726-6933.
Vendor(s): BRS. *3270*

YEAR BOOK OF DRUG THERAPY.
Mosby - Year Book, Inc., Continuity Division, 200 N. LaSalle, Chicago, IL 60601. TEL 312-726-9733.
Vendor(s): BRS. *3746*

YEAR BOOK OF EMERGENCY MEDICINE.
Mosby - Year Book, Inc., Continuity Division, 200 N. LaSalle, Chicago, IL 60601. TEL 312-726-9733. FAX 312-726-6075.
Vendor(s): BRS. *3312*

YEAR BOOK OF FAMILY PRACTICE.
Mosby - Year Book, Inc., Continuity Division, 200 N. LaSalle, Chicago, IL 60601. TEL 312-726-9733. FAX 312-726-6075.
Vendor(s): BRS. *3163*

YEAR BOOK OF GERIATRICS AND GERONTOLOGY.
Mosby - Year Book, Inc. (Chicago) 200 N. LaSalle
St., Chicago, IL 60601-1080. TEL 312-726-9733.
FAX 312-726-6075.
Vendor(s): BRS. *2280*

YEAR BOOK OF HAND SURGERY.
Mosby - Year Book, Inc., Continuity Division, 200 N.
LaSalle St., Chicago, IL 60601-1080. TEL 312-
726-9733. FAX 312-726-6075.
Vendor(s): BRS. *3386*

YEAR BOOK OF HEALTH CARE MANAGEMENT.
Mosby - Year Book, Inc. (Chicago) 200 N. LaSalle
St., Chicago, IL 60601-1080. TEL 312-726-9733.
FAX 312-726-6075.
Vendor(s): BRS. *2470*

YEAR BOOK OF HEMATOLOGY.
Mosby - Year Book, Inc., Continuity Division, 200 N.
LaSalle, Chicago, IL 60601. TEL 312-726-9733.
FAX 312-726-6075.
Vendor(s): BRS. *3274*

YEAR BOOK OF INFECTIOUS DISEASES.
Mosby - Year Book, Inc. (Chicago) 200 N. LaSalle
St., Chicago, IL 60601-1080. TEL 312-726-9733.
FAX 312-726-6075.
Vendor(s): BRS. *3224*

YEAR BOOK OF MEDICINE.
Mosby - Year Book, Inc., Continuity Division, 200 N.
LaSalle, Chicago, IL 60601. TEL 312-726-9733.
FAX 312-726-6075.
Vendor(s): BRS. *3163*

YEAR BOOK OF NEPHROLOGY.
Mosby - Year Book, Inc. (Chicago) 200 N. LaSalle
St., Chicago, IL 60601-1080. TEL 312-726-9733.
FAX 312-726-6075.
Vendor(s): BRS. *3390*

YEAR BOOK OF NEUROLOGY & NEUROSURGERY.
Mosby - Year Book, Inc., Continuity Division, 200 N.
LaSalle, Chicago, IL 60601. TEL 312-726-9733.
FAX 312-726-6075.
Vendor(s): BRS. *3356*

YEAR BOOK OF NEURORADIOLOGY.
Mosby - Year Book, Inc. (Chicago) 200 N. LaSalle
St., Chicago, IL 60601. TEL 312-726-9733.
Vendor(s): BRS. *3363*

YEAR BOOK OF NUCLEAR MEDICINE.
Mosby - Year Book, Inc., Continuity Division, 200 N.
LaSalle, Chicago, IL 60601. TEL 312-726-9733.
FAX 312-726-6075.
Vendor(s): BRS. *3363*

YEAR BOOK OF OBSTETRICS AND GYNECOLOGY.
Mosby - Year Book, Inc., Continuity Division, 200 N.
LaSalle, Chicago, IL 60601. TEL 312-726-9733.
FAX 312-726-6075.
Vendor(s): BRS. *3297*

YEAR BOOK OF OCCUPATIONAL MEDICINE.
Mosby - Year Book, Inc. (Chicago) 200 N. LaSalle
St., Chicago, IL 60601-1080. TEL 312-726-9733.
FAX 312-726-6075.
Vendor(s): BRS. *3163*

YEAR BOOK OF ONCOLOGY.
Mosby - Year Book, Inc., Continuity Division, 200 N.
LaSalle, Chicago, IL 60601. TEL 312-726-9733.
FAX 312-726-6075.
Vendor(s): BRS. *3203*

YEAR BOOK OF OPHTHALMOLOGY.
Mosby - Year Book, Inc., Continuity Division, 200 N.
LaSalle, Chicago, IL 60601. TEL 312-726-9733.
FAX 312-726-6075.
Vendor(s): BRS. *3306*

YEAR BOOK OF ORTHOPEDICS.
Mosby - Year Book, Inc., Continuity Division, 200 N.
LaSalle, Chicago, IL 60601. TEL 312-726-9733.
FAX 312-726-6075.
Vendor(s): BRS. *3312*

YEAR BOOK OF PATHOLOGY AND CLINICAL PATHOLOGY.
Mosby - Year Book, Inc., Continuity Division, 200 N.
LaSalle, Chicago, IL 60601. TEL 312-726-9733.
FAX 312-726-6075.
Vendor(s): BRS. *3163*

YEAR BOOK OF PEDIATRICS.
Mosby - Year Book, Inc., Continuity Division, 200 N.
LaSalle, Chicago, IL 60601. TEL 312-726-9733.
FAX 312-726-6075.
Vendor(s): BRS. *3327*

YEAR BOOK OF PERINATAL - NEONATAL MEDICINE.
Mosby - Year Book, Inc., Continuity Division, 200 N.
LaSalle, Chicago, IL 60601. TEL 312-726-9746.
FAX 312-726-6075.
Vendor(s): BRS. *3327*

YEAR BOOK OF PLASTIC, RECONSTRUCTIVE, AND AESTHETIC SURGERY.
Mosby - Year Book, Inc., Continuity Division, 200 N.
LaSalle, Chicago, IL 60601. TEL 312-726-9733.
FAX 312-726-6075.
Vendor(s): BRS. *3386*

YEAR BOOK OF PSYCHIATRY AND APPLIED MENTAL HEALTH.
Mosby - Year Book, Inc., Continuity Division, 200 N.
LaSalle, Chicago, IL 60601. TEL 312-726-9733.
FAX 312-726-6075.
Vendor(s): BRS. *3356*

YEAR BOOK OF PULMONARY DISEASE.
Mosby - Year Book, Inc., Continuity Division, 200 N.
LaSalle, Chicago, IL 60601. TEL 312-726-9746.
FAX 312-726-6075.
Vendor(s): BRS. *3368*

YEAR BOOK OF SURGERY.
Mosby - Year Book, Inc., Continuity Division, 200 N.
LaSalle, Chicago, IL 60601. TEL 312-726-9733.
FAX 312-726-6075.
Vendor(s): BRS. *3386*

YEAR BOOK OF TRANSPLANTATION.
Mosby - Year Book, Inc. (Chicago) 200 LaSalle St.,
Chicago, IL 60601. TEL 312-726-9733.
Vendor(s): BRS. *3386*

YEAR BOOK OF ULTRASOUND.
Mosby - Year Book, Inc. (Chicago) 200 N. LaSalle
St., Chicago, IL 60601-1080. TEL 312-726-9733.
FAX 312-726-6075.
Vendor(s): BRS. *3363*

YEAR BOOK OF UROLOGY.
Mosby - Year Book, Inc., Continuity Division, 200 N.
LaSalle, Chicago, IL 60601. TEL 312-726-9733.
FAX 312-726-6075.
Vendor(s): BRS. *3390*

YEAR BOOK OF VASCULAR SURGERY.
Mosby - Year Book, Inc., Continuity Division, 200 N.
LaSalle, Chicago, IL 60601. FAX 312-726-9733.
Vendor(s): BRS. *3163*

YOUTH MARKETS ALERT.
Alert Publishing, Inc., 37-06 30th Ave., Long Island
City, NY 11103-3808. TEL 718-626-3356.
Vendor(s): Data-Star, DIALOG, NewsNet. *1509*

Z V E I ELEKTRO UND ELEKTRONIK - EINKAUFSFUEHRER.
Verlag W. Sachon, Schloss Mindelburg, Postfach
1463, 8948 Mindelheim, Germany. TEL 08261-
999-0. FAX 08261-999-132.
Vendor(s): Data-Star, FIZ Technik. *1880*

ZAHRANICNE PERIODIKA V C S F R.
Univerzitna Kniznica, Michalska 1, 814 17
Bratislava, Czechoslovakia. TEL 0331151.
FAX 334246. *416*

ZASSHI SHINBUN SOKATAROGU.
Media Research Center, Inc., c/o Irimajiri Bldg., 6-
40 Shin-Ogawa-Machi, Shinjuku-ku, Tokyo 162,
Japan. *416*

ZEITSCHRIFTEN - DATENBANK (Z D B).
Deutsches Bibiotheksinstitut, Bundesallee 184-5,
1000 Berlin 31, Germany. TEL 030-8505130.
2791

ZENTRALBLATT FUER DIDAKTIK DER MATHEMATIK.
Fachinformationszentrum Karlsruhe, Gesellschaft
fuer wissenschaftlich-technische Information mbH,
7514 Eggenstein-Leopoldshafen 2, Germany.
TEL 07247-808-0. FAX 07247-808-666.
Vendor(s): STN International. *3062*

ZENTRALBLATT FUER MATHEMATIK UND IHRE GRENZGEBIETE.
Springer-Verlag, Heidelberger Platz 3, D-1000
Berlin 33, Germany. TEL 030-8207-1.
Vendor(s): STN International (MATH). *3063*

ZHONGGUO SHENGWUXUE WENZHAI.
Zhongguo Kexueyuan, Shanghai Wenxian Qingbao
Zhongxin, 319 Yueyang Lu, Shanghai 200031,
People's Republic of China. TEL 4336650.
FAX 0086-021-4718906. *468*

ZHONGGUO XINLI WEISHENG ZAZHI.
Beijing Yike Daxue, Jingshen Weisheng Yanjiusuo,
Huayuan Beilu, Beijing 100083, People's Republic
of China. TEL 2010890.
Vendor(s): DIALOG. *4051*

ZOO BIOLOGY.
John Wiley & Sons, Inc., Journals, 605 Third Ave.,
New York, NY 10158. TEL 212-850-6000.
FAX 212-850-6088. *594*

ZOOLOGICAL RECORD.
BIOSIS, 2100 Arch St., Philadelphia, PA 19103-
1399. TEL 215-587-4800. FAX 215-587-2016.
Vendor(s): DIALOG (File no.185). *468*

411 NEWSLETTER.
United Communications Group, 11300 Rockville
Pike, Ste. 1100, Rockville, MD 20852-3030.
TEL 301-816-8950.
Vendor(s): Data-Star (PTBN), DIALOG (File no.636),
NewsNet (TE94). *1368*

Vendor Listing/Serials Online

AUSINET
Information Management Group, 310 Ferntree Gully Rd., Clayton, Vic. 3168, Australia Tel: 554 8433
A L I S A.
  Australian Books in Print.
  Australian Education Index.
  Bibliography of Education Theses in Australia.
  The Business Who's Who of Australia.

BELINDIS (Subsidiary of: Belgian Ministry of Economic Affairs)
Data Processing Centre, 30 rue de Mot, 1040 Brussels, Belgium Tel: 32-22336737 Telex: 23509 energi B
Fax: 32-22304619.
  Bibliotheque Africaine. Liste des Acquisitions. (AFLI)
  Coal Abstracts.
  Economic Titles - Abstracts.
  I N I S Atomindex.
  Key to Economic Science.
  Recueil des Brevets d'Invention.

BRS INFORMATION TECHNOLOGIES
8000 Westpark Dr., McLean, VA 22102. Tel: 703-442-0900
Fax: 703-893-4632.
  A B A Banking Journal. (TSAP)
  A B I - INFORM. (INFO)
  A S F A Aquaculture Abstracts. (CSAL)
  A S F A Marine Biotechnology Abstracts. (CSAL)
  Abridged Readers' Guide to Periodical Literature.
  Academic Abstracts C D - R O M.
  Academic Index. (ACAD)
  Administrative Science Quarterly.
  Adweek (Los Angeles). (TSAP)
  Adweek (New York). (TSAP)
  Adweek's Marketing Week. (TSAP)
  Aerospace Daily. (TSAP)
  Age and Ageing.
  Agribusiness Worldwide. (TSAP)
  Agricultural Engineering Abstracts. (CABA)
  Agricultural Supply Industry. (TSAP)
  Agroforestry Abstracts.
  Agrow.
  Air Conditioning, Heating & Refrigeration News. (TSAP)
  American Banker.
  American College of Cardiology. Journal.
  American Doctoral Dissertations.
  American Family Physician.
  American Heart Journal.
  American Hospital Formulary Service Drug Information. (DIFT)
  American Journal of Cardiology.
  American Journal of Medicine.
  American Journal of Obstetrics and Gynecology.
  American Journal of Psychiatry.
  American Journal of Public Health.
  American Journal of Surgery.
  Anesthesia and Analgesia.
  Anesthesiology.
  Animal Behavior Abstracts. (CSAL)
  Animal Breeding Abstracts. (CABA)
  Animal Disease Occurrence. (VETR)
  Animal Pharm.
  Annals of Internal Medicine.
  Annals of Neurology.
  Annals of Surgery.
  Annals of the Rheumatic Diseases.
  Apparel Industry Magazine.
  Aquatic Sciences & Fisheries Abstracts. Part 1: Biological Sciences and Living Resources. (CSAL)
  Aquatic Sciences & Fisheries Abstracts. Part 2: Ocean Technology, Policy and Non-Living Resources. (CSAL)
  Aquatic Sciences & Fisheries Abstracts. Part 3: Aquatic Pollution and Environmental Quality. (CSAL)
  Archives of Diseases in Childhood.
  Art Index.
  Arthritis and Rheumatism.
  Arts & Humanities Citation Index. (AHCI)
  Biocontrol News and Information.
  Biodeterioration Abstracts.
  Biological Abstracts. (BIOL)
  Biological Abstracts - R R M. (BIOL)
  Biotechnology Research Abstracts. (CSAL)
  Blood.
  Books in Print. (BBIP)
  Books in Print Supplement. (BBIP)
  Books Out-of-Print. (BBIP)
  The Bowker Annual Library and Book Trade Almanac.
  British Heart Journal.
  British Journal of Obstetrics & Gynaecology.
  British Journal of Rheumatology.
  British Journal of Surgery.
  British Journal of Urology.
  British Medical Journal.
  Bulletin of Entomological Research.
  Business Index.
  C.A.B. International Bureau of Agricultural Economics. Annotated Bibliographies Series A.
  C.A.B. International Bureau of Agricultural Economics. Annotated Bibliographies. Series B: Agricultural Policy and Rural Development in Africa.
  C.A.B. International. Bureau of Nutrition. Annotated Bibliographies.
  C.A.B. International. Bureau of Soils. Annotated Bibliographies.
  C M I Descriptions of Fungi and Bacteria.
  C S A Neurosciences Abstracts. (CSAL)
  C S I Congressional Record Abstracts: Master Edition.
  C S I Federal Register Abstracts: Master Edition. (FREG)
  Calcified Tissue Abstracts. (CSAL)
  Cambridge Scientific Biochemistry Abstracts: Part 1. Biological Membranes. (CSAL)
  Cambridge Scientific Biochemistry Abstracts: Part 2. Nucleic Acids. (CSAL)
  Cambridge Scientific Biochemistry Abstracts: Part 3. Amino-Acids, Peptides & Proteins. (CSAL)
  Canadian Medical Association Journal.
  Cardiology Clinics.
  Chemical Abstracts - Section Groupings. (CHEM)
  Chemoreception Abstracts. (CSAL)
  Children's Books in Print. (BBIP)
  Ching Feng.
  Circulation. (JWAT)
  Circulation Research.
  Clinica.
  Clinical Diabetes.
  Clinical Orthopaedics and Related Research.
  Clinical Pediatrics.
  Clinical Pharmacology & Therapeutics.
  Compumath Citation Index.
  Computer & Control Abstracts. (INSP)
  Computer and Information Systems Abstracts Journal. (CSEN)
  Computer Database. (CMPT)
  Cotton and Tropical Fibres. (CABA)
  Crop Physiology Abstracts. (CABA)
  Cumulative Index to Nursing & Allied Health Literature. (NAHL)
  Current Advances in Applied Microbiology & Biotechnology. (CABS)
  Current Advances in Cancer Research. (CABS)
  Current Advances in Cell and Developmental Biology. (CABS)
  Current Advances in Clinical Chemistry. (CABS)
  Current Advances in Ecological and Environmental Sciences. (CABS)
  Current Advances in Endocrinology & Metabolism. (CABS)
  Current Advances in Genetics and Molecular Biology. (CABS)
  Current Advances in Immunology & Infectious Diseases. (CABS)
  Current Advances in Neuroscience. (CABS)
  Current Advances in Plant Science. (CABS)
  Current Advances in Protein Biochemistry. (CABS)
  Current Advances in Toxicology. (CABS)
  Current Awareness in Biological Sciences. (CABS)
  Current Awareness in Health Education.
  Current Contents: Agriculture, Biology & Environmental Sciences. (CCON,AGRI)
  Current Contents: Arts & Humanities. (CCON,ARTS)
  Current Contents: Clinical Medicine. (CCON,CLIN)

Current Contents: Engineering, Technology & Applied Sciences. (CCON,ENGI)
Current Contents: Life Sciences. (CCON,LIFE)
Current Contents: Physical, Chemical & Earth Sciences. (CCON,PHYS)
Current Contents: Social & Behavioral Sciences. (CCON,BEHA)
Current History.
Current Index to Journals in Education.
Current Index to Statistics. (MATH)
Current Law Index.
Current Mathematical Publications.
The Cyprus Review.
Dairy Science Abstracts. (CABA)
DataBase Alert. (KIPD)
DataBase Directory. (KIPD)
Defense & Aerospace Electronics. (TSAP)
Devices & Diagnostics Letter. (DIOG)
Diabetes.
Diabetes Care.
Dissertation Abstracts. (DISS)
Dissertation Abstracts International. Section A: Humanities and Social Sciences. (DISS)
Dissertation Abstracts International. Section B: Physical Sciences and Engineering. (DISS)
Dissertation Abstracts International. Section C: Worldwide. (DISS)
Ecology Abstracts. (CSAL)
Electrical & Electronics Abstracts. (INSP)
Electronics and Communications Abstracts Journal. (CSEN)
Emergency Medicine Clinics of North America.
Emergency Medicine Reports.
Engineering Index Annual. (COMP)
Engineering Index Monthly. (COMP)
Entomology Abstracts. (CSAL)
Epiphany Journal.
Exceptional Child Education Resources. (ECER)
Excerpta Medica Abstract Journals.
Excerpta Medica. Section 1: Anatomy, Anthropology, Embryology & Histology.
Excerpta Medica. Section 2: Physiology.
Excerpta Medica. Section 3: Endocrinology.
Excerpta Medica. Section 4: Microbiology: Bacteriology, Mycology, Parasitology and Virology.
Excerpta Medica. Section 5: General Pathology and Pathological Anatomy.
Excerpta Medica. Section 6: Internal Medicine.
Excerpta Medica. Section 7: Pediatrics and Pediatric Surgery.
Excerpta Medica. Section 8: Neurology and Neurosurgery.
Excerpta Medica. Section 9: Surgery.
Excerpta Medica. Section 10: Obstetrics and Gynecology.
Excerpta Medica. Section 11: Otorhinolaryngology.
Excerpta Medica. Section 12: Ophthalmology.
Excerpta Medica. Section 13: Dermatology and Venereology.
Excerpta Medica. Section 14: Radiology.
Excerpta Medica. Section 15: Chest Diseases, Thoracic Surgery and Tuberculosis.
Excerpta Medica. Section 16: Cancer.
Excerpta Medica. Section 17: Public Health, Social Medicine & Epidemiology.
Excerpta Medica. Section 18: Cardiovascular Diseases and Cardiovascular Surgery.
Excerpta Medica. Section 19: Rehabilitation and Physical Medicine.
Excerpta Medica. Section 20: Gerontology and Geriatrics.
Excerpta Medica. Section 21: Developmental Biology and Teratology.
Excerpta Medica. Section 22: Human Genetics.
Excerpta Medica. Section 23: Nuclear Medicine.
Excerpta Medica. Section 24: Anesthesiology.
Excerpta Medica. Section 25: Hematology.
Excerpta Medica. Section 26: Immunology, Serology and Transplantation.
Excerpta Medica. Section 27: Biophysics, Bio-Engineering and Medical Instrumentation.
Excerpta Medica. Section 28: Urology and Nephrology.
Excerpta Medica. Section 29: Clinical and Experimental Biochemistry.
Excerpta Medica. Section 30: Clinical and Experimental Pharmacology.
Excerpta Medica. Section 31: Arthritis and Rheumatism.
Excerpta Medica. Section 32: Psychiatry.
Excerpta Medica. Section 33: Orthopedic Surgery.
Excerpta Medica. Section 35: Occupational Health and Industrial Medicine.
Excerpta Medica. Section 36: Health Policy, Economics and Management.
Excerpta Medica. Section 38: Adverse Reactions Titles.
Excerpta Medica. Section 40: Drug Dependence, Alcohol Abuse and Alcoholism.
Excerpta Medica. Section 46: Environmental Health and Pollution Control.
Excerpta Medica. Section 48: Gastroenterology.
Excerpta Medica. Section 49: Forensic Science Abstracts.
Excerpta Medica. Section 50: Epilepsy Abstracts.
Excerpta Medica. Section 52: Toxicology.
F D A Enforcement Report. (DIOG)
F D A Medical Bulletin. (DIOG)
Faba Bean Abstracts. (CABA)
Family Relations.
Federal Applied Technology Database.
Federal Register. (DIOG)
Field Crop Abstracts. (CABA)
Food and Drug Letter. (DIOG)
Food Science and Technology Abstracts. (CABA)
Forest Products Abstracts. (CABA)
Forestry Abstracts. (CABA)
Forestry Abstracts. Leading Article Reprint Series.
Forthcoming Books. (BBIP)
G M P Letter. (DIOG)
Gastroenterology Journal.
Genetics Abstracts. (CSAL)
Genitourinary Medicine: The Journal of Sexual Health, STDs and HIV.
Government Reports Announcements and Index Journal.
Gut.
Handbook on Injectable Drugs. (DIFT)
Harvard Business Review. (HBRO)
Harvard Health Letter.
Health and Safety Science Abstracts. (CSEN)
Health Index. (HEAL)
Health News Daily. (HNDY)
Heart and Lung.
Helminthological Abstracts. (VETR)
Herbage Abstracts. (CABA)
Horticultural Abstracts. (CABA)
Human Genome Abstracts. (CSAL)
I S M E C: Mechanical Engineering Abstracts. (CSEN)
Immunology Abstracts. (CSAL)
Index Medicus. (MESH, MESZ)
Index of Current Research on Pigs.
Index of Fungi.
Index to Book Reviews in Religion.
Index to Dental Literature. (MESH, MESZ)
Index to U.S. Government Periodicals.
Index Veterinarius. (VETR)
Inpharma.
Institute of Muslim Minority Affairs. Journal.
International Biodeterioration.
International Nursing Index.
International Pharmaceutical Abstracts. (IPAB)
Inventory of Marriage and Family Literature.
Irrigation and Drainage Abstracts. (CABA)
J A M A: The Journal of the American Medical Association. (JWAT)
Journal of Allergy and Clinical Immunology.
Journal of Bone and Joint Surgery: American Volume.
Journal of Clinical Investigation.
Journal of Clinical Pathology.
Journal of Family History.
Journal of Family Issues.
Journal of Infectious Diseases. (JWAT)
Journal of Laboratory and Clinical Medicine.
Journal of Marriage and the Family.
Journal of Neurology, Neurosurgery and Psychiatry.
Journal of Pediatrics.
Journal of Psychology and Theology.
Journal of Technology Transfer.
Key Abstracts - Business Automation.
Lancet.
Lasers in Medicine.
Legal Resource Index. (LAWS)
Leisure, Recreation and Tourism Abstracts. (TOUR)
Lentils. (CABA)
Library & Information Science Abstracts. (LISA)
Library Literature.
Linguistics and Language Behavior Abstracts. (LLBA)
Magazine Article Summaries. (PMRO)
Magazine Index. (MAGS)
Maize Abstracts. (CABA)
Management Contents. (MGMT)
Masters Abstracts International.
Mathematical Reviews. (MATH)
Medical and Health Care Books and Serials in Print.
Medical Clinics of North America.
Medical Letter on Drugs and Therapeutics.
Medical Science Research.
Medicine (Baltimore).
Mental Measurements Yearbook. (MMYD)
Merck Index: An Encyclopedia of Chemicals and Drugs. (MRCK)
Microbiology Abstracts: Section A. Industrial & Applied Microbiology. (CSAL)
Microbiology Abstracts: Section B. Bacteriology. (CSAL)
Microbiology Abstracts: Section C. Algology, Mycology and Protozoology. (CSAL)
Monthly Catalog of United States Government Publications.
N T I S Bibliographic Data Base.
Nashville Business and Lifestyles. (BDLN)
National Cancer Institute. Journal.
National Council on Family Relations. Report.
National Newspaper Index. (NOOZ)
Nematological Abstracts. (CABA)
Neurology.
New England Journal of Medicine. (NEJM)
Nutrition Abstracts and Reviews. Series A: Human and Experimental. (NUTR)
Nutrition Abstracts and Reviews. Series B: Livestock Feeds and Feeding. (VETR)
Obstetrical & Gynecological Survey.
Obstetrics and Gynecology.
Occasional Papers on Religion in Eastern Europe.
Oceanic Abstracts. (CSAL)
Oncogenes and Growth Factors Abstracts. (CSAL)
Ornamental Horticulture.
Outlook (Year) Proceedings.
P A I S International in Print. (PAIS)
P N I.
Paperbound Books in Print. (BBIP)
Pediatric Clinics of North America.
Pediatrics.
Personnel Psychology.
Peterson's Guide to Four-Year Colleges (Year). (PETE)
Peterson's Guide to Two-Year Colleges (Year). (PETE)
Philosophical Forum.
Physical Therapy.
Physics Abstracts. (INSP)
Pig News & Information.
Plant Breeding Abstracts. (CABA)
Plant Growth Regulator Abstracts. (CABA)
Pollution Abstracts. (CSAL)
Potato Abstracts. (CABA)
Poultry Abstracts. (CABA)
Predicasts F & S Index Europe. (PTSI)
Predicasts F & S Index International. (PTSI)
Predicasts F & S Index of Corporate Change. (PTSI)
Predicasts F & S Index United States. (PTSI)
Predicasts Overview of Markets and Technology. (PTSP)
Protozoological Abstracts. (VETR)
Psychological Abstracts.
Quarterly Journal of Medicine.
Radiologic Clinics of North America.
Reactions.
Religion Index One: Periodicals. (RELI)
Religion Index Two: Multi-Author Works.
Religious and Inspirational Books and Serials in Print.
Resources in Education.
Respiratory Medicine.
Review of Agricultural Entomology.
Review of Medical and Veterinary Entomology. (VETR)
Review of Medical and Veterinary Mycology. (VETR)
Review of Plant Pathology.
Rice Abstracts. (CABA)
Roundsmanship (Year).
Rural Development Abstracts. (ECON)
Science. (SCIE)
Scientific American. (SAMM)
Scrip - World Pharmaceutical News.
Seed Abstracts. (CABA)
Seminars in Neurology.
Seminars in Respiratory Medicine.
Sexually Transmitted Diseases.
Shonika.
Small Animals. (VETR)
Social Planning - Policy & Development Abstracts. (SOCA)
Social Sciences Citation Index. (SSCI)
Social Work Research and Abstracts. (SWAB)
Sociological Abstracts. (SOCA)
Soils and Fertilizers.
Solid State and Superconductivity Abstracts. (CSEN)
Sorghum and Millets Abstracts. (CABA)
Southern Social Studies Journal.
Soyabean Abstracts. (CABA)

SportSearch. *(SFDB)*
Stroke.
Subject Guide to Books in Print. *(BBIP)*
Surgical Clinics of North America.
Thorax.
Toxicology Abstracts. *(CSAL)*
Trade & Industry Index. *(TSAP)*
Tropical Oil Seeds. *(CABA)*
Ulrich's International Periodicals Directory. *(ULRI)*
Ulrich's Update. *(ULRI)*
U.S. Centers for Disease Control. Morbidity and Mortality Weekly Report.
Vaard i Norden.
Veterinary Bulletin. *(VETR)*
Virology and A I D S Abstracts. *(CSAL)*
Washington Drug Letter (Washington, 1979). *(DIOG)*
Weed Abstracts. *(CABA)*
Wheat, Barley and Triticale Abstracts. *(CABA)*
World Agricultural Economics and Rural Sociology Abstracts. *(ECON)*
Year Book of Anesthesia.
Year Book of Cardiology.
Year Book of Dentistry.
Year Book of Dermatologic Surgery.
Year Book of Dermatology.
Year Book of Diagnostic Radiology.
Year Book of Digestive Diseases.
Year Book of Drug Therapy.
Year Book of Emergency Medicine.
Year Book of Family Practice.
Year Book of Geriatrics and Gerontology.
Year Book of Hand Surgery.
Year Book of Health Care Management.
Year Book of Hematology.
Year Book of Infectious Diseases.
Year Book of Medicine.
Year Book of Nephrology.
Year Book of Neurology & Neurosurgery.
Year Book of Neuroradiology.
Year Book of Nuclear Medicine.
Year Book of Obstetrics and Gynecology.
Year Book of Occupational Medicine.
Year Book of Oncology.
Year Book of Ophthalmology.
Year Book of Orthopedics.
Year Book of Pathology and Clinical Pathology.
Year Book of Pediatrics.
Year Book of Perinatal - Neonatal Medicine.
Year Book of Plastic, Reconstructive, and Aesthetic Surgery.
Year Book of Psychiatry and Applied Mental Health.
Year Book of Pulmonary Disease.
Year Book of Surgery.
Year Book of Transplantation.
Year Book of Ultrasound.
Year Book of Urology.
Year Book of Vascular Surgery.

BUREAU OF NATIONAL AFFAIRS
Data Base Publishing Unit, 1231 25th St., NW, Washington, DC 20037. Tel: 202-452-4132
Telex: 892692
Fax: 202-452-4062.
B N A's Banking Report.
Daily Labor Report.
Daily Tax Report.
S E C News Digest.
Securities Regulation & Law Report.

C E D O C A R
26 Bd. Victor, 75996 Paris Armees, France Tel: 33-145523456 Telex: 202778 F
Fax: 33-145524993.
Alloys Index.
Computer & Control Abstracts.
Electrical & Electronics Abstracts.
Engineering Index Annual.
Engineering Index Monthly.
Government Reports Announcements and Index Journal.
Key Abstracts - Business Automation.
Metals Abstracts.
Metals Abstracts Index.
Nonferrous Metals Alert.
Physics Abstracts.
Polymers, Ceramics, Composite Alert.

C I S T I (Subsidiary of: National Research Council of Canada)
Montreal Rd., Bldg. M55, Ottawa, Ont. K1A 0S2, Canada Tel: 613-993-1210 Telex: 0533115
Fax: 613-952-8244.
A S F A Aquaculture Abstracts.
Agricultural Engineering Abstracts.
Alloys Index.
Animal Breeding Abstracts.
Animal Disease Occurrence.
Aquatic Sciences & Fisheries Abstracts. Part 1: Biological Sciences and Living Resources.
Aquatic Sciences & Fisheries Abstracts. Part 2: Ocean Technology, Policy and Non-Living Resources.
Bibliography and Index of Geology.
Bibliography of Agriculture.
Biocontrol News and Information.
Biological Abstracts.
Biological Abstracts - R R M.
Bulletin of Entomological Research.
C.A.B. International Bureau of Agricultural Economics. Annotated Bibliographies Series A.
C.A.B. International Bureau of Agricultural Economics. Annotated Bibliographies. Series B: Agricultural Policy and Rural Development in Africa.
C.A.B. International. Bureau of Nutrition. Annotated Bibliographies.
C.A.B. International. Bureau of Soils. Annotated Bibliographies.
C M I Descriptions of Fungi and Bacteria.
Canada. Petawawa National Forestry Institute. Information Reports. *(MICROLOG)*
Canadian Business Index.
Canadian Magazine Index. *(Canadian Business and Current Affairs)*
Canadian News Index.
Canadian Theses.
Canadiana.
Canadiana on Microfiche.
Canadiana Pre-1901.
Chemical Abstracts - Section Groupings.
Chemical Titles.
Coal Abstracts.
Computer & Control Abstracts.
Cotton and Tropical Fibres.
Crop Physiology Abstracts.
Current Index to Journals in Education.
Dairy Science Abstracts.
Directory of Associations in Canada.
Electrical & Electronics Abstracts.
Engineering Index Monthly.
Faba Bean Abstracts.
Field Crop Abstracts.
Food Science and Technology Abstracts.
Forest Products Abstracts.
Forestry Abstracts.
Forestry Abstracts. Leading Article Reprint Series.
Government Reports Announcements and Index Journal.
Helminthological Abstracts.
Herbage Abstracts.
Horticultural Abstracts.
I N I S Atomindex.
Index of Current Research on Pigs.
Index of Fungi.
Index Veterinarius.
International Biodeterioration.
Irrigation and Drainage Abstracts.
Key Abstracts - Business Automation.
Leisure, Recreation and Tourism Abstracts.
Lentils.
Maize Abstracts.
Merck Index: An Encyclopedia of Chemicals and Drugs.
Metals Abstracts.
Metals Abstracts Index.
Microlog: Canadian Research Index.
Nematological Abstracts.
Nonferrous Metals Alert.
Nutrition Abstracts and Reviews. Series A: Human and Experimental.
Nutrition Abstracts and Reviews. Series B: Livestock Feeds and Feeding.
Ornamental Horticulture.
Packaging Science and Technology Abstracts.
Physics Abstracts.
Pig News & Information.
Plant Breeding Abstracts.
Plant Growth Regulator Abstracts.
Polymers, Ceramics, Composite Alert.
Potato Abstracts.
Poultry Abstracts.
Protozoological Abstracts.
Resources in Education.
Review of Agricultural Entomology.
Review of Medical and Veterinary Entomology.
Review of Medical and Veterinary Mycology.
Review of Plant Pathology.
Rice Abstracts.
Rural Development Abstracts.
Seed Abstracts.
Small Animals.
Soils and Fertilizers.
Sorghum and Millets Abstracts.
Soyabean Abstracts.
Steels Alert.
Tropical Oil Seeds.
Union List of Scientific Serials in Canadian Libraries.
Veterinary Bulletin.
Weed Abstracts.
Wheat, Barley and Triticale Abstracts.
World Agricultural Economics and Rural Sociology Abstracts.

C R E D O C
34 rue de la Montagne, BP 11, 1000 Brussels, Belgium Tel: 33 (2) 513 9213 Telex: 63129 CREDOC B
Fax: 32-25130911.
Steels Alert.

CENTRAL INSTITUTE FOR SCIENTIFIC AND TECHNICAL INFORMATION
52 A.G. Nasser, Sofia 1040, Bulgaria Tel: 71-91-91 Telex: 22404
Biological Abstracts.
Biological Abstracts - R R M.
Physical Therapy.

CHEMICAL INFORMATION SYSTEMS (Subsidiary of: Fein-Marquart Assocs., Inc.)
7215 York Rd., Baltimore, MD 21212. Tel: 410-321-8440 Telex: 9103801738
Fax: 301-296-0712.
Registry of Toxic Effects of Chemical Substances.

COMPUSERVE, INC.
5000 Arlington Centre Blvd., Columbus, OH 43220. Tel: 614-457-0802
Fax: 614-457-0348.
Aquariculture and Aquatic Sciences. Journal.
Book World.
CompuServe.
Current Business Reports: Monthly Retail Trade, Sales and Inventories.
Current Business Reports: Monthly Wholesale Trade: Sales and Inventories.
Current Construction Reports.
Current Construction Reports: Housing Starts.
Current Construction Reports: Housing Units Authorized by Building Permits.
Current Construction Reports: New One-Family Houses Sold and for Sale.
Current Construction Reports: Value of New Construction Put in Place.
Current Governments Reports: City Employment.
Current Governments Reports: County Government Employment.

VENDOR LISTING/SERIALS ONLINE

Current Governments Reports: Government Finances.

Current Governments Reports: Public Employment.

Current Governments Reports: State Government Tax Collections.

Current Housing Reports.

Current Housing Reports: Housing Characteristics.

Current Housing Reports: Housing Vacancies.

Current Industrial Reports: Broadwoven Fabrics (Gray).

Current Industrial Reports: Fats and Oils. Oilseed Crushings.

Current Industrial Reports: Fats and Oils. Production, Consumption, and Stocks.

Current Population Reports: Consumer Income. Money Income of Households, Families and Persons in the United States (Year).

Current Population Reports: Local Population Estimates.

Current Population Reports: Population Characteristics. Geographical Mobility.

Current Population Reports: Population Characteristics. Marital Status and Living Arrangements.

Current Population Reports: Population Characteristics. School Enrollment: Social and Economic Characteristics of Students.

Current Population Reports: Population Estimates and Projections.

Current Population Reports: Population Estimates and Projections. United States Population Estimates by Age, Sex, Race and Hispanic Origin.

FedWatch.

First Facts On the Currency Market.

Foreign Trade Reports. U.S. Export and Import Merchandise Trade and Supplement.

International Population Data.

Micro M D Newsletter.

One to One (Fresno).

Orphan Disease Update. *(GO NORD)*

Peterson's Guide to Four-Year Colleges (Year). *(PCG)*

Peterson's Guide to Two-Year Colleges (Year). *(PCG)*

Software Catalog: Microcomputers.

Statistical Abstract of the United States.

U.S. Bureau of the Census. Annual Survey of Manufactures.

U.S. Bureau of the Census. Census and You.

U.S. Bureau of the Census. Census of Agriculture.

U.S. Bureau of the Census. Census of Construction Industries.

U.S. Bureau of the Census. Census of Governments.

U.S. Bureau of the Census. Census of Manufactures.

U.S. Bureau of the Census. Census of Retail Trade.

U.S. Bureau of the Census. Census of Service Industries.

U.S. Bureau of the Census. Census of Wholesale Trade.

U.S. Bureau of the Census. County and City Data Book.

U.S. Bureau of the Census. County Business Patterns.

U.S. Bureau of the Census. State and Metropolitan Area Data Book.

Windows Journal.

Wine Investor: Buyers' Guide.

D I M D I (Subsidiary of: Deutsches Institut fuer Medizinische Dokumentation und Information) Box 42 05 60, Weisshausstrasse 27, D-5000 Cologne, Germany Tel: (49) 221-4721-1, (42) 221-4724-270 Telex: 88 81 364 dim D Fax: (49) 221411429.

A I D S Newsletter.
A S F A Aquaculture Abstracts.
Abstracts on Hygiene and Communicable Diseases.
Agricultural Engineering Abstracts.
Agrindex.
Agroforestry Abstracts.
Animal Breeding Abstracts.
Animal Disease Occurrence.
Aquatic Sciences & Fisheries Abstracts. Part 1: Biological Sciences and Living Resources.
Aquatic Sciences & Fisheries Abstracts. Part 2: Ocean Technology, Policy and Non-Living Resources.
Aquatic Sciences & Fisheries Abstracts. Part 3: Aquatic Pollution and Environmental Quality.
Bibliographie der Pflanzenschutzliteratur.
Biocontrol News and Information.
Biodeterioration Abstracts.
Biological Abstracts.
Biological Abstracts - R R M.
Bulletin of Entomological Research.
C.A.B. International Bureau of Agricultural Economics. Annotated Bibliographies Series A.
C.A.B. International Bureau of Agricultural Economics. Annotated Bibliographies. Series B: Agricultural Policy and Rural Development in Africa.
C.A.B. International. Bureau of Nutrition. Annotated Bibliographies.
C.A.B. International. Bureau of Soils. Annotated Bibliographies.
C M I Descriptions of Fungi and Bacteria.
Cotton and Tropical Fibres.
Crop Physiology Abstracts.
Dairy Science Abstracts.
Environment Abstracts.
Environment Abstracts Annual.
Excerpta Medica Abstract Journals.
Excerpta Medica. Section 1: Anatomy, Anthropology, Embryology & Histology.
Excerpta Medica. Section 2: Physiology.
Excerpta Medica. Section 3: Endocrinology.
Excerpta Medica. Section 4: Microbiology: Bacteriology, Mycology, Parasitology and Virology.
Excerpta Medica. Section 5: General Pathology and Pathological Anatomy.
Excerpta Medica. Section 6: Internal Medicine.
Excerpta Medica. Section 7: Pediatrics and Pediatric Surgery.
Excerpta Medica. Section 8: Neurology and Neurosurgery.
Excerpta Medica. Section 9: Surgery.
Excerpta Medica. Section 10: Obstetrics and Gynecology.
Excerpta Medica. Section 11: Otorhinolaryngology.
Excerpta Medica. Section 12: Ophthalmology.
Excerpta Medica. Section 13: Dermatology and Venereology.
Excerpta Medica. Section 14: Radiology.
Excerpta Medica. Section 15: Chest Diseases, Thoracic Surgery and Tuberculosis.
Excerpta Medica. Section 16: Cancer.
Excerpta Medica. Section 17: Public Health, Social Medicine & Epidemiology.
Excerpta Medica. Section 18: Cardiovascular Diseases and Cardiovascular Surgery.
Excerpta Medica. Section 19: Rehabilitation and Physical Medicine.
Excerpta Medica. Section 20: Gerontology and Geriatrics.
Excerpta Medica. Section 21: Developmental Biology and Teratology.
Excerpta Medica. Section 22: Human Genetics.
Excerpta Medica. Section 23: Nuclear Medicine.
Excerpta Medica. Section 24: Anesthesiology.
Excerpta Medica. Section 25: Hematology.
Excerpta Medica. Section 26: Immunology, Serology and Transplantation.
Excerpta Medica. Section 27: Biophysics, Bio-Engineering and Medical Instrumentation.
Excerpta Medica. Section 28: Urology and Nephrology.
Excerpta Medica. Section 29: Clinical and Experimental Biochemistry.
Excerpta Medica. Section 30: Clinical and Experimental Pharmacology.
Excerpta Medica. Section 31: Arthritis and Rheumatism.
Excerpta Medica. Section 32: Psychiatry.
Excerpta Medica. Section 33: Orthopedic Surgery.
Excerpta Medica. Section 35: Occupational Health and Industrial Medicine.
Excerpta Medica. Section 36: Health Policy, Economics and Management.
Excerpta Medica. Section 38: Adverse Reactions Titles.
Excerpta Medica. Section 40: Drug Dependence, Alcohol Abuse and Alcoholism.
Excerpta Medica. Section 46: Environmental Health and Pollution Control.
Excerpta Medica. Section 48: Gastroenterology.
Excerpta Medica. Section 49: Forensic Science Abstracts.
Excerpta Medica. Section 50: Epilepsy Abstracts.
Excerpta Medica. Section 52: Toxicology.
Faba Bean Abstracts.
Field Crop Abstracts.
Food Science and Technology Abstracts.
Forest Products Abstracts.
Forestry Abstracts.
Forestry Abstracts. Leading Article Reprint Series.
Helminthological Abstracts.
Herbage Abstracts.
Horticultural Abstracts.
Hospital Literature Index.
Index of Current Research on Pigs.
Index of Fungi.
Index to Scientific Book Contents. *(ISTP&B Search)*
Index Veterinarius.
Informationsdienst Krankenhauswesen.
International Biodeterioration.
International Pharmaceutical Abstracts.
Irrigation and Drainage Abstracts.
Lasers in Medicine.
Leisure, Recreation and Tourism Abstracts.
Lentils.
Maize Abstracts.
Medical Science Research.
Nematological Abstracts.
Nutrition Abstracts and Reviews. Series A: Human and Experimental.
Nutrition Abstracts and Reviews. Series B: Livestock Feeds and Feeding.
Ornamental Horticulture.
Packaging Science and Technology Abstracts.
Pig News & Information.
Plant Breeding Abstracts.
Plant Growth Regulator Abstracts.
Potato Abstracts.
Poultry Abstracts.
Protozoological Abstracts.
Psychological Abstracts.
Review of Agricultural Entomology.
Review of Medical and Veterinary Entomology.
Review of Medical and Veterinary Mycology.
Review of Plant Pathology.
Rice Abstracts.
Rural Development Abstracts.
Science Citation Index.
Seed Abstracts.
Small Animals.
Social Planning - Policy & Development Abstracts. *(SA63)*
Social Sciences Citation Index.
Sociological Abstracts. *(SA63)*
Soils and Fertilizers.
Sorghum and Millets Abstracts.
Soyabean Abstracts.
Tropical Diseases Bulletin.
Tropical Oil Seeds.
Veterinary Bulletin.
Vitis - Viticulture and Enology Abstracts.
Weed Abstracts.
Wheat, Barley and Triticale Abstracts.
World Agricultural Economics and Rural Sociology Abstracts.

DATA-STAR
114 Jermyn St., Plaza Suite, London SW1Y 6HJ, United Kingdom Tel: 44-71-930-5503, 44-71-930-2581
Radio Suisse AG, Laupenstr. 18A, CH-3008 Berne, Switzerland Tel: 41-31-509500 Fax: 41-31-509675.
A B B Review.
A B C der Deutschen Wirtschaft.

A B C Europ Production - Europex.
A B I - INFORM. *(INFO)*
A S S I A. *(ASSI)*
Abstracts in BioCommerce. *(CELL)*
Advanced Ceramics Report. *(PTBN)*
Advanced Coatings & Surface Technology. *(PTBN)*
Advanced Composites Bulletin. *(PTBN)*
Advanced Manufacturing Technology.
Advanced Recovery Week.
Aerospace Financial News.
Affluent Markets Alert.
Agrochemicals Handbook.
Agroforestry Abstracts.
Agrow.
Air Safety Week.
Air - Water Pollution Report.
Airline Business.
Airline Financial News.
Alliance Alert.
Alloys Index. *(META)*
Alternative Energy Digests.
American Banker. *(BANK)*
Analytical Abstracts. *(ANAB)*
Animal Pharm.
Annuaire Telexport.
Applied Genetics News.
Asbestos Control Report.
Audio Week.
Audiotex Update.
Autoparts Report.
The B B I Newsletter.
B D I Deutschland Liefert.
Battery & E V Technology News.
Biodeterioration Abstracts.
Biological Abstracts.
Biological Abstracts - R R M.
Biomedical Materials.
Biotech Business.
Biotechnology Investment Opportunities.
Branch Automation News.
Brazil Service. *(FSRI)*
Business and the Environment.
Business Law Brief.
Business Travel News.
Buyouts.
C A S E Strategies.
C D C - A I D S Weekly. *(PTS NEWSLETTER DATABASE)*
Card News.
Chem-Facts: Ammonia.
Chem-Facts: Belgium.
Chem-Facts: Ethylene & Propylene.
Chem-Facts: Federal Republic of Germany.
Chem-Facts: Methanol.
Chem-Facts: Netherlands.
Chem-Facts: Polyethylene.
Chem-Facts: Polypropylene.
Chem-Facts: United Kingdom.
Chemical Abstracts - Section Groupings.
Chemical Business.
Chemical Business Bulletins (Series): Fertilizers.
Chemical Engineering Abstracts. *(CEAB)*
Chemical Hazards in Industry. *(CHIN)*
Chemical Industry Notes. *(CIND)*
Clinica.
Coal & Synfuels Technology.
Communications Daily.
Communications Week International.
Commuter - Regional Airline News.
Composites & Adhesives Newsletter.
Computer & Control Abstracts.
Computer Database. *(CMPT)*
Computer Fraud and Security Bulletin.
Computer Protocols.
Corporate Venturing News.
Cosmetic Insider's Report.
Country Forecasts.
Cumulative Index to Nursing & Allied Health Literature.
Currency Confidential.
Current Biotechnology Abstracts. *(CUBI)*
The Cyprus Review.
C2C Abstracts: Japan - Analytical Chemistry. *(JPTC)*
C2C Abstracts: Japan - Ceramics. *(JPTC)*
C2C Abstracts: Japan - Chemical Engineering. *(JPTC)*
C2C Abstracts: Japan - Crystallography. *(JPTC)*
C2C Abstracts: Japan - Hydrocarbons. *(JPTC)*
C2C Abstracts: Japan - Inorganic Chemistry. *(JPTC)*
C2C Abstracts: Japan - Materials Science. *(JPTC)*
C2C Abstracts: Japan - Metals. *(JPTC)*
C2C Abstracts: Japan - Organic Chemistry. *(JPTC)*
C2C Abstracts: Japan - Physical Chemistry. *(JPTC)*

C2C Abstracts: Japan - Plastics. *(JPTC)*
C2C Abstracts: Japan - Polymer Chemistry. *(JPTC)*
C2C Abstracts: Japan - Surface Chemistry. *(JPTC)*
C2C Abstracts: Japan - Textiles. *(JPTC)*
C2C Currents: Japan - Chemistry. *(JPTC)*
C2C Currents: Japan - Computers. *(JPTC)*
C2C Currents: Japan - Electronics. *(JPTC)*
C2C Currents: Japan - Materials. *(JPTC)*
Dealing with Technology.
Defense & Aerospace Electronics. *(PTBN)*
Defense Cleanup.
Defense Marketing International.
Defense Technology Business.
Devices & Diagnostics Letter.
Directory of Federal Laboratories.
Directory of Online Databases. *(CUAD)*
Directory of Portable Databases.
E C Energy Monthly.
East European Markets.
Economic Titles - Abstracts.
Einkaufs 1x1 der Deutschen Industrie.
Electrical & Electronics Abstracts.
Electronic Bookstore for Executives.
Electronic Office.
Energy Books Quarterly.
Energy Conservation News.
Energy Daily.
Energy Information Abstracts. *(ENER)*
Energy Information Abstracts Annual. *(ENER)*
Energy Report.
Engineering Index Annual.
Engineering Index Monthly.
Environment Abstracts. *(NVER; Acid Rain Abstracts NVAR)*
Environment Abstracts Annual. *(NVER/Acid Rain Abstracts NVAR)*
Environment Week.
Environmental Compliance Update.
The European Community.
European Directory of Agrochemical Products.
Eventline.
Excerpta Medica Abstract Journals.
Excerpta Medica. Section 1: Anatomy, Anthropology, Embryology & Histology.
Excerpta Medica. Section 2: Physiology.
Excerpta Medica. Section 3: Endocrinology.
Excerpta Medica. Section 4: Microbiology: Bacteriology, Mycology, Parasitology and Virology.
Excerpta Medica. Section 5: General Pathology and Pathological Anatomy.
Excerpta Medica. Section 6: Internal Medicine.
Excerpta Medica. Section 7: Pediatrics and Pediatric Surgery.
Excerpta Medica. Section 8: Neurology and Neurosurgery.
Excerpta Medica. Section 9: Surgery.
Excerpta Medica. Section 10: Obstetrics and Gynecology.
Excerpta Medica. Section 11: Otorhinolaryngology.
Excerpta Medica. Section 12: Ophthalmology.
Excerpta Medica. Section 13: Dermatology and Venereology.
Excerpta Medica. Section 14: Radiology.
Excerpta Medica. Section 15: Chest Diseases, Thoracic Surgery and Tuberculosis.
Excerpta Medica. Section 16: Cancer.
Excerpta Medica. Section 17: Public Health, Social Medicine & Epidemiology.
Excerpta Medica. Section 18: Cardiovascular Diseases and Cardiovascular Surgery.
Excerpta Medica. Section 19: Rehabilitation and Physical Medicine.
Excerpta Medica. Section 20: Gerontology and Geriatrics.
Excerpta Medica. Section 21: Developmental Biology and Teratology.
Excerpta Medica. Section 22: Human Genetics.
Excerpta Medica. Section 23: Nuclear Medicine.
Excerpta Medica. Section 24: Anesthesiology.
Excerpta Medica. Section 25: Hematology.
Excerpta Medica. Section 26: Immunology, Serology and Transplantation.
Excerpta Medica. Section 27: Biophysics, Bio-Engineering and Medical Instrumentation.
Excerpta Medica. Section 28: Urology and Nephrology.
Excerpta Medica. Section 29: Clinical and Experimental Biochemistry.
Excerpta Medica. Section 30: Clinical and Experimental Pharmacology.
Excerpta Medica. Section 31: Arthritis and Rheumatism.
Excerpta Medica. Section 32: Psychiatry.
Excerpta Medica. Section 33: Orthopedic Surgery.

Excerpta Medica. Section 35: Occupational Health and Industrial Medicine.
Excerpta Medica. Section 36: Health Policy, Economics and Management.
Excerpta Medica. Section 38: Adverse Reactions Titles.
Excerpta Medica. Section 40: Drug Dependence, Alcohol Abuse and Alcoholism.
Excerpta Medica. Section 46: Environmental Health and Pollution Control.
Excerpta Medica. Section 48: Gastroenterology.
Excerpta Medica. Section 49: Forensic Science Abstracts.
Excerpta Medica. Section 50: Epilepsy Abstracts.
Excerpta Medica. Section 52: Toxicology.
F D A Medical Bulletin.
F T C Freedom of Information Log.
F X Week.
Financial Regulation Report.
Financial Technology Insight.
Financial World.
Firmen der Neuen Bundeslaender.
Flight International.
Food and Drug Letter.
Food Chemical News.
Food Science and Technology Abstracts. *(FSTA)*
Future Home Technology News.
G M P Letter.
Gas Daily.
General Accounting Office Reports and Technology.
General Practitioner. *(GPGP)*
Genetic Technology News.
Global Environmental Change.
Going Public - The I P O Reporter.
Government Reports Announcements and Index Journal.
Ground Water Monitor. *(PTBN)*
Handbuch der Grossunternehmen.
Harvard Business Review. *(HBRO)*
Health Index. *(HLTH)*
Health News Daily.
Helicopter News.
High Performance Plastics.
High Tech Ceramics News.
High Tech Separations News.
Holland Exports.
I S D N News.
Imaging Update.
Independent Telco News.
Industrial Bioprocessing.
Industrial Health & Hazards Update.
Industrial Specialties News.
Industries in Transition.
Information Management Report. *(PTBN)*
Innovation.
Inside Market Data.
Integrated Circuits International.
Intelligent Network News.
International Coal Report.
International Country Risk Guide.
International Industrial Opportunities.
International Packaging Abstracts.
International Product Alert.
International Reports. *(FSRI)*
International Solar Energy Intelligence Report.
International Tax Report.
International Venture Capital Network.
Item Processing Report.
Japanese Investment in U S Real Estate Review.
Key Abstracts - Business Automation.
Key to Economic Science.
Korea Automotive Review.
L A N Product News.
Laboratory Hazards Bulletin. *(CSNB)*
Lasers in Medicine.
Lookout - Foods.
Mainframe Computing.
Management and Marketing Abstracts.
Management Contents. *(MGMT)*
Management Matters.
Marketing Research Review.
Marketletter.
Martindale: the Extra Pharmacopoeia.
Medeconomics.
Media Monitor.
Medical Devices, Diagnostics & Instrumentation Reports: The Gray Sheet.
Medical Science Research.
Medical Textiles.
Medical Waste News.
Membrane & Separation Technology News.
Metals Abstracts. *(META)*
Metals Abstracts Index. *(META)*
Mexico Service. *(FSRI)*
Microcell Report.
Military & Commercial Fiber Business.
Mims Magazine.

VENDOR LISTING/SERIALS ONLINE

Minority Markets Alert.
Mittelstaendische Unternehmen.
Mobile Communications.
Mobile Data Report: Business Intelligence on Radio-Based Information Networks.
Mobile Satellite Reports.
Modem User News.
Morgan Report on Directory Publishing. (PTBN)
N A S A Software Directory.
N C I Cancer Weekly.
N I S T Update.
N T I S Bibliographic Data Base.
National Report on Computers and Health.
Navy News & Undersea Technology.
Netline.
Network Management Systems & Strategies.
Networks Update.
New Materials - Japan.
New Media Markets.
New Technology Week.
Nonferrous Metals Alert. (MBUS)
Nonwovens Abstracts.
North Sea Letter.
Octane Week.
Oil Spill Intelligence Report.
Online Libraries and Microcomputers.
Online Newsletter.
Open: O S I Product and Equipment News.
Optical & Magnetic Report.
Optical Materials and Engineering News.
Oxy-Fuel News.
P A I S International in Print. (PAIS)
P C Business Products.
Paper Sales.
Personal Computer Markets.
Pesticide & Toxic Chemical News.
Petroleum-Energy Business News Index. (PEAB)
Pharmaceutical Business News.
Physics Abstracts.
Political Risk Yearbook. (FSRI)
Political Risk Yearbook. Volume 1: North & Central America. (FSRI)
Political Risk Yearbook. Volume 2: Middle East & North Africa. (FSRI)
Political Risk Yearbook. Volume 3: South America. (FSRI)
Political Risk Yearbook. Volume 4: Sub-Saharan Africa. (FSRI)
Political Risk Yearbook. Volume 5: Asia & the Pacific. (FSRI)
Political Risk Yearbook. Volume 6: Europe - Countries of the E C. (FSRI)
Political Risk Yearbook. Volume 7: Europe - Outside the E C. (FSRI)
Pollution Abstracts. (POLL)
Polymers, Ceramics, Composite Alert. (MBUS)
Power in Asia.
Power in Europe.
Predicasts Basebook.
Predicasts F & S Index Europe.
Predicasts F & S Index International.
Predicasts F & S Index United States.
Predicasts Forecasts. (PTFC)
Predicasts Overview of Markets and Technology.
Prescription and O T C Pharmaceuticals: The Pink Sheet.
Product Alert.
Productivity Software.
Psychological Abstracts. (PSYC)
Quick Response News.
R I S C Management.
Real Estate Investment Situations.
Research Alert (New York).
Research in Ministry.
Rig Market Forecast.
S M T Trends.
Sales Pro.
Science Citation Index.
Screen Digest.
Scrip - World Pharmaceutical News. (PHIND)
Sensor Review.
Sensor Technology.
Shopper Report.
Side Effects of Drugs Annual. (SEDB)
Social Planning - Policy & Development Abstracts. (SOCA)
Social Sciences Citation Index.
Sociological Abstracts. (SOCA)
Software Markets.
Soviet Aerospace & Technology.
Space Commerce Week.
Space Exploration Technology.
SportSearch.
Steels Alert. (MBUS)
Superconductor Week.
Superfund.
Takeover Targets.
Tele-Service News.

Telecom Markets.
Telecom Today.
Theoretical Chemical Engineering Abstracts.
Toiletries, Fragrances and Skin Care: The Rose Sheet. (FDCR)
Tour and Travel News.
Trading Systems Technology.
Turing Institute Abstracts in Artificial Intelligence.
UNIX Today.
Utility Reporter: Fuels Energy & Power.
Vaard i Norden.
Video News International.
Video Technology News.
Voice Technology News.
Washington Drug Letter (Washington, 1979).
Waste Information Digests.
Wer Baut Maschinen und Anlagen.
Wer Liefert Was?
Wing Newsletter.
Working Papers in Business.
World Accounting Report.
Worldcasts: Product Edition.
Worldcasts: Regional Edition.
Worldwide Biotech.
Worldwide Databases.
Worldwide Telecom.
Worldwide Videotex Update.
Youth Markets Alert.
Z V E I Elektro und Elektronik - Einkaufsfuehrer.
411 Newsletter. (PTBN)

DIALOG INFORMATION SERVICES, INC. (Subsidiary of: Knight-Ridder, Inc.)
3460 Hillview Ave., Palo Alto, CA 94304. Tel: 415-858-2700 Telex: 334499 DIALOG
Fax: 415-858-7069.
A B A Banking Journal. (File no.648)
A B B Review.
A B I - INFORM. (File no.15)
A C M Guide to Computing Literature.
A D R I D.
A F L - C I O News.
A I Expert. (File no.675)
A P F Reporter.
A S F A Aquaculture Abstracts. (File no.44)
A S F A Marine Biotechnology Abstracts. (File no. 44 and 76)
Abstracts in BioCommerce. (File no.286)
Abstracts in Medicine and Key Word Index. (File 219)
Academic Index. (File no.88)
Academy of Marketing Science. Journal.
Accent on Living. (File no.149)
Administrative Management (New York).
Administrative Science Quarterly.
Advanced Ceramics Report. (File no.636)
Advanced Coatings & Surface Technology. (File no.636)
Advanced Composites Bulletin. (File no.636)
Advanced Manufacturing Technology.
Advanced Recovery Week.
Adweek (Los Angeles). (File no.648)
Adweek (New York). (File no.648)
Adweek's Marketing Week. (File no.648)
Aerospace Daily. (File nos.624,648)
Aerospace Financial News.
Affluent Markets Alert.
Aftermarket Business.
Agribusiness Worldwide. (File no.648)
Agricultural Engineering Abstracts.
Agricultural Supply Industry. (File no.648)
Agrindex. (File no.203)
Agrochemicals Handbook. (File no.306)
Agroforestry Abstracts.
Agroindex - Automated Information System.
Agrow.
Air Conditioning, Heating & Refrigeration News. (File no.648)
Air Safety Week.
Air Transport World.
Air - Water Pollution Report.
Airline Financial News.
Airports. (File no.624/McGRAW-HILL PULICATIONS ONLINE)
Alaska Business Monthly.
Alaska Journal of Commerce & Pacific Rim Reporter.
Alliance Alert.
Alloys Index. (File no.32/METADEX)
Alternative Energy Digests.
America: History and Life. Articles Abstract and Citations of Reviews and Dissertations Covering the United States and Canada. (File no.38)
American Banker. (File no.625)
American Demographics.
American Doctoral Dissertations. (File no.35)

American Fitness. (File no.149)
American Heritage.
American Hospital Formulary Service Drug Information. (File no.229)
American Libraries.
American Library Directory. (File no.460)
American Men and Women of Science. (File no.236)
American Metal Market.
American Review of Public Administration.
American Salesman.
American Statistics Index. (File no.102)
Amusement Business.
Analytical Abstracts. (File no.305)
Animal Behavior Abstracts. (File no.76/LIFE SCIENCES COLLECTION)
Animal Breeding Abstracts.
Animal Disease Occurrence.
Animal Pharm.
Apicultural Abstracts.
Apparel Industry Magazine.
Appliance Manufacturer.
Applied Genetics News.
Aqualine Abstracts.
Aquatic Sciences & Fisheries Abstracts. Part 1: Biological Sciences and Living Resources. (File no.44)
Aquatic Sciences & Fisheries Abstracts. Part 2: Ocean Technology, Policy and Non-Living Resources. (File no.44)
Aquatic Sciences & Fisheries Abstracts. Part 3: Aquatic Pollution and Environmental Quality. (File no.44)
Architectural Periodicals Index. (File no.179)
Arizona Business Gazette.
Arkansas Business and Economic Review.
Artbibliographies Modern. (File no.56)
Arts & Humanities Citation Index. (File no.439)
Asbestos Control Report.
Asia - Pacific Forecasting Service.
Atlanta Business Chronicle.
Atlantic.
Atlantic Economic Journal.
Audio Week.
Audiocassette Finder. (File no.46)
Audiotex Update.
Austin Business Journal.
Australian Journal of Dairy Technology. (File nos.50 & 53)
Automotive Industries.
Autoparts Report.
Avery Index to Architectural Periodicals.
Aviation Daily. (File no.624/McGRAW-HILL PUBLICATIONS ONLINE)
Aviation Week & Space Technology. (File no.624/McGRAW-HILL PUBLICATIONS ONLINE)
The B B I Newsletter.
B C Business.
B H A. (File no.191, Art Literature International)
B N A Labor Relations Reporter. (Laborlaw, File 244)
B N A Labor Relations Reporter. Labor Arbitration.
B N A Policy and Practice Series. Fair Employment Practices.
B O C Week.
B P Report.
Backpacker.
Bakery Production and Marketing.
Baltimore Business Journal.
Battery & E V Technology News.
Beilsteins Handbuch der Organischen Chemie. Supplement. (File no.390)
Best's Review. Life - Health Insurance Edition.
Best's Review. Property - Casualty Insurance Edition.
Beverage World (English Edition).
Bibliography and Index of Geology.
Bibliography of Economic Geology.
Billboard (New York).
Biocontrol News and Information.
Biodeterioration Abstracts.
Biography and Genealogy Master Index. (File nos.287,288)
Biological Abstracts. (File nos.5 & 55)
Biological Abstracts - R R M. (File nos.5 & 55)
Biomedical Materials.
Biotech Business.
Biotechnology Research Abstracts. (File no.76/LIFE SCIENCES COLLECTION)
Boating.
Boating Industry.
Bond Buyer. (File no.626)
Book Review Index. (File no.137)
Book World.
Books in Print. (File no.470)
Books in Print Supplement. (File no.470)
Books Out-of-Print. (File no.470)

Boston Business Journal.
The Bowker Annual Library and Book Trade Almanac.
Boys' Life (Inkprint Edition).
Branch Automation News.
Brands and Their Companies.
Brazil Service.
British Education Index. *(File no.121)*
Broadcasting (Washington).
Building Design & Construction.
Building Supply Home Centers.
Buildings.
Bulletin of Entomological Research.
Business America.
Business and Commercial Aviation.
Business and the Environment.
Business Asia.
Business Atlanta.
Business Aviation Weekly. *(File no.624/McGRAW-HILL PUBLICATIONS ONLINE)*
Business Digest of Delaware Valley.
Business Digest of Lehigh Valley.
Business Eastern Europe.
Business Europe.
Business First.
Business History Review.
Business Horizons.
Business Index. *(File no.148)*
Business International.
Business International Money Report.
Business Journal (Phoenix).
Business Journal Serving Greater Milwaukee.
Business Latin America.
Business New Hampshire Magazine.
Business: North Carolina.
Business Quarterly.
Business Record.
Business Travel News.
Business Week. *(File no.624/McGRAW-HILL PUBLICATIONS ONLINE)*
Buyouts.
Byte. *(File no.624/McGRAW-HILL PUBLICATIONS ONLINE)*
C.A.B. International Bureau of Agricultural Economics. Annotated Bibliographies Series A.
C.A.B. International Bureau of Agricultural Economics. Annotated Bibliographies. Series B: Agricultural Policy and Rural Development in Africa.
C.A.B. International. Bureau of Nutrition. Annotated Bibliographies.
C.A.B. International. Bureau of Soils. Annotated Bibliographies.
C A S E Strategies.
C D C - A I D S Weekly. *(file no.636)*
C D Computing News.
C D - R O M Databases.
C D - R O M Librarian.
C D - R O M Professional. *(File no.170)*
C I C's State School Directories.
C I S Index. *(File no.101)*
C M I Descriptions of Fungi and Bacteria.
The C P A Journal.
C S A Neurosciences Abstracts. *(File no.76/LIFE SCIENCES COLLECTION)*
C S I Congressional Record Abstracts: Master Edition.
C S I Federal Index. *(File no.20)*
C S I Federal Register Abstracts: Master Edition.
Calcified Tissue Abstracts. *(File no.76/LIFE SCIENCES COLLECTION)*
California Business.
Cambridge Scientific Biochemistry Abstracts: Part 1. Biological Membranes. *(File no.76/LIFE SCIENCES COLLECTION)*
Cambridge Scientific Biochemistry Abstracts: Part 2. Nucleic Acids. *(File no.76/LIFE SCIENCES COLLECTION)*
Cambridge Scientific Biochemistry Abstracts: Part 3. Amino-Acids, Peptides & Proteins. *(File no.76/LIFE SCIENCES COLLECTION)*
Canadian Business Index. *(File no.262)*
Canadian Business Review.
Canadian Magazine Index. *(File no.262)*
Canadian News Index. *(File no.262)*
Capital District Business Review.
Car and Driver.
Card News.
Central America Update.
Central America Update.
Central New York Business Journal.
Ceramic Abstracts. *(File no.335)*
Chem-Facts: Ammonia.
Chem-Facts: Belgium.
Chem-Facts: Ethylene & Propylene.
Chem-Facts: Federal Republic of Germany.
Chem-Facts: Methanol.
Chem-Facts: Netherlands.

Chem-Facts: Polypropylene.
Chemical Abstracts - Section Groupings. *(CA SEARCH)*
Chemical Business Bulletins (Series): Fertilizers.
Chemical Engineering. *(File no.624/McGRAW-HILL PUBLICATIONS ONLINE)*
Chemical Engineering Abstracts. *(File no.315)*
Chemical Hazards in Industry. *(File no.317)*
Chemical Industry Notes. *(File no.19)*
Chemical Marketing Reporter.
Chemoreception Abstracts. *(File no.76/LIFE SCIENCES COLLECTION)*
Children Today.
Children's Books in Print. *(File no.470)*
Chilton's Automotive Marketing.
Chilton's Distribution Magazine.
Chilton's Food Engineering.
Chilton's Food Engineering International.
Chilton's Hardware Age.
Chilton's Jewelers' Circular-Keystone.
Chilton's Motor Age.
China Business Review.
China Today.
Ching Feng.
Choices (New York).
Christian Science Monitor Index.
Chronicle of Latin American Economic Affairs.
Civil Engineering Hydraulics Abstracts. *(File no.96/FLUIDEX)*
Clean Coal - Synfuels Letter. *(File no.624/McGRAW-HILL PUBLICATIONS ONLINE)*
Clinica.
Coal & Synfuels Technology.
Coal Outlook.
Coal Week. *(File no.624/McGRAW-HILL PUBLICATIONS ONLINE)*
Coal Week International. *(File no.624/McGRAW-HILL PUBLICATIONS ONLINE)*
Colorado Business.
Columbus Business Journal.
Commerce Business Daily. *(File nos.194 & 195)*
Common Carrier Week.
Communication World.
Communications Daily.
Communications News.
Communications Week International.
Commuter - Regional Airline News.
Companies and Their Brands.
Compensation and Benefits Review.
Composites & Adhesives Newsletter.
Computer-Aided Engineering.
Computer-Aided Process Control Abstracts. *(File no. 96)*
Computer & Control Abstracts. *(File nos.2,3 & 4/INSPEC)*
Computer Book Review.
Computer Database. *(File no.275)*
Computer Design.
Computer Fraud and Security Bulletin.
Computer Graphics World.
Computer Language.
Computer Pictures.
Computer Protocols.
Computer - Readable Databases. *(File no.230)*
Computers in Banking.
Computers in Healthcare.
Computerworld. *(File no.674)*
Computing Reviews.
Conference Papers Annual Index. *(File no. 77)*
Conference Papers Index. *(File no.77)*
Construction Equipment.
Construction Review.
Consumer Reports. *(File no.646)*
Consumer Reports on Health. *(File no.646)*
Consumer Reports Travel Letter. *(File no.646)*
Controls and Systems.
Corporate Cleveland.
Corporate Detroit Magazine.
Corporate E F T Report.
Corporate Report Minnesota.
Corporate Venturing News.
Cosmetic Insider's Report.
Cotton and Tropical Fibres.
Country Forecasts.
Country Profiles.
Country Reports.
Courier (Paris).
Crain's Chicago Business.
Crain's Cleveland Business.
Crain's Detroit Business.
Crain's New York Business.
Cranberries.
Criminal Justice Periodical Index. *(File no.171)*
Crop Physiology Abstracts.
Cumulative Index to Nursing & Allied Health Literature. *(File no. 218)*
Currency Confidential.
Current Biotechnology Abstracts. *(File no.358)*

Current Business Reports: Monthly Retail Trade, Sales and Inventories.
Current Business Reports: Monthly Wholesale Trade: Sales and Inventories.
Current Construction Reports.
Current Construction Reports: Housing Starts.
Current Construction Reports: Housing Units Authorized by Building Permits.
Current Construction Reports: New One-Family Houses Sold and for Sale.
Current Construction Reports: Value of New Construction Put in Place.
Current Contents: Agriculture, Biology & Environmental Sciences. *(File no.440)*
Current Contents: Arts & Humanities. *(File no.440)*
Current Contents: Clinical Medicine. *(File no.440)*
Current Contents: Engineering, Technology & Applied Sciences. *(File no.440)*
Current Contents: Life Sciences. *(File no.440)*
Current Contents: Physical, Chemical & Earth Sciences. *(File no.440)*
Current Contents: Social & Behavioral Sciences. *(File no.440)*
Current Digest of the Post-Soviet Press. *(File no.645)*
Current Governments Reports: City Employment.
Current Governments Reports: County Government Employment.
Current Governments Reports: Government Finances.
Current Governments Reports: Public Employment.
Current Governments Reports: State Government Tax Collections.
Current History.
Current Housing Reports.
Current Housing Reports: Housing Characteristics.
Current Housing Reports: Housing Vacancies.
Current Index to Journals in Education. *(File no.1/ERIC)*
Current Index to Statistics.
Current Industrial Reports: Broadwoven Fabrics (Gray).
Current Industrial Reports: Fats and Oils. Oilseed Crushings.
Current Industrial Reports: Fats and Oils. Production, Consumption, and Stocks.
Current Law Index.
Current Mathematical Publications.
Current Physics Index.
Current Population Reports: Consumer Income. Money Income of Households, Families and Persons in the United States (Year).
Current Population Reports: Local Population Estimates.
Current Population Reports: Population Characteristics. Geographical Mobility.
Current Population Reports: Population Characteristics. Marital Status and Living Arrangements.
Current Population Reports: Population Characteristics. School Enrollment: Social and Economic Characteristics of Students.
Current Population Reports: Population Estimates and Projections.
Current Population Reports: Population Estimates and Projections. United States Population Estimates by Age, Sex, Race and Hispanic Origin.
Current Research in Library & Information Science. *(File no.61)*
Current Technology Index. *(File no.142)*
The Cyprus Review.
C2C Abstracts: Japan - Analytical Chemistry. *(File no.582)*
C2C Abstracts: Japan - Ceramics. *(File no.582)*
C2C Abstracts: Japan - Chemical Engineering. *(File no.582)*
C2C Abstracts: Japan - Crystallography. *(File no.582)*
C2C Abstracts: Japan - Hydrocarbons. *(File no.582)*
C2C Abstracts: Japan - Inorganic Chemistry. *(File no.582)*
C2C Abstracts: Japan - Materials Science. *(File no.582)*
C2C Abstracts: Japan - Metals. *(File no.582)*
C2C Abstracts: Japan - Organic Chemistry. *(File no.582)*
C2C Abstracts: Japan - Physical Chemistry. *(File no.582)*
C2C Abstracts: Japan - Plastics. *(File no.582)*
C2C Abstracts: Japan - Polymer Chemistry. *(File no.582)*
C2C Abstracts: Japan - Surface Chemistry. *(File no.582)*

VENDOR LISTING/SERIALS ONLINE

C2C Abstracts: Japan - Textiles. *(File no.582)*
C2C Currents: Japan - Chemistry. *(File no.582)*
C2C Currents: Japan - Computers. *(File no.582)*
C2C Currents: Japan - Electronics. *(File no.582)*
C2C Currents: Japan - Materials. *(File no.582)*
D G Review.
Daily News Record.
Dairy Foods.
Dairy Science Abstracts.
Dallas - Fort Worth Business Journal.
Data Based Advisor.
Data Channels.
Data Communications. *(File no.624/McGRAW-HILL PUBLICATIONS ONLINE)*
Database (Weston). *(File no.170)*
Database Searcher.
Datamation.
Dealerscope Merchandising.
Dealing with Technology.
Defense & Aerospace Electronics. *(File nos.636,648)*
Defense Cleanup.
Defense Daily.
Defense Electronics.
Defense Marketing International.
Defense Technology Business.
Denver Business.
Denver Post Index.
Detroit News Index.
Devices & Diagnostics Letter.
Digital Review.
Directories in Print.
Directory of Corporate Affiliations. *(File no.513)*
Directory of Leading Private Companies, Including Corporate Affiliations. *(File no. 513)*
Directory of Research Grants.
Discount Store News.
Discover (Burbank).
Dissertation Abstracts.
Dissertation Abstracts International. Section A: Humanities and Social Sciences. *(File no.35)*
Dissertation Abstracts International. Section B: Physical Sciences and Engineering. *(File no.35)*
Dissertation Abstracts International. Section C: Worldwide. *(File no.35)*
Distribution.
Doing Business with Eastern Europe.
Drug and Cosmetic Industry.
Drug Topics.
Drugs in Prospect.
Drugs in Research.
Drugs in Use.
Dutchess County Historical Society. Yearbook.
E D N Magazine.
E F T Report.
E N R. *(File no.624/McGRAW-HILL PUBLICATIONS ONLINE)*
East European Industrial Monitor.
Ecological Abstracts. *(File no.292)*
Ecology Abstracts. *(File no.76/LIFE SCIENCES COLLECTION)*
Economic Indicators (Washington).
Economic Inquiry.
Economic Titles - Abstracts.
Economist.
Educational Marketer.
Electric Utility Week. *(File no.624/McGRAW-HILL PUBLICATIONS ONLINE)*
Electrical & Electronics Abstracts. *(File nos.2,3 & 4/INSPEC)*
Electronic Business.
Electronic Design.
Electronic Learning.
Electronic News.
Electronics. *(File no.624/McGRAW-HILL PUBLICATIONS ONLINE)*
Employee Relations Law Journal.
Encyclopedia of Associations. *(File no.114)*
Energy Books Quarterly.
Energy Conservation News.
Energy Daily.
Energy Data Base.
Energy Information Abstracts. *(File no.69)*
Energy Information Abstracts Annual. *(File no.69)*
Energy Report.
Energy User News.
Engineered Materials Abstracts. *(File no.293)*
Engineering Index Annual. *(File no.8)*
Engineering Index Monthly. *(File no.8)*
Enhanced Services Outlook.
Entomology Abstracts. *(File no.76/LIFE SCIENCES COLLECTION)*
Environment Abstracts. *(File no.40)*
Environment Abstracts Annual. *(File no.40)*
Environment Week.
Environmental Periodicals Bibliography.
Epiphany Journal.
Euromoney.

European Directory of Agrochemical Products. *(File no.316)*
Eventline.
Exceptional Child Education Resources. *(File no.54)*
Excerpta Medica Abstract Journals.
Excerpta Medica. Section 1: Anatomy, Anthropology, Embryology & Histology.
Excerpta Medica. Section 2: Physiology.
Excerpta Medica. Section 3: Endocrinology.
Excerpta Medica. Section 4: Microbiology: Bacteriology, Mycology, Parasitology and Virology.
Excerpta Medica. Section 5: General Pathology and Pathological Anatomy.
Excerpta Medica. Section 6: Internal Medicine.
Excerpta Medica. Section 7: Pediatrics and Pediatric Surgery.
Excerpta Medica. Section 8: Neurology and Neurosurgery.
Excerpta Medica. Section 9: Surgery.
Excerpta Medica. Section 10: Obstetrics and Gynecology.
Excerpta Medica. Section 11: Otorhinolaryngology.
Excerpta Medica. Section 12: Ophthalmology.
Excerpta Medica. Section 13: Dermatology and Venereology.
Excerpta Medica. Section 14: Radiology.
Excerpta Medica. Section 15: Chest Diseases, Thoracic Surgery and Tuberculosis.
Excerpta Medica. Section 16: Cancer.
Excerpta Medica. Section 17: Public Health, Social Medicine & Epidemiology.
Excerpta Medica. Section 18: Cardiovascular Diseases and Cardiovascular Surgery.
Excerpta Medica. Section 19: Rehabilitation and Physical Medicine.
Excerpta Medica. Section 20: Gerontology and Geriatrics.
Excerpta Medica. Section 21: Developmental Biology and Teratology.
Excerpta Medica. Section 22: Human Genetics.
Excerpta Medica. Section 23: Nuclear Medicine.
Excerpta Medica. Section 24: Anesthesiology.
Excerpta Medica. Section 25: Hematology.
Excerpta Medica. Section 26: Immunology, Serology and Transplantation.
Excerpta Medica. Section 27: Biophysics, Bio-Engineering and Medical Instrumentation.
Excerpta Medica. Section 28: Urology and Nephrology.
Excerpta Medica. Section 29: Clinical and Experimental Biochemistry.
Excerpta Medica. Section 30: Clinical and Experimental Pharmacology.
Excerpta Medica. Section 31: Arthritis and Rheumatism.
Excerpta Medica. Section 32: Psychiatry.
Excerpta Medica. Section 33: Orthopedic Surgery.
Excerpta Medica. Section 35: Occupational Health and Industrial Medicine.
Excerpta Medica. Section 36: Health Policy, Economics and Management.
Excerpta Medica. Section 38: Adverse Reactions Titles.
Excerpta Medica. Section 40: Drug Dependence, Alcohol Abuse and Alcoholism.
Excerpta Medica. Section 46: Environmental Health and Pollution Control.
Excerpta Medica. Section 48: Gastroenterology.
Excerpta Medica. Section 49: Forensic Science Abstracts.
Excerpta Medica. Section 50: Epilepsy Abstracts.
Excerpta Medica. Section 52: Toxicology.
Executive Report.
F A S Report: Weekly Roundup of World Production and Trade.
F C C Week.
F D A Consumer.
F D A Medical Bulletin.
F T C Freedom of Information Log.
F T C: Watch.
F X Week.
Faba Bean Abstracts.
Facts on File World News Digest With Index. *(File no.264)*
Family Relations.
Federal Register. *(File no.669)*
Federal Research in Progress Database. *(File nos.265,266)*
Federal Reserve Bank of New York. Quarterly Review.
Federal Reserve Bulletin.
Fiber Optics News.
Field Crop Abstracts.
Film & Video Finder. *(File no.46)*
Financial Executive.

Financial Technology Insight.
Financial Times World Shipping Yearbook.
Financial Times World Tax Report.
Financial World.
Financing Foreign Operations: Global Edition.
Findex. *(File no.196)*
Firmen der Neuen Bundeslaender.
Florida Business - Southwest.
Florida Trend.
Flower and Garden.
Fluid Flow Measurement Abstracts. *(File no.96/FLUIDEX)*
Fluid Sealing Abstracts. *(File no.96/FLUIDEX)*
Flying.
Folio (Stamford).
Food and Drug Letter.
Food Chemical News.
Food, Cosmetics and Drugs Packaging.
Food Science and Technology Abstracts. *(File no.51)*
Foods Adlibra. *(File no.79)*
Footwear News.
Forbes.
Forecast (New York).
Foreign Trade Reports. U.S. Export and Import Merchandise Trade and Supplement.
Forest Industries.
Forest Products Abstracts.
Forestry Abstracts.
Forestry Abstracts. Leading Article Reprint Series.
Forthcoming Books. *(File no.470)*
Foundation Directory.
Foundation Grants Index.
Foundry Management & Technology.
From the State Capitals. Labor Relations.
Fund Raising Management.
Fusion Power Report.
Future Home Technology News.
The Futurist.
G M P Letter.
Gale Directory of Publications and Broadcast Media.
Gas Daily.
Genetic Technology News.
Genetics Abstracts. *(File no.76/LIFE SCIENCES COLLECTION)*
Geographical Abstracts: Human Geography. *(File no.292)*
Geographical Abstracts: Physical Geography. *(File no.292)*
Geological Abstracts. *(File no.292)*
Geological Society of India. Journal. *(File no.89)*
Georgia Trend.
Geoscience Documentation.
Geotitles.
Gifts & Decorative Accessories.
Global Environmental Change.
Going Public - The I P O Reporter.
Government Computer News.
Government Product News.
Government Reports Announcements and Index Journal. *(File no.6)*
Government Research Directory.
Grand Rapids Business Journal.
Graphic Arts Monthly.
Green Markets. *(File no.624/McGRAW-HILL PUBLICATIONS ONLINE)*
Ground Water Monitor.
Guns & Ammo.
H F D - Retailing Home Furnishings.
Handbook on Injectable Drugs. *(File no.229)*
Handbuch der Grossunternehmen.
Hangzhou Daxue Xuebao (Ziran Kexue Ban).
Harvard Business Review. *(File no.122)*
Hawaii Business.
Hazardous Waste News.
Health Devices Alerts. *(File no.198)*
Health Devices Sourcebook. *(File no.188)*
Health Index. *(File no.149)*
Health News Daily.
Healthcare Financial Management.
Helicopter News.
Helminthological Abstracts.
Herbage Abstracts.
Hewlett-Packard Journal.
High Performance Plastics.
High Performance Textiles.
High Tech Ceramics News.
High Tech Separations News.
Highway & Heavy Construction Products.
Historical Abstracts. Part A: Modern History Abstracts, 1450-1914. *(File no.39)*
Historical Abstracts. Part B: Twentieth Century Abstracts, 1914 to the Present. *(File no.39)*
Horticultural Abstracts.
Hospitalis.
Hospitals.
Hot Rod.

VENDOR LISTING/SERIALS ONLINE 5117

Houston Business Journal.
Houston Post Index.
Human Genome Abstracts. *(File no.76)*
Hydraulics & Pneumatics.
Hypatia. *(File no. 57)*
I C O Library Monthly Entries - Coffeeline. *(File no.164)*
I D P Report.
I S D N News.
I S M E C: Mechanical Engineering Abstracts. *(File no.14)*
Illinois Business Review.
Imaging Update.
Immunology Abstracts. *(File no.76/LIFE SCIENCES COLLECTION)*
Implement & Tractor.
Inc.
Independent Power Report. *(File no.624/McGRAW-HILL PUBLICATIONS ONLINE)*
Independent Telco News.
Index Medicus. *(File nos.154 & 155/MEDLINE)*
Index of Current Research on Pigs.
Index of Economic Articles in Journals and Collective Volumes. *(File no.139)*
Index of Fungi.
Index to Book Reviews in Religion. *(File no.190)*
Index to Dental Literature. *(File nos.154 & 155/MEDLINE)*
Index Veterinarius.
Indiana Business.
Indianapolis Business Journal.
Industrial Aerodynamics Abstracts. *(File no.96/FLUIDEX)*
Industrial and Labor Relations Review.
Industrial Bioprocessing.
Industrial Communications.
Industrial Corrosion Abstracts. *(File no. 96)*
Industrial Distribution.
Industrial Energy Bulletin. *(File no.624/McGRAW HIL- PUBLICATIONS ONLINE)*
Industrial Engineering.
Industrial Finishing.
Industrial Health.
Industrial Health & Hazards Update.
Industrial Researcher.
Industrial Specialties News.
Industries in Transition.
Industry Week.
Information Management Report. *(File no.636)*
Information Science Abstracts. *(File no.202)*
Informatique et Sciences Juridiques.
Ingram's Magazine.
Innovation.
Inside Energy With Federal Lands. *(File no.624/McGRAW-HILL PUBLICATIONS ONLINE)*
Inside F.E.R.C. *(File no.624/McGRAW-HILL PUBLICATIONS ONLINE)*
Inside F E R C's Gas Market Report. *(File no.624/McGRAW-HILL PUBLICATIONS ONLINE)*
Inside Market Data.
Inside N R C. *(File no.624/McGRAW-HILL PUBLICATIONS ONLINE)*
Inside R & D.
Institute of Muslim Minority Affairs. Journal.
Institute of Paper Science and Technology. Abstract Bulletin. *(File nos.240 & 840/PAPERCHEM)*
Institutional Distribution.
Instrumentation and Control Systems.
Insurance Periodicals Index. *(File no.169)*
Integrated Circuits International.
Integrated Waste Management. *(File no. 624/McGRAW-HILL PUBLICATIONS ONLINE)*
Intelligent Network News.
Interavia: Aerospace Review.
Interior Design.
International Aerospace Abstracts. *(File no.108)*
International Biodeterioration.
International Country Risk Guide.
International Defense Review.
International Development Abstracts. *(File no.292)*
International Directory of Brands and Their Companies.
International Directory of Corporate Affiliations. *(File no. 513)*
International Journal of Purchasing & Materials Management.
International Journal of Supercomputer Applications.
International Nursing Index. *(File nos.154 & 155/MEDLINE)*
International Pharmaceutical Abstracts. *(File no.74)*
International Population Data.
International Product Alert.
International Research Centers Directory.

International Solar Energy Intelligence Report.
Iron Age.
Irrigation and Drainage Abstracts.
Item Processing Report.
Jane's Airport Review.
Jane's Defence Weekly.
Jane's Intelligence Review.
Japanese Investment in U S Real Estate Review.
Journal of Commerce and Commercial.
Journal of Consumer Affairs.
Journal of Consumer Research.
Journal of Economic Literature. *(Economic Literature Index File no. 139)*
Journal of Mormon History. *(File nos.38,39)*
Journal of Psychology and Theology.
Journal of Retailing.
Journal of Risk and Insurance.
Journal of Technology Transfer.
Kaleidoscope: Current World Data.
Kansas Business News.
Kentucky Business Ledger.
Key Abstracts - Business Automation. *(File nos.12 & 13/INSPEC)*
Key to Economic Science.
Kiplinger's Personal Finance.
Korea Automotive Review.
L A N Product News.
L A N Times.
Labor Arbitration and Dispute Settlements. *(File no.244)*
Laboratory Hazards Bulletin. *(File no.317)*
Ladies Home Journal (Inkprint Edition).
Lasers in Medicine.
Legal Resource Index. *(File no.150)*
Leisure, Recreation and Tourism Abstracts.
Lentils.
Library & Information Science Abstracts. *(File no.61/LISA)*
Life (New York).
Linguistics and Language Behavior Abstracts. *(File no.36/LLBA)*
Literature Abstracts.
Literature Abstracts: Catalysts & Catalysis.
Lodging Hospitality.
London Business Monthly Magazine.
Lookout - Foods.
Los Angeles Times Index.
Louisville Magazine.
M L A International Bibliography of Books and Articles on the Modern Languages and Literatures.
McGraw-Hill's Biotechnology Newswatch. *(File no.624/McGRAW-HILL PUBLICATIONS ONLINE)*
Machine Design.
Magazine Index. *(File no.47)*
Magill's Cinema Annual.
Mainframe Computing.
Maize Abstracts.
Management and Marketing Abstracts.
Management Contents. *(File no.75)*
Management Matters.
Martindale: the Extra Pharmacopoeia. *(File no.141)*
Maryland. Police and Correctional Training Commissions. Report to the Governor, the Secretary of Public Safety and Correctional Services, and Members of the General Assembly.
Maryland Business & Living Journal.
Masters Abstracts International. *(File no.35)*
Materials Business Information. *(File no.269)*
Materials Information Translations Service.
Mathematical Reviews.
Media Week.
Medical and Health Care Books and Serials in Print.
Medical Devices, Diagnostics & Instrumentation Reports: The Gray Sheet. *(File no.187)*
Medical Economics.
Medical Textiles.
Medical Waste News.
Meetings and Conventions.
Membrane & Separation Technology News.
Memphis Business Journal.
Mercer Business Magazine.
Merck Index: An Encyclopedia of Chemicals and Drugs.
Metals Abstracts. *(File no.32/METADEX)*
Metals Abstracts Index. *(File no.32/METADEX)*
Metals Week. *(File no.624/McGRAW-HILL PUBLICATIONS ONLINE)*
Meteorological and Geoastrophysical Abstracts. *(File no.29)*
Metropolitan Toronto Business Journal.
Mexico Service.

Microbiology Abstracts: Section A. Industrial & Applied Microbiology. *(File no.76/LIFE SCIENCES COLLECTION)*
Microbiology Abstracts: Section B. Bacteriology. *(File no.76/LIFE SCIENCES COLLECTION)*
Microbiology Abstracts: Section C. Algology, Mycology and Protozoology. *(File no.76/LIFE SCIENCES COLLECTION)*
Microcell Report.
Microcomputer Index. *(File no. 233)*
Military & Commercial Fiber Business.
Military Robotics Newsletter. *(NL0650)*
Military Specifications and Standards Services Numeric Index.
Million Dollar Directory Series. *(File no.517)*
Mineralogical Abstracts. *(File no.292)*
Minority Markets Alert.
Mittelstaendische Unternehmen.
Mixing and Separation Technology Abstracts. *(File no. 96)*
Mobile Data Report: Business Intelligence on Radio-Based Information Networks.
Mobile Satellite Reports.
Modem User News.
Modern Bride.
Modern Office Technology.
Modern Tire Dealer.
Money.
Monthly Catalog of United States Government Publications. *(File no.66)*
Monthly Index to the Financial Times.
Morgan Report on Directory Publishing. *(File no.636)*
Motor Trend.
Mount Sinai Journal of Medicine.
Multimedia and Videodisc Monitor.
MuniWeek. *(File no.626)*
N C I Cancer Weekly.
N C J R S Document Retrieval Index.
N I O S H T I C Database.
N T I S Bibliographic Data Base.
Nashville Business and Lifestyles. *(File no.635)*
National Data Book of Foundations.
National Newspaper Index. *(File no.111)*
National Petroleum News.
National Report on Computers and Health.
National Review.
Nation's Business.
Nation's Restaurant News.
Natural History.
Navy News & Undersea Technology.
Nematological Abstracts.
Netline.
Network Management Systems & Strategies.
Network World. *(File no.674)*
Networks Update.
New Hampshire Business Review.
New Leader.
New Materials - Japan.
New Mexico Business Journal.
New Orleans Business.
New Orleans CityBusiness.
New Republic.
New Technology Week.
Newsletters in Print.
Nonferrous Metals Alert. *(File no.269)*
Nonwovens Abstracts.
NuclearFuel. *(File no.624/McGRAW-HILL PUBLICATIONS ONLINE)*
Nucleonics Week. *(File no.624/McGRAW-HILL PUBLICATIONS ONLINE)*
Nursing Homes and Senior Citizen Care.
Nutrition Abstracts and Reviews. Series A: Human and Experimental.
Nutrition Abstracts and Reviews. Series B: Livestock Feeds and Feeding.
O & M Intelligence. *(File no.587/DMS DEFENSE NEWSLETTERS)*
Oakland Business Monthly.
Occasional Papers on Religion in Eastern Europe.
Occupational Safety & Health Reporter. *(Laborlaw, File 244)*
Oceanic Abstracts. *(File no.28)*
Octane Week.
Offshore Engineering Abstracts. *(File no.96/FLUIDEX)*
Oil Daily.
Oil Spill Intelligence Report.
Oncogenes and Growth Factors Abstracts. *(File no.76)*
Online (Weston). *(File no 170)*
Online Libraries and Microcomputers.
Online Newsletter.
Open: O S I Product and Equipment News.
Opportunities Briefing.
Optical & Magnetic Report.
Optical Materials and Engineering News.
Orange County Business Journal.

VENDOR LISTING/SERIALS ONLINE

Ornamental Horticulture.
Outdoor Life.
Outlook (Year) Proceedings.
Oxy-Fuel News.
P A I S International in Print. *(File no.49/PAIS)*
P A S C A L Explore. E 30: Microscopie Electronique et Diffraction Electronique.
P C Business Products.
P C Magazin.
P C Week.
P N I.
Pacific Business News.
Packaging Science and Technology Abstracts. *(File no.252)*
Paper Sales.
Paperbound Books in Print. *(File no.470)*
Patient Care.
Performance Materials. *(File no.624/McGRAW-HILL PUBLICATIONS ONLINE)*
Personal Computer.
Personalist Forum.
Pesticide & Toxic Chemical News.
Petersen's Photographic.
Peterson's Guide to Four-Year Colleges (Year). *(File no.214)*
Peterson's Guide to Graduate and Professional Programs: An Overview (Year) (Book 1). *(File no.273)*
Peterson's Guide to Graduate Programs in Business, Education, Health, and Law (Year) (Book 6). *(File no.273)*
Peterson's Guide to Graduate Programs in Engineering and Applied Sciences (Year) (Book 5). *(File no.273)*
Peterson's Guide to Graduate Programs in the Biological and Agricultural Sciences (Year) (Book 3). *(File no.273)*
Peterson's Guide to Graduate Programs in the Humanities and Social Sciences (Year) (Book 2). *(File no.273)*
Peterson's Guide to Graduate Programs in the Physical Sciences and Mathematics (Year) (Book 4). *(File no.273)*
Peterson's Guide to Two-Year Colleges (Year). *(File no.214)*
Petroleum-Energy Business News Index.
Pharmaceutical Business News.
Philosopher's Index. *(File no.57)*
Physician and Sportsmedicine.
Physics Abstracts. *(File nos.2,3 & 4/INSPEC)*
Pig News & Information.
Pipelines Abstracts. *(File no.96/FLUIDEX)*
Plant Breeding Abstracts.
Plant Engineering.
Plant Growth Regulator Abstracts.
Platt's International Petrochemical Report. *(File no.624/McGRAW-HILL PUBLICATIONS ONLINE)*
Platt's Oilgram News. *(File no.624/McGRAW-HILL PUBLICATIONS ONLINE)*
Platt's Oilgram Price Report. *(File no.624/McGRAW-HILL PUBLICATIONS ONLINE)*
Playthings.
Pollution Abstracts. *(File no.41)*
Polymers, Ceramics, Composite Alert. *(File no.269)*
Popular Photography.
Popular Science.
Potato Abstracts.
Poultry Abstracts.
Power Letter.
Predicasts Basebook.
Predicasts F & S Index Europe.
Predicasts F & S Index International.
Predicasts F & S Index of Corporate Change.
Predicasts F & S Index United States.
Predicasts Forecasts.
Predicasts Overview of Markets and Technology.
Prescription and O T C Pharmaceuticals: The Pink Sheet. *(File no.187)*
Product Alert.
Productivity Software.
Professional Engineer.
Progressive Architecture.
Progressive Grocer.
Protozoological Abstracts.
Psychological Abstracts. *(File no.11/PsycINFO)*
Psychology Today.
Publishers Directory.
Publishers, Distributors & Wholesalers of the United States. *(File no.450)*
Puget Sound Business Journal.
Pumps and Other Fluids Machinery Abstracts. *(File no.96/FLUIDEX)*
Quarterly Coal Report.
Quick Response News.
R I L M Abstracts of Music Literature. *(File no.97)*

R I S C Management.
R N.
Regional Aviation Weekly. *(File no.624/McGRAW-HILL PUBLICATIONS ONLINE)*
Registry of Toxic Effects of Chemical Substances. *(File no.336)*
Religion Index One: Periodicals. *(File no.190)*
Religion Index Two: Multi-Author Works. *(File no.190)*
Religious and Inspirational Books and Serials in Print.
Research Alert (New York).
Research & Development.
Research Centers Directory.
Research in Ministry.
Research Services Directory.
Resources in Education. *(File no.1/ERIC)*
Restaurant Business.
Review of Agricultural Entomology.
Review of Medical and Veterinary Entomology.
Review of Medical and Veterinary Mycology.
Review of Plant Pathology.
Rice Abstracts.
Rural Development Abstracts.
S M T Trends.
S T A R. *(File no.108)*
St. Louis Business Journal.
Sales and Marketing Management.
Sales Pro.
San Diego Business Journal.
Santa Clara County Business Magazine.
Saturday Evening Post.
Scholastic Update.
School and College.
Schweizerische Zeitschrift fuer Volkswirtschaft und Statistik.
Science Citation Index. *(Files nos.34,432,433,434/SCISEARCH)*
Scouting.
Screen Digest.
Scrip - World Pharmaceutical News.
Searchable Physics Information Notices. *(File no.62/SPIN)*
Securities Week. *(File no.624/McGRAW-HILL PUBLICATIONS ONLINE)*
Seed Abstracts.
Selected Water Resources Abstracts. *(File no.117)*
Sensor Review.
Sensor Technology.
Shopper Report.
Side Effects of Drugs Annual. *(File 70/SEDBASE)*
Skiing Trade News.
Skin Diver Magazine.
Small Animals.
Smithsonian.
Smoking and Health Bulletin. *(File no.160)*
Social Planning - Policy & Development Abstracts. *(File No.37)*
Social Sciences Citation Index. *(File no.7/SOCIAL SCISEARCH)*
Social Security Bulletin.
Sociological Abstracts. *(File no.37)*
Software Catalog: Microcomputers.
Software Encyclopedia. *(File no.278)*
Software Markets.
Soils and Fertilizers.
Solid-Liquid Flow Abstracts. *(File no.96/FLUIDEX)*
Sorghum and Millets Abstracts.
SourceMex.
Southern Social Studies Journal.
Soviet Aerospace & Technology.
Soviet Perspectives.
Soyabean Abstracts.
Space Commerce Week.
Space Exploration Technology.
Sports Illustrated.
SportSearch.
SportStyle.
Standard & Poor's Corporation Records. *(File no.133/Corporate Descriptions)*
Standard Corporation Records Current News Edition. *(File no.133)*
Statistical Abstract of the United States.
Steels Alert. *(File no.269)*
Stereo Review.
Subject Guide to Books in Print. *(File no.470)*
Sunset.
Superconductor Week.
Superfund.
Supermarket News.
Survey of Current Business.
Technology and Learning.
Technology Review.
Teen.
Tekstilec.
Tele-Service News.
Telecom Today.

Telephone Engineer and Management.
Telephone Engineer & Management Directory.
Textile Technology Digest. *(File no.119)*
Theoretical Chemical Engineering Abstracts.
Thomas Register of American Manufacturers and Thomas Register Catalog File. *(File no.535)*
Tin International.
Toiletries, Fragrances and Skin Care: The Rose Sheet. *(File no.187)*
Tooling & Production.
Tour and Travel News.
Toxicology Abstracts. *(File no.76/LIFE SCIENCES COLLECTION)*
Trade & Industry Index. *(File no.148)*
Trading Systems Technology.
Transportation & Distribution.
Travel Weekly.
Tree Physiology.
Tribos - Tribology Abstracts. *(File no.96/FLUIDEX)*
Tropical Oil Seeds.
U S A Today.
U S News & World Report.
U S Oil Week.
Ulrich's International Periodicals Directory. *(File no.480)*
Ulrich's Update. *(File no.480)*
U.S. Bureau of Labor Statistics. Monthly Labor Review.
U.S. Bureau of the Census. Annual Survey of Manufactures.
U.S. Bureau of the Census. Census and You.
U.S. Bureau of the Census. Census of Agriculture.
U.S. Bureau of the Census. Census of Construction Industries.
U.S. Bureau of the Census. Census of Governments.
U.S. Bureau of the Census. Census of Manufactures.
U.S. Bureau of the Census. Census of Retail Trade.
U.S. Bureau of the Census. Census of Service Industries.
U.S. Bureau of the Census. Census of Wholesale Trade.
U.S. Bureau of the Census. County and City Data Book.
U.S. Bureau of the Census. County Business Patterns.
U.S. Bureau of the Census. State and Metropolitan Area Data Book.
U.S. Crop Reporting Board. Agricultural Prices.
U.S. Crop Reporting Board. Cattle on Feed.
U.S. Crop Reporting Board. Crop Production.
U.S. Department of Agriculture. Agricultural Income and Finance Situation and Outlook.
U.S. Department of Agriculture. Agricultural Outlook.
U.S. Department of Agriculture. Cotton and Wool Situation and Outlook.
U.S. Department of Agriculture. Dairy Situation and Outlook.
U.S. Department of Agriculture. Feed Situation and Outlook.
U.S. Department of Agriculture. Fruit and Tree Nuts Situation and Outlook Report.
U.S. Department of Agriculture. Livestock and Poultry Situation and Outlook.
U.S. Department of Agriculture. Oil Crops Situation and Outlook Report.
U.S. Department of Agriculture. Rice Situation and Outlook Report.
U.S. Department of Agriculture. Sugar and Sweetener Situation and Outlook.
U.S. Department of Agriculture. Tobacco Situation and Outlook Report.
U.S. Department of Agriculture. Vegetable and Specialty Crop Situation and Outlook.
U.S. Department of Agriculture. Wheat Situation and Outlook.
U.S. Department of State. Key Officers of Foreign Service Posts.
United States Patents Quarterly. *(Patlaw, File 243)*
United States Political Science Documents. *(File no.93)*
UNIX Today.
Utility Reporter: Fuels Energy & Power.
Vaard i Norden.
Vermont Business.
Veterinary Bulletin.
Video News International.
Video Technology News.
Virology and A I D S Abstracts. *(File no.76/LIFE SCIENCES COLLECTION)*
Vitis - Viticulture and Enology Abstracts.
Voice Technology News.
Washington Monthly.
Waste Information Digests.

Weed Abstracts.
Western Business.
Western Grower and Shipper.
Wheat, Barley and Triticale Abstracts.
Whitaker's Books in Print. *(File no.430)*
Whole Earth Review.
Who's Who in America. *(File no.234)*
Wing Newsletter.
Women's Wear Daily.
Workbasket.
Workbench.
Working Woman.
World Affairs Report. *(File no. 167)*
World Agricultural Economics and Rural Sociology Abstracts.
World Agricultural Supply and Demand Estimates.
World Aluminum Abstracts. *(File no.33)*
World Health.
World Ports and Harbours Abstracts. *(File no.96/FLUIDEX)*
World Textile Abstracts. *(File no.67)*
World Translation Index. *(File no.295)*
Worldcasts: Product Edition.
Worldcasts: Regional Edition.
Worldwide Biotech.
Worldwide Databases.
Worldwide Financial Regulations.
Worldwide Telecom.
Worldwide Videotex Update.
Youth Markets Alert.
Zhongguo Xinli Weisheng Zazhi.
Zoological Record. *(File no.185)*
411 Newsletter. *(File no.636)*

DOW JONES NEWS RETRIEVAL
PO Box 300, Princeton, NJ 08540. Tel: 609-452-1511 Fax: 609-520-4775.
A B A Banking Journal.
Administrative Science Quarterly.
Aerospace Daily.
Air Conditioning, Heating & Refrigeration News.
Airports.
American Demographics.
Arizona Business Gazette.
Aviation Daily.
Aviation Week & Space Technology.
Barron's National Business and Financial Weekly.
Book World.
Building Supply Home Centers.
Business America.
Business Aviation Weekly.
Business Week.
Byte.
Chemical Engineering. *(CE)*
Clean Coal - Synfuels Letter. *(CSL)*
Coal Week. *(COW)*
Coal Week International. *(CWI)*
Data Communications.
E N R. *(ENR)*
Economist.
Electric Utility Week. *(EUW)*
FedWatch.
Green Markets. *(GM)*
Independent Power Report. *(COG)*
Industrial Energy Bulletin.
Inside Energy With Federal Lands. *(IE)*
Inside F.E.R.C. *(FERC)*
Inside F E R C's Gas Market Report. *(GSMR)*
Inside N R C. *(NRC)*
Integrated Waste Management.
Japan Economic Daily.
L A N Times.
McGraw-Hill's Biotechnology Newswatch. *(BIO)*
Metals Week. *(MW)*
Nashville Business and Lifestyles.
NuclearFuel. *(NUF)*
Nucleonics Week. *(NUC)*
Peterson's Guide to Four-Year Colleges (Year). *(SCHOOL)*
Peterson's Guide to Two-Year Colleges (Year). *(SCHOOL)*
Physician and Sportsmedicine.
Platt's International Petrochemical Report.
Platt's Oilgram News. *(PON)*
Platt's Oilgram Price Report. *(POP)*
Regional Aviation Weekly.
Securities Week. *(SW)*
Time.
Wall Street Journal (Eastern Edition).

EUROPEAN SPACE AGENCY
Via Galileo Galilei, I-00044 Frascati (Rome), Italy Tel: 39-6-941801 Telex: 610637 ESRIN1
A B I - INFORM. *(File no.30)*
A S F A Aquaculture Abstracts.
A S F A Marine Biotechnology Abstracts.
Aerospace Daily. *(File no.72/AEROSPACE DAILY)*
Agricultural Engineering Abstracts. *(File nos.16 & 124/CAB)*
Agrindex. *(File no.29/AGRIS)*
Agroforestry Abstracts.
Alloys Index. *(File no.3)*
Animal Breeding Abstracts. *(File nos.16 & 124/CAB)*
Animal Disease Occurrence. *(File nos.16 & 124/CAB)*
Apicultural Abstracts. *(File nos.16 & 124/CAB)*
Aqualine Abstracts.
Aquatic Sciences & Fisheries Abstracts. Part 1: Biological Sciences and Living Resources.
Aquatic Sciences & Fisheries Abstracts. Part 2: Ocean Technology, Policy and Non-Living Resources.
Aquatic Sciences & Fisheries Abstracts. Part 3: Aquatic Pollution and Environmental Quality.
Biocontrol News and Information.
Biodeterioration Abstracts.
Biological Abstracts.
Biological Abstracts - R R M. *(File no.7/BIOSIS)*
The Bowker Annual Library and Book Trade Almanac.
Bulletin of Entomological Research.
Bulletin Signaletique. Part 522: Histoire des Sciences et des Techniques.
Bulletin Signaletique d'Information Administrative.
C.A.B. International Bureau of Agricultural Economics. Annotated Bibliographies Series A.
C.A.B. International Bureau of Agricultural Economics. Annotated Bibliographies. Series B: Agricultural Policy and Rural Development in Africa.
C.A.B. International. Bureau of Nutrition. Annotated Bibliographies.
C.A.B. International. Bureau of Soils. Annotated Bibliographies.
C M I Descriptions of Fungi and Bacteria.
C S E L T Infotel.
Chemical Abstracts - Section Groupings. *(File no.2/CHEMABS)*
Chemical Engineering Abstracts. *(File no.85/CHEMICAL ENGINEERING ABSTRACTS)*
Civil Engineering Hydraulics Abstracts. *(File no.48/FLUIDEX)*
Computer-Aided Process Control Abstracts. *(File no. 48)*
Computer & Control Abstracts. *(File no.8/INSPEC)*
Conference Papers Annual Index. *(File no. 36)*
Conference Papers Index. *(File no.36/CONFERENCE PAPERS INDEX)*
Convergence: International Congress on Transportation Electronics. Proceedings.
Cotton and Tropical Fibres. *(File nos.16 & 124/CAB)*
Crop Physiology Abstracts. *(File nos.16 & 124/CAB)*
Current Biotechnology Abstracts. *(File no.95/CURRENT BIOTECHNOLOGY ABSTRACTS)*
Current Index to Statistics.
Current Mathematical Publications.
C2C Abstracts: Japan - Analytical Chemistry. *(File no.241)*
C2C Abstracts: Japan - Ceramics. *(File no.241)*
C2C Abstracts: Japan - Chemical Engineering. *(File no.2410)*
C2C Abstracts: Japan - Crystallography. *(File no.241)*
C2C Abstracts: Japan - Hydrocarbons. *(File no.241)*
C2C Abstracts: Japan - Inorganic Chemistry. *(File no.241)*
C2C Abstracts: Japan - Materials Science. *(File no.241)*
C2C Abstracts: Japan - Metals. *(File no.241)*
C2C Abstracts: Japan - Organic Chemistry. *(File no.241)*
C2C Abstracts: Japan - Physical Chemistry. *(File no.241)*
C2C Abstracts: Japan - Plastics. *(File no.241)*
C2C Abstracts: Japan - Polymer Chemistry. *(File no.241)*
C2C Abstracts: Japan - Surface Chemistry. *(File no.241)*
C2C Abstracts: Japan - Textiles. *(File no.241)*
C2C Currents: Japan - Chemistry. *(File no.241)*
C2C Currents: Japan - Computers. *(File no.241)*
C2C Currents: Japan - Electronics. *(File no.241)*
C2C Currents: Japan - Materials. *(File no.241)*
Dairy Science Abstracts. *(File nos.16 & 124/CAB)*
Diffusion Express. *(File no.27)*
E U D I S E D - R & D Bulletin. *(File no.24/EUDISED R&D)*
Electrical & Electronics Abstracts. *(File no.8/INSPEC)*
Energy Information Abstracts. *(File no.19/ENERGYLINE)*
Energy Information Abstracts Annual. *(File no.19/ENERGYLINE)*
Engineered Materials Abstracts. *(File no.134)*
Engineering Index Annual.
Engineering Index Monthly.
Environment Abstracts. *(File no.11/ENVIROLINE and File no.109/Acid Rain Abstracts)*
Environment Abstracts Annual. *(File no.11/File no.109 Acid Rain Abstracts)*
Eventline.
Faba Bean Abstracts. *(File nos.16 & 124/CAB)*
Field Crop Abstracts. *(File nos.16 & 124/CAB)*
Fluid Flow Measurement Abstracts. *(File no.48/FLUIDEX)*
Fluid Sealing Abstracts. *(File no.48/FLUIDEX)*
Food Science and Technology Abstracts. *(File no.20/FSTA)*
Forest Products Abstracts. *(File nos.16 & 124/CAB)*
Forestry. *(File nos.16 & 124/CAB)*
Forestry Abstracts.
Forestry Abstracts. Leading Article Reprint Series.
Government Reports Announcements and Index Journal.
H T F S Digest. *(File no.138/HEATFLO)*
Heat Transfer & Fluid Flow Service Digest. *(File no.138/HEATFLO)*
Helminthological Abstracts. *(File nos.16 & 124/CAB)*
Herbage Abstracts. *(File nos.16 & 124/CAB)*
Horticultural Abstracts. *(File nos.16 & 124/CAB)*
I N I S Atomindex. *(File no.28/INIS)*
I S M E C: Mechanical Engineering Abstracts. *(File no.10/ISMEC)*
Index of Current Research on Pigs.
Index of Fungi.
Index Veterinarius. *(File nos.16 & 124/CAB)*
Industrial Aerodynamics Abstracts. *(File no.48/FLUIDEX)*
Industrial Corrosion Abstracts. *(File no. 48)*
Information Eaux. *(File no.73/AFEE)*
International Aerospace Abstracts. *(File no.1/NASA)*
International Biodeterioration. *(File nos.16 & 124/CAB)*
International Building Services Abstracts.
International Labour Documentation. *(File no.53/LABORDOC)*
International Packaging Abstracts.
International Pharmaceutical Abstracts. *(File no.102/IPA)*
Irrigation and Drainage Abstracts.
Key Abstracts - Business Automation. *(File no.8/INSPEC)*
Laboratory Hazards Bulletin. *(File no.90/LABORATORY HAZARDS BULLETIN)*
Leisure, Recreation and Tourism Abstracts. *(File nos.16 & 124/CAB)*
Lentils. *(File nos. 16 & 124/CAB)*
M I R A Automobile Abstracts.
M I R A Automotive Business Index.
Maize Abstracts. *(File nos.16 & 124/CAB)*
Management and Marketing Abstracts.
Mass Spectrometry Bulletin. *(File no.86/MASS SPECTROMETRY BULLETIN)*
Mathematical Reviews. *(File no.80/MATHSCI)*
Metals Abstracts. *(File no.3/METADEX)*
Metals Abstracts Index. *(File no.3/METADEX)*
Mixing and Separation Technology Abstracts. *(File no. 48)*
N A T O Advanced Science Institutes Series A: Life Sciences. *(File no.128)*
N A T O Advanced Science Institutes Series B: Physics. *(File no.128)*
N A T O Advanced Science Institutes Series C: Mathematical and Physical Sciences. *(File no.128)*
N A T O Advanced Science Institutes Series D: Behavioural and Social Sciences. *(File no.128)*
N A T O Advanced Science Institutes Series E: Applied Sciences. *(File no.128)*
N A T O Advanced Science Institutes Series F: Computer and Systems Sciences. *(File no.128)*
N A T O Advanced Science Institutes Series G: Ecological Sciences. *(File no.128)*
N A T O Advanced Science Institutes Series H: Cell Biology. *(File no.128)*
Nematological Abstracts. *(File nos.16 & 124/CAB)*
Nonferrous Metals Alert. *(File no.111)*
Nonwovens Abstracts.
Nutrition Abstracts and Reviews. Series A: Human and Experimental. *(File nos.16 & 124/CAB)*

VENDOR LISTING/SERIALS ONLINE

Nutrition Abstracts and Reviews. Series B: Livestock Feeds and Feeding. *(File nos.16 & 124/CAB)*
Oceanic Abstracts. *(File no.17/OCEANIC)*
Offshore Engineering Abstracts. *(File no.48/FLUIDEX)*
Ornamental Horticulture. *(File nos.16 & 124/CAB)*
P A S C A L Thema. T 215: Biotechnologies (Editions Francaise).
P A S C A L Thema. T 230: Energie.
P A S C A L Thema. T 235: Medecine Tropicale.
P A S C A L Thema. T 240: Metaux. Metallurgie.
P A S C A L Thema. T 260: Zoologie Fondamentale et Appliquee des Invertebres (Milieu Terrestre, Eaux Douces).
Packaging Science and Technology Abstracts. *(File no.55/PACKABS)*
Physics Abstracts. *(File no.8/INSPEC)*
Pig News & Information. *(File nos.16 & 124/CAB)*
Pipelines Abstracts. *(File no.48/FLUIDEX)*
Plant Breeding Abstracts. *(File nos.16 & 124/CAB)*
Plant Growth Regulator Abstracts.
Pollution Abstracts. *(File no.18/POLLUTION)*
Polymers, Ceramics, Composite Alert. *(File no.111)*
Potato Abstracts. *(File nos.16 & 124/CAB)*
Poultry Abstracts. *(File nos.16 & 124/CAB)*
Protozoological Abstracts. *(File nos.16 & 124/CAB)*
Pumps and Other Fluids Machinery Abstracts. *(File no.48/FLUIDEX)*
Recherche en Matiere d'Economie des Transports. *(File no.74/TRANSDOC Subfile: RESEARCH)*
Review of Agricultural Entomology. *(File nos.16 & 124/CAB)*
Review of Medical and Veterinary Entomology. *(File nos.16 & 124/CAB)*
Review of Medical and Veterinary Mycology. *(File nos.16 & 124/CAB)*
Review of Plant Pathology. *(File nos.16 & 124/CAB)*
Rice Abstracts. *(File nos.16 & 124/CAB)*
Rural Development Abstracts.
S A E Technical Papers.
S T A R.
Safety and Health at Work. *(File no.40/CISDOC)*
Securite et Sante au Travail.
Seed Abstracts.
Small Animals. *(File nos.16 & 124/CAB)*
Social and Labour Bulletin.
Soils and Fertilizers. *(File nos.16 & 124/CAB)*
Solid-Liquid Flow Abstracts. *(File no.48/FLUIDEX)*
Sorghum and Millets Abstracts. *(File nos.16 & 124/CAB)*
Soyabean Abstracts. *(File nos.16 & 124/CAB)*
Stapp Car Crash Conference Proceedings.
Steels Alert. *(File no.111)*
Theoretical Chemical Engineering Abstracts.
Tribos - Tribology Abstracts. *(File no.48/FLUIDEX)*
Tropical Oil Seeds. *(File nos.16 & 124/CAB)*
Ulrich's International Periodicals Directory. *(File no.103/ULRICH'S PERIODICALS)*
Ulrich's Update. *(File no.103/ULRICH'S PERIODICALS)*
Urban Abstracts.
Veterinary Bulletin. *(File nos.16 & 124/CAB)*
Vitis - Viticulture and Enology Abstracts.
Weed Abstracts. *(File nos.16 & 124/CAB)*
Wheat, Barley and Triticale Abstracts. *(File nos.16 & 124/CAB)*
World Agricultural Economics and Rural Sociology Abstracts. *(File nos.16 & 124/CAB)*
World Aluminum Abstracts. *(File no.9/ALUMINUM)*
World Ports and Harbours Abstracts. *(File no.48/FLUIDEX)*
World Translation Index. *(File no.33/WTI)*

F I Z TECHNIK
Ostbahnhofstrasse 13, D-6000 Frankfurt 60, Germany Tel: (069) 4308-1
Fax: 49-494308200.
A B C der Deutschen Wirtschaft.
A B C Europ Production - Europex.
Alloys Index. *(META)*
B D I Deutschland Liefert.
Coal Abstracts. *(COAL)*
Coal Research Projects. *(COALRIP)*
Convergence: International Congress on Transportation Electronics. Proceedings.
D K I Literatur-Schnelldienst Kunststoffe Kautschuk Fasern.
Einkaufs 1x1 der Deutschen Industrie.
International Packaging Abstracts.
Metals Abstracts. *(META)*
Metals Abstracts Index. *(META)*
Packaging Science and Technology Abstracts.
S A E Technical Papers.
Stapp Car Crash Conference Proceedings.
Wer Baut Maschinen und Anlagen.
Z V E I Elektro und Elektronik - Einkaufsfuehrer.

FINSBURY DATA SERVICES (Now: Reuters Ltd.)
85 Fleet St., London EC4P 4AJ, United Kingdom
Tel: 44-71-250-1122
Fax: 44-71-510-6227.
M E A L Tri-Media Digest for Brands Advertisers.

HUMAN RESOURCE INFORMATION NETWORK
(Subsidiary of: Executive Telecom System, Inc.)
9585 Valparaiso Ct., College Park N., Indianapolis, IN 46268. Tel: 317-872-2045
Fax: 317-872-2059.
A B I - INFORM. *(ETSI-HRIN)*
A I D S Policy and Law. *(Files CDD, HDD)*
Asbestos Abatement Report.
B N A Labor Relations Reporter. Labor Arbitration.
B N A Pension Reporter. *(CDD, HDD)*
B N A Policy and Practice Series. Fair Employment Practices.
B N A Special Report Series on Work & Family.
B N A's Banking Report. *(CDD,HDD)*
B N A's Employee Relations Weekly. *(CDD,HDD)*
Benefits Today.
Bulletin on Training. *(CDD, HDD)*
Bulletin to Management. *(CDD, HDD)*
Chemical Regulation Reporter.
Chemical Substances Control. *(CDD, HDD)*
Collective Bargaining Negotiations & Contracts.
Consultants and Consulting Organizations Directory. *(CCOD)*
Daily Labor Report. *(CDD, HDD)*
Daily Report for Executives. *(CDD, HDD)*
Employment Guide. *(EMPG, CDD, HDD)*
Employment Information in the Mathematical Sciences.
Environment Reporter.
Fair Employment Practices Summary of Latest Developments. *(CDD, HDD)*
From the State Capitals. Labor Relations.
Government Employee Relations Report. *(CDD, HDD)*
Government Manager. *(CDD, HDD)*
H R Magazine.
Harvard Business Review.
Human Resource Executive.
Immigration Policy & Law. *(CDD, HDD)*
Individual Employment Rights. *(CDD, HDD)*
Industrial Health & Hazards Update.
International Labour Documentation.
Job Safety & Health (Washington). *(CDD, HDD)*
Labor Relations Week. *(CDD, HDD)*
Management Matters.
National Report on Substance Abuse. *(CDD, HDD)*
National Report on Work & Family.
Newsletters in Print. *(NIP)*
Occupational Safety & Health Reporter. *(CDD, HDD)*
Social and Labour Bulletin.
Tax Management Weekly Report.
Toxics Law Reporter. *(CDD, HDD)*
Training.
Training and Development Alert.
Training and Development Organizations Directory. *(TDOD)*
Union Labor Report.
Union Labor Report Weekly Newsletter. *(CDD, HDD)*
Videos for Business and Training. *(Video)*

I N K A (Subsidiary of: Fachinformationszentrum Energie, Physik, Mathematik GMBH)
Leopoldshafen 2, D-7514 Eggentein, Germany Tel: 7247 82 4568, 49 7247 824553 Telex: 7826487 FIZED
Fax: 49-72147824568.
Coal Abstracts.
Referateorgan: Zerstoerungsfreie Pruefung.

IST-INFORMATHEQUE, INC.
1611 Cremazie Blvd., E., Montreal, PQ H2M 2P2, Canada Tel: 514-383-1611
Fax: 514-383-7233.
Canadian Business Index.
Canadian News Index.
Point de Repere.
Safety and Health at Work.
Securite et Sante au Travail.

INFORMATION ACCESS CO. (Subsidiary of: Ziff-Davis Publishing Co.)
362 Lakeside Dr., Foster City, CA 94404. Tel: 415-378-5000
Fax: 415-378-5369.
Academic Index.
Acknowledge the Window Letter.
Administrative Science Quarterly.
Advanced Wireless Communication.
American Spectator.
Apparel Industry Magazine.
Business History.
California Planning and Development Report.
Computer Gaming World.
Harvard Health Letter.
Health News (Toronto).
Hypatia.
Internal Auditor.
Journal of Development Studies.
Journal of Money, Credit & Banking.
Journal of Small Business Management.
Personnel Psychology.
Physical Therapy.
Political Risk Letter.
San Antonio Business Journal.
Second Opinion (Chicago).
Software Maintenance News.

JICST
c/o U S A C O Corp., Tsutsumi Bldg., 13-12 Shimbashi 1-chome, Minato-ku, Tokyo 105, Japan
Shirobu-Shushuka, 5-2 Nagatacho 2-chome, Chiyoda-ku, Tokyo 100, Japan Tel: 813-581-6411
Telex: 02223604 J
Audiology Japan.
Brain and Nerve.
Coal Abstracts.
Current Bibliography on Science and Technology: Chemistry and Chemical Engineering (Foreign).
Current Bibliography on Science and Technology: Chemistry and Chemical Engineering (Japanese).
Current Bibliography on Science and Technology: Earth Science, Mining and Metallurgy.
Current Bibliography on Science and Technology: Electronics and Electrical Engineering.
Current Bibliography on Science and Technology: Energy.
Current Bibliography on Science and Technology: Environmental Pollution.
Current Bibliography on Science and Technology: Life Sciences.
Current Bibliography on Science and Technology: Management Science and Systems Engineering.
Current Bibliography on Science and Technology: Mechanical Engineering.
Current Bibliography on Science and Technology: Nuclear Engineering.
Current Bibliography on Science and Technology: Pure and Applied Physics.
Current Science and Technology Research in Japan.
Electrical & Electronics Abstracts.
Excerpta Medica Abstract Journals.
Excerpta Medica. Section 1: Anatomy, Anthropology, Embryology & Histology.
Excerpta Medica. Section 2: Physiology.
Excerpta Medica. Section 3: Endocrinology.
Excerpta Medica. Section 4: Microbiology: Bacteriology, Mycology, Parasitology and Virology.
Excerpta Medica. Section 5: General Pathology and Pathological Anatomy.
Excerpta Medica. Section 6: Internal Medicine.
Excerpta Medica. Section 7: Pediatrics and Pediatric Surgery.
Excerpta Medica. Section 8: Neurology and Neurosurgery.
Excerpta Medica. Section 9: Surgery.
Excerpta Medica. Section 10: Obstetrics and Gynecology.
Excerpta Medica. Section 11: Otorhinolaryngology.
Excerpta Medica. Section 12: Ophthalmology.
Excerpta Medica. Section 13: Dermatology and Venereology.
Excerpta Medica. Section 14: Radiology.
Excerpta Medica. Section 15: Chest Diseases, Thoracic Surgery and Tuberculosis.
Excerpta Medica. Section 16: Cancer.

VENDOR LISTING/SERIALS ONLINE

Excerpta Medica. Section 17: Public Health, Social Medicine & Epidemiology.
Excerpta Medica. Section 18: Cardiovascular Diseases and Cardiovascular Surgery.
Excerpta Medica. Section 19: Rehabilitation and Physical Medicine.
Excerpta Medica. Section 20: Gerontology and Geriatrics.
Excerpta Medica. Section 21: Developmental Biology and Teratology.
Excerpta Medica. Section 22: Human Genetics.
Excerpta Medica. Section 23: Nuclear Medicine.
Excerpta Medica. Section 24: Anesthesiology.
Excerpta Medica. Section 25: Hematology.
Excerpta Medica. Section 26: Immunology, Serology and Transplantation.
Excerpta Medica. Section 27: Biophysics, Bio-Engineering and Medical Instrumentation.
Excerpta Medica. Section 28: Urology and Nephrology.
Excerpta Medica. Section 29: Clinical and Experimental Biochemistry.
Excerpta Medica. Section 30: Clinical and Experimental Pharmacology.
Excerpta Medica. Section 31: Arthritis and Rheumatism.
Excerpta Medica. Section 32: Psychiatry.
Excerpta Medica. Section 33: Orthopedic Surgery.
Excerpta Medica. Section 35: Occupational Health and Industrial Medicine.
Excerpta Medica. Section 36: Health Policy, Economics and Management.
Excerpta Medica. Section 38: Adverse Reactions Titles.
Excerpta Medica. Section 40: Drug Dependence, Alcohol Abuse and Alcoholism.
Excerpta Medica. Section 46: Environmental Health and Pollution Control.
Excerpta Medica. Section 48: Gastroenterology.
Excerpta Medica. Section 49: Forensic Science Abstracts.
Excerpta Medica. Section 50: Epilepsy Abstracts.
Excerpta Medica. Section 52: Toxicology.
Food Science and Technology Abstracts.
Government Reports Announcements and Index Journal.
I to Cho.
Industrial Health.
Iwate Medical University School of Liberal Arts & Sciences. Annual Report. *(JOIS-III)*
J I C S T Online Information System.
Japan Society for Simulation Technology. Journal. *(JOIS)*
Japanese Journal of Clinical Oncology.
Jibi Inkoka, Tokeibu Geka.
Kagaku Gijutsu Bunken Sokuho. Doboku, Kenchiku Kogaku Hen.
Key Abstracts - Business Automation.
Kokyo to Junkan.
Neurological Surgery.
Nippon Medical School. Journal.
Physics Abstracts.
Rigaku Ryoho Janaru.
Rihabiriteshon Igaku.
Seicho.
Seishin Igaku.
Shinshin-Igaku.

MEAD DATA CENTRAL, INC. (Subsidiary of: Mead Corp.)
9443 Springboro Pike, Miamisburg, OH 45342.
Fax: 513-865-1211.
A B A Banking Journal.
A B A Journal.
A B I - INFORM. *(ABI)*
A I Expert. *(AIEXPT)*
A J D C: American Journal of Diseases of Children.
Advanced Manufacturing Technology.
Advanced Recovery Week.
Advertising Age. *(ADAGE)*
Adweek (New York).
Adweek: Southeast.
Aerospace America. *(AEROAM)*
Aerospace Daily. *(AIRDLY)*
Airline Business.
Airports.
All England Law Reports.
Almanac of Famous People.
American Banker.
American Demographics.
American Family Physician.
American Hospital Formulary Service Drug Information.
American Journal of Cardiology.
American Journal of International Law.
American Journal of Medicine.
American Journal of Physical Medicine and Rehabilitation.
American Journal of Surgery.
American Maritime Cases.
Annals of Neurology.
Annals of Plastic Surgery.
Annals of Surgery.
Annals of Thoracic Surgery.
Antitrust & Trade Regulation Report. *(TRADRG)*
Antitrust Law Journal.
Archives of Dermatology.
Archives of General Psychiatry.
Archives of Internal Medicine.
Archives of Neurology.
Archives of Ophthalmology.
Archives of Otolaryngology - Head & Neck Surgery.
Archives of Pathology & Laboratory Medicine.
Archives of Surgery.
Arizona Business Gazette.
Arthritis and Rheumatism.
Asian Studies Center Backgrounder.
Automotive Industries.
AutoWeek.
Aviation Daily. *(AVDLY)*
Aviation Week & Space Technology.
B N A Labor Relations Reporter. Labor Arbitration.
B N A Pension Reporter. *(PENSN)*
B N A's Banking Report. *(BNABNK)*
B N A's Patent, Trademark & Copyright Journal.
Back Pain Monitor.
Backgrounder.
Backgrounder Update.
Bank Management.
Banking Expansion Reporter.
Beverage World (English Edition).
Blood.
Bond Buyer.
Book World.
British Journal of Surgery.
Brooklyn Law Review.
Bulletin on the Rheumatic Diseases.
Business Aviation Weekly. *(WBA)*
Business Index.
Business Insurance.
Business Law Brief.
Business Lawyer. *(BUSLAW)*
Business Week.
Byte.
Catholic University Law Review.
Central America Update.
Chemical Engineering. *(CHEMEN)*
Chemical Regulation Reporter. *(CHEMRG)*
Chemical Week.
Chilton's Automotive Marketing.
Chilton's Distribution Magazine.
Chilton's Food Engineering.
Chilton's Motor Age.
Chronicle of Latin American Economic Affairs.
Clean Coal - Synfuels Letter. *(SYNFLS)*
Clinical Laser Monthly.
Clinical Orthopaedics and Related Research.
Clinical Pediatrics.
Coal.
Coal Outlook.
Coal Week. *(COALWK)*
Coal Week International. *(COALIN)*
Columbia Law Review.
Communications Daily.
Communications Week International.
Computerworld.
Contemporary Musicians.
Contraceptive Technology Update.
Cornell Law Review.
Corporate Capital Transactions Coordinator.
Corporate E F T Report.
Crain's Chicago Business. *(CHIBUS)*
Crain's New York Business. *(NYBUS)*
Criminal Appeal Reports.
Critical Care Medicine.
Critical Issues.
Current Digest of the Post-Soviet Press.
Current Law Index.
Current Surgical Diagnosis & Treatment.
D M News.
Daily Labor Report. *(DLABRT)*
Daily Report for Executives. *(DREXEC)*
Daily Tax Report. *(BNADTR)*
Data Base Reports.
Data Communications.
Database Searcher.
Defense & Foreign Affairs.
Defense and Foreign Affairs Strategic Policy.
Defense and Foreign Affairs Weekly.
Defense Electronics.
Delaware Journal of Corporate Law.
Delta's New Product News.
Discover (Burbank).
Diseases of the Colon and Rectum.
Duke Law Journal.
E & M J Mining Activity Digest.
E C Energy Monthly.
E F T Report.
E N R. *(ENR)*
East European Markets.
Economic Week.
Economist.
Electric Utility Week. *(ELUTL)*
Electronic Design.
Electronic Media.
Electronic Office.
Electronics.
Employee Health and Fitness.
Energy Report.
Energy User News.
Engineering & Mining Journal.
Environment Reporter. *(ENVREP)*
Environmental Law (Portland).
Environmental Law Reporter.
Estate and Financial Planners Alert.
Estates Gazette.
Executive Memorandum.
Executive Speaker.
Expert and the Law.
Facts on File World News Digest With Index.
Family Law Reports.
Federal Contracts Report. *(FDCONT)*
Federal Register.
Federal Reserve Bulletin.
Federal Tax Coordinator 2d.
Financial Regulation Report.
Financial Times World Tax Report.
Financial World.
Flight International.
Forbes.
Fordham Law Review.
Foreign Affairs.
Forensic Services Directory.
Foster Natural Gas Report.
Genetic Technology News.
George Washington Law Review.
Georgetown Law Journal.
Government Employee Relations Report. *(GOVEMP)*
Green Markets. *(GRNMKT)*
Harvard Business Review.
Harvard Law Review. *(Lexis)*
Hastings Law Journal.
Health Policy & Biomedical Research: The Blue Sheet.
Heritage Foundation. Issue Bulletins.
Heritage Lectures.
High-Tech Materials Alert.
Hofstra Law Review.
Hospital Admitting Monthly.
Hospital Employee Health.
Hospital Infection Control.
Hospital Peer Review.
Hospital Risk Management.
Hospitals.
Inc.
Independent Power Report. *(IPR)*
Index to Legal Periodicals.
Indiana Law Journal.
Industrial Bioprocessing.
Industrial Cases Reports.
Industrial Energy Bulletin.
Industrial Relations Law Reports.
Industry Week.
Information Today.
InfoWorld.
Inside Energy With Federal Lands. *(INERGY)*
Inside F.E.R.C. *(INFERC)*
Inside F E R C's Gas Market Report. *(GASMKT)*
Inside N R C. *(INNRC)*
Inside R & D.
Institution Analysis.
Insurance Periodicals Index. *(NEXIS/LEXIS)*
Integrated Waste Management.
Interavia: Aerospace Review.
Interavia Air Letter.
International Coal Report.
International Defense Review.
International Environment Reporter.
International Lawyer.
International Legal Materials.
International Pharmaceutical Abstracts.
International Tax Report.
International Trade Reporter Current Reports. *(INTRAD)*
Investor's Daily.
Issues in Bank Regulation.
J A M A: The Journal of the American Medical Association.
Jack O'Dwyer's Newsletter.

Journal of Nervous and Mental Disease.
Journal of Pediatric Surgery.
Journal of Portfolio Management.
Kaleidoscope: Current World Data.
Kansas City Business Journal.
L A N Times.
Latin America Regional Reports - Brazil.
Latin America Regional Reports - Caribbean.
Latin America Regional Reports - Mexico & Central America.
Latin America Weekly Report.
Latin American Regional Reports - Andean Group.
Latin American Regional Reports - Southern Cone.
Law Practice Management.
Legal Resource Index. *(LGLIND)*
Legal Times.
Life (New York).
Link-Up.
Louisiana Law Review.
McGraw-Hill's Biotechnology Newswatch. *(BIOTEC)*
Maclean's.
MacWeek.
Magazine Index.
Managerial Law.
Manchester Guardian Weekly.
Marine Log.
Mechanical Engineering.
Medical Devices, Diagnostics & Instrumentation Reports: The Gray Sheet.
Medicine (Baltimore).
Metals Week. *(METLWK)*
Michigan Law Review.
Middle East Business Intelligence.
Middle East Executive Reports.
Military Law Review.
Mining Annual Review.
Mining Magazine.
Minnesota Law Review.
Mobile Communications.
Money.
Nashville Business and Lifestyles. *(ADV)*
National Association of Insurance Commissioners. Proceedings.
National Cancer Institute. Journal.
National Journal.
National Law Journal.
National Newspaper Index.
New Law Journal.
New Media Markets.
New York Law Journal.
New York University Law Review.
Newsmakers.
Newsweek.
The Nikkei Weekly.
North Carolina Law Review.
North Sea Letter.
Northwestern University Law Review.
Nuclear News.
NuclearFuel. *(NUFUEL)*
Nucleonics Week. *(NUWEEK)*
O'Dwyer's P R Services Report.
Offshore Incorporating the Oilman.
Ohio State Law Journal.
Oil & Gas Journal.
Pediatrics.
Pensions & Investments. *(PENINV)*
People Weekly.
Physician and Sportsmedicine.
Platt's International Petrochemical Report.
Platt's Oil Marketing Bulletin.
Platt's Oilgram News. *(PONEWS)*
Platt's Oilgram Price Report. *(PPRICE)*
Policy Review.
Political Risk Yearbook. *(COUNTRY REPORTS SERVICE)*
Political Risk Yearbook. Volume 1: North & Central America. *(COUNTRY REPORTS SERVICE)*
Political Risk Yearbook. Volume 2: Middle East & North Africa. *(COUNTRY REPORTS SERVICE)*
Political Risk Yearbook. Volume 3: South America. *(COUNTRY REPORTS SERVICE)*
Political Risk Yearbook. Volume 4: Sub-Saharan Africa. *(COUNTRY REPORTS SERVICE)*
Political Risk Yearbook. Volume 5: Asia & the Pacific. *(COUNTRY REPORTS SERVICE)*
Political Risk Yearbook. Volume 6: Europe - Countries of the E C. *(COUNTRY REPORTS SERVICE)*
Political Risk Yearbook. Volume 7: Europe - Outside the E C. *(COUNTRY REPORTS SERVICE)*
Power in Asia.
Power in Europe.
Prepared Foods.
Prescription and O T C Pharmaceuticals: The Pink Sheet.
Progress in Cardiovascular Diseases.
Property, Planning and Compensation Reports.
Prospective Payment Survival.
Public Health Reports.
Regional Aviation Weekly. *(RAWKY)*
Religious Leaders of America.
Rig Market Forecast.
Road Traffic Reports.
Same-Day Surgery.
Securities Regulation & Law Report. *(SECREG)*
Securities Week. *(SECWK)*
Seminars in Arthritis & Rheumatism.
Seminars in Hematology.
Seminars in Oncology.
Sensor Business Digest.
Sexually Transmitted Diseases.
SourceMex.
Sporting News.
Sports Illustrated.
Stanford Law Review.
Surgery, Gynecology & Obstetrics.
Tax Lawyer.
Tax Notes.
Telecom Markets.
Texas Law Review.
Time.
Toiletries, Fragrances and Skin Care: The Rose Sheet.
Tort & Insurance Law Journal.
Tulane Law Review.
Tulane Maritime Law Journal.
U C L A Law Review.
U S A Today.
U S News & World Report.
United States Banker.
United States Law Week. *(USLW)*
University of Chicago Law Review.
University of Pennsylvania Law Review.
University of Pittsburgh Law Review.
Vanderbilt Law Review.
Washington Law Review.
Washington Quarterly.
Weekly Law Reports.
Who's Who Among Black Americans.
Who's Who Among Hispanic Americans.
Who's Who in Technology.
Wisconsin Law Review.
World Accounting Report. *(WAR)*
The WorldPaper.
Yale Law Journal.

NATIONAL DATA CORP.
2 National Data Plaza, Corporate Sq., Atlanta, GA 30329. Tel: 404-728-2000
Fax: 609-667-5030.
  International Financial Statistics.

NATIONAL LIBRARY OF MEDICINE
8600 Rockville Pike, Bethesda, MD 20209. Tel: 301-496-6193
Fax: 301-496-4000.
  Academy of Medicine, Singapore. Annals.
  American Podiatric Medical Association. Journal.
  Bibliography of Bioethics.
  Bibliography of the History of Medicine.
  Chiropractic History.
  Current Bibliography of Plastic & Reconstructive Surgery.
  F A M L I.
  Health Sciences Serials.
  Hospital Literature Index.
  Index Medicus.
  Index to Dental Literature.
  International Nursing Index.
  International Pharmaceutical Abstracts.
  Issues in Law and Medicine.
  List of Serials Indexed for Online Users.
  Perspectives (Toronto). *(Perspectives - Toronto SR0051880, W1PE8705F)*
  Physical Fitness - Sports Medicine.
  Population Index.
  Psychopharmacology Bulletin.

NEWSNET (Subsidiary of: Independent Pubns.)
945 Haverford Rd., Bryn Mawr, PA 19010.
Tel: 215-527-8030
Fax: 215-527-0338.
  Advanced Coatings & Surface Technology. *(RD26)*
  Advanced Manufacturing Technology.
  Advanced Wireless Communication.
  Aerospace Financial News.
Affluent Markets Alert.
Africa News. *(IT15)*
Aging Research & Training News.
Air Safety Week.
Air Toxics Reports.
Air - Water Pollution Report.
Airline Financial News.
Airports.
American Banker.
American Marketplace.
Angola Peace Monitor.
Antitrust Freedom of Information Log.
Applied Genetics News.
Applied Networks Report.
Asbestos Control Report.
Audio Week.
Audiotex Update.
Autoparts Report.
B O C Week.
B P Report.
Battery & E V Technology News.
Biotech Business.
Biotechnology Investment Opportunities.
Boot Cove Economic Forecast.
Branch Automation News.
Business and the Environment.
Business Computer Digest.
C A D - C A M Update.
C A S E Strategies.
C D C - A I D S Weekly.
C D Computing News.
C D - R O M Databases.
C D - R O M Librarian.
C I M Strategies.
California Planning and Development Report.
Card News.
Cellular Sales & Marketing.
Central America Update.
Central America Update.
Child Protection Report.
Chronicle of Latin American Economic Affairs.
Coal & Synfuels Technology.
Commerce Business Daily.
Common Carrier Week.
Communications Daily.
Communications Week International.
Commuter - Regional Airline News.
Computer Protocols.
Computers in Libraries.
Construction Claims Monthly.
Construction Claims Training Guide.
Consumer Information Appliance.
Contractor Profit News.
Corporate E F T Report. *(FI12)*
Corporate Giving Watch.
Corporate Jobs Outlook! *(File no.GB.41)*
Country Forecasts.
Daily Report for Executives.
Daily Tax Report.
Data Broadcasting Report.
Data Channels. *(TE22)*
Dealing with Technology.
Defense & Aerospace Electronics. *(DE03)*
Defense Daily. *(DE01)*
Defense Marketing International.
Defense Technology Business.
Digest of Activities of Congress.
Directory of Federal Laboratories.
Document Image Automation Update. *(EC51)*
E F T Report. *(FI11)*
Eastern European and Soviet Telecom Report.
Economic Opportunity Report.
Editors Only. *(PB13)*
Education Daily.
Education of the Handicapped.
Education Technology News.
Educational Marketer.
Electro Manufacturing.
Electronic Bookstore for Executives.
Electronic Buyers' News.
Electronic Engineering Times.
Electronic Messaging News.
Electronic Trade & Transport News.
Electronic World News.
Emergency Preparedness News. *(GT34)*
Employment Opportunities (Englewood).
Energy Conservation News.
Energy Daily.
Energy Design Update.
Energy Report.
Enhanced Services Outlook.
Entrepreneurial Manager's Newsletter.
Environment Week.
Environmental Compliance Update.
Environmental Health Letter.
The European Community.
The Exporter.
F C C Week. *(TE52)*

F T C Freedom of Information Log.
F T C: Watch.
F X Week.
Fair Employment Report.
Federal Contract Disputes.
Federal Grants & Contracts Weekly.
Federal Research Report. (RD10)
Fiber Optics News. (TE29)
Fiber Optics Weekly Update.
Flame Retardancy News.
For Your Eyes Only.
Friday Memo. (PB15)
Fusion Power Report. (EY46)
Future Home Technology News.
Futuretech.
General Accounting Office Reports and Technology.
Genetic Technology News.
Global Environmental Change.
Greenhouse Effect Report. (EV01)
Ground Water Monitor. (EV18)
Hazardous Waste News. (CH10)
HazMat Transport. (CH14)
Health Care Competition Week.
Health Grants & Contracts Weekly.
Health News Daily.
Helicopter News. (AE12)
Heller Report on Education Technology and Telecommunications Markets.
High Tech Ceramics News.
High Tech Separations News.
Holt Advisory.
Hospital Patient Relations Report.
Hydrowire.
I D P Report.
I S D N News.
Ice Cream Reporter.
Imaging Update.
Independent Telco News.
Indoor Air Quality Update.
Industrial Bioprocessing.
Industrial Communications. (TE13)
Industrial Health & Hazards Update. (LA04)
Industries in Transition.
Information & Interactive Services Report. (TE41)
Information Report.
Information Week.
Innovator's Digest. (RD09)
Inside Market Data.
Intelligent Network News.
InterAmerican Opportunities Briefing. (File no. IT03)
International Industrial Opportunities.
International Merger Law: Events and Commentary.
International Solar Energy Intelligence Report.
International Venture Capital Network.
Item Processing Report.
Japan Free Press.
Japanese Investment in U S Real Estate Review.
Korea Automotive Review.
L A N Product News.
Land Use Law Report. (EV02)
Law Office Technology Review.
Legislative Network for Nurses.
Limited Partnership Investment Review.
Long-Distance Letter.
Mainframe Computing.
Managed Care Law Outlook.
Managed Care Outlook.
Management Matters.
Marketing Research Review. (AD06)
Medical Waste News.
Membrane & Separation Technology News.
Mental Health Law Reporter.
Mental Health Report.
Mergers and Corporate Policy.
Micro M D Newsletter.
Microcell Report.
Microcomputers in Education. (EC59)
Middle East Business Intelligence. (IT50)
Military & Commercial Fiber Business.
Military Robotics Newsletter. (DE14)
Military Robotics Sourcebook.
Military Space. (DE04)
Minority Markets Alert.
Mobile Data Report: Business Intelligence on Radio-Based Information Networks.
Mobile Phone News. (TE25)
Mobile Satellite Reports.
Modem User News.
Morgan Report on Directory Publishing. (PB30)
Multimedia and Videodisc Monitor.
MuniWeek.
N A S A Software Directory.
N C I Cancer Weekly.
N I S T Update. (GT32)
N T T Topics. (TE31)

Navy News & Undersea Technology.
Netline.
Network Management Systems & Strategies.
Networking Directory.
Networks Update.
NewsNet Action Letter. (PB99)
Noise Regulation Report. (EV19)
Northern Ireland News Service.
Nuclear Waste News. (EV03)
Occupational Health & Safety Letter.
Office Computing Report.
Oil Spill Intelligence Report.
Older Americans Report.
Online Libraries and Microcomputers.
Online Newsletter.
Online Product News.
Open: O S I Product and Equipment News.
Open Systems Report.
Opportunities Briefing. (File no.IT33)
Optical & Magnetic Report.
Optical Materials and Engineering News.
Origins, C N S Documentary Service.
P A Cs & Lobbies. (PO02)
P C Business Products.
Photobulletin. (PB26)
Photoletter.
Photomarket. (PB17)
Plastics Business News.
Political Risk Letter.
Product Safety Letter.
Productivity Software.
Prospective Payment Survival.
Public Broadcasting Report. (PB04)
Public Finance - Washington Watch.
Purpa Lines.
Quick Response News.
RateGram.
Real Estate Investment Situations.
Report on A T & T. (TE50)
Report on Disability Programs.
Report on Education of the Disadvantaged.
Report on Education Research.
Report on I B M.
Report on Preschool Programs.
Report on School-Aged Child Care.
Research Alert (New York).
Robotronics Age Newsletter. (EC16)
S D I Intelligence Report. (DE09)
S D I Monitor. (DE05)
S E C News Digest. (EV96)
S. Klein Newsletter on Computer Graphics. (EC02)
S M T Trends.
Sales Prospector.
Satellite News. (TE03)
Satellite Week. (AE01)
School Law News.
Security Intelligence Report.
Semiconductor Industry & Business Survey Newsletter. (EC35)
Seybold Outlook on Professional Computing. (EC20)
Sludge Newsletter. (CH13)
Small Business Tax Review.
Solid Waste Report. (EV20)
SourceMex.
Southscan.
Soviet Aerospace & Technology. (DE02)
Soviet Perspectives. (File no.IT17)
Space Business News. (AE11)
Space Calendar.
Space Commerce Week. (AE05)
Space Exploration Technology.
Space Fax Daily.
Space R & D Alert.
Spang Robinson Report.
Speednews.
State Regulation Report. (CH11)
State Tax Review.
State Telephone Regulation Report. (TE47)
Student Aid News.
Superconductor Week.
Superfund.
Surface Modification Technology News.
Systems and Networks Integration.
Takeover Targets.
Tax Management Weekly Report.
Technical Computing.
Tele-Service News.
Telecom Today.
Telecommunications Alert. (TE75)
Telecommunications Reports. (TE11)
Telecommunications Week. (TE59)
Telephone News. (TE04)
Television Digest with Consumer Electronics. (PB01)
Tour and Travel News.
Toxic Materials News. (CH12)

Trading Systems Technology.
U S Rail News. (TS11)
Unique (Denville).
U.S. Centers for Disease Control. Morbidity and Mortality Weekly Report.
UNIX Today.
Urban Transport News. (TS10)
Utility Reporter: Fuels Energy & Power. (EY12)
Video Marketing News.
Video News International.
Video Technology News.
Video Week. (EL01)
Vocational Training News.
Voice Technology News.
Wing.
Wing Newsletter.
Working Papers in Business.
World Satellite Directory.
Worldwide Databases.
Worldwide Telecom.
Worldwide Videotex Update. (PB08)
Youth Markets Alert.
411 Newsletter. (TE94)

ORBIT SEARCH SERVICE

8000 Westpark Drive, McLean, VA 22102. Tel: 703-442-0900
Fax: 703-893-4632.

A B I - INFORM. (INFORM)
Abstracts on Tropical Agriculture. (TROPAG)
Accountants' Index. (ACCOUNTANTS)
Adhesives Abstracts.
Alloys Index. (METADEX)
American Men and Women of Science. (AMWS)
Analytical Abstracts. (ANALYTICA)
Antarctic Bibliography. (COLD)
Aqualine Abstracts. (AQUALINE)
Bibliography and Index of Geology.
Bibliography on Cold Regions Science & Technology. (COLD)
The Bowker Annual Library and Book Trade Almanac.
C S I Federal Register Abstracts: Master Edition.
Ceramic Abstracts. (CERAB)
Chemical Abstracts - Section Groupings. (CAS82)
Chemical Abstracts Service Source Index. (CASSI)
Chemical Engineering Abstracts. (CEA)
Chemical Industry Notes. (CIN)
Computer & Control Abstracts. (INSPEC
Convergence: International Congress on Transportation Electronics. Proceedings.
Corporate Technology Directory. (CORP)
Current Index to Journals in Education. (ERIC)
Current Research in Library & Information Science.
C2C Abstracts: Japan - Analytical Chemistry. (JTEC)
C2C Abstracts: Japan - Ceramics. (JTEC)
C2C Abstracts: Japan - Chemical Engineering. (JTEC)
C2C Abstracts: Japan - Crystallography. (JTEC)
C2C Abstracts: Japan - Hydrocarbons. (JTEC)
C2C Abstracts: Japan - Inorganic Chemistry. (JTEC)
C2C Abstracts: Japan - Materials Science. (JTEC)
C2C Abstracts: Japan - Metals. (JTEC)
C2C Abstracts: Japan - Organic Chemistry. (JTEC)
C2C Abstracts: Japan - Physical Chemistry. (JTEC)
C2C Abstracts: Japan - Plastics. (JTEC)
C2C Abstracts: Japan - Polymer Chemistry. (JTEC)
C2C Abstracts: Japan - Surface Chemistry. (JTEC)
C2C Abstracts: Japan - Textiles. (JTEC)
C2C Currents: Japan - Chemistry. (JTEC)
C2C Currents: Japan - Computers. (JTEC)
C2C Currents: Japan - Electronics. (JTEC)
C2C Currents: Japan - Materials. (JTEC)
Directory of American Research and Technology. (DART)
Directory of Online Databases. (CUADRA)
Directory of Portable Databases.
Ecological Abstracts.
Electrical & Electronics Abstracts. (INSPEC)
Energy Information Abstracts. (Energyline)
Energy Information Abstracts Annual. (Energyline)
Engineered Materials Abstracts. (EMAB)
Engineering Index Annual.
Engineering Index Monthly.
Environment Abstracts. (ENVIROLINE)
Environment Abstracts Annual. (Enviroline)
Food Science and Technology Abstracts. (FSTA)
Geographical Abstracts: Human Geography.
Geographical Abstracts: Physical Geography.
Geological Abstracts.

VENDOR LISTING/SERIALS ONLINE

Government Reports Announcements and Index Journal. *(NTIS)*
Health and Safety Science Abstracts. *(ORBIT)*
Imaging Abstracts. *(IMABS)*
Index to Scientific & Technical Proceedings.
Index to the American Banker.
International Development Abstracts.
International Labour Documentation. *(LABORDOC)*
International Packaging Abstracts. *(PIRA)*
Investor's Digest of Canada.
Key Abstracts - Business Automation. *(INSPEC)*
Library & Information Science Abstracts. *(LISA)*
Literature Abstracts: Catalysts & Catalysis. *(APILIT)*
Literature and Patent Abstracts: Oilfield Chemicals.
Management and Marketing Abstracts. *(MMA)*
Metals Abstracts. *(METADEX)*
Metals Abstracts Index. *(METADEX)*
N I O S H T I C Database.
N T I S Bibliographic Data Base.
Nonferrous Metals Alert. *(MATERIALS/B)*
Nonwovens Abstracts.
P N I.
Packaging Science and Technology Abstracts.
Paper and Board Abstracts. *(PIRA)*
Patents Abstracts.
Petroleum Abstracts. *(TULSA)*
Petroleum-Energy Business News Index.
Physics Abstracts. *(INSPEC)*
Polymers, Ceramics, Composite Alert. *(MATERIALS/B)*
Printing Abstracts. *(PIRA)*
Professional Engineer.
Psychological Abstracts.
R A P R A Abstracts. *(RAPRA)*
R A P R A New Trade Names in the Rubber and Plastics Industries. *(RAPRA)*
S A E Handbook.
S A E Technical Literature Abstracts.
S A E Technical Papers.
S A E Transactions.
Safety and Health at Work.
Science Citation Index.
Scientific and Technical Books and Serials in Print. *(File name BIPS)*
Securite et Sante au Travail.
Stapp Car Crash Conference Proceedings.
Steels Alert. *(MATERIALS/B)*
Synthetic Methods of Organic Chemistry.
Theoretical Chemical Engineering Abstracts.
Vitis - Viticulture and Enology Abstracts.
Waste Management Today.
Welding Abstracts.
World Ceramic Abstracts.
World Publishing Monitor. *(EPA)*
World Surface Coating Abstracts. *(WSCA)*
World Textile Abstracts. *(WTA)*

PERGAMON INFOLINE (Now: Orbit Search Service)
8000 Westpark Dr., McLean, VA 22102. Tel: 703-442-0900
Achilles House, Western Ave., London W3 0UA, United Kingdom Tel: 44-81-992-3456Fax: 703-983-4632.
Aqualine Abstracts. *(AQUALINE)*
Ceramic Abstracts. *(CERAB)*
Chem-Facts: Ammonia.
Chem-Facts: Belgium.
Chem-Facts: Ethylene & Propylene.
Chem-Facts: Federal Republic of Germany.
Chem-Facts: Methanol.
Chem-Facts: Netherlands.
Chem-Facts: Polyethylene.
Chem-Facts: Polypropylene.
Chem-Facts: United Kingdom.
Chemical Age Project File. *(CAPF)*
Current Information in the Construction Industry.
Current Research in Britain. Biological Sciences. *(CRIB)*
Current Research in Britain. Humanities. *(CRIB)*
Current Research in Britain. Physical Sciences. *(CRIB)*
Directory of Corporate Affiliations.
I M M Abstracts and Index. *(IMMAGE)*
International Building Services Abstracts.
International Directory of Corporate Affiliations.
International Journal of Rock Mechanics and Mining Sciences & Geomechanics Abstracts.
International Petroleum Abstracts. *(IPA)*
Mass Spectrometry Bulletin.
Million Dollar Directory Series.
Paper and Board Abstracts.
Reference Book of Corporate Managements. *(RBCM)*
United States Patents Quarterly.
Who's Who in Technology. *(WHOTECH)*
World Surface Coating Abstracts. *(WSCA)*
World Textile Abstracts. *(WTA)*

PRENTICE-HALL INFORMATION NETWORK
(Now: Research Institute of America; Subsidiary of: Thompson Professional)
910 Sylvan Ave., Englewood Cliffs, NJ 07632-3310.
Cumulative Changes 1986 Code and Regulations.
Federal Estate and Gift Taxes.
Federal Excise Tax.
Federal Tax Guide.
Federal Tax Regulations.
Federal Taxes Citator.
Federal Taxes 2nd.
I R S Memoranda and Letter Rulings.
Internal Revenue Code of 1986 as Amended.
Private Letter Rulings.
S Corporations (Englewood Cliffs).
State and Local Taxes.
State and Local Taxes: Property Taxes.
State and Local Taxes: Sales and Use Taxes.
State Inheritance Taxes.

QL SYSTEMS, LTD.
1819 Granville St., Halifax, Nova Scotia B3, Canada
275 Sparks St., Ste. 901, St. Andrews Tower, Ottawa, ON KIR7X9, Tel: 613-238-3499
A S T I S Bibliography.
A S T I S Current Awareness Bulletin.
A S T I S Occasional Publications.
Alberta Reports.
Canadian Business Index.
Canadian Foreign Relations.
Canadian News Index.
Canadian Sales Tax Reporter.
Coal Abstracts.
Film - Video Canadiana. *(FVC,FVPD)*
International Bibliography of the Social Sciences. Economics.
International Bibliography of the Social Sciences. Social and Cultural Anthropology.
International Bibliography of the Social Sciences. Sociology.
Investor's Digest of Canada.
Manitoba Reports.
National Reporter.
New Brunswick Reports.
Newfoundland & Prince Edward Island Reports.
Nova Scotia Reports.
Ontario Appeal Cases.
Ontario Reports.
Polar and Glaciological Abstracts.
Saskatchewan Reports.
Tax Profile.
Western Weekly Reports.

RESEARCH LIBRARIES GROUP INFORMATION NETWORK
1200 Villa St., Mountain View, CA 94041-1100.
Tel: 415-691-2211
Fax: 415-964-0943.
Avery Index to Architectural Periodicals.

S T N INTERNATIONAL
c/o Chemical Abstracts Service, 2540 Olentengy River Rd., Box 3012, Columbus, OH 43210. Tel: 614-421-3600, 800-848-6533 Telex: 6842086 CHMAB
A O A C International Journal. *(CJAOAC)*
Accounts of Chemical Research. *(CJACS)*
Agroforestry Abstracts.
Alloys Index.
American Chemical Society. Journal. *(CJACS)*
Analyst. *(CJRSC)*
Analytica Chimica Acta.
Analytical Abstracts. *(ANABSTR)*
Analytical Chemistry. *(CJACS)*
Angewandte Chemie. *(CJVCH)*
Applied Catalysis.
Bibliography and Index of Geology. *(GeoRef)*
Biochemistry. *(CJACS)*
Biodeterioration Abstracts.
Biological Abstracts. *(BIOSIS)*
Biological Abstracts - R R M. *(BIOSIS)*
Biopolymers. *(CJWILEY)*
Carbohydrate Research.
Ceramic Abstracts.
Chem Sources International.
Chem Sources U S A.
Chemical Abstracts - Applied Chemistry and Chemical Engineering Sections. *(CA)*
Chemical Abstracts - Biochemistry Sections. *(CA)*
Chemical Abstracts - Macromolecular Sections. *(CA)*
Chemical Abstracts - Organic Chemistry Sections. *(CA)*
Chemical Abstracts - Physical, Inorganic and Analytical Chemistry Sections. *(CA)*
Chemical Abstracts - Section Groupings. *(CA)*
Chemical Abstracts Service Source Index. *(CA)*
Chemical Hazards in Industry.
Chemical Industry Notes. *(CIN)*
Chemical Research in Toxicology.
Chemical Reviews. *(CJACS)*
Coal Abstracts.
Coal Research Projects.
Computer & Control Abstracts. *(INSPEC)*
D K I Literatur-Schnelldienst Kunststoffe Kautschuk Fasern.
Electrical & Electronics Abstracts. *(INSPEC)*
Energy & Fuels. *(CJACS)*
Energy Data Base.
Energy Research Abstracts. *(ENERGY)*
Engineered Materials Abstracts. *(EMA)*
Engineering Index Annual.
Engineering Index Monthly. *(COMPENDEX)*
Environmental Science & Technology. *(CJACS)*
Faraday Discussions. *(CJRSC)*
Findex.
Government Reports Announcements and Index Journal. *(NTIS)*
I N I S Atomindex. *(ENERGY)*
I N I S Newsletter.
Index Medicus. *(MEDLINE)*
Index to Dental Literature. *(MEDLINE)*
Industrial & Engineering Chemistry Research. *(CJACS)*
Inorganic Chemistry. *(CJACS)*
International Nursing Index. *(MEDLINE)*
Journal of Agricultural and Food Chemistry. *(CJACS)*
Journal of Analytical Atomic Spectrometry. *(CJRSC)*
Journal of Applied Polymer Science. *(CJWILEY)*
Journal of Chemical and Engineering Data. *(CJACS)*
Journal of Chemical Information and Computer Sciences. *(CJACS)*
Journal of Chemical Research. *(CJRSC)*
Journal of Medicinal Chemistry. *(CJACS)*
Journal of Organic Chemistry. *(CJACS)*
Journal of Organometallic Chemistry.
Journal of Physical Chemistry. *(CJACS)*
Journal of Polymer Science. Part A: Polymer Chemistry. *(CJWILEY)*
Journal of Polymer Science. Part B: Polymer Physics. *(CJWILEY)*
Journal of Polymer Science. Polymer Symposia Edition.
Journal of the Chemical Society. Chemical Communications. *(CJRSC)*
Key Abstracts - Business Automation. *(INSPEC)*
Laboratory Hazards Bulletin. *(LHB)*
Langmuir. *(CJACS)*
Literature Abstracts.
Literature and Patent Abstracts: Oilfield Chemicals.
Macromolecules. *(CJACS)*
Metals Abstracts. *(METADEX)*
Metals Abstracts Index. *(METADEX)*
N T I S Bibliographic Data Base.
Nonferrous Metals Alert. *(MATBUS)*
Organometallics. *(CJACS)*
Patents Abstracts.
Physics Abstracts. *(INSPEC)*
Physics Briefs - Physikalische Berichte. *(PHYS)*
Polymers, Ceramics, Composite Alert. *(MATBUS)*
Royal Society of Chemistry. Journal: Dalton Transactions. *(CJRSC)*
Royal Society of Chemistry. Journal: Faraday Transactions. *(CJRSC)*
Royal Society of Chemistry. Journal: Perkin Transactions 1. *(CJRSC)*
Royal Society of Chemistry. Journal: Perkin Transactions 2. *(CJRSC)*
Steels Alert. *(MATBUS)*
Vademecum Deutscher Lehr- und Forschungsstaetten. Staetten der Forschung.
Zentralblatt fuer Didaktik der Mathematik.
Zentralblatt fuer Mathematik und ihre Grenzgebiete. *(MATH)*

SOURCE TELECOMPUTING CORP.
1616 Anderson Rd., McLean, VA 22102.
E R I C Clearinghouse on Urban Education. Digest.

VENDOR LISTING/SERIALS ONLINE 5125

TELESYSTEMES-QUESTEL
83-85 blvd. Vincent Auriol, Paris 75013, France
Tel: 33-144236464 Telex: 204594 TELQUES F
Fax: 33-144236465.
- Bibliographie Geographique Internationale.
- Bibliography of Bioethics. (BIOETHICS)
- Bulletin Signaletique. Part 519: Philosophie.
- Bulletin Signaletique. Part 520: Sciences de l'Education.
- Bulletin Signaletique. Part 522: Histoire des Sciences et des Techniques.
- Bulletin Signaletique. Part 523: Histoire et Sciences de la Litterature.
- Bulletin Signaletique. Part 524: Sciences du Langage.
- Bulletin Signaletique. Part 525: Prehistoire et Protohistoire.
- Bulletin Signaletique. Part 526: Art et Archeologie.
- Bulletin Signaletique. Part 527: Histoire et Sciences des Religions.
- Bulletin Signaletique. Part 528: Bibliographie Internationale de Science Administrative.
- Bulletin Signaletique. Part 529: Ethnologie.
- Bulletin Signaletique. Part 529: Sociologie.
- Bulletin Signaletique des Telecommunications.
- Catalogue Afnor (Normes Francaises).
- Chemical Abstracts - Section Groupings. (CAS)
- Diffusion Express. (Base EDF.DOC)
- Directory of Online Databases. (CUADRA)
- Directory of Portable Databases.
- Informatique et Sciences Juridiques.
- Merck Index: An Encyclopedia of Chemicals and Drugs.
- P A S C A L Thema. T 215: Biotechnologies (Editions Francaise).
- P A S C A L Thema. T 230: Energie.
- P A S C A L Thema. T 235: Medecine Tropicale.
- P A S C A L Thema. T 240: Metaux. Metallurgie.
- P A S C A L Thema. T 260: Zoologie Fondamentale et Appliquee des Invertebres (Milieu Terrestre, Eaux Douces).
- Repertoire des Banques de Donnees Teletel Pour l'Entreprise.
- Safety and Health at Work.
- Securite et Sante au Travail.
- Social and Labour Bulletin.
- Travail et Emploi.

UNITED COMMUNICATIONS GROUP
11300 Rockville Pike, Ste. 1100, Rockville, MD 20852. Tel: 301-816-8950
Fax: 301-816-8945.
- Commerce Business Daily. (CBD OnLine)
- Oil Price Information Service. (PETROSCAN)

UNIVERSITY OF TSUKUBA
Gakujutsu Joho Shori Center, Tennodai, Sakuramura, Niihari-gun, Ibaraki, Japan Tel: 81-298532111
- Computer & Control Abstracts.
- Electrical & Electronics Abstracts.
- International Pharmaceutical Abstracts.
- Key Abstracts - Business Automation.
- Physics Abstracts.

VU/TEXT INFORMATION SERVICES, INC. (Subsidiary of: Knight-Ridder, Inc.)
325 Chestnut St., Suite 1300, Philadelphia, PA 19106. Tel: 215-574-4400
- Arizona Business Gazette.
- Book World.
- Campaign.
- Discover (Burbank).
- Economist.
- Entertainment Weekly.
- Film - Video Canadiana.
- Fortune Magazine.
- Journal of Commerce and Commercial.
- Kansas City Business Journal.
- Life (New York).
- Marketing.
- Money.
- Nashville Business and Lifestyles. (BDL,ADV)
- New Scientist.
- People Weekly.
- Sports Illustrated.
- Time.
- U S A Today.
- Wall Street Transcript.

WEST SERVICES, INC. (Subsidiary of: West Publishing Co.)
58 W. Kellogg Blvd., Box 64779, Saint Paul, MN 55164-0779. Tel: 612-228-2786
Fax: 612-688-3570.
- A B A Journal.
- Alabama Law Review.
- Alabama Lawyer.
- American Criminal Law Review. (ACRIMLREV)
- American Indian Law Review.
- American Journal of Legal History.
- American University Law Review.
- Antitrust. (ANTITR)
- Antitrust & Trade Regulation Report. (BNA-ATRR)
- Antitrust Law Journal. (ANTITRLJ)
- Arizona State Law Journal.
- B N A Labor Relations Reporter. Labor Arbitration.
- B N A Pension Reporter. (BNA-PEN)
- B N A's Banking Report. (BNA-BNK)
- B N A's Patent, Trademark & Copyright Journal. (BNA-PTCJ)
- Benefits Today.
- Boston College Law Review.
- Boston University Law Review.
- Brief (Chicago). (BRIEF)
- Brigham Young University Law Review.
- Brooklyn Journal of International Law.
- Buffalo Law Review.
- Business Lawyer. (BUSLAW)
- C B A Record.
- Case Western Reserve Law Review.
- Chemical Regulation Reporter.
- Chicago - Kent Law Review.
- Chicano - Latino Law Review.
- Cincinnati Law Review.
- Cleveland State Law Review.
- Collective Bargaining Negotiations & Contracts.
- Columbia Journal of Transnational Law.
- Connecticut Law Review.
- Constitutional Commentary.
- Cornell International Law Journal.
- Cornell Law Review.
- Creighton Law Review.
- Criminal Justice Abstracts.
- Cumberland Law Review.
- Current Law Index.
- Daily Labor Report. (BNA-DLR)
- Daily Report for Executives. (BNA-DER)
- Daily Tax Report. (BNA-DTR)
- Delaware Journal of Corporate Law.
- Denver Journal of International Law and Policy.
- Denver University Law Review.
- Dickinson Law Review.
- Drake Law Review.
- Duke Law Journal.
- Emory Law Journal.
- Environment Reporter. (BNA-ER)
- Environmental Law (Portland).
- Environmental Law Reporter.
- Family Advocate. (FAMADVO)
- Family Law Quarterly. (FAMLQ)
- Federal Bar News & Journal.
- Federal Contracts Report.
- Federal Register.
- Federal Rules of Evidence News.
- Fletcher Forum of World Affairs.
- Florida Bar Journal.
- Florida Law Review.
- Florida State University Law Review.
- Fordham International Law Journal.
- Fordham Law Review.
- Fordham Urban Law Journal.
- Forensic Services Directory.
- From the State Capitals. Civil Rights.
- From the State Capitals. Insurance Regulation.
- From the State Capitals. Justice Policies.
- From the State Capitals. Labor Relations.
- From the State Capitals. Public Utilities.
- From the State Capitals. Taxation and Revenue Policies.
- From the State Capitals. Taxes - Property.
- From the State Capitals. Waste Disposal and Pollution Control.
- From the State Capitals. Women and the Law.
- George Washington Journal of International Law and Economics.
- George Washington Law Review.
- Georgetown Law Journal.
- Georgia Law Review.
- Golden Gate University Law Review.
- Government Employee Relations Report.
- Gower Federal Service - Mining.
- Gower Federal Service - Outer Continental Shelf.
- Hamline Law Review.
- Harvard Civil Rights - Civil Liberties Law Review.
- Harvard Environmental Law Review.
- Harvard International Law Journal.
- Harvard Journal of Law and Public Policy.
- Harvard Journal on Legislation.
- Harvard Law Review.
- Harvard Women's Law Journal.
- Hastings Communications and Entertainment Law Journal (Comm - Ent).
- Hastings Constitutional Law Quarterly.
- Hastings International and Comparative Law Review.
- Hastings Law Journal.
- Hofstra Law Review.
- Houston Journal of International Law.
- Houston Law Review.
- Howard Law Journal.
- Human Rights. (HUMRT)
- Idaho Law Review.
- Illinois Legal Times.
- Index to Legal Periodicals.
- Indiana Law Journal.
- Indiana Law Review.
- Insurance Periodicals Index.
- Inter-American Law Review.
- International Lawyer.
- International Trade Reporter Current Reports. (BNA-ITR)
- Iowa Law Review.
- Issues in Law and Medicine.
- John Marshall Law Review.
- Journal of Air Law and Commerce.
- Journal of Corporation Law.
- Journal of Criminal Law & Criminology.
- Journal of Law & Commerce.
- Judicature.
- Judicial Conduct Reporter.
- Kentucky Law Journal.
- Labor - Management Relations Analysis. (File LLR-NEWS)
- Law & Business Directory of Corporate Counsel.
- Law and Policy in International Business.
- Law Practice Management.
- Legal Resource Index. (LRI)
- Litigation.
- Louisiana Law Review.
- Loyola Law Review.
- Loyola of Los Angeles International and Comparative Law Journal.
- Maine Law Review.
- Marquette Law Review.
- Maryland Law Review.
- Mercer Law Review.
- Michigan Bar Journal.
- Michigan Law Review.
- Minnesota Law Review.
- Mississippi College Law Review.
- Mississippi Law Journal.
- Missouri Law Review.
- Natural Resources & Environment.
- Naval Law Review.
- Nebraska Law Review.
- New Jersey Lawyer.
- New York State Bar Journal. (NYSTBJ)
- New York University Law Review.
- North Carolina Law Review.
- North Dakota Law Review.
- Northern Kentucky Law Review.
- Northwestern Journal of International Law & Business.
- Northwestern University Law Review.
- Notre Dame Law Review.
- Nova Law Review.
- Ohio State Journal on Dispute Resolution.
- Ohio State Law Journal.
- Oklahoma City University Law Review.
- Oklahoma Law Review.
- Oregon Law Review.
- Pacific Law Journal.
- Pepperdine Law Review.
- Preview of United States Supreme Court Cases.
- Probate & Property.
- Public Contract Law Journal.
- Public Utilities Fortnightly.
- Real Property, Probate and Trust Journal.
- S E C Docket.
- S E C News Digest.
- Saint Louis University Law Journal.
- Santa Clara Law Review.
- Securities Regulation & Law Report. (BNA-SRLR)
- South Carolina Law Review.
- South Dakota Law Review.
- South Texas Law Review.
- Southwestern Law Journal.
- Stanford Journal of International Law.
- Stanford Law Review.
- Stetson Law Review.
- Suffolk Transnational Law Journal.
- Suffolk University Law Review.

5126 VENDOR LISTING/SERIALS ONLINE

Syracuse Journal of International Law & Commerce.
Tax Lawyer.
Tax Management Compensation Planning. *(File TM-CP, TM-CP-OLD, TM-CPJ)*
Tax Management Compensation Planning Journal. *(File TM-CPJ)*
Tax Management Estates, Gifts and Trusts. *(File TM-EGT, TM-EGT-OLD, TM-EGTJ)*
Tax Management Estates, Gifts and Trusts Journal. *(File TM-EGTJ)*
Tax Management Foreign Income Portfolios. *(File TM-FOR)*
Tax Management Memorandum. *(File TM-TMM)*
Tax Management Real Estate. *(File TM-RE, TM-RE-OLD, TM-REJ)*
Tax Management Real Estate Journal. *(File TM-REJ)*
Tax Management U S Income. *(File TM-US, TM-US-OLD, TM-TMWR)*
Tax Notes.
Temple Law Review.
Tennessee Bar Journal.
Tennessee Law Review.
Texas Tech Law Review.
Thurgood Marshall Law Review.
Tort & Insurance Law Journal.
Tulane Law Review.
Tulane Maritime Law Journal.
Tulsa Law Journal.
United States Law Week.
United States Tax Court Reports.

University of Baltimore Law Review.
University of Chicago Legal Forum.
University of Illinois Law Review.
University of Kansas Law Review.
University of Pittsburgh Law Review.
University of Richmond Law Review.
University of San Francisco Law Review.
Utah Law Review.
Vanderbilt Journal of Transnational Law.
Vanderbilt Law Review.
Villanova Law Review.
Virginia Environmental Law Journal.
Virginia Journal of International Law.
Virginia Tax Review.
Washington & Lee Law Review.
Washington Law Review.
William Mitchell Law Review.
Wisconsin Law Review.
Yale Journal on Regulation.

WILSONLINE (Subsidiary of: H. W. Wilson Co.)
950 University Ave., Bronx, NY 10452. Tel: 718-588-8400
Fax: 718-538-2746.
   Abridged Readers' Guide to Periodical Literature.
   Applied Science and Technology Index. *(File AST)*
   Art Index. *(File ART)*
   Bibliographic Index. *(File BIB)*
   Biography Index. *(File BIO)*
   Biological & Agricultural Index.
   Book Review Digest. *(File BRD)*
   Business Periodicals Index. *(File BPI)*
   China Business Review.
   Cumulative Book Index. *(File CBI)*
   Education Index. *(File EDI)*
   Essay and General Literature Index. *(File EGL)*
   General Science Index. *(File GSI)*
   Humanities Index. *(File HUM)*
   I R S Publications.
   Index to Book Reviews in Religion.
   Index to Legal Periodicals. *(File ILP)*
   Index to U.S. Government Periodicals.
   Library Literature. *(File LIB)*
   M L A International Bibliography of Books and Articles on the Modern Languages and Literatures.
   New York Law Journal.
   North Carolina Journal of International Law and Commercial Regulation.
   Ohio State Journal on Dispute Resolution.
   Ohio State Law Journal.
   Readers' Guide Abstracts. Microfiche Edition. *(File RGA)*
   Readers' Guide to Periodical Literature. *(File RDG)*
   Religion Index One: Periodicals.
   Religion Index Two: Multi-Author Works.
   Research in Ministry.
   Short Story Index.
   Social Sciences Index. *(File SSI)*
   U C Davis Law Review.
   Vertical File Index. *(File VFI)*

Cessations

This index includes entries for titles in the Bowker International Serials Database which were reported ceased during the past three years.

687   US
A A M A. TECHNICAL ADVISORY COMMITTEE. BULLETIN. ceased. irreg. American Apparel Manufacturers Association, Technical Advisory Committee, 2500 Wilson Blvd., Ste. 301, Arlington, VA 22201.

687   US
A A M A. TECHNICAL ADVISORY COMMITTEE. RESEARCH PAPER. ceased. a. American Apparel Manufacturers Association, Technical Advisory Committee, 2500 Wilson Blvd., Ste. 301, Arlington, VA 22201.

687   US
A A M A. WASHINGTON LETTER. ceased. 3/m. American Apparel Manufacturers Association, 2500 Wilson Blvd., Ste. 301, Arlington, VA 22201.

674   CN   ISSN 0065-0013
A B C BRITISH COLUMBIA LUMBER TRADE DIRECTORY AND YEAR BOOK. 1916-19?? biennial. Progress Publishing Co. Ltd., C-310 Marine Bldg., 355 Burrard St., Vancouver, B.C. V6C 2G6, Canada.

310 659.1   US
A B C CASE BOOK. 1981-198? q. (back issues avail.) Audit Bureau of Circulations, 900 N. Meacham Rd., Schaumburg, IL 60173-4968.

070.5   US   ISSN 0065-0048
A B C OF BOOK TRADE. 1966-1990. quinquennial. A B Bookman Publications, Inc., Box AB, Clifton, NJ 07015.

380   YU
A B C PRIVREDE JUGOSLAVIJE. 1973-1989. a. (Chamber of Economy Croatia) Privredni Vjesnik, Rooseveltov Trg 2, Box 631, Zagreb, Croatia.

028.5 602   PL
A B C TECHNIKI/A B C OF TECHNICS; magazine for children. 1964-19??; suspended. 4/yr. Wydawnictwo Czasopism i Ksiazek Technicznych SIGMA - NOT, Ul. Biala 4, P.O. 1004, 00-950 Warsaw, Poland.

011   AT   ISSN 0815-0303
A B N CATALOGUE. 1985-19?? s-a. (also avail. in microfiche) National Library of Australia, Australian Bibliographic Network, Canberra, A.C.T. 2600, Australia.

418.02   BL
A B R A T E S. 1976-19?? bi-m. Associacao Brasileira de Tradutores, Av. Almirante Barroso 97, Rio de Janeiro, Brazil.

001.6 621.381   AT
A C A D S QUARTERLY; the magazine of technical computing. 1968-19?? q. (A C A D S Association) National Publications Pty. Ltd., P.O. Box 297, Homebush West, N.S.W. 2140, Australia.

388.3   UK
A C E. (Accessories Components & Equipment) 1982-198? bi-m. Haymarket Publishing Ltd., 38-42 Hampton Rd., Teddington, Middx. TW11 0JE, England.

364.4   AT   ISSN 0155-8862
A.C.P.C. FORUM. ceased. bi-m. (Australian Crime Prevention Council) Magazine Art Pty. Ltd., 35 Willis St., Hampton, Vic. 3188, Australia.

011   BE   ISSN 0771-5137
A C P STATES YEARBOOK. ceased 1980. a. Editions Delta, Rue Scailquin 55, B-1030 Brussels, Belgium.

574.192   UK   ISSN 0260-1117
A C T H AND RELATED PEPTIDES. ceased 1990. m. Sheffield University Biomedical Information Service (SUBIS), The University, Sheffield S10 2TN, England.

331.8   AT   ISSN 0314-2868
A C T U BULLETIN. ceased 1990 (Dec.). irreg. Australian Council of Trade Unions, 393-397 Swanston St., Melbourne, Vic. 3000, Australia.

331   AT
A C T U NATIONAL YOUTH BROCHURE. ceased 1990. a. Australian Council of Trade Unions, 393-397 Swanston St., Melbourne, Vic. 3000, Australia.

331   AT
A C T U YOUTH BOOK. ceased. a? Australian Council of Trade Unions, 393-397 Swanston St., Melbourne, Vic. 3000, Australia.

630   UK   ISSN 0027-5670
A D A S QUARTERLY REVIEW. 1971-1980. q. Agricultural Development and Advisory Service, Whitehall Place, London SW1, England.
Supersedes: N A A S Quarterly Review.

336.2   US   ISSN 0091-553X
KF6464.A1
A D & D: TAX INTERPRETATIONS. 1973-1976. m. (looseleaf format) Alexander Hamilton Institute, 605 Third Ave., New York, NY 10016.

327 355   UK   ISSN 0264-0643
A D I U REPORT. 1979-1988. bi-m. Armament and Disarmament Information Unit, Science Policy Research Unit, University of Sussex, Brighton, Sussex BN1 9RF, England.

962   SX
A.D.K. BOOKLET: FACTS AND FIGURES/A.D.K. SCHRIFTENREIHE: DATEN AND FAKTEN. 1978-19?? irreg. (back issues avail.) Afrikaans Duitse Kultuurunie (SWA), Box 2185, 9100 Windhoek, Namibia.

028.5   AT   ISSN 1030-178X
A.D. MAGAZINE. (Supplement avail.: A.D. Youthleader) 1988-19?? 4/yr. (back issues avail.) Joint Board of Christian Education, 10 Queen St., Melbourne, Vic. 3000, Australia.

312   UN   ISSN 0252-4422
A D O P T. (Asian-Pacific and Worldwide Documents on Population Topics) 1979-1988 (vol.10, no.12). m. United Nations Economic and Social Commission for Asia and the Pacific (ESCAP), Population Division, The United Nations Bldg., Rajadamnern Ave., Bangkok 10200, Thailand.

001.64   US   ISSN 0044-5649
A D P NEWSLETTER. (Automatic Data Processing) 1967-1976 (Dec.). fortn. Management Science Publishing Inc., 430 Park Ave., New York, NY 10022.

369.4 371.3   AT   ISSN 1030-1798
A.D. YOUTHLEADER. (Supplememt to: A.D. Magazine) 1988-19?? 5/yr. (back issues avail.) Joint Board of Christian Education, 10 Queen St., Melbourne, Vic. 3000, Australia.

531.64 621.48   SW   ISSN 0519-3346
TK9008
A E. (Atomenergi) ceased. irreg. Studsvik A B, Fack, S-611 82 Nykoeping, Sweden.

674   US   ISSN 0099-1716
TA419.A1
A-E CONCEPTS IN WOOD DESIGN. 1975-1982. bi-m. American Wood Preservers Institute, 1651 Old Meadow Rd., Suite 105, McLean, VA 22102.
Supersedes (1923-1972): Wood Preserving (ISSN 0043-7697)

370 310   US   ISSN 0001-1045
CODEN: AEDMAD
A E D S MONITOR. 1962-1986? bi-m. (also avail. in microform from UMI; reprint service avail. from UMI) International Association for Computing in Education, c/o William J. Runnell, 1230 17th St., N.W., Washington, DC 20036.

CESSATIONS

371.3 US
A E D S NEWSLETTER. 1982-19?? bi-m. International Association for Computing in Education, c/o University of Oregon, 1787 Agate St., Eugene, OR 97403.

621.3 GW ISSN 0043-6801
TK6600 CODEN: WBATB3
A E G-TELEFUNKEN. WISSENSCHAFTLICHE BERICHTE. (Allgemeine Elektrizitaets Gesellschaft) 1911-1982. 5/yr. A E G-Telefunken, Firmenverlag, Theodor-Stern-Kai 1, 6000 Frankfurt 70, Germany.
Formerly: Telefunken-Zeitung.

621.38 GW ISSN 0001-107X
TK3 CODEN: ATFPB2
A E G - TELEFUNKEN PROGRESS. (Allgemeine Elektrizitaets Gesellschaft) 1952-1982. q. A E G-Telefunken, Firmenverlag, Theodor-Stern-Kai 1, 6000 Frankfurt 70, Germany.
Formerly: A E G Progress.

330 US ISSN 0149-9785
A E I ECONOMIST. ceased. m. American Enterprise Institute for Public Policy Research, 1150 17th St., N.W., Washington, DC 20036.

178 NE ISSN 0006-4645
A EN D. (Alcohol en Drugs) 1959-19?? q. Nationale Commissie Tegen het Alkoholisme en Andere Verslavingen, Corn. Houtmanstraat 21, 3572 LT Utrecht, Netherlands.

301 360 AT ISSN 0813-877X
A F I T BULLETIN. (Australian Families Income Transfer) 1984-1990 (no.8). irreg. Australian Institute of Family Studies, 300 Queen St., Melbourne, Vic. 3000, Australia.

331.88 US ISSN 0149-2489
HD8055.A5
A F L - C I O AMERICAN FEDERATIONIST. 1894-198? m. (also avail. in microform from UMI) American Federation of Labor - Congress of Industrial Organizations, 815 16th St., N.W., Washington, DC 20006.
Formerly (until 1976): American Federationist (ISSN 0001-1169)

331.88 US ISSN 0001-1177
A F L - C I O FREE TRADE UNION NEWS. 1944-1984 (vol.39, no.9). m. (tabloid format) A F L - C I O, 815 16th St., N.W., Washington, DC 20006.

637 UK
A F R C INSTITUTE OF FOOD RESEARCH TECHNICAL BULLETINS. (Former name of issuing body: National Institute for Research in Dairying) 1979-1986 (no.8). irreg. Agriculture & Food Research Council, Institute of Food Research, Reading Laboratory, Shinfield, Reading RG2 9AT, England.
Former titles: N I R D Technical Bulletins; N I R D - H R I Technical Bulletins.

331.88 371.1 US
A F T IN THE NEWS. ceased. m. (reprint service avail. from UMI) American Federation of Teachers, 555 New Jersey Ave., N.W., Washington, DC 20001.

635 CN ISSN 0829-5247
A FLEUR DE POT; la revue des amateurs de plantes d'interieur. 1985-19?? 6/yr. HortiCom Inc., 1449 Ave. William, Sillery, Que. G1S 4G5, Canada.

796 US ISSN 0361-5898
GV439
A I A W HANDBOOK - DIRECTORY. ceased. a. (Association for Intercollegiate Athletics for Women) American Alliance for Health, Physical Education, Recreation, and Dance, National Association for Girls and Women in Sport, 1900 Association Dr., Reston, VA 22091.
Formed by the merger of: A I A W Handbook of Policies and Operating Procedures (ISSN 0090-9106); A I A W Directory, Charter Member Institutions.

610 551.5 US ISSN 1040-6018
A I B C BULLETIN. 1988-1990 (vol.3, no.1). 3/yr. (looseleaf format; back issues avail.) American Institute of Biomedical Climatology, 1023 Welsh Rd., Philadelphia, PA 19115.

325 US ISSN 0001-1517
A I C C NEWS. (Former name of issuing body: American Immigration and Citizenship Conference) 1955-198? bi-m. (processed) National Immmigration, Refugee and Citizenship Forum, 277 Massachusettes Ave., N.E., Ste. 210, Washington, DC 20002.

657 US ISSN 0146-9770
A I C P A WASHINGTON REPORT. 1975-198? w. American Institute of Certified Public Accountants, 1211 Ave. of the Americas, New York, NY 10036-8775.

660 US ISSN 0065-8812
CODEN: ACSSCQ
A I CH E SYMPOSIUM SERIES. 1951-19?? a. (back issues avail.) American Institute of Chemical Engineers, 345 E. 47th St., New York, NY 10017.
Supersedes: Chemical Engineering Progress Symposium Series (ISSN 0069-2948)

610 614.8 US ISSN 0894-931X
A I D S: A QUARTERLY BIBLIOGRAPHY FROM ALL FIELDS OF PERIODICAL LITERATURE. (Acquired Immune Deficiency Syndrome) 1987-198?; suspended. q. Lincoln Associates, Box 507, Madison, WI 53701.

616.9 SZ
A I D S AND ASSOCIATED DISEASES. 1988-19?? irreg. S. Karger AG, Allschwilerstr. 10, Postfach, CH-4009 Basel, Switzerland.

616.9 011 US ISSN 0895-3201
A I D S RESEARCH TODAY. 1987-1991. m. BIOSIS, 2100 Arch St., Philadelphia, PA 19103-1399.

616.9 US
A I D S SCAN; current literature in perspective. 1989-1990 (Nov.). q. Mosby - Year Book, Inc. (Subsidiary of: Times Mirror Company), 11830 Westline Industrial Dr., St. Louis, MO 63146.

368 AT ISSN 0084-697X
A.I.J. MANUAL OF AUSTRALASIAN LIFE ASSURANCE. (Australasian Insurance Journal) 1930-198? a. Bushell Publishing Co. Pty. Ltd., 1987 Pittwater Rd., Bayview, N.S.W. 2104, Australia.

614.7 US
A I N NEWS. ceased 1987 (vol.26, no.6). 6/yr. (looseleaf format) Association of Interpretive Naturalists, Inc., Box 1892, Ft. Collins, CO 80522.
Supersedes: Association of Interpretive Naturalists. Employment Opportunities Listing.

001.6 651.8 US
A I S P DIALOGUE. (Former name of issuing body: International Information-Word Processing Association) 1972-1990. bi-m. Association of Information Systems Professionals, 104 Wilmot Rd., Ste. 201, Deerfield, IL 60015-5195.
Former titles (until 1988): A I S P Newsline; Words (ISSN 0164-4742)

296 US
A J C JOURNAL. 1978-19?? q. American Jewish Committee, 165 E. 56th St., New York, NY 10022-2746.
Formerly: American Jewish Committee News and Views.

917.3 US ISSN 0090-8614
E158
A L A SIGHTS TO SEE BOOK. 1971-198? a. (Automobile Legal Association) A L A Auto & Travel Club, 888 Worcester St., Wellesley, MA 02181.
Formerly: A L A Green Book.

020 US ISSN 0065-907X
A L A STUDIES IN LIBRARIANSHIP. 1971-1983 (no.10). irreg. (reprint service avail. from UMI) American Library Association, 50 E. Huron St., Chicago, IL 60611.

020.6 US ISSN 0364-1597
Z673.A5
A L A YEARBOOK; a review of library events of previous year. 1976-1989. a. (reprint service avail. from UMI) American Library Association, 50 E. Huron St., Chicago, IL 60611.

635.9 630 US
A L I; the allied landscape industry magazine. (Allied Landscape Industry) 1974-19?? q. American Association of Nurserymen, 1250 I St., N.W., Ste. 500, Washington, DC 20005.

622 US
A M A PRODUCT DIRECTORY. ceased 1986. biennial. American Monument Association, 933 High St., Ste. 200, Worthington, OH 43085.
Former titles: American Monument Association. Retailer's Guide; Granite and Marble Directory (ISSN 0731-4094)

378 620 US
A M C E E MONITOR; educating technical professionals worldwide. ceased. 10/yr. Association for Media-Based Continuing Education for Engineers, 613 Cherry St., Ste. 307, Atlanta, GA 30332.

001.681 629.8 JA ISSN 0388-1423
A M J NEWSLETTER. 1967-1991. bi-w. (tabloid format) Genyosha Publications, Inc., 18-2, Shibuya 3-chome, Shibuya-ku, Tokyo 150, Japan.
Formerly (until Aug. 1975): Automation Journal of Japan (ISSN 0005-1225)

737 US
A N A COMMUNIQUE. ceased 1989 (vol.3). 4/yr. American Numismatic Association, 818 N. Cascade Ave., Colorado Springs, CO 80903.

384.54 US ISSN 0739-0351
A N A R C NEWSLETTER. 1964-1990 (Mar.). bi-m. Association of North American Radio Clubs, 1218 Huntington Rd., San Marcos, CA 92609.

737.4 380.1 US
A N A RESOURCE DIRECTORY. ceased. every 18 mos. American Numismatic Association, 818 N. Cascade Ave., Colorado Springs, CO 80903-3279.

020 UK
A N S L I C S NEWS. 1980-1990. q. Aberdeen and North of Scotland Library and Information Co-operative Service, RGIT Library, St. Andrew St., Aberdeen, Scotland AB1 1HG.

994 AT ISSN 0001-2068
D1
A N U HISTORICAL JOURNAL. 1964-1986. a. (back issues avail.) Australian National University, Historical Society, G.P.O. Box 4, Canberra, A.C.T. 2601, Australia.

387.7 US ISSN 0744-2629
A O P A GENERAL AVIATION NATIONAL REPORT. 1948-198? m. Aircraft Owners and Pilots Association, 421 Aviation Way, Frederick, MD 21701.
Formerly: A O P A Newsletter.

363.6 US
A P C A GOVERNMENT AGENCIES DIRECTORY. 1970-197? a. (reprint service avail. from UMI) (Air Pollution Control Associates, The Association Dedicated to Air Pollution Control and Hazardous Waste Management) A P C A, Box 2861, Pittsburgh, PA 15230.
Former titles: Directory of Governmental Air Pollution Agencies; A P C A Directory and Resource Book (ISSN 0094-9191); Supersedes: A P C A Directory.

338.1 AT ISSN 0156-1766
A P M A REPORT (NO.). ceased. irreg? University of New England, Department of Agricultural Economics and Business Management, Armidale, N.S.W. 2351, Australia.

595.7 US ISSN 0882-8431
A R P E NEWS. 1973-1991 (Dec.). m. (back issues avail.) American Registry of Professional Entomologists, 9301 Annapolis Rd., Lanham, MD 20706.

610 US ISSN 0893-4762
RD130
A S A I O PRIMERS IN ARTIFICIAL ORGANS. 1987-1988 (Apr.-Jun.). q. (American Society of Artifical Internal Organs) J.B. Lippincott Co., E. Washington Sq., Philadelphia, PA 19105.

333 368 US ISSN 0569-7840
A S A MONOGRAPH (WASHINGTON). 1969-1979 (no.8). irreg. American Society of Appraisers, Box 17265, Washington, DC 20041.

737.4 US
A S P N NEWSLETTER. 1980-198? q. American Society for Portuguese Numismatics, 3491 Clearview Ave., Columbus, OH 43220.

CESSATIONS

629.8 GW
A S R. (Antrieb mit Steuerung und Regelung) 1973-1980. 10/yr. Vereinigte Fachverlage Krausskopf Ingenieur-Digest, Lessingstr. 12, P.F. 2760, 6500 Mainz, Germany.

629.2 US
A T V NEWS. (All Terrain Vehicle) 1981-19?? bi-w. (back issues avail.) Cycle News, Inc., Box 1030, 2201 Cherry Ave., Long Beach, CA 90801.
Formerly: Biker.

388.3 US
A T V SPORTS. (All Terrain Vehicle) ceased. m. Wright Publishing Co., 2949 Century Place, Box 2260, Costa Mesa, CA 92628.

720 CL ISSN 0567-428X
A U C A. (Arquitectura, Urbanismo, Construccion y Arte) 1965-1986; suspended. 3/yr. (back issues avail.) Ediciones A U C A, Monsenor Miller 15, Of. 126, Santiago, Chile.

340 GW ISSN 0933-4718
A V A - ARBEITSMATERIALIEN ZUR VERWALTUNGS- UND HOCHSCHULAUSBILDUNG. 1982-1991. bi-m. W. Kohlhammer GmbH (Subsidiary of: Deutscher Gemeindeverlag GmbH), Max-Planck-Str. 12, D-5000 Cologne 40, Germany.

614.85 GW
A W IM BLICKPUNKT. 1980-1989. bi-m. Arbeiterwohlfahrt Kreisverband Koeln e.V., Rubensstr. 7-13, D-5000 Cologne 1, Germany.

659.1 US
A W N Y NEWS. ceased. 3/yr. Advertising Women of New York, 153 E. 57th St., New York, NY 10022.

657 AT
A Y BUSINESS. 1975-19?? bi-m. Arthur Young, Ed. & Pub., 83 Clarence St., Sydney, N.S.W. 2000, Australia.

378 FI ISSN 0355-5798
LF4435.A33
AABO AKADEMI. AARSSKRIFT. 1917-1986. a. Aabo Akademi, Domkyrkotorget 3, 20500 Aabo, Finland.

630 334.683 NE
AAN- EN VERKOOPOST. ceased. m. Nationale Cooperatieve Aan- en Verkoopvereniging voor Land-en Tuinbouw Cebeco-Handelsraad, Blaak 31, 3011 GA Rotterdam, Netherland.

796 SW
AARETS BANDY. ceased. a. Stroembergs Idrottsboecker, Vittangigatan 27, Vaellingby, Stockholm, Sweden.

970 DK ISSN 0109-9035
AARHUS UNIVERSITET. CENTER FOR LATINAMERIKASTUDIER. NYHEDSBREV. ceased. 2/yr. Aarhus Universitet, Center for Latinamerikastudier, Willemoesgade 15, 8200 Aarhus N, Denmark.

910 DK ISSN 0106-9047
AARHUS UNIVERSITET. GEOGRAFISK INSTITUT. NOTAT. 1979-1989 (no.71). irreg., no.63, 1987. (back issues avail.) Aarhus Universitet, Geografisk Institut, DK-8000 Aarhus C, Denmark.

320 DK ISSN 0901-5213
AARHUS UNIVERSITET. INSTITUT FOR STATSKUNDSKAB. ARBEJDSPAPIR. ceased. irreg. Aarhus Universitet, Institut for Statskundskab - University of Aarhus, Institute of Political Science, Universitetsparken, DK-8000 Aarhus C, Denmark.

001.6 621.381 US ISSN 0724-6722
QA75.5
ABACUS (NEW YORK); the magazine for the computer professional. 1984-198? 5/yr. (back issues avail.) Springer-Verlag, Journals, 175 Fifth Ave., New York, NY 10010.

967.11 CM ISSN 0001-3102
ABBIA; revue culturelle Camerounaise. 1963-19?? q. (reprint service avail. from KTO) (Centre de Litterature Evangelique) Editions C L E, B.P. 1501, Yaounde, Cameroon.

028.5 333.7 GW ISSN 0934-8549
ABGESAEGT; Jugendzeitschrift fuer Natur- und Umweltschutz. 1985-1991. q. (back issues avail.) Naturschutzjugend Niedersachsen, Seilwinderstr. 4-5, 3000 Hannover 1, Germany.

323.4 919.406 AT
ABORIGINAL LAW NOTES. ceased. 8/yr. Aboriginal Law Centre, University of New South Wales, Faculty of Law, P.O. Box 1, Kensington, N.S.W. 2033, Australia.

950 NE ISSN 0065-0390
ABR-NAHRAIN. SUPPLEMENTS. 1964; ceased same year. irreg. (University of Melbourne, Department of Middle Eastern Studies, AT) E.J. Brill, P.O. Box 9000, 2300 PA Leiden, Netherlands.

282 US ISSN 0737-3457
ABRIDGED CATHOLIC PERIODICAL AND LITERATURE INDEX. 1983-1991. bi-m. Catholic Library Association, 461 W. Lancaster Ave., Haverford, PA 19041.

658.5 621 016 US
ABSTRACT NEWSLETTER: INDUSTRIAL & MECHANICAL ENGINEERING. ceased 1984. w. U.S. National Technical Information Service, 5285 Port Royal Rd., Springfield, VA 22161.
Former titles: Weekly Abstract Newsletter: Industrial and Mechanical Engineering; Weekly Government Abstracts. Industrial and Mechanical Engineering (ISSN 0364-6483)

616.2 016 JA ISSN 0389-7389
ABSTRACTS OF THE CURRENT LITERATURE ON RESPIRATORY DISEASES AND T B/KOKYUKI SHIKKAN KEKKAKU BUNKEN NO SHOROKU SOKUHO. 1950-1992 (Mar.). m. Japan Anti-Tuberculosis Association - Kekkaku Yobokai, 1-3-12 Misaki-cho, Chiyoda-ku, Tokyo 101, Japan.
Formerly: Abstracts of the Current Literature on T B and Other Respiratory Diseases (ISSN 0001-3668)

614.7 016 US ISSN 0044-5819
RA565.A1
ABSTRACTS ON HEALTH EFFECTS OF ENVIRONMENTAL POLLUTANTS; all abstracts and references on environmental research from Biological Abstracts and B A-R R M (Reports, Reviews, Meetings). 1972-1989. m. (reprint service avail.) BIOSIS, 2100 Arch St., Philadelphia, PA 19103-1399.

591 CU
ACADEMIA DE CIENCIAS DE CUBA. INSTITUTO DE ZOOLOGIA. INFORME CIENTIFICO-TECNICO. 1978-1982 (no.68). irreg. Academia de Ciencias de Cuba, Instituto de Zoologia, Industria 452, Havana 2, Cuba.

400 AG ISSN 0001-3862
ACADEMIA PORTENA DEL LUNFARDO. BOLETIN. 1966-1983 (vol.20). q. Libreria Pardo, Estados Unidos 1379, C.P. 1101 Buenos Aires, Argentina.

621.381 US ISSN 0892-4694
LB2395.7
ACADEMIC COMPUTING. 1986-199? 8/yr. Academic Computing Publications, Inc., 200 W. Virginia, Box 804, McKinney, TX 75069.

500 060 PL ISSN 0079-3159
ACADEMIE POLONAISE DES SCIENCES. CENTRE SCIENTIFIQUE, PARIS. CONFERENCES. 1953-1988 (no.137). irreg. (Polska Akademia Nauk, Centre Scientifique, Paris, FR) Panstwowe Wydawnictwo Naukowe, Ul. Miodowa 10, 00-251 Warsaw, Poland.

284 051 US ISSN 0362-708X
AS30
ACADEMY. 1943-1986 (vol.42, no.2). s-a. Lutheran Academy for Scholarship, c/o Richard Jeske, Ed., Lutheran Theological Seminary, 7301 Germantown Ave., Philadelphia, PA 19119.
Former titles: Academy: Lutherans in Profession; Lutheran Scholar (ISSN 0024-7502)

610 US ISSN 0001-4249
Z881
ACADEMY BOOKMAN. 1948-1982. s-a. (Friends of the New York Academy of Medicine, Friends of the Rare Book Room, Inc.) New York Academy of Medicine, Library, 2 E. 103rd St., New York, NY 10029.

536 US ISSN 0888-6881
QC276 CODEN: IVREEW
ACADEMY OF SCIENCES OF THE U S S R. HIGH TEMPERATURE INSTITUTE. I V T A N REVIEWS. 1987-1991. q. (back issues avail., reprint service avail. from UMI) Hemisphere Publishing Corporation (Subsidiary of: Taylor & Francis Group), 1900 Frost Rd., Ste. 101, Bristol, PA 19007.

388.3 CN ISSN 0315-3339
ACCELERATOR (OTTAWA). 1971-1975. q. Ontario Motor League, Ottawa Club, 1354 Richmond Rd., Ottawa, Ont. K2B 7Z3, Canada.

268 US ISSN 0001-4516
ACCENT ON YOUTH. 1968-19?? q. (United Methodist Church) United Methodist Publishing House, Graded Press, 201 Eighth Ave. S., Nashville, TN 37203.
Formerly: Twelve - Fifteen.

617.6 US ISSN 0065-079X
RK701
ACCEPTED DENTAL THERAPEUTICS. 1934-198? biennial. American Dental Association, 211 E. Chicago Ave., Chicago, IL 60611.
Formerly: Accepted Dental Remedies.

070.5 US
ACCESS (NEW YORK); what's new in reference publishing and information systems. ceased. q. R.R. Bowker, A Reed Reference Publishing Company, Division of Reed Publishing (USA) Inc., 121 Chanlon Rd., New Providence, NJ 07974.

384.5 US ISSN 0149-9262
ACCESS (WASHINGTON, 1975); the citizens journal of telecommunications. 1975-1986. m. (tabloid format; also avail. in microfilm) Telecommunications Research and Action Center, Box 12038, Washington, DC 20005.

616.99 US ISSN 0887-056X
RC261.A1 CODEN: ACONER
ACCOMPLISHMENTS IN ONCOLOGY. 1986-198? s-a. J.B. Lippincott Co., E. Washington Sq., Philadelphia, PA 19105.

621.381 657 US
ACCOUNTANTS MICROCOMPUTER NEWS. 1982-1990. m. Professional Publications, 50 S. 9th St., Ste. 200, Minneapolis, MN 55402.
Formerly: Accountants I B Micro Report (ISSN 8750-2798)

358.4 US
ACCOUNTING AND FINANCE TECH DIGEST. 1950-1986 (vol.37, no.9). m. (also avail. in microform from UMI) U.S. Air Force Accounting and Finance Center, AFAFC/DAPL, Denver, CO 80279-5000.
Formerly: Air Force Accounting and Finance Technical Digest (ISSN 0002-2330)

332.2 US
ACCOUNTING INSIGHT. ceased 1990 (May). m. National Council of Savings Institutions, 1101 15th St., N.W., Ste. 400, Washington, DC 20005-5070.

657 US
ACCOUNTING NEWS (NEW YORK, 1981). 1981-199? q. Warren, Gorham & Lamont Inc., One Penn Plaza, New York, NY 10119.

330 CN
ACHIEVERS. 1987-1990. q. 550-1500 W. Georgia, Vancouver, B.C. V6G 2Z6, Canada.

614.7 US
ACID RAIN FICHE. ceased 1990 (Nov.-Dec.). m. (microfiche) R.R. Bowker, A Reed Reference Publishing Company, Division of Reed Publishing (USA) Inc., 121 Chanlon Rd., New Providence, NJ 07974.

614.7 UK ISSN 0267-6222
ACID RAIN UPDATE. 1985-198? s-a. (back issues avail.) Technical Communications, 100 High Ave., Letchworth, Herts SG6 3RR, England.

614.7 SW ISSN 0282-1540
ACIDIFICATION RESEARCH IN SWEDEN. ceased 1990 (no.9). s-a. National Environmental Protection Board, Box 1302, S-17125 Solna, Sweden.

500 355 AG ISSN 0001-5490
ACTA CIENTIFICA. 1967-19?? q. Ministerio de Defensa, Instituto de Investigaciones Cientificas y Tecnicas de las Fuerzas Armadas, Zufriategui y Varela, Villa Martelli, Buenos Aires, Argentina.

621.38 530 FR ISSN 0001-558X
TK7800 CODEN: ACELAZ
ACTA ELECTRONICA. 1956-1989; suspended. a. Laboratoires d'Electronique et de Physique Appliquee (LEP), B.P. 15, 94451 Limeil-Brevannes cedex, France.

CESSATIONS

616.994   SP   ISSN 0001-589X
ACTA IBERICA RADIOLOGICA - CANCEROLOGICA. ceased 1966 (vol.21). q. Vitrubio 11, Madrid 6, Spain.

616.988   NE   ISSN 0065-1362
RC960   CODEN: ALSMAZ
ACTA LEIDENSIA; mededelingen uit het Instituut voor Tropische Geneeskunde te Leiden; communicitions from the Institute for Tropical Disease at Leiden. 1964-19?? irreg. (Instituut voor Tropische Geneeskunde te Leiden) Leiden University Press, c/o E.J. Brill Publishers, Postbus 9000, 2300 PA Leiden, Netherlands.

610   JA   ISSN 0001-611X
CODEN: AMUKAC
ACTA MEDICA UNIVERSITATIS KAGOSHIMAENSIS. 1958-1989 (vol.31, no.2). s-a. Kagoshima Daigaku, Igakubu - Kagoshima University, Faculty of Medicine, 8-1 Usuki-cho 12-chome, Kagoshima 890, Japan.

300   MX
ACTA MEXICANA DE CIENCIAS SOCIALES. 1978-198? q. Instituto Politecnico Nacional, Escuela Superior de Medicina, Prolongacion de S. Diaz Miron y Plan de San Luis, Mexico 17, D.F., Mexico.

618   JA   ISSN 0001-6330
ACTA OBSTETRICA ET GYNAECOLOGICA JAPONICA. 1954-19?? q. Japan Publications Trading Co. Ltd., Box 5030, Tokyo International, Tokyo, Japan.
Formerly: Japanese Obstetrical and Gynecological Society. Journal.

551.46   US   ISSN 0325-5182
ACTA OCEANOGRAPHICA ARGENTINA. published only once, 1977. s-a. International Association for the Physical Sciences of the Ocean, Comite Nacional, c/o Dr. Robert E. Stevenson, Box 1161, Del Mar, CA 92014-1161.

615.1   SW   ISSN 0001-6675
CODEN: APSXAS
ACTA PHARMACEUTICA SUECICA; Svensk farmaceutisk tidskrift. 1964-1988. 6/yr. (back issues avail.; reprint service avail. from UMI) (Swedish Academy of Pharmaceutical Sciences) Swedish Pharmaceutical Press, P.O. Box 1136, S-111 81 Stockholm, Sweden.

439   DK   ISSN 0001-6691
PD1503
ACTA PHILOLOGICA SCANDINAVICA; tidsskrift for nordisk sprogforskning. 1926-1985; resumed 1987-1988 (vol.35). irreg. (also avail. in microform from SWZ; reprint service avail. from ISI) P.O. Box 2571, DK-2100 Copenhagen OE, Denmark.

016   PL
ACTA POLYTECHNICAE WRATISLAVIENSIS. 1972-19?? q. Politechnika Wroclawska, Wybrzeze Wyspianskiego 27, 50-370 Wroclaw, Poland.

155   SW   ISSN 0065-1605
ACTA PSYCHOLOGICA - GOTHOBURGENSIA. 1956-1966. irreg. Goeteborgs Universitet, Department of Psychology, Fack, S-400 20 Goeteborg 14, Sweden.

577   IT   ISSN 0300-8924
QP801.V5   CODEN: AVEZA6
ACTA VITAMINOLOGICA ET ENZYMOLOGICA; rivista internazionale di vitaminologia e di enzimologia. 1947; N.S. 1979-1985. q. Via M. D'Aviano 2-5, 20131 Milan, Italy.
Formerly: Acta Vitaminologica (ISSN 0001-7248)

333.7   US
ACTION (CONCORD). ceased 1988. q. Society for the Protection of New Hampshire Forests, 54 Portsmouth St., Concord, NH 03301.

616.86   US   ISSN 0001-7396
ACTION (RENSSELAERVILLE). 1954-198? m. Alcohol Education for Youth and Community, Inc., Box 122, Rensselaerville, NY 12147.

640.73   US
ACTION FOR CORPORATE ACCOUNTABILITY. ACTION NEWS. 1987-19?? bi-m. Action for Corporate Accountability, 212 3rd Ave. N., Ste. 300, Minneapolis, MN 55401.

001.64   CN
ACTION INFORMATIQUE. 1988-19?? 22/yr. (tabloid format) Publications Transcontinental Inc., 465 St.-Jean St., 9th fl., Montreal, Que. H2Y 3S4, Canada.

330 370   US   ISSN 0162-5306
ACTION LINE (MEMPHIS). 1973-19?? s-a. (looseleaf format; back issues avail.) Southeastern American Institute for Decision Sciences, College of Business Administration, Memphis State University, Memphis, TN 38152.

612.67 362.6 296   US
ACTION MEMO & SENIOR CITIZENS ADVOCATE; and aspects of aging. 1981-19??; suspended. q. (back issues avail.) Jewish Association for Services for the Aged, 40 W. 68th St., New York, NY 10023.
Formerly: Senior Citizens Advocate (ISSN 0882-9403)

362   UK
ACTION RESEARCH. 1971-199?; suspended. 3/yr. Action Research for the Crippled Child, Vincent House, N. Parade, Horsham, W. Sussex RH12 2DA, England.
Formerly: Action (Horsham) (ISSN 0309-2658)

384.5 384.5   UK
ACTION STATIONS: THE DIRECTORY OF SOCIAL ACTION PROGRAMMES. 1977-1989. s-a. (back issues avail.) Media Project, Volunteer Centre, 29 Lower King's Rd., Berkhamsted, Herts. HP4 2AB, England.
Formerly: Directory of Social Action Programmes (ISSN 0262-3153)

330   NQ
ACTIVIDAD ECONOMICA. 1978-1984. m. Banco de America, Avda. Sandino y 40, Calle Sur Este, Apdo. 285, Managua, D.N., Nicaragua.

338.2   VE   ISSN 0001-7582
ACTIVIDADES PETROLERAS. ceased. q. Ministerio de Energia y Minas, Torre Norte, Centro Simon Bolivar, Caracas, Venezuela.

792   US
ACTOR'S COMPLETE SUMMER THEATER GUIDE. 1982-19?? biennial. Allen Theatrical Publications, Box 2129, Rockefeller Center Sta., New York, NY 10185.
Formerly: Summer Theater Guide.

318   CR
ACTUALIDAD ESTADISTICA. ceased 1986. 3/yr. Centro de Informacion Estadistica, Direccion General de Estadistica y Censos, Apdo. 10 163, 1000 San Jose, Costa Rica.

330.1   CU   ISSN 0864-1439
ACTUALIDADES DE LA ECONOMIA SOCIALISTA; revista de traducciones. 1986-1989 (Jun.). m. Junta Central de Planificacion (JUCEPLAN), Centro de Informacion Cientifico-Tecnica, 20 de Mayo y Ayestaran, Plaza de la Revolucion, Havana, Cuba.

610.28   SZ   ISSN 0254-0819
QH324.9.B5
ACUTE CARE; international review of critical care medicine incorporating patient monitoring. 1964-19?? q. (also avail. in microform from RPI) S. Karger AG, Allschwilerstrasse 10, P.O. Box, CH-4009 Basel, Switzerland.
Former titles (until vol.9, 1982): Biotelemetry and Patient Monitoring (ISSN 0378-309X); (until vol.5, 1978): Biotelemetry (ISSN 0301-5912)

659.1   US
AD DAY; the national newsletter of advertising and marketing. 1965-1990. d. A S M Communications, Inc. (New York), 49 E. 21st St., New York, NY 10010.
Former titles: Ad Day - U S A & Ad Daily.

659.1   US   ISSN 0192-7922
AD EAST. 1970-1988. m. (newspaper) Ad East Enterprises Inc., 100 Boylston St., 2nd Fl., Boston, MA 02116-4610.

659   US
AD-PRO. ceased 1991. m. National Retail Merchants Association, 100 W. 31st St., New York, NY 10001.
Supersedes: Radio Broadcaster & Retail Broadcaster & Newspaper Newsletter & Promotion Exchange.

340   IQ
ADALA. 1975-19?? q. Ministry of Justice, Legal Drafting Department, Baghdad, Iraq.
Supersedes: Diwan al-Tadween al-Qanouni. Nashrat; Diwan al-Tadween al-Qanouni Majallat (ISSN 0025-1038)

054.1   FR
ADAM. 1925-1974. m. 14 rue Brunel, 75017 Paris, France.

621.381   US
ADD-ON BUYER'S GUIDE & HANDBOOK. ceased 1989. s-a. Bedford Communications, Inc., 150 Fifth Ave., New York, NY 10011.

016 616.861   CN   ISSN 0065-1885
ADDICTION RESEARCH FOUNDATION OF ONTARIO. BIBLIOGRAPHIC SERIES. 1967-19?? irreg. Addiction Research Foundation of Ontario, Marketing Services, 33 Russell St., Toronto, Ont. M5S 2S1, Canada.

910.4   US
ADIRONDACK BITS'N PIECES. ceased 1985. 4/yr. Bannister Publications, 22 Prospect, Box 63, Port Henry, NY 12974.

350   PP   ISSN 0311-4511
ADMINISTRATION FOR DEVELOPMENT. 1974-1987; suspended. s-a. Administrative College of Papua New Guinea, PO Box 1216, Boroko, Papua New Guinea.

342   CN   ISSN 0826-8754
KE5015.A13
ADMINISTRATIVE LAW JOURNAL; developments in administrative law. ceased 1991. 4/yr. Butterworths Canada Ltd., 75 Clegg Rd., Markham, Ont. L6G 1A1, Canada.

371.2   US   ISSN 0742-6542
ADMINISTRATOR'S UPDATE. 1979-1992. 3/yr. (E R I C Clearinghouse on Higher Education) American Association of University Administrators, c/o Susan Kaplan, Gen. Sec., George Washington University, 2121 Eye St., N.W., Washington, WA 20052.

235   US
ADOLESCENT MENTAL HEALTH ABSTRACTS. 1983-1988 (vol.5, no.4). q. Center for Adolescent Mental Health, Columbia University, School of Social Work, 622 W. 113th St., New York, NY 10025.

155.5   US
ADOLINKS. 1983-19?? q. Washington University, Center for Adolescent Mental Health, Box 1196, St. Louis, MO 63130.

612 616.4   UK   ISSN 0142-8551
ADRENAL GLANDS. ceased 1990. m. (looseleaf format; back issues avail.) Sheffield University Biomedical Information Service (SUBIS), The University, Sheffield S10 2TN, England.

268   US
ADULT BIBLE STUDY. PUPIL. FRENCH EDITION. ceased. q. Southern Baptist Convention, Sunday School Board, 127 Ninth Ave., N., Nashville, TN 37234.

268   US   ISSN 0162-4164
ADULT BIBLE TEACHER. LARGE PRINT EDITION. ceased. q. (large print in 13 pt.) Southern Baptist Convention, Sunday School Board, Customer Service Department, 127 Ninth Ave. N., Nashville, TN 37234.

374   UK   ISSN 0001-849X
LC5201
ADULT EDUCATION. 1926-1989. q. (also avail. in microform from UMI; reprint service avail. from UMI, SWZ) National Institute of Adult Continuing Education, 19B De Montfort St., Leicester LE1 7GE, England.

374   US
ADULT LEARNER. 1975-1990. q. General Educational Development Institute, 16211 Sixth Ave., N.E., Seattle, WA 98155.

370 001.642   US
ADULT LITERACY & TECHNOLOGY: GUIDE TO LITERACY SOFTWARE (YEAR). published only once, 1989. a. People's Computer Co., Inc., 1 Spinnaker Way, Berkeley, CA 94710-1612.

268   US   ISSN 0149-998X
ADULT PLANBOOK; resources for adult Christian education in United Methodist Churches. 1959-19?? a. (United Methodist Church) United Methodist Publishing House, Graded Press, 201 Eighth Ave. S., Nashville, TN 37203.
Formerly: United Methodist Church (United States) Division of Education. Adult Planbook (ISSN 0082-7983)

CESSATIONS 5131

360   US   ISSN 0899-1995
ADULT RESIDENTIAL CARE JOURNAL. 1987-1991? q. (reprint service avail. from UMI) Human Sciences Press, Inc. (Subsidiary of: Plenum Publishing Corp.), 233 Spring St., New York, NY 10013-1578.
    Formerly (until 1988): Adult Foster Care Journal (ISSN 8756-6559)

621   UK
ADVANCED MANUFACTURING TECHNOLOGY. 1985-19?? irreg. Jordan & Sons Ltd., 21 St. Thomas St., Bristol BS1 6JS, England.

668.4   UK   ISSN 0957-9559
ADVANCED MATERIALS ABSTRACTS. 1989-1991. m. (Rubber and Plastics Research Association of Great Britain, R A P R A Technology Ltd.) Pergamon Press plc, Headington Hill Hall, Oxford OX3 0BW, England.

510   NE
ADVANCED STUDIES IN PURE MATHEMATICS. 1983-1987 (vol.12). irreg. Elsevier Science Publishers B.V., Books Division, P.O. Box 211, 1000 AE Amsterdam, Netherlands.

610 620   US   ISSN 0888-2215
ADVANCES IN BIOMEDICAL COMPUTING SERIES. 1987-19?? irreg. (back issues avail.) Computer Science Press, Inc., 41 Madison Ave., 37th Fl., New York, NY 10010-3546.

658.403   US   ISSN 0196-870X
QA76.6
ADVANCES IN COMPUTER PROGRAMMING MANAGEMENT. ceased 1984. irreg. John Wiley & Sons, Inc., 605 Third Ave., New York, NY 10158-0012.

574.8   US   ISSN 0084-5949
    CODEN: ADCYB4
ADVANCES IN CYTOPHARMACOLOGY. 1971-198? irreg. Raven Press, 1185 Ave. of the Americas, New York, NY 10036.

658.403   US   ISSN 0196-8718
QA76.9.D3
ADVANCES IN DATA BASE MANAGEMENT. ceased 1984. irreg. John Wiley & Sons, Inc., 605 Third Ave., New York, NY 10158-0012.

541.37 660   US   ISSN 0567-9907
QD552   CODEN: AEEEAS
ADVANCES IN ELECTROCHEMISTRY AND ELECTROCHEMICAL ENGINEERING. 1961-19?? (vol. 16). irreg. Krieger Publishing Co. Inc., P.O. Box 9542, Melbourne, FL 32901.

614.7   US   ISSN 0065-2563
TD180   CODEN: AESTC9
ADVANCES IN ENVIRONMENTAL SCIENCE AND TECHNOLOGY. 1969-1988. irreg. John Wiley & Sons, Inc., 605 Third Ave., New York, NY 10158-0012.
    Formerly: Advances in Environmental Sciences (ISSN 0095-4535)

155.937 616.89   US   ISSN 0747-6353
HV6001
ADVANCES IN FORENSIC PSYCHOLOGY AND PSYCHIATRY. 1984-198? (vol.2). irreg. Ablex Publishing Corporation, 355 Chestnut St., Norwood, NJ 07648.

616.4 618   US
ADVANCES IN HUMAN FERTILITY & REPRODUCTIVE ENDOCRINOLOGY. 1982-198? (vol.3). a. Raven Press, 1185 Ave. of the Americas, New York, NY 10036.

615.19   SZ   ISSN 0253-2093
    CODEN: ADPHDK
ADVANCES IN PHARMACOTHERAPY/FORTSCHRITTE IN DER PHARMAKOTHERAPIE. 1981-19?? irreg. S. Karger AG, Allschwilerstr. 10, CH-4009 Basel, Switzerland.

320   US
ADVANCES IN POLITICAL SCIENCE. 1982-198? irreg. Sage Publications, Inc., 2111 W. Hillcrest Dr., Newbury Park, CA 91320.

612.015   US   ISSN 0160-2179
QP801.P638   CODEN: APLRDC
ADVANCES IN POLYAMINE RESEARCH. 1978-1983 (vol.4). irreg. Raven Press, 1185 Ave. of the Americas, New York, NY 10036.

620 380.3   US   ISSN 0888-2207
ADVANCES IN SATELLITE COMMUNICATIONS SERIES. 1987-19?? irreg. (back issues avail.) Computer Science Press, Inc., 41 Madison Ave., 37th Fl., New York, NY 10010-3546.

621.3   US   ISSN 0888-4536
TK1191   CODEN: APMDEA
ADVANCES IN SOVIET POWER SYSTEMS. PART 1: THERMAL AND MECHANICAL. 1986-1990. bi-m. (U.S.S.R. Ministry of Power and Electrification, UR) Allerton Press, Inc., 150 Fifth Ave., New York, NY 10011.

621.3   US   ISSN 0888-4544
TK3001   CODEN: ASPDEC
ADVANCES IN SOVIET POWER SYSTEMS. PART 2: ELECTRICAL GENERATION AND DISTRIBUTION. 1986-1990. bi-m. (U.S.S.R. Ministry of Power and Electrification, UR) Allerton Press, Inc., 150 Fifth Ave., New York, NY 10011.

613.7 610   US   ISSN 0889-3977
RC1200
ADVANCES IN SPORTS MEDICINE AND FITNESS. 1987-1989 (Dec.). a. Mosby - Year Book, Inc. (Chicago) (Subsidiary of: Times Mirror Company), 200 N. LaSalle St., Chicago, IL 60601-1080.

621.3 001.644   US   ISSN 0888-2223
ADVANCES IN TELECOMMUNICATIONS NETWORKS SERIES. 1982-19?? q. Computer Science Press, Inc., 41 Madison Ave., 37th Fl., New York, NY 10010-3546.
    Formerly: Journal of Telecommunication Networks (ISSN 0276-0037)

661   US   ISSN 0271-2334
QC319.8   CODEN: ATRPDU
ADVANCES IN TRANSPORT PROCESSES. 1980-1986 (vol.4). irreg. John Wiley & Sons, Inc., 605 Third Ave., New York, NY 10158-0012.

621.381   US   ISSN 0888-224X
ADVANCES IN V L S I AND COMPUTER SYSTEMS. (Very Large Scale Integration) 1983-19?? irreg. Computer Science Press, Inc., 41 Madison Ave., 37th Fl., New York, NY 10010-3546.
    Supersedes: Journal of V L S I and Computer Systems (ISSN 0733-5644); Journal of Digital Systems (ISSN 0195-4350); Journal of Design Automation and Fault-Tolerant Computing (ISSN 0099-1708)

610.73   US   ISSN 1042-9565
ADVANCING CLINICAL CARE. 1986-1991 (Nov.). bi-m. (also avail. in microform from UMI; reprint service avail. from UMI) Data Design, Inc., 2901 Oakhurst Ln., Franksville, WI 53126.
    Formerly (until vol.4, no.3, 1989): Ad Nurse (ISSN 0887-2198)

284   GW   ISSN 0232-6086
ADVENTGEMEINDE; church paper of the Seventh Day Adventists. 1980-1990. m. (Gemeinschaft der Siebenten-Tags-Adventisten in der DDR) Union Druckerei, Charlottenstr. 79, 1080 Berlin, Germany.

371.3   US
ADVENTURES IN LEARNING. 1985-1988. bi-m. (back issues avail.) Dragon Quest, Box 1635, Sebastopol, CA 95473-1635.
    Formerly: Dragon Smoke.

659.1   US   ISSN 0276-9751
HF5802
ADVERTISING AGE YEARBOOK. 1981-1984. a. Crain Books (Subsidiary of: Crain Communications, Inc.), 740 Rush St., Chicago, IL 60611.

362 301.4   US
ADVICE FOR ADULTS WITH AGING PARENTS OR A DEPENDENT SPOUSE. ceased 1989. bi-m. Helpful Publications, Box 339, Glenside, PA 09038.

332.6   US
ADVISOR (CHICAGO). 1986-198? s-m. Capital Futures Associates, Ltd., Box 2618, Chicago, IL 60690.

659.1   US   ISSN 0894-3052
ADWEEK'S WINNERS. ceased 1990 (Apr.). m. A S M Communications, Inc. (New York), 49 E. 21st St., New York, NY 10010.

629.13   GW   ISSN 0001-9100
AERO; unabhaengige Monatsschrift fuer die gesamte Luft- und Raumfahrt. 1950-1988. bi-m. c/o Marshall Cavendish, Paulstr. 3, 2000 Hamburg 1, Germany.

387.73   US   ISSN 0001-9097
AERO; the aircraft owner's magazine. 1968-198? m. Fancy Publications, Inc., Box 6050, Mission Viejo, CA 92690.

700 627.137   US
AEROART. 1988; ceased same year. q. American Society of Aviation Artists, 15 W. 44th St., New York, NY 10036.

551.65   AU   ISSN 0001-9224
AEROLOGISCHE BERICHTE/AEROLOGICAL REPORT; Radiosondenaufstiege und Hoehenwindmessungen. 1952-19?? q. Zentralanstalt fuer Meteorologie und Geodynamik, Hohe Warte 38, A-1190 Vienna, Austria.

629.13   UK
AERONAUTICS AND FLIGHT. 1986-198? m. Brenard Press Ltd., Bldg. 221, Heathrow Airport, Hounslow, Middlesex, England.

355 011   US   ISSN 0738-0461
UF530
AEROSPACE DEFENSE MARKETS & TECHNOLOGY. 1982-1991 (Dec.). m. with q. and a. cumulations. (back issues avail.) Predicasts, A Ziff Communications Company, 11001 Cedar Ave., Cleveland, OH 44106.
    Formerly: Defense Markets and Technology.

629.4 658 363.35   US
AEROSPACE INTELLIGENCE. ceased 1990. w. (back issues avail.) Forecast International Inc. - D M S, 22 Commerce Rd., Newtown, CT 06470.

531.64   US
AESOP INSTITUTE NEWSLETTER. ceased. irreg. Aesop Institute, Box 880, Sebastopol, CA 95473.
    Formerly: Sunwind.

378   US
AFFAIRS OF STATE. 1983-19?? 3/yr. Mississippi State University, Alumni Association, Drawer AA, Mississippi State, MS 39765.

659.1   US
AFFILIATED ADVERTISING AGENCIES INTERNATIONAL. NEWS. ceased 1991 (Sep.). bi-m. Affiliated Advertising Agencies International, 2280 S. Xanadu Way, Ste. 300, Aurora, CO 80014-1330.

323.4   CN   ISSN 0441-4128
AFFIRMATION. 1979-19?? q. Ontario Human Rights Commission, Ministry of Labour, Suite M159A Ave., Macdonald Block, Queens's Park, Toronto, Ont. M7A 1A2, Canada.
    Formerly (until 1981): Human Relations.

636.7   US
AFGHAN WORLD; a bimonthly magazine for Afghan lovers. 1979-198? bi-m. Hoflin Publishing Ltd., 4401 Zephyr St., Wheat Ridge, CO 80033-3299.
    Formerly: Afghan Quarterly (ISSN 0199-2678)

956.006   GW   ISSN 0931-3583
AFGHANISTANBLAETTER. 1980-19??; suspended. q. (back issues avail.) Komitee zur Unterstuetzung der Fluechtlinge in Afghanistan und zum Wiederaufbau des zerstoerten Landes e.V. - Assistance Committee for Afghan Refugees and Reconstruction of the Country, Klosterallee 78, D-2000 Hamburg 13, Germany.

052   UK   ISSN 0266-2701
AFKAR INQUIRY; magazine of events and ideas. 1984-1988; suspended. m. Tropvale Ltd., 55 Banner St., London EC1Y 8PX, London.

015   UK   ISSN 0266-6731
Z3503.
AFRICA BIBLIOGRAPHY. 1985-1988. a. (International African Institute) Manchester University Press, Oxford Rd., Manchester M13 9PL, England.

916.02   PO
AFRICA ECONOMICA. 1984-1989. 4/yr. Centro de Estudos Economia e Sociedade, Direccao, Redaccao e Assinaturas, Av. Elias Garcia, 123, 4 Piso, 1000 Lisbon, Portugal.

CESSATIONS

960 309 US
AFRICA IN THE MODERN WORLD. ceased. irreg. Cornell University Press, 124 Roberts Place, Ithaca, NY 14850.

016 309 UK
AFRICA INDEX TO CONTINENTAL PERIODICAL LITERATURE. 1977-19??; suspended. irreg. (back issues avail.) Hans Zell Publishers (Subsidiary of: Bowker-Saur Ltd.-Butterworths), P.O. Box 56, Oxford OX1 3EL, England.
Continues: Africa Index (ISSN 0378-4797)

968 330.1 SA ISSN 0250-0116
AFRICA SEMINAR: COLLECTED PAPERS. 1978-1985 (vol.5). irreg. University of Cape Town, Centre for African Studies, Private Bag, Rondebosch 7700, South Africa.

382 US
AFRICAN-AMERICAN CHAMBER OF COMMERCE. NEWS. 1973-19?? q. New York Chamber of Commerce and Industry, African-American Chamber of Commerce, 200 Madison Ave., New York, NY 10016-3989.

627 UK
AFRICAN AND ASIAN WATER & SEWAGE. 1982-198? q. International Trade Publications Ltd., Queensway House, 2 Queensway, Redhill, Surrey RH1 1QS, England.
Formerly: African Water and Sewage.

355 FR ISSN 0244-0342
UA855
AFRICAN DEFENCE JOURNAL. 1980-1990. m. S A P E F, 11 rue de Teheran, 75008 Paris, France.

614.7 UK ISSN 0309-345X
AFRICAN ENVIRONMENT SPECIAL REPORTS. 1974-1977. irreg. International African Institute, Lionel Robbins Bldg., 10 Portugal St., London WC2A 2HD, England.

616.97 SA
AFRICAN JOURNAL OF CLINICAL AND EXPERIMENTAL IMMUNOLOGY. 1980-1984? q. Box 399, Bloemfontein 9300, South Africa.

323.4 UK ISSN 0263-1989
DT763
AFRICAN NATIONAL CONGRESS OF SOUTH AFRICA. NEWSBRIEFINGS. 1977-1990 (Dec.). w. African National Congress of South Africa, P.O. Box 38, 28 Penton St., London N19 PR, England.

327 UA
AFRICAN NEWSLETTER. 1973-19?? m. African Society, 5 Ahmed Hishmat Street, Zamalek, Cairo, Egypt.

355 FR ISSN 0182-2322
UA855
AFRIQUE DEFENSE; mensuel d'information militaire. 1978-1991. m. S A P E F, 11 rue de Teheran, 75008 Paris, France.

330 FR
AFRIQUE INDUSTRIE. ceased. bi-m. Ediafric, 10 rue Vineuse, 75116 Paris cedex 16, France.

371.0025 UK
AFTER SCHOOL; a guide to post school opportunities. ceased (2nd ed.). irreg. Kogan Page Ltd., 120 Pentonville Rd., London N1 9JN, England.

200 UK ISSN 0261-5630
AGAPE. 1982-1988. m. Emmaus Family of Prayer, 11 York Rd., Birkdale, Southport, Merseyside PR8 2AD, England.
Formerly: Maranatha.

636.1 CN
AGENDA CANADIAN AMERICAN ALMANAC. 1985-1991. a. Club Jockey du Quebec, 14 Pagnuelo St., Outremont, Que. H2V 3B9, Canada.
Former titles: Agenda American Almanac (Year); American Racehorse Owners & Breeders Almanac.

268 US ISSN 0275-9667
AGES 3-4 CHURCH AND HOME LEAFLETS. 1982-19?? m. (United Methodist Church) United Methodist Publishing House, Graded Press, 201 Eighth Ave. S., Box 801, Nashville, TN 37202.
Formerly: Nursery Days (ISSN 0029-6414)

268 US
AGES 5-6 CHURCH AND HOME LEAFLETS. 1982-19?? q. (United Methodist Church) United Methodist Publishing House, Graded Press, 201 Eighth Ave. S., Box 801, Nashville, TN 37202.
Former titles (until 1988): Ages 4-6 Church and Home Leaflets (ISSN 0276-3435); Kindergartner (ISSN 0023-1517)

800 US ISSN 0896-1964
AGINCOURT IRREGULAR; stories, poems, pictures. 1986-1989 (Dec.). irreg. (back issues avail.) Agincourt Press, 1869 Woodridge Ct., Middleburg, FL 32068-4134.

200 US ISSN 0748-6677
AGLOW; for the contemporary Christian woman. 1969-1991 (Apr.). bi-m. (Women's Aglow Fellowship, International) Aglow Publications, Box 1548, Lynnwood, WA 98046-1556.

001.6 IT ISSN 0392-8306
AGORA (ROME); informatics in a changing world. 1982?-198? q. Intergovernmental Bureau of Informatics, 23, Viale Civilta del Lavoro, 00144 Rome, Italy.

630 GW
HD1491.G33
AGRAR-INFORM; zeitschrift fuer die sozialistische Landwirtschaft und Nahrunggueterswirtschaft. 1967-1991. m. Deutscher Landwirtschaftsverlag Berlin, Reinhardstr. 14, 1040 Berlin, Germany.
Formerly: Kooperation (ISSN 0023-3811); Formed by the merger of: Deutsche Landwirtschaft (ISSN 0012-0391); Zeitschrift fuer Agraroekonomik.

630 GW ISSN 0323-3308
AGRARTECHNIK (BERLIN); landtechnische Zeitschrift der DDR. 1950-1991. m. (Kammer der Technik, Fachverband Land-, Forst- und Nahrungsguetertechnik) VEB Verlag Technik, Postfach 201, Oranienburger Str. 13-14, 1020 Berlin, Germany.
Formerly: Deutsche Agrartechnik (ISSN 0011-9784)

630 HU ISSN 0238-8197
AGRARVILAG. 1988-1990 (vol.3, no.2). bi-m. Agroinform, Karolyi Mihaly Orszagos Mezogazdasagi Konyvtar, Attila ut 93, H-1253 Budapest 13, Hungary.

630 UK
AGRI-TECHNOLOGY BUYERS GUIDE. 1984-1990. a. International Trade Publications Ltd., Queensway House, 2 Queensway, Redhill, Surrey RH1 1QS, England.
Former titles (until 1989): Asian Agribusiness Buyers Guide; Asian Agriculture Buyers Guide (ISSN 0265-833X)

630.24 668.6 US ISSN 0044-6769
CODEN: AGCACM
AGRICHEMICAL AGE; for dealers, applicators, and consultants. 1958-1991. 11/yr. H B J Farm Publications, Inc. (San Francisco) (Subsidiary of: Harcourt Brace Jovanovich, Inc.), 731 Market St., San Francisco, CA 94103-2011.
Formerly: Agrichemical West.

630 BL
AGRICOLAS. 1969-1987. s-a. (tabloid format) Comissao Brasileira de Documentacao Agricola, Avenida Padua Dias, 11, Caixa Postal 09, 13400 Piracicaba, SP, Brazil.

630 BL ISSN 0002-1318
AGRICULTOR; informative mensal da acares a familia rural capixaba. 1965-1985. m. (processed) Acares, Caixa Postal 644, Vitoria, Espirito Santo, Brazil.

630 631.381 US ISSN 0882-9284
AGRICULTURAL COMPUTING. 1981-1990 (no.9). m. Doane Publishing, 11701 Borman Dr., St. Louis, MO 63146.

338.1 CN ISSN 0708-5206
HD9014.C4
AGRICULTURAL DEVELOPMENT CORPORATION OF SASKATCHEWAN. ANNUAL REPORT. ceased 1990. a. Agricultural Development Corporation of Saskatchewan, 2500 Victoria Ave., Ste. 1106, Regina, Sask. S4P 3V, Canada.

631.3 US
AGRICULTURAL ELECTRONICS. 1985-1990. s-a. American Society of Agricultural Engineers, 2950 Niles Rd., St. Joseph, MI 49085-9659.

630 II ISSN 0970-2962
AGRICULTURAL ENGINEERING TODAY. 1976-19?? 6/yr. Indian Society of Agricultural Engineers, Satya Mansion, Flat, Nos. 305-306, Community Centre, Ranjit Nagar, New Delhi 100 008, India.

575.1 US ISSN 0278-9736
CODEN: AGEREH
AGRICULTURAL GENETICS REPORT; crop and animal biotechnology, food production, and bioremediation. 1982-1990. bi-m. Mary Ann Liebert, Inc., 1651 Third Ave., New York, NY 10128.

631 CN ISSN 0707-7793
AGRICULTURAL SCIENCE BULLETIN. 1964-19?? irreg. University of Saskatchewan, Extension Division, Saskatoon, Sask. S7N 0W0, Canada.
Former titles: Agricultural Science (ISSN 0381-5927); Information (ISSN 0381-5919); Supersedes: Saskatchewan Farm Science (ISSN 0048-9174)

338.1 US
AGRICULTURE REVIEW. ceased 1987. q. (back issues avail.) D R I - McGraw-Hill, 24 Hartwell Ave., Lexington, MA 02173.

338.1 BL ISSN 0100-4298
AGROANALYSIS. 1977-1989; suspended. m. (Instituto Brasileiro de Economia, Centro de Estudos Agricolas) Fundacao Getulio Vargas, Caixa Postal 9052, 20250 Rio de Janeiro, R.J., Brazil.

630 668.6 YU ISSN 0002-1865
CODEN: AGHJA4
AGROHEMIJA; casopis za hemizaciju poljoprivrede i sumarstva. 1959-1989. bi-m. Jugoslovensko Drustvo za Proucavanje Zemljista, Nemanjina 6, 11080 Zemun, Yugoslavia.

631.3 FR
AGROMATIQUE. 1982-19?? s-m. Editions du Boisbaudry, B.P. 6359, 35063 Rennes Cedex, France.

053.5 SZ
AHA!; das Magazin fuer Spielen und mehr. 1989-1991. bi-m. Kanzleistr. 127, Postfach 49, CH-8026 Zurich, Switzerland.

059.94 FI ISSN 0044-6920
AIKAMERKKI. 1927-1992. 8/yr. Tyovaen Sivistysliitto TSL r.y. - Workers Educational Association, Paasivuorenkatu 5 B, 00530 Helsinki 53, Finland.

387.744 FR
AIR CARGO. 1972-1980. q. Editions Jacques Bereny, 107 rue de l'Universite, 75007 Paris, France.

358.4 UK
AIR FORCES OF THE WORLD. ceased 1988. a. Interavia S.A. (Subsidiary of: Jane's Information Group), Sentinel House, 163 Brighton Rd., Coulsdon, Surrey CR3 2NX, England.

614.7 US
AIR POLLUTION CONTROL PROGRESS. 1967-198? q. Department of Public Health, Air Management Services, 500 S. Broad St., Philadelphia, PA 19146.

387.7 CN
AIR TRANSPORT MANAGEMENT; Canada's magazine for the commercial aviation executive. 1988-1991. 6/yr. Baxter Publishing Co., 310 Dupont St., Toronto, Ont. M5R 1V9, Canada.

658 US
AIRCRAFT DEALER. 1990; ceased same year. bi-m. Aircraft Dealers Network, 5211 S. Washington Ave., Titusville, FL 32708.

629.133 UK ISSN 0002-2705
TT154
AIRFIX; for modellers. 1960-19?? m. (also avail. in microform from UMI; reprint service avail. from UMI) Palitoy Company, Baker St., Coalville, Leics., England.

387.7 US
AIRPORT QUARTERLY. ceased after one issue. q. Airport Operators Council International, 1220 19th St., N.W., Ste. 800, Washington, DC 20036.

658　　　　　　US
AISLE VIEW; the newsletter of tips, tactics and how-to's for small and novice exhibitors. 1990-1991? m. Exhibitor Publications, Inc., 745 Marquette Bank Bldg., Rochester, MN 55904.

794.1　　　　　　AG
AJEDREZ 2000. ceased. 6/yr. Casa del Ajedrecista S.A., Peru 84-5-piso - oficina 72, 1067 Buenos Aires, Argentina.

610　　　　PL　ISSN 0084-277X
AKADEMIA MEDYCZNA WE WROCLAWIU. PRACE NAUKOWE. 1967-1981 (vol.15). irreg. Akademia Medyczna we Wroclawiu, Ul. Pasteura 1, 50-367 Wroclaw, Poland.

338.1　　　　　　PL
AKADEMIA ROLNICZA W SZCZECINIE. ZESZYTY NAUKOWE. EKONOMIKA, ORGANIZACJA I KIEROWANIE. 1975-19?? irreg. Akademia Rolnicza, Janosika 8, 71-424 Szczecin, Poland.

630　　　　　　PL
AKADEMIA ROLNICZA W SZCZECINIE. ZESZYTY NAUKOWE. ROLNICTWO. SERIA AGROTECHNICZNA. 1977-1988 (no.135). irreg. Akademia Rolnicza, Janosika 8, 71-424 Szczecin, Poland.

630 581　　　　　　PL
AKADEMIA ROLNICZA W SZCZECINIE. ZESZYTY NAUKOWE. ROLNICTWO. SERIA PRZYRODNICZA. 1977-1989 (no.139). irreg. Akademia Rolnicza, Janosika 8, 71-424 Szczecin, Poland.

630　　　　　　PL
AKADEMIA ROLNICZA W SZCZECINIE. ZESZYTY NAUKOWE. ROLNICTWO. SERIA TECHNICZNA. 1978-198? irreg. Akademia Rolnicza, Janosika 8, 71-424 Szczecin, Poland.

300　　　　UR　ISSN 0131-3843
AS262
AKADEMIYA NAUK LITOVSKOI S.S.R. TRUDY. SERIYA A. OBSHCHESTVENNYE NAUKI/LIETUVOS T.S.R. MOKSLU AKADEMIJOS DARBAI. A SERIJA. VISUOMENES MOKSLAI. 1955-1990. q. Izdatel'stvo Mokslas, Zvaigzdziu 23, Vilnius 232050, Lithuanian S.S.R., U.S.S.R.

540 620 550　　UR　ISSN 0132-2729
Q4　　　　　　CODEN: LMDBAL
AKADEMIYA NAUK LITOVSKOI S.S.R. TRUDY. SERIYA B. KHIMIYA, TEKHNIKA, FIZICHESKAYA GEOGRAFIYA/LIETUVOS T.S.R. MOKSLU AKADEMIJOS DARBAI. B SERIJA. CHEMIJA, TECHNIKA, FIZINE GEOGRAFIJA. 1955-1990. 6/yr. Izdatel'stvo Mokslas, Zvaigzdziu 23, Vilnius 232050, Lithuanian S.S.R., U.S.S.R.

574　　　　UR　ISSN 0131-3851
QH301　　　　　CODEN: LMDCAO
AKADEMIYA NAUK LITOVSKOI S.S.R. TRUDY. SERIYA C. BIOLOGICHESKIE NAUKI/LIETUVOS T.S.R. MOKSLU AKADEMIJOS DARBAI. C SERIJA. BIOLOGIJOS MOKSLAI. 1955-1990. q. Izdatel'stvo Mokslas, Zvaigzdziu 23, Vilnius 232050, Lithuanian S.S.R., U.S.S.R.
Supersedes in part (from 1960): Akademiya Nauk Litovskoi S.S.R. Trudy. Seriya B (ISSN 0024-3000)

384.54　　　　　　II
AKASHVANI. 1936-1987. fortn. (All India Radio) Akashvani Group of Journals, PTI Building, Parliament St., New Delhi 110001, India.

059.927　　　　　　TS
AKHBAR DUBAI. 1965-19?? w. Department of Information, P.O. Box 17, Dubai, United Arab Emirates.

330　　　　US　ISSN 0044-7048
　　　　　　CODEN: ABERDF
AKRON BUSINESS AND ECONOMIC REVIEW. 1969-1991 (vol. 22, no.4). q. (also avail. in microfilm from UMI; reprint service avail. from UMI) University of Akron, College of Business Administration, College of Business, Rm. 419, Akron, OH 44325.

614　　　　DK　ISSN 0107-7619
AKTIVITETEN I SYGEHUSVAESENET. 1979-1985. a. Sundhedsstyrelsen, Amaliegade 13, 1012 Copenhagen K, Denmark.

491　　　　UR　ISSN 0320-734X
AKTUAL'NYE PROBLEMY LEKSIKOLOGII I SLOVOOBRAZOVANIYA. 1972-1980 (no.9). a. Novosibirskii Gosudarstvennyi Universitet, Kafedra Obshchego Yazykoznaniya, Redaktsionno-Izdatel'skii Otdel, Novosibirsk, 90 Akademgorodok, Russian S.F.S.R., U.S.S.R.

621.38　　　　　　DK
AKTUEL DATA - E D B. (Supplement to: Aktuel Elektronik) 1984-1985. 6/yr. Teknisk Forlag A-S, Skelbaekgade 4, DK-1717 Copenhagen V, Denmark.

297　　　　GW　ISSN 0724-2735
AKTUELLE FRAGEN; aus der Welt des Islam. 1981-1989. q. (Christlich-Islamische Gesellschaft) Zentralinstitut Islam-Archiv-Deutschland, Postfach 1528, Am Kuhfuss 8, 4770 Soest, Germany.

690　　　　DK　ISSN 0108-6669
AKTUELT OM BYGGELITTERATUR. 1983-19?? 4/yr. Byggecentrums Litteraturjeneste, PO Box 300, 1501 Copenhagen V, Denmark.

371.2 373　　　US　ISSN 0002-4139
ALABAMA ASSOCIATION OF SECONDARY SCHOOL PRINCIPALS. BULLETIN. 1964-1990 (Dec.). a. Alabama Association of Secondary School Principals, Box 428, Montgomery, AL 36101.

621.47　　　　　　US
ALABAMA SUNRISE. 1983-1987. irreg. Alabama Solar Association, c/o University of Alabama in Huntsville, Johnson Research Center, Huntsville, AL 35899.

338.4　　　　　　US
ALASKA. DEPARTMENT OF FISH AND GAME. COMMERCIAL OPERATORS. 1961-198? a. Department of Fish and Game, Box 3-2000, Juneau, AK 99802.

330.9　　　　　　US
ALASKA. OFFICE OF THE GOVERNOR. PERFORMANCE REPORT. 1972-199? a. Office of the Governor, Division of Policy, Box AD, Juneau, AK 99811.
Formerly: Performance Report of the Alaska Economy.

070.5 700 051　　US　ISSN 0893-505X
ALASKA ASSOCIATION OF SMALL PRESSES NEWSLETTER. 1984-199? irreg. (looseleaf format; back issues avail.) Alaska Association of Small Presses, Box 821, Cordova, AK 99574.

663　　　　US　ISSN 0191-5320
ALASKA BEVERAGE ANALYST. (Subseries of: Northwest Beverage Analyst) 1936-1990 (Dec.). m. Bell Publications, Beverage Analyst Group, 2403 Champa St., Denver, CO 80205.

605.5 622　　　US　ISSN 0887-2279
ALASKA BUSINESS NEWSLETTER. 1985-1990. w. Todd Communications, 203 W. 15th Ave., Ste. 102, Anchorage, AK 99501.
Formerly: Alaska Business.

690 622　　　　　　US
ALASKA CONSTRUCTION & OIL. 1959-19?? m. Vernon Publications Inc., 3000 Northup Way, Ste. 200, Bellevue, WA 98004.
Former titles: Alaska Construction and Oil Report (ISSN 0002-4473); Alaska Construction.

387.7 799　　　　　US
ALASKA FLYING. ceased. m. 808 E St., Ste. 200, Anchorage, AK 99501.

338.1　　　　　　CN
ALBERTA. DEPARTMENT OF AGRICULTURE. MARKET SITUATION AND OUTLOOK. 1971-1985. q. (looseleaf format) Department of Agriculture, Market Analysis Branch, 7000-113 St., Edmohton, Alta. T6H 5T6, Canada.
Formerly: Alberta Farm Market Analysis.

647.94　　　　　　CN
ALBERTA HOTEL ASSOCIATION. MEMBERSHIP ROSTER & BUYERS GUIDE. ceased. a. Naylor Communications Ltd., 920 Yonge St., 6th fl., Toronto, Ont. M4W 3C7, Canada.

025　　　　CN　ISSN 0705-6087
ALBERTA LIBRARY NEWS. 1972-1991. 2/yr. (back issues avail.) Alberta Culture and Multiculturalism, Library Services Branch, 16214-114 Ave., Edmonton, Atla. T5M 2Z5, Canada.

CESSATIONS 5133

790.019　　　　　　CN
ALBERTA PARENT MAGAZINE. 1985-1991 (Mar.). bi-m. c/o Ruth Kelly, 5308 Calgary Trail, Edmonton, Alta. T6H 4J8, Canada.
Formerly: P I N Magazine.

340　　　　　　CN
ALBERTA REGULATIONS SERVICE. ceased 1991 (Feb.). 4/yr. (looseleaf format) Butterworths Canada Ltd., 75 Clegg Rd., Markham, Ont. L6G 1A1, Canada.

001.3　　　　　　CN
ALBERTA: STUDIES IN THE ARTS AND SCIENCES. 1988-1992 (vol.3, no.2). s-a. University of Alberta Press, 141 Athabasca Hall, Edmonton, Alta. T6G 2E8, Canada.

011　　　　US　ISSN 1052-522X
Z6941
ALBERTSEN'S - INTERNATIONAL EDITION. 1990-1992. a. Albertsen's, Box 339, Nevada City, CA 95959.

800　　　　　　US
ALCATRAZ. 1979-1985 (no.3). irreg. (back issues avail.) (A E Foundation) Alcatraz Editions, 354 Hoover Rd., Soquel, CA 95073.

956.40 296　　　SA　ISSN 0002-5127
ALEH. 1965-1986; suspended. 4/yr. Habonim Dror S.A., Zionist Centre, 84 de Villiers St., Johannesburg, South Africa.
Supersedes in part: Kol Hatnua.

028.5　　　　　　US
ALF. ceased 1990. q. Welsh Publishing Group, Inc., 300 Madison Ave., New York, NY 10017.

387.7　　　　　　HK
ALIA. ROYAL WINGS. ceased. 4/yr. (Royal Jordanian Airlines) Thomson Press Hong Kong Ltd., 19th Fl., Tai Sang Commercial Bldg., 24-34 Hennessy Rd., Hong Kong.

811　　　　US　ISSN 0147-5762
ALIVE & KICKING. 1976-1978 (no.2). 2/yr. c/o Selma Sklar, Ed., 35-50 85th St., Jackson Heights, NY 11372.

616.97 615.37　　US　ISSN 0883-7767
ALLERGY RELIEF NEWSLETTER. 1986-1989. m. (back issues avail.) Rodale Press, Inc., 33 E. Minor, Emmaus, PA 18049.

520　　　　US　ISSN 0191-3867
QB12
ALMANAC FOR COMPUTERS. 1977-1991. a. U.S. Naval Observatory, Washington, DC 20392.

320　　　　　　US
ALMANAC OF CALIFORNIA GOVERNMENT AND POLITICS. 1975-1989 (7th ed.). biennial. California Journal, Inc., 1714 Capitol Ave., Sacramento, CA 95814.
Formerly: California Journal Almanac of State Government and Politics.

200 800　　　DK　ISSN 0900-1573
ALMANAK FOR TEOLOGI OG LITTERATUR. 1985-1987. a. Anis Publishing, Frederiksberg Alle 10A, DK-1820 Frederiksberg C, Denmark.

388.3　　　　　　IT
ALMANNACO AUTO. ceased. a. Edigamma s.r.l., Piazza dei Sanniti, 9, 00185 Rome, Italy.

811　　　　US　ISSN 0162-8208
ALTADENA REVIEW. 1978-1989 (no.11). irreg. (back issues avail.) Altadena Review, Inc., Box 212, Altadena, CA 91001.

531.64 380.5　　US　ISSN 0271-9029
ALTERNATE ENERGY TRANSPORTATION NEWSLETTER; the newsletter of technology in motion. 1979-199? m. Campbell Publishing (Subsidiary of: Electric Vehicle Consultants, Inc.), 327 Central Park W., New York, NY 10025.
Incorporates: Chopper Noise (ISSN 0275-0198)

808.81　　　US　ISSN 0893-2581
ALTERNATIVE FICTION & POETRY. 1986-19?? irreg. (back issues avail.) Philip Athans, Ed. & Pub., 7783 Kensington Lane, Hanover Park, IL 60103.

051　　　　US　ISSN 0730-1766
ALTERNATIVE MEDIA MAGAZINE. 1974-1985? q. (also avail. in microfilm; back issues avail.; reprint service avail. from BLH) Alternative Press Syndicate, 211 E. 43rd St, New York, NY 10017.
Former titles: Alternative Press Review; Alternative Journalism Review; Underground Press Review;
Supersedes: Free Ranger Inter-Tribal News Service (ISSN 0016-044X)

CESSATIONS

619 NE ISSN 0168-8448
CODEN: ALTMEA
ALTERNATIVE MEDICINE. 1986-198? (vol.3). q. (back issues avail.) (International Society of Alternative Medicine) V S P, P.O. Box 346, 3700 AH Zeist, Netherlands.

800 US ISSN 0748-9463
E839.5
ALTERNATIVE PRESS ANNUAL. 1983-1986 (vol. IV). a. (back issues avail.) Temple University Press, Broad & Oxford Sts., Philadelphia, PA 19122.

362 US
ALTERNATIVES (ELLENWOOD); an alternate lifestyle newsletter. 1973-1991 (vol.17, no.4). q. (back issues avail.) Alternate Lifestyles, Inc., Box 429, 5263 Bouldercrest Rd., Ellenwood, GA 30049.

943 GW ISSN 0342-8699
ALTFRAENKISCHE BILDER UND WAPPENKALENDER. 1895-1991. a. (Freunde Mainfraenkischer Kunst und Geschichte, Gesellschaft Mainfraenkischer Kunst und Geschichte) Verlag Stuertz, Beethovenstr. 5, 8700 Wuerzburg, Germany.
Formerly: Altfraenkische Bilder.

820 821 UK ISSN 0266-8521
ALTRIVE CHAPBOOKS. 1984-1989 (no.6). a. (back issues avail.) James Hogg Society, Department of English Studies, University of Stirling, Stirling FK9 4LA, Scotland.

700 900 IT
L'ALTRO PIEMONTE. 1982-199? m. (back issues avail.) Stammer S.P.A., Centro Commerciale, Milano S. Felice, 20090 Segrate (Milan), Italy.

622 669 AT
ALUMINIUM IN USE. 1965-19?? q. (back issues avail.) Comalco Ltd., 440 Collins St., Melbourne, Vic. 3000, Australia.

669 US
ALUMINIUM INDUSTRY IN THE SOVIET UNION. ceased after one issue, 1981. Metal Bulletin Inc., 220 Fifth Ave., 10th Fl., New York, NY 10001.

669.722 SA
ALUMINUM REVIEW. 1957-1988 (no.95). q. Huletts Aluminum Ltd., Box 2430, Johannesburg 2000, South Africa.
Formerly (until 1974): Alcan Review (ISSN 0002-5003)

808.81 US
ALURA. 1975-1991 (vol.16, no.1). q. (back issues avail.) Alura Press, Box 44, Novinger, MO 63559.

331 BA
AMAL; ijtimaiyah, ummaliyah, shahriyah. ceased 1980 (vol.16). m. Wizarat al-Amal wa-al-Shuun al-Ijtimiyah, P.O. Box 753, Manama, Bahrain.

796.82 US ISSN 0160-7332
AMATEUR BOXER. 1978-19?? 6/yr. (back issues avail.) Diversified Periodicals, Box 249, Cobalt, CT 06414.

011 BL ISSN 0100-0977
AMAZONIA - BIBLIOGRAFIA. 1963-1977. irreg. Instituto Brasileiro de Informacao em Ciencia e Tecnologia, IBICT SCN Quadra 2, Bloco K, 70710 Brasilia, D.F., Brazil.

362.18 UK
AMBULANCE BULLETIN. 1963-1976 (Sep.). q. Electricity Supply Ambulance Centre, Electricity Council, 30 Millbank, London S.W.1., England.
Formerly: British Electricity Ambulance Bulletin.

368 US ISSN 0193-6581
AMERICAN ACADEMY OF ACTUARIES. JOURNAL. ceased. a. American Academy of Actuaries, 1720 I St., N.W., 7th Fl., Washington, DC 20006.

362 US ISSN 0002-7324
CODEN: AMRHA
AMERICAN ARCHIVES OF REHABILITATION THERAPY. 1952-1987 (vol.35, no.7). 3/yr. (also avail. in microform from UMI; reprint service avail. from UMI) American Association for Rehabilitation Therapy, Inc., 32 Ferndale Rd., W., Paramus, NJ 07652.

550 US ISSN 0569-2393
CODEN: ACDABW
AMERICAN ASSOCIATION FOR THE ADVANCEMENT OF SCIENCE. COMMITTEE ON DESERT AND ARID ZONE RESEARCH. CONTRIBUTIONS. ceased. irreg. American Association for the Advancement of Science, Southwestern and Rocky Mountain Division, Box 3AF, Las Cruces, NM 88001.

636.089 US ISSN 0098-3543
SF771 CODEN: PAMDDZ
AMERICAN ASSOCIATION OF VETERINARY LABORATORY DIAGNOSTICIANS. PROCEEDINGS OF ANNUAL MEETING. 1957-1986 (29th ed.). a. American Association of Veterinary Laboratory Diagnosticians, c/o Charlotte L. Fox, Ex. Dir., 3900 E. Timrod, Tucson, AZ 85712.

917.806 US
AMERICAN CITIZEN. 1923-19?? q. (tabloid format) American Citizen Press, 8262 Hascall St., Box 944 DTS, Omaha, NE 68101.

690 US
AMERICAN CLIPPER. 1913-1987. q. American Hoist & Derrick Co., 345 St. Peter, Ste. 1800, St. Paul, MN 55102.
Formerly: American Crosby Clipper (ISSN 0002-8134)

796.077 US ISSN 0894-4210
AMERICAN COACH. 1987-1988 (Sep.). bi-m. (American Coaching Effectiveness Program) Human Kinetics Publishers, Inc., Box 5076, Champaign, IL 61825-5076.

616.8 US ISSN 0002-7995
AMERICAN COLLEGE OF NEUROPSYCHIATRISTS. BULLETIN. ceased. irreg. (2-3/yr.). American College of Neuropsychiatrists, 28595 Orchard Lake Rd., Ste. 200, Farmington Hills, MI 48013-4715.

691 US ISSN 0097-4145
TA680
AMERICAN CONCRETE INSTITUTE. PROCEEDINGS. 1905-1987. a. (also avail. in microform from UMI) American Concrete Institute, Box 19150, Redford Sta., Detroit, MI 48219.

747 US
AMERICAN COUNTRY. 1987-19?? bi-m. Mother Earth News, Inc. (Hendersonville), 105 Stoney Mountain Rd., Box 70, Hendersonville, NC 28791.

070 US
AMERICAN COURT AND COMMERCIAL NEWSPAPERS. BULLETIN. ceased. q. American Court and Commercial Newspapers, 210 S. Spring St., Box 54026, Los Angeles, CA 90054.

070 US
AMERICAN COURT AND COMMERCIAL NEWSPAPERS. CONVENTION PROCEEDINGS. ceased. a. American Court and Commercial Newspapers, 210 S. Spring St., Box 54026, Los Angeles, CA 90054.

070 US
AMERICAN COURT AND COMMERCIAL NEWSPAPERS. NEWS SERVICE. ceased. m. American Court and Commercial Newspapers, 210 S. Spring St., Box 54026, Los Angeles, CA 90054.

379 US ISSN 0002-8304
L11
AMERICAN EDUCATION. 1965-1985. m. (Jan.-Feb. & Aug.-Sep. nos. are combined). (also avail. in microform from UMI,MIM) U.S. Department of Education, Washington, DC 20202.
Supersedes: Higher Education and School Life.

350
AMERICAN ENTERPRISE INSTITUTE FOR PUBLIC POLICY RESEARCH. MEMORANDUM. no.8, 1973-1991. q. American Enterprise Institute for Public Policy Research, c/o Pat Ford, 1150 17th St. N.W., Washington, DC 20036.

791.43 US
PN1993
AMERICAN FILM; the magazine of the film and television arts. 1975-1992 (Jan.). 10/yr. (also avail. in microfilm from UMI; microfiche) (American Film Institute) B P I Communications, Inc. (New York) (Subsidiary of: Affiliated Publications, Inc.), 1515 Broadway, 39th Fl., New York, NY 10036.

Former titles: American Film Magazine (Washington) (ISSN 0361-4751); A F I News; Incorporates (in 1975): Dialogue on Film; Which was formerly: Discussion (ISSN 0046-0346)

796.352 US
AMERICAN GOLF MAGAZINE. ceased 1991. bi-m. American Golf Corporation, 1633 26th St., Santa Monica, CA 90404.

636.3 US
AMERICAN HAMPSHIRE SHEEP ASSOCIATION. FLOCK BOOK. ceased 1984 (vol.82). a. American Hampshire Sheep Association, Box 345, Ashland, MO 65010.

798 658 US
AMERICAN HORSE EXCHANGE. ceased. m. Heartland Communications Group, Inc., 900 Central Ave., Box 916, Fort Dodge, IA 50501.

362 US ISSN 0360-5167
RA960
AMERICAN HOSPITAL ASSOCIATION. HOUSE OF DELEGATES. PROCEEDINGS. ceased 1987. a. American Hospital Association, 840 N. Lake Shore Dr., Chicago, IL 60611.

635 US
AMERICAN HOSTA SOCIETY. NEWSLETTER. ceased. a. American Hosta Society, 5300 Whiting Ave., Edina, MN 55435.

340 970 US
AMERICAN INDIAN TREATIES PUBLICATIONS SERIES. 1975-19?? irreg. (back issues avail.) University of California, Los Angeles, American Indian Studies Center, 3220 Campbell Hall, U.C.L.A., Los Angeles, CA 90024-1548.

629.13 629.4 US ISSN 0065-8685
AMERICAN INSTITUTE OF AERONAUTICS AND ASTRONAUTICS. A I A A LOS ANGELES SECTION. MONOGRAPHS. 1967-19?? irreg. American Institute of Aeronautics and Astronautics, 370 L'Enfant Promenade, S.W., Washington, DC 20024.

320 US
AMERICAN JEWISH COMMITTEE. DOMESTIC AFFAIRS DEPARTMENT. PERTINENT PAPERS. 1978-19?? irreg. (approx. 2/yr.). American Jewish Committee, Domestic Affairs Department, 165 E. 56th St., New York, NY 10022.

296 US
AMERICAN JEWISH COMMITTEE. RECENT ADDITIONS TO THE LIBRARY. 1939-19?? q. (back issues avail.) American Jewish Committee, 165 E. 65th St., New York, NY 10022.

152 616.891 US
AMERICAN JOURNAL OF CLINICAL ASSESSMENT. ceased. q. P S G Publishing Company, Inc., 545 Great Rd., Box 6, Littleton, MA 01460.

617.7 615.19 US
AMERICAN JOURNAL OF OPTOMETRIC MEDICINE. 1981-1989. m. (back issues avail.) American College of Optometric Physicians, Box 41774, Memphis, TN 38714.

616.21 US ISSN 0065-9037
AMERICAN LARYNGOLOGICAL, RHINOLOGICAL AND OTOLOGICAL SOCIETY TRANSACTIONS. 1896-1991. a. (also avail. in microform from UMI; back issues avail.) (American Laryngological, Rhinological and Otological Society) Triological Foundation, Inc., 10 S. Broadway, 14th fl., St. Louis, MO 63102-1712.

330.1 808.8 US ISSN 0897-2176
AMERICAN LIBERTARIAN; an independent Libertarian newspaper. 1986-1989 (Oct.). m. (tabloid format; back issues avail.) 21715 Park Brook Dr., Katy, TX 77450.

020 US ISSN 0002-9793
AMERICAN LIBRARY DIRECTORY UPDATING SERVICE. (Supplement to: American Library Directory) 1969-1989 (Jul.). bi-m. R.R. Bowker, A Reed Reference Publishing Company, Division of Reed Publishing (USA) Inc., 121 Chanlon Rd., New Providence, NJ 07974.

020 340 US
AMERICAN LIBRARY LAWS. ceased 1984 (5th ed.). irreg. (reprint service avail. from UMI) American Library Association, 50 E. Huron St., Chicago, IL 60611.

658.8 US
AMERICAN MARKETING ASSOCIATION. INTERNATIONAL MEMBERSHIP DIRECTORY AND MARKETING SERVICES GUIDE. ceased. a. American Marketing Association, 250 S. Wacker Dr., Ste. 200, Chicago, IL 60606.
Former titles: American Marketing Association. Membership Roster and Directory of International Marketing Service Organizations; American Marketing Association. Membership Roster Including the Advertising Section of Marketing Service Organizations; American Marketing Association. Marketing Service Organization and Membership Roster; American Marketing Association. Directory of Marketing Services and Membership Roster (ISSN 0093-1454)

398 US
AMERICAN MATERIAL CULTURE AND FOLKLIFE. ceased 1991 (Jun.). irreg., unnumbered. U M I Research Press, 300 N. Zeeb Rd., Ann Arbor, MI 48106-1346.

614.7 US
AMERICAN METEOROLOGICAL SOCIETY AND AMERICAN INSTITUTE OF AERONAUTICA AND ASTRONAUTICS. INTERNATIONAL CONFERENCE ON THE ENVIRONMENTAL IMPACT OF AEROSPACE OPERATIONS IN THE HIGH ATMOSPHERE. (PROCEEDINGS). 1973-1983 (9th, Omaha). irreg. American Meteorological Society, 45 Beacon St., Boston, MA 02108.

382 US
AMERICAN MIDEAST BUSINESS ASSOCIATION. BULLETIN. 1970-1992. 10/yr. (back issues avail.) American Mideast Business Association, 1137 S. Green St., Tuckertom, NJ 08087.
Former titles: American-Arab Association. Bulletin; American-Arab Association of Commerce and Industry. Bulletin (ISSN 0044-7528)

539 US
AMERICAN NUCLEAR SOCIETY. PROCEEDINGS OF THE EXECUTIVE CONFERENCE. ceased 1983. irreg. American Nuclear Society, 555 N. Kensington Ave., La Grange Park, IL 60525.

539 US
AMERICAN NUCLEAR SOCIETY. PROCEEDINGS OF THE NATIONAL TOPICAL MEETING. ceased. irreg. American Nuclear Society, 555 N. Kensington Ave., La Grange Park, IL 60525.

651.2 US ISSN 0584-455X
HF5548
AMERICAN OFFICE DEALER. 1908-1990. m. Allen-Abernathy Co. (Subsidiary of: A S M Communications, Inc. (New York)), 49 E. 21st St., 9th Fl., New York, NY 10010.
Former titles: Western Office Dealer (ISSN 0199-5529); Southern Office Dealer.

380.1 US
AMERICAN PACKAGE EXPRESS CARRIERS ASSOCIATION. SERVICE DIRECTORY. ceased. biennial. American Package Express Carriers Association, 2200 Mill Rd., Alexandria, VA 22314.

676 US
AMERICAN PAPER INSTITUTE. WOOD PULP AND FIBER STATISTICS. 1936-1990. a. American Paper Institute, Inc., 260 Madison Ave., New York, NY 10016.

100 US
AMERICAN PHILOSOPHICAL ASSOCIATION. NEWSLETTER ON PHILOSOPHY AND MEDICINE. 1979-199? 3/yr. American Philosophical Association, c/o Rosamond Rhodes, Ed., Mt. Sinai School of Medicine, One Gustave Levy Place, Box 1193, New York, NY 10029.

811 US ISSN 0737-3635
PS301
AMERICAN POETRY. 1983-19?? 3/yr. (back issues avail.) (University of New Mexico, Department of English) McFarland & Company, Inc., Box 611, Jefferson, NC 28640.

658 US
AMERICAN PRODUCTIVITY & QUALITY CENTER. DIGEST (YEAR). 1984-1991. a. American Productivity & Quality Center, 123 N. Post Oak Ln., Houston, TX 77024.
Formerly: Productivity Digest (ISSN 0741-6466)

808.81 US ISSN 0737-5905
AMERICAN PROMETHEUS; a journal of young people's poetry. 1983-1986. 9/yr. (Sep.-May). Eterna International, Inc., 27 W. 560 Warrenville Rd., Warrenville, IL 60555.

320 US ISSN 0891-446X
AMERICAN PURPOSE. 1987-198? 10/yr. (also avail. in microform from UMI) (James Madison Foundation) Heldref Publications, 4000 Albemarle St., N.W., Washington, DC 20016.

658 338 US
AMERICAN RETAILER. 1987-1990. bi-m. American Retailer, Inc., 21 W. Delilah Rd., Pleasantville, NJ 08232.

949 US ISSN 0193-8118
E184.R8
AMERICAN ROMANIAN REVIEW. 1977-1989. bi-m. American Romanian Heritage Foundation, Inc., c/o Theodore Andrica, Ed., 10710 Lake Ave., Cleveland, OH 44102-1212.

387.54 US
AMERICAN SAILINGS. 1929-1990. w. International Thomson Transport Press, 424 W. 33rd St., New York, NY 10001.
Formerly: Brandon's Shipper & Forwarder (ISSN 0006-9086)

368.32 US ISSN 0742-9517
HG8751
AMERICAN SOCIETY OF C L U. JOURNAL. (Chartered Life Underwriters) 1946-1986. bi-m. (also avail. in microform from UMI; back issues avail.; reprint service avail. from UMI,WSH) American Society of C L U & Ch F C, 270 Bryn Mawr Ave., Bryn Mawr, PA 19010.
Formerly: C L U Journal (ISSN 0007-8573)

385.264 US
AMERICAN SOCIETY OF TRAFFIC AND TRANSPORTATION. NEWSLETTER. 1946-1982 (vol.18). bi-m. American Society of Traffic and Transportation, Box 33095, Louisville, KY 40232.

646.724 051 US
AMERICAN STYLE. 1987-1991. bi-m. Whittle Communications L.P., 333 Main Ave., Knoxville, TN 37902.
Supersedes (in 1989): Southern Style.

910.09 979 US ISSN 0003-1534
F591
AMERICAN WEST; travel & life. 1964-1990. bi-m. (also avail. in microform from UMI; reprint service avail. from UMI) American West Publishing Co., 7000 E. Tanque Verde Rd., Ste. 30, Tucson, AZ 85715-5319.

956.94 US ISSN 0044-8079
AMERICAN ZIONIST FEDERATION. NEWS AND VIEWS. 1972-197? m. American Zionist Federation, 515 Park Ave., New York, NY 10022.

629.286 AT ISSN 1032-6499
AMERICAR AUSTRALIA. 1989-19?? q. (back issues avail.) Eddie Ford Publications, Private Bag, Newstead, Vic. 3462, Australia.

621.381 US
AMIGA USER. ceased 1989 (May). m. Haymarket Group Ltd., 45 W. 34th St., Ste. 407, New York, NY 10001.

336 350 IT ISSN 0569-9479
AMMINISTRAZIONE TRIBUTI E FINANZE. 1951?-1989 (Dec.). m. Societa Edizioni Pubblicazioni s.r.l., Via Ticino 14-16, 00198 Rome, Italy.

778.534 US
AMPERSAND'S ENTERTAINMENT GUIDE. 1977-19?? 4/ yr. Alan Weston Communications, Inc., 303 N. Glenoaks Blvd., Ste. 600, Burbank, CA 91502.

813 US ISSN 0044-8168
AMRA; swordplay & sorcery. 1956-1981. irreg. (back issues avail.; reprint service avail. from UMI) (Hyborean Legion) Terminus, Owlswick & Ft. Mudge Electrick St. Railway Gazette, Box 8243, Philadelphia, PA 19101.

370 DK ISSN 0900-3096
AMTSKOMMUNALE ENKELTFAGSKURSER. 1984-198? a. Undervisningsministeriet, Direktoratet for Folkeoplysning, Copenhagen, Denmark.

617.96 UK ISSN 0261-4510
ANAESTHESIA (SHEFFIELD). ceased 1989. m. (looseleaf format; back issues avail.) Sheffield University Biomedical Information Service (SUBIS), The University, Sheffield S10 2TN, England.

296 AG
ANALES DE LA COMUNIDAD ISRAELITA DE BUENOS AIRES. 1953-1969. a. Asociacion Mutual Israelita Argentina, Kultur Departament bay der Kehile in Buenos Ayres, Pasteur 633, Buenos Aires, Argentina.

614.7 CN ISSN 0707-5723
ANALYSIS. 1977-19?? irreg. Ministry of the Environment, Laboratory Services Branch, Box 213, Rexdale, Ont. M9W 5L1, Canada.

547 US
ANALYSIS OF ORGANIC MATERIALS: AN INTERNATIONAL SERIES OF MONOGRAPHS. 1972-1982 (vol.18). irreg. (reprint service avail. from ISI) Academic Press, Inc., 1250 Sixth Ave., San Diego, CA 92101.
Formerly: Monographs in Organic Functional Group Analysis (ISSN 0077-0906)

536 621 US ISSN 0066-1538
QD79.T38
ANALYTICAL CALORIMETRY. 1968-19?? irreg. Plenum Publishing Corp., 233 Spring St., New York, NY 10013.

330 UK
ANBAR CUMULATIVE JOINT INDEX. 1984-19?? 8/yr. Anbar Abstracts (Subsidiary of: M C B University Press Ltd.), 62 Toller Ln., Bradford, W. Yorks BD8 9BY, England.

051 US
ANCHORAGE MAGAZINE. 1989-1990. 12/yr. Ship Creek Publishing, 733 W. 4th, Ste. 792, Anchorage, AK 99501-2192.

623.82 US ISSN 0097-8442
VM351
ANCIENT INTERFACE. (Subseries of: American Institute of Aeronautics and Astronautics, Los Angeles Section. Monographs) 1970-19?? a. American Institute of Aeronautics and Astronautics, Western Headquarters, 370 L'Enfant Promenade, S.W., Washington, DC 20024.

340 II
ANDHRA WEEKLY REPORTER. 1955-19?? w. Madras Law Journal Office, Box 604, Mylapore, Madras 4, India.

614.8 344.07 690.24 US 340 ISSN 0887-7866
ANDREWS SCHOOL ASBESTOS ALERT; the national journal alerting school districts to student and teacher asbestos exposure and resulting legal proceedings, construction problems, medical developments and Environmental Protection Agency actions. 1984-1989 (Apr.). m. (looseleaf format; back issues avail.) Andrews Publications, 1646 West Chester Pike, Box 1000, Westtown, PA 19395.

320 UK ISSN 0345-0295
DR1
ANEKS; kwartalnik polityczny/political quarterly. 1973-1990 (no.53). q. Aneks Press, 61 Dorset Rd., London W5 4HX, England.

051 US
ANGELES. ceased 1991. m. California Magazine, Inc., 11601 Wilshire Blvd., Ste. 1800, Los Angeles, CA 90025.

800 US
ANGELSTONE. 1978-19?? a. Angelstone Press, 316 Woodland Dr., Birmingham, AL 35209.

510 IT
ANGOLO ACUTO. 1969?-1982. s-a. Via Cairoli 78, 50131 Florence, Italy.

CESSATIONS

636　　　　　　UK　ISSN 0144-3879
ANIMAL DISEASE OCCURRENCE - DATA TABLES. 1980-1989. s-a. C.A.B. International, Wallingford, Oxon OX10 8DE, England.

636　　　　　　US
ANIMAL SCIENCE RESEARCH REPORT. 1961-19??; suspended. a. Louisiana State University, Animal Science Department, Baton Rouge, LA 70803.
　Formerly: Livestock Producer's Day Report (ISSN 0076-1052)

590.74　　　　US　ISSN 0019-3127
QL1
ANIMALAND. 1934-19?? 3/yr. Staten Island Zoological Society, Inc., 614 Broadway, Staten Island, NY 10310.
　Formerly: In Animaland.

791.43 384.5　　US　ISSN 0889-5589
ANIMATOR. 1971-1988 (no.43); suspended. q. (back issues avail.) Oregon Art Institute, Northwest Film & Video Center, 1219 S.W. Park Ave., Portland, OR 97205.

370　　　　　　DK　ISSN 0106-8172
ANMELDELSER I PAEDAGOGISKE TIDSSKRIFTER. 1971-1988. irreg. Bibliotekscentrale, Tempovej 7-11, 2750 Ballerup, Denmark.

630　　　　　　FI　ISSN 0570-1538
　　　　　　　　　　　CODEN: ANAFA6
ANNALES AGRICULTURAE FENNIAE. 1962-1991 (vol. 30, no.4). 4/yr. Maatalouden Tutkimuskeskus - Agricultural Research Centre, 31600 Jokioinen, Finland.

327　　　　　　BE　ISSN 0066-2135
ANNALES D'ETUDES INTERNATIONALES. 1970-1991. a. (Universite de Geneve, Institut Universitaire de Hautes Etudes Internationales, SZ - University of Geneva. Graduate Institute of International Studies) Etablissements Emile Bruylant, 67 rue de la Regence, B-1000 Brussels, Belgium.

615.1　　　　　FR　ISSN 0066-2186
ANNALES MOREAU DE TOURS. 1962-19?? irreg. (reprint service avail. from KTO) Presses Universitaires de France, Departement des Revues, 14 Avenue du Bois-de-l'Elpine, B.P.90, 91003 Evry Cedex, France.

510 658　　　　PL　ISSN 0324-8429
QA267　　　　　　　　CODEN: FUMAAJ
ANNALES SOCIETATIS MATHEMATICAE POLONAE. SERIA 4: FUNDAMENTA INFORMATICAE. 1977-19?? q. (Polskie Towarzystwo Matematyczne) Panstwowe Wydawnictwo Naukowe, Ul. Miodowa 10, 00-251 Warsaw, Poland.

614　　　　　　IT
ANNALI DI STUDI GIURIDICI E SOCIO-ECONOMICI SUI SERVIZII SANITARI NAZIONALE E REGIONALE. 1975-198? irreg. Maria Ragno, Via Crescenzio 43, Rome, Italy.

576 616.15 616.97　IT
ANNALI SCLAVO MONOGRAPH. ceased 1989. s-a. Sclavo S.p.A., Via Fiorentina 1, 53100 Siena, Italy.
　Supersedes (1959-1983): Annali Sclavo (ISSN 0003-472X)

617　　　　　　US　ISSN 0734-1997
　　　　　　　　　　　CODEN: ASMEEY
ANNALS OF SPORTS MEDICINE. 1982-1990 (vol.5, no.4). q. Raven Press, 1185 Ave. of the Americas, New York, NY 10036.

015　　　　　　US　ISSN 0066-2445
Z6958.F6
ANNOTATED GUIDE TO TAIWAN PERIODICAL LITERATURE. 1966-1973 (2nd ed.). irreg. Chinese Materials Center Publications, 633 Post St., Ste. 251, San Francisco, CA 94109-8299.

630　　　　　　FR　ISSN 0243-6825
ANNUAIRE DE STATISTIQUE AGRICOLE. ceased 1989. a. Ministere de l'Agriculture (Direction des Affaires Financieres et Economique), Service Central des Enquetes et Etudes Statistique, 4, Av. Saint-Mande, 75570 Paris Cedex 12, France.

663　　　　　　FR　ISSN 0066-2763
ANNUAIRE DES BOISSONS ET DES LIQUIDES ALIMENTAIRES/JAHRBUCH DER GETRAENKE UND FLUESSIGEN NAHRMITTEL. 1945-19?? a. Editions du Gonfalon, 29 Route de Dourdan, 91670 Angerville, France.

200 954　　　　II　ISSN 0970-3861
ANNUAL BIBLIOGRAPHY OF CHRISTIANITY IN INDIA. 1980-1991; suspended. a. Heras Institute of Indian History and Culture, St. Xavier's College, Bombay 400 001, India.

571 060　　　　NE　ISSN 0066-3794
ANNUAL BIBLIOGRAPHY OF INDIAN ARCHAEOLOGY. 1928-19?? irreg. (Kern Institute of Indology) E. J. Brill, P.O. Box 9000, 2300 PA Leiden, Netherlands.

327　　　　　　CN　ISSN 0384-1103
ANNUAL CANADIAN-AMERICAN SEMINAR. PROCEEDINGS. (Each issue has distinctive title) 1961-1989. a. University of Windsor, Centre for Canadian-American Studies, 401 Sunset Ave., Windsor, Ont. N9B 3P4, Canada.
　Former titles: Institute for Canadian-American Relations (Papers); Seminar on Canadian-American Relations (Papers) (ISSN 0080-8814)

655.5　　　　　UK　ISSN 0066-3913
Z327
ANNUAL DIRECTORY OF BOOKSELLERS IN THE BRITISH ISLES SPECIALISING IN ANTIQUARIAN AND OUT-OF-PRINT BOOKS. 1970-198? a. Stoate & Bishop Ltd., St. James Sq., Cheltenham GL50 3PU, England.

330　　　　　　US　ISSN 0090-4309
HF5343
ANNUAL EDITIONS: BUSINESS AND MANAGEMENT. 1973-1989. a. Dushkin Publishing Group, Inc., Sluice Dock, Guilford, CT 06437-9989.
　Former titles: Business Management (ISSN 0276-3923); Annual Editions: Readings in Business.

384.5　　　　　UN
ANNUAL HIGH FREQUENCY BROADCASTING FREQUENCY LIST. ceased. a. (microform) International Telecommunication Union, International Frequency Registration Board, Place des Nations, CH-1211 Geneva 20, Switzerland.

150　　　　　　US　ISSN 0092-5055
RC500　　　　　　　　CODEN: APSACT
ANNUAL OF PSYCHOANALYSIS. 1973-19?? a. (Chicago Institute for Psychoanalysis) Analytic Press, Inc., 365 Broadway, Hillsdale, NJ 07642.

410 950　　　　US　ISSN 0734-5348
PK2151
ANNUAL OF URDU STUDIES. 1981-1990 (No.7). a. (back issues avail.) 1130 E. 59th St., Chicago, IL 60637.

660.2　　　　　US　ISSN 0140-9115
ANNUAL REPORTS ON FERMENTATION PROCESSES. 1977-1985 (vol.8). irreg. (reprint service avail. from ISI) Academic Press, Inc., 1250 Sixth Ave., San Diego, CA 92101.

618.92 617　　　US
ANNUAL REVIEW OF BIRTH DEFECTS; the fetus and the newborn. ceased. a. John Wiley & Sons, Inc., 605 Third Ave., New York, NY 10158-0012.

001.6 621.381　　US　ISSN 8756-7016
QA75.5
ANNUAL REVIEW OF COMPUTER SCIENCE. 1986-1991; suspended. a. Annual Reviews Inc., 4139 El Camino Way, Box 10139, Palo Alto, CA 94306-0897.

785.4　　　　　US　ISSN 0731-0641
ML3505.8
ANNUAL REVIEW OF JAZZ STUDIES. 1982-1987. a. (also avail. in microform from MIM,UMI; reprint service avail. from UMI) (Institute of Jazz Studies) Transaction Periodicals Consortium, Rutgers University, New Brunswick, NJ 08903.
　Supersedes (1973-1981) (vol.6): Journal of Jazz Studies; Incorporates: Studies in Jazz Discography (ISSN 0093-3686)

530 621　　　　US　ISSN 0892-6883
QA901　　　　　　　　CODEN: ARNTE9
ANNUAL REVIEW OF NUMERICAL FLUID MECHANICS AND HEAT TRANSFER. 1987-1988. a. (reprint service avail. from UMI) Hemisphere Publishing Corporation (Subsidiary of: Taylor & Francis Group), 1900 Frost Rd., Ste. 101, Bristol, PA 19007-1598.

382　　　　　　UK　ISSN 0072-5846
ANNUAL STATEMENT OF THE OVERSEAS TRADE OF THE UNITED KINGDOM. ceased 1989. a. Department of Trade and Industry, 1 Victoria St., London SW1, England.

813　　　　　　US
ANNUAL WORLD'S BEST S F. 1965-1990 (Jul.). a. (back issues avail.) DAW Books, Inc., 1633 Broadway, New York, NY 10014-3658.

659.1　　　　　IT
ANNUARIO ITALIANO PUBBLICITA MARKETING RELAZIONI PUBBLICHE. 1982-1987. a. Ediemme srl, Via della Scrofa, 14, I-00186 Rome, Italy.

027.4　　　　　IT
ANNUARIO STATISTICO DELLE BIBLIOTECHE LOMBARDE; biblioteche comunali. 1985-199? irreg. (Regione Lombardia, Settore Cultura e Informazione) Editrice Bibliografica s.r.l., Viale Vittorio Veneto 24, 20124 Milan, Italy.

808.81　　　　US
ANOTHER PLACE TO PUBLISH. 1987-1989 (Dec.). q. Box 102, Delafield, WI 53018.

800　　　　　　US　ISSN 0735-8202
ANOTHER SEASON. 1982-1986. a. Gothaholm House, c/o Becknell Family, 6734 N. 31st Ave., Omaha, NE 68112.

374　　　　　　GW　ISSN 0003-522X
ANS WERK. 1964-1989. bi-m. (Neuwerk-Gemeinschaft e.V.) Roether Verlag, Berliner Allee 56, Postfach 4101, D-6100 Darmstadt 1, Germany.

780.42　　　　GW　ISSN 0344-2667
ANSCHLAEGE. 1978-1991. irreg. Archiv fuer Populaere Musik GmbH, Ostertorsteinweg 3, 2800 Bremen 1, Germany.

973　　　　　　US　ISSN 0066-4618
ANSON G. PHELPS LECTURESHIP ON EARLY AMERICAN HISTORY. 1932-1984. irreg. New York University Press, 70 Washington Square So., New York, NY 10012.

051　　　　　　US　ISSN 0736-2684
ANSWER MAN NEWSLETTER. 1983-198? (back issues avail.) Gary Warne, Ed. & Pub., Box 11263, San Francisco, CA 94101.

001.6 621.381　　US　ISSN 0745-2527
ANTIC: THE ATARI RESOURCE. 1982-1990 (Jun.). m. Antic Publishing, Inc., 544 Second St., San Francisco, CA 94107.

914　　　　　　IT
ANTICHITA PISANE; rivista di archeologia e di topografia storica. 1974-1976. irreg. (Universita degli Studi di Pisa, Scuola Speciale per Archeologi Preistorici) Pacini Editore S.R.L., Via della Gherardesca, 56014 Ospedaletto (Pisa), Italy.

612.015 616.97　UK　ISSN 0142-8462
ANTIGEN ANTIBODY REACTIONS. ceased 1990. m. (looseleaf format; back issues avail.) Sheffield University Biomedical Information Service (SUBIS), The University, Sheffield S10 2TN, England.

745.1 747　　　AT
ANTIQUE SHOPS OF AUSTRALIA. 1981-19?? biennial. Bomilhold Pty. Ltd., 2-27 Dale St., Brookvale, N.S.W. 2100, Australia.

745.1　　　　　UK
ANTIQUES. 1963-19?? q. Antique & General Advertising, Old Rectory, Hopton Castle, Craven Arms, Salop SY7 0QJ, England.
　Absorbed: Antiques World.

305.412　　　　FR　ISSN 0402-6233
ANTOINETTE. 1955-1990. m. Confederation Generale du Travail, 263 rue de Paris, 93516 Montreuil Cedex, France.

636.5　　　　　BL
ANUARIO AVICOLA. 1912-198? a. Gessulli Editores Ltda., Caixa Postal 8034, 01051 Sao Paulo, SP, Brazil.

720　　　　　　MX
ANUARIO DE ARQUITECTURA MEXICANA. 1977-19??; suspended. a. Instituto Nacional de Bellas Artes, Museo de Arte Moderno, Paseo de la Reforma y Gandhi, Chalpultepec, Mexico 5, D.F., Mexico.

CESSATIONS

340 301 SP ISSN 0210-1785
ANUARIO DE SOCIOLOGIA Y PSICOLOGIA JURIDICAS.
1974-1987? a. (Colegio de Abogados de Barcelona) Instituto de Psicologia y Sociologia Juridicas, Calle Mallorca 283, Barcelona, Spain.

382 AG ISSN 0066-5118
ANUARIO DEL COMERCIO EXTERIOR LATINO-AMERICANO; guide to the industry and foreign trade of Latin America. 1966-197? a. (Latin American Free Trade Association) E.P.I.S.A., Rivadavia 825, 2 Piso, Buenos Aires, Argentina.
Formerly: Anuario de los Paises de A L A L C (ISSN 0571-3846)

860 CR ISSN 0587-5196
ANUARIO DEL CUENTO COSTARRICENSE. 1967-198? a. Editorial Costa Rica, Calles la y 3a, Apdo 2014, San Jose, Costa Rica.

330 318 VE ISSN 0066-5185
ANUARIO ESTADISTICO DE LOS ANDES: VENEZUELA. 1966-198? a. Universidad de Los Andes, Instituto de Investigaciones Economicas, La Hechicera, Edif. B, C.P. 5101, Merida, Venezuela.

370 300 320 GW
ANUARIO: MUENSTERANER BEITRAEGE ZUR LATEIN AMERIKA FORSCHUNG. 1978-1986 (vol.6). irreg. (back issues avail.) (University of Muenster, Research Group on Latin America) Verlag Achim Schrader, Hiltruperstr. 93, 4400 Muenster, Germany.
Formerly (until 1986): Education, Sociedad y Politica. Anuario (ISSN 0172-8296)

538.7 SP
ANUARIOS DE GEOMAGNETISMO (YEAR). (In three regional parts: San Pablo, Almeria, Santa Cruz de Tenerife) 1962-1989; suspended. a. Instituto Geografico Nacional, Servicio de Geomagnetismo, General Ibanez de Ibero, 3, Apdo. 3007, 28003 Madrid, Spain.
Former titles (until 1985): Anuarios de Geomagnetismo de San Pablo y Almeria y del Centro Geofisico de Canarias; (until 1983): Anuario de Geomagnetismo - Observatorios de San Pablo (Toledo) y Almeria; (until 1981): Anuario de Geomagnetismo - Centro Geogisico de Canarias; (until 1975): Anuarios del Servicio de Geomagnetismo y Aeronomia.

374 IE ISSN 0332-1568
AONTAS REVIEW; an Irish journal of adult education. 1979-1985 (vol.5, no.1). 2/yr. National Association of Adult Education, 65 Fitzwilliam Sq., Dublin 2, Ireland.

617.6 UK ISSN 0003-6439
APEX. 1903-19?? 3/yr. University College Hospital Dental School, Dental Society, Mortimer Market, London WC1E 6JD, England.

687 US
APPAREL FACTORY OUTLET STORES SURVEY. ceased. a. American Apparel Manufacturers Association, 2500 Wilson Blvd., Ste. 301, Arlington, VA 22201.

792 US
APPLAUSE; San Diego magazine of the arts. ceased. m. (back issues avail.) (San Diego Applause Magazine, Inc.) Performing Arts Magazine, 612 Pennsylvania Ave., San Diego, CA 92103.

800 US ISSN 0896-7245
APPLE BLOSSOM CONNECTION. ceased 1989. m. Peak Output Unlimited, Box 325, Stacyville, IA 50476.

380.1 US
APPLIANCE NEW PRODUCT DIGEST. 1986-19?? q. (tabloid format) Dana Chase Publications, Inc., 1110 Jorie Blvd., CS-9019, Oak Brook, IL 60522-9019.

510 CN ISSN 0700-9224
APPLIED MATHEMATICS NOTES/NOTES DE MATHEMATIQUES APPLIQUEES. 1975-1990 (vol. 15). q. Canadian Applied Mathematics Society, University of Alberta, Edmonton, Alta. T6A 1A1, Canada.
Formerly: University of British Columbia. Department of Mathematics. Applied Mathematics Notes - Notes de Mathematiques Appliquees.

621 US
APPLIED MECHANISMS CONFERENCE PROCEEDINGS. 1969-19?? biennial? Oklahoma State University, College of Engineering, Engineering Extension, 512 Engineering North, Stillwater, OK 74078.

616.07 SZ ISSN 0252-1172
 CODEN: APTHDM
APPLIED PATHOLOGY. 1983-19?? bi-m. (also avail. in microform from RPI) S. Karger AG, Allschwilerstrasse 10, P.O. Box, CH-4009 Basel, Switzerland.

615.842 US ISSN 0160-9963
APPLIED RADIOLOGY DIRECTORY. 1984-1990. a. Romaine Pierson Publishers, Inc., 80 Shore Rd., Port Washington, NY 11050.
Formerly: Applied Radiology Buyer's Guide.

639.34 US
AQUARIUM DIGEST INTERNATIONAL. 1972. q. Tetra Press, 201 Tabor Rd., Morris Plains, NJ 07950.

574.92 US
AQUATIC TOXICOLOGY. 1982-1984 (vol.2). irreg. (also avail. in microform from RPI; back issues avail.; reprint service avail. from SWZ) Raven Press, 1185 Ave. of the Americas, New York, NY 10036.

627 333.91 II ISSN 0970-0366
AQUAWORLD; monthly on water from India. 1986-19?? m. (back issues avail.) Dipak B.R. Chaudhuri, G-82 Sujan Singh Park, New Delhi 110003, India.

332 FR
ARAB BANKS. ceased. m. Ediafric, 10 rue Vineuse, 75116 Paris Cedex 16, France.

664 GW
ARAB FOOD & BEVERAGE; alamussina'atulghizaiyah. (Supplement to: Arab Tech) 1985-198? q. Beta Publishing, P.O. Box 140121, D-5300 Bonn 2, Germany.

327 US ISSN 0896-2146
DS63.1
ARAB PRESS BULLETIN. 1986-198? d. American-Arab Affairs Council, American-Arab Press Institute, 1730 M St., N.W., Ste. 512, Washington, DC 20036.

600 GW ISSN 0722-4303
ARAB TECH; alamussina'a walteknologia. (Supplements avail.: Arab Food & Beverage; Arab Automotive) 1982-198? bi-m. (back issues avail.) Beta Publishing, P.O. Box 140121, 5300 Bonn 1, Germany.

327 UK ISSN 0518-1852
ARAB WORLD. 1972-1981. q. Anglo Arab Association, 21 Collingham Rd., London SW5 0NU, England.

001.3 GW ISSN 0724-6994
ARBEITSGESTALTUNG FUER BEHINDERTE. 1982-1988. bi-m. (back issues avail.) Friedr. Vieweg und Sohn Verlagsgesellschaft mbH, Postfach 5829, D-6200 Wiesbaden 1, Germany.

613.62 344 GW ISSN 0232-7287
ARBEITSHYGIENISCHE INFORMATION BAUWESEN. 1965-1990. 10/yr. (back issues avail.) Institut fuer Arbeitssicherheit und Umweltschutz, Arbeitsstudium und Betriebsorganisation e.V., Rhinstr. 48, 1140 Berlin-Marzahn 1, Germany.

613.62 614.85 610 GW ISSN 0232-5160
ARBEITSMEDIZININFORMATION. 1974-1991. q. Gesellschaft fuer Arbeitshygiene und Arbeitsschutz, Zentralinstitut fuer Arbeitsmedizin, Noeldnerstr. 40-42, 1134 Berlin, Germany.

613.62 GW ISSN 0138-1555
ARBEITSSCHUTZ, ARBEITSHYGIENE; Zeitschrift fuer Theorie und Praxis. 1967-1990. q. Zentralinstitut fuer Arbeitsschutz, Gerhart-Hauptmann-Str. 1, 8020 Dresden, Germany.

331 DK ISSN 0109-1158
ARBEJDERMUSEET. AARBOG. 1983-1988 (vol.3). a. Arbejdermuseet, Roemersgade 22, 1362 Copenhagen K, Denmark.

331 DK ISSN 0109-1514
HD5949
ARBEJDSDIREKTORATET BERETNING OM ARBEJDSFORMIDLINGEN OG ARBEJDSLOESHEDSFORSIKRINGEN. 1978-1984. a. Arbejdsdirektoratet, Adelgade 13, 1304 Copenhagen K, Denmark.

331 DK ISSN 0107-9735
ARBEJDSMARKEDET OG ARBEJDSMARKEDSPOLOTIK/ LABOR MARKET AND LABOR MARKET POLICY. 1978-1987 (Dec.). a. Arbejdsministeriet, Oekonomisk-Statistisk Konsulent, Laksegade 19, 1063 Copenhagen K, Denmark.

500 IC
ARBOK VISINDAFELAGS ISLENDINGA. 1975-19?? irreg. Visindafelag Islendinga - Societas Scientiarum Islandica (Icelandic Scientific Society), Haskolabokasafn, 101 Reykjavik, Iceland.

701.18 US ISSN 0882-3588
ARC; the rural arts newsletter. 1979-19?? bi-m. (tabloid format; back issues avail.) Rural Arts Services, Box 1547, Mendocino, CA 95460.
Formerly: Newsletter from Rural Arts Services.

913 BE ISSN 0772-7488
ARCHAELOGIA BELGICA. 1950-19?? irreg. Service National des Fouilles - Nationale Dienst voor Opgravingen, Parc de Cinquantenaire 1, B-1040 Brussels, Belgium.

913 770 UK ISSN 0143-0661
ARCHAEOLOG. 1978-1980. 6/yr. Royal Photographic Society of Great Britain, Archaeological Group, The Octagon, Milsom St., Bath BA1 1DN, England.

913 GW
ARCHAEOLOGIA MUSICALIS. 1987-19?? s-a. Moeck Verlag & Musikinstrumentenwerk, Postfach 143, 3100 Celle 1, Germany.

913 BE
ARCHAEOLOGICUM BELGII SPECULUM. 1968-1979 (no.11). irreg. Service National des Fouilles - Nationale Dienst voor Opgravingen, Parc du Cinquantenaire 1, B-1040 Brussels, Belgium.

913 KO
ARCHAEOLOGY IN KOREA. 1973-1987 (vol.14). a. Seoul National University, University Museum, Seoul Taehakkyo Pangmulgwan, S. Korea.

913 UK ISSN 0952-1240
ARCHAEOLOGY TODAY. 1979-19?? m. Carphone Consultants Ltd., 28 Woodcock Industrial Estate, Warminster, Wiltshire BA12 9DY, England.
Formerly: Popular Archaeology (ISSN 0143-0262)

913 BE ISSN 0066-6025
ARCHEOLOGISCHE KAARTEN VAN BELGIE. 1968-19?? irreg. Service National des Fouilles - Nationale Dienst voor Opgravingen, Parc du Cinquantenaire 1, B-1040 Brussels, Belgium.

720 UK ISSN 0066-6092
ARCHIGRAM. 1961-1972. irreg. 59, Aberdare Gardens, London N.W.6, England.

720 SA
ARCHITECTS DIRECTORY. 1981-1990. a. Institute of South African Architects, Professional Promotion Directorate, Box 3952, Cape Town 8000, South Africa.

720 690 UK
ARCHITECTURAL & BUILDING INFORMATION SELECTOR. 1971-19?? s-a. B & M Publications (London) Ltd., Box 13, Hereford House, Bridle Path, Croydon, Surrey CR9 4NL, England.

720 US
ARCHITECTURE AND URBAN DESIGN. ceased 1991 (Jun.). irreg. U M I Research Press, 300 N. Zeeb Rd., Ann Arbor, MI 48106-1346.

850 016 US ISSN 0194-1356
Z5941
ARCHITECTURE SERIES: BIBLIOGRAPHY. 1978-1990 (Dec.). 20/m. (back issues avail.) Vance Bibliographies, 112 N. Charter St., Box 229, Monticello, IL 61856.

720 US
ARCHITECTURES. 1985-198? (no.4); suspended. q. (International Network for Art & Architecture) Eastview Editions, Inc., Box 783, Westfield, NJ 07091.

616.994 016 GW ISSN 0003-911X
 CODEN: ARGEAR
ARCHIV FUER GESCHWULSTFORSCHUNG. 1949-19?? bi-m. Verlag Gesundheit GmbH, Neue Gruenstr. 18, 1020 Berlin, Germany.

CESSATIONS

929   GW   ISSN 0003-9403
CS610
ARCHIV FUER SIPPENFORSCHUNG; und alle verwandten Gebiete. (Includes supplement: Praktische Forschungshilfe) 1928-1991. irreg. C.-A. Starke Verlag, Frankfurter Str. 51, Postfach 1310, 6250 Limburg, Germany.

534   PL   ISSN 0066-6823
ARCHIWUM AKUSTYKI. 1966-19?? q. (Polska Akademia Nauk, Komitet Akustyki) Panstwowe Wydawnictwo Naukowe, Ul. Miodowa 10, 00-251 Warsaw, Poland.

367   UK   ISSN 0142-5498
ARENA. 1979-19??; suspended. bi-m. Standing Conference of Youth Organisations in Northern Ireland, 86 Lisburn Rd., Belfast BT9 6AF, N. Ireland.

790.1   US   ISSN 0735-1267
ARENA REVIEW. 1977-1990 (vol.14, no.1). s-a. (back issues avail.) Center for the Study of Sport in Society, c/o Michael A. Malec, Ed., Department of Sociology, Boston College, Chestnut Hill, MA 02167.

370   AG
ARGENTINA. CENTRO NACIONAL DE DOCUMENTACION E INFORMACION EDUCATIVA. INFORMACIONES Y DOCUMENTOS. 1963-19??; suspended. q. (Ministerio de Cultura y Educacion) Centro de Documentacione Informacion Educativa, Paraguay 1657-1er. piso, 1062-Capital Federal, Argentina.
Formerly: Informacion Educativa (ISSN 0019-9788)

332   AG
ARGENTINA. COMISION NACIONAL DE VALORES. BOLETIN INFORMATIVO. 1971-198? q. Comision Nacional de Valores, Hippolito Yrigoyen 250, Oficina 1004, Buenos Aires, Argentina.

318   AG
ARGENTINA. COMISION NACIONAL DE VALORES. INFORMACION ESTADISTICA. suspended. irreg. Comision Nacional de Valores, 215 Hippolito Yrigoyen, Buenos Aires, Argentina.

331.11   AG
ARGENTINA. CONSEJO NACIONAL DE DESARROLLO. RECURSOS HUMANOS. ceased. irreg. Consejo Nacional de Desarrollo, Buenos Aires, Argentina.

500   AG   ISSN 0010-6364
ARGENTINA. CONSEJO NACIONAL DE INVESTIGACIONES CIENTIFICAS Y TECNICAS. INFORMACIONES. 1963-1983 (Jan.). bi-m. Consejo Nacional de Investigaciones Cientificas y Tecnicas, Rivadavia 1917, 1033 Buenos Aires, Argentina.

600   AG   ISSN 0325-6278
ARGENTINA. INSTITUTO NACIONAL DE TECNOLOGIA INDUSTRIA. BOLETIN TECNICO. 1967-1984. irreg. Instituto Nacional de Tecnologia Industrial, Leandro N. Alem 1067, Casilla de Correo 1359, 1001 Buenos Aires, Argentina.

800   UK   ISSN 0143-0246
PN2
ARGO (OXFORD); an international review of new art and writing from Britain and America. 1952-1991 (vol.9, no.1). 3/yr. (Southern Arts Association) Argo Publishing Co., Museum of Modern Art, 30 Pembroke St., Oxford OX1 1BP, England.
Incorporating (as of 1979): Delta.

053   GW   ISSN 0722-964X
ARGUMENT-BEIHEFT. 1979-1986. a. Argument-Verlag GmbH, Rentzelstr. 1, 2000 Hamburg 13, Germany.

334   FR   ISSN 0004-119X
ARGUS DES COLLECTIVITES; equipement, entretien, securite, tourisme, loisirs. 1952-19?? 9/yr. Editions Garon, 60 rue du Landy, 93210 La Planie St. Denis, France.

665.5   FR   ISSN 0398-7515
ARGUS DU PETROLE. ceased. s-w. S.O.C.I.D.O.C., 142 rue Montmartre, 75002 Paris, France.

368   FR   ISSN 0153-3614
L'ARGUS INTERNATIONAL. 1977-19?? bi-m. Securitas, 2 rue de Chateaudun, 75009 Paris, France.
Formerly: Reassurance (ISSN 0034-1096)

949.7   YU
ARHIV JUGOSLAVIJE. BILTEN. 1980-1986 (no.9). s-a. Arhiv Jugoslavije - Archives of Yugoslavia, Vase Pelagica 33, P.C. 65, 11000 Belgrade, Yugoslavia.

557 622   US
ARIZONA. OIL AND GAS CONSERVATION COMMISSION. REPORT OF INVESTIGATION. ceased 1979 (no.7). irreg. (Oil and Gas Conservation Commission) Arizona Geological Survey, 5150 N. 16th St., Ste. B-141, Phoenix, AZ 85016-3203.

970.1   US
ARIZONA INDIAN MONTHLY. 1978-1981 (vol.3, no.12). m. Indian Development, 4560 N. 19th Ave., Ste. 200, Phoenix, AZ 85015-4113.

620   US   ISSN 0194-7435
ARIZONA PROFESSIONAL ENGINEER. 1949-19?? bi-m. Arizona Society of Professional Engineers, 100 W. Camelback Rd., Ste. 100, Phoenix, AZ 85013-2530.

330.9   US
ARIZONA PROGRESS. 1945-1990. q. Valley National Bank of Arizona, Economic Planning Division, Box 71, 241 N. Central Ave., Phoenix, AZ 85001.

330 658 350   US   ISSN 0004-1629
HC107.A6
ARIZONA REVIEW. 1952-199? s-a. University of Arizona, College of Business and Public Administration, Division of Economic and Business Research, Tucson, AZ 85721.
Formerly: Arizona Review of Business and Public Administration.

330 317   US   ISSN 0518-6242
HA245
ARIZONA STATISTICAL REVIEW. 1945-1989 (Dec.). a. Valley National Bank of Arizona, Economic Planning Division, Box 71, 241 N. Central Ave., Phoenix, AZ 85001.
Formerly: Statistical Review of Arizona.

975   US   ISSN 0889-5481
HC107.A6
ARIZONA TREND; magazine of Arizona business & finance. 1986-1990. m. Trend Magazines, Inc., 3003 N. Central Ave., Ste. 2004, Phoenix, AZ 85012.

796.332   US
ARKANSAS FOOTBALL MAGAZINE. 1963-19?? a. (back issues avail.) Host Communications, Inc., 7621 Little Ave., No.516, Charlotte, NC 28226-8162.

355   UK   ISSN 0142-4696
UA647
ARMED FORCES. 1978-1989. m. (reprint service avail. from UMI) Ian Allan Ltd., Terminal House, Station Approach, Shepperton, Surrey TW17 8AS, England.

378   AT   ISSN 0811-7098
ARMIDALE COLLEGE OF ADVANCED EDUCATION. ANNUAL REPORT. 1973-1988. a. University of New England, C.B. Newling Centre, Mossman St., Armidale, N.S.W. 2351, Australia.

011   UK
ARMSTRONG'S MONTHLY BULLETIN. 1977-19?? 10/yr. Alan Armstrong Ltd., 2 Arkwright Rd., Reading RG2 0SQ, England.
Formerly (until 1988): New Editions - Directories, Annuals & Reference Books.

355 069   UK
ARMY MUSEUM. 1981-1987. a. (back issues avail.) National Army Museum, Royal Hospital Rd., London SW3 4HT, England.

355   US
ARMY ORGANIZATIONAL EFFECTIVENESS JOURNAL. ceased. q. U.S. Department of the Army, Office of the Chief of Public Affairs, Washington, DC 20310-1508.
Formerly: O E Communique.

355   RM
ARMY'S LIFE. (Supplement avail.: Entire People's Struggle) ceased. s-a. Ministerul Apararii Nationale, Str. Cobalcescu Nr. 28A, sector 1, Bucharest 70768, Rumania.

581   US   ISSN 0004-2625
QK475   CODEN: JAARAG
ARNOLD ARBORETUM. JOURNAL. 1919-1990; suspended. q. (back issues avail.; reprint service avail. from KTO) Harvard University, Arnold Arboretum, 125 Arbor Way, Jamiaca Plain, MA 02130-2795.

914.2   UK
AROUND CANTERBURY. ceased. q. Around Kent Publications, Newspaper House, Railway Rd., Sheerness, Kent ME12 1PU, England.

052   HK
AROUND HONG KONG. (Extracted from the Sunday edition of "South China Morning Post") ceased. w. South China Morning Post Ltd., G.P.O. Box 37, Hong Kong.

158   BL   ISSN 0100-8692
BF5
ARQUIVOS BRASILEIROS DE PSICOLOGIA. 1949-1990 (vol.42, no.3). q. Fundacao Getulio Vargas, C.P. 9052, 22250 Rio de Janeiro R.J., Brazil.
Former titles (until 1978): Arquivos Brasileiros de Psicologia Aplicada (ISSN 0004-2757); (until 1968): Arquivos Brasileros de Psicotecnica.

745.1 747   IT   ISSN 0393-5132
ARREDOSTILE MIDDLE EAST. 1983-19?? s-a. Editore Rima s.r.l., Via Luigi Barzini 20, 20125 Milan, Italy.

016.7   SZ
ART/KUNST; international bibliography of art books-internationale bibliographie des kunstbuchs-bibliographie internationale des livres d'art. 1972-1988 (vol. 17). a. W. Jaeggi AG, Postfach, CH-4001 Basel, Switzerland.

700   US
ART & CINEMA; the V R I slide library. 1975-19?? 3/yr. V R I Arts Publishers, Box 1208, Imperial Beach, CA 92032.
Former titles: Visual and Performing Arts; Art and Cinema (ISSN 0363-2911)

709.7   US
ART INSIGHT SOUTHWEST; a journal devoted to recognition of the arts in the West and Southwest. 1966-1978 (vol.7, no.1). q. (also avail. in microform from UMI; reprint service avail. from UMI) Art Insight, Inc., Box 1763, Austin, TX 78767.
Former titles: A I Art Insight (ISSN 0194-9071); (until vol.7, no.1, 1978): Southwestern Art (ISSN 0038-4739)

700   UK
ART MAGAZINE. 1971-1991. q. Federation of British Artists, 17 Carlton House Terrace, London SW1Y 5BD, England.
Formerly: F.B.A. Quarterly.

808   US   ISSN 0277-7053
ART ON THE LINE SERIES. 1981-1984. a. Curbstone Press, 321 Jackson St., Willimantic, CT 06226.

700 914   SP
ART ROMANIC. (Contains 2 series: Monografies and Tematica) ceased 1979 (no.10). irreg. Artestudi Edicions, Provenca 552, Barcelona 26, Spain.

700   IT   ISSN 0004-3451
ARTERAMA. 1969-1984. 10/yr. Mimar S.A.S., Piazza Santa Francesca Romana 1, 20129 Milan, Italy.

700   UK
ARTFUL REPORTER; the arts newspaper for the North West. 1977-198? m. North West Arts, 12 Harter St., Manchester M1 6HY, England.

296 323.4   US
ARTICLES OF INTEREST IN CURRENT PERIODICALS. ceased. 7/yr. American Jewish Committee, 165 E. 56th St., New York, NY 10022.

708.11 CN
ARTISTS IN CANADA: A UNION LIST OF ARTISTS FILES/ARTISTES DU CANADA: UNE LISTE COLLECTIVE DES DOSSIERS D'ARTISTES. 1970-19?? irreg. National Gallery of Canada, Library, Ottawa, Ont. K1N 9N4, Canada.
Former titles: Artists in Canada; National Gallery of Canada. Library. Checklist of Canadian Artists Files (ISSN 0078-6993)

700 069 US
ARTISTS RESOURCE GUIDE TO NEW ENGLAND GALLERIES, GRANTS AND SERVICES. published only once; 1988. a. Artist Foundation, Inc., 8 Park Plaza, Boston, MA 02116-3902.

730 US ISSN 0164-1298
N6530.N7
ARTPARK. 1976-1989. a. Artpark, Inc., Public Relations Department, Box 371, Lewiston, NY 14092.

720 US ISSN 0730-9481
NA1
ARTS & ARCHITECTURE. 1981-1988. bi-m. (also avail. in microform from UMI; reprint service avail. from UMI) Arts & Architecture, Inc., c/o Barbara Goldstein, Ed., 1223 Wilshire Blvd., Ste. 472, Santa Monica, CA 90403.

700 330 US
ARTS & BUSINESS COUNCIL. ANNUAL REPORT. ceased. a. Arts & Business Council, 130 E. 40th St., New York, NY 10016.

792 US
ARTS AND LEISURE MAGAZINE. 1975-1986. m. (back issues avail.) Hagen Publishing Co., Box 707, Custer, SD 57730.

378 US ISSN 0738-9361
ARTS & SCIENCES (EVANSTON). 1978-1988. a. Northwestern University, College of Arts and Sciences, 1918 Sheridan Rd., Evanston, IL 60208.

700 UK
THE ARTS BUSINESS. 1980-1991. irreg. Southern Arts, 13 St. Clement St., Winchester, Hampshire SO23 9DQ, England.
Former titles: Southern Arts Association. Publication & Southern Arts Bulletin (ISSN 0262-1169)

700 UK ISSN 0143-4519
ARTS COUNCIL OF GREAT BRITAIN. EDUCATION BULLETIN. 1979-1986. 3/yr. Arts Council of Great Britain, 105 Piccadilly, London W1V 0AU, England.

792 UK ISSN 0951-1121
ARTS FESTIVALS IN BRITAIN AND IRELAND. 1970-1989. a. Rhinegold Publishing Ltd., 241 Shaftesbury Ave., London WC2H 8EH, England.
Formerly (until 1986): Festivals in Great Britain.

700 706 US
ARTS JOURNAL. 1975-1992. m. Arts Journal Co., 324 Charlotte St., Asheville, NC 28801.

700 792 780 UK ISSN 0260-8723
ARTS REPORT. 1981-1988. m. West Midlands Arts, 82 Granville St., Birmingham B1 2LH, England.
Supersedes: West Midlands Arts News Sheet.

700 780 792 US ISSN 0741-4579
NX735
ARTS REVIEW. 1983-1988 (Jan.). q. National Endowment for the Arts, Office of Communication, 1100 Penn Ave., N.W., Washington, DC 20506.
Supersedes (1975-1983): Cultural Post.

700 793.32 AT ISSN 0814-883X
ARTSWEST. 1981-1988. m. (back issues avail.) Artswest Foundation Ltd., Room 402, Westpoint Shoppingtown, Patrick St., Blacktown, N.S.W. 2148, Australia.

701.18 CN ISSN 0381-9515
ARTVIEWS. 1975-1989. 4/yr. (also avail. in microfiche; reprint service avail. from MML) Visual Arts Ontario, 439 Wellington St., 2nd Fl., Toronto, Ont. M5V 1E7, Canada.

300 JA ISSN 0387-2785
ASAHI AJIA REBYU/ASAHI ASIA REVIEW. 1970-19?? q. Asahi Shinbunsha - Asahi Shinbun Publishing Co., 3-2, Tsukiji 5-chome, Chuo-ku, Tokyo 104, Japan.

520 JA
ASAHI KOSUMOSU/ASAHI COSMOS. ceased in 1987. a. Asahi Shinbunsha - Asahi Shimbun Publishing Co., 3-2, Tsukiji 5-chome, Chuo-ku, Tokyo 104, Japan.

340 US ISSN 1053-0231
KF3964.A73
ASBESTOS ABATEMENT LITIGATION REPORTER. 1990-1991 (May). m. (looseleaf format; back issues avail.) Andrews Publications, 1646 West Chester Pike, Box 1000, Westtown, PA 19395.

614.7 US ISSN 0897-1501
ASBESTOS ISSUES. ceased 1991 (Aug.). m. P H Publishing, Inc., 760 Whalers Way, Ste. 100-A, Fort Collins, CO 80525.

810.8 US ISSN 0098-9363
PS501
ASCENT. 1973-19??; suspended. 3/yr. University of Illinois at Urbana-Champaign, English Department, 608 S. Wright St., Urbana, IL 61801.

614.7 US
ASH AT WORK. ceased. irreg. American Coal Ash, 1913 I St., N.W., Ste. 600, Washington, DC 20036.

332.1 621.381 001.642
ASHTON-TATE QUARTERLY. 1985-198? q. Ashton-Tate Publishing Group, Box 3729, Escondido, CA 92025-0929.

664 GW
ASIA AND MIDDLE EAST FOOD TRADE. 1984-1991. 4/yr. Beta Publishing, Postfach 140121, 5300 Bonn 1, Germany.
Formerly: Middle East Food Trade and Catering Equipment (ISSN 0265-6469)

950 CN ISSN 0835-3336
ASIA HORIZON AZIE; Asia Pacific studies newsletter. 1987-1991 (May). s-a. Canadian Asian Studies Association, c/o University of Montreal, C.P. 6128, Succ. A, Montreal, Que. H3C 3J7, Canada.
Formerly: Canadian Asian Studies Association. Revue.

323.4 AT ISSN 0815-6344
ASIA PACIFIC CONTEXT. 1985-19?? 4/yr. Asian Bureau Australia, 173 Royal Parade, Parkville, Vic. 3052, Australia.

332 US ISSN 0739-6244
ASIA - PACIFIC CURRENCY REPORT. 1983-19?? s-m. (back issues avail.) International Business Information, Inc., 700 Walnut St., Ste. 202, Cincinnati, OH 45202.

327 SI
ASIA - PACIFIC INTERNATIONAL AND STRATEGIC STUDIES NEWSLETTER. 1984-19?? q. (back issue avail.) Institute of Southeast Asian Studies, Heng Mui Keng Terrace, Pasir Panjang, Singapore 0511, Singapore.

330 UK ISSN 0954-7525
ASIA PACIFIC INTERNATIONAL JOURNAL OF BUSINESS RESEARCH. announced, never published. a. (University of Queensland, Graduate School of Management, AT) M C B University Press Ltd., 62 Toller Ln., Bradford, W. Yorks BD8 9BY, England.

658 UK ISSN 0954-7533
ASIA PACIFIC INTERNATIONAL JOURNAL OF MANAGEMENT DEVELOPMENT. announced, never published. s-a. M C B University Press Ltd., 62 Toller Ln., Bradford, W. Yorks BD8 9BY, England.

658 UK
ASIA PACIFIC INTERNATIONAL MANAGEMENT FORUM. ceased 1992. 3/yr. (International Management Centres) M C B University Press Ltd., 62 Toller Ln., Bradford, W. Yorks BD8 9BY, England.
Formerly: Asia Pacific International Management Review (ISSN 0954-2957)

658 UK ISSN 0955-1484
ASIA PACIFIC TOP MANAGEMENT DIGEST. announced, never published. m. M C B University Press Ltd., 62 Toller Ln., Bradford, W. Yorks BD8 9BY, England.

070.5 II ISSN 0066-8362
ASIAN BOOK TRADE DIRECTORY. (Prepared with the assistance of UNESCO) 1964; ceased same year. irreg. Popular Prakashan Pvt. Ltd., 35-C, Pandit Madan Mohan Malaviya Marg, Popular Press Bldg., Tardeo, Bombay 400034, India.
Formerly: Directory of Asian Book Trade.

323.4 AT
ASIAN BUREAU AUSTRALIA. NEWSLETTER. 1971-19?? 4/yr. Asian Bureau Australia, 173 Royal Pde., Parkville, Vic. 3052, Australia.

001.6 621.381 HK ISSN 0254-217X
CODEN: ASCMD7
ASIAN COMPUTER MONTHLY. 1977-1991; suspended. m. Computer Publications Ltd., Washington Plaza, 1st Fl., 230 Wanchai Rd., Wanchai, Hong Kong.

332 338.9 PH ISSN 0066-8397
ASIAN DEVELOPMENT BANK. OCCASIONAL PAPERS. 1969-198? irreg. Asian Development Bank, P.O. Box 789, 1099 Manila, Philippines.

332 HK
ASIAN FINANCE. ceased in Nov. 1991. q. Asian Finance Publications Ltd., 3 Floor Hollywood Centre, 233 Hollywood Rd., Hong Kong.

684.3 SI
ASIAN FURNITURE. 1986-19?? 5/yr. (back issues avail.) Asian Business Press Pte. Ltd. (Subsidiary of: Asian Business Press Group), 100 Beach Road, No. 26-00 Shaw Towers, Singapore 0718, Singapore.

340 US
ASIAN LAW SERIES. 1969-198? irreg. University of Washington Press, Box 50096, Seattle, WA 98105.

994 327 AT
ASIAN PACIFIC REVIEW; Australia, Asia and the World. 1950-1989 (no.8). 4/yr. (reprint service avail. from UMI) Australian Institute of International Affairs, Victorian Branch, 124-6 Jolimont Rd., East Melbourne, Vic. 3002, Australia.
Former titles: Dyason House Papers; Australia's Neighbors (ISSN 0005-0474)

333.33 HK
ASIAN PROPERTY. 1990-1991 (vol.2, Sept.). m. Travel and Trade Publishing (Asia) Ltd., 16-F, Capitol Centre, 5-19 Jardine's Bazaar, Causeway Bay, Hong Kong.

294.3 US ISSN 0888-5869
Z7757.A8
ASIAN RELIGIOUS STUDIES INFORMATION. 1987-1989. s-a. (back issues avail.) Institute for Advanced Studies of World Religions, RD 2, Route 301, Carmel, NY 10512.
Incorporates: Buddhist Research Information (ISSN 0192-396X) & Sikh Religious Studies Information (ISSN 0193-1466) & Hindu Text Information (ISSN 0277-1349)

950 338.91 SZ
ASIAN STUDIES SERIES. 1979-1987. irreg. Centre de Recherche sur l'Asie Moderne, Institut Universitaire de Hautes Etudes Internationales, Institut Universitaire d'Etudes du Developpement - Modern Asia Research Center, Graduate Institute of International Studies, Institute of Development Studies, Case Postale 36, CH-1211 Geneva 21, Switzerland.

674.2 SI
ASIAN TIMBER. 1982-19?? m. (back issues avail.) Toucan Publications Pte Ltd., 322-C King George's Avenue, Singapore 0820, Singapore.
Formerly: Asian Timber Trades Journal (ISSN 0264-4134)

950 960 980 GW ISSN 0232-8410
ASIEN - AFRIKA - LATEINAMERIKA. JAHRBUCH; Bilanz und Chronik. 1969-1989. a. Zentraler Rat fuer Asien-, Afrika- und Lateinamerikawissenschaften in der DDR, Rosa-Luxemburg-Str. 3, 1020 Berlin, Germany.
Formerly: Asien - Afrika - Lateinamerika (ISSN 0066-8508)

808.81 SP ISSN 0213-7585
H53.S7
ASIMETRIA. 1986-1988 (no.7). s-a. (tabloid format; back issues avail.) Virgen de la Salud, 78, 08024 Barcelona, Spain.

327 CU
ASOCIACION CUBANA DE LA NACIONES UNIDAS. BOLETIN. 1969-1990 (no.2); suspended. 3/yr. Asociacion Cubana de las Naciones Unidas, Calle J y 25 Vedado, Havana, Cuba.

677.2 SP ISSN 0571-3609
ASOCIACION DE INVESTIGACION TEXTIL ALGODONERA. COLECCION DE MANUALES TECNICOS. ceased 199? irreg. Asociacion de Investigacion Textil Algodonera, Gran via de les Corts Catalanes 670, 08010 Barcelona, Spain.

677.2 SP
ASOCIACION DE INVESTIGACION TEXTIL ALGODONERA. ESTUDIOS Y DOCUMENTOS. 1975?-199? irreg. Asociacion de Investigacion Textil Algodonera, Gran via de les Corts Catalanes 670, 08010 Barcelona, Spain.

930 880 US
ASPECTS OF GREEK AND ROMAN LIFE. ceased. irreg. Cornell University Press, 124 Roberts Place, Ithaca, NY 14850.

808 US
ASSAYS. 1981-1990. a. University of Pittsburgh Press, 127 N. Bellefield Ave., Pittsburgh, PA 15260.

333.3 336.2 US ISSN 0090-6352
KF6759.5.A59
ASSESSMENT AND VALUATION LEGAL REPORTER. 1971-1990? m. (looseleaf format; back issues avail.) International Association of Assessing Officers, 1313 E. 60th St., Chicago, IL 60637-2892.

332.63 US
ASSET-BACKED SECURITIES REPORT. 1985-199? m. Warren, Gorham and Lamont Inc., One Penn Plaza, New York, NY 10119.

330 PO
ASSOCIACAO INDUSTRIAL PORTUENSE. BOLETIM INFORMATIVO. 1849-19?? m. Associacao Industrial Portuense, Av. da Boavista 2671, P.O. Box 1092, 4102 Porto Codex, Portugal.

332 658 FR
ASSOCIATION EUROPEENNE DE MANAGEMENT ET DE MARKETING FINANCIERS. BANK AND MANAGEMENT. ceased. q. Association Europeenne de Management et de Marketing Financiers - European Financial Management and Marketing Association, 16, rue d'Aguesseau, F-75008 Paris, France.

621.381 001.6 US ISSN 0066-9091
ASSOCIATION FOR COMPUTING MACHINERY. PROCEEDINGS OF NATIONAL CONFERENCE. 1946-1987. a. Association for Computing Machinery, 1515 Broadway, 17th Fl., New York, NY 10036.

370.28 371.394 US ISSN 0147-9296
ASSOCIATION FOR EDUCATIONAL DATA SYSTEMS. ANNUAL CONVENTION PROCEEDINGS. 1973-19?? a. (reprint service avail. from UMI) International Association for Computing in Education, c/o University of Oregon, 1787 Agate St., Eugene, OR 97403.

658 US
ASSOCIATION LEADER (WASHINGTON). 1988-19?? bi-m. Institute of Association Management Companies, 1133 15th St., N.W., Washington, DC 20005.

658 UK ISSN 0144-9613
ASSOCIATION MANAGEMENT. 1980-19?? 6/yr. Hamerville Magazines Ltd., Regal House, Regal Way, Watford, Herts. WD2 4YJ, England.

285 US
ASSOCIATION OF ADVENTIST FORUMS NEWSLETTER. 1969-199? q. (tabloid format; back issues avail.) Association of Adventist Forums, Box 5330, Takoma Park, MD 20912.

910 US
ASSOCIATION OF AMERICAN GEOGRAPHERS. DIRECTORY. 1956-1990. irreg. Association of American Geographers, 1710 16th St., N.W., Washington, DC 20009-3198.

Formerly: Association of American Geographers. Handbook-Directory (ISSN 0571-5962)

625 US
ASSOCIATION OF AMERICAN RAILROADS. DATA SYSTEMS DIVISION. PAPERS. ceased. a. Association of American Railroads, Library Rm., 50 F St., N.W., Washington, DC 20001.

378 CN ISSN 0702-5378
ASSOCIATION OF CANADIAN COMMUNITY COLLEGES. JOURNAL. ceased. q. Association of Canadian Community Colleges, 110 Eglinton Ave. W., 2nd Floor, Toronto, Ont. M4R 1A3, Canada.

620 UK
ASSOCIATION OF CONSULTING ENGINEERS WHO'S WHO & YEAR BOOK. 19??-1992. a. Municipal Journal Ltd., 32 Vauxhall Bridge Rd., London SW1V 2SS, England.

338 659.1 US
ASSOCIATION OF FREE COMMUNITY PAPERS. NEWS BULLETIN. ceased. irreg. Association of Free Community Papers, 111 E. Wacker Dr., Ste. 600, Chicago, IL 60601.

371.3 US
ASSOCIATION OF TEACHER EDUCATORS. PUBLICATIONS. ceased. 3/yr. (unnumbered). Association of Teacher Educators, 1900 Association Dr., Reston, VA 22091-1599.

Supersedes (as of 1977): Association of Teacher Educators. Bulletin.

643.7 698.9 US
ASSOCIATION OF THE WALL AND CEILING INDUSTRIES INTERNATIONAL. BULLETIN. ceased. 17/yr. Association of the Wall and Ceiling Industries International, 1600 Cameron St., Alexandria, VA 22314-2705.

020 IT ISSN 0519-2048
ASSOCIAZIONE ITALIANA BIBLIOTECHE. QUADERNI DEL BOLLETTINO D'INFORMAZIONI. (Supplement to: Associazione Italiana Biblioteche. Bollettino d'Informazioni) 1965-1978 (no.6). irreg. (back issues avail.) Associazione Italiana Biblioteche, Casella Postale 2461, 00100 Rome A-D, Italy.

312 MR
AS-SOUKAN. 1973-1980 (no.7). s-a. (also avail. in microfiche) Direction de la Statistique, B.P. 178, Rabat, Morocco.

841 CN
ASTROLABE. 1979-19?? irreg. University of Ottawa Press, 603 Cumberland, Ottawa, Ont. K1N 6N5, Canada.

520 GW ISSN 0587-565X
ASTRONOMIE UND RAUMFAHRT. 1963-1991. bi-m. Kulturbund der D.D.R., Postfach 61, 9630 Crimmitschau, Germany.

745.5 AT
AT THE CENTRE. 1979-19??; suspended. bi-m. Footscray Community Arts Centre, 45 Moreland St., Footscray, Vic. 3011, Australia.

Formerly: Community Arts News.

808.81 US ISSN 0731-8987
ATAVIST. 1982-1990 (Spring). s-a. Atavist, Box 5643, Berkeley, CA 94705.

100 CS
ATEIZMUS. ceased 1989. bi-m. (Slovenska Akademia Vied, Ustav Vedeckeho Ateizmu) Veda, Publishing House of the Slovak Academy of Sciences, Klemensova 19, 814 30 Bratislava, Czechoslovakia.

808.18 700 US
ATHENA INCOGNITO MAGAZINE; a journal of surrealistic writing. 1980-1991 (no.12). a. (back issues avail.) Athena Press (San Francisco), 1442 Judah St., San Francisco, CA 94122.

616.1 US
ATHEROSCLEROSIS. 1977-1983 (vol.6). irreg. (reprint service avail. from ISI) Springer-Verlag, 175 Fifth Ave., New York, NY 10010.

338 US
ATLANTA PROFESSIONAL. 1988-19?? 12/yr. (tabloid format) Small Business Media Network, Inc., 1858-C Independence Sq., Dunwoody, GA 30338.

051 CN ISSN 0004-6744
AP5
ATLANTIC ADVOCATE. 1909-1992. m. University of New Brunswick Press, Box 3370, Fredericton, N.B. E3B 5A2, Canada.

Incorporates: Marine Advocate & Busy East; Atlantic Guardian.

330 CN
ATLANTIC BUSINESS. 1982-1989. 6/yr. (also avail. in microfilm from MML) Canasus Communications Inc. (Halifax), 402-1668 Barrington St., Halifax, N.S. B3S 2AS, Canada.

387 CN
ATLANTIC CANADA SHIPPING PROJECT. ANNUAL CONFERENCE. PROCEEDINGS. 1978-1985. a. Memorial University of Newfoundland, Maritime History Group, St. John's, Nfld. A1C 5S7, Canada.

794.1 US
ATLANTIC CHESS NEWS. 1975-199? 6/yr. New Jersey State Federation, Box 334, Piscataway, NJ 08854.

327 US
ATLANTIC COMMUNITY NEWS. 1962-1990. bi-m. (also avail. in microform from UMI; reprint service avail. from UMI) Atlantic Council of the United States, Inc., 1616 H St., N.W., 3rd Fl., Washington, DC 20006.

327 US ISSN 0004-6760
D839
ATLANTIC COMMUNITY QUARTERLY. 1962-1990. q. (also avail. in microfilm; microfiche; reprint service avail.) Atlantic Council of the United States, Inc., 1616 H St., N.W., 3rd Fl., Washington, DC 20006.

327 UK ISSN 0571-7795
ATLANTIC PAPERS. 1969-19?? q. (back issues avail.) (Atlantic Institute for International Affairs) Croom Helm Ltd., Provident House, Burnell Row, Beckenham, Kent BR3 1AT, England.

621.5 CN
ATLAS COPCO COMMENTS; commentary on the applications of compressed air, gas and hydraulics. 1958-1991. q. Atlas Copco Canada Inc., P.O. Box 745, Pointe Claire-Dorval, Que. H9R 4S8, Canada.

Formerly: Canadian Air Comments (ISSN 0045-4338)

617.96 BL ISSN 0034-7094
ATLAS DE TECNICAS DE BLOQUEIOS REGIONAIS. (Supplement to: Revista Brasileira de Anestesiologia) published only once. bi-m. Cidade - Editora Cientifica Ltda., c/o Dr. Antonio Leite Oliva Filho, Ed., R. Pe Anchieta 1500 Ap. 401, 80730 Curitiba Pr., Brazil.

580 PL ISSN 0067-0324
ATLAS ROZMIESZCZENIA DRZEW I KRZEWOW W POLSCE. 1963-1982 (vol.32). irreg. (Polska Akademia Nauk, Zaklad Dendrologii) Panstwowe Wydawnictwo Naukowe, Ul. Miodowa 10, 00-251 Warsaw, Poland.

796.4 CS ISSN 0323-1364
ATLETIKA. vol.36, 1984-1992. m. (Ceskoslovensky Svaz Telesne Vychovy) Olympia, Klimentska 1, 115 88 Prague 1, Czechoslovakia.

539.7 PH ISSN 0115-3757
TK9113.P6
ATOMEDIA. 1976-19?? biennial. (back issues avail.) Philippine Atomic Energy Commission, Don Marianos Marcas Ave., Diliman, Quezon City, Philippines.

539.7 US ISSN 0090-6360
QC173 CODEN: ATPHDU
ATOMIC PHYSICS. 1969-19?? irreg. Plenum Publishing Corp., 233 Spring St., New York, NY 10013.

659 DK
ATT:. 1988-19?? m. Thomson Communications (Scandinavia) A-S, Struenseegade 7-9, DK-2200 Copenhagen N, Denmark.

800 070.5 US ISSN 0147-7129
ATTIC PRESS. 1977-1978. bi-m. (looseleaf format; back issues avail.) Attic Press Co., 235 Adams St., Apt. 14F, Brooklyn, NY 11201.

340 US
ATTORNEY SANCTIONS NEWSLETTERS. ceased 1991. m. Shepard's - McGraw-Hill, Inc., Box 35300, Colorado Springs, CO 80935-3530.

CESSATIONS

340 621.381   US   ISSN 0745-421X
KF320.A9
ATTORNEYS COMPUTER REPORT. 1982-1990. m. Professional Publications, 50 S. 9th St., Ste. 200, Minneapolis, MN 55402.

616.8 340   US   ISSN 0278-0879
RA1151
ATTORNEY'S DIRECTORY OF FORENSIC PSYCHIATRISTS IN THE UNITED STATES AND CANADA; a biographical professional and reference directory of legal psychiatrists. 1983-198? biennial. (back issues avail.) (American College of Forensic Psychiatry) Edward Miller, Ed. & Pub., 26701 Quail Creek, No. 295, Laguna Hills, CA 92656.

340 150 614.19   US   ISSN 0887-4905
RA1151
ATTORNEY'S DIRECTORY OF FORENSIC PSYCHOLOGISTS. 1986-198? biennial. (back issues avail.) (American College of Forensic Psychology) Edward Miller, Ed. & Pub., 26701 Quail Creek, No. 295, Laguna Hills, CA 92656.

340 001.6 629.8   US
ATTORNEY'S GUIDE TO LAW OFFICE AUTOMATION. ceased. m. Cumberland Data Services, Inc., Legal Graphics, Drawer 1590, Grundy, VA 24614.

028.5   GW   ISSN 0323-8903
ATZE. ceased 1991. m. Verlag Junge Welt GmbH, Mauerstr. 39-40, 1080 Berlin, Germany.

674   CN   ISSN 0383-0047
AU FIL DU BOIS. 1974-1992. bi-m. Association des Manufacturiers de Bois de Sciage du Quebec - Quebec Lumber Manufacturer's Association, 5055 W., Hamel Blvd., Ste. 200, Quebec, Que. G2E 2G6, Canada.

388.3   US   ISSN 1046-4573
TL7.A1
AUCTION RESULTS QUARTERLY. 1989-1990 (Dec). q. Krause Publications, Inc., 700 E. State St., Iola, WI 54990.

796.9   UK
AUDI - DAILY MAIL SKIER'S HOLIDAY GUIDE. 1961-198? a. Ocean Publications Ltd., 34 Buckingham Palace Rd., London SW1W ORE, England.
Former titles: Daily Mail Skier's Holiday Guide (ISSN 0309-5134); Peter Stuyvesant Travel Ski Guide.

001.5   US   ISSN 0164-8985
AUDIO & ELECTRONICS DIGEST. 1976-1985. m. (Society of Audio Consultants) Audio-Sac, c/o Jerry Joseph, General Delivery, Beverly Hills, CA 90210.
Formerly (until vol.2, no.7, Sep. 1977): Audio Digest and Personal Communications.

617.8   GW   ISSN 0571-8678
AUDIO-TECHNIK. 1958-1988. irreg. Robert Bosch GmbH, Geschaeftsbereich Mobile Kommunikation, Forckenbeckstr. 9-13, D-1000 Berlin 33, Germany.

620.2   US
AUDIO TIMES. 1958-1990. m. Retail Press, Inc. (Subsidiary of: Capital Cities - ABC), 825 Seventh Ave., 6th Fl., New York, NY 10019.

051   US
AUDIO VIDEO REVIEW DIGEST. 1989; announced, never published. 3/yr. Gale Research Inc., 835 Penobscot Bldg., Detroit, MI 48226.

659.1   US
AUDIT PROCEDURE FOR OUT-OF-HOME MEDIA. 1985-1990. irreg. Out-of-Home Measurement Bureau, Inc., 100 Barnegat Rd., Box 1201, New Canaan, CT 06840.

001.64   US
AUERBACH D P TRAINING. 1981-1984. bi-m. Auerbach Publishers Inc., 6560 N. Park Dr., Pennsauken, NJ 08109.

001.64   US
AUERBACH DISTRIBUTED DATA PROCESSING MANAGEMENT. 1979-1984. bi-m. Auerbach Publishers, Inc., 6560 N. Park Dr., Pennsaken, NJ 08109.

001.64   US
AUERBACH FINANCIAL - RETAIL SYSTEMS REPORTS. 1979-1984. m. Auerbach Publishers, Inc., 6560 N. Park Dr., Pennsauken, NJ 08109.

001.6   US
AUERBACH OFFICE SYSTEMS REPORTS. 1979-1984. m. Auerbach Publishers, Inc., 6560 N. Park Dr., Pennsauken, NJ 08109.
Supersedes: Auerbach Microform Reports.

621.381   US
AUERBACH PLUG-COMPATIBLE PERIPHERALS REPORT. 1979-1984. base vol. (plus m. updates). Auerbach Publishers, Inc., 6560 N. Park Dr., Pennsauken, NJ 08109.
Supersedes: Auerbach Peripherals and Data Handling Reports.

261   SZ   ISSN 0004-7821
AUFBAU; Schweizerische Zeitschrift fuer Recht, Freiheit und Frieden. 1919-1988 (no.24). fortn. Verein der Freunde des "Aufbau", Postfach 1008, CH-8036 Zurich, Switzerland.

617.7   GW   ISSN 0004-7910
AUGENOPTIK; Fachzeitschrift fuer Augenoptiker, Ophthalmologen und Arbeitshygieniker. 1884-1991. bi-m. VEB Verlag Technik, Postfach 201, Oranienburger Str. 13-14, 1020 Berlin, Germany.

378.1   US   ISSN 0004-7996
AUGUSTANA COLLEGE BULLETIN. 1929-1980? 3/yr. Augustana College, Rock Island, IL 61201.

301.412 028.1   US
AUNT EDNA'S READING LIST. 1987-1989 (Nov.). m. 2002-H Hunnewell St., Honolulu, HI 96822.

133   US
AUREA FLAMMA. ceased 1987. m. (back issues avail.) Ordo Templi Baphe-Metis, Box 1219, Corpus Christi, TX 78403-1219.

708   SZ   ISSN 0067-0618
AUS DEM SCHWEIZERISCHEN LANDESMUSEUM. 1953-1978 (no.41). irreg. Paul Haupt AG, Falkenplatz 14, CH-3001 Berne, Switzerland.

374.013   GW
AUSBILDER-INFORMATIONEN. 1976-1991. bi-m. Industrie und Handelskammer Mittlerer Neckar, Sitz Stuttgart, Jaegerstr. 30, 7000 Stuttgart 1, Germany.

327   GW   ISSN 0004-8208
AUSSENPOLITISCHE KORRESPONDENZ. 1956-1991. w. (Ministerium fuer Auswaertige Angelegenheiten, Presseabteilung) Staatsverlag, Otto-Grotewohl-Str. 17, 1086 Berlin, Germany.

747 659.152   US   ISSN 0199-1531
AUSTIN HOMES & GARDENS. 1979-1988 (Mar.). q. (back issues avail.; reprint service avail.) Marlo Media, Inc., Box 1684, Austin, TX 78767.

027.7   AT   ISSN 0811-112X
AUSTRALASIAN COLLEGE LIBRARIES (SOUTH AUSTRALIA). 1983-1989. q. (back issues avail.) Auslib Press, P.O. Box 622, Blackwood, S.A. 5051, Australia.

929   AT   ISSN 0815-4597
AUSTRALASIAN FAMILY HISTORY GAZETTE. 1986-1991; suspended. s-a. (back issues avail.) Australasian Federation of Family History Organisations, 120 Kent St., Syndney, N.S.W. 2000, Australia.

368   AT   ISSN 0045-0073
AUSTRALASIAN INSURANCE JOURNAL. 1920-198? m. Bushell Publishing Co. Pty. Ltd., 1987 Pittwater Rd., Bayview, N.S.W. 2104, Australia.

100   AT
AUSTRALASIAN JOURNAL OF PHILOSOPHY. MONOGRAPH SERIES. 1982-198? irreg. Australasian Association of Philosophy, Philosophy Department, La Trobe University, Bundoora, Vic. 3083, Australia.

387.7   AT   ISSN 0727-2731
AUSTRALIA. AIR TRANSPORT STATISTICS. AIRLINE AIRCRAFT UTILISATION. 1965-1988. s-a. (back issues avail.) Department of Transport & Communications, Domestic Aviation Information Section, P.O. Box 594, Canberra City, A.C.T. 2601, Australia.

387.7   AT   ISSN 0727-2774
AUSTRALIA. AIR TRANSPORT STATISTICS. FLIGHT CREW LICENCES. 1978-1987 (Dec). a. (back issues avail.) Department of Transport & Communications, Aviation Industry Statistics Section, Box 594, Canberra City, A.C.T. 2601, Australia.

551.4   AT   ISSN 0067-219X
GB821   CODEN: AWRHAO
AUSTRALIA. AUSTRALIAN WATER RESOURCES COUNCIL. HYDROLOGICAL SERIES. 1966-19?? irreg. Australian Government Publishing Service, G.P.O. Box 84, Canberra, A.C.T. 2601, Australia.

526   AT
AUSTRALIA. BUREAU OF MINERAL RESOURCES, GEOLOGY, AND GEOPHYSICS. PUBLICATIONS. (In two parts: Part 1: Publications; Part 2: Maps) ceased. irreg. Bureau of Mineral Resources, Geology, and Geophysics, G.P.O. Box 378, Canberra, A.C.T. 2601, Australia.

549   AT   ISSN 1031-7295
AUSTRALIA. BUREAU OF STATISTIC. QUEENSLAND OFFICE. SAND, GRAVEL AND QUARRY PRODUCTION, QUEENSLAND. 1967-1990. s-a. Australian Bureau of Statistics, Queensland Office, 313 Adelaide St., Brisbane, Qld. 4000, Australia.

362.734 319.4   AT
AUSTRALIA. BUREAU OF STATISTICS. ADOPTIONS. 1979-1984. a. Australian Bureau of Statistics, P.O. Box 10, Belconnen, A.C.T. 2616, Australia.

382.6 319   AT   ISSN 0705-0534
AUSTRALIA. BUREAU OF STATISTICS. AUSTRALIAN EXPORTS, COUNTRY BY COMMODITY. 1958-1984. a. Australian Bureau of Statistics, P.O. Box 10, Belconnen, A.C.T. 2616, Australia.
Formerly: Australia. Bureau of Statistics. Australian Exports Bulletin (ISSN 0067-186X)

338   AT   ISSN 1033-2618
AUSTRALIA. BUREAU OF STATISTICS. AUSTRALIAN NATIONAL ACCOUNTS: GROSS PRODUCT, EMPLOYMENT AND HOURS WORKED. 1987-1990. a. Australian Bureau of Statistics, P.O. Box 10, Belconnen, A.C.T. 2616, Australia.
Former titles: Australia. Bureau of Statistics. Australian National Accounts: Gross Product by Industry; Australia. Bureau of Statistics. Estimates of Gross Product by Industry at Current and Constant Prices; Australia. Bureau of Statistics. Australian National Accounts: Gross Product by Industry at Current and Constant Prices.

332.1 319   AT
AUSTRALIA. BUREAU OF STATISTICS. BANKING, AUSTRALIA. 1945-19?? q. Australian Bureau of Statistics, P.O. Box 10, Belxonnen, A.C.T. 2616, Australia.
Formerly: Australia. Bureau of Statistics. Banking Statistics.

350 362.7   AT   ISSN 0728-4543
AUSTRALIA. BUREAU OF STATISTICS. CHILD CARE ARRANGEMENTS, AUSTRALIA, PRELIMINARY. 1969-1987. irreg. Australian Bureau of Statistics, Ground Floor, Wing 5, Cameron Offices, Belconnen, A.C.T. 2617, Australia.
Formerly (until 1980): Australia. Bureau of Stastistics. Child Care, Preliminary (ISSN 0728-4551)

350   AT   ISSN 0816-0627
AUSTRALIA. BUREAU OF STATISTICS. DIGEST OF CURRENT ECONOMIC STATISTICS. 1959-1989. m. Australian Bureau of Statistics, P.O. Box 10, Belconnen, A.C.T. 2616, Australia.

332 319   AT
AUSTRALIA. BUREAU OF STATISTICS. FINANCE COMPANIES, AUSTRALIA. 1965-1989. m. Australian Bureau of Statistics, P.O. Box 10, Belconnen, A.C.T. 2616, Australia.

382 319   AT
AUSTRALIA. BUREAU OF STATISTICS. FOREIGN TRADE, AUSTRALIA, PART 1: EXPORTS AND IMPORTS. 1904-1984. a. (also avail. in microfiche from BHP) Australian Bureau of Statistics, P.O. Box 10, Belconnen, A.C.T. 2616, Australia.
Formerly: Australia. Bureau of Statistics. Overseas Trade, Australia, Part 1: Exports and Imports (ISSN 0705-0518)

CESSATIONS

370 319.4   AT
AUSTRALIA. BUREAU OF STATISTICS. NEW SOUTH WALES OFFICE. TERTIARY EDUCATION, NEW SOUTH WALES. 1972-1986. a. Australian Bureau of Statistics, New South Wales Office, St. Andrews House, Sydney Square, George St., Sydney, N.S.W. 2000, Australia.

352.7   AT
AUSTRALIA. BUREAU OF STATISTICS. QUEENSLAND OFFICE. BUILDING APPROVALS: PRELIMINARY FIGURES FOR DWELLING UNITS APPROVED. 1970-1988. m. Australian Bureau of Statistics, Queensland Office, 313 Adelaide St., Brisbane, Qld. 4000, Australia.

312   AT
AUSTRALIA. BUREAU OF STATISTICS. QUEENSLAND OFFICE. CENSUS OF POPULATION AND HOUSING: CHARACTERISTICS OF PERSONS AND DWELLINGS IN SUBURBS OF BRISBANE CITY AND LOCAL AUTHORITY AREAS WITHIN BRISBANE STATISTICAL DIVISION. 1981-19?? irreg. Australian Bureau of Statistics, Queensland Office, 313 Adelaide St., Brisbane, Qld. 4000, Australia.

312   AT
AUSTRALIA. BUREAU OF STATISTICS. QUEENSLAND OFFICE. CENSUS (YEAR) - ABORIGINAL AND TORRES STRAIT ISLANDER PEOPLE IN QUEENSLAND. published only once, 1986. irreg. Australian Bureau of Statistics, Queensland Office, 313 Adelaide St., Brisbane, Qld. 4000, Australia.

312   AT
AUSTRALIA. BUREAU OF STATISTICS. QUEENSLAND OFFICE. CENSUS (YEAR) - FAMILIES AND HOUSEHOLDS. 1986-19?? irreg. Australian Bureau of Statistics, Queensland Office, 313 Adelaide St., Brisbane, Qld. 4000, Australia.

365.64   AT
AUSTRALIA. BUREAU OF STATISTICS. QUEENSLAND OFFICE. COMMUNITY CRIME PREVENTION ATTITUDES, QUEENSLAND. published only once, 1987. irreg. Australian Bureau of Statistics, Queensland Office, 313 Adelaide St., Brisbane, Qld. 4000, Australia.

330   AT
AUSTRALIA. BUREAU OF STATISTICS. QUEENSLAND OFFICE. ESTABLISHMENT SIZE STATISTICS. 1979-19?? irreg. (also avail. on floppy disk) Australian Bureau of Statistics, Queensland Office, 313 Adelaide St., Brisbane, Qld. 4000, Australia.

360   AT   ISSN 1031-2277
AUSTRALIA. BUREAU OF STATISTICS. QUEENSLAND OFFICE. HEALTH AND WELFARE ESTABLISHMENTS, QUEENSLAND, PRELIMINARY. 1975-1990. a. Australian Bureau of Statistics, Queensland Office, 313 Adelaide St., Brisbane, Qld. 4000, Australia.

312   AT
AUSTRALIA. BUREAU OF STATISTICS. QUEENSLAND OFFICE. HOSPITAL MORBIDITY RATES, QUEENSLAND. 1966-1986. irreg. Australian Bureau of Statistics, Queensland Office, 313 Adelaide St., Brisbane, Qld. 4000, Australia.

658.8   AT
AUSTRALIA. BUREAU OF STATISTICS. QUEENSLAND OFFICE. INDEXES OF RETAIL PRICES OF FOOD IN QUEENSLAND TOWNS. 1975-1987. irreg. Australian Bureau of Statistics, Queensland Office, 313 Adelaide St., Brisbane, Qld. 4000, Australia.

382   AT
AUSTRALIA. BUREAU OF STATISTICS. QUEENSLAND OFFICE. INTERSTATE AND FOREIGN TRADE. 1974-1987. a. Australian Bureau of Statistics, Queensland Office, 313 Adelaide St., Brisbane, Qld. 4000, Australia.

319   AT   ISSN 0312-7397
Z4019
AUSTRALIA. BUREAU OF STATISTICS. QUEENSLAND OFFICE. LIST OF PUBLICATIONS. 1972-1990. a. Australian Bureau of Statistics, Queensland Office, 313 Adelaide St., Brisbane, Qld. 4000, Australia.

331.11 331.2   AT
AUSTRALIA. BUREAU OF STATISTICS. QUEENSLAND OFFICE. MANUFACTURING ESTABLISHMENTS: EMPLOYMENT SIZE STATISTICS. 1968-1985. a. Australian Bureau of Statistics, Queensland Office, 313 Adelaide St., Brisbane, Qld. 4000, Australia.

330   AT   ISSN 0818-979X
AUSTRALIA. BUREAU OF STATISTICS. QUEENSLAND OFFICE. MANUFACTURING ESTABLISHMENTS: SMALL AREA STATISTICS, QUEENSLAND. 1968-1988. a. Australian Bureau of Statistics, Queensland Office, 313 Adelaide St., Brisbane, Qld. 4000, Australia.
Formerly (until 1984): Australia. Bureau of Statistics. Queensland Office. Census of Manufacturing Establishments: Small Area Statistics by Industry, Queensland (ISSN 0729-1531)

330   AT
AUSTRALIA. BUREAU OF STATISTICS. QUEENSLAND OFFICE. MANUFACTURING ESTABLISHMENTS: SUMMARY OF OPERATIONS. 1971-1985. a. Australian Bureau of Statistics, Queensland Office, 313 Adelaide St., Brisbane, Qld. 4000, Australia.

622 665.5   AT   ISSN 1031-2714
AUSTRALIA. BUREAU OF STATISTICS. QUEENSLAND OFFICE. MINERAL PRODUCTION, QUEENSLAND. 1969-1990. a. Australian Bureau of Statistics, Queensland Office, 313 Adelaide St., Brisbane, Qld. 4000, Australia.

362.7   AT   ISSN 0818-1993
AUSTRALIA. BUREAU OF STATISTICS. QUEENSLAND OFFICE. PRE-SCHOOLS AND CHILD CARE CENTRES, QUEENSLAND. 1973-1990. a. Australian Bureau of Statistics, Queensland Office, 313 Adelaide St., Brisbane, Qld. 4000, Australia.
Formerly (until 1985): Australia. Bureau of Statistics. Queensland Office. Pre-schools Training and Child Minding, Queensland (ISSN 0313-3133)

330   AT
AUSTRALIA. BUREAU OF STATISTICS. QUEENSLAND OFFICE. RETAIL INDUSTRY: DETAILS OF OPERATIONS. 1979-1986. irreg. (also avail. on floppy disk) Australian Bureau of Statistics, Queensland Office, 313 Adelaide St., Brisbane, Qld. 4000, Australia.
Formerly: Australia. Bureau of Statistics. Queensland Office. Census of Retail Establishments and Selected Service Establishments: Details of Operations by Industry Class.

368.2   AT   ISSN 1031-3893
AUSTRALIA. BUREAU OF STATISTICS. QUEENSLAND OFFICE. ROAD TRAFFIC ACCIDENTS, QUEENSLAND (ANNUAL). 1945-1990. a. Australian Bureau of Statistics, Queensland Office, 313 Adelaide St., Brisbane, Qld. 4000, Australia.

368.2   AT   ISSN 1031-2803
AUSTRALIA. BUREAU OF STATISTICS. QUEENSLAND OFFICE. ROAD TRAFFIC ACCIDENTS, QUEENSLAND (QUARTERLY). 1984-1990. q. Australian Bureau of Statistics, Queensland Office, 313 Adelaide St., Brisbane, Qld. 4000, Australia.

674.2   AT   ISSN 0314-3287
AUSTRALIA. BUREAU OF STATISTICS. QUEENSLAND OFFICE. SAWMILL STATISTICS, QUEENSLAND. 1948-1990. q. Australian Bureau of Statistics, Queensland Office, 313 Adelaide St., Brisbane, Qld. 4000, Australia.

370   AT   ISSN 0818-2582
AUSTRALIA. BUREAU OF STATISTICS. QUEENSLAND OFFICE. SCHOOLS, QUEENSLAND. 1989-1990. a. Australian Bureau of Statistics, Queensland Office, 313 Adelaide St., Brisbane, Qld. 4000, Australia.
Formerly (until 1984): Australia. Bureau of Statistics. Queenslnad Office. Primary and Secondary Education, Queensland (ISSN 0313-8518)

370   AT   ISSN 0818-2132
AUSTRALIA. BUREAU OF STATISTICS. QUEENSLAND OFFICE. SCHOOLS, QUEENSLAND, PRELIMINARY. 1976-1988. a. Australian Bureau of Statistics, Queensland Office, 313 Adelaide St., Brisbane, Qld. 4000, Australia.
Formerly (until 1985): Australia. Bureau of Statistics. Queensland Office. Government School, Queensland, Preliminary.

647.97   AT
AUSTRALIA. BUREAU OF STATISTICS. QUEENSLAND OFFICE. SELECTED ACCOMMODATION ESTABLISHMENTS, QUEENSLAND. 1984-19?? irreg. Australian Bureau of Statistics, Queensland Office, 313 Adelaide St., Brisbane, Qld. 4000, Australia.

614.42   AT
AUSTRALIA. BUREAU OF STATISTICS. QUEENSLAND OFFICE. SMOKING BEHAVIOUR. published only once, 1985. irreg. Australian Bureau of Statistics, Queensland Office, 313 Adelaide St., Brisbane, Qld. 4000, Australia.

331.11   AT
AUSTRALIA. BUREAU OF STATISTICS. QUEENSLAND OFFICE. THE LABOUR FORCE: REGIONAL ESTIMATES. 1984-19?? q. Australian Bureau of Statistics, Queensland Office, 313 Adelaide St., Brisbane, Qld. 4000, Australia.

331.11   AT
AUSTRALIA. BUREAU OF STATISTICS. QUEENSLAND OFFICE. TYPE AND CONDITIONS OF PART-TIME EMPLOYMENT. 1988-19?? irreg. Australian Bureau of Statistics, Queensland Office, 313 Adelaide St., Brisbane, Qld. 4000, Australia.

345.01   AT
AUSTRALIA. BUREAU OF STATISTICS. QUEENSLAND OFFICE. USAGE OF LEGAL SERVICES, QUEENSLAND. published only once, 1986. irreg. Australian Bureau of Statistics, Queensland Office, 313 Adelaide St., Brisbane, Qld. 4000, Australia.

380.5   AT   ISSN 1031-8097
AUSTRALIA. BUREAU OF STATISTICS. QUEENSLAND OFFICE. TRANSPORT, QUEENSLAND. 1974-1989. a. Australian Bureau of Statistics, Queensland Office, 313 Adelaide St., Brisbane, Qld. 4000, Australia.

312.274   AT   ISSN 1031-1084
AUSTRALIA. BUREAU OF STATISTICS. ROAD TRAFFIC ACCIDENTS INVOLVING FATALITIES, AUSTRALIA. 1970-1990 (Dec.). m. (processed) Australian Bureau of Statistics, P.O. Box 10, Belconnen, A.C.T. 2616, Australia.
Formerly: Australia. Bureau of Statistics. Road Accident Fatalities (ISSN 0035-7162)

350   AT   ISSN 0571-964X
HC601
AUSTRALIA. BUREAU OF STATISTICS. SEASONALLY ADJUSTED INDICATORS. 1967-1983. a. Australian Bureau of Statistics, P.O. Box 10, Belconnen, A.C.T. 2616, Australia.

350 319.4   AT
AUSTRALIA. BUREAU OF STATISTICS. TECHNICAL PAPERS. ceased. irreg. Australian Bureau of Statistics, P.O. Box 10, Belconnen, A.C.T 2616, Australia.

350   AT
AUSTRALIA. BUREAU OF STATISTICS. TERTIARY EDUCATION. 1983-1985. a. Australian Bureau of Statistics, P.O. Box 10, Belconnen, A.C.T. 2616, Australia.

310   AT
AUSTRALIA. BUREAU OF STATISTICS. TIME SERIES SERVICE. 1979-1989. q. (avail. on magnetic tape and microfiche) Australian Bureau of Statistics, P.O. Box 10, Belconnen, A.C.T. 2616, Australia.
Formerly: Australia. Bureau of Statistics. Time Series Data on Magnetic Tape and Microfiche.

370 310   AT   ISSN 1031-7767
AUSTRALIA. BUREAU OF STATISTICS. VICTORIAN OFFICE. SCHOOLS, VICTORIA. 1967-1990. a. Australian Bureau of Statistics, Victorian Office, Box 2796Y, G. P.O., Melbourne, Vic. 3001, Australia.
Former titles (until 1984): Australia. Bureau of Statistics. Victorian Office. National Schools Statistics, Victoria; Australia. Bureau of Statistics. Victorian Office. Primary and Secondary Education, Victoria (ISSN 0067-1150)

338.4 319   AT   ISSN 0727-2200
AUSTRALIA. BUREAU OF STATISTICS. WESTERN AUSTRALIAN OFFICE. CENSUS OF MANUFACTURING ESTABLISHMENTS. SUMMARY OF OPERATIONS BY GROUP, WESTERN AUSTRALIA. 1968-1989. a. Australian Bureau of Statistics, Western Australian Office, 30 Terrace Rd., Perth, W.A. 6000, Australia.
Former titles: Australia. Bureau of Statistics. Western Australia Office. Census of Manufacturing Establishments. Summary of Operations by Industry Class; Australia. Bureau of Statistics. Western Australian Office. Economic Censuses: Manufacturing Establishments: Summary of Operations by Industry Class.

CESSATIONS 5143

336.1   AT
AUSTRALIA. COMMONWEALTH GRANTS COMMISSION. GRANTS COMMISSION REPORT ON FINANCIAL ASSISTANCE FOR LOCAL GOVERNMENT. 1974-19?? irreg. Australian Government Publishing Service, G. P.O. Box 84, Canberra, A.C.T. 2601, Australia.
Former titles: Australia. Grants Commission. Grants Commission Report on Financial Assistance for Local Government; Australia. Grants Commission. Grants Commission Report on Special Assistance for States.

690   AT
AUSTRALIA. DEPARTMENT OF ADMINISTRATIVE SERVICES. AUSTRALIAN CONSTRUCTION SERVICES. TECHNICAL BULLETIN. 1972-1979; resumed 19??-1990 (vol.59). q. Department of Administrative Services, Australian Construction Services, 470 Morthbourne Ave., Dickson, A.C.T. 2602, Australia.
Formerly (until 1988): Australia. Department of Housing and Construction. Technical Bulletin (ISSN 0816-1321)

331 658.3   AT   ISSN 0811-1863
AUSTRALIA. DEPARTMENT OF EMPLOYMENT AND INDUSTRIAL RELATIONS. EMPLOYEE PARTICIPATION NEWS. 1981-19?? q. (back issues avail.) (Department of Employment and Industrial Relations, Working Environment Branch) Australian Government Publishing Service, G.P.O. Box 84, Canberra, A.C.T. 2601, Australia.

333.91   AT
AUSTRALIA. DEPARTMENT OF PRIMARY INDUSTRIES AND ENERGY. STREAMLINE UPDATE. 1983-19?? irreg. (approx. 8/yr.). Department of Primary Industries and Energy, G.P.O. Box 858, Canberra, A.C.T. 2601, Australia.
Formerly: Australia. Department of Resources and Energy. Streamline Update (ISSN 0812-7735)

350 382   AT
AUSTRALIA. DEPARTMENT OF PRIMARY INDUSTRY. CONDITIONS FOR EXPORT OF EXPERIMENTAL SHIPMENTS. 1972-19?? a. Department of Primary Industry, Quarantine and Inspection Service, Edmund Barton Bldg., Broughton St., Barton, A.C.T. 2600, Australia.

350 382   AT
AUSTRALIA. DEPARTMENT OF PRIMARY INDUSTRY. CONDITIONS FOR EXPORT OF GRAPES. 1972-19?? a. Department of Primary Industry, Quarantine and Inspection Service, Edmund Barton Bldg., Broughton ST., Barton, A.C.T. 2600, Australia.

350 382   AT
AUSTRALIA. DEPARTMENT OF PRIMARY INDUSTRY. CONDITIONS FOR EXPORT OF PRIMARY PRODUCTS. 1972-19?? a. Department of Primary Industry, Quarantine and Inspection Service, Edmund Barton Bldg., Broughton St., Barton, A.C.T. 2600, Australia.
Formerly (until 1987): Australia. Department of Primary Industry. Conditions for Export of Pears.

350 679.7   AT   ISSN 0404-181X
HD9148.A8
AUSTRALIA. DEPARTMENT OF PRIMARY INDUSTRY. TOBACCO INDUSTRY TRUST. ACCOUNT ANNUAL REPORT. 1956-198? a. Department of Primary Industry, Field Crop Division, Edmund Barton Bldg., Broughton St., Barton, A.C.T. 2600, Australia.

370   AT
AUSTRALIA. EDUCATION RESEARCH AND DEVELOPMENT COMMITTEE. ANNUAL REPORT. 1970-19?? a. Australian Government Publishing Service, G.P.O. Box 84, Canberra, A.C.T. 2601, Australia.
Formerly: Australia. Advisory Committee on Research and Development in Education. Annual Report.

338.994   AT
AUSTRALIA. INDUSTRIES ASSISTANCE COMMISSION. ANNUAL REPORT. 1974-1989. a. Australian Government Publishing Service, G.P.O. 84, Canberra, A.C.T. 2601, Australia.

370   AT   ISSN 0156-9643
AUSTRALIA. LIBRARY INFORMATION SERVICE. CATALOGUE OF SERIALS. 1984-1988. a. Ministry of Education, 151 Royal St., E. Perth, W.A. 6000, Australia.

711   AT   ISSN 0067-1517
NA9280.C3
AUSTRALIA. NATIONAL CAPITAL DEVELOPMENT COMMISSION. ANNUAL REPORT. 1958-19?? a. National Capital Development Commission, G.P.O. Box 373, Canberra, A.C.T. 2601, Australia.

352.7 620 614.7   AT   ISSN 0313-9948
AUSTRALIA. NATIONAL CAPITAL DEVELOPMENT COMMISSION. TECHNICAL PAPERS. 1974-19?? irreg. National Capital Development Commission, G.P.O. Box 373, Canberra, A.C.T. 2601, Australia.

301.412   AT
AUSTRALIA. NATIONAL WOMEN'S ADVISORY COUNCIL. ANNUAL REPORT. 1979-19?? a. Australian Government Publishing Service, G.P.O. Box 84, Canberra, A.C.T. 2601, Australia.

994   AT
AUSTRALIA. NORTHERN TERRITORY PROTOCOL AND PUBLIC RELATIONS BRANCH. TERRITORY DIGEST. 1968-1990 (vol.12, no.3). q. Northern Territory Protocol and Public Relations Branch, Mitchell St., P.O. Box 4396, Darwin, N.T. 5790, Australia.
Former titles: Australia. Northern Territory Protocol and Public Relations Service. Territory Digest; Australia. Northern Territory Information Service. Territory Digest (ISSN 0728-4276); Australia. Northern Territory Division. Northern Newsletter (ISSN 0045-0189)

539 621.48   AT
AUSTRALIA. NUCLEAR SCIENCE AND TECHNOLOGY ORGANISATION. A N S T O - M. 1959-1984 (vol.27). irreg. Nuclear Science and Technology Organisation, Menai, N.S.W. 2234, Australia.
Formerly: Australia. Atomic Energy Commission. Research Establishment. A A E C - M (ISSN 0067-1665)

387.165 310   AT
AUSTRALIA. STEVEDORING STATISTICS. STEVEDORING LABOUR REVIEW. ceased 1989. q. Department of Transport and Communications, Stevedoring Statistics, G.P.O. Box 594, Canberra, A.C.T. 2601, Australia.
Formerly: Australia. Sea Transport Statistics. Stevedoring Labour Review (ISSN 0156-7381)

296   AT
AUSTRALIA & NEW ZEALAND JEWISH YEAR BOOK. ceased 1988. a. B'nai B'rith District 21 Australia and New Zealand, 99 Hotham St., Balaclava, Vic. 3183, Australia.

052   US
AUSTRALIA BULLETIN. ceased. s-m. Australian Overseas Information Service, 630 Fifth Ave., New York, NY 10111.
Formerly: Australian Weekly News Roundup.

994   AT   ISSN 0067-1495
DU80
AUSTRALIA HANDBOOK. 1969-19?? a. Australian Government Publishing Service, G.P.O. Box 84, Canberra, A.C.T. 2601, Australia.

551 559.8   AT
AUSTRALIAN ACADEMY OF SCIENCE. NATIONAL COMMITTEE FOR ANTARCTIC RESEARCH. AUSTRALIAN ANTARCTIC AND SUB-ANTARCTIC RESEARCH PROGRAMMES. 1976-19?? a. Australian Academy of Science, National Committee for Antarctic Research, G.P.O. Box 783, Canberra, A.C.T. 2601, Australia.

745.1 747   AT
AUSTRALIAN ANTIQUES TRADE GAZETTE. 1981-19?? m. (back issues avail.) Bomilhold Pty. Ltd., 2-27 Dale St., Brookvale, N.S.W. 2100, Australia.

690   AT   ISSN 0310-1045
AUSTRALIAN ASSOCIATION OF PERMANENT BUILDING SOCIETIES. NATIONAL NEWSLETTER. 1973-1986. bi-m. Australian Association of Permanent Building Societies, P.O. Box 21, Deakin, A.C.T. 2600, Australia.

338   AT   ISSN 0311-323X
AUSTRALIAN AUDIO-VISUAL REFERENCE BOOK. 1974-1987. a. D.W. Thorpe (Subsidiary of: Butterworths), 18 Salomon St., Port Melbourne, Vic. 3207, Australia.

286   AT   ISSN 0004-8739
AUSTRALIAN BAPTIST. 1913-19?? m. Australian Baptist Publishing House Ltd., 68 Arundel St., Glebe, N.S.W. 2037, Australia.

920 929 990   AT
AUSTRALIAN BIOGRAPHICAL AND GENEALOGICAL RECORD. NEWSLETTER. 1983-19?? q. (back issues avail.) Australian Biographical and Genealogical Record, P.O. Box 1788, North Sydney N.S.W. 2060, Australia.

382   AT
AUSTRALIAN BRITISH BUSINESS DIRECTORY. 1984-198? q. International Public Relations Pty. Ltd., 33 Walsh St., West Melbourne, Vic. 3003, Australia.
Formerly: Directory of U.K. Subsidiaries and Affiliates in Australia.

347 336   AT
AUSTRALIAN BUSINESS AND ASSETS PLANNING REPORTER. (In 2 vols.) 1979-19?? 12/yr. C C H Australia Ltd., P.O. Box 230, North Ryde, N.S.W. 2113, Australia.

384.55 028.5   AT   ISSN 0812-1621
AUSTRALIAN CHILDREN'S TELEVISION FOUNDATION. INFORMATION PAPERS. 1983-1987 (no.7). irreg. (back issues avail.) Australian Children's Television Foundation, 199 Grattan St., Carlton, Vic. 3053, Australia.

650   AT   ISSN 0726-6065
AUSTRALIAN COMPANY LAW & PRACTICE. (In 3 vols.) 1982-1990? irreg. C C H Australia Ltd., P.O. Box 230, N. Ryde, N.S.W. 2113, Australia.
Formerly: Australian Corporate Affairs Reporter (ISSN 0310-8813)

780   AT   ISSN 0311-2764
AUSTRALIAN COMPOSER. 1972-1989. irreg. Fellowship of Australian Composers, P.O. Box 522, Strathfield, N.S.W. 2135, Australia.
Formerly: Fellowship of Australian Composers. Newsletter.

370   AT   ISSN 0067-1835
LA2102
AUSTRALIAN COUNCIL FOR EDUCATIONAL RESEARCH. OCCASIONAL PAPERS. ceased 1987. irreg. Australian Council for Educational Research, P.O. Box 210, Hawthorn, Vic. 3122, Australia.

658   AT
AUSTRALIAN DIRECTOR. 1971-1990. m. Institute of Directors in Australia, 16 O'Connell St., Sydney, N, S.W. 2000, Australia.

330   AT   ISSN 1030-6560
AUSTRALIAN ECONOMIC BRIEF. 1988-19?? q. (back issues avail.) Australian Chamber of Manufactures, Victorian Division, 380 St. Kilda Rd., Melbourne, Vic. 3004, Australia.

621.38   AT   ISSN 0815-5046
AUSTRALIAN ELECTRONICS MONTHLY. 1985-198? m. (back issues avail.) Kedhorn Holdings Pty. Ltd., 1st Fl., 347 Darling St., Balmain, N.S.W. 2041, Australia.

340   AT
AUSTRALIAN FAMILY LAW GUIDE. 1985-1990 (Jun.). bi-m. C C H Australia Ltd., P.O. Box 230, North Ryde, N.S.W. 2113, Australia.

791.43   AT   ISSN 0045-0448
AUSTRALIAN FILMS; a catalogue of scientific, educational and cultural films. 1959-1981; suspended. a. National Film & Sound Archive, McCoy Circuit, Acton, A.C.T. 2601, Australia.

634.9   AT   ISSN 0004-914X
CODEN: AUFRAE
AUSTRALIAN FOREST RESEARCH. 1966-19?? q. (back issues avail.) C.S.I.R.O., 314 Albert St., E. Melbourne, Vic. 3002, Australia.

360   AT   ISSN 0818-5352
AUSTRALIAN INSTITUTE OF FAMILY STUDIES. POLICY BACKGROUND PAPER (NO.). ceased. irreg. Australian Institute of Family Studies, 300 Queen St., Melbourne, Vic. 3000, Australia.

CESSATIONS

301.4　　　　　　AT　　ISSN 0817-6345
AUSTRALIAN INSTITUTE OF FAMILY STUDIES. WORKING PAPER. 1981-198? irreg. (back issues avail.) Australian Institute of Family Studies, 300 Queen St., Melbourne, Vic. 3000, Australia.

798.4 636.1　　　　AT　　ISSN 0155-6134
AUSTRALIAN JOCKEY CLUB THOROUGHBRED STALLION REGISTER. 1978-1989 (vol.9). a. (back issues avail.) Australian Jockey Club, Randwick Racecourse, Alison Rd., Randwick, N.S.W. 2031, Australia.

600　　　　　　　AT　　ISSN 0819-3355
　　　　　　　　　　　　CODEN: AJBIEU
AUSTRALIAN JOURNAL OF BIOTECHNOLOGY. 1987-19?? q. (back issues avail.) Australian Industrial Publishers Pty. Ltd., 2 Wilford Ave., Underdale, S.A. 5033, Australia.

685　　　　　　　AT
AUSTRALIAN LEATHER JOURNAL. 1898-19?? bi-m. (Footwear Manufacturers Association of Australia) Hamilton Press Pty. Ltd., P.O. Box 58, Killara, N.S.W. 2071, Australia.
　　Formerly: Australian Leather Journal, Boot and Shoe Recorder (ISSN 0004-962X)

621.381　　　　　　AT
AUSTRALIAN MICRO C W. 1983-1986. m. Computerworld Pty. Ltd., 37-43 Alexander St., Crows Nest, N.S.W. 2065, Australia.

622　　　　　　　AT　　ISSN 0084-7488
HD9506.A7
AUSTRALIAN MINERAL INDUSTRY. ANNUAL REVIEW. 1948-1987. a. Bureau of Mineral Resources, Geology and Geophysics, G.P.O. Box 378, Canberra, A.C.T. 2601, Australia.
　　Formerly: Australia Mineral Industry Review (ISSN 0067-1509)

622　　　　　　　AT　　ISSN 0155-9419
HD9506.A7
AUSTRALIAN MINERAL INDUSTRY. QUARTERLY. (Includes: Quarterly Statistics) 1948-1989 (vol.41, no.2). q. Bureau of Mineral Resources, Geology and Geophysics, G.P.O. Box 378, Canberra, A.C.T. 2601, Australia.
　　Formerly: Australian Mineral Industry. Quarterly Review. (ISSN 0004-9751)

300　　　　　　　AT　　ISSN 0157-5767
AUSTRALIAN NATIONAL UNIVERSITY. DEVELOPMENT STUDIES CENTRE. MONOGRAPH. 1975-1984 (no. 33). irreg. Australian National University, Development Studies Centre, G.P.O. Box 4, Canberra, A.C.T. 2601, Australia.

796.72　　　　　　AT　　ISSN 0813-4952
AUSTRALIAN OFF-ROAD YEAR. 1982-1989. a. (back issues avail.) Chevron Publishing Group Pty.Ltd., P.O. Box 206, Hornsby, N.S.W. 2077, Australia.

658　　　　　　　AT　　ISSN 1031-5217
AUSTRALIAN PRACTICE MANAGEMENT; the business magazine for doctors. 1988-19?? m. (back issues avail.) Adis Press Australasia Pty. Ltd., 404 Sydney Rd., Balgowlah, N.S.W. 2093, Australia.

664　　　　　　　AT　　ISSN 1030-5920
AUSTRALIAN REGIONAL IMPACT ANALYSIS SERIES (NO.). ceased. irreg. University of New England, Department of Agricultural Economics and Business Management, Armidale, N.S.W. 2351, Australia.

636.7　　　　　　US
AUSTRALIAN SHEPHERD QUARTERLY. ceased. q. Hoflin Publishing Ltd., 4401 Zephyr St., Wheat Ridge, CO 80033-3299.

623.8 387　　　　　AT
AUSTRALIAN SHIPPING AND SHIPBUILDING. 1947-19?? a. Australian Government Publishing Service, G.P.O. Box 84, Canberra, A.C.T. 2601, Australia.

631.3 636　　　　　AT
AUSTRALIAN SMALL FARMS HANDBOOK; services, supplies, equipment. 1984-19?? irreg. Second Back Row Press, P.O. Box 43, Leura, N.S.W. 2780, Australia.
　　Formerly: Australian Small Farms Directory (ISSN 0812-955X)

686.2　　　　　　AT
AUSTRALIAN SMALL OFFSET INPLANT PRINTER. ceased 1986 (vol.11, no.6). bi-m. Calmor & Associates Pty. Ltd., P.O. Box 1316, North Sydney, N.S.W. 2069, Australia.
　　Formerly: Small Offset Australia.

336　　　　　　　AT
AUSTRALIAN STAMP DUTIES. (In 3 vols.) 1985-1990. irreg. (approx. 10-12/yr.) C C H Australia Ltd., P.O. Box 230, N. Ryde, N.S.W. 2113, Australia.

050 990　　　　　　AT
AUSTRALIAN STUDIES NEWSLETTER. 1984-1988 (no.8). s-a. (back issues avail.) Australian Studies Association, Centre for Australian Studies, Curtin University, G.P.O. Box 1987, Perth, W.A. 6001, Australia.

600　　　　　　　AT　　ISSN 0819-5943
AUSTRALIAN TECHNOLOGY REVIEW. 1987-1989 (vol.3, no.9). m. Riddell Publishing, 100 Alexander St., Crows Nest, N.S.W. 2065, Australia.

380.5　　　　　　AT　　ISSN 0311-628X
HE289
AUSTRALIAN TRANSPORT. 1973-19?? a. Australian Government Publishing Service, G.P.O. Box 84, Canberra, A.C.T. 2601, Australia.
　　Formerly: Australia. Department of Civil Aviation. Civil Aviation Report (ISSN 0572-0400)

990　　　　　　　AT
AUSTRALIAN WAR MEMORIAL NEWSLETTER. 1982-19?? 3/yr. (back issues avail.) Australian War Memorial, G.P.O. Box 345, Canberra, A.C.T. 2601, Australia.

331.88　　　　　　AT
AUSTRALIAN WORKERS' UNION. OFFICIAL REPORT OF THE ANNUAL CONVENTION. 1886-19?? a. Australian Workers' Union, P.O. Box a-252, Sydney S., N.S.W. 2000, Australia.

690　　　　　　　AU
AUSTRIA. BUNDESMINISTERIUM FUER BAUTEN UND TECHNIK. WOHNBAUFORSCHUNG. 1971-1985. m. Sparkassenverlag GmbH, Grimmelshausengasse 1, A-1030 Vienna, Austria.

910.202　　　　　　AU
AUSTRIAN AIRLINES. FLIGHT GUIDE. 1957-1988. s-a. (Oestereichische Luftverkehrs AG) Austrian Airlines, Catering Division, Schwechat Airport, A-1300 Vienna, Austria.
　　Formerly: Route Maps and Board Price List.

808 920　　　　　US　　ISSN 0145-1499
CT220
AUTHORS IN THE NEWS; compilation of news stories and feature articles from American newspapers and magazines, covering prominent writers in all fields. 1975-1976 (vol.2). irreg. Gale Research Inc., 835 Penobscot Bldg., Detroit, MI 48226.
　　Formerly: Contemporary Authors News.

692.286　　　　　GW　　ISSN 0178-4811
AUTO AND SERVICE; reply card export publication for automotive engineering. 1984-1990. s-a. (back issues avail.) Vogel-Verlag und Druck KG, P.O. Box 6740, 8700 Wuerzberg, Germany.

388　　　　　　　SZ
AUTO ILLUSTRIERTE. ceased 1990. m. Powerslide AG, Kreuzstr. 60, P.O. Box 282, CH-8032 Zurich, Switzerland.

388.3　　　　　　DK　　ISSN 0106-0473
AUTO NYT. 1979-1988. m. Thomson Communications (Scandinavia) A-S, Struenseegade 7-9, DK-2200 Copenhagen, Denmark.

388　　　　　　　US
AUTOBODY. (In two parts) 1990; ceased same year. bi-m. Gemini Communications, 306 N. Cleveland Massillon Rd., Akron, OH 44313-9302.

800 700　　　　　PL　　ISSN 0860-8091
AUTOGRAF. ceased 1990 (no.8). m. (back issues avail.) Gdanskie Towarzystwo Przyjaciol Sztuki, Ul. Chlebnicka 2, 80-830 Gdansk, Poland.

388.3　　　　　　US
AUTOGUIDE. 1988-1989. a. Edgell Communications, 7500 Old Oak Blvd., Cleveland, OH 44130.

385　　　　　　　PL　　ISSN 0137-2858
AUTOMATYKA KOLEJOWA. 1953-1991. m. Wydawnictwa Komunikacji i Lacznosci, Ul. Kazimierzowska 52, Warsaw, Poland.
　　Formerly (until 1978): Przeglad Kolejowy Elektrotechniczny (ISSN 0033-2216)

796.77　　　　　　AT
AUTOMOBILE. 1980-198? q. (back issues avail.) Western Publishers Pty. Ltd., 10 Joseph St., Toowoomba, Qld. 4350, Australia.

382　　　　　　　FR
AUTOMOBILE INTERNATIONAL. ceased. bi-m. Ediafric, 10 rue Vineuse, 75116 Paris cedex 16, France.

388.3 621.38　　　　US
AUTOMOTIVE ELECTRONIC NEWS. 1989-19?? bi-w. (newspaper) Rich Bambarck, Ed. & Pub., 7 E. 12th St., New York, NY 10003.

658.8　　　　　　CN　　ISSN 0702-8318
AUTOMOTIVE MARKETER. 1962-1991 (Jul.). q. Wadham Publications Ltd., 1450 Don Mills Rd., Don Mills, Ont. M3B 2X7, Canada.
　　Former titles: Automotive Mass Marketer (ISSN 0067-2572); Petroleum Automotive and T.B.A. Marketer.

388.476 658　　　　US
AUTOMOTIVE MARKETING RETAIL AFTERMARKET GUIDE. 1986-1990. a. Chilton Co., Chilton Way, Radnor, PA 19089.

670　　　　　　　US　　ISSN 0745-3043
HF5487
AUTOMOTIVE PRODUCTS REPORT. 1984-1990. m. (also avail. in tabloid format) Irving-Cloud Publishing Co., 7300 N. Cicero Ave., Lincolnwood, IL 60646.

629.286　　　　　CN　　ISSN 0068-9629
AUTOMOTIVE SERVICE DATA BOOK. 1935-19?? a. Maclean-Hunter Ltd., Business Publication Division, Maclean-Hunter Bldg., 777 Bay St., Toronto, Ont. M5W 1A7, Canada.

612 616.1　　　　　UK　　ISSN 0142-856X
AUTONOMIC NERVOUS SYSTEM. ceased 1990. m. (looseleaf format; back issues avail.) Sheffield University Biomedical Information Service (SUBIS), The University, Sheffield S10 2TN, England.

621.3 658.8　　　　US
AUTOSOUND & COMMUNICATIONS. 1975-1990. 12/yr. (tabloid format) Capital Cities, 825 Seventh Ave., 6th Fl., New York, NY 10019.

618　　　　　　　SP　　ISSN 0210-7171
　　　　　　　　　　　　CODEN: AOGIEM
AVANCES EN OBSTETRICIA Y GINECOLOGIA. 1974-19?? irreg. (approx. biennial). Salvat Publicaciones Cientificas, S.A., Mallorca 45, 08029 Barcelona, Spain.

615　　　　　　　SP　　ISSN 0210-3397
　　　　　　　　　　　　CODEN: AVTPBI
AVANCES EN TERAPEUTICA. 1969-19?? a. (Universidad Autonoma de Barcelona) Salvat Publicaciones Cientificas, S.A., Mallorca 45, 08029 Barcelona, Spain.

338.1 331　　　　　PH
AVERAGE WAGE RATES OF FARM WORKERS IN THE PHILIPPINES. ceased. irreg. Bureau of Agricultural Economics, Ben-Lor Building, 1184 Quezon Ave., Quezon City, Philippines.

629.13　　　　　　NE　　ISSN 0005-2035
AVIA; maandblad voor lucht- en ruimtevaart. 1911-19?? m. (Koninklijke Nederlandse Vereniging voor Luchtvaart) Wijt en Zn. B.V., Postbus 268, Rotterdam, Netherlands.

636.089　　　　　US　　ISSN 8750-037X
AVIAN - EXOTIC PRACTICE; a journal of specialty medicine and surgery for the practitioner. 1984-19?? (vol.1, no. 4). q. Veterinary Practice Publishing Co., Box 4457, Santa Barbara, CA 93140.

629.13　　　　　　US
AVIATION AND COMPUTER ENTHUSIASTS NEWSLETTER. 1985-1990 (no.5). bi-m. Aviation and Computer Enthusiasts, 2009 Camelot Dr., Las Cruces, NM 88005.

CESSATIONS

629.13   FR
AVIATION - C L A P. 1965-19?? bi-m. Ligue Francaise de l'Enseignement et de l'Education Permanente, 3 rue Recamier, 75007 Paris, France.

614.8   AT   ISSN 0045-1207
AVIATION SAFETY DIGEST. 1953-1991. q. Civil Aviation Authority, P.O. Box 367, Canberra, A.C.T. 2601, Australia.

629.132   US
AVIATION U S A (TUSCALOOSA). 1984-19?? fortn. Randall Publishing Co., Box 2029, Tuscaloosa, AL 35403.

621.381   US
AVION NEWS. 1990; ceased same year. bi-m. Data Base Publications, 8310 Capital of Texas Hwy., Ste. 385, Austin, TX 78731.

629.13   SP   ISSN 0005-2272
AVION. 1946-19?? m. (with supplements). Real Aero Club de Espana, Arlaban 1, Madrid, Spain.

700 069 708   US
AWARDS IN THE VISUAL ARTS. 1982-1991; suspended. a. (back issues avail.) Southeastern Center for Contemporary Arts, 750 Marguerite Dr., Winston-Salem, NC 27106.

954   II   ISSN 0005-2485
AYURVEDA-BHARATI; a multilingual quarterly journal of Ayurveda & Indian culture. 1961-1991; suspended. q. (back issues avail.) Institute of Ayurvedic Studies and Research - Ayurveda Bijnan Parishad, 52 Mahatma Gandhi Rd., Calcutta 700 009, India.

636.089 591   JA   ISSN 0389-1836
                         CODEN: ADJHDO
AZABU DAIGAKU JUIGAKUBU KENKYU HOKOKU/AZABU UNIVERSITY. VETERINARY MEDICINE. BULLETIN. 1954-1986 (vol.7 no.2); suspended. s-a. Azabu University, School of Veterinary Medicine - Azabu Daigaku Juigakubu, 1-17-71 Fuchinobe, Sagamihara-shi, Kanagawa-ken 229, Japan.
Formerly: Azabu Veterinary College. Bulletin.

574.191   NE   ISSN 0005-2744
QD1
B B A - ENZYMOLOGY. (Biochimica et Biophysica Acta) ceased. m. Elsevier Science Publishers B.V., P.O. Box 211, 1000 AE Amsterdam, Netherlands.

574.192   NE   ISSN 0067-2734
                         CODEN: BBALAJ
B B A LIBRARY. (Biochimica et Biophysica Acta) 1963-19?? irreg. Elsevier Science Publishers B.V., Books Division, P.O. Box 211, 1000 AE Amsterdam, Netherlands.

574.191   NE   ISSN 0304-4173
B B A REVIEWS ON BIOENERGETICS. (Biochimica et Biophysica Acta) 1947-1987. 4/yr. (also avail. in microform from RPI) Elsevier Science Publishers B.V., P.O. Box 211, 1000 AE Amsterdam, Netherlands.

621.38   UK   ISSN 0068-1377
B B C ANNUAL REPORT AND HANDBOOK. 1928-1986. a. British Broadcasting Corporation, 35 Marylebone High St., London W1M 4AA, England.

780   US   ISSN 0084-8018
B B C MUSIC GUIDES. (British Broadcasting Corporation) 1969-198? irreg. University of Washington Press, Box 50096, Seattle, WA 98105.

371.42   US
B C. (Before College) 1989-1990. s-a. CareerVision, Inc., 900 Broadway, Ste. 203, New York, NY 10003-1210.

500   CN
B C DISCOVERY. 1982-1991. bi-m. Discovery Foundation, 400 The Station, 601 West Cordova St., Vancouver, B.C. V6B 1G1, Canada.

338   CN   ISSN 0821-0020
B.C. ECONOMIC BULLETIN. ceased. bi-m. Ministry of Industry and Small Business Development, 1405 Douglas St., Victoria, B.C. V8V 1X4, Canada.

Former titles: B.C. Business Bulletin (ISSN 0228-6211); British Columbia. Ministry of Industry and Small Business Development. Monthly Bulletin of Business Activity; British Columbia. Department of Economic Development. Monthly Bulletin of Business Activity (ISSN 0524-5370); British Columbia. Department of Industrial Development, Trade and Commerce. Monthly Bulletin of Business Activity.

330   CN   ISSN 0706-3601
B.C. ECONOMIC DEVELOPMENT. 1978-19?? q. Ministry of Industry and Small Business Development, 1405 Douglas St., Vancouver, B.C. V8V 1X4, Canada.

658   CN
B.C. HEALTH MANAGEMENT REVIEW. 1985-1990. q. Canada Wide Magazines Ltd., 4180 Lougheed Hwy., No. 401, Burnaby, B.C. V5C 6A7, Canada.

615.9   CN
B C PHARMACIST. 1987-1991. 6/yr. Canada Wide Magazines Ltd., 4180 Lougheed Hwy., Ste. 401, Burnaby, B.C. V5C 6A7, Canada.

574.28 015   UK   ISSN 0142-0674
R856.A1
B E C A N. (Bioengineering Current Awareness Notification) 1972-19?? m. (back issues avail.) (Brunel Institute for Bioengineering) Taylor & Francis Ltd., Rankine Rd., Basingstoke, Hants. RG24 0PR, England.

574.28   UK   ISSN 0262-7779
B E C A N BIOMECHANICS & ORTHOPAEDICS. (Bioengineering Current Awareness Notification) 1982-198? m. (Brunel Institute for Bioengineering) Taylor & Francis Ltd., Rankine Rd., Basingstoke, Hants RG24 0PR, England.

574 620   UK   ISSN 0261-8281
B E C A N ELECTRODES FOR MEDICINE AND BIOLOGY. (Bioengineering Current Awareness Notification) 1982-198? m. (back issues avail.) (Brunel Institute for Bioengineering) Taylor & Francis Ltd., Rankine Rd., Basingstoke, Hants RG24 0PR, England.

574.28   UK   ISSN 0262-7760
B E C A N EQUIPMENT FOR THE DISABLED POPULATION. (Bioengineering Current Awareness Notification) 1972-19?? m. (back issues avail.) (Brunel Institute for Bioengineering) Taylor & Francis Ltd., Rankine Rd., Basingstoke, Hants RG24 0PR, England.

574.28   UK   ISSN 0261-8273
B E C A N INSTRUMENTATION AND TECHNIQUES IN CARDIOLOGY. (Bioengineering Current Awareness Notification) 1982-198? m. (back issues avail.) (Brunel Institute for Bioengineering) Taylor & Francis Ltd., Rankine Rd., Basingstoke, Hants RG24 0PR, England.

621.4 016   UK   ISSN 0001-3447
B I C E R I ABSTRACTS FROM TECHNICAL AND PATENT PUBLICATIONS.. 1949-19?? w. (processed) British Internal Combustion Engine Research Institute Ltd., 111-112 Buckingham Ave., Slough, Berks. SL1 4PH, England.

613.7 011.8 614.8   US   ISSN 0278-2340
Z5814.H43
B I H E P. (Bibliographic Index of Health Education Periodicals) 1981-1985 (vol.6). q. (back issues avail.) Indiana University, Center for Health & Safety Studies, HPER Bldg. Rm. 116, Indiana University, Bloomington, IN 47405.

658.8   US   ISSN 0194-0406
HD9350.1
B I N CALIFORNIA GOLDBOOK. (Beverage Industry News) 1961-19?? a. Industry Publications, Inc., 703 Market St., San Francisco, CA 94103.
Formerly: Beverage Industry News California Goldbook.

668.4   UK   ISSN 0144-5014
B I P PLASTICS REVIEW. (British Imperial Plastics) 1979-1989 (no.1). 3/yr. B I P Chemicals Ltd., P.O. Box 6, Popes Lane, Oldbury, Warley, W. Midlands B69 4PD, England.

658.8 016   US
B I T S. (Bibliographic Index of the Tobacco Scene) 1970-198? bi-w. (or more frequently). (looseleaf format; back issues avail.) Tobacco Merchants Association of the United States, Inc., 231 Clarksville Rd., Ste. 6, Box 8019, Princeton, NJ 08543-8019.

Formerly (until 1981): Bi-weekly Index to the Tobacco Scene.

384.554 382   US
B M E'S TELEVISION ENGINEERING. (Broadcast Management Engineering) ceased. m. Act III Publishing, 401 Park Ave. S., New York, NY 10016.
Formery (until Jan. 1990): B M E.

623.82 016   UK
B M T CORTEC BIBLIOGRAPHIES. 1963-19?? irreg. (British Maritime Technology Ltd.) B M T Cortec Ltd., Wallsend Research Station, Wallsend, Tyne and Wear NE28 6UY, England.
Formerly: British Ship Research Association. B.S.R.A. Bibliographies.

629.2   UK
B M W MAGAZINE. 1982-19?? m. Specialist Publications (Regional) Ltd., Hodge House, St. Mary St., Cardiff CF1 1QO, England.
Formerly: B M V Car Club Magazine.

070.5 658.403   US   ISSN 0747-5438
B N A ONLINE. 1984-198? irreg. (back issues avail.) The Bureau of National Affairs, Inc., 1231 25th St., N.W., Washington, DC 20037.

331 340   US   ISSN 0893-1704
KF9084.A15
B N A'S ALTERNATIVE DISPUTE RESOLUTION REPORT. 1987-1991. bi-w. (back issues avail.) The Bureau of National Affairs, Inc., 1231 25th St., N.W., Washington, DC 20037.

720 620   UK   ISSN 0264-4606
                         CODEN: BBCDD8
B O C A A D. (Bulletin of Computer Aided Architectural Design) 1969-19?? q. University of Strathclyde, Department of Architecture & Building Science, 131 Rottenrow, Glasgow G4 0NG, Scotland.

388.324   BL   ISSN 0006-6087
B R. (Boletin Rodoviario) (Temporarily suspended during 1977) 1964-1982 (no.196). m. Associacao Nacional das Empresas de Transportes Rodoviarios de Carga, 04038- Rua Borges Lagoa 1341, Sao Paulo, Brazil.

623.82   UK
B S C BULLETIN. 1965-19?? m. British Shipbuilders Council, Hermes House, St. John's Rd., Tunbridge Wells, Kent TN4 9UZ, England.

896 496 700   US   ISSN 0045-1282
BA SHIRU. 1970-1989 (vol.13, no.1). s-a. University of Wisconsin-Madison, Department of African Languages and Literature, 866 Van Hise Hall, Madison, WI 53706.

649   US
BABY TIMES; the magazine for caring mothers. 1989-1991; suspended. q. Busch Publishing Co., Inc., 5005 Riveria Court, Fort Wayne, IN 46825.

617.3   US
BACK PAIN. 1987-1988 (Dec.). m. Back Pain Magazine, Inc., 405 N.W. 44th Ter., St. 101, Deerfield Beach, FL 33442-9203.

301.412 808.81   US   ISSN 0888-6520
BACKBONE; a journal for women's literature. 1984-1988. s-a. (back issues avail.) Backbone Magazine, Inc., Box 95315, Seattle, WA 98145.

384.1 791.4   US   ISSN 0098-5481
PN1998.A1
BACKSTAGE T V FILM - TAPE & SYNDICATION DIRECTORY. 1965-198? a. Backstage Publications, Inc., 330 W. 42th St., New York, NY 10036.

374.4   GW
BACKUP; Informatikzeitschrift fuer Schule und Weiterbildung. 1986-1990. bi-m. Verlag Moritz Diesterweg, Hochstrasse 29-31, 6000 Frankfurt a.M. 1, Germany.

576 616.76   UK   ISSN 0263-7227
BACTERIAL CELL SURFACE. ceased 1990. m. (looseleaf format; back issues avail.) Sheffield University Biomedical Information Service (SUBIS), The University, Sheffield S10 2TN, England.

CESSATIONS

384.54   DK   ISSN 0109-3088
BAEREBOELGEN. 1977-1990. s-a. Danmarks Radio, Shortwave Department - Kortboelgetjenesten, Radiohuset, Rosenoernsallee 22, 1999 Frederiksberg C, Denmark.
    Formerly (until Sept. 1983): Radio Denmark (ISSN 0107-8623)

320   DK   ISSN 0900-3134
BAG KULISSERNE; informationsorgan til Fredsbevaegelserne. 1984-1986. q. S F's Fredspolitiske Udvalg, c/o Jens Thoft, Christiansborg, 1240 Copenhagen K, Denmark.

289.9   US   ISSN 0195-9212
BP300
BAHA'I NEWS. 1924-19?? m. (back issues avail.) National Spiritual Assembly of the Baha'is of the United States, 536 Sheridan Rd., Wilmette, IL 60091.

799   US
BAKER DEER HUNTING ANNUAL. ceased. a. Aqua-Field Publishing Co., Inc., 66 W. Gilbert St., Shrewsbury, NJ 07702.

540   US
BAKER SERIES IN CHEMISTRY. ceased. irreg. Cornell University Press, 124 Roberts Place, Ithaca, NY 14850.

664.772   US   ISSN 0005-416X
TX761
BAKING INDUSTRY. 1887-1989. m. (also avail. in microform from UMI) Putman Publishing Co., 301 E. Erie St., Chicago, IL 60611.

332.1   UK
BALANCES OF LONDON AND SCOTTISH BANKS' GROUPS. 1973-1991. m. Committee of London and Scottish Bankers, 10 Lombard St., London EC3V 9AP, England.
    Formed by the merger of: Balances of London Clearing Banks' Groups; Balances of Scottish Clearing Banks' Groups.

810   US   ISSN 0888-188X
LH1.B18
BALL STATE UNIVERSITY FORUM. 1960-1989 (vol.30, no.4). q. (also avail. in microform from UMI; reprint service avail. from UMI) Ball State University, Department of English, Muncie, IN 47306.
    Formerly: Ball State Teachers College Forum (ISSN 0005-433X)

001.6 621.381   US
BALTIMORE COMPUTER DIGEST. ceased. m. Clark Publishing Company, 1001 N. Highland, 4th Fl., Arlington, VA 22201.

778.534   FR   ISSN 0184-8895
BANC-TITRE - ANIMATION STAND; le magazine du cinema graphique et du film d'animation. 1978-1985 (Jun.). 10/yr. Tarcus, 17 rue Jourbert, 75009 Paris, France.
    Formerly (until Dec. 1981): Banc-Titre.

330.9   IT
BANCA NAZIONALE DEL LAVORO. CONDENSED STATEMENT OF CONDITION. ceased 1985. a. Banca Nazionale del Lavoro, Via Vittorio Veneto 119, 00187 Rome, Italy.

630   BL   ISSN 0101-0697
Z5075.B795
BANCO DE BIBLIOGRAFIAS. 1978-1988; resumed 1989-1991 (vol.11, no.1). irreg. Empresa Brasileira de Pesquisa Agropecuaria, Departamento de Informacao e Editoracao, Sain Parque Rural, Trecho B, Caixa Postal 040315, 70770 Brasilia DF, Brazil.

332   BL   ISSN 0005-4879
HC186
BANCO DO BRASIL. BOLETIM. 1966-19?? q. Banco do Brasil S.A., Setor Bancario Sul, Lote 32, Quadra 4, C.P. 562, Brasilia, D.F., Brazil.

330   UK   ISSN 0306-9338
BANGOR OCCASIONAL PAPERS IN ECONOMICS. 1973-1989 (vol.22). irreg. University of Wales Press, 6 Gwennyth St., Cathays, Cardiff CF2 4YD, Wales.

332.1 001.64   US   ISSN 0572-5933
BANK AUTOMATION NEWSLETTER. 1967-199? m. (looseleaf format; also avail. in microform from UMI) Warren, Gorham and Lamont Inc., One Penn Plaza, New York, NY 10119.

332.1   US   ISSN 0522-2494
HG1501
BANK DIRECTOR'S REPORT. 1969-199? m. (also avail. in microform from UMI) Warren, Gorham and Lamont Inc., One Penn Plaza, New York, NY 10119.

332.1   US
BANK - FINANCIAL SERVICES MARKETING REPORT. 1973-199? m. Warren, Gorham and Lamont Inc., One Penn Plaza, New York, NY 10119.

332.1   US   ISSN 0162-7422
BANK LOAN OFFICERS REPORT. 1971-199? m. (looseleaf format; also avail. in microform from UMI) Warren, Gorham and Lamont Inc., One Penn Plaza, New York, NY 10119.

332.1 658.8   US   ISSN 0162-7430
BANK MARKETING REPORT. 1967-199? m. (looseleaf format; also avail. in microform from UMI) Warren, Gorham and Lamont Inc., One Penn Plaza, New York, NY 10119.

332.1   JA
BANK OF JAPAN. ANNUAL REPORT. ceased. a. Bank of Japan, Foreign Department - Nihon Ginko, C.P.O. Box 203, Tokyo 100-91, Japan.
    Formerly: Bank of Japan. Annual Report of the Policy Board (ISSN 0067-3676)

330.9   JA   ISSN 0067-3684
BANK OF JAPAN. BUSINESS REPORT. ceased. s-a. Bank of Japan, Foreign Department - Nihon Ginko, C.P.O. Box 203, Tokyo 100-91, Japan.

332.1   US
BANK OPERATIONS MANAGEMENT SERVICE. 1986-1991. 3/yr. (looseleaf format) Warren, Gorham and Lamont Inc., One Penn Plaza, New York, NY 10119.

332.1 378   US   ISSN 0084-9855
BANKERS SCHOOLS DIRECTORY (YEAR). ceased. biennial. American Bankers Association, Education Policy & Development, 1120 Connecticut Ave., N.W., Washington, DC 20036.

286   NO   ISSN 0005-5565
BANNERET. 1879-19?? 24/yr. (tabloid format) Norske Baptistsamfunn - Baptist Union of Norway, P.O. Box 2061, 4004 Stavanger, Norway.

332   CN   ISSN 0225-2910
BANQUE NATIONALE DU CANADA. REVUE ECONOMIQUE. 1980-1990. (vol.11, no.1). irreg. National Bank of Canada, Department of Economic Analysis, 600 de la Gauchetiere St., W., 11th Fl., Montreal, Que. H3B 4L2, Canada.

020   HU   ISSN 0237-0719
BARANYAI KONYVTAROS. 1972-1988 (vol.17, no.2). s-a. (tabloid format; back issues avail.) Baranya Megyei Konyvtarkozi Bizottsag Tajekoztatoja, Baranya Megyei Konyvtar, Geisler E.u.8, H-7621 Pecs, Hungary.

658   US   ISSN 1042-993X
BARE KNUCKLES; the survival guide for private companies. 1989; ceased same year (vol.1, no.8). m. Canterbury Group, Inc., Box 691, Summit, NJ 07902.

617.6   US
BASAL FACTS; the international journal of stress and chronic disease. 1976-1987. q. (back issues avail.) Medico-Dental Arts, 303 W. 2nd St., Rock Falls, IL 61071.

796.357   US
BASEBALL (YEAR). 1976-1990. a. (back issues avail.) (National Association of Professional Baseball Leagues) American Sports Publishing, 600 S. Duke St., Box 2089, Durham, NC 27702.

795.4 796.357   US
BASEBALL CARD SHOWS. 1988; ceased same year. q. Krause Publications, Inc., 700 E. State St., Iola, WI 54990.
    Formerly: Baseball Card Show Calendar (ISSN 0897-2834)

796.357 384.554   US
BASEBALL VIDEO MAGAZINE. ceased. q. (video cassette only) Box 9807, Englewood, NJ 07631.

150   US
BASIC CONCEPTS IN PSYCHOLOGY SERIES. 1970-1979. irreg. Brooks - Cole Publishing Co., 511 Forest Lodge Rd., Pacific Grove, CA 93950-5098.

960   SZ   ISSN 0171-0087
BASLER AFRIKA BIBLIOGRAPHIEN. NACHRICHTEN/ BASEL AFRICA BIBLIOGRAPHY. NEWSLETTER. ceased 1991. q. (processed) Basler Afrika Bibliographien, Postfach 2037, CH-4001 Basel, Switzerland.

747   UK
BATHROOMS, KITCHEN & TILES. 1985-19?? m. B & M Publications (London) Ltd., P.O. Box 13, Hereford House, Bridle Path, Croydon, Surrey CR9 4NL, England.

691   GW   ISSN 0723-6506
BAU TRICHTER. AUSGABE A. ceased 1988. m. Erich Schmidt Verlag GmbH & Co. (Bielefeld), Viktoriastr. 44A, Postfach 4330, 4800 Bielefeld, Germany.

609   GW
BAUBEDARF EINKAUFEN, BERATEN, VERKAUFEN. ceased 1990. m. Verlag und Druckerei Meininger GmbH, Maximilianstr. 7-17, 6730 Neustadt, Germany.
    Formerly: Baubedarf Manager (ISSN 0174-1985)

690 016   GW   ISSN 0323-8490
BAUINFORMATION WISSENSCHAFT UND TECHNIK. 1966-1990. bi-m. Bauakademie der D.D.R., Bauinformation, Wallstr. 27, 1020 Berlin, Germany.
    Formerly (until 1976): Bauinformation (ISSN 0005-6642)

891.7   CN   ISSN 0005-6952
BAYAVAYA USKALOS; Byelorussian literary magazine. 1950-1990; suspended. a. Byelorussian Literary Association, 24 Tarlton Rd., Toronto, Ont. M5P 2M4, Canada.

630.24 668.6   UK
BAYER AGROCHEM COURIER. 1962-1984. 3/yr. Bayer UK Ltd., Agrochem Division, Eastern Way, Bury St. Edmunds, Suffolk IP32 7AH, England.

350   GW
BAYERISCHE STAATSREGIERUNG. GRENZLANDBERICHT. ceased 1990. a. Bayerisches Staatsministerium fuer Landesentwicklung und Umweltfragen, Postfach 810140, 8000 Munich 81, Germany.

614   SA
BE SAFE AT HOME/WEES VEILIG TUIS. ceased. a. Medical Association of South Africa, Medical House, Central Square, Pinelands 7405, South Africa.

799   US
BEACH CULTURE. 1989-1991. Surfer Publications, Inc., 33046 Calle Aviador, Juan Capistrano, CA 92675.

633   US
BEAN COMMISSION JOURNAL. ceased 1990. q. Bean Commission, Box 473, Leslie, MI 49251-0473.

917.8   US
BEAR FLAG REPUBLIC. 1972-197? m. (looseleaf format) Bear Flag Productions, Inc., c/o Western States Associates, 101 California, No. 930, San Francisco, CA 94111.

910.202   CN   ISSN 0838-1895
BEAUTIFUL BRITISH COLUMBIA MAGAZINE'S GUIDEBOOK. 1988-19??; suspended. a. Beautiful British Columbia Magazine Ltd., 929 Ellery St., Victoria, B.C. V9A 7B4, Canada.

747   ISSN 1043-5468
BEAUTIFUL GLASS FOR HOME & OFFICE. 1990; suspended in same year. q. Albert Lewis, Ed. & Pub., Box 69, Brewster, NY 10509.

658 646.7   US
BEAUTY PRODUCT MARKETING. 1972-1990. m. (tabloid format) Capital Cities - A B C, Inc., 825 Seventh Ave., 6th Fl., New York, NY 10019.

647.9   US
BED & BREAKFAST GUEST; the B & B travelclub newsletter. 1982-198? bi-m. (looseleaf format; back issues avail.) American Bed & Breakfast Association, 16 Village Green, No. 203, Crofton, MD 21114.
    Formerly: Bed and Breakfast Guestletter.

647　　　　　US　　ISSN 0887-7505
BED & BREAKFAST UPDATE; an international information exchange for B & B travelers, innkeepers, reservation services, and homestay hosts. 1984-1988 (Dec.). q. (looseleaf format; back issues avail.) Rocky Point Press, Box 4814, N. Hollywood, CA 91607.

052　　　　　UK
BEDFORDSHIRE LIFE. 1976-19??; suspended. m. County Life Ltd., P.O. Box 18, Lincoln, Lincolnshire LN5 7DY, England.
Supersedes in part: Northamptonshire and Bedfordshire Life (ISSN 0306-9001)

820　　　　　UK　　ISSN 0005-7673
BEDSITTER; a labour of love. 1959-198? 2/yr. Olive Rhodes Teugels, Ed.& Pub., 6 Clapham Mansions, Nightingale Lane, London SW4 9AQ, England.

636.2　　　　　US
BEEFMASTER TIMES; a special publication for members of Beefmaster Breeders Universal and other interested cattlemen. 1986-1991 (Jan.). q. Beefmaster Breeders Universal, 6800 Park Ten Blvd., No. 290 W., San Antonio, TX 78213.

338.47　　　　　US　　ISSN 0734-970X
BEER MARKETING MANAGEMENT. 1982-1989 (vol.7, no.2). q. (back issues avail.) National Beer Wholesalers' Association, 5205 Leesburg Pike, Ste. 1600, Falls Church, VA 22041.

616.8　　　　　DK　　ISSN 0107-4156
RC450.D4
BEFOLKNINGENS FORBRUG AF PSYKIATRISKE SENGEPLADSER. (Subseries of: Sygehusstatistik) 1976-1985. triennial. Sundhedsstyrelsen, Amaliegade 13, 1012 Copenhagen K, Denmark.

808　　　　　US　　ISSN 0739-6694
BEGINNING (IOWA CITY); the magazine for the writer in the community. 1983-1989. q. (back issues avail.) (Institute for Human Potential and Social Development) Writers House Press, Box 3071, Iowa City, IA 52244.

590　　　　　NE　　ISSN 0169-7544
BF671
BEHAVIOUR. SUPPLEMENTS; an international journal of comparative ethology. 1950-1977 (vol.20). irreg. E.J. Brill, P.O. Box 9000, 2300 PA Leiden, Netherlands.

150　　　　　UK　　ISSN 0262-4109
BEHAVIOURAL APPROACHES WITH CHILDREN. 1977-1989. 3/yr. Association for Behavioural Approaches with Children, c/o Centre for Child Study, Dept. of Educational Psychology, University of Birmingham, Birmingham B15 2TT, England.

338　　　　　US
BEHIND SMALL BUSINESS. ceased. bi-m. Dona M. Risdall, Ed. & Pub., Box 37147, Minneapolis, MN 55431.

384.5　　　　　GW　　ISSN 0138-113X
HE8680.G4
BEITRAEGE ZUR GESCHICHTE DES RUNDFUNKS. 1967-1989. q. Rundfunk der D.D.R., Staatliches Komitee fuer Rundfunk, Nalepastr. 18-50, 1160 Berlin, Germany.

320 158　　　　　GW　　ISSN 0045-169X
JX5
BEITRAEGE ZUR KONFLIKTFORSCHUNG; psycho-politische Aspekte. 1971-1991. q. Markus Verlagsgesellschaft mbH, Hohenzollernring 85-87, 5000 Cologne 1, Germany.

100 320　　　　　GW　　ISSN 0232-2803
BEITRAEGE ZUR KRITIK DER BUERGERLICHEN IDEOLOGIE UND DES REVISIONISMUS. 1976-198? irreg. Akademie-Verlag Berlin, Leipziger Str. 3-4, 1086 Berlin, Germany.

617.3　　　　　GW　　ISSN 0005-8149
CODEN: BOTRAJ
BEITRAEGE ZUR ORTHOPAEDIE UND TRAUMATOLOGIE. 1954-19?? m. (Gesellschaft fuer Orthopaedie der DDR) Verlag Gesundheit GmbH, Neue Gruenstr. 18, 1020 Berlin, Germany.

574　　　　　GW
BEITRAEGE ZUR WIRKSTOFFORSCHUNG. ceased 1990. s-a. Institut fuer Wirkstoffforschung, Alfred-Kowalke-Str. 4, 1136 Berlin-Friedrichsfelde, Germany.

332.6　　　　　BE
BELGIUM. MINISTERE DES AFFAIRES ECONOMIQUES. RAPPORT ANNUEL SUR LES INVESTISSEMENTS ETRANGERS EN BELIQUE/BELGIUM. MINISTERIE VAN ECONOMISCHE ZAKEN. JAARLIJKS RAPPORT OVER DE BUITENLANDSE INVESTERINGEN. ceased 1984. a. Ministere des Affaires Economiques, Rue del'Industrie 6, B-1040 Brussels, Belgium.
Formerly (until 1984): Investissements Etrangers en Belgique (ISSN 0075-0247)

635　　　　　BE　　ISSN 0303-903X
BELGIUM. RIJKSSTATION VOOR SIERPLANTENTEELT. MEDEDELINGEN. 1961-1984 (no.50). irreg. Rijksstation voor Sierplantenteelt, Caritasstraat 21, B-9090 Melle, Belgium.

384　　　　　US　　ISSN 0096-8692
TK1
BELL TELEPHONE MAGAZINE. 1941-1986. bi-m. (also avail. in microform from UMI) American Telephone and Telegraph Company, 195 Broadway, New York, NY 10007.
Formerly: Bell Telephone Quarterly.

020　　　　　IS
BEN GURION UNIVERSITY. INSTITUTES FOR APPLIED RESEARCH. LIBRARY ACQUISITIONS. ceased. 3/yr. Ben Gurion University, Institutes for Applied Research, P.O. Box 1025, Beersheva 84 110, Israel.

332.678　　　　　US
BENCH INVESTMENT LETTER. 1979-1989. m. Bench Corporation, 222 Bridge Plaza South, Fort Lee, NJ 07024.
Formerly: Total Return Strategies.

642.5　　　　　US
BENENSON RESTAURANT GUIDE (YEAR). 1986-198? a. Sterling Publishing Co., Inc., 387 Park Ave. S., New York, NY 10016-8810.

658　　　　　AT
BENETAX REMUNERATION PLANNER. 1985-1991 (Sep.). 5/yr. (looseleaf format; back issues avail.) Cullen Egan Dell Ltd., 168 Walker St., North Sydney, N.S.W. 2060, Australia.

746.92　　　　　IT
BENISSIMO SPECIALE. ceased. m. Gruppo Editoriale Fabbri SPA, Divisione Periodici, Via Mecenate 91, 20138 Milan, Italy.

070.5 658　　　　　US
BENJAMIN PUBLISHING - MARKETING REPORT; news of business-building book programs. 1964-1987; suspended. irreg. (tabloid format) Benjamin Company, Inc., 21 Dupont Ave., White Plains, NY. 10604-3537.
Formerly (until 1984): Benco Report.

683　　　　　UK　　ISSN 0265-069X
BENN'S HARDWARE PRICE LIST. 1960-1987. m. Indoces Ltd., 22 Northefield Ave., London W13, England.

616.8　　　　　DK　　ISSN 0108-7819
BERETNING FOR PSYKIATRISKE INSTITUTIONER I DANMARK. 1979-1981. irreg. Sundhedsstyrelsen, Amaliegade 13, 1012 Copenhagen K, Denmark.

320　　　　　GW
BERICHTE AUS NAMIBIA. 1981-1990. bi-m. Exclusiv-Verlag Meissner GmbH, Venusbergweg 35, 5300 Bonn, Germany.

332.7　　　　　NE　　ISSN 0005-9110
BERICHTEN VAN DE AFDELING VOLKSKREDIETWEZEN. 1964-19?? irreg. Ministerie van Welzijn, Volksgezondheid en Cultuur, Postbus 5406, 2280 HK Rijswijk, Netherlands.

510　　　　　US
BERKELEY SYMPOSIA ON MATHEMATICAL STATISTICS AND PROBABILITY. ceased 1972 (vol.6). irreg. University of California Press, 2120 Berkeley Way, Berkeley, CA 94720.

352　　　　　GW　　ISSN 0523-0144
BERLINER FORUM. 1968-1990. irreg. Presse- und Informationsamt des Landes Berlin, Rathaus Schoeneberg, John-F.-Kennedy-Platz, 1000 Berlin 62, Germany.

943　　　　　GW
BERLINER HISTORISCHE KOMMISSION. VEROEFFENTLICHUNGEN. 1960-1984 (vol.57). irreg. Walter de Gruyter und Co., Genthiner Str. 13, 1000 Berlin 30, Germany.

330.943　　　　　GW
BERLINER WIRTSCHAFTSDATEN. 1973-1991. irreg. (looseleaf format) Senatsverwaltung fuer Wirtschaft, Martin Luther Str. 105, 1000 Berlin 62, Germany.

301　　　　　SZ　　ISSN 0067-6136
BERNER BEITRAEGE ZUR SOZIOLOGIE. 1959-1991. irreg. (Universitaet Bern, Institut fuer Soziologie und Sozio-Oekonomische Entwicklungsfragen) Paul Haupt AG, Falkenplatz 14, CH-3001 Berne, Switzerland.

364　　　　　SZ　　ISSN 0067-6144
BERNER KRIMINOLOGISCHE UNTERSUCHUNGEN. 1962-1991. irreg. Paul Haupt AG, Falkenplatz 14, CH-3001 Berne, Switzerland.

910 330　　　　　SZ　　ISSN 0067-6152
BERNER STUDIEN ZUM FREMDENVERKEHR. 1966-198? irreg. (Universitaet Bern, Forschungsinstitut fuer Fremdenverkehr) Verlag Peter Lang AG, Jupiterstr. 15, CH-3015 Bern, Switzerland.

070.5　　　　　US　　ISSN 8755-9633
Z1035
BEST BOOKS BY CONSENSUS (YEAR). 1981-198?; suspended. a. (back issues avail.) Info Digest, 9302 Parkside, Box 165, Morton Grove, IL 60053.
Supersedes (in 1982): Best Sellers and Best Choices (Year) (ISSN 0275-0945)

330　　　　　US
BEST OF BUSINESS INTERNATIONAL. 1979-1991. q. (Xerox Corporation) Whittle Communications L.P., 333 Main Ave., Knoxville, TN 37902.
Formerly: Best of Business.

330　　　　　US
BEST OF BUSINESS QUARTERLY. 1986-1991. q. Whittle Communications L.P., 333 Main Ave., Knoxville, TN 37902.

792　　　　　US
BEST PLAYS OF ... (YEAR). 1920-1986. a. (back issues avail.) Siena Publishers, 45 W. 36th St., New York, NY 10008.

028.5　　　　　US
BESTSELLERS; books and authors in the news. 1989-1990. q. Gale Research Inc., 835 Penobscot Bldg., Detroit, MI 48226.

641.53 613　　　　　US
RA784
BESTWAYS TO HEALTH; food, health & fitness. 1973-19?? m. (also avail. in microform) Bestways Magazine, Inc., 1140 Lake St., Oak Park, IL 60301.
Formerly: Bestways Magazine (ISSN 0362-4250)

615.19 576　　　　　UK　　ISSN 0263-7235
BETA LACTAMS. ceased 1989. m. (looseleaf format; back issues avail.) Sheffield University Biomedical Information Service (SUBIS), The University, Sheffield S10 2TN, England.

020　　　　　US　　ISSN 0067-6357
BETA PHI MU CHAPBOOK. 1953-1974 (no.10). irreg. Beta Phi Mu, International Library Honor Society, c/o University of Pittsburgh, School of Library and Information Science, Pittsburgh, PA 15260.

690 016　　　　　DK　　ISSN 0409-2694
BETON-LITTERATUR REFERATER. 1971-1989. q. Aalborg Portland, CtO., Roerdalsvej 44, Box 165, DK-9100 Aalborg, Denmark.

338 016　　　　　AU
BETRIEBSWIRTSCHAFTLICHE O P W Z - DOKUMENTATION. 1959-1991. 10/yr. (looseleaf format) Oesterreichisches Produktivitaets- und Wirtschaftlichkeits-Zentrum (OPWZ), Rockhgasse 6, A-1014 Vienna, Austria.
Former titles: O P W Z - Dokumentation; O P Z - Dokumentation (ISSN 0029-7208)

650　　　　　US
BETTER BUSINESS BUREAU. ceased. m. (also avail. in microfilm) (Consumer Affairs Foundation) Consumer Affairs Foundation, Inc., Box 70, Essex St. Station, Boston, MA 02112.

CESSATIONS

Formerly (until 1975): B B B Tribune (ISSN 0005-2809)

613.7　　　　　US
BETTER HEALTH & LIVING. 1985-1988 (June). bi-m. (back issues avail.) Decathlon Corp., c/o Gallery Magazine, 401 Park Ave. South, 3rd Fl., New York, NY 10016-8802.
Formerly (until 1986): Bruce Jenner's Better Health and Living.

640
BETTER HOMES AND GARDENS MICROWAVE RECIPES. 1986-1988. a. Meredith Corporation, Special Interest Publications, 1716 Locust St., Des Moines, IA 50336.

746　　　　　US
BETTER HOMES AND GARDENS NEEDLEWORK & CRAFT IDEAS. 1977-1988. a. Meredith Corporation, Special Interest Publications, 1716 Locust St., Des Moines, IA 50336.
Formerly: Better Homes and Gardens 100's of Needlework and Craft Ideas (ISSN 0278-7504)

658　　　　　US　　ISSN 0736-7171
BETTER REP MANAGEMENT. 1983-1991. m. Talk Publications Inc., Box 26277, San Jose, CA 95159.

800　　　　　US
BETWEEN C AND D; post-modern lower east side fiction magazine. 1984-1991. 3/yr. (back issues avail.) 255 E. Seventh St., New York, NY 10009.

327
BETWEEN THE LINES (LOS ANGELES). ceased. 6/yr. Guatemala Information Center, Box 57027, Los Angeles, CA 90057.

028.5　　　　　US　　ISSN 0745-1172
BETWEEN TIMES. 1919-1989 (vol.73, no.2). q. Warner Press, Inc., Box 2499, Anderson, IN 46018.
Formerly: Reach (ISSN 0034-0308)

338.47　　　　　US
BEVERAGE PROFIT IDEAS. 1983-1989? 3/yr. Beverage Profit Ideas, Inc., 67 Broadway, Greenlawn, NY 11740.

658.8
BEVERAGE RETAILER WEEKLY. 1933-19?? w. Box 917, Paramus, NJ 07653-0917.

051　　　　　US
BEYOND AVALON. ceased. q. (back issues avail.) Beyond Avalon - Judith Tarnpool Associates, 93 Jackson Ave., Bridgeport, CT 06606.

808.838　　　　　GW
BEYOND S F ANTHOLOGY. 1983-198?; suspended. irreg. (back issues avail.) Fabula Press Agency, Bezgenrieter Str. 85, 7326 Heiningen, Germany.

630　　　　　II　　ISSN 0067-6454
BHARAT KRISHAK SAMAJ. YEAR BOOK. 1964-19??; suspended. a. Bharat Krishak Samaj - Farmer's Forum, India, A-1 Nizamuddin West, New Delhi 110013, India.

410　　　　　II　　ISSN 0250-975X
BHASHAVIMARSA. 1978-1989 (Dec.). q. Gujarati Sahitya Parishad, P.O. Box 4060, Ashram Rd., River Side, Ahmedabad 380000, India.

630　　　　　BL
BIBLIOGRAFIA BRASILEIRA DE AGRICULTURA (YEAR). 1978-1979. irreg. Instituto Brasileiro de Informacao em Ciencia e Tecnologia, IBICT SCN Quadra 2, Bloco K, 70710 Brasilia, D.F., Brazil.
Supersedes (1969-1975): Bibliografia Brasileira de Ciencias Agricolas (ISSN 0067-6594); Bibliografia Brasileira de Agricultura (ISSN 0100-6800)

300 016　　　　　BL　　ISSN 0067-6608
BIBLIOGRAFIA BRASILEIRA DE CIENCIAS SOCIAIS. 1954-1979. a. Instituto Brasileiro de Informacao em Ciencia e Tecnologia, IBICT SCN Quadra 2, Bloco K, 70710 Brasilia, D.F., Brazil.
Supersedes: Bibliografia Economico-Social.

340 016　　　　　BL　　ISSN 0067-6616
BIBLIOGRAFIA BRASILEIRA DE DIREITO. (Formerly issued in Bibliografia Brasileira de Ciencias Sociais) 1967-1981. irreg. Instituto Brasileiro de Informacao em Ciencia e Tecnologia, IBICT SCN Quadra 2, Bloco K, 70710 Brasilia, D.F., Brazil.

015 029.7　　　　　BL　　ISSN 0067-6624
BIBLIOGRAFIA BRASILEIRA DE DOCUMENTACAO. 1811; N.S. 1960-1980. irreg. Instituto Brasileiro de Informacao em Ciencia e Tecnologia, IBICT SCN Quadra 2, Bloco K, 70710 Brasilia, D.F., Brazil.

620 016　　　　　BL　　ISSN 0100-0705
Z5852
BIBLIOGRAFIA BRASILEIRA DE ENGENHARIA. 1972-1979. a. Instituto Brasileiro de Informacao em Ciencia e Tecnologia, IBICT SCN Quadra 2, Bloco K, 70710 Brasilia, D.F., Brazil.

530 016　　　　　BL　　ISSN 0067-6640
BIBLIOGRAFIA BRASILEIRA DE FISICA. 1961-1979. irreg. Instituto Brasileiro de Informacao em Ciencia e Tecnologia, IBICT SCN Quadra 2, Bloco K, 70710 Brasilia, D.F., Brazil.
Supersedes in part: Bibliografia Brasileira de Matematica e Fisica.

510　　　　　BL　　ISSN 0067-6667
Z6653
BIBLIOGRAFIA BRASILEIRA DE MATEMATICA. 1961-1979. irreg. Instituto Brasileiro de Informacao em Ciencia e Tecnologia, IBICT SCN Quadra 2, Bloco K, 70710 Brasilia, D.F., Brazil.
Supersedes in part: Bibliografia Brasileira de Matematica e Fisica.

610 016　　　　　BL　　ISSN 0067-6675
BIBLIOGRAFIA BRASILEIRA DE MEDICINA. 1937-1979. irreg. Instituto Brasileiro de Informacao em Ciencia e Tecnologia, IBICT SCN Quadra 2, Bloco K, 70710 Brazilia DF, Brazil.
Formerly (until 1958): Indice-Catalogo Medico Brasileiro.

540 016　　　　　BL　　ISSN 0100-0756
Z5521
BIBLIOGRAFIA BRASILEIRA DE QUIMICA E QUIMICA TECNOLOGICA. 1972-1979. irreg. Instituto Brasileiro de Informacao em Ciencia e Tecnologia, IBICT SCN Quadra 2, Bloco K, 70710 Brasilia, D.F., Brazil.
Supersedes: Bibliografia Brasileira de Quimica (ISSN 0067-6683) & Bibliografia Brasileira de Quimica Tecnologia (ISSN 0405-721X)

590 016　　　　　BL　　ISSN 0067-6691
BIBLIOGRAFIA BRASILEIRA DE ZOOLOGIA. 1950-1979. irreg. Instituto Brasileiro de Informacao em Ciencia e Tecnologia, IBICT SCN Quadra 2, Bloco K, 70710 Brasilia, D.F., Brazil.

015　　　　　BL　　ISSN 0100-722X
Z1679
BIBLIOGRAFIA DE PUBLICACOES OFICIAIS BRASILEIRAS. 1981-1987; suspended. irreg. Camara dos Deputados, Centro de Documentacao e Informacao, Palacio do Congresso Nacional, 70160 Brasilia DF, Brazil.

410　　　　　IT
BIBLIOGRAFIA LINGUISTICA ITALIANA. 1975-1985. 3/yr. Pacini Editore S.R.L., Via della Gherardesca, 56014 Ospedaletto (Pisa), Italy.

949.4 016　　　　　SZ　　ISSN 0067-6772
BIBLIOGRAFIA TICINESE. 1957-1960. a. Biblioteca Cantonale Lugano, Viale Carlo Cattaneo, CH-6900 Lugano, Switzerland.

610 340 016　　　　　CS
BIBLIOGRAFICKY VYBER: ZDRAVOTNICTVI A PRAVO/ABSTRACTS OF HEALTH LEGISLATURE. 1970-1991. bi-m. Ustav Vedeckych Lekarskych Informaci, Vitezneho Unora 31, 121 32 Prague 2, Czechoslovakia.

015　　　　　YU
BIBLIOGRAFIJA PRINOVLJENIH DOMACIH PUBLIKACIJA. 1975-1976 (vol.5). bi-m. Narodna Biblioteka Srbije, Skerliceva 1, 11000 Belgrade, Yugoslavia.

630　　　　　CE　　ISSN 0379-1564
BIBLIOGRAPHICAL SERIES ON COCONUT. 1967-19??; suspended. a. Coconut Research Institute, Coconut Information Centre, Bandirippuwa Estate, Lunuwila, Sri Lanka.

020　　　　　GW　　ISSN 0138-2225
BIBLIOGRAPHIE AKTUELL. 1978-1990. 3/yr. Deutsche Buecherei, Deutscher Platz 1, 7010 Leipzig, Germany.

300 016　　　　　US
BIBLIOGRAPHIE COURANTE D'ARTICLES DE PERIODIQUES POSTERIEURS A 1944 SUR LES PROBLEMES POLITIQUES, ECONOMIQUES ET SOCIAUX/INDEX TO POST-1944 PERIODICAL ARTICLES ON POLITICAL, ECONOMIC AND SOCIAL PROBLEMS. 1968-1981. a. (Fondation Nationale des Sciences Politiques, FR) G.K. Hall & Co., 70 Lincoln St., Boston, MA 02111.

300 054.1　　　　　FR
BIBLIOGRAPHIE DES TRAVAUX EN LANGUE FRANCAISE SUR L'AFRIQUE AU SUD DU SAHARA, SCIENCES HUMAINES ET SOCIALES. ceased 1992. a. (back issues avail.) Centre d'Etudes Africaines, 54 bd. Raspail, 75006 Paris, France.

100 016　　　　　GW　　ISSN 0034-2262
Z7127
BIBLIOGRAPHIE PHILOSOPHIE. 1967-1987. q. Zentralstelle fuer Philosophische Information und Dokumentation, 1086 Berlin, Germany.
Incorporates: Referatekartei Philosophie mit Bibliographischem Anhag & Bibliographie Nichtmarxistischer Philosophischer Zeitschriften.

320　　　　　GW
BIBLIOGRAPHIE POLITIKWISSENSCHAFT UND VOELKERRECHT. ceased 1990. s-m. Hochschule fuer Recht und Verwaltung, August-Bebel-Str. 89, 1590 Potsdam, Germany.
Formerly: Bibliographie Voelkerrecht und Internationale Beziehungen (ISSN 0138-1334)

649　　　　　GW　　ISSN 0342-3964
Z7164.Y8
BIBLIOGRAPHIE SOZIALISATION UND SOZIALPAEDAGOGIK. 1968-1991. q. (Deutsches Jugendinstitut, Arbeitsgruppe Dokumentation) D J I Verlag Deutsches Jugendinstitut, Freibadstr. 30, 8000 Munich 90, Germany.
Formerly (until 1975): Dokumentation - Jugendforschung, Jugendhilfe, Jugendpolitik (ISSN 0012-5113)

301　　　　　GW　　ISSN 0138-5038
BIBLIOGRAPHIE SOZIOLOGIE. 1962-1990. 10/yr. Akademie fuer Gesellschafts-Wissenschaften, Zentralstelle fuer Soziologische Information und Dokumentation, Johannes-Dieckmann Strasse 19-23, Postfach 1270, 1086 Berlin, Germany.

913 016.9301　　　　　GW　　ISSN 0232-4865
Z5133.R46
BIBLIOGRAPHIE ZUR ARCHAEO-ZOOLOGIE UND GESCHICHTE DER HAUSTIERE. 1971-1991. a. Zentralinstitut fuer Alte Geschichte und Archaeologie, Leipziger Str. 3-4, Postfach 1322, 1086 Berlin, Germany.

011　　　　　GW　　ISSN 0070-3931
Z2250
BIBLIOGRAPHISCHER INFORMATIONSDIENST DER DEUTSCHEN BUECHEREI. 1963-1990. irreg. Deutsche Buecherei, Deutscher Platz 1, 7010 Leipzig, Germany.

028.5 016　　　　　US　　ISSN 0147-250X
Z1037
BIBLIOGRAPHY OF BOOKS FOR CHILDREN. 1935-1989. quadrennial. (reprint service avail. from UMI) Association for Childhood Education International, 11141 Georgia Ave., Ste. 200, Wheaton, MD 20902.

576 016　　　　　US
BIBLIOGRAPHY OF GERMFREE RESEARCH. 1962-198? a. (tabloid format; back issues avail.) (Gnotobiotic Society) Ave Marie Press, c/o B.A. Teah, Ed., Dept. of Microbiology, Lobund Laboratory, University of Notre Dame, Notre Dame, IN 46556.

016 947 387　　　　　US
BIBLIOGRAPHY OF MARITIME AND NAVAL HISTORY PERIODICAL ARTICLES. 1972-19?? irreg. Texas A & M University, Sea Grant College Program, College Station, TX 77843-4115.

016　　　　　SA　　ISSN 0067-7256
BIBLIOGRAPHY OF SOUTH AFRICAN GOVERNMENT PUBLICATIONS. 1969-1989. irreg. Government Printer, Bosman St., Private Bag X85, Pretoria 0001, South Africa.

CESSATIONS

617   US   ISSN 0067-7264
BIBLIOGRAPHY OF SURGERY OF THE HAND. 1967-1988. a. (back issues avail.) American Society for Surgery of the Hand, c/o Lynne C. Brescia, 3025 S. Parker Rd., Ste. 65, Aurora, CO 80014.

021   IT   ISSN 0006-1700
BIBLIOTECA LABRONICA NOTIZIARIO. (Supplement to: Indicatore di Livorno) 1969-1971. bi-m. (also avail. in microfilm) (Comune di Livorno) Biblioteca Labronica "F.D. Guerrazzi", Piazza Matteotti 6, 57100 Livorno, Italy.

913   SP   ISSN 0067-7507
BIBLIOTECA PREHISTORICA HISPANA. 1958-1986 (no. 23). irreg. Centro de Estudios Historicos, Departamento de Prehistoria, Palacio del Museo Arqueologico Nacional, Serrano, 13, 28001 Madrid, Spain.

015   SP
BIBLIOTECA UNIVERSITARIA Y PROVINCIAL, BARCELONA. BOLETIN DE NOTICIAS. ceased 1980 (no.1). irreg. Universidad de Barcelona, Biblioteca, Gran Via de les Corts Catalanes, 585, Barcelona-7, Spain.

020   MX   ISSN 0185-0083
BIBLIOTECAS Y ARCHIVOS. 1967-1985 (no.16); suspended. irreg. (back issues avail.) Escuela Nacional de Biblioteconomia y Archivonomia, Miguel Angel 94, Col. Mixcao, 03910 Mexico D.F., Mexico.

629   CN   ISSN 0825-9658
BIBLIOTECH. 1985-1991. bi-m. (looseleaf format) National Library of Canada, 395 Wellington St., Ottawa, Ont. K1A 0N4, Canada.
Formerly (until 1985): National Library of Canada. Technical News (ISSN 0820-8093)

020   GW   ISSN 0006-1964
Z671
DER BIBLIOTHEKAR; Zeitschrift fuer das Bibliothekswesen. 1946-1991. 12/yr. (also avail. in microfilm from UMI; reprint service avail. from UMI) (Zentralinstitut fuer Bibliothekswesen) V E B Bibliographisches Institut, PSF 130, Gerichtsweg 26, 7010 Leipzig, Germany.

020   GW
BIBLIOTHEKSSTUDIEN. ceased. irreg. K.G. Saur Verlag KG, Heilmannstrasse 17, Postfach 711009, 8000 Munich 71, Germany.

796.6   UK
BICYCLE ACTION. 1988-1991. 8/yr. Stonehart Leisure Magazines, 67-71 Goswell Rd., London EC1V 7EN, England.

613.7   US
BICYCLE GUIDE'S COMPLETE CYCLING FITNESS. 1989; ceased same year. a. Raban Publishing, 711 Boylston St., Boston, MA 02116.

350
BID DATA ON CURRENT MUNICIPAL PUBLIC WORKS. ceased. s-a. University of Tennessee, Municipal Technical Advisory Service, 600 Henley, Ste. 120, Knoxville, TN 37996-4105.

800 016   DK   ISSN 0067-8473
BIDRAG TIL H. C. ANDERSENS BIBLIOGRAFI. 1966-1978 (vol.11). irreg. Kongelige Bibliotek, Christians Brygge 8, DK-1219 Copenhagen K, Denmark.

331.2   US   ISSN 0525-4620
HD4966.B262
BIENNIAL SURVEY OF BANK OFFICER SALARIES. ceased. biennial. Bank Administration Institute, Personnel Administration Commission, 1 N. Franklin St., Chicago, IL 60606-3401.
Formerly: Bank Officer Salary Survey (ISSN 0067-3528)

332.1 658.3   US
BIENNIAL SURVEY OF BANK PERSONNEL POLICIES AND PRACTICES. 1962-19?? biennial. Bank Administration Institute, Personnel Administration Commission, 1 N. Franklin St., Chicago, IL 60606-3401.
Formerly: Bank Administration Institute. Personnel Policies and Practices (ISSN 0067-3536)

301.412   US
BIG APPLE DYKE NEWS. 1981-1988. irreg. B.A.D. News, 192 Spring St., No.15, New York, NY 10012.

799   CN
BIG FISH COUNTRY FISHING GUIDE. ceased. a. Big Fish Country Publishers, Box 684, Terrace, B.C. V8G 4B8, Canada.

808   US   ISSN 0892-0842
BIG TWO-HEARTED. 1985-1991 (vol.5). 3/yr. (back issues avail.) (Mid-Peninsula Library Cooperative) Ralph W. Secord Press, 424 Stephenson Ave., Iron Mountain, MI 49801.

268.1   NE   ISSN 0006-2235
BIJBELLESSEN VOOR DE KINDEREN. 1912-19?? q. (Zevende-Dags Adventisten - Seventh-Day Adventists) Stichting Uitgeverij "Veritas", Biltseweg 14, 3735 ME Boschen Duin, Netherlands.

681.11 739.27   CN   ISSN 0006-2316
BIJOU MAGAZINE. 1952-19?? bi-m. (Corporation des Bijoutiers du Quebec) Canam Publications Ltd., 8270 Mountain Sights, Ste. 201, Montreal, Que. H4P 2B7, Canada.
Incorporates: Loupe; Bijoutier.

621 531 796.6   US   ISSN 0734-5992
BIKE TECH; bicycling magazine's newsletter for the technical enthusiast. 1982-19?? bi-m. Rodale Press, Inc., 33 E. Minor St., Emmaus, PA 18098.

388.347   US
BIKER PARTIES. ceased 1988 (vol.1). 4/yr. Outlaw Biker Magazine, 450 Seventh Ave., Ste. 2305, New York, NY 10001.

659.152   US
BIKINI. 1987-198? bi-m. Ujena Inc., 1400 N. Shoreline Blvd., Mountain View, CA 94043.

621   DK   ISSN 0900-8659
BIL TESTEN. published only once, 1985. a. L N B Boeger, Aabenraa 29, DK-1124 Copenhagen K, Denmark.

791.43   GW   ISSN 0006-2383
TR845
BILD UND TON; Zeitschrift fuer visuelle und auditive Medien. 1948-1991. m. Fotokinoverlag Leipzig, Postfach 67, 7031 Leipzig, Germany.

940 069   GW
BILDUNG IM GESCHICHTSMUSEUM. 1974-19?? a. Museum fuer Geschichte der Stadt Dresden, Ernst-Thaelmann-Str. 2, 8010 Dresden, Germany.

338.476   DK   ISSN 0108-5018
BILENS AARSREVY. ceased 1988 (no.88). a. Bonniers Specialmagasiner, Strandboulevarden 130, 2100 Copenhagen OE, Denmark.

612 616.3   UK   ISSN 0261-4561
BILIARY TRACT. ceased 1989. m. (looseleaf format; back issues avail.) Sheffield University Biomedical Information Service (SUBIS), The University, Sheffield S10 2TN, England.

550   GW
BIO; Zeitschrift fuer Mensch und Natur. 1987-19?? m. Magazinpresse Verlag GmbH, Elisenstr. 3, D-8000 Munich 2, Germany.

635   GW   ISSN 0176-2494
BIO GARTEN. 1984-1989. bi-m. (back issues avail.) Bio Garten-Verlag, Am Eichwald 24, D-6117 Schaafheim, Germany.

612.015 617   UK   ISSN 0266-6316
BIOCOMPATIBLE MATERIALS. ceased 1990. m. (looseleaf format; back issues avail.) Sheffield University Biomedical Information Service (SUBIS), The University, Sheffield S10 2TN, England.

610   GW   ISSN 0232-3516
BIOGRAPHIEN HERVORRAGENDER NATURWISSENSCHAFTLER, TECHNIKER UND MEDIZINER. 1962-1991. 2/yr. B.G. Teubner Verlagsgesellschaft mbH, Sternwartenstr. 8, 7010 Leipzig, Germany.

574   IO   ISSN 0126-0758
BIOINDONESIA. 1975-1984 (no.10). irreg. (back issues avail.) Indonesian Institute of Sciences, Research and Development Centre for Biology - Lembaga Ilmu Pengetahuan Indonesia, Pusat Penelitian dan Pengembangan Biologi, Jalan Juanda 18, Bogor 16122, Indonesia.

551.46   US   ISSN 0196-5581
QH91.A1   CODEN: BOJODV
BIOLOGICAL OCEANOGRAPHY JOURNAL. 1981-1990. q. Taylor & Francis, 1900 Frost Rd., Ste. 101, Bristol, PA 19007.

574 150   FR   ISSN 0397-7153
QL751   CODEN: BIBEDL
BIOLOGIE DU COMPORTEMENT/BIOLOGY OF BEHAVIOUR. ceased 1990 (vol.15, nos.3-4). q. (also avail. in microform from UMI; reprint service avail. from ISI) Masson, 120 bd. St. Germain, 75280 Paris Cedex 06, France.

574 016   GW   ISSN 0006-3290
    CODEN: BIRUAA
BIOLOGISCHE RUNDSCHAU; Zeitschrift fuer die gesamte Biologie und ihre Grenzgebiete. 1963-1990. bi-m. (reprint service avail. from ISI) Gustav Fischer Verlag, Villengang 2, Postfach 176, 6900 Jena, Germany.

573.21 312   UK   ISSN 0266-3880
BIOLOGY AND SOCIETY. 1969-1990 (Dec.). q. (back issues avail.) Galton Institute, 19 Northfields Prospect, Northfields, London SW18 1PE, England.
Formerly (until Dec. 1983): Eugenics Society Bulletin (ISSN 0306-8471)

574   US
BIOLOGY SERIES (SEATTLE). 1967-19?? irreg. University of Washington Press, Box 50096, Seattle, WA 98105.

613.9   US
BIOMEDICAL BULLETIN. 1980-198? irreg. (back issues avail.) Association for Voluntary Surgical Contraception, Inc., 122 E. 42nd St., New York, NY 10168.
Formerly: A V S Biomedical Bulletin (ISSN 0271-6771)

610.28 614   US
BIOMEDICAL ENGINEERING AND HEALTH SYSTEMS: A WILEY-INTERSCIENCE SERIES. (Issues not published consecutively) 1968-1983. irreg., unnumbered. John Wiley & Sons, Inc., 605 Third Ave., New York, NY 10158-0012.
Formerly: Biomedical Engineering Series of Monographs (ISSN 0067-8848)

616.86   US   ISSN 0149-1008
BIORESEARCH TODAY: ADDICTION. 1972-1990 (Dec.). m. BIOSIS, 2100 Arch St., Philadelphia, PA 19103-1399.

574.028 016   US   ISSN 0149-0990
BIORESEARCH TODAY: BIO ENGINEERING & INSTRUMENTATION. 1972-1991 (Dec.). m. BIOSIS, 2100 Arch St., Philadelphia, PA 19103-1399.

574 016 616.04   US   ISSN 0149-0982
BIORESEARCH TODAY: BIRTH DEFECTS. 1972-1990 (Dec.). m. (reprint service avail.) BIOSIS, 2100 Arch St., Philadelphia, PA 19103-1399.

616.994   US   ISSN 0149-1016
BIORESEARCH TODAY: CANCER A - CARCINOGENESIS. 1972-1991 (Dec.). m. BIOSIS, 2100 Arch St., Philadelphia, PA 19103-1399.

616.994   US   ISSN 0149-1024
BIORESEARCH TODAY: CANCER B - ANTICANCER AGENTS. 1972-1991 (Dec.). m. BIOSIS, 2100 Arch St., Philadelphia, PA 19103-1399.

616.994 615   US   ISSN 0149-1032
BIORESEARCH TODAY: CANCER C - IMMUNOLOGY. 1972-1991 (Dec.). m. BIOSIS, 2100 Arch St., Philadelphia, PA 19103-1399.

664.06 016   US   ISSN 0149-0958
BIORESEARCH TODAY: FOOD ADDITIVES & RESIDUES. 1972-1991 (Dec.). m. BIOSIS, 2100 Arch St., Philadelphia, PA 19103-1399.

576 016   US   ISSN 0149-0974
BIORESEARCH TODAY: FOOD MICROBIOLOGY. 1972-1991 (Dec.). m. BIOSIS, 2100 Arch St., Philadelphia, PA 19103-1399.

612.67   US   ISSN 0149-0966
BIORESEARCH TODAY: HUMAN & ANIMAL AGING. 1972-1991 (Dec.). m. BIOSIS, 2100 Arch St., Philadelphia, PA 19103-1399.

CESSATIONS

610 016   US   ISSN 0149-094X
BIORESEARCH TODAY: HUMAN AND ANIMAL PARASITOLOGY. 1972-1991 (Dec.). m. BIOSIS, 2100 Arch St., Philadelphia, PA 19103-1399.

301.3 574.5 016   US   ISSN 0149-0931
BIORESEARCH TODAY: HUMAN ECOLOGY. 1972-1990 (Dec.). m. BIOSIS, 2100 Arch St., Philadelphia, PA 19103-1399.

613.62 016   US   ISSN 0149-0923
BIORESEARCH TODAY: INDUSTRIAL HEALTH & TOXICOLOGY. 1972-1991 (Dec.). m. BIOSIS, 2100 Arch St., Philadelphia, PA 19103-1399.

668.6 016 632.9   US   ISSN 0149-0907
BIORESEARCH TODAY: PESTICIDES. 1972-1991 (Dec.). m. BIOSIS, 2100 Arch St., Philadelphia, PA 19103-1399.

613.94 016   US   ISSN 0149-0915
BIORESEARCH TODAY: POPULATION, FERTILITY & BIRTH CONTROL. 1972-1990 (Dec.). m. BIOSIS, 2100 Arch St., Philadelphia, PA 19103-1399.

615.19 011   US
BIOSIS CAS SELECTS: ANTIARRYTHMIC DRUGS. 1988-1989. bi-w. BIOSIS, 2100 Arch St., Philadelphia, PA 19103-1399.

573 011   US
BIOSIS CAS SELECTS: BACTERIAL & VIRAL GENETICS. 1984-1989. bi-w. BIOSIS, 2100 Arch St., Philadelphia, PA 19103-1399.

591.192   US
BIOSIS CAS SELECTS: BIOCHEMISTRY OF DAIRY PRODUCTS. 1987-1989. bi-w. BIOSIS, 2100 Arch St., Philadelphia, PA 19103-1399.

664   US   ISSN 0276-3109
    CODEN: BSBFDQ
BIOSIS CAS SELECTS: BIOCHEMISTRY OF FERMENTED FOODS. 1981-1989. bi-w. (reprint service avail.) BIOSIS, 2100 Arch St., Philadelphia, PA 19103-1399.

630 011   US
BIOSIS CAS SELECTS: BIOCHEMISTRY OF FRUITS & VEGETABLES. 1987-1989. bi-w. BIOSIS, 2100 Arch St., Philadelphia, PA 19103-1399.

574   US   ISSN 0276-3117
    CODEN: BSCLDF
BIOSIS CAS SELECTS: BIOLOGICAL CLOCKS. 1981-19?? bi-w. BIOSIS, 2100 Arch St., Philadelphia, PA 19103-1399.

616.99   US   ISSN 0276-3125
    CODEN: BSCID6
BIOSIS CAS SELECTS: CANCER IMMUNOLOGY. 1981-1990 (Dec.). bi-w. BIOSIS, 2100 Arch St., Philadelphia, PA 19103-1399.

615.19   US   ISSN 0276-3133
    CODEN: BSERD9
BIOSIS CAS SELECTS: ENDORPHINS. 1981-1989. bi-w. (reprint service avail.) BIOSIS, 2100 Arch St., Philadelphia, PA 19103-1399.

574   US
BIOSIS CAS SELECTS: ENZYME METHODS. 1984-1989. bi-w. BIOSIS, 2100 Arch St., Philadelphia, PA 19103-1399.

340   US
BIOSIS CAS SELECTS: FOOD AND DRUG LEGISLATION. 1985-1989. bi-w. BIOSIS, 2100 Arch St., Philadelphia, PA 19103-1399.

574 011   US
BIOSIS CAS SELECTS: GENETIC MANIPULATION IN PLANTS. 1985-1989. bi-w. BIOSIS, 2100 Arch St., Philadelphia, PA 19103-1399.

574.8   US   ISSN 0276-315X
    CODEN: BHCYDB
BIOSIS CAS SELECTS: HISTOCHEMISTRY AND CYTOCHEMISTRY. 1981-19?? bi-w. BIOSIS, 2100 Arch St., Philadelphia, PA 19103-1399.

575.1 011   US
BIOSIS CAS SELECTS: HORMONE & HORMONE RECEPTOR INTERACTIONS. 1984-1989. bi-w. BIOSIS, 2100 Arch St., Philadelphia, PA 19103-1399.

575.1 011   US
BIOSIS CAS SELECTS: HORMONES & GENE EXPRESSION. 1984-1989. bi-w. BIOSIS, 2100 Arch St., Philadelphia, PA 19103-1399.

615.19   US   ISSN 0276-3176
    CODEN: BSEIDG
BIOSIS CAS SELECTS: INTERFERON. 1981-1989. bi-w. (reprint service avail.) BIOSIS, 2100 Arch St., Philadelphia, PA 19103-1399.

610   US
BIOSIS CAS SELECTS: LYMPHOKINES. 1985-1989. bi-w. BIOSIS, 2100 Arch St., Philadelphia, PA 19103-1399.

618   US   ISSN 0276-3184
    CODEN: BSMDD7
BIOSIS CAS SELECTS: MAMMALIAN BIRTH DEFECTS. 1981-1989. bi-w. (reprint service avail.) BIOSIS, 2100 Arch St., Philadelphia, PA 19103-1399.

616.8 011   US
BIOSIS CAS SELECTS: NEURORECEPTORS. 1984-1989. bi-w. BIOSIS, 2100 Arch St., Philadelphia, PA 19103-1399.

616.97 011   US
BIOSIS CAS SELECTS: NUTRITION & IMMUNOLOGY. 1988-1989. bi-w. BIOSIS, 2100 Arch St., Philadelphia, PA 19103-1399.

574.192 011   US
BIOSIS CAS SELECTS: PEPTIDE AND PROTEIN SEQUENCES. 1985-1989. bi-w. BIOSIS, 2100 Arch St., Philadelphia, PA 19103-1399.

575.1   US   ISSN 0276-3206
    CODEN: BSPGDV
BIOSIS CAS SELECTS: PLANT GENETICS. 1981-1989. bi-w. (reprint service avail.) BIOSIS, 2100 Arch St., Philadelphia, PA 19103-1399.

157   US   ISSN 0276-3214
    CODEN: BSCHD3
BIOSIS CAS SELECTS: SCHIZOPHRENIA. 1981-19?? bi-w. BIOSIS, 2100 Arch St., Philadelphia, PA 19103-1399.

574   US   ISSN 0276-3222
    CODEN: BSTRDG
BIOSIS CAS SELECTS: TRANSPLANTATION. 1981-19?? bi-w. BIOSIS, 2100 Arch St., Philadelphia, PA 19103-1399.

574.28   US   ISSN 0572-6565
    CODEN: BIBSBR
BIOTECHNOLOGY & BIOENGINEERING SYMPOSIA. 1969-198? irreg. (also avail. in microform from UMI; reprint service avail. from UMI) John Wiley & Sons, Inc., 605 Third Ave., New York, NY 10158-0012.

574   US
BIOTECHNOLOGY WEEK; the news magazine of biotechnology. 1992; announced, never published. fortn. (tabloid format) Cahners Publishing Company (Newton) (Subsidiary of: Reed International PLC), Division of Reed Publishing (USA) Inc., 275 Washington St., Newton, MA 02158.

581   MX   ISSN 0185-0326
QH107   CODEN: BIOTDT
BIOTICA. 1976-1988. q. (back issues avail.) Instituto Nacional de Investigaciones sobre Recursos Bioticos (INIREB), Apdo. Postal 63, Km. 25 Antigua Carr. A Coatepec, 9100 Xalapa, Veracruz, Mexico.

598.2   CN   ISSN 0229-5024
BIRDFINDING IN CANADA. 1981-1989. bi-m. Box 519, Kleinburg, Ont. L0J 1C0, Canada.

598.2 500.9   UK   ISSN 0006-3673
BIRDS AND COUNTRY. 1949-198? q. 79 Surbiton Hill Park, Surbiton, Surrey, England.

694   GW
BIRKNER EUROLIGNUM; the European timber market. 1985-19?? biennial. Birkner & Co. Verlag, Winsbergring 38, Postfach 540750, 2000 Hamburg 54, Germany.

976
BIRMINGHAM HISTORICAL SOCIETY. JOURNAL. 1960-1987. a. Birmingham Historical Society, One Sloss Quarters, Birmingham, AL 35222-1243.

382 382   US
BIRMINGHAM INTERNATIONAL TRADE DIRECTORY. 1982-198? quadrennial. Birmingham Area Chamber of Commerce, Research and Trade Division, 2027 First Ave. N., Birmingham, AL 35203.

616.043   US   ISSN 0547-6844
RG626   CODEN: BTHDAK
BIRTH DEFECTS ORIGINAL ARTICLE SERIES. (Former name of issuing body: National Foundation, March of Dimes) ceased. irreg. (March of Dimes Birth Defects Foundation) Alan R. Liss, Inc., 41 E. 11th St., New York, NY 10003.

355   IS
BITAON CHEL RIFUAH. ceased. 3/yr. Ministry of Defense Publishing House, Subscription Dept., 25 David Eleazer St., Hakirya, Tel Aviv 64 734, Israel.

811   US   ISSN 0006-3908
BITTERROOT; an international magazine of poetry. 1962-1991. 3/yr. (back issues avail.) Menke Katz, Ed. & Pub., Box 489, Spring Glen, NY 12483.

028.5   SW   ISSN 0345-1593
BLAAKLINT - LIVLINAN. 1969-1990. 8/yr. Sveriges Blaablandsungdom, Koepmangatan, 3, S-702 10 Oerebro, Sweden.
    Formed by the merger of: Blaaklint (ISSN 0006-4556); Livlinan.

622   AT
BLACK COAL IN AUSTRALIA. 1977-1987. a. Australia and New South Wales Joint Coal Board, 1 Chifley Square, 11th Fl., Sydney, N.S.W. 2000, Australia.

780 910.03   US   ISSN 0898-8536
ML3556
BLACK MUSIC RESEARCH BULLETIN. 1978-19?? s-a. Center for Black Music Research, Columbia College Chicago, 600 S. Michigan Ave., Chicago, IL 60605.
    Formerly: Black Music Research Newsletter (ISSN 0898-851X)

910.03   US
BLACK NATION. 1981-198?; suspended. s-a. Getting Together Publications, Box 29293, Oakland, CA 94604.

361.8   US
BLACK PAPERS. ceased. irreg. New York Urban League, Inc., 218 W. 40th St., 6th Fl., New York, NY 10018.

780   US   ISSN 0090-7790
ML3556
BLACK PERSPECTIVE IN MUSIC. 1973-1990 (vol.18). a. (also avail. in microform from UMI; reprint service avail. from UMI) Foundation for Research in the Afro-American Creative Arts, Drawer I, Cambria Heights, NY 11411.

301 323   US   ISSN 0084-7909
E185.5
BLACK POSITION. 1971-1974 (nos.3-4). irreg. Broadside Press, Box 04257, Northwestern Station, Detroit, MI 38204-0257.

700 320   US
BLACK STAR; a quarterly magazine of arts & anarchist opinion. ceased 1987. q. (back issues avail.) J. Gallagher, Ed. & Pub., Box 3506, Tucson, AZ 85722.

920   SA   ISSN 0250-0817
HF3901
BLACK WHO'S WHO OF SOUTHERN AFRICA. ceased. a. African Business Publications (Pty) Ltd., Box 2901, Johannesburg 2001, South Africa.

273   US
BLACKBERRY. (Chapbook series) 1974-198? irreg. (approx. 20/yr.). Blackberry Books, Chimney Farm, Nobleboro, ME 04555.

371   GW   ISSN 0006-4394
BLAETTER FUER DEN DEUTSCHLEHRER. 1957-1989. 4/yr. Verlag Moritz Diesterweg, Hochstr. 29-31, D-6000 Frankfurt-Main 1, Germany.

349 333   GW   ISSN 0006-4440
BLAETTER FUER GRUNDSTUECKS, BAU- UND WOHNUNGSRECHT. 1951-198? m. Luchterhand Verlag, Heddesdorfer Str. 31, Postfach 1780, 5450 Neuwied, Germany.

371.3 GW
BLAETTER FUER LEHRERFORTBILDUNG; Zeitschrift fuer das Seminar. (Supplement to: Lehrerjournal, Grundschulmagazin, Lehrerjournal Hauptschulmagazin) 1948-198? m. Ehrenwirth Verlag GmbH, Schwanthaler Str. 91, D-8000 Munich 2, Germany.

349 332 GW ISSN 0006-4475
BLAETTER FUER STEUERRECHT, SOZIAL VERSICHERUNG UND ARBEITSRECHT. 1950-19?? s-m. Luchterhand Verlag, Heddesdorfer Str. 31, Postfach 1780, 5450 Neuwied, Germany.

847 FR ISSN 0006-4513
BLAGUES. 1953-19?? bi-m. Editions Rouff, 36 rue du Vieux-Pont-De-Sevres, 92100 Boulogne Billancourt, France.

700 770 NE ISSN 0923-6511
BLIND. 1980-19?? q. Stichting Pretentieus, Prinsengracht 218, 1016 HD Amsterdam, Netherlands.
Formerly: Zien Magazine (ISSN 0167-5966)

340 US
BLIND JUSTICE. 1937-1990. q. National Lawyers Guild, New York City Chapter, 55 Sixth Ave., 3rd Fl., New York, NY 10013-1601.

371.911 GW
BLINDOC. ceased. q. Deutsche Blindenstudienanstalt e.V., Postfach 1160, 3550 Marburg, Germany.

778.53 US
BLOCKBUSTER; the video magazine. 1989-1992 (Mar.). m. Blockbuster Entertainment Corporation, 1 E. Broward Blvd., Ste. 710, Fort Lauderdale, FL 33301.

929 US ISSN 0889-9479
BLOIS VOICE. ceased 1980 (no.49). q. (back issues avail.) 501 Aspen Way, McMinnville, OR 97128.

616.15 612.014 UK ISSN 0142-8586
BLOOD COAGULATION. ceased 1991. m. (looseleaf format; back issues avail.) Sheffield University Biomedical Information Service (SUBIS), The University, Sheffield S10 2TN, England.

612.015 616.76 UK ISSN 0142-8594
BLOOD PROTEINS. ceased 1991. m. (looseleaf format; back issues avail.) Sheffield University Biomedical Information Service (SUBIS), The University, Sheffield S10 2TN, England.

616.1 612 UK ISSN 0268-1536
BLOOD VESSEL WALLS. ceased 1990. m. (looseleaf format; back issues avail.) Sheffield University Biomedical Information Service (SUBIS), The University, Sheffield S10 2TN, England.

820 IT
BLUE GUITAR; rivista annuale di letteratura inglese e americana. 1975-1989. a. (Universita di Roma "La Sapienza", Facolta di Magistero) Herder Editrice e Libreria s.r.l., Piazza Montecitorio, 120, 00186 Rome, Italy.

800 US ISSN 0743-2917
BLUE MOON. 1987-1989. a. Red Herring Press, Channing-Murray Foundation, 1209 W. Oregon St., Urbana, IL 61801.

781.573 UK ISSN 0006-5161
BLUES WORLD. 1965-198? m. Amon-Ra Fine Art Ltd., Meeting House, Frenchay, Bristol BS16 1NT, England.

796.95 US
BOAT. 1989-199? q. Diamandis Communications, Inc. (Subsidiary of: Hachette Publications), 1633 Broadway, New York, NY 10009.

796.95 US
BOATING DIGEST. ceased. bi-m. (tabloid format) United Publications, Inc., Box 996, Yarmouth, ME 04096.

796.95 011 US
BOATING INFORMATION; a bibliography and source list. 1986-1989. biennial. American Boat & Yacht Council, Inc., Box 747, Millersville, MD 21108.

623.82 US ISSN 0190-4507
BOATING PRODUCT NEWS; the marine industry's product newspaper. 1977-1990. 6/yr. (tabloid format) Communication Channels, Inc., 6255 Barfield Rd., Atlanta, GA 30328-4369.

797.14 US
BOATRACING. 1981-1989. bi-m. Muncey Productions, Inc., Box 707, Monroe, WA 98272.

796.95 US
BOATS & GEAR. 1990; ceased same year. bi-m. Taunton Press, Inc., 63 S. Main St., Box 355, Newtown, CT 06470.

796.95 AT ISSN 1032-5360
BOATS, BOATS, BOATS.... 1988-19?? a. Baird Publications Pty. Ltd., 10 Oxord St., South Yarra, Vic. 3141, Australia.

332.6 US
BOB JENNINGS CONFIDENTIAL REPORT. 1985-198? q. American Media Group, 951 Broken Sound Pkwy., N.W., Boca Raton, FL 33431.

338.9 GW ISSN 0170-1916
BOCHUMER MATERIALEN ZUR ENTWICKLUNGSFORSCHUNG UND ENTWICKLUNGSPOLITIK. 1976-1986 (no.32). irreg. (Ruhr-Universitaet, Bochum, Institut fuer Entwicklungsforschung und Entwicklungspolitik) K. Thienemanns Verlag, Edition Erdmann, Blumenstr. 36, 7000 Stuttgart, Germany.

327 338.9 GW ISSN 0572-6654
BOCHUMER SCHRIFTEN ZUR ENTWICKLUNGSFORSCHUNG UND ENTWICKLUNGSPOLITIK. 1968-1981 (no.21). irreg. (Ruhr-Universitaet, Bochum, Institut fuer Entwicklungsforschung und Entwicklungspolitik) K. Thienemanns Verlag, Edition Erdmann, Blumenstr. 36, 700 Stuttgart 1, Germany.

574.5 GW ISSN 0006-5455
BODEN UND GESUNDHEIT; Schriftenfolge fuer angewandte Oekologie. 1953-198? q. Gesellschaft Boden und Gesundheit, 7183 Langenburg, Germany.

613 US ISSN 0145-6210
BODY FORUM. 1976-1981. 6/yr. World Healthee Ways Inc., Box 420375, Atlanta, GA 30342.

613 US
BODYBUILDING WOMAN. 1987-198?; suspended. bi-m. Symmetry Publishing, Inc., Box 179, Grafton, NH 03240-0179.

949.8 US ISSN 0045-2351
BOIAN NEWS SERVICE; Romanian news and world report. vol.4, 1971-199? w. (processed) Boian News Service, 300 E. 91st St., New York, NY 10028.

028 SW ISSN 0005-2833
Z1035.5
BOKREVY. 1970-1990. q. Bibliotekstjaenst AB, Box 200, 221 00 Lund, Sweden.
Supersedes: B B L - Revy.

620 BL ISSN 0067-9607
BOLETIM DE ENGENHARIA DE PRODUCAO. 1962-1963 (vol.3). irreg. Universidade de Sao Paulo, Departamento de Engenharia de Electricidade, Cidade Universitaria, "Armando de Salles Oliveira", C.P.8191, Sao Paulo, Brazil.

639.2 BL ISSN 0006-5927
BOLETIM DE ESTUDOS DE PESCA. 1961-1969. 3/yr. Superintendencia do Desenvolvimento do Nordeste, Av. Prof., Moraes Rego, Cidade Universitaria, 50000 Recife PE, Brazil.

531 BL
BOLETIM DE INDICADORES ENERGETICOS. 1984-198? irreg. Companhia Paulista de Forca e Luz, Assessoria de Pesquisa e Desenvolvimento, Caixa Postal 1808, 13100 Campinas, Brazil.

551.22 PO
BOLETIM MENSUEL DES SEISMES PROCHES. 1974-1976. m. Instituto Nacional de Meteorologia e Geofisica, Rua Cao Aeroporto, 1700 Lisbon, Portugal.

382 MX
BOLETIN DE ECONOMIA INTERNACIONAL. ceased 1989 (Dec.). q. Banco de Mexico, Direccion de Investigacion Economica y Bancaria, Av. Juarez 90, Col. Centro, Delegacion Cuauhtemoc, 06059 Mexico DF, Mexico.
Supersedes (in 1985): Boletin de Indicadores Economicos Internacionales.

572 PY ISSN 0560-4168
BOLETIN DE LA SOCIEDAD CIENTIFICA DEL PARAGUAY Y DEL MUSEO ETNOGRAFICO. 1957-1962 (vol.6). irreg. Museo Etnografico "Andres Barbero", Espana 217, Asuncion, Paraguay.

318 BO
BOLIVIA. INSTITUTO NACIONAL DE ESTADISTICA. BOLETIN ESTADISTICO MENSUAL. 1945; N.S. 1980-198? m. Instituto Nacional de Estadistica, Casilla de Correo No. 6129, La Paz, Bolivia.

318 BO
BOLIVIA. INSTITUTO NACIONAL DE ESTADISTICA. BOLETIN ESTADISTICO TRIMESTRAL. 1981-198? q. Instituto Nacional de Estadistica, Casilla de Correo No. 6129, La Paz, Bolivia.

410 015 NE ISSN 0168-7298
BOLLETTINO DI ITALIANISTICA; bibliografia e informazione culturale. 1983-1991. irreg. (back issues avail.) (Centro di Calcolo) E.J. Brill, P.O. Box 9000, 2300 PA Leiden, Netherlands.

574.92 639.3 IT
BOLLETTINO DI PESCA, PISCICOLTURA E IDROBIOLOGIA. 1925; N.S. 1946-1976. s-a. Laboratorio Centrale di Idrobiologia, Viale del Caravaggio, 107, 00147 Rome, Italy.
Formerly: Bollettino di Pesca (ISSN 0006-6575)

914.504 IT
BOLOGNA INCONTRI. 1970-1986 (no.12). m. Ente Provinciale per Il Turismo di Bologna, Via Marconi 45, 40122 Bologna, Italy.

633.1 338.1 AG ISSN 0045-2467
BOLSA DE CEREALES. REVISTA INSTITUCIONAL. 1872-1991 (vol.119, no.3000). q. Bolsa de Cereales, Avda. Corrientes 127, 1043 Buenos Aires, Argentina.
Formerly: Bolsa de Cereales. Revista (ISSN 0325-1276)

690 AT
BOMA MAGAZINE. ceased. m. Rala Publications, 203-205 Darling St., Balamin, N.S.W. 2041, Australia.

811 US
BOMBAST. 1977-19?? 3/yr. 642 E. Weldon Ave., Fresno, CA 93704.

630 IC ISSN 1017-3528
BONDINN. 1983-1992. 2/yr. Frodi Ltd., Armuli 18, 108 Reykjavik, Iceland.

301 GW ISSN 0068-0044
BONNER BEITRAEGE ZUR SOZIOLOGIE. 1964-1991. irreg. (Rheinische Friedrich-Wilhelms-Universitaet, Institut fuer Soziologie) Ferdinand Enke Verlag, Postfach 101254, 7000 Stuttgart 10, Germany.

929 US ISSN 0899-2339
BONNER COUNTY GENEALOGICAL SOCIETY QUARTERLY. 1983-1989 (vol.7, no.1). q. Bonner County Genealogical Society, Box 27, Dover, ID 83825.

635 AT ISSN 0045-2483
BONSAI IN AUSTRALIA. 1970-1991. bi-m. Bonsai Society of Australia, Teffer Rd., Castle Hill, N.S.W. 2154, Australia.

016 800 US ISSN 0000-0280
BOOK - GUIDE: MYSTERY, DETECTIVE AND SUSPENSE STORIES. ceased. bi-m. Holt Information Systems, Division of Holt, Rinehart & Winston, Inc, 383 Madison Ave, New York, NY 10017.

658.8 UK
BOOK MARKETS IN THE AMERICAS, AFRICA, ASIA AND AUSTRALASIA. 1984-198? irreg. Euromonitor Publications Ltd., 87-88 Turnmill St., London EC1M 5QU, England.

070.5 658.8 UK
BOOK MARKETS IN WESTERN AND EASTERN EUROPE. 1978-1984. irreg. Euromonitor Publications Ltd., 87-88 Turnmill St., London EC1M 5QU, England.

CESSATIONS

010 US
BOOK NOTES. 1971-1983. 4/yr. (looseleaf format) University of Pittsburgh, College of Arts and Sciences, Book Center, Pittsburgh, PA 15260.

800 920 US
BOOK REVIEW NEWSLETTER; for people who love to read. 1983-19?? 3/yr. Creative Press, Manchester Mall, 811 Main St., Box 10, CT 06040.

028.1 301.412
BOOK REVIEWERS GUIDE. 1985-1986. q. R and B Enterprises, Manchester Mall, 811 Main St., Box 10, Manchester, CT 06040.
Formerly: Spirit of the Muse.

028.1 UK ISSN 0950-9089
BOOKQUEST. 1976-1990. 3/yr. Literacy Centre, Brighton Polytechnic, Falmer, Brighton BN1 9PH, England.

028.8 US
BOOKS FOR WORLD EXPLORERS SERIES. 1979-19?? 4/yr. National Geographic Society, 17th & M Sts., N.W., Washington, DC 20036.

016 892.7 CN ISSN 0705-7172
BOOKS IN ARABIC. ceased 1988. irreg. Metropolitan Toronto Library Board, 789 Yonge St., Toronto, Ont. M4W 2G8, Canada.

016 891.992 CN ISSN 0705-8209
BOOKS IN ARMENIAN. ceased 1988. irreg. Metropolitan Toronto Library Board, Regional Multilanguage Department, 789 Yonge St., Toronto, Ont. M4W 2G8, Canada.

016 890 CN ISSN 0316-7437
BOOKS IN BENGALI. ceased 1988. irreg. (processed) Metropolitan Toronto Library Board, Regional Multilanguage Department, 789 Yonge St., Toronto, Ont. M4W 2G8, Canada.

016 890 CN
BOOKS IN CHINESE. ceased 1988. irreg. (processed) Metropolitan Toronto Library Board, Regional Multilanguage Department, 789 Yonge St., Toronto, Ont. M4W 2G8, Canada.

016 839 CN ISSN 0705-2332
BOOKS IN DANISH. ceased 1988. irreg. Metropolitan Toronto Library Board, Regional Multilanguage Department, 789 Yonge St., Toronto, Ont. M4W 2G8, Canada.

016 839 CN ISSN 0705-2294
BOOKS IN DUTCH. 1974-1988. irreg. Metropolitan Toronto Library Board, Regional Multilanguage Department, 789 Yonge St., Toronto, Ont. M4W 2G8, Canada.

016 894.541 CN ISSN 0705-1883
BOOKS IN FINNISH. ceased 1988. irreg. Metropolitan Toronto Library Board, Regional Multilanguage Department, 789 Yonge St., Toronto, Ont. M4W 2G8, Canada.

016 890 CN ISSN 0705-8373
BOOKS IN HINDI. ceased 1988. irreg. Metropolitan Toronto Library Board, Regional Multilanguage Department, 789 Yonge St., Toronto, Ont. M4W 2G8, Canada.

016 894.511 CN ISSN 0705-6494
BOOKS IN HUNGARIAN. ceased 1988. irreg. Metropolitan Toronto Library Board, Regional Multilanguage Department, 789 Yonge St., Toronto, Ont. M4W 2G8, Canada.

016 860 CN ISSN 0705-7156
BOOKS IN SPANISH. ceased. irreg. Metropolitan Toronto Library Board, Regional Multilanguage Department, 789 Yonge St., Toronto, Ont. M4W 2G8, Canada.

016 896 CN ISSN 0705-825X
BOOKS IN URDU. 1972-19?? irreg. Metropolitan Toronto Library Board, Regional Multilanguage Department, 789 Yonge St., Toronto, Ont. M4W 2G8, Canada.

050 II ISSN 0006-7555
BOOKSELLER PUSTAK VIKRETA BARODA; sahitya - pracharak Baroda. 1950-197? m. Jaideva Bros., Atmaram Marg, Baroda 1, India.

666.1 UK ISSN 0006-7822
BORON IN GLASS. 1950-1985. q. (Borax Consolidated Ltd.) Borax Consolidated Ltd., Borax House, Carlisle Place, London SW1P 1HT, England.

676 AU
BOSS - OESTERREICH. 1894-19?? s-m. Verlagsbuchhandlung Brueder Hollinek und Co. GmbH, Feldgasse 13, A-1238 Vienna, Austria.
Formerly: Papiershandels-Fachblatt (ISSN 0031-1391)

330 US
BOSTON BUSINESS MAGAZINE. ceased 1991 (Feb.). bi-m. (Bergenheim & Associates) M C P, Inc., 5500 Wayzata Blvd., Ste. 800, Minneapolis, MN 55416.
Formerly: Boston Business.

974 US ISSN 0190-3586
F73.1
BOSTONIAN SOCIETY. PROCEEDINGS.. 1881-1983. irreg. Bostonian Society, Old State House, 206 Washington St., Boston, MA 02109.

200 GW
BOTSCHAFT UND DIENST; Zeitschrift fuer Erwachsenbildung. 1950-1991. bi-m. (Maennerarbeit der Evangelischen Kirche Deutschlands) Verlag Kirche und Mann, Neue Schlesingergasse 22-24, 6000 Frankfurt a.M. 1, Germany.

790.13 FR
BOUQUET; le sport de l'esprit. ceased. bi-m. Publications Guy Hachette, La Petite Motte Senille, 86100 Chatellerault, France.
Incorporates: Sport de l'Esprit (ISSN 0395-9066)

796.32 CN ISSN 0835-7447
BOWBENDER MAGAZINE'S HUNTING ANNUAL (YEAR). ceased. a. (back issues avail.) Bill Windsor, Pub., P.O. Box 912, 65 McDonald Close, Carstairs, Alta. T0M 0N0, Canada.

101 US
BOWLING GREEN STUDIES IN APPLIED PHILOSOPHY. 1979-1986 (vol.8). a. Bowling Green State University, Department of Philosophy, Bowling Green, OH 43403.

793 747 US
BOXING BEAT. 1986-19??. m. Jems, Inc., 55 Ave of the Americas No. 309, New York, NY 10013.

796.83 GW ISSN 0138-1245
BOXRING. 1949-1990. m. Deutscher Boxverband der D D R, c/o Dietrich Denz, Am Danewend 10, 1123 Berlin-Karow, Germany.

028.5 200
BRAILLE PILOT. ceased. q. Gospel Association for the Blind, Inc., Box 62, Delray Beach, FL 33447.

332.1 US ISSN 0162-7481
BRANCH BANKER'S REPORT. 1968?-199? m. (also avail. in microform from UMI) Warren, Gorham and Lamont Inc., One Penn Plaza, New York, NY 10119.

378 GW ISSN 0939-3986
BRANDENBURGISCHEN LANDESHOCHSCHULE POTSDAM. WISSENSCHAFTLICHE ZEITSCHRIFT. 1956-1992. 10/yr. Brandenburgische Landeshochschule Potsdam, Am Neuen Palais, 1571 Potsdam, Germany.
Formerly: Paedagogische Hochschule "Karl Liebknecht" Potsdam. Wissenschaftliche Zeitschrift (ISSN 0138-290X)

387.7 US
BRANIFF DESTINATION. 1985-19?? m. Skies America Publishing Company, 7730 S.W. Mohawk, Tualatin, OR 97062.

634.9 BL ISSN 0045-270X
SD159
BRASIL FLORESTAL. suspended. s-a. Instituto Brasileiro de Desenvolvimento Florestal, Setor de Areas Isoladas, L4 Norte, Palacio do Desenvolvimento, 70000 Brasilia, DF, Brazil.

338.2 BL
BRAZIL. CONSELHO NACIONAL DO PETROLEO. ATUALIDADES. (Supplement avail.: Dados Estatisticos) 1971-1985 (Mar-Apr). bi-m. Conselho Nacional do Petroleo, Secao de Relacoes Publicas, SGA Norte Quadra 603 Modulo J, Brasilia DF, Brazil.

028.5 016 BL ISSN 0100-7238
Z1037.A1
BRAZIL. FUNDACAO NACIONAL DO LIVRO INFANTIL E JUVENIL. BOLETIM INFORMATIVO. 1969-1985; 1987-198? q. Fundacao Nacional do Livro Infantil e Juvenil, Rua da Imprensa 16, 20030 Rio de Janeiro, Brazil.

980 BL
BRAZIL. PATRIMONIO HISTORICO E ARTISTICO NACIONAL. REVISTA. 1937-1990; suspended. s-a. (Secretaria do Patrimonio Historico e Artistico Nacional) Fundacao Nacional Pro-Memoria, Avda. Rio Branco 46 - 2 andar, 20090- Rio de Janeiro, R.J., Brazil.
Formerly: Brazil. Diretoria do Patrimonio Historico e Artistico Nacional. Revista (ISSN 0068-0788)

011 BL
BRAZIL. SERVICO SOCIAL DO COMERCIO. COLECAO BIBLIOGRAFICA. 1970-1987 (vol.18). a. Servico Social do Comercio, Rua Voluntarios da Patria 169, 22270 Rio de Janeiro, Brazil.

332.6 BL
BRAZIL. SUPERINTENDENCIA DO DESENVOLVIMENTO DO NORDESTE. NORDESTE, OPORTUNIDADES DE INVESTIMENTOS. 1975-1982. a. Superintendencia do Desenvolvimento do Nordeste, Av. Prof. Moraes Rego, Cidade Universitaria, 50000 Recife PE, Brazil.

627 BL
BRAZIL. SUPERINTENDENCIA DO DESENVOLVIMENTO DO NORDESTE. RELATORIO SINTETICO, ANDAMENTO DO PROGRAMA DE IRRIGACAO DO NORDESTE. 1971-19?? irreg. Superintendencia do Desenvolvimento do Nordeste, Servico Publico Federal, Recife, Pernambuco, Brazil.

600 US
BREAKTHROUGH (NEW YORK). ceased. 24/yr. Boardroom Reports, Inc., 330 W. 42nd St., New York, NY 10036.

500 US
Q1
BREAKTHROUGHS IN HEALTH & SCIENCE. 1937-1991 (Jan.). m. (also avail. in microform from UMI) Family Media, Inc., Men's and In-Home Group, 3 Park Ave., New York, NY 10016.
Formerly (until 1990): Science Digest (ISSN 0036-8296)

806 US ISSN 0734-8665
PT2603.R397
BRECHT YEARBOOK. (Title varies for each volume) ceased 1987 (vol. 13). a. (International Brecht Society) Wayne State University Press, 5959 Woodward Ave., Detroit, MI 48202.

630 UK ISSN 0006-954X
BRECON AND RADNOR FARMER. 1962-198? m. N.F.U. Publications Ltd., 5 High East St., Dorchester, Dorset DT1 1HJ, England.

913 GW ISSN 0068-0907
D80
BREMER ARCHAEOLOGISCHE BLAETTER. 1960-1990; suspended. irreg. (Bremer Gesellschaft fuer Vorgeschichte) Dr. Rudolf Habelt GmbH, Am Buchenhang 1, 5300 Bonn 1, Germany.

266 GW ISSN 0006-9574
BREMER MISSIONSSCHIFF; Kinderbrief aus der Weltmission. 1904-19?? m. Norddeutsche Mission, Vahrer Str. 243, 2800 Bremen 44, Germany.
Incorporates: Kinderbrief aus der Weltmission.

338.1 664 FR
BREVES DE SOLAGRAL. ceased 1989. m. Solidarite Agro-Alimentaire, 13, bd. Saint-Martin, 75003 Paris, France.

051 US ISSN 0006-9892
BRIDGEPORT NEWS. 1937-199? w. Bridgeport News Inc., 3252 S. Halsted, Chicago, IL 60608.

200 US ISSN 1042-2234
BRIDGES (COLUMBIA); an interdisciplinary journal of theology, philosophy, history, and science. 1988-1991 (Aug.). s-a. Robert Seitz Frey, Nancy Thomson-Frey, Eds. & Pubs., Box 943, Columbia, MD 20783-0943.

334 CS
BRIEF INFORMATION ON THE CO-OPERATIVE MOVEMENT IN CZECHOSLOVAKIA. 1957-1990. irreg. Ustredni Rada Druzstev, Tesnov 5, 110 06 Prague 1, Czechoslovakia.
Formerly: Czechoslovak Cooperative Movement in Figures.

053.1 SZ ISSN 0006-999X
BRIEFE AN DEN MITMENSCHEN. 1970-1989. m. Emil F. Oesch Verlag AG, Klausstr. 10, CH-8008 Zuerich, Switzerland.

200 340 US ISSN 0896-8713
BRIEFLY. 1981-1989. q. (back issues avail.; reprint service avail. from UMI) Christian Legal Society, Box 1492, Merrifield, VA 22116.

333.33 US ISSN 0899-8779
BRIEFS. 1965-1990. fortn. Society of Real Estate Appraisers, 225 N. Michigan Ave., Ste. 724, Chicago, IL 60601-7601.
Former titles: S R E A Briefs (ISSN 0273-8236); (until 1980): Appraisal Briefs.

370 SP
BRISAS ALFONSINAS; revista literaria escolar del instituto. 1957-198? s-a. (also avail. in microform) Instituto Nacional de Ensenanza Media "Alfonso X el Sabio", Vista Alegre, Murcia, Spain.

808.81 US
BRISTLECONE. 1988-1990. q. Western Nevada Community College, 2201 W. Nye Lane, Carson City, NV 89703.

941 UK
BRITAIN IN BRIEF. ceased. a. H.M.S.O., P.O. Box 276, London SW8 5DT, England.

910.2 UK
BRITAIN WELCOMES COACHES. 1978-19?? a. Lewis Productions Ltd., Unit 3, River Gardens Business Centre, Spur Rd., Feltham, Middx TW14 0SN, England.

338 621.381 UK
BRITAIN'S P.C. MANUFACTURERS. 1984-1991. irreg. Jordan & Sons Ltd., 21 St. Thomas St., Bristol BS1 6JS, England.
Formerly (until 1990): Computer Services Software.

387.7 UK ISSN 0068-1342
BRITISH AVIATION YEAR BOOK. 197?-197? a. Hanover Press Ltd., 80 Highgate Rd., London NW5 1PB., England.

796.815 UK
BRITISH BOXING YEARBOOK. 1945-19?? a. R & D Publications Ltd., 30-34 Langham St., London W1N 5LB, England.
Formerly (until 1985): Boxing News Annual.

380 338 UK ISSN 0143-9111
HF3501
BRITISH BUSINESS. 1886-1989. w. (also avail. in microform from UMI; reprint service avail. from UMI) Oakfield House, Perrymount Rd., Haywards Heath, W. Sussex RH16 3DH, England.
Formerly: Trade and Industry (ISSN 0006-5323)

687 UK ISSN 0007-0467
BRITISH CLOTHING MANUFACTURER. 1965-1989. q. (also avail. in microform from UMI; reprint service avail. from UMI) International Thomson Business Publishing, 100 Avenue Rd., Swiss Cottage, London NW3 3TP, England.

630 338.91 CN ISSN 0227-3802
BRITISH COLUMBIA. MINISTRY OF AGRICULTURE AND FOOD. AGRICULTURAL AID TO DEVELOPING COUNTRIES. 1972-19?? a. Ministry of Agriculture and Food, Publications Office, Parliament Bldgs., Victoria, B.C. V8W 2Z7, Canada.

350 CN ISSN 1180-0429
BRITISH COLUMBIA. PROVINCIAL GOVERNMENT. B C NEWS. 1953-1991; suspended. irreg. (6-8/yr.). (tabloid format) Provincial Government, Parliament Buildings, Victoria, B.C. V8V 1X4, Canada.
Former titles: British Columbia. Provincial Government. Provincial Report (ISSN 0829-7975); British Columbia Government News (ISSN 0007-0513)

340 CN
BRITISH COLUMBIA FAMILY LAW QUANTUM SERVICE. ceased 1991 (Feb.). q. (looseleaf format) Butterworths Canada Ltd., 75 Clegg Rd., Markham, Ont. L6G 1A1, Canada.

634.9 674.2 CN ISSN 0007-0548
HD9764.C4
BRITISH COLUMBIA LUMBERMAN; truck logging, saw milling, plywoods, general forestry (regional). 1917-19?? m. Journal of Commerce Ltd. (Subsidiary of: Southam Communications Ltd.), P.O.B. 82230, North Burnaby, B.C. V5C 6E7, Canada.

371 CN
BRITISH COLUMBIA TEACHERS' FEDERATION. EFFECTIVE BARGAINING COMMITTEE. INFORMATION REPORT; bargaining bulletin. 1981-1988. m. (looseleaf format) B.C. Teachers' Federation, 105-2235 Burrard St., Vancouver, B.C. V6J 3H9, Canada.
Incorporates (in 1982): British Columbia Teachers' Federation. Arguments Bulletin; British Columbia Teachers' Federation. Effective Teaching and Learning Conditions Committee. Information Report.

333.91 CN
BRITISH COLUMBIA WATER AND WASTE ASSOCIATION. PROCEEDINGS OF THE ANNUAL CONFERENCE. ceased. a. Department of Fisheries & Oceans, 200 Kent St., Ottawa, Ont. K1A 0E6, Canada.

001.64 621.381 UK
BRITISH COMPUTER SOCIETY. MICROFORM SPECIALIST GROUP. ANNUAL PROCEEDINGS. 1976-19?? a. British Computer Society, Microform Specialist Group, 13 Mansfield St., London W1M 0BP, England.

551.4 UK ISSN 0306-3380
CODEN: BGTBAH
BRITISH GEOMORPHOLOGICAL RESEARCH GROUP. TECHNICAL BULLETIN. 19??-19??; suspended. irreg. (2-3/yr.). (back issues avail.) Environmental Publications, c/o Prof. K.M. Clayton, School of Environmental Sciences, Univ. of East Anglia, Norwich NR4 7TJ, England.

798 UK
BRITISH HORSE SOCIETY DIARY. 19??-19?? ceased. a. British Horse Society, British Equestrian Centre, Stoneleigh, Kenilworth, Warks CV8 2LR, England.

610 UK
BRITISH JOURNAL OF ACCIDENT & EMERGENCY MEDICINE. 1983-1990 (Mar.). q. Media Publishing Co., Erith Business Centre, High Street, Erith, Kent DA8 1RT, England.
Formerly: A and E News.

615 619 UK ISSN 0144-8803
Discard
BRITISH JOURNAL OF PHARMACEUTICAL PRACTICE. 1979-1991 (vol.13,no.1). m. Medical Tribune UK Ltd., Tower House, Southampton St., London WC2E 7LS, England.

020 UK
BRITISH LIBRARY. SUBJECT AUTHORITY FICHE. ceased 1990. a.(plus bi-m and q. cums.). (microfiche) British Library, Bibliographic Services, 2 Sheraton St., London W1V 4BH, England.

029 947 016 UK ISSN 0140-4113
BRITISH LIBRARY OF POLITICAL AND ECONOMIC SCIENCE. QUARTERLY LIST OF ADDITIONS IN RUSSIAN AND EAST EUROPEAN LANGUAGES. 1973-19?? q. (processed) British Library of Political and Economic Science, 10 Portugal St., London WC2A 2HD, England.

610 016 US ISSN 0140-2722
BRITISH MEDICINE. 1972-1990 (vol.19). m. (also avail. in microform from MIM,UMI) Pergamon Press, Inc., Journals Division, 660 White Plains Rd., Tarrytown, NY 10591-5153.
Formed by the merger of: British Medical Index (ISSN 0007-1439); British Medical Book List (ISSN 0007-1412)

574 550 UK ISSN 0068-2306
CODEN: BBMHAX
BRITISH MUSEUM (NATURAL HISTORY) BULLETIN. HISTORICAL. 1953-199? a. British Museum (Natural History), Cromwell Rd., London SW7 5BD, England.

676 UK
BRITISH PAPER. 1985-19?? 3/yr. (back issues avail.) (Association of Manufacturers of Printings & Writings) A.F.L. Deeson Publishing Ltd., Ewell House, Faversham, Kent ME13 8UP, England.

620.106 UK ISSN 0140-2145
BRITISH PUMP MANUFACTURERS ASSOCIATION. TECHNICAL CONFERENCE PROCEEDINGS. ceased 1989 (11th). irreg. B H R A Fluid Engineering, Cranfield, Bedford MK43 0AJ, England.

769.56 UK
BRITISH STAMP VALUES. 1979-198? a. Link House Magazines Ltd., Link House, Dingwall Ave., Croydon, Surrey CR9 2TA, England.

621.38 UK ISSN 0141-9471
BROADCAST ENGINEERING NOTES. 1978-19?? irreg. Independent Broadcasting Authority, Engineering Information Service, Crawley Ct., Winchester, Hants. SO21 2QA, England.

340 US
BRODER NEW YORK TORT REPORTER. ceased 1991. m. Shepard's - McGraw-Hill, Inc., Box 35300, Colorado Springs, CO 80935-3530.

635 US
BROMELIAD HOBBYIST. 1986-1987 (vol.2). 12/yr. Bromeliad Study Group of Northern California, 1334 S. Van Ness, San Francisco, CA 94110.

808.8 US ISSN 0732-9709
PS501
BROOKLYN COLLEGE ALUMNI LITERARY REVIEW. 1981-1985. s-a. (back issues avail.) Brooklyn College Alumni Association, 1234 Boylan Hall, Brooklyn, NY 11210.

821.8 US ISSN 0092-4725
PR4229
BROWNING INSTITUTE STUDIES. 1973-199? a. Browning Institute, Inc., Box 2983, Grand Central Sta., New York, NY 10163-2983.

053.1 GW ISSN 0007-2605
BRUECKE (NEUSTADT); Magazin fuer Jugend, Wirtschaft, Politik, Kultur, Unterhaltung, Mode, Sport. 1952-1982. m. Akademos-Verlag, Postfach 87, D-8632 Neustadt B. Coburg, W. Germany.

929 US
BRYAN NEWSLETTER. 1981-199? q. Box 1144, Enterprise, AL 36331.

929 US ISSN 0146-1990
CS71
BRYANT BACKTRAILS. 1977-1982. q. Kenma Publishing Co., Box 2786, Evansville, IN 47714-0786.

919 CJ
BUCCANEER; official in-flight magazine of Cayman Airways. ceased. m. (Cayman Airways) Northwester Company, Ltd., 1 Crewe Rd., P.O. Box 243, Georgetown, Grand Cayman, Cayman Islands, British, W.I.

658.8 GW
BUCHWOCHE. (Supplement avail.) 1834-1991. w. Fachbuchverlag GmbH, Karl-Heine-Str. 16, 7031 Leipzig, Germany.
Formerly (until 1990): Boersenblatt fuer den Deutschen Buchhandel (ISSN 0006-5641)

384 681.38 HU ISSN 0007-2907
CODEN: BUTRAR
BUDAVOX TELECOMMUNICATION REVIEW. (Supplement avail.: Budavox News) 1965-198? q. BUDAVOX Telecommunication Foreign Trading Company Ltd., Budafoki tu 79, H-1392 Budapest XI, Hungary.
Formerly: B H G Telecommunication Review.

622 PL ISSN 0239-9679
BUDOWNICTWO WEGLOWE. PROJEKTY - PROBLEMY. 1956-1989. m. (Wspolnota Wegla Kamiennego) Wydawnictwo "Slask", Ul. W. Korfantego 51, 40-161 Katowice, Poland.
Formerly: Projekty, Problemy, Budownictwo Weglowe.

574 AG ISSN 0068-340X
BUENOS AIRES. CENTRO DE INVESTIGACION DE BIOLOGIA MARINA. CONTRIBUCION CIENTIFICA. 1962-19?? irreg. Centro de Investigacion de Biologia Marina, Libertad 1235, Buenos Aires, Argentina.

CESSATIONS

633   AG   ISSN 0068-3418
BUENOS AIRES. INSTITUTO DE FITOTECNIA. BOLETIN INFORMATIVO. 1954-198?; suspended. irreg. Instituto Nacional de Tecnologia Agropecuaria, Centro de Investigaciones en Ciencias Agronomicas, Departamento de Genetica, Casilla de Correo No. 25, 1712 Castelar, Argentina.

382   SZ
BUERO UND VERKAUF. ceased 1989. m. Schweizerischer Kaufmaennischer Verband, Hans-Huber-Str. 4, Postfach 692, CH-8027 Zurich, Switzerland.

610   PR   ISSN 0045-3374
BUHITI. 1970-19?? q. Universidad de Puerto Rico, School of Medicine, Box 5067, San Juan, PR 00936.

720   US
BUILD YOUR DREAM HOME DESIGNS. 1990; suspended same year. 12/yr. Garlinghouse Company, Inc., 34 Industrial Park Pl., Box 1717, Middletown, CT 06457.

690   UK
BUILDERS' MERCHANTS INFORMATION SELECTOR. 1976-19?? 3/yr. B & M Publications (London) Ltd., P.O. Box 13, Hereford House, Bridle Path, Croydon CR9 4NL, England.

691   AT
BUILDING PRODUCTS INDEX (SYDNEY). 1988-19?? a. Peter Isaacson Publications Pty. Ltd., 45-50 Porter St., Prahran, Vic. 3181, Australia.

690   US
BUILDING PRODUCTS REPORT. 1990; ceased same year. m. (tabloid format) McGraw-Hill, Inc., 1221 Ave. of the Americas, New York, NY 10020.

690   SA
BUILDING PRODUCTS SELECTOR. ceased. 6/yr. Westbourne MacLean-Hunter (Pty) Ltd., P.O. Box 6110, Johannesburg, South Africa.

690   CN   ISSN 0826-595X
BUILDING RENOVATION. ceased. 6/yr. Maclean-Hunter Ltd., Business Publication Division, Maclean-Hunter Bldg., 777 Bay St., Toronto, Ont. M5W 1A7, Canada.

690   CN   ISSN 0007-361X
BUILDING RESEARCH NEWS. 1962-19??. 3/yr. National Research Council of Canada, Division of Building Research, Ottawa, Ont. K1A 0R6, Canada.

690   SA
BUILDINGS FOR HEALTH AND WELFARE SERVICES. ceased 1988 (Apr.). irreg. Council for Scientific and Industrial Research, Division of Building Technology, P.O. Box 395, Pretoria 0001, South Africa.

947   BU
BULGARIA IN FIGURES. 1983-1987. irreg. Bulgarian Chamber of Commerce and Industry, 11-a Al. Stamboliiski Blvd., Sofia, Bulgaria.
    Formerly (until 1987): Bulgarian Chamber of Commerce and Industry. Statistical Reference Book.

380.52 387   UK
BULK HANDLING & TRANSPORT. 1977-198? biennial. C.S. Publications Ltd., 54 Cheam Common Rd., Worcester Park, Surrey KT4 8RJ, England.

015   FR
BULLETIN BIBLIOGRAPHIQUE. ceased 1990 (May). bi-m. Ministere de l'Industrie, Bibliotheque Central, 101 rue de Grenelle, 75007 Paris, France.

667.6   BE
BULLETIN BIBLIOGRAPHIQUE DES LABORATOIRES PROFESSIONNELS FRANCAIS ET BELGE. 1952-19?? 11/yr. Industrie des Vernis, Peintures, Mastics, Encres d'Imprimerie et Couleurs d'Art, Laboratoire I. V.P., Ave. Pierre Holoffe, B-1342 Limelette, Belgium.
    Formerly: Digest des Revues Techniques (ISSN 0012-2718)

631.3 016   FR   ISSN 0007-4160
BULLETIN BIBLIOGRAPHIQUE INTERNATIONAL DU MACHINISME AGRICOLE/INTERNATIONAL FARM MACHINERY ABSTRACTS. (Includes: Quarterly Supplement - ISSN 0150-6544) 1966-1989. 11/yr. (International Commission of Agricultural Engineering) Centre National de Machinisme Agricole du Genie Rural, des Eaux et des Forets (CEMAGREF), Parc de Tourvoie, 92160 Antony, France.

633.1   FR
BULLETIN D'INFORMATION DES RIZICULTEURS DE FRANCE. ceased 1980 (no.183). q. Paysan du Midi, B.P.1098, 34007 Montpellier, France.

340   CS
BULLETIN DE DROIT TCHECOSLOVAQUE. 1925-19?? q. Jednota Ceskoslovenskych Pravniku, Nam. Curieovych 7, 116 40 Prague 1, Czechoslovakia.

870   NE
BULLETIN DU CANGE. 1924-1978 (vol.41). a. E. J. Brill, P.O. Box 9000, 2300 PA Leiden, Netherlands.

320   US   ISSN 0163-7789
BULLETIN EXTERIEUR. 1977-198? q. Mouvement Haitien de Liberation, c/o Haitian Information Center, 1218 Flatbush Ave., Brooklyn, NY 11226.
    Formerly: Bulletin pour l'Exterieur.

541.36 016   US   ISSN 0149-2268
QD511   CODEN: BCTHDA
BULLETIN OF CHEMICAL THERMODYNAMICS (1977). 1958-1990 (vol.28); suspended. a. (International Union of Pure and Applied Chemistry, Commission on Thermodynamics) Thermochemistry, Inc., Oklahoma State University, Department of Chemistry, Stillwater, OK 74078.
    Former titles (until 1976): Bulletin of Thermodynamics and Thermochemistry (ISSN 0068-4139); (until 1961): Bulletin of Chemical Thermodynamics; Which superseded: Thermochemical Bulletin and Bulletin of Unpublished Thermal Material.

297   UK   ISSN 0267-2669
BULLETIN OF ISLAMIC STUDIES. suspended. q. Muslim Institute, 6 Endsleigh, London WC1H 0DS, England.

780   US
BULLETIN OF RESEARCH IN MUSIC EDUCATION. 1969-1989. a. Pennsylvania Music Educators Association, Inc., 823 Old Westtown Rd., W. Chester, PA 19382.

020 001.3   US   ISSN 0160-0168
Z881
BULLETIN OF RESEARCH IN THE HUMANITIES. 1897-19?? (vol.87, no.4); suspended. 4/yr. New York Public Library, 5th Ave. at 42nd St., New York, NY 10018.
    Formerly (until vol.81, 1978): New York Public Library. Bulletin (ISSN 0028-7466)

591   UK   ISSN 0007-5167
CODEN: BZONAP
BULLETIN OF ZOOLOGICAL NOMENCLATURE. (Former name of issuing body: Commonwealth Agricultural Bureaux) 1943-19?? 4/yr. C.A.B. International, Commission on Zoological Nomenclature, Wallingford, Oxon OX10 8DE, England.

613.62 614.85   FR   ISSN 0759-9161
RC964
BULLETIN ON APPLIED RESEARCH FOR THE PROTECTION OF MAN AT WORK. 1983-1987. q. Institut National de Recherche et de Securite pour la Prevention des Accidents du Travail et des Maladies Professionnelles, 30 rue Olivier Noyer, 75680 Paris Cedex 14, France.

301   US   ISSN 0897-5809
BULLETIN ON THE 15 T F P S. 1982-199? 2/yr. American Society for the Defense of Tradition, Family and Property, Box 121, Pleasantville, NY 10570.
    Formerly: Bulletin on the T F P's.

371.9   US   ISSN 0731-5775
BULLETINS ON SCIENCE AND TECHNOLOGY FOR THE HANDICAPPED. 1980-1985. q. (back issues avail.; also avail. on tape) American Association for the Advancement of Science, Project on Science, Technology and Disability, 1333 H Street, N.W., Washington, DC 20005.

620.1   GW
BUNDESANSTALT FUER MATERIALFORSCHUNG UND -PRUEFUNG. AMTS- UND MITTEILUNGSBLATT. 1970-1988. q. Bundesanstalt fuer Materialforschung und -pruefung, Unter den Eichen 87, D-1000 Berlin 45, Germany.
    Formerly: Bundesanstalt fuer Materialpruefung. Amts- und Mitteilungsblatt (ISSN 0340-7551)

355   GW
BUNDESWEHR UND WIRTSCHAFT. 1987-19?? q. Media-Mail Verlagsgesellschaft mbH, Postfach 91 07 08, Laegenfeldstr. 8, 3003 Ronnenberg 3, Germany.

371.912   GW   ISSN 0007-5965
DAS BUNTE BLATT; Monatsschrift in einfacher Sprache. (Illustrated paper for deaf children) 1951-1990. m. Bund Deutscher Taubstummenlehrer, Eichendorffstr. 111, 8440 Straubing, Germany.

651   CN   ISSN 0007-604X
LE BUREAU. 1965-19?? 6/yr. Maclean-Hunter Ltd., Business Publication Division, Maclean-Hunter Bldg., 777 Bay St., Toronto, Ont. M5W 1A7, Canada.

001.6   FR   ISSN 0766-5229
BUREAU ET INFORMATIQUE; revue de l'actualite de l'informatique et de l'organisation du bureau. 1970-19??; suspended. bi-m. B.I. Magazine, 14, rue du Champ-de-Mars, 75007 Paris, France.

929   UK
BURKE'S ROYAL FAMILIES OF THE WORLD. VOL. 1: EUROPE AND LATIN AMERICA. 1977-199? irreg. Burke's Peerage, 46 Royal Ave., London SW3 4QF, England.

330   BD
BURUNDI. MINISTERE DE L'ECONOMIE ET DES FINANCES. BULLETIN ECONOMIQUE ET FINANCIER. 1977-1979 (vol.10). bi-m. Ministere de l'Economie et des Finances, B.P. 492-2790, Bujumbura, Burundi.

388.322   UK
BUS & COACH MANAGEMENT. ceased 1991. 6/yr. Trinity Publishing Ltd., Times House, Station Approach, Ruislip, Middx. HA4 8NB, England.

330   US   ISSN 0163-531X
HC108.A75   CODEN: BUSIDW
BUSINESS (ATLANTA); the magazine of managerial thought and action. 1951-1991 (Jan.). q. (also avail. in microform from UMI; back issues avail.) Georgia State University, College of Business Administration, GSU Business Press, University Plaza, Atlanta, GA 30303.
    Formerly (until 1979): Atlanta Economic Review (ISSN 0004-671X)

651.2   SA
BUSINESS & OFFICE EQUIPMENT SELECTOR. ceased. q. Selector Magazine Publications (Pty) Ltd. (Subsidiary of: Westbourne-MacLean Hunter (Pty) Ltd.), P.O. Box 6110, Johannesburg 2000, South Africa.

330   US   ISSN 0146-4744
BUSINESS ASSISTANCE MONOGRAPH SERIES. ceased. irreg. Federal Reserve Bank of Boston, Research Department, 600 Atlantic Ave., Boston, MA 02106.

330   US
BUSINESS BULLETIN. ceased. 8/yr. Prudential Publishing Co., 7089 Crystal Blvd., Diamond Springs, CA 95619.

658.8   CN
BUSINESS COMPUTER RESELLER NEWS. ceased. fortn. Moorshead Publications Ltd., 1300 Don Mills Rd., North York, Ont. M3B 3M8, Canada.

330 380.3   UK
BUSINESS COMPUTING & COMMUNICATIONS. 1983-198? m. Morgan-Grampian (Publishers) Ltd., 30 Calderwood St., London SE18 6QH, England.

330.9   US   ISSN 0146-7735
HC101
BUSINESS CONDITIONS DIGEST. 1961-1990 (Apr.). m. (also avail. in microform from MIM,KTO; reprint service avail. from UMI) U.S. Bureau of Economic Analysis, Statistical Indicators Division, U.S. Dept. of Commerce, Washington, DC 20230.
    Former titles (until 1971): Business Cycle Digest (ISSN 0007-6597); (until 1969): B.C.D. Business Cycle Development (ISSN 0093-6804)

001.64 US
BUSINESS DATA PROCESSING: A WILEY SERIES. 1971-1980. irreg., unnumbered. John Wiley & Sons, Inc., 605 Third Ave., New York, NY 10158-0012.

650.07 370 ISSN 0007-6686
BUSINESS EDUCATION JOURNAL. ceased. s-a. (Emporia State University, Division of Business and Business Education) Emporia State Press, 1200 Commercial St., Emporia, KS 66801.

651.2 US
BUSINESS ELECTRONICS DEALER. 1986-19?? m. Vance Publishing Corporation, 400 Knightsbridge Pkwy., Lincolnshire, IL 60069.

330.9 II
BUSINESS ENVIRONMENT. 19??-1987. w. Tata Economic Consultancy Services, Orient House, Mangalore Estate, Ballard Estate, Bombay 400038, India.

330 US ISSN 0889-6674
HC101 CODEN: BUEEEJ
BUSINESS EXECUTIVES' EXPECTATIONS. 1977-1990. q. Conference Board, Inc., 845 Third Ave., New York, NY 10022.

332.1 US
BUSINESS FORECASTS. ceased Sep. 1990. w. Weiss Research, Inc., Box 2923, W. Palm Beach, FL 33402.
Formerly: Weekly Bank Clearings.

330 US
BUSINESS INFORMATION FOR DALLAS. 1976-1984 (vol.7). irreg. Dallas Public Library, Business and Technology Division, 1515 Young St., Dallas, TX 75201.

020 UK ISSN 0951-9971
BUSINESS LIBRARY MANAGEMENT. 1987-1991. 8/yr. Headland Press, 1 Henry Smith's Terrace, Headland, Cleveland TS24 0PD, England.

332 US ISSN 0892-4090
HF1 CODEN: BUMOEL
BUSINESS MONTH. 1893-1990. m. (also avail. in microform from UMI,MIM; reprint service avail. from UMI) Goldhirsh Group, Inc., 38 Commercial Wharf, Boston, MA 02110.
Former titles (until 1987): Dun's Business Month (ISSN 0279-3040); Dun's Review (ISSN 0012-7175)

685 US
BUSINESS OF FUR; the magazine of fur retailing. 1983-1991. 11/yr. (reprint service avail.) Fur Publishing Plus, Inc., 19 W. 21st St., Ste. 403, New York, NY 10010.

330 CN
BUSINESS REVIEW. 1981-199? bi-m. (Saskatchewan Chamber of Commerce) Naylor Communications Ltd. (Winnipeg), 100 Sutherland Ave., Winnipeg, Man. R2W 3C7, Canada.

330.9 US ISSN 0895-4615
BUSINESS STARTS RECORD. ceased. a. Dun & Bradstreet, Economic Analysis Department, 299 Park Ave., New York, NY 10171.

336 US ISSN 0897-9979
KF6450.A15
BUSINESS TAX REPORT. 1988-1990 (Jun.). bi-w. Tax Management, Inc. (Subsidiary of: The Bureau of National Affairs, Inc.), 1231 25th St., N.W., Washington, DC 20037.

942 UK
BUSINESS TODAY. 1985-1988; suspended. m. (back issues avail.) Sheffield Chamber of Commerce & Manufacturers Inc., 33 Earl St., Sheffield S1 3FX, England.

910.09 US ISSN 1040-4635
BUSINESS TRAVELER'S NEWSLETTER. 1984-1989. m. (looseleaf format) Runzheimer International, Runzheimer Park, Rochester, WI 53167.

338 UK
BUSINESS WORLD. 1974-1990. w. Europress Ltd., 17 Ridgemont Rd., Bramhall, Cheshire, England.

621.381 US ISSN 0193-6832
BUSS; the independent newsletter of Heath/Zenith computers. 1977-198? 16/yr. Sextant Publishing Company, 716 E St., S.E., Washington, DC 20003.

929 US ISSN 0743-4235
BUTSON FAMILY NEWSLETTER. 1979-19? (no.10); suspended. a. c/o W. Wesley Johnston, Ed., 3140 Montevideo Dr., San Ramon, CA 94583-2630.

616.4 UK ISSN 0260-0072
CODEN: CLEYDQ
BUTTERWORTHS INTERNATIONAL MEDICAL REVIEWS: CLINICAL ENDOCRINOLOGY. 1982-199? a. (also avail. in microform from UMI; back issues avail.) Butterworth & Co. (Publishers) Ltd. (Subsidiary of: Reed International PLC), 88 Kingsway, London WC2B 6AB, England.

616.3 UK ISSN 0260-0110
CODEN: GASTDE
BUTTERWORTHS INTERNATIONAL MEDICAL REVIEWS: GASTROENTEROLOGY. 1981-199? a. (also avail. in microform from UMI; back issues avail.) Butterworth & Co. (Publishers) Ltd. (Subsidiary of: Reed International PLC), 88 Kingsway, London WC2B 6AB, England.

616.8 UK ISSN 0260-0137
CODEN: BMRNDK
BUTTERWORTHS INTERNATIONAL MEDICAL REVIEWS: NEUROLOGY. 1981-199? a. (also avail. in microform from UMI; back issues avail.) Butterworth & Co. (Publishers) Ltd. (Subsidiary of: Reed Imternational PLC), 88 Kingsway, London WC2B 6AB, England.

618 UK ISSN 0144-9478
BUTTERWORTHS INTERNATIONAL MEDICAL REVIEWS: OBSTETRICS AND GYNECOLOGY. 1981-199? a. (also avail. in microform from UMI; back issues avail.) Butterworth & Co. (Publishers) Ltd. (Subsidiary of: Reed International PLC), 88 Kingsway, London WC2B 6AB, England.

617.3 UK ISSN 0260-0153
BUTTERWORTHS INTERNATIONAL MEDICAL REVIEWS: ORTHOPAEDICS. 1983-199? a. (also avail. in microform from UMI; back issues avail.) Butterworth & Co. (Publishers) Ltd. (Subsidiary of: Reed International PLC), 88 Kingsway, London WC2B 6AB, England.

618.92 UK ISSN 0260-0161
CODEN: BIMPD7
BUTTERWORTHS INTERNATIONAL MEDICAL REVIEWS: PEDIATRICS. 1982-199? a. (also avail. in microform from UMI; back issues avail.) Butterworth & Co. (Publishers) Ltd. (Subsidiary of: Reed International PLC), 88 Kingsway, London WC2B 6 AB, England.

340 UK ISSN 0269-2805
BUTTERWORTHS TRADING LAW CASES. 1986-1989 (Dec.). bi-m. Butterworth & Co. (Publishers) Ltd., Borough Green, Sevenoaks, Kent TN15 8PH, England.

360 NE ISSN 0167-5303
BUUT. 1979-1988 (Dec.). 15/yr. Landelijke Organisatie voor Sociaal-Cultureel Werk Gamma, Postbus 14004, Utrecht 3508 SB, Netherlands.
Formerly: Attak (ISSN 0044-9962)

651.2 US
BUYING OFFICE PRODUCTS. 1988; ceased same year. m. Data Base Publications, 8310 Capital of Texas Hwy., Ste. 385, Austin, TX 78731.

809 US ISSN 0363-5236
BYE CADMOS; journal of aesthetic analogies. 1975-1987. s-a. American Institute for Writing Research, Corp., Box 1364, Grand Central Station, New York, NY 10163.

690 DK ISSN 0007-7488
BYGGE NYT. 1972-1981. 12/yr. Thomson Communications (Scandinavia) A-S, Struenseegade 7-9, DK-2200 Copenhagen N, Denmark.

690 DK ISSN 0007-7488
BYGGE NYTS LEVERANDOERREGISTER. ceased 1989. a. Thomson Communications (Scandinavia) A-S, Struenseegade 7-9, DK-2200 Copenhagen N, Denmark.

690 674 NO
BYGNINGSARBEIDEREN. ceased. m. (9/yr.). Norsk Bygningsindustriarbeiderforbund, Henrik Ibsens Gate 7, Oslo 1, Norway.

621.381 US
BYTE ENGINEERS. 1990; announced, never published. m. McGraw-Hill Information Services Co., Byte Publications, One Phoenix Mill Lane, Peterborough, NH 03458.

616 UR
BYULLETEN' SIGNAL'NOI INFORMATSII O ZHURNALE "LABORATORNOE DELO/BULLETIN OF CURRENT AWARENESS INFORMATION ON THE JOURNAL "LABORATORY TECHNIQUE". 1980-1989 (no.12). m. (Vsesoyuznoe Nauchnoe Obshchestvo Vrachei-Laborantov) Izdatel'stvo Meditsina, Petroverigskii pereulok 6-8, 101838 Moscow, Russian S.F.S.R., U.S.S.R.

367 US
C A A MAGAZINE. 1894-19?? q. Chicago Athletic Association, 12 S. Michigan Ave., Chicago, IL 60603.
Formerly (until 1980): Cherry Circle (ISSN 0009-3238)

636 UK
C.A.B. INTERNATIONAL. BUREAU OF ANIMAL BREEDING AND GENETICS. TECHNICAL COMMUNICATIONS. 1932-19?? irreg. C.A.B. International, Bureau of Animal Breeding and Genetics, Wallingford, Oxon OX10 8DE, England.
Formerly: Commonwealth Bureau of Animal Breeding and Genetics. Technical Communications (ISSN 0069-6919)

612.3 UK
C.A.B. INTERNATIONAL. BUREAU OF NUTRITION. TECHNICAL COMMUNICATIONS. 1939-19?? irreg. C.A.B. International, Bureau of Nutrition, Wallingford, Oxon OX10 8DE, England.
Formerly: Commonwealth Bureau of Nutrition. Technical Communications (ISSN 0069-6943)

633 UK
C.A.B. INTERNATIONAL. BUREAU OF PASTURES AND FIELD CROPS. BULLETIN. 1948-19?? irreg. C.A.B. International, Bureau of Pastures and Field Crops, Wallingford, Oxon OX10 8DE, England.
Formerly: Commonwealth Bureau of Pastures and Field Crops. Bulletin (ISSN 0069-701X)

631.4 UK
C.A.B. INTERNATIONAL. BUREAU OF SOILS. TECHNICAL COMMUNICATIONS. 1929-19?? irreg., no.55, 1975. C.A.B. International, Bureau of Soils, Wallingford, Oxon OX10 8DEN, England.
Formerly: Commonwealth Bureau of Soils. Technical Communications (ISSN 0069-7036)

634.9 UK
C.A.B. INTERNATIONAL. FORESTRY BUREAU. TECHNICAL COMMUNICATIONS. 1942-19?? irreg. C.A.B. International, Forestry Bureau, Wallingford, Oxon OX10 8DE, England.
ormerly: Commonwealth Forestry Bureau. Technical Communications (ISSN 0069-7060)

574 UK
C.A.B. INTERNATIONAL. INSTITUTE OF BIOLOGICAL CONTROL. TECHNICAL COMMUNICATIONS. 1960-19?? irreg. C.A.B. International, Institute of Biological Control, Wallingford, Oxon OX10 8DE, England.
Formerly: Commonwealth Institute of Biological Control. Technical Communications (ISSN 0069-7125)

020 UK ISSN 0954-9196
C A B L I S. (Current Awareness Bulletin for Library and Information Staff) 1974-1990. m. British Library, Research and Development Department, 2 Sheraton St., London W1, England.
Formerly: Current Awareness Bulletin for Librarians and Information Scientists (ISSN 0261-2992)

581 UK
C A B'S ANNUAL REPORT. 1976-19?? a. C.A.B. International, Mycological Institute, Wallingford, Oxon OX10 8DE, England.
Supersedes: Commonwealth Mycological Institute. Annual Review (ISSN 0140-4636)

CESSATIONS

001.644 US
C A D - C A M DIGEST. 1977-19?? m. C A D - C A M, Box 8100, Dallas, TX 75205.

001.6 629.8 US ISSN 0741-0042
C A D - C A M: MANAGEMENT STRATEGIES. (Computer Aided Design - Computer Aided Manufacturing) 1983-1988. a. (plus q. updates). (looseleaf format) Auerbach Publishers Inc. (Subsidiary of: Warren, Gorham & Lamont, Inc.), One Penn Plaza, New York, NY 10119.

658 352.7 US ISSN 0276-0428
C A I NEWS. 1973-1991 (vol.18, no.1). m. (back issues avail.) Community Association Institute, 1423 Powhatan St., Ste. 7, Alexandria, VA 22314.

338 AT
C A I NEWS BRIEFS. 1977-198? fortn. Confederation of Australian Industry, Industry House, National Circuit, Barton, A.C.T. 2600, Australia.
Formerly (until 1985): C A I News (ISSN 0155-2090); Formed by the merger of: Associated Chambers of Manufacturers of Australia. Industry News; Australian Council of Employers Federation. Economic Newsletter (ISSN 0310-3064)

001.6 621.381 GW ISSN 0179-7379
C A K. (Computer Anwendungen - Computer Applications - Universitaet Karlsruhe) 1986-1989. q. (back issues avail.) (Universitaet Karlsruhe) Friedr. Vieweg und Sohn Verlagsgesellschaft mbH, P.O. Box 5829, D-6200 Wiesbaden 1, Germany.

686.2 US
C A P INTERNATIONAL OUTLOOK. (Charles A. Pesko) ceased. bi-m. C A P International, Inc., One Longwater Circle, Norwell, MA 02061.

630 US ISSN 0271-7190
C A R D REPORT (AMES, 1971). 1971-19?? irreg. (3-4/yr.) Iowa State University, Center for Agricultural and Rural Development, Ames, IA 50010.
Formerly: C A E D Report (ISSN 0270-6091)

629.286 CN
C A T. (Canadian Automotive Training) ceased 1991 (Nov.). 6/yr. Wadham Publications Ltd., 1450 Don Mills Rd., Don Mills, Ont. M3B 2X7, Canada.

384.55 UK
C.A.T.S. REPORTS. 1973-1981. irreg. (back issues avail.) Centre for Advanced T V Studies, 42 Theobald's Rd., London WC18 XNW, England.
Supersedes (in 1980, vol.8): J C A T S (ISSN 0308-6801)

790 AT
C A T S TALES. 1966-19?? m. (Childrens Activities Time Society, Inc.) Catapult Press, 76 Boulton St., Dianella, W.A. 6062, Australia.

720 SP
C A U. (Construccion Arquitectura Urbanismo) 1970-1987. 6/yr. Colegio de Aparejadores y Arquitectos Tecnicos de Barcelona, Buen Pastor, 5, Barcelona-21, Spain.

352 US ISSN 0731-8758
HJ9013.N5
C B C QUARTERLY. 1981-1990 (vol.10, no.3). q. (back issues avail.) Citizens Budget Commission, 11 Penn Plaza, Ste. 900, New York, NY 10001-2006.

384.54 790.13 SP
C B FUNK MAGAZIN. 1978-19?? w. Alantas, Calle Gerona 20-22, 17480 Figueres, Spain.

621.38 US ISSN 0007-795X
C B MAGAZINE. 1964-1982. m. (also avail. in microform from UMI) Robb and Associates, 2778 Industrial Blvd. Ste.101, Norman, OK 73069.

690 016 II ISSN 0007-7968
C.B.R.I. ABSTRACTS. 1964-19?? s-a. Central Building Research Institute, Roorkee, Uttar Pradesh, India.

070 US ISSN 0362-3238
PN4888.T4
C B S NEWS INDEX. 1975-1987. q. (with a. cum.). (Dataflow Systems, Inc.) University Microfilms International, Research Collections, c/o James Ritchey, Ed., 300 N. Zeeb Rd., Ann Arbor, MI 48106.

362 CN
C C B OUTLOOK (BRAILLE EDITION). ceased 1989. q. (Braille; also avail. in audio cassette; large print) Canadian Council of the Blind, Ste. 610, 220 Dundas St., London, Ont. N6A 1H3, Canada.

052 362 CN ISSN 0007-7984
HV1571
C C B OUTLOOK (LARGE PRINT EDITION); information for and by sightless Canadians. 1948-1989. q. (also avail. in Braille; audio cassette) Canadian Council of the Blind, P.O. Box 2310 Station D., Ottawa, Ont. K1P 5W5, Canada.

917.4 US
C C I ACTION. 1973-19?? w. New York Chamber of Commerce and Industry, Inc., 200 Madison Ave., New York, NY 10016-3989.

617.6 US
C D H A JOURNAL. 1985-1989 (vol.4, no.2). 4/yr. (also avail. in microform from UMI) (California Dental Hygienists Association) Adler Droz, Inc., 2081 Business Ctr. Dr. No. 290, Irvine, CA 92715-1128.
Formerly (until 1985): Dental Hygienist (ISSN 0045-9933)

658 GW
C D H KONTAKTER. ceased 1990. 8/yr. Wirtschaftsverband der Handelsvertreter und Handelsmakler Bergisch-Land, Islandufer 21, 5600 Wuppertal 1, Germany.

001.642 US
C D - I NEWS; issued monthly for the consumer electronics, entertainment, publishing, information and education industries. (Compact Disc Interactive) 1986-1989. m. (back issues avail.) Link Resources Corp. (Subsidiary of: Emerging Technologies Publications), 79 Fifth Ave., 12th Fl., New York, NY 10003.

001.642 621.381 US ISSN 0891-3188
C D - R O M REVIEW. (Compact Disc - Read Only Memory) 1986-1988 (Dec.). bi-m. I D G Communications (Peterborough), 80 Elm St., Peterborough, NH 03458.

384.54
ML156.9
C D REVIEW'S COMPACT DISC YEARBOOK. ceased. a. W G E Publishing, Inc. (Subsidiary of: International Data Group), Forest Rd., Hancock, NH 03449.
Formerly: Digital Audio and Compact Disc Review Yearbook (ISSN 1041-8342)

330.9 CK
C.E.D.E. COLECCION-DEBATES. 1980-1982. irreg. Universidad de los Andes, Centro de Estudios sobre Desarrollo Economico, Apdo. Aereo 4976, Bogota 3, Colombia.

330 CK
C E D E DOCUMENTOS DE TRABAJO. 1973-1986 (Nov., no.85). irreg. Universidad de los Andes, Centro de Estudios sobre Desarrollo Economico, Facultad de Economia, Apdo. Aereo 4976, Bogota, Colombia.

371.42 EI ISSN 0252-855X
C E D E F O P NEWS; vocational training in Europe. 1975-1991. 3/yr. European Centre for the Development of Vocational Training (CEDEFOP), Bundesallee 22, 1000 Berlin 15, Germany.
Former titles (until 1981): Vocational Training (ISSN 0378-5068); Vocational Training Information Bulletin.

621.38 CN ISSN 0008-3461
C E E. (Canadian Electronics Engineering) 1956-19?? 12/yr. (also avail. in microform from UMI; reprint service avail. from UMI) Maclean-Hunter Ltd., Business Publication Division, Maclean-Hunter Bldg., 777 Bay St., Toronto, Ont. M5W 1A7, Canada.

621.3 539.7 UK ISSN 0267-0372
C E G B ABSTRACTS. 1948-1989 (vol.5, no.5-6). m. Central Electricity Generating Board, 15 Newgate St., London EC1A 7AU, England.
Formerly (until 1984): C E G B Digest.

621.3 UK ISSN 0305-7194
TK1 CODEN: CEREDG
C E G B RESEARCH. 1974-198? (no.22). irreg. (approx. 2/yr.). (back issues avail.) Central Electricity Generating Board, Technology Planning and Research Division, Courtenay House, 18 Warwick Lane, London EC4P 4EB, England.

631.3 FR ISSN 0249-5686
C E M A G R E F NOUVELLES. 1965-1987. q. Centre National du Machinisme Agricole du Genie Rural, des Eaux et des Forets, Parc de Tourvoie, 92160 Antony, France.
Formerly: C N E E M A Nouvelles (ISSN 0007-8743)

282 301.4 CK
C E N P A F A L BULETIN. 1976-1977 (Dec.); suspended. q. Centro de Pastoral Familiar para America Latina, Avda. 28 No. 37-21, Apdo. Aereo No. 54569, Bogota, Colombia.

338 US
C E O NEWSLETTER. (Chief Executive Officer) 1982-1989 (Sep.). m. (back issues avail.) National Fluid Power Association, 333 N. Mayfair Rd., Milwaukee, WI 53222.
Formerly (until 1986): Fluid Power Manager.

410 US
C E T A BULLETIN. 1972-19?? irreg. Chinese-English Translation Assistance Group, 3910 Knowles Ave., Box 400, Kensington, MD 20895.

636 GW
C G KURIER. 1935-1988. q. Centralgenossenschaft fuer Viehverwertung e.G., Adenauerallee 18, 3000 Hannover 1, Germany.
Former titles: C G Information (ISSN 0007-8360); C G Monatsspiegel fuer Vieh und Fleisch.

001.642 US
C GAZETTE. ceased 1992. bi-m. Oakley Publishing Co., Box 70167, Eugene, OR 97401.

312 AT ISSN 0312-200X
C H O M I - DAS. (Clearing House on Migration Issues) 1975-1990 (July). q. Ecumenical Migration Centre, Attn: Sarah-Bassett, Librarian, 125 Leicester St., Fitzroy, Vic. 3065, Australia.

641.5 US ISSN 1040-5585
C I A O; the definitive Italian food newsletter. 1982-1991 (Sep.). 4/yr. (back issues avail.) (Cuisine International America & Overseas) C I A O, Ltd., 136 Sky-Hi Dr., W. Seneca, NY 14224.

382 US
C I B & T ANALYST; a non-partisan, strategic view of critical international business issues. 1985-1990. q. (Georgetown University, School of Business Administration) Center for International Business and Trade, 1242 35th St. N.W., Ste. 501, Washington, DC 20057.
Formerly (until 1987): N C E I S Trade Analyst.

026 UK
C I C R I S DIRECTORY. 1968-1989 (7th ed.). irreg. Cooperative Industrial and Commercial Reference and Information Service, Shepherds Bush Rd., London W6 7AT, England.
Formerly: C I C R I S Directory and Guide to Resources (ISSN 0069-9829)

621.32 AU ISSN 0252-9246
TH7700
C I E - JOURNAL. 1981-1989. s-a. (back issues avail.) Commission Internationale de l'Eclairage, Central Bureau, Kegelgasse 27, A-1030 Vienna, Austria.

664 GW ISSN 0340-2002
C.I.I.A. SYMPOSIA. (Commission Internationale des Industries Agricole et Alimentaires) published only once, 1974. irreg. Dr. Dietrich Steinkopff Verlag, Saalbaustr. 12, Postfach 11 1008, 6100 Darmstadt 11, Germany.

330 SP ISSN 0214-0446
C I M; revista de gestion de las nuevas tecnologias de produccion. (Computer Integrated Manufacturing) 1987-19?? 8/yr. Compania Espanola de Editoriales Tecnologicas Internacionales, S.A., Concepcion Arenal 5, 08027 Barcelona, Spain.

621 001.6 US ISSN 0745-9726
TJ153
C I M E. (Computers in Mechanical Engineering) 1983-1989 (vol.7). bi-m. (also avail. in microform from UMI; reprint service avail. from ISI) (American Society of Mechanical Engineers) Springer-Verlag, 175 Fifth Ave., New York, NY 10010.

633.1 633.15 MX ISSN 0304-5463
SB189
C I M M Y T REVIEW. 1975-19?? a. Centro Internacional de Mejoramiento de Maiz y Trigo, Londres 40, Apdo. Postal 6-641, Mexico 6, D.F., Mexico.

621.381 001.644 US
C I M TECHNOLOGY. (Computer Integrated Manufacturing) (Supplement to: Manufacturing Engineering Magazine) 1981-1988. q. (also avail. in microform from UMI) Society of Manufacturing Engineers, Computer and Automated Systems Association, One S M E Dr., Box 930, Dearborn, MI 48121.
Formerly: C A D - C A M Technology (ISSN 0737-660X)

658.4 001.5 US ISSN 0891-4044
C I O LETTER. (Chief Information Officer) 1987-198? m. Controlled Publishing & Marketing, Inc., 2811 Wilshire Blvd., Ste. 430, Santa Monica, CA 90403.

658 500 US
C I O MONTHLY. (Chief Information Officer) 1987; ceased same year. m. (back issues avail.) Macmillan Professional Journals, 30 Vreeland Rd., Florham Park, NJ 07932.

591 UK ISSN 0305-2729
C I P KEYS TO THE NEMATODE PARASITES OF VERTEBRATES. (Former name of issuing body: Commonwealth Agricultural Bureaux) 1974-19?? s-a. (back issues avail.) C.A.B. International, Institute of Parasitology, Wallingford, Oxon OX10 8DE, England.

352.7 US
C.I.P. NEWSLETTER. (Capital Improvement Project) ceased. s-m. Department of Business and Economic Development, Box 2359, Honolulu, HI 96804.

020 US ISSN 0162-492X
C L A S S FORUM. ceased 1991 (vol.13, no.2). m. Cooperative Library Agency for Systems and Services, 1415 Koll Circle, Ste. 101, San Jose, CA 95112-4698.

020 UK ISSN 0269-056X
C L W CONTENTS MONTHLY; contents of serials for the library and information professions. 1986-1989. m. College of Librarianship Wales, Library, Llanbadarn Fawr, Aberystwyth SY23 3AS, Wales.

011 UK
C L W LIBRARY CATALOGUE. 1981-1989. 11/yr. College of Librarianship Wales, Library, Llanbadarn Fawr, Aberystwyth SY23 3AS, Wales.

610 US ISSN 0007-862X
R11 CODEN: CMDIDE
C M D. (Current Medical Dialog) 1934-1975 (vol.42, no.3). m. Williams & Wilkins Co., 428 E. Preston St., Baltimore, MD 21202.

789.99 US
C M E ANNUAL REPORT. 1972-1991. a. (back issues avail.) Center for Music Experiment, Q-037, University of California, San Diego, La Jolla, CA 92093.

681.11 658.8 US
C M M A INDUSTRY UPDATE. ceased. q. Clock Manufacturers and Marketing Association, 710 E. Ogden, Ste. 113, Naperville, IL 60563.

770 US ISSN 0731-2377
TR640
C M P BULLETIN. 1982-19?? q. (back issues avail.) University of California, Riverside, California Museum of Photography, Riverside, CA 92521.

640.73 US
C N A: THE NUTRITION CONNECTION. 1989-1990. Consumers for Nutrition Action, Inc., 18 W. 25th St., Ste. 203, Baltimore, MD 21218.

610.73 US
C N R VOICE. (Center for Nursing Research) 1973-1989. q. Ohio State University, College of Nursing, Newton Hall, 1585 Neil Ave., Columbus, OH 43210.

178 UK ISSN 0260-6429
C O A D WORDS. 1980-1990. q. Churches Council on Alcohol and Drugs, 1 Stockwell Green, London SW9 9HP, England.
Supersedes: Fact Finder (ISSN 0425-5860); Focus (Drink and Gambling) (ISSN 0071-6308)

378 US
C O E EVENTS. 1971-19?? bi-w. Memphis State University, College of Education, Room 302, Memphis, TN 38152.
Supersedes (in 1980): B E R S Newsletter.

020 001.539 US ISSN 0198-8840
T58.64
C O I N T REPORTS; a multidisciplinary approach. (Communication and Information Technology) 1980-198?; suspended. q. (back issues avail.) Info Digest, 9302 Parkside, Box 165, Morton Grove, IL 60053.

621.381 US ISSN 0093-8270
TK7874
C O S - M O S DIGITAL INTEGRATED CIRCUITS. ceased. irreg. Radio Corporation of America, Solid State Division, Box 3200, Somerville, NJ 08876.

620 US
C P I EQUIPMENT REPORTER. 1987-1988. q. (tabloid format) McGraw-Hill, Inc., 1221 Ave. of the Americas, New York, NY 10020.

400 GW ISSN 0007-8921
C P S REPORTER. (Cultural - Political - Scientific) 1956-19?? 11/yr. (tabloid format) Beacon-Verlag Koerber oHG, Birkental 13, Postfach 1420, 6702 Bad Duerkheim, Germany.

332.6 US
C R B OUTLOOK. ceased. m. Commodity Research Bureau, 100 Church St., Ste. 1850, New York, NY 10007.

630 UK
C R I NEWS. 1978-1988. 2/yr. Cranfield Rural Institute, Silsoe, Bedford MK45 4DT, England.
Former titles: Silsoe College News; (until 1984): National College of Agricultural Engineering News (ISSN 0144-6991)

618 376 US
C S E C NEWSLETTER. 1974-1990 (vol.6, no.1). q. (back issues avail.) (Cesareans, Support, Education and Concern) C S E C, Inc., 22 Forest Rd., Framingham, MA 01701.

350 US
C S G BACKGROUNDER. 1982-199? irreg. Council of State Governments, Iron Works Pike, Box 11910, Lexington, KY 40578-9989.

500 600 AT ISSN 0069-7192
C S I R O FILM CATALOGUE. ceased. irreg. Commonwealth Scientific and Industrial Research Organization, 314 Albert St., E. Melbourne, Vic. 3002, Australia.

500 600 016 SA ISSN 0301-6145
Z7403
C S I R PUBLICATIONS/W N N R PUBLIKASIES; list of publications arising from work undertaken or supported by C S I R. 1951-1989 (no.63). s-a. Council for Scientific and Industrial Research, Division of Information Services, P.O. Box 395, Pretoria 0001, South Africa.
Supersedes: C S I R Research Review (ISSN 0007-9162)

943.7 CS ISSN 0303-2221
DB215.6
C S S R. KRONIKA VNITROPOLITICKYCH UDALOSTI. 1970-1988; suspended. a. Nakladatelstvi Svoboda, Na Florenci 3-1420, Nove Mesto, 113 03 Prague 1, Czechoslovakia.

334.2 US
C U I S RESOURCES. (Credit Union Information Service) (Supplement to: Credit Union Information Service) 1973-19?? m. United Communications Group, 11300 Rockville Pike, Ste. 1100, Rockville, MD 20852-3030.

338.91 CN ISSN 0821-1272
HC59.69
C U S O JOURNAL. 1983-19??: suspended. a. C U S O, 135 Rideau St., Ottawa, Ont. K1N 9K7, Canada.

331.1 US ISSN 1042-3672
AP2
C V: THE COLLEGE MAGAZINE. 1989-1990 (Dec.). 5/yr. (back issues avail.) CareerVision, Inc., 215 Park Ave. S., New York, NY 10010.

266 US
C W S CONNECTIONS. 1984-198? bi-m. (National Council of the Churches of Christ) Church World Service, Office of C S W Communications, 475 Riverside Dr., Rm. 620, New York, NY 10115.

797.124 CN
C Y A NEWSLETTER. 1979-19?? q. (tabloid format) Canadian Yachting Association, 333 River Rd., Ottawa, Ont. K1L 8B9, Canada.

821 820 UK
CABARET 246. 1983-1989 (no.10). 3/yr. (back issues avail.) Red Sharks Press, 122 Clive St., Grangetown, Cardiff CF1 7JE, Wales.

028.5 US
CABBAGE PATCH KIDS. ceased 1988. q. Butterick Co., Inc., 161 Ave. of the Americas, New York, NY 10013.

684.1 US
CABINET MANUFACTURING & FABRICATING. 1987-1992 (Feb.). 10/yr. (tabloid format) K B C Publications, Inc., Two University Plaza, Hackensack, NJ 07601.
Formerly: Cabinet Manufacturing and Fabricating Today.

384.55 658 US ISSN 0279-8891
HE8700.7.C6
CABLE MARKETING; management magazine for cable television executives. 1981-1990. m. Associated Cable Enterprises, Inc., 352 Park Ave. S., New York, NY 10010.

384.55 US
CABLE REPORTS. ceased. m. Cable Television Information Center, 397 Herndon Pkwy., Ste. 25, Herndon, VA 22070.

621.388 384 US ISSN 0745-2802
TK6675
CABLE T V BUSINESS; business magazine for the cable television industry. 1963-1991. s-m. (also avail. in microform from UMI; reprint service avail. from UMI) Cardiff Publishing Co., 6300 S. Syracuse Way, Ste. 650, Englewood, CO 80111.
Former titles (1976-1982): T V C (ISSN 0164-8489); (1964-1971): T V Communications (ISSN 0039-8519); T V; Communications.

384.55 US ISSN 0363-1915
HE8700.7.C6
CABLEFILE; the standard reference for the cable television industry. 1976-1991. a. Cable Publishing Group, 600 S. Cherry St., Ste. 400, Denver, CO 80222.

796.77 790.13 SP
CABRIO. 1980-19?? w. Alantas, Calle Gerona 20-22, 17480 Figueres, Spain.

808.8 US ISSN 0734-8428
CACHE REVIEW. 1982-1991 (vol.6, no.1). a. Cache Press, Box 19794, Seattle, WA 98109-6794.

301.412 PO
CADERNOS CONDICAO FEMININA. 1975-198? irreg. Comissao para a Igualdade e Direitos das Mulheres, Av. da Republica, 32, 2 Esq, 1093 Lisbon Codex, Portugal.

CESSATIONS

981   BL
CADERNOS DE ESTUDOS BRASILEIROS. 1972-1980 (no.10). irreg. Universidade Federal do Rio de Janeiro, Forum de Ciencia e Cultura, Av. Pasteur 250, Praia Vermelha, Rio de Janeiro, Brazil.

301.35 301.364   BL   ISSN 0304-2669
CADERNOS DE ESTUDOS RURAIS E URBANOS. 1968-1986 (N.S. no.2). a. Centro de Estudos Rurais e Urbanos, Cidade Unversitaria, Caixa Postal 8105, Sao Paulo, Brazil.

615.1   FR   ISSN 0007-9715
CAHIERS DE BIBLIOGRAPHIE THERAPEUTIQUE FRANCAISE. EDITION MEDICALE. (Supplement to: Dictionnaire Vidal) 1962-1991 (Oct.). 10/yr. (Centre d'Etudes de Documentation et de Recherches) Editions du Vidal, 11, rue Quentin Bauchart, 75384 Paris Cedex 8, France.

320   BE   ISSN 0575-0571
CAHIERS DE BRUGES/BRUGES QUARTERLY. 1951-1991. irreg. (reprint service avail. from KTO) (College d'Europe) Uitgeverij de Tempel, 41 Tempelhof, Bruges, Belgium.

841   FR   ISSN 0032-1974
CAHIERS DE LITTERATURE ET DE POESIE: POETES ET LEURS AMIS. 1963-1990 (Apr.). q. 7 rue des Wallons, 75013 Paris, France.

333.77   BE   ISSN 0575-0970
CAHIERS DU SART TILMAN. 1963-19?? irreg. Universite de Liege, Batiment B 12, 4000 Sart-Tilman, Liege, Belgium.

800 900   CN   ISSN 0708-6431
LES CAHIERS NICOLETAINS. 1979-1990 (vol.12, no.4). q. Societe d'Histoire Regionale de Nicolet, 2705 du Fleuve-Ouest, R.R. 1, Nicolet, Que. JOG 1E0, Canada.

574.524 616.96   FR   ISSN 0029-7224
                                CODEN: CAOEA4
CAHIERS O R S T O M SERIE ENTOMOLOGIE MEDICALE ET PARASITOLOGIE. 1963-1987 (vol.25, no.4). q. (back issues avail.) O R S T O M, Institut Francais de Recherche Scientifique pour le Developpement en Cooperation, 70-74 Route d'Aulnay, 93143 Bondy cedex, France.

841   FR
CAHIERS SAINT-JOHN PERSE. 1978-1990; suspended. a. (back issues avail.) Fondation St.-John Perse, Hotel de Ville, 1316 Aix-en-Provence, France.

840   SZ
CAHIERS SUISSES ROMAIN ROLLAND. 1977; ceased same year. irreg. (reprint service avail. from UMI) Editions de la Baconniere S.A., P.O. Box 185, CH-2017 Boudry, Switzerland.

681.14 001.6   US   ISSN 0164-7830
CALCULATORS - COMPUTERS MAGAZINE. 1977-19?? 7/yr. (back issues avail.) Dymax, Box 310, 1010 Doyle No. 9, Menlo Park, CA 94025.

301.412   CN
CALENDHER. 1983-19?? m. (tabloid format) (Web Collective) On the Go Marketing Inc., 100 Wellesley St. E., Toronto, Ont. M4Y 1H5, Canada.
   Formerly (until 1990): Web.

914.1   UK   ISSN 0307-2029
CALGACUS; the Scottish review of politics, current affairs, history and the arts. ceased 1976. q. (back issue avail.) West Highland Publishing Co. Ltd., Breakish, Isle of Skye 1V42 8PY, Scotland.

051   CN   ISSN 0707-4409
CALGARY MAGAZINE. 1978-1988 (Dec.). m. Telemedia West Publishing, 240-1509 Center St., Calgary, Alta. T2G 2E6, Canada.

338.4   US
CALGON AIR - WATER REPORT. 1969-19?? q. (processed) Calgon Corporation, Calgon Center, Box 1346, Pittsburgh, PA 15230.
   Formerly: Calgon Water Report.

364   US   ISSN 0093-8912
KFC1102
CALIFORNIA. COUNCIL ON CRIMINAL JUSTICE. COMPREHENSIVE PLAN FOR CRIMINAL JUSTICE. ceased. a. Office of Criminal Justice Planning, 1130 K St., Ste. 300, Sacramento, CA 95814.

051   US   ISSN 0279-3768
F869.L8
CALIFORNIA (LOS ANGELES). 1976-1991. m. (also avail. in microfiche from UMI; back issues avail.; reprint service avail. from UMI) California Magazine, Inc., 11601 Wilshire Blvd., Ste. 1800, Los Angeles, CA 90025.
   Formerly (until 1983): New West (ISSN 0362-1146)

070.5   US   ISSN 0198-8433
CALIFORNIA ACADEMIC LIBRARIES LIST OF SERIALS. 1976-1989. biennial. (microfiche) University of California, Division of Library Automation, Kaiser Bldg., 8th Fl., 300 Lakeside Dr., Oakland, CA 94612-3550.

620   US
CALIFORNIA INSTITUTE OF TECHNOLOGY. DIVISION OF ENGINEERING AND APPLIED SCIENCE. RESEARCH REPORT. 1953-19?? biennial. California Institute of Technology, Division of Engineering and Applied Science, Mail Code 104-44, Pasadena, CA 91125.
   Former titles: California Institute of Technology. Division of Engineering and Applied Science. Annual Report; California Institute of Technology. Division of Engineering and Applied Science. Report of Research and Other Activities (ISSN 0068-5658)

647.9   US
CALIFORNIA LODGING INDUSTRY. 1983-1990. a. Laventhol & Horwath, 1845 Walnut St., Philadelphia, PA 19103.

635   US
CALIFORNIA RARE FRUIT GROWERS. ANNUAL JOURNAL. ceased. a. California Rare Fruit Growers, Inc., c/o Dianne M. Hand, 9233 Dorrington Place, Arleta, CA 91331.

635   US
CALIFORNIA RARE FRUIT GROWERS. ANNUAL YEARBOOK. ceased. a. California Rare Fruit Growers, Inc., c/o Dianne M. Hand, 9233 Dorrington Place, Arleta, CA 91331.

647.9   US
CALIFORNIA RESTAURANT OPERATIONS. 1976-1990. a. Laventhol & Horwath, 1845 Walnut St., Philadelphia, PA 19103.

285
CALLED OUT; a journal devoted to building the local church. 1982-1990 (Fall). q. (back issues avail.) (Christian Fellowship) Cityhill Publishing, 4600 Christian Fellowship Rd., Columbia, MO 65203.

784.7   TR
CALYPSO. ceased. irreg. (Unique Services) Unique Services Printers & Publishers, 17 Cassia Ave., Pleasantville, San Fernando, Trinidad, W.I.

381   VE   ISSN 0008-1876
CAMARA DE COMERCIO DE LA GUAIRA. BOLETIN ESTADISTICO.. 1946-1988. a. Camara de Comercio de La Guaira, Edificio "Camara de Comercio", Plaza El Consul, piso 2, Maiquetia, Apdo. 150, La Guaira, Venezuela.

946   SP
CAMARA OFICIAL DE COMERCIO INFORMACION. ceased. m.(with supplements). Camara Oficial de Comercio, Industria y Navegacion de Bilbao, Rodriguez Arias, 6, Bilbao (Vizcaya), Spain.

791.43   GW   ISSN 0008-2066
CAMERA. 1963-1990. q. Bundesarchiv, Filmarchiv, Hausvogteiplatz 3-4, 1080 Berlin, Germany.

381   IT
CAMERA DI COMMERCIO, INDUSTRIA, ARTIGIANATO E AGRICOLTURA DI PADOVA. NOTIZIARIO ESTERO. suspended. irreg. Camera di Commercio, Industria, Artigianato e Agricoltura di Padova, Via E. Filiberto 34, Padua, Italy.

770   GR   ISSN 0259-8280
CAMERA INTERNATIONAL. 1985-1990. q. (back issues avail.) Moressopulos & Associates, 2, Cherefontos Str., GR-105 58 Athens, Greece.

369.4   US   ISSN 0092-1289
HS3353.C3
CAMP FIRE LEADERSHIP; a magazine for leaders of Camp Fire Starflight, Adventure, Discovery and Horizon Clubs. vol.52, 1973-1987. q. Camp Fire, Inc., 4601 Madison Ave., Kansas City, MO 64112-1278.
   Formerly: Camp Fire Girl (ISSN 0008-2287)

320   US   ISSN 0361-056X
KF4885.A15
CAMPAIGN PRACTICES REPORTS. 1974-1991 (Sept.). 24/yr. (back issues avail.) Congressional Quarterly Inc., 1414 22nd St., N.W., Washington, DC 20037.

790.13   FR   ISSN 0220-2425
CAMPOS. ceased. bi-m. Publications Guy Hachette, La Petite Motte Senille, 86100 Chatellerault, France.

378.198   US
CAMPUS U S A. 1987-1990. q. Collegiate Marketing & Communications, Inc., 1801 Rockville Pike, Rockville, MD 20852-1633.

619   CN
CANADA. AGRICULTURE CANADA. ANIMAL RESEARCH CENTRE. RESEARCH REPORT. 1964-1989. a. Agriculture Canada, Animal Research Centre, Ottawa, Ont. K1A OC6, Canada.
   Formerly: Canada. Agriculture Canada. Animal Research Institute. Research Report (ISSN 0066-1899)

338.2   CN
CANADA. DEPARTMENT OF ENERGY, MINES AND RESOURCES. CANADA OIL AND GAS LANDS ADMINISTRATION ANNUAL REPORT (YEAR). 1965-1991. a. (tabloid format) Department of Energy, Mines and Resources, Canada Oil and Gas Lands Administration, 355 River Road, Ottawa, Ont. K1A 0E4, Canada.
   Formerly: Canada. Department of Indian and Northern Affairs. Oil and Gas Land and Exploration Section. Oil and Gas Activities. North of 60.

354.71 310   CN
CANADA. DEPARTMENT OF FISHERIES AND OCEANS. COMMUNICATIONS DIRECTORATE. STATISTICS ON SALES OF SPORT FISHING LICENCES IN CANADA. 1971-1972. a. Department of Fisheries and Oceans, Communications Directorate, 200 Kent St., 14th floor, Ottawa, Ont. K1A OE6, Canada.
   Formerly: Canada. Fisheries and Marine Service. Recreational Fisheries Branch. Statistics on Sales of Sport Fishing Licences in Canada.

338.2   CN
CANADA. DEPARTMENT OF INDIAN AFFAIRS AND NORTHERN DEVELOPMENT. MINES AND MINERALS STATISTICS: CLAIMS ACTIVITIES. 1967-1988. m. Department of Indian Affairs and Northern Development, Mining Resources Section, Les Terrasses de la Chaudiere, Ottawa, Ont. K1A 0H4, Canada.
   Former titles: Canada. Department of Indian Affairs and Northern Development. Mines and Minerals Statistics: North of 60; Canada. Northern Economic Development Branch. Mining Section. Mining Statistics: North of 60.

361.6 016   CN
CANADA. DEPARTMENT OF NATIONAL HEALTH AND WELFARE. LIBRARY. ACQUISITIONS. 1947-1985. irreg. Department of National Health and Welfare., Library, Ottawa, Ont., Canada.

634.9   CN   ISSN 0228-9989
CANADA. ENVIRONMENT CANADA. FORESTRY SERVICE RESEARCH NOTES. 1981-1984. q. Environment Canada, Department Canada, 351 St. Joseph Blvd., Ottawa, Ont. K1A 1C7, Canada.
   Supersedes: Canada. Forestry Service. Bi-Monthly Research Notes (ISSN 0317-6908); **Formerly:** Canada. Department of Fisheries and Forestry. Bi-Monthly Research Notes (ISSN 0008-2643)

333.7   CN   ISSN 0840-4666
CANADA. ENVIRONMENT CANADA. SUSTAINABLE DEVELOPMENT. 1980-1991 (vol.12, no.1). 3/yr. (back issues avail.) Environment Canada, Corporate Policy Group, Place Vincent Massey, Ottawa, Ont. K1A 0H3, Canada.
   Formerly (until vol.9, no.1): Canada. Environment Canada. Land (ISSN 0707-9850)

CESSATIONS

363.6   CN
CANADA. FISHERIES AND ENVIRONMENT CANADA. OCCASIONAL PAPER. 1975-19?? irreg. Department of Fisheries & Oceans, 200 Kent St., Ottawa, Ont. K1A 0E6, Canada.

550 551.46   CN   ISSN 0706-2354
VK794
CANADA. HYDROGRAPHIC SERVICE. WATER LEVELS. VOL. 1: DAILY MEANS. 1962-1984. a. Department of Fisheries and Oceans, Information & Publications Branch, 200 Kent St., Ottawa, Ont. K1A 0E6, Canada.
Supersedes in part: Canada. Hydrographic Service. Water Levels (ISSN 0068-7669)

550 551.46   CN   ISSN 0706-2346
V794
CANADA. HYDROGRAPHIC SERVICE. WATER LEVELS. VOL. 2: TIDAL HIGHS AND LOWS. 1962-1984. a. Department of Fisheries and Oceans, Information & Publications Branch, 200 Kent St., Ottawa, Ont. K1A 0E6, Canada.
Supersedes in part: Canada. Hydrographic Service. Water Levels (ISSN 0068-7669)

352   CN   ISSN 0381-0976
CANADA. INFORMATION CANADA. MUNICIPAL REPORT. 1973-19?? m. Information Canada, P.O. Box 5738, Sta. F, Ottawa, Ont. K2C 3M1, Canada.

331   CN
CANADA. LABOUR CANADA. ANNUAL REVIEW - REVUE ANNUELLE. ceased 1990. a. (reprint service avail. from MML) Labour Canada, Publications Distribution, Ottawa, Ont. K1A 0J2, Canada.

574.92   CN   ISSN 0068-7995
QH91.A1   CODEN: NMBOB5
CANADA. NATIONAL MUSEUMS, OTTAWA. PUBLICATIONS IN BIOLOGICAL OCEANOGRAPHY. 1970-1982 (no.11). irreg. (National Museum of Natural Sciences) National Museums of Canada, Ottawa, Ont. K1A 0M8, Canada.

600   CN
CANADA. NATIONAL RESEARCH COUNCIL OF CANADA. PUBLICATIONS/CANADA. CONSEIL NATIONAL DE RECHERCHES. PUBLICATIONS. 1936-19??; suspended. irreg. (National Research Council of Canada - Conseil National de Recherches) C.I.S.T.I. Publicity and Communications, Ottawa, Ont. K1A 0S2, Canada.

634.9   CN   ISSN 0709-9959
CODEN: CFRTBW
CANADA. NORTHERN FORESTRY CENTRE. FORESTRY REPORT. 1971-19?? irreg. (back issues avail.; reprint service avail. from MML) Northern Forestry Centre, 5320-122 St., Edmonton, Alta. T6H 3S5, Canada.
Formerly: Canadian Forestry Service. Prairies Region. Forestry Report.

368   CN
CANADA. OFFICE OF THE SUPERINTENDENT OF FINANCIAL INSTITUTIONS. LIST OF SECURITIES. 1972-19?? a. Financial Institutions Canada, Office of the Superintendent, 255 Slater St., 13th Fl., Ottawa, Ont. K1A 0H2, Canada.
Formerly: Canada. Department of Insurance. List of Securities (ISSN 0380-1020)

623.82   CN   ISSN 0527-4834
CANADA. STATISTICS CANADA. BOATBUILDING AND REPAIR/CONSTRUCTION ET REPARATION D'EMBARCATIONS. (Catalogue 42-205) 1920-1980. a. (also avail. in microform from MML) Statistics Canada, Communications Division, 3rd Fl., R.H. Coats Bldg., Ottawa, Ont. K1A 0T6, Canada.

338.4   CN   ISSN 0527-4869
HD9397.C2
CANADA. STATISTICS CANADA. BREWERIES/BRASSERIES. (Catalog 32-205) 1919-1980. a. (also avail. in microform from MML) Statistics Canada, Communications Division, 3rd Fl., R.H. Coats Bldg., Ottawa, Ont. K1A 0T6, Canada.

312   CN   ISSN 0380-7533
RA407.5.C2
CANADA. STATISTICS CANADA. CAUSES OF DEATH, PROVINCES BY SEX AND CANADA BY SEX AND AGE. (Catalogue 84-203) 1965-1988. a. (also avail. in microform from MML) Statistics Canada, Communications Division, 3rd Fl., R.H. Coats Bldg., Ottawa, Ont. K1A 0T6, Canada.

338.4   CN   ISSN 0527-4915
CANADA. STATISTICS CANADA. COFFIN AND CASKET INDUSTRY/INDUSTRIE DES CERCEUILS. (Catalogue 35-210) 1960-1980. a. (also avail. in microform from MML) Statistics Canada, Communications Division, 3rd Fl., R.H. Coats Bldg., Ottawa, Ont. K1A 0T6, Canada.

338.4   CN   ISSN 0833-2002
HD9697.C333
CANADA. STATISTICS CANADA. COMMUNICATIONS AND ENERGY WIRE AND CABLE INDUSTRY. (Catalogue 43-209) 1960-19?? a. (also avail. in microform from MML) Statistics Canada, Communications Division, 3rd Floor, R.H. Coats Bldg., Ottawa, Ont. K1A 0T6, Canada.
Formerly: Canada. Statistics Canada. Manufacturers of Electric Wire and Cable - Fabricants de Fils et de Cables Electriques (ISSN 0527-5504)

338.4   CN   ISSN 0828-9824
HD9696.A3
CANADA. STATISTICS CANADA. COMMUNICATIONS AND OTHER ELECTRONIC INDUSTRIES. (Catalogue 43-206) 1960-19?? a. (also avail. in microform from MML) Statistics Canada, Communications Division, 3rd Floor, R.H. Coats Bldg., Ottawa, Ont. K1A 0T6, Canada.
Formerly: Canada. Statistics Canada. Communications Equipment Manufacturers - Fabricants d'Equipement de Telecommunication (ISSN 0527-494X)

236 317   CN   ISSN 0575-8254
HJ13
CANADA. STATISTICS CANADA. CONSOLIDATED GOVERNMENT FINANCE: FISCAL YEAR ENDED NEAREST TO DECEMBER 31. (Catalogue 68-202) 1954-1987. a. (also avail. in microform from MML) Statistics Canada, Communications Division, 3rd Floor, R.H. Coats Bldg., Ottawa, Ont. K1A 0T6, Canada.

381 663   CN   ISSN 0705-4319
HD9364.C3
CANADA. STATISTICS CANADA. CONTROL AND SALE OF ALCOHOLIC BEVERAGES IN CANADA. (Catalogue 63-202) 1928-19??; suspended. a. (also avail. in microform from MML) Statistics Canada, Publications Sales and Services, Ottawa, Ont. K1A 0T6, Canada.

677.7   CN   ISSN 0527-4990
HD9999
CANADA. STATISTICS CANADA. CORDAGE AND TWINE INDUSTRY/CORDERIE ET FICELLERIE (FABRICATION). (Catalogue 34-203) 1919-1980. a. (also avail. in microform from MML) Statistics Canada, Communications Division, 3rd Fl., R.H. Coats Bldg., Ottawa, Ont. K1A 0T6, Canada.

338.4   CN   ISSN 0527-5016
HD9884.C18
CANADA. STATISTICS CANADA. COTTON YARN AND CLOTH MILLS/FILATURE ET TISSAGE DU COTON. (Catalogue 34-205) 1918-1980. a. (also avail. in microform from MML) Statistics Canada, Communications Division, 3rd Fl., R.H. Coats Bldg., Ottawa, Ont. K1A 0T6, Canada.

378   CN   ISSN 0382-411X
CANADA. STATISTICS CANADA. EDUCATIONAL STAFF IN COMMUNITY COLLEGES/PERSONNEL D'ENSEIGNEMENT DES COLLEGES COMMUNAUTAIRES. (Catalog 81-227) 1970-197? a. Statistics Canada, Communication Division, 3rd Fl., R.H. Coats Bldg., Ottawa, Ont. K1A 0T6, Canada.
Formerly: Canada. Statistics Canada. Statistical Profiles of Educational Staff in Community Colleges (ISSN 0382-4128)

338.4   CN   ISSN 0384-4161
CANADA. STATISTICS CANADA. ELECTRIC LAMP AND SHADE MANUFACTURERS/INDUSTRIE DES LAMPES ELECTRIQUES ET DES ABAT-JOUR. (Catalogue 35-214) 1960-1980. a. (also avail. in microform from MML) Statistics Canada, Communications Division, 3rd Fl., R.H. Coats Bldg., Ottawa, Ont. K1A 0T6, Canada.

312   CN   ISSN 0708-7012
HA741
CANADA. STATISTICS CANADA. ESTIMATES OF POPULATION FOR CANADA AND THE PROVINCES - ESTIMATIONS DE LA POPULATION DU CANADA ET DES PROVINCES. (Catalog 91-201) 1922-1983. a. (also avail. in microform from MML) Statistics Canada, Communications Division, 3rd Floor, R.H. Coats Bldg., Ottawa, Ont. K1A 0T6, Canada.

338.1 317   CN   ISSN 0068-712X
HD1781
CANADA. STATISTICS CANADA. FARM NET INCOME. (Catalog 21-202) 1940-19?? a. (also avail. in microform from MML) Statistics Canada, Communications Division, 3rd Floor, R.H. Coats Bldg., Ottawa, Ont. K1A 0T6, Canada.

331.7   CN   ISSN 0575-8491
JL105
CANADA. STATISTICS CANADA. FEDERAL GOVERNMENT EMPLOYMENT. (Catalog 72-004) 1952-1989. q. (also avail. in microform from MML) Statistics Canada, Communications Division, 3rd Floor, R.H. Coats Bldg., Ottawa, Ont. K1A 0T6, Canada.

351 317   CN   ISSN 0527-5148
JL105
CANADA. STATISTICS CANADA. FEDERAL GOVERNMENT EMPLOYMENT IN METROPOLITAN AREAS. (Catalogue 72-205) 1968-1988. a. (also avail. in microform from MML) Statistics Canada, Communications Division, 3rd Fl., R.H. Coats Bldg., Ottawa, Ont. K1A 0T6, Canada.

336 317   CN   ISSN 0575-8521
HJ13
CANADA. STATISTICS CANADA. FEDERAL GOVERNMENT FINANCE: REVENUE AND EXPENDITURE, ASSETS AND LIABILITIES. (Catalogue 68-211) 1953-1989. a. (also avail. in microform from MML) Statistics Canada, Communications Division, 3rd Floor, R.H. Coats Bldg., Ottawa, Ont. K1A 0T6, Canada.

687.2   CN   ISSN 0384-2967
HD9969.U6
CANADA. STATISTICS CANADA. FOUNDATION GARMENT INDUSTRY/INDUSTRIE DES CORSETS ET SOUTIENS-GORGE. (Catalogue 34-212) 1920-1980. a. (also avail. in microform from MML) Statistics Canada, Communications Division, 3rd Floor, R.H. Coats Bldg., Ottawa, Ont. K1A 0T6, Canada.

364.1   CN   ISSN 0825-432X
HV6535.C3
CANADA. STATISTICS CANADA. HOMICIDE IN CANADA: A STATISTICAL PERSPECTIVE. (Catalog 85-209) 1961-1988. a. (also avail. in microform from MML) Statistics Canada, Communications Division, 3rd Fl., R.H. Coats Bldg., Ottawa, Ont. K1A 0T6, Canada.
Former titles: Canada. Statistics Canada. Homicide Statistics (ISSN 0706-2788); Canada. Statistics Canada. Murder Statistics (ISSN 0575-917X)

690   CN   ISSN 0319-8278
HD9715.C3
CANADA. STATISTICS CANADA. HOUSING STARTS AND COMPLETIONS. (Catalogue 64-002) 1946-1990. m. (also avail. in microform from MML) Statistics Canada, Communications Division, 3rd Floor, R.H. Coats Bldg., Ottawa, Ont. K1A 0T6, Canada.

687.3   CN   ISSN 0384-3343
CANADA. STATISTICS CANADA. KNITTING MILLS - BONNETERIE. (Catalogue 34-215) 1918-1980. a. (also avail. in microform from MML) Statistics Canada, Communications Division, 3rd Fl., R.H. Coats Bldg., Ottawa, Ont. K1A 0T6, Canada.

338.4   CN   ISSN 0384-3300
CANADA. STATISTICS CANADA. LEATHER GLOVE FACTORIES/FABRIQUES DE GANTS EN CUIR. (Catalogue 33-204) 1924-197? a. Statistics Canada, Communications Division, 3rd Fl., R.H. Coats Bldg., Ottawa, Ont. K1A 0T6, Canada.

362.1   CN   ISSN 0831-7313
RA978.C2
CANADA. STATISTICS CANADA. LIST OF CANADIAN HOSPITALS. (Catalogue 83-201) 1942-1988. a. (also avail. in microform from MML) Statistics Canada, Communications Division, 3rd Fl., R.H. Coats Bldg., Ottawa, Ont. K1A 0T6, Canada.

CESSATIONS

Former titles: Canada. Statistics Canada. List of Canadian Hospitals and Special Care Facilities (ISSN 0225-5642); Canada. Statistics Canada. Hospitals Section. List of Canadian Hospitals and Related Institutions and Facilities (ISSN 0319-8014)

336.71   CN   ISSN 0703-2749
HJ9014
CANADA. STATISTICS CANADA. LOCAL GOVERNMENT FINANCE: REVENUE AND EXPENDITURE, ASSETS AND LIABILITIES, ACTUAL. (Catalogue 68-204) 1944-1988. a. (also avail. in microform from MML) Statistics Canada, Communications Division, 3rd Fl., R.H. Coats Bldg., Ottawa, Ont. K1A 0T6, Canada.

338.4   CN   ISSN 0527-5539
HD9655.C2
CANADA. STATISTICS CANADA. MANUFACTURERS OF INDUSTRIAL CHEMICALS/FABRICANTS DE PRODUITS CHIMIQUES INDUSTRIELS. (Catalog 46-219) 1960-1980. a. (also avail. in microform from MML) Statistics Canada, Communications Division, 3rd Fl., R.H. Coats Bldg., Ottawa, Ont. K1A 0T6, Canada.

338.4   CN   ISSN 0384-3912
HD9999.S9
CANADA. STATISTICS CANADA. MANUFACTURERS OF SOAP AND CLEANING COMPOUNDS/FABRICANTS DE SAVON ET DE PRODUITS DE NETTOYAGE. (Catalog 46-214) 1918-1980. a. (also avail. in microform from MML) Statistics Canada, Communications Division, 3rd Fl., R.H. Coats Bldg., Ottawa, Ont. K1A 0T6, Canada.

338.2   CN   ISSN 0382-4020
HD9660.P7
CANADA. STATISTICS CANADA. MANUFACTURING INDUSTRIES DIVISION. POTASH MINES/MINES DE POTASSE. (Catalog 26-222) 1974-197? a. Statistics Canada, Communications Division, 3rd Fl., R.H. Coats Bldg., Ottawa, Ont. K1A 0T6, Canada.

338.4   CN   ISSN 0384-4811
HD9780.C2
CANADA. STATISTICS CANADA. MISCELLANEOUS LEATHER PRODUCTS MANUFACTURERS/FABRICANTS D'ARTICLES DIVERS EN CUIR. (Catalogue 33-205) 1920-1980. a. (also avail. in microform from MML) Statistics Canada, Communications Division, 3rd Fl., R.H. Coats Bldg., Ottawa, Ont. K1A 0T6, Canada.

338   CN   ISSN 0527-5822
CANADA. STATISTICS CANADA. MOTOR VEHICLE, PART 1, RATES AND REGULATIONS/VEHICULES A MOTEUR, PARTIE 1, CHARGES FISCALES ET REGLEMENTATION. (Catalogue 53-217) 1960-19?? a. Statistics Canada, Communications Division, 3rd Fl., R.H. Coats Bldg., Ottawa, Ont. K1A 0T6, Canada.

388.3   CN   ISSN 0527-5849
CANADA. STATISTICS CANADA. MOTOR VEHICLE, PART 4, REVENUES/VEHICULES A MOTEUR, PARTIE 4, RECETTES. (Catalogue 53-220) 1960-19?? a. Statistics Canada, Communications Division, 3rd Fl., R.H. Coats Bldg., Ottawa, Ont. K1A 0T6, Canada.

388   CN   ISSN 0527-5865
CANADA. STATISTICS CANADA. MOTOR VEHICLE TRAFFIC ACCIDENTS/ACCIDENTS DE LA CIRCULATION ROUTIERE. (Catalogue 53-206) 1952-1975. a. Statistics Canada, Communications Division, 3rd Fl., R.H. Coats Bldg., Ottawa, Ont. K1A 0T6, Canada.

338.4   CN   ISSN 0384-4080
CANADA. STATISTICS CANADA. OFFICE FURNITURE MANUFACTURERS/INDUSTRIE DES MEUBLES DE BUREAU. (Catalogue 35-212) 1960-1980. a. (also avail. in microform from MML) Statistics Canada, Communications Division, 3rd Fl., R.H. Coats Bldg., Ottawa, Ont. K1A 0T6, Canada.

350   CN   ISSN 0825-9224
JL198
CANADA. STATISTICS CANADA. PROVINCIAL AND TERRITORIAL GOVERNMENT EMPLOYMENT/EMPLOI DANS LES ADMINISTRATIONS PROVINCIALES ET TERRITORIALES. (Catalogue 72-007) 1959-1989. q. (also avail. in microform from MML) Statistics Canada, Communications Division, 3rd Fl., R.H. Coats Bldg., Ottawa, Ont. K1A 0T6, Canada.
Formerly: Canada. Statistics Canada. Provincial Government Employment (ISSN 0527-608X)

336 317   CN   ISSN 0710-1023
HJ13
CANADA. STATISTICS CANADA. PROVINCIAL GOVERNMENT FINANCE: ASSETS, LIABILITIES, SOURCE AND APPLICATION OF FUNDS. (Catalogue 68-209) 1950-1988. a. (also avail. in microform from MML) Statistics Canada, Communications Division, 3rd Floor, R.H. Coats Bldg., Ottawa, Ont. K1A 0T6, Canada.
Formerly: Canada. Statistics Canada. Provincial Government Finance: Assets, Liabilities, Sources and Uses of Funds (ISSN 0318-8876)

388   CN   ISSN 0706-3105
HE357
CANADA. STATISTICS CANADA. ROAD AND STREET LENGTH AND FINANCING/VOIES PUBLIQUES, LONGUEUR ET FINANCEMENT. (Catalogue 53-201) 1928-197? a. Statistics Canada, Communications Division, 3rd Fl., R.H. Coats Bldg., Ottawa, Ont. K1A 0T6, Canada.
Formerly: Canada. Statistics Canada. Road and Street Mileage and Expenditure - Voies Publiques: Longueur et Depenses (ISSN 0410-5869)

623.82   CN   ISSN 0527-6144
CANADA. STATISTICS CANADA. SHIPBUILDING AND REPAIR/CONSTRUCTION ET REPARATION DE NAVIRES. (Catalogue 42-206) 1937-1980. a. (also avail. in microform from MML) Statistics Canada, Communications Division, 3rd Fl., R.H. Coats Bldg., Ottawa, K1A 0T6, Canada.

387   CN   ISSN 0527-6160
CANADA. STATISTICS CANADA. SHIPPING STATISTICS/STATISTIQUES MARITIME. (Catalogue 54-002) 1957-197? m. Statistics Canada, Communications Division, 3rd Fl., R.H. Coats Bldg.., Ottawa, Ont. K1A 0T6, Canada.

338.4   CN   ISSN 0384-4951
HD9424.C2
CANADA. STATISTICS CANADA. SLAUGHTERING AND MEAT PROCESSORS/ABATTAGE ET CONDITIONNEMENT DE LA VIANDE. (Catalogue 32-221) 1917-1980. a. (also avail. in microform from MML) Statistics Canada, Communications Division, 3rd Fl., R.H. Coats Bldg., Ottawa, Ont. K1A 0T6, Canada.

664.9   CN   ISSN 0703-7333
CANADA. STATISTICS CANADA. STOCKS OF FROZEN MEAT PRODUCTS/STOCKS DE VIANDES CONGELEES. (Catalogue 32-012) 1934-1988. m. (also avail. in microform from MML) Statistics Canada, Communications Division, 3rd Floor, R.H. Coats Bldg., Ottawa, Ont. K1A 0T6, Canada.

614 617   CN   ISSN 0317-3720
RD27.3.C3
CANADA. STATISTICS CANADA. SURGICAL PROCEDURES AND TREATMENTS/INTERVENTIONS CHIRURGICALES ET TRAITEMENTS; a report on the surgical operations and non-surgical procedures performed on in-patients in Canadian hospitals - un rapport sur les interventions chirurgicales et les actes non chirurgicaux, effectues sur les malades hospitalises dans les hopitaux Canadiens. (Catalog 82-208) 1969-1987. a. (also avail. in microform from MML) Statistics Canada, Communications Division, 3rd Floor, R.H. Coats Bldg., Ottawa, Ont. K1A 0T6, Canada.

338.4   CN   ISSN 0300-0265
CANADA. STATISTICS CANADA. WOOL PRODUCTION AND SUPPLY. (Catalogue 23-205) 1939-1987. a. (also avail. in microform from MML) Statistics Canada, Communications Division, 3rd Fl., R.H. Coats Bldg., Ottawa, Ont. K1A 0T6, Canada.

327   CN   ISSN 0068-7685
F1029
CANADA IN WORLD AFFAIRS. ceased 1973 (vol.17). irreg. Canadian Institute of International Affairs, 15 King's College Circle, Toronto, Ont. M5S 2V9, Canada.

333.7   CN   ISSN 0068-7693
HD107
CANADA LAND INVENTORY. REPORT. 1965-19?? irreg. Environment Canada, Canadian Wildlife Service, 10th Floor P.V.M., Ottawa, Ont. K1A 0E7, Canada.

381   CN   ISSN 0384-9252
CANADA REPORT. 1970-1988. w. (looseleaf format; back issues avail.) Micro Media, 158 Pearl St., Toronto, Ont. M5H 1L3, Canada.

336   CN   ISSN 0712-6662
CANADA TAX LETTER. ceased. 6/yr. Richard De Boo Publishers, 81 Curlew Dr., Don Mills, Ont. M3A 3P7, Canada.

917   CN   ISSN 0709-9762
CANADA: TRAVEL INFORMATION. ceased. a. Tourism Canada, Publications, 4E - 235 Queen St., 4th Fl. East, Ottawa, Ont. K1A 0H6, Canada.

971 317   CN   ISSN 0068-8142
HA744
CANADA YEARBOOK. (Catalog 11-202) 1867-197? a. (also avail. in microfilm from MML) Statistics Canada, Communications Division, 3rd Floor, R.H. Coats Bldg., Ottawa, Ont. K1A 0T6, Canada.

330 658   CN
CANADIAN AUTOMOTIVE AFTERMARKET DIRECTORY - MARKETING GUIDE. ceased 1991 (Jun.). a. Wadham Publications Ltd., 1450 Don Mills Rd., Don Mills, Ont. M3B 2X7, Canada.

690 016   CN   ISSN 0008-3089
TA1
CANADIAN BUILDING ABSTRACTS. 1960-1986. 3/yr. National Research Council of Canada, Institute for Research in Construction, Ottawa, Ont. K1A 0R6, Canada.

690   CN   ISSN 0045-4508
CANADIAN BUILDING NEWS. 1937-1989. s-a. Canadian Gypsum Co. Ltd., Box 4034, Terminal A, Toronto, Ont. M5W 1K8, Canada.

346.066   CN
CANADIAN BUSINESS LAW NEWSLETTER. 1987-1990. 10/yr. Carswell Publications, 2330 Midland Ave., Aginourt, Ont. M1S 1P7, Canada.

799   CN   ISSN 0834-325X
CANADIAN CAMPING. ceased. q. (back issues avail.) Canadian Camping Association, 1806 Avenue Rd., Toronto, Ont. M5M 3Z1, Canada.

540   CN
CANADIAN CHEMICAL INDUSTRY: A CORPUS SURVEY. 1986-198? irreg. Corpus Information Services, Division of Southam Business Information & Communications Group Inc., 1450 Don Mills Road, Don Mills, Ont. M3B 2X7, Canada.

742   CN
CANADIAN CIRCUMPOLAR LIBRARY. MISCELLANEOUS PUBLICATIONS. 1969-1984. irreg. Canadian Circumpolar Library, University of Alberta, Edmonton, Alta. T6G 2E9, Canada.
Formerly: Boreal Institute, Edmonton. Miscellaneous Publications (ISSN 0068-029X)

350   CN
CANADIAN CO-OPERATIVE ASSOCIATION. WORKING PAPERS. 1986-19?? bi-m. Canadian Co-Operative Association, 510-119 44th Ave. S., Saskatoon, Sask. S7K 5X2, Canada.
Formerly: Co-Operative College of Canada. Working Papers.

621.38   CN
CANADIAN COMMUNICATIONS REPORTS. 1973-19?? s-m. Maclean-Hunter Ltd., Business Publication Division, Maclean-Hunter Bldg., 777 Bay St., Toronto, Ont. M5W 1A7, Canada.

780   CN
CANADIAN COMPOSERS SERIES. 1975-19?? irreg. University of Toronto Press, Front Campus, Toronto, Ont. M5S 1A6, Canada.

346.066   CN   ISSN 0835-9245
CANADIAN CORPORATE LAW REPORTER. 1987-1990 (Nov.). 6/yr. (looseleaf format; back issues avail.) Butterworths Canada Ltd., 75 Clegg Rd., Markham, Ont. L6G 1A1, Canada.

620   CN   ISSN 0008-3313
CANADIAN COUNCIL OF PROFESSIONAL ENGINEERS. NEWS BRIEF - COMMUNIQUE. 1958-1977 (vol.19). m. Canadian Council of Professional Engineers, 401-116 Albert St., Ottawa, Ont. K1P 5G3, Canada.
Formerly: Canadian Professional Engineer.

378 CN ISSN 0711-8635
LB2338
CANADIAN DIRECTORY OF AWARDS FOR GRADUATE STUDY (YEAR)/REPERTOIRE CANADIEN DES BOURSES D'ETUDES SUPERIEURES (YEAR). ceased. biennial. Association of Universities and Colleges of Canada, 151 Slater St., Ottawa, Ont. K1P 5N1, Canada.

792 CN ISSN 0317-9044
PR9191.2
CANADIAN DRAMA/ART DRAMATIQUE CANADIEN. 1975-1990. (vol.2, no.16). s-a. University of Guelph, Department of English, Guelph, Ont. N1G 2W1, Canada.

001.3 CN ISSN 0225-6932
CANADIAN FEDERATION FOR THE HUMANITIES. ANNUAL REPORT. 1945-1982. a. Canadian Federation for the Humanities, 151 Slater St., Ste. 407, Ottawa, Ont. K1P 5H3, Canada.
Formerly: Humanities Research Council of Canada. Report (ISSN 0073-3946)

791.43 CN ISSN 0705-2162
CANADIAN FEDERATION OF FILM SOCIETIES. NEWSLETTER. 1977-1990. q. Canadian Federation of Film Societies, P.O. Box 6536, Sta. "D", Calgary, Alta. T2P 2E1, Canada.

639.2 551.46 CN
CANADIAN FISHERMAN. 1914-19?? m. Sentinel Business Publications, 6420 Victoria Ave., Unit 8, Montreal, Que. H3W 2S7, Canada.
Former titles: Canadian Fisherman and Ocean Science; Canadian Fisherman (ISSN 0317-2023)

665.5 CN ISSN 0315-8233
HD9581.C3
CANADIAN GAS ASSOCIATION. MEMBERSHIP DIRECTORY. suspended 1989. a. Canadian Gas Association, 55 Scarsdale Rd., Don Mills, Ont. M3B 2R3, Canada.

929 CN ISSN 0707-3232
CS80
CANADIAN GENEALOGIST. 1979-1988 (vol.10, no.2). q. (back issues avail.) Generation Press, 172 King Henrys Blvd., Agincourt, Ont. M1T 2V6, Canada.

320 CN ISSN 0068-8835
CANADIAN GOVERNMENT SERIES. 1947-19?? irreg. University of Toronto Press, 63A St. George St., Toronto, Ont. M5S 1A6, Canada.

333.7 CN ISSN 0225-1485
CANADIAN HERITAGE. 1979-1990 (vol.15). 4/yr. Heritage Canada, P.O. Box 1358, Sta. B, Ottawa, Ont. K1P 5R4, Canada.
Supersedes: Heritage Canada (ISSN 0315-1298)

388.314 CN ISSN 0702-8733
CANADIAN HIGHWAY CARRIERS GUIDE. 1972-1988. a. Southam Business Information and Communications Group Inc., 450 Don Mills Rd., Don Mills, Ont. M3B 2X7, Canada.

658.91 CN
CANADIAN HOTEL & RESTAURANT (ANNUAL). 1923-19?? a. Maclean-Hunter Ltd., Business Publication Division, Maclean-Hunter Bldg., 777 Bay St., Toronto, Ont. M5W 1A7, Canada.
Formerly: Canadian Hotel and Restaurant's Product Hot Lines - Produits Vedettes.

323.4 CN ISSN 0828-7252
CANADIAN HUMAN RIGHTS ADVOCATE. (Includes quarterly supplement (which continues): Rights and Freedoms) 1972-1990 (vol.6, no.10). 10/yr. (also avail. in microfilm) R.R. 1, Maniwaki, Que. J9E 3A8, Canada.
Formerly (until 1986): Rights and Freedoms.

340 608.7 CN ISSN 0824-2623
KE2775.8
CANADIAN INTELLECTUAL PROPERTY REPORTS. 1983-199? (vol.27). 12/yr. (6 vols./yr.). Carswell Publications, 2330 Midland Ave., Agincourt, Ont. M1S 1P7, Canada.

371.3 410 CN ISSN 0045-4613
PE1068.C2
CANADIAN JOURNAL OF ENGLISH LANGUAGE ARTS. 1978-19?? 3/yr. Canadian Council of Teachers of English, P.O. Box 3382, Stn. "B", Calgary, Alta. T2M 4M1, Canada.
Formerly (until 1986): Highway One.

610.736 CN ISSN 0008-4247
CANADIAN JOURNAL OF PSYCHIATRIC NURSING. 1961-1991; suspended. q. (also avail. in microform from UMI; reprint service avail. from UMI) Psychiatric Nurses Association of Canada, 509 Pandora Ave. West, Winnipeg, Man. R2C 1M8, Canada.

368 CN
CANADIAN LIFE AND HEALTH INSURANCE ASSOCIATION. QUARTERLY REVIEW. 1985-1990 (vol.6, no.3). q. (back issues avail.) Canadian Life & Health Insurance Association, 20 Queen St., W., Ste. 2500, Toronto, Ont. M5H 3S2, Canada.
Formerly: Current Topics.

338 CN
CANADIAN MANUFACTURER. 1985-199? 10/yr. (tabloid format; back issues avail.) Canadian Manufacturer's Association, 1 Yonge St., Toronto, Ont. M5E 1J9, Canada.

636 664.9 CN
CANADIAN MEAT COUNCIL. FACTS, FIGURES, COMMENT. ceased 1989. s-m. Canadian Meat Council - Conseil des Viandes du Canada, 5233 Dundas St. W., Ste. 304, Islington, Ont. M9B 1A6, Canada.
Formerly: Meat Packers Council of Canada. Facts, Figures, Comment (ISSN 0047-6358)

338.2 622 CN ISSN 0068-9297
CANADIAN MINES REGISTER OF DORMANT AND DEFUNCT COMPANIES. 1960-19??; suspended. irreg. Northern Miner (Subsidiary of: Southam Business Communications, Inc.), 1450 Don Mills Rd., Don Mills, Ont. M3B 2X7, Canada.

338.2 622 CN ISSN 0068-9300
HD9506.C22
CANADIAN MINES REGISTER OF DORMANT AND DEFUNCT COMPANIES. SUPPLEMENT. 1966-19??; suspended. irreg. Northern Miner (Subsidiary of: Southam Business Communications, Inc.), 1450 Don Mills Rd., Don Mills, Ont. M3B 2X7, Canada.

340 622.8 CN
CANADIAN MINING LAW. ceased 1989 (no.66). q. (looseleaf format) Butterworths Canada Ltd., 75 Clegg Rd., Markham, Ont. L6G 1A1, Canada.

622 665.5 CN ISSN 0710-622X
HD9574.C2
CANADIAN OIL & GAS HANDBOOK. ceased 1991. a. Northern Miner (Subsidiary of: Southam Business Communications, Inc.), 1450 Don Mills Rd., Don Mills, Ont. M3B 2X7, Canada.

331.2 CN ISSN 0705-6680
CANADIAN PERSPECTIVE. 1976-1980. irreg. Association of Canadian Pension Management, 1075 Bay St., Ste. 730, Toronto, Ont. M5S 2B1, Canada.

665.5 CN ISSN 0008-4735
CODEN: CNPEAW
CANADIAN PETROLEUM. 1956-1989. m. Southam Business Communications Inc. (Subsidiary of: Southam Inc.), 1450 Don Mills Rd., Don Mills, Ont. M3B 2X7, Canada.

320 CN
CANADIAN POLITICAL SCIENCE ASSOCIATION. UPDATING THESES IN CANADIAN POLITICAL SCIENCE, COMPLETED AND IN PROGRESS. (Includes biennial supplements) 1970-1987. biennial. (back issues avail.) Canadian Political Science Association, 12 Henderson Ave., University of Ottawa, Ottawa, Ont. K1N 6N5, Canada.

386 CN ISSN 0068-9467
CANADIAN PORTS AND SEAWAYS DIRECTORY. 1934-1989. a. Southam Business Information Communications Group Inc., 1450 Don Mills Rd., Don Mills, Ont. M3B 2X7, Canada.

796.332 CN
CANADIAN PRO FOOTBALL. ceased. a. PaperJacks Ltd., 330 Steelcase Rd. E., Markham, Ont. L3R 2MI, Canada.

640.73 CN
CANADIAN PRODUCT LAW GUIDE. 1978-1991 (Nov.). m. C C H Canadian Ltd., 6 Garamond Ct., Don Mills, Ont. M3C 1Z5, Canada.
Formerly: Canadian Product Safety Guide.

CESSATIONS 5161

676 CN
CANADIAN PULP AND PAPER ASSOCIATION. WOODLANDS SECTION. PUBLICATIONS. 1927-19?? irreg. Canadian Pulp and Paper Association, Sun Life Bldg., 19th Fl., 1155 Metcalfe St., Montreal, Que. H3B 4T6, Canada.

380.5 790.1 CN ISSN 0847-9283
CANADIAN R V TRADE. 1989-19?? q. (back issues avail.) Formula Publications Ltd., 447 Speers Rd., Ste. 4, Oakville, Ont. L6K 3S7, Canada.

500 CN ISSN 0319-1974
Q180.C2 CODEN: CAREDM
CANADIAN RESEARCH. ceased. 8/yr. (also avail. in microform from UMI) Maclean-Hunter Ltd., Business Publication Division, Maclean-Hunter Bldg., 777 Bay St., Toronto, Ont. M5W 1A7, Canada.
Former titles: Canadian Research and Development (ISSN 0008-493X); Canadian Nuclear Technology.

651.3 CN ISSN 0709-5236
CANADIAN SECRETARY. (Supplement to: O E & M Office Equipment & Methods) ceased 1991. 4/yr. Maclean-Hunter Ltd., Business Publication Division, Maclean-Hunter Bldg., 777 Bay St., Toronto, Ont. M5W 1A7, Canada.

664 658 CN
CANADIAN SPECIALTY FOODS RETAILER. 1985-198? bi-m. (back issues avail.) Naef Publishing Inc., 106 Lakeshore Rd. E., Ste. 208, Port Credit, Ont. L5G 1E3, Canada.

370 016 CN
CANADIAN TEACHERS' FEDERATION. BIBLIOGRAPHIES IN EDUCATION. 1969-1987 (no.81). irreg. (also avail. in microform from UMI; reprint service avail. from UMI) Canadian Teachers' Federation, 110 Argyle Ave., Ottawa, Ont. K2P 1B4, Canada.

917 CN ISSN 0319-7093
CANADIAN TRAVEL NEWS WEEKLY. 1961-19??; suspended. w. Rodney Publications Ltd., P.O. Box 370, Stn. Q, Toronto, Ont. M4T 2M5, Canada.
Formerly: Canadian Travel News (ISSN 0045-5482)

388.324 CN
CANADIAN TRUCKERS' GUIDE. 1981-1991 (Jun.). a. (back issues avail.) Wadham Publications Ltd., 1450 Don Mills Rd., Don Mills, Ont M3B 2X7, Canada.

340 CN
CANADIAN UNEMPLOYMENT INSURANCE LEGISLATION. vol.8, 1984-19?? irreg. C C H Canadian Ltd., 6 Garamond Court, Don Mills, Ont. M3C 1Z5, Canada.

388.4 CN ISSN 0316-7933
HE4501
CANADIAN URBAN TRANSIT ASSOCIATION. PROCEEDINGS. 1973-19?? a. Canadian Urban Transit Association, 55 York St., Ste. 901, Toronto, Ont. M5J 1R7, Canada.
Formerly: Canadian Transit Association. Proceedings (ISSN 0316-7941)

616.99 US ISSN 0198-6473
RC261.A1 CODEN: CBRVDC
CANCER BIOLOGY REVIEWS. 1980-1982 (vol.3). irreg. Marcel Dekker, Inc., 270 Madison Ave., New York, NY 10016.

616.99 US
CANCER CALENDAR. 1979-198? m. Fox Chase Cancer Center, 7701 Burholme Ave., Philadelphia, PA 19111.

616.99 GW ISSN 0342-8893
CODEN: CCAMD9
CANCER CAMPAIGN. 1978-1991. irreg. Gustav Fischer Verlag, Wollgrasweg 49, Postfach 720143, 7000 Stuttgart 70, Germany.

616.994 US ISSN 0361-090X
RC268 CODEN: CDPRD4
CANCER DETECTION AND PREVENTION. 1976-19?? m. (also avail. in microfilm; reprint service avail. from ISI) Alan R. Liss, Inc., 41 E. 11th St., New York, NY 10003.

610 DK ISSN 0109-5668
RC261.A1 CODEN: CAREEN
CANCER REVIEWS. 1985-1988 (vol.12). bi-m. (back issues avail.) Munksgaard International Publishers Ltd., P.O. Box 2148, DK-1016 Copenhagen K, Denmark.

616.994 US ISSN 0361-5960
RC261 CODEN: CTRRDO
CANCER TREATMENT REPORTS. 1959-1987 (Dec.). m. (also avail. in microform from MIM,UMI,PMC) U.S. National Cancer Institute, Bethesda, MD 20892.
Formerly (until 1976): Cancer Chemotherapy Reports.

636 020.75 688 069 US ISSN 0748-9188
CANINE COLLECTORS COMPANION. 1985-1990. bi-m. R.L. Taylor, Ed. & Pub., 6305 S.W. Roundtree Ct., Portland, OR 97219.

378 CN ISSN 0711-4370
CANNON. ceased 1989. m. University of Toronto Engineering Society, Faculty of Applied Science and Engineering, 10 Kings College Rd., Rm. B670, Toronto, Ont. M5S 1A1, Canada.

811 US
CANVASS. 1979-1982? q. R. Kay Hejny, Ed. & Pub., 534 Richey Rd., Houston, TX 77090.

910.202 IT
CAORLESPIAGGIA. 1970-1990. w. (back issues avail.) Pubblistudio de Zorzi Casa Editrice s.r.l., Via Marinoni 53, Udine, Italy.

381 US
CAPITAL (DENVER, 1989). 1989; ceased same year. m. Denver Business Journal, 2401 15th St., Ste. 350, Denver, CO 80202.

339 US ISSN 0008-588X
CAPITAL GOODS REVIEW. 1950-1987. irreg. Machinery and Allied Products Institute (M A P I), 1200 18th St., N.W., Washington, DC 20036.

370 US ISSN 0272-8931
L11
CAPSTONE JOURNAL OF EDUCATION. 1980-1989 (vol.9, no.4). q. (also avail. in microform from UMI) University of Alabama, College of Education, Box 870231, Tuscaloosa, AL 35487-0231.

333.33 388.3 US
CAR CARE MALL NEWS. 1987-1990 (Oct.). q. (back issues avail.) Automotive Week Publishing Co., Box 3495, Wayne, NJ 07474-3495.
Formerly: Car Care Center News.

629.2 UK
CAR CHOICE. 1983-198? m. Car Choice Magazines, Sovereign House, Brentwood, Essex, England.

388.3 US ISSN 1045-7216
CAR CORRAL. 1989-1991 (Apr.). m. Krause Publications, Inc., 700 E. State St., Iola, WI 54990.

629.222 US
CAR SHOWS AND AUCTIONS. 1988-1990 (Dec.). q. Krause Publications, Inc., 700 E. State St., Iola, WI 54990.
Formerly: Old Cars Show (ISSN 0897-2842)

799.3 SZ ISSN 0008-6096
CARABINIER DE LAUSANNE. 1955-19?? 3/yr. Societe des Carabiniers de Lausanne, Case Postale 321, 1001 Lausanne, Switzerland.

055.1 IT
CARAVEL AMERICA. ceased 1989. m. Editorial Caravel, Via Ravizza 16, 20146 Milan, Italy.

669 US ISSN 0192-8333
TJ1186 CODEN: CTJOD9
CARBIDE AND TOOL JOURNAL. 1969-19?? bi-m. (reprint service avail.) C T E Publications Inc., 464 Central Ave., IL 60093.
Formerly: Carbide Journal (ISSN 0045-5733)

612.015 616.97 UK ISSN 0952-0309
CARBOHYDRATE ANTIGENS. ceased Dec., 1990. m. (looseleaf format; back issues avail.) Biomedical Information Service, The University, Sheffield S10 2TN, England.

612.3 612.015 UK ISSN 0142-8470
CARBOHYDRATE METABOLISM. ceased 1990. m. (looseleaf format; back issues avail.) Sheffield University Biomedical Information Service (SUBIS), The University, Sheffield S10 2TN, England.

610 US
CARDIAC IMPULSE. 1978-1989 (July). 6/yr. Matrix Communications, Inc., 7239 Lake St., River Forest, IL 60305-2238.

616.1 GW ISSN 0179-7166
CODEN: CANBES
CARDIOLOGISCH-ANGIOLOGISCHES BULLETIN. 1964-1990. q. Verlag fuer Medizin Dr. Ewald Fischer GmbH, Fritz-Frey-Str. 21, 6900 Heidelberg, Germany.
Formerly: Cardiologisches Bulletin (ISSN 0084-8603)

616.1 US
CARDIOLOGY PRODUCT NEWS. 1981-198? bi-m. (tabloid format) P W Communications, Inc., 400 Plaza Dr., Secaucus, NJ 07094.

616.1 US ISSN 0394-073X
CARDIOMYOLOGY. ceased. w. (University of Naples, Faculty of Medicine and Surgery) Idelson Scientific Publishers, Via Alcide De Gasperi, 55, 80133 Naples, Italy.

616.2 US
CARDIOPULMONARY NEWS AND INTERVIEWS. 1986-1990 (Dec.). q. (back issues avail.) American College of Chest Physicians, 911 Busse Hwy., Park Ridge, IL 60068.

616.858 UK
CARE MAGAZINE. 1973-19?? a. Care for Mentally Handicapped People, c/o T.S. Doggett, 9a Weir Rd., Kibworth, Leics. LE8 0LQ, England.

371.42 US
CAREER EDUCATION NEWS. vol.4, 1975-1991 (vol.15). s-m. (looseleaf format; back issues avail.) Diversified Learning, Inc., 72-300 Vallat Rd., Rancho Mirage, CA 92270.

387.164 HK
CARGONEWS YEARBOOK. 1987-19?? a. Far East Trade Press Ltd., Kai Tak Commercial Bldg., 2nd Fl., 317 Des Voeux Rd., Central, Hong Kong.

330 TR ISSN 0069-0481
CARIBBEAN ECONOMIC ALMANAC; a collection of economic and statistical data covering the Caribbean area. 1962-1964. irreg. Economic and Business Research Information and Advisory Service, P.O. Box 780, Port-of-Spain, Trinidad & Tobago, W.I.

917.203 015 GY
CARICOM BIBLIOGRAPHY. 1977-1986 (vol.10). s-a. Caribbean Community Secretariat, Information and Documentation Section, Bank of Guyana Bldg., Ave. of the Republic, Georgetown, Guyana.

658 610 US
CARING (ROCHESTER). 1975-1989. q. (back issues avail.) St. Mary's Hospital, 1216 Second St., S.W., Rochester, MN 55902.

574.192 DK ISSN 0105-1938
TP500 CODEN: CRCODS
CARLSBERG RESEARCH COMMUNICATIONS. 1878-1989 (vol.54, no.6). bi-m. (also avail. in microform from UMI; reprint service avail. from ISI) Carlsberg Laboratoriet, Gl. Carlsbergvej 8-10, 2500 Copenhagen (Valby), Denmark.
Formerly (until 1976): Laboratoire Carlsberg. Comptes Rendus des Travaux (ISSN 0008-6657)

327 US
CARNEGIE ENDOWMENT FOR INTERNATIONAL PEACE IN THE 1970'S. ceased. irreg. (reprint service avail. from UMI) Carnegie Endowment for International Peace, 2400 N St., N.W., Ste. 700, Washington, DC 20037.
Supersedes (in 1979): Carnegie Endowment for International Peace Report (ISSN 0069-0643); Which was formerly (until 1911): Carnegie Endowment for International Peace. Annual Report.

613.7 370 UK
CARNEGIE RESEARCH PAPERS. 1966-19?? s-a. (Carnegie School of Physical Education) Foster Print Group, 152 Canal Road, Bradford BD1 4SS, England.
Formerly: Research Papers in Physical Education (ISSN 0034-5350)

914 AU ISSN 0411-129X
CARNUNTUM JAHRBUCH. 1955-19?? a. Boehlau Verlag GmbH & Co.KG., Dr. Karl Lueger-Ring 12, Postfach 581, A-1011 Vienna, Austria.
Formerly: Roemische Forschungen in Niederoesterreich. Beiheft.

677 UK
CARPET MANUFACTURER INTERNATIONAL. 1966-198? s-a. World Textiles Publications, 76 Kirkgate, Bradford, W. Yorkshire BD1 1TB, England.
Incorporates (in 1985): Tufting Year Book (ISSN 0082-674X); Superseded: Skinner's Record Tufting Yearbook.

790.13 FR ISSN 0220-6137
CARROUSEL. ceased. bi-m. Publications Guy Hachette, La Petite Motte Senille, 86100 Chatellerault, France.

380.5 US
CARTEL. 1989; ceased same year. bi-w. Box 2291, Topeka, KS 66603.

382 BL ISSN 0019-9737
CARTERIA DE COMERCION EXTERIOR. INFORMACAO SEMANAL. 1966-1990 (Mar. no.1116). w. Banco do Brasil S.A., Carteria de Comercio Exterior, Avda. Rio Branco 65, Caixa Postal 1150, 20090 Rio de Janeiro, Brazil.

639.3 CN
CARTES DE PECHES DE CHALUTIERS QUEBECOIS. CAHIER SPECIAL D'INFORMATION. 1977-1981. irreg. Ministere de l'Agriculture, des Pecheries et de l'Alimentation, Bureau des Echanges, 96 Montee Sandy Beach, C.P. 1070, Gaspe, Que. G0C 1R0, Canada.

388.3 US
CARTOONS. 1959-1991. bi-m. Petersen Publishing Co., 8490 Sunset Blvd., Los Angeles, CA 90069.

737 UK
CARTWHEEL. 1964-1978. bi-m. Birmingham Numismatic Society, 17 Roughley Dr., Four Oaks, Sutton Coldfield, West Midlands, England.

333.33 SZ ISSN 1010-5786
CASA. 1972-1989 (vol.17, no.3). bi-m. SHZ-Forster Fachverlag AG, Alte Landstrasse 43, CH-8700 Kuesnacht, Switzerland.
Formerly: Stockwerk - Eigentum.

747 IT ISSN 0393-5140
CASARREDO MIDDLE EAST. 1977-19?? s-a. Editore RIMA s.r.l., Via Luigi Barzini 20, 20125 Milan, Italy.

619 US
CASE STUDIES IN EMERGENCY MEDICINE. 1985-1992. m. Aspen Publishers, Inc., 200 Orchard Ridge Dr., Gaithersburg, MD 20878.

341 US ISSN 0008-7254
JX1
CASE WESTERN RESERVE JOURNAL OF INTERNATIONAL LAW. 1968-1988. 3/yr. (also avail. in microfilm from RRI) Case Western Reserve University, School of Law, 11075 East Blvd., Cleveland, OH 44106.

320 UK
CASEBOOK SERIES ON EUROPEAN POLITICS AND SOCIETY. 1981-19?? irreg. (Harvard University, Center for European Studies) George Allen & Unwin (Publishers) Ltd., 40 Museum St., London WC1, England.

340 CN ISSN 0709-6968
CASES TO BE HEARD BY THE SUPREME COURT OF CANADA. 1976-19?? irreg. (4-5/yr.). (back issues avail.) Canadian Legal Information Centre, 161 Laurier Ave., West, 5th Fl., Ottawa, Ont. K1P 5J2, Canada.

330 DK ISSN 0107-5586
CASESAMLING. 1976-19?? a. Handelshoejskolen i Koebenhavn, Institut for Informatik og Oekonomistyring, Namrensgade 19, DK-1366 Copenhagen K, Denmark.

371.9 UK ISSN 0260-0544
CASTLE LODGE NEWS AND VIEWS. 1980-198? q. Castle Hill Hospital, Unit for Younger Disabled, c/o Mr. C. Bibby, Castle Lodge, Cottingham, North Humberside HU16 5JQ, England.

070.5 US
CATALOG BUSINESS. 1985-1990 (Aug.). bi-m. Mill Hollow Corporation, 19 W. 21st St., New York, NY 10010.

581 561.13 US ISSN 0148-642X
CODEN: CFPOA6
CATALOG OF FOSSIL SPORES AND POLLEN. 1957-1985 (vol.45); suspended. irreg. (looseleaf format; also avail. in cards) Pennsylvania State University, College of Earth & Mineral Sciences, Coal Research Section, 517 Deike Bldg., University Park, PA 16802.

658 US
CATALOG PRODUCT NEWS. 1988-199? q. (reprint service avail. from UMI) Cowles Business Media (Subsidiary of: Cowles Media Company), Six River Bend Center, 911 Hope St., Box 4949, Stamford, CT 06907-0949.

581 CK
CATALOGO ILUSTRADO DE LAS PLANTAS DE CUNDINAMARCA. 1966-1987. irreg. Universidad Nacional de Colombia, Instituto de Ciencias Naturales, Apdo. 7495, Bogota, Colombia.

629.13 II ISSN 0077-2968
CATALOGUE OF N A L TECHNICAL TRANSLATIONS. 1972-19?? a. (processed) National Aeronautical Laboratory, P.O. Box 1779, Kodihalli, Bangalore 560017, India.

791.43 PL
CATALOGUE OF POLISH FEATURE FILMS. ceased. biennial. Film Polski Ltd., Ul. Mazowiecka 6-8, 00-048 Warsaw, Poland.
  Formerly (until 1969): Polish Film Production.

617.7 US ISSN 0740-6967
CATARACT; INTERNATIONAL JOURNAL OF CATARACT SURGERY. 1983-1986. 8/yr. (back issues avail.) Park Row Publishers, 1457 Broadway, No. 901, New York, NY 10036.

282 979 US
CATHOLIC HERITAGE. 1988; ceased same year. bi-m. Box 02112, Portland, OR 97202.

282 US ISSN 0008-8331
HN51
CATHOLIC RURAL LIFE. 1922-19?? 5/yr. National Catholic Rural Life Conference, 4625 Beaver Ave., Des Moines, IA 50310.

020 IE
CATSNIPS. ceased 1980. q. Library Association of Ireland, Cataloguing and Indexing Group, 53 Upper Mount St., Dublin 2, Ireland.

305.412 800 AT
CAULDRON; feminist journal. 1974-1975 (vol.1, no.3). q. Cauldron Collective, 70 Midwera St., Villawood, N. S.W. 2163, Australia.

100 CK
CAUSA Y EFECTO; revista de filosofia. 1984-1985. bi-m. Estudiantes Universidad Nacional, Apdo. Aereo 14.490, Bogota, Colombia.

338 CJ
CAYMAN ISLANDS HANDBOOK AND BUSINESSMAN'S GUIDE. 1973-199? a. Northwester Company Ltd., Box 243, George Town, Grand Cayman, B.W.I.

918 CJ
CAYMAN ISLANDS HOLIDAY GUIDE. 1972-199? a. (Department of Tourism) Northwester Company Ltd., P.O. Box 243, George Town, Grand Cayman, British W.I.

917.2 CJ
CAYMAN ISLANDS NOR'WESTER. 1971-199? m. Northwester Company Ltd., Box 243, George Town, Grand Cayman, British West Indies.

333.33 CJ
CAYMAN ISLANDS REAL ESTATE REVIEW. 1977-1988. a. Cayman Free Press Ltd., Special Publications Division, Box 1365, Grand Cayman, Cayman Islands, British W.I.

051 US ISSN 0897-4381
CELEBRITY PLUS. 1987-198? m. (tabloid format; back issues avail.) Globe Communications Corp. (New York), 441 Lexington Ave., New York, NY 10017.
  Formerly: Celebrity Focus.

301.412 US ISSN 0735-4398
CELIBATE WOMAN; a journal for women who are celibate or considering this liberating way of relating to others. 1982-1988 (vol.4, no.2). irreg. (back issues avail.) Martha Allen, Ed. & Pub., 3306 Ross Place, N.W., Washington, DC 20008.

574 CC ISSN 1001-0602
CELL RESEARCH/XIBAO YANJIU. 1990; ceased after the trial issue. q. (Shanghai Xibao Shengwusuo) Kexue Chubanshe, Qikan Bu, 16 Donghuangchenggen Beijie, Beijing 100707, People's Republic of China.

574.192 NE
CELL SURFACE REVIEWS. 1976-1982 (vol.8). a. (back issues avail.) Elsevier Science Publishers B.V., P.O. Box 211, 1000 AE Amsterdam, Netherlands.

574.8 BE ISSN 0008-8757
CODEN: CELLA4
CELLULE; recueil de cytologie et d'histologie. 1884-1987 (no.74). irreg. (also avail. in microfilm from PMC) Editions Nauwelaerts S.A., Rue de l'Eglise St. Suplice 19, B-5998 Beauvechain, Belgium.

101 IT ISSN 0393-5442
B4
CENTAURO; rivista quadrimestrale di filosofia e teoria politica. 1981-1986. 3/yr. Guida Editori S.p.A., Via D. Morelli 16-B, 80121 Naples, Italy.

658 US
CENTER MANAGEMENT. 1990-1991 (Jan.). 8/yr. Engel Communications, Inc., 820 Bear Tavern Rd., W. Trenton, NJ 08628.

370 028.5 US
CENTER POINT. 1980-1990 (vol.10, no.1). q. (back issues avail.) Citizens Education Center, 310 First Ave. S., Ste. 330, Seattle, WA 98104-2536.

330 NE
CENTRAAL ORGAAN VOOR DE ECONOMISCHE BETREKKINGEN MET HET BUITENLAND. REPORT OF ACTIVITIES. ceased 1988. a. Centraal Orgaan voor de Economische Betrekkingen met het Buitenland, Prinses Beatrixlaan 5, 2595 Gravenhage, Netherlands.

322.4 327 US ISSN 0893-7699
CENTRAL AMERICA BULLETIN. 1981-1990 (vol.9, no.3). m. (back issues avail.) Central America Research Institute, Box 4797, Berkeley, CA 94704.
  Formerly (until 1984): El Salvador Bulletin (ISSN 0738-3223)

330.9 CE
CENTRAL BANK OF SRI LANKA, REVIEW OF THE ECONOMY/ARTHIKA VIVARANAYA. 1975-1988. a. Central Bank of Sri Lanka, Department of Economic Research, Director of Information, Janadhipathi Mawathi, Colombo 1, Sri Lanka.

100 US
CENTRAL ISSUES IN PHILOSOPHY SERIES. 1970-1987. irreg. Prentice Hall, Inc., Box 500, Englewood Cliffs, NJ 07632.

338.9 US ISSN 0069-1674
CENTRAL NAUGATUCK VALLEY REGIONAL PLANNING AGENCY. ANNUAL REPORT. 1960-19?? a. (processed) Central Naugatuck Valley Regional Planning Agency, 20 E. Main St., Waterbury, CT 06702.

782.1 US ISSN 0008-9508
ML27.U5
CENTRAL OPERA SERVICE BULLETIN. 1954-1990 (vol. 30). q. (back issues avail.) Metropolitan Opera National Council, Central Opera Service, Lincoln Center, New York, NY 10023.

625 385 PL
CENTRALNY OSRODEK BADAN I ROZWOJU TECHNIKI KOLEJNICTWA. PRACE. 1959-1991. irreg. (approx. 4-5/yr.). Wydawnictwa Komunikacji i Lacznosci, Kazimierzowska 52, Warsaw, Poland.

634.9 574.5 BE
CENTRE D'ECOLOGIE FORESTIERE ET RURALE. COMMUNICATIONS. 1943; N.S. no.56, 1988-19?? irreg. Centre d'Ecologie Forestiere et Rurale, Passage des Deportes no.2, B-5800 Gembloux, Belgium.
  Formerly: Centre de Cartographie Phytosociologique. Communications (ISSN 0069-1747)

CESSATIONS 5163

668.4 016 FR ISSN 0008-9702
CENTRE D'ETUDE DES MATIERES PLASTIQUES. BULLETIN DE DOCUMENTATION. 1964-198? m. (processed) Centre d'Etude des Matieres Plastiques, 65 rue de Prony, 75854 Paris Cedex 17, France.

070 FR ISSN 0008-9648
CENTRE DE FORMATION DES JOURNALISTES. FEUILLETS. 1953-1982. q. Centre de Formation des Journalistes, 29 rue du Louvre, 75002 Paris, France.

740 745.2 FR
CENTRE NATIONAL D'ART ET DE CULTURE GEORGES POMPIDOU. ANNUAIRE DES CONCEPTEURS. ceased 1979. a. Centre National d'Art et de Culture Georges Pompidou, Centre de Creation Industrielle, Centre Beaubourg, 75004 Paris, France.

913 016 BE ISSN 0069-1992
CENTRE NATIONAL DE RECHERCHES ARCHEOLOGIQUES EN BELGIQUE. REPERTOIRES ARCHEOLOGIQUES. SERIE A: REPERTOIRES BIBLIOGRAPHIQUES/ NATIONAAL CENTRUM VOOR OUDHEIDKUNDIGE NAVORSINGEN IN BELGIE. OUDHEIDKUNDIGE REPERTORIA. REEKS A: BIBLIOGRAFISCHE REPERTORIA. 1960-1989. irreg. (approx. a.). Centre National de Recherches Archeologiques en Belgique, 1 Parc du Cinquantenaire, 1040 Brussels, Belgium.

913 BE ISSN 0069-200X
CENTRE NATIONAL DE RECHERCHES ARCHEOLOGIQUES EN BELGIQUE. REPERTOIRES ARCHEOLOGIQUES. SERIE B: REPERTOIRES DES COLLECTIONS. 1965-1989. irreg. Centre National de Recherches Archeologiques en Belgique, 1 Parc du Cinquantenaire, 1040 Brussels, Belgium.

913 BE ISSN 0069-2018
CENTRE NATIONAL DE RECHERCHES ARCHEOLOGIQUES EN BELGIQUE. REPERTOIRES ARCHEOLOGIQUES. SERIE C: REPERTOIRES DIVERS. 1964-1989. irreg. Centre National de Recherches Archeologiques en Belgique, 1 Parc du Cinquantenaire, 1040 Brussels, Belgium.

200 NZ ISSN 0111-5308
CENTREPOINT. 1980-1991 (Mar.). q. (back issues avail.) Centrepoint Community Growth Trust, P.O. Box 35, Albany, Auckland, New Zealand.

621.8 US
CENTRIFUGAL PUMP SPEC BOOK. 1981-198? a. Gordon Publications, Inc., 301 Gibraltar Dr., Morris Plains, NJ 07950.

546 US
CENTRIFUGAL PUMP SPECIFICATIONS. 1981-198? a. (also avail. in magnetic tape; back issues avail.) Gordon Publications, Inc., Reference Book Group, 301 Gibraltar Dr., Morris Plains, NJ 07950.

338.1 551 SP ISSN 0210-8623
S542.S692 CODEN: AIOOD3
CENTRO DE EDAFOLOGIA Y BIOLOGIA APLICADA. ANUARIO. 1975-1989 (vol.14). a. (back issues avail.) Centro de Edafologia y Biologia Aplicada, Instituto de Recursos Naturales y Agrobiologia (C.S. I.C.), c/o Cordel de Merinas, 40-52, 37071 Salamanca, Spain.

330 CK
CENTRO DE ESTUDIOS SOBRE DESARROLLO ECONOMICO. CUADERNOS. 1982-1983. bi-m. Universidad de los Andes, Centro de Estudios sobre Desarrollo Economico, Apdo. Aereo 4976, Bogota, Colombia.
  Formerly: Centro de Estudios Sobre Desarrollo Economico. Estudios Laborales.

781.7 IE ISSN 0009-0174
CEOL; a journal of Irish music. 1963-1985. irreg. (also avail. in microfilm) Breandan Breathnach, Ed. & Pub., 47 Frascati Park, Blackrock, Dublin, Ireland.

666 US ISSN 0009-0247
CERAMIC SCOPE. 1964-1990. bi-m. (back issues avail.) 87 Wall St., 2nd Fl., Seattle, WA 98121-1330.

666 US
CERAMIC WORLD. 1971-1987. bi-m. Daisy Publishing Inc., 3824 Smith Ave., Everett, WA 98201.

CESSATIONS

913 572   US   ISSN 0577-3334
CERAMICA DE CULTURA MAYA. 1961-1988 (no.15). irreg. (back issues avail.) Ceramica De Cultura Maya, c/o Muriel Kirkpatrick, Coordinator, Laboratory of Anthropology, Temple University, Philadelphia, PA 19122.

616.8   US
CEREBRAL FUNCTION SYMPOSIUM. PROCEEDINGS. 1970-1972 (2nd). irreg. Charles C. Thomas, Publisher, 2600 S. First St., Springfield, IL 62794-9265.

791.4 384.5   CS   ISSN 0009-0735
CESKOSLOVENSKY ROZHLAS A TELEVIZE. vol.32, 1965-19?? w. Ceskoslovensky Rozhlas, Vinohradska 12, 120 99 Prague 2, Czechoslovakia.

794.1   CS   ISSN 0009-0743
CESKOSLOVENSKY SACH. 1906-1992. m. (Ceskoslovensky Svaz Telesne Vychovy) Olympia, Klimentska 1, 115 88 Prague 1, Czechoslovakia.

630   IS
CHADASHOT HA-CHAKLAUT. ceased 1991 (Mar.). w. Merav Publishing Industries Ltd., 6 Tushia St., Tel Aviv 67218, Israel.

663.94   JA   ISSN 0366-6123
CHAGYO GIJUTSU KENKYU/STUDY OF TEA. 1941-1987. s-a. National Research Institute of Vegetables, Ornamental Plants and Tea, 2769 Kanaya, Haibara, Shizuoka 428, Japan.

685.31 658.8   US   ISSN 0069-2387
HD9787.U4
CHAIN SHOE STORES AND LEASED SHOE DEPARTMENT OPERATORS. 1962-19?? a. Nickerson & Collins Co., Rumpf Publishing Division, 850 Busse Hwy., Park Ridge, IL 60068-5980.

658.870   US
CHAIN STORE AGE GENERAL MERCHANDISE TRENDS. 1925-1988 (Jan.). m. Lebhar-Friedman, Inc., 425 Park Ave., New York, NY 10022.
   Former titles: Chain Store Age General Merchandise Edition; 1976-1979: Chain Store Age General Merchandise Group (ISSN 0193-1350); 1975-1976: Chain Store Age: Newsmagazine for the General Merchandise Group; Which was formed by the merger of: Chain Store Age General Merchandise - Variety Executives Edition; Chain Store Age General Merchandise - Variety Store Edition.

370   US
CHALLENGE OF EXCELLENCE ANNUAL REPORT. ceased. a. Department of Education, Bureau of Publications, 721 Capitol Mall, Box 944272, Sacramento, CA 94244-2720.

200   US
CHALLENGE OF THE '80S UPDATE. ceased. q. Conservative Baptist Association of America, Box 66, Wheaton, IL 60189.
   Formerly: Conservative Baptist Association of America. Update.

623.8   SW   ISSN 0009-112X
CHALMERS TEKNISKA HOEGSKOLA. INSTITUTIONEN FOER SKEPPSHYDROMEKANIK. RAPPORT/CHALMERS UNIVERSITY OF TECHNOLOGY. DEPARTMENT OF SHIP HYDROMECHANICS. REPORT. 1959-1989. irreg. Chalmers Tekniska Hoegskola, Institutionen foer Skeppshydromekanik, Fack, S-412 96 Goeteborg, Sweden.

976   US
CHAMBER MESSAGE. 1961-1989 (Oct.). m. Meridian - Lauderdale County Chamber of Commerce, 2000 9th St., Meridian, MS 39302.

990   NL
CHAMBRE DE COMMERCE ET D'INDUSTRIE DE NOUVELLE CALEDONIE. BULLETIN. 1972-19?? bi-m. Chambre de Commerce et d'Industrie de Nouvelle Caledonie, P.O. Box M3, Noumea, New Caledonia.

380 338   FR   ISSN 0009-1219
CHAMBRE DE COMMERCE ET D'INDUSTRIE DE PARIS. BULLETIN MENSUEL. 1894-1990; suspended. m. Chambre de Commerce et d'Industrie de Paris (CEDIP), 2 place de la Bourse, 75002 Paris, France.

622   FR   ISSN 0009-126X
TN400
CHAMBRE SYNDICALE DES MINES DE FER DE FRANCE. BULLETIN TECHNIQUE. 1939-1982. q. Chambre Syndicale des Mines de Fer de France, 15 bis, rue de Marignan, 75008 Paris, France.

338   FR   ISSN 0069-259X
CHAMBRE SYNDICALE DES MINES DE FER DE FRANCE. RAPPORT D'ACTIVITE. ceased. a. Chambre Syndicale des Mines de Fer de France, 15 bis rue de Marignan, 75008 Paris, France.

790.1   CN   ISSN 0229-3455
CHAMPION. ceased 1991 (vol.14, no.3). q. Athlete Information Bureau, 1600 James Naismith Dr., Ottawa, Ont. K1B 5N4, Canada.

614.7   GW
CHANCEN; fuer Leben, Umwelt, Technik. 1987-1989. m. (back issues avail.) Bauer Spezialzeitschriften Verlag, Industriestr. 16, D-5000 Cologne 60, Germany.

952   JA
CHANGING JAPAN. 1973-19?? (no.3). irreg. (back issues avail.) International Society for Educational Information, Inc. - Kokusai Kyoiku Joho Senta, Royal Wakaba 5F, 22 Wakaba 1-chome, Shinjuku-ku, Tokyo 160, Japan.

658   US   ISSN 0195-3508
CHANNEL (LOS ANGELES). 1975-198? q. University of California, Los Angeles, John E. Anderson Graduate School of Management, Computers & Information Systems, 405 Hilgard Ave., Los Angeles, CA 90024.

791.4   UI
CHANNEL T V TIMES. 1962-1991 (Oct.). w. Channel Television Ltd., c/o Gordon de Ste. Croix, Television Centre, La Pouquelaye, St. Helier, Jersey, Channel Islands.
   Former titles: Channel Television Times; Channel Viewer (ISSN 0009-1499)

384.55   US
CHANNELS: THE BUSINESS OF COMMUNICATIONS. 1981-1990. s-m. Act III Publishing, 401 Park Ave. S., New York, NY 10016.
   Formerly: Channels of Communications (ISSN 0276-1572)

690 331.88   FR
CHANTIERS MAGAZINE. ceased 1984. m. (9/yr.). 17 rue d'Uzes, 75002 Paris, France.

372   CN   ISSN 0009-1618
CHANTIERS PEDAGOGIQUES. 1967-1972. 8/yr. 140 Ouest, 94 rue, Charlesbourg, Que., Canada.

929   US   ISSN 0883-1181
CHAPMAN CHATTER. 1983-1988 (no.20). q. 1403 Kingsford Dr., Florissant, MO 63031.

370   US   ISSN 0883-1718
CHARACTER II (CHICAGO); a newsletter about the policies shaping American youth. 1976-1989 (Sep.). 6/yr. Character, Inc., c/o A R L Services Inc., 1455 S. Michigan Ave., Chicago, IL 60605-2810.
   Former titles: Character (ISSN 0162-8933); (until 1980): Socializer.

622.33   FR   ISSN 0009-1685
CHARBONNAGES DE FRANCE. PUBLICATIONS TECHNIQUES. 1965-1989. irreg. Unite des Services Techniques des Charbonnages de France, 2 rue de Metz, 57802 Freyming Merlebach, France.

659.1   UK
CHARTERED INSTITUTE OF MARKETING. MARKETER. ceased. q. Chartered Institute of Marketing, Moor Hall, Cookham SL6 9QH, England.

370   UK   ISSN 0264-7125
LB2830.3.G7
CHARTERED INSTITUTE OF PUBLIC FINANCE AND ACCOUNTANCY. EDUCATION STATISTICS. UNIT COSTS. 1980-1988. a. (back issues avail.) Chartered Institute of Public Finance and Accountancy, 3 Robert St., London WC2N 6BH, England.

380.5   UK   ISSN 0260-9886
CHARTERED INSTITUTE OF PUBLIC FINANCE AND ACCOUNTANCY. HIGHWAYS AND TRANSPORTATION. ACTUALS. 1980-1989. a. (back issues avail.) Chartered Institute of Public Finance and Accountancy, 3 Robert St., London WC2N 6BH, England.

352.7   UK   ISSN 0260-4078
CHARTERED INSTITUTE OF PUBLIC FINANCE AND ACCOUNTANCY. HOUSING REVENUE ACCOUNTS STATISTICS. ACTUALS. 1951-1990. a. (back issues avail.) Chartered Institute of Public Finance and Accountancy., 3 Robert St., London WC2N 6BH, England.
   Formerly: Chartered Institute of Public Finance and Accountancy. Housing Part 2: Revenue Accounts. Actuals Statistics (ISSN 0307-1316)

362.2   UK   ISSN 0144-9915
CHARTERED INSTITUTE OF PUBLIC FINANCE AND ACCOUNTANCY. POLICE STATISTICS. ACTUALS. 1949-1989. a. (back issues avail.) Chartered Institute of Public Finance and Accountancy, 3 Robert St., London WC2N 6BH, England.

370   UK   ISSN 0266-2949
CHARTERED INSTITUTE OF PUBLIC FINANCE AND ACCOUNTANCY. SCHOOL MEALS STATISTICS. 1967-1989. a. (back issues avail.) Chartered Institute of Public Finance and Accountancy, 3 Robert St., London WC2N 6BH, England.

380.5   UK   ISSN 0306-9559
HE243.A1
CHARTERED INSTITUTE OF TRANSPORT. HANDBOOK. 1930-1990. a. Chartered Institute of Transport, 80 Portland Place, London W1N 4DP, England.

327   UK   ISSN 0143-5795
CHATHAM HOUSE PAPERS. 1979-19?? irreg. Pinter Publications, 25 Floral St., London WC2 9DS, England.

340   CS
CHEKHOSLOVATSKOGO PRAVA BIULETEN. 1951-19?? q. Jednota Ceskoslovenskych Pravniku, Nam. Curieovych 7, 116 40 Prague 1, Czechoslovakia.

540   SA
CHEM NEWS. ceased 1988. irreg. Council for Scientific and Industrial Research, P.O. Box 395, Pretoria 0001, South Africa.

540   UK
CHEMFACTS: SCANDINAVIA. 1981-198? a. Chemical Data Services, 39A Bowling Green Lane, London EC1R 0BJ, England.

540   SW   ISSN 0004-2056
QD1   CODEN: CSRPB9
CHEMICA SCRIPTA; an international journal on progress in chemistry and biochemistry. 1971-199? irreg., vol. 29, 1989. (also avail. in microfilm from PMC; back issues avail.) Kungliga Vetenskapsakademien - Royal Swedish Academy of Sciences, P.O. Box 50005, S-104 05 Stockholm, Sweden.
   Supersedes: Arkiv for Kemi.

630   GW
CHEMIE UND TECHNIK IN DER LANDWIRTSCHAFT UND GENOSSENSCHAFTLICHE RATSCHLAEGE. 1949-1991. m. (back issues avail.) Deutsche Raiffeisen-Warenzentrale GmbH, Reuterweg 51-53, Postfach 100643, 6000 Frankfurt a.M. I, Germany.

540   GW   ISSN 0411-8987
                               CODEN: CGDMBG
CHEMISCHE GESELLSCHAFT DER DDR. MITTEILUNGSBLATT. 1953-1991. m. Chemische Gesellschaft der DDR, Redaktionskollegium Mitteilungsblatt, Clara-Zetkin-Str. 105, Postfach 1327, 1086 Berlin, Germany.

660   GW   ISSN 0009-2967
CHEMISCHE INDUSTRIE INTERNATIONAL. 1956-1991. q. (reprint service avail. from UMI) (Verband der Chemischen Industrie) Handelsblatt GmbH, Kasernenstr. 67, Postfach 102717, 4000 Duesseldorf 1, Germany.

540 615.19   US
CHEMISTRY AND PHARMACOLOGY OF DRUGS. 1982-1992; suspended. irreg. John Wiley & Sons, Inc., 605 Third Ave., New York, NY 10158-0012.

540 AT ISSN 0314-4240
TP1 CODEN: CHAUDY
CHEMISTRY IN AUSTRALIA. 1931-19?? m. (also avail. in microfiche) (Royal Australian Chemical Institute) Rala Publications, 203-205 Darling St., Balamin, N.S.W. 2041, Australia.
 Formerly (until July 1977): Royal Australian Chemical Institute. Proceedings (ISSN 0035-8746)

794.1 US
CHESS GAZETTE. 1980-1991 (Mar.). 6/yr. Chessco, 308 Union Arcade Bldg., Davenport, IA 52801.

794.1 US ISSN 0897-7305
GV1313
CHESS INTERNATIONAL; a journal for the correspondence chessplayer. 1986-1991. bi-m. (back issues avail.) (World Correspondence Chess Federation) Chess International, Ste. 99, 8530 Steilacoom Rd., S.E., Lacey, WA 98503-1793.

794.1 SZ
CHESS NOTES. 1982-1989. 6/yr. (back issues avail.) 9 rue de la Maladiere, CH-1205 Geneva, Switzerland.

572 US
CHICAGO ANTHROPOLOGY EXCHANGE. ceased. s-a. University of Chicago, Department of Anthropology, 1126 E. 59th St., Chicago, IL 60637.

378.1 US ISSN 0009-3572
CHICAGO ILLINI. 1946-1988 (June). s-w. (Sep.-May); bi-w. (Jun.-Aug.). (tabloid format) Commuter, Inc., 1626 W. North Shore, Chicago, IL 60626.
 Formerly: Commuter Illini.

380 US ISSN 0577-7259
HG6046
CHICAGO MERCANTILE EXCHANGE YEARBOOK. 1984-1989. a. Chicago Mercantile Exchange, Statistics Department, 30 S. Wacker Dr., Chicago, IL 60606.
 Incorporates (1972-1983): International Monetary Market Yearbook.

616.89 011 US ISSN 0009-3661
Z6664.N5
CHICAGO PSYCHOANALYTIC LITERATURE INDEX. 1958-198? q. Chicago Institute for Psychoanalysis, 180 N. Michigan, Chicago, IL 60601.

051 US ISSN 0894-5640
CHICAGO TIMES. 1987-1990 (Apr.); suspended. bi-m. Chicago Times Company, 180 N. Michigan Ave., Ste. 1440, Chicago, IL 60601.

361.8 US ISSN 0009-3793
CHICORY (BALTIMORE). 1966-197? 10/yr. Enoch Pratt Free Library, Urban Services Program, 400 Cathedral St., Baltimore, MD 21201.

330.9 US
CHIEF ECONOMIST COMMENTARY. ceased 1988. w. (back issues avail.) D R I - McGraw-Hill, 24 Hartwell Ave., Lexington, MA 02173.

155.4 364 SZ ISSN 0251-2467
CHILD HEALTH AND DEVELOPMENT. ceased. irreg. S. Karger AG, Allschwilerstr. 10, P.O. Box, CH-4009 Basel, Switzerland.

616.89 II ISSN 0009-3998
 CODEN: CPQUDY
CHILD PSYCHIATRY QUARTERLY; a journal devoted to the mental health of child and youth. 1967-1990; suspended. q. (also avail. in microfilm from UMI; back issues avail. reprint service avail. from ISI and UMI) Community Mental Health Centre (Indira Health Home), Road 7, Banjara Hills, Hyderabad 530 034, Andhra Pradesh, India.

155.4 US ISSN 0099-0116
LB1101
CHILD STUDY JOURNAL MONOGRAPH. 1980, ceased same year. irreg. (reprint service avail. from UMI) State University of New York, College at Buffalo, Bacon Hall 312J, 1300 Elmwood Ave., Buffalo, NY 14222.

028.5 340 US
CHILD WELFARE LEAGUE OF AMERICA. FROM THE DESK OF THE EXECUTIVE DIRECTOR. ceased. q. Child Welfare League of America, Inc., 440 First St., N.W., Washington, DC 20001-2085.

618 US ISSN 0272-6319
CHILDBIRTH ALTERNATIVES QUARTERLY. 1979-1988. q. (back issues avail.) Janet Isaacs Ashford, Ed. & Pub., 327 Glenmont Dr., Solana Beach, CA 92075.

618.2 610.73 US ISSN 0279-490X
RG651
CHILDBIRTH EDUCATOR. 1981-1990. q. (back issues avail.) Cahners Publishing Company (New York), American Baby Group (Subsidiary of: Reed International PLC), Division of Reed Publishing (USA) Inc., 475 Park Ave. S., New York, NY 10016-6999.

028.5 US
CHILDHOOD IN POETRY. 1967-1980. irreg. Gale Research Inc., 835 Penobscot Bldg., Detroit, MI 48226.

028.5 649 US
CHILDREN. ceased. bi-m. (also avail. in microfilm from KTO) Rodale Press, Inc., 33 E. Minor St., Emmaus, PA 18098.

179.3 179.4 US
CHILDREN AND ANIMALS. 1975-1989. 4/yr. Humane Society of the United States, National Association for the Advancement of Humane Education, Box 362, East Haddam, CT 06423.
 Former titles (until 1985): Humane Education (ISSN 0149-8061); N A A H E Journal.

028.5 CN
CHILDREN'S CHOICES OF CANADIAN BOOKS. 1979-1991 (vol.7). every 9 mos. (back issues avail.) Citizens' Committee on Children, Box 6133, Sta. J, Ottawa, Ont. K2A 1T2, Canada.

614.7 150 155.4 US ISSN 0886-0505
CHILDREN'S ENVIRONMENTS QUARTERLY. 1984-1989. 4/yr. (Center for Human Environments) Lawrence Erlbaum Associates, Inc., 365 Broadway, Hillsdale, NJ 07642.
 Former titles: Childhood City Quarterly; Childhood City Newsletter.

323.4 UK
CHILE FIGHTS. 1973-19?? q. Chile Solidarity Campaign, 129 Seven Sisters Rd., London N7 7QG, England.

323.4 US
CHILENET. 1987-1990. q. (back issues avail.) (Chile Center for Education & Development) Chile Information Network, Chile Center, Box 20179, Cathedral Finance Sta., New York, NY 10025.

387.7 HK
CHINA AVIATION JOURNAL. 1986-1989; suspended. s-m. (back issues avail.) Conmilit Press Ltd., Sing Pao Bldg., 22 Fl., 101 King's Road, North Point, Hong Kong, Hong Kong.
 Formerly: Airport Equipment and Aviation.

917.306 US ISSN 0889-9002
CHINA DAILY NEWS. 1940-19?? d. (newspaper; also avail. in microfilm from BHP; back issues avail.) China Daily News, Inc., 15 Mercer St., Ste. 102, New York, NY 10013.

382 GW ISSN 0178-7438
CHINA-HANDEL. 1985-198? bi-m. (back issues avail.) Verlag Ute Schiller, P.O.B. 650 648, D-1000 Berlin 65, Germany.

622.33 CH
CHINA, REPUBLIC. MINING RESEARCH AND SERVICE ORGANISATION. M R S O SPECIAL REPORT. 1977-19?? irreg. Mining Research and Service Organization, Industrial Technology Research Institute, Taipei, Taiwan, Republic of China.

327 052 HK
CHINA REVIEW; monthly news magazine on China. 1989-1990 (ceased Feb.). m. China Review Publications Ltd. (Subsidiary of: Sing Tao Group), Guardian House, Ste. 1005, 32 Oi Kwan Rd., Morrison Hill, Hong Kong.

382 US ISSN 0258-977X
HF1040.9.C6
CHINA SOURCES. 1980-19?? m. Asian Sources Trade Journals, c/o Wordright Enterprises Inc., 1020 Church St., Box 3062, Evanston, IL 60204-3062.

915.1 US ISSN 0896-2979
CHINESE GEOGRAPHY AND ENVIRONMENT. 1988-1991; suspended. q. M. E. Sharpe, Inc., 80 Business Park Dr., Armonk, NY 10504.

536.56 US ISSN 1044-1085
CHINESE JOURNAL OF LOW TEMPERATURE PHYSICS. 1989-1990. q. (back issues avail.) (Zhongguo Kexue Jishu Daxue, CC - University of Science and Technology of China) Allerton Press, Inc., 150 Fifth Ave., New York, NY 10011.

621.3 US ISSN 0899-9988
TK7871.85 CODEN: PTTPDZ
CHINESE JOURNAL OF SEMICONDUCTORS. ceased. q. (back issues avail.) (Academia Sinica (Chinese Academy of Sciences), Institute of Semiconductors, CC - Zhongguo Kexueyuan, Bandaoti Yanjiusuo) Allerton Press, Inc., 150 Fifth Ave., New York, NY 10011.

621 US ISSN 1040-6174
CHINESE MECHANICAL ENGINEERING ABSTRACTS. 1989-1991. 8/yr. (also avail. in microform; back issues avail.) Pergamon Press, Inc., Journals Division, 660 White Plains Rd., Tarrytown, NY 10591-5153.

530 US ISSN 0887-3518
QC685 CODEN: CPLAEI
CHINESE PHYSICS - LASERS. 1986-198? m. (Optical Society of America, Inc.) American Institute of Physics, 335 E. 45th St., New York, NY 10017.

951 CH ISSN 0009-465X
CH'ING DOCUMENTS/KU KUNG WEN HSIEN. 1969-1973. q. National Palace Museum - Kuo Li Ku Kung Po Wu Yuan, Wai Shuang Hsi, Shih Lin, Taipei, Taiwan, Republic of China.

621.381 IT ISSN 0392-9353
CHIP. 1984-1989. m. Tecniche Nuove s.p.a., Via Ciro Menotti 14, 20129 Milan, Italy.

617.3 PL ISSN 0009-479X
 CODEN: CNROA4
CHIRURGIA NARZADOW RUCHU I ORTOPEDIA POLSKA. 1928-19?? bi-m. (Polskie Towarzystwo Ortopedyczne i Traumatologiczne) Panstwowy Zaklad Wydawnictw Lekarskich, Dluga 38-40, Warsaw, Poland.

610 GW ISSN 0720-3462
CHIRURGISCHEN ARBEITSGEMEINSCHAFT. VERHANDLUNG. 1980-1991. irreg. (Chirurgischen Arbeitsgemeinschaft (CAO)) Ferdinand Enke Verlag, Postfach 101254, 7000 Stuttgart 10, Germany.

052 AT
CHISHOLM GAZETTE. 1987-1990 (vol.7, no.1). 3/yr. (back issues avail.) Chisholm Institute of Technology, P.O. Box 197, Caulifield E., Vic. 3145, Australia.

340 CN ISSN 0009-4889
CHITTY'S LAW JOURNAL. 1950-1981. m.(except July & Aug.). (also avail. in microfilm from RRI; reprint service avail. from RRI) Jonah Publications Ltd., 620 Sheppard Ave. W., Downsview, Ont. M3H 2S1, Canada.

640.73 UK ISSN 0953-1475
CHOICES. 1979-1988. 3/yr. Community Education Development Centre (CEDC), Lyng Hall, Blackberry Lane, Coventry CV2 3JS, England.
 Formerly (until 1987): Consumer Education Newsletter - Cylchlythyr Addysg Defnyddwyr (ISSN 0261-7129)

320 US
CHOICES (BIRMINGHAM). 1983-19?? q. (back issues avail.) Educational Perspectives, Inc., 1100 Columbiana Road, Birmingham, AL 35209.

780 UR
CHOIR DIRECTOR'S LIBRARY. 1966-1988 (no.52). a. Izdatel'stvo Muzyka, Ul. Neglinnaya 14, Moscow 103031, Russian S.F.S.R., U.S.S.R.

940 AU
CHORHERRENSTIFT KLOSTERNEUBURG. JAHRBUCH. 1961-19?? a. Boehlau Verlag GmbH & Co.KG., Dr. Karl Lueger-Ring 12, Postfach 581, A-1011 Vienna, Austria.

CESSATIONS

200 384.55   US   ISSN 0890-3387
CHRISTIAN FILM & VIDEO. 1984-1989 (vol.2). bi-m. (back issues avail.) Carstin Mark Communications, 785 Cressman Rd., Box 181, Harleysville, PA 19438.

658   US   ISSN 0892-4708
CHRISTIAN MANAGEMENT REVIEW; a management tool in Christian enterprise. 1987-1989. q. (back issues avail.) J. Alan Youngren, Ed. & Pub., Box 9150, Downers Grove, IL 60515.

200   UK
CHRISTIAN NEWS WORLD. 1988-198? 12/yr. Herald House Ltd., Dominion Rd., Worthing, West Sussex BN14 8JP, England.

808.81   US   ISSN 0897-5590
CHRISTIAN OUTLOOK. 1988-198? q. (back issues avail.) Hutton Publications, Box 1870, Hayden, ID 83835.

327 200   CS   ISSN 0009-5567
CHRISTIAN PEACE CONFERENCE. 1962-1990 (no. 101). q. Christian Peace Conference, International Secretariat, Jungmannova 9, 110 00 Prague 1, Czechoslovakia.

220   US
CHRISTIAN UNITY MAGAZINE. ceased. q. James P. Thompson Publishers, 7095 South St., Webster, FL 33597.

200 266   US
CHURCH MINISTRIES WORKERS; journal for church leaders. 1986-1991. q. (General Conference of Seventh-Day Adventists) Pacific Press Publishing Association, 1350 N. Kings Rd., Nampa, ID 83202.

200   UK   ISSN 0009-6474
CHURCH NEWS. 1946-1989. m. Home Words Printing & Publishing Co. Ltd., Box 44, Guildford, Surrey GU1 1XL, England.

808   US
CHURCHYARD; an anthology of Christian weird tales. 1984-198? (vol.1, no.2). irreg. Fandom Unlimited, c/o Robert M. Price, Pub., 216 Fernwood Ave., Upper Montclair, NJ 07043.
  Formerly (until 1989): Reborn (ISSN 0277-7843)

691   FR
CIMENTS ET CHAUX. 1970-1991. m. Syndicat National des Fabricants de Ciments et de Chaux, 41, Avenue de Friedland, 75008 Paris, France.

200   US
CINCINNATI BIBLE SEMINARY. SEMINARY REVIEW. 1954-198?; suspended. q. (back issues avail.) Cincinnati Bible Seminary, 2700 Glenway Ave., Cincinnati, OH 45204.
  Formerly: Cincinnati Christian Seminary. Seminary Review.

778.5   US   ISSN 0277-5891
CINEFAN; science fiction, fantasy & horror in films. 1974-198? 3/yr. (back issues avail.) Fandom Unlimited Enterprises, c/o R.D. Larson, Box 23069, San Jose, CA 95153-0306.

778.534   II
CINEMA INDIA - INTERNATIONAL. 1984-1990 (no.2). q. T.M. Ramachandran, Ed. & Pub., A-15, Anand Nagar, Juhu Tara Rd., Juhu, Bombay 400 049, India.

791.43   AT   ISSN 0158-698X
PN1993.5.A8
CINEMA PAPERS YEARBOOK. 1980-1984. a. M T V Publishing Ltd., 43 Charles St., Abbotsford, Vic. 3067, Australia.
  Formerly (until 1985): Australian Motion Picture Yearbook.

778.5   IT
CINEMASESSANTA. 1960-1987. bi-m. Editore Pironti, P.za Dante 30, 80135 Naples, Italy.

808 778.5   IT   ISSN 0412-5568
CINEROMANZO. 1950-19?? m. Casa Editrice Universo S.p.A., Via de Vizzi 35, 20092 Cinisello Balsamo, Italy.

658   CN
CIRCUIT INDUSTRIEL. 1980-1989. 5/yr. Promotions Andre Pageau Inc., 1627, boul. St. Joseph Charlesbourg ouest, Quebec, Que. G2K 1H1, Canada.
  Formerly: Outilite.

020   CS   ISSN 0009-7438
CITATEL; casopis pre knihovnikov a pracu kniznic. 1951-1991. m. Matica Slovenska, Ul. Mudronova 26, 036 52 Martin, Czechoslovakia.

332.6   US
CITICORP REPORT TO INVESTORS. (Includes section: Citiviews) q. Citicorp, 399 Park Ave., New York, NY 10043.

332   US
CITILIFE. 1972-1982? s-m. Citicorp, Public Affairs Dept., 399 Park Ave., New York, NY 10043.

350   US   ISSN 0578-3283
E185.61
CITIZEN (JACKSON); a journal of fact and opinion presenting a conservative view of the civil rights revolution. 1956-1989 (Sep.). bi-m. (also avail. in microfilm from UMI) (Citizens Councils of America) Citizens Council, Inc., c/o William S. Purvis, Ed., 666 North St., No. 102A, Jackson, MS 39202-3196.

055.1   IT
CITTA CALABRIA. suspended 1989 (no.32). bi-m. (back issues avail.) Rubbettino Editore, Viale dei Pini, 88049 Soveria Mannelli, Italy.

323 301   US   ISSN 0009-7683
CITY ALMANAC. 1966-1989 (vol.21, no.1). q. New School for Social Research, Center for New York City Affairs, 66 Fifth Ave., New York, NY 10011.

026.65   UK   ISSN 0009-7713
CITY BUSINESS COURIER; news-letter of the City Business Library. 1954-1989 (Spring). s-a. (Corporation of London) City Business Library, 106 Fenchurch St., London EC3M 5JB, England.
  Formerly: C R R Courier.

309.2   CN
CITY OF TORONTO PLANNING AND DEVELOPMENT DEPARTMENT. CITY PLANNING. 1978-1990. irreg. Planning and Development Department, East Tower, 20th Fl., City Hall, Toronto, Ont. M5H 2N2, Canada.
  Formerly: City of Toronto Planning Board. City Planning (ISSN 0705-887X)

301.4157   AT
CITY RHYTHM. 1981-19?? bi-m. Janek Pty. Ltd., P.O. Box 408, Richmond, 3121, Australia.

332   UK   ISSN 0266-7339
CITY UNIVERSITY BUSINESS SCHOOL. ECONOMIC REVIEW. 1979-19?? s-a. (also avail. in microform) (City University Business School) Basil Blackwell Ltd., 108 Cowley Rd., Oxford OX4 1JF, England.
  Formerly (until Apr. 1983): Annual Monetary Review (ISSN 0144-4220)

624   US   ISSN 0277-3775
TA1
CIVIL ENGINEERING FOR PRACTICING & DESIGN ENGINEERS. 1982-1986. m. (also avail. in microfilm; microfiche) Pergamon Press, Inc., Journals Division, 660 White Plains Rd., Tarrytown, NY 10591-5153.

624   UK   ISSN 0263-0257
   CODEN: CESYEE
CIVIL ENGINEERING SYSTEMS; decision making & problem solving. 1983-1991 (vol.8). q. (back issues avail.) E. & F.N. Spon, Ltd., 2-6 Boundary Row, London SE1 8HN, England.

301   FR   ISSN 0007-957X
CIVILISATION LIBERTAIRE; cahiers d'etudes sociologiques. 1969-198? m. 21 rue des Mathurius, 91570 Bievres, France.
  Formerly: Cahier de l'Humanisme Libertaire.

613.7   US
CLARITY MAGAZINE. 1976-1990 (Dec.). q. Ananda World Brotherhood Village, Church of God-Realization, 14618 Tyler Foote Rd., Nevada City, CA 95959.
  Formerly (until 1982): Spirit and Nature Magazine.

378.1   US   ISSN 0009-8272
CLARK NOW. 1970-199?; suspended. a. Clark University, 950 Main St., Worcester, MA 01610.

769.7   UK
CLASSIC MOTOR CYCLE. ceased 1986. bi-m. Business Press International Ltd., Quadrant House, The Quadrant, Sutton, Surrey SM2 5AS, England.

629.2
TL7
CLASSIC OLD CAR VALUE GUIDE. 1967-1990 (vol.23). a. Gold Book, Inc., 430 Tenth St., N.W., Ste. S-202, Atlanta, GA 30318.
  Formerly: Old Car Value Guide (ISSN 0475-1876)

384.554   US
CLASSIC T V. ceased. m. 2980 College Ave., Ste. 2, Box 25MG, Berkeley, CA 94705.

181.45   II
CLASSIC YOGA INTERNATIONAL. 1980-19?? q. International Board of Yoga, Santa Cruz East, Bombay 400 055, India.

150.19   US
CLASSICS IN PSYCHOANALYSIS. 1984-19??. irreg. (Chicago Institute for Psychoanalysis) International Universities Press, Inc., 59 Boston Post Rd., Box 1524, Madison, CT 06443-1524.

372   ISSN 0888-9376
CLASSMATE. 1985-1990 (Apr.). 4/yr. (back issues avail.) Frank Schaffer Publications, Inc., 19771 Magellan Dr., Torrance, CA 90502.

370   CN   ISSN 0825-4729
CLASSROOM. 1984-19?? bi-m. Scholastic-TAB Publications Ltd., 123 Newkirk Rd., Richmond Hill, Ont. L4C 3G5, Canada.

340   CN   ISSN 0704-0393
CLIC'S LEGAL MATERIALS LETTER. 1977-19??. bi-m. (back issues avail.) Canadian Law Information Council, 600 Eglinton Ave. East, Ste. 205, Toronto, Ont. M4P 1P3, Canada.

697   II   ISSN 0009-8930
   CODEN: CLCOAH
CLIMATE CONTROL; serving the air conditioning and refrigeration industry. 1968-1985. bi-m. All India Air Conditioning and Refrigeration Association, c/o S. Sajjan Singh, 7-17 Kirti Nagar, New Delhi 110 015, India.

616.07   IT   ISSN 0366-6778
LA CLINICA. 1935-1990. bi-m. (back issues avail.) Nuova Casa Editrice Licinio Cappelli S.p.a., Via Farini, 14, 40124 Bologna, Italy.

617.96   SP   ISSN 0210-4660
CLINICA ANESTESIOLOGICA. 1977-199? 4/yr. Salvat Publicaciones Cientificas, S.A., Muntaner 262, 08021 Barcelona, Spain.

618.1   SP   ISSN 0210-4938
CLINICA GINECOLOGICA. 1976-1988 (Mar.). 3/yr. (Instituto Dexeus) Salvat Editores, S.A., Mallorca 45, 08029 Barcelona, Spain.

612.015   US
CLINICAL BIOCHEMISTRY (SAN DIEGO); contemporary theories and techniques. ceased after vol.3, 1984. irreg. (reprint service avail. from ISI) Academic Press, Inc., 1250 Sixth Ave., San Diego, CA 92101.

574   US
CLINICAL BIOCHEMISTRY REVIEWS (MELBOURNE). ceased. irreg. Kreiger Publishing, Box 9542, Melbourne, FL 32902.

612.015   US   ISSN 0272-9881
RB40   CODEN: CLBRDO
CLINICAL BIOCHEMISTRY REVIEWS (TARRYTOWN). 1987; ceased same year. s-a. Pergamon Press, Inc., Journals Division, 660 White Plains Rd., Tarrytown, NY 10591-5153.

616.1   US
CLINICAL CARDIOLOGY MONOGRAPHS. 1972-19?? irreg., latest 1978. W.B. Saunders Co. (Subsidiary of: Harcourt Brace Jovanovich, Inc.), Curtis Center, Independence Square W., Philadelphia, PA 19106.
  Formerly (vol.1): Cardiovascular Diseases; Current Status and Advances.

615.37 574 US
CLINICAL IMMUNOBIOLOGY. 1972-1980 (vol.4). irreg. (reprint service avail. from ISI) Academic Press, Inc., 1250 Sixth Ave., San Diego, CA 92101.

618 US
CLINICAL MONOGRAPHS IN OBSTETRICS AND GYNECOLOGY. 1975-1981. irreg. John Wiley & Sons, Inc., 605 Third Ave., New York, NY 10158-0012.

612 SZ ISSN 0252-1164
CODEN: CPBIDP
CLINICAL PHYSIOLOGY AND BIOCHEMISTRY. 1982-1991. bi-m. (also avail. in microform from RPI) S. Karger AG, Allschwilerstr. 10, P.O. Box, CH-4009 Basel, Switzerland.

618.97 US ISSN 0890-2267
CLINICAL REPORT ON AGING. 1987-1989 (vol.3, no.4). bi-m. (tabloid format; back issues avail.) (American Geriatrics Society) Elsevier Science Publishing Co., Inc. (New York), 655 Ave. of the Americas, New York, NY 10010.

658.896 UK ISSN 0009-9422
CLIQUE; the antiquarian booksellers' medium. 1890-19?? w. Stoate & Bishop Ltd., St. James Sq., Cheltenham GL50 3PU, England.

338 332 US
CLOSELY HELD BUSINESS. 1973-1989. m. (looseleaf format; also avail. in microform from UMI) Maxwell Macmillan, Professional and Business Reference Publishing, 910 Sylvan Ave., Englewood Cliffs, NJ 07632.
Supersedes (in 1977): Closely Held Corporations.

621.385 US
CO. 1986-1987 (Oct.). m. Telecom Library, Inc., 12 W. 21st St., New York, NY 10010.

796.3 US ISSN 0894-4237
COACHING VOLLEYBALL. 1987-1990 (vol.3). bi-m. (American Volleyball Coaches Association) Human Kinetics Publishers Inc., 1607 N. Market St., Box 5076, Champaign, IL 61825-5076.

796.323 US ISSN 0894-4245
COACHING WOMEN'S BASKETBALL. 1987-1990 (vol.3). bi-m. (Women's Basketball Coaches Association) Human Kinetics Publishers, Inc., 1607 N. Market St., Box 5076, Champaign, IL 61825-5076.

531.64 US ISSN 0741-7713
COAL-BASED SYNFUELS; a current awareness bulletin. ceased. s-m. U.S. Department of Energy, Office of Scientific and Technical Information, Box 62, Oak Ridge, TN 37831.

614.85 614.7 US ISSN 0741-5257
COAL PREPARATION AND POLLUTION CONTROL; a current awareness bulletin. ceased. s-m. U.S. Department of Energy, Office of Scientific and Technical Information, Box 62, Oak Ridge, TN 37831.

531.64 US
COAL SITUATION. 1980-198? m. Chase Manhattan Bank, One New York Plaza, New York, NY 10081.

917 US ISSN 0010-0005
COAST. 1955-1989. w. (Mar.-Oct.), m. (Nov.-Feb.). (also avail. in microform from UMI; reprint service avail.) (Guide Magazines Group) Resort Publications, Ltd., Kings Highway at 50th Ave. N., Drawer 2448, Myrtle Beach, SC 29577.

340 333.7 US
COASTAL LAW MEMO. 1980-1986 (no.5). irreg. University of Oregon, School of Law, Ocean and Coastal Law Center, Eugene, OR 97403-1221.

929 US
COATNEY-COURTNEY EXCHANGE. 1984-19?? 4/yr. Box 536, Freeman, SD 57029.

334 640 FR
COCLICO. (Consommateurs, Clients, Consommateurs) 1976-19?? 11/yr. Groupe L S A, 91 rue du Faubourg, St. Honore, 75008 Paris, France.

001.6 621.381 US
CODEWORKS. 1985-1990 (Nov.). bi-m. 80-Northwest Publishing, Inc., 3838 S. Warner St., Tacoma, WA 98409-4698.

616.1 FR ISSN 0010-0226
COEUR. 1970-1989. bi-m. Masson, 120 Bd. St-Germain, 75280 Paris Cedex 06, France.

737.4 769.56 SI ISSN 0129-0967
COIN DIGEST. 1987-1991 (Oct.). q. Taisei Stamps and Coins, Liang Court Complex, no.01-33, 177 River Valley Rd., Singapore 0617, Singapore.

665.5 VE
COLECCION LA ALQUITRANA. 1975-19?? irreg. Ministerio de Energia y Minas, Torre Norte, Centro Simon Bolivar, Caracas, Venezuela.

332 SP ISSN 0522-3822
COLEGIO DE AGENTES DE CAMBIO Y BOLSA DE BARCELONA. SERVICIO DE ESTUDIOS E INFORMACION. BOLETIN FINANCIERO. 1962-1987. q. Colegio de Agentes de Cambio y Bolsa de Barcelona, Servicio de Estudios e Informacion, Paseo Isabel II, s-n, 08003 Barcelona, Spain.

796 US
COLEMAN OUTDOOR ANNUAL. ceased. a. Aqua-Field Publishing Co., Inc., 66 W. Gilbert St., Shrewsbury, NJ 07702.
Formerly: Coleman Camping Annual.

362.7 CN
COLLAGE. ceased 1988 (vol.1, no.10). m. Canadian Council on Children and Youth, 2211 Riverside Dr., Ste. 11, Ottawa, Ont. K1H 7X2, Canada.

350.086 IT
COLLANA DI STUDI SU PROBLEMI URBANISTICI FIORENTINO. ceased 1974 (no.2). irreg. Ufficio della Provincia, Florence, Italy.

700 SP
COLLECCIO DE MATERIALS. 1977-19?? irreg. Artestudi Edicions, Provenca 552, Barcelona 26, Spain.

780.9 IT ISSN 0069-5270
COLLECTANEA HISTORIAE MUSICAE. 1953-1966 (vol.4). irreg. Casa Editrice Leo S. Olschki, Casella Postale 66, 50100 Florence, Italy.

362.8 US
COLLECTIVE NETWORKER NEWSLETTER. 1978-1988. 12/yr. Networker Collective, Box 5446, Berkeley, CA 94705.
Formerly (until 1981): Grapevine.

790.13 UK
COLLECTORS WORLD. 1983-198? bi-m. Focus Magazines Ltd., Greencoat House, Francis St., London SW1P 1DG, England.

780 371.42 US
COLLEGE MUSICIAN. 1986-198? 4/yr. Alan Weston Communications, Inc., 303 N. Glenoaks Blvd., Ste. 600, Burbank, CA 91502.

610 CN ISSN 0045-7388
COLLEGE OF PHYSICIANS AND SURGEONS OF ONTARIO. INTERIM REPORT. 1963-1987. s-a. College of Physicians and Surgeons of Ontario, 80 College St., Toronto, Ont. M5G 2E2, Canada.
Formerly: College of Physicians and Surgeons of Ontario. Semi-Annual Report.

371.42 301.412 US
COLLEGE WOMAN. 1985-198? 4/yr. Alan Weston Communications, Inc., 303 N. Glenoaks Blvd., Ste. 600, Burbank, CA 91502.

100 GW
COLLEGIUM PHILOSOPHICUM JENENSE. 1977-1990. irreg., vol.7, 1987. (back issues avail.) (Friedrich-Schiller-Universitaet, Sektion Marxistisch-Leninistische Philosophie) Hermann Boehlaus Nachfolger, Meyerstr. 50a, 5300 Weimar, Germany.

636.7 US
COLLIE CUES; the international collie magazine. 1948-1986. bi-m. Halamar, Inc., 9800 Flint Rock Rd., Manassas, VA 22111.

370 CK
COLOMBIA. MINISTERIO DE EDUCACION NACIONAL. EDUCACION PARA DESARROLLO. ceased. irreg. Ministerio de Educacion Nacional, Division de Educacion de Adultos, Bogota, Colombia.

917 US
COLONIAL WILLIAMSBURG OCCASIONAL PAPERS IN ARCHAEOLOGY. 1973-1977. irreg. Colonial Williamsburg Foundation, Box 1776, Williamsburg, VA 23187-1776.

975 US
COLONIAL WILLIAMSBURG STUDIES IN COLONIAL CHESAPEAKE HISTORY AND CULTURE. published only once, 1991. irreg. Princeton University Press, 3175 Princeton Pike, Lawrenceville, NJ 08648.

799.2 US ISSN 0364-071X
TS537
COLT AMERICAN HANDGUNNING ANNUAL. 1975-19?? a. Aqua-Field Publishing Co., Inc., 66 W. Gilbert St., Shrewsbury, NJ 07702.

330 US ISSN 0069-6323
COLUMBIA ESSAYS ON THE GREAT ECONOMISTS. 1971-1976. irreg. Columbia University Press, 562 W. 113th St., New York, NY 10025.

947 US
COLUMBIA UNIVERSITY. HARRIMAN INSTITUTE. STUDIES. published only once, 1991. irreg. Princeton University Press, 3175 Princeton Pike, Lawrenceville, NJ 08648.

305.3 051 US
COMBAT MISSION. ceased 1990. bi-m. Pilot Communications, Inc., Box 304, Brookfield, CT 06804.

301.16 384.5 070.5 UK
COMEDIA; reports on the media and communications industry. 1980-1988. bi-m. (back issues avail.) Association for Media Education, c/o Scottish Film Council, 74 Victoria Crescent Rd., Glasgow G12 9JH, Scotland.
Former titles: Comedia Series; Minority Press Group Reports. Media Education Journal; A M E S Journal.

327 US ISSN 0146-8537
COMENTARIOS SOBRE EL DESARROLLO INTERNACIONAL. 1971-197? bi-m. (also avail. in microform from UMI) Society for International Development, 1346 Connecticut Ave. N.W., Washington, DC 20036.

370 371.4 CN ISSN 0315-4351
COMMENT ON EDUCATION. 1971-19?? 4/yr. (University of Toronto, Guidance Centre) Oise Publishing, 252 Bloor St.W., Toronto, Ont. M5S 1V5, Canada.

332 US
COMMENTS. 1975-198? bi-m. Kansas City Association of Trusts and Foundations, 406 Board of Trade Bldg., Kansas City, MO 64105.

380 US ISSN 0010-2741
HF1
COMMERCE. 1904-199? m. (back issues avail.; reprint service avail. from KTO) Chicago Association of Commerce and Industry, 200 N. LaSalle St., 6th Fl., Chicago, IL 60601-1014.

382 BE
COMMERCE EXTERIEUR DE L'U.E.B.L. AVEC LES PAYS D'AFRIQUE. ceased 1976. a. Office Belge du Commerce Exterieur, 162 Blvd. Emile Jacqmain, 1210 Brussels, Belgium.

382 BE
COMMERCE EXTERIEUR DE L'U.E.B.L. AVEC LES PAYS D'AMERIQUE LATINE/BUITENLANDSE HANDEL VAN DE B.L.E.U. MET DE LANDEN VAN LATIJNS AMERIKA. ceased 1976. a. Office Belge du Commerce Exterieur, 162 Blvd. Emile Jacqmain, 1210 Brussels, Belgium.

382 BE
COMMERCE EXTERIEUR DE L'U.E.B.L. AVEC LES PAYS D'ASIE/BUITENLANDSE HANDEL VAN DE B.L.E.U. MET DE LANDEN VAN AZIE. ceased 1976. a. Office Belge du Commerce Exterieur, 162 Blvd. Emile Jacqmain, 1210 Brussels, Belgium.

382 BE
COMMERCE EXTERIEUR DE L'U.E.B.L. AVEC LES PAYS DE L'EST/BUITENLANDSE HANDEL VAN DE B.L.E.U. MET DE OOSTLANDEN. ceased 1976. a. Office Belge du Commerce Exterieur, 162 Blvd. Emile Jacqmain, 1210 Brussels, Belgium.

CESSATIONS

382 BE
COMMERCE EXTERIEUR DE L'U.E.B.L. AVEC LES PAYS DE LA C.E.E./BUITLANDSE HANDEL VAN DE B.L.E.U. MET DE E.E.G.-LIDSTATEN. ceased 1976. a. Office Belge du Commerce Exterieur, 162 Blvd. Emile Jacqmain, 1210 Brussels, Belgium.

382 BE
COMMERCE EXTERIEUR DE L'U.E.B.L. AVEC LES PAYS INDUSTRIALISES (AUTRE QUE LES PAYS DE LA C.E.E. ET L'A.E.L.E.)/BUITENLANDSE HANDEL VAN DE B.L.E.U. MET DE INDUSTRIELANDEN (NIET E.E.G.- EN E.V.A.- LIDSTATEN). ceased 1976. a. Office Belge du Commerce Exterieur, 162 Blvd. Emile Jacqmain, 1210 Brussels, Belgium.

387.7 UK
COMMERCIAL AIR TRANSPORT INDUSTRY. ceased 1988. a. Interavia S.A. (Subsidiary of: Jane's Information Group), Sentinel House, 163 Brighton Rd., Coulsdon, Surrey CR3 2NX, England.
Former titles: World Commercial Aircraft; World Helicopter Systems; Military Avionic Equipment.

690 UK ISSN 0262-5334
HD1393.5
COMMERCIAL AND INDUSTRIAL FLOORSPACE STATISTICS. 1981-1989. a. Welsh Office, Economic and Statistical Services Division, New Crown Bldg., Cathays Park, Cardiff CF1 3NQ, Wales.

332.1 333.33 US
COMMERCIAL CONSTRUCTION REPORT. ceased. m. American Bankers Association, Real Estate Finance Center, 1120 Connecticut Ave., N.W., Washington, DC 20026.

639.2 US
COMMERCIAL FISHING NEWSLETTER. 1980-1989. q. (back issues avail.) Virginia Institute of Marine Science, Gloucester Point, VA 23062.

340 CN ISSN 0832-235X
KE916.22
COMMERCIAL LAW DIGEST. 1987-1990. w. (50/yr.). Carswell Publications, 2330 Midland Ave., Agincourt, Ont. M1S 1P7, Canada.

332.3 US
COMMERCIAL LENDER'S ALERT. ceased 1991. m. Warren, Gorham and Lamont Inc., One Penn Plaza, New York, NY 10119.

380.1 US ISSN 0270-2460
HD69.N4
COMMERCIAL NEWS U S A. NEW PRODUCTS ANNUAL DIRECTORY; international marketing information for the foreign service. ceased 1986. a. U.S. Department of Commerce, 14th St. between Constitution and E. St., N.W., Washington, DC 20230.

380 US ISSN 0010-3098
COMMERCIAL RECORD. ceased 199? w. Warren, Gorham and Lamont Inc., One Penn Plaza, New York, NY 10119.

387 UK
COMMERCIAL SHIPPER. ceased 1985 (Mar.). m. British Shippers Council, Hermes House, St. John's Rd., Tunbridge Wells, Kent TN4 9UZ, England.

629.1 US
COMMERCIAL SPACE. 1985-1986. q. McGraw-Hill, Inc., 1221 Ave. of the Americas, New York, NY 10020.

330 US ISSN 0735-9314
COMMERCIAL SPACE REPORT; a monthly newsletter on free enterprise in space. 1977-1989 (vol.13, no. 12). m. (looseleaf format; back issues avail.) Box 60547, Sunnyvale, CA 94088.

327 EI
COMMISSION OF THE EUROPEAN COMMUNITIES. INDEX TO (YEAR) C O M DOCUMENTS. (Council of Ministers) ceased 1987. a. Eurofi plc, Guidgate House, Pelican Lane, Newbury, Berkshire RGi3 1NX, England.
Formerly: Commission of the European Communities. Index to (Year) Documents.

354 EI ISSN 0256-7121
Z7165.E8
COMMISSION OF THE EUROPEAN COMMUNITIES. MONTHLY CATALOGUE. PART A: PUBLICATIONS. 1985-19?? m. Office for Official Publications of the European Communities, 2 rue Mercier, L-2985 Luxembourg, Luxembourg.

330 320 EI
COMMISSION OF THE EUROPEAN COMMUNITIES. STUDIES: SOCIAL POLICY SERIES. 1963-19?? irrege. Office for Official Publications of the European Communities, L-2985 Luxembourg, Luxembourg.
Formerly: Commission of the European Communities. Etudes: Serie Politique Sociale (ISSN 0069-6730)

323.4 301.412 US
COMMITTEE FOR HUMAN RIGHTS IN GRENADA. BULLETIN. 1987-1991. q. Committee for Human Rights in Grenada, Box 20714, Cathedral Finance Sta., New York, NY 10025.
Formerly: Grenada Bulletin.

621.381 UK ISSN 0953-0614
COMMODORE DISK USER. 1987-19?? bi-m. Argus Specialist Publications Ltd., Argus House, Boundary Way, Hemels, Hampstead, Herts HP2 7ST, England.

621.381 001.6 US ISSN 0744-8724
QA76.8.C63
COMMODORE MAGAZINE. 1981-19?? m. Commodore Magazine, Inc., 1200 Wilson Dr., West Chester, PA 19380.
Supersedes in part: Power - Play Magazine; Former titles: Commodore Microcomputers; Commodore - The Microcomputer Magazine; Commodore Interface.

155.5 US
COMMON FOCUS; an exchange of information about early adolescence. 1978-1989 (vol.9, no.1). irreg. (back issues avail.) University of North Carolina, Center for Early Adolescence, Ste. 211, Carr Mill Mall, Carrboro, NC 27510.

540 GW ISSN 0138-4074
COMMON NAME - KARTEI PFLANZENSCHUTZ- UND SCHAEDLINGSBEKAEMPFUNGSMITTEL. 1966-1990. a. V E B Fahlberg-List, Direktion Forschung, Informationsstelle, Alt Salbke 60-63, 3013 Magdeburg-SO, Germany.

330.1 CN ISSN 0319-7549
HB1
COMMON SENSE ECONOMICS. 1974-1985 (no.14). a. (back issues avail.) University of Waterloo, Department of Economics, Waterloo, Ont. N2L 3G1, Canada.

813 US ISSN 0010-3314
COMMONPLACE BOOK. 1964-19?? q. (looseleaf format) c/o Andrew Peck, Ed., 185 West End Ave., Apt. 11F, New York, NY 10023.

942 UK ISSN 0010-3411
DA10
COMMONWEALTH. 1958-1988. bi-m. (Royal Commonwealth Society and Commonwealth Foundation) World of Information, 21 Gold St., Saffron Walden, Essex CB10 1ES, England.
Formerly: Commonwealth Journal.

636 UK ISSN 0069-6927
COMMONWEALTH BUREAU OF ANIMAL HEALTH. REVIEW SERIES. (Former name of issuing body: Commonwealth Agricultural Bureaux) 1952-19?? irreg. (also avail. in microfiche; back issues avail.) C.A.B. International, Bureau of Animal Health, Wallingford, Oxon OX10 8DE, England.

635 UK ISSN 0069-6986
COMMONWEALTH BUREAU OF HORTICULTURE AND PLANTATION CROPS. HORTICULTURAL REVIEW. (Former name of issuing body: Commonwealth Agricultural Bureaux) 1969-19?? irreg. C.A.B. International, Bureau of Horticulture and Plantation Crops, Wallingford, Oxon OX10 8DE, England.

635 UK ISSN 0069-6994
COMMONWEALTH BUREAU OF HORTICULTURE AND PLANTATION CROPS. RESEARCH REVIEWS. (Former name of issuing body: Commonwealth Agricultural Bureaux) 1966-19?? irreg. C.A.B. International, Bureau of Horticulture and Plantation Crops, Wallingford, Oxon OX10 8DE, England.

633 635 UK ISSN 0069-7001
COMMONWEALTH BUREAU OF HORTICULTURE AND PLANTATION CROPS. TECHNICAL COMMUNICATIONS. (Former name of issuing body: Commonwealth Agricultural Bureaux) 1930-19?? irreg. C.A.B. International, Bureau of Horticulture and Plantation Crops, Wallingford, Oxon OX10 8DE, England.

320 US
COMMONWEALTH REPORT. 1989-1991; suspended. 10/yr. Commonwealth Institute, 186 Hamphire St., Cambridge, MA 02139.

690 AT
COMMONWEALTH SCIENTIFIC AND INDUSTRIAL RESEARCH ORGANIZATION. DIVISION OF BUILDING RESEARCH. TECHNICAL PAPER. 1954-1988 (vol.12, no.4). irreg. C.S.I.R.O., Division of Building Research, Graham Rd., Highett, Vic. 3190, Australia.

595.7 AT ISSN 0069-7338
COMMONWEALTH SCIENTIFIC AND INDUSTRIAL RESEARCH ORGANIZATION. DIVISION OF ENTOMOLOGY. TECHNICAL PAPER. 1957-19?? irreg. C.S.I.R.O., Editorial and Publications Service, P.O. Box 89, East Melbourne, Vic. 3002, Australia.

664 AT
COMMONWEALTH SCIENTIFIC AND INDUSTRIAL RESEARCH ORGANIZATION. DIVISION OF FOOD PROCESSING. TECHNICAL PAPER. 1956-19??; suspended. irreg. C.S.I.R.O., Division of Food Processing, P.O. Box 52, North Ryde, N.S.W. 2113, Australia.
Formerly: Commonwealth Scientific and Industrial Research Organization. Division of Food Research. Technical Paper (ISSN 0069-7427)

677 530 AT
COMMONWEALTH SCIENTIFIC AND INDUSTRIAL RESEARCH ORGANIZATION. DIVISION OF TEXTILE PHYSICS. ANNUAL REPORT. 1971-1987. a. C.S.I.R.O., Division of Textile Physics, P.O. Box 7, Ryde, N.S.W. 2112, Australia.

639.9 AT
COMMONWEALTH SCIENTIFIC AND INDUSTRIAL RESEARCH ORGANIZATION. DIVISION OF WILDLIFE AND ECOLOGY. TECHNICAL PAPER. 1958-1987; suspended. irreg. C.S.I.R.O., Division of Wildlife and Ecology, P.O. Box 84, Lyneham, A.C.T. 2602, Australia.
Former titles (until no.37, 1987): Commonwealth Scientific and Industrial Research Organization. Division of Wildlife and Rangelands Research. Technical Paper (ISSN 0812-2237); Commonwealth Scientific and Industrial Research Organization. Division of Wildlife Research. Technical Paper.

620 600 AT ISSN 0045-7647
COMMONWEALTH SCIENTIFIC AND INDUSTRIAL RESEARCH ORGANIZATION. INDUSTRIAL RESEARCH NEWS. 1957-1991. bi-m. C.S.I.R.O. (Dickson), P.O. Box 225, Dickson, A.C.T. 2602, Australia.

639 AT ISSN 0157-8081
COMMONWEALTH SCIENTIFIC AND INDUSTRIAL RESEARCH ORGANIZATION. MARINE LABORATORIES. FISHERY SITUATION REPORT. 1979-1987. irreg. C.S.I.R.O., Marine Laboratories, G.P.O. Box 1538, Hobart, Tas. 7001, Australia.

639 AT ISSN 0726-4283
COMMONWEALTH SCIENTIFIC AND INDUSTRIAL RESEARCH ORGANIZATION. MARINE LABORATORIES. MICROFICHE REPORT. 1978-19?? irreg. C.S.I.R.O., Marine Laboratories, G.P.O. Box 1538, Hobart, Tas. 7001, Australia.

633 AT ISSN 0069-7680
SB191.W5
COMMONWEALTH SCIENTIFIC AND INDUSTRIAL RESEARCH ORGANIZATION. WHEAT RESEARCH UNIT. REPORT. 1960-19?? a. C.S.I.R.O., Editorial & Publications Service, 314 Albert St., E. Melbourne, Vic. 3002, Australia.

330 327 UK ISSN 0950-7043
DA10
COMMONWEALTH TODAY. ceased. bi-m. (back issues avail.) World of Information, 21 Gold St., Saffron Walden, Essex CB10 1EJ, England.

250 BE
COMMUNAUTES ET LITURGIES; revue d'action liturgique et pastorale. 1919-1987 (no.6). 6/yr. Monastere de Saint Andre, Allee de Clerlande 1, B-1340 Ottignies, Belgium.
Formerly (until 1975): Paroisse et Liturgie (ISSN 0031-2347)

266 US ISSN 0279-1196
COMMUNICARE. 1926-1990. bi-m. (also avail. in microform from UMI) Christian Communications, Inc., Box 1601, Wichita, KS 67201.

Formerly (until 1981): Defender.

621.38 UK ISSN 0305-3601
TK5101.A1 CODEN: COBRDB
COMMUNICATION & BROADCASTING; information, practice, technique. 1974-198?; suspended. irreg. (reprint service avail. from UMI) Marconi Co. Ltd., Marconi House, Chelmsford, Essex CM1 1PL, England.
Formed by the merger of: Point to Point Communication (ISSN 0032-2334); Sound and Vision (ISSN 0038-1829)

301.16 US
COMMUNICATION: THE HUMAN CONTEXT. 1988-1990 (vol.4). irreg. Ablex Publishing Corporation, 355 Chestnut St., Norwood, NJ 07648.

634.9 FI ISSN 0358-9609
SD1
COMMUNICATIONES INSTITUTI FORESTALIS FENNIAE. 1919-1988 (vol.146). 10/yr. Metsantutkimuslaitos - Finnish Forest Research Institute, Unioninkatu 40 A, SF-00170 Helsinki, Finland.

301.16 SZ ISSN 0340-0158
COMMUNICATIONS; European Journal of Communication, Le Journal Europeen de la Communication, Die Europaeische Zeitschrift fuer Kommunikation. 1974-1988. 3/yr. (reprint service avail. from ISI) (Deutsche Gesellschaft fuer Kommunikationsforschung) Verlag Peter Lang AG, Jupiterstr. 15, CH-3000 Bern 15, Switzerland.

001.6 621.381 659.1US
COMMUNICATIONS CONSULTANT. 1985-1990. m. Jobson Publishing Corp., 352 Park Ave. S., New York, NY 10010.

621.38 JA
COMMUNICATIONS IN JAPAN. ceased. a. (Ministry of Posts and Telecommunications) Japan Times, Ltd., 4-5-4 Shibaura, Minato-ku, Tokyo 108, Japan.

621 US
COMMUNICATIONS PRODUCTS & SYSTEMS. 1985-198? bi-m. (tabloid format) Gordon Publications, Inc., 301 Gibraltar Dr., Morris Plains, NJ 07950.

621.38 US
COMMUNICATIONS STANDARDS MANAGEMENT. ceased 1991. base vol. (plus bi-m. updates). (looseleaf format) Auerbach Publishers (Subsidiary of: Warren, Gorham & Lamont), One Penn Plaza, New York, NY 10119.

621.3 380.3 US ISSN 1051-2691
COMMUNICATIONS SYSTEMS ENGINEERING: POSTAL APPLICATIONS. 1991-1992. q. Hemisphere Publishing Corporation (Subsidiary of: Taylor & Francis Group), 1900 Frost Rd., Ste. 101, Bristol, PA 19007-1598.

384.5 384.1 380.3 UK ISSN 0267-1395
COMMUNICATIONS SYSTEMS WORLDWIDE; international magazine of communications design. 1984-19?? m. (back issues avail.) Morgan-Grampian (Publishers) Ltd., 30 Calderwood St., London SE18 6QH, England.

621.3 US
COMMUNICATOR (INDIANAPOLIS); a TV technicians newsletter. 1958-198? irreg. (looseleaf format) R C A Corporation, Technical Services Training, 600 North Sherman Drive, Indianapolis, IN 46201.
Supersedes: R C A Plain Talk and Technical Tips (ISSN 0048-6582)

350 US
COMMUNIQUE (INDIANAPOLIS). ceased. q. Hudson Institute, Herman Kahn Center, 5395 Emerson Way, Box 26-919, Indianapolis, IN 46226-0919.
Formerly (until 1975): Hudson Newsletter.

305.412 CN ISSN 0710-5118
COMMUNIQU'ELLES. 1974-1991. bi-m. (back issues avail.) Editions Communiqu'elles, 3585 St. Urbain, Montreal, Que. H2X 2N6, Canada.

320.532 CN
COMMUNIST AND WORKERS PARTIES. INFORMATION BULLETIN. 1963-1989. m. (back issues avail.) Progress Books, 71 Bathurst St., 3rd Fl., Toronto, Ont. M5V 2P6, Canada.

320.532 CN ISSN 0010-3756
COMMUNIST VIEWPOINT. 1969-19?? q. (reprint service avail. from UMI) Progress Books, 72 Tecumseth St., Toronto, Ont. M5V 2R8, Canada.
Supersedes: Horizons.

320.532 CN ISSN 0709-3845
LE COMMUNISTE; revue theorique et politique. 1980-19?? q. 4164 rue Parthenais, Montreal, Que. H2K 3T9, Canada.

374 AT ISSN 0156-2878
COMMUNITY EDUCATION NEWSLETTER. 1976-1989 (vol.14, no.4). bi-m. (back issues avail.) Australian Association for Community Education, c/o Chisholm Institute, McMahon's Rd., Frankston, Vic. 3199, Australia.

001.644 US
COMMUNITY MEMORY NEWS. 1983-1988. a. (back issues avail.) Community Memory Project, 2617 San Pablo, Berkeley, CA 94702.

352.7 UK
COMMUNITY NETWORK. 1984-19?? 4/yr. Town & Country Planning Association, 17 Carlton House Terrace, London SW1Y 5AS, England.
Formerly: Network (London, 1984) (ISSN 0266-9129)

051 US
COMMUNITY NEWS (BOULDER); great places, faces and events. ceased 1988. bi-w. New Hope Communications, Inc., 1301 Spruce St., Boulder, CO 80302-4832.

658 US ISSN 0747-6086
COMMUNITY SERVICE BUSINESS. 1978-1989. 12/yr. M L P Enterprises, 236 E. Durham St., Box 18918, Philadelphia, PA 19119.
Formerly (until July 1984): C B O Management Report (ISSN 0272-6300)

610.73 UK ISSN 0260-5244
COMMUNITY VIEW; a journal for nurses working in the community. 1979-19?? q. Smith & Nephew, P.O. Box 81, Messle Rd., Hull HU3 2BN, England.

640.73 780 US
COMPACT DISC. 1986-1989. q. A B C Leisure Magazines, Inc., 825 Seventh Ave., New York, NY 10019.

621.31 BL
COMPANHIA PAULISTA DE FORCA E LUZ. BOLETIM ESTATISTICO; acompanhamento do mercado de energia eletrica relatorio estatistico anual. 1970-198? irreg. Companhia Paulista de Forca e Luz, Assessoria de Planejamento e Gestao Empresarial, Rodovia Campinas Mogi-Mirim, Km. 2,5 n. 1755, Caixa Postal 1808, Campinas - SP, Brazil.

051 US ISSN 0895-1721
COMPASSION MAGAZINE; a literary quarterly for social responsibility. 1988-198? 3/yr. Pittenbruach Press, 15 Walnut St., Box 553, Northampton, MA 01061.

317 GT ISSN 0588-912X
COMPENDIO ESTADISTICO CENTROAMERICANO. 1957-19?? a. General Treaty on Central American Economic Integration, Permanent Secretariat - Tratado General de Integracion Economica Centroamericana, 4a Avenida 10-25, Zona 14, Guatemala City, Guatemala.

612.015 616.97 UK ISSN 0263-7286
COMPLEMENT (SHEFFIELD). ceased 1991. m. (looseleaf format; back issues avail.) Sheffield University Biomedical Information Service (SUBIS), The University, Sheffield S10 2TN, England.

616.97 SZ ISSN 1012-8204
CODEN: CMPIE7
COMPLEMENT AND INFLAMMATION; laboratory and clinical research. 1984-1991. bi-m. (also avail. in microform from RPI) S. Karger AG, Allschwilerstr. 10, P.O. Box, CH-4009 Basel, Switzerland.
Formerly: Complement (ISSN 0253-5076)

780 UR
COMPOSER AND HIS SONGS. ceased 1986. 2/yr. Izdatel'stvo Muzyka, Ul. Neglinnaya 14, Moscow 103031, Russian S.F.S.R., U.S.S.R.

780 UK
COMPOSERS OF WALES SERIES. 1978-1980 (no.4). irreg. (Welsh Arts Council) University of Wales Press, 6 Gwennyth St., Cathays, Cardiff CF2 4YD, Wales.

618.97 DK
COMPREHENSIVE GERONTOLOGY. SECTION A: CLINICAL AND LABORATORY SCIENCES. 1987-198? (vol.2). 3/yr. Munksgaard International Publishers Ltd., Journals Division, 35 Noerre Soegade, P.O. Box 2148, DK-1016 Copenhagen K, Denmark.
Formerly: Comprehensive Gerontology. Serie A: Clinical Laboratory Sciences (ISSN 0902-0071)

155.67 DK
COMPREHENSIVE GERONTOLOGY. SECTION B: BEHAVIOURAL, SOCIAL AND APPLIED SCIENCES. 1987-198? (vol.2). 3/yr. Munksgaard International Publishers Ltd., Journals Division, 35 Noerre Soegade, P.O. Box 2148, DK-1016 Copenhagen K, Denmark.
Formerly: Comprehensive Gerontology. Serie B: Behavioural, Social and Applied Sciences (ISSN 0902-008X)

301.435 DK
COMPREHENSIVE GERONTOLOGY. SECTION C: INTERDISCIPLINARY TOPICS. 1987-198? (vol.2). a. Munksgaard International Publishers Ltd., Journals Division, 35 Noerre Soegade, P.O. Box 2148, DK-1016 Copenhagen K, Denmark.
Formerly: Comprehensive Gerontology. Serie C: Interdisciplinary Topics (ISSN 0902-0098)

384 US
COMPTEL MAGAZINE. 1991; announced, never published. q. (Competitive Telecommunications Association) Leo Douglas, Inc., 9607 Gayton Rd., Richmond, VA 23233.

624 621 US ISSN 0957-2899
COMPUTATIONAL MECHANICS COMMUNICATIONS. 1990; announced, never published. bi-m. Computational Mechanics Inc., 25 Bridge St., Billerica, MA 01821-1007.

001.644 DK ISSN 0573-9985
COMPUTER AIDED DESIGN I DANMARK. ceased 1985. a. Statens Byggeforskningsinstitut, P.O. Box 119, DK-2970 Hoersholm, Denmark.

658.8 658 621.381 US
COMPUTER & SOFTWARE NEWS. 1983-1989 (May). w. Lebhar-Friedman, Inc., 425 Park Ave., New York, NY 10022.

621.381 UK ISSN 0264-4479
COMPUTER ANSWERS; solves your micro queries & problems. 1982-1991. 12/yr. V N U Business Publications BV, 32-34 Broadwick St., London W1A 2HG, England.

651.8 UK ISSN 0308-4221
CODEN: CPUABQ
COMPUTER APPLICATIONS. 1969-198? s-a. University of Nottingham, Department of Geography, Nottingham NG7 2RD, England.
Formerly: Computer Applications in the Natural and Social Sciences (ISSN 0069-8105)

387 623.82 NE
COMPUTER APPLICATIONS IN SHIPPING AND SHIPBUILDING. 1974-1989 (vol.13). irreg. Elsevier Science Publishers B.V., Books Division, P.O. Box 211, 1000 AE Amsterdam, Netherlands.

001.6 011.7 621.381US
COMPUTER CONTENTS; semi-monthly compilation of tables of contents from more than 250 of the latest computer periodicals. 1983-1989 (Dec.). 24/yr. Institute for Scientific Information, 3501 Market St., Philadelphia, PA 19104.

001.64 338 021.381 US
COMPUTER DAILY; the daily newspaper for the computer industry. 1972-1989 (Apr.). d. Computer Age & E D P News Services (Subsidiary of: Millin Publishing Group, Inc.), 3918 Prosperity Ave., Ste. 310, Fairfax, VA 22031-3300.

651.8 001.6 US ISSN 0010-4558
QA76 CODEN: CODCB8
COMPUTER DECISIONS; information systems, automated data processing, problem solving, office automation. 1969-1990. m. (also avail. in microfilm from UMI) F M Computer Publications, 25 W. 43rd St., Ste. 707, New York, NY 10036.

CESSATIONS

621.381 US ISSN 0010-4582
COMPUTER DISPLAY REVIEW. 1966-1989. 2/yr. (looseleaf format) G M L Corporation, 594 Marrett Rd., Lexington, MA 02173.

001.644 IT
COMPUTER GRAFICA E APPLICAZIONI. ceased Dec. 1991. m. (11/yr.). Gruppo Editoriale Jackson S.p.A., Via Pola 9, 20124 Milan, Italy.

001.644 621.381 US ISSN 1041-2263
CODEN: CGREEV
COMPUTER GRAPHICS REVIEW. 1985-19?? m. Intertec Publishing Corp., 9221 Quivira Rd., Box 12901, Overland Park, KS 66212.

001.644 US
COMPUTER GRAPHICS SYSTEMS. 1988-19?? q. P T N Publishing Corp., 445 Broad Hollow Rd., Ste. 25, Melville, NY 11747.

001.644 AT
COMPUTER GRAPHICS TECHNOLOGY. 1981-19?? bi-m. Business Press International Pty. Ltd., 162 Goulburn St., Darlinghurst, N.S.W. 2010, Australia.
Former titles: Graphics Technology; Graphics Today.

001.644 US ISSN 0747-9670
T385 CODEN: CGTOE3
COMPUTER GRAPHICS TODAY. 1984-1989. m. (National Computer Graphics Association) Media Horizons, Inc., 445 Broadhollow Rd., Ste.21, Melville, NY 11747-4722.

658.8 621.381 US
COMPUTER HOT LINE. ceased. w. Heartland Communications Group, Inc., 900 Central Ave., Box 916, Fort Dodge, IA 50501.

621.381 001.642 US
COMPUTER HOT LINE WEEKLY (NEWSSTAND EDITION). ceased. w. Heartland Communications Group, Inc., 900 Central Ave., Box 916, Fort Dodge, IA 50501.
Supersedes: Micro-Line.

338 621.381 US ISSN 0748-0474
TS155.6 CODEN: CIREEB
COMPUTER-INTEGRATED MANUFACTURING REVIEW. 1984-198? q. (back issues avail.; reprint service avail.) Auerbach Publishers Inc. (Subsidiary of: Warren, Gorham & Lamont, Inc.), One Penn Plaza, New York, NY 10119.

658.8 US
COMPUTER MARKETPLACE MAGAZINE. 1986-198? bi-m. R K Productions, Inc., 16175 Monterey Rd., Morgan Hill, CA 95037-5452.

001.644 US
COMPUTER NETWORKING SYMPOSIUM. PROCEEDINGS. 1977-1988. a. (Institute of Electrical and Electronics Engineers, Inc.) I E E E Computer Society Press, 10662 Los Vaqueros Circle, Los Alamitos, CA 90720-1264.

001.6 621.381 UK
COMPUTER NEWSLETTER (BRACKNELL); application of computers to the building services industry. 1982-198? 4/yr. Building Services Research and Information Association, Old Bracknell Lane West, Bracknell, Berks. RG12 4AH, England.
Formerly: Microcomputer Newsletter (ISSN 0263-8908)

535 621.381 US ISSN 0955-355X
TA1630 CODEN: COOPE3
COMPUTER OPTICS. 1989-1991. 4/yr. (also avail. in microform; back issues avail.) (International Centre for Scientific and Technical Information, UR) Pergamon Press, Inc., Journals Division, 660 White Plains Rd., Tarrytown, NY 10591-5153.

380.3 659.1 US ISSN 0893-5947
COMPUTER P R UPDATE. 1983-19?? q. Cycon Communications Inc., Box 591, Addison, IL 60101-0591.

530.15 NE ISSN 0167-7977
CODEN: CPHREF
COMPUTER PHYSICS REPORTS; international review journal devoted to methods and algorithms in computational physics. (Supplement to: Computer Physics Communications) 1983-1990 (vol.12). bi-m. North-Holland (Subsidiary of: Elsevier Science Publishers B.V.), P.O. Box 211, 1000 AE Amsterdam, Netherlands.

338 658.182 US
COMPUTER PRODUCT SELLING. 1988-1989. 9/yr. Lebhar-Friedman, Inc., 425 Park Ave., New York, NY 10022.

001.6 US ISSN 0161-6862
COMPUTER PRODUCTS. 1979-198? 10/yr. (tabloid format) Gordon Publications, Inc., 301 Gibraltar Dr., Morris Plains, NJ 07950.

001.642 US ISSN 0736-3621
COMPUTER PROGRAMMING MANAGEMENT. (Sub-series of: Auerbach Information Management Series) 1974-1991. bi-m. (looseleaf format) Auerbach Publishers (Subsidiary of: Warren, Gorham & Lamont), One Penn Plaza, New York, NY 10119.

070.5 US
COMPUTER PUBLISHING. 1986-1991 (Apr.). m. Pacific Magazine Group, 513 Wilshire Blvd., Santa Monica, CA 90401.
Formerly (until Aug., 1990): Electronic Publishing and Printing.

658.8 US ISSN 0890-3980
CODEN: CORME9
COMPUTER RESELLER MONTHLY; the magazine for systems & software resellers. 1981-198? m. International Thomson Retail Press, Inc. (Subsidiary of: International Thomson Business Press, Inc.), 345 Park Ave., S., New York, NY 10010-1707.
Formerly: Computer Merchandising.

658.478 US
COMPUTER SECURITY PRODUCTS REPORT. 1986-1991. q. (also avail. in microfiche) Assets Protection Publishing, Box 5323, Madison, WI 53705.

001.6 621.381 US
COMPUTER STANDARDS CONFERENCE. PROCEEDINGS. 1986-1988. biennial. (Institute of Electrical and Electronics Engineers, Inc.) I E E E Computer Society Press, 10662 Los Vaqueros Circle, Los Alamitos, CA 90720-1264.

001.6 621.381 CN ISSN 0382-1005
COMPUTERS. 1971-19?? irreg. National Research Council of Canada, Division of Mechanical Engineering - Conseil National de Recherches du Canada, Montreal Road Laboratories, Ottawa, Ont. K1A 0R6, Canada.

001.6 US
COMPUTERS & INDUSTRIAL ENGINEERING ANNUAL CONFERENCE. PROCEEDINGS. ceased. a. Pergamon Press, Inc., Journals Division, 660 White Plains Rd., Tarrytown, NY 10591-5153.

370 510 US ISSN 0888-2193
COMPUTERS AND MATH SERIES. 1984-19?? irreg. (back issues avail.) Computer Science Press, Inc., 41 Madison Ave., 37th Fl., New York, NY 10010-3546.

001.6 900 CN ISSN 0384-5060
CODEN: CMDPDZ
COMPUTERS AND MEDIEVAL DATA PROCESSING/ INFORMATIQUE ET ETUDES MEDIEVALES. 1971-1987 (vol.17, no.2). 2/yr. Universite de Montreal, Institut d'Etudes Medievales, C.P. 6128, Succursale A, Montreal, Que. H3G 3J7, Canada.

001.3 621.381 100 US
COMPUTERS & PHILOSOPHY. 1986-1990. 3/yr. (also avail. on diskette; back issues avail.) Carnegie Mellon University, CDEC Bldg. B, Pittsburgh, PA 15213.
Formerly: Computers and Philosophy Newsletter (ISSN 0893-3278)

620 US ISSN 0734-5402
TA174
COMPUTERS FOR DESIGN & CONSTRUCTION. 1982-198? m. MetaData Inc., Box 585, Locust, NJ 07760.

370 US ISSN 0888-2177
COMPUTERS IN EDUCATION SERIES. 1982-19?? irreg. (back issues avail.) Computer Science Press, Inc., 41 Madison Ave., 37th Fl., New York, NY 10010-3546.

330 US ISSN 0887-980X
HF5549.5.D37
COMPUTERS IN PERSONNEL. 1986-1989. q. Auerbach Publishers Inc. (Subsidiary of: Warren, Gorham & Lamont, Inc.), One Penn Plaza, New York, NY 10119.

621.381 500 US ISSN 0893-1909
COMPUTERS IN SCIENCE. 1987-198? bi-m. (also avail. in microform; microfilm; back issues avail.) I D G Communications (Peterborough), 80 Elm St., Peterborough, NH 03458.

621.381 US
COMPUTERS - R - DIGITAL. 1979-198? m. Directory Database, Box 8669, Redbank, NJ 07701.

371.394 621.381 US ISSN 0737-500X
LB1028.5
COMPUTERS, READING AND LANGUAGE ARTS; a teaching resource. 1983-198? q. Modern Learning Publishers, Inc., 1308 East 38th St., Oakland, CA 94602.

370 GW
COMPUTERSTUNDE; Lehrblaetter fuer den Informationstechnischen Unterricht. 1987-1990. s-a. (looseleaf format; back issues avail.) A L S Verlag GmbH, Justus-von-Liebig-Str. 19, 6057 Dietzenbach, Germany.

001.6 621.381 629.8US
COMPUTERWORLD FOCUS. 1985-1989 (Dec.). 10/yr. (also avail. in microfilm) C W Communications, Inc., 375 Cochituate Rd., Box 9171, Framingham, MA 01701-9171.
Formerly (until 1985): Computerworld's Office Automation.

001.642 621.381 US ISSN 1043-0792
COMPUTE'S AMIGA RESOURCE. 1989-1990. m. Compute Publications, Inc. (Subsidiary of: General Media International Limited), 324 W. Wendover Ave., Ste. 200, Greensboro, NC 27408.

001.6 621.381 US ISSN 0895-9595
QA76.8.A66
COMPUTE'S APPLE APPLICATIONS. 1985-198? 6/yr. (back issues avail.) Compute! Publications, Inc. (Subsidiary of: American Broadcasting Companies, Inc.), 324 W. Wendover Ave., Ste. 200, Box 5406, Greensboro, NC 27408.
Formerly: Compute's Apple: Special Applications Issue.

621.381 US ISSN 0737-3716
QA76.8.V5
COMPUTE'S GAZETTE; for Commodore Personal Computer users. 1983-1990. m. (also avail. in microform from UMI; back issues avail.; reprint service avail. from UMI; avail. on diskette) Compute Publications, Inc. (Subsidiary of: General Media International Limited), 324 W. Wendover Ave., Ste. 200, Greensboro, NC 27408.

621.381 US
COMPUTE'S GAZETTE DISK & MAGAZINE. ceased 1990. m. Compute Publications, Inc. (Subsidiary of: General Media International Limited), 324 W. Wendover Ave., Ste. 200, Greensboro, NC 27408.

001.6 621.381 US ISSN 0893-8261
COMPUTE'S P C MAGAZINE; for IBM, Tandy, & PC compatibles. 1987-1990. m. Compute Publications, Inc. (Subsidiary of: General Media International Limited), 324 W. Wendover Ave., Ste. 200, Greensboro, NC 27408.

001.6 621.381 330 US ISSN 0276-5756
COMPUTING RESOURCES FOR THE PROFESSIONAL. 1981-198? bi-m. University of Washington, Academic Computing Services, HG-45, 3737 Brooklyn Ave., N.E., Seattle, WA 98105.

001.6 UK ISSN 0142-7210
CODEN: COMTD4
COMPUTING TODAY. 1979-19?? m. Argus Specialist Publications Ltd., Argus House, Boundary Way, Hemels, Hampstead, Herts HP2 7ST, England.
Incorporates: Business Micro.

800 US ISSN 1042-9948
COMSTOCK QUARTERLY; the portfolio of Western culture. 1989-1990. q. (back issues avail.) Comstock Chronicle Inc., Box 436, Virginia City, NV 89440.

314 IT ISSN 0010-4957
COMUNE DI ROMA. UFFICIO DI STATISTICA E CENSIMENTO. BOLLETTINO STATISTICO. 1877-1968. irreg. Comune di Roma, Ufficio di Statistica e Censimento, Via della Greca 5, 00186 Rome, Italy.

CESSATIONS 5171

785.06 CN ISSN 0707-5103
CON BRIO. 1977-198? s-a. National Arts Centre Orchestra, Ottawa, Ont. K1P 5W1, Canada.

618 616.4 370.15 US ISSN 1042-1297
CONCEIVE MAGAZINE; the magazine of infertility issues. 1989-19?? bi-m. (back issues avail.) Knipper Publishing, Inc., Box 2047, Danville, CA 94526.

615.9 SZ ISSN 0254-8739
CONCEPTS IN TOXICOLOGY. 1984-19?? irreg. S. Karger AG, Allschwilerstrasse 10, P.O. Box, CH-4009 Basel, Switzerland.

333.7 US
CONCERN BULLETIN. ceased. q. Concern, 1749 Columbia Rd., N.W., Washington, DC 20009.

780 UR
CONCERT REPERTOIRE OF BAYAN PLAYER. ceased 1989 (no.9). irreg. Izdatel'stvo Muzyka, Ul. Neglinnaya 14, Moscow 103031, Russian S.F.S.R., U.S.S.R.
  Formerly: Album of Concert Pieces for Bayan-Accordion.

352.7 US
CONDOMINIUM DEVELOPMENT GUIDE. ceased 199? a. (to update base volume). Warren, Gorham and Lamont Inc., One Penn Plaza, New York, NY 10119.

664.15 658.8 US ISSN 0010-5457
CONFECTIONER; candy technology, marketing, merchandising. 1916-19?? bi-m. Confectioner Publishing Co., c/o Gertrude Kluck, Ed., 1960 S. 90th St., Milwaukee, WI 53227.

970 355 US ISSN 0734-3671
CONFEDERATE HISTORICAL INSTITUTE JOURNAL. 1979-1990. q. (back issues avail.) Confederate Historical Institute, Box 7388, Little Rock, AR 72217.

690 BE ISSN 0045-8023
CONFEDERATION NATIONALE DE LA CONSTRUCTION. ANNUAIRE. 1948-1985. a. Confederation Nationale de la Construction, Lombardstraat 34-42, B-1000 Brussels, Belgium.

332.6 US ISSN 0896-2510
CONFERENCE BOARD. UTILITY INVESTMENT REPORT. 1958-1988 (vol.2). q. Conference Board, Inc., 845 Third Ave., New York, NY 10022.
  Former titles: Conference Board. Utility Investment Statistics. Utility Appropriations (ISSN 0360-523X); Conference Board. Investment Statistics. Utility Appropriations (ISSN 0547-7301)

330.9 US ISSN 0010-5554
HC101   CODEN: SBCBEK
CONFERENCE BOARD STATISTICAL BULLETIN. 1968-1989 (Dec.). m. Conference Board, Inc., 845 Third Ave., New York, NY 10022.

658 US ISSN 0896-2553
    CODEN: CBMFE8
CONFERENCE BOARD'S MANAGEMENT BRIEFING: BUSINESS FINANCE. 1986-1990 (Jan.-Feb.). bi-m. Conference Board, Inc., 845 Third Ave., New York, NY 10022.

330.9 US
CONFERENCE ON AMERICAN ECONOMIC ENTERPRISE. PAPERS. ceased 1985 (vol.4). irreg. Sleepy Hollow Restorations, Inc., Tarrytown, NY 10591.

331.1 II ISSN 0069-8555
CONFERENCE ON HUMAN RELATIONS IN INDUSTRY. PROCEEDINGS. 1959-1976. a. South India Textile Research Association, Coimbatore 641014, India.

011 UK ISSN 0260-8316
T391
CONFERENCES AND EXHIBITIONS INTERNATIONAL. 1954-1989. m. International Trade Publications Ltd., Queensway House, 2 Queensway, Redhill, Surrey RH1 1QS, England.
  Former titles (until 1980): Conferences and Exhibitions (ISSN 0306-9397); Conferences, Exhibitions and Executive Travel (ISSN 0010-5597); Conference News.

011 910.2 UK ISSN 0260-776X
CONFERENCES MEETINGS & EXHIBITIONS WELCOME. 1979-19?? a. Lewis Productions Ltd., Unit 3, River Gardens Bus. Centre, Spur Rd., Feltham, Middx TW14 0SN, England.

646.724 659.152 US
CONFETTI. (Six different eds. avail.) 1989-1991. bi-m. Communications Venture Group, Ltd., 208 E. 51st St., New York, NY 10022.

054.1 FR
CONFIDENCES MAGAZINE. ceased. w. Edi-Monde, 25 Rue de Berri, 75388 Paris Cedex 8, France.
  Formerly: Mon Journal Confidences (ISSN 0026-9174)

332.6 US
CONFIDENTIAL REPORT FROM ZURICH. 1985-198? m. American Media Group, 951 Broken Sound Pkwy., N.W., Boca Raton, FL 33431.

301.2 PE
CONGRESO INTERNACIONAL DE AMERICANISTAS. ACTAS. 1971-1975 (no.6). irreg. (back issues avail.) (Instituto de Estudios Peruanos) I E P Ediciones, Horacio Urteaga 694 (Campe de Marte), Lima 11, Peru.

296 AG
CONGRESO JUDIO LATINOAMERICANO. COLOQUIO. 1979-1990 (no.23). 3/yr. Congreso Judio Latinoamericano - World Jewish Congress, Larrea 744, 1030 Buenos Aires, Argentina.

011 GW ISSN 0233-2213
CONGRESS CALENDAR G D R; Kongresse, Symposien, Tagungen, Messen und Austellungen in der DDR. (German Democratic Republic) 1985-1991. a. Zentralinstitut fuer Information und Dokumentation der D D R, Koepenicker Str. 80-82, 1020 Berlin, Germany.

331 US ISSN 0010-6143
CONNECTICUT. LABOR DEPARTMENT. BULLETIN. 1936-19?? bi-m. Labor Department, 200 Folly Brook Blvd., Wethersfield, CT 06109.
  Formerly: Connecticut Labor Department. Monthly Bulletin.

614.7 US
CONNECTICUT ENVIRONMENT. 1973-1991 (Jun.). m. (11/yr.). Department of Environmental Protection, State Office Bldg., Rm. 112, Hartford, CT 06106.
  Formerly: Connecticut. Department of Environmental Protection. Citizens' Bulletin.

011 US
CONNECTICUT PERIODICAL INDEX. 1981-1986. q. (plus s-a. & a. cum.). Box 4050, Stamford, CT 06907-0050.

974 US ISSN 0090-8517
TG1
CONNECTICUT RIVER VALLEY COVERED BRIDGE SOCIETY. BULLETIN. 1954-1989. q. Connecticut River Valley Covered Bridge Society, 73 Ash St., Manchester, NH 03104.

910.09 US
CONNECTICUT TRAVELS. ceased. m. Totoket Communications, Inc., 245 College St., New Haven, CT 06510.

001.644 621.381 US ISSN 0894-170X
CONNECTIONS (FULLERTON, 1987); the newsletter for networking Macintoshes. 1987-1992. 8/yr. (back issues avail.) Box 5894, Fullerton, CA 92635.

312 AG
CONSEJO LATINOAMERICANO DE CIENCIAS SOCIALES. SERIE POBLACION. INFORME DE INVESTIGACION. 1973-19?? irreg. Consejo Latinoamericano de Ciencias Sociales, Callao 875, 1023 Buenos Aires, Argentina.

001 502 AG
CONSEJO NACIONAL DE INVESTIGACIONES CIENTIFICAS Y TECNICAS. INFORME SOBRE UN ANO DE LABOR. ceased. irreg. Consejo Nacional de Investigaciones Cientificas y Tecnicas, Rivadavia 1917, 1033 Buenos Aires, Argentina.

025 US ISSN 0190-3608
Z699.4.C25
CONSER TABLES. 1979-19?? irreg. (looseleaf format) U.S. Library of Congress, Serial Record Division, Washington, DC 20541.

320 US ISSN 0146-0978
AP2
CONSERVATIVE DIGEST. 1975-19?? 11/yr. (reprint service avail. from UMI) Second Opinion Publications, 1201 S. Eads St., Ste. 1802, Arlington, VA 22202-2845.

352.7 US
CONSERVE NEIGHBORHOODS. 1978-19?? 10/yr. (back issues avail.) National Trust for Historic Preservation, 1785 Massachusetts Ave. N.W., Washington, DC 20036.

379 US ISSN 0095-5329
LA246
CONSOLIDATED REPORT ON ELEMENTARY AND SECONDARY EDUCATION IN COLORADO. ceased. a. Department of Education, State Office Bldg., 201 E. Colfax Ave., Denver, CO 80203.

320 US ISSN 0882-5955
KF4546.A3
CONSTITUTION (WASHINGTON). 1971-1988. m. (tabloid format; back issues avail.) National Center for Constitutional Studies, Box 37110, Washington, DC 20013.
  Formerly (until 1985): Freemen Digest (ISSN 8755-4364); **Supersedes (in 1982):** Freemen Report.

342 US
CONSTITUTIONAL LIMITATIONS ON CRIMINAL PROCEDURES. ceased. base vol. (plus a. suppl.). Shepard's - McGraw-Hill, Inc., Box 35300, Colorado Springs, CO 80935-3500.

690 622 SA
CONSTRUCTION & MINING EQUIPMENT SELECTOR. ceased. 6/yr. Westbourne-Maclean Hunter (Pty.) Ltd., Nedbank East City, 120 End St., P.O. Box 6110, Johannesburg 2000, South Africa.

690 GW
CONSTRUCTION ANNUAL. 1984-1990. a. Vogel-Verlag und Druck KG, Max-Planck-Str. 7-9, Postfach 67 40, 8700 Wuerzburg 1, Germany.

690 340 US ISSN 0892-4619
CONSTRUCTION CONSULTANT. 1987-198? bi-m. (back issues avail.) Professional Education Systems, Inc., 200 Spring St., Box 1208, Eau Claire, WI 54702.

616.8 301.1 US
CONSTRUCTIVE ACTION NEWSLETTER. 1960-1989 (Dec.). m. (processed) (American Conference of Therapeutic Self Help, Self Health, Social Clubs A. C.T.) A.C.T.-Action Press, c/o Sr. Shirley Mae Burghard, Ed., Ross Towers Apt. B-1104, 710 Lodi St., Syracuse, NY 13203.
  Supersedes: Constructive Action for Good Health; **Formerly:** Constructive Action for Good Mental Health (ISSN 0010-6992)

610 SP ISSN 0210-5632
CONSULTA. ceased. w. (back issues avail.) Editores Medicos, S.A., Paseo de la Castellana, 53, 28046 Madrid, Spain.

385.264 US
CONSULTANT EXCHANGE. 1975-1990. 9/yr. National Moving and Storgae Association., 1500 N. Beauregard St., Alexandria, VA 22311-1715.

370.15 500 150 US ISSN 8756-6508
CONSULTATION; an international journal. 1980-1990 (vol.9). q. (reprint service avail. from UMI) Human Sciences Press, Inc. (Subsidiary of: Plenum Publishing Corp.), 233 Spring St., New York, NY 10013-1578.

687 640.73 US
CONSUMER AFFAIRS NEWSLETTER. ceased. irreg. American Apparel Manufacturers Association, 2500 Wilson Blvd., Ste. 301, Arlington, VA 22201.

332.7 346.066 US
CONSUMER CREDIT LAW REVIEW. 1989; published only once. q. N I L S Publishing Company (Subsidiary of: Capital Cities - A B C, Inc. Company), Box 2507, Chatsworth, CA 91311.

332.3 US
CONSUMER CREDIT LETTER; for all consumer lenders. 1974-1987. w. (back issues avail.) Business Publishers, Inc., 951 Pershing Dr., Silver Spring, MD 20910-4464.

5172 CESSATIONS

Formerly: Washington Credit Letter (ISSN 0742-2008)

621.38   US   ISSN 0362-4722
HD9696.A3
CONSUMER ELECTRONICS. 1972-1990 (Feb.). m. Fairchild Publications, Inc., 7 E. 12th St., New York, NY 10003.

640.73   NZ   ISSN 0114-5436
CONSUMER FOOD AND HEALTH. 1989-1990. bi-m. Consumers' Institute, Private Bag, Te Aro, Wellington, New Zealand.

312 658   US   ISSN 0893-3561
HB871
CONSUMER MARKETS ABROAD. 1981-1988 (vol.7, no. 11). m. (also avail. in microfiche; back issues avail.; reprint service avail. from UMI) American Demographics, Inc., (Subsidiary of: Dow Jones & Co., Inc.), 108 N. Cayuga St., Ithaca, NY 14851.
Formerly: International Demographics (ISSN 0731-5414)

330.9   UK
CONSUMER MARKETS IN CENTRAL AND EAST AFRICA. published only once, 1986. biennial. Euromonitor Publications Ltd., 87-88 Turnmill St., London EC1M 5QU, England.

330.9   UK
CONSUMER MARKETS IN THE FAR EAST. published only once, 1985. irreg. Euromonitor Publications Ltd., 87-88 Turnmill St., London EC1M 5QU, England.

640.73   NZ   ISSN 0114-541X
CONSUMER VOICE. (Supplement to: Consumer) ceased 1990 (no.16). m. Consumers' Institute, Private Bag, Te Aro, Wellington, New Zealand.

327 943.6 970   AU   ISSN 0010-7239
CONTACT. 1954-1990. q. Oesterreichisch-Amerikanische Gesellschaft - Austro-American Society, Stallburggasse 2, A-1010 Vienna, Austria.

333.7   AT   ISSN 0728-7569
CONTACT (GOODNA, QLD.). 1971-1988. q. Conservation and Bush Rescue Association, c/o Marcel Morain, Ed., 13 Curtin St., Bethalia, Qld. 4205, Australia.

051   US
CONTACT (GRAWN). ceased 1990 (Feb.). m. c/o TV Contact Publishing, 2701 W. Waters Ave., Ste. 102, Tampa, FL 33614-1832.

617.752   UK
CONTAX. 1986-1991. bi-m. (back issues avail.) Reed Business Publishing Ltd., Enterprise Publishing, Quadrant House, The Quadrant, Sutton, Surrey SM2 5AS, England.

700   US
CONTEMPORARY AMERICAN ART CRITICS. ceased 1991 (Jun.). irreg. U M I Research Press, 300 N. Zeeb Rd., Ann Arbor, MI 48106-1346.

614   US
CONTEMPORARY COMMUNITY HEALTH SERIES. ceased. irreg. University of Pittsburgh Press, 127 N. Bellefield Ave., Pittsburgh, PA 15260.

614   NZ
CONTEMPORARY HEALTH ISSUES. ceased 1989. irreg. Health Statistical Sevices, 133 Molesworth St., Wellington, New Zealand.
Formerly: Trends in Health and Health Services (ISSN 0550-824X)

616.02   US   ISSN 1050-9607
CODEN: CIMDEH
CONTEMPORARY MANAGEMENT IN INTERNAL MEDICINE. 1990-1992 (Feb.). bi-m. Churchill Livingstone Medical Journals, 650 Ave. of the Americas, New York, NY 10011.

100   US   ISSN 0414-7790
CONTEMPORARY PHILOSOPHY SERIES. ceased. irreg. Cornell University Press, 124 Roberts Pl., Ithaca, NY 14850.

616.89   US   ISSN 0277-8041
RC321   CODEN: CPCHDR
CONTEMPORARY PSYCHIATRY; a journal of critical review. ceased 1990 (vol.9). q. (also avail. in microfilm from JSC) Plenum Press, 233 Spring St., New York, NY 10013.

615.842   CN   ISSN 0835-4545
CONTEMPORARY RADIOLOGY; international radiology news. 1987-19?? q. Medicopea International Inc., 8200 Decarie Blvd., Suite 220, Montreal, PQ H4P 2P5, Canada.

200   US
CONTEMPORARY RELIGIOUS MOVEMENTS: A WILEY-INTERSCIENCE SERIES. 1974-1980. irreg., unnumbered. John Wiley & Sons, Inc., 605 Third Ave., New York, NY 10158-0012.

792 800   US
CONTEMPORARY SCRIPTS. (Subseries of: V R I Theater Library) 1986-198? 10/yr. (back issues avail.) V R I Arts Publishers, Box 1208, Imperial Beach, CA 92032.

340   US
CONTEMPT. ceased. bi-m. National Lawyers Guild (Seattle), 411 Smith Tower, Seattle, WA 98104.

808.8   US   ISSN 1041-1771
E183.8.S65
CONTENTIONS (NEW YORK). 1981-1990 (Dec.). 11/yr. (combined Jul.-Aug.). Committee for the Free World, 120 E. 81st St., Ste. 7H, New York, NY 10028-1428.

374.8   CN   ISSN 0045-8384
CONTINUING EDUCATION DIRECTORY FOR METROPOLITAN TORONTO. 1969-1989. s-a. Metropolitan Toronto Library Board, 789 Yonge St., Toronto, Ont. M4W 2G8, Canada.

800   US
CONTRABAND (SUMAS). 1971-1985; suspended. irreg. Contraband Press, c/o Kilgore, 5136 Reese Hill Rd., Sumas, WA 98295-8603.

355 363.35   US
CONTRACTING INTELLIGENCE. ceased 1990. bi-w. (back issues avail.) Forecast International Inc. - D M S, 22 Commerce Rd., Newtown, CT 06470.

001.642   US
CONTRACTS REFERENCE DIRECTORY. ceased. irreg. (Association of Data Processing Service Organizations) A D A S P O, The Computer Software and Services Industry Association, 1300 N. 17th St., Ste. 300, Arlington, VA 22209.

200   US   ISSN 0164-5587
CONTRAST. 1982-1990 (Jul.). bi-m. (back issues avail.) Bible Science Association, Box 32457, Minneapolis, MN 55432-0457.

069   CN
CONTRIBUTIONS TO MUSEUM STUDIES. announced, never published. irreg. Royal British Columbia Museum, 675 Bellville St., Victoria, B.C. V8V 1X4, Canada.
Supersedes in part: Syesis (ISSN 0082-0601)

560 551   NE   ISSN 0165-280X
CONTRIBUTIONS TO TERTIARY AND QUATERNARY GEOLOGY. 1978-1989 (vol.26). q. E.J. Brill, P.O. Box 9000, 2300 PA Leiden, Netherlands.

575   SZ   ISSN 0376-4230
CODEN: CVEVDJ
CONTRIBUTIONS TO VERTEBRATE EVOLUTION. ceased. irreg. (reprint service avail. from ISI) S. Karger AG, Allschwilerstrasse 10, P.O. Box, CH-4009 Basel, Switzerland.

612.387   US   ISSN 0892-4295
CONTROL DATA WORLD; the independent publication for Control Data systems users. 1987-1989. m. (tabloid format; reprint service avail.) Publications & Communications, Inc., 12416 Hymeadow Dr., Austin, TX 78750-1896.

657 370   US   ISSN 8756-5684
CONTROLLERS QUARTERLY. 1985-1991. 4/yr. (back issues avail.) National Association of Accountants, Controllers Council, 10 Paragon Dr., Montvale, NJ 07645-1760.

642.59 610 658   US   ISSN 0887-0144
CONVENIENCE CARE UPDATE. 1984-1990. m. (back issues avail.; reprint service avail.) American Health Consultants, Six Piedmont Center, Ste. 400, 3525 Piedmont Rd., N.E., Atlanta, GA 30305.
Formerly (until 1986): Urgent Care Update.

658.87   US
HF5469.5
CONVENIENCE STORE MANAGEMENT; the national magazine for convenience stores executives and suppliers. 1974-1990. m. Capital Cities, 825 Seventh Ave., 6th Fl., New York, NY 10019.
Formerly: Convenience Store Merchandiser (ISSN 0095-7151)

359   UK
CONVENTIONAL AND NUCLEAR SUBMARINES OF THE WORLD. ceased 1988. a. Interavia S.A. (Subsidiary of: Jane's Information Group), Sentinel House, 163 Brighton Rd., Coulsdon, Surrey CR3 2NX, England.

282   SZ   ISSN 0010-8154
BX801
CONVERGENCE. 1935-1991; suspended. s-a. International Catholic Movement for Intellectual and Cultural Affairs - Pax Romana, General Secretariat, B.P. 85, 37-39 Rue de Vermont, CH-1211 Geneva 20-CIC, Switzerland.

664   US   ISSN 0886-943X
TX1
COOK'S; America's food authority. 1980-1990. 10/yr. Pennington Publishing, Inc., 2710 North Ave., Bridgeport, CT 06604.

500 641.5 301.42   US
COOKSTOVE NEWS. 1981-1988. q. (back issues avail.) Aprovecho Institute, 80574 Hazelton Rd., Cottage Grove, OR 97424-9711.

334   SZ
COOP FACHBLATT FUER UNTERNEHMUNGSFUEHRUNG/ REVUE D'ECONOMIE D'ENTERPRISE. 1968-1982. m. Coop Schweiz, Postfach 2550, 4002 Basel, Switzerland.

420 810   GW   ISSN 0069-9780
COOPER MONOGRAPHS ON ENGLISH AND AMERICAN LANGUAGE AND LITERATURE. 1956-1991. irreg. K.G. Saur Verlag KG, Ortlerstr. 8, 8000 Munich 70, Germany.

334   II   ISSN 0045-8503
COOPERATOR'S BULLETIN. ceased 1986. m. Jammu and Kashmir Cooperative Union, Vir Marg, Jammu, India.

616   US
COPE; oncology news for professionals. 1986-1989 (vol.3, no.6). 10/yr. Pulse Publications, Inc., Box 1700, Franklin, TN 37065.

651.2   US
COPIER DUPLICATOR NEWS. (Update to: Datapro Reports on Copiers and Duplicators) ceased. Datapro Information Services Group (Subsidiary of: McGraw-Hill, Inc.), 600 Delran Pkwy., Delran, NJ 08075.

070 659.1   GW
COPY; Magazin fuer Medien, Kommunikation, und Kreation. (Supplements avail.) 1903-1989. w. Handelsblatt GmbH, Postfach 102717, 4000 Duesseldorf 1, Germany.
Formerly (until 1987): Z V und Z V (Zeitungsverleger und Zeitschriftenverleger) (ISSN 0044-1511)

616.1   GW   ISSN 0721-393X
COR & CORONARIEN; Herz und Kreislauf aktuell. 1981-19?? irreg. (back issues avail.) (Bayer AG, P M I Verlag GmbH) August-Schanz-Str. 21, 6000 Frankfurt a.M. 50, Germany.

623.4   US   ISSN 0590-6776
TS532
CORD SPORTFACTS GUNS GUIDE. ceased 1985. a. Cord Communications Corp., 130 W. 42nd St., New York, NY 10036.

799.2   US   ISSN 0092-8216
SK1
CORD SPORTFACTS: HUNTING. ceased 1985. a. Cord Communications Corp., 130 W. 42nd St., New York, NY 10036.

615.37 616.97   US
CORE SERIES IN PRIMARY CARE: ALLERGY - IMMUNOLOGY GUIDE. 1987; ceased same year. m. Core Medical Journals (Subsidiary of: Excerpta Medica, Inc.), 3131 Princeton Pike, Bldg. 2A, Lawrenceville, NJ 08648.

616.7 US
CORE SERIES IN PRIMARY CARE: ARTHRITIS - RHEUMATOLOGY GUIDE. 1987; ceased same year. m. Core Medical Journals (Subsidiary of: Excerpta Medica, Inc.), 3131 Princeton Pike, Bldg. 2A, Lawrenceville, NJ 08648.

616.1 US
CORE SERIES IN PRIMARY CARE: CARDIOLOGY GUIDE. 1987; ceased same year. m. Core Medical Journals (Subsidiary of: Excerpta Medica, Inc.), 3131 Princeton Pike, Bldg. 2A, Lawrenceville, NJ 08648.

616.462 US
CORE SERIES IN PRIMARY CARE: DIABETES MANAGEMENT GUIDE. 1987; ceased same year. m. Core Medical Journals (Subsidiary of: Excerpta Medica, Inc.), 3131 Princeton Pike, Bldg. 2A, Lawrenceville, NJ 08648.

616.3 US
CORE SERIES IN PRIMARY CARE: GASTROENTEROLOGY GUIDE. 1987; ceased same year. m. Core Medical Journals (Subsidiary of: Excerpta Medica, Inc.), 3131 Princeton Pike, Bldg. 2A, Lawrenceville, NJ 08648.

618.97 US
CORE SERIES IN PRIMARY CARE: GERIATRIC MEDICINE GUIDE. 1987; ceased same year. m. Core Medical Journals (Subsidiary of: Excerpta Medica, Inc.), 3131 Princeton Pike, Bldg. 2A, Lawrenceville, NJ 08648.

616.9 US
CORE SERIES IN PRIMARY CARE: INFECTIOUS DISEASE GUIDE. 1987; ceased same year. m. Core Medical Journals (Subsidiary of: Excerpta Medica, Inc.), 3131 Princeton Pike, Bldg. 2A, Lawrenceville, NJ 08648.

616.8 US
CORE SERIES IN PRIMARY CARE: PSYCHIATRY IN PRIMARY CARE GUIDE. 1987; ceased same year. m. Core Medical Journals (Subsidiary of: Excerpta Medica, Inc.), 3131 Princeton Pike, Bldg. 2A, Lawrenceville, NJ 08648.

610 155.3 US
CORE SERIES IN PRIMARY CARE: SEXUAL MEDICINE GUIDE. 1987; ceased same year. m. Core Medical Journals (Subsidiary of: Excerpta Medica, Inc.), 3131 Princeton Pike, Bldg. 2A, Lawrenceville, NJ 08648.

630 US
CORNELL INTERNATIONAL AGRICULTURE MIMEOGRAPHS. 1963-198? irreg. (3-4/yr.). Cornell University, Program in International Agriculture, 384 Caldell Hall, Ithaca, NY 14853.
Formerly: Cornell International Agricultural Development Mimeographs (ISSN 0070-0010)

614.8 US
CORNELL RECOMMENDATIONS TO HOMEOWNERS FOR CHEMICAL CONTROL OF BITING FLIES IN NEW YORK STATE. ceased. irreg. Cornell University, Media Services, 7-8 Business and Technology Park, Ithaca, NY 14850.

632.9 US
CORNELL RECOMMENDATIONS TO MUNICIPALITIES FOR CHEMICAL CONTROL OF BITING FLIES IN NEW YORK STATE. ceased. irreg. Cornell University, Media Services, 7-8 Business and Technology Park, Ithaca, NY 14850.

891.85 NZ ISSN 0113-2644
CORNUCOPIA MAGAZINE. 1983-1989. q. (back issues avail.) Cornucopia Magazine Society Inc., P.O. Box 13-335, Christchurch 1, New Zealand.

657 US ISSN 0745-5119
HF5686.C7
CORPORATE ACCOUNTING. 1983-199? q. (also avail. in microform from UMI) Warren, Gorham and Lamont Inc., One Penn Plaza, New York, NY 10119.

330.9 US
CORPORATE BARTER & COUNTERTRADE. 1985-1989 (Feb). m. BarterNews Publications, Box 3024, Mission Viejo, CA 92690.

331 US
CORPORATE BENEFIT PLANS (YEAR). 1980-1989. a. International Foundation of Employee Benefit Plans, 18700 W. Bluemound Rd., P.O. Box 69, Brookfield, WI 53008-0069.
Formerly: Managing Corporate Benefit Plans.

331 US
CORPORATE COMMENTARY. ceased. q. Medical Economics Company Inc., 680 Kinderkamack Rd., Oradell, NJ 07649.

650 659.2 US ISSN 0010-8952
CORPORATE COMMUNICATIONS REPORT. 1969-19?? q. Addison Corporate Annual Reports, 112 E. 31st St., New York, NY 10016.

330 US ISSN 0274-6107
CORPORATE CONTROLLERS REPORT. 1979-199? m. Warren, Gorham and Lamont Inc., One Penn Plaza, New York, NY 10119.
Formerly: Corporate Controller's and Treasurer's Report.

338.4 660 US ISSN 0574-1181
CORPORATE DIAGRAMS AND ADMINISTRATIVE PERSONNEL OF THE CHEMICAL INDUSTRY. 1958-199? (14th ed.). irreg. (back issues avail.) Chemical Economic Services, Box 468, Palmer Sq., Princeton, NJ 08540.

330 170 CN ISSN 0841-1956
CORPORATE ETHICS MONITOR. 1989-199? 6/yr. Carswell Publications, 2330 Midland Avenue, Agincourt, Ont. M1S 1P7, Canada.

613.7 CN ISSN 0892-9319
HD7395.P45
CORPORATE FITNESS. 1982-19?? bi-m. (back issues avail.) College Edouard-Montpetit, 945, Chemin de Chambly, Longueuil, Que. J4H 3M6, Canada.
Formerly: Corporate Fitness and Recreation.

332 US
CORPORATE FUND RAISING DIRECTORY (YEAR). 1980-198? a. Public Service Materials Center, 5130 Macarthur Blvd., N.W., Apt. 200, Washington, DC 20016-3316.
Formerly: Corporate Fund Raising Directory.

368.382 US
CORPORATE HEALTH. 1985-1989 (vol.2, no.1). bi-m. A M C Publisher, 5700 Old Orchard Rd., Skokie, IL 60077-1024.

340 US
CORPORATE LAW LOCATOR. 1988-1990. a. R.R. Bowker, A Reed Reference Publishing Company, Division of Reed Publishing (USA) Inc., 121 Chanlon Rd., New Providence, NJ 07974.

370 330 US
CORPORATE PHILANTHROPY; an information service. ceased 1989. q. (back issues avail.) Independent Sector, 1828 L St., N.W., Ste. 1200, Washington, DC 20036.

380 US
CORPORATE REPORT FACT BOOK WISCONSIN; a directory of publicly held companies in the state of Wisconsin. 1984-1987. a. M C P, Inc., 5500 Wayzata Blvd., Ste. 800, Minneapolis, MN 55416.

332.6 382 330 US ISSN 0896-775X
CORPORATE RESTRUCTURING, the authoritative report on the reshaping of American companies. 1988-1990 (Aug.). m. (back issues avail.) M L R Publishing Company (Subsidiary of: M L R Enterprises Inc.), 229 S. 18th St., Philadelphia, PA 19103.

790.1 US
CORPORATE SPORTS. 1989; announced, never published. bi-m. Ed Ayres, Ed. & Pub., 9171 Wilshire Blvd., Ste. 300, Beverly Hills, CA 90210.

384.55 US ISSN 0889-4523
TK6630.A1
CORPORATE TELEVISION. 1986-1989. bi-m. (International Television Association) P S N Publications (Subsidiary of: United Newspapers Publications Ltd.), 2 Park Ave., 4th Fl., New York, NY 10016.

330 US
CORPORATE TRENDTRACT. ceased 1989 (May). bi-m. Gale Research Inc., Dept. 77748, Detroit, MI 48277-0748.

384.55 658 US
CORPORATE VIDEO DECISIONS. 1988-1990. m. Act III Publishing, 410 Park S., 7th Fl., New York, NY 10016.

346.066 US
CORPORATION LAW GUIDE. ceased. 2 base vols. (plus fortn. updates). Commerce Clearing House, Inc., 4025 W. Peterson Ave., Chicago, IL 60646.

974 US
CORPUS VEXILLORUM MUNDI; national flags. 1986-1987; suspended. a. Flag Research Center, Box 580, Winchester, MA 01890.

621 US
TA462
CORROSION ENGINEER'S SOURCE BOOK; NACE member directory and guide to corrosion control products - services. 1940-19?? a. (reprint service avail. from UMI) National Association of Corrosion Engineers (NACE), Box 218340, Houston, TX 77218.
Formerly: Materials Performance Buyer's Guide (ISSN 0095-7976)

620.112 US
CORROSION MONOGRAPH SERIES. 1966-1986. irreg., unnumbered. John Wiley & Sons, Inc., 605 Third Ave., New York, NY 10158-0012.

100 US
COSMIC SCIENCE RESEARCH CENTER. NEWSLETTER. 1964-1989. 12/yr. Cosmic Science Research Center, 6255 S.W. King Blvd., Beaverton, OR 97005-5310.

646.7 US
COSMOPOLITAN'S BEAUTY GUIDE. 1976-1987. s-a. (Cosmopolitan Special Publications) Hearst Magazines, Cosmopolitan, 959 8th Ave., New York, NY 10019.

613.7 US
COSMOPOLITAN'S SUPER DIET & EXERCISE GUIDE. 1978-1987. s-a. (Cosmopolitan Special Publications) Hearst Magazines, Cosmopolitan, 959 8th Ave., New York, NY 10019.

310 CR
COSTA RICA. CENTRO DE INFORMACION ESTADISTICA. ANUARIO ESTATISTICO. ceased 1982. a. Centro de Informacion Estadistica, Direccion General de Estadistica y Censos, Apdo. 10163, 1000 San Jose, Costa Rica.

910 CR ISSN 0045-8740
COSTA RICA. INSTITUTO GEOGRAFICO NACIONAL. INFORME SEMESTRAL. 1955-1983. s-a. Instituto Geografico Nacional, Ap. 2272, San Jose, Costa Rica.

633.51 631 II ISSN 0045-8759
COTTON DEVELOPMENT. 1971-1989 (vol.18, nos.3-4). q. (also avail. in microform from UMI) Directorate of Cotton Development, Ministry of Agriculture, 14 Ramajibhai Kamani Marg, Ballard Estate, Box 1002, Bombay 400038, India.

633 US
COTTON GINNINGS BY STATES. (Series A10) 1900-1991 (Oct.). 13/yr. (also avail. in microfiche) U.S. Bureau of the Census, Customer Services, Washington, DC 20233.
Former titles: Cotton Ginnings in the United States (ISSN 0093-433X); Cotton Production in the United States.

677 310 JA ISSN 0574-2374
COTTON STATISTICS MONTHLY/MENKA TOKEI GEPPO. 1964-1987. m. Japan Cotton Traders' Association - Nihon Menka Kyokai, 2-9 Awaji-machi 3-chome, Chuo-ku, Osaka 541, Japan.

332.1 US
COUNCIL CONNECTION. 1985-1990 (vol.6, no.3). bi-m. (back issues avail.) Credit Union Executives Society, 2801 Coho St., Ste. 300, Madison, WI 53713.

301.426 US ISSN 0146-1117
COUNCIL NOTES. 1977-19?? q. Indiana Family Health Council, Inc., 21 Beachway Dr., Ste. B, Indianapolis, IN 46224.
Supersedes: Indiana Family Planner (ISSN 0019-6606)

CESSATIONS

333.7   FR
COUNCIL OF EUROPE. CENTRE NATUROPA. DOCUMENTATION SERIES. 1976-199?; suspended. irreg. Council of Europe, Centre Naturopa, B.P. 431R6, 67006 Strasbourg cedex, France.
  Formerly: Council of Europe. Documentation and Information Centre for the Environment and Nature. Documentation Series.

378   CN
COUNCIL OF ONTARIO UNIVERSITIES QUADRENNIAL REVIEW. 1975-19?? quadrennial. (reprint service avail. from UMI) Council of Ontario Universities, Suite 8039, 130 St. George Street, Toronto, Ont. M5S 2T4, Canada.
  Former titles: Council of Ontario Universities Triennial Review (ISSN 0315-9590); Council of Ontario Universities Biennial Review (ISSN 0084-8972); Council of Ontario Universities. Annual Review (ISSN 0315-9000)

370   US
COUNCIL ON OUTDOOR EDUCATION. NEWSLETTER. 1954-19?? irreg. (1-2/yr.). American Alliance for Health, Physical Education, Recreation and Dance, Council on Outdoor Education, 1900 Association Dr., Reston, VA 22091.
  Formerly: Outdoor Education (ISSN 0030-7033)

330 669   US   ISSN 0951-7588
COUNTERTRADE & BARTER. ceased. bi-m. Metal Bulletin Inc., 220 Fifth Ave., New York, NY 10001.
  ormerly: Countertrade and Barter Quarterly.

200   UK   ISSN 0011-0124
COUNTRY CHURCHMAN. 1953-1990. m. Country Churchman Ltd., Abbey Press, Abingdon, Berkshire, England.

690 747   US
COUNTRY LIVING DREAM HOMES. 1988-1989. a. Hearst Corporation, 1700 Broadway, Ste. 2801, New York, NY 10019.

630   CN
COUNTRY SUN. 1985-199? m. Woodroe Nicholson Publishing Ltd., Box 2440, 884 Ford St., Peterborough, Ont. K9J 7Y8, Canada.

646.724   CN
COUP DE PEIGNE. 1983-1989. 4/yr. 612 St.Jacques W., Montreal, Que. H3C 4M8, Canada.

500   FR
COURRIER DU C N R S SUPPLEMENT. 1973-19?? irreg. (approx. 2-3/yr). (Centre National de la Recherche Scientifique) Editions du C N R S, 1 Place Aristide Briand, 92195 Meudon Cedex, France.

760   FR
COURRIER TECHNIQUE ARTS GRAPHIQUES. ceased 1975 (no.26). irreg. Kodak-Pathe, Division Marches et Graphiques, 8 et 14 rue Villiot, 75580 Paris Cedex 12, France.

340   CN   ISSN 0227-6178
COURT CASES OF INTEREST TO THE OMBUDSMAN INSTITUTION. ceased 1982. a. International Ombudsman Institute, Faculty of Law, University of Alberta, Edmonton, Alta. T6G 2H5, Canada.

347   US
COURT IMPROVEMENT BULLETIN. 1981-1988 (no.15). s-a. (back issues avail.; reprint service avail. from UMI,ISI) American Judicature Society, 25 E. Washington, Ste. 1600, Chicago, IL 60602-1805.

347   US   ISSN 0276-1661
KF8732.A15
COURT MANAGEMENT JOURNAL. 1978-1985. a. National Center for State Courts, 300 Newport Ave., Williamsburg, VA 23187-8798.

347   US
COURT OF APPEALS FOR THE FEDERAL CIRCUIT NEWSLETTER. ceased. bi-m. American Bar Association, Litigation Section, 750 N. Lake Shore Dr., Chicago, IL 60611.

942   UK
COVENTRY EVENING TELEGRAPH YEAR BOOK & WHO'S WHO. 1966-1990. a. Coventry Newspapers Ltd., Corporation St., Coventry CV1 1FP, England.

330   US
COWLES FOUNDATION MONOGRAPHS. 1970-198? irreg. Yale University Press, 92A Yale Sta., New Haven, CT 06520.
  Formerly: Cowles Foundation for Research in Economics at Yale University. Monographs (ISSN 0084-9413)

330.9   SP   ISSN 0211-5379
COYUNTURA COMERCIAL. ALAVA. ceased 1989. bi-m. Camara Oficial de Comercio e Industria de Alava, Dato 38, 01005 Vitoria, Spain.

338   SP
COYUNTURA INDUSTRIAL. (Supplement to: Economia Industrial) ceased. m. Ministerio de Industria, Paseo de la Castellana 160, Madrid 28046, Spain.

330.9   SP   ISSN 0211-1284
COYUNTURA INDUSTRIAL Y UTILIZACION DE LA CAPACIDAD PRODUCTIVA DE ALAVA. ceased 1989. bi-m. Camara Oficial de Comercio e Industria de Alava, Dato 38, 01005 Vitoria, Spain.

745.5   US
CRAFT - ART - NEEDLEWORK DIGEST. ceased. bi-m. Kalmbach Publishing Co., Box 1612, Waukesha, WI 53187.

700   AT   ISSN 0311-046X
NK1089
CRAFT AUSTRALIA. 1971-19?? q. (also avail. in microfiche) Crafts Council of Australia, 35 George St. The Rocks, Sydney, N.S.W. 2000, Australia.

666 745.5   AT   ISSN 0816-360X
CRAFTS COMPETITIONS AND PRIZES. 1976-198? irreg. Crafts Council of Australia, 35 George St., The Rocks, N.S.W. 2000, Australia.

745.5   AT
CRAFTS COUNCIL NEWS. 1971-19?? m. (looseleaf format) Crafts Council of Tasmania, 77 Salamanca Pl., Hobart, Tas. 7000, Australia.

382   US
CRAIN'S INTERNATIONAL BUSINESS. 1990; ceased same year. m. Crain Communications, Inc., 740 N. Rush St., Chicago, IL 60611-2590.

800   US
CRAWL OUT YOUR WINDOW. 1975-1990. a. Foundation for New Literature, 4641 Park Blvd., San Diego, CA 92116.

371.3   UK
CREATIVE ARTS & CRAFTS HANDBOOK. ceased. biennial. Educational Institute of Design Craft & Technology, c/o P.E. Dawson, Ed., 52 Locarno Ave., Gillingham, Kent ME8 6ES, England.

745.5   US
CREATIVE IDEAS FOR LIVING. 1970-1990? bi-m. Sampler Publications, Inc., 707 Kautz Rd., St. Charles, IL 60174.
  Former titles (until 1984): Decorating and Craft Ideas (ISSN 0192-3706); Decorating Craft Ideas Made Easy (ISSN 0011-7382)

746   US
CREATIVE IDEAS NEEDLE AND CRAFT. ceased. bi-m. P S C Games Limited Partnership, 810 Seventh Ave., New York, NY 10019.
  Former titles: American HomeArts Needlecraft for Today (ISSN 0895-2175); (until 1987): Needlecraft for Today; Incorporates (in 1987): Needle and Thread.

658   US
CREATIVE MEETINGS. ceased. s-a. American Society of Association Executives, 1575 I St., N.W., Washington, DC 20005.

686.2   JA
CREATOR. ceased. q. Japan Printing News Co., Ltd. - Nippon Insatsu Shinbunsha, 1-16-8 Shintomi, Chuo-ku, Tokyo 104, Japan.

330   US
CREDIT PROFESSIONAL. 1940-1991. s-a. (back issues avail.) Credit Professionals International, 50 Crestwood Executive Center, Ste. 204, St. Louis, MO 63126.
  Formerly (until 1990): C W I Credit Professional.

334.2   US   ISSN 0074-4468
HG2037
CREDIT UNION YEARBOOK. 1954-198? a. Credit Union National Association, Inc., Box 431, Madison, WI 53701.
  Formerly: International Credit Union Yearbook.

658.88 332   US   ISSN 0045-9011
CREDITALK. 1969-198? bi-m. (tabloid format) National Retail Merchants Association, Credit Management Division, 100 W. 31st St., New York, NY 10001.

780.904   US
CREEM CLOSE-UP METAL ROCK 'N' ROLL. ceased. m. Cambray Publishing Inc., Box 931869, Sunset Sta., Los Angeles, CA 90093.

780.42 028.5   US
CREEM ROCK SHOTS. ceased. m. Cambray Publishing Inc., Box 931869, Sunset Sta., Los Angeles, CA 90093.

133.9   US
CRESCENDO (GARRETT PARK). 1980-198? q. (looseleaf format; back issues avail.) (Institute for Consciousness & Music) I C M West Press, c/o Institute for Music & Imagery, Box 557, Garrent Park, MD 20896-9999.
  Formerly: Institute for Consciousness and Music Newsletter.

069   RM
CRESTEREA PATRIMONIULUI MUZEAL. 1978-19?? irreg. Muzeul de Istorie al Republicii Socialiste Romania, Calea Victoriei 12, Bucharest, Rumania.

342 361   CN
CRIMINAL INJURIES COMPENSATION. 1980-19?? irreg. (also avail. in microfilm; microfiche; magnetic tape) Statistics Canada, Health Division, R.H. Coats Bldg., 18th floor, Ottawa K1A 0T6, Ont., Canada.
  Formerly (until 1986): Criminal Injury Compensation.

364   US   ISSN 0362-8353
HV7296
CRIMINAL JUSTICE PLAN (RICHMOND). 1969-1985. irreg. Department of Criminal Justice Services, Attn: Librarian, 805 E. Broad St., Richmond, VA 23219.

343   US
CRIMINAL LAW DIGEST; digests of leading federal and state cases. ceased 199? 2/yr. to update base volume. Warren, Gorham and Lamont Inc., One Penn Plaza, New York, NY 10119.

181.45   US
CRIMSON DAWN. ceased 1988 (May). 6/yr. Ananda Marga Inc., 97-38 42nd Ave., Ste. 1F, Corona, NY 11368-2145.

200 133.5   US
CRIMSON FULLMOON; a newsletter of the white goddess religion. 1987-19?? m. (looseleaf format; back issues avail.) Malkuthian Rite Temple Society, 2507 Hilton Court, Augusta, GA 30909.

301.16   US
CRITICAL COMMUNICATIONS REVIEW. 1983-198? (vol.3). irreg. Ablex Publishing Corporation, 335 Chestnut St., Norwood, NJ 07648.

800   US   ISSN 0070-153X
CRITICAL ESSAYS IN MODERN LITERATURE. 1957-1989. irreg. University of Pittsburgh Press, 127 N. Bellefield Ave., Pittsburgh, PA 15260.

778   US
CRITICAL STUDIES IN FILM AND TELEVISION. ceased 1991 (Jun.). irreg. U M I Research Press, 300 N. Zeeb Rd., Ann Arbor, MI 48106-1346.
  Formerly: Studies in Cinema.

350.6   US
CRITIQUE: SOUTHERN CALIFORNIA PUBLIC POLICY AND ADMINISTRATION. 1976-1980. q. California State University, Long Beach, Graduate Center for Public Policy and Administration, 1250 Bellflower Blvd., Long Beach, CA 90840.

797.21   SP   ISSN 0011-1694
CROL. 1965-19?? m. (Federacion Espanola de Natacion) Prensa XXI, S.A., Avda Paral.lel, 180, Apdo. No. 350 F.D., 08015 Barcelona, Spain.

CESSATIONS

800 US
CROP DUST. 1980-1984 (no.5); suspended. 2/yr. Crop Dust Press, Rt. 5, Box 75, Warrenton, VA 22186-8614.

631 US ISSN 0162-5098
SB1 CODEN: CRSOA3
CROPS AND SOILS MAGAZINE. 1948-198? m. (bi-m. Apr.-Sept.). American Society of Agronomy, Inc., 677 S. Segoe Rd., Madison, WI 53711.
Formerly: Crops and Soils (ISSN 0011-1864)

631 CN
CROPS GUIDE. (Supplement to: Country Guide) 1972-1991 (Mar.). a. (microform; also avail. in microfilm from UMI) Farm Business Communications, 1760 Ellice Ave., Winnipeg, Man. R3H OB6, Canada.

808 US ISSN 0748-0164
PG13
CROSS CURRENTS. ceased. a. (University of Michigan, Department of Slavic Languages and Literatures) Yale University Press, 92A Yale Sta., New Haven, CT 06520.

746 US
CROSS QUICK. 1988-19??; suspended. bi-m. Meredith Corporation, 1716 Locust St., Des Moines, IA 50336.

800 700 NZ
CROSSCURRENT. 1972-19??; suspended. q. (back issues avail.) Outrigger Publishers Ltd., P.O. Box 1198, Hamilton, New Zealand.
Incorporates: Rimu & Matrix; Former titles: Pacific Quarterly Moana (ISSN 0110-3970); New Quarterly Cave (ISSN 0110-0076); Cave.

051 US
CROSSROADS MONTROSE. 1989-1990 (Apr.). m. Asarum Inc., 1110 Lovett Blvd., Ste. 212, Houston, TX 77006.

800 700 US ISSN 0741-6210
CROTON REVIEW. 1978-1988 (no.1). a. (back issues avail.) Croton Council on the Arts, Inc., Box 277, Croton-on-Hudson, NY 10520.

808.81 US
CROWDANCING QUARTERLY. 1983-19??; suspended. s-a. (back issues avail.) Crowdancing, 570 W. 10th Ave., Eugene, OR 97401.

361.77 614 PO ISSN 0870-3701
CRUZ VERMELHA PORTUGESA. BOLETIM DE INFORMACAO. 1975-1986. q. Cruz Vermelha Portugesa - Portuguese Red Cross, Jardim 9 de Abril, 1293 Lisbon Codex, Portugal.
Formerly: Humanidade.

016 460 SP ISSN 0590-1545
Z2687
CUADERNOS BIBLIOGRAFICOS. ceased 1988 (no.50). irreg. Consejo Superior de Investigaciones Cientificas (C.S.I.C.), Instituto de Filologia, Vitruvio, 8, 28006 Madrid, Spain.

410 UY
CUADERNOS DE SEMIOTICA. published only once, 1978. irreg. Editorial Anfora Solar, Garibaldi 2844, Montevideo, Uruguay.

374 MX
CUADERNOS DEL C R E F A L. 1976-1987 (no.19). irreg. Centro Regional de Educacion de Adultos y Alfabetizacion Funcional para America Latina, Quinta Erendira, 61600 Patzcuaro, Mich., Mexico.

700 940 001.3 SP
CUADERNOS INTERNACIONALES DE HISTORIA PSICOSOCIAL DEL ARTE. 1982-198?; suspended. s-a. Centro de Estudios Postuniversitarios, Paris 118, 08036 Barcelona, Spain.

320 MX ISSN 0185-027X
CUADERNOS POLITICOS. 1974-1990 (no.59-60). 3/yr. Ediciones Era, Avena 102, 09810 Mexico, D.F., Mexico.

330 CU ISSN 0011-2607
HC157.C8
CUBA NOTICIAS ECONOMICAS. 1965-1987 (vol.23, no.158). bi-m. Chamber of Commerce, Calle 21 No. 701, esq. A, Vedado, Havana 4, Cuba.

676 CU
CUBA PAPEL. ceased, 1986. q. Union del Papel, Departamento Tecnico, Via Blanca Km 50, Santa Cruz del Norte, Havana, Cuba.

200 UK ISSN 0260-2202
CUBIT; Christian magazine for students. 1980-198? 3/yr. Universities and Colleges Christian Fellowship, 38 De Montfort St., Leicester LE1 7GP, England.
Formerly: C.U. News.

378.0025 664 331.1 US ISSN 0734-7073
CULINARY ARTS NEWS; the worldwide guide to cooking schools. 1982-19?? q. (back issues avail.) Culinary and Fine Arts Ltd., Box 153, Western Springs, IL 60558.

630 635 FR
CULTIVER EN PROVENCE COTE D'AZUR. ceased. m. Societe Centrale d'Agriculture, d'Horticulture et d'Acclimatation de Nice et des Alpes-Maritimes, Palais de l'Agriculture, 113 Promenade des Anglais, Nice, France.
Formerly (until 1988): Cote d'Azur Agricole et Horticole (ISSN 0010-9681)

301 IT ISSN 0392-2111
CULTURA E MASS MEDIA. 1979-1985 (no.9). irreg. Liguori Editore s.r.l., Via Mezzocannone 19, 80134 Naples, Italy.

700 US
CULTURAL CLIMATE. 1974-198? m. Arts Council of Hawaii, Box 38000, Honolulu, HI 96837-1000.
Former titles: Hawaii Council for Culture and the Arts. Newsletter; (1976-1981): Cultural Climate.

780 US ISSN 0161-1186
ML1
CUM NOTIS VARIORUM. 1976-1989 (no.136). 10/yr. University of California, Berkeley, Music Library, Berkeley, CA 94720.

539.7 011 US
CUMULATIVE BIBLIOGRAPHY OF LITERATURE EXAMINED BY THE RADIATION SHIELDING INFORMATION CENTER. 1965-1983 (vol.7). irreg. (also avail. in microfiche; back issues avail.) Oak Ridge National Laboratory, Radiation Shielding Information Center, Box 2008, Oak Ridge, TN 37831-6362.

622.33 PL
CUPRUM. 1974-19?? bi-m. (Zaklad Projektowych Miedzi "Cuprum") Wydawnictwo Czasopism i Ksiazek Technicznych SIGMA - NOT, Ul. Biala 4, P.O. 1004, 00-950 Warsaw, Poland.

621.3 SA
CURRENT. 1963-1991 (Apr.). m. Thomson Publications (Subsidiary of: Times Media Ltd.), P.O. Box 56182, Pinegowrie 2123, South Africa.
Formed by the 1983 merger of: Electrical Engineer; Electronics and Instrumentation (ISSN 0013-5186); Formerly: S.A. Engineer and Electrical Review (ISSN 0081-2420); Which was formed by the merger of: South African Electrical Review; South African Engineer (ISSN 0038-2140)

629.1 UK
CURRENT AIRCRAFT PRICES. ceased 1988. a. Interavia S.A. (Subsidiary of: Jane's Information Group), Sentinel House, 163 Brighton Rd., Coulsdon, Surrey CR3 2NX, England.

011 UK
CURRENT ASIAN & AUSTRALASIAN DIRECTORIES; a guide to directories published in or relating to all countries in Asia, Australasia & Oceania. 1978-1989. irreg. C.B.D. Research Ltd., 15 Wickham Rd., Beckenham, Kent BR3 2JS, England.

658.3 US ISSN 0011-3360
CURRENT COMPENSATION REFERENCES. 1968-198? m. (looseleaf format) Executive Compensation Service Inc., Two Executive Dr., Ft. Lee, NJ 07024.

641.1 US ISSN 0090-0443
CODEN: CCNTBP
CURRENT CONCEPTS IN NUTRITION. 1972-1988 (vol. 15). irreg. John Wiley & Sons, Inc., 605 Third Ave., New York, NY 10158-0012.

616.1 US ISSN 0884-4194
CODEN: CCCDAN
CURRENT CONCEPTS OF CEREBROVASCULAR DISEASE: STROKE. 1966-1991 (Dec.). bi-m. (also avail. in microform from UMI; back issues avail.; reprint service avail. from UMI) American Heart Association, 7272 Greenville Ave., Dallas, TX 75231-4596.

658 US ISSN 0893-5165
CURRENT CONTENTS - HEALTH SERVICES ADMINISTRATION. (Includes: Journal Index and Title Word Index) 1988-1989. m. Institute for Scientific Information, 3501 Market St., Philadelphia, PA 19104.

331 CN ISSN 0707-5766
HC111
CURRENT ECONOMIC AND INDUSTRIAL RELATIONS INDICATORS. 1977-1988. s-a. Queen's University, Industrial Relations Centre, Kingston, Ont. K7L 3N6, Canada.

608.7 531.64 US ISSN 0273-298X
TJ163.2
CURRENT ENERGY PATENTS. 1980-19?? m. U.S. Department of Energy, Office of Scientific and Technical Information, Box 62, Oak Ridge, TN 37831.

011 UK ISSN 0070-1955
CURRENT EUROPEAN DIRECTORIES. 1969-198? C.B.D. Research Ltd., 15 Wickham Rd., Beckenham, Kent BR3 2JS, England.

336 US
CURRENT GOVERNMENTS REPORTS: LOCAL GOVERNMENT FINANCES IN MAJOR COUNTY AREAS. (Series GF-6) ceased in 1986. a. (also avail. in microfiche) U.S. Bureau of the Census, Customer Services, Washington, DC 20233.
Formerly: Current Governments Reports: Local Government Finances in Selected Metropolitan Areas and Large Counties.

616.15 616.99 US ISSN 0739-4810
RC633.A1 CODEN: CHONEG
CURRENT HEMATOLOGY AND ONCOLOGY. 1982-1988 (vol.6). a. Year Book Medical Publishers, Inc., 200 N. LaSalle St., Chicago, IL 60601-1080.

331.1 CN ISSN 0318-952X
HD8106.5
CURRENT INDUSTRIAL RELATIONS SCENE IN CANADA. 1973-1991. a. Queen's University, Industrial Relations Centre, Kingston, Ont. K7L 3N6, Canada.

610 US ISSN 0070-2005
R123
CURRENT MEDICAL INFORMATION AND TERMINOLOGY. 1963-1981 (5th ed.). irreg. (also avail. in microfiche) American Medical Association, 535 N. Dearborn St., Chicago, IL 60610.
Formerly: Current Medical Terminology.

616.00 NE
CURRENT ONCOLOGY SERIES. 1986; published only once. irreg. (reprint service avail. from ISI) Elsevier Science Publishers B.V., Books Division, P.O. Box 211, 1000 AE Amsterdam, Netherlands.

312 US
CURRENT POPULATION REPORTS: POPULATION CHARACTERISTICS. SOCIAL AND ECONOMIC CHARACTERISTICS OF THE BLACK POPULATION. (Series P-20) ceased. irreg. U.S. Bureau of the Census, Customer Services, Washington, DC 20233.
Formerly: U.S. Bureau of the Census. Current Population Reports: Negro Population (ISSN 0082-951X)

618.97 US ISSN 1052-4002
CURRENT PROBLEMS IN GERIATRICS. 1991-19?? bi-m. Mosby - Year Book, Inc. (Littleton) (Subsidiary of: Times Mirror Company), 545 Great Rd., Littleton, MA 01460.

616.12 US
CURRENT PROBLEMS IN PULMONOLOGY. 1979-1988. a. Mosby - Year Book, Inc. (Subsidiary of: Times Mirror Company), 11830 Westline Industrial Dr., St. Louis, MO 63146.

CESSATIONS

327   FI   ISSN 0356-7893
JX1901
CURRENT RESEARCH ON PEACE AND VIOLENCE. 1971-1990. q. (back issues avail.; reprint service avail. from ISI) Tampere Peace Research Institute, Hameenkatu 13 B, Box 447, 33101 Tampere 10, Finland.
     Formerly (until 1978): Instant Research on Peace and Violence (ISSN 0046-967X)

610   CN
CURRENT THERAPY. 1988-1990 (Mar.). 8/yr. Medical Post, Maclean-Hunter Bldg., 777 Bay St., Toronto, Ont. M5W 1A7, Canada.

616.97   NE   ISSN 0169-1244
                   CODEN: CTAAEP
CURRENT TITLES AND ABSTRACTS IN IMMUNOLOGY, TRANSPLANTATION AND ALLERGY. 1985-1989 (vol. 22). s-m. (reprint service avail. from ISI) Elsevier Science Publishers B.V., P.O. Box 211, 1000 AE Amsterdam, Netherlands.

551.46 333.91 011   US   ISSN 0883-4725
CURRENT TITLES IN OCEAN, COASTAL, LAKE & WATERWAY SCIENCES; reader's information bulletin and service. 1986-1989. q. (back issues avail.) Coastal Education & Research Foundation, Inc., Box 8068, Charlottesville, VA 22906.

001.642   US
CURRENT TRENDS IN PROGRAMMING METHODOLOGY. 1977-1978. irreg. Prentice Hall, Inc., Box 500, Englewood Cliffs, NJ 07632.

371.3 375   AT   ISSN 0815-4678
CURRICULUM AUSTRALIA. 1985-1989 (no.7). s-a. Curriculum Development Centre, P.O. Box 26, Woden, A.C.T. 2606, Australia.
     Formerly: Curriculum Development in Australian Schools.

388   AT   ISSN 0313-5276
CUSTOM VANS & TRUCKS. 1976-19?? q. (back issues avail.) Eddie Ford Publications, Private Bag, Newstead, Vic. 3462, Australia.

052   UK   ISSN 0951-5127
CUT. 1986-1989. 12/yr. c/o Bill Sinclair, Ed., 1 St. Bernard's Row, Edinburgh EH4 1HW, Scotland.

808.81   US   ISSN 0882-6951
CUTTING EDGE QUARTERLY (ANN ARBOR). 1985-1990 (vol.3, no.4). q. (back issues avail.) Empty Mirror Press, Box 3430, Ann Arbor, MI 48106.

796.6   US   ISSN 0011-4278
TL440
CYCLE GUIDE. 1967-1987. m. 20916 Higgins Ct., Torrance, CA 90501.

301.1 616.4   US   ISSN 0896-7636
CYCLES (SHARON); a P M S support newsletter. 1984-1989. bi-m. (back issues avail.) Box 524, Sharon, MA 02067-0005.

900   UK
CYFRES LLYGAD Y FFYNNON. 1972-1978 (vol.11). irreg. (Welsh Joint Education Committee) University of Wales Press, 6 Gwennyth St., Cathays, Cardiff CF2 4YD, Wales.

796.6   CS   ISSN 0011-4413
CYKLISTIKA. 1884-1992. m. (Ceskoslovensky Svaz Telesne Vychovy) Olympia, Klimentska 1, 115 88 Prague 1, Czechoslovakia.

799.2   US   ISSN 0160-2543
CYNEGETICUS; a publication devoted to the interdisciplinary study of hunting. 1977-1987 (vol. 11, no.1). q. (back issues avail.) Douglas Stange, Ed. & Pub., Box 493, Ekalaka, MT 59324.

636.089   CY
CYPRUS. CHIEF VETERINARY OFFICER. ANNUAL REPORT. 1967-1990. a. Department of Veterinary Services, Nicosia, Cyprus.

361   CY   ISSN 0070-2404
CYPRUS. DEPARTMENT OF SOCIAL WELFARE SERVICES. ANNUAL REPORT. 1952-1973. a. Department of Social Welfare Services, c/o Director, Nicosia, Cyprus.

314   CY
CYPRUS. DEPARTMENT OF STATISTICS AND RESEARCH. STATISTICAL POCKET BOOK. 1978-19?? irreg. Ministry of Finance, Department of Statistics and Research, Nicosia, Cyprus.

551.6   CY   ISSN 0379-0916
QC990.C9
CYPRUS. METEOROLOGICAL SERVICE. SUMMARY OF THE WEATHER IN CYPRUS. 1971-1989. a. Meteorological Service, Nicosia, Cyprus.

622   CY
CYPRUS. MINES SERVICE. ANNUAL REPORT. 1921-1989. a. Ministry of Commerce and Industry, Mines Department, Government Printing Office, Nicosia, Cyprus.
     Formerly: Cyprus. Mines Department. Annual Report of the Senior Mines Officer for the Year.

331 368.4   CY
CYPRUS. MINISTRY OF LABOUR AND SOCIAL INSURANCE. DEPARTMENT OF SOCIAL WELFARE SERVICES. SOCIAL WELFARE REPORT. ceased 1982. q. Ministry of Labour and Social Insurance, Department of Social Welfare Services, Nicosia, Cyprus.

331 368.4   CY   ISSN 0256-8314
CYPRUS. MINISTRY OF LABOUR AND SOCIAL INSURANCE. LABOUR REVIEW. 1962-1990 (vol.47). q. Ministry of Labour and Social Insurance, Public Relations Department, Nicosia, Cyprus.
     Supersedes (until 1974): Cyprus. Ministry of Labour and Social Insurance. Quarterly Review (ISSN 0011-4480)

616.2   US   ISSN 0196-2418
CYSTIC FIBROSIS G A P CONFERENCE REPORTS. 1969-19?? a. Cystic Fibrosis Foundation (Rockville), 6931 Arlington Rd., Ste. 200, Bethesda, MD 20814-5205.

574.8   SZ
CYTOBIOLOGISCHE REVUE/CYTOBIOLOGICAL REVIEW/ REVUE CYTOBIOLOGIQUE/REVISTA CITOBIOLOGICA; internationale Zeitschrift fuer Zellforschung, Zell- und Organtherapie. 1977-1989 (Jul.). q. Ott Verlag AG, Postfach 22, CH-3600 Thun 7, Bern, Switzerland.

334   CS
CZECHOSLOVAK COOPERATOR. 1957-1990. q. Ustredni Rada Druzstev, Tesnov 5, 110 06 Prague 1, Czechoslovakia.

330   CS   ISSN 0045-9461
CZECHOSLOVAK ECONOMIC DIGEST; commentaries, essays. 1966-1989. 6/yr. (processed) Orbis, Vinohradska 46, 12041 Prague 2, Czechoslovakia.
     Formerly: New Trends.

284   CS
CZECHOSLOVAK ECUMENICAL NEWS/ TSCHECHOSLOWAKISCHE OEKUMENISCHE NACHRICHTEN. 1954-1990; suspended. bi-m. Ecumenical Council of Churches in C S S R, Vitkova 13, 186 00 Prague - Karlin, Czechoslovakia.
     Former titles (until no.2, 1984): Czech Ecumenical News (ISSN 0013-077X); (until 1964): Protestant Churches in Czechoslovakia.

388.3   CS   ISSN 0011-4650
CZECHOSLOVAK MOTOR REVIEW. 1954-198? m. (Ceskoslovenska Obchodni Komora) Rapid, Foreign Trade Publicity Corporation, 28 Rijna 13, 112 79 Prague 1, Czechoslavakia.

500 600 016   CS   ISSN 0045-9488
Z7403
CZECHOSLOVAK SCIENTIFIC AND TECHNICAL PERIODICALS CONTENTS. 1971-1991 (no.10). 10/yr. Statni Technicak Knihovna, Klementinum, Marianske Nam. 5, 11307 Prague, Czechoslovakia.

352.7   US
D B E D NEWSLETTER. ceased. irreg. Department of Business and Economic Development, Information Office, Box 2359, Honolulu, HI 96804.
     Formerly: D P E D Newsletter.

970.1   US   ISSN 0740-3984
E78.D6
D.C. DIRECTORY. 1979-1985. a. Phelps-Stokes Fund, American Indian Program, 11 Dupont Circle, N.W., No.802, Washington, DC 20036.

371.928   US
D C UPDATE. ceased. m. The Association for Persons with Severe Handicaps (TASH), 7010 Roosevelt Way, N.E., Seattle, WA 98115.

610   GW   ISSN 0323-4614
D D R - MEDIZIN-REPORT. 1972-19?? m. (Ministerium fuer Gesundheitswesen) Verlag Gesundheit GmbH, Neue Gruenstr. 18, 1020 Berlin, Germany.

320 016   GW   ISSN 0341-5457
D D R REPORT; Zeitschriften und Buecher der DDR - Referatezeitschrift zur politischen Bildung in der Bundesrepublik Deutschland. ceased. m. (Gesellschaft fuer Politische Bildung e.V.) Verlag Neue Gesellschaft GmbH, Postfach 20 13 52, D-5300 Bonn 2, Germany.

600   DK   ISSN 0107-5403
D D V - ANALYSEN. 1981-198? a. Danske Vedligeholdelsesforening, c/o Danmarks Tekniske Hoejskole, Bybning 301, 2800 Lyngby, Denmark.

200   CR
D E I CUADERNOS. 1980-1988 (no.10). irreg. Departamento Ecumenico de Investigaciones, Apdo. 339, S. Pedro Montes de Oca, San Jose, Costa Rica.

385   GW   ISSN 0323-3553
TF3   CODEN: DETEBZ
D E T; wissenschaftlich-technische Zeitschrift fuer Bau, Betrieb und Instandhaltung schienengebundener Verkehrseinrichtungen. 1953-1983. m. (Kammer der Technik, Fachverband Fahrzeugbau und Verkehr) VEB Verlag Technik, Postfach 201, 1020 Berlin, Germany.
     Formerly: Deutsche Eisenbahntechnik (ISSN 0012-0057)

378   US
D.H.E. DATA BRIEFS. 1973-1976; resumed 1981-1983 (Dec.). irreg. Department of Higher Education, 20 W. State St., CN 542, Trenton, NJ 08625.

378   US
D.H.E. RESEARCH NOTE. 1975-1980. irreg. Department of Higher Education, 20 W. State St., CN 542, Trenton, NJ 08625.

011   US
D.H. HILL LIBRARY SERIALS CATALOG. 1971-19??; suspended. irreg. (microfiche) North Carolina State University, Libraries, Box 7111, Raleigh, NC 27695-7111.

025.4 001.539   GW   ISSN 0011-4987
D K - MITTEILUNGEN. 1956-1990. bi-m. (Deutsches Institut fuer Normung e.V. (D I N), Ausschuss fuer Klassifikation) Beuth Verlag GmbH, Burggrafenstr. 6, 1000 Berlin 30, Germany.

658.8   US
D M A MATTERS. 1985-198? q. Direct Marketing Association, 11 W. 42nd St., New York, NY 10036.

355 629.13   US
D M S MARKET INTELLIGENCE REPORTS: GAS TURBINE ENGINES. GAS TURBINE MARKETS. ceased 1990. m. updated suppl. (looseleaf format; back issues avail.) Forecast International Inc. - D M S, 22 Commerce Rd., Newtown, CT 06470.

614.7   DK
D M U LUFT. A. 1978-1991. irreg. Ministry of the Environment, National Environmental Research Institute, Division of Emissions and Air Pollution, Fredriksborgvej 399, DK-4000 Roskilde, Denmark.
     Formerly: M S T Luft (ISSN 0106-343X)

610   US   ISSN 0741-6512
D R G MONITOR. (Diagnosis Related Group) 1983-1990 (Dec.). m. Hanley & Belfus, Inc., 210 S. 13th St., Philadelphia, PA 19107.

500 330 630   NZ   ISSN 0110-5221
                  CODEN: DDPAEX
D S I R DISCUSSION PAPER. 1978-19?? irreg. (back issues avail.) (Department of Scientific and Industrial Research) D S I R Publishing, P.O. Box 9741, Wellington, New Zealand.

620 338 658   NZ   ISSN 0111-8587
D S I R INDUSTRIAL INFORMATION SERIES. 1982-19?? irreg. (back issues avail.) (Department of Scientific and Industrial Research) D S I R Publishing, P.O. Box 9741, Wellington, New Zealand.

CESSATIONS

636.7 US
DACHSHUND REPORTER. 1980-19?? bi-m. Reporter Publications, Box 827, Culver City, CA 90230.

200 DK ISSN 0900-1581
DAGDRYP; daglig bibellaesning. 1984-1989. a. (K F U M i Danmark) Unitas Forlag, Valby Langgade 19, DK-2500 Valby, Denmark.

382 US
DAILY COMMERCIAL NEWS AND SHIPPING GUIDE; Southern California's steamship information newspaper. 1921-1991. d. (tabloid format) C.A. Page Publishing Co., 1117 W. Manchester Blvd, Ste. A, Inglewood, CA 90301-1500.

637 US
DAIRY. 1944-198?; suspended. m. Webb Publishing Company, 1999 Shepard Rd., St. Paul, MN 55116.

637 US
DAIRYMAN BUYERS GUIDE AND DIRECTORY. 1984-19?? a. (reprint service avail.) c/o Robert M. McCune, Pub., 14970 Chandler, Box 819, Corona, CA 91718.

637 AT
DAIRYMAN'S DIGEST AND PRIMARY PRODUCER; a complete coverage of the dairying industry, farm factory and home. 1935-19?? m. (tabloid format) (New South Wales Dairy Farmers Association) D F A Newspapers Ltd., 491 Elizabeth St., Surry Hills, N. S.W. 2010, Australia.
Formed by the merger of: Dairyman's Digest; Primary Producer (ISSN 0032-8308)

799.1 US ISSN 0145-613X
SH401
DAIWA FISHING ANNUAL. 1975-19?? a. Aqua-Field Publishing Co., Inc., 66 W. Gilbert St., Shrewsbury, NJ 07702.
Formerly: Daiwa Sportfishing Annual.

954.9 II
DAKSHINESIA. 1970-1974. s-a. Gandhian Institute of Studies, Department of Political Science, P.O. Box 116, Rajghat, Varanasi 1, India.
Formerly (until 1972): Pakistan Survey (ISSN 0048-2749)

708.1 US
DALLAS MUSEUM OF ART. ANNUAL REPORT. 1953-1987. a. Dallas Museum of Art, 1717 N. Harwood, Dallas, TX 75201.

782.1 US ISSN 0731-8529
ML1699
DALLAS OPERA MAGAZINE. 1977-1988 (Dec.). a. Dallas Opera, Majestic Theatre, Ste. 400, 1925 S. Elm, Dallas, TX 75201.
Formerly: Dallas Civic Opera Magazine (ISSN 0277-0113)

792.8 US ISSN 0737-0997
GV1587
DANCE NOTATION JOURNAL. 1983-198? a. (back issues avail.) Dance Notation Bureau, 33 W. 21st St., 3rd Fl., New York, NY 10010.

020 DK
DANMARKS BIBLIOTEKSSKOLE. STUDIER. 1974-1990. irreg., 8-10/yr. Danmarks Biblioteksskole, 6 Birketinget, 2300 Copenhagen S, Denmark.

554 DK ISSN 0105-063X
QE278 CODEN: DGUAB8
DANMARKS GEOLOGISKE UNDERSOEGELSE. AARBOG/ GEOLOGICAL SURVEY OF DENMARK. YEARBOOK. 1973-1982. a. Danmarks Geologiske Undersoegelse, 8 Thoravej, DK-2400 Copenhagen, Denmark.

658.8 DK ISSN 0045-9585
DANMARKS HANDELS TIDENDE. 1905-1989. bi-m. Danske Handelsforeningers Faelles-Organisation, Ehlersvej 9, 2900 Hellerup, Denmark.

685.31 DK
DANMARKS SKOTIDENDE. 1900-19?? 4/yr. Danmarks Skomagerkaug - Danish Guild of Shoemakers, Kaerlundevej 52,1, DK-2730 Herlev, Denmark.

839.5 DK
DANSK KULTURHISTORIE OG BEVIDSTHEDSDANNELSE 1880-1920. 1977-199? (vol.20). 2/yr. (back issues avail.) Odense University Press, Campusvej 55, DK-5230 Odense M, Denmark.

327 DK
DANSKE KULTURINSTITUT. NYT; oplysning om Danmark og kulturelt samvirke med andre nationer. 1983-1989 (no.16). irreg. (4-5/yr.). Danske Kulturinstitut, 2 Kultorvet, 1175 Copenhagen K, Denmark.
Formerly: Danske Selskab. Nyt (ISSN 0900-2871)

028.5 GW ISSN 0177-1531
DU DARFST. 1982-19?? bi-m. (back issues avail.) Initiative Jugendmagazin, Postfach 1446, 6070 Langen, Germany.

800 US
DARK VISIONS. announced; never published. irreg. Cornell University, Risley Hall, Rm. 422, Ithaca, NY 14853.

651 US ISSN 0011-6769
DARTNELL OFFICE ADMINISTRATION SERVICE. 1959-19?? m. Dartnell Corp., 4660 Ravenswood Ave., Chicago, IL 60640.

375 300 US ISSN 0747-4857
HG1
DATA BOOK OF SOCIAL STUDIES MATERIALS AND RESOURCES. 1971-1989 (vol.13). a. (also avail. in microform from EDR) Social Science Education Consortium, Inc., 855 Broadway, Boulder, CO 80302.
Former titles: Social Studies Materials and Resources Data Book. Annual; (until vol.4, 1979): Social Studies Curriculum Materials Data Book Supplement.

001.64 UK
DATA BUSINESS. 1981-1991. m. V N U Business Publications BV, 32-34 Broadwick St., London W1A 2HG, England.

368 US
DATA COMMUNICATIONS SOURCE BOOK. ceased. a. (plus q. supplements). Merritt Company, 1661 Ninth St., Box 955, Santa Monica, CA 90406.

651.8 658.403 US
DATA MANAGEMENT. 1951-198? m. (also avail. in microfilm from UMI; reprint service avail. from UMI) Data Processing Management Association, 505 Busse Highway, Park Ridge, IL 60068-3191.
Former titles (until 1983): D M: Data Management (ISSN 0148-5431); (until 1975): Data Management (ISSN 0022-0329); Journal of Data Management.

621.381 UK ISSN 0267-5447
DATA STORAGE REPORT. 1985-1991. m. (back issues avail.) Elsevier Science Publishers Ltd., Crown House, Linton Rd., Barking, Essex IG11 8JU, England.

001.64 NE ISSN 0167-1340
DATABUS; maandblad voor microcomputer techniek. 1979-1990. 10/yr. (back issues avail.) Kluwer Technische Tijdschriften BV, Gedempte Gracht 6, Postbus 23, 7400 GA Deventer, Netherlands.

001.64 UK
DATABUSINESS. 1981-1991. m. V N U Business Publications BV, 32-34 Broadwick St., London W1A 2HG, England.

001.64 UK
DATALINK. 1977-1991. w. V N U Business Publications BV, 32-34 Broadwick St., London W1A 2HG, England.

001.64 US
DATALINK. (Update to: Datapro Reports on Data Communication) ceased. m. Datapro Information Services Group (Subsidiary of: McGraw-Hill, Inc.), 600 Delran Pkwy., Delran, NJ 08075.

338 US ISSN 0730-7071
DATAPRO DIRECTORY OF ON-LINE SERVICES. 1982-19?? 2 base vols. plus m. issues. (looseleaf format) Datapro Information Services Group (Subsidiary of: McGraw-Hill, Inc.), 600 Delran Pkwy., Delran, NJ 08075.

001.64 US
DATAPRO NEWSCOM. (Update to: Datapro 70) 1972-19?? m. Datapro Information Services Group (Subsidiary of: McGraw-Hill, Inc.), 600 Delran Pkwy., Delran, NJ 08075.

001.6 621.381 US ISSN 0275-0813
DATAPRO REPORTS ON MINICOMPUTERS. ceased. 3 base vols. plus m. issues. Datapro Informtion Services Group (Subsidiary of: McGraw-Hill, Inc.), 600 Delran Pkwy., Delran, NJ 08075.

001.642 US
DATAPRO REPORTS ON SOFTWARE. 1986-19?? 1 base vol. plus m. issues. Datapro Information Services Group (Subsidiary of: McGraw-Hill, Inc.), 600 Delran Pkwy., Delran, NJ 08075.

621.3 US ISSN 0735-8458
DATAPRO REPORTS ON TELECOMMUNICATIONS. ceased. 3 base vols. plus m. issues. Datapro Information Services Group (Subsidiary of: McGraw-Hill, Inc.), 600 Delran Pkwy., Delran, NJ 08075.

001.6 651.8 US ISSN 0272-3336
DATAPRO REPORTS ON WORD PROCESSING. ceased. base vols. (plus m. updates). Datapro Information Services Group (Subsidiary of: McGraw-Hill, Inc.), 600 Delran Pkwy., Delran, NJ 08075.

001.64 US ISSN 0045-9704
DATAPRO 70; E D P buyer's bible. 1970-19?? 3 base vols. plus m. issues. (looseleaf format) Datapro Information Services Group (Subsidiary of: McGraw-Hill, Inc.), 600 Delran Pkwy., Delran, NJ 08075.

410 PE
DATOS ETNO-LINGUISTICOS. 1975-198? irreg. (microfiche; back issues avail.) Instituto Linguistico de Verano, Departamento de Estudios Etno-Linguisticos, Casilla 2492, Lima 100, Peru.

929 US ISSN 0883-8550
DAUGHERTY FAMILY NEWSLETTER. 1984-198? q. (looseleaf format; back issues avail.) Daugherty Family Association, 1704 Sweetbriar, Bloomington, IL 61701.

900 US ISSN 0733-5946
DAVID MCCALDEN REVISIONIST NEWSLETTER. 1981-19?? m. (looseleaf format; back issues avail.) c o Truth Missions, Box 3849, Manhattan Beach, CA 90266.

378 US
DAVIDSON UPDATE. 1971-1989 (Dec.). 6/yr. Davidson College, Box 1678, Davidson, NC 28036.

296 US ISSN 0011-7048
DS101
DAVKA; the West Coast Jewish quarterly. ceased 1977. 4/yr. Los Angeles Hillel Council, Jewish Federation-Council, Los Angeles, 900 Hilgard Ave., Los Angeles, CA 90024.

052 PK
DAWN OVERSEAS WEEKLY. 1975-1989 (Jul.). w. Pakistan Herald Publications (Pvt.) Ltd., Haroon House, Dr. Ziauddin Ahmed Rd., G.P.O. Box 3740, Karachi 1, Pakistan.

069 708 CN ISSN 0703-6507
DAWSON AND HIND. 1971-19??; suspended. 3/yr. Association of Manitoba Museums, 422-167 Lombard Ave., Winnipeg, Man. R3B 0T6, Canada.

929 US ISSN 0743-216X
CS71
DAY RESEARCHER. 1983-19?? 4/yr. c/o Addie P. Howell, Ed., 319 Houston Lake Blvd., Centerville, GA 31028.

150 301 US
DEATH AND DYING A TO Z. ceased. base vol. (plus q. supplements). Croner Publications, Inc., 34 Jericho Turnpike, Jericho, NY 11753.

133 US
DEATH RATTLE. 1972-1988 (vol.18, Oct.). bi-m. Kitchen Sink Press, Inc., 2 Swamp Rd., Princeton, WI 54968.

610 617 US ISSN 1040-1733
DEBATES IN CLINICAL SURGERY. 1989-1990. a. Mosby - Year Book, Inc. (Chicago) (Subsidiary of: Times Mirror Company), 200 N. LaSalle St., Chicago, IL 60601-1080.

610 170 US
DEBATES IN MEDICINE. 1988-1991 (Apr.). a. Mosby - Year Book, Inc. (Chicago) (Subsidiary of: Times Mirror Company), 200 N. LaSalle St., Chicago, IL 60601-1080.

CESSATIONS

610　　　　　　　　HU　　ISSN 0133-9060
DEBRECENI ORVOSTUDOMANYI EGYETEM EVKONYVE.
1966-19??; suspended. a. Debreceni Orvostudomanyi Egyetem - University Medical School of Debrecen, Nagyerdei korut 98, 4012 Debrecen, Hungary.

301.435 700　　　　US　　ISSN 0748-1195
DECEMBER ROSE; a magazine for creative seniors. 1984-1988. bi-m. (back issues avail.) Retirement Housing Foundation, Inc., 401 E. Ocean Blvd., No. 300, Long Beach, CA 90802-4934.

747　　　　　　　　　CN
DECORATING AMBIANCE. ceased 1986. 2/yr. Marc Andre Turmel, Ed. & Pub., 3117 St. Catherine E., Ste. 1, Montreal, Que. H1W 2C1, Canada.

667.6 678.24　　　　US　　ISSN 1045-5914
TP934
DECORATIVE PRODUCTS WORLD. 1908-1991. 9/yr. Chilton Co. (Subsidiary of: A B C Publishing), Chilton Way, 201 King of Prussia Rd., Radnor, PA 19089.
Former titles: American Paint and Wallcoverings Dealer (ISSN 0199-4328); American Paint and Wallpaper Dealer (ISSN 0003-0309)

522.63　　　　　　　US　　ISSN 0735-3073
QB63
DEEP SKY. 1983-1992 (Jan). q. (back issues avail.) Kalmbach Publishing Co., Box 1612, Waukesha, WI 53187.

630　　　　　　　　　AT
DEER FARMERS JOURNAL OF N.S.W. 1977-19??; suspended. q. N.S.W. Deer Farmers Association, Inc., P.O. Box 380, Gosford, N.S.W. 2250, Australia.
Formerly: Deer Talk.

355　　　　　　　　　UK　　ISSN 0952-908X
DEFENCE MINISTER AND CHIEF OF STAFF. 1983-1989 (no.3). q. Defence Profile Ltd., 150 Regent St. Ste. 500, London W1R 5FA, England.

355　　　　　　　　　IT　　ISSN 1120-1665
DEFENCE TODAY; international armed forces and military technology. 1977-1990. m. (9/yr.). (back issues avail.) Publi & Consult S.P.A., Via Tagliamento 29, 00198 Rome, Italy.

355 621.38　　　　　SP
DEFENSA ELECTRONICA. 1985-19?? 2/yr. (back issues avail.) Defensa Edefa, S.A., Editorial de Publicaciones, Jorge Juan 98, 28009 Madrid, Spain.

355 327　　　　　　US　　ISSN 1044-3177
UF530
DEFENSE & DIPLOMACY; the magazine of world leaders. 1983-1991. bi-m. (back issues avail.) Defense & Diplomacy, Inc., 6849 Old Dominion Dr., Ste. 200, McLean, VA 22101-3705.
Formerly (until 1989): Journal of Defense and Diplomacy (ISSN 0736-5810)

355　　　　　　　　　US
DEFENSE BUDGET INTELLIGENCE. ceased 1990. w. (back issues avail.) Forecast International Inc. - D M S, 22 Commerce Rd., Newtown, CT 06470.

355　　　　　　　　　US
DEFENSE BUDGET SERVICE. 1990-1991. base vol. (plus q. updates). (looseleaf format) Carroll Publishing Company, 1058 Thomas Jefferson St., N.W., Washington, DC 20007.

355 350　　　　　　US
DEFENSE ORGANIZATION SERVICE - PROCUREMENT. ceased. base vol. (plus updates 6/yr.). (looseleaf format) Carroll Publishing Company, 1058 Thomas Jefferson St., N.W., Washington, DC 20007.

355 350　　　　　　US
DEFENSE ORGANIZATION SERVICE - R D T & E. (Research Development Test & Evaluation) ceased. base vol. (plus updates 6/yr.). (looseleaf format) Carroll Publishing Company, 1058 Thomas Jefferson St., N.W., Washington, DC 20007.

355　　　　　　　　　US
DEFENSE TECHNOLOGY INTERNATIONAL. 1989; announced never published. bi-m. Horizon - House - Microwave, Inc., 685 Canton St., Norwood, MA 02062.

350.71 355　　　　　US
DEFENSE WORLD; the magazine of defense issues and technologies. 1989 (Jan.); suspended the same year with Dec. issue. bi-m. McGraw-Hill, Inc., 1221 Ave. of the Americas, 42nd Fl., New York, NY 10020.

700 830 069 780　　　GW
DEINE STADT; Kunst, Kultur und Leben in Braunschweig. 1979-1989. a. Stadt Braunschweig, Kulturamt, Steintorwall 3, 3300 Braunschweig, Germany.

800 700　　　　　　US　　ISSN 0011-7714
DEKALB LITERARY ARTS JOURNAL. 1966-1989. 4/yr. (also avail. in microform from UMI; reprint service avail. from ISI,UMI) Dekalb Community College, 555 N. Indian Creek Dr., Clarkston, GA 30021.

706　　　　　　　　　US
DELAWARE ART MUSEUM. ANNUAL REPORT. 1912-1990? a. Delaware Art Museum, 2301 Kentmere Parkway, Wilmington, DE 19806.
Formerly: Wilmington Society of the Fine Arts. Report (ISSN 0084-0327)

340　　　　　　　　　US
DELAWARE VALLEY COUNSELOR. 1987-19?? q. (back issues avail.) Legal Communications, Ltd., 1617 JFK Blvd., Ste. 1245, Philadelphia, PA 19103.

380.14　　　　　　　US
DELI-DAIRY. 1972-1990. bi-m. Box 373, Cedarhurst, NY 11516.
Formerly: Deli-Dairy Management.

362.2　　　　　　　　CN
DELLCREST NEWS. 1966-1989 (vol.27, no.1). q. Dellcrest Children's Centre, 1645 Sheppard Ave. W., Downsview, Ont. M3M 2X4, Canada.
Formerly: Dellcrest Children's Centre Newsletter; **Supersedes:** Boys Village Report (ISSN 0045-2688)

980　　　　　　　　　US
DELLPLAIN LATIN AMERICAN STUDIES. ceased. irreg. Westview Press, 5500 Central Ave., Boulder, CO 80301.

810　　　　　　　　　FR　　ISSN 0396-7549
DELTA. 1975-1989 (no.28). 2/yr. Universite de Montpellier (Universite Paul Valery), Centre d'Etudes et de Recherches sur les Ecrivains du Sud des Etats-Unis, B.P. 5043, 34032 Montpellier Cedex, France.

329.3　　　　　　　　US　　ISSN 0011-8192
DEMOCRAT (WASHINGTON). 1968-19?? m. Democratic National Committee, 2600 Virginia Ave. N.W., Washington, DC 20037.

616.8　　　　　　　　UK　　ISSN 0142-8373
DEMYELINATING DISEASES. ceased 1990. m. (looseleaf format; back issues avail.) Sheffield University Biomedical Information Service (SUBIS), The University, Sheffield S10 2TN, England.

332　　　　　　　　　IT
DENARO CAPITAL. ceased. m. Rizzoli Editore s.p.a., Via A. Rizzoli 2, 20132 Milan, Italy.

100　　　　　　　　　GW　　ISSN 0070-3419
DENKEN, SCHAUEN, SINNEN. 1962-198? irreg. Verlag Freies Geistesleben GmbH, Haussmannstr. 76, 7000 Stuttgart, Germany.

027.4　　　　　　　　DK　　ISSN 0106-3626
DENMARK. BIBLIOTEKSTILSYNET INFORMERER. 1975-1989 (no.3). 4/yr. Bibliotekstilsynet, Nyhavn 31 E, 3, DK-1051 Copenhagen K, Denmark.

331.11 314　　　　　DK　　ISSN 0070-346X
HD5799
DENMARK. DANMARKS STATISTIK. ARBEJDSLOESHEDEN. 1910-1984. a. Danmarks Statistik, Sejroegade 11, 2100 Copenhagen OE, Denmark.

331.1　　　　　　　　DK　　ISSN 0105-0788
DENMARK. DANMARKS STATISTIK. ARBEJDSMARKEDSSTATISTIK: KVARTALSVIS REGIONALSTATISTIK. ceased 1988. q. (back issues avail.) Danmarks Statistik, Sejroegade 11, 2100 Copenhagen OE, Denmark.

690　　　　　　　　　DK　　ISSN 0108-7568
DENMARK. DANMARKS STATISTIK. BYGNINGSOPGOERELSEN. 1977-1982. quadrennial. Danmarks Statistik, Sejroegade 11, 2100 Copenhagen OE, Denmark.

Supersedes in part: Denmark. Danmarks Statistik. Folke- og Boligtaellingen.

314　　　　　　　　　DK　　ISSN 0105-9750
DENMARK. DANMARKS STATISTIK. STATISTIKE EFTERRENINGER/DANMARKS STATISTICS. STATISTICAL NEWS. 1976-1982. a. Danmarks Statistik, Sejroegade 11, 2100 Copenhagen OE, Denmark.

350　　　　　　　　　DK　　ISSN 0107-0371
DENMARK. DANMARKS STATISTIK. VALGENE TIL DE KOMMUNALE OG AMTSKOMMUNALE RAAD. 1971-1983. irreg. Danmarks Statistik, Sejroegade 11, 2100 Copenhagen OE, Denmark.
Formerly: Denmark. Danmarks Statistik. Valgene til de Kommunale Raad.

336.2　　　　　　　　DK　　ISSN 0109-6672
HJ6971
DENMARK. DIREKTORATET FOR TOLDVAESENET. TOLDVAESENETS AARSBERETNING. 1971-1989. a. Direktoratet for Toldvaesenet, Amaliegade 44, DK-1256 Copenhagen K, Denmark.
Former titles: Denmark. Direktoratet for Toldvaesenet. Toldvaesenet Aktiviteter; Denmark. Direktoratet for Toldvaesenet. Toldvaesenet.

614.7　　　　　　　　DK　　ISSN 0108-7487
DENMARK. MILJOEKREDITRAADET. BERETNING. 1977-1990. a. Miljoekreditraadet, Miljoestyrelsen, Strandgade 29, 1401 Copenhagen K, Denmark.

500　　　　　　　　　DK　　ISSN 0105-452X
DENMARK. PLANLAEGNINGSRAADET FOR FORSKNINGEN - DANDOK - STATENS 6 FORSKNINGSRAAD. BERETNING. 1974-1988. biennial. Forskningsafdelingen - Danish Research Administration, H.C. Andersens Boulevard 40, DK-1553 Copenhagen V, Denmark.

352.7　　　　　　　　DK　　ISSN 0105-9602
DENMARK. PLANSTYRELSEN. REGIONPLANORIENTERING. 1975-1983 (vol.13). irreg. Miljoeministeriet, Planstyrelsen - Danish National Agency for Physical Planning, Ministry of the Environment, Haraldsgade 53, DK-2100 Copenhagen Oe, Denmark.

630　　　　　　　　　DK　　ISSN 0589-6665
DENMARK. STATENS BYGGEFORSKNINGSINSTITUT. LANDBRUGSBYGGERI. 1956-1991 (vol.76). irreg. Statens Byggeforskninginstitut, SBI-Publikationer, P.O. Box 119, DK-2970 Hoersholm, Denmark.

690　　　　　　　　　DK　　ISSN 0904-2253
DENMARK. STATENS BYGGEFORSKNINGSINSTITUT. PROJEKTRESUMEER. 1983-1987. a. Statens Byggeforskninginstitut - Danish Building Research Institute, Dr. Neergards Vej 15, Postbox 119, DK-2970 Hoersholm, Denmark.
Formerly: Denmark. Statens Byggeforskninginstitut. Program Resumeer (ISSN 0109-0321)

778.5　　　　　　　　DK　　ISSN 0105-5526
DENMARK. STATENS FILMCENTRAL. S F C, 16MM FILM. ceased. biennial. Statens Filmcentral, Vestergade 27, 1456 Copenhagen K, Denmark.
Formerly: Denmark. Statens Filmcentral. Katalog over 16mm Film.

338.1　　　　　　　　DK　　ISSN 0107-5683
HD2001
DENMARK. STATENS JORDBRUGSOEKONOMISKE INSTITUT. SERIE B: OEKONOMIEN I LANDBRUGETS DRIFTSGRENE/ECONOMICS OF AGRICULTURAL ENTERPRISES. 1982-1989; suspended. a. Statens Jordbrugsoekonomiske Institut, Toftegards Plads, Gl. Koege Landevej 1-3, 2500 Valby, Denmark.
Formerly: Regnkabsresultater.

637　　　　　　　　　DK　　ISSN 0366-3221
　　　　　　　　　　　　　　CODEN: BSFJAL
DENMARK. STATENS MEJERIFORSOEG. BERETNING. 1925-1990 (vol.276). irreg. Statens Mejeriforsoeg - Danish Research Institute for Dairy Industry, Roskildevej 56, DK-3400 Hilleroed, Denmark.

336　　　　　　　　　DK　　ISSN 0106-4908
DENMARK. STATSSKATTEDIREKTORATET OG LIGNINGSRAADET. MEDDELELSER 1. HAEFTE: INDKOMST- OG FORMUEANSAETTELSER. 1976-19?? a. Statsskattedirektoratet, Copenhagen, Denmark.
Formerly: Denmark. Statens Ligningsdirektorat og Ligningsraadet. Indkomst- og Formueskat.

CESSATIONS

336 DK
DENMARK. STATSSKATTEDIREKTORATET OG LIGNINGSRAADET. MEDDELELSER 2. HAEFTE: VURDERING AF FAST EJENDOM. 1976-19?? a. Statsskattedirektoratet, Copenhagen, Denmark.
Formerly: Denmark. Statsskatedirektoratet og Ligningsraadet. Vurdering af Fast Ejendom.

020 DK ISSN 0107-8003
DENMARK BIBLIOTEKSTILSYNET. BERETNING. 1974-1988. a. Bibliotekstilsynet, Nyhavn 31 E, 3, DK-1051 Copenhagen K, Denmark.

617.6 GW ISSN 0011-8559
DENTAL-DIENST. 1948-1990. m. Bielefelder Verlagsanstalt GmbH & Co. KG, Niederwall 53, Postfach 1140, 4800 Bielefeld, Germany.

617.6 US ISSN 0011-8672
DENTAL LABORATORY REVIEW. 1925-1991 (Aug.). m. (also avail. in microform from UMI; reprint service avail. from UMI) Edgell Communications, 7500 Old Oak Blvd., Cleveland, OH 44130.

617.6 US ISSN 0011-8680
DENTAL MANAGEMENT. 1960-1991 (Aug.). m. Edgell Communications, 7500 Old Oak Blvd., Cleveland, OH 44130.

617.6 AT ISSN 0418-694X
DENTAL OUTLOOK. 1962-1991. q. Dental Outlook Publications Ltd., P.O. 679, Glebe, N.S.W. 2037, Australia.

617.6 US
DENTIST'S DESK REFERENCE; materials, instruments & equipment. 1962-1991. biennial. American Dental Association, 211 E. Chicago Ave., Chicago, IL 60611.
Formerly: Guide to Dental Materials and Devices (ISSN 0093-9706)

617.6 US ISSN 0196-2701
DENTISTS MEDICAL DIGEST. 1979-1989 (Dec.). 12/yr. (looseleaf format; back issues avail.) D M D, Inc., 603 Bayville Rd., Box 402, Locust Valley, NY 11560.

929 US
DENTON DISPATCH; a newsletter for Denton and related families. 1986-1990 (Oct.). q. 3218 Robin Rd., White Pine, TN 37890.

658.871 US
DEPARTMENT STORE ECONOMIST. 1838-19?? 8/yr. Retail Directions, Inc., 48 E. 43 St., New York, NY 10017.
Former titles: Retail Directions; Department Store Management (ISSN 0011-8893)

051 CN ISSN 0383-7521
PQ3912.5
DERIVES; tiers-monde-Quebec une nouvelle conjoncture culturelle. 1975-1988 (no.57-58). 4/yr. Editions Derives, C.P. 398 Succ., Montreal, Que. H1V 3M5, Canada.

616.5 UK ISSN 0262-5504
DERMATOLOGY IN PRACTICE. 1982-1990 (vol.8, no.3). bi-m. Medical Tribune UK Ltd., Tower House, Southampton St., London WC2E 7LS, England.

630 CR ISSN 0046-0028
DESARROLLO RURAL EN LAS AMERICAS. 1969-1984. 2/yr. (also avail. in microfilm from UMI; reprint service avail. from UMI) Instituto Interamericano de Cooperacion para la Agricultura - O E A, Apdo. 55, 2200 Coronado, San Jose, Costa Rica.

320 330 BO
DESARROLLO Y HUMANISMO. 1981-1988 (vol.8). s-a. Fundacion "Ricardo Bacherer", Casilla Postal 3835, La Paz, Bolivia.

632 UK ISSN 0305-2680
DESCRIPTIONS OF PLANT VIRUSES. 1970-19?? irreg. (back issues avail.) Association of Applied Biologists, Horticultural Research International, Wellesbourne, Warwick CV35 9EF, England.

330 331 BL
DESEMPENHO RECENTE DA INDUSTRIA DA CONSTRUCAO CIVIL DO RS. 1982-1988 (1st sem.). s-a. Fundacao de Economia e Estatistica, Rua Duque De Caxias, No. 1691, CEP 90010 Porto Alegre RS, Brazil.

645 747 US ISSN 0882-1526
DESIGN HORIZONS. 1984-198? q. Communications - Today Publishing Ltd. (Subsidiary of: Reed International PLC), 200 S. Main St., Box 2754, High Point, NC 27261-2411.

747 745.5 UK ISSN 0265-1092
DESIGN INTERNATIONAL; an information and bibliographic data base. 1984-198? a. (microfiche) Emmett Publishing, 21 West St., Haslemere, Surrey GU27 2AB, England.

747 GW
DESIGN INTERNATIONAL. ISSUE A. 1976-1988. bi-m. Design International, Kantering 57, 5330 Koenigswinter, Germany.
Supersedes in part: Design International (ISSN 0011-9393)

740 GW
DESIGN INTERNATIONAL. ISSUE B. 1967-1988. q. Design International, Kaufering 57, 5330 Koenigswinter, Germany.
Supersedes in part: Design International (ISSN 0011-9393)

747 US
DESIGN TODAY; the business magazine for interior design. (Avail. only as supplement to: Furniture - Today) 1983-1990. q. Cahners Business Newspapers (Subsidiary of: Reed International PLC), Division of Reed Publishing (USA) Inc., 200 S. Main St., Box 2754, High Point, NC 27261-2411.

745.2 UK ISSN 0011-9423
DESIGNER. 1931-1988. bi-m. (Society of Industrial Artists & Designers) Designer Publication, 29 Bedford Sq., London WC13 3EG, England.
Formerly: S I A D Journal.

747 US
DESIGNER SPECIFIER. 1957-1992 (Jan.). m. North American Publishing Co., 401 N. Broad St., Philadelphia, PA 19108.
Incorporates (in Jan. 1990): Professional Office Design; **Formerly (until Aug. 1989):** Designer (ISSN 0011-9431)

747 US
DESIGNERS' KITCHENS & BATHS. 1988-1989. q. Gralla Publications, 1515 Broadway, New York, NY 10036.

133.5 FR
DESTIN INTERNATIONAL. ceased. m. (Institut de Technologie Previsionnelle Appliquee) Editions Astres, 10 rue de Grussol, 75011 Paris, France.
Formerly: Destin (ISSN 0011-9555)

910.4 CN ISSN 0834-017X
DESTINATION CANADA MEETINGS AND CONVENTIONS. 1981-1988. bi-m. (back issues avail.) (Destination Canada Inc.) Baxter Publishing Co., 310 Dupont St., Toronto, Ont. M5R 1V9, Canada.
Former titles (until 1986): Travel Destination Canada, Meetings and Conventions (ISSN 0834-0161); (until 1985): Travel Destination Canada (ISSN 0712-1261)

910.2 MX
DESTINOS. 1983-1988. m. Internacional de Revistas, S.A. de C.V., Torcuato Tasso, 231 Col. Polanco, C.P. 11560 Mexico, D.F., Mexico.

133.5 UK ISSN 0266-3120
DESTINY. 1984-198? m. Sovereign International, Sovereign House, Brentwood, Essex CM14 4SE, England.

658.8 CN
DETAILLANT EN ALIMENTATION; le guide des panneurs-epiceries. 1982-1991 (vol.2, no.3). q. Publicor Inc., 7, Chemin Bates, Outremont, Que. H2V 1A6, Canada.
Formerly: Accommodeur.

020 US
DETROIT PUBLIC LIBRARY. M R L BULLETIN. 1945-1991 (Apr.); suspended. bi-m. Detroit Public Library, Municipal Reference Library, 1004 City-County Bldg., Detroit, MI 48226.

327 GW ISSN 0080-7125
DEUTSCH-AUSLAENDISCHE BEZIEHUNGEN. SCHRIFTENREIHE. 1961-1979. irreg. (Institut fuer Auslandsbeziehungen, Stuttgart) K. Thienemanns Verlag, Edition Erdmann, Blumenstr. 36, 7000 Stuttgart 1, Germany.

015 350 GW
DEUTSCHE BIBLIOGRAPHIE. VERZEICHNIS AMTLICHER DRUCKSCHRIFTEN; Veroeffentlichungen der Behoerden, Koerperschaften, Anstalten und Stiftungen des oeffentlichen Rechts sowie der wichtigsten halbamtlichen Institutionen in der Bundesrepublik Deutschland und West-Berlin. 1957-1982. irreg. (Deutsche Bibliothek) Buchhaendler-Vereinigung GmbH, Gr. Hirschgraben 17-21, 6000 Frankfurt a.M. 1, Germany.

070.5 GW ISSN 0459-004X
Z319
DEUTSCHE BUECHEREI. JAHRBUCH. 1965-1990. a. Deutsche Buecherei, Deutscher Platz, 7010 Leipzig, Germany.

323.4 GW
DEUTSCHE DEMOKRATISCHE REPUBLIK. KOMITEE FUER MENSCHENRECHTE. SCHRIFTEN UND INFORMATIONEN. 1975-1989. 3/yr. Komitee fuer Menschenrechte, Otto-Grotewohl-Str. 19D, 1080 Berlin, Germany.

780 015 GW ISSN 0012-0502
DEUTSCHE MUSIKBIBLIOGRAPHIE. 1943-1990. m. (Deutsche Buecherei) Friedrich Hofmeister Musikverlag GmbH, Karlstr. 10, 7010 Leipzig, Germany.

383 GW ISSN 0012-0588
DEUTSCHE POST (BERLIN); Zeitschrift fuer das Post- und Fernmeldewesen der D D R. 1955-1990. 6/yr. Transpress VEB Verlag fuer Verkehrswesen, Franzoesische Str. 13-14, 1086 Berlin, Germanmy.

914 GW ISSN 0034-3668
DEUTSCHE REISEBUERO-ZEITUNG. 1965-1989. w. Langener Druck- und Verlags GmbH, Robert-Bosch-Str. 13, Postfach 1429, 6070 Langen, Germany.

940 GW ISSN 0340-8396
DEUTSCHES MITTELALTER, KRITISCHE STUDIENTEXTE DER MONUMENTA GERMANIAE HISTORICA. 1937-1949. irreg. Anton Hiersemann Verlag, Rosenbergstr. 113, Postfach 140155, 7000 Stuttgart 1, Germany.

608.7 GW
DEUTSCHES PATENTAMT. BEKANNTMACHUNGEN. 1960-1990. w. Deutsches Patentamt, Dienststelle Berlin, Gitschinerstr. 97, 1000 Berlin 61, Germany.
Formerly: Germany (Democratic Republic). Amt fuer Erfindungs- und Patentwesen. Bekanntmachungen (ISSN 0005-8246)

790.1 GW ISSN 0323-8628
DEUTSCHES SPORTECHO: REIHE A. (Issued in 2 parts) 1947-1991. 6/w. Sportverlag GmbH, Neustaedtische Kirchstr. 15, 1086 Berlin, Germany.

790.1 GW ISSN 0232-4814
DEUTSCHES SPORTECHO: REIHE B. (Issued in two parts) ceased 1991. 6/w. Sportverlag GmbH, Neustadtische Kirchstr. 15, 1086 Berlin, Germany.

300 US
DEVELOPING NATIONS MONOGRAPH SERIES ONE. ceased (no.7). irreg. Wake Forest University, Overseas Research Center, Box 7206, Reynolds Sta., Winston Salem, NC 27109.

338 380 RH
DEVELOPMENT. 1962-19?? m. Modus Publications (Pvt) Ltd., Throgmorton House, Samora Michel Ave., PO Box 1819, Harare, Zimbabwe.
Formerly: Industrial and Commercial Development.

338.91 NZ
DEVELOPMENT CO-OPERATION: REVIEW OF N.Z. OFFICIAL DEVELOPMENT ASSISTANCE. 1974-1988. a. Ministry of External Relations and Trade, Wellington, New Zealand.
Former titles: Annual Development Assistance Review, Memorandum of New Zealand; Annual Aid Review, Memorandum of New Zealand.

CESSATIONS

338.91 327 US
DEVELOPMENT FORUM. 1986-19?? s-a. Overseas Development Network, Harvard-Radcliffe International Development Forum, 333 Valencia St., Ste. 330, San Fransisco, CA 94103.

520 629.4 NE
DEVELOPMENTS IN SOLAR SYSTEM AND SPACE SCIENCE. 1975-1979. irreg. Elsevier Science Publishers B.V., P.O. Box 211, 1000 AE Amsterdam, Netherlands.

330 CN
LE DEVOIR ECONOMIQUE. ceased June 1990. 8/yr. 211 St-Sacrement St., Montreal, Que. H2Y 1X1, Canada.

282 US
DIACONATE MAGAZINE. ceased 1991 (Nov.). bi-m. Liturgical Publications Inc., 2875 S. James Dr., New Berlin, WI 53151-3662.

613.2 GW ISSN 0722-0448
DIAET - THERAPIE; bei Hypertonie - Hyperlipoproteinaemie - Diabetes mellitus. 1981-19?? bi-m. (tabloid format; back issues avail.) P M I Verlag GmbH, August-Schanz-Str. 21, 6000 Frankfurt a.M. 50, Germany.

770 IT
DIAFRAMMA INTERNATIONAL PHOTOGRAPHERS. (Includes supplements) 1958-1985 (Jan.). m. EditPhoto, Via degli Imbriani, 20158 Milan, Italy.
Former titles (until Dec. 1984): Diaframma Fotografia Italiana. Newsletter; (until 1982): Diaframma Fotografia Italiana; (until 1976): Skema il Diaframma Fotografia Italiana; (until 1975): Fotografia Italiana; (until 1972): Popular Photography Italiana; (until 1966): Popular Photography.

610 US ISSN 0163-3228
RC71
DIAGNOSIS. 1979-1988. 12/yr. (also avail. in microform from UMI; reprint service avail. from UMI) Medical Economics Company Inc., 680 Kinderkamack Rd., Oradell, NJ 07649.

616.97 US
DIAGNOSTIC AND CLINICAL IMMUNOLOGY. 1984-198? 6/yr. (back issues avail.; reprint service avail. from ISI) Wiley-Liss, Inc., 41 E. 11th St., New York, NY 10003.
Formerly: Diagnostic Immunology.

330.9 BL
DIAGNOSTICOS A P E C. ceased 1986. irreg. Associacao Promotora de Estudos de Economia, Rua Sorocaba 295, Rio de Janeiro, Botafogo, Brazil.

616 US
Q183 CODEN: LABMAS
DIAGNOSTICS & CLINICAL TESTING. 1963-1990 (July). m. Nature Publishing Co., 65 Bleecker St., New York, NY 10012.
Formerly (until Apr. 1989): Laboratory Management (ISSN 0023-6845); Incorporates (in 1977): Medical Lab (ISSN 0025-7311)

380 UK
DIAL SAFETY, SECURITY, HEALTH & HYGIENE. 1989-199? a. Dial Industry Publications (Subsidiary of: Reed Information Services Ltd.), Windsor Court, East Grinstead House, East Grinstead, W. Sussex RH19 1XA, England.

021 CN ISSN 0700-3048
DIALOGUE (OTTAWA). 1973-1988. 4/yr. Ontario Library Service - Rideau - Service des Bibliotheques de L'Ontario, 1675 Russell Rd., Unit 8, Ottawa, Ont. K1G 0N1, Canada.

026 011 US
DICTIONARY CATALOG OF OFFICIAL PUBLICATIONS OF THE STATE OF NEW YORK; monographs catalogued by the New York State Library. 1977-1991. q. New York State Library, Albany, NY 12230.

920 UK ISSN 0070-4733
DICTIONARY OF LATIN AMERICAN AND CARIBBEAN BIOGRAPHY. 1969-19?? irreg. Melrose Press Ltd., 3 Regal Lane, Soham, Ely, Cambridgeshire CB7 5BA, England.

500 IT
DIDATTICA SCIENTIFICA. 1971-1982. 3/yr. Istituto Italiano Edizioni Atlas, Via Crescenzi 88, 24100, Bergamo, Italy.

250 GW ISSN 0720-9916
DIENST AM WORT - GEDANKEN ZUR SONNTAGSPREDIGT. 1950-1988. 8/yr. Religioese Bildungsarbeit Stuttgart GmbH-Verlag, Boeheimstr. 44, 7000 Stuttgart 1, Germany.

613.2 610 UK ISSN 0142-8624
DIET. ceased 1990. m. (looseleaf format; back issues avail.) Sheffield University Biomedical Information Service (SUBIS), The University, Sheffield S10 2TN, England.

327 US ISSN 0896-2138
DIGEST OF THE ARAB PRESS. 1986-198? s-m. American-Arab Affairs Council, American-Arab Press Institute, 1730 M St., N.W., Ste. 512, Washington, DC 20036.

658.8 621.381 US
DIGITAL REVIEW BUYERS GUIDE. ceased. a. Ziff-Davis Publishing Co., One Park Ave., New York, NY 10016.

382 PH
DIMENSIONS OF PHILIPPINE EXPORTS. 1974-19?? a. Ministry of Trade, Trade & Industry Bldg., 361 Gil J. Puyat Ave. Ext., Makati, Metro Manila, Philippines.

001.3 BL
DIOGENES. 1981-1986 (no.10). s-a. Editora Universidade de Brasilia, Caixa Postal 153001, CEP 70910 Brasilia D.F., Brazil.

948.9 DK ISSN 0070-4938
DIPLOMATARIUM DANICUM. 1938-19?? irreg. Danske Sprog- og Litteraturselskab - Danish Society of Language and Literature, Frederiksholms Kanal 18 A, 1220 Copenhagen K, Denmark.

531.64 US ISSN 0735-2484
DIRECT ENERGY CONVERSION (OAK RIDGE, 1982). 1982-19?? s-m. U.S. Department of Energy, Office of Scientific and Technical Information, Box 62, Oak Ridge, TN 37831.

338 US ISSN 0094-209X
Z7165.U5
DIRECTORIES OF HAWAII. ceased. irreg. Department of Business and Economic Development, Information Office, Box 2359, Honolulu, HI 96804.

020 011 US ISSN 0146-7085
Z5771
DIRECTORY INFORMATION SERVICE; an annotated guide to business and industrial directories, professional and scientific rosters, directory databases, and other lists and guides of all kinds. (Supplement to: Directory of Directories) 1977-198? irreg. (2 every 18 months). Gale Research Inc., Dept. 77748, Detroit, MI 48277-0748.

200 US
DIRECTORY OF CHURCHES AND SYNAGOGUES. 1934-198?; suspended. a. Council of Churches of the City of New York, 475 Riverside Dr., Ste. 439, New York, NY 10115.

378 CN ISSN 0705-8160
TX911.5
DIRECTORY OF COURSES: TOURISM, HOSPITALITY, RECREATION. 1976-19?? biennial. Tourism Canada, 4E - 235 Queen Canada, Ottawa, Ont. K1A 0H6, Canada.

011 US ISSN 0890-5525
Z5771
DIRECTORY OF DIRECTORIES: PUBLISHERS VOLUME. 1987-1988 (2nd ed.). a. Gale Research Inc., Dept. 77748, Detroit, MI 48277-0748.

920 US
DIRECTORY OF DISTINGUISHED AMERICANS. 1982-19?? a. American Biographical Institute, Inc., Governing Board of Editors, 5126 Bur Oak Circle, Box 31226, Raleigh, NC 27622.

500 CN ISSN 0316-0297
Q180.C2
DIRECTORY OF FEDERALLY SUPPORTED RESEARCH IN UNIVERSITIES/REPERTOIRE DE LA RECHERCHE DANS LES UNIVERSITES SUBVENTIONNEE PAR LE GOUVERNEMENT FEDERAL. 1972-19?? a. (National Research Council of Canada) C.I.S.T.I. Publicity and Communications, Ottawa, Ont. K1A 0S2, Canada.

371.4 376 US ISSN 0732-5215
LB2338
DIRECTORY OF FINANCIAL AIDS FOR WOMEN. 1978-19?? biennial. A B C-Clio Information Services, 2040 Alameda Padre Serra, Box 4397, Santa Barbara, CA 93103.

370 US ISSN 0732-2755
P95
DIRECTORY OF GRADUATE PROGRAMS IN THE COMMUNICATION ARTS AND SCIENCES. 1967-19?? every 5 yrs. Speech Communication Association, 5105 Backlick Rd., Bldg. E., Annandale, VA 22003.
Formerly: Directory of Graduate Programs in the Speech Communication Arts and Sciences (ISSN 0070-5616)

510 540 US ISSN 0890-541X
Q180.U5
DIRECTORY OF GRANTS IN THE PHYSICAL SCIENCES. 1986-1987. irreg. Oryx Press, 4041 N. Central at Indian School Rd., Phoenix, AZ 85012-3397.

330 US ISSN 0278-0119
Z7165.U5
DIRECTORY OF INDUSTRY DATA SOURCES, U.S. AND CANADA. 1981; ceased same year. a. Ballinger Publishing Co., 10 E. 53rd St., New York, NY 10022-5244.

610 MY
DIRECTORY OF INFORMATION ON MEDICAL PRACTITIONERS IN MALAYSIA. (Supplement avail.) 1969-1979. triennial. (back issues avail.) Malaysian Medical Association, 4th Fl., MMA House, 124 Jalan Pahang, 53000 Kuala Lumpur, Malaysia.

382 US
DIRECTORY OF INTERNATIONAL TRADE. 1984-19?? irreg. Produce Marketing Association, 1500 Casho Mill Rd., Box 6036, Newark, DE 19714-6036.

669.14 US
DIRECTORY OF IRON AND STEEL WORKS OF THE UNITED STATES AND CANADA. ceased. triennial. American Iron and Steel Institute, 1133 15th St., N.W., Ste. 300, Washington, DC 20005.

360 614 US ISSN 0419-2818
DIRECTORY OF JEWISH HEALTH AND WELFARE AGENCIES. 1952-1990. s-a. Council of Jewish Federations, Inc., 730 Broadway, 2nd Fl., New York, NY 10003.

624 UK ISSN 0260-5007
DIRECTORY OF LAND AND HYDROGRAPHIC SURVEY SERVICES IN THE UNITED KINGDOM. 1979-1991. a. Royal Institution of Chartered Surveyors, 12 Great George St., Parliament Square, London SW1P 3AD, England.

778.1 US ISSN 0160-6077
DIRECTORY OF LIBRARY REPROGRAPHIC SERVICES. 1959-19?? biennial. Meckler Corporation, 11 Ferry Lane W., Westport, CT 06880-5808.

338 US ISSN 0190-3047
HD9727.H3
DIRECTORY OF MANUFACTURERS, STATE OF HAWAII. 1969-1984. irreg. Chamber of Commerce of Hawaii, Dillingham Bldg., 735 Bishop St., Honolulu, HI 96813.

020 US
DIRECTORY OF MASSACHUSETTS LIBRARIES AND MEDIA CENTERS INCLUDING BUYER'S GUIDE. 1985-1987. a. L D A Publishers, 42-36 209 St., Bayside, NY 11361.
Former titles: Directory of Massachusetts Libraries and Media Centers and Buyers' Guide; (until 1985): Directory of Massachusetts Libraries and Media Centers.

658 US ISSN 0731-8510
RA977
DIRECTORY OF MULTIHOSPITAL SYSTEMS. 1980-1986. a. American Hospital Association, 840 N. Lake Shore Dr., Chicago, IL 60611.

CESSATIONS

707.4　　　　　UK　　ISSN 0267-9698
DIRECTORY OF MUSEUMS & LIVING DISPLAYS. 1985-1989 (3rd ed.). quinquennial. Macmillan Press Ltd., Houndmills, Basingstoke, Hampshire RG21 2XS, England.

610.73　　　　　US
DIRECTORY OF NURSES WITH DOCTORAL DEGREES. ceased. irreg. (reprint service avail. from UMI) American Nurses' Association, 2420 Pershing Rd., Kansas City, MO 64108.

371.42　　　　　UK　　ISSN 0070-6019
HF5382.5.G7
DIRECTORY OF OPPORTUNITIES FOR GRADUATES. 1957-1991. a. V N U Business Publications BV, 32-34 Broadwick St., London W1A 2HG, England.

020 025　　　　　US　　ISSN 0884-089X
Z6941
DIRECTORY OF PERIODICALS ONLINE: NEWS, LAW & BUSINESS; indexed, abstracted & full-text. 1985-1991; suspended. a. Library Alliance, Inc., 264 Lexington Ave., Ste. 4C, New York, NY 10016-4182.

500　　　　　US　　ISSN 0884-0911
Q1.A1
DIRECTORY OF PERIODICALS ONLINE: SCIENCE & TECHNOLOGY. 1989-1991; suspended. a. Library Alliance, Inc., 264 Lexington Ave., Ste. 4C, New York, NY 10016-4182.

621.3　　　　　US
DIRECTORY OF POWER PLANT MANAGERS. ceased 1991. a. Utility Data Institute, Inc. (Subsidiary of: Halliburton Co.), 1700 K St., N.W., Ste. 400, Washington, DC 20006.

380.5　　　　　US　　ISSN 0270-8264
HE4421
DIRECTORY OF RESEARCH, DEVELOPMENT AND DEMONSTRATION PROJECTS. 1988-19?? a. U.S. Urban Mass Transportation Administration, 400 Seventh St. S.W., Washington, DC 20590.
　Former titles: Improving Urban Mobility (ISSN 0270-8248) & Directory of Research, Development, and Demonstrations.

362.8　　　　　US　　ISSN 0362-7179
HV98.I15
DIRECTORY OF SERVICES FOR MIGRANT FAMILIES/ DIRECTORIO DE SERVICIOS PARA FAMILIAS MIGRANTES. 1975-1977. irreg. Office of Education, Migrant Education Section, Springfield, IL 62777.

658.7　　　　　US
DIRECTORY OF SHOP-BY-MAIL BARGAIN SOURCES. 1978-1986. irreg. Pilot Books, 103 Cooper St., Babylon, NY 11702.

371.9　　　　　NZ
DIRECTORY OF SPECIAL EDUCATION AND GUIDANCE SERVICES IN NEW ZEALAND. 1960-1988. a. Department of Education, Education Services, Box 1379, New Zealand.

331.4　　　　　US　　ISSN 0273-2157
DIRECTORY OF SPECIAL OPPORTUNITIES FOR WOMEN. 1981-198? irreg. Garrett Park Press, Box 190F, Garrett Park, MD 20896.

650　　　　　US　　ISSN 0070-640X
DIRECTORY OF STATE AND FEDERAL FUNDS AVAILABLE FOR BUSINESS DEVELOPMENT. 1966-1985. irreg. Pilot Books, 103 Cooper St., Babylon, NY 11702.

362.7　　　　　US
DIRECTORY OF STATE AND LOCAL CHILD SUPPORT ADVOCACY GROUPS. 1986-1989. a. Children's Foundation, 725 15th St., N.W., Ste. 505, Washington, DC 20005.

610　　　　　US
DIRECTORY OF SUDDEN INFANT DEATH SYNDROME PROGRAMS AND RESOURCES. 1984-198? irreg. National Sudden Infant Death Syndrome Clearinghouse, 8201 Greensboro Dr., Ste. 600, McLean, VA 22102.

380.1 530　　　　　US
DIRECTORY OF THE SOLAR INDUSTRY. 1976-19?? a. Solar Data, 13 Evergreen Rd., Hampton, NH 03842.

910.202　　　　　US
DIRECTORY OF TRAVEL INFORMATION SOURCES FOR THE PACIFIC ISLANDS; comprehensive resource guide. published only once, 1988. irreg. Pilot Books, 103 Cooper St., Babylon, NY 11702.

025　　　　　US
DIRECTORY OF WESTCHESTER LIBRARIES AND MEDIA CENTERS INCLUDING BUYERS' GUIDE. ceased 1985. a. L D A Publishers, 42-36 209 St., Bayside, NY 11361.
　Formerly: Directory of Westchester Libraries and Media Centers and Buyers' Guide.

380.1　　　　　US
DIRECTORY PUBLISHERS BUYERS GUIDE. 1988-1991. a. Morgan-Rand Publishing Co., 2200 Sansom St., Philadelphia, PA 19103.
　Formerly: Directory Industry Buyers Guide.

658　　　　　IT
DIRITTO DELL'IMPRESA (NAPLES, 1987); imprese pubbliche e imprese private con partecipazione pubblica. 1987-198?; suspended. q. Edizioni Scientifiche Italiane, Via Casalini, 80121 Naples, Italy.

724 747　　　　　US
DIRSMITH GROUP. PUBLICATION; the promise of tomorrow. 1980-198? q. (back issues avail.) Dirsmith Group, Inc., 318 Maple Ave., Highland Park, IL 60035.

300　　　　　US　　ISSN 0894-9573
DIRTY BUM: A MAGAZINE. 1987-19?? q. Joyce Stokes, Ed. & Pub., 4309 N. Morada, Covina, CA 91722.

340　　　　　US　　ISSN 1042-2099
DIS - ABILITY LAW BRIEFS. ceased. q. American Bar Association, Commission on Mental & Physical Disability Law, 750 N. Lake Shore Dr., Chicago, IL 60611.

790.1　　　　　US
DISC SPORTS. 1983-19?? bi-m. Sports Ink Magazines, Inc., Box 159, 2 South Park Pl., Fair Haven, VT 05743.

915.204　　　　　UK
DISCOVER THE FAR EAST. 1986-198?; suspended. a. Discovery Press, 33-35 Crouch End Hill, London N8 8DH, England.

284　　　　　US
DISCOVERIES (KANSAS CITY). 1920-1988. w. Church of the Nazarene, Nazarene Headquarters, Christian Life & Sunday School, 6401 The Paseo, Kansas City, MO 64131.

977　　　　　US　　ISSN 0899-8329
DISCOVERY FIVE HUNDRED. 1986-1992 (Dec.). q. (looseleaf format; back issues avail.) International Columbian Quincentenary Alliance, Ltd., Box 1492, Columbus, NJ 08022.

917.2　　　　　UK
DISNEYLAND ANNUAL. 1983-1991. a. World International Publishing Co., P.O. Box 111, Gt. Ducie St., Manchester, M60 3BL, England.

028.5　　　　　US
DISNEY'S DUCK TALES. ceased 1990. q. Welsh Publishing Group, Inc., 300 Madison Ave., New York, NY 10017.

614 640.73　　　　　CN
DISPATCH/DEPECHE. 1969-19?? q. (back issues avail.) Department of Health and Welfare, Health Protection Branch, Educational Services, Rm. 1-6, Health Protection Branch Bldg., Holland Ave., Ottawa, Ont. K1A 0L2, Canada.

914　　　　　BE　　ISSN 0419-4241
DISSERTATIONES ARCHAEOLOGICAE GANDENSES. 1953-1991. irreg. Uitgeverij de Tempel, 41 Tempelhof, Bruges, Belgium.

001.6 658.403　　　　　US
DISTRIBUTED PROCESSING PRODUCT REPORTS. 1976-19?? m. (back issues avail.; m. index avail. on diskette) Management Information Corporation, 401 E. Route 70, Ste. 104, Box 5062, Cherry Hill, NJ 08034-5062.
　Formerly: Distributed Processing Report (ISSN 0161-7508)

620.8　　　　　US
DISTRICT OF COLUMBIA. AIR MONITORING SECTION. ANNUAL REPORT ON THE QUALITY OF THE AIR IN WASHINGTON, D.C. 1974-1982; suspended. a. Department of Consumer and Regulatory Affairs, Air Monitoring Section, 5010 Overlook Ave., S.W., Washington, DC 20032.
　Formerly: District of Columbia. Air Monitoring Division. Annual Report on the Quality of the Air in Washington, D.C.

797.21　　　　　US
DIVING WORLD (VAN NUYS). 1988-1990. m. Creative Age Publications, 7628 Densmore Ave., Van Nuys, CA 91406.

282 301.428　　　　　US
DIVORCE MINISTRY NEWSLETTER. 1982-1989. s-a. North American Conference of Separated and Divorced Catholics, 1100 S. Goodman St., Rochester, NY 14620.

799　　　　　US　　ISSN 0146-6143
TS536.6.M8
DIXIE GUN WORKS MUZZLELOADERS' ANNUAL. ceased. a. Aqua-Field Publishing Co., Inc., 66 W. Gilbert St., Shrewsbury, NJ 07702.

610.73 378　　　　　US
DOCTORAL PROGRAMS IN NURSING. ceased 1989. a. National League for Nursing, 350 Hudson St., New York, NY 10014.

001.64　　　　　US
DOCUMENT MANAGEMENT; the journal of records automation and image processing. 1989; announced never published. q. Frost & Sullivan, Inc., 106 Fulton St., New York, NY 10038-2786.

020　　　　　AG　　ISSN 0070-6841
DOCUMENTACION BIBLIOTECOLOGICA. 1970-1974? irreg. Universidad Nacional del Sur, Centro de Documentacion Bibliotecologica, Av. Alem 1253, 8000 Bahia Blanca, Argentina.

842 792　　　　　FR
DOCUMENTATION THEATRALE; fiches analytiques. 1974-1986 (vol.8). a. Universite de Paris X (Paris-Nanterre), Centre d'Etudes Theatrales, 200 Av. de la Republique, 92001 Nanterre Cedex, France.

910.202 016　　　　　FR　　ISSN 0767-2640
DOCUMENTATION TOURISTIQUE: BIBLIOGRAPHIE ANALYTIQUE INTERNATIONALE. 1969-19?? q. (cards) Universite d'Aix-Marseille III (Universite de Droit, d'Economie et des Sciences), Centre des Hautes Etudes Touristiques, Fondation Vasarely, 1 Av. Marcel Pagnol, 13090 Aix-en-Provence, France.

669 016　　　　　II
DOCUMENTED SURVEY ON METALLURGICAL DEVELOPMENTS. 1970-19?? m. National Metallurgical Laboratory, P.O. Burmamines, Jamshedpur 7, India.

320　　　　　VE　　ISSN 0012-4753
D839.3
DOCUMENTOS; revista de informacion politica. 1960-1975 (no.63). q. Universidad Central de Venezuela, Instituto de Estudios Politicos, Caracas, Venezuela.

320.531　　　　　UK
DOCUMENTS IN SOCIALIST HISTORY. no.2, 1974-1991. irreg. (Bertrand Russell Peace Foundation) Spokesman Books, Bertrand Russell House, Gamble St., Nottingham, England.

709　　　　　CN　　ISSN 0383-4514
DOCUMENTS IN THE HISTORY OF CANADIAN ART/ DOCUMENTS D'HISTOIRE DE L'ART CANADIEN. 1974-19?? irreg. National Gallery of Canada, 380 Sussex Drive, Ottawa, Ont. K1N 9N4, Canada.

320 900　　　　　US
DOCUMENTS OF REVOLUTION. ceased. irreg. Cornell University Press, 124 Roberts Place, Ithaca, NY 14850.

636.7　　　　　UK　　ISSN 0268-9502
DOG & COUNTRY. 1897-1990. q. Gilbertson & Page Ltd., P.O. Box 321, Welwyn Garden City, Herts AL7 1LF, England.
　Incorporates: Countryside Monthly (ISSN 0261-2208); Formerly (until May 1981): Gamekeeeper and Countryside (ISSN 0016-4321)

CESSATIONS

636.7   US
DOG WEEK. ceased. w. Hoflin Publishing Ltd., 4401 Zephyr St., Wheat Ridge, CO 80033-3299.

616.86 016   GW   ISSN 0341-8022
HV4997
DOKUMENTATION GEFAEHRDUNG DURCH ALKOHOL, RAUCHEN, DROGEN, ARZNEIMITTEL. 1972-1989. 4/yr. Institut fuer Dokumentation und Information, Sozialmedizin und Oeffentliches Gesundheitswesen, Westerfeldstr. 35-37, Postfach 201012, 4800 Bielefeld 1, Germany.
    Formerly (until 1974): Dokumentation Drogengefaehrdung und Alkoholmissbrauch.

407   GW   ISSN 0343-3420
DOKUMENTATION NEUSPRACHLICHER UNTERRICHT. 1976-1991. a. (reprint service avail. from UMI) (Informationszentrum fuer Fremdsprachenforschung Marburg) Max Hueber Verlag, Max-Hueber-Str. 4, 8045 Ismaning, Germany.

620.1   GW   ISSN 0340-3475
DOKUMENTATION TRIBOLOGIE/DOCUMENTATION TRIBOLOGY. 1967-1987. a. (back issues from no.5, 1968 avail.) Bundesanstalt fuer Materialforschung und -pruefung, Unter den Eichen 87, 1000 Berlin 45, Germany.
    Formerly: Dokumentation Verschleiss, Reibung und Schmierung (ISSN 0070-7023).

320   GW   ISSN 0418-9906
DD261.4
DOKUMENTE ZUR AUSSENPOLITIK DER DEUTSCHEN DEMOKRATISCHEN REPUBLIK. ceased 1990. a. Staatsverlag der D D R, Otto-Grotewohl-Str. 17, 1086 Berlin, Germany.

790.13   UK   ISSN 0955-1646
DOLLS & DOLLS' HOUSE. 1988-1990. s-a. (Guild of Master Craftsman) Guild of Master Craftsman Publications Ltd., 166 High St., Lewes, East Sussex BN7 1XU, England.

340   CN
DOMINION REPORT SERVICE. ceased 1990. m. C C H Canadian Ltd., 6 Garamond Ct., Don Mills, Ont. M3C 1Z5, Canada.

746.92   CN
DOMINO. 1988-1991 (Apr.). 4/yr. Globe and Mail Ltd., 444 Front St. W., Toronto, Ont. M5V 2S9, Canada.

943   GW   ISSN 0070-7074
DONAUSCHWAEBISCHES SCHRIFTTUM. 1953-19?? irreg. Landsmannschaft der Donauschwaben, Goldmuehlestr. 30, 7032 Sindelfingen, Germany.

051   US
DONNELLEY DIRECTORY RECORD. 1970-199?; suspended. irreg. Donnelley Directory (Purchase), 287 Bowman Ave., Purchase, NY 10577.

808.838   US
DOSSIER (ONEONTA). 1981-1983; suspended. q. International Spy Society, English Department, State University College, Oneonta, NY 13820.

051   US   ISSN 0891-5741
AP2
DOSSIER (WASHINGTON, D.C.). 1975-1991 (Mar.). m. Haan Enterprises, 1015 31st St., N.W., Ste. 500, Washington, DC 20007.
    Formerly (until 1986): Washington Dossier (ISSN 0149-7936)

621.3   SP
DOSSIER - CATALOGO EQUIPO ELECTRICO. suspended. a. Tecnipublicaciones, S.A., Fernando VI, 27, 28004 Madrid, Spain.

330.5 350   FR   ISSN 0769-3478
DOSSIERS DE L'OUTRE-MER. 1970-1987 (no.86). q. (also avail. in microfiche) Centre National de Documentation des Departements d'Outre-Mer (CENADDOM), Bt. du Centre d'Etudes de Geographie Tropicale, Domaine Universitaire, 33405 Talence, France.
    Formerly: C E N A D D O M Bulletin d'Information (ISSN 0337-4084)

615.1   JA   ISSN 0012-5660
DOTAITO NYUSU RETA/DOTITE NEWS LETTER. 1953-19?? q. (tabloid format) Dojindo Co. Ltd., 2861, Murazoe, Kengun-machi, Kumamoto-shi 862, Japan.

391.412   US
DOUGLASS SERIES ON WOMEN'S LIVES AND THE MEANING OF GENDER. ceased 1987. irreg. Rutgers University Press, 109 Church St., New Brunswick, NJ 08901.

332.6   US
DOWSE MARKET LETTER. 1978-1989 (Feb.). m. Dowse Securities Management Corporation, 230 California St., Ste. 501, San Francisco, CA 94111.

796.72   US   ISSN 0894-5187
DRAG RACING. 1984-1991 (Mar.). m. (also avail. in microfiche from UMI) Petersen Publishing Co., 8490 Sunset Blvd., Los Angeles, CA 90069.

800   DK   ISSN 0900-7350
DRAMAPAEDAGOGIK I NORDISK PERSPEKTIV. ceased. a. Teaterforlaget Drama, Grasten, Denmark.

792   US
DRAMATIST'S BIBLE. 1980-19?? a. (International Society of Dramatists) St. James Press, 233 E. Ontario, Ste. 600, Chicago, IL 60611.

133   US
DREAMSHORE; a psychedelic journal. 1982-1989; suspended. a. (back issues avail.; reprint service avail. from UMI) Dreamshore Press, Box 1387, Bloomington, IN 47402.

910.2   GW   ISSN 0012-6101
DRESDNER MONATS-BLAETTER; Zeitschrift der Freunde Dresdens. 1949-1990. m. Bund der Mitteldeutschen e.V., Poppelsdorfer Allee 82, 5300 Bonn 1, Germany.

178   UK
DRIFT. 1988-1991. 2/yr. Western Temperance League, 6 Gloucester St., Upper Eastville, Bristol BS5 6QE, England.

622.338   US
DRILLING; the Wellsite publication. 1939-1989. bi-m. Edgell Communications, 7500 Old Oak Blvd., Cleveland, OH 44130.
    Former titles: Drilling-D C W (ISSN 0012-6241); Drilling International.

665.5 338.2   CN   ISSN 0228-7587
                                                      CODEN: DRLSET
DRILLSITE. 1980-19?? bi-m. Maclean-Hunter Ltd. (Calgary), 200-1015 Centre St. N., Calagary, Alta. T2E 2P8, Canada.

808   US
DRISHTI. ceased 1987. q? Church Center for the United Nations, 777 U.N. Plaza Lobby, New York, NY 10017.

388.324   US
DRIVE! (CHATSWORTH). 1961-198? m. (tabloid format) 9800 Topanga Canyon Blvd., Ste. 345, Chatsworth, CA 91311.

385   PL   ISSN 0137-284X
DROGI KOLEJOWE. 1953-1991. m. Wydawnictwa Komunikacji i Lacznosci, Ul. Kazimierzowska 52, Warsaw, Poland.
    Formerly (until 1978): Przeglad Kolejowy Drogowy (ISSN 0033-2208)

380.14   FR
DROGUERIE COULEURS; menage. 1946-19?? m. Societe d'Edition et de Presse, 106 bd. Malesherbes, 75828 Paris Cedex 17, France.

323.4   FR   ISSN 0012-6411
DROIT ET LIBERTE. 1949-1987. m. (Mouvement Contre le Racisme et pour l'Amitie Entre les Peuples) Societe Droit et Liberte, 89, rue Oberkampf, 75543 Paris Cedex 11, France.

616.86   UK   ISSN 0142-8381
DRUG ADDICTION. ceased 1990. m. (looseleaf format; back issues avail.) Sheffield University Biomedical Information Service (SUBIS), The University, Sheffield S10 2TN, England.

615   US
DRUG AND THERAPEUTICS LETTER. 1973-1990 (vol.8, no.2). q. (newspaper) University of Tennessee, Drug Information Center, 877 Madison Ave., Ste. 210, Memphis, TN 38163.
    Formerly (until 1982): Drug Information Newsletter.

615.19 664   US   ISSN 0272-3530
RM302.4   CODEN: DNIND4
DRUG-NUTRIENT INTERACTIONS; a journal of research in nutritional pharmacology and toxicology. 1981-19?? q. Alan R. Liss, Inc., 41 E. 11th St., New York, NY 10003.

615   US
DRUG TRADE NAME CROSS REFERENCE LIST. 1973-1988. a. (reprint service avail.) American Society of Hospital Pharmacists, 4630 Montgomery Ave., Bethesda, MD 20814.

157.63 616.863   AT   ISSN 0817-3052
DRUGS: AUSTRALIA; news and views of the national campaign against drug abuse. 1986-19?? q. Commonwealth Department of Health, P.O. Box 100, Woden, A.C.T. 2606, Australia.

367   PP
DRUM. 1964-19?? m. Girl Guides Association of Papua New Guinea, Box 79, Konedobu, Papua New Guinea.

020   US
DRUMM BIBLIOGRAPHIES. 1988-199? irreg. Borgo Press, Box 2845, San Bernardino, CA 92406.

052   IE   ISSN 0012-687X
PR8844
DUBLIN MAGAZINE. 1923-1958 (Dec.). q. (also avail. in microform from IMI; reprint service avail. from KTO) New Square Publications Ltd., Elstow, Knapton Rd., Dun Laoghaire, Dublin, Ireland.

796.7   IT
DUE RUOTE. ceased. bi-m. Edigamma, S.r.l., Piazza dei Sanniti, 9, 00185 Rome, Italy.

612.67   US
DUKE UNIVERSITY. CENTER FOR THE STUDY OF AGING AND HUMAN DEVELOPMENT. REPORTS ON ADVANCES IN RESEARCH. 1977-1989 (vol.12, no.4). 4/yr. Duke University, Center for the Study of Aging and Human Development, Box 2920, Duke University Medical Center, Durham, NC 27710.

330   SA
DURBAN METROPOLITAN ECONOMY PROJECT; a survey of educational facilities & social rates of return. 1984-19?? irreg. University of Natal, Department of Economics, King George V Ave., Durban, South Africa.

651.2 371.3   US   ISSN 0743-4200
DVORAK DEVELOPMENTS. 1973-1988 (Winter). q. Freelance Communications, Box 1895, Upland, CA 91785-1895.
    Formerly: Quick Strokes.

621.38   GW
E; Elektronik-Technologie, Elektronik-Anwendungen, Elektronik-Marketing. 1963-1991. fortn. (back issues avail.) Konradin-Verlag Robert Kohlhammer GmbH, Ernst-Mey-Str. 8, 7022 Leinfelden-Echterdingen, Germany.
    Former titles: Elektronik-Technologie & Elektronik-Zeitung (ISSN 0012-8074)

621.389   US   ISSN 0734-5542
E A R FOR CHILDREN. (Evaluation of Audio Recordings) 1983-19?? q. Sound Advice Enterprises, 40 Holly Lane, Roslyn Heights, NY 11577.

371.26   CN   ISSN 0703-6892
E & M NEWSLETTER. ceased 1989 (no.45). 2/yr. (back issues avail.) (Ontario Institute for Studies in Education) Educational Evaluation Centre, 252 Bloor St. W., Toronto, Ont, M5S 1V6, Canada.

384 340   SZ
PN1991.3.E8
E B U REVIEW. (PROGRAMMES, ADMINISTRATION, LAW EDITION). (Technical Edition: Technical Information) 1950-1990. bi-m. European Broadcasting Union, Ancienne Route 17A, Case Postale 67, CH-1218 Grand-Saconnex, Geneva, Switzerland.
    Former titles: E B U Review. Geneva Edition. (Programmes, Administration, Law) (ISSN 0012-7493); E B U Review. Part B: General and Legal.

621.3   UK
E C A YEAR BOOK DESK DIARY. 1918-19?? a. Electrical Contractors' Association, 34 Palace Court, London W2 4HY, England.
    Formerly: Electrical Contractors' Year Book (ISSN 0070-9654)

341 UK ISSN 0262-5156
LAW
E C J R: EUROPEAN COURT OF JUSTICE REPORTER; a digest of all decisions of the European Court of Justice. 1982-1991. 10/yr. (back issues avail.) (E S C Publishing Ltd.) Sweet & Maxwell, South Quay Plaza, 8th Fl., 183 Marsh Wall, London E14 9FT, England.

614.7 016 CN ISSN 0704-4062
E C O - L O G INFORMATION SERVICES. 1971-19?? 6/ yr. Corpus Information Services Ltd., Division of Southam Communications Ltd., 1450 Don Mills Rd., Don Mills, Ont. M3B 2X7, Canada.

350 DK ISSN 0108-9900
E D B - KURSUSKATALOG; oversigt over brugerorienterede edb-kurser for medarbejdere i den offentlige forvaltning. 1983-1989. a. Forvaltningens Edb-Kursusudvalg, Administrationsdepartementet - Ministry of Finance, Department of Administration, Holmens Kanal 20-3, 1060 Copenhagen K, Denmark.

330 382 UK ISSN 0955-1255
E D I WORLD; journal on paperless trade and transport. 1987-19?? (vol.2). 6/yr. Elsevier Science Publishers Ltd., Crown House, Linton Road, Barking, Essex IG11 8JU, England.
Formerly: Trade Facilitation (ISSN 0920-6434)

001.64 CN
E D P BUYER'S GUIDE. (Electronic Data Processing) 1975-1987. a. Laurentian Media Inc., 501 Oakdale Rd., Downsview, Ont. M3N 1W7, Canada.

340 UK ISSN 0262-9380
E E C INFORMATION SERVICES; the advisory service for business enquiries about EEC directives, regulations, agreements or documents. (European Economic Community) 1982-1991. q. Monitor Press, Rectory Rd., Great Waldingfield, Sudbury, Suffolk CO10 OTL, England.

382 341.57 UK
E E C INFORMATION SERVICES. BULLETIN. (European Economic Community) ceased 1990. q. Monitor Press, Rectory Rd., Great Waldingfield, Sudbury, Suffolk CO10 OTL, England.

338.1 314 NE
E E G VADEMECUM/SELECTED AGRI-FIGURES OF THE E.E.C. 1960-1983 (Nov.). biennial. Landbouw - Economisch Instituut, Postbus 29701, 2502 LS 's-Gravenhage, Netherlands.
Formerly: Geselecteerde Agrarische Cijfers van de E E C (ISSN 0072-4211)

621.3 US
E E I ENVIRONMENTAL JOURNAL. ceased 1984 (vol.2, no.2). 6/yr. Edison Electric Institute, 701 Pennsylvania Ave., N.W., Washington, DC 20004-2696.

331 323.4 US
E E O C COMPLIANCE MANUAL (WEEKLY). 1975-19?? w. U.S. Equal Employment Opportunity Commission, 2401 E Street, N.W., Washington, DC 20037.

658 323.4 US ISSN 0276-5853
E E O REPORT. (Equal Employment Opportunity) 1974-1990. m. (back issues avail.) (Institute for Management) Panel Publishers, Inc., 36 W. 44th St., No.1316, New York, NY 10036-8102.

683 GW ISSN 0046-0877
E F B; Hausrat, Werkzeuge, Beschlaege, Kunststoffe, Elektrogerate. (Eisenhaendler Fachblatt) 1897-19?? m. E F B - Verlag GmbH, Breslauer Str. 23, 6450 Hanau, Germany.

332 US
E F T PRESS ALERT. (Electronic Fund Transfer) ceased. m. Warren, Gorham and Lamont Inc., One Penn Plaza, New York, NY 10119.

600 US
E G & G MONITOR. 1968-1988 (no.4). bi-m. E G & G Inc., Corporate Communication Department, 45 William St., Wellesley, MA 02181.

320 GW ISSN 0343-6667
E G MAGAZIN. (Europaeische Gemeinschaft) ceased 1989. m. (10/yr.). (Kommission der Europaeischen Gemeinschaften) Nomos Verlagsgesellschaft mbH und Co. KG, Postfach 610, 7570 Baden-Baden, Germany.

621.3 CS ISSN 0007-4594
E G U BULLETIN. 1960-1989 (no.104). s-a. Vyzkumny Ustav Energeticky, Partyzanska 7A, Prague 7, Czechoslovakia.

371.3 UK ISSN 0266-9544
E.I.D.C.T. - C.D.T. YEAR BOOK. 1984-19?? biennial. Educational Institute of Design Craft & Technology, c/o P.E. Dawson, 52 Locarno Ave., Gillingham, Kent. ME8 6ES, England.
Incorporates: Craft Buyer's Guide; Which was formerly: E.I.D.C.T. Year Book.

790.13 GW ISSN 0341-4175
E L O; Technik erleben und verstehen. 1975-1989. m. (back issues avail.) Franzis-Verlag GmbH, Karlstr. 37, 8000 Munich 2, Germany.
Former titles: E L O. Magazine fuer Praxis und Hobby; E L O Magazine fuer die Welt der Elektronik.

778.5 US
E M C. (Special issue of Lifelong Learning) 1970-19?? s-a. (back issues avail.) University of California, Berkeley, Extension Media Center, 2176 Shattuck Ave., Berkeley, CA 94704.

610 011 US ISSN 1040-4929
Z6675.E45
E M S ACCESS (YEAR); an index to (year) Emergency Medical Services periodicals. (Emergency Medical Service) 1986-1987. a. (back issues avail.) Next Question Please, 323 S. Marquette St., Ironwood, MI 49938.

378 US
E R I C CLEARINGHOUSE FOR JUNIOR COLLEGES. HORIZONS ISSUES. MONOGRAPH SERIES. 1968-1986. irreg. E R I C Clearinghouse for Junior Colleges, 8118 Math Sciences Bldg., University of California, Los Angeles, CA 90024.

372.4 US
E R I C - R C S NEWSLETTER. ceased. s-a. ERIC Clearinghouse on Reading and Communication Skills, 1111 Kenyon Rd., Urbana, IL 61801.

651.37 UK
E.S.A. QUARTERLY NEWS BULLETIN. ceased. q. Executive Secretaries' Association, 34 Chestnut Ave., Gosfield, Halstead CO9 1TD, England.

621.381 794 US ISSN 0893-2565
TK7885.A1 CODEN: EESMEY
E S D: THE ELECTRONIC SYSTEM DESIGN MAGAZINE. 1971-1989. 13/yr. (also avail. in microfiche from UMI) Sentry Publishing Company, Inc., 1900 W. Park Dr., Ste. 200, Westborough, MA 01581-3907.
Formerly: Digital Design (ISSN 0147-9245)

070.5 GW
E S V PROGRAMMBEREICHE PHILOLOGIE- VOLKSKUNDE-GESCHICHTE; Neuerscheinungen und Neuauflagen mit Terminuebersicht. (Erich Schmidt Verlag) 1960-19?? m. Erich Schmidt Verlag GmbH & Co. (Bielefeld), Viktoriastr. 44a, Postfach 7330, 4800 Bielefeld 1, Germany.

020 UK
EALING MISCELLANY. 1973-198? (no.31). irreg. Ealing College of Higher Education, St. Mary's Rd., Ealing W5 5RF, England.

929 US
EARLY RECORDS OF UPPER EAST TENNESSEE. 1987-1990 (Oct.). q. 3218 Robin Rd., White Pine, TN 37890.

629.1 016.3337 US ISSN 0145-5605
Z6033.A8
EARTH RESOURCES: A CONTINUING BIBLIOGRAPHY WITH INDEXES. ceased 1990. q. U.S. National Aeronautics and Space Administration, Washington, DC 20546.

550 560 549 US ISSN 0012-8228
QE1 CODEN: EARSAF
EARTH SCIENCE. 1946-19?? q. (also avail. in microform from MIM,UMI; reprint service avail. from ISI,UMI) American Geological Institute, 4220 King St., Alexandria, VA 22302-1507.
Formerly: Earth Science Digest (ISSN 0095-8514)

550 US ISSN 0012-8236
QE79 CODEN: ESCBAF
EARTH SCIENCE BULLETIN. 1968-1988 (vol. 20); suspended. irreg. Wyoming Geological Association, Box 545, Casper, WY 82602.

910.09 770 US
EARTHTREKS MAGAZINE. 1990-199?; suspended. 4/yr. (back issues avail.) Five Corners Publications, Ltd., Rte.100, HCR 70, Box 2, Plymouth, VT 05056.
Formerly: Earthtreks Digest (ISSN 1051-1814)

011 US
EAST ASIA LIBRARY SERIES. suspended. irreg. (Hoover Institution, East Asian Collection) Stanford University, 219 Lou Henry Hoover Bldg., Stanford, CA 94305-6012.

323.4 US
EAST TIMOR UPDATE. 1980-198? s-a. (also avail. in microform) East Timor Human Rights Committee, 133 1-2 South St., Auburn, NY 13021-4811.

310 BE
EAST-WEST STATISTICS SERVICE. ceased. m. Europe Information Service, 46, Av. Albert-Elisabeth, 1040 Brussels, Belgium.

917.306 US
EAST WIND. 1982-198?; suspended. s-a. Getting Together Publications, Box 29293, Oakland, CA 94604.

617.7 II ISSN 0301-469X
EASTERN ARCHIVES OF OPHTHALMOLOGY. 1973-1981. bi-m. C.B.S. Publishers and Distributors, 485 Jain Bhanan, Bhola Nath Nagar, Shahdra, Delhi 32, India.

387.74 US
EASTERN REVIEW (NEW YORK); featuring selected works from America's most notable publications. 1976-19?? m. (Eastern Airlines) East-West Network, Inc. (New York), 34 E. 51st St., New York, NY 10022.

332 US
EASY LIVING. 1975-19?? q. (Creative Marketing Enterprises, Inc.) Webb Co., Creative Communications Division, 7900 International Dr., Ste. 300, Bloomington, MN 55425.

796.77 GW
EASY RIDER; Motorrad-Magazin fuer junge Leute. 1979-1984. m. Syburger Verlag GmbH, Hertinger Str. 60, 4750 Unna, Germany.

551.46 AT ISSN 0729-0403
EBB AND FLOW. 1982-19?? irreg. (tabloid format) Great Barrier Reef Marine Park Authority, P.O. Box 1379, Townsville, Qld. 4810, Australia.

362.7 CN ISSN 0705-1123
ECHO (OTTAWA). 1977-19?? q. Children's Aid Society of Ottawa, Foster Parent Association, 1370 Bank St., Ottawa, Ont. K1H 7Y3, Canada.
Formerly: Children's Aid Society of Ottawa. Information Bulletin (ISSN 0709-0706);
Incorporates: Foster Parent Nourricier (ISSN 0046-4767); Foster News.

675.2 IT ISSN 0012-9437
L'ECO CUOIO. (Bi-m supplement available) 1921-19??; suspended. fortn. (newspaper) Casa Editrice Edimark, Via Anfossi 36, 20135 Milan, Italy.

614.7 US
ECO-NEWS; environmental newsletter for children. 1971-1985. m. (also avail. in microform from UMI; back issues avail.; reprint service avail. from UMI) Environmental Action Coalition, 625 Broadway, New York, NY 10012.

614.7 AT ISSN 0812-843X
ECOFILE. 1983-19?? q. Department of the Arts, Sport, the Environment, Tourism and Territories, 15, Moore St., Canberra, A.C.T. 2601.

338.1 631 FR ISSN 0374-6003
CODEN: BAIABK
ECOLE NATIONALE SUPERIEURE D'AGRONOMIE ET DES INDUSTRIES ALIMENTAIRES. BULLETIN. 1959-1982. a. (Institut National Polytechniques de Nancy, Ecole National Superieure d'Agronomie et des Industries Alimentaires) Bibliotheque Agronomique, 2 Av. de la Foret de Haye, 54500 Vandoeuvre, France.

500 SZ
ECOLE POLYTECHNIQUE FEDERALE DE LAUSANNE. PUBLICATION. 1971-19?? (no.120). irreg. Ecole Polytechnique Federale de Lausanne, CH-1015 Lausanne, Switzerland.

CESSATIONS

340 US ISSN 8755-9013
ECOLOGICAL ILLNESS LAW REPORT. 1983-1990; suspended. bi-m. (back issues avail.) Box 1976, Evanston, IL 60204-1796.
  Formerly: Ecological Health Law Report.

331 IT ISSN 0392-1212
ECONOMIA DEL LAVORO (ROME); rivista trimestrale di economia e politica del lavoro. 1975-1991 (no.4). q. (back issues avail.) Centro di Ricerche Economiche e Sociali (CERES), Via Nomentana 201, 00161 Rome, Italy.
  Formerly: Quaderni di Economia del Lavoro.

330 ES ISSN 0012-9860
ECONOMIA SALVADORENA (SAN SALVADOR, 1946). 1946-1984 (no.47-48). a. Universidad de El Salvador, Instituto de Estudios Economicas, Ciudad Universitaria, Final 25 Av. Norte, San Salvador, El Salvador.

330 016 US ISSN 0093-2485
ECONOMIC BOOKS: CURRENT SELECTIONS. 1974-1991. q. University of Pittsburgh, Department of Economics, University Libraries, 4P25 Forbes Quadrangle, Pittsburgh, PA 15260.

382 AT
ECONOMIC BULLETIN. 1970-1986 (vol.18). fortn. Australia - Japan Economic Institute, 719 Tower Bldg., Australia Square, Sydney, N.S.W. 2000, Australia.

330.9 US
ECONOMIC-BUSINESS REVIEW. 1980-1988 (Dec.). q. Sangamon State University, Springfield, IL 62708.
  Formerly: Central Illinois Economic-Business Review.

330 CN ISSN 0225-8013
ECONOMIC COUNCIL OF CANADA. DISCUSSION PAPERS. 1973-19??. irreg. Economic Council of Canada, Publications Division, Box 527, Ottawa, Ont. K1P 5V6, Canada.

338.9 SA ISSN 0070-8518
ECONOMIC DEVELOPMENT PROGRAMME FOR THE REPUBLIC OF SOUTH AFRICA. 1964-1989. irreg. Government Printer, Bosman St., Private Bag X85, Pretoria 0001, South Africa.

332.6 US
ECONOMIC INDEX MARKET. ceased. m. Coffee, Sugar & Cocoa Exchange, Inc., Four World Trade Center, New York, NY 10048.

330 US
ECONOMIC OUTLOOK FOR NEW JERSEY. ceased 1990. a. Office of Economic Policy, 20 W. State St., CN 830, Trenton, NJ 08625.

338.9 US ISSN 0095-3830
HC106.6 CODEN: EOUSDT
ECONOMIC OUTLOOK U.S.A. 1974-198? (vol.16, no.1). q. (also avail. in microform from UMI; reprint service avail. from UMI) University of Michigan, Institute for Social Research, Survey Research Center, Box 1248, Ann Arbor, MI 48106.

338 CN
ECONOMIC REVIEW AND OUTLOOK. 1945-19?? a. Ministry of Industry and Small Business Development, 1405 Douglas St., Victoria, B.C. V8W 1X4, Canada.
  Former titles: British Columbia Economic Activity; British Columbia Economic Outlook Survey (ISSN 0319-0412)

330 US ISSN 0884-4887
  CODEN: ERMAEP
ECONOMIC ROAD MAPS. 1919-1990 (Dec.). irreg. Conference Board, Inc., 845 Third Ave., New York, NY 10022.
  Formerly: Road Maps of Industry (ISSN 0035-7227)

330.9 II
ECONOMIC SCENE. 1976-1987. m. Tata Economic Consultancy Services, Orient House, Mangalore House, Ballard Estate, Bombay 400038, India.

330.9 PO
ECONOMIC SITUATION IN THE YEAR. 1976-19?? a. Ministerio do Planeamento e Administracao Territorio, Departamento Central de Planeamento, Avenida D. Carlos I, 126, 1200 Lisbon, Portugal.
  Former titles: Portugal. Ministerio das Financas e do Plano. Departamento Central de Planeamento. Plano; Portugal. Ministerio do Plano e da Coordenacao Economica. Departamento Central de Planeamento. Plano.

330 JA ISSN 0021-4833
ECONOMIC SURVEY OF JAPAN. 1969-19?? a. (processed) (Ministry of Finance, Economic Planning Agency - Okura-sho) Japan Times, Ltd., 4-5-4 Shibaura, Minato-ku, Tokyo 108, Japan.
  Supersedes: Japanese Economic Statistics.

330 US
ECONOMICS AND BUSINESS LETTER. 1974-197? s-a. (back issues avail.) Slippery Rock State College, Department of Economics and Business, Slippery Rock, PA 16057.

330.9 FR
ECONOMIE ALGERIENNE. 1978-19?? a. I C Publications, 10 rue Vineuse, 75116 Paris Cedex 16, France.

330.9 FR
ECONOMIE GABONAISE. 1977. a. I C Publications, 10 rue Vineuse, 75116 Paris, France.

330 LH
ECONOMY OF THE PRINCIPALITY OF LIECHTENSTEIN. 1962-19?? irreg. Press and Information Office, Government Palace, FL-9490 Vaduz, Liechtenstein.
  Formerly: Liechtenstein Economy.

800 FR ISSN 0293-9320
P211
ECRIT DU TEMPS. 1982-1989. s-a. Editions de Minuit, 7 rue Bernard-Palissy, 75006 Paris, France.

318 370 EC
ECUADOR. INSTITUTO NACIONAL DE ESTADISTICA Y CENSOS. ENCUESTA ANUAL DE RECURSOS Y ACTIVIDADES DE SALUD. 1967-19?? Instituto Nacional de Estadistica y Censos, 10 de Agosto No. 229, Quito, Ecuador.

270 US ISSN 0013-080X
BX1
ECUMENIST; a journal for promoting Christian unity. 1962-1991. 3/yr. (also avail. in microform from UMI; reprint service avail. from UMI) Paulist Press, 997 Macarthur Blvd., Mahwah, NJ 07430.

001.6 DK ISSN 0109-6109
EDB NYT. 1984-1988. m. Thomson Communications (Scandinavia) A-S, Struenseegade 7-9, DK-2200 Copenhagen N, Denmark.

330 US
EDGE; the manager's magazine of corporate computing. 1988-1990 (Nov.). bi-m. (back issues avail.) International Computer Programs, Inc., P.O. Box 40946, Indianapolis, IN 46240-0946.

070.5 070 IT
EDITORE. ceased. m. (11/yr.). Gruppo Editoriale Fabbri SPA, Via Mecenate 91, 20138 Milan, Italy.

070.5 070 US
EDITSPEAK; the resource for magazine editors. 1988-1989 (vol.1, no.6). m. (back issues avail.) EditSpeak Publishing Company, 736 Jones St., Ste. 31, San Francisco, CA 94109.

370.196 SP
EDUCACION; noticias de educacion, ciencia y cultura iberoamericanas. 1984-1990. m. Organizacion de Estados Iberoamericanos para la Educacion, la Ciencia y la Cultura (OEI), Ciudad Universitaria, 28040 Madrid, Spain.

378 CK ISSN 0120-3819
EDUCACION SUPERIOR Y DESARROLLO. 1982-1987 (vol.5, no.3). q. (also avail. in microfiche) Instituto Colombiano para el Fomento de la Educacion Superior, Calle 17 No. 3-40, Bogota, D.E., Colombia.

371.9 US ISSN 0889-9657
EDUCATION AND SELF MANAGEMENT OF THE PSYCHIATRIC PATIENT. 1987-1989 (Oct.). q. Gallery Press, 117 N. Main St., Essex, CT 06426.

370 US
EDUCATION AROUND THE WORLD. 1958-19?? irreg. U.S. Department of Education, Washington, DC 20202.

370 340 US ISSN 0276-718X
KF4114
EDUCATION LAW BULLETIN. 1975-19?? irreg. (also avail. in microform from UMI; back issues avail.; reprint service avail. from UMI) Center for Law and Education, Inc., 955 Massachusetts Ave., Cambridge, MA 02139.

370 US ISSN 0197-5374
EDUCATION TIMES; the national newspaper serving education leaders. 1980-19?? w. Institute for Educational Leadership, 1001 Connecticut Ave. N.W., Ste. 310, Washington, DC 20036.

370 US
EDUCATION UPDATE (WASHINGTON). ceased. q. (tabloid format; back issues avail.) Heritage Foundation, 214 Massachusetts Ave., N.E., Washington, DC 20002.

371.3 374 AT ISSN 0817-0975
EDUCATION VICTORIA. 1986-1990 (Dec.). m. (tabloid format; back issues avail.) Ministry of Education, G. P.O. Box 4367, Melbourne, Vic. 3001, Australia.

371.394 621.381 US
EDUCATIONAL COMPUTING CHRONICLE; resources for integrating computers into today's elementary classrooms. 1981-198? 4/yr. (also avail. in looseleaf format) Association of Computer Using Educations, Stayer Research and Learning Center, Millersville University, Millersville, PA 17551.
  Former titles: Lesson Plans Plus; (until May 1988): Computer Curriculum Resources; School Microcomputing Bulletin (ISSN 0735-9969)

370 315 KO
EDUCATIONAL DEVELOPMENT IN KOREA; a graphic presentation. ceased 1975. a. Ministry of Education, Korean Educational Development Institute, 92-6 Umyeon-dong, Seocho-gu, Seoul 137-791, S. Korea.

621.381 US
EDUCATIONAL MICROCOMPUTING ANNUAL. published only once, 1985. irreg. Oryx Press, 4041 N. Central at Indian School Rd., Phoenix, AZ 85012-3397.

375 US
EDUCATIONAL R & D REPORT. 1978-198? q. (U.S. National Institute of Education) Council for Educational Development and Research, 1201 16th St., N.W., Ste. 305, Washington, DC 20036.

370 150 US
EDUCATIONAL USER'S GROUP NEWSLETTER. 1974-19?? m. Hewlett Packard Co. (Santa Clara), 5301 Stevens Creek Blvd., Santa Clara, CA 95052-8059.

371.33 016 US
EDUCATIONAL VIDEO AND FILM. 1950-1990. triennial (with a. supplements). University of Michigan, Film and Video Library, 919 S. University Ave., Ann Arbor, MI 48109-1185.
  Former titles: Educational Film and Video (Year); Educational Films.

800 US
EGAD!. 1986-1989 (vol.5). s-a. (back issues avail.) Bizarre Press, D19 Maple Hill Estates, Hamel, MN 55340.

051 US
EGG (NEW YORK). 1990-1991 (Mar.). 10/yr. Forbes, Inc., 7 W. 18th St., New York, NY 10011.

320.531 GW ISSN 0013-2659
HX6
EINHEIT; Zeitschrift fuer Theorie und Praxis des wissenschaftlichen Sozialismus. 1946-1991. m. (Sozialistische Einheitspartei Deutschlands, Zentralkomitee) Dietz Verlag, Wallstr. 76-79, Postfach 273, 1020 Berlin, Germany.

625.1 GW ISSN 0013-2837
EISENBAHN-TECHNISCHE PRAXIS. 1949-1989. s-a. (also avail. in microfilm from UMI) Gewerkschaft der Eisenbahner Deutschlands, Beethovenstr. 12-16, 6000 Frankfurt, Germany.

625.19 GW
EISENBAHN ZEITSCHRIFT. 1987-1991. 10/yr, E K Verlag, Mercystr. 15, Postfach 5560, 7800 Freiburg, Germany.

929 US
EKELL ARCHIVES. 1985-1987. 4/yr. Arlene H. Eakle, Ed.& Pub., Box 22045, Salt Lake City, UT 84122.

338 658.5 UR
EKONOMIKO-MATEMATICHESKIE METODY PLANIROVANIYA I UPRAVLENIYA. 1972-19?? irreg. Akademiya Nauk S.S.S.R., Dal'nevostochnyi Nauchnyi Tsentr, Ul. Leninskaya 50, Vladivostok, Russian S.F.S.R., U.S.S.R.

385 PL ISSN 0137-219X
EKSPLOATACJA KOLEI. 1953-1991. m. Wydawnictwa Komunikacji i Lacznosci, Ul. Kazimierzowska 52, Warsaw, Poland.
Formerly (until 1978): Przeglad Kolejowy Przewozowy (ISSN 0552-4199)

318 ES
EL SALVADOR EN CIFRAS. ceased 1981. biennial. Direccion General de Estadistica y Censos, 1 Calle Poniente y 43 Avenida Sur, San Salvador, El Salvador.

338.476 BL
ELASTOMEROS. 1975-1981 (vol.2). bi-m. Expert Editora Tecnica Ltda., Caixa Postal 18-281, 04699 Sao Paulo, Brazil.

332.6 US
ELDER VIEWPOINT ON FUTURES. 1985-1989 (no.305). 44/yr. Word'sworth Publishing, Inc., Box 5909, Santa Monica, CA 90405.

324 US ISSN 0742-5279
JK1976
ELECTION POLITICS; a journal of political campaigns and elections. 1984-1989 (vol.6, no.7). 4/yr. Free Congress Research and Education Foundation, Center for Government and Politics, 721 Second St., N.E., Washington, DC 20002.

621.3 US
ELECTRIC POWER INDUSTRY ABSTRACTS. 1975-1984. bi-m. Utility Data Institute, Inc., 1700 K St., N.W., Ste. 400, Washington, DC 20006.
Former titles: Inforum: Energy-Environment Information System; Inforum: Environmental Report Data System (ISSN 0360-4985)

531 US
ELECTRIC POWER QUARTERLY. 1983-19?? q. U.S. Energy Information Administration, National Energy Information Center, Forrestal Bldg., IF-048, 1000 Independence Ave., S.W., Washington, DC 20585.

621.313 US
ELECTRIC UTILITY GENERATION PLANBOOK. 1972-19?? a. (reprint service avail. from UMI) McGraw-Hill, Inc., 1221 Avenue of Americas, New York, NY 10020.

621.3 531.64 UK ISSN 0142-0615
TK1 CODEN: IEPSDC
ELECTRICAL POWER AND ENERGY SYSTEMS. 1979-19?? q. (also avail. in microform from UMI; back issues avail.) Butterworth - Heinemann Ltd. (Subsidiary of: Reed International PLC), Linacre House, Jordan Hill, Oxford OX2 8DP, England.

621.3 658.7 UK
ELECTRICAL RETAILING. 1983-199? m. Argus Specialist Publications Ltd., Argus House, Boundary Way, Hemels, Hampstead, Herts HP2 7ST, England.

621.32 US
ELECTRICAL SYSTEMS DESIGN. 1921-1990 (vol.70, no.5). 10/yr. (also avail. in microform from UMI; reprint service avail. from UMI) Andrews Communications, Inc., 5123 W. Chester Pike, Box 556, Edgemont, PA 19028.
Formerly: Electrical Consultant (ISSN 0361-4972)

621.3 UK
ELECTRICAL TRADER. 1925-1990. 11/yr. (also avail. in microform from UMI) Reed Business Publishing Ltd., Consumer Industries Press, Quadrant House, The Quadrant, Sutton, Surrey SM2 5AS, England.
Former titles: Electrical and Electronic Trader (ISSN 0013-418X); Wireless; Electrical Trader.

621.309 UK ISSN 0268-5949
CODEN: GDGOET
ELECTRICITY FOR CHINA. 1985-19?? m. Reed Business Publishing Ltd., Enterprise Division, Quadrant House, The Quadrant, Sutton, Surrey SM2 5AS, England.

621.3 SI
ELECTRO. 1973-19?? biennial. Electrical & Electronic Engineering Society, Ngee Ann Technical College, 535 Clementi Rd., Singapore 2159, Singapore.

541.37 UK ISSN 0305-9979
QD551 CODEN: ECHMBU
ELECTROCHEMISTRY. 1970-198? a. Royal Society of Chemistry, Thomas Graham House, Science Park, Milton Rd., Cambridge CB4 4WF, England.

681 617 US
ELECTROMEDICAL & ELECTROSURGICAL EQUIPMENT SPEC BOOK. 1985-198? a. Gordon Publications, Inc., 301 Gibraltar Dr., Morris Plains, NJ 07950.

578 574.8 UK
ELECTRON MICROSCOPY OF PROTEINS. 1981-1987. irreg. Academic Press Ltd., 24-28 Oval Rd., London NW1 7DX, England.

537 US
ELECTRONIC DESIGN'S GOLD BOOK. 1974-19?? a. V N U Business Publications, Inc., Ten Holland Dr., Hasbrouck Heights, NJ 07604.

794 793 621.381 US ISSN 0733-6039
ELECTRONIC GAMES HOTLINE. 1982-198? fortn. Reese Communications, Inc., 460 W. 34th St., New York, NY 10001.

794 793 621.381 US
ELECTRONIC GAMES SOFTWARE ENCYCLOPEDIA. 1982-198? a. Reese Communications, Inc., 460 W. 34th St., New York, NY 10001.

658.403 US
ELECTRONIC INFORMATION REPORT; the monthly newsletter for executives concerned with the electronic information industry. 1979-1988. m. (back issues avail.) Link Resources Corp. (Subsidiary of: International Data Corp.), 79 Fifth Ave., New York, NY 10003-2025.
Formerly (until 1985): Online Database Report.

621.38 US ISSN 0895-3708
TK7836 CODEN: ELMAEH
ELECTRONIC MANUFACTURING. (Supplement avail.: Desk Manual) 1955-1990 (Sept.) m. (also avail. in microfilm from UMI; back issues avail.; reprint service avail. from UMI) Lake Publishing Corporation, 17730 W. Peterson Rd., Box 159, Libertyville, IL 60048-0159.
Former titles: Electri-Onics (ISSN 0745-4309); (until 1978): Insulation - Circuits (ISSN 0020-4544); (until 1970): Insulation.

621.38 691 US
ELECTRONIC MANUFACTURING DESK MANUAL; for the electrical - electronic industries. (Supplement to: Electronic Manufacturing (ISSN 0895-3708)) 1961-19?? a. (also avail. in microform) Lake Publishing Corporation, 17730 W. Peterson Rd., Box 159, Libertyville, IL 60048-0159.
Former titles: Electri-Onics Desk Manual (ISSN 0745-4309); Insulation - Circuits Desk Manual; Insulation - Circuits Directory - Encyclopedia (ISSN 0074-0659); Insulation Directory-Encyclopedia.

621.3 US
ELECTRONIC MANUFACTURING NEWS. ceased 1991. m. Cahners Publishing Company (Des Plaines) (Subsidiary of: Reed International PLC), Division of Reed Publishing (USA) Inc., 1350 E. Touhy Ave., Box 5080, Des Plaines, IL 60017-5080.

370 780 US ISSN 1044-3150
ML73
ELECTRONIC MUSIC EDUCATOR. 1988-1991 (Jun.). q. Instrumentalist Company, 200 Northfield Rd., Northfield, IL 60093.

070.5 US ISSN 0888-0948
CODEN: EPBUEG
ELECTRONIC PUBLISHING BUSINESS. 1983-19?? m. (except Aug.). (back issues avail.) 885 N. San Antonio Rd., Los Altos, CA 94022.
Formerly: E P B: Electronic Publishing and Bookselling (ISSN 0737-5336)

546.1 UK ISSN 0305-9766
QD475 CODEN: ESMICK
ELECTRONIC STRUCTURE & MAGNETISM OF INORGANIC COMPOUNDS. 1972-198? every 18 mos. Royal Society of Chemistry, Thomas Graham House, Science Park, Cambridge CB4 4WF, England.

621.38 UK ISSN 0141-061X
CODEN: ETSTDN
ELECTRONIC TECHNOLOGY. 1965-1990. m. Society of Electronic and Radio Technicians, 57-61 Newington Causeway, London SE1 6BL, England.
Formerly: S.E.R.T. Journal (ISSN 0013-4805)

658.8 UK
ELECTRONICS & INSTRUMENTS DIRECTORY. 1965-198? a. Morgan-Grampian Book Publishing Co. Ltd., 30 Calderwood St., London SE18 6QH, England.
Former titles (until Mar. 1988): Directory of Electronics, Instruments and Computers (ISSN 0267-1441); (until 1984): Directory of Instruments, Electronics, Automation; Instruments, Electronics and Automation Purchasing Directory (ISSN 0074-0578)

621.38 670 US ISSN 0090-5291
TK7870
ELECTRONICS BUYERS' GUIDE. 1945-1987. a. (also avail. in microfilm) Penton Publishing (Hasbrouck Heights), 611 Rt. 46 W., Hasbrouck Heights, NJ 07004.

621.3 US
HD9696.A1
ELECTRONICS DISTRIBUTION TODAY. 1916-198? m. (back issues avail.) Intertec Publishing Corp. (White Plains), 707 Westchester Ave., White Plains, NY 10604.
Formerly: E E's Electronic Distributor (ISSN 0734-175X)

621.38 US
ELECTRONICS TRENDS (CLEVELAND). 1966-19?? q. Predicasts, Inc., 200 University Circle Research Center, 11001 Cedar Ave., Cleveland, OH 44106.
Formerly: Predicasts Electronic Trends (ISSN 0032-7174)

574.191 JA
ELECTROPHYSIOLOGY/DENKI SEIRIGAKU. 1951-1976 (vol.31). irreg. Showa University, School of Medicine, Department of Physiology - Showa Daigakubu Igakubu Seirigaku Kyoshitsu, 1-5-8 Hatanodai, Shinagawa-ku, Tokyo 142, Japan.

621.3 GW ISSN 0037-4687
ELEKTRODIENST. 1959-1991. q. Siemans Verlag AG, Postfach 3240, 8520 Erlangen 2, Germany.
Formerly: Siemens Elektrodienst.

621 UR
ELEKTROTECHNIKA IR MECHANIKA. 1963-1973. irreg. Kaunas Polytechnic Institute, Editing and Publishing Group - Kauno Politechnikos Institutas, K. Donelaicio 73, 233006 Kaunas, Lithuanian S.S.R., U.S.S.R.
Formerly: Mechanika.

372 CN ISSN 0046-1792
ELEMENTS; a journal for elementary education. 1969-1988. s-a. (also avail. in microform from MIM,MML; reprint service avail.) University of Alberta, Department of Elementary Education, Education South, Rm. 551, Edmonton, Alta. T6G 2G5, Canada.

621.38 BL
ELETRONICA/ELECTRONICS. 1963-19?? m. Santamaria & Correa Ltd., Rua Tavares Bastos 702, 05012 Sao Paulo, SP, Brazil.

621.3 IT
ELETTRONICA; compratori e fornitori di elettonica e strumentazione. ceased 1990 (Apr.). m. Gruppo Editoriale Fabbri SPA, Divisione Periodici, Via Mecenate 91, 20138 Milan, Italy.
Formerly: Giornale dei Componenti Elettronici.

330 US
ELIOT JANEWAY LECTURES ON HISTORICAL ECONOMICS. 1974-197? irreg. (reprint service avail. from UMI) (Princeton University, Woodrow Wilson School) Princeton University Press, 3175 Princeton Pike, Lawrenceville, NJ 08648.

378 AT
ELLAMATTA. ceased. a. University of New England, Armidale Students' Association, Armidale, N.S.W. 2351, Australia.

813 US ISSN 0013-6301
PZ1.A1
ELLERY QUEEN'S ANTHOLOGY. 1960-198? s-a. Davis Publications, Inc., 380 Lexington Ave., New York, NY 10017.

CESSATIONS

388.3 NE ISSN 0013-6409
ELSEVIER SELECT. 1970-1986. q. B.V. Uitgeversmaatschappij Bonaventura, P.O. Box 152, Amsterdam, Netherlands.

947 322.4 US ISSN 0013-6417
ELTA. 1945-1991. m. (processed) Lithuanian National Foundation, Inc., Elta Information Service, 1611 Connecticut Ave., N.W., Washington, DC 20009.

663.19 FR
EMBOUTEILLAGE CONDITIONNEMENT. 1949-1988. 10/yr. S I M E I C, 7 rue de la Boetie, 75008 Paris, France.

289.9 US
EMERGENCE: JOURNAL FOR EVOLVING CONSCIOUSNESS. 1981-1990 (Jan.). q. Sufi Order, Box 1112, Nederland, CO 80466.
Formed by the 1987 merger of: Message & Heart and Wings Journal; Which was formerly (until 1986): Mureeds' Newsletter.

642.59 US
EMERGENCY CARE QUARTERLY. 1985-1992. q. Aspen Publishers, Inc., 200 Orchard Ridge Dr., Gaithersburg, MD 20878.

388.3 US ISSN 0894-4156
EMERGING AUTOMOTIVE INDUSTRIES REVIEW. 1987-198? m. Mead Ventures, Inc., Box 44952, Phoenix, AZ 85064.

325 DK ISSN 0900-7679
EMIGRANTEN. 1985-1988. a. Dansk Udvandrerhistorisk Selskab, Postboks 1731, DK-9100 Aalborg, Denmark.

360 301 IT ISSN 0013-6700
EMIGRAZIONE; informazioni sociali del Patronato Acli. 1967-19??; suspended. m. Patronato Acli, Via G. Marcora 18-20, Rome, Italy.
Formerly: Informazioni Sociali per l'Emigrazione.

378 US
EMORY TODAY. 1980-1992. 4/yr. Emory University, Office of University Periodicals, 1655 N. Decatur Rd., Atlanta, GA 30322.
Formerly (until 1986): Emorandum.

331 US
EMPLOYEE RELATIONS BULLETIN (NEW YORK). ceased 198? m. National Retail Merchants Association, 100 W. 31st St., New York, NY 10001.

338 US
EMPLOYMENT OUTPUT AND TRADE OF U.S. MANUFACTURING INDUSTRIES. 1958-1985. a. (back issues avail.) Trade Relations Council of the United States, One Church St., Ste. 601, Rockville, MD 20850.

331 914.206 323.4 UK ISSN 0142-2197
EMPLOYMENT REPORT. 1978-198? q. (back issues avail.) Commission for Racial Equality, Elliot House, 10-12 Allington St., London SW1E 5EH, England.

338.1 AG ISSN 0325-9153
ENCUESTA DE EXPECTATIVAS AGROPECURIAS. ceased. s-a. Banco Rio de la Plata, Gerencia de Investigaciones Economicas, Bartolome Mitre 480 P. 13, 1036 Capital, Argentina.

330.9 331.11 CL
ENCUESTA NACIONAL DEL EMPLEO TOTAL PAIS. 1966-19?? s-a. Instituto Nacional de Estadisticas, Av. Bulnes 418, Casilla 498, 3 Santiago, Chile.

781.57 US
ENCYCLOPEDIC YEARBOOK OF JAZZ. announced, never published. a. DaCapo Press, Inc., 233 Spring St., New York, NY 10013.

322.4 UK ISSN 0267-0224
END JOURNAL. 1982-1989. q. (back issues avail.) 11 Goodwin St., London N4 3HQ, England.

622.33 IT
ENERGIA ED IDROCARBURI/ENERGY AND HYDROCARBONS. ceased. irreg. Ente Nazionale Idrocarburi, Rome, Italy.
Formerly: Energia ed Idrocarburi. Sommario Statistico.

531.6 016 US ISSN 0098-5104
TJ163.2
ENERGY ABSTRACTS FOR POLICY ANALYSIS. 1975-19?? m. (back issues avail.) U.S. Department of Energy, Office of Scientific and Technical Information, Box 62, Oak Ridge, TN 37831.

370 US
ENERGY AND EDUCATION. (Supplement avail.: Directory of Energy Education Materials) 1977-19?? bi-m. (back issues avail.) National Science Teachers Association, 5112 Berwyn Rd., 3rd Fl., College Park, MD 20740.

531.64 614.7 SA
ENERGY & THE ENVIRONMENT. ceased. m. (Institute of Energy) Keeble Publishing Co. Pty. Ltd., P.O. Box 3080, Johannesburg 2000, South Africa.

531.64 614.7 US ISSN 0275-5289
Z5853.P83
ENERGY AND THE ENVIRONMENT. 1980-19?? m. U.S. Department of Energy, Office of Scientific and Technical Information, Box 62, Oak Ridge, TN 37831.

612.015 613.2 UK ISSN 0268-1528
ENERGY BALANCE. ceased 1990. m. (looseleaf format; back issues avail.) Sheffield University Biomedical Information Service (SUBIS), The University, Sheffield S10 2TN, England.

613.7 CN
ENERGY: CANADA HEALTH & FITNESS. ceased. 6/yr. Success in Fitness Inc., One Pacifique, St. Anne de Bellevue, Que. H9X 1C5, Canada.

531.64 US ISSN 0273-3102
ENERGY CLEARINGHOUSE. ceased. w. Business Publishers, Inc., 951 Pershing Dr., Silver Spring, MD 20910-4464.

531.64 US ISSN 0161-8091
TJ163.25.J3 CODEN: EDJADD
ENERGY DEVELOPMENTS IN JAPAN. 1978-1984. q. (also avail. in microform from MIM,UMI) Pergamon Press, Inc., Journals Division, 660 White Plains Rd., Tarrytown, NY 10591-5153.

531.64 SW ISSN 0281-8515
ENERGY, ENVIRONMENT AND DEVELOPMENT IN AFRICA. 1984-1988 (no.11). irreg. Nordiska Afrikainstitutet, P.O. Box 1703, S-751 47 Uppsala, Sweden.

531.64 US
CODEN: ENBIEY
ENERGY FROM BIOMASS AND MUNICIPAL WASTE; a current awareness bulletin. ceased. m. U.S. Department of Energy, Office of Scientific and Technical Information, Box 62, Oak Ridge, TN 37831.
Formerly: Energy from Biomass (ISSN 8755-0245)

665.5 622 539.7 US
ENERGY INFORMATION. 1972-19?? w. (looseleaf format) Petroleum Information Corp., Box 2612, Denver, CO 80201-2612.

621 660 US ISSN 0278-4521
TJ163.13 CODEN: ENPGDT
ENERGY PROGRESS. 1981-198? q. (also avail. in microform from UMI; reprint service avail. from UMI) American Institute of Chemical Engineers, 345 E. 47th St., New York, NY 10017.

530 600 US ISSN 0190-4876
ENERGY RESEARCH REPORTS. 1975-19?? s-m. (22/yr.). (back issues avail.) International Data Corp., 5 Speen St., Box 9015, Framingham, MA 01701.

531.64 EI
ENERGY SAVING AND ALTERNATIVE ENERGY SOURCES NEWSLETTER. 1981-1985. q. Commission of the European Communities, Directorate General for Energy, Service des Renseigements, 200 rue de la Loi, Brussels, Belgium.
Formerly: Rational Use of Energy.

531.64 US
ENERGY SENSE. 1983-198? q. General Learning Corporation, Custom Publishing Group, 60 Revere Dr., Northbrook, IL 60062-1563.

600 US
ENERGY SYSTEMS PRODUCT NEWS. 1976-19?? bi-m. Business Communications, Inc. (Subsidiary of: Thomas Publishing Co.), One Penn Plaza, 250 W. 34th St., New York, NY 10001.

600 SW ISSN 0348-7369
ENERGY TECHNOLOGY. ceased 1990. q. Swedish National Board for Technical Development - Styrelsen foer Teknisk Utveckling, Box 43200, 100 72 Stockholm, Sweden.

614.7 DK
ENERGY - TEKNIK & MILJOE. 1972-1986. m. (tabloid format) Fagbladsforlaget Teknik & Viden aps, P.O. Box 80, Algade 10, 4500 Nykoebing, Sjaelland, Denmark.
Formerly: Teknik og Miljoe.

531.6 US ISSN 0731-6291
ENERGYGRAMS; brief descriptions of energy technology. ceased. q. U.S. Department of Energy, Office of Scientific and Technical Information, Box 62, Oak Ridge, TN 37831.

531.6 DK ISSN 0900-419X
ENERGYLAB NEWSLETTER. 1985-198? irrege. (approx. 3-4/yr.). Energy Research Laboratory, Niels Bohr Alle 25, 5230 Odense M, Denmark.

531.64 NZ
ENERGYWIDE. ceased. bi-m. Ministry of Energy, P.O. Box 2337, Wellington, New Zealand.

980 US
ENFOQUE; en las americas. 1981-1986. bi-m. Southeastern Council for Latin American Educational Exchange, 61 Patillo Rd., Stockbridge, GA 30281.

620 US ISSN 0742-3101
TA710.A1
ENGINEERING GEOLOGY ABSTRACTS. 1984-1991 (Spring). q. American Geological Institute, 4220 King St., Alexandria, VA 22302-1507.

624.151 US ISSN 0071-0326
TA705 CODEN: EGCHAH
ENGINEERING GEOLOGY CASE HISTORIES. (Each vol. has distinctive title) 1957-1978 (vol.11). irreg. Geological Society of America, 3300 Penrose Pl., Box 9140, Boulder, CO 80301.

536.7 US ISSN 0196-5964
CODEN: ETCHD9
ENGINEERING THERMOPHYSICS IN CHINA/CHUNG-KUO KUNG CH'ENG JE WU LI. 1980-198? q. Rumford Publishing Co., Box 5370, Chicago, IL 60680.

620 621.381 US
ENGINEERING TOOLS. 1988-1989. m. V N U Business Publications, Inc., Ten Holland Dr., Hasbrouck Heights, NJ 07604.

362 UK
ENGLAND AND WALES NATIONAL HEALTH SERVICE. HEALTH SERVICES COSTING RETURNS. 1976-1987. a. (also avail. in microform) Department of Health, Alexander Fleming House, Elephant and Castle, London SE1 6BY, England.
Former titles: Great Britain. National Health Service. Health Services Costing Returns; Great Britain National Health Service. Hospital Costing Returns (ISSN 0072-6966)

914.2 UK ISSN 0267-3398
ENGLAND'S BEST HOLIDAYS. 1974-199? a. F.H.G. Publications Ltd., Abbey Mill Business Centre, Seedhill, Paisley PA1 1JN, Scotland.

929 US ISSN 0898-5464
ENGLISH ENQUIRIES. 1988-1991 (vol.5). irreg. (back issues avail.) Name Game Enterprises, S. 4204 Conklin St., Spokane, WA 99203-6235.
Formerly: English Lineages and Queries.

631 UK ISSN 0261-2674
ENGLISH HOPS. 1981-1988; suspended. 6/yr. English Hops Ltd., Hop Pocket Lane, Paddock Wood, Tonbridge, Kent, England.

792 780 US
ENJOYING THE ARTS. 1975-19?? irreg. Rosen Publishing Group, 29 E. 21st St., New York, NY 10010.

800 US ISSN 0148-8627
PQ6150
ENSAYISTAS; Georgia series on Hispanic thought. 1976-1991 (nos.30-31). a. (back issues avail.) University of Georgia, Latin American Studies Center, Athens, GA 30602.

917 IT ISSN 0013-8622
ENTE PROVINCIALE PER IL TURISMO DI NUORO. NOTIZIARIO. 1963-19?? 5/yr. (looseleaf format) Ente Provinciale per Il Turismo di Nuoro, Nuoro 08100, Italy.

338 350 US ISSN 0191-5215
HC101
ENTERPRISE (WASHINGTON). 1955-1987. q. National Association of Manufacturers, 1331 Pennsylvania Ave., N.W. Ste. 1500, Washington, DC 20004-1703.
  Supersedes (in 1977): N A M Reports (ISSN 0027-5921)

630 UK
ENTERPRISE FARMING. 1967-199? q. Food from Britain, Market Towers, New Covent Garden Market, London SW8 5NQ, England.
  Formerly (until March, 1988): Farming Business.

338.1 FR ISSN 0046-2152
ENTERPRISES AGRICOLES. ceased. m. (10/yr.). Societe de Publications et d'Editions Reunies, 21 rue du Faubourg St. Antoine, 75550 Paris Cedex 11, France.

051 US
ENTERTAINMENT AT LARGE. 1990; suspended same year. m. Entertainment at Large, Inc., Box 616626, Orlando, FL 32861.

792 US
ENTERTAINMENT FACILITIES BUYERS GUIDE. ceased. a. Billboard Publications, Inc., Amusement Business Division, Box 24970, Nashville, TN 37202.
  Former titles: Facility Supplies Sourcebook; Buyers' Guide for the Mass Entertainment Industry (ISSN 0362-6180); Amusement Equipment Buyers Guide; Incorporating: Facility Manager's Buyer's Guide; A B's Guide to Souvenirs and Novelties.

369.4 630 CN
ENTHUSIAST. 1939-19?? q. Ministry of Agriculture and Food, Rural Organizations and Services Branch, P.O. Box 1030, Guelph, Ont. N1H 6N1, Canada.
  Former titles: Junior Farmer and 4-H Enthusiast (ISSN 0022-6572); Junior Farmer and 4-H Quarterly.

338 US
ENTREPRENEUR'S GUIDE TO HOMEBASE BUSINESS. 1988-19?? s-a. Entrepreneur Inc., 2392 Morse Ave., Irvine, CA 92714.

387 347.75 GW
ENTSCHEIDUNGEN DES BUNDESOBERSEEAMTES UND DER SEEAMTER DER BUNDESREPUBLIK DEUTSCHLAND. 1975-1989. m. K.O. Storck Verlag, Stahltwiete 7, 2000 Hamburg 50, Germany.

614.7 917.9 US
ENVIRONMENTAL ASSESSMENT OF THE ALASKAN CONTINENTAL SHELF. ANNUAL REPORTS SUMMARY. ceased. a. U.S. National Oceanic and Atmospheric Administration, Environmental Research Laboratories, 6010 Executive Blvd., Rockville, MD 20852.

614.7 UK ISSN 0305-7712
QD1 CODEN: ENCHDZ
ENVIRONMENTAL CHEMISTRY. 1975-1984. irreg. Royal Society of Chemistry, Thomas Graham House, Science Park, Milton Rd., Cambridge CB4 4WF, England.

614 AT ISSN 0818-5670
ENVIRONMENTAL HEALTH REVIEW, AUSTRALIA. 1968-1988; suspended. bi-m. (Australian Institute of Health Surveyors) Trend Publishing Pty. Ltd., P.O. Box 97, Camperdown, N.S.W. 2050, Australia.
  Former titles: Australian Health Surveyor; Australian Institute of Health Surveyors. Journal.

614.7 US
ENVIRONMENTAL IMPACT ASSESSMENT WORLDLETTER; the international newsletter for environmental assessment. 1983-1988. bi-m. Environmental and Ground Water Institute, 200 Felgar St., Rm. 127, Norman, OK 73019.

612.015 UK ISSN 0142-8659
ENVIRONMENTAL PHYSIOLOGY. ceased 1990. m. (looseleaf format; back issues avail.) Sheffield University Biomedical Information Service (SUBIS), The University, Sheffield S10 2TN, England.

614.7 340 US
ENVIRONMENTAL PROTECTION: THE LEGAL FRAMEWORK. ceased 1991. base vol. (plus a. suppl.). Shepard's - McGraw-Hill, Inc., Box 35300, Colorado Springs, CO 80935-3530.

612.015 UK ISSN 0261-4626
ENZYME ISOLATION AND PURIFICATION. ceased 1990. m. (looseleaf format; back issues avail.) Sheffield University Biomedical Information Service (SUBIS), The University, Sheffield S10 2TN, England.

528 US ISSN 0071-0962
EPHEMERIS OF THE SUN, POLARIS AND OTHER SELECTED STARS WITH COMPANION DATA AND TABLES. 1910-1988. a. U.S. Naval Observatory, Dept. of the Navy, Washington, DC 20392.

616.8 UK ISSN 0261-4634
EPILEPSY. ceased 1990. m. (looseleaf format; back issues avail.) Sheffield University Biomedical Information Service (SUBIS), The University, Sheffield S10 2TN, England.

283 US ISSN 0013-9629
EPISCOPALIAN. ceased 1990. m. (tabloid format) (Episcopal Church) Episcopalian, Inc., 1201 Chestnut St., Ste. 1200, Philadelphia, PA 19107-4101.

574.8 UK ISSN 0269-4565
EPITHELIA. 1987-19?? q. Oxford University Press, Walton St., Oxford OX2 6DP, England.

658.8 361.73 US
EPSILON LETTER. 1978-1985. q. (back issues avail.) Epsilon, 50 Cambridge St., Burlington, MA 01803.

658 001.6 US
EPSILON MARKETING LETTER. 1983-1987. q. (back issues avail.) Epsilon, 50 Cambridge St., Burlington, MA 01803.

378 US
EPSILON NON-PROFIT LETTER. 1982-1986. q. (back issues avail.) Epsilon, 50 Cambridge St., Burlington, MA 01803.

621.381 CN ISSN 0830-9434
EPSON TODAY. 1985-1990 (Jun.). m. (back issues avail.) C-Way Publications, 95 Mural St., Richmond Hill, Ont., L4B 3G3, Canada.

798 UK ISSN 0260-8111
EQUESTRIAN YEAR. 1980-198? a. Hazleton Publishing, 3 Richmond Hill, Richmond, Surrey TW10 6RE, England.

636.089 GW ISSN 0176-8018
EQUINE ABSTRACTS. 1984-1990. q. (Deutsche Reiterliche Vereinigung) F N - Verlag, Freiherr-von-Langen-Str. 13, Postfach 110363, 4410 Warendorf 1, Germany.

382 BL ISSN 0046-239X
EQUIPE; revista dos servidores da Sudene. 1968-1974. m. Superintendencia do Desenvolvimento do Nordeste, Av. Prof. Moraes Rego, Cidade Universitaria, 50000 Recife PE, Brazil.

621.9 CN
EQUIPMENT CONNECTION. 1987-19?? m. Sanford Evans Communications Ltd., 1077 St. James St., Box 6900, Winnipeg, Man. R3C 3B1, Canada.

332 UK
EQUITIES. 1987-198? w. (back issues avail.) I F R Publishing Ltd., 7th Fl., South Quay Plaza 2, 183 Marsh Wall, London E14 9FU, England.
  Formerly: Equities International (ISSN 0953-6477)

820 US
ERA OF ARNOLD BENNETT. ceased. 3/yr. (back issues avail.) c/o Anita Miller, Ed., 334 Hawthorn, Glencoe, IL 60022.
  Formerly: Arnold Bennett Newsletter.

530 GW
ERGEBNISSE DER PLASMAPHYSIK UND DER GASELEKTRONIK. SCHRIFTENREIHE. 1967-198? irreg. Akademie-Verlag Berlin, Leipziger Str. 3-4, 1086 Berlin, Germany.

640.73 DK ISSN 0105-5992
ERHVERVFREMMENDE OG FORBRUGERPOLITISKE FORANSTALTNINGER. 1977-1985. irreg. Industriministeriet, Biblioteket, Slotholmsgade 12, 1216 Copenhagen K, Denmark.
  Formerly: Denmark. Handelsministeriet. Oversigt over Erhvervfremmende og Forbruger Politiske Foranstaltninger.

372 US ISSN 0014-0163
ERIC - CRIER NEWSLETTER. ceased. 3/yr. ERIC Clearinghouse on Retrieval of Information & Evaluation on Reading, 200 Pine Hall, School of Education, Indiana University, Bloomington, IN 47401.

400 300 GW ISSN 0138-1016
AS182
ERNST-MORITZ-ARNDT-UNIVERSITAET GREIFSWALD. WISSENSCHAFTLICHE ZEITSCHRIFT. GESELLSCHAFTSWISSENSCHAFTLICHE REIHE. 1951-1990 (vol.39, no.3). q. (back issues avail.) Ernst-Moritz-Arndt-Universitaet, Domstrasse 11, 2200 Greifswald, Germany.
  Formerly: Greifswald. Universitaet. Wissenschaftliche Zeitschrift. Gesellschafts- und Sprachwissenschaftliche Reihe (ISSN 0072-7504)

574 540 510 GW ISSN 0138-2853
Q49 CODEN: WZEMAX
ERNST-MORITZ-ARNDT-UNIVERSITAET GREIFSWALD. WISSENSCHAFTLICHE ZEITSCHRIFT. MATHEMATISCH-NATURWISSENSCHAFTLICHE REIHE. 1951-1990 (vol.39, no.3). q. (back issues avail.) Domstrasse 11, Fr.-Ludwig-Jahn-Strasse 15a, 2200 Greifswald, Germany.

100 900 410 700 GW ISSN 0138-1067
  CODEN: WZERDH
ERNST-MORITZ-ARNDT-UNIVERSITAET GREIFSWALD. WISSENSCHAFTLICHE ZEITSCHRIFT. MEDIZINISCHE REIHE. 1951-1990 (vol.39, no.2). q. (back issues avail.) Ernst-Moritz-Arndt-Universitaet, Domstrasse 11, 2200 Greifswald, Germany.

630 BL ISSN 0071-1292
ESCOLA SUPERIOR DE AGRICULTURA "LUIZ DE QUEIROZ". BOLETIM DE DIVULGACAO. 1962-19??; suspended. irreg. Universidade de Sao Paulo, Escola Superior de Agricultura "Luiz de Queiroz", Box 9, 13400 Piracicaba, Sao Paulo, Brazil.

133.9 UK
ESOTERIC SCIENCE JOURNAL. 1979-1990. 6/yr. Dr. Douglas M. Baker, Pub., Little Elephant, High Road, Essendon, Herts., England.

800 GW ISSN 0931-3818
ESOTERIK-ALMANACH. 1986-1989. biennial. Dr. Lothar Rossipaul Verlagsgesellschaft mbH, Bavariaring 24, 8000 Munich 2, Germany.

499.992 GW ISSN 0014-0619
DER ESPERANTIST. 1965-1991. bi-m. Kulturbund der DDR, Esperanto-Verband, Otto-Nuscke-Strasse 1, 1080 Berlin, Germany.

499.992 UK
ESPERANTO LOBBY NEWS. 1979-1987. q. Esperanto Lobby, 140 Holland Park Ave., London W11 4UF, England.
  Formerly (until 1986): Esperanto in Parliament.

382 630 IT
ESPORTARE; informazioni per il commercio estero. 1982-1990 (no.6). m. Istituto Nazionale per il Commercio Estero, Via Liszt 21, 00100 Rome (EUR), Italy.
  Incorporates: Export Alimentare e dei Prodotti Agricoli; Former titles: Notiziario Ortofrutticolo e dei Prodotti Agricoli-Alimentarii e Floricoli; Notiziario Ortofrutticolo dei Prodotti Agricoli-Alimentari (ISSN 0029-4403)

380.5 052 SA
ESPRIT DE CORPS. 1984-1989 (Dec.). m. South African Transport Services, Public Relations Department, Private Bag X47, Johannesburg 2000, South Africa.

CESSATIONS

530   US   ISSN 0071-1438
QC1   CODEN: ESPHAU
ESSAYS IN PHYSICS. 1970-1990. irreg. (reprint service avail. from ISI) Academic Press, Inc., 1250 Sixth Ave., San Diego, CA 92101.

780   US
ESSAYS ON MODERN MUSIC. 1984-1987 (vol.3, No.4); suspended. a. League of Composers, International Society for Contemporary Music, Boston Inc., Box 172, West Somerville, MA 02144.

370   UK
ESSEX EDUCATION. 1947-198? s-a. (Essex County Council) Essex Education Committee, County Hall, Chelmsford Essex, England.

282
ESSEX RECUSANT. 1958-1988. a. Essex Recusant Society, 1 Cliffsea Grove, Leigh-on-Sea, Essex SS9 1NG, England.

332.6 318   PN
ESTADISTICA PANAMENA. INVERSIONES DIRECTAS EXTRANJERAS EN PANAMA. 1960-19?? irreg. Direccion de Estadistica y Censo, Contraloria General, Apdo. 5213, Panama 5, Panama.

312 310   PN   ISSN 0378-6749
ESTADISTICA PANAMENA. SITUACION DEMOGRAFICA. SECCION 221. ESTADISTICAS VITALES - CIFRAS PRELIMINARES. 1955-1988. s-a. Direccion de Estadistica y Censo, Contraloria General, Apartado 5213, Panama 5, Panama.
    Formerly: Estadistica Panamena. Seccion 221. Movimento de Poblacion (ISSN 0078-8902)

340   US
ESTATE PLANNING LAW LOCATOR. 1988-1990. a. R.R. Bowker, A Reed Reference Publishing Company, Division of Reed Publishing (USA) Inc., 121 Chanlon Rd., New Providence, NJ 07974.

614.35 614.28   UN   ISSN 0082-8327
ESTIMATED WORLD REQUIREMENTS OF NARCOTIC DRUGS. SUPPLEMENT. ceased. 12/yr. (International Narcotics Control Board - Organe International de Controle des Stupefiants) United Nations Publications, Room DC2-0853, New York, NY 10017.

301   MX
ESTUDIOS FRONTERIZOS MEXICO - ESTADOS UNIDOS. 1984-1986. irreg. CEFNOMEX, Abelardo L. Rodriguez No. 21, Zona del Rio, Tijuana, Baja California 22320, Mexico.

001.3   BL   ISSN 0100-2635
F2501
ESTUDOS BRASILEIROS. 1976-1982 (vol.8, no.13). s-a. Universidade Federal do Parana, Centro de Estudos Brasileiros, Rua General Carneiro 460, 80000 Curitiba, Parana, Brazil.

170   US   ISSN 1011-3878
ETHICS & PERSPECTIVES!. 1987-1991; suspended. q. (back issues avail.) International Association of Ethicists, Inc., 117 W. Harrison Bldg., Ste. I-104, 6th fl., Chicago, IL 60605.

352   CN
ETHICS IN EDUCATION. 1981-1990. 5/yr. (Ontario Institute for Studies in Education) O I S E Press, 252 Bloor Street West, Toronto, Ont. M5S 1V6, Canada.

361.77   ET
ETHIOPIAN RED CROSS SOCIETY NEWSLETTER. 1981-1990 (vol.9, no.29). q. Ethiopian Red Cross Society, Addis Ababa, Ethiopia.

917.306   US   ISSN 0894-0932
E184.M5
ETHNIC AFFAIRS. 1987-1988 (no.2). s-a. University of Texas at Austin, Center for Mexican American Studies, Austin, TX 78712.

971.004   CN
ETHNIC DIRECTORY OF CANADA. 1976-19?? irreg. Western Publishers, Box 30193, Sta. "B", 526 16th Ave. N.W., Calgary, Alta. T2M 4P1, Canada.

398 301.2   NE   ISSN 0071-1845
ETHNOLOGIA. 1959-19?? irreg. (Gesellschaft fuer Voelkerkunde, GW) E. J. Brill, P.O. Box 9000, 2300 PA Leiden, Netherlands.

574.5   CN
ETUDES ECOLOGIQUES. 1979-1985. s-a. (back issues avail.) Universite Laval, Laboratoire D'Ecologie Forestiere, Quebec, Que. G1K 7P4, Canada.

614.8   UN   ISSN 0250-8710
    CODEN: ERSODS
EURO REPORTS AND STUDIES. 1979-19?? (no.112). irreg. World Health Organization, Regional Office for Europe, Scherfigsvej 8, 2100 Copenhagen 0, Denmark.

380 658.7   GW
EURO TRANSPORT JOURNAL. 1962-1989. m. Kirschbaum-Verlag, Siegfriedstr. 28, Postfach 210209, 5300 Bonn 2, Germany.
    Formerly: Transport und Lager (ISSN 0041-1566)

330   UK   ISSN 0954-4011
EUROBRIEF. 1989-1991. 24/yr. Paradigm Europe, Science and Technology Letters, P.O. Box 81, Northwood, Middlesex HA6 3DN, England.

621.3 540   UK
EURODOC FILE. 1980-198? q. Technical Indexes Ltd., Willoughby Rd., Bracknell, Berkshire RG12 4DW, England.

332   UK
EUROMARKET REPORT. ceased. w. Financial Times Business Information Ltd., Tower House, Southampton St., London WC2E 7HA, England.

320   GW
EUROPA U. JUGEND; eine Zeitschrift fuer junge Europaeer. 1965-198? q. (back issues avail.) Europa Union Verlag GmbH, Bachstr. 32, Postfach 1529, 5300 Bonn 1, Germany.

020   GW   ISSN 0723-4384
EUROPAEISCHE INTEGRATION - DOKUMENTATION; Informationen fuer Bibliothekare. 1982-198? a. (back issues avail.) Kommission der Europaeischen Gemeinschaft, Presse- und Informationsbuero, Zitelmannstr. 22, D-5300 Bonn 1, Germany.

780   GW   ISSN 0073-0025
EUROPAEISCHE VOLKSMUSIKINSTRUMENTE. HANDBUCH. 1967-1983. irreg. VEB Deutscher Verlag fuer Musik, Karlstr. 10, 7010 Leipzig, Germany.

540   GW
EUROPAEISCHER WIRTSCHAFTSDIENST. CHEMIE-DIENST. 1926-1991. w. Casimir Katz Verlag, Bleichstr. 20-22, 7562 Gernsbach, Germany.

677   GW
EUROPAEISCHER WIRTSCHAFTSDIENST. TEXTIL- UND CHEMIEFASER-DIENST. 1926-1991. w. Casimir Katz Verlag, Bleichstr. 20-22, 7562 Gernsbach, Germany.

632   FR   ISSN 0071-2396
EUROPEAN AND MEDITERRANEAN PLANT PROTECTION ORGANIZATION. PUBLICATIONS. SERIES B: PLANT HEALTH NEWSLETTER. 1950-1988 (vol.92). irreg. (processed) European and Mediterranean Plant Protection Organization, 1 rue le Notre, 75016 Paris, France.
    Formerly: Surveys of the Position of Various Pests and Diseases in Europe and the Mediterranean Area.

614.7   US   ISSN 0272-4626
TD1   CODEN: EAPRD5
EUROPEAN APPLIED RESEARCH REPORTS: ENVIRONMENTAL AND NATURAL RESOURCES SECTION; a journal of European science and technology. ceased. 10/yr. (in 2 vols., 5 nos./vol.). Harwood Academic Publishers, 50 W. 23rd St., New York, NY 10010.

973   BE
EUROPEAN ASSOCIATION FOR AMERICAN STUDIES. BIENNIAL REPORT. 1977-19?? s-a. Center for American Studies, 4 bd. de l'Empereur, 1000 Brussels, Belgium.

614.7   EI
EUROPEAN ATOMIC ENERGY COMMUNITY. CONTAMINATION RADIOACTIVE DES DENREES ALIMENTAIRES DANS LES PAYS DE LA COMMUNAUTE. 1965-19?? a. Office for Official Publications of the European Communities, L-2985 Luxembourg, Luxembourg.

200   SP
EUROPEAN CHALLENGE. 1988-19?? bi-m. (Church of Christ in Europe) Juan Antonio Monroy, Ed. & Pub., Apdo. 2029, 28080 Madrid, Spain.

330   EI
EUROPEAN COMMUNITIES. ECONOMIC AND SOCIAL COMMITTEE. YEARBOOK. 1960-198? irreg. European Communities, Economic and Social Committee, Press and Information Division, 2 rue Ravenstein, 1000 Brussels, Belgium.

338 016   UK   ISSN 0071-2582
EUROPEAN COMPANIES; a guide to sources of information. 1961-198? irreg. C.B.D. Research Ltd., 15 Wickham Rd., Beckenham, Kent BR3 2JS, England.

677.2 314   IT   ISSN 0423-7269
HD9885.A2
EUROPEAN COTTON INDUSTRY STATISTICS. 1958-1985. a. Istituto per Assistenza e Servizi alle Aziende Tessili s.r.l. (I.A.S.A.T.), Via Borgonuovo 11, 20121 Milan, Italy.

340 016   UK   ISSN 0305-8476
LAW
EUROPEAN LAW DIGEST. 1973-1991. m. (European Law Centre Ltd.) Sweet & Maxwell, South Quay Plaza, 8th Floor, 183 Marsh Wall, London E14 9FT, England.

332   FR   ISSN 0071-2957
HG3881
EUROPEAN MONETARY AGREEMENT. REPORT OF THE BOARD OF MANAGEMENT. (Supersedes European Payment Union. Annual Report) 1959-19?? a. (also avail. in microfiche) Organization for Economic Cooperation and Development, 2 rue Andre-Pascal, 75775 Paris Cedex 16, France.

320   NO   ISSN 0333-273X
EUROPEAN POLITICAL DATA NEWSLETTER. 1971-1988 (Dec.). q. Norwegian Social Science Data Services, Hans Holmboesgt. 22, N-5007 Bergen, Norway.

330   BE   ISSN 0261-8249
EUROPEAN REVIEW. 1981-1991. q. Arthur Andersen & Co., 56 av. des Arts, 1040 Brussels, Belgium.

362.8   EI
EUROPEAN SOCIAL FUND. ANNUAL REPORT ON THE ACTIVITIES OF THE NEW EUROPEAN SOCIAL FUND. 1972-19?? a. Office for Official Publications of the European Communities, L-2985 Luxembourg, Luxembourg.

320   UK
EUROPEAN SOCIALIST THOUGHT SERIES. 1974-1991. irreg. Spokesman Books, Bertrand Russell House, Gamble St., Nottingham, England.

658   UK
EUROPEAN SPENDING QUARTERLY; forecasts and analysis of consumer demand in 12 countries. 1990-1991. q. (Economist Intelligence Unit) Business International Ltd., 40 Duke St., London W1A 1DW, England.

332.6   FR   ISSN 0995-2721
EUROPEAN SPONSORSHIP NEWSLETTER. 1989-1990. bi-m. Editions des Trois Rives, 23, Av. Corentin Cariou, 75019 Paris, France.

914   GW
EUROPEAN TOURISM & CONGRESS - DER FREMDENVERKEHR. 1949-19?? m. Jaeger Verlag GmbH, Holzhofallee 38, Postfach 110452, 6100 Darmstadt, Germany.
    Former titles: Fremdenverkehr - Tourismus and Kongress (ISSN 0930-6269); Fremdenverkehr und das Reisebuero (ISSN 0342-4774); Fremdenverkehr (ISSN 0016-0962)

388.324   GW   ISSN 0175-6281
EUROPEAN TRUCK & TRAILER; special edition of Verkehrs-Rundschau. 1983-1986. irreg. (back issues avail.) Heinrich Vogel Fachzeitschriften GmbH, Postfach 802020, Neumarkterstr.18, 8000 Munich 80, Germany.

338   UK
EUROPICK NEWS. 1990-1991. bi-m. Pick Systems Europe, P.O. Box 232, Northampton NN1 5PL, England.

314 EI ISSN 0378-4207
HA1107.5
EUROSTAT NEWS. 1976-19?? q. Statistical Office of the European Communities, L-2985 Luxembourg, Luxembourg.

600 FR
EUROTECHNOLOGIES. announced, never published. 18/yr. A Jour, 11 rue du Marche St. Honore, 75001 Paris, France.

690 NE ISSN 0920-8437
EUROTRADE (DUTCH EDITION); vraag & aanbod voor toelevering en exportindustrie. 1987-1991. m. Kluwer Technische Tijdschriften BV, Postbus 23, 7400 GA Deventer, Netherlands.

690 NE ISSN 0920-8453
EUROTRADE (ENGLISH EDITION); monthly for subcontractors and the exporting industry. 1987-1991. m. Kluwer Technische Tijdschriften BV, Postbus 23, 7400 GA Deventer, Netherlands.

690 NE ISSN 0920-8445
EUROTRADE (FRENCH EDITION); offres et demandes pour la sous-traitance et l'exportation. 1987-1991. m. Kluwer Technische Tijdschriften BV, Postbus 23, 7400 GA Deventer, Netherlands.

690 NE ISSN 0920-8461
EUROTRADE (GERMAN EDITION); Angebot und Nachfrage fuer Zulieferung und Export. 1987-1991. m. Kluwer Technische Tijdschriften BV, Postbus 23, 7400 GA Deventer, Netherlands.

610 340 US ISSN 0884-2981
R726 CODEN: EUREEF
EUTHANASIA REVIEW. 1987-1990. s-a. (reprint service avail. from UMI) (Hemlock Society) Human Sciences Press, Inc. (Subsidiary of: Plenum Publishing Corp.), 233 Spring St., New York, NY 10013-1578.

058.81 DK ISSN 0014-3278
EVA. 1962-1989 (no.4). 8/yr. Bonniers Specialmagasiner, Strandboulvarden 130, 2100 Copenhagen OE, Denmark.

289 UK ISSN 0046-2853
EVANGELICAL MAGAZINE. 1959-1975. bi-m. Providence House, 118 Falcon Rd., London S.W.11., England.

284 GW ISSN 0014-3553
EVANGELISCHER NACHRICHTENDIENST IN DER D D R. 1947-1990. w. Evangelische Verlagsanstalt GmbH, Ziegelstr. 30, 1040 Berlin, Germany.

327 YU ISSN 0353-2976
EVROPA DANAS/EUROPE TODAY. 1988-1989 (no.3-4). q. Institut za Medjunarodnu Politiku i Privredu, Makedonska 25, P.O. Box 750, 11000 Belgrade, Yugoslavia.

615.7 NE ISSN 0921-4496
  CODEN: EMCPE
EXCERPTA MEDICA. SECTION 130: CLINICAL PHARMACOLOGY. 1988-1991. 16/yr.(in 2 vols.; 8 nos./vol.). Excerpta Medica (Subsidiary of: Elsevier Science Publishers B.V.), P.O. Box 548, 1000 AM Amsterdam, Netherlands.

617.95 016 NE ISSN 0014-438X
RD118.A1 CODEN: EXMPB
EXCERPTA MEDICA. SECTION 34: PLASTIC SURGERY. 1970-1991 (vol.22). 6/yr. Excerpta Medica (Subsidiary of: Elsevier Science Publishers B.V.), P.O. Box 548, 1000 AM Amsterdam, Netherlands.

615 016 NE ISSN 0376-5091
RS51 CODEN: DGLIA
EXCERPTA MEDICA. SECTION 37: DRUG LITERATURE INDEX. 1969-1990 (vol.22, no.24). 24/yr. Excerpta Medica (Subsidiary of: Elsevier Science Publishers B.V.), P.O. Box 548, 1000 AM Amsterdam, Netherlands.

616.9 NE ISSN 0922-6532
EXCERPTA MEDICA. SECTION 54: A I D S. (Acquired Immune Deficiency Syndrome) 1989-1991. 10/yr. Excerpta Medica (Subsidiary of: Elsevier Science Publishers B.V.), P.O. Box 548, 1000 AM Amsterdam, Netherlands.

658 US
EXECU-TIME; the newsletter on effective use of executive time. 1979-199? s-m. Timlet Corp., Box 631, Lake Forest, IL 60045.

658 US
EXECUTIVE ADMINISTRATOR. ceased 1988. m. Center for Management Systems, Box 159, Akron, IA 51001.

388.3 US
EXECUTIVE AND OWNERSHIP REPORT. ceased 1988. a. American Trucking Associations, Inc., Statistical Analysis Department, 2200 Mill Rd., Alexandria, VA 22314.

650 US ISSN 0745-4783
EXECUTIVE COMMUNICATIONS; increasing your personal impact. 1981-198? m. (back issues avail.) Magna Publications, Inc., 2718 Dryden Dr., Madison, WI 53704-3006.
  Formerly: Decker Communication Report.

658 US
EXECUTIVE COMPENSATION ALERT. ceased 1988. m. Research Institute of America, Inc., 90 Fifth Ave., New York, NY 10011.

658 US ISSN 0095-4144
HD4965.5.A7
EXECUTIVE COMPENSATION SERVICE. REPORTS ON INTERNATIONAL COMPENSATION. ARGENTINA. ceased 1980. a. Executive Compensation Service Inc., Two Executive Dr., Ft. Lee, NJ 07024.

331.2 US
EXECUTIVE COMPENSATION SERVICE. REPORTS ON INTERNATIONAL COMPENSATION. BRAZIL. ceased 1980. a. Executive Compensation Service Inc., Two Executive Dr., Ft. Lee, NJ 07024.

331.2 US ISSN 0090-9971
HD4965.5.U6
EXECUTIVE COMPENSATION SERVICE. REPORTS ON INTERNATIONAL COMPENSATION. PUERTO RICO. ceased 1980. a. Executive Compensation Service Inc., Two Executive Dr., Ft. Lee, NJ 07024.

340 US
EXECUTIVE DISCLOSURE GUIDE. 1976-198? m. Commerce Clearing House, Inc., 4025 W. Peterson Ave., Chicago, IL 60646.

051 US
EXECUTIVE LIVING. 1988-1991. bi-m. Business Journal Publishing Co. (Cleveland), 1720 Euclid Ave., Ste. 300, Cleveland, OH 44115.

651.2 US
EXECUTIVE MART. 1970-1988. 6/yr. Hamel Publishing Co., Inc., 27B Woodland St., Natick, MA 01760-5413.

330 UK
EXECUTIVE ON SUNDAY. 1979-1989. m. W P Publications, Newspaper House, Derngate, Northampton, England.
  Formerly (until Feb. 1988): South Midlands Business and Commerce Digest.

613.7 US
EXECUTIVE PRODUCTIVITY. 1981-19?? m. Newsletter Management Corporation, 951 Broken Sound Pkwy., N.W., Ste. 300, Boca Raton, FL 33431.
  Incorporates (1981-1985): Executive's Personal Health Advisor (ISSN 0277-1667)

336 AT
EXECUTIVE TAX RETURN. 1978-1990 (Sep.). s-a. Cullen Egan Dell Ltd., 168 Walker St., N. Sydney, N.S.W. 2000, Australia.

301.16 310 US
EXECUTIVE TREND WATCH; public exposure in the national media. 1982-1991 (May). s-m. (looseleaf format; back issues avail.) Conference on Issues & Media, Inc., 300 N. Washington St., Ste. 401, Alexandria, VA 22314.
  Formerly (until 1988): Issues Management Letter (ISSN 0882-1798)

331 US
EXECUTIVES ON THE MOVE. ceased. q. Gale Research Inc., 835 Penobscot Bldg., Detroit, MI 48226.

378.1 UK ISSN 0014-4622
EXETER UNIVERSITY GAZETTE. 1953-19?? a. University of Exeter, Hailey Wing, Reed Hall, Streatham Drive, Exeter EX4 4QR, England.

336 UK ISSN 0269-4921
EXPATRIATES TAX & INVESTMENT INTELLIGENCE. 1986-1989 (Mar.). bi-m. Longman Group (UK) Ltd., 21-27 Lamb's Conduit St., London WC1N 3NJ, England.

500 BL ISSN 0014-4762
EXPERIENTIAE. 1961-1989 (vol.30, no.10); suspended. irreg. Universidade Federal de Vicosa, 36570 Vicosa, Minas Gerais, Brazil.

574 US
EXPERIMENTAL BIOLOGY; environmental and sensory aspects. 1942-19?? (vol.48). 6/yr. (also avail. in microform from MIM; reprint service avail. from UMI) Springer-Verlag, Journals, 175 Fifth Ave., New York, NY 10010.
  Former titles: Revue Canadienne de Biologie et Biologie Experimentale (ISSN 0714-6140); Revue Canadienne de Biologie (ISSN 0035-0915)

340 US
EXPERT EVIDENCE REPORTER. ceased 1990. m. Shepard's - McGraw-Hill, Inc., Box 35300, Colorado Springs, CO 80935-3530.

001.539 US
EXPERT SYSTEMS; planning, implementation, integration. 1989-1991. q. Auerbach Publishers (Subsidiary of: Warren, Gorham & Lamont), One Penn Plaza, New York, NY 10119.

001.535 US
EXPERT SYSTEMS IN GOVERNMENT CONFERENCE. 1985-1987. a. (Institute of Electrical and Electronics Engineers, Inc.) I E E E Computer Society Press, 10662 Los Vaqueros Circle, Los Alamitos, CA 90720-1264.
  Formerly (until 1986): Expert Systems in Government Symposium.

255 US ISSN 0362-0867
BR1
EXPLOR. 1975-1988. a. Garrett - Evangelical Theological Seminary, c/o Alva R. Caldwell, 2121 Sheridan Rd., Evanston, IL 60201.

330.9 US
EXPLORATIONS IN THE WORLD ECONOMY. 1982-198? irreg. (back issues avail.) Sage Publications, Inc., 2111 W. Hillcrest Dr., Newbury Park, CA 91320.

977 US
EXPLORE MINNESOTA TRAVELER. ceased 1991. biennial. Office of Tourism, 375 Jackson St., Ste. 250, St. Paul, MN 55101.
  Formerly: Explore Minnesota Arts and Attractions.

940 UK
EXPLORING EUROPE. (Teacher's Series) 1977-1983. 3/yr. University of Sussex, School of European Studies, Schools Unit, Arts Area, Brighton BN1 9QN, England.
  Supersedes: European Studies (ISSN 0014-3103)

745.1 US ISSN 0888-4722
EXPO INFO; the world's fair world. 1971-19?? q. (tabloid format; back issues avail.) Expo-Collectors Historians Organization (ECHO), 1415 Randall Ct., Los Angeles, CA 90065-1815.

380 CN ISSN 0708-1332
HF3223
EXPORT CANADA; the marketing directory of Canadian trade. 1978-19?? a. Canex Enterprises, Inc., Box 1048, Sta. A., Surrey, B.C. V3S 4P5, Canada.

380.1 SI
EXPORT LINES. 1986- 19?? a. Times Trade Directories Pte. Ltd., Times Centre, 1 New Industrial Road, Singapore 1953, Singapore.

382 GW ISSN 0724-4509
EXPORT-MARKT, EURO-REVUE. 1921-19?? irreg. Vogel-Verlag und Druck KG, Max-Planck-Str. 7-9, Postfach 6740, 8700 Wuerzburg 1, Germany.
  Formerly (until 1983): Euro-Revue (ISSN 0341-7581)

382 JA
EXPORTERS OF JAPANESE PRODUCTS. DIRECTORY. ceased. irreg. Japan Textile Products Exporters Association - Nihon Seni Seihin Yushutsu Kumiai, Textile Exporters House, 4-4, Bingo-machi, Higashi-ku, Osaka 541, Japan.

CESSATIONS

382 US ISSN 0556-3585
HF3161.P4
EXPORTS BY PENNSYLVANIA MANUFACTURERS. 1972-198? irreg. Department of Commerce, Bureau of Policy, Planning & Systems Development, 474 Forum Bldg., Harrisburg, PA 17120.

796.357 CN ISSN 0835-3743
LES EXPOS. 1969-1992. 6/yr. (Montreal Baseball Club Ltd.) Conseillers Communicatec Inc., 536 Dawson, Mt. Royal, Que. H3R 1C6, Canada.
Former titles (until 1987): Baseball - Revue du Baseball; Montreal Expos Baseball Program.

268 US ISSN 0014-5238
EXPOSITOR BIBLICO (TEACHER EDITION). 1893-1991. a. Casa Bautista de Publicaciones, Box 4255, El Paso, TX 79914.

051 US
EXPOSURE (LOS ANGELES). ceased 1990 (Oct.). bi-m. Planet Publishing, 1155 N. LaBrea, Los Angeles, CA 90210.

800 US
EXPRESSO TILT. 1984-198? 2/yr. (back issues avail.) 737 Wharton St., Philadelphia, PA 19147.

332 SP ISSN 0014-5378
EXTEBANK MONTHLY ECONOMIC REPORT/ INFORMACION ECONOMICA. BOLETIN. 1977-1989 (Mar.). m. (reprint service avail. from UMI) Banco Exterior de Espana, Economic Research Department, Carrera de San Jeronimo, 36, Madrid 14, Spain.

332 UK
EXTEL PROSPECTUSES AND NEW ISSUES FICHE SERVICE. ceased 1990. m. (also avail. in microfiche; back issues avail.) Extel Financial Ltd., Fitzroy House, 13-17 Epworth St., London EC2A 4DL, England.
Former titles: Extel Book of Prospectuses and New Issues Fiche Service; (until 1984): Extel Book of Prospectuses and New Issues (ISSN 0308-7387)

747 US ISSN 0886-5949
EXTERIORS. 1983-198? q. Edgell Communications, 7500 Old Oak Blvd., Cleveland, OH 44130.

617.7 AT ISSN 1032-4070
EYECARE AUSTRALIA. 1988-19?? m. (tabloid format; back issues avail.) Medicine Group Publishing House, 199 Comdamine St., Balgowlah, N.S.W. 2092, Australia.

630 UN ISSN 0071-6960
F A O AGRICULTURAL DEVELOPMENT PAPER. 1954-1979 (no.99). irreg. Food and Agriculture Organization of the United Nations, c/o UNIPUB, 4611-F Assembly Dr., Lanham, MD 20706-4391.

634.9 676 UN ISSN 0532-0283
F A O FORESTRY STUDIES. 1950-19?? irreg. Food and Agriculture Organization of the United Nations, c/o UNIPUB, 4611-F Assembly Dr., Lanham, MD 20706-4391.
Formerly (until 1973): F A O Forestry and Forest Products Studies (ISSN 0099-9857)

639 UN ISSN 0071-7061
F A O MANUALS IN FISHERIES SCIENCE. 1965-19?? irreg. Food and Agriculture Organization of the United Nations, Via delle Terme de Caracalla, 00100 Rome, Italy.

375 636 UN ISSN 0429-9388
F A O - W H O EXPERT PANEL ON VETERINARY EDUCATION. REPORT OF THE MEETING. 1962-19?? a? Food and Agriculture Organization of the United Nations, Distribution and Sales Section, Via delle Terme di Caragalla, I-00100 Rome, Italy.

630 US ISSN 0195-3346
F C X CAROLINA COOPERATOR. 1922-19?? 10/yr. F C X, Inc., 609 St. Marys St., Raleigh, NC 27605-1703.
Formerly: Carolina Cooperator (ISSN 0008-6738)

331.88 GW ISSN 0323-5750
F D G B. RUNDSCHAU. 1956-198? q. (Confederation of Free German Trade Unions) Verlag Tribuene, Am Treptower Park 28-30, 1193 Berlin, Germany.
Formerly: Freien Deutschen Gewerkschaftsbundes. Rundschau (ISSN 0014-5769)

671 UK ISSN 0014-5785
F E & Z N. 1960-19?? irreg. Zinc Development Association, 34 Berkeley Sq., London W1X 6AJ, England.

281.6 US ISSN 0361-0810
F G C QUARTERLY. 1968-19?? q. Friends General Conference, 1216 Arch St., Ste. 2B, Philadelphia, PA 19107.

020 010 GW ISSN 0074-5804
F I D - C R REPORT SERIES. 1964-1986. irreg. (International Federation for Documentation, Committee on Classification Research) Indeks Verlag, Woogstr. 36a, D-6000 Frankfurt 50, Germany.

029 NE
F I D - R I MEETINGS REPORTS. 1970-1974 (no.2). irreg. Federation Internationale d'Information et de Documentation - International Federation for Information and Documentation, P.O. Box 90402, 2509 LK The Hague, Netherlands.

029 NE ISSN 0203-6495
F I D - R I SERIES ON PROBLEMS OF INFORMATION SCIENCE. 1969-1981 (no.7). irreg. Federation Internationale d'Information et de Documentation - International Federation for Information and Documentation, Postbus 90402, 2509 LK The Hague, Netherlands.
Formerly: F I D - R I Series of Collected Articles.

639.2 AT ISSN 0726-0741
F.I.N.S.. (Fishing Industry News Service) 1968-19?? 6/yr. Fisheries Department, 108 Adelaide Tce., Perth, W.A. 6000, Australia.

028.5 US
F L I P MAGAZINE. (Future Literature in Progress) 1986-198? 4/yr. Art Center of Battle Creek, 265 E. Emmett St., Battle Creek, MI 49017.

348 CN
F M COMPILATION OF THE STATUTES OF CANADA. REVISED STATUTES. 1972-1987. a. (looseleaf format) Supply and Services Canada, 45 Boulevard Sacre Coeur, Hull, Que. K1A 0S9, Canada.
Formerly: F M Compilation of the Statutes of Canada (ISSN 0380-2639)

157.734 616.6 US
F Q. (Foreskin Quarterly) ceased. q. (back issues avail.) Desmodus Inc., Box 11314, San Francisco, CA 94101.

266 US
F S M LINKS. 1974-1988. q. Franciscan Sisters of Mary, 1100 Bellevue Ave., St. Louis, MO 63117.

054 FR ISSN 0755-0960
PR823
FABULA. 1983-19?? 2/yr. Presses Universitaires de Lille, Rue du Barreau, B.P. 199, 59654 Villeneuve d'Ascq, France.

053 GW
FABULA PRESS AWARD READER. 1983-1988. irreg. (back issues avail.) Fabula Press Agency, Bezgenrieter Str. 85, 7326 Heiningen, Germany.

200 US ISSN 0361-6061
FACE-TO-FACE (NEW YORK); an interreligious bulletin. ceased. 3/yr. (reprint service avail. from UMI) Anti-Defamation League of B'nai B'rith, 823 United Nations Plaza, New York, NY 10017.

800 US ISSN 0893-7974
FACET; a creative writing magazine. ceased 1986. bi-m. Judith C. Porter, Ed. & Pub. (Hualapai), Box 4950, Hualapai, AZ 86412.

830 AU
FACETTEN. 1970-1987. a. (Kulturamt) Jugend und Volk Verlagsgesellschaft, Anschuetzg. 1, A-1153 Vienna, Austria.

373.246 SW ISSN 0014-6463
FACKLAERAREN. 1953-19?? s-m. (22/yr.). Laerarnas Tidning, Box 12 239, 102 26 Stockholm, Sweden.

331.88 SW ISSN 0014-6471
FACKLIGA VAERLDSRORELSEN. 1953-19?? m. Box 9144, S-102 72 Stockholm, Sweden.

382 US
FACSIMILE USERS' DIRECTORY; key FAX numbers in the US, Canada and overseas. 1989-1990. s-a. Monitor Publishing Company, 104 Fifth Ave., 2nd Fl., New York, NY 10011.

338.91 US
FACTS FOR ACTION. ceased. bi-m. Oxfam America, 115 Broadway, Boston, MA 02116.

910 DK ISSN 0108-996X
FACTS OM DANMARK. 1984-198? irreg. Udenrigsministeriet, Asiatisk Plads 2, 1448 Copenhagen K, Denmark.

388.31 DK ISSN 0106-4517
FAERDSELSORIENTERING; faerdselspaedagogisk tidsskrift. 1973-1989. q. Raadet for Stoerre Faerdselssikkerhed, Valbygaardsvej 62, DK 2500 Valby, Copenhagen, Denmark.

388.3 AU ISSN 0014-6870
DER FAHRZEUGHANDEL; Fachzeitschrift fuer den Fahrzeughandel. 1948-198? m. Oesterreichischer Wirtschaftsverlag, Nikolsdorfer Gasse Nr. 7-11, 1051 Vienna, Austria.

332.7 US
FAIR CREDIT REPORTING MANUAL. 1971-199? irreg. Warren, Gorham and Lamont Inc., One Penn Plaza, New York, NY 10119.

051 330 US ISSN 0885-1999
FAIRFAX. 1986-19?? q. Hough Communications, Inc., 1701 Pennsylvania Ave. N.W., Ste. 940, Washington, DC 20006-5873.

051 US
FAME. 1988-1991 (Dec.). m. 140 W. 22nd St., New York, NY 10011.

301.426 DR
FAMILIA. ceased. s-a. Asociacion Dominicana Pro Bienestar de la Familia, Apdo. 1053, Santo Domingo, Dominican Republic.

917.206 US ISSN 0741-7403
FAMILIA LATINA. 1984-1991. m. American International Hispanic Communications, 1219 Palo Verde, Carson City, NV 89701-4338.

640.73 DK ISSN 0900-2049
FAMILIEN DANMARKS FORBRUGER. HAANDBOG; kend dine muligheder og rettigheder. 1984; published only once. a. Forlag for Social & Sundhedssektor, Albertslund, Denmark.

320 US
FAMILY, LAW AND DEMOCRACY. 1980-1990 (Nov.). m. (back issues avail.) Free Congress Research & Education Foundation, Inc., 721 Second St., N.E., Washington, DC 20002.
Formed by the 1980 merger of: Family Protection Report; Initiative and Referendum Report; Journal of Family and Culture.

301.4 UK ISSN 0538-9089
HQ763
FAMILY PLANNING IN FIVE CONTINENTS. 1965-198? irreg. (processed) International Planned Parenthood Federation, Regent's College, Inner Circle, Regent's Park, London NW1 4NS, England.

344 US ISSN 0090-0923
KF3771.A73
FAMILY PLANNING - POPULATION REPORTER. 1972-1981 (vol.10, no.3). bi-m. (also avail. in microform from UMI; reprint service avail. from UMI) Alan Guttmacher Institute, 360 Park Ave. So., New York, NY 10010.

613.7 US
FAMILY PRACTICE ALERT. ceased 1990 (Dec.). m. (also avail. in audio cassette) American Health Consultants, Six Piedmont Center, Ste. 400, 3525 Piedmont Rd., N.E., Atlanta, GA 30305.

610 UK ISSN 0305-9669
FAMILY PRACTITIONER SERVICES. 1974-1990. m. Society of Administrators of Family Practitioner Services, 111 The Ropewalk, Nottingham NG1 5EP, England.

301.4 US ISSN 0887-9109
FAMILY THERAPY TODAY. 1986-19?? m. (back issues avail.) P.M. Inc., 14545 Friar, No. 106, Box 2468, Van Nuys, CA 91404.

387   UK ISSN 0144-8781
HE890.5
FAR EAST SHIPPING. 1980-198? a. Seatrade Publications Ltd., Fairfax House, Causton Rd., Colchester, Essex CO1 1RJ, England.

016 630 US ISSN 0193-8487
FARM AND GARDEN INDEX. 1978-1986. q. University Microfilms International, Serials Data Management, 300 N. Zeeb Rd., Ann Arbor, MI 48106-1346.

635   US
FARM AND GARDEN PERIODICALS ON MICROFILM. 1978-1986. a. University Microfilms International, Serials Data Management, 300 N. Zeeb Rd., Ann Arbor, MI 48106-1346.

630 636 658.8 US ISSN 0014-813X
FARM SUPPLIER; serving farm supply, feed, and fertilizer dealers. 1927-1988 (Jun.). 10/yr. (also avail. in microform from UMI; reprint service avail. from UMI) A B C Consumer Magazines, Inc., Farm Supplier (Subsidiary of: A B C Publishing, Inc.), 825 Seventh Ave., New York, NY 10019.
 Formerly: Feed and Farm Supplier.

630   US
FARMERS FASTLINE: WISCONSIN EDITION. 1988-198? m. HowFine Publishing Co., Inc., 4900 Fox Run Rd., Buckner, KY 40010.
 Formerly (until 1989): Wisconsin Farmers Fastline.

338.1 657 US
FARMERS FEDERAL TAX ALERT. ceased 1988. m. Research Institute of America, Inc., 90 Fifth Ave., New York, NY 10011.

630   AT ISSN 0014-8466
FARMERS WEEKLY. 1917-1990 (Aug.). w. (newspaper; also avail. in microform from UMI; reprint service avail. from UMI) (Western Australia Farmers Federation) Farmers Weekly Newspaper Co. Ltd., 239 Adelaide Terrace, Perth, W.A. 6000, Australia.

631   ZA ISSN 0014-8504
FARMING IN ZAMBIA; voice of Zambian agriculture. 1965-1984 (vol.15, no.1). q. Ministry of Agriculture and Water Development, P.O. Box 50197, Lusaka, Zambia.

312   DK ISSN 0108-5557
HF3649.F3
FAROERNE OG GROENLAND. 1984-1989. irreg. (9-10/yr.). (back issues avail.) Danmarks Statistik, Sejroegade 11, 2100 Copenhagen OE, Denmark.

623.89 DK ISSN 0109-5811
FARVANDVAESENETS TRAFIKANALYSE. 1981-1984 (vol.4). a. Farvandvaesenet, Farvandsinspektoratet, P.O. Box 1919, 1023 Copenhagen K, Denmark.

659.152 UK ISSN 0142-2081
FASHION INDEX. 1979-1985 (vol.3). irreg. (back issues avail.) (Newcastle upon Tyne Polytechnic Library) Newcastle upon Tyne Polytechnic Products Ltd., Ellison Building, Ellison Place, Newcastle upon Tyne NE1 8ST, England.

681.11 746.92 US
FASHION TIME QUARTERLY. 1991-1992. bi-m. (tabloid format) Miller Freeman Inc. (New York) (Subsidiary of: United Newspapers Group), 1515 Broadway, New York, NY 10036.

370   US ISSN 0896-2332
FAST FORWARD. 1987-1989 (Sep.). 8/yr. Department of Education, Office of Press and Communications, 333 Market St., Harrisburg, PA 17126-0333.

669 338 US ISSN 0895-4895
TJ1320
FASTENER AGE; serving the precision forming and fabricating industries. 1987-198?; suspended. bi-m. (Wire Association International) Fastener Age, Inc., 1570 Boston Post Rd., Box H, Guilford, CT 06437.

332.6 US
FASTEST GROWING STOCKS. 1961-19?? 36/yr. F G S Research Ltd., Box 3458, Chapel Hill, NC 27515.

912.16 US ISSN 0192-1347
G1797.21.E635
FASTFACTS EUROPEAN HOTEL LOCATOR. 1978-1991. a. Reed Travel Group (Subsidiary of: Reed Publishing USA), 500 Plaza Dr., Secaucus, NJ 07096.

647.94 US ISSN 0197-9477
TX907
FASTFACTS U S A HOTEL MOTEL LOCATOR. 1979-1991. a. Reed Travel Group (Subsidiary of: Reed Publishing USA), 500 Plaza Dr., Secaucus, NJ 07096.

388.324 US
FASTLINE FOR ARKANSAS - OKLAHOMA TRUCKERS. 1984-1991. m. Fastline Publications, Inc., 4900 Fox Run Rd., Buckner, KY 40010.
 Formerly: Arkansas - Oklahoma Trucker.

910   SW ISSN 0349-0823
FAUNA NORRLANDICA. 1978-1987. irreg. University of Umeo, Department of Ecological Zoology, c/o Prof. Karl Muller, S-90187 Umea, Sweden.

781.7 US
FAVORITE COUNTRY STARS. 1988-198? a. Southeast Magazines, Inc., 545 Mainstream Dr., Ste. 101, Nashville, TN 37228.

929 977 US ISSN 0739-8093
F497.F2
FAYETTE CONNECTION. 1981-1992. q. (looseleaf format; back issues avail.) Fayette County Genealogical Society, Box 342, Washington C.H., OH 43160.

808.838 UK ISSN 0954-8017
FEAR. no.21, 1990-1991 (Oct.). m. (back issues avail.) Newsfield, Ludlow, Shropshire SY8 1JW, England.

332.1 US
FEDERAL HOME LOAN BANK OF CINCINNATI. FIFTH DISTRICT REVIEW. 1978-198? q. Federal Home Loan Bank of Cincinnati, Box 598, 2000 Atrium Two, Cincinnati, OH 45201.
 Formerly (until 1986): Federal Home Loan Bank of Cincinnati. Quarterly Review.

332.1 US
FEDERAL HOME LOAN BANK OF DALLAS. QUARTERLY. 1982-198? q. Federal Home Loan Bank of Dallas, Office of the Corporate Secretary, Box 619026, Dallas-Ft. Worth, TX 75261-9026.

332.1 US
FEDERAL HOME LOAN BANK OF SAN FRANCISCO. PROCEEDINGS OF THE ANNUAL CONFERENCE. 1975-1990. a. Federal Home Loan Bank of San Francisco, Box 7948, San Francisco, CA 94120.

332.1 US
FEDERAL HOME LOAN BANK OF SEATTLE. BANK NOTES. ceased. s-a. Federal Home Loan Bank of Seattle, 1501 Fourth Ave., Ste. 1900, Seattle, WA 98101-1693.

350   US
FEDERAL NEWS CLIPSHEET. ceased 198? m. U.S. Office of Personnel Management, Office of Public Affairs, Washington, DC 20415.

614.7 CN ISSN 0069-0007
FEDERAL - PROVINCIAL WILDLIFE CONFERENCE. TRANSACTIONS. 1922-1989. a. Environment Canada, Canadian Wildlife Service, Ottawa, Ont. K1A 0E7, Canada.

330.9 US
FEDERAL RESERVE BANK OF ATLANTA. RESEARCH PAPER SERIES. 1976-198? irreg. Federal Reserve Bank of Atlanta, 104 Marietta N.W., Atlanta, GA 30303.

350   US ISSN 0734-4651
FEDERAL - STATE EXECUTIVE DIRECTORY. ceased. a. Carroll Publishing Company, 1058 Thomas Jefferson St., N.W., Washington, DC 20007.

011 336 US
FEDERAL TAX LOCATOR. ceased. 6 base vols. (plus. q. suppl.). Shepard's - McGraw-Hill, Inc., Box 35300, Colorado Springs, CO 80935-3530.

374   US
FEDERAL TRAINER. ceased. 4/yr. U.S. Office of Personnel Management, Training Resources Management Division-W E D, Box 7230, Washington, DC 20044.

679.7 FR
FEDERATION DES DEBITANTS DE TABAC DE L'ILE-DE-FRANCE. ANNUAIRE OFFICIEL. 1952-19?? a. Societe Pym, 27 rue Hermel, 75018 Paris, France.

798   FR
FEDERATION EQUESTRE FRANCAISE. GUIDE OFFICIEL DU CAVALIER. ceased. irreg. (Federation Equestre Francaise) Editions Bastin-Lavauzelle, 164 Fg. Saint-Honore, 75008 Paris, France.
 Formerly: Federation Francaise des Sports Equestres. Annuaire Officiel (ISSN 0071-4232)

574.192 GW ISSN 0071-4402
     CODEN: FEBPBY
FEDERATION OF EUROPEAN BIOCHEMICAL SOCIETIES. (PROCEEDINGS OF MEETING). 1964-1985. irreg. Federation of European Biochemical Societies, c/o Prof. Karl Decker, Biochemisches Institut, Universitat Freiburg, Hermann-Herder-Str. 7, 7800 Freiburg, Germany.

633 658 CN ISSN 0046-3604
TS2120
FEED AND FARM SUPPLY DEALER. 1920-1988. 4/yr. Sanford Evans Communications Ltd., 1077 St. James St., Box 6900, Winnipeg, Man. R3C 3B1, Canada.

681   GW ISSN 0014-9683
     CODEN: FGRTA3
FEINGERAETETECHNIK; Wissenschaftlich-technische Zeitschrift fuer Entwicklung, Fertigung und Anwendung von Feingeraeten. 1952-1991. m. (Kammer der Technik, Wissenschaftlich-Technische Gesellschaft fuer Mess- und Automatisierungstechnik) Verlag Technik GmbH, Postfach 201, Oranienburger Str. 13-14, 1020 Berlin, Germany.

574   DK ISSN 0109-856X
FELTUNDERSOEGELSE; noter og meddelelser. 1967-1990; suspended. irreg. Midtsjaellands Naturhistoriske Forening, Dronning Margarethesvej 33, DK-4100 Ringsted, Denmark.

305.412 US
FEMINIST WRITERS' GUILD NATIONAL NEWSLETTER. 1977-198? 4/yr. (back issues avail.) Feminist Writers Guild, Box 9396, Berkeley, CA 94709.

613.7 618 UK ISSN 0268-1609
FERTILISATION. ceased 1990. m. (looseleaf format; back issues avail.) Sheffield University Biomedical Information Service (SUBIS), The University, Sheffield S10 2TN, England.

631.8 US ISSN 0071-4631
FERTILIZER TRENDS. 1956-1986. biennial. Tennessee Valley Authority, National Fertilizer & Environmental Research Center, Muscle Shoals, AL 35660-1010.

631.85 FR
FERTILIZERS AND AGRICULTURE. 1947-19?? 3/yr. (processed) International Superphosphate Manufacturers' Association Ltd., 28 rue Marbeuf, 75008 Paris, France.
 Former titles: Bulletin de Documentation; Phosphorus in Agriculture (ISSN 0031-8434)

800 700 US ISSN 0883-9166
E169.12
FESSENDEN REVIEW. vol.10, 1985-1989 (Oct.). q. Reginald A. Fessenden Educational Fund, Inc., Box 7272, San Diego, CA 92107.

398   US
FESTIVALS. 1982-1989 (Mar.). 6/yr. Resource Publications, Inc., 160 E. Virginia St., Ste. 290, San Jose, CA 95112.
 Formerly: Family Festivals (ISSN 0277-6448)

917   US
FESTIVALS SOURCEBOOK; a reference guide to fairs, festivals and celebrations in agriculture, antiques, the arts, theatre and drama, arts and crafts, community, dance, ethnic events, film, folk, food and drink, history, Indians, marine, music, seasons and wildlife. 1977-1990 (3rd ed.). irreg. Gale Research Inc., 835 Penobscot Bldg., Detroit, MI 48226.

658   US
FESTIVITY!. 1988-1990 (vol.3 no.6, June). m. Festivities Publications, Inc., 1205 W. Forsyth St., Jacksonville, FL 32204.

CESSATIONS

612 618 UK ISSN 0261-4650
FETAL PHYSIOLOGY. ceased 1990. m. (looseleaf format; back issues avail.) Sheffield University Biomedical Information Service (SUBIS), The University, Sheffield S10 2TN, England.

305.3
FETISH TIMES. 1974-1991 (Dec.). m. B & D Co., Box 7109, Van Nuys, CA 91409.

665.5 GW
FEUERUNGSTECHNIK, ENERGIE & UMWELT; internationale Fachzeitschrift fuer Oel- und Gasfeuerung. 1963-1989. m. Bundesverband Energie-Umwelt-Feuerungen e.V., Boblingerstr. 18, Stg. 10, Postfach 102731, 7000 Stuttgart 1, Germany.
  Formerly: Feuerungstechnik - Gebaeudetechnik (ISSN 0015-0401)

551.5 CN
FEUILLET METEOROLOGIQUE. 1952-1988 (vol.26). q. Ministere de l'Environnement du Quebec, Direction de la Meteorologie, 2360 Chemin Sainte-Foy, Sainte-Foy, Que. G1V 4H2, Canada.

800 US ISSN 0741-6024
FICTION NETWORK MAGAZINE. 1983-1990. 2/yr. (back issues avail.) Fiction Network, 870 Market St., San Francisco, CA 94102.

808.38 US
FICTION WRITER'S MONTHLY. 1983-1989. 12/yr. Romantic Times Publishing Group, 55 Bergen St., Brooklyn, NY 11201.

640 US ISSN 0898-0039
FIERY FOODS FRONT; a chile industry newsletter. 1988-19?? 10/yr. (back issues avail.) Out West Publishing, 3414-B Constitution N.E., Box 4278, Albuquerque, NM 87196.

800 US
FIFTH SUN. 1979-19?? irreg. Quincunx Press, c/o Max and Nora Benavidez, 3325 Descanso Dr., Los Angeles, CA 90026.

322.4 US
FIGHT THE RIGHT. 1981-198? irreg. Center for Constitutional Rights, 666 Broadway, New York, NY 10012.

382 FJ
FIJI. BUREAU OF STATISTICS. QUARTERLY DIGEST OF OVERSEAS TRADE. 1967-1986 (Sep.); suspended. q. Bureau of Statistics, Box 2221, Suva, Fiji.

919.6 FJ
FIJI HOLIDAY. ceased. m. (tabloid format) Fiji Times Ltd., P.O. Box 1167, Suva, Fiji.
  Formerly: N. Bula Mai.

015 FJ
FIJI NATIONAL BIBLIOGRAPHY. 1979-1986; suspended. a. (back issues avail.) Ministry of Education, Youth and Sport, Library Service of Fiji, P.O. Box 2526, Government Bldg., Suva, Fiji.

800 FR ISSN 0298-7139
FILIGRANE; recherches litteraires et spirituelles. 1986-1989 (vol.4). 2/yr. (back issues avail.) (Centre National des Lettres) Editions Argel, 7 rue Chaudron, 75010 Paris, France.

791.43 US
FILM AND VIDEO MAKERS DIRECTORY. 1973-198? a. Carnegie, Museum of Art, Section of Film and Video, 4400 Forbes Ave., Pittsburgh, PA 15213.

778.5 900 US ISSN 0892-2160
PN1993 CODEN: FIHIE6
FILM HISTORY; an international journal. 1987-1990 (vol.4, no.4). q. Taylor & Francis, 1900 Frost Rd., Ste. 101, Bristol, PA 19007.

150 301 US
FILM - PSYCHOLOGY REVIEW. 1977-1980 (vol.4, no.2). q. (also avail. in microform from UMI; reprint service avail. from UMI) Redgrave Publishing Co. (Subsidiary of: Docent Corp.), Box 67, South Salem, NY 10590.
  Former titles: Film - Psychology (ISSN 0145-9759); (until 1980): Psychocultural Review.

791.43 UK ISSN 0071-4917
FILM REVIEW (LONDON, 1970). 1970-19?? a. W.H. Allen & Co. Ltd., 44 Hill St., London W1X 8LB, England.

791.43 FR ISSN 0294-0957
FILMO. 1983-19?? q. Edition de la Ligue Francaise de l'Enseignement et de l'Education (Edilig), 3 rue Recamier, 75431 Paris Cedex 07, France.

384 UK
FILMS ON VIDEO. 1982-19?? a. Argus Specialist Publications Ltd., Argus House, Boundary Way, Hemels, Hamsptead, Herts HP2 7ST, England.

791.43 AT ISSN 0158-3778
FILMVIEWS; the film users quarterly. 1955-19?? q. (back issues avail.) Australian Catalogue, P.O. Box 204, Albert Park, Vic. 3206, Australia.
  Formerly (until 1980): Federation of Victorian Film Societies. Federation News (ISSN 0046-3582)

491.9 891.9 PL
FILOLOGIA BALTYCKA/BALTIC PHILOLOGY. 1977-1978 (no.3); suspended. irreg. Adam Mickiewicz University Press, Marchlewskiego 128, 61-874 Poznan, Poland.

330.9 UK
THE FINANCE DIRECTOR. 1991-1991(vol.1, issue 14). m. (back issues avail.) Monitor Press, Rectory Rd., Great Waldingfield, Sudbury, Suffolk CO10 OTL, England.
  Formerly: Corporate Financial Letter.

330.9 UK
FINANCE FOR NEW PROJECTS IN UK; guide to private and public sector initiatives and grants. 1975-1985. biennial. Peat Marwick Mitchell & Co., 1 Puddle Dock, Blackfriars, London EC4V 3PD, England.

332.65 US
FINANCIAL ANALYSIS OF A GROUP OF PETROLEUM COMPANIES. 1945-1987. a. Chase Manhattan Bank, Energy Economics Division, One Chase Manhattan Plaza, New York, NY 10015.

388.3 US ISSN 0099-2445
HE5623
FINANCIAL ANALYSIS OF THE MOTOR CARRIER INDUSTRY. 1946-198? a. American Trucking Associations, Inc., Statistical Analysis Department, 2200 Mill Rd., Alexandria, VA 22314.

332 059 RH
FINANCIAL GAZETTE. 1970-19?? w. (newspaper; back issues avail.) Modus Publications (Pvt) Ltd., Throgmorton House, Samora Machel Ave., P.O. Box 1819, Harare, Zimbabwe.
  Formerly: Rhodesian Financial Gazette.

340 CN
FINANCIAL LITIGATION REVIEW. 1987-19?? q. Canadian Institute of Chartered Accountants, 150 Bloor Street West, Toronto, Ont. M5S 2Y2, Canada.

332.1 US
FINANCIAL MANAGER. ceased 1991 (Oct.). m. American Bankers Association, Financial Management Center, 1120 Connecticut Ave., N.W., Washington, DC 20036.
  Formerly (until Jan. 1988): Bank Investments and Funds Management Newsletter.

657 US ISSN 0744-9062
FINANCIAL MANAGERS' STATEMENT. 1979-1992 (Jan.). bi-m. Financial Managers Society, Inc., 8 S. Michigan Ave., K 500, Chicago, IL 60603-3307.
  Formerly: Quarterly Statement.

330 CN
FINANCIAL POST REPORT ON THE NATION; Canada: outlook. 1984-19?? a. Maclean-Hunter Ltd., Business Publication Division, Maclean-Hunter Bldg., 777 Bay St., Toronto, Ont. M5W 1A7, Canada.

330 CN
FINANCIAL POST SURVEY OF PREDECESSOR AND DEFUNCT COMPANIES. 1981-19?? biennial. (Financial Post Co., Ltd.) Maclean-Hunter Ltd., Business Publication Division, Maclean-Hunter Bldg., 777 Bay St., Toronto, Ont. M5W 1A7, Canada.

310 US
FINANCIAL REGISTER. 1987-198? 2/yr. Crain Communications, Inc., 740 N. Rush St., Chicago, IL 60611.

332 340 US ISSN 0895-6359
HG1
FINANCIAL SERVICES YEARBOOK. 1988-1991 (Jan.). a. (reprint service avail. from UMI) (National Center of Financial Services) University of California Press, Journals Division, 2120 Berkeley Way, Berkeley, CA 94720.

330 001.64 US
FINANCIAL TECHNOLOGY NEWS. 1990-1991. 12/yr. Technology News Inc., 150 Nassau St., New York, NY 10038.

330.9 UK ISSN 0142-162X
HF5001
FINANCIAL TIMES WORLD BUSINESS WEEKLY. 1978-19?? w. (back issues avail.) Financial Times Business Information Ltd., Tower House, Southampton St., London WC2E 7HA, England.

332.6 US ISSN 0040-4195
FINANCIAL TREND; the newsweekly of Southwestern industry and investments. 1970-198? w. (tabloid format; also avail. in microfilm from UMI; reprint service avail. from UMI) (Financial Trend, Inc.) Dougery, Jones & Wilder Communications, Inc., 17950 Preston Rd. Ste. 990, Preston Plaza, Dallas, TX 75252.

378 US
FINANCING HIGHER EDUCATION. 1959-1987. irreg. Southern Regional Education Board, 592 Tenth St., N.W., Atlanta, GA 30318-5790.
  Supersedes in part: Southern Regional Education Board. State and Local Revenue Potential (ISSN 0090-8649)

332 PL
FINANSE. 1950-1989 (no.10-12). m. Panstwowe Wydawnictwo Ekonomiczne, Niecala 4A, 00-098 Warsaw, Poland.

332 DK ISSN 0015-2153
FINANSTIDENDE. 1915-1989 (vol.74, no.34). w. Store Kannikestraede 16, DK-1169 Copenhagen K, Denmark.

640 658.8 US
FINDERS KEEPERS (KINSMAN). 1972-19?? m. c/o Fran Verina, Ed., Box 96, Kinsman, OH 44428.

700 US
FINE ARTS WORK CENTER IN PROVINCETOWN. VISUAL CATALOGUE. ceased. a. Fine Arts Work Center in Provincetown, Inc., 24 Pearl St., Box 565, Provincetown, MA 02657.
  Formerly: Fine Arts Work Center in Provincetown. Newsletter.

546 US ISSN 0740-3739
FINE CHEMICALS DIRECTORY. 1985-1986. a. (also avail. in microform from MIM,UMI) Pergamon Press, Inc., 660 White Plains Rd., Tarrytown, NY 10591-5153.

780 US
FINE TIMES. 1979-19?? m. Bam Publications, Inc., 3470 Buskirk Ave., Pleasant Hill, CA 94523.

070 US
FINELINE; the newsletter on journalism ethics. 1989-1991 (Dec.). m. (reprint service avail.) Billy Goat Strut Publishing, Inc., 600 E. Main St., Louisville, KY 40202.

360 FI ISSN 0071-5336
HD7197.3
FINLAND. SOSIAALI- JA TERVEYSMINISTERIO. TUKIMUSOSASTO. SOSIAALISIA ERIKOISTUTKIMUKSIA/FINLAND. MINISTRY OF SOCIAL AFFAIRS AND HEALTH. RESEARCH DEPARTMENT. SPECIAL SOCIAL STUDIES. (Section XXXII of Official Statistics of Finland) 1921-1987. irreg. Ministry of Social Affairs and Health, Research Department - Sosiaali- ja Terveysministerio. Tukimusosasto, Box 303, SF-00171 Helsinki 17, Finland.

314 352.7 FI ISSN 0355-2152
FINLAND. TILASTOKESKUS. ASUNTOTUOTANTO/ FINLAND. STATISTIKCENTRALEN. BOSTADSPRODUKTIONEN/FINLAND. CENTRAL STATISTICAL OFFICE. CONSTRUCTION OF DWELLINGS. (Section XVIII D of Official Statistics of Finland) 1968-1987. a. Central Statistical Office, P.O. Box 504, SF-00101 Helsinki, Finland.

331   FI   ISSN 0430-5280
FINLAND. TYOVOIMAMINISTERIO. TYOVOIMAKATSAUS/ FINLAND. MINISTRY OF LABOUR. LABOUR REPORTS. 1957-1989. 4/yr. Ministry of Labour, Planning Department, P.O. Box 524, SF-00101 Helsinki, Finland.

330   FI   ISSN 0015-2412
FINNFACTS. 1960-1991; suspended. q. Finnfacts Instituutti r.y., Etelainen Makasiinkatu 4, 00130 Helsinki, Finland.

540   FI   ISSN 0303-4100
QD1   CODEN: FCMLAS
FINNISH CHEMICAL LETTERS; short chemical and biochemical communications. 1974-1989. 6/yr. (also avail. in microform from UMI; reprint services avail. from ISI,UMI) Suomen Kemian Seura - Association of Finnish Chemical Societies, Hietaniemenkatu 2, 00100 Helsinki, Finland.
    Formed by the merger of: Suomen Kemistilehti B (ISSN 0371-4101); Finska Kemistsamfundet. Meddelanden.

614.84   UK
FIRE & SECURITY PROTECTION. (Directory avail.) 1938-1991. m. A.E. Morgan Publications Ltd., 9 West St., Epsom, Surrey KT18 7RL, England.
    Formerly: Fire Protection Review (ISSN 0015-2641); Incorporates: Accident Prevention.

614.84   AT
FIRE JOURNAL. 1960-19?? q. (back issues avail.) (Australian Fire Protection Association) General Magazine Company (Australia) Pty. Ltd., P.O. Box 1024, Richmond North, Vic. 3121, Australia.

016.6289 614.84   UK
FIRE SCIENCE ABSTRACTS. 1947-1985 (no.3). q. (also avail. in microfiche) Fire Research Station, Boreham Wood, Herts WD6 2BL, England.
    Formerly (until 1981): References to Scientific Literature on Fire (ISSN 0306-5766)

352.3   US   ISSN 0071-5468
FIRE YEARBOOK. 1961-19?? a. Davis Publishing Co., 2015 McFarland Blvd., E., Tuscaloosa, AL 35405.

617   IT   ISSN 0393-2214
FIRENZE CHIRURGICA/FLORENCE JOURNAL OF SURGERY. (Supplement avail.) 1983-1987. s-a. Akos S.r.L., Via Curtatone, 12, 50123 Florence, Italy.

639.2   GW   ISSN 0428-5018
FISCHWIRT; Zeitschrift fuer die Binnenfischerei. 1948-198? m. Chmielorz GmbH, Postfach 22 29, D-6200 Wiesbaden, Germany.

639.2   US   ISSN 0015-2900
FISH BOAT - SEA FOOD MERCHANDISING; the national magazine of the commercial fishing industry. 1940-19?? q. Journal Publications, Box 1348, Mandevillle, LA 70470.

639.2   US
FISH HEALTH NEWS; a service to the field of fish health research. 1972-1985. q. U.S. Fish & Wildlife Service, Department of the Interior, Washington, DC 20240.

639 016   US
FISHERIES REVIEW; an abstracting service for fishery research and management. 1955-1989 (Sep.). q. U.S. Fish and Wildlife Service, 1025 Penock Pl., Ste. 212, Fort Collins, CO 80524.
    Formerly: Sport Fishery Abstracts (ISSN 0038-786X)

639.2   AT   ISSN 0155-4786
FISHERMAN'S JOURNAL. 1977-19?? bi-m. (Union of Fishermen's Co-Operatives) Rala Publications, 203-205 Darling St., Balmain, N.S.W. 2041, Australia.

639.2   US
FISHERY PRODUCTS REPORT - CALIFORNIA. 1947-19?? 3/wk. (back issues avail.) U.S. National Marine Fisheries Service, Terminal Island Office, Box 3266, Terminal Island, CA 90731.

799.1   US
FISHING AND BOATING ILLUSTRATED; reporting on fresh and salt water fishing. ceased. a. (reprint service avail.) Gallant - Charger Publications, Inc., 34249 Camino Capistrano, Box HH, Capistrano Beach, CA 92624.
    Formerly: Bob Zwirz' Fishing Annual (ISSN 0363-5538)

929   US
FISHING FOR BASS. 1983-1990. q. (looseleaf format; back issues avail.) 5835 Village Forest Ct., Houston, TX 77092.

613.7 641.1   US
FITNESS & DIET. ceased. 4/yr. Runner's World Magazine, Inc., Box 366, Mountain View, CA 94042.

613.7 330   US   ISSN 0887-817X
FITNESS IN BUSINESS. ceased, 1989. bi-m. (also avail. in microform; back issues avail.) Association for Fitness in Business, 310 N. Alabama, Ste. A100, Indianapolis, IN 46204.

810   US   ISSN 0071-5654
PS3511.I9
FITZGERALD - HEMINGWAY ANNUAL. 1969-1979. a. Gale Research Inc., 835 Penobscot Bldg., Detroit, MI 48226.

500   CN   ISSN 0832-6002
FLABBERGAST; the magazine for curious young minds. 1987-19?? 11/yr. Youth Science Foundation, 151 Slater St., Ste. 904, Ottawa, Ont. K1P 5H2, Canada.

949 410   IT
FLAMURI/FLAG. 1950-1988 (no.265-268). irreg. (back issues avail.) Balli Kombetar, Albanian Agrarian-Democratic Party, Casella Postale 525, 00100 Rome, Italy.

659.1   US   ISSN 0882-1925
FLASH (CHICAGO); the magazine for creative information. 1983-1991 (Feb.). bi-m. Macmillan Creative Services Group, 212 W. Superior, Chicago, IL 60610.

027.4   US   ISSN 0015-3508
FLASH (SEATTLE). 1935-1986 (vol.41, no.3). bi-m. Seattle Public Library Staff Association, 1000 4th Ave., Seattle, WA 98104.

051   US
FLATIRON; covering the Flatiron, Gramercy and Union Square historic districts. 1989-1990. m. Flatiron Press, Inc., 56 W. 22nd St., New York, NY 10010.

388.324   US   ISSN 0162-1025
TL165
FLEET OWNER: SMALL FLEET EDITION. 1979-198? m. (also avail. in microform from UMI) McGraw-Hill, Inc., 1221 Ave. of the Americas, New York, NY 10020.

637 636   GW
FLEISCHLEISTUNGSPRUEFUNG FUER RINDER, LEGELEISTUNGSPRUEFUNG FUER HUEHNER, FLEISCHLEISTUNGSPRUEFUNG FUER SCHAFE. 1966-1989. a. Anstalt fuer Leistungspruefungen in der Tierzucht fuer das Land Nordrhein-Westfalen, Im Woeholz 1, 4780 Lippstadt-Eickelborn, Germany.

310   GW
FLENSBURGER STATISTISCHE BLAETTER. 1975-1991. irreg. (2-4/yr.). Stadt Flensburg, Der Magistrat, Amt fuer Stadtentwicklung, Postfach 2742, 2390 Flensburg, Germany.

001.6 629.8   US   ISSN 0732-7471
FLEXIBLE AUTOMATION; the newsletter of automated systems. 1982-1990 (Dec.). m. Box 175, Ho-Ho-Kus, NJ 07423.

000.642   US
FLEXNOTES; the independent newsletter for DataFlex programmers. 1985-1990 (no.15). irreg. (looseleaf format; back issues avail.) Caldwell Computer Enterprises, 1564-A Fitzgerald Dr., Ste. 408, Pinole, CA 94564.

747.4   US   ISSN 1041-2433
N520   CODEN: FCBUE4
FLOOR COVERING BUSINESS. 1928-1990. m. Capital Cities, 825 Seventh Ave., 6th Fl., New York, NY 10019.
    Formerly: Modern Floor Coverings.

362.2   US   ISSN 0094-2294
RC445
FLORIDA. MENTAL HEALTH PROGRAM OFFICE. STATISTICAL REPORT OF HOSPITALS. (Former name of issuing body: Division of Mental Health) 1960-1987; suspended. a. Department of Health and Rehabilitative Services, Alcohol, Drug Abuse and Mental Health Program Office, 1323 Winewood Blvd., Tallahassee, FL 32301.

340   US   ISSN 0164-6427
FLORIDA BAR CASE SUMMARY SERVICE. 1976-1991 (July). w. (back issues avail.) Florida Bar, 650 Apalachee Parkway, Tallahassee, FL 32399-2300.

975   US
FLORIDA ECONOMY. 1977-19?? irreg. Department of Commerce, 107 W. Gaines St., Tallahassee, FL 32399-2000.
    Formerly (until 1984): Florida's Economy.

645   US   ISSN 0274-8983
FLORIDA HOMEFURNISHINGS. 1980-198? 6/yr. Rabcom International, 530 Fifth Ave., Pelham, NY 10806.

051   US   ISSN 0271-6100
F317.M7
FLORIDA KEYS MAGAZINE. 1978-19?? m. Crain Associated Enterprises, 500 N. Dearborn St., Chicago, IL 60610.

647.9   US
FLORIDA LODGING INDUSTRY. 1979-1990. a. Laventhol & Horwath, 1845 Walnut St., Philadelphia, PA 19103.

621   US
FLOW LINES; the fluid mechanics magazine. 1977-19?? s-a. (back issues avail.) T S I Incorporated, 500 Cardigan Rd., Box 64394, St. Paul, MN 55164.
    Supersedes in part (in 1986): T S I Quarterly.

352.7   DK
FLYTNINGER. published only once, 1984. a. Soenderjyllands Amtskommune, Storegade 19, DK-6200 Aabenraa, Denmark.

614   ISSN 0278-1808
FOCAL POINTS. 1975-1981; resumed 1983-19?? irreg. (approx. 6/yr.) U.S. Centers for Disease Control, Center for Health Promotion and Education, 1600 Clifton Rd., Atlanta, GA 30333.

796.357   HU   ISSN 0238-4000
FOCI. 1988-199? w. Hirlapkiado Vallalat, Blaha Lujza ter 3, 1959 Budapest 8, Hungary.

616.863   US
FOCUS - EDUCATION PROFESSIONALS IN FAMILY RECOVERY. 1977-1992. 6/yr. (back issues avail.) U.S. Journal Inc., 3201 S.W. 15th St., Deerfield Beach, FL 33442.
    Former titles: Focus on Family and Chemical Dependence; (until 1984): Focus on Alcohol and Drug Issues (ISSN 0161-4428)

352   US
FOCUS ON.... ceased. irreg. (6-8/yr.). Intergovernmental Health Policy Project, 2021 K St., N.W., Ste. 800, Washington, DC 20006.

950   US   ISSN 0046-4295
DS1
FOCUS ON ASIAN STUDIES. 1963-19?? 3/yr. (Association for Asian Studies, Inc.) Asia Society, 725 Park Ave., New York, NY 10021.

374 338.91   US   ISSN 0899-188X
FOCUS ON BASICS; innovative teaching practices for adults. 1987-1990 (vol.2, no.3). 3/yr. (back issues avail.) World Education, Inc., 210 Lincoln St., Boston, MA 02111.

610.73   US   ISSN 0736-3605
FOCUS ON CRITICAL CARE. 1973-1992 (Apr.). bi-m. (also avail. in microfilm from UMI; back issues avail.; reprint service avail. from UMI) (American Association of Critical-Care Nurses (AACN)) Mosby - Year Book, Inc. (Subsidiary of: Times Mirror Company), 11830 Westline Industrial Dr., St. Louis, MO 63146.
    Formerly (until 1983): Focus on A A C N.

770   AT
FOCUS ON PHOTOGRAPHY. 1979-19?? a. Australian Hi-Fi & Specialist Magazines Group Pty. Ltd., P.O. Box 341, Mona Vale, N.S.W. 2103, Australia.
    Former titles (until 1988): Photoworld Annual (ISSN 0727-3967); Photographic World Annual.

635   US
FOCUS ON PLANTS. 1987-1991. 4/yr. (back issues avail.) Thompson & Morgan, Box 1308, Jackson, NJ 08527.
    Formerly: Growing From Seed.

CESSATIONS

500 600   US
FOCUS ON SCI-TECH. 1972-19?? irreg. Carnegie Library of Pittsburgh, Science and Technology Department, 4400 Forbes Ave., Pittsburgh, PA 15213.

370 970   US
FOCUS ON THE AMERICAS; a newsletter to promote the teaching of the Americas in the schools. 1968-1990. q. Center for the Teaching of the Americas, c/o Sister Mary Consuela, I.H.M., Director, Immaculata College, Immaculata, PA 19345.

370   DK   ISSN 0108-7746
FOCUS PAA UNDERVISNING. 1982-19?? irreg. Arbejderbevaegelsens Skolekontaktudvalg--AOF, Teglvaerksgade 27, 2100 Copenhagen OE, Denmark.

331.88   ISSN 0744-1177
FOCUS QUARTERLY. 1967-1986. q. (tabloid format) Ohio A F L - C I O, 271 E. State St., Columbus, OH 43215.
    Formerly: Focus (Columbus, 1967) (ISSN 0015-5047)

796.332   DK   ISSN 0108-5077
FODBOLDENS AARSREVY. 1957-1988 (no.88). a. Bonniers Specialmagasiner, Strandboulvarden 130, 2100 Copenhagen OE, Denmark.
    Formerly (until 1982): Fodbold Jul.

910.09   US
FODOR'S AMSTERDAM. ceased. a. Fodor's Travel Publications, Inc. (Subsidiary of: Random House, Inc.), 201 E. 50th St., New York, NY 10022.

910.09   US
FODOR'S BED & BREAKFAST GUIDE. ceased. a. Fodor's Travel Publications, Inc. (Subsidiary of: Random House, Inc.), 201 E. 50th St., New York, NY 10022.

917.804   US   ISSN 0276-9018
F774.3
FODOR'S COLORADO. 1981-19?? a. Fodor's Travel Publications, Inc. (Subsidiary of: Random House, Inc.), 201 E. 50th St., New York, NY 10022.

910.09   US
FODOR'S DALLAS - FORT WORTH. ceased. a. Fodor's Travel Publications, Inc. (Subsidiary of: Random House, Inc.), 201 E. 50th St., New York, NY 10022.

917   US   ISSN 0192-3730
F852.2
FODOR'S FAR WEST. 1975-19?? a. Fodor's Travel Publications, Inc. (Subsidiary of: Random House, Inc.), 201 E. 50th St., New York, NY 10022.

910.09   US
FODOR'S FUN IN NEW ORLEANS. ceased. irreg. Fodor's Travel Publications, Inc. (Subsidiary of: Random House, Inc.), 201 E. 50th St., New York, NY 10022.

910.09   US
FODOR'S FUN IN RIO. ceased. irreg. Fodor's Travel Publications, Inc. (Subsidiary of: Random House, Inc.), 201 E. 50th St., New York, NY 10022.

910.09   US
FODOR'S FUN IN SAINT MARTIN. ceased. a. Fodor's Travel Publications, Inc. (Subsidiary of: Random House, Inc.), 201 E. 50th St., New York, NY 10022.

910.09   US
FODOR'S FUN IN THE BAHAMAS. ceased. a. Fodor's Travel Publications, Inc. (Subsidiary of: Random House, Inc.), 201 E. 50th St., New York, NY 10022.

910.09   US
FODOR'S FUN IN THE RIVIERA. ceased. irreg. Fodor's Travel Publications, Inc. (Subsidiary of: Random House, Inc.), 201 E. 50th St., New York, NY 10022.

917.304   US
FODOR'S GREAT TRAVEL VALUES: AMERICAN CITIES. 1971-19?? a. Fodor's Travel Publications, Inc. (Subsidiary of: Random House, Inc.), 201 E. 50th St., New York, NY 10022.
    Former titles: Fodor's American Cities on a Budget; Fodor's Budget Travel in America (ISSN 0192-8287)

917.104   US
FODOR'S GREAT TRAVEL VALUES: CANADA. 1982-19?? a. Fodor's Travel Publications, Inc. (Subsidiary of: Random House, Inc.), 201 E. 50th St., New York, NY 10022.
    Former titles: Fodor's Budget Travel Canada; Fodor's Budget Canada.

919.604   US
FODOR'S GREAT TRAVEL VALUES: CARIBBEAN. 1979-19?? a. Fodor's Travel Publications, Inc. (Subsidiary of: Random House, Inc.), 201 E. 50th St., New York, NY 10022.
    Former titles: Fodor's Budget Travel Caribbean; Fodor's Budget Caribbean (ISSN 0193-9122)

910.09   US
FODOR'S GREAT TRAVEL VALUES: HAWAII. ceased. a. Fodor's Travel Publications, Inc. (Subsidiary of: Random House, Inc.), 201 E. 50th St., New York, NY 10022.

915.204   US
FODOR'S GREAT TRAVEL VALUES: JAPAN. 1980-19?? a. Fodor's Travel Publications, Inc. (Subsidiary of: Random House, Inc.), 201 E. 50th St., New York, NY 10022.
    Former titles: Fodor's Budget Travel Japan; Fodor's Budget Japan (ISSN 0276-2552)

910.09   US
FODOR'S GREAT TRAVEL VALUES: LONDON. ceased. a. Fodor's Travel Publications, Inc. (Subsidiary of: Random House, Inc.), 201 E. 50th St., New York, NY 10022.

917.204   US
FODOR'S GREAT TRAVEL VALUES: MEXICO. 1979-19?? a. Fodor's Travel Publications, Inc. (Subsidiary of: Random House, Inc.), 201 E. 50th St., New York, NY 10022.
    Former titles: Fodor's Budget Travel Mexico; Fodor's Budget Mexico (ISSN 0196-1829)

914.604   US
FODOR'S GREAT TRAVEL VALUES: SPAIN. 1979-19?? a. Fodor's Travel Publications, Inc. (Subsidiary of: Random House, Inc.), 201 E. 50th St., New York, NY 10022.
    Former titles: Fodor's Budget Travel Spain; Fodor's Budget Spain (ISSN 0270-7888)

910.202   US
FODOR'S HOUSTON & GALVESTON. ceased. a. Fodor's Travel Publications, Inc. (Subsidiary of: Random House, Inc.), 201 E. 50th St., New York, NY 10022.

910.09   US
FODOR'S INTERSTATE - 10. ceased. irreg. Fodor's Travel Publications, Inc. (Subsidiary of: Random House, Inc.), 201 E. 50th St., New York, NY 10022.

910.09   US
FODOR'S INTERSTATE - 55. ceased. irreg. Fodor's Travel Publications, Inc. (Subsidiary of: Random House, Inc.), 201 E. 50th St., New York, NY 10022.

910.202   US
FODOR'S INTERSTATE - 75. ceased. irreg. Fodor's Travel Publications, Inc. (Subsidiary of: Random House, Inc.), 201 E. 50th St., New York, NY 10022.

210.202   US
FODOR'S INTERSTATE - 80. ceased. irreg. Fodor's Travel Publications, Inc. (Subsidiary of: Random House, Inc.), 201 E. 50th St., New York, NY 10022.

210.202   US
FODOR'S INTERSTATE - 95. ceased. irreg. Fodor's Travel Publications, Inc. (Subsidiary of: Random House, Inc.), 201 E. 50th St., New York, NY 10022.

210.202   US
FODOR'S JORDAN & THE HOLY LAND. ceased. irreg. Fodor's Travel Publications, Inc. (Subsidiary of: Random House, Inc.), 201 E. 50th St., New York, NY 10022.

914.69   US
FODOR'S LISBON. 1984-19?? a. Fodor's Travel Publications, Inc. (Subsidiary of: Random House, Inc.), 201 E. 50th St., New York, NY 10022.

910.202   US
FODOR'S LOIRE VALLEY. ceased. irreg. Fodor's Travel Publications, Inc. (Subsidiary of: Random House, Inc.), 201 E. 50th St., New York, NY 10022.

910.202   US
FODOR'S MEXICO CITY & ACAPULCO. ceased. a. Fodor's Travel Publications, Inc. (Subsidiary of: Random House, Inc.), 201 E. 50th St., New York, NY 10022.

910.202   US
FODOR'S NINETEEN THIRTY-SIX ON THE CONTINENT. ceased. irreg. Fodor's Travel Publications, Inc. (Subsidiary of: Random House, Inc.), 201 E. 50th St., New York, NY 10022.

910.202   US
FODOR'S PROVINCE OF QUEBEC. ceased. irreg. Fodor's Travel Publications, Inc. (Subsidiary of: Random House, Inc.), 201 E. 50th St., New York, NY 10022.

910.202   US
FODOR'S ROCKIES. ceased. irreg. Fodor's Travel Publications, Inc. (Subsidiary of: Random House, Inc.), 201 E. 50th St., New York, NY 10022.

910.202   US
FODOR'S ROYALTY WATCHING GUIDE. ceased. irreg. Fodor's Travel Publications, Inc. (Subsidiary of: Random House, Inc.), 201 E. 50th St., New York, NY 10022.

910.202   US
FODOR'S SELECTED HOTELS OF EUROPE. ceased. irreg. Fodor's Travel Publications, Inc. (Subsidiary of: Random House, Inc.), 201 E. 50th St., New York, NY 10022.

910.202   US
FODOR'S SELECTED RESORTS & HOTELS OF THE U.S.. ceased. irreg. Fodor's Travel Publications, Inc. (Subsidiary of: Random House, Inc.), 201 E. 50th St., New York, NY 10022.

910.202   US
FODOR'S SYDNEY. ceased. a. Fodor's Travel Publications, Inc. (Subsidiary of: Random House, Inc.), 201 E. 50th St., New York, NY 10022.

910.202   US
FODOR'S TEXAS. ceased. a. Fodor's Travel Publications, Inc. (Subsidiary of: Random House, Inc.), 201 E. 50th St., New York, NY 10022.

910.202   US
FODOR'S VIEWS TO DINE BY AROUND THE WORLD. ceased. irreg. Fodor's Travel Publications, Inc. (Subsidiary of: Random House, Inc.), 201 E. 50th St., New York, NY 10022.

910.202   US
FODOR'S WILLIAMSBURG, JAMESTOWN & YORKTOWN. ceased. irreg. Fodor's Travel Publications, Inc. (Subsidiary of: Random House, Inc.), 201 E. 50th St., New York, NY 10022.

320   AU
FOEDERALISMUS-STUDIEN. 1977-1978. irreg. Boehlau Verlag GmbH & Co.KG., Dr. Karl Lueger-Ring 12, Postfach 581a, A-1011 Vienna, Austria.

676.3   US   ISSN 0738-761X
FOLDING CARTON. 1968-19?? 10/yr. (back issues avail.) E. Gilbert Mathews, Inc., 274 Tanner Marsh Rd., Guilford, CT 06437.

616.97   IT   ISSN 0303-8432
CODEN: FAICAZ
FOLIA ALLERGOLOGICA ET IMMUNOLOGICA CLINICA. 1953-1990. bi-m. (also avail. in microform) (Societa Italiana di Allergologia e Immunologia Clinica) Lombardo Editore, Via Verona, 22, 00161 Rome, Italy.
    Formerly: Folia Allergologica (ISSN 0015-5470)

616.15   GW   ISSN 0323-4347
FOLIA HAEMATOLOGICA; internationales Magazin fuer klinische und experimentelle Blutforschung. 1904-1991. 6/yr. (Gesellschaft fuer Haematologie und Bluttransfusion) Akademische Verlagsgesellschaft Geest und Portig K.G., Sternwartenstr. 8, 7010 Leipzig, Germany.

616.8   IT
FOLIA NEUROPSYCHIATRICA. suspended. s-a. (back issues avail.) Direzione Sanitatria, Via Miglietta, Lecce, Italy.

410   US   ISSN 0160-9394
PG1
FOLIA SLAVICA. 1977-198? (vol.8); suspended. irreg. (approx. 3/yr.). (back issues avail.) Slavica Publishers, Inc., Box 14388, Columbus, OH 43214.

781.7   UK
FOLK MUSIC NEWS. 1982-19?? m. Goldcity Ltd., 28 Gordon Mansions, Torrington Place, London WC1E 7HF, England.

027.4   DK   ISSN 0105-6077
FOLKEBIBLIOTEKSSTATISTIK, BUDGETTER, VIRKSOMHED. 1977-1988. a. Bibliotekstilsynet - Directorate for Public Libraries, Nyhavn 31 E,3, DK-1051 Copenhagen K, Denmark.

948.9   DK   ISSN 0900-3037
FOLKESAGN I TEKST OG BILLED FRA NOERREHERRED. 1983-1988. a. Forlag i Stalden, Nyboelle Strand, 4913 Horslunde, Denmark.

055.1   IT
FONDAZIONE GIORGIO CINI. NOTIZIE. 1977-198?; suspended. s-a. (tabloid format; back issues avail.) Fondazione Giorgio Cini, Isola S. Giorgio Maggiore, I-30124 Venice, Italy.

664.06 340   UK
FOOD ADDITIVES - DESCRIPTIONS, FUNCTIONS AND U.K. LEGISLATIONS. 1976-198? irreg. British Food Manufacturing Industries Research Association, Randalls Rd., Leatherhead, Surrey, KT22 7RY, England.

630 338.1   UN   ISSN 0532-0194
FOOD AND AGRICULTURE ORGANIZATION OF THE UNITED NATIONS. AGRICULTURAL PLANNING STUDIES. 1963-198? irreg. Food and Agriculture Organization of the United Nations, c/o UNIPUB, 4611-F Assembly Dr., Lanham, MD 20706-4391.

664 615   CN
FOOD & DRUG PACKAGING NEWS. 1981-1990. q. Maclean Hunter Ltd., Business Publication Division, Maclean-Hunter Bldg., 777 Bay St., Toronto, Ont. M5W 1A7, Canada.
   Formerly: Food and Drug Product News.

331 614.7   US   ISSN 0885-0704
FOOD & JUSTICE. 1984-1992; suspended. m. (back issues avail.) United Farm Workers of America, Box 62, La Paz, Keene, CA 93531.

664   UN   ISSN 0304-8942
TX341
FOOD AND NUTRITION. 1974-19??; suspended. 2/yr. Food and Agriculture Organization of the United Nations, Sales & Distribution Section, Via delle Terme di Caracalla, 00100 Rome, Italy.
   Supersedes: Nutrition Newsletter (ISSN 0428-9447)

664   US   ISSN 0895-3090
HV696.F6
FOOD FIRST DEVELOPMENT REPORTS. 1987-1989 (no.6). 4/yr. (Institute for Food and Development Policy) Food First Books, 145 Ninth St., San Francisco, CA 94103.

362.8 641.1   US
FOOD FOR THOUGHT (ANN ARBOR). ceased 198? 4/yr. Michigan Federation of Food Co-Operatives, 209 S. Fourth Ave., Ann Arbor, MI 48104.

664 382   PL   ISSN 0015-6418
TX360.P7
FOOD FROM POLAND; review of exports of agricultural products and foodstuffs from Poland. 1964-19?? q. AGPOL - Polexportpress, Ul. Marszalkowska 124, 00-950 Warsaw, Poland.

664   SA
FOOD INDUSTRIES YEARBOOK AND BUYERS' GUIDE. 1952-19?? biennial. Thomson Publications (Subsidiary of: Times Media Ltd.), Thomson House, 83 Hendrik Verwoerd Dr., Randburg 2194, P.O. Box 56182, Pinegowrie 2123, South Africa.
   Former titles: Food Industries Yearbook and Buyers' Directory; Food Industries of S.A. Buyers' Guide (ISSN 0071-7185); Food Industries of South Africa Manual and Buyer's Guide.

664 658.8   UK
FOOD PROCESSING (BRISTOL). 1984-19?? irreg. Jordan & Sons Ltd., 21 St. Thomas St., Bristol BS1 6JS, England.

647.95   US   ISSN 0892-757X
FOOD SERVICE FORUM. 1986-198? m. (back issues avail.) Chase Communications Group, Ltd., 25-35 Beechwood Ave., Box 9001, Mount Vernon, NY 10552-9001.

305.2   US
FOOT WORSHIP. 1984-1991 (Dec.). s-a. B & D Co., Box 7109, Van Nuys, CA 91409.

305.2   US
FOOT WORSHIP NEWS. 1989-1991 (Dec.). bi-m. B & D Co., Box 7109, Van Nuys, CA 91409.

796.332   US
FOOTBALL INSIGHT; inside stats for serious fans. 1985-19?? w. (looseleaf format; back issues avail.) Parrish Publishers, Box 23205, Portland, OR 97223.

020 910.09   US   ISSN 0733-3196
FOOTLOOSE LIBRARIAN. 1981-1991 (May). bi-m. (except Jul.-Aug.). (back issues avail.) Balmy Press, Box 972, Minneapolis, MN 55458.

685.31   US
FOOTWEAR COUNCIL. BULLETINS. ceased. irreg. Footwear Council, 51 E. 42nd St., Rm. 1803, New York, NY 10017.

685.31   US
FOOTWEAR COUNCIL. NEWSLETTER. ceased. irreg. Footwear Council, 51 E. 42nd St., Rm. 1803, New York, NY 10017.

675 685.31   FR
FOOTWEAR, RAW HIDES AND SKINS, AND LEATTHER INDUSTRY IN O E C D COUNTRIES.. 1950-1985. irreg. (also avail. in microfiche) Organization for Economic Cooperation and Development, 2 rue Andre-Pascal, 75775 Paris Cedex 16, France.
   Formerly: Hides, Skins and Footwear Indusrty in O E C D Countries - Industrie des Cuirs et Peaux et de la Chaussure dans les Pays de l'O C D E (ISSN 0474-585X)

323.4   US
FOR THE PEOPLE. 1976-1982. 4/yr. (when Congress is in session). Congressional Black Caucus, 306 House of Representatives, Annex 1, Washington, DC 20515.

362.11   DK   ISSN 0107-7627
RA989.D4
FORBRUGET AF SOMATISKE SENGEPLADSER. 1982-1985. a. Sundhedsstyrelsen, Amaliegade 13, 1012 Copenhagen K, Denmark.

629.13 016   JA   ISSN 0454-191X
FOREIGN AERO-SPACE LITERATURE/GAIKOKU KOKU UCHU BUNKEN MOKUROKU. 1962-1983; suspended. a. National Diet Library - Kokuritsu Kokkai Toshokan, 1-10-1 Nagata-cho, Chiyoda-ku, Tokyo 100, Japan.

327   GW   ISSN 0015-7139
FOREIGN AFFAIRS BULLETIN. 1960-1991. every 10 days. Ministerium fuer Auswaertige Angelegenheiten, Hauptabteilung Presse, Marz-Engels-Platz 2, 1020 Berlin, Germany.

608.7 500 600 016   JA   ISSN 0015-721X
FOREIGN CHEMICAL PATENT NEWS/GAIKOKU TOKKYO SOKUHO, KAGAKU-HEN. 1958-1988 (vol.30, no.52). w. Japan Information Center of Science and Technology - Nihon Kagaku Gijutsu Joho Senta, 5-2 Nagata-cho, 2-chome, Chiyoda-ku, Tokyo 100, Japan.

330.9   US   ISSN 0090-9467
HC10
FOREIGN ECONOMIC TRENDS AND THEIR IMPLICATIONS FOR THE UNITED STATES. ceased. irreg. (also avail. in microform from UMI; reprint service avail. from UMI) U.S. National Technical Information Service, 5285 Port Royal Rd., Springfield, VA 22161.
   Formerly: Economic Trends and Their Implications for the United States.

327   US
FOREIGN POLICY PREVIEW. 1986-1991. m. Foreign Policy Association, 729 Seventh Ave., New York, NY 10019.

327   US
FOREIGN POLICY RESEARCH INSTITUTE ANNUAL REPORT. 1957-1989. a. Foreign Policy Research Institute, 3615 Chestnut St., Philadelphia, PA 19104.

382 665   US   ISSN 0363-6798
FOREIGN TRADE REPORTS. BUNKER FUELS. (Series FT-810) 1948-1989. m. and a. (also avail. in microform) U.S. Bureau of the Census, Foreign Trade Division, Washington, DC 20233.

382 677.2   US
FOREIGN TRADE REPORTS. GENERAL IMPORTS OF COTTON, WOOL AND MANMADE FIBER MANUFACTURERS. (Series FT-130) 1957-1986 (Dec.). m. U.S. Bureau of the Census, Foreign Trade Division, Washington, DC 20233.
   Formerly: Foreign Trade Reports. General Imports of Cotton Manufactures (ISSN 0094-7520)

382   US   ISSN 0095-7771
HF105
FOREIGN TRADE REPORTS. U.S. AIRBORNE EXPORTS AND GENERAL IMPORTS. (Series FT 986) ceased. m. U.S. Bureau of the Census, Foreign Trade Division, Washington, DC 20233.

382   US
FOREIGN TRADE REPORTS. U.S. IMPORTS FOR CONSUMPTION AND GENERAL IMPORTS-TSUSA COMMODITY BY COUNTRY OF ORIGIN: ANNUAL (YEAR). (Tariff Schedules of the United States Annotated) (Series FT-246) 1965-1988 (Dec.). a. U.S. Bureau of the Census, Foreign Trade Division, Washington, DC 20233.
   Formerly: Foreign Trade Reports. U.S. Imports for Consumption and General Imports; Tariff Schedules Annotated by Country (ISSN 0565-1190)

382   US
FOREIGN TRADE REPORTS. VESSEL ENTRANCES AND CLEARANCES. (Series FT 975) 1945-1987 (Dec.). a. (m. until 1951). U.S. Bureau of the Census, Foreign Trade Div., Washington, DC 20233.

382 316   UN   ISSN 0071-7401
FOREIGN TRADE STATISTICS OF AFRICA. SERIES B: TRADE BY COMMODITY. 1962-1982 (no.32). irreg. United Nations Economic Commission for Africa - Commission Economique pour l'Afrique, P.O. Box 3001, Addis Ababa, Ethiopia.

658.3   US   ISSN 0015-7333
FOREMAN'S LETTER. 1943-198? s-m. (looseleaf format) Bureau of Business Practice, 24 Rope Ferry Rd., Waterford, CT 06386.

624   UK   ISSN 0888-8817
TA219
FORENSIC ENGINEERING; structures, foundations, materials, construction, machinery and policy. 1987-1991. q. (also avail. in microform) Pergamon Press plc, Headington Hill Hall, Oxford OX3 0BW, England.

614.19   US   ISSN 0046-4570
         CODEN: FSGADC
FORENSIC SCIENCE GAZETTE. 1970-1980; N.S. 1984-1986 (vol.3, no.3); suspended. 4/yr. (also avail. in microform from UMI; reprint service avail. from UMI) Southwestern Institute of Forensic Sciences, Box 35728, Dallas, TX 75235.

658   US
FORESIGHT (NEW YORK). 1986-198? m. American Management Association, 135 W. 50th St., New York, NY 10020-1201.

634.96 595.7   CN   ISSN 0826-0532
FOREST PEST MANAGEMENT INSTITUTE. TECHNICAL NOTE SERIES. 1984-1987 (no.9). irreg. Forestry Canada, Forest Pest Management Institute, P.O. Box 490, 1219 Queen St. E., Sault Ste. Marie, Ont. P6A 5M7, Canada.

574 540 614.7 634.9CN
FOREST PEST MANAGEMENT INSTITUTE PROGRAM REVIEW. 1982-1988. a. Forest Pest Management Institute, Forestry Canada, 1219 Queen St. E., P.O. Box 490, Sault Ste. Marie, Ont. P6A 5M7, Canada.

634.9   US
FOREST WORLD. 1985-1990. a. World Forestry Center, 4033 S.W. Canyon Rd., Portland, OR 97221.
   Formerly (until 1984): Western Forestry Center. Annual Report.

CESSATIONS

332.6   US
FOREX WAVES AND CYCLES. 1987-1990. s-m. M M S International, 1301 Shoreway Rd., Ste. 300, Belmont, CA 94002.

674   CN   ISSN 0821-1841
FORINTEK REVIEW. 1981-1989 (vol.3, no.3). 6/yr. Forintek Canada Corp., 6620 N.W. Marine Dr., Vancouver, B.C. V6T 1X2, Canada.
    Formerly (until 1983): Wood Technology Notes (ISSN 0227-1001)

001.64   GW
FORKEL - NACHRICHTEN AUS INFORMATIK UND WIRTSCHAFT. 1988-1991. 2/yr. (back issues avail.) Forkel Verlag GmbH, Felsenstr. 23, Postfach 2120, 6200 Wiesbaden-Dotzheim, Germany.

809   IT   ISSN 0390-2153
FORME DEL SIGNIFICATO. 1972-1984 (no.31). irreg. Liguori Editore s.r.l., Via Mezzocannone 19, 80134 Naples, Italy.

658   NO   ISSN 0071-7630
FORRETNINGS- OG BEDRIFTSLEDEREN. 1959-198? a. Forlaget Tanum-Norli A-S, Kr. Augustsgt. 7A, Oslo 1, Norway.

371.42   GW   ISSN 0323-4711
FORSCHUNG DER SOZIALISTISCHEN BERUFSBILDUNG. 1967-19?? 6/yr. Zentralinstitut fuer Berufsbildung der Deutschen Demokratischen Republik, Reinhold-Huhn-Str. 5, 1086 Berlin, Germany.

370   GW   ISSN 0323-326X
FORSCHUNG, LEHRE, PRAXIS. ceased 1990. m. Tribune Verlag, Am Treptower Park 28-30, 1193 Berlin, Germany.

800   GW   ISSN 0071-7703
FORSCHUNGSPROBLEME DER VERGLEICHENDEN LITERATURGESCHICHTE. 1951-1978 (no.7). irreg. (back issues avail.) Max Niemeyer Verlag, Pfrondorfer Str. 4, 7400 Tuebingen, Germany.

635   DK   ISSN 0106-2573
FORSKNINGSLABORATORIET FOR FRUGT OG GROENTINDUSTRI. AARSBERETNING. 1970-198? a. Ministry of Agriculture, Institut of Pomology, Kirstinebjergvej 12, DK-5792 Aarslev, Denmark.

355   DK   ISSN 0106-2093
FORSVAR: MILITAER KRITISK MAGASIN. 1980-1985. 3/yr. Militar- og Noegterforeningen, Dramingesngade 14, DK-1420 Copenhagen K, Denmark.

028.5   US   ISSN 0000-0965
FORTHCOMING CHILDREN'S BOOKS; pre-K through grade 12. 1987-1989 (vol.3, no.4). bi-m. R.R. Bowker, A Reed Reference Publishing Company, Division of Reed Publishing (USA) Inc., 121 Chanlon Rd., New Providence, NJ 07941.

616.6   GW
FORTSCHRITTE DER UROLOGIE UND NEPHROLOGIE. 1970-1987 (vol.26). irreg. Dr. Dietrich Steinkopff Verlag, Saalbaustr. 12, Postfach 11 14 42, 6100 Darmstadt 11, Germany.

296   IS   ISSN 0334-2506
DS149.A1
FORUM; a quarterly on the Jewish people, Zionism and Israel. 1963-19?? q. (also avail. in microform from UMI; reprint service avail. from UMI) World Zionist Organization, Department of Information, P.O. Box 92, Jerusalem 91920, Israel.
    Formerly: Dispersion and Unity (ISSN 0070-6701)

200   GW   ISSN 0722-7647
FORUM (AACHEN); mit Pfarrgemeineraeten unterwegs. 1973-19?? q. (looseleaf format; back issues avail.) Bergmoser und Hoeller Verlag GmbH, Karl-Friedrich-Str. 76, 5100 Aachen, Germany.

684.1   US
FORUM (WAYLAND). 1980-1987 (Oct.). q. Gunlocke Company, One Gunlocke Dr., Wayland, NY 14572.

581   SA   ISSN 0015-847X
FORUM BOTANICUM. 1962-1990 (vol.28, no.2). bi-m. (processed) South African Association of Botanists, Private Bag X101, Pretoria 0001, South Africa.
    Formerly: South African Forum Botanicum.

370   BL   ISSN 0100-9591
LB7
FORUM EDUCACIONAL. 1977-1990 (vol.14, no.3). 4/yr. (Instituto de Estudos Avancados en Educacao) Fundacao Getulio Vargas, C.P. 9052, 22250 Rio de Janeiro, Brazil.

320   GW
FORUM EUROPA; Zeitschrift fuer transnationale Politik. 1972-1989. q. (back issues avail.) (Junge Europaeische Foederalisten) Forum Europa Verlag, Berliner Platz 1, 5300 Bonn 1, Germany.

331.1   US
FORUM U S A. ceased. irreg. (World Arbitration Institute) American Arbitration Association, 140 W. 51st St., New York, NY 10020-1203.

320   US   ISSN 0896-2707
FORWARD (OAKLAND); journal of Socialist thought. 1978-198?; suspended. s-a. Getting Together Publications, Box 29293, Oakland, CA 94604.

694   IT   ISSN 0393-5167
FORWOOD INTERNATIONAL. 1977-19?? s-a. Editore Rima s.r.l., Via Luigi Barzini 20, 20125 Milan, Italy.
    Formerly: Informobili Middle East.

665.5   US   ISSN 0146-4299
Z5853.P83
FOSSIL ENERGY UPDATE. 1976-19?? m. U.S. Department of Energy, Office of Scientific and Technical Information, Box 62, Oak Ridge, TN 37831.

770   IO   ISSN 0126-057X
FOTO INDONESIA. 1972-19?? bi-m. Yayasan Foto Indonesia, Jalan Pandu 28, Bandung, Indonesia.

770   DK   ISSN 0108-0016
FOTO-REVYEN. 1982-1985. a. Bonnier Specialmagasiner, Strandboulevarden 130, 2100 Copenhagen Oe, Denmark.

770   GW   ISSN 0015-8836
FOTOGRAFIE; Zeitschrift fuer kulturpolitische, aesthetische und technische Probleme der Fotografie. 1947-1991. m. Fotokinoverlag Leipzig, Postfach 67, 7031 Leipzig, Germany.

010 060   US
FOUNDATION DIRECTORY SUPPLEMENT. 1982-198? biennial. Foundation Center, 79 Fifth Ave., New York, NY 10003.

361.73   US   ISSN 0735-2522
FOUNDATION GRANTS INDEX BIMONTHLY. 1983-198? bi-m. Foundation Center, 79 Fifth Ave., New York, NY 10003.
    Formerly: Foundation Grants Index Bibliography.

310   US
FOUNDATION 500. 1974-1986. a. (Foundation Research Service) Douglas M. Lawson Associates, Inc., 545 Madison Ave., New York, NY 10022.

669   US   ISSN 0269-7890
FOUNDRY FOCUS. 1986-1990. 3/yr. (back issues avail.) Metal Bulletin Inc., 220 Fifth Ave., 10 Fl., New York, NY 10001.

671   UK   ISSN 0015-9050
FOUNDRY WORKER. ceased. bi-m. Amalgamated Union of Engineering Workers, Foundry Section, 43 Crescent, Salford, Manchester M5 4PE, England.

388.3   US
FOUR WHEELER SPECIALS. ceased 198? q. Penthouse International Ltd., 1965 Broadway, New York, NY 10023.

810   US   ISSN 0362-0247
FOUR ZOAS; journal of poetry and letters. 1972-1990? irreg. High Meadow Press, Middletown Springs, VT 05757.

616.99 616.99   US
FOX CHASE. 1980-198?; suspended. q. Fox Chase Cancer Center, 7701 Burholme Ave., Philadelphia, PA 19111.

621.381   US
FOX 20. ceased 1983. m. Foxfire Systems, Inc., c/o Ronald K. Wray, 3109 Park Shadow, Deer Park, TX 77536-5281.

796.7 305.412   US
FOXYRIDERS. 1989-19?? 2/yr. Paisano Publications, Inc., Box 3000, Agoura Hills, CA 91301.

339   GW
FRAGEN DES SOZIALISTISCHEN WELTSYSTEMS. ceased 1990. a. Akademie fuer Staats- und Rechtswissenschaft, August-Bebel-Str. 89, 1502 Potsdam-Babelsberg, Germany.

847   FR   ISSN 0015-9379
FRANC-RIRE. 1957-19?? bi-m. Editions Rouff, 36 rue du Vieux-Pont-De-Sevres, 92100 Boulogne-Billancourt, France.

551   FR   ISSN 0755-6365
FRANCE. BUREAU DE RECHERCHES GEOLOGIQUES ET MINIERES. AGENCE FRANCAISE POUR LA MAITRISE DE L'ENERGIE. GEOTHERMIE-ACTUALITES. 1961; N.S. 1968-19?? q. Bureau de Recherches Geologiques et Minieres, Division Edition et Vente, B.P. 6009, 45060 Orleans cedex, France.
    Supersedes (in 1983): France. Bureau de Recherches Geologiques et Minieres. Bulletin. Section 2: Geologie des Cite Mineraux (ISSN 0153-6540); Former titles: France. Bureau de Recherches Geologiques et Minieres. Bulletin. Section 2. Geologie Appliquee-Chronique des Mines (ISSN 0300-9351); France. Bureau de Recherches Geologiques et Minieres. Bulletin. Section 2. Geologie Appliquee (ISSN 0007-6090); Chronique des Mines et de la Recherche Miniere (ISSN 0009-6075)

636.089   FR   ISSN 0249-5740
FRANCE. CENTRE DE RECHERCHE ZOOTECHNIQUE. DEPARTEMENT DE GENETIQUE ANIMALE. BULLETIN TECHNIQUE. 1968-19?? irreg. Centre de Recherche Zootechnique, Departement de Genetique Animale, 78352 Jouy en Josas, France.
    Formerly: France. Centre de Recherche Zoologique. Departement de Genetique Animale. Bulletin Technique.

944 338.9   FR   ISSN 0071-8491
FRANCE. COMMISSION NATIONALE DE L'AMENAGEMENT DU TERRITOIRE. RAPPORT. 1964-1981. irreg. Documentation Francaise, 29-31 Quai Voltaire, 75340 Paris cedex 07, France.

330 310   FR   ISSN 0533-0793
HC271
FRANCE. INSTITUT NATIONAL DE LA STATISTIQUE ET DES ETUDES ECONOMIQUES. COLLECTIONS. SERIE C, COMPTES ET PLANIFICATION. 1968-1989 (no.153). 8/yr. Institut National de la Statistique et des Etudes Economiques, 18 bd. A. Pinard, 75675 Paris 14, France.

312 331   FR   ISSN 0533-0807
HC271
FRANCE. INSTITUT NATIONAL DE LA STATISTIQUE ET DES ETUDES ECONOMIQUES. COLLECTIONS. SERIE D, DEMOGRAPHIE ET EMPLOI. 1969-1989 (no.131). irreg. Institut National de la Statistique et des Etudes Economiques, 18 bd. A. Pinard, 75675 Paris, France.

330 314   FR   ISSN 0533-0815
HC271
FRANCE. INSTITUT NATIONAL DE LA STATISTIQUE ET DES ETUDES ECONOMIQUES. COLLECTIONS. SERIE E, ENTERPRISES. ceased 1988 (no.117). 8/yr. Institut National de la Statistique et des Etudes Economiques, 18 bd. A. Pinard, 75675 Paris 14, France.

330 310   FR   ISSN 0533-0823
FRANCE. INSTITUT NATIONAL DE LA STATISTIQUE ET DES ETUDES ECONOMIQUES. COLLECTIONS. SERIE M, MENAGES. 1968-1989 (no.140). 10/yr. Institut National de la Statistique et des Etudes Economiques, 18 bd. A. Pinard, 75675 Paris 14, France.

314   FR   ISSN 0533-0831
FRANCE. INSTITUT NATIONAL DE LA STATISTIQUE ET DES ETUDES ECONOMIQUES. COLLECTIONS. SERIE R, REGIONS. 1968-1989 (no.68). 4/yr. Institut National de la Statistique et des Etudes Economiques, 18 bd. A. Pinard, 75675 Paris 14, France.

CESSATIONS

330 016   FR
FRANCE. SERVICE DE RELATIONS PUBLIQUES ET D'INFORMATION. BIBLIOTHEQUE CENTRALE. LISTE MENSUELLE D'ACQUISITIONS D'OUVRAGES. SELECTION HEBDOMADAIRE D'ARTICLES ECONOMIQUES. ceased. w. Ministere de l'Industrie et de la Recherche, Service de Relations Publiques et d'Information, Bibliotheque Centrale, 101 rue de Grenelle, 75007 Paris, France.

330 016   FR
FRANCE. SERVICE DU TRAITEMENT DE L'INFORMATION ET DES STATISTIQUES INDUSTRIELLES. BIBLIOTHEQUE CENTRALE. BULLETIN BIBLIOGRAPHIQUE. 1978-19?? m. Service du Traitement de l'Information et des Statistiques Industrielles, Bibliotheque Centrale, 101 rue de Grenelle, 75007 Paris, France.

330 016   FR
FRANCE. SERVICE DU TRAITEMENT DE L'INFORMATION ET DES STATISTIQUES INDUSTRIELLES. BIBLIOTHEQUE CENTRALE. SELECTION HEBDOMADAIRE D'ARTICLES ECONOMIQUES. ceased. w. Service du Traitement de l'Information et des Statistiques Industrielles, Bibliotheque Centrale, 101 rue de Grenelle, 75007 Paris, France.

297 914.406   FR
FRANCE - ISLAM. ceased 1977. m. Amicale des Musulmans en Europe, 59 rue Claude Bernard, 75005 Paris, France.

440 370   UK   ISSN 0015-9417
FRANCE - LOISIRS. ceased. m.(during school term). Mary Glasgow Publications Ltd., 140 Kensington Church St., London W.8, England.
Formerly: France.

338   US
FRANCHISING IN THE ECONOMY. (Formerly issued by U.S. Bureau of Industrial Economics) ceased. a. U.S. Department of Commerce, I T A Service Industries Division, Washington, DC 20230.

658.8   US
FRANCHISING OPPORTUNITIES HANDBOOK. ceased. a. U.S. Department of Commerce, I T A-Service Industries Division, Washington, DC 20230.

491.7   GW   ISSN 0473-5277
FRANKFURTER ABHANDLUNGEN ZUR SLAVISTIK. ceased 1977 (vol.24). irreg. Franz Steiner Verlag Wiesbaden GmbH, Birkenwaldstr. 44, Postfach 10 15 26, 7000 Stuttgart 1, Germany.

901   GW
FRANZ DELITZSCH - VORLESUNGEN. NEUE FOLGE. 1978-1990. irreg. Verlag Lambert Schneider, Hausackerweg 16, 6900 Heidelberg, Germany.

322   GW   ISSN 0016-0229
FRAUEN DER GANZEN WELT. 1952-1990. q. (Women's International Democratic Federation) Verlag fuer die Frau, Friedrich-Ebert-Str. 76-78, 7010 Leipzig, Germany.

376   GW   ISSN 0177-4042
FRAUEN UND SCHULE; Zeitschrift fuer Maedchen- und Frauenbildung. 1984-1989. q. Frauen und Schule Verlag, Lachmannstr. 4, 1000 Berlin 61, Germany.

570 610   GW   ISSN 0342-1953
FRAUNHOFER-GESELLSCHAFT. BERICHTE. 1977-1990. q. (looseleaf format) Fraunhofer-Gesellschaft, Leonzodstr. 54, 8000 Munich 19, Germany.
Supersedes: Fraunhofer Gesellschaft. Mitteilungsblatt.

333.33   US   ISSN 0749-4645
FREDDIE MAC REPORTS; a monthly review of events occurring in the secondary mortgage market. 1983-1991 (Dec.). m. Federal Home Loan Mortgage Corporation, 8200 Jones Branch Dr., McLean, VA 22102-3107.

948.9   DK   ISSN 0107-9476
FREDERIKSVAERKEGNENS MUSEUMSFORENING. AARSSKRIFT. 1986-1989. a. Frederiksvaerkegnens Museumsforening, Jernbanegade 4, 3300 Frederiksvaerk, Denmark.
Formerly: Frederiksvaerkegnens Museumsforening. Aarbog.

340   CN
FREEDOM OF INFORMATION SERVICE. announced, never published. a. (looseleaf format) Butterworths Canada Ltd., 75 Clegg Rd., Markham, Ont. L6G 1A1, Canada.

070   US
FREEDOM TO EXPRESS. 1982-19?? m. (back issues avail.) Freedom to Express, Inc., 422 S.W. 5th, Ste. B, Grants Pass, OR 97526.

330.9   GW   ISSN 0071-9412
CB478
FREIBERGER FORSCHUNGSHEFTE. MONTANWISSENSCHAFTEN. REIHE D: ECONOMIC SCIENCES. 1951-1991. irreg. (Bergakademie Freiberg) Deutscher Verlag fuer Grundstoffindustrie, Karl-Heine-Str. 27, 7031 Leipzig, Germany.

053.1   GW   ISSN 0427-5217
FREIE WELT; illustrierte Wochenzeitung. 1954-19?? 26/yr. Berliner Verlag, Karl-Liebknecht-Str. 29, 1026 Berlin, Germany.

380.52   UK
FREIGHT GUIDE. 1915-1991. m. Wilkinson Bros. Ltd., 230-234 Long Lane, London SE1 4QE, England.

798.2   GW   ISSN 0341-7182
FREIZEIT PFERDE. ceased 1991. m. Verlag Eugen Ulmer GmbH, Postfach 700561, Wollgrasweg 41, 7000 Stuttgart 70, Germany.

382   US   ISSN 0016-1039
FRENCH - AMERICAN COMMERCE; an economic, industrial and financial review. 1898-1988. q. French-American Chamber of Commerce of the United States, Inc., 509 Madison Ave., Ste. 1900, New York, NY 10022-5501.

658.8 630 641.1   US
FRESH FACTS FOR FOODSERVICE NEWSLETTER. ceased. m. (looseleaf format) United Fresh Fruit & Vegetable Association, 727 N. Washington St., Alexandria, VA 22314.
Formerly: Foodservice Newsletter.

664 658.8   US
FRESH PRODUCE FOODSERVICE DIRECTORY. 1985-1990. a. Vance Publishing Corporation (Kansas City), Box 2939, Shawnee Mission, KS 66201.

574   UK   ISSN 0374-7646
QH90   CODEN: FBARAD
FRESHWATER BIOLOGICAL ASSOCIATION. ANNUAL REPORT. 1932-1990. a. (also avail. in microfiche; back issues avail.) Freshwater Biological Association, The Ferry House, Ambleside, Cumbria LA22 0LP, England.

799   US
FRESHWATER FISHERMAN. ceased. a. Aqua-Field Publishing Co., Inc., 66 W. Gilbert St., Shrewsbury, NJ 07702.
Formerly: Ferber's Freshwater Fisherman.

787   US   ISSN 0162-0401
ML1
FRETS MAGAZINE; the magazine of acoustic string instruments. 1979-1989 (Aug.). m. (also avail. in microfilm from UMI; reprint service avail. from UMI) G P I Publications, 20085 Stevens Creek, Cupertino, CA 95014.
Incorporates: Pickin' (ISSN 0098-1761)

500.9   GW   ISSN 0043-6836
Q3   CODEN: WZFMA4
FRIEDRICH-SCHILLER-UNIVERSITAET JENA. MATHEMATISCH-NATURWISSENSCHAFTLICHE REIHE. WISSENSCHAFTLICHE ZEITSCHRIFT. vol.22, 1973-1990. 6/yr. Friedrich-Schiller-Universitaet Selbstverlag, Ernst-Thaelmann-Ring 24a, Jena 6900, Germany.

500   GW   ISSN 0138-1652
AS182
FRIEDRICH-SCHILLER-UNIVERSITAET JENA. WISSENSCHAFTLICHE ZEITSCHRIFT; gesellschaftswissenschaftliche Reihe. ceased 1990. 6/yr. Friedrich-Schiller-Universitaet, Ernst-Thaelmann-Ring 24a, 6900 Jena, Germany.

649 371.4   US
FRIENDS (SURRY). ceased 1987. q. Special Children's Friends, Rd. 1, Box 84, Surry, ME 04684.

790.1   US
FRISBEE DISC WORLD. 1976-1982 (vol.7 no.4). q. International Frisbee Disc Association, Box 970, San Gabriel, CA 91778.
Formerly: Frisbee World.

370   DK   ISSN 0108-4259
LC53.D4
FRISKOLER OG PRIVATE GRUNDSKOLER; noegletal og finansieringskilder. 1980-1984. a. Undervisningsministeriet, Datakontoret, Frederiksholms Kanal 21-25, DK-1220 Copenhagen K, Denmark.

028.5   GW   ISSN 0323-8806
FROESI. ceased 1991. m. Verlag Junge Welt GmbH, Mauerstr. 39-40, 1080 Berlin, Germany.

332   US   ISSN 0749-2812
FROM THE STATE CAPITALS. BANKING POLICIES. 1946-1989 (Dec.). fortn. (processed) Wakeman-Walworth, Inc., 300 N. Washington St., Alexandria, VA 22314.
Former titles: From the State Capitals. Banking (ISSN 0741-3548); From the State Capitals. Small Loans, Sales Finance, Banking (ISSN 0016-1934)

574   SZ   ISSN 0301-0155
     CODEN: FMXBAL
FRONTIERS OF MATRIX BIOLOGY. 1973-19?? irreg. (approx. 1/yr.). (reprint service avail. from ISI) S. Karger AG, Allschwilerstrasse 10, P.O. Box, CH-4009 Basel, Switzerland.

329.9   US
FRONTLINE (OAKLAND); on the frontline in the struggle against war and racism. 1984-1989 (vol.7, no.10). bi-w. Box 2809, Oakland, CA 94609.

640   GW   ISSN 0323-5947
FUER DICH; illustrierte Wochenzeitung fuer die Frau. 1962-19?? w. Berliner Verlag, Karl-Liebknecht-Str. 29, 1026 Berlin, Germany.

200   US   ISSN 0276-4679
FULNESS. 1978-1990 (Feb.). bi-m. Fulness House, Inc., Box 79350, Fort Worth, TX 76179.

301   AG
FUNDACION BARILOCHE. DESARROLLOS HUMANO SOCIAL PUBLICACIONES. ceased. irreg. Fundacion Bariloche, Casilla de Correo 138, 8400 San Carlos de Bariloche - Rio Negro, Argentina.
Former titles: Fundacion Bariloche. Desarrollos Sinergicos. Publicaciones; Fundacion Bariloche. Departamento de Sociologia. Publicaciones; Fundacion Bariloche. Departamento de Sociologia. Documentos de Trabajo (ISSN 0071-9838)

100   DR
FUNDACION RODRIGUEZ DEMORIZI. BOLETIN. 1978-198? irreg. Editora Taller, Isabel la Catolica 309, Apdo. de Correos 2190, Z-1, Santo Domingo, Dominican Republic.

285   US
FUNDAMENTALIST JOURNAL. 1982-1989 (Dec.). m. (back issues avail.) 2220 Langhorne Rd., Lynchburg, VA 24514.

675.3   UK   ISSN 0260-2393
FUR REVIEW. 1963-19?? m. Fur Review Publishing Co., Worcester House, 2nd Fl., Vintners Place, London EC4V 3AU, England.
Former titles: Fur and Leather Review (ISSN 0016-2957); Fur Market Review (ISSN 0016-2930)

645 338   US
FURNITURE RETAILER (NASHVILLE). ceased. m. Production Publishing Co., 804 Church St., Nashville, TN 37203.

645   US
FURNITURE - TODAY'S MANUFACTURING - TODAY. (Avail. only as supplement to: Furniture - Today) 1984-1990. 4/yr. (reprint service avail.) Cahners Business Newspapers (Subsidiary of: Reed International PLC), Division of Reed Publishing (USA) Inc., 200 S. Main St., Box 2754, High Point, NC 27261.
Former titles: Today's Furniture Design; Design Horizons.

398 808   JA   ISSN 0386-1465
FURUSATO TENBO. 1977-19?? m. (back issues avail.; reprint service avail. from ISI, UMI) (Chiiki Bunka Kenkyukai) Sensu Sha Inc., 9-14 Nishi Kanda 3-chome, Chiyoda-ku, Tokyo 101, Japan.

CESSATIONS

665.5   US   ISSN 0163-3856
TK9204
FUSION ENERGY UPDATE. 1977-19?? m. U.S. Department of Energy, Office of Scientific and Technical Information, Box 62, Oak Ridge, TN 37831.

001.539   UK   ISSN 0266-7207
QA75.5   CODEN: FCSYEX
FUTURE COMPUTING SYSTEMS. 1985-1989. q. Oxford University Press, Walton St., Oxford OX2 6DP, England.

338 621.381   US
FUTURE VIEWS (DALLAS); a newsletter on emerging issues in the personal computer industry. 1982-198? m. (back issues avail.) Future Computing Datapro, 8111 LBJ Freeway, Dallas, TX 75251.
    Incorporates (in Dec. 1986): Software Views; Hardware Views; Distribution Views; Home Views; Office Views. Hardware Views was formerly (until 1985): Technology Views.

301.415   US
G A L A REALIST. 1978-1990 (Jan.). m. (back issues avail.) Gay and Lesbian Atheists, Box 14142, San Francisco, CA 94114.
    Former titles (until Oct. 1989): G A L A Review (ISSN 0277-3236); (until Feb. 1985): G A L A.

760   US
G A T F EDUCATION REPORT. 1968-198? q. (looseleaf format) Graphic Arts Technical Foundation, 4615 Forbes Ave., Pittsburgh, PA 15213-3796.

360   US
G F MAGAZINE. 1989-199? q. Gannett Foundation, 1101 Wilson Blvd., Arlington, VA 22209.

621   SZ
G F SPECTRUM; technische Mitteilungen aus dem GF Konzern. 1978-1985. s-a. Georg Fischer Aktiengesellschaft, Postfach, CH-8201 Schaffhausen, Switzerland.

614   US   ISSN 0888-4250
RA413
G H A A JOURNAL. 1980-1989 (vol.10, no.1). s-w. Group Health Association of America, Inc., 1129 Twentieth St., N.W., Ste. 600, Washington, DC 20036.
    Formerly: Group Health Journal (ISSN 0196-6332)

910 001.642   US   ISSN 1041-2697
G70.2
G I S FORUM. (Geographic Information Systems) 1988-1992. m. (back issues avail.) T H G Publishing Company, Box 1621, St. Petersburg, FL 33731.

300 988.1   GY
G I S R A. 1970-1974 (vol.5, no.4). q. (tabloid format) Guyana Institute for Social Research and Action, P.O. Box 528, Georgetown, Guyana.

338   BE
G O M - ECONOMIE IN LIMBURG. 1960-1989. q. Gewestelijke Ontwikkelingsmaatschappij Limburg - Regional Development Authority Limburg, Kunstlaan 18, B-3500 Hasselt, Belgium.
    Formerly (until 1978): Economie in Limburg (ISSN 0013-0532)

301.425   BE   ISSN 0770-6138
HQ1102
G R I F. 1974-1982. 5/yr. Groupe de Recherche et d'Information Feministes, 59 rue Henri van Zuylen, 1180 Brussels, Belgium.
    Formerly (until 1980): Cahier du Grif (ISSN 0770-6081)

621.38   US   ISSN 0273-141X
TK1   CODEN: GAEJDG
G T E AUTOMATIC ELECTRIC WORLD-WIDE COMMUNICATIONS JOURNAL. (General Telephone & Electronics) 1948-19?? q. (also avail. in microform from UMI; reprint service avail. from UMI) G T E-Automatic Electric, 400 N. Wolf Rd., Melrose Park, IL 60164.
    Former titles: G T E Automatic Electric Technical Journal (ISSN 0147-3328); Automatic Electric Technical Journal (ISSN 0005-1063)

621.3   US   ISSN 0097-7721
TK7800
G T E JOURNAL OF RESEARCH AND DEVELOPMENT. (General Telephone & Electronics) ceased after one issue, 1974. q. G T E Laboratories, Inc., 40 Sylvan Rd., Waltham, MA 02154.

330   SA
G T E S NEWSLETTER. ceased. irreg. Council for Scientific and Industrial Research, Division of Information Services, P.O. Box 395, Pretoria 0001, South Africa.

790.13   US
G W T W COLLECTORS CLUB NEWSLETTER. 1979-198? q. Gone With The Wind Collectors Club, c/o Marlene Ridenoir, Ed., 8105 Woodview Rd., Ellicott City, MD 21043-6742.

510   SP   ISSN 0016-3805
QA1
GACETA MATEMATICA. ceased 1982. 8/yr. Instituto Jorge Juan de Matematicas, Serrano 123, Madrid-6, Spain.

621.9   US
GADGET. 1975-198? m. 116 W. 14th St., New York, NY 10011.

808.838   US
GALACTIC DISCOURSE. 1977-1991. irreg. (back issues avail.) Satori Press, 29881 Greens Ct., Menifee, CA 92355.

813 808.838   US   ISSN 0016-4003
GALAXY. (Several foreign editions) 1950-1980 (July). bi-m. (also avail. in microfiche from UMI; reprint service avail. from UMI) Avenue Victor Hugo Publishing, 339 Newbury St., Boston, MA 02115.

700   GW   ISSN 0323-8865
GALERIE - INFORMATIONEN. 1979-1990. q. Staatliche Kunstsammlungen Cottbus, Spremberger Str. 1, 7500 Cottbus, Germany.

800 808.838   US   ISSN 0162-8305
PS648.S3
GALILEO (BOSTON). 1976-1980 (Jan.). 6/yr. Avenue Victor Hugo Publishing, 339 Newbury St., Boston, MA 02115.

659.1   US   ISSN 0016-4070
GALLAGHER REPORT; a confidential letter to marketing, sales, advertising and media executives. 1951-1989 (June). w. Gallagher Report, Inc., 230 Park Ave., New York, NY 10017.
    Incorporating: Gallagher Presidents' Report.

700   SA
GALLERY. ceased 1989 (Dec.). q. (back issues avail.) Seven Arts Publishers (Pty) Ltd., Box 72161, Parkview 2122, Johannesburg, South Africa.

808.81   US
GALLERY WORKS. 1973-1991 (no.8). irreg. (back issues avail.) Poet's Commune Publications, 218 Appleton Dr., Aptos, CA 95003.

794   US
GAME PLAYER'S; the leading magazine of video and computer entertainment. 1988-1991 (Oct.). m. Signal Research Inc., 300-A Westgate Dr., Greensboro, NC 27407.

808.838   UK   ISSN 0960-1325
GAMES MASTER INTERNATIONAL. 1990-1991 (Oct.). m. Newsfield, Ludlow, Shropshire SY8 1JW, England.
    Supersedes (in 1990): Games Master.

574   US   ISSN 0148-7280
QP273   CODEN: GAMRDC
GAMETE RESEARCH. 1978-19?? m. Wiley-Liss, Inc., 41 E. 11th St., New York, NY 10003.

581   US   ISSN 0191-3999
SB1
GARDEN (BRONX). 1951-1990 (vol.14, no.6). bi-m. (also avail. in microform from UMI; reprint service avail. from UMI) Garden Society, New York Botanical Garden, Bronx, NY 10458.
    Supersedes: Garden Journal (ISSN 0016-4585); Which was formerly (until 1977): Garden Journal of the New York Botanical Garden.

635   CN
GARDEN FAX. 1976-19?? irreg. Department of Agriculture, Printmedia Branch, 7000 113th St., Edmonton, Alta. T6H 5T6, Canada.

910 917.404   US   ISSN 1044-3576
GARDEN STATE HOME & GARDEN. 1987-1991 (Sep.). 13/yr. N B T Corp. (Subsidiary of: Micromedia Affiliates), 50 Rte. 9 N., Morganville, NJ 07751-9976.
    Incorporates: New Jersey Home and Garden (ISSN 0890-3921)

635 658.8   US   ISSN 0195-1386
SB403
GARDEN SUPPLY RETAILER; merchandising and management magazine for garden centers and distributors. 1949-1991. 10/yr. (also avail. in microfilm from UMI; reprint service avail. from UMI) Chilton Co., 201 King of Prussia Rd., Radnor, PA 19089.
    Formerly: Home and Garden Supply Merchandiser (ISSN 0018-3954)

635   SA
GARDENER/TUINIER. 1915-19?? m. Pretoria Horticultural Society, Box 1186, Pretoria, South Africa.

635   SA
GARDENER MAGAZINE. 1980-1989; suspended. m. Cotswold Publications, 208 Gale St., Box 1925, Durban 4000, South Africa.

635   US
GARDENS SOUTHWEST. 1989-1990 (vol.2). s-a. (Phoenix Home & Garden, Inc.) P H G, Inc., Box 34308, Phoenix, AZ 85067.

331 338
GARMENT WORKER. 1926-19?? m. National Union of Tailors & Garment Workers, 16 Charles Sq., London N1 6HP, England.

635   NO
GARTNERYRKET - G-UTGAVE. ceased. 10/yr. Norsk Gartnerforbund, Motzfeldtsgate 1, 0187 Oslo 1, Norway.

027.4   US
GARY GRAPHIQUE. 1943-198? m. (10/yr.). (processed) Gary Public Library, 220 West 5th Ave., Gary, IN 46402.
    Formerly (until Dec. 1976): Gary Library Bulletin (ISSN 0016-4801)

531.6   US
GAS CALORIMETER WORKSHOP. PROCEEDINGS. 1982-1985. irreg. Fermi National Accelerator Laboratory, Batavia, IL 60510.
    Former titles (until 1985): Gas Sampling Calorimeter Workshop II; (until 1982): Gas Calorimeter Workshop.

830   GW
GASOLIN 23. 1973-19?? irreg. Nova Press, Friedrichstr. 60, 6000 Frankfurt, Germany.

612 616.3   UK   ISSN 0261-4669
GASTRIC AND DUODENAL ULCER. ceased 1990. m. (looseleaf format; back issues avail.) Sheffield University Biomedical Information Service (SUBIS), The University, Sheffield S10 2TN, England.

616.3   US   ISSN 0016-5085
RC799   CODEN: GASTAB
GASTROENTEROLOGY. 1943-198? m. (plus supplement). (also avail. in microform from MIM, UMI; reprint service avail. from UMI) (American Gastroenterological Association) Elsevier Science Publishing Co., Inc. (New York), 655 Ave. of the Americas, New York, NY 10010.

641.013   IT   ISSN 0016-514X
GASTRONOMO; rivista gastronomica. ceased. q. Casa Editrice Luigi Veronelli, Via degli Alerami 5, 20148 Milan, Italy.

301.4157   CN
GAY ASSOCIATION IN NEWFOUNDLAND. NEWSLETTER. 1984-1990. m. (back issues avail.) Gay Association in Newfoundland, P.O. Box 1364, Stn. C, St. John's, Nfld. A1C 5N5, Canada.

Cessations

301.415   US
GAY BIBLIOGRAPHY. 1971-1980 (6th ed.). irreg. (every 3-4 yrs.). Gay & Lesbian Task Force, Library Information Clearinghouse, c/o Ankha Shamin, 4716 Fourth Ave. S., Minneapolis, MN 55409.

301.4157 323.4   US
GAY WRITES. 1985-198? q. Gay and Lesbian Democrats of America, 5123 Fifth St., N.W., Washington, DC 20011-4040.

800 821   UK   ISSN 0308-7999
DS41
GAZELLE REVIEW OF LITERATURE ON THE MIDDLE EAST. ceased. irreg. Ithaca Press, P.O. Box 362, Oxford OX2 6ET, England.

910.202   MX
GAZETA TURISTICA. 1961-1989. 6/yr. Roberto de la Parra Loya, Ed. & Pub., Av. Juarez No. 157-405, Mexico 06030, D.F., Mexico.

330.9   FR
GAZETTE ECONOMIQUE. ceased 1986. m. La Gazette, 7 rue Jacquemars-Gielee, 59815 Lille Cedex, France.

792   PL
GDANSKIE ZESZYTY TEATRALNE. 1973-19?? a. Gdanskie Towarzystwo Przyjaciol Sztuki, Ul. Chlebnicka 2, 80-830 Gdansk, Poland.

800   GW   ISSN 0072-0550
GEISTIGE BEGEGNUNG; Moderne Erzaehler der Welt. 1962-1983 (no. 59). irreg. (Institut fuer Auslandsbeziehungen, Stuttgart) K. Thienemanns Verlag, Edition Erdmann, Blumenstr. 36, 7000 Stuttgart, Germany.

362.42   GW   ISSN 0138-2586
GEMEINSAM; Zeitschrift der Hoergeschaedigten. 1957-1991. m. Gehoerlosen- und Schwerhoerigenverband der DDR, Schiffbauerdamm 13, 1040 Berlin, Germany.
    Formerly: Deutsche Gehoerlosen-Zeitschrift.

929 900   US
GENEALOGICAL AND HISTORICAL MAGAZINE OF THE SOUTH. 1984-1991. a. Carroll Ainsworth Enterprises, 956 W. Pajaro Rd., Las Cruces, NM 88005-3532.

639   UN   ISSN 0072-0747
SH1
GENERAL FISHERIES COUNCIL FOR THE MEDITERRANEAN. PROCEEDINGS AND TECHNICAL PAPERS/CONSEIL GENERAL DES PECHES POUR LA MEDITERRANEE. DEPATS ET DOCUMENTS TECHNIQUES. 1952-198? irreg. Food and Agriculture Organization of the United Nations, c/o UNIPUB, 4611-F Assembly Dr., Lanham, MD 20706-4391.

382   GW
GENERAL MERCHANDISE. ARABIC EDITION. ceased 1990. 2/yr. Vogel-Verlag und Druck KG, P.O. Box 6740, 8700 Wuerzburg, Germany.

055.1   IT   ISSN 0046-5615
GENERAZIONE ZERO; istanze e verifiche nella societa in movimento. 1970-1974 (no.23). bi-m. Casa Editrice G. D'Anna, Via dei Della Robbia 26, 50132 Florence, Italy.

371.2   IT
GENITORI E SCUOLA. 1975-19?? m. (9/yr.). Editrice la Scuola S.p.A., Via Cadorna 11, 25186 Brescia, Italy.

948   DK
GENTOFTE-BOGEN. 1924-19?? a. Historisk Topografisk Selskab for Gentofte, Ahlmanns Alle 6, 2900 Hellerup, Denmark.
    Formerly: Historisk-Topografisk Selskab for Gjentofte Kommune. Meddelelser.

557   CN   ISSN 0823-1257
GEOLOGY IN BRITISH COLUMBIA. ceased 1981. a. (back issues avail.) Ministry of Energy, Mines and Petroleum Resources, Mineral Resources Division, Parliament Bldgs., Victoria, B.C. V8V 1X4, Canada.
    Supersedes in part: Geology, Exploration and Mining in British Columbia (ISSN 0085-1027); Which was formerly: Lode Metals in British Columbia.

551   NO   ISSN 0072-1174
    CODEN: GFPBAB
GEOPHYSICA NORVEGICA. 1934-198? irreg. (back issues avail.) Universitetsforlaget, Box 2959-Toeyen, 0608 Oslo 1, Norway.

551   II   ISSN 0378-6307
QE500   CODEN: GRBUDH
GEOPHYSICAL RESEARCH BULLETIN. 1963-1990. q. National Geophysical Research Institute, Uppal Rd., Hyderabad 500007, Andhra Pradesh, India.
    Formerly: National Geophysical Research Institute. Bulletin (ISSN 0027-9382)

551   US   ISSN 0959-3071
GEOPHYSICS ABSTRACTS. 1991; announced, never published. 12/yr. (also avail. in microform; back issues avail.) (Scitechinform, UR) Pergamon Press, Inc., Journals Division, 660 White Plains Rd., Tarrytown, NY 10591-5153.

378.198   US   ISSN 0746-9403
GEORGE STREET JOURNAL. ceased. bi-w. (Brown University) Brown News Bureau, 71 George St., Providence, RI 02912.

330   US   ISSN 0196-1098
HT393.G4
GEORGIA. OFFICE OF PLANNING AND BUDGET. STATE INVESTMENT PLAN. ceased. a. Office of Planning and Budget, 270 Washington St., Atlanta, GA 30334.

363.2   US
GEORGIA F O P NEWS. 1971-199? q. (also avail. in microform from UMI) (Georgia Fraternal Order of Police, Labor Council) Dale Corporation, 84 Executive Dr., Troy, MI 48083-4504.

690 333.33
GEORGIA HOUSING NETWORK; the monthly magazine for Georgia housing professionals. 1987-19?? m. Leo Douglas, Inc., 9607 Gayton Rd., Ste. 201, Richmond, VA 23233.

657   US   ISSN 0275-8911
HF5601
GEORGIA JOURNAL OF ACCOUNTING. 1980-1989. a. University of Georgia, J.M. Tull School of Accounting, Athens, GA 30602.

340 323.4   US
GEORGIA PEACE AND JUSTICE REPORT. ceased. q. (tabloid format) Atlanta Clergy and Laity Concerned, 222 E. Lake Dr., Decatur, GA 30030.

929   US   ISSN 0898-5413
GEORGIA QUERIES. 1988-1991 (vol.4). irreg. (back issues avail.) Name Game Enterprises, S. 4204 Conklin St., Spokane, WA 99203-6235.
    Formerly: Georgia Lineages and Queries.

621.44 551   US   ISSN 0733-9100
GEOTHERMAL REPORT. 1971-19?? 24/yr. Warne and Blanton Publishers, Inc., 3225 Freeport Blvd., Sacramento, CA 95818-4203.

618.97
GERIATRIC MEDICINE. 1987-1989. biennial. (back issues avail.) Medical Economics Books, 680 Kinderkamack Rd., Oradell, NJ 07649.

334 381 338   GW   ISSN 0138-5410
GERMAN DEMOCRATIC REPUBLIC. CONSUMER CO-OPERATIVE SOCIETIES. MAGAZINE. 1967-1991. a. Verband der Konsumgenossenschaften der DDR, Stresemannstr. 128, PF 1269, 1086 Berlin, Germany.

383   GW
GERMANY (FEDERAL REPUBLIC, 1949-). BUNDESMINISTERIUM FUER DAS POST- UND FERNMELDEWESEN. HAUSHALTSRECHNUNG, NACHWEISUNG UEBER DIE EINNAHMEN UND AUSGABEN DER DEUTSCHEN BUNDESPOST. 1959-1991. a. Bundesministerium fuer das Post-und Fernmeldewesen, Postfach 8001, 5300 Bonn, Germany.
    Former titles: Germany (Federal Republic, 1949-). Bundesministerium fuer das Post- und Fernmeldewesen. Jahresrechnung, Nachweisung ueber die Einnahmen und Ausgaben der Deutschen Bundespost (ISSN 0435-7329); Germany (Federal Republic). Bundesministerium fuer das Post- und Fernmeldewesen. Jahresnachweisung ueber die Einnahmen und Ausgaben der Deutschen Bundespost.

943   GW   ISSN 0032-7794
GERMANY (FEDERAL REPUBLIC, 1949-) PRESSE- UND INFORMATIONSAMT. BULLETIN. 1953-1985. w. Presse- und Informationsamt, Welckerstr. 11, 5300 Bonn, Germany.

769.56   CN   ISSN 0016-8963
GERMANY STAMP NEWS. 1961-19?? m. (processed) German Philatelic Society, 374 Hazel St., Waterloo, Ont., Canada.

617.6   DK   ISSN 0109-565X
GERODONTICS; a journal for the treatment of the older adult. 1985-1988 (vol.4, no.6). bi-m. (back issues avail.) Munksgaard International Publishers Ltd., P.O. Box 2148, DK-1016 Copenhagen K, Denmark.

617.6   US   ISSN 0734-0664
    CODEN: GRDND6
GERODONTOLOGY; an international journal. 1982-1991. q. (also avail. in microform) Beech Hill Enterprises, Inc., Box 40, Mt. Desert, ME 04660-0040.

013   AU   ISSN 0072-4165
GESAMTVERZEICHNIS OESTERREICHISCHER DISSERTATIONEN. 1967-19?? irreg., no.18, 1983. Verband der Wissenschaftlichen Gesellschaften Oesterreichs, Lindengasse 37, A-1070 Vienna, Austria.

943 301   GW
GESCHICHTSDIDAKTIK; Probleme Projekte Perspektiven. 1978-1987. 4/yr. Dr. Michael Sauer Friedrich Verlag, Postfach 7640, 4000 Duesseldorf 1, Germany.

340 938   AU
GESELLSCHAFT FUER GRIECHISCHE UND HELLENISTISCHE RECHTSGESCHICHTE. AKTEN. ceased. irreg. Boehlau Verlag GmbH & Co.KG., Dr. Karl Lueger-Ring 12, Postfach 581, A-1011 Vienna, Austria.

971   GW   ISSN 0722-849X
GESELLSCHAFT FUER KANADA-STUDIEN. ZEITSCHRIFT. 1981-1991. s-a. (back issues avail.) Karl Wachholtz Verlag, Rungestr. 4, 2350 Neumuenster, Germany.

613   GW
GESUNDHEITSBLATT A O K AKTUELL; Gesundheitsblatt der Allgemeinen Ortskrankenkasse Berlin. 1956-1991. 3/yr. Allgemeine Ortskrankenkasse Berlin, Information und Gesundheit, Mehringplatz 15, 1000 Berlin 61, Germany.
    Formerly (until 1989): A O K Aktuell; *Supersedes* (in 1976): A O K Gesundheitsblatt (ISSN 0514-9886)

331   US
GETTING JOBS. ceased 1989. bi-m. (back issues avail.) M P C Educational Publishers (Subsidiary of: John Wiley & Sons Company), 3839 White Plains Rd., Bronx, NY 10467.
    Supersedes (as of vol.3, 1986): New Dimensions (Bronx); (until 1985): Fashion Merchandising Newsletter.

331.8   GW   ISSN 0138-2691
GEWERKSCHAFTSLEBEN. ceased 1989. m. Tribune Verlag, Am Treptower Park 28-30, 1193 Berlin, Germany.

651.2   US
GEYER'S OFFICE DEALER. 1877-1992 (Jan.). m. (plus directory). (reprint service avail. from UMI, ISI) Geyer-McAllister Publications, Inc., 51 Madison Ave., New York, NY 10010.
    Formerly (until 1984): Geyer's Dealer Topics (ISSN 0016-948X)

614   NE   ISSN 0016-9501
GEZOND LIMBURG. 1947-1990. m. (8/yr.). Provinciaal Samenwerkingsverband van het Limburgse Groene Kruis, Kleine Steeg 7, Postbus 125, 6130 AC Sittard, Netherlands.

380.1   GH
GHANA ENTERPRISE. 1976-199?; suspended. q. (Ghana National Chamber of Commerce) Hensteve Publications Ltd., P.O. Box 2325, Accra 21162, Ghana.
    Supersedes: Ghana National Chamber of Commerce. Newsletter.

5200 CESSATIONS

978 001.3   US
GHOST TOWN QUARTERLY. 1988-1991; suspended. q. (back issues avail.) McLean Enterprises, Box 714, Philipsburg, MT 59858.

640   US
GIFT DIGEST. 1976-198? 4/yr. Market Place Publications, Box 58421, 170 World Trade Mart, Dallas, TX 75258.

688 730   US   ISSN 0163-2175
HD9773.A1
GIFTS & TABLEWARE(NEW YORK). 1962-198? m. (tabloid format; also avail. in microform from UMI; reprint service avail. from UMI) Billboard Publications, Inc. (New York), 1515 Broadway, 39th Fl., New York, NY 10036.
Formerly (until 1978?): Gift and Tableware Reporter (ISSN 0016-9846)

618.1   PL   ISSN 0017-0011
CODEN: GIPOA3
GINEKOLOGIA POLSKA. 1922-19?? m. (Polskie Towarzystwo Ginekologiczne - Polish Society of Gynaecology) Panstwowy Zaklad Wydawnictw Lekarskich, Ul. Dluga 38-40, Warsaw, Poland.

616.1   IT
GIORNALE DI EMODINAMICA; rivista di fisiopatologia cardiocircolatoria, diagnostica emodinamica, angiografia. 1981-19?? s-a. (Gruppo Italiano di Studi Emodinamici) Edizioni Minerva Medica, Corso Bramante 83-85, 10126 Turin, Italy.

388.324   IT
GIORNALE DI TRASPORTI INDUSTRIALI. (Supplement to: Trasporti Industriali) ceased. m. Etas Kompass S. p.A., Via Mantegna 6, 20154 Milan, Italy.

150.5   IT
GIORNALE ITALIANO DI PSICOLOGIA. QUADERNI. ceased 1977 (no.2). irreg. Societa Editrice il Mulino, Via Santo Stefano 6, 40125 Bologna, Italy.

336   IT
GIORNALE TRIBUTARIO - ESPANSIONE. 1980-198? fortn. Arnoldo Mondadori Editore S.p.A., Casella Postale 1772, 20090 Segrate (Milan), Italy.

450 375.4   US   ISSN 0434-0299
GIORNALINO. 1958-1969; resumed 1977-1989 (vol. 12, no.5). m. (Nov.-Apr.). (back issues avail.) c/o Prof. Remo Trivelli, Department of Modern English, University of Rhode Island, Kingston, RI 02881.

367   UK   ISSN 0262-9208
GIRL ANNUAL. ceased. a. Fleetway Annuals, IPC Magazines, Kings Reach Tower, Stamford St., London SE1 9LS, England.

327 382   US   ISSN 0895-1012
JC599.S58
GLASNOST NEWS AND REVIEW. 1987-1991 (Sep.). bi-m. (back issues avail.) Center for Democracy in the U S S R, 358 W. 30th St., Ste. 1-A, New York, NY 10001.
Formerly (until Oct-Dec. 1990): Glasnost.

620.86   US
GLASS AND CERAMICS NEWSLETTER. ceased 1990. bi-m. National Safety Council, Industrial Section, 444 N. Michigan Ave., Chicago, IL 60611.
Formerly: Safety Newsletter: Glass and Ceramics Section.

970.1   CN
GLENBOW MUSEUM. ARCHIVES SERIES. no.6, 1974-19?? irreg. Glenbow-Alberta Institute, 130-9th Ave, S.E., Calgary, Alta. T2G 0P3, Canada.
Formerly: Glenbow Foundation. Archives Series (ISSN 0436-0605)

808   US
GLENS FALLS REVIEW. 1983-19?? a. Loft Press, 42 Sherman Ave., Glens Falls, NY 12801-2753.

914.104   UK
GLIMPSE OF LONDON WITH AMERICAN EXPRESS. 1965-1988. a. (American Express International, US) Clarke & Hunter (London) Ltd., 61 London Rd., Staines, Middx. TW18 4BN, England.

382   CN
GLOBAL BUSINESS ISSUES. 1984-1990 (vol.2, no.4). q. Conference Board of Canada, 255 Smyth Road, Ottawa, Ont. K1H 8M7, Canada.
Formerly: International Business Perspectives (ISSN 0825-3706)

001.644   US
GLOBAL NETWORKS. 1990-1991. q. Network World Inc., 161 Worcester Rd., Framingham, MA 01701.

327   US   ISSN 0741-0204
D839
GLOBAL PERSPECTIVES; an interdisciplinary journal of international relations. 1983-198? s-a. (back issues avail.) Transnational Studies Association, Box 361, Orlando, FL 32802.

668.4   CN   ISSN 0835-1791
GLOBAL PLASTICS REPORT. 1987-1991. m. (back issues avail.) 233 Dupras Ave., LaSalle, Que. H8R 3S4, Canada.

769.56   DK   ISSN 0900-078X
GLOBALIA NYT; maanadsblad for seriose filatelister. 1983-1988. m. Forlaget Globalia, Bogensevej 26, 5270 Odense N, Denmark.

612.015 616.97   UK   ISSN 0143-4314
GLYCOPROTEINS. ceased 1990. m. (looseleaf format; back issues avail.) Sheffield University Biomedical Information Service (SUBIS), The University, Sheffield S10 2TN, England.

051   US   ISSN 0896-7121
GMAC QUEST; pursuing America's dreams. 1988-19?? bi-m. (back issues avail.) Aegis Group - Publishers (Subsidiary of: Lintas - Ceco Communications), 30400 Van Dyke Ave., Warren, MI 48093.

284   GW   ISSN 0232-489X
GNADAUER MITTEILUNGEN; fuer die landeskirchlichen Gemeinschaften. 1949-1990. bi-m. Envangelisch-Kirchliches Gnadauer Gemeinschaftswerk in der DDR, Schleusenstr. 55, 1255 Woltersdorf, Germany.

910.202 051   US
GO - ATLANTA. 1987-198? m. Go Magazine, Ltd., 541 Julia St., New Orleans, LA 70130-3623.
Formerly: Go: The Authentic Guide to Atlanta.

910.202 051   US
GO - DALLAS. 1986-198? m. Go Magazine, Ltd., 541 Julia St., New Orleans, LA 70130-3623.
Former titles: Go: The Authentic Guide to Dallas; Go: The Authentic Guide to San Antonio.

910.202   US
GO - NEW ORLEANS. 1973-198? m. (back issues avail.) Go Magazine, Ltd., 541 Julia St., New Orleans, LA 70130-3623.
Formerly: Go: The Authentic Guide to New Orleans.

910.202 051   US
GO - WASHINGTON, DC. 1987-198? m. Go Magazine, Ltd., 541 Julia St., New Orleans, LA 70130-3623.
Formerly: Go: The Authentic Guide to the Nation's Capital.

020   SW   ISSN 0347-884X
GOETEBORGS UNIVERSITET. UNIVERSITETSBIBLIOTEK. AARSBERAETTELSE. 1907-27; N.S 1930-1977. a. Goeteborgs Universitet, Universitetsbibliotek, Centralbiblioteket, Box 5096, S-402 22 Goeteborg, Sweden.

028.5 371.4   US
GOING PLACES! (WASHINGTON). 1976-1991. s-a. (back issues avail.) Wave, Inc., 501 School St. S.W., Ste. 600, Washington, DC 20024-2754.

052   UK
GOING SHOPPING MAGAZINE. 1982-19?? bi-m. C P R Publishing, Northern Rock House, 20 Market Place, Guisborough, Cleveland TS14 6HF, England.

622   US
GOLD IN CATALYSIS. ceased 1983. irreg. Gold Institute, Administrative Office - Institut de l'Or, Bureau Administratif, 1026 16th St., N.W., Ste. 101, Washington, DC 20036.

770   SA   ISSN 0017-1581
GOLDEN EYE. 1969-1985. m. South African Photographic Trade Association Ltd., P.O. Box 10425, 2000 Johannesburg, South Africa.

739.27   US   ISSN 0274-7456
HD9747.U5
GOLDSMITH. 1903-1989 (Apr.). m. Allen-Abernathy Co. (Subsidiary of: A S M Communications, Inc. (New York)), 49 E. 21st St., 9th Fl., New York, NY 10010.
Former titles: Southern Jeweler (ISSN 0038-4232); Pacific Goldsmith (ISSN 0191-8397)

796.352   US   ISSN 0742-4485
GV981
GOLF DIGEST ALMANAC (YEAR). 1984-1989. a. Golf Digest - Tennis, Inc. (Subsidiary of: New York Times Company), 5520 Park Ave., Box 395, Trumbull, CT 06611-0395.

796.352   US
GOLFLIFESTYLE. ceased. q. C F W Enterprises, Inc., 4201 W. Van Owen Pl., Burbank, CA 91505.
Formerly: Golfwest.

616.4   UK   ISSN 0143-425X
GONADOTROPHINS. ceased 1991. m. (looseleaf format; back issues avail.) Sheffield University Biomedical Information Service (SUBIS), The University, Sheffield S10 2TN, England.

664   US   ISSN 0885-0690
GOOD FOOD. 1986-1988. m. Murdoch Magazines, 500 Plaza Dr., Secaucus, NJ 07096.

350   US   ISSN 0017-2065
GOOD GOVERNMENT. 1881-1992; suspended. q. (also avail. in microfilm from UMI; reprint service avail. from UMI) National Civil Service League, 3600 Gunston Rd., Alexandria, VA 22302.

070 200   US
GOOD NEWS: CHRISTIAN IN JOURNALISM. 1960-1989. q. (back issues avail.) Crown Communications (St. Paul), Box 11626, St. Paul, MN 55111.

028.5   GW
GOOFY. 1979-198? m. Ehapa Verlag GmbH, Im Riedenberg 54, 7022 Leinfelden-Echterdingen 3, Germany.

333.33 658.8   US
GORDON DOWNTOWN MARKETVIEW. ceased. q. Edward S. Gordon Co., Inc., 200 Park Ave., New York, NY 10166.

622   PL   ISSN 0043-2075
GORNICTWO ODKRYWKOWE. 1959-1990. bi-m. (Centralny Osrodek Badawczo-Projektowy Gornictwa Odkrywkowego "Poltegor") Panstwowe Wydawnictwo Naukowe, Miodowa 10, Warsaw, Poland.
Formerly: Wegiel Brunatny Gornictwo Odkrywkowe.

800 808.838   US
GOTHIC. 1979-1980; resumed 1983-198? a. (also avail. in microform from UMI; back issues avail.; reprint service avail. from UMI) Gary William Crawford, Ed. & Pub., Box 80051, Baton Rouge, LA 70898.
Former titles: Gothic Chapbook Series (ISSN 0193-0184); Gothic.

658.7   US
GOVERNMENT BUYER; what's new in products and prices. 1980-1985. bi-m. (tabloid format) Morgan-Grampian Publishing Co. (Boston), 1050 Commonwealth Ave., Boston, MA 02215.

002   US
GOVERNMENT DOCUMENTS AND INFORMATION CONFERENCE. PROCEEDINGS. ceased 1982. irreg. Meckler Corporation, 11 Ferry Lane W., Westport, CT 06880-5808.
Formerly: Library Government Documents and Information Conference. Proceedings.

001.644   US
GOVERNMENT GRAPHICS SYSTEMS. 1988-19?? q. P T N Publishing Corp., 445 Broad Hollow Rd., Ste. 21, Melville, NY 11747.

026 950   II
GOVERNMENT ORIENTAL MANUSCRIPTS LIBRARY. BULLETIN. 1948-1990; suspended. a. Government Oriental Manuscripts Library, Curator, University Library Buildings, Chepauk, Madras 600 005, India.

368   US
GOVERNMENT RELATIONS WATCH. ceased. m. American Academy of Actuaries, 1720 I St., N.W., 7th Fl., Washington, DC 20006.

CESSATIONS

791.43   US
GRAFFITI; a bimonthly review of film and video animation. ceased 1988 (vol.8, no.3). 8/yr. International Animated Film Society, c/o A S I F A, Box 787, Burbank, CA 91503.
Incorporates: Inbetweener.

796.357   CN   ISSN 0701-0745
GRAND SLAM. ceased. bi-m. Canadian Amateur Softball Association, 1600 James Naismith Dr., Gloucester, Ont. K1B 5N4, Canada.

378   US   ISSN 0160-9734
H62.A1
GRANTS MAGAZINE; the journal of sponsored research and other programs. 1978-1991 (vol.14). q. (also avail. in microfilm from JSC; back issues avail.) Plenum Publishing Corp., 233 Spring St., New York, NY 10013-1578.

760   US   ISSN 0096-1159
                          CODEN: RGAFA8
GRAPHIC ARTS TECHNICAL FOUNDATION. RESEARCH PROJECT REPORT. 1947-198? irreg. (6-8/yr.). Graphic Arts Technical Foundation, 4615 Forbes Ave., Pittsburgh, PA 15213-3796.
Formerly (until no.101., 1974): Graphic Arts Technical Foundation. Research Progress Report.

301   UK   ISSN 0262-4753
GRASS-ROOTS (POOLE); God's people, a force for renewal in society today. 1982-198? 6/yr. Celebration Publishers, 57 Dorchester Rd., Lytchett Minster, Poole, Dorset BH16 6JE, England.

929   US
GRAYSON GATEWAY. ceased. q. Denison Library, History and Genealogy Society, Rt. 1, Box 273C, Denison, TX 75020.

551.46   AT
GREAT BARRIER REEF MARINE PARK AUTHORITY NEWSLETTER. 1980-19?? 3/yr. Great Barrier Reef Marine Park Authority, P.O. Box 1379, Townsville, Qld. 4810, Australia.
Formerly: Great Barrier Reef Marine Park Authority Bulletin (ISSN 0705-8764)

628 614.7   UK   ISSN 0140-170X
GREAT BRITAIN. DEPARTMENT OF THE ENVIRONMENT AND DEPARTMENT OF TRANSPORT. LIBRARY. LIBRARY BULLETIN.. 1972-1990 (no.12); suspended. s-m. Department of the Environment & Department of Transport, Publications Sales Unit, Building 1, Victoria Road, Middlesex HA4 0NZ, England.
Former titles: Great Britain. Departments of the Environment and Transport. Library. Library Bulletin (ISSN 0306-1043); Great Britain. Department of the Environment. Library. Library Bulletin; Ministry of Housing and Local Government's Index to Periodical Articles and Classified Accessions List; Ministry of Transport's Library Accessions List and Guide to Periodical Articles.

621.3   UK   ISSN 0307-1146
TK57
GREAT BRITAIN. ELECTRICITY COUNCIL. ANNUAL REPORT AND ACCOUNTS. 1959-1990. a. Electricity Council, 30 Millbank, London SW1P 4RD, England.

690   UK   ISSN 0306-0152
GREAT BRITAIN. PROPERTY SERVICES AGENCY. CONSTRUCTION REFERENCES. ceased 1991. s-a. Property Services Agency, Library Sales Office CO05, Whitgift Centre, Wellesley Rd., Croydon CR9 3LY, England.

520   UK   ISSN 0308-3322
QB82.G72
GREAT BRITAIN. ROYAL GREENWICH OBSERVATORY. ANNUAL REPORT. 1974-1979; N.S. 1985-198? irreg. (Science and Engineering Research Council) Royal Greenwich Observatory, Madingley Road, Cambridge CB3 0EZ, England.

614   UK   ISSN 0080-7877
GREAT BRITAIN. SCOTTISH HEALTH SERVICES PLANNING COUNCIL. ANNUAL REPORT. 1974-1989. a. Scottish Health Service Planning Council, St. Andrews House, Regent Rd., Edinburgh, Scotland.

631.4   UK   ISSN 0072-7199
GREAT BRITAIN. SOIL SURVEY OF ENGLAND AND WALES. REPORT. 1967-1986. a. Soil Survey and Land Research Centre, Silsoe Campus, Silsoe, Bedford MK45 4DT, England.

378   UK   ISSN 0072-7237
GREAT BRITAIN. UNIVERSITY GRANTS COMMITTEE. ANNUAL SURVEY. 1964-1989. a. University Grants Committee, 14 Park Crescent, London W1N 4DH, England.

636.7   US
GREAT DANE REVIEW; a bimonthly magazine for Great Dane lovers. 1979-198? bi-m. Hoflin Publishing Ltd., 4401 Zephyr St., Wheat Ridge, CO 80033-3299.
Formerly: Great Dane Quarterly.

641.53   US
GREAT FOODS MAGAZINE. 1984-198? bi-m. 158 Linwood Plaza, Fort Lee, NJ 07024.

020   US
GREAT PLAINS LIBRARIES. published only once; 1982. a. (Emporia State University, School of Library and Information Management) Emporia State Press, 1200 Commercial St., Emporia, KS 66801.
Supersedes: Library School Review (ISSN 0453-2406)

658.8   US   ISSN 0192-2467
GREATER OHIO VALLEY RETAILER; serving the retailers and suppliers of major home goods products. 1969-198? m. 11214 Enyart Rd., Loveland, OH 45140.

382 314   GR   ISSN 0256-3614
GREECE. NATIONAL STATISTICAL SERVICE. BULLETIN DE STATISTIQUE DU COMMERCE EXTERIEUR. ceased 1984. q. National Statistical Service of Greece, Statistical Information and Publications Division, 14-16 Lycourgou St., 10166 Athens, Greece.
Formerly (until 1974): Greece. National Statistical Service. Bulletin Mensuel du Statistique de Commerce Exterieur.

929   US
GREEN GRAPEVINE. 1980-1982. q. Kenma Publishing Co., Box 2786, Evansville, IN 47714-0786.

028.5 974   US
GREEN MOUNTAINEER. 1981-19?? 3/yr. (back issues avail.) Vermont Historical Society, Pavilion Bldg., 109 State St., Montpelier, VT 05602.

974   US
GREENE HILLS ECHO. ceased 1985 (Mar.). q. (looseleaf format; back issues avail.) Greene County Historical Society, Box 127, Waynesburg, PA 15370.

635   US
GREENER GARDENING, EASIER. 1974-1991; suspended. m. (tabloid format; back issues avail.) E. Dexter Davis, Ed.& Pub., 26 Norfolk St., Holliston, MA 01746.

310   DK   ISSN 0106-2875
GREENLAND IN FIGURES. 1978-1987. irreg. (back issues avail) Statministeriet, Groenlandsdepartementet, Hausergade 3, DK 1128 Copenhagen K, Denmark.

310   DK   ISSN 0106-0899
GROENLAND I TAL. 1975-1986. a. Statsministeriet, Groenlandsdepartementet, Hausergade 3, 1128 Copenhagen K, Denmark.

301.32   DK
GROENLANDSDEPARTEMENTET. STATISTIKE MEDDELELSER. 1960-1989. a. Statsministeriet, Groenlandsafdelingen, Hausergade 3, 1128 Copenhagen K, Denmark.
Former titles: Denmark. Ministeriet for Groenland. Statistike Meddelelser (ISSN 0900-2510); Denmark. Ministeriet for Groenland. Statistisk Kontor. Meddelelser (ISSN 0106-2891); Denmark. Ministeriet for Groenland. Oekonomisk-Statistisk Kontor. Meddelelser.

641   NE
GROEPSVOEDINGSINFORMATIE. 1980-1989 (Oct.). q. Voorlichtingsbureau voor de Voeding, Laan Copes van Cattenburch 42, 2585 GB The Hague, Netherlands.
Formerly: Groepsvoeding Informatiekrant.

810   US   ISSN 8756-9094
GROUNDSWELL (ALBANY). 1984-1989 (vol.3, no.2). 2/yr. Guild Press, 19 Clinton Ave., Albany, NY 12207.

150   US   ISSN 0093-4763
GROUPS: A JOURNAL OF GROUP DYNAMICS AND PSYCHOTHERAPY. ceased. a. Association of Medical Group Psychoanalysts, c/o David Weisselberger, M.D., Ed., 185 E. 85th St., New York, NY 10028.
Formerly: Journal of Psychoanalysis in Groups (ISSN 0022-3964)

634 635   AT   ISSN 0046-6476
GROWER. 1946-19?? m. Horticultural Association of S.A. Inc., 11 Ebenezer Place, Adelaide, S.A. 5000, Australia.

371.42   US   ISSN 0741-4498
GROWING EDGE; pathways to career transformations. 1984-1990 (vol.6). bi-m. (looseleaf format; back issues avail.) Lifecareer Foundation, 933 "C" S. Santa Fe Ave., Vista, CA 92083.

332.6   US
GROWTH STOCK ADVISORY. 1982-1988 (Jun.). s-m. Growth Stock Outlook, 4405 East-West Hwy., Bethesda, MD 20814.

332.63   US
GROWTH STOCK REPORT. 1984-19?? m. Newsletter Management Corporation, 951 Broken Sound Pkwy., N.W., Ste. 300, Boca Raton, FL 33431.
Incorporates (1984-1987): New Issue Alert; High-Tech Stock Digest.

322.4 327 614.7 333GW
DIE GRUENEN. 1979-1990. w. (back issues avail.) Talpa Verlag GmbH, Gartenstr. 13, 8890 Aichach, Germany.

574   GW   ISSN 0085-1299
GRUNDBEGRIFFE DER MODERNEN BIOLOGIE. 1967-1991. irreg. Gustav Fischer Verlag, Wollgrasweg 49, Postfach 720143, 7000 Stuttgart 70, Germany.

338.9   PE
GRUPO ANDINO; revista informativa. 1972-1989 (no. 181); suspended. m. Junta del Acuerdo de Cartagena, Apdo. Aereo 18-1177, Lima 18, Peru.

996   GU   ISSN 0046-6522
GUAM RECORDER. 1924; N.S. 1971-1979 (vol.9). q. (University of Guam, Micronesian Area Research Center) University of Guam Press, UOG Station, Mangilao, Guam.

380   GU
GUAM TRADE WITH THE UNITED STATES AND FOREIGN COUNTRIES. 1976-1983. irreg. Department of Commerce, Office of Trade Statistics, GITC Bldg., 590 S. Marine Dr., Ste. 601, Tammuning, Guam 96911.

332.64   SP
GUIA BURSATIL. 1978-1989 (Jan.). q. Banco Hispano Americano, Division de Tesoreria y Mercado de Capitales, Plaza de Canalejas, 1, 28014 Madrid, Spain.

918   BL
GUIA CAMPING. 1980-19?? a. Editora Abril, S.A., Rua Geraldo Flausino Gomes, 61, 11 andar, 04575 Sao Paulo, Brazil.

972   MX
GUIA INTERNACIONAL DE INVESTIGACIONES SOBRE MEXICO. 1985-1989. biennial. Colegio de la Frontera Norte, Blvd. Abelardo Rodriguez, 21, Zona del Rio, 22320 Tijuana, Mexico.

918   BL
GUIA SUL. 1976-19?? a. Editora Abril, S.A., Rua Geraldo Flausino Gomes, 61, 11 andar, 04575 Sao Paulo, Brazil.

918.704   VE
GUIA TURISTICA DE CARACAS, LITORAL Y VENEZUELA. suspended. a. (Camara Nacional de Turismo) Corporacion de Turismo Venezuela, Centro Capriles, 7o, Plaza Venezuela, Apdo. 50200, Caracas, Venezuela.

985   PE
GUIAS BIBLIOGRAFICAS. 1971-1980 (no.3). irreg. (Instituto de Estudios Peruanos) I E P Ediciones, Horacio Urteaga 694 (Campe de Marte), Lima 11, Peru.

CESSATIONS

371.4 US ISSN 0146-1168
GUIDANCE CLINIC. 1969-1991; suspended. 10/yr. Princeton Educational Publishers, Box 280, Plainsboro, NJ 08536.

387 JA
GUIDE & DIRECTORY OF PORT OF YOKOHAMA. ceased. a. Port and Harbor Bureau, Industry and Trade Center Bldg., Yamashita-cho, Naka-ku, Yokohama, Japan.

362.7 649 FR
GUIDE DE LA JEUNE MAMAN. ceased 1989. a. 17 rue Viete, 75017 Paris, France.

681.11 SZ
GUIDE DES ACHETEURS: HORLOGERIE, BIJOUTERIE ET BRANCHES ANNEXES/BUYERS' GUIDE: WATCH INDUSTRY, JEWELLERY AND ALLIED TRADES. 1930-1986. a. Hugo Buchser S.A., Tour-de-l'Ile 4, 1211 Geneva 11, Switzerland.
Formerly: Guide des Acheteurs pour l'Horlogerie et les Branches Annexes.

700 323.4 US
GUIDE MAGAZINE (DENVER). 1982-1988. m. (back issues avail.) La Cite Guide Inc., 432 S. Broadway, Denver, CO 80209.

371.9 US
GUIDE TO C O P A RECOGNIZED ACCREDITING BODIES. 1980-1988. biennial. Council on Postsecondary Accreditation, One Dupont Circle, N.W., Ste. 305, Washington, DC 20036.
Formerly: Guide to Recognized Accrediting Agencies (ISSN 0196-4402)

916.7 UK
GUIDE TO EAST AFRICA. 1984-198? irreg. Michael Haag Ltd., P.O. Box 369, London NW3 4ER, England.

629
GUIDE TO ENGINEERED MATERIALS. 1986-1991. a. A S M International, Periodical Publications, Materials Park, OH 44073.

332.1 US
GUIDE TO FEDERAL INCOME TAXES FOR SAVINGS INSTITUTIONS. 1982-198? irreg. Ernst & Young, 787 Seventh Ave., New York, NY 10019.

914.9 UK
GUIDE TO GREECE. 1978-198? irreg. Michael Haag Ltd., Box 369, London NW3 4ER, England.
Formerly: Travelaid Guide to Greece.

910.09 UK
GUIDE TO PARTY BOOKING. ceased. a. British Leisure Publications (Subsidiary of: Reed Information Services Ltd.), Windsor Court, East Grinstead, West Sussex RH19 1XA, England.
Formerly: A B C Guide to Party Booking.

691
GUIDE TO STABILITY DESIGN CRITERIA FOR METAL STRUCTURES. (Former name of issuing body: Column Research Council) 197-19??; suspended. irreg. (Structural Stability Research Council) John Wiley & Sons, Inc., Fritz Engineering Laboratory No. 13, Lehigh University, Bethlehem, PA 18015.
Formerly: Guide to Design Criteria for Metal Structures.

016 960 NE
GUIDE TO THE SOURCES OF THE HISTORY OF AFRICA. ceased 1971 (vol.8). irreg. I D C Microform Publishers B.V., P.O. Box 11205, 2301 EE Leiden, Netherlands.
Formerly: Guide to the Sources of the History of the Nations. B: Africa.

320 US
GUIDE TO U S GOVERNMENT DIRECTORIES. 1981-1985 (vol.2). irreg. Oryx Press, 4041 N. Central at Indian School Rd., Phoenix, AZ 85012-3397.

747.78 US
GUIDE TO WHIRLPOOL BATHS. ceased. q. Avanstar Communications, Inc. (Santa Ana), 1700 E. Dyer Rd., Ste. 250, Santa Ana, CA 92705.

649 US
GUIDE TO YOUR CHILD'S DEVELOPMENT. 1986-1990. a. Educational Programs, Inc., 8003 Old York Rd., Elkins Park, PA 19117-1410.

910.202 UK
GULF GUIDE & DIARY. 1972-198? a. World of Information, 21 Gold St., Saffron Walden, Essex CB10 1EJ, England.

355 CN ISSN 0319-2776
GULF WINGS. 1972-1990 (Feb.). 6/yr. (Canadian Forces Base) Journal Pioneer, Summerside, P.E.I. COB 2A0, Canada.

355 US ISSN 0279-4268
U1
GUNG-HO; the magazine for the international military man. 1981-198? bi-m. Charlton Publications, Inc., 1 Division St., Derby, CT 06418.

799.3 US ISSN 0072-906X
GUNS AND AMMO ANNUAL. ceased 1984. a. Petersen Publishing Co., 8490 Sunset Blvd., Los Angeles, CA 90069.

621.9 GW ISSN 0177-9796
GUSS PRODUKTE. ceased 1991. a. Verlag Hoppenstedt und Co., Havelstr. 9, Postfach 4006, 6100 Darmstadt, Germany.

910.2 SZ ISSN 0017-579X
GUTE REISE; Kurzinformationen fuer Tourismus und Verkehr. 1967-19?? s-m. Wild-Service, Neugasse 55, CH-9000 St. Gallen, Switzerland.

686.2 FR
GUTENBERG; annuaire des industries graphiques. 1936-19??; suspended. biennial. Editions Technorama, 31 Place Saint Ferdinand, 75017 Paris, France.

686.2 US
GUTENBERG & FAMILY. 1985-198? 3/yr. Type Directors Club, 60 E. 42nd St., No. 1130, New York, NY 10165-0015.

338 GY ISSN 0017-5854
GUYANA BUSINESS. 1889-19??; suspended. q. Georgetown Chamber of Commerce & Industry, Box 10110, 156 Waterloo St., Georgetown, Guyana.
Supersedes: Commercial Review.

796.077 AT
GYM COACH. ceased. q. Australian Gymnastic Federation, 2-6 Redwood Dr., Dingley, Vic. 3172, Australia.

372 613.7 US ISSN 0887-1027
GYM DANDIES; the physical education series for grades 4-8. 1986-1991. a. Great Activities Publishing Co., Box 51158, Durham, NC 27717-1158.

796.41 US ISSN 0895-2914
GYMNASTICS TODAY. ceased. bi-m. (tabloid format) Health Management Publications, Inc., 550 American Ave., King of Prussia, PA 19406-1441.

690 016 HU ISSN 0209-9853
GYORSINDEX - EPITES. 1969-19?? m. Orszagos Muszaki Informacios Kozpont es Konyvtar (O.M.I.K.K.) - National Technical Information Centre and Library, Muzeum u. 17, Box 12, H-1428 Budapest, Hungary.

001.6 016 HU ISSN 0133-9966
GYORSINDEX - SZAMITASTECHNIKA, AUTOMATIZALAS. 1970-19?? m. Orszagos Muszaki Informacios Kozpont es Konyvtar (O.M.I.K.K.) - National Technical Information Centre and Library, Muzeum u. 17, Box 12, 1428 Budapest, Hungary.

657 US ISSN 0017-6117
H & S REPORTS. 1963-19?? q. Haskins & Sells, 1633 Broadway, Ste. 2C, New York, NY 10019.

917.306 398 US ISSN 1040-6654
F205.S75
H I F P A GUIDE TO HISPANIC CULTURAL WORLD. ceased. biennial. Hispanic Institute for the Performing Arts, Box 32249, Washington, DC 20007.

332.6 HK
H K F E NEWSLETTER. ceased 1990 (no.161). m. Hong Kong Futures Exchange Ltd., Rm. 911, New World Tower, 16-18 Queen's Rd., Central, Hong Kong.

020 US
H L A JOURNAL. 1944-198?; suspended. irreg. (also avail. in microfilm from UMI; reprint service avail. from UMI) Hawaii Library Association, Box 4441, Honolulu, HI 96812-4441.
Formerly: Hawaii Library Association Journal (ISSN 0017-8586)

330.9 US
H S DENT BUSINESS FORECAST. 1989-1990 (Jun.). m. (back issues avail.) H S Business Forecast, Inc., 203 Calle del Oaks, Monterey, CA 93940.

353.8 US ISSN 0017-6311
HT167.2
H U D NEWSLETTER. 1970-198? w. (also avail. in microform from UMI; reprint service avail. from UMI) U.S. Department of Housing and Urban Development, 451 Seventh St. N.W., Washington, DC 20410.

697 UK
H V A C RED BOOK OF HEATING, VENTILATING AND AIR CONDITIONING EQUIPMENT. 1971-1990. biennial. Heating and Ventilating Publications Ltd., Faversham House, 111 St. James's Rd., Croydon, Surrey CR9 2TH, England.
Formerly (until 1979): Air Conditioning, Ventilating and Heating Equipment (ISSN 0065-4809)

374 GW ISSN 0932-8300
H V V EXTRA; Informationsdienst fuer hauptberufliche VHS-Leiter und -Mitarbeiter in Hessen. 1980-1991. a. Hessischer Volkshochschulverband, Winterbachstr. 38, 6000 Frankfurt a.M. 1, Germany.

300 001.3 TU ISSN 0441-6058
AS348.A3
HACETTEPE BULLETIN OF SOCIAL SCIENCES AND HUMANITIES. ceased with vol.6, no.1&2. s-a. (also avail. in microform from UMI; reprint service avail. from UMI) Hacettepe University Press, Ankara, Turkey.

616.5 IT ISSN 0017-6575
HAEMATOLOGICA LATINA. ceased. q. International Archives of Experimental and Clinical Haematology, Via S. Senatore 6-2, 20122 Milan, Italy.

574 II
HAFFKINE INSTITUTE. BULLETIN. 1973-1984 (vol.12). 3/yr. Haffkine Institute for Research Training & Testing, Acharya Donde Marg. Parel, Bombay 400 012, India.

808.81 070.5 020 US
HAIKU REVIEW. 1980-1987. biennial. High-Coo Press, 4634 Hale Dr., Decatur, IL 62526-1117.

646.7 US
HAIR. 1986-1990 (Jun.). q. Go-Stylish Publishing Co., 475 Park Ave. S., New York, NY 10016.

646.7 HK
HAIR INTERNATIONAL. ceased. q. Far East Trade Press Ltd., 2-F Kai Tak Commercial Bldg., 317 Des Voeux Rd., Central, Hong Kong.

051 US ISSN 0163-7770
HAITI REPORT. 1975-198? q. Friends of Haiti, c/o Haitian Information Center, 1218 Flatbush Ave., Brooklyn, NY 11226.
Formerly (until vol.1, no.3, 1976): Friends of Haiti. Bulletin.

330.9 CN
HALTON BUSINESS REPORT. ceased. m. 191 Main St. E., Milton, Ont. L9T 4N9, Canada.

621.384 US ISSN 0148-5989
HAM RADIO MAGAZINE. 1968-1990 (Jun.). m. (also avail. in microform from UMI; reprint service avail. from UMI) C Q Communications, Inc., 76 N. Broadway, Hicksville, NY 11801.
Formerly (until 1969): Ham Radio (ISSN 0017-6842); *Incorporates:* Ham Radio Horizons (ISSN 0147-8818)

821 UK
HAMPSHIRE POETS. 1969-19?? 2/yr. Southern Arts Association, 19 Southgate St., Winchester, Hants. SO23 9EB, England.

340 350 GW ISSN 0438-5004
HANDAKTEN FUER DIE STANDESAMTLICHE ARBEIT.
1962-1986. irreg. Verlag fuer Standesamtswesen GmbH, Hanauer Landstr. 197, 6000 Frankfurt 1, Germany.

340 DK ISSN 0901-0602
HANDBOG I SOCIALLOVGIVNING; Social Legislation Handbook. ceased. a. Retsinformation, Axeldorv 6, DK-1609 Copenhagen V, Denmark.

618.92 US
HANDBOOK OF COMMON POISONINGS IN CHILDREN.
1976-1983 (2nd ed.). irreg. American Academy of Pediatrics, 141 Northwest Point Blvd., Box 927, Elk Grove Village, IL 60009-0927.

641.5 US ISSN 0278-906X
TX355
HANDBOOK OF FOOD PREPARATION. ceased 1980 (8th). irreg. American Home Economics Association, 1555 King St., Alexandria, VA 22314.

069 UK ISSN 0260-5570
HANDBOOKS IN MARITIME ARCHAEOLOGY. ceased. irreg. National Maritime Museum, Romney Rd., Greenwich SE10 9NF, England.

355 GW
HANDBUCH ZUR DEUTSCHEN MILITAERGESCHICHTE.
1964-1981. irreg. (Militaergeschichtliches Forschungsamt) Bernard und Graefe Verlag, Karl-Mund-Str. 2, Postfach 2060, 5400 Koblenz, Germany.

658.8 380 GW
HANDEL. 1947-1985. m. Wirtschaftsvereinigung Gross- und Aussenhandel, Landesverband Nordrhein-Westfalen e.V., Adlerstr. 34-40, 4000 Duesseldorf, Germany.
Former title: Grosshandelskaufmann (ISSN 0046-6441)

330 DK ISSN 0105-533X
HANDELSHOEJSKOLEN I AARHUS. INSTITUT FOR MARKEDSOEKONOMI. SKRIFTSERIE E. ceased 1984 (no.13). irreg. Handelshoejskolen i Aarhus, Institut for Markedsoekonomi, Aarhus, Denmark.

330 DK
HANDELSHOEJSKOLEN I KOEBENHAVN. INSTITUT FOR TRAFIK-, TURIST- OG REGIONALOEKONOMI. PUBLIKATION. 1984-1988 (no.47). irreg. Copenhagen School of Economics and Business Administration, Copenhagen, Denmark.

531.64 DK
HANDELSMINISTERIETS ENERGIFORSKNINGSPROGRAM.
1978-198? a. Energistyrelsen, Landemaerket 11, DK-1119 Copenhagen K, Denmark.

660 NE
HANDLING CHEMICALS SAFELY. 1980-1988. a. Nederlandse Instituut voor Arbeidsomstandigheden - Dutch Institute for the Working Environment, Postbus 5665, 1007 AR Amsterdam, Netherlands.

332.63 US
HARD MONEY DIGEST; a summary and comparison of expert opinion. 1980-1989. m. (tabloid format) Hard Money Digest, Ltd., Box 37, Corte Madera, CA 94925.

683 US ISSN 0017-7709
HARDWARE MERCHANDISER. 1949-19?? 12/yr. (also avail. in tabloid format) Irving-Cloud Publishing Co., 7300 N. Cicero Ave., Lincolnwood, IL 60646.

783.7 US ISSN 0099-0604
ML1
HARMONY (HARMONY); contemporary Christian music magazine. 1974-1977 (Oct.). m. (back issues avail.) Acts 29, R.R. 2, Box 218, Harmony, PA 16037.

798.4 US ISSN 0017-7857
HARNESS HORSE; newsweekly of the standardbred industry. 1935-1991. w. Commonwealth Communications Services, Inc., Cameron and Kelker Sts., Box 10779, Harrisburg, PA 17105.
Incorporates (in 1988): Hub Rail (ISSN 0193-8630)

599.01 US
HAROLD C. MACK SYMPOSIUM. PROCEEDINGS. ceased 1972. irreg. Harper Hospital (Detroit), Department of Gynecology and Obstetrics, c/o Charles C. Thomas, Pub., 2600 S. First St., Springfield, IL 62794-9265.
Continues: Symposium on the Physiology and Pathology of Human Reproduction (ISSN 0085-7076)

338 DK ISSN 0107-7724
HARVARD BOERSEN. (Published in collaboration with Harvard Business Review) 1981-1989 (Nov., vol. 23). q. A-S Forlaget Boersen, Moentergade 19, Box 2103, 1014 Copenhagen K, Denmark.

016 650 US
HARVARD BUSINESS SCHOOL. BAKER LIBRARY. CURRENT PERIODICAL PUBLICATIONS IN BAKER LIBRARY. 1971-198? a. Harvard Business School, Baker Library, Soldiers Field Rd., Boston, MA 02163.
Formerly: Harvard University. Graduate School of Business Administration. Baker Library. Current Periodical Publications in Baker Library.

330 US
HARVARD BUSINESS SCHOOL. BAKER LIBRARY. KRESS LIBRARY OF BUSINESS AND ECONOMICS. PUBLICATIONS. 1939-1984 (no.24). irreg. (back issues avail.) Harvard Business School, Baker Library, Soldiers Field Rd., Boston, MA 02163.
Formerly: Harvard University. Graduate School of Business Administration. Baker Library. Kress Library of Business and Economics. Publications (ISSN 0073-0777)

917.306 US ISSN 0362-8078
DK508.A2
HARVARD UKRAINIAN RESEARCH INSTITUTE. MINUTES OF THE SEMINAR IN UKRAINIAN STUDIES. 1970-19?? a. (back issues avail.) Harvard University, Ukrainian Research Institute, 1581-1583 Massachusetts Ave., Cambridge, MA 02138.

021 US ISSN 0095-4721
Z732.H3
HAWAII. STATE PUBLIC LIBRARY SYSTEM. L S C A ANNUAL PROGRAM. (Library Services and Construction Act) ceased. a. State Public Library System, Research Evaluation Services, 465 S. King St., Rm. B-1, Honolulu, HI 96813.

539.721 US
HAWAII CONFERENCE ON HIGH ENERGY PHYSICS.
1972-1991 (Nov.). biennial. (reprint service avail. from UMI,ISI) (University of Hawaii, High Energy Physics Group) University of Hawaii Press, 2840 Kolowalu St., Honolulu, HI 96822.
Formerly: Hawaii Topical Conference in Particle Physics. Proceedings (ISSN 0073-1153)

020.6 US
HAWAII LIBRARY ASSOCIATION NEWSLETTER. 1958-198? q. Hawaii Library Association, Box 4441, Honolulu, HI 96812-4441.

598.2 US
HAWK MIGRATION ASSOCIATION OF NORTH AMERICA. JOURNAL. ceased. irreg. Hawk Migration Association of North America (HMANA), Box 3482, Rivermont Sta., Lynchburg, VA 24503.

796.95 IS
EL-HAYAM; Israeli marine sports magazine. 1981-1991. bi-m. El- Hayam Tikshoret Ltd., P.O. Box 32238, Tel Aviv 61321, Israel.

387.164 380.1 GW
HAZARDOUS CARGO CONTACTS. 1976-1989. a. K.O. Storck Verlag, Stahltwiete 7, 2000 Hamburg 50, Germany.
Formerly: Gefahrgut Kontakte.

600 660 US
HAZARDOUS CHEMICALS INFORMATION ANNUAL.
1986-19?? (vol.2). a. Van Nostrand Reinhold Company, 115 Fifth Ave., New York, NY 10003.

370 US ISSN 0017-8713
HEAD, HEART, HANDS & HEALTH IN VIRGINIA. 1918-198? m. Virginia Polytechnic Institute and State University, Cooperative Extension Service, 4-H Department, c/o Cecil M. McBride, Smyth Hall, Blacksburg, VA 24061.

CESSATIONS 5203

362 CN ISSN 0226-5788
HEALTH CARE (DON MILLS). 1959-1991. 8/yr. (also avail. in microform from MIM,UMI; reprint service avail. from UMI) Southam Business Communications Inc. (Subsidiary of: Southam Inc.), 1450 Don Mills Rd., Don Mills, Ont. M3B 2X7, Canada.
Former titles: Health Care in Canada (ISSN 0706-0726); Hospital Administration in Canada (ISSN 0018-554X)

368.3 US
HEALTH CARE VIEWPOINT. 1961-19?? irreg. Health Insurance Association of America, Public Relations Div., 1850 K St., N.W., Washington, DC 20006.
Formerly: Health Insurance Viewpoints (ISSN 0017-9027)

610 US
HEALTH CAREER NEWS. 1990-1991. bi-m. (tabloid format) Elsevier Communications, 301 Gibraltar Dr., Box 650, Morris Plains, NJ 07950.

362 US
HEALTH CARESYSTEMS. 1965-198? m. (tabloid format) Gralla Publications, 1515 Broadway, New York, NY 10036.
Former titles: Health Care Product News (ISSN 0018-5566); Hospital and Nursing Home Product News.

613.7 UK
HEALTH EXPRESS. 1982-198? m. Argus Health Publications Ltd., Victory House, 14 Leicester Pl., London WC2H 7QP, England.

615.543 US ISSN 0046-7057
HEALTH FOR LIFE. 1967-19?? q. (tabloid format) (Life Foundation, Inc.) Si-Nel Publishing, 1377 Barclay Circle, Marietta, GA 30068.

615.53 658 US
HEALTH HIGHLIGHTS. ceased. fortn. American Osteopathic Hospital Association, 1454 Duke St., Alexandria, VA 22314-3403.

368 US ISSN 0883-6671
HEALTH INSURANCE MEDICAL RECORDS RISK MANAGEMENT REPORT. 1983-1990. q. Cox Publications, Box 20316, Billings, MT 59104-0316.
Incorporates: Public Sector - Health Care Risk Management (ISSN 0270-8973); Formerly (until 1985): Risk Management Report - Medical Records (ISSN 0273-3617)

610 340 US
HEALTH MATRIX. 1983-1990 (Feb.). q. (back issues avail.) National Health Publishing, 99 Painters Mill Rd., Owings Mills, MD 21117.

613.7 US ISSN 0276-606X
RA407.4 .K3
HEALTH OF KANSAS CHART BOOK. 1978-19?? irreg. Department of Health and Environment, Topeka, KS 66620.

613.7 628 US
HEALTH REPORTER. 1980-1990. q. Department of Health, Division of Health Promotion, Box 90, Harrisburg, PA 17108.

640.73 613.7 US
HEALTH RESOURCES; reviewing the best in health promotion. 1986-19?? m. (back issues avail.) Kelly Communications (Charlottesville), 410 E. Water St., Charlottesville, VA 22901.

614.8 US
HEALTH REVIEW. 1987-1989 (vol.3). a. City Health Department, Public Information Office, 303 E. Fayette St., 8th Fl., Baltimore, MD 21202.

610 378 UK
HEALTH STUDENT. 1973-1991. 6/yr. National Union of Students, 461 Holloway Rd., London N7 6LJ, England.
Former titles (until 1976): Health Team; British Medical Students' Journal; Scope (ISSN 0036-8989)

610 US ISSN 0891-1924
R855
HEALTH TECHNOLOGY. 1987-1990. q. (Emergency Care Research Institute) E C R I, 5200 Butler Pike, Plymouth Meeting, PA 19462.

CESSATIONS

610   US
HEALTH WATCH. 1991-199? bi-m. Health Watch, Inc., 455 S. 4th Ave., Ste 1515, Louisville, KY 40202-2513.

610 658   US
HEALTHCARE MARKETING AND HOSPITAL NATIONAL ACCOUNT MANAGEMENT. ceased. 12/yr. Biomedical Business International, Inc., 17722 Irvine Blvd., Tustin, CA 92680.
    Formerly: Healthcare Marketing.

613.9 618   AT   ISSN 0725-1688
HEALTHRIGHT; journal of family planning, women's health and sexuality. 1981-1990 (vol.9, no.4). q. (back issues avail.) Family Planning Association of N.S.W., 161 Broadway, N.S.W. 2007, Australia.

613.7
HEALTHWEEK. 1987-1992 (Jan.). bi-w. (tabloid format; also avail. in microfilm) Healthweek Publications, Inc. (Subsidiary of: C M P Publications), 600 Community Dr., Manhasset, NY 11030.

614.85
HEALTHY COMPANIES. ceased. q. Medical Economics Company Inc., 680 Kinderkamack Rd., Oradell, NJ 07649.

051   US
HEALTHY MAN. 1990; ceased same year. bi-m. Reese Communications, Inc., 460 W. 34th St., New York, NY 10001.

929   US   ISSN 0886-4969
HEARD JOURNAL; & Herd, Hird, Hurd, too. 1984-1989 (no.19). 3/yr. (looseleaf format; also avail. in microfilm; back issues avail.) Family Tree Helpers, 1486 Oriental Ave., Bellingham, WA 98226.

612   UK   ISSN 0263-7324
HEARING. ceased 1990. m. (looseleaf format; back issues avail.) Sheffield University Biomedical Information Service (SUBIS), The University, Sheffield S10 2TN, England.

700 301.435   US   ISSN 0887-2597
HEARTLAND JOURNAL (MADISON). 1983-199?; suspended. 4/yr. (back issues avail.) Wisconsin Academy of Science, Arts and Letters, 1922 University Ave., Box 55115, Madison, WI 53705.

614   US
HEATING, AIR CONDITIONING & PLUMBING PRODUCTS. 1963-198? bi-m. (tabloid format) Gordon Publications, Inc., 301 Gibraltar Dr., Morris Plains, NJ 07950.
    Former titles (until Sep. 1980): Heating and Plumbing Product News; H P M (Heating and Plumbing Merchandiser) (ISSN 0194-5874)

593.7   US   ISSN 8756-1964
HEAVY-ION REACTIONS; a current awareness bulletin. ceased. s-m. U.S. Department of Energy, Office of Scientific and Technical Information, Box 62, Oak Ridge, TN 37831.

551.5   IS
HEBREW UNIVERSITY OF JERUSALEM. DEPARTMENT OF ATMOSPHERIC SCIENCES. LIST OF CONTRIBUTIONS. 1970-1987. a. Hebrew University of Jerusalem, Department of Atmospheric Sciences, Terra Santa College Bldg., Jerusalem, Israel.

371.2 330   GW
HEILBRONNER HOCHSCHUL-INFORMATIONEN. 1978-1991. s-a. (back issues avail.) Fachhochschule Heilbronn, Max-Planck-Str. 39, 7100 Heilbronn, Germany.

667.6   GW
HEIM UND FARBE. 1949-1989. m. (also avail. in microfiche) (Bundesverband Grosshandel Heim und Farbe e.V.) Rechtsverlag GmbH, Oststr. 119, 4000 Duesseldorf, Germany.
    Formerly (until 1987): Farbenhaendler (ISSN 0046-3280)

613   DK   ISSN 0107-3575
HEL; tidsskrift for holistisk Sundhed. 1981-1985. q. (Holistisk Netvaerk) Bavnebanke, Gerlev Idraetshoejskole, Skaelskoer Landevej 28, DK-4200 Slagelse, Denmark.
    Supersedes: Tvaerfagligt Forum for Sundhedspaedagogik og -Politik. Nyhedsbrev (ISSN 0106-9446)

810   US   ISSN 0197-3371
NX164.W65
HELICON NINE; the journal of women's arts and letters. 1979-1989 (no.20). 3/yr. (back issues avail.) Helicon Nine, Box 22412, Kansas City, MO 64113.

635   US
HELPING EACH OTHER. ceased 1989. 12/yr. Judy Huber, Ed. & Pub., HCR, Box 275, Bowdle, SD 67428.

649   DK   ISSN 0108-934X
HELSES BOERNEBLAD; sundhedsoplysning for boern. 1983-1990 (vol.8). 8/yr. Helse. Familiens Laegemagasin, Classensgade 36, DK-2100 Copenhagen OE, Denmark.
    Formerly: Boernebladet (Ringkoebing).

808.8   US   ISSN 0737-7169
HEMLOCKS AND BALSAMS. 1980-1992. a. Lees-McRae College, Box 128, Banner Elk, NC 28604.

332 330.9   UK
HENLEY CENTRE FOR FORECASTING. DIRECTOR'S GUIDE TO THE E E C ECONOMIES. 1978-19?? m. Henley Centre for Forecasting, 2 Tudor St., Blackfriars, London EC4Y 0AA, England.

352   US   ISSN 0018-0386
HENNEPIN REPORTER. 1965-1979? 10/yr. Hennepin County Board of Commissioners, A301 Government Center, Minneapolis, MN 55487.

635.98   US   ISSN 8750-1090
HERB BASKET. 1984-1989. q. Practical Press, Box 548, Boiling Springs, PA 17007.

635   US
HERBAL KITCHEN. ceased 1989. 5/yr. c/o Diane Lea Mathews, Box 134, Salisbury Center, NY 13454.

943   GW   ISSN 0437-3014
HERBERGEN DER CHRISTENHEIT; Beitraege zur Deutschen Kirchengeschichte. 1965-1990. biennial. (Arbeitsgemeinschaft fuer Kirchengeschichte der Evangelischen Landeskirchen der DDR) Evangelische Verlagsanstalt GmbH, Burgstr. 1-5, 7010 Leipzig, Germany.

910.09   UK
HERITAGE HOLIDAYS AND VISITS IN BRITAIN. 1984-1987. a. F H G Publications Ltd., Abbey Mill Business Centre, Seedhill, Paisley PA1 1JN, England.

301   US   ISSN 0073-1986
HERITAGE OF SOCIOLOGY. 1964-1984 (no.43). irreg. (reprint service avail. from UMI,ISI) University of Chicago Press, 5720 S. Woodlawn Ave., Chicago, IL 60637.

301.4157 780   US
HERIZON NEWSLETTER. 1976-1991 (no.9). m. (looseleaf format; back issues avail.) Box 1082, Binghamton, NY 13902.

200   GW   ISSN 0723-8673
HERMETIKA; Jahrbuch fuer estoerisches Christentum. 1983-1990. a. (back issues avail.) Hermetika-Verlag, Herzogstr. 1, 8921 Kinsau, Germany.

910.07   US
HERTZ TRAVEL GUIDE. (Avail. in 22 regional editions.) 1988-1991. q. Continental Publishing Services, Inc., 1450-C Enea Cir., Concord, CA 94520-5212.

547   UK   ISSN 0144-8773
                                   CODEN: HCHED7
HETEROCYCLIC CHEMISTRY. 1980-1984 (vol.5). irreg. Royal Society of Chemistry, Thomas Graham House, Science Park, Milton Rd., Cambridge CB4 4WF, England.

621.389   UK
HI-FI NOW!. 1983-19?? m. Argus Specialist Publications Ltd., Argus House, Boundary Way, Hemels, Hampstead, Herts HP2 7ST, England.

791.43   US
HI-TECH TERROR. 1985-1989 (no.43). m. c/o Craig Ledbetter, Ed., Box 5367, Kingwood, TX 77325.

810   US   ISSN 0748-3015
HIBISCUS; short stories and poetry for people who like to read. 1985-1989 (Sep.). 3/yr. Hibiscus Press, Box 22248, Sacramento, CA 95822.

581   AG   ISSN 0325-3732
QK1   CODEN: HICKD8
HICKENIA; boletin del Darwinion. 1976-1984 (vol.2, no.8). irreg. (back issues avail.) (Academia Nacional de Ciencias Exactas, Fisicas y Naturales) Instituto de Botanica Darwinion, Labarden y del Campo, Casilla Correo 22, San Isidro 1642, Buenos Aires, Argentina.

613.7 531.64   US
HICKORY STUMP. 1982-1990. irreg. (looseleaf format) Middle Tennessee Land Trust Association, 8070 Regency Dr., Nashville, TN 37221.

978   US   ISSN 0018-1420
F869.T43
HIGH COUNTRY. 1967-1985; suspended. q. (back issues avail.) William A. Harker, Ed. & Pub., Box 178, Temecula, CA 92390.

028.5 370   US   ISSN 0191-2283
HIGH - LOW REPORT; for professionals concerned with literature for teenage and adult nonreaders. 1979-1983. m. (10/yr.). Riverhouse Publications, 20 Waterside Plaza, New York, NY 10010.

001.6 621.815   US
HIGH PERFORMANCE SYSTEMS. 1980-1990 (Jul.). m. (microfilm; also avail. in microfiche; back issues avail.) C M P Publications, Inc., 600 Community Dr., Manhasset, NY 11030.
    Former titles (until 1989): V L S I Systems Design; V L S I Design (ISSN 0279-2834); Lambda (ISSN 0273-8414)

709.1 373   US
HIGH SCHOOL SPORTS. 1985-1991; suspended. 5/yr. 12 E. 49th St. Ste. E16, New York, NY 10017-1028.

671   US   ISSN 0146-4752
                        CODEN: HSCODM
HIGH SOLIDS COATINGS; magazine and buyer's guide. 1976-1991; suspended. a. (back issues avail.) Technology Marketing Corporation, One Technology Plaza, Norwalk, CT 06854.

338   US
HIGH STANDARDS IN PRODUCTIVITY AND PERFORMANCE. 1980-1990. m. Bureau of Business Practice, 24 Rope Ferry Rd., Waterford, CT 06386.
    Formed by the 1988 merger of: High Standards & Productivity and Performance.

380.31 332.6   US
HIGH TECH INVESTOR (ELKVIEW). 1988-19?? bi-m. (back isses avail.) Yellowstone Information Services, 104 Frame Rd., Elkview, WV 25071.

658   US
HIGH-TECH MANAGER'S BULLETIN. ceased. s-m. Bureau of Business Practice, 24 Rope Ferry Rd., Waterford, CT 06386.

658   US   ISSN 0743-4294
HIGH-TECH MARKETING. 1984-1988. m. (reprint service avail.) Technical Marketing Corp., 1460 Post Rd. E., Wesport, CT 06880-5509.

600 621.381   US   ISSN 0895-8432
T1   CODEN: HTBUE9
HIGH TECHNOLOGY BUSINESS. 1981-1990 (Jan.). m. (also avail. in microfiche from UMI; back issues avail.; reprint service avail. from UMI) Infotechnology Publishing, 9990 Lee Hwy., No.301, Fairfax, VA 22030.
    Formerly (until 1987): High Technology (ISSN 0277-2981)

330   US
HIGH TECHNOLOGY EXPORT & IMPORT. ceased 1991 (Mar.). bi-m. Hunter Publishing Limited Partnership, 950 Lee St., Des Plaines, IL 60016.

352.7 360   US
HIGHLIGHTS (CHARLOTTESVILLE). ceased. bi-m. University of Virginia, Center for Public Service, 2015 Ivy Rd., Charlottesville, VA 22903-1795.

331   CN   ISSN 0714-4571
HIGHLIGHTS OF INDUSTRIAL RELATIONS LITERATURE. 1975-19?? 2/yr. Queen's University, Industrial Relations Centre, Kingston, Ont. K7L 3N6, Canada.

CESSATIONS

600 GW ISSN 0933-9280
HIGHTECH; Trends, Maerkte, Management. 1986-1991. m. Management Presse Verlag, Baierbrunner Str. 33, 8000 Munich 70, Germany.

388 AT ISSN 0046-7383
HIGHWAY. 1963-19??; suspended. q. (reprint service avail. from ISI) Highways Department, Box 1, Walkerville, S.A. 5081, Australia.

133 PK ISSN 0065-5627
AL-HIKMA. 1964-19?? irreg. Shah Waliullah Academy, Hyderabad, Pakistan.

001.3 US
HILANDAR BULLETIN. ceased. 3/yr. Center for Slavic, Byzantine and East European Studies, Hilandar Research Library, 227 Main Library, Ohio State University, 1858 Neil Ave. Mall, Columbus, OH 43210.

929 US ISSN 0890-0612
HILLIARD HISTORY; a family history newsletter for Hilliard, Hillyard, Hillard and other variations of the surname. 1986-1989 (no.10). 3/yr. (back issues avail.) Hilliard Consulting Services, Box 819, Hilmar, CA 95324.

616.8 US ISSN 0193-5216
RC321 CODEN: HJCPDU
HILLSIDE JOURNAL OF CLINICAL PSYCHIATRY. 1979-1990. s-a. (reprint service avail. from UMI) (Long Island Jewish Hillside Medical Center, Department of Psychiatry) Human Sciences Press, Inc. (Subsidiary of: Plenum Publishing Corp.), 233 Spring St., New York, NY 10013-1578.
Supersedes: Hillside Hospital Journal (ISSN 0440-8152)

647.94 HK
HILTON HORIZON. 1978-1989 (Apr.). 4/yr. Hilton International (Hong Kong), 2 Queen's Road Central, G.P.O. Box 42, Hong Kong, Hong Kong.

613.7 200 US ISSN 0276-4148
RA781.7
HIMALAYAN INTERNATIONAL INSTITUTE. ELEANOR N. DANA LABORATORY. RESEARCH BULLETIN. 1980-198? a. Himalayan International Institute of Yoga Science & Philosophy of the U.S.A., R.R. 1, Box 400, Honesdale, PA 18431.

720 352.7 IT
HINTERLAND. ceased 1985. q. Programma S.r.l., Via Revere, 7, 20123 Milan, Italy.

285 CN ISSN 0229-7175
HIS DOMINION. 1974-1990; suspended. q. (back issues avail.) Canadian Theological Seminary, 4400 4th Ave., Regina, Sask. S4T 0H8, Canada.

612.015 616.3 UK ISSN 0143-4209
HISTAMINE RECEPTORS. ceased 1990. m. (looseleaf format; back issues avail.) Sheffield University Biomedical Information Service (SUBIS), The University, Sheffield S10 2TN, England.

500.9 GT ISSN 0018-2346
HISTORIA NATURAL Y PRO NATURA. 1964-1989. q. c/o Jorge a Ibarra, Apdo Postal 987, Guatemala, Guatemala.

912 US
HISTORIC COUNTRY HOUSE HOTELS: GREAT BRITAIN. ceased. a. Globe Pequot Press, 138 W. Main St., Box Q, Chester, CT 06412.

332.1 US
HISTORICAL CHART BOOK. ceased 1989. a. U.S. Federal Reserve System, Board of Governors, Publications Services, Rm. MS-138, Washington, DC 20551.

990 AT ISSN 0311-8924
HISTORICAL JOURNAL. 1975-1976. irreg. Wollongong University, Historical Society, P.O. Box 1144, Wollongong, N.S.W. 2500, Australia.

900 US
HISTORICAL PERIODICALS DIRECTORY. 1982-1986 (no.5). irreg. A B C-Clio, 130 Cremona, Box 1911, Santa Barbara, CA 93116-1911.
Former titles: Clio Historical Periodicals Directory; Clio Periodicals Directory.

901 UK ISSN 0073-2621
HISTORICAL PROBLEMS: STUDIES AND DOCUMENTS. 1968-19?? irreg. George Allen & Unwin (Publishers) Ltd., 40 Museum St., London WC1, England.

283 209 US ISSN 0018-2591
BX5917.C8
HISTORIOGRAPHER. 1952-1989 (vol.150). q. Episcopal Diocese of Connecticut, 1335 Asylum Ave., Hartford, CT 06105.

942 572 UK ISSN 0269-9591
HISTORY AND ARCHAEOLOGY REVIEW. ceased. s-a. (back issues avail.) Allan Sutton Publishing Ltd., 30 Brunswick Rd., Gloucester, GL1 1JJ, England.

150.19 US ISSN 0734-9831
HISTORY OF PSYCHOANALYSIS. 1984-19?? irreg. (Chicago Institute for Psychoanalysis) International Universities Press, Inc., 59 Boston Post Rd., Box 1524, Madison, CT 06443-1524.

621.38 UK
HOBBY ELECTRONICS. 1978-19?? m. Argus Specialist Publications Ltd., Argus House, Boundary Way, Hemels, Hampstead, Herts HP2 7ST, England.

500 GW ISSN 0138-2098
HOCHSCHULE FUER BAUWESEN COTTBUS. WISSENSCHAFTLICHE ZEITSCHRIFT. 1978-1991. s-a. Hochschule fuer Bauwesen Cottbus, Karl-Marx-Str. 17, 7500 Cottbus, Germany.

330 GW ISSN 0067-5954
HOCHSCHULE FUER OEKONOMIE "BRUNO LEUSCHNER" BERLIN. WISSENSCHAFTLICHE ZEITSCHRIFT. 1946-1991. q. Hochschule fuer Oekonomie "Bruno Leuschner" Berlin, Hermann-Duncker-Str. 8, 1157 Berlin, Germany.

388.31 GW ISSN 0233-0016
Z7164.T81
HOCHSCHULE FUER VERKEHRSWESEN "FRIEDRICH LIST". BIBLIOGRAPHIE VERKERSWESEN; Teil Verkehrssicherheit. 1982-1990. 6/yr. Hochschule fuer Verkehrswesen "Friedrich List", Friedrich-List-Platz 1, 8010 Dresden, Germany.

790.1 378.198 US
HOG CALL FANLETTER. 1979-1990 (Aug.). 26/yr. (back issues avail.) (Razorback Fan Club) Hog Call Publishers, Box 7281, Little Rock, AR 72217.

636.4 CN ISSN 0018-3199
HOG GUIDE. (Supplement to: Country Guide) 1965-1989. bi-m. Public Press Ltd., 1760 Ellice Ave., Winnipeg, Man. R3H 0B6, Canada.

631.4 JA ISSN 0073-2923
CODEN: HONKAY
HOKKAIDO NOGYO SHIKENJO DOJO CHOSA HOKOKU/ HOKKAIDO NATIONAL AGRICULTURAL EXPERIMENT STATION. SOIL SURVEY REPORT. 1951-1988 (vol. 32). a. (also avail. in microform) Hokkaido National Agricultural Experiment Station - Hokkaido Nogyo Shikenjo, 1 Hitsujigaoka, Toyohira-ku, Sapporo 004, Japan.

621.3 JA ISSN 0439-3465
CODEN: MSHUAF
HOKKAIDO UNIVERSITY. RESEARCH INSTITUTE OF APPLIED ELECTRICITY. MONOGRAPH SERIES. 1950-19?? (vol.25). a. Hokkaido University, Research Institute of Applied Electricity - Hokkaido Daigaku Oyo Denki Kenkyusho, Nishi-6-chome, Kita-12-jo, Kita-ku, Sapporo 060, Japan.

639.2 JA ISSN 0385-1362
HOKKAIDO WAKKANAI FISHERIES EXPERIMENTAL STATION. COLLECTED REPRINTS. 1972-1990. biennial. Hokkaido Wakkanai Fisheries Experimental Station, Horai 4-5-4, Wakkanai, Hokkaido 097, Japan.

615.53 US
HOLISTIC HEALTH NEWS. ceased. 6/yr. Berkeley Holistic Health Center, 3099 Telegraph Ave., Berkeley, CA 94705.

797.172 NE
HOLLAND WINDSURFING. ceased 1984 (vol.6). 9/yr. N. Odijckstraat 8, 2596 AH The Hague, Netherlands.

778 384 US
HOLLYWOOD MAGAZINE. 1988-1991. bi-m. 7000 Hollywood Blvd., Hollywood, CA 90028.

133 GW
HOLOGRAMM. 1977-1990. q. (back issues avail.) Verlag Bruno Martin, Auf der Hoehe 10, 2121 Suedergellersen, Germany.

690 TZ ISSN 0856-0366
HOME BUILDERS JOURNAL. 1980-1986. q. Home Builders Ltd., Box 25119, Dar es Salaam, Tanzania.

640 US ISSN 0893-7621
HOME BUSINESS ADVISOR; helping parents work at home. 1987-1990. bi-m. (back issues avail.) Next Step Publications, 1485 Third St., Astoria, WA 98103-5305.
Incorporates (in Jan. 1989): New Families (ISSN 0892-4554)

338 US
HOME BUSINESS MONTHLY; the management magazine for home business owners. 1984-1989 (Dec.). m. (Home Business Research Center) Home Business, Inc., 38 Briarcliffe Rd., Rochester, NY 14617.

338 659.1 US
HOME BUSINESS NEWS. 1985-1988 (Dec.). bi-m. (back issues avail.) 12221 Beaver Pike, Jackson, OH 45640.

360 US
HOME CARE SERVICES IN NEW YORK STATE. 1979-1982. irreg. Office of Health Systems Management, Department of Health, Tower Bldg., Gov. Nelson A. Rockefeller Empire State Plaza, Albany, NY 12237.

643 US
HOME CENTER PRODUCTS REPORT. 1985-1987. bi-m. (also avail. in tabloid format; reprint service avail.) Irving-Cloud Publishing Co., 7300 N. Cicero Ave., Lincolnwood, IL 60646.

621.381 UK
HOME COMPUTING WEEKLY. 1983-19?? w. Argus Specialist Publications Ltd., Argus House, Boundary Way, Hemels, Hampstead, Herts HP2 7ST, England.

640 US ISSN 0073-3105
TX173
HOME ECONOMICS IN INSTITUTIONS GRANTING BACHELORS OR HIGHER DEGREES. 1965-1981. biennial. American Home Economics Association, 1555 King St., Alexandria, VA 22314.

332.3 US
HOME EQUITY LENDING SERVICE. 1988-199? q. (looseleaf format) (Consumer Bankers Association) Warren, Gorham and Lamont Inc., One Penn Plaza, New York, NY 10119.

747 UK
HOME FURNISHINGS SURVEY. 1981-1986. biennial. Euromonitor Publications Ltd., 87-88 Turnmill St., London EC1M 5QU, England.

749 CN ISSN 0018-4055
HOME GOODS RETAILING. 1955-19?? m. (tabloid format) Maclean-Hunter Ltd., Business Publication Division, Maclean-Hunter Bldg., 777 Bay St., Toronto, Ont. M5W 1A7, Canada.

615.53 658 US
HOME HEALTH MANAGEMENT ADVISOR. 1986-198? m. Aspen Publishers, Inc., 1600 Research Blvd., Rockville, MD 20850.

640 US
HOME MICROWAVE. ceased 1988. bi-m. M L S Publications, Division St., Derby, CT 06418.

370 US
HOME SCHOOLER'S WEEKLY. ceased. w. Home Education Press, Box 1083, Tonasket, WA 98855.

374.4 UK ISSN 0441-7445
HOME STUDY. 1967-198? q. National Extension College, 18 Brooklands Ave., Cambridge, England.

929 US
HOME SWEET HOME. 1984; ceased same year. q. Family Historical and Research Organizations, Inc., Box 30, Sugar City, ID 83448.

664 US
HOMEOPATHIC DIGEST. 1983-1988. q. (back issues avail.) Bionatural Health Media, Inc., Box 318, Greenwich, CT 06870.

CESSATIONS

643.7 US ISSN 0195-2196
TH4817
HOMEOWNER; America's how-to magazine. 1974-1991. 10/yr. (also avail. in microform from UMI; reprint service avail. from UMI) Family Media, Inc., Men's and In-Home Group, 3 Park Ave., New York, NY 10016.
Former titles: Homeowners How-To Magazine; Homeowners How-To Handbook (ISSN 0148-3161); Which was formed by the merger of: Homeowners Handbook (ISSN 0094-8675); How To.

666.1 US
HOMEOWNER'S GUIDE TO GLASS. published only once, 1988. irreg. National Glass Association, 8200 Greensboro Dr., Ste. 302, McLean, VA 22102.

615.532 BE
HOMOEOPATHIE CARACTERISTIQUE. 1988-1989 (vol.2, no.6). q. Association Patients pour l'Homoeopathie Uniciste (APHU), 45, rue A. De Boeck, B-1140 Brussels, Belgium.

600 001.6 621.38 US
HONEYWELL BULL SOURCE MAGAZINE. 1984-19?? q. (back issues avail.) Honeywell Bull, Inc., Technology Park, Mail stop 314N, Billerica, MA 01821-4199.
Formerly: Honeywell Source Magazine.

382
HONG KONG CABLE. 1969-1988. m. Hong Kong Trade Development Council, 573 Fifth Ave., New York, NY 10036.

387 HK
HONG KONG PORT SERVICES INDEX (YEAR). ceased. a. Far East Trade Press Ltd., Kai Tak Commercial Bldg., 2nd Fl., 317 Des Voeux Rd., Central, Hong Kong.
Formerly: Lloyd's Hong Kong Port Services Index (Year).

011 HK ISSN 0379-5853
HONGKONGIANA; an index to selected Hong Kong periodicals. 1978-1987. a. (back issues avail.) Hong Kong Polytechnic Library, Hung Hom, Kowloon, Hong Kong.

581 UK
HOOKER'S ICONES PLANTARIUM. 1837-1990 (vol.40). irreg. Bentham-Moxon Trust, Royal Botanic Gardens, Kew, Richmond, Surrey TW9 3AB, England.

929 US ISSN 0886-3601
CS71
HOOKS FAMILY CHRONICLES; a newsletter for Hook(e), Hooks. 1980-1989. q. (looseleaf format; back issues avail.) M.R. Stultz, Ed. & Pub., 5800 Swarthmore Dr., College Park, MD 20740.

360 US ISSN 0018-4721
E184.A7
HOOSHARAR. 1914-198? m. (except Jul. & Aug.). Armenian General Benevolent Union, 585 Saddle River Rd., Saddle Brook, NJ 07662.

362 355.72 FR ISSN 0018-487X
HOPITAUX CIVILS ET MILITAIRES. GAZETTE. (Supplements avail.) 1828-19?? q. 49 rue Saint Andre des Arts, 75006 Paris, France.

910.4 NE
HOPPER. 1978-19?? 6/yr. (K L M Dutch Airlines) Multi Media International, P.O. Box 469, 1180 AL Amstelveen, Netherlands.
Formerly: City Hopper.

052 IE
HORIZON. 1983-1990. q. Jude Publication Ltd., 2-6 Tara St., Dublin 2, Ireland.

320.531 GW ISSN 0046-791X
HORIZONT (BERLIN); sozialistische Wochenzeitung fuer internationale Politik und Wirtschaft. 1968-19?? m. Berliner-Verlag, Karl-Liebknecht-Str. 29, 1026 Berlin, Germany.

798.2 US
HORSE ACTION. 1979-1988. a. Rich Publications (Subsidiary of: Cowles Media Company), 941 Calle Negocio, San Clemente, CA 92672-6202.

791.8
HORSE & RIDER'S RODEO ACTION. 1973-1988. a. Rich Publications (Subsidiary of: Cowles Media Company), 941 Calle Negocio, San Clemente, CA 92672-6202.
Formerly: Horse and Rider All-Western Yearbook.

636.1 US ISSN 0162-8127
SF285.3
HORSE CARE. 1979-1991 (Jul.). 10/yr. Rich Publications (Subsidiary of: Cowles Media Company), 941 Calle Negocio, San Clemente, CA 92672-6202.

636.1 US
HORSE WOMAN. 1978-1989. 4/yr. Rich Publications, Inc. (Subsidiary of: Cowles Media Company), 41919 Moreno, 941 Calle Negocio, San Clemente, CA 92672-6202.
Formerly (until 1989): Horse Women.

798.2 US ISSN 0018-5221
HORSEMAN. 1956-1990. m. (also avail. in microform from UMI; reprint service avail. from UMI) Horseman Publishing Corp., 25025 I-45 N., Ste. 390, Spring, TX 77380.
Formerly: Texas and Southwestern Horseman.

798
HORSEMAN'S SERVICE DIRECTORY AND DESK REFERENCE. 1980-1990; suspended. a. H P Partnership, 11 Park Ave., Gaithersburg, MD 20877.

635.9 US
HORTLINE. ceased 1988 (Aug.). 12/yr. Tom's World Horticulture Consulting, Box 5238, Charleston, WV 25361.

362 UK ISSN 0300-5461
HOSPITAL AND HEALTH SERVICE PURCHASING; guide to equipment and supplies. 1967-19?? m. (Institute of Health Service Administrators) T.G. Scott & Son Ltd., 30-32 Southampton St., London WC2E 7HR, England.
Formerly: Hospital Purchasing (ISSN 0018-5825)

614 UK
HOSPITAL & HEALTH SERVICES NEWS & APPOINTMENT REVIEW. 1982-19?? fortn. T.G. Scott & Son Ltd., 30-32 Southampton St., London WC2E 7HR, England.

657.832 US
HOSPITAL CAPITAL FORMATION MANAGEMENT LETTER. 1982-1991. 12/yr. (back issues avail.) Health Resources Publishing, Brinley Professional Plaza, 3100 Hwy. 138, Box 1442, Wall Township, NJ 07719-1442.
Formerly: Hospital Capital Formation and Reorganization Report (ISSN 0738-6370)

618.92 US
HOSPITAL CARE OF CHILDREN AND YOUTH. 1986-198? irreg. American Academy of Pediatrics, 141 Northwest Point Blvd., Box 927, Elk Grove Village, IL 60009-0927.

642.59 UK
HOSPITAL CATERER. ceased 1990. m. (Hospital Caterers Association) T.G. Scott & Son Ltd., 30-32 Southampton St., London WC2E 7HR, England.

658.8 US
HOSPITAL GIFT SHOP MANAGEMENT. 1983-19?? m. Creative Age Publications, 7628 Densmore Ave., Van Nuys, CA 91406-2088.

658 SA
HOSPITAL OFFICIAL/HOSPITAAL BEAMPTE. 1960-1989. 3/yr. (back issues avail.) Hospital Personnel Association of South Africa, P.O. Box 86, Howard Place, Capetown 7450, South Africa.

542 CN ISSN 0823-6798
HOSPITAL PRODUCTS & TECHNOLOGY. ceased 1991. 6/yr. Southam Business Inc., 1450 Don Mills Rd., Don Mills, Ont. M3B 2X7, Canada.

647.94 US
HOSTELING; a greater understanding of the world and its people through out-of-doors, educational and recreational travel. ceased. bi-m. American Youth Hostels, Inc., Metropolitan New York Council, 891 Amsterdam Ave., New York, NY 10025-4403.
Formerly: Metropolitan New York Council. Hostel News.

647.94 US
HOSTELING HOLIDAYS. 1956-1990. a. American Youth Hostels, Inc., Metropolitan New York Council, 891 Amsterdam Ave., New York, NY 10025-4403.

797.14 US
HOT ROD PERFORMANCE BOATS. ceased. bi-m. Petersen Publishing Co., 8490 Sunset Blvd., Los Angeles, CA 90069.

051 US
HOT SHOTS (NEW YORK). ceased 1990. bi-m. Leisure Plus Publications, Inc. (Subsidiary of: Mavety Media Group Ltd.), 462 Broadway, Ste. 4000, New York, NY 10013.

338 US ISSN 0898-7521
HOT TIPS. 1988-1989 (Feb.). bi-m. (back issues avail.) American Institute of Small Business, 7515 Wayzata Blvd., Minneapolis, MN 55426.

647.94 910.09 US
HOTEL MAGAZINE NETWORK. 1987-199? bi-m. Hotel Magazine Network, Inc., 1729 H St., N.W., Washington, DC 20006.

642.47 SA
HOTEL, RESTAURANT & CATERING SELECTOR. ceased. 4/yr. Westbourne-Maclean Hunter (Pty) Ltd., Nedbank East City, 120 End St., Box 6110, Johannesburg 2000, South Africa.

690 US
HOUSE BEAUTIFUL'S BUILDING & REMODELING PRODUCTS ANNUAL BUYER'S GUIDE. 1988-1989. a. Hearst Corporation, 1700 Broadway, Ste. 2801, New York, NY 10019.

617.89 US ISSN 0197-3657
HOUSE EAR INSTITUTE. PROGRESS REPORT. 1973-19?? a. House Ear Institute, 256 S. Lake St., Los Angeles, CA 90057.
Formerly: Los Angeles Foundation of Otology. Progress Report.

616.21 US
HOUSE EAR INSTITUTE. RESEARCH BULLETIN. 1982-198? s-a. House Ear Institute, 256 S. Lake St., Los Angeles, CA 90057.

929 US
HOUSER HUNTERS: FAMILY OF CHARLES FRANKLIN HOUSER. 1982-1984. a. (back issues avail.) Houser Enterprises, Box 25872, Fort Lauderdale, FL 33320-5872.

929 US
HOUSER HUNTERS NEWSLETTER. 1983-1986 (Mar.). q. (back issues avail.) Houser Enterprises, Box 25872, Fort Lauderdale, FL 33320-5872.

643 US ISSN 0162-8836
HF6201.H8 CODEN: HOUSET
HOUSEWARES. (Directory number avail.) 1892-1990 (Dec.). 21/yr. Edgell Communications, 7500 Old Oak Blvd., Cleveland, OH 44130.

352.7 US
HOUSING AMERICA. ceased 1980. m. National Association of Home Builders of the United States, Home Manufacturers Council, 15th and M Sts., N.W., Washington, DC 20005.

352.7 016 US ISSN 0018-6570
Z7165.U5
HOUSING AND PLANNING REFERENCES. 1948-198? bi-m. U. S. Department of Housing and Urban Development, Washington, DC 20410.

333.7 US ISSN 0276-4415
HD7293.A1
HOUSING FINANCE REVIEW. 1982-198? 4/yr. (also avail. in microfiche) (Federal Home Loan Mortgage Corporation (Freddie Mac)) Elsevier Science Publishing Co., Inc. (New York), 655 Ave. of the Americas, New York, NY 10010.

674 SA ISSN 0367-6447
HOUTIM. 1963-1987 (no.95). q. Processing and Chemical Manufacturing Technology - C S I R, Box 395, Pretoria 0001, South Africa.

286 NE
HOUVAST. 1970-19?? m. (10/yr.). (Zevende-Dags Adventisten - Seventh-Day Adventists) Stichting Uitgeverij "Veritas", Box 630, The Hague, Netherlands.

811 810　　　　　US
HOW(EVER). 1983-1992 (Jan.). 4/yr. c/o Meredith Stricker, Ed., 1171 E. Jefferson, Iowa City, IA 52245.

371.9　　　　　US　　ISSN 0275-4819
HOW TO GET HELP FOR KIDS; reference guide to services for handicapped children. 1980-198? irreg. Gaylord Professional Publications, Box 4901, Syracuse, NY 13221.

059.951　　　　　CC
HUAREN SHIJIE; daxing zonghexing wenhua shuangyuekan. ceased. bi-m. P.O. Box 3823, Beijing 100038, People's Republic of China.

974　　　　　US　　ISSN 0193-4791
HUDSON FORUM. 1971-1989 (Oct.). bi-m. Hudson County Chamber of Commerce and Industry, 574 Summit Ave., Jersey City, NJ 07306.

640.73　　　　　GW
DER HUETTENMANN. 1935-1991. irreg. Saarstahl Voelkingen GmbH, Postfach 101980, 6620 Volklingen-Saar, Germany.

954　　　　　NE
HULL MONOGRAPHS ON SOUTH-EAST ASIA. ceased 1971 (vol.4). irreg. I D C Microform Publishers B.V., P.O. Box 11205, 2301 EE Leiden, Netherlands.

575.1　　　　　UK　　ISSN 0952-0325
HUMAN GENOME. ceased 1990. m. (looseleaf format; back issues avail.) Sheffield University Biomedical Information Service (SUBIS), The University, Sheffield S10 2TN, England.

150 370　　　　　US　　ISSN 0741-5745
HUMAN INTELLIGENCE INTERNATIONAL NEWSLETTER. 1978-19?? q. (tabloid format; back issues avail.) Oakland University, 544 O'Dowd Hall, Rochester, MI 48309-4401.

312　　　　　UK　　ISSN 0951-1172
HUMAN LIFE MATTERS. 1985-1989 (no.6). irreg. Human Life Council, Humanae Vitae House, Chapel Brae, Braemar, Aberdeenshire AB3 5YS, Scotland.

658　　　　　HK
HUMAN RESOURCES JOURNAL. 1985-1992; suspended. s-a. Asian Research Service, G.P.O. Box 2232, Hong Kong.

658.3 340　　　　　US
HUMAN RESOURCES MANAGEMENT REPORTER. 1987-199? m. (looseleaf format) Warren, Gorham and Lamont Inc., One Penn Plaza, New York, NY 10119.

300　　　　　SA
HUMAN SCIENCES RESEARCH COUNCIL. COMPASS. 1982-19?? s-a. Human Sciences Research Council, Private Bag X41, Pretoria 0001, South Africa.

360　　　　　US　　ISSN 0745-2616
HUMAN SERVICES (WOODHAVEN). ceased. 11/yr. Leader Observer, Inc., 80-34 Jamaica Ave., Woodhaven, NY 11421.

331　　　　　GW　　ISSN 0172-8334
HUMANE PRODUKTION, HUMANE ARBEITSPLAETZE. ceased 1990. m. Friedr. Vieweg und Sohn Verlagsgesellschaft mbH, Postfach 5829, D-6200 Wiesbaden 1, Germany.

001.3　　　　　PO
HUMANIDADES. 1982-198? irreg. Universidade do Porto, Associacao de Estudantes da Faculdade de Letras, Porto, Portugal.

015　　　　　HU　　ISSN 0324-3451
Z2143
HUNGARIAN BOOK REVIEW. 1959-1990. q. Magyar Konyvkiadok es Konyvterjesztok Egyesulese - Hungarian Publishers' and Booksellers' Association, Vorosmarty ter 1, 1051 Budapest, Hungary.
　　Formerly: Books from Hungary (ISSN 0006-7504)

690　　　　　HU　　ISSN 0018-7720
　　　　　　　　　　CODEN: HBUBDN
HUNGARIAN BUILDING BULLETIN. 1958-1987. q. Epitesugyi Tajekoztatasi Kozpont - Information Centre of Building, Harsfa u. 21, 1074 Budapest, Hungary.

791.43　　　　　HU
HUNGARIAN CINEMA. 1965-1990 (vol.2). 5/yr. (processed) Hungarofilm, Bathory u. 10, 1054 Budapest, Hungary.
　　Formerly (until 1988): Hungarofilm Bulletin (ISSN 0018-7798)

340　　　　　HU　　ISSN 0441-4411
HUNGARIAN LAW REVIEW. 1968-1986. a. Magyar Jogasz Szovetseg, Szemere u. 10, 1054 Budapest 5, Hungary.

330.9　　　　　HU
HUNGARIAN PRESS REVIEW AND ECONOMIC NEWS. ceased 198? w. Magyar Tavirati Iroda, Kiado Hivatal, P.O. Box 3, 1426 Budapest, Hungary.

382　　　　　HU　　ISSN 0238-602X
HF13
HUNGARIAN TRADE JOURNAL. 1975-198? m. (Magyar Kereskedelmi Kamara - Hungarian Chamber of Commerce) Lapkiado Vallalat, Lenin krt. 9-11, 1073 Budapest, Hungary.
　　Formerly: New Hungarian Exporter (ISSN 0324-7473); Supersedes (1953-1975): Hungarian Exporter (ISSN 0018-7739)

015　　　　　HU　　ISSN 0133-7505
HUNGARIKA IRODALMI SZEMLE; kulfoldon, idegen nyelven megjelent magyar vonatkozasu konyvek es folyoiratcikkek valogatott bibliografiaja. 1971-1989 (vol.19, no.4). q. Orszagos Szechenyi Konyvtar, Budavari Palota F epulet, H-1827 Budapest, Hungary.
　　Supersedes (in 1977): Hungarica Kulfoldi Folyoiratszemle (ISSN 0200-0156)

382　　　　　HU
HUNGAROPRESS ECONOMIC INFORMATION. ceased 198? bi-m. Magyar Kereskedelmi Kamara - Hungarian Chamber of Commerce, Kossuth Lajos Ter 6-8, 1055 Budapest, Hungary.

330 314　　　　　HU　　ISSN 0209-6919
HUNGARY. KOZPONTI STATISZTIKAI HIVATAL. AGAZATI KAPCSOLATOK MERLEGE. ceased 1987. irreg. Statisztikai Kiado Vallalat, Kaszasdulo u. 2, P.O. Box 99, 1300 Budapest 3, Hungary.

338.47　　　　　HU　　ISSN 0237-0298
HUNGARY. KOZPONTI STATISZTIKAI HIVATAL. EPITOIPARI ARAK ALAKULASA. 1970-1982. irreg. Statisztikai Kiado Vallalat, Kaszasdulo u. 2, P.O. Box 99, 1300 Budapest, Hungary.

071　　　　　US
HUNTING HOUSE NEWS. 1978-1988. s-a. Andes Society for History and Culture, Andes, NY 13731.

929 900　　　　　US
HUNTINGTON HISTORICAL SOCIETY. QUARTERLY. 1961-198?; suspended. q. Huntington Historical Society, 209 Main St., Huntington, NY 11743.

333.33　　　　　NO　　ISSN 0333-3329
HUSEIERENS MAGASIN. 1975-19?? bi-m. Norges Huseierforbund, Media-Centrum A-S, P.O. Box 9172, 0134 Oslo 1, Norway.

301.412　　　　　US
HUSTLER LETTERS MAGAZINE. 1985-19?? 6/yr. Larry Flynt Publications, Inc., 9171 Wilshire Blvd., Ste. 300, Beverly Hills, CA 90210.

691　　　　　US
HUTTON'S BUILDING PRODUCTS CATALOG. 1978-1992. a. Hutton Publications, Box 1870, Hayden, ID 83835.
　　Formerly: B P C (Building Products Catalog) (ISSN 0161-6293)

690.24　　　　　US
HUTTON'S MECHANICAL PRODUCTS CATALOG. 1963-1992. a. Hutton Publications, Box 1870, Hayden, ID 83835.

600　　　　　US
HUTTON'S PLUMBING, HEATING, COOLING CATALOG. 1970-1992. a. Hutton Publications, Box 1870, Hayden, ID 83835.

574.92　　　　　NO　　ISSN 0073-4128
QH91.A1　　　　　　　　CODEN: HVALAL
HVALRAADETS SKRIFTER/SCIENTIFIC RESULTS OF MARINE BIOLOGICAL RESEARCH. 1931-198? irreg. (Norske Videnskaps-Akademi - Norwegian Academy of Science and Letters) Universitetsforlaget, Kolstadgt. 1, Box 2959-Toeyen, 0608 Oslo 6, Norway.

647.94 910.09　　　　　US
HYATT MAGAZINE. 1987-19?? bi-m. Hotel Magazine Network, Inc., 1729 H St., N.W., Washington, DC 20006.

621.381　　　　　US　　ISSN 0740-4859
HYATT'S P C NEWS REPORT; a monthly reader service covering the personal computer market. 1983-199? m. (Hyatt Research Corp.) DataTrends Publications, Inc., 8130 Boone Blvd., Ste. 210, Vienna, VA 22182.
　　Formerly: P C News Watch.

616.97　　　　　UK　　ISSN 0142-8497
HYPERSENSITIVITY. ceased 1990. m. (looseleaf format; back issues avail.) Sheffield University Biomedical Information Service (SUBIS), The University, Sheffield S10 2TN, England.

612 616.8　　　　　UK　　ISSN 0142-8683
HYPOTHALAMUS. ceased 1991. m. (looseleaf format; back issues avail.) Sheffield University Biomedical Information Service (SUBIS), The University, Sheffield S10 2TN, England.

368　　　　　US
I A D A WATCH LINE. ceased. q. Independent Automotive Damage Appraisers Association, 710 E. Ogden Ave., Ste. 113, Naperville, IL 60563-8603.

551.5　　　　　AU
I A M P NEWS BULLETIN. ceased. irreg. International Association of Meteorology and Atmospheric Physics, c/o Prof. M. Kuhn, Institut fuer Met. und Geophys., Univ. Innsbruck, Innrain 52, A-6020 Innsbruck, Austria.

314　　　　　NE
I A R U S OCCASIONAL PAPERS. 1986-19?? irreg. (International Association for Regional and Urban Statistics) International Statistical Institute, Postbus 950, Princes Beatrixlaan 485, 2270 AZ Voorburg, Netherlands.

677　　　　　US
I A W C M BULLETIN. vol.39, 1975-1991 (Sep.). m. (International Association of Wiping Cloth Manufacturers) Bernard D. Brill, Ed. & Pub., 7910 Woodmont Ave., Ste. 1212, Bethesda, MD 20814.
　　Formerly: N A W C M Bulletin.

110　　　　　US
I AM NEWS. ceased 1989 (Winter). q. Ananda Ashram, R.D. 3, Box 141, Monroe, NY 10950.

620 681　　　　　US
I & C S BUYERS' GUIDE. 1935-19?? a. (also avail. in microform from UMI) Chilton Co., Chilton Way, Radnor, PA 19089.
　　Formerly: Instruments and Control Systems Buyers' Guide.

641　　　　　IT　　ISSN 0018-8530
I.B.A. NEWS. 1964-19?? 3/yr. (International Bartenders Association) Editoriale Selepress, Corso Plebisciti 1, 20129 Milan, Italy.

384　　　　　UK　　ISSN 0308-423X
　　　　　　　　　　CODEN: IBARBD
I B A TECHNICAL REVIEW. (Independent Broadcasting Authority) 1972-1982. irreg. Independent Television Commission, 70 Brompton Rd., London SW3 1EY, England.

690　　　　　BE　　ISSN 0018-8603
I.B. FLASH-EDITION BATIMENT. (Supplement: Export Express) ceased. Confederation Generale des Cadres, 29 Bd. de la 2e Armee Britannique, Brussels 19, Belgium.

610　　　　　UK　　ISSN 0260-0765
　　　　　　　　　　CODEN: JIBDD4
I B I D. (Journal of International Biomedical Information and Data) 1980-198? q. M C S Consultants, Chapel Place, Tunbridge Wells, Kent TN1 1BP, England.

CESSATIONS

651.8 001.6   IT
I B I NEWSLETTER. 1963-198? bi-m. Intergovernmental Bureau for Informatics, Viale Civilta del Lavoro 23, 00144 Rome, Italy.
    Former titles: I B I-I C C Newsletter; I C C Newsletter (ISSN 0018-8840)

510.78   US   ISSN 0085-2082
I B M RESEARCH SYMPOSIA SERIES. 1971-19?? irreg. Plenum Publishing Corp., 233 Spring St., New York, NY 10013.

374   CN   ISSN 0018-8891
I.C.E.A. CAHIERS. 1966-19?? (vol.9, no.2). irreg. Institut Canadien d'Education des Adultes, 506 Est rue Catherine, Suite 800, Montreal, Que. H2L 2C7, Canada.
    Formerly: Education des Adultes (ISSN 0424-5393)

331.8   BE   ISSN 0018-8921
I C F T U ECONOMIC & SOCIAL BULLETIN. 1953-1986 (vol.24, Dec.). 4/yr. International Confederation of Free Trade Unions, 37-47 rue Montagne aux Herbes Potageres, B-1000 Brussels, Belgium.

296   UK
I C J C NEWSLETTER. 1970-1991 (vol.20). irreg. International Council of Jews from Czechoslovakia, 31 Craven St., London WC2N 5NP, England.

619   GW   ISSN 0333-2241
I C L A S BULLETIN. 1957-1991. s-a. (International Council for Laboratory Animal Science) Gustav Fischer Verlag, Wollgrasweg 49, Postfach 720143, 7000 Stuttgart 70, Germany.
    Formerly (until no.46, Mar., 1980): I C L A Bulletin.

325   SZ
I C M C NEWSLETTER/C I C M INFORMATIONS/BOLETIN INFORMATIVO. 1977-1989; suspended. q. International Catholic Migration Commission - Commission Internationale Catholique pour les Migrations, 37-39 rue de Vermont, CH-1211 Geneva 20 CIC, Switzerland.

325   SZ
I C M MONTHLY DISPATCH FOR THE PRESS. 1979-198? m. Intergovernmental Committee for Migration, 17 Route des Morillons, Case Postale 71, CH-1211 Geneva 19, Switzerland.
    Formerly: Intergovernmental Committee for European Migration. Monthly Dispatch for the Press.

616.99 574.87 016   US
I C R D B CANCERGRAM: CANCER RESEARCH TECHNIQUES AND APPLICATIONS. 1977-1990 (Mar.). m. U.S. National Cancer Institute, International Cancer Research Data Bank, International Cancer Information Center, Bldg. 82, National Institutes of Health, Bethesda, MD 20892.
    Formerly: I C R D B Cancergram: Cytology - Techniques, Applications.

616.99 574 016   US
I C R D B CANCERGRAM: CELL BIOLOGY - CELL KINETICS. 1977-1990 (Mar.). m. U.S. National Cancer Institute, International Cancer Research Data Bank, International Cancer Information Center, Bldg. 82, National Institutes of Health, Bethesda, MD 20892.
    Former titles: I C R D B Cancergram: Cell Biology - Kinetics; I C R D B Cancergram: Cell Biology - Cell Kinetics.

616.99 574.87 016   US
I C R D B CANCERGRAM: CELL BIOLOGY - CYTOGENETICS. 1977-1990 (Mar.). m. U.S. National Cancer Institute, International Cancer Research Data Bank, International Cancer Information Center, Bldg. 82, National Institutes of Health, Bethesda, MD 20892.

616.99 574 016   US
I C R D B CANCERGRAM: CELL BIOLOGY - GROWTH REGULATION AND DIFFERENTIATION. 1977-1990 (Mar.). m. U.S. National Cancer Institute, International Cancer Research Data Bank, International Cancer Information Center, Bldg. 82, National Institutes of Health, Bethesda, MD 20892.

616.99 016   US
I C R D B CANCERGRAM: CHEMICAL CARCINOGENESIS - AROMATIC HYDROCARBONS AND HETEROCYCLIC ANALOGS. 1977-1990 (Mar.). m. U.S. National Cancer Institute, International Cancer Research Data Bank, Bldg. 82, International Cancer Information Center, National Institutes of Health, Bethesda, MD 20892.
    Former titles: I C R D B Cancergram: Chemical Carcinogenesis - Aromatic Hydrocarbons and Related Compounds; I C R D B Cancergram: Chemical Carcinogenesis - Polycyclic Aromatic Hydrocarbons, and Related Compounds.

616.99 016   US
I C R D B CANCERGRAM: CHEMICAL CARCINOGENESIS - AZO DYES, ARYL AMINES, AND RELATED COMPOUNDS. 1977-1990 (Mar.). m. U.S. National Cancer Institute, International Cancer Research Data Bank, International Cancer Information Center, Bldg. 82, National Institutes of Health, Bethesda, MD 20892.

616.99 016   US
I C R D B CANCERGRAM: CHEMICAL CARCINOGENESIS - MISCELLANEOUS AGENTS. 1977-1990 (Mar.). m. U.S. National Cancer Institute, International Cancer Research Data Bank, International Cancer Information Center, Bldg. 82, National Institutes of Health, Bethesda, MD 20892.

616.99 614.7 016   US
I C R D B CANCERGRAM: CHEMICAL CARCINOGENESIS - NITROSO COMPOUNDS. 1977-1990 (Mar.). m. U.S. National Cancer Institute, International Cancer Research Data Bank, International Cancer Information Center, Bldg. 82, National Institutes of Health, Bethesda, MD 20892.

616.99 016   US
I C R D B CANCERGRAM: CLINICAL CANCER IMMUNOLOGY AND BIOLOGICAL THERAPY. 1977-1990 (Mar.). m. U.S. National Cancer Institute, International Cancer Research Data Bank, International Cancer Information Center, Bldg. 82, National Institutes of Health, Bethesda, MD 20892.
    Formerly: I C R D B Cancergram: Clinical Cancer Immunology and Immunotherapy.

616.99 575.1 016   US
I C R D B CANCERGRAM: D N A TUMOR VIRUSES IN NON-PRIMATE SYSTEMS. 1977-1990 (Mar.). m. U.S. National Cancer Institute, International Cancer Research Data Bank, International Cancer Information Center, Bldg. 82, National Institutes of Health, Bethesda, MD 20892.

616.99 016   US
I C R D B CANCERGRAM: DIETARY ASPECTS OF CARCINOGENESIS. 1977-1990 (Mar.). m. U.S. National Cancer Institute, International Cancer Research Data Bank, International Cancer Information Center, Bldg. 82, National Institutes of Health, Bethesda, MD 20892.

616.89 614.7 016   US
I C R D B CANCERGRAM: ENVIRONMENTAL AND OCCUPATIONAL CARCINOGENESIS. 1977-1990 (Mar.). m. U.S. National Cancer Institute, International Cancer Research Data Bank, International Cancer Information Center, Bldg. 82, National Institutes of Health, Bethesda, MD 20892.
    Formerly (until 1978): I C R D B Cancergram: Etiology of Cancer in the General Population.

616.99 575.1   US
I C R D B CANCERGRAM: GENETIC ASPECTS OF CARCINOGENESIS. 1981-1990. m. U.S. National Cancer Institute, International Cancer Research Data Bank, International Cancer Information Center, Bldg. 82, National Institutes of Health, Bethesda, MD 20892.

616.99 574 016   US
I C R D B CANCERGRAM: HORMONES IN CANCER-RELATED BIOLOGY - NON-STEROID HORMONES. 1977-1990 (Mar.). m. U.S. National Cancer Institute, International Cancer Research Data Bank, International Cancer Information Center, Bldg. 82, National Institutes of Health, Bethesda, MD 20892.

616.99 574 016   US
I C R D B CANCERGRAM: HORMONES IN CANCER-RELATED BIOLOGY - STEROID HORMONES. 1977-1990 (Mar.). m. U.S. National Cancer Institute, International Cancer Research Data Bank, International Cancer Information Center, Bldg. 82, National Institutes of Health, Bethesda, MD 20892.

616.99 016   US
I C R D B CANCERGRAM: HUMAN RETROVIRUSES. 1987-1990 (Mar.). m. U.S. National Cancer Institute, International Cancer Research Data Bank, International Cancer Information Center, Bldg. 82, National Institutes of Health, Bethesda, MD 20892.

616.99 016   US
I C R D B CANCERGRAM: IMMUNOBIOLOGY AND CANCER - FUNCTIONAL ASPECTS OF CELL-MEDIATED IMMUNITY. 1977-1990 (Mar.). m. U.S. National Cancer Institute, International Cancer Research Data Bank, International Cancer Information Center, Bldg. 82, National Institutes of Health, Bethesda, MD 20892.
    Formerly: I C R D B Cancergram: Immunobiology and Cancer - Functional Aspects of Cellular Immunity.

616.99 016   US
I C R D B CANCERGRAM: IMMUNOBIOLOGY AND CANCER - HUMORAL IMMUNITY. 1977-1990 (Mar.). m. U.S. National Cancer Institute, International Cancer Research Data Bank, International Cancer Information Center, Bldg. 82, National Institutes of Health, Bethesda, MD 20892.
    Formerly: I C R D B Cancergram: Immunobiology and Cancer - Antibodies and Humoral Immunity.

616.99 016   US
I C R D B CANCERGRAM: IMMUNOBIOLOGY AND CANCER - IDENTIFICATION AND CHARACTERIZATION OF IMMUNE CELLS. 1977-1990 (Mar.). m. U.S. National Cancer Institute, International Cancer Research Data Bank, International Cancer Information Center, Bldg. 82, National Institutes of Health, Bethesda, MD 20892.

616.99 016   US
I C R D B CANCERGRAM: IMMUNOBIOLOGY AND CANCER - TUMOR-ASSOCIATED ANTIGENS. 1977-1990 (Mar.). m. U.S. National Cancer Institute, International Cancer Research Data Bank, International Cancer Information Center, Bldg. 82, National Institutes of Health, Bethesda, MD 20892.

616.99 016   US
I C R D B CANCERGRAM: IMMUNOLOGY AND CANCER - THE MAJOR HISTOCOMPATIBILITY COMPLEX. 1977-1990 (Mar.). m. U.S. National Cancer Institute, International Cancer Research Data Bank, International Cancer Information Center, Bldg. 82, National Institutes of Health, Bethesda, MD 20892.

616.99 016   US
I C R D B CANCERGRAM: MECHANISMS OF CARCINOGENESIS - ACTIVATION AND METABOLISM OF CARCINOGENS. 1977-1990. m. U.S. National Cancer Institute, International Cancer Research Data Bank, International Cancer Information Center, Bldg. 82, National Institutes of Health, Bethesda, MD 20892.

616.99 016   US
I C R D B CANCERGRAM: MECHANISMS OF CARCINOGENESIS - MACROMOLECULAR ALTERATION AND REPAIR. 1977-1990 (Mar.). m. U.S. National Cancer Institute, International Cancer Research Data Bank, International Cancer Information Center, Bldg. 82, National Institutes of Health, Bethesda, MD 20892.

616.99 016   US
I C R D B CANCERGRAM: MECHANISMS OF CARCINOGENESIS - ONCOGENIC TRANSFORMATION. 1977-1990 (Mar.). m. U.S. National Cancer Institute, International Cancer Research Data Bank, International Cancer Information Center, Bldg. 82, National Institutes of Health, Bethesda, MD 20892.

616.15 016   US
I C R D B CANCERGRAM: METASTASIS. 1985-1990 (Mar.). m. U.S. National Cancer Institute, International Cancer Research Data Bank, International Cancer Information Center, Bldg. 82, National Institutes of Health, Bethesda, MD 20892.

616.99 016   US
I C R D B CANCERGRAM: MODIFICATION OF CARCINOGENESIS. 1977-1990 (Mar.). m. U.S. National Cancer Institute, International Cancer Research Data Bank, International Cancer Information Center, Bldg. 82, National Institutes of Health, Bethesda, MD 20892.

616.99 574.88 016   US
I C R D B CANCERGRAM: MOLECULAR BIOLOGY - CYCLIC NUCLEOTIDES. 1977-1990 (Mar.). m. U.S. National Cancer Institute, International Cancer Research Data Bank, International Cancer Information Center, Bldg. 82, National Institutes of Health, Bethesda, MD 20892.

616.99 574.88 016   US
I C R D B CANCERGRAM: MOLECULAR BIOLOGY - D N A. 1977-1990 (Mar.). m. U.S. National Cancer Institute, International Cancer Research Data Bank, International Cancer Information Center, Bldg. 82, National Institutes of Health, Bethesda, MD 20892.

616.99 574.88 016   US
I C R D B CANCERGRAM: MOLECULAR BIOLOGY - PROTEINS, POLYPEPTIDES, AMINO ACIDS. 1977-1990 (Mar.). m. U.S. National Cancer Institute, International Cancer Research Data Bank, International Cancer Information Center, Bldg. 82, National Institutes of Health, Bethesda, MD 20892.

616.99 574.88 016   US
I C R D B CANCERGRAM: MOLECULAR BIOLOGY - R N A. 1977-1990 (Mar.). m. U.S. National Cancer Institute, International Cancer Research Data Bank, International Cancer Information Center, Bldg. 82, National Institutes of Health, Bethesda, MD 20892.

616.99 016   US
I C R D B CANCERGRAM: ORGAN SITE CARCINOGENESIS - GASTROINTESTINAL TRACT AND PANCREAS. 1977-1990 (Mar.). m. U.S. National Cancer Institute, International Cancer Research Data Bank, International Cancer Information Center, Bldg. 82, National Institutes of Health, Bethesda, MD 20892.

616.99 016   US
I C R D B CANCERGRAM: ORGAN SITE CARCINOGENESIS - KIDNEY AND URINARY TRACT. 1977-1990 (Mar.). m. U.S. National Cancer Institute, International Cancer Research Data Bank, International Cancer Information Center, Bldg. 82, National Institutes of Health, Bethesda, MD 20892.

616.99 016   US
I C R D B CANCERGRAM: ORGAN SITE CARCINOGENESIS - LIVER. 1977-1990 (Mar.). m. U.S. National Cancer Institute, International Cancer Research Data Bank, International Cancer Information Center, Bldg. 82, National Institutes of Health, Bethesda, MD 20892.

616.99 016   US
I C R D B CANCERGRAM: ORGAN SITE CARCINOGENESIS - LYMPHATIC AND HEMATOPOIETIC TISSUES. 1977-1990 (Mar.). m. U.S. National Cancer Institute, International Cancer Research Data Bank, International Cancer Information Center, Bldg. 82, National Institutes of Health, Bethesda, MD 20892.

616.99 016   US
I C R D B CANCERGRAM: ORGAN SITE CARCINOGENESIS - MAMMARY GLAND. 1977-1990 (Mar.). m. U.S. National Cancer Institute, International Cancer Research Data Bank, International Cancer Information Center, Bldg. 82, National Institutes of Health, Bethesda, MD 20892.

616.99 016   US
I C R D B CANCERGRAM: ORGAN SITE CARCINOGENESIS - REPRODUCTIVE TRACT. 1977-1990 (Mar.). m. U.S. National Cancer Institute, International Cancer Research Data Bank, International Cancer Information Center, Bldg. 82, National Institutes of Health, Bethesda, MD 20892.

616.99 016   US
I C R D B CANCERGRAM: ORGAN SITE CARCINOGENESIS - RESPIRATORY TRACT. 1977-1990 (Mar.). m. U.S. National Cancer Institute, International Cancer Research Data Bank, International Cancer Information Center, Bldg. 82, National Institutes of Health, Bethesda, MD 20892.

616.99 016   US
I C R D B CANCERGRAM: ORGAN SITE CARCINOGENESIS - SKIN. 1986-1990 (Mar.). m. U.S. National Cancer Institute, International Cancer Research Data Bank, International Cancer Information Center, Bldg. 82, Rm. 103, National Institutes of Health, Bethesda, MD 20892.

616.99 575.1 016   US
I C R D B CANCERGRAM: R N A VIRUSES ASSOCIATED WITH CANCER. 1977-1990 (Mar.). m. U.S. National Cancer Institute, International Cancer Research Data Bank, International Cancer Information Center, Bldg. 82, National Institutes of Health, Bethesda, MD 20892.
   Incorporates (in 1986): I C R D B Cancergram: R N A Viruses Associated with Cancer - Molecular Biology.

616.99 615.8 016   US
I C R D B CANCERGRAM: RADIATION CARCINOGENESIS. 1977-1990 (Mar.). m. U.S. National Cancer Institute, International Cancer Research Data Bank, International Cancer Information Center, Bldg. 82, National Institutes of Health, Bethesda, MD 20892.

616.99 016   US
I C R D B CANCERGRAM: SHORT-TERM TEST SYSTEMS FOR CARCINOGENICITY AND MUTAGENICITY. 1977-1990 (Mar.). m. U.S. National Cancer Institute, International Cancer Research Data Bank, International Cancer Information Center, Bldg. 82, National Institutes of Health, Bethesda, MD 20892.

616.99 574 016   US
I C R D B CANCERGRAM: STRUCTURAL AND FUNCTIONAL ASPECTS OF CELL MEMBRANES. 1977-1990 (Mar.). m. U.S. National Cancer Institute, International Cancer Research Data Bank, International Cancer Information Center, National Institutes of Health, Bethesda, MD 20892.

616.99 016   US
I C R D B CANCERGRAM: VIRAL IMMUNOLOGY. 1977-1990 (Mar.). m. U.S. National Cancer Institute, International Cancer Research Data Bank, International Cancer Information Center, Bldg. 82, National Institutes of Health, Bethesda, MD 20892.

616.99 016   US
I C R D B CANCERGRAM: VIRUS STUDIES IN HUMANS AND OTHER PRIMATES. 1977-1990 (Mar.). m. U.S. National Cancer Institute, International Cancer Research Data Bank, International Cancer Information Center, Bldg. 82, National Institutes of Health, Bethesda, MD 20892.

327   US
I D A F NEWS NOTES. 1982-1989 (May). q. International Defense and Aid Fund for Southern Africa, United States Committee, Box 17, Cambridge, MA 02138.

333.91   US
I.D.A. JOURNAL. 1974-19?? s-a. International Desalination Association, 10 S. Main St., Ste. 206, Box 387, Topsfield, MA 01983.
   Former titles (until 1985): W S I A Journal; N W S I A Journal.

284   IT
I D E A. 1975-1989 (Feb.). m. (looseleaf format; back issues avail.) Alleanza Evangelica Italiana, Casella Postale 680, I-50100 Florence, Italy.

370   US   ISSN 0073-8697
I D E A MONOGRAPHS. 1967-19?? irreg. Institute for Development of Educational Activities, Inc., 259 Regency Ridge, Dayton, OH 45459.

370   US   ISSN 0073-8700
I D E A OCCASIONAL PAPERS. 1967-19?? irreg. Institute for Development of Educational Activities, Inc., 259 Regency Ridge, Dayton, OH 45459.

378   CN   ISSN 0382-0769
I D E E S. (Innovations, Demarches, Experiences dans l'Enseignement Superieur) 1975-1987 (vol.6, no.1). irreg. Association des Universites Partiellement Ou Entierement de Langue Francaise, Universite de Montreal, B.P. 6128, Montreal, Que. H3C 3J7, Canada.

355 327   IS   ISSN 0333-8428
UA853.I8
I D F JOURNAL. 1982-19?? q. Israel Defense Forces, Military Post 01025, Israel.

621.381
I E E E CONFERENCE ON COMPUTER WORKSTATIONS. PROCEEDINGS. 1985-1988. irreg. (also avail. in microfiche) (Institute of Electrical and Electronics Engineers, Inc.) I E E E Computer Society Press, 10662 Los Vaqueros Circle, Los Alamitos, CA 90720-1264.
   Formerly: International Conference on Computer Workstations. Proceedings.

621.3   US   ISSN 0748-9196
TK7800
I E E E ELECTROTECHNOLOGY REVIEW. 1984-1986. irreg. Institute of Electrical and Electronics Engineers, Inc., 345 E. 47th St., New York, NY 10017.

001.6   US
I E E E WORKSHOP ON LANGUAGES FOR AUTOMATION (PROCEEDINGS). 1983-1988. a. (Institute of Electrical and Electronics Engineers, Inc.) I E E E Computer Society Press, 10662 Los Vaqueros Circle, Los Alamitos, CA 90720-1264.

011   US
I E NEWS: PROCESS INDUSTRIES. ceased. q. (tabloid format) Institute of Industrial Engineers, 25 Technology Park-Atlanta, Norcross, GA 30092.
   Formerly: Steel Industry.

621.32   AT   ISSN 0018-9618
        CODEN: IELRBL
I.E.S. LIGHTING REVIEW. ceased. bi-m. (Illuminating Engineering Society of Australia) Thomson Publications (Australia) Pty. Ltd., 47 Chippen St., Chippendale N.S.W. 2008, Australia.

690   GW   ISSN 0018-9693
I F L - MITTEILUNGEN. 1961-1991. bi-m. (tabloid format) Institut fuer Leichtbau und Oekonomische Verwendung von Werkstoffen, Karl-Marx-Str., PSF 44, 8080 Dresden, Germany.

320.9   US   ISSN 0018-9758
E740
I.F. STONE'S WEEKLY. 1953-1971. fortn. (reprint service avail. from KTO) 4420 29th St. N.W., Washington, DC 20008.

621.37   US   ISSN 0095-1021
TK399
I.F.T. JOURNAL. ceased. bi-m. International Foundation for Telemetering, 21031 Ventura Blvd., Ste. 1001, Woodland Hills, CA 91364.

769.56   US
I G P C PHILATELIC REPORT. 1981-1988. q. Inter-Governmental Philatelic Corporation, 460 W. 34th St., New York, NY 10001.

633.63   BE   ISSN 0018-9898
I.I.R.B. 1965-1976 (vol.7, no.2). 4/yr. International Institute for Sugar Beet Research, 47 rue Montoyer, B-1040 Brussels, Belgium.

620   CK   ISSN 0049-3201
I I T TECNOLOGIA. 1959-19?? bi-m. Instituto de Investigaciones Tecnologicas, Apdo. Aereo 7031-Nacional 2062, Av. 30, 52-A-77, Bogota D.E., Colombia.

400   US   ISSN 0361-3399
I J A L NATIVE AMERICAN TEXTS SERIES. (International Journal of American Linguistics) 1976-19??; suspended. irreg. (reprint service avail. from UMI,ISI) University of Chicago Press, 5720 S. Woodlawn Ave., Chicago, IL 60637.

800   GW
I J B - BULLETIN; Neue internationale Kinder- und Jugendliteratur. 1983-1989. a. Internationale Jugendbibliothek - International Youth Library, Schloss Blutenburg, 8000 Munich 60, Germany.

370   UK   ISSN 0306-1981
I L E A CONTACT. 1972-1986. 36/yr. Inner London Education Authority, County Hall, Rm. 59, London SE1 7PB, England.

301.435   US
I M C JOURNAL. 1984-199? q. International Medical Centers, 1515 N.W. 167th St., Miami, FL 33169.

614.7   NE
I M G - T N O RESEARCH INSTITUTE FOR ENVIRONMENTAL HYGIENE. ANNUAL REPORT. 1942-1985. a. I M G - T N O Research Institute for Environmental Hygiene, Box 214, Schoemakerstraat 97, 2600 AE Delft, Netherlands.
   Formerly: I G - T N O Research Institute for Environmental Hygiene. Annual Report.

CESSATIONS

790.1   US
I M I S COUNCIL NEWSLETTER. 1983-1992; suspended. q. (back issues avail.) Sporting Goods Manufacturers Association, 200 Castlewood Dr., N. Palm Beach, FL 33408.

658.3   US
I M P A C T. (Information for Managers on Personnel and Current Trends in Human Resources) ceased 1990. bi-w. Maxwell Macmillan, Professional and Business Reference Publishing, 910 Sylvan Ave., Englewood Cliffs, NJ 07632-3310.

658.8   US
I M P O DISTRIBUTOR NEWS. 1959-19?? bi-m. (tabloid format; also avail. in microform from UMI; reprint service avail. from UMI) Chilton Co., One Chilton Way, Radnor, PA 19089.
    Formerly (until 1984): Industrial Distributor News (ISSN 0019-8161)

370   US
I N E T UP-DATE. ceased 1985. a. Michigan State University, International Networks in Education and Development (INET), College of Education, 237 Erickson Hall, E. Lansing, MI 48824.
    Formerly: N F E Exchange (Non-Formal Education).

020   DK
I N F A A RAPPORT. 1983-19?? irreg. Aabenraa Proevecenter for Ny Informationsteknologi, c/o Det Soenderjydske Landsbibliotek, Haderslevvej 3, 6200 Aabenraa, Denmark.

387   PL
I N S A BULLETIN. ceased. q. International Shipowners' Association, Sieroszewskiego 7, 81-376 Gdynia, Poland.

301   FR   ISSN 0758-7724
I N S E E PREMIERS RESULTATS. 1983-1989. s-m. Institut National de la Statistique et des Etudes Economiques, 18 bd. Adolphe Pinard, 75675 Paris cedex 14, France.

500   AG   ISSN 0325-934X
I N T I. 1979-1986. q. Instituto Nacional de Tecnologia Industrial, Leandro N. Alem 1067, Casilla de Correo 1359, 1001 Buenos Aires, Argentina.
    Supersedes (1961-1980): Argentina. Instituto Nacional de Tecnologia Industrial. Boletin I N T I (ISSN 0019-0225)

539   JA
I P C R CYCLOTRON TECHNICAL REPORT. (Institute of Physical and Chemical Research) 1971-1973 (No. 8). irreg. Rikagaku Kenkyujo, Saikurotoron Kenkyushitsu - Cyclotron Laboratory, 2-1 Hirosawa, Wako-shi, Saitama-ken 351-01, Japan.

658.3   UK   ISSN 0019-0330
I P M DIGEST. 1965-1990. m. Institute of Personnel Management, IPM House, Camp Rd., Wimbledon, London SW19 4UX, England.

370.15 150   GW   ISSN 0445-9121
I P N L. (Individual Psychology News Letter) ceased 1990. q. (back issues avail.) International Association of Individual Psychology, c/o Horst Groener, Ed., Ruffinstr. 10, 8000 Munich 19, Germany.

301 016   UK   ISSN 0309-6904
I P P F CO-OPERATIVE INFORMATION SERVICE. 1964-1990. q. International Planned Parenthood Federation, Regent's College, Inner Circle, Regent's Park, London NW1 4NS, England.
    Formerly: International Planned Parenthood Federation. Library Bulletin (ISSN 0047-0880)

636.089   BL   ISSN 0019-0411
I.P.V.D.F. BOLETIM MENSAL; dos trabalhos relatados pelos tecnicos. 1949-1974. m. (processed) Instituto de Pesquisa Veterinarias Desiderio Finamor, Caixa Postal 2076, Porto Alegre-R S, Brazil.

320 330.1   GW   ISSN 0323-3901
HC281
I P W FORSCHUNGSHEFTE. 1965-1990. q. Institut fuer Internationale Politik und Wirtschaft der D.D.R., Breite Str. 11, 1020 Berlin, Germany.
    Formerly: Deutsches Wirtschafts Institut, Berlin. D W I Forschungshefte (ISSN 0046-015X)

331.1 658   US   ISSN 0019-0454
I.R. CONCEPTS; developments in management & industrial relations. ceased. 4/yr. Organization Resources Counselors, Inc., 1270 Ave. of the Americas, New York, NY 10020.
    Supersedes: I.R.C. Current News.

280   US   ISSN 0887-1043
I R F NEWSLETTER. 1985-1989. q. International Religious Foundation, Inc., JAF Box 2347, New York, NY 10116.
    Supersedes (in May-June, 1986): New E R A Newsletter (ISSN 0277-3082)

678   UK   ISSN 0019-0462
I.R.I. JOURNAL. 1924-1975. bi-m. (also avail. in microfilm from UMI; reprint service avail. from UMI) (Institution of the Rubber Industry) Rubber & Technical Press Ltd., Tenterden, Kent, Eng.
    Formerly: Institution of the Rubber Industry. Transactions and Proceedings.

621.387   US   ISSN 0892-094X
I S I ONLINE NEWS. 1984-1991 (Sep.). 3/yr. Institute for Scientific Information, 3501 Market St., Philadelphia, PA 19104.

020   II
I S I S BULLETIN. 1976-19?? q. Indian Society for Information Science, c/o Library, Indian Institute of Science, Bangalore 560012, India.

629.13   BL   ISSN 0019-0772
I T A - ENGENHARIA. 1958-1970. bi-m. Instituto Tecnologico de Aeronautica, Sao Jose dos Campos, Sao Paulo, Brazil.

338.9   IS   ISSN 0047-1216
HC60
I T C C REVIEW. (International Technical Cooperation Centre) 1972-1984. irreg. (also avail. in microform from MIM) Association of Engineers and Architects in Israel, 200 Dizengoff Rd., P.O. Box 3082, Tel Aviv, Israel.

621.38   UK   ISSN 0268-3954
I T INTELLIGENCE. (Information Technology) ceased. m. Elsevier Science Publishers Ltd., Crown House, Linton Rd., Barking, Essex IG11 8JU, England.

800 700 770   US   ISSN 1047-5249
I: THE FIRST PERSON; writings & art in the first person point of view. 1989-1990. q. (back issues avail.) Zeugma Press, Box 663, Graton, CA 95444.

627   US
I W R A NEWSLETTER. 1985-1989. q. International Water Resources Association, University of Illinois, 205 North Mathews Ave., Urbana, IL 61801.

370   SP   ISSN 0536-2512
IBERO-AMERICAN BUREAU OF EDUCATION. INFORMATION AND PUBLICATIONS DEPARTMENT SERIES V: TECHNICAL SEMINARS AND MEETINGS. 1964-198? irreg. Ibero-American Bureau of Education, Avenida de los Reyes Catolicos, Ciudad Universitaria, Madrid 3, Spain.

051   US
ICE RIVER; a magazine of speculative writing, fantastic art and contemporary music. 1985-1990. 3/yr. (back issues avail.) Ice River, Inc., 953 N. Gale, Union, OR 97883.
    Formed by the 1989 merger of: Ice River - A Quarterly Review and Market Tabloid for Speculative Writing, Fantastic Art and Electronic Music & Ice River - A Journal of Speculative Writing.

353.9   US   ISSN 0362-3912
HD7655.I2
IDAHO. DEPARTMENT OF LABOR AND INDUSTRIAL SERVICES. ANNUAL REPORT. 1974-19?? a. Department of Labor and Industrial Services, 277 N. Sixth, Statehouse Mall, Boise, ID 83720.

663   US
IDAHO BEVERAGE ANALYST. (Subseries of: Northwest Beverage Analyst) 1936-1990 (Dec.). m. Bell Publications, Beverage Analyst Group, 2403 Champa St., Denver, CO 80205.

363.2   US
IDAHO PEACE OFFICER. 1946-19?? q. Idaho Peace Officers Association, 9355 Lyle St., Boise, ID 83709-4844.

621.389   US
IDEAS IN SOUND. 1972-198? s-a. (also avail. in microform from UMI; reprint service avail. from UMI) Hoke Communications, Inc., 224 Seventh St., Garden City, NY 11530.

659.1   US
IDEASWORTH. 1965-1991 (Jan.). a. Specialty Advertising Association International, 3125 Skyway Cir N, Irving, TX 75038-3526.
    Formerly: Specialty Advertising Report (ISSN 0038-6871)

054.1   FR
IDEES POUR TOUS - SPECIALE HEBDO. (Avail. also in 9 supplements and annual directory) 1963-1986. w. (processed) Route de Bethanie, Boisset et Gaujac, 30140 Anduze, France.
    Formerly: Idees pour Tous (ISSN 0019-1434)

658.788   US   ISSN 0747-962X
IDENTIFICATION JOURNAL. 1984-198? 7/yr. Marking Devices Publishing, Inc., 113 Adell Pl., Elmhurst, IL 60126-3301.

207.11   US   ISSN 0019-1795
BR1
ILIFF REVIEW. ceased 1988. 3/yr. (back issues avail.) Iliff School of Theology, 2201 S. University Blvd., Denver, CO 80210.

929   US
ILL-IA-MO SEARCHER. 1973-1992 (vol.26, no.2). q. (back issues avail.) Mary Alma Kay, Ed. & Pub., R. R.1, Box 182, Keokuk, IA 52632-9708.

378.1   US   ISSN 0362-5524
LB3223.4.I3
ILLINOIS. BOARD OF HIGHER EDUCATION. STATEWIDE SPACE SURVEY. 1962-1989 (Fall). irreg. Board of Higher Education, 500 Reisch Bldg., 4 W. Old Capitol Sq., Springfield, IL 62701.

640   US   ISSN 0739-148X
TX165.A1
ILLINOIS TEACHER OF HOME ECONOMICS. 1957-1991 (vol.34, no.5). bi-m. (back issues avail.) University of Illinois at Urbana-Champaign, Division of Home Economics Education, 347 Education Bldg., 1310 S. 6th St., Champaign, IL 61820.
    Formerly: Illinois Teacher for Contemporary Roles (ISSN 0536-5139)

917   US
ILLINOIS TRAVEL AND RECREATION GUIDE. ceased. a. Rockford Map Publishers, Inc., 4525 Forest View Ave., Box 6126, Rockford, IL 61125.

593   US
ILLUSTRATED GUIDE TO THE PROTOZOA. 1983-198? irreg. (Society of Protozoologists) Allen Press, Inc., 1041 New Hampshire Ave., Box 368, Lawrence, KS 66044.
    Formerly (until 1985): Society of Protozoologists. Special Publication.

741.6   UK   ISSN 0307-319X
ILLUSTRATORS. 1973-1991. bi-m. (back issues avail.) Association of Illustrators, 1 Colville Place, London W1, England.

740   UK   ISSN 0260-8324
ILLUSTRATORS DESPATCH. 1980-1989. 12/yr. Association of Illustrators, 1 Colville Place, London W1, England.

796.72   SW   ISSN 0019-249X
ILLUSTRERAD MOTOR SPORT. 1961-198? m. Lerums Boktryckeri AB, Box 333, 44300 Lerum, Sweden.

796.72 796.75   GW   ISSN 0442-3054
ILLUSTRIERTER MOTORSPORT. 1951-1991. m. Sportverlag GmbH, Neustaedtische Kirchstr. 15, 1086 Berlin, Germany.

370   PR
IMAGENES. 1985-1987 (Dec.). s-a. Universidad Interamericana de Puerto Rico, Recinto Metropolitano, Decanato de Estudiantes, Apdo. 1293, Hato Rey, PR 00919.

808.81   US
IMAGES. 1974-1990. 3/yr. (tabloid format) Wright State University, English Department, Dayton, OH 45435.

325.1 658.3   US
IMMIGRATION MANAGEMENT ALERT. 1986-19?? s-m. Business Research Publications, Inc., 817 Broadway, New York, NY 10003.

610 616.97   JA   ISSN 0285-0796
CODEN: IMDVDH
IMMUNO-ADVANCE. 1970-1988 (vol.17, no.1). 3/yr. Sanko Junyaku Co. Ltd., TMM Bldg., 10-6, Iwamoto-Cho 1, 1 Chome, Chiyoda-ku, Tokyo 101, Japan.

612 616.99   UK   ISSN 0266-6340
IMMUNODEFICIENCY. ceased 1989. m. (looseleaf format; back issues avail.) Sheffield University Biomedical Information Service (SUBIS), The University, Sheffield S10 2TN, England.

616.97   UK   ISSN 0268-1587
IMMUNOLOGIC RECEPTORS. ceased 1991. m. (looseleaf format; back issues avail.) Sheffield University Biomedical Information Service (SUBIS), The University, Sheffield S10 2TN, England.

576   US   ISSN 0092-6019
CODEN: IMSED7
IMMUNOLOGY: AN INTERNATIONAL SERIES OF MONOGRAPHS AND TREATISES. 1971-1981 (vol.6). irreg. (reprint service avail. from ISI) Academic Press, Inc., 1250 Sixth Ave., San Diego, CA 92101.
Formerly: Monographs on Immunology (ISSN 0077-1023)

616.97   US   ISSN 0271-3284
IMMUNOLOGY TRIBUNE. ceased. m. (tabloid format; back issues avail.) M D T Publications, Box 581, Sheffield, MA 01257-0581.

616.76 576   UK   ISSN 0264-9551
IMMUNOPARASITOLOGY. ceased 1990. m. (looseleaf format; back issues avail.) Sheffield University Biomedical Information Service (SUBIS), The University, Sheffield S10 2TN, England.

616.76 616.99   UK   ISSN 0264-956X
IMMUNOSUPPRESSION. ceased 1989. m. (looseleaf format; back issues avail.) Sheffield University Biomedical Information Service (SUBIS), The University, Sheffield S10 2TN, England.

659.1   US
IMPACT (EVANSTON). 1959-1989 (Jan.). m. (back issues avail.) Impact Publications (Evanston), Box 1896, Evanston, IL 60204-1896.

347   US
IMPACT (SAN FRANCISCO). 1979-198? q. (tabloid format; back issues avail.) Public Interest Clearinghouse, 200 McAllister St., San Francisco, CA 94102.
Formerly: Public Interest Clearinghouse. Newsletter.

054.1   SZ
L'IMPACT SUISSE. 1968-1991. 11/yr. Hugo Buchser S.A., P.O. Box 402, 1211 Geneva 11, Switzerland.

380.01 663.1   US   ISSN 0749-7946
HD9353
IMPACT YEARBOOK; a directory of the U.S. wine & spirits industry. 1985-19?? a. M. Shanken Communications, Inc., Attn.: Lynn Rittenband, 387 Park Ave. S., New York, NY 10016.

320.531   DR
IMPACTO SOCIALISTA. 1975-197?; N.S. 1985-198? bi-m. (Partido Comunista Dominicano) Editora Taller, C. por A., Isabel la Catolica 309, Santo Domingo, Dominican Republic.

382   US   ISSN 0073-5604
IMPORTERS AND EXPORTERS TRADE PROMOTION GUIDE. 1967-19?? irreg. World Wide Trade Service, Box 283, Medina, WA 98039.

381   US   ISSN 1041-6056
IN DELAWARE; Delaware's international magazine. published only once, 1989. q. Gauge Corporation, 1300 N. Market St., Ste. 501, Wilmington, DE 19801.

647.94   IT
IN DESIGN. 1960-198? m. Stammer S.p.A., Centro Commerciale Milano San Felice, 20090 Segrate-Milan, Italy.
Formerly: Am Albergo Moderno (ISSN 0392-2847)

910.202   RH
IN FLIGHT WITH AIR ZIMBABWE. ceased. 6/yr. (Air Zimbabwe) Modus Publications (Pvt) Ltd, Throgmorton House, Samora Michel Ave., P.O. Box 1819, Harare, Zimbabwe.

910.202   US
IN PARADISE. 1981-1990. m. Hawaiian Airlines, 7 Waterfront Plaza, Ste. 400, 500 Ala Moana Blvd., Honolulu, HI 96813.
Formerly (until 1987): Hawaii.

220   US
IN STEP. ceased 1991 (Jan.). q. Prairie Bible Institute, Three Hills, Alberta TOM 2AO, Canada.

287   US
IN TOUCH (INDIANAPOLIS). 1971-1991 (Aug.). w. (Wesleyan Church) Wesley Press, c/o In Touch Editor, Box 50434, Indianapolis, IN 46250.
Former titles: Encounter (Indianapolis, 1971); Venture.

378   US
IN VIEW. 1989-1991. 5/yr. (tabloid format) Whittle Communications L.P., Corporate Communications, 333 Main Ave., Knoxville, TN 37902.

612.015 616.4   UK   ISSN 0142-8691
INBORN ERRORS OF METABOLISM. ceased 1990. m. (looseleaf format; back issues avail.) Sheffield University Biomedical Information Service (SUBIS), The University, Sheffield S10 2TN, England.

336.2   US
INCOME, EMPLOYMENT, ESTATE AND GIFT TAX PROVISIONS: INTERNAL REVENUE CODE. ceased. a. Commerce Clearing House, Inc., 4025 W. Peterson Ave., Chicago, IL 60646.
Formerly: Income, Estate and Gift Tax Provisions: Internal Revenue Code (ISSN 0073-5671)

336.24   II   ISSN 0019-3437
INCOME-TAX JOURNAL. 1963-19?? fortn. Madras Law Journal Office, P.O. Box 604, Madras 4, India.

384.54   UK   ISSN 0309-0175
INDEPENDENT BROADCASTING AUTHORITY. ANNUAL REPORT AND ACCOUNTS. 1954-1991. a. Independent Television Commission, 70 Brompton Rd., London SW3 1EY, England.

378.73   US   ISSN 0734-6735
INDEPENDENT HIGHER EDUCATION. 1976-1980. a. National Institute of Independent Colleges and Universities, 122 C St., N.W., Ste. 750, Washington, DC 20001.
Formerly: Private Higher Education (ISSN 0364-3735)

332.678   US   ISSN 1042-3346
INDEPENDENT INVESTOR. 1985-1989 (vol.5, no.19). 24/yr. (back issues avail.) Strategic Advisers, Inc., 82 Devonshire St., Dept. L8A, Boston, MA 02109.
Former titles (until 1987): Independent Investor's Personal Investing Newsletter (ISSN 8755-7185); Personal Investing.

070.5   US   ISSN 0898-784X
INDEPENDENT PUBLISHERS TRADE REPORT. 1987-198? m. (back issues avail.) Greenfield Press, Box 176, Southport, CT 06490.

388.324   CN
INDEPENDENT TRUCKER. 1981-1991. m. (back issues avail.) Wadham Publications Ltd., 1450 Don Mills Rd., Don Mills, Ont. M3B 2X7, Canada.
Former titles: Trucking Canada; Western Trucking; Trucking Canada (East and West).

540 016   US   ISSN 0019-3828
INDEX CHEMICUS REGISTRY SYSTEM. 1964-1988. 12 monthly tapes plus annual cumulation tape. (magnetic tape) Institute for Scientific Information, c/o Shelly Rahman, 3501 Market St., Philadelphia, PA 19104.

551.4   CN
INDEX DE REFERENCES: INVENTAIRE DES STATIONS HYDROMETRIQUES. 1968-1972. irreg. Department of Energy and Resources, 5700, 4e av. Ouest, Charlesbourg, Que. G1H 6R1, Canada.

700   US   ISSN 0085-1760
INDEX OF ART IN THE PACIFIC NORTHWEST. 1970-19?? irreg. (University of Washington, Henry Art Gallery) University of Washington Press, Box 50096, Seattle, WA 98105.

331 016   CN   ISSN 0226-1537
Z7164.L1
INDEX OF INDUSTRIAL RELATIONS LITERATURE. 1976-19?? a. Queen's University, Industrial Relations Centre, Kingston, Ont. K7L 3N6, Canada.

150   US   ISSN 0073-5884
INDEX OF PSYCHOANALYTIC WRITINGS. ceased. irreg. International Universities Press, Inc., 59 Boston Post Rd., Box 1524, Madison, CT 06443-1524.

001.3 028   US   ISSN 0073-5892
Z1035.A1
INDEX TO BOOK REVIEWS IN THE HUMANITIES. 1960-1991 (Aug.). a. (back issues avail.) Phillip Thomson, Ed. & Pub., 836 Georgia St., Williamston, MI 48895.

340   US   ISSN 0000-104X
INDEX TO LEGAL BOOKS. ceased. a. R.R. Bowker, A Reed Reference Publishing Company, Division of Reed Publishing (USA) Inc., 121 Chanlon Rd., New Providence, NJ 07974.

380   II   ISSN 0536-7506
INDIA. OFFICE OF THE COMPTROLLER AND AUDITOR-GENERAL. REPORT: UNION GOVERNMENT (POSTS AND TELEGRAPHS). 1970-19?? a. Office of the Comptroller and Auditor-General, Controller of Publications, Civil Lines, Delhi 110054, India.

665.5   UK   ISSN 0957-2384
INDIA ENERGY. 1989-198? bi-m. Knighton Enterprises Ltd., P.O. Box 213, Swindon SN6 8UA, England.

028.1 970.1   CN   ISSN 0709-9010
DS407
INDIAN BOOK REVIEW DIGEST. 1977-19?? a. LITIR Database, c/o Department of English, University of Alberta, Edmonton, Alta. T6G 2E5, Canada.

600   II   ISSN 0073-6503
INDIAN INSTITUTE OF TECHNOLOGY, BOMBAY. SERIES. 1968-1980. irreg. Indian Institute of Technology, Bombay, Central Library, Powai, Bombay 400 076, India.

616.988   II   ISSN 0019-5898
INDIAN MEDICAL RECORD. 1880-19?? m. S.C. Mookerjee, 14 Purand Chand Nahar Ave., Calcutta 13, India.

320 954   US
INDIAN REVIEW (CHICAGO); a review of India & the neighbouring countries. 1978-19?? q. 33 N. LaSalle St., Ste. 2323, Chicago, IL 60602-2604.

338.1   II   ISSN 0970-4981
INDIAN TOBACCO JOURNAL. 1969-1979 (vol. 20). q. Ministry of Agriculture, Department of Agriculture and Cooperation, Directorate of Tobacco Development - Tambaku Vikas Nideshalaya, 27 Eldams Rd., Teynampet, Madras 600 018, India.
Formerly (until 1977): Indian Tobacco Bulletin.

368.4 331   US
INDIANA. DEPARTMENT OF EMPLOYMENT AND TRAINING SERVICES. MONTHLY SUMMARY OF UNEMPLOYMENT INSURANCE ACTIVITIES. ceased 1990. m. Department of Employment and Training Services, Statistical Services, 10 Senate Ave., Rm. 313, Indianapolis, IN 46204.

368.4 331   US
INDIANA. DEPARTMENT OF EMPLOYMENT AND TRAINING SERVICES. SOME SIGNIFICANT STATISTICS ABOUT UNEMPLOYMENT INSURANCE. ceased 1990. a. Department of Employment and Training Services, Statistical Services, 10 Senate Ave., Rm. 313, Indianapolis, IN 46204.

977.2   US   ISSN 0019-6649
F521
INDIANA HISTORY BULLETIN. 1923-19?? (vol.63). m. Indiana Historical Bureau, 408 State Library and Historical Bldg., 140 N. Senate Ave., Indianapolis, IN 46204.

CESSATIONS

331.1   US
HD5725.I6
INDIANA LABOR MARKET LETTER. ceased 1988. m. Department of Employment and Training Services, Labor Market Information, 10 N. Senate Ave., Rm. 101, Indianapolis, IN 46204.
   Formerly: Labor Force Status of Indiana Residents (ISSN 0362-3793)

331   US
INDIANA REPORT. ceased. m. Department of Employment and Training Services, Labor Market Information, 10 Senate Ave., Rm. 101, Indianapolis, IN 46204.

371.26   US
INDIANA STUDIES IN HIGHER EDUCATION. 1961-1987 (Nov.). irreg. Indiana University, Bureau of Evaluative Studies and Testing, Bloomington, IN 47404.
   Formerly: Indiana Studies in Prediction (ISSN 0073-6945)

020 027.7   US   ISSN 0019-6800
Z1007
INDIANA UNIVERSITY BOOKMAN. 1956-1988 (no.17). irreg. (also avail. in microform from UMI) Indiana University, Lilly Library, Bloomington, IN 47405.
   Supersedes: Indiana Quarterly for Bookmen.

330.9   MX
INDICADORES DEL SECTOR FINANCIERO. ceased 1988 (Oct.). m. Banco de Mexico, Direccion de Investigacion Economica y Bancaria, Av. Juarez 90, Col. Centro, Delegacion Cuauhtemoc, 06059 Mexico DF, Mexico.
   Formerly (until 1985): Indicadores de Moneda y Banca.

918.102   BL   ISSN 0101-8353
INDICADORES I B G E/I B G E INDICATORS. 1982-1990; suspended. m. (also avail. in microform) Fundacao Instituto Brasileiro de Geografia e Estatistica, Divisao de Comercializacao e Promocao, Rua General Canabarro, 666 Bloco B, 2o andar, CEP 20271 Maracana Rio de Janeiro, Brazil.

658.5   SZ
INDICATEUR INDUSTRIEL; revue europeenne de la machine-outil, d'electronique et d'electrotechnique. 1912-1991. m. La Planta, 1163 Efoy, Switzerland.
   Formerly: Revue de la Technique Europeenne (ISSN 0035-4252)

686.2 016   IT   ISSN 0019-6967
Z117
INDICATORE GRAFICO; rassegna bibliografica mensile. 1960-1984 (vol.25, no.9). m. Ente Nazionale per la Cellulosa e per la Carta, Viale Regina Margherita 262, 00198 Rome, Italy.

011 610   GW   ISSN 0340-8094
INDICES NATURWISSENSCHAFTLICH-MEDIZINISCHER PERIODICA BIS 1850. 1971-1981 (vol.3). irreg. Anton Hiersemann Verlag, Rosenbergstr. 113, Postfach 140155, 7000 Stuttgart 1, Germany.

332.6   US
INDIVIDUALIZED PORTFOLIOS. 1987-1989. m. Analytic Systems, Inc., 625 N. Michigan Ave., Ste. 1920, Chicago, IL 60611.

100   GW   ISSN 0179-7565
AP32
INDIVIUALITAET; Europaeische Vierteljahresschrift. 1982-1990. q. (back issues avail.) Verlag Urachhaus Johannes M. Mayer GmbH, Postfach 13 10 89, 7000 Stuttgart 1, Germany.
   Formerly (until 1985): Kaspar Hauser - Europaeische Halbjahresschrift.

591   NE   ISSN 0168-6259
INDO-MALAYAN ZOOLOGY. 1984-19?? (vol.6). s-a. A.A. Balkema, P.O. Box 1675, 3000 BR Rotterdam, Netherlands.

639   UN   ISSN 0537-3654
INDO-PACIFIC FISHERIES COUNCIL. REGIONAL STUDIES. 1965-1975. irreg. Indo-Pacific Fisheries Council, F A O Regional Office for Asia and the Pacific, Maliwan Mansion, Phra Atit Road, Bangkok 10200, Thailand.

591 562   US   ISSN 0073-7240
QL401   CODEN: IPMOAP
INDO-PACIFIC MOLLUSCA. 1959-1976 (no.17). irreg. Delaware Museum of Natural History, Box 3937, Wilmington, DE 19807.

500   IO
INDONESIA. CENTRE FOR SCIENTIFIC DOCUMENTATION AND INFORMATION. ANNUAL REPORT/INDONESIA. PUSAT DOKUMENTASI DAN INFORMASI ILMIAH. LAPORAN TAHUNAN. 1965-1988. a. Indonesian Institute of Sciences, Centre for Scientific Documentation and Information - Pusat Dokumentasi dan Informasi Ilmiah - Lembaga Ilmu Pengetahuan Indonesia, Jalan Jenderal Gatot Subroto 10, Box 269-JKSMG-88, Jakarta 12790, Indonesia.
   Formerly: Indonesia. National Scientific Documentation Center. Annual Report (ISSN 0126-0812)

631   US
INDOOR CITRUS & RARE FRUIT SOCIETY. NEWSLETTER. 1981-1990 (no.34). q. Indoor Citrus & Rare Fruit Society, 490 Spring Grove Rd., Hollister, CA 95023.

330.9   YU   ISSN 0353-0973
INDOS; glasilo delovne organizacije. 1974-1989. bi-m. (looseleaf format) Industrijska c.3, 61110 Ljubljana, Yugoslavia.

614   UK
INDUSAFE. 1976-198? bi-m. (Northern Ireland Industrial Safety Group) Carnaghan Associates, 8 Collinbridge Drive, Glengormley, Newtownabbey, N. Ireland.

615   IT   ISSN 0446-0243
INDUSTRIA DEI FARMACI. 1955-198? bi-m. (Associazione Nazionale dell' Industria Farmaceutica Italiana) Pieraldo Editore s.r.l., Piazza di Pietra 34, 00186 Rome, Italy.

600   IT
INDUSTRIA OGGI. ceased. m. Gruppo Editoriale Jackson S.p.A., Via Pola 9, 20124 Milan, Italy.

614.85   US   ISSN 0073-7313
INDUSTRIAL ACCIDENT PREVENTION ASSOCIATION. GUIDE TO SAFETY. 1965-19?? a. Industrial Accident Prevention Association, 2 Bloor St. W., Toronto, Ont. M4W 3N8, Canada.

660   US   ISSN 0273-9313
TP1
INDUSTRIAL CHEMICAL NEWS. 1980-19??; suspended. m. (tabloid format; also avail. in microform from UMI; reprint service avail. from UMI) Chemical Week Associates, 810 Seventh Avenue, New York, NY 10019.

338   US   ISSN 0882-9454
HC107.A135
INDUSTRIAL DEVELOPMENT IN THE TENNESSEE VALLEY REGION. 1959-1989. a. Tennessee Valley Authority, Industrial Development Staff, 3B4 Old City Hall, Knoxville, TN 37902.
   Formerly (until 1983): Industrial Development in the T V A Area (ISSN 0495-145X)

620   BE
INDUSTRIAL ENGINEERING NEWS. 1975-19?? 10/yr. Pan European Publishing Co., Rue Verte 216, B-1210 Brussels, Belgium.
   Formerly: International Equipment News. Europe.

338   SA
INDUSTRIAL EQUIPMENT SELECTOR. 1971-19?? m. Keeble Publishing Co. Pty. Ltd., P.O. Box 3080, Johannesburg 2000, South Africa.

634.9   US
INDUSTRIAL FORESTRY ASSOCIATION. NEWSLETTER. 1934-19?? 16/yr. Industrial Forestry Association, 1500 SW First, Ste. 770, Portland, OR 97201.

338   PH   ISSN 0019-8587
INDUSTRIAL PHILIPPINES. 1950-1978? m. Philippine Chamber of Industries, P.O. Box 3873, Manila, Philippines.

346.066   UK
INDUSTRIAL PROPERTY LAW. ANNUAL. 1975-198? irreg. (European Law Centre Ltd.) Sweet & Maxwell, South Quay Plaza, 8th Floor, 183 Marsh Wall, London E14 9FT, England.

613.62   II   ISSN 0019-8765
INDUSTRIAL SAFETY & HEALTH BULLETIN. 1958-19?? q. Directorate General of Factory Advice and Labour Institutes, Central Labour Institute Bldg., Sion, Bombay 22, India.

747   US
INDUSTRIAL SEWING NEWS. 1990-1991. q. Bobbin Blenheim Media Corp., 1110 Shop Rd., Box 1986, Columbia, SC 29202.

621.9   AT
INDUSTRIAL TECHNOLOGY AND MACHINE TOOLS. 1949-19?? 6/yr. (tabloid format) Prince Publishing Group Pty. Ltd. (Subsidiary of: TecPress Ltd. (Hong Kong)), St. James Centre, 111 Elizabeth St., 17th Fl., Sydney, N.S.W. 2000, Australia.
   Supersedes: Machine Tool Monthly; Manufacturing Engineer (ISSN 0047-5815)

338   UK
INDUSTRIAL TYNE & WEAR. 1920-198? m. Tyne & Wear Chamber of Commerce, 65 Quayside, Newcastle Upon Tyne NE1 3DS, England.
   Formerly: Industrial Tyneside (ISSN 0019-8846)

338   IQ   ISSN 0046-9270
INDUSTRIALIST/SINAI. 1960-19?? q. Iraqi Federation of Industries, Khullani Sq., P.O. Box 5665, South Gate, Baghdad, Iraq.

332.6   US   ISSN 0094-1352
HG4915
INDUSTRISCOPE. 1973-1990 (Feb.). m. (tabloid format) Media General Financial Services, 301 E. Grace St., Box C-32333, Richmond, VA 23293.
   Supersedes: Financial Weekly Industriscope.

338   US   ISSN 0019-9435
HC107.M4
INDUSTRY. 1918-1991 (Jul.). m. (Associated Industries of Massachusetts) A I M Service Corporation, 441 Stuart St., Box 763, Boston, MA 02116.

382   US
INDUSTRY INTERNATIONAL. 1981-198? bi-m. Johnston International (Subsidiary of: Hunter Publishing L.P.), 386 Park Ave., S., New York, NY 10016.

640.73   US
INFACT UPDATE. ceased. s-a. Infact, 256 Hanover St., 3rd Fl., Boston, MA 02113-2303.

616.9   CN   ISSN 0833-076X
INFECTION CONTROL CANADA. 1986-1989. q. Health Media Inc., 14453 29A Ave., White Rock, B.C. V4A 9K8, Canada.

610   US   ISSN 0090-6549
RC110   CODEN: IFDRAL
INFECTIOUS DISEASE REVIEWS. 1971-1981. irreg. Futura Publishing Co., 295 Main St., Box 330, Mount Kisco, NY 10549.

330   CN   ISSN 0824-801X
INFLATION MONITOR. 1983-1990 (no.5). irreg. C.D. Howe Institute, 125 Adelaide St. East, Toronto, Ont. M5C 1L7, Canada.

052 054.1   CN
INFLUENCE; for Canadians of ideas, style and action. ceased 1988. bi-m. (back issues avail.) Sound & Vision, 99 Atlantic Ave., Ste.302, Toronto, Ont. M6K 3J8, Canada.

621.381   US
INFO (IOWA CITY). 1983-1992. m. (also avail. in microfiche) Info Publications, Inc., 705 Hwy. 1 W., Iowa City, IA 52246-4221.
   Formerly: Info 64.

385   BE
INFO S T I B/INFO M I V B. 1979-1988 (no.51). bi-m. Societe des Transports Intercommunaux de Bruxelles, Av. de la Toison d'Or, 1060 Brussels, Belgium.

677   DK   ISSN 0901-4233
INFO-TEX. 1984-19?? 6/yr. Bredgade 41, DK-7400 Herning, Denmark.

052   SA   ISSN 0250-1910
INFORMA. 1953-19?? m. (back issues avail.) Department of Development Planning, Private Bag X644, Pretoria 0001, South Africa.
   Formerly: Mvelaphanda (ISSN 0025-6242)

700   PO
INFORMACAO CULTURAL. 1976-19?? irreg. Secretaria da Estado da Cultura, Av. da Republica 16, Lisbon 1, Portugal.

056.1 SP
INFORMACION CULTURAL. 1978-1990? m. Ministerio de Cultura, Secretaria General Tecnica, Plaza del Rey, 1, 28071 Madrid, Spain.
Formerly (until 1981): Cuaderno de Cultura.

338.1 CN
L'INFORMATEUR AGRICOLE. 1982-1988. m. 1500 Laframboise, Saint-Hyacinthe, Que. J2S 7Z3, Canada.

708.3 GW ISSN 0171-6913
INFORMATION; Theater und Musik, Kunst und Wissenschaft in Kassel. 1969-19?? m. Baerenreiter Verlag, Heinrich-Schuetz-Allee 31-37, 3500 Kassel, Germany.
Formerly: Informationen aus Kassel.

665.5 UK ISSN 0019-9931
INFORMATION ABOUT THE OIL INDUSTRY - FOR THE OIL INDUSTRY. 1961-1990. m. Associated Octel Company Ltd., 20 Berkeley Sq., London W1X 6DT, England.

658 621.381 US ISSN 0883-315X
CODEN: ICENEV
INFORMATION CENTER. 1985-1991. q. Weingarten Publications, Inc., 38 Chauncy St., Boston, MA 02111.

972.9 MQ
INFORMATION ECONOMIQUE. ceased. irreg. Chambre de Commerce et d'Industrie de la Martinique, 50 Rue Ernest Deproge, P.O. Box 478, 97241 Fort-de-France Cedex, Martinique, W.I.

001.64 658.4031 US ISSN 1041-9098
T58.64 CODEN: IEXEEB
INFORMATION EXECUTIVE. 1988-19??; suspended. q. Data Processing Management Association, 505 Busse Hwy., Park Ridge, IL 60068-3191.

792 GW ISSN 0046-9343
Z6935.
INFORMATION G. 1970-1971. bi-m. Wolfgang Gielow Verlag, Theatinerstr. 35, 8000 Munich 2, Germany.

025 US ISSN 1049-9326
INFORMATION INDUSTRY ALERT; tracking the application of information delivery technology. 1990-1991. m. Industry News Service Inc., Box 457, Wilton, CT 06897-0457.

658 US
INFORMATION MANAGEMENT REVIEW. 1985-198? q. Aspen Publishers, Inc., 200 Orchard Ridge Dr., Gaithersburg, MD 20878.

340 658.403 US
INFORMATION MARKETING NEWS. 1983-198? bi-w. Paul Lowell, 88 Bleecker St., New York, NY 10012.

914 382 US
INFORMATION MOSCOW, WESTERN EDITION. 1978-1988; suspended. irreg. Sovus Business Consultants, 40 W. 67th St., Ste.7C, New York, NY 10023.
Former titles: U S Information Moscow; Information Moscow (ISSN 0163-5093)

915.1 US
INFORMATION PEKING (BEIJING). 1980-198? irreg. Welt Publishing Co., 1413 K. St., N.W., Ste. 800, Washington, DC 20005.

020 US
INFORMATION SCIENCES SERIES. 1963-1988? irreg. John Wiley & Sons, Inc., 605 Third Ave., New York, NY 10158-0012.
Formerly: Hayes and Becker Information Sciences Series.

362.7 US
INFORMATION SHARING INDEX. ceased. a. U.S. Department of Health and Human Services, Office of Child Support Enforcement, National Child Support Enforcement Reference Center, 330 C St., S.W., Ste. 2094, Washington, DC 20201-0001.

330 US
HF5548.2 CODEN: IFSYAF
INFORMATION SYSTEMS (CAROL STREAM). 1958-1988. m. (also avail. in microform from UMI; reprint service avail. from UMI) Hitchcock Publishing Co. (Subsidiary of: American Broadcasting Companies, Inc.), 191 S. Gary Ave., Carol Stream, IL 60188.
Former titles: Infosystems (ISSN 0364-5533); Business Automation.

621.381 UK
INFORMATION TECHNOLOGY, COMPUTER & COMMUNICATIONS. HARDWARE INDEX. 1985-1991. 2/yr. Technical Indexes Ltd., Willoughby Rd., Bracknell, Berkshire RG12 8DW, England.

338.91 UK ISSN 0268-1102
HC59.72.I55
INFORMATION TECHNOLOGY FOR DEVELOPMENT. 1986-1990. q. (UNESCO Informatics Division, UN) Oxford University Press, Oxford Journals, Pinkhill House, Southfield Road, Eynsham, Oxford OX8 1JJ, England.

020 GW ISSN 0138-5739
INFORMATION UND DOKUMENTATION: ANNOTIERTE TITELLISTE. 1968-1991. q. Zentralinstitut fuer Information und Dokumentation der D D R, Koepenicker Str. 80-82, 1020 Berlin, Germany.

636 CN ISSN 0581-3263
INFORMATION VETERINAIRE. ceased. irreg. Universite de Montreal, Faculte de Medecine Veterinaire, C.P. 5000, St. Hyacinthe, Que. J2S 7C6, Canada.

301 GW ISSN 0020-0395
INFORMATIONEN ZUR SOZIOLOGISCHE FORSCHUNG IN DER D.D.R.. 1965-1990. irreg. Akademie fuer Gesellschaftswissenschaften beim ZK der SED, Zentralstelle fuer Soziologische Information und Dokumentation, Johannes-Dieckmann-Str. 19-23, 1086 Berlin, Germany.

352 301 FR ISSN 0396-9975
INFORMATIONS D'ILE DE FRANCE. 1970-1991 (no.87). 4/yr. Prefecture de la Region d'Ile de France, 29 rue Barbet de Jouy, 75700 Paris, France.
Former titles: Bulletin d'Information de la Region Parisienne (ISSN 0018-8506); I.A.U.R.P. Bulletin.

574 GW ISSN 0344-4430
INFORMATIONSAUFNAHME UND INFORMATIONSVERARBEITUNG IM LEBENDEN ORGANISMUS. 1971-1975. irreg. (Akademie der Wissenschaften und der Literatur, Mainz, Mathematisch-Naturwissenschaftliche Klasse) Franz Steiner Verlag Wiesbaden GmbH, Birkenwaldstr. 44, Postfach 10 15 26, D-7000 Stuttgart 1, Germany.

913 GW
INFORMATIONSBLAETTER ZU NACHBARWISSENSCHAFTEN DER UR- UND FRUEHGESCHICHTE. 1970-19?? a. Dr. Rudolf Habelt GmbH, Am Buchenhang 1, 5300 Bonn 1, Germany.

388.324 GW ISSN 0342-4960
INFORMATIONSDIENST FUER DEN K F Z-ZUBEHOER UND ERSATZTEILE-FACHHANDEL. 1953-1991. m. Gert Wohlfarth GmbH Verlag Fachtechnik und Mercator-Verlag, Stresemannstr. 20-22, 4100 Duisburg 1, Germany.

020 GW
INFORMATIONSDIENST UEBERSETZUNGEN. ceased 1991. irreg. (microfiche) Zentralinstitut fuer Information und Dokumentation der D D R, Koepenicker Str. 80-82, 1020 Berlin, Germany.

616.5 GW ISSN 0930-6803
INFORMATIONSZENTRUM HAUT. 1986-1989. bi-m. (back issues avail.) P M I Verlag GmbH, August-Schanz-Str. 21, D-6000 Frankfurt 50, Germany.

385 BL
INFORMATIVO R N. 1971-19?? Rede Ferroviaria Federal, S.A., Regional do Nordeste, Praca Procopio Ferreira 86, 20.224 Rio de Janeiro, Brazil.

327 MX ISSN 0185-4399
E183.8.M6
INFORME; relaciones Mexico-Estados Unidos. ceased (vol.2, no.4). 3/yr. Centro de Estudios Economicos y Sociales del Tercer Mundo, Programa de Estudio de las Relaciones Mexico-Estados Unidos, Porfirio Diaz No. 50, San Jeronimo, Mexico 10200, Mexico.

615 610 US ISSN 0730-6636
INFORMED. 1970-19?? w. (looseleaf format; back issues avail.) M D T Publications, Box 581, Sheffield, MA 01257-0581.

340 US
INFORMER (EAU CLAIRE). ceased. q. 200 Spring St., Eau Claire, WI 54702.

380.3 001.6 HK
INFOTEC CHINA; magazine of telecommunication, computer and automation. 1985-1989 (vol.15). 3/yr. Adsale Publishing Company, Tung Wai Commercial Bldg., 21st Fl., 109-111 Gloucester Rd., Wanchai, Hong Kong.

530 US
INFRARED AND MILLIMETER WAVES. 1981-1986 (vol. 16). irreg. Academic Press, Inc., 1250 6th Ave., San Diego, CA 92101.

620 IT ISSN 0035-6263
CODEN: IGGRBA
INGEGNERIA; rivista di scienza e tecnica. 1951-1986 (Dec.). m. Editore Ulrico Hoepli, Via Hoelpi 5, 20121 Milan, Italy.

370 US ISSN 0073-800X
INGLIS LECTURE. 1926-1965. a. Harvard University Press, 79 Garden St., Cambridge, MA 02138.

332.64 US ISSN 1053-7163
HG4961
INITIAL PUBLIC OFFERINGS ANNUAL. 1990; published only once. a. Omnigraphics, Inc., 2500 Penobscot Bldg., Detroit, MI 48226.

322.4 340 US
INITIATIVE AND REFERENDUM: THE POWER OF THE PEOPLE!. 1986-1989. q. (back issues avail.) Initiative Resource Center, 235 Douglass St., San Francisco, CA 94114.

811 810 US
INK (BUFFALO). 1974-1987; suspended. a. 111 Elmwood Ave., Buffalo, NY 14201.

610 SP
INMUNOLOGIKA. ceased 1987 (vol.7, no.2). bi-m. Grutesa, Arzobispo Morcillo 24, Apartado 19 182, Madrid 34, Spain.

780 621.389 US ISSN 1047-2363
ML1049.8
INMUSIC. 1990-1991 (Apr.). m. Schwann Publications, 535 Boylston St., Boston, MA 02116.

633 AT ISSN 0020-1588
INNISFAIL CANEGROWER. suspended. m. Innisfail District Canegrowers' Executive, P.O. Box 32, Innisfail, Qld., Australia.

624 GW
INNOVATION. 1962-1991. m. Verlag fuer Technik und Wirtschaft GmbH & Co., Lise-Meitner-Str. 2, Postfach 4029, 6500 Mainz, Germany.
Formerly: Ingenieur Digest (ISSN 0579-6407)

001.6 620 GW ISSN 0721-4405
DER INNOVATIONS-BERATER; Ideen fuer neue und bessere Produkte und Dienstleistungen. 1982-1989. bi-m. Rudolf Haufe Verlag & Co. KG, Postfach 740, 7800 Freiburg im Breisgau, Germany.

668.4 540 US ISSN 1045-1889
INNOVATIONS IN POLYMERS - ENGINEERING PLASTICS. 1989-199? m. (back issues avail.) Technical Insights, Inc., 32 N. Dean St., Englewood, NJ 07631.

338 AT
INNOVATORS DIRECTORY. 1985-19?? irreg. Department of Industry Development, G.P.O. 1141, Brisbane, Qld. 4001, Australia.

800 AT ISSN 0314-285X
INPRINT; the short story journal. 1977-1989 (vol.10). a. (back issues avail.) Australian Council Literature Board, P.O. Box 666, Broadway, N.S.W. 2007, Australia.

627 TU ISSN 0300-2721
INSAAT MUHENDISLERI ODASI. TEKNIK BULTEN. ceased 1978 (vol.8). q. Turkish Chamber of Civil Engineers - Insaat Muhendisleri Odasi, Selanik Caddesi 19-1, Kizilay 06650 Ankara, Turkey.

070.5 US
INSIDE BOOKS. 1988-1989; suspended. m. Miami Media, Inc., 18 E. 12th St., New York, NY 10003.

796.6 US
INSIDE CYCLING. ceased. m. Inside Communications, 5595 Arapahoe Ave., Ste. G, Boulder, CO 80303.

CESSATIONS

340   US   ISSN 0747-6213
KF3890.A15
INSIDE DRUG LAW; an independent publication for drug-law professionals. 1984-19?? 10/yr. (looseleaf format) Vanguard Information Publications, Box 667, Chapel Hill, NC 27514.

635   CN
INSIDE GREEN. ceased. 10/yr. Indoor Gardening Society of Canada, 16 Edgar Woods Rd., Willowdale, Ont. M2H 2Y7, Canada.

808 808.838   US
INSIDE JOKE; a newsletter of comedy and creativity. 1980-19?? 8/yr. (every 6 wks.). Pen-Elayne Enterprises, Box 1609, Madison Sq. Sta., New York, NY 10159.

364 360   UK
INSIDE OUT. 1972-1990. q. Society of Voluntary Associates, Brixton Hill Pl., London SW2 1HJ, England.
    Formerly (until 1988): S O V A News.

001.642   US
INSIDE 1 2 3 - G. 1990; ceased same year. m. Cobb Group, Inc., 9420 Bunsen Pkwy., Ste. 300, Louisville, KY 40220.

796.357   US   ISSN 0731-8146
GV877
INSIDERS BASEBALL FACT-BOOK EXTRA. 1982-19?? a. Research Analysis Publications, 3339 McLaughlin Rd., Los Angeles, CA 90006.

741.43   US
INSIDER'S BOX OFFICE REPORT ANNUAL. 1987-1988. a. VerDugo Press, 6715 Sunset Blvd., Hollywood, CA 90028.

373   AT   ISSN 0811-4188
INSIGHT. 1983-1989 (no.2). s-a. Department of School Education, G.P.O. Box 33, Sydney, N.S.W. 2001, Australia.

378   UK   ISSN 0144-8471
INSIGHT (LONDON, 1978). 1978-1983. q. Hipper Teachers' Centre, Markham Rd., Chesterfield, Derbyshire, England.

296 323.4   UK   ISSN 0307-353X
DS135.E8
INSIGHT: SOVIET JEWS. 1975-1988. irreg. 31 Percy St., London W. 1, England.

364   FR   ISSN 0020-2134
INSTANTANES CRIMINOLOGIQUES. 1967-19??; suspended. q. (Association Francaise de Criminologie) Centre Francais de Criminologie, 12 av. Rockefeller, 69008 Lyon, France.

630   SP
INSTITUT AGRICOLA CATALA DE SANT ISIDRE. BUTLLETI. 1978-198? m. Institut Agricola Catala de Sant Isidre, Plaza de Sant Josep Oriol, 4, 08002 Barcelona, Spain.

368   FR   ISSN 0020-2223
INSTITUT DES ACTUAIRES FRANCAIS. BULLETIN TRIMESTRIEL. 1890-19?? q. Dulac et Cie, 8 Rue Lamartine, 75009 Paris, France.

800   FR   ISSN 0073-8263
INSTITUT DES ETUDES OCCITANES. PUBLICATIONS. 1970-19?? irreg. (reprint service avail. from KTO) Presses Universitaires de France, Departement des Revues, 14 Avenue du Bois-de-l'Epine, B.P.90, 91003 Evry Cedex, France.

960   SG   ISSN 0070-2633
INSTITUT FONDAMENTAL D'AFRIQUE NOIRE. MEMOIRES. 1939-1982. irreg. (reprint service avail. from SWZ) Institut Fondamental d'Afrique Noire - Cheikh Anta Diop, Boite Postale 206, Dakar, Senegal.

658.8   DK   ISSN 0108-1489
INSTITUT FOR AFSAETNINGSOEKONOMI. NYT. 1974-1989. irreg. (approx. 8/yr). Handelshoejskolen i Koebenhavn, Institut for Afsaetningsoekonomi - Copenhagen School of Economics and Business Administration, Rosenoerns Alle 31,4.sal, DK-1970 Frederiksberg C, Denmark.

300   AU   ISSN 0046-9696
INSTITUT FUER GESELLSCHAFTSPOLITIK. MITTEILUNGEN. 1970-1988. irreg. Ploesslgasse 2, A-1040 Vienna, Austria.

980   GW   ISSN 0073-8948
INSTITUT FUER IBEROAMERIKA-KUNDE. SCHRIFTENREIHE. 1963-1983 (no.31). irreg. K. Thienemanns Verlag, Edition Erdmann, Blumenstr. 36, 7000 Stuttgart, Germany.

380.5 387   FR
INSTITUT MEDITERRANEEN DES TRANSPORTS MARITIMES. 1984-1989. a. (back issues avail.) Edisud, La Calade, RN 7, 13090 Aix-en-Provence, France.

500   RW
INSTITUT NATIONAL DE RECHERCHE SCIENTIFIQUE. RAPPORT POUR L'ANNEE. ceased 1989. a. Institut National de Recherche Scientifique, BP 218, Butare, Rwanda.

956.94   LE
INSTITUTE FOR PALESTINE STUDIES. ARABIC ANNUAL DOCUMENTARY SERIES. 1965-1981. a. Institute for Palestine Studies, P.O. Box 11-7164, Beirut, Lebanon.

956.94   LE
INSTITUTE FOR PALESTINE STUDIES. ARABS UNDER ISRAELI OCCUPATION SERIES. 1969-1981. a. Institute for Palestine Studies, P.O. Box 11-7164, Beirut, Lebanon.

956.94   LE
INSTITUTE FOR PALESTINE STUDIES. I.P.S. PAPERS SERIES. 1979-1990. irreg. Institute for Palestine Studies, P.O. Box 11-7164, Beirut, Lebanon.

956.94   LE   ISSN 0073-8808
INSTITUTE FOR PALESTINE STUDIES. INTERNATIONAL ANNUAL DOCUMENTARY SERIES. 1967-1981. a. Institute for Palestine Studies, P.O. Box 11-7164, Beirut, Lebanon.

150   US
INSTITUTE FOR PSYCHOANALYSIS. NEWSLETTER. 1932-198? 3/yr. Chicago Institute for Psychoanalysis, 180 N. Michigan Ave., Chicago, IL 60601.
    Formerly: Institute for Psychoanalysis. Report (ISSN 0073-8875)

368   UK   ISSN 0020-269X
INSTITUTE OF ACTUARIES STUDENTS' SOCIETY. JOURNAL. 1916-19?? a. Alden Press Ltd., Osney Mead, Oxford OX2 OEF, England.

657   UK   ISSN 0073-9030
INSTITUTE OF CHARTERED ACCOUNTANTS IN ENGLAND AND WALES. MANAGEMENT INFORMATION SERIES. 1968-1985 (no.5). irreg. Institute of Chartered Accountants in England and Wales, P.O. Box 620, Central Milton Keynes, London MK9 2JX, England.

336   UK   ISSN 0143-5205
INSTITUTE OF CHARTERED ACCOUNTANTS IN ENGLAND AND WALES. QUARTERLY TAXATION BULLETIN. 1976-1990. q. Institute of Chartered Accountants in England and Wales, P.O. Box 620, Central Milton Keynes MK9 2JX, England.

664.9   UK
INSTITUTE OF FOOD RESEARCH - BRISTOL LABORATORY BIENNIAL REPORT. 1977-1989. biennial. Institute of Food Research - Bristol, Langford, Bristol BS18 7DY, England.
    Former titles: Food Research Institute Bristol. Biennial Report; Meat Research Institute. Biennial Report.

621   US
INSTITUTE OF INDUSTRIAL ENGINEERS. FACILITIES PLANNING AND DESIGN DIVISION. MONOGRAPH SERIES. ceased. irreg. (reprint service avail. from UMI) Institute of Industrial Engineers, Facilities Planning and Design Division, 25 Technology Park-Atlanta, Norcross, GA 30092.

620   US
INSTITUTE OF INDUSTRIAL ENGINEERS. OPERATIONS RESEARCH DIVISION. MONOGRAPH SERIES. ceased. irreg. (reprint service avail. from UMI) Institute of Industrial Engineers, Operations Research Division, 25 Technology Park-Atlanta, Norcross, GA 30092.

676 016   US
    CODEN: IPCBA4
INSTITUTE OF PAPER SCIENCE AND TECHNOLOGY. BIBLIOGRAPHIC SERIES. 1929-1986 (no.292). irreg. Institute of Paper Science and Technology, 575 14th St., N.W., Atlanta, GA 30318.
    Formerly: Institute of Paper Chemistry. Bibliographic Series (ISSN 0073-9480)

676 016   US
INSTITUTE OF PAPER SCIENCE AND TECHNOLOGY. KEYWORD INDEX TO ABSTRACT BULLETIN. 1966-198? m. (plus s-a. issues). Institute of Paper Science and Technology, 575 14th St., N.W., Atlanta, GA 30318.
    Former titles (until Jul. 1989): Institute of Paper Chemistry. Keyword Index to Abstract Bulletin; Institute Paper Chemistry. Keyword Supplement (ISSN 0020-3041)

301.1   US
INSTITUTE ON PLURALISM AND GROUP IDENTITY. WORKING PAPER SERIES. ceased 1990. irreg. Institute on Pluralism and Group Identity, 165 E. 56th St., New York, NY 10022.

624   UK   ISSN 0307-8353
    CODEN: PEDCEG
INSTITUTION OF CIVIL ENGINEERS. PROCEEDINGS. PART 1: DESIGN AND CONSTRUCTION. vol.52, 1972-1991. bi-m. (back issues avail.) Thomas Telford Ltd., Thomas Telford House, 1 Heron Quay, London E14 4JD, England.

624   UK   ISSN 0307-8361
    CODEN: PETEEY
INSTITUTION OF CIVIL ENGINEERS. PROCEEDINGS. PART 2: RESEARCH AND THEORY. vol.53, 1972-1991. q. (back issues avail.) Thomas Telford Ltd., Thomas Telford House, 1 Heron Quay, London E14 4JD, England.

630   SP   ISSN 0046-9890
INSTITUTO AGRICOLA CATALAN DE SAN ISIDRO. REVISTA. 1852-1989. q. Instituto Agricola Catalan de San Isidro, Plaza de San Jose Oriol, 4, 08002 Barcelona, Spain.

630 016   CK
INSTITUTO COLOMBIANO AGROPECUARIO. CATALOGO DE PUBLICACIONES PERIODICAS. (Supplements avail.) 1975-1982. irreg. Instituto Colombiano Agropecuario, Biblioteca Agropecuaria, Division de Comunicacion Rural, Apdo. Aereo 151123, Bogota, D.E., Colombia.

630   BL   ISSN 0046-9947
INSTITUTO DE PESQUISA AGROPECUARIA DO L'ESTE. PESQUISA E EXPERIMENTOS. COMUNICADO TECNICO. 1971-19?? 40/yr. Instituto de Pesquisa Agropecuaria do l'Este, Cruz das Almas, Bahia 44380, Brazil.

368   BL   ISSN 0100-5790
INSTITUTO DE RESSEGUROS DO BRASIL. SECRETARIA GERAL DA PRESIDENCIA. RELATORIO DO EXERCICIO. 1940-1989. a. Instituto de Resseguros do Brasil, Secretaria Geral da Presidencia (SECR-GP), Av. Marechal Camara, 171, Rio de Janeiro, 171, CEP 20023, Brazil.
    Formerly: Instituto de Resseguros do Brasil. Assessoria de Comunicacao Social. Relatorio do Exercicio.

634.9   BL   ISSN 0100-3151
SD1   CODEN: IFBTBI
INSTITUTO FLORESTAL. BOLETIM TECNICO. 1972-1988 (vol.42). irreg. Instituto Florestal, C.P. 1322, Sao Paulo 01051, Brazil.

407   CK
INSTITUTO LINGUISTICO DE VERANO. SERIE SINTACTICA. 1975-198? irreg. (also avail. in microfiche) Instituto Linguistico de Verano, Apdo. Aereo 100602, Bogota, Colombia.

665.5   MX   ISSN 0186-3266
INSTITUTO MEXICANO DEL PETROLEO. BOLETIN INFORMATIVO. ceased. bi-m. Instituto Mexicano del Petroleo, Av. Lazaro Cardenas, No. 152, Delegacion Gustavo A. Madero, 07730, Mexico, D.F., Mexico.

200   MX
INSTITUTO SUPERIOR DE ESTUDIOS ECLESIASTICOS. LIBRO ANUAL. ceased 1981. a. Instituto Superior de Estudios Eclesiasticos, Victoria 21, Mexico 22, D.F., Mexico.

200   UY
INSTITUTO TEOLOGICO DEL URUGUAY. CUADERNOS. ceased 1982 (no.7). irreg. Instituto Teologico del Uruguay, San Fructuoso 1019, Montevideo, Uruguay.

300   RM
INSTITUTUL POLITEHNIC IASI. BULETINUL. SECTIA VIII. STIINTE SOCIAL-ECONOMICE. 1946-1981 (vol.27). q. Institutul Politehnic "Gheorghe Asachi" din Iasi, Calea 23 August 11, 6600 Jassy, Rumania.

028.5   SA
INSTITUUT VIR NAVORSING IN KINDER- EN JEUGLEKTUUR. BULLETIN/INSTITUTE FOR RESEARCH IN CHILDREN'S LITERATURE. BULLETIN. 1979-1990 (vol.12, no.2). s-a. Instituut vir Navorsing in Kinder- en Jeuglektuur - Institute for Research in Children's Literature, Potchefstroom University for Christian Higher Education, Potchefstroom 2520, South Africa.

631.6   NE
INSTITUUT VOOR CULTUURTECHNIEK EN WATERHUISHOUDING. MEDEDELING. NIEUWE SERIE. 1958-1988 (no.61). irreg. (back issues avail.) Instituut voor Cultuurtechniek en Waterhuishouding - Institute for Land and Water Management Research, P.O. Box 35, 6700 AA Wageningen, Netherlands.
Formerly: Instituut voor Cultuurtechniek en Waterhuishouding. Mededeling (ISSN 0074-0411); Incorporates (after no.262, 1981): Instituut voor Cultuurtechniek en Waterhuishouding. Verspreide Overdrukken (ISSN 0074-0438)

631.6 614.7 333.91   NE
INSTITUUT VOOR CULTUURTECHNIEK EN WATERHUISHOUDING. TECHNICAL BULLETINS. NEW SERIES. 1958-1988 (no.80). irreg. (back issues avail.) Instituut voor Cultuurtechniek en Waterhuishouding - Institute for Land and Water Management Research, P.O. Box 35, 6700 AA Wageningen, Netherlands.
Formed by the merger of: Instituut voor Cultuurtechniek en Waterhuishouding. Technical Bulletin (ISSN 0074-042X); Instituut voor Cultuurtechniek en Waterhuishouding. Miscellaneous Reprints.

581   NE
INSTITUUT VOOR DE VEREDELING VAN TUINBOUWGEWASSEN. JAARVERSLAG. PROJECTEN VAN ONDERZOEK/INSTITUTE FOR HORTICULTURAL PLANT BREEDING. ANNUAL REPORT. RESEARCH PROJECTS. 1948-1989. a. Instituut voor de Veredeling van Tuinbouwgewassen - Institute for Horticultural Plant Breeding, Mansholtlaan 15, Postbus 16, 6700 AA Wageningen, Netherlands.

632 581   NE   ISSN 0019-0349
INSTITUUT VOOR PLANTENZIEKTENKUNDIG ONDERZOEK. MEDEDELING/INSTITUTE OF PHYTOPATHOLOGICAL RESEARCH. COMMUNICATIONS. 1950-1987 (no.1040). irreg. Instituut voor Planteziektenkundig Onderzoek, P.O. Box 9060, 6700 GW Wageningen, Netherlands.

333.9   PL   ISSN 0074-0586
INSTYTUT GOSPODARKI WODNEJ. PRACE. 1961-1991. irreg. Wydawnictwa Komunikacji i Lacznosci, Ul. Kazimierzowska 52, 02-546 Warsaw, Poland.

621.38   PL   ISSN 0020-451X
INSTYTUT LACZNOSCI. PRACE. 1954-1991. irreg. (also avail. in microfilm) Wydawnictwa Komunikacji i Lacznosci, Kazimierzowska 52, Warsaw, Poland.

669   PL   ISSN 0137-589X
INSTYTUT METALI NIEZELAZNYCH. PRACE. 1971-1989 (no.3). q. Instytut Metali Niezelaznych, Ul. Sowinskiego 5, 44-101 Gliwice, Poland.

368 340   US
INSURANCE LAW BRIEFINGS. ceased 1989. m. Shepard's - McGraw-Hill, Inc., Box 35300, Colorado Springs, CO 80935-3530.

181.45 294.5   US
INTEGRAL LIGHT. suspended. q. Yoga Research Foundation, 6111 S.W. 74th Ave., Miami, FL 33143.

600 380.3   US
INTEGRATED NETWORKS UPDATE. 1987-1988. m. (back issues avail.) Link Resources Corp., 79 Fifth Ave., New York, NY 10003-2025.
Formerly: Thruput.

621.381 338   US
INTEL YELLOW PAGES. ceased. a. Intel Corporation, Literature Department, 3065 Bowers Ave., Santa Clara, CA 95051.

052   UK
INTELLIGENCE DIGEST (EDINBURGH). 1960-19?? m. (also avail. in Braille) Scottish Braille Press, Craigmillar Park, Edinburgh EH16 5NB, Scotland.

600 658
INTELLIGENT BUILDINGS CONFERENCE PROCEEDINGS. 1984-1986. s-a. Cross Communications, 1881 9th St., Ste. 302, Boulder, CO 80302-5151.

001.6 621.381   US
INTELLIGENT MAC; publication of the smartmac user group. 1986-198? bi-m. (back issues avail.) (American Mensa Ltd.) Crown Communications (St. Paul), Box 11626, St. Paul, MN 55111.
Formerly: Mac Intelligencer.

610   UK   ISSN 0264-7494
INTENSIVE THERAPY & CLINICAL MONITORING. 1979-1990 (vol.12, no.1). bi-m. Medical Tribune UK Ltd., Tower House, Southampton St., London WC2E 7LS, England.
Former titles: British Journal of Parenteral Therapy; British Journal of Intravenous Therapy (ISSN 0144-879X)

301.16   CN   ISSN 0020-4927
INTER; information et documentation sur les moyens de communication sociale. 1967-19?? m. Office des Communications Sociales, 4005 rue de Bellechasse, Montreal, Que. H1X 1J6, Canada.

696   CN
INTER - MECANIQUE DU BATIMENT. 1985-19?? 6/yr. Ideo Productions Inc., 2095 Charest Blvd. W., Ste. 226, Sainte-Foy, Que. G1N 4L8, Canada.

614.58   US   ISSN 1041-911X
INTERACT (WYNDMOOR). 1990-1992. q. (back issues avail.) Psychology Exchange, 8810 Delphine Rd., Wyndmoor, PA 19118.

636   US
INTERACTIONS. 1986-1988 (May). s-a. (tabloid format) Delta Society, 321 Burnett Ave., S., Ste. 3030, Renton, WA 98055.

960 944   FR   ISSN 0020-5125
INTERAFRIQUE PRESSE. 1954-19?? w. Societe Afrique Information, 93 rue Lafayette, 75010 Paris, France.

371.8   NE
INTERAKTIE; tijdschrift voor onderwijs, vorming en opleiding. 1971-198? 11/yr. J.B. van den Brink en Co. B.V., Postbus 14, 7240 BA Lochem, Netherlands.
Formerly: Karakter.

630 016   CR   ISSN 0301-438X
INTER-AMERICAN CENTRE FOR AGRICULTURAL DOCUMENTATION AND INFORMATION. DOCUMENTACION E INFORMACION AGRICOLA. 1973-198? irreg. (also avail. in microform) Instituto Interamericano de Cooperacion para la Agricultura - O E A, Apdo. 55, 2200 Coronado, San Jose, Costa Rica.
Formed by the merger of: Inter-American Institute of Agricultural Sciences. Center for Training and Research. Bibliotecologia y Documentacion (ISSN 0074-0926) & Inter-American Institute of Agricultural Sciences. Bibliografias (ISSN 0085-1949)

327   US
INTERCONTINENTAL PRESS. 1963-198? fortn. (also avail. in microfilm from UMI; back issues avail.; reprint service avail. from UMI) 408 Printing & Publishing Co., 408 West St., New York, NY 10014.
Former titles: Intercontinental Press Combined with Imprecor (ISSN 0162-5594); (until Jan. 1978): Intercontinental Press (ISSN 0020-5303)

300 016   II   ISSN 0020-5338
INTERDISCIPLINE. ceased 1984. q. Gandhian Institute of Studies, PO Box 116, Rajghat, Varanasi 1, India.
Formerly: Social Science Abstracts.

378   CN
L'INTERDIT. ceased. m. Publi-Peq, 1581 Dufresne, Montreal, Que. H2K 3J6, Canada.

669 001.6   IT   ISSN 0393-4470
INTERFACCIA. 1985-1990 (Nov.). m. Gruppo Editoriale Fabbri SPA, Divisione Periodici, Via Mecenate, 91, 20138 Milan, Italy.

001.6 621.381   NZ   ISSN 0113-3462
INTERFACE. 1981-1990. 11/yr. (Computer Society of New Zealand) Associated Group Media Ltd., Private Bag 15, Newmarket, Auckland, New Zealand.

200 301.412   US   ISSN 0892-6719
INTERFAITH WOMEN'S NEWS & NETWORK. 1980-1990 (vol.10, no.2). q. (also avail. in microform; back issues avail.) 790 11th Ave., Apt. 32H, New York, NY 10019.

693   AT
INTERLOCKING CONCRETE PAVING REVIEW. 1980-19?? s-a. Concrete Masonry Association of Australia, 25 Berry St., North Sydney, N.S.W. 2060, Australia.

330   US
INTERMARKET. ceased. m. InterMarket Publishing Corporation, 2 First National Plaza, Ste. 2020, Chicago, IL 60603.

368   SZ   ISSN 0074-1264
INTERNATIONAL ACTUARIAL CONGRESS. TRANSACTIONS. (Published by host country) ceased 1984 (vol.22). quadrennial. (Association of Swiss Actuaries) Staempfli & Cie AG, Bern, c/o Prof. Heinz Schmid, Institut fuer math. Statistik, Sidlerstr. 5, CH-3012 Bern, Switzerland.

659.1   US
INTERNATIONAL ADVERTISING ASSOCIATION. INTELLIGENCE SUMMARY. ceased. bi-m. International Advertising Association, 342 Madison Ave., Ste. 2000, New York, NY 10017.

659.1   US
INTERNATIONAL ADVERTISING ASSOCIATION AIRLETTER. ceased. bi-m. International Advertising Association, 342 Madison Ave., Ste. 2000, New York, NY 10017.

384   US
INTERNATIONAL AND COMPARATIVE BROADCASTING. 1976-19?? irreg. Temple University Press, Philadelphia, PA 19122.

660 536   US   ISSN 1044-5102
INTERNATIONAL ARCHIVES OF HEAT AND MASS TRANSFER. 1991-1992. q. (International Centre for Heat and Mass Transfer) Hemisphere Publishing Corporation (Subsidiary of: Taylor & Francis Group), 1900 Frost Rd., Ste. 101, Bristol, PA 19007-1598.

616.8 618.928   US
INTERNATIONAL ASSOCIATION OF CHILD AND ADOLESCENT PSYCHIATRY AND ALLIED PROFESSIONS. YEARBOOK. 1970-19?? irreg. John Wiley & Sons, Inc., 605 Third Ave., New York, NY 10158-0012.
Former titles: International Association for Child Psychiatry and Allied Professions. Yearbook (ISSN 0074-963X); International Yearbook for Child Psychiatry and Allied Disciplines.

332 341   UK   ISSN 0266-3147
INTERNATIONAL BANKING & FINANCIAL LAW BULLETIN. 1984-198? m. (tabloid format; back issues avail.) International Business Communications Ltd., 12-13 Little Newport St., London WC2H 7PP, England.
Formerly: International Banking Law Bulletin.

363.2 016   UK
INTERNATIONAL BIBLIOGRAPHY OF SELECTED POLICE LITERATURE. 1968-19?? a. International Police Association, Country Police Hqtrs., Sutton Rd., Maidstone, Kent, England.

016 200 Z7833   NE   ISSN 0538-5105
INTERNATIONAL BIBLIOGRAPHY OF THE HISTORY OF RELIGIONS/BIBLIOGRAPHIE INTERNATIONAL DE L'HISTOIRE DES RELIGIONS. 1954-1987 (vol.20). a. E.J. Brill, P.O. Box 9000, 2300 PA Leiden, Netherlands.

576   US
INTERNATIONAL BIODETERIORATION SYMPOSIUM. PROCEEDINGS. BIODETERIORATION OF MATERIALS. ceased 1983 (vol.5). irreg. Halsted Press (Subsidiary of: John Wiley & Sons, Inc.), 605 Third Ave., New York, NY 10016.

090.75   US   ISSN 0741-9953
INTERNATIONAL BOOK COLLECTORS ALMANAC. NEWSLETTER; a cornucopia for booklovers. 1984-19?? m. (back issues avail.) Pegasus Publishers, Inc., Box 913, Vashon, WA 98070.

CESSATIONS

332 340   US
INTERNATIONAL BUSINESS REGULATIONS REPORT. 1939-1989. m. International Reports, Inc. (Subsidiary of: I B C U.S.A.), 114 E. 32nd St., Ste. 602, New York, NY 10016-5506.
Formerly: Forex Service (ISSN 0015-7627)

338   US
INTERNATIONAL C A D - C A M - C A E SOFTWARE PRODUCTS DATABASE. 1983-19?? a. TecSpec, Box 617024, Orlando, FL 32861-7024.
Former titles: International C A D - C A M Software Directory; International C A D - C A M Software; International Engineering - Scientific Software Directory.

616.99   SZ
INTERNATIONAL CATALOGUE OF FILMS, FILMSTRIPS AND SLIDES ON PUBLIC EDUCATION ABOUT CANCER. 1977-19?? irreg. International Union Against Cancer, 3 rue de Conseil-General, 1205 Geneva, Switzerland.

301.32   SZ
INTERNATIONAL CATHOLIC MIGRATION COMMISSION. ANNUAL REPORT/COMMISSION INTERNATIONALE CATHOLIQUE POUR LES MIGRATIONS. RAPPORT ANNUEL/COMISION CATOLICA INTERNACIONAL DE MIGRATION. INFORME ANUAL. ceased 1988. a. International Catholic Migration Commission - Commission Internationale Catholique pour les Migrations, 37-39 rue de Vermont, CH-1211 Geneva 20 CIC, Switzerland.

668.4   US   ISSN 0579-5400
INTERNATIONAL CELLULAR PLASTICS CONFERENCE. PROCEEDINGS. ceased. irreg. Society of Plastics Industry, Inc., 1275 K St., N.W., Ste. 400, Washington, DC 20005.

536   US   ISSN 0888-6911
QC319.8
INTERNATIONAL CENTRE FOR HEAT & MASS TRANSFER. BULLETIN. 1987-1991. a. (back issues avail.; reprint service avail. from UMI) Hemisphere Publishing Corporation (Subsidiary of: Taylor & Francis Group), 1900 Frost Rd., Ste. 101, Bristol, PA 19007-1598.

287   US   ISSN 0890-4081
INTERNATIONAL CHRISTIAN DIGEST. 1987-19?? 10/yr. United Methodist Publishing House, 201 Eighth Ave. S., Box 801, Nashville, TN 37202.

629.1   UN   ISSN 0074-252X
INTERNATIONAL CIVIL AVIATION ORGANIZATION. OBSTACLE CLEARANCE PANEL. REPORT OF MEETING. ceased 1971. irreg. International Civil Aviation Organization, 1000 Sherbrooke St. W., Montreal, Que. H3A 2R2, Canada.

629.1   UN   ISSN 0074-2228
INTERNATIONAL CIVIL AVIATION ORGANIZATION. (PANEL ON) APPLICATION OF SPACE TECHNIQUES RELATING TO AVIATION. REPORT OF MEETING. ceased 1971. irreg. International Civil Aviation Organization, 1000 Sherbrooke St. W., Montreal, Que. H3A 2R2, Canada.

629.1   UN
INTERNATIONAL CIVIL AVIATION ORGANIZATION. SONIC BOOM COMMITTEE. REPORT OF THE MEETING. ceased 1973. irreg. International Civil Aviation Organization, Sonic Boom Committee, Attn: Document Sales Unit, 1000 Sherbrooke St. W., Montreal, Que. H3A 2R2, Canada.
Formerly: International Civil Aviation Organization. Sonic Boom Panel. Report of the Meeting (ISSN 0074-2562)

629.1   UN   ISSN 0074-2589
INTERNATIONAL CIVIL AVIATION ORGANIZATION. VISUAL AIDS PANEL. REPORT OF MEETING. ceased 1980. irreg. International Civil Aviation Organization, 1000 Sherbrooke St. W., Montreal, Que. H3A 2R2, Canada.

616.8   SZ
INTERNATIONAL COLLEGE OF PSYCHOSOMATIC MEDICINE. PROCEEDINGS OF THE CONGRESS. ceased. irreg. (reprint service avail. from ISI) S. Karger AG, Allschwilerstrasse 10, P.O. Box, CH-4009 Basel, Switzerland.

623.4   US
INTERNATIONAL COMBAT ARMS. 1983-1989 (Nov.). bi-m. (also avail. in microfiche from UMI) Petersen Publishing Co., 8490 Sunset Blvd., Los Angeles, CA 90069.

616.15   GW
INTERNATIONAL COMMITTEE FOR STANDARDIZATION IN HEMATOLOGY. SYMPOSIA. ceased 1972 (13th). irreg. Institut fuer Standardisierung und Dokumentation im Med Laboratorium, Hugstetter Str. 55, 7800 Freiburg im Breisgau, Germany.

001.6 629.8   US
INTERNATIONAL COMPUTER VISION PRODUCTS DATABASE. 1984-19?? a. TecSpec, Box 617024, Orlando, FL 32861-7024.
Formerly: International Computer Vision Directory.

001.6 621.381   US
INTERNATIONAL CONFERENCE ON COMPUTERS AND APPLICATIONS. 1984-1987. triennial. (Institute of Electrical and Electronics Engineers, Inc.) I E E E Computer Society Press, 10662 Los Vaqueros Circle, Los Alamitos, CA 90720-1264.

539.7   US   ISSN 0534-8676
INTERNATIONAL CONFERENCE ON ELECTRON AND ION BEAM SCIENCE AND TECHNOLOGY. ABSTRACTS. ceased 1970 (4th). irreg. Electrochemical Society, Inc., 10 S. Main St., Pennington, NJ 08534-2896.

137   US   ISSN 0534-9044
INTERNATIONAL CONGRESS OF GRAPHOANALYSTS. PROCEEDINGS. 1929-19?? a. International Graphoanalysis Society, 111 N. Canal St., Chicago, IL 60606.

610   GW   ISSN 0074-3704
INTERNATIONAL CONGRESS OF HISTORY OF MEDICINE. PROCEEDINGS. (Proceedings Published in Host Country) 1920-1986 (30th). biennial. International Society for the History of Medicine, c/o Dr. Hans Schadewaldt, Moorenstrabe 5, 4000 Dusseldorf 1, Germany.

576   GW
INTERNATIONAL CONGRESS OF MICROBIOLOGY. PROCEEDINGS. (Supplement to: Zentralblatt fuer Bakteriologie) 12th, 1978-1992. irreg. Gustav Fischer Verlag, Wollgrasweg 49, Postfach 720143, 7000 Stuttgart 70, Germany.

780   US
INTERNATIONAL CONGRESS ON WOMEN IN MUSIC. NEWSLETTER. 1983-1990 (Mar.). q. International Congress on Women in Music, Box 12164, La Crescenta, CA 91214.

320.52   CN   ISSN 0831-4268
INTERNATIONAL CONSERVATIVE INSIGHT; strategic, political and economic news & conservative commentary. 1986-1989. bi-m. (also avail. in microform from UMI) Canadian Conservative Centre, Box 8200, Vancouver, B.C. V6B 4E8, Canada.

690 620   US   ISSN 0149-5585
INTERNATIONAL CONSTRUCTION WEEK. 1975-198? w. McGraw-Hill, Inc., 1221 Ave. of the Americas, New York, NY 10020.

690   US
INTERNATIONAL CONSTRUCTION WEEK: AFRICA CONSTRUCTION BUSINESS REPORT. 1980-198? m. (International Construction Week) McGraw-Hill, Inc., 1221 Ave. of the Americas, New York, NY 10020.

690   US   ISSN 0278-2448
INTERNATIONAL CONSTRUCTION WEEK: ASIA CONSTRUCTION BUSINESS REPORT. 1979-198? m. (International Construction Week) McGraw-Hill, Inc., 1221 Ave. of the Americas, New York, NY 10020.

690   US   ISSN 0278-2456
INTERNATIONAL CONSTRUCTION WEEK: LATIN AMERICA CONSTRUCTION BUSINESS REPORT. 1979-198? m. (International Construction Week) McGraw-Hill, Inc., 1221 Ave. of the Americas, New York, NY 10020.

690   US   ISSN 0278-2464
INTERNATIONAL CONSTRUCTION WEEK: MIDEAST CONSTRUCTION BUSINESS REPORT. 1979-198? m. (International Construction Week) McGraw-Hill, Inc., 1221 Ave. of the Americas, New York, NY 10020.

001.6 629.8   US
INTERNATIONAL CONTROL PRODUCTS DATABASE. 1984-19?? a. TecSpec, Box 617024, Orlando, FL 32861-7024.
Formerly: International Programmable Controllers Directory.

616.97   SZ   ISSN 0074-4220
INTERNATIONAL CONVOCATION ON IMMUNOLOGY. PAPERS. 1968-1985 (9th). irreg. (reprint service avail. from ISI) (Center for Immunology) S. Karger AG, Allschwilerstrasse 10, P.O. Box, CH-4009 Basel, Switzerland.

334   SZ   ISSN 0074-4247
INTERNATIONAL COOPERATIVE ALLIANCE. CONGRESS REPORT. 1895-1988 (29th, Stockholm). quadrennial. (reprint service avail. from UMI) International Co-Operative Alliance, Rte. des Morillons 15, 1218 Grand Saconnex, Geneve, Switzerland.

052   II
INTERNATIONAL COOPERATIVE ALLIANCE. DOCUMENTATION BULLETIN FOR SOUTHEAST ASIA. ceased. q. International Cooperative Alliance, Regional Office for South-East Asia, Bonow House, 43 Friends' Colony East, New Delhi 110 065, India.

677.2   SZ
INTERNATIONAL COTTON-SYSTEM FIBRE CONSUMPTION STATISTICS. 1974-1988. a. (also avail. in microform) International Textile Manufacturers Federation, Am Schanzengraben 29, Postfach, CH-8039 Zurich, Switzerland.

619   GW
INTERNATIONAL COUNCIL FOR LABORATORY ANIMAL SCIENCE. PROCEEDINGS OF THE SYMPOSIUM. 1958-1992. triennial. (also avail. in microfiche from NTI) (International Council for Laboratory Animal Science) Gustav Fischer Verlag, Wollgrasweg 49, Postfach 720143, 7000 Stuttgart 70, Germany.
Formerly: International Committee on Laboratory Animals. Proceedings of Symposium (ISSN 0074-2805)

574.92 639.3   DK   ISSN 0106-1003
INTERNATIONAL COUNCIL FOR THE EXPLORATION OF THE SEA. ANNALES BIOLOGIQUES. 1943-1986. a. (back issues avail.) International Council for the Exploration of the Sea, Palaegade 2, DK-1261 Copenhagen K, Denmark.

790   CN   ISSN 1013-4468
INTERNATIONAL COUNCIL OF KINETOGRAPHY LABAN. PROCEEDINGS. 1959-19?? biennial. (back issues avail.) International Council of Kinetography Laban, c/o Ann Kipling Brown, Chairperson, 705 Galbraith House, Michener Park, Edmonton, Alta. T6H 4M5, Canada.

355 621.38   US
INTERNATIONAL DEFENSE IMAGES; the journal with a modern look at defense. 1986-198? q. International Defense Images, Ltd., 2419 Mt. Vernon Ave., Alexandria, VA 22301.

355   US
INTERNATIONAL DEFENSE INTELLIGENCE. ceased 1990. w. (back issues avail.) Forecast International Inc. - D M S, 22 Commerce Rd., Newtown, CT 06470.

332.6 338.91   US
INTERNATIONAL DEVELOPMENT REVIEW. 1988-1990. q. International Media Partners Inc., Cable Bldg., Ste. 322, 611 Broadway, New York, NY 10012.

621.3   UK   ISSN 0267-9299
INTERNATIONAL ELECTRONICS FOR CHINA. 1985-19?? m. Reed Business Publishing Ltd., Quadrant House, The Quadrant, Sutton, Surrey SM2 5AS, England.

364   FR   ISSN 0252-063X
INTERNATIONAL EXCHANGE OF INFORMATION ON CURRENT CRIMINOLOGICAL RESEARCH PROJECTS IN MEMBER STATES. 1966-1991 (vol.28). a. Council of Europe, Directorate of Legal Affairs, Division of Crime Problems, Publishing and Documentation Service, 67000 Strasbourg, France.

700   US
INTERNATIONAL EYE. 1979-1987. m. (tabloid format; also avail. in microfiche; back issues avail.) East Village Eye, Inc., 611 Broadway, No. 609, New York, NY 10012.
Formerly: East Village Eye (ISSN 0748-3066)

CESSATIONS

658.8 659.1   US
INTERNATIONAL FACT BOOK ON DIRECT MARKETING. ceased. a. Direct Marketing Association, Information Central Department, 11 W. 42nd St., New York, NY 10036-8092.

664.028   US
INTERNATIONAL FROZEN FOOD ASSOCIATION. BULLETIN BOARD. 1974-198? m. (looseleaf format) (International Frozen Food Association) American Frozen Food Institute, 1764 Old Meadow Lane, Ste. 350, McLean, VA 22102.
Supersedes: International Frozen Food Association. Letter.

549   US
INTERNATIONAL GEMOLOGICAL SYMPOSIUM PROCEEDINGS. published only once, 1982. irreg. Gemological Institute of America, 1660 Stewart St., Santa Monica, CA 90404.

658.8   UK
INTERNATIONAL GIFTS NEWS. 1967-19?? q. Trade Promotion Services Ltd., Exhibition House, 6 Warren Lane, Woolwich, London SE18 6BW, England.

620   US
INTERNATIONAL HEAT TRANSFER CONFERENCE. ceased. irreg., 8th, 1986. (reprint service avail. from UMI) Hemisphere Publishing Corporation (Subsidiary of: Taylor & Francis Group), 1900 Frost Rd., Ste. 101, Bristol, PA 19007-1598.

001.642
INTERNATIONAL I E E E CONFERENCE ON ADA APPLICATIONS AND ENVIRONMENTS. 1984-1988. biennial. (Institute of Electrical and Electronics Engineers, Inc., Computer Language Technical Committee) I E E E Computer Society Press, 10662 Los Vaqueros Circle, Los Alamitos, CA 90720-1264.
Former titles (until 1986): I E E E Computer Society Conference on Ada Applications and Environments International; (until 1984): I E E E Computer Society Conference on Ada Applications and Environments.

620   US
HD9696.A96
INTERNATIONAL INDUSTRIAL SENSOR PRODUCTS DATABASE. 1983-19?? a. TecSpec, Box 617024, Orlando, FL 32861.
Former titles: International Industrial Sensor Directory (ISSN 0736-1831); Industrial Sensor Directory.

331   UN
INTERNATIONAL INSTITUTE FOR LABOUR STUDIES. PUBLIC LECTURE SERIES. 1975-19?? irreg. International Institute for Labour Studies, Box 6, CH-1211 Geneva 22, Switzerland.

370   US   ISSN 0192-5318
BF309
INTERNATIONAL INTERDISCIPLINARY SEMINAR ON PIAGETIAN THEORY AND ITS IMPLICATIONS FOR THE HELPING PROFESSIONS. PROCEEDINGS; emphasis: the handicapped child. 1970-19?? a. (back issues avail.) Children's Hospital of Los Angeles, University Affiliated Program, Piaget Conference Committee, Box 54700, Los Angeles, CA 90054.

621.381   US
INTERNATIONAL JOURNAL OF COMPUTER AIDED V L S I DESIGN. (Very Large Scale Integration) 1989-1990. q. Ablex Publishing Corporation, 355 Chestnut St., Norwood, NJ 07648.

617.643   US
INTERNATIONAL JOURNAL OF ORTHODONTICS. 1962-1991 (vol.29). s-a. (also avail. in microform from UMI; back issues avail.; reprint service avail. from UMI) (Federation of Orthodontic Associations) Town and Country Printers, 3953 N. 76th, Milwaukee, WI 53222.

020   US   ISSN 0740-5138
Z666
INTERNATIONAL JOURNAL OF REVIEWS IN LIBRARY AND INFORMATION SCIENCE. 1984-1988 (vol.4, no.2). s-a. Rosary College, Graduate School of Library and Information Sciences, River Forest, IL 60305.

695   US
INTERNATIONAL JOURNAL OF ROOFING TECHNOLOGY. 1989-1990. a. National Roofing Contractors Association, 10255 W. Higgins Rd., Ste. 600, Rosemont, IL 60018.
Formerly: Journal of Roofing Technology.

331   UK   ISSN 0266-2140
INTERNATIONAL LABOUR REPORTS. 1984-1990. bi-m. Mayday Publications Ltd., Box 45, Stainborough, Barnsley, S. Yorks S75 3EA, England.

520 515   JA   ISSN 0536-3403
INTERNATIONAL LATITUDE OBSERVATORY OF MIZUSAWA. PROCEEDINGS. 1954-1987 (vol.26). a. International Latitude Observatory of Mizusawa, 2-12 Hoshogaoka, Mizusawa-shi, Iwate-ken 023, Japan.

520 551   JA   ISSN 0386-0779
INTERNATIONAL LATITUDE OBSERVATORY OF MIZUSAWA. PUBLICATIONS. 1951-1987 (vol.20, nos.1-2). a. International Latitude Observatory of Mizusawa, 2-12 Hoshigaoka, Mizusawashi, Iwateken 023, Japan.

636.2   US
INTERNATIONAL LIMOUSIN JOURNAL. 1971-19?? m. (North American Limousin Foundation) Limousin World, Inc., 1241 S. Eleventh St., Yukon, OK 73099-5305.

658   UK
INTERNATIONAL MANAGEMENT (ARABIC EDITION)/ ALAM AL-IDARAH. 1946-1988 (Dec.). m. McGraw-Hill International Publications Co. Ltd., 34 Dover St., London W1X 4BR, England.

341   CN
INTERNATIONAL MARITIME LAW SEMINAR. PUBLICATION. (Title changes with each no.) 1979-1988 (no.4). irreg. (looseleaf format; also avail. in audio cassette; back issues avail.) Continuing Legal Education Society of B.C., 200-1148 Hornby St., Vancouver, B.C. V6Z 2C3, Canada.

658.8 301.16   US
INTERNATIONAL MARKETING COMMUNICATIONS NEWSLETTER. ceased 1989. irreg. Business - Professional Advertising Association, 100 Metroplex Dr., Edison, NJ 08817.

610   BE
INTERNATIONAL MEDICAL NEWSLETTER. 1985-1987 (vol.3, no.6). 11/yr. Pan European Publishing Co., Rue Verte 216, B-1210 Brussels, Belgium.

025   US
INTERNATIONAL MICRO NEWS. 1978-1987; suspended. q. (tabloid format; back issues avail.) Norman Ross Publishing, Inc., 1995 Broadway, New York, NY 10023.
Formerly: Micro News.

340.6   US
INTERNATIONAL MICROFORM JOURNAL OF LEGAL MEDICINE AND FORENSIC SCIENCES. 1965-1985. q. (microform; reprint service avail. from UMI) (Milton Helpern Library of Legal Medicine) University Microfilms International, Publisher Relations Department, c/o Sheila Branham, Publisher Rep., 300 N. Zeeb Rd., Ann Arbor, MI 48106.
Formerly: International Microform Journal of Legal Medicine (ISSN 0020-7977)

331.88   US   ISSN 0020-8019
INTERNATIONAL MOLDERS' AND ALLIED WORKERS' JOURNAL. 1863-198? bi-m. International Molders' and Allied Workers' Union, 608 E. Baltimore Pk., Box 607, Media, PA 19063.

649   US   ISSN 0140-668X
INTERNATIONAL MONOGRAPH SERIES ON EARLY CHILD CARE. ceased 1980 (vol.9). a. Gordon & Breach Science Publishers, 270 Eighth Ave., New York, NY 10011.

745.1 700   US   ISSN 0095-2591
NK6050
INTERNATIONAL NETSUKE COLLECTORS SOCIETY JOURNAL. 1973-1985 (vo.12, no.4). q. (back issues avail.) International Netsuke Collectors Society, c/o B Hurtigs Oriental, P.O. Box 10698, Honolulu, HI 96816.

327   SW   ISSN 0308-762X
DJK35
INTERNATIONAL NEWSLETTER. 1976-1992 (Feb.); suspended. s-a. (back issues avail.) (International Committee for Soviet and East European Studies) St Olofsgatan 18, S-75221 Uppsala, Sweden.

340 016   CN
INTERNATIONAL OMBUDSMAN INSTITUTE BIBLIOGRAPHY. ceased 1982. a. (cum. vol. every 5 yrs.). International Ombudsman Institute, Faculty of Law, University of Alberta, Edmonton, Alta. T6G 2H5, Canada.

370.196 327   US
INTERNATIONAL PEACE STUDIES NEWSLETTER. 1971-1989; suspended. q. (Center for Peace Studies) University of Akron, 302 E. Buchtel Ave., Akron, OH 44325-6201.

618.92   FR   ISSN 0245-9337
INTERNATIONAL PEDIATRIC ASSOCIATION. BULLETIN. 1975-1989 (vol.10, no.4). q. International Pediatric Association, Chateau de Longchamp, Bois de Boulogne, 75016 Paris, France.

351.74   UK   ISSN 0579-5567
INTERNATIONAL POLICE ASSOCIATION. MEETING OF THE INTERNATIONAL EXECUTIVE COUNCIL. 1950-19?? a. International Police Association, County Police Hqtrs., Sutton Rd., Maidstone, Kent, England.

351.74   UK   ISSN 0579-6881
INTERNATIONAL POLICE ASSOCIATION. TRAVEL SCHOLARSHIPS. 1970-19?? a. International Police Association, County Police Hqtrs., Sutton Rd., Maidstone, Kent., England.

531.64   US
INTERNATIONAL POWER SYSTEMS. ceased. a. (American Business Press, Inc.) McGraw-Hill, Inc., 1221 Ave. of the Americas, New York, NY 10020.

333.33   UK   ISSN 0267-744X
INTERNATIONAL PROPERTY REVIEW. 1976-1987; suspended. q. Jones Lang Wootton, 22 Hanover Sq., London W1R OJL, England.

133   US   ISSN 0147-782X
BF1024.5
INTERNATIONAL PSYCHIC REGISTER; a directory of practitioners of the psychic arts in the United States, Canada & Great Britain. 1977-1979. a. Ornion Press, 1114 1-2 Pennsylvania Ave., Erie, PA 16507.

616.8   US
INTERNATIONAL PSYCHO-ANALYTICAL ASSOCIATION. MONOGRAPH. ceased. irreg. (International Psychoanalytical Association) International Universities Press, Inc., 59 Boston Post Rd., Box 1524, Madison, CT 06443-1524.

620   US
INTERNATIONAL Q C FORUM. 1982-198? (no.24); suspended. q. (back issues avail.) Media International Promotions, Inc., 114 E. 32nd St., New York, NY 10016.

643   TU   ISSN 0259-8388
INTERNATIONAL QUARTERLY OF ANALYTICAL CHEMISTRY. published only once, 1987. q. Tahsin Yazicioglu, P. Kutusu 1318, Sirkeci, Istanbul 34438, Turkey.

620   UK   ISSN 0269-5839
TA166
INTERNATIONAL REVIEW OF ERGONOMICS: CURRENT TRENDS IN HUMAN FACTORS RESEARCH AND PRACTICE. 1987-1989. a. Taylor & Francis Ltd., Rankine Rd., Basingstoke, Hants RG24 0PR, England.

152.8   US   ISSN 0741-0131
BF367
INTERNATIONAL REVIEW OF MENTAL IMAGERY. 1984-198? a. Human Sciences Press, Inc. (Subsidiary of: Plenum Publishing Corp.), 233 Spring St., New York, NY 10013-1578.

500   US   ISSN 0074-7866
INTERNATIONAL SCIENCE REVIEW SERIES. 1961-1972 (vol.15). irreg. Gordon & Breach Science Publishers, 270 Eighth Ave., New York, NY 10011.

CESSATIONS

327 US
INTERNATIONAL SECURITY NEWS CLIPPING SERVICE. 1987-19?? bi-w. Topsfield Foundation, Inc., Rt. 169, Box 203, Pomfret, CT 06258.

331 US
INTERNATIONAL SERIES ON THE QUALITY OF WORKING LIFE. 1976-19?? irreg. Kluwer Nijhoff Publishing, 101 Philip Dr., Assinippi Park, Norwell, MA 02061.

616 SZ ISSN 0074-8544
INTERNATIONAL SOCIETY OF INTERNAL MEDICINE. CONGRESS PROCEEDINGS. 1950-1986. biennial. International Society of Internal Medicine, c/o Dr. Rolf A. Streuli, Regionalspital, CH-4900 Langenthal, Switzerland.

330 US
INTERNATIONAL SPACE BUSINESS REVIEW. 1985-1989. q. Media Dimensions, Inc., 41 E. 23rd St., New York, NY 10010.

370 UN
INTERNATIONAL STUDIES IN EDUCATION. 1961-1980. irreg. Unesco Institute for Education - Unesco Institut fuer Paedagogik, c/o Head of the Publications Unit, Feldbrunnenstr. 58, D-2000 Hamburg 13, Germany.

338.1 UK ISSN 0074-8706
INTERNATIONAL SUGAR ORGANIZATION. ANNUAL REPORT. 197?-1987. irreg. International Sugar Organization, 1 Canada Sq., Canary Wharf, London E14 5AA, England.

797.21 AT ISSN 0020-8876
INTERNATIONAL SWIMMER. 1964-1989 (vol.26, no.2). bi-m. Wallacia (Sales) Pty. Ltd., 4 Coppabella Rd., Dural, N.S.W 2158, Australia.

627 UK ISSN 0140-1769
INTERNATIONAL SYMPOSIUM ON DREDGING TECHNOLOGY. PROCEEDINGS. 1976-1983 (4th). irreg. B H R A Fluid Engineering, Cranfield, Bedford MK43 0AJ, England.

541.37 US ISSN 0091-391X
TK7871.85
INTERNATIONAL SYMPOSIUM ON SILICON MATERIALS SCIENCE AND TECHNOLOGY. PROCEEDINGS. 1969; ceased same year. irreg. Electrochemical Society, Inc., 10 S. Main St., Pennington, NJ 08534-2896.

621.38 US
INTERNATIONAL TELECONFERENCING SYMPOSIUM (PROCEEDINGS). 1980-1986. a. (back issues avail.) Cross Communications, 1881 9th St., Ste. 302, Boulder, CO 80302-5151.

677 UK ISSN 0074-9087
INTERNATIONAL TEXTILE MACHINERY. 1967-198? a. World Textiles Publications, 76 Kirkgate, Bradford, W. Yorkshire BD1 1TB, England.
  Supersedes: Textile Recorder Annual and Machinery Review.

387 382 US
INTERNATIONAL TRADE AND TRANSPORT. (Formerly issued as a supplement to American Sailings) 1987-1988. m. K-III Press, Inc., 424 W. 33rd St., New York, NY 10001.

320.56 331.88 CS
INTERNATIONAL TRADE UNION CONFERENCE FOR ACTION AGAINST APARTHEID. RESOLUTION. published only once, 1977. irreg. World Federation of Trade Unions, Branicka 112, 140 00 Prague 4, Czechoslovakia.

610 SZ ISSN 0074-9192
INTERNATIONAL UNION AGAINST CANCER. MANUAL/ UNION INTERNATIONALE CONTRE LE CANCER. MANUEL. 1963-198? irreg. International Union Against Cancer, 3 rue de Conseil-General, 1205 Geneva, Switzerland.

352 NE ISSN 0074-9443
INTERNATIONAL UNION OF LOCAL AUTHORITIES. REPORTS OF CONGRESS. 1913-19?? irreg. International Union of Local Authorities, Wassenaarseweg 41, 2596 CG The Hague, Netherlands.

920 UK
INTERNATIONAL WHO'S WHO IN ENGINEERING. 1984-19?? irreg. Melrose Press Ltd., 3 Regal Lane, Soham, Ely, Cambridgeshire CB7 5BA, England.

301.42 US
INTERNATIONAL WOMEN'S WRITING GUILD YEARBOOK. 1976-19?? International Women's Writing Guild, Box 810, Gracie Sta., New York, NY 10028.

619 GW
INTERNATIONAL WORKSHOP ON NUDE MICE. PROCEEDINGS. 1974-1992. irreg. (International Council for Laboratory Animal Science) Gustav Fischer Verlag, Wollgrasweg 49, Postfach 720143, 7000 Stuttgart 70, Germany.

320 US
INTERNATIONAL YEARBOOK OF ORGANIZATIONAL DEMOCRACY. 1982-1986. irreg. John Wiley & Sons, Inc., 605 Third Ave., New York, NY 10158-0012.

797 FR ISSN 0074-9648
INTERNATIONAL YEARBOOK OF THE UNDERWATER WORLD/ANNUAIRE INTERNATIONAL DU MONDE SOUS-MARIN. 1967-1983. q. World Underwater Federation, 47 rue du Commerce, 75015 Paris, France.

669 US ISSN 0264-9438
INTERNATIONAL ZINC & GALVANISING SURVEY. 1967-198? irreg. Metal Bulletin Inc., 220 Fifth Ave., 10th Fl., New York.

630 658 GW ISSN 0863-1840
INTERNATIONALE-AGRAR-INDUSTRIEZEITSCHRIFT. ceased 1990. 6/yr. V E B Deutscher Landwirtschaftsverlag, Reinhardtstr. 14, 1040 Berlin, Germany.

500 GW ISSN 0172-3146
INTERNATIONALE AUFGABEN DER D G D. ceased 1989. 8/yr. Deutsche Gesellschaft fuer Dokumentation e.V., Westendstr. 19, 6000 Frankfurt, Germany.

362 SZ
INTERNATIONALER ARZT- UND SPITALBEDARF. 1958-19?? a. Vogt-Schild AG, Zuchwilerstr. 21, 4501 Solothurn 1, Switzerland.
  Formerly: Internationaler Spitalbedarf (ISSN 0074-977X)

341 GW ISSN 0020-9503
INTERNATIONALES RECHT UND DIPLOMATIE. 1956-1980. irreg. Verlag Wissenschaft und Politik Berend von Nottbeck, Salierring 14, 5000 Cologne 1, Germany.

910.2 UK
INTERNATIONALLY SPEAKING. 1947-1989. bi-m. Thomas Cook Ltd., Box 36, Peterborough PE3 6SB, England.
  Former titles (until Aug. 1985): World of Thomas Cook; Thomas Cook News (ISSN 0305-0904); Cooks Staff Magazine (ISSN 0010-8294)

621.9 BE
INTER-TECHNIC. 1953-19?? (French ed.); 1970-19?? (Dutch ed.). m. (10/yr.). Chambre Syndicale des Importateurs et Negociants en Machines - Federation of Belgian Importers and Merchants of Machine-Tools and Tools, 203 av. Slegers, B-1050 Brussels, Belgium.
  Formerly: Inter-Techniek; Alle Internationale Technische Nieuwigheden.

615.842 UK ISSN 0954-3317
INTERVENTIONAL RADIOLOGY. ceased 1991. m. Sheffield University Biomedical Information Service (SUBIS), The University, Sheffield S10 2TN, England.

616.3 612.3 UK ISSN 0261-4723
INTESTINAL MALFUNCTION. ceased 1990. m. (looseleaf format; back issues avail.) Sheffield University Biomedical Information Service (SUBIS), The University, Sheffield S10 2TN, England.

330 US
INTRAPRENEURIAL EXCELLENCE; how to harness the force reshaping American business. ceased. 12/yr. American Management Association, 135 W. 50th St., New York, NY 10020-1201.

914.106 058.7 SW ISSN 0280-8773
INVANDRARFRAAGOR. AARSBOK. 1983-198? a. Immigrant Institutet, Kvarngatan 16, S-502 33 Boras, Sweden.

058.7 SW ISSN 0349-554X
INVANDRARTIDNINGEN (MONTHLY); Arabic edition. 1972-1990. m. Stiftelsen Invandrartidningen, Box 1352, S-111 83 Stockholm, Sweden.

  Supersedes (in 1980): Invandrartidningen Information (ISSN 0345-4983)

929 US
INVESTIGATOR. 1986-1988. q. Learning Place, Box 3261, Beaumont, CA 92223.
  Formerly: Pass Genealogical Reporter.

332.6 US
INVESTING. 1990; ceased same year. q. Research Services, Inc., 2201 Third St., San Francisco, CA 94107.

332.6 UK ISSN 0021-0048
HG4502
INVESTMENT ANALYST. 1962-19?? q. (Society of Investment Analysts) Longman Group (UK) Ltd., Fourth Ave., Harlow, Essex CM19 5AA, England.

332.6 US ISSN 0075-0271
HG4530
INVESTMENT COMPANIES; mutual funds and other types. 1941-199? a. with m. & q. updating. (Wiesenberger Services, Inc.) Warren, Gorham and Lamont Inc., One Penn Plaza, New York, NY 10119.

332.6 US
INVESTMENT MONTHLY. 1986-198? m. K C I Communications, Inc., 1101 King St., Ste. 400, Alexandria, VA 22314.

332.6 UK ISSN 0953-8453
HG5436
INVESTMENT TRUST DIRECTORY (YEAR). 1978-1990. a. (tabloid format) (Association of Investment Trust Companies) Woodhead-Faulkner (Publishers) Ltd., Fitzwilliam House, 32 Trumpington St., Cambridge CB2 1QY, England.
  Formerly: Investment Trust Year Book (ISSN 0261-3891)

332.6 US
INVESTOR RELATIONS (SAN FRANCISCO). 1991-1992 (Jan.). m. (National Investor Relations Institute) Research Services, Inc., 2201 Third St., San Francisco, CA 94107.

332.6 US
INVESTOR RELATIONS (WASHINGTON); a practical guide for NASDAQ companies. ceased 1988. irreg. National Association of Securities Dealers, Inc., 1735 K St., N.W., Washington, DC 20006.

332.6 US
INVESTOR RELATIONS REPORT. ceased. q. National Association of Securities Dealers, Inc., 1735 K St., N.W., Washington, DC 20006.

621.38 UK
INVISION. 1986-1989. m. International Thomson Business Publishing, 100 Avenue Road, London NW3 3TP, England.

200 150 US ISSN 0021-0250
INWARD LIGHT. 1937-19?? irreg. (Friends Conference on Religion and Psychology) Inward Light, 749 Polo Rd., Bryn Mawr, PA 19010.

379 US ISSN 0091-8962
LB2826.I8
IOWA. DEPARTMENT OF PUBLIC INSTRUCTION. SUMMARY OF FEDERAL PROGRAMS. 1971-1982. a. Department of Public Instruction, Grimes State Office Bldg, Des Moines, IA 50319.

630 658 US
IOWA AGRI-NEWS. 1984-1991. w. Agri-News Publications, 420 Second St., LaSalle, IL 61301-2334.

633 US
IOWA AGRICULTURAL STATISTICS. 1976-1990; suspended. a. Agricultural Statistics, Federal Bldg., Rm. 833, 210 Walnut St., Des Moines, IA 50309.
  Supersedes: Iowa. Crop and Livestock Reporting Service. Weather and Field Crops (ISSN 0163-4976)

610.7 US ISSN 0075-0387
IOWA NURSES' ASSOCIATION. BULLETIN. ceased. a. Iowa Nurses' Association, 100 Court Ave., Ste. 9 LL, Des Moines, IA 50309-2200.
  Formerly: Iowa State Nurses' Association. Bulletin.

614.7 322.4 900 IT
L'IPPOGRIFO; politica ed economia dei beni culturali e ambientali. 1988-198? q. (back issues avail.) Societa Editrice Il Mulino, Strada Maggiore, 37, 40125 Bologna, Italy.

315 338 IR
IRAN. MINISTRY OF INDUSTRIES AND MINES. TRENDS IN INDUSTRIAL AND COMMERCIAL STATISTICS. 1965-1975. q. Ministry of Industries and Mines, Arg Square, Teheran, Iran.

791.43 IR
IRANIAN CINEMA. published only once, 1985. a. National Film Archive of Iran - Film-khane-ye Melli-e Iran, P.O. Box 5158, Teheran 11365, Iran.

052 IE
IRELAND TODAY. 1949-19?? s-m. (reprint service avail. from KTO) Department of External Affairs, Information Section, IE , Ivengh House, St. Stephen's Green, Dublin 1, Ireland.
 Former titles: Weekly Bulletin of Ireland; Ireland (ISSN 0021-0935)

914 UK
IRISH ARCHAEOLOGICAL RESEARCH FORUM. 1974-1977. 2/yr. Queen's University, Ulster Museum Conservation Laboratory, 13 University Sq., Belfast BT7 1NN, Antrim, Northern Ireland.

929
IRISH CREEK COUSINS NEWSLETTER; of Thompson family history and genealogy. 1982-19?? m. (looseleaf format; back issues avail.) 4231 Lowe, Toledo, OH 43612.

301 338.1 IE ISSN 0021-1249
IRISH JOURNAL OF AGRICULTURAL ECONOMICS AND RURAL SOCIOLOGY. 1967-1991. a. T.E.A.G.A.S.C., 19 Sandymount Ave., Dublin 4, Ireland.

614.7 IE ISSN 0332-1665
CODEN: IESCDD
IRISH JOURNAL OF ENVIRONMENTAL SCIENCE. 1980-1987; suspended. 2/yr. Foras Forbartha, St. Martin's House, Waterloo Rd., Dublin 4, Ireland.

669 ISSN 0140-8402
IRON & MANGANESE ORES SURVEY. 1978-198? irreg. Metal Bulletin Inc., 220 Fifth Ave., 10th Fl., New York.

811 US ISSN 0047-150X
PN6099.6
IRONWOOD. 1972-1988 (Nov.). s-a. Ironwood Press, Box 40907, Tucson, AZ 85717.

631.3 US
IRRIGATION ASSOCIATION. MANAGEMENT BULLETIN. ceased 1991. bi-m. Irrigation Association, 1911 N. Ft. Myer Dr., Ste. 1009, Arlington, VA 22209.

631.3 US
IRRIGATION NEWSLETTER. ceased 1991. bi-m. Irrigation Association, 1911 N. Ft. Myer Dr., Ste. 1009, Arlington, VA 22209.

910.5 SA
ISIZWE. 1974-19?? a. University of Natal, Students Geographical Society, Durban 4001, South Africa.

808 US ISSN 0277-593X
ISMAEL REED AND AL YOUNG'S QUILT. 1981-1986 (no.5). s-a. (back issues avail.) Quilt-Ybird, 660 13th St., No. 203, Oakland, CA 94812-1241.

690 534 IT
ISOLARE. 1971-19?? bi-m. BE-MA Editore, Via Teocrit, 50, 20128 Milan, Italy.

050 070 IS ISSN 0078-0448
ISRAEL. GOVERNMENT PRESS OFFICE. NEWSPAPERS AND PERIODICALS APPEARING IN ISRAEL. 1965-1966. a. Government Press Office, Agron House, 37 Hillel St., Jerusalem, Israel.

332.6 IS ISSN 0334-3898
HC497.P2
ISRAEL BUSINESS. 1961-1991 (no.481). m. (processed) A G Publications Ltd., P.O. Box 7422, Haifa 31070, Israel.
 Former titles: Israel Business and Investors' Report; Israel Investors' Report (ISSN 0021-2113)

387 IS
ISRAEL PORTS AUTHORITY. ANNUAL REPORT. ceased 1984. a. Israel Ports Authority, Box 20121, Tel Aviv, Israel.

332.6 US ISSN 0147-4316
HG4503
ISRAEL SECURITIES REVIEW. 1973-198?; suspended. 6/yr. American Israel Ventures Corp., 461 Beach 124 St., Belle Harbor, NY 11694.
 Formerly (until 1975): Israel Securities Review Monthly Magazine (ISSN 0147-4308)

336 IS
ISRAEL TAX LAW LETTER. 1980-1990. irreg. (approx. 15/yr.). A G Publications Ltd., Box 7422, 31070 Haifa, Israel.

320 IS
ISRAELI DEMOCRACY (ENGLISH EDITION). 1987-19?? q. Israel Democracy Institute, P.O. Box 4702, 91040 Jerusalem, Israel.

200 CN
ISSUE (TORONTO). 1974-19?? irreg. United Church of Canada, 85 St. Clair Ave. E., Toronto, Ont. M4T 1M8, Canada.

332.1 US
ISSUES FOR BANK COUNSEL. ceased 1987 (Sep.). m. American Bankers Association, Member Communications, 1120 Connecticut Ave., N.W., Washington, DC 20026.

657 UK
ISSUES IN ACCOUNTABILITY. 1977-1985; suspended. s-a. (back issues avail.) Strathclyde Convergencies, 15 Spence St., Glasgow G20 0AW, Scotland.

360
ISSUES IN CANADIAN SOCIAL POLICY/POLITIQUE SOCIALE AU CANADA. 1982-1984. biennial. Canadian Council on Social Development, 55 Parkdale Ave., Box 3505, Station C, Ottawa, Ont. K1Y 4G1, Canada.

945 011 US ISSN 0020-4064
ISTITUTO ITALIANO DI CULTURA. BULLETIN. ceased. m. Istituto Italiano di Cultura, 686 Park Ave., New York, NY 10021.

800 400 IT ISSN 0077-2763
PN5
ISTITUTO UNIVERSITARIO ORIENTALE DI NAPOLI. ANNALI. SEZIONE GERMANICA. 1958-1974. 8/yr. Herder Editrice e Libreria s.r.l., Piazza Montecitorio 117-121, 00186 Rome, Italy.

616.07 IT ISSN 0391-7452
ISTO CITO PATOLOGIA; documentazione casistica. 1979-1988 (vol.10). q. Edi. Ermes, Via Timavo 12, 20124 Milan, Italy.

694 IT
L'ITALIA DEL LEGNO. 1990-1991 (Mar.). m. Gruppo Editoriale Fabbri SPA, Divisione Periodici, Via Mecenate 91, 20128 Milan, Italy.

330 IT ISSN 0021-2911
ITALIAN ECONOMIC SURVEY. 1946-1979. bi-m. Associazione fra le Societa Italiane per Azioni, Piazza Venezia 11, Rome, Italy.

617 IT ISSN 0392-3525
CODEN: IJSSET
ITALIAN JOURNAL OF SURGICAL SCIENCES. 1970?-1989 (vol.19). q. (also avail. in microform from UMI; reprint service avail. from ISI) Masson Italia Periodici, Via Statuto 2-4, 20121 Milan, Italy.
 Formerly: Surgery in Italy.

380 IT ISSN 0021-2997
ITALIAN TRADE TOPICS. 1957-1987. q. Italian Embassy in the United States, Commercial Office, 1601 Fuller St., N.W., Washington, DC 20009.

574.92 639.3 IT ISSN 0006-6753
ITALY. LABORATORIO DI IDROBIOLOGIA. BOLLETTINO DI PESCA PISCICOLTURA E IDROBIOLOGIA. 1925; N.S. 1946-1984. s-a. Laboratorio Central di Idrobiologia, Libreria Dello Stato, Viala del Caravaggio 107, 00147 Rome, Italy.

355 792 780 UK
IT'S NTERTAINMENT. 1977-198? 4/yr. Navy, Army and Air Force Institutes, Kennington, London S.E.11, England.

333 JA
IWATE UNIVERSITY. MOUNTAINS LAND USE RESEARCH LABORATORY. BULLETIN. 1968-1991. irreg. Iwate University, Faculty of Agriculture, Mountains Land Use Research Station - Iwate Daigaku Nogakubu Fuzoku Sanchi Riyo, 3-18-8 Ueda, Morioka 020, Iwate, Japan.

976.704 US
IZARD COUNTY HISTORIAN. 1970-1989. q. (back issues avail.) Izard County Historical Society, c/o Helen C. Lindley, Ed., Dolph, AR 72528.

769.56 800 US ISSN 0278-436X
HE6183.L59
J A P O S BULLETIN. (Journalists, Authors, Poets on Stamps) 1974-1988. q. (back issues avail.; reprint service avail. from UMI) (J A P O S Study Group) Gustav Detjen Jr., Pub., 154 Laguna Court, St. Augustine Shores, FL 32086-7031.

708.1 069.7 US ISSN 0021-356X
J.B. SPEED ART MUSEUM BULLETIN. 1940-19??; suspended. irreg. (2-3/yr.). J.B. Speed Art Museum, 2035 S. Third St., Box 2600, Louisville, KY 40201-2600.

792 BE
J E B THEATRE. ceased. irreg. (2-3/yr.). Direction Generale de la Jeunesse et des Loisirs, Galerie Ravenstein 78, 1000 Brussels, Belgium.

369.4 FR ISSN 0021-583X
J.E.M.. (Jeunes en Marche) 1967-19?? m. Scouts de France, 23, rue Ligner, 75020 - Paris, France.

370 331 296 US
J L C EDUCATOR. 1975-19?? 5/yr. Jewish Labor Committee, Educators Chapter, Atran Center, 25 E. 21st St., 2nd Fl., New York, NY 10010.

658 JA
J M A NEWSLETTER. 1978-1990? q. (back issues avail.) Japan Management Association, 3-1-22 Shiba-koen, Minato-Ku, Tokyo 105, Japan.

621.9 382 JA
J M E A NEWSLETTER. ceased. m? Japan Machinery Exporters' Association - Nihon Kikai Yushutsu Sogo, 5-8, 3-chome, Shiba Koen, Minato-ku, Tokyo, Japan.

001.53 029.7 US ISSN 0021-3748
Z678.9.A1
J O L A TECHNICAL COMMUNICATIONS. (Journal of Library Automation) 1970-1972 (July-Aug.). m. American Library Association, Information Science & Automation Div., 50 E. Huron St., Chicago, IL 60611.

361.75 US ISSN 0364-4103
J S A C GRAPEVINE. 1969-19??; suspended. m. (tabloid format) Joint Strategy and Action Committee, 815 Second Ave., New York, NY 10017-4503.

028.5 SP
J-20. (Juventud Siglo XX) 1969-1990 (June). m. Ediciones Don Bosco (Edebe), Paseo San Juan Bosco 62, Barcelona-17, Spain.

810 US ISSN 0021-3837
PS3523.046
JACK LONDON NEWSLETTER. 1967-1989 (vol.21); suspended. 3/yr. (also avail. in microfilm from UMI; reprint service avail. from UMI) c/o Dept. of Cinema, Southern Illinois University, Carbondale, IL 62901.

929 US ISSN 0738-6648
CS71
JACKSONIANA; a Jackson family newsletter. 1978-19?? q. (back issues avail.) Ernest H. Jackson, Ed. & Pub., 730 Parker Woods Dr., Rockford, IL 61102.

808.81 US
JACKSONVILLE POETRY QUARTERLY. 1960-1992. q. (looseleaf format; also avail. in microfiche; back issues avail.) Arcane Order Press, 2904 Rosemary Ln., Falls Church, VA 22042.

820 AU
JACOBEAN DRAMA STUDIES. 1972-198? irreg. Universitaet Salzburg, Institut fuer Englische Sprache, Akademiestr. 24, A-5020 Salzburg, Austria.

5220 CESSATIONS

340   AT   ISSN 0727-7946
JACOBS' COUNTY COURT PRACTICE. 1980-198? s-a. (looseleaf format) Law Book Co. Ltd., 44-50 Waterloo Rd., N. Ryde, N.S.W. 2113, Australia.

020   SA   ISSN 0256-0070
Z858.U417
JAGGER JOURNAL. 1980-1989 (No.10). a. University of Cape Town, Libraries, Rondebosch 7700, South Africa.

943   GW   ISSN 0341-9177
JAHRBUCH DER HISTORISCHEN FORSCHUNG IN DER BUNDESREPUBLIK DEUTSCHLAND. 1974-1991. a. (Arbeitsgemeinschaft Ausseruniversitaren Historischen Forschungsrichtungen der Bundesrepublik) K.G. Saur Verlag KG, Ortlerstr. 8, Postfach 701620, 8000 Munich 70, Germany.

657 658   GW
JAHRBUCH FUER BETRIEBSWIRTE. 1975-1991. a. Taylorix Fachverlag Stiegler & Co., Zazenhaeuserstr. 106, 7000 Stuttgart 40, Germany.

155   GW
JAHRBUCH FUER ENTWICKLUNGSPSYCHOLOGIE. ceased. a. Klett-Cotta, Rotebeuhlstr. 77, Postfach 809, D-7000 Stuttgart 1, Germany.

320   GW   ISSN 0304-2197
JAHRBUCH INTERNATIONALE POLITIK UND WIRTSCHAFT. ceased 1989. a. Staatsverlag der D D R, Otto-Grotewohl-Str. 17, 1086 Berlin, Germany.

385   GW   ISSN 0177-5529
JAHRBUCH SCHIENENVERKEHR; Berichte-Statistik-Fotografien-Aktuelles von der Schiene. 1982-1991. a. (back issues avail.) Verlag Dr. Bernhard Abend, Altenbergstr. 1, 7000 Stuttgart 1, Germany.

940   GW
JAHRBUCH ZUR GESCHICHTE DRESDENS. (Subseries of: Institute's Informationsdienst) ceased 1989. a. Institut und Museum fuer Geschichte der Stadt Dresden, Ernst-Thaelmann-Str. 2, 8010 Dresden, Germany.

811   US   ISSN 0362-8302
PS501
JAM TO-DAY. 1973-1990 (no.15). a. (back issues avail.) 372 Dunstable Rd., Tyngsboro, MA 01879.

338   JM
JAMAICAN MANUFACTURER. ceased. 2/yr. Jamaican Manufacturer Association, Ltd., 85A Duke St., Kingston, Jamaica, W.I.

658.788   JM
JAMAICAN PACKAGING DIRECTORY. 1982-198? quinquennial. (back issues avail.) Bureau of Standards, Packaging Centre, 6 Winchester Rd., P.O. Box 113, Kingston 10, Jamaica, W.I.

658.8   US   ISSN 0162-9107
JANUZ DIRECT MARKETING LETTER; a monthly portfolio of useful direct marketing ideas. 1974-19?? m. Januz Consultants Division, Box 631, Lake Forest, IL 60045.

636   JA   ISSN 0453-0535
JAPAN. NORIN-SHO KACHIKU EISEI SHIKENJO NENPO/ JAPAN. NATIONAL INSTITUTE OF ANIMAL HEALTH. ANNUAL REPORT. 1960-1985. a. National Institute of Animal Health - Norin-sho Kachiku Eisei Shikenjo, Section 1-1, Kannondai 3-chome, Yatabe-machi, Tsukuba-gun, Ibaraki-ken 305, Japan.

915.206   US
JAPAN AND AMERICA; a journal of cultural studies. ceased. 3/yr. Pacific Institute of Cultural Studies, 561 E. Wilson Ave., Salt Lake City, UT 84105-2918.

616.2   JA   ISSN 0075-3165
JAPAN ANTI-TUBERCULOSIS ASSOCIATION. REPORTS ON MEDICAL RESEARCH PROBLEMS/KEKKAKU YOBOKAI KENKYU GYOSEKI. 1951-1984 (vol.32). a. Japan Anti-Tuberculosis Association - Kekkaku Yobokai, 1-3-12 Misaki-cho, Chiyoda-ku, Tokyo 101, Japan.

330   US   ISSN 0895-6731
HC461
JAPAN BUSINESS. ceased 1988. m. Ciber Inc., International Trade Commission Bldg., 8th Fl., 500 E St., S.W., Washington, DC 20024.

540   US   ISSN 0895-674X
QD1
JAPAN CHEMISTRY. 1988; ceased same year. m. Ciber Inc., International Trade Commission Bldg., 8th Fl., 500 E St., S.W., Washington, DC 20024.

001.6 621.381 001.7US   ISSN 0890-1406
QA75.5
JAPAN COMPUTER TECHNOLOGY AND APPLICATIONS ABSTRACTS. 1987; ceased same year. m. University Publications of America (Subsidiary of: Congressional Information Service), 4520 East-West Hwy., Ste. 800, Bethesda, MD 20814-3389.

001.6 621.381   US   ISSN 0895-6715
QA75.5
JAPAN COMPUTERS. 1988; ceased same year. m. Ciber Inc., International Trade Commission Bldg., 8th Fl., 500 E St., S.W., Washington, DC 20024.

621.3   US   ISSN 0895-6723
TK7800
JAPAN ELECTRONICS (WASHINGTON). 1988; ceased same year. m. Ciber Inc., International Trade Commission Bldg., 8th Fl., 500 E St., S.W., Washington, DC 20024.

531.64   US   ISSN 0895-6774
TJ163.13
JAPAN ENERGY. 1988; ceased same year. m. Ciber Inc., International Trade Commission Bldg., 8th Fl., 500 E St., S.W., Washington, DC 20024.

600   US   ISSN 0895-6685
TS1
JAPAN MANUFACTURING. ceased 1988. m. Ciber Inc., International Trade Commission Bldg., 8th Fl., 500 E St., S.W., Washington, DC 20024.

620.11   US   ISSN 0895-6707
TA401
JAPAN MATERIALS. 1988; ceased same year. m. Ciber Inc., International Trade Commission Bldg., 8th Fl., 500 E St., S.W., Washington, DC 20024.

669   US
JAPAN MATERIALS NEWS. ceased. 12/yr. A S M International, Materials Park, OH 44073.

011   JA
JAPAN PERIODICALS. 19??-19?? triennial. Keizai Koho Center, Otemachi Bldg. 6-1, Ote-machi 1-chome, Chiyoda-ku, Tokyo 100, Japan.

769.56   JA
JAPAN PHILATELY. suspended 1991 (Dec). m. Japan Philatelic Society, P.O. Box 1, Shinjuku, Tokyo 163-91, Japan.

320.531   JA   ISSN 0021-4655
HX9
JAPAN SOCIALIST REVIEW. 1961-1983. m. Social Democratic of Japan - Nihon Shakaito, 1-8-1 Nagata-cho, Chiyoda-ku, Tokyo, Japan.

600   US
T1
JAPAN TECHNOLOGY SERIES. 1986-1989. m. Ciber Inc., International Trade Commission Bldg., 8th Fl., 500 E St., S.W., Washington, DC 20024.
Formerly (until 1988): Japanese Technical Abstracts (ISSN 0882-5246)

621.38   US   ISSN 0895-6766
TK5101.A1
JAPAN TELECOMMUNICATIONS. 1988; ceased same year. m. Ciber Inc., International Trade Commission Bldg., 8th Fl., 500 E St., S.W., Washington, DC 20024.

382   JA
JAPAN TIMES DIRECTORY. ceased. a. Japan Times, Ltd., 4-5-4 Shibaura, Minato-ku, Tokyo 108, Japan.

617.96   NE   ISSN 0169-1066
CODEN: JAJREV
JAPANESE ANAESTHESIA JOURNALS REVIEW. 1985-1988 (vol.4). q. V S P, P.O. Box 346, 3700 AH Zeist, Netherlands.

745.92   US   ISSN 1041-5912
JAPANESE FLOWER ARRANGING. 1987-1989. bi-m. (looseleaf format; back issues avail.) c/o Shirley C. Pototsky, Ed., 44 Lane Park, Ste. 1, Brighton, MA 02135.

610   JA   ISSN 0021-5031
R97   CODEN: JJEMAG
JAPANESE JOURNAL OF EXPERIMENTAL MEDICINE. 1922-1990 (vol.60, no.6). bi-m. University of Tokyo, Institute of Medical Science - Tokyo Daigaku Ikagaku Kenkyusho, 4-6-1 Shirokanedai, Minato-ku, Tokyo 108, Japan.

382   JA
JAPAN'S ECONOMY AND JAPAN - U S TRADE. 1982-19?? a. (Japan-US Study Group) Japan Times Ltd., 5-4 Shibaura, 4-Chome, Minato-ku, Tokyo 1D8, Japan.
Formerly: Japan's Economy and Trade.

781.57   UK
JAZZ MUSIC NEWS. 1982-19?? m. Goldcity Ltd., 28 Gordon Mansions, Torrington Place, London WC1E 7HF, England.

681   GW   ISSN 0448-9497
TS510   CODEN: JNRVAY
JENA REVIEW/JENAER RUNDSCHAU. 1956-1991. q. Jenoptik Carl Zeiss JENA GmbH, Carl-Zeiss-Str. 1, 6900 Jena, Germany.

943   GW   ISSN 0138-3604
JENAER BEITRAEGE ZUR PARTEIGESCHICHTE; Mitteilungsblatt der Forschungsgemeinschaft Geschichte der Buergerlichen Parteien in Deutschland. 1957-1990. irreg. Historisches Institut der Friedrich-Schiller-Universitaet Jena, Goetheallee 1, 6900 Jena, Germany.
Formerly: Arbeitsgemeinschaft der Sektion Geschichte der Akademie der Wissenschaften Geschichte der Buergerlichen Parteien in Deutschland. Mitteilungsblatt.

332 677   US   ISSN 0731-9444
JENKS SOUTHEASTERN BUSINESS LETTER. 1981-198? s-m. (back issues avail.) Jenks Enterprises, Box 7664, Atlanta, GA 30357.

052   UK   ISSN 0268-5000
JENNINGS MAGAZINE. 1985-1988 (Spring). q. (back issues avail.) Jennings Magazine Ltd., 336 Westbourne Park Rd., London W11 1EQ, England.

739.27   US
JEWEL. 1988-1989. q. Collector Communications Corp., 170 Fifth Ave., New York, NY 10010.

745.594 745.5   SA
JEWELLERY, CURIOS, ARTS & CRAFTS (YEAR). ceased. a. South African Foreign Trade Organisation, Publishing Division, P.O. Box 782706, Sandton 2146, South Africa.

296 320.52   AT
JEWISH COMMENTARY. 1983-198?; suspended. irreg. (2-3/yr.). (back issues avail.) Torah News Digest, 55 Dover Rd., Rose Bay, N.S.W. 2029, Australia.

023   US
JEWISH LIBRARIANS TASK FORCE. NEWSLETTER. 1976-198? s-a. (processed) American Library Association, Ethnic Materials Information Exchange Round Table, Jewish Librarians Task Force, c/o Steven Mitchel, Ed., 6069 California Cir., Ste 203, Rockyville, MD 20852.
Formerly: Jewish Librarians Caucus Newsletter.

781.7 296   US
JEWISH MUSIC NOTES. 1949-198? q. J W B Jewish Music Council, 15 E. 26 St., New York, NY 10010.

388.3   US   ISSN 1047-2312
HD9710.A1
JOBBER EXECUTIVE; for active management in automotive aftermarket distribution. 1957-1991 (Apr.). m. Hunter Publishing Limited Partnership, 950 Lee St., Des Plaines, IL 60016.
Formerly: Jobber and Warehouse Executive (ISSN 0021-7042)

371.42   US   ISSN 0738-0208
JOBLESS NEWSLETTER; how to make a living without a job. 1982-198? m. (looseleaf format; back issues avail.) Baker Publishing, c/o Albert Baker, Ed., 14902 Running Deer Trail, Austin, TX 78734.

020   US
JOBS IN PRINT. ceased. 21/yr. Rutgers University, School of Communication, Information, and Library Studies, 4 Huntington St., New Brunswick, NJ 08903.

371.42 US ISSN 1040-9300
JOBS TODAY; youth. 1989; ceased same year. q. OmniGraphics, Inc., 2500 Penobscott Bldg., Detroit, MI 48226.

296 DK ISSN 0107-7333
JOEDISK REVY. 1981; ceased same year. irreg. Joedisk Revy, Dan Melchior, Enighedsvej 10, 2920 Charlottenlund, Denmark.

347 GW ISSN 0532-596X
JOHANN-WOLFGANG-GOETHE UNIVERSITAET, FRANKFURT. OSTASIATISCHE SEMINAR. VEROEFFENTLICHUNGEN. REIHE A. SUEDOSTASIENKUNDE. 1965-1976 (vol.5). irreg. Verlag Otto Harrassowitz, Taunusstr. 14, Postfach 2929, 6200 Wiesbaden 1, Germany.

950 GW
JOHANN-WOLFGANG-GOETHE-UNIVERSITAET, FRANKFURT. OSTASIATISCHE SEMINAR. VEROEFFENTLICHUNGEN. REIHE B: OSTASIENKUNDE. 1970-19?? irreg. Verlag Otto Harrassowitz, Taunusstr. 14, Postfach 2929, 6200 Wiesbaden 1, Germany.
Formerly: Universitaet Frankfurt am Main. Ostasiatischen Seminars. Veroeffentlichungen (ISSN 0340-6652)

617 US ISSN 0075-3815
JOHN ALEXANDER MONOGRAPH SERIES ON VARIOUS PHASES OF THORACIC SURGERY. ceased. irreg. Charles C. Thomas, Publisher, 2600 S. First St., Springfield, IL 62794-9265.

331 US ISSN 0021-7190
HD4802
JOHN HERLING'S LABOR LETTER. 1948-1989 (vol.38, no.36). w. John Herling's Labor Letter, Inc., 1010 Vermont Ave., N.W., Ste. 1002, Washington, DC 20005.

325 US
JOHNS HOPKINS UNIVERSITY. POPULATION INFORMATION PROGRAM. POPULATION REPORTS. ARABIC EDITION. 1973-1986. irreg. (looseleaf format; back issues avail.) Johns Hopkins University, Population Information Program, 527 St. Paul Place, Baltimore, MD 21202.
Formerly: George Washington University. Population Information Program. Population Reports.

929 US ISSN 8755-1721
CS71
JOHNSON JOURNAL. 1982-19?? 4/yr. (back issues avail.; reprint service avail.) Box 96, Broderick, CA 95605.

797.1 US ISSN 0271-2040
GV835.8
JOHNSON OUTBOARDS BOATING. ceased 1986. a. Acqua Field Publications, Inc., 656 Shrewsbury Ave., Shrewsbury, NJ 07701.

671.52 UK
JOINING AND MATERIALS. 1969-1989. m. (back issues avail.) Welding Institute, Abington Hall, Cambridge CB1 6AL, England.
Former titles: Metal Construction (ISSN 0307-7896); Metal Construction and British Welding Journal (ISSN 0026-0541); British Welding Journal.

614.8 US ISSN 0277-8327
JOINT COMMISSION PERSPECTIVES. 1952-1986. bi-m. (back issues avail.) Joint Commission on Accreditation of Healthcare Organization, 875 N. Michigan Ave., Chicago, IL 60611.
Formerly: J C A H Perspectives.

808.8 US
JOINT ENDEAVOR. 1973-19?? q. Box 99, Huntsville, TX 77340.

327 EI ISSN 0447-8452
JN22
JOINT MEETING OF THE MEMBERS OF THE CONSULTATIVE ASSEMBLY OF THE COUNCIL OF EUROPE AND OF THE MEMBERS OF THE EUROPEAN PARLIAMENTARY ASSEMBLY. OFFICIAL REPORT OF DEBATES. 1953-19?? a. Office for Official Publications of the European Communities, P.O. Box 1003, L-2985 Luxembourg, Luxembourg.

028.5 DK
JONAH HEX. ceased. m. Interpresse, Krogshoejvej 32, 2880 Bagsvaerd, Denmark.

929 US
JONES OF AMERICA. ceased. 4/yr. Inkwell Publications, 1661 Lauranceae Way, Riverdale, GA 30296.

382 JO
JORDAN. DEPARTMENT OF STATISTICS. MONTHLY BULLETIN OF EXTERNAL TRADE STATISTICS. 1988-1990. m. Department of Statistics, P.O. Box 2015, Amman, Jordan.

915 US ISSN 0164-4777
DS153.A2
JORDAN (WASHINGTON). 1976-1988. irreg. (approx. 2/yr.). (back issues avail.) (Ministry of Information, Amman, JO) Jordan Information Bureau, 2319 Wyoming Ave., N.W., Washington, DC 20008.

336 JO ISSN 0449-1491
JORDAN ECONOMY IN FIGURES. 1971-1988. m. Department of Statistics, Amman, Jordan.

910 SW ISSN 0021-7476
G149
JORDEN RUNT; lander, folk, resor. 1929-19?? m. Bengt Pleijel, Ed. & Pub., Narvavaegen 30, 11523 Stockholm, Sweden.

618.92 BL ISSN 0021-7557
JORNAL DE PEDIATRIA; orgao oficial da sociedade brasileira de pediatria. 1934-19?? 10/yr. (also avail. in microform from UMI; reprint service avail. from UMI) (Sociedade Brasileira de Pediatria) Editora de Publicacoes Cientificas Ltda., Rua Major Suckow, 30 a 36, 20911 Rio de Janeiro RJ, Brazil.

630.091 FR ISSN 0183-5173
CODEN: JATADT
JOURNAL D'AGRICULTURE TRADITIONNELLE ET DE BOTANIQUE APPLIQUEE; travaux d'ethnobiologie. 1954-1991. a. Museum National d'Histoire Naturelle, Laboratoire d'Ethnobiologie-Biogeographie, 57 rue Cuvier, 75231 Paris Cedex 05, France.
Formerly: Journal d'Agriculture Tropical et de Botanique Appliquee (ISSN 0021-7662)

616.8 FR
JOURNAL DE PSYCHIATRIE BIOLOGIQUE ET THERAPEUTIQUE. ceased 1988. 4/yr. Masson, 120 bd. Saint-Germain, 75280 Paris, France.

615.84 FR ISSN 0243-1203
CODEN: JEURDB
JOURNAL EUROPEEN DE RADIOTHERAPIE. 1980-1989. q. (also avail. in microform from UMI) Masson, 120 bd. Saint-Germain, 75280 Paris Cedex 06, France.

960 300 001.3 US ISSN 0095 4993
DT1
JOURNAL OF AFRICAN STUDIES. 1974-1989. q. (also avail. in microform; back issues avail.; reprint service avail.) (Helen Dwight Reid Educational Foundation) Heldref Publications, 4000 Albemarle St., N.W., Washington, DC 20016.

368 US ISSN 0021-874X
HG8011
JOURNAL OF AMERICAN INSURANCE. (Former name of issuing body (until 1977): American Mutual Insurance Alliance) 1924-1990 (vol.66, no.4). q. (also avail. in microform from UMI; reprint service avail. from UMI) Alliance of American Insurers, 1501 Woodfield Rd., Schaumburg, IL 60173-4980.

616.12 UK ISSN 0883-2935
CODEN: JACAED
JOURNAL OF APPLIED CARDIOLOGY. 1986-1991. bi-m. (also avail. in microform; back issues avail.) Pergamon Press plc, Headington Hill Hall, Oxford OX3 0BW, England.

700 US
JOURNAL OF ART. ceased 1991. 9/yr. Rizzoli International Publications, Inc., 300 Park Ave. S., New York, NY 10010-5313.

947 UK ISSN 0075-4161
DK507.A2
JOURNAL OF BYELORUSSIAN STUDIES. 1965-1990. a. Anglo-Byelorussian Society, 39 Holden Rd., London N12 8HS, England.

155.4 362.7 US ISSN 0276-6256
HQ767.8
JOURNAL OF CHILDREN IN CONTEMPORARY SOCIETY; advances in theory and applied research. 1967-1990. q. (also avail. in microfiche; back issues avail.) (Carnegie - Mellon University Child Care Center) Haworth Press, Inc., 10 Alice St., Binghamton, NY 13904.
Formerly (until May 1980): Children in Contemporary Society (ISSN 0276-6264)

530 US ISSN 1044-8357
QC1
JOURNAL OF CHINESE PHYSICS. 1989-1990. bi-m. (back issues avail.) (Zhongguo Wuli Xuehui, CC - Chinese Physical Society) Allerton Press, Inc., 150 Fifth Ave., New York, NY 10011.

301.16 US ISSN 0194-2158
HM258
JOURNAL OF COMMUNITY COMMUNICATIONS. 1973-19?? q. (back issues avail.) Village Design, Box 1220, Berkeley, CA 94701.

610 616.89 US ISSN 0887-6509
JOURNAL OF COMPLIANCE IN HEALTH CARE. 1986-1989. s-a. Springer Publishing Company, 536 Broadway, New York, NY 10012.

310 US ISSN 1044-0755
JOURNAL OF COMPUTING AND SOCIETY. 1990-1991. s-a. Ablex Publishing Corporation, 355 Chestnut St., Norwood, NJ 07648.

300 SA ISSN 0258-9001
JOURNAL OF CONTEMPORARY AFRICAN STUDIES. 1981-199? 2/yr. (reprint service avail. from UMI) Africa Institute of South Africa, P.O. Box 630, Pretoria 0001, South Africa.

610.07 US ISSN 0894-1912
R845 CODEN: JCHPET
JOURNAL OF CONTINUING EDUCATION IN THE HEALTH PROFESSION. 1981-19?? q. (back issues avail.) Taylor & Francis New York, 79 Madison Ave., Ste. 1110, New York, NY 10016.
Formerly (until 1987): Moebius (ISSN 0272-3425)

700 720 069 US ISSN 0888-7314
NK1
JOURNAL OF DECORATIVE AND PROPAGANDA ARTS. 1986-1990 (no.17); suspended. q. (back issues avail.) Wolfson Foundation of Decorative and Propaganda Arts, 2399 N.E. Second Ave., Miami, FL 33137.

338.91 US ISSN 0897-1862
HD72
JOURNAL OF ECONOMIC GROWTH. 1986-1990. q. National Chamber Foundation, 1615 H St., N.W., Washington, DC 20062.

616.1 US ISSN 0892-1059
JOURNAL OF ELECTROPHYSIOLOGY. 1983-198? bi-m. Futura Publishing Company, Inc., Bedford Ridge Rd., Box 330, Mt. Kisco, NY 10549.
Formerly (until 1985): Clinical Progress in Pacing and Electrophysiology (ISSN 0736-6108)

620 US ISSN 0191-9539
TA1 CODEN: JOASDI
JOURNAL OF ENGINEERING & APPLIED SCIENCES. 1981-1985. q. (also avail. in microform from MIM, UMI) Pergamon Press, Inc., Journals Division, 660 White Plains Rd., Tarrytown, NY 10591-5153.

629 US
JOURNAL OF ENGINEERING & COMPUTER APPLICATIONS. 1986-1991. q. Auerbach Publishers (Subsidiary of: Warren, Gorham & Lamont), One Penn Plaza, New York, NY 10119.

621 II ISSN 0251-1770
JOURNAL OF ENGINEERING PRODUCTION. 1981-199? q. (Indian Society of Mechanical Engineers) Wiley Eastern Ltd., 4835-24 Ansari Rd., Darya Ganj, New Delhi - 110 022, India.

001.3 US ISSN 0091-3219
E184.A1
JOURNAL OF ETHNIC STUDIES. 1973-1991. q. (also avail. in microform from UMI; reprint service avail. from UMI) Western Washington University, Bellingham, WA 98225.

CESSATIONS

619   US   ISSN 0730-8485
CODEN: JEPAD3
JOURNAL OF EXPERIMENTAL PATHOLOGY. 1983-1990. q. Mary Ann Liebert, Inc., 1651 Third Ave., New York, NY 10128.

333.91 614.7   US   ISSN 0276-0142
QH96.A1
JOURNAL OF FRESHWATER. 1977-198? s-a. Freshwater Foundation, 2500 Shadywood Rd., Box 90, Navarre, MN 55392.

780   US
JOURNAL OF GUITAR ACOUSTICS & TECHNOLOGY. 1980-1983 (vol.2, no.3). q. (back issues avail.) Timothy White, Ed. & Pub., c/o Northeast Robotics, Inc., Box 421, New Boston, NH 03070.
Formerly: Journal of Guitar Acoustics.

627   US   ISSN 1051-2705
JOURNAL OF HYDRAULIC ENGINEERING (BRISTOL). ceased 1991. q. Hemisphere Publishing Corporation (Subsidiary of: Taylor & Francis Group), 1900 Frost Rd., Ste. 101, Bristol, PA 19007-1598.

539.7   US   ISSN 0735-7923
TP249   CODEN: JIITDJ
JOURNAL OF INDUSTRIAL IRRADIATION TECHNOLOGY. 1983-1988 (vol.4). 2/yr. (also avail. in microform from RPI) Marcel Dekker Journals, 270 Madison Ave., New York, NY 10016.

614.7   US
JOURNAL OF INTERPRETATION (DERWOOD). ceased 1979 (vol.4). s-a. Association of Interpretive Naturalists, Inc., 6700 Needwood Rd., Derwood, MD 20855.

371.912   US   ISSN 0882-7893
HV2402
JOURNAL OF INTERPRETATION (ROCKVILLE). 1985-1987 (vol.4). a. Registry of Interpreters for the Deaf, Inc., 8719 Colesville Rd., Ste. 310, Silver Spring, MD 20910.

617.6 340   US   ISSN 0894-8879
JOURNAL OF LAW AND ETHICS IN DENTISTRY; a forum for clinicians, attorneys and risk managers. 1988-19?? a. (National Society of Dental Practitioners) Mosby - Year Book, Inc. (Littleton) (Subsidiary of: Times Mirror Company), 545 Great Rd., Littleton, MA 01460.

001.535   US   ISSN 1049-2976
JOURNAL OF NEURAL NETWORK COMPUTING; technology, design, and applications. ceased 1991. q. Auerbach Publishers (Subsidiary of: Warren, Gorham & Lamont), One Penn Plaza, New York, NY 10119.

616.4   US   ISSN 0731-4361
RC628   CODEN: JOWRDN
JOURNAL OF OBESITY AND WEIGHT REGULATION. 1980-1990. s-a. (also avail. in microform from UMI; reprint service avail. from ISI, UMI) Human Sciences Press, Inc. (Subsidiary of: Plenum Publishing Corp.), 233 Spring St., New York, NY 10013-1578.
Formerly (until 1981): Obesity and Metabolism (ISSN 0190-2318)

800 100   CN   ISSN 0381-6524
JOURNAL OF OUR TIME. 1977-19?? (no.4); suspended. irreg. Traditional Studies Press, Box 984, Adelaide St. Post Office, Toronto, Ont. M5C 2K4, Canada.

617.632   DK   ISSN 0075-4331
CODEN: JPRSB6
JOURNAL OF PERIODONTAL RESEARCH. SUPPLEMENTUM. 1966-1986. irreg. (reprint service avail. from ISI) Munksgaard International Publishers Ltd., 35 Noerre Soegade, P.O. Box 2148, DK-1016 Copenhagen K, Denmark.

800 700   CN   ISSN 0835-7099
JOURNAL OF PRE-RAPHAELITE & AESTHETIC STUDIES. 1977-1989. s-a. (back issues avail.) Foundation for Pre-Raphaelite & Aesthetic Studies, Department of English, University of British Columbia, Vancouver, B.C. V6T 1W5, Canada.
Supersedes (in 1987): Journal of Pre-Raphaelite Studies (ISSN 0271-1435); (until 1980): Pre-Raphaelite Review (ISSN 0162-8488)

616.8   US   ISSN 1049-6343
RA790.A1   CODEN: JPADEF
JOURNAL OF PREVENTIVE PSYCHIATRY AND ALLIED DISCIPLINES. 1981-1990 (vol.4). q. (reprint service avail. from ISI) (Center for Preventive Psychiatry) Human Sciences Press, Inc. (Subsidiary of: Plenum Publishing Corp.), 233 Spring St., New York, NY 10013.
Formerly (until 1987): Journal of Preventive Psychiatry (ISSN 0197-9353)

333.33   US   ISSN 0887-5812
HD1390
JOURNAL OF REAL ESTATE DEVELOPMENT. 1985-1989 (Summer). q. Federal Research Press, 210 Lincoln St., Ste. 700, Boston, MA 02111-2491.

617.8   US   ISSN 0022-4677
RC423   CODEN: JSHDAX
JOURNAL OF SPEECH AND HEARING DISORDERS. 1936-19?? q. (also avail. in microform from UMI; reprint service avail. from UMI) American Speech - Language - Hearing Association, 10801 Rockville Pike, Rockville, MD 20852.
Formerly (until 1947): Journal of Speech Disorders.

133   US
JOURNAL OF SPIRITUAL AND NATURAL HEALING. ceased 1990 (vol.15, Dec.). q. Aetherius Society, 6202 Afton Pl., Los Angeles, CA 90028-8298.
Formerly: Spiritual Healing Bulletin.

610   NO   ISSN 0030-6207
CODEN: JOCIAT
JOURNAL OF THE OSLO CITY HOSPITALS. 1951-1989. m. (back issues avail.) Oslo City Health Authorities, Ullevaal Hospital, c/o Institute for Experimental Medical Research, 0407 Oslo 4, Norway.

636.089   US   ISSN 0748-0512
JOURNAL OF VETERINARY ONCOLOGY. 1986-19?? q. Mary Ann Liebert, Inc., 1651 Third Ave., New York, NY 10128.

540   US   ISSN 0163-4526
CODEN: JWBCDV
JOURNAL OF WATER BORNE COATINGS; magazine and buyer's guide. 1978-1991. q. Technology Marketing Corporation, One Technology Plaza, Norwalk, CT 06854.
Incorporates: Journal of Water Borne Coatings Buyer's Guide.

073   GW
JOURNALISTEN - HANDBUCH. ceased. irreg. Verlag Chmielorz GmbH und Co, Wilhelmstr. 42, 6200 Wiesbaden, Germany.
Formerly: Wer Schreibt Worueber? Journalisten-Handbuch.

286   US
JOVENES "A" (STUDENT EDITION). 1890-1991. a. Casa Bautista de Publicaciones, Box 4255, El Paso, TX 79914.
Former titles: Jovenes Biblicos (Student Edition); Expositor Biblico (Student Edition).

635   US
JOY OF HERBS. 1988-19?? q. (back issues avail.) Brook Publishing Co., 201 E. Fourth St., Loveland, CO 80537-5655.

053   GW
JUGENDPOLITIK. 1975-1989. q. (Deutscher Bundesjugendring) Forum Europa Verlag, Berliner Platz 1, 5300 Bonn 1, Germany.

028.5   GW   ISSN 0022-6297
HQ799.G5
JUNGE GENERATION. ceased 1990. m. (Zentralrat der Freien Deutschen Jugend) Verlag Junge Welt GmbH, Mauerstr. 39-40, 1080 Berlin, Germany.

947 028.5   UK
JUNI DRUZI. 1955-198? 4/yr. (tabloid format) Association of Ukrainian Former Combatants in Great Britain, 49 Linden Gardens, London W2 4HG, England.
Formerly: Juni.

792.8   UK   ISSN 0960-720X
JUNIOR FRIENDS. 1987-19?? 3/yr. Royal Academy of Dancing, 48 Vicarage Crescent, Battersea, London SW11 3LT, England.

929 398   US   ISSN 0892-791X
CS71
JUNK JOURNAL. 1986-1989. a. (looseleaf format; back issues avail.) Paul W. Jones, Ed. & Pub., 217 N. Prospect St., Bowling Green, OH 43402-2411.

332.6   FR   ISSN 0154-8840
JURI-SOCIAL. ceased. m. (Societe Europeenne de Presse Fiscale et Juridique) La Villeguerin Editions, 54 rue de Chabrol, 75480 Paris Cedex 10, France.

323.4   US
JURISDICTION JOURNAL & SOVEREIGN REVIEW. 1980-198? 10/yr. (tabloid format; back issues avail.) Journal & Review Publishers, Box 299, Provo, UT 84603.
Formerly: Jurisdiction Journal.

633.895   MY   ISSN 0126-6136
SB291.H4   CODEN: JSPMDZ
JURNAL SAINS INSTITUT PENYELIDIKAN GETAH MALAYSIA. ceased in 1985 (vol.7, no.1). s-a. Rubber Research Institute of Malaysia - Institut Penyelidikan Getah Malaysia, 260 Jalan Ampang, 50450 Kuala Lumpur, Malaysia.

020   US
JUST B"TWX US: AN INTERLIBRARY LOAN INFORMATION BULLETIN. 1970-1986 (vol.6, no.4). irreg. (processed) University of Colorado, Boulder, University Libraries, Interlibrary Loan Service, Boulder, CO 80309-0184.
Former titles: Just B'twx Us: An Interlibrary Loan Newsletter; Just B'twx Us: An Interlibrary Loan Service Newsletter (ISSN 0075-4587)

574   GW
JUSTUS-LIEBIG-UNIVERSITAET GIESSEN-LAHN. ARBEITSKREIS FUER WILDBIOLOGIE UND JAGDWISSENSCHAFT. SCHRIFTEN. 1977-1988 (vol. 19). irreg. (Justus-Liebig-Univeristaet Giessen-Lahn, Arbeitskreis fuer Wildbiologie und Jagdwissenschaft) Ferdinand Enke Verlag, Postfach 10 12 54, D-7000 Stuttgart 10, Germany.

028.5   AG   ISSN 0022-7196
JUVENTUD. 1936-1990. m. (Iglesia Adventista del Septimo Dia) Asociacion Casa Editora Sudamericana, Avda. San Martin 4555, 1602 Florida, Buenos Aires, Argentina.

133.4 200 398   US
K.A.M.; a journal of traditional Wicca. 1976-1991 (Aug.). 2/yr. Keepers of the Ancient Mysteries, Box 2513, Kensington, MD 20891.
Formerly: K.A.M. Newsletter.

526   US
K G S - N C I C NEWSLETTER. ceased 1988. irreg. (Kentucky Geological Survey) National Cartographic Information Center, 228 MMR Bldg., University of Kentucky, Lexington, KY 40506-0107.

330   JA   ISSN 0289-890X
K K C BRIEF. 1982-1990 (no.60). irreg. Keizai Koho Center, Japan Institute for Social and Economic Affairs, Otemachi Bldg. 6-1, Ote-machi 1-chome, Chiyoda-ku, Tokyo 100, Japan.

352.7   DK   ISSN 0107-2692
K M D PLANNYT; information om planlaegning. 1980-1988. q. Kommunedata, Aalborg-Centralen, Hadsundvej 184, 9100 Aalborg, Denmark.

100   CN   ISSN 0319-1648
KABALARIAN COURIER. 1930-1980. q. (back issues avail.) (Society of Kabalarians of Canada) Kabalarian Philosophy Ltd., 908 W. 7th Ave, Vancouver, B.C. V5Z 1C3, Canada.

333.9   AU   ISSN 0022-7595
KAERNTNER NATURSCHUTZBLAETTER. 1962-1990. a. Amt der Kaerntner Landesregierung, Abteilung Landesplanung, Wulfengasse 13, A-9020 Klagenfurt, Austria.

350   JA   ISSN 0453-0675
KAGAKU KEISATSU KENKYUJO SHIRYO/NATIONAL RESEARCH INSTITUTE OF POLICE SCIENCE. DATA. ceased. irreg. Kagaku Keisatsu Kenkyujo - National Research Institute of Police Science, 6 Sanban-cho, Chiyoda-ku, Tokyo 102, Japan.

CESSATIONS

660   JA   ISSN 0451-2030
CODEN: KAKJAJ
KAGAKU KOJO/CHEMICAL FACTORY. 1957-1985. m. Industrial Daily News Ltd. - Nikkan Kogyo Shinbun Ltd., 1-8-10 Kudan Kita, Chiyoda-ku, Tokyo 102, Japan.

794.1   GR
KAISSA. 1988-1990. 11/yr. Kaissa Chess Center, 8 Kalidromiou St., Gr-114 72, Athens, Greece.

636.089   MY   ISSN 0126-9437
KAJIAN VETERINAR MALAYSIA. 1967-1989. s-a. Association of Veterinary Surgeons Malaysia - Persatuan Doktor Veterinar Malaysia, University Pertanieu Malaysia, Faculty of Veterinary Medicine & Animal Science, 43 400 Serdang, Selangor, Malaysia.
Formerly: Kajian Veterinar (ISSN 0047-309X)

700   II
KALAKSHETRA QUARTERLY. 1959-1989 (vol.9); suspended. q. Besant Cultural Centre, Kalakshetra (International Arts Centre), Tiruvanmiyur, Madras 600 041, India.
Formerly (until Apr. 1978): Kalakshetra (ISSN 0047-3111)

028.5 602   PL   ISSN 0137-8856
KALEJDOSKOP TECHNIKI. 1957-19??; suspended. m. Wydawnictwo Czasopism i Ksiazek Technicznych SIGMA - NOT, Ul. Biala 4, P.O. Box 1004, 00-950 Warsaw, Poland.

200   US
KALENDAR JEDNOTA. 1897-1989 (vol.92). a. (First Catholic Slovak Union) Jednota Press, P.O. Box 150, Rosedale Ave. & Jednota Lane, Middletown, PA 17057.
Formerly: Jednota Kalendar.

677   UR
KALININSKII NAUCHNO-ISSLEDOVATEL'SKII INSTITUT TEKSTIL'NOI PROMYSHLENNOSTI. NAUCHNO-ISSLEDOVATEL'SKIE TRUDY. 1971-1973 (vol.3). irreg. Kalininskii Nauchno-Issledovatel'skii Institut Tekstil'noi Promyshlennosti, Kalinin, Russian S.F.S.R., U.S.S.R.

790.1   FR
KALKI; action et tradition. ceased. s-a. Editions Pardes, B.P. 47, 45390 Puiseaux, France.

860   PE
KANAN; revista anual de cultura. 1978-19?? a. Instituto Nacional de Cultura, Filial Ancash, Plaza de Armas s-n, Huaras, Peru.

615.842   JA   ISSN 0022-8311
KANAZAWA IRIGAKU SOSHO/JOURNAL OF RADIOLOGY AND PHYSICAL THERAPY. 1946-1975 (vol.99). 2-3/yr. Kanazawa Daigaku, Igakubu, Hoshasen Igaku Kyoshitsu - Kanazawa University, School of Medicine, Department of Radiology, 13-1 Takara-machi, Kanazawa-shi, Ishikawa-ken 920, Japan.

301   NR   ISSN 0567-4840
AP9
KANO STUDIES; journal of Saharan and Sudanic research. 1973-19?? a. (Abdullahi Bayero College) Oxford University Press (Nigerian Branch), P.M.B. 5095, Oxford House, Iddo Gate, Ibadan, Nigeria.

364.36   US
KANSAS. JUVENILE JUSTICE INFORMATION CENTER. ANNUAL REPORT. 1976-1984. a. Bureau of Investigation, Statistical Analysis Center, 1620 S.W. Tyler St., Topeka, KS 66612-1837.

610   US
KANSAS CITY MEDICAL GUIDE. 1989; suspended same year. bi-m. 8940 Oak St., Kansas City, MO 64144.

340   US
KANSAS JUSTICE INFORMATION SYSTEM. RESOURCE DIRECTORY (YEAR). discontinued 1986. a. Bureau of Investigation, Statistical Analysis Center, 1620 S.W. Tyler St., Topeka, KS 66612-1837.

796   MY
KARATE BUDOKAN INTERNATIONAL ANNIVERSARY. 1971-19?? a. (Karate Association of Malaysia) Karate Budokan International Inc., No. 5, Jalan Taman (7-6), Petaling Jaya 46050, Malaysia.
Formerly: Karate International Anniversary (ISSN 0085-2481)

796.815   US
KARATE FORUM. ceased. q. Jems, Inc., 55 Ave of the Americas No. 309, New York, NY 10013.

616.89   SZ   ISSN 0254-5373
KARGER BIOBEHAVIORAL MEDICINE SERIES. 1983-1984 (vol.4). s-a. S. Karger AG, Allschwilerstr. 10, CH-4009 Basel, Switzerland.

374.8   SZ   ISSN 0254-1270
CODEN: KCESDX
KARGER CONTINUING EDUCATION SERIES. 1982-1986 (vol.8). irreg. S. Karger AG, Allschwilerstr. 10, P.O. Box, CH-4009 Basel, Switzerland.

301 914   US   ISSN 0164-2537
KARIKAZO; Hungarian folklore newsletter. 1975-1987. q. American-Hungarian Folklore Centrum, Box 262, Bogota, NJ 07603.

636   FI   ISSN 0047-3251
KARJATALOUS. 1924-198? m. Valio Meijerien Keskusosuusliike - Valio Finnish Co-Operative Dairies' Association, Meijeritie 4, PL 69, 00371 Helsinki, Finland.

400   GW
KARL MARX UNIVERSITAET, LEIPZIG. WISSENSCHAFTLICHE ZEITSCHRIFT; gesellschaftswissenschaftliche Reihe. 1951-1990. 6/yr. Karl Marx Universitaet Leipzig, Goethestr. 3-5, 7010 Leipzig, Germany.
Formerly: Karl Marx Universitaet, Leipzig. Wissenschaftliche Zeitung (ISSN 0043-6879)

016 282   NE
KATHOLIEK DOCUMENTATIE CENTRUM. SLEUTELS. ceased. irreg. Katholiek Documentatie Centrum, Erasmuslaan 36, 6525 GG Nijmegen, Netherlands.
Incorporates: Katholiek Documentatie Centrum. Archieven; Katholiek Documentatie Centrum. Bibliografieen.

282   IT   ISSN 0022-9431
KATOLIKUS SZEMLE. 1949-1991 (Oct.). q. Actio Catholica Hungarorum in Exteris, Piazza Cavalieri di Malta, 5, 00153 Rome, Italy.

948.9   DK   ISSN 0280-8463
KATTEGAT-SKAGERRAK-PROJECTET. MEDDELELSER; regionens kulturudvikling under 1800-tallet. 1982-1988 (no.16). irreg. Kattegat-Skagerrak-Projectet, c/o Fiskeri og Soefartsmuseet, 6700 Esbjerg, Denmark.

572   CK
KATXA - TA. 1976-1977 (no.4). q. Asociacion Colombiana Indigenista, Apdo. Aereo 92099, Bogota, Colombia.

301.412   US
KEEPSAKE (SCOTTSDALE); magazine for brides. ceased 1985. s-a. 123 East Echo Lane, Phoenix, AZ 85020.

651.8   US
KELLY - GRIMES BUYERS GUIDE FOR WORD PROCESSING. 1984-198? a. John Wiley & Sons, Inc., 605 Third Ave., New York, NY 10158-0012.

380   UK   ISSN 0950-6160
KELLY'S AUTOMATED OFFICE & BUSINESS EQUIPMENT DIRECTORY. 1987-1990. a. Kelly's Directories (Subsidiary of: Reed Information Services Ltd.), Windsor Court, East Grinstead House, East Grinstead, W. Sussex RH19 1XB, England.

621.3 681 530   NE   ISSN 0167-8590
KEMA SCIENTIFIC & TECHNICAL REPORTS. 1983-1990 (no.8). bi-m. (back issues avail.) N.V. tot Keuring van Elektrotechnische Materialen (KEMA), Utrechtseweg 310, 6812 AR Arnhem, Netherlands.

686.2 070.5   US
KEMBLE OCCASIONAL. 1964-198?; suspended. 3/yr. Kemble Collections, California Historical Society, 2099 Pacific Ave., San Francisco, CA 94109-2235.

333.33   UK
KEMPS PROPERTY INDUSTRY YEARBOOK. 1974-1987. a. Kemps Group (Printers & Publishers) Ltd., Westbury House, 701-705 Warwick Rd., Solihull, West Midlands B91 3DA, England.
Formerly: Kemps Estate Agents Yearbook and Directory.

170 610   US
KENNEDY INSTITUTE OF ETHICS. NEWSLETTER. 1986-1990. q. Kennedy Institute of Ethics, Georgetown University, Washington, DC 20057.
Formerly: Kennedy Institute of Bioethics. Newsletter.

340   US
KENTUCKY. COURT OF JUSTICE. BIENNIAL REPORT. ceased 1985. biennial. Court of Justice, Press and Public Information Office, Bush Bldg., 403 Wapping St., Frankfort, KY 40601.
Formerly: Kentucky. Court of Justice. Annual Report.

338   US   ISSN 0363-5198
HC107.K4
KENTUCKY DIRECTORY OF SELECTED INDUSTRIAL SERVICES. 1970-1987. biennial. Department of business Development, Capital Plaza Tower, Frankfort, KY 40601.

380.1   US
KENTUCKY INTERNATIONAL TRADE DIRECTORY. 1978-1987. irreg. Economic Development Cabinet, Capital Plaza Tower, Frankfort, KY 40601.

811   US   ISSN 0889-647X
KENTUCKY POETRY REVIEW. 1964-1990. 2/yr. Bellarmine College, Louisville, KY 40205-0671.
Formerly: Approaches; a Periodical of Poems by Kentuckians (ISSN 0003-7133)

354   KE   ISSN 0065-1966
KENYA INSTITUTE OF ADMINISTRATION. JOURNAL. 1965-19??; suspended. a. Kenya Institute of Administration, P.O. Lower Kabete, Nairobi, Kenya.
Formerly: Administration in Kenya.

610   KE
KENYA MEDICAL ABSTRACTS. 1980-1985 (vol.2). irreg. University of Nairobi, Medical Library, Box 30588, Nairobi, Kenya.

666   GW
KERAMIK BOUTIQUE. 1977-198? 2/yr. Stolberger Str. 84, D-5000 Cologne 41, Germany.

666   GW
KERAMIK CREATIV. 1977-1991. q. Verlagsanstalt Handwerk GmbH, Auf'm Tetelberg 7, Postfach 8120, 4000 Duesseldorf 1, Germany.

301.435   IS
KESHER (JERUSALEM). ceased 1989. s-a. J D C - Brookdale Institute of Gerontology and Adult Human Development in Israel, P.O. Box 13087, Jerusalem 91130, Israel.

500   CC   ISSN 1000-3088
Q111
KEXUE BOLAN/SCIENCE PANORAMA. ceased 1990 (Oct.). m. (Zhongguo Kexueyuan - Academia Sinica) Kexue Chubanshe, 16 Donghuangchenggen Beijie, Beijing 100707, People's Republic of China.

616.12   US   ISSN 0899-8019
KEY CARDIOLOGY. 1987-1988. q. Mosby - Year Book, Inc. (Chicago) (Subsidiary of: Times Mirror Company), 200 N. LaSalle St., Chicago, IL 60601-1080.

780   NE
KEY NOTES; musical life in the Netherlands. 1975-1989 (no.25). a. Donemus Amsterdam, Paulus Potterstraat 14, 1071 CZ Amsterdam, Netherlands.
Formerly: Sonorum Speculum (ISSN 0038-1438)

380 330   CY
KEY OF THE MIDDLE EAST. 1990; ceased same year. biennial. Chatila Publishing House, P.O. Box 5122, Limassol, Cyprus.

800 700   US   ISSN 1041-5254
KEY WEST REVIEW. ceased 1991. q. (back issues avail.) Key West Review, Inc., Box 2082, Key West, FL 33045-2082.

780   US
KEYNOTE: A MAGAZINE FOR THE MUSICAL ARTS; including the WNCN program guide. 1977-1990 (Mar.). m. G A F Broadcasting Company, Inc., 1180 Ave. of the Americas, New York, NY 10036.

5224 CESSATIONS

398 US ISSN 0149-8444
GR1
KEYSTONE FOLKLORE. 1956; N.S. 1982-1991. 2/yr. (also avail. in microform from UMI; reprint service avail. from UMI) Pennsylvania Folklore Society, 415 Logan Hall-CN, University of Pennsylvania, Philadelphia, PA 19104.
   Formerly (until 1972): Keystone Folklore Quarterly (ISSN 0023-0987)

327 338.91 IS ISSN 0334-2212
KIDMA; Israel journal of development. 1972-1989; suspended. 3/yr. Society for International Development, Israel Chapter, 11 Lamparonti St., P.O.B. 13130, Jerusalem 91131, Israel.

616.6 UK ISSN 0142-8705
KIDNEY DISEASES. ceased 1990. m. (looseleaf format; back issues avail.) Sheffield University Biomedical Information Service (SUBIS), The University, Sheffield S10 2TN, England.

616 UK ISSN 0261-4731
KILLER CELLS AND CYTOTOXICITY. ceased 1990. m. (looseleaf format; back issues avail.) Sheffield University Biomedical Information Service (SUBIS), The University, Sheffield S10 2TN, England.

581 AT ISSN 0819-1247
CODEN: KNGAEX
KINGIA. 1978-19?? irreg. Department of Conservation and Land Management, Western Australian Herbarium, P.O. Box 104, Como, W.A. 6152, Australia.
   Supersedes (in 1988): Western Australian Herbarium. Research Notes.

200 UK ISSN 0143-5922
KING'S THEOLOGICAL REVIEW. 1978-1990 (vol.8, no.2). 2/yr. King's College, Faculty of Theology and Religious Studies, Strand, London WC2R 2LS, England.

340 UK ISSN 0453-8854
K11
KINGSTON LAW REVIEW. 1968-1987 (vol.16, no.1). s-a. (back issues avail.) Kingston Polytechnic School of Law, Kenry House, Kingston Hill, Kingston upon Thames, Surrey KT2 7LB, England.

778.5 SZ
KINO-FILM. 1936-1989. m. Schweizerisches Filmzentrum, Muenstergasse 18, CH-1800 Zuerich, Switzerland.
   Former titles (until 1983): Kino-Film mit Werbung Heute; (until 1980): Film.

769.56 US
KIRIBATI REPORT. 1979-19?? q. Kiribati Philatelic Society, Box 2792, Boston, MA 02208.

209 DK ISSN 0450-3171
KIRKEHISTORISKE SAMLINGER. 1849-19?? a. (Selskabet for Danmarks Kirkehistorie) Akademisk Forlag, Store Kannikestraede 8, P.O. Box 54, 1002 Copenhagen K, Denmark.

780.42 US
KISS ROCKS. 1985-1991 (Jan.). bi-m. (looseleaf format; back issues avail.) Kiss Rocks Fan Club, Box 308 H, Scarsdale, NY 10583.

783 SZ ISSN 0023-2068
KLEINE CHORZEITUNG; Mitteilungsblatt fuer die katholischen Kirchenchoere. (Supplement to: Katholische Kirchenmusik) 1950-1985. irreg. (2-3/ yr.). Paulus-Verlag GmbH, Murbacherstr. 29, 6003 Lucerne, Switzerland.
   Formerly: Kirchensaenger.

746 NE
KNIPPLUS. 1974-198? 6/yr. De Kreatieve Pers B.V., Keizersgracht 489, 1017 DM Amsterdam, Netherlands.
   Former titles (until 1986): Handwerken met Steek; Handwerken; Steek.

677 338.4 US ISSN 0085-2562
KNITTING TIMES YEARBOOK. ceased. a. National Knitwear and Sportswear Association, 386 Park Ave. So., New York, NY 10016.

020 CS ISSN 0322-807X
Z671 CODEN: KVIFA8
KNIZNICE A VEDECKE INFORMACIE. 1968-1991. q. Matica Slovenska, Ul. Mudronova 26, 036 52 Martin, Czechoslovakia.

658.3 UK
KNOW YOUR TRAINING FILMS. (In two volumes) 1975-1988. biennial. Management Update Ltd., 99A Underdale Rd., Shrewsbury, Shropshire SY2 5EE, England.

600 IS ISSN 0792-2035
KNOWHOW. 1988-1989. m. A.G. Publications, P.O. Box 7422, Haifa 31 070, Israel.

910 DK ISSN 0106-3618
KOEBENHAVNS UNIVERSITET. GEOGRAFISK CENTRALINSTITUT. LABORATORIUM FOR GEOMORFOLOGI. 1972-1982 (vol.8). irreg. University of Copenhagen, Intittute of Geography, Library, Oester Voldgade 10, DK-1350 Copenhagen K, Denmark.

338 JA
KOGYO RITCHI HANDOBUKKU/INDUSTRIAL LOCATION HANDBOOK. 1966-19?? triennial. Japan Industrial Location Center - Nihon Kogyo Ritchi Senta, 2-1 Shiba-Kotohira-machi, Minato-ku, Tokyo, Japan.

500 JA
KOKYO SHIKEN KENKYU KIKAN KADAI ANNAI. KAGAKU GIJUTSU TEMA HEN. 1973-19?? 2/yr. Japan Information Center of Science and Technology - Nihon Kagaku Gijutsu Joho Senta, 5-2 Nagato-cho 2-chome, Chiyoda-ku, Tokyo 100, Japan.

378.198 296 US
KOLENU. 1972-1989. 2/yr. (back issues avail.) Cornell University, Student Finance Commission, G34 Anabel Taylor Hall, Ithaca, NY 14853.

352.7 DK ISSN 0106-7362
KOMMUNEPLANORIENTERING. 1979-1985 (vol.13). irreg. Miljoeministeriet, Planstyrelsen - Danish National Agency for Physical Planning, Ministry of the Environment, Haraldsgade 53, DK-2100 Copenhagen Oe, Denmark.

500 GW ISSN 0233-2264
KONGRESSTERMINDIENST: NATURWISSENSCHAFTLICH-TECHNISCHE VERANSTALTUNGEN IM SOZIALISTISCHEN AUSLAND. 1985-1991. q. Zentralinstitut fuer Information und Dokumentation der D D R, Koepenicker Str. 80-82, 1020 Berlin, Germany.

320 070 GW
KONSERVATIV HEUTE. 1969-19?? bi-m. (Gesellschaft fuer Konservative Publizistik e.V.) Criticon Verlag GmbH, Knoebelstr. 36, D-8000 Munich 22, Germany.

500 GW ISSN 0452-4918
KONSTANZER BLAETTER FUER HOCHSCHULFRAGEN. 1963-1990. q. Universitaetsverlag Konstanz GmbH, Taegermoosstr. 1, Postfach 102051, 7750 Konstanz, Germany.

629.2 UR
KONSTRUKTORSKO-TEKHNOLOGICHESKII INSTITUT AVTOMATIZATSII AVTOMOBILESTROENIYA. SBORNIK TRUDOV. ceased 1971. irreg. Konstruktorsko-Tekhnologicheskii Institut Avtomatizatsii Avtomobilestroeniya, 454080, Chelyabinsk, Ul. Entuziastov, 2, Russian S.F.S.R., U.S.S.R.

790.019 GW ISSN 0323-6021
KONTAKT. ceased 1990. bi-m. Verlag Junge Welt GmbH, Mauerstr. 39-40, 1080 Berlin, Germany.

929 DK ISSN 0108-5190
KONTAKT (COPENHAGEN, 1977); blade af slaegtens historie. 1977-19?? irreg. (1-2/yr.). Kaerbyholmslaegten, Hejrevej 38, 2400 Copenhagen NV, Denmark.

890 GW
KONTINENT. 1974-1991. q. Kontinent Verlag GmbH, Lindenstr. 76, 1000 Berlin 61, Germany.

690 SW ISSN 0075-6776
KONTROLLRAADET FOER BETONGVAROR. MEDDELANDE. 1950-1988. a. Kontrollraadet foer Betongvaror - Swedish Council for Precast Concrete Control, Box 14104, S-161 14 Bromma, Sweden.

027 016 HU ISSN 0454-3491
KONYVTARI ES DOKUMENTACIOS SZAKIRODALOM/ LIBRARY AND DOCUMENTATION LITERATURE ABROAD; referalo lap - abstracting journal. 1968-19?? q. Orszagos Szechenyi Konyvtar, Konyvtartudomanyi es Modszertani Kozpont - Centre for Library Science and Methodology at the National Szechenyi Library, Budavari Palota F epulet, H-1827 Budapest, Hungary.

020 HU ISSN 0236-5200
KONYVTARI ES INFORMATIKAI KOZPONTI GYARAPODASI JEGYZEK/CENTRAL ACCESSIONING LIST ABOUT LIBRARY AND INFORMATION SCIENCE. 1984-19?? q. Orszagos Szechenyi Konyvtar, Konvtartudomanyi es Modszertani Kozpont - Centre for Library Science and Methodology at the National Szechenyi Library, Budavari Palota F epulet, H-1827 Budapest, Hungary.
   Formerly: Orszagos Szechenyi Konyvtar Konyvtartudomanyi es Modszertani Kozpont. Gyarapodasi Jegyzek - Accession List.

020 HU ISSN 0209-8393
KONYVTARI KIADVANYOK; osszesitett jegyzek. 1973-1992. a. Hajdu-Bihar Megyei Konyvtar, Voros Hadsereg utja 8, HU-4026 Debrecen, Hungary.

380 315 KO ISSN 0075-6857
KOREA (REPUBLIC). NATIONAL BUREAU OF STATISTICS. WHOLESALE AND RETAIL TRADE CENSUS REPORT/ TOSOMAEUP CENSUS BOGO SEO. 1968-19?? triennial. National Bureau of Statistics, Economic Planning Board, 90, Gyeongun-dong, Jongro-gu, Seoul 110-310, S. Korea.

323.4 327 951.9 US
KOREA BI-WEEKLY REPORT. 1988-19?? s-m. (tabloid format; back issues avail.) North American Coalition for Human Rights in Korea, 110 Maryland Ave., N.E., Box 68, Washington, DC 20002.
   Formerly: Korea Weekly Report.

315 KO ISSN 0081-4806
HA4630.5
KOREA STATISTICAL KOREA/TONGGYE SUCHUP. 1962-19?? a. National Bureau of Statistics, Economic Planning Board, 90, Gyeongun-dong, Jongro-gu, Seoul 110-310, S. Korea.

620.162 GW ISSN 0233-0741
KORROSION. 1970-1991. bi-m. (also avail. in microfiche) Zentralstelle fuer Korrosionsschutz, Karl-Marx-Str., Gebaeude 418, Postfach 92, 8080 Dresden, Germany.

943.7 CS
KRAJSKE KULTURNI STREDISKO V HRADCI KRALOVE. KOMENTOVANA VYROCI. ceased 1979. a. Krajske Kulturni Stredisko v Hradci Kralove, Hradci Kralove, Czechoslovakia.

059.8 UK ISSN 0023-4656
KRIKOS; a quarterly international Greek review. (English supplement: The Link) 1950-1988 (Sep.). q. Krikos Ltd., 33 Mapesbury Rd., London NW2 4HT, England.

364 301 016 AU ISSN 0255-3678
KRIMINALSOZIOLOGISCHE BIBLIOGRAPHIE. 1973-1991. q. Institut fuer Rechts- und Kriminalsoziologie, Museumstr. 12, A-1016 Vienna, Austria.

282 US ISSN 0023-477X
KRISTAUS KARALIAUS LAIVAS/SHIP OF CHRIST THE KING. 1922-1990. s-m. Congregation of Marian Fathers, 4545 W. 63rd St., Chicago, IL 60629.

100 GW ISSN 0138-3612
KRITIK DER BUERGERLICHEN IDEOLOGIE. 1971-198? irreg. (Akademie der Wissenschaften der DDR) Akademie-Verlag Berlin, Leipziger Str. 3-4, 1086 Berlin, Germany.

330 016 HU ISSN 0237-0840
KULFOLDI KOZGAZDASAGI IRODALMI SZEMLE. SERIES A. 1956-198? m. (back issues avail.) Marx Karoly Kozgazdasagtudomanyi Egyetem, Dimitrov ter 8, Budapest 9, Hungary.
   Formerly (until 1985): Tajekoztato a Kulfoldi Kozgazdasagi Irodalomrol. Series A, Referatumok - Information on the Foreign Economic Literature, Series A (ISSN 0020-0166); Which was superseded in part (in 1969): Tajekoztato a Kulfoldi Kozgazdasagi Irodalomrol (ISSN 0492-1755)

CESSATIONS

330   HU   ISSN 0237-0859
KULFOLDI KOZGAZDASAGI IRODALMI SZEMLE. SERIES B. 1956-198? m. (back issues avail.) Marx Karoly Kozgazdasagtudomanyi Egyetem, Dimitrov Ter 8, Budapest 9, Hungary.
Formerly (until 1985): Tajekoztato a Kulfoldi Kozgazdasagi Irodalomrol. Series B, Bibliografia (ISSN 0133-1655); Which was superseded in part (in 1969): Tajekoztato a Kulfoldi Kozgazdasagi Irodalomrol (ISSN 0492-1755)

016   HU   ISSN 0133-333X
AI19.H8
KULFOLDI MAGYAR NYELVU KIADVANYOK; kulfoldon magyar nyelven megjelent konyvek es folyoiratcikkek valogatott bibliografiaja. 1972-1989 (vol.19, no.4). q. Orszagos Szechenyi Konyvtar, Budavari Palota F, H-1827 Budapest, Hungary.
Supersedes (in 1976): Kulfoldi Magyar Nyelvu Folyoiratok Repertoriuma (ISSN 0133-0438)

640.73   FI   ISSN 0359-9329
KULUTTAJATIETOA. 1967-1990. bi-m. Elinkeinohallitus - National Board of Trade and Consumer Affairs, Haapaniemenkatu 4 A, 00530 Helsinki, Finland.

796.815   DK
KUNG FU. ceased. m. Interpresse, Krogshoejvej 32, 2880 Bagsvaerd, Denmark.

709.5   GW   ISSN 0023-5393
N8
KUNST DES ORIENTS/ART OF THE ORIENT. 1950-1979. a. (back issues avail.) Franz Steiner Verlag Wiesbaden GmbH, Birkenwaldstr. 44, Postfach 10 15 26, 7000 Stuttgart 1, Germany.

700 800   GW   ISSN 0023-544X
N3
KUNST UND LITERATUR; Zeitschrift fuer Fragen der Aesthetik und Kunsttheorie. 1953-1991. 6/yr. Verlag Volk und Welt, Otto-Nuschke-Str. 10-11, 1086 Berlin, Germany.

701.18   GW
KUNSTBLATT. 1972-1990. q. (reprint service avail. from KTO) Interessengemeinschaft Berliner Kunstgalerien e.V., Ludwigkirchstr. 11a, 1000 Berlin 15, Germany.
Formerly: Berliner Kunstblatt (ISSN 0170-1665)

725   GW
KUNSTHANDWERK IN EUROPA; Vierteljahresschrift fuer Architektur-Kunst am Bau-Kunsthandwerk. 1978-1985. q. Ludwig Schultheiss Verlag, Heilwigstr. 64, 2000 Hamburg 20, Germany.

790   GW   ISSN 0138-5569
KUNTERBUNT; die lustige Gedankenschaukel-knifflige Kreuzwort-, silben-, und schachprobleme. 1947-1990. q. Blumenstein Verlag, Am Michelsbach 27, 5900 Eisenach, Germany.

677 746.92   GW
KURSBUCH-TEXTIL (YEAR); Terminplaner Industrie - Handwerk, Design, Kunst, Handel. 1988-19?? a. (back issues avail.) Textil-Werkstatt-Verlag, P.O. Box 5944, Friedenstr. 5, 3000 Hannover 1, Germany.

950   CE
KURUKSHETRA. 1975-1979; suspended (vol.5). s-a. (Siri Lak-Indo Study Group) Sri Lanka Kshattriya Maha Sabha, 12 Claessen Place, Colombo 5, Sri Lanka.

636.7   US
KUVASZ NEWSLETTER. 1966-19?? m. Kuvasz Club of America, Inc., 18 S. Terrace Ave., Mt. Vernon, NY 10550.

305.425   DK   ISSN 0900-2073
KVINDER. 1975-1985 (vol.6). bi-m. Redstockings, Kvindehuset, Gothersgade 37, 1123 Copenhagen, Denmark.

331.4   DK   ISSN 0109-0356
KVINDER PAA TINDER. 1982-198? q. Kvindehusforeningen, Kvindehuset, Havnegade 22, 8000 Aarhus C, Denmark.

808   JA   ISSN 0388-0532
KYOTO REVIEW. 1976-1990 (no.23). a. Kyoto Seika College, 137 Kino, Iwakura, Sakyo-ku, Kyoto 606, Japan.

980   CN   ISSN 0704-1217
JL966
L A R U STUDIES. 1976-1982 (vol.5, no.1). 3/yr. Latin American Research Unit, P.O. Box 673, Adelaide Sta., Toronto, Ont. M5C 2J8, Canada.

980   CN
L A R U WORKING PAPER. ceased 1981 (no.31). irreg. (3-4/yr.). Latin American Research Unit, P.O. Box 673, Adelaide Sta., Toronto, Ont. M5C 2J8, Canada.

322.4   US
L.A. W I S P. 1962-198? every 6 wks. Southern California Women Strike for Peace, 1431 Ocean Ave., No. B, Santa Monica, CA 90401.

347   US
L C A QUARTERLY. 1981-1987 (vol.3, no.1). irreg. Lawyers for the Creative Arts, 213 W. Institute Pl., No. 411, Chicago, IL 60610-3125.
Formerly: Lawyers for the Creative Arts. Bulletin.

624.176   NE   ISSN 0023-6276
TA710.A1
L G M MEDEDELINGEN. 1956-19?? q. Delft Geotechnics, Stieltjesweg 2, Postbus 69, 2600 AB Delft, Netherlands.

641.1   US
L.I.F.E. NEWSLETTER. 1968-19?? bi-m. League for International Food Education, 1815 N. Lynn St., Ste. 200, Arlington, VA 22209.

020   US   ISSN 0075-9821
Z669.7   CODEN: LITODD
L I S T. (Library and Information Services Today) ceased 1975 (vol.5). a. Gale Research Co., Book Tower, Detroit, MI 48226.

500   SW
L K B NEWS. 1981-1987. s-a. L K B Produkter AB, Box 305, S-161 26 Bromma, Sweden.
Formerly: L K B News with Science Tools (ISSN 0280-4557)

322.4 020.6   US
L N A C ALMANAC. 1984-1989 (vol.6, no.2). irreg. (2-3/yr.). (tabloid format; back issues avail.) Librarians for Nuclear Arms Control, Box 60552, Pasadena, CA 91116.
Incorporates: Study Peace.

378.1   UK   ISSN 0023-639X
HB1
L S E MAGAZINE. 1951-1990. q. (reprint service avail. from KTO) London School of Economics and Political Science, Houghton St., London WC2A 2AE, England.

500 300   UK   ISSN 0269-9710
H1
L.S.E. QUARTERLY. 1987-1990. q. (London School of Economics) Basil Blackwell Ltd., 108 Cowley Rd., Oxford OX4 1JF, England.

052   UK   ISSN 0262-575X
L T P. 1982-1986. a. (back issues avail.) L T P Cambridge, New Hall, Cambridge, England.

051   US
L V; the magazine of Las Vegas. ceased. m. Associated Magazines Publishers, 3800 Howard Hughes Pkwy., Ste. 120, Las Vegas, NV 89109.

664.09 658.8   US
LABELING REQUIREMENTS FOR CONSUMER PACKAGES OF FRESH FRUITS AND VEGETABLES. 1958-19?? s-a. Produce Marketing Association, 1500 Casho Mill Rd., Box 6036, Newark, DE 19714-6036.

610   SP   ISSN 0023-6691
LABORATORIO. 1946-1988. m. c/o Eduardo Suarez Peregrin, Apdo. Correos 193, 18080 Granada, Spain.

606   US   ISSN 0160-8584
CODEN: LRMMDZ
LABORATORY AND RESEARCH METHODS IN BIOLOGY AND MEDICINE. 1977-19?? irreg. Wiley-Liss, Inc., 41 E. 11th St., New York, NY 10003.

542   UK   ISSN 0308-8367
LABORATORY EQUIPMENT INDEX. 1976-198? a. Technical Indexes Ltd., Willoughby Rd., Bracknell, Berks. RG12 4DW, England.

610   UK
LABORATORY EQUIPMENT INTERNATIONAL. 1980-1982. 4/yr. Reed Business Publishing Developments, Times House, 4th floor, Throwley Way, Sutton, Surrey SM1 4AF, England.

616.97   US
LABORATORY IMMUNOLOGY. 1989-1990. 2/yr. (Association of Medical Laboratory Immunologists) Plenum Publishing Corp., 233 Spring St., New York, NY 10013-1578.

619   US   ISSN 1040-7677
LABORATORY PLANNING & DESIGN. ceased after one issue, 1989. q. Aster Publishing Corporation, 859 Wilamette St., Box 10955, Eugene, OR 97440.

301 331   UN   ISSN 0378-5408
HD4811
LABOUR AND SOCIETY. 1976-19?? 4/yr. (International Institute for Labour Studies) I L O Publications, PO Box 6, CH-1211 Geneva 22, Switzerland.
Supersedes: I I L S Bulletin (ISSN 0435-2874)

331 340   PK
LABOUR LAW CASES. 1947-1980 (vol.21). irreg. (back issues avail.) Bureau of Labour Publications, 8, Business Centre, P.O. Box 5833, Karachi-2, Pakistan.

340 330   AT
LABOUR LAW IN NEW ZEALAND. 1989-1991. 4/yr. Law Book Co. Ltd., 44-50 Waterloo Rd., North Ryde, N. S.W. 2113, Australia.

052   UK   ISSN 0140-1270
LABOUR REVIEW. 1978-1985. m. (back issues avail.) Workers' Revolutionary Party, 21-25 Beehive Place, London SW9, England.

378   AT   ISSN 0155-2856
LABYRINTH. 1978-1991. s-a. (back issues avail.) University of Queensland, Tertiary Education Institute, St. Lucia, Qld. 4072, Australia.

618.92   US   ISSN 0362-3173
LACTATION REVIEW. 1976-1982 (vol.6, no.1). irreg. (back issues avail.) Human Lactation Center Ltd., 666 Sturges Hwy., Westport, CT 06880.

551.46   VE   ISSN 0023-7256
CODEN: LGBWAW
LAGENA. 1964-198?; suspended. s-a. Universidad de Oriente, Instituto Oceanografico, Biblioteca, Apdo. Postal 94, Cumana, Sucre, Venezuela.

929   US
LAIR; Cunningham family newsletter. 1982-1988. q. (back issues avail.) 673 High St., Charlestown, IN 47111.

977   US
LAKE COUNTY HISTORICAL QUARTERLY. 1959-1989 (vol.31). q. (looseleaf format; back issues avail.) Lake County Historical Society, 8610 King Memorial Rd., Mentor, OH 44060.

800   US   ISSN 0889-6410
LAKE STREET REVIEW. 1976-1991 (no.25). a. Lake Street Review Press, Box 7188, Powderhorn Sta., Minneapolis, MN 55407.

614.7   US
LAND - L E A F. Ceased. 4/yr. Land Educational Association, 3368 Oak Ave., Stevens Point, WI 54481.

333.33   US   ISSN 0889-0498
LAND OPPORTUNITY REVIEW. 1970-1991 (vol.22, no.7). m. (back issues avail.) International Publications (Subsidiary of: Mid-America Marketing Inc.), Box 5730, Pompano Beach, FL 33074-5730.

340   CN
LAND USE PLANNING; practice, procedure, policy. ceased 1991. a. (looseleaf format) Butterworths Canada Ltd., 75 Clegg Rd., Markham, Ont. L6G 1A1, Canada.

630   NE
LANDBOUWMAAND. 1971-1989. 10/yr. Stichting Boerengroep, Postbus 265, 6700 AG Wageningen, Netherlands.

CESSATIONS

929   US   ISSN 0739-134X
CS71.L256494
LANDERS LANDING. 1981-1991. q. (also avail. in microfilm; back issues avail.) Jo Landers, Ed. & Pub., 3110 Y 2 St., Vancouver, WA 98661.

621.3   SZ   ISSN 0023-7949
LANDIS UND GYR MITTEILUNGEN. 1953-1988. irreg. L G Z Landis und Gyr Zug AG, CH-6301 Zug, Switzerland.

333.7   CN   ISSN 0715-1489
S934.C3
LANDMARKS. 1982-198? q. Ministry of Natural Resources, Circulation Department, Ground Fl., 511 King St. W., Toronto, Ont. M5V 2Z4, Canada.

712   SA
LANDSCAPE SOUTHERN AFRICA. 1986-19?? bi-m. (back issues avail.) (Institute of Landscape Architects of South Africa) Phase Four (Pty) Ltd., P.O. Box 784279, Sandton 2146, South Africa.

016   DK   ISSN 0106-7737
LANDSCENTRALEN FOR UNDERVISNINGSMIDLER. BAANDCENTRALEN. BAANDKATALOG. 1978-1989. a. Landscentralen for Undervisningsmidler - National Institute for Educational Media, Oernevej 30, 2400 Copenhagen NV, Denmark.

387   DK   ISSN 0108-7231
LANDSHAVNEPLANBIDRAG; Aalborg Havn. published only once, 1982. a. Havnevaesen, Administrationsbygningen, Vesterbro 104, 9000 Aalborg, Denmark.

630   GW
LANDTECHNIK; vereinigt mit Die Landarbeit. 1946-1991. m. (Kuratorium fuer Technik und Bauwesen in der Landwirtschaft e.V) Verlag Eduard F. Beckmann KG, Postfach 1120, Heidecker Weg 112, 3160 Lehrte, Germany.
Formerly: Fachzeitschrift fuer Alle Bereiche der Agrartechnik und Laendliches Bauen (ISSN 0023-8082)

341   FR   ISSN 0085-2686
LANGUE INTERNATIONALE. 1950-1989. a. (processed) Societe Idiste Francaise, c/o Georges Moureaux, Ed., 18 rue Emile Ecuyer, 01100 Oyonnax, France.

630   SW   ISSN 0345-7001
LANTBRUKSNYTT. 1966-1990 (Sep.). 16/yr. Skaanska Dagbladet AB, Box 165, S-20121 Malmoe 1, Sweden.

658   UK   ISSN 0263-4228
LARGE MIXED RETAILING. 1982-1985. m. Benn Publications Ltd., Sovereign Way, Tonbridge, Kent TN9 1RW, England.

028.5   US
LASER; the kids' peace newsletter. 1982-198? m. (exc. Jul. & Aug.). Pittenbruach Press, 15 Walnut St., Box 553, Northampton, MA 01060.

621.366   US
LASER APPLICATIONS. 1971-1984 (vol.5). irreg. (reprint service avail. from ISI) Academic Press, Inc., 1250 Sixth Ave., San Diego, CA 92101.

531.64   US   ISSN 0741-5222
LASER RESEARCH; a current awareness bulletin. ceased. s-m. U.S. Department of Energy, Office of Scientific and Technical Information, Box 62, Oak Ridge, TN 37831.

200   US   ISSN 0023-8635
LAST DAY MESSENGER. 1963-1990 (Jan.); suspended. q. (Interstate Bible Chapel, Inc.) Gospel Tract Distributors, Box 17406, Portland, OR 97217.

011 613.9   UK   ISSN 0308-8774
LATEST LITERATURE IN FAMILY PLANNING. 1974-1990 (no.99). bi-m. Family Planning Association, 27-35 Mortimer St., London W1N 7RJ, England.

299   US
LATTER-DAY SENTINEL. (3 separate editions: 1 for Arizona; 1 for Southern California, 1 for Southern Nevada) 1979-1989. bi-w. (tabloid format; back issues avail.) Latter-Day Sentinel Newspapers, Inc., 13705 N.E. Airport Way, Portland, OR 97230-1043.

305.412 289.2   US   ISSN 0889-9185
LATTER - DAY WOMAN. 1986-198? bi-m. (back issues avail.) Latter - Day Woman, Inc., Box 126, Sandy, UT 84070.

410   UR   ISSN 0201-8039
LATVIESU VALODAS KULTURAS JAUTAJUMI. 1965-1990; suspended. a. Avots, 24, Padomju Blvd., 226047 Riga, Latvian S.S.R., U.S.S.R.

811   US   ISSN 0363-2164
LAUGHING BEAR. 1976-1978; resumed 1983; ceased same year. irreg. Laughing Bear Press, Box 14, Woodinville, WA 98072.

657   US   ISSN 0147-2208
HF5686.H75
LAVENTHOL AND HORWATH PERSPECTIVE; semiannual publication covering subjects of general business and financial interest. 1921-1990. s-a. Laventhol & Horwath, 1845 Walnut St., Philadelphia, PA 19103.
Former titles: L K H H Accountant (ISSN 0023-6314); Horwath Accountant.

340 296   US
LAW AND LEGISLATION IN ISRAEL. ceased. irreg. American Jewish Congress, Stephen Wise Congress House, 15 E. 84th St., New York, NY 10028.

614.58 340   US   ISSN 0890-5037
LAW AND MENTAL HEALTH. 1985-1990. a. Pergamon Press, Inc., Journals Division, 660 White Plains Rd., Tarrytown, NY 10591-5153.

340 621.381 001.642US
LAW OFFICE GUIDE IN COMPUTERS (YEAR) DIRECTORY. 1984-1987 (Dec.). a. Ziegler Ross Inc., 3772 Sacramento St., San Franscisco, CA 94118.

658.8   US   ISSN 0091-4665
HD9999.G36
LAWN & GARDEN MARKETING; the merchandising magazine for lawn, garden and leisure living products. 1961-1991 (Mar.). 10/yr. Intertec Publishing Corp., 9221 Quivira Rd., Box 12901, Overland Park, KS 66212-9981.
Formerly: Lawn, Garden, Outdoor Living; Incorporates: Modern Garden Center.

635   US   ISSN 0746-9152
LAWN SERVICING. 1984-1989 (Mar.). 10/yr. Intertec Publishing Corp., Box 12901, 9221 Quivira Rd., Overland Park, KS 66212.

296 301   US
LEADERS' DIGEST. 1981-19?? 5/yr. American Jewish Committee, Institute of Human Relations, 165 E. 56 St., New York, NY 10022.

334   US
LEADERSHIP DIRECTIONS. ceased. 3/yr. (back issues avail.) North American Students of Cooperation, Box 7715, Ann Arbor, MI 48107.

635.9   US
LEAF & LEISURE. ceased 1986. m. Wordcraft, Inc., Box 6472, Austin, TX 78762.

614.7   CN   ISSN 0832-7580
LEAKING UNDERGROUND STORAGE TANK NEWSLETTER/BULLETIN RESERVOIRS SOUTERRAINS NON ETANCHES. 1986-1989. q. Environment Canada, Industrial Programs Branch, Ottawa, Ont. K1A 0H3, Canada.

370 658   US
LEARN & PLAY. 1988-198? bi-m. Edgell Communications, 7500 Old Oak Blvd., Cleveland, OH 44130.

685.31   US   ISSN 0023-9747
TS940
LEATHER AND SHOES. 1891-198? m. Locksmith Publishing Corp., Rumpf Publishing Division, 850 Busse Hwy., Park Ridge, IL 60068-5980.

675.2   US   ISSN 0075-8345
HD9780.U5
LEATHER BUYERS GUIDE AND LEATHER TRADE MARKS. 1963-198? a. Locksmith Publishing Corp., Rumpf Publishing Division, 850 Busse Hwy., Park Ridge, IL 60068-5980.

338   US
LEATHER TODAY ADDITIONS. published only once, 1987. 10/yr. Fur Publishing Plus, Inc., 19 W. 21st St., Ste. 403, New York, NY 10010.

289.9   SA
LEBONE LA KGALALELO. 1954-19?? q. (Church of the Nazarene) Africa Nazarene Publications, P.O. Box 1288, Florida, Transvaal 1710, South Africa.
Formerly: Lebone la Kgalalelo Isibani Sobu Ngcwele (ISSN 0024-0060)

637   US
LECHERO LATINOAMERICANO. 1987-1990 (vol.2, no.3). bi-m. Holstein-Friesian World, Inc., 8036 Lake St., Box 299, Sandy Creek, NY 13145.
Formerly: Holstein Latinoamericano.

510   NE
LECTURE NOTES IN NUMERICAL AND APPLIED ANALYSIS. 1983-1989 (vol.10). irreg. Elsevier Science Publishers B.V., Books Division, P.O. Box 211, 1000 AE Amsterdam, Netherlands.

617.96   UK   ISSN 0267-0003
LECTURES IN ANAESTHESIOLOGY. 1984-1988. 2/yr. (World Federation of Societies of Anaesthesiologists) Blackwell Scientific Publications Ltd., Osney Mead, Oxford OX2 OEL, England.
Formerly (until 1985): W F S A Lectures (ISSN 0265-1858)

369.4   SW   ISSN 0345-7044
LEDARBLADET SAMSPEL. 7/yr. Svenska Scoutfoerbundet, P.O. Box 49 005, 100 28 Stockholm, Sweden.

977   US
LEE COUNTY HISTORICAL SOCIETY. HISTORICAL YEARBOOK. 1972?-1977. a. Lee County Historical Society, Box 58, Dixon, IL 61021.

800 792 942   UK   ISSN 0140-8089
LEEDS MEDIEVAL STUDIES. 1975-1981; suspended. irreg. (back issues avail.) University of Leeds, Centre for Medieval Studies, Leeds LS2 9JT, England.

340.6   US   ISSN 0190-2350
KF3821.A15
LEGAL ASPECTS OF MEDICAL PRACTICE. 1972-1990; suspended. m. (also avail. in microfilm from UMI, WSH; reprint service avail. from UMI,WSH) (American College of Legal Medicine) Shugar Publishing, 32 Mill Rd., Westhampton Beach, NY 11978.

340 624   US   ISSN 0730-952X
LEGAL BRIEFS FOR THE CONSTRUCTION INDUSTRY. 1975-1989. s-m. (looseleaf format; back issues avail.) McGraw-Hill, Inc., 1221 Ave. of the Americas, New York, NY 10020.
Formerly: Legal Briefs for Architects, Engineers, and Contractors.

332   US
LEGAL BULLETIN (CHICAGO). ceased 1989. bi-m. United States League of Savings Institutions, 111 E. Wacker Dr., Chicago, IL 60601.

340 016   US   ISSN 0279-5787
K33
LEGAL CONTENTS; semi-monthly compilation of tables of contents from more than 320 business magazines and journals. 1972-1989. s-m. (also avail. in microform from UMI; reprint service avail. from UMI) Institute for Scientific Information, 3501 Market St., Philadelphia, PA 19104.
Former titles (until 1980): C C L P: Contents of Current Legal Periodicals (ISSN 0147-0493); (until 1976: Contents of Current Legal Periodicals (ISSN 0300-7391); Incorporates: Survey of Law Reviews (ISSN 0360-7372)

340   CN   ISSN 0225-2287
LEGAL INFORMATION SERVICE REPORTS. 1979-1986. irreg. (back issues avail.) University of Saskatchewan, Native Law Centre, Diefenbaker Centre, Saskatoon, Sask. S7N 0W0, Canada.

340 352.7   US
LEGAL SERVICES OCCASIONAL. 1969-19?? irreg., approx. 3/yr. Massachusetts Law Reform Institute, 69 Canal St., Boston, MA 02114.
Formerly: Legal Services Monthly.

340   US
LEGISLATIVE ISSUES IN FOCUS. 1982-198? q. (looseleaf format) American Academy of Allergy & Immunology, 611 E. Wells St., Milwaukee, WI 53202.

610　　　　　　SP
LEGUAS. 1965-1987 (no.1127). bi-m. Laboratorio Aldo-Union, Angel Guimera, 123-125, Esplugas (Barcelona), Spain.

700　　　　NE　　ISSN 0169-8575
LEIDSE KUNSTHISTORISCHE REEKS. 1966-1969 (vol.2). irreg. Leiden University Press, c/o E.J. Brill Publishers, Postbus 9000, 2300 PA Leiden, Netherlands.

591 616.9　　UK　　ISSN 0952-0333
LEISHMANIASIS. ceased 1991. s-m. (looseleaf format; back issues avail.) Sheffield University Biomedical Information Service (SUBIS), The University, Sheffield S10 2TN, England.

794　　　　　　US
LEISURE TIME ELECTRONICS. ceased 1986. m. C B S Magazines, Leisure Time Electronics Department, 1515 Broadway, New York, NY 10036.

917　　　　　　US
LEISUREGUIDE - LOUISVILLE. 1979-19?? a. L I N Cellular Communications Corp., 21200 Irwin St., Woodland Hills, CA 91367.

910.4　　　　　US
LEISUREGUIDE - MILWAUKEE. 1982-19?? a. L I N Cellular Communications Corp., 21200 Irwin St., Woodland Hills, CA 91367.

658　　　　GW　　ISSN 0138-2845
LEITUNG UND PLANUNG VON WISSENSCHAFT UND TECHNIK. 1969-1991. a. Zentralinstitut fuer Information und Dokumentation der D D R, Koepenicker Str. 80-82, 1020 Berlin, Germany.

345 388.3
LEMON FILE; an auto warranty litigation case reference service. 1982-1991. q. (looseleaf format) Center for Auto Safety, 2001 S St., N.W., Ste. 410, Washington, DC 20009.

332
LENDING FOR THE COMMERCIAL BANKER. ceased. q. Warren, Gorham and Lamont Inc., One Penn Plaza, New York, NY 10119.

301.4157 301.412　US
LESBIAN POSITION. 1982-198? m. Box 3075, New Haven, CT 06515.

316　　　　　　LO
LESOTHO. BUREAU OF STATISTICS. HALF-YEARLY STATISTICAL BULLETIN. ceased 1976 (June). s-a. Bureau of Statistics, Box MS 455, Maseru 100, Lesotho.
Formerly: Lesotho. Bureau of Statistics. Quarterly Statistical Bulletin.

781.57　　　　UK
LET IT ROCK. 1972-197? m. Hanover Press Ltd., 80 Highgate, London NW5 1PB, England.

282　　　　US　　ISSN 0740-9613
LET'S PRAY TOGETHER. 1979-1989 (vol.11). w. Families for Prayer, Inc., 775 Madison Ave., Albany, NY 12208.

267　　　　FR　　ISSN 0397-0167
LETTRE AUX EDUCATEURS. 1981-1991 (Jul.); suspended. 9/yr. (back issues avail.) Enfance Missionnaire, 15 Villa Molitor, 75016 Paris, France.

054.1　　　　　FR
LETTRE CULTURELLE. 1973-1991. m., with supplements. (also avail. in microfilm; microfiche) Fondation Nationale pour l'Encouragement de la Creativite (F.N.E.C.), 4 rue Lefevre, 78390 Bois d'Arcy, France.

610 574　　　　FR
LETTRE DE L'INFORMATIQUE MEDICALE. 1987-19?? 11/yr. (back issues avail.) E C 2, 269, rue de la Garenne, 92000 Nanterre, France.

616.99 616.15　UK　ISSN 0261-474X
LEUKEMIA RESEARCH. ceased 1990. m. (looseleaf format; back issues avail.) Sheffield University Biomedical Information Service (SUBIS), The University, Sheffield S10 2TN, England.

613　　　　　　NE
LEVEN EN GEZONDHEID. 1972-19?? m. (11/yr.). Stichting Uitgeverij "Veritas", Box 630, The Hague, Netherlands.

338.9　　　　　PE
LEYES ECONOMICAS DE LOS PAISES MIEMBROS. 1971-1974; resumed 1977-1986 (Dec.). m. (back issues avail.) Junta del Acuerdo de Cartagena, Departamento de Comunicaciones e Informacion, Paseo de la Republica 3895, San Isidro, Lima, Peru.
Formerly (until 1976): Junta del Acuerdo de Cartagena. Grupo Andino: Legislacion Economica y Social de los Paises Miembros.

991.4　　　　PH　　ISSN 0024-1679
DS688.L4
LEYTE-SAMAR STUDIES. 1967-1987 (vol.21). s-a. (also avail. in microfiche) Divine Word University, Tacloban City 7101, Philippines.

368　　　　US　　ISSN 0889-4469
LIABILITY & INSURANCE BULLETIN. 1986-1987. w. (back issues avail.) Buraff Publications (Subsidiary of: The Bureau of National Affairs, Inc.), 1350 Connecticut Ave. N.W., Ste. 1000, Washington, DC 20036.

327　　　　　　US
LIBERATION BULLETIN. 1987-1988; suspended after vol.9. irreg. National Center for Public Policy Research, 300 Eye St., N.E., Ste. 3, Washington, DC 20002.

179.3　　　　　UK
LIBERATOR. 1976-199? q. British Union for the Abolition of Vivisection, 16A Crane Grove, London N7 8LB, England.
Former titles (until 1981): Animal Welfare; A V Times; Anti-Vivisectionist (ISSN 0003-5610)

380.3 320 100　US　ISSN 0893-2115
LIBERTARIAN E-MAIL DIRECTORY; a guide to freedom-lovers reachable by computerized communications. 1986-1988 (no.6). s-a. (back issues avail.) Daniel Tobias, Ed. & Pub., 447 Merrick St., Shreveport, LA 71104-2305.

331.88　　　　IE　　ISSN 0790-5068
LIBERTY NEWS. 1953-1989 (Dec.). bi-m. Irish Transport & General Workers' Union, Liberty Hall, Dublin 1, Ireland.
Formerly (until 1985): Liberty (ISSN 0024-2063)

020　　　　　　US
LIBRARY AND INFORMATION SCIENCE ANNUAL. 1985-1989. a. Libraries Unlimited, Inc., Box 3988, Englewood, CO 80155-3988.
Formerly (until 1986): Library Science Annual (ISSN 8755-2108)

025　　　　　　US
LIBRARY AUTOMATION NEWS. 1983-1990. m. Hennepin County Library, Technical Services Division, 12601 Ridgedale Dr., Minnetonka, MN 55343.
Formerly: Online Catalog News.

029　　　　　　US
LIBRARY BIBLIOGRAPHIES AND INDEXES. 1975; ceased same year. irreg. Gale Research Inc., 835 Penobscot Bldg., Detroit, MI 48226.

020 016　　　UK　　ISSN 0263-3612
LIBRARY LINK. 1970-1989; suspended. m. College of Librarianship Wales, Library, Llanbadarn Fawr, Aberystwyth SY23 3AS, Wales.

020　　　　　　US
LIBRARY MEDIA OUTPUT. published only once, 1975. irreg. Department of Education, Montgomery, AL 36104.

020　　　　US　　ISSN 0162-6426
Z733
LIBRARY OF CONGRESS; a brief summary of major activities. 1976-1987. a. U.S. Library of Congress, Washington, DC 20540.

026　　　　　　US
LIBRARY SERVICE TO THE PEOPLE OF NEW YORK STATE: A LONG RANGE PLAN. 1978-1989. a. New York State Library, State Education Department, Cultural Education Center, Albany, NY 12230.

070.5　　　　　CK
LIBROS. ceased. bi-m. Camara Colombiana de la Industria Editoriale, Carrera 7a, No. 17-51, Apdo. Aereo 8998, Bogota, Colombia.

658.8　　　　　US
LICENSING BUSINESS YEARBOOK. ceased 1990. a. (back issues avail.) New Market Enterprises, Inc., Box 1665, Scottsdale, AZ 85252.

602.7　　　　　US
LICENSING INTERNATIONAL. 1984-198? bi-m. W F C, Inc., 3000 Hadley Rd., S. Plainfield, NJ 07080.

268　　　　　　NE
LICHTHOEVE. 1932-198? q. Lichthoeve, Oude Barnevelderweg 7, 3886 PT Garderen, Netherlands.
Formerly: Lichthoeve-Kinderwerk (ISSN 0024-2853)

830　　　　　　GW
LICHTWARK-STIFTUNG. VEROEFFENTLICHUNG. ceased. irreg. Hans Christians Verlag, Kl. Theaterstr. 9, 2000 Hamburg 36, Germany.

368 310　　　　US
LIFE RATES & DATA. 1971-1989. a. National Underwriter Co., 505 Gest St., Cincinnati, OH 45203.

542　　　　　　US
LIFE SCIENCE LAB PRODUCTS. 1988-1991 (Jul.). bi-m. (reprint service avail.) Knolls Publishing Group, 240 Cedar Knolls Rd., Ste. 220, Cedar Knolls, NJ 07927.

296 947　　　　US
LIFELINES (NEW YORK). (Former name of issuing body (until 1985): Greater N.Y. Conference on Soviet Jewry) 1981-1987. m. Coalition to Free Soviet Jews, 8 W. 40th St., New York, NY 10018.
Formerly: Currents (New York).

052　　　　　　UK
LIFESTYLE (NEWBURY). 1988-198? a. Kingsclere Publications Ltd., Highfiled House, 2 Highfield Ave., Newbury, Berkshire RG14 5DS, England.

028.5 284　　　US　　ISSN 0737-8173
LIGHTED PATHWAY. 1929-1990 (Jan.). m. (Church of God) Pathway Press, 922-1080 Montgomery Ave., Cleveland, TN 37311.

633.71　　　　CN　　ISSN 0024-340X
LIGHTER/BRIQUET. 1931-1987 (vol.27, no.3-4). irreg. Agriculture Canada, Communications Branch, 930 Carling Ave., Ottawa, Ont. K1A 0C7, Canada.

301.1　　　　　US
LIMERENCE FORUM; open forum and research instrument. suspended after one issue, 1982. irreg. c/o Randall Tennov, Ed., Rd. 2, Box 251, Millsboro, DE 19966.

591 595.7　　AG　　ISSN 0325-7592
LIMNOBIOS. 1976-1989 (vol.2, no.10). a. (back issues avail.) Instituto de Limnologia "Dr. Raul A. Ringuelet", Casilla de Correo 712, 1900 La Plata, Argentina.

630　　　　NZ　　ISSN 0069-3839
LINCOLN COLLEGE. FARMERS' CONFERENCE. PROCEEDINGS. 1951-19?? a. Lincoln College, Canterbury, New Zealand.

350　　　　　　US
LINCOLN INSTITUTE OF LAND POLICY. BASIC CONCEPT SERIES. 1978-19?? Lincoln Institute of Land Policy, 26 Trowbridge St., Cambridge, MA 02138.

929 942　　　　UK
LINCOLNSHIRE FAMILY HISTORIAN. no.10, 1981-19?? 4/yr. Society for Lincolnshire History and Archaeology, Jew's Court, Steep Hill, Lincoln LN2 1LS, England.
Formerly (until Apr., 1985): Family History Newsletter (ISSN 0142-3460)

929　　　　　　US
LINDSAY LINKS & LEGACY. 1980-1982. q. Kenma Publishing Co., Box 2786, Evansville, IN 47714-0786.

796.332　　　　US
LINDY'S SOUTHEASTERN RECRUITING GUIDE. 1986-1990. a. D M D Publications, Inc., 2700 Highway 280, Ste. 108, Birmingham, AL 35223.

950　　　　PH　　ISSN 0459-4835
LIPUNAN JOURNAL. 1965-1981 (vol.3, no.1). a. University of the Philippines, Asian Center, Diliman, Quezon City 1101, Philippines.

CESSATIONS

789.913 US ISSN 0024-4309
LIST-O-TAPES; loose-leaf tape catalog covering all tape releases, open reel, cartridge and cassette. 1964-1990. base vol. serviced with w. revised replacement sheets. (looseleaf format) Phonolog Publishing (Subsidiary of: Trade Service Corporation), 10996 Torreyana Rd., Box 85007, San Diego, CA 92138.

630 FR ISSN 0078-6292
LIST OF RESEARCH INSTITUTES AND SCIENTISTS IN O E C D MEMBER COUNTRIES. (Special number of its Documentation dans l'Agriculture et l'Alimentation) 1958-197? irreg. (also avail. in microfiche) Organization for Economic Cooperation and Development, 2 rue Andre-Pascal, 75775 Paris Cedex 16, France.

663.3 US
LISTEN TO YOUR BEER. 1983-1986 (vol2, no.2). irreg. (back issues avail.) American Brewing Information Service (ABIS), Box 546, Portland, OR 97207.

791.4 UK ISSN 0024-4392
AP4
LISTENER. 1929-19?? w. Listener Publications Ltd., 199 Old Marylebone Rd., London NW1 5QS, England.
  Formerly: Listener and B B C Television Review.

282 255 US ISSN 0024-4465
BX3601
LISTY SV. FRANTISKA/LEAFLETS OF ST. FRANCIS. 1924-1988 (June). q. Franciscan Friars of the Custody of the Most Holy Savior, 232 S. Home Ave., Pittsburgh, PA 15202.

621.382 US
LITE RATE. 1985-1990. q. (back issue avail.) Intelco Corp., 20410 Observation Dr., Germantown, MD 20876-4024.

800 831 GW ISSN 0172-0457
LITERARISCHES ARBEITSJOURNAL. 1979-1990. q. Kanalpresse im Verlag Karl Pfortner, Postfach 450, 8832 Weissenburg, Germany.

830 GW ISSN 0323-3766
LITERARISCHES SONDERHEFT; der Zeitschrift Deutsch als Fremdsprache. 1971-1991. a. (Karl Marx Universitaet Leipzig, Herder Institut) Verlag Enzyklopaedie, Gerichtsweg 26, 7010 Leipzig, Germany.

338 070.5 CN ISSN 0712-4384
LITERARY MARKETS. 1982-19?? bi-m. Literary Markets, 4340 Coldfall Rd., Richmond, B.C. V7C 1P8, Canada.

800 GW ISSN 0177-2074
LITERATUR IM HISTORISCHEN PROZESS (NEUE FOLGE). 1981-19?? 3/yr. Argument-Verlag GmbH, Rentzelstr. 1, 2000 Hamburg 13, Germany.

700 800 GW ISSN 0024-4775
NX1
LITERATURE, MUSIC, FINE ARTS; a review of German-language research contributions on literature, music, and fine arts. 1968-1991. s-a. (also avail. in microform from MIM; reprint service avail. from ISI) Institut fuer Wissenschaftliche Zusammenarbeit - Institute for Scientific Co-Operation, Landhausstr. 18, 7400 Tuebingen, Germany.

621.3 016 SZ ISSN 0024-4872
LITERATURRUNDSCHAU. 1953-1989 (vol.36, no.4). q. Electrowatt Engineering Services Ltd., Library, Postfach, 8022 Zurich, Switzerland.

615.842 SZ ISSN 1011-2928
  CODEN: LTMOEM
LITHIUM THERAPY MONOGRAPHS. 1987-1991. irreg. S. Karger AG, Allschwilerstr. 10, P.O. Box, CH-4009 Basel, Switzerland.

821 UK
LITTLE WORD MACHINE. 1971-1981 (no.11). irreg. L. W.M. Publications, 5 Beech Terrace, Undercliffe, Bradford, West Yorkshire BD3 0PY, England.

330.9 UR ISSN 0207-1266
LITUANISTIKA V S.S.S.R. EKONOMIKA; nauchno-referativnyi sbornik. 1978-1990. a. Akademiya Nauk Litovskoi S.S.R., Nauchno-Informatsionnyi Tsentr, Michurino g-ve 1-46, Vilnius, Lithuanian S.S.R., U.S.S.R.

100 301.1 150 UR ISSN 0202-2001
LITUANISTIKA V S.S.S.R. FILOSOFIYA I PSIKHOLOGIYA; nauchno-referativnyi sbornik. 1977-1990. a. Akademiya Nauk Litovskoi S.S.R., Nauchno-Informatsionnyi Tsentr, Michurino g-ve 1-46, Vilnius, Lithuanian S.S.R., U.S.S.R.

700 UR
LITUANISTIKA V S.S.S.R. ISKUSSTVOVEDENIE; nauchno-informatsionnyi sbornik. 1978-1990. a. Akademiya Nauk Litovskoi S.S.R., Nauchno-Informatsionnyi Tsentr, Michurino g-ve 1-46, Vilnius, Lithuanian S.S.R., U.S.S.R.

949.6 UR
LITUANISTIKA V S.S.S.R. ISTORIYA; nauchno-referativnyi sbornik. 1977-1990. a. Akademiya Nauk Litovskoi S.S.R., Nauchno-Informatsionnyi Tsentr, Michurino g-ve 1-46, Vilnius, Lithuanian S.S.R., U.S.S.R.

890 UR ISSN 0207-1274
PG8701
LITUANISTIKA V S.S.S.R. LITERATUROVEDENIE; nauchno-referativnyi sbornik. 1978-1990. a. Akademiya Nauk Litovskoi S.S.R., Nauchno-Informatsionnyi Tsentr, Michurino g-ve 1-46, Vilnius, Lithuanian S.S.R., U.S.S.R.

340 UR ISSN 0202-2028
LITUANISTIKA V S.S.S.R. PRAVO; nauchno-referativnyi sbornik. 1978-1990. a. Akademiya Nauk Litovskoi S.S.R., Nauchno-Informatsionnyi Tsentr, Michurino g-ve 1-46, Vilnius, Lithuanian S.S.R., U.S.S.R.

410 UR ISSN 0202-201X
PG8501
LITUANISTIKA V S.S.S.R. YAZYKOZNANIE; nauchno-referativnyi sbornik. 1978-1990. a. Akademiya Nauk Litovskoi S.S.R., Nauchno-Informatsionnyi Tsentr, Michurino g-ve 1-46, Vilnius, Lithuanian S.S.R., U.S.S.R.

100 200 575 600 US
LIVE AND LET LIVE. 1977-1988. irreg. (2-4/yr.). c/o Patrick A. Heller, Ed., 300 Frandor Ave., Lansing, MI 48912-5202.

612 612.015 UK ISSN 0261-4758
LIVER FUNCTION. ceased 1990. m. (looseleaf format; back issues avail.) Sheffield University Biomedical Information Service (SUBIS), The University, Sheffield S10 2TN, England.

052 SI
LIVING. 19??-1987. m. M P H Media Services, 601 Sims Dr. 03-21, 03 Pan I, Warehouse Complex 1438, Singapore.

333.33 352.7 US ISSN 0741-5516
LIVING (PHOENIX EDITION). 1979-19?? bi-m. (back issues avail.) Baker Publications, Inc., 5501 LBJ Frwy., No. 400, Dallas, TX 75240-6202.
  Formerly: Phoenix Living (ISSN 0164-5870)

352.7 AT ISSN 0047-4835
LIVING CITY. 1967-1986. 2/yr. Melbourne & Metropolitan Board of Works, Box 4342 G.P.O., Melbourne, Vic. 3001, Australia.

530 US ISSN 0893-8067
LIVING PHYSICS. 1972-19?? q. Tesla Foundation, 330 A West Vintah, Colorado Springs, CO 80905.
  Former titles: Adventures in Science; Adventures in Experimental Physics (ISSN 0044-6386)

616.97 US ISSN 0192-995X
LIVING WITH ALLERGIES. 1979-1989 (vo.11). a. (looseleaf format; back issues avail.) American Allergy Association, Box 7273, Menlo Park, CA 94026.
  Formerly: Allergy Information Exchange (ISSN 0163-0660)

745.1 747 AT
LIVING WITH ANTIQUES. 1981-19?? 3/yr. (back issues avail.) Bomilhold Pty. Ltd., 2-27 Dale St., Brookvale, N.S.W. 2100, Australia.

616.99 US
LIVING WITH CANCER. 1987-1991. 3/yr. American Cancer Society, Inc., Florida Division, 1001 S. MacDill Ave., Tampa, FL 33629.

800 CN ISSN 0076-0153
PQ3900
LIVRES ET AUTEURS QUEBECOIS. 1936-1980. a. Presses de l'Universite Laval, Cite universitaire, Quebec, Que. G1K 7P4, Canada.
  Formerly: Livres et Auteurs Canadiens.

636.296 US
LLAMA WORLD MAGAZINE. 1979-19?? q. (processed) 921 First Ave. W., No. 309, Seattle, WA 98119-3702.
  Formerly: Llama Newsletter (ISSN 0730-7802)

332.3 US ISSN 0277-1497
HG2040.5.U5
LOANS CLOSED AND SERVICING VOLUME FOR THE MORTGAGE BANKING INDUSTRY. 1971-1989. a. Mortgage Bankers Association of America, Economics and Education Department, 1125 15th St., N.W., Washington, DC 20005.
  Formerly: Mortgage Banking: Loans Closed and Servicing Volume (ISSN 0363-1710)

338 UK
LOCAL AREA HOUSING STATISTICS. 1985-1989 (Dec.). irreg. (approx. 1-2/m.). (back issues avail.) Nationwide Anglia Building Society, Chesterfield House, Bloomsbury Way, London WC1V 6PW, England.

331.1 352 UK ISSN 0957-5111
LOCAL GOVERNMENT EMPLOYMENT. 1953-1991 (Feb). bi-m. (back issues avail.) (Local Authorities Conditions of Service Advisory Board) Centurion Press, 41 Belgrave Sq., London SW1X 8NZ, England.
  Formerly: Local Government Manpower (ISSN 0140-1017)

352 320 NE
LOCAL GOVERNMENT NEWSLETTER. 1966-19?? m. International Union of Local Authorities, P.O. Box 90646, 2509 LP The Hague, Netherlands.
  Supersedes: I U L A Newsletter (ISSN 0019-087X); Which was formerly: Local Government Throughout the World.

642 US
LOCALNETTER UPDATE SERVICE. ceased. 4/yr. Architecture Technology Corporation, Box 24344, Minneapolis, MN 55424.

629.13 US ISSN 0024-5704
LOCKHEED ORION SERVICE DIGEST. 1962-19?? irreg. Lockheed-California Co., Burbank, CA 91510.

390 572 PL ISSN 0076-0382
GN585.P6
LODZKIE STUDIA ETNOGRAFICZNE. 1959-1973. a. (Polskie Towarzystwo Ludoznawcze, Oddzial w Lodzi) Panstwowe Wydawnictwo Naukowe, Ul. Miodowa 10, 00-251 Warsaw, Poland.

510 500 PL ISSN 0076-0412
LODZKIE TOWARZYSTWO NAUKOWE. WYDZIAL III NAUK MATEMATYCZNO-PRZYRODNICZYCH. PRACE. 1947-1973. irreg. Panstwowe Wydawnictwo Naukowe, Ul. Miodowa 10, 00-251 Warsaw, Poland.

610 PL ISSN 0076-0420
LODZKIE TOWARZYSTWO NAUKOWE. WYDZIAL IV. NAUK LEKARSKICH. PRACE. 1951-1973. irreg. Panstwowe Wydawnictwo Naukowe, Ul. Miodowa 10, 00-251 Warsaw, Poland.

600 PL ISSN 0076-0439
LODZKIE TOWARZYSTWO NAUKOWE. WYDZIAL V. NAUK TECHNICZNYCH. PRACE. 1963-1973. irreg. Panstwowe Wydawnictwo Naukowe, Ul. Miodowa 10, 00-251 Warsaw, Poland.

690 US
THE LOG. 1988-19?? m. (Log Home Guide Information Center) Muir Publishing Co., Inc., Middle Creek Rd., Box 581, Cosby, TN 37722.

690 US ISSN 0894-0355
TH4840
LOG HOMES DESIGN, CONSTRUCTION & FINANCE ISSUE. 1987-1989 (vol.6, no.2). a. Home Buyer Publications, Inc., 4451 Brookfield Corporate Dr., Ste. 101, Chantilly, VA 22021.
  Formerly (until 1989): Construction and Finance Guide.

720 690   CN   ISSN 0315-8756
LOG HOUSE. 1974-1980. a. (back issues avail.) Log House Publishing Co. Ltd., R.R. 1, Pender Island, B.C. VON 2M0, Canada.
  Formerly: Canadian Log House.

380.3 621.381   US   ISSN 0743-2445
LOGO AND EDUCATION COMPUTING JOURNAL. 1983-1988 (vol.3). 4/yr. (back issues avail.) Interactive Education Foundation, Flowerfield Bldg. 7, St. James, NY 11780-1502.

200 060   PH   ISSN 0076-0471
LOGOS; a series of monographs in scripture, theology, philosophy. 1966-1979. irreg., no.14, 1985. Loyola School of Theology, Ateneo de Manila University, Box 4082, Manila, Philippines.

378   UK
LONDON AND SOUTH EASTERN REGIONAL ADVISORY COUNCIL FOR FURTHER EDUCATION. BULLETIN OF SPECIAL COURSES. ceased 1988. a. London and South Eastern Regional Advisory Council for Further Education, Tavistock House South, Tavistock Square, London WC1H 9LR, England.
  Formerly: London and Home Counties Regional Advisory Council for Technological Education. Bulletin of Special Courses.

300 016   UK   ISSN 0076-051X
Z7161
LONDON BIBLIOGRAPHY OF THE SOCIAL SCIENCES. ceased (last issue: Vol. 47, 1989 published Mar. 1990). a. (reprint service avail. from SCH) (British Library of Political and Economic Science) Mansell Publishing Ltd., Villiers House, 41-47 Strand, London WC2N 5JE, England.

330 378   UK
LONDON BUSINESS SCHOOL. JOURNAL. ceased. 2/yr. London Business School, Sussex Place, Regent's Park, London NW1 4SA, England.

382   UK
LONDON CREATIVE LISTINGS (YEAR). 1985-1986. a. Kogan Page Ltd., 120 Pentonville Rd., London N1 9JN, England.

910.202   UK
LONDON DELEGATE. 1979-198? s-a. Where Publications, 55-57 Great Marlborough St., London W1V 1DD, England.
  Formerly: London Life for Delegates.

670   UK
LONDON DIRECTORY OF INDUSTRY AND COMMERCE. ceased 1991. a. Kemps Group (Printers & Publishers) Ltd., Westbury House, 701-705 Warwick Rd., Solihull, W. Midlands B91 3DA, England.
  Former titles: London Directory; Trades Register of London (ISSN 0082-5808)

610   UK
LONDON MEDICINE. 1986-1988 (Dec.). q. (back issues avail.) Hermiston Publications Ltd., 2 Hill Square, Edinburgh EH8 9DR, Scotland.

910   UK   ISSN 0076-0641
LONDON SCHOOL OF ECONOMICS AND POLITICAL SCIENCE. DEPARTMENT OF GEOGRAPHY. GEOGRAPHICAL PAPERS. 1964-19?? irreg. London School of Economics & Political Science, Dept. of Geography, Houghton St., Aldwych, London WC2A 2AE, England.

914   UK   ISSN 0024-6190
LONDON WEEKLY DIARY OF SOCIAL EVENTS. 1921-1991. w. London Diary Publications Ltd., 25 Park Row, Greenwich, London SE10 9NL, England.

910.09   AT   ISSN 1030-5459
LONELY PLANET UPDATE. 1981-1989 (no.30). q. (back issues avail.) Lonely Planet, Building 4, 64 Balmain St., Richmond, Vic. 3121, Australia.
  Formerly: Lonely Planet Newsletter.

051   US   ISSN 0898-557X
LONG ISLAND MONTHLY. 1988-1990. m. C M P Publications, Inc., 600 Community Dr., Manhasset, NY 11030.

610   US
LONG TERM CARE. ceased. m. American Health Consultants, Inc., Six Piedmont Center, Ste. 400, 3525 Piedmont Rd., N.E., Atlanta, GA 30305.

821   UK   ISSN 0144-6436
LOOT. 1979-1987. 4/yr. Spectacular Diseases, 83B London Rd., Peterborough, Cambs., England.

368   US   ISSN 0191-2763
LOSS PREVENTION AND CONTROL. 1979-1987. bi-w. (looseleaf format) Buraff Publications (Subsidiary of: The Bureau of National Affairs, Inc.), 1350 Connecticut Ave. N.W., Ste. 1000, Washington, DC 20036.

658.8   US
LOSS PREVENTION NEWSLETTER FOR DISTRIBUTION CENTER EXECUTIVES. ceased. q. Food Marketing Institute, 1750 K St., N.W., Washington, DC 20006.

368   US
LOUISIANA AVENT. ceased 1970. s-m. Chase Communications Group, Ltd., 25-35 Beechwood Ave., Box 9001, Mount Vernon, NY 10552-9001.
  Formerly: Louisiana Insurer (ISSN 0024-6832)

634.9   US
LOUISIANA STATE UNIVERSITY. SCHOOL OF FORESTRY, WILDLIFE, AND FISHERIES. ANNUAL FORESTRY SYMPOSIUM. PROCEEDINGS. 1952-198? a. Louisiana State University, School of Forestry, Wildlife, and Fisheries, 227 Forestry-Wildlife-Fisheries Bldg., Baton Rouge, LA 70803-6202.
  Formerly: Louisiana State University. School of Forestry and Wildlife Management. Annual Forestry Symposium. Proceedings. (ISSN 0076-1095)

929   US
LOVE HISTORICAL AND GENEALOGICAL QUARTERLY. vol.6, 1977-19?? q. Love Historical and Genealogical Association, 3300 Woodmont Blvd. Ste. A, Nashville, TN 37215-1832.

001.6 629.8   US
LOW COST C A D - C A M SYSTEMS. (Computer Aided Design - Computer Aided Machinery) ceased 1987. a. Engineering Software Exchange, 41 Travers Ave., Yonkers, NY 10705.
  Formerly: C A D Systems Update.

970   US   ISSN 0458-4201
LOWER CAPE FEAR HISTORICAL SOCIETY. BULLETIN. 1957-1988 (vol.31). s-a. Lower Cape Fear Historical Society, Box 813, Wilmington, NC 28401.

613.2   US   ISSN 0893-3383
LOWFAT LIFELINE; a monthly newsletter dedicated to the conviction that we can cut down on fat and eat very well. 1985-198? m. (looseleaf format; back issues avail.) 52 Condolea Court, Lake Oswego, OR 97035-1002.

808.1   UK   ISSN 0047-5157
LUDD'S MILL. 1971-19?? s-a. Eight Miles High Publications, 44 Spa Croft Rd., Teall St., Ossett, W. Yorkshire WF5 0HE, England.

387.7   GW
LUFTHANSA'S GERMANY. 1983-1990. 6/yr. Deutsche Lufthansa AG, Von-Gablenz-Str. 2-6, 5000 Cologne 21, Germany.

615.19   UK   ISSN 0950-0529
LUMINESCENCE. ceased 1990. m. (looseleaf format; back issues avail.) Sheffield University Biomedical Information Service (SUBIS), The University, Sheffield S10 2TN, England.

629.13   US   ISSN 0892-7782
LUNAR ENTREPRENEURS DIRECTORY. ceased 1987. a. Space Age Publishing Co., 20431 Stevens Creek Blvd., No. 210, Cupertino, CA 95014-2225.

910 526   SW
GA9
LUND STUDIES IN GEOGRAPHY. SERIES C. GENERAL, MATHEMATICAL AND REGIONAL GEOGRAPHY. 1962-1988. (Lunds Universitet, Department of Geography) Lund University Press, P.O. Box 141, S-221 00 Lund, Sweden.
  Formerly: Lund Studies in Geography. Series C. General and Mathematical Geography (ISSN 0076-1486)

581   SW   ISSN 0348-2456
LUND UNIVERSITET. VAEXTEKOLOGISKA INSTITUTIONEN. MEDDELANDEN. 1973-1990 (vol. 52). irreg. (back issues avail.) Lund University, Department of Plant Ecology, Oestra Vallgaten 14, S-223 61 Lund, Sweden.

749   GW   ISSN 0138-5518
DER LUSTIGE GRILLENFAENGER; Denksportprobleme - Geschicklichkeitsaufgaben - Froehliche Kurzweil. 1951-1990. q. Blumenstein Verlag, Am Michelsbach 27, 5900 Eisenach, Germany.

200   IT
LUX. 1962-197? s-a. African Association of St. Augustine, Via Urbano VIII, 16, Rome, Italy.

796.93   CS   ISSN 0323-1445
LYZARSTVI. vol.70, 1984-1992. m. (Ceskoslovensky Svaz Telesne Vychovy) Olympia, Klimentska 1, 115 88 Prague 1, Czechoslovakia.

687   UK
M A B FASHION PREVIEW. 1983-1989. s-a. (Menswear Association of Britain) M A B Communications Ltd., 19-20 Grosvenor St., London WIX OAS, England.

621.381   US
M A C AZINE. 1984-1989 (Mar.). m. Icon Concepts, 8008 Shoal Creek Blvd., Austin, TX 78758.

011   GW   ISSN 0723-3078
M & A INFODIENST. 1919-1989 (Dec.). m. Grosse Eschenheimer Str. 16, Postfach 101528, D-6000 Frankfurt 1, Germany.

614.7   UK   ISSN 0952-4711
M & Q ENVIRONMENT. 1987-19?? 6/yr. Ashire Publishing Ltd., 42 Grays Inn Rd., London WC1X 8LR, England.

658   US   ISSN 0024-7952
    CODEN: MBATAS
M B A. (Masters in Business Administration) 1966-1979 (vol. 12, no. 9). 6/yr. (also avail. in microfilm from UMI) M B A Communications, 730 Third Ave., New York, NY 10017.

574.92   US
M B L SCIENCE. 1985-19?? 2/yr. (back issues avail.) Marine Biological Laboratory, Public Information Office, Woods Hole, MA 02543.

382   FR   ISSN 1145-2447
M C I. (Marches Contrats Investissements) 1988-1991. w. E S I Publications (Subsidiary of: Masson), 5 et 7, rue Laromiguiere, 75005 Paris, France.

780 001.642   US
M C S. (Music, Computers & Software) 1985-19?? (vol.3, no.3). bi-m. 31 Lewis Rd., Northport, NY 11763-1617.

069   UK   ISSN 0309-6653
M D A INFORMATION. 1977-19?? 4/yr. Museum Documentation Association, Building O, 347 Cherry Hinton Road, Cambridge CB1 4DH, England.

910.04 956   UK
M E E D PRACTICAL GUIDE. U A E. (United Arab Emirates) 1981-198? irreg. Middle East Economic Digest Ltd., 21 John St., London WC1N 2BP, England.

305.412 300   UK   ISSN 0141-948X
HQ1101
M - F; a feminist journal. 1978-1986. 2/yr. (also avail. in microfilm; back issues avail.) 24 Ellerdale Road, London NW3 6BB, England.

614.58   US   ISSN 0025-9683
RA790.A1   CODEN: MHGNB
M H. (Mental Hygiene) 1917-19?? q. (microform; also avail. in microfilm from UMI) National Association for Mental Health, 1800 N. Kent St., Rosslyn, VA 22209.

780   CN
M I A C COMMUNIQUE. 1980-1989. 3/yr. Music Industries Association of Canada, 1210 Shepard Ave. E., Ste. 109, North York, Ont. M2K 1E3, Canada.
  Formerly: M I A C Newsletter.

380.3   US
M I C - ALERT. 1989-19?? w. Management Information Corporation, 401 E. Rte. 70, Box 5062, Cherry Hill, NJ 08034.

5230 CESSATIONS

600   FR
M I D I S T RAPPORT D'ACTIVITE (YEAR). ceased 1983. a. Ministere de la Recherche et de la Technologie, Mission Interministerielle de l'Information Scientifique et Technique, 9 rue Georges Pitard, 75015 Paris, France.

001.6 658.403   US   ISSN 0199-8838
M I S WEEK; the newspaper for information management. (Management Information Systems) 1980-1990 (Jun.). w. Fairchild Publications, Inc., M I S Week (Subsidiary of: Capital Cities/A B C Inc.), 7 E. 12th St., New York, NY 10003.

621.3   US
M P AND L NEWS. 1939-1991 (vol.56, no.3). m. (back issues avail.) Mississippi Power and Light, Box 1640, Jackson, MS 39215-1640.

670   US
M P I BUYERS GUIDE. ceased. a. Meeting Planners International, 1950 Stemmons Freeway, Dallas, TX 75207.

333.33   US
M S H D A HOUSING TRENDS AND ACTIVITY. ceased 1988. q. Michigan State Housing Development Authority, Plaza One, 4th Fl., 401 S. Washington Sq., Box 30044, Lansing, MI 48909.

384.5   US
M S O; the magazine for cable system operations. 1986-1991. m. (back issues avail.) Communications Technology Publications Corp. (Subsidiary of: Transmedia Partners), 50 S. Steele St., Ste. 700, Denver, CO 80209-2812.
    Formerly (until 1989): Cable Strategies.

350   US
M T A S MUNICIPAL REPORT. 1973-1991. q. (also avail. in microform) University of Tennessee, Municipal Technical Advisory Service, 600 Henley, Ste. 120, Knoxville, TN 37996-4105.
    Former titles: M T A S Municipal Technical Report; University of Tennessee. Institute for Public Service. M T A S Municipal Technical Report.

658.5   US   ISSN 0024-8509
M T M JOURNAL OF METHODS-TIME MEASUREMENT. 1955-1988 (vol.14). a. (also avail. in microform from UMI) Methods-Time Measurement Association for Standards and Research, 16-01 Broadway, Fair Lawn, NJ 07410.

610   IT
M T MEDICAL TOP. 1986-19?? m. Masson Italia Periodici, Via Statuto 2-4, 20121 Milan, Italy.

620   GW   ISSN 0935-8080
M T U HEUTE. 1972-19?? q. (Motoren - und Turbinen - Union Heute) M T U Gruppe Muenchen GmbH, Dachauer Str. 665, 8000 Munich 50, Germany.

330   DK
MAANEDS BOERSEN. 1978-19?? m. Boersen Magazine, Moentergade 19, P.O. Box 2103, DK-1140 Copenhagen, Denmark.

694   IT
MACCHINE DEL LEGNO. 1970-19?? m. Ribera Editore & C. s.a.s., Via Don Sturzo 35-C, 20020 Lainate MI, Italy.

551.46   CN
MCGILL UNIVERSITY, MONTREAL. MARINE SCIENCES CENTRE. MANUSCRIPT REPORT. 1966-1987. irreg. McGill University, Marine Science Centre, Box 6070, Sta. A, Montreal, Que. H3C 3G1, Canada.

621.9   US   ISSN 0024-9106
                          CODEN: MTBBA3
MACHINE AND TOOL BLUE BOOK; the magazine of manufacturing technology and management. 1906-1990. m. (also avail. in microform from UMI; reprint service avail. from UMI) Hitchcock Publishing Co., 191 S. Gary Ave., Carol Stream, IL 60188.

621   II   ISSN 0541-6434
TJ1180.A1
MACHINE TOOL ENGINEER. 1958-19??; suspended. q. (also avail. in microfilm) H M T Limited, R & D Centre (Metal Cutting), Yeshwanthapur Post, Bangalore 560 022, India.

621.8   SA
MACHINE TOOLS & PRODUCTION ENGINEERING. 1976-1987 (Feb.). m. (Numerical Control Society) National Publishing (Pty) Ltd., P.O. Box 2735, Johannesburg 2000, South Africa.

620 600   US
MACHINE VISION PRODUCT BUYER'S GUIDE. 1987-1990. biennial. Automated Vision Association, 900 Victor's Way, Box 3724, Ann Arbor, MI 48106.

621.9   JA
MACHINERY JAPAN. ceased. s-a. Japan Machinery Exporters' Association - Nihon Kikai Yushutsu Sogo, 5-8, 3-chome, Shiba Koen, Minato-ku, Tokyo 105, Japan.

620 621.9 380.5   KO
MACHINERY KOREA. 1979-1988 (Dec.). m. (back issues avail.) Korea Institute of Machinery and Metals (KIMM), P.O. Box 27, Gurodanji, Seoul, S. Korea.

631.3   FR   ISSN 0024-9246
MACHINISME AGRICOLE TROPICAL. 1963-1989 (no. 108). q. Centre d'Etudes et d'Experimentation du Machinisme Agricole Tropical, Parc de Tourvoie, 92160 Antony (Hauts de Seine), France.

950   LE   ISSN 0002-4023
AP95.A6
AL-MACHRIQ. 1898-1971. bi-m. (reprint service avail. from KTO) (Saint Joseph University, Beirut) Imprimerie Catholique, B.P. 946, Beirut, Lebanon.

001.681 621.381   US
QA76.8.M3
MACINTOSH HANDS ON; the magazine for Macintosh enthusiasts. 1984-1990 (Jan.). m. (back issues avail.) Mindcraft Publishing Corporation, 52 Domino Dr., Concord, MA 01742.
    Formerly (until 1988): Nibble Mac (ISSN 0884-3929)

621.381   US
MACINTOSH NEWS. 1988-1990 (Aug.). bi-w. (tabloid format) C M P Publications, Inc., 600 Community Dr., Manhasset, NY 11030.

027.7   CN   ISSN 0024-9270
MCMASTER UNIVERSITY LIBRARY RESEARCH NEWS. 1969-1989. s-a. (back issues avail.) McMaster University Library Press, Mills Memorial Library, Hamilton, Ont. L8S 4L6, Canada.

929   US
MCNEILL MEMORANDA. 1983-198? irreg. (back issues avail.) McNeill Enterprises, c/o Rubu Simonson McNeill, Ed., N. 4015 Marguerite Rd., Spokane, WA 99212-1818.

547 541.39   US   ISSN 0076-2091
QD262   CODEN: MASYAO
MACROMOLECULAR SYNTHESES. 1963-1985 (vol.9). irreg. John Wiley & Sons, Inc., 605 Third Ave., New York, NY 10158-0012.

621.381   US
MCWILLIAMS LETTER. 1983-198? 10/yr. Prelude Press, 8165 Mannix Dr., Los Angeles, CA 90046.

747 382   GW   ISSN 0171-6042
MADE IN EUROPE. FURNITURE AND INTERIORS; a decorator's import guide. 1978-19?? bi-m. Made in Europe Marketing Organization GmbH & Co. KG, Unterlindau 21-29, 6000 Frankfurt 1, Germany.

282   IT   ISSN 0024-9580
MADONNA DI BARBANA; peridico mensile del santuario. 1910-19?? m. Santuario Madonna di Barbana, Isola di Barbana, 34073 Grado (Go), Italy.

811   US   ISSN 0047-5432
MADRONA; a quarterly of poetry. 1971-19?? irreg. (also avail. in microform from UMI) Gemini Foundation, c/o Charles Webb, 3232 Palmer Dr., Los Angeles, CA 90065-4925.

943   GW
MAERKISCHEN MUSEUM. JAHRBUCH. 1975-1984. a. Maerkisches Museum, Kultur Historisches Museum der Stadt Berlin, Am Koellinischen Park 5, 1020 Berlin, Germany.

378.1 500   II   ISSN 0024-9726
MAGADH UNIVERSITY JOURNAL. 1964-1988. s-a. Magadh University, Registrar, Bodh Gaya, Camp Gaya, Bihar, India.

640.73   GW   ISSN 0174-5735
MAGAZIN FUER HEIMWERKER. 1968-19?? 10/yr. (back issues avail.) Verlagsgesellschaft Siegfried Rohn GmbH, Stolbergerstr. 84, 5000 Cologne 41, Germany.
    Formerly: Heimwerkstatt Vereinigt mit Magazin fuer Heim und Ausbau.

640   CN
MAGAZINE VIVRE. 1969-19?? bi-m. Publicor Inc., 7, Chemin Bates, Outremont, Que. H2V 1A6, Canada.

910.4   CN   ISSN 0838-6838
LE MAGAZINE VOYAGES PLUS. 1986. q. (back issues avail.) Publications Transcontinental Inc., 465 Saint-Jean, 9e Etage, Montreal, Que. H2Y 3S4, Canada.

800 900   US
MAGILL'S LITERARY ANNUAL: HISTORY AND BIOGRAPHY. ceased. a. Salem Press, Box 1097, Englewood Cliffs, NJ 07632.
    Formerly: Magill's History Annual.

574.88   US
MAGNETIC RESONANCE IN BIOLOGY. suspended 1983. irreg. John Wiley & Sons, Inc., 605 Third Ave., New York, NY 10158-0012.

536.7   US   ISSN 0891-9801
TK2970   CODEN: MPGEED
MAGNETOHYDRODYNAMICS. 1988-1990. q. (also avail. in microform from UMI; back issues avail.; reprint service avail. from UMI) Hemisphere Publishing Corporation (Subsidiary of: Taylor & Francis Group), 1900 Frost Rd., Ste. 101, Bristol, PA 19007-1598.

025   HU   ISSN 0133-1949
MAGYAR KONYVTAROSOK EGYESULETENEK EVKONYVE. 1973-1984. a. (Magyar Konyvtarosok Egyesulete) Nepmuvelesi Propaganda Iroda, Kartacs u. 24-26, H-1139 Budapest, Hungary.

335   HU   ISSN 0076-2415
HD8419.H9
MAGYAR MUNKASMOZGALMI MUZEUM. EVKONYV. 1967-198? biennial. Muzsak Kozmuvelodesi Kiado, 1139 Kartacs ul. 24-26, Budapest, Hungary.

658   US
MAIL ORDER SUCCESS NEWSLETTER; mail marketing ideas that work. 1985-1989 (Nov.). 8/yr. (back issues avail.) Teague Publishing Group, c/o Bob E. Teague, Ed., Box 191, Dayton, OH 45404.

657.46 336.2   US
MAIN HURDMAN & CRANSTOUN NEWS SUMMARY. ceased. irreg. Main Hurdman & Cranstoun (Certified Public Accountants), 767 Fifth Ave., 46th Fl., New York, NY 10153.

336.2   US
MAIN HURDMAN & CRANSTOUN TAX NEWSLETTER. ceased. irreg. Main Hurdman & Cranstoun (Certified Public Accountants), 767 Fifth Ave., 46th Fl., New York, NY 10153.

332.9   US
MAIN STREET JOURNAL. 1985-198? m. Claremont Economics Institute, 250 W. First St., Ste. 220, Claremont, CA 91711.

974.1   US
MAINE HISTORICAL SOCIETY. RESEARCH SERIES. 1977-19?? irreg. Maine Historical Society, 485 Congress St., Portland, ME 04101.

051   US   ISSN 0025-0678
F16
MAINE LIFE MAGAZINE. 1946-198? bi-m. Atlantic Publishing Group, Inc., One Auburn Center, The Goff Wing, Auburn, ME 04210.

974.1   US
MAINE TODAY MAGAZINE. ceased. m. Maine Chamber of Commerce and Industry, 126 Sewall St., Augusta, ME 04330.

651   US
MAINSTREAM (RUTHERFORD). ceased. 7/yr. (Eastern Regional Office Machine Dealers Association) C N C Enterprises, 112 Park Ave., Rutherford, NJ 07070.

620   CN ISSN 0827-5637
MAINTAINER. 1984-1990 (Oct.). m. (tabloid format) Maitainer Publishing Co., Ltd., 217-B E. 16th Ave., Vancouver, B.C. V5T 2T5, Canada.

796.352   US
MAINTENANCE TRENDS REPORT. ceased. a. Golf Course Superintendents Association of America, 1421 Research Park Dr., Lawrence, KS 66049.

028.5   US
MAJED. 1978-1991. m. Medialink International, 191 Atlantic Ave., Brooklyn, New York, NY 11201.

382   UK ISSN 0268-2338
HG4057
MAJOR COMPANIES OF THE UNITED STATES OF AMERICA (YEAR). 1986-1989. a. Graham & Trotman Ltd., Sterling House, 66 Wilton Rd., London SW1V 1DE, England.

531.64   AT ISSN 0727-260X
MAJOR ENERGY STATISTICS. 1981-1988. m. Department of Primary Industries and Energy, G.P.O. Box 858, Canberra, A.C.T. 2601, Australia.

330.9   US
MAJOR INDUSTRIAL NATIONS EXECUTIVE REPORT. ceased 1989. q. D R I - McGraw-Hill, 24 Hartwell Ave., Lexington, MA 02173.

332.1   AT
MAJOR TRADING BANK STATISTICS. 1960-1989. m. Australian Bureau of Statistics, P.O. Box 10, Belconnen, A.C.T. 2616, Australia.

641 684.1   FI ISSN 0356-8202
MAKASIINI. 1978-19?? m. A-Lehdet Oy, Hitsaajankatu 10, SF-00810 Helsinki, Finland.

020   SU ISSN 0256-4971
MAKTABAT AL-IDARAH. 1970-1988 (vol.15). 3/yr. (also avail. in microfilm) Institute of Public Administration, Library and Documents Center, P.O. Box 205, Riyadh 11141, Saudi Arabia.

616.15   UK ISSN 0952-0341
MALARIA. ceased 1990. m. (looseleaf format; back issues avail.) Sheffield University Biomedical Information Service (SUBIS), The University, Sheffield S10 2TN, England.

959.5   MY ISSN 0047-5610
MALAYSIA IN HISTORY. ceased. q. Malaysian Historical Society, c/o Muzium Negara, Jalan Petalawati, Kuala Lumpur, Malaysia.

657   SI ISSN 0217-717X
MALAYSIAN ACCOUNTANT. 1986-1989. q. (Malaysian Association of Certified Public Accountants) Longman Singapore Publishers (Pte) Ltd., Professional Books Division, 25 First Lok Yang Road, Jurong Town, Singapore 2262, Singapore.

636.089   MY ISSN 0126-5652
           CODEN: MVEJDP
MALAYSIAN VETERINARY JOURNAL. 1955-1989. a. Malaysian Veterinary Association, University of Malaya, Lembah Pantai, Kuala Lumpur 22-11, Malaysia.

791   US
MALCOLM HULKE STUDIES IN CINEMA & TELEVISION. 1992; announced, never published. irreg. Borgo Press, Box 2845, San Bernardino, CA 92406.

630 338.1   MM
MALTA. CENTRAL OFFICE OF STATISTICS. CENSUS OF AGRICULTURE AND FISHERIES. ceased. a. Central Office of Statistics, Auberge d'Italie, Valletta, Malta.
 Formerly: Malta. Office of Statistics. Census of Agriculture (ISSN 0076-3454)

301   RH
MAMBO OCCASIONAL PAPERS. SOCIO-ECONOMIC SERIES. 1974-1987 (vol.22). irreg. Mambo Press, Box 779, Gweru, Zimbabwe.

612   UK ISSN 0266-6375
MAMMARY GLAND. ceased 1990. m. (looseleaf format; back issues avail.) Sheffield University Biomedical Information Service (SUBIS), The University, Sheffield S10 2TN, England.

100   US
MAN, ENVIRONMENT, SPACE AND TIME. 1981-199?; suspended. s-a. World Research Center, Inc., c/o Prof. Walter Isard, B-4 West Sibley Hall, Cornell University, Ithaca, NY 14853.

338.4   JA
MAN-MADE FIBERS OF JAPAN. ceased. a. Japan Chemical Fibres Association, No. 3 Nihonbashi-Honcho 3-chome, Chuo-ku, Tokyo 103, Japan.

658   US ISSN 0278-999X
HD28
MANAGEMENT (LOS ANGELES). 1981-198? q. University of California, Los Angeles, John E. Anderson Graduate School of Management, GSM Rm. 4250M, 405 Hilgard Ave., Los Angeles, CA 90024.

657 658   US
MANAGEMENT ADVISOR. ceased. q. Warren, Gorham and Lamont Inc., One Penn Plaza, New York, NY 10119.

658.8   AT
MANAGEMENT AND MARKETING UPDATE. 1962-19??; suspended. m. Rydge Publications (Australia) Pty. Ltd. (Subsidiary of: B R W Publications), 35 Mountain St., Ultimo, N.S.W. 2007, Australia.
 Formed by the merger of: Rydge's Sales and Marketing Service; Rydge's Management To-day; Which was formerly: Rydge's Management Service.

658   US
MANAGEMENT DEVELOPMENT GUIDE. 1970-19?? s-a. (back issues avail.) American Management Association (New York), 135 W. 50th St., New York, NY 10020.

629.8   US ISSN 0076-3624
MANAGEMENT GUIDE TO N C (Numerical Control) 1964-1971 (no.2). irreg. AIM Tech, 5411 E State St., Rockford, IL 61108-2376.

330   US
MANAGEMENT NETWORK PERSPECTIVE; the single source for information on multivendor network management technology. 1988-1991 (Jan.). m. Communications Solutions, Inc., 3165 Kifer Rd., Santa Clara, CA 95051-0804.

658   GW ISSN 0340-4137
MANAGEMENT WISSEN. 1982-1991. m. Management Presse Verlag, Baierbrunner Str. 33, 8000 Munich 70, Germany.

658   GW
MANAGEMENT WISSEN JAHRBUCH. 1974-19?? a. Management Presse Verlag, Baierbrunner Str. 33, 8000 Munich 70, Germany.

658   US ISSN 0090-3825
HD28
MANAGEMENT WORLD; dedicated to innovative management of people and careers in the office. 1960-1990 (vol.19, no.2). 6/yr. (also avail. in microform from UMI; reprint service avail.) Administrative Management Society, 1101 14th St., N.W., Ste. 1100, Washington, DC 20005.
 Supersedes (in 1972): A M S Management Bulletin (ISSN 0001-1967)

658 614.85   US
MANAGING FOR HEALTH. ceased. q. Medical Economics Company Inc., 680 Kinderkamack Rd., Oradell, NJ 07649.

330   US
MANAGING M I S PERSONNEL; ideas and advice for people who manage people. (Management Information Systems) 1986-19?? m. Auerbach Publishers Inc. (Subsidiary of: Warren, Gorham & Lamont, Inc.), One Penn Plaza, New York, NY 10119.

300   US ISSN 0025-1976
           CODEN: MJSPDT
MANAS. 1948-1988 (vol.41). w. (also avail. in microfilm from UMI; reprint service avail. from UMI) Manas Publishing Co., Box 32112, El Sereno Sta., Los Angeles, CA 90032.

810   US
MANASSAS REVIEW. 1977-1984 (vol.4). irreg. Northern Virginia Community College, Manassas Campus, Manassas, VA 22110.

610   UK
MANCHESTER MEDICINE. ceased 1991. 6/yr. Hermiston Publications Ltd., 2 Hill Sq., Edinburgh EH8 9DR, Scotland.

382   US ISSN 0095-0688
HF5068.M3
MANHATTAN DIRECTORY OF COMMERCIAL & INDUSTRIAL PROPERTIES. 1937-19?? a. Standard Abstract Corp., c/o Benjamin Scheckner, 70 E. 10th St., No. 12F, New York, NY 10003.

346.066 342   US ISSN 0893-8911
K13
MANHATTAN LAWYER. 1987-1991. 10/yr. (tabloid format) American Lawyer Media, L.P. (New York), 600 Third Ave., 3rd Fl., New York, NY 10016.

614   CN ISSN 0383-3925
MANITOBA. HEALTH SERVICES COMMISSION. ANNUAL REPORT. 1971-1992. a. Manitoba Health Services Commission, Box 925, 599 Empress St., Winnipeg, Man. R3C 2T6, Canada.

614 310   CN
MANITOBA. HEALTH SERVICES COMMISSION. ANNUAL STATISTICS. 1971-1992. a. Manitoba Health Services Commission, Box 925, 599 Empress St., Winnipeg, Man. R3C 2T6, Canada.
 Formerly: Manitoba. Health Services Commission. Statistical Supplement to the Annual Report (ISSN 0383-3933)

642.5   CN
MANITOBA RESTAURANT & FOODSERVICES ROSTER. ceased. a. (Manitoba Restaurant & Foodservice Association) Naylor Communications Ltd. (Winnipeg), 100 Sutherland Ave., Winnipeg, Man. R2W 3C7, Canada.

380.1   CN ISSN 0076-390X
HC117.M3
MANITOBA TRADE DIRECTORY. 1956-1991. a. Sanford Evans Communications Ltd., 1077 St. James St., Box 6900, Winnipeg, Man. R3C 3B1, Canada.

746.92   GW ISSN 0344-5631
DER MANN MAGAZIN. ceased 1991. bi-m. Verlag Bode GmbH & Co. KG, Turnstr. 1-3, 7530 Pforzheim, Germany.

658   GW
MANNESMANN KIENZLE KURIER; aktuelle Nachrichten fuer Geschaeftsfreunde und Partner. 1979-1990. s-a. Mannesmann Kienzle GmbH, Postfach 1640, 7730 Villingen-Schwenningen, Germany.
 Former titles: Kurier; Kienzle Kurier.

157.734   US
MANSCAPE 2. 1985-1989 (Aug.). bi-m. (back issues avail.) First Hand Ltd., 310 Cedar Lane, Box 1314, Teaneck, NJ 07666.

685.11   CN
MANSTYLE. 1909-1990; suspended. 2/yr. (also avail. in microform from UMI) Laurentian Media Inc., 501 Oakdale Rd., Downsview, Ont. M3N 1W7, Canada.
 Formerly: Men's Wear of Canada (ISSN 0025-9535)

388.3   US
MANUFACTURED HOUSING REPORTER. 1957-19?? m. (tabloid format) Romac Corporation, 316 Stone Ridge, Kerrville, TX 78028.
 Former titles: Mobile Home Reporter and Travel Home News; Mobile Home Reporter and Recreation Vehicle News (ISSN 0026-7163)

621.8 016   UK
MANUFACTURING AND MATERIALS HANDLING INDEX. 1973-198? 2/yr. Technical Indexes Ltd., Willoughby Rd., Bracknell, Berks RG12 4DW, England.
 Formerly: Materials Handling Index (ISSN 0308-8359)

338 658   SA
MANUFACTURING & MATERIALS MANAGEMENT. ceased. m. Keeble Publishing Co. Pty. Ltd., P.O. Box 3080, Johannesburg 2000, South Africa.

338   US
MANUFACTURING APPLICATIONS: THE D P MANAGER'S REPORT. 1987-1988. m. Auerbach Publishers Inc. (Subsidiary of: Warren, Gorham & Lamont, Inc.), One Penn Plaza, New York, NY 10119.

CESSATIONS

332 US ISSN 0896-2529
CODEN: MIOUEI
MANUFACTURING INVESTMENT OUTLOOK. 1953-1989. q. Conference Board, Inc., 845 Third Ave., New York, NY 10022.
 Former titles: Investment Statistics: Capital Investment Conditions (ISSN 0092-4210); Incorporates (in Jul. 1978): Manufacturing Investment Statistics: Capital Investment and Supply Conditions (ISSN 0362-9708); National Industrial Conference Board. Investment Statistics. Capital Appropriations (ISSN 0547-7271); Conference Board. Manufacturing Investment Statistics. Capital Appropriations (ISSN 0361-4239); Manufacturing Investment Statistics: Capital Appropriations and Capital Investment and Supply Conditions (ISSN 0195-8313).

330 AT ISSN 1031-296X
MANUFACTURING REPORT. 1988-19?? 9/yr. (back issues avail.) Australian Chamber of Manufactures, Victorian Division, 370 St. Kilda Rd., Melbourne, Vic. 3004, Australia.

600 338 US ISSN 0278-4424
MANUFACTURING TECHNOLOGY HORIZONS. 1982-1988 (vol.7, no.3). bi-m. Manufacturing Technology Press, Inc., Box 220, Lake Geneva, WI 53147.

628 IT
MANUTENZIONE. 1979-1988. bi-m. MO.ED.CO. s.r.l., Via Paolo da Cannobio 9, 20122 Milan, Italy.

327 RM
MAPAMOND. 1945-19?? m. (National Center for Promoting the Friendship and Co-operation with other Nations) Foreign Languages Press Group, Piata Presei libere Nr. 1, P.O. Box 33, Bucharest 71341, Rumania.
 Formerly: Veac Nou.

745.592 FR
MAQUETTES PLASTIQUE MAGAZINE. 1968-19?? m. Perlor Radio, 25 rue Herold, 75001 Paris, France.
 Formerly: Maquettes-Plastiques (ISSN 0047-5858)

608 FR ISSN 0153-9019
MARCHE DE L'INNOVATION. 1971-19?? m. (back issues avail.) Agence Nationale de Valorisation de la Recherche, 43 rue Caumartin, 75436 Paris Cedex 09, France.

300 CE
MARGA INSTITUTE. PROGRESS REPORT. 1973-1987 (no.5). irreg. Marga Institute, Sri Lanka Centre for Development Studies, Box 601, 61 Isipathana Mawatha, Colombo 5, Sri Lanka.

282 CN ISSN 0381-7946
MARIA. ceased. m. P.O. Box 195, Sta. C, Toronto, Ont. M6J 3M9, Canada.

574.92 US
MARINE ECOLOGY; a comprehensive, integrated treatise on life in oceans and coastal waters. 1970-198? (vol.5, part 4). irreg. John Wiley & Sons, Inc., 605 Third Ave., New York, NY 10158-0012.

387 US
MARINE ENGINEERING LOG MARINE DIRECTORY. 1878-1986. a. (also avail. in microform from UMI; reprint service avail.) Simmons-Boardman Publishing Corp., 345 Hudson St., New York, NY 10014.

551.46 US
MARINE RESOURCE ECONOMICS. 1983-1990. q. Taylor & Francis, 1900 Frost Rd., Ste. 101, Bristol, PA 19007.
 Formerly: Journal of Marine Resource Economics (ISSN 0738-1360)

359 GW ISSN 0720-8103
MARINE-RUNDSCHAU INTERNATIONAL. 1890-1989. bi-m. (back issues avail.) Moench Verlagsgesellschaft mbH, Heilsbachstr. 26, 5300 Bonn 1, Germany.

387 CN
MARITIME HISTORY GROUP NEWSLETTER. 1976-1987; suspended. a. Memorial University of Newfoundland, Maritime History Group, St. John's, Nfld. A1C 5S7, Canada.
 Supersedes (in 1984): Canadian Shipping Project Newsletter (ISSN 0708-0727)

069 387 UK ISSN 0307-8590
MARITIME MONOGRAPHS AND REPORTS. 1970-19?? irreg. National Maritime Museum, Romney Rd., Greenwich SE10 9NF, England.

942 UK
MARITIME STORY OF SOUTHERN ENGLAND. ceased. irreg. James Dunning Publications, 20 Riverside Gardens, Romsey, Hants. SO51 8HN, England.

332.6 US ISSN 0360-1773
HG4501
MARKET CHRONICLE. 1967-1991; suspended. w. (also avail. in microform from UMI) William B. Dana Company, Box 958, New York, NY 10277.
 Formerly: O.T.C. Market Chronicle (ISSN 0029-7305)

677 HK
MARKET REPORT FOR CHINA'S TEXTILE AND APPAREL INDUSTRY. 1985-19??; suspended. q. Adsale Publishing Company, 21st Fl., Tung Wai Commercial Bldg., 109-111 Gloucester Rd., Wanchai, Hong Kong.

658.83 CN ISSN 0025-360X
MARKET RESEARCH FACTS AND TRENDS. 1958-19?? m. Maclean-Hunter Ltd., Business Publication Division, Maclean-Hunter Bldg., 777 Bay St., Toronto, Ont. M5W 1A7, Canada.

741.67 US
MARKET RESEARCH REPORT. 1982-1988. irreg. Graphic Arts Technical Foundation, 4615 Forbes Ave., Pittsburgh, PA 15213-3796.

658.8 796 US
MARKET WATCH. 1982-1990. q. (looseleaf format) National Sporting Goods Association, 1699 Wall St., Mt. Prospect, IL 60056-5780.

658.8 US
THE MARKETER. 1990; ceased same year. m. Act III Publishing, 410 Park Ave., S., New York, NY 10016.

659.1 301.10 658 US
MARKETING - ADVERTISING - RESEARCH NEWSLETTER; a newsletter on marketing, sales, advertising, public relations, and market research. 1965-19?? bi-m. (tabloid format; back issues avail.) Business-Professional Advertising Association, Metroplex Corporate Center, 100 Metroplex Dr., Edison, NJ 08817.

381.41 CN ISSN 0527-6624
HD9014.C2
MARKETING BOARDS IN CANADA/OFFICES DE COMMERCIALISATION AU CANADA. 1973-19?? a. Agriculture Canada, Economics Branch, Sir John Carling Building, Carling Ave., Ottawa K1A 0C5, Canada.

381.41 US ISSN 0094-2510
HD9247.C2
MARKETING CALIFORNIA DRIED FRUITS: PRUNES, RAISINS, DRIED APRICOTS & PEACHES. ceased 1991. a. (back issues avail.) (U.S. Department of Food & Agriculture) Federal-State Market News Service (Sacramento), Box 942871, Sacramento, CA 94271-0001.

659.1 301.10 330 US
MARKETING COMMUNICATIONS REPORT. 1975-19?? bi-m. (tabloid format; back issues avail.) Business-Professional Advertising Association, Metroplex Corporate Ctr., 100 Metroplex Dr., No. 401, Edison, NJ 08817-2684.

381 615 US ISSN 0093-125X
HD9666.5
MARKETING GUIDE. 1973-198? a. Medical Economics Company Inc., 680 Kinderkamack Rd., Oradell, NJ 07649.

659.1 US
MARKETING - HIGH TECH TRENDS. ceased 1985. irreg. Business - Professional Advertising Association, 100 Metroplex Dr., Edison, NJ 08817.

665.5 US
MARKETING TRENDS (DES PLAINES). vol.11, 1974-19?? bi-m. Midwest Petroleum Marketers Association, 17th and Dixie Hwy., East Hazel Crest, IL 60429.

312 US
MARKETRENDS. 1984-19??; suspended. bi-m. Greater Washington Research Center, 1717 Massachusetts Ave., N.W., Ste. 403, Washington, DC 20036.

622.33 US
MARKETS FOR COAL AND COAL TECHNOLOGIES. 1988-1990. w. Utility Data Institute, Inc. (Subsidiary of: Halliburton Co.), 1700 K St. N.W., no.400, Washington, DC 20006.

810 US ISSN 0025-3820
PS2363
MARKHAM REVIEW. 1968-1987. 2/yr. (also avail. in microform from UMI; reprint service avail. from UMI) Wagner College, Horrmann Library, Staten Island, NY 10301.

659.1 658.8 GW
MARKT KOMMUNIKATION. 1970-1991. m. Verlag fuer Technik und Wirtschaft GmbH & Co., Lise-Meitner-Str. 2, Postfach 4029, 6500 Mainz, Germany.

630 338.1 MR
MAROC AGRICOLE; revue mensuelle technique et economique au service des agriculteurs. 1968-19?? m. Loghlam Presse, 27 rue d'Epinal, Casablanca, Morocco.

620 US ISSN 0025-3960
MARQUETTE ENGINEER. 1925-19?? q. Marquette University, School of Engineering, 1515 W. Wisconsin Ave., Milwaukee, WI 53233.

301.42 US ISSN 0276-4512
MARRIAGE & FAMILY. 1959-1991 (Aug.). m. (reprint service avail. from UMI) (St. Meinrad Archabbey) Abbey Press, Hill Dr., St. Meinrad, IN 47577.
 Former titles: Marriage and Family Living; (until 1974): Marriage (ISSN 0025-4010)

658 910.202 US
MARRIOTT PORTFOLIO. 1986-19?? bi-m. Hotel Magazine Network, Inc., 1729 H St., N.W., Washington, DC 20006.

705 US ISSN 0076-4701
N380
MARSYAS. 1941-1985 (vol. 22). biennial. (also avail. in microform from UMI; reprint service avail. from KTO) New York University, Institute of Fine Arts, 14 E. 78th St., New York, NY 10021.

658.8 338.47 US ISSN 0025-4061
HD9999.H83
MART; magazine of consumer electronics and appliance. (Also includes bimonthly supplements of Telecommunications Retailer) 1922-198? m. (tabloid format; also avail. in microform from UMI) Gordon Publications, Inc., 301 Gibraltar Dr., Morris Plains, NJ 07950.

320.532 UK ISSN 0025-4118
AP4
MARXISM TODAY; theoretical and discussion journal of the Communist Party of Great Britain. 1957-1991. m. Marxism Today Ltd., 6 Cynthia St., London N1 9JF, England.

943.7 331 CS ISSN 0323-164X
MARXISMUS A SOUCASNOST. 1971-1989 (Dec.). 4/yr. Rude Pravo Vydavatelstvi UV KSC, Na Porici 30, 112 86 Prague 1, Czechoslovakia.

340 US
MARYLAND. ATTORNEY GENERAL. ATTORNEY GENERAL'S DIGEST. 1979-1991 (vol.12, no.4). q. (looseleaf format; back issues avail.) Attorney General, State Law Department, 200 St. Paul Place, Baltimore, MD 21202.

344 US ISSN 0092-9476
KFM1549.A73
MARYLAND. DEPARTMENT OF HUMAN RESOURCES. INFORMATION PAMPHLET. ceased. irreg. Department of Human Resources, Social Services Administration, 1100 N. Eutaw St., Baltimore, MD 21201.

350 US
MARYLAND. DEPARTMENT OF LEGISLATIVE REFERENCE. UPDATE. 1982-19?? irreg. Department of Legislative Reference, 90 State Circle, Annapolis, MD 21401.

975 069 US
MARYLAND. STATE ARCHIVES. NEWSLETTER. 1984-1985 (vol.3). irreg. State Archives, 350 Rowe Blvd., Annapolis, MD 21401.

929 US ISSN 0025-4150
CS42
MARYLAND AND DELAWARE GENEALOGIST. 1959-1990. q. (back issues avail.) Raymond B. Clark, Jr., Ed. & Pub., Box 352, St. Michaels, MD 21663.

657 US ISSN 0025-4185
MARYLAND C.P.A. QUARTERLY. ceased. q. Maryland Association of Certified Public Accountants, Keyser Bldg., Baltimore, MD 21202.

340 US
MARYLAND LAW FORUM. 1971-19?? 3/yr. (also avail. in microfilm from RRI; reprint service avail. from RRI) University of Maryland School of Law, Student Bar Association, 500 West Baltimore St., Baltimore, MD 21201.

621.9 GW ISSN 0025-4495
TJ3 CODEN: MTECAL
MASCHINENBAUTECHNIK; Wissenschaftlich-technische Zeitschrift fuer Forschung, Entwicklung und Konstruktion. 1952-1991. m. (Kammer der Technik, Fachverband Maschinenbau) Verlag Technik GmbH, Oranienburger Str. 13-14, 1020 Berlin, Germany.

977 929 US ISSN 0735-4754
MASON MEMORIES. 1973-19??; suspended. q. Mason County Historical Society, 1687 S. Lakeshore Dr., Ludington, MI 49431-9355.

820 UK ISSN 0025-4711
MASQUE. 1918-198? a. University of Strathclyde, Students' Association, 90 John St., Glasgow G1 1JH, Scotland.
Formerly: Mask.

535.84 SZ
MASS SPECTROMETRY; European journal of mass spectrometry in biochemistry. 1980-1987. q. Medecine et Hygiene, P.O. Box 456, CH-1211 Geneva 4, Switzerland.

051 910.09 US
MASTER CARD. 1989-19?? q. North-South Net, Inc., 100 Almeria Ave., Ste.200, Coral Gables, FL 33134.

870 UR
MASTER PERFORMERS. 1977-1991. 2/yr. Izdatel'stvo Muzyka, Ul. Neglinnaya 14, Moscow 103031, Russian S.F.S.R., U.S.S.R.

725 US
MASTERGUIDE. 1985-1988. a. (American Institute of Architects) North American Publishing Co., 401 N. Broad St., Philadelphia, PA 19108.

572 390 970 US ISSN 0887-6665
E51
MASTERKEY, for Indian lore and history. 1927-1989. q. (back issues avail.) Southwest Museum, Box 128, Highland Park Sta., Los Angeles, CA 90042.

610.73 378 US
MASTER'S EDUCATION: ROUTE TO OPPORTUNITIES IN CONTEMPORARY NURSING. 1966-198? a. National League for Nursing, 350 Hudson St., New York, NY 10014.
Formerly: Master's Education: Route to Opportunities in Modern Nursing (ISSN 0076-5104)

890 UR
MASTERSKAYA; uroki literaturnogo masterstva. 1975-19?? irreg. Izdatel'stvo Molodaya Gvardiya, Ul. Sushevskaya, 21, 101503, GSP-4 Moscow, Russian S.F.S.R., U.S.S.R.

320 GW ISSN 0340-0476
MATERIALIEN ZUR POLITISCHEN BILDUNG; Analysen - Berichte - Dokumente. 1973-19?? q. (Arbeitskreis Deutscher Bildungsstaetten e.V.) Leske Verlag und Budrich GmbH, Postfach 300 406, 5090 Leverkusen 3, Germany.

531.64 333.7 CN ISSN 1180-4246
MATERIALS & ENERGY ADVANTAGE. 1990-1991. 20/yr. Evert Communications Ltd., 982 Wellington St., Ottawa, Ont. K1Y 2X8, Canada.

600 500 US ISSN 0146-6399
TA401 CODEN: MSOCDX
MATERIALS AND SOCIETY. 1977-1991. q. (also avail. in microform from MIM,UMI) (Acta Metallurgica, Inc.) Pergamon Press, Inc., Journals Division, 660 White Plains Rd., Tarrytown, NY 10591-5153.

620.1 US ISSN 0079-8126
TA404.2
MATERIALS RESEARCH IN SCIENCE AND ENGINEERING AT PURDUE UNIVERSITY. PROGRESS REPORT. 1962-1988. a. Purdue University, Materials Research Business Office, Physics Bldg., West Lafayette, IN 47907.
Supersedes: Materials Research in Science and Engineering at Purdue University. Annual Report.

618 618.92 BL ISSN 0025-5491
MATERNIDADE E INFANCIA; arquivos medico-sociais. 1943-1977. q. (cards) Legiao Brasileira de Assistencia, Rua Guaianazes 1385, Sao Paulo, Brazil.

510 BU ISSN 0205-3217
MATHEMATICA BALKANICA. 1936-1966; N.S. 1987-1991 (vol.4, no.1). q. (back issues avail.) Bulgarian Academy of Sciences, National Committee of Mathematics, Akad. G. Bonchev Str. 9, Sofia 1113, Bulgaria.
Formerly: Revue Mathematiques de l'Union Interbalkaniques.

510 CN ISSN 0076-5333
MATHEMATICAL EXPOSITIONS. 1946-19?? irreg. (University of Toronto Press) University of Toronto Press, 63A St. George St., Toronto, Ont. M5S 1A6, Canada.

370 621.381 US
MATHEMATICS AND MICROCOMPUTER MATERIALS CATALOG 7-12, ADULT. 1980-1986. a. Educat Publishers, Inc., Box 4006, New Canaan, CT 06840.

574 US
MATHEMATICS IN BIOLOGY. 1981-1984 (vol.2). irreg. (reprint service avail. from ISI) Academic Press, Inc., 1250 Sixth Ave., San Diego, CA 92101.

510 AT ISSN 0810-6142
MATHEMATICS STUDENTS' GAZETTE. 1966-1990. 4/yr. Mathematical Association of Western Australia, P.O. Box 492, Subiaco, W.A. 6008, Australia.

510 GW ISSN 0465-3769
MATHEMATISCH-NATURWISSENSCHAFTLICHE BIBLIOTHEK. 1956-1991. a. B.G. Teubner Verlagsgesellschaft mbH, Sternwartenstr. 8, 7010 Leipzig, Germany.

510 AT ISSN 0810-6150
MATHMAG. 1981-1990. 4/yr. Mathematical Association of Western Australia, P.O. Box 492, Subiaco, W.A. 6008, Australia.

808.81 CN
MATTAWA CHRONICLE. 1988, ceased same year. s-a. Box 1208, Mattawa, Ont. P0H 1V0, Canada.

612.67 US
MATURE HEALTH. 1986-1989 (Sep.). 10/yr. Haymarket Group Ltd., 45 W. 34th St., New York, NY 10001.
Formerly: A I M Plus.

737.4 US
MAURICE ROSEN'S RARE COIN CONFIDENTIAL. 1987-1988 (Sep.). m. Target, Inc., 6612 Owens Dr., Pleasanton, CA 94566.

969.82 MF
MAURITIUS CHAMBER OF COMMERCE AND INDUSTRY. NEWSLETTER. suspended. m. Mauritius Chamber of Commerce and Industry, 3 Royal Street, Port Louis, Mauritius.

330.9 MF
MAURITIUS ECONOMIC BULLETIN. ceased 1985. m. Ministry of Finance, Government House, Port Louis, Mauritius.

910.9 500 CN
MAWDSLEY MEMOIRS. 1973-1981. irreg. University of Saskatchewan, Department of Geography, Saskatoon, Sask. S7N 0W0, Canada.

320.531 US
MAY DAY!. 1981-1986? q. Socialist Party, U.S.A., 5502 W. Adams Blvd., Los Angeles, CA 90016-2504.

341 382 US ISSN 1050-897X
KJC6242.A52
MEALEY'S EUROPEAN ENVIRONMENTAL LAW REPORT. 1990-1992. s-m. Mealey Publications, Inc., Box 446, Wayne, PA 19087.

341 US ISSN 0742-4655
JX238.I7
MEALEY'S LITIGATION REPORT: IRANIAN CLAIMS. 1984-1991 (Jan.). s-m. Mealey Publications, Inc., Box 446, Wayne, PA 19087.

637 636 UK
MEAT AND DAIRY PRODUCTS. 1978-1988. s-a. Commonwealth Secretariat, Publications Division, Marlborough House, London SW1Y 5HX, England.

636 UK ISSN 0076-5716
MEAT AND LIVESTOCK COMMISSION, BUCKS, ENGLAND. INDEX OF RESEARCH. 1961-19?? a. Meat and Livestock Commission, Box 44, Queensway House, Bletchley, Milton Keynes MK2 2EF, England.
Formerly: Index of Pig Research.

612.67 IS
MEBROOKDALE/HIGHLIGHTS. ceased. s-a. J D C - Brookdale Institute of Gerontology and Human Development in Israel, P.O. Box 13087, Jerusalem 91130, Israel.

380 HK ISSN 0258-3038
MECHANICAL & ELECTRONIC INDUSTRIES YEARBOOK OF CHINA. published only once, 1986. a. Economic Information & Agency, 342 Hennessy Rd., 10th Fl., Hong Kong, Hong Kong.

621 US ISSN 0025-651X
TJ1 CODEN: MEENBI
MECHANICAL ENGINEERING NEWS. 1964-1992. q. (processed; reprint service avail. from UMI) American Society for Engineering Education, 11 Dupont Circle, Ste. 200, Washington, DC 20036.

620 AU
MECHANIK. 1947-198? m. (Bundesinnung Wien der Mechaniker) Oesterreichischer Wirtschaftsverlag, Nikolsdorfer Gasse 7-11, A-1051 Vienna, Austria.
Formerly: Oesterreichische Mechaniker (ISSN 0029-9294)

624 621.8 CS ISSN 0025-6595
MECHANIZACIA. (Supplement to: Inzinierske Stavby) 1953-19?? m. Alfa, Hurbanovo nam. 3, 815 89 Bratislava, Czechoslovakia.

020 651 940 SW ISSN 0039-6893
MEDDELANDEN FRAAN SVENSKA RIKSARKIVET. 1877-19?? irreg. Riksarkivet - National Archives, Box 12541, 102 29 Stockholm, Sweden.

070.43 CN
MEDIA ACTION; monthly journalism review from the AIDS Committee of Toronto. 1985-19?? m. (back issues avail.) A I D S Committee of Toronto, Box 55, Station "F", Toronto, Ont. M4Y 2L4, Canada.

791.4 778 US ISSN 0889-8928
MEDIA ARTS. 1983-1990. 4/yr. (tabloid format) National Alliance of Media Arts Centers, 1212 Broadway, No. 816, Oakland, CA 94612.

791.43 US
MEDIA EXHIBITORS' DIRECTORY FOR INDEPENDENT ARTISTS. 1986-198? a. Carnegie, Museum of Art, Section of Film and Video, 4400 Forbes Ave., Pittsburgh, PA 15213.

332.6 US ISSN 0279-0734
HG4501
MEDIA GENERAL FINANCIAL WEEKLY; market digest. 1971-1990 (Feb.). w. (also avail. in microfilm) Media General Financial Services, 301 E. Grace St., Box C-32333, Richmond, VA 23293.
Former titles: M - G Financial Weekly; Financial Daily (ISSN 0046-3876); Incorporates: Media General Stockchart.

371.3 US ISSN 0730-3262
MEDIA MONITOR (ARDSLEY). 1977-1981? 4/yr. Informedia, Box 7130, Ardsley on Hudson, NY 10503.

070 US
MEDIA PERSONNEL DIRECTORY. 1979-198? irreg. Gale Research Inc., 835 Penobscot Bldg., Detroit, MI 48226.

CESSATIONS

659.1   US
MEDIA PLANNING GUIDE. 1990; ceased same year. bi-m. J B & Me Publishing, Box 3879, Manhattan Beach, CA 90266.

371.3   US   ISSN 0199-9273
MEDIA REVIEW; professional evaluations of instructional materials. 1977-1988 (Jun.). m. (looseleaf format; back issues avail.) Education Funding Research Council, 1611 N. Kent St., Ste. 508, Arlington, VA 22209-4331.
    Formerly: Media Index (ISSN 0162-0223)

384   US
MEDIA USER'S NEWSLETTER. 1984-19?? q. Public Interest Video Network, New Voices Radio, 1642 R St., N.W., Washington, DC 20009.

610   US   ISSN 0300-7200
MEDIC ALERT NEWSLETTER. 1960-1991. 3/yr. Medic Alert Foundation International, Box 1009, Turlock, CA 95380-1009.

610   US   ISSN 0025-7001
                        CODEN: MAHSA
MEDICAL ASPECTS OF HUMAN SEXUALITY. 1967-1992 (Feb.). m. Cahners Publishing Company (New York), Medical-Health Care Group (Subsidiary of: Reed International PLC), Division of Reed Publishing (USA) Inc., 249 W. 17th St., New York, NY 10011.

610 574   FI   ISSN 0302-2137
R850.A1   CODEN: MDBYAS
MEDICAL BIOLOGY. 1974-1987. bi-m. (also avail. in microform from UMI) Finnish Medical Society Duodecim, Kalevankatu 11 A, 00100 Helsinki, Finland.
    Supersedes: Annales Medicinae Exeprimentalis et Bilogiae Fenniae (ISSN 0003-4479)

610   HK   ISSN 0258-3267
MEDICAL CHINA. 1985-1989; suspended. q. (People's Medical Publishing House, CC) Medical China Publishing Ltd., 4306 China Resources Building, 26 Harbour Road, Wanchai, Hong Kong.

610   UK   ISSN 0143-4330
MEDICAL COMPUTING. ceased 1990. m. (looseleaf format; back issues avail.) Sheffield University Biomedical Information Service (SUBIS), The University, Sheffield S10 2TN, England.

681   US
MEDICAL DESIGN AND MATERIAL. 1991; ceased same year. m. Aster Publishing Corporation, 859 Willamette St., Box 10955, Eugene, OR 97440.

615.845 610.28 016 UK   ISSN 0025-7222
R856.A1
MEDICAL ELECTRONICS & COMMUNICATIONS ABSTRACTS. 1966-1989. q. Parjon Information Services, P.O. Box 144, Haywards Heath, Sussex RH16 2YX, England.

610   UK   ISSN 0261-3646
MEDICAL FORUM. 1981-19?? q. Medical Education (International) Ltd., Publishing House, 62 Stert St., Abingdon, Oxon OX14 3UQ, England.

610   US
MEDICAL GROUP NEWS & IN-OFFICE TESTING ADVANCES; and health services report. 1968-19?? bi-m. (tabloid format; also avail. in microform from UMI; reprint service avail. from UMI) Medical Group News, Inc., Box 36, Glencoe, IL 60022.
    Formerly: Medical Group News (ISSN 0025-7265)

610 600   UK
MEDICAL HORIZONS. 1987-1991 (vol.5, no.3). q. (Association of British Health-Care Industries) F S G Communications Ltd., 57-59 Whitechapel Road, London E1 1DU, England.

616.97 011   US
MEDICAL INFORMATION SYSTEMS: ABSTRACTS IN MEDICINE AND KEY WORK INDEX. 1966-1989 (Oct.). m. (also avail. in cards) References & Index Services, Inc., 3951 N. Meridian St., Ste. 100, Indianapolis, IN 46208-4011.
    Formerly: Medical Information Systems: Allergy.

616.12 011   US
MEDICAL INFORMATION SYSTEMS: CARDIOLOGY. 1966-1989 (Oct.). m. (also avail. in cards) (Methodist Hospital Graduate Medical Center of Indianapolis) References & Index Services, Inc., 3951 N. Meridian, Ste. 100, Indianapolis, IN 46208.

610 011   US
MEDICAL INFORMATION SYSTEMS: CLINICAL PATHOLOGY. 1966-1989 (Oct.). m. (also avail. in cards) (Methodist Hospital Graduate Medical Center of Indianapolis) References & Index Services, Inc., 3941 N. Meridian, Ste. 100, Indianapolis, IN 46208.

610 011   US
MEDICAL INFORMATION SYSTEMS: CRITICAL CARE AND EMERGENCY MEDICINE. 1966-1989 (Oct.). m. (also avail. in cards) (Methodist Hospital Graduate Medical Center of Indianapolis) References & Index Services, Inc., 3951 N. Meridian, Ste. 100, Indianapolis, IN 46208.
    Formed by the merger of: Medical Information Systems: Emergency Medicine; Medical Information Systems: Critical Care.

616.5 011   US
MEDICAL INFORMATION SYSTEMS: DERMATOLOGY. 1966-1989 (Oct.). m. (also avail. in cards) (Methodist Hospital Graduate Medical Center of Indianapolis) References & Index Services, Inc., 3951 N. Meridian, Ste. 100, Indianapolis, IN 46208.

616.4 011   US
MEDICAL INFORMATION SYSTEMS: ENDOCRINOLOGY. 1966-1989 (Oct.). m. (also avail. in cards) (Methodist Hospital Graduate Medical Center of Indianapolis) References & Index Services, Inc., 3951 N. Meridian, Ste. 100, Indianapolis, IN 46208.

616.3 011   US
MEDICAL INFORMATION SYSTEMS: GASTROENTEROLOGY. 1966-1989 (Oct.). m. (also avail. in cards) (Methodist Hospital Graduate Medical Center of Indianapolis) References & Index Services, Inc., 3951 N. Meridian, Ste. 100, Indianapolis, IN 46208.

616.15 011   US
MEDICAL INFORMATION SYSTEMS: HEMATOLOGY-ONCOLOGY. 1966-1989 (Oct.). m. (also avail. in cards) (Methodist Hospital Graduate Medical Center of Indianapolis) References & Index Services, Inc., 3951 N. Meridian, Ste. 100, Indianapolis, IN 46208.

610 011   US
MEDICAL INFORMATION SYSTEMS: INFECTIOUS DISEASE. 1966-1989 (Oct.). m. (also avail. in cards) (Methodist Hospital Graduate Medical Center of Indianapolis) References & Index Services, Inc., 3951 N. Meridian, Ste. 100, Indianapolis, IN 46208.

616.8 011   US
MEDICAL INFORMATION SYSTEMS: NEPHROLOGY. 1966-1989 (Oct.). m. (also avail. in cards) (Methodist Hospital Graduate Medical Center of Indianapolis) References & Index Services, Inc., 3951 N. Meridian, Ste. 100, Indianapolis, IN 46208.

616.8 011   US
MEDICAL INFORMATION SYSTEMS: NEUROLOGY. 1966-1989 (Oct.). m. (also avail. in cards) (Methodist Hospital Graduate Medical Center of Indianapolis) References & Index Services, Inc., 3951 N. Meridian, Ste. 100, Indianapolis, IN 46208.

616.2 011   US
MEDICAL INFORMATION SYSTEMS: PULMONARY. 1966-1989 (Oct.). m. (also avail. in cards) (Methodist Hospital Graduate Medical Center of Indianapolis) References & Index Services, Inc., 3951 N. Meridian, Ste. 100, Indianapolis, IN 46208.

615.842 011   US
MEDICAL INFORMATION SYSTEMS: RADIOLOGY. 1966-1989 (Oct.). m. (also avail. in cards) (Methodist Hospital Graduate Medical Center of Indianapolis) References & Index Services, Inc., 3951 N. Meridian, Ste. 100, Indianapolis, IN 46208.

616.7 011   US
MEDICAL INFORMATION SYSTEMS: RHEUMATOLOGY. 1966-1989 (Oct.). m. (also avail. in cards) (Methodist Hospital Graduate Medical Center of Indianapolis) References & Index Services, Inc., 3951 N. Meridian, Ste. 100, Indianapolis, IN 46208.

610.28 542   SA
MEDICAL INSTRUMENT AND EQUIPMENT SELECTOR. ceased. bi-m. Westbourne Maclean-Hunter (Pty) Ltd., Nedbank East City, 120 End St., PO Box 6110, Johannesburg 2000, South Africa.

610 381   US
MEDICAL PRODUCTS MARKETERS DIRECTORY. 1981-198? a. C P S Communications, Inc., Directories Division, 7200 W. Camino Real, Ste. 215, Boca Raton, FL 33433.

615.842   US   ISSN 0025-746X
                        CODEN: MRPHA9
MEDICAL RADIOGRAPHY AND PHOTOGRAPHY. 1925-1988. 2/yr. Eastman Kodak Co., 343 State St., Rochester, NY 14650.

610   US
MEDICAL ROUNDS; review journal for the staff physician. ceased 1990 (May). 6/yr. Little, Brown and Company, 34 Beacon St., Boston, MA 02108.

613   US   ISSN 0162-2285
MEDICAL SELFCARE. 1976-1990. bi-m. (also avail. in microform from UMI) Island Publishing Company, Inc., Box 701, Providence, RI 02901.

610   US   ISSN 0025-7583
MEDICAL TIMES; journal for the family physician. 1872-1990. m. (also avail. in microform from UMI; back issues avail.; reprint service avail.) Romaine Pierson Publishers, Inc., 80 Shore Rd., Port Washington, NY 11050.

616.07 658   US   ISSN 0892-8185
MEDICENTER MANAGEMENT. 1984-1988 (vol.5, no.7). m. (back issues avail.; reprint service avail.) Brentwood Publishing, 30 Vreeland Rd., Florham Park, NJ 07932.

616.988   SP   ISSN 0025-7958
MEDICINA TROPICAL. ceased 1973. bi-m. (Centro Espanol de Medicina Tropical, Pabellon 2, Facultad de Medicina (Ciudad Universitaria), Madrid 3, Spain.

615   US   ISSN 0076-6054
                        CODEN: MDCHAG
MEDICINAL CHEMISTRY; series of monographs. 1963-1985 (vol.20). irreg. (reprint service avail. from ISI) Academic Press, Inc., 1250 Sixth Ave., San Diego, CA 92101.

615.1   DK   ISSN 0025-8040
MEDICINSK FORUM. 1948-1988. 6/yr. Foreningen af Danske Medicinfabrikker - Association of the Danish Pharmaceutical Industry, Landemaerket 25, DK-1119 Copenhagen K, Denmark.

340.6   US   ISSN 0025-8164
KFV2926.C65   CODEN: MLBUD
MEDICO-LEGAL BULLETIN. 1951-1990 (vol.39, no.3); suspended. bi-m. (processed) Department of Health, Medical Examiner Division, 9 N. 14th St., Richmond, VA 23219.

070   AU
MEDIEN JOURNAL; Informationen aus Medienarbeit und -forschung. 1977-1989 (vol.3). q. Oesterreichische Gesellschaft fuer Kommunikationsfragen, Rudolfskai 42, A-5020 Salzburg, Austria.

301.16   GW   ISSN 0937-7417
MEDIEN MEMO. 1989-1991. q. Georg Thieme Verlag, Ruedigerstr. 14, Postfach 104853, 7000 Stuttgart 10, Germany.

380.1   IT   ISSN 0047-6609
MEDITERRANEO; mensile di economia e cultura. 1967?-1976. m. Camera di Commercio Industria Artigianato e Agricoltura di Palermo, Via Emerico Amari 11, Palermo 90139, Italy.

610 020   GW   ISSN 0343-1002
MEDIZIN BIBLIOTHEK DOKUMENTATION. 1977-1980. q. (Arbeitsgemeinschaft fuer Medizinisches Bibliothekswesen) Medizin Bibliothek Dokumentation-Verlag, Loheide 35, 4800 Bielefeld 1, Germany.

100   US
MEET THE LORDS. 1969-1991. q. Awareness Research Foundation, Inc., c/o Helen Hoag, Ed., 35 Ritter Rd., Apt. 29, Desoto Sq., Hayesville, NC 28904.

CESSATIONS

056.1   AG
MEGAFON; revista interdisciplinaria de estudios latinoamericanos. 1975-199? s-a. (Centro de Estudios Latinoamericanos) Fernando Garcia Cambeiro, Cochabamba 244, 1150 Buenos Aires, Argentina.

617.6   US   ISSN 0025-8725
MEHARRI-DENT. vol.23, 1966-198? 3/yr. (during school term). (Ewell Neil Dental Society) Meharry Medical College, School of Dentistry, 1005 18th Ave. N., Nashville, TN 37208.

618   US
MEHARRY MEDICAL COLLEGE. SCHOOL OF DENTISTRY. PROCEEDINGS OF AN ORAL RESEARCH SEMINAR. 1973-198? biennial. (back issues avail.) Meharry Medical College, School of Dentistry, 1005 18th Ave. N., Nashville, TN 37208.

334   FI
MEIDAN LIIKE/OUR MOVEMENT; kuluttaja & osuustoiminta. 1970-19?? bi-m. (back issues avail.) Viestintarengas Oy, P.O. Box 72, 00501 Helsinki, Finland.
Formerly (until 1989): E - Lehti (ISSN 0355-3817)

637   FI   ISSN 0784-1736
MEIJERITEOLLISUUS; meijeritaloudellinen aikakauslehti. 1918-198? 7/yr. Valio Meijerien Keskusosuusliike - Valio Finnish Co-Operative Dairies' Association, Meijeritie 4, PL 69, 00371 Helsinki, Finland.
Formerly: Karjantuote (ISSN 0047-3243)

621   UR
MEKHANICHESKAYA TEKHNOLOGIYA/MECHANINE TECHNOLOGIJA. 1968-1990 (no.19). irreg. Kaunas Politechnic Institute, Editing and Publishing Group - Kauno Politechnikos Institutas, K. Donelaicio 73, 233006 Kaunas, Lithuanian S.S.R., U.S.S.R.

338.9   UN   ISSN 0252-5348
MEKONG BULLETIN. 1968-1986 (vol.18, no.2). a. United Nations Economic and Social Commission for Asia and the Pacific (ESCAP), Mekong Committee, United Nations Bldg., Rajadamnern Ave., Bangkok 10200, Thailand.
Formerly: Mekong Monthly Bulletin (ISSN 0047-6668)

574.875   US   ISSN 0160-2462
QH509   CODEN: MTPRDM
MEMBRANE TRANSPORT PROCESSES. 1978-1979 (vol.3). irreg. Raven Press, 1185 Ave. of the Americas, New York, NY 10036.

663   FR   ISSN 0085-221X
MEMENTO DE L'O.I.V.. 1928-1975. quinquennial. Office International de la Vigne et du Vin, 11 rue Roquepine, 75008 Paris, France.

331.88   US   ISSN 0032-3160
MEMO FROM C O P E. ceased. fortn. Committee on Political Education, A F L - C I O, 815 16th St., N.W., Washington, DC 20006.

607   FR   ISSN 0071-9005
MEMOIRES O.R.S.T.O.M.. 1961-1988. irreg. O R S T O M, Institut Francais de Recherche Scientifique pour le Developpement en Cooperation, 70-74 Route d'Aulnay, 93143 Bondy cedex, France.

051   US   ISSN 0898-9184
MEMORIES; the magazine of then and now. 1988-1990. bi-m. Diamandis Communications, Inc. (Subsidiary of: Hachette Publications), 1633 Broadway, New York, NY 10009.

614.7   NE
MENS EN MILIEU. ceased. irreg. Van Gorcum, Box 43, 9400 AA Assen, Netherlands.

305.3   US
MEN'S LIFE. ceased after one issue, 1990. q. Murdoch Magazines (Subsidiary of: News America Publishing, Inc.), 200 Madison Ave., New York, NY 10016.

305.4   US
MEN'S REPORT; a magazine about men. 1986-1989 (Feb.). bi-m. (back issues avail.) Center for Men's Studies, 2600 Dwight Way, Berkeley, CA 94704.
Formerly: M R Magazine (ISSN 0885-470X)

687   US
MEN'S RETAILER. 1975-1984? 4/yr. Fashion Retailer Publications, 6G44 Apparel Mart, Box 586398, Dallas, TX 75258.

133.9   GW   ISSN 0175-9809
MENSCH GUTEN WILLENS; Zeitschrift fuer Cosmospsychologie. 1979-198?; suspended. q. (back issues avail.) Cosmospsychologischer Verlag, Moerikestr. 8, D-7898 Lauchringen, W. Germany (B.R.D.).

301.32   SZ
MENSCHEN UNTERWEGS. ceased 1988. s-a. International Catholic Migration Commission, 37-39 rue de Vermont, CH-1211 Geneva 20 CIC, Switzerland.

616.8 618.92   UK   ISSN 0143-7550
MENTAL RETARDATION. ceased 1989. m. (looseleaf format; back issues avail.) Sheffield University Biomedical Information Service (SUBIS), The University, Sheffield S10 2TN, England.

364   US   ISSN 0890-7005
LE MERCENAIRE INTELLIGENCE NEWSLETTER. 1978-198? m. (tabloid format; back issues avail.) Box 507, Fredericktown, MO 63645-0507.

929   US
MERCER MEMORIES; for Mercer Family researchers. ceased. bi-m. Next Question Please, 323 S. Marquette St., Ironwood, MI 49938.

382   NZ
MERCHANDISE TRADE WITH AUSTRALIA. 1983-19?? q. (back issues avail.) New Zealand Department of Statistics Information Service, P.O. Box 2922, Wellington, New Zealand.

915   IS
MERCHAVIM; collection of geographical research about Israel and the Middle East. 1974-19?? irreg. Tel Aviv University, Department of Geography, Tel Aviv, Israel.

001.6 621.381   CN
MERCURY; newsletter of the computer centre. 1969-1985 (vol.16, issue 85). irreg. University of Manitoba, Computer Services, Engineering Bldg., Rm. 603, Winnipeg, Man. R3T 2N2, Canada.

338.91 327   US
MERGING WORLD. 1987-19?? m. (back issues avail.) Overseas Development Network, 333 Valencia St., Ste. 300, San Francisco, CA 94103-3547.

530 520   SA   ISSN 0257-1994
MESON. 1980-1988. q. (back issues avail.) South African Institute of Physics, c/o National Accelerator Center, P.O. Box 72, Faure 7131, South Africa.

913.031   NE   ISSN 0920-4989
QE675
MESOZOIC RESEARCH. 1987-1989 (vol.3). 4/yr. (back issues avail.) E.J. Brill, P.O.Box 9000, 2300 PA Leiden, Netherlands.

281.9   FR   ISSN 0026-0266
MESSAGER DE L'EXARCHAT DU PATRIARCHE RUSSE EN EUROPE OCCIDENTALE. 1950-19?? a. (Union des Associations Culturelles de l'Eglise Orthodoxe) Exarchat du Patriarche de Moscou, 26 rue Preclet, 75015 Paris, France.

620.1 389   GW
MESSEN PRUEFEN AUTOMATISIEREN. 1965-19?? 10/yr. Hans Holzmann Verlag KG, Gewerbestr. 2, Postfach 1342, 8939 Bad Woerishofen, Germany.
Former titles: Messen und Pruefen (ISSN 0026-0339); Automatik (ISSN 0005-1136)

331.88 670   SA   ISSN 0026-072X
METAL WORKER/METAAL WERKER. 1906-19?? bi-m. Amalgamated Engineering Union, P.O. Box 1168, Johannesburg 2000, South Africa.

669   AU   ISSN 0047-6889
METALLBERICHT. 1967-19?? m. (Fachverband der Eisen- und Metallwarenindustrie Oesterreichs) Oesterreichischer Wirtschaftsverlag, Nikolsdorfergasse 7-11, A-1051 Vienna, Austria.

669   II   ISSN 0369-061X
METALLURGICAL ENGINEER. 1969-1983; suspended. a. (Metallurgical Engineering Association) Indian Institute of Technology, Bombay, Central Library, Powai, Bombay 400 076, India.

621.75   US
METALWORKING DISTRIBUTOR. ceased 1990. q. Penton Publishing (Subsidiary of: Pittway Company), 1100 Superior Ave., Cleveland, OH 44114.

669   US   ISSN 0891-4036
HD9506.U6
METALWORKING NEWS. 1960-1990. w. (tabloid format; also avail. in microfilm) Fairchild Publications, Inc., Metal Working News (Subsidiary of: Capital Cities Media, Inc.), 7 E. 12th St., New York, NY 10003.
Incorporates: Chilton's Iron Age: Manufacturing Management; (in 1987): Chilton's Iron Age Management (ISSN 0026-1025) Chilton's Iron Age: Manufacturing News supersedes in part (in 1984) and continues numbering of: Chilton's Iron Age (ISSN 0164-5137); Which was formerly (1873-1976): Iron Age (ISSN 0021-1508); Which incorporates (in Jul. 1977): N C Management Report.

551   GW   ISSN 0543-5927
QE39   CODEN: MFRCBN
"METEOR" FORSCHUNGSERGEBNISSE. REIHE C. GEOLOGIE UND GEOPHYSIK. 1968-1986. irreg. (Deutsche Forschungsgemeinschaft) Gebrueder Borntraeger Verlagsbuchhandlung, Johannesstr. 3A, D-7000 Stuttgart 1, Germany.

510   NE
METHODS IN GEOMATHEMATICS. ceased. irreg. Elsevier Science Publishers B.V., PO Box 211, 1000 AE Amsterdam, Netherlands.

616.01 576.64   US   ISSN 0076-6933
QR360   CODEN: MTVIAM
METHODS IN VIROLOGY. 1967-1984 (vol.8). irreg. (reprint service avail. from ISI) Academic Press, Inc, 1250 Sixth Ave., San Diego, CA 92101.

612.015   UK   ISSN 0950-0537
METHYL TRANSFERASES. ceased 1990. m. (looseleaf format; back issues avail.) Sheffield University Biomedical Information Service (SUBIS), The University, Sheffield S10 2TN, England.

020 500 600 330   CS   ISSN 0322-7243
METODICKY ZPRAVODAJ CS. SOUSTAVY VEDECKYCH, TECHNICKYCH A EKONOMICKYCH INFORMACI. 1973-1990. q. Ustredi Vedeckych Technickych a Ekonomickych Informaci (UVTEI), Konviktska 5, 113 57 Prague 1, Czechoslovakia.

630   CS   ISSN 0026-1319
    CODEN: MZVPDK
METODIKY PRO ZAVADENI VYSLEDKU VYZKUMU DO PRAXE/METHODS FOR THE APPLICATION OF RESEARCH RESULTS INTO PRACTICE. 1957-19?? 25/yr. (tabloid format; also avail. in microform) Ustav Vedeckotechnickych Informaci pro Zemedelstvi, Slezska 7, 120 56 Prague 2, Czechoslovakia.

020   US   ISSN 0887-1973
METRO HANDBOOK AND DIRECTORY OF MEMBERS (YEAR). 1980-1988. a. (back issues avail.) (New York Metropolitan Reference & Research Library Agency) L D A Publishers, 42-36 209 St., Bayside, NY 11361.
Former titles: METRO; New York Metropolitan Reference and Research Agency. Handbook and Directory of Members; New York Metropolitan Reference and Research Agency. Directory of Members (ISSN 0362-8744)

330.9   US
METRO INSIGHTS. 1987-1990. a. D R I - McGraw-Hill, 24 Hartwell Ave., Lexington, MA 02173.

200 301.3   US
METRO - MINISTRY NEWS; interdenominational newsletter. 1985-1991. q. Institute on the Church in Urban-Industrial Society, 4750 N. Sheridan Rd., Ste. 327, Chicago, IL 60640.

352.7   US
METRO MONITOR. 1979-1991 (Oct.). every 6 wks. (tabloid format) Metropolitan Council of the Twin Cities Area, 230 E. 5 St. 4th Fl., St. Paul, MN 55101.

051   US
METRONORTH. 1989-1990 (vol.1, no.3). q. MetroNorth Publishing Inc., 29 School St., Danvers, MA 01923-2924.

CESSATIONS

708.147   US   ISSN 0192-6950
N610
METROPOLITAN MUSEUM OF ART. NOTABLE ACQUISITIONS. ceased. a. Metropolitan Museum of Art, Fifth Ave. & 82nd St., New York, NY 10028.

305.412   US
METROPOLITAN WOMAN. 1989-1990. bi-m. Talcott Corporation, 208 W. Huron St., Chicago, IL 60610.
Formerly (until Aug. 1990): Minneapolis Woman.

598.2   NE   ISSN 0026-1688
MEVO; internacia revuo ornitologia. 1964-1984. 4/yr. (back issues avail.) Ornitologia Rondo Esperantlingva, Floraplein 23, 5644 JS Eindhoven, Netherlands.

972   US   ISSN 0730-2584
MEXICAN FORUM/FORO MEXICANO. 1981-1986. q. Institute of Latin American Studies, Office for Mexican Studies, University of Texas, Sid Richardson Hall 1310, Austin, TX 78712.

972   MX   ISSN 0543-7741
F1209
MEXICO; facts, figures, trends. 1960-1976. irreg. Banco Nacional de Comercio Exterior, S.A., Departamento de Publicaciones, Venustiano Carranza 32, Mexico 1, D.F., Mexico.

972   MX   ISSN 0185-1926
F1203
MEXICO. ARCHIVO GENERAL DE LA NACION. BOLETIN. ceased (vol.9, no.10). q. (back issues avail.) Archivo General de la Nacion, Apdo. Postal 1999, 06010 Mexico, D.F., Mexico.

338 318   MX
MEXICO. DIRECCION GENERAL DE ESTADISTICA. ESTADISTICA INDUSTRIAL MENSUAL. 1964-1978. m. Secretaria de Programacion y Presupuesto, Palacio Nacional, Col. Centro, 06000 Mexico, D.F., Mexico.

331 318   MX   ISSN 0076-7492
MEXICO. SECRETARIA DE PROGRAMACION Y PRESUPUESTO. 1938-19?? a. Secretaria de Programacion y Presupuesto, Departamento de Estadisticas Industriales, Palacio National, Col. Centro, 06000 Mexico, D.F., Mexico.

972   MX   ISSN 0026-1793
MEXICO HEROICO. 1962-1975 (vol.119). m. Editorial Jus, S.A., Plaza de Abasolo 14, Colonia Guerrero, Mexico 3, D.F., Mexico.

301.4157   US   ISSN 0889-7042
MICHAELS ON ETIQUETTE; a journal on manners, morals, values, attitudes and other behaviors. 1985-1989. 10/yr. (back issues avail.) M L P Enterprises, 236 E. Durham St., Box 18918, Philadelphia, PA 19119.

914.404   FR
MICHELIN GREEN GUIDE SERIES: BELGIUM - LUXEMBOURG. ceased. irreg. Michelin, Services de Tourisme, 46 av. de Breteuil, 75346 Paris Cedex 7, France.

914.2   FR
MICHELIN GREEN GUIDE SERIES: LONDRES. ceased. irreg. Michelin, Services de Tourisme, 46 av. de Breteuil, 75346 Paris cedex 7, France.

914.4   FR
MICHELIN GREEN GUIDE SERIES: NORMANDY. ceased. irreg. Michelin, Services de Tourisme, 46 av. de Breteuil, 75346 Paris cedex 7, France.

353.9   US
MICHIGAN. DEPARTMENT OF COMMERCE. ANNUAL REPORT. 1963-19?? a. Department of Commerce, Lansing, MI 48913.
Formerly: Michigan. Department of Commerce. Annual Report Summary (ISSN 0094-3479)

330 016   US   ISSN 0091-9047
Z7164.E2
MICHIGAN BUSINESS AND ECONOMIC RESEARCH BIBLIOGRAPHY. ceased 1981. irreg. University of Michigan, Institute of Science & Technology, Division of Research, 851 Senda Plata, Venice, FL 33595.

650   US   ISSN 0076-7840
HF5006
MICHIGAN BUSINESS PAPERS. 1937-1986 (no.68). irreg. (reprint service avail. from UMI) University of Michigan, Graduate School of Business Administration, Division of Research, Ann Arbor, MI 48109.

650   US   ISSN 0076-7859
MICHIGAN BUSINESS REPORTS. 1938-1979 (no.63). irreg. (reprint service avail. from UMI) University of Michigan, Graduate School of Business Administration, Division of Research, Ann Arbor, MI 48109.

650   US   ISSN 0076-7867
HF5006
MICHIGAN BUSINESS STUDIES. 1926; N.S. 1975-1982 (vol.2). irreg. (reprint service avail. from UMI) University of Michigan, Graduate School of Business Administration, Division of Research, Ann Arbor, MI 48109.

330.9   US   ISSN 0730-272X
HC107.M5
MICHIGAN ECONOMY. 1982-19?? (vol.6, no.1). 4/yr. Wayne State University, School of Business Administration, Bureau of Business Research, Detroit, MI 48202.

301.412   US   ISSN 1055-856X
MICHIGAN FEMINIST STUDIES. 1974-19?? irreg. University of Michigan, Women's Studies Department, 230 W. Engineering, Ann Arbor, MI 48109-1902.
Former titles (until 1987): New Occasional Papers in Women's Studies (ISSN 1050-4893); (until 1983): Michigan Occasional Papers (ISSN 0731-163X); Supersedes (in 1978): University of Michigan Papers in Women's Studies.

650   US   ISSN 0076-7972
MICHIGAN INTERNATIONAL BUSINESS STUDIES. 1963-1981 (vol.18). irreg. (reprint service avail. from UMI) University of Michigan, Graduate School of Business Administration, Division of Research, Ann Arbor, MI 48109.

332   US
MICHIGAN INVESTOR. 1902-198? w. Contractor Publishing Co., 1629 W. Lafayette, Detroit, MI 48216.

051 015   US   ISSN 0026-2250
MICHIGAN MAGAZINE INDEX. 1967-1988. q. (microfiche) Library of Michigan, Box 30007, Lansing, MI 48909.

374   US
MICHIGAN STATE UNIVERSITY. COOPERATIVE EXTENSION SERVICE. ANNUAL REPORT. 1915-19?? a. Michigan State University, Cooperative Extension Service, East Lansing, MI 48824.

317   US   ISSN 0076-8308
HA441
MICHIGAN STATISTICAL ABSTRACT. 1955-1986. a. (also avail. in microfiche from BHP) Wayne State University, Bureau of Business Research, Detroit, MI 48202.

917   US
MICHIGAN TRAVEL AND RECREATION GUIDE. ceased. a. Rockford Map Publishers, Inc., 4525 Forest View Ave., Box 6126, Rockford, IL 61125.

811   US   ISSN 0194-1313
PS3224
MICKLE STREET REVIEW. 1979-19?? a. Walt Whitman Association, Box 1493, Camden, NJ 08101.

621.38   UK
MICRO AND DIGITAL ELECTRONICS. 1983-19?? q. Argus Specialist Publications Ltd., Argus House, Boundary Way, Hemels, Hampstead, Herts HP2 7ST, England.

572   GW
MICRO-BIBLIOTHECA ANTHROPOS. 1953-1977. irreg. (microfilm) Anthropos Institut, D-5205 St. Augustin (bei Bonn), Germany.

621.381   GW
MICRO COMPUTER COLLEGE; Computer in Schule, Studieren und Freizeit. 1984-1989. m. Fachzeitschriften GmbH, Neumarkterstr. 18, 8000 Munich 80, Germany.

621.381   US   ISSN 0747-587X
MICRO CORNUCOPIA. 1981-19?? bi-m. (also avail. in microfilm) Micro Cornucopia, Inc., Box 223, Bend, OR 97709.

001.6 621.381   FR
MICRO ORDINATEURS/MICRO COMPUTERS. 1984-1989. m. S P S, 49 rue de l'Universite, 75007 Paris, France.

070.5 029   US
MICRO PUBLISHER. 1983-198? 5/yr. (tabloid format; also avail. in microform) Bell & Howell Co., Microphoto Division, Old Mansfield Rd., Wooster, OH 44691.

001.642 621.381   US   ISSN 8755-5794
Z678.93.M53
MICRO SOFTWARE EVALUATIONS. ceased. a. Meckler Corporation, 11 Ferry Lane W., Westport, CT 06880-5808.

612 616.1   UK
MICROCIRCULATION. ceased 1989. m. (looseleaf format; back issues avail.) Sheffield University Biomedical Information Service (SUBIS), The University, Sheffield S10 2TN, England.

621.381   US
MICROELECTRONIC MANUFACTURING AND TESTING DESK MANUAL. 1982-19?? a. Lake Publishing Corporation, 17730 West Peterson Rd., Box 159, Libertyville, IL 60048-0159.

621.381   US
MICROGRAM NEWSLETTER; the consumer's newsletter for computing educators. 1983-1988. 9/yr. (back issues avail.) Educational Products Information Exchange (EPIE) Institute, 103-3 W Montauk Hwy. 3, Hampton Bays, NY 11946-4006.

789.91 781.57   NE
MICROGRAPHY; jazz and blues on microgroove. 1968-1989 (no.78). q. Golden Age Records, Nieuwezijds Voorburgwal 51-53, 1012 RD Amsterdam, Netherlands.

370   UK
MICROS IN SCOTTISH EDUCATION. 1980-1988 (vol.2, no.1). q. Scottish Council for Educational Technology, 74 Victoria Crescent Rd., Glasgow G12 9JN, Scotland.
Formerly (until 1986): Phase Two (ISSN 0260-5562)

578 574.8   UK   ISSN 0268-151X
MICROSCOPY AND 3D IMAGING. ceased 1990. m. (looseleaf format; back issues avail.) Sheffield University Biomedical Information Service (SUBIS), The University, Sheffield S10 2TN, England.

574.8 612.015   UK   ISSN 0264-9594
MICROSOMES. ceased 1989. m. (looseleaf format; back issues avail.) Sheffield University Biomedical Information Service (SUBIS), The University, Sheffield S10 2TN, England.

621.38   US
TK7876   CODEN: MSNTEC
MICROWAVE SYSTEMS NEWS. 1971-1990. m. (also avail. in microfilm from UMI; reprint service avail.) Cardiff Publishing Co., 6300 S. Syracuse Way, Ste. 650, Englewood, CO 80111.
Former titles: Microwave Systems News and Communications Technology (ISSN 8750-7935); M S N Microwave Systems News (ISSN 0164-3371); Microwave Systems News (ISSN 0047-7214)

330   CN
MID-CANADA COMMERCE. 1981-19?? 10/yr. (Winnipeg Chamber of Commerce) Naylor Communications Ltd. (Winnipeg), 100 Sutherland Ave., Winnipeg, Man. R2W 3C7, Canada.

810   US   ISSN 0272-717X
PN2
MID-HUDSON LANGUAGE STUDIES. 1978-19?? a. Mid-Hudson Modern Language Association, c/o George J. Sommer, Ed., Marist College, Poughkeepsie, NY 12601.

615.19   US   ISSN 0734-6506
MID-WEEK REPORT. 1982-1989 (Jan.). w. (looseleaf format; back issues avail.) F-D-C Reports, Inc., 5550 Friendship Blvd., Ste. One, Chevy Chase, MD 20815.

330.9 US
MIDAMERICAN OUTLOOK; a review of MidAmerican business. 1978-19?? q. AmeriTrust Corporation, 900 Euclid Ave., Cleveland, OH 44101.
   Supersedes: Clevetrust Corporation Business Bulletin.

700 CN
MIDCONTINENTAL. ceased. q. P.O. Box 129, Station M, Toronto, Ont. M6S 9Z9, Canada.

915.6 016   US   ISSN 0162-766X
DS41
MIDDLE EAST: ABSTRACTS AND INDEX. 1978-1985. a. Northumberland Press, 1717 Boulevard of the Allies, Pittsburgh, PA 15219.

630   UK   ISSN 0266-5905
MIDDLE EAST AGRIBUSINESS. ceased 1990. q. International Trade Publications Ltd., Queensway House, 2 Queensway, Redhill, Surrey RH1 1QS, England.

327   US   ISSN 0733-5350
DS63.1
MIDDLE EAST ANNUAL. 1981-1985. a. G.K. Hall & Co., 70 Lincoln St., Boston, MA 02111.

001.6 621.381   UK   ISSN 0263-9203
MIDDLE EAST COMPUTING. 1982-198? bi-m. Reed Business Publishing Ltd., Enterprise Division, Quadrant House, The Quadrant, Sutton, Surrey SM2 5AS, England.

370   UK   ISSN 0265-5292
MIDDLE EAST EDUCATION & TRAINING. 1979-19?? bi-m. International Trade Publications Ltd., Queensway House, 2 Queensway, Redhill, Surrey RH1 1QS, England.
   Formerly: Middle East Education.

332   UK   ISSN 0266-2094
HG3256.A5
MIDDLE EAST FINANCIAL DIRECTORY. ceased. a. (back issues avail.) Middle East Economic Digest Ltd., 21 John St., London WC1N 2BP, England.

956.9 LE
MIDDLE EAST FORUM/KULLIYAH. 1925-1973. q. American University of Beirut, Alumni Association, Box 1786, Beirut, Lebanon.

658 UA
MIDDLE EAST MANAGEMENT REVIEW. 1977-19?? s-a. American University in Cairo, Graduate Managaement Programme, P.O. Box 2511, Cairo, Egypt.

628.05   UK   ISSN 0140-5098
TD311.A1
MIDDLE EAST WATER & SEWAGE. 1977-198? bi-m. Industrial & Marine Publications Ltd., Queensway House, 2 Queensway, Redhill, Surrey RH1 1QS, England.

382 956   US   ISSN 0262-818X
DS42.4   CODEN: MIFID4
MIDEAST FILE. 1982-1988. 4/yr. Learned Information, Inc., 143 Old Marlton Pike, Medford, NJ 08055.

770   FR   ISSN 0047-7273
MIDI-MINUIT FANTASTIQUE. 1970-197? 10/yr. (back issues avail.) Librairie le Terrain Vague, 14-16 rue de Verneuil, 75007 Paris, France.

052 UK
MIDLAND CARDOWNER. 1976-1991. 5/yr. Midland Bank Ltd., 164 Station Rd., Redhill RH1 1HF, England.
   Formerly: Access Magazine.

630   US   ISSN 0047-7281
HD2951
MIDLAND COOPERATOR. 1933-198? bi-w. (tabloid format; also avail. in microform from UMI) Cenex - Land O'Lakes, Box 64089, St. Paul, MN 55164-0089.

540   US   ISSN 0141-0342
            CODEN: MMMODH
MIDLAND MACROMOLECULAR MONOGRAPHS. 1974-1980 (vol.7). irreg. Gordon and Breach Science Publishers, 270 Eighth Ave., New York, NY 10011.

001.642 US
MIDRANGE. 1981-1990 (Dec.). 12/yr. (also avail. in microform from UMI) Robert A. Cozzi, Jr., Ed. & Pub., Box 2158, Glen Ellyn, IL 60138.
   Former titles (until 1988): Q 38 Technical Journal (ISSN 0748-3392); Q 38.

387.7   US   ISSN 1051-7375
MIDWAY. 1986-199? m. (Midway Airlines) Skies America Publishing Company, 7730 S.W. Mohawk, Tualatin, OR 97062.

808   US   ISSN 0741-3149
MIDWAY REVIEW; a magazine of contemporary arts. 1980-198? s-a. (back issues avail.) Southwest Area Cultural Arts Council, 2358 W. 63rd St., 2nd Fl., Chicago, IL 60636.

636 US
MIDWEST BORZOI CLUB BULLETIN. 1937-1988. q. Midwest Borzoi Club, Inc., 33594 Overland Ln., Solon, OH 44139.

325   SZ   ISSN 0026-3583
MIGRATION NEWS; an international biannual on migration and refugees. 1952-1988; suspended. s-a. International Catholic Migration Commission, 37-39 rue de Vermont, CH-1211 Geneva 20 CIC, Switzerland.

578 616   AU   ISSN 0026-3702
QH201   CODEN: MIKSAM
MIKROSKOPIE; Zentralblatt fuer mikroskopische Forschung und Methodik. 1946-1985 (vol.42). bi-m. Verlag Georg Fromme and Co., Spengergasse 39, A-1051 Vienna, Austria.

637.1   GW   ISSN 0323-5424
            CODEN: MFMPB3
MILCHFORSCHUNG - MILCHPRAXIS. 1958-1990. bi-m. Deutscher Landwirtschaftsverlag GmbH, Reinhardtstr. 14, 1040 Berlin, Germany.

637.1   GW   ISSN 0933-0682
MILCHSTRASSE; Neues ueber Kaese, Sahne, Milch. 1987-1990. bi-m. Milchwirtschaftlicher Fachverlag GmbH, Bonner Str. 28, Postfach 624, 5480 Rm-Rolandseck, Germany.

629.222 US
MILESTONE CAR. 1972-1982. s-a. (Milestone Car Society Inc.) Dragonwyck Publishing Co., Burrage Rd., Contoocook, NH 03229.

355.27 UK
MILITARY COMMUNICATIONS. ceased 1988. a. Interavia S.A. (Subsidiary of: Jane's Information Group), Sentinel House, 163 Brighton Rd., Coulsdon, Surrey CR3 2NX, England.

739.7 355 US
MILITARY DEALERS AND COLLECTORS DIRECTORY. 1981-1987. a? Haas Publications, Box 775, Worthington, OH 43085.

355   US   ISSN 0885-1972
UC263
MILITARY FORUM. 1984-1989 (Dec.). 10/yr. (also avail. in microfilm from UMI; reprint service avail.) National Journal, Inc., 1730 M St., N.W., Ste. 1100, Washington, DC 20036.

790.13 355 US
MILITARY HISTORY ARCHIVES BULLETIN. 1987-1990. m. (looseleaf format; back issues avail.) Merriam Press, 218 Beech St., Bennington, VT 05201.
   Formerly (until 1990): Military Portfolio.

355 US
MILITARY LOGISTICS FORUM. 1984-19?? bi-m. E W Communications, Inc., 6300 S. Syracuse Way, Ste. 650, Englewood, CO 80111-9912.

614.7   DK   ISSN 0107-8550
MILJOEVAERN. 1978-1990 (Dec.). irreg. (1-2/yr.). Kongelige Veterinaer- og Landbohoejskole, Miljoevaernscentret, Institut for Matematik og Fysik, Thorvaldsenvej 40, 1871 Frederiksberg C, Denmark.

809 860 BL
MIMESIS. 1975-1978 (no.4). irreg. Instituto de Biociencias, Letras e Ciencias Exatas de Sao Jose do Rio Preto, Faculdade de Filosofia, Ciencias e Letras, Rua Cristovao Colombo 2265, 15000 Sao Jose do Rio Preto, Sao Paulo, Brazil.
   Formerly: Etudos Anglo-Hispanico.

808.838 IT
MINA. ceased 1990 (June). m. Edizioni Lancio, Via Tiburtina km 11.550, Rome, Italy.

610   US   ISSN 0898-3127
MIND-BODY-HEALTH DIGEST. 1987-1990 (vol.4, no.3). q. (back issues avail.) Institute for the Advancement of Health, 423 Washington St., 3rd fl., San Francisco, CA 94111-2339.

811 US
MINDPRINT REVIEW; a literary journal from the Central Sierra. 1983-1989 (no.8). a. Glen Hill Publications, Box 62, Soulsbyville, CA 95372.

808.81 US
MIND'S EYE. 1985-19??; suspended. irreg. (2-3/yr.). (back issues avail.) Box 656, Glenview, IL 60025.

622   UK   ISSN 0950-6098
MINERAL RESOURCES ENGINEERING. 1988-1991. q. Taylor & Francis Ltd., Rankine Rd., Basingstoke, Hants RG24 0PR, England.

612.015 616.4   UK   ISSN 0142-873X
MINERALOCORTICOIDS AND GLUCOCORTICOIDS. ceased 1990. m. (looseleaf format; back issues avail.) Sheffield University Biomedical Information Service (SUBIS), The University, Sheffield S10 2TN, England.

549 AT
MINERALOGICAL SOCIETY OF NEW SOUTH WALES. JOURNAL. published only once, 1979. a. Mineralogical Society of New South Wales, Box R35, Royal Exchange, Sydney, N.S.W., Australia.

549 531.64   US   ISSN 0890-1392
MINERGIA. 1983-198? 10/yr. (looseleaf format; back issues avail.) Hugh Douglas & Co., Ltd., 124 Sixteenth Ave., San Francisco, CA 94133.

622 US
MINES IN WEST VIRGINIA. 1964-198? irreg. Geological and Economic Survey, Box 879, Morgantown, WV 26507-0879.

338 621.381 US
MINI. 1984-198? bi-m. Para Research, Inc., 85 Eastern Ave., Gloucester, MA 09130.

880 UK
MINIBUS. 1989-1990 (no. 4). 2/yr. Joint Association of Classical Teachers, 31-34 Gordon Square, London WC1H 0PY, England.

001.6 621.381 US
MININEWS. (Update to: Datapro Reports on Microcomputers) ceased. m. Datapro Information Services Group (Subsidiary of: McGraw-Hill, Inc.), 600 Delran Pkwy., Delran, NJ 08075.

622 US
MINING INDUSTRY OF IDAHO. ANNUAL REPORT. 1899-19?? a. (processed) Department of Labor and Industrial Services, Mine Safety Bureau, 277 North 6th St., Statehouse, Boise, ID 83720.

622 SA
MINING SUN. ceased. m. (also avail. in microfilm from PSL) Chamber of Mines of South Africa, P.O. Box 809, Johannesburg 2000, South Africa.

282   BE   ISSN 1013-4549
MINISTRIES AND COMMUNITIES. ceased 1989 (Oct.). q. Pro Mundi Vita, Abdij van't Park, Abdijdreef 7A, B-3030 Leuven, Belgium.

769.56 US
MINKUS (YEAR) SPECIALIZED AMERICAN STAMP CATALOG. 1953-1988. a. Minkus Publications, Inc., 1935 Trillium Ln., Charlotte, NC 23211-4444.
   Formerly: Minkus New American Stamp Catalog (ISSN 0076-9061)

769.56 US
MINKUS STAMP JOURNAL. 1966-1987. q. (also avail. in microform from UMI) Minkus Publications, Inc., 1935 Trillium Ln., Charlotte, NC 23211-4444.
   Former titles: Minkus Stamp and Coin Journal; (until 1980): Minkus Stamp Journal (ISSN 0026-5357)

350   US   ISSN 0741-9449
MINNESOTA JOURNAL. 1983-1992; suspended. 22/yr. Citizens League, 708 3rd St., S., Ste. 500, Minneapolis, MN 55415.

CESSATIONS

340 US ISSN 0734-7537
KFM5870.A15
MINNESOTA TAX JOURNAL. 1982-1989. 4/yr. (looseleaf format) Butterworth Legal Publishers (St. Paul), 289 E. 5th St., St. Paul, MN 55101.
Formerly: Minnesota Tax Law Journal.

910.202 US
MINNESOTA TRAVEL AND RECREATION GUIDE. ceased. a. Rockford Map Publishers, Inc., 4525 Forest View Ave., Box 6126, Rockford, IL 61125.

015 910.03 US ISSN 0748-2302
Z1361.E4
MINORITIES IN AMERICA. ANNUAL BIBLIOGRAPHY. 1985-19?? irreg. (back issues avail.) Pennsylvania State University Press, 215 Wagner Bldg., University Park, PA 16802.

613 US ISSN 0886-876X
MINUTE-A-DAY HEALTH NEWSLETTER. 1984-1990 (Nov.). m. Crisis Prevention Institute, Inc., Box 15338, Plantation, FL 33318-5338.
Incorporates (1987-1990): Minute-a-Day Drug Letter (ISSN 0890-7366); Formerly (until 1986): Nitty-Gritty Health Newsletter.

574.92 JA ISSN 0493-4334
MISAKI MARINE BIOLOGICAL STATION. CONTRIBUTIONS. 1940-1988 (vol.34). a. Misaki Marine Biological Station - Tokyo Daigaku Rigakubu Fuzoku Rinkai Jikkensho, University of Tokyo, Koajiro, Miura 238-02, Japan.

052 IS
MISHKENOT SHA'ANANIM NEWSLETTER. 1984-1990 (no.13). q. (back issues avail.) Mishkenot Sha'ananim Ltd., P.O. Box 8215, Guest House, Cultural Center, Yemin Moshe, Israel.

370 IS
MISIFRUT HA-HINUKH; translations from the educational literature. 1969-19?? irreg. (approx. 3/yr.). Hebrew University of Jerusalem, School of Education, Jerusalem, Israel.

746.96 GW
MISS VOGUE. ceased 1990. m. Conde Nast Verlag GmbH, Leopoldstr. 44, 8000 Munich 40, Germany.

266 AT ISSN 0155-2902
MISSION REVIEW. ceased 1989. q. (back issues avail.) Uniting Church in Australia, Commission for Mission, 222 Pitt St., 5th Fl., Sidney, N.S.W. 2000, Australia.

268 UK ISSN 0021-4167
MISSIONLAND. 1955-1988. a. Pontifical Mission Aid Society of Holy Childhood, 23 Eccleston Square, London SW1V 1NU, England.
Formerly: Jambo.

378 016 US
MISSISSIPPI STATE UNIVERSITY ABSTRACTS OF THESES AND DISSERTATIONS. 1953-19?? biennial. Mississippi State University, Graduate School, c/o Mitchell Memorial Library, Box 5408, Mississippi State, MS 39762.
Formerly: Mississippi State University Abstracts of Theses (ISSN 0540-3847)

970 US ISSN 0076-9630
MISSOURI HANDBOOK SERIES. 1961-1976. irreg. University of Missouri Press, 2910 LeMone Blvd., Columbia, MO 65202.

296 US ISSN 0746-1291
MISSOURI JEWISH POST AND OPINION. ceased. w. (reprint service avail. from UMI) Spokesman Co., Inc., c/o Gabriel M. Cohen, Pub., 2120 N. Meridian St., IN 46202.

810 US ISSN 0076-9649
MISSOURI LITERARY FRONTIERS SERIES. 1968-1989. irreg. University of Missouri Press, 2910 LeMone Blvd., Columbia, MO 65202.

336 US
MISSOURI TAX REVIEW. 1978-1986. q. Department of Revenue, Box 629, Jefferson City, MO 65105.
Supersedes (in 1982): Missouri. Department of Revenue. Tax Information Bulletin.

620 627 JA
MITSUI ENGINEERING & SHIPBUILDING TECHNICAL BULLETIN. ceased. m. Mitsui Engineering and Shipbuilding Co. Ltd., Technical Research and Development Headquarters, 6-4, Tsukiji 5-chome, Chuo-ku, Tokyo, Japan.

020 GW ISSN 0043-6763
MITTEILUNGEN AUS DEM WISSENSCHAFTLICHEN BIBLIOTHEKSWESEN DER DDR. 1963-1989. m. (Ministerium fuer Hoch- und Fachshulwesen der DDR, Methodisches Zentrum fuer Wissenschaftliche Bibliotheken und Informations- und Dokumentationseinrichtungen) Beirat fuer das Wissenschaftliche Bibliothekswesen und die Wissenschaftliche Information, Unter den Linden 8, Postfach 1312, 1086 Berlin, Germany.

383 GW ISSN 0323-6315
MITTEILUNGEN P T. 1956-1991. bi-m. Deutsche Bundespost Telekom Zentrum fuer Telekommunikation, Oranienburgerstr. 70, 1040 Berlin, Germany.

616.7 GW ISSN 0341-5112
MOBIL; das Rheuma-Magazin. ceased 1990. bi-m. (Deutsche Rheuma-Liga e.V.) Verlag fuer Medizin Dr. Ewald Fischer GmbH, Fritz-Frey-Str. 21, Postfach 10 57 67, 6900 Heidelberg 1, Germany.

658.5 745.2 UK
MOBILE PLANT DESIGN AND COMPONENTS. 1979-198? bi-m. Trinity Publishing Ltd., Trinity House, Hercies Rd., Hillingdon, Middlesex UB10 9NA, England.

510 AT
MOBIUS. 1967-19?? a. Mathematical Association of South Australia, 163a Greenhill Rd., Parkside, S.A. 5066, Australia.
Formerly: Mathematical Association of South Australia. S.A. Mathematics Teacher (ISSN 0047-6242)

028.5 IT
MODA IN BABY. 1972-19?? q. Zanfi Editori s.r.l., Via Ganaceto 121, 41100 Modena, Italy.
Formerly: Linea Baby Junior.

646 GW ISSN 0026-7279
DIE MODE. 1958-1990. s-a. Zeitschriftenverlag fuer die Frau, Friedrich-Ebert-Str. 76-78, 7010 Leipzig, Germany.

659.152 US ISSN 0898-4980
MODEL; fashion & entertainment. 1989-1991. 10/yr. Family Media, Inc., Women's and Fashion Group, 3 Park Ave., New York, NY 10016.

790.13 US
MODEL SHOPPER; money saving ads and articles for the model hobbyist. 1987-199? m. Antic Publishing, Inc., 544 Second St., San Francisco, CA 94107.

790.13 UK ISSN 0955-1689
MODELLING AND MINIATURE CRAFTS. 1983-1990. s-a. (Guild of Master Craftsmen) Guild of Master Craftsman Publications Ltd., 166 High St., Lewes, East Sussex BN7 1XU, England.

371.9 NE ISSN 0076-9916
MODERN APPROACHES TO THE DIAGNOSIS AND INSTRUCTION OF MULTI-HANDICAPPED CHILDREN. 1971-1989 (vol.22). irreg. Swets Publishing Service (Subsidiary of: Swets en Zeitlinger B.V.), Heereweg 347, 2161 CA Lisse, Netherlands.

332.1 US
MODERN BANKING CHECKLISTS (SUPPLEMENT). ceased 199? base vols. (s-a. updates). Warren, Gorham and Lamont, One Penn Plaza, New York, NY 10119.

820 US
MODERN BRITISH LITERATURE. 1976-1980. s-a. (back issues avail.) Edward A. Kopper, Ed. & Pub., 108 Farmington Drive, Butler, PA 16001.

616.1 US ISSN 0026-7600
RC631.A1
MODERN CONCEPTS OF CARDIOVASCULAR DISEASE. 1932-1991 (Dec.). m. (also avail. in microform from UMI; back issues avail.; reprint service avail. from UMI) American Heart Association, 7272 Greenville Ave., Dallas, TX 75231-4596.

617.6 US ISSN 0894-7953
MODERN DENTAL PRACTICE. 1988-1989; suspended. q. Williams & Wilkins, 428 E. Preston St., Baltimore, MD 21202.

617.6 US
MODERN DENTALAB. 1983-1991. bi-m. Stevens Publishing Corp., 225 N. New Rd., Waco, TX 76710.

671.37 US
MODERN DEVELOPMENTS IN POWDER METALLURGY. 1960-1989 (vol.21). quadrennial. (reprint service avail. from UMI) Metal Powder Industries Federation, 105 College Rd. E., Princeton, NJ 08540.
Formerly: International Powder Metallurgy Conference. Proceedings - Modern Developments in Powder Metallurgy (ISSN 0074-7513)

950 CN
MODERN EAST ASIAN STUDIES. 1980-19?? irreg. University of Toronto Press, 63A St. George St., Toronto, Ont. M5S 1A6, Canada.

420 375.4 JA
MODERN ENGLISH JOURNAL/EIGO KYOIKU JAANARU. 1970-19?? a. (also avail. in microform from UMI) Seido Language Institute, 12-6 Funado-cho, Ashiya, Hyogo 659, Japan.

340 GW ISSN 0026-7953
LAW
MODERN LAW AND SOCIETY; a review of German-language research contributions on law, political science, and sociology. (Also issued as: German Studies, Section II) 1968-1991. s-a. (reprint service avail from ISI) Institut fuer Wissenschaftliche Zusammenarbeit - Institute for Scientific Co-Operation, Landhausstr. 18, 7400 Tuebingen, Germany.

610 CN ISSN 0026-8097
MODERN MEDICINE OF CANADA; the journal of diagnosis and treatment. 1946-1991. m. South Times Publishing Ltd., 1450 Don Mills Rd., Don Mills, Ont. M3B 2X7, Canada.

610 UK ISSN 0026-8100
MODERN MEDICINE OF GREAT BRITAIN. 1956-1991. m. (also avail. in microfilm from UMI) Findlay Publications Ltd., Franks Hall, Horton Kirby, Kent DA9 4LL, England.

651 AT ISSN 0810-9451
HF5548.2 CODEN: MOOFDE
MODERN OFFICE. 1961-19?? 11/yr. (also avail. in microform from UMI) Peter Isaacson Publications Pty. Ltd., 45-50 Porter St., Prahran, Vic. 3181, Australia.
Formerly: Modern Office and Data Management (ISSN 0311-7731); Which was formed by the merger of: Modern Office Administration; Modern Office (ISSN 0047-7737); Data Trend (ISSN 0011-6947)

770 US ISSN 0026-8240
TR1 CODEN: MPHOAA
MODERN PHOTOGRAPHY. 1937-1989 (Jul.). m. (also avail. in microform from UMI) Diamandis Communications, Inc., 1633 Broadway, New York, NY 10009.

770 US
MODERN PHOTOGRAPHY VIDEO MAGAZINE. 1987-1989. q. (avail. only on video caassette) Hachette Magazines, Inc., 1633 Broadway, New York, NY 10009.

779.05 US
MODERN PHOTOGRAPHY'S PHOTO BUYING GUIDE. 1969-1989. a. Hachette Magazines, Inc., 1633 Broadway, New York, NY 10009.

800 US
MODERN SHORT STORIES. 1988-1991. q. Claggk Publications, Inc., Bldg. A, Ste. 101, 4820 Alpine Pl., Las Vegas, NV 89017.

617 US ISSN 0196-1918
MODERN TECHNICS IN SURGERY. ABDOMINAL SURGERY. 1980-198? irreg. (approx. a.). Futura Publishing Company, Inc., 2 Bedford Ridge Rd., Box 330, Mount Kisco, NY 10549.

CESSATIONS

617.54   US   ISSN 0163-7029
MODERN TECHNICS IN SURGERY. CARDIAC - THORACIC SURGERY. 1979-198? irreg. (approx. a.). Futura Publishing Company, Inc., 2 Bedford Ridge Rd., Box 330, Mount Kisco, NY 10549.

617.95   US   ISSN 0276-9387
MODERN TECHNICS IN SURGERY. PLASTIC SURGERY. 1981-198? irreg. (approx a.). Futura Publishing Company, Inc., 2 Bedford Ridge Rd., Box 330, Mount Kisco, NY 10549.

300   US
MODERN TIMES. 1973-198? 10/yr. (also avail. in microform from UMI,MIM) 186 Hampshire St., Cambridge, MA 02139.
   Supersedes (in 1983): Working Papers Magazine (ISSN 0744-9836); Formerly (until 1981): Working Papers for a New Society (ISSN 0091-1615)

355   US   ISSN 1041-4967
MODERN WARFARE. 1989-199? bi-m. Empire Press, 602 S. King St., Ste. 300, Leesburg, VA 22075.

647.9   AU   ISSN 0026-8704
MODERNES HOTEL; Hotel und Restaurant im Dienste des Fremdenverkehrs. 1925-19?? m. (tabloid format) Hotel Verlag, Leopold Steinergasse 50, A-1190 Vienna, Austria.

380.1   US   ISSN 0276-0959
HD9999.B253
MODERN'S MARKET GUIDE. 1966-19?? a. Vance Publishing Corporation, 400 Knightsbridge Parkway, Lincolnshire, IL 60069.

054.1   FR   ISSN 0026-8747
MODES DE PARIS. ceased. w. Publications Editions Mondiales, 2 rue des Italiens, 75009 Paris, France.

574   US
MOLECULAR BIOLOGY (SAN DIEGO); an international series of monographs and textbooks. 1961-1987 (vol.24, part 7). irreg. (reprint service avail. from ISI) Academic Press, Inc., 1250 Sixth Ave., San Diego, CA 92101.

615.9   US
MOLECULAR TOXICOLOGY. 1986-1992. q. (also avail. in microform from UMI; reprint service avail. from UMI) Hemisphere Publishing Corporation (Subsidiary of: Taylor & Francis Group), 1900 Frost Rd., Ste. 101, Bristol, PA 19007-1598.
   Formerly (until 1987): Molecular Biology and Toxicology (ISSN 0883-9492)

639.3   US
MOLLUSK FARMING U S A. 1976-1990. bi-m. Aquaculture Digest, 11057 Negley Ave., San Diego, CA 92131.
   Supersedes in part (in 1989): Aquaculture Digest (ISSN 0193-3140)

669   US
MOLYBDENUM MOSAIC; the journal of molybdenum technology. ceased 1987 (vol.10). q. Climax Molybdenum Co. of MI, Box 407, Ypsilanti, MI 48197.

378   AT   ISSN 0159-950X
MONASH REVIEW; what's new in education, research and community service. 1969-1989. 6/yr. (back issues avail.) Monash University, Information Office, Wellington Rd., Clayton, Vic. 3168, Australia.

510 310   JA
MONBU-SHO TOKEI SURI KENKYUJO NENPO/INSTITUTE OF STATISTICAL MATHEMATICS. ANNUAL REPORT. 1967-19?? a. Monbu-sho Tokei Suri Kenkyujo - Ministry of Education, Institute of Statistical Mathematics, 6-7, Minami-Azabu 4-chome, Minato-ku, Tokyo 106, Japan.

551   FR
MONDE ET MINERAUX; mineralogie, paleontologie, geologie. 1974-19?? bi-m. c/o Pascal Entremont, 18, Passage Verdeau, 75009 Paris, France.

332.6   US
MONEY DYNAMICS LETTER. 1982-1990 (Oct.). m. Money Dynamics Letter Publishing Co., 675 Bering Dr., Ste. 160, Houston, TX 77057.

330.9   US
MONEY: MARKETS AND POLICY. 1986-1989. 6/yr. Conference Board, Inc., 845 Third Ave., New York, NY 10022.

338   US   ISSN 0077-040X
MONITOR (ALBANY); the voice of industry in New York State. 1914-19?? irreg. Business Council of New York State, Inc., 152 Washington Ave., Albany, NY 12210.

001.6   US   ISSN 0882-3944
MONITOR (ARLINGTON). 1983-199? m. Community Computers of Virginia, Inc., 2704 N. Pershing Dr., Arlington, VA 22201.

591   IT   ISSN 0391-1632
MONITORE ZOOLOGICO ITALIANO. MONOGRAFIE/ITALIAN JOURNAL OF ZOOLOGY. MONOGRAPHS. 1975-1987 (no.3). irreg. (back issues avail.; reprint service avail. from ISI) Universita degli Studi di Firenze, Dipartimento di Biologia Animale e Genetica, c/o L. Pardi, Ed., Via Romana 17, 50125 Florence, Italy.

551 560   US   ISSN 0077-085X
MONOGRAPHS IN GEOLOGY AND PALEONTOLOGY. 1967; ceased same year. irreg. (reprint service avail. from UMI) Princeton University Press, Princeton, NJ 08540.

574.19 612   US   ISSN 0094-8950
MONOGRAPHS IN LIPID RESEARCH. 1974-19?? irreg. Plenum Publishing Corp., 233 Spring St., New York, NY 10013.

940   US
MONOGRAPHS ON EUROPE. 1980-1981 (no.4). irreg. Harvard University, Center for European Studies, 27 Kirkland St., Cambridge, MA 02138-2043.

668.4   US
MONOGRAPHS ON PLASTICS SERIES. 1972-1973 (vol.1, pt.2). irreg. Marcel Dekker, Inc., 270 Madison Ave., New York, NY 10016.

659.1   US
MONOGRAPHS ON SEVERELY RESTRICTED OR FORBIDDEN ADVERTISING PRACTICES. ceased. s-a. International Advertising Association, 342 Madison Ave., Ste. 2000, New York, NY 10017.

051   US
MONROE. 1988-19?? m. Miotke Media & Marketing, Inc., RR 1 Box 128, Gulliver, MI 49840-9801.

388.324   US
MONSTER TRUCKS. ceased 198? q. Penthouse International Ltd., 1965 Broadway, New York, NY 10023.

616.8   CN
MONTAGE. 1975-198? bi-m. (tabloid format; back issues avail.) Clarke Institute of Psychiatry, Public Relations Office, 250 College St., Toronto, Ont. M5T 1R8, Canada.

663   US
MONTANA BEVERAGE ANALYST. (Subseries of: Northwest Beverage Analyst) 1935-1990 (Dec.). m. Bell Publications, Beverage Analyst Group, 2403 Champa St., Denver, CO 80205.

070   US
MONTANA FOURTH ESTATE. 1938-19?? m. Montana Press Association, 1900 N. Main, Ste. C, Helena, MT 59601.

633.11   US
MONTANA WHEAT SCOOP. ceased. m. (Montana Grain Growers Association) W E B P C O Publications, Box 2027, Wenatchee, WA 98801.

051   US
MONTEREY LIFE. 1979-199? m. Monterey Bay Magazine Co., Box 12135, Altanta, GA 30355-2135.

630   UK
MONTGOMERYSHIRE FARMER. 1980-198? m. N.F.U. Publications Ltd., 5 High East St., Dorchester, Dorset DT1 1HJ, England.

330.9   US
MONTHLY BUSINESS STARTS. 1986-1989. m. Dun & Bradstreet, Economic Analysis Department, 299 Park Ave., New York, NY 10171.

289.9   DK   ISSN 0901-2982
MONTHLY JOURNAL OF SCIENTOLOGY. ceased. m. Church of Scientology, Advanced Organisation Saint Hill Europe and Africa, Jernbanegade 6, DK-1608 Copenhagen V, Denmark.

336   US
MONTHLY TAX REPORT. ceased 1990. m. (back issues avail.) Laventhol & Horwath, 1845 Walnut St., Philadelphia, PA 19103.

700   SP
MONUMENTS DE LA CATALUNYA ROMANICA. (Contains 2 series: Comarques and Museus) 1978-19?? irreg. Artestudi Edicions, Provenca 552, Barcelona 26, Spain.

780   UR
MONUMENTS OF RUSSIAN MUSIC ART. 1972-1988 (no.12). irreg. Izdatel'stvo Muzyka, Ul. Neglinnaya 14, Moscow 103031, Russian S.F.S.R., U.S.S.R.

332.6   US   ISSN 0275-0201
HG3741
MOODY'S COMMERCIAL PAPER RECORD. 1981-198? m. Moody's Investors Service (Subsidiary of: Dun & Bradstreet Corporation), 99 Church St., New York, NY 10007-0300.
   Formed by the merger of: Moody's Commercial Paper Record. Monthly Statistical Supplement; Moody's Commercial Paper Record. Quarterly Reference Edition.

929   UK
MOOT: THIRKILL - THRELKELD FAMILY NEWSLETTER. 1973-1985. irreg., (approx. a.). c/o Eunice Wilson, Ed., 143 Harbord St., London SW6 6PN, England.
   Formerly: Moot.

808.81   US   ISSN 0882-147X
MORNING COFFEE CHAPBOOK SERIES. 1984-1991 (no. 30). 5/yr. (back issues avail.) Coffee House Press, 27 N. 4th St., Ste. 400, Minneapolis, MN 55401.

929   US   ISSN 0889-7247
MORRELL, MORRILL FAMILIES ASSOCIATION NEWSLETTER. 1981-1989. q. Morrell, Morrill Families Association, 3312 E. Costilla Ave., Littleton, CO 80122.

616.89   US
MORTON PRINCE DIGEST OF HYPNOTHERAPY. 1983-1990 (no.3); suspended. q. (back issues avail.) Institute for Research in Hypnosis & Psychotherapy, 1991 Broadway, Ste. 188, New York, NY 10023.

500   US   ISSN 0027-1284
Q11   CODEN: MOSAAG
MOSAIC (WASHINGTON). 1970-1992. 4/yr. (also avail. in microform from MCA,UMI) U.S. National Science Foundation, Science Resource Studies, Washington, DC 20550.

629.13   US   ISSN 1044-5129
MOSCOW AVIATION INSTITUTE. JOURNAL. 1991-1992. q. Hemisphere Publishing Corporation (Subsidiary of: Taylor & Francis Group), 1900 Frost Rd., Ste. 101, Bristol, PA 19007-1598.

647.9   US   ISSN 0148-7078
MOTEL - HOTEL INSIDER. 1968-19?? bi-m. (back issues avail.; reprint service avail. from UMI) Magna Publications, Inc., 2718 Dryden Dr., Madison, WI 53704.

658   CN
MOTIVATIONAL MARKETING. 1985-1986. 6/yr. Motivational Marketing Publishing Inc., 173 Waverly Rd., Toronto, Ont. M4L 3T4, Canada.

796.7   CN
LE MOTOCYCLISTE. ceased. 8/yr. Jevco Publishing Inc., 2021 Union St., Ste. 1150, Montreal, Que. H3A 2S9, Canada.

612 616.8   UK   ISSN 0263-7340
MOTOR ACTIVITY. ceased 1989. m. (looseleaf format; back issues avail.) Sheffield University Biomedical Information Service (SUBIS), The University, Sheffield S10 2TN, England.

629.2   UK
MOTOR AGENTS ASSOCIATION YEAR BOOK AND DIARY. 1983-198? a. Motor Agents Association Ltd., 201 Great Portland St., London W1N 6AB, England.

629.28   US   ISSN 0094-1514
TL152
MOTOR HANDBOOK. ceased. a. Hearst Corporation, Motor Manuals Department, 5600 Crooks Rd., Troy, MI 48098.
   Formerly: Motor's Handbook.

CESSATIONS

388.3   CN   ISSN 0027-190X
MOTOR IN CANADA; in the interests of the automotive trade in western Canada. 1915-1991 (Oct.). m. Sanford Evans Communications Ltd., 1077 St. James St., Box 6900, Winnipeg, Man. R3C 3B1, Canada.

629.2   SA
MOTOR INDUSTRY NEWS DIGEST. N.S. 1985-198? fortn. Ramsay, Son & Parker (Pty) Ltd., Box 180, Howard Place 7450, Cape Town, South Africa.

910.09   NO
DE MOTOR NYTT. 1972-1989. 4/yr. MoMagazine, Box 473, 2301 Hamar, Norway.
    Formerly: Norsk Motor Nytt; Incorporates: Du Store Verden.

796.75   UK   ISSN 0268-0831
MOTOR RACING; Britain's only monthly racing magazine. ceased. m. Motor Racing Magazines, Sovereign House, Brentwood, Essex CM14 4SE, England.

388   SZ
MOTOR SPORT AKTUELL. 1975-1990. w. Powerslide AG, Kreuzstrasse 60, 8032 Zurich, Switzerland.

796.7   US
MOTORCYCLE INDUSTRY BUSINESS JOURNAL. ceased. 8/yr. Hancock-Brown Corporation, Box 4295, Irvine, CA 92716-4295.

388.3   IE   ISSN 0027-2256
MOTORING LIFE. 1949-1991. m. Private Motorist Protection Association, Wolfe Tone St., Dublin 1, Ireland.

910   SP
MOTORMADRID. ceased. m. Tecnipublicaciones, S.A., Fernando VI, 27, 28004 Madrid, Spain.

796.7 910.202   GW
MOTORRAD TOUREN. 1988-1992. bi-m. Motor-Presse Stuttgart, Leuschnerstr. 1, Postfach 106036, 7000 Stuttgart 10, Germany.

610   US   ISSN 0077-1740
MOUNT ZION HOSPITAL AND MEDICAL CENTER, SAN FRANCISCO. BULLETIN. 1953-1986? 4/yr. Mount Zion Hospital and Medical Center, Box 7921, San Francisco, CA 94120.

051   US   ISSN 0027-2558
MOUNTAIN LIFE AND WORK; magazine of the Appalachian South. 1925-19?? q. (also avail. in microform from UMI; reprint service avail. from UMI) Council of the Southern Mountains, Inc., Box 546, Pineville, KY 40977.
    Formerly: Southern Mountain Life and Work.

051   US   ISSN 0191-9482
MOUNTAINWEST MAGAZINE; from the Grand Teton to the Grand Canyon. ceased 1980? m. Mountainwest Publications, c/o Reed H. Blake, Ed., 2883 Indian Hills Dr., Provo, UT 84604.

371.42   US
MOVING UP. 1986-198? 4/yr. Alan Weston Communications, Inc., 303 N. Glenoaks Blvd., Ste. 600, Burbank, CA 91502.
    Incorporates: Ampersand.

301.412 640   US
MOXIE. 1989-1990; suspended. m. Wieder Health & Fitness, Inc., 21100 Erwin St., Woodland Hills, CA 91367.

612.015 616.3   UK   ISSN 0142-8748
MUCOPOLYSACCHARIDES. ceased 1990. m. (looseleaf format; back issues avail.) Sheffield University Biomedical Information Service (SUBIS), The University, Sheffield S10 2TN, England.

576   UK   ISSN 0952-035X
MULTI DRUG RESISTANCE. ceased 1990. m. (looseleaf format; back issues avail.) Sheffield University Biomedical Information Service (SUBIS), The University, Sheffield S10 2TN, England.

690   US   ISSN 0146-0919
MULTI HOUSING NEWS. 1966-1991 (Jun.). m. (tabloid format) Gralla Publications, 1515 Broadway, New York, NY 10036.
    Formerly: Apartment Construction News (ISSN 0003-6358)

613.7 790.1   US
MULTI - SPORT FACILITY NEWS. 1977-1990. 4/yr. Sterling Southeast Inc., 1450 N.E. 123rd St., N. Miami, FL 33161-6051.
    Formerly: Fitness Industry Magazine.

332.6   US
MUNICIPAL BOND INTEREST RECORD. ceased 1991 (Mar.). w. Standard & Poor's Corporation, 25 Broadway, New York, NY 10004.
    Formerly: Municipal Registered Bond Interest Record.

346.006   US   ISSN 1055-5862
MUNICIPAL LIABILITY LITIGATION REPORTER; the national journal reporting civil rights litigation brought against public officials. 1987-1991 (Aug.). m. (looseleaf format; back issues avail.) Andrews Publications, 1646 West Chester Pike, Box 1000, Westtown, PA 19395.
    Formerly: Public Officials Liability Litigation Reporter (ISSN 0899-1472)

352   US   ISSN 0276-489X
JS39
MUNICIPAL YEAR BOOK DIRECTORIES. 1981-1988. a. International City Management Association, 1120 G St., N.W., Ste. 300, Washington, DC 20005.

331.8   HU   ISSN 0027-3600
MUNKA. 1951-1988 (Dec.). m. Szakszervezetek Orszagos Tanacsa, Dozsa Gyorgy ut 84 B, Budapest 6, Hungary.

033   DK   ISSN 0109-3347
MUNKSGAARDS SOCIAL AARBOG. 1984-198? a. Munksgaard International Publishers Ltd., P.O. Box 2148, DK-1016 Copenhagen K, Denmark.

028.5   US   ISSN 0737-6855
MUPPET MAGAZINE. 1982-1989 (no.25). q. Welsh Publishing Group, Inc., 300 Madison Ave., New York, NY 10017.

612.015 617.1   UK   ISSN 0261-4766
MUSCLE BIOCHEMISTRY. ceased 1990. m. (looseleaf format; back issues avail.) Sheffield University Biomedical Information Service (SUBIS), The University, Sheffield S10 2TN, England.

612 617.1   UK   ISSN 0261-4774
MUSCLE PHYSIOLOGY. ceased 1989. m. (looseleaf format; back issues avail.) Sheffield University Biomedical Information Service (SUBIS), The University, Sheffield S10 2TN, England.

800
MUSE. 1990-1991. irreg. (3/yr.) (back issues avail.) University of Arkansas at Little Rock, Office of Communications, 2801 S. University Ave., Little Rock, AR 72204.

808.81   US   ISSN 0898-2392
MUSE (BURLINGTON); the magazine for poets. 1987-1990; suspended. bi-m. Muse Magazine, Inc., Box 45, Burlington, NC 27216-0045.
    Formerly: Muse Letter.

708.4   FR   ISSN 0027-3767
MUSEE CARNAVALET. BULLETIN. 1948-1983 (no.36). s-a. (back issues avail.) Societe des Amis du Musee Carnavalet, 23 rue de Sevigne, 75003 Paris, France.

572   SZ   ISSN 0072-0828
MUSEE D'ETHNOGRAPHIE DE LA VILLE DE GENEVE. BULLETIN ANNUEL. 1958-1990. a. Musee d'Ethnographie de la Ville de Geneve, 65-67 Bd. Carl-Vogt, 1205 Geneva, Switzerland.

500.9 915   FR
MUSEE NATIONAL D'HISTOIRE NATURELLE, PARIS. NOTES ET MEMOIRES SUR LE MOYEN-ORIENT. 1933-19?? irreg. Museum National d'Histoire Naturelle, 38 rue Geoffroy Saint-Hilaire, 75005 Paris, France.
    Formerly (until vol.5): Musee National d'Histoire Naturelle, Paris. Notes et Memoires de la Section d'Etudes Geologiques de Haut-Commissariat Francais en Syrie et au Liban.

301.2   DR
MUSEO DEL HOMBRE DOMINICANO. SERIE ESTUDIO Y ARTE. 1977-1978 (no.4). irreg. Museo del Hombre Dominicano, Calle Pedro Henriquez Urena, Plaza de la Cultura, Santo Domingo, Dominican Republic.

500.9 069   UY
MUSEO NACIONAL DE HISTORIA NATURAL. ANALES. ceased 1972 (vol.7, no.5). irreg. Museo Nacional de Historia Natural, Casilla de Correo 399, Montevideo, Uruguay.
    Formerly: Montevideo. Museo de Historia Natural. Anales.

069   IT
MUSEOLOGIA (FLORENCE). 1972-198? (no.18). a. Universita Internazionale dell'Arte, Centro di Studi per la Museologia, Via Incontri, 3, 50139 Florence, Italy.

069   IT
MUSEOLOGIA (NAPLES). 1977-1988. s-a. Edizioni Scientifiche Italiane s.p.a., Via Chiatamone, 7, I-80121 Naples, Italy.

069   US   ISSN 0027-397X
MUSEOLOGIST. 1935-1989 (no.181). q. (processed; also avail. in microfilm; reprint service avail.) Mid-Atlantic Association of Museum, Box 817, Newark, DE 19715-0817.

500   BL   ISSN 0077-2240
    CODEN: MPEPAW
MUSEU PARAENSE EMILIO GOELDI. PUBLICACOES AVULSAS. 1964-1986 (no.40). irreg. Conselho Nacional de Desenvolvimento Cientifico e Tecnologico, Museu Paraense Emilio Goeldi, Av. Magalhaes Barata, 376, C.P. 399, 66000 Belem, Para, Brazil.

913   NR
MUSEUM AFRICUM; West African journal of classical and related studies. 1972-1987 (vol.8). a. University of Ibadan, Department of Classics, Ibadan, Nigeria.
    Supersedes: Nigeria and the Classics (ISSN 0549-2629)

708   US   ISSN 0884-1918
AM13.W3
MUSEUM & ARTS WASHINGTON. 1985-1991. bi-m. Museum & Arts Washington, Inc., 1707 L St., N.W., Ste. 222, Washington, DC 20036.

069   CN   ISSN 0701-9548
MUSEUM METHODS MANUALS. 1973-19?? irreg. Royal British Columbia Museum, 675 Belleville St., Victoria, B.C. V8V 1X4, Canada.

500.9   FR   ISSN 0078-9720
MUSEUM NATIONAL D'HISTOIRE NATURELLE, PARIS. ANNUAIRE. 1939-1982 (no.13). a. Museum National d'Histoire Naturelle, 38 rue Geoffroy Saint-Hilaire, 75005 Paris, France.

500.9   FR   ISSN 0078-9739
    CODEN: AMNNAK
MUSEUM NATIONAL D'HISTOIRE NATURELLE, PARIS. ARCHIVES. 1802-19?? irreg. Museum National d'Histoire Naturelle, 38 rue Geoffroy Saint-Hilaire, 75005 Paris, France.

016   FR   ISSN 0085-476X
MUSEUM NATIONAL D'HISTOIRE NATURELLE, PARIS. BIBLIOTHEQUE CENTRALE. LISTE DES PERIODIQUES FRANCAIS ET ETRANGERS. SUPPLEMENT. 1971-1980. a. Museum National d'Histoire Naturelle, Bibliotheque Centrale, 38 rue Geoffrey St. Hilaire, 75005 Paris, France.

500.907   FR
MUSEUM NATIONAL D'HISTOIRE NATURELLE, PARIS. LABORATOIRE D'ETHNOBOTANIQUE. PUBLICATIONS DIVERSES. 1933-1988 (vol.35). irreg. Museum National d'Histoire Naturelle, Laboratoire d'Ethnobotanique, 57 rue Cuvier, 75005 Paris, France.

530 541   FR   ISSN 0078-9771
MUSEUM NATIONAL D'HISTOIRE NATURELLE, PARIS. MEMOIRES. NOUVELLE SERIE. SERIE D. SCIENCES PHYSICO-CHIMIQUES. 1950-1969 (vol.4). irreg. Museum National d'Histoire Naturelle, 38 rue Geoffroy Saint-Hilaire, 75005 Paris, France.

850 100   IT
MUSEUM PATAVINUM. SEMESTRALE. 1983-19?? s-a. (Universita degli Studi di Padova. Facolta di Lettere e Filosofia) Casa Editrice Leo. S. Olschki, Viuzzo del Pozzetto (Viale Europa), 50126 Florence, Italy.

069　　　　　　　US　　ISSN 0733-0960
AM1
MUSEUM STUDIES JOURNAL. 1983-198? (vol.3, no.2). s-a. John F. Kennedy University, Center for Museum Studies, 1500 Sixteenth St., San Francisco, CA 94103.

631　　　　　　　US
MUSHROOM NEWSWIRE. 1980-1990. irreg. American Mushroom Institute, 907 E. Baltimore Pike, Kennett Sq., PA 19348.

780　　　　　　　UK　　ISSN 0952-2697
MUSIC & MUSICIANS INTERNATIONAL. 1952-1990. m. Orpheus Publications (Subsidiary of: Filmtrax Plc.), Unit 8 Primrose Mews, 1a Sharpleshall St., London NW1 8YL, England.
　　Formerly (until Jun. 1987): Music and Musicians (ISSN 0027-4232); Incorporates: Records and Recordings.

780　　　　　　　US　　ISSN 0273-8902
ML3469
MUSIC & SOUND OUTPUT. 1980-1989. m. Testa Communications, Inc., 25 Willowdale Ave., Port Washington, NY 11050.

780.42　　　　　　US
MUSIC BUSINESS CONTACTS. 1980-19?? bi-m. Music-by-Mail, Box 6101, Long Island City, NY 11106.

785　　　　　　　US
MUSIC EDUCATORS NATIONAL CONFERENCE. SELECTIVE MUSIC LISTS: INSTRUMENTAL SOLOS AND ENSEMBLES. 1972-1979. irreg. Music Educators National Conference, 1902 Association Dr., Reston, VA 22091.

788　　　　　　　US　　ISSN 0077-2402
MUSIC EDUCATORS NATIONAL CONFERENCE. SELECTIVE MUSIC LISTS: VOCAL SOLOS AND ENSEMBLES. 1968-1974. irreg. Music Educators National Conference, 1902 Association Dr., Reston, VA 22091.

780　　　　　　　US
MUSIC INDUSTRY PRODUCTS. 1983-198? q. Steve Tolin Enterprises, Inc., Box 2772, Palm Springs, CA 92263-2772.

780　　　　　　　US
MUSIC MART. 1990-1991 (May). m. Krause Publications, Inc., 700 E. State St., Iola, WI 54990.

781.6　　　　　　CN　　ISSN 0380-5131
ML5
MUSIC SCENE. 1967-1990 (Jan.-Feb.). bi-m. (also avail. in microform from MML) Performing Rights Organization of Canada Ltd., 41 Valleybrook Dr., Don Mills, Ont. M3B 2S6, Canada.

780　　　　　　　US　　ISSN 0027-447X
ML1
MUSIC TEMPO. 1961-19?? bi-m. King Enterprises, 4136 Peak St., Toledo, OH 43612.

789.91　　　　　　US　　ISSN 0735-777X
TK7881.7
MUSICAL AMERICA; the journal of classical music. (In 2 eds.: Consumer Edition, Trade Edition) 1898-1992. bi-m. (also avail. in microform from UMI,MIM; reprint service avail. from UMI) Musical America Publishing Inc., 825 Seventh Ave., 8th Fl., New York, NY 10019.
　　Incorporates (in Apr. 1988): Opus (ISSN 8750-488X); Formerly (until 1987): High Fidelity - Musical America (ISSN 0018-1463)

780　　　　　　　CN　　ISSN 0700-4745
ML5
MUSICANADA. 1976-1990. q. Canadian Music Council - Conseil Canadien de la Musique, 36 Elgin St., Ottawa, Ont. K1P 5K5, Canada.
　　Formerly: Canada Music Book (ISSN 0007-9634)

780 016　　　　　　GW　　ISSN 0323-438X
MUSIK - INFORMATION; bibliographische Titeluebersicht. (Two introductory numbers called Jahrg. O, Heft A, were issued in 1970) 1971-1990. m. (Deutsche Hochschule fuer Musik "Hanns Eisler") Leitstelle fuer Information und Dokumentation "Musik", Otto-Grotewohl-Strasse 19, 1080 Berlin, Germany.

780　　　　　　　DK　　ISSN 0900-1204
MUSIK NYT. 1985-198? m. Musikexpressen, Meterbuen 6-12, 2740 Skovlunde, Denmark.

781.7　　　　　　GW　　ISSN 0323-5106
ML5
MUSIKFORUM; Zeitschrift fuer musikalisches Volksschaffen. 1956-1989. 4/yr. Zentralhaus fuer Kulturarbeit, Dittrichring 4, Postfach 1051, 701 Leipzig, Germany.
　　Formerly: Volksmusik (ISSN 0042-8558)

636.1　　　　　　US
MUSTANG! (ROLLINGSTONE); an adventure in our Western heritage. 1989-19?? q. Mustang Creek, Inc., RR 1, Box 112AA, Rollingstone, MN 55969.

332.6327　　　　　　US
MUTUAL FUND ADVANTAGE. 1986-1988 (vol.2, no. 22). m. Triversal Marketing Co., Box 4689, Medford, OR 97501.

332.6　　　　　　　US
MUTUAL FUND QUARTERLY. 1988-198? q. Gryphon Publishing Co., 819 Second St., Ste. B-284, Manchester, NH 03102-5211.

289.9　　　　　　　SA
MUTWALISI. ceased. q. (Church of the Nazarene) Africa Nazarene Publications, P.O. Box 1288, Florida, Transvaal 1710, South Africa.

333.7　　　　　　RM
MUZEUL DE ISTORIE AL REPUBLICII SOCIALISTE ROMANIA. CERCETARI DE CONSERVARE SI RESTAURARE A PATRIMONIULUI MUZEAL. 1981-19?? irreg. Muzeul de Istorie al Republicii Socialiste Romania, Calea Victoriei 12, Bucharest, Rumania.

940.8　　　　　　RM
MUZEUL DE ISTORIE AL REPUBLICII SOCIALISTE ROMANIA. CERCETARI ISTORICE. 1979-19?? irreg. Muzeul de Istorie al Republicii Socialiste Romania, Calea Victoriei 12, Bucharest, Rumania.

708　　　　　　　RM
MUZEUL NATIONAL. 1974-19?? a. Muzeul de Istorie al Republicii Socialiste Romania, Calea Victoriei Nr.12, Bucharest, Rumania.

069　　　　　　　RM
MUZEUL SI EDUCATIA SOCIALISTA. 1977-19?? irreg. Muzeul de Istorie al Republicii Socialiste Romania, Calea Victoriei 12, Bucharest, Rumania.

069　　　　　　　PL　　ISSN 0509-6936
MUZEUM NARODOWE W WARSZAWIE. ROCZNIK/MUSEE NATIONAL DE VARSOVIE. ANNUAIRE. 1938-1988; suspended. a. (back issues avail.) Muzeum Narodowe w Warszawie, Al. Jerozolimskie 3, Warsaw, Poland.

914.706　　　　　　CN　　ISSN 0027-5417
AP58.U5
MY I SVIT/WE AND THE WORLD. 1950-1985 (vol.36). m. (back issues avail.) Mykola Kolankiwsky, Ed. & Pub., c/o Niagara Falls Art Gallery and Museum, Queen Elizabeth Way, R.R.2., Niagara Falls, Ont. L2E 6S5, Canada.

612 616.1　　　　　UK　　ISSN 0261-4790
MYOCARDIUM. ceased 1989. m. (looseleaf format; back issues avail.) Sheffield University Biomedical Information Service (SUBIS), The University, Sheffield S10 2TN, England.

808.838　　　　　　US
MYSTERY TIME ANTHOLOGY. 1983-1992. a. (back issues avail.) Hutton Publications, Box 1870, Hayden, ID 83835.
　　Formerly: Mystery Time (ISSN 0886-2958)

332 301.412　　　　　US
N A B W EXCHANGE. 1975-1989. bi-m. (National Association of Bank Women) P.M. Haeger & Associates, Inc., 500 N. Michgan Ave., Ste. 1400, Chicago, IL 60611.

796.41　　　　　　US　　ISSN 0363-9282
GV464
N A G W S GUIDE. GYMNASTICS. 1963-19?? quadrennial. (American Alliance for Health, Physical Education, Recreation, and Dance, National Association for Girls and Women in Sport) A A H P E R D Publications, 1900 Association Dr., Reston, VA 22091.
　　Formerly: Gymnastics Guide.

CESSATIONS 5241

796.342　　　　　　US　　ISSN 0272-863X
GV991
N A G W S GUIDE. TENNIS. 1938-1988. biennial. American Alliance for Health, Physical Education, Recreation, and Dance, National Association for Girls and Women in Sport, 1900 Association Dr., Reston, VA 22091.
　　Supersedes in part: Tennis - Badminton - Squash Guide (ISSN 0065-7042); Tennis - Badminton Guide.

368　　　　　　　US　　ISSN 0027-5867
N A I I PRESS SAMPLINGS. 1967-1991. bi-m. National Association of Independent Insurers, 2600 River Rd., Des Plaines, IL 60018.

657　　　　　　　US　　ISSN 0077-3360
N A M F ACCOUNTING MANUAL; a uniform accounting system for metal finishers. 1968-19?? irreg. National Association of Metal Finishers, 111 E. Wacker Dr., Chicago, IL 60601.

380　　　　　　　US
N A M - N I C SPEAKERS DIRECTORY. 1983-1987. every 2-3/yrs. National Association of Manufacturers, 1331 Pennsylvania Ave. NW, Ste. 1500-North, Washington, DC 20004-1703.

613.7　　　　　　US　　ISSN 0276-461X
GV223
N A P E H E PROCEEDINGS. 1979-1986 (vol.6). a. (back issues avail.) (National Association for Physical Education in Higher Education) Human Kinetics Publishers, Inc., Box 5076, Champaign, IL 61820.
　　Former titles: National Association for Physical Education for College Women; (until 1978): N C P E A M Proceedings (National College Physical Education Association for Men).

332　　　　　　　US
N A P FORUM. 1966-19?? q. (National Association of the Professions) Physicians Planning Services Corp., 292 Madison Ave., New York, NY 10017.

615.19　　　　　　US　　ISSN 0736-5233
N A R D HOME HEALTH CARE PHARMACY BULLETIN. 1983-1988. bi-m. National Association of Retail Druggists, 205 Daingerfield Rd., Alexandria, VA 22314.

332.6　　　　　　　US
N A S D A Q NOTES. (National Association of Securities Dealers Automated Quotations) ceased. m. National Association of Securities Dealers, Inc., 1735 K St., N.W., Washington, DC 20006.

332.6 658　　　　　　US
N A S D EXECUTIVE DIGEST. ceased. bi-m. National Association of Securities Dealers, Inc., 1735 K St., N.W., Washington, DC 20006-1506.

332.6　　　　　　　US
N A S D NEWSLETTER. 1975-198? s-a. National Association of Securities Dealers Inc., 1735 K St. N.W., Washington, DC 20006.
　　Formerly: N A S D News.

020　　　　　　　II
N A S S D O C RESEARCH INFORMATION SERIES. SOCIAL SCIENCE NEWS; index to select Indian newspapers in English. (National Social Science Documentation Centre) 1986-19?? suspended. m. Indian Council of Science Documentation Centre, Indian Council of Social Sciences Research, 35, Ferozshah Road, New Delhi 110 001, India.

677　　　　　　　US
N A T A D NEWSLETTER. ceased. q. National Association of Textile and Apparel Distributors, P.O. Box 759, Mamaroneck, NY 10543.

332　　　　　　　US
N B A NEWS REPORT. ceased. bi-m. National Bankers Association, 122 C St., N.W., Ste. 580, Washington, DC 20001.

020　　　　　　　US
N C L I S NEWS. ceased after one issue, 1990. irreg. U.S. National Commission on Libraries and Information Science, 1111 18th St. NW, Ste. 310, Washington, DC 20036.

540　　　　　　　SA
N C R L NEWS. ceased. 6/m. (National Chemical Research Laboratory) Council for Scientific and Industrial Research, Publishing Division, P.O. Box 395, Pretoria 0001, South Africa.

CESSATIONS

658.3 US
N C S L EXCHANGE. vol.4, 1974-1992; suspended. m. National Civil Service League, Center for Public Personnel Management, 3600 Gunston Rd., Alexandria, VA 22302.

621 669 US ISSN 0271-1079
TJ1189
N C SHOPOWNER. (Numerical Control) 1980-19?? 12/yr. (also avail. in microform from UMI; back issues avail.; reprint service avail.) McGraw-Hill, Inc., 1221 Ave. of the Americas, New York, NY 10020.

300 PH
N D S P - U P RESEARCH ILLUSTRATED. 1976-1981 (vol.5, no.1). q. University of the Philippines, Office of Research Coordination, Quezon City 3004, Philippines.

620 UK ISSN 0262-0057
N E I NEWS. 1977-1989. q. Northern Engineering Industries plc., N.E.I. House, Regent Centre, Newcastle-upon-Tyne NE3 3SB, England.

539.7 614.7 US
N E S P NEWSLETTER. 1973-1987. q. (back issues avail.) (National Environmental Studies Project) Nuclear Management and Resources Council, Inc., 1776 Eye St., N.W., Washington, DC 20006.

700 780 US
N F A A ARTS ALUMNI DIRECTORY; roster of awards of the arts recognition and talent search. 1983-1987. a. National Foundation for Advancement in the Arts, 3915 Biscayne Blvd., 2nd Fl., Miami, FL 33137.

500 016 US
N F A I S BULLETIN. 1987-198? (vol.3, no.6). bi-m. National Federation of Abstracting and Information Services, 1429 Walnut St., Philadelphia, PA 19102.

370 PH ISSN 0115-8473
N F E - W I D EXCHANGE - ASIA. OCCASIONAL PAPER. 1981-1984. irreg. (back issues avail.) University of the Philippines at Los Banos, College of Agriculture, Department of Agricultural Education and Rural Studies, Laguna 4031, Philippines.

380.5 US
N F T A ON THE MOVE. 1967-19?? q. Niagara Frontier Transportation Authority, 181 Ellicott St., Buffalo, NY 14205.
Formerly (until 1973): N F T A Newsletter.

621.38 JA ISSN 0027-6553
CODEN: NHKTAT
N H K GIJUTSU KENKYU/N H K TECHNICAL JOURNAL. (Nippon Hoso Kyokai) 1949-19?? 2/yr. Japan Broadcasting Corp., Science & Technical Research Laboratories, 41-1 Udagawa-cho, Shibuya-ku, Tokyo 150, Japan.

621.38 JA ISSN 0027-6561
N H K GIKEN GEPPO/N H K TECHNICAL REPORT. (Nippon Hoso Kyokai) 1958-19?? m. Japan Broadcasting Corp., Science & Technical Research Laboratories, Information Services & Patents Division, 1-10-11 Kinuta, Setagaya-ku, Tokyo 157, Japan.

621.38 JA ISSN 0027-657X
N H K LABORATORIES NOTE. (Nippon Hoso Kyokai) 1966-19?? irreg. (10-12/yr.). (processed) Japan Broadcasting Corp., Science & Technical Research Laboratories, Information Services & Patents Division, 1-10-11 Kinuta, Setagaya-ku, Tokyo 157, Japan.

621.38 JA ISSN 0077-2631
CODEN: NHOKAM
N H K TECHNICAL MONOGRAPH. (Nippon Hoso Kyokai) 1963-1987 (no.37). a. Japan Broadcasting Corp., Science & Technical Research Laboratories, Information Services & Patents Division, 1-10-11 Kinuta, Setagaya-ku, Tokyo 150, Japan.

796 CN ISSN 0079-5569
N.H.L. PRO HOCKEY. 1969-19?? a. PaperJacks Ltd., 330 Steelcase Rd. E., Markham, Ont. L3R 2M1, Canada.

301.4157 301.412 US
N H LAMBDA NEWSLETTER. (New Hampshire) ceased 1989. m. TriFleg Press, 10 Piermont St., Nashua, NH 03063.

333.91 SA
N I W R INFORMATION SHEET. 1974-1985 (no.20). irreg. Division of Water Technology, Box 395, Pretoria 0001, South Africa.

338.47 647.95 US
N L B A NEWS. ceased 1989. bi-m. National Licensed Beverage Association, 4214 King St., W., Alexandria, VA 22302.

651.2 747 US
N O P A SPECIAL REPORT. ceased 1989 (Dec.). 6/yr. National Office Products Association, 301 N. Fairfax St., Alexandria, VA 22314.

361 NE
N O W NIEUWS. 1971-1988 (Dec.). m. Nederlandse Organisatie van Welzijnswerkers, Postbus 578, 3500 AN Utrecht, Netherlands.
Former titles: N V M W Nieuws; Sleutelaar (ISSN 0049-0725)

658.8 US ISSN 0027-6901
N P N BULLETIN; a weekly information service for important people in oil marketing. (National Petroleum News) 1961-1980. w. Hunter Publishing Co., Inc., 950 Lee St., Des Plaines, IL 60016.

530 SA
N P R L NEWSLETTER. ceased. a. (National Physical Research Institute) Council for Scientific and Industrial Research, Publishing Division, P.O. Box 395, Pretoria 0001, South Africa.

510 SA
N R I M S CURRENT ACTIVITIES. ceased. q. (National Research Institute for Mathematical Sciences) Council for Scientific and Industrial Research, Publishing Division, P.O. Box 395, Pretoria 0001, South Africa.

350 US
N R P A WASHINGTON ACTION REPORT. 1972-19?? fortn. National Recreation and Park Association, 3101 Park Center Dr., Alexandria, VA 22302.

370 US
N S T F REPORT. 1971-198? s-a. (National Scholarship Trust Fund) Graphic Arts Technical Foundation, 4615 Forbes Ave., Pittsburgh, PA 15213-3796.

786 US
N Y CITY OPERA SPOTLIGHT. (New York) suspended 1989. 4/yr. New York City Opera Guild, New York State Theater, Lincoln Center, New York, NY 10023.

051 US
N Y N Y: THE BEST OF NEW YORK. 1986-1987. m. P.J. Vane, Pub., 170 Second Ave., New York, NY 10003.

327 US
N.Y. PEACELETTER. ceased. q. (looseleaf format) Women Strike for Peace, 1930 Chestnut St., Ste. 1500, Philadelphia, PA 19103.

632.9 US
N Y S PESTICIDES RECOMMENDS (REDBOOK). (New York State) ceased. a. Cornell University, Media Services, 7-8 Business and Technology Park, Ithaca, NY 14850.

378.198 US
N Y U ALUMNI NEWS. 1955-1989. q. (tabloid format; back issues avail.) Alumni Federation of New York University, Inc., 25 West 4th St., Ste. 516, New York, NY 10012.
Formerly: New York University Alumni News.

380.5 NZ ISSN 0027-7193
N.Z.H. MAANDBLAD. ceased. bi-m. Noord-Zuid-Hollandse Vervoer Mij - North-South-Holland Transport Co., Leidsevaart 396, Haarlem, Netherlands.

387.7 GW ISSN 0027-7428
NACHRICHTEN FUER DIE ZIVILE LUFTFAHRT, DEUTSCHE DEMOKRATISCHE REPUBLIK. 1958-1990 (no.1). m. Ministerium fuer Verkehrswesen, Hauptverwaltung der Zivilen Luftfahrt, 108 Berlin, Germany.

300 UN
NAMIBIA STUDIES SERIES. 1978-19?? irreg. (back issues avail.) United Nations Institute for Namibia, Publications Section, P.O. Box 33811, Lusaka, Zambia.

320.9 PY ISSN 0047-8644
NANDE. 1959-198?; suspended. m. Editorial Emegebe S.A., Alberdi 1393, Asuncion, Paraguay.

929 US
NASE DEJINY; Czech genealogy and culture. 1980-198? bi-m. Old Homestead Publishing Co., Rt. 3, Box 7688, Hallettsville, TX 77964.

330 SA
NATAL BUSINESS NEWS. ceased. bi-m. George Warman Publications (Pty.) Ltd., Box 3847, Cape Town 8000, South Africa.

629.1 II
NATIONAL AERONAUTICAL LABORATORY. CASE STUDIES. 1980-19?? irreg. National Aeronautical Laboratory, P.O. Box 1779, Kodihalli, Bangalore 560017, India.

629.1 011 II
NATIONAL AERONAUTICAL LABORATORY. SELECTED ABSTRACTS FROM RUSSIAN AND OTHER FOREIGN SCIENTIFIC LITERATURE. 1978-19?? n. National Aeronautical Laboratory, P.O. Box 1779, Kodihalli, Bangalore 560017, India.

629.13 US ISSN 0891-1703
TL506.U6
NATIONAL AIR AND SPACE MUSEUM. RESEARCH REPORT. ceased 1986. a. (National Air and Space Museum) Smithsonian Institution Press, 470 L'Enfant Plaza, Ste. 7100, Washington, DC 20560.

610.73 US
NATIONAL ASSOCIATION OF PEDIATRIC NURSE ASSOCIATES AND PRACTITIONERS. CHAPTERS' BULLETIN. ceased. bi-m. National Association of Pediatric Nurse Associates and Practitioners, 1101 Kings Hwy. N., No. 206, Cherry Hill, NJ 08034.

520 JA
QB4 CODEN: TKABAC
NATIONAL ASTRONOMICAL BULLETIN. 1927-1946; N.S. 1947-1988 (no.281). irreg. National Astronomical Observatory - Kokuritsu Tenmondai, Mitaka-shi, Tokyo 181, Japan.
Formerly: Tokyo Astronomical Bulletin (ISSN 0082-4690)

646.7 US
NATIONAL BARBER STYLING SCHOOL BULLETIN. 1950-1983. bi-m. (National Barber Styling School) Milady Publishing Company, 220 White Plains Rd., Tarrytown, NY 10591.

616.99 US ISSN 0195-8690
RC267
NATIONAL CANCER INSTITUTE. ANNUAL REPORT. ceased. a. U.S. National Cancer Institute, Department of Health and Human Services, Bldg. 31, Rm. 11A52, Bethesda, MD 20892.

551 CH
NATIONAL CENTRAL UNIVERSITY. BULLETIN OF GEOPHYSICS. 1967-1987 (vol.27-28). National Central University, Institute of Geophysics, Chungli, Taiwan 320, Republic of China.

790.2 II
NATIONAL CENTRE FOR THE PERFORMING ARTS. QUARTERLY JOURNAL. 1972-1988 (Mar.); suspended. q. National Centre for the Performing Arts, Nariman Point, Bombay 400021, India.

331 US ISSN 0077-3735
NATIONAL CIVIL SERVICE LEAGUE. ANNUAL REPORT. ceased 1992. a. National Civil Service League, 3600 Gunston Rd., Alexandria, VA 22302.

616.858 US
NATIONAL COALITION OF GAY S.T.D. SERVICES. OFFICIAL NEWSLETTER. 1979-1988 (vol.9). q. National Coalition of Gay S.T.D. Services, Box 239, Milwaukee, WI 53201.
Formerly: Sexual Health Reports.

001.64 621.381 US
NATIONAL COMPUTER CONFERENCE (PROCEEDINGS). (Subseries of: A F I P S Conference Proceedings) 1973-1987 (vol.56). a. (also avail. in microfiche; microfilm; back issues avail.) (American Federation of Information Processing Societies) Springer-Verlag, 175 Fifth Ave., New York, NY 10010.
Formerly: National Computer Conference and Exposition (Proceedings) (ISSN 0095-6880)

690 AT
NATIONAL CONSTRUCTOR. 1977-19?? m. (back issues avail.) Peter Isaacson Publications Pty. Ltd., 45-50 Porter St., Prahran, Vic. 3181, Australia.

300 US ISSN 0085-3712
NATIONAL COUNCIL FOR THE SOCIAL STUDIES. HOW TO DO IT SERIES. ceased. irreg. National Council for the Social Studies, 3501 Newark St., N.W., Washington, DC 20016.

332.1 US
NATIONAL COUNCIL OF SAVINGS INSTITUTIONS. ANNUAL REPORT OF THE PRESIDENT. ceased. a. National Council of Savings Institutions, 1101 15th., N.W., Ste.400, Washington, DC 20005-5070.
Formerly: National Association of Mutual Banks of the United States. Report.

051 US
NATIONAL DATING SCENE. ceased. bi-m. Box 1307, Skokie, IL 60076.

371.912 UK
NATIONAL DEAF CHILDREN'S SOCIETY. ANNUAL ACCOUNTS. 1948-19?? a. National Deaf Children's Society, 45 Hereford Rd., London W2 5AH, England.

617.6 US ISSN 0097-1901
NATIONAL DENTAL ASSOCIATION. JOURNAL. 1941-19?? q. (also avail. in microform from UMI; reprint service avail. from UMI) National Dental Association, 5506 Connecticut Ave., N.W., Ste. 24, Washington, DC 20015.
Former titles: N.D.A. Quarterly (ISSN 0027-9129); National Dental Association. Bulletin.

378.002 US
NATIONAL DIRECTORY OF CATHOLIC HIGHER EDUCATION. ceased. a. Catholic News Publishing Co., Inc., 210 N. Ave., New Rochelle, NY 10801.

712 US ISSN 0272-247X
SB469.33
NATIONAL DIRECTORY OF LANDSCAPE ARCHITECTURE FIRMS. ceased. biennial. American Society of Landscape Architects, 4401 Connecticut Ave., NW, Washington, DC 20008-2302.

350 US ISSN 0095-3113
JK2443
NATIONAL DIRECTORY OF STATE AGENCIES. ceased 1990. a. Carroll Publishing Company, 1058 Thomas Jefferson St., N.W., Washington, DC 20007.

621.38 UK ISSN 0305-2257
TK7800 CODEN: NEREBX
NATIONAL ELECTRONICS REVIEW; technical articles & a survey of progress in electronics over the previous year. ceased 1990. a. National Electronics Council, Savoy Place, London WC2R 0BL, England.
Formerly: National Electronics Council. Review (ISSN 0047-8857)

332.1 US ISSN 8756-9043
HG1881
NATIONAL FACT BOOK OF SAVINGS INSTITUTIONS. ceased 1988. a. National Council of Savings Institutions, 1101 15th St., N.W., Rm. 400, Washington, DC 20005-5070.
Formerly: National Fact Book of Savings Banking (ISSN 0738-260X)

382 US
NATIONAL FOREIGN TRADE COUNCIL. POLICY DECLARATION. ceased 1986. bi-w. National Foreign Trade Council, 100 E. Second St., New York, NY 10017.

052 UK
NATIONAL FRONT NEWS. 1973-1990. fortn. (tabloid format) Third Way Publications, P.O. Box 228, London E12, England.

616 301 US ISSN 0547-7115
RC321
NATIONAL GUILD OF CATHOLIC PSYCHIATRISTS. BULLETIN. 1948-1989; suspended. a. (back issues avail.) National Guild of Catholic Psychiatrists, Inc., c/o Dr. Robert McAllister, Taylor Manor Hospital, Box 396, Ellicott City, MD 21043.

370 US
NATIONAL HEAD INJURY FOUNDATION ANNUAL REPORT. 1985-198? biennial. National Head Injury Foundation, 333 Turnpike Rd., Southborough, MA 01772.

301.54 UK
NATIONAL HOUSING AND TOWN PLANNING COUNCIL. CONFERENCE AND EXHIBITION GUIDE. 1950-19?? a. National Housing and Town Planning Council, 14-18 Old St., London EC1V 9AB, England.
Formerly: National Housing and Town Planning Council. Handbook and Year Book (ISSN 0077-4707)

301.54 UK
NATIONAL HOUSING AND TOWN PLANNING COUNCIL. HANDBOOK AND YEAR BOOK. 1900-19?? a. National Housing and Town Planning Council, 14-18 Old St., London EC1V 9AB, England.
Formerly: Housing and Planning Year Book (ISSN 0073-3644)

301.435 US
NATIONAL INDIAN COUNCIL ON AGING. 1976-19?? biennial. National Indian Council on Aging, Inc., Box 2088, Albuquerque, NM 87103.

686.2 SA
NATIONAL INDUSTRIAL COUNCIL OF THE PRINTING AND NEWSPAPER INDUSTRY OF SOUTH AFRICA. MONTHLY RECORD. 1919-1989 (Dec.). m. National Industrial Council of the Printing and Newspaper Industry of South Africa, Pearl House, Heerengracht, Box 6776, Roggebaai 8012, Cape Town, South Africa.

664 US
NATIONAL INSTITUTE FOR THE FOODSERVICE INDUSTRY. NEWS. 1971-19?? s-a. Educational Foundation of the National Restaurant Association, 250 S. Wacker Dr., Chicago, IL 60606.

631 UK ISSN 0140-4199
NATIONAL INSTITUTE OF AGRICULTURAL BOTANY, CAMBRIDGE, ENGLAND. TECHNICAL LEAFLETS. 1977-19?? a. National Institute of Agricultural Botany, Huntingdon Rd., Cambridge CB3 0LE, England.

631 JA ISSN 0077-4863
S562.J3
NATIONAL INSTITUTE OF AGRICULTURAL SCIENCES, TOKYO. BULLETIN. SERIES H (FARM MANAGEMENT, LAND UTILIZATION, RURAL LIFE). 1951-1981 (vol. 55). irreg. Department of Agricultural Development, Agricultural Research Center, Kannondai 3-1-1, Tsukuba, Ibaraki-ken 305, Japan.

360 UK ISSN 0077-4774
NATIONAL INSTITUTE SOCIAL SERVICES LIBRARY. 1964-19?? irreg. (National Institute for Social Work) George Allen & Unwin (Publishers) Ltd., 40 Museum St., London WC1, England.
Formerly: National Institute for Social Work Training Series.

331 340 CN ISSN 0835-8087
NATIONAL LABOUR REVIEW. 1987-1991. q. (back issues avail.) Butterworths Canada Ltd., 75 Clegg Rd., Markham, Ont. L6G 1A1, Canada.

340 US
NATIONAL LAW JOURNAL INDEX. 1983-1985. a. New York Law Publishing Co., Marketing Dept., 111 Eighth Ave., New York, NY 10011.

610 016 US ISSN 0025-7346
NATIONAL LIBRARY OF MEDICINE. CURRENT CATALOG PROOFSHEETS. 1966-1992. w. (U.S. National Library of Medicine) Medical Library Association, Six N. Michigan Ave., Ste. 300, Chicago, IL 60602.

797 CN
NATIONAL LIFELINER. 1977-19?? q. (back issues avail.) Royal Life Saving Society Canada, 191 Church Street, Toronto, Ont. M5B 1Y7, Canada.

069 387 UK ISSN 0141-1268
NATIONAL MARITIME MUSEUM. OCCASIONAL LECTURES SERIES. 1978-19?? irreg. National Maritime Museum, Romney Rd., Greenwich SE10 9NF, England.

570 PH ISSN 0076-3772
NATIONAL MUSEUM OF THE PHILIPPINES. MONOGRAPH SERIES. 1970-1991? (no.14); suspended. irreg. National Museum of the Philippines, Padre Burgos Street, Manila, Philippines.

620 610 371.9 CN ISSN 0706-568X
NATIONAL RESEARCH COUNCIL, CANADA. DIVISION OF ELECTRICAL ENGINEERING. BULLETIN/CONSEIL NATIONAL DE RECHERCHES DU CANADA. DIVISION DE GENIE ELECTRIQUE. BULLETIN. 1975-19?? a. (also avail. in microfilm; back issues avail.) National Research Council of Canada, Division of Electrical Engineering, Rm. 301, Ottawa, Ont., K1A OR8, Canada.

690 016 CN
NATIONAL RESEARCH COUNCIL, CANADA. INSTITUTE FOR RESEARCH IN CONSTRUCTION. BIBLIOGRAPHY. 1951-1985? irreg. National Research Council of Canada, Institute for Research in Construction, Ottawa, Ont. K1A OR6, Canada.
Formerly: National Research Council, Canada. Division of Building Research. Bibliography (ISSN 0085-3828)

690 CN
NATIONAL RESEARCH COUNCIL, CANADA. INSTITUTE FOR RESEARCH IN CONSTRUCTION. BUILDING PRACTICE NOTE. 1976-1987. irreg. (back issues avail.) National Research Council of Canada, Institute for Research in Construction, Ottawa, Ont. K1A OR6, Canada.
Formerly: National Research Council, Canada. Division of Building Research. Building Practice Note (ISSN 0701-5216)

690 CN
CODEN: DPNRDL
NATIONAL RESEARCH COUNCIL, CANADA. INSTITUTE FOR RESEARCH IN CONSTRUCTION. PAPER. 1975-19?? irreg. National Research Council of Canada, Institute for Research in Construction, Ottawa, Ont. K1A OR6, Canada.
Formerly: National Research Council, Canada. Division of Building Research. D B R Paper (ISSN 0381-4319)

690 CN
NATIONAL RESEARCH COUNCIL, CANADA. INSTITUTE FOR RESEARCH IN CONSTRUCTION. SPECIAL TECHNICAL PUBLICATION. 1973-1985. irreg. National Research Council of Canada, Institute for Research in Construction, Ottawa, Ont. K1A OR6, Canada.
Formerly: National Research Council, Canada. Division of Building Research. Special Technical Publication (ISSN 0701-5208)

610 US ISSN 0276-2293
NATIONAL REYE'S SYNDROME FOUNDATION. 1980-1987 (vol.7); suspended. a. (back issues avail.) National Reye's Syndrome Foundation, 426 N. Lewis, Box 829, Bryan, OH 43506.

332.6 US ISSN 0077-5703
NATIONAL SECURITIES AND RESEARCH CORPORATION. ANNUAL FORECAST. 1948-198? a. National Securities & Research Corp., 605 Third Ave., New York, NY 10016.

355 US ISSN 0162-3206
NATIONAL SECURITY RECORD. 1978-198? m. (looseleaf format; back issues avail.) Heritage Foundation, 214 Massachusetts Ave., N.E., Washington, DC 20002.

657 US
NATIONAL SOCIETY OF PUBLIC ACCOUNTANTS. ANNUAL REPORT. ceased. a. National Society of Public Accountants, 1010 N. Fairfax St., Alexandria, VA 22314.

790.1 US ISSN 1052-1232
NATIONAL SPORTS DAILY; ludud aequus omnibus iocus ludique/fun, games and fair play for all. 1990-1991 (Jun.). d. (except Saturday). National American Sports Communications L.P., 15 W. 52nd St., New York, NY 10019-6105.

355 US
NATIONAL STRATEGY INFORMATION CENTER. AGENDA PAPERS. 1969-1985 (no.15). irreg. (2-3/yr.). National Strategy Information Center, 140 E. 56th St., Ste. 5-H, New York, NY 10022.
Formerly: National Strategy Information Center. Strategy Papers.

CESSATIONS

990   AT   ISSN 0047-911X
NATIONAL TIMES; Australia's national weekly newspaper of business and affairs. 1971-19?? w. (tabloid format) John Fairfax & Sons Ltd., 235 Jones St., Broadway, Sydney, N.S.W. 2007, Australia.

658 647.94   US
NATIONAL TREND OF BUSINESS IN THE LODGING INDUSTRY. 1928-1990. m. Laventhol & Horwath, 1845 Walnut St., Philadelphia, PA 19103.
 Formerly: Trend of Business in the Lodging Industry.

329.9   GW   ISSN 0028-0437
DER NATIONALE DEMOKRAT. 1961-1991. m. (National-Demokratische Partei Deutschlands) Zeitungsverlag National, Prenzlauer Allee 36, 1055 Berlin, Germany.

371.2   US   ISSN 0194-2263
NATION'S SCHOOLS REPORT. 1928-1990. 22/yr. (looseleaf format; also avail. in microform from UMI; reprint service avail. from UMI) Capitol Publications, Inc., 1101 King St., Ste. 444, Box 4155, Alexandria, VA 22313-2055.
 Former titles: Nation's Schools (ISSN 0028-0526); Nation's Schools and Colleges (ISSN 0095-3326); College and University Business (ISSN 0010-0900)

996.9 979 800   US
NATIVE HAWAIIAN REPORT. 1977-1989. m. (tabloid format; back issues avail.) Alu Like, Inc., 1024 Mapunapuna, Honolulu, HI 96819-4417.

970.1 700   US
NATIVE VISION. 1984-199? irreg. American Indian Contemporary Arts, The Monadnnock Bldg., 685 Market St., Ste. 250, San Francisco, CA 94105-4212.

613   US   ISSN 0047-9152
NATURAL HEALTH BULLETIN. 1970-1991; suspended. m. Princeton Educational Publishers, Box 280, Plainsboro, NJ 08536.

500.9   CN   ISSN 0068-1628
NATURAL HISTORY HANDBOOK SERIES. 1942-19?? irreg. Royal British Columbia Museum, 675 Belleville St., Victoria, B.C. V8V 1X4, Canada.

614.7   SP
NATURALIA HISPANICA. suspended. irreg. (back issues avail.) Instituto Nacional para la Conservacion de la Naturaleza, Gran via San Francisco 35, Madrid 5, Spain.

028.5 333.7   CN   ISSN 0836-0928
LES NATURALISTES; une force de la nature. 1980-19?? q. Cercles des Jeunes Naturalistes, 4101 Sherbrooke East, Ste. 124, Montreal, Que. H1X 2B2, Canada.
 Formerly (until 1987): Cercles des Jeunes Naturalistes. Bulletin de Nouvelles (ISSN 0827-1364)

333.7   UK
NATURE CONSERVANCY COUNCIL. CHIEF SCIENTIST DIRECTORATE REPORTS. 1978-1991. irreg. (also avail. in microfiche) Nature Conservancy Council, Information and Library Services, Northminster House, Peterborough PE1 1UA, England.
 Formerly: Nature Conservancy Council. Chief Scientist Team Reports (ISSN 0143-0378)

505   US   ISSN 0085-3860
Q1
NATURE - SCIENCE ANNUAL. 1970-1978. a. Time-Life Books, Inc. (Subsidiary of: Time, Inc.), 777 Duke Street, Alexandria, VA 22314.

910   CS
NAUKA O ZEMI. SERIA GEOGRAPHICA. 1966-1984. irreg. (Slovenska Akademia Vied) Veda, Publishing House of the Slovak Academy of Sciences, Klemensova 19, 814 30 Bratislava, Czechoslovakia.

500   UR
NAUKA SEGODNYA. 1973-1989. a. Izdatel'stvo Znanie, Novaya pl. 3-4, 101835 Moscow, Russian S.F.S.R., U.S.S.R.

796.95   US   ISSN 0199-0837
GV771
NAUTICAL QUARTERLY. 1977-1990 (no.50). q. Box 549, Essex, CT 06426.

520   GW   ISSN 0433-681X
NAUTISCHES JAHRBUCH. 1950-1990. a. Seehydrographischer Dienst, Dierkower Damm 45, 2540 Rostock 40, Germany.

970.1   US
NAVAJO AREA NEWSLETTER. vol.7, 1977-19?? m. U.S. Bureau of Indian Affairs, Navajo Area Office, Box M, Window Rock, AZ 86515.
 Formerly: Navajo Education Newsletter (ISSN 0193-4503)

028.5   II   ISSN 0028-1492
PK1858
NAVALKATHA. 1962-19?? m. Savita Exports, Evergreen Industrial Estate, Shakti Mill Lane, Mahalaxmi, Bombay 400 011, India.

059.992   MY
NAVJIWAN PUNJABI NEWS. 1950-1991 (Dec.). w. 52 Jalan 8-18, Petaling Jaya, 46050 Selangor, Malaysia.

296   CN   ISSN 0705-7822
NAYER DOR/NEW GENERATION; magazine en Yiddish pour les jeunes et les adultes. 1978-1982. irreg. David Botwinik, Ed.& Pub., 5775 Wentworth, Cote St. Luc, Montreal, Que. H4W 2S3, Canada.

015   US   ISSN 0091-0406
Z1223.5.N4
NEBRASKA STATE PUBLICATIONS CHECKLIST. 1973-1991. bi-m. (microfiche; back issues avail.) (Library Commission) Nebraska Publications Clearinghouse, 1420 P St., Lincoln, NE 68508.

312   NE
NEDERLANDS INTERUNIVERSITAIR DEMOGRAFISCH INSTITUUT. WORKING PAPERS. 1973-1988 (no.76). irreg. Nederlands Interdisciplinair Demografisch Instituut - Netherlands Interdisciplinary Demographic Institute, Lange Houtstraat 19, 2511 CV The Hague, Netherlands.

322.4   NE   ISSN 0028-2278
NEDERLANDSE GEDACHTEN. 1955-19?? w. Anti-Revolutionaire Partij, Dr. Kuyperstraat 3, 2514 BA The Hague, Netherlands.

796   FR   ISSN 0247-1906
NEIGE MAGAZINE. 1979-19?? q. Publications Jean Suard, B.P. 4, 74320 Sevrier, France.

929   US
NELSON NOTES. ceased. q. (back issues avail.) Ancestor's Attic, 4041 Pedley Rd., No. 18, Riverside, CA 92509.

332.63   US   ISSN 0897-6538
HG4907
NELSON'S GUIDE TO "NEGLECTED" STOCKS. 1988-198? a. Nelson Publications, One Gateway Plaza, Box 591, Port Chester, NY 10573.

741.5   US   ISSN 0746-9438
NEMO: THE CLASSIC COMICS LIBRARY. 1983-198? bi-m. Fantagraphics Books, Inc., 7563 Lake City Way, Seattle, WA 98115.

331   JA
NENPO NIHON NO ROSHI KANKEI. 1968-1989. a. Japan Institute of Labour - Nihon Rodo Kyokai, Chutaikin Bldg., 1-7-6 Shibakoen, Minato-ku, Tokyo, Japan.

440   CN   ISSN 0380-9366
PC3631
NEOLOGIE EN MARCHE. SERIE A. LANGUE GENERALE. 1973-1987 (no.43). irreg. Office de la Langue Francaise, 700 bd. Saint-Cyrille Est, 2e, Quebec, Que. G1R 5A9, Canada.

051   US
NEON. 1989-1990 (Aug.). q. Chicago Magazine, Inc., 414 N. Orleans St., Ste. 800, Chicago, IL 60610.

618.92 612   UK   ISSN 0263-7359
NEONATAL PHYSIOLOGY. ceased 1989. m. (looseleaf format; back issues avail.) Sheffield University Biomedical Information Service (SUBIS), The University, Sheffield S10 2TN, England.

616.76 616.99   UK   ISSN 0142-8500
NEOPLASM IMMUNOLOGY. ceased 1990. m. (looseleaf format; back issues avail.) Sheffield University Biomedical Information Service (SUBIS), The University, Sheffield S10 2TN, England.

340   MY
NERACA. 1973-19?? a. University of Malaya, Law Society - Universiti Malaya, Persatuan Undang-Undang, Lembah Pantai, 59100 Kuala Lumpur, Malaysia.

382 314   NE   ISSN 0168-4094
NETHERLANDS. CENTRAAL BUREAU VOOR DE STATISTIEK. NAAMLIJSTEN VOOR DE STATISTIEK VAN DE BUITENLANDSE HANDEL/LIST OF GOODS FOR THE STATISTICS OF FOREIGN TRADE. SUPPLEMENT. 1962-1986. a. Centraal Bureau voor de Statistiek, Prinses Beatrixlaan 428, Voorburg, Netherlands.

639   NE   ISSN 0168-4167
NETHERLANDS. CENTRAAL BUREAU VOOR DE STATISTIEK. STATISTIEK VAN DE VISSERIJ/STATISTICS OF FISHERIES. 1950-1978. a. Centraal Bureau voor de Statistiek, Prinses Beatrixlaan 428, Voorburg, Netherlands.

371 379   NE   ISSN 0168-5244
NETHERLANDS. CENTRAAL BUREAU VOOR DE STATISTIEK. STATISTIEK VAN DE GEMEENTEWEGE PER LEERLING BESCHIKBAAR GESTELDE BEDRAGEN VOOR HET LAGER ONDERWIJS/STATISTICS OF THE AMOUNTS PER PUPIL PROVIDED FOR PRIMARY EDUCATION. 1949-1981. a. Centraal Bureau voor de Statistiek, Prinses Beatrixlaan 428, Voorburg, Netherlands.
 Formerly: Netherlands. Centraal Bureau voor de Statistiek. Statistiek van de Gemeentewege per Leerling Beschikbaar Gestelde Bedragenter Bestrijding van de Materiele Exploitatiekosten der Lagere Scholen. (ISSN 0077-7226)

371.3 314   NE   ISSN 0168-423X
NETHERLANDS. CENTRAAL BUREAU VOOR DE STATISTIEK. STATISTIEK VAN DE VOORLICHTING BIJ SCHOLEN EN BEROEPSKEUZE/STATISTICS OF VOCATIONAL GUIDANCE. 1946-1978. a. Centraal Bureau voor de Statistiek, Prinses Beatrixlaan 428, Voorburg, Netherlands.
 Formerly: Netherlands. Centraal Bureau voor de Statistiek. Statistiek van de Voorlichting Bij Beroepskeuze (ISSN 0077-7218)

338 314   NE   ISSN 0077-751X
NETHERLANDS. CENTRAAL BUREAU VOOR DE STATISTIEK. WINSTSTATISTIEK DER GROTERE NAAMLOZE VENNOOTSCHAPPEN/PROFIT-STATISTICS OF THE LIMITED LIABILITY COMPANIES. 1939-1970. a. Centraal Bureau voor de Statistiek, Prinses Beatrixlaan 428, Voorburg, Netherlands.

001.642   US   ISSN 1040-4503
NETWARE TECHNICAL JOURNAL. 1989-1990. q. McGraw-Hill, Inc., 1221 Avenue of the Americas, New York, NY 10020.

200   UK   ISSN 0261-1708
NETWORK (LONDON, 1965). 1965-1990 (Oct.). q. United Society for the Propagation of the Gospel, Partnership House, 157 Waterloo Rd., London SE1 8XA, England.

362.7   CN   ISSN 0831-0254
NETWORK (TORONTO). 1976-19?? 4/yr. Save the Children - Canada, 3080 Yonge St., Ste. 6020, Toronto, Ont. M4N 3P4, Canada.
 Formerly (until 1985): Promises (ISSN 0703-9115)

338   US   ISSN 1040-3388
NETWORK (WASHINGTON, 1986). 1986-1989 (vol.4, no.4). bi-m. U.S. Small Business Administration, Office of Public Communications, 1441 L St., N.W., Rm.926, Washington, DC 20416.

380.3 001.644   US
NETWORK COMPUTING (CEDAR KNOLLS). ceased. m. Probe Research, Inc., Three Wing Dr., Ste. 240, Cedar Knolls, NJ 07927-1097.
 Formerly: I B M - D E C.

333.7   US
NETWORK NEWSLETTER. ceased 1987. 6/yr. Santa Barbara Network, 924 Anacapa St., Ste. B, Santa Barbara, CA 93101.

350.86 323.4   US   ISSN 0047-9373
NETWORK - URBAN COALITION. 1972-1988. m. National Urban Coalition, 8601 Georgia St., Ste. 500, Silver Spring, MD 20910.

384.54 384.554   UK   ISSN 0954-9145
NETWORKS; a current awareness bulletin on broadcasting and social action. 1988-1989. bi-m. (back issues avail.) Media Project, Volunteer Centre, 29 Lower Kings Rd., Berkhamsted, Herts. HP4 2AB, England.

028.5   GW   ISSN 0863-3045
NEU LEBEN. ceased 1991. m. Verlag Junge Welt GmbH, Mauerstr. 39-40, 1080 Berlin, Germany.
Formerly: Neues Leben (ISSN 0323-5815)

610   GW   ISSN 0178-787X
NEUE AERZTLICHE; allgemeine Zeitung fuer Klinik und Praxis. 1985-1991. d. (back issues avail.) Aerztliche Allgemeine Verlagsgesellschaft mbH, Hellerhofstr. 2-4, Postfach 10 01 49, 6000 Frankfurt a.M. 1, Germany.

053.1   GW   ISSN 0028-3142
AP30
NEUE DEUTSCHE HEFTE. 1954-1990. q. Verlag Neue Deutsche Hefte, Kindelbergweg 7, 1000 Berlin 46, Germany.

371.3   GW   ISSN 0723-3280
NEUE DIDAKTISCHE MODELLE. 1972-198? (vol.5). irreg. Colloquium Verlag, Unter den Eichen 93, 1000 Berlin 45, Germany.

621.381 001.6   GW   ISSN 0028-3401
HF5547.A2   CODEN: NTBUB4
NEUE TECHNIK IM BUERO; Fachzeitschrift fuer Informationsverarbeitung. 1957-1991. bi-m. (Russian edition q.). Verlag Technik GmbH, Oranienburger Str. 13-14, 1020 Berlin, Germany.

320   GW
NEUER WEG; Organ des Zentralkomitees der S E D fuer Fragen des Parteilebens. 1946-1991. s-m. (Sozialistische Einheitspartei Deutschlands, Zentralkomitee) Dietz Verlag, Wallstr. 76-79, Postfach 273, Berlin 1020, Germany.

020   GW   ISSN 0457-3897
NEUJAHRSGABE DER DEUTSCHEN BUECHEREI. 1956-1990. a. Deutsche Buecherei, Deutscher Platz 1, 7010 Leipzig, Germany.

616.8 612.015   UK   ISSN 0264-9403
NEURAL CIRCULATION AND C S F. ceased 1991. m. (looseleaf format; back issues avail.) Sheffield University Biomedical Information Service (SUBIS), The University, Sheffield S10 2TN, England.

616.8   US   ISSN 0896-436X
QA76.5   CODEN: NNREEV
NEURAL NETWORK REVIEW. ceased. q. Lawrence Erlbaum Associates, Inc., 365 Broadway, Hillsdale, NJ 07642.

612 616.8   UK   ISSN 0264-9411
NEURAL ORGANISATION. ceased 1990. m. (looseleaf format; back issues avail.) Sheffield University Biomedical Information Service (SUBIS), The University, Sheffield S10 2TN, England.

618.92 616.8   UK   ISSN 0261-4804
NEURAL TUBE DEFECTS. ceased 1989. m. (looseleaf format; back issues avail.) Sheffield University Biomedical Information Service (SUBIS), The University, Sheffield S10 2TN, England.

616.4 616.93   UK   ISSN 0950-0553
NEUROIMMUNOENDOCRINOLOGY. ceased 1991. s-m. (looseleaf format; back issues avail.) Sheffield University Biomedical Information Service (SUBIS), The University, Sheffield S10 2TN, England.

612.78   NE   ISSN 0301-6412
CODEN: NEURDL
NEUROLINGUISTICS; international series devoted to speech physiology and speech pathology. 1973-1984 (vol.13). irreg. Swets Publishing Service (Subsidiary of: Swets en Zeitlinger B.V.), Heereweg 347, 2161 CA Lisse, Netherlands.

616.8   PL   ISSN 0028-3843
CODEN: NNPOBE
NEUROLOGIA I NEUROCHIRURGIA POLSKA. 1951-19?? bi-m. Panstwowy Zaklad Wydawnictw Lekarskich, Dluga 38-40, Warsaw, Poland.

616.8 617   US   ISSN 0887-9842
NEUROSURGERY (PHILADELPHIA); state of the art reviews. ceased. s-a. (plus supplement). Hanley & Belfus, Inc., 210 S. 13th St., Philadelphia, PA 19107.

615.9   US   ISSN 0160-2748
NEUROTOXICOLOGY. 1977; ceased same year. irreg. Raven Press, 1185 Ave. of the Americas, New York, NY 10036.

352   US   ISSN 0360-9731
JS451.N35
NEVADA GOVERNMENT TODAY. 1973-1989 (vol.15, no.2). q. Nevada League of Cities, Box 2307, Carson City, NV 89702-2307.

051 621.381   US
NEW ALADDIN. 1987-198? 6/yr. (avail. only on disk) Disk Publications, Inc., 11701 Pine Forest Dr., Dallas, TX 75230-2832.

614.7 600   US   ISSN 0895-1497
NEW ALCHEMY QUARTERLY. 1980-1992. q. (back issues avail.) New Alchemy Institute, 237 Hatchville Rd., East Falmouth, MA 02536.

028.1   CN
NEW & FORTHCOMING CANADIAN BOOKS. 1973-1990. s-a. (back issues avail.) Quill & Quire (Subsidiary of: Key Publishers Co. Ltd.), 70 The Esplanade, 4th fl., Toronto, Ont. M5E 1R2, Canada.

284 028.5   US
NEW BEGINNINGS (PISGAH FOREST). 1982-198? bi-m. 1211 Williamson Creek Rd., Pisgah Forest, NC 28768.

574   US   ISSN 1043-4674
QH506   CODEN: NEBIE2
THE NEW BIOLOGIST. ceased. m. W.B. Saunders Co. (Subsidiary of: Harcourt Brace Jovanovich, Inc.), Curtis Center, Independence Square W., Philadelphia, PA 19106.

612.015   CN   ISSN 0832-6614
NEW BIOTECH. 1986-1991. 16/yr. (back issues avail.) Winter House Scientific Publications, P.O. Box 7131, Sta. J, Ottawa, Ont. K2A 4C5, Canada.

917.1   CN   ISSN 0839-6434
G155.C3
NEW BRUNSWICK. DEPARTMENT OF TOURISM, RECREATION AND HERITAGE. ANNUAL REPORT. 1972-1991. a. Department of Tourism, Recreation and Heritage, Public Relations Branch, P.O. Box 12345, Fredericton, N.B. E3B 5C3, Canada.
Formerly: New Brunswick. Department of Tourism. Annual Report (ISSN 0703-6566)

338.9   CN   ISSN 0548-4065
HC117.N3
NEW BRUNSWICK DEVELOPMENT CORPORATION. ANNUAL REPORT. ceased. a. New Brunswick Development Corporation, 238 Waterloo Rd., Fredericton, N.B. E3B 4Y2, Canada.
Formerly: New Brunswick Development Corporation. Report.

659.1 720 330   US
NEW BUSINESS. 1983-1987. bi-m. (back issues avail.) Clubhouse Publishing, Inc., Box 3312, Sarasota, FL 34230.

792 793   UK   ISSN 0950-4303
NEW DANCE; magazine of experimental and progressive dance. 1977-1988. 4/yr. New Dance Publishing Ltd., 48 Ash Grove, West Yorkshire, Leeds LS6 1AY, England.

745.5   US
NEW DIMENSIONS IN GLASS. ceased. q. (processed) A F G Industries, Inc., Box 929, Kingsport, TN 37662.
Formerly: Creative Ideas in Glass.

287 028.5   US
NEW DISCIPLES. 1982-19?? q. (United Methodist Board of Discipleship) United Methodist Publishing House, Graded Press, 201 Eighth Ave. S., Box 801, Nashville, TN 37202.

330   US   ISSN 0164-3533
HC107.A11   CODEN: NENBA3
NEW ENGLAND BUSINESS. 1952-1992 (Apr.). 12/yr. (also avail. in microform from UMI; reprint service avail. from UMI) New England Business Corp., 20 Park Plaza, Ste. 1120, Boston, MA 02116-4303.
Supersedes (in 1979): New Englander (ISSN 0028-4947); Which incorporated: New England Business Journal.

330.9   US   ISSN 0895-5662
NEW ENGLAND ECONOMIC INDICATORS MONTHLY UPDATE. (Supplement to: New England Economic Indicators) ceased. m. Federal Reserve Bank of Boston, Research Department, 600 Atlantic Ave., Boston, MA 02106-2076.

051   US   ISSN 0884-5166
NEW ENGLAND LIVING MAGAZINE. 1979-1991 (Oct.). 6/yr. New England Lifestyle Publications, Inc., 177 E. Industrial Dr., Manchester, NH 03103.

051   US   ISSN 8750-216X
F1
NEW ENGLAND MONTHLY. 1984-1990. m. New England Monthly, Inc., Box 446, Haydenville, MA 01039.

333.33   US
NEW ENGLAND REAL ESTATE NEWS DIRECTORY. 1980-1989 (Dec.). a. Communication Channels, Inc., 6255 Barfield Rd., Atlanta, GA 30328-4369.

301.435   US   ISSN 0163-2248
NEW ENGLAND SENIOR CITIZEN. 1970-1988. m. Prime National Publishing Corp., 470 Boston Post Rd., Weston, MA 02193.

385   US   ISSN 0162-1599
HE2714
NEW ENGLAND STATES LIMITED. 1977-1983 (vol.5, no.1). s-a. New England Rail Service, Box 249, Newbury, VT 05051.

051   US
NEW HAMPSHIRE LIFE; four-color regional magazine for New Hampshire. 1985-19?? bi-m. (reprint service avail.) Masthead Communications Inc., Box 1200, N. Hampton, NH 03862.
Formerly (until vol.5, no.6, 1990): Seacoast Life (ISSN 0885-6435)

266   US   ISSN 0896-3150
NEW HEAVEN - NEW EARTH. 1983-1992 (Feb.). m. (11/yr.). (back issues avail.) People of Praise, Inc., 107 S. Greenlawn Ave., South Bend, IN 46617-3429.

640   US
NEW HOME. 1988-1991 (vol.3, no.6). bi-m. Box 2008, Village W., Laconia, NH 03247.

333.33 643.7   CN
NEW HOME MAGAZINE; a consumer guide to new home buying in British Columbia. 1986-19?? q. (Greater Vancouver Home Builders' Association) Clarion Holdings Inc., c/o Canadian Home Builders Association of B.C., B.C.I.T. Campus Housing Industry Training Center, 3700 Willingdon Ave., Burnaby, B.C. V5G 3H2, Canada.

382   HU
NEW HUNGARIAN EXPORTER TECHNICAL SERIES. ceased 1990. q. Magyar Kereskedelmi Kamara - Hungarian Chamber of Commerce, Kossuth Lajos ter 608, 1055 Budapest V, Hungary.

378   US
NEW JERSEY. DEPARTMENT OF HIGHER EDUCATION. RESEARCH REPORT. 1976-1984 (Aug.). irreg. Department of Higher Education, 20 W. State St., CN 542, Trenton, NJ 08625.

338.9   US   ISSN 0077-8478
NEW JERSEY. ECONOMIC POLICY COUNCIL. ANNUAL REPORT OF ECONOMIC POLICY COUNCIL AND OFFICE OF ECONOMIC POLICY. 1968-1990. a. Office of Economic Policy, 20 W. State St., CN 830, Trenton, NJ 08625.

330   US
NEW JERSEY. OFFICE OF ECONOMIC POLICY. ECONOMIC REPORT OF THE GOVERNOR. 1982-1988. a. Office of Economic Policy, 20 W. State St., CN 830, Trenton, NJ 08625.

364   US
NEW JERSEY. STATE LAW ENFORCEMENT PLANNING AGENCY. APPLICANTS GUIDE. 1972-199? a. State Law Enforcement Planning Agency, CN083, Trenton, NJ 08625-0083.
Formerly: Criminal Justice Plan for New Jersey (ISSN 0092-4652); **Supersedes**: New Jersey Plan for Criminal Justice.

CESSATIONS

370   US
NEW JERSEY EDUCATION BULLETIN. 1982-1991; suspended. m. (looseleaf format) Department of Education, 225 W. State St., CN 500, Trenton, NJ 08625-0500.

330   US   ISSN 0886-9995
NEW JERSEY SUCCESS. 1980-1989 (Nov.). m. New Jersey Success, Inc., Attn: Norman B. Tomlinson, Jr., Pub., 55 Park Pl., Box 920, Morristown, NJ 07963.

028.1   US
NEW LETTERS REVIEW OF BOOKS. suspended. 3/yr. (tabloid format) University of Missouri, Kansas City, 5100 Rockhill Rd., Kansas City, MO 64110.

352   UK
NEW LOCAL GOVERNMENT SERIES. ceased. irreg. George Allen & Unwin (Publishers) Ltd., 40 Museum St., London W.C.1, England.

070.5   US   ISSN 0192-2319
NEW MAGAZINE REVIEW. 1979-198? bi-m. New Magazine Review Publishing Co., Box 3699, North Las Vegas, NV 89030.

658   US
NEW MANAGEMENT. 1983-1988 (vol.6, no.2). q. (also avail. in microform from RPI) (University of Southern California, Graduate School of Business Administration) Wilson Learning Corporation, c/o Diane Ewart, 6950 Washington Ave. S., Eden Prairie, MN 55344.

666 668.4   UK   ISSN 0952-6196
NEW MATERIALS - KOREA. 1987-1990. bi-m. (back issues avail.) Elsevier Science Publishers Ltd., Crown House, Linton Rd., Barking, Essex IG11 8JU, England.

289.3   US
NEW MESSENGER (TALKING BOOK). 1953-1976. bi-m. Church of Jesus Christ of Latter-day Saints, 50 E. North Temple, Salt Lake City, UT 84150.

622   US
NEW MEXICO. BUREAU OF MINES AND MINERAL RESOURCES. CIRCULAR. 1930-1986 (no.200). irreg. Bureau of Mines and Mineral Resources, Socorro, NM 87801.

781.58   US
NEW MUSIC DISTRIBUTION SERVICE MANUAL. suspended. a. Jazz Composers Orchestra Association, 598 Broadway, 7th Fl., New York, NY 10012-3210.

970   US
NEW NATIVE AMERICAN NOVEL. 1974-19?? q. University of New Mexico, American Studies Department, Alburquerque, NM 87131.
Formerly (until 1986): New America: A Review.

700 792   US   ISSN 1040-3892
NEW NORTH ARTSCAPE; Minnesota's arts magazine. 1984-1992. bi-m. (tabloid format; back issues avail.) (St. Paul Art Collective) New North Artscape, 420 Fifth St. N., Ste. 990, Minneapolis, MN 55401.
Formerly (until 1988): Vinyl Arts Magazine.

327   FI
NEW PERSPECTIVES. 1970-19?? bi-m. World Peace Council, Lonnrotinkatu 25 A, Box 114, Helsinki 18, Finland.

370   AT   ISSN 1034-4284
NEW PERSPECTIVES. 1978-1991 (Nov.). 4/yr. Department of School Education, Community Relations Unit, G.P.O. Box 33, Sydney, N.S.W. 2001, Australia.
Supersedes (in 1989): Perspectives (ISSN 0155-2821)

800 792   US   ISSN 0731-4523
PS634
NEW PLAYS U S A. 1982-19?? biennial. (back issues avail.) Theatre Communications Group, Inc., 355 Lexington Ave., New York, NY 10017.

658.8   US   ISSN 0733-8252
NEW PRODUCT DEVELOPMENT; creativity, research, development, marketing. 1981-19?? m. (back issues avail.) Point Publishing Co., Inc., Box 1309, Point Pleasant, NJ 08742.

338   DK   ISSN 0108-1497
NEW PRODUCTS FROM DENMARK. 1982-1985. irreg. Udenrigsministeriet - Ministry of Foreign Affairs, Asiatisk Plads 2, DK-1448 Copenhagen K, Denmark.

016 720   US   ISSN 0271-0994
Z5945
NEW PUBLICATIONS FOR ARCHITECTURE LIBRARIES. (Subseries of: Architecture Series: Bibliography) 1979-1990 (Dec.). m. (back issues avail.) Vance Bibliographies, 112 N. Charter St., Box 229, Monticello, IL 61856.

384.55   US   ISSN 0738-3371
NEW-RADIO CABLE AUDIO & PAY RADIO REPORT. 1980-198? m. (back issues avail.) Waters Information Services, Inc., Box 2248, Binghamton, NY 13902-2248.

133.91   US   ISSN 0147-7625
BF1001
NEW REALITIES. 1969-1991. bi-m. Heldref Publications, 1319 Eighteenth St., N.W., Washington, DC 20036-1802.
Formerly (until 1977): Psychic (ISSN 0033-2798)

384.55   CN
NEW RELEASE MAGAZINE. ceased. m. International Video Advertising Inc., 825 Granville St., Ste. 508, Vancouver, B.C. V6Z 1K9, Canada.

016   US
NEW SCIENTIFIC & TECHNICAL BOOKS IN AMERICA. 1974-19?? s-a. Beverly Books Inc., 19 Meridian Rd., Edison, NJ 08820-2823.

669.23 016   US   ISSN 0095-9286
QD181.A3
NEW SILVER TECHNOLOGY; silver summaries from the current world literature. 1974-19?? m. (back issues avail.) Silver Institute, 1026 16th St., N.W., Ste. 101, Washington, DC 20036.

340   AT   ISSN 0729-5987
NEW SOUTH WALES STATUTES ANNOTATION AND REFERENCES; annotations to the N.S.W. public acts and cross references to other acts of N.S.W. and the Commonwealth. 1982-1991? 4/yr. Law Book Co. Ltd., 44-50 Waterloo Rd., N. Ryde, N.S.W. 2113, Australia.

371.9   US   ISSN 0882-9659
NEW WAYS (EVANSTON); bringing a better life for people who are mentally retarded. 1986-199? q. First Publications, Inc., Box 5072, Evanston, IL 60204.

811   US   ISSN 0197-4874
NEW WILDERNESS LETTER. 1977-1983 (vol. 11). 2/yr. (back issues avail.) 325 Spring St., Apt. 208, New York, NY 10013.

808.81 800   JA
NEW YARN. 1983-1989 (vol.7). irreg. (back issues avail.) Bank of Creativity (BOC), Fuji-cho 6-5-20, Hoya-shi, Tokyo 202, Japan.

381   US
NEW YORK (STATE) DEPARTMENT OF ECONOMIC DEVELOPMENT. RESEARCH BULLETIN. 1960-1987 (no.55). irreg. Department of Economic Development, Bureau of Business Research, Statistics Unit, One Commerce Plaza, Albany, NY 12245.
Formerly: New York (State). Department of Commerce. Research Bulletin (ISSN 0077-9156)

368   US   ISSN 0467-6769
NEW YORK (STATE). INSURANCE DEPARTMENT. LOSS AND EXPENSE RATIOS. 1951-1981 (Dec.). a. (back issues avail.) Insurance Department, Publications Unit, Empire State Plaza, Agency Bldg. No. 1, Albany, NY 12257.

610   US   ISSN 0028-7105
NEW YORK ACADEMY OF MEDICINE. NEWS NOTES. 1962-19?? 3/yr. New York Academy of Medicine, 2 E. 103rd St., New York, NY 10029.

333.33 340   US
NEW YORK CO-OP & CONDO INSIDER. ceased. m. Brownstone Publishers, Inc., 304 Park Ave. S., New York, NY 10010.

639.9 333.7   US   ISSN 0028-7210
SK111   CODEN: NFGJAX
NEW YORK FISH AND GAME JOURNAL. 1954-198? s-a. Department of Environmental Conservation, 50 Wolf Rd., Albany, NY 12233.

807   US   ISSN 0149-1040
NEW YORK LITERARY FORUM. 1978-19?? (vol.14). s-a. New York Literary Forum, Box 1091, New York, NY 10021-0036.

610   US   ISSN 0196-6871
R11   CODEN: NYMQDG
NEW YORK MEDICAL QUARTERLY. 1979-1989 (vol.9). q. New York Medical College, Valhalla, NY 10595.

330   US
NEW YORK STATE DIRECTORY OF BUSINESS PERMITS. ceased. a. Matthew Bender & Co., Inc. (Albany), Dept. DM, Box 989, Albany, NY 12201-9990.

614.7   US   ISSN 0048-0053
NEW YORK STATE ENVIRONMENT. 1970-1990 (June). s-m. (back issues avail.) Department of Environmental Conservation, 50 Wolf Rd., Albany, NY 12233.

332.6   US   ISSN 0275-4479
NEW YORK STOCK EXCHANGE. STATISTICAL HIGHLIGHTS. 1955-19?? m. New York Stock Exchange, 11 Wall St., New York, NY 10005.
Supersedes (in 1978): New York Stock Exchange Monthly Review (ISSN 0548-7390)

051   US
NEW YORK STYLE & DESIGN. 1989-1991. bi-m. Manso Communications, 535 41st St., Union City, NJ 07087.

028.1   US
NEW YORK TIMES BOOK REVIEWS. 1896-1979. s-a. Times Books (Subsidiary of: Random House, Inc.), 201 E. 50th St., New York, NY 10022-7703.

026   US
NEW YORK UNIVERSITY. BULLETIN OF THE TAMIMENT INSTITUTE - BEN JOSEPHSON LIBRARY. 1957-1983 (no.50). irreg. (also avail. in microfilm; back issues avail.) New York University, Tamiment Library, 70 Washington Sq. So., New York, NY 10012.
Formerly: New York University. Libraries. Bulletin of the Tamiment Library (ISSN 0077-9490)

610   US   ISSN 0028-789X
NEW YORK UNIVERSITY MEDICAL CENTER NEWS. 1964-19?? m. (except summer). (tabloid format) New York University Medical Center, 550 First Ave., New York, NY 10016.

809 808.8   US   ISSN 0077-9504
NEW YORK UNIVERSITY STUDIES IN COMPARATIVE LITERATURE. 1967-19?? irreg. New York University Press, 70 Washington Square So., New York, NY 10012.

305.4   US
NEW YORK WOMAN. 1986-1992 (Jan.). 10/yr. American Express Publishing Corp., 1120 Ave. of the Americas, New York, NY 10036.

301.412   US
NEW YORK WOMAN'S NEWS. ceased. m. Good Businesskeeping, Box 471, Forest Hills, NY 11375.

808.02   US
NEW YORK WRITER. 1989-1991. q. American Exposition, Inc., 110 Green St., Ste. 703, New York, NY 10012.

641.1 630 574   US   ISSN 0362-0069
     CODEN: NYFSBJ
NEW YORK'S FOOD AND LIFE SCIENCES BULLETIN. 1971-199? irreg. (back issues avail.) (New York State College of Agriculture and Life Sciences) Cornell University, New York's Food and Life Sciences Bulletin, 1150 Comstock Hall, Ithaca, NY 14853.

354 NZ
NEW ZEALAND. DEPARTMENT OF MAORI AFFAIRS. ANNUAL REPORT. 1930-1989. a. Department of Maori Affairs, P.O. Box 273, Wellington, New Zealand.
Formerly: New Zealand. Department of Maori Affairs. Report.

500 NZ ISSN 0077-961X
S381 CODEN: NEZSAC
NEW ZEALAND. DEPARTMENT OF SCIENTIFIC AND INDUSTRIAL RESEARCH. BULLETIN. 1927-1986. irreg. (back issues avail.) (Department of Scientific and Industrial Research) D S I R Publishing, Box 9741, Wellington, New Zealand.

551 NZ ISSN 0113-2903
NEW ZEALAND. DEPARTMENT OF SCIENTIFIC AND INDUSTRIAL RESEARCH. GEOPHYSICS DIVISION. RESEARCH REPORT. 1952-198? irreg. Department of Scientific and Industrial Research, Geophysics Division, P.O. Box 1320, Wellington, New Zealand.
Formerly (until 1986): New Zealand. Department of Scientific and Industrial Research. Geophysics Division. Report (ISSN 0110-6112)

551 NZ ISSN 0113-3055
NEW ZEALAND. DEPARTMENT OF SCIENTIFIC AND INDUSTRIAL RESEARCH. GEOPHYSICS DIVISION. TECHNICAL REPORT. 1952-198? irreg. Department of Scientific and Industrial Research, Geophysics Division, P.O. Box 1320, Wellington, New Zealand.
Formerly (until 1986): New Zealand. Department of Scientific and Industrial Research. Geophysics Division. Technical Note (ISSN 0110-7089)

500 NZ ISSN 0077-9636
CODEN: NZIBAN
NEW ZEALAND. DEPARTMENT OF SCIENTIFIC AND INDUSTRIAL RESEARCH. INFORMATION SERIES. 1948-1988. irreg. (back issues avail.) D S I R Publishing, Box 9741, Wellington, New Zealand.

300 NZ ISSN 0112-2339
NEW ZEALAND. DEPARTMENT OF SCIENTIFIC AND INDUSTRIAL RESEARCH. SOCIAL SCIENCE SERIES. 1984-1988. irreg. D S I R Publishing, P.O. Box 9741, Wellington, New Zealand.

319 NZ ISSN 0077-9652
NEW ZEALAND. DEPARTMENT OF STATISTICS. ANNUAL REPORT OF THE GOVERNMENT STATISTICIAN. ceased 1989. a. Department of Statistics, P.O. Box 2922, Wellington, New Zealand.

338.4 NZ ISSN 0110-3490
HD9715.N4
NEW ZEALAND. DEPARTMENT OF STATISTICS. BUILDING STATISTICS. ceased 1987. a. Department of Statistics, P.O. Box 2922, Wellington, New Zealand.

690 NZ ISSN 0110-4640
HD9715.N4
NEW ZEALAND. DEPARTMENT OF STATISTICS. CENSUS OF BUILDING AND CONSTRUCTION. ceased 1984. quinquennial. Department of Statistics, P.O. Box 2922, Wellington, New Zealand.

380.5 NZ ISSN 0112-3629
NEW ZEALAND. DEPARTMENT OF STATISTICS. CENSUS OF TRANSPORT, STORAGE & COMMUNICATION. 1979-1984. irreg. Department of Statistics, P.O. Box 2922, Wellington, New Zealand.

331 319 NZ ISSN 0112-6598
HD8861
NEW ZEALAND. DEPARTMENT OF STATISTICS. CONSUMERS PRICE INDEX. ceased 1987. a. Department of Statistics, P.O. Box 2922, Wellington, New Zealand.
Formerly: New Zealand. Department of Statistics. Part A: Prices (ISSN 0110-5019); Supersedes in part: New Zealand. Department of Statistics. Prices, Wages and Labour (ISSN 0077-9911)

312 NZ ISSN 0112-6709
JV9261
NEW ZEALAND. DEPARTMENT OF STATISTICS. EXTERNAL MIGRATION STATISTICS. ceased 1987. a. Department of Statistics, P.O. Box 2922, Wellington, New Zealand.
Formerly: New Zealand. Department of Statistics. Population and Migration. Part B: External Migration (ISSN 0110-3768); Which superseded in part: New Zealand. Department of Statistics. Population and Migration.

368 319 NZ ISSN 0110-3474
NEW ZEALAND. DEPARTMENT OF STATISTICS. INSURANCE STATISTICS. ceased. a. Department of Statistics, P.O. Box 2992, Wellington, New Zealand.

340 310 NZ ISSN 0112-4447
NEW ZEALAND. DEPARTMENT OF STATISTICS. JUSTICE STATISTICS: PART A. ceased. a. Department of Statistics, P.O. Box 2922, Wellington, New Zealand.
Supersedes in part: New Zealand. Department of Statistics. Justice Statistics (ISSN 0110-3482)

340 310 NZ ISSN 0112-4501
NEW ZEALAND. DEPARTMENT OF STATISTICS. JUSTICE STATISTICS: PART B. ceased. a. Department of Statistics, P.O. Box 2922, Wellington, New Zealand.
Supersedes in part: New Zealand. Department of Statistics. Justice Statistics (ISSN 0110-3482)

352 NZ ISSN 0110-3466
NEW ZEALAND. DEPARTMENT OF STATISTICS. LOCAL AUTHORITY STATISTICS. ceased. a. Department of Statistics, P.O. Box 2922, Wellington, New Zealand.

382 339 319 NZ ISSN 0112-5117
HG3883.N45
NEW ZEALAND. DEPARTMENT OF STATISTICS. OVERSEAS BALANCE OF PAYMENTS. ceased. a. Department of Statistics, P.O. Box 2922, Wellington, New Zealand.
Formerly: New Zealand. Department of Statistics. Balance of Payments (ISSN 0110-4616)

312 NZ ISSN 0110-4586
NEW ZEALAND. DEPARTMENT OF STATISTICS. VITAL STATISTICS. 1964-1987. a. Department of Statistics, P.O. Box 2922, Wellington, New Zealand.

362 NZ ISSN 0110-1900
RA992.5
NEW ZEALAND. HEALTH STATISTICAL SERVICES. HOSPITAL MANAGEMENT DATA. 1926-1988. a. Health Statistical Services, c/o Josephine Ryan, 133 Molwesworth St., P.O. Box 5013, Wellington, New Zealand.
Formerly: Hospital Statistics of New Zealand (ISSN 0073-3466)

531.64 NZ
NEW ZEALAND. MINISTRY OF ENERGY. ANNUAL REPORT. 1978-1989. a. Ministry of Energy, P.O. Box 2337, Wellington, New Zealand.
Incorporates: New Zealand. Ministry of Energy. Mines Division. Annual Report.

380.5 614.86 NZ
NEW ZEALAND. MINISTRY OF TRANSPORT. TRAFFIC RESEARCH CIRCULAR. 1974-1985 (no.27). irreg. Ministry of Transport, P.O. Box 3175, Wellington, New Zealand.

380.5 388.413 NZ ISSN 0110-6872
NEW ZEALAND. MINISTRY OF TRANSPORT. TRAFFIC RESEARCH REPORT. 1974-1990. irreg. Ministry of Transport, Land Transport Division, P.O. Box 27489, Wellington, New Zealand.

333.7 NZ ISSN 0111-686X
NEW ZEALAND. NATURE CONSERVATION COUNCIL. NEWSLETTER. 1972-1988. 5/yr. (processed) Nature Conservation Council, P.O. Box 12-200, Wellington, New Zealand.

388.1 NZ ISSN 0549-0030
NEW ZEALAND. ROAD RESEARCH UNIT. BULLETIN. 1965-19?? irreg. Road Research Unit, P.O. Box 12446, Wellington, New Zealand.

388.1 NZ ISSN 0111-0756
NEW ZEALAND. ROAD RESEARCH UNIT. OCCASIONAL PAPER. 1978-19?? irreg. Road Research Unit, P.O. Box 12446, Wellington, New Zealand.

388.1 NZ ISSN 1170-4683
NEW ZEALAND. TRANSIT NEW ZEALAND. ROAD RESEARCH UNIT. NEWSLETTER. 1963-1990 (Dec.). q. Transit New Zealand, Road Research Unit, P.O. Box 12446, Wellington, New Zealand.
Formerly: New Zealand. Road Research Unit. Newsletter (ISSN 0549-0014)

630 627 NZ ISSN 0111-0829
NEW ZEALAND AGRICULTURAL ENGINEERING INSTITUTE. CURRENT PUBLICATIONS. ceased 1987. a. New Zealand Agricultural Engineering Institute, Lincoln College, Canterbury, New Zealand.

630 310 NZ ISSN 0112-3718
HD2195.5
NEW ZEALAND CENSUS OF AGRICULTURAL CONTRACTING SERVICES; a volume of statistics consolidating earlier releases, with some additions. 1982-1984. irreg. Department of Statistics, P.O. Box 2922, Wellington, New Zealand.

621.38 NZ
NEW ZEALAND ELECTRONICS REVIEW. 1967-1987 (vol. 20); suspended. a. (National Electronics Development Association) Associated Group Media Ltd., Private Bag 15, Newmarket, Auckland, New Zealand.

614 NZ ISSN 0110-5264
NEW ZEALAND HEALTH STATISTICS REPORT. ceased. a. Health Statistical Services, c/o Josephine Ryan, 133 Molesworth St., P.O. Box 5013, Wellington, New Zealand.

374 NZ ISSN 0112-224X
NEW ZEALAND JOURNAL OF ADULT LEARNING. 1970-1988; suspended. s-a. National Council of Adult Education, 192 Tinakori Rd., P.O. Box 12114, Wellington North, 6038, New Zealand.
Formerly (until 1983): Continuing Education in New Zealand (ISSN 0110-6619)

637 NZ ISSN 0300-1342
CODEN: NZJDAY
NEW ZEALAND JOURNAL OF DAIRY SCIENCE AND TECHNOLOGY. 1966-1988. 3/yr. New Zealand Dairy Research Institute, Private Bag, Palmerston North, New Zealand.
Formerly: New Zealand Journal of Dairy Technology (ISSN 0028-8268)

330.9 NZ ISSN 0545-7785
NEW ZEALAND NEWS REVIEW. 1960-1990. s-m. Reserve Bank of New Zealand, Public Affairs & Information Service Section, Box 2498, Wellington, New Zealand.

330.9 NZ ISSN 0112-2061
NEW ZEALAND PLANNING COUNCIL. MONITORING REPORTS. 1983-19?? irreg. (back issues avail.) New Zealand Planning Council, P.O. Box 5066, Wellington, New Zealand.
Incorporates: New Zealand Planning Council. Planning Papers.

633.11 NZ ISSN 0078-0219
NEW ZEALAND WHEAT REVIEW. 1945-19?? triennial. Department of Scientific and Industrial Research, Crop Research Division, Private Bag, Christchurch, New Zealand.

711.4 US
NEWCOMER HOUSING GUIDE. 1986-198? bi-m. Visitor Publications, Inc., 6200 Courtney Campbell, Ste. 990, Tampa, FL 33607.

929 US ISSN 0882-6773
CS71
NEWKIRK NOTES. 1982-1988 (no.25). q. 1403 Kingsford Dr., Florissant, MO 63031.

640 US
NEWLYWED. 1989-1991. 3/yr. 3 - C Publishing, 1853 Post Rd. E., Westport, CT 06880.

300 375 US
NEWS AND NOTES ON THE SOCIAL SCIENCES. 1965-19?? 3/yr. (processed; also avail. in microfiche) Indiana University, Coordinator for School Social Studies, 1127 Atwater, Bloomington, IN 47401.

600 371.9 US
NEWS AND VIEWS (SANTA MONICA). 1988-19?? q. (back issues avail.) VTEK, 1625 Olympic Blvd., Santa Monica, CA 90404.

664.752 AT
NEWS FOR THE BREAD MANUFACTURERS AND PASTRY COOKS OF QUEENSLAND. 1947-19?? m. Bread Manufacturers of Queensland, 51 Gregory Terrace, Brisbane, Qld. 4000, Australia.

791.43 US
NEWS FROM CALLY CURTIS. ceased. 4/yr. Cally Curtis Co., 1111 N. Las Palmas Ave., Hollywood, CA 90038.

5248 CESSATIONS

791.43   YU   ISSN 0448-021X
NEWS - JUGOSLAVIJA FILM. 1962-1987. q. (back issues avail.) Jugoslavija Film, Import-Export of Motion Pictures, Knez Mihailova 19, 11000 Belgrade, Yugoslavia.

658.8   UK   ISSN 0028-9353
NEWS TRADE WEEKLY. 1925-1991 (no. 3329). w. John Menzies (GB) Ltd., Hanover Bldgs., Rose St., Edinburgh EH2 2YQ, Scotland.

338   US   ISSN 1040-8193
NEWSLETTER FOR FAMILY-OWNED BUSINESS. ceased 1991 (Jan.). bi-w. McGraw-Hill, Inc., Business Week Management Information Center, 1221 Ave. of the Americas, 36th Fl., New York, NY 10020.

001.6 621.381   US   ISSN 0896-4912
NEWSLETTER FOR INFORMATION EXECUTIVES. ceased. bi-w. McGraw-Hill, Inc., Business Week Management Information Center, 1221 Ave. of the Americas, 36th Fl., New York, NY 10020.

638.1   US
NEWSLETTER ON BEEKEEPING; the world of bees and honey. 1984-1989 (vol.6, no.4). q. Bee Specialist, 6100 Shadow Hills Rd., Las Cruces, NM 88001.

200 327
NEWSLETTER ON CHURCH AND STATE ABROAD. 1983-198? a. (back issues avail.) Carnegie Council on Ethics and International Affairs, Merrill House, 170 E. 64th St., New York, NY 10021-7478.

622   AT
NEWSPAN MINERALS. ceased. d. (back issues avail.) Newspan Publications, 237 Stirling Hwy., Unit 4, Claremont, W.A. 6010, Australia.

665.5   AT
NEWSPAN PETROLEUM. ceased. w. (back issues avail.) Newspan Publications, 237 Stirling Hwy., Unit 4, Claremont, W.A. 6010, Australia.

020   NQ
NICARAGUA. ARCHIVO NACIONAL. BOLETIN. 1979-1986. 5/yr. Arquivo Nacional, Ministerio de Cultura, Managua, Nicaragua.
    Former titles (until 1983): Nicaragua. Archivo Nacional. Boletin Informativo; (until 1982): Nicaragua. Archivo Nacional. Boletin Tecnico Informativo; (until 1981): Nicaragua. Archivo General de la Nacion. Boletin.

917.2   NR
NICARAGUA, CENTRAL AMERICA: A COUNTRY TO DISCOVER. 1983-199?; suspended. m? Instituto Nicaraguense de Turismo - Nicaragua Institute of Tourism, P.O. Box 122, Managua, Nicaragua.

830   GW   ISSN 0933-3282
DD1
NIEMANDSLAND; Zeitschrift Zwischen den Kulturen. 1987-1989. q. Verlag Dirk Nishen GmbH und Co. KG, Am Tempelhofer Berg 6, 1000 Berlin 61, Germany.

052   NR   ISSN 0029-0033
NIGERIA MAGAZINE. 1927-1988 (vol.55, no.4). q. (back issues avail.) Ministry of Culture and Social Welfare, Federal Department of Culture, P.M.B. 12524, Lagos, Nigeria.

052   UK   ISSN 0142-9272
NIGERIA NEWSLETTER. ceased. fortn. Frank Cass & Co. Ltd., Gainsborough House, 11 Gainsborough Rd., London E11 1RS, England.

910.202   US
NIGHT & DAY. 1989-1990. w. Sasquatch Publishing Company, Inc., 1931 Second Ave., Seattle, WA 98101.

621.381   JA
NIKKEI DATAPRO: MINICOMPUTERS. ceased. data file with m. or q. supplements plus newsletter. Nikkei Business Publications, Inc., 3-3-23, Misakicho, Chiyoda-ku, Tokyo 101, Japan.

621.38 380.1   UK
NIKKEI HIGH TECH REPORT. 1985-19?? fortn. (Nikkei Industry Research Institute (NIRI), JA) Elsevier Science Publishers Ltd., Crown House, Linton Rd., Barking, Essex IG11 8JU, England.
    Incorporates: Japan Electronics Today News (ISSN 0261-3506)

780   US
NINE-O-ONE NETWORK. ceased 1988. bi-m. Box 17011, Memphis, TN 38187-0011.

709.03   US   ISSN 0097-5184
N6450
NINETEENTH CENTURY (PHILADELPHIA). 1975-1984 (vol.9, nos.1-2). 4/yr. (also avail. in microform from UMI; reprint service avail. from UMI) Victorian Society in America, 219 S. Sixth St., Philadelphia, PA 19106.

820   UK   ISSN 0264-6773
NINTH DECADE. 1980-1990. 3/yr. Ninth Decade, 12 Stevenage Road, London SW6 6ES, England.
    Former titles (until 1983): Atlantic Review (London) (ISSN 0142-7024); Shearsman (ISSN 0260-8049); Telegram (London) (ISSN 0261-1260)

050   NO   ISSN 0107-752X
NIPPON NYT. 1979-19??; suspended. irreg. (3-5/yr.). Skandinavisk Japan Samlerforening, Skolegt. 46, N-9000 Tromsoe, Norway.

630   JA   ISSN 0029-0904
NOGYO NO KAIRYO/IMPROVEMENT OF AGRICULTURE. 1954-1976. m. Nogyo no Kairyo Kyokai, 3 Takasago, Urawa-shi, Japan.

388.31   US
NOISE MANUAL. published only once, 1980. irreg. (also avail. in looseleaf format) Department of Transportation, Publications Section, 1900 Royal Oaks Dr., Sacramento, CA 95815.

530.4   US   ISSN 0078-0995
NON-METALLIC SOLIDS; a series of monographs. 1971-1972 (vol.3). irreg. (reprint service avail. from ISI) Academic Press, Inc., 1250 Sixth Ave., San Diego, CA 92101.

677   US   ISSN 0888-1979
NONWOVENS WORLD. 1986-199? bi-m. (also avail. in microform from UMI; reprint service avail. from UMI) Miller Freeman, Inc., 600 Harrison St., San Francisco, CA 95407.

677.4   US
NONWOVENS WORLD BUYERS GUIDE. ceased 1991. a. Miller Freeman, Inc., 600 Harrison St., San Francisco, CA 94107.

646.72   US   ISSN 0090-1903
NORDA BRIEFS. 1935-19?? m. (looseleaf format) Norda Inc., 271 Rte. 46 West, No. D105, Fairfield, NJ 07006.
    Formerly: Norda Schimmel Briefs (ISSN 0036-6080)

381   GW
NORDFRIESLAND (FLENSBURG); Chronik in Wort und Bild; Handbuch fuer den Kreis Nordfriesland. ceased 1984. a. Flensburger Zeitungsverlag GmbH, Nikolaistr. 7, 2390 Flensburg, Germany.

691.3   SW   ISSN 0029-1307
NORDISK BETONG. 1957-1991. 4/yr. Nordiska Betongfoerbundet, S-100 44, Stockholm, Sweden.
    Incorporates: Cement og Beton (ISSN 0008-8870)

200   SW   ISSN 0085-4212
NORDISK EKUMENISK AARSBOK. 1972-1990. biennial. Nordiska Ekumeniska Institutet - Nordic Ecumenical Institute, Box 640, S-75127 Uppsala, Sweden.

363.2   NO   ISSN 0029-1390
NORDISK KRIMINALTEKNISK TIDSSKRIFT. ceased. q. c/o Lars l'Abee-Lund, Box 8017, Oslo, Norway.

737   NO   ISSN 0078-107X
NORDISK NUMISMATISK AARSSKRIFT/SCANDINAVIAN NUMISMATIC JOURNAL. 1936-1984. biennial. (Kungliga Vitterhets- , Historie- och Antikvitets Akademien, SW - Royal Academy of Letters, History and Antiquities) Norwegian University Press, Kolstadgt. 1, Box 2959-Toeyen, 0608 Oslo 6, Norway.

410   DK   ISSN 0108-7789
NORDISK TIDSSKRIFT FOR FAGSPROG OG TERMINOLOGI/NORRAENT TIMARIT UM FAGMAAL OG IDORD/NORDISK TIDSSKRIFT FOR FAGSPRAAK OG TERMINOLOGI/POHJOISMAINEN ERIKOISKIELTEN JA TERMINOLOGIAN AIKAKAUSLEHTI/NORDISK TIDSKRIFT FOR FACKSPRAAK OCH TERMINOLOGI/ NORDIC JOURNAL OF L S P AND TERMINOLOGY. 1983-1990 (vol.1-2). s-a. Bondehavevej 11, DK-2880 Bagsvaerd, Denmark.

636.089   DK   ISSN 0029-1579
       CODEN: NOVTAV
NORDISK VETERINAERMEDICIN/SCANDINAVIAN JOURNAL OF VETERINARY SCIENCE. 1949-19?? m. (also avail. in microform from UMI; reprint service avail. from UMI) Danske Dyrlaegeforening, Alhambravej 15, DK-1826 Copenhagen V, Denmark.

960   SW   ISSN 1100-6749
DT19.9.S3
NORDISKA AFRIKAINSTITUTET. ANNUAL REPORT. 1963-1987 (no.26). a. (back issues avail.) Nordiska Afrikainstitutet - Scandinavian Institute of African Studies, P.O. Box 1703, S-751 47 Uppsala, Sweden.
    Formerly (until 1987): Scandinavian Institute of African Studies. Newsletter (ISSN 0549-6330)

053.981   DK   ISSN 0107-2188
NORDSCHLESWIG; Berichte-Daten-Meinungen. 1978-1986. a. (Bund Deutscher Nordschleswiger) Deutsches Generalsekretariat, Vestergade 30, DK-6200 Aabenraa, Denmark.

690   NO   ISSN 0065-0226
NORGES LANDBRUKSHOEGSKOLE. INSTITUTT FOR BYGNINGSTEKNIKK. AARSMELDING/AGRICULTURAL UNIVERSITY OF NORWAY. DEPARTMENT OF BUILDING TECHNOLOGY IN AGRICULTURE. ANNUAL REPORT. 1964-1989. a. Norges Landbrukshoegskole, Instituut for Bygningsteknikk - Agricultural University of Norway, Department of Building Technology in Agriculture, P.O. Box 65, N-1432 Aas-NLH, Norway.

631.2   NO   ISSN 0065-0218
NORGES LANDBRUKSHOEGSKOLE. INSTITUTT FOR BYGNINGSTEKNIKK. BYGGEKOSTNADSINDEKS FOR DRIFTSBYGNINGER I JORDBRUKET. PRISUTVIKLINGEN. 1958-1989. a. Norges Landbrukshoegskole, Instituut for Bygningsteknikk - Agricultural University of Norway, Department of Building Technology in Agriculture, P.O. Box 65, N-1432 Aas-NLH, Norway.

690   NO   ISSN 0065-0234
NORGES LANDBRUKSHOEGSKOLE. INSTITUTT FOR BYGNINGSTEKNIKK. MELDING. 1951-1989. irreg. Norges Landbrukshoegskole, Instituut for Bygningsteknikk - Agricultural University of Norway, Department of Building Technology in Agriculture, P.O. Box 65, N-1432 Aas-NLH, Norway.

636.089   NO
NORGES VETERINAERHOEGSKOLE. AARSMELDING/ NORWEGIAN COLLEGE OF VETERINARY MEDICINE. ANNUAL REPORT. 1985-1986. a. Norges Veterinaerhoegskole, P.O. Box 8146, 0033-Oslo 1, Norway.

015   NO   ISSN 0029-1862
HF6015
NORSK BIBLIOGRAFISK BIBLIOTEK. 1936-198? Norwegian University Press, P.O. Box 2959, 0608 Oslo 6, Norway.

574 614.7 312   NO
NORSK VILTFORSKNING. MEDDELELSER. 1935-198? irreg. (back issues avail.) Directorate for Nature Management, Tungasletta 2, N-7000 Trondheim, Norway.

382 338   US
NORTH AFRICA MONITOR. ceased. 10/yr. Business International Corp., 215 Park Ave. S., New York, NY 10003.
    Formerly: Algeria Monitor - Algeria Information.

614.7   CN   ISSN 0840-5662
GF28.N7
NORTH AMERICAN ENVIRONMENT. 1973-1989. 4/yr. (American Society for Environmental Education, Inc.) Pallister Resource Management Ltd., 4116 - 64th St., Suite 105, Calgary, Alta. T2C 2B3, Canada.

Former titles: American Environment; Environmental Education Report and Newsletter; Environmental Education Report (ISSN 0199-6916); E E Report (ISSN 0162-0606); Environmental Education Report (ISSN 0091-1712)

323.4   JC571   US   ISSN 0270-2282
NORTH AMERICAN HUMAN RIGHTS DIRECTORY; directory of groups in the United States and Canada active in international human rights. 1980-198? (2nd ed.). irreg. Garrett Park Press, Box 190F, Garrett Park, MD 20896.
Formerly: Human Rights Directory (ISSN 0197-8101)

360   US
NORTH CAROLINA. DEPARTMENT OF HUMAN RESOURCES. PUBLICATION. ceased 1978. irreg. Department of Human Resources, c/o Janet Lucas, Office Mgr., 101 Blair Dr., Raleigh, NC 27603.

551   US
NORTH CAROLINA. DEPARTMENT OF NATURAL RESOURCES AND COMMUNITY DEVELOPMENT. DIVISION OF LAND RESOURCES. ECONOMIC PAPER. ceased 1990 (no.68). irreg. North Carolina Geological Survey, Box 27687, Raleigh, NC 27611.
Formerly: North Carolina. Division of Mineral Resources. Economic Paper.

551   US
NORTH CAROLINA. DEPARTMENT OF NATURAL RESOURCES AND COMMUNITY DEVELOPMENT. DIVISION OF LAND RESOURCES. REGIONAL GEOLOGY SERIES. 1975-1982 (no.2). irreg. North Carolina Geological Survey, Box 27687, Raleigh, NC 27611-7687.

551   US
NORTH CAROLINA. DEPARTMENT OF NATURAL RESOURCES AND COMMUNITY DEVELOPMENT. DIVISION OF LAND RESOURCES. SPECIAL PUBLICATION. 1965-1983 (no.8). irreg. North Carolina Geological Survey, Box 27687, Raleigh, NC 27611.
Formerly: North Carolina. Division of Mineral Resources. Special Publication (ISSN 0078-1398)

720   US   ISSN 0029-2427
NORTH CAROLINA ARCHITECT. 1954-19?? bi-m. (American Institute of Architects, North Carolina Chapter) Spectator Publications, Inc., Box 12887, Raleigh, NC 27605.
Formerly: Southern Architect.

378   US
NORTH CAROLINA STATE UNIVERSITY. COLLEGE OF TEXTILES NEWS. 1976-1989. s-a. North Carolina State University, College of Textiles, Box 8301, Raleigh, NC 27695-8301.
Formerly: North Carolina State University. School of Textiles News.

551.46   US   ISSN 0164-6761
NORTH CAROLINA TARHEEL COAST. 1969-1991. bi-m. Division of Marine Fisheries, Box 769, Morehead City, NC 28557.

051   US
NORTH COUNTRY ANVIL. 1972-1990. 4/yr. (also avail. in microform from UMI) North Country Anvil Inc., Box 37, Milville, MN 55957.

338   HA561   US   ISSN 0549-8368
NORTH DAKOTA GROWTH INDICATORS. 1959-19?? irreg. Economic Development Commission, Liberty Memorial Bldg., Bismarck, ND 58505.

370   US   ISSN 0029-2737
NORTH DAKOTA JOURNAL OF EDUCATION. ceased 1990 (Apr.). 4/yr. North Dakota Education Association, Box 5005, Bismarck, ND 58502.
Formerly: North Dakota Teacher.

548   NE
NORTH-HOLLAND SERIES IN CRYSTAL GROWTH. ceased 1979. irreg. North-Holland (Subsidiary of: Elsevier Science Publishers B.V.), P.O. Box 211, 1000 AE Amsterdam, Netherlands.

621.381   NE
NORTH-HOLLAND SERIES IN GENERAL SYSTEMS RESEARCH. 1978-1979; suspended. irreg. North-Holland (Subsidiary of: Elsevier Science Publishers B.V.), P.O. Box 211, 1000 AE Amsterdam, Netherlands.

510   NE
NORTH-HOLLAND SERIES IN PROBABILITY AND APPLIED MATHEMATICS. 1979-1984. irreg. North-Holland (Subsidiary of: Elsevier Science Publishers B.V.), P.O. Box 211, 1000 AE Amsterdam, Netherlands.

914.1   UK   ISSN 0260-2415
NORTH OF SCOTLAND VISITOR; tourist guide to north of Scotland. 1980-19?? a. Scotsman Publications, 20 North Bridge, Edinburgh EH1 1YT, Scotland.

387   NO   ISSN 0332-6144
NORTH SEA OBSERVER. 1978-19?? 6/yr. Norwegian Technical Press A S, P.O. Box 235, Skoeyen, 0212 Oslo 2, Norway.

052   UK
NORTHAMPTONSHIRE LIFE. 1976-19??; suspended. m. County Life Ltd., P.O. Box 18, Lincoln, Lincolnshire LN5 7DY, England.
Supersedes in part: Northamptonshire and Bedfordshire Life (ISSN 0306-9001)

917   US
NORTHERN ARIZONA SCENE; a pictorial and prose profile of Arizona's northlands. 1976-1986. a. Halamar, Inc., 9800 Flint Rock Rd., Manassas, VA 22111.

020 015   UK   ISSN 0144-123X
Z2024.N853
NORTHERN BIBLIOGRAPHY. 1979-198? (vol.10, part 1). q. Northern Regional Library System, Central Library, Newcastle upon Tyne NE99 1DX, England.

630   UK   ISSN 0078-1754
CODEN: RARIAQ
NORTHERN IRELAND. DEPARTMENT OF AGRICULTURE. RECORD OF AGRICULTURAL RESEARCH. 1963-1988 (vol.36). irreg. Department of Agriculture, Dundonald House, Upper Newtownards Rd., Belfast BT4 3SB, N. Ireland.

971   CN   ISSN 0029-3199
DK1
NORTHERN NEIGHBORS. 1956-1989. 11/yr. (also avail. in microform from UMI; reprint service avail. from UMI; back issues avail.) Northern Neighbors Ltd., Box 1000, Gravenhurst, Ont. P0C 1G0, Canada.

913   US   ISSN 0277-0997
QH84.1
NORTHERN RAVEN. 1981-1988 (Spring). a. Center for Northern Studies, Wolcott, VT 05680 9726.
Formerly: Raven (Wolcott).

371.1 375   UK   ISSN 0048-0797
NORTHERN TEACHER. 1953-1983. s-a. (tabloid format) Irish National Teachers Organization, 23 College Gardens, Belfast BT9 6BS, N. Ireland.

051   US
NORTHWEST MAGAZINE (PORTLAND); the Sunday Oregonian magazine. 1950-1991. w. (back issues avail.) Oregonian Publishing Company, 1320 S.W. Broadway, Portland, OR 97201.

614 310   NO   ISSN 0332-7965
NORWAY. STATISTISK SENTRALBYRAA. ALKOHOL OG ANDRE RUSMIDLER/ALCOHOL AND DRUGS. (Subseries of its Norges Offisielle Statistikk) ceased. a. Statistisk Sentralbyraa, Box 8131 Dep., 0033 Oslo 1, Norway.

301.4   NO   ISSN 0332-7957
NORWAY. STATISTISK SENTRALBYRAA. FAMILIE STATISTIKK/FAMILY STATISTICS. (Subseries of its Norges Offisielle Statistikk) 1974-19?? irreg. Statistisk Sentralbyraa, Box 8131 Dep., 0033 Oslo 1, Norway.

312   NO   ISSN 0332-8015
NORWAY. STATISTISK SENTRALBYRAA. FRAMSKRIVING AV FOLKEMENGDEN: REGIONALE TALL/NORWAY. CENTRAL BUREAU OF STATISTICS. POPULATION PROJECTIONS: REGIONAL FIGURES. (Subseries of its Norges Offisielle Statistikk) ceased. irreg. Statistisk Sentralbyraa - Central Bureau of Statistics, Box 8131 Dep., 0033 Oslo 1, Norway.

330 314   NO   ISSN 0078-1924
NORWAY. STATISTISK SENTRALBYRAA. OEKONOMISK UTSYN/ECONOMIC SURVEY. (Subseries of its Norges Offisielle Statistikk) 1936-1987. quadrennial. Statistisk Sentralbyraa, Box 8131 Dep., 0033 Oslo 1, Norway.

364.4   NO   ISSN 0550-0532
NORWAY. STATISTISK SENTRALBYRAA. SIVILRETTSSTATISTIKK/CIVIL JUDICIAL STATISTICS. (Subseries of: Norges Offisielle Statistikk) 1886-1988. a. Statistisk Sentralbyraa, Box 8131-Dep., 0033 Oslo 1, Norway.

382   US   ISSN 0029-3644
HF29
NORWEGIAN AMERICAN COMMERCE. 1934-1989. q. Norwegian American Chamber of Commerce, Inc., 800 Third Ave., New York, NY 10022.

658.3   US
NOT JUST THE CLASSIFIEDS. 1987-1989 (Jan.). q. Shomex Productions, 2601 Ocean Park Blvd., Santa Monica, CA 90405-5990.

800 780 700   GW
NOTES FROM EUROPE/CAHIERS EUROPEENS/ EUROPAEISCHE HEFTE; European literature cultural review. 1974-1989. q. Bertelsmann Fachzeitschriften GmbH, Postfach 5555, 4830 Gutersloh 100, Germany.

630   CN   ISSN 0380-5735
NOTES ON AGRICULTURE. 1966-1988. s-a. University of Guelph, Ontario Agricultural College, Guelph, Ont. N1G 2W1, Canada.

361.8   GW
NOTGROSCHEN. 1987-1991. q. Sozialhilfeverein Raunheim e.V., Uhlandstr. 39, 6096 Raunheim, Germany.

374   MX
NOTI C R E F A L INTERNACIONAL. 1953-1986 (Dec.). q. Centro Regional de Educacion de Adultos y Alfabetizacion Funcional para America Latina, Quinta Erendira, 61600 Patzcuaro, Mich., Mexico.
Formerly (until 1980): Boletin Informativo C R E F A L.

917.306   US
NOTICIARIO. 1979-198? q. National Council of La Raza, 810 First St., N.E., No. 300, Washington, DC 20002-4272.

051   CN   ISSN 0384-2282
NOTICIARIO DE CANADA. ceased 1985. fortn. Department of External Affairs, External Communications Division (BFE), 125 Sussex Dr., Ottawa, Ont. K1A 0G2, Canada.

617.6   BL   ISSN 0029-4144
NOTICIARIO - ODONTOLOGIA SANITARIA NAS AMERICAS. 1963-1967 (no.8). 2/yr. (processed) Universidade de Sao Paulo, Escola de Saude Publica, Caixa Postal 8099, Cidade Universitaria, Sao Paulo, Brazil.

051   CN   ISSN 0228-5843
NOTICIAS DO CANADA. 1980-1985. fortn. Department of External Affairs, 125 Sussex Dr., Ottawa, Ont. K1A 0G2, Canada.

610.73
NOTIZIARIO AGGIORNAMENTI PROFESSIONALI. vol.10, 1988-19?? bi-m. Masson Italia Periodici, Via Statuto 2-4, 20121 Milan, Italy.

799.1   IT
NOTIZIARIO F.I.P.S.. ceased 1990 (Mar.). m. Federazione Italiana Pesca Sportiva ed Attivita Subacquee, Viale Abruzzi 79, 20131 Milan, Italy.

639.9   GW
NOTSCHREI DER TIERE. 1980-1991. q. (looseleaf format; back issues avail.) Foerderverein Hilfswerk Salem e.V., Alte Presseckerstr. 51, 8652 Stadtsteinach, Germany.

100 320   IT
NOTTOLA; rivista quadrimestrale di filosofia. 1982-1987. q. Associazione Culturale "La Nottola", Via Marco Evangelista 2, 61045 Pergola (PS), Italy.

809   US   ISSN 0889-0803
NOTUS NEW WRITING. 1986-1990. s-a. (back issues avail.) OtherWind Press, Inc., 2420 Walter Dr., Ann Arbor, MI 48103.

CESSATIONS

630   FR
LE NOUVEL AGRICULTEUR; moniteur agricole. 1964-19?? w. Societe de Publications et d'Editions Reunies, 21 rue du Faubourg St. Antoine, 75550 Paris Cedex 11, France.
   Formerly: Agri Sept (ISSN 0044-6750); Incorporates (1925-1986): Producteur Agricole Francais (ISSN 0555-3121)

972.9   MQ
LA NOUVELLE LETTRE D'INFORMATION. ceased. irreg. Chambre de Commerce et d'Industrie de la Martinique, 50, rue Ernest Deproge, B.P. 478, 97241 Fort-de-France Cedex, Martinique.

388.324   CN   ISSN 0822-5435
LA NOUVELLE VOIX DE L'ANCAI. 1983-19?? m. Ideo Productions Inc., 2095 Blvd. Charest W., Ste-Foy, Que. G1N 4L8, Canada.

500   DK   ISSN 0108-3333
NOUVELLES SCIENTIFIQUES FRANCO-DANOISES. 1978-1987. 5/yr. Association Franco-Danoise pour la Recherche et le Developpement, c/o Knud Loensted, Matematisk Institut, Universitetsparken 5, 2100 Copenhagen OE, Denmark.

647.94   CN
NOVA SCOTIA HOSTELLER. 1963?-19?? q. (looseleaf format) Canadian Hostelling Association - Nova Scotia, P.O. Box 3010, South Halifax, N.S. B3J 3G6, Canada.

890   DK   ISSN 0107-8941
NOVELLE MAGASINET. 1981-198? fortn. Interpresse, Bagsvaerd, Denmark.

070   CS   ISSN 0029-5167
NOVINAR/JOURNALIST. (Supplement avail.: Obrazova Priloha) 1949-19?? m. (Ceskoslovensky Svaz Novinaru) Novinar, Narodni tr. 17, Prague 1, Czechoslovakia.
   Formerly: Ceskoslovensky Novinar.

330 016   CS   ISSN 0139-5203
NOVINKY LITERATURY: EKONOMIE. 1960-1990. m. Statni Knihovna C S R, Klementinum 190, 110 01 Prague 1, Czechoslovakia.
   Former titles (until 1974): Novinky Literatury: Bibliografie Ekonomicke Literatury; Novinky Literatury: Spolecenske Vedy. Rada 2: Bibliografie Ekonomicke Literatury (ISSN 0006-1123)

591   US   ISSN 0278-3274
                      CODEN: NOARDP
NOVITATES ARTHROPODAE. 1980-19?? irreg. J-B Publishing Co., 430 Ivy Ave., Crete, NE 68333.

615.842   GW
NUCCOMPACT: EUROPEAN-AMERICAN COMMUNICATIONS IN NUCLEAR MEDICINE. 1970-1991. bi-m. G I T Verlag GmbH, Roesslerstr. 90, 6100 Darmstadt 11, Germany.

539.7   SA   ISSN 0048-1025
                     CODEN: NULABZ
NUCLEAR ACTIVE. 1969-1989 (Aug.). s-a. Atomic Energy Corporation, P.O. Box 256, Pretoria 0001, South Africa.

539.7   US
NUCLEAR PHYSICS MONOGRAPHS. 1978-19?? irreg. Plenum Publishing Corp., 233 Spring St., New York, NY 10013.

539   US
NUCLEAR REPORT. 1978-1989. m. American Nuclear Society, 555 N. Kensington Ave., La Grange Park, IL 60525.

539.7 621.3   CN   ISSN 0838-3871
NUCLEAR SECTOR FOCUS. 1987-1991. a. Atomic Energy of Canada Ltd., 344 Slater St., Ottawa, Ont. K1A 0S4, Canada.

539.7   AT   ISSN 0815-0249
QC792.78.A8   CODEN: NUSPEG
NUCLEAR SPECTRUM. 1985-198?; suspended. s-a. Australian Nuclear Science and Technology Organisation, Menai, N.S.W. 2234, Australia.

296   US
NUESTRO ENCUENTRO. 1980-1991. q. Anti-Defamation League of B'nai B'rith, 823 United Nations Plaza, New York, NY 10017.

282   VC
NUNTIA. ceased 1990. s-a. (Pontifical Commission for the Revision of the Oriental Code of Canon Law) Libreria Editrice Vaticana, 00120 Vatican City (Rome), State of the Vatican City.

649   IT   ISSN 0033-1570
NUOVE PROSPETTIVE. 1960-198? m. (Federazione Circoli Giovanili Catolici di Milano) Fondazione Oratori Milanesi, Via S. Antonio 5, Milan 20122, Italy.
   Formerly: Prospettive Giovanili.

659.1   IT   ISSN 0394-9583
NUOVO; comunicazione e immagine. 1982-19??; suspended. q. Ediforum srl, Viale Beatrice D'Este, 37, 20122 Milan, Italy.

542   IT
IL NUOVO LABORATORIO. 1956-198? 5/yr. (plus 1 special issue). Edizioni Ariminum, Via Negroli 51, 20133 Milano, Italy.
   Formerly: Laboratorio (ISSN 0456-9814)

610.73 340   US
NURSING ADMINISTRATION & LAW MANUAL. 1985-198? s-a. Aspen Publishers, Inc., 1600 Research Blvd., Rockville, MD 20850.

610.73   US
NURSING FORMS MANUAL. 1985-198? s-a. Aspen Publishers, Inc., 1600 Research Blvd., Rockville, MD 20850.

364.4   US
NURSING HOME LOSS CONTROL; a newsletter of loss prevention, crime prevention, and accident prevention. ceased. m. Rusting Publications, 403 Main St., Box 1032, Port Washington, NY 11050.
   Formerly: Nursing Home Security and Safety Management.

610.73   US   ISSN 0894-3184
NURSING SCIENCE QUARTERLY. 1988-1990. q. Williams & Wilkins, 428 E. Preston St., Baltimore, MD 21202.

613.2   US   ISSN 0160-2470
                     CODEN: NHDIDW
NUTRITION IN HEALTH AND DISEASE. 1979; ceased same year. irreg. Raven Press, 1185 Ave. of the Americas, New York, NY 10036.

641.1   US
NUTRITIONAL SUPPORT SERVICES; the journal of practical application in clinical nutrition. 1981-198? m. Creative Age Publications, 7628 Densmore Ave., Van Nuys, CA 91406-2088.

378   US
NUTSHELL (KNOXVILLE); a handbook for college. 1969-19?? s-a. 13-30 Corporation, 505 Market St., Knoxville, TN 37902.
   Incorporates (in 1982): Graduate: A Handbook for Leaving School.

700   DK   ISSN 0109-5544
NY ABSTRAKTION. 1977-1985. a. c/o Finn Mickelborg, Noerregade 45 A, DK-1165 Copenhagen K, Denmark.

621.38   DK   ISSN 0105-4880
NY ELEKTRONIK. 1927-1989. m. St. Kongensgade 72, DK-1264 Copenhagen K, Denmark.
   Incorporates: Populaer Radio; Which was formerly: Populaer Radio og TV Teknik (ISSN 0032-4442)

617.6   DK
DET NY INFODONT. 1980-1989; suspended. irreg. (6-8/yr.). Odontologisk Forening, Aarhus Tandlaegehoejskole, Vennelyst Blvd, 8000 Aarhus C, Denmark.
   Formerly: Infodont (ISSN 0107-8097); Which was formed by the merger of: Info; Odont (ISSN 0105-189X)

808   US
NYCTALOPS. 1970-1991 (vol.1, no.19). irreg. Silver Scarab Press, 502 Elm S.E., Albuquerque, NM 87102.

614   DK   ISSN 0900-2685
NYHEDSBREV FOR SOCIAL OG SUNDHEDSSEKTOR. 1984-1986. fortn. Forlag for Social og Sundhedssektor, Ibertslund, Denmark.

643.6 651.2   DK   ISSN 0109-6222
NYT OM MOEBLER. ceased. m. Danish Furniture Manufacturer Association, Center Boulevard 5, DK-2300 Copenhagen S, Denmark.

020.6   SW   ISSN 0349-3210
NYTT FRAAN D F I. 1980-1986 (no.4). irreg., (3-4/yr.). Delegationen foer Vetenskaplig och Teknisk Informationsfoersoerjning - Delegation for Scientific and Technical Information, Box 43 033, 100 72 Stockholm, Sweden.

001.6 629.8   US   ISSN 0737-7592
O A - F A UPDATE; a monthly report on Japanese office and factory automation. 1983-1984 (vol.2, no.1). m. Japan Information Service (Austin), Box 4700 N. Austin Sta., Austin, TX 78765-4700.

338.47 666   FR   ISSN 0474-5493
O E C D. CEMENT INDUSTRY/O C D E. INDUSTRIE DU CIMENT. 1954-1975. irreg. (also avail. in microfiche) Organization for Economic Cooperation and Development, 2 rue Andre-Pascal, 75775 Paris Cedex 16, France.

331.11   FR
O E C D. DEVELOPMENT CENTRE. EMPLOYMENT SERIES. 1971-19?? irreg. (also avail. in microfiche) Organization for Economic Cooperation and Development, 2 rue Andre-Pascal, 75775 Paris Cedex 16, France.

338.39   FR   ISSN 0474-5477
O E C D. ELECTRICITY SUPPLY INDUSTRY/O C D E. INDUSTRIE DE L'ELECTRICITE. ceased. irreg. (also avail. in microfiche) Organization for Economic Cooperation and Development, 2 rue Andre-Pascal, 75775 Paris Cedex 16, France.

338.39   FR   ISSN 0474-5876
O E C D. ENGINEERING INDUSTRIES IN O E C D COUNTRIES. 1955-1983. irreg. (also avail. in microfiche) Organization for Economic Cooperation and Development, 2 rue Andre-Pascal, 75775 Paris Cedex 16, France.
   Formerly: O E C D. Machinery Committee. Engineering Industries in North America - Europe - Japan.

382   FR   ISSN 0304-3282
O E C D. GUIDE TO LEGISLATION ON RESTRICTIVE BUSINESS PRACTICES SUPPLEMENTS. ceased. 2/yr. (also avail. in microfiche) Organization for Economic Cooperation and Development, 2 rue Andre-Pascal, 75775 Paris Cedex 16, France.

338   FR   ISSN 0474-5450
HC10
O E C D. INDUSTRIAL PRODUCTION/O C D E. PRODUCTION INDUSTRIELLE. ceased. irreg. (also avail. in microfiche) Organization for Economic Cooperation and Development, 2 rue Andre-Pascal, 75775 Paris Cedex 16, France.

338 314   FR   ISSN 0474-5469
O E C D. INDUSTRIAL STATISTICS/O C D E. STATISTIQUES INDUSTRIELLES. 1955-198? irreg. (also avail. in microfiche) Organization for Economic Cooperation and Development, 2 rue Andre-Pascal, 75775 Paris Cedex 16, France.

539   FR
O E C D. NEWSLETTER ON R & D IN URANIUM EXTRACTION TECHNOLOGY/O C D E. BULLETIN D'INFORMATION RELATIF A LA R & D SUR LES TECHNIQUES D'EXTRACTION DE L'URANIUM. 1983-1984. s-a. Organization for Economic Cooperation and Development, Nuclear Energy Agency, 38 bd. Suchet, 75016 Paris, France.

331.11   FR   ISSN 0474-5892
O E C D. SOCIAL AFFAIRS DIVISION. DEVELOPING JOB OPPORTUNITIES. 1965-198? irreg. (also avail. in microfiche) Organization for Economic Cooperation and Development, 2 rue Andre-Pascal, 75775 Paris Cedex 16, France.

382   FR   ISSN 0474-5396
HF1016
O E C D. STATISTICS OF FOREIGN TRADE. SERIES B: TABLES BY REPORTING COUNTRIES/O C D E. STATISTIQUES DU COMMERCE EXTERIEUR. SERIE B: TABLEAUX PAR PAYS DECLARANTS. 1974-19?? a. (also avail. in microfiche) Organization for Economic Cooperation and Development, 2 rue Andre-Pascal, 75775 Paris Cedex 16, France.

Former titles: Organization for Economic Cooperation and Development. Statistics of Foreign Trade. Series B. Trade by Commodities. Country Summaries; O E C D Foreign Trade Statistics. Series B.

350   FR
O E C D. STUDIES IN RESOURCE ALLOCATION. 1974-198? (vol. no. 5). irreg. (also avail. in microfiche) Organization for Economic Cooperation and Development, 2 rue Andre-Pascal, 75775 Paris Cedex 16, France.

338.47 621.3   FR   ISSN 0474-5353
O E C D. SURVEY OF ELECTRIC POWER EQUIPMENT/O C D E. ENQUETE SUR L'EQUIPEMENT ELECTRIQUE. 1950-19?? irreg. (also avail. in microfiche) Organization for Economic Cooperation and Development, 2 rue Andre-Pascal, 75775 Paris Cedex 16, France.

331   FR   ISSN 0474-5620
O E C D. WAGES AND LABOUR MOBILITY SUPPLEMENT. 1966-19?? irreg. (also avail. in microfiche) Organization for Economic Cooperation and Development, 2 rue Andre-Pascal, 75775 Paris Cedex 16, France.

539 621.48   FR   ISSN 0078-6284
O E C D HALDEN REACTOR PROJECT. 1960-1981. a. (also avail. in microfiche) Organization for Economic Cooperation and Development, Nuclear Energy Agency, 38 bd. Suchet, 75016 Paris, France.

558   BL   ISSN 0078-2874
O.I.G.G.; revista do Instituto Geografico e Geologico. 1943-1968 (vol.20). irreg. Instituto Geologico, Caixa Postal 8772, Sao Paulo, Brazil.

685   AU   ISSN 0029-7151
O L W. (Oesterreichische Lederwaren) 1948-19?? m. Manstein Verlag Ges.m.b.H., Gusshausstr. 12, 1040 Vienna, Austria.

266   IT   ISSN 0029-7178
O.M.I. MISSIONS. 1862-1972. q. Missionary Oblates of Mary Immaculate, General House, 290 via Aurelia, 00165 Rome, Italy.

025   US   ISSN 0278-7946
Z675.U5
O M S ANNUAL REPORT. 1971-1989. a. Association of Research Libraries, Office of Management Services, 1527 New Hampshire Ave., N.W., Washington, DC 20036.

600   FR   ISSN 0071-9021
    CODEN: ORSIAF
O.R.S.T.O.M. INITIATIONS DOCUMENTATIONS TECHNIQUES. (Office de la Recherche Scientifique et Technique Outre-Mer) 1962-1989. irreg. O R S T O M, Institut Francais de Recherche Scientifique pour le Developpement en Cooperation, 70-74 Route d'Aulnay, 93143 Bondy cedex, France.

949   NE
O S G N WETENSCHAPPELIJKE PUBLIKATIE. 1967-1989. irreg. Organisatie van Studenten in de Geschiedenis van Nederland, Groningen, Netherlands.

384   US
O U T - LINE. 1974-1990 (Jul.). irreg. (looseleaf format) Organization for Use of the Telephone, 3417 Volta Pl., N.W., Washington, DC 20007-2783.

917.904
OAHU, A PARADISE GUIDE. (Supplement avail.: Oahu Update) ceased 1989. biennial. Paradise Publications, 8110 S.W. Wareham, Portland, OR 97223.

917.904   US   ISSN 1042-8038
OAHU UPDATE. (Supplement to: Oahu, a Paradise Guide) 1989-1990. q. Paradise Publications, 8110 S.W. Wareham, Portland, OR 97223.

332.6   US
OAKLEY'S AGGRESSIVE STOCK ALERT. 1987-198? m. American Media Group, 951 Broken Sound Pkwy., N.W., Boca Raton, FL 33431.

618   US   ISSN 0198-9197
OB-GYN DIGEST (YEAR). 1959-1979 (vol.21, no.11). 10/yr. (also avail. in microform from UMI; reprint service avail. from UMI) Medical Digest, Inc., 445 Central Ave., Northfield, IL 60093.

Former titles: Journal of Continuing Education in Obstetrics and Gynecology (ISSN 0148-5164); Ob-Gyn Digest (ISSN 0029-7429) Incorporates: Ob-Gyn Abstracts.

618 340   US   ISSN 0735-9551
KF2910.G943
OB-GYN LITIGATION REPORTER; the national reporting service of litigation concerning obstetrical and gynecological products. 1982-1991 (Mar.). s-m. (looseleaf format; back issues avail.) Andrews Publications, 1646 West Chester Pike, Box 1000, Westtown, PA 19395.

636.7   UK
OBEDIENCE COMPETITOR MAGAZINE. ceased 1991. fortn. Our Dogs Publishing Co. Ltd., 5 Oxford Rd., Station Approach, Manchester M60 1SX, England.

943.6   AU   ISSN 0572-192X
DB153
OBEROESTERREICHISCHES LANDESARCHIV. MITTEILUNGEN. 1950-19?? a. Boehlau Verlag GmbH & Co.KG., Dr. Karl Lueger-Ring 12, Postfach 581, A-1011 Vienna, Austria.

554   GW   ISSN 0078-2939
    CODEN: OGABAV
OBERRHEINISCHE GEOLOGISCHE ABHANDLUNGEN. 1929-1985. a. Verlag C.F. Mueller GmbH (Karlsruhe), Amalienstr. 29, 7500 Karlsruhe 1, Germany.

380   FR
OBJECTIF, INTER 8000. 1971-1990. 10/yr. Chambre de Commerce et d'Industrie de Dunkerque, 1, Quai Freycinet, Boite Postale 1501, 59383 Dunkerque Cedex 1, France.
Formerly: Inter 8000.

520   FR
OBSERVATIONS ET TRAVAUX (SPECIAL ISSUES). published only once, 1989. 4/yr. Societe Astronomique de France, 3, rue Beethoven, 75016 Paris, France.

133   US   ISSN 0731-7840
OCCULTISM UPDATE. (Supplement to the Encyclopedia of Occultism and Parapsychology) 1978-1986 (2nd ed.). irreg. Gale Research Inc., 835 Penobscot Bldg., Detroit, MI 48226.

330   US
OCEAN COUNTY BUSINESS TODAY. 1984-198? m. Pentacle Publishing Co., 1830 US Rte. 9, Toms River, NJ 08755.

614.7 340   CN
OCEAN DUMPING CONTROL ACT ANNUAL REPORT. 1984-1988. a. (also avail. in microfiche) Environment Canada, Conservation and Protection, Ottawa, Ont. K1A 0H3, Canada.

551.46   US   ISSN 0890-5460
GC1   CODEN: OPHEE6
OCEAN PHYSICS AND ENGINEERING. 1974-19?? 3/yr. (also avail. in microform from RPI) Marcel Dekker Journals, 270 Madison Ave., New York, NY 10016.
Former titles: Ocean Science and Engineering (ISSN 0275-2220); Marine Science Communications (ISSN 0098-8383)

614.70   US   ISSN 0029-8174
GC1   CODEN: OCMGA
OCEANS. 1960-19?? bi-m. (also avail. in microform from UMI; reprint service avail. from UMI) Oceans Magazine Associates, Inc., 2001 W. Marin St., Stamford, CT 06902.

340 330   DK   ISSN 0903-5079
ODENSE UNIVERSITY. DEPARTMENT OF COMMERCIAL LAW AND POLITICAL SCIENCE. PUBLICATIONS. 1982-1988 (no.1). irreg. Odense University, Department of Commercial Law and Political Science, Odense Universitetsbibliotek, Campusvej 5, 5230 Odense, Denmark.
Formerly (until 1984): Odense Universitet. Institut for Offentlig Oekonomi og Politik. Occasional Paper (ISSN 0109-0976)

960   NR
ODUMA. 1973-19??; suspended. s-a. Rivers State Council for Arts & Culture, 74-76 Bonny St., P.M.B. 5156, Port Harcourt, Nigeria.

330.05   PL   ISSN 0137-5806
HB9
OECONOMICA POLONA. 1974-1989 (3-4). q. (Polska Akademia Nauk, Komitet Nauk Ekonomicznych - Polish Academy of Sciences) Panstwowe Wydawnictwo Ekonomiczne, Niecala 4a, 00-098 Warsaw, Poland.

330   GW
OEFFENTLICHE WIRTSCHAFT UND GEMEINWIRTSCHAFT. 1951-1985. q. (Gesellschaft fuer Oeffentliche Wirtschaft und Gemeinwirtschaft e.V.) Hammonia-Verlag GmbH, Postfach 620228, 2000 Hamburg 62, Germany.
Formerly: Oeffentliche Wirtschaft (ISSN 0029-8603)

200   GW   ISSN 0175-5838
OEKUMENE AM ORT; Blaetter fuer oekumenische Basisarbeit. 1972-1990. m. (looseleaf format; back issues avail.) Verlag der Action 365, Kennedyallee 111a, 6000 Frankfurt a.M. 70, Germany.

028.5   FI
OESTERBOTTNISKA POSTEN. 1968-198? w. (tabloid format) (Svenska Oesterbottens Ungdomsfoerbund) Jakobstads Tryckeri och Tidnings AB, Jakobsg. 13, SF-68600 Jakobstad, Finland.

635.9   AU
OESTERREICH FLORIST; Fachzeitschrift der oesterreichischen Blumenbinder. ceased 1990. 10/yr. Bohmann Druck und Verlag GmbH & Co. KG, Leberstr. 122, A-1110 Vienna, Austria.

300   AU
OESTERREICHISCHE AKADEMIE DER WISSENSCHAFTEN. KOMMISSION FUER SOZIAL- UND WIRTSCHAFTWISSENSCHAFTEN. VEROEFFENTLICHUNGEN. (Subseries of its Philosophisch-Historische Klasse. Sitzungsberichte) 1973-1989. irreg. Verlag der Oesterreichischen Akademie der Wissenschaften, Dr. Ignaz Seipel-Platz 2, 1010 Vienna, Austria.

617   AU
OESTERREICHISCHE GESELLSCHAFT FUER CHIRURGIE. MITTEILUNGEN. 1972-19?? 4/yr. Verlag Dieter Goeschl GmbH, Andergasse 10, A-1170 Vienna, Austria.

685.31   AU
DER OESTERREICHISCHER SCHUHMARKT. 1949-198? m. (Bundesinnung der Schuhmacher) Oesterreichischer Wirtschaftsverlag, Nikolsdorfergasse 7-11, A-1051 Vienna, Austria.
Formerly: Oesterreichische Schuhmacher - Zeitung (ISSN 0029-9464)

330   AU   ISSN 0078-3595
OESTERREICHISCHES WIRTSCHAFTSINSTITUT FUER STRUKTURFORSCHUNG UND STRUKTURPOLITIK. SCHRIFTENREIHE. 1968-1990. irreg. Oesterreichisches Wirtschaftsinstitut fuer Strukturforschung und Strukturpolitik, Hessenplatz, A-4020 Linz, Austria.
Formerly: Oesterreichisches Institut fuer Mittelstandspolitik. Schriftenreihe.

947   DK   ISSN 0108-4380
OESTNYT. ceased. s-a. Selskabet for Oesteuropastudier, Slavisk Institut, Ny Munkegade 116-4, 8000 Aarhus C, Denmark.
Formerly: Solskabet for Oesteuropastudier. Nyhedsbrev.

910.2   US
OFF BEAT. 1977-1991. q. (back issues avail.) 1250 Vallejo St., No.9, San Francisco, CA 94109.

651.3   UK
OFFICE PRIDE. 1956-198? 6/yr. 6 Wimpole St., London W1M 8AS, England.

651.2   US
HF5547.A2   CODEN: TOOFDN
OFFICE TECHNOLOGY MANAGEMENT. 1966-1992. m. Business Technology Management, Inc., 1225 Franklin Ave., Ste. 210, Garden City, NY 11530.
Former titles (until 1991): Today's Office (ISSN 0744-2815); Office Products News (ISSN 0030-0241)

5252 CESSATIONS

001.64 US
OFFICENEWS. (Update to: Datapro Reports on Office Automation) C. m. Datapro Information Services Group (Subsidiary of: McGraw-Hill, Inc.), 600 Delran Pkwy., Delran, NJ 08075.

746 677 645 FR
OFFICIEL DES TEXTILES (AMEUBLEMENT). ceased. s-a. Publication Mandel, 3, rue de l'Arrivee, 75749 Paris, France.

970.1 US
OH HI YOH NOH. 1970-1988. m. Seneca Nation of Indians, Box 231, Plummer Bldg., Salamanca, NY 14779.

016 632 US
OHIO AGRICULTURAL RESEARCH AND DEVELOPMENT CENTER, WOOSTER. LIST OF REFERENCES: MAIZE VIRUS AND MYCOPLASMA DISEASES. 1971-1988. a. Ohio State University, Ohio Agricultural Research and Development Center, 1680 Madison Ave., Wooster, OH 44691-4096.
Formerly: Ohio Agricultural Research and Development Center, Wooster. Library. List of References: Maize Virus Diseases and Corn Stunt.

910 US ISSN 0094-9043
G1
OHIO GEOGRAPHERS: RECENT RESEARCH THEMES. (Supplement avail.) 1973-1989 (vol.17). a. (also avail. in microform from UMI) Miami University, Department of Geography, 218 Shideler Hall, Oxford, OH 45056.

810 US
OHIO RENAISSANCE REVIEW. 1974-198? q. (back issues avail.) Infinity Press and Publications, Box 804, Ironton, OH 45638.
Formerly (until 1984): N I R (New Infinity Review).

630 640 US ISSN 0749-1492
S101
OHIO REPORT; research and development in agriculture, home economics, and natural resources. 1916-1986 (vol.71, no.1). bi-m. Ohio State University, Ohio Agricultural Research and Development Center, Wooster, OH 44691.
Formerly: Ohio Report on Research and Development in Biology, Agriculture and Home Economics (ISSN 0030-1043)

647.94 US
OHIO RESTAURANT JOURNAL. 1983-1991 (Feb.). 3/yr. (Ohio Restaurant Association) Marbro Advertising Inc., 303 East Livingston Ave., Columbus, OH 43215.

970.1 US
OHOYO; for American Indian-Alaska native women. ceased 1983. bi-m. Ohoyo Resource Center, Box 4073, Wichita Falls, TX 76308.

657 US
OIL & GAS FEDERAL TAX ALERT. 1981-1990. m. Research Institute of America, Inc., 90 Fifth Ave., New York, NY 10011.

665.5 UK
OIL AND OIL FIELD EQUIPMENT & SERVICE COMPANIES WORLDWIDE. 1985-19?? a. E. & F.N. Spon Ltd., 2-6 Boundary Row, London SE1 8HN, England.
Formerly: Oil and Gas Industry (ISSN 0265-640X)

665.5 US
OIL IN TEXAS. ceased 1992. m. Petroleum Information Corporation, Box 2612, Denver, CO 80201-2612.

662 US
OIL PRICE DATABOOK. 1977-1981. irreg. (back issues avail.) Bloomberg Petroleum Publications, Box 998, Lakewood, NJ 08701.

665.5 016 AT
OILSCAN. ceased. w. (back issues avail.) Newspan Publications, P.O. Box 158, Claremont, W.A. 6010, Australia.

620 JA ISSN 0475-0071
TA1 CODEN: MSEOBH
OKAYAMA UNIVERSITY. SCHOOL OF ENGINEERING. MEMOIRS. 1966-1987 (vol.21). s-a. Okayama Daigaku, Kogakubu - Okayama University, School of Engineering, Tsushima, Okayama 700, Japan.

331 317 US
OKLAHOMA. EMPLOYMENT SECURITY COMMISSION. ACTUARIAL DIVISION. HANDBOOK OF EMPLOYMENT SECURITY PROGRAM STATISTICS. 1952-1985. a. Employment Security Commission, Actuarial Division, Will Rogers Bldg., Oklahoma City, OK 73105.

657 US ISSN 0030-168X
OKLAHOMA C.P.A. ceased. q. Oklahoma Society of Certified Public Accountants, 265 W. Court, Lincoln Office Plaza, 4545 N. Lincoln Blvd., Oklahoma City, OK 73105.

333.33 US
OKLAHOMA HOME AND LIFESTYLE. 1976-1990 (Dec.). bi-m. Tulsa Home and Garden, Inc., 4129 S. 72nd E. Ave., Tulsa, OK 74145.
Formerly: Oklahoma Home - Garden.

331.1 US ISSN 0030-1744
HD5725.035
OKLAHOMA LABOR MARKET. 1949-1990 (Mar.). m. Employment Security Commission, Research Department, Will Rogers Bldg., 2401 Lincoln Blvd., Oklahoma City, OK 73105.

821 CN
OLD NUN. ceased 1975. bi-m. Old Nun Publications, 129 Seaton St., Toronto, Ont. M5A 2T2, Canada.

975.6 US ISSN 0078-4540
OLD SALEM GLEANER. 1957-1990. 3/yr. Old Salem, Inc., Box F, Salem Station, Winston-Salem, NC 27108.
Formerly (until 1962): Old Salem Newsletter.

621.384 US ISSN 0030-204X
OLD TIMERS' BULLETIN. 1960-199? q. Antique Wireless Association Inc, Main St., Holcomb, NY 14469.

612.67 US
OLDER TEXAN. 1977-19?? s-a. Department on Aging, Box 12786, Capitol Sta., Austin, TX 78711.
Formerly: Encore (Austin).

331.1 US
OLDER WORKER. 1988-1989. m. (back issues avail.) (Community Development Services, Inc.) C D Publications, 8204 Fenton St., Silver Spring, MD 20910-2889.

929 US ISSN 0162-0800
CS71
OLMSTEAD'S GENEALOGY RECORDED. 1976-1983. q. Olmstead Family Association, 2989 Lodi Rd., Interlaken, NY 14847.

069.9 US
OMAHA (NEBRASKA). 1975-198? m. (tabloid format) (Western Heritage Museum, Omaha History Museum) Western Heritage Society, Inc., Omaha Union Station, 801 S. 10th St., Omaha, NE 68108.
Former titles (until 1986): Stagecoach; (until 1980): Western Heritage Bee.

500 600 JA ISSN 0286-5300
OMNI JAPAN/OMUNI. 1982-1989 (no.84, Apr.). m. Obunsha Publishing Co., Ltd., 55 Yokodera-cho, Shinjuku-ku, Tokyo 162, Japan.

697 UK ISSN 0305-5981
OMNIBUS (BRACKNELL); free member's newsletter. 1974-19?? 4/yr. Building Services Research and Information Association, Old Bracknell Lane West, Bracknell, Berks. RG12 4AH, England.
Formerly: H V R A Newsletter.

352.7 US
OMNIBUS (PITTSBURGH). 1971-1986. bi-m. Southwestern Pennsylvania Regional Planning Commission, 200 First Ave., Waterfront Bldg., Pittsburgh, PA 15222-1573.
Formerly (until 1978): S P R P C Reports (ISSN 0049-1691)

621.38 360 UK ISSN 0953-9492
ON AIR - OFF AIR. 1977-19??; suspended. 6/yr. Media Project, Volunteer Centre, 29 Lower Kings Rd., Berkhansted, Herts. HP4 2AB, England.
Formerly: Media Project News (ISSN 0263-1911)

621.38 US
ON - LINE (NEW YORK). 1982-19?? q. Computer Services Center, Department of General Services, Manhattan Municipal Bldg., 17th fl., 1 Centre St., New York, NY 10007.
Formerly: Wires.

800.81 US
ON THE EDGE (CAMBRIDGE). 1983-1990. 3/yr. 29 Concord Ave., No. 603, Cambridge, MA 02138.

910.202 UK ISSN 0269-3208
ON THE MOVE; the guide for independent travellers. 1985-1988. bi-m. (back issues avail.) Transit Publications Ltd., South Band Business Centre, 13 Park House, 140 Battersea Park Rd., London SW11 4NB, England.

380.5 381 US
ON THE MOVE (BUFFALO). 1973-1989; suspended. q. Niagara Frontier Transportation Authority, Public Affairs Division, 181 Ellicott St., Box 5008, Buffalo, NY 14205.
Formerly (until 1981): Metro Newsletter.

200 AT ISSN 0310-9348
ON THE MOVE (MELBOURNE, 1973). 1973-19?? 4/yr. (back issues avail.) Joint Board of Christian Education, 10 Queen St., 2nd Fl., Melbourne, Vic. 3000, Australia.

616.4 US
ONCOLOGY ABSTRACTS. 1986-1988. m. Cambridge Scientific Abstracts, 720 Wisconsin Ave., 6th Fl., Bethesda, MD 20814.

616.99 US
ONCOLOGY & BIOTECHNOLOGY NEWS. 1987-1990. m. (tabloid format) Med Publishing, Inc., Office Center at Princeton Meadows, Bldg. 1000, Plainsboro, NJ 08536.

100 UK ISSN 0143-8247
ONE EARTH. 1980-1990 (vol.9, no.4). q. (back issues avail.) Findhorn Foundation, The Park, Forres 1V36 0TZ, Scotland.

362.8 320 US
ONE FAMILY. ceased 1989. irreg. Planetary Citizens, Box 1503, Mt. Shasta, CA 96067.

179.3 US
ONE WORLD. 1981-1983 (vol.2, no.3-4). irreg. (back issues avail.) Trans-Species Unlimited, Box 1553, Williamsport, PA 17703-1553.

380.5 IT
ONERI FISCALI SULLA MOTORIZZAZIONE. ceased 1986. biennial (updates every six months). Associazione Nazionale fra le Industrie Automobilistiche, Corso G. Ferraris 61, 10128 Turin, Italy.

700 CN ISSN 0380-285X
ONION. 1975-1982 (vol.5, no.8). m. (tabloid format) Arteditorial Co., Box 261, Sta. Z, Toronto, Ont. M5N 2Z4, Canada.

284.2 SA ISSN 0030-2694
ONS JEUG. 1951-1991 (vol.40). m. Nederduitse Gereformeerde Kerk, Kerkjeugaksie - Dutch Reformed Church, Youth Commission, Box 396, Bloemfontein 9300, South Africa.

305.412 BE
ONS VOLK; weekblad voor vrouw en gezin. 1911-19?? w. Standaard Vitgeverij, NV, Belgeilei 147-A, B-2000 Antwerp, Belgium.

630 CN
ONTARIO. MINISTRY OF AGRICULTURE AND FOOD. FACTS AND FIGURES ON THE AGRI-FOOD SECTOR. ceased. irreg. (2-3/yr.). Ministry of Agriculture and Food, Consumer Information Centre, Legislative Bldgs., Queen's Park, Toronto, Ont. M7A 2B2, Canada.

630 658 CN
ONTARIO. MINISTRY OF AGRICULTURE AND FOOD. FARM INPUT REVIEW. ceased. q. Ministry of Agriculture and Food, Consumer Information Centre, Legislative Bldgs., Queen's Park, Toronto, Ont. M7A 2B2, Canada.

354 CN
ONTARIO. MINISTRY OF THE ENVIRONMENT. ANNUAL REPORT. 1973-1984. a. Ministry of the Environment, Communications Branch, 135 St. Clair Ave. W., 2nd fl., Toronto, Ont. M4V 1P5, Canada.

340   CN
ONTARIO LABOUR RELATIONS BOARD LAW AND PRACTICE; citation up-dater. ceased 1988 (no.8). a. (looseleaf format; back issues avail.) Butterworths Canada Ltd., 75 Clegg Rd., Markham, Ont. L6G 1A1, Canada.

610   CN   ISSN 0228-877X
ONTARIO MEDICAL TECHNOLOGIST. 1965-1988 (vol.9, no.4). q. Ontario Society of Medical Technologists, 234 Eglinton Ave. E., Ste. 600, Toronto, Ont. M4P 1K5, Canada.
Formerly (until Jan. 1980): Ontario Society of Medical Technologists. Newsletter (ISSN 0380-1888)

317   CN   ISSN 0319-7751
HA748.O55
ONTARIO STATISTICS. 1964-1986. a. Ministry of Treasury and Economics, Sectoral & Regional Policy Br., Statistics Section, Toronto, Ont. M7A 1Y7, Canada.
Formerly: Ontario Statistical Review (ISSN 0078-5113)

811   US   ISSN 0894-265X
OPEN MAGAZINE. 1985-1991. a. (back issues avail.) Open Dialogues, Inc., 215 North Ave. W., Ste. 21, Westfield, NJ 07090.

052   CN
OPEN ROAD; international anarchist newsjournal. 1976-19?? q. (tabloid format; back issues avail.) Open Road Collective, Box 46135, Sta. G, Vancouver, B.C. V6R 4G5, Canada.

621.381   US
OPEN SYSTEMS; managing office technology. 1979-198? m. (plus 4 special reports). William R. Schulhof, Ed. & Pub., Box 1231, Stamford, CT 06904.

001.539 380.3   NE   ISSN 0921-8327
OPEN SYSTEMS INFORMATION SYSTEMS. 1988-1990 (vol.2, no.8). m. I O S Press, Van Diemenstraat 94, 1013 CN Amsterdam, Netherlands.

323.4 614.8   GY
OPEN WORD. 1982-1990 (July, no.409). w. (looseleaf format; back issues avail.) Working Peoples Alliance, 45 Croal St., Georgetown, Guyana.

780 647.968   US
OPERA AMERICA. MANAGEMENT RESOURCE VOLUME. suspended 1987. biennial. (back issues avail.) Opera America, 777 14th St., N.W., Ste. 520, Washington, DC 20005.

001.6 621.381   NE
OPERATING AND PROGRAMMING SYSTEMS SERIES. 1974-1982. irreg. Elsevier Science Publishers B.V., P.O. Box 211, 1000 AE Amsterdam, Netherlands.

323.4   CN
OPERATION LIBERTE. 1978-1979. irreg. (back issues avail.) Ligue des Droits et Libertes, 1825 de Champlain, Montreal, Que. H2L 2S9, Canada.

617.7   US   ISSN 8756-0402
CODEN: OLTHED
OPHTHALMIC LASER THERAPY. 1985-1990. q. Mary Ann Liebert, Inc., 1651 Third Ave., New York, NY 10128.

617.7   AT
OPHTHALMOLOGISTS' EXCHANGE. ceased. q. Royal Australian College of Ophthalmologists, 27 Commonwealth St., Sydney, N.S.W. 2010, Australia.
Formerly: Australian College of Ophthalmologists. Newsletter.

658   US   ISSN 0746-1070
OPHTHALMOLOGY MANAGEMENT. 1983-1991 (Apr.). 10/yr. Viscom Publications, Inc., 50 Washington St., Norwalk, CT 06854.

001.64   US   ISSN 0886-4659
OPS: THE DATA CENTER NEWSLETTER. (Operations) 1986-1989. m. Auerbach Publishers Inc. (Subsidiary of: Warren, Gorham & Lamont, Inc.), One Penn Plaza, New York, NY 10119.

282   NE   ISSN 0169-7269
OPSTAP; werkschrift voor geloofsvorming. 1981-1992 (Jan.). 4/yr. (back issues avail.) Katholiek Pedagogisch Centrum, Postbus 482, 5201 AL 's-Hertogenbosch, Netherlands.

535   GW
OPTICAL ENGINEERING REPORTS: EUROPEAN EDITION. ceased 1987. 4/yr. (International Society for Optical Engineering) Spectrum Communications GmbH, Xantener Str. 22, D-1000 Berlin 15, Germany.

617.75   UK   ISSN 0267-4041
OPTICAL MANAGEMENT. 1984-199? m. (back issues avail.) Reed Business Publishing Group, Carew Division (Subsidiary of: Reed International PLC), Quadrant House, The Quadrant, Sutton, Surrey SM2 5AS, England.

617.752   BE   ISSN 0030-3976
OPTICIEN BELGE/BELGISCHE OPTICIEN. 1953-1991. 10/yr. 30 av. Vital Riethijisen, 1080 Brussels, Belgium.

658   US   ISSN 0885-4858
OPTIMAL HEALTH. 1984-1989 (Jan.-Feb.). bi-m. Athletic Business Publications, Inc., 1842 Hoffman St., Ste. 201, Madison, WI 53704.
Incorporates: Wellness Center Management.

332.6   CN   ISSN 0831-4853
OPTIONPROFITS. 1986-19?? s-m. (back issues avail.) Hume Publishing Company Ltd., 4100 Yonge St., Ste. 502, Willowdale, Ont. M2P 3B9, Canada.

610   US
OPTIONS (VAN NUYS); the changing world of medical practice. ceased. m. Creative Age Publications, 7628 Densmore Ave., Van Nuys, CA 91406.

617.75   US
OPTOMETRY TIMES. 1983-1987. m. Edgell Communications, 7500 Old Oak Blvd., Cleveland, OH 44130.

612 617.6   UK   ISSN 0261-4820
ORAL BIOLOGY. ceased 1989. m. (looseleaf format; back issues avail.) Sheffield University Biomedical Information Service (SUBIS), The University, Sheffield S10 2TN, England.

333.7   SA
ORANGE FREE STATE. NATURE CONSERVATION BRANCH. ANNUAL REPORT. 1971-1986. a. Nature Conservation Branch, P.O. Box 517, Bloemfontein 9300, South Africa.
Formerly: Orange Free State. Nature Conservation Division. Annual Report.

574   SA
ORANGE FREE STATE. NATURE CONSERVATION BRANCH. MISCELLANEOUS PUBLICATIONS SERIES. 1970-198? irreg. Nature Conservation Branch, P.O. Box 517, Bloemfontein 9300, South Africa.
Formerly: Orange Free State. Nature Conservation Division. Miscellaneous Publications Series.

378   IS
ORANIM. 1967-198? s-a. Haifa University, Oranim College of Education, Tivon 36 805, Israel.

810   US   ISSN 0474-3326
PZ1.A1
ORBIT (NEW YORK); a science fiction anthology. 1966-197? irreg. Harper and Row Publishers, Inc., 10 E. 53rd St., New York, NY 10022.

355 970.1   US
ORDER OF THE INDIAN WARS JOURNAL. 1980-19?? (vol.2, no.4). q. (back issues avail.) Order of the Indian Wars, Box 7401, Little Rock, AR 72217.

282   GW   ISSN 0323-7532
ORDINARIATE UND BISCHOEFLICHE AEMTER IN DER D D R. KIRCHLICHE AMTSBLATT. AUSGABE DER APOSTLICHEN ADMINISTRATUR GOERLITZ. 1952-1990. m. (Berliner Bischofskonferenz) St. Benno-Verlag GmbH, Thueringer Str. 1-3, 7033 Leipzig, Germany.

282   GW   ISSN 0323-763X
ORDINARIATE UND BISCHOEFLICHE AEMTER IN DER D D R. KIRCHLICHE AMTSBLATT. AUSGABE DES BISCHOEFLICHEN AMTES ERFURT-MEININGEN. 1952-1990. m. (Berliner Bischofskonferenz) St. Benno-Verlag GmbH, Thueringer Str. 1-3, 7033 Leipzig, Germany.

282   GW   ISSN 0323-7737
ORDINARIATE UND BISCHOEFLICHE AEMTER IN DER D D R. KIRCHLICHE AMTSBLATT. AUSGABE DES BISCHOEFLICHEN AMTES SCHWERIN. 1952-1990. m. (Berliner Bischofskonferenz) St. Benno-Verlag GmbH, Thueringer Str. 1-3, 7033 Leipzig, Germany.

282   GW   ISSN 0323-7680
ORDINARIATE UND BISCHOEFLICHE AEMTER IN DER D D R. KIRCHLICHE AMTSBLATT. AUSGABE DES BISTUMS DRESDEN-MEISSEN. 1952-1990. m. (Berliner Bischofskonferenz) St. Benno-Verlag GmbH, Thueringer Str. 1-3, 7033 Leipzig, Germany.

282   GW   ISSN 0323-7583
ORDINARIATE UND BISCHOEFLICHEN AEMTER IN DER D D R. KIRCHLICHE AMTSBLATT. AUSGABE DES BISCHOEFLICHEN AMTES MAGDEBURG. 1952-1990. m. (Berliner Bischofskonferenz) St. Benno-Verlag GmbH, Thueringer Str. 1-3, 7033 Leipzig, Germany.

663   US   ISSN 0030-462X
OREGON BEVERAGE ANALYST. (Subseries of: Northwest Beverage Analyst) 1936-1990 (Dec.). m. Bell Publications, Beverage Analyst Group, 2403 Champa St., Denver, CO 80205.

350   PL   ISSN 0860-4673
ORGANIZACJA - METODY - TECHNIKA W ADMINISTRACJI PANSTWOWEJ. 1958-19?? m. (also avail. in microform) Instytut Administracji i Zarzadzania, Ul. Wawelska 56, 02-067 Warsaw, Poland.
Formerly: Organizacja - Metody - Technika (ISSN 0030-5057)

338.2 665.5   AU
ORGANIZATION OF THE PETROLEUM EXPORTING COUNTRIES. ANNUAL REPORT. 1967-19?? a. Organization of the Petroleum Exporting Countries, Public Information Department, Obere-Donaustr. 93, A-1020 Vienna, Austria.
Formerly: Organization of the Petroleum Exporting Countries. Annual Review and Record (ISSN 0474-6317)

616.4   NE   ISSN 0030-5162
ORGANORAMA. 1964-1990 (no.4). q. Organon Nederland B.V., Postbus 20, Oss, Netherlands.
Incorporates: Hormoon.

070.5   UK
ORIEL. 1987-19?? 3/yr. Welsh Arts Council, Oriel Bookshop, 53 Charles Street, Cardiff, Wales.

659.1   DK   ISSN 0030-5499
ORIENTERING. 1963-19?? q. Danske Reklamebureauers Brancheforening - Danish Association of Advertising Agencies, Snaregade 12, DK-1205 Copenhagen K, Denmark.

808.839   US
ORIGINAL ROMANCE DIGEST. ceased. bi-m. 158 Linwood Plaza, Ft. Lee, NJ 07024.

617.3   US
ORTHOPEDIC PRODUCTS NEWS. 1983-1991. m. (back issues avail.) Lippincott Healthcare Publications, 130 Madison Ave., New York, NY 10016.

664.94   US
OSPREY'S SEAFOOD NEWSLETTER. 1985-1988. irreg. Osprey Books, 1454 S. E. Camano Dr., Stanwood, WA 98292-7634.

320   GW
OSTEUROPA-FORUM. 1973-1989. q. (back issues avail.) Junius Verlag, Stresemannstr. 375, 2000 Hamburg 50, Germany.

053.1   GW   ISSN 0030-6479
OSTFRIESLAND; Zeitschrift fuer Kultur, Wirtschaft und Verkehr. 1950-1989. q. (Ostfriesische Landschaft) Verlag Gerhard Rautenberg, Blinke 8, Postfach 909, 2950 Leer, Germany.

658.7   FI   ISSN 0356-7931
OSTO. 1965-1989. m. (also avail. in microfiche) Kustannusliike Liikejulkaisut Oy, Fredrikink 27, 00120 Helsinki 12, Finland.
Formerly: Osto ja Materiaalijohto (ISSN 0030-6509)

370   PL   ISSN 0472-2191
OSWIATA DOROSLYCH. 1957-1990. 10/yr. (Ministerstwo Edukacji Narodowej) Wydawnictwa Szkolne i Pedagogiczne, Ul. Pankiewicza 3, 00-696 Warsaw, Poland.

CESSATIONS

591   NZ
OTAGO MUSEUM BULLETIN: ZOOLOGY. SPIDERS OF N.Z. ceased 1988 (vol.6). irreg. Otago Museum Trust Board, Great King St., Dunedin, New Zealand.

821   UK   ISSN 0144-5847
OTHER POETRY. 1978-1990 (no.27-28). 3/yr. 2 Stoneygate Ave., Leicester LE2 3HE, England.

051   CN   ISSN 0826-0265
OTTAWA NEWCOMER; the magazine for people moving to Ottawa. 1983-19??; suspended. m. 347474 Ontario Ltd., 400 Cumberland St., Ottawa, Ont. K1N 8X3, Canada.

268   IE   ISSN 0030-6797
OUR BOYS. 1914-1990. m. (10/yr.). Irish Christian Brothers Congregation, Dilmnagh Castle, Dublin 12, Ireland.

352.7   SI
OUR HOME. 1972-19?? bi-m. Housing and Development Board, Ministry of National Development Bldg., Maxwell Road, Singapore 0106, Singapore.

052 283   UK
OUR MAG. ceased 1991. q. (Braille; also avail. in large print) Torch Trust for the Blind, Torch House, Hallaton, Market Harborough, Leicestershire LE16 8UJ, England.

387   JA
OUR PORT - PORT OF YOKOHAMA. ?-19?? a. Port and Harbor Bureau, Industry and Trade Center Bldg., Yamashita-cho, Naka-ku, Yokohama, Japan.

323.4 342   US
OUR RIGHT TO KNOW. 1979-198? q. Fund for Open Information and Accountability, Inc., 145 W. Fourth St., New York, NY 10012.

796.5 799
OUTDOOR DIGEST; archery, camping, clothing, cutlery, firearms, footwear, hunting, sports optics. 1981-1988 (Sep.). m. (back issues avail.) (A F I Communications Group, Inc.) National Association of Federally Licensed Firearms Dealers, 2801 E. Oakland Park, No. 307, Ft. Lauderdale, FL 33306.
    Former titles: Arms and Outdoor Digest; F F L Business News.

614.7   US
OUTDOOR REVIEW. ceased. q. (back issues avail.) Recreational Equipment, Inc., 18200 Segale Park Dr., Box C-88126, Seattle, WA 98188.

796 301.412   US
OUTDOOR WOMAN. 1990-1992. 10/yr. Gentian Mountain, Inc., R.R. 6, Katonah, NY 10536-7806.

633.1 636.5   CN
OUTLOOK. 1976-1989. a. Canada Grains Council, 760-360 Main St., Winnipeg, Man. R3C 3Z3, Canada.

658.8   US   ISSN 0161-2131
OUTLOOK (ALEXANDRIA, 1974). 1974-19?? 6/yr. United Fresh Fruit and Vegetable Association, 727 N. Washington St., Alexandria, VA 22314.

338 330   US   ISSN 0742-9916
OUTLOOK ON I B M. ceased 198? fortn. Phillips Publishing, Inc., 7811 Montrose Rd., Potomac, MD 20854.

378 340   US
OUTPUT (CLEVELAND). 1987-1989. q. American College of Computer Lawyers, 23811 Chagrin Blvd., Ste. 245, Cleveland, OH 44122.

301   US
OUTREACH NEWSLETTER. 1979-1991; suspended. 3/yr. Boston University, African Studies Center, 270 Bay State Rd., Boston, MA 02215.

790   US
OUTSIDE BUSINESS MAGAZINE; the business magazine of the outdoor sports industry. 1976-1991 (Apr.). 12/yr. Mariah Publications Corporation, 1165 N. Clark St., 7th Fl., Chicago, IL 60610-2845.
    Former titles: Outside Magazine; (until Mar. 1986): N O O N (National Outdoor Outfitters News) (ISSN 0192-7000)

332.6   US
OUTTEN QUARTERLY STOCK EVALUATION. 1975-1991 (Mar.). q. Edgar C. Outten, Jr., Ed. & Pub., 435 Winslow Ave., Long Beach, CA 90814.

051   US   ISSN 1047-8442
HQ76.3.U5
OUTWEEK; the lesbian and gay news magazine. 1989-1991 (Jun.). w. OutWeek Publishing Corporation, 159 W. 25th St., 7th Fl., New York, NY 10001.

780.43   US   ISSN 0196-433X
ML1
OVATION; the magazine for classical music listeners. 1980-1989 (Sep.). m. (back issues avail.) Concert Music Group, Ltd., 271 Madison Ave., New York, NY 10017.

059.951   CH
OVERSEAS DIGEST SEMIMONTHLY/HAI WAI WEN CHAI PAN YUEH K'AN. ceased 1991 (Apr.). s-m. 4F, no. 44, Lane 25, Hsinglung Rd Sec. 2, Taipei, Taiwan 11713, Republic of China.

352.7   DK   ISSN 0108-4151
OVERSIGT OVER BY- OG REGIONFORSKNING. 1980-1984. biennial. Statens Byggeforskningsinstitut, Postboks 119, 2970 Hoersholm, Denmark.

581   DK   ISSN 0107-8801
QC989.D4
OVERSIGT OVER DE METEOROLOGISKE FORHOLD PAA FORSOEGSSTATIONERNE. 1981-198? a. Statens Planteavlsforsoeg, Statens Planteavlskontor, Virumgaard, Skovbrynet 18, 2800 Lyngby, Denmark.

627   DK   ISSN 0107-4997
TK1525.5
OVERSIGT OVER RAPPORTER M.M. VEDROERENDE VANDKRAFTUNDERSOEGELSER I GROENLAND. 1981-1989 (Jun.). a. Ministry of Energy, Mineral Resources Administration for Greenland, Slotsholmsgade 1, 4, 1216 Copenhagen K,. Denmark.

782.1   CN
OVERTURES (TORONTO). 1968-19?? q. Canadian Opera Company, 417 Front St. East, Toronto, Ont. M5A 1E28, Canada.
    Formerly: Canadian Opera Guild. Guild News (ISSN 0045-5229)

016 362.7   NE
OVERZICHT BOEKEN. ceased. 6/yr. Documentatiecentrum Jeugdvoorzieningen, Postbus 19272, 3501 DG Utrecht, Netherlands.

362.7   NE
OVERZICHT TIJDSCHRIFTARTIKELEN. ceased. 6/yr. Documentatiecentrum Jeugdvoorzieningen, Postbus 19272, 3501 DG Utrecht, Netherlands.

616.7   US   ISSN 0747-5551
P A. (Physician Assistant) 1984-1989. 10/yr. S C P Communications, Inc., 134 W. 29th St., New York, NY 10001-5304.

200   US
P A C E. (Professional Approaches for Christian Educators) 1970-1987 (no.18). 8/yr. (looseleaf format; back issues avail.) St. Mary's Press, Terrace Heights, Winona, MN 55987.

052   TZ
P A C WORLD. ceased. q. Pan Africanist Congress of Azania, Box 2412, Dar es Salaam, Tanzania.

630 016   FR
P A S C A L THEMA. T 210: INDUSTRIES AGROALIMENTAIRES. 1985-1989 (Dec.). 10/yr. Centre National de la Recherche Scientifique, Institut de l'Information Scientifique et Technique, B.P. 54, 54514 Vandoeuvre-Les-Nancy Cedex, France.
    Formerly: P A S C A L Thema. Part 210: Industries Agroalimentaires; Which supersedes (1982-1984): Bulletin Signaletique. Part 210: Industries Agro-Alimentaires: Bibliographie Internationale.

362 610   US   ISSN 0078-7353
                          CODEN: PASRC
P A S REPORTER. (Professional Activity Study) 1962-19?? irreg. Commission on Professional and Hospital Activities, 1968 Green Rd., Ann Arbor, MI 48105.
    Formerly: Commission on Professional and Hospital Activities. Record.

686.2 676.2   AT
P A T E F A PRINTING INDUSTRY QUARTERLY. 1985-1990. q. Printing & Allied Trades Employers Federation of Australia, 77 Lithgow Street, St. Leonards, N.S.W. 2065, Australia.

615.19
P.A. UPDATE; continuing education for the physician assistant. 1981-198? m. Excerpta Medica, Inc., Core Publishing Division (Subsidiary of: Elsevier Science Publishers B.V.), 105 Raider Blvd., Belle Mead, NJ 08052.
    Formerly: P.A. Drug Update.

001.642 330   US
HF5548.125
P C ACCOUNTING. 1984-198? m. (also avail. in microfilm) M & T Publishing, Inc. (Subsidiary of: Markt & Technik), 501 Galveston Dr., Redwood City, CA 94063-4728.
    Former titles (until 1988): Business Software Magazine (ISSN 0742-1214); Power of E S Magazine.

621.381   US   ISSN 1054-867X
P C ADVISOR. 1990-1991 (Aug.). m. (audio cassette; back issues avail.) Mosaic Media, Inc., 999 Main St., Ste. 200, Glen Ellyn, IL 60137.

621.381 001.642   US
P C CLONES. (Personal Computer) 1987-1988. q. Patch Communications, 5211 S. Washington Ave., Box F, Titusville, FL 32780.

778.3   US   ISSN 0030-7866
TP249.5   CODEN: PCMPBF
P C M - P C E. (Photochemical Machining Photochemical Etching) 1966-1975. m. Scientech Publishing Co., 1303 N. Harris St., Champaign, IL 61820.
    Formerly: P C E (Photochemical Etching).

621.381 001.642   US
P C PRODUCTS. 1984-1986. m. (also avail. in microfilm) Cahners Publishing Co., Inc. (Newton) (Subsidiary of: Reed Holdings, Inc.), 275 Washington St., Newton, MA 02158-1630.

621.381   US   ISSN 0738-0194
QA76.8.I2594
P C TECH JOURNAL; for the IBM systems professional. 1983-1989. m. (also avail. in microform from UMI; back issues avail.) Ziff-Davis Publishing Co., 10 President's Landing, Medford, MA 02155.

749   US   ISSN 0030-7963
P F M; the business magazine for progressive furniture retailers. (Professional Furniture Merchant) 1969-19?? m. Gralla Publications, 1515 Broadway, New York, NY 10036.

200   US
P F N A NEWS. 1960-198? q. (tabloid format) (Pentecostal Fellowship of North America) Gospel Publishing House, 1445 Boonville Ave., Springfield, MO 65802-1894.

658.4031   US
P I C K AND U N I X GUIDE. ceased after one issue. a. (International Data Base Management Association) I D B M A, Inc., 10675 Treena St., Ste. 103, San Diego, CA 92131.

621.381   US   ISSN 0890-6246
QA76.5   CODEN: PCOOEP
P I C O LAPTOPS & PORTABLES MAGAZINE. 1983-198? m. Portable Computing International Corp., 145 Grove St., Extension, Box 428, Peterborough, NH 03458-0428.

371.3 410   US   ISSN 0078-7388
P I - L T; OCCASIONAL PAPERS ON PROGRAMMED INSTRUCTION AND LANGUAGE TEACHING. ceased 197? irreg. Behavioral Research Laboratories, Ladera Professional Center, Box 577, Palo Alto, CA 94302.

630.2   PL   ISSN 0020-0670
P.I.M.R. INFORMATOR PATENTOWY. 1954-19?? bi-m. (looseleaf format) Przemyslowy Instytut Maszyn Rolniczych, Branzowy Osrodek Informacji Naukowej, Technicznej i Ekonomicznej, Starolecka 31, 61-361 Poznan, Poland.

020 US ISSN 0146-2237
AS36.P865
P L A REPORT. 1973-1988 (vol.10). a. Post Library Association, Long Island Univ., C.W. Post Center, Greenvale, NY 11548.

913 UK ISSN 0260-7751
P.P.A. NORTH WEST REGION NEWSLETTER. ceased. q? Pre-School Playgroups Association, North West Region, Hotspur House, Gloucester St., Manchester M1 5QR, England.

621 660 US ISSN 0747-2722
TJ844
P - P M TECHNOLOGY. 1978-1992. bi-m. P - P M Technology, Box 8096, Incline Village, NV 89450.
Former titles: Practical Lubrication and Maintenance; (until 1984): Fluid and Lubricant Ideas (ISSN 0194-4444)

100 US ISSN 0030-8250
BF1995
P R S JOURNAL. 1941-1990 (vol.50, no.4). q. (also avail. in microfilm from UMI; reprint service avail. from UMI) Philosophical Research Society Inc., 3910 Los Feliz Blvd., Los Angeles, CA 90027.
Formerly: Horozon (Los Angeles).

370.193 US
P T A IN FOCUS. ceased 1990. 3/yr. National Parent - Teacher Association, 700 N. Rush St., Chicago, IL 60611.

383 384 NE ISSN 0030-8366
HE6009.N4 CODEN: PTBDA8
P T T BEDRIJF; denkbeelden, methoden, onderzoekingen. 1947-1987. irreg. (3-4/yr.). Staatsbedrijf der Posterijen Telegrafie en Telefonie, Kortenaerkade 12, The Hague, Netherlands.

378.1 SA ISSN 0030-8412
P.U.-KANER. 1968-19?? m. (tabloid format) Potchefstroom University for Christian Higher Education, Department of Development - Potchefstroomse Universiteit vir Christelike Hoer Onderwys, Posbus 156, Potchefstroom, South Africa.

331 DK ISSN 0107-6949
PAA JOBBET; et liberalt loenmodtagerblad. 1981-19?? q. Venstre, Soelleroedvej 30, 2840 Holte, Denmark.

629.1 AT ISSN 0156-3726
PACIFIC AVIATION YEARBOOK. 1979-19?? a. Peter Isaacson Publications Pty. Ltd., 45-50 Porter St., Prahran, Vic. 3181, Australia.

320 UK
PACIFIC BUSINESS GUIDE. 1984-198? a. World of Information, 21 Gold St., Saffron Walden, Essex CB10 1EJ, England.

664 NL
PACIFIC FOODS. 1989-1990 (no.2). irreg. South Pacific Commission, B.P. D5, Noumea, Cedex, New Caledonia.

300 FJ ISSN 0379-525X
PACIFIC PERSPECTIVE. 1972-1990 (vol.14). 2/yr. South Pacific Social Sciences Association, Box 5083, Suva, Fiji.

333.33 UK
PACIFIC PROPERTY. (Supplement to: World Property) 1989-199? q. Builder Group plc, 1 Millharbour, London E13 9RA, England.

658.7 US ISSN 0030-8846
HF5437.A2
PACIFIC PURCHASOR. 1918-1988 (Nov.). m. (Purchasing Management Association of Northern California, Inc.) Polar Communications, Inc., 819 S. Main St., Burbank, CA 91506-3305.

382 US ISSN 0738-9035
PACIFIC RIM INTELLIGENCE REPORT; and independent analysis of forces shaping Pacific markets and trade. 1980-198? bi-w. Government Information Services, 1611 N. Kent, Ste. 508, Arlington, VA 22209.

380.5 US ISSN 0030-8943
TL720.7
PACIFIC TRAFFIC; the magazine of Western transportation & distribution. 1943-1988 (vol.35, no.7). m. International Thomson Transport Press (San Francisco), 562 Mission, San Francisco, CA 94105.
Formerly: Pacific Air and Truck Traffic.

910.2 CN ISSN 0030-8951
G155.P25
PACIFIC TRAVEL NEWS. 1957-19?? m. Baxter Publishing Co., 310 Dupont St., Toronto, Ont. M5B 1V9, Canada.

950 US ISSN 1043-8130
PACIFICA; a journal of Pacific and Asian studies. 1989-1990 (vol.2, no.2). s-a. Alaska Pacific University, Pacific Rim Studies Center, 4101 University Dr., Anchorage, AK 99508.

658.7884 US
TS195.A1
PACKAGING LINE PLANNING GUIDE. 1929-1992. a. Cahners Publishing Company (Des Plaines) (Subsidiary of: Reed International PLC), Division of Reed Publishing (USA) Inc., 1350 E. Touhy Ave, Box 5080, Des Plaines, IL 60017-5080.
Former titles (until 1991): Packaging Encyclopedia; Packaging Reference Issue and Encyclopedia (Year); (until 1986): Packaging Encyclopedia and Yearbook; (until 1985): Packaging Encyclopedia; Modern Packaging Encyclopedia (ISSN 0736-0908)

499 GW
PACO; bulteno de la Mondpaca Esperantista Movado, sekcio de GDR. 1966-1991. a. Kulturbund der DDR, Esperanto-Verband, Otto-Nuschke-Str. 1, 1080 Berlin, Germany.

370 BE ISSN 0079-0370
PAEDAGOGICA BELGICA ACADEMICA; periodical survey of the Belgian University Studies in Education. 1951-1985. a. Rijksuniversiteit te Gent, Seminaries voor Historische en voor Vergelijkende Pedagogiek, A. Baertsoenkaai 3, B-9000 Ghent, Belgium.

378 GW ISSN 0138-1768
PAEDAGOGISCHE HOCHSCHULE LISELOTTE HERRMANN GUESTROW. PAEDAGOGISCHE FAKULTAET. WISSENSCHAFTLICHE ZEITSCHRIFT. ceased 1991. s-a. Paedagogische Hochschule Liselotte Herrmann Guestrow, Direktorat fuer Forschung, Goldberger Str. 12, 2600 Guestrow, Germany.
Supersedes in part: Paedagogische Hochschule Liselotte Herrmann Guestrow. Wissenschaftliche Zeitschrift (ISSN 0138-1563)

618.92 SZ ISSN 0078-7795
CODEN: PFPXA6
PAEDIATRISCHE FORTBILDUNGSKURSE FUER DIE PRAXIS. 1961-1988 (vol.62). irreg. (approx. 2/yr.). (reprint service avail. from ISI; back issues avail.) S. Karger AG, Allschwilerstrasse 10, P.O. Box, CH-4009 Basel, Switzerland.

595.7 591 LU ISSN 0257-7046
PAIPERLEK; letzebuerger Entomologesch Zaeitschreift. 1979-19?? (vol.12, no.2). s-a. (back issues avail.) Musee National d'Histoire Naturelle, Groupement des Entomologistes Luxembourgeois, c/o Marc Meyer, Marche-aux-Poissons, L-2345 Luxembourg, Luxembourg.

910.4 II
PAKISTAN TOURISM REVIEW. 1977-1980. m. Pakistan Tourism Development Corporation, Hotel Metropole, Club Rd., Karachi 4, Pakistan.

355.31 BE
PALLAS. ceased 1989. q. Association des Officiers en Service Actif, 77 Avenue Milcamps, 1040 Brussels, Belgium.

796.325 IT
PALLAVOLO. 1964-1989. m. Federazione Italiana Pallavolo, V.le Tiziano 70, Rome, Italy.

910 387.742 US
PAN AM CLIPPER. 1961-199? m. (Pan American Airways) East-West Network, Inc. (New York), 34 E. 51st St., New York, NY 10022.

621.9 US ISSN 0300-6514
PAN-AMERICAN TRADER. ceased 1987. m. (tabloid format) Hopkins Publications, Box 324, Needham Heights, MA 02194.

808 US ISSN 0897-7941
PANGLOSS PAPERS. 1982-1989 (Oct.). q. Pangloss, 1681 W. 25th St., Los Angeles, CA 90007.

001.3 UN
PANORAMA; cultural newsletter. 1984-1987. 3/yr. Unesco, Cultural Documentation and Information Centre, Place de Fontenoy, 75700 Paris, France.

330.9 BL
PANORAMA A P E C OF THE BRAZILIAN ECONOMY. 1972-1986. m. Associacao Promotora de Estudos de Economia, Rua Sorocaba 295, Botofugo, Rio de Janeiro, Brazil.

630 SP
PANORAMA DE AGRICULTURA EN (YEAR). ceased. a. Ministerio de Agricultura, Pesca y Alimentacion, Secretaria General Tecnica, Centro de Publicaciones, Paseo de la Infanta Isabel, 1, 28014 Madrid, Spain.

015 SP
PANORAMAS BIBLIOGRAFICOS DE ESPANA. no.2, 1976-19?? irreg. (Biblioteca Nacional) Ministerio de Cultura, Of. del Secretario General, Madrid, Spain.

636.7 US
PAP TALK. ceased. m. Papillon Club of America, c/o Roseann Fucillo, Corr. Sec., 2600 Kennedy Blvd., Jersey City, NJ 07306.

410 811 US ISSN 0890-4359
PAPER AIR. 1976-1990. a. (back issues avail.) Singing Horse Press, Box 40034, Philadelphia, PA 19106.

800 US
PAPER CURTAIN. ceased. a. Athena Press (Westlake Village), 31220 La Baya Dr., Ste. 110, Westlake Village, CA 91362.

676 US ISSN 0031-1197
TS1080 CODEN: PTJOAD
PAPER TRADE JOURNAL. 1872-19?? m. (also avail. in microform from UMI; reprint service avail. from UMI) Vance Publishing Corporation, 400 Knightsbridge Pkwy., Lincolnshire, IL 60069.

802 US
PAPERBACK QUARTERLY; journal of mass market paperback history. 1978-1982. q. Paperback Quarterly Publications, 1710 Vincent St., Brownwood, TX 76801.

499 AT ISSN 0078-9070
P11
PAPERS IN BORNEO LINGUISTICS. (Subseries of Pacific Linguistics. Series A: Occasional Papers) 1969-198? irreg. Australian National University, Research School of Pacific Studies, Dept. of Linguistics, G.P.O. Box 4, Canberra, A.C.T. 2601, Australia.

499.5 AT ISSN 0078-9127
P11
PAPERS IN LINGUISTICS OF MELANESIA. (Subseries of Pacific Linguistics. Series A: Occasional Papers) 1968-198? irreg. Australian National University, Research School of Pacific Studies, Pacific Linguistics, Dept. ot Linguistics, G.P.O. Box 4, Canberra, A.C.T. 2601, Australia.

499 AT ISSN 0078-9135
P11
PAPERS IN NEW GUINEA LINGUISTICS. (Subseries of Pacific Linguistics. Series A: Occasional Papers) 1964-198? irreg. Australian National University, Research School of Pacific Studies, Pacific Linguistics, Dept. of Linguistics, G.P.O. Box 4, Canberra, A.C.T. 2601, Australia.

499 AT ISSN 0078-9143
P11
PAPERS IN PHILIPPINE LINGUISTICS. (Subseries of Pacific Linguistics. Series A: Occasional Papers) 1966-198? irreg. Australian National University, Research School of Pacific Studies, Pacific Linguistics, Dept. of Linguistics, G.P.O. Box 2601, Canberra, A.C.T. 2601, Australia.

350 US ISSN 0078-916X
PAPERS IN PUBLIC ADMINISTRATION (ANN ARBOR). 1948-19?? irreg. University of Michigan, Institute of Public Policy Studies, 1516 Rackham Bldg., Ann Arbor, MI 48104.

410 UK ISSN 0263-5798
PAPERS IN SLAVONIC LINGUISTICS. 1982-1984 (vol.2); resumed 1989-1990; suspended. irreg. Aston Modern Languages Club, Aston University, Department of Modern Languages, Aston Triangle, Birmingham B4 7ET, England.

CESSATIONS

301   IS
PAPERS IN SOCIOLOGY. 1972-19?? a. (back issues avail.) Hebrew University of Jerusalem, Department of Sociology, Givat Ram Campus, Jerusalem, Israel.

572 301   NE   ISSN 0317-8382
PAPERS ON EUROPEAN AND MEDITERRANEAN SOCIETIES. 1974-1985. irreg. Universiteit van Amsterdam, Antropologisch-Sociologisch Centrum, Euromed, Oudezijds Achterburgwal 185, 1012 DK Amsterdam, Netherlands.

319.5   PP
PAPUA NEW GUINEA. NATIONAL STATISTICAL OFFICE. SUMMARY OF STATISTICS. 1970-1979; suspended. a. National Statistical Office, P.O. Wards Strip, Papua New Guinea.

510   PP
PAPUA NEW GUINEA UNIVERSITY OF TECHNOLOGY. MATHEMATICS EDUCATION CENTRE. REPORTS. 1978-1986. 6/yr. Papua New Guinea University of Technology, Mathematics Education Centre, Private Mail Bag, Lae, Papua New Guinea.

790.132   US
PAR EXCELLENCE. 1980; ceased same year (vol.1, no.2). bi-m. Unicover Corporation, One Unicover Center, Cheyenne, WY 82008.

130   US   ISSN 0031-1804
BF1001   CODEN: PAREDT
PARAPSYCHOLOGY REVIEW. 1970-1990 (Mar.). bi-m. (back issues avail.) Parapsychology Foundation, 228 E. 71st St., New York, NY 10021.
Supersedes: Parapsychology Foundation. Newsletter.

616.4 612.015   UK   ISSN 0261-4847
PARATHYROID HORMONES. ceased 1989. m. (looseleaf format; back issues avail.) Sheffield University Biomedical Information Service (SUBIS), The University, Sheffield S10 2TN, England.

618 362   US   ISSN 0888-2843
PARENT CARE; resources to assist family caregivers. 1985-1991 (vol.6, no.6). 6/yr. University of Kansas Gerontology Center, 4089 Dole, Lawrence, KS 66045.

370   US
PARENTS' GUIDE TO HIGHLY-RATED EDUCATIONAL SOFTWARE. 1988-199? a. Educational Products Information Exchange Institute, 103 W. Montauk Hwy., Ste.3, Hampton Bays, NY 11946-4006.

054.1 053.1   FR   ISSN 0031-2053
PARISER KURIER; Deutsche Zeitung in Frankreich periodique Allemand bilingue. 1952-1991 (Nov.). bi-m. (tabloid format) 84, rue de Rennes, 75006 Paris, France.

329.9   HU   ISSN 0464-476X
JN2191.S92
PARTTORTENETI KOZLEMENYEK. ceased. 4/yr. Kossuth Konyvkiado, Revay U. 16, 1065 Budapest 6, Hungary.

330   US   ISSN 0743-6610
PASADENA JOURNAL OF BUSINESS. 1982-19?? m. (back issues avail.) (Kelly, Peck Associates, Inc.) Pasadena Publications, 155 S. El Molino Ave., No. 101, Pasadena, CA 91101.

001.642   US
PASCAL NEWSLETTER. 1980-1988. q. Oregon Software Inc., 6915 S.W. Macadam Ave., Portland, OR 97219.

330   US
EL PASO MAGAZINE. ceased 198? m. (Greater El Paso Chamber of Commerce) Philip J. Laven and Associates, Inc., 10 Civic Center Plaza, El Paso, TX 79944.

028.5   IT
PASSATEMPI MARVEL; mensile di giochi per il tempo libero. ceased. m. Edigamma s.r.l., Piazza Dei Sanniti 9, 00185 Rome, Italy.

800   FR   ISSN 0031-2711
AP20
PASSERELLE; revue litteraire trimestrielle a sens unique. 1969-19?? (no.64). q. Pierre Bearn, Ed. & Pub., 60 rue Monsieur le Prince, 75006 Paris, France.

001.3 320 900 100   CN
PAST & PRESENT. 1976-19?? 3/yr. University of Waterloo, Faculty of Arts, Waterloo, Ont. N2L 3G1, Canada.

608.7   GW
PATENTSPIEGEL METALLBAU. ceased 1991. m. (Aluminium-Zentrale e.V.) Aluminium-Verlag GmbH, Koenigsallee 30, Postfach 101262, 4000 Duesseldorf 1, Germany.

371.9   US
PATHFINDER (WASHINGTON); information resources and technology in rehabilitation. 1979-19?? bi-m. (tabloid format) National Rehabilitation Information Center, 4407 8th St., N.E., Washington, DC 20017.

333.78   US
PATHFINDERS. BIENNIAL REPORT. ceased. biennial. Department of Parks and Recreation, 1405 Resources Bldg., 1416 9th St., Box 2390, Sacramento, CA 95811.
Formerly: Pathfinders. Annual Report.

616.07 574.2   US   ISSN 0362-3025
RB6   CODEN: PBANBA
PATHOBIOLOGY ANNUAL. 1972-1982. a. Raven Press, 1185 Ave. of the Americas, New York, NY 10036.

617.6   US   ISSN 0882-6471
PATIENT PLEASERS! DENTAL EDITION. 1985-198? m. (back issues avail.) American Health Consultants, Inc., 67 Peachtree Park Dr., N.E., Atlanta, GA 30309.

610   US   ISSN 0882-6471
PATIENT PLEASERS! HEALTH CARE EDITION. 1985-198? m. (back issues avail.) American Health Consultants, Inc., 67 Peachtree Park Dr., N.E., Atlanta, GA 30309.

658 340   US
PATIENTS' RIGHTS REPORTER. 1983-198? m. Cox Publications, Box 20316, Billings, MT 59104-0316.
Formerly: Patients' Rights in California (ISSN 0736-2544)

330 658   US
PATUXENT BUSINESS DIGEST. 1989-1990. m. 10750 Little Patuxent Pkwy., Columbia, MD 20144.

780   NE   ISSN 0031-3246
PAUKENSLAG. 1962-198? bi-m. (also avail. in microfilm) (Stichting Frysk Orkest) Vereniging Vrienden Frysk Orkest, Vredeman de Vriesstraat 19, Postbus 666, 8900 BJ Leeuwarden, Netherlands.

267   SZ   ISSN 0079-0281
PAX ROMANA. ceased 1991. quadrennial. International Catholic Movement for Intellectual and Cultural Affairs - Pax Romana, General Secretariat, B.P. 85, 37-39 Rue de Vermont, CH-1211 Geneva 20-CIC, Switzerland.

384.6   US   ISSN 0886-5396
PAY PHONE NEWS. 1985-1988. m. TeleStrategies Publishing, Inc., 1355 Beverly Rd., Ste. 100, McLean, VA 22101.

618.92   PL   ISSN 0031-3939
     CODEN: PEPOA6
PEDIATRIA POLSKA. ceased. m. (Polskie Towarzystwo Pediatryczne) Panstwowy Zaklad Wydawnictw Lekarskich, Ul. Dluga 38-40, Warsaw, Poland.

618.92   SZ   ISSN 0300-1245
     CODEN: PEDIEY
PEDIATRICIAN; international journal of child and adolescent health. 1972-1991. q. (also avail. in microform from RPI) S. Karger AG, Allschwilerstr. 10, P.O. Box, CH-4009 Basel, Switzerland.

675   GW
PELZ INTERNATIONAL; Fachzeitschrift fuer das Kuerschnerhandwerk und die Rauchwarenwirtschaft. 1947-1991. bi-m. (Zentralverband des Kuerschnerhandwerks) Rhenania-Fachverlag GmbH, Possmoorweg 5, 2000 Hamburg 60, Germany.
Formerly: Rund Um den Pelz International (ISSN 0048-8755)

051   US   ISSN 0031-4293
PENINSULA LIVING. 1954-197? w. (tabloid format; also avail. in microfilm) Peninsula Newspapers, Inc., Box 300, Palo Alto, CA 94302.

378   US
PENN STATE UPDATE. 1984-19?? s-a. Penn State Alumni Association, 105 Old Main, University Park, PA 16802.

792.8   US
PENNSYLVANIA BALLET. 1980-198? q. Pennsylvania Ballet Association, c/o Pennsylvania Ballet School, 1101 S. Broad St., Philadelphia, PA 19147.

333.7   US   ISSN 0164-7822
PENNSYLVANIA NATURALIST. 1978-198? bi-m. RD 2, Box 87, Huntingdon, PA 16652-9001.

338.4   US   ISSN 0476-1103
HA607
PENNSYLVANIA STATISTICAL ABSTRACT. 1958-198? a. (also avail. in microfiche from BHP) Department of Commerce, Bureau of Policy, Planning & Systems Development, 474 Forum Bldg., Harrisburg, PA 17120.

841   FR   ISSN 0031-479X
LA PENSEE FRANCAISE. 1946-1989. bi-m. Union Litteraire et Artistique de France, 35 rue Gayet, 42000 Saint-Etienne (Loire), France.

360   US
PENSION BRIEFINGS. ceased. m. Federal Publications, Inc. (Subsidiary of: Longman Company), 1120 20th St., N.W., Ste. 500 S., Washington, DC 20036.

368   US
PENSION FACTS. 1974-198? biennial. American Council of Life Insurance, Information Department, 1001 Pennsylvania Ave., N.W., Washington, DC 20004.

916.89   RH
PEOPLE. ceased. fortn. Ministry of Information, Posts and Telecommunications, P.O. Box 8122, Causeway, Harare, Zimbabwe.
Supersedes (in 1979): African Times.

301.16   US
PEOPLE, COMMUNICATION ORGANIZATION. 1986-199? irreg. Ablex Publishing Corporation, 355 Chestnut St., Norwood, NJ 07648.

320   SJ
PEOPLE'S LOCAL GOVERNMENT JOURNAL/AL-HUKM AL-SHABI AL-MAHALLI. ceased 1977 (vol.5). m. Ministry of People's Local Government, PO Box 94, Khartoum, Sudan.

796.4   CN   ISSN 0832-8196
PERFORMANCE. 1986-19?? 6/yr. Canadian Weightlifting Federation, 1600 James Naismith Dr., Gloucester, Ont. K1B 5N4, Canada.
Formerly: Canadian Weightlifting Journal - Journal Canadien d'Halterophilie (ISSN 0705-1727)

332.6   US   ISSN 0300-7693
PERFORMANCE GUIDE PUBLICATIONS. MUTUAL FUNDS AND TIMING. 1967-19?? m. (looseleaf format) Performance Guide Publications, Inc., Box 2604, Palos Verdes Peninsula, CA 90274.

620   FR
PERFORMANCES. 1972-19?? q. (tabloid format) Matra Defense, 37 av. Louis Breguet, Velizy 78140, France.

792 780   US   ISSN 0480-0257
PERFORMING ARTS MAGAZINE (SAN FRANCISCO EDITION); San Francisco music & theatre monthly. 1967-198? m. Theatre Publications, Inc., 2999 Overland Ave., Ste. 201, Los Angeles, CA 90064.

658   AT
PERMAIL HOSPITAL BOOK. 1965-19?? biennial. Permail Pty. Ltd., P.O. Box 56, Artarmon, N.S.W. 2064, Australia.

362.7   US
PERMANENCY REPORT. 1983-198? q. Child Welfare League of America, Inc., Permanent Families for Children, 67 Irving Pl., New York, NY 10003.
Formerly (until 1983): Adoption Report.

400   NE   ISSN 0553-6812
PERMANENT INTERNATIONAL COMMITTEE OF LINGUISTS. COMMITTEE ON LINGUISTIC STATISTICS. PUBLICATION. 1950-19?? irreg. Permanent International Committee of Linguists, Sint-Annastraat 40, Nijmegen, Netherlands.

CESSATIONS

808 US
PERRY RHODAN SCIENCE FICTION PAPERBACK MAGAZINE. 1969-198? m. 2495 Glendower Ave., Hollywood, CA 90027.
Supersedes (after no.137, 1979): Perry Rhodan Science Fiction Magazine.

150 US ISSN 0883-2293
PERSON-CENTERED REVIEW; an international journal of research, theory, and application. 1985-1990 (vol.5., no.4). q. Sage Publications, Inc., 2455 Teller Rd., Newbury Park, CA 91320.

001.6 621.381 NE
PERSONAL COMPUTER KOOPGIDS. ceased. 2/yr. V N U Business Publications B.V., Rijnsburgstr. 11, 1059 AT Amsterdam, Netherlands.

001.6 621.381 US
PERSONAL COMPUTING. 1976-1990 (Aug.). m. (also avail. in microfilm from UMI; microfiche; reprint service avail. from UMI) V N U Business Publications, Inc., Ten Holland Dr., Hasbrouck Heights, NJ 07604.
Formerly: Personal Computing Plus; Formed by the 1984 merger of: Personal Computing (ISSN 0192-5490); Personal Software Magazine (ISSN 0740-0438)

510 US ISSN 0888-3262
CODEN: PCOSE3
PERSONAL COMPUTING SERIES. 1984-19?? irreg. (back issues avail.) Computer Science Press, Inc., 41 Madison Ave., 37th Fl., New York, NY 10010-3546.

368 US
PERSONAL LINES LETTER. ceased 1989 (May). m. Shelby Publishing Corp., 210 Lincoln St., Ste. 700, Boston, MA 02111-2491.

658 US ISSN 0048-3443
PERSONAL REPORT FOR THE EXECUTIVE. 1972-198? s-m. Research Institute of America, Inc., 90 Fifth Ave., New York, NY 10011.

001.642 UK
PERSONAL SOFTWARE. 1982-19?? q. Argus Specialist Publications Ltd., Argus House, Boundary Way, Hemels, Hampstead, Herts HP2 7ST, England.

621.381 US ISSN 1047-4013
QA76.525
PERSONAL WORKSTATION; where powerful PC's and workstations meet. 1989-1991 (June). m. Computer Metrics, Inc. (Subsidiary of: Markt & Technik), 501 Galveston Dr., Redwood City, CA 94063-4728.
Formerly (until 1990): M I P S (Magazine of Intelligent Personal Systems).

367 US
PERSPECTIVE (NEWTON). ceased. 8/yr. Association of Professional Y M C A, 2139 Commonwealth Ave., Newton, MA 02166.

384.6 US ISSN 0740-5324
PERSPECTIVE ON A T & T AND BOC PRODUCTS AND MARKETING. 1983-1989 (Jul.). m. (also avail. in microfilm; back issues avail.) B C R Enterprises, Inc., 950 York Rd., Hinsdale, IL 60521.

614.8 US
PERSPECTIVES (BALTIMORE). 1921-1986. bi-m. City Health Department, Bureau of Health Information, 303 E. Fayette St., 2nd Fl., Baltimore, MD 21202.
Supersedes (in 1976): Baltimore Health News (ISSN 0045-1363)

378 US
PERSPECTIVES (DES MOINES). 1968-1989. a. Drake University, Office of Marketing and Communications, 200 Old Main, Des Moines, IA 50311.

658 US
PERSPECTIVES (HAMPTON). 1978-19?? q. Independent Community Consultants, Inc., Box 141, Hampton, AR 71744.
Formerly: Mt. Ida Reporter.

800 028.5 US ISSN 0883-6086
Z1037.A1
PERSPECTIVES (NORWOOD). N.S. 1990-199? 5/yr. Christopher - Gordon Publishers, Inc., 480 Washington St., Norwood, MA 02062.

370 500 US ISSN 0273-4621
Q180.55.E4 CODEN: PSCGDI
PERSPECTIVES IN COMPUTING (ARMONK); applications in the academic, scientific community. 1981-198? s-a. (back issues avail.) International Business Machines Corp., Armonk, NY 10504.

364 US
PERSPECTIVES IN CRIMINAL JUSTICE. 1981-198? a. Sage Publications, Inc., 2111 W. Hillcrest Dr., Newbury Park, CA 91320.

620 UK
PERSPECTIVES IN STRUCTURAL SCIENCE. 1984-198?; suspended. a. Freund Publishing House, Ltd., Suite 500, Chesham House, 150 Regent St., London W1R 5FA, England.

615.9 US
PERSPECTIVES IN TOXICOLOGY. ceased. irreg. Raven Press, 1185 Ave. of the Americas, New York, NY 10036.

301 GW ISSN 0171-3183
PERSPEKTIVEN. 1978-198? q. (reprint service avail. from KTO) Lothar Ulsamer, Kelterstr. 35, 7300 Esslingen-Sulzgries, Germany.
Incorporates: Gesellschaft.

011 PE
PERU. BIBLIOTECA NACIONAL. BIBLIOGRAFIA NACIONAL. 1978-1983. bi-m. Biblioteca Nacional del Peru, Digbine, Apartado 2335, Lima, Peru.

330.9 PE
PERU: COMPENDIO ESTADISTICO. 1980-1987. a. Instituto Nacional de Estadistica, Ave. 28 de Julio 1056, Lima, Peru.

632.9 II ISSN 0031-6148
SB951 CODEN: PSTDAN
PESTICIDES. 1967-19??; suspended. m. (also avail. in microfilm from UMI; reprint service avail. from UMI) Colour Publications Pvt. Ltd., 126-A Dhurunadi, Off Dr. Nariman Rd., Bombay 400 025, India.

632.9 UK ISSN 0956-0602
PESTICIDES DISC. 1991; ceased same year. 2/yr. (Royal Society of Chemistry) Pergamon Press plc, Headington Hill Hall, Oxford OX3 0BW, England.

636.089 179.3 US
PET HEALTH NEWS. 1970-199? m. Fancy Publications, Inc., Box 6050, Mission Viejo, CA 92690.
Former titles (until Aug. 1985): Today's Animal News; (until Jan.-Feb. 1981): Today's Animal Health; (until Jan. 1977): Animal Cavalcade.

799.1 US ISSN 1041-4703
PETERSEN'S FISHING. 1987-1991 (Apr.). bi-m. Petersen Publishing Co., 8490 Sunset Blvd., Los Angeles, CA 90069.

378.0025 US ISSN 0890-3085
L901
PETERSON'S APPLYING TO COLLEGES AND UNIVERSITIES IN THE UNITED STATES: A HANDBOOK FOR INTERNATIONAL STUDENTS. 1985-1988. a. Peterson's Guides, Inc., 202 Carnegie Center, Box 2123, Princeton, NJ 08543-2123.

780 US
LE PETIT BATON. 1972-199? 4/yr. Sir Thomas Beecham Society, Inc., 664 South Irena Ave., Redondo Beach, CA 90277.
Incorporates: Beecham Society Bulletin (ISSN 0084-7763); Which was formerly: Beecham Society Newsletter.

665.5 US ISSN 0884-4550
HD9560.1
PETROLEUM MANAGEMENT. 1978-1992 (Jan.). m. (back issues avail.) Management Publishing Services, P.O. Box 55829, Houston, TX 77255-5829.

531.64 US
PETROLEUM SITUATION. 1950-19?? irreg. Chase Manhattan Bank, Energy Economics Division, One Chase Manhattan Plaza, New York, NY 10015.
Incorporates: Energy Report from Chase.

662 US
PETROLEUM WHOLESALER. ceased. fortn. Oil Buyers' Guide, Box 998, Lakewood, NJ 08701.

332.6 US
PETZOLD ON STOCKS. 1984-19?? s-m. Heinz A. Petzold & Associates, Inc., 216 Rheem Blvd., Orinda, CA 94563.

798 GW ISSN 0138-1342
PFERD UND SPORT. 1957-1990. m. Deutscher Pferdesport-Verband, Storkower Str. 118, 1055 Berlin, Germany.

798 GW
PFERDEMARKT; Deutschlands grosse Pferdeschau. 1977-1989. bi-m. Verlag E.E. Timm und Sohn GmbH, Grosseneumarkt 45, D-2000 Hamburg 11, Germany.

053.1 GW ISSN 0031-6784
DIE PFORTE; Zeitschrift und Schriften fuer wertidealistische Philosophie und Kultur. 1947-1983. a. Dr. Kurt Port Verlag GmbH, Dulkweg 9, 7300 Esslingen, Germany.

616.76 616.99 UK ISSN 0142-8519
PHAGOCYTES. ceased 1990. m. (looseleaf format; back issues avail.) Sheffield University Biomedical Information Service (SUBIS), The University, Sheffield S10 2TN, England.

332.6 US
PHARMACIST'S ASSETS. 1983-198? bi-m. Medical Publishing Enterprises, 15-22 Fairlawn Ave., Fairlawn, NJ 07410.

615 GW ISSN 0344-7154
CODEN: PHKTDK
PHARMAKOTHERAPIE. 1978-198? irreg. Dustri-Verlag Dr. Karl Feistle, Bahnhofstr. 9, 8024 Deisenhofen, Germany.

950 490 890 US
PHI THETA PAPERS. 1950-19?? a. (back issues avail.) (Oriental Languages Student Association) University of California, Berkeley, Department of East Asian Languages, Durant Hall, Berkeley, CA 94720.

327 US
PHILADELPHIA PAPERS. 1964-198? irreg. Foreign Policy Research Institute, 3615 Chestnut St., Philadelphia, PA 19104.
Former titles: Foreign Policy Research Institute. Monograph Series; Foreign Policy Research Institute. Research Monograph Series (ISSN 0553-5743)

769.56 CN ISSN 0048-3737
PHILATOPIC MAGAZINE. ceased. bi-m. Empire Stamp Corporation Ltd., 1150 Yonge St., Toronto, Ont. M4W 2M2, Canada.

806 US
PHILIP K. DICK SOCIETY NEWSLETTER. 1983-1992 (Dec.). 3/yr. (looseleaf format; back issues avail.) Box 611, Glen Ellen, CA 95442.

338.1 PH ISSN 0031-7446
HD2086
PHILIPPINE AGRICULTURAL SITUATION. ceased 1983 (no.2). s-a. Bureau of Agricultural Economics, Ben-Lor Bldg., 1184 Quezon Ave., Quezon City, Philippines.

636.089 PH ISSN 0048-3761
SF1 CODEN: PJAIAG
PHILIPPINE JOURNAL OF ANIMAL INDUSTRY. 1934-1984 (vol.39). s-a. Bureau of Animal Industry, Diliman, Quezon City, Philippines.

551 PH ISSN 0116-0109
PHILIPPINE JOURNAL OF VOLCANOLOGY. 1983-19?? s-a. Philippine Institute of Volcanology and Seismology, Hizon Bldg., 5th Fl., 29 Quezon Ave., Quezon City, Philippines.

361.77 PH ISSN 0031-7713
PHILIPPINE JUNIOR RED CROSS MAGAZINE. 1948-1990 (vol.45). 6/yr. (during school year). Philippine National Red Cross, 860 United Nations Ave., Manila, Philippines.

677 PH ISSN 0115-2351
PHILIPPINE TEXTILE DIGEST. 1971-1981 (vol.9). q. Philippine Textile Research Institute, Ministry of Trade and Industry, General Santos Ave., Bicutan, Taguig, Metro Manila, Philippines.

CESSATIONS

338.1   PH
PHILIPPINES. BUREAU OF AGRICULTURAL ECONOMICS. CROP AND LIVESTOCK STATISTICS. 1954-1981. a. Bureau of Agricultural Economics, Ben-Lor Bldg., 1184 Quezon Ave., Quezon City, Philippines.
Formerly: Philippines. Bureau of Agricultural Economics. Crop, Livestock and Natural Resources Statistics (ISSN 0079-1512)

338.1   PH   ISSN 0079-1520
PHILIPPINES. BUREAU OF AGRICULTURAL ECONOMICS. REPORT. 1953-198? a. Bureau of Agricultural Economics, Ben-Lor Bldg., 1184 Quezon Ave., Quezon City, Philippines.

331   PH
PHILIPPINES. BUREAU OF LABOR AND EMPLOYMENT STATISTICS. SELECTED LABOR INDICATORS. 1975-1988. s-a. Bureau of Labor and Employment Statistics, Dole Bldg., Intramuros, Manila, Philippines.
Formerly: Philippines. Labor Statistics Service. Selected Labor Indicators.

630   PH
PHILIPPINES. DEPARTMENT OF AGRICULTURE. BUREAU OF AGRICULTURAL STATISTICS. CROP STATISTICS BULLETIN. suspended. m. (processed) Department of Agriculture, Bureau of Agricultural Statistics, BEN-LOR Bldg., 1184 Quezon City, Philippines.

630   PH
PHILIPPINES. DEPARTMENT OF AGRICULTURE. BUREAU OF AGRICULTURAL STATISTICS. RICE AND CORN INVENTORY. suspended. m. (processed) Department of Agriculture, Bureau of Agricultural Statistics, BEN-LOR Bldg., 1184 Quezon City, Philippines.

382   PH
PHILIPPINES. MINISTRY OF TRADE. TREND ANALYSIS OF THE TWENTY LEADING EXPORTS AND PROSPECTS IN THE YEAR AHEAD. 1974-19?? irreg. Ministry of Trade, Trade & Industry Bldg., 361 Gil J. Puyat Ave. Ext, Makati, Metro Manila, Philippines.

382   PH
PHILIPPINES. MINISTRY OF TRADE. TWENTY LEADING IMPORTS. 1974-19?? irreg. Ministry of Trade, Trade & Industry Bldg., 361 Gil J. Puyat Ave. Ext, Makati, Metro Manila, Philippines.

381 315   PH
PHILIPPINES. NATIONAL CENSUS AND STATISTICS OFFICE. ANNUAL SURVEY OF WHOLESALE AND RETAIL ESTABLISHMENTS. ceased 1969. a. National Census and Statistics Office, Ramon Magsaysay Blvd., Box 779, Manila, Philippines.

382 315   PH
PHILIPPINES. NATIONAL CENSUS AND STATISTICS OFFICE. COASTWISE TRADE REPORT. ceased 1974. a. National Statistics Office, Ramon Magsaysay Blvd., Box 779, Manila, Philippines.

350.865 312   PH
PHILIPPINES. NATIONAL CENSUS AND STATISTICS OFFICE. LISTING OF CITIES, MUNICIPALITIES AND MUNICIPAL DISTRICTS BY PROVINCE. ceased. irreg. National Statistics Office, Ramon Magsaysay Blvd., P.O. Box 779, Manila, Philippines.

312   PH
PHILIPPINES. NATIONAL CENSUS AND STATISTICS OFFICE. SOCIAL INDICATOR. ceased. a. National Census and Statistics Office, Ramon Magsaysay Blvd., Manila, Philippines.

315   PH
PHILIPPINES. NATIONAL CENSUS AND STATISTICS OFFICE. SPECIAL REPORT. 1970. ceased 1970. National Census and Statistics Office, Ramon Magsaysay Blvd., P.O. Box 779, Manila, Philippines.

633   PH
PHILIPPINES. NATIONAL FOOD AUTHORITY. GRAINS JOURNAL. 1976-1982 (Jul.). bi-m. National Food Authority, E. Rodriguez Ave., Quezon City, Philippines.
Formerly: Philippines. National Grain Authority. Grains Journal.

336.2   PH   ISSN 0040-0068
PHILIPPINES. NATIONAL TAX RESEARCH CENTER. TAX MONTHLY. 1960-1988. m. (processed) National Tax Research Center, First BF Condominium, Aduana St., Intramuros, Manila, Philippines.

500   NE   ISSN 0031-7926
TK1   CODEN: PTREAN
PHILIPS TECHNICAL REVIEW. 1936-1989 (Nov.). m. N.V. Philips' Gloeilampenfabrieken, Research Laboratories, Eindhoven, Netherlands.

100 900   GW   ISSN 0016-884X
Z7127
PHILOSOPHY AND HISTORY; a review of German-language research contributions on philosophy, history and cultural developments. 1968-1991. s-a. (also avail. in microform from MIM; reprint service avail. from ISI) Institut fuer Wissenschaftliche Zusammenarbeit, Landhausstr. 18, 7400 Tuebingen, Germany.

100 206   US   ISSN 0739-1218
PHILOSOPHY AND THE ARTS; a literary and philosophical review. 1975-19?? a. Philosophy and the Arts, Box 431, Jerome Ave. Sta., Bronx, NY 10468.
Incorporates: Bertrand Russell Today.

610   US   ISSN 0894-9565
RC535   CODEN: PPRRE4
PHOBIA PRACTICE AND RESEARCH JOURNAL. 1988-1990. s-a. (reprint service avail. from UMI) Human Sciences Press, Inc. (Subsidiary of: Plenum Publishing Corp.), 233 Spring St., New York, NY 10013-1578.

378   UK
PHOENIX. 1975-1987. w. (during school term). University of East Anglia, University House, University Plain, Norwich NR4 7TJ, England.

327   US
PHOENIX (DUMONT). 1984-1990 (Nov.). irreg. (approx. 4/yr.). Phoenix Publications, Box 132, Dumont, NJ 07628.

770   UK
PHOTO & VIDEO TRADER. 1973-1989 (Dec.). fortn. Henry Greenwood & Co. Ltd., 58 Fleet St., London EC4Y 1JU, England.
Former titles: Photo Trader (ISSN 0031-8612); (until 1974): Photo Trade World; Photographic Trade Bulletin.

384.554 770   GR
PHOTO, CINE, VIDEO BUYER'S GUIDE. 1983-19?? biennial. Moressopulos & Associates, P.O. Box 30564, GR-100 33 Athens, Greece.

770 028.5   CN   ISSN 0708-5435
TR640
PHOTO COMMUNIQUE. 1979-19?? q. (back issues avail.) (Holocene Foundation) Gail Fisher-Taylor, Ed. & Pub., Box 155, Station "B", Toronto, Ont. M5T 2T3, Canada.

770.5   US   ISSN 0093-1365
TR150
PHOTO INFORMATION ALMANAC. 1960-1989. a. A B C Consumer Magazines, Inc., Photographic Publishing Division, 825 Seventh Ave., New York, NY 10019.

700   AT
PHOTO TRAVELLER. ceased. a. (reprint service avail.) Australian Hi-Fi & Specialist Magazines Group Pty. Ltd., P.O. Box 341, Mona Vale, N.S.W. 2103, Australia.

616.99   UK   ISSN 0952-0368
PHOTOCHEMOTHERAPY. ceased 1990. m. (looseleaf format; back issues avail.) Sheffield University Biomedical Information Service (SUBIS), The University, Sheffield S10 2TN, England.

770   US   ISSN 0278-2790
PHOTOGRAPHER'S MARKET NEWSLETTER. 1981-1985. m. (back issues avail.) F & W Publications, Inc., 9933 Alliance Rd., Cincinnati, OH 45242.

770 011   US
PHOTOGRAPHY MAGAZINE INDEX. 1984-19?? a. Paragon Publishing, Box 53, Santa Rosa, CA 95402.

770   UK
PHOTOGRAPHY REPORT. 1980-1986. biennial. Euromonitor Publications Ltd., 87-88 Turnmill St., London EC1M 5QU, England.

530   US   ISSN 1049-5290
PHOTONICS: TECHNOLOGY AND APPLICATIONS. 1990-1991. m. (back issues avail.) Technical Insights, Inc., 32 N. Dean St., Englewood, NJ 07631.

778.53   UK   ISSN 0269-8293
PHOTOPLAY. 1950-19?? m. Argus Specialist Publications Ltd., Argus House, Boundary Way, Hemels, Hampstead, Herts HP2 7St, England.
Former titles: Photoplay Movies and Video; Photoplay Movie and Video Monthly; Photoplay Film and TV Scene.

700 770   US   ISSN 0893-4835
PHOTOSTATIC MAGAZINE; audio and print culture. 1983-1989 (Dec.); suspended. bi-m. (also avail. in magnetic tape; video cassette; back issues avail.) PhotoStatic Retrofuturism, 911 North Dodge St., Iowa City, IA 52245.

610   US
PHYSICIAN COMPUTER MONTHLY. 1983-198? m. American Health Consultants, Inc., 67 Peachtree Park Dr., Atlanta, GA 30309.

378 530   US   ISSN 0569-5716
QC29
PHYSICS MANPOWER - EDUCATION AND EMPLOYMENT STATISTICS. 1964-199? irreg. American Institute of Physics, 335 E. 45th St., New York, NY 10017.

574.1   US   ISSN 0148-4427
   CODEN: MPPADB
PHYSIOLOGICAL SOCIETY OF PHILADELPHIA. MONOGRAPHS. 1976-19?? irreg. Halsted Press (Subsidiary of: John Wiley & Sons, Inc.), 605 Third Ave., New York, NY 10016.

615.53 617.533   UK   ISSN 0266-6154
   CODEN: PHPRE6
PHYSIOTHERAPY PRACTICE. 1985-198? 4/yr. (back issues avail.) Churchill Livingstone Medical Journals, Robert Stevenson House, 1-3 Baxter's Place, Leith Walk, Edinburgh EH1 3AF, Scotland.

387.7   US   ISSN 0193-211X
PILOT NEWS. 1971-198? m. Suburban Pilot, Inc., 5320 N. Jackson Ave., Kansas City, MO 64119.

379   US   ISSN 0079-2071
LB1028
PILOT STUDIES APPROVED FOR STATE AID IN PUBLIC SCHOOL SYSTEMS IN VIRGINIA. 1964-19?? a. Department of Education, Division of Educational Research, Box 6-Q, Richmond, VA 23216.

028.5   FR
PILOTE. 1959-1989. m. Dargaud Editeur, 71417 Dourdan Cedex, France.

056.1   US   ISSN 0146-2075
PIMIENTA. 1958-198? m. Fiesta Publishing Corp., 6443 N.W. 82nd Ave., Miami, FL 33166-2735.

811   US
PINCHPENNY. 1979-1988. q. (back issues avail.) Pinchpenny Press, 4851 Q. St., Sacramento, CA 95819.

612 612.015   UK   ISSN 0268-1501
PINEAL GLAND. ceased 1989. m. (looseleaf format; back issues avail.) Sheffield University Biomedical Information Service (SUBIS), The University, Sheffield S10 2TN, England.

917.4   US
PINERY. 1956; N.S. 1977-1985. irreg. (3-4/yr.). Portage County Historical Society, University of Wisconsin, Stevens Point, WI 54481.

051   US
PINK!. 1989-1991. q. Leisure Plus Publications, Inc. (Subsidiary of: Mavety Media Group Ltd.), 462 Broadway, Ste. 4000, New York, NY 10013.

659.1   US
PINWHEEL PINK PAGES. 1971-19?? q. (back issues avail.) Schaedler Quinzel, Inc., 404 Park Ave. South, New York, NY 10016-8462.

371.83   GW   ISSN 0476-8612
PIONIERLEITER. ceased 1990. s-m. Verlag Junge Welt GmbH, Mauerstr. 39-40, 1080 Berlin, Germany.

CESSATIONS

533 CN
PIPELINE. 1985-1990 (Jun.). w. (tabloid format) Oil Pipeline News Inc., P.O. Box 1397, Estevan, Sask. S4A 2K9, Canada.

420 375.4 US
PITT SERIES IN ENGLISH AS A SECOND LANGUAGE. 1974-19?? irreg. University of Pittsburgh Press, 127 North Bellefield Ave., Pittsburgh, PA 15260.

929 US ISSN 0882-3189
F157.A4
PITTS CHOICE; Pittsburgh's choice cemeteries. 1984-198? q. W A B Genealogical Services, 322 Greenway Dr., Pittsburgh, PA 15235-3748.

331 US
PLACEMENT BULLETIN. ceased 1991 (Jan.). m. American Compensation Association, 14040 N. Northsight Blvd., Scottsdale, AZ 85260.

305.142 US ISSN 0148-902X
PLAINSWOMAN. 1977-198? (vol.12, no.10); suspended. 10/yr. (back issues avail.) Plainswoman, Inc., Box 8027, Grand Forks, ND 58202.

636.1 798 FR ISSN 0032-051X
PLAISIRS EQUESTRE; la revue de l'homme de cheval. 1962-19?? 6/yr. Editions Crepin-Leblond et Cie, 14, rue du Patronage, 52003 Chaumont Cedex, France.

379 US
PLAN REVIEW PROCESS FOR CONSOLIDATED PROGRAM SCHOOLS. ceased 1980. a. State Department of Education, Superintendent of Public Instruction, 721 Capitol Mall, Sacramento, CA 95814.

352.7 BL
PLANEJAMENTO. 1974-1980 (vol.8, no.2). bi-m. Fundacao para o Desenvolvimento da Ciencia na Bahia, Av. Luiz Filho, CEP 4000 - Salvador, Bahia, Brazil.
Formerly (until 1977): Planejamento na Bahia.

322.4 US
PLANET EARTH. ceased 1986. a. Planetary Citizens, Box 1509, Mt. Shasta, CA 96067.

350 AT
PLANNER MAGAZINE. ceased. q. Rala Publications, 203-205 Darling St., Balmain, N.S.W. 2041, Australia.

352.7 UK
PLANNING AND DEVELOPMENT DIGEST. 1984-1991. m. Planning Exchange, 186 Bath St., Glasgow G2 4HG, Scotland.
Formerly: Planning Information Digest (ISSN 0267-7385)

574.88 630 NE ISSN 0167-6857
CODEN: PTCEDJ
PLANT CELL, TISSUE AND ORGAN CULTURE; an international journal on in vitro culture of higher plants. 1981-1989 (vol.3). m. (reprint service avail. from SWZ) Kluwer Academic Publishers, Postbus 17, NE-3300 AA Dordrecht, Netherlands.

635 US
PLANT LORE. ceased 1985. 2/yr. 16 Oak St., Genesse, NY 14454.

658 US
PLANT MANAGERS SURVEY. ceased. q. Dun & Bradstreet, Economic Analysis Department, 299 Park Ave., New York, NY 10171.

630 016 IS ISSN 0032-0897
PLANT PROTECTION ABSTRACTS. 1965-198? q. Makhteshim Agan, P.O. Box 60, Beersheva, Israel.

581 574.1 UK ISSN 0952-3855
PLANTS TODAY. ceased 1989. 6/yr. Blackwell Scientific Publications Ltd., P.O. Box 88, Oxford OX2 0EL, England.

658.788 668.4 US
PLASTICS PACKAGING. 1988; ceased same year. bi-m. Edgell Communications, 7500 Old Oak Blvd., Cleveland, OH 44130.

668.4 US
PLASTICS TODAY. 1989; ceased Dec. of same year. s-m. J S D Publishing Co., 5827 Columbia Pike, Ste. 310, Falls Church, VA 22041.

668.4 US
PLASTICTRENDS. ceased. bi-m. Miramar Publishing Co., 6133 Bristol Parkway, Box 3640, Culver City, CA 90231-3640.

790.1 US
PLAYER'S SPORTS FOR KIDS. 1990-1991 (vol.2, no.4). bi-m. Signal Research Inc., 300-A S. Westgate Dr., Greensboro, NC 27407.

796.333 SA
PLAYFAIR S.A. RUGBY YEARBOOK. ceased. a. Promco (Pty) Ltd., 1202 Radio City, Tulbagh Square, Cape Town 8001, South Africa.

028.5 UK
PLAYHOUR ANNUAL. ceased. a. Fleetway Annuals, Kings Reach Tower, Stamford St., London SE1 9LS, England.

910.202 US
PLEASANT HAWAII; the Aloha State magazine. 1988-1991. q. Pleasant Hawaii, Inc., 270 Lewers St., Penthouse, Honolulu, HI 96815.

054.1 FR
PLEIN NORD; revue historique et culturelle du Nord de la France. 1973-1986. 10/yr. La Gazette, 7 rue Jacquemars-Gielee, 59015 Lille Cedex, France.

808 US
PLOUGH (HURON); North Coast review. 1983-198? a. (back issues avail.) Firelands Writing Center, Firelands College, Huron, OH 44839.

895.61 JA
PLOVER/CHIDORI. 1989-1991 (Dec.). s-a. (back issues avail.) P.O. Box 122, Ginowan-shi, Okinawa-ken 901-22, Japan.

696 US ISSN 0192-1711
TH6101 CODEN: PLENDY
PLUMBING ENGINEER. 1973-1990 (June). 9/yr. (also avail. in microform from UMI; reprint service avail. from UMI) (American Society of Plumbing Engineers) Delta Communications Inc. (Chicago) (Subsidiary of: Elsevier Business Press, Inc. (New York)), 400 N. Michigan Ave., Ste. 1200, Chicago, IL 60611.

317.3 US ISSN 0079-2403
HA195
POCKET DATA BOOK, USA. 1967-1979. irreg. (also avail. in microform) U.S. Bureau of the Census, Customer Service, Washington, DC 20233.

811 US
POETESSA; the new woman's poetry journal. 1984-198? irreg. (back issues avail.) Poetessa Press, Box 420, East Rockaway, NY 11518.

811 US
POETRY NOW. 1973-1988 (no.37). q. (tabloid format; also avail. in microform from UMI; reprint service avail. from UMI) E.V. Griffith, Ed. & Pub., 3118 K St., Eureka, CA 95501.

811 US
POETRY TEXAS. 1977-199? s-a. College of the Mainland, Division of Humanities, 8001 Palmer Hwy., Texas City, TX 77590.

808.81 UK ISSN 0268-1390
POETRY WORLD. 1966-198? s-a. Anvil Press Poetry Ltd., 69 King George St., London SE10 8PX, England.
Formerly (until 1986): Modern Poetry in Translation (ISSN 0026-8291)

811 US ISSN 0197-6338
PS551
POETS IN THE SOUTH; conversation within the word. 1977-1984 (vol.2, no.2). 3/yr. University of South Florida, Center for Writers, LET 141, University of South Florida, Tampa, FL 33620.

388.3 629.2 FR ISSN 0032-227X
POIDS LOURD; revue technique du vehicule industriel. 1906-19?? m. Compagnie Generale de Developpement, 11 rue Godefroy Cavaignac, 75541 Paris Cedex 11, France.

790.1 US
POKER PLAYER. 1981-198? w. (tabloid format) Gambling Times, Inc., 16760 Stagg St., Ste. 213, Van Nuys, CA 91406.
Incorporates: Pan Player Plus.

914 PL
POLAND - TOURISM. 1975-19?? m. Polska Agencja Interpress, Ul. Bagatela 12, 00-585 Warsaw, Poland.

320 US ISSN 0892-2519
POLAND WATCH REPORTS. 1982-19?? 3/yr. Poland Watch Center, Box 18216, Washington, DC 20036.
Formerly: Poland Watch (ISSN 0736-0061)

947 323.4 DK ISSN 0108-7371
POLEN-NYT/POLAND NEWS. 1982-19?? bi-m. Stoet Solidarnosc - Support Solidarite Committee, H.C. Oerstedsvej 50B, 1879 Frederiksberg C, Denmark.

800 YU ISSN 0032-2520
POLET. 1962-1990. w? Savez Socialisticke Omladine Hrvatske, Opaticka 10, PP 99, 41001 Zagreb, Yugoslavia.

364 US ISSN 0271-7565
POLICE AND SECURITY BULLETIN; monthly review of new ideas and publications in law enforcement, criminal justice, industrial security and public safety. 1969-1989 (vol.21, no.3). m. (also avail. in microfiche from UMI; back issues avail.) Lomond Publications, Inc., Box 88, Mt. Airy, MD 21771.
Former titles (until 1980): Systems, Technology and Science for Law Enforcement and Security; Systems, Technology and Science for Law Enforcement and Security Newsletter (ISSN 0039-8055)

351.74 US ISSN 0079-2950
HV8143
POLICE YEARBOOK. 1961-19?? a. (Davis Publishing Co.) Davis Publishing Co., Law Enforcement Division, 6016 E. Shirley Lane, Montgomery, AL 36117.

338.91 US ISSN 8755-9412
POLICY NOTES. 1975-1990. irreg. (looseleaf format; back issues avail.) Interfaith Action for Economic Justice, 110 Maryland Ave., N.E., Washington, DC 20002.
Formerly (until Aug. 1983): Food Policy Notes.

910.09 CU
POLIMITAS. ceased. a. Instituto Nacional del Turismo, Malecon y G, Vedado, Havana, Cuba.

551 PL ISSN 0208-8061
POLISH ACADEMY OF SCIENCES. INSTITUTE OF GEOPHYSICS. PUBLICATIONS. SERIES G. NUMERICAL METHODS IN GEOPHYSICS. ceased 1987 (no.3-203). irreg. Polska Akademia Nauk, Instytut Geofizyki - Polish Academy of Sciences, Institute of Geophysics, Ul. Ksiecia Janusza 64, 01-452 Warsaw, Poland.
Supersedes in part: Polska Akademia Nauk. Instytut Geofizyki. Materialy i Prace (ISSN 0079-3574)

791.43 PL
POLISH FILM. 1963-1981; N.S. 1988-19?? q. Film Polski Ltd., Ul. Mazowiecka 6-8, 00-048 Warsaw, Poland.
Formerly: Polish Film - Film Polonais (ISSN 0015-136X)

387 PL ISSN 0032-2911
HE730
POLISH MARITIME NEWS. 1958-1982; resumed 1984-1989; suspended. m. Polish Chamber of Foreign Trade, Maritime Branch, Pulaskiego 6, 81-368 Gdynia, Poland.

621 PL
POLITECHNIKA GDANSKA. INSTYTUT ORGANIZACJI I PROJEKTOWANIA. RAPORT. 1982-19?? a. (reprint service avail.) Politechnika Gdanska, Ul. Majakowskiego 11-12, 80-592 Gdansk 6, Poland.

011 PL ISSN 0551-651X
POLITECHNIKA POZNANSKA. ZESZYTY NAUKOWE. BIBLIOGRAFIA. 1962-1989 (no.17); suspended. irreg. Politechnika Poznanska, Pl. Curie-Sklodowskiej 5, Poznan, Poland.

016 PL
POLITECHNIKA WROCLAWSKA. BIBLIOTEKA GLOWNA I OSRODEK INFORMACJI NAUKOWO-TECHNICZNEJ. PRACE NAUKOWE. PRACE BIBLIOGRAFICZNE. 1975-1989 (no.18). irreg. Politechnika Wroclawska, Wybrzeze Wyspianskiego 27, 50-370 Wroclaw, Poland.

5260 CESSATIONS

330   PL   ISSN 0137-6306
POLITECHNIKA WROCLAWSKA. OSRODEK BADAN PROGNOSTYCZNYCH. PRACE NAUKOWE. KONFERENCJE. 1975-1980 (no.7). irreg. Politechnika Wroclawska, Wybrzeze Wyspianskiego 27, 50-370 Wroclaw, Poland.

330.9   PL   ISSN 0137-6314
POLITECHNIKA WROCLAWSKA. OSRODEK BADAN PROGNOSTYCZNYCH. PRACE NAUKOWE. MONOGRAFIE. 1978-1989 (no.9). irreg. Politechnika Wroclawska, Wybrzeze Wyspianskiego 27, 50-370 Wroclaw, Poland.

330.9   PL   ISSN 0137-6322
POLITECHNIKA WROCLAWSKA. OSRODEK BADAN PROGNOSTYCZNYCH. PRACE NAUKOWE. STUDIA I MATERIALY. 1977-1990 (no.6). irreg. Politechnika Wroclawska, Wybrzeze Wyspianskiego 27, 50-370 Wroclaw, Poland.

330.9   PL   ISSN 0137-6330
POLITECHNIKA WROCLAWSKA. OSRODEK BADAN PROGNOSTYCZNYCH. PRACE NAUKOWE. WSPOLPRACA/SOTRUDNICHESTVO. 1973-1974 (no.2). irreg. Politechnika Wroclawska, Wybrzeze Wyspianskiego 27, 50-370 Wroclaw, Poland.

320 156   US
POLITICAL BEHAVIOR ANNUAL. ceased. a. Westview Press, 5500 Central Ave., Boulder, CO 80301.

301.412   US   ISSN 0896-7202
POLITICAL WOMAN. 1986-198? q. 4521 Campus Dr., Ste. 388, Irvine, CA 92715.

053   GW
POLITICUM; Stuttgarter Zeitschrift fuer Politik und Gesellschaft. 1981-1989; suspended. q. (back issues avail.) Foerderverein Politicum e.V., Schurwaldstr. 24, D-7000 Stuttgart 1, Germany.

327   GW   ISSN 0340-5869
POLITIK UND KULTUR. 1974-1990. bi-m. Colloquium Verlag, Luetzowstr. 105, 1000 Berlin 30, Germany.

362   US
POLLING. 1974-19?? irreg? United Cerebral Palsy of New York City, Inc., 122 E. 23rd St., New York, NY 10010.

943.8 327   PL   ISSN 0032-3675
POLOGNE ET LES AFFAIRES OCCIDENTALES. 1965-19?? s-a. Instytut Zachodni, Stary Rynek 78-79, 61-772 Poznan, Poland.

617   PL   ISSN 0032-373X
POLSKI PRZEGLAD CHIRURGICZNY. 1922-19?? m. (Towarzystwo Chirurgow Polskich) Panstwowy Zaklad Wydawnictw Lekarskich, Ul. Dluga 38-40, Warsaw, Poland.

574.192   UK   ISSN 0263-7367
POLYAMINES. ceased 1989. m. (looseleaf format; back issues avail.) Sheffield University Biomedical Information Service (SUBIS), The University, Sheffield S10 2TN, England.

620   US   ISSN 0032-406X
TA1
POLYTECHNIC ENGINEER. 1901-1913; N.S. 1958-19?? 2/yr. Polytechnic Institute of New York, 333 Jay St., Brooklyn, NY 11201.

200 300 001.3   BL
PONTIFICIA UNIVERSIDADE CATOLICA DE SAO PAULO. REVISTA. suspended. q. Editora da Pontificia Universidade Catolica de Sao Paulo, Rua Monte Alegre 984, 05014 Sao Paulo, SP, Brazil.

572   VC
PONTIFICO MUSEO MISSIONARIO ETNOLOGICO. ANNALI. 1937-1976. a. Pontificio Museo Missionario Etnologico, 00120 Vatican City (Rome), State of the Vatican City.
    Formerly (until 1962): Annali Lateranensi.

798.2   GW   ISSN 0930-1186
PONY. ceased 1991. m. Verlag Eugen Ulmer GmbH, Postfach 70 05 61, 7000 Suttgart 70, Germany.

301.32 312   CS
POPULACNI ZPRAVY. 1976-1990. irreg. (1-2/yr.). Federalni Ministerstvo Prace a Socialnich Veci - Federal Ministry of Labour and Social Affairs, Palackeho nam. 4, 12801 Prague 2, Czechoslovakia.

796   UK   ISSN 0262-4001
POPULAR CARAVAN. 1982-198? m. Sovereign International, Sovereign House, Brentwood, Essex CM14 4SE, England.

799.1   US   ISSN 0889-4752
POPULAR LURES. 1986-19?? 6/yr. National Reporter Publications, Inc., 15115 S. 76th E. Ave., Bixby, OK 74008.

301.426 613.9   US   ISSN 0161-0902
HQ763
POPULATION AND FAMILY PLANNING PROGRAMS. 1969-198? irreg. (reprint service avail. from UMI) Population Council, One Dag Hammarskjold Plaza, New York, NY 10017.

370 301.32   US
POPULATION EDUCATION INTERCHANGE. 1972-1988. 4/yr. (reprint service avail. from UMI) Population Reference Bureau, Inc., 777 14th St. N.W., Washington, DC 20005.
    Formerly: Interchange (ISSN 0047-0465)

312   IR
POPULATION GROWTH OF IRAN. published only once, 1974. irreg. Statistical Centre, Dr. Fatemi Ave, Teheran 14144, Iran.

387   US   ISSN 0032-4817
PORT OF BALTIMORE BULLETIN. 1928-19?? m. Maryland Port Administration, World Trade Center Baltimore, Baltimore, MD 21202.

387   US
HF3163.N5
PORT OF NEW ORLEANS RECORD. (Overseas edition avail.) 1942-1991 (Jul.). m. Board of Commissioners Port of New Orleans, 2 Canal St., Box 60046, New Orleans, LA 70160.
    Formerly: New Orleans Port Record (ISSN 0028-6397)

387   JA
PORT OF YOKOHAMA. PLANS FOR FUTURE. ceased. irreg. Port and Harbor Bureau, Industry & Trade Center Bldg., Yamashita-cho, Naka-ku, Yokohama, Japan.

979   US   ISSN 0197-1085
PORTAGE. 1979-1989 (vol.10, no.1). q. (back issues avail.) Museum of History and Industry, 2700 - 24th Ave. East, Seattle, WA 98112.

658.8   US
PORTFOLIO OF SALES AND MARKETING PLANS. ceased. a. Sales and Marketing Management, (Subsidiary of: Bill Communications, Inc.), 633 Third Ave., New York, NY 10017.

387   IT   ISSN 0032-4965
PORTO DI VENEZIA. 1929-1982. m. Provveditorato al Porto di Venezia, Zattere N. 1401, C.P. 30123, Venice, Italy.

623.82 620.009   US   ISSN 0032-5015
PORTS O'CALL. 1968-199? quinquennial. Society of Wireless Pioneers, Box 530, Santa Rosa, CA 95402.

380.1   US
PORTSMOUTH CHAMBER OF COMMERCE. REPORT; Portsmouth area business news. 1924-19?? m. Portsmouth Chamber of Commerce, Box 70, 524 Middle St., Portsmouth, VA 23705.
    Formerly: Portsmouth Chamber of Commerce. Newsletter (ISSN 0032-5023)

531.64   PO   ISSN 0377-2233
HD9502.P8
PORTUGAL. ESTATISTICAS DA ENERGIA: CONTINENTE, ACORES E MADEIRA. 1969-19?? a. Instituto Nacional de Estatistica, Servicos Centrais, Av. Antonio Jose de Almeida, 1078 Lisbon Codex, Portugal.
    Formerly: Estatisticas da Energia: Continente e Ilhas Adjacentes.

338 314   PO
PORTUGAL. INSTITUTO NACIONAL DE ESTATISTICA. ESTATISTICAS DAS SOCIEDADES: CONTINENTE, ACORES E MADEIRA. 1939-19?? a. Instituto Nacional de Estatistica, Av. Antonio Jose de Almeida, 1078 Lisbon Codex, Portugal.
    Formerly: Portugal. Instituto Nacional de Estatistica. Estatisticas das Sociedades. Continente e Ilhas Adjacentes (ISSN 0870-3205)

320   US
PORUNCA VREMII. ceased. m. Boian News Service, 300 E. 91st St., New York, NY 10028.

769.56   US   ISSN 0032-5325
POSTAL BELL/EKIREI. 1939-19?? 6/yr. (processed; also avail. in microfilm) Japanese American Society for Philately, Box 2730, Santa Clara, CA 95051.

350   US   ISSN 0888-0794
POSTAL EMPLOYEES' NEWSLETTER. 1986-19?? w. Federal Employees News Digest, Inc., Box 7528, Falls Church, VA 22046.

383   US   ISSN 0146-9983
HE6371
POSTAL HISTORY U.S.A. 1972-198? q. (looseleaf format) (Fourth Class Cancellation Club) J-B Publishing Co., 430 Ivy Ave., Crete, NE 68333.
    Formerly: Fourth Class Cancellation Club Newsletter.

630   AT   ISSN 0032-5589
POTATO GROWER NEWS. 1945-19?? w. (tabloid format) (Victorian Potato Growers Association) Baxter & Stubbs Pty. Ltd., P.O. Box 51, Ballarat, Vic. 3350, Australia.

633   UK   ISSN 0265-7015
POTATO WORLD. 1984-19?? 2/yr. Potato Marketing Board, Broad Field House, 4 Between Towns Rd., Cowley, Oxford OX4 3NA.
    Formerly: Potato Quarterly.

616.2   CN   ISSN 0318-9236
POUMONS. 1967-1986. 4/yr. Association Pulmonaire du Quebec - Quebec Lung Association, 4837 rue Boyer, Bureau 100, Montreal, Que. H2J 3E6, Canada.
    Formerly: Observation, Opinion, Orientation (ISSN 0029-7674)

544.66   US   ISSN 0092-1300
QC482.D5
POWDER DIFFRACTION FILE SEARCH MANUAL. FINK METHOD. INORGANIC. (Subseries of the Committee's Publication SMF) ceased. a. Joint Committee on Powder Diffraction Standards, International Centre for Diffraction Data, 1601 Park Lane, Swarthmore, PA 19081.

669   US   ISSN 0149-3922
TN695   CODEN: PMDTDK
POWDER METALLURGY IN DEFENSE TECHNOLOGY. ceased 1987 (vol.7). irreg. Metal Powder Industries Federation, 105 College Rd. E., Princeton, NJ 08540.

797   UK
POWER BOAT AND WATERSKIING. 1966-1989. m. c/o Coach House, Medcroft Rd., Tackley, Oxford OX5 3AH, England.

621.3 613.1   US   ISSN 1044-5137
POWER ENERGY ECOLOGY. 1992; announced, never published. q. Hemisphere Publishing Corporation (Subsidiary of: Taylor & Francis Group), 1900 Frost Rd., Ste. 101, Bristol, PA 19007-1598.

621.2 621.5   UK   ISSN 0950-1487
TJ840   CODEN: PIHEE2
POWER INTERNATIONAL. 1955-1990. 12/yr.(in 4 vols.). Elsevier Science Publishers Ltd., Crown House, Linton Rd., Barking, Essex IG11 8JU, England.
    Former titles (until 1985): Hydraulic Pneumatic Mechanical Power (ISSN 0306-4069); Hydraulic Pneumatic Power (ISSN 0018-8131)

780.42   US
POWER METAL. 1987-198? m. (back issues avail.) Charlton Publications, Inc., 60 Division St., Derby, CT 06418.

531.64 621.3   US   ISSN 0079-4457
TK2921   CODEN: PSSYAD
POWER SOURCES SYMPOSIUM. PROCEEDINGS. 1956-19?? biennial. Electrochemical Society, Inc., 10 S. Main St., Pennington, NJ 08534-2896.

690   CS   ISSN 0477-8685
TH4
POZEMNI STAVBY/CONSTRUCTION ENGINEERING. (Supplement avail.) 1953-1990. m. Ministerstvo Stavebnictvi Ceske Socialisticke Republiky, Spalena 51, 113 02 Prague 1, Czechoslovakia.

330.9   PL
PRACE POPULARNONAUKOWE. EKONOMIA I ORGANIZACJA. (Subseries of: Prace Popularnonaukowe (ISSN 0079-4805)) 1978-19?? irreg. Towarzystwo Naukowe w Toruniu, Ul. Wysoka 16, 87-100 Torun, Poland.

330   US
PRACTICAL GUIDE TO COUNTERTRADE. 1985-198? irreg. Metal Bulletin Inc., 220 Fifth Ave., New York, NY 10001.

371.42   US   ISSN 0032-6410
PRACTICAL KNOWLEDGE. 1939-1991. m. Nelson-Hall Publishing Co., 111 N. Canal St., Chicago, IL 60606.

340   US   ISSN 0160-8177
KF1
PRACTICAL LAW BOOKS REVIEW; a quick reference to new legal publications by field of specialization. 1978-1990 (Nov.). q. (back issues avail.) Library Management & Services, 5914 Highlands Hills Dr., Austin, TX 78731.

610.73   US
PRACTICAL NURSING CAREER. 1968-198? a. National League for Nursing, 350 Hudson St., New York, NY 10014.

155.5   US
PRACTICE APPLICATIONS. 1983-19?? q. Washington University, Center for Adolescent Mental Health, Box 1196, St. Louis, MO 63130.

610 658   US
PRACTICE MARKETING & MANAGEMENT. HEALTH CARE EDITION. 1982-198? m. (looseleaf format; back issues avail.) American Health Consultants, Inc., 67 Peachtree Park Dr., N.E., Atlanta, GA 30309.

371.3 600   II   ISSN 0032-6690
HG1505
PRAJNAN. 1967-1986 (vol.18). a. Technical Teachers Training Institute, Block FC, Sector III, Calcutta 700 091, India.

551.22   GW   ISSN 0933-7660
PRAKLA SEISMOS REPORT. 1971-1990. s-a. (back issues avail.) Prakla Seismos AG, Buchholzerstr. 100, 3000 Hannover 51, Germany.

610   SA
PRAKTISYN. 1984-1988 (Sep.). m. National Publishing (Pty) Ltd., P.O. Box 2735, Johannesburg 2000, South Africa.

600 070   PL
PRASA TECHNICZNA. 1971-19??; suspended. bi-m. (Rada Prasy Technicznej) Wydawnictwo Czasopism i Ksiazek Technicznych SIGMA - NOT, Ul. Biala 4, P.O. Box 1004, 00-950 Warsaw, Poland.

618.92   US
PRE-PARENT ADVISER. ceased. a. (Johnson & Johnson) Whittle Communications L.P., Corporate Communications, 505 Market St., Knoxville, TN 37902.

371.3 659.1   US
PRE-SCHOOL & KINDERGARTEN MARKET-CENTER. 1981-198? 3/yr. Randall Publishing Co., Box 2029, Tuscaloosa, AL 35403.

669   US   ISSN 0032-714X
     CODEN: PCMEBG
PRECISION METAL; the magazine of metal component design and production. 1943-1989. m. (also avail. in microform from UMI; reprint service avail. from UMI) Penton Publishing, 1100 Superior Ave., Cleveland, OH 44114.
     Formerly: Precision Metal Molding.

637   BL   ISSN 0100-5162
PRECOS MEDIOS DO BOI GORDO E LA. ceased 1988. s-a. (Instituto Brasileiro de Economia, Centro de Estudos Agricolas) Fundacao Getulio Vargas, C.P. 9052, 22250 Rio de Janeiro, Brazil.

028   UK   ISSN 0032-7263
PREFACE; an introduction to books. 1965-1984. bi-m. (processed) (Hackney Junior Libraries) Hackney Library Services, Mare St., Hackney, London E. 8, England.

910.202   US
PREFERRED TRAVELLER. 1981-19?? q. American Leisure Industries, Inc., 4501 Forbes Blvd., Ste. 100, Lanham, MD 20706.
     Formerly (until vol.12, no.3, 1989): Touring and Travel.

340   YU
PREGLED PRAVA ZEMALJA U RAZVOJU. 1977-19?? q. Institut za Uporedno Pravo, Belgrade, Terazije 41, 11000 Belgrade, Yugoslavia.

340   YU   ISSN 0032-731X
PREGLED ZAKONODAVSTVA U STRANIM DRZAVAMA. 1958-19?? q. Institut za Uporedno Pravo, Belgrade, Terazije 41, 11000 Belgrade, Yugoslavia.

612 618   UK   ISSN 0261-4898
PREGNANCY. ceased 1989. m. (looseleaf format; back issues avail.) Sheffield University Biomedical Information Service (SUBIS), The University, Sheffield S10 2TN, England.

282   AG
PREGON DE LA T F P. 1969-1989 (Oct.). s-m. Sociedad Argentina de Defensa de la Tradicion, Familia y Propiedad, Reconquista 657, Primer piso, 1371 Buenos Aires, Argentina.
     Formerly (until 1979): Tradicion, Familia, Propiedad; Supersedes: Cruzada.

634.9 581 591 016   CS   ISSN 0032-7336
PREHLED LESNICKE A MYSLIVECKE LITERATURY/ REVIEW OF LITERATURE ON FORESTRY AND GAME MANAGEMENT. 1957-19?? m. Ustava Vedeckotechnickych Informaci pro Zemedelstvi, Slezska 7, 120 56 Prague 2, Czechoslovakia.

011   CS   ISSN 0862-1187
PREHLEDY INFORMATIVNI LITERATURY. 1963-1989. s-a. Statni Knihovna C S R, Klementinum 190, 110 01 Prague 1, Czechoslovakia.
     Former titles (until 1986): Novinky Literatury: Prehledy Informativni Literatury (ISSN 0029-5191); (until 1968): Novinky Literatury. Prehledy Literatury.

375 028.5   US
PRESCHOOL PATTERNS. ceased 1990 (Nov.). bi-m. Warren Publishing House, Inc., Box 2250, Everett, WA 98203.

372.21   US   ISSN 0748-4054
PRESCHOOL PERSPECTIVES; the monthly newsletter for educators of young children. 1984-1992. m. Business Publishers, Inc., 951 Pershing Dr., Silver Spring, MD 20910-4464.

296 059.62   US   ISSN 0092-4091
DS101
PRESENT TENSE; the magazine of world Jewish affairs. 1973-19?? bi-m. (also avail. in microform from UMI; reprint service avail. from UMI) American Jewish Committee, 165 E. 56th St., New York, NY 10022.

659.1   US
PRESENTATION BUSINESS NEWS. 1989-1991. bi-m. Pacific Magazine Group, 513 Wilshire Blvd., Ste. 344, Santa Monica, CA 90401.

320 970   US
THE PRESIDENT'S TEAM. 1981-1991; suspended. irreg. (every 2-4 yrs.). Braddock Communications, Inc., 909 N. Washington St., Alexandria, VA 22314-1555.
     Formerly: Executive Bio-Pictorial Directory (Year) (ISSN 0272-345X)

070   UK
PRESS AND THE PEOPLE. 1953-1990 (37th ed.). a. Press Council, 1 Salisbury Sq., London EC4Y 8AE, England.

070 621.384   UK   ISSN 0269-1752
PRESS BRIEFING. 1986-198? s-a. Carrick Publishing, 28 Miller Rd., Ayr KA7 2AY, Scotland.

070   GW   ISSN 0032-7840
PRESSE DER SOWJETUNION. 1950-1990. w. (Presseamt beim Vorsitzenden des Ministerrates der DDR) Verlag Volk und Welt, Glinkastr. 13-15, 1086 Berlin, Germany.

613.7 613.2   IT
PREVENIRE. ceased 1988 (no.12). m. Nesi Editore S. r.l., Via Pergolesi, 29, 20124 Milan, Italy.

616   US
PREVENTIVE MEDICINE QUARTERLY. ceased 1986 (vol. 10, no.2). q. Department of Health and Environmental Control, 2600 Bull St., Columbia, SC 29201.

659.152   FI   ISSN 0359-6079
PRIMA. 1982-198? s-a. Kustannus Oy Faktum, Hitsaajankatu 7, 00810 Helsinki 81, Finland.

792.8   US
PRIMA BALLERINA. 1989-199? bi-m. Prima Publishing Group, 5695 Peachtree Pkwy., Norcross, GA 30092.

610   US
PRIMARY CARE RECORDS. ceased. m. American Health Consultants, Inc., 67 Peachtree Park Dr., N.E., Atlanta, GA 30309.

372   AT
PRIMARY JOURNAL K-7. 1973-1989 (no.2); suspended. 2/yr. Department of School Education, G.P.O. Box 33, Sydney, N.S.W. 2001, Australia.
     Formerly: Primary Journal (ISSN 0311-1342)

333.33   CN
PRINCE EDWARD ISLAND. AGRICULTURAL DEVELOPMENT CORPORATION. ANNUAL REPORT. 1971-1989. a. Agricultural Development Corporation, Box 1390, Charlottetown, P.E.I., Canada.
     Formerly: Prince Edward Island. Land Development Corporation. Annual Report.

330 510   US   ISSN 0079-5240
PRINCETON STUDIES IN MATHEMATICAL ECONOMICS. 1964-1980 (no.7). irreg. (reprint service avail. from UMI) Princeton University Press, 3175 Princeton Pike, Lawrenceville, NJ 08540.

780   US   ISSN 0079-5259
PRINCETON STUDIES IN MUSIC. 1964-1980 (no.7). irreg. (reprint service avail. from UMI) Princeton University Press, 3175 Princeton Pike, Lawrenceville, NJ 08648.

341 327   US   ISSN 0079-5267
PRINCETON UNIVERSITY. CENTER OF INTERNATIONAL STUDIES. POLICY MEMORANDUM SERIES. 1952-1988 (no.43). irreg. (reprint service avail. from UMI) Princeton University, Center of International Studies, Bendheim Hall, Princeton University, Princeton, NJ 08544.

341 327   US   ISSN 0555-1501
PRINCETON UNIVERSITY. CENTER OF INTERNATIONAL STUDIES. RESEARCH MONOGRAPH SERIES. 1959-1989 (no.51). irreg. (back issues avail.; reprint service avail. from UMI) Princeton University, Center of International Studies, Bendheim Hall, Princeton University, Princeton, NJ 08544.

379.15 296   US
PRINCIPAL (NEW YORK). 1955-19?? m. (10/yr.). (Association of Yeshivah-Day School Principals of General Studies) Board of Jewish Education of Greater New York, 426 W. 58th St., New York, NY 10019.

943.64   LH   ISSN 0048-5306
PRINCIPALITY OF LIECHTENSTEIN - A DOCUMENTARY HANDBOOK. 1966-198? irreg. Press and Information Office, Government Palace, FL-9490 Vaduz, Liechtenstein.

370   NE   ISSN 0032-8499
PRINSEJAGT. 1962-19?? m. Algemene Speeltuinvereniging Prinsejagt, Van Aitzemastraat 31, Eindhoven, Netherlands.

655   AT   ISSN 0048-5322
PRINTERS NEWS. 1961-197? fortn. (Printing and Allied Trades Employers' Federation) Printers News Pty. Ltd., 507 Kent St., Sydney, N.S.W. 2000, Australia.

686.2   US
PRINTER'S NEWS. 1975-1990. m. (tabloid format) The Printer, 3200 S. John Redditt, Lufkin, TX 75901.

686.2   CN
PRINTING PRODUCT GUIDE. 1980-19?? q. Maclean Hunter Ltd., Maclean-Hunter Bldg., 777 Bay St., Toronto, Ont. M5W 1A7, Canada.

CESSATIONS

800   US
PRISMAL-CABRAL. 1977-1984. s-a. (back issues avail.) c/o Aleido Rodriguez, University of Maryland, Department of Spanish and Portuguese, College Park, MD 20742.
    Formerly: Prismal.

332.6   US
PRIVATE PLACEMENT ADVISORY. 1987-1988. m. Merit Communications Inc., 8605 Westwood Center Dr., Ste. 204, Vienna, VA 22180.

370 340   US
PRIVATE SCHOOL LAW DIGEST. 1982-1990 (May). 5/yr. (looseleaf format; back issues avail.) National Catholic Education Association, 1077 30th St., N.W., Ste. 100, Washington, DC 20007.

371.002   US   ISSN 0885-1603
L901
PRIVATE SCHOOLS OF THE UNITED STATES. 1985-1988. a. (Curriculum Information Center) Market Data Retrieval, Inc., 16 Progress Dr., Shelton, CT 06484.

910.09   US
PRIVILEGED TRAVELER. ceased. bi-m. 42 Usonia Rd., Pleasantville, NY 10570.

338.1   CN
PRO-FARM. ceased. 6/yr. (Western Canadian Wheat Growers Association) Ag-Com Publications Inc., P.O. Box 517, White City, Sask. S0G 5B0, Canada.

282   BE   ISSN 1012-4543
BX801
PRO MUNDI VITA STUDIES. 1963-1991. bi-m. (also avail. in microform from UMI; reprint service avail. from UMI) Pro Mundi Vita, International Information and Research Centre, Abdij van't Park, Abdijdreef 7A, B-3001 Leuven, Belgium.
    Formerly: Pro Mundi Vita Bulletin; Incorporates: Pro Mundi Vita Dossiers; Which was formerly (until 1975): Pro Mundi Vita. Special Notes (ISSN 0079-5593)

796   US   ISSN 0032-9126
PRO-SPORTS. 1965-198? q. Reese Communications, Inc., 460 W. 34th St., New York, NY 10001.

614.7   CN   ISSN 0707-1922
PROBE POST; Canada's environmental magazine. 1978-1991 (vol.14, no.2); suspended. q. Pollution Probe Foundation, 12 Madison Ave., Toronto, Ont. M5R 2S1, Canada.

320.531   GW   ISSN 0032-9258
HX6
PROBLEME DES FRIEDENS UND DES SOZIALISMUS; Zeitschrift der kommunistischen und Arbeiterparteien fuer Theorie und Information. ceased 1991. m. Dietz Verlag, Wallstr. 76-79, Postfach 273, Berlin 1020, Germany.

382 338.5   YU   ISSN 0032-938X
HF37.Y8
PROBLEMI SPOLJNE TRGOVINE I KONJUNKTURE/ FOREIGN TRADE & BUSINESS CYCLES PROBLEMS. 1962-19?? q. Institut za Spoljnu Trgovinu, Mose Pijade 8, Belgrade, Yugoslavia.

574   CS
PROBLEMY BIOLOGIE KRAJINY/QUESTIONES GEOBIOLOGICAE. ceased 1982 (no.28). irreg. (Slovenska Akademia Vied) Veda, Publishing House of the Slovak Academy of Sciences, Klemensova 19, 814 30 Bratislava, Czechoslovakia.

370   PL
PROBLEMY OSWIATY NA WSI. 1974-19?? 5/yr. (Ministerstwo Edukacji Narodowej) Wydawnictwa Szkolne i Pedagogiczne, Ul. Pankiewicza 3, 00-696 Warsaw, Poland.
    Formerly: Zbiorcza Szkola Gminna (ISSN 0209-0112)

610   PL   ISSN 0137-7183
PROBLEMY SZKOLNICTWA I NAUK MEDYCZNYCH. 1966-19?? q. (Ministerstwo Zdrowia i Opieki Spolecznej) Panstwowy Zaklad Wydawnictw Lekarskich, Dluga 38-40, Warsaw, Poland.
    Formerly: Problemy Uczelni i Instytutow Medycznych (ISSN 0032-9541)

341   US
PROCEDURAL ASPECTS OF INTERNATIONAL LAW. ceased. irreg. University Press of Virginia, Box 3608, University Sta., Charlottesville, VA 22903.

621.381   UK   ISSN 0954-4917
PROCESS INDUSTRY INTERNATIONAL; international bulletin for suppliers and users of process instrumentation. 1988-1990. m. Elsevier Science Publishers Ltd., Crown House, Linton Rd., Barking, Essex IG11 8JU, England.

636.5   US
PROCESSED POULTRY. 1988-199? bi-m. Watt Publishing Co., Sandstone Bldg., Mt. Morris, IL 61054.

330   LE   ISSN 0254-9379
PROCHE-ORIENT ETUDES ECONOMIQUES. 1967-1989. q. Universite St. Joseph, Faculte de Sciences Economiques, Rue Huvelin, Box 293, Beirut, Lebanon.
    Formerly: Travaux du Seminaire d'Etudes Economiques.

388   VE   ISSN 0032-9681
PRODUCCION. 1942-198?; suspended. m. Camara de Industriales de Caracas, Edificio Camara de Industriales, Esq. Pte. Anauco, Caracas, Venezuela.

630   AG   ISSN 0079-5852
HD1862
PRODUCCION RURAL ARGENTINA. 1964-1985. s-a. Banco Rio de la Plata, Gerencia de Investigaciones Economicas, Bartolome Mitre 480 P.13, 1036 Capital, Argentina.

674   US
PRODUCT ACCEPTANCE NEWS. 1976-19?? q. Society of American Wood Preservers, Inc., 7297 Lee Hwy., Unit P, Fall Church, VA 22042.

681   US   ISSN 0882-2700
PRODUCT DIRECTORY & BUYERS' GUIDE. 1981-19?? a. (reprint service avail.) Miramar Publishing Co., Box 3640, Culver City, CA 90231-3640.

630   CN
LE PRODUCTEUR HORTICOLE. 1985-1991 (Jul.). 10/yr. Societe d'Editions S E L C Inc., P.O. Box 1320, 1 Philipsburg, Bedford, Que. J0J 1A0, Canada.
    Formerly: Horticulteur (ISSN 0827-1496)

658   US   ISSN 1057-2341
TS156.A1   CODEN: PINMEM
PRODUCTION & INVENTORY MANAGEMENT; the magazine of manufacturing performance. 1980-1992. m. (also avail. in microform from UMI; back issues avail.) (American Production and Inventory Control Society) T D A Publications, Inc., 2021 Coolidge St., Hollywood, FL 33020-2012.
    Former titles: P and I M Review (ISSN 1057-8803); P and I M Review with A P I C S News; Production and Inventory Management Review with A P I C S News; P I M Review; Incorporates: A P I C S News (ISSN 0274-9874)

770 380.1   AT
PROFESSIONAL AND INDUSTRIAL PHOTOGRAPHIC EQUIPMENT. 1971-19?? a. Yaffa Publishing Group, 17-21 Bellevue St., Surry Hills, N.S.W. 2010, Australia.
    Formerly: Australian Photography Professional and Industrial Catalogue.

371.42   US
PROFESSIONAL CAREERS MAGAZINE. 1986-19?? bi-m. (tabloid format) Westech Corporation, 4701 Patrick Henry Dr., Ste. 1901, Santa Clara, CA 95054.

720 620   US   ISSN 0160-0362
PROFESSIONAL MARKETING REPORT. 1976-1989 (Nov.). m. (also avail. in microfiche; back issues avail.) Gerre Jones Associates, Inc., Box 14302, Albuquerque, NM 87191.

340   US
PROFESSIONAL MONITOR. 1959-1989 (vol.23, no.7). m. Michigan Association of the Professions, 530 W. Ionia, Ste. C, Lansing, MI 48933.
    Formerly: Legislative Monitor (ISSN 0279-8743)

658 651.2   US
PROFESSIONAL OFFICE MANAGER. 1985-1987 (Oct.). m. Professional Publications, 50 S. 9th St., Ste. 20D, Minneapolis, MN 55402.

    Former titles: Office Management Report; C P A Office Managment Report; Incorporates: Attorneys Office Management Report (ISSN 0883-5713)

350 720   UK
PROFESSIONAL PRACTICE DEVELOPMENT. 1989-1992. q. (looseleaf format) 62 Toller Ln., Bradford, W. Yorks BD8 9BY, England.

384.55   UK   ISSN 0267-5528
PROFESSIONAL PROMOTION MEDIA DIRECTORY. 1984-198? s-a. Professional Books Ltd., 46 Milton Trading Estate, Abingdon, Oxon OX14 4SY, England.
    Formerly: Marketing Directory.

070.5   UK
PROFESSIONAL PUBLISHING MEDIA DIRECTORY. 1983-198? s-a. Professional Books Ltd., 46 Milton Trading Estate, Abingdon, Oxon OX14 4SY, England.
    Formerly: Publishing and Bookselling Directory (ISSN 0266-0210)

373.246 650   UK   ISSN 0957-5936
PROFESSIONAL SECRETARY. 1968-19?? m. Pitman Publishing, 128 Long Acre, London WC2E 9AN, England.
    Formerly (until 1989): Memo (ISSN 0025-9071)

651.3   US
PROFESSIONAL SECRETARY - ADMINISTRATIVE SUPPORT LETTER. 1960-199? s-m. Bureau of Business Practice, 24 Rope Ferry Rd., Waterford, CT 06386.
    Former titles: P.S. for Professional Secretaries (ISSN 0273-9682); P.S. for Private Secretaries (ISSN 0030-8285)

658.8 332   US
PROFESSIONAL SELLING: FINANCIAL SERVICES EDITION. 1983-198? s-m. Bureau of Business Practice, 24 Rope Ferry Rd., Waterford, CT 06386.

384.55   UK
PROFESSIONAL T V & RADIO MEDIA DIRECTORY. 1982-198? s-a. Professional Books Ltd., 46 Milton Trading Estate, Abingdon, Oxon OX14 4SY, England.
    Formed by the merger of: T V Directory & Radio Directory; Formerly: Information on TV Directory (ISSN 0263-9874)

371.42   US
PROFESSIONAL TRAINER. 1982-198? q. (tabloid format) McGraw-Hill Training Systems, Box 641, Del Mar, CA 92014.

747.5   US
PROFESSIONAL UPHOLSTERER. 1984-198? 6/yr. (reprint service avail.) (National Association of Professional Upholsterers) Communications Today Publishing Ltd., 200 S. Main St, Box 2754, High Point, NC 27261.

332.6   BL
PROFILE OF THE SAO PAULO STOCK EXCHANGE. 1983-1988. a. Bolsa de Valores de Sao Paulo - Sao Paulo Stock Exchange, Rua Alvares Penteado, 151, Sao Paulo, SP 01012, Brazil.
    Formerly: Bolsa de Valores de Sao Paulo. Relatorio.

621.381   US   ISSN 8755-464X
QA76.8.K38
PROFILES (SOLANA BEACH). 1983-198?; suspended. 12/yr. (back issues avail.) Kaypro Corporation, 533 Stevens Ave., Solana Beach, CA 92075.

340   US
PROFILES OF OHIO LAWYERS. 1989-1991. a. Anderson Publishing Co., 2035 Reading Rd., Cincinnati, OH 45202.

330   US
PROFIT (STUDIO CITY). 1981-1990. m. (looseleaf format; back issues avail.) Players Press Inc., Box 1132, Studio City, CA 91604.

658   US
PROFITMAKER. ceased 1990. bi-m. National Retail Merchants Association, 100 W. 31 St., New York, NY 10001.

631.5   BL   ISSN 0100-5316
HD1875.S3
PROGNOSTICO REGIAO CENTRO-SUL. 1974-1985. a. Instituto de Economia Agricola, Servico de Biblioteca e Documentacao, Av. Miguel Estefano 3900, Caixa Postal 8114, 04301 Sao Paulo S.P., Brazil.

677 US
PROGRAM NEWS. ceased. bi-m. Clemson University, College of Industrial Management and Textile Science, Office of Professional Development, Clemson, SC 29631.

001.642 US
PROGRAMMER'S JOURNAL; the resource journal for IBM micro programmers. 1983-1991. bi-m. (also avail. in microfiche; back issues avail.) Miller Freeman Inc., 600 Harrison St., San Francisco, CA 94107.

631.8 US ISSN 0730-7322
S631
PROGRESS (MUSCLE SHOALS). 1966-1986. a. Tennessee Valley Authority, Office of Agriculture and Chemical Development, National Fertilizer Development Center, Muscle Shoals, AL 35660.
Former titles: National Fertilizer Development Center. Annual Report (ISSN 0077-4510); Tennessee Valley Authority. Agricultural and Chemical Development Annual Report.

630 CN
PROGRESS IN AGRICULTURE. (Supplement to: Lethbridge Magazine) 1984-1990. a. 248684 Alberta Ltd., Box 1203, Lethbridge, Alta. T1J 4A4, Canada.

618 US ISSN 0361-0233
QP93.5 CODEN: PCFTDS
PROGRESS IN CHEMICAL FIBRINOLYSIS AND THROMBOLYSIS. 1975-1978 (vol.3). irreg. Raven Press, 1185 Avenue of the Americas, New York, NY 10036.
Formerly: International Conference on Synthetic Fibronolytic--Thrombolytic Agents. Proceedings.

615.9 US ISSN 0079-6158
RA1221 CODEN: PCTXA5
PROGRESS IN CHEMICAL TOXICOLOGY. 1963-1975 (no.5). irreg. (reprint service avail. from ISI) Academic Press, Inc., 1250 Sixth Ave., San Diego, CA 92101.

616.8 612 SZ ISSN 0378-4045
CODEN: PCNEDN
PROGRESS IN CLINICAL NEUROPHYSIOLOGY. 1977-1983 (vol.10). irreg. (back issues avail.) S. Karger AG, Allschwilerstr. 10, P.O. Box, CH-4009 Basel, Switzerland.

621.381 US ISSN 1052-6692
PROGRESS IN COMPUTER-AIDED V L S I DESIGN. 1989-199? irreg. Ablex Publishing Corporation, 355 Chestnut St., Norwood, NJ 07648.

610 SZ ISSN 0254-623X
PROGRESS IN CRITICAL CARE MEDICINE. 1984-19?? irreg. (reprint sevice avail.; back issues avail.) S. Karger AG, Alschwilerstr. 10, P.O. Box, CH-4009 Basel, Switzerland.

001.53 US ISSN 0275-8717
CODEN: PCSREK
PROGRESS IN CYBERNETICS AND SYSTEMS RESEARCH. 1975-1982 (no.9). irreg. (back issues avail.; reprint service avail. from UMI) Hemisphere Publishing Corporation (Subsidiary of: Taylor & Francis Group), 1900 Frost Rd., Ste. 101, Bristol, PA 19007-1598.

658.8 UK ISSN 0952-4452
PROGRESS IN MARKETING. 1989-1991. a. Pinter Publishers Ltd., 25 Floral St., London WC2E 9DS, England.

618 UK ISSN 0261-0140
PROGRESS IN OBSTETRICS AND GYNAECOLOGY. 1981-198? a. Churchill Livingstone Medical Journals, Robert Stevenson House, 1-3 Baxter's Pl., Leith Walk, Edinburgh EH1 3AF, Scotland.

530 US
PROGRESS IN PHYSICS. 1981-1991; suspended. irreg. Birkhaeuser Boston, Inc., 675 Massachusetts Ave., Cambridge, MA 02139-3309.

671 US ISSN 0079-6719
TN695 CODEN: PPWMAA
PROGRESS IN POWDER METALLURGY. 1947-1987 (vol. 43). a. Metal Powder Industries Federation, 105 College Rd. E., Princeton, NJ 08540.

551.4 623.82 UK ISSN 0959-2822
PROGRESS IN UNDERWATER SCIENCE. N.S. 1974?-1990? a. Underwater Association, 59 Ramsgate Rd., Margate, Kent CT9 5SA, England.

636.089 SZ ISSN 0255-3686
PROGRESS IN VETERINARY MICROBIOLOGY AND IMMUNOLOGY. 1985-1989 (vol.5). irreg. (approx. 1/yr.). (reprint service avail.) S. Karger AG, Allschwilerstr. 10, P.O. Box, CH-4009 Basel, Switzerland.

379.73 US
PROGRESS OF EDUCATION IN THE UNITED STATES OF AMERICA. ceased 1984. biennial. U.S. Department of Education, Washington, DC 20202.
Formerly: Progress of Public Education in the United States (ISSN 0079-6891)

940 UK
PROJECT DEFNYDDIAU AC ADNODDAU Y SWYDDFA GYMREIG. 1982-1988. irreg. (Welsh Joint Education Committee) University of Wales Press, 6 Gwennyth St., Cathays, Cardiff CF2 4YD, Wales.

331 NE
PROJECT PERSONEELSVOORZIENING KWARTAIRE SECTOR. BULLETIN. 1979-1989 (no.13). irreg. Sociaal en Cultureel Planbureau, J.C. van Markenlaan 3, 2285 VL Rijswijk, Netherlands.

333.9 US ISSN 0079-6956
PROJECT SKYWATER. ANNUAL REPORT. 1967-1986. a. U.S. Bureau of Reclamation, Denver Office, Box 25007, Denver Federal Center, Denver, CO 80225.

658 US
PROJECT UPDATE. 1988-1989. m. American Management Association, 135 W. 50th St., New York, NY 10020.

669 SP ISSN 0214-3135
PROMECANICA; revista internacional, sobre temas de maquinas-herramienta y metalurgia en general. ceased. 4/yr. Prensa XXI, S.A., Avda Paral.lel, 180, Apdo. No. 350 F.D., 08015 Barcelona, Spain.

055.1 IT
PROMETEO (MESSINA); rivista di cultura. 1981-1989 (no.37). q. Edizioni Prometeo, Piazza A.M. di Francia, 9, I-98100 Messina, Italy.

659.1 US ISSN 0891-1681
PROMOTION DIGEST. 1984-199? bi-m. (looseleaf format; back issues avail.) Commerce Communications, Inc., 5247 Washburn Ave., S., Minneapolis, MN 55410.

551.46 JA
PROMPT REPORT OF THE SCIENTIFIC SURVEY OF THE SOUTH PACIFIC. 1984-1987. irreg. Kagoshima Daigaku, Nanpo Kaiiki Kenkyu Senta - Kagoshima University, Research Center for the South Pacific, 21-24 Koorimoto 1-chome, Kagoshima-shi, Kagoshima-ken 890, Japan.

820 808.81 UK ISSN 0305-7992
PROOF. 1974-1989. 2/yr. Lincolnshire and Humberside Arts, St. Hughs, Newport, Lincoln LN1 3DN, England.

530 US ISSN 0888-6903
QD65 CODEN: PDUPEV
PROPERTY DATA UPDATE. 1987-198? q. (also avail. in microform from UMI; reprint service avail. from UMI) (National Standard Reference Data Service of the U S S R, UR) Hemisphere Publishing Corporation (Subsidiary of: Taylor & Francis Group), 1900 Frost Rd., Ste. 101, Bristol, PA 19007-1598.

333.33 UK ISSN 0267-4173
PROPERTY MONTHLY REVIEW. 1979-198? m. (back issues avail.) Industrial Newspapers Ltd., Queensway House, 2 Queensway, Redhill, Surrey RH1 1QS, England.

617.6 613.7 US
PROPHYWAYS. 1949-198? s-a. (tabloid format; back issues avail.) Florida Dental Hygienists' Association, Inc., Box 948113, Maitland, FL 32794-8113.

370 UK ISSN 0033-1511
PROSPECTIVES. 1965-1989 (vol.25, no.4). 4/yr. Centre d'Animation, de Developpement et de Recherche en Education (C.A.D.R.E.), 1940 Est, bd. Henri Bourassa, Montreal, Que. H2B 1S2, Canada.

808.81 UK ISSN 0308-2776
PROSPICE. 1973-19?? q. Prospice Publishing Ltd., P.O. Box 18, Buxton, Derbys. SK17 6YP, England.
Incorporates: Moorlands Review.

640.73 CN ISSN 0701-8525
PROTECT YOURSELF. 1973-1991 (Apr.). m. Office de la Protection du Consommateur, 5199 Sherbrooke St., E., Ste. 2580, Montreal, Que. H1T 3X1, Canada.

574.2 US ISSN 0736-4547
CODEN: PRABDK
PROTEIN ABNORMALITIES. 1982-19?? irreg. Wiley-Liss, Inc., 41 E. 11th St., New York, NY 10003.

612.015 612 UK ISSN 0950-0596
PROTEIN SECRETION. ceased 1989. m. (looseleaf format; back issues avail.) Sheffield University Biomedical Information Service (SUBIS), The University, Sheffield S10 2TN, England.

612.015 UK ISSN 0261-4901
PROTEIN SEPARATION. ceased 1990. m. (looseleaf format; back issues avail.) Sheffield University Biomedical Information Service (SUBIS), The University, Sheffield S10 2TN, England.

574.192 UK ISSN 0142-8306
PROTEIN SYNTHESIS. ceased 1990. m. (looseleaf format; back issues avail.) Sheffield University Biomedical Information Service (SUBIS), The University, Sheffield S10 2TN, England.

809 IT ISSN 0033-1848
PROVE DI LETTERATURA. 1960-1983. bi-m. (tabloid format) Nino Palumbo, Ed. & Pub., Via Ai Castagneti 4, San Michele di Pagana (Rapallo), Italy.

338 IT ISSN 0033-1910
PROVINCIA DI PADOVA IN CIFRE. 1935-19??; suspended. q. Camera di Commercio, Industria, Artigianato e Agricoltura di Padova, Via F. Filiberto 64, Padua, Italy.

331.1 US
PROVISIONS OF CALIFORNIA COLLECTIVE BARGAINING AGREEMENTS. 1977-19?? biennial. (back issues avail.) Department of Industrial Relations, Division of Labor Statistics and Research, Box 603, San Francisco, CA 94101.

330 016 PL ISSN 0032-8138
PRZEGLAD BIBLIOGRAFICZNY PISMIENNICTWA EKONOMICZNEGO. 1946-1989 (nos.4-6). bi-m. Panstwowe Wydawnictwo Ekonomiczne, Niecala 4a, 00-098 Warsaw, Poland.

330 PL
PRZEGLAD GOSPODARCZY. 1968-19?? m. (Polskie Towarzystwo Ekonomiczne, Oddzial we Wroclawiu) Wydawnictwa Czasopism Technicznych, N.O.T, Czackiego 3-5, Warsaw, Poland.

630 PL ISSN 0324-8739
PRZEMYSLOWY INSTYTUT MASZYN ROLNICZYCH. PRACE. 1960-1990; suspended. q. Przemyslowy Instytut Maszyn Rolniczych, Branzowy Osrodek Informacji Naukowej, Technicznej i Ekonomicznej, Ul. Starolecka 31, 60-963 Poznan, Poland.

616.97 SZ ISSN 0250-8087
PSEUDO-ALLERGIC REACTIONS; involvement of drugs and chemicals. 1980-1985 (vol.4). irreg. (reprint service avail. from ISI) S. Karger AG, P.O. Box, CH-4009 Basel, Switzerland.

616.89 PL ISSN 0033-2674
CODEN: PSPOB3
PSYCHIATRIA POLSKA. 1967-19?? bi-m. (Polskie Towarzystwo Psychiatryczne) Panstwowy Zaklad Wydawnictw Lekarskich, Dluga 38-40, Warsaw, Poland.

616.8 011 US ISSN 1042-041X
PSYCHIATRIC ABSTRACT AND COMMENT. 1989-1991 (Oct.). 10/yr. Churchill Livingstone Medical Journals, 650 Ave. of the Americas, New York, NY 10011.

616.8 UK ISSN 0262-9283
RC321
PSYCHIATRIC DEVELOPMENTS; advances and prospects in research and clinical practice. 1983-19?? 4/yr. (also avail. in microform from UMI) Oxford University Press, Oxford Journals, Pinkhill House, Southfield Road, Eynsham, Oxford OX8 1JJ, England.

616.8 GW ISSN 0033-2739
PSYCHIATRIE, NEUROLOGIE UND MEDIZINISCHE PSYCHOLOGIE; Zeitschrift fuer die gesamte Nervenheilkunde und Psychotherapie. 1949-1991. m. S. Hirzel Verlag Leipzig, Sternwartstr. 8, 7010 Leipzig, Germany.

5264 CESSATIONS

700 150.19 974 US
PSYCHOANALYTIC PERSPECTIVES ON ART. 1985-1988 (vol.3). a. (back issues avail.) Analytic Press, 365 Broadway, Hillsdale, NJ 07642.

150.19 AG ISSN 0325-6502
PSYCHOLOGICA; revista argentina de psicologia realista. suspended 1983 (no.6). s-a. Fundacion Arche de Altos Etudios Antropologicos, Rodriguez Pena 778, 1020 Buenos Aires, Argentina.

616.89 GW
PSYCHOLOGIE-ALMANACH. 1987-1989. biennial. Dr Lothar Rossipaul Verlagsgesellschaft mbH, Bavariaring 24, 8000 Munich 2, Germany.

150 SZ
PSYCHOLOGIE IM GESPRAECH; ein Forum der psychologischen Auseinandersetzung. 1964-1990 (vol.26). bi-m. Ausbildungszentrum fuer Individualpsychologische Psychotherapie und -analyse, Schaffhauserstr. 345, CH-8050 Zurich, Switzerland.
   Formerly: Psychologische Menschenkenntnis (ISSN 0033-3034)

301.1 900 GW ISSN 0935-0179
PSYCHOLOGIE UND GESCHICHTE. 1989-1991. q. Asanger Verlag GmbH, Rohrbacher Str. 89, 6900 Heidelberg, Germany.

615.19 616.8 UK ISSN 0142-8411
PSYCHOPHARMACOLOGY. ceased 1990. m. (looseleaf format; back issues avail.) Sheffield University Biomedical Information Service (SUBIS), The University, Sheffield S10 2TN, England.

616.8 UK ISSN 0143-7593
PSYCHOTHERAPY. ceased 1989. m. (looseleaf format; back issues avail.) Sheffield University Biomedical Information Service (SUBIS), The University, Sheffield S10 2TN, England.

616.89 US ISSN 0737-0938
PSYCHOTHERAPY NEWSLETTER. 1983-198? q. Center for Gestalt Development, Inc., Box 990, Highland, NY 12528.

350 016 US ISSN 0193-970X
PUBLIC ADMINISTRATION SERIES: BIBLIOGRAPHY. (Subseries avail.: Recent Transportation Literature for Planning and Engineering Librarians) 1978-1991. 20/m. (back issues avail.) Vance Bibliographies, 112 N. Charter St., Box 229, Monticello, IL 61856.

350 340 320 US ISSN 0735-4703
KF5401.A75
PUBLIC ADMINISTRATOR AND THE COURTS. 1985-1991. q. (back issues avail.) Research Publications, Inc. (Asheville), 92 Fairway Dr., Asheville, NC 28805.

350 320 US
PUBLIC AFFAIRS BULLETIN. 1959-198? 5/yr. University of South Carolina, Institute of Public Affairs, Columbia, SC 29208.
   Supersedes (in 1978): University of South Carolina Governmental Review (ISSN 0042-0050)

350 026 US
PUBLIC DOCUMENTS HIGHLIGHTS FOR TEXAS. 1978-1989 (Spr.). q. State Library, Information Services Division, Box 12927, Austin, TX 78711.

370 US
PUBLIC EDUCATION IN VIRGINIA. 1965-1987 (Winter). q. (back issues avail.) Department of Education, Box 6-Q, Richmond, VA 23216.

331 US
PUBLIC EMPLOYEE BARGAINING. 1977-1990 (May). bi-w. Commerce Clearing House, Inc., 4025 W. Peterson Ave., Chicago, IL 60646.

610 614 UN ISSN 0300-4880
CODEN: PHEUDR
PUBLIC HEALTH IN EUROPE. 1972-19?? (no.29). irreg. World Health Organization, Regional Office for Europe, Scherfigsvej 8, 2100 Copenhagen OE, Denmark.

020 US ISSN 0555-6031
Z671
PUBLIC LIBRARY REPORTERS. 1954-1985 (no.21). irreg. (reprint service avail. from UMI) (Public Library Association) American Library Association, 50 E. Huron St., Chicago, IL 60611-2795.

659.1 UK ISSN 0263-6166
PUBLIC RELATIONS. 1982-19?? q. (Institute of Public Relations) Longman Group (UK) Ltd., Fourth Ave., Harlow, Essex CM19 5AA, England.

659.1 330 US
PUBLIC RELATIONS CUES & COUPS. 1983-1989; suspended. bi-m. (looseleaf format) Jerryend Communications, Inc., RD 2, Box 356H, Birdsboro, PA 19508-9328.

600 352 US ISSN 0882-1445
PUBLIC TECHNOLOGY. 1979-1991. m. Public Technology, Inc., 1301 Pennsylvania Ave., N.W., Washington, DC 20004.
   Formerly: Public Technology News.

663.4 UK
PUBLICAN MONITOR. ceased 1991 (Oct.). q. (back issues avail.) Euromonitor, 87-88 Turnmill St., London EC1M 5QR, England.
   Formerly: Pub Monitor.

301.45 US
PUBLICATIONS ON ETHNICITY AND NATIONALITY. 1979-198? irreg. University of Washington Press, Box 50096, Seattle, WA 98105.

659 US
PUBLICIST. 1976-19?? bi-m. (Public Relations Aids) P R A Group, c/o P R Aids, Inc., 307 W. 36th St., New York, NY 10018.
   Former titles: Publicity Break; Publicist.

001.647 659.1 US
PUBLICITY OPPORTUNITIES. ceased. m. (Association of Data Processing Service Organization) A D A S P O, The Computer Software and Services Industry Association, 1300 N. 17th St., Ste. 300, Arlington, VA 22209.

382 UK
PUBLISHED DATA ON EUROPEAN INDUSTRIAL MARKETS. 1971-1985. irreg. I A L Consultants Ltd., 14 Buckingham Palace Rd., London SW1W 0QP, England.

382 UK
PUBLISHED DATA ON MIDDLE & FAR EAST INDUSTRIAL MARKETS. 1983-1985. irreg. I A L Consultants Ltd., 14 Buckingham Palace Rd., London SW1W 0QP, England.

070.5 US ISSN 0885-6214
PUBLISHING AND NEW MEDIA TECHNOLOGY NEWSLETTER. ceased 1990. 26/yr. (also avail. in microform; back issues avail.) (Research Association for the Paper and Board, Printing and Packaging Industries, UK) Pergamon Press, Inc., Journals Division, 660 White Plains Rd., Tarrytown, NY 10591-5153.

073 GW
PUBLIZISTIK-HISTORISCHE BEITRAEGE. ceased 1991. irreg. K.G. Saur Verlag KG, Ortlerstr. 8, Postfach 701620, 8000 Munich 70, Germany.

070 016 GW ISSN 0552-6981
PUBLIZISTIKWISSENSCHAFTLICHER REFERATEDIENST. 1966-1991. a. (Freie Universitaet Berlin, Institut fuer Publizistik und Dokumentationswissenschaft) K.G. Saur Verlag KG, Ortlerstr. 8, Postfach 701620, 8000 Munich 70, Germany.

056.1 PE
PUEBLO INDIO. 1981-1988 (no.15). bi-m. (Consejo Indio de Sud America - Indian Council of South America) Empresa Editora Alternativa, Apdo. Postal 2054, Correo Central, Lima 100, Peru.

056.1 US ISSN 1041-2026
PUERTA DEL SOL. 1988-1991 (May). m. (audio cassette; with printed transcription) Champs-Elysees Inc., Box 158067, Nashville, TN 37215-8067.

350 PR
PUERTO RICO. OFICINA DE PRESUPUESTO Y GERENCIA. REVISTA. 1952-1984. irreg. (approx. 1-2/yr.). Oficina de Presupuesto y Gerencia - Office of Budget and Management, Cruz 254, Apto. 3228, San Juan, PR 00902.
   Former titles: Puerto Rico. Oficina de Presupuesto y Gerencia. Boletin de Presupuesto y Gerencia; Puerto Rico. Negociado del Presupuesto. Boletin de Gerencia Administrativa.

621.381 US
PUGET SOUND SMALL SYSTEM USERS GROUP NEWSLETTER. ceased. m. (Puget Sound Small System Users Group) K F H Publications, Inc., 3530 Bagley Ave. N., Seattle, WA 98403.

659.152 IT
PULL. ceased. q. Zanfi Editori s.r.l., Via Ganaceto 121, P.O. Box 433, 41100 Modena, Italy.

388.3 US
PULLING POWER. ceased. bi-m. Four Wheeler Publishing (Subsidiary of: General Media Publishing Group), 6718 Eton Ave., Conoga Park, CA 91303.

616.2 US ISSN 0272-7900
RC756
PULMONARY DISEASE REVIEWS. 1980-1984 (vol.5). irreg. John Wiley & Sons, Inc., 605 Third Ave., New York, NY 10158-0012.

676 US ISSN 0277-0156
HD9821
PULP & PAPER WEEK PRICE - EXPORT-IMPORT DATABOOK. ceased 1980. a. Miller Freeman Publications, Inc., 500 Howard St., San Francisco, CA 94105.

808.838 US
PULPHOUSE: THE HARDBACK MAGAZINE. 1988-1992 (no.12). irreg. (back issues avail.) Pulphouse Publishing, Inc., Box 1227, Eugene, OR 97440.

051 US ISSN 0276-0436
AP2
PULPSMITH (YEAR). 1964-1990. a. (also avail. in microform from UMI; microfilm) (Generalist Association) Harry Smith, Ed. & Pub., 69 Joralemon St., Brooklyn, NY 11201.
   Former titles (until 1981): Smith; Pulpsmith.

827 UK ISSN 0033-4278
AP101
PUNCH. 1841-1992. w. (also avail. in microform from UMI; reprint service avail. from UMI) Punch Publications Ltd., 23-27 Tudor St., London EC4Y 0HR, England.

610 UK
PUNCH DIGEST FOR DOCTORS. 1982-1991. m. Punch Publications Ltd., Ludgate House, 245 Blackfriars Rd., London SE1 9UZ, England.

028.5 053.1 GW ISSN 0178-9953
DER PUNKT; Schuelerzeitung am Karlsgymnasium. 1981-1986. q. (back issues avail.) Karlsgymnasium, Tuebingerstr. 38, 7000 Stuttgart 1, Germany.

700 780 DK ISSN 0901-5469
PUNKT 95. 1985-1989 (Dec.). 3/yr. Herluf Trollesvej 15 A, DK-4200 Slagelse, Denmark.

658 US
PURCHASINGWORLD. 1958-1991. m. Huebcore Communications, Inc., 29100 Aurora Rd., Ste. 200, Solon, OH 44139.

530 621 ISSN 0079-8193
CODEN: PAPHAP
PURE AND APPLIED PHYSICS; a series of monographs and textbooks. ceased 1986 (vol.43). irreg. (reprint service avail. from ISI) Academic Press, Inc., 1250 Sixth Ave., San Diego, CA 92101.

574.192 UK ISSN 0260-1141
PURINES. (Current awareness service for researchers in clinical and life sciences) ceased 1990. m. Sheffield University Biomedical Information Service (SUBIS), The University, Sheffield S10 2TN, England.

181.45 US ISSN 0930-8857
PURNA YOGA. 1977-199? 2/yr. Atmaniketan Ashram, 1291 Weber St., Pomona, CA 91769.

CESSATIONS

309.2   MY
PURNAMA RAYA. 1974; ceased same year. q. Urban Development Authority - Perbadanan Pembangunan Bandar, Peti Surat 10080, 50704 Kuala Lumpur, Malaysia.

636.8   US   ISSN 0731-0366
PURRRRR!; the newsletter for cat lovers. 1982-1990? bi-m. (back issues avail.) Islesboro Publishing, HCR 227, Islesboro, ME 04848.

793   UK
PUZZLES FOR PLEASURE. 1975-19?? m. A I M Publications, Carnaby House, 27-29 Beak St., London W1, England.

320 301 330 100   US   ISSN 0738-9752
B823.3
Q J I. (Quarterly Journal of Ideology) 1976-19?? q. University of Auburn, Department of Sociology, Montgoery, AL 36193.

362   UK   ISSN 0265-7848
Q P S REPORTER. 1968-1991. q. Quaker Peace and Service, Friends House, Euston Rd., London NW1 2BJ, England.
Former titles: Quaker Peace and Service (ISSN 0141-5352); Peace Action Newsletter; Quaker Service (ISSN 0306-283X)

001.3 300   US   ISSN 0950-0332
Q X. (Questioning Exchange) 1987-198? 3/yr. Taylor & Francis, Inc., 242 Cherry St., Philadelphia, PA 19106-1906.

808 851   IT   ISSN 0393-7496
PQ4001
QUADERNI DI RETORICA E POETICA. 1985-1987 (vol.3, no.2). s-a. Liviana Editrice s.r.l., Via L. Dottesio 1, 35138 Padua, Italy.

940   IT
QUADERNI DI STUDI STORICI TOSCANI. ceased. irreg., 3-4/yr. (Centro di Studi Storici Toscani) Libreria L. del Re, Via dei Pucci 45 R., 50122 Florence, Italy.

055.1 056.9   IT
QUADERNI LATINOAMERICANI. 1988-198? (no.9-10). s-a. Edizioni Scientifiche Italiane s.p.a., Via Chiatamone, 7, I-80121 Naples, Italy.

616.075   IT   ISSN 0033-4979
CODEN: QSDCAJ
QUADERNI SCLAVO DI DIAGNOSTICA CLINICA E DI LABORATORIO. 1965-1989; suspended. q. Sclavo S. p.A., Via Fiorentina 1, 53100 Siena, Italy.

913   SP   ISSN 0210-8291
QUADERNS DE TREBALL. ceased 1982 (no.5). irreg. Universidad Autonoma de Barcelona, Departament de Prehistoria i Arqueologia, Servici de Publicacion, Apdo. de Correos, 28, 08193 Bellatera, Spain.

595.7   CN   ISSN 0033-5037
CODEN: QUENB4
QUAESTIONES ENTOMOLOGICAE; a periodical record of entomological investigation. 1965-1990 (vol.26). q. (also avail. in microform from UMI) University of Alberta, Department of Entomology, Edmonton, Alta. T6G 2E3, Canada.

289.6   UK
QUAKER INFORMATION NETWORK. 1986-1991 (Apr.). 6/yr. Friends World Committee for Consultation, Drayton House, 30 Gordon St., London WC1H 0AX, England.

289.6   UK
QUAKER SOCIAL RESPONSIBILITY & EDUCATION JOURNAL. 1979-1990. 3/yr. Quaker Social Responsibility & Education, Friends House, Euston Rd., London NW1 2BJ, England.

360   UK
QUALITY ASSURANCE ABSTRACTS. 1986-1992 (vol.6). bi-m. Departments of Health and Social Security, Hannibal House, Elephant and Castle, London SE1 6TE, England.

616.1   US   ISSN 0748-6901
QUALITY OF LIFE AND CARDIOVASCULAR CARE. 1984-19?? q. (also avail. in microform from UMI) (Emory University, School of Medicine) Haymarket Doyma Inc., 53 Park Pl., New York, NY 10007.

658   US   ISSN 0892-0087
TS156.A1
QUALITY REVIEW. 1987-1990. q. American Society for Quality Control (New York), 253 W. 73rd St., New York, NY 10023.

660   US
QUANTUM (CINCINNATI). 1960-19?? q. Quantum Chemical Corporation, U S I Division, 11501 Northlake Dr., Cincinnati, OH 45249.
Formerly: U S I News (United States Industrial Chemicals Co.).

301.412   US   ISSN 8756-520X
QUARANTE; magazine for the woman who has arrived. 1984-1991. q. Box 2875, Arlington, VA 22202.

315   UN   ISSN 0125-0019
JX1977
QUARTERLY BULLETIN OF STATISTICS FOR ASIA AND THE PACIFIC. 1973-1987 (vol.17, no.4). q. United Nations Economic and Social Commission for Asia and the Pacific (ESCAP), United Nations Bldg., Rajadamnern Ave., Bangkok 2, Thailand.
Formerly: Quarterly Bulletin of Statistics for Asia and the Far East (ISSN 0048-6159)

330.9
QUARTERLY BUSINESS STARTS. 1978-19?? q. Dun & Bradstreet, Economic Analysis Department, 299 Park Ave., New York, NY 10171.
Formerly: Quarterly Business Starts Report.

636.089   US   ISSN 0740-2430
QUARTERLY INDEX: INFORMATION ACCESS FOR THE SMALL ANIMAL PRACTITIONER. 1983-199? q. Veterinary Interface, 5679 Claribel Rd., Oakdale, CA 95361-9353.

574 016   US   ISSN 0196-5530
Z5321
QUARTERLY INDEX TO CURRENT CONTENTS - LIFE SCIENCES. (Includes Author Index, Journal Index, and Permuterm Subject Index) 1980-1983. 4/yr. Institute for Scientific Information, 3501 Market St., Philadelphia, PA 19104.

360   US
QUARTERLY PUBLIC ASSISTANCE STATISTICS. (ORS Report A-12) ceased. q. U.S. Social Security Administration, Office of Research, Statistics and International Policy, 1875 Connecticut Ave., N.W., Washington, DC 20009.
Formed by the merger of: U.S. Social Security Administration. Office of Research and Statistics. Public Assistance Statistics (ISSN 0145-952X); U.S. Social Security Administration. Applications and Case Dispositions for Public Assistance (ISSN 0360-6848)

651.8   US   ISSN 0882-8679
QUARTERLY REPORT; a word processing newsletter. 1985-1986 (Apr.). q. (looseleaf format; back issues avail.) c/o Janet R. Wilson, Ed., 817 30th Ave. S., Seattle, WA 98144-3205.

658.8   UK   ISSN 0307-7667
HF5415
QUARTERLY REVIEW OF MARKETING. 1961-1990 (Oct.). q. (Chartered Institute of Marketing) Marketing House Publishers Ltd, Moor Hall, Cookham, Maidenhead, Berks. SL6 9QH, England.
Incorporates: Marketing Forum (ISSN 0542-7363)

070.5 011   UK   ISSN 0265-5837
QUARTERLY SERIAL BULLETIN. 1983-1991. 4/yr. Dawson UK Ltd., Cannon House, Folkestone, Kent CT19 5EE, England.

333.7 016   CN
QUEBEC (PROVINCE). DEPARTEMENT D'ENERGIE ET RESOURCES. REPERTOIRE DES PUBLICATIONS. ceased. a. Department of Energy and Resources, 3700 4e Ave. Ouest, Charlesbourg, Que. G1H 6R1, Canada, Canada.
Formerly: Quebec (Province). Ministere des Richesses Naturelles. Repertoire des Publications.

574   CN
QUEBEC (PROVINCE). MINISTERE DE L'AGRICULTURE, DES PECHERIES ET DE L'ALIMENTATION. DIRECTION GENERALE DES PECHES MARITIMES. TRAVAUX SUR LES PECHERIES. 1964-1984 (no.50). irreg. (3-4/yr.). Ministere de l'Agriculture, des Pecheries et de l'Alimentation, Bureau des Echanges, C.P. 340, Grande Riviere, Cte. de Gaspe, Que. G0C 1V0, Canada.

331 340   CN   ISSN 0700-1681
LAW
QUEBEC (PROVINCE) MINISTERE DU TRAVAIL ET DE LA MAIN D'OEUVRE. JURISPRUDENCE EN DROIT DU TRAVAIL: TRIBUNAL DU TRAVAIL. 1970-19?? q. Ministere du Travail et de la Main d'Oeuvre, Centre de Recherche et de Statistiques sur le Marche du Travail, 425 rue St. Amable, Quebec City, Que. G1R 4Z1, Canada.

368.4 658.3   CN   ISSN 0712-8231
HD7105.45.C2
QUEBEC (PROVINCE). REGIE DES RENTES DU QUEBEC. STATISTICAL OUTLOOK. 1982-1984. a. Regie des Rentes du Quebec, C.P. 5200, Quebec, Que. G1K 7S9, Canada.

338   CN   ISSN 0033-5975
QUEBEC INDUSTRIEL. 1946-19?? m. (also avail. in microfilm) Maclean-Hunter Ltd., Business Publication Division, 1001 ouest, blvd de Maisonneuve, Ste. 1000, Montreal, Que. H3A 3E1, Canada.

572   US
QUEENS COLLEGE PUBLICATIONS IN ANTHROPOLOGY. 1975-198? a. (back issues avail.) Queens College Press, c/o Dyanne Maue, Kiely 1309, Flushing, NY 11367.

020   US   ISSN 0146-8677
QUEENS COLLEGE STUDIES IN LIBRARIANSHIP. 1977-19?? irreg. (approx. 1/yr.). (back issues avail.) Queens College Press, c/o Dyanne Maue, Kiely 1309, Flushing, NY 11367.

331.1   CN   ISSN 0317-2546
QUEEN'S UNIVERSITY. INDUSTRIAL RELATIONS CENTRE. RESEARCH AND CURRENT ISSUES SERIES. 1964-1990. irreg. Queen's University, Industrial Relations Centre, Kingston, Ont. K7L 3N6, Canada.
Formerly: Queen's University. Industrial Relations Centre. Research Series (ISSN 0075-6164)

027.7   CN
QUEEN'S UNIVERSITY AT KINGSTON. ANNUAL REPORT ON THE LIBRARIES. ceased 197? a. Queen's University, Kingston, Ont. K7L 3N6, Canada.

331.1   CN   ISSN 0075-6156
HD8102
QUEEN'S UNIVERSITY AT KINGSTON. INDUSTRIAL RELATIONS CENTRE. REPRINT SERIES. 1961-1991. irreg. Queen's University, Industrial Relations Centre, Kingston, Ont. K7L 3N6, Canada.

371.2   AT
QUEENSLAND. DEPARTMENT OF EDUCATION. INFORMATION AND PUBLICATIONS BRANCH. DOCUMENT. 1973-19?? irreg. Department of Education, Information and Publications Branch, P.O. Box 33, North Quay, Qld. 4000, Australia.
Formerly: Queensland. Department of Education. Research and Curriculum Branch. Document (ISSN 0310-4087)

375   AT
QUEENSLAND. DEPARTMENT OF EDUCATION. INFORMATION AND PUBLICATIONS BRANCH. INFORMATION STATEMENT. ceased. irreg. Department of Education, Information and Publications Branch, P.O. Box 33, North Quay, Qld. 4000, Australia.
Formerly: Queensland. Department of Education. Research and Curriculum Branch. Information Statement (ISSN 0310-5121)

375   AT
QUEENSLAND. DEPARTMENT OF EDUCATION. RESEARCH BRANCH. REPORTING RESEARCH. 1971-19?? irreg. Department of Education, Research Branch, P.O. Box 33, North Quay, Qld. 4000, Australia.
Formerly: Queensland. Department of Education. Research and Curriculum Branch. Reporting Research (ISSN 0310-4095)

630   AT   ISSN 0157-7786
QUEENSLAND AGRICULTURAL JOURNAL. 1897-1989; suspended. bi-m. Department of Primary Industries, Brisbane, Australia.

319   AT   ISSN 1031-279X
QUEENSLAND IN RELATION TO AUSTRALIA. 1971-1990. a. Australian Bureau of Statistics, Queensland Office, 313 Adelaide St., Brisbane, Qld. 4000, Australia.

CESSATIONS

670 AT
QUEENSLAND MANUFACTURERS DIRECTORY. ceased. irreg. Department of Industry Development, Enterprise House, 46 Charlotte St., Brisbane, Qld. 4000, Australia.

330.9 AT
QUEENSLAND PROFILE. 1984-1988. a. Department of Industry Development, Enterprise House, 46 Charlotte St., Brisbane, Qld. 4000, Australia.

388 AT ISSN 0048-6388
QUEENSLAND ROADS. 1962-1989. a. Main Roads Department, Box 1412, Brisbane, Qld. 4001, Australia.

808.81 US
QUERCUS. ceased. a. Sacramento Poetry Center, 1727 I St., Sacramento, CA 95814.

808 US
QUI-LIGHT. 1983-198?; suspended. q. (back issues avail.) Twilight Society of America, 140-10 Franklin Ave., Flushing, NY 11355.

664.028 US ISSN 0033-6408
TP493.5
QUICK FROZEN FOODS. 1938-1985. m. (also avail. in microform from UMI; reprint service avail. from UMI) Harcourt Brace Jovanovich, Inc., 7500 Old Oak Blvd., Cleveland, OH 44130.

664.028 US ISSN 0079-9289
QUICK FROZEN FOODS DIRECTORY OF FROZEN FOOD PROCESSORS. 1945-1985. a. Harcourt Brace Jovanovich, Inc., 7500 Old Oak Blvd., Cleveland, OH 44130.

800 700 770 US
QUIMBY. 1985-19?? (no.33). bi-m. (back issues avail.) Quimby Archives, Box 281, Astor Sta., Boston, MA 02123.

683 FR
QUINCAILLERIE MODERNE. ceased. m. Societe d'Edition et de Presse, 106 bd. Malesherbes, 75828 Paris, France.

793 UK ISSN 0952-8148
QUIZ TRIVIA. 1985-19?? q. Keesing (UK) Ltd., Brabazon House, Linkfield Corner, Redhill, Surrey RH1 1SW, England.
Formerly (until Dec. 1987): Quiz Corner.

617 NZ ISSN 0033-6696
R.A.C.S. NEWSLETTER. 1925-19?? q. (Royal Australasian College of Surgeons) Otago Daily Times Ltd., P.O. Box 181, Dunedin, New Zealand.

387.7 UK ISSN 0033-6718
R A E NEWS. 1948-1991. bi-m. Royal Aerospace Establishment, Building Q101, Farnborough, Hampshire GU14 6TD, England.

375.4 420 US ISSN 0884-3740
R A L REPORT; a communication on research focusing on reading and the language arts. 1984-1991. q. (back issues avail.) United Scholastic Services, Inc., Box 706, East Lansing, MI 48826.

218 US
R A R CHALLENGE. 1980-1989 (Fall). q. (back issues avail.) Interfaith Center to Reverse the Arms Race, 132 N. Euclid, Pasadena, CA 91101.
Formerly: R A R Newsletter.

600 016 US ISSN 0361-753X
R & D MANAGEMENT DIGEST; news & literature: science policy, technology assessment and transfer, federal programs, international development, programs and project management. 1971-1989 (vol.19, no.1). m. (also avail. in microform from UMI; back issues avail.; reprint service avail. from UMI) Lomond Publications, Inc., Box 88, Mt. Airy, MD 21771.

919.604 GU
R & R PACIFIC; the serviceman's guide of rest & relaxation. 1986-1990 (Dec.). m. Glimpses of Guam, Inc., P.O. Box 3191, Agana, Guam 96910.

020 371.2 AT
R B R O T A L. (Resource-Based Resource-Oriented Teaching and Learning) 1976-19?? q. Ministry of Education, 15 Royal St., East Perth, W.A. 6004, Australia.

616.858 NE
R E A P. (Research Exchange and Practice in Mental Retardation) 1975-197? 4/yr. Swets Publishing Service (Subsidiary of: Swets en Zeitlinger B.V.), Heereweg 347B, Lisse, Netherlands.

624 620 US ISSN 0885-9809
R E T S DIGEST. (Research Engineering Technical Services) 1971-1987. 3/yr. (back issues avail.) National Stone Association, 1415 Elliot Place, N.W., Washington, DC 20007.

621.3 GW ISSN 0040-1455
TK6540 CODEN: TMRFAL
R F Z. TECHNISCHE MITTEILUNGEN. 1957-1991. q. Rundfunk- und Fernsehtechnisches Zentralamt, Agastr., 1199 Berlin-Adlershof, Germany.

381 GW
R G H REFLEXE. ceased 1991. bi-m. Rationalisierungs - Gemeinschaft des Handels beim R K M, Spichernstr. 55, 5000 Cologne 1, Germany.

378 GW
R I A S-FUNKUNIVERSITAET, BERLIN. SCHRIFTENREIHE. FORSCHUNG UND INFORMATION. 1967-198? (vol. 38). irreg. Colloquium Verlag, Unter den Eichen 93, 1000 Berlin 45, Germany.
Formerly: R I A S-Funkuniversitaet, Berlin. Forschung und Information (ISSN 0067-5997)

700 US
R I L A NEWS. (Repertoire International de la Litterature de l'Art/International Repertory of the Literature of Art) ceased. irreg. (R I L A) J. Paul Getty Trust, c/o Sterling and Francine Clark Art Institute, Williamstown, MA 01267.

133.9 US
R K M PUBLISHING TAPE & BOOK CLUB BULLETIN. 1981-198? 4/yr. R K M Publishing Co., Box 23042, Euclid, OH 44123.
Formerly: R K M Publishing Newsletter.

240 CN ISSN 0079-9351
R.M. BUCKE MEMORIAL SOCIETY FOR THE STUDY OF RELIGIOUS EXPERIENCE. PROCEEDINGS OF THE CONFERENCE. 1965-1974. irreg. (back issues avail.) R.M. Bucke Memorial Society, 1033 Pine Ave. W., Montreal, Que. H3A 1A1, Canada.

612.015 UK ISSN 0142-8799
R N A. ceased 1990. m. (looseleaf format; back issues avail.) Sheffield University Biomedical Information Service (SUBIS), The University, Sheffield S10 2TN, England.

610.73 CN ISSN 0048-7112
R N A O NEWS. 1945-1991 (Oct.). bi-m. Registered Nurses Association of Ontario, 33 Price St., Toronto, Ont. M4W 1Z2, Canada.

914 FR ISSN 0033-703X
R O C. 1966-1990. w. (processed) Reseau d'Organisme Culturels, 3 rue Pasteur, 78800 Houilles, France.

300 001.3 SA
R S A 2000: DIALOGUE WITH THE FUTURE/R S A 2000: GESPREK MET DIE TOEKOMS. 1974-199? 2/yr. Centre for Science Development, Human Sciences Research Council - Sentrum vir Wetensekapontwikkeling, Raad vir Geestesetenskaplike Navorsing, Private Bag X270, Pretoria 0001, South Africa.
Formerly: R S A: Dialogue with the Future (ISSN 1011-1913)

540 UK
R S C PAPERBACK SERIES. MONOGRAPHS FOR TEACHERS. 1959-1985. irreg. Royal Society of Chemistry, Thomas Graham House, Science Park, Milton Rd., Cambridge CB4 4WF.
Former titles (until 1982): Royal Society of Chemistry. Monographs for Teachers (ISSN 0080-4428); Royal Institute of Chemistry. Monographs for Teachers.

384.5 US
R T T Y JOURNAL. BEGINNERS HANDBOOK. 1975-19?? irreg. R T T Y Journal, 9085 La Casita Ave., Fountain Valley, CA 92708.

388.3 CN
R V GUIDE. (Recreational Vehicle) 1989-1991; suspended. a. (back issues avail.) Formula Publications Ltd., 447 Speers Rd., Ste. 4, Oakville, Ont. L6K 3S7, Canada.

808 UK ISSN 0140-9069
RABIES MAGAZINE. 1977-19?? Bonefold Imprint, 68 Parkhill Rd., London NW3, England.

929 US
RADER RELATIVES NEWSLETTER. 1986-1987 (no.3); suspended. q. (looseleaf format; back issues avail.) Nathan's Writings, Box 81, Mt. Aukum, CA 95656.

540 US ISSN 0197-8039
TP156.C8
RADIATION CURING BUYER'S GUIDE. 1977-1990. a. Technology Marketing Corporation, One Technology Plaza, Norwalk, CT 06854.
Formerly: U V Curing Buyer's Guide (ISSN 0146-5031)

200 US
RADICAL OPTION. 1985-198? bi-m. (looseleaf format) Growth Associates, Box 247, Bolton, MA 01740.

051 US ISSN 0360-8212
RADICAL RELIGION; a quarterly journal of critical thought. 1973-19?? q. (also avail. in microfilm) Community for Religious Research and Education, Inc., Religious Studies Department, St. Francis College, Loretto, PA 15940-0001.

052 UK ISSN 0262-6993
RADICAL SCOTLAND. 1983-1991. bi-m. (back issues avail.) Radical Scotland Publishing Co-operative, 48 Pleasance, Edinburgh EH8 9TJ, Scotland.

621.3 UK ISSN 0262-2572
TK6540 CODEN: RELWDZ
RADIO & ELECTRONICS WORLD. 1981-198? m. (back issues avail.) Radio & Electronics World Magazines, Sovereign House, Brentwood, Essex CM14 4SE, England.
Incorporates: Radio and Electronics Constructor.

384.5 791.4 621.38 CS ISSN 0033-7676
CODEN: RDTLAW
RADIO - TELEVISION. 1950-19?? (vol.40, no.4); suspended. bi-m. International Radio and Television Organization, Skokanska 1, 169 56 Prague 6, Czechoslovakia.

384.5 US
RADIO WEEK. 1933-1992 (Mar.). w. National Association of Broadcasters, 1771 N St., N.W., Washington, DC 20036.
Incorporates (in 1988): Radioactive (ISSN 0747-4032); (in 1985): N A B Highlights; Formerly: N A B Today (Radio Edition).

615.832 GW ISSN 0033-8184
RM845 CODEN: RDBGAT
RADIOBIOLOGIA - RADIOTHERAPIA; Internationale Zeitschrift fuer das Gebiet der Strahlentherapie, Strahlenbiologie, Strahlenphysik. 1960-1990. bi-m. (reprint service avail. from ISI) Verlag Gesundheit GmbH, Neue Gruenstr. 18, 1020 Berlin, Germany.

615.8 US ISSN 0161-7516
RADIOLOGY - NUCLEAR MEDICINE INTERNATIONAL. 1979-1981. bi-m. W. G. Holdsworth & Associates, Inc., 625 E. Seegers Rd., Des Plaines, IL 60016.

800 DK ISSN 0108-8491
RADISEN; radikalt debatblad. 1982-19?? 3/yr. c/o Ejvind Mortensen, Frederikssundvej 22, Sundbylille, 3600 Frederikssund, Denmark.

200 371.8 GW ISSN 0033-8532
RADIUS. 1955-1990. q. (Evangelische Akademikerschaft in Deutschland) Radius-Verlag GmbH, Kniebisstr. 29, 7000 Stuttgart 1, Germany.

630 GW ISSN 0033-8710
RAIFFEISENBOTE. 1895-1990. m. (Bundesverband der Deutschen Volksbanken und Raiffeisenbanken e.V.) Verlag Bildpost, Alboinstr. 17-23, 1000 Berlin 42, Germany.

331.88 385 US ISSN 0033-8850
HD6350.R25
RAILWAY CARMEN'S JOURNAL. 1891-1986 (Aug.). m. Brotherhood Railway Carmen of the United States and Canada, 4929 Main St., Kansas City, MO 64112.

385 UK
RAILWAY ENGINEER. ceased 1990. 4/yr. Institution of Mechanical Engineers, Railway Division, 1 Birdcage Walk, London SW1H 9JJ, England.
Formerly (until 1980): Railway Engineering International.

027 UR
RAIONNYE BIBLIOTEKI BELORUSSII; analiz sostoyaniya raboty i metodicheskie rekomendatsii. 1957-1978. a. (also avail. in microfilm) Gosudarstvennaya Biblioteka Belorusskoi S.S.R. im V.I. Lenina, Krasnozmanennaya ul., 9, Minsk, Byelorussian S.S.R., U.S.S.R.

636.089 BL
RAIZES. 1972-198? m. Gessulli Editores Ltda., Caixa Postal 8034, 01051 Sao Paulo, SP, Brazil.
Supersedes (in 1980): Atualidades Agroveterinarias; Which was formed by the merger of: Atualidades Agronomicas & Atualidades Veterinarias.

636.2 CN
RANCHER. 1970-19?? m. Rancher Publishing, Box 1060, Adergrove, B.C. V0X 1A0, Canada.

910.202 US
RAND MCNALLY INTERSTATE ROAD ATLAS; United States, Canada, Mexico. ceased. a. Rand McNally & Co., 8255 N. Central Park, Skokie, IL 60076.

370 SA
RANDSE AFRIKAANSE UNIVERSITEIT. PROSPEKTUS. 1968-19?? a. (processed) Rand Afrikaans University, Box 524, Johannesburg 2000, South Africa.

780.42 US
RAPPIN'. 1989-1991. bi-m. Charlton Publications, Inc., Box 185, 60 Division St., Derby, CT 06418-0158.

331.1 368.4 IT ISSN 0033-9385
RASSEGNA DEL LAVORO. 1955-19?? m. (Ministero del Lavoro e della Previdenza Sociale) Istituto Poligrafico dello Stato, Libreria Dello Stato, Piazza Verdi 10, 00100 Rome, Italy.

617 IT
RASSEGNA DI MEDICINA D'URGENZA. suspended. q. Casa Editrice Idelson, Via A. De Gasperi 55, Naples 80133, Italy.

616.891 IT
RASSEGNA DI PSICOTERAPIE - IPNOSI. ceased. 3/yr. Edizioni Minerva Medica, Corso Bramante 83, 10126 Turin, Italy.

700 IT ISSN 0033-975X
RASSEGNA LUCCHESE; periodico di cultura. 1950-1986. q. Maria Pacini Fazzi, Piazza S. Alessandro 2, 55100 Lucca, Italy.

610 IT
RASSEGNA MEDICA. ENGLISH EDITION. 1923-19?? Gruppo Lepetit S.p.A., Via Roberto Lepetit 8, 20124 Milan, Italy.
Former titles (until 1974): Rassegna: Medical and Cultural Review; (until 1961): Rassegna Medica-Convivium Sanitatis.

619 US ISSN 0309-1848
CODEN: RNLEDA
RAT NEWS LETTER. 1977-1989; suspended. irreg. University of Pittsburgh School of Medicine, Department of Pathology, Pittsburgh, PA 15261.

615.1 US ISSN 0031-7020
CODEN: RDGTAP
RATIONAL DRUG THERAPY. 1967-19?? m. (also avail. in microform from UMI) American Society for Pharmacology & Experimental Therapeutics, 9650 Rockville Pike, Bethesda, MD 20814.
Formerly: Pharmacology for Physicians.

676.2 US
RAW MATERIALS FOR THE PULP AND PAPER INDUSTRY. published only once, 1984. irreg. Metal Bulletin Inc., 220 Fifth Ave., 10th Fl., New York, NY 10001.

917.306 US
LA RAZA HABLA MAGAZINE. 1975-1988. bi-m. (also avail. in microfiche; microfilm; back issues avail.) New Mexico State University, Chicano Program, Box 4188, Las Cruces, NM 88003.

100 SP ISSN 0212-5978
RAZON ESPANOLA. 1983-19?? bi-m. Fundacion Balmes, Genova, 12, Madrid 4, Spain.

700 US ISSN 0161-5114
RE-VIEW; artists on art. 1977-1982 (vol.4). s-a. Ambrose Arts Foundation, Inc., 85 Mercer St., New York, NY 10012.

616.89 616.8 UK ISSN 0143-7585
REACTIVE PERSONAL DISTRESS. (Current awareness service for researchers in clinical and life sciences) 1980-1989. m. Sheffield University Biomedical Information Service (SUBIS), The University, Sheffield S10 2TN, England.

800 US ISSN 0899-5044
READ ME. 1988-1990 (vol.3). q. 1118 Hoyt Ave., Everett, WA 98201.

059.8 GR
READER'S DIGEST (GREEK EDITION). ceased. m. (Epiloges Apo to Reader's Digest) Selected Publications Ltd., 188 Hymittou St., GR-116 36 Athens, Greece.

059.956 JA ISSN 0034-043X
READER'S DIGEST (JAPANESE EDITION). 1946-1986. m. Reader's Digest of Japan, Ltd., 1-1-1 Hitotsubashi, Chiyoda-ku, Tokyo 100, Japan.

370 US ISSN 0146-1176
READING CLINIC. 1974-1987. 10/yr. Princeton Educational Publishers, Box 280, Plainsboro, NJ 08536.

621.48 SW ISSN 0034-057X
REAKTORN. 1958-19?? q. Studsvik A B, Fack, 61182 Nykoeping 1, Sweden.

333.33 US
REAL ESTATE BULLETIN. (Former name of issuing body: Commerce and Industry Association of New York, Inc.) 1972-19?? s-m. New York Chamber of Commerce and Industry, Inc., 200 Madison Ave., New York, NY 10016-3989.

333.33 US ISSN 0194-6900
REAL ESTATE INTELLIGENCE REPORT. 1978-198? m. Phillips Publishing, Inc., Consumer Publishing, 7811 Montrose Rd., Potomac, MD 20854.

340 333.33 US
REAL ESTATE LAW LOCATOR. 1988-1990. a. R.R. Bowker, A Reed Reference Publishing Company, Division of Reed Publishing (USA) Inc., 121 Chanlon Rd., New Providence, NJ 07974.

333.33 US
REAL ESTATE OUTLOOK. 1979-199? q. Warren, Gorham and Lamont Inc., One Penn Plaza, New York, NY 10119.

333.33 US ISSN 0742-2644
HD1361
REAL ESTATE QUARTERLY; residential and investment markets, mortgage finance and special topics. ceased. q. National Association of Realtors, Economics and Research Division, Economics and Research Division, 777 14th St., N.W., Washington, DC 20005.

333.3 US
REAL ESTATE SYNDICATION ALERT. 1984-199? m. Warren, Gorham and Lamont Inc., One Penn Plaza, New York, NY 10119.

808.87 US
REAL FUN MAG; humor and mass media. 1984-19?? q. (back issues avail.) Box 15243, Philadelphia, PA 19125.

813 US ISSN 0034-0898
F596
REAL WEST. 1957-19?? bi-m. Charlton Publcations, Inc., 60 Division St., Derby, CT 06418.

055.1 IT
REALTA SUDAFRICANA. 1966-1991 (Apr.). m. Embassy of the Republic of South Africa, c/o Information Counsellor, Via Tanaro 14, 00198 Rome, Italy.
Supersedes (in 1980): Sud Africa - Ieri, Oggi, Domani (ISSN 0039-4505)

333.33 US
REALTOR. 1936-198? m. Washington Area Real Estate Council, Inc., 777 14th St., N.W., Ste. 200, Washington, DC 20005.

333.33 US
REALTORS REVIEW. 1977-1978 (Dec.). m. (also avail. in Braille; record; back issues avail.) National Association of Realtors (Chicago), 430 N. Michigan Ave., Chicago, IL 60611.

333.33 US
REALTY ROUNDUP. no.197, 1969-1989 (Sep.). w. Real Estate Forum, Inc., 12 W. 37th St., New York, NY 10018.

800 811 US ISSN 0882-6757
REAPER. 1981-1991. a. (back issues avail.) Story Line Press, Inc., Three Oaks Farm, 27006 Gap Rd., Brownsville, OR 97327-9718.

616.9 UK ISSN 0144-1078
RC111 CODEN: RAIFD9
RECENT ADVANCES IN INFECTION. 1979-198? irreg. Laurence Erlbaum Associates Ltd., 116 Pentonville Rd., London N1 9JB, England.

610.73 UK ISSN 0144-6592
RECENT ADVANCES IN NURSING. 1981-1990 (Mar.). 4/yr. Churchill Livingstone Medical Journals, Robert Stevenson House, 103 Baxter's Pl., Leith Walk, Edinburgh EH1 3AF, Scotland.

613.62 UK
RECENT ADVANCES IN OCCUPATIONAL HEALTH. 1981-198? irreg. Churchill Livingstone Medical Journals, Robert Stevenson House, 1-3 Baxter's Pl., Leith Walk, Edinburgh EH1 3AF, Scotland.

388 311 US ISSN 0737-772X
Z7164.T8
RECENT TRANSPORTATION LITERATURE FOR PLANNING AND ENGINEERING LIBRARIANS. (Subseries of: Public Administration Series: Bibliography) 1982-1991. m. (back issues avail.) Vance Bibliographies, 112 N. Charter St., Box 229, Monticello, IL 61856.

900 US ISSN 0145-5311
Z6205
RECENTLY PUBLISHED ARTICLES. (Previously published as a section of American Historical Review) 1976-198? 3/yr. American Historical Association, 400 A St., S.E., Washington, DC 20003.

612 617.7 UK ISSN 0142-8802
RECEPTORS (SENSORY). ceased 1989. m. (looseleaf format; back issues avail.) Sheffield University Biomedical Information Service (SUBIS), The University, Sheffield S10 2TN, England.

340 NE ISSN 0169-9806
RECHTSHISTORISCHE STUDIES. 1976-1988 (vol.15). irreg. Leiden University Press, c/o E.J. Brill Publishers, Postbus 9000, 2300 PA Leiden, Netherlands.

683.83 US
RECIPROCATING PUMP SPECIFICATIONS. ceased. a. Gordon Reference Book Group (Subsidiary of: Gordon Publications, Inc.), c/o Gordon Publications, Inc., Box 650, Morris Plains, NJ 07950-0650.

780 US
RECORD REVIEW (LOS ANGELES). 1976-1984. bi-m. (back issues avail.) Ashley Communications, Inc., Box 88427, Los Angeles, CA 90009.

157.63 US
RECOVERY NOW. 1988-19?? m. Box 280, Throgs Neck Sta., New York, NY 10465.

790.1 AT ISSN 1030-763X
RECREATION AND SPORT IN THE HOLIDAYS. 1976-1988. 4/yr. Department of Recreation and Sport, Adelaide, Australia.

919.404 AT ISSN 0156-6962
RECREATION AND TOURISM RESEARCH UNIT. OCCASIONAL PAPER. ceased. irreg. University of New England, Department of Agricultural Economics and Business Management, Recreation and Tourism Research Unit, Armidale, N.S.W. 2351, Australia.

790.1 658 UK ISSN 0144-624X
RECREATION MANAGEMENT HANDBOOK. 1975-19?? biennial. E. & F.N. Spon Ltd., 11 New Fetter Lane, London EC4P 4EE, England.
Formerly: Recreation Management Yearbook (ISSN 0306-3062)

CESSATIONS

614 790.1   US
RECREATIONAL SAFETY NEWSLETTER. ceased 1990. bi-m. National Safety Council, 444 N. Michigan Ave., Chicago, IL 60611.

658.3   US   ISSN 1040-6271
HF5549.5.R44
RECRUITMENT TODAY; the magazine of recruitment strategies. 1988-1991 (Jan.). bi-m. A C C Communications, Inc., Box 2440, Costa Mesa, CA 92628.

616.1 016   US   ISSN 0090-1326
RECURRING BIBLIOGRAPHY OF HYPERTENSION. 1969-1990 (Dec.). bi-m. (also avail. in microform from UMI,MIM; reprint service avail. from UMI; back issues avail.) American Heart Association, 7320 Greenville Ave., Dallas, TX 75231-4599.

332.6   US
RED HERRING. 1985-19?? m. Market Mania, Box 1234, Pacific, CA 94044.

322.4   US
RED LINE. 1961-1989. q. Cardinal Mindszenty Foundation, Inc., Box 11321, St. Louis, MO 63105.

649 370   US
REDBOOK'S YOUNG MOTHER. 1969-198? 3/yr. Hearst Corporation, Redbook, 224 W. 57th St., New York, NY 10019.

385   BL   ISSN 0100-3941
REDE FERROVIARIA FEDERAL. LISTA DE ARTIGOS SELECIONADOS. 1973-1986 (vol.14, no.4); suspended. q. Rede Ferroviaria Federal, S.A. Gerencia de Documentacao, Praca Procopio Ferreira 86, sala 1020, 20224 Rio de Janeiro RJ, Brazil.

301   GW   ISSN 0138-5836
REFERATBLATT SOZIOLOGIE. 1969-1990. q. Akademie fuer Gesellschafts-Wissenschaften, Zentralstelle fuer Soziologische Information und Dokumentation, Johannes-Dieckmann Str. 19-23, 1086 Berlin, Germany.

100   GW   ISSN 0138-2721
REFERATEBLATT PHILOSOPHIE. REIHE E. AKTUELLE PROBLEME UND KRITIK DER BUERGERLICHEN PHILOSOPHIE. 1965-19?? 3/yr. Zentralstelle fuer Philosophische Information und Dokumentation, J.-Dieckmann-Str. 19-23, 1080 Berlin, Germany.
Formerly: Aktuelle Probleme der Buergerlichen Philosophie (ISSN 0002-3833)

155.4   GW   ISSN 0138-3655
REFERATEDIENST JUGENDFORSCHUNG. 1971-1989. s-a. (looseleaf format) Zentralinstitut fuer Jugendforschung, Stallbaumstr.9, 7022 Leipzig, Germany.

371.9   GW   ISSN 0232-7503
REFERATEDIENST REHABILITATIONSPAEDAGOGIK. 1982-1990. 3/yr. Humboldt-Universitaet zu Berlin, Universitaetsbibliothek, Clara-Zetkin-Str. 27, 1086 Berlin, Germany.

616.4 016   CS   ISSN 0034-2726
REFERATOVY VYBER Z ENDOKRINOLOGIE/ABSTRACTS OF ENDOCRINOLOGY. 1957-19?? q. Ustav Vedeckych Lekarskych Informaci, Vitezneho Unora 31, 121 32 Prague 2, Czechoslovakia.

612 016   CS   ISSN 0034-2734
REFERATOVY VYBER Z FYSIOLOGIE/ABSTRACTS OF PHYSIOLOGY. 1969-19?? s-a. Ustav Vedeckych Lekarskych Informaci, Vitezneho Unora 31, 121 32 Prague 2, Czechoslovakia.

618.97 016   CS   ISSN 0034-2750
REFERATOVY VYBER Z GERONTOLOGIE A GERIATRIE/ABSTRACTS OF GERONTOLOGY AND GERIATRICS. 1968-19?? s-a. Ustav Vedeckych Lekarskych Informaci, Vitezneho Unora 31, 121 32 Prague 2, Czechoslovakia.
Formerly: Referatovy Vyber z Geriatrie.

616.992 016   CS   ISSN 0034-2815
REFERATOVY VYBER Z ONKOLOGIE/ABSTRACTS OF ONCOLOGY. 1969-19?? q. Ustav Vedeckych Lekarskych Informaci, Vitezneho Unora 31, 121 32 Prague 2, Czechoslovakia.

616.21 016   CS   ISSN 0034-2831
REFERATOVY VYBER Z OTORHINOLARYNGOLOGIE A FONIATRIE/ABSTRACTS OF OTORHINOLARYNGOLOGY AND PHONIATRICS. 1960-19?? q. Ustav Vedeckych Lekarskych Informaci, Vitezneho Unora 31, 121 32 Prague 2, Czechoslovakia.

616.07 016   CS   ISSN 0034-284X
REFERATOVY VYBER Z PATOLOGICKE ANATOMIE/ABSTRACTS OF PATHOLOGY. 1959-19?? q. Ustav Vedeckych Lekarskych Informaci, Vitezneho Unora 31, 121 32 Prague 2, Czechoslovakia.

332.64   US
REFERENCE GUIDE FOR N A S D A Q COMPANIES. (National Association of Securities Dealers Automated Quotations) ceased 1988. irreg. National Association of Securities Dealers, Inc., 1735 K St., N.W., Washington, DC 20006.

330   FR
REFLETS ECONOMIQUES ET COMMERCIAUX. 1952-19??; suspended. m. E S S E C, 34, rue de Liege, 75008 Paris, France.

771   IT
REFLEX FOTO. ceased. q. Editrice Reflex s.r.l., Via DiVilla Severini 54, 00101 Rome, Italy.

200   CN   ISSN 0025-3065
REGARD DE FOI; revue religieusse d'actualite. 1904-1989. bi-m. Montfort Fathers, 5875 Est rue Sherbrooke, Montreal, Que. H1N 1B6, Canada.
Formerly: Marie Reine des Coeurs.

630 333.7   US   ISSN 8756-3002
REGENERATION NEWSLETTER. 1981-1991 (vol.7, no.1). bi-m. (tabloid format; back issues avail.) Rodale Institute, Regeneration Project, 222 E. Main St., Emmaus, PA 10049.
Formerly (until 1985): Cornucopia Project Newsletter.

780   CN   ISSN 0714-4369
REGGAE. 1982-1988? irreg. (1-2/yr.). (back issues avail.) Live Good Today, 10 Walmer Rd., No. 1501, Toronto, Ont. M5R 2W4, Canada.
Formerly: Reggae Quarterly.

368.382   CN
REGIE DE L'ASSURANCE MALADIE DU QUEBEC. BULLETIN. 1970-1987. (vol.18). bi-m. (looseleaf format) Regie de l'Assurance-Maladie du Quebec, 1125 Chemin Saint-Louis, Quebec, Que. G1K 7T3, Canada.

917   CN
REGINA. 1976-19?? a. Tourism Regina, Regina Convention and Visitors Bureau, Box 3355, Regina, Sask. S4P 3H1, Canada.

971   CN
REGINA CHAMBER OF COMMERCE EXCHANGE. 1985-19?? m. Regina Chamber of Commerce, 2145 Albert, Regina, Sask. S4P 2V1, Canada.

792   US
REGIONAL & DINNER THEATER GUIDE. 1986-19?? biennial. Allen Theatrical Publications, Box 2129, Rockefeller Center Sta., New York, NY 10185.

352   FR   ISSN 0253-1968
REGIONAL AND LOCAL AFFAIRS NEWS. 1982-1986. 10/yr. Council of Europe, Directorate of Environment and Local Authorities, B.P. 431 R6, Strasbourg 67006, France.
Formerly: Council of Europe. Information Bulletin - Municipal and Regional Matters (ISSN 0252-0753)

352   US
REGIONAL PLAN NEWS. 1929-1986; 1987-19??; suspended. irreg. Regional Plan Association, Inc., 1040 Ave. of the Americas, New York, NY 10018.
Former titles: R P A News; R P A Bulletin (ISSN 0483-7738); Regional Plan News (ISSN 0034-3374); Regional Plan Association. News Letter.

320   US   ISSN 0147-0590
K18   CODEN: REGUD4
REGULATION (WASHINGTON, 1977); A E I journal on government and society. 1977-198? bi-m. American Enterprise Institute for Public Policy Research, 1150 17th St., N.W., Washington, DC 20036.

371.9   GW   ISSN 0931-8224
REHAB-REPORT; Nachrichten-Magazin fuer Rehabilitation. 1987-19?? 12/yr. Verlag Modernes Lernen - Dortmund, Borgmann KG, Hohe Str. 39, PF 10 05 55, 4600 Dortmund, Germany.

371.9   US   ISSN 0740-5294
REHABFILM NEWSLETTER. 1978-198? q. Rehabilitation International U S A, c/o National Health Council, 22 E. 21st St., New York, NY 10010.

610   US   ISSN 0885-1123
REHABILITATION REPORT; a survey of the medical literature for rehabilitation professionals. ceased 1988. m. Demos Publications, Inc., 156 Fifth Ave., Ste. 1018, New York, NY 10010.

371.9 362.4   US   ISSN 0360-0726
HD7255.A2
REHABILITATION - WORLD; U S journal of international news and information. 1975-198? q. Rehabilitation International U S A, c/o National Health Council, 25 E. 21st St., New York, NY 10010.

900 890   JA
REKISHI TO BUNGAKU/HISTORY AND LITERATURE. 1972-19?? q. Heibonsha Ltd., 4 Yonban-cho, Chiyoda-ku, Tokyo 102, Japan.

799   US
REMINGTON HUNTING & SHOOTING GUIDE. ceased. a. Aqua-Field Publishing Co., Inc., 66 W. Gilbert St., Shrewsbury, NJ 07702.

530 621.38   UK   ISSN 0267-6133
G70.4
REMOTE SENSING YEARBOOK. ceased 1989. a. Taylor & Francis Ltd., Rankine Rd., Basingstoke, Hants RG24 0PR, England.

800 500   IT   ISSN 0034-4419
RENDICONTI; rivista di letteratura e scienza. 1961-1977 (no.29-30). bi-m. Via Castiglione 35, Bologna, Italy.

674.9   US
RENEWABLE MATERIALS INSTITUTE SERIES. ceased. irreg. Syracuse University Press, 1600 Jamesville Ave., Syracuse, NY 13244.

629.2   US   ISSN 0192-3153
RENEWS. ceased 1989. m. Babcox Publications, Inc., 11 S. Forge St., Akron, OH 44304.

051   US
RENO. ceased. m. Associated Magazines Publishers, 3800 Howard Hughes Pkwy., Ste. 120, Las Vegas, NV 89109.

320 362.971   CN
REPERTOIRE ADMINISTRATIF. 1975-19??; ceased. irreg. Ministere des Communications, Direction Generale des Publications Gouvernementales, 2e etage, 1279 bd. Charest Ouest, Quebec, Que. G1N 4K7, Canada.
Formerly: Collection l'Etat et le Citoyen.

389 690   FR   ISSN 0335-3559
TA368
REPERTOIRE DE MATERIAUX ET ELEMENTS CONTROLES DU BATIMENT. 1965-19?? a. Association Francaise de Normalisation, Tour Europe - Cedex 7, 92049 Paris La Defense, France.

334   CN   ISSN 0080-097X
REPERTOIRE DES COOPERATIVES DU QUEBEC. 1969-19?? a. (Ministere des Communications, Directions Generale des Publications Gouvernementales) Ministere des Communications, 2e etage, 1279 boul. Charest Ouest, Quebec, Que. G1N 4K7, Canada.

650   BE
REPERTOIRE DES GROUPES D'ENTREPRISES. 1979-19?? a. Centre de Recherche et d'Information Socio-Politiques (CRISP), Rue du Congres 35, B-1000 Brussels, Belgium.
Formerly (until 1989): Repertoire Permanent des Groupes Financiers et Industriels (ISSN 0034-4583)

001.3 340   FR
REPERTOIRE DES THESES AFRICANISTES FRANCAISES. ceased 1991. a. Centre d'Etudes Africaines, 54, bd. Raspail, 75006 Paris, France.

792　　　　CN　　ISSN 0226-1804
REPERTOIRE THEATRAL DU QUEBEC (YEAR). ceased 1989. a. Cahiers de Theatre Jeu Inc., 426 rue Sherbrooke Est, Bur.102, Montreal, Que. H2L 1J6, Canada.

660　　　　IT
REPERTORIO CHIMICO ITALIANO; industriale e commerciale. ceased 1988. quadrennial. Edizioni Ragno, Via Crescenzio 43, 00193 Rome, Italy.

669　　　　　　ISSN 0080-1216
REPERTORIO DELLE INDUSTRIE SIDERURGICHE ITALIANE. 1949-1980. quinquennial. Associazione Industrie Siderurgiche Italiane, Piazza Velasca 8, 20122 Milan, Italy.

616.863　　　　IT
REPERTORIO TERAPEUTICO; medicamenta-drugs international index. 1963-19?? (7th ed.). irreg. Organizzazione Editoriale Medico-Farmaceutica, Via Edolo 42, P.O. Box 10434, 20125 Milan, Italy.

330.1　　　　CN
REPORT ON CANADA. ceased. a. MacLean Hunter Ltd., Business Publication Division, MacLean Hunter Bldg., 777 Bay St., Toronto, Ont. M5W 1A7, Canada.

549　　　　KO
REPORT ON GEOSCIENCE AND MINERAL RESOURCES. 1977-1982 (vol.14). s-a. (Ministry of Science and Technology) Korea Institute of Geology, Mining and Materials, 30 Kajungdong, Yusongku, Taejon 305-350, S. Korea.

330 301.16　　　　US
REPORT ON I B M IN COMMUNICATIONS. ceased. s-m. DataTrends Publications, Inc., 8130 Boone Blvd., Ste. 210, Vienna, VA 22182.

658　　　　US
REPORTER (CLINTON). 1979-198? 3/yr. Nielsen Clearing House, 1900 N. 3rd St., Clinton, IA 52732.

612.015　　　US　　ISSN 1048-2008
QD461　　　　　　CODEN: RMTHEJ
REPORTS IN MOLECULAR THEORY. 1990-1991. q. C R C Press, Inc., 2000 Corporate Blvd., N.W., Boca Raton, FL 33431.

340　　　　US　　ISSN 0890-3271
REPORTS OF INTEREST TO LAWYERS. 1984-19?? bi-m. (tabloid format; back issues avail.) Merton Allen Associates, InfoTeam Inc., Box 15640, Plantation, FL 33318-5640.

616.97　　　UK　　ISSN 0266-660X
REPRODUCTIVE IMMUNOLOGY. ceased 1989. m. (looseleaf format; back issues avail.) Sheffield University Biomedical Information Service (SUBIS), The University, Sheffield S10 2TN, England.

572 301 900 910　　GW　　ISSN 0722-6349
GN1
RESEARCH; contributions to interdisciplinary anthropology. 1982-1991. a. (Association for International Scientific Communication) Edition Herodot, Kongressstr.5, 5100 Aachen, Germany.

630　　　　UK　　ISSN 0264-5467
　　　　　　　　　　　CODEN: RDAGES
RESEARCH AND DEVELOPMENT IN AGRICULTURE. 19??-19?? 3/yr. Longman Group (UK) Ltd., Fourth Ave., Harlow, Essex CM19 5AA, England.

331　　　　AT　　ISSN 0158-9830
RESEARCH DISCUSSION PAPERS. 1979-19?? irreg. (back issues avail.) Australian Chamber of Manufactures, 370 St. Kilda Rd., Melbourne 3004, Australia.

658.8 659.1　　　　SA
RESEARCH FOR MARKETING. (Title and numbering of former title resumed with vol.5, 1978) 1970-1991; suspended. s-a. University of South Africa, Bureau of Market Research, Box 392, Pretoria 0001, South Africa.
　Supersedes (in 1978): Marketing Research and Media; Research for Marketing.

636.089　　　UK　　ISSN 0958-823X
RESEARCH HIGHLIGHTS IN ANIMAL NUTRITION. 1990-1991. q. Chalcombe Publications, Honey Lane, Hurley, Maidenhead, Burks. SO6 5LR, England.

020　　　AT　　ISSN 0034-5245
Z671
RESEARCH IN LIBRARIANSHIP. 1965-1991. 3/yr. Office of Research in Librarianship, Box 744, Wagga Wagga, N.S.W. 2650, Australia.

574.3　　　UK　　ISSN 0034-5253
QP251
RESEARCH IN REPRODUCTION. 1969-1990. q. International Planned Parenthood Federation, Regent's College, Inner Circle, Regent's Park, London NW1 4NS, England.

336 340　　　US　　ISSN 0163-9994
KF6352
RESEARCH INSTITUTE LAWYERS TAX ALERT. 1978-198? m. Research Institute of America, Inc., 90 Fifth Ave., New York, NY 10011.

370 686.2　　　US　　ISSN 0737-0083
RESEARCH PUBLICATIONS. REPORT. 1983-198? q. Gale Research Inc., 835 Penobscot Bldg., Detroit, MI 48226.

574.5 333.7　　　UK　　ISSN 0143-0386
RESEARCH REPORTS DIGEST. 1978-1991. irreg. Nature Conservancy Council, Information and Library Services, Northminster House, Peterborough PE1 1UA, England.

636.089 574　　　　US
RESEARCH REVIEWS IN ANIMAL AND PLANT SCIENCES. 1988-1989. q. Institute for Scientific Information, 3501 Market St., Philadelphia, PA 19104.
　Formerly: I S I Atlas of Science: Animal and Plant Sciences (ISSN 0894-3761)

574　　　　US
RESEARCH REVIEWS IN BIOCHEMISTRY. 1988-1989. q. Institute for Scientific Information, 3501 Market St., Philadelphia, PA 19104.
　Formerly: I S I Atlas of Science: Biochemistry (ISSN 0894-3753)

610　　　　US
RESEARCH REVIEWS IN MEDICINE. 1989; ceased same year. q. Institute for Scientific Information, 3501 Market St., Philadelphia, PA 19104.

616.8　　　　US
RESEARCH REVIEWS IN NEUROSCIENCE. 1989; ceased same year. q. Institute for Scientific Information, 3501 Market St., Philadelphia, PA 19104.

610　　　　BL
RESIDENCIA MEDICA. 1972-19?? 9/yr. Editora de Publicacoes Medicas Ltda. (Subsidiary of: Editora de Publicacoes Cientificas Ltda.), Rua Major Suckow, 30 a 36, 20911 Rio de Janeiro RJ, Brazil.

910.09　　　　US
RESORTS & INCENTIVES. 1990-1992. 6/yr. Miller Freeman Inc. (New York) (Subsidiary of: United Newspapers Group), 1515 Broadway, New York, NY 10036.

370 371.3　　　　CN
RESOURCE BOOK/RESSOURCES. 1958-19?? a. Maclean Hunter Ltd., Business Publication Division, Maclean-Hunter Bldg., 777 Bay St., Toronto, Ont. M5W 1A7, Canada.

157.61　　　　US
RESOURCE DIRECTORY OF NATIONAL ALCOHOL-RELATED ASSOCIATIONS, AGENCIES AND ORGANIZATIONS. 1985-1991 (no.2). a. U.S Department of Health and Human Services, Alcohol, Drug Abuse, and Mental Health Administration, 5600 Fishers Lane, Rockville, MD 20857.

910　　　　AT
RESOURCES AND INDUSTRY OF CENTRAL QUEENSLAND. 1984-19?? irreg. Department of Industry Development, Enterprise House, 46 Charlotte St., Brisbane, Qld. 4000, Australia.

630　　　　AT
RESOURCES AND INDUSTRY OF FAR NORTH QUEENSLAND. 1971-19?? irreg. Department of Industry Development, Enterprise House, 46 Charlotte St., Brisbane, Qld. 4000, Australia.

615.9 610　　　UK　　ISSN 0954-5271
RESOURCES PHARMACEUTICAL AND HEALTHCARE INFORMATION NEWS. ceased 1989 (Apr.). m. P J B Publications Ltd., 18-20 Hill Rise, Richmond, Surrey TW10 6UA, England.

286　　　　US
RESPUESTA. 1965-1991. q. Casa Bautista de Publicaciones, Box 4255, El Paso, TX 79914.

647.95　　　　US
RESTAURANT SOUTH. 1947-198? m. Southern Trade Publications Co., Box 18343, Greensboro, NC 27419.

070　　　　VE
RESUMEN. 1973-198? w. Grupo Editor Olavarria, Edificio el Cigarral, piso 7, Apdo. 62236, Avenida Principal de Bello Monte, Caracas 106, Venezuela.

658.8　　　　CN
RETAIL MERCHANDISING. 1949-1990. 6/yr. Canadian Engineering Publications Ltd., 111 Peter St., Suite 411, Toronto, Ont. M5V 2W2, Canada.
　Formerly: Volume Retail Merchandising.

001.6 658.8　　　　US
RETAILNEWS. (Update to: Datapro Reports on Retail Automation) ceased. m. Datapro Information Services Group (Subsidiary of: McGraw-Hill, Inc.), 600 Delran Pkwy., Delran, NJ 08075.

362.6　　　　US
RETIREMENT HOUSING INDUSTRY. 1981-1990. a. Laventhol & Horwath, 1845 Walnut St., Philadelphia, PA 19103.
　Former titles: Industry Study; Lifecare Industry.

332.6　　　　US
RETIREMENT MONEY. ceased 1991. 10/yr. 2204 Sensensey Ln., Falls Church, VA 22043-3116.

330.9　　　RE　　ISSN 0750-0750
REUNION. INSTITUT NATIONAL DE LA STATISTIQUE ET DES ETUDES ECONOMIQUES. INDICATEURS CONJONCTURELS. 1982-1990. q. Observatoire Economique de la Reunion, 15 rue de l'Ecole, 97490 Ste. Clotilde, Reunion.

133　　　UK　　ISSN 0143-0181
REVELATION. 1972-1987. irreg. (1-2/yr.). 2 Rose Cottage, Farm Rd., Ruardean Woodside, Ruardean, Gloucestershire, GL17 9XL, England.

860 791.43　　　　CR
REVENAR. 1980-1988 (no.14). s-a. Asociacion de Autores de Costa Rica, Apdo. 425, 2050 Montes de Oca, San Jose, Costa Rica.

720.5　　　CN　　ISSN 0705-1913
REVIEW OF ARCHITECTURE AND LANDSCAPE ARCHITECTURE. 1977-19?? irreg. c/o Irving Grossman, Alumni Association, Faculty of Architecture and Landscape Architecture, 9 Sultan St., Toronto, Ont. M5S 1L6, Canada.

312　　　AT　　ISSN 0727-6982
HB3675
REVIEW OF AUSTRALIA'S DEMOGRAPHIC TRENDS. 1981-19?? a. (Department of Immigration and Ethnic Affairs) Australian Government Publishing Service, Canberra, Australia.

616.8　　　US　　ISSN 0095-7550
QP351　　　　　　CODEN: RENEDP
REVIEWS OF NEUROSCIENCE. 1974-1978 (vol.3). irreg. Raven Press, 1185 Avenue of the Americas, New York, NY 10036.

301.16　　　　CL
REVISTA ARTES DE LA COMUNICACION. 1972-1974 (vol.4). s-a. (back issues avail.) Universidad Catolica de Chile, Escuela Artes de la Comunicacion, Diagonal Oriente 3300, Santiago, Chile.

410 869　　　BL　　ISSN 0101-8248
PC5001
REVISTA BRASILEIRA DE LINGUA E LITERATURA. 1978-19?? (no.15). a. Sociedade Brasileira de Lingua e Literatura, Av. Epitacio Pessoa 2094-102, 22471 Rio de Janeiro, Brazil.

798 636.089　　　　BL
REVISTA CENTAURUS. 1984-1985. m. Editora Centaurus Ltda., Av. Getulio Vargas 1556 e 1558, Caixa Postal 2890, CEP 90000 Porto Alegre RS, Brazil.

CESSATIONS

320   BL   ISSN 0716-1417
JA5
REVISTA DE CIENCIA POLITICA. 1958-1990 (vol.33, no.3). q. (Instituto de Direito Publico e Ciencia Politica) Fundacao Getulio Vargas, C.P. 9052, 22250 Rio de Janeiro, R.J., Brazil.
Formerly (until 1966): Revista de Direito Publico e Ciencia Politica (ISSN 0034-8023)

340   BL   ISSN 0034-8007
REVISTA DE DIREITO ADMINISTRATIVO. 1945-1989 (no.178). q. (Instituto de Direito Publico e Ciencia Politica) Fundacao Getulio Vargas, C.P. 9052, 22250 Rio de Janeiro, R.J., Brazil.
Formerly: Revista de Servico Publico.

616.89   BL   ISSN 0034-8767
REVISTA DE PSIQUIATRIA DINAMICA. 1960-1974 (vol. 10). q. Universidade Federal do Rio Grande do Sul, Faculdade de Medicina, Rua Sarmento Leite s-n, 90000 Porto Alegre, R.S., Brazil.

355   AG
REVISTA DE TEMAS MILITARES. 1982-1984; suspended. q. Ediciones A P, Maipu 621, 4 C, 1006 Buenos Aires, Argentina.

800   BL   ISSN 0035-0605
REVISTA DO LIVRO (RIO DE JANEIRO). 1956-19?? q. (also avail. in microfilm from UMI; reprint service avail. from UMI) Instituto Nacional do Livro, Avda. Rio Branco 219-239, 4 Andar, 20000-Rio de Janeiro-RJ, Brazil.

384.5 792 778.5   CL   ISSN 0302-8003
REVISTA E A C. ceased 1974 (vol.4). s-a. Universidad Catolica de Chile, Escuela de Teatro, Cine y Television, Biblioteca, Diagonal Oriente 3300, Casilla 114 D, Santiago, Chile.

770   BL
REVISTA FOTOPTICA. 1950-198?; suspended. bi-m. Bela Vista Editorial Ltda., Rua Conego Eugenio Leite 920, 05414 Sao Paulo SP, Brazil.
Formerly: Novidaded Fotoptica (ISSN 0029-5159)

982   AG
REVISTA HISTORICA. 1977-19?? q. (Instituto Historica de la Organizacion Nacional) Emece Editores S.A., Apdo Especial Numero 84, 1000 Buenos Aires, Argentina.

860 972.86   CR
REVISTA HISTORICO: CRITICA DE LITERATURA CENTROAMERICANA. 1974-19?? s-a. Universidad de Costa Rica, Instituto de Estudios Centroamericanos, Apdo. 41, Ciudad Universitaria R. Facio, San Jose, Costa Rica.

615.842   US   ISSN 0034-9704
R895.A1
REVISTA INTERAMERICANA DE RADIOLOGIA. 1976-1987 (vol.12, no. 4). q. Interamerican College of Radiology - Colegio Interamericano de Radiologia, c/o Dr. Luis O. Martinez, Ed., Dept. of Radiology, Mt. Sinai Hospital, Miami, FL 33140.

350.865   VE
REVISTA INTERNACIONAL DE VIVIENDA RURAL/ INTERNATIONAL RURAL HOUSING JOURNAL. 1970-1978 (no.7). a. (with bi-m. supplements). International Rural Housing Association, Apt. 16224, Caracas, Venezuela.

660   AG   ISSN 0325-0474
TP1   CODEN: RLIQAE
REVISTA LATINOAMERICANA DE INGENIERIA QUIMICA Y QUIMICA APLICADA/LATIN AMERICAN JOURNAL OF CHEMICAL ENGINEERING AND APPLIED CHEMISTRY. 1971-1987 (vol.17). s-a. Asociacion Argentina de Investigadores en Ciencias de la Ingenieria Quimica y Quimica Aplicada, Av. 1 No. 867, La Plata, Argentina.

616.99   SP   ISSN 0482-640X
RC261.A1
REVISTA NACIONAL DE ONCOLOGIA. 1952-19?? q. Instituto Nacional de Oncologia, Bartolome Cossio, s-n, Ciudad Universitaria, Madrid 3, Spain.

658   CU   ISSN 0138-6921
REVISTA REFERATIVA. ORGANIZACION DE LA DIRECCION. 1974-1987. s-a. Academia de Ciencias, Instituto de Documentacion e Informacion Cientifico-Tecnica (IDICT), Capitolio Nacional, Prado y San Jose, Apdo. 2291, Havana 2, Cuba.

366   US   ISSN 0035-0443
REVISTA ROTARIA; una publicacion internacional. 1933-1990 (July). bi-m. (also avail. in microform from UMI; reprint service avail. from UMI) Rotary International, 1560 Sherman Ave., Evanston, IL 60201.

620.2   FR   ISSN 0557-7713
TA365
REVUE D'ACOUSTIQUE. ceased. 4/yr. (Societe Francaise d'Acoustique) Information Promotion Francaises, 12 rue Pascal, 75005 Paris, France.

340   HU   ISSN 0139-2026
REVUE DE DROIT HONGROIS. 1968-1986. 2/yr. Magyar Jogasz Szovetseg, Szemere u. 10, 1054 Budapest 5, Hungary.

616.86   FR   ISSN 0035-130X
            CODEN: REALAC
REVUE DE L'ALCOOLISME. 1954-1989. 4/yr. (also avail. in microform; reprint service avail. from ISI) (Groupement Medical d'Etudes sur l'Alcoolisme) Masson, 120 bd. Saint-Germain, 75280 Paris Cedex 06, France.

663.19   FR
REVUE DE L'EMBOUTEILLAGES ET DES INDUSTRIES CONNEXES. 1949-1988. 10/yr. S I M E I C, 7 rue la Boetie, 75008 Paris, France.

971   CN   ISSN 0713-7958
PQ3900
REVUE DE L'HISTOIRE DU QUEBEC ET DU CANADA FRANCAIS. 1983-1987 (no.14). 2/yr. University of Ottawa Press, 603 Cumberland, Ottawa, Ont. K1N 6N5, Canada.

610   FR
REVUE DU JEUNE MEDECIN. (Includes Supplements) 1977-19?? w. (also avail. in microform from MIM) Edition E P R A L, 130 bd. Saint-Germain, 75006 Paris, France.

770   CS   ISSN 0232-0576
REVUE FOTOGRAFIE. 1957-1990. q. (processed) Orbis, Vinohradska 46, 120 41 Prague 2, Czechoslovakia.

371.912   FR   ISSN 0035-3124
REVUE GENERALE DE L'ENSEIGNEMENT DES DEFICIENTS AUDITIFS. ceased 1989 (vol.81, no.4). 4/yr. Association Francaise des Enseignants et Reeducateurs de Langage et Audition, 254 rue Saint-Jacques, 75005 Paris, France.
Formerly: Revue Generale de l'Enseignement des Sourds-Muets.

332.1   SZ   ISSN 0080-2611
HG1531
REVUE INTERNATIONALE D'HISTOIRE DE LA BANQUE. 1968-1990. a. (Banco di Napoli, IT) Librairie Droz S.A., 11, rue Massot, CH-1211 Geneva 12, Switzerland.

301 440   FR   ISSN 0986-6426
REVUE LANGUEDOCIENNE DE SOCIOLOGIE ETHNOLOGIE. 1986-1990 (no.2). irreg. Universite de Montpellier (Universite Paul Valery), Centre de Recherche sur le Changement Social Regional, B.P. 5043, 34032 Montpellier Cedex, France.

320   LE   ISSN 0557-9414
REVUE LIBANAISE DES SCIENCES POLITIQUES. 1970-19?? s-a. Association Libanaise des Sciences Politiques, Librairie du Liban, Place Riad Solh, Beirut, Lebanon.

550   GW   ISSN 0080-2689
RHEINISCHE SCHRIFTEN. 1963-19?? irreg. Rheinland Verlag GmbH Koeln, Abtei Brauweiler, 5024 Pulheim 2, Germany.

616.7   GW   ISSN 0930-5580
RHEUMA PRAXIS-AKTUELL. 1985-1989 (vol.5, no.3). 8/yr. (back issues avail.) P M I Verlag GmbH, August-Schanz-Str. 21, D-6000 Frankfurt 50, Germany.

917.306   US   ISSN 0893-181X
RHODE ISLAND QUERIES. 1987-1991 (vol.3). irreg. Topp of the Line, W. 1304 Cliffwood Court, Spokane, WA 99218-2917.

610   US
RHODES DIRECTORY OF BLACK PHYSICIANS IN THE UNITED STATES. 1976-198? triennial. Aqua Dynamics Ltd., 1317 E. Brambleton Ave., Norfolk, VA 23504.

808.81   US
RHYME TIME POETRY NEWSLETTER. 1981-1992. bi-m. (back issues avail.) Hutton Publications, Box 1870, Hayden, ID 83835.

945   IT
RICERCHE DI STORIA MODERNA. 1976; ceased same year. irreg. (Universita degli Studi di Pisa, Istituto di Storia Medioevale e Moderna) Pacini Editore S.R.L., Via della Gherardesca, 56014 Ospedaletto (Pisa), Italy.

378.198 800   UK   ISSN 0261-6505
RICHMOND COLLAGE. 1978-1988. s-a. Richmond upon Thames College, Library, Egerton Rd., Twickenham, Middx. TW2 7SJ, England.

052   AT
RICHMOND TIMES. 1983-1990 (Dec.). w. (back issues avail.) C P I Publications, 45-50 Porter St., Prahran, Vic. 3181, Australia.

368   SP
RIESGO; seguros, ahorro, finanzas. 1956-19?? m. Santa Engracia 151, 28003 Madrid, Spain.

374 500   JA   ISSN 0286-4487
RIGAKU SENKOKA ZASSHI. 1980-1987 (vol.8). a. Tokyo Rika Daigaku, Rigaku Senkoka - Science University of Tokyo, 1-3 Kagurazaka, Shinjuku-ku, Tokyo 162, Japan.

051   US   ISSN 0895-3139
RIGHT HERE; the hometown magazine. 1984-1990. 5/yr. (back issues avail.) Right Here Publications, Box 1014, Huntington, IN 46750.

070.5   CN
RIGHTS CANADA. 1976-198?; suspended. a. Canadian Book Publishers Council, 45 Charles St. E., Toronto, Ont. M4Y 1S2, Canada.

639.2   FI   ISSN 0355-0648
RIISTA- JA KALATALOUDEN TUTKIMUSLAITOS. KALANTUTKIMUSOSASTO. TIEDONANTOJA. 1971-19?? irreg. (back issues avail.) Finnish Game and Fisheries Research Institute, Fisheries Division, P.O. Box 202, SF-00151 Helsinki 15, Finland.

150   BE   ISSN 0085-1078
RIJKSUNIVERSITEIT TE GENT. LABORATORIUM VOOR EXPERIMENTELE, DIFFERENTIELE EN GENETISCHE PSYCHOLOGIE. MEDEDELINGEN EN WERKDOCUMENTEN. 1961-19?? irreg. Rijksuniversiteit te Gent, Laboratorium voor Experimentele, Differentiele en Genetische Psychologie, H. Dunantlaan 2, B-9000 Ghent, Belgium.

970   US   ISSN 0146-1869
RIO GRANDE HISTORY. 1973-19??; suspended. irreg. New Mexico State University Library, Rio Grande Historical Collections, Box 30006, Las Cruces, NM 88003.

808.87   US
RIP OFF COMIX; international review of comics. 1977-1991 (vol.31). q. (back issues avail.) Rip Off Press, Inc., Box 4686, Auburn, CA 95604.

056.1   MX
RITMO. 1982-19?? fortn. Lucio Blanco 435, Azcapotzalco, 02400 Mexico D.F., Mexico.

540   IT
RIVISTA DE CHIMICA. 1990-1991 (Mar.). m. Gruppo Editoriale Fabbri SPA, Divisione Periodici, Via Mecenate 91, 20138 Milan, Italy.

618   IT
RIVISTA DI OSTETRICIA, GINECOLOGIA PRATICA E MEDICINA PERINATALE. ceased 1991. 5/yr. (Associazione Ostetrici Ginecologi Ospedalieri Italiani) C I C Edizioni Internazionali s.r.l., Via L. Spallanzani 11, 00161 Rome, Italy.

155.3 610   IT
RIVISTA DI SESSUOLOGIA. 1960-1990. q. (Centro Italiano di Sessuologia) C I C Edizioni Internazionali s.r.l., Via L. Spallanzani, 11, 00161 Rome, Italy.
Formerly: Sessuologia (ISSN 0037-2838)

150 154.7　　　IT　　ISSN 0035-6743
BF1
RIVISTA INTERNAZIONALE DI PSICOLOGIA E IPNOSI. 1955-19??; suspended. q. (International University of New Medicine) Istituto di Indagini Psicologiche, Corso XXII Marzo 57, 20129 Milan, Italy.
Formerly: Rivista di Psicologia della Scrittura.

616.2　　　IT　　ISSN 0035-7049
RIVISTA SICILIANA DELLA TUBERCOLOSI E DELLE MALATTIE RESPIRATORIE. 1947-1973. bi-m. (Associazione Siciliana contro la Tubercolosi) Universita degli Studi di Palermo, Clinica Tisiologica, Via Trabucco 180, Palermo 90146, Italy.

336.2　　　SZ　　ISSN 0048-8429
RIVISTA TRIBUTARIA TICINESE. 1968-1990. q. Cancelleria Dello Stato, 6500 Bellinzona, Switzerland.

335 658　　　CS
RIZENI EKONOMIKY; mesicni vyber z ceskoslovenskeho a zahranicniho tisku. 1966-1989 (Jan.). m. Ceskoslovenska Tiskova Kancelar, Ekonomicka Redakce - Czechoslovak News Agency, Opletalova 5, 111 44 Prague 1, Czechoslovakia.
Former titles: Rizeni Ekonomiky v Socialistickych Zemich (ISSN 0035-7146); Nova Soustava Rizeni.

388.324　　　AT
ROAD TRANSPORTER OF AUSTRALIA. 1953-19?? q. Victorian Road Transport Association, 17 Raglan St., South Melbourne, Vic. 3205, Australia.
Formerly: Road Transporter (ISSN 0035-7308)

001.6 629.8　　　US
ROBOTICS TECHNICAL DIRECTORY (YEAR). 1984-1986. a. I S A Services, Inc., 67 Alexander Dr., Box 12277, Research Triangle Park, NC 27709.
Formerly: Robotics - C A D - C A M Directory.

780.42　　　US
ROCK. ceased Jan. 1990. bi-m. Edrei Communications Company, 1086 Teaneck Rd., Teaneck, NJ 07666.
Former titles (until 1907): Daytimers - Real Life; Rona Barrett's Daytimers TV.

780.42　　　US　　ISSN 1058-9848
ROCK BEAT. ceased 1992. 6/yr. Larry Flynt Publications, Inc., 9171 Wilshire Blvd., Ste. 300, Beverly Hills, CA 90210.

780.904　　　US
ROCK SHOT. ceased. m. Cambray Publishing Inc., Box 931869, Sunset Sta., Los Angeles, CA 90093.

551.5　　　PL　　ISSN 0080-3448
ROCZNIK ELEKTRYCZNOSCI ATMOSFERYCZNEJ I METEOROLOGII. (Subseries of: Prace Obserwatorium Geofizycznego Im. St. Kalinowskiego w Swidrze) 1961-1965. irreg. (Polska Akademia Nauk, Instytut Geofizyki) Panstwowe Wydawnictwo Naukowe, Miodowa 10, 00-251 Warsaw, Poland.

551 538.7　　　PL　　ISSN 0082-0458
ROCZNIK MAGNETYCZNY/ANNUAIRE MAGNETIQUE. 1949-19?? irreg. (Polska Akademia Nauk, Instytut Geofizyki) Panstwowe Wydawnictwo Naukowe, Miodowa 10, Warsaw, Poland.

286　　　DK　　ISSN 0109-2952
ROEDDERNE. 1982-1990 (Aug.). 9/yr. (Baptisternes Soendagsskoler) Danske Baptisters Ungdomsforbund, Toelloese, Denmark.

930　　　GW
ROEMER PELIZAEUS MUSEUM. ZEITSCHRIFT DES MUSEUMS ZU HILDESHEIM. ceased 1978. irreg. Roemer und Pelizaeus Museum, Am Steine 1-2, 3200 Hildesheim, Germany.

993　　　NZ　　ISSN 0111-2805
ROLL BACK THE YEARS. 1980-1987 (vol.3, no.54). bi-m. (back issues avail.) C & S Publications, P.O. Box 148, Taumarunui, New Zealand.

945　　　NE　　ISSN 0169-975X
ROMA AETERNA. 1964-1978 (vol.10). irreg. E.J. Brill, P.O. Box 9000, 2300 PA Leiden, Netherlands.

840　　　FR　　ISSN 0754-2275
ROMAN. 1982-1989 (no.26). q. (back issues avail.) Presses de la Renaissance, 37 rue du Four, 75006 Paris, France.

332.6　　　US
ROMAN REPORTS. 1972-1987. 12/yr. Harry H. Peck, Ed. & Pub., 7125 Liberty Rd., Solon, OH 44134.

870　　　GW　　ISSN 0035-7979
ROMAN-ZEITUNG. 1952-1990. m. Verlag Volk und Welt, Glinkastr. 13-15, 1086 Berlin, Germany.

808　　　US
ROMANCE GROUP. ceased. 3/w. Digest Publishing Inc., 158 Linwood Plaza, Fort Lee, NJ 07024.

440 840　　　GW　　ISSN 0005-8181
PC3
ROMANISCHE PHILOLOGIE. BEITRAEGE. 1961-19?? s-a. Verlag Ruetten und Loenig, Franzoesische Str. 32, 1080 Berlin, Germany.

400　　　GW
ROMANISTISCHE VERSUCHE UND VORARBEITEN. 1956-1991. irreg. Universitaet Bonn, Romanisches Seminar, Am Hof 1, 5300 Bonn 1, Germany.

820　　　AU
ROMANTIC REASSESSMENT. 1972-198? irreg. Universitaet Salzburg, Institut fuer Englische Sprache, Akademiestr. 24, A-5020 Salzburg, Austria.

642.5　　　GW
ROMANTIK. 1979-1991. q. (Romantik Hotels & Restaurants GmbH & Co. KG) G W Verlag GmbH, Postfach 101088, 5000 Cologne 1, Germany.

796.75　　　UK
ROTHMANS GRAND PRIX MOTORCYCLE YEARBOOK. 1986-198? a. (back issues avail.) Queen Anne Press Ltd., 66 Shoe Lane, London EC4P 4AB, England.

387.7　　　US
ROTORNEWS. 1968-198? bi-m. Helicopter Association International, 1619 Duke St., Alexandria, VA 22314-3406.

388.411　　　SZ　　ISSN 1017-0448
ROUTES DU MONDE. ceased 1991. 6/yr. International Road Federation - Federation Routiere Internationale, 63 Rue de Lausanne, CH-1202 Geneva, Switzerland.

355　　　UK　　ISSN 0035-8673
ROYAL ARMY PAY CORPS JOURNAL. 1931-1992. s-a. Royal Army Pay Corps, Corps Headquarters, Worthy Down, Winchester, Hants, England.

069 574　　　CN　　ISSN 0068-1636
ROYAL BRITISH COLUMBIA MUSEUM. OCCASIONAL PAPERS SERIES. 1939-1985. irreg. (back issues avail.) Royal British Columbia Museum, 675 Bellville St., Victoria, B.C. V8V 1X4, Canada.

610　　　UK
ROYAL COLLEGE OF SURGEONS OF ENGLAND. HANDBOOK. ceased 1984. quinquennial. Royal College of Surgeons of England, 35-43 Lincoln's Inn Fields, London WC2A 3PN, England.

020　　　UK　　ISSN 0035-8851
ROYAL COMMONWEALTH SOCIETY LIBRARY NOTES. (Includes List of Accessions) 1957-1991. 6/yr. (processed) Royal Commonwealth Society Library, Commonwealth Trust, Northumberland Ave., London WC2, England.

913　　　CN
ROYAL ONTARIO MUSEUM. ARCHAEOLOGY OCCASIONAL PAPERS. 1959-1974 (no.26). irreg. Royal Ontario Museum, Publication Services, 100 Queen's Park, Toronto, Ont. M5S 2C6, Canada.
Formerly: Royal Ontario Museum. Art and Archaeology. Occasional Papers (ISSN 0082-5077)

572　　　CN　　ISSN 0316-1277
ROYAL ONTARIO MUSEUM. ETHNOGRAPHY MONOGRAPH. published only once, 1973. irreg. Royal Ontario Museum, Publication Services, 100 Queen's Park, Toronto, Ont. M5S 2C6, Canada.

540 020　　　UK
ROYAL SOCIETY OF CHEMISTRY. DATABASE NEWSLETTER. 1979-198?; suspended. 3/yr. Royal Society of Chemistry, Information Services, Thomas Graham House, Science Park, Milton Rd., Cambridge CB4 4WF, England.
Former titles: Royal Society of Chemistry. Information Services. Newsletter (ISSN 0260-4140) & U K C I S Newsletter (ISSN 0144-2570)

384　　　UK
ROYAL TELEVISION SOCIETY TALKBACK. ceased. 12/yr. Royal Television Society, Tavistock House East, Tavistock Square, London WC1H 9HR, England.
Formerly: Royal Television Society Bulletin.

338.476 310　　　US
RUBBER MANUFACTURERS ASSOCIATION. STATISTICAL REPORT. INDUSTRY RUBBER REPORT. ceased 1990 (Dec.). m. Rubber Manufacturers Association, 1400 K St. N.W., 9th Fl., Washington, DC 20005.

800　　　CN　　ISSN 0715-8610
RUBICON. 1983-1988. s-a. (back issues avail.) McGill University, 853 rue Sherbrooke St. W., Montreal, Que. H3A 2T6, Canada.

796.333　　　DK　　ISSN 0108-1233
RUGBY NYT. 1974-19?? q. Dansk Rugby Union, Idraettens Hus, Broendby Stadion 20, DK-2605 Broendby, Denmark.

200　　　CN　　ISSN 0829-0067
RUMORS; a good humored magazine for Christians. 1982-19?? q. (tabloid format; back issues avail.) Wood Lake Books Inc., Box 700, Winfield, B.C. V0H 2C0, Canada.

001.6 621.381　　　DK
RUN. 1984-198? 8/yr. C.W. Communications Inc., Torvegade 52, 1400 Copenhagen K, Denmark.

410　　　US
RUNDBRIEF. 1980-1989 (May). 8/yr. American Association of Teachers of German, 112 Haddontowne Court, Ste. 104, Cherry Hill, NJ 08034.

282　　　GW
RUNDBRIEF DER DOBRUDSCHA-DEUTSCHEN. 1949-1989. bi-m. Koenigsberger Str. 6, 7929 Gerstetten, Germany.

384　　　GW　　ISSN 0035-9882
RUNDFUNKJOURNALISTIK IN THEORIE UND PRAXIS. 1965-1989. s-a. Rundfunk der D.D.R., Staatliches Komitee fuer Rundfunk, Nalepastr. 18-50, 116 Berlin, Germany.

289.9 917.306 398　　　US
RUNESTONE (BRECKENRIDGE). 1972-1987 (no.63). 6/yr. Asatru Free Assembly, Box 1754, Breckenridge, TX 76024.

796　　　UK
RUNNING REVIEW. 1981-1987. m. Ron Hill Sports Ltd., 8-14 Church St., Hyde, Cheshire SK14 1LL, England.
Incorporates: Athletic Event & Marathon Running.

387.736　　　US
RUNWAYS. 1990-199? bi-w. (tabloid format) (Knight - Ridder, Inc.) Runways Publications, Inc., 2221 Rosecrans Ave., Ste. 236, El Segundo, CA 90245.

630   CN   ISSN 0838-9357
RURAL CONSTRUCTION. 1984-198? q. Wicklow Hills Publishing Co. Inc., P.O. Box 150, Acton, Ont. L7J 2M3, Canada.
    Formerly (until 1987): Farm Builder of Canada (ISSN 0825-8570)

630
RURAL DEVELOPMENT. no.26, Oct. 1978-198? bi-m. University of Massachusetts, Berkshire Cooperative Extension Service, 46 Summer St., Pittsfield, MA 01003.

330 334   AT   ISSN 0816-5173
RURAL DEVELOPMENT WORKING PAPERS. 1985-1987 (no.2). irreg. Australian National University, National Centre for Development Studies, G.P.O. Box 4, Canberra, A.C.T. 2601, Australia.

370   UK   ISSN 0140-4776
RURAL EXTENSION, EDUCATION AND TRAINING ABSTRACTS. 1978-1989. bi-m. (also avail. in microfiche; back issues avail.) C.A.B. International, Wallingford, Oxon OX10 8DE, England.

973   US
RURAL FOLIO. 1976-1980. q. Rensselaerville Historical Society, Box 8, Rensselaerville, NY 12147.

631   AT
RURAL NEWSLETTER. 1965-19??; suspended. bi-m. (back issues avail.) Central Coast Agricultural Research and Extension Committee, P.O. Box 362, Gosford, N.S.W. 2250, Australia.

780   UR
RUSSIAN AND SOVIET COMPOSERS. 1978-1991. 2/yr. Izdatel'stvo Muzyka, Ul. Neglinnaya 14, Moscow 103031, Russian S.F.S.R., U.S.S.R.

891.72   US   ISSN 0048-881X
RUSSIAN LITERATURE TRIQUARTERLY. 1971-1991 (vol. 24). a. (back issues avail.; reprint service avail. from ISI) Ardis Publishers, 2901 Heatherway, Ann Arbor, MI 48104.

150   US
RUTGERS SYMPOSIA IN APPLIED PSYCHOLOGY. 1988-1989. irreg. Rutgers University Press, 109 Church St., New Brunswick, NJ 08901.

610   US
RX BEING WELL; the waiting room magazine. 1983-1987. bi-m. B M I - McGraw-Hill, Health Care Group, 800 Second Ave., New York, NY 10017.

610   US   ISSN 0191-961X
RA645.3
RX HOME CARE. 1979-1990. m. (back issues avail.) Bill Communications, Inc. (Akron), 341 White Pond Dr., Akron, OH 44320.

615.9 642.59   US
RX HOME CARE DIRECTORY. 1983-1990. a. (back issues avail.) Bill Communications, Inc. (Akron), 341 White Pond Dr., Akron, OH 44320.
    Formerly: Rx Home Care Buyer's Guide

624   AT
RYDGE'S C C E M - CONSTRUCTION, CIVIL ENGINEERING AND MINING. 1967-1988. m. Rydge Publications Pty. Ltd., 72 Clarnece St., Sydney, N.S.W. 2000, Australia.
    Formerly: Rydge's Construction, Civil Engineering and Mining Review (ISSN 0048-8887)

796.357   US   ISSN 0888-8124
GV863.A1
S A B R REVIEW OF BOOKS; a forum of baseball literary opinion. 1986-1990. a. Society for American Baseball Research, Inc., Box 93183, Cleveland, OH 44101.

371.394   US
S A I N T. (Special and Individual Needs Technology) ceased 1988 (Spring). m. (large print edition) Leaders Digest, Inc., 6803 Whittier Ave., Ste. 200, McLean, VA 22101.

630 016   US
S A T R A: AGRICULTURAL SCIENCES. (Science and Technology Research Abstracts) 1974-1975. q. (microfiche) G.K. Hall & Co., 70 Lincoln Street, Boston, MA 02111.

338.1   GW
S - AGRAR-AKTUELL. 1981-1991. m. Bayerischer Sparkassen-Verband, Karolinenplatz 5, 8000 Munich 2, Germany.
    Formerly (until 1987): S - Landspiegel.

384.554   US
S B C A WEEKLY. 1987-19?? w. (looseleaf format; back issues avail) Satellite Broadcasting & Communications Association, 225 Reinekers Ln., Ste. 600, Alexandria, VA 22314-2322.

350   US
S C A N. (Superior California Administration Newsletter) 1974-19?? a. (back issues avail.) California State University, Chico, School of Behavioral and Social Sciences, Chico, CA 95929.

020   UK   ISSN 0307-6903
S C O C L I S NEWS. 1975-1983. 3/yr. Standing Conference of Co-Operative Library and Information Services, c/o Angela Allott, Ed., Sheffield City Libraries, Surrey SI 1XZ, England.

370 621.381   US   ISSN 0735-8296
                             CODEN: SCOPER
S C O P E; humanities computing update. (Scholarly Communication: Online Publishing and Education) 1983-1987; suspended. bi-m. (back issues avail.) Paradigm Press, Inc., Box 1057, Osprey, FL 34229-1057.

340 657   US   ISSN 0897-800X
K23
S CORPORATIONS (NEW YORK); the journal of tax, legal and business strategies. 1988-1991. q. (also avail. in microform from WSH; reprint service avail. from UMI,WSH) Executive Enterprises Publications Co., Inc., 22 W. 21st St., New York, NY 10010-6904.

068   AT   ISSN 0158-1953
S E A R M G NEWSLETTER. 1972-19?? (no.38). 3/yr. (also avail. in microfiche) Southeast Asian Research Materials Group, Australia National University Library, P.O. Box 4, Canberra City, A.C.T. 2601, Australia.
    Formerly: Southeast Asian Research Materials Group. Newsletter (ISSN 0311-290X)

051   US
S F (SAN FRANCISCO). 1988-1991. m. California Magazine Partnership, 1045 Sansome, San Francisco, CA 94111.

020.9   US   ISSN 0273-2343
Z720.A4
S H A R E; a directory of feminist library workers. (Sisters Have Resources Everywhere) 1975-19?? irreg. Women Library Workers, 2027 Parker, Berkeley, CA 94704.

697 628   GW   ISSN 0931-7775
S H - TECHNIK. (Sanitaeinstallation und Heizungsbau) 1958-1990. bi-m. R. Oldenbourg Verlag GmbH, Rosenheimer Str. 145, 8000 Munich 80, Germany.
    Former titles: Sanitaer-Installateur und Heizungsbauer (ISSN 0340-4439); Sanitaer-und Gas-Installateur.

621.381   US
S I G C O S I M NEWSLETTER. 1972-199? q. Association for Computing Machinery, Special Interest Group on Computer Systems Installation Management, 1515 Broadway, 17th Fl., New York, NY 10036.

418.028   US
S I G L A S H NEWSLETTER. 1968-19?? q. (processed) Association for Computing Machinery, Special Interest Group on Language Analysis and Studies in the Humanities, 1515 Broadway, 17th Fl., New York, NY 10036.
    Formerly: S I C A S H Newsletter (ISSN 0036-147X)

001.539   US
S I M - I M EXCHANGE. (Institutional Member) 1986-19?? q. Society for Information Management, 401 N. Michigan Ave., Chicago, IL 60611-4267.

615.8   SZ
S I N MEDICAL NEWSLETTER. 1978-1987. a. Schweizerisches Institut fuer Nuklearforschung, CH-5234 Villigen PSI, Switzerland.

539.7   SZ
S I N NEWSLETTER. (Included in: Schweizerisches Institut fuer Nuklearforschung. Jahresbericht) ceased 1987. a. Schweizerisches Institut fuer Nuklearforschung, CH-5234 Villigen PSI, Switzerland.
    Formerly: S I N Physics Report.

333.33   US   ISSN 0894-5594
S I O R REPORTS. ceased 1990. bi-m. (back issues avail.) Society of Industrial and Office Realtors, 777 14th St., N.W., Washington, DC 20005-3271.

574.92   UK   ISSN 0080-8121
S.M.B.A. COLLECTED REPRINTS. 1948-1980. a. Scottish Marine Biological Association, Dunstaffage Marine Research Laboratory, P.O.B. 3, OBAN, Argyll, Scotland.

380.3 621.381   US   ISSN 1040-1393
S N A COMMUNICATIONS REPORT; new products, trends, and analysis in the SNA environment. (Systems Network Architecture) 1986-199? bi-w. (back issues avail.) DataTrends Publications, Inc., 8130 Boone Blvd., Ste. 210, Vienna, VA 22182.

674   FR
S O E - BOIS; service d'observation economique des industries du bois. ceased 1982. m. Centre de Perfectionnement pour les Industries du Bois, Service d'Observation Economique, 10 av. de Saint Mande, 75012 Paris, France.

381   US   ISSN 0276-6701
HF5421
S.O.S. DIRECTORY. 1979-19?? a. Save on Shopping Directory, 9109 San Jose Blvd., Jacksonville, FL 32217-5016.
    Formerly: Save On Shopping (ISSN 0092-8003)

711   AT
S.P.A.N.. (State Planning Authority News) 1966-1973. irreg. Department of Environment and Planning, G. P.O. Box 3927, Sydney, N.S.W. 2001, Australia.

020 016   UK   ISSN 0307-5354
Z666
S P E L; a pointer to selected articles and books in European languages. (Selected Publications in European Languages) 1973-1989; suspended. 3/yr. (back issues avail.) College of Librarianship Wales, Library, Llanbadarn Fawr, Aberystwyth SY23 3AS, Wales.

621.381   US   ISSN 0734-0133
QA76.8.T145
S Q. (Syntax Quarterly) 1982-1983. q. (back issues avail.) Syntax ZX80, Inc., (Subsidiary of: Harvard Group), Bolton Rd., R.D. 2, Box 457, Harvard, MA 01451.

614.5 616.9   US
S T D FACT SHEET. (Sexually Transmitted Diseases) ceased 1979. irreg. (also avail. in microfiche) U.S. Centers for Disease Control, Information Services, 1600 Clifton Rd., Atlanta, GA 30333.
    Formerly: V.D. Fact Sheet (ISSN 0095-6937)

621.381   US
S T - LOG; the Atari ST monthly magazine. 1987-19?? m. Larry Flynt Publications, Inc., 9171 Wilshire Blvd., Ste. 300, Beverly Hills, CA 90210.

791.4   US   ISSN 0885-6745
S T V GUIDE. (Satellite Television) 1982-1990 (June). m. Triple D Publishing, Inc., 1300 S. DeKalb St., Box 2347, Shelby, NC 28151-2384.

625   DK   ISSN 0106-3111
S V LEVERINGSBETINGELSER OG PROEVNINGSMETODER. vol.12, 1981-19?? irreg. Statens Vejlaboratorium, Roskilde, Denmark.

384.54   US
S W L SWAPPER. 1991-1992. m. Brendale's - S W L S, Box 1135, Pepperell, MA 01463-1135.

780   GW   ISSN 0080-519X
SAARBRUECKER STUDIEN ZUR MUSIKWISSENSCHAFT. 1966-1985. irreg. (Universitaet des Saarlandes, Musikwissenschaftliches Institut) Baerenreiter Verlag, Heinrich-Schuetz-Allee 31-37, 3500 Kassel-Wilhelmshoehe, Germany.

631   GW   ISSN 0323-4436
SAAT- UND PFLANZGUT. 1959-1991. m. Kombinat Pflanzenzuechtung und Saatgutwirtschaft, c/o Gorkistr. 9, Postfach 951, 5020 Erfurt, Germany.

796.357   US   ISSN 0889-2997
GV877
SABERMETRIC REVIEW; monthly empirical analysis of baseball. 1986-198? m. Meckler Publishing Corporation, 11 Ferry Lane W., Westport, CT 06880-5808.

808.838   IT
SABRINA. ceased 1990 (Dec.). m. Edizioni Lancio, Via Tiburtina km 11.550, Rome, Italy.

338   US   ISSN 0036-2204
SACRAMENTO BUSINESS. 1968-1989 (Dec.). m. (exc. Nov./Dec.). Sacramento Metropolitan Chamber of Commerce, 917 Seventh St., Sacramento, CA 95814.
 Formerly: At Work.

621.381   US
SACRAMENTO SANYO USER'S GROUP NEWSLETTER. ceased 1987 (Feb.). m. Sacramento Sanyo User's Group, c/o Eric Brubakken, Ed., 7433 Auspicious Way, Sacramento, CA 95842.

615.19   SZ   ISSN 0256-730X
SAFETY EVALUATION AND REGULATION OF CHEMICALS. 1983-1986 (vol.3). irreg. (reprint service avail. from ISI) S. Karger AG, Allschwilerstr. 10, P.O Box, CH-4009 Basel, Switzerland.

614.8   US
SAFETY FORUM. 1974-1987. 3/yr. (tabloid format) American Alliance for Health, Physical Education, Recreation, and Dance, 1900 Association Dr., Reston, VA 22091.

658   US
SAFETY MANAGEMENT NEWSLETTER. ceased. m. Merritt Company, 1661 Ninth St., Box 955, Santa Monica, CA 90406.

100   IT
SAGGI FILOSOFICI. 1979-1983 (vol.4). irreg. Casa Editrice Leo S. Olschki, Casella Postale 66, 50100 Florence, Italy.

674   FI   ISSN 0036-262X
SAHAMIES. 1949-1988. 9/yr. Suomen Sahat r.y. - Finnish Sawmills, Saastopankinranta 4 C 24, SF-00530 Helsinki 53, Finland.

797.124   US
SAILBOARD NEWS; the international trade journal of windsurfing. 1979-19?? m. Sports Ink Magazines, Inc., Box 159, 2 South Park Pl., Fair Haven, VT 05743.

920   UK
ST. DAVID'S DAY BILINGUAL SERIES. 1928-1989. a. University of Wales Press, 6 Gwennyth St., Cathays, Cardiff CF2 4YD, Wales.

282   GW   ISSN 0487-2088
ST. HEDWIGSBLATT; katholisches Kirchenblatt im Bistum Berlin. 1954-1990. 52/yr. (Bischofliches Ordinariat Berlin) St. Benno Verlag GmbH, Thueringer Str. 1-3, 7033 Leipzig, Germany.

382   XK
ST. LUCIA. STATISTICAL DEPARTMENT. ANNUAL OVERSEAS TRADE REPORT: PART 1. 1960-1987. a. Statistical Department, New Government Bldg., 2nd Fl., Castries, St. Lucia, W.I.

642   UK
ST. PIERRE PARK HOTEL MAGAZINE. 1986-198? a. Kingsclere Publications Ltd., Highfield House, 2 Highfield Ave., Newbury, Berkshire RG14 5DS, England.

200   US   ISSN 0082-4208
ST. THOMAS MORE LECTURES. 1964-19?? irreg. Yale University Press, 92A Yale Station, New Haven, CT 06520.

646   GW   ISSN 0036-3294
SAISON. 1959-1990. q. Zeitschriftenverlag fuer die Frau, Friedrich-Ebert-Str. 76-78, 7010 Leipzig, Germany.

664.1   UR   ISSN 0036-3340
        CODEN: SAPRAK
SAKHARNAYA PROMYSHLENNOST. 1923-19?? m. (tabloid format) Ministerstvo Sel'skogo Khozyaistva, Moscow, Russian S.F.S.R., U.S.S.R.

658   US   ISSN 0741-6601
SALES & MARKETING DIGEST (BOCA RATON). 1983-19?? m. Newsletter Management Corporation, 951 Broken Sound Pkwy., N.W., Ste. 300, Boca Raton, FL 33431.
 Formerly: Modern Sales Technology.

658.8   US   ISSN 0891-1622
SALES PROMOTION MONITOR. 1983-199? m. (looseleaf format; back issues avail.) Commerce Communications, Inc., 5247 Washburn Ave., S., Minneapolis, MN 55410.

646.7   US
SALON BIZ. 1989; ceased same year (vol.2, no.7). m. (tabloid format) Canon Communications, Inc., 3340 Ocean Park Blvd., Ste. 1000, Santa Monica, CA 90405-3207.

800   US   ISSN 0737-5506
SALTHOUSE. 1987-1989 (no. 18). irreg. (back issues avail.) Salthouse Press, c/o Dept. of English, 800 W. Main, Univ. of Wisconsin, Whitewater, WI 53190-1790.

800   US   ISSN 0226-840X
PS615
SAMISDAT. 1973-1992. a. 456 Monroe Tpke., Monroe, CT 06468.
 Supersedes (until vol.40, no.4): Fourth Dimension; Formerly: Berkeley Samisdat Review.

323.4   US   ISSN 0361-1302
DK274.A2
SAMIZDAT BULLETIN. 1973-19?? m. (looseleaf format; also avail. in microfiche) Samizdat Publications, Inc., Box 6128, San Mateo, CA 94403-0928.

747 659.152   US   ISSN 0893-2697
SAN ANTONIO HOMES & GARDENS. 1985-1989? m. (back issues avail.) Posada Publishing, Box 1684, Austin, TX 78767.

621.381   US
SAN - B U G. ceased. m. Bowie Sanyo Users Group, c/o Carl Katz, Ed., 404 Golf Course Dr., Arnold, MD 21012.

312   US
SAN DIEGO POPULATION AND LAND USE BULLETIN. 1964-1989. s-a. (tabloid format) City Planning Department, 1010 Second Ave., Ste. 600, San Diego, CA 92101.

500.9 500   US   ISSN 0080-5920
QH1   CODEN: SDNMAG
SAN DIEGO SOCIETY OF NATURAL HISTORY. MEMOIRS. 1931-1990 (vol.21, no.19). irreg. San Diego Society of Natural History, San Diego Natural History Museum Library, Box 1390, San Diego, CA 92112.

500.9   US   ISSN 0080-5947
QH1   CODEN: TSDSAW
SAN DIEGO SOCIETY OF NATURAL HISTORY. TRANSACTIONS. 1905-1989 (memoir 16). irreg. (back issues avail.) San Diego Society of Natural History, San Diego Natural History Museum Library, Box 1390, San Diego, CA 92112.
 Incorporates: San Diego Society of Natural History. Occasional Papers (ISSN 0080-5939)

341.1   UK   ISSN 0036-4444
SANITY. 1961-1991. m. Campaign for Nuclear Disarmament, 22-24 Underwood St., London N1 7JG, England.

677.39   JA   ISSN 0036-4495
SF553.J3   CODEN: SAKEAO
SANSHI KENKYU/ACTA SERICOLOGICA. 1952-1988 (no.142). q. National Institute of Sericultural and Entomological Science, 1-2 Owashi, Ibaraki 305, Japan.

333.7   US
SANTA CRUZ ISLAND PRESERVE NEWS. ceased. 2/yr. Santa Cruz Nature Conservancy, 213 Sternwhorf, Santa Barbara, CA 93101.

388.3 625.7   CN
SASKATCHEWAN. DEPARTMENT OF HIGHWAYS AND TRANSPORTATION. TECHNICAL REPORT. 1966-19?? 2/yr. (processed) Department of Highways and Transportation, 1855 Victoria Ave., Regina, Sask. S4P 3V5, Canada.
 Formerly: Saskatchewan. Department of Highways. Technical Report.

690   CN
SASKATCHEWAN BUILDING TRADES YEARBOOK. 1972-19?? a. (back issues avail.) (South Saskatchewan Building and Construction Trades Council) Naylor Communications Ltd. (Winnipeg), 100 Sutherland Ave., Winnipeg, Man. R2W 3C7, Canada.

362.7 613.2   CN
SASKATOON PARENT. ceased 1989. 4/yr. Ad Ventures Magazines, Box 5048, Saskatoon, Sask. S7K 4E3, Canada.

677   II
SASMIRA TECHNICAL DIGEST. 1980-1989 (Dec.). s-a. Silk and Art Silk Mill's Research Association, Sasmira Marg, Worli, Bombay 400 025, India.

677   II   ISSN 0970-6739
SASMIRA'S BULLETIN. 1962-1989 (Aug.). m. Silk and Art Silk Mills' Research Association, Sasmira Marg, Worli, Bombay 400 025, India.

384.55   US
SATELLITE AGE. 1978-19??; suspended. q. (back issues avail.) Martin Roberts & Associates, Inc., Box 5254, Beverly Hills, CA 90210.
 Formerly: Satellite Telecommunications Newsletter.

621.385   US   ISSN 0739-1935
SATELLITE AUDIO REPORT. 1983-19?? m. Waters Information Service, Box 2248, Binghamton, NY 13902-2248.

621.38   US   ISSN 0743-0361
SATELLITE BUSINESS. 1984-19?? m. Video Publishing Company, Box 2772, Palm Springs, CA 92263.

800   US
SATORI; fact & fiction. 1988-19?? q. Hands Off Press, Box 318, Tivoli, NY 12583.

382   US
SAUDI ARABIA MARKET CONDITIONS. 1982-19?? a. Business International Corp., 215 Park Ave. S., New York, NY 10003.
 Formerly: B I Middle East Marketing Conditions: Saudi Arabia; Supersedes in part: B I - Memo.

028.5   YU   ISSN 0036-5092
SAVEZ OMLADINE. 1954-19?? m. Savez Socijalisticke Omladine Vojvodine, Pokrajinska Konferencija, Ljubice Gerovac 1, 41000 Zagreb, Yugoslavia.

331.4   US
HF5500.3.U54
SAVVY WOMAN. 1980-1991 (Feb.). m. (also avail. in microform from UMI; reprint service avail. from UMI) Family Media, Inc., Women's and Fashion Group, 3 Park Ave., New York, NY 10016.
 Formerly (until 1988): Savvy (ISSN 0194-2581)

625.19   US
SCALE COUPLER. 1987-1990. bi-m. Green Lantern Press Ltd., Box 7032, Fairfax Station, VA 22039-7032.

058   GW   ISSN 0721-2089
SCANDICA MAGAZIN; Zeitschrift fuer Kultur und Gesellschaft Skandinaviens. 1981-19?? q. Nordis Holding GmbH, Christophstr. 18-20, 4300 Essen 1, Germany.

792   SW   ISSN 0036-5718
SCEN OCH SALONG. 1915-1990 (vol.7). 5/yr. Folkparkernas Centralorganisation, P.O. Box 17194, S-104 62 Stockholm, Sweden.

791.4   AT
SCENE. 1925-19?? w. (tabloid format; also avail. in microfilm) Herald & Weekly Times Ltd., 44-74 Flinders St., Melbourne, Vic. 3000, Australia.
 Formerly: Listener in T V (ISSN 0024-4406)

CESSATIONS

332.6 US ISSN 0882-2190
SCHABACKER INVESTMENT MANAGEMENT. WEEKLY ADVISORY BULLETIN. 1982-198? w. (back issues avail.) Schabacker Investment Management, 15245 Shady Grove Rd., No. 100, Rockville, MD 20850-3222.

622.338 CN ISSN 0380-4305
TN873.C22
SCHEDULE OF WELLS DRILLED FOR OIL AND GAS IN ALBERTA. 1938-1990. a. (microfiche) Energy Resources Conservation Board, 640 5th Ave. S.W., Calgary, Alta. T2P 3G4, Canada.

830 GW ISSN 0085-5952
SCHMANKERL; Blaetter fuer bayrisch-oesterreichische Heimatliteratur. 1969-19?? 3/yr. Verlag Friedl Brehm, Woerthstr. 18, 8000 Munich 80, Germany.

665.538 GW ISSN 0036-6226
CODEN: SHRGAC
SCHMIERUNGSTECHNIK; Fachzeitschrift fuer Tribotechnik. 1970-1991. m. (Kammer der Technik, Praesidium, Kommission fuer Schmierungstechnik) Verlag Technik GmbH, Oranienburger Str. 13-14, 1020 Berlin, Germany.

070.5 GW
DIE SCHOENSTEN BUECHER DER DEUTSCHEN DEMOKRATISCHEN REPUBLIK. 1963-1987. a. Fachbuchverlag, Karl-Heine-Str. 16, 7031 Leipzig, Germany.
Formerly: Spiegel Deutscher Buchkunst (ISSN 0081-3702)

379 330 US
SCHOOL - BUSINESS PARTNERSHIPS REPORT. 1990; ceased same year. s-m. (Community Development Services, Inc.) C D Publications, 8204 Fenton St., Silver Spring, MD 20910.

375 UK
SCHOOL CURRICULUM DEVELOPMENT COMMITTEE. ANNUAL REPORT (YEAR). ceased 1988. a. School Curriculum Development Committee, Newcombe House, 45 Notting Hill Gate, London W11 3JB, England.

379 US
SCHOOL IMPROVEMENT EXCHANGE. 1989-1991. a. State Department of Education, 721 Capitol Mall, Sacramento, CA 95814.

027.8 370 AT ISSN 0158-9172
SCHOOL LIBRARIES IN AUSTRALIA. 1971-19?? (vol.13, no.2). q. Australian School Library Association, P.O. Box 450, Belconnen, A.C.T. 2617, Australia.

027.8 CN ISSN 0706-2915
SCHOOL LIBRARY NEWSLETTER. 1972-19??; suspended. irreg. Prince Edward Island Provincial Library, Enman Cres., Box 7500, Charlottetown, P.E.I. C1A 8T8, Canada.
Formerly (until Apr. 1978): School Library Association Newsletter (ISSN 0706-2907)

376 AT ISSN 0158-6289
SCHOOL MATHEMATICS JOURNAL. 1976-19?? 3/yr. Newcastle Mathematical Association, Newcastle College of Advanced Education, P.O. Box 84, Waratah, N.S.W. 2298, Australia.

375 UK ISSN 0140-7732
SCHOOL TECHNOLOGY. 1972-1989 (vol.90). 4/yr. Trent Polytechnic, Trent International Centre for School Technology, Burton St., Nottingham NG1 4BU, England.

910.2 UK
SCHOOLS AND COLLEGES WELCOME. 1978-198? a. Lewis Productions Ltd., Unit 3, River Gardens Bus. Centre, Spur Rd., Feltham, Middx TW14 OSN, England.

551.46 US
SCHOOLWORD. 1974-1992. 4/yr. (back issues avail.) Mystic Marinelife Aquarium, Attn.: Education Dept., 55 Coogan Blvd., Mystic, CT 06355-1997.

830 GW ISSN 0179-6429
SCHREISSE; 'pataphysische Nachrichten. 1985-1990. s-a. Franz und Segebrecht, Walther-Rathenau-Str. 35, 7410 Reutlingen, Germany.

940 320 322.4 GW
SCHRIFTENREIHE DAS ANDERE DEUTSCHLAND. 1981-19?? irreg. Donat & Temmen Verlag, Hohenlohestr. 21, 2800 Bremen 1, Germany.

700 GW ISSN 0723-0788
SCHRIFTENREIHE DER HOCHSCHULE DER KUENSTE BERLIN. 1980-1984 (vol.7). irreg. (Hochschule der Kuenste Berlin) Colloquium Verlag, Unter den Eichen 93, 1000 Berlin 45, Germany.

630 340 AU
SCHRIFTENREIHE FUER AGRARWIRTSCHAFT. 1973-1979. irreg. Oesterreichische Gesellschaft Agrarrecht, Peter Jordan Str. 82, A-1190 Vienna, Austria.

711.4 338.9 AU ISSN 0558-9746
SCHRIFTENREIHE FUER RAUMFORSCHUNG UND RAUMPLANUNG. 1957-1990. irreg. Amt der Kaerntner Landesregierung, Abteilung Landesplanung, Wulfengasse 13, A-9020 Klagenfurt, Austria.

053.1 AU
SCHRIFTTUMSSPIEGEL. 1971-1990. q. Gesellschaft fuer Ganzheitsforschung, Augasse 2-6, A-1090 Vienna, Austria.

610 DK ISSN 0109-260X
SCHULTZ MEDICINALBIBLIOTEK. PUBLIKATION. ceased. a. Schultz Jurist-Forbundet, Mondergade 21, DK-1116 Copenhagen K, Denmark.

789.91 US ISSN 0893-0449
ML156.2
SCHWANN. 1949-1989 (Dec.). q. (back issues avail.) Schwann Publications, 535 Boylston St., Boston, MA 02116.

780.65 US ISSN 0893-0430
ML156.2
SCHWANN C D; your guide to compact discs. ceased 1989 (vol.4, no.12). m. N I L S Publishing, 21625 Prairie St., Chatsworth, CA 91311.

669.722 SZ ISSN 0036-7257
TS554 CODEN: SALRAY
SCHWEIZER ALUMINIUM RUNDSCHAU/REVUE SUISSE DE L'ALUMINIUM. 1951-1989. bi-m. Swiss Aluminium Ltd., Klausstrasse 10, CH-8008 Zurich, Switzerland.

687 677 SZ
SCHWEIZERISCHER ARBEITGEBERVERBAND FUER DAS SCHNEIDERGEWERBE. NEWSLETTER. ceased 1988. bi-m. Schweizerischer Arbeitgeberverband fuer das Schneidergewerbe - Syndicat Suisse des Maitres-Tailleurs, Marktgass 6, CH-9229 Bischofszell, Switzerland.

070 SZ
SCHWEIZERISCHER VERBAND DER ZEITUNGS- UND ZEITSCHRIFTENVERLEGER. BULLETIN. 1921-1991. 6/yr. Schweizerischer Verband der Zeitungs- und Zeitschriftenverleger - Swiss Newspaper Publishers Association, Baumackerstr. 42, Postfach, CH-8050 Zurich, Switzerland.
Formerly: Schweizerischer Zeitungsverleger-Verband. Bulletin (ISSN 0036-7923)

610 GW
SCHWERPUNKT-MEDIZIN. 1978-1990. bi-m. Selecta-Verlag, Pasinger Str. 8, 8033 Planegg, Germany.

700 500 300 001.3 US
SCIARTS. 1984-198? q. University of Alaska, College of Arts and Sciences, 3211 Providence Dr., Anchorage, AK 99508.

500 600 330 UK
SCIENCE & BUSINESS. 1984-19?? bi-m. Mark Allen Scientific Publishing Ltd., Croxted News, 288 Croxted Rd. Hill, London SE24 9DA, England.
Former titles: Science and Business Link-Up (ISSN 0267-8837); Science - Technology - Industry Link-Up.

200 US ISSN 0193-3396
Q174
SCIENCE AND NATURE; the annual of Marxist philosophy for natural scientists. 1978-1989; suspended. a. (back issues avail.) c/o Lloyd Motz, Columbia University, Pupin Hall, Box 57, New York, NY 10027.

500 620 US ISSN 0036-8245
Q1
SCIENCE AND TECHNOLOGY (NEW YORK); an interdisciplinary monthly magazine for professional scientists and engineers. 1962-1969. m. International Communications, 48 E. 43rd St., 4th Fl., New York, NY 10017.
Formerly: International Science and Technology.

500 600 US ISSN 1041-2557
SCIENCE & TECHNOLOGY ANNUAL REFERENCE REVIEW. ceased 1991. a. Oryx Press, 4041 N. Central at Indian School Rd., Phoenix, AZ 85012-3397.

500 CN
SCIENCE AND TECHNOLOGY DIMENSIONS. 1969-19??; both eds. suspended. 11/yr. (also avail. in microform from UMI; reprint service avail. from UMI) (National Research Council) Science & Technologie Mondex Inc., P.O. Box 250, Toronto, Ont. M5C 9Z9, Canada.
Former titles: Science Dimension (ISSN 0036-830X); N R C Research News.

500 600 US
SCIENCE & TECHNOLOGY UPDATE. 1976-1990 (June). q. E G & G, Inc., Corporate Communication Department, 45 William St., Wellesley, MA 02181.
Formerly (until 1985): Energy and Environmental Update.

500 600 US
SCIENCE & TECHNOLOGY VIDEO MAGAZINE. 1989-1990. 9/yr. (avail. only on video cassette) Encyclopaedia Britannica, Inc., 310 S. Michigan St., Chicago, IL 60604.

809 AT ISSN 0156-6342
SCIENCE FICTION NEWS. 1953-1983; suspended. irreg. Australian Science Fiction Association, Box 4440, Sydney, N.S.W. 2001, Australia.
Supersedes: Australian Science Fiction Association. Journal (ISSN 0084-7585)

300 UK ISSN 0144-8447
SCIENCE FOR PEOPLE. 1973-1989. q. (also avail. in microform from UMI; reprint service avail. from UMI) Science for People, 25 Horsell Rd., London N5 1XL, England.

029.7 500 US
SCIENCE TECHNOLOGY: INFORMATION. 1969-19?? bi-m. Trends Publishing Inc., National Press Bldg., Washington, DC 20045.
Formerly: Scientific Information Notes (ISSN 0036-8784)

681.1 SW ISSN 0036-8598
CODEN: SCTOAB
SCIENCE TOOLS; the L K B instrument journal. 1954-1987 (vol.34, no.1). 2/yr. L K B - Produkter AB, Box 305, S-161 26 Bromma, Sweden.

621.3 SZ ISSN 0036-8695
TK1.A1 CODEN: SCELAT
SCIENTIA ELECTRICA; journal for modern problems of theoretical and applied electrical engineering. 1955-1990. 4/yr. (Eidgenoessische Technische Hochschule Zuerich, Abteilung fuer Elektrotechnik - Swiss Federal Institute of Technology, Department of Electrical Engineering) Birkhauser Verlag AG, Klosterberg 23, P.O. Box 133, CH-4010 Basel, Switzerland.

505 HK ISSN 0586-5751
SCIENTIFIC DIRECTORY OF HONG KONG. 1968-1978. quadrennial. Government Information Services, Beaconsfield House, Queen's Rd., Central, Victoria, Hong Kong.

778 HU ISSN 0236-9702
SCIENTIFIC FILMS AND VIDEOCASSETTES. 1985-19?? q. Orszagos Muszaki Informacios Kozpont es Konyvtar (O.M.I.K.K.) - National Technical Information Centre and Library, Muzeum u. 17, P.O. Box 12, 1428 Budapest, Hungary.
Formerly: Technical and Scientific Films (ISSN 0231-4932)

170 317.3 US
SCIENTIFIC INTEGRITY. 1982-1989. q. National Association of Biology Teachers, Inc., 11250 Roger Bacon Dr., Ste. 19, Reston, VA 22090.

500 IT
SCIENZA 82. ceased. m. (10/yr.). Gruppo Editoriale Fabbri SPA, Via Mecenate 91, 20138 Milan, Italy.

687.11 US
SCOREBOARD. ceased 1978. q. Young Menswear Association of Men's Apparel Industry, 1328 Broadway, New York, NY 10001.

799 US
SCOTCH GAME CALL HUNTING ANNUAL. ceased. a. Aqua-Field Publishing Co., Inc., 66 W. Gilbert St., Shrewsbury, NJ 07702.

914.2 UK ISSN 0267-338X
SCOTLAND'S BEST HOLIDAYS. 1974-199? a. F.H.G. Publications Ltd., Abbey Mill Business Centre, Seedhill, Paisley PA1 1JN, Scotland.

929 US ISSN 0730-4986
CS71
SCOTT SCANNER. 1977-1982. q. Kenma Publishing Co., Box 2786, Evansville, IN 47714-0786.

052 UK ISSN 0268-053X
SCOTTISH AMBASSADOR. 1986-1987. q. Wilton Kindalloch Ltd., Comrie, Perthshire PH6 2LJ, Scotland.

630 UK
SCOTTISH FARMING LEADER. 1948-1990. m. National Farmers' Union of Scotland, 17 Grosvenor Crescent, Edinburgh EH12 5EN, Scotland.

782.1 UK ISSN 0309-7323
SCOTTISH OPERA NEWS. 1976-198? 6/yr. Scottish Opera Ltd., 39 Elmbank Crescent, Glasgow G2 4PT, Scotland.
Supersedes: Scottish Opera Magazine.

751.6 UK ISSN 0264-9039
SCOTTISH SOCIETY FOR CONSERVATION AND RESTORATION. BULLETIN. 1983-1989. irreg. Scottish Society for Conservation and Restoration, Department of Conservation and Analytical Research, Royal Museum of Scotland, Chambers Street, Edinburgh EH1 1JA, Scotland.
Formerly (until 1983): Scottish Society for the Conservation and Restoration of Historic and Artistic Works. Newsletter (ISSN 0260-5597)

001.94 US
SEARCH - FLYING SAUCERS. ceased 1990. q. (also avail. in microfilm from UMI; reprint service avail. from BLH, UMI) Palmer Publications, Inc., Box 296, Amherst, WI 54406.
Formed by the 1976 merger of: Search (Amherst) (ISSN 0037-0290); Flying Saucers (ISSN 0015-489X) Incorporating: Ray Palmer's Forum.

929 US
SEARCHING ILLINOIS ANCESTORS - TRAVEL ILLINOIS. 1984-19?? bi-m. Helen Cox Tregillis, Ed. & Pub., Box 107, Cowden, IL 62423-0107.
Formerly: Searching Illinois Ancestors (ISSN 0886-7763)

382 UK
SEATRADE ARAB SHIPPING GUIDE. 1978-1991. a. Seatrade Publications Ltd., Seatrade House, 42-48 North Station Rd., Colchester CO1 1RB, England.
Former titles: Arab Shipping; Seatrade Guide to Arab Shipping (ISSN 0141-4151)

387 UK
SEATRADE TURKISH SHIPPING GUIDE. 1979-1991. a. Seatrade Publications Ltd., Seatrade House, 42-48 North Station Rd., Colchester CO1 1RB, England.
Former titles: Turkish Shipping; (until 1984): Latin American Shipping; Seatrade Guide to Latin American Shipping (ISSN 0142-5064)

387 UK
HE561
SEATRADE U.S. SHIPPING GUIDE. 1979-1991. a. Seatrade Publications Ltd., Seatrade House, 42-48 North Station Rd., Colchester CO1 1RB, England.
Formerly: Seatrade U.S. Yearbook (ISSN 0142-5056) 1985 edition published as: Seatrade North America Yearbook.

650 US ISSN 0037-0444
SEATTLE BUSINESS. vol.54, 1970-1990 (Aug.). m. Vernon Publications Inc., 3000 Northup Way, Ste. 200, Bellevue, WA 98004.

811 US ISSN 0048-9956
SECOND COMING. 1972-1989 (Dec.). 2/yr. (back issues avail.; reprint service avail. from UMI) Second Coming, Inc., 118 Laidley St., Box 31249, San Francisco, CA 94131.

323.4 US ISSN 0748-9528
SECOND OPINION (SAN FRANCISCO). 1974-1986. q. (looseleaf format; back issues avail.) Coalition for the Medical Rights of Women, 2845 24th St., San Francisco, CA 94110.

373 371 UK
SECONDARY HEADS ASSOCIATION REVIEW. 1902-1988. 2/yr. Secondary Heads Association, 130 Regent Rd., Leicester LE1 7P6, England.
Formerly: Headmasters Association Review (ISSN 0046-6980)

373 AT ISSN 0728-9006
SECONDARY JOURNAL (SYDNEY); years 6-12. 1982-1989 (no.2). 2/yr. Department of School Education, G.P.O. Box 33, Sydney, N.S.W. 2001, Australia.

332 US
SECONDARY MORTGAGE MARKET ANALYSIS. ceased. m. Warren, Gorham and Lamont Inc., One Penn Plaza, New York, NY 10119.

670 US
SECONDARY WOOD PRODUCTS MANUFACTURERS DIRECTORY. 1989-199? irreg. Miller Freeman Publications, Inc., 600 Harrison St., San Francisco, CA 94107.

346 US
SECURITIES LAW ANTHOLOGY. 1988; announced, never published. a. International Library Law Book Publishers, Inc., 101 Lakeforest Blvd., Ste. 270, Gaithersburg, MD 20877.

327 US
SECURITY AND INTELLIGENCE FOUNDATION. NIGHTWATCH. 1986-1990. q. (tabloid format; back issues avail.) Security and Intelligence Foundation, 301 S. Columbus St., Alexandria, VA 22314-3603.

327 US
SECURITY AND INTELLIGENCE FOUNDATION. SITUATION REPORT. 1977-19?? s-a. (tabloid format; back issues avail.) Security and Intelligence Foundation, 2800 Shirlington Rd., No. 405, Arlington, VA 22206.

651 364.4 US
SECURITY SYSTEMS. 1971-1988 (Jan.); suspended. m. P T N Publishing Corp., 210 Crossways Park Dr., Woodbury, NY 11797.
Former titles: Security Systems Administration; Security Industry and Product News.

631 UK
SEED POTATO. ceased 1991. s-a. National Association of Seed Potato Merchants, Palmer House, Suite A, Palmer Lane, Coventry CV1 1FN, England.

635 US
SEEDPEOPLE NETWORK. NEWSLETTER. ceased. 4/yr. Seedpeople Network, Box 1466, Chelan, WA 98816.

283 SA ISSN 0037-0827
SEEK. 1961-1990. m. Church of the Province of Southern Africa, Seek Board, P.O. Box 4849, Johannesburg 2000, South Africa.

616.89 JA ISSN 0037-1076
SEISHIN BUNSEKI/TOKYO JOURNAL OF PSYCHOANALYSIS. 1933-1977 (vol.35, no.1). q. Tokyo Institute for Psychoanalysis - Tokyo Seishin Bunsekigaku Kenkyujo, 281 Nishinasuno, Tochigi 329-27, Japan.

614.7 JA ISSN 0386-8141
CODEN: SKGKDR
SEITAI KAGAKU/AQUATIC ECOLOGICAL CHEMISTRY. 1978-1989 (vol.9, no.4). q. (back issues avail.) Scientist Inc. - Saientistosha, Yamazaki Bldg., 3-2, Kanda Surugadai, Chiyoda-ku, Tokyo 101, Japan.

200 294 US
SELBST-VERWIRKLICHUNG: JAHRESHEFT. 1959-1991. a. Self-Realization Fellowship, Inc., 3880 San Rafael Ave., Los Angeles, CA 90065.
Formerly (until 1969): Gemeinschaft der Selbst-Verwirklichung. Jahresheft (ISSN 0072-0577)

069 016 CS
SELECTED BIBLIOGRAPHY OF MUSEOLOGICAL LITERATURE. 1970-1990 (vol.21). a. Slovenske Narodne Muzeum, Muzeologicky Ustav, Vajanskeho Nabrezie 2, 814 36 Bratislava, Czechoslovakia.

Formerly: Bibliographical Selection of Museological Literature (ISSN 0067-6861)

665.5 AU ISSN 0080-858X
SELECTED DOCUMENTS OF THE INTERNATIONAL PETROLEUM INDUSTRY. 1966-1978. irreg. Organization of the Petroleum Exporting Countries, Public Information Department, Obere-Donaustr. 93, A-1020 Vienna, Austria.

011 US
SELECTION GUIDE SERIES. ceased. irreg. Neal-Schuman Publishers, Inc., 100 Varick St., New York, NY 10013.

658.8 US ISSN 1040-9742
SELLING RED. ceased 1990. m. McGraw-Hill, Inc., 1221 Ave. of the Americas, New York, NY 10020.

200 UK ISSN 0266-3392
SELLY OAK JOURNAL. 1984-1989. 2/yr. Selly Oak Colleges, Bristol Rd., Birmingham B29 6LQ, England.

330.9 621.3 US
SEMICONDUCTOR ECONOMICS REPORT; covering the economics of the microelectronics industry. 1986-1989 (vol.4, no.4). m. (looseleaf format; back issues avail.) D M Data, Inc., 6900 E. Camelback Rd., Ste. 1000, Scottsdale, AZ 85251.
Formerly: Technology Trends Newsletter.

020 US ISSN 0361-9966
SEMINAR ON THE ACQUISITION OF LATIN AMERICAN LIBRARY MATERIALS. RESOLUTIONS AND LISTS OF COMMITTEES. ceased 1978 (no.23). irreg. University of Massachusetts, Seminar on the Acquisition of Latin American Library Materials, Amherst, MA 01002.

610 US ISSN 0748-6480
SEMINARS IN ADOLESCENT MEDICINE. 1985-19?? (vol.3). q. (also avail. in microfilm) Thieme Medical Publishers, Inc., 381 Park Ave. S., Ste. 1501, New York, NY 10016.

610 US
SEMINARS IN OCCUPATIONAL MEDICINE. 1986-1987 (vol.2, no.4). q. (also avail. in microfilm) Thieme Medical Publishers, Inc., 381 Park Ave., So., Ste. 1501, New York, NY 10016.

492 892 SA ISSN 0256-6044
PJ3001
SEMITICS. (Subseries of University of South Africa. Miscellanea) 1970-198? (vol.10). irreg. University of South Africa, Box 392, Pretoria 0001, South Africa.

320 US
SENATE ISSUES YEARBOOK. 1980-1987. a. Conservative Caucus Research Analysis and Education Foundation, 450 Maple Ave. E., Vienna, VA 22180.

301.435 US
SENIOR AMERICAN NEWS. 1975-1989. m. Prime National Publishing Corp., 470 Boston Post Rd., Weston, MA 02193.

362.6 US
SENIOR PATIENT. 1989-1991 (Mar.-Apr.). m. (Postgraduate Medicine) McGraw-Hill, Inc., 1221 Avenue of the Americas, New York, NY 10020.

301.435 US
SENIOR WORLD OF THE CENTRAL COAST; serving active older adults of Santa Barbara, Ventura, San Luis Obispo Counties. 1985-1991 (Dec.). m. Californian Publishing Co., 1000 Pioneer Way, Box 1565, El Cajon, CA 92022.

332.678 US
SENIORS' MONEY ALERT. 1983-1991 (Dec.). m. (looseleaf format; back issues avail.) Myrtle Brickman, Ed. & Pub., 11905 Bennett Rd., Herndon, VA 22071.
Formerly: Brickman Letter (ISSN 0748-1853)

630 US
SENSIBLE AGRICULTURE. ceased 1991 (May). m. Northcutt Communications, Box 134, Port Orchard, WA 98366-0134.

CESSATIONS

588.2   JA   ISSN 0037-2277
SENTAI CHII ZAPPO/MISCELLANEA BRYOLOGICA ET LICHENOLOGICA. 1955-1983. 3/yr. (back issues avail.) Hattori Botanical Laboratory - Hattori Shokubutsu Kenkyujo, Obi, Nichinan-shi, Miyazaki-ken 889-25, Japan.

330   KO
SEOUL NATIONAL UNIVERSITY. ECONOMIC REVIEW. 1967-1988. a. Seoul National University, Institute of Economic Research - Seoul Daehakkyo Kyeongje Yeonguso, Seoul 151-742, S. Korea.

808.81   US
SEPARATE DOORS. 198?-1986. s-a. Jelm Mountain Press, 209 Park St., Laramie, WY 82070.

325   AT   ISSN 0310-740X
SERBIAN BULLETIN. 1972-19?? m. Serbian National Defence, c/o Gvozden Bralovic, Box 236, Canberra City, A.C.T. 2601, Australia.

639.9   TZ
SERENGETI RESEARCH INSTITUTE. ANNUAL REPORT. 1966-1977. a. Serengeti Research Institute, P.O. Seronera, via Arusha, Arusha, Tanzania.

011   UK
SERIALS IN C L W LIBRARY. 1981-1988; suspended. a. College of Librarianship Wales, Library, Llanbadarn Fawr, Aberystwyth SY23 3AS, Wales.

638   JA   ISSN 0581-5908
SERICULTURAL EXPERIMENT STATION. ANNUAL REPORT/SANSHI SHIKENJO NENPO. 1960-19?? a. National Institute of Sericultural and Entomological Science - Sanshi Shikenjo, 1-2 Owashi, Ibaraki 305, Japan.

581   SP
SERIE BOTANICA. 1982-1987 (no.6). irreg. (Universidad de Navarra, Facultad de Ciencias) Ediciones Universidad de Navarra, S.A., Apdo. 396, 31080 Pamplona, Spain.

677.2   SP
SERIE DE INGENIERIA DE LA CALIDAD. ceased. Asociacion de Investigacion Textil Algodonera, Gran via de les Corts Catalanes 670, 08010 Barcelona, Spain.

370   AG
SERIE LEGISLACION EDUCATIVA ARGENTINA. suspended. irreg. (Ministerio de Educacion y Justicia) Centro Nacional de Documentacion e Informacion Educativa, Paraguay 1657-ler. piso, 1062-Capital Federal, Argentina.

028.5   DK
SERIE MAGASINET. ceased. 18/yr. Interpresse, Krogshoejvej 32, 2880 Bagsvaerd, Denmark.

332.6 336   UK   ISSN 0267-7571
SERVICE COMPRIS. 1983-1991. s-a. (back issues avail.) Mary Glasgow Publications, Avenue House, 131 Holland Park Ave., London W11 4UT, England.

332.1   US
SERVICE CORPORATION DIRECTORY. 1976-19?? irreg. United States League of Savings Institutions, 111 E. Wacker Dr., Chicago, IL 60601.

380.5   DK   ISSN 0109-7334
SERVICE- OG VAREVOGNE; service and delivery vans. 1979-1990. q. Thomson Communications (Scandinavia) A-S, Stueneegade 7-9, DK-2200 Copenhagen N, Denmark.

820   SA
SESAME. 1982-1992 (no.15). irreg. (2-3/yr.). Renoster Books, P.O. Box 260, Rivonia 2128, South Africa.

636.7   US   ISSN 0199-6738
SETTER QUARTERLY. 1979-198? q. Hoflin Publishing Ltd., 4401 Zephyr St., Wheat Ridge, CO 80033-3299.

051   US   ISSN 0271-3012
PR471
SEVEN (LAKEWOOD); an Anglo-American literary journal. 1980-1991. a. (also avail. in microfilm; microfiche from BHP; back issues avail.) (Marion E. Wade Collection at Wheaton College) Bookmakers Guild, Inc., 9655 W. Colfax Ave., Lakewood, CO 80215.

811   US
SEVEN (OKLAHOMA CITY). 1958-1982? irreg. 3630 N.W. 22, Oklahoma City, OK 73107-2893.

677   US   ISSN 0029-4292
SEW BUSINESS. 1866-1989 (Dec.). m. Gralla Publications (Dallas), 15400 Knoll Trail, Ste. 112, Dallas, TX 75248.
Formerly: Home Sewing.

614.7   US   ISSN 0149-5879
SEWAGE TREATMENT CONSTRUCTION GRANTS MANUAL. 1976-1989 (Jun.). m. (looseleaf format; back issues avail.) The Bureau of National Affairs, Inc., 1231 25th St., N.W., Washington, DC 20037.

687 670   AT
SEWTRADE C F I YEARBOOK. 1989-19?? a. (Clothing and Footwear Institute) Publishing and Production Projects, Edgecliff Centre, P.O. Box 343, Edgecliff, N.S.W. 2027, Australia.

621.381   US   ISSN 0731-2180
SEXTANT; independent magazine for the users of Heath-Zenith microcomputers. 1982-198? 8/yr. Sextant Publishing Company, 716 E St., S.E., Washington, DC 20003.

360   IS
SHACHAR. ceased. q. Association for the Development and Advancement of Personnel in the Social Services, Givat Joint, Jerusalem, Israel.

929   US   ISSN 1055-4653
SHACKELFORD NEWSLETTER. 1953-1992 (Oct.). q. Mary Jane Shackelford Kaiser, Ed. & Pub., 5752 Wheelock Rd., Fort Wayne, IN 46835.

289.9   US   ISSN 1041-0198
SHAKER SPIRIT. 1989-19?? bi-m. Point Publishing Co., Inc., Box 1309, Point Pleasant, NJ 08742.

808.81   US   ISSN 0037-329X
PN6010.5
SHANTIH; new international writings. 1971-1982 (vol.4, no.4); suspended. irreg. c/o Irving Gottesman, Box 1930, Canal St. Sta., New York, NY 10013-0872.

332.6   AT   ISSN 0037-3311
SHAREHOLDER. 1966-1991 (Oct.). irreg. Australian Shareholders Association, N.S.W. Branch, 51 Pitt St., Sydney, N.S.W. 2000, Australia.

663.2   UK   ISSN 0307-1170
SHAW'S WINE GUIDE. 1972-198? s-a. Shaw's Price Guide Ltd., P.O. 32, Abingdon, Oxfordshire OX14 3LJ, England.

669.1   GW   ISSN 0178-6849
SHEET METAL TUBES SECTIONS; technical journal for production, treatment and refinement of strip, sheet metal, tubes and sections including all related subjects. 1982-1990; suspended. 2/yr. Meisenbach GmbH, Hainstr. 18, Postfach 2069, 8600 Bamberg, Germany.

780   US   ISSN 0197-3495
M1630.18
SHEET MUSIC. STANDARD ORGAN EDITION. 1976-1991. 6/yr. Sheet Music Magazine, Inc., 223 Katonah Ave., Katonah, NY 10536.
Formerly: Sheet Music (ISSN 0164-386X)

340   US
SHEPARD'S UNITED STATES SUPREME COURT CASE COMMENTARIES. ceased 1989. a. (also avail. in audio cassette) Shepard's - McGraw-Hill, Inc., Box 35300, Colorado Springs, CO 80935-3530.

361   US   ISSN 0037-3605
SHEPHERD'S CALL. 1951-19?? bi-m. Little Brothers of the Good Shepherd, Box 260, Momence, IL 60954-0260.

614.7 639.2 574.5   IE   ISSN 0332-2629
SHERKIN ISLAND. JOURNAL. 1980-19?? s-a. (back issues avail.) Sherkin Island Marine Station, Sherkin Island, Co. Cork, Ireland.

052   UK
SHERLOCK HOLMES MYSTERY BOOK. ceased 1981. irreg. World Distributors Ltd., P.O. Box 111, 12 Lever St., Manchester M60 1TS, England.

133   US
SHETOTEM. 1984-1991 (vol.7, no.2). q. (tabloid format) Panic Press, Box 27465, San Antonio, TX 78227-0465.

339   CC
SHIJIE JINGJI DAOBAO/WORLD ECONOMIC HERALD. ceased. d. (newspaper) Shijie Jingji Daobao She, Shanghai, People's Republic of China.

621.3   JA   ISSN 0037-3745
CODEN: SNDKBV
SHIN NIPPON DENKI GIHO/NEW NIPPON ELECTRIC TECHNICAL REVIEW. 1972-1981. a. N E C Kansai, Ltd., 2-9-1 Seiran, Otsu-shi, Shiga-ken 520, Japan.

623.82   US
SHIPBUILDERS COUNCIL OF AMERICA. STATISTICAL QUARTERLY. ceased. q. Shipbuilders Council of America, 4301 Fairfax Dr., No. 330, Arlington, VA 22201-1627.

352   AT   ISSN 0037-3966
SHIRE & MUNICIPAL RECORD. 1908-1991. m. Law Book Co. Ltd., 44-50 Waterloo Rd., North Ryde, N. S.W. 2112, Australia.

677   UK
CODEN: SIPUDK
SHIRLEY PUBLICATIONS. S: SERIES. 1972-1988. irreg. (reprint service avail.) British Textile Technology Group, Shirley Towers, Manchester M20 8RX, England.
Formerly: Shirley Institute Publications. S: Series (ISSN 0306-5154)

500   JA   ISSN 0910-5190
SHIZEN HAKUBUTSUEN KIYO. published only once, 1984. a. Toyama-ken Shizen Hakubutsuen - Toyama Field Museum, 1-1 Yoshizumi, Fuchu-machi, Nei-gun, Toyama-ken 939-26, Japan.

808.87   CN   ISSN 0824-7870
DER SHMAISER/SPANKER. published only once, 1984. irreg. David Botwinik, Ed. & Pub., 5775 Wentworth, Cote St. Luc, Montreal, Que. H4W 2S3, Canada.

296   US   ISSN 0885-8659
DS101
SHMATE. 1982-19?? 4/yr. (also avail. in microform from UMI; back issues avail.) Box 4228, Berkeley, CA 94704.

340   IS
SHNATON HAMISHPAT HAIVRI. 1974-1988. a. Institute for the Study of Hebrew Law, Hebrew University, Mount Scopus, Jerusalem 91 905, Israel.

940   US
SHOAH; a journal of Holocaust resources. 1978-19?? 3/yr. National Jewish Center for Learning & Leadership, c/o C L A L, 47 W. 34th St., 2nd fl., New York, NY 10001-3012.

800   US
SHOCK SUSPENSTORIES; extra-large comics. 1991; announced, never published. bi-m. Russ Cochran Publisher, Ltd., Box 469, W. Plains, MO 65775-0469.

639.9   UK
SHOOTING & CONSERVATION. 1955-19??; suspended. q. (The British Association for Shooting and Conservation) Litharne Ltd., P.O. Box 9, Stratford Upon Avon, Warwickshire, England.
Formerly: W A G B I Magazine; Incorporates: Gamekeepers' Gazette (ISSN 0016-433X)

338   US
SHOP BY MAIL DIRECTORY FOR PERSONAL COMPUTER USERS. published only once, 1986. irreg. Pilot Books, 103 Cooper St., Babylon, NY 11702.

333.33   UK   ISSN 0037-4199
SHOP PROPERTY. 1967-1990. m. Newman Books Ltd., 32 Vauxhall Bridge Rd., London SW1V 2SS, England.

658   CN   ISSN 0226-7551
SHOPPING CENTRE CANADA. 1979-1988 (Mar.). a. Maclean Hunter Ltd., Business Publication Division, Maclean Hunter Bldg., 777 Bay St., Toronto, Ont. M5W 1A7, Canada.

658   US
SHOW & SELL. 1986-198? m. (back issues avail.) ProTech Publishing & Communications, Box 212, SR 245, Santa Claus, IN 47579.

792 FR ISSN 0037-430X
SHOW-BUSINESS. ceased. w. 22 rue Huyghens, Paris (16e), France.

613.62 GW
SICHERHEIT BERGBAU, ENERGIEWIRTSCHAFT, GEOLOGIE, METALLURGIE. 1954-19?? 4/yr. Deutscher Verlag fuer Grundstoffindustrie, Karl-Heine-Str. 27, 7031 Leipzig, Germany.
Former titles: Sicherheit Bergbau, Energiewirtschaft, Metallurgie (ISSN 0037-4520); Sicherheit.

368.4 IT ISSN 0037-4598
SICUREZZA SOCIALE; dottrina, giurisprudenza, informazioni. 1945-19??; suspended. bi-m. Patronato ACLI, Via G. Marcora 1820, 00153 Rome, Italy.

338 US
SIDELINE BUSINESS NEWSLETTER. 1982-1987. m. (looseleaf format; back issues avail.) J G Press, Inc., Box 351, Emmaus, PA 18049.

625.19 DK ISSN 0900-470X
SIDESPORET; det danske modelbaneblad. 1979-1986 (Nov.). q. U K - Modeller, Liljehaven 19, 2760 Maaloev, Denmark.
Formerly: U K - Modelinformation (ISSN 0108-7258)

531.64 621.3 GW
SIEMENS ENERGY AND AUTOMATION WITH PRODUCT NEWS. ceased 1991. 10/yr. Siemens Verlag AG, Postfach 3240, 8520 Erlangen, Germany.
Former titles: Siemens Power Engineering and Automation Product News; Siemens Power Engineering Product News (ISSN 0721-5681)

651.8 001.64 GW
SIEMENS-MAGAZIN COM. 1966-1990. 6/yr. Siemans Verlag AG, Postfach 3240, 8520 Erlangen, Germany.
Former titles: Data Report (ISSN 0374-289X); Siemens Data Report (ISSN 0037-4652)

809 CN ISSN 0380-6693
SIFT. 1974-19?? St. Mary's University, English Department, Halifax, N.S. B3H 3C3, Canada.

617.7 US
SIGHT. 1986-1990. 3/yr. (reprint service avail.) Co-Optics of America, Inc., 413 River Street Service Road, Oneonta, NY 13820.

980 MX
SIGLO 19; revista de historia. 1986-19?? (vol.5, no. 10). s-a. Universidad Autonoma de Nuevo Leon, Facultad de Filosofia y Letras, Apdo. Postal 3024, 64000 Monterrey, Nuevo Leon, Mexico.

028.5 UK
SIGNAL SELECTION OF CHILDREN'S BOOKS. 1985-1991. a. Thimble Press, Lockwood Station Rd., South Woodchester, Nr. Stroud, Glos. GL5 5EQ, England.
Supersedes: Signal Review (ISSN 0264-2212)

348.7 US ISSN 0162-0444
KF4547.8
SIGNIFICANT DECISIONS OF THE SUPREME COURT. ceased. a. (American Enterprise Institute for Public Policy Research) Fred B. Rothman & Co., 10368 W. Centennial Rd., Littleton, CO 80127.

286 SA ISSN 0037-5071
SIGNS OF THE TIMES/TEKENS VAN DIE TYE. 1923-1989. q. (Seventh-Day Adventist Church) Southern Publishing Association, Rosmead Ave., Kenilworth, Cape Town, South Africa.

621.381 001.642 US ISSN 0149-7898
SILICON GULCH GAZETTE. 1977-1987; suspended. q. (tabloid format) Jim Warren, Ed. & Pub., 345 Swett Rd., Woodside, CA 94062.

634.9 BL ISSN 0583-3132
SD23.S2 CODEN: SLVPAJ
SILVICULTURA EM SAO PAULO. 1962-1988 (vol.20-22). irreg. Instituto Florestal, C.P. 1322, Sao Paulo 01051, Brazil.

746 US
SIMPLICITY KNITTING. 1985-1989. 3/yr. Simplicity Pattern Co., Inc., 200 Madison Ave., New York, NY 10016.
Formerly: Knitting with Simplicity.

646.4 US
SIMPLICITY MAGAZINE. 1967-1989. 2/yr. Simplicity Pattern Co., Inc., 200 Madison Ave., New York, NY 10016.
Former titles (until 1987): Simplicity Sewing for Today; Simplicity Today; Simplicity Today Incorporating Home Catalog (ISSN 0198-7100); Supersedes: Simplicity Home Catalog (ISSN 0364-1732)

668.54 659.152 US
SIMPLY YOU. 1985-198? q. (back issues avail.) Brainstorm Communications, 407 S. Dearborn, Ste. 1500, Chicago, IL 60605.

500 614.7 610 PH
SINAG-AGHAM; a popular science magazine. 1983-1986. q. (back issues avail.) University of the Philippines, Office of Research Coordination, P N B Bldg. U.P. Campus, Diliman, Quezon City, Philippines.

335 368 SI
SINGAPORE BANKING, FINANCE & INSURANCE. 1979-19?? a. Times Directories Private Ltd., 422 Thomson Rd., Singapore 1129, Singapore.

388 SI
SINGAPORE MOTORING GUIDE. 1980-19?? a. Times Directories Private Ltd., 422 Thomson Rd., Singapore 1129, Singapore.

200 051 US ISSN 0888-3335
SINGLE IMPACT. 1985-1990 (Dec.). q. 7245 College St., Lima, NY 14485.

051 US
SINGLE SCENE (SALEM). ceased 1989 (vol.8). m. Box 5027, Salem, OR 97304.

051 US
SINGLE SOURCE. 1987-1989. bi-m. Box 460127, Aurora, CO 80015.

330 IT ISSN 0037-5780
DC301
SINTESI ECONOMICA. 1948-1979. s-m. Unione Italiana delle Camere di Commercio, Industria, Artigianato e Agricoltura, Piazza Sallustio 21, Rome, Italy.

382 UY
SINTESIS - A L A D I. ceased 198? q. (with supplements). Asociacion Latinoamericana de Integracion - Latin American Integration Association, Cebollati 1461, Casilla de Correo 577, 10001 Montevideo, Uruguay.
Supersedes (in 1981): Sintesis - A L A L C; Which was formerly (until 1965): Sintesis (ISSN 0037-5802)

330 333.33 US
SITE DEVELOPMENT NEWS. 1989-1990. s-m. Gordon Publications, Inc., 301 Gibraltar Dr., Box 650, Morris Plains, NJ 07950-0650.

338.1 AG ISSN 0325-9161
HD9014.A7
SITUACION COYUNTURAL DEL SECTOR AGROPECUARIO. ceased. bi-m. Banco Rio de la Plata, Gerencia de Investigaciones Economicas, Bartolome Mitre 480 P. 13, 1036 Capital, Argentina.

796.21 US ISSN 0037-6124
SKATE. 1940-1990. q. (also avail. in microform from LCP) Roller Skating Rink Operators Association, 7700 "A" St., Box 81846, Lincoln, NE 68501.

336 DK
SKATTEBREV; til studiebrug. 1983-1986. a. Skattekartotek, Palaegade 4, 1261 Copenhagen K, Denmark.

796.92 DK
SKI MAGASINET DANMARK. 1984-19?? 3/yr. Sports Media A.S., Gl. Klausdalsbrovej 480, DK-2730 Herlev, Denmark.

796.93 FR
SKI MAGAZINE. ceased. 6/yr. Edimonde-Loisirs, 23-25 rue de Berri, 75388 Paris Cedex 08, France.

796.93 US
SKIING UTAH. ceased. m. (Nov.-Apr.). Coles Publishing Company, 419 E. 100 S., Salt Lake City, UT 84111.

700 SZ
SKIRA MAGAZINE. 1986-19?? s-a. Editions d'Art Albert Skira S.A., 89, Route de Chene, 1208 Geneva, Switzerland.

674 NO
SKOGBRUKETS OG SKOGINDUSTRIENES FORSKNINGSRAAD. AARBOK. ceased 1988. a. Skogbrukets og Skogindustrienes Forskningsraad, Box 115, Vinderen, Oslo 3, Norway.
Formelrys: Skogbrukets og Skogindustrienes Forsknings-Forening. Arbok.

370 DK ISSN 0900-2006
SKOLE OG EDB. 1985-1986. a. Munksgaard International Publishers Ltd., 35 Noerre Soegade, P.O. Box 2148, DK-1016 Copenhagen K, Denmark.

370 DK ISSN 0108-3872
SKOLE OG FREMTID. 1981-19?? bi-m. Center for Skole og Fremtid ApS, Bagsvaerdvej 35-37, 2800 Lyngby, Denmark.
Formerly: P-75 Posten.

780 DK ISSN 0108-4402
SKOLEMUSIKHAANDBOGEN. 1982-1989. a. Folkeskolens Musiklaererforening, Gudenaavej 162, 7400 Herning, Denmark.

370 NO ISSN 0080-9950
SKOLENS AARBOK. 1965-198? a. Aschehoug et Co., Sehestedsgt. 3, 0164 Oslo 1, Norway.

051 US
SKYLANDER MAGAZINE. 1986-1990 (Dec.); suspended. m. Jade Associates, RR 3 Box 12, Hackettstown, NJ 07840-9409.
Formerly: Warren County Magazine.

001.3 CI ISSN 0352-8650
SLAVONSKI POVIJESNI ZBORNIK. 1963-1988 (no.25). s-a. (back issues avail.) Centar za Povijest Slavonje i Baranje (C.P.S.B.), Starceviceva 8, 55000 Slavonski Brod, Croatia.
Former titles: Centar za Drustvena Istrazivanja Slavonije i Baranje. Zbornik (ISSN 0352-1168); (until 1983): Historijski Institut Slavonije i Baranje. Zbornik.

612.015 UK ISSN 0268-1498
SLEEP (SUBSTANCES). ceased 1990. m. (looseleaf format; back issues avail.) Sheffield University Biomedical Information Service (SUBIS), The University, Sheffield S10 2TN, England.

550 CS ISSN 0036-1372
SLOVENSKA AKADEMIA VIED. GEOLOGICKY USTAV D. STURA: ZBORNIK: ZAPADNE KARPATY. ceased 1970. irreg. (1-2/yr.). Veda, Publishing House of the Slovak Academy of Sciences, Klemensova 19, 814 30 Bratislava, Czechoslovakia.
Supersedes: Slovenska Akademia Vied. Geologicky Ustav D. Stura. Geologicke Prace.

780 CS ISSN 0037-6965
ML5
SLOVENSKA HUDBA. 1957-1971 (no.9-10). irreg. (Svaz Ceskych a Slovenskych Skladatelu) Slovensky Muzicky Fond, Fucikova 29, 80100 Bratislava, Czechoslovakia.

059.918 CS
SLOVENSKO; kulturno-spolocensky mesacnik. 1977-1991 (Apr.). m. Matica Slovenska, Slovenska Narodna Kniznica, Ul. L. Novomeskeho 32, 036 52 Martin, Czechoslovakia.

001.3 YU
SLOVENSKO MORJE IN ZALEDJE. 1977-1984 (no.7). biennial. Zalozba Lipa, Muzejski trg. 7, 66000 Koper, Yugoslavia.

917.109 CN ISSN 0037-7015
SLOVENSKY HLAS/SLOVAK VOICE. 1949-1989 (vol. 41). m. (tabloid format) Canadian Slovak Benefit Society, 250 Villaire, Windsor, Ont. N8S 2J2, Canada.

001.6 621.381 US ISSN 0736-6957
 CODEN: SBCNDL
SMALL BUSINESS COMPUTER NEWS. 1975-19?? m. Management Information Corporation, 401 E. Route 70, Cherry Hill, NJ 08034.

CESSATIONS

330   AT   ISSN 0811-5680
SMALL BUSINESS REVIEW. 1980-1987. q. Council of Small Business Organisations of Australia Ltd. (COSBOA), Commerce House, Brisbane Ave., Barton, A.C.T. 2600, Australia.

336.2 338   US
SMALL BUSINESS TAXATION. 1988-199? bi-m. Warren, Gorham and Lamont Inc., One Penn Plaza, New York, NY 10119.

338   US   ISSN 0094-2464
SMALL BUSINESSMAN'S CLINIC. 1972-1991. m. (processed) Small Businessman's Clinic, 113 Vista del Lago, Scotts Valley, CA 95066.

796.95   UK
SMALL CRAFT. (Supplement to: Naval Architect) 1981-19?? q. (back issues avail.) Royal Institution of Naval Architects, 10 Upper Belgrave St., London SW1X 8BQ, England.

028.1   US   ISSN 1052-2697
SMALL PRESS BOOK REVIEW ANNUAL. 1990; announced, never published. a. Meckler Publishing Corporation, 11 Ferry Lane W., Westport, CT 06880-5808.

378   US
SMALL TALK (WASHINGTON). 1983-199? irreg. Council of Independent Colleges, One Dupont Circle, Ste. 320, Washington, DC 20036.

970.1   US
SMALL TRAIL. ceased. irreg. (4-5/yr.). American Indian Community House, 842 Broadway, New York, NY 10003.

069 700   US
SMITH COLLEGE MUSEUM OF ART. JOURNAL. 1982-19?? irreg. Smith College Museum of Art, Northampton, MA 01063.

700   US
SMITHSONIAN INSTITUTION. ARCHIVES OF AMERICAN ART. NEWSLETTER. 1971-19?? irreg. (1-2/yr.). Smithsonian Institution, Archives of American Art, Washington, DC 20560.

523.01   US   ISSN 0081-0320
TL796.A1
SMITHSONIAN INSTITUTION. ASTROPHYSICAL OBSERVATORY. S A O SPECIAL REPORT. 1957-19?? irreg. Smithsonian Institution Astrophysical Observatory, 60 Garden St., Cambridge, MA 02138.

323.4   US   ISSN 0193-5755
SMOLOSKYP; a quarterly dealing with human rights affairs in Ukraine and Eastern Europe. 1978-1989 (vol.9, no.41). q. (also avail. in microfiche; back issues avail.) (Ukrainian Information Service) Smoloskyp Publishers, Box 561, Ellicott City, MD 21043.

001.6 621.381   US
SNOBOL4 INFORMATION BULLETIN. 1968-19?? (no. 31). irreg. (back issues avail.) University of Arizona, Department of Computer Science, SNOBOL4 Project, Tucson, AZ 85721.

028.5   US
SNOOPY MAGAZINE. 1987-1990 (no.10). q. Welsh Publishing Group, Inc., 300 Madison Ave., New York, NY 10017.

380.1   CN   ISSN 0707-9184
HE5614.5.C2
SNOWMOBILE ACCIDENTS, MANITOBA. 1972-19?? a. Manitoba Public Insurance Corporation, Box 6300, 9th Floor, 330 Graham Ave., Winnipeg, Man. R3C 4A4, Canada.

797   AT   ISSN 0310-9399
SOARING IN THE A.C.T. (Australian Capital Territory) ceased. irreg. (Australian National University Gliding Club) Canberra Gliding Club, P.O. Box 1130, Canberra, A.T.C. 2601, Australia.

150 300   US
SOCIAL AND BEHAVIORAL SCIENCES DOCUMENTS. 1971-1988. 2/yr. (back issues avail.) Select Press, Box 37, Corte Madera, CA 94925.

600 301 330.9   UK   ISSN 0267-6230
SOCIAL AND ECONOMIC IMPACT OF NEW TECHNOLOGY; a review and information service. 1985-198? q. Technical Communications, 100 High Ave., Letchworth, Herts. SG6 3RR, England.

381   PH   ISSN 0115-2661
SOCIAL DEVELOPMENT NEWS. 1972-1987. q. Philippine Business for Social Progress, Public Information Office, Yutivo Building, 4th Fl., 270 Dasmarinas St., Binondo, Manila, Philippines.

301   CN
SOCIAL DEVELOPMENT OVERVIEW. 1972-1991. irreg. Canadian Council on Social Development, 55 Parkdale Avenue, P.O. Box 3505, Sta. C, Ottawa, Ont. K1Y 4G1, Canada.
  Formerly: Social Development (ISSN 0316-313X)

301 289.6   US
SOCIAL ORDER SERIES. 1985-1990. irreg. (back issues avail.) Religious Society of Friends, Pacific Yearly Meeting, 7899 St. Helena Rd., Santa Rosa, CA 95404.

360   US
SOCIAL PERSPECTIVES. vol.4, 1976-19?? s-a. University of Alabama, School of Social Work, Box 870314, Tuscaloosa, AL 35487-0314.

300   US   ISSN 0886-280X
F251
SOCIAL SCIENCE (CHAPEL HILL). 1914-198? q. University of North Carolina at Chapel Hill, Institute for Research in Social Science, Manning Hall 026A, Chapel Hill, NC 27514.
  Former titles (until vol.71, no.1, 1986): Social Science News Letter (ISSN 0743-8974); University of North Carolina News Letter.

300   US   ISSN 0195-7791
SOCIAL SCIENCE MONITOR; for public relations executives. 1979-1991. m. Communication Research Associates, Inc., 10606 Mantz Rd., Silver Spring, MD 20903.
  Incorporates (1986-1989): Hi-Tech Alert for the Professional Communicator (ISSN 0888-9511); (1983-1989): Video Monitor (ISSN 0888-9538)

320   II
SOCIAL SCIENCE PROBINGS. 1984-198? q. People's Publishing House Private Ltd., 5-E Rani Jhansi Road, New Delhi 110 055, India.

300   CN   ISSN 0049-092X
SOCIAL SCIENCES IN CANADA. 1971-198? 7/yr. Social Science Federation of Canada, 151 Slater St., Ste. 415, Ottawa, Ont. K1P 5H3, Canada.

634.9 016   US
SOCIAL SCIENCES IN FORESTRY; a current selected bibliography and index. 1962-1991 (no.89, Dec.). 4/yr. (processed; also avail. in microfiche from EDR) University of Minnesota, Forestry Library, c/o Jean Albrecht, Forestry Library, B50 NRAB, 2003 Upper Buford Circle, St. Paul, MN 55108.

614   DK   ISSN 0900-2030
SOCIAL SIKRING; lovsamling for praktikere og til studier. 1984-1986. a. Forlag for Social og Sundhedssektor, Albertslund, Denmark.

320.531   NZ   ISSN 0037-816X
SOCIALIST ACTION. 1969-1988 (vol.20); suspended. fortn. (tabloid format) Socialist Action Publishing Association, Box 8852, Auckland, New Zealand.

509   MX
SOCIEDAD MEXICANA DE HISTORIA DE LA CIENCIA Y DE LA TECNOLOGIA. ACTAS. 1969-1979 (vol.5). irreg. Sociedad Mexicana de Historia de la Ciencia y de la Tecnologia, Apartado Postal 21-873, Coyoacan, 04000 Mexico, D.F., Mexico.
  Formerly: Sociedad Mexicana de Historia de la Ciencia y de la Tecnologia. Anales.

819   CN   ISSN 0049-1055
SOCIETE DES ECRIVAINS CANADIENS. BULLETIN. 1970-1976. q. Societe des Ecrivains Canadiens, c/o Michel Champagne, 473 Dolbeau, Quebec, Que. G1S 2R6, Canada.

332   BE
SOCIETE GENERALE DE BELGIQUE. INFORMATION BULLETIN. ceased 1987. q. Societe Generale de Belgique, Information Department, Rue Royale 30, B-1000 Brussels, Belgium.
  Formerly: Societe Generale de Belgique. Quarterly Information Bulletin.

910   BE   ISSN 0770-7576
SOCIETE GEOGRAPHIQUE DE LIEGE. BULLETIN. 1965-1987. a. Societe Geographique de Liege, 7, Place du Vingt-Aout, B-4000 Liege, Belgium.
  Supersedes: Universite de Liege. Seminaire de Geographie. Travaux; Travaux Geographigues de Liege.

510 520 530   BE   ISSN 0037-959X
Q56   CODEN: ASSBAH
SOCIETE SCIENTIFIQUE DE BRUXELLES. ANNALES. SCIENCES MATHEMATIQUES, ASTRONOMIQUES ET PHYSIQUES. 1875-1992. 4/yr. Societe Scientifique de Bruxelles, Rue de Bruxelles 6, B-5000 Namur, Belgium.
  Formerly: Societe Scientifiques de Bruxelles. Annales. Serie 1: Sciences Mathematiques, Astronomiques et Physiques.

001.6   FR
SOCIETES DE SERVICE ET DE CONSEIL EN INFORMATIQUE. ceased. irreg. (Direction des Industries Electroniques et de l'Informatique) Documentation Francaise, 29-31 Quai Voltaire, 75340 Paris, France.

917   US
SOCIETY FOR AMERICAN ARCHAEOLOGY. MEMOIR SERIES. ceased. irreg. Society for American Archaeology, 808 17th St., N.W., Ste. 200, Washington, DC 20006.

700   US
SOCIETY FOR FOLK ARTS PRESERVATION. NEWSLETTER. 1980-1989; suspended. 3/yr. (tabloid format) Society for Folk Arts Preservation, Inc., 308 E. 79 St., New York, NY 10021.

635   US
SOCIETY FOR LOUISIANA IRISES. SPECIAL PUBLICATIONS. 1952-1991. irreg. Society for Louisiana Irises, Box 4-0175, U.S.L., Lafayette, LA 70504.

600   US   ISSN 0081-1491
SOCIETY FOR THE HISTORY OF TECHNOLOGY. MONOGRAPH SERIES. 1962-19?? irreg. Society for the History of Technology, c/o Bruce Seely, Sec., Dept. of Social Sciences, Michigan Technological Univ., Houghton, MI 49931.

574.1   US
SOCIETY OF GENERAL PHYSIOLOGISTS. DISTINGUISHED LECTURE SERIES. 1978-19?? irreg. Raven Press, 1185 Ave. of the Americas, New York, NY 10036.

612   US   ISSN 0094-7733
         CODEN: SGPHAW
SOCIETY OF GENERAL PHYSIOLOGISTS SERIES. 1945-1984 (vol.38). a. Raven Press, 1185 Ave. of the Americas, New York, NY 10036.

301 410   NE   ISSN 0049-1217
P40
SOCIOLINGUISTICS. 1966-19?? (vol.19). s-a. I C G Publications, P.O. Box 509, 3300 AM Dordrecht, Netherlands.

370   SW   ISSN 1100-5491
SOEDOK; nyfoervaervslista. 1983-1991; suspended. m. Swedish National Board of Education, 10D Section, S-106 42 Stockholm, Sweden.
  Former titles: Skolvux-soe (ISSN 0282-4736); Skola och Vuxenutbilning (ISSN 0281-0891)

028.5   DK
SOEREN SPAETTE. ceased. m. Interpresse, Krogshoejvej 32, 2880 Bagsvaerd, Denmark.

001.642   DK   ISSN 0109-9531
SOFT; alt om data store programblad. 1985-19?? bi-m. Forlaget Audio A-S, St. Kongensgade 72, 1264 Copenhagen K, Denmark.

001.642 621.381   CN
SOFTWARE CANADA. (Supplement to: Canadian Datasytems (ISSN 0008-3364)) 1982-19?? 11/yr. Maclean-Hunter Ltd., Business Publication Division, Maclean-Hunter Bldg., 777 Bay St., Toronto, Ont. M5W 1A7, Canada.

001.539 011 020   US   ISSN 0740-5022
SOFTWARE PUBLISHERS' CATALOGS ANNUAL. 1983-1991. a. (microfiche) Meckler Publishing Corporation, 11 Ferry Lane W., Westport, CT 06880-5808.

001.642 370   US
SOFTWARE REPORTS: GUIDE TO EVALUATED EDUCATIONAL SOFTWARE. 1983-198? a. Trade Service Publications, Inc, Software Reports, 10996 Torreyana Rd., San Diego, CA 92121.

001.642   US
SOFTWARENEWS. (Update to: Datapro Directory of Software) ceased. m. Datapro Information Services Group (Subsidiary of: McGraw-Hill, Inc.), 600 Delran Pkwy., Delran, NJ 08075.

551   UK   ISSN 0260-9088
SOIL SURVEY AND LAND EVALUATION. 1981-1989. 3/yr. Geo Books, Regency House, 34 Duke St., Norwich, Norfolk NR3 3AP, England.

635   US
SOLANACEAE QUARTERLY. 1984-1990 (vol.6, no.4). q. Solanaceae Enthusiasts, 3370 Princeton Ct., Santa Clara, CA 95051.

621.47   US
SOLAR BIBLIOGRAPHY. 1976-198? irreg. U.S. Department of Housing and Urban Development, Office of Policy Development and Research, 451 Seventh St., S.W., Washington, DC 20410.

531.6   US   ISSN 0364-6998
Z5853.P83
SOLAR ENERGY UPDATE. 1976-19?? m. U.S. Department of Energy, Office of Scientific and Technical Information, Box 62, Oak Ridge, TN 37831.

355.31   US
SOLDIER SUPPORT ADVOCATE. 1972-1989 (Dec.). q. Bldg. 600, ATZ-AOJ, Ft. Harrison, IN 46216-5048.

621.38   US
SOLID STATE PROCESSING AND PRODUCTION BUYERS GUIDE AND DIRECTORY. ceased. a. Cahners Publishing Company (Des Plaines) (Subsidiary of: Reed International PLC), Division of Reed Publishing (USA) Inc., 1350 Touhy Ave., Box 5080, Des Plaines, IL 60017-5080.

360 310   FR
SOLIDARITE - SANTE; etudes statistiques. (Supplements: Revue Francaise des Affaires Sociales) ceased 1986. 6/yr. (also avail. in microfiche) Documentation Francaise, 29-31 Quai Voltaire, 75340 Paris Cedex 07, France.
  Former titles: France. Ministere des Affaires Sociales et de la Solidarite Nationale. Sante, Securite Sociale, Statistiques et Commentaires; France. Ministere de la Sante et de la Securite Sociale. Sante, Securite Sociale. Statistiques et Commentaires (ISSN 0338-3423); France. Ministere de la Sante et de la Famille. Bulletin de Statistiques et Sante (ISSN 0376-6128); France. Ministere de la Sante et de la Famille. Sante, Securite Sociale; France. Ministere de la Sante et de la Securite Sociale. Sante, Securite Sociales Statistiques et Commentaires; France. Ministere de la Sante. Bulletin de Statistiques de Sante, Securite Sociales.

051 202   US
SOLOING. ceased 1988. bi-m. (tabloid format) 4118 Tenth Ave. N., Lake Worth, FL 33461.

620 612   US   ISSN 0886-8034
R856.A1
SOMA: ENGINEERING FOR THE HUMAN BODY. ceased 1990. q. Hemisphere Publishing Corporation (Subsidiary of: Taylor & Francis Group), 1900 Frost Rd., Ste. 101, Bristol, PA 19007-1598.

810   US   ISSN 1044-6710
THE (SOMETHING). 1985-1990 (no.4). bi-m. (looseleaf format; back issues avail.) 1520 Bryn Mawr Ave., Racine, WI 53403.
  Formerly: Sumari Bulletin.

784.61   US
SONG HITS' HEARTBREAKERS. 1942-1991. bi-m. Charlton Publications, Inc., 60 Division St., Derby, CT 06418.
  Former titles: Song Hits (ISSN 0038-1365); Song Hits Combination.

780   UR
SONGS FROM RADIO, TV AND FILM PRODUCTIONS. 1979-1991 (no.94). 6/yr. Izdatel'stvo Muzyka, Ul. Neglinnaya 14, Moscow 103031, Russian S.F.S.R., U.S.S.R.

630   US
SONOMA MARIN FARMER. 1971-198? m. Box 722, Healdsburg, CA 95448.

051   US
SONOMA READER. 1989-199? m. Box 2572, Santa Rosa, CA 95405.

700   CH   ISSN 0259-3742
SOOCHOW UNIVERSITY JOURNAL OF CHINESE ART HISTORY. 1973-1987 (vol.15). q. Soochow University, Wai Shuang Hsi, Shih Lin, Taipei Hsien, Taiwan, Republic of China.

100   IR
SOPHIA PERENNIS. 1975-19?? s-a. Imperial Iran Academy of Philosophy, Avenue France Kucheh Nezami 6, P.O. 14-1699, Teheran, Iran.

613.9   US   ISSN 1043-4186
SORROW'S REWARD. 1989-199? q. Human Life International, 7845-E Airpark Rd., Gaithersburg, MD 20879.

745.1 700   US
SOTHEBY'S INTERNATIONAL PRICE GUIDE: ANTIQUES AND COLLECTIBLES. ceased. a. Apollo Book (Distributor), Box 3839, Poughkeepsie, NY 12603-0839.

659.1   US   ISSN 8755-0555
SOUND MANAGEMENT. 1984-1992 (Jan.). 6/yr. Radio Advertising Bureau, 304 Park Ave. S., 7th Fl., New York, NY 10010.

800   US   ISSN 0273-0324
SOURCE (JAMAICA). 1976-19?? s-a. Queens Council on the Arts, Literary Arts Division, 161-04 Jamaica Ave., Jamaica, NY 11432.

296   US
SOURCE (NEW YORK). 1973-19?? fortn. City College of New York, Finley 235, 133rd St. & Convent Ave., New York, NY 10031.

384.5   US
SOURCE TAB: A DIRECTORY OF PROGRAM RESOURCES FOR PUBLIC RADIO. ceased. irreg. National Federation of Community Broadcasters, 666 11th St. N.W., Ste. 805, Washington, DC 20001.

133   US   ISSN 0732-6696
SOURCEFINDER. 1981-1988; suspended. q. (back issues avail.) Center of Light, Box 6232, Augusta, GA 30906.
  Formerly: New Age Guide to Events and Resources.

001.539   US
SOURCES FILE; resources for computer industry marketers. ceased 1991 (Feb.). bi-m. Applied Computer Research, Inc., Box 82266, Phoenix, AZ 85071-2266.
  Formerly: Sources.

370   SA
SOUTH AFRICA. CENTRAL STATISTICAL SERVICE. EDUCATION: ASIAN. (Report No. 21-03) ceased. a. Central Statistical Service, Private Bag X44, Pretoria 0001, South Africa.
  Former titles: South Africa. Department of Statistics. Education: Asian; South Africa. Department of Statistics. Education: Coloureds and Asians.

370   SA
SOUTH AFRICA. CENTRAL STATISTICAL SERVICE. EDUCATION: WHITES. (Report No. 21-02) ceased 1984. a. Central Statistical Service, Private Bag X44, Pretoria 0001, South Africa.
  Formerly: South Africa. Department of Statistics. Education: Whites.

331.1   SA
SOUTH AFRICA. CENTRAL STATISTICAL SERVICE. LABOUR STATISTICS: WAGE RATES, EARNINGS AND AVERAGE HOURS WORKED IN THE PRINTING AND NEWSPAPER INDUSTRY, ENGINEERING INDUSTRY, BUILDING INDUSTRY AND COMMERCE. (Report No. 01-20) ceased 1980. a. Central Statistical Service, Private Bag X44, Pretoria 0001, South Africa.
  Formerly: South Africa. Department of Statistics. Labour Statistics: Wage Rates, Earnings and Average Hours Worked in the Printing and Newspaper Industry, Engineering Industry, Building Industry and Commerce.

378   SA   ISSN 0081-220X
SOUTH AFRICA. DEPARTMENT OF HIGHER EDUCATION. ANNUAL REPORT. 1910-1989. a. Government Printer, Bosman St., Private Bag X85, Pretoria 0001, South Africa.

370   SA
SOUTH AFRICA. DEPARTMENT OF NATIONAL EDUCATION. ANNUAL REPORT. ceased 1989. a. Department of National Education, Bosman St., Private Bag X85, Pretoria 0001, South Africa.

388.31 625   SA
SOUTH AFRICA. DIVISION OF ROADS AND TRANSPORT TECHNOLOGY. ANNUAL REPORT/DIVISIE VIR PAD- EN VERTOERTEGNOLOGIE. 1961-19??; suspended. a. Division of Roads and Transport Technology, P.O. Box 395, Pretoria 0001, South Africa.
  Former titles: National Institute for Transport and Road Research. Annual Report (ISSN 0379-6124); National Institute for Road Research. Annual Report.

556   SA
SOUTH AFRICA. GEOLOGICAL SURVEY. RESEARCH DIGEST. 1986-199? s-a. Geological Survey, Private Bag X112, Pretoria 0001, South Africa.

365.6   SA
SOUTH AFRICA. PRISONS DEPARTMENT. ANNUAL STATISTICS BY THE COMMISSIONER OF PRISONS. (Report year ends June 30) ceased. a. Government Printer, Bosman St., Private Bag X85, Pretoria 0001, South Africa.

364.4   SA   ISSN 0300-1555
SOUTH AFRICA. PRISONS DEPARTMENT. REPORT OF THE COMMISSIONER OF PRISONS. (Order and language of titles varies) ceased. a. Government Printer, Bosman St., Private Bag X85, Pretoria 0001, South Africa.
  Continues its: Annual Report of the Director of Prisons.

333.9   SA
SOUTH AFRICA. WATER RESEARCH COMMISSION. RESEARCH PROJECTS. ceased 1988. 3/yr. Water Research Commission, P.O. Box 824, Pretoria 0001, South Africa.

331 332.1   SA   ISSN 0036-0570
SOUTH AFRICAN BANKING. 1917-19?? m. South African Society of Bank Officials, S A S B O House, 97 Simmonds St., Braamfontein, Johannesburg, South Africa.

540   SA
SOUTH AFRICAN CHEMICALS. ceased. m. Keeble Publishing Co. Pty. Ltd., P.O. Box 3080, Johannesburg 2000, South Africa.

794.1   SA   ISSN 0038-2094
SOUTH AFRICAN CHESSPLAYER. 1953-19?? m. (back issues avail.) Box 4513, Cape Town, South Africa.

052   SA   ISSN 0038-2132
DT751
SOUTH AFRICAN DIGEST. 1956-1989 (Dec.). w. Bureau for Information, 356 Vermeulen St., Pretoria 0002, South Africa.
  Incorporates: Comment and Opinion: A Weekly Survey of the South African Press and Radio.

610   SA
SOUTH AFRICAN MEDICAL POST. ceased. m. Westbourne-Maclean Hunter (Pty) Ltd., Nedbank East City, 120 End St., Box 6110, Johannesburg 2000, South Africa.

610   SA   ISSN 1015-2377
SOUTH AFRICAN MEDICAL RESEARCH COUNCIL. BIENNIAL RESEARCH REPORT. 1969-199? biennial. South African Medical Research Council, P.O. Box 19070, Tygerberg 7505, South Africa.
  Supersedes in part (in 1989): South African Medical Research Council. Research Report (ISSN 0081-248X)

622 620   SA   ISSN 0081-2498
SOUTH AFRICAN MINING AND ENGINEERING YEARBOOK. 1915-19?? a. Thomson Publications (Subsidiary of: Times Media Ltd.), Box 56182, Pinegowrie 2123, South Africa.

CESSATIONS

059.951   SA   ISSN 1016-1384
SOUTH AFRICAN PANORAMA (CHINESE EDITION)/NANFI JINGGUAN. 1987-1991. bi-m. Bureau for Information, Private Bag X745, Pretoria 0001, South Africa.

053.931   SA   ISSN 0167-9767
SOUTH AFRICAN PANORAMA (DUTCH EDITION). ceased 1991. bi-m. Bureau for Information, Private Bag X745, Pretoria 0001, South Africa.

054.1   SA   ISSN 0259-9198
SOUTH AFRICAN PANORAMA (FRENCH EDITION). 1963-1991. bi-m. Bureau for Information, Private Bag X745, Pretoria 0001, South Africa.

053.1   SA   ISSN 0259-9236
SOUTH AFRICAN PANORAMA (GERMAN EDITION). 1963-1991. bi-m. Bureau for Information, Private Bag X745, Pretoria 0001, South Africa.

055.1   SA   ISSN 0259-9201
SOUTH AFRICAN PANORAMA (ITALIAN EDITION). 1974-1991. bi-m. Bureau for Information, Private Bag X745, Pretoria 0001, South Africa.

056.9   SA   ISSN 0259-9228
SOUTH AFRICAN PANORAMA (PORTUGUESE EDITION). 1974-1991. bi-m. Bureau for Information, Private Bag X745, Pretoria 0001, South Africa.

056.1   SA   ISSN 0259-921X
SOUTH AFRICAN PANORAMA (SPANISH EDITION). 1969-1991. bi-m. Bureau for Information, Private Bag X745, Pretoria 0001, South Africa.

352.7   US
SOUTH ATLANTIC URBAN STUDIES. 1977-1981 (vol.5). a. College of Charleston, Urban Studies Center, Charleston, SC 29401.

634.9   AT
SOUTH AUSTRALIA. WOODS AND FORESTS DEPARTMENT. BULLETIN. 1928-1981 (no.26). irreg. Woods and Forests Department, 135 Waymouth St., Adelaide, S.A., Australia.

808   US   ISSN 0742-8936
SOUTH DAKOTA AUTHORS' CATALOG. 1981-198?; suspended. biennial. South Dakota State Poetry Society, Box 326, Harrisburg, SD 57032.

977   US
SOUTH DAKOTA HISTORICAL COLLECTIONS. 1902-1989. irreg. (reprint service avail. from UMI) South Dakota State Historical Society, 800 Governors Dr., Pierre, SD 57501.
    Former titles: South Dakota State Historical Society. Collections (ISSN 0081-2773); South Dakota. Department of History. Historical Collections; (until 1974): South Dakota. Department of History. Report and Historical Collections (ISSN 0092-198X)

630   UK
SOUTH LINCOLNSHIRE FARMER. 1923-198? m. N.F.U. Publications Ltd., 5 High East St., Dorchester, Dorset DT1 1HJ, England.

327   NL
SOUTH PACIFIC COMMISSION. ANNUAL REPORT. 1948-1981. a. South Pacific Commission, B.P. D5, Noumea, Cedex, New Caledonia.
    Formerly: South Pacific Commission. South Pacific Report (ISSN 0081-2854)

052 054.1   NL
SOUTH PACIFIC COMMISSION. MONTHLY NEWS OF ACTIVITIES. 1979-1987. m. (back issues avail.) South Pacific Commission, B.P. D5, Noumea, Cedex, New Caledonia.

639.2 338.1   NL
SOUTH PACIFIC COMMISSION. OCCASIONAL PAPER. 1977-1983. irreg. South Pacific Commission, B.P. D5, Noumea, Cedex, New Caledonia.

330 320   UK   ISSN 0956-0955
SOUTH EAST ASIA DIGEST. 1989; ceased same year. 26/yr. South East Asia Research Ltd., Ivebury Court no.2, 325 Latimer Rd., London W10 6RA, England.

020   CN   ISSN 0707-6894
SOUTHEAST REGIONAL LIBRARY (SASKATCHEWAN) LIBRARY DIRECTORY. 1975-1987. a. Southeast Regional Library (Saskatchewan), Box 550, Weyburn, Sask. S4H 2K7, Canada.

639.2   US
SOUTHEASTERN LOG. 1971-1989 (Dec.). m. Box 7900, Ketchikan, AK 99901.

338.91 361   US
SOUTHERN AFRICA DEVELOPMENT NEWS. ceased. bi-m. (American Council for Voluntary International Action) InterAction, 200 Park Ave. S., New York, NY 10003.

622   US
SOUTHERN AFRICAN METALS & MINERALS CONFERENCE. PROCEEDINGS. 1981-198? irreg. Metal Bulletin Inc., 220 Fifth Ave., 10th Fl., New York, NY 10001.

799   US   ISSN 0081-2986
SOUTHERN ANGLER'S AND HUNTER'S GUIDE. 1961-1989. a. Southern Angler's Guide Publications, 100 Nell St., Hot Springs, AR 71913-4364.

332.1   US   ISSN 0038-383X
HG1501
SOUTHERN BANKER. 1904-1991 (vol.173, no.4). 10/yr. Thomson Publishing Corporation, One State St. Plaza, New York, NY 10004.

747   US   ISSN 1041-5696
SOUTHERN CALIFORNIA HOME & GARDEN. 1988-1991 (May). m. Westar Media, Inc., 656 Bair Island Rd., 2nd fl., Redwood City, CA 94063.

637   US   ISSN 0038-402X
SOUTHERN DAIRY PRODUCTS JOURNAL. 1927-198? bi-m. Box 6126, Clearwater, FL 33518.

635   US
SOUTHERN HERBS. ceased 1987 (no.9). 4/yr. c/o Eve Elliott, 1729 Unice Ave., Lehigh Acres, FL 33971.

800 051   US   ISSN 0889-9304
SOUTHERN MAGAZINE. 1986-198? m. Arkansas Writers' Project, Box 34010, Little Rock, AR 72203.

633.71 679.7   US   ISSN 0300-6239
SOUTHERN TOBACCO JOURNAL. ceased. m. Southern Trade Publications Co., Box 9377, Greensboro, NC 27419.

051   US
SOUTHPOINT. suspended 1990. m. Southern Progress Corp. (Subsidiary of: Time, Inc. Magazine Co.), c/o Don Logan, Pres., 2100 Lakeshore Dr., Birmingham, AL 35209.

350   SX
SOUTH WEST AFRICA ADMINISTRATION: WHITE PAPER ON THE ACTIVITIES OF THE DIFFERENT BRANCHES. 1961-1979. irreg. (processed) Ministry of Education and Culture, Estorff Reference Library, Private Bag 13349, Windhoek, Namibia.

628.1   US   ISSN 0196-0717
TD201   CODEN: STWJDV
SOUTHWEST & TEXAS WATER WORKS JOURNAL. 1918-198? m. American Water Works Association, Southwest and Texas Sections, 306 E. Adams Ave., Temple, TX 76501.
    Former titles (until 1979): Water (ISSN 0099-8729); (until 1977): Southwest Water Works Journal (ISSN 0038-4720)

300.7   US   ISSN 0049-1683
SOUTHWESTERN JOURNAL OF SOCIAL EDUCATION. 1970-19?? s-a. (also avail. in microform from UMI; reprint service avail. from UMI) Texas Council for Social Studies, North Texas State Univ., Box 5427, Denton, TX 76203.

608.7   US   ISSN 0553-3864
KF3114.A2
SOUTHWESTERN LEGAL FOUNDATION. PATENT LAW ANNUAL. 1964-19?? a. (also avail. in microform from RRI; reprint service avail. from RRI) Southwestern Legal Foundation, Box 830707, Richardson, TX 75083.

730   RU
SOVETSKAYA SKUL'PTURA. vol.74, 1976-19?? irreg. Izdatel'stvo Sovetskii Khudozhnik, Ul. Chernyakhovskogo, 4a, Moscow a-319, Russia.

581 630   US   ISSN 0892-6999
SB112.5
SOVIET AGRICULTURAL BIOLOGY. PART 1: PLANT BIOLOGY. 1986-1990. bi-m. (All-Union Academy of Agricultural Sciences) Allerton Press, Inc., 150 Fifth Ave., New York, NY 10011.

591   US   ISSN 0892-7006
SF1
SOVIET AGRICULTURAL BIOLOGY. PART 2: ANIMAL BIOLOGY. 1986-1990. bi-m. (All-Union Academy of Agricultural Sciences, UR) Allerton Press, Inc., 150 Fifth Ave., New York, NY 10011.

355   IS
SOVIET ARMY; digest from the Soviet press. ceased 1985. m. International Research Center on Contemporary Society, P.O. Box 687, Jerusalem 91 006, Israel.

327   US   ISSN 0887-0500
DJK50
SOVIET - EAST EUROPEAN SURVEY; selected research and analysis from Radio Free Europe-Radio Liberty. 1985-19?? a. (back issues avail.) Westview Press, 5500 Central Ave., Boulder, CO 80301.

621   US   ISSN 0891-334X
TS225
SOVIET FORGING AND SHEET METAL STAMPING TECHNOLOGY. 1986-1990. bi-m. (Soviet Machine Tool Industry and Scientific-Technical Society for the Engineering Industry, UR) Allerton Press, Inc., 150 Fifth Ave., New York, NY 10011.

551.4   US   ISSN 0038-5425
GB651   CODEN: SHSPBB
SOVIET HYDROLOGY: SELECTED PAPERS. (English translation from the Russian) 1962-198? irreg. (4 nos./vol.). (also avail. in microfilm; reprint service avail. from ISI) American Geophysical Union, 2000 Florida Ave. N.W., Washington, DC 20009.

616.97   US   ISSN 0739-8433
QR181
SOVIET IMMUNOLOGY. 1982-1990. bi-m. (U.S.S.R. Academy of Medical Sciences, UR) Allerton Press, Inc., 150 Fifth Ave., New York, NY 10011.

322.4 323.1 296   US   ISSN 0038-5468
SOVIET JEWRY ACTION NEWSLETTER. 1969-19?? fortn. (processed) Student Struggle for Soviet Jewry, c/o Glenn Richter, Ed., 240 Cabrini Blvd., No. 5B, New York, NY 10033-1114.

051   US   ISSN 0038-5549
DK1
SOVIET LIFE. 1956-1992; suspended. m. (also avail. in microform from UMI; reprint service avail. from UMI) (Novosti Press Agency, RU) Soviet Life, Box 578, Frederisksburg, VA 22404-9989.
    Incorporates in 1977: Soviet Panorama (ISSN 0038-5611); **Formerly:** U S S R

530   US   ISSN 0888-689X
TA404.2   CODEN: SMSREL
SOVIET MATERIALS SCIENCE REVIEWS. 1987-198? q. (also avail. in microform from UMI; back issues avail.; reprint service avail. from UMI) Hemisphere Publishing Corporation (Subsidiary of: Taylor & Francis Group), 1900 Frost Rd., Ste. 101, Bristol, PA 19007-1598.

622   NE   ISSN 0970-2458
SOVIET MINING JOURNAL. 1987-1989 (vol.3, no.4). q. A.A. Balkema, P.O. Box 1675, NE-3000 BR Rotterdam, Netherlands.

947   UK   ISSN 0038-5603
SOVIET NEWS. 1941-1991. w. (also avail. in microform from UMI; reprint service avail. from UMI) Soviet Embassy in London, Press Dept., 3 Rosary Gardens, London SW7 4NW, England.

629.1   US   ISSN 0889-020X
SOVIET SPACEFLIGHT REPORT. 1987-1989. bi-m. (back issues avail.) Starwise Publications, Box 25-WB, Pulaski, NY 13142.

600   UK
SOVIET TECHNOLOGY ALERT. ceased 1990. m. Elsevier Science Publishers Ltd., Crown House, Linton Rd., Barking, Essex IG11 8JU, England.

947   UK   ISSN 0038-5905
SOVIET WEEKLY. 1942-1991. w. (tabloid format) Soviet Embassy in London, Press Dept., 3 Rosary Gardens, London SW7 4NW, England.

947   GW   ISSN 0038-6006
H5
SOWJETWISSENSCHAFT; gesellschaftswissenschaftliche Beitraege. 1948-1989. 6/yr. Verlag Volk und Welt, Glinkastr. 13-15, 1086 Berlin, Germany.

CESSATIONS

301   GW   ISSN 0340-9201
SOZIALISATION UND KOMMUNIKATION. 1974-1991. irreg. (Universitaet Erlangen-Nuernberg) Ferdinand Enke Verlag, Postfach 101254, 7000 Stuttgart 30, Germany.

335   GW   ISSN 0038-6111
HD4809
SOZIALISTISCHE ARBEITSWISSENSCHAFT; theoretische Zeitschrift fuer arbeitswissenschaftliche Disziplinen. 1957-19?? 6/yr. (Zentrales Forschunginstitut fuer Arbeit, Staatssekretariat fuer Arbeit und Loehne) Verlag Die Wirtschaft, Am Friedrichshain 22, 1055 Berlin, Germany.
Formerly: Arbeitsoekonomik.

629.1   US
SPACE BENEFITS: SECONDARY APPLICATION OF AEROSPACE TECHNOLOGY IN OTHER SECTORS OF THE ECONOMY. ceased 1981. a. U.S. National Aeronautics and Space Administration, Washington, DC 20546.

330 600   US
SPACE ENTERPRISE. ceased 198? m. Pasha Publications Inc., 1401 Wilson Blvd., Ste. 900, Arlington, VA 22209-9970.
Formerly: Space Ventures Report.

629.13   US
SPACE ENTREPRENEURS DIRECTORY. (Supplement to: Space Calendar and Space Daily) ceased 1985. a. Space Age Publishing Co., 20431 Stevens Creek Blvd., No.210, Cupertino, CA 95014-0975.

629.13   US
SPACE FOR ALL PEOPLE. 1980-198? bi-m. (back issues avail.) Progressive Space Forum, 1724 Sacramento St., No.9, San Francisco, CA 94109.

629.1   UK   ISSN 0258-4212
TL787
SPACE MARKETS. 1986-19?? bi-m. Interavia S.A. (Subsidiary of: Jane's Information Group), Sentinel House, 163 Brighton Rd., Coulsdon, Surrey CR5 2NH, England.

520   US
SPACE ORNITHOLOGY NEWSLETTER. 1988-1991 (Oct.). q. Astronomical Data Service, 3922 Leisure Lane, Colorado Springs, CO 80917.

629.13   US   ISSN 0038-6332
TL787
SPACE WORLD (AMHERST). 1957-1989. 12/yr. (also avail. in microform from UMI) Palmer Publications, Inc., 318 Main St., Amherst, WI 54406.

629.1   UK   ISSN 0268-4713
SPACEFLIGHT NEWS. ceased 1991. m. Spaceflight News Ltd., P.O. Box 15, Grantham, Lincolnshire NG32 2LL, England.
Formerly (until 1985): Shuttle Story (ISSN 0266-2175)

629.13 327 355   US
SPACELINE. 1986-198? m. (back issues avail.) Institute for Security and Cooperation in Outer Space, 1352 Q St. N.W., Ste. 2E, Washington, DC 20004-4320.

811   US   ISSN 0038-6367
SPAFASWAP; some poetry, a few anecdotes, some wisdom and philosophy. 1969-19?? 6/yr. c/o Lois J. Long, Ed., 1070 Ahern Dr., La Puente, CA 91746.
Incorporates: Guardino's Gazette.

314   SP
SPAIN. INSTITUTO NACIONAL DE ESTADISTICA. ANUARIO ESTADISTICO: EDICION MANUAL. 1912-1988. a. Instituto Nacional de Estadistica, P. de la Castellana, 183, 28071 Madrid, Spain.

330   SP
SPAIN. INSTITUTO NACIONAL DE INDUSTRIA. PROGRAMA DE INVESTIGACIONES ECONOMICAS: SERIE E. 1977-1983 (no.18). irreg. Instituto Nacional de Industria, Programa de Investigaciones Economicas, Plaza del Marque de Salamanca 8-30, Madrid 6, Spain.

630   SP
SPAIN. MINISTERIO DE AGRICULTURA, PESCA Y ALIMENTACION. INFORMACION AGRARIA. ceased. s-a. Ministerio de Agricultura, Pesca y Alimentacion, Secretaria General Tecnica, Centro de Publicaciones, Paseo de la Infanta Isabel, 1, 28014 Madrid, Spain.

630 380   SP
SPAIN. MINISTERIO DE AGRICULTURA, PESCA Y ALIMENTACION. REGISTRO DE VARIEDADES PROTEGIDAS. BOLETIN. ceased. q. Ministerio de Agricultura, Pesca y Alimentacion, Secretaria General Tecnica, Centro de Publicaciones, Paseo de la Infanta Isabel, 1, 28014 Madrid, Spain.

354   SP
SPAIN. MINISTERIO DE ECONOMIA Y HACIENDA. SUBDIRECCION GENERAL DE ORGANIZACION E INFORMACION. ESTADISTICA DE LA INFORMACION AL PUBLICO. 1971-19?? irreg. Ministerio de Economia y Hacienda, Secretaria General Tecnica, Centro de Publicaciones, Plaza del Campillo del Mundo Nuevo, 3, 28005 Madrid, Spain.
Formerly: Spain. Ministerio de Hacienda. Subdireccion General de Organizacion e Informacion. Estadistica de la Informacion al Publico.

350   SP
SPAIN. MINISTERIO DE RELACIONES CON LAS CORTES Y DE LA SECRETARIA DE ESTADO. COLECCION INFORME. ceased. irreg. (Ministerio de Relaciones con las Cortes y de la Secretaria de Estado) Boletin Oficial del Estado, Servicio Central de Publicaciones, Ayala, 5, 28001 Madrid, Spain.
Formerly: Spain. Servicio Central de Publicaciones de la Presidencia del Gobierno. Coleccion Informe.

344.46   SP
SPAIN. TRIBUNAL CENTRAL DE TRABAJO. REPERTORIO DE SENTENCIAS. 1973-1989. s-a. Editorial Aranzadi, S.A., Avda. Carlos III, 34, Apdo. 111, 31080 Pamplona, Spain.

332   SW   ISSN 0346-1602
SPARBANKERNA. 1973-1990. 14/yr. Swedish Savings Banks Association, Box 16426, S-103 27 Stockholm, Sweden.
Supersedes: Sparfraemjaren (ISSN 0038-6545); Svensk Sparbankstidskrift (ISSN 0039-6737)

791.44   US
SPARKS (SANTA ROSA). 1968-199? s-a. Society of Wireless Pioneers, Box 530, Santa Rosa, CA 95402.
Formerly (until 1976): Wireless Pioneer (ISSN 0084-0440)

791   US
SPARKS JOURNAL. 1977-199? q. (tabloid format) Society of Wireless Pioneers, Box 530, Santa Rosa, CA 95402.
Formerly: Sparks Journal Quarterly.

052   JA   ISSN 0389-3510
HC462.9
SPEAKING OF JAPAN. 1981-1990. m. Keizai Koho Center, Speakers' Bureau, Otemachi Bldg. 6-1, Otemachi 1-chome, Chiyoda-ku, Tokyo 100, Japan.

373   AT   ISSN 0813-2402
SPECIAL EDUCATION JOURNAL. 1984-1991 (no.2). s-a. Department of School Education, G.P.O. Box 33, Sydney, N.S.W. 2001, Australia.

371.9   US   ISSN 0049-1837
SPECIAL EDUCATION NEWSLETTER. 1961-1988. 4/yr. (processed) National Catholic Educational Association, Special Education Department, c/o Suzanne Hall, Ed., 1077 - 30th St., N.W., Washington, DC 20007.

282   US
SPECIAL NEWS FOR SPECIAL PEOPLE. ceased 1990. irreg. (3-4/yr.). Our Sunday Visitor, Inc., Religious Education Department, 200 Noll Plaza, Huntington, IN 46750.

332.6   US
SPECIAL SITUATIONS UNDER FIVE DOLLARS. 1983-198? m. (looseleaf format; back issues avail.) Dow Theory Forecasts, Inc., 7412 Calumet Ave., Hammond, IN 46324-2692.
Formerly: Penny Stock Plays.

338.91   UN   ISSN 0257-7860
SPECIAL UNITED NATIONS SERVICES. 1980-19?? d. International Foundation for Development Alternatives, 4 place du Marche, 1260 Nyon, Switzerland.

301 380.5   US   ISSN 0276-8631
HV1553   CODEN: STPPDE
SPECIALIZED TRANSPORTATION PLANNING AND PRACTICE. 1982-1991. 4/yr. (in 1 vol., 4 nos./vol.). (also avail. in microform) Gordon and Breach Science Publishers, 270 Eighth Ave., New York, NY 10011.

380.5   US
SPECIALIZED TRANSPORTATION SERVICES, SERVICES GUIDE. 1983-19?? irreg. J.J. Keller and Associates, Inc., 145 W. Wisconsin Ave., Box 368, Neenah, WI 54957-0368.

070.5 380.1   US   ISSN 0895-254X
SPECIALTY BOOKSELLERS DIRECTORY. 1987-1991. a. (Avail. in database formats for IBM-PC, Macintosh, or compatibles) Ad-Lib Publications, 51 1-2 W. Adams, Box 1102, Fairfield, IA 52556-1102.

658.8   US
SPECIALTY RETAILER. published only twice, 1990. m. Creative Age Publications, Inc., 7628 Densmore Ave., Van Nuys, CA 91406-2088.

370   US
SPECIALWARE DIRECTORY; a guide to software sources for special education. 1983-1985. irreg. (Linc Associates, Inc.) Oryx Press, 4041 N. Central at Indian School Rd., Phoenix, AZ 85012-3397.

615   HU   ISSN 0138-9238
SPECTRUM PHARMACEUTICUM. 1963-1989. q. Orszagos Orvostudomanyi Informacios Intezet es Konyvtar, P.O. Box 278, Szentkiralyi u.21, 1444 Budapest, Hungary.

100 200   US   ISSN 0895-7517
SPECTRUM REVIEW; book reviews, interviews, and views. 1987-1991 (no.17). q. (back issues avail.) Integral Publishing, Box 1030, Lower Lake, CA 95457.

332.6   US
SPECULATIVE INVESTOR. 1980-1988 (Mar.). irreg. Arete Activities Inc., 101 St. Marks Pl., New York, NY 10009.

617.7   UK   ISSN 0268-148X
SPEECH. ceased 1989. m. (looseleaf format; back issues avail.) Sheffield University Biomedical Information Service (SUBIS), The University, Sheffield S10 2TN, England.

646.7   SW
SPEGELN. ceased 1989 (Dec.). bi-m. Frisoerarstaelldas Foerbund, Box 1146, 111 81 Stockholm, Sweden.

778.534   GW   ISSN 0176-4594
SPEKTRUM FILM. 1983-1986 (Dec.). m. Jugendfilmclub Koeln, Hansaring 82-86, 5000 Cologne 1, Germany.

372 410   AT
SPELLING ACTION. 1971-1990. q. (back issues avail.) Spelling Action Society, 58 Raeside St., Westlake, Qld. 4074, Australia.

684.1   US
SPELMANEWS. 1978-1990. bi-m. Spelmans Home Furnishings Services, 3001 Veazy Terr., N.W., Washington, DC 20008.

338.2   CN   ISSN 0700-7426
SPHERE. 1970-1990 (no.6). bi-m. Shell Canada Ltd., 400-4th Ave. S.W., Calgary, Alta. T2P 2H5, Canada.

642.5   US
SPICE (FORT LAUDERDALE). 1991; ceased same year (Fall). bi-m. Sterling Southeast Inc., 3230 W. Commercial Blvd., Ste. 250, Fort Lauderdale, FL 33309.

664 631   II   ISSN 0377-547X
SPICES NEWSLETTER. 1967-1989. m. Spices Board, St. Vincent Cross Rd., Ernakulam, Cochin 682 018, India.

796.42   SZ
SPIRIDON; international running magazine. 1972-1989 (Jun.). 9/yr. Noel Tamini, Ed. & Pub., 1922 Salvan, Switzerland.
Former titles: Foulees - le Nouveau Spiridon; Spiridon.

CESSATIONS

808   US   ISSN 0886-7267
SPIRIT (PRINCETON). 1971-1992 (no.87). m. (back issues avail.) Kitchen Sink Press, Inc., Rt. 1, Box 329, Princeton, WI 54968.
Formerly (until 1974): Will Eisner's Spirit (ISSN 0279-5523)

917.404   US
SPIRIT OF MASSACHUSETTS GUIDEBOOK. 1988-1992. a. (Massachusetts Office of Travel and Tourism) G T E Discovery Publications, Inc., 22026 20th St., Ste. 101, Bothell, WA 98021.

200 808.81   US
SPIRIT WINGS. 1986-198? a. (back issues avail.) Broken Streets, 57 Morningside Dr., E., Bristol, CT 06010.

028.5   US
SPIRITQUEST. ceased 1990 (Dec.). 6/yr. (Lutheran Church - Missouri Synod, Board for Youth Services) Concordia Publishing House, 3558 S. Jefferson Ave., St. Louis, MO 63118.
Formerly (until 1988): Teen Time.

200 BP602   US   ISSN 0160-0354
SPIRITUAL COMMUNITY GUIDE; the new consciousness source book. 1972-1985 (no.6). irreg. Arcline Publications, 1800 S. Robertson Blvd., Ste. 182, Los Angeles, CA 90035.

658 285   US   ISSN 0745-6352
SPIRITUAL FITNESS IN BUSINESS; a forum of ideas for Christians in the workplace. 1983-1990 (Feb.). m. (back issues avail.) Probe Ministries International, 1900 Firman Dr., Ste. 100, Richardson, TX 75081.

133.9   UK
SPIRITUALIST GAZETTE. 1972-1991. m. S A G B, 33 Belgrave Square, London SW1 8QV, England.

230 282 BX2350.A1   US   ISSN 0162-6760
SPIRITUALITY TODAY; a quarterly of spiritual theology. 1949-1992 (Summer). q. (also avail. in microform from UMI; reprint service avail. from UMI) (Dominicans, Province of St. Albert the Great) Spirituality Today Journal, Inc., 3642 Lindell Blvd., St. Louis, MO 63108.
Formerly (until 1977): Cross and Crown (ISSN 0011-1910)

338.91   NE   ISSN 0167-319X
SPONSORBULLETIN. 1974-1988 (no.27). 2/yr. Stichting Mensen in Nood, Postbus 1041, 5200 BA's Hertogenbosch, Netherlands.

016 790.1   CN   ISSN 0838-4061
SPORT & LEISURE; a journal of social science abstracts. 1980-1990 (vol.2, no.3). 3/yr. University of Waterloo Press, Waterloo, Ont. N2L 3G1, Canada.
Formerly (until 1989): Sociology of Leisure and Sport Abstracts (ISSN 0167-580X)

790.1   IT
SPORT CAPITAL. ceased. bi-m. Rizzoli Editore S.p.A., Via A. Rizzoli 2, 20132 Milan, Italy.

796.48   RM   ISSN 0007-5191
SPORT EN ROUMANIE/SPORT IN ROMANIA. 1957-1989 (Dec.). 4/yr. Romanian Olympic Committee, Str. Vasile Conta Nr. 16, Bucharest, Rumania.
Formerly: Bulletin Olympique Roumain: Romanian Olympic Bulletin.

796   US   ISSN 0038-7940
SPORT WORLD. ceased. bi-m. (also avail. in microform from UMI; reprint service avail. from UMI) Reese Communications, Inc., 460 W. 34th St., New York, NY 10001.

688.76   IT
SPORTIMPIANTI. 1980-19?? s-a. Edizioni Il Falasco s. n.c., Lunomare G. Marconi 34-35, 3-126 Lido di Venezia, Italy.

790.1   CN
SPORTING TIMES. 1990-1991 (Apr.). m. Adams Enterprises Ltd., P.O. Box 117, Vernon, B.C. V1T 6M1, Canada.

796   GW   ISSN 0138-144X
SPORTKEGLER. ceased 1991. m. Deutscher Kegler Verband der D.D.R., Storkower Str. 118, 1055 Berlin, Germany.

796.41   CS
SPORTOVNI A MODERNI GYMNASTIKA. 1951-1991. m. (Ceskoslovensky Svaz Telesne Vychovy) Olympia, Klimentska 1, 115 88 Prague 1, Czechoslovakia.
Former titles: Gymnastika; Sportovni a Umelecka Gymnastika (ISSN 0038-8114)

796.6   GW
SPORTRAD. 1988-1992. m. Motor-Presse Stuttgart, Leuschnerstr. 1, Postfach 106036, 7000 Stuttgart 10, Germany.

910.09 790.1   US
SPORTREKS; the newsletter for active travelers. 1988-1990; suspended. m. (back issues avail.) Symmetry Publishing, Box 221, Barnard, VT 05031.

799.1   US
SPORTS AFIELD BASS & PANFISH. 1977-1990. a. (also avail. in microfiche from UMI) Hearst Magazines, Sports Afield, 250 W. 55th St., New York, NY 10019.
Formerly: Sports Afield Bass (ISSN 0742-0609)

799.2 SK301   US   ISSN 0160-1830
SPORTS AFIELD DEER. ceased 1990. a. (also avail. in microfiche from UMI) Hearst Magazines, Sports Afield, 250 W. 55th St., New York, NY 10019.

799.1   US
SPORTS AFIELD FISHING. 1938-1990. a. (also avail. in microfiche from BLH) Hearst Magazines, Sports Afield, 250 W. 55th St., New York, NY 10019.
Formerly: Sports Afield Fishing Annual (ISSN 0742-0587)

799.1 SH401   US   ISSN 0742-0595
SPORTS AFIELD FISHING SECRETS. 1977-1990. a. (also avail. in microfiche from UMI) Hearst Magazines, Sports Afield, 250 W. 55th St., New York, NY 10019.

799.2 SK7   US   ISSN 0276-8895
SPORTS AFIELD HUNTING. 1977-1989. a. Hearst Magazines, Sports Afield, 250 W. 55th St., New York, NY 10019.

799.1   US
SPORTS AFIELD KNOW YOUR FISH. 1960-1989. a. Hearst Magazines, Sports Afield, 250 W. 55th St., New York, NY 10019.

790.1   US
SPORTS AFIELD SPECIAL PUBLICATIONS. ceased. a. Hearst Magazines (Subsidiary of: Hearst Corporation), 250 W. 55th St., New York, NY 10019.

790.1 975   US
SPORTS HISTORY. 1987-199? bi-m. Empire Press, 602 S. King St., Ste. 300, Leesburg, VA 22075.

790.1 658.8   US
SPORTS MARKETING NEWS. 1986-1988. bi-w. Technical Marketing Corp., Box 453, Winchester, MA 01890.

617 011   US   ISSN 0897-9340
SPORTS MEDICINE RESEARCH TODAY. 1988-1991 (Dec.). m. BIOSIS, 2100 Arch St., Philadelphia, PA 19103-1399.

796.332   US
SPORTS QUARTERLY - FOOTBALL PROS. 1962-198? a. Lopez Publications, Inc., 111 E. 35th St., New York, NY 10016.

790   US
SPORTS TRAVEL. 1989-1990. m. Reed Travel Group, 500 Plaza Dr., Secaucus, NJ 07096.

796   II
SPORTS WEEK. 1968-1988; suspended. w. Inquilab Publications, 245 Ripon Rd., Bombay 400034, India.

790.1 613.7   US
SPORTSCAPE. 1980-198? 10/yr. City Sports, Inc., 118 King St., San Francisco, CA 94107.

790.1   FI   ISSN 0785-6695
SPORTTI. ceased. 6/yr. Yhtyneet Kuvalehdet Oy, Maistraatinportti 1, 00240 Helsinki, Finland.

796   GW   ISSN 0340-0956
SPORTWISSENSCHAFTLICHE DISSERTATIONEN. 1975-1989 (vol.30). irreg. Verlag Ingrid Czwalina, Reesenbuettler Redder 75, 2070 Ahrensburg, Germany.

274 301.412   UK
SPOTLIGHT (EDINBURGH). 1968-1990 (Spring). s-a. Church of Scotland Woman's Guild, Editorial Board of Spotlight, 121 George St., Edinburgh EH2 4YN, Scotland.

431   GW
SPRACHPFLEGE AND SPRACHKULTUR; Zeitschrift fuer gutes Deutsch. 1952-1991. 4/yr. (back issues avail.) V E B Bibliographisches Institut, PSF 130, Gerichtsweg 26, 7010 Leipzig, Germany.
Formerly: Sprachpflege (ISSN 0049-2019)

634   NE
SPRENGER INSTITUUT. COMMUNICATIONS. ceased. irreg. (back issues avail.) Sprenger Instituut, Postbus 17, 6700 AA Wageningen, Netherlands.

634 664   NE   ISSN 0081-3850
SPRENGER INSTITUUT. JAARVERSLAG/SPRENGER INSTITUTE. ANNUAL REPORT. 1956-19?? a. Sprenger Instituut, Postbus 17, 6700 AA Wageningen, Netherlands.

634   NE
SPRENGER INSTITUUT. RAPPORTEN. ceased. irreg. (back issues avail.) Sprenger Instituut, Postbus 17, 6700 AA Wageningen, Netherlands.

020   US   ISSN 0038-8599
SPRINGFIELD. MASSACHUSETTS. CITY LIBRARY BULLETIN. 1887-19?? bi-m. Springfield Library and Museums Association, 220 State St., Springfield, MA 01103.

800   CN   ISSN 0383-283X
SQUATCHBERRY JOURNAL. 1975-19?? a. Box 205, Geraldton, Ont. P0T 1M0, Canada.

330.9   CE
SRI LANKA. MINISTRY OF PLAN IMPLEMENTATION. PERFORMANCE. 1978-1988. q. Ministry of Plan Implementation, Central Bank Bldg., Colombo 1, Sri Lanka.

792 380   US
STAGE MANAGERS DIRECTORY. 1983-1990. a. Broadway Press, 12 W. Thomas St., Shelter Island, NY 11964-1037.
Formerly: Stage Managers' Association Directory.

026 929 CS42   US   ISSN 1042-2080
STAGECOACH; bulletin for genealogists. 1981-1990. q. Kinship, 60 Cedar Heights Rd., Rhinebeck, NY 12572.

636.2   DK   ISSN 0108-0903
STAMBOG OVER KOEER AF ROED DANSK MALKERACE. 1981-1986. a. Landbrugets Raadgivningscenter, Landsudvalget for Kvaeg, Stambogsfoereningen for RDM, Udkaervej 15, Skejby, DK-8200 Aarhus N, Denmark.

636.2   DK   ISSN 0105-0281
STAMBOG OVER KVAEG AF ROED DANSK MALKERACE. 1972-1988. a. Landbrugets Raadgivningscenter, Landsudvalget for Kvaeg, Udkaervsej 15, Skejby, DK-8200 Aarhus N, Denmark.
Former titles: Stambog og Elitestambog over Tyre af Roed Dansk Malkerace; Elitestambog over Koeer af Roed Dansk Malkerace.

769.56   US   ISSN 0273-978X
STAMP DEALER. 1977-19?? m. Hentzell Publications, 1050 Essex St., Ste. 205, San Diego, CA 92103-3346.

769.56   UK
STAMPS AND FOREIGN STAMPS. 1980-19?? m. E M A P Pursiut Publications Ltd., Bushfield House, Orton Centre, Peterborough PE2 0UW, England.
Formed by the merger of: Stamps (ISSN 0143-7011) & Foreign Stamps.

389.6   GW
STANDARDISIERUNG UND QUALITAET. 1954-1991. m. (Amt fuer Standardisierung, Messwesen und Warenpruefung) Verlag fuer Standardisierung, Postfach 840, 1020 Berlin, Germany.

CESSATIONS

551   US   ISSN 0081-4350
QE1   CODEN: SSGEAS
STANFORD UNIVERSITY. PUBLICATIONS. GEOLOGICAL SCIENCES. suspended 1986 (vol.20). irreg. Stanford University, School of Earth Sciences, Stanford, CA 94305.

808   DK   ISSN 0109-2588
STAR; fotoroman. 1982-198? m. Interpresse, Krogshoejvej 32, 2880 Bagsvaerd, Denmark.

658.8 621.381   US
STAR NEWS (SAN RAFAEL). 1982-1984. q. Micropro International Corp., 33 San Pablo Ave., San Rafael, CA 94903.

821   UK
STARDANCE. 1972; ceased same year. a. c/o Marek Urbanowicz, Ed., 49 Sheen Park, Richmond, Surrey, England.

808.838   US
STARSHORE; a magazine for the SF reader. 1990-1991 (Spring). q. McAlpine Publishing, 800 Seahawk Circle, Ste. 116, Virginia Beach, VA 23452.

621.381   US   ISSN 0889-6216
START (SAN FRANCISCO); guide to Atari. 1986-1991 (Apr.); suspended. m. (back issues avail.) Antic Publishing, Inc., 544 Second St., San Francisco, CA 94107.

796   SW   ISSN 0038-9943
START & SPEED. 1967-19?? 10/yr. Lerums Boktryckeri AB, Box 333, 44300 Lerum, 443 01 Lerum 1, Sweden.

361   US   ISSN 0899-1944
STATE CHILD CARE FACT BOOK (YEAR). 1986-1988. a. Children's Defense Fund, 122 C St., N.W., Washington, DC 20001.
 Formerly: Child Care: Whose Priority.

362.8   US
STATE COURT CASELOAD STATISTICS. 1975-19?? a. U.S. Department of Justice, Bureau of Justice Statistics, 633 Indiana Ave., N.W., Washington, DC 20531.

020   US
STATE UNIVERSITY COLLEGE OF ARTS & SCIENCE AT GENESEO. SCHOOL OF LIBRARY AND INFORMATION SCIENCE. NEWSLETTER. 1967-1983. 3/yr. (processed) State University of New York, College at Geneseo, School of Library and Information Science, Geneseo, NY 14454-1498.
 Formerly: State University College of Arts and Science at Geneseo. School of Library Science. Newsletter (ISSN 0039-0194)

388.413   DK   ISSN 0901-0963
STATENS VEJLABORATORIUM. NYE PUBLIKATIONER. ceased. q. Statens Vejlaboratorium, Elisagardsvej 5, Postboks 235, 4000 Roskilde, Denmark.

318   US   ISSN 0585-1432
HA175
STATISTICAL COMPENDIUM OF THE AMERICAS. 1969-1971. irreg. Organization of American States, 1889 F St., N.W., Washington, DC 20006.

338.4 669 310   EI   ISSN 0081-4954
STATISTICAL OFFICE OF THE EUROPEAN COMMUNITIES. SIDERURGIE ANNUAIRE. 1964-19?? a. Statistical Office of the European Communities, L-2985 Luxembourg, Luxembourg.

301 310   EI   ISSN 0039-0488
STATISTICAL OFFICE OF THE EUROPEAN COMMUNITIES. SOCIAL STATISTICS. 1969-19?? 6/yr. Statistical Office of the European Communities, L-2985 Luxembourg, Luxembourg.

338.4 314   EI   ISSN 0081-4970
STATISTICAL OFFICE OF THE EUROPEAN COMMUNITIES. STATISTIQUES INDUSTRIELLES ANNUAIRE. ceased. a. Statistical Office of the European Communities, L-2985 Luxembourg, Luxembourg.

910 011 370 380.5   TH
STATISTICAL REPORTS OF CHANGWAT. 1964-1986. a. National Statistical Office, Statistical Information Division, Larn Luang Rd., Bangkok 10100, Thailand.

310   US   ISSN 0732-6971
HA37
STATISTICAL SERVICES DIRECTORY. 1982-1984 (2nd ed.). a. Gale Research Inc., 835 Penobscot Bldg., Detroit, MI 48226.

314   UK   ISSN 0081-5098
STATISTICS - AFRICA; sources for market research. 1970-198? irreg. C.B.D. Research Ltd., 15 Wickham Rd., Beckenham, Kent BR3 2JS, England.

310 015   UK   ISSN 0309-5371
STATISTICS - ASIA & AUSTRALASIA: SOURCES FOR MARKET RESEARCH. 1974-198? irreg. C.B.D. Research Ltd., 154 High St., Beckenham, Kent BR3 1EA, England.

338.4   US
STATISTICS FOR ELECTRIC UTILITIES IN PENNSYLVANIA. ceased. a. Department of Commerce, Bureau of Policy, Planning, & Systems Development, 474 Forum Bldg., Harrisburg, PA 17120.

310   US
STATISTICS FOR GAS UTILITIES IN PENNSYLVANIA. 1956-198? a. Department of Commerce, Bureau of Policy, Planning, & Systems Development, 474 Forum Bldg., Harrisburg, PA 17120.

338.4   US   ISSN 0094-4335
TD224.P4
STATISTICS FOR WATER UTILITIES INCLUDING WATER AUTHORITIES IN PENNSYLVANIA. ceased. a. Department of Commerce, Bureau of Policy, Planning, & Systems Development, 474 Forum Bldg., Harrisburg, PA 17120.

616.861   CN   ISSN 0715-7657
HV5306
STATISTICS ON ALCOHOL AND DRUG USE IN CANADA AND OTHER COUNTRIES. 1983-19?? irreg. Addiction Research Foundation of Ontario, 33 Russell St., Toronto, Ont. M5S 2S1, Canada.

910.03   US
STATUS OF BLACK NEW YORK REPORT. ceased. a. New York Urban League, Inc., 218 W. 40th St., 6th Fl., New York, NY 10018.

790.1   GW   ISSN 0138-5666
STECKENPFERD; das bunte Raetselbuechlein. 1955-1990. q. Blumenstein Verlag, Am Michelsbach 27, 5900 Eisenach, Germany.

628   US
STEEL CAN RECYCLING NEWSLETTER. 1972-19?? 4/yr. American Iron and Steel Institute, Committee of Tin Mill Products Producers, 1133 15th St., N.W., Ste. 300, Washington, DC 20005.
 Formerly: Steel Can Recycling.

669.142 382   US
STEEL COMMENTS. 1982-198? irreg. (back issues avail.) American Iron and Steel Institute, 1133 15th St., N.W., Ste. 300, Washington, DC 20005.

669.142   US
STEEL FOUNDERS' RESEARCH JOURNAL. ceased. q. (back issues avail.) Steel Founders' Society of America, Cast Metals Federation Bldg., 455 State St., Des Plains, IL 60016.

634.9   US   ISSN 0082-318X
STEPHEN F. AUSTIN STATE UNIVERSITY. SCHOOL OF FORESTRY. BULLETIN. 1957-1972 (no.25). irreg. Stephen F. Austin State University, School of Forestry, Nacogdoches, TX 75961.

808.81   US   ISSN 0735-4789
PS508.N3
STEPPINGSTONES. 1982-1985. q. Steppingstones Press, Box 1690, New York, NY 10011.

598.2   NO   ISSN 0039-1247
    CODEN: SRNAAA
STERNA. 1951-1987. a. Stavanger Museum Biblioteket, N-4005 Stavanger, Norway.

616.4   UK   ISSN 0142-8527
STEROIDOGENESIS. ceased 1990. m. (looseleaf format; back issues avail.) Sheffield University Biomedical Information Service (SUBIS), The University, Sheffield S10 2TN, England.

340   GW
STEUER- UND ZOLLBLATT FUER BERLIN. 1951-1991. w. (back issues avail.) (Senatsverwaltung fuer Finanzen) Kulturbuch-Verlag GmbH, Passauer Str. 4, 1000 Berlin 30, Germany.

370   UK   ISSN 0144-0764
STIRLING TECHNICAL REPORTS IN EDUCATION. 1980-19?? irreg. University of Stirling, Department of Education, Stirling FK9 4LA, Scotland.

746.4   US
STITCH. ceased. m. Crow Publications, Inc., 650 S. Lipan, Denver, CO 80223.

332.5   US   ISSN 1042-5799
REVPAR
STOCKHOLDERS AND CREDITORS NEWS SERVICE CONCERNING THE PUBLIC SERVICE COMPANY OF NEW HAMPSHIRE; the national journal of record reporting details of the P S N H bankruptcy. 1987-198? s-m. (looseleaf format; back issues avail.) Andrews Publications, 1646 West Chester Pike, Box 1000, Westtown, PA 19395.

152   SW   ISSN 0345-021X
STOCKHOLMS UNIVERSITET. PSYKOLOGISKA INSTITUTIONEN. REPORTS. SUPPLEMENT SERIES. 1970-1989. irreg. (approx. 5/yr.). Stockholms Universitet, Psykologiska Institutionen, S-106 91 Stockholm, Sweden.

332.6   US   ISSN 0749-9779
STOCKOWNERS' NEWS. 1984-19?? q. (looseleaf format; back issues avail.) Fund for Stockowners Rights, Box 65563, Washington, DC 20035.

642.5   US
STOKES REPORT. 1981-1991. m. (back issues avail.) Judy Ford Stokes & Associates, Inc., 14 N. Parkway Sq., Ste. 300, 4200 Northside Pkwy., Atlanta, GA 30327.

811   US
THE STONE. 1967-1988 (no.15). irreg. Stone Press (Santa Cruz), 1112-B Ocean St., Santa Cruz, CA 95060.

811   US   ISSN 0146-1397
PS580
STONE COUNTRY; a magazine of poetry, reviews and graphics. 1974-19?? 2/yr. (double issues). (back issues avail.) Nathan Mayhew Seminars of Martha's Vineyard, Box 132, Menemsha, MA 02552.
 Formerly: Patterns (ISSN 0031-3211)

959 808   US
STONE LION REVIEW. 1978-1986. irreg. Harvard University, Undergraduates and Graduates of Asian Studies, 2 Divinity Ave., Cambridge, MA 02138.

690   US   ISSN 1045-4519
STONE THROUGH THE AGES. 1984-19??; suspended. q. Marble Institute of America, Inc., 33305 State St., Farmington, MI 48335.
 Formerly: Through the Ages.

385   NE
DE STOOMTRAM. 1977-1989 (no.39). q. Stichting MuseumStoomtram, Postbus 137, 1620 AC Hoorn, Netherlands.

621.86   SA
STORAGE, HANDLING & DISTRIBUTION. ceased. m. Westbourne-Maclean Hunter (Pty) Ltd., Nedbank East City, 120 End St., Box 6110, Johannesburg 2000, South Africa.

350.865   UK
STORETALK. 1979-1990 (Feb.). bi-m. (back issues avail.) British Home Stores PLC, Marylebone House, 129-137 Marylebone Rd., London NW1 5QD, England.
 Formerly (until 1986): B H S Parade.

390   IT   ISSN 0081-5837
STORIA, COSTUMI E TRADIZIONI. 1962-198? (vol.15). irreg. ALFA Edizioni, Via Santo Stefano 13, I-40125 Bologna, Italy.

028.5   US
STORK. 1985-1989. 8/yr. Children's Better Health Institute, 110 Waterway Blvd., Box 567, Indianapolis, IN 46202.

818.005   CN
STORY SO FAR. 1971-19??; suspended. irreg. Coach House Press, 401(Rear) Huron St., Toronto, Ont. M5S 2G5, Canada.

910.09   AT   ISSN 0811-191X
STORYLINES. 1982-1991 (Apr.). m. (back issues avail.) Northern Territory Tourist Commission, 99 Todd Street, Alice Springs. N.T. 0870, Australia.

808.81   US   ISSN 1047-2622
STRAIGHT AHEAD. 1987-1991 (vol. 5). m. Box 2091, La Habra, CA 90632.

388.31   GW   ISSN 0039-2146
TE3
DIE STRASSE; Zeitschrift fuer Forschung und Praxis des Strassenwesens. 1960-1990. m. (Leitstelle fuer Information und Dokumentation) Transpress VEB Verlag fuer Verkehrswesen, Franzoesische Str. 13-14, 1086 Berlin, Germany.

330   US   ISSN 0748-4895
STRATEGIC PLANNING MANAGEMENT. 1983-199? m. (looseleaf format; back issues avail.) Commerce Communications, Inc., 5247 Washburn Ave., S., Minneapolis, MN 55410.

929   US
STRATTON NOTES. 1985-1991 (vol.6). irreg. Topp of the Line, c/o Mrs. Bette Butcher Topp, Ed., W. 1304 Cliffwood Ct., Spokane, WA 99218-2917.

810   US   ISSN 0190-1737
STREET MAGAZINE. 1975-1981 (vol.3, no.3). irreg. (back issues avail.) Street Press, Box 772, Sound Beach, NY 11789-0772.

352.7   US
STREET TALK; Connecticut's neighborhood magazine and resource guide. 1978-1984. q. (back issues avail.) Regional Housing Rehabilitation Institute, 280 Norton St., New Haven, CT 06511-3036.

823 821   UK   ISSN 0262-9267
STRIDE. 1981-1989. q. (back issues avail.) Stride Publications, 37 Portland St., Newton, Exeter, Devon EX1 2EG, England.

621   US   ISSN 0146-2059
TA350
STRUCTURAL MECHANICS SOFTWARE SERIES. 1977-19?? irreg. (University of Virginia, Department of Engineering Science and Systems) University Press of Virginia, Box 3608 University Sta., Charlottesville, VA 22903.

780   UR
STUDENT CHOIR DIRECTOR'S LIBRARY. 1951-1991 (no. 21). a. Izdatel'stvo Muzyka, Ul. Neglinnaya 14, Moscow 103031, Russian S.F.S.R., U.S.S.R.

378   US
STUDENT LIFE. 1984-1989 (Feb.). s-a. The Time Inc. Magazine Company, Time & Life Bldg., Rockefeller Center, 1271 Ave. of the Americas, New York, NY 10020.
    Formerly: Dorm Magazine (ISSN 0743-2860)

070   US   ISSN 0274-9777
STUDENT PRESS SERVICE. 1979-1990 (Mar.); suspended. 7/yr. Youth Policy Institute, 1221 Massachusetts Ave., N.W., Ste. B, Washington, DC 20005.

378   US
STUDENT TRAVEL CATALOG. 1974-1992. a. Council on International Educational Exchange, 205 E. 42nd St., New York, NY 10017.
    Formerly: Student Work Study Travel Catalog.

910.202   US   ISSN 1043-0709
STUDENT TRAVELER; student travel guide. ceased 1991. 2/yr. (back issues avail.; reprint service avail.) Whittle Communications L.P., Corporate Communications, 333 Main Ave., Knoxville, TN 37902.
    Formerly (until 1989): America (Knoxville).

378 327   US
STUDENTS UNITED FOR PEACE NEWSLETTER. ceased. 6/yr. 1724 H St., No. 36, Sacramento, CA 95814-2134.

100   IT
STUDI FILOSOFICI. 1978-1981 (vol.4); suspended. a. (Istituto Universitario Orientale) Casa Editrice Leo. S. Olschki, Viuzzo del Pozzetto (Viale Europa), 50136 Florence, Italy.

945   IT   ISSN 0081-6264
STUDI VENEZIANI. 1959-1976. a. (Fondazione Giorgio Cini, Istituto Venezia e l'Oriente) Giardini Editori e Stampatori, Via Santa Bibbiana 28, 56100 Pisa, Italy.
    Formerly (until 1965): Societa e Stato Veneziano. Istituto di Storia. Bollettino.

901   GW
STUDIA DELITZSCHIANA. NEUE FOLGE. 1980-1990. irreg. Verlag Lambert Schneider, Hausackerweg 16, D-6900 Heidelberg, Germany.

930   NE   ISSN 0169-8311
STUDIA GAIANA. 1948-1981 (vol.6). irreg. E.J. Brill, P.O. Box 9000, 2300 PA Leiden, Netherlands.

540   PL   ISSN 0082-5530
STUDIA SOCIETATIS SCIENTIARUM TORUNENSIS. SECTIO B. CHEMIA. 1954-1972 (vol.8). irreg. (Towarzystwo Naukowe w Toruniu) Panstwowe Wydawnictwo Naukowe, Ul. Miodowa 10, Warsaw, Poland.

574   PL   ISSN 0082-5581
STUDIA SOCIETATIS SCIENTIARUM TORUNENSIS. SECTIO G. PHYSIOLOGIA. 1961-19??; suspended. irreg. Towarzystwo Naukowe w Toruniu, Ul. Wysoka 16, 87-100 Torun, Poland.

100 800   GW   ISSN 0081-735X
STUDIEN ZUR PHILOSOPHIE UND LITERATUR DES NEUNZEHNTEN JAHRHUNDERTS. 1968-1979 (vol. 36). irreg. Vittorio Klostermann, Frauenlobstr. 22, 6000 Frankfurt a.M. 90, Germany.

970.1 342   CN   ISSN 0226-3491
STUDIES IN ABORIGINAL RIGHTS. 1980-1986. irreg. University of Saskatchewan, Native Law Centre, Diefenbaker Centre, Saskatoon, Sask. S7N 0W0, Canada.

700 913   US
STUDIES IN ANCIENT ART AND ARCHAEOLOGY. ceased. irreg. Cornell University Press, 124 Roberts Pl., Ithaca, NY 14850.

930   NE
STUDIES IN ANCIENT CIVILIZATION. 1972-1980; suspended. irreg. Elsevier Science Publishers B.V., P.O. Box 211, 1000 AE Amsterdam, Netherlands.

301.2   US   ISSN 0585-6523
STUDIES IN ANTHROPOLOGICAL METHOD. ceased. irreg. Holt, Rinehart and Winston, Inc., c/o Harcourt Brace Jovanovich, 6277 Sea Harbor Dr., Orlando, FL 32887.

600   US
STUDIES IN APPLIED REGIONAL SCIENCE. 1976-19?? irreg. Kluwer Nijhoff Publishing, 101 Philip Dr., Assinippi Park, Norwell, MA 02061.

780.01   US
STUDIES IN BRITISH MUSICOLOGY. ceased 1991 (Jun.). irreg. U M I Research Press, 300 N. Zeeb Rd., Ann Arbor, MI 48106-1346.

930   US
STUDIES IN CHRISTIAN ANTIQUITY. ceased 1981 (vol. 21). irreg. (reprint service avail. from UMI) Catholic University of America Press, 620 Michigan Ave., N.E., Washington, DC 20064.

330   UK   ISSN 0081-7856
STUDIES IN ECONOMICS. 1970-1976 (no.11). irreg. George Allen & Unwin (Publishers) Ltd., 40 Museum St., London W.C.1, England.

830   GW   ISSN 0081-797X
STUDIES IN GERMAN LITERATURE. 1964-198? irreg. Walter de Gruyter & Co., Mouton Publishers, Postfach 110240, D-1000 Berlin 11, Germany.

378   CN   ISSN 0081-7988
STUDIES IN HIGHER EDUCATION IN CANADA. 1960-19?? irreg. (Association of Universities and Colleges of Canada) University of Toronto Press, Front Campus, Toronto, Ont. M5S 1A6, Canada.

327   US
STUDIES IN LATIN AMERICAN REVOLUTION. 1981-198? q. Global Options, Box 40601, San Francisco, CA 94140-0601.

890   US
STUDIES IN MODERN HEBREW LITERATURE. ceased. irreg. Cornell University Press, 124 Roberts Place, Ithaca, NY 14850.

800   US
STUDIES IN MODERN LITERATURE. ceased 1991 (June). irreg. U M I Research Press, 300 N. Zeeb Rd., Ann Arbor, MI 48106-1346.

417 480   UK   ISSN 0081-8275
Z7009.L5
STUDIES IN MYCENAEAN INSCRIPTIONS AND DIALECT. 1956-1991 (no.23); suspended. irreg. British Association for Mycenaean Studies, Faculty of Classics, Sidgwick Ave., Cambridge CB3 9DA, England.

800   US   ISSN 0743-7889
STUDIES IN ROMANTIC AND MODERN LITERATURE. 1985-1988 (vol.2). irreg. Peter Lang Publishing, Inc., 62 W. 45th St., 4th Fl., New York, NY 10036.

301   US   ISSN 0081-8518
STUDIES IN SOCIAL LIFE. 1953-19?? irreg. Kluwer Nijhoff Publishing, 101 Philip Dr., Assinippi Pk., Norwell, MA 02061.

800   US
STUDIES IN SPECULATIVE FICTION. ceased 1991 (Jun.). irreg. U M I Research Press, 300 N. Zeeb Rd., Ann Arbor, MI 48106-1346.

700   US
STUDIES IN THE FINE ARTS: ART PATRONAGE. ceased 1991 (Jun.). irreg. U M I Research Press, 300 N. Zeeb Rd., Ann Arbor, MI 48106-1346.

700   US
STUDIES IN THE FINE ARTS: ART THEORY. ceased 1991 (Jun.). irreg. U M I Research Press, 300 N. Zeeb Rd., Ann Arbor, MI 48106-1346.

700   US
STUDIES IN THE FINE ARTS: AVANT-GARDE. ceased 1991 (Jun.). irreg. U M I Research Press, 300 N. Zeeb Rd., Ann Arbor, MI 48106-1346.

700   US
STUDIES IN THE FINE ARTS: CRITICISM. ceased 1991 (Jun.). irreg. U M I Research Press, 300 N. Zeeb Rd., Ann Arbor, MI 48106-1346.

700   US
STUDIES IN THE FINE ARTS: ICONOGRAPHY. ceased 1991 (Jun.). irreg. U M I Research Press, 300 N. Zeeb Rd., Ann Arbor, MI 48106-1346.

700   US
STUDIES IN THE FINE ARTS: STUDIES IN BAROQUE ART HISTORY. ceased 1991 (June). irreg. U M I Research Press, 300 N. Zeeb Rd., Ann Arbor, MI 48106-1346.

770   US
STUDIES IN THE FINE ARTS: STUDIES IN PHOTOGRAPHY. ceased 1991 (June). irreg. U M I Research Press, 300 N. Zeeb Rd., Ann Arbor, MI 48106-1346.

700   US
STUDIES IN THE FINE ARTS: STUDIES IN RENAISSANCE ART HISTORY. ceased 1991 (June). irreg. U M I Research Press, 300 N. Zeeb Rd., Ann Arbor, MI 48106-1346.

370 150   FR
STUDIES IN THE LEARNING SCIENCES. 1973-19?? irreg. (also avail. in microfiche) Organization for Economic Cooperation and Development, Centre for Educational Research and Innovation, 2 rue Andre-Pascal, 75775 Paris Cedex 16, France.

500   US
STUDIES IN THE NATURAL SCIENCES. 1973-19?? irreg. (University of Miami, Center for Theoretical Studies) Plenum Publishing Corp., 233 Spring St., New York, NY 10013.

646.3   AT
STUDIO BEAUTY. ceased. s-a. Buying Systems Australia Pty. Ltd., 23-25 Bay St., Double Bay, Sydney, N.S.W. 2028, Australia.

701.18 UK ISSN 0039-4114
STUDIO INTERNATIONAL. 1893-1988. 4/yr. (also avail. in microform from MIM,WMP) Medical Tribune Group, Tower House, Southampton St., London WC2E 7LS, England.
   Formerly: Studio.

410 GW ISSN 0342-8982
P3
STUDIUM LINGUISTIK. 1976-1987. s-a. (back issues avail.) Verlag Anton Hain Meisenheim GmbH, Savignystr. 53, D-6000 Frankfurt-Main 1, Germany.

500 600 SW
STUDSVIK TECHNICAL NEWS. 1972-19?? q. Studsvik A B, Fack, 61182 Nykoeping 1, Sweden.

610 US
STUDY GUIDE IN QUALITY ASSURANCE AND UTILIZATION REVIEW. 1981-199? irreg. (looseleaf format) American College of Utilization Review Physicians, 1531 S. Tamiami Trail, Ste. 703, Venice, FL 34292.

870.196 US ISSN 0893-0511
LB2376.3.G7
STUDY IN THE UNITED KINGDOM AND IRELAND. ceased 1989 (3rd ed.). biennial. (reprint service avail. from UMI) Institute of International Education, 809 United Nations Plaza, New York, NY 10017.
   Formerly: Study in the United Kingdom.

793 US
STUDY OF FINANCIAL RESULTS AND REPORTING TRENDS IN THE GAMING INDUSTRY. 1981-1990. a. Laventhol & Horwath, 1845 Walnut St., Philadelphia, PA 19103.

746 UK
STYLE MAGAZINE. 1968-19?? 3/yr. Style Patterns Ltd., Radley House, 35-39 S. Ealing Rd., London W5 4QT, England.
   Formerly: Style Pattern Book (ISSN 0309-4898)

016 310 UK
SUBJECT INDEX TO SOURCES OF COMPARATIVE INTERNATIONAL STATISTICS. 1978-198? irreg. C.B.D. Research Ltd., 15 Wickham Rd., Beckenham, Kent BR3 2JS, England.

808 UK ISSN 0049-2442
SUCCESS (PETERBOROUGH); magazine for creative writers. 1968-1990. q. Success Magazine, 17 Andrews Cres., Peterborough PE4 6XL, England.

658 301.435 US ISSN 8755-321X
SUCCESSFUL MARKETING TO SENIOR CITIZENS. 1981-1991; suspended. m. Senior World Publications, Inc., 2117 Garnet Ave., San Diego, CA 92109.

330.9 SJ
SUDAN JOURNAL OF DEVELOPMENT RESEARCH. 1977-1982 (vol.6). s-a. National Council for Research, Economic and Social Research Council, P.O. Box 1166, Khartoum, Sudan.

338 BL ISSN 0039-453X
SUDENE INFORMA. 1962-1977. q. Superintendencia do Desenvolvimento do Nordeste, Av. Prof Moraes Rego, Cidade Universitaria, 50000 Recife PE, Brazil.

371 GW ISSN 0340-2355
SUEDWESTDEUTSCHE SCHULBLAETTER. ceased 1986. 2/yr. (Philologenverband Baden-Wuerttemberg) Ernst Klett Verlag, Rotenbuehlstr. 77, Postfach 809, 7000 Stuttgart 1, Germany.

664 633 NE ISSN 0081-9204
TP375 CODEN: SUTRBB
SUGAR TECHNOLOGY REVIEWS. 1971-1989 (vol.14). 3/yr. (also avail. in microform from RPI) Elsevier Science Publishers B.V., P.O. Box 211, 1000 AE Amsterdam, Netherlands.

053.93 052 SA
SUID-AFRIKAANSE OORSIG. 1954-1989 (Dec.). s-m. Bureau for Information, 356 Vermeulen St., Pretoria 0002, South Africa.

340.3 SA
SUID-AFRIKAANSE REGSKOMMISSIE. JAARVERSLAG/ SOUTH AFRICAN LAW COMMISSION. ANNUAL REPORT. 1974-1989. a. Government Printer, Bosman St., Private Bag X85, Pretoria 0001, South Africa.

617.6 016 BL ISSN 0039-4947
SUMARIOS DE ODONTOLOGIA. 1967-1991. bi-m. (processed) Universidade de Sao Paulo, Faculdade de Odontologia, Seccao de Documentacao Odontologica, Caixa Postal 8216, 01000 Sao Paulo, Brazil.

340 US
SUMMARY OF RECENT DECISIONS AND LEGISLATION RELATING TO THE LAW OF REAL PROPERTY. vol.39, 1975-1991. q. (looseleaf format) Ticor Title Guarantee, 39 Broadway, New York, NY 10006-3084.
   Formerly: Summary of Recent Decisions Relating to the Law of Real Property.

808.81 US ISSN 0893-9381
SUMMERFIELD JOURNAL. 1987-1989? q. Box 499, Riverdale, GA 30274-0499.

531.64 621.47 US
SUN-ECLIPSE. 1976-1985. m. Alabama Solar Energy Association, c/o University of Alabama in Huntsville, Kenneth E. Johnson Environmental and Energy Center, Huntsville, AL 35899.

059.945 FI ISSN 0039-548X
SUOMALAINEN. 1966-1977. q. Maanpuolustuslehden Kustannus Oy, P. Hesperiankatu 15 A, Helsinki 26, Finland.

001.6 621.381 US
SUPER GROUP MAGAZINE (FRENCH EDITION). 1990; ceased same year (vol.5). q. 1787 E. Fort Union Blvd., Ste. 107, Salt Lake City, UT 84121.

796.75 US
SUPER - MOTO CROSS. 1987-1989 (Dec.). m. Petersen Publishing Co., 8490 Sunset Blvd., Los Angeles, CA 90069.

796 US ISSN 0039-5684
SUPER SPORTS. 1968-198? 6/yr. Reese Communications, Inc., 460 W. 34th St., New York, NY 10001.

700 791.43 AT
SUPER 8 READER; acme! projecting the Nineties. 1984-19?? a. (Australian Film Commission) Sydney Super 8 Film Group, P.O. Box 424, Kings Cross, N.S.W. 2011, Australia.

531 621.3 US ISSN 0897-6279
SUPERCONDUCTIVITY; theory and applications. 1988; announced, never published. 8/yr. Elsevier Science Publishing Co., Inc., 655 6th Ave., New York, NY 10010.

530 US ISSN 0959-308X
SUPERCONDUCTIVITY ABSTRACTS. 1991; announced, never published. m. (also avail. in microform; back issues avail.) (Scitechinform, UR) Pergamon Press, Inc., Journals Division, 660 White Plains Rd., Tarrytown, NY 10591-5153.

621.3 US
SUPERCONDUCTOR ADVANCE. 1988-19?? m. Box C, Tenafly, NJ 07670.

332.6 US
SUPERGROWTH TECHNOLOGY U S A. 1981-1988. m. 21st Century Research, 8200 Blvd. E., N. Bergen, NJ 07047.

658.8 AT
SUPERMARKET CIRCLE. 1982-198? 7/yr. (back issues avail.) Supermarket Magazines Distributors Pty. Ltd., 14 Herbert St., Artarmon, N.S.W. 2064, Australia.

621.381 US ISSN 0740-4816
SUPERMICRO. 1982-19??; suspended. m. (looseleaf format; back issues avail.) I T O M International Co., Box 1450, Los Altos, CA 94022.

658 US ISSN 0740-0411
SUPERVISOR'S NEWSLETTER; a guide to supervisory action. 1960-19?? m. (reprint service avail. from UMI) A.C. Croft, Inc., Box 2440, Costa Mesa, CA 92627.
   Former titles (until 1981): Assignments in Management Supervisor's Newsletter; (until 1979): Assignments in Management (ISSN 0004-5116)

658.3 US ISSN 0194-8717
SUPERVISOR'S SAFETY CLINIC. ceased. s-m. Bureau of Business Practice, 24 Rope Ferry Rd., Waterford, CT 06386.

581 GW
SUPPLEMENT PILZE. ceased. s-a. G I T Verlag GmbH, Alsfelder Str. 10, Postfach 11 05 64, D-6100 Darmstadt 11, Germany.

336 340 II ISSN 0253-6560
SUPREME COURT CASES (TAXATION). 1973-1990. m. (back issues avail.) Eastern Book Company, 34 Lalbagh, Lucknow 226 001, India.

347 II
SUPREME COURT JOURNAL. 1950-19?? fortn. Madras Law Journal Office, Box 604, Mylapore, Madras 4, India.

537.5 UK ISSN 0959-9517
  CODEN: SRMIEX
SURFACE MOUNT INTERNATIONAL; an international journal. 1990-1991 (Oct.). 6/yr. Elsevier Science Publishers Ltd., Crown House, Linton Rd., Barking, Essex IG11 8JU, England.

617 US
SURGERY REPORT. 1990; ceased same year. 4/yr. Mosby - Year Book, Inc. (Subsidiary of: Times Mirror Company), 11830 Westline Industrial Dr., St. Louis, MO 63146.

616.3 IT
SURGICAL GASTROENTEROLOGY. suspended 1980. q. (Collegium Internationale Chirugiae Digestivae) Piccin Editore, Via Porciglia 10, 35100 Padua, Italy.

617.3 US ISSN 0891-1800
SURGICAL ROUNDS FOR ORTHOPAEDICS. 1987-1990. m. (also avail. in microform from UMI; back issues avail.) Romaine Pierson Publishers, Inc., 80 Shore Rd., Port Washington, NY 11050.

332 US
SURVEY OF FINANCIAL INDICATORS. 1976-1989 (Oct.). s-a. Conference Board, Inc., 845 Third Ave., New York, NY 10022.
   Formerly: Financial Indicators and Corporate Financing Plans: A Semi-Annual Survey.

060 US
SURVEY OF GRANT-MAKING FOUNDATIONS. 1975-198? a. Public Service Materials Center, 5130 Macarthur Blvd., N.W., Apt. 200, Washington, DC 20016-3316.

658.8 310 US
SURVEY OF INDUSTRIAL PURCHASING POWER. 1974-1988. a. (reprint service avail. from UMI) Bill Communications, Inc., 633 Third Ave., New York, NY 10017.
   Former titles: Sales and Marketing Management Survey of Industrial and Commercial Buying Power; Sales and Marketing Management Survey of Industrial Purchasing Power; Sales Management Survey of Industrial Purchasing Power.

540 US ISSN 0081-976X
QD1 CODEN: SPGCAZ
SURVEY OF PROGRESS IN CHEMISTRY. 1963-1983 (vol.10). irreg. (reprint service avail. from ISI) Academic Press, Inc., 1250 Sixth Ave., San Diego, CA 92101.

616.95 011 US
Z6664.V45
SURVEY OF RESEARCH FOR SEXUALLY TRANSMITTED DISEASES. no.2, 1978-19?? irreg. U.S. Centers for Disease Control, 1600 Clifton Rd., N.E., Atlanta, GA 30333.
   Former titles: Sexually Transmitted Diseases. Abstracts and Bibliography (ISSN 0195-7708); Current Literature on Venereal Disease (ISSN 0001-3544)

336 US
SURVEY OF STATE TAXATION. ceased. q. (Association of Data Processing and Services Organizations) A D A S P O, The Computer Software and Services Industry Association, 1300 N. 17th St., Ste. 300, Arlington, VA 22209.

310 US ISSN 0737-545X
Z7554.U5
SURVEYS, POLLS, CENSUSES AND FORECASTS DIRECTORY. 1983-198? a. Gale Research Inc., 835 Penobscot Bldg., Detroit, MI 48226.

360 US
SURVIVAL BULLETIN. 1969-19?? q. United Presbyterian Church, USA, United Presbyterian Church in the U.S.A., Health, Education and Welfare Asociation, 100 Weatherspoon St., Louisville, KY 40202.
Formerly: Survival News Bulletin.

572 UK ISSN 0307-823X
SUSSEX ANTHROPOLOGY. 1976-198? irreg. University of Sussex, Students' Union, Falmer, Brighton, Sussex BN1 9QN, England.
Formerly: Sussex Essays in Anthropology.

929 UK
SUSSEX GENEALOGICAL CENTRE. OCCASIONAL PAPERS. 1979-19?? irreg. Sussex Genealogical Centre, 105 Springett Ave., Ringmer, Lewes, East Sussex BN8 5QS, England.

338 SW
SVENSK INDUSTRITIDNING. ceased 1990. 8/yr. Svensk Industrifoerening, P.O. Box 1133, 111 81 Stockholm, Sweden.

674 676.12 SW ISSN 0039-6796
SVENSK TRAEVARU- OCH PAPPERSMASSETIDNING/ SWEDISH TIMBER AND WOOD PULP JOURNAL. 1885-198? m. AB Svensk Traevarutidning, Midskoggraend 5, S-115 43 Stockholm, Sweden.
Formerly: Svensk Travarutidning.

614 SW ISSN 0303-6537
SWEDEN. SJUKVAARDENS OCH SOCIALVAARDENS PLANERINGS- OCH RATIONALISERINGSINSTITUT. S P R I RAAD 7. 1971-19?? irreg. Sjukvaardens och Socialvaardens Planerings- och Rationaliseringsinstitut - Swedish Planning and Rationalization Institute of the Health and Social Services, Box 27310, S 102 54 Stockholm, Sweden.

620 SW ISSN 0282-2024
SWEDEN. STATENS JAERNVAEGARS HUVUDKONTOR. GEOTEKNIK OCH INGENJOERGEOLOGI. MEDDELANDEN. 1917-1987 (no.47). irreg. Statens Jaernvaegars Huvudkontor, Geoteknik och Ingenjoergeolgi - State Railways Head Office, Geotechnical Department, S-105 50 Stockholm, Sweden.
Former titles: Sweden. Statens Jaernvaegars Centralfoervaltning. Geoteknik och Ingenjoergeologi. Meddelanden; Sweden. Statens Jaernvaegars Centralfoervaltning. Geotekniska Kontoret. Meddelanden.

551 SW ISSN 0284-1711
SWEDISH INSTITUTE OF SPACE PHYSICS. PREPRINT. 1969-1989. irreg. (back issues avail.) Swedish Institute of Space Physics, P.O. Box 812, S-91828 Kiruna, Sweden.
Formerly: Kiruna Geophysical Institute. Preprint (ISSN 0349-2656)

314.94 338.4 SZ
SWITZERLAND. BUNDESAMT FUER STATISTIK. EINGEFUEHRTE MOTORFAHRZEUGE - VEHICULES A MOTEUR IMPORTES. ceased 1987. a. Bundesamt fuer Statistik, Hallwylstr. 15, CH-3003 Berne, Switzerland.
Continues in part: Switzerland. Statistisches Amt. Eingefuehrte Motorfahrzeuge: in Verkehr Gesetzte Neue Motorfahrzeuge.

382 600 SZ
SWITZERLAND YOUR PARTNER; hi-tec "high technology products of Switzerland". 1979-1992. s-a. Swiss Office for Trade Promotion, Avenue Avant Poste 4, C.P. 1128, CH-1001 Lausanne, Switzerland.

628.1 AT ISSN 0039-761X
SYDNEY WATER BOARD JOURNAL. 1951-19?? s-a. Metropolitan Water Sewerage and Drainage Board, 341 Pitt St., Sydney, N.S.W., Australia.

332.678 US ISSN 0738-4173
SYLVIA PORTER'S PERSONAL FINANCE MAGAZINE. 1983-1989 (May). 10/yr. Sylvia Porter's Personal Finance Magazine Co., 380 Lexington Ave., New York, NY 10017.

160 GW ISSN 0082-0660
BL600
SYMBOLON; Jahrbuch fuer Symbolforschung. (Vols.1-7 published by Schwabe-Verlag, Basel) 1955; N.S. 1975-19?? a. (Gesellschaft fuer Wissenschaftliche Symbolforschung) DuMont Buchverlag GmbH & Co. KG, Mittelstr. 12-14, 5000 Cologne 1, Germany.

622 US ISSN 0085-7068
CODEN: PSCRDH
SYMPOSIUM ON COAL MINE DRAINAGE RESEARCH. PAPERS. 1965-19?? a. or biennial. (Coal Industry Advisory Committee to the Ohio River Valley Water Sanitation Commission) B C R National Laboratory, 500 William Pitt Way, Pittsburgh, PA 15238.

333.7 665 UK
SYMPOSIUM ON FLAMES AND INDUSTRY. PROCEEDINGS. ceased. irreg. Institute of Fuel, British Flame Research Committee, 18 Devonshire St., London W1N 2AU, England.

621.2 UK
SYMPOSIUM ON JET PUMPS & EJECTORS AND GAS LIFT TECHNIQUES. PROCEEDINGS. ceased. irreg., 2nd 1975 Cambridge. B H R A Fluid Engineering, Cranfield, Bedford MK43 OAJ, England.

001.642 US
SYMPOSIUM ON LOGIC PROGRAMMING PROCEEDINGS. 1984-1987. a. (Institute of Electrical and Electronics Engineers, Inc.) I E E E Computer Society Press, 10662 Los Vaqueros Circle, Los Alamitos, CA 90720-1264.
Formerly (until 1984): International Symposium on Logic Programming. Proceedings.

622 US
SYMPOSIUM ON SURFACE MINING AND RECLAMATION (PROCEEDINGS). 1973-1977. a. (National Coal Association) B C R National Laboratory, 500 William Pitt Way, Pittsburgh, PA 15238.

378 UK
SYNAPSE (EDINBURGH). ceased 1991. 2/yr. University of Edinburgh, Student Publications Board, 48, The Pleasance, Edinburgh EH8 9TJ, Scotland.

547 GW ISSN 0723-3655
QD262 CODEN: SNFMDF
SYNFORM. 1983-19?? q. (also avail. in microfilm; back issues avail.) V C H Verlagsgesellschaft mbH, Postfach 10 11 61, 6940 Weinheim, Germany.

621.381 US ISSN 0273-2696
SYNTAX. 1980-1984 (vol.4, no.11). m. (back issues avail.) Harvard Group, Box 667 T, Harvard, MA 01451.
Formerly: Syntax ZX80.

282 US ISSN 0279-781X
SYNTHESIS (BOLTON). 1981-199? q. (looseleaf format) Growth Associates, Box 247, Bolton, MA 01740.

808.8 051 US ISSN 0276-6345
AS30
SYRACUSE SCHOLAR; an interdisciplinary journal of ideas and research. 1980-1991 (vol.11, no.1). (back issues avail.) Syracuse University, Syracuse Scholar, 306-308 Sims Hall, Syracuse, NY 13244.

299 US
SYRACUSE UNIVERSITY. FOREIGN AND COMPARATIVE STUDIES. SOUTH ASIAN SPECIAL PUBLICATIONS. 1976-1983 (no.4); suspended. irreg. Syracuse University, Foreign and Comparative Studies, c/o Joanna C. Giansanti, Man. Ed., 321 Sims Hall, Syracuse, NY 13244-1230.

674 US
SYRACUSE WOOD SCIENCE SERIES. ceased. irreg. Syracuse University Press, 1600 Jamesville Ave., Syracuse, NY 13244.

001.642 US
SYSTEM BUILDER; the manager's guide for applications development. 1988-1990 (Apr.). bi-m. (back issues avail.) International Computer Programs, Inc., Box 40946, Indianapolis, IN 46240-0946.

001.535 US
SYSTEMS A I. 1990; ceased same year. bi-m. A I Week, Inc., 2555 Cumberland Pkwy., Ste. 299, Atlanta, GA 30339.

700 UK ISSN 0143-1064
SYZYGY. ceased 1979. q. (back issues avail.) Syzygy Publications, 5 Lorne St., Reading, Berkshire, England.

794.1 PL ISSN 0137-8198
SZACHY. 1947-1990 (Sep.). m. Ul. Czerniakowska 126A, 00-454 Warsaw, Poland.

629.13 US ISSN 0888-1812
T A C BULLETIN. 1961-1987. bi-m. Texas Department of Aviation, Box 12607, Austin, TX 78711.

001.3 US ISSN 0564-7169
AS36
T A I U S. (Texas A & I University Studies) 1968-1979 (vol.12). a. (tabloid format) Texas A & I University, Jernigan Library, Kingsville, TX 78363.

356 FR ISSN 0018-8395
T A M; periodique des forces armees. 1955-1987. bi-m. Association pour le Developpement et la Diffusion de l'Information Militaire, 6, Rue Saint-Charles, 75015 Paris, France.

368 US
T A P REPORT. 1970-1988 (Oct.). irreg. American Council of Life Insurance, Trend Analysis Program, 1001 Pennsylvania Ave., N.W., Washington, DC 20004-2599.

690 694 AT
T D A TIMBER NEWS. 1981-1991 (vol.51, no.1). s-a. Timber Development Association (NSW) Ltd., P.O. Box 50, Surry Hills, N.S.W. 2010, Australia.

629.8 US
T E A M. (Training and Education for Advanced Manufacturing) ceased. 4/yr. Industrial Technology Institute, Box 1485, Ann Arbor, MI 48106.

621.38 CS
T.E.S.L.A. ELECTRONICS. ceased 1987 (vol.20, no.3-4). q. T.E.S.L.A. Electronics Research Institute, Novodvorska 994, Prague 4, Czechoslovakia.

572 US
T H E T A. (Tsimshian, Haida, Eskimo, Tlingit, Aleut) 1973-1987 (vol.12); suspended. irreg. University of Alaska, Cross Cultural Communications, Gruening Bldg., 5th Fl., Fairbanks, AK 99701.

621.381 330 US ISSN 0892-2837
T I COMPUTING; a P C I publication for Texas Instruments computer users and VARs. 1984-1989. m. (tabloid format; back issues avail.) Publications & Communications, Inc., 12416 Hymeadow Dr., Austin, TX 78750-1896.
Formerly: T I Professional Computing (ISSN 0743-9512)

331.88 CS
T N C'S BULLETIN. 1988-1989. bi-m. World Federation of Trade Unions, Branicka 112, 140 00 Prague 4, Czechoslovakia.

821 UK ISSN 0144-2848
T O P S: THE OLD POLICE STATION. 1979-1990. q. St. Michaels & Lark Lane Community Association, The Old Police Station, 80 Lark Lane, Liverpool L17 8UU, England.

028.5 FR
T R I O. ceased 1978. m. Societe Parisienne d'Edition, 2-12 rue de Bellevue, 75019 Paris, France.

001.642 NE ISSN 0167-7888
T R W SERIES OF SOFTWARE TECHNOLOGY. 1978-1984. Elsevier Science Publishers B.V., P.O. Box 211, 1000 AE Amsterdam, Netherlands.

780 US
T.U.B.A. SERIES. 1975-198? irreg. (Tubists Universal Brotherhood Association) Brass Press, 136 Eighth Ave., N., Nashville, TN 37203.

791.4 GW ISSN 0934-3180
T V I. (Television International) 1985-19?? m. Tele-Audiovision, Postfach 1234, 8043 Unterfoehring, Germany.

791.4 790.1 US
T V SPORTS. 1988-1991. m. Crosby Vandenburgh Group, 309 Lakeside Dr., Horsham, PA 19044-2313.

Cessations

621.882   GW   ISSN 0170-9577
TS200   CODEN: TZMEDJ
T Z FUER METALLBEARBEITUNG. 1890-1989. m. Konradin-Industrieverlag GmbH, Postfach 100252, 7022 Leinfelden-Echterdingen, Germany.
Formerly: T Z fuer Praktische Metallbearbeitung (ISSN 0039-8667)

679.7   AU   ISSN 0039-8756
DER TABAKPFLANZER OESTERREICHS; Mitteilungsblatt fuer den oesterreichischen Tabakanbau. 1950-1986. irreg. Austria Tabakwerke A.G., Porzellangasse 51, A-1091 Vienna, Austria.

796   CN   ISSN 0828-4539
TABLE TENNIS TECHNICAL/TECHNIQUE TENNIS DE TABLE. 1981-1989. (Feb.). 6/yr. Canadian Table Tennis Association, 1600 James Naismith Dr., Gloucester, Ont. K1B SN4, Canada.

059.92   IS
TAFNIT. 1987-1990. bi-m. Rosh Pina Local Council, Rosh Pina 12000, Israel.

361.73   US   ISSN 0882-5521
TAFT NONPROFIT EXECUTIVE. ceased. m. Taft Group, 12300 Twinbrook Pkwy., Ste. 450, Rockville, MD 20852.
Formerly: Non-Profit Executive (ISSN 0735-1402)

796   CN   ISSN 0821-0160
TAKE FIVE. 1972-1988. m. Turner-Warwick Publications Inc., No. 13, 1715 Idylwyld Drive N., Saskatoon, Sask. S7L 1B4, Canada.
Supersedes (in 1983): Recreation Saskatchewan (ISSN 0708-0743)

663   UK   ISSN 0956-2710
TAKE-HOME DRINKS. 1989-199? bi-w. (tabloid format; back issues avail.) Reed Business Publishing Group, Carew Division (Subsidiary of: Reed International PLC), Quadrant House, The Quadrant, Sutton, Surrey SM2 5AS, England.

332.6 338   US   ISSN 8755-4755
TAKEOVER TARGET WEEKLY FORECAST. 1983-198? w. (back issues avail.) Quality Services Company, 5290 Overpass Rd., Ste. 127, Santa Barbara, CA 93111-9950.
Formerly: Santa Barbara Stock Market Report.

370 780   US   ISSN 0889-4175
ML1
TALENT EDUCATION JOURNAL. 1979-19?? q. Talent Education of St. Louis, 236 Spring Ave., St. Louis, MO 63119.

331.8 398   US   ISSN 0738-7911
TALKIN' UNION. 1981 1991. irreg. (back issues avail.) Box 5349, Takoma Park, MD 20912.

026   US   ISSN 0082-1519
Z5347
TALKING BOOKS, ADULT (LARGE PRINT EDITION). 1935-1987. biennial. (large print edition in 14 pt.) U.S. Library of Congress, National Library Service for the Blind and Physically Handicapped, Washington, DC 20542.

639.9   US   ISSN 0070-833X
TALL TIMBERS CONFERENCE ON ECOLOGICAL ANIMAL CONTROL BY HABITAT MANAGEMENT. PROCEEDINGS. 1969-1980 (no.7); suspended. irreg. (reprint service avail. from UMI) Tall Timbers Research Station, Route 1, Box 678, Tallahassee, FL 32312.

001.642   US
TALMIS INDUSTRY UPDATE; concise trends, news and analysis for the computer or software executive. 1980-1988. m. (back issues avail.) Link Resources Corp., 79 Fifth Ave., New York, NY 10003-2025.
Formerly: Talmis Update.

051   US
TAMPA BAY NEW HOMES. 1988-19?? 9/yr. Tampa Bay Media Affiliates (Subsidiary of: Micromedia Affiliates, Inc.), Bayport Plaza, Ste. 9900, 6200 Courtney Campbell Causeway, Tampa, FL 33607.

301.4157 301.412   US
TAPESTRY (MISSOULA). 1981-1988. q. 1013 Sherwood, Missoula, MT 59802-2601.

789.91 020   US   ISSN 0272-9520
TARAKAN MUSIC LETTER; the librarian's guide to audio collection development. 1979-19?? 5/yr. Sound Advice Enterprises, 40 Holly Lane, Roslyn Heights, NY 11577.

614.7 333.7 574   DK   ISSN 0496-8859
TARAXACUM. ceased. 3/yr. International Youth Federation, Klostermoellevej 48 A, Skanderborg, Denmark.

643.6   CH
TARGET HOUSEWARES & GIFTS. ceased 1989. m. United Pacific International Inc., P.O. Box 81-417, Taipei, Taiwan, Republic of China.

382.7 380.5   GW   ISSN 0492-2700
TARIF- UND VERKEHRS-ANZEIGER. ceased 1990. irreg. (approx. 35/yr.). Ministerium fuer Verkehrswesen, Tarifamt, Vossstr. 33, 1086 Berlin, Germany.

783   GW   ISSN 0344-1407
TASCHENBUCH FUER LITURGIE KIRCHENMUSIK UND MUSIKERZIEHUNG. (Not published in 1978) 1958-1991. a. Verlag Friedrich Pustet, Gutenbergstr. 8, 8400 Regensburg 1, Germany.
Former titles: Taschenbuch fuer Liturgie und Kirchenmusik (ISSN 0082-187X); Taschenbuch fuer den Kirchenmusiker.

632.9 595.7   AT
TASMANIA. DEPARTMENT OF PRIMARY INDUSTRY. INSECT PEST SURVEY. 1969-1989. a. Tasmanian Department of Primary Industry, G.P.O. Box 192B, Hobart, Tas. 7001, Australia.
Formerly: Tasmania. Department of Agriculture. Insect Pest Survey.

610 636.089   AT
TASMANIAN HYDATID DISEASE NEWSLETTER. 1964-1991 (Sep.). a. (back issues avail.) Tasmanian Hydatids Eradication Council, c/o Health Dept., 3 Brooke St., Hobart, Tas. 7000, Australia.

700 974   US   ISSN 0896-8063
GT2345
TATTOO ADVOCATE; journal of international tattoo arts. 1988-199? s-a. (back issues avail.) Tattoo Advocacy, Inc., 380 Belmont Ave., Haledon, NJ 07508.

979 700   US
TATTOO HISTORIAN. 1982-1987 (no.11). s-a. (back issues avail.) Tattoo Art Museum, 837 Columbus Ave., San Francisco, CA 94133.

343.73   US   ISSN 0196-8882
KF6272
TAX ALERT FOR MANAGEMENT. ceased 198? w. Research Institute of America, Inc., 90 Fifth Ave., New York, NY 10011.

347   US   ISSN 0892-4430
TAX LAW ANTHOLOGY. suspended after one issue, 1989. a. International Library Law Book Publishers, Inc., 101 Lakeforest Blvd., Ste. 270, Gaithersburg, MD 20877.

340 336   US
TAX LAW LOCATOR. 1988-1990. a. R.R. Bowker, A Reed Reference Publishing Company, Division of Reed Publishing (USA) Inc., 121 Chanlon Rd., New Providence, NJ 07974.

336.2   US   ISSN 0040-0084
TAX PLANNING. 1965-1990. m. (looseleaf format) Macmillan Information Company Inc., 910 Sylvan Ave., Englewood Cliffs, NJ 07632.

336   US
TAX PREPARERS LIABILITY SERVICE. ceased 1990. 5 base vols. (plus m. supplements). Research Institute of America, Inc., 90 Fifth Ave., New York, NY 10011.

340 336   US
TAX SHELTER LITIGATION REPORT; the national journal of record of tax shelter proceedings in federal and state courts. 1987-1989 (July). m. (looseleaf format; back issues avail.) Andrews Publications, 1646 West Chester Pike, Box 1000, West Chester Pike, PA 19395.

336   US
TAX YEAR IN REVIEW. ceased 1987. a. Research Institute of America, Inc., 90 Fifth Ave., New York, NY 10011.

336   US
TAXATION DIGEST. JOURNAL. 1981-199? a. Warren, Gorham & Lamont Inc., One Penn Plaza, New York, NY 10119.

742.92   US
TAXI. ceased 1991. m. Family Media, Inc., Women's and Fashion Group, 3 Park Ave., New York, NY 10016.

388.321   UK
TAXI DRIVERS COMPENDIUM. 1947-1990. a. Britannic Publicity Ltd., 8 Harewood Row, London NW1 6SE, England.

388.321   US   ISSN 0040-0211
TAXI NEWS DIGEST; voice of the taxi industry. 1948-198? m. (processed) (Wheel and Meter Society) Taxi News Digest Publishing Co., 17 Stillings St., Rear, Boston, MA 02210.

370   UK   ISSN 0040-0408
TEACHER. 1872-1989. w. (also avail. in microform from UMI; reprint service avail. from UMI) (National Union of Teachers) Teacher Publishing Co. Ltd., Derbyshire House, Lower St., Kettering, Northants. NN16 8BB, England.

380 371   UK
TEACHER IN COMMERCE; national journal of the commerical teaching profession. 1882-1991. 3/yr. Faculty of Teachers in Commerce Limited, 141 Bedford Rd., Sutton Coldfield, West Midlands B75 6DB, England.

370   UK
TEACHER'S TIME. 1970-19?? 5/yr. Eye to Eye Publications Ltd., 107-111 Fleet St., London EC4A 2AB, England.

929   US   ISSN 0899-5397
TEACHING GENEALOGY. 1988-1990. q. (back issues avail.) (Genealogical Institute) Family History World, Box 22045, Salt Lake City, UT 84122.

268   US   ISSN 0040-0645
TEACHING PICTURES FOR BIBLE SEARCHERS. ceased. q. Southern Baptist Convention, Sunday School Board, 127 Ninth Ave., N., Nashville, TN 37234.
Formerly: Junior Teaching Pictures.

001.644   US
TECHKNOWLEDGE. 1982-1991. m. Wang Laboratories, Inc., M-S 019-31A, One Industrial Ave., Lowell, MA 01851.

338.9 016   UK   ISSN 0040-0904
TECHNICAL CO-OPERATION; a monthly bibliography of Commonwealth official publications. 1964-1989. m. (with q. supplements). (also avail. in microfiche) Overseas Development Administration, Statistics Library, Eland House, Stag Place, London SW1E 5DH, England.

791.43   HU   ISSN 0138-9157
TECHNICAL FILM CARDS - INTERNATIONAL SELECTION. 1965-1982. q. Orszagos Muszaki Informacios Kozpont es Konyvtar - National Technical Information Centre and Library, Muzeum u. 17, Box 12, 1428 Budapest, Hungary.
Formerly: Technical Film International Bulletin (ISSN 0040-0947)

001.6 629.8 621.3   GW
TECHNICAL INFORMATION; process automation - electrical power installations. 1984-1991. s-a. (back issues avail.) V E B Kombinat Automatisierungsanlagenbau, Rhinstr. 100, 1140 Berlin, Germany.

770   US   ISSN 0040-0971
TR1
TECHNICAL PHOTOGRAPHY. 1969-198? m. P T N Publishing Corp., 210 Crossways Park Dr., Woodbury, NY 11797.

028.5   GW   ISSN 0497-0594
TECHNIKUS. ceased 1990. m. Verlag Junge Welt GmbH, Mauerstr. 39-40, 1080 Berlin, Germany.

576   US   ISSN 0082-2515
TECHNIQUES IN PURE AND APPLIED MICROBIOLOGY. 1969-1980. irreg., unnumbered. John Wiley & Sons, Inc., 605 Third Ave., New York, NY 10158-0012.

CESSATIONS

629.132 387.7 GW
TECHNISCH-OEKONOMISCHE INFORMATION DER ZIVILEN LUCHTFAHRT. 1964-1990. bi-m. (back issues avail.) Interflug, Flughafen Schoenefeld 1, 1189 Berlin, Germany.

571 GW ISSN 0067-4974
TECHNISCHE BEITRAEGE ZUR ARCHAEOLOGIE. 1959-19?? irreg. (Roemisch-Germanisches Zentralmuseum, Mainz) Dr. Rudolf Habelt GmbH, Am Buchenhang 1, 5300 Bonn 1, Germany.

500 540 530 510 GW ISSN 0323-5270
QD1 CODEN: WZHLDE
TECHNISCHE HOCHSCHULE CARL SCHORLEMMER LEUNA-MERSEBURG. WISSENSCHAFTLICHE ZEITSCHRIFT.. 1958-1991. bi-m. Technische Hochschule Carl Schorlemmer Leuna-Merseburg, Geusaerstr., 4200 Merseburg, Germany.

510 621.3 GW ISSN 0043-6917
CODEN: WZTHAP
TECHNISCHE HOCHSCHULE ILMENAU. WISSENSCHAFTLICHE ZEITSCHRIFT. 1954-1991. 5/yr. Technische Hochschule, Ilmenau, Postfach 327, 6300 Ilmenau, Germany.

621.9 GW ISSN 0040-1420
TECHNISCHE INFORMATION ARMATUREN. 1966-1991. 4/yr. Magdeburger Armaturenwerke M A W AG, Liebknechtstr. 65-91, 3031 Magdeburg, Germany.

658.5 745.2 GW ISSN 0341-5570
TECHNO-TIP. 1970-19?? 13/yr. Vogel-Verlag und Druck KG, Max-Planck-Str. 7-9, 8700 Wuerzburg 1, Germany.

370 600 US ISSN 0890-7889
TECHNOLOGY AND LEARNING. ceased 1989. bi-m. Lawrence Earlbaum Associates, Inc., 365 Broadway, Hillsdale, NJ 07642.

001.6 621.381 UK
TECHNOLOGY GRADUATE. 1987-199? 3/yr. (tabloid format; back issues avail.) Reed Business Publishing Group, Horizon Division (Subsidiary of: Reed International PLC), Quadrant House, The Quadrant, Sutton, Surrey SM2 5AS, England.

600 US
TECHNOLOGY ON CAMPUS. 1988-1989; suspended. q. Peter Li, Inc., 2451 E. River Rd., Dayton, OH 45439.

658 US ISSN 0882-2611
TECHNOLOGY REIMBURSEMENT REPORTS: THE BEIGE SHEET. 1985-1989 (Dec.). w. F-D-C Reports, Inc., 5550 Friendship Blvd., Ste. One, Chevy Chase, MD 20815.

639.2 MX ISSN 0304-2499
TECNICA PESQUERA. 1968-1990 (Sep.). m. Ediciones Mundo Marino S.A., Cruz Verde No. 40, Coyoacan, 04000 Mexico, D.F., Mexico.

780 792 IT ISSN 0393-8204
TECNO SHOW. 1985-199? bi-m. (back issues avail.) Stammer S.P.A., Centro Commerciale, Milano S. Felice, 20090 Segrate (Milan), Italy.

791.4 US ISSN 0731-9991
TEEN BAG. 1977-198? bi-m. Lopez Publications, Inc., 111 E. 35th St., New York, NY 10016.
Former titles: Movieland Presents Day TV; Movieland and TV Time (ISSN 0027-2787)

028.5 US ISSN 0040-201X
TEEN PIN-UPS. 1963-198? q. Reese Communications, Inc., 460 W. 34th St., New York, NY 10001.

028.5 200 US ISSN 1042-7953
TEENAGE. 1983-1990 (Apr.). 10/yr. (back issues avail.) Group Publishing, Inc., Box 481, 2890 N. Monroe, Loveland, CO 80539.
Formerly: Group Members Only (ISSN 0736-2188)

200 US
TEENS TODAY. 1969-1988. w. Church of the Nazarene, Nazarene Headquarters, Christian Life & Sunday School, 6401 The Paseo, Kansas City, MO 64131.

333.77 NO ISSN 0332-5938
TEKNIKK OG MILJOE. 1970-19?? q. Norwegian Technical Press A S, P.O.Box 235, Skoeyen, 0212 Oslo 2, Norway.
Formerly: Industri og Miljoe.

378 IS
TEL AVIV UNIVERSITY. PH.D. DEGREES AND ABSTRACTS. 1972-19?? irreg. Tel-Aviv University, Tel Aviv, Israel.

384.6 US
TELE-SCOPE. 1983-1990 (Mar.). m. Aries Group - M P S G, 1350 Piccard Dr., Ste. 300, Rockville, MD 20850.

301.16 658 US
TELECOM MANAGER; the complete guide to voice, data and information services. 1987-1990 (May). m. Capitol Publications, Inc., 1101 King St., Ste. 444, Alexandria, VA 22314.

384.6 US
TELECOMMANAGER. ceased. m. Telecom Publishing Group, 1101 King St., Ste. 444, Alexandria, VA 22314.

384 NE ISSN 0030-8382
TELECOMMUNICATIE; informatieblad voor handel en industrie. 1971-19?? m. Wijt en Zn. B.V., Box 268, Rotterdam, Netherlands.
Supersedes: P T T-Nieuws.

301.16 US ISSN 0882-1429
TK5101.A1
TELECOMMUNICATIONS ABSTRACTS. 1985-1989 (Dec.). m. R.R. Bowker, A Reed Reference Publishing Company, Division of Reed Publishing (USA) Inc., 121 Chanlon Rd., New Providence, NJ 07974.

574 US ISSN 0000-1252
TK5101.A1
TELECOMMUNICATIONS ABSTRACTS ANNUAL. ceased 1989 (Dec.). a. R.R. Bowker, A Reed Reference Publishing Company, Division of Reed Publishing (USA) Inc., 121 Chanlon Rd., New Providence, NJ 07974.
Formerly (until 1988): Telecommunications Index.

384 US ISSN 0735-388X
TELECOMMUNICATIONS COUNSELOR. 1981-1988 (Apr.). m. Voice & Data Resources, Inc., 236 West County Line, Jackson, NJ 08527.

621.38 US
TELECOMMUNICATIONS FICHE. ceased 1989 (Dec). m. (microfiche) R.R. Bowker, A Reed Reference Publishing Company, Division of Reed Publishing (USA) Inc., 121 Chanlon Rd., New Providence, NJ 07974.

621.38 US
TELECOMMUNICATIONS SURVEYS & FORECASTS. ceased 1989. q. Phillips Publishing, Inc., 7811 Montrose Rd., Potomac, MD 20854.
Formerly: Telecommunications (Potomac).

621.387 001.644 US
TELECOMMUTING REPORT; the monthly newsletter of trends & developments in location-independent work. 1984-1988 (May). m. Electronic Services Unlimited (Subsidiary of: Link-International Data Corp.), 79 Fifth Ave., New York, NY 10003.

574 US ISSN 0000-118X
TP248.2
TELEGEN ABSTRACTS; worldwide biotechnology and genetic engineering intelligence network. 1982-1989 (Dec.). m. (also avail. in microform) R.R. Bowker, A Reed Reference Publishing Company, Division of Reed Publishing (USA) Inc., 121 Chanlon Rd., New Providence, NJ 07974.
Formerly: Telegen Reporter (ISSN 0743-8443)

574 US
TP248.13
TELEGEN ABSTRACTS ANNUAL. 1973-1989 (Dec.). a. R.R. Bowker, A Reed Reference Publishing Company, Division of Reed Publishing (USA) Inc., 121 Chanlon Rd., New Providence, NJ 07974.
Former titles (until 1989): Telegen Reporter Annual (ISSN 0000-1201); (until 1988): Telegen Index and Yearbook.

574 011 US
TELEGEN FICHE. ceased 1989 (Dec.). m. (microfiche) R.R. Bowker, A Reed Reference Publishing Company, Division of Reed Publishing (USA) Inc., 121 Chanlon Rd., New Providence, NJ 07974.

791.4 CN ISSN 0049-3295
TELEGUIDE. 1959-19?? w. Williams Publishers Ltd., 1420 Mountain Ave., Kelowna, B.C. V1Y 7H5, Canada.

057.8 YU ISSN 0350-7564
TELEKS; informativni tednik dela. 1944-1990 (no.13). w. Delo, Titova 35, 61001 Ljubljana, Yugoslavia.
Supersedes (in 1977): I T D (ISSN 0350-4034); Which was formerly (until 1953): Tedenska Tribuna (ISSN 0040-196X)

658.8 384.6 US
TELEMARKETING MANAGEMENT. ceased 1989. m. (Conference Management Corporation) C M C Publishing, 200 Connecticut Ave., Norwalk, CT 06856-4990.

621.38 IT
TELEMATICA. 1981-198? 5/yr. Etas Kompass S.p.A., Via Rivoltana 95, 20090 Limito (Milan), Italy.

520 US ISSN 0190-5570
QB88
TELESCOPE MAKING. 1978-1992 (Jan.). q. (back issues avail.; reprint service avail. from UMI, BLH) Kalmbach Publishing Co., Box 1612, Waukesha, WI 53187.

535 522 US
TELESCOPE MAKING TECHNIQUES. 1977; ceased same year (vol.4). q. (William Charles Communications) Willmann-Bell, Inc., c/o Perry Remaklus, Box 3125, Richmond, VA 23235.

791.4 778.5 US
TELEVISION NETWORK MOVIES. ceased. a. Television Index, Inc., 40-29 27th St., Long Island City, NY 11101.

791.4 UK
TELEVISION: THE NEW ERA; U.K. consumer electronics market. 1983-198? irreg. Euromonitor Publications Ltd., 87-88 Turnmill St., London EC1M 5QU, England.
Formerly: Home Entertainment (ISSN 0260-6534)

600 330 HU ISSN 0521-4602
TEMADOKUMENTACIOS KIADVANYOK/THEMATICAL REVIEWS. 1959-1981 (no.132). irreg. Orszagos Muszaki Informacios Kozpont es Konyvtar (O.M.I. K.K.) - National Technical Information Centre and Library, Muzeum u. 17, Box 12, 1428 Budapest, Hungary.

178 AT
TEMPERANCE ADVOCATE. 1935-1989 (vol.54, no.2). q. (Australian and South Pacific Temperance Council) Queensland Temperance League, c/o T.A. Harwood, Ed., Box 590, Brisbane, Qld. 4001, Australia.
Formerly: Australian Temperance Advocate (ISSN 0005-0342)

782.1 CN
TEMPO. ceased 1990 (vol.6, no.1). a. Vancouver Opera, 1132 Hamilton St., Vancouver, B.C. V6B 2S2, Canada.
Formerly: Vancouver Opera Journal.

792 US
TENAZ TALKS TEATRO. 1977-1980. q. University of California, La Jolla, Chicano Studies Program, D-009, La Jolla, CA 92093.

338 US ISSN 0040-3121
TENNECO. 1967-1987 (vol.22). q. Tenneco Inc., Box 2511, Houston, TX 77001.

340 US
TENNESSEE BANKRUPTCY SERVICE. ceased. m. M. Lee Smith Publishers & Printers, 162 Fourth Ave. N., Box 2678, Nashville, TN 37219.

051 US
TENNESSEE ILLUSTRATED. 1988-1990 (Aug.). bi-m. Whittle Communications L.P., Corporate Communications, 505 Market St., Knoxville, TN 37902.

340 US
TENNESSEE JUDICIAL NEWSLETTER. 1974-1989 (vol. 15, no.5). bi-m. (Public Law Institute) University of Tennessee, College of Law, 1505 W. Cumberland Ave., Knoxville, TN 37996-1800.
Formerly (until 1984): Judicial Newsletter (ISSN 0163-2078)

001.3 US ISSN 0082-2779
AS36
TENNESSEE TECH JOURNAL. 1966-19?? a. (back issues avail.) Tennessee Technological University, Box 5183, Cookeville, TN 38501.

621.3 US ISSN 0082-2809
TENNESSEE VALLEY AUTHORITY. TECHNICAL MONOGRAPHS. 1934-19??; suspended. irreg. Tennessee Valley Authority, Treasury Services, Knoxville, TN 37902.

621.3 US ISSN 0082-2817
TK1425.M8
TENNESSEE VALLEY AUTHORITY. TECHNICAL REPORTS. 1940-19??; suspended. irreg. Tennessee Valley Authority, Treasury Services, Knoxville, TN 37902.

800 US
TENNESSEE WILLIAMS NEWSLETTER. vol.2, 1980-1983 (vol.4). 2/yr. University of Michigan, College of Engineering, Department of Humanities, Ann Arbor, MI 48109.

796.342 SW ISSN 0040-3431
TENNIS TIDNINGEN. 1945-1990. 10/yr. Svenska Tennisfoerbundets - Svenska Racket & Boll AB, Box 19022, 104 32 Stockholm, Sweden.

796.346 US ISSN 0040-3466
GV991
TENNIS U.S.A. 1928?-1989 (Dec.). m. (also avail. in microform from UMI) (United States Tennis Association) Family Media, Inc., 3 Park Ave., NY 10016.
 Supersedes (in 1979): U.S.L.T.A. Official News (United States Lawn Tennis Association).

100 IT ISSN 0040-3563
TEORESI; rivista di cultura filosofica. 1946-198? q. Universita degli Studi di Catania, Facolta di Lettere e Filosofia, Catania, Italy.

972.9 CU ISSN 0138-6212
TEORIA Y PRACTICA DE PRECIOS. 1979-1990 (vol.12, no.2). q. Comite Estatal de Precios, Amistad 552nd, Monte y Estrella, Habana 2, Havana, Cuba.

613.7 370 796 CS ISSN 0040-358X
TEORIE A PRAXE TELESNE VYCHOVY. 1952-1991. m. (Ceskoslovensky Svaz Telesne Vychovy) Olympia, Klimentska 1, 115 88 Prague 1, Czechoslovakia.

212.5 AG
TEOSOFO. 1946-19?? q. (Sociedad Theosofica) Editorial Teosofica, Casilla de Correo 36, 5800 Rio Cuarto, Cordoba, Argentina.

792 AG
TERCER ROSTRO. 1983-199? 5/yr. (back issues avail.) Centro Latinoamericano de Creacion e Investigacion Teatral de la Argentina, Lavalle 2237, Piso 6, No. 12, 1051 Buenos Aires, Argentina.
 Formerly: Informacion C E L C I T.

410 EI
TERMINOLOGICAL INFORMATION. 1965-1986. s-a. (back issues avail.) European Parliament, Terminology Office, Secretariat, Centre Europeen, Case Postale 1601, Luxembourg, Luxembourg.

551 560 NE ISSN 0308-9649
QE691
TERTIARY RESEARCH. 1976-1987 (vol.9). 4/yr. (back issues avail.) (Tertiary Research Group, UK) E.J. Brill, P.O. Box 9000, 2300 PA Leiden, Netherlands.

551 560 NE
TERTIARY RESEARCH SPECIAL PAPERS. ceased 1986 (vol.7). irreg. (Tertiary Research Group, UK) E.J. Brill, P.O. Box 9000, 2300 PA Leiden, Netherlands.
 Formerly: Tertiary Research Group. Special Papers (ISSN 0308-7506)

332.6 US
TEST & MEASUREMENT WORLD MARKET OUTLOOK. 1987-1991. bi-m. Cahners Publishing Company (Newton) (Subsidiary of: Reed International PLC), Division of Reed Publishing (USA) Inc., 275 Washington St., Newton, MA 02158-1630.

945 IT
TESTI MEDIEVALI DI INTERESSE DANTESCO. 1977-1978 (vol.2). irreg. (Istituto Dantesco Europeo) Casa Editrice Leo S. Olschki, Casella Postale 66, 50100 Florence, Italy.

547 621.381 US ISSN 0898-5529
 CODEN: TCMTE6
TETRAHEDRON COMPUTER METHODOLOGY; the international electronic journal for rapid publication of original research in computer chemistry. 1988-1991. 6/yr. Pergamon Press, Inc., Journals Division, 660 White Plains Rd., Tarrytown, NY 10591-5153.

387.7 IS
TEUFAH. 1985-1987; suspended. a. Haifa University, Wydra Shipping and Aviation Research Institute, Suite 2318, Eshkol Tower, Haifa 31 999, Israel.

338 US ISSN 0361-2597
HC107.T43
TEXAS. INDUSTRIAL COMMISSION. ANNUAL REPORT. 1962-1987. a. Industrial Commission, Box 12728, Capital Sta., Austin, TX 78711.

658 US
TEXAS A & M BUSINESS FORUM. 1975-1988. 2/yr. Texas A & M University, College of Business Administration, College Station, TX 77843.
 Formerly: Texas Business Executive.

378.198 US
TEXAS COLLEGE STUDENT. 1987-198? m. Waterloo Publishing Group, 604 W. 11th St., Austin, TX 78701.

917.604 US
TEXAS DEPARTMENT OF COMMERCE. TOURISM DIVISION. NEWSLETTER. 1964-198? m. Department of Commerce, Tourism Division, Congress Sq. II, 611 S. Congress, Ste. 201, Box 12008, Capitol Sta., Austin, TX 78711-2008.

338 621.381 US
TEXAS DESKTOP NEWS; Texas' computer newspaper. 1985-1989 (May). m. (tabloid format; reprint service avail.) Computer Street Journal, Inc. (Subsidiary of: Publications & Communications, Inc.), 12416 Hymeadow Dr., Austin, TX 78750-1896.
 Formerly: Computer Street Journal.

634.9 US ISSN 0082-304X
 CODEN: TXFPAY
TEXAS FORESTRY PAPERS. 1970-1972 (no.16). irreg. Stephen F. Austin State University, School of Forestry, Nacogdoches, TX 75961.

332 US ISSN 0882-0384
TEXAS LEAGUE SAVINGS ACCOUNT. 1972-1991. bi-m. (back issues avail.) S & L Communications, Inc., 408 W. 14th St., Austin, TX 78701.

029 US
TEXAS LIST OF SCIENTIFIC AND TECHNICAL SERIAL PUBLICATIONS. 1965-1989. s-a. (also avail. in microfiche; back issues avail.) Wilson Data Services, 477 W. 38th St., Houston, TX 77018.

647.9 US
TEXAS LODGING INDUSTRY. 1979-19?? a. Laventhol & Horwath, 1845 Walnut St., Philadelphia, PA 19103.

375.4 US
TEXAS PAPERS IN FOREIGN LANGUAGE EDUCATION. 1988-19?? irreg. University of Texas at Austin, Foreign Language Education Center, Education Bldg., 528 South, Austin, TX 78712-1295.

333.33 352.7 US ISSN 0884-7827
TEXAS REAL ESTATE. 1984-1986. bi-m. (plus a. issue). Greystone Publishing, 4665 Sweetwater Blvd., Ste. 100, Sugar Land, TX 77479.

026 US ISSN 0082-3163
Z732.T25
TEXAS SPECIAL LIBRARIES DIRECTORY. 1969-1987. irreg. State Library, Library Development Division, Texas Archives and Library Bldg., Box 12927, Capitol Sta., Austin, TX 78711.

677 US
TEXAS TEXTILE MAINTENANCE REPORTER; Arkansas, Colorado, Kansas, Illinois, Louisiana, Missouri, New Mexico, Oklahoma, Texas. 1959-19?? m. Henderson & Henderson, 1806 Treadwell St., Austin, TX 78704-2148.
 Formerly: Textile Maintenance Reporter (ISSN 0040-5094)

371.3 070.5 US ISSN 0733-8228
TEXTBOOK NEWS; the monthly newsletter on el-hi textbooks. 1982-1990. m. (except Jul./Aug.). (back issues avail.) Box 507, Lisle, IL 60532.

675 016 677 HU ISSN 0209-9578
TEXTIL- ES TEXTILRUHAZATI IPARI SZAKIRODALMI TAJEKOZTATO/ABSTRACT JOURNAL FOR TEXTILE AND CLOTHING INDUSTRY. 1949-19??. m. Orszagos Muszaki Informacios Kozpont es Konyvtar (O.M.I. K.K.) - National Technical Information Centre and Library, Muzeum u. 17, Box 12, 1428 Budapest, Hungary.
 Supersedes (in 1981): Muszaki Lapszemle. Textilipar, Eob- es Eorfeldolgozoipar - Technical Abstracts. Textile Industry, Leather and Leatherprocessing Industry (ISSN 0027-5069)

338.47 FR ISSN 0474-6023
TEXTILE INDUSTRY IN O E C D COUNTRIES. 1953-1983. irreg. (also avail. in microfiche) Organization for Economic Cooperation and Development, 2 rue Andre-Pascal, 75775 Paris Cedex 16, France.

385.264 UK
TEXTILE WORKER. 1936-1986. q. Textile and General Workers Union, Textile Trade Group, National House, Sunbridge Rd., Bradford BD1 2QB, England.

677 NE
TEXTILIA JOURNAAL. ceased. w. V N U Business Publications B.V., Rijnsburgstraat 11, 1059 AT Amsterdam, Netherlands.

800 NE ISSN 0169-8273
TEXTUS MINORES. 1948-1955 (vol.55). irreg. E.J. Brill, P.O. Box 9000, 2300 PA Leiden, Netherlands.

315 338 TH
THAILAND. NATIONAL STATISTICAL OFFICE. REPORT OF INDUSTRIAL SURVEY IN NORTHEAST REGION/ THAILAND. SAMNAKNGAN SATHITI HAENG CHAT. ceased 1972. irreg. National Statistical Office, Statistical Information Division, Larn Luang Rd., Bangkok, Thailand.

792 US ISSN 1052-0511
THEATER THREE. 1986-1991 (no.10). s-a. Carnegie - Mellon University, Department of Drama, Pittsburgh, PA 15213.

792.02 US
THEATRE AND DRAMATIC STUDIES. ceased 1991 (Jun.). irreg. U M I Research Press, 300 N. Zeeb Rd., Ann Arbor, MI 48106-1346.

792 FR
THEATRE EN EUROPE. 1984-1988; suspended. 3/yr. Theatre de l'Europe, 1, Place Paul Claudel, 75006 Paris, France.

792 UK ISSN 0309-8036
THEATRE PAPERS. 1978-19?? irreg. Dartington College of Arts, Department of Theatre, Devon, England.

792 US ISSN 0082-3848
THEATRE STUDENT SERIES. 1968-198? irreg. Rosen Publishing Group, 29 E. 21st St., New York, NY 10010.

792 US ISSN 0732-300X
THEATRE TIMES. 1982-199? 6/yr. Alliance of Resident Theatres - New York, Inc., c/o Art - New York, 131 Varick St., Ste. 904, New York, NY 10013.
 Supersedes: O O B A Newsletter; O O B A Guidebook to Theatres (ISSN 0361-6606)

250 GW ISSN 0138-2144
THEMATISCHE INFORMATION PHILOSOPHIE. 1965-1989. irreg. Zentralstelle fuer Philosophische Information und Dokumentation, J.-Dieckmann-Str. 19-23, 1086 Berlin, Germany.
 Formerly (1974-1976): Sonderinformation Philosophie; **(until 1970):** Informationen Philosophie.

541 UK ISSN 0305-9995
QD450 CODEN: THCHDM
THEORETICAL CHEMISTRY. 1972-198? biennial. Royal Society of Chemistry, Thomas Graham House, Science Park, Milton Rd., Cambridge CB4 4WF, England.
 Formerly: Quantum Chemistry.

541.2 US ISSN 0361-0551
QD450 CODEN: TCAPDZ
THEORETICAL CHEMISTRY: ADVANCES AND PERSPECTIVES. 1975-1981 (vol.6B). irreg. (reprint service avail. from ISI) Academic Press, Inc., 1250 Sixth Ave., San Diego, CA 92101.

CESSATIONS

212.5 UK ISSN 0951-497X
THEOSOPHICAL HISTORY. 1985-1989. q. 12 Bury Pl., London WC1A 2LA, England.

610 US
THERAPAEIA. (Supplement to: Medical Tribune) ceased 1986. m. Medical Tribune, Inc., 275 Park Ave. S., New York, NY 10010.

362.7 US
THINKING FAMILIES. 1988-1990. bi-m. Communications Plus, Inc., 605 Worcester Rd., Towson, MD 21204.

944 US
THIRD REPUBLIC/TROISIEME REPUBLIQUE. 1976-1989 (no.10). irreg. (microfiche) c/o William Logue, Ed., Northern Illinois University, Department of History, Dekalb, IL 60115.

860 US ISSN 0889-0722
THIRD WOMAN. 1981-19?? a. (back issues avail.) Third Woman Press, Chicano Studies, Dwinelle Hall 3412, University of California, Berkeley, CA 94720.

300 330 UK ISSN 0267-2499
D880
THIRD WORLD AFFAIRS. ceased. a. Third World Foundation for Social and Economic Studies, New Zealand House, 13th Fl., 80 Haymarket, London SW1Y 4TS, England.

919 910.202 AT
THIS WEEK IN CAIRNS. ceased. w. Peter Isaacson Publications Pty. Ltd., 45-50 Porter St., Prahran, Vic. 3181, Australia.

380.5 UK
THOMAS COOK BERLIN TRANSIT; a travel trade guide. 1986-1991. irreg. Thomas Cook Publishers, P.O. Box 227, Peterborough PE3 6SB, England.

380.5 UK
THOMAS COOK RAILPASS GUIDE; including city transit passes and national bus passes. 1987-1991. a. Thomas Cook Publishing, P.O. Box 227, Peterborough PE3 6SB, England.

806 US
THOMAS HARDY ANNUAL. 1982-1987 (vol.5). a. Humanities Press, 165 First Ave., Atlantic Highlands, NJ 07716-1289.

810 100 US ISSN 0730-868X
PS3053
THOREAU QUARTERLY. 1969-19??; suspended. q. (processed; also avail. in microform from MIM) (Thoreau Quarterly, Inc.) University of Minnesota, 355 Ford Hall, 224 Church St., N.E., Minnesota, MN 55455.
Formerly: Thoreau Journal Quarterly (ISSN 0040-6392)

636.1 798.4 US
THOROUGHBRED RECORD. 1875-1990 (June). m. (also avail. in microfilm from UMI) Thoroughbred Publications, Inc., 801 Corporate Dr., Ste. 101, Box 8237, Lexington, KY 40503.
Formerly: Thoroughbred Record and the Racing Calendar (ISSN 0040-6414)

821
THROUGH CASA GUIDI WINDOWS; the bulletin of the Browning Institute. 1975-19?? irreg. Browning Institute Inc., Box 2983, Grand Central Sta., New York, NY 10163-2983.

365 US
THROUGH THE LOOKING GLASS; a women's prison newsletter. 1976-19?? q. 2900 E. Madison St., Ste. B1, Seattle, WA 98112-4243.

917.13 796.5 CN ISSN 0380-6197
THUNDER BAY CAMPING GUIDE. 1972-1974. irreg. Amethyst Holdings Ltd., 1126 Roland St., Thunder Bay, Ont. P7B 5M4, Canada.

616.97 612 UK ISSN 0266-6618
THYMUS. ceased 1989. m. (looseleaf format; back issues avail.) Sheffield University Biomedical Information Service (SUBIS), The University, Sheffield S10 2TN, England.

616.4 618.92 UK ISSN 0226-6628
THYROID DISORDERS. ceased 1990. m. (looseleaf format; back issues avail.) Sheffield University Biomedical Information Service (SUBIS), The University, Sheffield S10 2TN, England.

381 US
TIDEWATER VIRGINIAN. 1963-19?? m. (also avail. in microfiche) Norfolk Chamber of Commerce, 403 Boush St., No. 350, Norfolk, VA 23510-1228.
Formerly (until 1977): New Norfolk (ISSN 0028-6389)

070.5 SW ISSN 0040-6805
TIDNINGS NYTT. 1951-1991. 9/yr. Presam, S-112 89 Stockholm, Sweden.

641 DK ISSN 0040-7224
TIDSSKRIFTET NY TID OG VI. 1936-1990 (July). 6/yr. Svend Olaf Voldan, Ed. & Pub., Frederiksborgvej 60, DK-3450 Alleroed, Denmark.

332.6 US ISSN 0149-5887
TIGER REPORT. (Timely Investments Get Excellent Results) 1977-197? m. Dennis D. Murphy, Ed. & Pub., 3404 North Romero Rd, Box B, Tucson, AZ 85705.

360 301 AT ISSN 1031-8283
TIGHTROPE. 1988-1989 (vol.1, no.4). q. (back issues avail.) Tasmanian Council of Social Service (TASCOSS), 82 Hampden Rd., Battery Point, Tas. 7004, Australia.

610 614.8 NE ISSN 0167-8647
TIJDSCHRIFT VOOR GEZONDHEID EN POLITIEK. 1983-19?? q. Van Gorcum en Co. B.V., P.O. Box 43, 9400 AA Aasen, Netherlands.

338.2 MY ISSN 0126-5547
TIMAH MALAYSIA/MALAYSIAN TIN. 1972-1989 (vol. 16, no.4). q. Tin Industry (Research and Development) Board, Ming Building, 9th Fl., Jalan Bukit Nanas, Box 12560, 50782 Kuala Lumpur, Malaysia.

800 US ISSN 0896-3878
TIMBUKTU. 1988-199? s-a. Box 469, Charlottesville, VA 22902.

052 UK ISSN 0040-7828
TIME AND TIDE; independent monthly. 1920-1990. w. Europress Ltd., 17 Ridgemont Rd., Bramhall, Cheshire, England.

681.11 UK ISSN 0260-5988
TIMECRAFT; clocks & crafts. 1981-19?? m. Watch & Clock Book Society, Box 22, Ashford, Kent TN23 1DN, England.

681.11 UK
TIMEPIECE REGISTER; price guide to longcase clocks. 1980-19?? q. Watch & Clock Book Society, P.O. Box 22, Ashford, Kent TN23 1DN, England.
Formerly: Timepiece (ISSN 0144-6894)

621.381 US
TIPS & TECHNIQUES. 1982-1990. 12/yr. Britz Publishing Inc., Box 1156, Madison, MS 39103-1155.

266 US
TO FOCUS ON UNREACHED PEOPLES (YEAR). 1979-198? a. (Missions Advanced Research and Communication Center) M A R C (Subsidiary of: World Vision International), 919 W. Huntington Dr., Monrovia, CA 91016.

613 US
TOBACCO-FREE YOUNG AMERICA REPORTER. 1983-1988 (vol.5, no.1). q. (back issues avail.) (National Interagency Council on Smoking and Health) Center for Health & Safety Studies, Office of Publications and Editorial Services, H P E R Bldg., Rm. 116, Indiana University, Bloomington, IN 47405.
Formerly: Smoking and Health Reporter (ISSN 0738-4920)

633.71 679.7 US
TOBACCO OBSERVER. 1976-19?? 12/yr. Tobacco Institute, 1875 I St., N.W., Ste. 800, Washington, DC 20006.

633.71 US
TOBACCO REPRINT SERIES. 1954-19?? irreg. (tabloid format) Tobacco Literature Service, North Carolina State University, Box 7111, 2314 D.H. Hill Library, Raleigh, NC 27695.

679.7 US
TOBACCO UPDATE. 1972-198? q. (looseleaf format) Tobacco Merchants Association of the United States, Inc., 231 Clarksville Rd., Box 8019, Princeton, NJ 08543-8019.

028.5 362.7 AT
TODAY'S CHILD LEAFLETS. 1944-1991; suspended. 10/yr. (back issues avail) Australian Early Childhood Association, P.O. Box 105, Watson, A.C.T. 2602, Australia.
Formerly (until 1979): Today's Child.

658 657 001.6 330 US
TODAY'S EXECUTIVE; trends and techniques in managing. 1978-1987. q. (back issues avail.) Price Waterhouse, Management Consulting Services Department, 1251 Ave. of the Americas, New York, NY 10020.

630 JA ISSN 0040-8697
TOHOKU DAIGAKU NOGAKU KENKYUJO HOKOKU/ TOHOKU UNIVERSITY. INSTITUTE FOR AGRICULTURAL RESEARCH. BULLETIN. 1949-1988 (vol.39). s-a. Tohoku Daigaku, Nogaku Kenkyujo - Tohoku University, Institute for Agricultural Research, 1-1 Katahira 2-chome, Sendai-shi, Miyagi-ken 980, Japan.
Formerly: Tohoku Daigaku Nogaku Kenkyujo Iho.

620 JA ISSN 0040-8816
CODEN: TRTUA9
TOHOKU UNIVERSITY. FACULTY OF ENGINEERING. TECHNOLOGY REPORTS/TOHOKU DAIGAKU KOGAKU HOKOKU. 1920-1988 (vol.52, no.2). s-a. Tohoku Daigaku, Kogakubu - Tohoku University, Faculty of Engineering, Library, Faculty of Engineering, Tohoku University, Sendai 980, Japan.

382 US ISSN 1047-0530
TOKYO BUSINESS MONTH. 1990-1991. m. (back issues avail.) Buraff Publications (Subsidiary of: Millin Publications, Inc.), 1350 Connecticut Ave., N.W., Ste. 1000, Washington, DC 20036.

371.9 JA
TOKYO METROPOLITAN GOVERNMENT. FUCHU REHABILITATION SCHOOL. ANNUAL REPORT. 1971-1988. a. Tokyo Metropolitan Government, Fuchu Rehabilitation School, 9-2, 2-chome, Musashidai, Fuchu-shi, Tokyo 183, Japan.

639 JA ISSN 0082-4836
TOKYO UNIVERSITY OF FISHERIES JOURNAL. SPECIAL EDITION/TOKYO SUISAN DAIGAKU TOKUBETSU KENKYU HOKOKU. 1958-1968. irreg. Tokyo University of Fisheries - Tokyo Suisan Daiguku, 4-5-7 Minato-ku, Tokyo 108, Japan.

700 UK ISSN 0040-9103
TOLPOLSKI'S CHRONICLE. 1953-1967. 24/yr. (oversized) Bridge Arch, 158 Sutton Walk, London S.E.1, England.

028.5 DK
TOM OG JERRY. ceased. m. Interpresse, Krogshoejvej 32, 2880 Bagsvaerd, Denmark.

683 GW ISSN 0179-5341
TOOLS AND HARDWARE. 1984-1990. s-a. (back issues avail.) Vogel-Verlag und Druck KG, Max-Planck-Str. 7-9, Postfach 6740, 8700 Wuerzburg 1, Germany.

338.1 US ISSN 0730-6318
TOP FARMER INTELLIGENCE; confidental weekly farm business and marketing advisor. 1966-198? w. AgriData Resources, Inc., 330 E. Kilbourn Ave., Ste. 200, Milwaukee, WI 53202.

658 UK ISSN 0953-5187
TOP MANAGEMENT DIGEST. ceased. m. M C B University Press Ltd., 62 Toller Ln., Bradford, W. Yorks BD8 9BY, England.

780.42 US
TOP TENS AND TRIVIA OF ROCK AND ROLL AND RHYTHM AND BLUES. ANNUAL SUPPLEMENT. 1974-1991. a. Blueberry Hill Publishing Co., 6504 Delmar, St. Louis, MO 63130.

333.7 UK ISSN 0268-2494
TOPICAL ISSUES. 1985-1990. q. Nature Conservancy Council Publications, Northminster House, Peterborough PE1 1UA, England.

769.56 US ISSN 0090-7286
HE6187
TOPICAL NEW ISSUES. (Subseries of: American Topical Association. Topical Handbook) ceased. a. American Topical Association, Inc., Box 630, Johnstown, PA 15907.

574.192 US
TOPICS IN BIOELECTROCHEMISTRY AND BIOENERGETICS. 1977-1983 (vol.5). irreg. John Wiley & Sons, Inc., 605 Third Ave, New York, NY 10158-0012.

917.1 CN
TORONTO. 1986-1991 (June). m. Globe and Mail Ltd., 444 Front St. W., Toronto, Ont. M5V 2S9, Canada.

950 CN ISSN 0082-5123
TORONTO SEMITIC TEXTS AND STUDIES. 1971-19?? irreg. University of Toronto Press, Front Campus, Toronto, Ont. M5S 1A6, Canada.

639 607 UK ISSN 0082-5352
TORRY RESEARCH STATION, ABERDEEN, SCOTLAND. ANNUAL REPORT. 1958-1988. a. Torry Research Station, P.O. Box 31, 135 Abbey Rd., Aberdeen AB9 8DG, Scotland.

100 GW
TOTOK: HANDBUCH DER GESCHICHTE DER PHILOSOPHIE. ceased 1990 (vol.6). irreg. Vittorio Klostermann, Frauenlobstr. 22, 6000 Frankfurt a.M. 90, Germany.

051 US
TOUCH OF CLASS. ceased. m. 12603 Prima Vista, San Antonio, TX 78233.

910.09 GW ISSN 0138-3973
DER TOURIST. 1962-1990. m. Deutscher Verband fuer Wandern, Bergsteigen und Orientierungslauf der D. D.R. (D.W.B.O.), Redaktion der "Tourist", Reichenberger str. 11, Dresden 8023, Germany.

917.104 CN
TOURIST GUIDE/GUIDE TOURISTIQUE. ceased. a. Editeur Limite-Ltd., 300 Arran Ave., St. Lambert, Que. J4R 1K5, Canada.

910.202 016 FR ISSN 0767-2659
TOURISTIC ANALYSIS REVIEW. 1973-199? (no.35). q. (cards; back issues avail.) Universite d'Aix-Marseille III (Universite de Droit, d'Economie et des Sciences), Centre des Hautes Etudes Touristiques, Fondation Vasarely, 1 Av. Marcel Pagnol, 13090 Aix-en-Provence, France.

020 CN ISSN 0382-0912
TOWN AND COUNTRY LIBRARIAN. 1964-1988 (vol.24, no.2). 2/yr. Middlesex County Library, Arva, Ont., Canada.

615.9 US ISSN 0146-1559
TOX-TIPS; notices of research projects. 1977-1989. m. U.S. National Library of Medicine, Toxicology Information Program, 8600 Rockville Pike, Bethesda, MD 20894.

615.9 FR ISSN 0249-6402
 CODEN: TOERD9
TOXICOLOGICAL EUROPEAN RESEARCH. 1978-1984; suspended. bi-m. (back issues avail.) Centre National de la Research Scientifique, Societe des Publications Essentielles, 15 Quai Anatole France, 75700 Paris, France.

615.19 UK ISSN 0142-8535
TOXINS. ceased 1989. m. (looseleaf format; back issues avail.) Sheffield University Biomedical Information Service (SUBIS), The University, Sheffield S10 2TN, England.

591 616.9 UK ISSN 0142-8829
TOXOPLASMOSIS. ceased 1990. m. (looseleaf format; back issues avail.) Sheffield University Biomedical Information Service (SUBIS), The University, Sheffield S10 2TN, England.

602.6 001.535 US
TRAC: GLOBAL YEARBOOK OF ISSUES, EVENTS, AND DISCOVERIES IN TELECOMMUNICATIONS, ROBOTICS, ARTIFICIAL INTELLIGENCE, C A D - C A M. 1987; announced, never published. a. E I C - Intelligence, 48 W. 38th St., New York, NY 10018.

612.3 UK ISSN 0268-1463
TRACE ELEMENTS. ceased 1989. m. (looseleaf format; back issues avail.) Sheffield University Biomedical Information Service (SUBIS), The University, Sheffield S10 2TN, England.

700 US
TRACKS (CHICAGO); a journal of artists' writings. 1974-1977. 3/yr. Herbert George, Ed. & Pub., 431 W. Oakdale Ave., No. 114, Chicago, IL 60657.

621.3 BE
TRACTEBEL NEWS. 1975-19?? 2/yr. (back issues avail.) Tractebel s.a., Services Relations Exterieures, 1 place du Trone, B-1000 Brussels, Belgium.
 Former titles: Tractionel News (ISSN 0770-9412); T.E. News.

346.066 382 CN ISSN 0827-5513
TRADE LAW TOPICS. ceased 1989 (vol.3, no.6). m. (looseleaf format) Butterworths Canada Ltd., 75 Clegg Rd., Markham, Ont. L6G 1A1, Canada.

382 CN ISSN 0836-0820
TRADE MONITOR. 1987-1989 (no.11). irreg. C.D. Howe Institute, 125 Adelaide St. E., Toronto, Ont. M5C 1L7, Canada.

382 CH ISSN 0082-5778
TRADE OF CHINA; Taiwan district. (Subseries of its Maritime Customs. I. Statistical Series) 1950-1989 (Dec.). a. (also avail. in microfilm from BHP) Inspectorate General of Customs, Statistical Department, 3rd floor, 85 Hsin-Sheng Rd., Section 1, Taipei, Taiwan 10626, Republic of China.

382 PH ISSN 0115-2394
TRADE POST. ceased. m. Ministry of Trade, Trade & Industry Bldg., 361 Gil J. Puyat Ave. Ext., Makati, Metro Manila, Philippines.

382 US
TRADE WINDS. ceased. q. World Trade Center of New Orleans, 2 Canal St., Ste. 2900, New Orleans, LA 70130.

011 658 US
TRADESHOW MARKETING JOURNAL. (Supplement to: Meeting Planners Alert) 1987-1989 (vol.3, no.4). q. M P A Communications Inc., Box 404, Derry, NH 03038.

382 US
TRADING POST (NEW ORLEANS). ceased. q. International House, Box 52020, New Orleans, LA 70152.

796.5 388.324 US
TRAILER LIFE'S RECREATIONAL VEHICLE BUYERS GUIDE. ceased. a. T L Enterprises, Inc., 29901 Agoura Rd., Agoura, CA 91301.

979 929 US ISSN 8756-7075
F847.C4
TRAILS TO CHURCHILL COUNTY. 1983-1989. q. Churchill County Historical & Genealogical Society, 1050 S. Maine, c/o Churchill Museum, Fallon, NV 89406.

378 CN ISSN 0712-7456
TRAINING RESOURCES TOURISM, HOSPITALITY, RECREATION. 1979-198? biennial. Tourism Canada, 4E - 235 Queen St., Ottawa, Ont. K1A 0H6, Canada.
 Supersedes in part: Resources for Tourism, Hospitality, Recreation.

380.5 UK
TRAINING TODAY. 1987-198? s-a. Road Transport Industry Training Board, Capitol House, Empire Way, Wembley, Middx. HA9 0NG, England.

625.19 US ISSN 0899-7217
TF1
TRAINS ILLUSTRATED. 1988-1991 (Fall). 4/yr. Kalmbach Publishing Co., Box 1612, Waukesha, WI 53187.

830 GW
TRAJEKT. 1970-1989. a. Hinstorff Verlag GmbH, Lagerstr. 7, 2500 Rostock, Germany.

385 PL ISSN 0137-2963
TRAKCJA I WAGONY. 1953-1991. m. Wydanictwa Komunikacji i Lacznosci, Ul. Kazimierzowska 52, Warsaw, Poland.
 Formerly (until 1978): Przeglad Kolejowy Mechaniczny (ISSN 0033-2224)

331 US
TRANSCRIPT. ceased. q. Niagara Frontier Transportation Authority, Public Affairs Division, 181 Ellicott St., Box 5008, Buffalo, NY 14205.

575.1 UK ISSN 0952-0376
TRANSCRIPTION REGULATION. ceased 1990. m. (looseleaf format; back issues avail.) Sheffield University Biomedical Information Service (SUBIS), The University, Sheffield S10 2TN, England.

910 US ISSN 0747-5020
G1
TRANSITION (CINCINNATI). ceased 1990 (vol.17, no.2). s-a. Socially & Ecologically Responsible Geographers, c/o Dept. of Geography, University of Cincinnati, Cincinnati, OH 45221.

720 AU ISSN 0041-1302
TRANSPARENT; Manuskripte fuer Architektur, Theorie, Umraum, Kunst. 1970-1988 (vol.19, no.11-12). m. (tabloid format) (Bundesministerium fuer Wissenschaft und Forschung) Guenther Feuerstein, Ed. & Pub., Wiedner Hauptstr. 40, A-1040 Vienna, Austria.

617 616.97 UK ISSN 0142-8446
TRANSPLANTATION IMMUNOLOGY. ceased 1990. m. (looseleaf format; back issues avail.) Sheffield University Biomedical Information Service (SUBIS), The University, Sheffield S10 2TN, England.

617 CN
TRANSPLANTATION - IMPLANTATION TODAY. 1984-1991 (vol.8). q. Multimed Inc., 3995 Bathurst St., Ste. 301, Downsview, Ont. M3H 5V3, Canada.

617 US ISSN 0074-3984
TRANSPLANTATION TODAY. 1967-1985 (vol.8). biennial. (Transplantation Society) Appleton & Lange (Subsidiary of: Simon & Schuster Company), 25 Van Zant St., Box 5630, Norwalk, CT 06856.

380.5 CN ISSN 0706-3962
TRANSPO. 1974-1989 (vol.12, no.2). q. Transport Canada, Public Affairs Branch, Ottawa, Ont. K1A 0N5, Canada.
 Formerly: Transport Canada.

388.1 US
TRANSPO NEWS. ceased 1982 (no.8). bi-m. (tabloid format) Department of Transportation, Public Affairs Office, Highways Administration Bldg., Olympia, WA 98504.
 Formerly (until Sep. 1975): Washington Highway News (ISSN 0511-3180)

380.5 DK ISSN 0108-8157
TRANSPORT (AARLIG). 1983-1985. a. Teknisk Forlag A-S, Skelbaekgade 4, DK-1717 Copenhagen V, Denmark.

380.5 AU
TRANSPORT AKTUELL. 1970-19?? q. Manstein Verlag Ges.m.b.H., Gusshausstrasse 12, 1040 Vienna, Austria.

380 388 SA
TRANSPORT & TRAFFIC/VERVOER & VERKEER. 1973-19?? s-a. (Chartered Institute of Transport, Southern Africa Division) Keeble Publishing Co. Pty. Ltd., P.O. Box 3080, Johannesburg 2000, South Africa.

658.8 UK ISSN 0951-3531
TRANSPORT MARKETING. ceased. 2/yr. M C B University Press Ltd., 62 Toller Ln., Bradford, W. Yorks BD8 9BY, England.

380.5 UK
TRANSPORT TRAINING. 1968-1992. bi-m. Road Transport Industry Training Board, Capitol House, Empire Way, Wembley, Middx. HA9 0NG, England.

CESSATIONS

380.5 614.7   US
TRANSPORTATION (BALTIMORE). 1976-1984. 3/yr. Regional Planning Council, 2225 N. Charles St., Baltimore, MD 21218.

658.7   US
TRANSPORTATION & DISTRIBUTION PRESIDENTIAL ISSUE. ceased 1990. a. (reprint service avail. from UMI) Penton Publishing, 1100 Superior Ave., Cleveland, OH 44114.
   Former titles: Handling and Shipping Managements Presidential Issue; Handling and Shipping. Presidential Issue.

380.5   SW   ISSN 0280-1183
TRANSPORTRAADET RAPPORT. 1980-1992. irreg. Transportraadet, Box 1329, 171 26 Solna, Sweden.

382   IT
TRASPORTI MARE TERRITORIO; rivista di informazioni marittime. 1979-1990. q. Casa Editrice Dott. A. Giuffre, Via Busto Arsizio 40, 20151 Milan, Italy.
   Formerly: Porti Mare Territorio.

380.5   IT   ISSN 0041-1817
TRASPORTI PUBBLICI. 1953-198?; suspended. m. Ministero dei Trasporti e dell'Aviazione Civile, Viale del Policlinico 2, 00161 Rome, Italy.

639   CN   ISSN 0082-609X
SH224.Q4   CODEN: TPEZA3
TRAVAUX SUR LES PECHERIES DU QUEBEC. 1964-1984 (no. 50). irreg. Ministere de l'Agriculture, des Pecheries et de l'Alimentation, C.P. 340, Grand-Riviere, Cte de Gaspe, Que. G0C 1V0, Canada.

917   UK
TRAVEL ASIA PACIFIC. 1969-19?? bi-m. A B C Travel Publications Ltd., 242 Vauxhall Bridge Rd., London SW1V 1AU, England.

330   US
TRAVEL BUSINESS REPORT; for those who manage the point of sale. 1982-19?? m. (looseleaf format) Walter Mathews Associates, Inc., 28 W. 38th St., New York, NY 10018.
   Formerly: Travel Business.

910   US
TRAVEL PHOTO SOURCE BOOK. 1983-1991. biennial. Society of American Travel Writers, 1155 Connecticut Ave., Ste. 500, Washington, DC 20036.

910.2   US   ISSN 0741-5818
TRAVEL SMART FOR BUSINESS; your personal advisor for business travel. ceased. m. Communications House, Inc., 40 Beechdale Rd., Dobbs Ferry, NY 10522.

917.9   US
TRAVEL UTAH. ceased. 6/yr. (May-Oct.). Coles Publishing Company, 419 E. 100 S., Salt Lake City, UT 84111.

910   US
TRAVELDAY. 1976-1982. m. Fimebrock Publishing, Inc., Box 1258, San Rafael, CA 94902.

910.9   SA
TRAVELLER'S FRIEND. 1990; ceased same year. m. Thomson Publications (Subsidiary of: Times Media Ltd.), P.O. Box 56182, Pinegowrie, South Africa.

910.202   GR
TRAVELLING. 1968-1982; resumed 1990-1991. q. Technical Press S.A., 6 Gorgiou St., Athens 11636, Greece.

917   CN
TRAVELLING ON BUSINESS. 1984-1991 (Feb.). 12/yr. Baxter Publishing Co., 310 Dupont St., Toronto, Ont. M5R 1V9, Canada.

910.202   AT
TRAVELWEEK BLUE BOOK. 1983-19?? a. Peter Isaacson Publications Pty. Ltd., 45-50 Porter St., Prahran, Vic. 3181, Australia.

919.4   AT   ISSN 0813-4790
HF3943
TRAVELWEEK HOTEL, MOTEL INDEX. 1965-19?? biennial. Peter Isaacson Publications Pty. Ltd., 45-50 Porter St., Prahran, Vic. 3181, Australia.
   Former titles: Travelweek Hotel, Motel Directory (ISSN 0813-4782); Travelweek Hotel, Motel and Travel Directory (ISSN 0156-3696).

700   FR   ISSN 0336-9730
TRAVERSES. ceased 1989 (no.47). q. (Centre National d'Art et de Culture, Centre de Creation Industrielle) Editions de Minuit, 7 rue Bernard-Palissy, 75006 Paris, France.

301   PE
TRAVESIA. ceased. s-a. Sociologia de la Pontificia Universidad Catolica, Lima, Peru.

543   US   ISSN 0082-6243
TREATISE ON ANALYTICAL CHEMISTRY. PART 1: THEORY AND PRACTICE OF ANALYTICAL CHEMISTRY. 1959-199? irreg. John Wiley & Sons, Inc., 605 Third Ave, New York, NY 10158-0012.

543   US   ISSN 0082-6251
TREATISE ON ANALYTICAL CHEMISTRY. PART 2: ANALYTICAL CHEMISTRY OF THE ELEMENTS; ANALYTICAL CHEMISTRY OF INORGANIC AND ORGANIC COMPOUNDS. 1961-19?? irreg. John Wiley & Sons, Inc., 605 Third Ave., New York, NY 10158-0012.

543   US   ISSN 0082-626X
TREATISE ON ANALYTICAL CHEMISTRY. PART 3: ANALYTICAL CHEMISTRY IN INDUSTRY. 1967-198? irreg. John Wiley & Sons, Inc., 605 Third Ave., New York, NY 10158-0012.

370   US
TREE. 1968-198? 3/yr. Independent Educational Services, 80 Nassau St., Princeton, NJ 08540.

051   US   ISSN 0894-3044
TREETOP PANORAMA. 1983-19?? 4/yr. (back issues avail.) Treetop Panorama Publications, R. Rt. 1, Box 160, Payson, IL 62360.

387.7   GW
TREFFPUNKT; Flughafen-Magazin. 1981-1991. q. (back issues avail.) Flughafen Frankfurt - Main AG, Postfach, 6000 Frankfurt a.M. 75, Germany.

800   US
TRELLIS (SAN MARINO). 1988-1990. q. Quadriga Publishing, 1613 Chelsea Rd., Ste. 311, San Marino, CA 91108.

746.92   US
TRENDING. 1990-1991? m. Gralla Publications (Dallas), Box 801470, Dallas, TX 75380.

332.6   US
TRENDS & FORECASTS. 1985-1990 (Jan.). m. Cambridge Reports, Inc., 955 Massachussetts Ave., Cambridge, MA 02139-3107.

330.9   US
TRENDS & PROJECTIONS BULLETINS. ceased. m. Standard & Poor's Corporation, 25 Broadway, New York, NY 10004.

621   JA
TJ1075.A2
TRIBOLOGIST. INTERNATIONAL EDITION. 1980-1989. a. (reprint service avail. from UMI) Japanese Society of Tribologists, Kikaishinko Kaikan, Rm. 407-2, 5-8 Shibakoen 3-chome, Minato-ku, Tokyo 105, Japan.
   Former titles: (until no.10, 1989): Japanese Society of Tribologists. Journal. International Edition; Japanese Society of Lubrication Engineers. Journal. International Edition (ISSN 0389-5483)

700 669   US
TRIBOLOGY NEWS. 1985-198? q. Gavarti Associates, Ltd., 9240 N. Sleepey Hollow Ln., Milwaukee, WI 53217.

056.9   GW   ISSN 0170-8058
TRIBUNA ALEMA; resenha mensal da imprensa Alema. ceased 1989. m. Friedrich Reinecke Verlag GmbH, Hartwicusstr. 3-4, D-2000 Hamburg 76, Germany.

055.1   GW   ISSN 0344-9033
TRIBUNA TEDESCA; rassegna mensile della stampa Tedesca. 1969-1989. m. Friedrich Reinecke Verlag GmbH, Hartwicusstr. 3-4, D-2000 Hamburg 76, Germany.

329.9   AT
TRIBUNE. 1923-1991 (Apr.). w. (Communist Party of Australia) Red Pen Publications, 635 Harris St., Ultimo, N.S.W. 2007, Australia.
   Formerly: Workers Weekly.

664.9   FR
TRIPERIE FRANCAISE. ceased. m. Confederation Nationale de la Triperie Francaise, 60, rue des Prouvaires, V209 9H535 Rungis, France.

332.1   AT
TRIPLE A. 1980-1989. m. G.P.O.Box 55A, Melbourne, Vic. 3001, Australia.
   Incorporates (in 1985): Triple A Asiabanking Almanac; Formerly: Asian Banking Directory (ISSN 0252-1024)

910.09   US
TRIPS (COLUMBUS); the travel advantage. ceased 1988. s-m. c/o Field Publications, 4343 Equity Dr., Columbus, OH 43228.

051   US   ISSN 0041-3127
TRIUMPH. 1966-1984. m.(except July-Aug.). (Society for the Christian Commonwealth) Triumph Magazine, Inc., 31 Winchester St., Warrenton, VA 22186.

310.4157   US
TROIS; three rivers one in six. ceased. irreg. Gay-Lesbian Organization at Ft. Wayne, Inc., 3426 Broadway, Ft. Wayne, IN 46807.

028.5   GW   ISSN 0323-8709
TROMMEL. ceased 1991 (no.4). w. Verlag Junge Welt GmbH, Mauerstr. 39-40, 1080 Berlin, Germany.

631.091   MX
TROPICAL ANIMAL PRODUCTION. 1976-1986. q. (Consejo Estatal de Azucar, DR) Universidad de Yucatan, Facultad de Medicina Veterinaria y Zootecnia, Apdo. 116D, Merida, Yucatan, Mexico.

616.9   SZ
TROPICAL DISEASES RESEARCH SERIES. 1979-1991. irreg. (Special Programme for Research and Training in Tropical Diseases, UN) Schwabe und Co. AG, Steinentorstr. 13, CH-4010 Basel, Switzerland.

633.1   NR   ISSN 0304-5765
    CODEN: TGLBD8
TROPICAL GRAIN LEGUME BULLETIN. 1975-1989 (no. 36). irreg. (International Grain Legume Information Centre) International Institute of Tropical Agriculture, P.M.B. 5320, Ibadan, Nigeria.

332.6   US
TROUBLED COMPANY INVESTOR; investment advice for sophisticated investors in securities of troubled companies. 1988-198? s-m. (looseleaf format; back issues avail.) Audit Investments, Inc., 136 Summit Ave., Ste. 200, Montvale, NJ 07645-1720.

929   US
TROUP COUNTY, GEORGIA AND HER PEOPLE. 1981-1988 (Oct.). q. (Martha Anderson & Associates) Family Tree Publications, 100 Shamrock Dr., LaGrange, GA 30240.

690 747   CN
TROWEL. 1949-19?? bi-m. Journal of Commerce Ltd., 2000 W. 12th Ave., Vancouver, B.C. V6J 2G2, Canada.

388.324   US
TRUCKING DIGEST. 1990-1991 (Mar.). m. Hammond Communications, 3387 Poplar, Ste. 221, Memphis, TN 38111.

388.324   US
TRUCKING - SOUTH. 1989-19?? bi-m. Georgia Motor Trucking Association, Box 2029, Tuscaloosa, AL 35403.

621.381 001.644   US
TRUE IMAGING; advanced graphics applications. 1988-1989. m. Ariel Communications, Inc., 12710 Research Blvd., Ste. 250, Austin, TX 78759.

810   US
TRUMPET. 1965-19?? irreg. Trumpet Publications, 1131 White, Kansas City, MO 64126.
   Former titles: Nickelodeon; Trumpet.

051   US   ISSN 0278-1263
TL720.9.P313
TRUMP'S; the magazine of the power corridor. 1990-1991. m. (Trump Shuttle) East - West Network, 54 E. 51st St., New York, NY 10022.

CESSATIONS

332.1 US
TRUST MARKETING RESOURCE NEWSLETTER. ceased. bi-m. Bank Marketing Association, 309 W. Washington St., Chicago, IL 60606.

371.2 CN
TRUSTEE. 1931-1991 (vol.61, no.2). 3/yr. Alberta School Boards Association, 12310-105 Ave., Edmonton, Alta. T5N 0Y4, Canada.
Formerly: Alberta School Trustee (ISSN 0002-4880)

051 US
TUBE. 1990; ceased same year. m. Tube Publications, 9865 Santa Monica Blvd., Beverly Hills, CA 90212.

929 US
TUCKERS OF AMERICA. ceased. 4/yr. Inkwell Publications, 1661 Lauranceae Way, Riverdale, GA 30296.

029 HU ISSN 0373-5354
TUDOMANYOS TAJEKOZTATAS ELMELETE ES GYAKORLATA/THEORY AND PRACTICE OF SCIENTIFIC INFORMATION. 1966-1976 (no.21). irreg. Orszagos Muszaki Informacios Kozpont es Konyvtar (O.M.I.K.K.) - National Technical Information Centre and Library, Muzeum u. 17, Box 12, 1428 Budapest, Hungary.

930 GW
TUEBINGER AEGYPTOLOGISCHE BEITRAEGE. 1973-1976 (no.2). irreg. Dr. Rudolf Habelt GmbH, Am Buchenhang 1, 5300 Bonn 1, Germany.

380.1 US ISSN 0041-4042
TULSA. 1959-1990. bi-m. (also avail. in microform from UMI; reprint service avail. from UMI) Metropolitan Tulsa Chamber of Commerce, 616 S. Boston, Tulsa, OK 74119.

384.5 US
TUNE IN THE WORLD WITH HAM RADIO KIT. ceased. a. American Radio Relay League, Inc., 225 Main St., Newington, CT 06111.

355 US
TURBINE INTELLIGENCE. ceased 1990. w. (back issues avail.) Forecast International Inc. - D M S, 22 Commerce Rd., Newtown, CT 06470.

796.5 CS ISSN 0496-4845
TURISTA; mesicnik na cestu. vol.23, 1984-1991. m. (back issues avail.) (Ceskoslovensky Svaz Telesne Vychovy) Olympia, Klimentska 1, 115 88 Prague 1, Czechoslovakia.
Formerly: Turistika a Horolezectvi.

489 400 FI ISSN 0082-7029
TURUN YLIOPISTO. KLASSILLISEN FILOLOGIAN LAITOS. OPERA EX INSTITUTO PHILOLOGIAE CLASSICAE UNIVERSITATIS TURKUENSIS EDITA. (Subseries of Turun Yliopisto. Julkaisuja. Sarja B. Humaniora) 1969-1986 (vol. 7). irreg. Turun Yliopisto, Klassillisen Filologian Laitos - University of Turku, Department of Classical Philology, SF-20500 Turku 50, Finland.

948 FI
TURUN YLIOPPILAS. 1929-1970. irreg. Turun Yliopiston Ylioppilaskunta, Rehtorinpellontie 4, 20500 Turku 50, Finland.

780 IT
TUTTO CASALINGHI & FERRAMENTO. 1981-199? bi-m. (back issues avail.) Stammer S.P.A., Centro Commerciale, Milano S. Felice, 20090 Segrate (Milan), Italy.
Formerly: Tutto Casalinghi.

780 IT
TUTTO MUSICA. ceased. m. Rizzoli Editore s.p.a., Via A. Rizzoli 2, 20132 Milan, Italy.

340 330 US ISSN 0082-7088
TWENTIETH CENTURY LEGAL PHILOSOPHY SERIES. ceased 1970 (no.8). irreg. Harvard University Press, 79 Garden St., Cambridge, MA 02138.

929 US ISSN 0891-3706
TWIGS MAGAZINE; genealogy for children. 1982-1991 (Jan.). irreg. (back issues avail.) Juniper Tree Press, 4830 Carol Dr., Troy, MI 48098.

800 CN ISSN 0829-7010
TYRO MAGAZINE. 1984-1991 (Oct.). 3/yr. (back issues avail.) Tyro Publishing, 194 Carlbert Str., Sault Ste. Marie, Ont. P6A 5E1, Canada.

330.9 US ISSN 0007-6740
U B S BUSINESS FACTS AND FIGURES. 1955-1989. m. Union Bank of Switzerland, Bahnhofstr. 45, 8021 Zurich, Switzerland.
Incorporates: Economic Panorama.

378 US ISSN 0745-3213
U C CLIP SHEET. 1925-19?? m. (newspaper) University of California, University Relations, c/o of Paul West, Ed., 300 Lakeside Dr., 22nd Fl., CA 94612.
Former titles: University of California U C News Clip Sheet (ISSN 0041-9435); University of California Clip Sheet.

791.43 746.92 MY
U F F. (Utusan Filem dan Feshen) no.25, 1972-19?? m. Utusan Melayu (Malaysia) Berhad, 46 M Jalan Chan Sow Lin, Kuala Lumpur, Malaysia.

001.94 US ISSN 0162-8046
TL789.A1
U F O ANNUAL. (Unidentified Flying Objects) ceased. a. Lexington Library Inc., 355 Lexington Ave., New York, NY 10017.

001.94 DK ISSN 0109-2596
U F O FORSKNING. 1983; published only once. irreg. Skandinavisk U F O Information, Postbox 6, 2820 Gentofte, Denmark.

001.94 GW ISSN 0041-5081
U F O - NACHRICHTEN. 1956-1988. bi-m. (newspaper) (Deutsche UFO-Studiengesellschaft (DUIST e.V.)) Ventla-Verlag, Postfach 130185, 6200 Wiesbaden 13, Germany.

769.56 UK ISSN 0142-7954
U H STAMP DIGEST. 1972-1987. m. Urch, Harris & Co. Ltd., Clifton Heights, Triangle West, Bristol BS8 1BQ, England.

720 UK
U I A - INTERNATIONAL ARCHITECT; an international review of architectural projects, theory, practice and criticism. 1979-1985. bi-m. (back issues avail.) (Union Internationale des Architectes, FR - International Union of Architects) International Architect Publishing Ltd., Box 85, 36 Bedford Square, London W1B 3EH, England.
Formerly: International Architect.

616.994 SZ
U I C C MAGAZINE. 1963-1990. q. International Union Against Cancer, 3 rue de Conseil-General, 1205 Geneva, Switzerland.
Former titles (until 1988): International Cancer News; (until 1986): U I C C News; U I C C Bulletin (ISSN 0041-5111)

616.9 SZ ISSN 0074-9222
RC261 CODEN: UICTA5
U I C C TECHNICAL REPORT SERIES. 1968-1987 (vol. 79). irreg. International Union Against Cancer, 3 rue de Conseil-General, 1205 Geneva, Switzerland.

370 UK
U K INITIAL TEACHING ALPHABET FEDERATION NEWSLETTER. ceased 1989. 3/yr. United Kingdom Initial Teaching Alphabet Federation, 181 Fleetwood Ave., Holland-on-Sea, Essex CO15 5RA, England.

668.4 UK
U K PLASTICS NEWS. 1989-1990 (Nov.). m. (back issues avail.) Reed Business Publishing Group, Quadrant House, The Quadrant, Sutton, Surrey SM2 5AS, England.

250 US
U M E CONNEXION. 1973-1989 (vol.17, no.1). 3/yr. (tabloid format; back issues avail.) United Ministries in Education, 1801 Las Lomas N.E., Albuquerque, NM 87106.
Former titles: Connexion; U M H E Connexion.

720 CU
U N A I C C BOLETIN. ceased. 3/yr. Union Nacional de Arquitectos e Ingenieros de la Construccion de Cuba, Humboldt No. 104, Esq. a Infanta, Vedado, Havana, Cuba.

649.1 UN ISSN 0049-4984
U N I C E F INFORMATION BULLETIN. 1972-19?? 5/yr. United Nations Childrens Fund - Fonds des Nations Unies pour l'Enfance, 3 United Nations Plaza, New York, NY 10017.

362.7 UN ISSN 0041-5340
U N I C E F NEWS. 1963-19?? 4/yr. United Nations Childrens Fund, 3 United Nations Plaza, New York, NY 10017.

630 016 US
U S - CANADIAN RANGE MANAGEMENT; a selected bibliography on ranges, pastures, wildlife, livestock, and ranching. 1978-1981. irreg. Oryx Press, 4041 N. Central at Indian School Rd., Phoenix, AZ 85012-3397.

551.46 US
U S DIRECTORY OF MARINE SCIENTISTS. 1950-1982. irreg. National Academy of Sciences, 2101 Constitution Ave., N.W., Washington, DC 20418.
Former titles: Directory of Marine Scientists in the United States; (until 1975): Directory of Oceanographers in the United States (ISSN 0070-5969); (until 1964): International Directory of Oceanographers.

647.9 US
U S ECONOMY LODGING INDUSTRY. 1981-1990. a. Laventhol & Horwath, 1845 Walnut St., Philadelphia, PA 19103.

796.332 US ISSN 0742-4299
GV955.5.U8
U S F L GUIDE AND REGISTER. (United States Football League) 1984-198? a. Sporting News Publishing Co., 1212 N. Lindbergh Blvd., St. Louis, MO 63132.

382 327
U S - JAPAN ECONOMIC AGENDA; mutual benefits from expanding trade. 1985-1991. q. (back issues avail.) Carnegie Council on Ethics and International Affairs, c/o Olivia Wakeman, Dir., Public Relations, Merrill House, 170 E. 64th St., New York, NY 10021-7478.

327 382 US ISSN 0091-407X
HF1456.5.J3
U S - JAPAN OUTLOOK; digest of American views of Japan. 1970?-1975? s-a. International Marketing Center, Ltd., 166 E. Superior St., Chicago, IL 60611.

157.61 US ISSN 0148-8619
U S JOURNAL OF DRUG AND ALCOHOL DEPENDENCE. 1977-1991. m. (tabloid format) U.S. Journal Inc., 3201 S.W. 15th St., Deerfield Beach, FL 33442.

330.9 US
U S - KOREA SOCIETY. ECONOMIC NEWSLETTER. 1974-19??; resumed 1985-19?? m. U S-Korea Society, 725 Park Ave., New York, NY 10021.

658.91 US ISSN 0361-2198
TX901
U S LODGING INDUSTRY; annual report on hotel and motor hotel operations. 1932-1990. a. Laventhol & Horwath, 1845 Walnut St., Philadelphia, PA 19103.
Formerly: Lodging Industry.

663.2 US ISSN 1044-8780
HD9377.C2
U S MARKET FOR CALIFORNIA VARIETAL WINE: IMPACT DATABANK REVIEW AND FORECAST. 1990-199? a. M. Shanken Communications, Inc., 387 Park Ave. S., New York, NY 10016.

051 US ISSN 0885-176X
F786
U S - MEXICO REPORT. 1982-1990 (vol.9, no.12). m. (back issues avail.) (New Mexico State University) Border Research Institute, 1200 University Ave., Box 3001, Dept. 3BRI, Las Cruces, NM 88003.

338.47 US ISSN 1044-8772
HD9348.U5
THE U S NON-ALCOHOLIC BEVERAGE MARKET: IMPACT DATABANK REVIEW AND FORECAST. 1983-19?? a. M. Shanken Communications, Inc., Attn.: Lynn Rittenband, 387 Park Ave. S., New York, NY 10016.
Formerly: Impact (New York, 1983) (ISSN 0882-6277).

CESSATIONS

333.33 US
U S REAL ESTATE WEEK. 1987-199? w. Warren, Gorham and Lamont Inc., One Penn Plaza, New York, NY 10119.

600 US ISSN 0892-497X
U S S R TECHNOLOGY UPDATE; a bi-weekly report on Soviet and Eastern European developments. 1986-19?? bi-w. (back issues avail.) Delphic Associates Incorporated, 7700 Leesburg Pike, Ste. 218, Fall Church, VA 22043.

796.346 US
U S TABLE TENNIS NEWS. 1933-19?? bi-m. (processed) United States Table Tennis Association, U.S. Olympic Complex, 1750 E. Boulder St., Colorado Springs, CO 80909.

621.38 US
U S TELECOM DIGEST. ceased 1990. s-m. Capitol Publications, Inc., Telecom Publishing Group, 1101 King St., Ste. 444, Box 1455, Alexandria, VA 22313-2055.

388 016 FR
U T A C BULLETIN DE DOCUMENTATION. 1945-1992. m. (Union Technique de l'Automobile du Motocycle et du Cycle, Service Documentation) Societe Auxiliaire Technique de l'Automobile, du Motocycle et du Cycle, 157 rue Lecourbe, 75015 Paris, France.
Formerly: Union Technique de l'Automobile du Motocycle et du Cycle. Bulletin Mensuel de Documentation (ISSN 0041-705X)

535 UK ISSN 0144-2317
CODEN: UVSGAZ
U.V. SPECTROMETRY GROUP. BULLETIN. (Ultra Violet) 1949-1984 (vol.11). a. (back issues avail.) U.V. Spectrometry Group, c/o Dr. M. Barnard, Perkin-Elmer Ltd., Beaconsfield, England.
Formerly (until 1973): Photoelectric Spectrometry Group Bulletin (ISSN 0079-1814)

371.002 DK ISSN 0107-1629
UDDANNELSE INSTITUTIONER OVER GRUNDSKOLENIVEAU. 1979-1987. a. Undervisningministeriet, Oekonomisk-Statistike Konsulent, Copenhagen, Denmark.

284 GW
UEBERGAENGE. 1974-1990. bi-m. (back issues avail.) Wichern-Verlag, Bachstr. 1-2, 1000 Berlin 21, Germany.
Formerly: Kirche im Sozialismus (ISSN 0173-4784)

333.7 UG
UGANDA. GAME DEPARTMENT. ANNUAL REPORT. 1925-198? a. Ministry of Tourism and Wildlife, Game Department, Box 4241, Kampala, Uganda.

011 UG
UGANDA. PUBLIC LIBRARIES BOARD. ACCESSION LIST. ceased 1976. bi-m. Public Libraries Board, P.O. 4262, Kampala, Uganda.

681.11 GW ISSN 0082-7290
UHRMACHER - JAHRBUCH FUER HANDWERK UND HANDEL. 1950-1990. a. Bielefelder Verlagsanstalt GmbH & Co. KG, Niederwall 53, Postfach 1140, 4800 Bielefeld, Germany.

742.92 US
UJENA FASHION. ceased. bi-m. Ujena Inc., 1400 N. Shoreline Blvd., Mountain View, CA 94043.

613.7 US
UJENA GIRL. ceased. bi-m. Ujena Inc., 1400 N. Shoreline Blvd., Mountain View, CA 94043.
Formerly: Fit (ISSN 0278-9760)

058.398 NO
UKENS NYTT. 1889-19?? 3/w. (tabloid format) Aftenposten, Akersgaten 51, Oslo 1, Norway.

011 US ISSN 0000-1163
ULRICH'S NEWS. 1988-1992. 4/yr. R.R. Bowker, A Reed Reference Publishing Company, Division of Reed Publishing (USA) Inc., 121 Chanlon Rd., New Providence, NJ 07974.

051 US
ULTRA MAGAZINE. ceased 1991 (Mar.). m. 1400 Post Oak Blvd., Ste. 850, Houston, TX 77056-3009.

620.11 GW
UMFORM PRODUKTE; Konstuktionen nach Zeichnung oder Muster. ceased 1991. a. Verlag Hoppenstedt und Co., Havelstr. 9, 6100 Darmstadt, Germany.

289.9 SA
UMPHAKO WABASHUMAYELI. ceased. q. (Church of the Nazarene) Africa Nazarene Publications, P.O. Box 1288, Florida, Transvaal 1710, South Africa.

289.9 SA
UMPHAPHAMISI. 1920-19?? q. (Church of the Nazarene) Africa Nazarene Publications, P.O. Box 1288, Florida, Transvaal 1710, South Africa.

600 GW ISSN 0722-8562
CODEN: UMSCDV
UMSCHAU, DAS WISSENSCHAFTS MAGAZIN. (Die Umschau, das Wissenschafts Magazin) 1897-1986. s-m. Broenner Verlag Breidenstein GmbH, Stuttgarter Str. 18-24, 6000 Frankfurt, Germany.
Formerly (until 1982): Umschau in Wissenschaft und Technik; Which incorporated: Weltraumfahrt - Raketentechnik (ISSN 0041-6347)

700 IT
UMUS. ceased. bi-m. Maggioli Editore, Via Crimea 1, 47037 Rimini, Italy.

658 SZ
UN PAYS, UN MARCHE. ceased 1987. 20/yr. Office Suisse d'Expansion Commercial, 4 Av. de l'Avant-Post, 1001 Lausanne, Switzerland.

320 UK ISSN 0264-6501
DK4442
UNCENSORED POLAND NEWS BULLETIN. 1981-1991 (no.17, Dec.). fortn. Information Centre for Polish Affairs (U.K.), 45 Kent Gardens, London W13 8BU, England.

808.87 US
UNCOMMON READER. 1986-1989. q. (back issues avail.) 1220 Taransay, Henderson, KY 42420.

665.5 US ISSN 0741-7721
UNCONVENTIONAL PETROLEUM; a current awareness bulletin. ceased. s-m. U.S. Department of Energy, Office of Scientific and Technical Information, Box 62, Oak Ridge, TN 37831.

027.7 US
UNDERGRADUATE FORUM; a university library newsletter for Northwestern. 1973-1987. irreg. Northwestern University Library, Undergraduate Services Department, 1935 Sheridan Rd., Evanston, IL 60201.

943.91 GW ISSN 0082-755X
UNGARN - JAHRBUCH; Zeitschrift fuer die Kunde Ungarns und Verwandte Gebiete. 1969-19?? a. (Ungarisches Institut) Verlag Dr. Anton Kovac, Elisbethstr. 22, 8000 Munich 40, Germany.

370 DK ISSN 0108-2426
UNGDOMSSKOLEN I TAL. 1981-19?? a. Kulturministeriet, Vestergade 29-31, 1456 Copenhagen K, Denmark.

810 700 US
UNICORN (BALTIMORE); a semi-annual of new literature and art. 1975-19?? s-a. Loyola College of Baltimore, Baltimore, MD 21210.

013 SA ISSN 0079-4325
UNION CATALOGUE OF THESES AND DISSERTATIONS OF THE SOUTH AFRICAN UNIVERSITIES. (Cumulated microfiche edition covers 1918-1989) 1918-1989. a. (also avail. in microfiche) Potchefstroom University for Christian Higher Education - Potchefstroomse Universiteit vir Christelike Hoer Onderwys, Potchefstroom, South Africa.

340 US
UNION LIST OF LEGISLATIVE HISTORIES. ceased with 5th ed. biennial. (back issues avail.) (Law Librarian's Society of the District of Columbia) Fred B. Rothman & Co., 10368 W. Centennial Rd., Littleton, CO 80120.

618.9 US
UNION OF EUROPEAN PEDOPSYCHIATRISTS. PROCEEDINGS. ceased 1971 (4th, Stockholm). irreg. Halsted Press, 605 Third Ave., New York, NY 10016.

350 CN ISSN 0082-7762
UNION OF NOVA SCOTIA MUNICIPALITIES. PROCEEDINGS OF THE ANNUAL CONVENTION. 1906-19?? biennial. Union of Nova Scotia Municipalities, Suite 132, 136 Roy Bldg., 1657 Barrington St., Halifax, N.S. B3J 2A1, Canada.

945 IT
UNIONCAMERE. ceased 1988 (Apr.). m. Unione Italiana delle Camere di Commercio, Industria, Artigianato e Agricoltura, Piazza Sallustio, 21, 00187 Rome, Italy.

051 US
UNIQUE (BRIDGEVIEW). 1990; ceased same year. m. Unique Magazine, Inc., Box 1224, Bridgeview, IL 60455.

320.531 FR
UNITE. 1972-1986. w. Parti Socialiste, 10 rue Solferino, 75333 Paris Cedex 07, France.

796.72 US
UNITED FLATHEAD RACERS ASSOCIATION NEWSLETTER. 1972-1980 (Dec.). m. United Flathead Racers Association, 23748 1-2 Lyons Ave., Newhall, CA 91321.

526 551 UK
UNITED KINGDOM RESEARCH ON GEODESY. 1963-198? triennial. Royal Institution of Chartered Surveyors (R I C S), L S Division, 12 Great George St., London SW1P 3AD, England.
Formerly: United Kingdom Geodesy Report.

287 371.3 US ISSN 0160-0885
BX8225.A1
UNITED METHODIST CHURCH. CURRICULUM PLANS. 1941-1992. a. (United Methodist Church, General Board of Discipleship, Curriculum Resources Committee) United Methodist Publishing House, Graded Press, Box 801, Nashville, TN 37202.

338.91 UN ISSN 0250-801X
UNITED NATIONS INDUSTRIAL DEVELOPMENT ORGANIZATION. DEVELOPMENT AND TRANSFER OF TECHNOLOGY SERIES. 1977-19?? irreg. United Nations Industrial Development Organization, P.O. Box 300, A-1400 Vienna, Austria.

300 UN
UNITED NATIONS INSTITUTE FOR NAMIBIA. OCCASIONAL PAPERS. 1985-19?? irreg. United Nations Institute for Namibia, Publications Section, P.O. Box 33811, Lusaka, Zambia.

370 UN
UNITED NATIONS INSTITUTE FOR NAMIBIA. PROSPECTUS. ceased. a. United Nations Institute for Namibia, Publications Section, P.O. Box 33811, Lusaka, Zambia.

309.2 US ISSN 0098-4035
E159
U.S. ADVISORY COUNCIL ON HISTORIC PRESERVATION. REPORT. 1972-1977 (Sep.). 8/yr. U.S. Advisory Council on Historic Preservation, 1522 K St. N.W., Suite 430, Washington, DC 20005.
Formerly: U.S. Advisory Council on Historic Preservation. Newsletter (ISSN 0091-9748)

338.9 US ISSN 0082-8637
U.S. AGENCY FOR INTERNATIONAL DEVELOPMENT. PROPOSED FOREIGN AID PROGRAM, SUMMARY PRESENTATION TO CONGRESS. 1963-19?? a. U.S. Agency for International Development, Dept. of State, Washington, DC 20523.

356.1 US
U.S. ARMY INFANTRY SCHOOL. HISTORY; ANNUAL SUPPLEMENT. ceased. a. U.S. Army Infantry School, Attn: ATSH-SE, Fort Benning, GA 31905-5452.
Formerly: U.S. Army Infantry Center. History; Annual Supplement (ISSN 0091-2271)

616.9 US ISSN 0093-5654
RA1231.R2
U.S. BUREAU OF RADIOLOGICAL HEALTH. RESEARCH GRANTS PROGRAM. (Subseries of U.S. Dept. of Health, Education, and Welfare. DHEW Publications) ceased. irreg. U.S. Bureau of Radiological Health, Dept. of Health, Education and Welfare, 330 Independence Ave., S.W., Washington, DC 20201.

333.91 US
U.S. BUREAU OF RECLAMATION. DENVER OFFICE. RESEARCH REPORTS. 1963-1969. irreg. (back issues avail.) U.S. Bureau of Reclamation, Denver Office, Box 25007, Denver Federal Center, Denver, CO 80225.
Former titles: U.S. Bureau of Reclamation. Engineering and Research Center. Research Reports; U.S. Water and Power Resources Service. Engineering and Research Center. Research Reports; U.S. Bureau of Reclamation. Engineering and Research Center. Research Reports (ISSN 0501-7467)

616.82 US
U.S. CENTERS FOR DISEASE CONTROL. NEUROTROPIC VIRAL DISEASES SURVEILLANCE: ASEPTIC MENINGITIS. ceased 198? a. U.S. Centers for Disease Control, 1600 Clifton Rd., Atlanta, GA 30333.

616.832 US
U.S. CENTERS FOR DISEASE CONTROL. NEUROTROPIC VIRAL DISEASES SURVEILLANCE: ENCEPHALITIS. ceased 198? a. U.S. Centers for Disease Control, 1600 Clifton Rd., Atlanta, GA 30333.

616.8 US
U.S. CENTERS FOR DISEASE CONTROL. NEUROTROPIC VIRAL DISEASES SURVEILLANCE: ENTEROVIRUS. ceased 198? a. U.S. Centers for Disease Control, 1600 Clifton Rd, Atlanta, GA 30333.

350 US
U.S. CIVIL SERVICE COMMISSION. 1961-197? m. U.S. Office of Personnel Management, 1900 E. St. N.W., Washington, DC 20415.

350 US ISSN 0190-9797
JK631
U.S. CIVIL SERVICE COMMISSION. ANNUAL REPORT. 1884-1979. a. U.S. Office of Personnel Management, 1900 E Street, N.W., Washington, DC 20415.

658.3 US ISSN 0361-6797
JK765
U.S. CIVIL SERVICE COMMISSION. BUREAU OF PERSONNEL MANAGEMENT EVALUATION. EVALUATION METHODS SERIES. 1975-197? irreg. U.S. Office of Personnel Management, Washington, DC 20415.

353.001 658.3 US ISSN 0093-366X
JK765
U.S. CIVIL SERVICE COMMISSION. PERSONNEL RESEARCH AND DEVELOPMENT CENTER. TECHNICAL STUDY. 1974-197? irreg. U.S. Office of Personnel Management, 1900 E. St., N.W., Washington, DC 20415.

320 US
U.S. CONGRESS. CONGRESSIONAL DIRECTORY. (Avail. in 3 eds.: paperbound; clothbound; thumb-indexed) ceased. a. (also avail. in microform from UMI) U.S. Government Printing Office, Superintendent of Documents, Washington, DC 20402-9371.

658.8 US
U.S. DEPARTMENT OF COMMERCE. CONSUMER GOODS AND SERVICES DIVISION. FRANCHISE OPPORTUNITIES HANDBOOK. 1965-1988. a. U.S. Department of Commerce, Room 1104, Washington, DC 20230.

330 016 US ISSN 0277-7207
Z1223
U.S. DEPARTMENT OF COMMERCE. PUBLICATIONS CATALOG. 1950-1982. a. U.S. Department of Commerce, Office of Publications, Washington, DC 20230.
Former titles: U.S. Department of Commerce. Publications; a Catalog and Index Supplement (ISSN 0091-9039); U.S. Department of Commerce. Publications. Supplement (ISSN 0499-0994)

608.7 531.64 US
U.S. DEPARTMENT OF ENERGY. D.O.E. PATENTS AVAILABLE FOR LICENSING. 1980-19?? s-a. U.S. Department of Energy, Office of Scientific and Technical Information, Box 62, Oak Ridge, TN 37831.
Formerly: U.S. Department of Energy. Patents Available for Leasing (ISSN 0277-3074)

371.9 US
U.S. DEPARTMENT OF HEALTH AND HUMAN SERVICES. ANNUAL REPORT TO THE CONGRESS OF THE UNITED STATES ON SERVICES PROVIDED TO HANDICAPPED CHILDREN IN PROJECT HEAD START. 1973-19?? a. U.S. Administration for Children, Youth and Families, 330 Independence Ave., S.W., Washington, DC 20201.
Formerly: U.S. Department of Health, Education and Welfare. Annual Report to the Congress of the United States on Services to Handicapped Children in Project Head Start (ISSN 0093-3430)

362 US ISSN 0082-9889
U.S. DEPARTMENT OF HEALTH, EDUCATION, AND WELFARE. CATALOG OF H E W ASSISTANCE PROVIDING FINANCIAL SUPPORT AND SERVICE TO STATES, COMMUNITIES, ORGANIZATIONS, INDIVIDUALS. ceased. a. U.S. Department of Health, Education, and Welfare., Washington, DC 20201.

360 US ISSN 0082-9897
HA211
U.S. DEPARTMENT OF HEALTH, EDUCATION AND WELFARE. HEALTH, EDUCATION AND WELFARE TRENDS. 1959-19?? a. U.S. Department of Health, Education and Welfare, Washington, DC 20201.

614.7 US
U.S. DEPARTMENT OF HOUSING AND URBAN DEVELOPMENT. INTERIM GUIDE FOR ENVIRONMENT ASSESSMENT. ceased. irreg. U.S. Department of Housing and Urban Development, Washington, DC 20410.

352.7 310 US ISSN 0147-7870
HD7293.A49
U.S. DEPARTMENT OF HOUSING AND URBAN DEVELOPMENT. STATISTICAL YEARBOOK. ceased. a. U.S. Department of Housing and Urban Development, Washington, DC 20410.
Formerly: H U D Statistical Yearbook (ISSN 0190-275X)

960 US ISSN 0083-0003
U.S. DEPARTMENT OF STATE. AFRICAN SERIES. (Subseries of its Departmental Series) 1960-19?? irreg. U.S. Department of State, Bureau of Public Affairs, 2201 C St. N.W., Washington, DC 20520.

353.1 US ISSN 0041-7610
JX232 CODEN: DSBUAM
U.S. DEPARTMENT OF STATE. BULLETIN; official monthly record of United States foreign policy. 1939-1989 (Dec.). m. (also avail. in microform from UMI,MCA, MIM,BHP; reprint service avail. from UMI; back issues avail.) U.S. Department of State, Bureau of Public Affairs, Washington, DC 20502.

327 US ISSN 0083-0038
U.S. DEPARTMENT OF STATE. DEPARTMENT AND FOREIGN SERVICE SERIES. 1948-19?? irreg. U.S. Department of State, Bureau of Public Affairs, 2201 C St. N.W., Washington, DC 20520.

327 US ISSN 0083-0054
U.S. DEPARTMENT OF STATE. EAST ASIAN AND PACIFIC SERIES. 1932-19?? irreg. U.S. Department of State, Bureau of Public Affairs, Washington, DC 20250.
Formerly: Far Eastern Series (ISSN 0083-0089)

940 US ISSN 0083-0070
U.S. DEPARTMENT OF STATE. EUROPEAN AND BRITISH COMMONWEALTH SERIES. 1948-19?? irreg. U.S. Department of State, Bureau of Public Affairs, 2201 C St. N.W., Washington, DC 20520.

327 382 US ISSN 0083-0097
U.S. DEPARTMENT OF STATE. GENERAL FOREIGN POLICY SERIES. 1948-19?? irreg. U.S. Department of State, Bureau of Public Affairs, 2201 C St. N.W., Washington, DC 20520.

327 US ISSN 0083-0143
U.S. DEPARTMENT OF STATE. INTER-AMERICAN SERIES. 1929-19?? irreg. U.S. Department of State, Bureau of Public Affairs, 2201 C St., N.W., Washington, DC 20520.

327 US ISSN 0083-0119
U.S. DEPARTMENT OF STATE. INTERNATIONAL INFORMATION AND CULTURAL SERIES. 1948-19?? irreg. U.S. Department of State, Bureau of Public Affairs, 2201 C St. N.W., Washington, DC 20520.

327 US ISSN 0083-0127
U.S. DEPARTMENT OF STATE. INTERNATIONAL ORGANIZATION AND CONFERENCE SERIES. 1959-19?? irreg. U.S. Department of State, Bureau of Public Affairs, 2201 C St. N.W., Washington, DC 20520.

327 US ISSN 0083-0135
U.S. DEPARTMENT OF STATE. INTERNATIONAL ORGANIZATION SERIES. 1968-19?? irreg. U.S. Department of State, Bureau of Public Affairs, 2201 C St., N.W., Washington, DC 20520.

950 956 US
U.S. DEPARTMENT OF STATE. NEAR EAST AND SOUTH ASIAN SERIES. 1948-19?? irreg. U.S. Department of State, Bureau of Public Affairs, Washington, DC 20250.
Supersedes: U.S. Department of State. Near and Middle Eastern Series (ISSN 0083-0151)

614.84 US ISSN 0083-0682
U.S. FEDERAL FIRE COUNCIL. FEDERAL FIRE EXPERIENCE FOR FISCAL YEAR. ceased. irreg. (also avail. in microfiche from NTI) U.S. Federal Fire Council, Rm. A07, Bldg. 225, National Bureau of Standards, Washington, DC 20234.

614.84 US ISSN 0083-0690
U.S. FEDERAL FIRE COUNCIL. MINUTES OF ANNUAL MEETING. ceased. irreg. (also avail. in microform from NTI) U.S. Federal Fire Council, Rm. A07, Bldg. 225, National Bureau of Standards, Washington, DC 20234.

614.84 US ISSN 0083-0704
U.S. FEDERAL FIRE COUNCIL. RECOMMENDED PRACTICES. 1962-1975? irreg. (also avail. in microform from NTI) U.S. Federal Fire Council, Rm. A07 - Bldg. 225, National Bureau of Standards, Washington, DC 20234.

338 US ISSN 0083-078X
HD1694
U.S. FEDERAL POWER COMMISSION. ANNUAL REPORT. ceased. a. (also avail. in microfilm from BHP) U.S. Federal Power Commission, 411 G St., N.W., Washington, DC 20426.

338.4 US ISSN 0098-681X
HD9724
U.S. FEDERAL TRADE COMMISSION. QUARTERLY FINANCIAL REPORT FOR MANUFACTURING, MINING AND TRADE CORPORATIONS. ceased. q. U.S. Federal Trade Commission, Office of Public Affairs, Sixth St. and Pennsylvania Ave., N.W., Washington, DC 20580.
Formerly: U.S. Federal Trade Commission. Quarterly Financial Report: United States Manufacturing Corporations (ISSN 0033-5509)

371.33 US ISSN 0083-1166
U.S. GOVERNMENT FILMS FOR PUBLIC EDUCATIONAL USE. 1955-19?? irreg. U.S. Office of Education, Dept. of Health, Education, and Welfare, Washington, DC 20202.

381 US ISSN 0083-1522
U.S. INTERSTATE COMMERCE COMMISSION. INTERSTATE COMMERCE ACTS ANNOTATED. 1930-19?? irreg. U.S. Interstate Commerce Commission, 12th St. and Constitution Ave., N.W., Washington, DC 20423.

353 US ISSN 0091-2646
KF5365
U.S. LABOR - MANAGEMENT SERVICES ADMINISTRATION. DECISIONS AND REPORTS ON RULINGS OF THE ASSISTANT SECRETARY OF LABOR FOR LABOR - MANAGEMENT RELATIONS. 1970-19?? w. U.S. Labor - Management Services Administration, New Department of Labor Building, 200 Constitution Ave., Washington, DC 20216.

355 US
U.S. M A LIBRARY BULLETIN. 1945-19?? irreg. U.S. Military Academy Library, West Point, NY 10996.

620.1 389 US ISSN 0022-4316
CODEN: JNBCAX
U.S. NATIONAL BUREAU OF STANDARDS. JOURNAL OF RESEARCH. SECTION C: ENGINEERING AND INSTRUMENTATION. ceased. q. Superintendent of Documents, Government Printing Office, Washington, DC 20402.

CESSATIONS

616.8 US ISSN 0083-2162
U.S. NATIONAL INSTITUTE OF NEUROLOGICAL DISEASES AND STROKE. N I N D S RESEARCH PROFILES: SUMMARY OF RESEARCH. 1968-19?? a. U.S. National Institute of Neurological and Communicative Disorders and Stroke, Dept. of Health, Education, and Welfare, Bethesda, MD 20014.

551.6 551.46 US ISSN 0091-8512
QC993.83
U.S. NATIONAL OCEANIC AND ATMOSPHERIC ADMINISTRATION. NATIONAL CLIMATIC CENTER. MARINE CLIMATOLOGICAL SUMMARIES. 1961-198? irreg. (also avail. in microfiche) U.S. National Climatic Data Center, Federal Building, MC-02, Asheville, NC 28801-2696.

387.7 US ISSN 0360-3954
HE17
U.S. NATIONAL TRANSPORTATION SAFETY BOARD. LISTING OF AIRCRAFT ACCIDENTS-INCIDENTS BY MAKE AND MODEL, U.S. CIVIL AVIATION. (Subseries of: United States. National Transportation Safety Board. Report) ceased. a. U.S. National Transportation Safety Board, 800 Independence Ave., S.W., Washington, DC 20594.

528 US ISSN 0083-243X
U.S. NAVAL OBSERVATORY. ASTRONOMICAL PAPERS PREPARED FOR USE OF AMERICAN EPHEMERIS AND NAUTICAL ALMANAC. 1882-19?? irreg. U.S. Naval Observatory, Washington, DC 20392.

520 US ISSN 0083-2448
QB4
U.S. NAVAL OBSERVATORY. PUBLICATIONS. SECOND SERIES. ceased. irreg. U.S. Naval Observatory, Department of the Navy, Washington, DC 20392.

370.025 US ISSN 0083-2618
U.S. OFFICE OF EDUCATION. ACCREDITED HIGHER INSTITUTIONS. 1917-19?? quadrennial. U.S. Office of Education, Department of Health, Education, and Welfare, Washington, DC 20202.

370.025 US ISSN 0083-2715
U.S. OFFICE OF EDUCATION. GUIDE TO ORGANIZED OCCUPATIONAL CURRICULUMS IN HIGHER EDUCATION. ceased. a. U.S. Office of Education, Dept. of Health, Education, and Welfare, Washington, DC 20202.

370 371.142 US ISSN 0083-2723
U.S. OFFICE OF EDUCATION. INTERNATIONAL TEACHER DEVELOPMENT PROGRAM. ANNUAL REPORT TO BUREAU OF EDUCATION AND CULTURAL AFFAIRR, DEPARTMENT OF STATE. 1956-19?? a. U.S. Office of Education, Dept. of Health, Education, and Welfare, Washington, DC 20202.

379 US ISSN 0083-2774
U.S. OFFICE OF EDUCATION. PUBLIC SCHOOL FINANCE PROGRAM. 1947-19?? irreg. U.S. Office of Education, Department of Health, Education, and Welfare, Washington, DC 20202.

378.15 US ISSN 0083-2790
U.S. OFFICE OF EDUCATION. RESIDENCE AND MIGRATION OF COLLEGE STUDENTS, ANALYTIC REPORT. ceased. irreg. U.S. Office of Education, Dept. of Health, Education, and Welfare, Washington, DC 20202.

370 US ISSN 0083-2855
U.S. OFFICE OF EDUCATION. STUDIES IN COMPARATIVE EDUCATION. EDUCATION IN (COUNTRY). ceased. irreg. U.S. Office of Education, Dept. of Health, Education, and Welfare, Washington, DC 20202.

370 US ISSN 0083-288X
U.S. OFFICE OF EDUCATION. TITLE VII: NEW EDUCATIONAL MEDIA NEWS AND REPORTS. 1959-19?? irreg. U.S. Office of Education, 400 Maryland Ave., S.W., Washington, DC 20202.

333.9 US ISSN 0083-2901
TD478.3
U.S. OFFICE OF SALINE WATER. DESALTING PLANTS INVENTORY REPORT. 1968-197? a. U.S. Office of Saline Water, Department of the Interior, Washington, DC 20240.

333.9 US ISSN 0083-291X
TD433
U.S. OFFICE OF SALINE WATER. SALINE WATER CONVERSION REPORT. 1952-197? a. U.S. Office of Saline Water, Department of the Interior, Washington, DC 20240.

350 360 US ISSN 0083-3134
U.S. RENEWAL ASSISTANCE ADMINISTRATION. TECHNICAL GUIDES. 1960-19?? irreg. U.S. Renewal Assistance Administration, Dept. of Housing and Urban Development, Washington, DC 20411.

350 360 US ISSN 0083-3142
U.S. RENEWAL ASSISTANCE ADMINISTRATION. URBAN RENEWAL PROJECT CHARACTERISTICS. 1954-19?? irreg. U.S. Renewal Assistance Administration, Dept. of Housing and Urban Development, Washington, DC 20411.

350 US ISSN 0083-3150
U.S. RENEWAL ASSISTANCE ADMINISTRATION. URBAN RENEWAL SERVICE BULLETINS. ceased. irreg. U.S. Renewal Assistance Administration, Dept. of Housing and Urban Development, Washington, DC 20411.

360 US ISSN 0566-0327
HD7123
U.S. SOCIAL SECURITY ADMINISTRATION. O R S I P NOTES. 1978-198? irreg. U.S. Social Security Administration, Office of Research, Statistics and International Policy, Universal North Bldg., Rm. 1120, 1875 Connecticut Ave., N.W., Washington, DC 20009.
Formerly (until 1985): U.S. Social Security Administration. Research and Statistics Notes.

332.4 US ISSN 0098-3896
HJ2052
U.S. TREASURY DEPARTMENT. BUREAU OF GOVERNMENT FINANCIAL OPERATIONS. REPORT ON FOREIGN CURRENCIES HELD BY THE U.S. GOVERNMENT. ceased. s-a. U.S. Department of the Treasury, Bureau of Government Financial Operations, Washington, DC 20226.
Formerly: U.S. Treasury Department. Bureau of Accounts. Report on Foreign Currencies in the Custody of the United States.

341 US
JX236.5
UNITED STATES INTERNATIONAL TREATIES TODAY. 1986-19?? a. William S. Hein & Co., Inc., 1285 Main St., Buffalo, NY 14209.
Formerly: Unpublished and Unnumbered Treaties Index (ISSN 0894-1564)

665.5 FR ISSN 0396-2644
UNITES PETROCHIMIQUES DANS LES PAYS DE L'O P E C ET DE L'O P A E P/PETROCHEMICAL UNITS IN THE O P E C AND O A P E C COUNTRIES. 1976-1978. a. (Institut Francais du Petrole) Editions Technip, 27 rue Ginoux, 75737 Paris Cedex 15, France.

917.3 US ISSN 0740-4603
UNITY (OAKLAND). 1978-198?; suspended. bi-w. (tabloid format; back issues avail.) Getting Together Publications, Box 29293, Oakland, CA 94604.

378.198 US
UNIVERCITY. 1980-198? w. (tabloid format) National News Bureau, 1318 Chancellor St., Philadelphia, PA 19107.

011 VE
UNIVERSIDAD DE LOS ANDES. VICERRECTORADO ACADEMICO. SERVICIOS BIBLIOTECARIOS DE CIENCIAS FORESTALES Y SERVICIOS BIBLIOTECARIOS DE GEOGRAFIA. OBRAS INGRESADAS. 1967-198?; suspended. q. Universidad de Los Andes, Vicerrectorado Academico, Servicios Bibliotecarios de Geografia, Merida, Venezuela.
Former titles: Universidad de Los Andes. Vicerrectorado Academico. Servicios Bibliotecarios de Geografia. Obras Ingresadas; Universidad de Los Andes. Instituto de Geografia y Conservacion de Recursos Naturales. Biblioteca. Obras Ingresadas.

574 SP ISSN 0213-3938
UNIVERSIDAD DE MURCIA. ANALES DE BIOLOGIA. SECCION ESPECIAL. (Subseries of: Anales de Biologia) 1984; ceased same year (no.2). irreg. Universidad de Murcia, Secretariado de Publicaciones e Intercambio Cientifico, Santo Cristo, 1, 30001 Murica, Spain.

340 SP ISSN 0210-539X
UNIVERSIDAD DE MURCIA. ANALES DE DERECHO. 1930-198? a. Universidad de Murcia, Secretariado de Publicaciones e Intercambio Cientifico, Santo Cristo, 1, 30001 Murcia, Spain.
Supersedes (in 1977): Universidad de Murcia. Anales. Derecho; (in 1954): Universidad de Murcia. Anales: Anales de Derecho.

370 100 SP
UNIVERSIDAD DE MURCIA. ANALES DE FILOSOFIA Y CIENCIAS DE LA EDUCACION. ceased. irreg. Universidad de Murcia, Secretariado de Publicaciones e Intercambio Cientifico, Santo Cristo, 1, 30001 Murcia, Spain.

001.3 SP
UNIVERSIDAD DE MURCIA. ANALES DE LETRAS. 1930-1985 (vol.43). irreg. Universidad de Murcia, Secretariado de Publicaciones e Intercambio Cientifico, Santo Cristo, 1, 30001 Murcia, Spain.
Supersedes in part (in 1980): Universidad de Murcia. Filosofia y Letras. Anales (ISSN 0463-9863); (until 1954): Universidad de Murcia. Anales de Letras.

910 SP ISSN 0210-492X
UNIVERSIDAD DE MURCIA. DIDACTICA GEOGRAFICA. 1972-1986 (vol.14). irreg. Universidad de Murcia, Secretariado de Publicaciones e Intercambio Cientifico, Santo Cristo, 1, 30001 Murcia, Spain.

574 SP
UNIVERSIDAD DE NAVARRA. PUBLICACIONES DE BIOLOGIA. 1980-1987 (no.22). irreg. (back issues avail.) (Universidad de Navarra, Facultad de Ciencias) Ediciones Universidad de Navarra, S.A., Apdo. 396, 31080 Pamplona, Spain.

010 080 CK
UNIVERSIDAD DEL VALLE. DEPARTAMENTO DE BILIOTECAS. BOLETIN DE ADQUISICIONES. 1955-19?? q. Universidad del Valle, Departamento de Bibliotecas, Apdo. Aereo 6641, Cali, Colombia.
Supersedes: Universidad del Valle Biblioteca. Publicaciones (ISSN 0068-5453)

610 MX
UNIVERSIDAD NACIONAL AUTONOMA DE MEXICO, FACULTAD DE MEDICINA. REVISTA. 1974-19?? m. Intersistemas, S.A. de C.V., Fernando Alencastre no. 110, Mexico 10 D.F., Mexico.

025.2 AG ISSN 0076-6399
UNIVERSIDAD NACIONAL DE CUYO. BIBLIOTECA CENTRAL. BOLETIN BIBLIOGRAFICO. 1940-1988 (no. 53). irreg. Universidad Nacional de Cuyo, Biblioteca Central, Centro Universitario-C.C. 420, Mendoza, Argentina.

020 010 AG ISSN 0076-6402
UNIVERSIDAD NACIONAL DE CUYO. BIBLIOTECA CENTRAL. CUADERNOS DE LA BIBLIOTECA. 1961-1986 (no.10). irreg. Universidad Nacional de Cuyo, Biblioteca Central, Centro Universitario-C.C. 420, Mendoza, Argentina.

001.3 VE ISSN 0076-4345
UNIVERSIDAD NACIONAL DEL ZULIA. FACULTAD DE HUMANIDADES Y EDUCACION. CONFERENCIAS Y COLOQUIOS. ceased. irreg. Universidad del Zulia, Facultad de Humanidades y Educacion, Apartado 526, Maracaibo, Venezuela.

378 BL
UNIVERSIDADE ESTADUAL PAULISTA. DEPARTAMENTO DE EDUCACAO. BOLETIM. ceased 1974. irreg. Universidade Estadual Paulista, Departamento de Educacao, Rua Roberto Simonsen 305, C.P. 957, Presidente Prudente, Brazil.

610 BL ISSN 0041-8838
UNIVERSIDADE FEDERAL DE MINAS GERAIS. ESCOLA DE ENGENHARIA. REVISTA. 1962-1980 (vol.3). s-a. Universidade Federal de Minas Gerais, Escola de Engenharia, Rua Espirito Santo 35, 4 Andar-Sala 7, Belo Horizonte, Minas Gerais, Brazil.

610 BL ISSN 0301-7729
UNIVERSIDADE FEDERAL DE MINAS GERAIS. FACULDADE DE MEDICINA. ANAIS. 1929-1987 (vol. 36); suspended. s-a. Universidade Federal de Minas Gerais, Faculdade de Medicina, Biblioteca "J. Baeta Vianna", Av. Alfredo Balena, 190-C.P. 340, 30.000 Belo Horizonte, Minas Gerais, Brazil.

946.9 BL ISSN 0101-0352
UNIVERSIDADE FEDERAL DO PARANA. CENTRO DE ESTUDOS PORTUGUESES. ARQUIVOS; publicacao semestral para a divulgacao da cultura portuguesa. 1970-1985 (vol.4, no.3). s-a. Universidade Federal do Parana, Centro de Estudos Portugueses, Caixa Postal 441, 80001 Curitiba, Parana, Brazil.

630 BL
UNIVERSIDADE FEDERAL DO RIO GRANDE DO SUL. FACULDADE DE AGRONOMIA. BOLETIM TECNICO. 1985; ceased same year. irreg. Universidade Federal do Rio Grande do Sul, Faculdade de Agronomia, Departamento de Solos, Bento Goncalves 7712, Caixa Postal 776, 90000 Porto Alegre, R.S., Brazil.

610 BL ISSN 0085-042X
UNIVERSIDADE FEDERAL DO RIO GRANDE DO SUL. FACULDADE DE MEDICINA. ANAIS. 1938-1978 (vol. 38). irreg. Universidade Federal do Rio Grande do Sul, Faculdade de Medicina, Rua Sarmento Leite s-n, 90000 Porto Alegre, R.S, Brazil.

981 BL
UNIVERSIDADE FEDERAL DO RIO GRANDE DO SUL. GABINETE DE PESQUISA DE HISTORIA. BOLETIM. 1973-1981 (no.17). irreg. Universidade Federal do Rio Grande do sul, Gabinete de Pesquisa de Historia, Av. Benito Gonzalves 9.500, 91500 Porto Alegre, Rio Grande do Sul, Brazil.

150 IT ISSN 0076-874X
UNIVERSITA CATTOLICA DEL SACRO CUORE, MILAN. SAGGI E RICERCHE. SERIE TERZA. SCIENZE PSICOLOGICHE. 1970-197? irreg. (Universita Dell Sacro Cuore) Vita e Pensiero, Largo A. Gemelli, 1, 20123 Milano, Italy.

330 IT
UNIVERSITA DEGLI STUDI DI CAGLIARI. ISTITUTO SCIENZE ECONOMICHE. STUDI DI ECONOMIA. 1970-198? 3/yr. Universita degli Studi di Cagliari, Istituto Scienze Economiche, N.B. Libr. Cosentino, Via Gallura 15-17, 09100 Cagliari, Italy.
  Formerly: Universita degli Studi di Cagliari. Istituto Economico Statistico. Studi di Economia.

510 GW
UNIVERSITAET GIESSEN. MATHEMATISCHES INSTITUT. VORLESUNGEN. 1974-19?? irreg. Universitaet Giessen, Mathematisches Institut, Arndtstr. 2, 6300 Giessen, Germany.

001.3 CN ISSN 0041-9206
BX802
UNIVERSITE D'OTTAWA. REVUE/UNIVERSITY OF OTTAWA QUARTERLY. 1931-1987 (vol.57, no.4). q. University of Ottawa Press, 603 Cumberland, Ottawa, Ont. K1N 6N5.

591 FR ISSN 0069-4681
UNIVERSITE DE CLERMONT-FERRAND II. ANNALES SCIENTIFIQUES. SERIE BIOLOGIE ANIMALE. 1963-1985 (vol.83); suspended. irreg. (back issues avail.) Universite de Clermont-Ferrand II, Departement de Mathematiques, 63177 Aubiere, France.

581 FR ISSN 0069-469X
UNIVERSITE DE CLERMONT-FERRAND II. ANNALES SCIENTIFIQUES. SERIE BIOLOGIE VEGETALE. 1965; ceased same year. irreg. Universite de Clermont-Ferrand II, Departement de Mathematiques, 63177 Aubiere, France.

540 FR ISSN 0069-4703
UNIVERSITE DE CLERMONT-FERRAND II. ANNALES SCIENTIFIQUES. SERIE CHEMIE. 1960; ceased same year. irreg. Universite de Clermont-Ferrand II, Departement de Mathematiques, 63177 Aubiere, France.

554 549 FR ISSN 0069-4711
QE1
UNIVERSITE DE CLERMONT-FERRAND II. ANNALES SCIENTIFIQUES. SERIE GEOLOGIE ET MINERALOGIE. 1959-1985 (vol.86). irreg. (back issues avail.) Universite de Clermont-Ferrand II, Departement de Mathematiques, 63177 Aubiere, France.

591.1 FR ISSN 0069-4746
UNIVERSITE DE CLERMONT-FERRAND II. ANNALES SCIENTIFIQUES. SERIE PHYSIOLOGIE ANIMALE. 1967; ceased same year. irreg. Universite de Clermont-Ferrand II, Unite d'Enseignement et de Recherche de Sciences Exactes et Naturelles, B.P. 45, 63170 Aubiere, France.

530 FR ISSN 0069-4738
UNIVERSITE DE CLERMONT-FERRAND II. ANNALES SCIENTIFIQUES. SERIE PHYSIQUE. 1963-1978 (vol. 64). irreg. (back issues avail.) Universite de Clermont-Ferrand II, Unite d'Enseignement et de Recherche de Sciences Exactes et Naturelles, B.P. 45, 63170 Aubiere, France.

440 RE ISSN 0337-6176
P381.R46
UNIVERSITE DE LA REUNION. CAHIER. 1971-19?? irreg. Universite de la Reunion, 24-26 av. de la Victoire, 97489 Saint-Denis, Reunion.
  Formerly: Centre Universitaire de la Reunion. Cahier.

709 FR ISSN 0563-9794
UNIVERSITE DE TOULOUSE II (LE MIRAIL). INSTITUT D'ART PREHISTORIQUE. TRAVAUX. 1958-1991; suspended. a. (back issues avail.) (Universite de Toulouse II (le Mirail)) Presses Universitaires du Mirail, 56 rue du Taur, 31069 Toulouse Cedex, France.

971 CN ISSN 0079-8347
UNIVERSITE LAVAL. CENTRE D'ETUDES NORDIQUES. TRAVAUX ET DOCUMENTS. 1963-1975. irreg. Presses de l'Universite Laval, C.P. 2447, Quebec, Que. G1K 7R4, Canada.

530 CN
UNIVERSITE LAVAL. CENTRE DE RECHERCHES SUR LES ATOMES ET LES MOLECULES. RAPPORT ANNUEL; physics and chemistry of atoms and molecules. 1968-1988. a. Universite Laval, Centre de Recherches sur les Atomes et les Molecules, Quebec, Que. G1K 7P4, Canada.

950 BE
UNIVERSITE LIBRE DE BRUXELLES. INSTITUT DE PHILOLOGIE ET D'HISTOIRE ORIENTALES ET SLAVES. ANNUAIRE. 1933-1983 (vol.27). irreg. (also avail. in microfiche from BHP) Universite Libre de Bruxelles, Institut de Philologie et d'Histoire Orientales et Slaves, Section de Slavistique, C.P. 133, Av. F.D. Roosevelt 50, 1050 Brussels, Belgium.

510 NE
UNIVERSITEIT VAN AMSTERDAM. MATHEMATISCH INSTITUUT. REPORT. 1970-19?? irreg. Universiteit van Amsterdam, Mathematisch Instituut, Roetersstraat 15, 1018 WB Amsterdam, Netherlands.

020 SA ISSN 0379-7104
UNIVERSITEIT VAN PRETORIA. BIBLIOTEEKDIENS. VERSLAGREEKS. 1979-1985 (no.8). irreg. University of Pretoria, Library Services, Pretoria 0002, South Africa.

378 052 UK ISSN 0265-4512
UNIVERSITY (BRISTOL). 1983-19?? irreg. (2-3/yr); no.7, 1987. (back issues avail.) University of Bristol, Information Office, 8 Priory Rd., Bristol BS8 1TZ, England.

808.8 US
UNIVERSITY JOURNAL. 1974-1992; suspended. s-a. California State University, Chico, Graduate School, Chico, CA 95926.

610 US ISSN 0042-014X
UNIVERSITY MEDICAL. 1970-1983 (vol.13, no.2). 4/yr. University of Texas at Galveston, Medical Branch. Division of Institutional Services, Ste. 633, Administration Bldg., Galveston, TX 77550.
  Supersedes: University of Texas Medical Branch Newsletter and Alumni Bulletin.

634.9 UK ISSN 0065-0277
UNIVERSITY OF ABERDEEN. DEPARTMENT OF FORESTRY. ECONOMIC SURVEY OF PRIVATE FORESTRY. 1952-1988. a. University of Aberdeen, Department of Forestry, St. Machar Dr., Old Aberdeen AB9 2UU, Scotland.

352 US
UNIVERSITY OF ALASKA. COOPERATIVE EXTENSION SERVICE. LOCAL GOVERNMENT HI-LITES. 1972-19?? irreg. University of Alaska, Cooperative Extension Service, Fairbanks, AK 99701.

630 634.9 CN ISSN 0705-3983
  CODEN: AFBUD3
UNIVERSITY OF ALBERTA. AGRICULTURE AND FORESTRY BULLETIN. 1962-1991. (vol.14). q. University of Alberta, Faculty of Extension, Edmonton, Alta. T6G 2J7, Canada.
  Formerly: University of Alberta. Faculty of Agriculture. Agriculture Bulletin (ISSN 0568-9074)

700 016 NZ ISSN 0041-9400
UNIVERSITY OF AUCKLAND. FINE ARTS LIBRARY BULLETIN. 1965-1989 (no.59); suspended. 2/yr. (processed) University of Auckland Library, Fine Arts Library, Private Bag, Auckland, New Zealand.

150 NO ISSN 0333-4325
UNIVERSITY OF BERGEN. INSTITUTE OF PSYCHOLOGY. PSYCHOLOGICAL REPORT SERIES. 1968-1978. irreg. (6-10/yr.). Universitetet i Bergen, Psykologisk Institutt, Box 25, 5014 Bergen-U, Norway.
  Formerly: University of Bergen. Institute of Psychology. Report.

624 CN
UNIVERSITY OF BRITISH COLUMBIA. DEPARTMENT OF CIVIL ENGINEERING. WATER RESOURCES RESEARCH SERIES. 1969-19?? irreg. University of British Columbia, Department of Civil Engineering, 2324 Main Mall, Vancouver, B.C. V6T 1W5, Canada.

634.9 CN
UNIVERSITY OF BRITISH COLUMBIA. FACULTY OF FORESTRY. RESEARCH REVIEW. 1984-1989. biennial. University of British Columbia, Faculty of Forestry, 270-2357 Main Mall, Vancouver, B.C. V6T 1W5, Canada.
  Formerly: University of British Columbia. Faculty of Forestry. Research and Publications (ISSN 0820-2923)

100 II
UNIVERSITY OF CALCUTTA. DEPARTMENT OF PHILOSOPHY. JOURNAL. 1975-19?? a. University of Calcutta, Department of Philosophy, Asutosh Bldg., Calcutta 700073, India.

913 US
UNIVERSITY OF CALIFORNIA, LOS ANGELES. INSTITUTE OF ARCHAEOLOGY. OCCASIONAL PAPERS. 1974-1988 (no.16). irreg. University of California, Los Angeles, Institute of Archaeology, 405 Hilgard Ave., Los Angeles, CA 90024-1510.

621.3 JA
UNIVERSITY OF ELECTRO-COMMUNICATIONS. RESEARCH INSTITUTE FOR COMMUNICATION SCIENCES. ANNUAL REPORT/DENKI TSUSHIN DAIGAKU DENKI TSUSHIN KENKYU SHISETSU NENPO. 1961-1987. a. University of Electro-Communications, Research Institute for Communication Sciences., 1-5-1 Chofugaoka, Chofu-shi, Tokyo 182, Japan.
  Formerly: University of Telecommunications. Research Laboratory of Communication Sciences. Annual Report.

610 020 IR
UNIVERSITY OF ESFAHAN. FACULTY OF MEDICINE. LIBRARY BULLETIN/DANESHGAH-E ESFAHAN. DANESHKADE-YE PEZESHKI. NASHRIYE-YE KETABKHANEH. 1972-1976 (vol.5). q. University of Esfahan, Faculty of Medicine, Esfahan, Iran.

301.435 US
UNIVERSITY OF FLORIDA. CENTER FOR GERONTOLOGY. RESEARCH SERIES. ceased. irreg. (University of Florida, Center for Gerontological Studies) University Presses of Florida, 15 N.W. 15th St., Gainesville, FL 32603.

618.97 301.435 US ISSN 0071-6103
UNIVERSITY OF FLORIDA. CENTER FOR GERONTOLOGY. STUDIES AND PROGRAMS. 1951-1979 (vol.26). irreg. (University of Florida, Center for Gerontology) University Presses of Florida, 15 N.W. 15th St., Gainesville, FL 32603.

020 GH
UNIVERSITY OF GHANA. DEPARTMENT OF LIBRARY AND ARCHIVAL STUDIES. OCCASIONAL PAPERS. ceased 1978 (vol.15). irreg. University of Ghana, Department of Library and Archival Studies, Box 60, Legon, Ghana.

CESSATIONS

551.46   US   ISSN 0199-137X
GC1021.H3
UNIVERSITY OF HAWAII. SEA GRANT COLLEGE PROGRAM. SEA GRANT QUARTERLY. ceased. q. University of Hawaii, Sea Grant College Program, 1000 Pope Rd., Rm. 220, Honolulu, HI 96822.

338.1   US   ISSN 0073-523X
UNIVERSITY OF ILLINOIS AT URBANA-CHAMPAIGN. DEPARTMENT OF AGRICULTURAL ECONOMICS. RESEARCH REPORT. 1954-19?? irreg. University of Illinois at Urbana-Champaign, Department of Agricultural Economics, Urbana, IL 61801.

620   US   ISSN 0073-5272
CODEN: UIBBAE
UNIVERSITY OF ILLINOIS AT URBANA - CHAMPAIGN. ENGINEERING EXPERIMENT STATION. BULLETIN. 1904-1970 (no.505). (back issues avail.) University of Illinois at Urbana-Champaign, Engineering Publications Office, 112 Engineering Hall, 1308 W. Green St., Urbana, IL 61801.

020   US
UNIVERSITY OF ILLINOIS AT URBANA-CHAMPAIGN. GRADUATE SCHOOL OF LIBRARY AND INFORMATION SCIENCE. DOWNS FUND PUBLICATIONS SERIES. 1972-1984 (no.8). irreg. University of Illinois at Urbana-Champaign, Graduate School of Library and Information Science, 249 Armory Bldg., 505 E. Armory St., Champaign, IL 61820.
Former titles: University of Illinois at Urbana-Champaign. Graduate School of Library and Information Science. Down Fund Publications Series; University of Illinois at Urbana-Champaign Graduate School of Library Science. Downs Fund Publications Series.

910   UK   ISSN 0309-2178
UNIVERSITY OF LONDON KING'S COLLEGE. DEPARTMENT OF GEOGRAPHY. OCCASIONAL PAPER. 1973-19?? irreg. University of London King's College, Department of Geography, Strand, London WC2R 2LS, England.

500   US
UNIVERSITY OF MIAMI. CENTER FOR THEORETICAL STUDIES. QUARTERLY BULLETIN. 1967-19??; suspended. q. (tabloid format) University of Miami, Center for Theoretical Studies, Box 249055, Coral Gables, FL 33124.

001.3   US   ISSN 0076-9703
AS36
UNIVERSITY OF MISSOURI STUDIES. 1926-1980 (no. 69). irreg. University of Missouri Press, 2910 LeMone Blvd., Columbia, MO 65202.

330   SA
UNIVERSITY OF NATAL. LOW-INCOME HOUSING SERIES. 1983; ceased same year. irreg. University of Natal, Department of Economics, King George V Ave., Durban, South Africa.

330   SA
UNIVERSITY OF NATAL. MONOGRAPH SERIES; transport policies and economic development in Southern Africa. 1984-19?? irreg. University of Natal, Department of Economics, King George V Ave., Durban, South Africa.

330   SA
UNIVERSITY OF NATAL. OCCASIONAL PAPERS; distribution of personal wealth in South Africa. 1982-19?? (no.21). irreg. University of Natal, Department of Economics, King George V Ave., Durban, South Africa.

371.2   AT
UNIVERSITY OF NEW ENGLAND. DEPARTMENT OF ADMINISTRATIVE, HIGHER AND ADULT EDUCATION STUDIES. CENTRE NEWS. 1985-1989. a. University of New England, Department of Administrative, Higher and Adult Education Studies, Armiche, N.S.W. 2351, Australia.

338.1   AT   ISSN 1036-4161
UNIVERSITY OF NEW ENGLAND. DEPARTMENT OF AGRICULTURAL ECONOMICS AND BUSINESS MANAGEMENT. WOOL ECONOMICS RESEARCH REPORTS (NO.). ceased. irreg. University of New England, Department of Agricultural Economics and Business Management, Armidale, N.S.W. 2351, Australia.

260   US   ISSN 0081-7708
UNIVERSITY OF NOTRE DAME. DEPARTMENT OF THEOLOGY. STUDIES IN CHRISTIAN DEMOCRACY. 1965-19?? irreg. University of Notre Dame Press, Notre Dame, IN 46556.

800 974   US   ISSN 0169-0361
UNIVERSITY OF PENNSYLVANIA STUDIES ON SOUTH ASIA. 1984-1986 (vol.3). irreg. (University of Pennsylvania) John Benjamins Publishing Co., 821 Bethlehem Pike, Philadelphia, PA 19118.

500   II   ISSN 0551-4932
AS472.P6   CODEN: JUPOAI
UNIVERSITY OF POONA SCIENCE AND TECHNOLOGY. JOURNAL. 1952-1983 (vol.56). biennial. University of Poona, Ganeshkhind, Poona 411 007, India.

551.46 574.92
UNIVERSITY OF RHODE ISLAND. GRADUATE SCHOOL OF OCEANOGRAPHY. COLLECTED REPRINTS. 1958-19?? irreg. University of Rhode Island, Graduate School of Oceanography, Kingston, RI 02881.
Formerly (until vol. 1-6): University of Rhode Island. Narragansett Marine Laboratory. Collected Reprints (ISSN 0077-281X)

551.46 574.92   US
UNIVERSITY OF RHODE ISLAND. GRADUATE SCHOOL OF OCEANOGRAPHY. MARINE TECHNICAL REPORTS. 1950-19?? irreg. University of Rhode Island, Graduate School of Oceanography, Kingston, RI 02881.
Formerly: Narragansett Marine Laboratory. Technical Reports (ISSN 0077-2836)

020 800   CN   ISSN 0380-9676
UNIVERSITY OF SASKATCHEWAN. LIBRARY. NOTABLE WORKS AND COLLECTIONS. 1975-19?? (no.18); suspended. a. University of Saskatchewan, Library, Saskatoon, Sask. S7N 0W0, Canada.

330   US
UNIVERSITY OF SOUTH CAROLINA. BUREAU OF BUSINESS AND ECONOMIC RESEARCH. OCCASIONAL STUDIES. 1972-198? irreg., no.15, 1983. University of South Carolina, College of Business Administration, Division of Research, Columbia, SC 29208.

025   UK   ISSN 0081-2935
UNIVERSITY OF SOUTHAMPTON. LIBRARY. AUTOMATION PROJECT REPORT. 1970-1975 (vol.5). irreg. University of Southampton, Library, Highfield, Southampton, Hants S09 5NH, England.

360   US   ISSN 0272-9016
HV13
UNIVERSITY OF SOUTHERN CALIFORNIA. SCHOOL OF SOCIAL WORK. SOCIAL WORK PAPERS. 1953-1988 (vol.21). irreg. University of Southern California, School of Social Work, Montgomery Ross Fisher Bldg., Rm. 214, University Park-MC 0411, Los Angeles, CA 90089-0411.
Formerly: University of Southern California. School of Social Work. Social Work Papers of the Faculty, Alumni and Students.

330   AT   ISSN 0085-7025
UNIVERSITY OF SYDNEY. ECONOMICS SOCIETY. ECONOMIC REVIEW. 1955-19?? 3/yr. University of Sydney, Economics Society, Sydney, N.S.W. 2006, Australia.

610   AT   ISSN 0042-0115
UNIVERSITY OF SYDNEY. POSTGRADUATE COMMITTEE IN MEDICINE. BULLETIN. 1945-1990 (May). m. Postgraduate Committee in Medicine, University of Sydney, D02, Sydney, N.S.W. 2006, Australia.

636.089   IR   ISSN 0042-0123
CODEN: JVFTDR
UNIVERSITY OF TEHERAN. FACULTY OF VETERINARY MEDICINE. JOURNAL. ceased. q. (looseleaf format) University of Teheran, Faculty of Veterinary Medicine, P.O. Box 14155-6453, Teheran, Iran.

636.089 020   IR
UNIVERSITY OF TEHERAN. FACULTY OF VETERINARY MEDICINE. LIBRARY BULLETIN/DANESHGAH-E TEHRAN. DANESHKADE-YE DAM'EZESHKI. NASHRIYE-YE KETABKHANEH. 1966-19?? q. University of Teheran, Faculty of Veterinary Medicine, Ayzenhover Ave., Box 3262, Teheran, Iran.

520   US   ISSN 0276-1106
UNIVERSITY OF TEXAS PUBLICATIONS IN ASTRONOMY. 1969-1984. irreg. University of Texas at Austin, Department of Astronomy, RLM 15.308, Austin, TX 78712.

634.9   PH   ISSN 0115-1266
UNIVERSITY OF THE PHILIPPINES AT LOS BANOS. COLLEGE OF FORESTRY. CONSERVATION CIRCULAR. 1965-1988. q. University of the Philippines at Los Banos, College of Forestry, Institute of Forest Conservation, P.O. Box 434, College, 4031 Laguna, Philippines.

591   JA   ISSN 0368-220X
QL1   CODEN: JFNZA4
UNIVERSITY OF TOKYO. FACULTY OF SCIENCE. JOURNAL. SECTION 4: ZOOLOGY/TOKYO DAIGAKU RIGAKUBU KIYO, DAI-4-RUI, DOBUTSUGAKU. 1926-1986 (vol. 16, no.2); suspended. a. University of Tokyo, Faculty of Science - Tokyo Daigaku Rigakubu, Hongo, Tokyo, Japan.

621.3   CN   ISSN 0082-514X
UNIVERSITY OF TORONTO. DEPARTMENT OF ELECTRICAL ENGINEERING. RESEARCH REPORT. 1954-19?? irreg. University of Toronto, Department of Electrical Engineering, Toronto, Ont., Canada.

310   UK
UNIVERSITY OF WARWICK BUSINESS INFORMATION SERVICE. OCCASIONAL REVIEW. 1980-198? irreg. University of Warwick Business Information Service, University of Warwick Library, Coventry CV4 7AL, England.
Formerly: Warwick Statistics Service. Occasional Review (ISSN 0144-6738)

001.6 621.381   US   ISSN 0744-8821
UNIVERSITY OF WASHINGTON. ACADEMIC COMPUTING SERVICES. NEWSLETTER. 1964-19?? every 6 wks. (looseleaf format) University of Washington, Academic Computing Services, 3737 Brooklyn Ave. N.E., Seattle, WA 98105.
Formerly: University of Washington. Academic Computing Center. Newsletter.

610   US   ISSN 0094-2006
UNIVERSITY OF WASHINGTON MEDICINE. 1974-1989 (vol.15, no.2). q. University of Washington School of Medicine, Health Sciences Information Services, C-301, Health Sciences Center SC-60, Seattle, WA 98195.

639.2   US   ISSN 0085-7939
UNIVERSITY OF WASHINGTON PUBLICATIONS IN FISHERIES. 1962-19?? irreg. (University of Washington, College of Fisheries) University of Washington Press, Box 50096, Seattle, WA 98105.

954 959   AT   ISSN 1032-9684
UNIVERSITY OF WESTERN AUSTRALIA. ASIAN STUDIES CENTRE. MONOGRAPHS. ceased 1988 (no.7). irreg. University of Western Australia, Asian Studies Centre, Nedlands, W.A. 6009, Australia.

990 330   AT   ISSN 0313-9581
UNIVERSITY OF WESTERN AUSTRALIA. CENTRE FOR EAST ASIAN STUDIES. OCCASIONAL PAPERS. 1975-1988 (no.9). irreg. University of Western Australia, Centre for East Asian Studies, Nedlands, W.A. 6009, Australia.

954 959 572   AT   ISSN 0155-0179
UNIVERSITY OF WESTERN AUSTRALIA. CENTRE FOR SOUTH AND SOUTHEAST ASIAN STUDIES. RESEARCH PAPERS. 1978-1986. irreg. University of Western Australia, Centre for South and Southeast Asian Studies, Nedlands, W.A. 6009, Australia.

378   AT   ISSN 0726-4844
UNIVERSITY OF WOLLONGONG. LEGISLATION. ceased. irreg. University of Wollongong, P.O. Box 1144, Wollongong, N.S.W. 2500, Australia.
Supersedes in part: University of Wollongong. Calendar (ISSN 0312-0007)

001.3   US
UNIVERSITY OF WYOMING AMERICAN STUDIES CONFERENCE. PROCEEDINGS. ceased 1982. irreg. University of Wyoming, School of American Studies, Laramie, WY 82071.

CESSATIONS

028.1 US ISSN 0191-4146
Z1033.U64
UNIVERSITY PUBLISHING; an international quarterly review of books published by university presses. 1975-1984 (vol.12). q. (tabloid format; back issues avail.) 2430 Bancroft, Berkeley, CA 94704.

320.5322 335.43 CS
UNIVERZITA KOMENSKEHO. FILOZOFICKA FAKULTA. ZBORNIK: MARXIZMU-LENINIZMUS. 1962-19?? irreg. (approx. a.). Univerzita Komenskeho, Filozoficka Fakulta, c/o Study and Information Center, Safarikova nam. 6, 818 06 Bratislava, Czechoslovakia.

943.7 CS
UNIVERZITA PAVLA JOZEFA SAFARIKA. USTAV MARXIZMU-LENINIZMU. ZBORNIK PRAC UCITELOV. 1974-1988 (no.15). a. Vychodoslovenske Vydavatel'stvo v Kosiciach, Alejova 3, 040 01 Kosice 1, Czechoslovakia.
Formerly: Univerzita P.J. Safariny. Ustav Mrxizmu-Leninizmu. Zbornik: Marxizmus-Leninizmus.

322.4 US
UNMASK. 1984-1986 (no.4). irreg. (back issues avail.) The Nerve Center, 1917 E. 29th St., Oakland, CA 94606.

799.2 GW ISSN 0566-2621
UNSERE JAGD. ceased 1990. m. (tabloid format) Deutscher Landwirtschaftsverlag GmbH, Reinhardtstr. 14, 1040 Berlin, Germany.

055.1 IT
UNSIN; no Vus per la Geiso e la Muntagno. 1981-1989 (vol.9, no.4). q. (tabloid format; back issues avail.) Unsin, Via Provinciale 3, 12030 Oncino, Italy.

811 US ISSN 0049-559X
PS536
UNSPEAKABLE VISIONS OF THE INDIVIDUAL. 1971-19?? irreg. Tuvoti, Box 439, California, PA 15419.

610 AT
UPDATE. ceased. m. Business Press International Pty. Ltd., 162 Goulburn St., Darlinghurst, N.S.W. 2010, Australia.

374.013 US ISSN 0162-945X
UPDATE (ALEXANDRIA); the newspaper for vocational educators. 1978-19?? 6/yr. (tabloid format) American Vocational Association, 1410 King St., Alexandria, VA 22314-2715.

614 US
UPDATE (COLUMBIA, 1971). 1971-1989 (Fall). q. Department of Health and Environmental Control, 2600 Bull St., Columbia, SC 29201.

332.6 US
UPDATE (LANSING). 1980-1988; suspended. irreg. Department of Commerce, Corporation & Securities Bureau, PO Box 30222, 6546 Mercantile Way, Lansing, MI 48909.
Formed by the merger of: Michigan. Department of Commerce. Corporation and Securities Bureau. Securities Bulletin (ISSN 0047-7109) & Blue Sky Bulletin.

617.6 US
UPDATE: DENTAL EDITION. vol.17, 1980-198? m. American Health Consultants, Inc., 61 Peachtree Park Dr., N.E., Atlanta, GA 30309.

610 CN
UPDATE IN CRITICAL CARE MEDICINE. 1990-199? bi-m. Decker Periodicals, One James St., S., P.O. Box 620, Sta. 1, Hamilton, Ont. L8N 3K7, Canada.

747.5 US ISSN 0744-138X
TT198
UPHOLSTERING TODAY; the manufacturing magazine of the upholstering industry. 1888-1990. 6/yr. (tabloid format) Cahners Business Newspapers (Subsidiary of: Reed International PLC), Division of Reed Publishing (USA) Inc., 200 S. Main St., Box 2754, High Point, NC 27261.
Formerly (until 1981): Upholstering Industry (ISSN 0042-0700)

975 US
UPPER SOUTH CAROLINA GENEALOGY & HISTORY. 1983-1988. q. Piedmont Historical Society, Box 8096, Spartanburg, SC 29305.
Formerly (until Apr. 1985): Piedmont Historical Society Quarterly.

929.2 US ISSN 0098-8960
CS71
UPSHAW FAMILY JOURNAL. 1974-1981 (vol.8, no.3). irreg. (back issues avail.) 408 Colchester Dr., Stone Mountain, GA 30088.

810 US ISSN 0197-8381
UPTON SINCLAIR QUARTERLY. 1977-1988 (vol.12). q. (back issues avail.) Sinclairiana, c/o Robert. O. Hahn, 3190 Valley Rd., No. P, Aptos, CA 95003-2176.
Formerly (until 1979): Uppie Speaks.

914 GW ISSN 0170-5725
UR- UND FRUEHZEIT; Zeitschrift fuer populaere Archaeologie. 1974-1991. 4/yr. Hagenberg Verlag, Hornburg, Germany.

500 GW ISSN 0049-562X
Q3 CODEN: URAAAZ
URANIA; populaerwissenschaftliche Zeitschrift. 1924-1991. m. Urania-Verlag, Salomonstr. 26, 7010 Leipzig, Germany.

500.9 540 530 320 GW
URANIA UNIVERSUM. 1955-1990. a. Urania Verlag, Salomonstrasse 26-28, 7010 Leipzig, Germany.

352.7 DK ISSN 0105-9459
URBAN AND REGIONAL RESEARCH IN DENMARK. 1972-1984. biennial. Danish Building Research Institute, Urban and Regional Planning Division, Statens Byggeforskningsinstitut, SBI-Publikationer, P.O. Box 119, DK-2970 Hoersholm, Denmark.

352.7 364 US ISSN 0736-6272
URBAN INSIGHTS MONOGRAPH SERIES. 1979-19?? irreg. Loyola University of Chicago, Center for Urban Policy, 820 N. Michigan Ave., Chicago, IL 60611.

301.364 334.77 US ISSN 0741-1308
URBAN RESOURCES. 1983-1988 (vol.5, no.4). 3/yr. (looseleaf format; back issues avail.) University of Cincinnati, Division of Metropolitan Services, Mail Location 175, Cincinnati, OH 45221.

711 AT ISSN 0310-5601
URBANOLOGY. 1971-1979. irreg. University of New South Wales, School of Town Planning, P.O. Box 1, Kensington, N.S.W. 2033, Australia.

059 US ISSN 0198-635X
AL URDUN; a Jordan newsletter. 1976-1987? irreg. (back issues avail.) (Embassy of the Hashemite Kingdom of Jordan) Jordan Information Bureau, 2319 Wyoming Ave., N.W., Washington, DC 20008.

001.6 621.381 US ISSN 0742-9789
USING PERSONAL COMPUTERS IN NONPROFIT AGENCIES. 1984-1990. irreg. (back issues avail.) Center for Community Futures, Box 5309, Elmwood Sta., Berkeley, CA 94705.

663 US
UTAH BEVERAGE ANALYST. 1936-1990 (Dec.). m. Bell Publications, Beverage Analyst Group, 2403 Champa St., Denver, CO 80205.

612 618 UK ISSN 0268-1455
UTERUS. ceased 1989. m. (looseleaf format; back issues avail.) Sheffield University Biomedical Information Service (SUBIS), The University, Sheffield S10 2TN, England.

621.3 FI
UUSI ELEKTRONIIKKA. ceased 1991 (Mar.). 32/yr. Insinoorilehdet Oy, Asemapaallikonkatu 12B, 00520 Helsinki, Finland.
Formerly: I.D.E.A. (ISSN 0781-8602); Which was formed by the merger of: Elektroniikka ja Automaatio; Elektronikkauutiset.

026 US ISSN 0042-1723
Z675.A2
V A S L A. 1966-19?? 4/yr. (processed) Special Libraries Association, Virginia Chapter, c/o Reynolds Metals Co., Exec. Office Library, 6601 W. Broad St., Richmond, VA 23261.

370 AT
V A T - C H A T. 1976-1989 (Mar.). q. (back issues avail.) Victorian Affiliated Teachers Federation, P.O. Box 200, 11 Glenwood Ave., Glen Waverley, Vic. 3150, Australia.
Formerly (until 1988): V A T Journal (ISSN 0811-0875)

629.286 UK
V B R A INDUSTRY YEARBOOK. 1960-1991. a. Vehicle Builders and Repairers Association (VBRA), Belmont House, 102 Finkle Ln., Gildersome, Leeds LS27 7TW, England.
Former titles: V B R A Directory of Members (ISSN 0263-1083); V B R A Directory of the Vehicle Bodybuilding and Accident Repair Industries.

620 GW ISSN 0042-174X
TA3 CODEN: VDIFA3
V D I - FORSCHUNGSHEFTE. 1930-1991. 6/yr. (Verein Deutscher Ingenieure) V D I-Verlag GmbH, Heinrichstr. 24, Postfach 101054, 4000 Duesseldorf 1, Germany.
Formerly: Forschung mit V D I-Forschungsheft.

070.172 US ISSN 0748-4976
AI3
V I NEWSPAPERS - SUBSTANTIVE INDEX. 1982-1988 (vol.13). m. (looseleaf format; back issues avail.) Aye-Aye Press, Ltd., P.O. Box 1122 Christiansted, St. Croix, VI 00821.

011 US
V I P. (Supplement to: Meeting News) 1990-1992. q. Miller Freeman Inc. (New York) (Subsidiary of: United Newspapers Group), 1515 Broadway, New York, NY 10036.

338.91 US ISSN 0882-0937
V I T A NEWS. 1960-1991. q. (also avail. in microfiche) Volunteers in Technical Assistance, 1815 N. Lynn St., Ste. 200, Arlington, VA 22209-2079.
Formerly (until 1971): V I T A Newsletter (ISSN 0042-1863)

629.2 GW ISSN 0177-9761
V K G - NACHRICHTEN. 1962-1990. bi-m. Verband der Kraftfahrzeugteile- und Zweiradgrosshaendler e.V., Postfach 1861, Oberstr. 36-42, 4030 Ratingen, Germany.

625.19 AT ISSN 0814-7078
V - LINE NEWS. 1930-19?? bi-m. 589 Collins St., Melbourne, Vic. 3000, Australia.
Former titles: Victorian Rail Ways; Vic Rail News (ISSN 0049-6197)

621.381 US ISSN 1040-970X
V M E NEWS. 1987-1991 (Jul.). 12/yr. Carefree Communications, Inc., Box 5268, Carefree, AZ 85377.

371.0025 AT
V S T A GUIDE TO VICTORIAN STATE SECONDARY SCHOOLS. 1965-1973. irreg. Victorian Secondary Teachers Association, 112 Trenerry Crescent, Abbotsford, Vic. 3067, Australia.

388 SW ISSN 0280-896X
V T I TOPICS. (Vaeg och Trafik Institutet) 1982-1988 (vol.7, no.3). q. (back issues avail.) Swedish Road and Traffic Research Institute, S-58101 Linkoping, Sweden.

001.64 SZ
V T X; magazin fuer Bildschirmtext. 1982-19?? m. Basler Zeitung, Hochbergerstr. 15, CH-4002 Basel, Switzerland.
Formerly: V T.

746.92 CN
V - THE STYLE OF THE CITY. 1987-1989. m. V.M. Publishing Ltd. (Subsidiary of: Pacific West Equities Ltd.), 1178 W. Pender St., Vancouver, B.C. V6E 2R9, Canada.

332.6 US
VALUE LINE NEW ISSUES SERVICE. 1984-1989. bi-m. Value Line Publishing, Inc., 711 Third Ave., New York, NY 10017.

332 SZ
VALUES AND MEASURES OF THE WORLD. ceased 1991. q. Schweizerischer Bankverein - Swiss Bank Corporation, 6 Aeschenplaz, CH-4002 Basel, Switzerland.

378 016 US
VANDERBILT UNIVERSITY. ABSTRACTS OF THESES. 1950-1986. irreg. Vanderbilt University, Publications Office, 117 Alumni Hall, Nashville, TN 37240.

5300 CESSATIONS

929 US
VANDERPOOL NEWSLETTER. 1974-198? q. (back issues avail.) Ancestor's Attic, 4041 Pedley Rd., No. 18, Riverside, CA 92509.

332.6
VANGUARD (ORLANDO). 1987-198? m. W M P Enterprises, 3443 Parkway Center Ct., Orlando, FL 32808.

708.1 CN ISSN 0315-5226
VANGUARD (VANCOUVER). 1972-1989. 6/yr. (also avail. in microfiche) Society for Critical Arts Publications, 40 E. Cordova St., Vancouver, B.C. V6A 1K2, Canada.
Supersedes: Vancouver Art Gallery. Bulletin (ISSN 0042-2479)

305.412 IT
VANITY. suspended 1989 (no.37). bi-m. Edizioni Conde Nast S.p.A., Piazza Castello 27, 20121 Milan, Italy.

700 US ISSN 0748-6723
NX503
VANTAGE POINT. 1984-1991. q. (back issues avail.) American Council for the Arts, 1285 6th Ave., 3rd Fl., New York, NY 10019.
Formerly (until 1989): Vantage Point: Issues in American Arts; Supersedes (in 1984): American Arts (ISSN 0194-1305); (until 1968): A C A Reports (ISSN 0044-9393); Incorporates: Arts in Common (ISSN 0300-6948)

792.43 US
VARIETY INTERNATIONAL MOTION PICTURE MARKETPLACE. ceased 1982. a. Garland Publishing, Inc., 1000A Sherman Ave., Hamden, CT 06514.

778.53 US ISSN 0000-1015
PN1992.95
VARIETY'S COMPLETE HOME VIDEO DIRECTORY. (Supplement avail.: Adult Supplement) 1988-1989. base vol. (plus 3 q. cum. supplements). R.R. Bowker, A Reed Reference Publishing Company, Division of Reed Publishing (USA) Inc., 121 Chanlon Rd., New Providence, NJ 07964.

778.53 US ISSN 0000-1007
VARIETY'S COMPLETE HOME VIDEO DIRECTORY. ADULT SUPPLEMENT. 1988-1990. base vol. (plus 3 q. cum. supplements). R.R. Bowker, A Reed Reference Publishing Company, Division of Reed Publishing (USA) Inc., 121 Chanlon Rd., New Providence, NJ 07974.

531.64 DK ISSN 0108-4615
VARMEFORSYNINGSPLANLAEGNING: STATUS. 1981-198? a. Energistyrelsen, Landemaerket ll, 1119 Copenhagen K, Denmark.

305.412 II
VARSHANK. 1983-19?? m. Savita Exports, Evergreen Industrial Estate, Shakti Mill Lane, Mahalaxmi, Bombay 400 011, India.

581 634.9 HU ISSN 0083-5323
DIE VEGETATION UNGARISCHER LANDSCHAFTEN. 1957-19?? irreg. (Magyar Tudomanyos Akademia) Akademiai Kiado, Publishing House of the Hungarian Academy of Sciences, P.O. Box 24, H-1363 Budapest, Hungary.

629.2 UK
VEHICLE BUILDERS & REPAIRERS ASSOCIATION. INDUSTRY YEARBOOK. ceased 1991. a. Vehicle Builders & Repairers Association (VBRA), Belmont House, 102 Finkle Lane, Gildersome, Leeds LS27 7TW, England.
Former titles: Vehicle Builders and Repairers Association. Directory of Members and Buyers Guide; Vehicle Builders and Repairers Association. Yearbook (ISSN 0083-5331); Vehicle Builders and Repairers Association. Directory.

948.9 DK ISSN 0108-867X
VENDSYSSEL HISTORISKE MUSEUM. 1981-1985. a. Vendsyssel Historiske Museum, Museumsgade 2, DK-9800 Hjoerring, Denmark.

055.1 IT
VENETO NOTIZIE. ceased 1990 (Nov.). m. Giunta Regionale del Veneto Cannaregio, 168, 168 Palazzo Sceriman, 30121 Venice, Italy.

020 HU ISSN 0133-7319
VENGERSKAJA LITERATURA PO BIBLIOTEKOVEDENIJU I INFORMATIKE; referativnyj zurnal. 1972-19?? s-a. (back issues avail.) Orszagos Szechenyi Konyvtar, Konyvtartudomanyi es Modszertani Kozpont - Centre for Library Science and Methodology at the National Szechenyi Library, Budavari Palota F epulet, 1827 Budapest, Hungary.

330 US ISSN 0191-3530
HG4961 CODEN: VENTDC
VENTURE (NEW YORK); for entrepreneurial business owners and investors. 1979-19?? m. (also avail. in microform from UMI; back issues avail.) Venture Magazine, Inc., 521 Fifth Ave., New York, NY 10175-0105.

332.6 CN
VENTURE LINK. 1987-1990. m. Canadian New Venture and Investments Group, Ltd., 221 Front St. E., Toronto, Ont., Canada.

910.09 US
VENUE. 1988; announced, never published. bi-m. Laux Company, Inc., 63 Great Rd., Maynard, MA 01754.

296 GW
VERBAND DER JUEDISCHE GEMEINDEN IN DER D.D.R. NACHRICHTENBLATT. 1961-1990. q. Verband der Juedischen Gemeinden, Bauzenerstr. 20, 8060 Dresden, Germany.

621.88 GW ISSN 0049-5921
CODEN: VERBDC
VERBINDUNGSTECHNIK; Kennziffer-Fachzeitschrift fuer thermisches und mechanisches Verbinden-Handhaben-Montieren. 1969-1980. m. Vereinigte Fachverlage Krausskopf Ingenieur-Digest, Lessingstr. 12, P.F. 2760, 6500 Mainz, Germany.

616.994 SZ ISSN 0042-3777
VEREIN FUER KREBSFORSCHUNG. MITTEILUNGEN; aus der Behandlung maligner Tumoren mit Viscum Album. 1969-1988. 3/yr. Verein fuer Krebsforschung, CH-4144 Arlesheim, Switzerland.

613.62 GW ISSN 0042-4021
VERKEHRSMEDIZIN UND IHRE GRENZGEBIETE. 1953-1990. bi-m. Transpress VEB Verlag fuer Verkehrswesen, Franzoesische Str. 13-14, 1080 Berlin, Germany.

051 US ISSN 0895-2329
VERMONT WOMAN; for Vermont women of achievement. 1985-1990 (July). m. (tabloid format; back issues avail.) Vermont Woman Publications, P.O. Box 940, Shelburne, VT 05482-0940.

821 UK
VERMOUTH. ceased 1991. irreg. Ver Poets, 61 & 63 Chiswell Green Lane, St. Albans, Herts, AL2 3AL, England.

629.133 US ISSN 0360-5450
CODEN: VERTDW
VERTICA; the international journal of rotorcraft and powered lift aircraft. 1977-1990 (vol.14). q. (also avail. in microform from MIM,UMI) Pergamon Press, Inc., Journals Division, 660 White Plains Rd., Tarrytown, NY 10591-5153.

658 US
VETERINARY MANAGEMENT UPDATE. ceased 1990. m. (back issues avail.) American Health Consultants, Six Piedmont Center, Ste. 400, 3525 Piedmont Rd., N.E., Atlanta, GA 30305.
Formerly: Practice Marketing and Management. Veterinary Edition (ISSN 0740-6983)

636.089 US ISSN 0895-7703
VETERINARY MEDICINE REPORT. 1989-1991. q. Mosby - Year Book, Inc. (Subsidiary of: Times Mirror Company), 11830 Westline Industrial Dr., St. Louis, MO 63146.

930 GW
VETUS TESTAMENTUM COPTICE. 1973-19?? irreg. Dr. Rudolf Habelt GmbH, Am Buchenhang 1, 5300 Bonn 1, Germany.

410 FR ISSN 0563-9786
DC607.1
VIA DOMITIA. 1954-1984. s-a. Universite de Toulouse II (le Mirail), Service des Publications, 56 rue du Taur, 31069 Toulouse Cedex, France.

629 BO
VIA LIBRE. 1938-1983; resumed 1985-1988 (Apr.). 6/yr. Automovil Club Bolivano, Casilla 602, La Paz, Bolivia.
Former titles: Autoclub; Via Libre.

624 AG ISSN 0042-5028
VIALIDAD. 1957-1987 (no.92). q. (processed) Ministerio de Obras Publicas, Calle 7, No. 1175, La Plata, Buenos Aires, Argentina.

530 US ISSN 0883-9506
TA355 CODEN: VINEEU
VIBRATION ENGINEERING; an international journal. 1987-1991. q. (also avail. in microform from UMI; back issues avail.; reprint service avail. from UMI) Hemisphere Publishing Corporation (Subsidiary of: Taylor & Francis Group), 1900 Frost Rd., Ste. 101, Bristol, PA 19007-1598.

979 US ISSN 0738-8586
VICTOR VALLEY MAGAZINE. 1982-198? 6/yr. Desert Alive Publishing Co., Box 618, Victorville, CA 92392.

375 AT ISSN 0085-7726
VICTORIA, AUSTRALIA. EDUCATION DEPARTMENT. CURRICULUM AND RESEARCH BRANCH. RESEARCH REPORTS. 1967-19?? irreg. Department of Education, Curriculum & Research Branch, 234 Queensberry St., Carlton, Vic. 3053, Australia.

621.3 AT
VICTORIA, AUSTRALIA. STATE ELECTRICITY COMMISSION. SCIENCE REPORT. 1971-1986 (no. 15). irreg. (back issues avail.) State Electricity Commission of Victoria, Herman Research Laboratory, Howard St., Richmond, Vic. 3121, Australia.

350 360 AT ISSN 0727-5803
VICTORIAN CONSULTATIVE COMMITTEE ON SOCIAL DEVELOPMENT. ANNUAL REVIEW. 1979-19?? a. (back issues avail.) Victoria Consultative Committee on Social Development, 290 Wellington St., Collingwood, Vic. 3066, Australia.

371.0025 373.246 AT
VICTORIAN TEACHER. 1984-198? q. (back issues avail.) Victorian Secondary Teachers Association, 112 Trenerry Crescent, Abbotsford, Vic. 3067, Australia.

330 AT
VICTORIAN UPDATE. 1986-1990. m. Victorian Government Printing Office, P.O. Box 203, North Melbourne, Vic. 3051, Australia.

914.8 IC
VID SEM FLJUGUM. ceased. 12/yr. (Icelandair) Frodi Ltd., Armuli 18, 108 Reykjavik, Iceland.

370 SP ISSN 0506-872X
VIDA ESCOLAR. 1959-198? m. (except Jul. & Aug.). Ministerio de Educacion, Ciencia, Direccion General de Ensenanza Basica, Servicio de Publicaciones, Madrid 3, Spain.

384.55 DK ISSN 0109-7717
VIDEO. VAERD AT SE. 1985-198? a. Forlag Carlsen, Krogrhej Vej 32, DK-2880 Bagvord, Denmark.

384.55 AT ISSN 0814-2769
VIDEO & AUDIO MARKETING. 1984-198? bi-m. Iris Publishing Co., Horwitz Cammerary, 506 Miller St., Cammeray, N.S.W. 2062, Australia.

384.55 US
VIDEO GAMES. 1982-1989. q. Pumpkin Press, Inc., 350 Fifth Ave., Ste. 8216, New York, NY 10118.

382.55 US ISSN 0740-4247
HD9696.T463
VIDEO MARKETING SURVEYS AND FORECASTS. 1983-1990. m. (looseleaf format; back issues avail.) Phillips Publishing, Inc., 7811 Montrose Rd., Ste. 100, Potomac, MD 20854-3363.

384.55 US
VIDEO PROPHILES. published only once, 1991. irreg. I D G Communications (Peterborough), 80 Elm St., Peterborough, NH 03458.

CESSATIONS

791.43   US   ISSN 0196-8793
VIDEO REVIEW (NEW YORK). 1980-1992 (Apr.). m. (also avail. in microform from UMI; reprint service avail. from UMI) Viare Publishing Co., 902 Broadway, New York, NY 10010.

791.43 621.38   US
VIDEO TIMES (SKOKIE); for home viewing on tape & disc. 1984-198? m. (back issues avail.) Publications International, Ltd. (Skokie), 3841 W. Oakton St., Skokie, IL 60076.
Formerly: Video Movies (ISSN 0742-8111)

791.4   CN
VIDEO TRADE. 1989-19?? s-m. (tabloid format) Moorshead Publications Ltd., 1300 Don Mills Rd., North York, Ont. M3B 3M8, Canada.

384.55 658.8   US
VIDEO TRADE NEWS. 1975-19?? m. Charles Tepfer, 56 Branchville Rd.., Box 597, Ridgefield, CT 06877.

384.55   UK
VIDEO WORLD. 1979-19?? m. Galaxy Publications Ltd., Box 312, Witham, Essex CM8 3SZ, England.

384.55   AT
VIDEO-X. 1984-19?? q. (back issues avail.) Luhaze (ACT) Pty. Ltd., 66-70 Maryborough St., Fyshwick, A.C.T. 2609, Australia.

384.55   UK   ISSN 0264-6358
VIDEODISC NEWSLETTER. 1983-1989. 3/yr. British Universities Film and Video Council, 55 Greek St., London W1V 5LR, England.

384.554   GR
VIDEOTAPES SOURCE BOOK. 1986-19?? s-a. Moressopulos & Associates, 2, Cherefontos Str., GR-105 58 Athens, Greece.

791.4   AT   ISSN 0729-1957
VIDEOWORLD. 1982-19?? m. Australian Hi-Fi & Specialist Magazines Group Pty. Ltd., P.O. Box 341, Mona Vale, N.S.W. 2103, Australia.

791.4   AT   ISSN 0729-1965
VIDEOWORLD BUYER'S GUIDE ANNUAL. 1982-19?? a. Australian Hi-Fi & Specialist Magazines Group Pty. Ltd., P.O. Box 341, Mona Vale, N.S.W. 2103, Australia.

917.106   CN   ISSN 0382-0262
VIE FRANCAISE. 1946-1989. q. (back issues avail.) Conseil de la Vie Francaise en Amerique, 56 rue St. Pierre, Ste. 301, Quebec, Que. G1K 4A1, Canada.

355.15   US
VIETNAM VETERAN; all about Vietnam. 1986-1989 (Oct.). m. c/o Michael A. Kukler, 1001 Rambling Rd., Nashville, TN 37501.

621.387   US
VIEWDATA - VIDEOTEX REPORT; the monthly newsletter monitoring viewdata - videotex, teletext, and related systems of information distribution. 1983-1988. m. (back issues avail.) Link Resources Corp., 79 Fifth Ave., New York, NY 10003-2025.

001.6 621.381   US
VIEWPOINT (ATLANTA). ceased 1986. m. I B M Corporation, G S D, Box 2068, Atlanta, GA 30055.

338   US
VIEWPOINT (NEW YORK). 1966-198? s-a. Main Hurdman & Cranstoun (Certified Public Accountants), 767 Fifth Ave., 46th Fl., New York, NY 10153.

052   IS
VIEWPOINT (TEL AVIV); socialist-zionist perspective on the Middle East. 1975-198?; suspended. m. World Union of Mapam, P.O. Box 1777, Tel Aviv 610 16, Israel.
Former titles (until 1986): Progressive Israel; Brit Mapam.

374 370 330   US
VIEWPOINTS IN BUSINESS AND OFFICE EDUCATION. 1975-1989 (vol.14, no.6). m. (Sep.-Apr.). Milady Publishing Corp., 220 White Plains Rd., Tarrytown, NY 10591.

001.642 621.381   US   ISSN 0275-0686
VIEWTEXT (POTOMAC). 1980-1991. m. (back issues avail.) Phillips Publishing, Inc., 7811 Montrose Rd., Potomac, MD 20854.

614 636.089   UN
VIGILANCIA EPIDEMIOLOGICA DE LAS ENCEFALITIS EN LAS AMERICAS. 1969-1979. s-a. Centro Panamericano de Zoonosis, Casilla 3092, 1000 Correo Central, Buenos Aires, Argentina.
Supersedes in part: Vigilancia Epidemiologica.

808.7   UK
VING. 1980-1983. irreg. Outcrowd, 3 Pleasant Villas, 189 Kent St., Mereworth, Maidstone, Kent ME18 5QN, England.

305.412   US   ISSN 0742-1494
VINTAGE '45; a uniquely supportive quarterly journal for women. 1983-19?? q. Vintage '45 Press, Box 266, Orinda, CA 94563.

342   US   ISSN 0360-7453
LAW
VIOLATIONS OF HUMAN RIGHTS IN SOVIET OCCUPIED LITHUANIA. 1971-1986. a. (also avail. in microfiche) Lithuanian American Community of USA, Inc., 1357 Gantt Dr., Huntington, PA 19006.

353.9   US
VIRGINIA. CRIMINAL JUSTICE SERVICES COMMISSION. ANNUAL REPORT. ceased. a. Criminal Justice Services Commission, 805 E. Broad St., 12th Fl., Richmond, VA 23219.
Former titles (until 1976): Virginia. Criminal Justice Officers Training and Standards Commission. Biennial Report; (until 1974): Virginia. Law Enforcement Officers Training Standards Commission. Biennial Report (ISSN 0095-1846)

353.9   US   ISSN 0095-1978
TD224.V8
VIRGINIA. STATE WATER CONTROL BOARD. ANNUAL REPORT. 1973-1981. a. State Water Control Board, 4900 Cox Rd., Glen Allen, VA 23233.

333.33   US
VIRGINIA HOUSING NETWORK; the monthly magazine for Virginia housing professionals. 1986-19?? m. Leo Douglas, Inc., 9607 Gayton Rd., Ste. 201, Richmond, VA 23233.

340   US
VIRGINIA LEGAL STUDIES. ceased. irreg. University Press of Virginia, Box 3608 University Sta., Charlottesville, VA 22903.

013   US   ISSN 0083-6451
VIRGINIA MILITARY INSTITUTE, LEXINGTON. PUBLICATIONS, THESES, AND DISSERTATIONS OF THE STAFF AND FACULTY. 1963-19??; suspended. irreg. Virginia Military Institute, Preston Library, Lexington, VA 24450.

790.1   US
VIRGINIA OUTDOORS. 1967-198? q. (back issues avail.) Virginia Outdoors Foundation, c/o Tyson Van Auken, 221 Governor St., Richmond, VA 23219.

348.73   US   ISSN 0049-6499
KFV2457
VIRGINIA RESEARCHER; digests of recent Virginia case law. 1970-198? m. (looseleaf format) National Legal Research Group, Inc, 2421 Ivy Rd., Box 7187, Charlottesville, VA 22906-7187.

625.7   US   ISSN 0161-6730
VIRGINIA ROAD BUILDER. 1945-198? a. (Virginia Road and Transportation Builders Association) V R B A Publishing Co., Inc., 30 LaBrook Dr., Richmond, VA 23225.

614   US
VIRGINIAIR. 1970-1987. q. State Air Pollution Control Board, Box 10089, Richmond, VA 23240.

371.42   US   ISSN 0083-6575
VIRGINIA'S SUPPLY OF PUBLIC SCHOOL INSTRUCTIONAL PERSONNEL. 1968-198? a. Department of Education, Division of Teacher Education, Box 6-Q, Richmond, VA 32316.

220 376   US
VIRTUOUS WOMAN. 1987-198? m. (looseleaf format; back issues avail.) Hanna Publications, 1229 Oak, Box 278, Eudora, KS 66025.

661   US
VISCOUS PRODUCTS. 1986-198? bi-m. Machalek Publishing Co., 15 S. Ninth St., Minneapolis, MN 55402.

301.4157   US   ISSN 0892-7375
VISIBILITIES. 1987-1992. bi-m. (back issues avail.) Visibility Press, Ltd., P.O. Box 1169, Olney, MD 20830-1169.

284   US
VISION (GRAND RAPIDS). ceased. 6/yr. Young Calvinist Federation, Box 7259, Grand Rapids, MI 49510.
Formerly: Y A M.

535   IT
VISION &. 1982-198? bi-m. Associazione Ottica Italiana, Sezione Oftalmica Autonoma, Via S. Felice a Ema, 20, 50125 Florence, Italy.
Supersedes: Luce e Immagini (ISSN 0024-7197)

028.5 600   GW
VISION & TECHNIK; popular technical journal. 1953-1991. m. Verlag Junge Welt GmbH, Mauerstr. 39-40, 1080 Berlin, Germany.
Formerly: Jugend und Technik (ISSN 0022-5878)

371.911   US
VISION VIEWS; newsletter for the visually impaired. 1977-19?? a. (tabloid format; also avail. in audio cassette; back issues avail.; large print edition in 14 pt.) Vision Foundation, Inc., 818 Mt. Auburn St., Watertown, MA 02172.

910.2   UK   ISSN 0260-910X
VISIT CALIFORNIA WITH FYFE ROBERTSON. 1981-19?? a. Lewis Productions Ltd., Unit 3, River Gardens Bus. Centre, Spur Rd., Feltham, Middx TW14 OSN, England.

612.3   UK   ISSN 0143-120X
VITAMIN D. ceased 1989. m. (looseleaf format; back issues avail.) Sheffield University Biomedical Information Service (SUBIS), The University, Sheffield S10 2TN, England.

634.9   YU
VJESNIK RADNIKA SUMARSTVA - SLAVONSKE POZEGE. 1973-1991 (Jan.). m. (back issues avail.) Pozesko Gorje Slavonska Pozega, Aleja Petra Drapsina 1, 55300 Slavonska Pozega, Yugoslavia.

440   CN
VOCABULAIRE DES IMPRIMES ADMINISTRATIFS. 1965-19?? irreg. Office de la Langue Francaise, 700 Bd. Saint-Cyrille Est, 2e, Quebec, Que. G1R 5A9, Canada.
Formerly: Quebec (Province) Office de la Langue Francaise. Cahiers (ISSN 0079-8770)

327   IT   ISSN 0049-6626
VOCE DELL'AFRICA. 1957-19?? m. Istituto Italo-Africano, Via Aldrovandi 16, 00197 Rome, Italy.

797   CS   ISSN 0139-6765
VODNI SPORTY. vol.36, 1984-1991. m. (Ceskoslovensky Svaz Telesne Vychovy) Olympia, Klimentska 1, 115 88 Prague 1, Czechoslovakia.

646 613   US   ISSN 0161-2190
VOGUE BEAUTY & HEALTH GUIDE. 1973-1981. a. (reprint service avail. from UMI) Conde Nast Publications Inc., Vogue Magazine, 350 Madison Ave., New York, NY 10017.

668.55   IT
VOGUE BELLEZZA. ceased 1989 (no.35). bi-m. Edizioni Conde Nast S.p.A., Piazza Castello 27, 20121 Milan, Italy.

646.4   GR
VOGUE PATTERNS (ATHENS). 1983-19?? bi-m. (back issues avail.) 387 Vouliagmenis Ave., Athens 163 46, Greece.

687.1 685.2   IT
VOGUE PELLICCE. ceased 1990 (Oct.). s-m. Edizioni Conde Nast S.p.A., Piazza Castello 27, 20121 Milan, Italy.

796 799   FR   ISSN 0757-0090
VOGUE SPORT. 1983-19?? 6/yr. (back issues avail.) Editions Conde Nast S.A., 4 Place du Palais Bourbon, 75007 Paris, France.

296 338.91   US
VOICE FROM JERUSALEM. 1981-19?? q. B'nai B'rith World Centre, B'nai B'rith International Israel Lodge, P.O. Box 7522, 91074 Jerusalem, Israel.

CESSATIONS

613 US
VOICE IN THE WILDERNESS; Nutritional Science News. 1979-19?? q. (back issues avail.) Nutritional Science Association, 188 Beechwood Dr., Youngstown, OH 44572.

630 CN
VOICE OF THE ELGIN FARMER. 1979-1988. s-m. Leader Publications Ltd., Box 490, Main St., Dresden, Ont. NOP 1M0, Canada.

630 CN
VOICE OF THE HURON FARMER. 1981-1988. bi-m. Leader Publications Ltd., P.O. Box 490, Main St., Dresden, Ont. NOP 1M0, Canada.

630 CN
VOICE OF THE OXFORD FARMER. 1985-1988. s-m. Leader Publications Ltd., P.O. Box 490, Main St., Dresden, Ont. NOP 1M0, Canada.

100 US ISSN 0744-7884
VOICE OF UNIVERSARIUS. 1960-19?? m. (back issues avail.) Universarius Foundation, Inc., Box 890, Taylor, AZ 85939.

281.9 US
VOICES IN THE WILDERNESS. 1986-1990 (Apr.). 6/yr. (back issues avail.; reprint service avail.) Box 4486, Salem, MA 01970-6486.

797.124 FR
VOILE MAGAZINE. N.S. 1970-1991. bi-m. (back issues avail.) Federation Francaise de Voile, 55 Av. Kleber, 75784 Paris Cedex 16, France.
  Formerly: Yachting a Voile.

646.7 FR
VOIX DE LA COIFFURE FRANCAISE. 1958-19?? q. (Federation Nationale de la Coiffure) S.E.I.D., 1-3 Place de la Bourse, 75002 Paris, France.

740 GW
VOLKSKUNST; Zeitschrift fuer volkstuemliche Sachkultur. 1978-1990. q. Verlag D.W. Callwey, Streitfeldstr. 35, Postfach 800409, 8000 Munich 80, Germany.

266 US
VOLUNTEER (NEW YORK, 1961). 1961-1988. 4/yr. Lutheran World Ministries, Volunteer Service Office, 360 Park Ave. S., New York, NY 10010.
  Formerly: Challenger.

338.1 UR
VOPROSY EKONOMIKI SEL'SKOGO KHOZYAISTVA DAL'NEGO VOSTOKA. ceased. irreg. Akademiya Nauk S.S.S.R., Dal'nevostochnyi Nauchnyi Tsentr, Ul. Leninskaya 50, Vladivostok, Russian S.F.S.R., U.S.S.R.

700 DK ISSN 0107-136X
VORE KUNSTNERE. ceased 1990 (vol.20). a. Skolernes Kunstforening Alssund-Kredsen, Eksp. Poul Berg, Roennebaervej 6, 6430 Nordborg, Denmark.
  Formerly: Skolernes Kunstforening Alssund-Kredsen. Katalog.

746.96 SZ
VOUS. (Supplement to 4 newspapers) 1941-1991. w. Hallwag AG, Nordring 4, CH-3001 Berne, Switzerland.
  Formerly (until 1988): Bouquet.

900 800 US
VOX MEDIAEVALIS. ceased. a. Medieval Institute Publications, Western Michigan University, Kalamazoo, MI 49008-3851.

791.45 016 CS
VYBEROVA ANOTOVANA BIBLIOGRAFIE STUDIJNICH MATERIALU. 1968-1989. biennial. Ceskoslovenska Televize, Odbor Vyzkumu Programu CST a Divaku CSR, Oddeleni Dokumentace a Odborne Informace, Jindrisska 16, 111 50 Prague 1, Czechoslovakia.

658 685.31 US
W A E M A WRAPUP. 1980-1990. bi-m. Western and English Manufacturers Association, 789 Sherman St., Ste. 160, Denver, CO 80203.
  Formerly: W A E M A Bulletin.

658.8 US
W B. 1984-1989. w. Waldenbooks, 201 High Ridge Rd., Stamford, CT 06904.

200 327 US
W C R P REPORT. 1985-199? s-a. World Conference on Religion and Peace, 777 United Nations Plaza, New York, NY 10017.

388.324 US ISSN 0042-9589
HF5487
W D; for automotive warehouse distributors, redistributing jobbers and their salesmen. (Warehouse Distribution) 1967-19?? 10/yr. Irving-Cloud Publishing Co., 7300 N. Cicero Ave., Lincolnwood, IL 60646.

374 UK ISSN 0141-0660
W E A SOUTHERN DISTRICT JOURNAL. 1977-19?? s-a. (back issues avail.) Worker's Educational Association, Southern District, Temple House, 9 Upper Berkeley St., London W1H 8BY, England.

621 GW ISSN 0171-5038
W E M A BEZUGSQUELLENVERZEICHNIS. 1950-1991. irreg. Wirtschaftsverband Eisen-Maschinen-und Apparatebau e. V.(WEMA), Karolingerplatz 10-11, 1000 Berlin 19, Germany.

687.11 US
W E R A BUSINESS NEWSLETTER. ceased 1992. m. Menswear Retailers of America, Western - English Retailers of America, 2011 I St., N.W., Ste. 600, Washington, DC 20011.

910.4 305.412 US
W E X I T A EXEC. 1984-1989 (Apr.). q. Women Executives International Tourism Association, 26 Court St., c/o M. Vidockler-Sath, Brooklyn, NY 11242.

791.4 US
W F L N PHILADELPHIA GUIDE TO EVENTS AND PLACES. 1960-1988 (Sep.). m. Franklin Broadcasting Co., 8200 Ridge Ave., Philadelphia, PA 19128.
  Formerly: W F L N Philadelphia Guide (ISSN 0042-9643)

336 US
W G & L TAX NEWS. 1980-199? 4/yr. Warren, Gorham & Lamont Inc., One Penn Plaza, New York, NY 10119.

069.5 AT ISSN 1030-6196
W.H.A.T.; the first comprehensive guide to Australia's cultural collections. (What's Here and There) 1988-19?? a.? Campbell Publishing (Subsidiary of: Campbell Group Ltd.), 20 Barcoo St., Roseville, N.S.W. 2069, Australia.

323 US ISSN 0741-5796
W O H R C NEWS. 1978-19?? q. (back issues avail.) Women's Occupational Health Resource Center, 117 St. Johns Pl., Brooklyn, NY 11217.

797.21 GW
W S V - AKTUELL. (Wuerttemburgischer Schwimmverband) 1979-1988. 3/yr. (back issues avail.) Wuerttembergischer Schwimmverband, Geschaeftsstelle, Struempfelbacherstr. 38, 7000 Stuttgart 60, Germany.

333.7 US
QH540
W W F & C F LETTER; a report on environmental issues. 1966-19?? bi-m. (looseleaf format; back issues avail.) World Wildlife Fund, 1250 24th St., N.W., Washington, DC 20037.
  Former titles: Conservation Foundation Letter (ISSN 0091-536X); C F Letter (ISSN 0007-8344)

739 391 GW ISSN 0042-9945
NK6600
WAFFEN- UND KOSTUMKUNDE. 1959-1987. s-a. (Gesellschaft fuer Historische Waffen- und Kostuemkunde) Deutscher Kunstverlag GmbH, Vohburger Str. 1, 8000 Munich 21, Germany.

015 UK ISSN 0065-0293
WALES. NATIONAL LIBRARY. HANDLIST OF MANUSCRIPTS IN THE NATIONAL LIBRARY OF WALES. (Supplement Series 2 of the National Library of Wales Journal) 1940-199? a. (occasionally irreg.). National Library of Wales, Aberystwyth, Dyfed SY23 3BU, Wales.

796 AT
WALK. 1949-1987. a. Melbourne Bushwalkers, G.P.O. Box 1751q, Melbourne, Vic. 3001, Australia.

040 US
WALKER - AMES LECTURES. 1958-19?? irreg. University of Washington Press, Box 50096, Seattle, WA 98105.

910.202 PR
WALKING TOURS OF SAN JUAN & RESTAURANT MENU GUIDE. 1980-1990. s-a. Publishing Resources, Inc., First Federal Bldg., Ste. 605, 1519 Ponce de Leon Ave., Santurce, PR 00909.
  Formerly: Walking Tours of San Juan.

677 US
WALLCOVERING INDUSTRY NEWS. 1984-1991. m. (back issues avail.) National Decorating Products Association, 1050 N. Lindbergh Blvd., St. Louis, MO 63132.

693 AT
WALLING REVIEW. 1981-19?? irreg. Concrete Masonry Association of Australia, 25 Berry St., North Sydney, N.S.W. 2060, Australia.

629.13 358.4 UK
WAR IN THE AIR. 1989-199? m. I P C Magazines Ltd., Prospect Magazines, Prospect House, 9-13 Ewell Rd., Cheam, Surrey SM1 4QQ, England.

360 UK
WAR ON WANT NEWS. 1985-1986. q. War on Want, Fenner Brockway House, 37-39 Grat Guildford St., London SE1 0ES, England.

322.4 US
WAR RESISTER. 1966-1987. 4/yr. War Resisters League, 339 Lafayette St., New York, NY 10012.

658.8 629 US
WARD'S AUTO DEALER. 1987-19?? m. Ward's Communications, Inc., 28 W. Adams St., Detroit, MI 48226.

338 US ISSN 0882-8016
HG4009
WARD'S BUSINESS DIRECTORY OF MAJOR INTERNATIONAL COMPANIES; 15,000 leading worldwide corporations. 1985-198? a. (also avail. in magnetic tape; avail. on floppy disk) Information Access Company, 362 Lakeside Dr., Foster City, CA 94404.

050 PL
WARSAW NEWSLETTER. 1969-1976 (Dec., no. 48). m. (w. in Spanish). Polska Agencja Interpress, Ul. Bagatela 12, 00-585 Warsaw, Poland.

050 PL
WARSAW POST. 1969-1976 (Dec., no. 48). w. Polska Agencja Interpress, Ul. Bagatela 12, 00-585 Warsaw, Poland.

330 UK ISSN 0083-7350
WARWICK ECONOMIC RESEARCH PAPERS. 1968-1991 (Dec.). irreg. (approx. 20/yr.). (also avail. in microfilm) University of Warwick, Department of Economics, Coventry CV4 7AL, England.

350 614.8 US
WASHINGTON. STATE HEALTH PLAN. 1980-1990. biennial. State Health Coordinating Council, Mail Stop OB-43F, Olympia, WA 98504.

385 614.85 US
WASHINGTON. UTILITIES AND TRANSPORTATION COMMISSION. RAILROAD-HIGHWAY GRADE CROSSING ACCIDENTS. SUMMARY AND ANALYSIS. ceased 1983. a. Utilities and Transportation Commission, Mail Stop FY-11, 1300 S. Evergreen Pk. Dr. S.W., Olympia, WA 98504.

657 US
WASHINGTON ACCOUNTANT. 1987-1990 (vol.4). bi-m. Accounting Promotions Inc., Box 9751, Arlington, VA 22209.

663.4 US
WASHINGTON BEVERAGE ANALYST. 1936-1990 (Dec.). m. Bell Publications, Beverage Analyst Group, 2403 Champa St., Denver, CO 80205.

338.1 US
WASHINGTON FORMLETTER. ceased. w. Business Publishers, Inc., 951 Pershing Dr., Silver Spring, MD 20910-4464.

CESSATIONS 5303

353　　　　　　US　ISSN 0277-8548
WASHINGTON HEALTH COSTS LETTER. 1974-1988 (Aug.). bi-w. (looseleaf format) Washington Business Information, Inc., c/o Karen Harrington, 1117 N. 19th St., Ste. 200, Arlington, VA 22209.
Formerly: P-S-R-O Reports (ISSN 0163-6618); Incorporates: Stat (Arlington).

333.33 340
WASHINGTON PROPERTY LAW REPORTER. 1982-19?? bi-m. (back issues avail.) Butterworth Legal Publishers (Salem), 90 Stiles Rd., Salem, NH 03079.

333.91　　　　　SP
WATER INTERNATIONAL/AGUA; international magazine of the techniques of the collection, distribution, treatment and purification of urban, industrial and irrigation waters. ceased. 4/yr. Prensa XXI, S.A., Avda Paral.lel, 180, Apdo. No. 350 F.D., 08015 Barcelona, Spain.

333.91　　　UK　ISSN 0043-129X
TD511　　　　　　CODEN: WPOCAH
WATER POLLUTION CONTROL. 1901-19?? 4/yr. (also avail. in microform from UMI; reprint service avail. from UMI) Institution of Water and Environmental Management, 15 John St., London WC1N 2EB, England.
Formerly: Institute of Sewage Purification Journal and Proceedings.

628.1 016　　　US
WATER QUALITY CONTROL DIGEST. 1969-1988 (Dec.). bi-m. University Digest Services, P.O. Box 343, Troy, MI 48099.
Formerly: U D S Water Quality Control Digest (ISSN 0043-1346)

624　　　　　　US
WATER RIGHTS. ceased. m. American Society of Civil Engineers, 345 E. 47th St., New York, NY 10017-2398.

333.91　　　　　US
WATER SUPPLY OUTLOOK FOR MONTANA. 1936-19?? 3/yr. U.S. Soil Conservation Service (Bozeman), 10 E. Babcock St, Fed. Bldg., Rm. 443, Bozeman, MT 59715.

333.91　　　　　US
WATER SUPPLY OUTLOOK FOR OREGON. 1935-1989 (June). a. U.S. Soil Conservation Service (Portland), 1220 S.W. Third Ave., Federal Bldg., Rm. 1640, Portland, OR 97204.

799.2　　　　　US
WATERFOWLER'S WORLD. 1977-19?? bi-m. Waterfowl Publications, c/o Cindy Conner, 4191 Blacksmith CV, Memphis, TN 38125-2611.

796.172 797.173　UK
WATERSPORT TRADE NEWS. 1986-198? q. (back issues avail.) Underwater World Publications Ltd., 40 Grays Inn Rd., London WC1X 8LR, England.

305.2　　　　　US
WATERSPORTS NEWS. 1989-1991 (Dec.). bi-m. B & D Co., Box 7109, Van Nuys, CA 91409.

350　　　　　　US
WE THE PEOPLE. 1985-1991 (Dec.). bi-m. Commission on the Bicentennial of the United States Constitution, 808 17th St., N.W., Washington, DC 20006.

551.5
WEATHER UPDATE. ceased 1981. q. Weathermeasure Corporation, Box 41257, Sacramento, CA 95841.

028.5　　　　US　ISSN 0043-1710
WEE WISDOM; a children's magazine from Unity. 1893-1991 (Dec.). 10/yr. (also avail. in Braille; microform from UMI) Unity School of Christianity, Unity Village, MO 64065.

028.5　　　　　US
WEE WISDOM (BRAILLE EDITION). 1893-1991. 10/yr. Unity School of Christianity, Unity Village, MO 64065.

052　　　　UK　ISSN 0043-1818
WEEKEND. 1904-198? w. Mail Newspapers Plc., Attention: Dir. Sally Cartwright, Carmelite House, London EC4Y 0JA, England.

910.202　　　　　GW
WEEKEND (YEAR) IN KOELN - IN COLOGNE; confidential tariff for agents. 1980-198? a. (looseleaf format) Verkehrsamt - Cologne Tourist Office, Unter Fettenhennen 19, D-5000 Cologne 1, Germany.

808.87　　　　　UK
WEEKEND BOOK OF JOKES. 1961-198? a. Mail Newspapers Plc., Attn: Dir. Sally Cartwright, Carmelite House, London EC4Y 0JA, England.

635　　　　　US　ISSN 1042-9972
WEEKEND GARDENER. 1984-1991 (Apr.). 6/yr. Tel-A-Cast Group, Drawer Q, Griffin, GA 30224.
Formerly: Weekend Gardener Journal.

330.9　　　　　US
WEEKLY BUSINESS STARTS. 1986-19?? w. Dun & Bradstreet, Economic Analysis Department, 299 Park Ave., New York, NY 10171.

028.5　　　　US　ISSN 0899-6121
WEEKLY READER. SUMMER EDITION C. GRADES 3-5. ceased. 6/yr. (issued during summer vacation). (tabloid format; also avail. in microfilm from UMI; reprint service avail. from UMI) Field Publications, 245 Long Hill Rd., Middletown, CT 06457.
Former titles: Weekly Reader. Summer Edition. Grades 3-5 (ISSN 0745-9149); D.J.'s Summer Weekly Reader; Bubblegum Gazette. Summer Weekly Reader (ISSN 0191-295X); Supersedes in part: My Weekly Reader (Summer Editions) (ISSN 0027-5484)

070.5 016　　　US　ISSN 0094-257X
Z1219
WEEKLY RECORD. 1974-1991. w. R.R. Bowker, A Reed Reference Publishing Company, Division of Reed Publishing (USA) Inc., 121 Chanlon Rd., New Providence, NJ 07974.
Formerly included in: Publishers Weekly.

913　　　　　　GW
WEGE VOR- UND FRUEHGESCHICHTLICHER FORSCHUNG. 1972-19?? irreg. Dr. Rudolf Habelt GmbH, Am Buchenhang 1, 5300 Bonn 1, Germany.

914.1　　　　UK　ISSN 0262-9941
WELCOME TO LONDON. 1982-1988. q. Where Publications, 55-57 Great Marlborough St., London W1V 1DD, England.

618.1　　　　　US
WELL AWARE. 1988-1991. q. Gynecology Center of Florida, 7330 S.W. 63rd Place, Ste. 410, S. Miami, FL 33143.

327　　　　　　CN
WELLESLEY PAPERS. 1973-19?? irreg. Canadian Institute of International Affairs, 15 King's College Circle, Toronto, Ont. M5S 2V9, Canada.

332　　　　　US　ISSN 0043-2415
WELLS FARGO BANK BUSINESS REVIEW. 1917-199? q. (tabloid format) Wells Fargo Bank, Economics Department No. 0188-057, 111 Sutter St., San Francisco, CA 94104.

800　　　　　　UK
WELLSIANA; world of H. G. Wells. 1908-19?? a. (looseleaf format) H.G. Wells Society, Polytechnic of North London, Prince of Wales Rd., London NW5 3LB, England.

370　　　　　UK　ISSN 0083-7946
WELSH STUDIES IN EDUCATION SERIES/YSGRIFAM AR ADDYSG. 1968-1976 (vol.6). irreg. (University College of Wales, Aberystwyth, Faculty of Education) University of Wales Press, 6 Gwennyth St., Cathays, Cardiff CF2 4YD, Wales.

327 341　　　AU　ISSN 0013-2640
EINE WELT DER VEREINTEN NATIONEN/UNITED NATIONS WORLD. 1947-1980. 4/yr. (tabloid format) United Nations World, Graben 27, A-1010 Vienna, Austria.

331.8　　　　GW　ISSN 0043-2601
WELTGEWERKSCHAFTSBEWEGUNG. 1949-1991. m. Verlag Tribune, Am Treptower Park 28-30, 1193 Berlin, Germany.

380　　　　　　GW
WERBE - MITTEL KATALOG. ceased. a. Goeller Verlag, Hauptstr. 4, Postfach 240, 7570 Baden-Baden, Germany.

331.88 690　　　NE
WERELDVERBOND VAN BOUWVAKARBEIDERS- EN HOUTBEWERKERSORGANISATIES. BULLETIN. 1954-19?? 3/yr. World Federation of Building and Woodworkers Union - Wereldverbond van Bouwvakarbeiders-en Houtbewerkersorganisaties, Oude Haven 1, 3984 KT Odijk, Netherlands.

633.18 016　　　LB
WEST AFRICA RICE DEVELOPMENT ASSOCIATION. CURRENT BIBLIOGRAPHY. 1974-19?? irreg. West Africa Rice Development Association, Box 1019, Monrovia, Liberia.

020　　　　　SG　ISSN 0850-430X
WEST AFRICAN ARCHIVIST. 1984; ceased same year. s-a. West African Regional Branch of the International Council on Archives, Direction des Archives du Senegal, Immeuble Administratif, Dakar, Senegal.

800　　　　　US　ISSN 0147-4502
PS569
WEST COAST PLAYS; outstanding new plays from the Coast. 1977-198? s-a. California Theatre Council, 135 N. Grand Ave., Los Angeles, CA 90012.

382　　　　　UK　ISSN 0142-646X
WEST EUROPEAN LIVING COSTS. 1972-1987. a. Confederation of British Industry, 103 New Oxford St., London WC1A 1DU, England.

649 051　　　　US
WEST MICHIGAN FAMILY. 1989-1990 (Dec.). m. 150 Fountain, N.E., Grand Rapids, MI 49503.

914.1　　　　UK　ISSN 0260-4426
WEST OF SCOTLAND VISITOR; a complete tourist guide to the West of Scotland. 1979-19?? a. Scotsman Publications, 20 North Bridge, Edinburgh EH1 1YT, Scotland.

622　　　　　　US
WEST VIRGINIA. MINERAL INDUSTRY STATUS. ceased. a. Geological and Economic Survey, Box 879, Morgantown, WV 26507-0879.

799　　　　　　US
WEST VIRGINIA HILLS & STREAMS. 1970-1990. bi-m. West Virginia Hills and Streams, Inc., Box 66, Renick, WV 24966.

960　　　　　US　ISSN 0035-7642
WESTERN ASSOCIATION OF AFRICANISTS. NEWSLETTER. 1969-1979. s-a. University of Nebraska, Lincoln, Political Science Department, Lincoln, NE 68508.
Formerly: Rocky Mountain Southwest African Studies Association. Newsletter.

614.85 319　　　AT
WESTERN AUSTRALIA. DEPARTMENT OF OCCUPATIONAL HEALTH, SAFETY AND WELFARE. INDUSTRIAL ACCIDENTS. 1962-19?? a. (processed) Department of Occupational Health, Safety and Welfare, Westcentre, 1240 Hay St., West Perth, W.A. 6005, Australia.
Formerly (until 1988): Australia. Bureau of Statistics. Western Australian Office. Industrial Accidents, Western Australia (ISSN 0067-1266)

330　　　　　　AT
WESTERN AUSTRALIA. ECONOMIC AND BUSINESS REVIEW. 1958-19?? q. University of Western Australia, Departments of Economics, Finance & Management, Nedlands, W.A. 6009, Australia.
Former titles: Economic Activity in Western Australia; Economic Activity (ISSN 0012-9925)

388　　　　　　CN
WESTERN AUTOBODY. 1988-1991 (Oct.). 5/yr. Sanford Evans Communications Ltd., 1077 St. James St., Box 6900, Winnipeg, Man. R3C 3B1, Canada.

796.95　　　US　ISSN 0738-8608
WESTERN BOATMAN. 1983-1990. bi-m. Poole Publications, Inc., 20700 Belshaw Ave., Carson, CA 90749-5427.

613.2　　　　　US
WESTERN HEMISPHERE NUTRITION CONGRESS. PROCEEDINGS. 1965-19?? triennial. (American Medical Association, Food & Nutrition Program) Wiley-Liss, Inc., 41 E. 11th St., New York, NY 10003.

5304 CESSATIONS

332.6 310   US   ISSN 0147-2410
WESTERN INVESTOR; investment information on publicly held companies in 13 Western States. (Supplement to: Western Investor Newsletter) 1971-1989. q. Willamette Publishing, Inc., 400 S.W. Sixth Ave., Ste. 1115, Portland, OR 97204.
Former titles: Northwest Stock Guide; Northwest Investment Tablistics (ISSN 0300-6840)

332.6   US   ISSN 0886-3768
HG4501
WESTERN INVESTOR NEWSLETTER; monitoring the publicly traded securities of the Great Northwest. 1971-1989. bi-w. Willamette Publishing, Inc., 400 S.W. Sixth Ave., Ste. 1115, Portland, OR 97204.
Formerly (until 1985): Northwest Investment Review (ISSN 0300-6824)

610   CN
WESTERN MEDICAL NEWS. 1978-1981. m. Western Medical News Ltd., 10216 128th St., Surrey, B.C. V3T 2Z3, Canada.

684.1   US
WESTERN MERCHANDISER. 1946-1989 (vol.12). s-a. Western Merchandise Mart, 1355 Market St., San Francisco, CA 94103.

674   CN
WESTERN RETAIL LUMBERMEN'S DIRECTORY. ceased. a. (Western Retail Lumbermen's Association) Naylor Communications Ltd. (Winnipeg) 100 Sutherland Ave., Winnipeg, Man. R2W 3C7, Canada.

330.9   AT   ISSN 0812-3470
WESTPAC BANKING CORPORATION. REVIEW. 1950-1990 (no.38). q. Westpac Banking Corporation, Economic Department, 60 Martin Place, Sydney, N.S.W. 2000, Australia.
Formerly (until 1982): Bank of New South Wales Review (ISSN 0522-2818)

179.3   US
WHALE CENTER JOURNAL. 1978-19?? q. (tabloid format) Whale Center, Fort Mason Center, No. F, San Francisco, CA 94123.
Formerly: Whale Center Newsletter.

387   AT
WHARFIE. 1967-1991. irreg. (Syndey Wharfie Group) Red Pen Publications, 635 Harris St., Ultimo, N.S.W. 2007, Australia.

384.5   UK   ISSN 0262-8481
WHAT C B; the citizens band magazine with the answers. (Citizens Band) 1981-1982 (Dec.). m. Link House Magazines Ltd., Link House, Dingwall Ave., Croydon, Surrey CR9 2TA, England.

791.4   US
WHAT C D?. (Compact Disc) ceased Apr. 1988. a. W G E Publishing, Box 278, Hancock, NH 03449.

770   UK
WHAT CAMERA?. 1988-1990 (vol.2, no.2). m. (back issues avail.) I P C Magzines Ltd., Prospect Magazines, Prospect House, 9-13 Ewell Rd., Cheam, Surrey SM1 4QQ, England.

630   US
WHAT'S DEVELOPING IN ALASKA. ceased. irreg. University of Alaska, Cooperative Extension Service, Fairbanks, AK 99701.

690   SI
WHAT'S NEW IN BUILDING. 1981-19?? m. (back issues avail.) Toucan Publications Pte Ltd., 322-C King George's Ave., Singapore 0820, Singapore.

581   US   ISSN 0193-0648
CODEN: WNPPDG
WHAT'S NEW IN PLANT PHYSIOLOGY. 1970-198? m. Houston Baker, 9411 Warfield Rd., Gaithersburg, MD 20760.

539.7   US
WHAT'S NEWS IN FUSION. 1980-1989. q. Fusion Power Associates, 2 Professional Dr., Ste. 248, Gaithersburg, MD 20879.

919.04   AT
WHAT'S ON IN AND AROUND TOOWOOMBA. ceased. fortn. Toowoomba and Golden West Regional Tourist Association Ltd., P.O. Box 3090, Town Hall, Toowoomba, Qld. 4350, Australia.

060   US   ISSN 0083-9167
WHERE AMERICA'S LARGE FOUNDATIONS MAKE THEIR GRANTS; who gets them and how much each receives. 1971-19?? irreg. Public Service Materials Center, 5130 Macarthur Blvd., N.W., Apt. 200, Washington, DC 20016-3316.

642.5 915   SI
WHERE TO EAT & ENTERTAIN - SINGAPORE. 1980-19?? a. Times Directories Private Ltd., 422 Thomson Rd., Singapore 1129, Singapore.

378.025   UK
WHICH DEGREE. 1963-1991. a. V N U Business Publications BV, 32-34 Broadwick St., London W1A 2HG, England.
Formerly: Which University (ISSN 0083-923X)

001.6 651.8   UK   ISSN 0265-6965
CODEN: WWPRDH
WHICH OFFICE SYSTEM?. (Supplement to: Which Computer?) 1980-1985. bi-m. E M A P National Publications Ltd., 20-22 Station Rd., Kettering, Northants NN15 7HH, England.
Former titles (until 1984): Which Word Processor and Office System? (ISSN 0263-7898); (until 1982): Which Word Processor? (ISSN 0143-6392)

384.55   UK   ISSN 0269-9354
WHICH VIDEO?. 1980-19?? m. (back issues avail.) Argus Specialist Publications Ltd., Argus House, Boundary Way, Hemels, Hampstead, Herts HP2 7ST, England.

028.1   UK   ISSN 0263-9432
WHITAKER'S CLASSIFIED MONTHLY BOOK LIST. 1983-198?; suspended. m. J. Whitaker & Sons Ltd., 12 Dyott St., London WC1A 1DF, England.

133   US   ISSN 0742-8820
WHITE LIGHT. 1974-1990 (vol.15, no.2). q. Light of Truth Church, Inc., Box 93124, Pasadena, CA 91109.

800   GW
WHITE RAVENS; A selection of international children's and youth literature. 1984-1991. a. Internationale Jugendbibliothek - International Youth Library, Schloss Blutenburg, 8000 Munich 60, Germany.

307   US   ISSN 0890-8028
WHOLE GAY CATALOG. (Supplement avail.: Lambda Rising News) 1983-1990; suspended. a. Lambda Rising, Inc., 1625 Connecticut Ave., N.W., Washington, DC 20009-1013.

613.2   US   ISSN 0888-2061
WHOLE LIFE; the journal of holistic health and natural living. 1986-1991. bi-m. (back issues avail.) Whole Life Enterprises, Inc., Box 2058, New York, NY 10159.

920   CN   ISSN 0847-2823
WHO'S SUCCEEDING. published only once, 1989. a. (back issues avail.) Info Globe, 444 Front St. W., Toronto, Ontario M5V 2S9, Canada.

657 370   US
WHO'S WHO AMONG CONTROLLERS TODAY. 1986-198? a. (back issues avail.) National Association of Accountants, Controllers Council, 10 Paragon Dr., Montvale, NJ 07645-1760.

780   US   ISSN 0362-3750
ML13
WHO'S WHO AMONG MUSIC STUDENTS IN AMERICAN HIGH SCHOOLS; a biographical dictionary of outstanding music students in American high schools. 1975-19?? irreg. Randall Publishing Co., Box 2029, Tuscaloosa, AL 35401.

378.1   US   ISSN 0148-6381
L901
WHO'S WHO AMONG VOCATIONAL AND TECHNICAL STUDENTS IN AMERICA. 1975-19?? a. Randall Publishing Co., Box 2029, Tuscaloosa, AL 35401.
Formerly: Who's Who Among Students in American Vocational and Technical Schools (ISSN 0360-5248)

338.47 658   US
WHO'S WHO IN BEER WHOLESALING. ceased 1989. irreg. National Beer Wholesalers Association, 5205 Leesburg Pike, Ste. 1600, Falls Church, VA 22041.

574 600   US   ISSN 0888-5982
WHO'S WHO IN BIOTECHNOLOGY. 1979-198? biennial. Gale Research Inc., Dept. 77748, Detroit, MI 48277-0748.

668.4 540   US   ISSN 0888-5958
WHO'S WHO IN CHEMISTRY & PLASTICS. 1979-198? biennial. Gale Research Inc., Dept. 77748, Detroit, MI 48277-0748.

624 550 531.64   US   ISSN 0888-5966
WHO'S WHO IN CIVIL ENGINEERING, EARTH SCIENCES & ENERGY. 1979-198? biennial. Gale Research Inc., Dept. 77748, Detroit, MI 48277-0748.

658 920   US   ISSN 0083-9485
HD69.C6
WHO'S WHO IN CONSULTING; a reference guide to professional personnel engaged in consultation for business, industry and government. 1968-1982. irreg. Gale Research Inc., Dept. 77748, Detroit, MI 48277-0748.

621.3 001.6 621.381US   ISSN 0888-5931
WHO'S WHO IN ELECTRONICS & COMPUTER SCIENCE. 1979-198? biennial. Gale Research Inc., Dept. 77748, Detroit, MI 48277-0748.

020 920   US
WHO'S WHO IN LIBRARY AND INFORMATION SERVICES. 1982; ceased same year. irreg. (reprint service avail. from UMI) American Library Association, 50 E. Huron St., Chicago, IL 60611-2795.

621 530   US   ISSN 0888-594X
WHO'S WHO IN MECHANICAL ENGINEERING & MATERIALS SCIENCE. 1979-198? biennial. Gale Research Inc., Dept. 77748, Detroit, MI 48277-0748.

535   US   ISSN 0888-5974
WHO'S WHO IN PHYSICS & OPTICS. 1979-198? biennial. Gale Research Inc., Dept. 77748, Detroit, MI 48277-0748.

920   UK
WHO'S WHO IN THE COMMONWEALTH. 1982-19?? irreg. Melrose Press Ltd., 3 Regal Lane, Soham, Ely, Cambridgeshire CB7 5BA, England.

791.4   UK
WHO'S WHO ON TELEVISION. 1984-1990. biennial. Boxtree Ltd., 36 Tavistock St., London WC2E 7PB, England.

330   US
WICHITA BUSINESS; Wichita's only magazine. 1967-1991. bi-m. Wichita Area Chamber of Commerce, 350 W. Douglas, Wichita, KS 67202.
Former titles: Wichita (ISSN 0043-5228); Wichita Trends.

283   GW
WIEDERHERSTELLUNG; dein Reich komme, dein Wille gesche, we im Himmel, so auf Erden. 1982-1989. q. (back issues avail.) Agape-Gemeinschaft e.V., Mathunistr. 23, D-8000 Munich 21, Germany.

053.1   AU   ISSN 0039-8934
WIENER TAGEBUCH; Zeitschrift fuer Kultur und Politik. 1970-1989. m. (Verein der Freunde des Wiener Tagebuch) Jentzsch & Co., Belvederegasse 10, A-1040 Vienna, Austria.
Formerly: Tagebuch.

330   AU
WIENER WIRTSCHAFTSBERICHTE. 1971-1986. 2/yr. Magistrat der Stadt Wien, Magistratsabteilung 4, Ebendorferstr. 2, A-1082 Vienna, Austria.
Formerly: Konjunkturbericht.

051   US   ISSN 1044-310X
WIGWAG. 1988-1991 (Dec.). m. Wigwag Magazine Company, Inc., 114 Horatio St., New York, NY 10014.

320 364 917.306   US
WILCOX REPORT NEWSLETTER. 1970-19??; suspended. irreg. (back issues avail.) Laird Wilcox, Box 2047, Olathe, KS 66061.
Formerly: Wilcox Report (ISSN 0049-7630)

574   GW
WILDBIOLOGISCHE INFORMATION FUER DEN JAEGER; Jagd und Hege Ausbildungsbuch. 1982-19?? irreg. Ferdinand Enke Verlag, Postfach 10 12 54, 7000 Stuttgart 10, Germany.

591 GW ISSN 0930-0856
WILDTIERE IN GEHEGEN. ceased 1991. bi-m. Verlag Eugen Ulmer GmbH, Postfach 700561, Wollgrasweg 41, 7000 Stuttgart 70, Germany.

001.64 621.381 US
WILEY SERIES IN COMPUTING. 1972-1992; suspended. irreg. John Wiley & Sons, Inc., 605 Third Ave., New York, NY 10158-0012.

620.7 US ISSN 0084-019X
WILEY SERIES ON SYSTEMS ENGINEERING AND ANALYSIS. 1980-19?? irreg. John Wiley & Sons, Inc., 605 Third Ave., New York, NY 10158-0012.

929 US ISSN 0883-9891
CS71
WILLETT HOUSE QUARTERLY. 1985-1989 (no.4). q. Willett House Ventures, Box 87, Foster, VA 23056-0087.

745.5 US
WILLIAMSBURG CRAFT SERIES. 1955-1965. irreg. Colonial Williamsburg Foundation, Box 1776, Williamsburg, VA 23187-1776.

917.1 CN
WILLOWDALE MONTH. 1979-1990 (Dec.). m. Thornhill Publications Ltd., P.O. Box 250, Thornhill, Ont. L3T 3N3, Canada.

621.387 US
WILSONLINES; the H.W. Wilson Company's Wilsonline Information System newsletter. 1986-198? irreg. H.W. Wilson Co., 950 University Ave., Bronx, NY 10452.

028.5 NE ISSN 0043-5678
WIMPEL. 1950-19?? 8/yr. Landelijk Centrum voor Gereformeerd Jeugdwerk, Postbus 99, 3970 AB Driebergen, Netherlands.

793 US
WIN THE LOTTERY TODAY. 1987-199?; suspended. m. Gambling Times, Inc., 16760 Stagg St., Ste. 213, Van Nuys, CA 91406.

808.81 US
WIND CHIMES. 1981-1989 (no.28). q. Wind Chimes Press, RR 1, Box 194A, Vienna, MD 21869-9735.

708.1 US ISSN 0049-7657
WIND ROSE. 1970-19?? bi-m. Mystic Seaport Museum, Inc., Mystic, CT 06355.

663.1 BE
WINES, ALCOHOL AND SPIRITS OF THE COMMON MARKET. YEARBOOK. ceased 1979. a. Editions Delta, Rue Scailquin 55, B-1030 Brussels, Belgium.

697 US ISSN 1045-8069
E169.04
WINTER LIVING; the essential guide to seasonal pleasures. 1978-1990. a. (back issues avail.) Guilford Publishing, Box 2008, Laconia, NH 03247.
Former titles (until 1990): Woodheat Woodstove Directory; Woodstove, Wood, Coal and Solar Equipment Directory (ISSN 0744-0820); Woodstove, Coalstove, Fireplace and Equipment Directory (ISSN 0271-5090)

807 700 US
WINTERFARE. 1973-198? a. Arts & Business Council, 130 E. 40th St., New York, NY 10016.

677 UK
WIRA SCAN. ceased. s-m. British Textile Technology Group Ltd., Wira House, West Park Ring Rd., Leeds LS16 6QL, England.

808.81 US
WIRE. 1981-19?? s-a. (back issues avail.) Progressive Press, 7320 Colonial, Dearborn Heights, MI 48127.

320 GW
WIRTSCHAFTS- UND GESELLSCHAFTSPOLITISCHE GRUNDINFORMATIONEN. 1959-19?? bi-m. Deutscher Instituts - Verlag GmbH, Gustav-Heinemann-Ufer 84-88, Postfach 510670, 5000 Cologne 51, Germany.
Formerly : Wirtschafts- und Sozialpolitische Grundinformationen.

330 AU ISSN 0259-0719
WIRTSCHAFTSUNIVERSITAET WIEN. DISSERTATIONEN. 1969-198? irreg. Verband der Wissenschaftlichen Gesellschaften Oesterreichs, Lindengasse 37, A-1070 Vienna, Austria.
Formerly: Hochschule fuer Welthandel in Wien. Dissertationen (ISSN 0507-7206)

330 GW ISSN 0043-633X
HB5
WIRTSCHAFTSWISSENSCHAFT. 1953-19?? m. Verlag Die Wirtschaft Berlin GmbH, Am Friedrichshain 22, 1055 Berlin 55, Germany.

810 370 US
WISCONSIN COUNCIL OF TEACHERS OF ENGLISH. SERVICE BULLETIN SERIES. no.24, 1979-198? irreg. Wisconsin Council of Teachers of English, Department of English, University of Wisconsin - Eau Claire, Eau Claire, WI 54701-4004.

614 US
WISCONSIN HEALTH CARE REPORT. 1968?-198? bi-m. Blue Cross & Blue Shield United of Wisconsin, Public Relations Department, 401 W. Michigan St., Milwaukee, WI 53201.
Supersedes (in 1980): Blue Cross of Wiscoonsin. News and Views.

910.202 US
WISCONSIN TRAVEL AND RECREATION GUIDE. ceased. a. Rockford Map Publishers, Inc., 4525 Forest View Ave., Box 6126, Rockford, IL 61125.

572 GW ISSN 0170-6977
CODEN: WUISD5
WISSENSCHAFT UND UMWELT. 1978-1988 (no.4). q. Friedr. Vieweg und Sohn Verlagsgesellschaft MbH, Postfach 5829, D-6200 Wiesbaden 1, Germany.

362 GW
WISSENSCHAFTLICHE BLAETTER ZU PROBLEMEN DES BLINDEN- UND SEHSCHWACHENWESENS. 1972-1991. s-a. Deutscher Blindenverband e.V., Bismarckallee 30, 5300 Bonn 2, Germany.

943 GW ISSN 0323-3499
WISSENSCHAFTLICHE MITTEILUNGEN. 1968-1991. 3/yr. Historiker Gesellschaft der DDR, Unter dem Linden 2, 1080 Berlin, Germany.
Formerly: Deutsche Historiker Gesellschaft, Berlin. Mitteilungen.

610 US ISSN 0271-9347
CODEN: WSYSD3
WISTAR SYMPOSIUM SERIES. 1980-19?? irreg. (Wistar Institute of Anatomy and Biology) Wiley-Liss, Inc., 41 E. 11th St., New York, NY 10003.

346 GW ISSN 0721-6890
K27
WISTRA. 1982-19?? s-m. (reprint service avail. from SCH) Verlag Dr. Peter Deubner GmbH, Fuerst-Puecklerstr. 30, Postfach 410268, 5000 Cologne, Germany.

747 645 GW ISSN 0138-2810
WOHNEN. 1978-1990. a. Zeitschriftenverlag fuer die Frau, Friedrich-Ebert-Str. 76-78, 7010 Leipzig, Germany.

053.1 GW ISSN 0138-2764
WOHNEN IM GRUENEN. ceased 1990. 3/yr. Zeitschriftenverlag fuer die Frau, Friedrich-Ebert-Str. 76, 7010 Leipzig, Germany.

051 US ISSN 0043-7239
WOMAN. 1980-1990 (Sep.). 9/yr. Conde Nast Publications, Inc., Woman Magazine, 350 Madison Ave., New York, NY 10017.

657 US ISSN 0043-7271
HF5601 CODEN: WCPAAR
WOMAN C P A. 1937-1990. q. (reprint service avail. from UMI) American Woman's Society of Certified Public Accountants, 111 E. Wacker Dr., No. 600, Chicago, IL 60601-4301.

747 US
WOMAN'S DAY COUNTRY DECORATING. 1988-19?? a. Hachette Magazines, Inc., Woman's Day Special Publications, 1633 Broadway, 45th Fl., New York, NY 10019.

641.5 US
WOMAN'S DAY DESSERT LOVER'S COOKBOOK. ceased. a. C B S Publications, Woman's Day, 1515 Broadway, New York, NY 10036.

635 US
WOMAN'S DAY HOUSE PLANTS. ceased. a. C B S Publications, Woman's Day, 1515 Broadway, New York, NY 10036.

658 330.1 US ISSN 0898-6126
WOMAN'S ENTERPRISE. 1988-19?? bi-m. Paisano Publications, Inc., 28210 Dorothy Dr., Box 3075, Agoura Hills, CA 91301.

305.412 US
WOMAN'S WEAL. 1984-198? m. J.R.H. Cruikshank Ltd., Box 264, Lynden, WA 98264.
Formerly: Woman's Advocate.

746.96 UK
WOMAN'S WORLD. 1977-1990. m. I P C Magazines Ltd., King's Reach Tower, Stamford St., London SE1 9LS, England.

028.5 US ISSN 0279-361X
WOMBAT; a journal of young people's writing and art. 1979-1991; suspended. 6/yr. (during school yr.). (also avail. in talking book; back issues avail.) Wombat, Inc., 365 Ashton Dr., Athens, GA 30606.

305.412 US
WOMEN; a world survey. 1985, published only once. irreg. World Priorities, Inc., Box 25140, Washington, DC 20007.

305.4 UN ISSN 0378-4770
HD6050
WOMEN AT WORK. ceased 1988. 2/yr. (also avail. in microform from UMI; microfiche from ILO) (International Labour Office) I L O Publications, CH-1211 Geneva 22, Switzerland.

052 054.1 053.1 GW ISSN 0043-7476
WOMEN OF THE WHOLE WORLD. 1951-1991. 6/yr. Women's International Democratic Federation, Unter den Linden 13, 1080 Berlin, Germany.

341.1 US ISSN 0042-9864
WOMEN STRIKE FOR PEACE. 1962-198? q. (also avail. in microform from UMI) 1930 Chestnut St., Ste. 1500, Philadelphia, PA 19103.

811 US
WOMEN TALKING, WOMEN LISTENING. 1975-19?? a. Women Talking, Women Listening Press, 420 N. Civic Dr., No. 302, Walnut Creek, CA 94596.

301.412 US ISSN 0276-7988
HQ1402
WOMEN'S ANNUAL. 1980-1985. a. G.K. Hall & Co., 70 Lincoln St., Boston, MA 02111.

613.7 US
WOMEN'S HEALTH & FITNESS NEWS. 1986-1991. 12/yr. Weight Watchers Magazine, 360 Lexington Ave., New York, NY 10017.

370 CN
WOMEN'S NETWORK/RESEAU FEMMES. ceased (vol.5, no.1). irreg. (approx. 4/yr.). Federation Nationale des Enseignants et des Enseignantes du Quebec, 1601 rue de Lorimer, Montreal, Que. H2K 4M5, Canada.
Former titles: Info-F N E E Q; (until 1983): Nouveau Pouvoir.

305.412 US ISSN 0882-1135
WOMEN'S QUARTERLY REVIEW. 1984-1989. q. (tabloid format; back issues avail.) Errante Publications, 165 Christopher St., New York, NY 10150.

790.1 UK
WOMEN'S SQUASH RACKETS ASSOCIATION. HANDBOOK. 1934-1989. a. Women's Squash Rackets Association, 345 Upper Richmond Rd. W., Sheen, London SW14 8QN, England.

910.09 US ISSN 0882-8458
WOMEN'S TRAVEL CONNECTIONS. 1983-19?? m. (looseleaf format; back issues avail.) Travel Trends Publishing, Inc., Box 6117, New York, NY 10150.
Formerly (until 1984): Connections, the Businesswoman's Travel Newsletter.

917.59 US
WOODALL'S CAMPGROUND DIRECTORY. ARIZONA, NEW MEXICO EDITION. ceased 1988. a. Woodall Publishing Co., 100 Corporate N., Ste. 100, Bannockburn, IL 60015.
Formerly: Woodall's Campground Directory. Arizona Edition (ISSN 0162-7384)

CESSATIONS

917.59   US   ISSN 0163-5328
WOODALL'S CAMPGROUND DIRECTORY. ARKANSAS, MISSOURI EDITION. ceased 1988. a. Woodall Publishing Co., 100 Corporate N., Ste. 100, Bannockburn, IL 60015.

917.59   US
WOODALL'S CAMPGROUND DIRECTORY. CALIFORNIA, NEVADA, MEXICO EDITION. ceased 1988. a. Woodall Publishing Co., 100 Corporate N., Bannockburn, IL 60015.
Formerly: Woodall's Campground Directory. California Edition (ISSN 0162-7392)

917.59   US   ISSN 0163-5344
WOODALL'S CAMPGROUND DIRECTORY. COLORADO EDITION. ceased 1988. a. Woodall Publishing Co., 100 Copporate N., Ste. 100, Bannockburn, IL 60015.

917.59   US
WOODALL'S CAMPGROUND DIRECTORY. DELAWARE, MARYLAND, VIRGINIA, DISTRICT OF COLUMBIA EDITION. ceased 1988. a. Woodall Publishing Co., 100 Corporate N., Ste. 100, Bannockburn, IL 60015.

917.59   US
WOODALL'S CAMPGROUND DIRECTORY. FLORIDA EDITION. 1973-1988. a. Woodall Publishing Co., 100 Corporate N., Ste. 100, Bannockburn, IL 60015.
Formerly: Woodall's Campground Directory. Florida Campgrounds Edition (ISSN 0090-5151)

917.59   US
WOODALL'S CAMPGROUND DIRECTORY. IDAHO, OREGON, WASHINGTON, BRITISH COLUMBIA EDITION. ceased 1988. a. Woodall Publishing Co., 100 Corporate N., Ste. 100, Bannockburn, IL 60015.
Formerly: Woodall's Campground Directory. Idaho, Oregon, Washington Edition (ISSN 0163-2493)

917.59   US   ISSN 0163-2485
WOODALL'S CAMPGROUND DIRECTORY. ILLINOIS, INDIANA EDITION. ceased 1988. a. Woodall Publishing Co., 100 Corporate N., Ste. 100, Bannockburn, IL 60015.

917.59   US   ISSN 0163-5336
WOODALL'S CAMPGROUND DIRECTORY. KENTUCKY, TENNESSEE EDITION. ceased 1988. a. Woodall Publishing Co., 100 Corporate N., Ste. 100, Bannockburn, IL 60015.

917.59   US   ISSN 0163-0121
WOODALL'S CAMPGROUND DIRECTORY. MICHIGAN EDITION. ceased 1988. a. Woodall Publishing Co., 100 Corporate N., Ste. 100, Bannockburn, IL 60015.

917.59   US
WOODALL'S CAMPGROUND DIRECTORY. MINNESOTA, WISCONSIN EDITION. ceased 1988. a. Woodall Publishing Co., 100 Corporate N., Ste. 100, Bannockburn, IL 60015.
Formerly: Woodall's Campground Directory. Wisconsin Edition (ISSN 0163-0105)

917.59   US   ISSN 0163-0083
WOODALL'S CAMPGROUND DIRECTORY. NEW ENGLAND STATES EDITION. ceased 1988. a. Woodall Publishing Co., 100 Corporate N., Ste. 100, Bannockburn, IL 60015.

917.59   US
WOODALL'S CAMPGROUND DIRECTORY. NEW JERSEY, OHIO, PENNSYLVANIA EDITIONS. ceased 1988. a. Woodall Publishing Co., 100 Corporate N., Ste. 100, Bannockburn, IL 60015.
Formerly: Woodall's Campground Directory. Ohio, Pennsylvania Editions (ISSN 0163-1950)

917.59   US
WOODALL'S CAMPGROUND DIRECTORY. NEW YORK EDITION. ceased 1988. a. Woodall Publishing Co., 100 Corporate N., Ste.100, Bannockburn, IL 60015.
Formerly: Woodall's Campground Directory. New Jersey, New York Edition (ISSN 0163-0113)

917.59   US   ISSN 0163-5352
WOODALL'S CAMPGROUND DIRECTORY. NORTH CAROLINA, SOUTH CAROLINA EDITION. ceased 1988. a. Woodall Publishing Co., 100 Corporate N., Ste. 100, Bannockburn, IL 60015.

917.59   US   ISSN 0163-240X
WOODALL'S CAMPGROUND DIRECTORY. ONTARIO EDITION. ceased 1988. a. Woodall Publishing Co., 100 Corporate N., Ste. 100, Bannockburn, IL 60015.

917.59   US
WOODALL'S CAMPGROUND DIRECTORY. TEXAS, MEXICO EDITION. ceased 1988. a. Woodall Publishing Co., 100 Corporate N., Bannockburn, IL 60015.
Formerly: Woodall's Campground Directory. Texas Edition (ISSN 0162-7376)

360   US   ISSN 0163-4321
WOODALL'S SENIOR EXCHANGE. ceased. bi-m. Woodall Publishing Co., 28167 N. Keith Dr., Lake Forest, IL 60045.

808.81   US
WOODRIDER. ceased. s-a. Lake City Community College, Rt. 3, Box 7, Lake City, FL 32055.

698.3   US
WOODSMITH SOURCEBOOK. 1986-19?? a. Woodsmith Publishing Co., 2200 Grand Ave., Des Moines, IA 50312.

338.4   UK
WOODWORKING INDUSTRY - BUYERS' GUIDE. 1945-19?? a. Benn Publications Ltd., Sovereign Way, Tonbridge TN9 1RW, England.
Formerly: Woodworking Industry - Directory (ISSN 0084-120X)

636   NZ
WOOL. ceased 1989. a. Massey Wool Association (Inc.), P.O. Box 12342, Wellington North, New Zealand.

800   US
WORD & IMAGE; the illustrated journal. 1986-1991 (vol.6, no.12). s-a. 436 Deer Lake Dr., Nashville, TN 37221-2107.

651.8   UK
WORD & INFORMATION PROCESSING. (Supplement to: Business Systems & Equipment) 1978-198? q. Maclean Hunter Ltd., Maclean Hunter House, Chalk Lane, Cockfosters Rd., Barnet, Herts. EN4 OBU, England.
Formerly: Word Processing Now (ISSN 0144-2066)

001.6 651.8   US
WORD PROCESSING NEWS. (Update to: Datapro Reports on Word Processing) ceased. m. Datapro Information Services Group (Subsidiary of: McGraw-Hill, Inc.), 600 Delran Pkwy., Delran, NJ 08075.

301.412   US
WORDS OF WOMEN. 1983-198? q. (back issues avail.) Hartford Feminist Library, c/o Hill Center, 33 Freeman St., Hartford, CT 06114.

338   US
WORK-AT-HOME REPORT. 1989-19?? bi-m. (back issues avail.) Home Business News, 12221 Beaver Pike, Jackson, OH 45640.

331   US
WORK LIFE REVIEW. 1982-198? 4/yr. (back issues avail.) Michigan Quality of Work Life Council, 11169 Glenish, Sterling Heights, MI 48077.

320   LU
WORK OF THE EUROPEAN PARLIAMENT; survey of the main activities of the European Parliament. 1984-19?? a. European Parliament, Directorate General for Research, L-2929 Luxembourg, Luxembourg.
Formerly: Progress Towards European Integration.

331.1   US
WORK STOPPAGES IN NEW YORK STATE. ceased. m. Department of Labor, Division of Research and Statistics, One Main St., 9th Fl., Brooklyn, NY 11201.

320   US
WORKERS TRIBUNE/TRIBUNA OBRERA. 1981-198? m. (back issues avail.) (Worker's Tribune) New International Distributors, Box 471, Ansonia Sta., New York, NY 10023.

320.532   UK
WORKERS WEEKLY. 1972-1988. w. (tabloid format) Workers Weekly Publications, 10 Athol St., Belfast BT12 4GX, Northern Ireland.

621.381 551.46   US
WORKING SYMPOSIUM ON OCEANOGRAPHIC DATA SYSTEMS. PROCEEDINGS. (1987 Symposium held as part of Oceans '87) 1975-1986. irreg. (Institute of Electrical and Electronics Engineers, Inc.) I E E E Computer Society Press, 10662 Los Vaqueros Circle, Los Alamitos, CA 90720-1264.
Formerly: Working Conference on Oceanographic Laboratory Systems. Proceedings.

613.7   US
WORKOUT; for fitness. 1984-1985 (vol.1). m. Stewart Publishing Co., c/o Stewart Communications, 9171 Wilshire Blvd., No. 525, Beverly Hills, CA 90210-5530.

690   NZ
WORKS NEWS. 1969-19?? bi-m. (Ministry of Works and Development) Percival Publishing Co. Ltd., P.O. Box 52-116, Kingsland, Auckland 3, New Zealand.

745.5   UK
WORKSHOP MASTERS. 1989-1991. bi-m. T E E Publishing, Edwards Centre, Regent St., Hinckley LE10 0BB, England.

621.815   US
WORKSHOP ON COMPUTER ARCHITECTURE FOR PATTERN ANALYSIS AND MACHINE INTELLIGENCE. 1981-1985. biennial. (Institute of Electrical and Electronics Engineers, Inc.) I E E E Computer Society Press, 10662 Los Vaqueros Circle, Los Alamitos, CA 90720-1264.
Formerly: I E E E Computer Society Workshop on Computer Architecture for Pattern Analysis and Image Database Management. Proceedings.

001.642   US
WORKSHOP ON SOFTWARE TESTING, VERIFICATION, AND ANALYSIS. PROCEEDINGS. 1986-1988. biennial. (Institute of Electrical and Electronics Engineers, Inc.) I E E E Computer Society Press, 10662 Los Vaqueros Circle, Los Alamitos, CA 90720-1264.
Formerly (until 1986): Workshop on Software Testing. Proceedings.

551.46   US
WORLD AQUACULTURE SOCIETY. PROCEEDINGS. ceased. q. World Aquaculture Society, 341 Pleasant Hall, Baton Rouge, LA 70803.

551.46   US
WORLD AQUACULTURE SOCIETY. SPECIAL PUBLICATIONS. ceased. irreg. World Aquaculture Society, 341 Pleasant Hall, Baton Rouge, LA 70803.

686   UK
WORLD BOOK INDUSTRY. published only once, 1986. irreg. Euromonitor Publications, 87-88 Turnmill St., London EC1M 5QU, England.

551.5   UK   ISSN 0957-9370
                                  CODEN: WCCREH
WORLD CLIMATE CHANGE REPORT. 1989-19?? m. (back issues avail.) B N A International, Inc. (Subsidiary of: The Bureau of National Affairs, Inc.), 17 Dartmouth St., London SW1H 9BL, England.

910.2   FR   ISSN 0070-6515
WORLD DIRECTORY OF TRAVEL AGENCIES. 1950-1988; suspended. a. International Hotel Association, 80 rue de la Roquette, 75011 Paris, France.

330   US
WORLD ECONOMIC HISTORY. ceased. irreg. Cornell University Press, 124 Roberts Place, Ithaca, NY 14850.

330.9   US   ISSN 0896-2545
                                  CODEN: WEMOE4
WORLD ECONOMIC MONITOR. 1986-1989. q. Conference Board, Inc., 845 Third Ave., New York, NY 10022.

374 613.9 338.91   US   ISSN 0300-7006
LC5163.D44
WORLD EDUCATION REPORTS; a journal of program developments in the field of Third World and US nonformal education for community development. 1972-1981 (Apr.); resumed 1985-1990 (no.29); suspended. 2/yr. (back issues avail.) World Education, Inc., 210 Lincoln St., Boston, MA 02111.

531.64 US
WORLD ENERGY SURVEY. 1979-19?? irreg. (Rockefeller Foundation) World Priorities, Inc., Box 25140, Washington, DC 20007.

312 NE
WORLD FERTILITY SURVEY. ANNUAL REPORTS. 1975-1985. a. International Statistical Institute, 428 Prinses Beatrixlaan, Box 950, 2270 AZ Voorburg, Netherlands.
 Former titles: World Fertility Survey. Progress Reports; Fertility Survey. Report.

338.1 UN ISSN 0084-179X
WORLD FOOD PROBLEMS. 1956-19?? irreg. Food and Agriculture Organization of the United Nations, c/o UNIPUB, 4611-F Assembly Dr., Lanham, MD 20706-4391.

664 US
WORLD FOOD PRODUCTION CONFERENCE SUMMARY REPORT. ceased. s-a. I M C Fertilizer Inc., 501 E. Lange St., Mundlein, IL 60060.
 Incorporates: Latin American Food Production Conference Summary Report.

634.9 SP ISSN 0084-1811
WORLD FORESTRY CONGRESS. PROCEEDINGS. ceased. irreg. Direccion General de Montes, Ministerio de Agricultura, Paseo de Infanta Isabel, Madrid, Spain.

685 380.1 HK
WORLD LEATHERLOGUE (YEAR). 1989; suspended in Apr. same year. a. (back issues avail) Headway International Publications Co., 9-F, Sing-Ho Finance Bldg., 168 Gloucester Rd., Hong Kong, Hong Kong.

320.531 CN ISSN 0043-8642
WORLD MARXIST REVIEW; problems of peace and socialism. 1958-1990. m. (also avail. in microform from UMI; reprint service avail. from UMI; back issues avail.) Progress Books, 71 Bathurst St. 3rd Floor, Toronto, Ont. M5V 2P6, Canada.

610 UK ISSN 0043-8669
WORLD MEDICINE; the medical newsmagazine. 1965-198? m. Reed Healthcare Commications Ltd., Fiary Court, 13-21 High St., Guilford, Surrey GU1 3DX, England.

551.3 UN ISSN 0251-8945
WORLD METEOROLOGICAL ORGANIZATION. COMMISSION FOR SPECIAL APPLICATIONS OF METEOROLOGY AND CLIMATOLOGY. ABRIDGED FINAL REPORT OF THE (NO.) SESSION. 1971-1978. World Meteorological Organization, Commission for Special Applications of Meteorology and Climatology, 41 Av. Giuseppe-Motta, CH-1211 Geneva 20, Switzerland.

283 US
WORLD MISSION. 1979-198? 10/yr. Episcopal Church of the United States, Mission Information Office, 815 Second Ave., New York, NY 10017.

636 633.2 UK
WORLD POULTRY. 1936-199? m. Reed Business Publishing Group, Carew Division (Subsidiary of: Reed International PLC), Quadrant House, The Quadrant, Sutton, Surrey SM2 5AS, England.

333.33 UK
WORLD PROPERTY. 198?-199? m? Builder Group plc, 1 Millharbour, London E13 9RA, England.

796.342 US ISSN 0043-910X
GV991
WORLD TENNIS. 1953-1991. m. (also avail. in microform from UMI; microfiche from KTO) Family Media, Inc., Men's and In-Home Group, 3 Park Ave., New York, NY 10016.
 Incorporates: American Lawn Tennis; Raquet.

382 UK
WORLD TRADE INDEX. 1975-1991. a. (back issues avail.) Eagle Commercial Publications Ltd., 185 Angel Place, Fore St., London N18 2UD, England.

382 US ISSN 0884-495X
WORLD TRADE REPORT. 1944; N.S. 1985-1989 (Dec.). m. New York Chamber of Commerce and Industry, Inc., 200 Madison Ave., New York, NY 10016-3989.
 Formerly: World Trade Bulletin (ISSN 0043-9150)

331.88 CS ISSN 0306-4824
WORLD TRADE UNION MOVEMENT. 1949-1992; suspended. q. World Federation of Trade Unions, Branicka 112, 140 00 Prague 4, Czechoslovakia.

621.381 001.535 UK
WORLD YEARBOOK OF NEW GENERATION COMPUTING RESEARCH AND DEVELOPMENT. 1988-19?? s-a. Kogan Page Ltd., 1120 Pentonville Rd., London N1 9JN, England.
 Formerly: World Yearbook of Fifth Generation Computing Research and Development.

808 US ISSN 0738-095X
WORLD'S GREATEST LOVE STORIES. ceased. 5/yr. Digest Publishing Inc., 158 Linwood Plaza, Fort Lee, NJ 07024.

700 US ISSN 0043-9363
N1
WORLDWIDE ART CATALOGUE BULLETIN. 1963-1992. q. Worldwide Books, 1001 W. Seneca St., Ithaca, NY 14850-3329.

620 US ISSN 0091-4800
HD69.I7
WORLDWIDE PROJECTS. 1967-198? 9/yr. Intercontinental Publications, Inc., 15 Ketchum St., Box 5017, Westport, CT 06881.
 Formerly: Worldwide Projects and Installation Planning (ISSN 0043-9398)

910.09 US
WORLDWIDE TRAVEL PLANNER. 1974-19?? bi-m. Wineberg Publications, 7842 N. Lincoln Ave., Skokie, IL 60077.
 Formerly: Happy Wanderer.

363.37 AT
WORMALD JOURNAL. 1967-19??; suspended. q. Wormald International Ltd., Alexander and Ernest Sts., Crows Nest, N.S.W. 2065, Australia.
 Formerly: Alert (Crows Nest) (ISSN 0044-7242)

808.8 CN ISSN 0709-4035
WOT. 1979-198? s-a. (back issues avail.) Wot Publications, 657 Ardmore Dr., R.R. 2, Sidney, B.C. V8L 3S1, Canada.

612 US ISSN 0892-9955
PS508.A44
WRITE AGE; first magazine of writing therapy. 1986-1990 (Fall-Winter). 2/yr. (back issues avail.) McCormick & Schilling, N82 W15855 Valley View Dr., Menomonee Falls, WI 53051.

820 US
WRITERS & THEIR WORK. 1950-19?? 6/yr. (back issues avail.) (British Council) British Book Centre (Subsidiary of: Pergamon Press Inc.), Maxwell House, Fairview Park, Elmsford, NY 10523.
 Formerly: Survey of the Work of British Writers (ISSN 0039-6311)

819 US
WRITERS' BAR-B-Q. 1987-1992. s-a. (back issues avail.) Sangamon Writers, Inc., 924 Bryn Mawr Blvd., Springfield, IL 62703.

800 US
WRITERS-IN-WAITING NEWSLETTER. 1986-19?? bi-m. (back issues avail.) B J O's Enterprises, 837 Archie St., Eugene, OR 97402.

800 US
WRITER'S INFO. 1985-1992. m. (back issues avail.) Hutton Publications, Box 1870, Hayden, ID 83835.

808 US ISSN 0741-9821
WRITERS WEST. 1982-199? bi-m. (back issues avail.) Box 16097, San Diego, CA 92116.

371 US
WRITING TEACHER (ORONO). 1983-1986. 2/yr. (back issues avail.) National Poetry Foundation, 302 Neville Hall, University of Maine, Orono, ME 04469.

973 016 US
WRITINGS ON AMERICAN HISTORY; a subject bibliography of articles. 1962-1990. a. (back issues avail.; reprint service avail. from KTO) (American Historical Association) Kraus International Publications (Subsidiary of: Kraus Organization Ltd.), Route 100, Millwood, NY 10546.

614.8 US
WYOMING. CHARACTERISTICS OF RECORDABLE OCCUPATIONAL INJURIES AND ILLNESSES (YEAR). 1978-1988. a. Department of Labor and Statistics, Herschler Building, Cheyenne, WY 82002.
 Formerly: Wyoming. Characteristics of Occupational Injuries and Illnesses (Year).

663 US ISSN 0043-9673
WYOMING BEVERAGE ANALYST. (Subseries of: Northwest Beverage Analyst) 1936-1990 (Dec.). m. Bell Publications, Beverage Analyst Group, 2403 Champa St., Denver, CO 80205.

020 US ISSN 0043-9738
Z671
WYOMING LIBRARY ROUNDUP. 1942-1990. 3/yr. (also avail. in microform from UMI; reprint service avail. from UMI) State Library, Supreme Court Bldg., Cheyenne, WY 82002.

001.3 PH ISSN 0084-3229
XAVIER UNIVERSITY. MUSEUM AND ARCHIVES PUBLICATIONS. 1970-19?? irreg. (processed) Xavier University, Cagayan de Oro 8401, Philippines.

794.1 GW ISSN 0934-5418
XIANG QI; Chinesisches Schach. 1986-198? q. (back issues avail.) Verlag Ute Schiller, Postfach 650 648, D-1000 Berlin 65, Germany.

294 US
Y O!; a global laserletter. (Yes Osho!) ceased 1991 (Jan.). w. Chidvilas, Inc., Box 17550, Dept. 99, Boulder, CO 80308.

334 FI ISSN 0355-9378
Y V. (Yhteisvoimin) 1949-1990. m. Op Julkaisut Oy - Central Association of the Co-Operative Banks, Arkadiankatu 23, SF-00100 Helsinki 10, Finland.
 Formerly: Yhteisvoimin - Together.

796.95 US ISSN 0748-805X
YACHT. 1983-1990. bi-m. (also avail. in microform from UMI; back issues avail.) Romaine Pierson Publishers, Inc., 80 Shore Rd., Port Washington, NY 11050.

797.1 US
YACHTING'S BOAT BUYERS GUIDE. 1959-1986. a. C B S Magazines, Yachting Department, One Park Ave., New York, NY 10016.
 Formerly: Boat Owners Buyers Guide (ISSN 0067-9321)

830 US ISSN 0084-3334
YALE GERMANIC STUDIES. 1964-19?? irreg. Yale University Press, 92A Yale Sta., New Haven, CT 06520.

879.9 US ISSN 0084-3423
YALE ROMANIC STUDIES. SECOND SERIES. 1951-19?? irreg. Yale University Press, 92A Yale Sta., New Haven, CT 06520.

891.8 US ISSN 0084-3431
YALE RUSSIAN AND EAST EUROPEAN STUDIES. 1966-19?? irreg. Yale University Press, 92A Yale Sta., New Haven, CT 06520.

001.6 621.381 IS
YARCHON YISRAELI LEMACHSHEVAI P C VETOAMIM. ceased 1990 (Apr.). bi-m. Technosdar Ltd., P.O. Box 31684, Tel Aviv 61316, Israel.

746 US ISSN 0882-7982
YARN MARKET NEWS. 1978-1988. 6/yr. Butterick Co., Inc., 161 Ave. of the Americas, New York, NY 10013.

610 371 US ISSN 8756-3460
RM930.A1
YEAR BOOK OF REHABILITATION. ceased. a. Year Book Medical Publishers, Inc., 200 N. LaSalle, Chicago, IL 60601.

745.5 AT ISSN 0818-917X
YEARBOOK OF SOUTH AUSTRALIAN CRAFTS (YEAR). 1985-19?? irreg. (back issues avail.) Crafts Council of South Australia Inc., 169 Payneham Rd., St. Peters, S.A. 5069, Australia.

CESSATIONS

610   US   ISSN 1050-219X
RC423.A1
YEAR BOOK OF SPEECH, LANGUAGE AND HEARING. 1990-1991. a. Mosby - Year Book, Inc. (Chicago) (Subsidiary of: Times Mirror Company), 200 N. LaSalle St., Chicago, IL 60601-1080.

811   US
YEARBOOK OF WORKS RE APPALACHIA. 1969-19?? a. (tabloid format; also avail. in record) Morris Harvey College Publications, Charleston, WV 25304.

327 335   US   ISSN 0084-4101
HX1
YEARBOOK ON INTERNATIONAL COMMUNIST AFFAIRS; parties and revolutionary movements. 1966-1991. a. (back issues avail.) (Hoover Institution on War, Revolution and Peace) Hoover Institution Press, Stanford University, Stanford, CA 94305-6010.

320.531 340   US   ISSN 0887-9117
K29
YEARBOOK ON SOCIALIST LEGAL SYSTEMS. 1986-19?? a. Transnational Juris Publications, Inc., Box 7282, Ardsley-on-Hudson, NY 10503.

342   II
YEARLY DIGEST. (Includes: Annual Consolidated Volume) 1950-19?? m. Madras Law Journal Office, Box 604, Mylapore, Madras 4, India.

364   II   ISSN 0513-2088
YEARLY DIGEST OF CRIMINAL CASES. (Includes: Annual Consolidated Volume) ceased. m. Madras Law Journal Office, Box 604, Mylapore, Madras 4, India.

808.838   US
YEAR'S BEST FANTASY STORIES. 1975-198? a. DAW Books, Inc., 1633 Broadway, New York, NY 10014-3658.

631   IS
YEDIOT HAMASKIRUT. 1968-199? m. Israel Fruit Growers Association, P.O. Box 40007, Tel Aviv 61400, Israel.

410 296 800   IS
YIDDISH LITERARY AND LINGUISTIC PERIODICALS AND MISCELLANIES; a selective annotated bibliography. 1982-198? irreg. Association for the Study of Jewish Languages, 1610 Eshkol Tower, University of Haifa, Mount Carmel, Haifa 31 999, Israel.

069 708   IS   ISSN 0334-1798
YISRAEL-AM VE-ERETZ/ISRAEL - PEOPLE AND LAND. 1984-1989. a. Ha-Aretz Museum - Eretz Israel Museum, P.O. Box 17068, Ramat Aviv, Tel Aviv, Israel.

929   US
YODER RESEARCH. 1982-1990. a. (looseleaf format) Yoder Family History Research, 1422 Wealthy S.E., Grand Rapids, MI 49506.
Formerly: Yoder Family History Research Newsletter.

387   JA
YOKOHAMA PORT ACTIVITIES. ?-19?? a. Port and Harbor Bureau, Industry & Trade Center Bldg., Yamashita-cho, Makaku, Yokohama, Japan.

614.42   US
YOU AND YOUR HEALTH. 1985-19?? 6/yr. Box AP, Los Altos, CA 94023.

051   US
YOU MAGAZINE. 1988-1990. m. America's 20th Century Beauty Pageant, Box 9217, Brae, CA 92622-9217.

643.3   US
YOUNG EXECUTIVES SOCIETY. ceased. q. National Appliance Parts Suppliers Association, 600 S. Federal St., Ste. 400, Chicago, IL 60605.

001.6 621.381   UK   ISSN 0269-8277
YOUR COMMODORE. 1984-19?? m. (back issues avail.) Argus Specialist Publications Ltd., Argus House, Boundary Way, Hemels, Hampstead, Herts HP2 7ST, England.

338 621.381   US
YOUR COMPUTER CAREER; the computer career planning newspaper. 1985-198? 3/yr. (back issues avail.) Data Processing Management Association, 505 Busse Highway, Park Ridge, IL 60068-3191.

362.7   US
YOUR FAMILY. 1989-1991. 10/yr. Family Media, Inc., Women's and Fashion Group, Three Park Ave., New York, NY 10016.

821   AT
YOUR FRIENDLY FASCIST. 1970-1986. irreg. Pig's Arse Press, P.O. Box 297, Summer Hill, N.S.W. 2130, Australia.

353.9 338.1   US   ISSN 0094-9914
HE356.A8
YOUR HIGHWAY DEPARTMENT, ARKANSAS. ceased. State Highway and Transportation Department, Box 2261, Little Rock, AR 72203.

636   US
YOUR PET PARADE. 1989-19?? 5/yr. (back issues avail.) Right Here Publications, Box 1014, Huntington, IN 46750.

658 338   AT   ISSN 0817-2455
YOUR PHARMACY. 1986-1990 (Dec.). m. (back issues avail.) Medicine Group Publishing House, 199 Condamine St., Balgowlah, N.S.W. 2093, Australia.

133.5   UK   ISSN 0267-4610
YOUR STARS. 1985-19?? 12/yr. Your Stars Magazines, Sovereign House, Brentwood, Essex CM14 4SE, England.

028.5 369.4   AT   ISSN 0814-4125
YOUTH AFFAIRS IN AUSTRALIA. 1985-19?? m. (back issues avail.) Youth Affairs Council of Australia, Suite 1, 250 Gore St., Fitzvory, Vic. 3065, Australia.

369.4   FR   ISSN 0254-9662
YOUTH OF THE 21. 1984-19?? s-a. (back issues avail) Council of Europe, B.P. 431 R6, 67006 Strasbourg, France.

155 362.7   CN
YOUTH POLICY TODAY. 1985-1989. q. Canadian Youth Foundation (C.Y.F.), 2211 Riverside Dr., Suite 11, Ottawa, Ont. K1H 7X2, Canada.
Former titles: Youth Policy Network; (until 1986): Friend's Network.

540   YU   ISSN 0351-0085
YUGOSLAV CHEMICAL PAPERS. 1977-1987. bi-m. Unija Kemijskih Drustava SFR Jugoslavije, Hrvatsko Kemijsko Drustvo, Marulicev trg 19, 41000 Zagreb, Croatia, Yugoslavia.

910 011   CN
YUKON BIBLIOGRAPHY UPDATE. 1970-1984. irreg. (back issues avail.) Canadian Circumpolar Library, B-03 Cameron, University of Alberta, Edmonton, Alta. T6G 2E9, Canada.

943.8 329.9   PL   ISSN 0137-6381
Z DZIEJOW STOSUNKOW POLSKO-RADZIECKICH I ROZWOJU WSPOLNOTY PANSTW SOCJALISTYCZNYCH. 1965-1987 (vol.11). 2/yr. Panstwowe Wydawnictwo Naukowe, Ul. Miodowa 10, 00-251 Warsaw, Poland.
Formerly (until 1977): Z Dziejow Stosunkow Polsko-Radzieckich (ISSN 0084-4438)

539.7   GW   ISSN 0323-8776
QD601.A1   CODEN: ZIMIDC
Z F I - MITTEILUNGEN. 1974-19?? irreg., no.18, 1979. (also avail. in microfiche) Akademie der Wissenschaften der DDR, Zentralinstitut fuer Isotopen- und Strahlenforschung, Permoserstr. 15, 7050 Leipzig, Germany.

671.52   GW   ISSN 0863-2162
    CODEN: ZISRE2
Z I S - REPORT. 1959-1990. m. Zentralinstitut fuer Schweisstechnik der DDR, Koethener Str. 33a, 4060 Halle-Saale, Germany.
Formerly: Z I S Mitteilungen (ISSN 0044-1465)

808.8 070   US   ISSN 0892-9696
Z MISCELLANEOUS. 1987-1990 (vol.4, no.2). q. (back issues avail.) Again & Again Press, Box 20041, Cherokee Sta., New York, NY 10028.

383 384   GW
Z P T. (Zeitschrift fuer das Post- und Telekommunikation) 1949-1991. m. (Deutsche Bundespost) Josef Keller Verlag, Postfach 1440, 8130 Starnberg, Germany.
Formerly: Z P F - Zeitschrift fuer das Post- und Fernmeldewesen (ISSN 0342-2119)

378 370   GW
Z V S - KURZINFO. 1979-1990. s-a. Zentralstelle fuer die Vergabe von Studienplaetzen, Sonnenstr. 171, Postfach 8000, 4600 Dortmund 1, Germany.

621.381   UK
Z X COMPUTING. 1982-19?? 6/yr. Argus Specialist Publications Ltd., Argus House, Boundary Way, Hemels, Hampstead, Herts. HP2 7ST, England.

286   NE   ISSN 0044-1562
ZAAIER. 1912-1990. m. Unie van Baptisten Gemeenten, c/o "De Vinkenhof", Biltseweg 10, 3735 MC Bosch en Duin, Netherlands.

617.6   GW   ISSN 0513-7926
ZAHNTECHNIK; Zeitschrift fuer Theorie und Praxis der stomatologischen Technik. 1960-19?? bi-m. (Medizinische Fachschule an der Fachpoliklinik fuer Stomatologie) Verlag Gesundheit GmbH, Neue Gruenstr. 18, 1020 Berlin, Germany.

323.4 327   BE
ZAIRE MONTHLY. 1986-1990 (vol.4). 10/yr. Comite Zaire, P.O. Box 25, B-3000 Leuven 3, Belgium.

943.9   HU   ISSN 0200-5344
ZALAI TUKOR. 1974-1975 (Jan.). 2/yr. Zala Megyei Tanacs V.B. Muvelodeusugyi Osztalya, 8901 Zalaegerszeg, P.F. 16, Hungary.

057   IT
ZALIV; revija za knjizevnost in kulturo. 1966-1990. q. Salita a Contovello 23, 34136 Trieste-Trst, Italy.

020 610   CS   ISSN 0139-6587
ZDRAVOTNICKA DOKUMENTACE. 1962-19?? bi-m. Ustav Vedeckych Lekarskych Informaci, Vitezneho Unora 31, 121 32 Prague 2, Czechoslovakia.

296   US
ZEIREI FORUM. 1971-19?? s-a. Zeirei Agudath Israel of America, 84 William St., New York, NY 10038.

800 700   AU
ZEIT UND KUNST. 1975; ceased same year. q. Wiener Secession, Friedrichstr. 5, A-1010 Vienna, Austria.

658.8   GW
ZEITRAUM. 1987-1991. a. (back issues avail.) Uniplan Internationaler Messebau, Postfach 2220, 5014 Kerpen, Germany.

612.67 618.97   GW   ISSN 0044-2224
    CODEN: ZEALAW
ZEITSCHRIFT FUER ALTERNSFORSCHUNG. 1939-19?? bi-m. Verlag Gesundheit GmbH, Neue Gruenstr. 18, 1020 Berlin, Germany.

639.2   GW   ISSN 0373-689X
SH1   CODEN: ZBFDAC
ZEITSCHRIFT FUER DIE BINNENFISCHEREI DER DDR. 1954-1990. m. (Ministerium fuer Land-, Forst- und Nahrungsgueterwirtschaft, Institut fuer Binnenfischerei) Deutscher Landwirtschaftsverlag GmbH, Reinhardt Str. 14, 1040 Berlin, Germany.
Formerly: Deutsche Fischerei-Zeitung (ISSN 0012-0111)

610   GW   ISSN 0049-8610
RA421   CODEN: ZHYGAM
ZEITSCHRIFT FUER DIE GESAMTE HYGIENE UND IHRE GRENZGEBIETE. 1955-19?? m. Verlag Gesundheit GmbH, Neue Gruenstr. 18, 1020 Berlin, Germany.

617   GW   ISSN 0232-7295
    CODEN: ZECODK
ZEITSCHRIFT FUER EXPERIMENTELLE CHIRURGIE; Transplantation und Kunstliche Organe. 1968-19?? 4/yr. (Gesellschaft fuer Chirurgie der DDR, Sektion Experimentelle Chirurgie) Verlag Gesundheit GmbH, Neue Gruenstr. 18, 1020 Berlin, Germany.

653   GW
ZEITSCHRIFT FUER FREUNDE DER STENOGRAFIE - DIE NEUWACHT. 1911-1991. bi-m. (back issues avail.) Ferdinand-Schrey-Gesellschaft, Grosser Schirnkamp 23, 4300 Essen 14, Germany.

616   GW   ISSN 0323-5637
    CODEN: ZMLADB
ZEITSCHRIFT FUER MEDIZINISCHE LABORATORIUMSDIAGNOSTIK. 1960-19?? irreg. (approx. 8/yr.). (reprint service avail. from ISI) Verlag Gesundheit GmbH, Neue Gruenstr. 18, 1020 Berlin, Germany.

Formerly: Zeitschrift fuer Medizinische Labortechnik (ISSN 0044-3069)

616.89 610   GW   ISSN 0723-1237
ZEITSCHRIFT FUER PERSONENZENTRIERTE PSYCHOLOGIE UND PSYCHOTHERAPIE. 1982-1987. q. (back issues avail.) Beltz Verlag, Postfach 1120, D-6940 Weinheim, Germany.

712   GW   ISSN 0170-5261
ZEITSCHRIFT FUER VEGETATIONSTECHNIK. ceased 1990. 4/yr. Patzer Verlag GmbH und Co. KG, Koenigsallee 65, 1000 Berlin 33, Germany.

666   GW   ISSN 0138-2233
ZEITSCHRIFTENSCHAU KERAMIK; Fachbibliographie fuer die gesamte Sintertechnik. 1969-1991. m. (also avail. in microfiche) Keramische Werke Hermsdorf - Tridelta AG, Postfach 2, 6530 Hermsdorf, Germany.

658   NE   ISSN 0169-7471
ZELFBESTUUR. 1981-1987 (vol.6). bi-m. Oude Gracht 322, 3511 PL Utrecht, Netherlands.

057.8   YU   ISSN 0044-3921
ZEMLJA SOVJETA; ilustrovani casopis. ceased 1991. fortn. Agentstvo Pechati "Novosti", Dopisnistvo u SFRJ, Strahinjica Bana 50, Belgrade, Yugoslavia.

615   GW   ISSN 0049-8696
RM1   CODEN: ZPPLBF
ZENTRALBLATT FUER PHARMAZIE, PHARMAKOTHERAPIE UND LABORATORIUMSDIAGNOSTIK. 1970-19?? m. (reprint service avail. from ISI) Verlag Gesundheit GmbH, Neue Gruenstr. 18, 1020 Berlin, Germany.

610 016   GW   ISSN 0931-4695
ZENTRALBLATT INNERE MEDIZIN/INTERNAL MEDICINE. 1973-1991. 26/yr. (in 2 vols., 13 nos./vol.). (also avail. in microform from UMI,BHP; reprint service avail. from ISI) (Deutsche Gesellschaft fuer Innere Medizin) Springer-Verlag, Heidelberger Platz 3, D-1000 Berlin 33, Germany.
Former titles: Zentralblatt Praktische Innere Medizin (ISSN 0722-9860); Zentralblatt Praktische Innere Medizin und Grenzgebiete; **Supersedes:** Kongresszentralblatt fuer die Gesamte Innere Medizin. Sektion A: Zentralblatt Praktische Innere Medizin und Grenzgebiete - Internal Medicine (ISSN 0301-584X); Which supersedes in part: Kongresszentralblatt fuer die Gesamte Innere Medizin (ISSN 0024-9998)

020 029   GW   ISSN 0433-6933
ZENTRALINSTITUT FUER BIBLIOTHEKSWESEN. MITTEILUNGEN UND MATERIALIEN. 1963-1990. bi-m. Zentralinstitut fuer Bibliothekswesen, Zentralstelle fuer die Information und Dokumentation Bibliothekswesen, Hermann-Matern-Str. 57, 104 Berlin, Germany.

372.21 362.7   IT
ZEROSEI. 1976-198? m. (10/yr.). Gruppo Editoriale Fabbri SPA, Via Mecenate 91, 20138 Milan, Italy.

020   IT
ZEROVENTI; bolletino di segnalazzioni da periodici di biblioteconomia e documentazione. 1982-1989 (no. 17). q. (back issues avail.) Regione Toscana Giunta Regionale, Via G. Modena 13, 50121 Florence, Italy.

330   US
ZEROWORK. 1975-1983 (no.3). irreg. (back issues avail.) Social Science Division, State University of New York, Purchase, NY 10577.

622   PL   ISSN 0044-4383
TN4
ZESZYTY PROBLEMOWE GORNICTWA. 1963-1979 (vol. 17, no.1). s-a. (Polska Akademia Nauk, Komitet Gornictwa) Panstwowe Wydawnictwo Naukowe, Ul. Miodowa 10, 00-251 Warsaw, Poland.

551.5   CC   ISSN 0217-9725
ZHONGGUO KEXUEYUAN DAQI WULISUO NIANBAO. (Issuing body also known as Chinese Academy of Sciences.) 1982-19?? a. (Zhongguo Kexueyuan, Daqi Wulisuo - Academia Sinica, Institute of Atmospheric Physics) Science Press - Kexue Chubanshe, 16 Donghuangchenggen Beijie, Beijing 100707, People's Republic of China.

539.7 016   GW
ZIDIS. 1979-19?? irreg. (also avail. in microfiche) Akademie der Wissenschaften der DDR, Zentralinstitut fuer Isotopen- und Strahlenforschung, Permoserstr. 15, 7050 Leipzig, Germany.
Formed by the merger of: Isotype Titles (ISSN 0047-1550) & Zidis-Information (ISSN 0323-4290)

551.5   RH   ISSN 0085-5693
QC925.6.Z55
ZIMBABWE. DEPARTMENT OF METEOROLOGICAL SERVICES. RAINFALL REPORT. suspended. a. Department of Meteorological Services, P.O. Box BE 150, Belvedere, Harare, Zimbabwe.

709 056   RH
ZIMBABWE INSIGHT. 1977-1988 (Dec.). 2/yr. National Gallery of Zimbabwe, P.O. Box 8155, Causeway, Harare, Zimbabwe.
Formerly: Insight (ISSN 0256-9728)

956.940   UK   ISSN 0084-5531
DS149
ZIONIST YEAR BOOK. 1951-1988. a. Zionist Federation of Great Britain and Northern Ireland, Balfour House, 741 High Rd., London N12 0BQ, England.

305 800   US   ISSN 0882-1658
PS509.F44
ZONE (WAVERLY); a feminist journal for women and men. 1986-1988 (vol.2). a. Box 103, Waverly, MA 02170-0103.

340 352.7   US   ISSN 0193-757X
K30
ZONING LAW ANTHOLOGY. 1978-198? a. International Library Law Book Publishers, Inc., 101 Lakeforest Blvd., Ste. 270, Gaithersburg, MD 20877.

591   DK   ISSN 0084-5655
ZOOLOGY OF ICELAND. 1938-198? irreg. (reprint service avail. from ISI) Munksgaard International Publishers Ltd., P.O. Box 2148, DK-1016 Copenhagen K, Denmark.

378   PL   ISSN 0591-2377
L51
ZYCIE SZKOLY WYZSZEJ. 1953-1991 (no.3). m. (Ministerstwo Edukacji Narodowej) Panstwowe Wydawnictwo Naukowe, Miodowa 10, 00-251 Warsaw, Poland.

700 913   GR   ISSN 0252-8150
N6891
ZYGOS (1982); annual edition on the Hellenic fine arts. (In 4 vols.) 1982-1985. a. Zygos Ltd., 33 Iofontos St., 11634 Athens, Greece.

808.81   CN   ISSN 0835-0264
ZYMERGY. 1987-1991; suspended. s-a. (back issues avail.) Sonja A. Skarstedt, Ed.& Pub., P.O. Box 1746, Place du Parc, Montreal, Que. H2W 2R7, Canada.

371.3   UK   ISSN 0943-612X
3-D EDUCATION. 1901-1990. q. Educational Institute of Design, Craft & Technology, c/o P.E. Dawson, Ed., 52 Locarno Ave., Gillingham, Kent. ME8 6ES, England.
Former titles (until 1988): Designing and Making (ISSN 0264-8156); (until 1983): Practical Education; Practical Education and School Crafts (ISSN 0048-5071)

796.7   US   ISSN 0196-5549
3 - WHEELING; the all terrain vehicle magazine. 1980-19?? m. Wright Publishing Co., 2949 Century Place, Box 2260, Costa Mesa, CA 92628.

380.3   US
3X - 400 INFORMATION MANAGEMENT. 1987-199? m. (back issues avail.) Duke Communications International, 221 E. 29th St., Ste. 242, Loveland, CO 80538.
Formerly (until 1990): Tech Exec (ISSN 1040-2586)

808   US   ISSN 0738-0941
5 GREAT ROMANCES. ceased. 5/yr. Digest Publishing Inc., 158 Linwood Plaza, Fort Lee, NJ 07024.

051   US   ISSN 1041-4355
F128.1
7 DAYS; a week in the life of New York. 1988-1990 (Apr.). w. 7 Days Publishing Enterprises, Inc., 36 Cooper Sq., New York, NY 10003.

200   US
7TH ANGEL. 1984-1985. 10/yr. J-S Arts & Features, Inc., Box 423, Pottstown, PA 19464-0423.

700   US
9-1-1 HOTLINE TO CONTEMPORARY CULTURE. 1983-198? 5/yr. Nine-One-One Media Arts Center, 105 S. Main, Ste. 204, Seattle, WA 98104.
Formerly: 9-1-1 Reports.

668.5   CN   ISSN 0828-1890
10; Canada's professional beauty magazine. 1984-19?? 7/yr. Audace Communications Inc., 237 Glengrove Ave. West, Toronto, Ont. M4R 1P4, Canada.

658.8   US
100 TOP LICENSED PROPERTIES. ceased 1990. q. (back issues avail.) New Market Enterprises, Inc., Box 1665, Scottsdale, AZ 85252.

658   US
225 - PORTFOLIO. 1979-1989. q. Talcott Corporation, 208 W. Huron St., Chicago, IL 60610.

747   US   ISSN 0278-0844
NK1700
1001 HOME IDEAS. 1941-1991. m. Family Media, Inc., Men's and In-Home Group, 3 Park Ave., New York, NY 10016.
Formerly: 1001 Decorating Ideas (ISSN 0030-2554)

331.88 615   US   ISSN 0012-6535
1199 NEWS. 1966-1989 (May). m. National Union of Hospital and Health Care Employees, A F L - C I O, 330 W. 42nd St., Ste. 1905, New York, NY 10036.

650.07 373.246   UK
2000. 1975-1989 (vol.14, no.12). m. Pitman Publishing, 128 Long Acre, London WC2E 9AN, England.

659.152   IT
3000 PUNTI. ceased. q. Zanfi Editori s.r.l., Via Ganaceto 121, P.O. Box 433, 41100 Modena, Italy.

Index to Publications of International Organizations

This index is divided into four sections: publications of international organizations, of international congresses, of the European Communities, and of the United Nations. Numbers refer to the page in the Classified List of Serials where the full entry appears.

INTERNATIONAL ORGANIZATIONS

A C A R T S O D. Monograph Series. (African Centre for Applied Research and Training in Social Development) 925

A C A R T S O D Newsletter. (African Centre for Applied Research and Training in Social Development) 4396

A D B Quarterly Review. (Asian Development Bank) 925

A I C A R C Bulletin. (Association Internationale de Critiques d'Art Recherche Centre) 310

A I L A Bulletin. (Association Internationale de Linguistique Appliquee) 2799

A I S M. Bulletin/I A L A Bulletin. (Association Internationale de Signalisation Maritime) 4723

A L A M A R Informativo. (Asociacion Latinoamericana de Armadores) 4723

A P O Annual Report. (Asian Productivity Organization) 1071

A P O News. (Asian Productivity Organization) 1071

A R N A B Newsletter. (African Research Network for Agricultural Byproducts) 67

A S A I H L Seminar Reports. (Association of Southeast Asian Institutions of Higher Learning) 1698

A S I F A News. (Association Internationale du Film d'Animation) 3503

Academie Internationale d'Histoire des Sciences. Collection des Travaux. 4296

Acta Colloquii Didactici Classici. 2800

Acta Geneticae Medicae et Gemellologiae: Twin Research. 3070

Acta Haematologica. 3270

Acta Musicologica. 3536

Acta Radiologica. 3356

Adelphi Papers. 3949

Advances in Space Research. 43

Aerospace U F O News. 44

African Development Bank. Report by the Board of Directors/Banque Africaine de Developpement. Rapport du Conseil d'Administration. 925

African Journal of Plant Protection/Revue Africaine de la Protection des Vegetaux. 166

African News Sheet. 2526

African Tax Systems. 1087

Afro Asian Economic Review. 926

Afro-Asian Publications. 2331

Alcoholism. 1533

Allergy & Clinical Immunology News. 3183

Ambito Empresarial. 899

America Cooperativa. 829

Americas. 2503

Amnesty International Report. 3950

Anales Galdosianos. 2894

Anciens Pays et Assemblees d'Etats. 3872

Andrologia. 3075

Animals International. 230

Annales de l'Economie Publique, Sociale et Cooperative. 829

Annals of Glaciology. 1554

Annotated Bibliography of Literature on Cooperative Movements in South-East Asia. 389

Annuaire des Arachnologistes Mondiaux. 528

Annuaire des Centres de Recherche Demographique/Directory of Demographic Research Centers. 3979

Annuaire des Chercheurs Francais du Fonds de Bourses de Recherche Scientifique et Technique de l'Organisation du Traite de l'Atlantique Nord. 1699

Annuaire Economique des Pays Membres de l'Organisation de l'Unite Africaine/Economic Yearbook of Member States of the Organization of African Unity. 843

Annual Report on the Results of Treatment in Gynecological Cancer. 3193

Anthos. 292

Anuario Estadistico Centroamericano de Comercio Exterior. 702

Anuario Estadistico Centroamericano de Comercio Exterior. 702

Anuario Interamericano de Derechos Humanos/Inter-American Yearbook on Human Rights. 2719

Apiacta. 76

Applied Geochemistry. 1554

Arab Affairs. 900

Arab Petroleum. 3682

Arab Struggle. 2428

Archiv fuer Rechts- und Sozialphilosophie/Archives de Philosophie du Droit et de Philosophie Sociale/Archives for Philosophy of Law and Social Philosophy. 3761

Archiv fuer Rechts- und Sozialphilosophie. Beihefte. 3761

Archiv fuer Religionspsychologie. 4163

Artificial Intelligence Communications. 1407

Asia - Pacific Scouting. 1232

Asian and Pacific Council. Food and Fertilizer Technology Center. Extension - Technical Bulletin. 77

Asian and Pacific Labour. 2580

Asian and Pacific Quarterly. 2804

Asian Bulletin/Bulletin d'Asie. 2336

Asian Development Bank. Annual Report. 759

Asian Development Bank. Board of Governors. Summary of Proceedings. 926

Asian Development Bank. Key Indicators of Asian and Pacific Countries. 759

Asian Institute of Technology. Annual Research and Activities Report. 4594

Asian News Sheet. 2527

Asian Pacific Anti-Communist League, China. Pamphlet. 3874

Asian Peoples' Anti-Communist League. Charts About Chinese Communists on the Mainland. 2336

Asociacion. 1232

Asociacion Interamericana de Bibliotecarios y Documentalistas Agricolas. Boletin Especial. 77

Asociacion Interamericana de Bibliotecarios y Documentalistas Agricolas. Boletin Informativo. 2744

Association Internationale d'Etudes du Sud-Est Europeen. Bulletin. 2350

Association Internationale d'Etudes Patristiques. Bulletin d'Information et de Liaison. 4163

Association Internationale pour l'Histoire du Verre. Bulletin. 1161

Association of Commonwealth Universities. Annual Report of the Council Together with the Accounts of the Association. 1700

Association of Institutes for European Studies. Annuaire. 2350

Association of Institutes for European Studies. Year-Book. 2350

Association of Southeast Asian Institutions of Higher Learning. Newsletter. 1700

Audiology. 3313

Automatica. 1411

B E N E L U X Economic Union. Conseil Central de l'Economie. Rapport du Secretaire sur l'Activite du Conseil. 1072

B I C - Code. (Bureau International des Containers) 3647

B I R D. (Base d'Information Robert-Debre) 1247

Babel. 2805

Bank for International Settlements. Annual Report. 763

Benelux Dossier/Dossier Benelux. 847

Benelux Publikatieblad/Bulletin Benelux. (Belgium Netherlands Luxembourg) 4054

Biblia Revuo. 4165

Bibliographie de la Philosophie/Bibliography of Philosophy. 3787

Bibliographie Internationale de l'Humanisme et de la Renaissance. 2519

Bibliography on Irrigation, Drainage, River Training and Flood Control/Bibliographie de la C I I D. Irrigation, Drainage et Maitrise des Crues. 4834

Biochemical Education. 472

Biology International: I U B S Newsmagazine. (International Union of Biological Sciences) 432

Blutalkohol. 1534

Boreas. 1555

Brahmavidya. 3635

Building and Wood. 2580

Building Research and Information. 607

Bulletin d'Archeologie Sud-Est Europeenne. 267

Bulletin de Philosophie Medievale. 3763

Bulletin for International Fiscal Documentation. 1089

Bulletin G C I D. (Greek National Committee) 4822

Bulletin Geodesique. 1587

Bulletin of Peace Proposals. 3876

Bulletin of Volcanology. 1587

Bureau International des Societes Gerant les Droits d'Enregistrement et de Reproduction Mecanique. Bulletin. 3998

C.A.B. International Bureau of Agricultural Economics. Annotated Bibliographies. Series B: Agricultural Policy and Rural Development in Africa. 134

C.A.B. International. Bureau of Nutrition. Annotated Bibliographies. 3613

C.A.B. International. Forestry Bureau. Annotated Bibliographies. (Commonwealth Agricultural Bureaux) 2111

C.A.B. International. Mycological Institute. Phytopathological Papers. (Commonwealth Agricultural Bureaux) 498

C C I A Background Information. (World Council of Churches, Commission of the Churches on International Affairs) 4167

C D - Info. (Christian Democrat International) 3877

C E R N Courier. 3846

C E R N - H E R A Reports. 3846

C E R N Reports. 3846

C E R N School of Computing. Proceedings. 4359

C E R N School of Physics. Proceedings. 3846

C I A Revue. (Confederation Internationale des Accordeonistes) 3543

C I A T Report/Informe CIAT. (Centro Internacional de Agricultura Tropical) 81

C.I.C.A.E. Bulletin d'Information. (Confederation Internationale des Cinemas d'Art et d'Essai) 3504

C I L E C T Newsletter. (Centre International de Liaison des Ecoles de Cinema et de Television) 1370

C I N D A. 3837

C I N T E R F O R - Documentacion. (Centro Interamericano de Investigacion y Documentacion sobre Formacion Profesional) 1619

C I N T E R F O R Estudios y Monografias. (Centro Interamericano de Investigacion y Documentacion sobre Formacion Profesional) 1619

C I R A Bulletin. (Centre International de Recherches sur l'Anarchisme) 3877

C.I.R.P. Annals. 1927

C M A S Bulletin d'Information/C M A S Newsletter. (Confederation Mondiale des Activites) 1602

C M I News Letter. (International Maritime Committee) 4725

C M I Year Book. 4725

C O D A T A Bulletin. (Committee on Data for Science and Technology) 4303

Cahiers de Droit Fiscal International. 2720

Cahiers Ligures de Prehistoire et de Protohistoire. 268

Catalogo de Publicaciones Latinoamericanas Sobre Formacion Profesional. 1620

Catalogus Musicus. 3544

Catalogus Translationem et Commentatorium. 2981

Centre for Plant Breeding and Reproduction Research. Annual Report. 83

Centre International de Documentation Arachnologique. Liste des Travaux Arachnologiques. 464

Centro de Estudios Monetarios Latinoamericanos. Ensayos. 771

Centro Interamericano de Investigacion y Documentacion sobre Formacion Profesional. Boletin. 1620

Centro Interamericano de Investigacion y Documentacion sobre Formacion Profesional. Informes. 1620

Centro Interamericano de Investigacion y Documentacion sobre Formacion Profesional. Serie Bibliografica. 1620

Centro Latinoamericano de Economia Humana. Publicaciones. 4431

Chemistry International. 1174

Chemoreception Abstracts. 1200

Child Abuse & Neglect. 1234

Children in the Tropics. 1235

Child's Nervous System. 3333

Christian Jewish Relations. 4169

Christianskaya Democratia. 3879

Chronicle of Parliamentary Elections and Developments. 3879

Chronobiologia. 435

Ciencia Interamericana. 4305

Cites Unies. 3953

Civilisations. 4431

Coal Prospects and Policies in I E A Countries. 3481

Colecciones Basicas C I N T E R F O R. 1621

Collection of Documents for the Study of International Non-Governmental Relations. 2720

Colombo Plan Bureau. The Colombo Plan Council Report. 927

Colombo Plan for Co-operative Economic and Social Development in Asia and the Pacific. Consultative Committee. Proceedings and Conclusions. 927

Colombo Plan for Co-operative Economic and Social Development in Asia and the Pacific. Development Perspectives. Country Issues Papers by Member Governments to the Consultative Committee. 927

Colombo Plan Newsletter. 927

Comite Consultatif pour la Masse et les Grandeurs Apparentees. 3445

Comite International de Cooperation dans les Recherches Nationales en Demographie. Actes des Seminaires. 3980

Comite International des Poids et Mesures. Comite Consultatif d'Electricite. (Rapport et Annexes). 3445

Comite International des Poids et Mesures. Comite Consultatif de Photometrie et Radiometrie. (Rapport et Annexes). 3445

Comite International des Poids et Mesures. Comite Consultatif de Thermometrie. Rapports et Annexes. 3445

Comite International des Poids et Mesures. Comite Consultatif des Unites (Rapport et Annexes). 3445

Comite International des Poids et Mesures. Comite Consultatif pour la Definition de la Seconde. (Rapport et Annexes). 3445

Comite International des Poids et Mesures. Comite Consultatif pour la Definition du Metre (Rapport et Annexes). 3445

INDEX TO PUBLICATIONS OF INTERNATIONAL ORGANIZATIONS 5313

Comite International des Poids et Mesures. Comite Consultatif pour les Etalons des Mesure des Rayonnements Ionisants (Rapport et Annexes). 3445

Comite International des Poids et Mesures. Proces-Verbaux des Seances. 3445

Comite International des Poids et Mesures. Systeme International d'Unites. 3445

Commission for the Geological Map of the World. Bulletin. 1558

Commonwealth Universities Yearbook. 1703

Communication Arts International. 1371

Communication World. 1005

Competition Policy in O E C D Countries. 927

Composers of the Americas/Compositores de America. 3547

CompStat Symposium. Proceedings. (Computational Statistics) 4569

Computers & Geosciences. 1878

Confederacion Latinoamericana de Asociaciones Cristianas de Jovenes. Carta. 4172

Conference Generale des Poids et Mesures. Comptes Rendus des Seances. 3445

Conscience et Liberte. 3941

Consejo Superior Universitario Centroamericano. Actas de la Reunion Ordinaria. 1704

The Controller. 50

Convenios Centroamericanos de Integration Economica. 927

Convergence: International Congress on Transportation Electronics. Proceedings. 4688

Cooperative Press in South-East Asia. 2568

Cooperative Trade Directory for Southeast Asia. 830

Cotton. Part 1: Bi-monthly Review of the World Situation. 4617

Cotton. Part 2: World Statistics. 4628

Council of Europe. Centre Naturopa. Newsletter. 1486

Council of Europe. Committee of Independent Experts on the European Social Charter. Conclusions. 4403

Council of Europe. Directorate of Legal Affairs. Information Bulletin on Legislative Activities. 2616

Council of Europe. Documentation Centre for Education in Europe. Newsletter. 1623

Council of Europe. Documentation Section. Biblio Bulletin. Series: East - West Relations. 3937

Council of Europe. Documentation Section. Biblio Bulletin. Series: Legal Affairs. 2698

Council of Europe. Documentation Section. Biblio Bulletin. Series: Political, Economic and Social Affairs. 3937

Council of Europe. European Treaty Series. 2722

Council of Europe. Parliamentary Assembly. Documents: Working Papers. 2722

Council of Europe. Parliamentary Assembly. Official Report of Debates. 2722

Council of Europe. Parliamentary Assembly. Orders of the Day, Minutes of Proceedings. 2722

Council of Europe. Parliamentary Assembly. Texts Adopted by the Assembly. 2722

Council of Europe. Standing Committee on the European Convention on Establishment (Individuals). Periodical Report. 3941

Council of Europe. Study Series: Local and Regional Authorities in Europe. 4086

Council of Europe. Symposium on Legal Processing. Proceedings. 2705

Council of Europe Forum. 3882

Cross-Cultural Psychology Bulletin. 4018

Cultural Policy. 3954

Current Dialogue. 4173

D E. 1624

Deep Sea Fisheries Development Project Reports. 2039

Democratic Journalist. 2568

Desert Locust Control Organization for Eastern Africa. Annual Report. 175

Development. 928

Development Hotline. 928

Developmental and Comparative Immunology. 3184

Dialogues et Cultures. 2811

Diamond World Review. 2563

Diarrhoeal Diseases/Maladies Diarrheiques. 3171

Directory of the National Productivity Organizations in A P O Member Countries. 1074

Division d'Aide et de Cooperation Francaise. Bulletin Trimestriel de Statistique. 713

Documentacion de la Seguridad Social Americana. 2530

Documentation Bulletin for South-East Asia. 399

Droit Nucleaire. 1804

Drug and Alcohol Dependence. 1535

E A A S Newsletter. (European Association for American Studies) 3955

E B U Monographs, Legal and Administrative Series. (European Broadcasting Union) 1372

E B U Seminars for Producers and Directors of Educational Television for Schools and Adults. (European Broadcasting Union) 1373

E B U Technical Review. (European Broadcasting Union) 1335

E B U Workshops for Producers and Directors of Television Programmes for Children and Young People. (European Broadcasting Union) 1373

E C M T Statistical Report on Road Accidents. (European Council of Ministers of Transport) 4663

E F I L Documentation. (European Federation for Intercultural Learning) 1721

E F I L Newsletter. (European Federation for Intercultural Learning) 1721

E F T A Bulletin. (European Free Trade Association) 906

E F T A Trade. (European Free Trade Association) 906

E P P O Bulletin. 176

E S A Bulletin. (European Space Agency) 51

E S A R B I C A Journal. (International Council on Archives, Eastern and Southern Africa Regional Branch) 2756

E U D I S E D - R & D Bulletin. (European Documentation and Information System for Education) 1676

Earth Sciences Programme Newsletter. 1559

Earthquake Engineering and Structural Dynamics. 1865

Echo. 1626

Economie Familiale/Home Economics. 2446

Ecumenical Review. 4175

Education and Culture. Section 1: Cultural Development. 1627

Education and Culture. Section 2: Higher Education and Research. 1627

Education in Europe. Cultural Development. 1628

Education in Europe. Section 1: Higher Education and Research. 1705

Education in O E C D Countries: Compendium of Statistical Information. 1629

Educational and Vocational Guidance - Bulletin A I O S P, I A E V G, I V S B B. (Association Internationale d'Orientation Scolaire et Professionelle) 3626

Electrochimica Acta. 1212

Electroencephalography and Clinical Neurophysiology Including Evoked Potentials and Electromyography and Motor Control. 3335

Electromyography and Motor Control. 3335

Encyclopedia of World Problems and Human Potential. 3956

Energy Policies of I E A Countries. 1788

Enfant en Milieu Tropical. 1236

Environment Features. 1950

Environment Newsletter. 1950

Environmental Policy and Law. 1952

Enzyme. 476

Epilepsia. 3336

Episodes (Herndon). 1560

Ergebnisse der Limnologie/Advances in Limnology. 1597

Estadistica. 4570

Estadisticas Macroeconomicas de Centroamerica. 715

Estudios de la Seguridad Social. 2531

Europastimme. 3956

European Aspects, Law Series. 2623

European Aspects, Social Studies Series. 4435

European Association for Animal Production. Publications. 216

European Bibliography of Soviet, East European and Slavonic Studies/Bibliographie Europeene des Travaux sur l'URSS et l'Europe de l'Est/Europaische Bibliographie der Sowjet- und Oesteuropastudien. 2328

European Co-Operation. 2723

European Commission of Human Rights. Decisions and Reports. 3941

European Conference on Controlled Fusion and Plasma Physics. Proceedings. 3847

European Convention on Human Rights. Yearbook. 3941

European Council of Jewish Community Services. Exchange. 4405

European Court of Human Rights. Publications. Series A: Judgments and Decisions/Cour Europeenne des Droits de l'Homme. Publications. Serie A: Arrets et Decisions. 3941

European Economic Review. 664

Int'l Org

INDEX TO PUBLICATIONS OF INTERNATIONAL ORGANIZATIONS

European Federation of Finance House Associations. Annual Report. 778

European Federation of Finance House Associations. Newsletter. 778

European Free Trade Association. Annual Report. 906

European Journal of Biochemistry. 476

European Journal of Cancer Part A. 3197

European Journal of Political Research. 3893

European Journal of Population/Revue Europeenne de Demographie. 3992

European League for Economic Cooperation. Publications. 929

European League for Economic Cooperation. Report of the Secretary General on the Activities of E.L.E.C. 929

European Organisation for Civil Aviation Equipment. General Assembly. Annual Report. 51

European Organization for Nuclear Research. Liste des Publications Scientifiques/List of Scientific Publications. 3837

European Respiratory Journal. 3365

European Southern Observatory. Annual Report. 364

European Taxation. 1093

European Water Pollution Control. 1977

European Yearbook. 929

Europhysics Conference Abstracts. 3837

Evoked Potentials. 3336

Exchange of Information on Research in European Law/Echange d'Informations sur les Recherches en Droit Europeen. 2698

Expression. 4842

Extensions and Corrections to the U D C. 2757

Eye to Eye. 3300

F A M L I. (Family Medicine Literature Index) 3174

F E M S. Microbiology. (Federation of European Microbiological Societies) 551

F E M S. Microbiology Ecology. (Federation of European Microbiological Societies) 551

F E M S. Microbiology Immunology. (Federation of European Microbiological Societies) 551

F E M S. Microbiology Letters. (Federation of European Microbiological Societies) 551

F E M S. Microbiology Reviews. (Federation of European Microbiological Societies) 465

F I D Directory. (Federation Internationale d'Information et de Documentation) 2757

F I D News Bulletin. (Federation Internationale d'Information et de Documentation) 2757

F I F A. Handbook. (Federation Internationale de Football Association) 4503

F I F A. Olympic Football Tournament. (Federation Internationale de Football Association) 4503

F I F A. Technical Reports. (Federation Internationale de Football Association) 4503

F I F A. U-17 World Tournament. 4503

F I F A. World Cup. 4503

F I F A. World Youth Championship. 4503

F I F A Magazine. 4503

F I F A News. 4503

F I O D S Revue. (Federation Internationale des Organisations de Donneurs de Sang Benevoles) 3208

F I P E S O Newsletter. (Federation Internationale des Professeurs de l'Enseignement Secondaire Officiel) 1633

F I S Bulletin. (International Ski Federation) 4545

F I T Newsletter/Nouvelles de la F I T. (Federation Internationale des Traducteurs) 2813

Faith and Order Papers. 4177

Farming for Development. 91

Federacion Panamericana de Asociaciones de Facultades de Medicina. Boletin. 3098

Federation Aeronautique International. Annual Information Bulletin. 52

Federation Internationale de Gymnastique. Bulletin. 4472

Federation Internationale de Rugby Amateur. Annuaire. 4503

Federation Internationale Motocycliste. Annuaire. 4518

Financing and External Debt of Developing Countries. 929

Flash. 2583

Flashes from the Trade Unions. 2583

Fluoride. 3174

Folia Linguistica. 2814

Folia Phoniatrica. 3314

Fontes Artis Musicae. 3588

Food Aid Shipments. 2067

Forage Network in Ethiopia Newsletter. 216

Free Labour World. 2583

Futuribles. 4436

Futurology. 4598

General Relativity and Gravitation. 3819

General Treaty for Central American Economic Integration. Permanent Secretariat. Carta Informativa. 929

General Treaty for Central American Economic Integration. Permanent Secretariat. Newsletter. 929

Genetic Counseling. 542

Geodex Retrieval System for Geotechnical Abstracts. 1844

Geographical Distribution of Financial Flows to Developing Countries. Disbursements - Commitments - Economic Indicators. 930

Geothermics. 1545

Germplasm Newsletter. 217

Giornale Storico della Lunigiana e del Territorio Lucense. 2364

Gold (Year). 3484

Gold Institute. International Conference on Gold & Silver in Medicine. Proceedings. 3484

Gold News/Nouvelles de l'Or. 3484

Grotiana. 2631

Guide - Annuaire de l'Equipement Agricole. 162

Guides to European Taxation: Taxation of Companies in Europe. 1096

Guides to European Taxation: Taxation of Patent Royalties, Dividends, Interest in Europe. 1096

Hague Conference on Private International Law. Actes et Documents/Hague Conference on Private International Law. Documents and Proceedings. 2723

Handbook on the 1989 Double Taxation Convention Between the Federal Republic of Germany and the United States of America. 1096

Hebrew Christian. 4180

Hegel - Studien Beihefte. 3768

Higher Education Management. 1708

Histopathology. 3197

History of European Ideas. 2367

Human Rights Bulletin (New York). 3943

Hydrological Sciences Journal/Journal des Sciences Hydrologiques. 1598

Hygie. 4104

I A B S E Report. (International Association for Bridge and Structural Engineering) 1867

I A G A News. (International Association of Geomagnetism and Aeronomy) 1590

I A J R C Journal. (International Association of Jazz Record Collectors) 3555

I A L News. (International Association of Laryngectomees) 1736

I A M C R Newsletter. (International Association for Mass Communications Research) 1336

I A S L Newsletter. (International Association of School Librarianship) 2760

I A T A Review. (International Air Transport Association) 4674

I B A Review. (International Bauxite Association) 3485

I C A A. International Institutes on the Prevention and Treatment of Alcoholism. Papers. (International Congress on Alcoholism and Addictions) 1536

I C A A News. (International Congress on Alcoholism and Addictions) 1536

I C A Regional Bulletin. (International Cooperative Alliance) 831

I C A S A L S Newsletter. (International Center for Arid and Semiarid Land Studies) 96

I C E L References. (International Council on Environmental Law) 1974

I C E M Review. (International Council for Educational Media) 1638

I C E S Cooperative Research Report/Rapport des Recherches Collectives. 1605

I C E S Fisheries Statistics/Bulletin Statistique des Peches Maritimes. 2051

I C E S Journal of Marine Science. 1605

I C E S Oceanographic Data Lists and Inventories. 1605

I C I D Bulletin. (International Commission on Irrigation and Drainage) 96

I C M A Newsletter. (International City - County Management Association) 4088

I C O M News. (International Council of Museums) 3525

I C P A Quarterly. (International Commission for the Prevention of Alcoholism and Drug Dependency) 1536

I C S U Newsletter. (International Council of Scientific Unions) 4313

I E C Bulletin. (International Electrotechnical Commission) 1893

I E C Catalogue of Publications. (International Electrotechnical Commission) 1772

I E E E International Conference on Acoustics, Speech and Signal Processing. Proceedings. 1894

I E E E International Symposium on Electrical Insulation. I E E E Conference Record. 1894

I E S A Information. (International Society for Electrosleep and Electroanaesthesia) 3338

I F A P Newsletter. (International Federation of Agricultural Producers) 96

I F I P Transactions A: Computer Science and Technology. (International Federation for Information Processing) 1396

I F I P Transactions B: Applications in Technology. 1396

I F I P Transactions C: Communications Systems. 1350

I F J Information. (International Federation of Journalists) 2570

I F L A Directory. (International Federation of Library Associations and Institutions) 2760

I F L A Journal. 2761

I F L A Publications. 2761

I F L Nieuws. (International Friendship League) 1298

I G F - Journal. (International Graphical Federation) 4001

I I A S A Annual Report. (International Institute for Applied Systems Analysis) 1437

I L C A Annual Report. (International Livestock Centre for Africa) 217

I L C A Bulletin. 217

I L C A Newsletter. 218

I L C A Proceedings. 218

I L C A Programme and Budget. 218

I L C A Research Report. (International Livestock Centre for Africa) 218

I M C Journal. (International Information Management Congress) 2797

I M F News. (International Metalworkers Federation) 3408

I M U Canberra Circular. (International Mathematical Union) 3037

I O J Newsletter. (International Organization of Journalists) 2570

I P D Cahier/P A I D Reports. (Institut Panafricain pour le Developpement) 931

I P I Report. (International Press Institute) 2570

I P R A Newsletter. (International Peace Research Association) 3959

I P S F News Bulletin. (International Pharmaceutical Students Federation) 3728

I P T C News. (International Press Telecommunications Council) 1363

I R R I Program Report. (International Rice Research Institute) 206

I S O Bulletin (English Edition). (International Organization for Standardization) 3446

I S O International Standards. (International Organization for Standardization) 3446

I S O Memento. (International Organization for Standardization) 3446

I S P R S Journal of Photogrammetry and Remote Sensing. (International Society for Photogrammetry and Remote Sensing) 2252

I S S A. Committee on Provident Funds. Reports. (International Social Security Association) 2533

I S S A. Social Security Documentation. Caribbean Series. (International Social Security Association) 2533

I S T A News Bulletin. (International Seed Testing Association) 179

I S U Constitution. (International Skating Union) 4475

I S U Regulations. (International Skating Union) 4475

I T C Journal. 2252

I T M F Country Statements. (International Textile Manufacturers Federation) 4619

I T M F Directory. (International Textile Manufacturers Federation) 4619

I T U Review. (International Typographical Union) 2584

I U C N Bulletin. (International Union for Conservation of Nature and Natural Resources) 1489

I U F R O World Series. (International Union of Forestry Research Organizations) 2102

I U G G Chronicle. (International Union of Geodesy and Geophysics) 1590

I U O M A Magazine. (International Union of Mail Artists) 329

I U P I W Views. (International Union of Petroleum & Industrial Workers) 3688

I U S S P Newsletter/U I E S P Bulletin de Liaison. (International Union for the Scientific Study of Population) 3983

I U S S P Papers/U I E S P Documents de l'Union. (International Union for the Scientific Study of Population) 3983

I W G I A Documents. (International Work Group for Indigenous Affairs) 241

I W G I A Newsletter. (International Work Group for Indigenous Affairs) 241

Ice. 1568

Immunizations/Vaccinations/Vacunaciones. 3175

Immunology Letters. 3186

Index to Plant Chromosome Numbers. 505

Individual Psychology News Letter. 4024

Industrial Policy in O E C D Countries. 869

Inform Quarterly Newsletter. 3264

Information and Management. 1445

Information Bulletin for Catholic Rural Organizations. 97

Information, Computer and Communications Policy. 931

Informations Recentes sur les Comptes Nationaux des Pays en Developpement/Latest Information on National Accounts of Developing Countries. 931

Infoterm Series. (International Information Centre for Terminology, Vienna) 2818

Ingenieria Sanitaria. 4104

Inspel. 2763

Institut International du Froid. Bulletin/International Institute of Refrigeration. Bulletin. 2300

Institut International du Froid. Comptes Rendus de Reunions de Commissions/International Institute of Refrigeration. Proceedings of Commiesion Meetings. 2300

Institut Panafricain pour le Developpement. Travaux d'Etudiants. Bulletin Analytique. 931

Institut Panafricain pour le Developpement. Travaux Manuscrits. 152

Instituto Indigenista Interamericano Serie de Ediciones Especiales. 242

Instituto Interamericano de Cooperacion para la Agricultura - O E A. Documentos Oficiales. 98

Instituto Interamericano del Nino. Boletin. 1239

Instituto Interamericano del Nino. Servicio Social. Informes Tecnicos. 4409

Instituto Panamericano de Geografia e Historia. Boletin Aereo. 2253

Inter American Press Association. Committee on Freedom on the Press. Report. 3899

Inter American Press Association. Minutes of the Annual Meeting. 2571

Inter-American Bar Association. Letter to Members. 2636

Inter-American Center of Tax Administrators. Informativo - Newsletter. 1098

Interamerican Children's Institute. Report of the General Director. 4409

Inter-American Commission of Women. News Bulletin. 4845

Inter-American Commission of Women. Noticiero. 4845

Inter-American Council for Education, Science, and Culture. Final Report. 1639

Inter-American Council of Commerce and Production. Uruguayan Section. Publicaciones. 931

Inter-American Development Bank. Annual Report. 785

Inter-American Development Bank. Institute for Latin American Integration. Annual Report. 931

Inter-American Economic and Social Council. Final Report of the Annual Meeting at the Ministerial Level. 2410

Inter-American Institute for Cooperation on Agriculture. Executive Committee. Yearly Meeting Report. 99

Inter-American Institute for Cooperation on Agriculture. Informe Anual. 99

Inter-American Review of Bibliography/Revista Interamericana de Bibliografia. 2520

Inter-American Tropical Tuna Commission. Annual Report/Comision InterAmericana del Atun Tropical. Informe Anual. 2043

Inter-American Tropical Tuna Commission. Bulletin/ Comision Interamericana del Atun Tropical. Boletin. 2043

Inter-American Tropical Tuna Commission. Data Report. 2043

InterMedia. 1375

International Abstracts in Operations Research. 1404

International Air Transport Association. Annual General Meeting. Reports and Proceedings. 4674

International Angiology. 3272

International Archery Federation. Bulletin Officiel. 4475

International Arthurian Society. Bibliographical Bulletin/ Societe Internationale Arthurienne. Bulletin Bibliographique. 2982

International Association for Byzantine Studies. Bulletin d'Information et de Coordination. 2368

International Association for Educational and Vocational Information. Studies and Reports. 1639

INDEX TO PUBLICATIONS OF INTERNATIONAL ORGANIZATIONS

International Association for Plant Tissue Culture. Newsletter. 506

International Association for Shell and Spatial Structures. Bulletin. 1868

International Association for the Exchange of Students for Technical Experience. Annual Report. 1722

International Association for the Physical Science of the Ocean. Proces-Verbaux. 1606

International Association of Agricultural Information Specialists. Quarterly Bulletin. 139

International Association of Engineering Geology. Bulletin. 1568

International Association of French Studies. Cahiers. 2925

International Association of Geodesy. Central Bureau for Satellite Geodesy. Bibliography. 2268

International Association of Geodesy. Central Bureau for Satellite Geodesy. Information Bulletin. 2253

International Association of Geodesy. Commission Permanente des Marees Terrestres. Marees Terrestres Bulletin d'Information. 1590

International Association of Labour History Institutions. Bibliographische Information. 722

International Association of Law Libraries. Directory. 2763

International Association of Liberal Religious Women. Newsletter. 4182

International Association of Literary Critics. Revue. 4130

International Association of Theoretical and Applied Limnology. Communications/Internationale Vereinigung fuer Theoretische und Angewandte Limnologie. Mitteilungen. 1598

International Association of Theoretical and Applied Limnology. Proceedings/Internationale Vereinigung fuer Theoretische und Angewandte Limnologie. Verhandlungen. 1598

International Astronomical Union. Transactions. 365

International Baccalaureate Organisation. Annual Bulletin. 1639

International Badminton Federation. Annual Statute Book. 4475

International Bibliography of the Forensic Sciences. 3176

International Brain Research Organization Monograph Series. 3339

International Bureau of Fiscal Documentation. Annual Report. 1098

International Cataloguing and Bibliographic Control. 2763

International Centre for Settlement of Investment Disputes. Annual Report. 950

International Centre of Insect Physiology and Ecology. Annual Report. 534

International Child Health: A Digest of Current Information. 3321

International Children's Centre. Paris. Report of the Director-General to the Executive Board. 4438

International Civil Defence Journal/Revue Internationale de Protection Civile/Revista Internacional de Proteccion Civil. 1273

International Classification. 2763

International College of Dentists. European Section. Newsletter. 3234

International Commission for Uniform Methods of Sugar Analysis. Report of the Proceedings of the Session (Year). 2073

International Commission of Jurists. Review. 2724

International Commission on Irrigation and Drainage. Congress Reports. 1924

International Commission on Irrigation and Drainage. Report. 4826

International Commission on Large Dams. Bulletin. 1868

International Commission on Radiological Protection. Annals. 3358

International Committee for Historical Science. Bulletin d'Information. 2314

International Committee of the Red Cross. Annual Report - Rapport d'Activite - Informe de Actividad - Taetigkeitsbericht. 4409

International Committee on Urgent Anthropological and Ethnological Research. Bulletin. 242

International Confederation of Free Trade Unions. World Congress Reports. 2584

International Confederation of Societies of Authors and Composers. 3675

International Conference on Data Processing in the Field of Social Security. Reports. 2535

International Congress Science Series. 3392

International Consumer Directory. 1505

International Cooperative Alliance. Cooperative Series. 831

International Copper Information Bulletin. 3425

International Cotton Industry Statistics. 4628

International Council for Bird Preservation. British Section. Report. 564

International Council of Scientific Unions. Year Book. 4315

International Council on Archives. Committee on Conservation and Restoration. Committee on Archival Reprography (Bulletin). 2764

International Customs Journal/Bulletin International des Douanes. 1098

International Dairy Federation. Annual Bulletin/Federation Internationale de Laiterie. Bulletin Annuel. 200

International Dairy Federation. Annual Memento/Federation Internationale de Laiterie. Memento Annuel. 200

International Dairy Federation. Catalogue of I D F Publications/Federation Internationale Laitiere. Catalogue des Publications. 139

International Dairy Federation. International Standard/Federation Internationale de Laiterie. Norme Internationale. 200

International Dairy Federation. Newsletter/Federation Internationale de Laiterie. Newsletter. 200

International Dental Journal. 3234

International Directory of Prisoners Aid Agencies. 1515

International Earth Rotation Service. Annual Report. 365

International Earth Rotation Service. Monthly Bulletin. 365

International Egg Commission. Market Review Situation & Outlook Report. 2073

International Egg Commission. Monthly Chick Placement Bulletin. 2073

International Egg Commission. Monthly News Letter. 2073

International Egg Commission. Six-Monthly Statistical Bulletin. 2073

International Electrotechnical Commission. Repertoire - Directory. 1900

International Electrotechnical Commission. Yearbook - Annuaire. 1900

International European Conference on High Energy Physics. Proceedings. 3847

International Federation for Documentation. P-Notes. 2764

International Federation for Housing and Planning. Directory. 2489

International Federation of Commercial Clerical, Professional and Technical Employees. Newsletter. 2585

International Federation of Journalists and Travel Writers. Official List/Repertoire Officiel. 4772

International Fiscal Association. Yearbook. 2724

International Graphical Federation. Report of Activities. 2585

International Gravimetrique Bureau. Bulletin d'Information. 1590

International Handbook of Universities and Other Institutions of Higher Education. 1709

International Hotel Guide. 2477

International Humanist. 3769

International Hydrographic Bulletin. 1606

International Hydrographic Organization. Yearbook. 1606

International Hydrographic Review. 1606

International Institute for Land Reclamation and Improvement. Annual Report. 181

International Institute for Land Reclamation and Improvement. Bibliography. 139

International Institute for Land Reclamation and Improvement. Publication. 181

International Institute of Administrative Sciences. Reports of the International Congress. 4064

International Institute of Seismology and Earthquake Engineering. Bulletin. 1591

International Institute of Seismology and Earthquake Engineering. Individual Studies by Participants at I I S E E. 1591

International Institute of Seismology and Earthquake Engineering. Year Book. 1591

International Institute on the Prevention and Treatment of Addictions. Selected Papers. 1536

International Journal of Biometeorology. 3436

International Journal of Cancer. 3198

International Journal of Continuing Engineering Education. 1826

International Journal of Dermatology. 3248

International Journal of Developmental Neuroscience. 3339

International Journal of Early Childhood. 1239

International Journal of Environment and Pollution. 1977

International Journal of Food Microbiology. 466

International Journal of Global Energy Issues. 1791

International Journal of Government Auditing/Revue Internationale de la Verification des Comptes Publics/Revista Internacional de Entidades Fiscalizadoras Superiores. 4064

International Journal of Group Tensions. 4025

International Journal of Gynaecology and Obstetrics. 3293

INDEX TO PUBLICATIONS OF INTERNATIONAL ORGANIZATIONS

International Journal of Hospitality Management. 4772

International Journal of Hydrogen Energy. 1791

International Journal of Legal Information. 2764

International Journal of Leprosy and Other Mycobacterial Diseases. 3220

International Journal of Oral & Maxillofacial Surgery. 3235

International Journal of Physical Education/Internationale Zeitschrift fuer Sportpaedagogik. 1752

International Journal of Psycho-Analysis. 4025

International Journal of Sport Psychology. 4476

International Journal of Systematic Bacteriology. 553

International Journal of University Adult Education. 1684

International League for Human Rights. Annual Report. 3944

International Linguistic Association. Monograph. 2819

International Linguistic Association. Special Publications. 2819

International Narcotics Control Board. Report for (Year). 3730

International Narcotics Control Board. Statistics on Psychotropic Substances for (Year). 3748

International Naturist Guide/Internationaler FKK-Reisefuehrer/Guide Naturiste Internationale. 4549

International Navigation Congress. Papers. 4729

International Navigation Congress. Proceedings. 4729

International Nursing Review. 3279

International Office of Cocoa, Chocolate and Sugar Confectionery. Annual Statistical Bulletin. 2088

International Oil Scouts Association. Official Publication. 3690

International Omega Association. Proceedings of Annual Meeting. 56

International Omega Association Newsletter. 4675

International Organization. 3961

International Organization for Migration. Annual Report. 3983

International Organization of Consumers Unions. Proceedings. 1505

International Orthopaedics. 3308

International Pacific Halibut Commission (U.S. and Canada). Annual Report. 2044

International Pacific Halibut Commission (U.S. and Canada). Scientific Reports. 2044

International Pediatric Association. Proceedings of Congress. 3321

International Pharmacy Journal. 3730

International Political Science Abstracts/Documentation Politique Internationale. 3938

International Political Science Association. World Congress. 3899

International Political Science Review/Revue Internationale de Science Politique. 3961

International Population Conference. Proceedings. 3983

International Prisoners Aid Association. Newsletter. 4409

International Psychologist. 4026

International Railway Statistics. Statistics of Individual Railways. 4664

International Rehabilitation Review. 3111

International Rescue Committee Annual Report. 4409

International Review for Business Education/Revue Internationale pour l'Enseignement Commercial/Internationale Zeitschrift fuer Kaufmaennisches Bildungswesen/Rivista Internazionale per la Cultura Commerciale/Revista Internacional la Ensenanza Comercial. 672

International Review of Administrative Sciences. 4064

International Review of Contemporary Law. 2636

International Review of Mission. 4183

International Review of the Red Cross. 2725

International Rubber Digest. 4292

International Seismological Centre. Bulletin. 1591

International Silk Association. Monthly Newsletter. 4620

International Skating Union. Ice Dancing Regulations. 4476

International Social Security Association. Studies and Research. 2535

International Social Security Review. 2535

International Social Work. 4409

International Society of Criminology. Bulletin. 1516

International Society of Plant Morphologists. Yearbook. 506

International Society of Soil Science. Bulletin. 181

International Statistical Handbook of Urban Public Transport/Recueil International de Statistiques des Transports Publics Urbains/Internationales Statistik-Handbuch fuer den Oeffentlichen Stadtverkehr. 4664

International Statistical Review. 4575

International Studies Notes. 3962

International Sugar Organization Statistical Bulletin. 2085

International Surgery. 3379

International Symposium on Canine Heartworm Disease. Proceedings. 4811

International Textile Machinery Shipment Statistics. 4628

International Textile Manufacturing. 4620

International Tin Research Institute. Annual Report. 3409

International Union for Inland Navigation. Annual Report. 4651

International Union for Vacuum Science, Technique and Applications. News Bulletin. 3821

International Union of Alpine Associations. Bulletin/Union Internationale des Associations d'Alpinisme. Bulletin. 4772

International Union of Crystallography. Abstracts of the Triennial Congress. 1210

International Union of Food and Allied Workers' Associations. News Bulletin. 2585

International Union of Geodesy and Geophysics. Monograph. 2254

International Union of Geodesy and Geophysics. Proceedings of the General Assembly. 1591

International Union of Public Transport. Technical Reports of the Congresses. 4651

International Union of Students. African Bulletin. 2169

International Union of Students. Sport Bulletin. 4476

International Union of Tenants. International Information. 2489

International V A T Monitor. 1098

International Whaling Commission. Annual Reports. 2044

International Wheat Council. Market Report. 152

International Wheat Council. Record of Shipments Wheat and Wheat Flour (Year). 99

International Wheat Council. Report for Crop Year. 99

International Wheat Council. Secretariat Papers. 99

Der Internationalen Gesellschaft fuer Geschichte der Pharmazie. Veroeffentlichungen. Neue Folge. 3730

Internationale Gesellschaft fuer Urheberrecht. Yearbook. 3676

Internationale Seilbahn-Rundschau/International Aerial Lift Review. 4651

Internationale Stiftung Mozarteum. Mitteilungen. 3557

Internationaler Verband Forstlicher Forschungsanstalten. Weltkongress Berichtswerk. 2102

Internationales Jahrbuch fuer Kartographie. 2254

Inter-Parliamentary Bulletin. 3962

Inter-Parliamentary Union. Series: "Reports and Documents". 3900

Interpressgraphic. 4002

Intervirology. 553

Inventaria Archaeologica Belgique. 274

Inventaria Archaeologica Ceskoslovensko. 274

Inventaria Archaeologica Denmark. 274

Inventaria Archaeologica Deutschland. 275

Inventaria Archaeologica Espana. 275

Inventaria Archaeologica France. 275

Inventaria Archaeologica Italia. 275

Inventaria Archaeologica Jugoslavija. 275

Inventaria Archaeologica Norway. 275

Inventaria Archaeologica Oesterreich. 275

Inventaria Archaeologica Pologne. 275

Inventaria Archaeologica Ungarn. 275

Jahrbuch fuer Liturgik und Hymnologie. 4183

Jazzforschung/Jazz Research. 3558

Jazzmen's Reference Book. 3558

Journal of Applied Crystallography. 1210

Journal of Cardiovascular Surgery. 3210

Journal of Cranio-Maxillo-Facial Surgery. 3380

Journal of Energy and Natural Resources Law. 2639

Journal of Environmental Pathology, Toxicology and Oncology. 1982

Journal of Glaciology. 1569

Journal of Heart and Lung Transplantation. 3380

Journal of Hydraulic Research. 1924

Journal of Magnetism and Magnetic Materials. 3822

Journal of Marine Systems. 1607

Journal of Medical & Veterinary Mycology. 3221

Journal of Oral Pathology & Medicine. 3236

Journal of Police Science and Administration. 1516

Journal of Reading. 1643

Journal of Rural Cooperation. 831

Journal of Sports Medicine and Physical Fitness. 3372

Journal of Structural Learning. 4033

Journal of Terramechanics. 3019

Journal of Traffic Medicine. 3309

Kidney International. 3388

Labor (Year). 985

Labor Press and Information. 2585

Latin American Bulletin/Boletin de America Latina. 2217

Lead and Zinc Statistics. 3427

Leben und Umwelt. 1491

Lethaia. 3658

Ligue Internationale Contre la Concurrence Deloyale. Annuaire. 916

Ligue Internationale Contre la Concurrence Deloyale. Communication. 1080

Local and Regional Authorities in Europe. Study Series. 4090

Log of the Star Class. 4525

Lotus. 2935

Al-Majallah al-Arabiyyah lil-Idarah/Arab Journal of Administration. 4066

Al-Majallah al-Bahriyyah/Maritime Magazine. 4732

Market Frontier News. 201

Marketing and Research Today. 1046

Materials Characterization. 3412

Mathematical and Computer Modelling. 3045

Ma'yanot. 2013

Meat Balances in O E C D Countries. 140

Medailles. 2438

Media Development. 1376

Medical & Biological Engineering & Computing. 470

Mercado Comun Centroamericano. Carta Informativa. 932

Meridian. 933

Message Olympique/Olympic Message. 4479

Metrologia. 3447

Microtables Imports - Exports of O E C D Countries. (Organization for Economic Cooperation and Development) 917

Microwave Power Symposium. Proceedings. 1903

Migration Today. 3985

Military Balance. 3464

Milk and Milk Products Balances in O E C D Countries. 140

Ministerial Formation. 4190

Modern Gold Coinage (Year). 3600

Monthly Letter on Evangelism. 4190

Music in the Media - I M Z Bulletin. 3564

Musikforum - Referate und Informationen des Deutschen Musikrates. 3568

Muslim World. 3908

N A T O. Annual Economic Colloquia. Proceedings. 918

N A T O Advanced Science Institutes Series A: Life Sciences. (North Atlantic Treaty Organization) 448

N A T O Advanced Science Institutes Series B: Physics. 3825

N A T O Advanced Science Institutes Series C: Mathematical and Physical Sciences. (North Atlantic Treaty Organization) 3048

N A T O Advanced Science Institutes Series E: Applied Sciences. (North Atlantic Treaty Organization) 4604

N A T O Basic Documents/O T A N Documents Fondamentaux. 3966

N A T O Final Communiques/O T A N Communiques Finals. 3966

N A T O Handbook. 3966

N A T O Review. (North Atlantic Treaty Organization) 3908

N A T O Scientific Publications. Newsletter. 4325

N E A Issue Brief. (Nuclear Energy Agency) 1807

Narcotic Drugs: Estimated World Requirements for (Year). 3811

National Accounts of O E C D Countries. Volume 1 Main Aggregates. 730

National Accounts of O E C D Countries. Volume 2 Detailed Tables. 730

Nature and Environment Series. 1493

Naturopa. 1493

Neural Networks. 1409

Neuroendocrinology. 3255

Neuroscience. 3348

News from I C S I D. (International Centre for Settlement of Investment Disputes) 958

News from O E C D. 875

Nordisk Statistisk Aarsbok/Yearbook of Nordic Statistics. 4581

Nordisk Statistisk Skriftserie/Statistical Reports of the Nordic Countries. 4581

Nordisk Statutsamling. 2661

North Atlantic Treaty Organization. Facts and Figures/ Alliance Atlantique. Structure, Faits et Chiffres. 3967

Noticias de Galapagos. 4330

Nuclear Law Bulletin. 1808

Nuclear Waste Bulletin/Bulletin sur les Dechets Nucleaires. 1986

Numen. 4193

Nutricion en Salud Publica. 4118

Nutrition de Sante Publique. 4118

O A S. General Secretariat. Annual Report. (Organization of American States) 2417

O E C D. Activities of the O E C D: Report by the Secretary General. 933

O E C D. Annual Oil Market Report. 3694

O E C D. Catalogue of Publications. 408

O E C D. Coal Information. 3492

O E C D. Code of Liberalization of Capital Movements/ O C D E. Code de la Liberation des Mouvements de Capitaux. 793

O E C D. Development Centre Seminars. 933

O E C D. Development Centre Studies. 933

O E C D. Development Cooperation. 933

O E C D. Economic Outlook Historical Statistics. 732

O E C D. Economic Surveys: Australia. 876

O E C D. Economic Surveys: Austria. 876

O E C D. Economic Surveys: Belgium - Luxembourg. 876

O E C D. Economic Surveys: Canada. 876

O E C D. Economic Surveys: Denmark. 876

O E C D. Economic Surveys: Finland. 876

O E C D. Economic Surveys: France. 876

O E C D. Economic Surveys: Germany. 876

O E C D. Economic Surveys: Greece. 876

O E C D. Economic Surveys: Hungary. 877

O E C D. Economic Surveys: Iceland. 877

O E C D. Economic Surveys: Ireland. 877

O E C D. Economic Surveys: Italy. 877

O E C D. Economic Surveys: Japan. 877

O E C D. Economic Surveys: Netherlands. 877

O E C D. Economic Surveys: New Zealand. 877

O E C D. Economic Surveys: Norway. 877

O E C D. Economic Surveys: Portugal. 877

O E C D. Economic Surveys: Spain. 877

O E C D. Economic Surveys: Sweden. 877

O E C D. Economic Surveys: Switzerland. 877

O E C D. Economic Surveys: Turkey. 877

O E C D. Economic Surveys: United Kingdom. 877

O E C D. Economic Surveys: United States. 877

O E C D. Economic Surveys: Yugoslavia. 877

O E C D. Employment Outlook. (Organization for Economic Cooperation and Development) 877

O E C D. Energy Statistics of O E C D Countries. 1800

O E C D. Environmental Data Compendium. 1974

O E C D. External Debt Statistics. 732

O E C D. Food Consumption Statistics. 2085

O E C D. Foreign Trade by Commodities. Series C. 732

O E C D. Industrial Structure Statistics. 732

O E C D. Iron and Steel Industry. 3417

O E C D. Labour Force Statistics/O C D E. Statistiques de la Population Active. 732

O E C D. Library. Special Annotated Bibliography: Automation/O C D E. Bibliotheque. Bibliographie Speciale Analytique: Automation. 1405

O E C D. Main Economic Indicators/O C D E. Principaux Indicateurs Economiques. 877

O E C D. Main Economic Indicators. Historical Statistics/O C D E. Principaux Indicateurs Economiques. Statistiques Retrospectives. 732

O E C D. Maritime Transport Committee. Maritime Transport. 4735

O E C D. Monthly Statistics of Foreign Trade Series A/O C D E. Statistiques Mensuel du Commerce Exterieur. 732

O E C D. Oil Statistics. Supply and Disposal. 3706

O E C D. Quarterly Labour Force Statistics/O C D E. Statistiques Trimestrielles de la Population Active. 990

O E C D. Revenue Statistics of O E C D Member Countries. 732

O E C D. Reviews of Manpower and Social Policies. 990

O E C D. Reviews of National Policies for Education. 1730

O E C D. Reviews of National Science and Technology Policy. 4605

O E C D. Social Policy Studies Series. 4069

O E C D. Steel Market in (Year) and Outlook for (Year). (Organization for Economic Cooperation and Development) 732

O E C D. Tourism Committee. Tourism Policy and International Tourism in O E C D Member Countries. 4780

O E C D. Uranium Resources, Production and Demand. 1809

O E C D. World Energy Statistics. (Organization for Economic Cooperation and Development) 1800

O E C D Economic Outlook. (Organization for Economic Cooperation and Development) 877

O E C D Economic Studies. 877

O E C D Financial Statistics/Statistiques Financieres de l'O C D E. 732

O E C D Financial Statistics. Part 1: Monthly Financial Statistics. 732

O E C D Financial Statistics. Part 2: Financial Accounts. 732

O E C D Financial Statistics. Part 3: Non-Financial Enterprises Financial Statements. 732

O E C D Liaison Bulletin Between Research and Training Institutes. 1082

O E C D Nuclear Energy Agency Activities in (Year). 1809

O E C D Observer. (Organization for Economic Cooperation and Development) 877

O E C D Oil and Gas Information. 3706

O I E C Bulletin. (Office International de l'Enseignement Catholique) 4193

O I V Bulletin. (Office International de la Vigne et du Vin) 384

O.I.V. Lettre. (Office International de la Vigne et du Vin) 384

O P E C Review. (Organization of the Petroleum Exporting Countries) 3694

Odonto-Stomatologie Tropicale/Tropical Dental Journal. 3239

Office International de la Vigne et du Vin. Reglements. 384

Olympic Review (Year). 4482

One World. 4193

Onoma. 2833

Orbis. 2833

Orbis Geographicus. 2258

Organ Building Periodical/Zeitschrift fuer Orgelbau. (International Society of Organbuilders) 3572

Organization of African Unity. Scientific Technical and Research Commission. Publication. 4332

Organization of American States. Department of Cultural Affairs. Manuales del Bibliotecario. 2778

Organization of American States. Department of Scientific Affairs. Report of Activities. 4332

Organization of American States. Department of Scientific Affairs. Serie de Biologia: Monografias. 450

Organization of American States. Department of Scientific Affairs. Serie de Fisica: Monografias. 3826

Organization of American States. Department of Scientific Affairs. Serie de Matematica: Monografias. 3050

Organization of American States. Department of Scientific Affairs. Serie de Quimica: Monografias. 1185

Organization of American States. General Assembly. Actas y Documentos. 3968

Organization of American States. Official Records. Indice y Lista General. 2418

Organization of the Petroleum Exporting Countries. Annual Statistical Bulletin. 3706

Osteoporosis International. 3138

P C R Information. (Programme to Combat Racism) 3945

P T T I Studies. (Postal Telegraph and Telephone International) 1353

Pacific Impact. 684

Pan American Federation of Engineering Societies. Bulletin. 1833

Pan American Institute of Geography and History. Commission on Geophysics. Boletin. 1592

Parlements et Francophonie. 2878

Participation. 3914

Pax et Libertas. 3968

Peace and the Sciences. 3968

Peace Courier. 3968

Pediatric Neurosurgery. 3350

Pedofauna. 187

People. 597

Permanent International Altaistic Conference (PIAC). Newsletter. 3643

Permanent International Association of Navigation Congresses. Bulletin. 4735

Personality and Individual Differences. 4038

Pest Advisory Leaflet. 187

Pharmacology and Therapeutics. 3739

Phonetica. 2834

Phycologia. 513

Physica A - Statistical and Theoretical Physics. 3826

Physica B - Physics of Condensed Matter. 3826

Physica C - Superconductivity. 3826

Physica D - Nonlinear Phenomena. 3826

Phytomorphology. 513

Plant Protection News. 189

Police Chief. 1520

Potash Review. 189

Prehospital and Disaster Medicine. 3143

Prison Information Bulletin. 1521

Prospect. 2494

Psychoneuroendocrinology. 3352

Psychotherapy and Psychosomatics. 3352

Public Health Nutrition. 4118

Public Transport International. 4655

Pulp and Paper Industry in O E C D Member Countries/Industrie des Pates et Papiers dans les Pays Membres de l'O C D E. 3666

Quality. 4607

Quarantine Advisory Leaflet. 190

Quarterly Bulletin on Solar Activity. 371

Quaternary International. 1578

Radiotherapy & Oncology. 3362

Rail International/Schienen der Welt. 4713

Reading Research Quarterly. 1658

Reading Teacher. 1758

Recherche en Matiere d'Economie des Transports/Research on Transport Economics. 4655

Reformation Review. 4197

Reformed World. 4248

Regional Tuna Bulletin. 2048

Regnum Vegetabile. 516

Rejuvenation. 2278

Repertorium Plantarum Succulentarum. 516

Resumenes de Formacion Profesional C I N T E R F O R. 1659

Review of Fisheries in O E C D Member Countries. 2048

Review of Income and Wealth. 1000

Review of International Cooperation. 3970

Review of Population Reviews. 3987

Revista FeLaBan. 798

Revista Geofisica. 1594

Revista Geografica. 2261

Revista Latinoamericana de Quimica. 1187

Revista W I Z O. 2204

Revue Africaine et Malgache de Psychologie. 4045

Revue de Bio-Mathematique/Biomathematics Review. 3052

Revue Internationale de Police Criminelle. 1522

Rivista di Studi Liguri/Revue d'Etudes Ligures. 2384

The Rotarian. 1300

Rubber Statistical Bulletin. 4294

S I E C A. Cuadernos. (Secretaria Permanente del Tratado General de Integracion Economica Centroamericana) 920

S P R E P Environmental Case Studies. (South Pacific Regional Environment Programme) 1967

S P R E P Fact Sheet. (South Pacific Regional Environment Programme) 1967

S P R E P Meeting Reports. (South Pacific Regional Environment Programme) 1967

S P R E P Occasional Papers. 1967

S P R E P Topic Review. 1967

S P R E P Training Reports. 1967

Salar. 2048

Scandinavian Journal of History. 2322

Scientia Horticulturae. 2138

Scientific World. 4341

Screening. 3326

Secondary Aluminium. 3495

Sedimentology. 1580

Seed Science and Technology. 517

Sennacieca Revuo. 3971

Series Estadisticas Seleccionadas de Centroamerica y Panama. 737

Situation de la Viticulture dans le Monde. 385

Societe Francaise de Psycho-Prophylaxie Obstetricale. Bulletin Officiel. 3296

Socio-Economic Differential Mortality in Industrialized Societies. 3987

Soil and Tillage Research. 120

Solnechnaya Radiatsiya i Radiatsionnyi Balans. Mirovaya Set/Solar Radiation and Radiation Balance Data. The World Network. 3441

Solubility Data Series. 1188

Sources of Contemporary Jewish Thought/Mekevot. 2884

South Pacific Commission. Handbook. 935

South Pacific Commission. Information Circular. 885

South Pacific Commission. Information Document. 935

South Pacific Commission. Report of Meetings. 885

South Pacific Commission. Statistical Bulletin. 4586

South Pacific Commission. Technical Paper. 4609

South Pacific Conference. Report. 3972

South Pacific Economies: Statistical Summary. 738

South Pacific Epidemiological and Health Information Service Annual Report. 4119

South Pacific Foods Leaflet. 2082

Southeast Asian Archives. 2342

Speakers' Papers: Speeches from the Gold and Silver Institutes' (Year) Annual Meeting. 3496

Speleological Abstracts/Bulletin Bibliographique Speleologique. 1552

Sport International. 4490

Statistical Theory and Method Abstracts. 4588

Stereotactic and Functional Neurosurgery. 3355

Strategic Survey. 3973

Students Life. 1325

Studi Genuensi. 286

Studies in Conservation. 345

Studies in Social History. 4389

Supplementary Service to European Taxation. 1107

Systems Research. 1837

T U I A F P W Information. (Trade Union International of Agricultural, Forestry and Plantation Workers) 2590

Tax - Benefit Position of Production Workers. 1107

Tax News Service. 1109

Taxation in Latin America. 1110

Taxon. 518

Teachers of the World. 1667

Terra et Aqua. 4740

Terra Nova. 1548

Terra Una. 4205

Theatre en Pologne/Theatre in Poland. 4640

Theosophist. 3784

Thrombosis and Haemostasis. 3212

Tidal Gravity Corrections. 1596

Torah Education. 4227

Toxicon. 3744

Trade Unions International of Workers in Commerce. Bulletin. 2590

Trade Unions International of Workers in Commerce. News. 2590

Transnational Associations/Associations Transnationales. 3974

Transport Museums. 4658

Transport Workers of the World. 2590

Trends in Pharmacological Sciences. 3744

Tropical Ecology. 519

Tuna and Billfish Assessment Programme Technical Report. 2050

Tunnelling and Underground Space Technology. 1839

Typographical Journal. 2590

U.I.A.M.S. Bulletin Trimestriel. (International Union for Moral and Social Action) 4422

U.I.A.M.S. Informations. (International Union for Moral and Social Action) 3930

U I A Newsletter. (Union Internationale des Architectes) 308

U I S Bulletin. (Union Internationale de Speleologie) 1583

U I T B B Bulletin. (Trade Unions International of Workers of the Building, Wood and Building Materials Industries) 2590

U I T Journal. (Union International de Tir) 4495

U I T P Biblio-Express. (International Union of Public Transport) 4668

U R S I Information Bulletin. (International Union of Radio Science) 1360

Uganda Freshwater Fisheries Research Organization. Annual Report. 2050

Union Mondiale des Organisations Syndicales sur Bases Economique et Sociale Liberales. Conferences: Rapport. 2591

Union of European Football Associations. Handbook of U E F A. 4514

United States Board on Books for Young People. Newsletter. 4138

Uranium: Resources, Production and Demand/Uranium: Ressources, Production et Demande. 3423

Veterinary Dermatology. 4818

Voice of Silence Newsletter. 2289

Volunteer. 2028

Vox Sanguinis. 3189

Vsemirnoe Profsoyuznoe Dvizhenie. 2591

W A Y Forum. (World Assembly of Youth) 1269

W C O T P Biennial Report. (World Confederation of Organizations of the Teaching Profession) 1732

W F D Y News. (World Federation of Democratic Youth) 1269

W I Z O Review. (Women's International Zionist Organization) 4855

Water Quality International. 1980

Water Research. 4832

Water Science and Technology. 4833

Welding in the World/Soudage dans le Monde. 3431

White Ribbon Bulletin. 1539

Widening Horizons. 4855

Women's News. 4857

Work Accomplished by the Inter-American Juridical Committee during its Meeting. 2695

World Advertising Expenditures. 39

World Agriculture - I F A P News. 130

World Air Transport Statistics. 4668

World Alliance of Y M C A's Directory. 1302

World Aluminum Abstracts. 3429

World Bibliography of Social Security/Bibliographie Universelle de Securite Sociale. 744

World Communique. 1246

World Council of Churches. Office of Education. Education Newsletter. 4210

World Development Report. 937

World Directory of Mathematicians. 3061

World Economic Outlook. 888

World Farmers' Times. 130

World Federation of Teachers' Unions. Information Letter. 1672

World Fertility Survey. Basic Documentation. 3989

World Grain Statistics Yearbook. 145

World Highways. 4723

World Hockey. 4497

World Journal of Surgery. 3386

World List of Family Planning Agencies. 598

World List of Universities, Other Institutions of Higher Education and University Organizations. 1698

World Methodist Historical Society. Historical Bulletin. 4253

World Mine Production of Gold. 3498

World Mining Congress. Report. 3498

The World of Music. 3587

World Patent Information. 3679

World Press Freedom Review. 2577

World Scout Organization Report. 1246

World Scouting News/Bulletin du Scoutisme Mondial. 1246

World Student News. 1672

World Transport Data/Statistiques Mondiales de Transport. 4669

World Union for the Safeguard of Youth. Bulletin. 1246

World Youth/Jeunesse du Monde/Juventud del Mundo. 1271

World Zionist Press Service. 3935

Yearbook for Traditional Music. 3587

Yearbook of International Congress Proceedings. 3978

Yearbook of International Organizations/Annuaire des Organisations Internationales. 3978

Yearbook of Tourism Statistics. 4801

Young Cinema and Theatre/Jeune Cinema et Theatre. 3519

Youthlink. 1272

Zahlentafeln der Physikalisch-Chemischen Untersuchungen des Rheinwassers/Tableaux Numeriques des Analyses Physico-Chimiques des Eaux du Rhin. 1980

Zeitschrift fuer Fremdenverkehr/Revue de Tourisme/ Tourist Review. 4798

Zhenshchiny Mira. 4858

Zionist Literature. 4143

Zshurnalist. 2577

INTERNATIONAL CONGRESS PROCEEDINGS

Acoustical Imaging. 3858

Acta Concilium Ophthalmologicum. 3297

Acta Endocrinologica Panamericana. 3250

Acta I M E K O. (International Measurement Confederation) 3445

Acta Medica et Sociologica. 4427

African Regional Trade Union Conference. Report. 2579

Afro-Asian Peoples' Conference. Proceedings. 2331

Afro-Asian Peoples' Solidarity Organization. Council. Documents of the Session. 2331

Aims of Education and Development of Personality. Comparative Aspects. Proceedings of the CESE Conference. 1614

Allergologicum; Transactions of the Collegium Internationale. 3183

Annuaire International des Jus de Fruits/Internation Directory of Fruit Juices. 377

Archivum. 2744

Asian Pacific Congress of Cardiology. Symposia. 3205

Assembly of Western European Union. Proceedings. 2719

Baptist World Alliance. Congress Reports. 4230

Biometeorology; Proceedings. 3433

Brown Boveri Symposia. Proceedings. 1883

Caribbean Congress of Labour. Report. 2581

Carnegie-Rochester Conference Series on Public Policy. 654

Carotenoids Other Than Vitamin A. 474

Chemistry of Natural Products. 1217

Clinical Neurosurgery: Proceedings. 3334

Colloques Internationaux d'Histoire Maritime. Travaux. 4726

Colloquium on the Law of Outer Space. Proceedings. 50

Colombo Plan for Co-operative Economic and Social Development in Asia and the Pacific. Consultative Committee. Proceedings and Conclusions. 927

Conference Internationale sur les Phenomenes d'Ionisation dans les Gaz. Comptes Rendus. 1225

Conferencia de Facultades Latinoamericanas de Derecho. (Documentos Oficiales). 2615

Congres International d'Histoire des Sciences. Actes. 4305

Congreso Latinamericano de Siderurgia. Memoria Tecnica. 3404

Congresos Indigenistas Interamericanos. Actas. 237

Congress in Park and Recreation Administration. Programme. 3391

Congress in Park and Recreation Administration. Reports. 4544

Congress of International Congress Organizers and Technicians. Proceedings. 3391

Congresso Europeo di Storia Ospitaliera. Atti. 2460

Congresso Latinoamericano de Hidraulica (Papers). 4823

Coordination Chemistry. 1175

Council for the Social Sciences in East Africa. Social Science Conference. Proceedings. 4369

Council of American Building Officials. One and Two Family Dwelling Code. 614

Developments in Biological Standardization. 3446

E A P R Abstracts of Conference Papers. (European Association for Potato Research) 176

Electra. 1886

Etudes Historiques. 2310

Eucarpia. 501

European Association for Personnel Management. Congress Reports. 1065

European Brewery Convention. Proceedings of the International Congress. 380

European Civil Aviation Conference (Report of Session). 4672

European Congress of Anaesthesiology. Proceedings. 3191

European Congress of Cardiology. (Proceedings). 3207

European Congress on Electron Microscopy. 559

European Grassland Federation. Proceedings of the General Meeting. 176

European League for Economic Cooperation. Reports of the International Congress. 929

European Organization for Quality. Conference Proceedings. 4597

EUROSIM - Simulation News Europe. 1435

Guetertransport in Seeverkehr. 4728

Hybrid Microelectronics Symposium. (Papers). 1771

I A B S E Congress Report. (International Association for Bridge and Structural Engineering) 1867

I A T A Annual Report. (International Air Transport Association) 4674

I C E S Marine Science Symposia/Actes du Symposium. 1605

I C E V H Educator. (International Council for Education of the Visually Handicapped) 1736

I C H P E R Congress Proceedings. (International Council on Health, Physical Education and Recreation) 3804

I E E E International Conference on Communications. Conference Record. 1337

I E E E International Conference on Systems, Man, and Cybernetics. Proceedings. 1441

I E E E International Symposium on Circuits and Systems. Proceedings. 1772

I F A C Symposia Series. (International Federation of Automatic Control) 1930

I F L A Annual. (International Federation of Library Associations and Institutions) 2760

I L S M H News. (International League of Societies for Persons with Mental Handicap) 4024

Index to Malaysian Conferences/Indeks Persidangan Malaysia. 3395

Instrumentation in the Pulp and Paper Industry. 3663

Inter-African Conference on Co-Operative Societies Meeting. Reunion. 831

Inter-African Conference on Food and Nutrition. Programa e Informacoes. 3607

Inter-African Conference on Food and Nutrition. Report. 3607

Inter-African Conference on Industrial Commercial and Agricultural Education Meeting. 1722

Inter-African Conference on Medical Co-Operation. Meeting. 3109

Inter-African Conference on Social Science Meeting. 4376

Inter-African Conference on the Treatment of Offenders. Meetings. Reunion. 1515

Inter-African Forestry Conference. Conference Forestiere Interafricaine (Communications). 2102

Inter-African Labour Conference Reports, Recommendations and Conclusions. 983

Inter-American Commission of Women. Special Assembly. Final Act/Comision Interamericana de Mujeres. Asamblea Extraordinaria. Acta Final. 3943

Inter-American Development Bank. Board of Governors. Proceedings of the Meeting. 785

International Academy of Legal Medicine and of Social Medicine. (Congress Reports). 3265

International Air Safety Seminar Proceedings. 55

International Anatomical Congress. Proceedings. 3110

International Association for Cereal Science and Technology. Congress Proceedings. 2073

International Association for Classical Archaeology. Proceedings of Congress. 274

International Association for Cross-Cultural Psychology. International Conference. Selected Papers. 4025

International Association for Dental Research. Abstracts of the General Meeting. 3234

International Association for Hydraulic Research. Congress Proceedings. 1924

International Association for Scientific Study of Mental Deficiency. Proceedings of International Congress. 3339

International Association of Democratic Lawyers. Congress Report. 2636

International Association of Logopedics and Phoniatrics. Reports of Congress. 3339

International Association of Meteorology and Atmospheric Physics. Report of Proceedings of General Assembly. 3436

INDEX TO PUBLICATIONS OF INTERNATIONAL ORGANIZATIONS

International
Association of Milk Control Agencies. Proceedings of Annual Meetings. 200

International Association of Museums of Arms and Military History. Congress Reports. 3525

International Association of Performing Arts Libraries and Museums. Congress Proceedings. 330

International Association of Physical Education and Sports for Girls and Women. Proceedings of the International Congress. 4475

International Association of State Lotteries. (Reports of Congress). 1098

International Association of Thalassotherapy. Congress Reports. 3110

International Association of Workers for Troubled Children and Youth. Congress Reports. 1736

International Astronomical Union. General Assembly. Highlights. 365

International Astronomical Union. Proceedings of Symposia. 365

International Basketball Federation. Official Report of the World Congress. 4507

International Beekeeping Congress. Reports. 99

International Biometeorological Congress. Summaries and Reports Presented to the Congress. 442

International Biophysics Congress. Abstracts. 466

International Center for Companies of the Food Trade and Industry. Congress Report. 1041

International Ceramic Congress. Proceedings. 1165

International Clean Air Congress. Proceedings. 1977

International Commission of Sugar Technology. Proceedings of the General Assembly. 2073

International Commission on Irrigation and Drainage. Congress Reports. 1924

International Commission on Large Dams. Transactions. 1868

International Commission on Trichinellosis. Proceedings. 3220

International Committee of Onomastic Sciences. Congress Proceedings. 2819

International Confederation for Agricultural Credit. Assembly and Congress Reports. 152

International Confederation of Free Trade Unions. World Congress Reports. 2584

International Conference of Agricultural Economists. Proceedings. 152

International Conference of Building Officials. Analysis of Revisions to the (Year) Uniform Codes. 621

International Conference of Building Officials. Building Department Administration. 621

International Conference of Building Officials. Code Changes Committee. Annual Report. 621

International Conference of Building Officials. Dwelling Construction Under the Uniform Building Code. 621

International Conference of Building Officials. Plan Review Manual. 621

International Conference of Building Officials. Uniform Code for the Abatement of Dangerous Buildings. 621

International Conference of Building Officials. Uniform Fire Code. 621

International Conference of Building Officials. Uniform Housing Code. 621

International Conference of Building Officials. Uniform Mechanical Code. 621

International Conference of Building Officials. (Year) Accumulative Supplement to the Uniform Codes and Related Publications. 621

International Conference of Ethiopian Studies. Proceedings. 2333

International Conference of Social Security Actuaries and Statisticians. Reports. 2535

International Conference of Social Work. Conference Proceedings. 4409

International Conference on Acoustics. Reports. 3859

International Conference on Aerospace Computers in Rockets and Spacecraft. Proceedings. 67

International Conference on Cloud Physics. Proceedings. 3436

International Conference on Computer Communications. (Proceedings). 1447

International Conference on Computing Fixed Points with Applications. Proceedings. 3039

International Conference on Cosmic Rays. (Proceedings). 3847

International Conference on Fluid Sealing. Proceedings. 1931

International Conference on Large High Voltage Electric Systems. Proceedings. 1900

International Conference on Lead. Proceedings. 3409

International Conference on Lighthouses and Other Aids to Navigation. Reports. 4729

International Conference on Liquefied Natural Gas. Papers. 3689

International Conference on Oral Biology. Proceedings. 3234

International Conference on Piagetian Theory and the Helping Professions. Proceedings. 1639

International Conference on the Physics of Electronic and Atomic Collisions. Abstracts of Contributed Papers and Invited Papers. 3847

International Conference on the Structural Design of Asphalt Pavements. Proceedings. 4719

International Conference on Thermoelectric Energy Conversion. Proceedings. 1900

International Conference on Vehicle Structural Mechanics. Proceedings. 4693

International Congress Calendar. 3392

International Congress for Byzantine Studies. Acts/ Congres International des Etudes Byzantines. Actes. 2368

International Congress for Cybernetics. Proceedings. Actes. 1441

International Congress for Papyrology. Proceedings. 274

International Congress for Stereology. Proceedings. 1917

International Congress for the Study of Pre-Columbian Cultures of the Lesser Antilles. Proceedings. 242

International Congress of Angiology. Proceedings. 3209

International Congress of Entomology. 534

International Congress of Hematology. Proceedings. 3272

International Congress of Histochemistry and Cytochemistry. Proceedings. 477

International Congress of Home Economics. Report. 2447

International Congress of Linguists. Proceedings. 2819

International Congress of Nephrology. Abstracts of Reports and Communications. 3388

International Congress of Occupational Therapy. Proceedings. 3618

International Congress of Parasitology. Proceedings. 584

International Congress of Pharmaceutical Sciences. Proceedings. 3729

International Congress of Primatology. Proceedings. 242

International Congress of Psychology. Proceedings. 4025

International Congress of Radiology. (Reports). 3358

International Congress of Sugarcane Technologists. Proceedings. 2073

International Congress of Verdi Studies. Proceedings. 3556

International Congress on Alcoholism and Addictions. Proceedings. 1536

International Congress on Animal Reproduction. Proceedings. 4811

International Congress on Clinical Chemistry. Abstracts. 477

International Congress on Clinical Chemistry. Papers. 477

International Congress on Combustion Engines. Proceedings. 1931

International Congress on Metallic Corrosion. (Proceedings). 3409

International Congress on Technology and Technology Exchange. Proceedings. 1826

International Congress on the History of Art. Proceedings. 330

International Congress Series. 3393

International Congresses on Tropical Medicine and Malaria. (Proceedings). 3220

International Council for Bird Preservation. Proceedings of Conferences. 564

International Council on Archives. East and Central Africa Regional Branch. General Conference Proceedings. 2764

International Diabetes Federation. Triennial Report. 3254

International Economic Association. Proceedings of the Conferences and Congresses. 671

International Electron Devices Meeting. I E D M Technical Digest. 1774

International Eucharist Congress. Proceedings. 4266

International Federation for Information and Documentation. Proceedings of Congress. 2764

International Federation for Medical Psychotherapy. Congress Reports. 3339

International Federation of Agricultural Producers. General Conference Proceedings. 99

International Federation of Asian and Western Pacific Contractors' Associations. Proceedings of the Annual Convention. 3393

International Federation of Associations of Textile Chemists and Colorists. Reports of Congress. 4620

International Federation of Catholic Universities. General Assembly. Report. 1709

International Federation of Fruit Juice Producers. Proceedings of Congress. Compte-Rendu du Congres. 382

International Federation of Fruit Juice Producers. Rapport Annuel d'Activite. 2073

International Federation of Medical Students' Associations. Minutes and Reports of the General Assembly. 3110

International Federation of Operational Research Societies. Airline Group (A G I F O R S) Proceedings. 4675

International Federation of Plantation, Agricultural and Allied Workers. Report of the Secretariat to the I F P A A W World Congress. 152

International Federation of Prestressing. Congress Proceedings. 1868

International Foundry Congress. Papers and Communications. 3409

International Gas Union. Proceedings of World Gas Conferences. 3689

International Grassland Congress. Proceedings. 181

International Hop Growers Convention. Report of Congress. 207

International Horticultural Congress. Proceedings. 2132

International Humanist and Ethical Union. Proceedings of the Congress. 3769

International Hydrographic Conference. Reports of Proceedings. 1606

International Institute for Sugar Beet Research. Reports of the Winter Congress. 181

International Institute of Administrative Sciences. Reports of the International Congress. 4064

International Institute of Ibero-American Literature. Congress Proceedings. Memoria. 2925

International Institute of Public Finance. Papers and Proceedings. 1098

International Institute of Synthetic Rubber Producers. Annual Meeting Proceedings. 4292

International Iron and Steel Institute. Report of Conference Proceedings. 3409

International Joint Conference on Artificial Intelligence. Advance Papers of the Conference. 1408

International Journal of Psycho-Analysis. 4025

International Law Association. Reports of Conferences. 2725

International Literary and Artistic Association. Proceedings and Reports of Congress. 2508

International Meeting of Animal Nutrition Experts. Proceedings. 219

International Metalworkers' Congress. Reports. 3409

International Mineralogical Association. Proceedings of Meetings. 3486

International Navigation Congress. Proceedings. 4729

International Office of Cocoa, Chocolate and Sugar Confectionery. Report of the General Assembly. 2088

International Olympic Academy. Report of the Sessions. 4476

International Organization for Cooperation in Health Care. General Assembly. Report. 3111

International Orthopaedics. 3308

International P.E.N. Congress. Report. 2925

International Pediatric Association. Proceedings of Congress. 3321

International Philatelic Federation. General Assembly. Proces-Verbal. 3753

International Political Science Association. World Congress. 3899

International Population Conference. Proceedings. 3983

International Potash Institute. Colloquium. Proceedings. 181

International Potash Institute. Congress Proceedings. 181

International Publishers Association. Proceedings of Congress. 4130

International Road Congresses. Proceedings. 4719

International Rubber Study Group. Summary of Proceedings of the Group Meetings and Assemblies. 4292

International School of Physics "Enrico Fermi". Italian Physical Society. Proceedings. 3820

International Sculpture Conference. Proceedings. 331

International Seaweed Symposium. Proceedings. 506

International Sedimentological Congress. Guidebook. 1569

International Skating Union. Minutes of Congress. 4476

International Social Security Association. Reports of the General Assemblies of the ISSA. 2535

International Society for Rock Mechanics. Congress. Proceedings. 1868

International Society for Soil Mechanics and Foundation Engineering. Proceedings. 1868

International Society for the Sociology of Religion. 4183

International Society of Blood Transfusion. Proceedings of the Congress. 3272

International Society of Urology. Reports of Congress. 3388

International Statistical Institute. Bulletin. Proceedings of the Biennial Sessions. 4575

International Symposium on Atherosclerosis. Proceedings. 3209

International Symposium on Canine Heartworm Disease. Proceedings. 4811

International Symposium on Chemical Reaction Engineering. Proceedings. 1855

International Symposium on Concrete Roads. Reports. 1868

International Symposium on Crop Protection. Proceedings. 181

International Symposium on Fault-Tolerant Computing. Digest of Papers. 1397

International Symposium on Regional Development. Papers and Proceedings. 2489

International Symposium on Subscriber Loop and Services. Proceedings. 1900

International Symposium on the Chemistry of Cement. Proceedings. 1179

International Television Symposium and Technical Exhibition, Montreux. Symposium Record. 1375

International Thermal Spraying Conference. Preprint of Papers. 3429

International Trade Conference of Workers of the Building, Wood and Building Materials Industries. (Brochure). 621

International Union against Tuberculosis. Conference Proceedings. 3365

International Union for Conservation of Nature and Natural Resources. Proceedings of the General Assembly. 1489

International Union of Anthropological and Ethnological Sciences Newsletter. 242

International Union of Biological Sciences. General Assemblies. Proceedings. 442

International Union of Crystallography. Abstracts of the Triennial Congress. 1210

International Union of Food and Allied Workers' Associations. Meeting of the Executive Committee. I. Documents of the Secretariat. II. Summary Report. 2585

International Union of Forestry Research Organizations. Congress Proceedings. 2102

International Union of Housing Finance Institutions. Congress Proceedings. 786

International Union of Latin Notaries. Proceedings of Congress. 4064

International Union of Radio Science. Proceedings of General Assemblies. 1357

International Union of School and University Health and Medicine. Congress Reports. 1640

International Union of Students. Congress and Executive Committee Meetings Resolutions. 1709

International Water Conference. Proceedings. 4826

Internationaler Weltkongress der U F O-Forscher. Dokumentarbericht. 56

Inter-Parliamentary Union. Summary Records of the Inter-Parliamentary Conferences. 3962

Istituto Internazionale di Studi Liguri. Collezione di Monografie Preistoriche e Archeologiche. 275

Journees Biochimiques Latines. Rapports. 479

K O W A N I News. (Kongres Wanita Indonesia) 4846

Kongres ha-Tsiyoni. Hahlatot/World Zionist Organization. Zionist Congress. 3903

Kongresa Libro. 3393

Macromolecular Chemistry (Oxford). 1220

Mathematics and Computers in Simulation. 1435

Mikroelektronik. 1775

Miles International Symposium. 525

Mushroom Science. 510

N A D C A International Die Casting Congress. Transactions. (North American Die Casting Association) 1921

Nobel Symposium Series. 2512

North Atlantic Treaty Organization. Expert Panel on Air Pollution Modeling. Proceedings. 1978

Open Door International for the Emancipation of the Woman Worker. Report of Congress. 990

Organization of American States. Permanent Council. Decisions Taken at Meetings (Cumulated Edition). 2418

Pacific Science Association. Congress and Inter-Congress Proceedings. 4332

Parapsychology Foundation. Proceedings of International Conferences. 3670

Perugia Quadrennial International Conferences on Cancer. Proceedings. 3201

Photochemistry (Oxford). 1229

Power Systems Computation Conference. P S C C Proceedings. 1834

Progress in Protozoology. 590

Rubber Research Institute of Malaysia. Rubber Growers' Conference - Proceedings. 4293

Social Welfare Services in Japan. 4420

Standing Conference of Local and Regional Authorities of Europe. Official Reports of Debates. 4074

Standing Conference of Local and Regional Authorities of Europe. Texts Adopted. 4074

Study of Time. 370

Symposia Foundation Merieux. 3155

Symposium (International) on Combustion. 1230

Trade Unions International of Chemical, Oil and Allied Workers. International Trade Conference. Documents. 2590

TropMed Seminars on Tropical Medicine. Proceedings. 3224

Unesco. Records of the General Conference. Proceedings. 3975

Unesco. Records of the General Conference. Resolutions. 3975

Union Academique Internationale. Compte Rendu de la Session Annuelle du Comite. 2516

Union Mondiale des Organisations Syndicales sur Bases Economique et Sociale Liberales. Conferences: Rapport. 2591

United Nations Issues Conference. Report. 3975

United Nations of the Next Decade Conference. Report. 3975

United Schools International. Documents of the Biennial Conference. 2688

Water Supply. 4833

Wenner Gren Center International Symposium Series. 4351

World Association for Educational Research. Congress Reports. 1672

World Buiatrics Congress. 4819

World Conference on Animal Production. Proceedings. 228

World Congress of Psychiatry. Proceedings. 3356

World Congress of the Deaf. Proceedings. 2290

World Congress of the W F D. Proceedings. (World Federation of the Deaf) 2290

World Congress on Fertility and Sterility. Proceedings. 460

World Congress on the Prevention of Occupational Accidents and Diseases. Proceedings. 3623

World Council of Churches. General Assembly. Assembly - Reports. 4210

World Council of Churches. Minutes and Reports of the Central Committee Meeting. 4210

World Council of Service Clubs. Minutes of the General Meeting. 4424

World Energy Conference. Plenary Conferences. Transactions. 1797

World Movement of Mothers. Reports of Meetings. 4424

World Muslim Conference. Proceedings. 4221

World Union for the Safeguard of Youth. Conference Proceedings. 4424

World Veterinary Congress. Proceedings. 4820

World Zionist Organization. General Council. Addresses, Debates, Resolutions. 3935

World's Poultry Science Association. Proceedings of World's Poultry Congress. 228

World's Woman's Christian Temperance Union. Triennial Report. 1540

EUROPEAN COMMUNITIES

A C P - E E C Council of Ministers. Annual Report (Year). 925

Agricultural Markets: Places. 71

Agricultural Statistics Series No.1: Crop Production. 132

Agricultural Statistics Series No.2: Animal Production. 132

Balance of Payments Statistical Yearbook. 704

Basic Statistics of the European Community. 706

Bulletin of the European Communities. 848

Bulletin of the European Communities and Supplements. 848

C E E International. Droit et Affaires. (Communaute Economique Europeenne) 2720

C O M Documents. 3952

Commission of the European Communities. Annual Reports on the Progress of Research Work Promoted by the ECSC. 4099

Commission of the European Communities. Collection of Agreements. 904

Commission of the European Communities. Community Law. 2721

Commission of the European Communities. Directorate of Taxation. Inventory of Taxes. 1091

Commission of the European Communities. Documentation Bulletin. 3936

Commission of the European Communities. Europa Transport. Annual Report. 4648

Commission of the European Communities. European Regional Development Fund. Annual Report. 927

Commission of the European Communities. Financial Report. 1091

Commission of the European Communities. Marches Agricoles: Serie "Prix". Notes Explicatif. 148

Commission of the European Communities. Marches Agricoles: Serie "Prix". Produits Animaux. 149

Commission of the European Communities. Marches Agricoles: Serie "Prix". Produits Vegetaux. 149

Commission of the European Communities. Operation of Nuclear Power Stations. 1804

Commission of the European Communities. Report on Competition Policy. 1073

Commission of the European Communities. Report on the Social Developments. 4369

Commission of the European Communities. Trade Union Information Bulletin. 2581

Commission of the European Communities, Directory. 2721

Community Report. 851

Council of the European Communities. Review of the Council's Work. 852

Court of Justice of the European Communities. Report of Cases of the Court. 2722

Debates of the European Parliament. 2722

Developments in the European Communities. Report. 860

Directory of Community Legislation in Force. 2619

Directory of European Community Trade and Professional Associations. 1130

Documentation Europeenne - Serie Agricole. 87

Documentation Europeenne - Serie Syndicale et Ouvriere. 977

Dossier Europa. 3891

E I B - Information. (European Investment Bank) 945

E L F. (European Labour Forum) 3955

E P News. 2722

E U F I - Journal. (European Financial Services) 776

Earnings - Industry and Services. 713

Energy in Europe. 1788

Etudes Universitaires sur l'Integration Europeenne/ University Studies on European Integration. 3956

Euro Abstracts Section I. Euratom and EEC Research. 3837

Euro Abstracts Section II. Coal and Steel. 3499

Eurolink Age. 2272

Europa Transport. 4649

Europe. 864

Europe Magazine. 906

European Access. 664

European Atomic Energy Community. Resultats des Mesures de la Radioactivite Ambiante dans les Pays de la Communaute: Air-Retombee-Eaux. 4100

European Coal and Steel Community. Consultative Committee. Handbook. 929

European Coal and Steel Community. Consultative Committee. Yearbook. 929

European Communities. Economic and Social Committee. Annual Report (Year). 664

European Communities. Economic and Social Committee. Bulletin. 664

European Communities. Economic and Social Committee. Commission Documents. 664

European Court of Human Rights. Publications. Series B: Pleadings, Oral Arguments and Documents/Cour Europeenne des Droits de l'Homme. Publications. Serie B: Memoires, Plaidoiries et Documents. 3942

European Economy. 864

European Economy. Series A: Recent Economic Trends. 864

European Economy. Series B: Business and Consumer Survey Results. 864

European File. 906

European Foundation for the Improvement of Living and Working Conditions. Annual Report. 4435

European Investment Bank. Annual Report. 778

European Parliament. Bulletin. 3956

European Parliament. Christian-Democratic Group. Report on the Activities. 3893

European Parliament. Committee Report. 3392

European Parliament. Research and Documentation Papers. 1954

European Parliament. Working Documents. 2723

European Safety and Reliability Association. Bulletin. 4100

European Savings Bank. Report. 778

European University News. 1633

Eurostatistics Data for Short Term Economic Analysis. 715

External Trade: Nomenclature of Goods/Commerce Exterieur: Nomenclature des Pays. 908

Fact Sheets on the European Parliament. 3894

General Commission on Safety and Health in the Iron and Steel Industry. Report. 3617

General Report on the Activities of the European Communities. 867

Green Europe. 94

Industrial Trends. 722

Information Service of the European Communities. Newsletter on the Common Agricultural Policy. 152

Information Service of the European Communities. Trade Union News. 2584

Innovation and Technology Transfer. 2763

Joint Nuclear Research Center, Ispra, Italy. Annual Report. 1806

Mines Safety and Health Commission. Report/Organe Permanent pour la Securite dans les Mines de Houille. Rapport. 3489

Official Journal of the European Communities. C Series: Information and Notices. 3967

Official Journal of the European Communities. L & C: Legislation and Competition. 3967

Practical Guide to the Use of the European Communities' Scheme of Generalized Tariff Preferences. 919

Recherches Universitaires sur l'Integration Europeenne. 1715

Results of the Business Survey Carried out Among Management in the Community. 1084

S C A D Bulletin. (Systeme Communautaire d'Acces a la Documentation) 411

Social Europe. 4419

Statistical Office of the European Communities. Agricultural Prices. 143

Statistical Office of the European Communities. Bulletin of Energy Prices. 1800

Statistical Office of the European Communities. Commerce Exterieur: Products C E C A. 739

Statistical Office of the European Communities. Energy Statistics. Yearbook. 1800

Statistical Office of the European Communities. Energy Statistics Monthly Bulletin. 1800

Statistical Office of the European Communities. External Trade. Analytical Tables: Import - Export. 739

Statistical Office of the European Communities. Foreign Trade: Standard Country Classification. 739

Statistical Office of the European Communities. Monthly External Trade Bulletin. 739

Statistical Office of the European Communities. Monthly Statistics Iron and Steel. 3428

Statistical Office of the European Communities. National Accounts Yearbook. 739

Statistical Office of the European Communities. Statistical Studies and Surveys. 739

Statistical Office of the European Communities. Statistical Yearbook. Agriculture. 143

Statistical Office of the European Communities. Transport, Communications, Tourisme - Annuaire Statistique. 4667

Statistical Office of the European Communities. Yearbook of Regional Statistics. 739

Steel Industry Safety and Health Commission. Information Bulletin. 3420

Terminologie et Traduction. 2847

Trade Union News from the European Community. 995

Unemployment Monthly Bulletin. 995

Vocational Training Information Bulletin. 3631

UNITED NATIONS

A B C Human Rights Teaching. 1721

A C E I D Newsletter. (Asian Centre of Educational Innovation for Development) 1721

A D I Quarterly News Letter. (Asian Development Institute) 925

A F R O Technical Papers. 4096

A F R O Technical Report Series. 4096

A I D S Health Promotion Exchange. 3216

Adult Education Information Notes. 1681

African Population Newsletter. 3979

African Trade/Commerce Africain. 899

Agricultural Review for Europe. 146

Agricultural Trade in Europe. 146

Agrindex. 73

Agro-Chemicals News in Brief. 167

Aircraft Accident Digest. 45

Animal Health Yearbook. 4805

Animal Production and Health Newsletter. 3357

Annotated Accessions List of Studies and Reports in the Field of Science Statistics. 389

Annual Bulletin of Coal Statistics for Europe. 3498

Annual Bulletin of Electric Energy Statistics for Europe. 1797

Annual Bulletin of Gas Statistics for Europe/Bulletin Annuel de Statistiques de Gaz pour l'Europe. 3704

Annual Bulletin of General Energy Statistics for Europe. 1797

Annual Bulletin of Housing and Building Statistics for Europe. 600

Annual Bulletin of Steel Statistics for Europe. 3424

Annual Bulletin of Trade in Chemical Products. 1071

Annual Bulletin of Transport Statistics for Europe. 4661

Annual Report on Development Assistance to Mauritius. 926

Annual Review of Engineering Industries and Automation. 1915

Annual Review of Project Performance Results. 926

Annual Review of the Chemical Industry. 1071

Anuario Estadistico de America Latina y el Caribe/ Statistical Yearbook for Latin America and the Caribbean. 4562

Anuario Hidrologico del Istmo Centroamericano. 1597

Art. 313

Asia - Pacific in Figures. 4562

Asia - Pacific Population Journal. 3979

Asian Bibliography. 2327

Asian Cultural Centre for Unesco. Organization and Activities. 3634

Asian - Pacific Book Development. 4120

Asian Pacific Culture. 3634

Assignment Children. 1232

B I B E Annual Summary. (International Bulletin of Bibliography on Education) 1674

B I B E Quarterly Bulletin. (International Bulletin of Bibliography on Education) 1674

Basic Facts about the United Nations. 3951

Bibliographical Services Throughout the World. 392

Biological Substances. 431

Boletin de Arte. 319

Bollettino per le Farmacodipendenze e l'Alcoolismo. 1534

Bulletin of Labour Statistics. 707

Bulletin on Ageing. 2271

Bulletin on Narcotics. 1535

C E P A L Review. (Comision Economica para America Latina y el Caribe) 849

C I F A Technical Papers. (Food and Agriculture Organization of the United Nations, Committee for Inland Fisheries of Africa) 2037

C I N D A. 3837

Caribbean Documentation Centre. Current Awareness Bulletin. 396

Catalogue of Reproductions of Paintings, 1860-1979. 321

Census of Motor Traffic on Main International Traffic Arteries. 4718

Centro Latinoamericano de Demografia. Boletin Demografico. 3980

Centro Latinoamericano de Demografia. Notas de Poblacion. 3980

Centro Latinoamericano de Demografia. Serie OI: Publicaciones Conjuntas con Instituciones Nacionales de Paises de America Latina. 3980

Centro Pan-Americano de Febre Aftosa. Boletin. 4099

Centro Panamericano de Zoonosis. Monografias Cientificas y Tecnicas. 4304

Centro Panamericano de Zoonosis. Notas Tecnicas. 4808

Centro Panamericano de Zoonosis. Publicaciones Especiales. 4808

Centro Panamericano de Zoonosis. Serie de Bibliografias. 4820

Ceres. 83

Codes and Abbreviations for the Use of the International Telecommunications Services. 1362

Commodity Trade and Price Trends. 927

Commodity Trade Statistics. 711

Composition of the W M O. 3434

Conditions of Work Digest. 975

Confluence. 4823

Connaissance de l'Orient. Collection Unesco d'Oeuvres Representatives. 2908

Connect. 1946

Copyright. 3674

Copyright Bulletin. 2616

Copyright Laws and Treaties of the World. 3674

Copyright Laws and Treaties of the World. Supplement. 3674

Corriere Unesco. 237

Cost of Social Security. 4403

Courier (Paris). 3954

Cuadernos de la C E P A L. 830

D O C P A L Resumenes Sobre Poblacion en America Latina/D O C P A L Latin American Population Abstracts. 3991

Date Palm Journal. 175

Demographic Handbook for Africa/Guide Demographie de l'Afrique. 3981

Demographic Yearbook. 3981

Development Business. 928

Development Forum. 928

Development Information Abstracts/Bulletin Analytique sur le Developpement/Resumenes de Informacion sobre el Desarrollo. 713

Diogenes (English Edition). 4433

Direction of Trade Statistics. 713

Directory: Organizations of the United Nations System in the United Republic of Tanzania. 929

Disarmament. 3457

Disarmament Newsletter. 3891

Disarmament Times. 3891

Documentation, Libraries and Archives: Bibliographies and Reference Works. 2793

Documentation, Libraries and Archives: Studies and Research. 2755

Droit d'Auteur. 3674

E E R. (Environmental Events Record) 1947

E S C A P Energy News. (United Nations Economic and Social Commission for Asia and the Pacific) 1785

E S C W A Population Bulletin. (Economic and Social Commission for Western Asia) 3981

Earth Sciences Series. 1543

Economic and Social Survey of Asia and the Pacific. 861

Economic Bulletin for Asia and the Pacific. 861

Economic Bulletin for Europe (Annual). 861

Economic Situation of Air Transport. Review and Outlook (Years). 4672

Economic Studies. 862

Economic Survey of Europe. 862

Economic Survey of Latin America and the Caribbean. 862

Educacion Medica y Salud. 1694

Education in Asia and the Pacific: Reviews, Reports and Notes. 1628

Educational Building Digest. 616

Educational Innovation and Information. 1721

Educational Studies and Documents. 1631

Electric Power in Asia and the Pacific. 1887

Energy Statistics Yearbook. 1799

Enfants du Monde. 4404

Epidemiological Surveillance of Rabies for the Americas. 4809

Estudios e Informes de la C E P A L/C E P A L Studies and Reports. 929

European Civil Aviation Conference (Report of Session). 4672

Everyone's United Nations. 3957

F A O Agricultural Services Bulletin. (Food and Agriculture Organization of the United Nations) 150

F A O Animal Production and Health Series. (Food and Agriculture Organization of the United Nations) 216

F A O Commodity Review and Outlook. 150

F A O Documentation - Current Bibliography. 2051

F A O Economic and Social Development Paper. 665

F A O Fertilizer and Plant Nutrition Bulletin. 150

F A O Fertilizer Yearbook. 176

F A O Fisheries Circulars. 2039

F A O Fisheries Reports. 2039

F A O Fisheries Series. 2039

F A O Fisheries Technical Paper. 2039

F A O Food and Nutrition Series. 3605

F A O Irrigation and Drainage Papers. 4824

F A O Legislative Studies. 89

F A O Plant Protection Bulletin (Miltilingual Edition). 502

F A O Quarterly Bulletin of Statistics/Bulletin Trimestriel F A O de Statistiques/Boletin Trimestral F A O de Estadisticas. 137

F A O Regional Conference for Africa. 89

F A O Regional Conference for Asia and the Pacific. Report. 89

F A O Regional Conference for Europe. Report of the Conference. 89

F A O Regional Conference for Latin America and the Caribbean. Report. 89

F A O Regional Conference for the Near East. Report. 89

F A O Terminology Bulletin. 89

Farm Management Notes for Asia and the Far East. 150

Fertilizer Trade Information Monthly Bulletin. 908

Finance and Development. 780

Food and Agricultural Legislation. 2627

Food and Agriculture Organization of the United Nations. Asia and Pacific Plant Protection Commission. Quarterly Newsletter. 177

Food and Agriculture Organization of the United Nations. Asia and Pacific Plant Protection Commission. Technical Document. 178

Food and Agriculture Organization of the United Nations. Asia and the Pacific Commission on Agricultural Statistics. Periodic Report. 137

Food and Agriculture Organization of the United Nations. Basic Texts. 92

Food and Agriculture Organization of the United Nations. European Inland Fisheries Advisory Commission. Occasional Papers. 2041

Food and Agriculture Organization of the United Nations. European Inland Fisheries Advisory Commission. Technical Papers. 2041

Food and Agriculture Organization of the United Nations. Production Yearbook. 150

Food and Agriculture Organization of the United Nations. Soils Bulletins. 178

Food and Agriculture Organization of the United Nations. Trade Yearbook. 150

Food and Agriculture Organization of the United Nations. World Soil Resources Reports. 178

Food and Agriculture Organization of the United Nations Conference. Report. 92

Food and Nutrition Bulletin. 3605

Food Irradiation Newsletter. 2069

Foreign Trade Statistics of Africa. Series A: Direction of Trade. 717

Foreign Trade Statistics of Africa. Series C: Summary Tables/Statistiques Africaines du Commerce Exterieur. Serie C: Tableaux Recapitulatifs. 717

Foreign Trade Statistics of Asia and the Pacific. 717

Forestry Newsletter of the Asia-Pacific Region. 2100

Freshwater and Aquaculture Contents Tables. 2041

Fundamentals of Educational Planning. 1721

G A T T Focus. (General Agreement on Tariffs and Trade) 666

G A T T Studies in International Trade. (General Agreement on Tariffs and Trade) 909

General Agreement on Tariffs and Trade. Basic Instruments and Selected Documents Series. Supplement. 909

General Agreement on Tariffs and Trade. G A T T Activities in (Year). 909

General Agreement on Tariffs and Trade. International Trade. 909

General Fisheries Council for the Mediterranean. Reports of the Sessions. 2041

General Fisheries Council for the Mediterranean. Studies and Reviews. 2041

Geological Correlation. 1562

Guide to National Bibliographical Information Centres. 2759

Guide to Sources of International Population Assistance. 3982

Guide to Training Opportunities for Industrial Development. 930

Guide to U N C T A D Publications. 719

Health Physics Research Abstracts. 4117

High Frequency Broadcasting Schedule. 1356

Higher Education in Europe. 1708

Human Rights Bulletin. 3943

Human Rights Newsletter. 3943

I A E A Library Film Catalog. (International Atomic Energy Agency) 3837

I A E A Technical Documents Series. (International Atomic Energy Agency) 1805

I A R C Monographs on the Evaluation of Carcinogenic Risks to Humans. (International Agency for Research on Cancer) 3197

I A R C Scientific Publications. (International Agency for Research on Cancer) 3197

I C A O Circulars. (International Civil Aviation Organization) 4674

I C A O Journal. (International Civil Aviation Organization) 54

INDEX TO PUBLICATIONS OF INTERNATIONAL ORGANIZATIONS

I C J Bibliography. (International Court of Justice) 2699

I F D A Dossier. (International Foundation for Development Alternatives) 3959

I I E P Occasional Papers. (International Institute for Educational Planning) 1722

I I E P Research Reports. (International Institute for Educational Planning) 1722

I I E P Seminar Papers. (International Institute for Educational Planning) 1722

I L C A Proceedings. 218

I L O Information. (International Labour Office) 981

I L O Judgements of the Administrative Tribunal. (International Labour Office) 2633

I L O Publications. (International Labour Office) 720

I L P E S Cuadernos. (Instituto Latinamericano y del Caribe de Planificacion Economica y Social) 999

I M F Survey. (International Monetary Fund) 720

I M O News. (International Maritime Organization) 4728

I M S Newsletter. (International Marine Science) 1605

I N I S Atomindex. 3837

I N I S Newsletter. 2761

I N I S Reference Series. 2761

I N S T R A W News. (International Research and Training Institute for the Advancement of Women) 4845

Ideas and Action Bulletin. 152

Impact of Science on Society. 4314

Index Translationum. 2793

Indicators for the Telegram Retransmission System (TRS) - Telex Identification Codes. 1363

Indo-Pacific Fishery Commission. Report. 2043

Industrial Development Abstracts. (United Nations Industrial Development Organization) 722

Industrial Property. 3675

Industrial Property, Statistics B. Part 1 - Patents/ Propriete Industrielle, Statistiques B. Partie 1 - Brevets. 3679

Industrial Property, Statistics B. Part 2 - Trademarks and Service Marks, Utility Models, Industrial Designs, Varieties of Plants, Microorganisms/ Propriete Industrielle, Statistiques B. Partie 2 - Marques de Produits et des Services, Modeles d'Utilit. 3680

Industry and Development. 931

Industry and Environment. 1958

Industry and Technology Development News - Asia and the Pacific. 931

Information Circular on Radiation Techniques and Their Applications to Insect Pests. 3358

Infoterra. 1958

Instituto de Nutricion de Centro America y Panama (INCAP). Informe Anual. 3607

Intergovernmental Oceanographic Commission. Technical Series. 1606

International Atomic Energy Agency. Annual Report. 1805

International Atomic Energy Agency. Bulletin. 1805

International Atomic Energy Agency. Legal Series. 2636

International Atomic Energy Agency. Nuclear Power Reactors in the World. 1806

International Atomic Energy Agency. Panel Proceedings Series. 1806

International Atomic Energy Agency. Proceedings Series. 1806

International Atomic Energy Agency. Safety Series. 4105

International Atomic Energy Agency. Technical Directories. 1806

International Atomic Energy Agency. Technical Report Series. 1806

International Bulletin on Atomic and Molecular Data for Fusion. 1806

International Bureau of Education. Bulletin. 1677

International Catalogue of Occupational Safety and Health Films. 3623

International Centre for Theoretical Physics. Annual Report. 3820

International Civil Aviation Organization. Aeronautical Agreements and Arrangements. Annual Supplement. 4674

International Civil Aviation Organization. Air Navigation Plan. Africa - Indian Ocean Region. 56

International Civil Aviation Organization. Air Navigation Plan. Caribbean and South American Regions. 56

International Civil Aviation Organization. Air Navigation Plan. Middle East and Asia Regions. 56

International Civil Aviation Organization. Air Navigation Plan. North Atlantic, North American and Pacific Regions. 56

International Civil Aviation Organization. Airworthiness Committee. Report of Meeting. 56

International Civil Aviation Organization. All-Weather Operations Panel. Report of Meeting. 56

International Civil Aviation Organization. Assembly. Report and Minutes of the Legal Commission. 4674

International Civil Aviation Organization. Assembly. Report of the Economic Commission. 4674

International Civil Aviation Organization. Assembly. Report of the Technical Commission. 56

International Civil Aviation Organization. Assembly. Resolutions. 4674

International Civil Aviation Organization. Automated Data Interchange Systems Panel. Report of Meeting. 56

International Civil Aviation Organization. Council. Annual Report. 4674

International Civil Aviation Organization. Digests of Statistics. Series AT. Airport Traffic. 4664

International Civil Aviation Organization. Digests of Statistics. Series F. Financial Data. 4664

International Civil Aviation Organization. Digests of Statistics. Series FP. Fleet, Personnel, Commercial Air Carriers. 4664

International Civil Aviation Organization. Digests of Statistics. Series R. Civil Aircraft on Register. 4664

International Civil Aviation Organization. Digests of Statistics. Series TF. Traffic by Flight Stage. 4664

International Civil Aviation Organization. Digests of Statistics. Series T. Traffic, Commercial Air Traffic. 4664

International Civil Aviation Organization. Index of I C A O Publications. Annual Cumulation. 4664

International Civil Aviation Organization. Legal Committee. Minutes and Documents (of Sessions). 4675

International Civil Aviation Organization. Library Information: Recent Accessions and Selected Articles. 66

International Conference on Education. Final Report/ Conference International de l'Education. Rapport Final. 1639

International Court of Justice. Yearbook. 2724

International Designs Bulletin. 3675

International Digest of Health Legislation. 4105

International Directory of Marine Scientists. 442

International Directory of New and Renewable Energy. 1140

International Finance Corporation. Report. 785

International Financial Statistics. 722

International Financial Statistics Yearbook. 722

International Frequency List. 1375

International Frequency List. Preface. 1375

International Institute for Labour Studies. Research Series. 983

International Labour Conference. Reports to the Conference and Record of Proceedings. 983

International Labour Documentation. 722

International Labour Office. Labour Law Documents. 984

International Labour Office. Official Bulletin. Series A. 984

International Labour Office. Official Bulletin. Series B. 984

International Labour Office. Special Report of the Director-General on the Application of the Declaration Concerning the Policy of Apartheid of the Republic of South Africa. 3944

International Labour Review. 984

International Monetary Fund. Annual Report of the Executive Board. 786

International Monetary Fund. Annual Report on Exchange Arrangements and Exchange Restrictions. 786

International Monetary Fund. Balance of Payments Statistics. 723

International Monetary Fund. Government Finance Statistics Yearbook. 723

International Monetary Fund. Occasional Papers. 786

International Monetary Fund. Pamphlet Series. 786

International Monetary Fund. Selected Decisions of the International Monetary Fund and Selected Documents. 786

International Monetary Fund. Staff Papers. 786

International Monetary Fund. Summary Proceedings of the Annual Meeting of the Board of Governors. 786

International Monetary Fund. World Economic and Financial Surveys. 786

International Narcotics Control Board. Report for (Year). 3730

International Narcotics Control Board. Statistics on Psychotropic Substances for (Year). 3748

International Oceanographic Tables. 1606

International Radio Consultative Committee. Plenary Assembly. Proceedings. 1356

International Review for the Sociology of Sport. 4439

International Review of Criminal Policy. 1516

International Rice Commission. Newsletter. 181

Int'l Org

International Social Science Journal. 4376

International Telecommunication Union. Booklets. 1338

International Telecommunication Union. Central Library. List of Annuals/Union Internationale des Telecommunications. Bibliotheque Centrale. Listes des Publications Annuelles/Union Internacional de Telecomunicaciones. Biblioteca Central. Lista de Publicaciones Anuales. 1348

International Telecommunication Union. Central Library. List of Periodicals/Union Internationale des Telecommunications. Bibliotheque Centrale. Liste des Periodique/Union International de Telcommunicaciones. Biblioteca Central. Lista de Revistas. 1348

International Telecommunication Union. Central Library. List of Recent Acquisitions/Union Internationale des Telecommunications. Bibliotheque Centrale. Liste des Acquisitions Recentes/Union Internacional de Telecomunicaciones. Biblioteca Central. Lista de Adquisiciones Recientes. 1348

International Telecommunication Union. List of Telegraph Offices Open for International Service. 1363

International Telecommunication Union. Operational Bulletin. 1363

International Telecommunication Union. Report on the Activities. 1363

International Telecommunication Union. Seminars. 1338

International Telegraph and Telephone Consultative Committee. Plans. 1363

International Telegraph and Telephone Consultative Committee. Plenary Assembly. Proceedings. 1363

International Trade Forum. 913

International Trade Statistics Yearbook. 723

International Travel and Health: Vaccination Requirements and Health Advice. 4105

International Understanding at School. 1640

Inventory of Population Projects in Developing Countries Around the World. 3984

Investment Africa. 932

Joint F A O - W H O Codex Alimentarius Commission. Report of the Session. 4106

Korean Social Science Journal. 4378

Labour Education. 986

Labour-Management Relations Series. 987

Land Reform, Land Settlement and Cooperatives/ Reforme Agraire, Colonisation et Cooperatives Agricoles/Reforma Agraria, Colonizacion y Cooperativas. 153

Lifelong Education Network. 1646

List of Cables Forming the World Submarine Network. 1363

List of E C A Documents Issued/Liste des Documents Publies par la C E A. 932

List of International Telephone Routes. 1364

List of Space Radiocommunication Stations and Radioastronomy Stations. 1357

List of Telecommunication Channels Used for the Transmission of Telegrams. 1364

Management Development Series. 1019

Marine Science Contents Tables. 466

Market Trends & Prospects for Chemical Products. 1183

Marques Internationales. 3676

Meetings on Atomic Energy. 3393

Migrant Pest Newsletter. 185

Monitoring Information Summary. 1357

Monographs on Oceanographic Methodology. 1608

Museums and Monuments Series. 3529

Mutation Breeding Newsletter. 185

N A T I S - News. (National Information System) 2774

Narcotic Drugs: Estimated World Requirements for (Year). 3811

Natural Resources Research. 1547

Nature and Resources. 1493

New Acquisitions in the U N E C A Library. 407

New Trends in Biology Teaching. 449

New Trends in Chemistry Teaching. 1184

New Trends in Integrated Science Teaching. 1756

New Trends in Mathematics Teaching. 3049

New Trends in Physics Teaching. 3825

New United Nations Publications. 3910

News from C C I V S. (Coordinating Committee for International Voluntary Service) 4415

Notas Sobre la Economia y el Desarrollo. 876

Nuclear Data Newsletter. 1807

Nuclear Fusion/Fusion Nucleaire. 3848

Objective: Justice. 3945

Occupational Safety and Health Series. 3620

Oficina Sanitaria Panamericana. Boletin. 4109

Operational Hydrology Reports. 1600

Our Planet. 1965

Ozone Layer Bulletin. 1978

P C T Gazette. (Patent Cooperation Treaty) 3680

P R E A L C Investigaciones sobre Empleo. (Programa Regional del Empleo para America Latina y el Caribe) 878

P R E A L C Newsletter. (Programa Regional del Empleo para America Latina y el Carige) 3630

Palestine Refugees Today. 4416

Pan American Health Organization. Bulletin. 4109

Periodicals of Asia and the Pacific. 2268

Permanent Missions to the United Nations/Missions Permanentes Aupres des Nations Unies a Geneve et Orga Principaux des Nations Unies. 3969

Personnel des Nations Unies et des Agences Specialisees en Republique de Rwanda. 934

Perspectives. 1654

Pesticide Residues in Food. 4110

Plant Genetic Resources Newsletter. 1495

Plant Variety Protection. 189

Population. 3985

Population Bulletin of the United Nations. 3986

Population Education in Asia and the Pacific Newsletter and Forum. 3986

Population Headliners. 3986

Population Studies. 3986

Populi. 3986

Prices of Agricultural Products and Selected Inputs in Europe and North America. 156

Propriete Industrielle. 3678

Prospects. 1656

Public Health Papers. 4110

R I S S: Regional Information Support Service. 142

Radiation Dosimetry Data: Catalogue. 3361

Rapport Annuel sur l'Assistance au Developpement: Rwanda. 934

Rapport Annuel sur la Cooperation au Developpement - Burundi. 934

Refugees. 3970

Refugees Magazine. 3970

Regional Development Dialogue. 934

Report on Development Assistance to Ethiopia. 934

Report on Development Cooperation to the Democratic Republic of the Sudan. 934

Report on the World Health Situation. 4111

Reports and Papers in the Social Sciences. 4384

Review of Maritime Transport. 4736

Revista Internacional del Trabajo. 992

Revue de Coree. 3643

Revue Internationale des Sciences Sociales. 4384

Revue Internationale du Travail. 992

Rural Progress. 935

Safety and Health at Work. 3623

Sample Surveys in the ESCAP Region. 737

Science Policy Studies and Documents. 4340

Securite et Sante au Travail. 3623

Selective Inventory of Social Science Information and Documentation Services. 4385

Siren. 1611

Small Industry Bulletin for Asia and the Pacific. 1028

Social and Labour Bulletin. 993

Social Development Newsletter. 4449

Soils Newsletter. 193

State of Food and Agriculture. 122

Statistical Indicators for Asia and the Pacific. 4587

Statistical Indicators of Short Term Economic Changes in E.C.E. Countries. 885

Statistical Information Bulletin for Africa/Bulletin d'Information Statistique pour l'Afrique. 739

Statistical Yearbook for Asia and the Pacific/Annuaire Statistique pour l'Asie et le Pacifique. 4588

Statistics of Road Traffic Accidents in Europe. 4667

Statistics of World Trade in Steel. 3428

Statistics on World Trade in Engineering Products. Bulletin. 3428

Steel Market. 3421

Studies and Reports in Hydrology Series. 1600

Studies in Mathematics Education. 1723

Studies in the Processing, Marketing and Distribution of Commodities. 1054

Studies on Selected Development Problems in Various Countries in the Middle East. 935

Study Abroad/Etudes a l'Etranger/Estudios en el Extranjero. 1723

Survey of Economic and Social Conditions in Africa. 935

Table of International Telex Relations and Traffic. 1366

Technical Papers in Hydrology Series. 1600

Telecommunication Journal. 1343

Trade and Development Report. 922

Trade in Natural Resource-Products. 922

Trade Policy Review. 922

Training for Agriculture and Rural Development. 1687

Transnational Corporations. 923

Transnational Corporations and Transborder Data Flows. 828

Transport & Communications Bulletin for Asia & the Pacific. 4657

Tungsten Statistics. 3428

U I E Case Studies. (Unesco Institute for Education) 1668

U I E Monographs. (Unesco Institute for Education) 1668

U I E Studies on Functional Illiteracy in Industrialized Countries. (Unesco Institute for Education) 1687

U I E Studies on Post-Literacy and Continuing Education. (Unesco Institute for Education) 1687

U N C H S Habitat News. (United Nations Centre for Human Settlements) 2497

U N C R D Bulletin. (United Nations Centre for Regional Development) 936

U N C R D Newsletter. (United Nations Centre for Regional Development) 936

U N C T A D Bulletin. (United Nations Conference on Trade and Development) 923

U N C T A D Commodity Yearbook. (United Nations Conference on Trade and Development) 741

U N C T A D Review. (United Nations Conference on Trade and Development) 923

U N Chronicle. 3974

U N D O C: Current Index. (United Nations Documents) 3938

U N E P Information. (United Nations Environment Programme) 1970

U N I C E F Policy Review Series. (United Nations Childrens Fund) 4422

U N I D I R Newsletter/Lettre de L'U N I D I R. (United Nations Institute for Disarmament Research) 3974

U N I D O Newsletter. (United Nations Industrial Development Organization) 936

U N I S I S T Boletin de Informacion. 2788

U N I S I S T Newsletter. (Unesco Programme of International Cooperation in Scientific and Technological Information) 2788

U N R I S D News. 4390

Unesco. Centro de Documentacion Cultural, Havana. Informaciones Trimestrales. 2516

Unesco. Comision Nacional Cubana. Boletin. 2516

Unesco. Principal Regional Office for Asia and Pacific. Abstract Bibliography Series on Population Education. 1680

Unesco. Principal Regional Office for Asia and the Pacific. Bulletin. 1669

Unesco. Records of the General Conference. Proceedings. 3975

Unesco. Records of the General Conference. Resolutions. 3975

Unesco. Regional Office for Science and Technology for Africa. Bulletin. 4349

Unesco. Regional Office for Science and Technology for Latin America and the Caribbean. Boletin. 4612

Unesco. Report of the Director-General on the Activities of the Organization. 3975

Unesco. Scientific Maps and Atlases and Other Related Publications. 414

Unesco. Statistics on Science and Technology/Statistiques Relatives aux Science et a la Technologie/Estadisticas Relativas a la Ciencia y a la Tecnologia. 4358

Unesco. Studies on Books and Reading. 4138

Unesco Australia. 936

Unesco List of Documents and Publications. 1680

Unesco Source Books on Curricula and Methods. 1762

Unesco Statistical Reports and Studies. 4591

Unesco Statistical Yearbook. 4591

Union Postale. 1354

Union Postale Universelle. Actes. 1354

Union Postale Universelle. Statistique des Services Postaux. 1354

United Nations. Conference on Trade and Development. Trade and Development Board. Official Records. 936

United Nations. Conference on Trade and Development. Trade and Development Board. Official Records. Supplements. 3975

United Nations. Dag Hammarskjold Library. Current Bibliographical Information. 3939

United Nations. Department of International Economic and Social Affairs. Statistical Office. Construction Statistic Yearbook. 639

United Nations. Development Programme. Compendium of Approved Projects. 936

United Nations. Division of Narcotic Drugs. Information Letter. 1539

United Nations. Economic and Social Commission for Asia and the Pacific. Asian Population Studies Series. 3988

United Nations. Economic and Social Commission for Asia and the Pacific. Development Papers. 1498

United Nations. Economic and Social Commission for Asia and the Pacific. Mineral Resources Development Series. 3497

United Nations. Economic and Social Commission for Asia and the Pacific. Natural Resources - Water Series. 4829

United Nations. Economic and Social Commission for Asia and the Pacific. Water Resources Series. 4829

United Nations. Economic and Social Council. Annexes. 696

United Nations. Economic and Social Council. Index to Proceedings. 3939

United Nations. Economic and Social Council. Official Records. 3975

United Nations. Economic Commission for Asia and the Pacific. Energy Resources Development Series. 1796

United Nations. Economic Commission for Europe. Information. 696

United Nations. Economic Commission for Europe. Statistical Journal. 1030

United Nations. General Assembly. Annexes. 696

United Nations. General Assembly. Index to Proceedings. 3939

United Nations. General Assembly. Official Records. 696

United Nations. General Assembly. Provisional Records. 696

United Nations. International Law Commission Yearbook. 2729

United Nations. Multilateral Treaties Deposited with the Secretary-General. 2729

United Nations. National Accounts Statistics. Analysis of Main Aggregates. 741

United Nations. National Accounts Statistics. Government Accounts and Tables. 742

United Nations. National Accounts Statistics. Main Aggregates and Detailed Tables. 742

United Nations. Population and Vital Statistics Report. 3996

United Nations. Regional Centre for Demographic Training and Research in Latin America. Serie A/Centro Latinoamericano de Demografia. Serie A. 3988

United Nations. Regional Centre for Demographic Training and Research in Latin America. Serie C/Centro Latinoamericano de Demografia. Serie C. 3988

United Nations. Regional Centre for Demographic Training and Research in Latin America. Serie D/Centro Latinoamericano de Demografia. Serie D. 3988

United Nations. Security Council. Index to Proceedings. 3939

United Nations. Security Council. Official Records. 3975

United Nations. Security Council. Official Records. Supplement. 3975

United Nations. Statistical Yearbook. 4591

United Nations. Treaty Series. 2729

United Nations. Treaty Series. Cumulative Index. 2701

United Nations. Trusteeship Council. Index to Proceedings. 3939

United Nations. Trusteeship Council. Offcial Records. Verbatim Records of Plenary Meetings. 3975

United Nations. Trusteeship Council. Official Records. 3975

United Nations. Trusteeship Council. Official Records. Annexes - Sessional Fascicle. 3975

United Nations. Trusteeship Council. Official Records. Resolutions. 3975

United Nations. Trusteeship Council. Official Records. Supplements. 3975

United Nations. Yearbook. 3975

United Nations Children's Fund. Programme Division. Conference Reports Series. 4422

United Nations Childrens Fund. Programme Division. Staff Working Papers Series. 4422

United Nations Commission on International Trade Law. Report on the Work of Its Session. 2729

United Nations Commission on International Trade Law. Yearbook. 2729

United Nations Conference on the Standardization of Geographical Names. Report of the Conference. 2264

United Nations Conference on Trade and Development: Proceedings. 923

United Nations Congress on the Prevention of Crime and the Treatment of Offenders. Report. 1523

United Nations Crime and Justice Research Institute. Publication. 1523

United Nations Disarmament Yearbook. 3473

United Nations Economic and Social Commission for Asia and the Pacific. Social Development Division. Social Work Education and Development. 4422

United Nations Economic and Social Commission for Asia and the Pacific. Statistical Newsletter. 742

United Nations Economic and Social Council. Disarmament Study Series. 3473

United Nations Economic and Social Council. Official Records. Supplements and Special Supplements. 696

United Nations Economic and Social Council. Resolutions and Decisions. 696

United Nations Economic and Social Council. Summary Records of Plenary Meetings. 696

United Nations Economic Commission for Africa. Annual Report. 936

United Nations Economic Commission for Africa. Statistical Newsletter. 742

United Nations Economic Commission for Europe. Occasional Studies. 887

United Nations Environment Programme. Evaluation Report (Year). 1970

United Nations Environment Programme. Feature. 1970

United Nations Environment Programme. Governing Council. Report on the Work of its Session. 1970

United Nations Environment Programme. The State of the Environment; Report of the Executive Director. 1970

United Nations Juridical Yearbook. 2730

United Nations Library. Monthly Bibliography. Part 1: Books, Official Documents, Serials. 3939

United Nations Library. Monthly Bibliography. Part 2: Selected Articles. 3939

United Nations Population Fund. Annual Review of Population Law. 3988

United Nations Regional Cartographic Conference for Asia and the Pacific. Report of the Conference. 2264

United Nations Regional Cartographic Conference for the Americas. Report of the Conference. 2264

United Nations Review. 3975

United Nations Statistical Office. Monthly Bulletin of Statistics. 4591

United Nations University. Work in Progress. 936

Vigilancia Epidemiologica de la Rabia para las Americas. 4819

W H O AIDS Series. (World Health Organization) 3224

W H O Offset Publications. (World Health Organization) 4119

W H O Technical Report Series. (World Health Organization) 3161

W M O Bulletin. (World Meteorological Organization) 3442

Waste Management Research Abstracts. 4119

Water Resources Journal. 4833

Weekly Epidemiological Record. 4115

World Bank. Abstracts of Current Studies. 744

World Bank. Annual Report. 937

World Bank. Monthly Operational Summary. 937

World Bank. Publications Update. 937

World Bank Atlas. 937

World Bank Economic Review. 888

World Bank Research News. 937

World Bank Research Observer. 804

World Cartography. 2266

World Debt Tables. 937

World Directory of Human Rights Teaching and Research. 1159

World Directory of Peace Research and Training Institutions. 3977

World Directory of Social Science Institutions. 4396

World Directory of Teaching and Research Institutions in International Law. 2730

World Economic Outlook. 888

World Food Programme Journal. 3613

World Health/Sante du Monde. 4115

World Health Forum. 3163

World Health Organization. Bulletin. 3163

World Health Organization. Handbook of Resolutions and Decisions of the World Health Assembly and the Executive Board. 4115

World Health Organization. Monograph Series. 4115

World Health Organization. Regional Office for Africa. Report of the Regional Committee. 4115

World Health Organization. Regional Office for Africa. Report of the Regional Director. 4115

World Health Organization. Regional Office for the Eastern Mediterranean. Annual Report of the Regional Director. 4115

World Health Organization. Regional Office for the Western Pacific. Annual Report of the Regional Director to the Regional Committee for the Western Pacific. 4115

World Health Organization. Work of W H O. 4115

World Health Organization A I D S Technical Bulletin. 3182

World Health Statistics Annual. 4119

World Health Statistics Quarterly/Rapport Trimestriel de Sanitares Mondiales. 4119

World List of Social Science Periodicals. 4396

World Market for Dairy Products. 130

World Meteorological Organization. Commission for Instruments and Methods of Observation. Abridged Final Report of the (No.) Session. 3442

World Meteorological Congress. Proceedings. 3442

World Meteorological Organization. Abridged Final Reports of Sessions of Technical Commissions. 3442

World Meteorological Organization. Annual Reports. 3442

World Meteorological Organization. Basic Documents. 3442

World Meteorological Organization. Commission for Aeronautical Meteorology. Abridged Final Report of the (No.) Session. 3442

World Meteorological Organization. Commission for Agricultural Meteorology. Abridged Final Report of the (No.) Session. 3443

World Meteorological Organization. Commission for Basic Systems. Abridged Final Report of the (No.) Session. 3443

World Meteorological Organization. Commission for Hydrology. Abridged Final Report of the (No.) Session. 3443

World Meteorological Organization. Commission for Marine Meteorology. Abridged Final Report of the (No.) Session. 3443

World Meteorological Organization. Congress. Abridged Report with Resolutions. 3443

World Meteorological Organization. Executive Council Session. Abridged Final Reports with Resolutions. 3443

World Meteorological Organization. Regional Association I (Africa). Abridged Final Report of the (No.) Session. 3443

World Meteorological Organization. Regional Association II (Asia). Abridged Final Report of the (No.) Session. 3443

World Meteorological Organization. Regional Association III (South America). Abridged Final Report of the (No.) Session. 3443

World Meteorological Organization. Regional Association IV (North America and Central America). Abridged Final Report of the (No.) Session. 3443

World Meteorological Organization. Regional Association V (South West Pacific). Abridged Final Report of the (No.) Session. 3443

World Meteorological Organization. Regional Association VI (Europe). Abridged Final Report of the (No.) Session. 3443

World Meteorological Organization. Reports on Marine Science Affairs. 1612

World Meteorological Organization. Special Environmental Reports. 1972

World Meteorological Organization. Technical Notes. 3443

World Meteorological Organization. Weather Reporting. Volume A: Observing Stations. 3443

World Meteorological Organization. Weather Reporting. Volume B: Data Processing. 3443

World Meteorological Organization. Weather Reporting. Volume C: Transmissions. 3444

World Meteorological Organization. Weather Reporting. Volume D: Information for Shipping. 3444

World Trade Annual. 924

World Trade Annual Supplement. 924

World Weather Watch Planning Reports. 3444

Yearbook of Common Carrier Telecommunication Statistics/Annuaire Statistique des Telecommunications du Secteur Public. 1346

Yearbook of Forest Products/Annuaire des Produits Forestiers/Anuario de Productos Forestales. 2119

Year Book of Labour Statistics. 744

Yearbook on Human Rights. 3948

Your United Nations. 2326

ISSN Index

Titles in the Bowker International Serials Database with ISSN are listed in this index. For title change, a reference is given to the ISSN of the new title. If a title has changed and a new ISSN has not been assigned (or has not been entered in the Bowker database serial record), a reference to the new title will be given. Duplicate listing of ISSN, with references to new titles and/or new ISSN, indicates that the serial has split. Ceased titles are identified by the symbol†.

ISSN	Title
0000-0019	Publishers Weekly
0000-0043	Irregular Serials and Annuals see 0000-0175
0000-0051	Previews†
0000-0078	L J - S L J Hot Line (Library Journal - School Library Journal) see 0740-736X
0000-0094	Bowker Serials Bibliography Supplement see 0000-1074
0000-0140	Subject Collections
0000-0159	Subject Guide to Books in Print
0000-0167	Subject Guide to Children's Books in Print
0000-0175	Ulrich's International Periodicals Directory
0000-0191	Who's Who in American Art
0000-0205	Who's Who in American Politics
0000-0213	Willing's Press Guide
0000-0221	Internationales Bibliotheks-Handbuch
0000-0248	Scientific and Technical Books in Print see 0000-054X
0000-0256	Who's Who in der Politik†
0000-0264	Subject Guide to Forthcoming Books see 0015-8119
0000-0280	Book - Guide: Mystery, Detective and Suspense Stories†
0000-0299	Biometeorological Research Centre. Reports
0000-0302	Mystery & Detection Annual
0000-0310	Books in Print Supplement
0000-0329	I B I D (International Bibliography, Information, Documentation) see 0256-1042
0000-0345	Canadian Serials Directory
0000-037X	Educational Media Yearbook see 8755-2094
0000-0388	International Index to Film Periodicals
0000-0434	Magazine Industry Market Place†
0000-0450	Information Industry Market Place changed to North American Online Directory.
0000-0469	Publishers Weekly Yearbook changed to Book Publishing Annual.
0000-0485	Small Press
0000-0507	Ulrich's Quarterly see 0000-1074
0000-0515	Books in Series in the United States see 0000-0906
0000-054X	Scientific and Technical Books and Serials in Print
0000-0574	Medical Books and Serials in Print see 0000-085X
0000-0590	Educational Film Locator see 0000-0973
0000-0612	Religious Books and Serials in Print see 0000-0868
0000-0620	Publishers and Distributors of the United States see 0000-0671
0000-0663	Associations' Publications in Print†
0000-0671	Publishers, Distributors & Wholesalers of the United States
0000-0701	Law Information see 0000-0752
0000-0728	Law Information Update see 0000-1031
0000-0736	Books Out-of-Print
0000-0752	Bowker's Law Books and Serials in Print
0000-0760	Bowker's Law Books and Serials in Print Update see 0000-1031
0000-0779	Computer Books and Serials in Print†
0000-0795	I B M Software Directory†
0000-0809	Business Mini-Micro Software Directory†
0000-0817	C P-M Software Directory†
0000-0825	El-Hi Textbooks and Serials in Print
0000-0833	Retailers Microcomputer Market Place†
0000-085X	Medical and Health Care Books and Serials in Print
0000-0868	Religious and Inspirational Books and Serials in Print
0000-0892	Bowker International Serials Database Update see 0000-1074
0000-0906	Books in Series
0000-0914	Magazines for Libraries
0000-0957	Magazines for School Libraries see 0000-1368
0000-0965	Forthcoming Children's Books†
0000-0973	Educational Film & Video Locator
0000-0981	Ulrich's and Irregular Serials and Annuals on Microfiche changed to Ulrich's on Microfiche.
0000-1007	Variety's Complete Home Video Directory. Adult Supplement†
0000-1015	Variety's Complete Home Video Directory†
0000-1023	Tradeshow Week Data Book
0000-1031	Bowker's Law Books and Serials in Print Supplement
0000-104X	Index to Legal Books†
0000-1058	Code of Federal Regulations Index
0000-1074	Ulrich's Update
0000-1112	Audio Video Market Place see 1044-0445
0000-1120	Complete Directory of Large Print Books and Serials
0000-1139	Robotics Abstracts
0000-1155	Literary Market Place see 0161-2905
0000-1163	Ulrich's News†
0000-118X	Telegen Abstracts†
0000-1198	Environment Abstracts Annual
0000-1201	Telegen Reporter Annual changed to Telegen Abstracts Annual.
0000-121X	Robomatix Reporter Annual see 1053-6051
0000-1228	Acid Rain Abstracts Annual see 0000-1198
0000-1236	C A D - C A M Abstracts Annual
0000-1244	Artificial Intelligence Abstracts Annual
0000-1252	Telecommunications Abstracts Annual†
0000-1279	Legal Publishing Preview
0000-1325	Volunteerism
0000-1341	Plus
0000-1368	Magazines for Young People
0000-1376	Of Cabbages and Kings
0001-0006	Mississippi News and Views†
0001-0022	A A A M Quarterly changed to A A A M Quarterly Journal.
0001-0049	A A C E Bulletin see 0274-9696
0001-0057	A A C S B Bulletin†
0001-0065	A A C T E Publications Service†
0001-0073	A.A.E.A. Byline
0001-009X	A A L C Reporter
0001-0111	A A M A Apparel Management Letter†
0001-012X	A A M A Newsletter†
0001-0146	A A M News
0001-0154	A A M V A Bulletin
0001-0162	A.A.P.M. Quarterly Bulletin see 0094-2405
0001-0170	A A P S News Letter see 8750-9687
0001-0189	A A Quarterly see 0261-6823
0001-0197	A.A.R.N. Newsletter
0001-0200	A A R P News Bulletin changed to A A R P Bulletin.
0001-0227	A A S Newsletter changed to Space Times.
0001-0235	Advertising Techniques see 0747-3168
0001-0243	A A T G Newsletter
0001-0251	A A T S E E L Newsletter
0001-026X	A A U P Bulletin see 0190-2946
0001-0278	A A U W Journal changed to A A U W Outlook.
0001-0286	A A U W New York Division. Newsletter changed to A A U W New Yorker.
0001-0308	A A Z P A Newsletter changed to A A Z P A Communique.
0001-0316	A et U†
0001-0340	A B Bookman's Weekly
0001-0367	A B C - Nieuwsmagazine†
0001-0375	A B C - Zeitung
0001-0383	A B C A Bulletin (American Business Communication Association) see 8756-1972
0001-0391	A B C Air Cargo Guide and Directory see 0141-6529
0001-0405	Schuhtechnik A B C see 0933-808X
0001-0413	A B C Film Review changed to Film Review (London, 1951).
0001-0421	A B C Goods Transport Guide see 0308-9304
0001-043X	B and C News see 0163-447X
0001-0456	A B C Pol Sci
0001-0464	A B C Radio Guide†
0001-0472	A B C Rail Guide
0001-0480	A B C Shipping Guide changed to A B C Passenger Shipping Guide.
0001-0502	A.B.D.
0001-0510	A B L C Journal changed to Textile Services.

0001-0529 A B M A C Bulletin *changed to* Taiwan Review.
0001-0545 A B N Correspondence
0001-0553 A B P - Association Belge des Paralyses. Bulletin
0001-0588 A C A News†
0001-0596 A C B Management *changed to* Communicator (Washington, 1953).
0001-060X A.C.C.A. Canberra Comment *see* 0817-4830
0001-0618 A. C. C. E. Reporter†
0001-0626 A C C E S S *changed to* A C C E L.
0001-0634 Chemical Abstracts Service Source Index
0001-0642 A. C. E.
0001-0650 A C E†
0001-0669 A C E C Review
0001-0677 A C E N News†
0001-0693 A C E Research†
0001-0707 A C H A News (American College of Hospital Administrators) *changed to* Executive News.
0001-0715 A C I Informazioni
0001-0723 A C I L Bulletin†
0001-0731 A C *changed to* Fibrecement Review.
0001-0766 A C M C Bulletin†
0001-0774 A C M C Newsletter *see* 0836-3463
0001-0782 Association for Computing Machinery. Communications
0001-0790 A C O S News
0001-0812 A C P A Newsletter *changed to* P I R I Newsletter.
0001-0847 A.D.A. Forecast *see* 0095-8301
0001-0855 A D A News
0001-0863 A D A Newsletter *changed to* A D A Leadership Bulletin.
0001-0871 A D A World *see* 0896-3134
0001-088X A D C Newsletter†
0001-0898 A D E Bulletin
0001-091X Adib†
0001-0928 A D K Nuusbrief *changed to* S A D K Nuusbrief.
0001-0936 A D L Bulletin *changed to* A D L on the Front Line.
0001-0944 A D M
0001-0960 A D T Transmitter
0001-0979 A D T V - Nachrichten
0001-0987 A D V - Informationsdienst
0001-0995 A D W - Umschau†
0001-1002 A E A M Newsletter Journal
0001-1010 A E B U
0001-1029 A E C L Review *see* 0707-5588
0001-1037 A E D S Journal *changed to* Journal of Research on Computing in Teacher Education.
0001-1045 A E D S Monitor†
0001-1053 A E G - Schakels
0001-1061 A E G - Telefunken al Dia†
0001-107X A E G - Telefunken Progress†
0001-1088 A E Rho Monitor *changed to* Playback.
0001-1096 A E Ue
0001-110X A U E W E S Journal
0001-1118 A E U Reports†
0001-1126 A F A Informationen
0001-1134 A F E R
0001-1150 A F L - C I O Library Acquisition List
0001-1169 American Federationist *see* 0149-2489
0001-1177 A F L - C I O Free Trade Union News†
0001-1185 A F L - C I O News
0001-1193 A F R A Boletin Informativo
0001-1207 A F R E
0001-1223 A F S Cast Metals Research Journal *see* 0008-7467
0001-1231 A.F. Universite *changed to* Aspects de la France.
0001-124X A F V - G2†
0001-1258 A F Z *changed to* Fischmagazin.
0001-1274 A G A
0001-1282 A G A News†
0001-1290 Agasvets†
0001-1304 A. G. Bush Library Abstracts†
0001-1320 A G E C O - Documentation Siderurgique
0001-1339 A G I E S
0001-1347 A G P Mitteilungen *see* 0723-2500
0001-1355 A G R A News
0001-1371 A G V A News *changed to* A G V A Newsletter.
0001-138X A.H.A. Newsletter *changed to* Perspectives (Washington).
0001-1398 A H A Review†
0001-1401 Aussenhandelsdienst der Industrie- und Handelskammern und Wirtschaftsverbaende
0001-1428 A H I L Quarterly *see* 0270-6717
0001-1436 A H R C Chronicle
0001-1452 A I A A Journal
0001-1460 A I A A Student Journal
0001-1479 A I A Journal *see* 0746-0554
0001-1487 A I A Memo *see* 0732-4073
0001-1495 Asociacion Interamericana de Bibliotecarios y Documentalistas Agricolas. Boletin Informativo
0001-1509 All India Congress Committee. Political and Economic Review†
0001-1517 A I C C News†
0001-1541 A I Ch E Journal
0001-155X American Industrial Development Council. A I D C Journal *see* 0279-6430
0001-1568 A.I. Digest *changed to* Advanced Animal Breeder.
0001-1576 A I F L D Report
0001-1584 A I L A
0001-1606 A I L Newsletter†
0001-1614 Modern Times
0001-1630 A I O E Labour News
0001-1649 A I P Educational Newsletter†
0001-1657 A. I. P. Information & Publication Newsletter†
0001-1665 A I P Newsletter *see* 0164-5420
0001-1673 A I Z *changed to* Allgemeine Immobilien-Zeitung.
0001-169X A K†
0001-1703 A L A F O. Revista
0001-1746 A L A Washington Newsletter
0001-1754 A L B A Bowls
0001-1762 A L E C Report *changed to* Philippine Journal of Labor and Industrial Relations.
0001-1789 A Lampada
0001-1800 Atualidades Medicas†
0001-1819 A.M.A. *see* 0142-3134
0001-1827 A M A Audio News Journal†
0001-1835 A M A International Health Bulletin†
0001-1843 American Medical News
0001-1851 A M A X Journal†
0001-186X A M B A C Noticiero
0001-1878 AmCham Newsletter
0001-1886 A. M. C. K. Mededelingsblad
0001-1908 A M D I Bollettino
0001-1916 A M I Newsletter *changed to* A M I News.
0001-1932 A M News - Southern Africa
0001-1940 Ampujainlehti
0001-1967 A M S Management Bulletin *see* 0090-3825
0001-1975 A M T D A Journal *see* 0308-9274
0001-1983 A M Z
0001-1991 A N A Club Bulletin *see* 0029-6090
0001-2025 A.N.F.I.A. Notiziario di Informazioni†
0001-2033 A N F I A Notiziario Statistico
0001-2041 A N N Y (Advertising News of New York) *see* 0199-2864
0001-205X American Newspaper Publishers Association, Research Institute. R I Bulletins *see* 0194-3243
0001-2068 A N U Historical Journal†
0001-2076 A N Z Bank Quarterly Survey†
0001-2084 A O P A Pilot
0001-2092 A O R N Journal
0001-2114 A P A Monitor
0001-2122 A.P.A.V.E. Revue Technique
0001-2130 A P C A Abstracts†
0001-2157 A P C D Report *see* 0092-8593
0001-2165 A P C O Bulletin
0001-2181 A P E C
0001-2203 A P L A Bulletin
0001-2211 A P L Technical Digest *see* 0270-5214
0001-2246 A P R A Journal†
0001-2262 A P W A Newsletter
0001-2270 A P W A Reporter
0001-2289 A R A Log
0001-2297 A R E R S
0001-2300 A R G R Journal
0001-2319 A R M P News†
0001-2327 A R S H A Bulletin
0001-2335 A R S Hai Sird
0001-2343 Archiv fuer Rechts- und Sozialphilosophie
0001-2351 A S A E Transactions
0001-2378 A S A Newsletter†
0001-2386 A S B Bulletin
0001-2394 A S B E Letter
0001-2408 A S B S D Bulletin
0001-2416 A S C A Newsletter *changed to* A S C A Counselor.
0001-2424 A S C A P *changed to* A S C A P in Action.
0001-2432 A S C E Publications Abstracts *see* 0734-1962
0001-2440 A S E A Bulletin†
0001-2459 A S E A Journal *see* 1013-3119
0001-2467 A S E E International Engineering Education Newsletter†
0001-2475 A S H A
0001-2483 A S H P Newsletter
0001-2491 A S H R A E Journal
0001-2505 A S H R A E Transactions
0001-2513 A S I S Newsletter *see* 0095-4403
0001-2521 Aslib Book List *changed to* Aslib Book Guide.
0001-253X Aslib Proceedings
0001-2548 A S L P Bulletin
0001-2556 A S M Bibliography Series *changed to* Materials Information Metallurgical Search-in-Print Series.
0001-2564 A S M T News†
0001-2580 A S P A C Newsletter of Cultural and Social Affairs†
0001-2599 A S P A C Quarterly of Cultural and Social Affairs *changed to* Asian and Pacific Quarterly.
0001-2602 A S P B A E Journal†
0001-2610 Planning
0001-2629 A S R C T Newsletter†
0001-2645 A S T E Bulletin *see* 0888-7233
0001-2653 A S T M S Journal
0001-2661 A T A Associazione Tecnica dell'Automobile
0001-2688 Auto Touring
0001-2696 Acta Technica Belgica. Revue A T B: Metallurgie
0001-2718 A T E Newsletter
0001-2726 A T F Monthly Report *changed to* A T F Annual Report.
0001-2734 A T G Bulletin
0001-2742 A T M N E Journal
0001-2750 A T O - A C E Newsletter†
0001-2769 A T P A S Bulletin *see* 0308-6895
0001-2777 A T R
0001-2785 A T Z
0001-2807 A U P E L F Revue *see* 0820-005X
0001-2815 Tissue Antigens
0001-2823 A U T Bulletin
0001-2831 A-V *see* 0274-7774
0001-2858 A V A Magazine *see* 0954-5611
0001-2866 A V A Member-Gram†
0001-2874 A V C Bulletin
0001-2890 A V Communication Review *see* 1042-1629
0001-2904 A V S News *changed to* A V S C News.
0001-2912 A Votre Sante†
0001-2920 A W A Technical Review†
0001-2947 A W R Bulletin
0001-2955 Hostelert
0001-2971 A A H E College and University Bulletin *see* 0162-7910
0001-298X Aakerifoeretagaren-Transportoeren *see* 0348-0356
0001-2998 Seminars in Nuclear Medicine
0001-3013 Aannemer *changed to* Bouwbedrijf.
0001-303X Aaraaichi
0001-3056 Arrow (Kenosha)
0001-3064 Aavesh
0001-3072 Abacus
0001-3099 Abacus
0001-3102 Abbia†
0001-3110 Abbigliamento Italiano *changed to* Abbigliamento.
0001-3129 Abeille & Erable†
0001-3137 Abeille de France *see* 0373-4625
0001-3153 Abel *changed to* Abel Value News.
0001-3161 Aberdeen-Angus Journal *see* 0194-9543
0001-317X Aberdeen - Angus Review
0001-3188 Aberdeen Chamber of Commerce Journal†
0001-3196 University of Aberdeen. African Studies Group. Bulletin
0001-320X University of Aberdeen Review
0001-3218 Abitare
0001-3234 Abolition News *changed to* Right to Know and the Freedom to Act.
0001-3242 About the House
0001-3285 Abrasive Methods *see* 0195-0932
0001-3307 Abraxas†
0001-3331 Abridged Index Medicus
0001-334X Abridged Readers' Guide to Periodical Literature
0001-3358 Abril†
0001-3374 Absatzwirtschaft
0001-3382 Abside
0001-3404 Abstracts and Book Title Index Card Service (ABTICS)†
0001-3412 Abstracts for Social Workers *see* 0148-0847
0001-3420 Abstracts for the Advancement of Industrial Utilization of Cereal Grains†
0001-3439 Abstracts from Current Scientific and Technical Literature
0001-3447 B I C E R I Abstracts from Technical and Patent Publications.†
0001-3455 Abstracts in Anthropology
0001-3463 Abstracts of Bulgarian Scientific Literature. Agriculture and Forestry. Veterinary Medicine
0001-3498 Abstracts of Bulgarian Scientific Literature. Geology and Geography *see* 0204-9406
0001-351X Abstracts of Bulgarian Scientific Literature. Mathematics, Physics, Astronomy, Geophysics, Geodesy *see* 0204-9449
0001-3528 Abstracts of Bulgarian Scientific Literature. Philosophy, Psychology and Pedagogics *changed to* Abstracts of Bulgarian Scientific Literature. Philosophy, Sociology, Science of Sciences, Psychology and Pedagogics.
0001-3536 Abstracts of Bulgarian Scientific Medical Literature
0001-3544 Current Literature on Venereal Disease *changed to* Survey of Research for Sexually Transmitted Diseases.
0001-3560 Abstracts of English Studies
0001-3579 Abstracts of Entomology
0001-3587 Abstracts of Folklore Studies†
0001-3595 Abstracts of Hospital Management Studies *see* 0194-4908
0001-3609 Abstracts of Instructional Materials in Vocational and Technical Education *see* 0160-2004
0001-3617 Abstracts of Mycology
0001-3625 Abstracts of North American Geology†
0001-3633 Abstracts of Photographic Science & Engineering Literature†
0001-3641 Abstracts of Research and Related Materials in Vocational and Technical Education *see* 0160-2004
0001-365X Abstracts of Romanian Scientific and Technical Literature
0001-3668 Abstracts of the Current Literature on T B and Other Respiratory Diseases *see* 0389-7389
0001-3676 Abstracts of Uppsala Dissertations in Science

ISSN INDEX 5333

0001-3684 Excerpta Criminologica *changed to* Criminology, Penology & Police Science Abstracts.
0001-3692 Abstracts on Hygiene *see* 0260-5511
0001-3714 Revista de Microbiologia
0001-3730 Acacia Clarion
0001-3749 Academe *see* 0190-2946
0001-3757 Academia Argentina de Letras. Boletin
0001-3765 Academia Brasileira de Ciencias. Anais
0001-3773 Academia Colombiana. Boletin
0001-3781 Academia das Ciencias de Lisboa. Boletim
0001-379X Academia de Artes y Ciencias de Puerto Rico. Boletin
0001-3803 Academia Medico Quirurgica Espanola. Anales†
0001-3811 Academia Militar de Chorrillos. Revista
0001-382X Academia Nacional de la Historia. Boletin
0001-3838 Academia Nacional de Medicina. Boletim
0001-3846 Academia Paulista de Letras. Revista
0001-3854 Academia Peruana de Cirugia Revista
0001-3862 Academia Portena del Lunfardo. Boletin†
0001-3889 Academia Republicii Socialiste Romania. Buletin de Informare Stiintifica, Geologia, Geografie†
0001-3897 Lingvistica-Filologie†
0001-3900 Academia Republicii Socialiste Romania. Buletin de Informare Stiintifica. Seria Matematica Astronomie†
0001-3919 Teoria si Istoria Literaturii si Artei; Buletin de Informare Stiintifica†
0001-3927 Academia Sinica. Institute of Chemistry. Bulletin
0001-3935 Academia Sinica. Institute of Ethnology. Bulletin
0001-3943 Academia Sinica. Institute of Zoology. Bulletin
0001-3951 Academic Achievement†
0001-396X Academic Therapy *changed to* Intervention in School and Clinic.
0001-3986 Academie d'Agriculture de France. Comptes Rendus Hebdomidaire des Seances *see* 0989-6988
0001-3994 Academie d'Architecture
0001-4001 Chirurgie
0001-401X Academie de Droit International de la Haye. Recueil des Cours
0001-4044 Academie des Sciences d'Outre-Mer, Paris. Comptes Rendus des Seances *see* 0221-0436
0001-4060 Academie Internationale du Tourisme. Revue
0001-4079 Academie Nationale de Medecine. Bulletin
0001-4087 Academie Polonaise des Sciences. Bulletin. Serie des Sciences Biologiques *see* 0239-751X
0001-4095 Academie Polonaise des Sciences. Bulletin. Serie des Sciences Chimiques *see* 0239-7285
0001-4109 Academie Polonaise des Sciences. Bulletin. Serie des Sciences de la Terre *see* 0239-7277
0001-4117 Academie Polonaise des Sciences. Bulletin. Serie des Sciences Mathematiques, Astronomiques et Physiques *see* 0239-7269
0001-4125 Academie Polonaise des Sciences. Bulletin. Serie des Sciences Techniques *see* 0239-7528
0001-4141 Academie Royale des Sciences des Lettres et des Beaux-Arts de Belgique. Classe des Sciences. Bulletin
0001-415X Commission Royale d'Histoire. Bulletin
0001-4168 Academie Royale de Medecine de Belgique. Bulletin *see* 0377-8231
0001-4176 Academie Royale des Sciences d'Outre-Mer. Bulletin des Seances
0001-4184 Academie Serbe des Sciences et des Arts. Classe des Sciences Mathematiques et Naturelles. Bulletin. Nouvelle Serie *changed to* Academie Serbe des Sciences et des Arts. Classe des Sciences Mathematiques et Naturelles. Bulletin. Sciences Mathematiques.
0001-4184 Academie Serbe des Sciences et des Arts. Classe des Sciences Mathematiques et Naturelles. Bulletin. Nouvelle Serie *see* 0352-5740
0001-4192 Academie Veterinaire de France. Bulletin
0001-4214 Revue Roumaine de Biochimie
0001-4249 Academy Bookman†
0001-4265 Academy of General Dentistry. Journal *see* 0363-6771
0001-4273 Academy of Management. Journal
0001-4281 Academy of Medicine of Cleveland. Bulletin *changed to* Cleveland Physician.
0001-4303 Academy of Toledo and Lucas County. Bulletin *changed to* Toledo Medicine.
0001-4311 Academy of Medicine, Toronto. Bulletin
0001-432X Academy of Sciences of the U S S R. Bulletin. Physical Series
0001-4338 Academy of Sciences of the U S S R. Izvestiya. Atmospheric and Oceanic Physics
0001-4346 Academy of Sciences of the U S S R. Mathematical Notes
0001-4354 Academy of Sciences of the U S S R. Izvestiya. Physics of the Solid Earth
0001-4362 Population Biocharacterist *see* 0098-8618
0001-4370 Academy of Sciences of the U S S R. Oceanology
0001-4389 Pharmacology and Therapeutics in Dentistry†
0001-4397 Acadiana Profile
0001-4400 Acao†
0001-4419 Accademia delle Scienze di Torino. Atti. Part 1. Classe di Scienze Fisiche, Matematiche e Naturali
0001-4427 Accademia Medica Lombarda. Atti
0001-4435 Reale Accademia dei Lincei. Classe di Scienze Fisiche, Matematiche e Naturali *see* 0392-7881
0001-4443 Accademia Nazionale di Agricoltura. Annali†
0001-4451 Accademie e Biblioteche d'Italia
0001-446X Accelerator (Saskatoon) *see* 0316-2893
0001-4478 Accelerator Newsletter
0001-4486 Accent†
0001-4508 Accent on Living
0001-4516 Accent on Youth†
0001-4559 Acciaio
0001-4567 L'Acciaio Inossidabile
0001-4575 Accident Analysis & Prevention
0001-4583 Accidents Claims Journal
0001-4591 Accidents, How They Are Caused and How to Prevent Them†
0001-4605 Accion
0001-4648 Accordion Horizons†
0001-4664 Accountancy
0001-4672 Accountancy Age
0001-4680 Accountancy, Business & Insurance Review
0001-4699 Accountancy Ireland
0001-4702 Accountant Journal *changed to* Institute of Chartered Accountants of Sri Lanka. Journal.
0001-4710 Accountant
0001-4729 Accountant
0001-4737 Accountants Digest†
0001-4745 Accountants' Journal
0001-4753 Accountants' Journal
0001-4761 Accountants Magazine
0001-4788 Accounting and Business Research
0001-4796 Accounting and Data Processing Abstracts *changed to* Accounting & Finance Abstracts.
0001-4818 Accounting Forum†
0001-4826 Accounting Review
0001-4834 Accounting Trends†
0001-4842 Accounts of Chemical Research
0001-4850 Acero y Energia
0001-4869 Achaab
0001-4877 Achats et Entretien du Materiel Industriel *see* 0396-6666
0001-4893 Acheteurs
0001-4907 Achievement
0001-4923 Acier†
0001-4931 Acier dans le Monde
0001-494X Acme
0001-4958 Aconcagua Iberoamerica-Europa†
0001-4966 Acoustical Society of America. Journal
0001-4974 Acoustics Abstracts
0001-4982 Inquinamento
0001-5008 Acquisitions Nouvelles en Pathologie Cardio-Vasculaire†
0001-5040 Acropole†
0001-5059 Across from City Hall *changed to* Citizens Union Reports.
0001-5067 Acrow Review
0001-5075 Act
0001-5083 Act
0001-5105 Acta Academiae Aboensis, Series B: Mathematica et Physica
0001-5113 Acta Adriatica
0001-5121 Acta Agriculturae Scandinavica
0001-513X Academia Scientiarum Hungarica. Acta Agronomica *see* 0238-0161
0001-5148 Acta Allergologica *see* 0105-4538
0001-5164 Acta Anaesthesiologica Belgica
0001-5172 Acta Anaesthesiologica Scandinavica
0001-5180 Acta Anatomica
0001-5199 Acta Apostolicae Sedis. Commentarium Officiale
0001-5202 Acta Arachnologica
0001-5210 Academia Scientiarum Hungarica. Acta Archaeologica
0001-5229 Acta Archaeologica Carpathica
0001-5237 Acta Astronomica
0001-5245 Tianwen Xuebao
0001-5253 Academia Scientiarum Hungarica. Acta Biochimica et Biophysica *see* 0237-6261
0001-5261 Acta Biochimica Iranica†
0001-527X Acta Biochimica Polonica†
0001-5288 Acta Biologica Hungarica
0001-5296 Acta Biologica Cracoviensia. Botanica
0001-530X Acta Biologica Cracoviensia. Zoologia
0001-5318 Acta Biologica et Medica Germanica *see* 0232-766X
0001-5326 Acta Biologica Venezuelica
0001-5334 Shiyan Shengwu Xuebao
0001-5342 Acta Biotheoretica
0001-5350 Academia Scientiarum Hungarica. Acta Botanica *see* 0236-6495
0001-5369 Acta Botanica Fennica
0001-5385 Acta Cardiologica
0001-5393 Acta Chemica Scandinavica *see* 0904-213X
0001-5407 Academia Scientiarum Hungarica. Acta Chimica *see* 0231-3146
0001-5415 Acta Chirurgiae Orthopaedicae et Traumatologiae Cechoslovaca
0001-5423 Acta Chirurgiae Plasticae
0001-5431 Academia Scientiarum Hungarica. Acta Chirurgica *see* 0231-4614
0001-544X Acta Chirurgica Austriaca
0001-5458 Acta Chirurgica Belgica
0001-5466 Acta Chirurgica Italica
0001-5474 Acta Chirurgica Jugoslavica
0001-5482 Acta Chirurgica Scandinavica *see* 1102-1101
0001-5490 Acta Cientifica†
0001-5504 Acta Cientifica Venezolana
0001-5520 Acta Crystallographica *see* 0108-7673
0001-5520 Acta Crystallographica *see* 0108-7681
0001-5520 Acta Crystallographica *see* 0108-2701
0001-5547 Acta Cytologica
0001-5555 Acta Dermato-Venereologica
0001-5563 Acta Diabetologica Latina
0001-5571 Acta Diurna†
0001-558X Acta Electronica†
0001-5601 Acta Entomologica Bohemoslovaca
0001-561X Acta Entomologica Fennica *see* 0785-8760
0001-5628 Academia Scientiarum Hungarica. Acta Ethnographica
0001-5636 Acta Forestalia Fennica
0001-5644 Acta Gastro-Enterologica Belgica
0001-5652 Human Heredity
0001-5660 Acta Geneticae Medicae et Gemellologiae: Twin Research
0001-5679 Academia Scientiarum Hungarica. Acta Geodaetica, Geophysica et Montanistica *see* 0374-1842
0001-5687 Acta Geographica
0001-5695 Academia Scientiarum Hungarica. Acta Geologica *see* 0236-5278
0001-5709 Acta Geologica Polonica
0001-5717 Dizhi Xuebao
0001-5725 Acta Geophysica Polonica
0001-5733 Diqiu Wuli Xuebao
0001-5741 Acta Gerontologica
0001-575X Acta Gerontologica et Geriatrica Belgica *changed to* Rejuvenation.
0001-5768 Acta Gerontologica Japonica *changed to* Yokufukai Chosa Kenkyu Kiyo.
0001-5776 Acta Ginecologica
0001-5784 Acta Obstetrica y Ginecologica Hispano-Lusitana
0001-5792 Acta Haematologica
0001-5806 Acta Haematologica Japonica *see* 0925-5710
0001-5814 Acta Haematologica Polonica
0001-5822 Acta Hepato- Splenologica *see* 0172-6390
0001-5830 Academia Scientiarum Hungarica. Acta Historiae Artium
0001-5849 Academia Scientiarum Hungarica. Acta Historica
0001-5857 Acta Historica Leopoldina
0001-5865 Acta Historica Medicinae, Stomatologiae, Pharmaciae, Veterinae
0001-5881 Acta Homeopathica *see* 0935-0853
0001-589X Acta Iberica Radiologica - Cancerologica†
0001-5903 Acta Informatica
0001-592X Academia Scientiarum Hungarica. Acta Juridica
0001-5938 Acta Leprologica
0001-5946 Academia Scientiarum Hungarica. Acta Linguistica
0001-5954 Academia Scientiarum Hungarica. Acta Mathematica *see* 0236-5294
0001-5962 Acta Mathematica
0001-5970 Acta Mechanica
0001-5989 Academia Scientiarum Hungarica. Acta Medica *see* 0236-5286
0001-5997 Acta Medica
0001-6004 Acta Medica Auxologica
0001-6012 Acta Medica Costarricense
0001-6039 Acta Medica Italica di Medicina Tropicale e Subtropicale e di Gastroenterologia
0001-6055 Acta Medica Nagasakiensia
0001-6071 Acta Medica Philippina
0001-608X Acta Medica Polona
0001-6098 Acta Medica Romana
0001-6101 Acta Medica Scandinavica *see* 0954-6820
0001-611X Acta Medica Universitatis Kagoshimaensis†
0001-6136 Acta Medica Veterinaria
0001-6152 Acta Medicinae Okayama *see* 0386-300X
0001-6160 Acta Metallurgica *see* 0956-7151
0001-6187 Academia Scientiarum Hungarica. Acta Microbiologica *see* 0231-4622
0001-6195 Acta Microbiologica Polonica
0001-6209 Weishengwu Xuebao
0001-6217 Academia Scientiarum Hungarica. Acta Morphologica *see* 0236-5391
0001-6225 Acta Morphologica Neelando-Scandinavica *see* 0924-3860
0001-6233 Acta Mozartiana
0001-6241 Acta Musicologica
0001-625X Acta Mycologica
0001-6268 Acta Neurochirurgica. Supplementa

ISSN

5334 ISSN INDEX

0001-6268 Acta Neurochirurgica
0001-6276 Acta Neurologica
0001-6284 Acta Neurologica et Psychiatrica Belgica *see* 0300-9009
0001-6284 Acta Neurologica et Psychiatrica Belgica *see* 0300-8967
0001-6306 Acta Neurologica Latinoamericana
0001-6314 Acta Neurologica Scandinavica
0001-6322 Acta Neuropathologica
0001-6330 Acta Obstetrica et Gynaecologica Japonica†
0001-6349 Acta Obstetrica et Gynecologica Scandinavica
0001-6357 Acta Odontologica Scandinavica
0001-6365 Acta Odontologica Venezolana
0001-6373 Academia Scientiarum Hungarica. Acta Oeconomica
0001-6381 Acta Oncologica†
0001-639X Acta Ophthalmologica
0001-6403 Acta Ophthalmologica Iugoslavica
0001-6411 Acta Ordinis Fratrum Minorum
0001-642X Acta Ordinis Sancti Augustini
0001-6438 Acta Orientalia
0001-6446 Academia Scientiarum Hungarica. Acta Orientalia
0001-6454 Acta Ornithologica
0001-6462 Acta Orthopaedica Belgica
0001-6470 Acta Orthopaedica Scandinavica
0001-6489 Acta Oto-Laryngologica
0001-6497 Acta Oto-Rhino-Laryngologica Belgica
0001-6500 Acta Oto-Rino-Laringologica Ibero-Americana *see* 0303-8874
0001-6519 Acta Otorrinolaringologica Espanola
0001-6527 Academia Scientiarum Hungarica. Acta Paediatrica *see* 0231-441X
0001-6535 Acta Paediatrica Belgica *see* 0340-6199
0001-6543 Acta Paediatrica Japonica
0001-6551 Acta Paediatrica Latina
0001-656X Acta Paediatrica Scandinavica *see* 0803-5253
0001-6578 Acta Paediatrica Sinica
0001-6586 Acta Paedopsychiatrica†
0001-6594 Acta Palaeobotanica
0001-6616 Gushengwu Xuebao
0001-6624 Acta Pathologica et Microbiologica Scandinavica *see* 0903-4641
0001-6632 Acta Pathologica Japonica
0001-6640 Acta Pediatrica Espanola
0001-6659 Acta Pharmaceutica Hungarica
0001-6667 Acta Pharmaceutica Jugoslavica
0001-6675 Acta Pharmaceutica Suecica†
0001-6683 Acta Pharmacologica et Toxicologica *see* 0901-9928
0001-6691 Acta Philologica Scandinavica†
0001-6705 Academia Scientiarum Hungarica. Acta Physica *see* 0231-4428
0001-6713 Acta Physica Austriaca *see* 0177-7963
0001-6721 Acta Universitatis Szegediensis de Attila Jozsef Nominatae. Acta Physica et Chemica
0001-673X Acta Physica Polonica *see* 0587-4246
0001-673X Acta Physica Polonica *see* 0587-4254
0001-6748 Acta Physioligica et Pharmacologia Neerlandica†
0001-6756 Academia Scientiarum Hungarica. Acta Physiologica *see* 0231-424X
0001-6764 Acta Physiologica et Pharmacologica Latinoamericana *changed to* Acta Physiologica Pharmacologica et Therapeutica Latinoamericana.
0001-6772 Acta Physiologica Scandinavica
0001-6780 Academia Scientiarum Hungarica. Acta Phytopathologica *see* 0238-1249
0001-6799 Acta Phytotaxonomica et Geobotanica
0001-6810 Acta Politica
0001-6829 Acta Poloniae Historica
0001-6837 Acta Poloniae Pharmaceutica
0001-6845 Acta Polytechnica Scandinavica. Electrical Engineering Series
0001-6853 Acta Polytechnica Scandinavica. Chemistry and Metallurgy Series *see* 0781-2698
0001-6861 Acta Polytechnica Scandinavica. Mathematics and Computing Machinery Series *see* 0355-2713
0001-687X Acta Polytechnica Scandinavica. Mechanical Engineering Series
0001-6888 Acta Polytechnica Scandinavica. Physics Including Nucleonics Series *see* 0355-2721
0001-6896 Acta Psiquiatrica y Psicologica de America Latina
0001-690X Acta Psychiatrica Scandinavica
0001-6918 Acta Psychologica
0001-6934 Acta Rheumatologica Scandinavica *see* 0300-9742
0001-6942 Acta Sagittariana
0001-6950 Acta Scholae Medicinalis Universitatis in Kioto†
0001-6969 Acta Universitatis Szegediensis de Attila Jozsef Nominatae. Acta Scientiarum Mathematicarum
0001-6977 Acta Societatis Botanicorum Poloniae
0001-6985 Acta Societatis Medicorum Upsaliensis *see* 0300-9734
0001-6993 Acta Sociologica
0001-7000 Acta Stomatologica Belgica
0001-7019 Acta Stomatologica Croatica
0001-7035 Academia Scientiarum Hungarica. Acta Technica
0001-7043 Ceskoslovenska Akademie Ved. Acta Technica
0001-7051 Acta Theriologica
0001-706X Acta Tropica
0001-7078 Acta Tuberculosa et Pneumologica Belgica *see* 0903-1936
0001-7094 Drug Therapy
0001-7108 Current Literature of Blood†
0001-7124 Acta Universitatis Carolinae: Biologica
0001-7132 Acta Universitatis Carolinae: Geologica
0001-7140 Acta Universitatis Carolinae: Mathematica et Physica
0001-7159 Acta Universitatis Lundensis Sectio: Medica, Mathematica, Scientiae Rerum Naturalium†
0001-7167 Acta Universitatis Palackianae, Facultatis Medicae *see* 0301-2514
0001-7175 Acta Universitatis Szegediensis de Attila Jozsef Nominatae. Acta Bibliothecaria
0001-7183 Acta Urologica Belgica
0001-7191 Acta Urologica Japonica
0001-7205 Academia Scientiarum Hungarica. Acta Veterinaria *see* 0236-6290
0001-7213 Acta Veterinaria
0001-7221 Acta Veterinaria Japonica
0001-723X Acta Virologica
0001-7248 Acta Vitaminologica *see* 0300-8924
0001-7264 Academia Scientiarum Hungarica. Acta Zoologica *see* 0236-7130
0001-7272 Acta Zoologica
0001-7280 Acta Zoologica et Pathologica Antverpiensia
0001-7299 Acta Zoologica Fennica
0001-7302 Dongwu Xuebao
0001-7310 Actas Dermosifiolograficas
0001-7329 Actas Luso Espanolas de Neurologia y Psiquiatria *see* 0300-5062
0001-7345 Actes Pontificaux†
0001-7353 Actinides and Lanthanides Reviews†
0001-737X Action (Louisville) *changed to* Update (Louisville).
0001-7388 Action (New York)†
0001-7396 Action (Rensselaerville)†
0001-740X Action†
0001-7418 Action Automobile et Touristique *changed to* Action Automobile.
0001-7426 Action et Pensee†
0001-7442 Action Line (Baltimore)
0001-7450 Action Municipale
0001-7469 Action Nationale
0001-7477 Action Poetique
0001-7485 Action - Reaction *see* 0360-1897
0001-7507 Action Sociale
0001-7523 Action Veterinaire
0001-754X Active Handicapped†
0001-7558 Active Service
0001-7566 Actividade Economica de Angola
0001-7574 C E E D. Actividades†
0001-7582 Actividades Petroleras†
0001-7590 Activist†
0001-7604 Activitas Nervosa Superior *see* 0960-7560
0001-7612 Activities of the Communist World Organizations†
0001-7620 A C Tivity
0001-7639 Actual
0001-7647 Actual Specifying Engineer *see* 0892-5046
0001-7655 Actualidad Economica
0001-7671 Actualidad Pediatrica†
0001-768X Actualidades de Japon
0001-7701 General Relativity and Gravitation
0001-771X Actualite Economique
0001-7728 Actualite Juridique: Edition Droit Administratif *changed to* L'Actualite Juridique: Droit Administratif.
0001-7736 Actualite Juridique: Edition Propriete Immobiliere *changed to* L'Actualite Juridique: Droit Administratif.
0001-7744 Actualite Missionnaire†
0001-7752 Actualite Pedagogique a l'Etranger†
0001-7779 Actualite Terminologique
0001-7787 Actualites Cereales *changed to* Actualites Agricoles.
0001-7795 Actualites et Culture Veterinaires†
0001-7809 Actualites Marines†
0001-7817 Actualites Odonto-Stomatologiques
0001-7825 Actuary
0001-7833 Actuel†
0001-7841 Actuele Onderwerpen-Reeks *changed to* A O.
0001-785X Aktuelle Chirurgie
0001-7868 Aktuelle Urologie
0001-7884 Acustica
0001-7892 Ad
0001-7906 AD-Cards†
0001-7914 Ad Change
0001-7949 Ad Lib
0001-7957 Ad Libs†
0001-7965 Ad Marginem
0001-7973 Ad Rem†
0001-7981 Behavioral Science in Progress†
0001-799X Adalbert-Stifter-Institut des Landes Oberoesterreich. Vierteljahresschrift
0001-8007 Adam
0001-8015 Adam International Review
0001-8023 Adam Magazine†
0001-804X Adansonia *see* 0240-8937
0001-8066 Adcrafter
0001-8074 Addiction and Drug Abuse Report *see* 1040-4163
0001-8082 Addictions†
0001-8090 Adding Life to Years†
0001-8112 A D E G - Kaufmann
0001-8120 A D E G - Kurier
0001-8139 Adelaar
0001-8147 Adelaide Church Guardian
0001-8163 University of Adelaide. Graduates Union. Monthly Newsletter and Gazette *changed to* Lumen.
0001-8171 Adem
0001-8198 Adhaesion
0001-8201 Adhesion Society of Japan. Journal
0001-821X Adhesives Age
0001-821X Adhesives Age Directory
0001-8228 Adhuna Sahitya
0001-8236 Adirondac
0001-8244 Behavior Genetics
0001-8252 Adirondack Life
0001-8260 Adler
0001-8279 Der Adler
0001-8295 Admap
0001-8317 Administratieve Arbeid†
0001-8325 Administration
0001-8333 Quarterly Journal of Administration
0001-835X Administrative Digest *changed to* Office Product News.
0001-8368 Administrative Law Review
0001-8376 Administrative Management *see* 0884-5905
0001-8384 Administrative Officer *changed to* Alert! Top Executive & The Administrative Officer.
0001-8392 Administrative Science Quarterly
0001-8406 Administrative Science Review *changed to* Bangladesh Journal of Public Administration.
0001-8414 Administrator Quarterly
0001-8422 Administrator's Digest *see* 0746-6129
0001-8430 Administrators Notebook
0001-8449 Adolescence
0001-8473 Adult & Continuing Education Today
0001-8481 Adult Education *see* 0741-7136
0001-849X Adult Education†
0001-8503 Adult Education in Finland *changed to* L E I F - Life and Education in Finland.
0001-8511 Adult Education in Nova Scotia†
0001-852X Adult Education in the Public Schools†
0001-8546 Adult Jewish Education†
0001-8562 Advance (Chicago) *changed to* Anglican Advance.
0001-8570 Advance (St. Louis) *see* 0360-7119
0001-8589 Advance (Springfield)
0001-8597 Advance (New York) *see* 0271-5848
0001-8600 Advance Abstracts of Contributions on Fisheries and Aquatic Sciences in India†
0001-8619 Advance Australia
0001-8627 Advanced Battery Technology
0001-8635 Advanced Documentation List†
0001-8651 Advanced Publications†
0001-8678 Advances in Applied Probability
0001-8686 Advances in Colloid and Interface Science
0001-8694 Advances in Education
0001-8708 Advances in Mathematics
0001-8716 Advances in Molecular Relaxation Processes *see* 0167-7322
0001-8724 Shinkei Kenkyu no Shinpo
0001-8732 Advances in Physics
0001-8740 Adveniat
0001-8759 Advent Christian Missions†
0001-8767 Adventbode *see* 0165-8603
0001-8775 Adventure†
0001-8783 Adventure (Nashville)
0001-8791 Journal of Vocational Behavior
0001-8805 Adventure Road
0001-8813 Adventure Time†
0001-8821 Adventurer *see* 0263-8894
0001-883X Adventures in Western New York History†
0001-8848 Excerpta Medica. Section 38: Adverse Reactions Titles
0001-8856 Advertentieblad
0001-8880 Adweek†
0001-8899 Advertising Age
0001-8902 Advertising & Marketing for Manufacturers†
0001-8910 Advertising and Marketing News *see* 0110-6813
0001-8929 Advertising and Newspaper News *see* 0814-6942
0001-8961 Advertising Quarterly *see* 0265-0487
0001-897X Advertising Statistical Review *changed to* T V Advertising Statistical Review.
0001-8988 Advertlink
0001-8996 Advocate (Los Angeles, 1967)
0001-9003 Advocate (New York)
0001-9011 Adyar
0001-902X Brahmavidya
0001-9038 Aegir
0001-9046 Aegyptus
0001-9054 Aequationes Mathematicae
0001-9062 Aerial†
0001-9070 Aerial Applicator
0001-9089 Sardegna-Agricoltura (Varese)
0001-9097 Aero†
0001-9100 Aero†
0001-9127 Aeroespacio
0001-9135 Aero Field†
0001-916X Aero Mundial
0001-9178 Aero Philatelist Annals†
0001-9186 Aero-Revue
0001-9194 Aerograph Research Notes†
0001-9216 Aerological Data of Japan
0001-9224 Aerologische Berichte†

ISSN

ISSN INDEX 5335

ISSN	Title
0001-9232	Aero Modeller
0001-9240	Aeronautical Journal
0001-9259	Aeronautical Quarterly see 0001-9240
0001-9267	Aeronautical Society of India. Journal
0001-9275	Aeronautique et l'Astronautique
0001-9283	Aeroporika Nea Kai Pathetike changed to Aeroporika Nea.
0001-9291	Aerosol Age see 1055-2340
0001-9313	Aerosol Report changed to Aerosol Spray Report.
0001-9321	Aerospace (Washington)†
0001-9364	Aerospace Historian see 1044-016X
0001-9372	Aerospace International†
0001-9380	Aerospace Maintenance Safety see 0364-7145
0001-9402	Aerospace Medicine see 0095-6562
0001-9410	Aerospace Medicine and Biology
0001-9429	Aerospace Safety see 0279-9308
0001-9445	Flieger-Revue
0001-9453	Aerotecnica changed to Aerotecnica, Missili e Spazio.
0001-9461	Aerovoz
0001-9488	Aerzteblatt Rheinland-Pfalz
0001-9496	Aerztliche Forschung†
0001-950X	Aerztliche Fortbildung†
0001-9518	Aerztliche Jugendkunde
0001-9526	Aerztliche Laboratorium see 0941-2131
0001-9534	Aerztliche Praxis
0001-9542	Aerztliche Tonbandzeitung†
0001-9550	Aersceala
0001-9569	Aesculape†
0001-9585	Aetnalzer
0001-9593	Aevum
0001-9607	Affaersekonomi changed to Affaersekonomi Management.
0001-9615	Affaires
0001-9623	Affairs of State†
0001-9658	Affaersvaerlden - Finanstidningen see 0345-3766
0001-9666	Affiches d'Alsace et de Lorraine - Moniteur des Soumissions et des Ventes de Bois de l'Est
0001-9674	Affirmation†
0001-9682	Afghanistan
0001-9690	Aficion Espanola
0001-9704	Afinidad
0001-9712	Afrasian Markets see 0970-6186
0001-9720	Africa (Edinburgh)
0001-9739	Africa†
0001-9747	Africa
0001-9755	Africa changed to Africa International.
0001-9763	Africa†
0001-978X	Africa Diary
0001-9798	Africa Digest see 0306-8412
0001-9828	Africa Quarterly
0001-9836	Africa Report
0001-9844	Africa Research Bulletin. Series A: Political, Social and Cultural changed to Africa Research Bulletin. Series A: Political.
0001-9852	Africa Research Bulletin. Series B: Economic, Financial and Technical changed to Africa Research Bulletin. Series B: Economic.
0001-9860	Africa Samachar
0001-9879	Africa Tervuren
0001-9887	Africa Today
0001-9909	African Affairs
0001-9925	African Aquarist†
0001-9933	African Arts
0001-9941	African Books Newsletter
0001-995X	African Bookshelf changed to Diplomatic Bookshelf & Review.
0001-9968	African Challenge see 0189-0557
0001-9976	African Communist
0001-9984	African Development see 0142-9345
0001-9992	African Historical Studies see 0361-7882
0002-001X	African Insurance Record changed to African Insurance & Finance Record.
0002-0028	African Journal of Medical Sciences see 0309-3913
0002-0044	African Labour News
0002-0052	African Law Digest
0002-0060	African Law Studies see 0732-9113
0002-0079	African M I M S see 0140-4415
0002-0087	African Notes
0002-0117	African Political Review see 0856-0056
0002-0133	African Recorder
0002-015X	African Scientist changed to African Scientist and Technologist.
0002-0168	African Social Research
0002-0184	African Studies
0002-0192	African Studies Association of the United Kingdom. Bulletin see 0305-862X
0002-0206	African Studies Review
0002-0214	African Studies Newsletter see 0278-2219
0002-0222	African Succulent Plant Society. Bulletin†
0002-0230	African Target†
0002-0249	African Trader
0002-0265	African Violet Magazine
0002-0273	African Wildlife
0002-0281	African†
0002-029X	Africana Bulletin
0002-0303	Africana Library Journal changed to Africana Journal.
0002-032X	Africana Notes and News
0002-0338	Africasia changed to Afrique-Asie.
0002-0346	Afrikat
0002-0397	Afrika Spectrum
0002-0400	Afrika-Spiegel
0002-0419	Afrika Studiecentrum. Documentatieblad see 0166-2694
0002-0427	Afrika und Uebersee
0002-0443	Journal of Nursing Administration
0002-046X	Afrique & Culture†
0002-0478	Afrique Contemporaine
0002-0486	Afrique et l'Asie see 0399-0370
0002-0508	Afrique Litteraire et Artistique changed to Afrique Litteraire.
0002-0516	Afrique Medicale
0002-0524	Afrique Mon Pays
0002-0532	Afrique Nouvelle†
0002-0540	Afrique Service
0002-0559	Afrique Urbaine†
0002-0575	Afro-American Studies see 0308-6860
0002-0591	Afro-Asia
0002-0613	Afro Asian Economic Review
0002-0621	Afro-Asian Journalist
0002-0648	Afro-Asia Peoples changed to Solidarity.
0002-0664	Lotus
0002-0672	Afrox News
0002-0699	After Beat†
0002-0710	Agrarische Rundschau
0002-0729	Age and Ageing
0002-0737	Age de la Science†
0002-0745	Age of Achievement†
0002-0753	Age of Tomorrow
0002-0761	Agence d'Informations Europeennes. Bulletin
0002-077X	Revue Parlementaire
0002-0788	Agency Items changed to Agency News.
0002-0796	Agenda
0002-080X	Agenor
0002-0826	Agent Commercial
0002-0834	Agente
0002-0869	Agenzia di Viaggi
0002-0877	Agenzia Economica Finanziaria
0002-0893	Agenzia Nazionale Informazioni Turistiche
0002-0907	Aggiornamenti Clinicoterapeutici changed to Gazzetta Medica Italiana Archivio per le Scienze Mediche.
0002-0915	Aggiornamenti di Terapia Oftalmologica
0002-0923	Aggiornamenti in Ematologia
0002-0931	Aggiornamenti di Ostetricia e Ginecologia see 0026-4784
0002-094X	Aggiornamenti Sociali
0002-0958	Aggiornamento Pediatrico
0002-0966	Aging (Washington)
0002-0974	Aging and Human Development see 0091-4150
0002-0982	Aging in the News†
0002-0990	A G M A Zine
0002-1008	Krankenpflege
0002-1024	Agra Europe
0002-1032	Agra University Journal of Research (Science).
0002-1040	Agradoot
0002-1059	Agraringenieur see 0341-2520
0002-1067	Agrarirodalmi Szemle
0002-1075	Agrarisch Weekoverzicht
0002-1105	Agrartorteneti Szemle
0002-1113	Magyar Tudomanyos Akademia. Agrartudomanyok Osztalya. Kozlemenyek changed to Agrartudomanyi Kozlemenyek.
0002-1121	Agrarwirtschaft
0002-113X	Agrekon
0002-1148	Agressologie
0002-1164	Agri Finance
0002-1172	Agri Hortique Genetica
0002-1180	Agri Marketing
0002-1199	Agri-Pick-Up
0002-1202	Agricoltore (Perugia)
0002-1210	Agricoltore Ferrarese
0002-1229	Agricoltore Trevisano
0002-1237	Agricoltura (Rome, 1952)
0002-1245	Agricoltura Aretina
0002-1253	Agricoltura Bergamasca†
0002-1261	Agricoltura delle Venezie
0002-127X	Agricoltura d'Italia
0002-1288	Agricoltura Nostra
0002-1296	Agricoltura Romagnola
0002-130X	Agriculteur du Sud-Est Magazine
0002-1318	Agricultor†
0002-1326	Agricultor Venezolano
0002-1334	Agricultura
0002-1342	Agricultura al Dia†
0002-1350	Agricultura de las Americas
0002-1369	Agricultural and Biological Chemistry changed to Bioscience, Biotechnology, and Biochemistry.
0002-1377	Agricultural and Veterinary Chemicals and Agricultural Engineering changed to Agricultural & Veterinary Chemicals.
0002-1393	South Africa. Department of Agricultural Technical Services. Agricultural Bulletins changed to South Africa. Department of Agriculture. Agricultural Bulletins.
0002-1407	Agricultural Chemical Society of Japan. Journal changed to Nippon Nogeikagaku Kaishi.
0002-1415	Agricultural Co-Operative Bulletin†
0002-1423	U.S. Department of Agriculture. Agricultural Economics Research see 1043-3309
0002-1458	Agricultural Engineering
0002-1466	Agricultural Finance Review
0002-1474	Agricultural Gazette of New South Wales†
0002-1482	Agricultural History
0002-1490	Agricultural History Review
0002-1504	A I C Review see 0840-8289
0002-1512	Agricultural Letter
0002-1520	Agricultural Literature of Czechoslovakia
0002-1539	Agricultural Machinery Journal†
0002-1547	Agricultural Marketing†
0002-1555	Agricultural Marketing
0002-1571	Agricultural Meteorology see 0168-1923
0002-158X	Agricultural News
0002-1598	Fertilizer Progress changed to Dealer Progress.
0002-1601	U.S. Crop Reporting Board. Agricultural Prices
0002-161X	Agricultural Research
0002-1628	Agricultural Research Journal of Kerala
0002-1660	Agricultural Situation see 0270-5672
0002-1679	Agricultural Situation in India
0002-1687	Agriculture
0002-1695	Agriculture†
0002-1709	Agriculture
0002-1717	Agriculture Abroad†
0002-1725	Agriculture and Agro-Industries Journal
0002-1733	Agriculture Checklist
0002-1741	Agriculture Decisions
0002-175X	Agriculture in Northern Ireland
0002-1776	Agriculture Pakistan see 0251-0480
0002-1784	Agrisul
0002-1792	Agro-Industrialist†
0002-1806	Israel. Meteorological Service. Agro-Meteorological Bulletin see 0333-7936
0002-1814	Agro-Service
0002-1822	Agroborealis
0002-1830	Agrochemia
0002-1849	Agrochemia
0002-1857	Agrochimica
0002-1865	Agrohemija†
0002-1873	Agrokemia es Talajtan
0002-1881	Agrokhimiya
0002-1903	Agronomia†
0002-1911	Agronomia Lusitana
0002-192X	Agronomia Tropical
0002-1938	Agronomics†
0002-1946	Agronomie Tropicale
0002-1954	Agronomski Glasnik
0002-1962	Agronomy Journal
0002-1970	Agros
0002-1989	Agrotehnicar
0002-1997	Agrotis
0002-2004	Aguat
0002-2012	Agway Cooperator
0002-2039	Ahijuna
0002-2047	Ahora
0002-2055	Ahorrot
0002-2063	Aid Newsletter changed to A M S A A Newsletter.
0002-208X	Aidai-Echoes
0002-2098	Aika see 0355-0303
0002-2101	Aikakan Himiakan Amsagir
0002-211X	Aikya†
0002-2136	Ain Agricole
0002-2144	Ain Shams Medical Journal
0002-2152	Air Actualites
0002-2160	Air Almanac
0002-2179	Air and Space Age†
0002-2187	Air and Water News†
0002-2195	Air B P†
0002-2209	Air Cadet News changed to Air Cadet Review.
0002-2225	Air Carrier Financial Statistics
0002-2241	Air Classics
0002-225X	Air Comprime
0002-2268	Air Conditioning & Refrigeration in India
0002-2276	Air Conditioning, Heating & Refrigeration News
0002-2284	Building Systems Design see 0199-8595
0002-2292	Air Currents changed to Citizens for Clean Air.
0002-2306	Air-Cushion Vehicles†
0002-2330	Air Force Accounting and Finance Technical Digest changed to Accounting and Finance Tech Digest.
0002-2349	Air Force and Space Digest see 0730-6784
0002-2357	Air Force Civil Engineer see 0362-188X
0002-2365	Air Force Comptroller
0002-2373	Air Force Driver changed to Driver.
0002-2403	Air Force Times
0002-2411	Air Line Employee
0002-242X	Air Line Pilot
0002-2454	Air Navigation Radio Aids†
0002-2462	Air Pictorial
0002-2470	Air Pollution Control Association. Journal see 1047-3289
0002-2489	Air Pollution Notes changed to Solid Waste Management Newsletter.
0002-2497	Air Pollution Titles
0002-2500	Air Progress
0002-2527	U D S Air Quality Control Digest changed to Air Quality Control Digest.
0002-2535	Air Reservist Magazine
0002-2543	Air Transport World
0002-2551	Air Transportation see 0745-5100
0002-256X	Air Transport Magazine see 0005-2132

ISSN INDEX

ISSN	Title
0002-2578	Air Travel *changed to* TravelScene.
0002-2586	Air University Library Index to Military Periodicals
0002-2594	Air University Review *see* 0897-0823
0002-2608	Air - Water Pollution Report
0002-2616	Air Weather Service Observer
0002-2640	Airconditioning and Refrigeration Business *see* 0279-4071
0002-2659	Aircraft *changed to* Aircraft & Aerospace.
0002-2667	Aircraft Engineering *changed to* Aircraft Engineering and Aerospace Technology.
0002-2675	Aircraft Illustrated
0002-2683	Aircraft Industry Record
0002-2691	A.O.P.A. Magazine
0002-2705	Airfixt
0002-2713	Airframe *changed to* British Aerospace News.
0002-2721	Airline Fleet Record
0002-273X	Airline Management and Marketing†
0002-2748	Airline Newsletter
0002-2756	Airman
0002-2764	Airman's Information Manual. Part 1. Basic Flight Manual and ATC Procedures *changed to* Airman's Information Manual. Official Guide to Basic Flight Information and A T C Procedures.
0002-2772	Airman's Information Manual. Part 2: Airport Directory†
0002-2802	Airport Forum
0002-2829	Airport Services Management
0002-2853	Airports International *changed to* Airports International Magazine.
0002-287X	Airways *see* 0032-0617
0002-2888	Airways International†
0002-2926	Aiton Review†
0002-2942	Asian Economies
0002-2969	Biologicheskii Zhurnal Armenii
0002-2977	Akademie der Wissenschaften und der Literatur. Geistes- und Sozialwissenschaftliche Klasse. Abhandlungen
0002-2985	Akademie der Wissenschaften und der Literatur, Mainz. Klasse der Literatur. Abhandlungen
0002-2993	Akademie der Wissenschaften und der Literatur, Mainz. Mathematisch-Naturwissenschaftliche Klasse. Abhandlungen
0002-3000	Akademische Monatsblaetter
0002-3027	Akademiya Meditsinskikh Nauk S.S.S.R. Vestnik
0002-3035	Akademiya Nauk Armyanskoi S.S.R. Izvestiya. Seriya Fizika
0002-3043	Akademiya Nauk Armyanskoi S.S.R. Izvestiya. Seriya Matematika
0002-3051	Akademiya Nauk Armyanskoi S.S.R. Izvestiya. Seriya Mekhanika
0002-306X	Akademiya Nauk Armyanskoi S.S.R. Izvestiya. Seriya Tekhnicheskikh Nauk
0002-3078	Akademiya Nauk Azerbaidzhanskoi S.S.R. Doklady
0002-3086	Akademiya Nauk Azerbaidzhanskoi S.S.R. Izvestiya. Seriya Biologicheskikh Nauk
0002-3094	Akademiya Nauk Azerbaidzhanskoi S.S.R. Izvestiya. Seriya Ekonomicheskikh Nauk
0002-3108	Akademiya Nauk Azerbaidzhanskoi S.S.R. Izvestiya. Seriya Fiziko-Tekhnicheskikh i Matematicheskikh Nauk
0002-3116	Akademiya Nauk Azerbaidzhanskoi S.S.R. Izvestiya. Seriya Istoriya, Filosofiya i Pravo
0002-3124	Akademiya Nauk Azerbaidzhanskoi S.S.R. Izvestiya. Seriya Nauki o Zemle
0002-3132	Akademiya Nauk Azerbaidzhanskoi S.S.R. Izvestiya. Seriya Yazykoznanie, Literatura i Iskusstvo
0002-3167	Akademiya Nauk Gruzinskoi S.S.R. Soobshcheniya
0002-3175	Akademiya Nauk Kazakhskoi S.S.R. Izvestiya. Seriya Geologicheskaya
0002-3183	Akademiya Nauk Kazakhskoi S.S.R. Izvestiya. Seriya Biologicheskaya
0002-3191	Akademiya Nauk Kazakhskoi S.S.R. Izvestiya. Seriya Fiziko - Matematicheskaya
0002-3205	Akademiya Nauk Kazakhskoi S.S.R. Izvestiya. Seriya Khimicheskaya
0002-3213	Akademiya Nauk Kazakhskoi S.S.R. Vestnik
0002-3221	Akademiya Nauk Kirgizskoi S.S.R. Izvestiya
0002-3248	Akademiya Nauk Latviiskoi S.S.R. Izvestiya. Seriya Khimicheskaya
0002-3264	Akademiya Nauk S.S.S.R. Doklady
0002-3299	Akademiya Nauk S.S.S.R. Institut Geologii Rudnykh Mestorozhdenii, Petrografii, Mineralogii i Geokhimii. Trudy†
0002-3302	Institut Teoreticheskoi Astronomii. Byulleten'
0002-3310	Akademiya Nauk S.S.S.R. Izvestiya. Energetika i Transport
0002-3329	Akademiya Nauk S.S.S.R. Izvestiya. Seriya Biologicheskaya
0002-3337	Akademiya Nauk S.S.S.R. Izvestiya. Seriya Fizika Zemli
0002-3345	Akademiya Nauk S.S.S.R. Izvestiya. Seriya Geologicheskaya
0002-3353	Akademiya Nauk S.S.S.R. Izvestiya. Seriya Khimicheskaya
0002-3361	Akademiya Nauk S.S.S.R. Izvestiya. Seriya Matematicheskaya
0002-337X	Akademiya Nauk S.S.S.R. Izvestiya. Seriya Neorganicheskie Materialy
0002-3388	Akademiya Nauk S.S.S.R. Izvestiya. Tekhnicheskaya Kibernetika
0002-3418	Akademiya Nauk S.S.S.R. Sibirskoe Otdelenie. Izvestiya. Seriya Biologicheskikh i Meditsinskikh Nauk
0002-3426	Akademiya Nauk S.S.S.R. Sibirskoe Otdelenie. Izvestiya. Seriya Khimicheskikh Nauk
0002-3434	Akademiya Nauk S.S.S.R. Sibirskoe Otdelenie. Izvestiya. Seriya Tekhnicheskikh Nauk
0002-3442	Akademiya Nauk S.S.S.R. Vestnik
0002-3450	Akademiya Nauk S.S.S.R. Institut Okeanologii. Trudy
0002-3469	Akademiya Nauk Tadzhikskoi S.S.R. Doklady
0002-3477	Akademiya Nauk Tadzhikskoi S.S.R. Izvestiya. Otdelenie Biologicheskikh Nauk
0002-3485	Akademiya Nauk Tadzhikskoi S.S.R. Izvestiya. Otdelenie Fiziko-Matematicheskikh i Geologo-Khimicheskikh Nauk
0002-3493	Akademiya Nauk Turkmenskoi S.S.R. Izvestiya. Seriya Biologicheskikh Nauk
0002-3507	Akademiya Nauk Turkmenskoi S.S.R. Izvestiya. Seriya Fiziko-Tekhnicheskikh, Khimicheskikh i Geologicheskikh Nauk
0002-3515	Akademiya Nauk S.S.S.R. Izvestiya. Seriya Fizika Atmosfery i Okeana
0002-354X	Akademiya Nauk Belarusskoi S.S.R. Doklady
0002-3558	Akademiya Navuk Belarusskai S.S.R. Vestsi. Seriya Biyalagichnykh Navuk
0002-3566	Akademiya Navuk Belarusskai S.S.R. Vestsi. Seriya Fizika-Tekhnichnykh Navuk
0002-3574	Akademiya Navuk Belarusskai S.S.R. Vestsi. Seriya Fizika-Matematychnykh Navuk
0002-3590	Akademiya Navuk Belarusskai S.S.R. Vestsi. Seriya Khimichnykh Navuk
0002-3612	Akaroa Mail
0002-3620	Akashi
0002-3639	Akhand Anand
0002-3655	Akher Saa
0002-368X	Akita Journal of Rural Medicine
0002-3698	Akrides
0002-3701	Akron Dental Society. Bulletin
0002-371X	Akron Law Review
0002-3728	Akros†
0002-3744	Aktie
0002-3752	Die Aktiengesellschaft
0002-3760	Aktion†
0002-3787	Aktualne Problemy Informacji i Dokumentacji
0002-3809	Aktuelle Freie Praxis†
0002-3825	Aktuelle Kulturpolitik†
0002-3833	Aktuelle Probleme der Buergerlichen Philosophie *see* 0138-2721
0002-3841	Aktuelle Sammlung†
0002-385X	Aktuelle Steuer-Informationen *see* 0170-7620
0002-3884	Aktuellt Politik och Samhaelle *see* 0345-0635
0002-3892	Akuntansi & Administrasi
0002-3914	Akusticheskii Zhurnal
0002-3922	Akvariet
0002-3930	Akvarium a Terarium
0002-3949	Akwesasne Notes
0002-3957	Akzente
0002-3965	Ousbou' al-Arabi
0002-3973	Al-Abhath
0002-3981	Ahad
0002-399X	Al-Dirasat al-Islamiyyah
0002-4015	Al-Ma'arif
0002-4023	Al-Machriqt
0002-4031	Majma' al-Lughah al-Arabiyyah. Majallah
0002-4058	Al-Maskukat
0002-4066	Ai Nostri Amici
0002-4074	Ta'awun
0002-4082	Turath al-Sha'bi
0002-4090	A L A
0002-4112	Alabama Academy of Science. Journal
0002-4120	Alabama Architect†
0002-4139	Alabama Association of Secondary School Principals. Bulletin†
0002-4147	Alabama Baptist Historian
0002-4155	Alabama Builder
0002-4163	Alabama Business†
0002-4171	Alabama Conservation
0002-418X	Alabama Contractor
0002-4198	Alabama Dental Association. Journal
0002-421X	Alabama Food Merchants Journal
0002-4228	Alabama Forest Products *see* 0275-6625
0002-4236	Alabama Historical Quarterly†
0002-4252	Alabama Journal of Medical Sciences†
0002-4260	Alabama Junior College Librarian *changed to* Alabama Junior College Library Association Newsletter.
0002-4279	Alabama Law Review
0002-4287	Alabama Lawyer
0002-4295	Alabama Librarian
0002-4309	Alabama Municipal Journal
0002-4325	Alabama Purchasor
0002-4333	Alabama Retail Trade *see* 0002-4163
0002-4341	Alabama Review
0002-435X	Alabama School Journal
0002-4368	Alabama Social Welfare†
0002-4384	Alabama Truckert
0002-4392	Alam Attijarat
0002-4406	Alambre
0002-4414	Alameda-Contra Costa Medical Association. Bulletin
0002-4422	Alamo
0002-4430	Alan Watts Journal†
0002-4465	Alaska Conservation Review†
0002-4473	Alaska Construction and Oil Report *changed to* Alaska Construction & Oil.
0002-449X	Alaska Industry *changed to* Alaska Business and Industry.
0002-4503	Alaska Journal†
0002-4511	Alaska Land Lines *changed to* Alaska's Resources.
0002-452X	Alaska Law Journal *changed to* Alaska Bar Rag.
0002-4538	Alaska Medicine
0002-4546	Alaska Nurse
0002-4554	A M U Press Alaskana Series (Alaska Methodist University) *changed to* A P U Press Alaskana Book Series.
0002-4562	Alaska
0002-4570	Sourdough
0002-4589	Alaska Teacher *changed to* Alaska Teacher Newsletter.
0002-4597	Alaska's Health and Welfare *changed to* Alaska. Department of Health and Social Services. Quarterly.
0002-4619	Alauda
0002-4627	Alba
0002-4643	Albania Oggi
0002-4651	Albania Report
0002-466X	Albany County Agriculture News *changed to* Extension News - Albany - Rensselaer - Saratoga - Washington Counties.
0002-4678	Albany Law Review
0002-4686	Albany Regional Medical Program. Report†
0002-4708	Albert Einstein Medical Center.Journal†
0002-4716	Alberta Amateur *see* 0049-5778
0002-4724	Alberta Business Trends *see* 0317-3925
0002-4740	Alberta Calls
0002-4759	Alberta Conservative†
0002-4767	Alberta Farm Economist†
0002-4775	Alberta Gazette
0002-4783	Alberta Historical Review *see* 0316-1552
0002-4805	Alberta Journal of Educational Research
0002-4821	Alberta Law Review
0002-483X	Library Association of Alberta. Bulletin†
0002-4848	Alberta Medical Bulletin†
0002-4856	Alberta Magazine *changed to* Westworld Alberta Magazine.
0002-4872	Alberta Oil and Gas Industry. Monthly Statistics *see* 0710-6874
0002-4880	Alberta School Trustee *changed to* Trustee.
0002-4902	Alberta Transport Reporter
0002-4910	Albertina Student
0002-4929	Albrecht-Thaer-Archiv *see* 0365-0340
0002-4937	Album
0002-4953	Albuquerque Archaeological Society Newsletter
0002-4961	Albus
0002-497X	Alcalde *changed to* Texas Alcalde.
0002-4988	Alcan Magazine†
0002-4996	Alcan News†
0002-5003	Alcan Review *changed to* Aluminum Review.
0002-5011	Alchimist†
0002-502X	Alcoholism
0002-5038	Alcoholism Review†
0002-5054	Alcool ou Sante
0002-5062	Alcor
0002-5089	Aldebaran Review
0002-5097	Alderley and Wilmslow and Knutsford Advertiser
0002-5100	Aldrichimica Acta
0002-5119	Aldus†
0002-5127	Aleh†
0002-5135	Alemanha Internacional†
0002-5143	Alemas
0002-5151	Alergia
0002-5178	Alerta†
0002-5186	Alerte Atomique
0002-5208	Alexanor
0002-5216	Alfa
0002-5224	Alfred Hitchcock's Mystery Magazine
0002-5232	Algebra and Logic
0002-5240	Algebra Universalis
0002-5267	Algemeen Maconniek Tijdschrift
0002-5275	Algemeen Nederlands Tijdschrift voor Wijsbegeerte
0002-5283	Algemeen Politieblad van het Koninkrijk der Nederlanden
0002-5291	Algeria. Institut Pedagogique National. Bureau de Documentation et d'Information Scolaires Universitaires et Professionnelles. Informations et Documents†

0002-5305 Algeria. Sous-Direction des Statistiques. Bulletin de Statistiques Generales *changed to* Algeria. Direction des Statistiques et de la Comptabilite Nationale. Bulletin Trimestriel de Statistiques.
0002-5313 Algerien en Europe
0002-5321 Universite d'Alger. Publications Scientifiques. Serie A: Mathematiques
0002-533X Universite d'Alger. Publications Scientifiques. Serie B: Sciences Physiques
0002-5348 Algo *see* 0214-0381
0002-5364 Algol *see* 0195-5365
0002-5380 Ali Nuove
0002-5399 Alieia
0002-5410 Alimentation au Quebec
0002-5429 Alimentazione Animale *see* 0390-0487
0002-5445 Aliupseeri *see* 0355-726X
0002-5453 Alive†
0002-5461 Alive (St. Louis)†
0002-547X Alive(Harrisonburg)†
0002-5488 Alkahest†
0002-5496 Alkohol-Industrie
0002-550X Alkoholdebatt
0002-5518 Alkoholfraagen *see* 0345-0732
0002-5526 Alkoholikysymys *changed to* Mutta.
0002-5534 All-Africa Church Music Association. Journal†
0002-5542 All-Church Press Newspapers
0002-5550 All Clear†
0002-5569 All England Law Reports
0002-5577 All Hands
0002-5585 All-India Anglo-Indian Association. Review
0002-5593 All India Reporter
0002-5607 All Outdoors
0002-5623 All the World
0002-5631 Alla Bottega
0002-564X Allam- es Jogtudomany
0002-5658 Allattani Kozlemenyek
0002-5666 Alle den Volcke
0002-5674 Alle Hens
0002-5682 Alle Kvinner†
0002-5690 Allegheny County Pharmacist
0002-5704 Allegro
0002-5712 Allemagne d'Aujourd'hui
0002-5720 Allemagne Internationale†
0002-5739 Allen Memorial Art Museum. Bulletin
0002-5747 Allergia
0002-5771 Allers
0002-578X Allers
0002-5798 Allgemeine Bau-Zeitung
0002-5801 Allgemeine Bauzeitung
0002-581X Allgemeine Deutsche Gesellen-Zeitung†
0002-5828 Allgemeine Deutsche Imkerzeitung
0002-5836 Allgemeine Deutsche Lehrerzeitung *see* 0342-0671
0002-5852 Allgemeine Forst- und Jagdzeitung
0002-5860 Allgemeine Forst Zeitschrift
0002-5879 Allgemeine Forstzeitung *changed to* Oesterreichische Forstzeitung.
0002-5895 Allgemeine Hotel- und Gaststaetten-Zeitung
0002-5909 Allgemeine Missionsnachrichten *see* 0723-6204
0002-5917 A P R
0002-5925 Allgemeine Schweizerische Militaerzeitschrift
0002-5933 Allgemeine Sparkasse Linz. Kurz Notiert *changed to* Allgemeine Sparkasse. Kurz Notiert.
0002-5968 Allgemeine Vermessungs-Nachrichten
0002-5976 Allgemeine Waermetechnik
0002-5984 Narichten der Fachorganisationen *see* 0342-3573
0002-5992 Allgemeiner Muehlen-Markt
0002-600X Allgemeiner Samen- und Pflanzen Anzeiger
0002-6018 Allgemeines Statistisches Archiv
0002-6050 Alliance Israelite Universelle en France. Cahiers
0002-6069 Alliance Journal†
0002-6093 Alliance Review
0002-6107 Allied Industrial Worker
0002-6123 Allis-Chalmers Engineering Review†
0002-614X Alloy Digest
0002-6158 Allpress
0002-6166 Allround-Collector Address-List
0002-6174 Allsvensk Samling *changed to* Sverigekontakt.
0002-6182 Allt i Hemmet
0002-6190 Allt om Hobby
0002-6204 Allt Om Mat
0002-6212 Alluminio e Nuova Metallurgia *see* 0365-3927
0002-6239 Alma *changed to* Paz e Alegria.
0002-6247 Alma Mater†
0002-6255 Almanac of Current World Leaders *see* 0192-6802
0002-6263 Current World Leaders - Biography and News *see* 0192-6802
0002-6271 Almanaque Aeronautico†
0002-628X Almas
0002-6298 Der Almbauer
0002-6301 Aloe
0002-631X Aloft†
0002-6328 Along the Boardwalk†
0002-6336 Alpen
0002-6344 Alpengarten†
0002-6352 Alpenlaendische Bienenzeitung
0002-6379 Alpha *changed to* Prisma.
0002-6395 Alpha-Mathematische Schuelerzeitschrift
0002-6409 Alpha News Digest *changed to* Alpha Digest.
0002-6417 Alpha Omegan
0002-6425 Alphabet†
0002-6433 Alphabet†
0002-6441 Alphabetic Subject Index to Petroleum Abstracts
0002-645X Alphian *changed to* Transportation Worldwide.
0002-6468 Alpi Venete
0002-6476 Alpine Garden Society. Quarterly Bulletin
0002-6484 Alpinismus *see* 0177-3542
0002-6492 Alpino
0002-6506 Alt for Damerne
0002-6514 Altkatholische Kirchenzeitung
0002-6522 Alt-Katholische Kirchenzeitung *see* 0930-5718
0002-6530 Microform Review
0002-6549 Alta Direccion
0002-6557 Alta Frequenza *see* 1120-3862
0002-6565 Alte und Moderne Kunst†
0002-6573 Altenheim
0002-6611 Alternative
0002-662X Alternative Press Index
0002-6638 Alternatives
0002-6646 Das Altertum
0002-6662 Altra Italia
0002-6670 Der Altsprachliche Unterricht
0002-6689 Aluminum
0002-6697 World Aluminum Abstracts
0002-6700 Johns Hopkins Hospital School of Nursing. Alumni Magazine
0002-6778 Amaru†
0002-6786 Amaterska Scena
0002-6794 Amatersky Film *changed to* Video plus Film.
0002-6816 Amateur Baseball News
0002-6832 Amateur Gardening
0002-6840 Amateur Photographer
0002-6859 Amateur Radio
0002-6867 Amateur Stage
0002-6875 Amateurtuinder
0002-6883 Amateur Winemaker†
0002-6905 Ambassade van de U.S.S.R. in Nederland. Informatie-Bulletin†
0002-6913 Ambassador†
0002-6948 Ambiance de Paris†
0002-6956 Ambience†
0002-6964 Ambienti†
0002-6972 Ambit
0002-6980 Ambix
0002-6999 Ambt en Plicht
0002-7006 Ambulatory Pediatric Association Newsletter
0002-7014 Ameghiniana
0002-7022 Amentia
0002-7049 America
0002-7057 Cooperative America *changed to* America Cooperativa.
0002-7065 America: History and Life. Part A: Article Abstracts and Citation *changed to* America: History and Life. Articles Abstract and Citations of Reviews and Dissertations Covering the United States and Canada.
0002-7081 America Indigena
0002-709X America Latina
0002-7103 Woman Physician *see* 0098-8421
0002-712X American Academy of Arts and Sciences. Bulletin
0002-7138 American Academy of Child Psychiatry. Journal *see* 0890-8567
0002-7146 American Academy of Gold Foil Operators. Journal *see* 0361-7734
0002-7154 American Academy of Ophthalmology and Otolaryngology. Transactions *see* 0161-6420
0002-7162 American Academy of Political and Social Science. Annals
0002-7170 Council on the Study of Religion. Bulletin†
0002-7189 American Academy of Religion. Journal
0002-7197 Independent Agent
0002-7200 American Agent and Broker
0002-7219 American Agriculturist and Rural New Yorker *see* 0161-8237
0002-7227 American Aircraft Modeler†
0002-7235 Alumni Register *changed to* Illinois State University Today.
0002-7243 American Analgesia Society. Journal
0002-7251 American Animal Hospital Association Bulletin *see* 0587-2871
0002-726X American Annals of the Deaf
0002-7286 American Anthropological Association. Newsletter *see* 0098-1605
0002-7294 American Anthropologist
0002-7316 American Antiquity
0002-7324 American Archives of Rehabilitation Therapy†
0002-7359 American Art Journal
0002-7367 American Artisan†
0002-7375 American Artist
0002-7413 American Association of Colleges for Teacher Education. Bulletin *see* 0731-602X
0002-7421 American Association of Dental Examiners. Board Bulletin
0002-743X American Association of Fund-Raising Counsel. Bulletin *see* 0899-3793
0002-7448 American Association of Nurse Anesthetists. Journal *see* 0094-6354
0002-7464 American Association of Petroleum Geologists. Bulletin *see* 0149-1423
0002-7472 American Association of State Libraries. President's Newsletter *see* 0044-9660
0002-7480 American Association of Teacher Educators in Agriculture. Journal *see* 1042-0541
0002-7499 American Association of Teachers of Esperanto Quarterly Bulletin
0002-7502 American Association of Workers for the Blind. Dictionary Catalogue†
0002-7510 American Association of Workers for the Blind. News and Views *changed to* A E R Report.
0002-7529 American Astrology
0002-7537 American Astronomical Society. Bulletin
0002-7545 American Automatic Merchandiser
0002-7561 American Banker
0002-757X American Baptist
0002-7596 American Bar Association Journal *see* 0747-0088
0002-760X American Bar News†
0002-7618 American Bard†
0002-7626 American Bee Journal
0002-7634 American Beef Producer†
0002-7642 American Behavioral Scientist
0002-7650 American Benedictine Review
0002-7669 American Bibliography of Agricultural Economics†
0002-7677 American Bicyclist & Motorcyclist
0002-7685 American Biology Teacher
0002-7707 American Book Publishing Record
0002-7715 American Breeds Magazine†
0002-7723 American Brewer†
0002-7731 American Building Supplies†
0002-7766 American Business Law Journal
0002-7774 Report on Alcohol *see* 0161-1267
0002-7782 American Cage-Bird Magazine
0002-7790 American Catholic Historical Society of Philadelphia. Records
0002-7804 American Cemetery
0002-7812 American Ceramic Society. Bulletin
0002-7820 American Ceramic Society. Journal
0002-7839 American Chamber of Commerce Executives. Journal†
0002-7847 American Chamber of Commerce in Japan. Journal
0002-7855 American Chamber of Commerce in Thailand. Review *see* 0125-0191
0002-7863 American Chemical Society. Journal
0002-788X American Choral Foundation. Research Memorandum Series
0002-7898 American Choral Review
0002-7901 American Christmas Tree Growers' Journal *see* 0569-3845
0002-791X American Church News *see* 0149-4244
0002-7928 American Cinematographer
0002-7936 American City *see* 0149-337X
0002-7944 American College Health Association. Journal *see* 0744-8481
0002-7952 A C H A Action
0002-7960 American College of Chest Physicians Bulletin *see* 0149-6719
0002-7979 American College of Dentists. Journal
0002-7987 American College of Foot Orthopedists Newsletter
0002-7995 American College of Neuropsychiatrists. Bulletin†
0002-8002 American College of Nurse-Midwives. Bulletin *see* 0091-2182
0002-8010 American College of Physicians. Bulletin *see* 0161-7478
0002-8029 American College of Preventive Medicine Newsletter *changed to* A C P M News.
0002-8037 American College of Radiology. Bulletin *see* 0098-6070
0002-8045 American College of Surgeons. Bulletin
0002-8053 American Comparative Literature Association Newsletter *see* 0891-3277
0002-8061 American Concrete Institute. Journal *see* 0889-3241
0002-8061 American Concrete Institute. Journal *see* 0889-325X
0002-807X American Cooner
0002-8088 American Corrective Therapy Journal *changed to* Clinical Kinesiology.
0002-810X American Craftmen's Council Outlook *changed to* A C C Outlook.
0002-8118 American Criminal Law Quarterly *see* 0164-0364
0002-8126 American Criminologist†
0002-8134 American Crosby Clipper *changed to* American Clipper.
0002-8142 American Dachshund†
0002-8150 American Dahlia Society. Bulletin
0002-8177 American Dental Association. Journal
0002-8185 American Dental Hygienists Association. Journal *see* 1043-254X
0002-8193 American Dialect Society. Newsletter
0002-8207 American Dialect Society. Publications
0002-8215 American Dialog†
0002-8223 American Dietetic Association. Journal
0002-8231 American Society for Information Science. Journal
0002-8258 American Drycleaner
0002-8266 American Dyestuff Reporter
0002-8274 American Ecclesiastical Review†
0002-8282 American Economic Review
0002-8290 American Economist
0002-8304 American Education†

ISSN

5338 ISSN INDEX

0002-8312 American Educational Research Journal
0002-8320 American Entomological Society. Transactions
0002-8339 American Esperanto Magazine†
0002-8347 American Stock Exchange Stock Reports
0002-8371 American Fabrics *see* 0091-0864
0002-838X American Family Physician
0002-8398 American Farm Bureau Federations Official News Letter *see* 0197-5617
0002-8401 American Farm Youth†
0002-8436 American Fencing
0002-8444 American Fern Journal
0002-8452 American Field
0002-8460 American Film Institute. Education Membership Newsletter†
0002-8487 American Fisheries Society. Transactions
0002-8525 American Flint
0002-8533 American Forensic Association. Journal *see* 1051-1431
0002-8541 American Forests
0002-855X American Foundation for the Blind Newsletter *changed to* A F B News.
0002-8568 American Fruit Grower
0002-8576 American Funeral Director
0002-8584 American Gas Association Monthly *changed to* A G A American Gas.
0002-8592 American Genealogist
0002-8606 American Geophysical Union. Transactions *see* 0096-3941
0002-8614 American Geriatrics Society. Journal
0002-8622 American-German Review†
0002-8630 American Girl (Inkprint Edition)†
0002-8649 American Glass Review
0002-8657 American Gold News *changed to* American Gold News and Western Prospector.
0002-8665 American Grocer
0002-8681 American Hampshire Herdsman
0002-869X American Harp Journal
0002-8703 American Heart Journal
0002-8711 American Helicopter Society. Journal
0002-872X American Hereford Journal
0002-8738 American Heritage
0002-8746 American Highways *see* 0147-4820
0002-8754 American Histadrut Cultural Exchange Institute. Bulletin†
0002-8762 American Historical Review
0002-8770 American History Illustrated
0002-8789 American Home†
0002-8797 American Horologist and Jeweler *see* 0279-6198
0002-8800 American Horticultural Magazine *see* 0096-4417
0002-8819 American Horticultural Society News and Views *see* 0096-4417
0002-8835 American Hungarian Review†
0002-8843 American Idea†
0002-886X American Import-Export Bulletin *changed to* Global Trade.
0002-8886 American Indian Law Newsletter
0002-8894 American Industrial Hygiene Association Journal
0002-8908 American Industry
0002-8916 American Inkmaker
0002-8940 Report on Food Markets *see* 0745-4503
0002-8959 American Institute of Food Distribution. Weekly Digest *see* 0745-4503
0002-8967 American Institute of Homeopathy. Journal
0002-8975 American Institute of Hypnosis. Journal
0002-8983 American Institute of Landscape Architects. Journal†
0002-8991 American Institute of Planners. Journal *see* 0194-4363
0002-9041 American Jewelry Manufacturer
0002-905X American Jewish Archives
0002-9068 American Jewish Historical Quarterly *see* 0164-0178
0002-9084 American Jewish World
0002-9092 American Journal of Agricultural Economics
0002-9106 American Journal of the Anatomy *see* 1058-8388
0002-9114 American Journal of Archaeology
0002-9122 American Journal of Botany
0002-9149 American Journal of Cardiology
0002-9157 American Journal of Clinical Hypnosis
0002-9165 American Journal of Clinical Nutrition
0002-9173 American Journal of Clinical Pathology
0002-919X American Journal of Comparative Law
0002-9203 American Journal of Correction *see* 0190-2563
0002-9211 American Journal of Digestive Diseases *see* 0163-2116
0002-922X A J D C: American Journal of Diseases of Children
0002-9238 American Journal of E E G Technology
0002-9246 American Journal of Economics and Sociology
0002-9254 American Journal of Enology and Viticulture
0002-9262 American Journal of Epidemiology
0002-9270 American Journal of Gastroenterology
0002-9289 American Journal of Hospital Pharmacy
0002-9297 American Journal of Human Genetics
0002-9300 American Journal of International Law
0002-9319 American Journal of Legal History
0002-9327 American Journal of Mathematics
0002-9335 American Journal of Medical Technology *see* 0741-5397
0002-9343 American Journal of Medicine
0002-9351 American Journal of Mental Deficiency *see* 0895-8017
0002-936X American Journal of Nursing
0002-9378 American Journal of Obstetrics and Gynecology
0002-9386 American Journal of Occupational Therapy *see* 0272-9490
0002-9394 American Journal of Ophthalmology
0002-9416 American Journal of Orthodontics and Oral Surgery *see* 0889-5406
0002-9432 American Journal of Orthopsychiatry
0002-9440 American Journal of Pathology
0002-9459 American Journal of Pharmaceutical Education
0002-9467 American Journal of Pharmacy and the Sciences Supporting Health *see* 0730-7780
0002-9475 American Journal of Philology
0002-9483 American Journal of Physical Anthropology
0002-9491 American Journal of Physical Medicine *see* 0894-9115
0002-9505 American Journal of Physics
0002-9513 American Journal of Physiology
0002-9521 American Journal of Proctology *see* 0162-6566
0002-953X American Journal of Psychiatry
0002-9548 American Journal of Psychoanalysis
0002-9556 American Journal of Psychology
0002-9564 American Journal of Psychotherapy
0002-9572 American Journal of Public Health and the Nation's Health *see* 0090-0036
0002-9580 American Journal of Roentgenology, Radium Therapy and Nuclear Medicine *see* 0361-803X
0002-9599 American Journal of Science
0002-9602 American Journal of Sociology
0002-9610 American Journal of Surgery
0002-9629 American Journal of the Medical Sciences
0002-9637 American Journal of Tropical Medicine and Hygiene
0002-9645 American Journal of Veterinary Research
0002-9653 Dimensions in American Judaism†
0002-967X American Killifish Association. Journal
0002-9688 American Labor†
0002-970X American Landrace *changed to* American Landrace.
0002-9718 American Laundry Digest
0002-9726 American Leather Chemists Association. Journal
0002-9734 American Legion Magazine
0002-9742 American Legion Press Association News-Letter
0002-9750 American Legislator†
0002-9769 American Libraries
0002-9777 American Library Association. Adult Services Division Newsletter†
0002-9785 American Library Association. Library Education Division. Newsletter†
0002-9793 American Library Directory Updating Service†
0002-9815 American Literary Accents†
0002-9823 American Literary Realism
0002-9831 American Literature
0002-9858 American Machinist (1963) *see* 1041-7958
0002-9866 American Marine Engineer
0002-9874 American Maritime Cases
0002-9882 American Maritime Officer
0002-9890 American Mathematical Monthly
0002-9904 American Mathematical Society. Bulletin. *see* 0273-0979
0002-9912 American Mathematical Society. New Publications *see* 0361-4794
0002-9920 American Mathematical Society. Notices
0002-9939 American Mathematical Society. Proceedings
0002-9947 American Mathematical Society. Transactions
0002-9955 American Medical Association. Journal *see* 0098-7484
0002-9963 American Medical Technologists. Journal *see* 0741-5397
0002-9971 American Medical Writers Association. Bulletin *changed to* A M W A Journal.
0002-9998 American Metal Market
0003-0007 American Meteorological Society. Bulletin
0003-0015 American-Mexican Medical Association. Journal
0003-0023 American Microscopical Society. Transactions
0003-0031 American Midland Naturalist
0003-0031 American Midland Naturalist Monograph Series
0003-004X American Mineralogist
0003-0066 American Motor Carrier†
0003-0074 A M A News *changed to* American Motorcyclist.
0003-0082 American Museum Novitates
0003-0090 American Museum of Natural History. Bulletin
0003-0104 American Music Center. Newsletter
0003-0112 American Music Teacher
0003-0139 American Musicological Society. Journal
0003-0147 American Naturalist
0003-0155 American Neptune
0003-0163 American Newspaper Boy *changed to* American Newspaper Carrier.
0003-0171 American Notes and Queries *see* 0895-769X
0003-018X American Nuclear Society Transactions
0003-0198 American Nurseryman
0003-0201 American Observer *see* 0745-7065
0003-021X American Oil Chemists' Society. Journal
0003-0228 American Old Time Fiddlers News *changed to* American Fiddlers News.
0003-0236 American Opinion *changed to* New American (Appleton).
0003-0244 American Optometric Association. Journal
0003-0252 American Orchid Society Bulletin
0003-0279 American Oriental Society. Journal
0003-0287 American Osteopathic Association. Journal *see* 0098-6151
0003-0295 American Oxonian
0003-0309 American Paint and Wallpaper Dealer *see* 1045-5914
0003-0317 American Paint Journal *see* 0098-5430
0003-0325 American Painting Contractor
0003-0333 American Paper Industry *see* 1046-4352
0003-0341 American Paper Institute. Paper, Paperboard, & Wood Pulp Monthly Statistical Summary
0003-0376 American Pen†
0003-0392 American Perfumer and Cosmetics *see* 0361-4387
0003-0406 Abstracts of Air and Water Conservation Literature†
0003-0422 Abstracts of Refining Literature *changed to* Literature Abstracts.
0003-0430 American Petroleum Institute. Abstracts of Refining Patents *changed to* Patents Abstracts.
0003-0457 American Petroleum Institute. Division of Statistics and Economics. Weekly Statistical Bulletin *changed to* American Petroleum Institute. Division of Statistics. Weekly Statistical Bulletin.
0003-0465 American Pharmaceutical Association. Journal *see* 0160-3450
0003-0473 American Philatelist
0003-0481 American Philosophical Quarterly
0003-049X American Philosophical Society. Proceedings
0003-0503 American Physical Society. Bulletin
0003-0511 American Pigeon Journal
0003-052X American Place Theatre. News†
0003-0538 American Podiatry Association. Journal *see* 8750-7315
0003-0546 American Poet
0003-0554 American Political Science Review
0003-0562 American Polygraph Association. Journal *see* 0197-7024
0003-0570 American Portuguese Cultural Society. Journal *see* 0098-4981
0003-0589 American Potato Journal
0003-0619 American Primrose, Primula and Auricula Society, Quarterly *see* 0162-6671
0003-0627 Pharmacy Times
0003-0635 American Protestant Hospital Association. Bulletin *changed to* American Protestant Health Association. Bulletin.
0003-0651 American Psychoanalytic Association. Journal
0003-066X American Psychologist
0003-0678 American Quarterly
0003-0686 American Racing Pigeon News
0003-0694 American Railway Engineering Association Bulletin
0003-0708 American Rationalist
0003-0716 American Record Guide
0003-0724 American Recorder
0003-0732 American Red Cross Youth Journal†
0003-0740 American Red Cross Youth News *changed to* Young Horizons.
0003-0775 American Report†
0003-0791 American Review of Eastern Orthodoxy
0003-0805 American Review of Respiratory Disease
0003-0813 American Review of World Health†
0003-0821 American Rhododendron Society. Quarterly Bulletin *see* 0745-7839
0003-083X American Rifleman
0003-0848 American Risk and Insurance Association. Commission on Insurance Terminology. Bulletin†
0003-0856 American Road Builder *see* 1043-4054
0003-0864 American Rock Garden Society Bulletin
0003-0872 American Rodding†
0003-0899 American Rose Magazine
0003-0902 American Salesman
0003-0910 American Scandinavian Review *see* 0098-857X
0003-0929 American Scene *see* 0730-5036
0003-0937 American Scholar
0003-0945 American School & University
0003-0953 American School Board Journal
0003-0961 American School News†
0003-097X American Schools of Oriental Research. Bulletin
0003-0988 American Scientific Affiliation. Journal: Evangelical Perspectives on Science and Christian Faith *see* 0892-2675
0003-0996 American Scientist
0003-1003 American Secondary Education
0003-1011 American Security Council Washington Report†

ISSN

ISSN	Title
0003-102X	American Sephardi
0003-1038	American Shoemaking
0003-1046	American Small Stock Farmer†
0003-1054	American Society for Geriatric Dentistry. Journal
0003-1062	American Society for Horticultural Science. Journal
0003-1070	American Society for Psychical Research. Journal
0003-1089	American Society for the Study of Orthodontics. Journal†
0003-1100	American Society of Civil Engineers. Engineering Mechanics Division. Newsletter†
0003-1119	American Society of Civil Engineers. Proceedings
0003-1135	American Society of Civil Engineers. Structural Division. Newsletter†
0003-1143	American Society of Civil Engineers. Surveying & Mapping Division. Newsletter†
0003-1151	American Society of Civil Engineers. Waterways & Harbors Division. Newsletter†
0003-116X	American Society of Farm Managers and Rural Appraisers. Journal
0003-1178	American Society of Newspaper Editors. Bulletin
0003-1186	American Society of Papyrologists. Bulletin
0003-1194	American Society of Psychosomatic Dentistry and Medicine. Journal see 0884-8297
0003-1208	American Society of Safety Engineers. Journal see 0099-0027
0003-1216	American Society of Sugar Beet Technologists. Journal see 0899-1502
0003-1224	American Sociological Review
0003-1232	American Sociologist
0003-1240	American Soft Drink Journal†
0003-1259	American Sokol
0003-1275	Soybean Profits†
0003-1283	American Speech
0003-1291	American Statistical Association. Journal see 0162-1459
0003-1305	American Statistician
0003-1313	American String Teacher
0003-1321	American Studies International
0003-1348	American Surgeon
0003-1356	American Surgical Dealer†
0003-1372	American Symphony Orchestra League. Newsletter see 0271-2687
0003-1380	American Teacher
0003-1399	American Theological Library Association. Newsletter
0003-1402	American Theosophist
0003-1410	American Transcendental Quarterly see 0149-9017
0003-1429	American Translator†
0003-1437	American Trial Lawyers Association Newsletter see 0364-8125
0003-1445	American Turf Monthly
0003-1453	American University Law Review
0003-1461	American Vegetable Grower
0003-147X	American Vegetarian-Hygienist†
0003-1488	American Veterinary Medical Association. Journal
0003-1496	American Vocational Journal see 0884-8009
0003-150X	American Water Works Association. Journal
0003-1518	AmericanWay
0003-1534	American West†
0003-1550	American Zionist
0003-1569	American Zoologist
0003-1593	America's Future
0003-1607	America's Textile Reporter†
0003-1615	The Americas
0003-1631	Amerikas Latvietis†
0003-1666	Amersfoortse Stemme†
0003-1674	A M E X changed to A M E X Canada.
0003-1682	Amgueddfa†
0003-1690	Amherst Alumni News changed to Amherst.
0003-1704	Ami du Peuple
0003-1712	Amica changed to A M I C A Bulletin.
0003-1720	Amicizia
0003-1739	Amicizia Ebraico-Cristiana di Firenze. Bollettino
0003-1747	Amico dell'Arte Cristiana
0003-1755	Amiga
0003-1763	Aminco Laboratory News†
0003-1771	Amis-Coop changed to Delta (Paris).
0003-178X	Amis de Han Ryner. Cahiers
0003-1798	Amis de la Radiesthesie
0003-1801	Amis de l'I.B.A.N.A. (Publication) changed to Ecole Nationale Superieure de Biologie Appliquee a la Nutrition et a l'Alimentation. Cahiers.
0003-181X	Amis de Milosz
0003-1828	Amis de Napoleon 3rd. Bulletin Interne changed to Nouveaux Cahiers du Second Empire.
0003-1844	Amis des Roses
0003-1852	Amis du Chateau de Pau. Bulletin
0003-1860	Amis du Film et de la Television changed to Visions.
0003-1879	Amistad†
0003-1887	S O S Amitie France. Bulletin National
0003-1895	Amities Catholiques Francaises
0003-1909	Amities Spirituelles. Bulletin
0003-1917	Amministrazione Socialista†
0003-1933	Amnesty Action
0003-1941	Amnesty International Monthly see 0308-6887
0003-195X	Among Friends
0003-1968	Among Ourselves
0003-1984	Amor Artis Bulletin†
0003-1992	Amperland
0003-200X	Amphora
0003-2018	Ampleforth Journal
0003-2026	Ampo
0003-2034	Amposta
0003-2069	Amsterdam in de Markt†
0003-2077	Amsterdam-Rotterdam Bank. Economic Quarterly Review†
0003-2093	Kursblatt der Amtlich Nicht Notierten Wertpapiere - Geregelter Freiverkehr an der Wiener Boerse changed to Kursblatt der Wiener Wertpapierboerse - Geregelter Freiverkehr.
0003-2107	Amtliche Veterinaernachrichten†
0003-2115	Amtlicher Anzeiger
0003-2131	Amtliches Kreisblatt fuer den Kreis Herzogtum Lauenburg
0003-214X	Berliner Wertpapierboerse. Amtliches Kursblatt
0003-2158	Wertpapierboerse in Stuttgart. Amtliches Kursblatt changed to Baden - Wuerttembergische Wertpapierboerse zu Stuttgart. Amtliches Kursblatt.
0003-2166	Wiener Warenboerse. Amtliches Kursblatt. Holz
0003-2174	Wiener Warenboerse. Amtliches Kursblatt. Rohhaeute und Felle, Leder Treibriemen und Technische Lederartikel
0003-2190	Amtliches Schulblatt fuer den Regierungsbezirk Duesseldorf
0003-2204	Amtliches Schulblatt fuer die Volks-, Real- und Berufsschulen fuer den Bezirksregierung Trier
0003-2220	Amtsblatt der Oesterreichischen Justizverwaltung
0003-2239	Amtsblatt der Stadt Kapfenberg
0003-2247	Wels, Stadt. Amtsblatt
0003-2255	Wiener Neustadt. Amtsblatt der Stadt changed to Wiener Neustadt. Amtsblatt der Statutarstadt.
0003-2263	Germany (Federal Republic, 1949-) Bundesministerium fuer das Post- und Fernmeldewesen. Amtsblatt changed to Germany (Federal Republic, 1949-). Bundesminister fuer das Post- und Telekommunikation. Amtsblatt.
0003-2271	Amtsblatt fuer das Land Vorarlberg
0003-228X	Amtsblatt fuer den Regierungsbezirk Aurich†
0003-2328	Amtsblatt fuer die Erzdioezese Bamberg
0003-2336	Der Amtsvormund
0003-2344	Amusement Business
0003-2360	An Lef Kernewek†
0003-2379	An-Nahar Arab Report changed to Memo.
0003-2387	Al-Nashra see 0889-8731
0003-2409	Anaesthesia (London)
0003-2417	Der Anaesthesist
0003-2425	Anais Azevedos†
0003-2441	Anais de Farmacia e Quimica de Sao Paulo
0003-245X	Anais Paulistas de Medicina e Cirurgia
0003-2468	Analecta Bollandiana
0003-2476	Analecta Cisterciensia
0003-2484	Anales Cientificos
0003-2492	Anales de Bromatologia
0003-2506	Anales de Mecanica y Electricidad
0003-2514	Anales de Medicina see 0210-7465
0003-2530	Anales del Instituto Corachan
0003-2549	Anales del Servicio de Psiquiatria
0003-2557	Anales Espanoles de Odontoestomatologia†
0003-2565	Beogradski Univerzitet. Pravni Fakultet. Anali
0003-2573	Analise Social
0003-2581	Analisis - Confirmado
0003-259X	Analisis de Actualidades Societicas†
0003-2603	Analog Science Fact - Science Fiction see 0161-2328
0003-262X	Analyse et Prevision see 0337-307X
0003-2638	Analysis
0003-2646	Analysis of Current Developments in the Soviet Union†
0003-2654	Analyst
0003-2662	Analyst
0003-2670	Analytica Chimica Acta
0003-2689	Analytical Abstracts
0003-2697	Analytical Biochemistry
0003-2700	Analytical Chemistry
0003-2719	Analytical Letters: Chemical Analysis - Clinical and Biomedical Analysis
0003-2727	Anaqueles†
0003-2751	Anarchy†
0003-276X	Anatomical Record
0003-2778	Anatomical Society of India. Journal
0003-2786	Anatomischer Anzeiger
0003-2794	Anbar Management Services Abstracts changed to Accounting & Finance Abstracts.
0003-2794	Anbar Management Services Abstracts see 0049-4100
0003-2794	Anbar Management Services Abstracts see 0305-067X
0003-2794	Anbar Management Services Abstracts see 0952-4614
0003-2816	Anbar Management Services Joint Index see 0261-0094
0003-2824	Anblick
0003-2832	Anchor changed to Golden Gate Aquarist.
0003-2840	Anchor
0003-2867	Ancilla changed to Mirjam.
0003-2883	Ancora†
0003-2891	Andar per Ceramiche
0003-2905	Andean Air Mail and Peruvian Times†
0003-2913	Andelsbladet
0003-2921	Esotera
0003-293X	Anderson College News changed to Signatures.
0003-2948	Andes
0003-2956	Andhra Agricultural Journal
0003-2964	Andhra Pradesh Productivity Council. Target
0003-2972	Andover Newton Quarterly†
0003-2980	Andrews University Seminary Studies
0003-2999	Anesthesia and Analgesia
0003-3006	Anesthesia Progress
0003-3014	Anesthesie, Analgesie, Reanimation see 0750-7658
0003-3022	Anesthesiology
0003-3049	Angeiologie
0003-3057	Angel Hair†
0003-3073	Angheliaforos changed to Anichti Orizontes-Angheliaforos.
0003-3081	Angelicum
0003-3103	Angels†
0003-3138	Angewandte Kosmetik see 0342-2968
0003-3146	Angewandte Makromolekulare Chemie
0003-3154	Angewandte Ornithologie
0003-3162	Angewandte Parasitologie
0003-3170	Angiologia
0003-3189	Angiologica see 1018-1172
0003-3197	Angiology
0003-3200	Angiopatias
0003-3219	Angle Orthodontist
0003-3227	Angler Tierzucht see 0171-7383
0003-3235	Anglers' Digest
0003-3243	Angler's Mail
0003-3251	Anglia
0003-326X	Anglica
0003-3278	Anglican Digest
0003-3286	Anglican Theological Review
0003-3308	Angling Times
0003-3316	Anglo American Trade News changed to Atlantic.
0003-3324	Anglo-Continental Dental Society. Journal changed to Restorative Dentistry.
0003-3332	Anglo-German Medical Review†
0003-3340	Anglo-German Review
0003-3359	Anglo-Israel Trade Journal see 0260-3985
0003-3367	Anglo-Jewish Art and History†
0003-3375	Anglo-Norwegian Trade Journal
0003-3383	Anglo-Spanish Quarterly Review
0003-3391	Anglo Swiss Times†
0003-3405	Anglo-Welsh Review†
0003-3413	Angola. Direccao dos Servicos de Estatistica. Boletim Mensal
0003-343X	Instituto de Investigacao Cientifica de Angola. Relatorios e Communicacoes
0003-3448	Laboratorio de Engenharia de Angola. Boletim Informativo†
0003-3456	Angola. Direccao Provincial dos Servicos de Geologia e Minas. Boletim
0003-3464	Angora Goat & Mohair Journal
0003-3472	Animal Behaviour
0003-3480	Animal Blood Groups and Biochemical Genetics see 0268-9146
0003-3499	Animal Breeding Abstracts
0003-3502	Animal Health see 0142-6591
0003-3510	Animal Health Age†
0003-3537	Animal Kingdom see 1048-4949
0003-3545	Animal Life†
0003-3553	Animal Nutrition and Health changed to Large Animal Veterinarian.
0003-357X	Animal Protection changed to A S P C A Report.
0003-3588	Animal Science Journal of Pakistan changed to Bangladesh Journal of Animal Science.
0003-3596	Animal Welfare Institute Information Report see 0743-0841
0003-360X	Animaldom
0003-3618	Wildlife see 0265-3656
0003-3634	Animals: Defender and Anti-Vivisection News changed to Campaigner & Animal's Defender.
0003-3642	Animals Magazine changed to Animal Forum.
0003-3650	Animaux de Laboratoire. Revue Bibliographique†
0003-3669	Animo
0003-3685	Ankara Universitesi. Veteriner Fakultesi. Dergisi
0003-3707	Ankh†
0003-3723	Ann Arbor Argus†
0003-3731	Ann Arbor Review†
0003-3758	Annabel
0003-3766	Annabella
0003-3774	Annabelle changed to Annabelle.
0003-3790	Annals of Science
0003-3804	Annalen der Physik
0003-3839	Annales Agronomiques†
0003-3847	Annales Botanici Fennici
0003-3855	Annales Chirurgiae et Gynaecologiae Fenniae see 0355-9521
0003-3863	Annales Collegii Medici Antverpiensis

0003-3871 Annales d'Anatomie Pathologique *see* 0242-6498
0003-388X Annales de Biologie Animale, Biochimie, Biophysique *see* 0181-1916
0003-3898 Annales de Biologie Clinique
0003-3901 Annales de Bourgogne
0003-391X Annales de Bretagne et des Pays de l'Ouest (Anjou, Maine, Touraine)
0003-3928 Annales de Cardiologie et d'Angeiologie
0003-3936 Annales de Chimie *see* 0151-9107
0003-3944 Annales de Chirurgie
0003-3952 Annales de Chirurgie Infantile *see* 0939-7248
0003-3960 Annales de Chirurgie Plastique *see* 0294-1260
0003-3979 Societe Francaise de Dermatologie et de Syphiligraphie. Bulletin *see* 0151-9638
0003-3987 Anales de Edafologia y Agrobiologia *changed to* Suelo y Planta.
0003-3995 Annales de Genetique
0003-4002 Annales de Genetique et de Selection Animale *see* 0999-193X
0003-4010 Annales de Geographie
0003-4037 Annales de la Nutrition et de l'Alimentation *see* 0250-6807
0003-4045 Annales de la Propagation de la Fois *changed to* Solidaires - Lumiere du Monde.
0003-4053 Annales de l'Amelioration des Plantes†
0003-4061 Annales de l'Anesthesiologie Francaise†
0003-407X Annales de l'Economie Collective *see* 0379-3699
0003-4088 Annales de Limnologie
0003-4096 Annales de Medecine et de Pharmacie de Reims *see* 0301-4444
0003-410X Annales de Medecine Interne
0003-4118 Annales de Medecine Veterinaire
0003-4126 Annales de Medecine des Accidents et du Trafic Traumatologie
0003-4134 Annales de Normandie
0003-4142 Annales de Paleontologie *see* 0753-3969
0003-4150 Annales de Parasitologie Humaine et Comparee
0003-4169 Annales de Physique
0003-4177 Annales de Phytopathologie†
0003-4185 Annales de Radiologie
0003-4193 Annales de Recherches Veterinaires
0003-4207 Annales de Sciences Economiques Appliquees
0003-4215 Annales de Speleologie†
0003-4223 Annales de Technologie Agricole *changed to* Sciences des Aliments.
0003-4231 Annales de Zoologie- Ecologie Animale†
0003-424X Annales de Zootechnie
0003-4266 Annales d'Endocrinologie
0003-4274 Annales des Falsifications de l'Expertise Chimique et Toxicologique
0003-4282 Annales des Mines *changed to* Realites Industrielles.
0003-4282 Annales des Mines *changed to* Gerer et Comprendre.
0003-4290 Annales des Mines de Belgique
0003-4312 Annales des Sciences Forestieres
0003-4320 Annales des Sciences Naturelles. Botanique et Biologie Vegetale
0003-4339 Annales des Sciences Naturelles. Zoologie et Biologie Animale
0003-4347 Annales des Telecommunications
0003-4355 Annales d'Histochimie *see* 0145-5680
0003-4363 Annales d'Hygiene de Langue Francaise *changed to* Medecine et Nutrition.
0003-4371 Annales d'Oculistique *see* 0181-5512
0003-438X Annales d'Oto-Laryngologie et de Chirurgie Cervico Faciale
0003-4398 Annales du Midi
0003-4401 Annales d'Urologie
0003-441X Annales - Economies, Societes, Civilisations
0003-4428 Annales Entomologici Fennici *see* 0785-8760
0003-4436 Annales Historiques de la Revolution Francaise
0003-4444 Annales Homeopathiques Francaises *changed to* Homeopathie.
0003-4452 Annales Internationales de Criminologie
0003-4479 Annales Medicinae Exeprimentalis et Bilogiae Fenniae *see* 0302-2137
0003-4487 Annales Medico-Psychologiques
0003-4495 Annales Paediatrici Japonici
0003-4509 Annales Pharmaceutiques Francaises
0003-4517 Annales Scientifiques Textiles Belges†
0003-4525 Annales Textiles†
0003-4533 Annales Universitatis Saraviensis. Reihe: Medizin *see* 0173-6973
0003-4541 Annales Zoologici
0003-455X Annales Zoologici Fennici
0003-4568 Annali della Carita
0003-4584 Italy. Ministero della Pubblica Istruzione. Annali della Pubblica Istruzione
0003-4592 Annali di Chimica
0003-4614 Annali di Idrologia†
0003-4622 Annali di Matematica
0003-4630 Annali di Medicina Navale
0003-4649 Annali di Microbiologia ed Enzimologia
0003-4657 Annali di Ostetricia e Ginecologia *see* 0300-0087
0003-4665 Annali di Ottamologia e Clinica Oculistica
0003-4673 Annali di Radiologia Diagnostica†
0003-469X Annali Italiani di Chirurgia
0003-4703 Annali Italiani di Dermatologia Clinica e Sperimentale
0003-4711 Annali Italiani di Pediatria†
0003-472X Annali Sclavo *changed to* Annali Sclavo Monograph.
0003-4738 Annals of Allergy
0003-4746 Annals of Applied Biology
0003-4762 Annals of Clinical Research *changed to* Annals of Medicine.
0003-4770 Annals of Dentistry
0003-4789 Annals of General Practice *see* 0300-8495
0003-4800 Annals of Human Genetics
0003-4819 Annals of Internal Medicine
0003-4827 Annals of Iowa
0003-4835 Annals of Library Science and Documentation
0003-4843 Annals of Mathematical Logic *see* 0168-0072
0003-4851 Annals of Mathematical Statistics *see* 0090-5364
0003-486X Annals of Mathematics
0003-4878 Annals of Occupational Hygiene
0003-4886 Annals of Ophthalmology
0003-4894 Annals of Otology, Rhinology and Laryngology
0003-4908 Rheumatology and Physical Medicine *see* 0263-7103
0003-4916 Annals of Physics
0003-4932 Annals of Surgery
0003-4940 Annals of the Holy Childhood *changed to* It's Our World.
0003-4967 Annals of the Rheumatic Diseases
0003-4975 Annals of Thoracic Surgery
0003-4983 Annals of Tropical Medicine and Parasitology
0003-4991 Annals of Wyoming
0003-5009 Annals of Zoology
0003-5017 L'Annee Biologique
0003-5033 Annee Psychologique
0003-505X Annonces de l'Industrie
0003-5076 Annotated Bibliography of Economic Geology†
0003-5084 Annotated Bibliography of Literature Produced by the Cooperative Movements in South-East Asia *changed to* Annotated Bibliography of Literature on Cooperative Movements in South-East Asia.
0003-5092 Annotationes Zoologicae Japonenses *see* 0289-0003
0003-5106 Announced Reprints†
0003-5114 Conference Board. Announcements of Mergers and Acquisitions†
0003-5130 Annual of Animal Psychology
0003-5149 Annuario di Diritto Comparato e di Studi Legislativi
0003-5157 Annuarium Historiae Conciliorum
0003-5165 Annunciatore Poligrafico
0003-519X Die Anregung
0003-5203 Annrinya
0003-5211 Anritsu Technical Bulletin
0003-522X Ans Werk†
0003-5238 Der Anschnitt†
0003-5246 Ansearchin' News *changed to* Tennessee Genealogical Magazine, "Ansearchin'" News.
0003-5254 Ansgarsjunioren *see* 0003-5262
0003-5262 Ansgarsposten
0003-5270 Anstoesse
0003-5289 Anstoss
0003-5300 Answer†
0003-5319 Antaeus
0003-5327 Antarctic
0003-5335 Antarctic Journal of the United States
0003-5351 Antarktiese Bulletin
0003-536X Antena
0003-5378 Antenna *see* 0101-9112
0003-5386 Antenna
0003-5394 Antenne Medicale
0003-5408 Antenni†
0003-5416 Anthologies of the Year *changed to* Poetry of the Year.
0003-5424 Anthos
0003-5440 Anthropologiai Kozlemenyek
0003-5459 Anthropologica
0003-5467 Royal Anthropological Institute of Great Britain and Ireland. Library. Anthropological Index *changed to* Anthropological Index to Current Periodicals in the Library of the Museum of Mankind Library.
0003-5475 Anthropological Journal of Canada†
0003-5483 Anthropological Linguistics
0003-5491 Anthropological Quarterly
0003-5505 Anthropological Society of Nippon. Journal
0003-5513 Anthropological Survey of India. Bulletin *see* 0970-3411
0003-5521 L'Anthropologie
0003-5548 Anthropologischer Anzeiger
0003-5556 Anthropologist
0003-5564 Anthropology U C L A
0003-5580 Anti-Apartheid News
0003-5599 Anti-Corrosion Methods and Materials
0003-5602 A R Staatkunde†
0003-5610 Anti-Vivisectionist *changed to* Liberator.
0003-5629 Antibiotica†
0003-5637 Antibiotiki *see* 0235-2990
0003-5645 Antichita Viva
0003-5653 Antiek
0003-5661 Antigonish Review
0003-567X Antik Tanulmanyok
0003-5688 Antike Kunst
0003-5696 Antike und Abendland
0003-5718 Antilliaanse Nieuwsbrief
0003-5742 Antioch College Reports *changed to* Antioch Report.
0003-5769 Antioch Review
0003-5785 Antiquarian Horology and the Proceedings of the Antiquarian Horological Society
0003-5793 Antiquariat†
0003-5815 Antiquaries Journal
0003-5823 Antique Airplane Association News
0003-5831 Antique Automobile
0003-584X Antique Collecting
0003-5858 Antique Collector
0003-5866 Antique Dealer and Collectors' Guide
0003-5874 Antique Finder *see* 0003-584X
0003-5882 Antique Monthly
0003-5890 Antique Motor News and Atlantic Auto Advertiser *see* 0888-1944
0003-5904 Antique Outboarder
0003-5912 Antique Trader *see* 0161-8342
0003-5939 Antiques *see* 0161-9284
0003-5947 Antiques Dealer†
0003-5955 Antiques in Britain *changed to* Antiques Folio.
0003-5963 Antiques Journal†
0003-598X Antiquity
0003-5998 The Antiseptic
0003-6021 Antitrust & Trade Regulation Report
0003-603X Antitrust Bulletin
0003-6048 Antitrust Law and Economics Review
0003-6056 Antitrust Law Journal
0003-6064 Antonianum
0003-6072 Antonie van Leeuwenhoek Journal of Microbiology and Serology *changed to* Antonie van Leeuwenhoek International Journal of General and Molecular Microbiology.
0003-6099 Antriebstechnik
0003-6102 Antropologia e Historia de Guatemala (I D A E H)
0003-6110 Antropologica
0003-6129 Antropolognytt *changed to* Antropologiska Studier.
0003-6137 Antropos
0003-6145 Antroposofia
0003-617X Antwerp Bee-Argus
0003-6188 Antwerps Havennieuws†
0003-620X Anukta
0003-6218 Anuvad
0003-6226 Anvil
0003-6234 Das Anwaltbuero†
0003-6242 Anyagmozgatas-Csomagolas
0003-6277 Anzeiger des Oesterreichischen Buchhandels
0003-6285 Anzeiger des Reiches der Gerechtigkeit
0003-6293 Anzeiger fuer die Altertumswissenschaft
0003-6307 Anzeiger fuer Schaedlingskunde und Pflanzenschutz *see* 0340-7330
0003-6315 Anzeiger Solothurn-Lebern
0003-6323 Aomori-ken Nogyo Kisho Junpo
0003-6331 Agriculture in Aomori
0003-634X Apalachee Diary†
0003-6358 Apartment Construction News *see* 0146-0919
0003-6366 Apartment Ideas *see* 0273-2858
0003-6390 Apeiron
0003-6412 Apercu Technique - Technisch Overzicht (A T O)
0003-6420 Aperture
0003-6439 Apex†
0003-6455 Apiacta
0003-6471 Apicultor†
0003-648X Apicultural Abstracts
0003-6498 Apka Swasthya
0003-6501 Aplikace Matematiky *see* 0862-7940
0003-651X Aplomb Zero
0003-6528 Apollo *changed to* Oeko.L.
0003-6536 Apollo
0003-6552 El Aposento Alto
0003-6560 Apothecary
0003-6579 Apothekersblad
0003-6587 Appalachia Journal
0003-6595 Appalachia
0003-6609 Appalachia Medicine†
0003-6617 Appalachian Lookout†
0003-6625 Appalachian Outlook
0003-6641 Appalachian Trailway News
0003-665X Appaloosa News *changed to* Appaloosa Journal.
0003-6668 Apparecchi Elettrodomestici Nella Casa Moderna
0003-6676 Apparecchiature Idrauliche e Pneumatiche *see* 0374-3225
0003-6684 Apparel Executive†
0003-6749 Appel de Saint Vincent de Paul†
0003-6757 Appita
0003-6765 Applet
0003-6773 Appliance Engineer *see* 0003-6781
0003-6781 Appliance
0003-679X Appliance Manufacturer
0003-6803 Appliance Service News
0003-6811 Applicable Analysis
0003-682X Applied Acoustics
0003-6838 Applied Biochemistry and Microbiology
0003-6846 Applied Economics
0003-6854 Applied Electrical Phenomena†
0003-6862 Applied Entomology and Zoology
0003-6870 Applied Ergonomics
0003-6889 Applied Graphics†
0003-6900 Applied Mechanics Reviews

ISSN	Title
0003-6919	Applied Microbiology see 0099-2240
0003-6935	Applied Optics
0003-6943	Applied Photography†
0003-6951	Applied Physics Letters
0003-696X	Applied Plastics†
0003-6978	Journal of Applied Pneumatics changed to International Journal of Applied Pneumatics.
0003-6986	Applied Science and Technology Index
0003-6994	Applied Scientific Research
0003-701X	Applied Solar Energy
0003-7028	Applied Spectroscopy
0003-7052	Appraisal
0003-7060	Appraisal Digest
0003-7079	Appraisal Institute Digest
0003-7087	Appraisal Journal
0003-7095	Appraiser see 1054-5999
0003-7109	Apprenticeship News
0003-7117	Approach
0003-7125	Approach Magazine†
0003-7133	Approaches; a Periodical of Poems by Kentuckians see 0889-647X
0003-7176	Apres - Demain
0003-7206	Aqua†
0003-7214	Aqua
0003-7222	Aqua Vite
0003-7230	New Aquarian Agent changed to Astrology - the New Aquarian Agent.
0003-7257	Aquarien Magazin see 0723-4066
0003-7265	Aquarien- und Terrarien-Zeitschrift see 0723-4066
0003-729X	Aquarium
0003-7303	Aquarius
0003-7311	Aquatic Biology Abstracts see 0140-5373
0003-7311	Aquatic Biology Abstracts see 0140-5381
0003-7338	Aqueduct News see 0092-0622
0003-7362	Aquinas
0003-7370	Ara
0003-7389	Arab
0003-7397	Arab Film and Television Center News
0003-7400	Arab Journal†
0003-7419	Arab News and Views†
0003-7435	Arab Oil Review
0003-7443	Arab Petroleum
0003-7451	A R R
0003-746X	Arab Veterinary Medical Association. Journal
0003-7478	Arab World†
0003-7486	Arabian Horse News†
0003-7494	Arabian Horse World
0003-7524	Arable Farmer see 0300-2829
0003-7540	Araksha
0003-7559	Araldo di S. Antonio
0003-7567	Aramco World see 1044-1891
0003-7583	A G B U Ararat
0003-7591	Arbeidskundig Tijdschrift changed to Bedrijfsvoering.
0003-7605	Die Arbeit
0003-7613	Die Arbeit†
0003-7621	Arbeit, Beruf, und Arbeitslosenhilfe changed to Arbeit und Beruf.
0003-763X	Arbeit und Leistung see 0340-2444
0003-7648	Arbeit und Recht
0003-7656	Arbeit und Wirtschaft
0003-7710	Arbeitsgemeinschaft fuer Jugendpflege und Jugendfuersorge. Mitteilungen changed to Forum Jugendhilfe.
0003-7737	Saarlaendischer Arbeitnehmer changed to Arbeitnehmer.
0003-7753	Arbeitsmedizin, Sozialmedizin, Arbeitshygiene see 0300-581X
0003-7761	Arbeitsrecht in Stichworten
0003-777X	Arbeitsrecht und Arbeitslosenversicherung
0003-7788	Arbeitsschutz changed to Bundesarbeitsblatt.
0003-7796	Arbeitstechnische Merkhefte der Waldarbeit
0003-780X	Arbeitsvorbereitung
0003-7818	Arbejdsgiveren
0003-7826	Arbejdslederen
0003-7834	Arbetsmiljoe
0003-7842	Arbetsledaren
0003-7850	Arbetsmarknaden†
0003-7869	Arbiter
0003-7877	Arbitration
0003-7885	Arbitration in the Schools
0003-7893	Arbitration Journal
0003-7907	Arbitro
0003-7915	Arbol de Fuego: Poesia
0003-7931	Arboricultural Association Journal see 0307-1375
0003-794X	Arboriculture Fruitiere
0003-7958	Arborist's News see 0278-5226
0003-7966	Arbos†
0003-7974	L'Arc
0003-7982	Arcadia
0003-7990	Arcadie
0003-8008	Archaeologia Austriaca
0003-8032	Archaeologiai Ertesito
0003-8059	Archaeological Society of Central New York. Bulletin†
0003-8067	Archaeological Society of Delaware. Bulletin
0003-8075	Archaeological Society of Japan. Journal
0003-8091	A S A Newsletter changed to A S A Journal.
0003-8105	Archaeologischer Anzeiger
0003-8113	Archaeology
0003-8121	Archaeology and Physical Anthropology in Oceania changed to Archaeology in Oceania.
0003-813X	Archaeometry
0003-8148	Archeia tes Pharmakeutikes (Athens)
0003-8156	Archeocivilisation†
0003-8164	Archeologia†
0003-8172	Archeologia Classica
0003-8180	Archeologia Polski
0003-8199	Archeological Newsletter†
0003-8202	Archeological Society of Virginia. Quarterly Bulletin
0003-8210	Archeologie see 0778-2837
0003-8229	Archeologie Vivante
0003-8237	Archer†
0003-827X	Archery World see 1043-5492
0003-8288	Archibald Newsletter†
0003-8296	Archidiocesi di Monreale. Bollettino Ecclesiastico
0003-8326	Archief voor de Geschiedenis van de Katholieke Kerk in Nederland changed to Trajecta.
0003-8369	Archimede
0003-8377	Archimedes†
0003-8385	Archimedes
0003-8393	Architect
0003-8407	Architect & Builder
0003-8415	Architect†
0003-8423	Architect & Contractor
0003-8431	Architect and Surveyor changed to Architect & Surveyor.
0003-844X	Architect Consulting Engineer-Product Bulletin Directory changed to Product Bulletin Directory.
0003-8458	Architekonike Kai Dikosmese†
0003-8466	Architects' Journal
0003-8490	Architecture Culture
0003-8504	Architectural Design
0003-8512	Architectural Design, Cost and Data changed to Design Cost & Data.
0003-8520	Architectural Digest
0003-8547	Architectural Glass & Aluminium†
0003-8555	Architectural Institute of Japan. Transactions
0003-858X	Architectural Record
0003-8598	Architectural Record Newsletter†
0003-8601	Architectural Research and Teaching changed to Journal of Architectural Research.
0003-861X	Architectural Review
0003-8628	Architectural Science Review
0003-8644	Arkhitektura
0003-8652	Architecture and Building Industry
0003-8679	Architecture Canada†
0003-8687	Architecture Concept
0003-8695	Architecture d'Aujourd'hui (Paris, 1930)
0003-8709	Architecture East Midlands†
0003-8717	Architecture Francaise see 0003-8695
0003-8725	Architecture in Australia changed to Architecture Australia.
0003-8733	Architecture New Jersey
0003-8741	Architecture Today
0003-875X	Der Architekt
0003-8768	Der Architekt und der Bauingenieur
0003-8784	Architektur und Kultiviertes Wohnen changed to Architektur und Wohnen.
0003-8792	Architektur und Wohnform see 0173-8046
0003-8806	Architektur Wettbewerbe changed to Architecture & Competitions.
0003-8814	Architektura
0003-8830	Architettura (Milan)
0003-8849	Archiv
0003-8857	Archiv†
0003-8865	Archiv der Gegenwart
0003-8873	Archiv der Internationalen Stefan Zweig-Gesellschaft
0003-8881	Julius Klaus- Stiftung. Archiv see 0300-984X
0003-889X	Archiv der Mathematik
0003-8911	Archiv des Oeffentlichen Rechts
0003-892X	Archiv des Voelkerrechts
0003-8938	Archiv for Pharmaci og Chemi changed to Farmaci.
0003-8946	Archiv fuer Begriffsgeschichte
0003-8962	Archiv fuer das Eisenhuettenwesen see 0177-4832
0003-8970	Archiv fuer das Studium der Neueren Sprachen und Literaturen
0003-8989	Archiv fuer Deutsche Postgeschichte
0003-8997	Archiv fuer die Civilistische Praxis
0003-9012	Archiv fuer die Gesamte Virusforschung see 0304-8608
0003-9020	Archiv fuer Druck und Papier†
0003-9039	Archiv fuer Elektrotechnik
0003-9047	Archiv fuer Energiewirtschaft
0003-9055	Archiv fuer Experimentelle Veterinaermedizin
0003-9063	Archiv fuer Fischereiwissenschaft
0003-908X	Archiv fuer Gartenbau
0003-9098	Archiv fuer Gefluegelkunde
0003-9101	Archiv fuer Geschichte der Philosophie
0003-911X	Archiv fuer Geschwulstforschung†
0003-9128	Archiv fuer Gynaekologie see 0932-0067
0003-9136	Archiv fuer Hydrobiologie
0003-9152	Archiv fuer Japanische Chirurgie
0003-9160	Archiv fuer Katholisches Kirchenrecht
0003-9179	Archiv fuer Kinderheilkunde see 0300-8630
0003-9187	Archiv fuer Dermatologische Forschung see 0340-3696
0003-9195	Archiv fuer Klinische und Experimentelle Ohren-, Nasen- und Kehlkopfheilkunde see 0302-9530
0003-9209	Archiv fuer Kommunalwissenschaften
0003-9225	Archiv fuer Kriminologie
0003-9233	Archiv fuer Kulturgeschichte
0003-925X	Archiv fuer Lebensmittelhygiene, Insbesondere fuer Fleisch-, Fisch- und Milchhygiene changed to Archiv fuer Lebensmittel Hygiene, Fleisch-, Fisch- und Milchhygiene.
0003-9268	Archiv fuer Mathematische Logik und Grundlagenforschung see 0933-5846
0003-9276	Archiv fuer Mikrobiologie see 0302-8933
0003-9284	Archiv fuer Molluskenkunde
0003-9292	Archiv fuer Musikwissenschaft
0003-9306	Archiv fuer Naturschutz und Landschaftsforschung
0003-9314	Archiv fuer Oeffentliche und Freigemeinnuetzige Unternehmen
0003-9330	Archiv fuer Orthopaedische und Unfallchirurgie see 0344-8444
0003-9357	Zeitschrift fuer Physiotherapie see 0940-6689
0003-9365	Archiv fuer Protistenkunde
0003-9373	Archiv fuer Psychiatrie und Nervenkrankheiten see 0175-758X
0003-9381	Archiv fuer Reformationsgeschichte
0003-9403	Archiv fuer Sippenforschung†
0003-9411	Archiv fuer Technisches Messen - A T M see 0171-8096
0003-942X	Archives of Animal Nutrition
0003-9438	Archiv fuer Tierzucht
0003-9446	Archiv fuer Toxikologie see 0340-5761
0003-9454	U F I T A
0003-9462	Archiv fuer Vaterlaendische Geschichte und Topographie
0003-9470	Archiv Ostdeutscher Familienforscher
0003-9489	Archiva Veterinaria†
0003-9497	Archivalische Zeitschrift
0003-9500	Der Archivar
0003-9519	Archive for History of Exact Sciences
0003-9527	Archive for Rational Mechanics and Analysis
0003-9535	Archives
0003-9543	Archives Advocate†
0003-9551	Archives and Manuscripts
0003-956X	Archives Belges de Dermatologie et de Syphiligraphie see 0301-8636
0003-9578	Archives Belges de Medecine Sociale, Hygiene, Medecine du Travail et Medecine Legale changed to Archives Belges de Medecine Sociale et d'Hygiene.
0003-9586	Archives d'Anatomie, d'Histologie et d'Embryologie
0003-9594	Archives d'Anatomie Microscopique et de Morphologie Experimentale see 0989-8972
0003-9608	Archives d'Anatomie Pathologique see 0395-501X
0003-9616	Archives de Biochimie et Cosmetologie†
0003-9624	European Archives of Biology
0003-9632	Archives de Philosophie
0003-9640	Archives de Psychologie
0003-9659	Archives de Sociologie des Religions see 0335-5985
0003-9667	Archives de Zoologie Experimentale et Generale†
0003-9675	Archives des Lettres Modernes
0003-9683	Archives des Maladies du Coeur et des Vaisseaux
0003-9691	Archives des Maladies Professionnelles de Medecine du Travail et de Securite Sociale
0003-9705	Archives des Sciences
0003-9721	Revue Diplomatique changed to Archives Diplomatiques et Consulaires.
0003-973X	Archives d'Ophtalmologie see 0181-5512
0003-9748	Archives et Bibliotheques de Belgique
0003-9756	European Journal of Sociology
0003-9764	Archives Francaises de Pediatrie
0003-9772	Archives Francaises des Maladies de l'Appareil Digestif see 0399-8320
0003-9780	Archives Internationales de Pharmacodynamie et de Therapie
0003-9799	Archives Internationales de Physiologie et de Biochimie changed to Archives Internationales de Physiologie, de Biochimie et de Biophysique.
0003-9802	Archives Internationales de Sociologie de la Cooperation et du Developpement
0003-9810	Archives Internationales d'Histoire des Sciences
0003-9829	Archives Italiennes de Biologie
0003-9837	Archives Juives
0003-9845	Archives Mediterraneennes de Medecine
0003-9853	Archives of American Art Journal
0003-9861	Archives of Biochemistry and Biophysics
0003-987X	Archives of Dermatology
0003-9888	Archives of Diseases in Childhood
0003-9896	Archives of Environmental Health
0003-990X	Archives of General Psychiatry
0003-9918	Archives of Hygiene†
0003-9926	Archives of Internal Medicine
0003-9934	Archives of Medical Hydrology
0003-9942	Archives of Neurology
0003-9950	Archives of Ophthalmology

5342 ISSN INDEX

0003-9969 Archives of Oral Biology
0003-9977 Archives of Otolaryngology *see* 0886-4470
0003-9985 Archives of Pathology *see* 0363-0153
0003-9993 Archives of Physical Medicine and Rehabilitation
0004-0002 Archives of Sexual Behavior
0004-0010 Archives of Surgery
0004-0029 Archives of Traditional Music. Trimester Report†
0004-0037 Archives Roumaines de Pathologie Experimentale et de Microbiologie *changed to* Roumanian Archives of Microbiology and Immunology.
0004-0053 Archivio Botanico e Biogeografico Italiano
0004-0061 Archivio de Vecchi†
0004-007X Archivio di Chirurgia Toracica e Cardiovascolare†
0004-0088 Archivio di Filosofia
0004-0096 Archivio di Fisiologia
0004-010X Archivio di Medicina Interna
0004-0118 Archivio di Ortopedia *see* 0390-7368
0004-0126 Archivio di Ostetricia e Ginecologia
0004-0134 Archivio di Ottalmologia *see* 0300-0109
0004-0142 Archivio di Patologia e Clinica Medica†
0004-0150 Archivio di Psicologia, Neurologia e Psichiatria
0004-0169 Archivio di Scienze Biologiche†
0004-0177 Archivio di Studi Urbani e Regionali
0004-0185 Archivio di Tisiologia e delle Malattie dell'Apparato Respiratorio *changed to* Archivio Monaldi per le Malattie del Torace.
0004-0193 Archivio E. Maragliano di Patologia e Clinica
0004-0207 Archivio Glottologico Italiano
0004-0215 Archivio Italiano delle Malattie dell'Apparato Digerente†
0004-0223 Archivio Italiano di Anatomia e di Embriologia
0004-0231 Archivio Italiano di Anatomia e Istologia Patologica†
0004-024X Archivio Italiano di Chirurgia†
0004-0258 Archivio Italiano di Otologia, Rinologia e Laringologia *changed to* Otorinolaringologica.
0004-0266 Archivio Italiano di Patologia e Clinica dei Tumori
0004-0274 Archivio Italiano di Pediatria e Puericoltura†
0004-0312 Archivio per le Scienze Mediche *changed to* Gazzetta Medica Italiana Archivio per le Scienze Mediche.
0004-0320 Archivio Stomatologico
0004-0347 Archivio Storico Lodigiano
0004-0355 Archivio Storico per la Calabria e la Lucania
0004-0363 Archivio Storico per la Sicilia Orientale
0004-0371 Archivio Storico Ticinese
0004-038X Archivmitteilungen
0004-0398 Archivni Casopis
0004-0401 Archivo de Ciencias Biologicas y Naturales, Teoricas y Aplicadas
0004-041X Archivio di Medicina Mutualistica†
0004-0428 Archivo Espanol de Arte
0004-0444 Archivo Historico de Miraflores. Boletin
0004-0452 Archivo Ibero-Americano
0004-0460 Archivio Italiano di Urologia e Nefrologia *changed to* Archivio Italiano di Urologia e Nefrologia, Andrologia.
0004-0479 Archivio Veterinario Italiano
0004-0495 Archivos Argentinos de Reumatologia†
0004-0509 Archivos Argentinos de Tisiologia y Neumonologia
0004-0517 Archivos Argentinos Enfermedades del Aparato Digestivo
0004-0525 Archivos Bolivianos de Medicina
0004-0533 Archivos de Biologia y Medicina Experimentales
0004-0541 Archivos de Criminologia, Neuro-Psiquiatria y Disciplinas Conexas
0004-055X Archivos de Historia Potosina
0004-0568 Archivos de Medicina Experimental†
0004-0576 Archivos de Neurobiologia
0004-0584 Archivos de Pediatria del Uruguay
0004-0592 Archivos de Zootecnia
0004-0606 Archivos Dominicanos de Pediatria
0004-0622 Archivos Latinoamericanos de Nutricion
0004-0630 Archivos Leoneses
0004-0649 Archivos Venezolanos de Puericultura y Pediatria
0004-0665 Archivum Franciscanum Historicum
0004-0673 Archivum Heraldicum†
0004-0681 Archivum Histologicum Japonicum *see* 0914-9465
0004-069X Archivum Immunologiae et Therapiae Experimentalis
0004-0711 Archiwista
0004-072X Archiwum Automatyki i Telemechaniki *changed to* Archiwum Automatyki i Robotyki.
0004-0738 Archiwum Budowy Maszyn†
0004-0754 Archiwum Gornictwa *changed to* Archives of Mining Sciences.
0004-0762 Archiwum Historii Medycyny *see* 0860-1844
0004-0770 Archiwum Hutnictwa *changed to* Archives of Metallurgy.
0004-0789 Archiwum Hydrotechniki *changed to* Archives of Hydrotechnic.
0004-0797 Archiwum Inzynierii Ladowej
0004-0800 Archiwum Mechaniki Stosowanej *see* 0373-2029
0004-0819 Arcispedale S. Anna di Ferrara†
0004-0835 Arcoscenico
0004-0843 Arctic
0004-0851 Arctic and Alpine Research
0004-086X Arctic Circular†
0004-0878 Resource Development *see* 0824-4952
0004-0894 Area
0004-0908 Area Development Magazine
0004-0916 U.S. Department of Labor. Employment and Training Administration. Area Trends in Employment and Unemployment
0004-0932 Arena
0004-0959 Arena
0004-0967 Arepo†
0004-0975 Arethusa
0004-0983 Argentina
0004-0991 Argentina Automotriz
0004-1009 Argentina. Congreso. Biblioteca. Boletin *changed to* Argentina. Congreso de la Nacion. Biblioteca. Boletin.
0004-1017 Argentina. Direccion Nacional de Estadistica y Censos. Boletin de Estadistica *see* 0325-1969
0004-1025 Argentina. Direccion Nacional de Asistencia Nacional. DAS
0004-1033 Pergamino, Argentine Republic. Estacion Experimental Agropecuario. Boletin de Divulgacion†
0004-1041 Argentina Futuro
0004-105X Argentina Grafica
0004-1068 Argentina. Ministerio de Trabajo y Prevision. Boletin de Biblioteca *see* 0403-0133
0004-1076 Argentina. Servicio de Hidrografia Naval. Boletin†
0004-1084 Argentine Science Fiction Review
0004-1106 Argentinos Lietuviu Balsas
0004-1114 Argosy†
0004-1130 Argot†
0004-1149 Argument for Frihet och Raett
0004-1157 Das Argument
0004-1165 Argus (Thunder Bay)
0004-1173 Argus
0004-1181 Argus (Bloomington)
0004-119X Argus des Collectivites†
0004-1203 Argus des Pharmaciens
0004-1211 Argus-Journal *changed to* Alliance (Ottawa).
0004-122X Argus Menager *see* 0537-5819
0004-1238 Arhitektura-Urbanizam *see* 0350-3666
0004-1246 Arhiv Bioloskih Nauka†
0004-1254 Arhiv za Higijenu Rada i Toksikologiju
0004-1262 Arhiv za Poljoprivredne Nauke
0004-1270 Arhiv za Pravne i Drustvene Nauke
0004-1289 Arhiv za Zastitu Majke i Djeteta
0004-1297 Arhivski Pregled
0004-1300 Aria Compressa
0004-1319 Arid Lands Research Newsletter†
0004-1327 A R I E L
0004-1335 Ariel
0004-1343 Ariel
0004-136X Arithmetic Teacher
0004-1378 Arizona Academy of Science Journal *see* 0193-8509
0004-1386 Arizona Advocate
0004-1394 Arizona Alumnus
0004-1408 Arizona and the West *see* 0894-8410
0004-1424 Arizona Bar Journal *see* 1040-4090
0004-1432 Arizona Beverage Journal *changed to* Arizona Beverage Analyst.
0004-1440 Arizona Business Bulletin *see* 0093-0717
0004-1459 Arizona Dental Journal†
0004-1467 Arizona Economic Indicators†
0004-1475 Arizona Education News *changed to* Alert (Phoenix).
0004-1483 Arizona English Bulletin
0004-1491 Arizona Farmer - Ranchman *changed to* Arizona Farmer - Stockman.
0004-1505 Arizona Grocer
0004-1521 Arizona Highways
0004-153X Arizona Law Review
0004-1548 Arizona Librarian†
0004-1556 Arizona Medicine *see* 0093-0415
0004-1564 Arizona Mobile Citizen
0004-1572 Arizona Modern Business and Industry *see* 0193-7480
0004-1580 Arizona-New Mexico Contractor and Engineer *changed to* Builder Architect.
0004-1599 Arizona Nurse
0004-1602 Arizona Pharmacist *changed to* Arizona Pharmacist.
0004-1610 Arizona Quarterly
0004-1629 Arizona Review†
0004-1637 Arizona Roadrunner†
0004-1653 Arizona Teacher *see* 0194-8849
0004-167X Ark
0004-1688 Ark *changed to* Ark (1978).
0004-1696 Ark-Light Newsletter *see* 0094-0488
0004-170X Ark/Ozark
0004-1718 Arkansas Archeologist
0004-1726 Arkansas Banker
0004-1742 Arkansas Business and Economic Review
0004-1750 Arkansas Cattle Business
0004-1769 Arkansas Dental Journal
0004-1777 Arkansas Department of Education Newsmagazine *changed to* Education Update (Little Rock).
0004-1785 Arkansas Farm Research
0004-1807 Arkansas Game & Fish Magazine
0004-1815 Arkansas Grocer
0004-1823 Arkansas Historical Quarterly
0004-1831 Arkansas Law Review
0004-184X Arkansas Libraries
0004-1858 Arkansas Medical Society. Journal
0004-1866 Arkansas Municipalities *see* 0193-8371
0004-1874 Arkansas Oil and Gas Statistical Bulletin
0004-1882 Arka-Tech
0004-1890 Arkansas Valley Journal
0004-1904 Arkham Collector†
0004-1920 Arkhimedes
0004-1939 Arkhitektura S.S.S.R.
0004-1947 Arkhiv Anatomii, Gistologii i Embriologii
0004-1955 Arkhiv Patologii
0004-1963 Arhiv za Farmaciju
0004-1971 Arkitekt
0004-198X Arkitekten
0004-1998 Arkitektnytt
0004-1998 Arkitektnytt *issued with* 0332-6578 A T
0004-2005 A T
0004-2013 Arkitektur DK
0004-2021 Arkitektur
0004-203X Arkiv
0004-2048 Arkiv for Astronomi†
0004-2056 Chemica Scripta†
0004-2064 Arkiv for Geofysik†
0004-2080 Arkiv foer Matematik
0004-2099 Arkiv for Mineralogi och Geologi†
0004-2110 Arkiv for Zoologi *see* 0300-3256
0004-2145 Arma
0004-2153 Armament Data Sheets
0004-217X Armchair Detective
0004-2188 Armed Forces Comptroller
0004-220X Armed Forces Journal *see* 0196-3597
0004-2218 Armed Forces Medical Journal, India *changed to* Medical Journal Armed Forces, India.
0004-2226 Armed Forces Writer & Journalist *changed to* National Association of Government Communicators. News.
0004-2234 Armee *changed to* Armees d'Aujourd'hui.
0004-2269 Armee-Motor
0004-2277 Armee-Rundschau
0004-2285 Armeiski Pregled
0004-2293 Armenya Segodnia
0004-2307 Armenian-American Outlook *changed to* A M A A News.
0004-2315 Armenian Church *see* 0199-8765
0004-2323 Armenian Digest
0004-2331 Armenian Guardian†
0004-234X Armenian Mirror - Spectator
0004-2358 Armenian Reporter
0004-2366 Armenian Review
0004-2374 Armenian Weekly
0004-2382 Armenian Welfare Association of New York News
0004-2404 Armenytt
0004-2412 Armieri *changed to* Armi e Pesca.
0004-2420 Armor
0004-2439 Arms and Armour Society Journal
0004-2447 Arms Control and National Security†
0004-2455 Army *see* 0899-2525
0004-2455 Army
0004-2463 Army, Air Force & Naval Air Statistical Record
0004-2471 United States Army Aviation Digest
0004-248X Army Aviation
0004-2498 Army Digest *see* 0093-8440
0004-251X Army Journal *changed to* Australian Defence Force Journal.
0004-2528 Army Logistician *changed to* Army Logistician.
0004-2536 Army Museum Newsletter†
0004-2544 Army Orders†
0004-2552 Army Quarterly and Defence Journal
0004-2560 Army Research and Development *see* 0162-7082
0004-2579 Army Reserve Magazine
0004-2595 Army Times
0004-2617 Arnold Air Letter
0004-2625 Arnold Arboretum. Journal†
0004-2633 Arnoldia
0004-265X Ars Sutoria
0004-2668 Arquipelago *changed to* Voz do Povo.
0004-2676 Arquitecto Peruano
0004-2706 Arquitectura
0004-2714 Arquivo de Patologia
0004-2722 Arquivo do Distrito de Aveiro†
0004-2730 Arquivos Brasileiros de Endocrinologia e Metabologia
0004-2749 Arquivos Brasileiros de Oftalmologia
0004-2757 Arquivos Brasileiros de Psicologia Aplicada *see* 0100-8692
0004-2765 Arquivos Brasileiros de Tuberculose e Doencas do Torax
0004-2773 Arquivos Catarinenses de Medicina
0004-2781 Arquivos de Angola
0004-279X Arquivos de Biologia†
0004-2803 Arquivos de Gastroenterologia
0004-2811 Arquivos de Higiene e Saude Publica†
0004-282X Arquivos de Neuro-Psiquiatria
0004-2838 Universidade Federal de Minas Gerais. Curso de Odontologia. Arquivos do Centro de Estudos
0004-2846 Arredare la Casa†

ISSN

ISSN INDEX

ISSN	Title
0004-2854	Arredorama
0004-2870	Ars Aequi
0004-2889	Ars Buddhica
0004-2897	Ars Medici
0004-2900	Ars Medici et Nouveautes Medicales
0004-2919	Ars Organi
0004-2927	Ars Pharmaceutica
0004-296X	Art Alliance Bulletin
0004-2986	Art and Archaeology Newsletter
0004-2994	Art and Archaeology Technical Abstracts
0004-301X	Art and Australia
0004-3028	Art and Craft in Education *see* 0262-7035
0004-3044	Art and Life
0004-3052	Art and Man
0004-3060	Indianapolis Museum of Art. Bulletin *changed to* Indianapolis Museum of Art. Previews Magazine.
0004-3079	Art Bulletin
0004-3087	Art Chretien
0004-3095	Art d'Eglise†
0004-3109	Art Direction
0004-3125	Art Education
0004-3133	Art Enfantin *changed to* Creations.
0004-315X	Art et Curiosite
0004-3168	Art et Decoration
0004-3184	Art Gallery†
0004-3206	Art Gallery of South Australia. Bulletin†
0004-3214	Art in America
0004-3222	Art Index
0004-3230	Art International
0004-3249	Art Journal *changed to* Art Journal (Year).
0004-3265	Art Material Trade News
0004-3273	Artnews
0004-329X	Art of the Americas. Bulletin†
0004-3303	Art Quarterly
0004-3354	Arta
0004-3389	De Arte
0004-3397	Qui Arte Contemporanea†
0004-3400	Arte Cristiana
0004-3419	Arte e Poesia†
0004-3443	Arte Lombarda
0004-3451	Arterama†
0004-346X	Arte Tipografico *changed to* Graficas Mundiales.
0004-3478	Arteregalo
0004-3486	Artes
0004-3494	Artes Graficas *see* 1054-2434
0004-3508	Artes Graficas en Mexico
0004-3516	Artes Hispanicas†
0004-3524	Artes/Letras
0004-3532	Artforum
0004-3540	Artha
0004-3559	Artha Vijnana
0004-3567	Artha-Vikas
0004-3575	Arthaniti
0004-3583	Arthritis and Rheumatic Diseases Abstracts†
0004-3591	Arthritis and Rheumatism
0004-3605	Arthur D. Little. Industrial Bulletin *changed to* Arthur D. Little Inc. Bulletin.
0004-3613	Arthur Young Journal†
0004-363X	Arti e Mercature
0004-3648	Artibus Asiae
0004-3664	Articles on Neoplasia *changed to* Current Articles on Neoplasia.
0004-3672	Articoli Casalinghi *changed to* Articoli Casalinghi ed Elettrocasalinghi.
0004-3680	Artifact
0004-3702	Artificial Intelligence
0004-3710	Artificial Kidney Bibliography *see* 0363-2369
0004-3729	Artificial Limbs†
0004-3737	Artigiano Modenese
0004-3745	Artigliere
0004-3753	Artigos Selecionados†
0004-377X	Artikkelindeks Foer Bygg†
0004-3788	Artilleri-Tidskrift
0004-3796	Artillerie, Armee & Technik
0004-380X	Artillerie Rundschau
0004-3818	Artilleriiskii Zhurnal
0004-3826	Artillery Journal
0004-3834	Artis *changed to* Dieren.
0004-3842	Artis
0004-3869	Artisan Staff Association Magazine *changed to* A S A Magazine.
0004-3877	Artist *changed to* The Artist Incorporating Art & Artists.
0004-3885	Artist
0004-3907	Artistes et Varietes
0004-3915	Artlook
0004-3931	Arts and Activities
0004-394X	Arts and Sciences *changed to* New Tech Times.
0004-3958	Arts Asiatiques
0004-3966	Arts en Auto
0004-3982	Arts et Industries
0004-3990	Arts et Manufactures
0004-4008	Arts et Metiers
0004-4024	Arts in Society†
0004-4032	Arts in Virginia
0004-4059	Arts Magazine (New York)
0004-4067	Arts Management
0004-4083	Arts of Asia
0004-4091	Arts Review
0004-4113	Artscanada
0004-4121	Artweek
0004-413X	Arunodayam†
0004-4148	Arx†
0004-4156	Aryan Path†
0004-4164	Aryana
0004-4172	Arzneimittel-Forschung
0004-4180	Arzt in Niederoesterreich
0004-4202	As We Are†
0004-4210	Asahi Glass Company. Research Laboratory. Reports *changed to* Asahi Glass Company. Research Center. Reports.
0004-4229	Asbarez
0004-4237	Asbestos†
0004-4245	Asbestos Worker
0004-4253	Asbury Seminarian *changed to* Asbury Theological Journal.
0004-427X	Ascent†
0004-4288	Aschehougs Leksikonservice†
0004-4296	Asecolda†
0004-430X	Aseguradores
0004-4318	Asfalt
0004-4326	Ashanti Times†
0004-4334	Ashford Advertiser *changed to* Ashford Extra.
0004-4342	Achkhar
0004-4350	Ashland Dealer†
0004-4377	Ashtree Echo
0004-4385	Asi†
0004-4407	Asia Bulletin *see* 0161-4355
0004-4423	Asia Bulletin†
0004-4431	Asia Calling†
0004-444X	Asia Christian Colleges Association. Bulletin†
0004-4458	Asia Foundation Program Quarterly†
0004-4466	Asia Letter
0004-4474	Asia Magazine
0004-4482	Asia Major†
0004-4490	Asia Notebook *see* 0387-3927
0004-4504	Asia Scene *changed to* Japan 21st.
0004-4520	Asian Almanac
0004-4539	Asian and Indian Skyways *changed to* Skyways.
0004-4547	Asian Books Newsletter
0004-4555	Asian Economic Review
0004-458X	Asian Industry *see* 0254-3729
0004-4598	Asian Institute of Technology. Newsletter *changed to* A I T Review.
0004-4601	Asian Labour *changed to* Asian and Pacific Labour.
0004-4628	Asian Outlook
0004-4636	Asian Printer†
0004-4644	Asian Recorder
0004-4652	Asian Review and Arts and Letters *see* 0038-2841
0004-4660	Asian Student†
0004-4679	Asian Studies
0004-4687	Asian Survey
0004-4695	Asiatic Research Bulletin†
0004-4709	Asiatic Society of Bombay. Journal
0004-4717	Asiatische Studien
0004-4725	Asie Nouvelle
0004-4733	Asien-Bibliographie†
0004-4741	Asociacion Argentina Criadores de Cerdos. Revista
0004-4768	Asociacion Bioquimica Argentina. Revista
0004-4776	Asociacion Colombiana de Facultades de Medicina. Cronica†
0004-4784	Asociacion Costarricense de Bibliotecarios. Boletin
0004-4792	Asociacion Cultural Humboldt. Boletin
0004-4806	Asociacion de Ex-Alumnos de la Escuela Nacional de Bibliotecarios. Boletin
0004-4814	Asociacion Franco-Mexicana de Ingenieros y Tecnicos. Boletin
0004-4822	Asociacion Geologica Argentina. Revista
0004-4830	Asociacion Medica Argentina. Revista†
0004-4849	Asociacion Medica de Puerto Rico. Boletin
0004-4857	Asociacion Mexicana de Facultades y Escuelas de Medicina. Boletin
0004-4865	Asociacion Nacional de Industriales. Revista Trimestral *see* 0120-9515
0004-4873	Asociacion Numismatica Argentina. Revista
0004-4881	Asociacion Odontologica Argentina. Revista
0004-489X	Asociacion para Evitar la Ceguera en Mexico. Archivos
0004-4911	Aspect†
0004-4954	Asphalt
0004-4962	Aspire†
0004-4970	Asprenas
0004-4989	Assam Information
0004-4997	Assam Review and Tea News
0004-5004	Assay *see* 0147-6629
0004-5012	Assayad
0004-5020	Assegai†
0004-5063	Assembly Engineering
0004-5071	Assessors Journal *see* 0731-0285
0004-508X	Assessors News Letter - A N L *see* 0731-0277
0004-511X	Assicurazioni
0004-5136	Assignments in Management *see* 0740-0411
0004-5144	Education Sanitaire et Nutritionnelle d'Afrique Centrale
0004-5152	Assistant Librarian
0004-5187	Associacao Bahiana de Bibliotecarios. Informa
0004-5195	Associacao Brasileira de Pesquisas sobre Plantas Aromaticas e Oleos Essenciais. Boletim
0004-5209	Associacao Comercial de Lourenco Marques. Boletim†
0004-5217	Associacao Comercial do Amazonas. Boletim
0004-5225	Associacao Medica Brasileira. Boletim†
0004-5233	Associacao Medica Brasileira. Jornal
0004-5241	Associacao Medica Brasileira. Revista
0004-525X	Associacao Medica de Minas Gerais. Revista
0004-5268	Associacao Medica do Rio Grande do Sul. Revista *changed to* Revista A M R I G S.
0004-5276	Associacao Paulista de Cirurgioes Dentistas. Revista
0004-5292	Association and Society Manager†
0004-5306	Association Canadienne d'Education. Bulletin
0004-5314	Association Canadienne des Bibliothecaires de Langue Francaise. Bulletin *see* 0315-2340
0004-5322	Association de Geographes Francais. Bulletin
0004-5349	Association des Anciens Eleves des Ecoles Techniques Superieures de Geneve. Bulletin Technique *changed to* Association des Anciens Eleves de l'Ecole d'Ingenieurs de Geneve. Bulletin Technique.
0004-5365	Association des Bibliothecaires Francais. Bulletin d'Informations
0004-5373	Association des Diplomes de Microbiologie de la Faculte de Pharmacie de Nancy. Bulletin *changed to* Microbia (Nancy).
0004-539X	Association des Medecins de Langue Francaise du Canada. Bulletin
0004-5403	Association for Asian Studies. Newsletter *changed to* Asian Studies Newsletter.
0004-5411	Association for Computing Machinery. Journal
0004-542X	Association for Psychoanalytic Medicine. Bulletin
0004-5438	A R S C Journal
0004-5446	Association for the Advancement of Medical Instrumentation. Journal (JAAMI) *see* 0899-8205
0004-5454	Association for the Study of Perception. Journal
0004-5462	Revue Technique des Industries du Cuir *see* 0980-1367
0004-5470	Association Francaise des Techniciens du Petrole. Revue *see* 0152-5425
0004-5489	Association Francaise pour les Recherches et Etudes Camerounaises. Bulletin *changed to* Office National de Recherches Scientifiques du Cameroun. Recherches et Etudes Camerounaises.
0004-5497	Association Francaise pour l'Etude du Cancer. Bulletin *see* 0007-4551
0004-5500	Association Francaise pour l'Etude du Quaternaire. Bulletin *see* 1142-2904
0004-5519	Association Generale des Medecins de France. Bulletin
0004-5527	Association Guillaume Bude. Bulletin
0004-5535	Art
0004-5543	Association Internationale des Numismates Professionels. Bulletin-Circular
0004-5551	Association Internationale d'Etudes du Sud-Est Europeen. Bulletin
0004-556X	Association Internationale Permanente des Congres de la Route. Bulletin *changed to* Routes - Roads.
0004-5578	Association Management
0004-5586	Feuillets de l'A N A S *see* 0121-4977
0004-5608	Association of American Geographers. Annals
0004-5616	Association of American Medical Colleges. Bulletin†
0004-5632	Annals of Clinical Biochemistry
0004-5640	Association of College and University Concert Managers. Bulletin *changed to* Association of Performing Arts Presenters Bulletin.
0004-5659	Association of College Unions - International. Bulletin
0004-5667	Association of College Unions - International. Union Wire
0004-5675	Association of Collegiate Schools of Planning. Bulletin†
0004-5683	Association of Economic Geographers. Annals
0004-5691	Association of Engineering Geologists. Bulletin
0004-5713	Association of Engineers, Kerala State. Journal *changed to* Association of Engineers, Kerala P.W.D. News Letter.
0004-5721	Association of Food and Drug Officials of the United States. Quarterly Bulletin *changed to* Association of Food and Drug Officials. Journal.
0004-573X	Association of Marshall Scholars and Alumni. Newsletter *changed to* Marshall News.
0004-5748	Association of Nova Scotia Land Surveyors *see* 0380-9242
0004-5756	Association of Official Analytical Chemists. Journal *changed to* A O A C International Journal.
0004-5764	Association of Official Seed Analysts. News Letter
0004-5772	Association of Physicians of India. Journal
0004-5780	Association of Public Analysts. Journal

5344 ISSN INDEX

0004-5799 Association of Public Passenger Transport Operators. Journal†
0004-5810 Association of Teachers of Japanese. Journal-Newsletter *see* 0885-9884
0004-5837 Association of the Bar of the City of New York. Record
0004-5845 Association of University Evening Colleges. Newsletter *changed to* Five Minutes with A C H E.
0004-5853 Association of Urban Universities Newsletter†
0004-5861 Association pour le Developpement International de l'Observatoire de Nice. Bulletin d'Information *see* 0249-7522
0004-587X Association Suisse des Electriciens. Bulletin
0004-5888 Association Technique de l'Industrie Papetiere. Feuillets Bibliographiques. *changed to* Centre Technique du Papier. Feuillets Bibliographiques.
0004-5896 Association Technique de l'Industrie Papetiere. Revue
0004-590X Associazione degli Africanisti Italiani. Bollettino
0004-5918 Notiziario (Arezzo)
0004-5934 Associazione Italiana Biblioteche. Bollettino d'Informazioni
0004-5950 Associazione Italiana Industriali Tintori, Stampatori e Finitori Tessili. Notiziario *changed to* Associazione Nobilitazione Tessile. Notiziario.
0004-5969 Associazione Italiana per l'Assistenza Agli Spastici. Notiziaro *changed to* Associazione Italiana Assistenza Spastici. Notiziaro.
0004-5977 Associazione Italiana Veterinari per Piccoli Animali. Bollettino
0004-5985 Associazione Nazionale Ex Internati. Bollettino Ufficiale
0004-5993 Associazione Nazionale Mutilati e Invalidi di Guerra. Sezione di Roma. Notiziario
0004-6000 Associazione Romana di Entomologia. Bollettino
0004-6019 Assurance Francaise
0004-6027 Assurances
0004-6035 Assurances Banques Transports†
0004-6043 Assureur Counseil *changed to* Revue du Courtage.
0004-6051 Assyrian Star
0004-606X Aste Giudiziarie
0004-6078 Asti Informazioni Economiche
0004-6086 Astma- og Allergi-Nytt *see* 0801-3799
0004-6094 Astra
0004-6108 Astra
0004-6116 Astrado
0004-6124 Astral Projection†
0004-6132 Astrolabio
0004-6140 Astrological Magazine
0004-6175 Astrologischer Auskunftsbogen
0004-6183 Astrology
0004-6191 Astrology Guide
0004-6205 Astronautica Acta *see* 0094-5765
0004-6213 Astronautics and Aeronautics *see* 0740-722X
0004-6221 Astronautik
0004-623X Astronautyka
0004-6248 Bulletin of the Astronomical Institutes of Czechoslovakia
0004-6256 Astronomical Journal
0004-6264 Astronomical Society of Japan. Publications
0004-6272 Astronomical Society of the Pacific. Leaflet†
0004-6280 Astronomical Society of the Pacific. Publications
0004-6299 Astronomicheskii Zhurnal
0004-6302 Astronomie
0004-6310 Astronomie in der Schule
0004-6337 Astronomische Nachrichten
0004-6345 Astronomisk Tidsskrift
0004-6353 Astronomy
0004-6361 Astronomy and Astrophysics
0004-637X Astrophysical Journal
0004-6388 Astrophysical Letters *see* 0888-6512
0004-6396 Astrophysics
0004-640X Astrophysics and Space Science
0004-6434 At Cooper Union
0004-6450 At Home with the South African Permanent†
0004-6469 New Packaging *see* 0288-3864
0004-6477 Atem *see* 0341-3403
0004-6485 Atemschutz-Informationen†
0004-6493 Atene e Roma
0004-6507 Atenea *see* 0716-1840
0004-6531 Ateneo Parmense. Acta Bio-Medica
0004-654X Ateneo Parmense. Sezione 2: Acta Naturalia *see* 0392-419X
0004-6558 Ateneo Veneto†
0004-6574 Athenaeum
0004-6582 Athene†
0004-6590 L'Athenee
0004-6604 Athens Annals of Archaeology
0004-6612 Athens Chamber of Commerce and Industry. Monthly Bulletin
0004-6620 Institut Pasteur Hellenique. Archives
0004-6647 Athletic Director
0004-6655 Athletic Journal *see* 0036-6382
0004-6663 Athletics Arena *changed to* Athletics Arena International.
0004-6671 Athletics Weekly
0004-668X Atletiekwereld
0004-6698 Athletik
0004-6701 Atlanta Magazine
0004-671X Atlanta Economic Review *see* 0163-531X
0004-6736 Atlante
0004-6744 Atlantic Advocate†
0004-6752 Atlantic Baptist
0004-6760 Atlantic Community Quarterly†
0004-6787 Atlantic Mirror†
0004-6795 Atlantic Monthly *see* 0276-9077
0004-6809 Atlantic Naturalist†
0004-6817 Atlantic Observer-Knickbocker International†
0004-6825 Atlantic Provinces Inter-University Committee on the Sciences. Newsletter
0004-6833 Atlantic Psychologist†
0004-6841 Atlantic Report
0004-685X Atlantic Sun
0004-6868 Atlantic Truck Transport Review *see* 0830-1808
0004-6914 Marine/Atlantische Welt†
0004-6922 Atlas (Paris, 1960) *changed to* Atlas - Air France.
0004-6930 Atlas *see* 0195-8895
0004-6965 Atmanirvrithi†
0004-6973 Atmosphere *see* 0705-5900
0004-6981 Atmospheric Environment *see* 0960-1686
0004-6981 Atmospheric Environment *see* 0957-1272
0004-699X Air Pollution Abstracts†
0004-7007 Atoka
0004-7015 Atom
0004-7023 Atom†
0004-7031 Atom-Informationen
0004-7058 Atom News *changed to* A E A Times.
0004-7066 Atom und Strom†
0004-7082 Atomic Data *see* 0092-640X
0004-7090 Atomic Energy in Australia†
0004-7104 Atomic Energy Law Journal
0004-7112 Atomic Energy Review†
0004-7120 Atomic Energy Society of Japan. Journal
0004-7139 I N I S Atomindex
0004-7147 Atomkernenergie *see* 0932-3902
0004-7155 A T O M K I Kozlemenyek†
0004-7163 Atomnaya Energiya
0004-7171 Atomo e Industria
0004-718X Atomo Petrolio Elettricita
0004-7198 Kerntechnik *see* 0932-3902
0004-7201 Izotoptechnika *see* 0865-0497
0004-721X Atomwirtschaft *see* 0365-8414
0004-7228 Atoomenergie en Haar Toepassingen *see* 0165-2117
0004-7244 Att Bo†
0004-7252 Attentie Met Oog en Oor *changed to* Attentie.
0004-7279 Atterraggio Forzato
0004-7287 Societa degli Ingegneri e degli Architetti in Torino. Atti e Rassegna Tecnica
0004-7309 Attualita di Laboratorio†
0004-7317 Attualita di Ostetricia e Ginecologia
0004-7325 Attualita Mediche
0004-7333 Attualita Mondiali *changed to* Informazioni e Attualita Mondiali.
0004-7376 Au Fil du Rail
0004-7384 Au Grand Air
0004-7392 Auberge de la Jeunesse
0004-7414 Auburn Pharmacist†
0004-7422 Auckland City Art Gallery Quarterly†
0004-7465 The Auctioneer
0004-7473 Audecibel
0004-7481 Audenshaw Papers
0004-749X Audience†
0004-7503 Audience†
0004-7546 Audio Amateur
0004-7554 Audio Engineering Society. Journal
0004-7562 Audio-Visual Communications *changed to* A V C Development and Delivery.
0004-7570 Audio Visual Journal
0004-7589 Audio-Visual Language Journal *see* 0957-1736
0004-7597 Audio-Visual Media *see* 0952-3987
0004-7600 Audio-Vizualis Technikai es Modszertani Kozlemenyek *changed to* A -V Kommunikacio.
0004-7619 Audiotecnica
0004-7627 Audiovisivi
0004-7635 Audiovisual Instruction *see* 8756-3894
0004-7643 Audit-Poetry
0004-7651 Auditor
0004-7686 American Birds
0004-7694 Audubon Magazine
0004-7708 Auerbach Computer Characteristics Digest *see* 0361-2783
0004-7716 Auerbach Computer Notebook International†
0004-7724 Auerbach Data Communications Reports *changed to* Data Communications Reports.
0004-7732 Auerbach Data Handling Reports†
0004-7740 Auerbach Graphic Processing Reports†
0004-7775 Auerbach Software Reports *changed to* Applications Software Reports.
0004-7775 Auerbach Software Reports *changed to* Systems Software Reports.
0004-7783 Auerbach Standard E D P Reports†
0004-7791 Auerbach Time Sharing Reports†
0004-7813 Aufbau
0004-7821 Aufbau†
0004-783X Aufbereitungs-Technik - Mineral Processing
0004-7848 Aufbruch
0004-7864 Der Aufstieg†
0004-7872 Der Auftrag
0004-7880 Auftrag
0004-7899 Ran
0004-7902 Der Augenarzt
0004-7910 Augenoptik†
0004-7929 Der Augenoptiker
0004-7937 Der Augenspiegel
0004-7945 Augsburg Echo
0004-7953 Augsburg in Zahlen
0004-7961 Augsburger Kulturnachrichten
0004-797X Augusta Magazine
0004-7996 Augustana College Bulletin†
0004-8003 Augustiniana
0004-8011 Augustinianum
0004-802X Augustinus
0004-8038 Auk
0004-8046 Aum *changed to* Aum: the Message of Sri Chinmoy.
0004-8054 Aural News
0004-8062 Aurea Parma
0004-8070 Auricle *see* 0377-9696
0004-8089 Aurora
0004-8097 Ausbau *changed to* Technik Heute.
0004-8100 Der Ausbilder
0004-8119 Ausblick (Dusseldorf)
0004-8127 Ausgrabungen und Funde
0004-816X Statistik des Aussenhandels Oesterreichs *changed to* Austria. Statistisches Zentralamt. Aussenhandel Oesterreichs.
0004-8178 Aussenhandelsdienst *see* 0171-8789
0004-8186 Der Aussenhandelskaufmann†
0004-8194 Aussenpolitik
0004-8208 Aussenpolitische Korrespondenz†
0004-8216 Aussenwirtschaft
0004-8232 Aussenwirtschaftsdienst des Betriebs-Berater *see* 0340-7926
0004-8240 Aussprache†
0004-8259 Aussteuer Bett und Couch *changed to* Haustex.
0004-8267 Austin Dental News *changed to* Tenth Times.
0004-8275 Austral News *changed to* Australian Trading News.
0004-8283 Australian Citrus News
0004-8291 Australian and New Zealand Journal of Medicine
0004-8305 Australasian Baker and Miller's Journal *changed to* Pastrycooks & Bakers News Monthly.
0004-8313 Australasian Beekeeper
0004-8321 Australasian Catholic Record
0004-8356 Australasian Grocer *see* 0156-0352
0004-8364 A I M M Proceedings *see* 1034-6775
0004-8372 Australasian Insurance and Banking Record *see* 0725-4644
0004-8380 Australasian Journal of Dermatology
0004-8399 Australian Journal of Pharmacy
0004-8402 Australasian Journal of Philosophy
0004-8410 Australasian Manufacturer
0004-8437 Australasian Post
0004-8453 Australasian Printer Magazine *see* 1033-1522
0004-8461 Australasian Radiology
0004-847X Australasian Soft Drink Journal *changed to* Hospitality Beverage.
0004-8488 Australasian Sportsgoods and Toy Retailer *see* 1035-915X
0004-8496 Australasian Stamp Collector
0004-850X A N Z Bank Business Indicators *see* 0727-2979
0004-8542 Australia. Bureau of Statistics. Western Australian Office. Monthly Statistical Summary *see* 0727-2367
0004-8577 Australia. Bureau of Statistics. National Income and Expenditure, Quarterly Estimates *see* 1031-5128
0004-8585 Australia. Bureau of Statistics. Western Australian Office. Quarterly Statistical Abstract†
0004-8607 Australia International†
0004-8615 Australia Newsletter†
0004-8623 Australian Academic and Research Libraries
0004-8631 Australian Accountant
0004-8658 Australian and New Zealand Journal of Criminology
0004-8666 Australian and New Zealand Journal of Obstetrics and Gynecology
0004-8674 Australian & New Zealand Journal of Psychiatry
0004-8682 Australian and New Zealand Journal of Surgery
0004-8690 Australian & New Zealand Journal of Sociology
0004-8704 Australian Antique Collector
0004-8712 V A C C Journal *changed to* Motor Industry Journal.
0004-8720 Australian Automotive Engineering and Equipment *changed to* Automotive Engineer.
0004-8739 Australian Baptist†
0004-8747 Australian Bird Bander *see* 0155-0438
0004-8763 Australian Bookseller and Publisher
0004-8771 Australian Bride Magazine *changed to* Mode Brides.
0004-878X Australian Builder
0004-8798 Australian Building Science and Technology
0004-8801 Australian Business Communications†
0004-881X Australian Ceramic Society. Journal

ISSN

ISSN INDEX 5345

0004-8828 Australian Chemical Engineering
0004-8836 Australian Chemical Processing and Engineering *see* 0728-3636
0004-8844 Australian Children Limited *see* 0818-6286
0004-8852 Australian Christian
0004-8887 Australian Coin Review
0004-8895 Australian College of Dental Surgeons. Annals. *see* 0158-1570
0004-8909 Australian College of Speech Therapists. Journal *changed to* Australian Journal of Human Communication Disorders.
0004-8917 Australian Computer Journal
0004-8933 Australian Country Magazine *changed to* Farm Equipment.
0004-8941 Australian Credit Manager *changed to* Credit Review.
0004-895X Australian Cricket *changed to* Australian Cricket.
0004-8992 Australian Economic History Review
0004-900X Australian Economic Papers
0004-9018 Australian Economic Review
0004-9026 Australian Education Index
0004-9034 Australian Electrical World *changed to* Australian, Asian & Pacific Electrical World.
0004-9042 Australian Electronics Engineering
0004-9050 Australian Entomological Society. Journal
0004-9069 Australian External Territories†
0004-9085 Australian Fashion News *see* 0312-0325
0004-9093 Australian Economic News†
0004-9107 Australian Fish Trades Review
0004-9115 Australian Fisheries
0004-9123 Australian Flying
0004-9131 Australian Food Manufacturer and Distributor†
0004-914X Australian Forest Research†
0004-9158 Australian Forestry
0004-9166 The Australian Gas Journal
0004-9174 Australian Gemmologist
0004-9182 Australian Geographer
0004-9190 Australian Geographical Studies
0004-9204 Australian Gliding
0004-9212 Australian Golf *changed to* Australian Golf Digest.
0004-9239 Australian Grapegrower *see* 0727-3606
0004-9255 Australian Hardware Journal
0004-9263 Australian Harness Sport
0004-928X Australian Home Beautiful
0004-9298 Australian Home Journal†
0004-9301 Australian Hot Rodding Review†
0004-931X Australian House and Garden
0004-9328 Australian Humanist†
0004-9344 A I A S Newsletter *see* 0729-4352
0004-9352 Australian Institute of Metals. Journal *changed to* Materials Forum.
0004-9360 Australian Jewish Historical Society. Journal of Proceedings
0004-9387 Australian Journal of Adult Education *see* 1035-0462
0004-9395 Australian Journal of Agricultural Economics
0004-9409 Australian Journal of Agricultural Research
0004-9417 Australian Journal of Biological Sciences *see* 1031-3613
0004-9425 Australian Journal of Chemistry
0004-9433 Australian Journal of Dairy Technology
0004-9441 Australian Journal of Education
0004-945X Australian Journal of Experimental Biology and Medical Science *see* 0818-9641
0004-9468 Australian Journal of French Studies
0004-9476 Australian Journal of Marketing Research
0004-9484 Australian Journal of Music Education *see* 0255-7614
0004-9492 Australian Journal of Physical Education *see* 0813-2283
0004-9506 Australian Journal of Physics
0004-9514 Australian Journal of Physiotherapy
0004-9522 Australian Journal of Politics and History
0004-9549 Search
0004-9557 Australian Journal of Social Issues
0004-9565 Australian Journal of Social Work *see* 0312-407X
0004-9573 Australian Journal of Soil Research
0004-9581 Australian Journal of Statistics
0004-959X Australian Journal of Zoology
0004-9603 Australian Lapidary Magazine
0004-9611 Australian Law Journal
0004-962X Australian Leather Journal, Boot and Shoe Recorder *changed to* Australian Leather Journal.
0004-9638 Australian Left Review
0004-9646 Australian Legal Monthly Digest
0004-9654 Australian Liberal†
0004-9662 Communion
0004-9670 Australian Library Journal
0004-9689 Australian Library News†
0004-9697 Australian Literary Studies
0004-9700 Australian Lithographer *see* 0159-2319
0004-9719 Australian Machinery and Production Engineering *changed to* Production Machinery.
0004-9727 Australian Mathematical Society. Bulletin
0004-9735 Australian Mathematical Society. Journal *see* 0263-6115
0004-9743 Australian Meteorological Magazine
0004-9751 Australian Mineral Industry. Quarterly Review. *see* 0155-9419
0004-976X Australian Mining
0004-9808 Australian Municipal Journal
0004-9816 Australian National Bibliography
0004-9832 Australian National University News†
0004-9840 Australian Natural History
0004-9867 Australian Newsagent and Stationer *see* 1036-7969
0004-9875 Australian Numismatic Journal
0004-9883 Australian Numismatic Society. Report
0004-9891 Australian Official Journal of Patents, Trade Marks and Designs *see* 1038-0671
0004-9905 Australian Outdoors
0004-9913 Australian Outlook *see* 1035-7718
0004-9921 Australian Packaging
0004-993X Australian Paediatric Journal *see* 1034-4810
0004-9956 Australian Parks *see* 0311-8223
0004-9964 Australian Photography
0004-9972 Australian Physicist
0004-9980 Australian Pistol Shooters' Bulletin
0004-9999 Royal Australian Planning Institute Journal *see* 0729-3682
0005-0008 Australian Plants
0005-0016 Australian Plastics and Rubber Journal†
0005-0024 Australian Police Journal
0005-0059 Australian Presbyterian Life
0005-0067 Australian Psychologist
0005-0075 Australian Public Affairs Information Service *see* 0727-8926
0005-0091 Australian Quarterly
0005-0105 Australian Railway Historical Society. Bulletin
0005-0113 Australian Rationalist *see* 1036-8191
0005-0148 Australian Refrigeration, Air Conditioning and Heating
0005-0164 Australian Road Research *changed to* Road and Transport Research.
0005-0199 Australian School Librarian *see* 1030-0155
0005-0229 Australian Science Index†
0005-0237 Australian Seacraft
0005-0253 Australian Skindivers *changed to* N.S.W. Skindiver.
0005-0261 Australian Society of Accountants. Bulletin†
0005-027X Australian Special Library News
0005-0296 Australian Stamp Monthly *changed to* Stamp News.
0005-030X Australian Student†
0005-0318 Australian Sugar Journal†
0005-0326 Australian Surveyor
0005-0334 Australian Teacher of the Deaf
0005-0342 Australian Temperance Advocate *changed to* Temperance Advocate.
0005-0350 Australian Thoroughbreds
0005-0377 Australian Tradition†
0005-0385 Australian Transport†
0005-0393 Australian Traveller†
0005-0407 Australian Trotting Register
0005-0415 Australian University†
0005-0423 Australian Veterinary Journal
0005-044X Australian Wine, Brewing & Spirit Review†
0005-0458 Australian Women's Weekly
0005-0474 Australia's Neighbors *changed to* Asian Pacific Review.
0005-0482 Australijas Latvietis
0005-0490 Austria Export
0005-0504 I F E F, Austria Sekcio. Bulteno
0005-0512 Austria-Philatelist
0005-0520 Austrian Information
0005-0539 Austro-Motor†
0005-0555 Austroflug
0005-0563 Austropack
0005-0571 Auszuege aus den Gebrauchsmustern
0005-058X Auszuege aus den Patentanmeldungen *see* 0178-4250
0005-0598 Auszuege aus Presseartikeln
0005-0601 Aut Aut
0005-0628 Author
0005-0652 Authority in Crisis†
0005-0660 Authorship
0005-0695 Autospark
0005-0709 Auto Age
0005-0717 Auto and Flat Glass Journal
0005-0725 Auto Club News Pictorial *see* 0746-8504
0005-0733 Auto Dealers' Digest *changed to* Auto Dealers' Guide.
0005-0768 Auto-Journal
0005-0776 Auto Laundry News
0005-0792 Auto-Motor
0005-0806 Auto Motor und Sport
0005-0814 Auto Noticias
0005-0822 Auto Racing†
0005-0830 Autorevue
0005-0857 Auto-Technik
0005-0865 Auto Trim News *changed to* Auto Trim & Restyling News.
0005-0873 Autovisie
0005-0881 Auto-Volt
0005-089X Auto-Writing *changed to* I I S T Bulletins.
0005-0903 Autoaccessorio
0005-0911 Autobody and the Reconditioned Car†
0005-092X Autocar *see* 0955-5889
0005-0938 Autocar et Cargo Routier†
0005-0946 Autoclub
0005-0954 Autoclub *changed to* Touring.
0005-0962 Autoclub and Via *changed to* Via!
0005-0989 Autohaus
0005-0997 Autokampioen
0005-1004 Autolinea†
0005-1012 Automat
0005-1020 Automated Education Letter†
0005-1039 Automaten-Markt
0005-1047 Automatic Control *see* 0146-4116
0005-1055 Automatic Documentation and Mathematical Linguistics
0005-1063 Automatic Electric Technical Journal *see* 0273-141X
0005-1071 Automatic Machining
0005-108X Automatic Welding†
0005-1098 Automatica
0005-1128 Automatie
0005-1136 Automatik *changed to* Messen Pruefen Automatisieren.
0005-1144 Automatika
0005-1152 Automation
0005-1160 Automation *changed to* Controls and Systems.
0005-1179 Automation and Remote Control
0005-1187 Automation Council News
0005-1217 Automation in Housing *see* 0899-5540
0005-1225 Automation Journal of Japan *see* 0388-1423
0005-1233 Automatisch-Verkaufen†
0005-125X Automatizace
0005-1268 Automatizacija Poslovanja
0005-1284 Automazione e Strumentazione
0005-1306 Automobil-Industrie
0005-1314 Revue Automobile
0005-1330 L'Automobile
0005-1349 Automobile
0005-1357 Automobile Abstracts *see* 0309-0817
0005-1373 Automobile Club di Milano. Notiziario Economico†
0005-139X Automobile in Southern Africa *see* 0304-8721
0005-1403 Automobile India
0005-1411 Automobile Law Reports Insurance Decisions *changed to* Automobile Law Reports - Insurance Cases.
0005-142X Automobile News
0005-1438 Automobile Quarterly
0005-1454 Automobilismo e Automobilismo Industriale *changed to* Automobilism.
0005-1470 Automotive Age *see* 0894-1270
0005-1489 Automotive Chain Store†
0005-1497 Automotive Cooling Journal
0005-1500 Automotive Design Engineering *see* 0307-6490
0005-1519 Automotive Fleet
0005-1527 Automotive Industries *changed to* Automotive Industries.
0005-1543 Automotive Market Report and Auto Week *changed to* Automotive Market Report.
0005-1551 Automotive News
0005-156X Automotive News of the Pacific Northwest
0005-1578 Automotive Retailer
0005-1586 Automotive Service *see* 0818-2884
0005-1594 Automobile International - Automovil Internacional *changed to* Auto & Truck International.
0005-1608 Automotor
0005-1616 Automovil de Venezuela
0005-1659 Autoparade†
0005-1675 Autoproducts *see* 0164-4904
0005-1683 Autorama
0005-1691 Auto Revista
0005-1713 Autorevue†
0005-173X Autosport
0005-1748 Autosprint
0005-1756 Autostrade
0005-1772 Autotoerist†
0005-1780 Autotransportes "Tres Estrellas de Oro"
0005-1799 Autoveteranen
0005-1802 AutoWeek
0005-1810 Autowelt†
0005-1829 Autoworld
0005-1845 Auvergne Litteraire†
0005-1853 Auxiliaire des Fabricants de Cartonnages, Transformateurs de Papier, Industries et Arts Graphiques *changed to* Cartonnages et Complexes.
0005-1861 Volunteer Leader
0005-1888 Avalanche†
0005-190X Avant-Garde†
0005-1918 Avant Garde
0005-1926 Avant Gardener
0005-1934 A M
0005-1942 A. D. Correspondence†
0005-1950 Avedik
0005-1969 Avenirs
0005-1977 Aventure Sous-Marine *changed to* Subaqua.
0005-1985 Avenue
0005-1993 Aves
0005-2000 Aves & Ovos
0005-2027 Avia
0005-2035 Avia†
0005-2043 Avia Aeroespacial
0005-206X Aviacao e Astronautica *changed to* Aviacao em Revista.
0005-2078 Aviacion

ISSN

ISSN	Title
0005-2086	Avian Diseases
0005-2094	Aviasport
0005-2116	National Aeronautics†
0005-2132	Aviation Magazine International
0005-2140	Aviation Mechanics Bulletin
0005-2159	Aviation Reports
0005-2167	Aviation Studies International. Official Price List
0005-2175	Aviation Week & Space Technology
0005-2183	Aviatsiya i Kosmonavtika
0005-2205	Aviazione di Linea Difesa e Spazio changed to Aviazione.
0005-2213	Rivista di Avicoltura
0005-2221	Aviculteur Quebecois
0005-2248	Avicultura Brasileira
0005-2256	Avicultural Magazine
0005-2264	Avio-Nieuws see 0017-6818
0005-2272	Avion†
0005-2280	Avis-Kronik-Index see 0106-147X
0005-2299	Labour and National Insurance
0005-2302	Avtomaticheskaya Svarka
0005-2310	Avtomatika i Telemekhanika
0005-2329	Avtomatika, Telemekhanika i Svyaz'
0005-2337	Avtomobil'naya Promyshlennost'
0005-2345	Avtomobil'nyi Transport
0005-2353	Avtomobil'nye Dorogi
0005-2361	Avvenire Agricolo (Parma)
0005-237X	Awake
0005-2388	Awakener
0005-2426	Axial
0005-2442	Ayrshire Cattle Society's Journal
0005-2450	Ayrshire Digest
0005-2469	Ayu
0005-2485	Ayurveda-Bharati†
0005-2493	Ayurveda Doot
0005-2515	Azad Mazdur
0005-2523	Azerbaidzhan Tibb Zhurnaly
0005-2531	Azerbaidzhanskii Khimicheskii Zhurnal
0005-254X	Azimut
0005-2558	Azione
0005-2566	Azione Cooperativa
0005-2574	Aziya i Afrika Segodnya
0005-2590	Aztec Engineer†
0005-2604	Aztlan changed to Aztlan: A Journal of Chicano Studies.
0005-2639	B A G - Nachrichten
0005-2647	B A R C News
0005-2655	B A S F Review†
0005-2671	British Amateur Scientific Research Association see 0141-6413
0005-268X	B & T
0005-2698	B-U Nachrichten
0005-2701	B & Z†
0005-2728	B B A - Bioenergetics
0005-2736	B B A - Biomembranes
0005-2744	B B A - Enzymology†
0005-2760	B B A - Lipids & Lipid Metabolism
0005-2779	B. B. A. Nieuws†
0005-2787	B B A-Nucleic Acids and Protein Synthesis†
0005-2795	B B A - Protein Structure see 0167-4838
0005-2809	B B B Tribune changed to Better Business Bureau.
0005-2817	British Broadcasting Corporation. B B C Engineering†
0005-2825	B B C Nachrichten see 1013-3119
0005-2833	Bokrevyt
0005-2841	B C A News
0005-2868	B C I R A Abstracts of Foundry Literature see 0268-3393
0005-2876	B C L A Reporter
0005-2884	B.C. Motorist changed to Going Places Magazine.
0005-2892	B C Power Engineer
0005-2906	B.C. Professional Engineer
0005-2930	B. C. Sports & Recreation Magazine†
0005-2949	B C Studies
0005-2957	B.C. Teacher
0005-2965	British Columbia Teachers' Federation. Newsletter see 0841-9574
0005-2981	B D K-Mitteilungen†
0005-299X	B D V-Dienst Niedersachsen†
0005-3015	B. E. A. Bulletin†
0005-3023	B E A Magazine changed to Topline.
0005-304X	B E M A Bulletin
0005-3058	B E N E L U X International
0005-3082	B I B - Liner
0005-3090	B I C C Bulletin†
0005-3112	B I I L†
0005-3120	Bibliotheque de Travail Junior
0005-3147	B I N O P Bulletin see 0249-6739
0005-3155	Bios
0005-3163	B.I.R.E.
0005-318X	B I T S
0005-3198	B L M
0005-3201	B M - E
0005-321X	B M G
0005-3228	B N A Policy and Practice Series
0005-3244	B N F Abstracts changed to B N F Nonferrous Metals Abstracts.
0005-3252	B O A C Review changed to British Airways News.
0005-3279	B R A Review see 0144-6339
0005-3287	Betriebssicherheit - B S changed to Neue B S.
0005-3295	B S C S Newsletter changed to B S C S: The Natural Selection.
0005-3309	B S I News
0005-3317	B.S.I. Quarterly see 0954-7207
0005-3325	B S P Magazine
0005-3333	B S R
0005-3341	B S S R Quarterly Newsletter changed to B S S R Newsletter.
0005-335X	Bibliotheque de Travail
0005-3368	B T A - Buerotechnik und Automation see 0343-2319
0005-3376	B T E - Werbedienst see 0171-838X
0005-3392	B T O News
0005-3414	Bibliotheque de Travail 2d Degre
0005-3430	B V A Bulletin
0005-3449	B V E A Reporter
0005-3457	B V N. Boletin Informativo
0005-3465	B Z
0005-3473	B Z B
0005-3503	Babel
0005-3538	Babson Alumni Bulletin changed to Babson Bulletin.
0005-3546	Babson's Washington Service†
0005-3554	Baby & Junior
0005-3562	Baby & Tiener†
0005-3570	Baby Care†
0005-3589	Baby Talk changed to Baby Talk Magazine.
0005-3600	Bach
0005-3643	Back to Godhead
0005-366X	Backstretch
0005-3678	Bacteriological Reviews see 0146-0749
0005-3686	Bad und Kueche†
0005-3708	Bad Homburger Veranstaltungsspiegel Kurzeitung†
0005-3724	Baden - Wuerttembergisches Verwaltungsblat see 0340-3505
0005-3740	Badger Farm Bureau News see 0887-9133
0005-3759	Badger History†
0005-3767	Badger Legionnaire
0005-3775	Badger Sportsman
0005-3783	Badia Greca di Grottaferrata. Bollettino
0005-3791	Badminton
0005-3805	Badminton Gazette changed to Badminton Now.
0005-3821	Archaeographie changed to Baecker - Zeitung.
0005-383X	Baecker und Konditor
0005-3848	Baender, Bleche, Rohre
0005-3856	Baessler Archiv
0005-3864	Baesta Ur Reader's Digest (Swedish Edition) see 1100-4843
0005-3872	Baeuerlicher Ratgeber†
0005-3880	Bagdala
0005-3899	Baghdad Chamber of Commerce. Weekly Bulletin changed to Baghdad Chamber of Commerce & Industry. Monthly Bulletin.
0005-3902	Baghdad Observer
0005-3910	Bagin
0005-3929	Bagolah changed to Batnua.
0005-3937	Bagvertising Weekly
0005-3945	Baha'i-Brief†
0005-3953	Bahamas
0005-3961	Bahamas Weekly and Nassau Tourist News changed to Nassau Cable Beach and Paradise Island. Tourist News.
0005-397X	Bahamian Review
0005-3988	Bahana
0005-3996	Hadshot Hahistadrut†
0005-4003	Baileya
0005-4011	Bajan and South Caribbean changed to The New Bajan.
0005-402X	Bakelite Review†
0005-4054	Baker, Confectioner, Caterer see 0005-4100
0005-4062	Baker - Konditor
0005-4070	Baker Street Journal
0005-4097	Bakers Journal
0005-4100	Bakers Review
0005-4119	Bakers Weekly see 0005-4127
0005-4127	Bakery Production and Marketing
0005-4135	New Student Baker changed to Student Baker.
0005-4143	Baking Research Association. Abstracts see 0430-7941
0005-4151	Baking Industries Journal see 0144-8374
0005-416X	Baking Industry†
0005-4178	Bakkersvakblad changed to Bakkerij.
0005-4186	Baksteen
0005-4194	Bal Bharati
0005-4208	Bal Sandesh
0005-4216	Balance
0005-4224	Balance of Payments Reports†
0005-4232	Balance Sheet
0005-4240	Banque Populaire Suisse. Balance Sheet Prospectus
0005-4259	Balans
0005-4267	Balcony Square changed to Underground.
0005-4275	Balde Branco
0005-4283	Bulgarski Ezik
0005-4291	Baljivan
0005-4313	Balkan Studies
0005-433X	Ball State Teachers College Forum see 0888-188X
0005-4348	Ballet - Who see 0705-8063
0005-4356	E M U Faculty-Staff News. Library Supplement changed to Eastern Michigan University Faculty-Staff News. Center of Educational Resources Supplement.
0005-4364	Ballon Kurier
0005-4380	Ballroom Dancing Times
0005-4399	Ballsout
0005-4402	Balneologia Polska
0005-4410	Balon
0005-4429	Balthazar
0005-4437	Baltic Exchange
0005-4453	Baltimore
0005-447X	Baltimore Bulletin of Education†
0005-4488	Baltimore City Public Schools Staff Newsletter and Community Newsletter changed to Baltimore City Public Schools Staff Newsletter.
0005-4496	Baltimore Engineer
0005-450X	Baltimore Jewish Times
0005-4518	Baltimore Museum of Art Record†
0005-4526	Baltische Briefe
0005-4534	Baltische Hefte
0005-4542	Bama'arakha
0005-4550	Chambre de Commerce et d'Industrie du Mali. Circulaire Mensuelle d'Information changed to Chambre de Commerce et d'Industrie du Mali. Bulletin Trimestriel.
0005-4569	Bamat Hatzarkhan†
0005-4577	Israel. Ministry of Agriculture. Department of Fisheries. Bamidgeh see 0792-156X
0005-4585	Banas
0005-4607	Banca Nazionale del Lavoro Quarterly Review
0005-4615	Banca y Comercio
0005-4623	Bancaria
0005-4631	Bancni Vestnik
0005-4658	Banco Central de Costa Rica. Revista†
0005-4666	Banco Central de Honduras. Revista Trimestral†
0005-4674	Banco Central de la Republica Argentina. Boletin Estadistico
0005-4682	Banco Central de la Republica Dominicana. Boletin Mensual
0005-4690	Banco Central de Nicaragua. Boletin Trimestral changed to Banco Central de Nicaragua. Boletin Anual.
0005-4704	Banco Central de Reserva de El Salvador. Revista Mensual changed to Banco Central de Reserva de El Salvador. Revista Trimestral.
0005-4712	Banco Central de Reserva del Peru, Boletin
0005-4720	Banco Central de Venezuela. Revista†
0005-4739	Banco Central del Ecuador. Boletin
0005-4747	Banco Central del Uruguay. Boletin Estadistico Mensual changed to Banco Central del Uruguay. Departamento de Estadisticas Economicas. Boletin Estadistico.
0005-4755	Banco Central del Uruguay. Seleccion de Temas Economicos changed to Banco Central del Uruguay. Seleccion de Temas.
0005-4763	Banco Central do Brazil. Boletim
0005-478X	Banco de Angola. Boletim Trimestral†
0005-4798	Banco de Espana. Boletin Estadistico
0005-4801	Banco de Fomento Nacional. Boletim de Informacao†
0005-481X	Banco de Guatemala. Boletin Estadistico
0005-4828	Banco de la Republica. Revista
0005-4852	Banco de Vizcaya. Noticiario Economico†
0005-4860	Banco di Sicilia. Informazioni Sulla Congiuntura
0005-4879	Banco do Brasil. Boletim†
0005-4887	Banco Nacional Ultramarino. Boletim Trimestral†
0005-4909	Band changed to K B M - Kantoormarkt.
0005-4917	Band†
0005-4925	Band- und Flechtindustrie
0005-4933	Band Journal
0005-4968	Bandwagon
0005-4976	Baner Ac Amserau Cymru changed to Y Faner.
0005-4984	Bangkok Bank. Monthly Review
0005-4992	Banif's Investment Bulletin
0005-500X	Banijya Barta
0005-5018	Bank- en Effectenbedrijf
0005-5026	Bank and Quotation Record
0005-5034	Bank-Betrieb changed to Die Bank.
0005-5042	Bank Board Letter
0005-5050	Bank Equipment News see 0146-0900
0005-5069	Bank Installment Lending Newsletter changed to Consumer Lending Report.
0005-5077	Bank Karamchari
0005-5085	Bankkaufmann
0005-5093	Bank Markazi Iran Bulletin changed to Bank Markazi Jomhouri Islami Iran. Bulletin.
0005-5115	Bank Negara Malaysia. Quarterly Economic Bulletin changed to Bank Negara Malaysia. Bulletin Ekonomi Suku Tahunan - Quarterly Economic Bulletin.
0005-5123	Bank News
0005-5131	Bank Notes
0005-514X	Bank of Canada Statistical Summary see 0045-1460
0005-5158	Bank of Canada. Weekly Financial Statistics
0005-5166	Bank of England Quarterly Bulletin
0005-5174	Bank of Finland. Monthly Bulletin see 0784-6509
0005-5182	Bank of Ghana. Quarterly Economic Bulletin
0005-5204	Bank of Hawaii Monthly Review see 0893-0732
0005-5212	Bank of India. Bulletin

ISSN INDEX 5347

ISSN	Title
0005-5220	Bank of Israel. Bulletin *changed to* Bank of Israel. Economic Review.
0005-5239	Bank of Jamaica. Bulletin
0005-5247	Bank of Japan. Economic Statistics Monthly
0005-5271	Bank of Libya. Economic Research Division. Economic Bulletin
0005-528X	Bank of London & South America. Revista Mensual†
0005-5298	Bank of London and South America Review†
0005-5301	Bank of Mauritius. Quarterly Review
0005-531X	Bank of Montreal Business Review
0005-5328	Bank of Nova Scotia. Monthly Review†
0005-5336	Bank of Sudan. Economic and Financial Bulletin *changed to* Bank of Sudan. Economic and Financial Statistics Review.
0005-5344	Bank of Taiwan Quarterly
0005-5352	Bank of Thailand. Monthly Bulletin *see* 0125-605X
0005-5360	Bank of Tokyo Semiannual Report *changed to* Bank of Tokyo Annual Report.
0005-5379	Bank of Tokyo Weekly Review *changed to* Tokyo Financial Review.
0005-5387	Bank One
0005-5395	Banker
0005-5409	Banker & Tradesman
0005-5417	Bankers Digest *changed to* Special Office Brief.
0005-5425	Bankers Digest
0005-5433	Banker's Letter of the Law
0005-5441	Bankers' Magazine (London) *see* 0737-6413
0005-545X	Bankers Magazine
0005-5468	Bankers' Magazine of Australasia *changed to* Australian Banker.
0005-5492	Banking *changed to* A B A Banking Journal.
0005-5506	Banking Law Journal
0005-5514	Banking News *changed to* Maryland Banking Quarterly.
0005-5522	Bankinsurance News
0005-5530	Bankruptcy Law Reports
0005-5549	Bankvaerlden
0005-5557	Banner (Grand Rapids)
0005-5565	Bannere†
0005-5573	Bano
0005-5581	Banque
0005-559X	Banque Centrale des Etats de l'Afrique de l'Ouest. Notes d'Information et Statistiques
0005-5603	Banque de Port-Said. Revue Economique Trimestrielle
0005-5611	Banque Nationale de Belgique. Bulletin
0005-562X	Banque Nationale de Paris. Revue†
0005-5662	Bantu Education Journal - Bantoe Onderwysblad *see* 0250-152X
0005-5670	Banyaszati es Kohaszati Lapok - Kohaszat
0005-5689	Baptist Bulletin
0005-5697	Baptist Challenge
0005-5700	Baptist Herald
0005-5719	Baptist History and Heritage
0005-5727	Baptist Leader
0005-5743	Baptist Program
0005-5751	Baptist Progress
0005-576X	Baptist Quarterly
0005-5778	Baptist Record
0005-5786	Baptist Times
0005-5794	Baptist Witness *see* 0726-4097
0005-5808	Baptist World
0005-5816	N A B E News†
0005-5824	Bar Examiner
0005-5840	Bar-Server†
0005-5859	Barat Review†
0005-5867	Baratz'ba
0005-5875	Baraza *changed to* Chemsa Bongo.
0005-5891	Barbados Museum and Historical Society. Journal
0005-5913	Barclays Trade Review *changed to* Business Brief.
0005-5921	Barco Pesquero†
0005-5948	Bardic Echoes†
0005-5956	Barid Hollanda
0005-5964	Barkai
0005-5972	Bark†
0005-5980	Barmer Ersatzkasse *changed to* Die Barmer.
0005-5999	Barmherzigkeit
0005-6006	Barn i Hem-Skola-Samhaelle
0005-6014	Barnard Bulletin
0005-6049	Baromfiipar *see* 0133-011X
0005-6057	Barre du Jour *changed to* Nouvelle Barre du Jour.
0005-6073	Barron's National Business and Financial Weekly
0005-609X	Baseball Digest
0005-6103	Basic Journal Abstracts†
0005-6111	Basilicata
0005-6138	Basis
0005-6146	Basis
0005-6154	Basketball *changed to* Play Off - Basketbal.
0005-6162	Basketball *changed to* Basketball Monthly.
0005-6170	Basketball Weekly
0005-6189	Basler Predigten
0005-6197	Basse Normandie Automobile
0005-6219	Basteria
0005-6227	Bat Research News
0005-6235	Bateaux
0005-626X	Baths Service *changed to* Recreation.
0005-6278	Batiment
0005-6308	Baatnytt
0005-6324	Baton Rouge *changed to* Baton Rouge's Commerce.
0005-6332	Battaglia Letteraria
0005-6340	Battaglie Postelegrafoniche
0005-6359	Battery Man
0005-6367	Batting the Breeze
0005-6375	Battleacts†
0005-6383	Baut
0005-6391	Bau; Fachzeitschrift fuer Bautechnik, Baupraxis und Baumaschinen *changed to* Bau; Fachzeitschrift fuer Baupraxis, Bautechnik, Baumaschinen, Betriebsfuehrung und Kalkulation.
0005-6413	Bau *see* 0172-2514
0005-6421	Bau & Bauindustrie†
0005-643X	Bau und Baustoff
0005-6448	Baustoffmarkt
0005-6472	Bauamt und Gemeindebau *see* 0005-6847
0005-6480	Baubeschlag Magazin mit Praktikus *changed to* Baubeschlag Magazin.
0005-6499	Bingo
0005-6510	Bauen und Fertighaus
0005-6545	Bauen mit Holz
0005-6553	Bauen und Siedeln
0005-6561	Der Bauer
0005-657X	Bauer und Gaertner†
0005-6596	Bauforum
0005-6618	Das Baugerue s t
0005-6626	Baugeschaeft und Bauunternehmer
0005-6634	Baugewerbe
0005-6642	Bauinformation *see* 0323-8490
0005-6650	Bauingenieur
0005-6677	Baum Bugle
0005-6685	Baumaschine Baugeraet Baustoff *changed to* Baumaschine - Baugeraet - Baustelle.
0005-6693	Baumaschine und Bautechnik *changed to* B M T.
0005-6707	Baumaschinen und Baugeraette Revue†
0005-6715	Baumaschinen- und Baugeraete-Handel
0005-6723	B D Baumaschinendienst
0005-674X	Baumeister
0005-6758	Bauplanung - Bautechnik
0005-6766	Baupraxis†
0005-6782	Bausparkasse der Rheinprovinz†
0005-6790	Baustein
0005-6804	Baustoff- und Baubedarfs-Grosshandel
0005-6839	Bauunternehmer *changed to* Bau; Fachzeitschrift fuer Baupraxis, Bautechnik, Baumaschinen, Betriebsfuehrung und Kalkulation.
0005-6847	Die Bauverwaltung
0005-6855	Bauwelt
0005-6863	Bauwirtschaft. Ausgabe B
0005-6871	Bauzeitung
0005-688X	Das Bauzentrum
0005-6928	New England Architect *changed to* Architecture: New England.
0005-6936	Bay State F L Bulletin *changed to* MA F L A Newsletter.
0005-6944	Bay State Librarian
0005-6952	Bayavaya Uskalost
0005-6960	Bayer Berichte
0005-6987	Bayer-Mitteilungen fuer die Gummi-Industrie†
0005-6995	Bayerische Akademie der Wissenschaften. Mathematisch-Naturwissenschaftliche Klasse. Abhandlungen
0005-7002	Bayerische Beamtenzeitung†
0005-7010	Bayerische Blaetter fuer Stenographie
0005-7029	Bayerische Boerse in Muenchen. Amtliches Kursblatt
0005-7045	Bayerische Gemeindezeitung
0005-7053	Bayerische Kleingaertner†
0005-7061	Das Bayerische Kraftfahrzeughandwerk
0005-707X	Bayerische Krippenfreund
0005-7088	Der Metzgermeister
0005-7096	Bayerische Standesamt *changed to* Das Standesamt.
0005-710X	Bayerische Akademie der Wissenschaften. Philosophisch-Historische Klasse. Abhandlungen, N.F.
0005-7118	Bayerischer Landesverein fuer Familienkunde. Blaetter
0005-7126	Bayerisches Aerzteblatt
0005-7142	Bayerisches Justizministerialblatt
0005-7150	Bayerisches Landwirtschaftliches Jahrbuch
0005-7169	Bayerisches Landwirtschaftliches Wochenblatt
0005-7177	Bayerisches Sonntagsblatt fuer die Katholische Familie
0005-7185	Bayerisches Staatsministerium des Innern. Ministerialamtsblatt der Bayerischen Innern Verwaltung *see* 0934-6465
0005-7193	Bayerisches Staatsministerium fuer Arbeit und Soziale Fuersorge Amtsblatt. *see* 0340-1790
0005-7207	Bayerisches Staatsministerium fuer Unterricht und Kultus. Amtsblatt
0005-7215	Bayern in Zahlen *changed to* Bayerisches Landesamt fuer Statistik und Datenverarbeitung. Zeitschrift - Bayern in Zahlen.
0005-7223	Bayern Nachrichten
0005-7231	Bayernturner
0005-724X	Baylor Business Studies†
0005-7258	Baylor Dental Journal
0005-7266	Baylor Geological Studies Bulletin
0005-7274	Baylor Law Review
0005-7282	Bayreuther Gemeindeblatt
0005-7312	De Bazuin
0005-7320	Beacon *changed to* Cityscape.
0005-7339	Beacon (New York)
0005-7347	Beacon
0005-7363	Beaconette
0005-7371	Be'ad Ve- Neged†
0005-738X	Beaken
0005-7398	Beam
0005-7401	Beamte im Lande Bremen *see* 0721-8206
0005-741X	Der Beamte in Rheinland-Pfalz
0005-7428	Bearing Engineer†
0005-7436	Beato Angelo
0005-7460	Beautiful British Columbia Magazine
0005-7495	Beauty Tips†
0005-7509	Beaux-Arts *changed to* Art and Culture.
0005-7517	The Beaver
0005-7525	Beaver
0005-7533	Bebidas
0005-755X	Beckman Report
0005-7568	Bedding *see* 0893-5556
0005-7576	Bedford Stuyvesant Youth in Action Monthly Newsletter
0005-7584	Bedford Transport†
0005-7592	Bedfordshire Magazine
0005-7630	Bedrijfsjournalist†
0005-7649	Bedrijfspluimveehouder *changed to* Pluimveehouderij.
0005-7657	Bedrijfsvervoer *changed to* Vervoer en Transporttechniek.
0005-7665	Bedside Nurse *changed to* Licensed Practical Nurse.
0005-7673	Bedsitter†
0005-7681	Det Bedste fra Reader's Digest (Danish Edition)
0005-769X	Beduin
0005-7703	Bee Craft
0005-7711	Bee-Hive *changed to* United Technologies Bee-Hive.
0005-772X	Bee World
0005-7738	Beef
0005-7754	Beekeeping
0005-7770	Beer Wholesaler
0005-7789	Beet†
0005-7797	F B U - Befael
0005-7800	Begegnung
0005-7819	Begegnung mit Polen
0005-7843	Behavioural Sciences and Community Development *see* 0970-3357
0005-786X	Behavioral Research in Highway Safety†
0005-7878	Behavior Research Methods and Instrumentation *see* 0743-3808
0005-7886	Behavior Science Notes *see* 0094-3673
0005-7894	Behavior Therapy
0005-7916	Journal of Behavior Therapy and Experimental Psychiatry
0005-7924	Behavior Today
0005-7932	Behavioral Neuropsychiatry
0005-7940	Behavioral Science
0005-7959	Behaviour
0005-7967	Behaviour Research and Therapy
0005-7983	Behind the Headlines
0005-7991	Behinderte Kind *see* 0939-4702
0005-8009	Bei Uns
0005-8017	Beihefte zum Geologischen Jahrbuch *see* 0341-6429
0005-8017	Beihefte zum Geologischen Jahrbuch *see* 0341-6410
0005-8017	Beihefte zum Geologischen Jahrbuch *see* 0341-6399
0005-8017	Beihefte zum Geologischen Jahrbuch *see* 0341-6402
0005-8025	Beitraege aus der Plasmaphysik *see* 0863-1042
0005-8041	Beitraege zur Biologie der Pflanzen
0005-805X	Beitraege zur Entomologie
0005-8068	Beitraege zur Geschichte der Arbeiterbewegung
0005-8076	Beitraege zur Geschichte der Deutschen Sprache und Literatur
0005-8084	Beitraege zur Linguistic und Informationsverarbeitung
0005-8092	Literaturkunde. Beitraege†
0005-8106	Musikwissenschaft. Beitraege
0005-8114	Beitraege zur Namenforschung
0005-8122	Beitraege zur Naturkundlichen Forschung in Suedwestdeutschland *see* 0176-3997
0005-8149	Beitraege zur Orthopaedie und Traumatologie†
0005-8157	Beitraege zur Paedagogischen Arbeit
0005-8165	Beitraege zur Pathologie *see* 0344-0338
0005-8173	Contributions to Atmospheric Physics
0005-8181	Romanische Philologie. Beitraege†
0005-819X	Beitraege zur Tabakforschung *see* 0173-783X
0005-8203	Beitraege zur Tropischen und Subtropischen Landwirtschaft und Tropen Veterinaermedizin *see* 0301-567X
0005-8211	Beitraege zur Vogelkunde
0005-822X	Bejaarden *changed to* Senior.
0005-8238	B E K - Bruecke *changed to* Barmer Bruecke.

ISSN	Title
0005-8246	Germany (Democratic Republic). Amt fuer Erfindungs- und Patentwesen. Bekanntmachungen *changed to* Deutsches Patentamt. Bekanntmachungen.
0005-8254	Bekhan Wa Bedan
0005-8262	Beklaednadsfolket
0005-8270	Bekleidung und Maschenware
0005-8289	Bekleidung und Waesche
0005-8297	Beku Nyusu
0005-8300	Bela Abela
0005-8327	Belaruskaja Carkva
0005-8335	Maandblad Belasting Beschouwingen
0005-8351	Belfagor
0005-8378	Belgian Chamber of Commerce in Great Britain Journal *changed to* Belgo-Luxembourg Chamber of Commerce in Great Britain. Journal.
0005-8386	Het Beste uit Reader's Digest (Belgian - Flemish Edition)
0005-8394	Belgian Trade Review *changed to* Belgian American Trade Review.
0005-8408	Belgicatom
0005-8416	Belgique Hoteliere
0005-8424	Belgique Laitiere *see* 0770-2515
0005-8440	Tijdschrift voor Geneeskunde
0005-8459	Belgische Duivensport
0005-8467	Belgische Fruitrevue
0005-8475	Belgische Textielreiniging
0005-8483	Belgische Tuinbouw
0005-8491	Belgium: Economic and Technical Information *see* 0775-1443
0005-8521	Belgium. Ministere des Affaires Economiques. Bibliotheque Centrale (Fonds Quetelet). Accroissements
0005-853X	Belgium. Ministere des Finances. Administration des Contributions. Bulletin des Contributions
0005-8556	Bell Journal of Economics and Management Science *see* 0741-6261
0005-8564	Bell Laboratories Record *changed to* A T & T Bell Laboratories Record.
0005-8572	Bell Ringer
0005-8580	Bell System Technical Journal *see* 8756-2324
0005-8602	Bella (Milan, 1947)
0005-8629	Belleza y Moda *changed to* Belleza y Moda - Votre Beaute.
0005-8637	Bellezza
0005-8645	Bellona†
0005-8653	Belmont Teachers Association. Newsletter *changed to* Beacon.
0005-8661	Beloit Poetry Journal
0005-867X	Belora†
0005-8696	Benavides
0005-8726	Benedictines
0005-8734	Benedictijns Tijdschrift
0005-8742	Benediktusbote
0005-8750	U.S. Unemployment Insurance Service. Benefit Series Service, Unemployment Insurance†
0005-8769	Benelux Economisch en Statistisch Kwartaalbericht - Bulletin Trimestriel Benelux Economique et Statistique *changed to* Benelux Dossier.
0005-8777	Benelux Publikatieblad
0005-8785	Benfica
0005-8793	Bengal Medical Journal
0005-8807	Bengal: Past and Present
0005-8815	Bengali Literature
0005-884X	Bent of Tau Beta Pi
0005-8858	Benzin & Olie Bladet
0005-8866	Beratende Ingenieure
0005-8874	Berea Alumnus
0005-8890	Berean Searchlight
0005-8904	Denmark. Forsoegslaboratoriet. Beretning *see* 0105-6883
0005-8912	B H M. Berg- und Huettenmaennische Monatshefte.
0005-8920	Bergbauwissenschaften und Verfahrenstechnik†
0005-8939	Winter-Bergkamerad *changed to* Alpin.
0005-8947	Das Bergmann-Echo
0005-8955	Bergomun
0005-8963	Der Bergsteiger
0005-8971	Bergverks-Nytt
0005-898X	Bergvriend
0005-9013	Berichte Biochemie und Biologie†
0005-9021	Bunsengesellschaft fuer Physikalische Chemie. Berichte
0005-9048	Berichte Physiologie, Physiologische Chemie und Pharmakologie†
0005-9056	Berichte ueber die Allgemeine und Spezielle Pathologie *see* 0722-9674
0005-9072	Berichte ueber Die Gesamte Biologie Abt. A: Berichte ueber Die Wissenschaftliche Biologie *see* 0005-9013
0005-9080	Berichte ueber Landwirtschaft
0005-9099	Berichte zur deutschen Landeskunde†
0005-9102	Berichte zur Raumforschung und Raumplanung
0005-9110	Berichten van de Afdeling Volkskredietwezent
0005-9129	Berita Bibliografi *see* 0216-1273
0005-9137	Berita L.I.P.I. *see* 0125-9156
0005-9145	Berita Selulosa
0005-9153	Berita Shell
0005-9161	Berkeley Barb†
0005-917X	Berkeley Monitor *changed to* Grassroots (Berkeley).
0005-9188	Berkeley Tribe†
0005-9196	Berkshire News *changed to* American Landrace.
0005-920X	Berkshire Review†
0005-9218	Magazine R V I - Info R V I *changed to* Virages.
0005-9226	Berlin
0005-9242	Berlin-Flugplan
0005-9250	Berlin Programm
0005-9269	Berliner Baer
0005-9277	Berliner Bank. Wirtschaftsbericht
0005-9285	Betten-Magazin
0005-9293	Berliner Lebent
0005-9307	Berliner Liberale Zeitung
0005-9323	Berliner Sozialversicherungs beamte und angestellte†
0005-9331	Berliner Statistik
0005-934X	Berliner Studentenzeitung
0005-9358	Berliner Turnzeitung
0005-9366	Berliner und Muenchener Tieraerztliche Wochenschrift
0005-9374	Sozialistische Politik†
0005-9382	The Bermudian
0005-9390	Sint Bernardus
0005-9404	Berner Briefmarken-Zeitung
0005-9412	Berner Wochen Bulletin
0005-9420	Berner Zeitschrift fuer Geschichte und Heimatkunde
0005-9439	Bernice P. Bishop Museum Bulletin *changed to* Bishop Museum Bulletins in Anthropology.
0005-9439	Bernice P. Bishop Museum Bulletin *see* 0893-3138
0005-9439	Bernice P. Bishop Museum Bulletin *see* 0893-312X
0005-9439	Bernice P. Bishop Museum Bulletin *see* 0893-3146
0005-9455	Bertelsmann Briefe
0005-9471	Beruf und Gesinnung
0005-948X	Berufliche Bildung *changed to* Gewerkschaftliche Bildungspolitik.
0005-9498	Berufs-Dermatosen *see* 0343-2432
0005-9501	Berufsberatung und Berufsbildung
0005-951X	Die Berufsbildende Schule
0005-9528	Berufsbildende Schule Oesterreich†
0005-9536	Berufsbildung
0005-9544	Berufsgenossenschaft *see* 0723-7561
0005-9560	Berufstaetige Frau Oesterreich†
0005-9579	Besco News†
0005-9587	Besier's Hauswirtschaftliche†
0005-9595	Besser Verpacken *changed to* O V Z - Mitteilungen.
0005-9609	Besseres Obst
0005-9617	Best in Documents†
0005-9625	Best Sellers†
0005-9641	Best Songs†
0005-965X	Best Wishes
0005-9668	Das Beste aus Reader's Digest (German Edition) *changed to* Reader's Digest - Das Beste (German Edition)
0005-9676	Das Beste aus Reader's Digest (Swiss-German Edition)
0005-9684	Det Beste fra Reader's Digest (Norwegian Edition)
0005-9692	Het Beste uit Reader's Digest (Dutch Edition)
0005-9706	Best's Review. Life - Health Insurance Edition
0005-9714	Best's Review. Property - Liability Insurance Edition *see* 0161-7745
0005-9722	Best's Weekly Digest *changed to* Best's Insurance Management Reports: Life - Health Edition.
0005-9730	Bestsellers *see* 0744-3102
0005-9749	Bet ha-Talmud†
0005-9765	Betail
0005-9773	Betar Jagat
0005-9781	Betelgeuse†
0005-979X	Bet Mikra
0005-9803	Bethany Guide†
0005-9811	Bethany Nazarene College Today†
0005-982X	Bethel College Bulletin
0005-9838	Bethlehem Express†
0005-9846	Beton
0005-9854	Beton Arme
0005-9889	Beton i Zhelezobeton
0005-9897	Beton-Landbau *see* 0171-7952
0005-9900	Beton- und Stahlbetonbau
0005-9919	Betonituote *see* 1235-2136
0005-9927	Betonstein-Zeitung *see* 0373-4331
0005-9935	Der Betrieb
0005-9943	Betrieb und Absatz†
0005-9951	Betriebliche Altersversorgung
0005-996X	Betriebsausruestung *changed to* Betriebs und Ausruestung.
0005-9986	Betriebswirtschafts-Magazin *see* 0932-3961
0006-0003	Buerotechnik *changed to* Sysdata.
0006-0011	Betriebswirtschaftliche Blaetter fuer die Praxis der Sparkassen und Girozentralen *changed to* Betriebswirtschaftliche Blaetter fuer die Praxis der Sparkassen und Landesbanken - Girozentralen.
0006-0046	Better Breeding
0006-0054	Better Broadcasts News *changed to* Telemedium.
0006-0062	Better Business†
0006-0070	Better Camping†
0006-0089	Better Crops with Plant Food
0006-0100	Better Driving†
0006-0119	Better Editing†
0006-0127	Better Education
0006-0151	Better Homes and Gardens
0006-016X	Better Investing
0006-0186	Better Management
0006-0194	Better Radio and Television
0006-0208	Better Roads
0006-0216	Better Supervision†
0006-0232	Better Tomorrows†
0006-0240	Better Transit Bulletin *see* 0029-4039
0006-0291	Between Ourselves *see* 0704-2965
0006-0305	Between the Lines *see* 0887-428X
0006-0313	Beursbengel
0006-033X	Bevart
0006-0356	Beverage Bulletin
0006-0364	Beverage Industry News *see* 0274-9041
0006-0372	Beverage Media
0006-0399	Beverages
0006-0410	Beverly Review
0006-0429	Bewusster Leben
0006-0453	Bezpecnost a Hygiena Prace
0006-0461	Bhagirath
0006-047X	Bharat Medical Journal†
0006-0488	Bharat Sevak
0006-0496	Bharatha Darshana
0006-050X	Bharati Te Videshi Sahita
0006-0518	Bhavan's Journal
0006-0526	Bhopal Regional College of Education. Journal†
0006-0542	Bhushan's World Trade Enquiries
0006-0577	Bianco e Nero
0006-0585	Bibbia e Oriente
0006-0593	Bibel Heute
0006-0607	Bibel-Journalen
0006-0615	Bibel und Gemeinde
0006-0623	Bibel und Kirche
0006-064X	Bibel und Liturgie
0006-0658	Bibeltrogna Vaenners Missionstidning
0006-0690	Bible Collector†
0006-0704	Bible et Son Message *see* 0761-7267
0006-0712	Bible et Terre Sainte *changed to* Monde de la Bible.
0006-0720	Bible et Vie Chretienne†
0006-0739	Bible Friend
0006-0747	Bible in New York *changed to* BibleWorld.
0006-0755	Bible Society News *changed to* Word in Action.
0006-0763	Bible Lands
0006-0771	Bible Readers' Union Bulletin *see* 0792-3910
0006-078X	Bible Searchers
0006-0798	Bible Searchers Teacher
0006-0801	American Bible Society Record
0006-081X	Bible Standard and Herald of Christ's Kingdom
0006-0828	Bible-Time
0006-0836	Bible Today
0006-0844	Bible Translator *see* 0260-0943
0006-0844	Bible Translator *see* 0260-0935
0006-0860	Biblia
0006-0879	Biblia Revuo
0006-0887	Biblica
0006-0895	Biblical Archaeologist
0006-0909	Biblical Missions
0006-0917	Biblical Theology
0006-0925	Biblical Viewpoint
0006-0941	Bibliofilia
0006-0968	Bibliografia Argentina de Artes y Letras†
0006-0976	Bibliografia Brasileira Mensal†
0006-0992	Bibliografia Classificada
0006-100X	Bibliografia Economica de Mexico *see* 0188-6673
0006-1018	Bibliografia Elettrotecnica†
0006-1026	Bibliografia Historica de Espana e Hispanoamerica *see* 0537-3522
0006-1034	Bibliografia Internazionale di Scienze ed Arti
0006-1042	Bibliografia Italiana di Idraulica
0006-1050	Bibliografia Medica Internacional†
0006-1069	Bibliografia Mexicana
0006-1077	Bibliografia Nazionale Italiana
0006-1085	Bibliografia Venezolana
0006-1093	Bibliografia Zawartosci Czasopism
0006-1107	Statni Knihovna C S R. Bibliograficky Casopis†
0006-1115	Bibliograficky Katalog C S S R: Clanky v Ceskych Casopisech *see* 0862-9269
0006-1123	Spolecenske Vedy. Rada 2: Bibliografie Ekonomicke Literatury *see* 0139-5203
0006-1158	Bibliografia Jugoslovenske Periodike *see* 0350-0349
0006-1166	Bibliografija Prispelih Knjiga Clanaka Iz Strucnih Casopisa i Drugih Dokumenata
0006-1182	Bibliographia I U L A - I F H P *changed to* Bibliographia I U L A.
0006-1190	Bibliographia Africana
0006-1204	Bibliographia Anastatica *see* 0303-4550
0006-1212	Bibliographia Asiatica
0006-1220	Bibliographia Asiatica *see* 0004-4733
0006-1239	Bibliographia Geodaetica
0006-1247	Bibliographia Neuroendocrinologica†
0006-1255	Bibliographic Index
0006-1271	Bibliographical Bulletin for Welding and Allied Processes†
0006-128X	Bibliographical Society of America. Papers

ISSN INDEX 5349

ISSN	Title
0006-1298	Bibliographie Africaine†
0006-1301	Bibliographie Agricole Courante Roumaine†
0006-131X	Bibliographie Americaniste†
0006-1328	Centre Technique du Cuir. Bibliographie Analytique et Signaletique†
0006-1336	Bibliographie de Belgique
0006-1344	Bibliographie de la France†
0006-1352	Bibliographie de la Philosophie
0006-1360	Bibliographie der Deutschen Bibliographien see 0301-4614
0006-1379	Bibliographie der Kunstblaetter†
0006-1387	Bibliographie der Pflanzenschutzliteratur
0006-1409	Bibliographie der Uebersetzungen Deutschsprachiger Werke
0006-1417	Bibliographie der Wirtschaftspresse
0006-1433	Bibliographie, Documentation, Terminologie†
0006-1441	Bibliographie du Quebec
0006-1468	Bibliographie Staat und Recht der Deutschen Demokratischen Republik (Vierteljahresbibliographie)†
0006-1476	World Bibliography of Social Security
0006-1484	Bibliographies of Atomic Energy Literature†
0006-1506	Bibliographische Berichte†
0006-1514	Bibliographische Zeitschrift fuer Aesthetik†
0006-1522	Bibliography and Index of Geology Exclusive of North America see 0098-2784
0006-1530	Bibliography of Agriculture
0006-1565	Bibliography of Reproduction
0006-1573	Bibliography of Systematic Mycology
0006-1581	Shu Mo Chi Kan
0006-159X	Bibliont
0006-1603	Bibliophilie see 0399-9742
0006-1611	Biblioteca
0006-162X	Biblioteca Americana de Autores. Boletin†
0006-1646	Biblioteca de Menendez Pelayo. Boletin
0006-1654	Biblioteca della Liberta
0006-1662	Biblioteca do Sejur. Boletim
0006-1670	Tribunal Justica Estado da Guanabara. Biblioteca. Boletim changed to Rio de Janeiro, Brazil (State). Tribunal de Justicia. Biblioteca. Boletim.
0006-1697	Biblioteca "Jose Artigas". Boletin
0006-1700	Biblioteca Labronica Notiziario†
0006-1719	Universidad Nacional Autonoma de Mexico. Instituto de Investigaciones Bibliograficas. Boletin
0006-1727	Biblioteca Nacional Jose Marti. Revista
0006-1751	Biblioteca y Hemeroteca de Servicios Electricos del Gran Buenos Aires. Boletin Bibliografico changed to Servicios Electricos del Gran Buenos Aires S.A. Boletin Bibliografico.
0006-176X	Bibliotecas
0006-1778	Biblioteconomia†
0006-1786	Bibliotek for Laeger
0006-1808	Bibliotekar'
0006-1816	Bibliotekar
0006-1824	Bibliotek 70 see 0905-4650
0006-1832	Bibliotekarstvo
0006-1840	Biblioteket Presenterar Nya Boecker†
0006-1859	Biblioteki Z.N.E.P.A.N. Biuletyn Informacyjny†
0006-1867	Biblioteksbladet
0006-1913	Bibliotheca Orientalis
0006-1921	Bibliotheca Sacra
0006-193X	Biblioteheck
0006-1948	Technische Hogeschool te Delft. Bibliotheek. Aanwinsten changed to Technische Universiteit te Delft. Bibliotheek. Aanwinsten.
0006-1956	Bibliotheekgids changed to Bibliotheek- en Archiefgids.
0006-1964	Der Bibliothekar†
0006-1972	Bibliotheksdienst
0006-1980	Bibliotheque de l'Ecole des Chartes
0006-1999	Bibliotheque d'Humanisme et Renaissance
0006-2006	Bulletin des Bibliotheques de France
0006-2014	Biblische Zeitschrift
0006-2022	Biblos
0006-2030	Biblos
0006-2057	Bichitra
0006-2065	Bicycle Journal see 0745-8126
0006-2073	Bicycling
0006-209X	Bielarus
0006-2103	Bielefelder Katalog changed to Bielefelder Katalog - Klassik.
0006-2111	Bien-Etre Social Canadien changed to Digeste Social.
0006-212X	Die Biene
0006-2146	Bienenvater
0006-2154	Bienenwelt
0006-2189	Big Farmer see 0274-6050
0006-2219	Bihar Industries
0006-2227	Bij de Haard changed to Eigen Aard.
0006-2235	Bijbellessen voor de Kinderen†
0006-2243	Bijbellessen voor de Sabbatschool
0006-2251	Bijblad bij de Industriele Eigendom
0006-226X	Bijblijven
0006-2278	Bijdragen
0006-2286	Bijdragen tot de Geschiedenis
0006-2294	Bijdragen tot de Taal-, Land- en Volkenkunde
0006-2308	Bijeen
0006-2316	Bijou Magazine†
0006-2324	Biken Journal†
0006-2332	Bil og Motor
0006-2340	Bilanz
0006-2359	Bilanz- und Buchhaltungspraxis see 0930-0597
0006-2367	Bilbransjen - Bilteknisk Fagblad
0006-2375	Bild der Wissenschaft
0006-2383	Bild und Ton†
0006-2391	Bildende Kunst
0006-2405	Bildermaerchen†
0006-2421	Bildmessung und Luftbildwesen changed to Z P F - Photogrammetrie und Fernerkundung.
0006-243X	Bildnerische Erziehung†
0006-2448	Bildor changed to Building Business and Apartment Management Bildor.
0006-2456	Bildung und Erziehung
0006-2464	Bilen og Baaden changed to Bilen.
0006-2472	Biliardo
0006-2502	Bill of Rights Newsletter see 0160-7731
0006-2510	Billboard (New York)
0006-2529	Bille-Anzeigen-Rundschau
0006-2537	Billed Bladet
0006-2545	Billiards & Snooker†
0006-2553	Billiken
0006-2561	Savez Sindikata Jugoslavije. Centralni Vec. Bilten changed to Savez Sindikata Jugoslavije. Veca S S J. Bilten.
0006-257X	Bilten Dokumentacije. Biljna Proizvodnja see 0351-2312
0006-2588	Bilten Dokumentacije. Elektrotehnika see 0351-238X
0006-2588	Bilten Dokumentacije. Elektrotehnika changed to Bilten Dokumentacije. Elektrotehnika i Elektronika. Proizvodnja Elektricnih Masina i Aparata. Ptt Usluge.
0006-2596	Bilten Dokumentacije. Goriva i Maziva†
0006-260X	Bilten Dokumentacije. Gradjevinarstvo i Arhitektura see 0352-1028
0006-260X	Bilten Dokumentacije. Gradjevinarstvo i Arhitektura see 0351-2576
0006-260X	Bilten Dokumentacije. Gradjevinarstvo i Arhitektura see 0351-2592
0006-2626	Bilten Dokumentacije. Industrija Tekstila i Papira†
0006-2634	Bilten Dokumentacije. Masinska Tehnologija i Radne Masine see 0351-8906
0006-2642	Bilten Dokumentacije. Metalurgija
0006-2650	Bilten Dokumentacije. Pogonske Masine i Masinski Delovi see 0351-8906
0006-2669	Bilten Dokumentacije. Prehrambena Industrija see 0351-2479
0006-2693	Bilten Dokumentacije. Silikatna Industrija see 0351-2509
0006-2707	Bilten Dokumentacije. Stocna Proizvodnja i Veterinarstvo see 0351-2320
0006-2715	Bilten Dokumentacije. Sumarstvo i Drvna Industrija†
0006-2731	Bilten Pravne Sluzbe J N A
0006-2758	Bilten Zavoda za Osnovno Obrazovanje i Obrazovanje Nastavnika Sr Srbije
0006-2766	Bim
0006-2774	Iranian Journal of Plant Pathology
0006-2790	Bimestre†
0006-2804	Binario
0006-2812	Binden en Bouwen
0006-2863	BioDynamics
0006-2871	Bio-Graphic Quarterly†
0006-2898	Biomedical Engineering see 0309-1902
0006-2901	Bioastronautics Report†
0006-291X	Biochemical and Biophysical Research Communications
0006-2928	Biochemical Genetics
0006-2944	Biochemical Medicine see 0885-4505
0006-2952	Biochemical Pharmacology
0006-2960	Biochemistry
0006-2979	Biochemistry
0006-2995	Biochemistry and Experimental Biology†
0006-3002	Biochimica et Biophysica Acta
0006-3029	Biofizika
0006-3037	Biogenic Amines and Transmitters in the Nervous System see 0193-5186
0006-3053	Biography Index
0006-3061	Bioinorganic Chemistry see 0162-0134
0006-307X	Biokhimiya
0006-3088	Biologia changed to Biologia. A: Botany.
0006-3088	Biologia changed to Biologia. B: Zoology.
0006-3088	Biologia changed to Biologia. C: General Biology.
0006-3088	Biologia changed to Biologia. D: Biochemistry and Molecular Biology.
0006-3096	Biologia
0006-310X	Biologia Culturale†
0006-3118	Biologia Gabonica
0006-3126	Biology of the Neonate
0006-3134	Biologia Plantarum
0006-3142	Biologiai Kozlemenyek - Biological Publications see 0133-3844
0006-3150	Biologica Latina†
0006-3169	Biological Abstracts
0006-3169	Biological Abstracts Cumulative Indexes
0006-3177	Biological & Agricultural Index
0006-3185	Biological Bulletin
0006-3193	Biological Bulletin
0006-3207	Biological Conservation
0006-3215	Biological Photographic Association. Journal see 0274-497X
0006-3223	Biological Psychiatry
0006-3231	Cambridge Philosophical Society. Biological Reviews
0006-324X	Biological Society of Washington. Proceedings
0006-3258	Biologie et Gastro-Enterologie see 0399-8320
0006-3266	Biologie Medicale
0006-3274	Der Biologieunterricht changed to Unterricht Biologie.
0006-3282	Biologische Abhandlungen
0006-3290	Biologische Rundschau†
0006-3304	Biologisches Zentralblatt
0006-3339	Biologist†
0006-3347	Biologist
0006-3355	Biology and Human Affairs see 0143-5051
0006-3363	Biology of Reproduction
0006-338X	Biomedical Electronics†
0006-3398	Biomedical Engineering
0006-341X	Biometrics
0006-3428	Biometrie Humaine see 0758-2714
0006-3436	Biometrie-Praximetrie
0006-3444	Biometrika
0006-3479	Bionomic Briefs†
0006-3487	Bionomica
0006-3495	Biophysical Journal
0006-3509	Biophysics
0006-3517	Biophysik see 0301-634X
0006-3517	Biophysik see 0175-7571
0006-3525	Biopolymers
0006-3533	Bioquimica Clinica changed to Acta Bioquimica Clinica Latinoamericana.
0006-3541	BioResearch Index see 0192-6985
0006-355X	Biorheology
0006-3568	BioScience
0006-3576	Biosophia
0006-3584	Biota†
0006-3592	Biotechnology and Bioengineering
0006-3606	Biotropica
0006-3614	Birbal
0006-3630	Bird-Banding see 0273-8570
0006-3649	Bird Life
0006-3657	Bird Study
0006-3665	Birds
0006-3673	Birds and Country†
0006-3681	Birlik
0006-369X	Birmingham
0006-3703	Birmingham ABC & Midland Counties Railway Time Tables†
0006-3711	Birmingham Bar Association. Bulletin
0006-3746	University of Birmingham Chemical Engineer†
0006-3754	Birmingham World
0006-3762	Birney Arrow†
0006-3770	Birra e Malto
0006-3797	Biscuits, Biscottes, Panification Industrielle, Produits Dietetiques, Chocolat, Confiserie changed to Magazine Strategies Gourmandes.
0006-3800	In the Field of Building†
0006-3827	Bismoi
0006-3835	Bit
0006-3843	B I T
0006-3851	Midwest Bridle and Bit see 1050-5741
0006-3878	Bitaon Heyl ha-Avir
0006-3886	Bitidningen
0006-3908	Bitterroot†
0006-3916	Bitumen
0006-3924	Bitumen, Teere, Asphalte, Peche changed to Strassen- und Tiefbau Vereinigt mit Strasse-Bruecke-Tunnel, Bitumen-Teere-Asphalts-Peche.
0006-3932	Bitzaron: The Hebrew Monthly of America changed to Bitzaron: A Quarterly of Hebrew Letters.
0006-3967	Biuletyn Historii Sztuki
0006-3975	Biuletyn Informacyjny†
0006-3983	Biuletyn Informacyjny Biblioteki Narodowej
0006-4017	Biuletyn Numizmatyczny
0006-4025	Poland. Glowny Urzad Statystyczny. Biuletyn Statystyczny
0006-4033	Zydowski Instytut Historyczny w Polsce. Biuletyn
0006-4068	Bjelovarski List
0006-4076	Blaa Stjaernan
0006-4084	Black Academy Review†
0006-4106	Black Belt Magazine
0006-4114	Black Business Digest†
0006-4122	Black Careers
0006-4165	Black Enterprise
0006-4173	Black Hills Anemone changed to Black Hills State Today.
0006-4203	Black News
0006-4246	Black Scholar
0006-4254	Black Student†
0006-4262	Black Swamp Review†
0006-4289	Black Times: Voices of the National Community†
0006-4297	Black Vanguard
0006-4319	Black World†
0006-4327	Blackboard Bulletin
0006-4335	Blackcountryman
0006-4351	Blackpool Hotel & Guest House Association. Journal
0006-4378	Blaetter der Freien Volksbuehne Berlin
0006-4386	Blaetter fuer Agrarrecht†
0006-4394	Blaetter fuer den Deutschlehrer†

5350 ISSN INDEX

0006-4408 Blaetter fuer Deutsche Landesgeschichte
0006-4416 Blaetter fuer Deutsche und Internationale Politik
0006-4440 Blaetter fuer Grundstuecks, Bau- und Wohnungsrecht†
0006-4459 Blaetter fuer Heimatkunde
0006-4475 Blaetter fuer Steuerrecht, Sozial Versicherung und Arbeitsrecht†
0006-4483 Blaetter fuer Volksliteratur
0006-4491 Blaetter fuer Zuercherische Rechtsprechung
0006-4505 Blagovest†
0006-4513 Blaguest†
0006-453X Blake Newsletter *see* 0160-628X
0006-4548 Blake Studies†
0006-4556 Blaaklint *see* 0345-1593
0006-4564 B T N†
0006-4580 B L A S A Newsletter *changed to* African Library Association of S.A. Newsletter.
0006-4610 Blaue, Alpwirtschaftliche Monatsblaetter
0006-4629 Blaue Kreuz
0006-4637 Der Blaue Peter
0006-4645 A en D†
0006-4653 Blauwe Kruis *see* 0921-3996
0006-4661 Blauwe Wimpel
0006-467X Bleb *changed to* Ark (Tiburon).
0006-4688 Blech-Rohre-Profile
0006-4696 Blessings of Liberty
0006-470X Bleter far Geszichte
0006-4718 Blick und Bild
0006-4734 Blick ins Fleischer-Fachgeschaeft *changed to* Blick.
0006-4742 Blick Ins Land
0006-4750 Blick vom Hochhaus
0006-4769 Blickpunkt
0006-4777 Blijde Boodschap†
0006-4785 Blijdorp Geluident†
0006-4793 Blikkenslager- Roer- og Sanitets Mesteren *see* 0902-5456
0006-4807 Blind Advocate *changed to* Advocate.
0006-4815 Blind Citizen
0006-4823 Blind Welfare
0006-4831 Blindas Tidskrift†
0006-4858 Zeitschrift fuer das Blinden- und Sehbehindertenbildungswesen *see* 0176-7836
0006-4866 Blindenwelt *changed to* Die Blindenselbsthilfe.
0006-4874 Blindmaker *see* 0305-733X
0006-4882 Blitz
0006-4890 Bloc
0006-4904 Der Block
0006-4912 Blodau'r Ffair†
0006-4920 Bloemenvriend
0006-4939 Bloemfontein Nuusbrief
0006-4947 Bloemheuwel-Nuus
0006-4955 Blomster
0006-4963 Blomster-Branschen
0006-4971 Blood
0006-498X Blood Group News†
0006-4998 The Blood-Horse
0006-5005 Blood Therapy Journal *changed to* Blood Therapy Journal International.
0006-5013 Bloodlines Journal *changed to* Bloodlines.
0006-5021 Blue Anchor *changed to* California Fruit Grower.
0006-503X Blue and Gold Triangle of Lambda Kappa Sigma
0006-5048 Blue and White†
0006-5056 Bluebook†
0006-5064 Blue Cloud Quarterly†
0006-5072 Blue Cross Reports. Research Series *see* 0095-6740
0006-5099 Blue Jay
0006-5102 Blue Triangle†
0006-5129 Bluegrass Music News
0006-5137 Bluegrass Unlimited
0006-5153 Blues Unlimited
0006-5161 Blues World†
0006-517X Bluestocking†
0006-5188 Bluestone†
0006-5196 Blumea
0006-5218 Blumenau em Cadernos
0006-5226 Blumenfreundin Blumenpost
0006-5242 Blut *see* 0939-5555
0006-5250 Blutalkohol
0006-5269 Blyttia
0006-5277 B'nai B'rith Messenger
0006-5307 Scripts†
0006-5323 Trade and Industry *see* 0143-9111
0006-5331 Board of Trade Newsletter *see* 0164-7059
0006-534X Board Manufacture Practice *see* 0306-4123
0006-5358 Boardman *changed to* Boardmember.
0006-5366 Boat & Motor Dealer
0006-5374 Boating
0006-5404 Boating Industry
0006-5404 Boating Industry Marine Buyers' Guide
0006-5420 Scientific Pest Control†
0006-5439 Bode van het Heil in Christus
0006-5455 Boden und Gesundheit†
0006-5463 Boden, Wand, Decke
0006-5471 Die Bodenkultur
0006-548X Bodensee Hefte
0006-5498 Bodine Motorgram
0006-5501 Body
0006-5528 National Defense Medical Journal
0006-5544 Boek der Boeken *changed to* Schrift.
0006-5560 Boekenband†
0006-5579 Boekengids
0006-5587 Boekverkoper†
0006-5595 Boer *see* 0772-7054
0006-5609 Boer en Tuinder
0006-5617 Boerderij
0006-5625 Boerenleenbank *changed to* Rabobank.
0006-5633 Boern & Unge
0006-5641 Boersenblatt fuer den Deutschen Buchhandel *changed to* BuchWoche.
0006-5692 Bogens Verden
0006-5706 Bogormen
0006-5714 Bogoslovlje
0006-5722 Bogoslovni Vestnik
0006-5730 Bogtrykkerbladet *see* 0017-2995
0006-5749 Bogvennen
0006-5773 Boi
0006-5781 Bois
0006-579X Bois et Forets des Tropiques
0006-5803 Boissons de France "Saines et Legeres" *see* 0760-1999
0006-5811 Bok og Bibliotek
0006-582X Bokbladet†
0006-5838 Bokmakierie *changed to* Birding in Southern Africa.
0006-5846 Bokvaennen
0006-5854 Boletim Cultural da Guine Portuguesa†
0006-5862 B I G (Boletim da Industria Grafica) *changed to* A B I G R A F em Revista.
0006-5870 Boletim da Pesca *changed to* Revista do Pescador.
0006-5897 Boletim de Bibliografia Portuguesa *see* 0253-3413
0006-5897 Boletim de Bibliografia Portuguesa *see* 0253-3421
0006-5897 Boletim de Bibliografia Portuguesa *see* 0253-343X
0006-5900 Boletim de Custos
0006-5919 Boletim de Desenvolvimento de Pessoal†
0006-5927 Boletim de Estudos de Pesca†
0006-5935 Boletim de Minas
0006-5943 Boletim de Psicologia
0006-5951 Boletim do Leite e Seus Derivados
0006-596X Boletim do Porto de Lisboa
0006-5978 Portos e Caminhos de Ferro de Mozambique *changed to* Mozambique. Direccao Nacional dos Portos e Caminhos de Ferro. Revista Trimestral.
0006-5994 Boletim Geoelectrico *see* 0870-4716
0006-6001 Mozambique. Servico Meteorologico. Boletim Geomagnetico Preliminar *changed to* Mozambique. Instituto Nacional de Geologia. Boletim Geomagnetico Preliminar.
0006-601X Boletim-Geral do Ultramar†
0006-6028 Boletim Geografico†
0006-6044 Mozambique. Servico Meteorologico. Boletim Meteorologico para a Agricultura *changed to* Mozambique. Instituto Nacional de Geologia. Boletim Meteorologico para a Agricultura.
0006-6060 Boletim Mineiro de Geografia†
0006-6079 Boletim Paulista de Geografia
0006-6087 B R†
0006-6095 Mozambique. Servico Meteorologico. Boletim Seismique *changed to* Mozambique. Instituto Nacional de Geologia. Boletim Seismique.
0006-6109 Boletim Sismico†
0006-6117 Boletim Tecnico da Petrobras *see* 0102-9304
0006-6125 Boletin Agropecuario del Alto Valle†
0006-6133 Boletin Bibliografice de Revista "Signos"†
0006-6141 Boletin Bibliografico Boliviano
0006-6176 Boletin Chileno de Parasitologia
0006-6184 Banco de la Republica. Biblioteca Luis Angel Arango. Boletin Cultural y Bibliografico
0006-6192 Escuela Interamericana de Bibliotecologia. Boletin de Adquisiciones†
0006-6206 Boletin de Arte
0006-6249 Boletin de Estudios Economicos
0006-6257 Boletin de Estudios Oaxaquenos†
0006-6265 Boletin de Filologia Espanola†
0006-6273 Boletin de Formacion Cooperativa
0006-6281 Venezuela. Ministerio de Energia y Minas. Boletin de Geologia
0006-629X Boletin de Higiene y Epidemiologia *changed to* Revista Cubana de Higiene y Epidemiologia.
0006-6303 Boletin de Historia y Antiguedades
0006-6311 Boletin de Informacion Dental *see* 1130-0094
0006-632X Boletin de Informacion Educativa†
0006-6338 Boletin de la Propiedad Industrial
0006-6346 Argentina. Ministerio de Trabajo y Seguridad Social. Boletin de Legislacion†
0006-6354 Boletin de Noticias†
0006-6362 Boletin del Deposito Legal de Obras Impresas *see* 0525-3675
0006-6389 Boletin Informativo†
0006-6397 Boletin Informativo sobre Estudios Latinoamericanos en Europa *see* 0924-0608
0006-6419 Boletin Juridico Militar
0006-6435 Boletin Mensual Climatologico†
0006-6451 Boletin Meteorologico de El Salvador†
0006-646X Boletin Naval
0006-6486 Boletin Produccion Animal†
0006-6494 Boletin Radiofonico T.V.
0006-6508 Boletin Uruguayo de Sociologia
0006-6524 Bolignyt *changed to* Vi Lejere.
0006-6532 Bolivarian Review†
0006-6540 Bolivia
0006-6559 Bolivia - Land of Promise†
0006-6567 Bollettino delle Malattie dell'Orecchio, della Gola, del Naso *changed to* Otorinolaringologica.
0006-6575 Bollettino di Pesca *changed to* Bollettino di Pesca, Piscicoltura e Idrobiologia.
0006-6583 Bollettino di Studi Latini
0006-6591 Bollettino Storico Piacentino
0006-6605 I S L Bollettino Bibliografico†
0006-6613 Bollettino Bibliografico Internazionale per l'Apostolato delle Edizioni†
0006-6621 Bollettino Bibliografico per le Scienze Morali e Sociale
0006-663X Bollettino Ceciliano
0006-6648 Bollettino Chimico Farmaceutico
0006-6656 D O X A Bollettino
0006-6664 Bollettino dei Brevetti per Invenzioni, Modelli e Marchi
0006-6680 Bollettino delle Accessioni di Periodici e Libri
0006-6699 Studio di Restauro Strini. Bollettino
0006-6710 Bollettino di Geodesia e Scienze Affini
0006-6729 Bollettino di Geofisica, Teorica ed Applicata
0006-6745 Bollettino di Libri Antichi e Moderni di Varia Cultura Esauriti e Rari
0006-6753 Italy. Laboratorio di Idrobiologia. Bollettino di Pesca Piscicoltura e Idrobiologia†
0006-6761 Bollettino di Psicologia Applicata
0006-677X Bollettino d'Oculistica
0006-6788 Bollettino Ecclesiastico *changed to* Arcidiocesi di Reggio Calabria. Rivista Pastorale.
0006-6796 Bollettino Economico
0006-680X Bollettino Emerografico di Economia Internazionale
0006-6826 Bollettino-Metallografico e di Odonto-Stoma-Tologia
0006-6834 Dati Meteorologico della Puglia e Luciania *changed to* Osservazioni di Meteorologia Agraria della Puglia e Basilicata.
0006-6842 Italy. Consiglio dell'Ordine dei Medici di Torino. Bollettino Ordine dei Medici†
0006-6850 Bollettino Quindicinale dell'Emigrazione†
0006-6869 Bollettino Storico della Svizzera Italiana
0006-6877 Bollettino Tecnico Geloso
0006-6885 Bollettino Termomeccanica
0006-6893 Bollettino Tributario d'Informazioni
0006-6907 Bollettino Vincenziano
0006-6915 Bolsa Mexicana de Valores. Weekly Bulletin
0006-6923 Bolsa de Comercio de Buenos Aires. Boletin *changed to* Bolsa.
0006-6931 Bolsa de Comercio de Rosario. Revista
0006-694X Bolsa de Valores do Rio de Janeiro. Boletim de Documentacao†
0006-6958 Bolwerk
0006-6966 Yelmo†
0006-6974 Bombay Market
0006-6982 Bombay Natural History Society. Journal
0006-6990 Bon Appetit
0006-7016 Bona
0006-7024 Bona Espero
0006-7040 Bond and Money Market Review†
0006-7059 Bondline†
0006-7067 Standard & Poor's Bond Outlook *see* 0731-1974
0006-7075 Bondholder's Register *see* 0961-8171
0006-7091 Bondsspaarbanken *see* 0169-5401
0006-7113 Bonifatiusblatt
0006-7121 Bonjour
0006-713X Bonne Cuisine
0006-7156 Bonner Meteorologische Abhandlungen
0006-7164 Bonner Zahlen†
0006-7172 Bonner Zoologische Beitraege
0006-7180 Bonsai Bulletin
0006-7199 Bonytt *see* 0800-1936
0006-7202 Book Club of California. Quarterly News-Letter
0006-7229 Book Collecting World
0006-7237 Book Collector
0006-7245 Book Exchange
0006-7253 Book-Keepers Journal *see* 0953-2579
0006-7261 Book Market†
0006-727X Book News†
0006-7288 Book News *changed to* Tartan Book Sales Catalog.
0006-7296 Book News Letter
0006-730X Book-Of-The-Month Club News
0006-7318 Book Production Industry *see* 0273-8724
0006-7326 Book Review Digest
0006-7334 Rucksack *changed to* Rambling Today.
0006-7342 Book Reviews of the Month†
0006-7350 Book Shopper Newsletter†
0006-7369 Book World
0006-7377 Bookbird
0006-7385 Booklist
0006-7393 Bookmark (Chapel Hill)
0006-7407 Bookmark (Albany)
0006-7415 Bookmark†
0006-7423 Books†
0006-7431 Books Abroad *see* 0196-3570

ISSN

0006-744X Books and Bookmen *changed to* Books Magazine.
0006-7458 Books and Libraries at the University of Kansas
0006-7474 Books at Iowa
0006-7482 Books for Your Children
0006-7490 Books from Finland
0006-7504 Books from Hungary *see* 0324-3451
0006-7512 Books in Polish or Relating to Poland
0006-7520 Books of the Southwest
0006-7539 Bookseller
0006-7547 Bookseller
0006-7555 Bookseller Pustak Vikreta Barodat†
0006-7563 Bookstore Journal
0006-7571 Boom-Pers Combinatie
0006-758X Boor
0006-7598 Boosey and Hawkes Newsletter
0006-7601 Boost
0006-761X Boot- und Schiffbau†
0006-7636 Boote
0006-7644 Bootswirtschaft
0006-7652 Bor- es Cipotechnika
0006-7660 Bordeaux Chirurgical†
0006-7679 Borden Review of Nutrition Research†
0006-7695 Borderline Magazine†
0006-7709 Bore Da
0006-7717 Boreal *changed to* Boreal International.
0006-7725 Borec
0006-7741 Borgazdasag
0006-775X Borghese
0006-7768 Borgyogyaszati es Venerologiai Szemle
0006-7784 Boris Kidric Institute of Nuclear Sciences. Bulletin†
0006-7792 Boern og Boeger
0006-7806 Borneo Research Bulletin
0006-7822 Boron in Glass†
0006-7849 Borsa dei Noli
0006-7857 Borsa Marmi
0006-7865 Borussen-Echo
0006-7873 Disaster Prevention
0006-789X Bosch Technische Berichte
0006-7903 Bose Institute. Transactions
0006-792X Boss†
0006-7938 Children's Hospital Medical Center, Boston. News *changed to* Children's World.
0006-7946 Boston City Record
0006-7954 Boston College Industrial and Commercial Law Review *see* 0161-6587
0006-7989 Boston Magazine
0006-7997 Boston Museum Bulletin *see* 0739-5736
0006-8004 Boston Public Schools Review *changed to* B P S News.
0006-8020 Boston Symphony Orchestra Program Book-Notes *changed to* Boston Symphony Orchestra Program.
0006-8039 Boston University Journal†
0006-8047 Boston University Law Review
0006-8055 Botanica Marina
0006-8063 Academia Sinica. Botanical Bulletin
0006-8071 Botanical Gazette *changed to* International Journal of Plant Sciences.
0006-808X Botanical Magazine *changed to* Botanical Magazine, Tokyo.
0006-8098 Botanical Museum Leaflets†
0006-8101 Botanical Review
0006-811X Botanical Society of Bengal. Bulletin
0006-8128 Botanical Survey of India. Bulletin
0006-8136 Botanicheskii Zhurnal
0006-8144 Botanikai Kozlemenyek
0006-8152 Botanische Jahrbuecher fuer Systematik, Pflanzengeschichte und Pflanzengeographie
0006-8160 Botanische Tuinen en Het Belmonte Arboretum der Landbouwhogeschool Te Wageningen Mededelingen†
0006-8179 Botanische Staatssammlung Muenchen. Mitteilungen
0006-8187 Botanisk Tidsskrift *see* 0107-055X
0006-8195 Botaniska Notiser *see* 0107-055X
0006-8209 Bote
0006-8217 Bote aus der Apotheke†
0006-8225 Bote fuer Tirol
0006-8233 Both Sides Now
0006-8241 Bothalia
0006-8276 Botschafter des Kommenden Koenigs
0006-8284 Boucherie Francaise
0006-8292 Boulanger-Patissier *see* 0224-5027
0006-8306 Boumi Temple News
0006-8314 Boundary-Layer Meteorology
0006-8330 Bouwbelangen
0006-8349 Bouwen aan de Nieuwe Aarde
0006-8365 Bouwliteratuur Documentatie†
0006-8373 Bouwmachines
0006-8381 Bouwondernemer
0006-839X Bovagblad
0006-8403 Bow and Arrow Hunting
0006-8411 Bowlers Journal and Billiard Revue *see* 0164-9183
0006-8438 Bowling Notizie
0006-8446 Bowling Proprietor
0006-8454 Bowls in N.S.W. *changed to* Bowls.
0006-8470 Box y Lucha
0006-8489 Boxboard Containers
0006-8497 Boxe Ring
0006-8519 Boxing News
0006-8527 Boxoffice
0006-8535 Boxwood Bulletin
0006-8543 Boyce Thompson Institute for Plant Research, Inc. Contributions†
0006-8551 Boys and Girls†
0006-856X Boys Baseball Bulletin *changed to* Pony Baseball - Softball Express.
0006-8578 Boys Brigade Gazette
0006-8586 Boys Club Bulletin *changed to* Boys & Girls Clubs of America Bulletin.
0006-8594 Boys Clubs of America. Journal *see* 0272-6513
0006-8608 Boys' Life (Inkprint Edition)
0006-8616 Brabant Tourisme
0006-8624 Brabantia
0006-8632 De Brabantse Leeuw
0006-8640 Bracara Augusta
0006-8667 Brackety - Ack
0006-8675 Bradfield College Chronicle
0006-8683 Bradford & Halifax Chambers of Commerce. Chamber of Commerce Journal
0006-8705 Bragantia
0006-8721 Brahmavadin
0006-873X Braille Book Review (Large Print Edition)
0006-8756 Braille Chess Magazine
0006-8772 Braille Forum
0006-8780 Braille Journal of Physiotherapy
0006-8799 Braille Mainichi *changed to* Braille Mainichi Weekly.
0006-8810 Braille Mirror
0006-8829 Braille Monitor (Inkprint Edition)
0006-8837 Braille Music Magazine
0006-8845 New Braille Musician *see* 0364-7501
0006-887X Braille Radio Times
0006-8888 Braille Rainbow *changed to* Rainbow.
0006-8896 Braille Science Journal
0006-890X Braille Sporting Record
0006-8918 Braille Star Theosophist
0006-8926 Braille Sunday School Quarterly†
0006-8942 Braille Variety News†
0006-8950 Brain
0006-8969 Brain and Nerve
0006-8977 Brain, Behavior and Evolution
0006-8985 Brain News
0006-9000 Brainstorms†
0006-9019 Brake and Front End Service *see* 0193-726X
0006-9027 Brand *changed to* Brand en Brandweer.
0006-9035 Brand Aus
0006-9043 Brandeis University Bulletin†
0006-9051 Brandfoersvar *see* 0283-1155
0006-906X Die Brandhilfe
0006-9078 Branding Iron
0006-9086 Brandon's Shipper & Forwarder *changed to* American Sailings.
0006-9094 Brandschutz
0006-9108 Brandverhuetung und Brandbekaempfung *see* 0343-3560
0006-9116 Brandwacht
0006-9124 Brandweert
0006-9132 Brangus Journal
0006-9140 Branicevo
0006-9159 Die Branntweinwirtschaft
0006-9167 Brazil Acucareiro
0006-9191 Brasil Jovem†
0006-9205 Brasil-Medico
0006-9248 Bratislavske Lekarske Listy
0006-9256 Bratrsky Vestnik
0006-9264 Bratstvo
0006-9272 Bratstvo
0006-9280 Brauereibesitzer und Braumeister *see* 0172-0589
0006-9299 Braunkohle Waerme und Energie *see* 0341-1060
0006-9310 Brautechnik Aktuell†
0006-9361 Brazil. Biblioteca da Camara dos Deputados. Boletim *changed to* Brazil. Camara dos Deputados. Documentacao e Informacao.
0006-9388 Brazil. Departamento de Agricultura. Boletim†
0006-9418 Faculdade de Farmacia e Odontologia de Rebeirao Preto. Revista *changed to* Universidade de Sao Paulo. Revista de Odontologia.
0006-9434 Brazil. Ministerio da Fazenda. Nucleo Regional de Administracao. Boletim Informativo *changed to* Brazil. Ministerio da Fazenda. Boletim Informativo da Secao de Documentacao.
0006-9442 Brazil. Ministerio da Saude. Departamento Nacional de Endemias Rurais. Divisao de Cooperacao e Divulgacao. Boletim Bibliografico†
0006-9469 Pernambuco. Secretaria do Saneamento, Habitacao e Obras. Boletim Tecnico
0006-9477 Brazila Esperantisto
0006-9485 Brazilian Bulletin†
0006-9493 Brazilian Business†
0006-9507 Brazilian News Briefs *changed to* American Chamber of Commerce - Sao Paulo. Update.
0006-9515 Bread of Life†
0006-9523 Break-In
0006-9531 Breakthru
0006-954X Brecon and Radnor Farmer†
0006-9566 Bref Rhone Alpes
0006-9574 Bremer Missionsschiff†
0006-9582 Bremer Schulblatt
0006-9604 Brennpunkt†
0006-9612 B W K
0006-9620 Brennstoffchemie *see* 0014-0058
0006-9639 Bres-Planete *changed to* Bres'
0006-9647 Bretagne Reelle
0006-9663 Brethren Life and Thought
0006-9671 Breton News *changed to* Carn.
0006-968X Breve, il Gruppo, la Cultura, l'Idee
0006-9698 Breviora
0006-9701 Brewers Bulletin
0006-971X Brewers Digest
0006-971X Brewers Digest Annual Buyers Guide and Brewery Directory
0006-9728 Brewers' Guardian†
0006-9736 Brewer
0006-9752 Brewing Trade Review *changed to* Brewing Review.
0006-9760 Brick and Clay Record†
0006-9779 Brickbats & Bouquets
0006-9787 Brides & Setting Up Home
0006-9795 Bride's Magazine *changed to* Bride's & Your New Home.
0006-9809 Bridge of Eta Kappa Nu
0006-9817 Bridge†
0006-9825 Bridge
0006-9833 Most
0006-9841 Bridge Bulletin *changed to* Bridge S A.
0006-985X Bridge d'Italia
0006-9868 Bridge Magazine *changed to* Bridge.
0006-9876 Bridge World
0006-9884 Bridgeport Hospital News *changed to* Resource Magazine (Bridgeport).
0006-9892 Bridgeport News†
0006-9914 Bridgeur
0006-9922 Brief *see* 0741-465X
0006-9930 Brief an Unsere Freunde *changed to* Enka Glanzstoff. Trend und Information.
0006-9949 Brief aus Wahlwies
0006-9965 Southern Methodist University School of Law. Brief
0006-9973 Briefe an den Chef†
0006-9981 Briefe an den Mitarbeiter†
0006-999X Briefe an den Mitmenschen†
0007-0009 Briefe fuer junge Steuerfachleute
0007-0017 Briefed†
0007-0025 Briefing Papers
0007-0033 Briefmarke
0007-0041 Briefmarken-Spiegel
0007-0068 Briefs†
0007-0076 Brieven Aan de Chef†
0007-0106 Brigham Young University Studies
0007-0122 Brighton Head and Freak Magazine
0007-0130 Brighton Historical Society. Newsletter *changed to* Brighton Newsletter.
0007-0149 Brighton Park Life
0007-0157 Brightonian
0007-0173 Brio
0007-0181 Bristol Building and Design Centre. Newsletter *changed to* Bristol Newsletter.
0007-019X Bristol Medico-Chirurgical Journal†
0007-0203 Britannia†
0007-0211 Brith *changed to* Covenant Voice.
0007-022X British Agents Review *changed to* British Commercial Agents Review.
0007-0238 British Amateur Journalist
0007-0262 British Antarctic Survey. Bulletin†
0007-0270 British Archaeological Abstracts *see* 0964-7104
0007-0289 British Archer
0007-0297 British Astronomical Association. Journal
0007-0300 British Baker
0007-0319 British Bandsman
0007-0327 British Bee Journal
0007-0335 British Birds
0007-0343 British Book News
0007-0351 British Boot and Shoe Institution. Journal *see* 0263-1008
0007-036X British Bulletin of Publications on Latin America, the West Indies, Portugal and Spain *see* 0268-2400
0007-0408 British Chamber of Commerce in Brazil. Information Circular *changed to* British Chamber of Commerce in Brazil. News & Views.
0007-0416 British Chamber of Commerce of Turkey. Trade Journal
0007-0432 British Chemist†
0007-0440 British Chess Magazine
0007-0459 British Citizen†
0007-0467 British Clothing Manufacturer†
0007-0475 B C U R A Monthly Bulletin†
0007-0483 British Columbia Catholic
0007-0513 British Columbia Government News *see* 1180-0429
0007-0521 British Columbia Hospital News *changed to* B C H A News.
0007-053X British Columbia Library Quarterly†
0007-0548 British Columbia Lumberman†
0007-0556 British Columbia Medical Journal
0007-0572 British Columbia Orchardist
0007-0580 British Columbia School Trustee†
0007-0599 British Corrosion Journal
0007-0602 British Deaf News
0007-0610 British Dental Journal
0007-0629 British Dental Surgery Assistant
0007-0637 British Education Index
0007-0653 British Endodontic Society Journal *see* 0143-2885
0007-0661 British Engineer†
0007-067X La Brita Esperantisto
0007-0688 British Farmer and Stockbreeder†
0007-0696 British Federation of Master Printers. Members Circular *see* 0307-7195
0007-070X British Food Journal
0007-0718 British Foundryman *see* 0953-6035

0007-0726 British Friesian Journal *see* 0954-6219
0007-0750 British Grassland Society. Journal *see* 0142-5242
0007-0769 British Heart Journal
0007-0777 British Homing World
0007-0785 British Homoeopathic Journal
0007-0807 B H R A Journal *changed to* Voice of the British Hospitality Association.
0007-0815 British Humanities Index
0007-0823 British Industry and Engineering
0007-0831 British Ink Maker *changed to* Ink & Print International.
0007-084X British Interplanetary Society Journal
0007-0858 British Italian Trade Review
0007-0866 British Jeweller *changed to* British Jeweller & Watch Buyer.
0007-0874 British Journal for the History of Science
0007-0882 British Journal for the Philosophy of Science
0007-0904 British Journal of Aesthetics
0007-0912 British Journal of Anaesthesia
0007-0920 British Journal of Cancer
0007-0939 British Journal of Chiropody†
0007-0947 British Journal of Clinical Practice
0007-0955 British Journal of Criminology
0007-0963 British Journal of Dermatology
0007-0971 British Journal of Diseases of the Chest *see* 0954-6111
0007-098X British Journal of Disorders of Communication *see* 0963-7273
0007-1005 British Journal of Educational Studies
0007-1013 British Journal of Educational Technology
0007-1021 British Journal of Experimental Pathology *see* 0959-9673
0007-1048 British Journal of Haematology
0007-1056 British Journal of Herpetology *see* 0268-0130
0007-1064 British Journal of Hospital Medicine
0007-1072 British Journal of Industrial Medicine
0007-1080 British Journal of Industrial Relations
0007-1099 British Journal of Marketing *see* 0309-0566
0007-1102 British Journal of Mathematical and Statistical Psychology
0007-1110 British Journal of Medical Education *see* 0308-0110
0007-1129 British Journal of Medical Psychology
0007-1137 British Journal of Non-Destructive Testing
0007-1145 British Journal of Nutrition
0007-1161 British Journal of Ophthalmology
0007-117X British Journal of Oral Surgery *see* 0266-4356
0007-1188 British Journal of Pharmacology
0007-1196 British Journal of Photography
0007-120X British Journal of Physical Education *see* 0954-6693
0007-1218 British Journal of Physiological Optics *see* 0275-5408
0007-1226 British Journal of Plastic Surgery
0007-1234 British Journal of Political Science
0007-1242 British Journal of Preventive and Social Medicine *see* 0141-7681
0007-1250 British Journal of Psychiatry
0007-1269 British Journal of Psychology
0007-1285 British Journal of Radiology
0007-1293 British Journal of Social and Clinical Psychology *see* 0144-6665
0007-1293 British Journal of Social and Clinical Psychology *see* 0144-6657
0007-1307 British Journal of Social Psychiatry†
0007-1315 British Journal of Sociology
0007-1323 British Journal of Surgery
0007-1331 British Journal of Urology
0007-134X British Journal of Venereal Diseases *changed to* Genitourinary Medicine: The Journal of Sexual Health, STDs and HIV.
0007-1358 British Kinematography, Sound and Television *see* 0950-2114
0007-1366 British Lawn Tennis *changed to* Tennis.
0007-1374 British Legion Journal *see* 0308-4949
0007-1390 British Master Patternmaker *changed to* British Pattern & Mould Maker.
0007-1404 British Medical Abstracts†
0007-1412 British Medical Book List *see* 0140-2722
0007-1420 British Medical Bulletin
0007-1439 British Medical Index *see* 0140-2722
0007-1447 British Medical Journal
0007-1455 British Medical Register of Holiday Accommodation†
0007-1463 British Mouthpiece
0007-1471 British Museum (Natural History) Bulletin. Geology
0007-148X British Museum (Natural History) Bulletin. Mineralogy *see* 0007-1471
0007-1498 British Museum (Natural History) Bulletin. Zoology
0007-151X British Museum Quarterly†
0007-1528 British Mycological Society. Bulletin *see* 0269-915X
0007-1536 British Mycological Society. Transactions *see* 0953-7562
0007-1544 British National Bibliography
0007-1552 British National Film Catalogue
0007-1587 British Nuclear Energy Society. Journal *see* 0140-4067
0007-1595 British Ornithologists' Club. Bulletin
0007-1617 British Phycological Journal
0007-1625 British Plastics *see* 0306-3534
0007-1633 British Polio Fellowship. Bulletin
0007-1641 British Polymer Journal *see* 0959-8103
0007-165X British-Portuguese Chamber of Commerce. Monthly Bulletin *changed to* Camara de Comercio Luso-Britanica. Bi-monthly Magazine.
0007-1668 British Poultry Science
0007-1676 British Practice in International Law†
0007-1684 British Printer
0007-1692 British Psychological Society. Bulletin *see* 0952-8229
0007-1706 British Racehorse *see* 0260-7468
0007-1714 British Railways Board. Monthly Review of Technical Literature†
0007-1722 British Record†
0007-1749 N L L Announcement Bulletin *see* 0959-4922
0007-1757 British Road Federation. Bulletin†
0007-1765 British Ship Research Association. Journal *see* 0268-9650
0007-1773 British Society for Phenomenology. Journal
0007-1781 British Society of Commerce. Review *changed to* Business Administration.
0007-179X British Society of Dowsers. Journal
0007-1803 British-Soviet Friendship
0007-1811 British Stationer *changed to* C T N.
0007-1846 British Studies Monitor†
0007-1854 British Sugar Beet Review
0007-1862 British Tax Guide
0007-1870 British Tax Review
0007-1889 British Technology Index *see* 0260-6593
0007-1897 British Toys *changed to* British Toys & Hobbies Briefing.
0007-1900 British Travel News†
0007-1927 British Vegetarian *changed to* Vegetarian Living.
0007-1935 British Veterinary Journal
0007-196X Brittonia
0007-1986 Public Health†
0007-1994 Broadcast Engineering
0007-1994 Broadcast Engineering Spec Book *changed to* Broadcast Engineering Equipment Reference Manual.
0007-2001 Broadcast Journal†
0007-201X Broadcasters Bulletin
0007-2028 Broadcasting (Washington)
0007-2036 Broadsheet
0007-2044 Broadsheet
0007-2052 China Policy Study Group. Broadsheet†
0007-2109 Broadside and the Free Press†
0007-2133 Broadway†
0007-215X Brodogradnja
0007-2168 Broed *changed to* Broed.
0007-2184 Bromeliad Society Bulletin *see* 0090-8738
0007-2192 Bromides in Agriculture
0007-2214 Bront
0007-2222 Bronches *changed to* Bronches-Broncho-Pneumologie.
0007-2230 Bronchi *changed to* Bronco-Pneumologia.
0007-2249 Bronx County Historical Society. Journal
0007-2257 Bronx County Medical Society. Bulletin *changed to* Bronx Medicine.
0007-2265 Bronx Real Estate and Building News *changed to* Bronx Realtor News.
0007-2273 Bronxboro†
0007-2281 Bronze
0007-229X Brookings Bulletin *see* 0745-1253
0007-2303 Brookings Papers on Economic Activity
0007-232X Brooklyn Barrister
0007-2346 Brooklyn Heights Press
0007-2354 Brooklyn Insurance Brokers Association. Bulletin *changed to* Messenger Reporter.
0007-2362 Brooklyn Law Review
0007-2370 Brooklyn Longshoreman *changed to* 1814 Union News.
0007-2397 Brooklyn Public Library Bulletin
0007-2400 Broom and Broom Corn News *changed to* Broom, Brush & Mop.
0007-2419 Brot und Gebaeck *see* 0367-4177
0007-2427 Broteria: Ciencias Naturais *see* 0870-7235
0007-2435 Brotherhood
0007-2443 Brotherhood of Maintenance of Way Employes. Journal *see* 1049-3921
0007-2451 Brothers Newsletter†
0007-2478 Brown Alumni Monthly
0007-2494 Brown Gold
0007-2516 Brown Swiss Bulletin
0007-2524 Brownie
0007-2532 Browning Newsletter *see* 0095-4489
0007-2559 Browser†
0007-2567 Brud ar Yez hag ar Vro *see* 0399-7014
0007-2583 Bruecke
0007-2605 Bruecke (Neustadt)†
0007-2648 Brug
0007-2656 Brug†
0007-2664 Bruehl
0007-2672 Brulot
0007-2680 Bruns' Beitraege fuer Klinische Chirurgie *see* 0023-8236
0007-2699 Brunswickan
0007-2702 Brushes *changed to* Brushes International.
0007-2710 Brushware
0007-2729 B. B. B. Agenda†
0007-2745 Bryologist
0007-2753 B't
0007-2761 Buch der Zeit
0007-277X Buch und Bildung
0007-2788 Druck und Verarbeitung†
0007-2796 Buchhaendler Heute
0007-280X Landesmuseum fuer Kaernten. Buchreihe.
0007-2818 Buck Investment Letter†
0007-2826 Buckeye Beverage Journal *changed to* Ohio Beverage Journal.
0007-2834 Buckeye Farm News
0007-2842 A D A C Motorwelt
0007-2869 Bucknell Review
0007-2885 Budapest
0007-2893 Budapester Rundschau
0007-2907 Budavox Telecommunication Review†
0007-294X Budget
0007-2958 Budget Decorating *see* 0360-4993
0007-2974 Budivel'ni Materialy i Konstruktsii *changed to* Stroitel'nye Materialy i Konstruktsii.
0007-2982 Budo-Sport
0007-2990 Budownictwo Okretowe
0007-3016 Buecherkommentare *changed to* Lektuere.
0007-3032 Buechergilde
0007-3040 Buecherschau
0007-3059 Buecherschiff
0007-3067 Der Buechsenmacher
0007-3075 Buehne
0007-3083 Die Buehnengenossenschaft
0007-3091 Buehnentechnische Rundschau
0007-3113 Buenos Aires Musical
0007-3121 Der Buerger im Staat
0007-313X Buero Modern *changed to* Carriere.
0007-3148 Bueromarkt
0007-3156 Bueromaschinen-Mechaniker *see* 0340-2185
0007-3164 Buerotechnische Praxis†
0007-3172 Buerotechnische Sammlung *see* 0935-0276
0007-3199 Buffalo Magazine *see* 0149-5070
0007-3210 Bugantics
0007-3245 Builder†
0007-3261 Builder (Columbus)
0007-327X Builder-Architect *changed to* Builder Architect.
0007-3296 Builders Report Pacific *see* 0194-6587
0007-330X Builders' Weekly Guide†
0007-3318 Building
0007-3326 Building Abstracts Service C I B†
0007-3334 Building Alaska†
0007-3342 Building & Construction
0007-3350 Building & Contract Journal
0007-3369 S.A. Building Products News *changed to* Building Products News.
0007-3377 Building & Heating Product Guide
0007-3385 Building and Management *changed to* Building Operating Manager.
0007-3393 Building & Realty Record†
0007-3407 Building Design & Construction
0007-3415 Building Construction in Texas†
0007-3423 Building Design
0007-3431 Building Economist
0007-344X Building Equipment and Materials for South Africa *changed to* Building Equipment & Materials.
0007-3458 Building Equipment News *changed to* Building Equipment and Materials.
0007-3466 Building Forum
0007-3490 Building Operating Management
0007-3504 Building Materials†
0007-3512 Building Materials and Equipment *see* 1031-3745
0007-3520 Building Materials Merchandiser *see* 1045-9367
0007-3539 Building Materials News
0007-3547 Building Official and Code Administrator
0007-3555 Building Permit Activity in Florida
0007-3563 Building Permit Values
0007-3571 Building Practice†
0007-358X Building Products News (Chippendale)
0007-3598 Building Progress†
0007-3601 Building Research†
0007-361X Building Research News†
0007-3628 Building Science *see* 0360-1323
0007-3636 Building Science Abstracts†
0007-3644 Building Services Contractor
0007-3652 Building Societies' Gazette *changed to* Mortgage Finance Gazette.
0007-3679 Building Stone News *changed to* Building Stone Magazine.
0007-3687 Building Supply Dealer *changed to* Hardware Merchandising's Canadian Hardware Handbook.
0007-3695 Building Supply News *changed to* Building Supply Home Centers.
0007-3709 Building Technology and Management *changed to* Chartered Builder.
0007-3717 Building Tradesman
0007-3725 Buildings
0007-375X Nieuwsbrief†
0007-3768 Buitenspoor
0007-3776 Bukhgalterskii Uchet
0007-3784 Buletin de Informare in Bibliologie *see* 1220-3092
0007-3792 Buletin de Informare Pedagogica *changed to* Probleme de Pedagogie Contemporana.
0007-3806 Buletin de Informare Stiintifica Biologie†

ISSN

ISSN INDEX 5353

0007-3822 Buletin de Informare Stiintifica. Fizica†
0007-3830 Istorie-Arheologie†
0007-3849 Buletin de Informare Stiintifica. Matematica, Mecanica, Astronomie†
0007-3857 Psihologie; Buletin de Informare Stiintifica†
0007-3865 Sociologie; Buletin de Informare Stiintifica†
0007-3873 Stiinte Economice; Buletin de Informare Stiintifica†
0007-3881 Stiinte Juridice; Buletin de Informare Stiintifica†
0007-389X Vyzkumny Ustav Rybarsky a Hydrobiologicky. Bulletin
0007-3903 Bulgaria Today
0007-3911 Bulgarian Films
0007-3938 Bulgarsko Geologichesko Druzhestvo. Spisanie
0007-3946 Bulgarian Review
0007-3954 Bulgarian Trade Unions
0007-3970 Bulgarska Akademiia na Naukite. Institut po Fiziologiia na Rasteniiata "Metodii Popov." Izvestiia *see* 0324-0290
0007-3989 Bulgarska Akademiia na Naukite. Spisanie
0007-3997 Bulgarski Knigopis *changed to* Bulgarski Knigopis. Seriia 1: Knigi, Notni, Graficheski i Kartografski.
0007-4004 Bulgarski Voin *see* 0861-7333
0007-4012 Bulgarsko Foto
0007-4020 Otkrytiya, Izobreteniya, Promyshlennye Obraztsy, Tovarnye Znaki *see* 0208-287X
0007-4020 Otkrytiya, Izobreteniya, Promyshlennye Obraztsy, Tovarnye Znaki *see* 0208-2888
0007-4039 Bulletin *changed to* Bulletin with Newsweek.
0007-4047 The Bulletin; the Newsweekly of the Capital of Europe
0007-4063 Centre de Documentation Siderurgique. Bulletin Analytique
0007-4071 Bulletin Analytique de Documentation Politique, Economique et Sociale Contemporaine
0007-408X Bulletin Analytique de Linguistique Francaise
0007-4098 Bulletin Analytique d'Entomologie Medicale et Veterinaire†
0007-4101 Bulletin Analytique Petrolier
0007-411X Bulletin Annote des Lois et Decrets
0007-4128 Bulletin Baudelairien
0007-4136 Bulletin Belge de Metrologie†
0007-4144 Bulletin Bi-Mensuel des Tirages†
0007-4152 Bulletin Bibliographique de Documentation Technique des Charbonnages de France *changed to* Bulletin Bibliographique de Documentation Technique du Groupement des Industries Extractives.
0007-4160 Bulletin Bibliographique International du Machinisme Agricole†
0007-4187 Bulletin Biologique de la France et de la Belgique†
0007-4209 Bulletin Critique du Livre Francais
0007-4217 Bulletin de Correspondance Hellenique
0007-4225 Belgium. Ministere des Communications. Bulletin de Documentation†
0007-4233 Laboratoire de Recherches et de Controle du Caoutchouc. Bulletin de Documentation Bibliographique *changed to* L R C C Bulletin Bibliographique.
0007-4241 Bulletin de Documentation Ceramique *changed to* CERINDEX: Bulletin de Documentation Ceramique.
0007-4268 Bulletin de Documentation Pratiques des Impots Directs et des Taxes sur le Chiffre d'Affaires *see* 0242-5912
0007-4276 Bulletin de Documentation Pratique des Taxes sur le Chiffre d'Affaires *see* 0242-5912
0007-4284 Bulletin de Geophysique†
0007-4292 Bulletin de la Librairie Ancienne et Moderne†
0007-4306 Belgium. Administration Penitentiaire. Bulletin
0007-4314 A I M Bulletin *see* 0758-8240
0007-4322 Bulletin de Litterature Ecclesiastique
0007-4330 Bulletin de l'Oeuvre Apostolique
0007-4349 Bulletin de l'Oeuvre d'Orient
0007-4357 Bulletin de Madagascar†
0007-4365 Bulletin de Medecine Legale et de Toxicologie Medicale *see* 0249-6208
0007-4373 A U P E L F Bulletin de Nouvelles Breves *see* 0226-7454
0007-4411 Bulletin de Psychologie Scolaire et d'Orientation
0007-442X Bulletin de Theologie Ancienne et Medievale
0007-4438 Institut de Science Financiere et d'Assurances. Bulletin des Actuaires Diplomes
0007-4446 Bulletin des Agriculteurs
0007-4462 Data from the Greek Economic Life *see* 0041-0543
0007-4489 Bulletin des Lettres†
0007-4497 Bulletin des Sciences Mathematiques
0007-4500 Bulletin des Soies et Soieries *changed to* Textilyon: Bulletin des Soies et Soieries.
0007-4519 Bulletin des Transports
0007-4535 Bulletin d'Information des Centrales Electriques†
0007-4543 France. Commissariat a l'Energie Atomique. Bulletin d'Informations Scientifiques et Techniques.†
0007-4551 Bulletin du Cancer
0007-456X Bibliographie de la France. Livres *changed to* Livres de France.
0007-4578 Bulletin Economique du Cambresis *changed to* Atout Cambresis.
0007-4586 Bulletin Economique et Social du Maroc *changed to* Signes du Present.
0007-4594 E G U Bulletin†
0007-4616 Bulletin Folklorique de l'Ile de France *changed to* Traditions de l'Ile de France.
0007-4624 Bulletin for International Fiscal Documentation
0007-4632 Bulletin Geodesique
0007-4640 Bulletin Hispanique
0007-4659 Bulletin Historique et Scientifique de l'Auvergne
0007-4667 Bulletin Hygiene du Travail†
0007-4675 Bulletin Immobilier
0007-4683 Japanese Communist Party. Central Committee. Bulletin: Information for Abroad
0007-4691 Bulletin Mathematique
0007-4705 Bulletin Medical Franco-Japonais
0007-4713 France. Institut National de la Statistique et des Etudes Economiques. Bulletin Mensuel de Statistique
0007-473X Bulletin Monumental
0007-4748 Service Central d'Organisation et Methodes. O et M Bulletin *changed to* Service Central d'Organisation et Methodes. Revue.
0007-4756 Bulletin of Applied Linguistics†
0007-4764 American Journal of Art Therapy
0007-4780 Bulletin of Bibliography and Magazine Notes *see* 0190-745X
0007-4799 Bulletin of Business Research†
0007-4802 Bulletin of Canadian Petroleum Geology
0007-4810 Bulletin of Concerned Asian Scholars
0007-4837 Bulletin of Dental Education
0007-4845 Bulletin of Endemic Diseases
0007-4853 Bulletin of Entomological Research
0007-4861 Bulletin of Environmental Contamination and Toxicology
0007-4888 Bulletin of Experimental Biology and Medicine
0007-4896 Bulletin of Grain Technology
0007-490X Bulletin of Hispanic Studies
0007-4918 Bulletin of Indonesian Economic Studies
0007-4926 Bulletin of Information on Current Research on Human Sciences Concerning Africa
0007-4942 Volunteer Service Bulletin *changed to* News from C C I V S.
0007-4950 Bulletin of Labour Statistics
0007-4969 Bulletin of Legal Developments
0007-4977 Bulletin of Marine Science
0007-4985 Bulletin of Mathematical Biophysics *see* 0092-8240
0007-4993 Bulletin of Mathematical Statistics *see* 0286-522X
0007-5000 Bulletin of Mechanical Engineering Education†
0007-5027 Laboratory Medicine
0007-5035 Bulletin of Peace Proposals
0007-5043 Bulletin of Physical Education
0007-5051 Bulletin of Polish Medical Science and History†
0007-506X Bulletin of Prosthetics Research *see* 0748-7711
0007-5078 Bulletin of Rural Economics and Sociology *changed to* Journal of Rural Economics & Development.
0007-5094 Science and Public Affairs Bulletin of the Atomic Scientists *see* 0096-3402
0007-5108 Bulletin of the Comediantes
0007-5116 Bulletin of the European Communities
0007-5124 Experimental Animals
0007-5132 Bulletin of the History of Dentistry
0007-5140 Bulletin of the History of Medicine
0007-5159 Bulletin of Tibetology
0007-5167 Bulletin of Zoological Nomenclature†
0007-5183 Bulletin Officiel de la Propriete Industrielle *see* 0223-4092
0007-5191 Sport en Roumanie†
0007-523X Bulletin on Narcotics
0007-5248 Bulletin on the Rheumatic Diseases
0007-5256 Bulletin Ornithologique
0007-5264 Bulletin Quotidien d'Afrique
0007-5272 Bulletin Quotidien d'Informations Textiles†
0007-5280 Belgium. Institut Royal Meteorologique. Bulletin Quotidien du Temps
0007-5302 Bulletin Signaletique des Telecommunications
0007-5329 Mathematiques Appliques-Informatique-Automatique *see* 0761-2060
0007-5345 Bulletin Signaletique. Part 130: Physique *changed to* P A S C A L Folio. F 10: Mecanique et Acoustique et Transfert de Chaleur.
0007-5353 Bulletin Signaletique. Part 140: Electricite-Electronique *see* 0246-1161
0007-537X Bulletin Signaletique. Part 160: Structure de la Matiere I *see* 0761-196X
0007-537X Bulletin Signaletique. Part 160: Structure de la Matiere I *see* 0761-1951
0007-5388 Bulletin Signaletique. Part 161. Structure de la Matiere II *see* 0761-1978
0007-5442 Bulletin Signaletique. Part 330: Sciences Pharmacologiques - Toxicologie *see* 0761-215X
0007-5442 Bulletin Signaletique. Part 330: Sciences Pharmacologiques - Toxicologie *see* 0761-1943
0007-5450 Bulletin Signaletique. Part 340: Microbiologie-Virologie-Immunologie *see* 0761-2133
0007-5450 Bulletin Signaletique. Part 340: Microbiologie-Virologie-Immunologie *see* 0761-2141
0007-5469 Bulletin Signaletique. Part 350. Pathologie Generale et Experimentale *see* 0761-2303
0007-5477 Bulletin Signaletique. Part 351: Revue Bibliographique Cancer *changed to* P A S C A L Thema. Part 251: Cancerologie (Cancernet).
0007-5493 Bulletin Signaletique. Part 361. Endocrinologie et Reproduction *see* 0761-1919
0007-5507 Bulletin Signaletique. 362: Diabete. Obesite. Maladies. *see* 0761-2281
0007-5515 Bulletin Signaletique. Part 370. Biologie et Physiologie Vegetales *see* 0761-1927
0007-5523 Bulletin Signaletique. Part 380: Agronomie-Zootechnie-Phytopathologie-Industries Alimentaires *see* 0181-0030
0007-5531 Bulletin Signaletique. Part 390: Psychologie. Psychopathologie. Psychiatrie *see* 0761-2176
0007-554X Bulletin Signaletique. Part 519: Philosophie
0007-5566 Bulletin Signaletique. Part 529: Sociologie - Ethnologie *changed to* Bulletin Signaletique. Part 529: Sociologie.
0007-5574 Bulletin Signaletique. Part 522: Histoire des Sciences et des Techniques
0007-5582 Bulletin Signaletique. Part 523: Histoire et Sciences de la Litterature
0007-5590 Bulletin Signaletique. Part 524: Sciences du Langage
0007-5612 Bulletin Signaletique. Part 526: Art et Archeologie
0007-5620 Bulletin Signaletique. Part 527: Sciences Religieuse *see* 0180-9296
0007-5639 Bulletin Signaletique. Part 528: Science Administrative *see* 0150-8695
0007-5647 Bulletin Signaletique. Part 730: Combustibles. Energie *see* 0761-1668
0007-5655 Bulletin Signaletique. Part 740: Metaux. Metallurgie *see* 0761-1684
0007-5663 Bulletin Signaletique. Part 761: Microscopie Electronique. Diffraction Electronique *see* 0761-2028
0007-5671 Polymeres *see* 0761-179X
0007-568X Bulletin Signaletique. Part 880: Genie Chimique. Industries Chimique et Parachimique *see* 0761-1781
0007-5698 Eau et Assainissement. Pollution Atmospherique *see* 0246-117X
0007-571X Bulletin Signaletique. Part 900. Bulletin des Traductions *see* 0259-8264
0007-5728 Bulletin Synoptique de Documentation Thermique *see* 0337-4092
0007-5736 Bulletin Technique
0007-5744 Bulletin Technique de la Suisse Romande *see* 0251-0979
0007-5752 Bureau Veritas. Bulletin Technique
0007-5779 Bulletins of American Paleontology
0007-5787 Bollettino delle Scienze Mediche
0007-5795 Bullettino Storico Empolese
0007-5809 Bullettino Storico Pistoiese
0007-5817 Bumazhnaya Promyshlennost'
0007-5833 Bund der Deutschen Katholischen Jugend. Informationsdienst
0007-5841 Bund der Oeffentlich Bestellten Vermessungsingenieure. Mitteilungsblatt *changed to* B D V I-Forum.
0007-585X Germany (Federal Republic, 1949-) Bundesanstalt fuer Arbeit. Amtliche Nachrichten
0007-5868 Bundesversorgungsblatt *changed to* Bundesarbeitsblatt.
0007-5876 Die Bundesbahn
0007-5884 Bundesbaublatt
0007-5892 Bundesforschungsanstalt fuer Forst- und Holzwirtschaft, Hamburg. Mitteilungen
0007-5914 Bundesgesundheitsblatt
0007-5922 Austria. Hoehere Bundeslehr- und Versuchsanstalt fuer Wein- und Obstbau. Mitteilungen Klosterneuburg
0007-5930 Die Bundesverwaltung
0007-5949 Die Bundeswehr
0007-5965 Das Bunte Blatt†
0007-5973 Bunte Blumenwelt
0007-5981 Bunte Oesterreich *changed to* Bunte.
0007-6007 Bur
0007-6015 Burbujas

ISSN

0007-6023 Burda Bunte Bild Rezepte†
0007-6031 Burda Moden
0007-604X Le Bureau†
0007-6066 Bureau Briefs†
0007-6074 Bureaux de France *see* 1148-5566
0007-6090 France. Bureau de Recherches Geologiques et Minieres. Bulletin. Section 2. Geologie Appliquee *see* 0755-6365
0007-6104 France. Bureau de Recherches Geologiques et Minieres. Bulletin. Section 1: Geologie de la France *changed to* France. Bureau de Recherches Geologiques et Minieres. Geologie de la France.
0007-6112 France. Bureau de Recherches Geologiques et Minieres. Bulletin Section 4: Geologie Generale *see* 0153-8446
0007-6120 Hydrogeologie *see* 0246-1641
0007-6155 Philippines. Bureau of Agricultural Economics. Bureau of Agricultural Economics Reporter†
0007-6163 Bureau of Government Research Bulletin†
0007-6171 University of Rhode Island. Bureau of Government Research. Newsletter *see* 0273-7884
0007-618X U.S. Bureau of the Census. Bureau of the Census Catalog *changed to* U.S. Bureau of the Census. Census Catalog and Guide.
0007-6201 Burgen und Schloesser†
0007-621X Burgenlaendische Forschungen
0007-6228 Burgenlaendische Gemeinschaft
0007-6236 Burgenlaendische Heimatblaetter
0007-6244 Burgenlaendische Landwirtschaftskammer. Mitteilungsblatt
0007-6252 Burgenlaendisches Leben
0007-6260 Buried History
0007-6279 Burlington County Times Advertiser†
0007-6287 Burlington Magazine
0007-6295 Burma Medical Journal
0007-6309 Burning Bush
0007-6325 B T O - Buerotechnik und Organisation *see* 0343-2319
0007-6333 Burroughs Bulletin
0007-6341 Burroughs Clearing House†
0007-635X Bus and Truck Transport *changed to* Truck Fleet.
0007-6376 Busara†
0007-6392 Buses
0007-6406 Business Abroad†
0007-6414 Business Administration *see* 0140-8453
0007-6422 Business Advertising†
0007-6430 Business Analyst
0007-6449 Business and Administration *changed to* Institute of Administration and Commerce of South Africa. Journal.
0007-6457 Business and Economic Dimensions†
0007-6465 Business & Economic Review
0007-6473 Business and Finance
0007-6481 Business and Financial Indicators†
0007-6503 Business and Society
0007-6511 Business and Society†
0007-652X Business and Technology Sources†
0007-6538 Business Archives
0007-6562 Business Comments†
0007-6570 Business and Commercial Aviation
0007-6589 Business Conditions *see* 0164-0682
0007-6597 Business Cycle Digist *see* 0146-7735
0007-6600 Business Conditions in Argentina†
0007-6627 Business Credit and Hire Purchase Journal
0007-6643 Zrak'or
0007-666X Business Economics
0007-6678 Business Education Forum
0007-6686 Business Education Journal†
0007-6694 Business Education World
0007-6708 Business Equipment Digest
0007-6716 Business Equipment Guide†
0007-6732 Business Systems & Equipment†
0007-6740 U B S Business Facts and Figures†
0007-6767 Business Forms Reporter *changed to* Business Forms, Labels and Systems.
0007-6775 Business Graphics†
0007-6783 Business Herald
0007-6791 Business History
0007-6805 Business History Review
0007-6813 Business Horizons
0007-6821 Business in Brief†
0007-683X Business in Nebraska
0007-6856 Business Inquiry†
0007-6864 Business Insurance
0007-6872 Business International
0007-6880 Business Latin America
0007-6899 Business Lawyer
0007-6902 Business Literature *changed to* Business Information.
0007-6929 Industrial Management & Data Systems
0007-6937 Business Management†
0007-6945 Business Memo from Belgium
0007-6953 Business Opportunities Digest
0007-6961 Business Periodicals Index
0007-6988 Business Products *changed to* N O P A Office Market Update.
0007-6996 Business Quarterly
0007-7011 Federal Reserve Bank of Philadelphia. Business Review
0007-702X Federal Reserve Bank of Dallas. Business Review *see* 0149-5364
0007-7038 Business Review and Economic News from Israel†
0007-7046 Business Screen *changed to* Backstage.
0007-7062 Business Service Checklist†
0007-7070 Business South Africa *changed to* Business S A.
0007-7097 Business Systems & Equipment
0007-7100 Business Today (Princeton)
0007-7119 Business Travel *changed to* Business Travel World.
0007-7127 Business Trends in New York State
0007-7135 Business Week
0007-7151 Businessman
0007-7178 Business Expectations *changed to* U S Survey of Business Expectations.
0007-7194 Buskap og Avdraatt
0007-7208 Bussi-Baer
0007-7216 Bustan†
0007-7224 Bustleton-Somerton News Gleaner *changed to* NewsGleaner - Bustleton - Somerton Edition.
0007-7232 Busy Bees' News†
0007-7240 Butane Propane
0007-7259 Butane - Propane News
0007-7267 Butcher Workman†
0007-7275 Butter-Fat
0007-7291 Butterfly
0007-7305 Butterick Home Catalog
0007-7313 Butterley Foundry News†
0007-7321 Butterworths Consolidated Legislation Service of South Africa. Monthly Bulletin *changed to* Butterworths Legislation Service. Monthly Bulletin.
0007-733X Buttons†
0007-7356 Buvar
0007-7364 Buxom Belle Courier
0007-7372 Buyer
0007-7380 Buyers' Guide
0007-7402 Buyers Purchasing Digest
0007-7429 Byarozka
0007-7437 Byelorussian-American Union. Bulletin†
0007-7445 Bygd
0007-7453 Bokvaennen *see* 0345-7982
0007-7461 Bygg *changed to* Byggaktuelt.
0007-7488 Bygge Nytt
0007-7488 Bygge Nyts Leverandoerregister†
0007-7496 Byggehaandvaerket
0007-750X Byggeindustrien
0007-7518 Byggekunst
0007-7542 Bygglitteratur†
0007-7550 Byggmaestaren†
0007-7569 Byggnadsarbetaren
0007-7577 Byggnadsindustrin *see* 0349-3733
0007-7585 Byggnadsingenjoren- Team
0007-7593 Byggnadskonst *see* 0281-658X
0007-7607 Byggnadstidningen
0007-7623 Bygmesteren
0007-7631 Byminner
0007-764X Hospital Equipment *changed to* Hospital Engineering Association of Japan. Journal.
0007-7658 Byplan
0007-7666 Gosudarstvennyi Komitet Soveta Ministrov S.S.S.R. po Voprosam Truda i Zarabotnoi Platy. Byulleten'
0007-7674 Byulleten' Inostrannoi Kommercheskoi Informatsii
0007-7682 Moskovskii Universitet. Moskovskoe Obshchestvo Ispytatelei Prirody. Geologicheskii Otdel. Byulleten *see* 0366-1318
0007-7690 Byulleten' Stroitel'noi Tekhniki
0007-7704 Byzantinische Zeitschrift
0007-7712 Byzantinoslavica
0007-7720 Canadian Review of American Studies
0007-7739 C A E News
0007-7763 C A H P E R Journal *see* 0273-6896
0007-7771 C A H S Journal
0007-778X Cal†
0007-7798 C A L F News *changed to* C A L F News Cattle Feeder.
0007-7801 C A M†
0007-7836 C A R D A N. Fiches Analytiques†
0007-7844 Council for the Advancement of Small Colleges. Newsletter†
0007-7852 C. A. S. I. Transactions†
0007-7860 C A T C A Journal†
0007-7879 C A T V Magazine *changed to* V U E Magazine.
0007-7887 C A U T Bulletin
0007-7925 Select†
0007-7933 C B E Bulletin *see* 0196-4984
0007-7941 C B M News
0007-795X C B Magazine†
0007-7968 C.B.R.I. Abstracts†
0007-7976 C C A R Journal *changed to* C C A R Journal.
0007-7984 C C B Outlook (Large Print Edition)†
0007-7992 Accounting Articles
0007-800X C C I T U Labour Bulletin†
0007-8018 C D A Newsletter *see* 0703-5764
0007-8034 C E A Forum
0007-8050 C E A Advisor
0007-8069 C E A Critic
0007-8077 O E C D. Isotope Generator Information Centre *changed to* O E C D. Newsletter on Isotopic Generators and Batteries.
0007-8093 C E A P Bulletin†
0007-8107 C E A Spotlight *see* 0882-5017
0007-8123 C E C Newsletter *changed to* Last Word.
0007-8131 C E C Update†
0007-814X C E D A G Informativo†
0007-8158 C E D A M Notiziario Bibliografico
0007-8166 C. E. D. Contact†
0007-8174 C. E. D. Dokumentoj†
0007-8204 English Education
0007-8212 C E F News *changed to* C E F Trailblazer.
0007-8220 C E F P Journal *changed to* Educational Facility Planner.
0007-8247 C E N (Construction Equipment News) *changed to* Thomson's Construction Australia.
0007-8255 Church of England Newspaper
0007-8271 C E N S I S Quindicinale di Note e Commenti *changed to* C E N S I S Note e Commenti.
0007-828X C E N T O Newsletter†
0007-8301 C E R I L H Bulletin Analytique
0007-8328 C E R N Reports
0007-8336 C E S I N News
0007-8344 C F Letter *changed to* W W F & C F Letter.
0007-8352 C G D Betriebstraete-Mitteilungen
0007-8360 C G Information *changed to* C G Kurier.
0007-8387 C I A S Centro de Investigacion y Accion *see* 0325-1306
0007-8395 Ciba Journal *changed to* Ciba-Geigy Journal.
0007-8409 Ciba Technical Notes *see* 0142-4904
0007-8417 C I C I A M S News - Nouvelles - Nachrichten
0007-8425 C.I.E. Newsletter
0007-8433 C I L Oval†
0007-8441 C I M M Y T Annual Report on Maize and Wheat Improvement *see* 0304-5439
0007-8441 C I M M Y T Annual Report on Maize and Wheat Improvement *see* 0304-548X
0007-845X C I M Notes *changed to* Cleveland Institute of Music (Newsletter).
0007-8468 C. I. M. Notiziario
0007-8484 C I R F Abstracts *changed to* T & D Abstracts.
0007-8506 C.I.R.P. Annals
0007-8514 C I S Index
0007-8530 C K of A Journal
0007-8549 C L A Journal
0007-8557 C L A Newsletter *see* 1056-1528
0007-8565 Cumann Leabharlannaithe Scoile. C L S Bulletin†
0007-8573 C L U Journal *see* 0742-9517
0007-8581 C. M. A. A. Newsletter†
0007-8603 C M A S Bulletin d'Information
0007-8611 C M B Newsletter
0007-862X C M D†
0007-8638 C M E A News
0007-8646 C.M.J. Quarterly *changed to* Shalom.
0007-8654 C M M
0007-8662 C - M News *changed to* C - M News.
0007-8670 C M R†
0007-8689 C M S News *see* 0311-0737
0007-8697 C M T Health Sciences TV Bulletin *changed to* H E S C A Feedback.
0007-8700 C. N. A. P. T. Bulletin†
0007-8743 C N E E M A Nouvelles *see* 0249-5686
0007-8751 C N E N Notiziario *see* 0393-716X
0007-8808 C O P H Bulletin
0007-8816 C O P N I P List†
0007-8824 C O P P E Boletim Informativo *changed to* C O P P E Noticiario.
0007-8832 C O S M E P Newsletter *changed to* C O S M E P Newsletter.
0007-8859 C O T A L
0007-8867 C P A†
0007-8875 C. P. C. Monthly Report†
0007-8883 C P C U News
0007-8891 C P E C Taxpayers News†
0007-8905 C P H Commentator *see* 0162-7929
0007-8921 C P S Reporter†
0007-893X C Q
0007-8948 C Q Elettronica & Computer
0007-8956 C Q Guide to Current American Government *see* 0196-612X
0007-8964 C Q Ham Radio
0007-8972 Foodservice and Hospitality
0007-8980 C R C Critical Reviews in Analytical Chemistry *see* 1040-8347
0007-8999 C R C Critical Reviews in Environmental Control *see* 1040-838X
0007-9006 C R C Critical Reviews in Food Technology *see* 1040-8398
0007-9014 C R C Critical Reviews in Radiological Sciences and Nuclear Medicine *see* 1040-8371
0007-9030 Illinois Drug Process *see* 0195-2099
0007-9049 C R E Information *see* 1011-9019
0007-9057 C R V Newsletter†
0007-9065 C S A Quarterly Review†
0007-9073 C S C Newsletter
0007-9081 C.S.E.R. Selezione *see* 0391-3457
0007-9103 C S I R O Wildlife Research *see* 1035-3712
0007-9111 C S I R Library Information & Accessions†
0007-912X C S I R O Abstracts *see* 0311-5836

ISSN INDEX 5355

0007-9138 C S I R O Food Preservation Quarterly *see* 0310-9070
0007-9154 C S I R Recorder†
0007-9162 C S I R Research Review *see* 0301-6145
0007-9197 C S U Collegian *changed to* Fort Collins Journal.
0007-9200 C T A Action *see* 0742-2121
0007-9219 C T V D: Cinema - T V - Digest
0007-9227 C W A News
0007-9235 Ca - A Cancer Journal for Clinicians
0007-9243 Ca Va
0007-926X Cabelliant†
0007-9278 Cabinet Maker and Retail Furnisher *changed to* Cabinet Maker.
0007-9286 Cable *changed to* O C International.
0007-9294 Cablecasting-Cable TV Engineering†
0007-9308 Cables and Transmission *see* 0242-1283
0007-9316 Cabore
0007-9332 Cacaos, Cafes, Sucres
0007-9340 Cacau Atualidades†
0007-9359 Cacciatore Siciliano
0007-9367 Cactus and Succulent Journal
0007-9375 Cactus and Succulent Journal of Great Britain *see* 0265-086X
0007-9391 Cad†
0007-9405 Cadenza
0007-9421 Cadernos de Biblioteconomia, Arquivistica e Documentacao
0007-943X Cadernos de Jornalismo e Comunicacao†
0007-9456 Cadet Journal and Gazette
0007-9472 Cadres and Profession *see* 0398-3145
0007-9480 Caducee
0007-9502 Caesaraugusta
0007-9510 Cafe, Cacao, The
0007-9537 Cafe Solo
0007-9545 Cafeteria Motel Bladet *changed to* Cafeteria Bladet.
0007-9553 Caffe†
0007-9561 Cage & Aviary Birds
0007-957X Civilisation Libertaire†
0007-9588 African Administrative Studies
0007-9596 Cahiers Astrologiques
0007-960X Cahiers Bibliques Trimestriels *see* 0222-9714
0007-9618 Cahiers Bourbonnais
0007-9626 Cahiers Bruxellois
0007-9634 Canada Music Book *see* 0700-4745
0007-9650 Cahiers d'Action Litteraire
0007-9669 Cahiers de l'Actualite Religieuse et Sociale *see* 0987-2213
0007-9677 Cahiers d'Agriculture Pratique des Pays Chauds *see* 0395-9481
0007-9685 Cahiers d'Anesthesiologie
0007-9693 Cahiers d'Archeologie et d'Histoire du Berry
0007-9715 Cahiers de Bibliographie Therapeutique Francaise. Edition Medicale†
0007-9723 Cahiers de Biologie Marine
0007-9731 Cahiers de Civilisation Medievale
0007-974X Cahiers de Droit
0007-9758 Cahiers de Droit Europeen
0007-9766 Cahiers de Geographie du Quebec
0007-9774 Cahiers de Josephologie
0007-9782 Cahiers de Kinesitherapie
0007-9790 Cahiers de la Ceramique, du Verre et des Arts du Feu
0007-9804 Association Belge de Documentation. Cahiers de la Documentation
0007-9812 Cahiers de la Methode Naturelle *changed to* Cahiers de la Methode Naturelle en Medecine.
0007-9820 Cahiers de la Puericultrice
0007-9839 Cahiers de la Reconciliation
0007-9847 Cahiers de la Renaissance Vaudoise
0007-9863 Cahiers de l'Enfance Inadaptee†
0007-9871 Cahiers de Lexicologie
0007-9898 Cahiers de l'Iroise
0007-991X Cahiers de l'Oronte
0007-9936 Cahiers de Medecine Interprofessionnelle
0007-9952 France. Institut National de Recherche et de Securite pour la Prevention des Accidents du Travail et des Maladies Professionnelles. Cahiers de Notes Documentaires
0007-9960 Cahiers de Nutrition et de Dietetique
0007-9979 Cahiers de Reeducation & de Readaptation Fonctionnelles†
0007-9987 Cahiers de Sociologie Economique *see* 0761-9871
0007-9995 Cahiers de Sociologie et de Demographie Medicales
0008-0004 Cahiers de Topologie et Geometrie Differentielle†
0008-0012 Cahiers de Tunisie
0008-0020 Cahiers des Ameriques Latines. Serie - Sciences de l'Homme *see* 1141-7161
0008-0039 Cahiers des Naturalistes
0008-0047 Cahiers des Religions Africaines
0008-0055 Cahiers d'Etudes Africaines
0008-0063 Cahiers d'Etudes Cathares
0008-008X Cahiers d'Histoire (Lyon)
0008-0101 Cahiers du Chemin†
0008-011X Cahiers du Cinema
0008-0128 Club de la Grammaire. Cahiers
0008-0136 Cahiers du Communisme
0008-0152 Caravelle
0008-0160 Cahiers du Monde Russe et Sovietique
0008-0179 Cahiers du Nursing *see* 0822-8558
0008-0195 Cahiers Economiques de Bruxelles
0008-0209 Cahiers Economiques et Sociaux
0008-0217 Cahiers Francais
0008-0233 Cahiers Galilee *changed to* Galilee.
0008-0241 Cahiers Geologiques
0008-025X Cahiers Haut-Marnais
0008-0268 Cahiers Integres de Medecine†
0008-0276 Cahiers Internationaux de Sociologie
0008-0284 Cahiers Internationaux de Symbolisme
0008-0292 Cahiers J E B *changed to* J E B.
0008-0292 Cahiers J E B *changed to* J E B Special.
0008-0292 Cahiers J E B *changed to* J E B-Points.
0008-0306 Cahiers Jean Tousseul†
0008-0314 Cahiers Laennec†
0008-0330 Cahiers Lyonnais d'Histoire de la Medecine†
0008-0365 Cahiers Naturalistes
0008-0373 Cahiers Numismatiques
0008-0381 Cahiers O R S T O M Serie Hydrologie *see* 0246-1528
0008-039X Cahiers O.R.S.T.O.M. Serie Oceanographie *see* 0245-9418
0008-0403 Cahiers O R S T O M Serie Sciences Humaines *see* 0768-9829
0008-0411 Cahiers Oceanographiques†
0008-042X Cahiers Pedagogiques
0008-0438 Cahiers Pierre Loti†
0008-0446 Cahiers pour l'Analyse†
0008-0454 Cahiers Raciniens
0008-0462 Cahiers Rationalistes
0008-0497 Cahiers Vilfredo Pareto
0008-0519 Caiet de Documentare Cinematografica
0008-0527 Caiet Pentru Literatura si Istoriografie
0008-0535 Cake and Cockhorse
0008-0543 Cal - Tax News
0008-056X Calabria Nobilissima
0008-0578 Calavo Newsletter *changed to* Calavo Newsletter.
0008-0586 Calcified Tissue Abstracts
0008-0594 Calcified Tissue Research *see* 0171-967X
0008-0616 Calcoin News
0008-0624 Calcolo
0008-0632 Calculi†
0008-0659 Calcutta Mathematical Society. Bulletin
0008-0667 Calcutta Medical Journal
0008-0675 Calcutta Municipal Gazette
0008-0683 Calcutta Statistical Association. Bulletin
0008-0691 University of Calcutta. Department of English. Bulletin *changed to* University of Calcutta. Department of English. Journal.
0008-0705 University of Calcutta. University College of Medicine. Bulletin
0008-0721 Calendar *changed to* C B C Features.
0008-073X Calendar of Coming Meetings of Interest to Historians†
0008-0756 Calendar of Events in the New Pennsylvania *changed to* Pennsylvania Quarterly Calendar of Events.
0008-0764 Calendar of Forthcoming Scientific and Technological Meetings to Be Held in Israel *see* 0333-6131
0008-0772 Calendar of Sports Events†
0008-0802 California A F L - C I O News
0008-0829 California Academy of Sciences. Academy Newsletter
0008-0837 California Agency Bulletin *changed to* California Insurance.
0008-0845 California Agriculture
0008-0853 California Agriculture Department Biennial Report†
0008-0861 California Air Environment†
0008-0896 California Apparel News
0008-090X California - Arizona Cotton
0008-0918 California Bowling News *changed to* Bowling News.
0008-0926 California Business
0008-0934 California C P A Quarterly *see* 0273-835X
0008-0942 California Cattleman
0008-0950 California Courier
0008-0969 California Covenanter *changed to* Pacific Southwest Covenanter.
0008-0977 California Dental Association. Journal
0008-0985 California Dental Association. Newsletter†
0008-1000 California. Division of Mines and Geology. Bulletin
0008-1019 California Elementary Administrator†
0008-1027 California Engineer
0008-1051 California Farmer
0008-106X Western Financial Journal†
0008-1078 California Fish and Game
0008-1094 California Forestry and Forest Products
0008-1108 California Future Farmer†
0008-1116 California Garden
0008-1124 California Grange News
0008-1140 California Highway Patrolman
0008-1167 California Historical Society. Notes *see* 0095-6465
0008-1175 California Historical Society Quarterly *see* 0162-2897
0008-1191 California Industrial Relations Reports
0008-1205 California Journal
0008-1213 California Journal of Educational Research *see* 0196-5042
0008-1221 California Law Review
0008-123X California Librarian†
0008-1248 California Livestock News *changed to* California Sheepman's Quarterly.
0008-1256 California Management Review
0008-1264 California Medicine *see* 0093-0415
0008-1272 California Men's and Women's Stylist *changed to* Men's Apparel News.
0008-1280 California Mental Health Research Digest†
0008-1299 California Mining Journal
0008-1302 California Monthly
0008-1310 California Nurse
0008-1329 Pacific Oil World
0008-1337 California Optometrist Association. Journal *see* 0273-804X
0008-1345 Nord Nytt
0008-1353 California Palace of the Legion of Honor. Bulletin†
0008-1361 California Pelican
0008-1388 California Pharmacy *changed to* California Pharmacist.
0008-140X California Probation, Parole and Correctional Association. Journal *changed to* Crime and Corrections.
0008-1418 California Professor *changed to* C C A Advocate.
0008-1426 California Public Survey†
0008-1434 California Publisher
0008-1442 California Rancher *changed to* California Grower & Rancher.
0008-1450 California Real Estate Magazine
0008-1477 California Safety News†
0008-1485 California Savings and Loan Journal *changed to* California Hotline.
0008-1493 California School Administrator†
0008-1507 California School Boards *changed to* California School Boards Journal.
0008-1515 California School Employee
0008-1523 California School Libraries *see* 0196-3309
0008-1558 California Southern Baptist
0008-1566 California State Employee *changed to* California Pride.
0008-1574 California State Publications
0008-1582 California Tech
0008-1604 California Vector Views†
0008-1612 California Veterinarian
0008-1620 California Water Pollution Control Association. Bulletin
0008-1639 California Western Law Review
0008-1647 Western Tide *changed to* Envoy (San Diego).
0008-1655 California Wineletter
0008-1663 California Woman
0008-1671 California Youth Authority Quarterly†
0008-1728 Call
0008-1736 Call Number†
0008-1744 Call Number
0008-1760 Calore
0008-1779 Calvary Review
0008-1787 Calvijn
0008-1795 Calvin Theological Journal
0008-1809 Calzado en Mexico *see* 0008-1817
0008-1817 Calzado y Teneria
0008-1833 Camag Bibliography Service
0008-1841 Camara Argentina de Productos Quimicos. Boletin Informativo
0008-185X Camara de Comercio de Bogota. Boletin
0008-1868 Comerciante
0008-1876 Camara de Comercio de La Guaira. Boletin Estadistico.†
0008-1884 Camara de Comercio de Lima. Boletin Semanal *changed to* Camara de Comercio de Lima. Boletin Semanal - Informativo Legal.
0008-1892 Comercio y Produccion
0008-1906 Camara de Comercio Luso-Americana. Boletim *changed to* Camara de Comercio Americana. Boletim.
0008-1914 Camara de Comercio Uruguayo-Britanica. Revista
0008-1922 Camara Nacional de Comercio de Managua. Boletin *changed to* Camara de Comercio de Nicaragua. Boletin Comercial.
0008-1930 Camara Oficial de Comercio, Industria y Navegacion de Barcelona. Boletin
0008-1949 Camera Textil de Mexico. Revista Tecnica *changed to* Revista Tecnica Textil-Vestido.
0008-1973 Cambridge Law Journal
0008-1981 Cambridge Philosophical Society. Proceedings. Mathematical and Physical Sciences *see* 0305-0041
0008-199X Cambridge Quarterly
0008-2007 Cambridge Review
0008-2023 Cambridgeshire, Huntingdon and Peterborough Life *changed to* Cambridgeshire Life Magazine.
0008-2031 Camden County Record
0008-204X Camellia Journal
0008-2058 Cameo Newsletter *changed to* Aging News.
0008-2066 Camera†
0008-2074 Camera†
0008-2082 CamerArt
0008-2090 Camera Canada
0008-2112 Camara de Industria y Comercio Argentino-Alemana. Boletin
0008-2120 Camera di Commercio di Milano *changed to* Realta Economica.
0008-2139 Camera di Commercio Industria Artigianato e Agricoltura. Dati e Notizie†

ISSN

ISSN INDEX

ISSN	Title
0008-2147	Camera di Commercio, Industria, Artigianato e Agricoltura di Belluno. Rassegna Economica
0008-2155	Camera Mainichi†
0008-2163	Camera Nu changed to Camera Palet.
0008-2171	Camera Thirty-Five†
0008-218X	Camera†
0008-2198	Chambre de Commerce, d'Industrie et des Mines du Cameroun. Bulletin d'Information
0008-221X	Camillusbode
0008-2236	Caminos changed to Mas Caminos.
0008-2244	Caminos del Aire†
0008-2252	Camion
0008-2260	Cammino
0008-2279	Cammino Economico
0008-2287	Camp Fire Girl see 0092-1289
0008-2295	Camp Management†
0008-2309	Campaign
0008-2317	Campaign Insight
0008-2325	Campeggio Italiano
0008-2341	Campesino
0008-235X	Campesino
0008-2376	Camping Magazine
0008-2384	Camping & Caravaning
0008-2406	C S E News
0008-2414	Camping-Caravanning-Revue
0008-2430	Camping Industry†
0008-2449	Camping Journal changed to Caravan Camping-Journal.
0008-2465	Campo
0008-2473	El Campo
0008-2481	Campus (Lennoxville)
0008-249X	Campus Call†
0008-2503	Campus Crier changed to Observer (Ellensburg).
0008-2511	Campus Estrien changed to Collectif (Sherbrooke).
0008-252X	Campus Leader
0008-2538	Campus Life
0008-2554	Canada Agriculture†
0008-2562	Canada Armenian Press changed to Canada Armenian Press. Newsletter.
0008-2570	Air Carrier Operations in Canada
0008-2589	Canada. Bureau of Statistics. Credit Statistics. see 0380-0741
0008-2597	Canada. Bureau of Statistics. Industry Division. Air Conditioning and Equipment changed to Canada. Statistics Canada. Air Conditioning & Refrigeration Equipment.
0008-2600	Canada. Statistics Canada. Biscuits and Confectionery†
0008-2619	Canada. Statistics Canada. Production of Canada's Leading Minerals†
0008-2627	Canada. Statistics Canada. Restaurant Statistics see 0226-2320
0008-2635	Canada Courier†
0008-2643	Canada. Department of Fisheries and Forestry. Bi-Monthly Research Notes see 0228-9989
0008-2651	Canada. Statistics Canada. Consumption, Production and Inventories of Rubber†
0008-266X	Canada. Statistics Canada. Service Bulletin. Energy Statistics†
0008-2686	Canada. Fisheries Research Board. Journal see 0706-652X
0008-2694	Canada Income Tax Guide
0008-2708	Canada Labour Service
0008-2716	Canada Lutheran see 0831-4446
0008-2732	Canada Poultryman
0008-2740	Canada Tax Cases
0008-2759	Canada Tax Service
0008-2775	Canadan Uutiset
0008-2791	Canada's Mental Health
0008-2805	Canadian (Belleville)
0008-2813	Canadian Administrator
0008-2821	Canadian Aeronautics and Space Journal
0008-283X	Canadian Affairs†
0008-2848	Canadian Aircraft Operator
0008-2856	Canadian Anaesthetists' Society. Journal see 0832-610X
0008-2864	Canadian Arabian News
0008-2872	Canadian Architect
0008-2880	Canadian Armed Forces Review changed to Government and Military Business.
0008-2902	Canadian Association of Radiologists. Journal
0008-2937	Canadian Author & Bookman
0008-2945	Canadian Automotive Trade
0008-2953	Canadian Aviation changed to Aviation & Aerospace.
0008-2961	Canadian Ayrshire Review
0008-297X	Canadian Banker see 0822-6830
0008-2988	Canadian Baptist
0008-3003	Canadian Bar Review
0008-3011	Canadian Beverage Review
0008-302X	Canadian Biochemical Society. Bulletin
0008-3038	Broadcaster
0008-3046	Canadian Botanical Association. Bulletin
0008-3054	Canadian Boy†
0008-3070	Canadian Building
0008-3089	Canadian Building Abstracts†
0008-3097	Canadian Building Digest
0008-3100	Canadian Business
0008-3127	Canadian Cartographer see 0317-7173
0008-3143	Cattlemen
0008-3151	Canadian Certified Accountant see 0318-742X
0008-316X	Canadian Chartered Accountant see 0317-6878
0008-3178	Canadian Chemical Education†
0008-3186	Canadian Chemical Processing changed to Process Industries Canada.
0008-3194	Canadian Chiropractic Association. Journal
0008-3208	Canadian Church Historical Society Journal
0008-3216	Canadian Churchman see 0847-978X
0008-3232	Canadian Clothing Journal†
0008-3240	Canadian Co-Operative Digest†
0008-3259	Canadian Composer
0008-3267	Canadian Consulting Engineer
0008-3275	Canadian Consumer
0008-3283	Canadian Controls & Instrumentation changed to Canadian Controls & Instrumentation (1983).
0008-3291	Canadian Copper
0008-3305	Canadian Council for International Co-Operation. Bulletin†
0008-3313	Canadian Council of Professional Engineers. News Brief - Communique†
0008-3321	Canadian Council of Resource Ministers. References†
0008-3348	Canadian Criminal Cases
0008-3364	Canadian Datasystems
0008-3372	Canadian Dental Association. Journal
0008-3380	Canadian Dental Hygienist see 0834-1494
0008-3399	Canadian Dietetic Association. Journal
0008-3402	Canadian Dimension
0008-3429	Canadian Doctor
0008-3437	Canadian Documentation Centre, Fitness and Sport. Bulletin†
0008-3445	Canadian Education Association. Newsletter
0008-3453	Canadian Education Index
0008-3461	C E E†
0008-3461	Canadian Electronics Engineering Annual Buyer's Guide
0008-347X	Canadian Entomologist
0008-3488	Canadian Estate and Gift Tax Reports changed to Canadian Estate Planning and Administration Reporter.
0008-3496	Canadian Ethnic Studies
0008-350X	Canadian Family Physician
0008-3518	Canadian Farm Economics
0008-3526	Canadian Farm Equipment Dealer†
0008-3534	Canadian Federation of Music Teachers' Associations. News Bulletin see 0319-6356
0008-3542	Canadian Feed & Grain Journal†
0008-3550	Canadian Field-Naturalist
0008-3577	Canadian Flight
0008-3585	Canadian Florist, Greenhouse and Nursery
0008-3631	Canadian Forum
0008-364X	Canadian Funeral Service see 0319-3225
0008-3658	Canadian Geographer
0008-3674	Canadian Geotechnical Journal
0008-3682	Canadian Golf Review†
0008-3690	Canadian Government Publications Monthly Catalogue see 0709-0412
0008-3704	Canadian Grocer
0008-3720	Canadian Hairdresser
0008-3739	Canadian Hereford Digest
0008-3747	Canadian High News see 0843-4557
0008-3755	Canadian Historical Review
0008-3763	Canadian Home Economics Journal
0008-3771	Canadian Home Leaguer changed to Sally Ann.
0008-378X	Canadian Horse see 0830-0593
0008-3798	Canadian Hospital changed to Leadership in Health Services.
0008-3801	Canadian Hotel & Restaurant
0008-3828	Canadian Independent Adjuster
0008-3836	Canadian Industrial Equipment News
0008-3844	Canadian Information Processing Society. Quarterly Bulletin see 0315-5986
0008-3852	Canadian Inhalation Therapy see 0831-2478
0008-3860	Canadian Institute of Food Technology Journal - Institut Canadien de Technologie Alimentaire Journal see 0963-9969
0008-3879	Canadian Insurance
0008-3887	Canadian Interiors
0008-3909	Canadian Jersey Breeder
0008-3917	Canadian Jeweller
0008-3925	Canadian Jewish Chronicle Review see 0008-3941
0008-3941	Canadian Jewish News
0008-395X	Canadian Jewish Weekly†
0008-3968	Canadian Journal of African Studies
0008-3976	Canadian Journal of Agricultural Economics
0008-3984	Canadian Journal of Animal Science
0008-3992	Canadian Journal of Arms Collecting see 0380-982X
0008-400X	Canadian Journal of Behavioural Science
0008-4018	Canadian Journal of Biochemistry see 0829-8211
0008-4026	Canadian Journal of Botany
0008-4034	Canadian Journal of Chemical Engineering
0008-4042	Canadian Journal of Chemistry
0008-4050	Canadian Journal of Comparative Medicine see 0830-9000
0008-4069	Canadian Journal of Corrections see 0704-9722
0008-4077	Canadian Journal of Earth Sciences
0008-4085	Canadian Journal of Economics
0008-4093	Canadian Journal of Genetics and Cytology - Journal Canadien de Genetique et de Cytologie see 0831-2796
0008-4107	Canadian Journal of History
0008-4115	Canadian Journal of History of Sport and Physical Education changed to Canadian Journal of History of Sport.
0008-4123	Canadian Journal of Hospital Pharmacy
0008-4131	Canadian Journal of Linguistics
0008-414X	Canadian Journal of Mathematics
0008-4158	Canadian Journal of Medical Technology
0008-4166	Canadian Journal of Microbiology
0008-4174	Canadian Journal of Occupational Therapy
0008-4182	Canadian Journal of Ophthalmology
0008-4190	Canadian Journal of Pharmaceutical Sciences†
0008-4204	Canadian Journal of Physics
0008-4212	Canadian Journal of Physiology and Pharmacology
0008-4220	Canadian Journal of Plant Science
0008-4239	Canadian Journal of Political Science
0008-4247	Canadian Journal of Psychiatric Nursing†
0008-4255	Canadian Journal of Psychology
0008-4263	Canadian Journal of Public Health
0008-4271	Canadian Journal of Soil Science
0008-428X	Canadian Journal of Surgery
0008-4298	Studies in Religion
0008-4301	Canadian Journal of Zoology
0008-4328	Canadian Labour Law Reporter
0008-4336	Canadian Labour - Monde Syndical changed to C L C Today.
0008-4344	Canadian Lacombe Breeders Association. Newsletter
0008-4352	Canadian Library Journal
0008-4360	Canadian Literature
0008-4379	Canadian Machinery & Metalworking
0008-4387	Canadian Marketer†
0008-4395	Canadian Mathematical Bulletin
0008-4409	Canadian Medical Association Journal
0008-4417	Canadian Mennonite†
0008-4433	Canadian Metallurgical Quarterly
0008-4441	Canadian Metalworking/Machine Production†
0008-445X	Canadian Military Engineer†
0008-4468	Canadian Military Journal
0008-4476	Canadian Mineralogist
0008-4492	Canadian Mining Journal
0008-4506	Canadian Modern Language Review
0008-4522	Canadian Motorcycling changed to Cycle C M A.
0008-4557	Canadian Commission for UNESCO. Bulletin
0008-4565	Canadian News Facts
0008-4573	Canadian Numismatic Journal
0008-4581	Canadian Nurse changed to Canadian Nurse - L'Infirmiere Canadienne.
0008-459X	Canadian Nurseryman see 0315-4874
0008-4611	Canadian Occupational Safety
0008-462X	Canadian Office Products and Stationery
0008-4638	Canadian Journal of Operational Research and Information Processing see 0315-5986
0008-4654	Canadian Packaging
0008-4662	Canadian Paint and Finishing†
0008-4670	Patent Office Record (Canada)
0008-4689	Canadian Patent Reporter
0008-4697	Peace Research
0008-4719	Canadian Periodical Index
0008-4727	Canadian Personnel & Industrial Relations Journal
0008-4735	Canadian Petroleum†
0008-4751	Canadian Physiotherapy Association Journal - Association Canadienne de Physiotherapie Revue see 0300-0508
0008-476X	Canadian Plant Disease Survey
0008-4778	Canadian Plastics
0008-4786	Canadian Podiatrist
0008-4794	Canadian Postmaster
0008-4808	Canadian Poultry Review†
0008-4816	Canadian Printer and Publisher see 0849-0767
0008-4824	Canadian Psychiatric Association Journal see 0706-7437
0008-4840	Canadian Public Administration
0008-4859	Canadian Publishers Directory
0008-4867	Canadian Pulp and Paper Industry see 0713-5807
0008-4867	Canadian Pulp and Paper Industry see 0225-7572
0008-4875	Canadian Rail
0008-4883	Canadian Railway Club. Official Proceedings see 0226-157X
0008-4891	Canadian Reader†
0008-4905	Canadian Realtor changed to Canadian Real Estate.
0008-4913	Canadian Register see 0383-1620
0008-493X	Canadian Research and Development see 0319-1974
0008-4948	Canadian Review of Sociology and Anthropology
0008-4956	Canadian Rockhound†
0008-4972	Canadian Sailor

ISSN INDEX

ISSN	Title
0008-4980	Canadian Shipping and Marine Engineering
0008-5006	Canadian Slavonic Papers
0008-5022	Canadian Society of Exploration Geophysicists. Journal *changed to* Canadian Journal of Exploration Geophysics.
0008-5030	Canadian Society of Forensic Science Journal
0008-5049	Canadian Sociology and Anthropology Association. Bulletin†
0008-5057	Canadian Spectroscopy *changed to* Canadian Journal of Applied Spectroscopy.
0008-5073	Canadian Sportsman
0008-509X	Canada. Statistics Canada. Canadian Statistical Review *see* 0835-9148
0008-5103	Canadian Surveyor - Geometre Canadien *see* 0841-8233
0008-5111	Canadian Tax Journal
0008-512X	Canadian Tax Papers
0008-5138	Canadian Tax Reporter
0008-5154	Canadian Technical Information News *changed to* Canadian Technical and Scientific Information News Journal.
0008-5162	Canadian Telephone and Cable Television Journal *see* 0318-0069
0008-5189	Canadian Tobacco Grower
0008-5197	Canadian Tourism†
0008-5200	Canadian Transportation and Distribution Management
0008-5219	Canadian Travel Courier *see* 1182-9699
0008-5235	Canadian Tuberculosis and Respiratory Disease Association. Bulletin *changed to* Canadian Lung Association. Bulletin.
0008-5243	Canadian U F O Report†
0008-5251	Canadian Underwriter
0008-5278	Canadian Vending
0008-5286	Canadian Veterinary Journal
0008-5294	Canadian Weather Review†
0008-5308	Canadian Weekly Law Sheet
0008-5316	Canadian Weekly Publisher *see* 0380-8025
0008-5324	Canadian Welder and Fabricator *changed to* Welding & Fabricating Canada.
0008-5332	Canadian Welfare *see* 0704-5263
0008-5340	Western Canadian Journal of Anthropology *see* 0706-4845
0008-5367	Canadian Wings *changed to* Wings.
0008-5383	Canadian Zionist
0008-5391	Canadiana
0008-5405	Canard Enchaine
0008-5413	Canberra Consumer
0008-5421	Canberra Post
0008-543X	Cancer
0008-5448	Cancer Bulletin *changed to* University of Texas. M.D. Anderson Cancer Center. Cancer Bulletin.
0008-5456	Cancer Chemotherapy Abstracts *see* 0095-7895
0008-5464	Cancer News
0008-5472	Cancer Research
0008-5480	Cancro
0008-5499	Canadian Charolais Banner *see* 0824-1767
0008-5502	Candle *changed to* Epilepsy Today.
0008-5510	Candle (Macomb)
0008-5537	Baked Snack Industry *see* 0745-1032
0008-5553	Cane Growers Quarterly Bulletin†
0008-5588	Canning and Packing *see* 0040-795X
0008-560X	Canning Trade *see* 0191-6181
0008-5618	Cannocchiale
0008-5626	Canoe - Camper
0008-5642	Canoeing in Britain *see* 0308-7565
0008-5650	Canon Law Abstracts
0008-5677	Canteras y Explotaciones
0008-5685	Canterbury Chamber of Commerce. Economic Bulletin
0008-5693	Canterbury Diocesan Notes *see* 0260-9924
0008-5715	Cantiere *see* 0029-6325
0008-5723	Canto dell'Assemblea†
0008-5731	Canto Gregoriano†
0008-5758	Canyon Cinemanews *changed to* Cinemanews.
0008-5774	Capaha Arrow
0008-5782	Cape Cod Illustrated†
0008-5790	Cape Librarian
0008-5804	Cape of Good Hope. Department of Nature Conservation. Newsletter *changed to* Cape of Good Hope. Department of Nature Conservation and Museum Services. Annual Report.
0008-5812	Cape Rock Journal *see* 0146-2199
0008-5820	Cape Town Photographic Society Syllabus
0008-5839	Capital
0008-5847	Capital
0008-5855	Capital Changes Reports
0008-5871	Capital en Accion *changed to* San Juan en Accion.
0008-588X	Capital Goods Review†
0008-5898	Capital Voice
0008-591X	Capitolium†
0008-5936	Capper's Weekly *see* 0892-1148
0008-5944	Capricho
0008-5952	C C C O News Notes
0008-5960	Capsule News†
0008-5979	Captions†
0008-5987	Car
0008-5995	Car
0008-6002	Car and Driver
0008-6010	Car Craft
0008-6029	Car-del Scribe
0008-6037	Car Mechanics
0008-6053	Car Rental & Leasing Insider Newsletter
0008-607X	Car Wash Review *changed to* American Carwash Review.
0008-6088	Cara
0008-6096	Carabinier de Lausanne†
0008-610X	Carabiniere
0008-6118	Caracola
0008-6126	Caractere
0008-6134	Caracteres
0008-6142	Caravan *see* 0268-0440
0008-6150	Caravan *changed to* Alive.
0008-6169	Caravan Bladet
0008-6177	Caravaning
0008-6185	Caravaning
0008-6193	Caravanner
0008-6207	Caravelt
0008-6215	Carbohydrate Research
0008-6223	Carbon
0008-6231	Carbon Black Abstracts†
0008-624X	Carcanet *see* 0144-7076
0008-6258	Carcinogenesis Abstracts *changed to* Cancergram.
0008-6266	Commonwealth Forestry Bureau. Card Title Service†
0008-6274	Cardamom News *changed to* Spice India.
0008-6290	Cardinal Poetry Quarterly†
0008-6312	Cardiology
0008-6320	Cardiologia nel Mondo
0008-6347	Cardiology Digest *changed to* Cardiology Digest (1979).
0008-6355	Cardiovascular Nursing
0008-6363	Cardiovascular Research
0008-6371	Cardiovascular Research Center Bulletin†
0008-638X	Caret
0008-641X	Cargill Crop Bulletin *changed to* Cargill Bulletin.
0008-6436	Caribbean Challenge
0008-6444	Caribbean Conservation Association. Newsletter *changed to* Caribbean Conservation News.
0008-6452	Caribbean Journal of Science
0008-6460	Caribbean Journal of Science and Mathematics†
0008-6487	Caribbean Educational Bulletin†
0008-6495	Caribbean Quarterly
0008-6509	Caribbean Report†
0008-6517	Caribbean Research Institute. Quarterly Report†
0008-6525	Caribbean Review
0008-6533	Caribbean Studies
0008-655X	Caridade
0008-6568	Caries Research
0008-6576	Carillon
0008-6592	Carinski Pregled
0008-6606	Carinthia 1
0008-6614	Caritas
0008-6622	Caritas-Korrespondenz
0008-6630	Carleton *see* 0315-1859
0008-6649	Carleton Miscellany†
0008-6657	Laboratoire Carlsberg. Comptes Rendus des Travaux *see* 0105-1938
0008-6665	Carmel
0008-6673	Carmelus
0008-6681	Carnegie Magazine
0008-669X	Carnets de Zoologie *changed to* Ecozoo.
0008-6703	Carnival
0008-6711	Carnivore Genetics Newsletter†
0008-672X	Carolina Christian
0008-6738	Carolina Cooperator *see* 0195-3346
0008-6746	Carolina Country
0008-6762	Carolina Genealogist†
0008-6770	Carolina Golfer
0008-6789	Carolina Highways
0008-6797	Carolina Quarterly
0008-6800	Carolina Sportsman
0008-6819	Carolinian†
0008-6835	Carovana†
0008-6843	Carpenter
0008-6851	Carpet Review *see* 0263-4236
0008-6886	Carrefour
0008-6894	Carrell
0008-6908	Carreteras
0008-6916	Carriage Journal
0008-6924	Carrier Reports
0008-6932	Carroll Business Bulletin
0008-6940	Carrosserie
0008-6959	Carrozziere Italiano
0008-6967	Cars & Car Conversions
0008-6975	Cars & Parts
0008-6975	Car & Parts Annual
0008-6983	Carta Cultural de Venezuela
0008-6991	Cartabianca
0008-7009	Cartactual
0008-7017	Carte Blanche†
0008-7025	Carte Segrete
0008-7033	Carthusian
0008-7041	Cartographic Journal
0008-705X	Cartonnagebedrijf *changed to* Kartoflexmarkt.
0008-7068	Cartoonist Profiles
0008-7076	Cartophilic Notes & News
0008-7092	Carwash Journal
0008-7114	Caryologia
0008-7122	Casa
0008-7149	Casa de la Cultura Ecuatoriana. Revista†
0008-7157	Casa de las Americas
0008-7165	Casa do Douro Boletim†
0008-7173	Casa Vogue
0008-7181	Casabella
0008-719X	Casana
0008-7203	Casas y Jardines
0008-7211	Cascade Caver
0008-722X	Cascades†
0008-7238	Case and Comment Magazine (Rochester)
0008-7246	Case & Counsel
0008-7254	Case Western Reserve Journal of International Law†
0008-7262	Case Western Reserve Law Review
0008-7270	Cash and Carry News *see* 0267-9361
0008-7289	Cash Box
0008-7297	Cash Crop Farming†
0008-7300	Cashew Bulletin
0008-7319	Cashier
0008-7327	C & S
0008-7335	Casopis Lekaru Ceskych
0008-7343	Narodni Muzeum v Praze. Casopis: Rada Historicka
0008-7351	Narodni Muzeum. Casopis: Oddil Prirodovedny *changed to* Narodni Muzeum v Praze. Casopis: Rada Prirodovedna.
0008-736X	Casopis pro Mezinarodni Pravo†
0008-7378	Casopis pro Mineralogii a Geologii
0008-7408	Cassa di Risparmio delle Provincie Lombarde Quarterly
0008-7416	Cassa di Soccorso e Malattia per i Dipendenti dell'Azienda Trasporti Municipali di Milano. Bollettino d'Informazione
0008-7424	Cassazione Penale
0008-7440	Cassella-Riedel Archiv
0008-7467	International Cast Metals Journal†
0008-7475	Castanea
0008-7483	Casteel†
0008-7491	Il Castello
0008-7505	Castillos de Espana
0008-7513	Casting Engineering *see* 0887-9060
0008-7521	Castings *changed to* Metal Casting and Surface Finishing.
0008-753X	Castorot
0008-7548	Burmah International†
0008-7556	Castrum Peregrini
0008-7564	Casual Living and Summer and Casual Furniture *changed to* Casual Living.
0008-7572	Casualty Return Statistical Summary *see* 0268-0815
0008-7580	Casualty Simulation
0008-7599	Cat
0008-7610	Catalogo Nacional del Envase, Embalaje y Artes Graficas Aplicadas *changed to* Catalogo Espanol del Envase, Embalaje y Artes Graficas Aplicadas.
0008-7629	Catalogue & Index
0008-7645	Catalysis Reviews *see* 0161-4940
0008-7661	Catalyst (Amherst)
0008-767X	Catalyst (Philadelphia)
0008-7688	Catalyst for Environmental Quality *see* 0194-1445
0008-7696	Catch
0008-770X	Catch Society of America. Journal†
0008-7726	Catechist
0008-7734	Catechistes *changed to* Temps et Paroles.
0008-7742	Catechistes d'Aujourd'hui *changed to* Points de Repere.
0008-7750	Universidad de Granada. Catedra Francisco Suarez. Anales
0008-7807	Catering Executive†
0008-7815	Catering Industry Employee
0008-7823	Catering Quarterly†
0008-784X	Caterpillar *see* 0730-305X
0008-7866	Cathcart Chronicle
0008-7874	Cathedral Age
0008-7882	Cathode Press†
0008-7890	Catholic Action News *changed to* New Earth.
0008-7904	Catholic Advance
0008-7912	Catholic Biblical Quarterly
0008-7920	Catholic Book Review *changed to* Canadian Book, Film and Record Review.
0008-7939	Religious Book Guide *see* 0279-9588
0008-7947	Catholic Business Education Review†
0008-7971	Catholic Chronicle
0008-7998	Catholic Digest
0008-8005	Catholic Documentation†
0008-8013	Catholic Education Today†
0008-8021	Catholic Film Newsletter *see* 0362-0875
0008-803X	Catholic Fireside
0008-8048	Catholic Forester
0008-8056	Catholic Free Press
0008-8064	Catholic Gazette
0008-8072	Catholic Herald
0008-8080	Catholic Historical Review
0008-8099	Catholic Hospital *see* 0226-5923 Medical Service *see* 0970-471X
0008-8102	Catholic Institutional Management†
0008-8110	Catholic Journalist
0008-8129	Catholic Lawyer
0008-8137	Catholic Library Association. Northern Illinois Chapter. Newsletter
0008-8161	

5358 ISSN INDEX

0008-8188 Parish and Lending Library News *changed to* Parish and Community Libraries News.
0008-820X Catholic Library World
0008-8218 Catholic Life *changed to* P I M E World.
0008-8226 Catholic Medical Quarterly
0008-8234 Catholic Messenger
0008-8242 Catholic Mind†
0008-8250 Catholic News†
0008-8269 Catholic Nurse†
0008-8277 Catholic Peace Fellowship Bulletin
0008-8285 Catholic Periodical and Literature Index
0008-8293 Catholic Pictorial
0008-8307 Catholic Press Directory
0008-8315 Catholic Review (Baltimore)
0008-8323 Catholic Review (New York)
0008-8331 Catholic Rural Life†
0008-834X Catholic School Editor†
0008-8366 Catholic Standard
0008-8390 Catholic University Law Review
0008-8404 Catholic Virginian
0008-8412 Catholic Voice
0008-8420 Catholic Weekly
0008-8439 Catholic Weekly
0008-8447 Catholic Witness
0008-8455 Catholic Woman's Journal†
0008-8463 Catholic Worker
0008-8471 Catholic Workman
0008-848X Catholic World *see* 1042-3494
0008-8498 Catholica†
0008-8501 Catholica
0008-851X Catholica Unio
0008-8528 Catolicismo†
0008-8536 Catonsville Roadrunner†
0008-8544 Cats Magazine
0008-8552 Cattleman
0008-8579 Caustic
0008-8609 Cavalier Daily
0008-8625 Caves and Karst†
0008-8641 Caxtonian†
0008-865X Cayuga County Farm and Home News *see* 0002-158X
0008-8668 Cebu y Derivados
0008-8676 Cecidologia Internationale
0008-8684 Cedars - Sinai Medical Center Compass
0008-8692 Ceiba
0008-8706 Celebriamo
0008-8714 Celestial Mechanics *see* 0923-2958
0008-8722 Celik
0008-8730 Cell and Tissue Kinetics *see* 0960-7722
0008-8749 Cellular Immunology
0008-8757 Cellulet
0008-8765 Cellulosa e Carta
0008-8773 Celtic News *changed to* Carn.
0008-8781 Celuloide
0008-879X Celuloza si Hirtie
0008-8811 Cement
0008-882X Cement
0008-8838 Cement & Concrete†
0008-8846 Cement and Concrete Research
0008-8854 Cement Technology *see* 0263-6050
0008-8862 Cement, Lime and Gravel *changed to* Quarry Management.
0008-8870 Cement og Beton *see* 0029-1307
0008-8889 Cement Special
0008-8897 Cement, Wapno, Gips
0008-8919 Cemento-Hormigon
0008-8927 Cemento Portland
0008-8935 Cenacolo
0008-8943 Cenhadwr†
0008-8951 Cenicafe
0008-896X Cenobio
0008-8978 Centaur†
0008-8986 Centauros
0008-8994 Centaurus
0008-9001 Centenary College Conglomerate
0008-901X Centennial Review *see* 0162-0177
0008-9036 Center for Children's Books. Bulletin
0008-9044 Center for Chinese Research Materials. Newsletter
0008-9052 University of Michigan. Center for Coordination of Ancient and Modern Studies. Newsletter†
0008-9079 Center for Law Enforcement Research Information†
0008-9087 Center for Research Libraries. Newsletter *see* 0275-4924
0008-9095 Center for Soviet and East-European Studies in the Performing Arts. Bulletin
0008-9117 Center Forum†
0008-9125 Center for the Study of Democratic Institutions. Center Magazine *see* 0893-7850
0008-9133 Center for Teaching About Peace and War. Newsletter *changed to* Center for Peace and Conflict Studies - Detroit Council for World Affairs. Newsletter.
0008-9141 Cento
0008-915X Centri Meccanografici ed Elettronici *changed to* Management e Informatica.
0008-9168 Centraal Orgaan voor de Handel in Aardappelen, Groenten en Fruit†
0008-9176 Central African Journal of Medicine
0008-9184 Central African Zionist Digest
0008-9192 Central Asiatic Journal
0008-9206 Central Bank News†
0008-9214 Central Bank News Digest *see* 0115-1401
0008-9222 Central Bank of Ceylon *changed to* Central Bank of Sri Lanka. Bulletin.
0008-9230 Central Bank of Cyprus. Bulletin
0008-9249 Central Bank of Egypt. Economic Review
0008-9257 Central Bank of Iraq. Quarterly Bulletin
0008-9265 Central Bank of Jordan. Quarterly Bulletin *changed to* Central Bank of Jordan. Monthly Statistical Bulletin.
0008-9273 Central Bank of Malta. Quarterly Review
0008-9281 Central Bank of Nigeria. Economic and Financial Review
0008-929X Central Bank of Nigeria. Monthly Report
0008-9311 Central Bible Quarterly†
0008-9346 Central Constructor†
0008-9362 Central Europe Journal†
0008-9389 Central European History
0008-9397 Central Glass and Ceramic Research Institute. Bulletin
0008-9400 Central Ideas†
0008-9419 Central Illinois Historical Messenger *changed to* Historical Messenger.
0008-9443 Central Japan Journal of Orthopaedic & Traumatic Surgery
0008-9451 Central Michigan Life
0008-946X Central New York Academy of Medicine. Bulletin
0008-9478 Central New York Regional Medical Program. Bulletin†
0008-9494 Central News†
0008-9508 Central Opera Service Bulletin†
0008-9524 Central Pennsylvania Labor News
0008-9559 Central States Archaeological Journal
0008-9575 Central State Speech Journal *changed to* Communication Studies.
0008-9583 Centralblatt fuer das Gesamte Forstwesen
0008-9591 Centralny Osrodek Informacji Budownictwa. Biuletyn-Informacja *see* 0867-4485
0008-9605 Centre Catholique des Intellectuels Francais. Recherches et Debats
0008-9621 Centre de Conjoncture Africaine et Malgache. Bulletin d'Information *changed to* C C A M Information.
0008-963X Centre de Documentation Siderurgique. Circulaire d'Informations *changed to* Revue de Metallurgie. Cahiers d'Information Techniques.
0008-9648 Centre de Formation des Journalistes. Feuillets†
0008-9664 Centre de Recherche et d'Information Socio-Politiques. Etudes Africaines†
0008-9672 Societe Nationale des Petroles d'Aquitaine. Centre de Recherches de Pau. Bulletin *see* 0396-2687
0008-9699 Universite Libre de Bruxelles. Centre d'Etude des Pays de l'Est. Revue du Centre d'Etude des Pays de l'Est et du Centre National pour l'Etude des Etats de l'Est *changed to* Universite Libre de Bruxelles. Centre d'Etude des Pays de l'Est. Revue des Pays de l'Est.
0008-9702 Centre d'Etude des Matieres Plastiques. Bulletin de Documentation†
0008-9710 Shikshak†
0008-9737 Universite Libre de Bruxelles. Centre d'Etudes de Recherche Operationnelle. Cahiers
0008-9761 Centre d'Etudes Socialistes. Cahiers†
0008-9788 Centre d'Information Civique, Paris. Etudes
0008-980X Centre International d'Etude des Textiles Anciens. Bulletin de Liaison *changed to* Centre International d'Etude des Textiles Anciens. Bulletin.
0008-9818 Centre International d'Etudes Romanes. Bulletin *changed to* Centre International d'Etudes Romanes. Revue Trimestrielle.
0008-9826 Centre Medical†
0008-9842 Federation Protestante de France. Centre d'Etudes et de Documentation. Bulletin *see* 0181-7671
0008-9869 Centre Technique du Bois et de l'Ameublement. Bulletin Bibliographique *changed to* Centre Technique du Bois et de l'Ameublement. Profils.
0008-9877 Centre Technique du Bois et de l'Ameublement. Bulletin d'Informations Techniques *see* 0296-8541
0008-9885 Centre Technique du Bois et de l'Ameublement. Cahiers
0008-9907 Centro America Odontologica
0008-9915 Instituto de Investigacao Cientifica de Mocambique. Centro de Documentacao Cientifica. Boletim†
0008-9931 Portugal. Ministerio do Ultramar. Centro de Documentacao Tecnico-Economica. Boletim Bibliografico
0008-994X Centro de Documentacion. Boletin
0008-9958 Centro de Estudios Monetarios Latinoamericanos. Boletin Mensual *see* 0186-7229
0008-9966 Centro de Estudios Sociales del Valle de los Caidos. Boletin *see* 0303-9889
0008-9990 Centro de Historia del Estado Falcon. Boletin
0009-000X Regno - Documenti
0009-0026 Centro di Documentazione Sul Movimento dei Disciplinati. Quaderni *changed to* Centro di Ricerca e di Studio Sul Movimento dei Disciplinati. Quaderni.
0009-0034 Centro Interamericano de Vivienda y Planeamiento. Lista de Nuevas Adquisiciones†
0009-0042 Centro Interamericano de Vivienda y Planeamiento. Suplemento Informativo *changed to* S I N D U. Noticiero.
0009-0050 Centro Latino Americano de Fisica Noticia†
0009-0069 Centro Latino Americano de Pesquisas em Ciencias Sociais. Boletim Bibliografia
0009-0085 Centro Nacional de Informacion de Ciencias Medicas. Revista de Resumenes. Cuaderno 2. Cirugia†
0009-0093 Centro Nacional de Informacion de Ciencias Medicas. Revista de Resumenes. Cuaderno 4. Higiene, Epidemiologia, Medios de Diagnostico y Otros†
0009-0107 Centro Nacional de Informacion de Ciencias Medicas. Revista de Resumenes. Cuaderno 1. Medicina†
0009-0115 Centro Nacional de Informacion de Ciencias Medicas. Revista de Resumenes. Cuaderno 3. Pediatria†
0009-0123 Centro Naval. Boletin
0009-0131 Centro Pan-Americano de Febre Aftosa. Boletin
0009-014X Centro Regional de Pesquisas Educacionais Jaoa Pinheiro. Boletim Informativo†
0009-0166 Century†
0009-0174 Ceol†
0009-0190 Ceramic Arts & Crafts
0009-0204 Ceramic Awareness Bulletin†
0009-0212 Ceramic Forum†
0009-0220 Ceramic Industry
0009-0220 Ceramic Industry Data Book Buyers Guide
0009-0247 Ceramic Scope†
0009-0255 Yogyo Kyokai Shi *see* 0914-5400
0009-0263 Ceramic Trade News and Catalog File *changed to* Ceramics (Livonia).
0009-0271 Ceramica Informazione
0009-028X Ceramic Italian nell'Edilizia *see* 0392-4890
0009-0301 Ceramics *changed to* Ceramic Industries International.
0009-031X Seramikkusu
0009-0328 Ceramics Monthly
0009-0336 Ceramique Moderne
0009-0344 Cercle d'Etudes Numismatiques. Bulletin
0009-0352 Cereal Chemistry
0009-0360 Cereal Science Today *see* 0146-6283
0009-0379 Ceres
0009-0387 Cerkev v Sedanjem Svetu
0009-0395 Cernakov Odkaz *changed to* Slobodne Slovensko.
0009-0409 Certificated Engineer
0009-0417 Certified Accountants Journal *see* 0306-2406
0009-0425 Certified General Accountant *see* 0318-742X
0009-0433 Certified Milk†
0009-0441 Cerveny Kvet
0009-045X Cervi's Rocky Mountain Journal *changed to* Rocky Mountain Business Journal.
0009-0468 Ceska Literatura
0009-0476 Ceska Mykologie
0009-0484 Ceske Listy†
0009-0492 Ceskoslovenska Akademie Ved. Vestnik
0009-0506 Ceskoslovenska Armada
0009-0514 Ceskoslovenska Dermatologie
0009-0522 Ceskoslovenska Epidemiologie, Mikrobiologie, Imunologie
0009-0530 Ceskoslovenska Farmacie
0009-0549 Ceskoslovenska Fotografie *changed to* Fotografie.
0009-0557 Ceskoslovenska Fysiologie
0009-0565 Ceskoslovenska Gastroenterologie a Vyziva
0009-0573 Ceskoslovenska Hygiena
0009-0581 Ceskoslovenska Neurologie *see* 0301-0597
0009-059X Ceskoslovenska Oftalmologie
0009-0603 Ceskoslovenska Otolaryngologie
0009-0611 Ceskoslovenska Patologie
0009-062X Ceskoslovenska Psychologie
0009-0638 Ceskoslovenska Rusistika *see* 0862-8459
0009-0638 Ceskoslovenska Rusistika *changed to* Svet Literatury.
0009-0646 Ceskoslovenska Spolecnost Mikrobiologicka. Bulletin
0009-0654 Ceskoslovenska Stomatologie
0009-0670 Rybarstvi
0009-0689 Ceskoslovenske Zdravotnictvi
0009-0697 Ceskoslovensky Architekt *changed to* Architekt.
0009-0700 Ceskoslovensky Casopis pro Fyziku
0009-0719 Ceskoslovensky Hornik a Energetik
0009-0727 Ceskoslovensky Kolorista
0009-0735 Ceskoslovensky Rozhlas a Televizet
0009-0743 Ceskoslovensky Sacht
0009-0751 Ceskoslovensky Vojak
0009-0778 Cesky Bratr
0009-0786 Cesky Jazyk a Literatura
0009-0794 Cesky Lid
0009-0808 Ceux des F F A

ISSN

ISSN	Title
0009-0816	Ceylon Coconut Planters' Review see 0255-4119
0009-0824	Ceylon Coconut Quarterly see 0255-4100
0009-0832	Sri Lanka Journal of Historical and Social Studies
0009-0840	Ceylon Journal of the Humanities changed to Sri Lanka Journal of the Humanities.
0009-0859	Ceylon Labour Gazette changed to Sri Lanka Labour Gazette.
0009-0875	Ceylon Medical Journal
0009-0883	Ceylon National Bibliography changed to Sri Lanka National Bibliography.
0009-0891	Ceylon Veterinary Journal changed to Sri Lanka Veterinary Journal.
0009-0905	Avicultura Industrial
0009-0913	Chacra changed to Campo Moderno y Chacra.
0009-0921	Chain Merchandiser
0009-093X	Chain Saw Age
0009-0948	Chain Saw Industry & Power Equipment Dealer†
0009-0972	Chalkmarks†
0009-0980	Challenge see 0045-849X
0009-0999	Challenge (London, 1961)
0009-1006	Challenge (London, 1960)
0009-1014	Challenge (Sandbach)
0009-1049	Challenge (New York)
0009-1057	Challenge†
0009-1065	New Stationer†
0009-1073	Challenge (Richmond)†
0009-1103	Chalmers†
0009-112X	Chalmers Tekniska Hoegskola. Institutionen foer Skeppshydromekanik. Rapport†
0009-1138	Dublin Chamber of Commerce Journal changed to Trade-Links Journal.
0009-1146	Chamber of Commerce of the U.S. Newsletter changed to Organization Dateline.
0009-1154	Chamber of Commerce of the U.S. Association Letter†
0009-1162	Product Safety News
0009-1189	Chambre de Commerce et d'Industrie de Meurthe et Moselle. Bulletin Mensuel see 0240-7426
0009-1197	Chambre de Commerce de Bruxelles. Bulletin Officiel changed to Entreprendre.
0009-1200	Chambre de Commerce et d'Industrie de Marseille. Cahiers de Documentation†
0009-1219	Chambre de Commerce et d'Industrie de Paris. Bulletin Mensuel†
0009-1227	Chambre de Commerce et d'Industrie de Rouen. Bulletin Economique
0009-1235	Chambre de Commerce Francaise du Japon. Bulletin†
0009-126X	Chambre Syndicale des Mines de Fer de France. Bulletin Technique†
0009-1286	Chaminade College Newsletter changed to Chaminade Newsletter.
0009-1294	Champagne News
0009-1308	Champignon
0009-1316	Champignoncultuur
0009-1324	Champion†
0009-1332	Champak
0009-1359	Chandrabhaga (West Bengal)
0009-1367	Change see 0335-1971
0009-1383	Change (Washington)
0009-1413	Changing Education†
0009-1421	Changing Schools†
0009-143X	Changing Times see 1056-697X
0009-1456	Channel changed to Maryknoll Fathers and Brothers.
0009-1464	Channel (New Paltz)†
0009-1480	Gambit†
0009-1499	Channel Viewer changed to Channel T V Times.
0009-1502	Channels (Omaha)†
0009-1510	Channels (Exeter)
0009-1529	Channels of Blessing
0009-1537	Chanoyu Quarterly
0009-1553	Chantecoq†
0009-1561	The Chanticleer
0009-1588	Chantiers†
0009-1596	Chantiers Cooperatifs
0009-160X	Les Chantiers du Cardinal
0009-1618	Chantiers Pedagogiques†
0009-1626	Children's Book Review†
0009-1634	Chapeaux et Coiffures de France see 0047-8512
0009-1642	Chaplain see 0149-4236
0009-1650	Chappaqua Speculator†
0009-1669	Character Potential†
0009-1685	Charbonnages de France. Publications Techniques†
0009-1707	Charing Cross Hospital Gazette changed to Charing Cross Medical Gazette.
0009-1715	Charisma changed to Touch.
0009-1723	Charity and Children
0009-1731	Charivari†
0009-174X	Charlatan: Interdisciplinary Journal†
0009-1758	Charles Buchan's Football Monthly changed to Football Monthly.
0009-1766	Charles C. Adams Center for Ecological Studies. Occasional Papers
0009-1774	Charles S. Peirce Society. Transactions
0009-1790	Charlotte-Mecklenburg School Report†
0009-1812	Charm†
0009-1820	Charmant†
0009-1839	Charme†
0009-1847	Charolais Banner
0009-188X	Chartered Accountant
0009-1898	Chartered Accountant in Australia see 1035-0748
0009-1901	Chartered Engineer†
0009-1928	Chartered Secretary see 1034-0408
0009-1936	Chartered Surveyor changed to Chartered Surveyor Weekly.
0009-1944	Chartotheca Translationum Alphabetica
0009-1952	Chase
0009-1960	Chasovoi
0009-1979	Chasse et Peche changed to Chasse-Peche-Tir.
0009-1987	Chat
0009-1995	Chatelaine (English edition)
0009-2002	Chaucer Review
0009-2010	Chaud - Froid - Plomberie see 0750-1552
0009-2029	Chauffage - Ventilation - Conditionnement
0009-2037	Chauffage-Plomberie†
0009-2053	Chaussure et la Mode see 0025-3898
0009-2061	Chavhata Weekly
0009-2096	Checklist of Congressional Hearings changed to Congress in Print.
0009-2126	Cheering Words
0009-2142	Cheese Reporter
0009-2150	Chef Magazine see 0192-7116
0009-2177	Chefs
0009-2185	Chelsea
0009-2207	Chemexcil Export Bulletin
0009-2223	Chemia Analityczna
0009-2231	Zagadnienia Technologii Chemicznej changed to Polish Journal of Applied Chemistry.
0009-224X	Chemia Stosowana. Seria B. Zagadnienia Inzynierii i Apartury Chemicznej changed to Inzynieria Chemiczna i Procesowa.
0009-2258	Chemical Abstracts - Section Groupings
0009-2266	Chemical Abstracts - Applied Chemistry Sections see 0090-8363
0009-2274	Chemical Abstracts - Macromolecular Sections
0009-2282	Chemical Abstracts - Organic Chemistry Sections
0009-2290	Chemical Abstracts - Physical and Analytical Chemistry Sections see 0278-1832
0009-2304	Chemical Abstracts - Biochemistry Sections
0009-2312	Chemical Age see 0262-4230
0009-2320	Chemical Age of India
0009-2347	Chemical and Engineering News
0009-2355	Chemical and Petroleum Engineering
0009-2363	Chemical & Pharmaceutical Bulletin
0009-2371	Chemical and Process Engineering see 0370-1859
0009-238X	Chemical-Biological Activities(CBAC)†
0009-2398	Chemical Bond
0009-2401	Chemical Bulletin
0009-241X	Chemical Communications see 0022-4936
0009-2452	Chemical Engineer and Transactions of the Institution of Chemical Engineers see 0302-0797
0009-2460	Chemical Engineering
0009-2479	Chemical Engineering Education
0009-2509	Chemical Engineering Science
0009-2517	Chemical Engineering World
0009-2525	Chemical Equipment
0009-2533	Chemical Era
0009-2541	Chemical Geology
0009-255X	Chemical Highlights
0009-2576	Chemical Industry News
0009-2584	Chemical Industry Report†
0009-2592	Chemical Instrumentation see 0743-5797
0009-2606	Chemical Market Abstracts see 0161-8032
0009-2614	Chemical Physics Letters
0009-2622	Chemical Processing see 0305-439X
0009-2630	Chemical Processing
0009-2649	Chemical Processing and Engineering changed to Chemical Business.
0009-2665	Chemical Reviews
0009-2673	Chemical Society of Japan. Bulletin
0009-2681	Chemical Society, London. Quarterly Reviews see 0306-0012
0009-269X	Chemical Substructure Index†
0009-2703	Chemical Technology changed to Chemtech.
0009-2711	Chemical Titles
0009-272X	Chemical Week
0009-2738	Chemicals & Allied Products Export News
0009-2746	Chemicals - International
0009-2754	Chemicals, Quarterly Industry Report†
0009-2770	Chemicke Listy
0009-2789	Chemicky Prumysl
0009-2797	Chemico-Biological Interactions
0009-2800	Chemie-Anlagen und Verfahren
0009-2819	Chemie der Erde
0009-2827	Chemie en Techniek†
0009-2843	Chemie in der Schule
0009-2851	Chemie in Unserer Zeit
0009-286X	Chemie-Ingenieur-Technik
0009-2886	Chemik
0009-2894	Chemiker-Zeitung see 0021-8383
0009-2908	Chemins
0009-2916	Cheminot
0009-2924	Chemins de Fer
0009-2932	Chemisch Weekblad see 0167-2746
0009-2932	Chemisch Weekblad changed to Chemisch Weekblad.
0009-2940	Chemische Berichte
0009-2959	Chemische Industrie
0009-2967	Chemische Industrie International†
0009-2975	Chemisches Informationsdienst see 0931-7597
0009-2983	Chemische Rundschau
0009-3017	Chemisier l'Elegance Masculine changed to Elegance Masculine-Mylord.
0009-3025	Chemist
0009-3033	Chemist & Druggist
0009-3041	Chemist & Drugstore News
0009-305X	Chemistry see 0190-597X
0009-3068	Chemistry and Industry
0009-3076	Chemistry and Industry in New Zealand changed to Chemistry in Industry.
0009-3084	Chemistry and Physics of Lipids
0009-3092	Chemistry and Technology of Fuels and Oils
0009-3106	Chemistry in Britain
0009-3114	Chemistry in Canada see 0823-5228
0009-3122	Chemistry of Heterocyclic Compounds (New York, 1965)
0009-3130	Chemistry of Natural Compounds
0009-3149	Chemists Review
0009-3157	Chemotherapy
0009-3165	Nihon Kagaku Ryoho Gakkai Zasshi
0009-3173	Chempress
0009-3203	Cherie Moda
0009-322X	Cherokee Phoenix changed to Cherokee Advocate.
0009-3238	Cherry Circle changed to C A A Magazine.
0009-3262	Chesapeake Science see 0160-8347
0009-3289	Cheshire Life
0009-3297	Cheshire Smile
0009-3300	Chesopiean
0009-3319	Chess changed to Chess.
0009-3327	Chess Correspondent
0009-3335	Chess Digest†
0009-3343	Chess in Australia
0009-3351	Chess Life and Review see 0197-260X
0009-336X	Chess 'n Checkers' changed to Pool Checker Masters.
0009-3378	Kyoto University. Chest Disease Research Institute. Bulletin
0009-3386	Chester White Journal
0009-3394	Chestnut Hill Local
0009-3408	Chetwynd Reporter changed to Chetwynd Echo.
0009-3424	Chez Nous
0009-3432	Chhandita
0009-3459	Chiba Medical Society. Journal see 0303-5476
0009-3483	Chict
0009-3491	Chicago Academy of Sciences. Bulletin
0009-3505	Chicago Bar Record see 0892-1822
0009-3513	Chicago Bowler
0009-3521	Chicago Daily Hide and Tallow Bulletin
0009-353X	Chicago Dental Society Fortnightly Review see 0091-1666
0009-3548	Chicago Fire Fighter†
0009-3556	Chicago Genealogist
0009-3564	Chicago Herpetological Society. Bulletin
0009-3572	Chicago Illini†
0009-3580	Chicago Journalism Review†
0009-3599	Chicago - Kent Law Review changed to Chicago - Kent Law Review.
0009-3602	Chicago Magazine†
0009-3610	Chicago Maroon
0009-3629	Chicago Medical School Quarterly†
0009-3637	Chicago Medicine
0009-3653	Chicago Police Star
0009-3661	Chicago Psychoanalytic Literature Index†
0009-367X	Chicago Purchasor
0009-3696	Chicago Review
0009-3718	Chicago Studies
0009-3734	University of Chicago. Pritzker School of Medicine. Alumni Association. Bulletin changed to University of Chicago. Pritzker School of Medicine. Alumni Association. Magazine.
0009-3742	Chicagoland Food News
0009-3769	Chicagoland's Real Estate Advertiser changed to Metro Chicago Real Estate.
0009-3777	Chicano Community Newspaper changed to El Chicano.
0009-3785	Chichester News changed to The Chichester Leaflet.
0009-3793	Chicory (Baltimore)†
0009-3807	Chief see 0746-7761
0009-3823	Jiefangjun Huabao
0009-3831	Education of Earth Science
0009-384X	Chiiki Fukushi
0009-3858	Chikitsak Samaj
0009-3866	Chikudenchi
0009-3874	Chikusan no Kenkyu
0009-3882	Child and Family
0009-3890	Child and Man
0009-3904	Child Care†
0009-3920	Child Development
0009-3939	Child Development Abstracts and Bibliography
0009-3947	Child Education
0009-3963	Child Health Investigation†
0009-3971	Child Life
0009-398X	Child Psychiatry and Human Development

5360 ISSN INDEX

ISSN	Title
0009-3998	Child Psychiatry Quarterly†
0009-4005	Child Study Journal
0009-4013	Child Weart
0009-4021	Child Welfare
0009-403X	Childbirth Education†
0009-4048	Childbirth Without Pain Education Association. Newsletter *changed to* Childbirth Without Pain Education Association. Memo.
0009-4056	Childhood Education
0009-4064	Children *see* 0361-4336
0009-4072	Mental Retardation News *see* 0199-9435
0009-4080	Children's Digest
0009-4099	Children's Digest (1950) *see* 0272-7145
0009-4102	Friend
0009-4129	Children's Hospital of the District of Columbia. Clinical Proceedings *see* 0092-7813
0009-4137	Children's House Magazine *changed to* Children's House - Children's World.
0009-4153	Children's Own
0009-4161	Children's Playmate
0009-417X	Children's Styles
0009-4196	Children's Theatre Review
0009-420X	Children's World
0009-4218	Child's Guardian
0009-4226	Chile - Economic Notes†
0009-4234	Chile-Economic Background Information†
0009-4242	Chile. Ejercito. Anexo Historico. Memorial
0009-4277	Chiltern Life†
0009-4285	Chimes (Notre Dame)
0009-4323	Chimie Actualites
0009-4331	Chimie Analytique *see* 0365-4877
0009-4366	Chimie et Technique
0009-4374	European Journal of Medicinal Chemistry
0009-4382	China Glass & Tableware
0009-4404	China News Analysis
0009-4412	China Notes
0009-4420	China Pictorial
0009-4439	China Quarterly
0009-4447	China Reconstructs *see* 1003-0905
0009-4455	China Report
0009-4471	China Today†
0009-448X	China Trade Report
0009-4498	China's Foreign Trade
0009-4501	Chinatown News
0009-451X	Chinchilla-Zucht†
0009-4528	Chinese Bulletin *changed to* Chinese-Canadian Bulletin.
0009-4536	Chinese Chemical Society. Journal (Taipei)
0009-4544	Chinese Culture
0009-4552	Chinese Economic Studies
0009-4560	Chinese Education
0009-4579	Chinese Journal of Administration
0009-4587	Chinese Journal of Microbiology *changed to* Chinese Journal of Microbiology and Immunology.
0009-4595	Chinese Language Teachers Association. Journal
0009-4609	Chinese Law and Government
0009-4617	Chinese Literature
0009-4625	Chinese Sociology and Anthropology
0009-4633	Chinese Studies in History
0009-4641	Chinese Voice
0009-465X	Ch'ing Documents†
0009-4668	Ching Feng
0009-4684	Chirimo
0009-4692	Chirogram†
0009-4706	Chiropodist *changed to* Journal of British Podiatric Medicine.
0009-4714	Chiropody Review
0009-4722	Der Chirurg
0009-4730	Chirurgia *changed to* Revista de Chirurgie, Oncologie, Radiologie, O.R.L., Oftalmologie, Stomatologie. Chirurgia.
0009-4749	Chirurgia degli Organi di Movimento
0009-4757	Chirurgia e Patologia Sperimentale
0009-4765	Chirurgia Gastroenterologica (Italian Edition)
0009-4773	Chirurgia Italiana
0009-4781	Chirurgia Maxillofacialis et Plastica
0009-479X	Chirurgia Narzadow Ruchu i Ortopedia Polska†
0009-4811	Chirurgia Triveneta
0009-482X	Chirurgia Veterinaria†
0009-4838	Chirurgien-Dentiste de France
0009-4846	Chirurgische Praxis
0009-4862	Chitalishte
0009-4870	Chitrali
0009-4889	Chitty's Law Journal†
0009-4897	Chizu
0009-4900	Map's Companion *changed to* Chizu no Tomo.
0009-4919	Chlodnictwo
0009-4935	Choc-Talk†
0009-4943	Chocolaterie, Confiserie de France *changed to* Magazine Strategies Gourmandes.
0009-4951	Chogin Research *see* 0287-2404
0009-496X	Choice
0009-4978	Choice (Middletown)
0009-4986	Choice†
0009-4994	Choisir
0009-5001	Choix Artistique et Litteraire
0009-501X	Choppers Magazine *see* 0194-9888
0009-5028	Choral Journal
0009-5036	Der Chordirigent
0009-5044	Chorleiter†
0009-5087	Christ und Buch
0009-5109	Christ und Welt *changed to* Deutsche Zeitung Christ und Welt.
0009-5117	Christadelphian
0009-5133	Christelijk-Historisch Tijdschrift†
0009-5141	Christelijk Oosten
0009-515X	Onze Vacature†
0009-5176	Christelijke Muziekbode *changed to* Muziekbode.
0009-5184	Die Christengemeinschaft
0009-5192	Christenlehre
0009-5206	Christian *see* 0092-8372
0009-5214	Christian Adventuret
0009-5222	Christian Advocate *changed to* Today's Ministry.
0009-5249	Christian Attitudes on Jews and Judaism *see* 0144-2902
0009-5265	Christian Beacon
0009-5273	Christian Bookseller *see* 0749-2510
0009-5281	Christian Century
0009-5303	Christian Communications
0009-5311	Christian Cynosure†
0009-532X	Christian Economics *changed to* Answers to Economic Problems.
0009-5338	Christian Endeavor World
0009-5346	Christian Family†
0009-5354	Christian Herald (Chappaqua)
0009-5362	Christian Heritage†
0009-5370	Christian Home†
0009-5389	Christian Home & School
0009-5397	Christian Institutes of Islamic Studies Bulletin *see* 0970-4698
0009-5400	Christian Labor Herald†
0009-5419	Christian Leader
0009-5427	Christian Life†
0009-5435	Christian Living
0009-5451	Christian Medical College Vellore Alumni Journal
0009-546X	Christian Medical Society Journal *changed to* Christian Medical & Dental Society Journal.
0009-5478	Christian Messenger
0009-5486	Christian Minister
0009-5494	Christian Monthly
0009-5508	Today's Christian Mother *changed to* Today's Christian Parent.
0009-5516	Christian News
0009-5524	Christian News Bulletin†
0009-5532	Christian News from Israel
0009-5540	Christian Nurse
0009-5559	Christian Order
0009-5567	Christian Peace Conference†
0009-5575	Christian Record
0009-5583	Christian Record Talking Magazine
0009-5591	Christian Recorder†
0009-5605	Christian Rural Fellowship. Bulletin†
0009-5613	Christian Science Journal
0009-563X	Christian Science Sentinel
0009-5648	Christian Socialist
0009-5656	Christian Standard
0009-5664	Christian Statesman
0009-5672	Christian Teacher†
0009-5680	Vanguard (Toronto)
0009-5699	Christian Voice
0009-5702	Christian Woman
0009-5710	Christianet
0009-5729	Christianisme au Vingtieme Siecle
0009-5737	Christianity and Crisis
0009-5753	Christianity Today
0009-5761	Christlich-Paedagogische Blaetter
0009-5788	Die Christliche Frau
0009-5796	Christliche Innerlichkeit
0009-580X	Christoffel-Blindenmission. Bericht
0009-5818	Christophorus
0009-5826	Youth Alive *see* 0190-6569
0009-5834	Christus
0009-5850	Christus in Israel†
0009-5869	Die Christus-Post
0009-5877	Christus Rex *changed to* Social Studies.
0009-5885	Christusruft
0009-5893	Chromatographia
0009-5907	Chromatographic Reviews *see* 0021-9673
0009-5915	Chromosoma
0009-5931	Chronica
0009-594X	Chronica *see* 1041-9764
0009-5958	Chronicle†
0009-5974	Chronicle†
0009-5982	Chronicle of Higher Education
0009-5990	Chronicle of the Horse
0009-6008	Chronicle of U S Classic Postal Issues
0009-6024	Chronicles of Oklahoma
0009-6040	Chronique de l'I R S A C
0009-6059	Chronique de Politique Etrangere *changed to* Studia Diplomatica.
0009-6067	Chronique d'Egypte
0009-6075	Chronique des Mines et de la Recherche Miniere *see* 0755-6365
0009-6083	Transport Echo
0009-6121	Chronique Sociale de France†
0009-6148	Chroniques de l'Art Vivant†
0009-6172	Chronmy Przyrode Ojczysta
0009-6180	Chronos†
0009-6199	Chrysalis†
0009-6202	Chubu Institute of Technology. Memoirs. Series A *see* 0910-8629
0009-6210	Chuck Wagon *see* 0891-0154
0009-6229	Chugoku Agricultural Research *changed to* Kinki Chugoku Agricultural Research.
0009-6237	Chugoku Electric Power Co. Technical Laboratory Report
0009-6245	Ch'ulpan Moonwha
0009-6253	Chung-Ang Herald
0009-6261	Chung Chi Bulletin
0009-6296	Chuo Law Review
0009-630X	Church Advocate
0009-6318	Church and Community†
0009-6334	Church & State
0009-6342	Church and Synagogue Libraries
0009-6350	Church Army Review *changed to* Church Army. Frontline News.
0009-6385	Church Growth Bulletin *see* 0731-1125
0009-6393	Church Herald
0009-6407	Church History
0009-6415	Church Labor Letter†
0009-6423	Media: Library Services Journal *see* 0884-6197
0009-6431	Clergy Journal
0009-644X	Church Music *see* 0305-4438
0009-6466	Church Musician
0009-6474	Church News†
0009-6482	Church Observer
0009-6490	Church of England Historical Society (Diocese of Sydney). Journal
0009-6504	Church of God Missions
0009-6512	Church of Ireland Gazette
0009-6520	Church of Light Quarterly
0009-6539	Church Panorama†
0009-6547	Church Quarterly†
0009-6555	Church Renewal†
0009-6563	Church Scene
0009-6571	Church Teacher *see* 0307-5982
0009-658X	Church Times
0009-6598	Churchwoman
0009-6601	Church World
0009-661X	Churchman
0009-6628	Churchman *changed to* Human Quest.
0009-6636	Churchman's Magazine
0009-6652	Casting and Forging *changed to* Chutanzo, Netsushori.
0009-6679	Cibles
0009-6687	Ciceroniana
0009-6709	Ciel et Terre
0009-6717	Ciencia Aeronautica
0009-6725	Ciencia e Cultura
0009-6733	Ciencia e Investigacion
0009-675X	Ciencia Interamericana
0009-6768	Ciencia y Naturaleza
0009-6776	Ciencias
0009-6784	Ciencias Administrativas†
0009-6792	Ciencias Neurologicas†
0009-6814	Cigar Makers' Official Journal†
0009-6822	Cigarette Card News and Trade Card Chronicle
0009-6830	Cimaise
0009-6849	Cimarron Review
0009-6873	Cincinnati Journal of Medicine *see* 0163-0075
0009-6881	Cincinnati Law Review
0009-6903	Cincinnati Purchasor
0009-6911	Cinderella Philatelist
0009-692X	Cine al Dia *changed to* Cine-Oja.
0009-6946	Cine Cubano
0009-6954	Cine News
0009-6970	Cine Technicians' Association of South India. Journal *changed to* C.T.A. Journal.
0009-7004	Cineaste
0009-7012	Cineclube do Porto. Boletim Circular *see* 0704-061X
0009-7020	Cinecronache
0009-7039	Cineforum
0009-7047	Cinemat
0009-7063	Cinemat
0009-7071	Cinema - Canada
0009-708X	Cinema de Amadores
0009-7101	Cinema Journal
0009-711X	Cinema Nuovo
0009-7144	Cinema Rangam†
0009-7152	Cinema e Societa
0009-7160	Cinemasud
0009-7179	Cinematografia in Presa†
0009-7187	Cinematografia Ita
0009-7195	Cines d'Orient†
0009-7209	Cinesiologie
0009-7225	Cinque Foil
0009-7241	Circolo Letterario†
0009-725X	Circolo Matematico di Palermo. Rendiconti
0009-7268	Circolo Speleologico Romano. Notiziario
0009-7284	Circuit Magazine†
0009-7292	Circuit News *changed to* Electricity U K.
0009-7306	Circuits Manufacturing *see* 1054-0407
0009-7314	Colegio Oficial de Farmaceutico. Circular Farmaceutica
0009-7322	Circulation
0009-7330	Circulation Research
0009-7349	Circulo
0009-7357	Circulo Odontologico de Rosario. Revista
0009-7365	Circus *changed to* Circus.
0009-7373	Cirque dans l'Univers
0009-7381	Cirugia del Uruguay
0009-739X	Cirugia Espanola
0009-7403	Cirugia Plastica Uruguaya
0009-7411	Cirugia y Cirujanos
0009-7438	Citatelt
0009-7446	Citation
0009-7489	Cahiers de Cite Libre
0009-7500	Cites et Villes†
0009-7527	Cithara

ISSN	Title
0009-7535	Cities and Villages
0009-7543	Citizen (Denver)
0009-7551	Citizen and Week End Review
0009-756X	Citizens' Business
0009-7578	Citrograph
0009-7586	Citrus and Vegetable Magazine
0009-7594	Citrus Industry Magazine
0009-7608	Citrus World†
0009-7616	Citta di Milano†
0009-7624	Patavium†
0009-7632	Citta di Vita
0009-7640	Citta e Societa
0009-7667	Cittadino Canadese
0009-7675	City†
0009-7683	City Almanac†
0009-7691	City Art Museum of Saint Louis. Bulletin changed to St. Louis Art Museum. Bulletin.
0009-7705	City Beautiful
0009-7713	City Business Courier†
0009-7721	City Club Comments changed to City Club Gadfly.
0009-7748	City Press†
0009-7756	Ciudad de Dios
0009-7764	Civic Administration see 0829-772X
0009-7772	Civic Affairs
0009-7780	Civic Forum
0009-7799	Civic Leader†
0009-7845	Civil Engineer in South Africa
0009-7853	Civil Engineering (New York) see 0360-0556
0009-787X	Civil Engineering, Construction & Public Works Journal†
0009-7888	Civil Engineering Contractor
0009-790X	Civil Liberties (New York)
0009-7918	Civil Liberties Bulletin†
0009-7926	Civil Liberties in New York see 0746-0201
0009-7934	Civil Liberties Reporter
0009-7942	Rights, Opportunities, Action Reporter†
0009-7969	Civil Rights Digest changed to New Perspectives.
0009-7985	Civil Service Journal see 0198-8557
0009-8000	Civil Service Leader
0009-8019	Civil Service News Releases changed to Civil Service News.
0009-8027	Civil Service Opinion changed to National Union for Civil and Public Servants. Journal.
0009-8035	Civil Service Review/Revue du Service Civil changed to Public Service Alliance of Canada. Review/Revue.
0009-8051	Civil Service Sports Quarterly†
0009-806X	Civil Transport Data Sheets
0009-8078	Civil War History
0009-8086	Civil War Round Table Digest
0009-8094	Civil War Times Illustrated
0009-8108	Civil War Token Society. Journal
0009-8132	Civilingenjoersfoerbundets Tidskrift see 0348-6087
0009-8140	Civilisations
0009-8159	Civilt Foersvar
0009-8167	Civilta Cattolica
0009-8175	Civilta' della Strada†
0009-8191	Civitas
0009-8205	Cizi Jazyky ve Skole changed to Cizi Jazyky.
0009-8213	Clan McLaren Society, U S A. Quarterly
0009-8221	Clare Market Review†
0009-823X	Claridad
0009-8256	Clarin Economico
0009-8264	Clark County School Letter changed to Educator.
0009-8272	Clark Now†
0009-8280	C L A S S: Reading†
0009-8299	Classe e Stato†
0009-8310	Classic Car
0009-8329	Classic Film Collector see 0275-8423
0009-8337	Classical Bulletin
0009-8345	Classical Folia†
0009-8353	Classical Journal
0009-8361	Classical Outlook
0009-837X	Classical Philology
0009-8388	Classical Quarterly
0009-840X	Classical Review
0009-8418	Classical World
0009-8426	Classici del Giallo
0009-8434	Classification Management
0009-8450	Classified Abstract Archive of the Alcohol Literature†
0009-8477	Classified Documentation List of Current Scientific Literature. Monthly Bulletin changed to C S M C R I Documentation List Monthly Bulletin.
0009-8485	Classroom Interaction Newsletter see 0749-4025
0009-8493	Claudia
0009-8507	Claudia
0009-8515	Claudia
0009-8523	Clausthaler Geologische Abhandlungen
0009-854X	Clavier
0009-8558	Clay Minerals
0009-8566	Canadian Clay and Ceramics see 0068-8444
0009-8574	Clay Science
0009-8582	Claycraft see 0959-6127
0009-8590	Claymore changed to Scottish Legion News.
0009-8604	Clays and Clay Minerals
0009-8620	Clean Water Report
0009-8639	Manual of Maintenance changed to Maintenance Buyers Guide.
0009-8647	Clean Air
0009-8655	Clearing House
0009-8663	Clearinghouse Announcements in Science & Technology†
0009-8671	Clearinghouse on Self-Instructional Materials for Health Care Facilities. Bulletin†
0009-868X	Clearinghouse Review
0009-8698	Clearway
0009-8701	Cleft Palate Journal see 1055-6656
0009-871X	Clemson University. College of Architecture. Semester Review changed to Clemson University. College of Architecture. Journal.
0009-8728	Cleo en la Moda
0009-8736	Clergy Review changed to Priests and People.
0009-8744	Clerk changed to A P E X.
0009-8752	Clessidra
0009-8787	Cleveland Clinic Quarterly see 0891-1150
0009-8809	Cleveland Engineering
0009-8817	Cleveland Food Dealer
0009-8825	Cleveland Jewish News
0009-8833	Cleveland Medical Library. Bulletin†
0009-8841	Cleveland Museum of Art. Bulletin
0009-885X	Cleveland Public Library Staff Association. News and Views
0009-8876	Cleveland State Law Review
0009-8884	Business Bulletin†
0009-8892	Clevelander
0009-8914	Clima Commerce International
0009-8930	Climate Control†
0009-8957	Climatological Data for Jakarta Observatory
0009-8965	Climb†
0009-8973	Climber and Rambler see 0955-3045
0009-8981	Clinica Chimica Acta
0009-899X	Clinica de Endocrinologia y Metabolismo. Boletin†
0009-9007	Clinica Europea
0009-9015	Clinica Gera†
0009-9023	Clinica Ortopedica†
0009-9031	Clinica Ostetrica e Ginecologica see 0304-0313
0009-904X	Clinica Otorinolaringoiatrica changed to Nuova, Clinica Otorinolaringoiatrica.
0009-9058	Clinica Pediatrica
0009-9066	Clinica Psichiatrica
0009-9074	Clinica Terapeutica
0009-9082	Clinica Veterinaria
0009-9090	Clinical Allergy see 0954-7894
0009-9104	Clinical and Experimental Immunology
0009-9112	Clinical Anesthesia†
0009-9120	Clinical Biochemistry (Tarrytown)
0009-9139	Quarterly Literature Reports. Clinical Biochemistry†
0009-9147	Clinical Chemistry
0009-9155	Clinical Electroencephalography
0009-9163	Clinical Genetics
0009-918X	Rinsho Shinkeigaku
0009-9201	Clinical Obstetrics and Gynecology
0009-921X	Clinical Orthopaedics and Related Research
0009-9228	Clinical Pediatrics
0009-9236	Clinical Pharmacology & Therapeutics
0009-9244	Clinical Psychologist
0009-9252	Clinical Radiology changed to Japanese Journal of Clinical Radiology.
0009-9260	Clinical Radiology
0009-9279	Clinical Research
0009-9295	Clinical Symposia
0009-9309	Clinical Toxicology see 0731-3810
0009-9317	Clinical Trends in Rheumatology†
0009-9325	Clinical Trials Journal changed to Clinical Trials and Meta-Analysis.
0009-9333	Clinicas Obstetricas y Ginecologicas de Norteamerica
0009-9341	Clinician
0009-935X	La Clinique, Ophtalmologique
0009-9368	Clio
0009-9376	Clio
0009-9384	Clio: Devoted to Commercials
0009-9414	Clipsheet†
0009-9422	Clique†
0009-9430	Clocktower
0009-9449	Close-Up see 0896-372X
0009-9465	Clothes see 0161-973X
0009-9473	Clothesline changed to National Clothesline.
0009-9503	Club
0009-9511	Club Alpino Italiano. Rivista Mensile changed to Club Alpino Italiano. Rivista.
0009-952X	Club and Institute Journal
0009-9538	Club Committee & Northern Free Trade News
0009-9546	Club du Griffon d'Arret a Poil Dur Korthal. Bulletin
0009-9554	Club Executive see 0192-2718
0009-9562	Club Folk†
0009-9570	Club Francais de la Medaille
0009-9589	Club Management
0009-9597	Club Managers Journal changed to Secretaries and Managers Journal of Australia.
0009-9600	Fussball Club Pforzheim. Club-Nachrichten
0009-9619	Club News see 0886-8832
0009-9627	Club Operations†
0009-9635	Club Secretary
0009-9651	Clube Filatelico de Portugal. Boletim
0009-966X	Clube Militar Naval. Anais
0009-9678	Salcofoon†
0009-9716	C M I Descriptions of Pathogenic Fungi and Bacteria changed to C M I Descriptions of Fungi and Bacteria.
0009-9724	Co-Ed see 0883-475X
0009-9740	Co-Op Highlights
0009-9759	Co-Op Maandbladt
0009-9767	Co-Op Report†
0009-9783	Cooperatie
0009-9805	Cooperative Information Bulletin changed to Cooperative Perspective.
0009-9813	Co-Operative Management and Marketing changed to Retail Marketing & Management.
0009-9821	Co-Operative News
0009-9848	Co-operative Review†
0009-9856	Co-Operatives Quarterly
0009-9864	Co-Partnership changed to Involvement of Participation.
0009-9872	Coach and Athlete changed to Coach and Athlete Magazine.
0009-9880	Coaching Clinic
0009-9899	Coaching Journal and Bus Review
0009-9902	Coagulation see 0301-0147
0009-9910	Coal Age see 1040-7820
0009-9929	Coal and Steel†
0009-9945	Coal Miner†
0009-9961	Coal Mining and Processing see 1040-7820
0009-997X	Coal News
0009-9988	Coal Research†
0009-9996	Canada. Statistics Canada. Coarse Grains Review†
0010-0005	Coast†
0010-003X	Coat of Arms
0010-0056	Cobbers†
0010-0064	Cobouw
0010-0080	Cock
0010-0099	Cockpit changed to Vliegtuigparade.
0010-0102	Cockpit changed to New Jersey Instructional Series.
0010-0110	Cockpit
0010-0137	Cocoa Statistics†
0010-0145	Coconut Bulletin changed to Indian Coconut Journal.
0010-0161	Cocuk Sagligi ve Hastaliklari Dergisi
0010-017X	Coda see 0820-926X
0010-0188	Codes Larcier
0010-0196	Codex†
0010-020X	Codicillus
0010-0226	Codeur†
0010-0234	Coeur et Medecine Interne see 0248-8663
0010-0250	Coffee Mazdoor Sahakari
0010-0277	Cognition
0010-0285	Cognitive Psychology
0010-0293	Cogwheel†
0010-0307	Cohesion†
0010-034X	Coiffure de Paris
0010-0358	Coiffure et Beaute†
0010-0366	Coimbra Medica†
0010-0374	Coin Dealer†
0010-0390	Coin Monthly changed to Coin Monthly (1980).
0010-0404	Coin-Op see 0092-2811
0010-0412	Coin Prices
0010-0420	Coin Slot see 0043-9304
0010-0439	Coin, Stamp, Antique News see 0702-3162
0010-0447	Coin World
0010-0455	Coinage
0010-0463	Coinamatic Age†
0010-0471	Coins
0010-0501	Coke and Chemistry U.S.S.R.
0010-0528	Coke Research Report see 0305-9545
0010-0536	Coke Review see 0305-8131
0010-0544	Colada
0010-0552	Colby Library Quarterly see 1050-5873
0010-0560	Colegio de Abogados de la Ciudad de Buenos Aires. Boletin Informativo see 0325-8955
0010-0579	Colegio de Abogados de Puerto Rico. Revista
0010-0587	Colegio de Abogados. Revista
0010-0595	Colegio de Bibliotecarios Colombianos.(Revista)†
0010-0609	Colegio de Ingenieros Arquitectos y Agrimensores de Puerto Rico. Revista
0010-0617	Colegio de Ingenieros de Caminos, Canales y Puertos. Boletin de Informacion
0010-0625	Colegio de Ingenieros de Venezuela. Boletin Informativo
0010-0633	Colegio de Profesores de Venezuela. Seccional No. 1. Boletin. Informativo
0010-0641	Colegio Medico de El Salvador. Archivas
0010-065X	Coleopterists Bulletin
0010-0676	Colfeian
0010-0684	Colgate changed to Colgate Scene.
0010-0692	Collage†
0010-0706	Collage
0010-0722	Collana di Monografie Turistiche†
0010-0730	Collectanea Botanica
0010-0749	Collectanea Franciscana
0010-0757	Collectanea Mathematica
0010-0765	Collection of Czechoslovak Chemical Communications
0010-0773	Femme Chic
0010-0781	Collections Baur. Bulletin
0010-079X	Collective Bargaining Negotiations & Contracts
0010-0803	Collective Bargaining Review

ISSN	Title
0010-0811	Collectivites-Express
0010-082X	Collector
0010-0838	Collectors Club Philatelist
0010-0854	Collector's World†
0010-0862	College see 0277-4720
0010-0870	College & Research Libraries
0010-0889	College and University
0010-0900	College and University Business see 0194-2263
0010-0919	College and University Business Officer see 0147-877X
0010-0935	College and University Personnel Association. Journal see 1046-9508
0010-0943	College and University Safety Newsletter changed to Campus Safety Newsletter.
0010-0951	College Board Review
0010-096X	College Composition and Communication
0010-0986	College Echoes†
0010-0994	College English
0010-1001	Education et Societe†
0010-101X	College Law Bulletin†
0010-1028	College Library Notes†
0010-1044	College of Dental Surgeons of the Province of Quebec. Information changed to Order of Dentists of Quebec. Information.
0010-1052	University of North Dakota. College of Education. Record see 0887-9486
0010-1060	College of Emporia Compass†
0010-1087	College of Physicians of Philadelphia. Transactions & Studies
0010-1095	College of Physicians, Surgeons and Gynecologists of South Africa. Transactions see 0375-3220
0010-1117	College Press Review see 0739-1056
0010-1125	College Press Service
0010-1133	Journal of College Radio
0010-1141	College Store Executive
0010-115X	College Store Journal
0010-1168	College Student Personnel Abstracts see 0748-4364
0010-1176	College Student Personnel Institute. Newsletter†
0010-1184	College Student Survey see 0146-3934
0010-1192	College Voice (Trenton)
0010-1206	Collegian (Elyria)
0010-1214	Collegiate Journalist†
0010-1222	Collegiate News and Views†
0010-1230	Collegiate Scene†
0010-1249	Collegio
0010-1265	Collezionista-Italia Filatelica
0010-1281	Colliery Guardian
0010-129X	Collins Signal Magazine†
0010-1303	Colloid Journal of the U S S R
0010-1311	Colloquium†
0010-132X	Colloqui Cremonese
0010-1338	Colloquia Germanica
0010-1346	Colloquium†
0010-1354	Colloquium Mathematicum
0010-1370	Colombia. Direccion General de Estadistica. Boletin Mensual de Estadistica see 0120-6281
0010-1389	Colombia. Ministerio de Defensa. Boletin
0010-1397	Colombia Today
0010-1419	Colombo Plan Newsletter
0010-1427	Colombophilie Belge
0010-1435	Colonial Courier
0010-1443	C N L
0010-1451	Colloquio: Letras
0010-146X	Color Engineering†
0010-1478	Color Engineering†
0010-1494	Colorado and Rocky Mountain Motor Carrier changed to Highland Highways.
0010-1516	Colorado Beverage Analyst
0010-1524	Colorado Business Review†
0010-1532	Colorado C P A Report†
0010-1540	Colorado Councillor changed to Colorado Kairos.
0010-1559	Colorado Dental Association. Journal
0010-1567	Colorado Editor
0010-1583	Colorado Engineer
0010-1605	Colorado F.P.†
0010-1613	Colorado Genealogist
0010-163X	Colorado Journal of Pharmacy
0010-1648	Colorado Magazine see 0272-9377
0010-1656	Colorado Manpower Review changed to Colorado Labor Force Review.
0010-1664	Colorado Municipalities
0010-1672	Colorado Music Educator
0010-1680	Colorado Nurse
0010-1699	Colorado Outdoors
0010-1702	Colorado Prospector
0010-1710	Colorado Quarterly†
0010-1729	Colorado Rancher and Farmer
0010-1745	Colorado School of Mines. Mineral Industries Bulletin see 0192-6179
0010-1761	Colorado State Library Newsletter changed to Centennial State Libraries.
0010-1788	Colores y Pinturas
0010-1796	Colorado-Rocky Mountain West†
0010-1818	Colour Review†
0010-1826	Colourage
0010-1834	Cols Bleus
0010-1842	Colstonian
0010-1850	Coltivatore e Giornale Vinicolo Italiano†
0010-1869	Columbia (New Haven)
0010-1877	Columbia Basin Farmer
0010-1885	Columbia College Pre-Med†
0010-1893	Columbia Daily Spectator
0010-1907	Columbia Forum†
0010-1915	Columbia Jester
0010-1923	Columbia Journal of Law and Social Problems
0010-1931	Columbia Journal of Transnational Law
0010-194X	Columbia Journalism Review
0010-1958	Columbia Law Review
0010-1966	Columbia Library Columns
0010-1982	Columbia Review (New York)
0010-1990	C.S.P.A.A. Bulletin†
0010-2016	Columbia University. Ancient Near Eastern Society. Journal changed to Ancient Near Eastern Society. Journal.
0010-2024	Columbian (Chicago)
0010-2032	Squires changed to Squires Newsletter.
0010-2059	Columbus Business Forum†
0010-2075	Column changed to S C A N.
0010-2091	The Columns (Fairmont)
0010-2105	Comarca de Suzano
0010-2113	Combat†
0010-2121	Combat
0010-213X	Combat Crew
0010-2164	International Laboratory
0010-2172	Combustion†
0010-2180	Combustion and Flame
0010-2199	Combustion Institute. Western States Section. Papers
0010-2202	Combustion Science and Technology
0010-2237	Comentarios Bibliograficos Americanos
0010-2245	Comercio
0010-2253	Comercio
0010-227X	Comercio & Mercados
0010-2288	Comercio Colombo Americano
0010-2296	Comercio Ecuatoriano
0010-2326	Comercio Hispano Britanico
0010-2334	Comercio Portugues changed to Comercio, Industria, Servicos.
0010-2342	Comercio y Produccion
0010-2350	Comercio y Produccion
0010-2369	Comhar
0010-2377	Coming up changed to Perspective (Berkeley).
0010-2385	Comin†
0010-2407	Comissao de Desenvolvimento Economico do Estado do Amazonas. Boletim Informativo
0010-2415	Comite Belge d'Histoire des Sciences. Notes Bibliographiques - Belgisch Komitee voor de Geschiedeis der Wetenschappen. Bibliographische Notas see 0771-6826
0010-2423	European Communities. Economic and Social Committee. Bulletin.
0010-2431	Olympic Review (Year)
0010-244X	Comites de Prevention du Batiment et des Travaux Publics. Cahiers
0010-2458	Officiel des Comites d'Entreprise et Services Sociaux
0010-2482	Commanders Digest see 0270-9015
0010-2504	Commando see 0031-1839
0010-2512	Commandos changed to Junior Life.
0010-2520	Comme les Autres
0010-2539	Comment†
0010-2547	Comment (London) changed to Focus (London, 1982).
0010-2555	Comment
0010-2571	Commentarii Mathematici Helvetici
0010-258X	Commentarii Mathematici Universitatis Sancti Pauli
0010-2598	Commentarium pro Religiosis et Missionariis
0010-2601	Commentary
0010-2628	Commentationes Mathematicae Universitatis Carolinae
0010-2644	Commentator†
0010-2652	Commentator
0010-2660	Comments on Argentine Trade
0010-2679	Comments on Astrophysics and Space Physics see 0146-2970
0010-2687	Comments on Atomic and Molecular Physics
0010-2695	Comments on Earth Sciences: Geophysics see 0276-8577
0010-2709	Comments on Nuclear and Particle Physics
0010-2725	Commerce see 0380-9811
0010-2733	Commerce International changed to London Commerce.
0010-2741	Commerce†
0010-275X	Commerce
0010-2768	Commerce†
0010-2776	Commerce†
0010-2784	Commerce & Industry†
0010-2792	Commerce & Industry Monthly Journal
0010-2806	Commerce des Combustibles†
0010-2814	Commerce du Levant
0010-2822	Commerce Education changed to Journal of Commerce Education.
0010-2830	Commerce Franco-Suisse
0010-2849	Commerce in France
0010-2865	Commerce Industrial and Mining Review
0010-2873	Commerce Moderne Urbanisme et Commerce see 0396-714X
0010-2881	Australia. Perth Chamber of Commerce. Commerce News†
0010-2911	Commercial Bulletin
0010-292X	Commercial Car Journal see 0734-1423
0010-2938	Commercial Courier
0010-2946	Decor and Contract Furnishing see 0020-5494
0010-2954	Commercial Expansion Reporter see 0036-3456
0010-2989	Commercial Fisheries Review see 0090-1830
0010-2997	Australian Commercial Fishing & Marketing
0010-3004	Commercial Grower see 0262-3765
0010-3012	Commercial Herald
0010-3039	Commercial Journal
0010-3047	Commercial Kitchen and Dining Room see 0190-8553
0010-3055	Commercial Law Journal
0010-3063	Commercial Motor
0010-3071	Allied Trades Association. Commercial News
0010-308X	Commercial Opinion changed to AssoCom Review.
0010-3098	Commercial Record†
0010-3101	Oregon Feed, Seed and Suppliers Association. Commercial Review changed to Commercial Review.
0010-311X	Commercial Teacher changed to Focus on Business Education.
0010-3136	Commercial Vehicles†
0010-3144	Northwestern Banker changed to Northwestern Financial Review.
0010-3160	Commercium
0010-3179	Commission
0010-3209	Commission on Accreditation of Service Experiences. Newsletter changed to American Council on Education. Center for Adult Learning and Educational Credentials Update.
0010-3217	Commitment†
0010-3225	Commodity Chart Service changed to C R B Futures Chart Service.
0010-3233	Commodity Trade Statistics
0010-3241	Commodity Yearbook Statistical Abstract Service changed to Commodity Yearbook Statistical Update.
0010-325X	Common Ground
0010-3276	Common Life
0010-3314	Commonplace Book†
0010-3322	Commons, Open Spaces and Footpaths Preservation Society. Journal changed to Open Spaces.
0010-3330	Commonweal
0010-3357	Commonwealth
0010-3365	Commonwealth Magazine
0010-3373	Commonwealth Education Liaison Committee Newsletter†
0010-3381	Commonwealth Forestry Review
0010-3403	Commonwealth Jeweller and Watchmaker changed to Jeweller, Watchmaker and Giftware.
0010-3411	Commonwealth†
0010-342X	Commonwealth Producer
0010-3438	Commonwealth Secretariat Rice Bulletin†
0010-3446	Communaute Autogestion†
0010-3454	Communaute Chretienne see 1188-5580
0010-3497	Communicatio Socialis
0010-3500	Communication Arts International
0010-3519	Communication Arts
0010-3527	Communication Disorders†
0010-3535	Communication: Journalism Education Today
0010-3543	Communication Reports†
0010-3551	Orvostorteneti Kozlemenyek
0010-356X	Communications
0010-3586	Communications Business changed to Communications and Cable T V Business.
0010-3608	Communications in Behavioral Biology see 0163-1047
0010-3616	Communications in Mathematical Physics
0010-3624	Communications in Soil Science and Plant Analysis
0010-3632	Communications News
0010-3640	Communications on Pure and Applied Mathematics
0010-3683	Communicator†
0010-3691	Communidades†
0010-3705	Communio
0010-3713	Communio Viatorum
0010-3721	Communique changed to Clipboard.
0010-3756	Communist Viewpoint†
0010-3772	Community (Chicago)
0010-3780	Community Comments see 0277-6189
0010-3802	Community Development Journal
0010-3829	Community Development Society. Journal
0010-3837	Community Health†
0010-3845	Community Health changed to Post Rock.
0010-3853	Community Mental Health Journal
0010-3861	Community Mental Health Services. Newsletter changed to Access (Tallahassee).
0010-3888	Community School and Its Administration†
0010-3896	Community Schools Gazette changed to Community Homes Gazette.
0010-3918	Community Teamwork†
0010-3926	Commutation et Electronique see 0242-1283
0010-3934	Compact see 0736-7511
0010-3942	Compact†
0010-3969	Companheiros

ISSN INDEX 5363

0010-3985 Companion of St. Francis and St. Anthony
0010-3993 Companion†
0010-4019 Company Law Journal†
0010-4027 Company News and Notes
0010-4035 Comparative and General Pharmacology *see* 0306-3623
0010-4043 Comparative and International Education Society. Newsletter
0010-4051 Comparative and International Law Journal of Southern Africa
0010-4078 Comparative Drama
0010-4086 Comparative Education Review
0010-4108 Comparative Group Studies *see* 1046-4964
0010-4116 Comparative Law Review
0010-4124 Comparative Literature
0010-4132 Comparative Literature Studies
0010-4140 Comparative Political Studies
0010-4159 Comparative Politics†
0010-4167 Comparative Romance Linguistics Newsletter
0010-4175 Comparative Studies in Society and History
0010-4191 Compass (Asbury Park) *changed to* Compass Magazine.
0010-4205 A I C S Compass (Association of Independent Colleges and Schools) *changed to* Career Education.
0010-4213 Compass (Norman)
0010-4248 Compensation Review *changed to* Compensation and Benefits Review.
0010-4299 Comple
0010-4310 Component Technology†
0010-4329 Comportamiento Humano
0010-4337 Composer†
0010-4353 Composers, Authors and Artists of America
0010-4361 Composites
0010-437X Compositio Mathematica
0010-4388 Compost Science *see* 0276-5055
0010-4396 Compostelle *changed to* Compostelle, Cahiers du Centre d'Etudes Compostellanes.
0010-440X Comprehensive Psychiatry
0010-4418 Comprendre
0010-4426 Compressed Air
0010-4450 Computable
0010-4469 Computer Abstracts
0010-4485 Computer-Aided Design
0010-4507 Computer and Information Systems *see* 0191-9776
0010-4523 Computer Applications Service†
0010-4531 Computer Bulletin
0010-4558 Computer Decisions†
0010-4566 Computer Design
0010-4574 Computer Digest *see* 0093-7290
0010-4582 Computer Display Review†
0010-4590 Computer Education
0010-4620 Computer Journal
0010-4639 Computer Management†
0010-4655 Computer Physics Communications
0010-4663 Computer Praxis *see* 0179-9738
0010-468X Computer Programs in Biomedicine *see* 0169-2607
0010-4728 Computer Science Newsletter *see* 0315-4661
0010-4736 Computer Services†
0010-4760 Computer Survey
0010-4787 Computer Weekly
0010-4795 Computers and Automation *see* 0361-1442
0010-4809 Computers and Biomedical Research
0010-4817 Computers and the Humanities
0010-4825 Computers in Biology and Medicine
0010-4833 Computers in Medicine Abstracts†
0010-4841 Computerworld
0010-485X Computing
0010-4868 Computing Newsletter for Schools of Business†
0010-4884 Computing Reviews
0010-4892 Computing Surveys *see* 0360-0300
0010-4906 Computopia
0010-4914 Comte de Jette Bulletin
0010-4922 Comune (Rome)
0010-4930 Comune Democratico
0010-4949 Comune di Bologna. Notiziario Mensile *changed to* Bologna.
0010-4957 Comune di Roma. Ufficio di Statistica e Censimento. Bollettino Statistico†
0010-4965 Comune di Roma. Ufficio di Statistica e Censimento. Notiziario Statistico Mensile
0010-4973 Comuni d'Europa
0010-5007 Instituto de Ciencias da Informacao Comunicacoes & Problemas
0010-5015 Comunicacoes Bioquimicas
0010-5023 Comunidad†
0010-504X Comunita
0010-5058 Comunita Europee *changed to* Dossier Europa.
0010-5066 Comunita Internazionale
0010-5074 Comunita Israelitica di Milano. Bollettino *changed to* Comunita Ebraica di Milano. Bollettino.
0010-5082 Combustion, Explosion, and Shock Waves
0010-5090 Con Edison Library Bulletin
0010-5104 Con Safos
0010-5112 Concept
0010-5120 Concept of Pakistan
0010-5147 Conceptos de Matematica
0010-5155 Conceptus
0010-5163 Concern (New York)†
0010-5171 Concern†
0010-5198 Concerning Food & Nutrition†
0010-5201 Concerning Poetry†
0010-5228 Conciliatore
0010-5236 Concilium
0010-5244 Concord†
0010-5252 Concordia
0010-5260 Concordia Historical Institute Quarterly
0010-5287 Concordia Torch
0010-5309 Concours Medical
0010-5317 Concrete
0010-5333 Concrete Construction
0010-5341 Concrete Construction and Architecture
0010-535X Concrete Industry Bulletin
0010-5368 Concrete Products
0010-5392 Conditional Reflex *changed to* Integrative Physiological and Behavioral Science.
0010-5414 Condor†
0010-5422 Condor (Tempe)
0010-5457 Confectioner†
0010-5465 Confectionery and Tobacco News *changed to* C T N.
0010-5473 Confectionery Production
0010-549X Confederacion de Camaras Nacionales de Comercio. Carta Semanal†
0010-5503 Confederacion Sudamericana de Asociaciones Cristianas de Jovenes. Noticias *changed to* Asociacion.
0010-5511 Confederate Historical Society. Journal†
0010-5546 Conference Board Record *see* 0147-1554
0010-5554 Conference Board Statistical Bulletin†
0010-5570 Conference on Latin American History Newsletter
0010-5589 Conferences du Cenacle
0010-5597 Conferences, Exhibitions and Executive Travel *see* 0260-8316
0010-5600 Conferencias
0010-5627 Confit
0010-5635 Confidencias†
0010-5651 Confidential Confessions†
0010-566X Confidential Detective Cases†
0010-5678 Confinia Neurologia *see* 1011-6125
0010-5686 Confinia Psychiatrica†
0010-5694 Confins *changed to* Lucre-Hatif.
0010-5708 Confort
0010-5716 Confrontation
0010-5732 Confronto†
0010-5740 Congiuntura Estera
0010-5759 Congiuntura Italiana
0010-5767 Congo-Afrique *see* 0049-8513
0010-5775 Congo Disque
0010-5783 Congo Magazine *changed to* Zaire Ya Sika.
0010-5805 Congo. Centre National de la Statistique et des Etudes Economiques. Bulletin Mensuel de la Statistique
0010-5821 Congregational Library. Bulletin
0010-583X Congregational Monthly *see* 0306-7262
0010-5848 Christian Leader†
0010-5856 Congregationalist
0010-5872 American Jewish Congress. Congress Bi-Weekly *see* 0163-1365
0010-5880 Congress Bulletin†
0010-5899 Congressional Digest
0010-5902 Congressional Monitor
0010-5910 Congressional Quarterly Service. Weekly Report
0010-5929 Rivista di Coniglicoltura
0010-5937 Conjunto
0010-5945 Conjuntura Economica
0010-5953 Connaissance de la Campagne†
0010-5961 Connaissance de la Mer†
0010-597X Connaissance de la Vigne et du Vin *see* 1151-0285
0010-5988 Connaissance des Arts *see* 0293-9274
0010-6003 Connaissance des Plastiques†
0010-602X Connaitre la Wallonie
0010-6038 Connchord
0010-6046 Connecticut Action†
0010-6054 Connecticut Antiquarian *changed to* The Landmark (Hartford).
0010-6070 Connecticut Bar Journal
0010-6089 Connecticut C P A *changed to* Connecticut C P A Quarterly.
0010-6097 Connecticut Conference Missioner†
0010-6100 Connecticut Conservation Reporter†
0010-6119 Connecticut Government
0010-6127 Connecticut Health Bulletin
0010-6135 Connecticut Industry *see* 0199-686X
0010-6143 Connecticut. Labor Department. Bulletin†
0010-6151 Connecticut Law Review
0010-616X Connecticut Libraries
0010-6178 Connecticut Medicine
0010-6208 Connecticut Purchaser *changed to* New England Purchaser.
0010-6216 Connecticut Review†
0010-6232 Connecticut State Dental Association. Journal
0010-6240 Connecticut Teacher†
0010-6259 Connecticut Woodlands
0010-6267 Connection†
0010-6275 Connoisseur *see* 0040-9952
0010-6283 Connoisseur's Guide†
0010-6291 Conocimiento de la Nueva Era
0010-6305 Conoscenza
0010-6313 Conparlist†
0010-6348 Conquiste del Lavoro
0010-6356 Conradiana
0010-6364 Argentina. Consejo Nacional de Investigaciones Cientificas y Tecnicas. Informaciones†
0010-6410 Conselho Estadual de Educacao de Sao Paulo. Acta
0010-6429 Consensus (Toronto) *changed to* Momentum.
0010-6445 Conservacionista†
0010-647X Conservation News†
0010-6488 Conservation Report *see* 0736-9522
0010-6496 Conservation Volunteer *changed to* The Minnesota Volunteer.
0010-650X Conservationist
0010-6518 Conservative and Unionist Central Office. Monthly News *changed to* Conservative News Line.
0010-6542 Conservative Judaism
0010-6550 Conservatoire de Musique de Geneve. Bulletin
0010-6569 Consiglio di Stato
0010-6577 Consol News
0010-6593 Consommation†
0010-6607 Constabulary Gazette
0010-6623 Constitutional and Parliamentary Information
0010-6631 Construcao Sao Paulo
0010-6658 De Constructeur
0010-6674 Construction *see* 1032-240X
0010-6690 Construction in Southern Africa†
0010-6704 Construction
0010-6712 Construction Advisor†
0010-6739 Construction Digest
0010-6755 Construction Equipment Distribution
0010-6763 Construction Equipment Magazine *see* 0192-3978
0010-6771 Construction Equipment Operation and Maintenance
0010-678X Construction Foreman's and Supervisor's Letter *see* 0744-7167
0010-6798 Construction Francaise *see* 0335-2021
0010-6828 Construction Industries and Trade Journal *changed to* Construction Industries and Trade Annual.
0010-6836 Construction Labor Report
0010-6844 Construction Methods and Equipment *see* 0270-1588
0010-6852 Construction Moderne
0010-6860 Construction News
0010-6879 Construction Plant Hire *changed to* Plant Hire.
0010-6887 Construction Products *changed to* Spectrum (Middletown).
0010-6895 Construction Products & Technology†
0010-6917 Construction Review
0010-6925 Construction Specifier
0010-6941 Construction West†
0010-695X Constructional Review
0010-6968 Constructioneer
0010-6976 Constructions Equipements pour les Loisirs
0010-6992 Constructive Action for Good Mental Health *changed to* Constructive Action Newsletter.
0010-700X Constructive Triangle *see* 1054-0040
0010-7018 Constructor
0010-7034 Construire
0010-7042 Consudel
0010-7050 Consulente Immobiliare
0010-7069 Consultant (Greenwich)
0010-7077 Consultant (Midland)†
0010-7085 Consultant (Columbia)
0010-7093 Consulting Engineer *see* 0956-9189
0010-7107 Consulting Engineer *see* 0892-5046
0010-7115 Consumers Affairs Bulletin *changed to* Co-Op Consumers.
0010-7123 Consumer Bulletin *changed to* Consumer's Research Magazine.
0010-7131 Consumer Buying Prospects *changed to* Economic Prospects.
0010-7158 Consumer Education Forum†
0010-7174 Consumer Reports
0010-7182 Consumers Digest
0010-7190 Consumers Voice
0010-7212 Contabilidad Administracion *changed to* Contaduria. Administracion.
0010-7220 Austria Contact
0010-7239 Contact†
0010-7247 Contact (London, 1955) *see* 0957-4883
0010-7255 Contact (Bromley)
0010-7263 Contact†
0010-7271 Contact Lens *see* 0306-9575
0010-728X Contact Lens Medical Bulletin *see* 0733-8902
0010-7301 Contact Point
0010-731X Contactblad
0010-7328 O A A G. Bulletin†
0010-7352 Container in Italia e nel Mondo *changed to* Eurotransports.
0010-7360 Container News
0010-7379 Containerisation International
0010-7387 Containers and Packaging†
0010-7395 Contamination Control *see* 0090-2519
0010-7409 Contamination Newsletter†
0010-7417 Contante y Sonante
0010-7468 Contemporary Authors
0010-7476 Contemporary Education
0010-7484 Contemporary Literature
0010-7492 Contemporary Literature in Translation†
0010-7514 Contemporary Physics

ISSN

5364 ISSN INDEX

0010-7522 Contemporary Poland
0010-7530 Contemporary Psychoanalysis
0010-7549 Contemporary Psychology
0010-7557 Contemporary Religions in Japan *see* 0304-1042
0010-7565 Contemporary Review
0010-7573 Contemporary Writers in Christian Perspective†
0010-7581 Contenido
0010-759X Contents of Contemporary Mathematical Journals *see* 0361-4794
0010-7603 Contents Pages: Electronics and Electricity†
0010-7611 Contents Pages of Iranian Science and Social Science Journals†
0010-762X Contenuti
0010-7646 Jaybee
0010-7662 Contigo *changed to* T V Contigo.
0010-7689 Continental *changed to* Hamilton History and Political Science Review.
0010-7697 Continental Bulletin
0010-7719 Continental Iron and Steel Trade Reports
0010-7727 Continental Magazine (Dearborn)†
0010-7735 Continental Paint and Resin News *see* 0266-7800
0010-7743 Contintentaler Stahlmarkt *changed to* Stahlmarkt.
0010-776X Continuing Education Report†
0010-7778 Continuous Learning†
0010-7794 Conto Dertien *changed to* Tussen Ons in.
0010-7816 Contra Costa County School Bulletin *changed to* Contra Costa Schools.
0010-7824 Contraception
0010-7832 Contract
0010-7840 Contract Bridge Bulletin
0010-7859 Contract Journal *changed to* Contract Journal (1979).
0010-7867 Contracting and Construction Engineer *see* 1032-0776
0010-7875 Contracting in the Carolinas
0010-7883 Contractor and Plant Manager†
0010-7913 Contractors' Electrical Equipment *changed to* Electrical Construction Technology.
0010-793X Contrary Investor
0010-7956 Contratista
0010-7964 Contrepoint
0010-7972 Instituto Ecuatoriano de Ciencias Naturales. Contribuciones
0010-7980 University of Wyoming. Contributions to Geology
0010-7999 Contributions to Mineralogy and Petrology
0010-8014 Controcorrente
0010-8022 Control and Instrumentation
0010-8030 Control and Science Record†
0010-8049 Control Engineering
0010-8065 Control Systems
0010-8073 The Controller
0010-8081 Controlli Numerici e Macchine *see* 0393-3911
0010-809X Controspazio†
0010-8103 Controvento
0010-8111 Convegno Musicale
0010-8138 Convenience Store Journal†
0010-8146 Convergence
0010-8154 Convergence†
0010-8170 Conversation et Traduction
0010-8189 Converter
0010-8197 Converting Industry *see* 0032-8707
0010-8200 Conveyancer and Property Lawyer
0010-8227 Convivium†
0010-8235 Convivium, Filosofia, Psicologia, Humanidades†
0010-8243 Convorbiri Literare
0010-8251 Cook County Highway News†
0010-826X Cookbook Digest
0010-8286 Cooks Continental Timetable *see* 0952-620X
0010-8294 Cooks Staff Magazine *changed to* Internationally Speaking.
0010-8308 Coop-Habitat
0010-8316 Cooperacion Libre
0010-8340 Cooperation *see* 0294-8303
0010-8359 Cooperation Agricole
0010-8367 Cooperation and Conflict
0010-8375 Cooperation et Developpement *see* 0395-9481
0010-8383 Cooperation Technique *see* 0395-9481
0010-8391 Cooperative Accountant
0010-8413 Cooperative Builder *see* 0896-9426
0010-843X Cooperative Education Association Newsletter
0010-8448 Cooperative Farmer
0010-8456 Cooperativismo & Nordeste†
0010-8464 Cooperator
0010-8472 Cooperator†
0010-8480 Cooperazione di Credito
0010-8499 Cooperazione e Societa
0010-8502 Cooperazione Educativa
0010-8510 Cooperazione Italiana
0010-8537 Cooper's Hero-Hobby†
0010-8545 Coordination Chemistry Reviews
0010-857X Copper†
0010-8596 Copper Abstracts *see* 0309-2216
0010-8626 Copyright
0010-8634 Copyright Bulletin
0010-8642 Copyright Society of the U.S.A. Bulletin *see* 0886-3520
0010-8650 Cor et Vasa
0010-8669 Coranto
0010-8677 Corcoran Gallery of Art Bulletin†
0010-8685 Cord
0010-8707 Corduroy†
0010-8723 C O R E S T A
0010-8731 Cork Historical and Archaeological Society. Journal
0010-874X Cork Weekly Examiner and Weekly Herald *changed to* Irish Weekly Examiner.
0010-8758 Cormorant†
0010-8766 Cormoran y Delfin
0010-8782 Cornell Countryman
0010-8790 Cornell Engineer
0010-8804 Cornell Hotel & Restaurant Administration Quarterly
0010-8812 Cornell International Law Journal
0010-8820 Cornell Journal of Social Relations†
0010-8839 Cornell Law Forum
0010-8847 Cornell Law Review
0010-8855 Cornell Newsletter, Chemicals-Pesticides Program†
0010-8863 Cornell Plantations
0010-8871 Cornell Program in Oral History. Bulletin *see* 0738-8128
0010-888X Cornell International Agricultural Development Bulletin *changed to* Cornell International Agricultural Bulletin.
0010-8898 Cornell University Medical College Alumni Quarterly
0010-8901 Cornell Veterinarian
0010-8936 Coronet†
0010-8944 Corpoandes *changed to* Corporacion de los Andes. Revista.
0010-8952 Corporate Communications Report†
0010-8960 Corporate Financing *see* 0020-3580
0010-8987 Corporate Planning: Formation, Operation and Management†
0010-8995 Corporate Practice Commentator
0010-9029 Correction Sidelights†
0010-9045 Corrections Digest
0010-9053 Corrective Psychiatry and Journal of Social Therapy *see* 0093-1551
0010-9061 Correio Agro-Pecuario
0010-9088 Correio Serrano
0010-910X Correo del Sur
0010-9118 Correo Economico
0010-9142 Corridor *changed to* Wordworks.
0010-9150 Corriere Nucleare†
0010-9169 Corriere dei Ciechi
0010-9177 Corriere dei Congressi†
0010-9185 Corriere dei Piccoli
0010-9193 Corriere dei Trasporti
0010-9207 Corriere del Farmacista
0010-9215 Corriere del Teatro
0010-9231 Corriere di Caracas
0010-924X Corriere d'Italia
0010-9258 Corriere Fitopatologico
0010-9266 Corriere Internazionale del Teatro
0010-9282 Corriere Sindacale†
0010-9290 Corriere Stenografico
0010-9304 Corrispondenza Socialista
0010-9312 Corrosion
0010-9320 Corrosion Abstracts†
0010-9339 Corrosion Abstracts
0010-9347 Corrosion Control Abstracts
0010-9355 Boshoku Gijutsu *see* 0917-0480
0010-9371 Corrosion Prevention and Control
0010-938X Corrosion Science
0010-941X Body Fashions *see* 0360-3520
0010-9428 Corset, Bra and Lingerie Magazine *changed to* Intimate Fashion News.
0010-9436 Corset de France *changed to* Dessous Mode International.
0010-9444 Corsetry and Underwear *see* 0308-9886
0010-9452 Cortex
0010-9525 Cosmic Research
0010-9541 Cosmopolitan
0010-955X Cosmopolitan Contact
0010-9568 Cosmorama Pictorial
0010-9576 Cosmos
0010-9592 Cost and Management *see* 0831-3881
0010-9606 Cost Engineer
0010-9614 Cost Engineering†
0010-9622 Value Engineering Digest - Defense Contract Guide *see* 0275-4371
0010-9630 Camara de Comercio. Boletin Informativo *changed to* Comercio.
0010-9649 Costruire Laterizi†
0010-9657 Costruttori Romani
0010-9665 Costruzioni
0010-9673 Costruzioni Metalliche
0010-9681 Cote d'Azur Agricole et Horticole *changed to* Cultiver en Provence Cote d'Azur.
0010-969X Cote des Coupons†
0010-9711 Coton et Fibres Tropicales
0010-972X Coton et Fibres Tropicales. Bulletin Bibliografique *see* 0010-9711
0010-9746 Cotswold Life
0010-9789 Cotton and General Economic Review *changed to* Cotton Outlook.
0010-9797 Cotton Digest *changed to* Cotton Digest International.
0010-9800 Cotton Gin and Oil Mill Press
0010-9819 Cotton Growing Review
0010-9835 Cotton's Progress†
0010-9843 Cottonwood *changed to* Cottonwood.
0010-9851 Couleurs
0010-986X Coulisse Diplomatique *see* 0015-3516
0010-9886 Council Fire†
0010-9894 Council for Research in Music Education. Bulletin
0010-9916 Council for the Protection of Rural England. Quarterly Bulletin *see* 0268-5795
0010-9924 Church Council of Greater Seattle. Occasional News *changed to* Source (Seattle).
0010-9932 Tanners' Council of America. Council News *changed to* Leather Industries of America. Newsbreak.
0010-9940 Council of Associations of University Student Personnel Services. Journal†
0010-9967 Council on America's Military Past. Periodical
0010-9975 A C C I Newsletter
0010-9983 Council of Library Technology. Newsletter *changed to* Council on Library - Media Technical Assistants. Newsletter.
0010-9991 Councilor
0011-0000 The Counseling Psychologist
0011-0019 My Counselor *changed to* Counselor (Wheaton).
0011-0027 Counselor (Langhorne)
0011-0035 Counselor Education and Supervision
0011-0043 Counselor's Information Service†
0011-0051 Count Dracula Society Quarterly *changed to* Castle Dracula.
0011-0086 Country & Western Express
0011-0094 Country and Western Roundabout
0011-0108 Country & Western Spotlight
0011-0124 Country Churchman†
0011-0159 Country Landowner
0011-0167 Country Life *changed to* National Country Life.
0011-0175 Country Life†
0011-0183 Country Life in British Columbia
0011-0191 Country Living (Owego)
0011-0205 Country Living (Covington)
0011-0213 Country Quest
0011-023X Country-Side
0011-0248 Country Song Roundup
0011-0256 Country Standard
0011-0264 Countryman
0011-0272 Countryman
0011-0299 Countrywide Sports†
0011-0302 Countrywoman
0011-0310 County Councils Gazette *changed to* County News.
0011-0353 County Progress
0011-037X Courage†
0011-0396 Courier (London)
0011-040X Courier (New York)†
0011-0418 Courier *changed to* Syracuse University Library Associates Courier.
0011-0426 Courier (Beaufort West)
0011-0434 Voedingsblad
0011-0442 Courrier Australien
0011-0450 Courrier Avicole†
0011-0469 Courrier: Cahiers d'Etudes et d'Informations *changed to* Association des Eleves et Anciens Eleves de l'Ecole Nationale Superieure des Postes et Telecomunications. Cahiers d'Etudes et d'Information.
0011-0477 Courrier de la Nature, l'Homme et l'Oiseau *changed to* Le Courrier de la Nature.
0011-0485 Courrier de la Normalisation *see* 0223-4866
0011-0493 Courrier de la Republique
0011-0507 Courrier des Echecs
0011-0515 Courrier des Messageries Maritimes *changed to* Compagnie Generale Maritime. Courrier.
0011-0523 Courrier d'Information-Rearmement Moral *see* 1017-2874
0011-054X Courrier du Littoral *changed to* Courrier du Littoral et de Bruges.
0011-0558 Courrier du Secretariat International de l'Enseignement Universitaire des Sciences Pedagogiques†
0011-0566 Courrier du Verre *changed to* Architecture de Lumiere Courrier du Verre.
0011-0574 Courrier Europeen
0011-0604 Courrier Industriel et Scientifique
0011-0620 Courrier Musical de France†
0011-0639 Courrier Vauclusien
0011-0647 Court Review
0011-0655 Couture†
0011-0671 Covenant Companion
0011-0701 Cover Note†
0011-071X Covered Bridge Topics
0011-0728 Covjek i Prostor
0011-0744 Craft Horizons *see* 0194-8008
0011-0752 Craft, Model and Hobby Industry *changed to* Craft and Needlework Age.
0011-0779 Craftsman *see* 1056-4225
0011-0787 Cranberries
0011-0795 Cranbrook Magazine†
0011-0809 Crane News†
0011-0825 Cranial Academy Newsletter *changed to* Cranial Letter.
0011-0833 Crawdaddy; Magazine of Rock *see* 0163-9404
0011-0841 Crazyhorse
0011-085X C R C Critical Reviews in Solid State Sciences *see* 1040-8436
0011-0868 Creationist†
0011-0876 Creative Camera
0011-0884 Creative Craft *see* 0146-6607

ISSN

0011-0892 Creative Drama†
0011-0906 Creative Plastics†
0011-0930 Creative Writing
0011-0973 Credit and Financial Management *see* 0897-0181
0011-0981 Credit and Financial Newsletter†
0011-099X Credit Communal de Belgique. Bulletin Trimestriel
0011-1007 Credit Executive
0011-1023 Credit Suisse. Bulletin
0011-1031 Credit Retailer
0011-1058 Credit Union Executive
0011-1066 Credit Union Magazine
0011-1074 Credit World
0011-1090 Credito Popolare
0011-1104 Creditreform *changed to* Creditinform.
0011-1139 Creel†
0011-1147 Creem
0011-1155 Creighton Law Review
0011-1171 Crescendo (Interlochen)
0011-1198 Cresset
0011-1201 Creuset, la Voix des Cadres *changed to* Cadres et Maitrise.
0011-121X Cri du Monde†
0011-1228 Crianca e Escola *changed to* Escola Fundamental.
0011-1236 Cricket
0011-1252 Cricket Quarterly†
0011-1260 Cricketer *see* 0266-7398
0011-1287 Crime & Delinquency
0011-1295 Crime Control Digest
0011-1309 Crime Detective†
0011-1317 Criminal Law Bulletin
0011-1325 Criminal Law Journal
0011-1333 Criminal Law Quarterly
0011-1341 Criminal Law Reporter
0011-135X Criminal Law Review
0011-1368 Criminalia†
0011-1376 Criminologist
0011-1384 Criminology
0011-1406 Crisi e Letteratura
0011-1422 Crisis (New York, 1910)
0011-1430 Crisis & Change
0011-1449 Cristallo
0011-1457 Cristianismo y Sociedad
0011-1465 Christ to the World
0011-1473 Criterio
0011-1481 Criterion†
0011-149X Critic (Chicago)
0011-1503 Critica
0011-1511 Critica d'Arte
0011-152X Critica Marxista
0011-1538 Critica Sociale†
0011-1546 Critica Sociologica
0011-1554 Critica Storica
0011-1562 Critical Quarterly
0011-1570 Critical Survey
0011-1589 Criticism
0011-1597 Criticon
0011-1600 Critique
0011-1619 Critique: Studies in Modern Fiction
0011-1627 Croatia Press†
0011-1643 Croatica Chemica Acta
0011-1651 Croce
0011-166X Crochet†
0011-1686 Croissance des Jeunes Nations *changed to* Croissance - Le Monde en Developpement.
0011-1694 Croit
0011-1708 Cromos
0011-1716 T T P I Trade Gazette
0011-1724 Cronaca Politica†
0011-1732 Cronache Calabresi†
0011-1740 Cronache d'Altri Tempi†
0011-1759 Chronica Dermatologica
0011-1767 Cronache di Archeologia e di Storia dell'Arte *changed to* Cronache di Archeologia.
0011-1775 Cronache Economiche†
0011-1783 Cronache Farmaceutiche
0011-1791 Cronica de Holanda
0011-1805 Cronica Medica†
0011-1813 Cronica Universitaria†
0011-183X Crop Science
0011-1848 Crop Science Society of Japan. Proceedings *changed to* Japanese Journal of Crop Science.
0011-1864 Crops and Soils *see* 0162-5098
0011-1872 Crops in India
0011-1880 Croquet Gazette
0011-1899 Cross†
0011-1902 Cross & Cockade Journal†
0011-1910 Cross and Crown *see* 0162-6760
0011-1945 Cross Country News
0011-1953 Cross Currents *changed to* Cross Currents: Religion and Intellectual Life.
0011-1961 Cross of Languedoc
0011-197X Cross Tie Bulletin *see* 0097-4536
0011-1988 Crossbow
0011-2011 Crossed Flags†
0011-202X Crossroads†
0011-2046 Crossroads (Newark) *changed to* Crossroads U.S.A. (Newark).
0011-2054 Crossroads (Pittsburgh)
0011-2070 Crow's Forest Products Digest†
0011-2089 Croydon Advertiser
0011-2100 Crucible
0011-2119 Crucible
0011-2143 Crusade Messenger *changed to* Crusader.
0011-2151 Crusader (Memphis)
0011-216X Crustaceana
0011-2186 Crux
0011-2194 Cruzada Eucaristica
0011-2208 Cruzado
0011-2216 Cruzeiro
0011-2224 Cry California *see* 0744-8686
0011-2232 Ceylon Journal of Medical Science
0011-2240 Cryobiology
0011-2259 Cryogenic Information Report *see* 1052-0139
0011-2275 Cryogenics
0011-2283 Cryogenics and Industrial Gases†
0011-2291 Immortality Magazine†
0011-2305 Crystal Lattice Defects *see* 0732-8699
0011-2313 C S A and the Consumer
0011-2321 Ctenar
0011-2348 Cuaderno Cultural†
0011-2364 Cuadernos de Arquitectura *changed to* Quaderns d'Arquitectura i Urbanisme.
0011-2372 Cuadernos de Botanica Canaria†
0011-2380 Cuadernos de Critica
0011-2429 Cuadernos de la Boca del Riachuelo
0011-2445 Cuadernos de Literatura†
0011-2453 Cuadernos de Orientacion Familiar *changed to* Delta (Barcelona).
0011-2488 Cuadernos de Ruedo Iberico
0011-250X Cuadernos Hispanoamericanos
0011-2526 Cuadernos Latinoamericanos de Economia Humana *changed to* Centro Latinoamericano de Economia Humana. Publicaciones.
0011-2534 Cuadernos para el Dialogo†
0011-2550 Cuadernos Trimestrales de Poesia
0011-2569 Cuadernos Universitarios
0011-2577 Cuadernos Valencianos de Historia de la Medicina y de la Ciencia
0011-2585 Cuba - Foreign Trade†
0011-2593 Cuba Internacional
0011-2607 Cuba Noticias Economicas†
0011-2615 Cuba. Oficina Nacional de Invenciones, Informacion Tecnica y Marcas. Boletin Oficial
0011-2623 Cuba Socialista†
0011-2631 Cuban Studies Newsletter - Boletin de Estudios Cubanos *see* 0361-4441
0011-264X Cucciolo
0011-2658 Cue *see* 0028-7369
0011-2666 Cue of Theta Alpha Phi
0011-2690 Le Cuir Paris
0011-2704 Cuisine et Vins de France
0011-2720 Cukoripar
0011-2739 Culinary Times
0011-2747 Cultivador Moderno
0011-2755 Cultura
0011-2763 Cultura Boliviana
0011-2771 Cultura e Scuola
0011-278X Cultura Hispanica
0011-2798 Cultura nel Mondo
0011-2801 Cultura Popolare†
0011-281X Cultura Turcica
0011-2828 Cultural Affairs†
0011-2836 Cultural Comercial
0011-2844 Cultural Events in Africa
0011-2852 Cultural Forum†
0011-2860 Cultural Hermeneutics *see* 0191-4537
0011-2879 Cultural News from Germany *changed to* Kulturbrief - A German Review.
0011-2887 Cultural News from India†
0011-2895 Cultural Research Institute. Bulletin
0011-2925 Culture Francaise
0011-2941 Groningen
0011-2976 Cumberland Presbyterian
0011-2984 Cumbria
0011-300X Cumulative Book Index
0011-3018 Cumulative Index to Nursing Literature *see* 0146-5554
0011-3026 Cumulative Stock Profits
0011-3034 Cuoio Pelli Materie Concianti
0011-3050 Cupula†
0011-3069 Curator
0011-3093 Curlew
0011-3107 Curling *changed to* Svensk Curling.
0011-3115 Northern Curling Review
0011-3123 Current Weekly
0011-3131 Current (Washington, 1960)
0011-3158 Current Abstracts of Chemistry and Index Chemicus *see* 0891-6055
0011-3166 Current Abstracts of the Soviet Press *changed to* Current Digest of the Post-Soviet Press.
0011-3174 University of Illinois at Urbana-Champaign. College of Agriculture. Current Affairs†
0011-3182 Current Affairs Bulletin
0011-3190 Indo-Pacific Fisheries Council. Current Affairs Bulletin†
0011-3204 Current Anthropology
0011-3212 Current Archaeology
0011-3220 Cryogenic Data Center. Current Awareness Service *see* 0364-0868
0011-3239 Current Bibliography for Aquatic Sciences and Fisheries *see* 0140-5373
0011-3239 Current Bibliography for Aquatic Sciences and Fisheries *see* 0140-5381
0011-3247 Current Bibliography of Epidemiology†
0011-3255 Current Bibliography on African Affairs
0011-3263 Current Bibliography on Science and Technology: Nuclear Engineering
0011-3271 Current Bibliography on Science and Technology: Chemistry and Chemical Engineering (Foreign)
0011-3298 Current Bibliography on Science and Technology: Electronics and Electrical Engineering
0011-3301 Current Bibliography on Science and Technology: Earth Science, Mining and Metallurgy
0011-331X Current Bibliography on Science and Technology: Mechanical Engineering
0011-3328 Current Bibliography on Science and Technology: Management Science and Systems Engineering
0011-3336 Current Bibliography on Science and Technology: Pure and Applied Physics
0011-3344 Current Biography
0011-3352 Current Books for Academic Libraries *see* 0360-473X
0011-3360 Current Compensation References†
0011-3379 C C A F V (Current Contents, Agricultural, Food and Veterinary Sciences) *see* 0090-0508
0011-3387 C C B S E (Current Contents, Behavioral, Social and Educational Sciences) *see* 0092-6361
0011-3395 Current Contents: Engineering and Technology *see* 0095-7917
0011-3409 Current Contents: Life Sciences
0011-3417 Current Contents, Physical and Chemical Sciences *see* 0163-2574
0011-3425 Current Digest of the Soviet Press *changed to* Current Digest of the Post-Soviet Press.
0011-3433 Current Documents from the German Democratic Republic†
0011-3468 Current Events (Fredericton) *changed to* N.B. Power News.
0011-3484 Current Events
0011-3492 Current Events
0011-3506 Current Food Additives Legislation†
0011-3514 Current Geographical Publications
0011-3522 Current Hawaiiana *changed to* Hawaiian Acquisition List.
0011-3530 Current History
0011-3557 Current Index to Conference Papers†
0011-3565 Current Index to Journals in Education
0011-3573 Current Indian Statutes
0011-359X Current Journals in Baker Library. Part One - Author and Title†
0011-3603 Current Journals in Baker Library. Part Two - Subject†
0011-3611 Current Laboratory Practice†
0011-362X Current Law
0011-3638 Current Leather Literature *changed to* Leather Science Abstracts.
0011-3646 Current Legal Bibliography†
0011-3654 Current Literature in Traffic and Transportation
0011-3662 Current Literature on Aging *see* 1047-4862
0011-3689 Current Medical Abstracts for Practitioners†
0011-3700 Current Medical Practice
0011-3719 Current Medicine for Attorneys†
0011-3727 Current Municipal Problems
0011-3735 Current Musicology
0011-3751 Current Notes on International Affairs *changed to* Australian Foreign Affairs and Trade: The Monthly Record.
0011-3778 Current Papers in Electrical & Electronics Engineering
0011-3786 Current Papers in Physics
0011-3794 Current Papers on Computers & Control
0011-3824 Current Podiatry *see* 0893-2034
0011-3832 Current Practices†
0011-3840 Current Problems in Surgery
0011-3859 Current Publications in Legal and Related Fields
0011-3867 Current Publications in Family Planning *see* 0039-3665
0011-3883 Current Scene†
0011-3891 Current Science
0011-3905 Current Science
0011-3913 Current Slang†
0011-3921 Current Sociology
0011-393X Current Therapeutic Research
0011-3948 Current Tissue Culture Literature *see* 0090-0753
0011-3964 Current Topics in Radiation Research†
0011-3972 U.S. Bureau of Labor Statistics. Current Wage Developments
0011-3999 Current Work in the History of Medicine
0011-4006 Currents *see* 0738-7776
0011-4014 Currents in Modern Biology *see* 0303-2647
0011-4022 Curriculum†
0011-4049 Curriculum Theory Network *see* 0362-6784
0011-4057 Cursillo
0011-4065 Curtain, Drapery and Bedspread Magazine *see* 0892-743X
0011-4073 Curtis's Botanical Magazine *see* 0265-3842
0011-409X Cushman Foundation for Foraminiferal Research. Contributions *see* 0096-1191
0011-4103 Custodian's Letter†
0011-4111 Custom Applicator
0011-412X Custom Tailor
0011-4146 Customs Bulletin
0011-4154 Customs Imports and Exports Journal
0011-4162 Cutis
0011-4170 Cutler-Hammer Record
0011-4189 Cutting Tool Engineering

ISSN INDEX

ISSN	Title
0011-4197	Cutting Tools
0011-4200	Cuvar Jadrana
0011-4219	Cybernetic Medicine
0011-4227	Cybernetica
0011-4235	Cybernetics *changed to* Cybernetics and Systems Analysis.
0011-4243	Cybernetics Abstracts
0011-426X	Cyclet
0011-4278	Cycle Guidet
0011-4286	Cycle World
0011-4294	Cycles (Irvine)
0011-4316	Cycling Weekly
0011-4324	Cycling and Motorcycling *changed to* Cycling & Motorcycling with the Scooter.
0011-4332	Cycling News *changed to* South African Cyclist.
0011-4359	Cyclo-Flamet
0011-4375	Cygnet
0011-4383	Cykel- och Sporthandlaren *see* 1100-052X
0011-4391	Cykel- och Mopednytt *see* 0280-3038
0011-4413	Cyklistikat
0011-4421	Cylchgrawn Llyfrgell Genedlaethol Cymru
0011-443X	Cylinder Theory Reports
0011-4448	Cymru'r Plantt
0011-4456	Cyprus Bulletin
0011-4464	Cyprus. Department of Statistics & Research. Quarterly Statistical Digestt
0011-4480	Cyprus. Ministry of Labour and Social Insurance. Quarterly Review *see* 0256-8314
0011-4499	Cyrano de Paris
0011-4510	Cystic Fibrosis. Quarterly Annotated Referencest
0011-4529	Cytobios
0011-4537	Cytogenetics *see* 0301-0171
0011-4545	Cytologia
0011-4553	Czasopismo Stomatologiczne
0011-4561	Czasopismo Techniczne *see* 0137-5911
0011-4561	Czasopismo Techniczne *see* 0137-592X
0011-457X	Czechoslovak Engineering Sciences Abstractst
0011-4588	Czechoslovak Film
0011-4596	Czechoslovak Film Press News *changed to* Film & Video News.
0011-460X	Czechoslovak Foreign Trade
0011-4626	Czechoslovak Journal of Physics. Section B *changed to* Czechoslovak Journal of Physics.
0011-4634	Czechoslovak Life
0011-4642	Czechoslovak Mathematical Journal
0011-4650	Czechoslovak Motor Reviewt
0011-4677	Czechoslovak Womant
0011-4685	Quattroruote Maret
0011-4693	D - A *see* 0161-5785
0011-4707	D A C News
0011-4723	D A Reviewt
0011-4731	D A S U P
0011-474X	D A V Magazine
0011-4758	D B - Kundenbrief
0011-4766	D B - Deutsche Bauzeitung - Die Bauzeitung *see* 0721-1902
0011-4782	D B Z
0011-4790	D B Z
0011-4804	D D F - Das Drogisten Fachblatt *changed to* D D F - Journal.
0011-4812	D D R - Sportt
0011-4820	DDR Verkehr *see* 0020-9511
0011-4839	D D Zt
0011-4847	D E C A Distributor *changed to* D E C A Dimensions.
0011-4871	D E S A L Reportajet
0011-4898	D E W Technische Berichte *see* 0724-7265
0011-4901	D F V L R - Nachrichten *see* 0937-0420
0011-491X	D F Zt
0011-4936	D H Lawrence Review
0011-4952	D I N Mitteilungen *see* 0722-2912
0011-4987	D K - Mitteilungent
0011-4995	D L - Q T C *see* 0178-269X
0011-5002	D L W Informationen zur Bau- und Einrichtungspraxis *see* 0172-2867
0011-5010	D L Z
0011-5029	D M
0011-5037	D M A Washington Newsletter *changed to* Marketing Advents.
0011-5045	D M G Newslettert
0011-5053	D M I - Nachrichten *see* 0342-0957
0011-5061	Deadline Data on World Affairs *changed to* Kaleidoscope: Current World Data.
0011-507X	D N Z International
0011-5088	D.O.
0011-510X	D P W V - Nachrichten *see* 0937-7425
0011-5118	D R C Newsletter *changed to* D R C News.
0011-5126	D R P A Log *changed to* Delaware Valley Business Magazine.
0011-5142	D S F - Journal
0011-5150	D S H Abstractst
0011-5169	D S T Z - Deutsche Stenografenzeitung
0011-5177	D.V.B.A. Publicaciones Tecnicas
0011-5185	D W I - Berichtet
0011-5193	D W V - Mitteilungen
0011-5207	Da-a - U dela
0011-5223	Dacca University Studies. Part A: Humanities *changed to* Dhaka University Studies. Part A: Arts, Humanities, and Social Science.
0011-5231	Dachshund
0011-524X	Dade County Teacher *changed to* U T D Today.
0011-5258	Dadost
0011-5266	Daedalus (Cambridge)
0011-5282	D A F Trucks Magazine *changed to* D A F Magazine.
0011-5290	Daffodil Journal
0011-5304	Dagspressen
0011-5320	Daheim bei der W A G
0011-5339	Dahl, Dunn & Hargitt's Moving Average Commodity Servicet
0011-5347	Dai Damu
0011-5355	Daiichi Kogyo Seiyaku Shaho
0011-5371	Daily Athenaeum
0011-538X	Daily Blessing
0011-5398	Daily Cardinal
0011-5401	Daily Construction Service
0011-541X	Daily Gleaner-Farmers Weekly
0011-5428	Daily Gleaner-Food Supplement
0011-5444	Daily Kent Stater
0011-5452	Daily Law Journal Record *changed to* Journal Record.
0011-5460	Daily News Record
0011-5495	Daily Telegraph Magazine *changed to* Telegraph Magazine.
0011-5509	Daily Variety
0011-5517	South Africa. Weather Bureau. Daily Weather Bulletin
0011-5525	Daily Word
0011-5533	Daily World *changed to* People's Daily World.
0011-5541	Dainichi-Nippon Densen Jiho - Dainichi-Nippon Cables Review *see* 0913-0101
0011-555X	Dairy and Ice Cream Field *see* 0198-9995
0011-5568	Dairy Council Digest
0011-5576	Dairy Farmer
0011-5592	Dairy Goat Journal
0011-5606	Dairy Guide
0011-5614	Dairy Herd Management
0011-5622	Dairy Industries *see* 0308-8197
0011-5657	Dairy, Natural and Dietary Food Industry Newsletter *changed to* Dairy Foods Newsletter.
0011-5673	Dairy Record *see* 0888-0050
0011-5681	Dairy Science Abstracts
0011-569X	Dairy Shorthorn Journal *changed to* Shorthorn Journal.
0011-5703	Dairy Situation *changed to* U.S. Department of Agriculture. Dairy Situation and Outlook.
0011-572X	Dairyman
0011-5738	Dairynews
0011-5746	Milk Reporter *changed to* Milk Marketer.
0011-5754	Dais *changed to* Monopoly.
0011-5762	Dak Tar
0011-5789	Minnesota Farmer *changed to* The Farmer - The Dakota Farmer.
0011-5800	Dalesman
0011-5819	Dalhousie Gazette
0011-5827	Dalhousie Review
0011-5835	Dallas
0011-5843	Dallas Bible College News *changed to* Dallas Bible College Herald.
0011-586X	Dallas Medical Journal
0011-5878	Dallas Notes *changed to* Iconoclast.
0011-5894	Daltons Weekly
0011-5908	Damals
0011-5916	Damernas Vaerld
0011-5940	Damn You
0011-5959	Het Damspel
0011-5975	Dan Smoot Reportt
0011-5983	Dance & Dancers
0011-5991	Dance Films Association and Dance Society Newsletter *changed to* Dance on Camera News.
0011-6009	Dance Magazine
0011-6017	Dance Newst
0011-6033	Dance Perspectivest
0011-6041	Dance Scopet
0011-605X	Dancing Times
0011-6068	Dandy
0011-6076	Danfoss Journal
0011-6084	Danish Journal
0011-6092	Danish Medical Bulletin
0011-6106	Danmarks Amtsraad
0011-6114	Danmarks Geologiske Undersoegelse
0011-6130	Danmarks Havfiskeri *see* 0011-6270
0011-6149	Danmarks Nationalbank. Monetary Review
0011-6157	Danmarksposten
0011-6165	Dansbalans *changed to* Volksdans.
0011-6173	Danses
0011-6181	Dansk Arbejde
0011-6203	Dansk Artilleri-Tidsskrift
0011-6211	Dansk Botanisk Arkiv *see* 0078-5237
0011-622X	Dansk Brandvaern *see* 0106-6072
0011-6238	Dansk Bridge
0011-6270	Dansk Fiskeritidende
0011-6297	Dansk Geologisk Forening. Bulletin
0011-6300	Dansk Grossist Tidende
0011-6319	Dansk Institutions Tidsskrift
0011-6327	Dansk Jagt *changed to* Jaeger.
0011-6335	Dansk-Kemi
0011-6351	Nye Dansk Landbrugt
0011-636X	Dansk Mejeritidendet
0011-6378	Dansk Missionsblad
0011-6386	Dansk Musiktidsskriftt
0011-6394	Dansk Ornitologisk Forenings Tidsskrift
0011-6408	Dansk Paedagogisk Tidsskrift
0011-6416	Dansk Patenttidende
0011-6424	Dansk Pelsdyravl
0011-6432	Dansk Psykolognyt *changed to* Psykolog Nyt.
0011-6440	Dansk Radio Industri *see* 0108-6626
0011-6459	Dansk Reklame *changed to* Markedsfoering.
0011-6475	Dansk Skovforenings Tidsskrift *see* 0905-295X
0011-6483	Dansk Smede-Tidende
0011-6491	Dansk Svejsetidende *changed to* Svejsetidende.
0011-6505	Dansk Teknisk Tidsskrift
0011-6513	Dansk Tiddskrift for Farmaci *see* 1100-1801
0011-6548	Dansk Vejtidsskrift
0011-6564	Danske Dyrlaegeforening. Medlemsblad *see* 0106-6854
0011-6572	Danske Kommuner
0011-6629	Danske Vognmaend
0011-6637	Darbininkas
0011-6645	Daring Confessions
0011-6653	Daring Romance *changed to* My Personal Love Secrets.
0011-667X	Dark Horset
0011-6688	Dark Shadowst
0011-6696	Umma
0011-6718	Darpon
0011-6726	D'Ars
0011-6734	Darshana International
0011-6750	Dartmouth College Library Bulletin
0011-6769	Dartnell Office Administration Servicet
0011-6777	Dartnell Sales and Marketing Servicet
0011-6793	Darwiniana
0011-6807	Dasein *see* 1045-2265
0011-6823	Data Journal *changed to* M S F Journal.
0011-6831	Data Managementt
0011-684X	Data Processing *see* 0950-5849
0011-6858	Data Processing Digest
0011-6866	Data Processing in Education *see* 0093-7290
0011-6874	Data Processing Magazinet
0011-6882	Data Processing Practitionert
0011-6890	Data Processort
0011-6939	Data Systems *see* 0046-6212
0011-6947	Data Trend *see* 0810-9451
0011-6963	Datamation
0011-6971	Dataweekt
0011-698X	Dateline Delhi
0011-7005	Datenjournal
0011-7013	Daughters of the American Revolution Magazine
0011-703X	Davar
0011-7048	Davkat
0011-7064	Dawnt
0011-7080	Day by Day
0011-7110	Israel. Ministry of Agriculture. Department of Fisheries. Dayig u-Midgeh be-Yisrael - Fisheries and Fishbreeding in Israel
0011-7145	Db, The Sound Engineering Magazine
0011-7153	D.C. Gazette *see* 0889-2202
0011-7161	Echo (De Aar)
0011-7188	De Paul Law Review
0011-7196	Deadwoodt
0011-720X	Deaf American
0011-7218	Dealerscope *see* 0888-4501
0011-7234	Dean Sherman's Forest Industry Affairs Letter *changed to* Forest Industry Affairs.
0011-7250	Decalogue Journal
0011-7269	Deccan Geographer
0011-7285	Deciduous Fruit Grower
0011-7293	Decimal Currency and Metrication Newst
0011-7307	Decision (Minneapolis)
0011-7315	Decision Sciences
0011-7323	Decisions of the Comptroller General of the United States
0011-7331	U.S. Department of the Interior. Decisions of the Department of the Interior
0011-734X	Deco Trefoilt
0011-7358	Decor
0011-7382	Decorating Craft Ideas Made Easy *changed to* Creative Ideas for Living.
0011-7404	Decorating Retailer
0011-7412	Decorating Your First Homet
0011-7420	Decoration - Ameublement
0011-7447	DECUScope
0011-7455	Dedalot
0011-7471	Deep-Sea Research and Oceanographic Abstracts *see* 0198-0149
0011-7471	Deep-Sea Research and Oceanographic Abstracts *see* 0198-0254
0011-748X	Defence Science Journal
0011-7498	Defender (Wilmington)
0011-7501	Defender
0011-7528	Defenders of Wildlife News *see* 0162-6337
0011-7552	Defense de l'Occidentt
0011-7579	Defense des Vegetaux *see* 0048-4091
0011-7587	Defense Law Journal
0011-7595	Defense Management Journalt
0011-7609	Defense Manager *see* 0092-1491
0011-7625	Defense Transportation Journal
0011-7633	Defensor-Chieftain

ISSN	Title
0011-765X	Defesa Nacional
0011-7668	Deficience Mentale - Mental Retardation see 0829-8815
0011-7676	Definition†
0011-7684	Dein Freund†
0011-7692	Dein Reich Komme
0011-7706	Deirdre†
0011-7714	Dekalb Literary Arts Journal†
0011-7722	Delavska Enotnost
0011-7730	Delaware Archaeology†
0011-7749	Delaware Geological Survey Reports of Investigations
0011-7765	Delaware History
0011-7773	Delaware Library Association Bulletin
0011-7781	Delaware Medical Journal
0011-779X	Delaware Today
0011-7803	D V I Magazine changed to Delaware Valley Business Magazine.
0011-782X	Delfts Bouwkundig Studenten Gezelschap Styles. Mededelingen
0011-7846	Delhi Law Times
0011-7854	Delhi Medical Journal
0011-7862	Deli News
0011-7870	Delinquency and Society†
0011-7889	Delirante
0011-7897	Deliverer
0011-7927	Delmarva Report†
0011-7935	Delo
0011-7943	Delo in Varnost
0011-7951	Delos
0011-796X	Delphin
0011-7978	Delta (Tigre)
0011-7986	Delta (Plymouth)
0011-7994	Delta (Budapest)
0011-801X	Delta (Washington) see 0025-570X
0011-8028	Delta Epsilon Sigma Bulletin see 0745-0958
0011-8036	Delta Farm Press
0011-8044	Delta Kappa Gamma Bulletin
0011-8052	Delta Pi Epsilon Journal
0011-8060	Paper Book
0011-8079	Deltawerken
0011-8087	Deltion Dieekiseos Epichiriseon
0011-8095	Deltion Dimotikis Vivliothikis Hermoupoleos†
0011-8109	International Committee on Irrigation and Drainage. Greek National Committee. Bulletin changed to Bulletin G C I D.
0011-8117	Greek Speleological Society. Deltion
0011-8133	National Foundation "King Paul." Deltion changed to Protovoulia.
0011-8141	DeLuxe General Rewind†
0011-815X	Demag Kurier
0011-8176	Demana see 0792-0814
0011-8184	D E Mly†
0011-8192	Democrat (Washington)†
0011-8206	Democratic German Report†
0011-8214	Democratic Journalist
0011-8222	Democratie Moderne
0011-8249	Demografia
0011-8265	Demografie
0011-8281	Demography and Development Digest†
0011-829X	Demokraat
0011-8303	Demokratische Gemeinde
0011-8311	Die Demokratische Schule
0011-832X	Demos
0011-8338	Demostat
0011-8346	Radio Waves and Examination
0011-8362	Den'gi i Kredit
0011-8370	Denken en Doen
0011-8389	Electric Furnace Steel
0011-8397	Denkisha no Kagaku
0011-8419	Denmark. Civilforsvarsstyrelsen. Orientation†
0011-8427	Denmark Quarterly Review
0011-8435	Radio, TV, HiFi & Electronics†
0011-8478	Electrophotography
0011-8486	Dental Abstracts
0011-8508	Dental Assistant Journal
0011-8516	Dental Association of South Africa. Journal
0011-8524	Dental Cadmos
0011-8532	Dental Clinics of North America
0011-8540	Dental Concepts†
0011-8559	Dental-Dienst†
0011-8567	Dental Digest see 0033-6572
0011-8575	Dental Echo
0011-8583	Dental Economics
0011-8591	Dental Guidance Council for Cerebral Palsy. Bulletin changed to Dental Guidance Council on the Handicapped. Journal.
0011-8605	Dental Health†
0011-863X	Dental Industry Newsletter†
0011-8656	Das Dental-Labor
0011-8664	Dental Laboratory News
0011-8672	Dental Laboratory Review†
0011-8680	Dental Management†
0011-8702	Dental Outlook
0011-8710	Dental Practice
0011-8729	Dental Practitioner and Dental Record see 0300-5712
0011-8737	Dental Products Report
0011-8745	National University of Iran. Dental School. Journal changed to Shaheed Beheshti University. Faculty of Dentistry. Journal.
0011-877X	Dental Student changed to Dentist (Waco).
0011-8788	Dental Survey†
0011-8796	Dental Technician
0011-8826	Denver Art Museum. Quarterly†
0011-8834	Denver Law Journal changed to Denver University Law Review.
0011-8850	Denver Public Library News see 0020-1405
0011-8869	Denver Quarterly
0011-8877	Osmania Medical College. Department of History of Medicine. Bulletin see 0304-9558
0011-8885	Department Store Employees Union. Local Twenty One Guide†
0011-8893	Department Store Management changed to Department Store Economist.
0011-8907	Department Store Suppliers changed to I.R.D.S.
0011-8915	Department Store Workers' Union. Local 1-S News
0011-8931	Depeche Commerciale et Agricole
0011-8958	Depeche Mode see 0299-3678
0011-8966	Depositaire de France
0011-8974	Derby changed to Esquire & Derby.
0011-8990	Derbyshire Life and Countryside
0011-9008	Derevoobrabatyvayushchaya Promyshlennost'
0011-9016	Dergi†
0011-9024	Dermato-Venerologie see 0028-386X
0011-9032	Dermatologia†
0011-9040	Dermatologia Ibero Latino-Americano see 0210-5187
0011-9059	International Journal of Dermatology
0011-9075	Dermatologica
0011-9083	Dermatologische Monatsschrift
0011-9091	Dermatology and Urology - Hifu to Hitsunyo changed to Nishi Nihon Journal of Dermatology.
0011-9105	Dermatology Digest see 0198-6643
0011-9113	Derriere le Miroir see 0761-4241
0011-9148	Deryn changed to Cip.
0011-9156	Des Moines. Public Library. Monthly Memo
0011-9164	Desalination
0011-9172	Desalination Abstracts†
0011-9199	Desarrollo†
0011-9202	Desarrollo Administrativo†
0011-9210	Descant
0011-9229	Desert Call
0011-9245	Design
0011-9253	Design see 0732-0973
0011-9261	Design
0011-927X	Design†
0011-9288	Design & Components in Engineering†
0011-9296	Design & Development†
0011-930X	Design and Environment changed to Urban Design Newsletter.
0011-9318	Design Australia†
0011-9342	Design Engineering
0011-9393	Design International changed to Design International. Issue B.
0011-9393	Design International changed to Design International. Issue A.
0011-9407	Design News
0011-9415	Design Quarterly
0011-9423	Designer†
0011-9431	Designer changed to Designer Specifier.
0011-944X	Designscape†
0011-9474	Desmos
0011-9490	Dessa Mina Minsta
0011-9512	Dessinateurs et Techniciens changed to Dessin et Technique.
0011-9520	Dessins et Modeles Internationaux see 0250-7730
0011-9539	Dessous Elegants changed to Dessous Mode International.
0011-9547	Destellos Evangelicos†
0011-9555	Destin changed to Destin International.
0011-9563	Destino†
0011-9571	Detail
0011-958X	Detergents and Specialties see 0090-8878
0011-9598	Detonator changed to Envoy (New York).
0011-9601	Detroit Dental Bulletin
0011-9628	Detroit Engineer see 8750-7811
0011-9636	Detroit Institute of Arts. Bulletin
0011-9644	Detroit Jewish News changed to Detroit Jewish News Ltd. Partnership.
0011-9652	The Detroit Lawyer
0011-9660	Detroit and Suburban Lutheran changed to Tri-County Lutheran.
0011-9679	Detroit Schools changed to Call to Action.
0011-9687	Detroit Society for Genealogical Research. Magazine
0011-9695	Detroit Teacher
0011-9709	Detroiter
0011-9725	Dettaglio Tessile e dell'Abbigliamento†
0011-9741	Deutsch als Fremdsprache
0011-9741	Deutsch als Fremdsprache issued with 0323-3715
0011-9741	Deutsch als Fremdsprache issued with 0323-3766
0011-975X	Die Deutsche Buehne
0011-9784	Deutsche Agrartechnik see 0323-3308
0011-9822	Deutsche Akademie fuer Staedtebau und Landesplanung. Mitteilungen
0011-9830	Deutscher Altphilologen-Verband. Mitteilungsblatt
0011-9849	Der Deutsche Apotheker
0011-9857	Deutsche Apotheker Zeitung
0011-9865	Deutsche Architektur see 0323-3413
0011-9873	Der Deutsche Arzt
0011-9881	Deutsche Aussenpolitik†
0011-989X	Deutsche Automobil Revue†
0011-9911	Deutsche Baumeister†
0011-992X	Deutsche Baumschule
0011-9938	Deutsche Beamte see 0933-0615
0011-9946	Deutsche Berufs- und Fachschule see 0172-2875
0011-9954	Deutsche Bibliographie. Das Deutsche Buch
0011-9989	Deutsche Buecherschau†
0011-9997	Deutsche Bundesbank. Mitteilungen
0012-0006	Deutsche Bundesbank. Monatsberichte
0012-0022	Deutsche Circus-Zeitung changed to Die Circuszeitung.
0012-0057	Deutsche Eisenbahntechnik see 0323-3553
0012-0073	Deutsche Entomologische Zeitschrift
0012-0081	Der Deutsche Fall Schirmjaeger†
0012-009X	Defazet
0012-0103	Sozialistische Finanzwirtschaft changed to Betrieb und Wirtschaft.
0012-0111	Deutsche Fischerei-Zeitung see 0373-689X
0012-012X	Der Deutsche Forstmann
0012-0138	Deutsche Gaertnerboerse see 0936-3734
0012-0162	Deutsche Gefluegelwirtschaft see 0340-3858
0012-0189	Deutsche Geologische Gesellschaft. Zeitschrift
0012-0197	Deutsche Gesellschaft fuer Geologische Wissenschaften. Berichte. Reihe A: Geologie und Palaeontologie, Reihe B: Mineralogie und Lagerstaettenforschung†
0012-0200	Deutsche Gesellschaft fuer Versicherungsmathematik. Blaetter
0012-0227	Deutsche Getraenke-Industrie see 0724-4266
0012-0235	Deutsche Gewaesserkundliche Mitteilungen
0012-0251	Deutsche Handelskammer in Oesterreich (Bulletin)
0012-026X	Deutsche Hebammen-Zeitschrift
0012-0286	Deutsche Hotel Zeitung changed to D G Deutsche Gaststaette - Deutsche Hotel-Zeitung Gastwirt und Hotelier.
0012-0294	Der Deutsche Hugenott
0012-0308	Deutsche Hydrographische Zeitschrift
0012-0316	Deutsche Ingenieurschule see 0340-448X
0012-0324	Deutsche Jaeger-Zeitung see 0720-4523
0012-0332	Deutsche Jugend
0012-0340	Deutsche Kameramann see 0343-5571
0012-0375	Deutsche Kunst und Denkmalpflege
0012-0391	Deutsche Landwirtschaft changed to Agrar-Inform.
0012-0413	Deutsche Lebensmittel-Rundschau
0012-0421	Deutsche Lehrerzeitung
0012-043X	Deutsche Literaturzeitung
0012-0448	Das Deutsche Malerblatt
0012-0456	Deutsche Mathematiker Vereinigung. Jahresbericht
0012-0464	Deutsche Mechaniker Zeitung†
0012-0472	Deutsche Medizinische Wochenschrift
0012-0480	Deutsche Milchwirtschaft
0012-0502	Deutsche Musikbibliographie†
0012-0510	Deutsche National-Zeitung
0012-0545	Deutsche Nationalbibliographie. Reihe C: Dissertationen und Habilitationsschriften
0012-0553	Der Deutsche Pelztierzuechter
0012-057X	Deutsche Polizei
0012-0588	Deutsche Post (Berlin)†
0012-0596	Deutsche Post (Frankfurt)
0012-060X	Deutsche Rechtsprechung
0012-0618	Deutsche Rentenversicherung
0012-0626	Deutsche Rheologische Gesellschaft. Berichte see 0340-8388
0012-0634	Der Deutsche Rundfunk- Einzelhandel
0012-0650	Deutsche Schachblaetter
0012-0677	Deutsche Schaefereizeitung
0012-0685	Deutscher Schreiner see 0341-8839
0012-0693	Die Deutsche Schrift
0012-0707	Deutsche Schuetzenzeitung
0012-0723	Das Deutsche Schuhmacherhandwerk see 0936-6121
0012-0731	Die Deutsche Schule
0012-074X	Deutsche Krankenpflege-Zeitschrift
0012-0758	Deutsche Seiler-Zeitung
0012-0766	Deutsche Sparkassenzeitung
0012-0774	Deutsche Steuer-Zeitung: Ausgabe A see 0724-5637
0012-0782	Deutsche Steuer-Zeitung. Ausgabe B changed to Steuer-Eildienst.
0012-0804	Der Deutsche Strassenverkehr
0012-0812	Deutsche Student
0012-0820	Der Deutsche Tabakbau
0012-0839	Deutsche Textiltechnik see 0323-3804
0012-0847	Deutsche Tieraerztliche Wochenschrift see 0341-6593
0012-0863	Deutsche Urmacher-Zeitschrift see 0932-464X
0012-0901	D V Z
0012-091X	Deutsche Versicherungszeitschrift†
0012-0936	Deutsche Vierteljahrsschrift fuer Literaturwissenschaft und Geistesgeschichte
0012-0944	Neue Volkskunst†

ISSN INDEX

ISSN	Title
0012-0960	Allgemeine Deutsche Weinfachzeitung see 0723-1350
0012-0979	Der Deutsche Weinbau
0012-0987	Deutsche Wissenschaftliche Kommission fuer Meeresforschung. Berichte see 0341-6836
0012-0995	Deutsche Wohnungswirtschaft
0012-1029	Deutsche Zahnaerztliche Zeitschrift
0012-1037	Zeitschrift fuer Neurologie see 0340-5354
0012-1045	Deutsche Zeitschrift fuer Philosophie
0012-1053	Deutsche Zeitschrift fuer Verdauungs- und Stoffwechselkrankheiten see 0863-1743
0012-107X	Deutscher Aerokurier see 0341-1281
0012-1088	Deutscher Alpenverein
0012-1096	Deutscher Drucker
0012-110X	Der Fass- und Weinkuefert
0012-1118	Deutscher Jaeger see 0340-7829
0012-1126	Deutscher Kantinen Anzeiger changed to Kantinen Anzeiger.
0012-1134	Deutscher Lebensmittelgrosshandel
0012-1142	Deutscher Lebensmittelhandel
0012-1169	Deutscher Palaestina-Verein. Zeitschrift
0012-1177	Deutscher Studenten-Anzeiger
0012-1185	Deutscher Verein fuer Oeffentliche und Private Fuersorge. Nachrichtendienst
0012-1193	Deutsches Adelsblatt
0012-1207	Deutsches Aerzteblatt
0012-1215	Deutsches Architektenblatt
0012-1223	Deutsches Archiv fuer Erforschung des Mittelalters
0012-1231	D A R
0012-124X	Deutsches Dachdecker-Handwerk changed to Das Dachdecker-Handwerk.
0012-1258	Deutsches Elektrohandwerk changed to D E - der Elektromeister und Deutsches Elektrohandwerk.
0012-1274	Deutsches Handwerksblatt
0012-1282	Deutsches Industrieinstitut Beitraeget
0012-1304	Deutsches Institut fuer Wirtschaftsforschung. Wochenbericht
0012-1312	Jahrbuch fuer Volkskunde und Kulturgeschichte see 0138-4503
0012-1320	Deutsches Medizinisches Journalt
0012-1339	Deutsches Museum. Abhandlungen und Berichte
0012-1347	Deutsches Steuerrecht
0012-1363	Deutsches Verwaltungsblatt
0012-1371	Deutsches Volksheimstaettenwerk. Informationsdienst
0012-138X	Deutsches Waffen-Journal
0012-1398	Deutschkurse
0012-1401	Deutschland - Frankreicht
0012-141X	Deutschland-Magazin
0012-1428	Deutschland Archiv
0012-1436	Deutschland-Berichte
0012-1444	Deutschland-Informationent
0012-1452	Der Deutschland- Sammlert
0012-1460	Deutschunterricht (Berlin)
0012-1487	Deutschunterricht in Suedafrika see 1016-4367
0012-1509	Deux Millet
0012-1525	Developer
0012-1533	Developing Economies
0012-155X	Development and Change
0012-1576	Development Digestt
0012-1592	Development, Growth and Differentiation
0012-1606	Developmental Biology
0012-1622	Developmental Medicine and Child Neurology
0012-1630	Developmental Psychobiology
0012-1649	Developmental Psychology
0012-1657	Developpement et Civilisationst
0012-1665	Devenir Historico
0012-1673	Devil's Advocatet
0012-1681	Devon and Cornwall Notes and Queries
0012-1711	Devotion au Saint-Esprit see 0396-969X
0012-172X	Dewey Newslettert
0012-1746	Dharma
0012-1754	Di Cyan and Brown Bulletin changed to Di Cyan Bulletin.
0012-1762	Dia Medico
0012-1770	Diabete see 0338-1684
0012-1789	Diabete et Nutrition
0012-1797	Diabetes
0012-1800	Diabetes in the News see 0893-5939
0012-1819	Diabetes Literature Indext
0012-1827	Diabetes Newsletter changed to Diabetes Update.
0012-1851	Diabetiker see 0341-8812
0012-186X	Diabetologia
0012-1878	Diafora
0012-1886	Diaghoniost
0012-1894	Diagnosi - Laboratorio e Clinicat
0012-1908	Internal Medicine and Diagnosis News see 0274-5542
0012-1916	Diagnosticat
0012-1924	Diagnostica
0012-1932	Diagnostyka Laboratoryjna
0012-1959	Diakoniat
0012-1967	Diakonia
0012-1975	Diakonie im Rheinland
0012-1983	Diakonische Werk see 0342-1643
0012-1991	Dialt
0012-2009	D A I R S and Systems for Instruction Newslettert
0012-2017	Dialectica
0012-2025	Dialetti d'Italia
0012-2033	Dialog (St. Paul)
0012-2041	Dialog
0012-2068	Dialogi
0012-2084	Dialogo
0012-2092	Dialogot
0012-2106	Dialogos
0012-2122	Dialogos
0012-2130	Dialoguet
0012-2157	Dialogue: A Journal of Mormon Thought
0012-2165	Dialoguet
0012-2173	Dialogue: Canadian Philosophical Review
0012-2181	Dialogue
0012-2203	Dialoguet
0012-2211	Dialogue (New York, 1962). Braille edition of 0012-222X
0012-222X	Dialogue (New York, 1962)†
0012-2238	Dialogue (New York, 1966)†
0012-2246	Dialogue (Milwaukee)
0012-2262	Dialogue (Washington)
0012-2270	Dialogue Calcutta changed to Dialogue India.
0012-2289	Dialogue on Campus
0012-2297	Dialoguer
0012-2300	Diamond News and South African Jeweller
0012-2319	Diamond Walnut News changed to Sun-Diamond Grower.
0012-2327	Diana
0012-2335	Diana (Marcianise)
0012-2343	Diana (Florence)
0012-2351	Diana Armi
0012-236X	Diapason
0012-2378	Diapason
0012-2386	Diario Italianot
0012-2416	Dibevo changed to Dibevo Vakblad.
0012-2432	Dickens Studies Newsletter see 0742-5473
0012-2440	Dickensian
0012-2459	Dickinson Law Review
0012-2467	Dictionnaire Permanent de la Construction
0012-2475	Dictionnaire Permanent Droit des Affaires
0012-2483	Dictionnaire Permanent Entreprise Agricole
0012-2491	Dictionnaire Permanent Fiscal
0012-2505	Dictionnaire Permanent Rural changed to Dictionnaire Permanent Rural (Droit, Social, Agricole).
0012-2513	Dictionnaire Permanent Social
0012-253X	Die Casting Engineer
0012-2548	Diecasting & Metal Mouldingt
0012-2556	Diemaking, Diecutting and Converting changed to Package Printing & Converting.
0012-2564	Dienen und Fuehren changed to Unterwegs (Leverkusen).
0012-2572	Dienender Glaube
0012-2580	Sonntagschulmitarbeiter
0012-2602	Diesel and Gas Turbine Progress see 1040-8878
0012-2610	Diesel Equipment Superintendent
0012-2629	Diesel - Lehti
0012-2637	Dietetique d'Aujourd'hui
0012-2645	Dietsche Warande en Belfort
0012-2653	Difesa Sociale
0012-2661	Differential Equations
0012-267X	Diffusion Data see 0377-6883
0012-2688	Difofu changed to Sedibeng.
0012-2696	Difusion Economica
0012-2718	Digest des Revues Techniques changed to Bulletin Bibliographique des Laboratoires Professionnels Francais et Belge.
0012-2734	U.S. National Labor Relations Board. Digest of Decisions of the National Labor Relations Board changed to Classified Index of N.L.R.B. and Related Court Decisions.
0012-2742	Digest of Investment Advices
0012-2750	Digest of Labour Cases
0012-2769	Digest of Neurology & Psychiatry
0012-2777	Digest of Opinions of the Attorney General
0012-2785	U.S. Library of Congress. Congressional Research Service. Digest of Public Bills and Resolutions changed to U.S. Library of Congress. Congressional Research Service. Digest of Public General Bills and Resolutions.
0012-2807	Journal for Special Educators of the Mentally Retarded see 0741-9325
0012-2815	Digest of the Soviet Ukrainian Presst
0012-2823	Digestion
0012-2831	Digital Integrated Circuit D.A.T.A. Book†
0012-284X	Dikobraz
0012-2858	Diliman Review
0012-2866	Dimanche
0012-2874	Dime Novel Round-Up
0012-2882	Dimension (Austin)
0012-2890	Dimension: Journal of Pastoral Concernt
0012-2904	Dimensioni
0012-2920	Dimossiotis changed to Nea Dimossiotis.
0012-2939	Dinamica Economica
0012-2971	Dines Letter
0012-3005	Dinaman
0012-3013	Dinteria
0012-3021	Diocesan Digestt
0012-303X	Diogenet
0012-3072	Diplomania see 0016-4364
0012-3080	Diplomatic Bookshelf changed to Diplomatic Bookshelf & Review.
0012-3099	U.S. Department of State. Diplomatic List
0012-3102	Diplomatic List of Arrivals & Departures
0012-3110	Diplomatist
0012-3129	Diplomlandwirt changed to V D L - Journal.
0012-3137	Dippy Postt
0012-3145	Spain. Direccion General de Archivos y Bibliotecas. Boletint
0012-3161	Power Electronicst
0012-3188	Reporter of Direct Mail Advertising changed to Direct Marketing Magazine.
0012-320X	Direction et Gestion des Entreprises
0012-3218	Direction for Youth Leaderst
0012-3226	Direction of Trade see 0252-306X
0012-3234	Directionst
0012-3242	Director
0012-3250	Director
0012-3277	Directory of Chemical Producers - U S A
0012-3293	Directory of Published Proceedings. Series S E M T - Science, Engineering, Medicine and Technology
0012-3307	Directory of Published Proceedings. Series S S H - Social Sciences - Humanities
0012-3323	Direttore Commerciale
0012-3331	Direzione Aziendalet
0012-334X	Dirigente Amministrativot
0012-3358	Dirigente Constructor
0012-3366	Dirigente Industrial
0012-3374	Dirigente Rural
0012-3390	Diritto Aereo
0012-3404	Diritto del Lavoro
0012-3412	Diritto delle Radiodiffusioni e delle Telecomunicazioni
0012-3420	Diritto di Autore
0012-3439	Diritto e Giurisprudenza
0012-3447	Diritto e Pratica Tributaria
0012-3455	Diritto Ecclesiastico changed to Diritto Ecclesiastico e Rassegna di Diritto Matrimoniale.
0012-3471	Diritto Internazionalet
0012-348X	Diritto Marittimo
0012-351X	Discipline and Grievances
0012-3528	Discobolo
0012-3544	Discographical Forum
0012-3560	Discoteca Alta Fedelta changed to Discoteca Hi Fi.
0012-3579	Discount Merchandiser
0012-3587	Discount Store News
0012-3595	Discours Social
0012-3625	Discovery (New Haven)
0012-3641	Discovery (Chicago)
0012-365X	Discrete Mathematics
0012-3668	Discretio
0012-3676	Discus
0012-3684	Discussion sur l'Alphabetisation see 0024-4503
0012-3692	Chest
0012-3706	Diseases of the Colon and Rectum
0012-3714	Diseases of the Nervous System see 0160-6689
0012-3730	Diskus
0012-3765	Dispatcher (San Francisco, 1942)
0012-3773	Dispensing Optician changed to Dispensing Optics.
0012-3781	Display Internationalt
0012-3803	Display World see 0745-4295
0012-3811	Disposables and Nonwovens
0012-382X	Disque-Tont
0012-3846	Dissent (New York)
0012-3862	Dissertationes Mathematicae
0012-3870	Dissertationes Pharmaceuticae et Pharmacologicae see 0301-0244
0012-3889	Distafft
0012-3900	Distributie en Zelfbediening,D6†
0012-3927	Distribution-Warehouse Cost Digest see 0894-7651
0012-3935	Distribution d'Aujourd'Hui
0012-3951	Distribution Worldwide see 0273-6721
0012-396X	C M I Distribution Maps of Plant Diseases
0012-3978	Distribuzione Modernat
0012-3986	Distributive Worker
0012-401X	District Heating changed to District Heating and Cooling.
0012-4028	District Mail
0012-4036	District Managementt
0012-4044	District Nursing see 0301-0821
0012-4060	District of Columbia Dental Society. Journalt
0012-4079	District of Columbia Nurses Association. Quarterly Reviewt
0012-4087	Distrofia Muscolare
0012-4109	D I T
0012-4125	Dithmarschen
0012-4133	Detail
0012-4141	Divadelni Noviny
0012-4206	Divine Life
0012-4214	Divine Word Messengert
0012-4222	Divinitas
0012-4230	Divorce Chats
0012-4249	Israel. Knesset. Divrei ha-Knesset
0012-4257	Divus Thomas
0012-4265	Divya Vani
0012-4273	Dix-Septieme Siecle
0012-4281	Dixie Contractor
0012-4303	Dixon Linet

ISSN INDEX 5369

ISSN	Title
0012-4311	Djezair
0012-432X	Djur-Expressen changed to Djurens Vaarld.
0012-4338	Djur och Natur†
0012-4346	Djurskyddet changed to Djurtidningen Djurskyddet.
0012-4354	Dnipro
0012-4370	Do It Yourself (Croydon)
0012-4389	Do It yourself-Markt changed to Muster und Farbe.
0012-4397	Do It Yourself Retailing†
0012-4400	Doberman News†
0012-4419	Dock and Harbour Authority
0012-4427	The Spectrum (Topeka)
0012-4435	Ad-Doctor
0012-4443	Doctor Communist
0012-446X	Doctrine and Life
0012-4478	Document Reproductie
0012-4486	Documenta Ophthalmologica
0012-4494	Documentacion Administrativa
0012-4508	Documentaliste - Sciences de l'Information
0012-4516	Documentatie†
0012-4524	Documentatie Verkeerseconomie en Aanverwante Onderwerpent
0012-4532	Documentatieblad see 0167-5850
0012-4540	Netherlands. Ministerie van Onderwijs en Wetenschappen. Documentatieblad see 0167-6644
0012-4559	Documentatio Geographica see 0341-2431
0012-4567	Societe Nationale des Chemins de Fer Belges. Documentaire see 0771-517X
0012-4583	Documentation - Technique, Scientifique et Commerciale
0012-4591	International Cooperative Alliance. Regional Office and Education Centre for South-East Asia. Documentation Bulletin changed to Documentation Bulletin for South-East Asia.
0012-4613	Documentation Catholique
0012-4621	Documentation Commerciale et Comptable
0012-463X	Documentation East-European Agricultural Literature†
0012-4648	Documentation Economique†
0012-4656	Documentation Francaise Illustree†
0012-4680	Documentation Rapide du Chef d'Enterprise see 0395-451X
0012-4699	Documentation Sociale†
0012-4702	Electricite de France. Documentation Technique see 1142-3153
0012-4710	Documentazione sui Paesi dell'Est
0012-4729	Documenti di Architettura†
0012-4737	Documenti di Vita Comunale
0012-4753	Documentos†
0012-477X	Documents et Debats
0012-4788	Documents et Statistiques†
0012-480X	Dodge Construction News. Chicago Edition
0012-4850	Dog News see 0309-1031
0012-4877	Dog Review of Southern Africa†
0012-4885	Dog World
0012-4893	Dog World
0012-4907	Dogar's General Knowledge Digest
0012-4931	Dohanyipar
0012-494X	Academy of Sciences of the U S S R. Doklady. Earth Science Sections see 0891-5571
0012-4958	Doklady Biochemistry
0012-4966	Doklady Biological Sciences
0012-4974	Doklady Biophysics
0012-4982	Doklady Botanical Sciences
0012-4990	Doklady Chemical Technology
0012-5008	Doklady Chemistry
0012-5016	Doklady Physical Chemistry
0012-5032	Dokumentacja Geograficzna
0012-5059	D F W Dokumentation-Information
0012-5067	Dokumentation der Deutschen Binnenschiffahrt†
0012-5075	Dokumentation der Gesetze und Verordnungen Osteuropas
0012-5091	Dokumentation der Zeit†
0012-5105	Dokumentation fuer Bodenmechanik - Grundbau - Felsmechanik - Ingenieurgeologie†
0012-5113	Dokumentation - Jugendforschung, Jugendhilfe, Jugendpolitik see 0342-3964
0012-513X	Dokumentation Sozialmedizin, Oeffentlicher Gesundheitsdienst, Arbeitsmedizin see 0932-5387
0012-5148	Dokumentation Strasse
0012-5156	Dokumentation Wasser
0012-5172	Dokumente
0012-5180	Documentation Study see 0913-3801
0012-5229	Doll Talk
0012-5245	Dollars & Sense
0012-5253	Dolphin changed to Dewan Perintis.
0012-5261	Dolphin Book Club News
0012-527X	Domei News†
0012-5288	Domenica
0012-5296	Domenica del Corriere
0012-530X	Domestic Equipment Trader
0012-5318	Domestic Heating see 0308-9614
0012-5326	Domestic Heating News changed to Domestic Heating Plus Plumbing: Bathrooms.
0012-5342	Dominion Engineer
0012-5350	Dominion Law Reports
0012-5369	Domov
0012-5377	Domus
0012-5393	Don
0012-5407	Don Universel du Sang see 0253-1321
0012-5415	Donauraum†
0012-5423	Der Donauschwabe
0012-544X	Dono
0012-5458	Dookola Swiata
0012-5474	Doorbraak
0012-5482	Doorkijk
0012-5490	Doors to Latin America†
0012-5504	Doortocht
0012-5512	Dopester†
0012-5520	Doprava
0012-5547	Dorf Aktuell see 0340-7837
0012-5555	Dorfschule†
0012-5563	Dornier Post
0012-5571	Road
0012-5598	Dorset Farmer
0012-561X	Doshkol'noe Vospitanie
0012-5636	Dostignuca†
0012-5652	Dotacion
0012-5660	Dotaito Nyusu Reta†
0012-5679	Dots and Taps
0012-5687	Dottore in Scienze Agrarie
0012-5695	Douai Magazine
0012-5709	Double Liaison
0012-5717	Douglas Library Notes†
0012-5725	Dow Diamond changed to Elements.
0012-575X	Dow Theory Comment
0012-5768	Down Beat
0012-5776	Down East Magazine
0012-5784	Down Library Lane†
0012-5806	Downside Review
0012-5814	Downstate Reporter†
0012-5822	Downtown Idea Exchange
0012-5849	Dr. Shelton's Hygienic Review†
0012-5857	Draegerheft
0012-5865	Draft Horse Journal
0012-5873	Drag Racing†
0012-5881	Dragoco Report
0012-589X	Dragon
0012-5911	Draht
0012-592X	Drahtwelt
0012-5938	Drake Law Review
0012-5946	Drama
0012-5954	Drama and Theatre†
0012-5962	T D R
0012-5989	Dramatics
0012-5997	Dramatika
0012-6004	Dramatists Guild Quarterly
0012-6012	Dramma
0012-6020	Drapers Records changed to D R: The Fashion Business.
0012-6055	Drehpunkt
0012-6063	Die Drei
0012-6071	Dreihammer
0012-608X	Dreikoenigsbote
0012-6098	Dreiser Newsletter see 0896-6362
0012-6101	Dresdner Monats-Blaetter†
0012-611X	Dressmaking
0012-6128	Dressvertising Weekly
0012-6136	Drevarsky Vyskum
0012-6144	Drevo
0012-6152	Drew Gateway
0012-6160	Drexel Library Quarterly†
0012-6179	Drexel Technical Journal†
0012-6187	Drie Talen
0012-6209	Rijksuniversiteit te Groningen. Nedersaksisch Instituut. Driemaandelijkse Bladen
0012-6225	Drill Bit see 0884-6219
0012-6241	Drilling-D C W changed to Drilling.
0012-625X	Drinks International
0012-6268	Der Dritte Weg
0012-6306	Droga changed to Droga Helvetica.
0012-6322	Drogerie-Journal†
0012-6330	Drogist
0012-6349	Drogistenblad Vergulde Gaper changed to D W.
0012-6357	Drogownictwo
0012-6365	Droit d'Auteur†
0012-6373	Droit de Vivre
0012-639X	Droit et Economie
0012-6411	Droit et Liberte†
0012-642X	Droit Maritime Francais
0012-6438	Droit Social
0012-6454	Drovers Journal
0012-6462	Druck-Print
0012-6470	Druck und Papier changed to I G Medien Forum.
0012-6489	Druckformenherstellung†
0012-6500	Der Druckspiegel
0012-6519	Druckwelt
0012-6527	Drug and Cosmetic Industry
0012-6535	1199 News†
0012-6543	Drug and Therapeutics Bulletin
0012-6551	Drug Digest†
0012-656X	Drug Information Bulletin see 0092-8615
0012-6578	Drug Intelligence and Clinical Pharmacy see 1042-9611
0012-6586	Drug Merchandising
0012-6608	Drug Research Reports: The Blue Sheet see 0162-3605
0012-6616	Drug Topics
0012-6624	Drug Trade News see 0278-1530
0012-6632	Drugarce
0012-6640	Druggist†
0012-6667	Drugs
0012-6683	Drugs Made in Germany
0012-6691	Drugs of Today changed to Medicamentos de Actualidad - Drugs of Today.
0012-6713	Drukkerswereld see 0922-1328
0012-6721	Drum
0012-6748	Drum Corps News
0012-6756	Druzhba Narodov
0012-6764	Druzina in Dom
0012-6772	Drvna Industrija
0012-6799	Dryade
0012-6802	Drycleaners News
0012-6829	Drycleaning World changed to Laundry Cleaning World.
0012-6837	Du
0012-6853	Dual Dictionary Coordinate Index to Petroleum Abstracts see 0162-329X
0012-6861	Dublin Historical Record
0012-687X	Dublin Magazine†
0012-6896	Dublin University Law Review†
0012-690X	Dubrovacki Vjesnik
0012-6918	Dubuque Leader
0012-6934	Duca Post
0012-6942	Duckett's Register†
0012-6950	Ducks Unlimited
0012-6977	Duepiut
0012-7019	Duesseldorfer Amtsblatt
0012-7027	Duesseldorfer Hefte
0012-7043	Duiker Krant
0012-7051	Duitse Kroniek
0012-706X	Duivengazet†
0012-7078	Duke Divinity School Review†
0012-7086	Duke Law Journal
0012-7094	Duke Mathematical Journal
0012-7108	Duke University Library Newsletter†
0012-7116	Duluthian
0012-7124	Dundee Chamber of Commerce Journal see 0306-0241
0012-7132	Dune Buggies & Hot VWs
0012-7159	Dunlop Industrial Rubber News†
0012-7167	Dunn & Hargitt's Commodity Service
0012-7175	Dun's Review see 0892-4090
0012-7183	Duodecim
0012-7191	Duquesne Hispanic Review†
0012-7205	Duquesne Review†
0012-7213	Duquesne University Law Review see 0093-3058
0012-7221	Durban High School Old Boys' Club. Bulletin
0012-723X	Durban Museum Novitates
0012-7264	Durez Molder changed to OxyChem Newsbriefs.
0012-7272	Durham County Local History Society. Bulletin
0012-7280	Durham University Journal
0012-7299	Duroc News
0012-7302	Dust†
0012-7310	Dutch-Australian Weekly
0012-7337	D V M Newsmagazine
0012-7353	Dyna
0012-7361	Dyna
0012-737X	Dynamic
0012-7388	Dynamic Maturity see 0148-799X
0012-7396	Dynamic Supervision
0012-7418	Dynamite International
0012-7434	Dysk Olimpijskit
0012-7450	E A R O P H News and Notes
0012-7469	E A S A changed to Engineers' News.
0012-7477	E A Z
0012-7485	E B B A News changed to North American Bird Bander.
0012-7493	E B U Review. Geneva Edition. (Programmes, Administration, Law) changed to E B U Review. (Programmes, Administration, Law Edition).
0012-7507	E D C†
0012-7515	E E E - Magazine of Circuit Design Engineering changed to E D N Magazine.
0012-7523	E D P Analyzer changed to I S Analyzer.
0012-7531	E D P Daily†
0012-754X	E D P Industry Report and Market Review see 0889-082X
0012-7558	E D P Weekly
0012-7590	E E G-E M G
0012-7604	E E I Bulletin see 0364-474X
0012-7612	E E I Statistical Releases. Electric Output
0012-7639	E E O†
0012-7647	E F D S S News see 0013-8231
0012-7655	E F T A Bulletin
0012-7671	E G
0012-768X	E I M Mededelingen
0012-7701	E L F Aquitaine
0012-771X	E L N A Bulteno changed to Esperanto - U S A.
0012-7744	E.M.G. Handmade Gramophones. Monthly Letter
0012-7760	E M N I D - Informationen changed to Umfrage und Analyse.
0012-7779	E M O Bulletin†
0012-7787	E M O National Digest see 0837-5771
0012-7795	E-M Synchronizer†
0012-7809	E N A P I†
0012-7817	E N P A S
0012-7825	Eos
0012-7841	E P I C Bulletin†
0012-7876	E.R.A. Journal†
0012-7884	E R B Newsletter changed to E R B Measures.
0012-7892	E R D A†
0012-7922	E R I C News Plus†
0012-7957	E R T (Electronics-Radio-TV) changed to Elektroniikka & Automaatio.
0012-7965	E S - Espana Semanal changed to Espana Hoy.

0012-7981 E S G - Nachrichten *changed to* Ansaetze.
0012-799X E S R O - E L D O Bulletin *see* 0376-4265
0012-8007 E S S A World *see* 0014-0821
0012-8015 Essor Economique et Commercial
0012-8023 E T V Newsletter
0012-8031 Elektrontechnische Zeitschrift. Ausgabe B *changed to* E T Z.
0012-804X E U R I S I†
0012-8066 E V
0012-8074 Elektronik-Zeitung *changed to* E.
0012-8082 Eagle (Washington)
0012-8104 Eagle and Boys' World
0012-8112 Eagle
0012-8139 Early American
0012-8147 Early American Industries Association. Chronicle
0012-8155 Early American Life
0012-8163 Early American Literature
0012-8198 Earnshaw's Infants' and Children's Review *see* 0161-2786
0012-821X Earth and Planetary Science Letters
0012-8228 Earth Science†
0012-8236 Earth Science Bulletin†
0012-8244 Earth Science Journal†
0012-8252 Earth Science Reviews
0012-8287 Earthquake Notes *see* 0895-0695
0012-8295 East
0012-8309 East Africa Journal
0012-8317 Journal of the East Africa Natural History Society and National Museum
0012-8325 East African Agricultural and Forestry Journal
0012-8333 East Africa Journal of Rural Development *changed to* Eastern Africa Journal of Rural Development.
0012-8341 East African Management Journal
0012-835X East African Medical Journal
0012-8368 East African Trade and Industry *changed to* Review of Trade and Industry.
0012-8376 East and West
0012-8384 East and West Series
0012-8392 East Anglian Magazine†
0012-8406 East Asia Millions *changed to* East Asia's Millions.
0012-8414 East Asian Cultural Studies *changed to* Asian Research Trends: a Humanities and Social Science Review.
0012-8430 East Europe†
0012-8449 East European Quarterly
0012-8457 East European Trade
0012-8465 East London Papers†
0012-8473 Perspective
0012-8481 East Midland Geographer
0012-849X Bangladesh. Bureau of Statistics. Monthly Bulletin of Statistics *see* 0377-1555
0012-8503 East Pakistan Bureau of Statistics. Weekly Information Service†
0012-852X East Riding Archaeologist
0012-8538 East Side Chamber of Commerce Newsletter
0012-8546 East Sussex Farmer
0012-8589 East - West
0012-8597 East-West Center Magazine†
0012-8600 East-West Commerce
0012-8627 East-West Digest
0012-8635 East-West Review†
0012-8643 Eastbournian
0012-8651 Easter Seal Bulletin *changed to* National Easter Seal Communicator.
0012-866X Eastern Africa Economic Review†
0012-8678 Eastern Africa Law Review
0012-8686 Eastern Anthropologist
0012-8708 Eastern Buddhist
0012-8724 Eastern Cape Naturalist *changed to* Naturalist.
0012-8732 Eastern Churches News Letter
0012-8740 Eastern Churches Review *see* 0144-8722
0012-8759 Eastern Dental Society Bulletin
0012-8767 Eastern Economist
0012-8775 Eastern European Economics
0012-8783 International Journal of Politics *see* 0891-1916
0012-8791 Eastern Evening News
0012-8805 Eastern Fruit Grower†
0012-8813 Eastern Horizon†
0012-8821 Eastern Journal of International Law
0012-883X Eastern Kansas Register
0012-8848 Eastern Librarian
0012-8856 Eastern Metals Review *changed to* Engineering & Metals Review.
0012-8864 Eastern News *changed to* Daily Eastern News.
0012-8872 Eastern Pharmacist
0012-8880 Eastern Railway Magazine
0012-8899 Eastern Massachusetts Regional Library System. Eastern Region News
0012-8902 Eastern Review (Brooklyn)
0012-8910 Eastern School Law Review†
0012-8937 Eastern Trade Gazette *changed to* Eastern Trade.
0012-8945 Eastern Utilization Research and Development Division. Publications and Patents *changed to* U.S. Department of Agriculture. Eastern Regional Research Center. Publications and Patents.
0012-8953 Eastern Worker
0012-8961 Eastern World
0012-897X Organic Chemical Bulletin *changed to* Eastman Fine Chemicals News.
0012-8996 Eaton Livia†
0012-9003 Information Eaux
0012-9011 Ebony
0012-902X Ecclesia†
0012-9038 Ecclesia
0012-9046 Ecclesia *changed to* Kiongozi.
0012-9054 Ecclesiastica Xaveriana *see* 0120-3649
0012-9089 Echo†
0012-9097 Echo†
0012-9119 Echo
0012-9127 Echo (Bethal)
0012-9135 Echo
0012-9143 Echo
0012-916X Economic Echo from Yugoslavia *changed to* Yugoslavia Echo.
0012-9178 Echo Africain
0012-9208 Echo de la Finance
0012-9224 Echo de la Liberte de l'Ouest
0012-9232 Echo de la Presse et de la Publicite
0012-9240 Echo de la Timbrologie
0012-9259 Echo de l'Imprimerie et des Arts Graphiques *see* 0012-9232
0012-9275 Echo des Eglises Wallonnes
0012-9283 Echo des Recherches
0012-9305 Echo uit Afrika *changed to* Echo uit Afrika en Andere Werelddelen.
0012-9321 Echoes
0012-933X Echoes
0012-9356 Echos du Monde Classique
0012-9372 Echo's voor de Textielkleinhandel†
0012-9380 Eclair†
0012-9402 Eclogae Geologicae Helvetiae
0012-9410 Eco
0012-9429 Eco Contemporaneo†
0012-9437 L'Eco Cuoio†
0012-9445 Eco de Nayarit
0012-9453 Eco degli Oratori e dei Circoli Giovanili
0012-947X Eco del Seguro
0012-9488 Eco della Riviera
0012-9496 Eco della Scuola Nuova
0012-9518 Eco dell'Educazione Ebraica
0012-9526 Eco dell'Industria Tessile
0012-9534 Eco d'Italia
0012-9542 Eco-Tessili
0012-9550 Ecole de Specialisation de l'Artillerie Anti-Aerienne. Bulletin d'Information
0012-9569 Ecole en Afrique†
0012-9577 Ecole et la Vie†
0012-9585 Ecole Maternelle Francaise
0012-9593 Ecole Normale Superieure. Annales Scientifiques
0012-9607 Ecologia Agraria
0012-9615 Ecological Monographs
0012-9623 Ecological Society of America. Bulletin
0012-9631 Ecologist†
0012-9658 Ecology
0012-9666 Ecology Today†
0012-9682 Econometrica
0012-9690 Economia†
0012-9704 Economia
0012-9712 Economia
0012-9747 Economia Aretina
0012-9763 Economia Dominicana
0012-978X Economia e Lavoro
0012-9798 Economia e Storia (Verona)
0012-9801 Economia Internacional
0012-981X Economia Internazionale
0012-9828 Economia Internazionale delle Fonti di Energia†
0012-9836 Economia Montana - Linea Ecologica
0012-9844 Economia Mundial
0012-9852 Economia Nuova per Un Mondo Nuovo
0012-9860 Economia Salvadorena (San Salvador, 1946)†
0012-9879 Economia Trentina
0012-9887 Economia y Administracion
0012-9895 Economia y Ciencias Sociales
0012-9917 Economic Abstracts *see* 0165-4748
0012-9925 Economic Activity *changed to* Western Australia. Economic and Business Review.
0012-9933 Economic and Business Bulletin *see* 0148-6195
0012-995X Economic & Business Review
0012-9968 Economic and Financial Review†
0012-9976 Economic and Political Weekly
0012-9984 Economic and Social Review
0012-9992 East African Community. Economic and Statistical Review
0013-0001 Economic Botany
0013-001X Economic Brief†
0013-0028 Commercial Bank of Greece. Economic Bulletin
0013-0044 Economic Bulletin of Ghana
0013-0079 Economic Development and Cultural Change
0013-0095 Economic Geography
0013-0109 Economic Geology *see* 0361-0128
0013-0117 Economic History Review
0013-0125 Economic Indicators (Washington)
0013-0133 Economic Journal
0013-0141 Economic Leaflets
0013-015X Economic News about Turkey†
0013-0168 Economic News
0013-0176 Economic News of Bulgaria
0013-0184 Economic Notes *see* 0895-5220
0013-0192 Economic Observer†
0013-0206 Economic Opportunity Report
0013-0249 Economic Record
0013-0257 Economic Report from Germany†
0013-0265 Economic Reporter
0013-0273 Economic Review
0013-0281 Economic Review
0013-029X Economic Review
0013-0303 Economic Review
0013-0311 Economic Review and Report *changed to* International Understanding.
0013-032X Economic Review of the Arab World
0013-0346 Economic Situation in the Community *see* 0379-217X
0013-0354 Economic Society of Australia and New Zealand. New South Wales and Victorian Branches. Economic Papers *see* 0812-0439
0013-0362 Economic Studies
0013-0370 Goetabanken *changed to* Gotabanken Economic Survey.
0013-0389 Economic Times
0013-0397 Economic Topics Series†
0013-0400 Economic Trends
0013-0419 Revista Economica
0013-0427 Economica
0013-0435 Economia de Cordoba
0013-0443 Economicos Tachydromos
0013-0451 Economics of Planning
0013-0478 Economie
0013-0494 Economie Appliquee
0013-0508 Economie Electrique†
0013-0524 Economie et Medecine Animales†
0013-0532 Economie in Limburg *changed to* G O M - Economie in Limburg.
0013-0540 Economie Libanaise et Arabe
0013-0559 Economie Rurale
0013-0567 Economies et Societes. Serie EM. Economie Mathematique et Econometrie
0013-0575 Economisch en Sociaal Tijdschrift
0013-0583 Economisch-Statistische Berichten
0013-0613 Economist
0013-0621 Economist
0013-063X De Economist
0013-0648 Economista
0013-0656 Economista
0013-0672 L'Economiste Egyptien
0013-0680 Ecos
0013-0699 Ecos de Portugal
0013-0702 Ecotass *see* 0733-5989
0013-0710 Ecrits de Paris
0013-0729 Ecrits du Canada Francais
0013-0761 Ecumenical Courier
0013-077X Czech Ecumenical News *changed to* Czechoslovak Ecumenical News.
0013-0788 National†
0013-0796 Ecumenical Review
0013-080X Ecumenist†
0013-0818 Edda
0013-0826 Die Edelkatze
0013-0842 Edesipar
0013-0877 Edilizia alle Fiere *see* 0393-8050
0013-0885 Edilizia Moderna†
0013-0893 Edinburgh Academy Chronicle
0013-0907 Edinburgh Dental Hospital Gazette†
0013-0923 Edition†
0013-0931 Editor†
0013-094X Editor & Publisher - the Fourth Estate
0013-0958 Editorial Research Reports *see* 1056-2036
0013-0966 Editorials on File
0013-0974 Editor's Notebook†
0013-0982 Edizioni Nostre *changed to* Pagine Aperte.
0013-0990 Edjer Grakanutian Yev Arvesdi
0013-1008 Edmonton Public Library. News Notes. *see* 0319-2156
0013-1016 Edmundite
0013-1024 EdPress Newsletter *changed to* EdPress News.
0013-1032 Edubusiness†
0013-1067 Educacion
0013-1075 Educacion
0013-1083 Educacion Dental†
0013-1091 Educacion Medica y Salud
0013-1105 Educador Social†
0013-1113 Educadores
0013-1121 Educate†
0013-113X Educateur
0013-1148 Educateur et Bulletin Corporatif *changed to* Educateur: Revue de Pedagogie et d'Education.
0013-1156 Education (Sydney)
0013-1164 Education
0013-1172 Education
0013-1180 Education
0013-1199 Education†
0013-1202 Education *changed to* Education News.
0013-1202 Education *see* 0259-207X
0013-1210 Education Abstracts†
0013-1229 Education and Culture *see* 0252-0958
0013-1237 Education and Training of the Mentally Retarded *changed to* Education and Training in Mental Retardation.
0013-1245 Education and Urban Society
0013-1253 Education Canada
0013-1261 Education Daily
0013-127X Education Digest
0013-1288 Education Enfantine
0013-1296 Education Equipment
0013-130X Education Equipment and Services Review†
0013-1318 Education et Developpement
0013-1326 Education for Teaching *see* 0309-877X
0013-1334 Education Gazette

ISSN

0013-1342 Education Gazette (Victoria)
0013-1350 Education in Chemistry
0013-1369 French News *changed to* France Education.
0013-1377 Education in Science
0013-1385 Education Index
0013-1407 Education Libraries Bulletin *see* 0957-9575
0013-1415 Education Musicale
0013-1423 Education
0013-1431 Education News
0013-144X Education Newsletter *changed to* Education San Diego County.
0013-1458 Education of the Visually Handicapped *see* 0899-1510
0013-1482 Education Quarterly
0013-1490 Education Quebecoise†
0013-1504 Education Recaps†
0013-1512 Education Reporter
0013-1520 Education Summary†
0013-1547 Education Today
0013-1563 Education Trends *changed to* Outlook in Education.
0013-1571 Education U S A
0013-158X Education Weekly†
0013-1598 Education Welfare Officer *see* 0263-0664
0013-1601 Educational Administration Abstracts
0013-161X Educational Administration Quarterly
0013-1628 Educational Administration Reporter†
0013-1644 Educational and Psychological Measurement
0013-1652 Educational Books and Equipment†
0013-1660 Educational Broadcasting Review *see* 0093-8149
0013-1679 Educational Bulletin *changed to* Dispatch (Des Moines).
0013-1687 Educational Courier†
0013-1695 Educational Development
0013-1725 Educational Forum
0013-1741 Educational Freedom
0013-175X Educational Horizons
0013-1768 Educational India
0013-1784 Educational Leadership
0013-1792 Educational Magazine†
0013-1806 Educational Marketer
0013-1814 Educational Media†
0013-1830 Transvaal. Education Department. Educational News Flashes
0013-1849 Educational Perspectives
0013-1857 Educational Philosophy and Theory
0013-1865 Educational Product Report *changed to* E P I E Publication Membership.
0013-1873 Educational Record
0013-1881 Educational Research
0013-189X Educational Researcher
0013-1911 Educational Review
0013-192X Educational Review
0013-1938 Educational Screen and Audio Visual Guide *see* 0091-360X
0013-1946 Educational Studies
0013-1954 Educational Studies in Mathematics
0013-1962 Educational Technology
0013-1970 Educational Broadcasting International *see* 0262-0251
0013-1989 Educational Theatre Journal *see* 0192-2882
0013-1997 Educational Theatre News
0013-2004 Educational Theory
0013-2012 Educator *changed to* Guru Malaysia.
0013-2020 Educator
0013-2047 Educators' Advocate
0013-2055 Educator's Dispatch†
0013-2071 Educazione alla Sicurezza
0013-208X Educazione Musicale†
0013-2098 Educazione Sanitaria *changed to* Educazione Sanitaria e Promozione della Salute.
0013-2101 Eendracht *changed to* W I K.
0013-211X Eendrachtbode†
0013-2128 Eerste Hulp†
0013-2144 Akademiya Nauk Estonskoi S.S.R. Izvestiya. Biologiya *changed to* Eesti Teaduste Akadeemia. Toimetised. Bioloogia.
0013-2152 Eesti Post†
0013-2160 Efemerides Costarricenses†
0013-2179 Effektivt Forsvar†
0013-2187 Effektivt Landbrug
0013-2195 Effeta
0013-2209 Efficacy†
0013-2217 Effluent and Water Treatment Journal
0013-2225 Effort *changed to* Jeu de Dames.
0013-2233 Efluvios†
0013-2241 Egerer Zeitung
0013-225X Egeszseg†
0013-2268 Egeszsegtudomany
0013-2276 Egeszsegugyi Gazdasagi Szemle
0013-2306 Egg Industry†
0013-2322 L'Eglise Canadienne
0013-2330 Eglise en Alsace
0013-2349 Eglise et Theologie
0013-2357 Eglise Qui Chante
0013-2365 Eglise Vivante†
0013-2373 Egretta
0013-2381 Egypt Travel Magazine
0013-239X L'Egypte Contemporaine
0013-2403 Egyptian Cotton Gazette
0013-2411 Egyptian Medical Association. Journal
0013-242X Egyptian Orthopaedic Journal *see* 1110-1148
0013-2438 Egyptian Pharmaceutical Journal†
0013-2446 Egyptian Public Health Association Journal
0013-2454 Egyptian Surgical Society Quarterly Review
0013-2462 Ehe *changed to* Partner Beratung.
0013-2470 Ehe und Familie
0013-2489 Rundbrief Ehemaliger Schueler und Freunde der Schulbrueder
0013-2497 Eichholzbrief
0013-2500 Eier-Wild-Gefluegel-Markt
0013-2519 Eigen Huis *changed to* Eigen Huis en Interieur.
0013-2527 Eigene Garten - Eigene Haus *changed to* Das Eigene Haus.
0013-2543 Film Making
0013-2551 Eight O'Clock *changed to* Sunday Star.
0013-2578 1860 Settler
0013-2586 Eighteenth-Century Studies
0013-2594 Eighteen Month Forecast of Japan's Economy *changed to* Quarterly Forecast of Japanese Economy.
0013-2608 Eigse
0013-2624 Eimreidin
0013-2632 Ein- und Verkaufsfuehrer der Oesterreichischen Uhren- und Schmuckwirtschaft *see* 0041-5839
0013-2640 Eine Welt der Vereinten Nationen†
0013-2659 Einheit†
0013-2667 Einheit und Fortschritt†
0013-2683 Eire - Ireland
0013-2705 Eisbericht
0013-2713 Eisdiele & Milchbar†
0013-273X Eisei Kagaku
0013-2756 Eisenbahn
0013-2764 Eisenbahn-Amateur
0013-2772 Eisenbahn-Landwirt
0013-2799 Eisenbahner
0013-2802 Eisenbahner. Ausgabe A & B *changed to* D B.
0013-2810 Der Eisenbahningenieur
0013-2829 Eisenbahntechnik *changed to* Neue Bahn.
0013-2837 Eisenbahn-technische Praxis†
0013-2845 Eisenbahntechnische Rundschau
0013-2853 Eisenwarenboerse
0013-2861 Eisenwaren-Zeitung *changed to* E Z - Eisenwaren und Hausrat.
0013-287X Eisma's Schildersblad *changed to* Eisma's Vakpers.
0013-2888 Either - Ort
0013-2896 Ejendomsmaegleren
0013-2918 Ejercito
0013-2926 Ekalabya
0013-2934 Ekistic Index
0013-2942 Ekistics
0013-2969 Wiadomosci Ekologiczne
0013-2977 Ekonomen
0013-2985 Ekonomia†
0013-2993 Ikonomiceska Misal
0013-3000 Ekonomicheskii Byulleten Niderlandov
0013-3019 Ekonomicheskie Nauki
0013-3027 Ekonomicko-Matematicky Obzor
0013-3035 Ekonomicky Casopis
0013-3051 Ekonomika i Zhizn'
0013-306X Ekonomika Poljoprivreda
0013-3094 Ekonomika Sel'skogo Khozyaistva
0013-3116 Ekonomika Stroitel'stva
0013-3124 Ekonomika Zemedelstvi *changed to* Ekonomika Polnohospodarstva.
0013-3132 Ekonomicheskaya Gazeta
0013-3167 Ekonomisk Revy†
0013-3175 Ekonomiska Laeget†
0013-3183 Ekonomiska Samfundets Tidskrift
0013-3191 Ekonomist
0013-3205 Ekonomista
0013-3213 Ekonomska Analiza - Economic Analysis *see* 0351-286X
0013-3221 Radna Jedinica *changed to* Organizacija Samoupravljanja OUR.
0013-323X Ekonomska Misao
0013-3248 Elektroprenos
0013-3256 Ekonomska Revija
0013-3264 Ekonomski Anali
0013-3272 Ekonomski Glasnik
0013-3299 Ekran *changed to* Media Reporter.
0013-3302 Ekran
0013-3310 Zhurnal Eksperimental'noi i Klinicheskoi Meditsiny
0013-3329 Eksperimental'naya Khirurgiya i Anesteziologiya *see* 0201-7563
0013-3353 Ekspress-Informatsiya. Automobilestroenie†
0013-3361 Ekspress-Informatsiya. Avtomobil'nyi Transport†
0013-3396 Ekspress-Informatsiya. Elektricheskie Mashiny i Apparaty†
0013-340X Ekspress-Informatsiya. Elektricheskie Stantsii, Seti i Sistemy†
0013-3426 Ekspress-Informatsiya. Fotokinoapparatura. Nauchnaya i Prikladnaya Fotografiya†
0013-3434 Ekspress-Informatsiya. Garazhi i Garazhnoe Oborudovanie†
0013-3442 Ekspress-Informatsiya. Gidroenergetika†
0013-3450 Ekspress-Informatsiya. Gornorudnaya Promyshlennost'†
0013-3477 Ekspress-Informatsiya. Iskusstvennye Sooruzheniya na Avtomobil'nykh Dorogakh†
0013-3493 Ekspress-Informatsiya. Khimicheskaya Tekhnologiya Pererabotki Vysokopolimernykh Materialov†
0013-3507 Ekspress-Informatsiya. Khimiya i Pererabotka Nefti i Gaza†
0013-3515 Ekspress-Informatsiya. Khimia i Tekhnologiya Neorganicheskikh Veshchestv†
0013-354X Ekspress-Informatsiya. Kozhevenno-Obuvnaya Promyshlennost' *changed to* Ekspress-Informatsiya. Kozhevennaya Promyshlennost'
0013-354X Ekspress-Informatsiya. Kozhevenno-Obuvnaya Promyshlennost' *changed to* Ekspress-Informatsiya. Obuvnaya Promyshlennost'
0013-3558 Ekspress-Informatsiya. Lokomotivostroenie Vagonostroenie†
0013-3574 Ekspress-Informatsiya. Myasnaya i Molochnaya Promyshlennost'†
0013-3582 Ekspress-Informatsiya. Nefte- i Gazodobyvayushchaya Promyshlennost'†
0013-3590 Ekspress-Informatsiya. Obogashchenie Poleznykh Iskopaemykh†
0013-3612 Ekspress-Informatsiya. Pishchevaya Promyshlennost'†
0013-3620 Ekspress-Informatsiya. Pod'emno-Transportnoe Mashinostroenie†
0013-368X Ekspress-Informatsiya. Protsessy i Apparaty Khimicheskikh Proizvodstv *see* 0207-5024
0013-3698 Ekspress-Informatsiya. Put' i Stroitel'stvo Zheleznykh Dorog *see* 0134-7683
0013-3701 Ekspress-Informatsiya. Radiolokatsiya, Televidenie, Radiosvyaz'†
0013-371X Ekspress-Informatsiya. Radiotekhnika Sverkhvysokikh Chastot i Kvantovaya Radiotekhnika *see* 0131-0437
0013-371X Ekspress-Informatsiya. Radiotekhnika Sverkhvysokikh Chastot i Kvantovaya Radiotekhnika *see* 0131-0208
0013-3736 Ekspress-Informatsiya. Rybnaya Promyshlennost'†
0013-3744 Ekspress-Informatsiya. Sel'skokhozyaistvennye Mashiny i Orudiya. Mekhanizatsiya Sel'skokhozyaistvennykh Rabot†
0013-3752 Ekspress-Informatsiya. Silikatnye Stroitel'nye Materialy†
0013-3787 Ekspress-Informatsiya. Steklo, Keramika i Ogneupory†
0013-3795 Ekspress-Informatsiya. Stroitel'stvo i Ekspluatatsiya Avtomobilnykh Dorog†
0013-3809 Ekspress-Informatsiya. Sudostroenie†
0013-3825 Ekspress-Informatsiya. Tara i Upakovka *see* 0131-0526
0013-3833 Ekspress-Informatsiya. Tekhnicheskaya Ekspluatatsiya Podvizhnogo Sostava i Tyaga Poezdov†
0013-3884 Ekspress-Informatsiya. Tekstil'naya Promyschlennost'†
0013-3892 Ekspress-Informatsiya. Teoriya i Praktika Nauchnoi Informatsii†
0013-3906 Ekspress-Informatsiya. Teploenergetika†
0013-3914 Ekspress-Informatsiya. Traktorostroenie†
0013-3922 Ekspress-Informatsiya. Transport i Khranenie Nefti i Gaza†
0013-3930 Ekspress-Informatsiya. Tsellyulozno-Bumazhnaya Promyshlennost'†
0013-3957 Ekspress-Informatsiya. Ugol'naya Promyshlennost'†
0013-3965 Ekspress-Informatsiya. Vodnyi Transport†
0013-3973 Ekspress-Informatsiya. Vozdushnyi Transport†
0013-3981 Ekspress-Informatsiya. Vychislitel'naya Tekhnika†
0013-399X El
0013-4007 El Branschen
0013-4023 El Paso Archaeology
0013-4031 El Paso Economic Review *see* 8750-6033
0013-404X El Salvador. Direccion General de Estadistica y Censos. Boletin Estadistico
0013-4058 Elam
0013-4066 Elan
0013-4074 Elder Statesman *changed to* Today's Times.
0013-4082 Elders
0013-4090 E L D O - E S R O Scientific and Technical Review *see* 0379-2285
0013-4104 Electra *changed to* Installatie Journaal.
0013-4112 Electric Heat and Air Conditioning *see* 0190-1370
0013-4139 Electric Power Statistics (Washington)†
0013-4147 Electric Railway Society. Journal
0013-4155 Electric Technology U.S.S.R.
0013-4163 Electric Traction *see* 0818-5204
0013-4171 Electric Vehicles for Industry *changed to* Electric Vehicles.
0013-418X Electrical and Electronic Trader *changed to* Electrical Trader.
0013-421X Electrical and Electronics Technician Engineers *see* 0306-8552
0013-4228 Electrical and Radio Trading
0013-4236 Electrical Apparatus Service - Volt-Age *see* 0190-1370
0013-4244 Electrical Business
0013-4252 Electrical Communication
0013-4279 Electrical Contractor (Sydney)
0013-4287 Electrical Contractor and Maintenance Supervisor *changed to* Electricity Canada.

5372 ISSN INDEX

0013-4295 Electrical Contractor and Retailer *see* 0308-7174
0013-4309 Electrical Engineer
0013-4317 Electrical Equipment
0013-4325 Electrical Equipment *changed to* E E Product News.
0013-4333 Electrical Equipment News
0013-435X Electrical India
0013-4376 Electrical Power Engineer *changed to* E P E.
0013-4384 Electrical Review
0013-4414 Electrical Times
0013-4422 Electrical Wholesaler
0013-4430 Electrical Wholesaling
0013-4449 Electrical Workers' Journal *see* 0897-2826
0013-4457 Electrical World
0013-4465 Electricidade *see* 0870-5364
0013-4481 Electricite
0013-449X Electricite de France. Direction des Etudes et Recherches. Bulletin. Serie A: Nucleaire, Hydraulique, Thermique *changed to* Electricite de France. Direction des Etudes et Recherches. Bulletin. Collection des Notes Internes. Production d'Energie (Hydraulique, Thermique et Nucleaire).
0013-4503 Electricite de France. Direction des Etudes et Recherches. Bulletin. Serie B: Reseaux Electriques, Materiels Electriques *see* 1161-0581
0013-4511 Electricite de France. Direction des Etudes et Recherches. Bulletin. Serie C: Mathematiques-Informatique *see* 1161-059X
0013-452X Electricite pour Vous *changed to* Pour Vous.
0013-4538 Electricity and Electronics
0013-4546 Electricity in Building *see* 0362-1324
0013-4562 Electrified Industry *see* 0194-4746
0013-4589 Electro Optics
0013-4597 Electrophysiological Technologists' Association. Proceedings and Journal *see* 0307-5095
0013-4600 Electro-Procurement *see* 0163-6197
0013-4619 Electro Radio Mercuur *changed to* E R M Journaal.
0013-4627 Elektrotechniek *changed to* Energietechniek.
0013-4635 Electro-Technology†
0013-4643 Electro-Technology
0013-4651 Electrochemical Society. Journal
0013-466X Electrochemical Society of India. Journal
0013-4678 Electrochemical Society of Japan. Journal - Denki Kagaku *see* 0366-9297
0013-4686 Electrochimica Acta
0013-4694 Electroencephalography and Clinical Neurophysiology *see* 0921-884X
0013-4708 Electrolysis Digest†
0013-4716 Electromechanical Design†
0013-4732 Electromyography *see* 0301-150X
0013-4740 Electron†
0013-4759 Electron *changed to* Sound & Vision.
0013-4767 Electron
0013-4775 Electroanalytical Abstracts†
0013-4783 Electronic Age†
0013-4791 Electronic & Appliance Specialist†
0013-4805 S.E.R.T. Journal *see* 0141-061X
0013-4813 Electronic Application News
0013-4821 Electronic Applications Bulletin *changed to* Electronic Components and Applications.
0013-483X Electronics Today *see* 0047-9624
0013-4848 Electronic Capabilities†
0013-4864 Electronic Components *see* 0307-2401
0013-4872 Electronic Design
0013-4880 Electronic Distributing and Marketing *changed to* Electronic Purchaser.
0013-4899 Electronic Engineer *changed to* E E Systems Engineering Today.
0013-4902 Electronic Engineering
0013-4910 Electronic Equipment News
0013-4929 Electronic Instrument Digest†
0013-4937 Electronic News
0013-4945 Electronic Packaging & Production
0013-4953 Electronic Products
0013-4961 Electronic Progress
0013-497X Electronic Servicing *see* 0278-9922
0013-4988 Electronic Technician *see* 0278-9922
0013-4996 Electronics Trends (Washington) *changed to* Electronic Market Trends.
0013-5011 Electronic Trends: International†
0013-502X Electronica†
0013-5046 Elternblatt†
0013-5054 Electronica y Fisica Aplicada†
0013-5062 Electronicien
0013-5070 Electronics *see* 0883-4989
0013-5097 Electronics Abstracts Journal *see* 0361-3313
0013-5100 Electronics and Communications†
0013-5119 Electronics and Communications Abstracts
0013-5127 Electronics and Power *changed to* I E E Review.
0013-5135 Electronics Australia
0013-5143 Electronics Digest†
0013-516X Electronics for You
0013-5178 Electronics Illustrated *see* 8755-0423
0013-5186 Electronics and Instrumentation *changed to* Current.
0013-5194 Electronics Letters
0013-5208 Electronics Record†
0013-5216 Electronics Today *see* 0957-0438
0013-5224 Electronics Weekly
0013-5232 Electronics World *see* 0745-1458
0013-5259 Electronique Industrielle *see* 0398-1851
0013-5267 Electronique Medicale†
0013-5283 Electronique Professionnelle Belge
0013-5305 Electroplating and Metal Finishing *see* 0264-2506
0013-5313 Electrotecnia Popular
0013-5321 Electrotehnica *changed to* Electrotehnica, Electronica si Automatica. Electrotehnica.
0013-5348 Eleftherotypia
0013-5372 Elektricheskie Stantsii
0013-5380 Elektrichestvo
0013-5399 Elektrie
0013-5402 Elektrik Muhendisligi
0013-5410 Elektrikeren
0013-5437 Elektrische Bahnen
0013-5445 E M A - Elektrische Maschinen
0013-5461 Elektrizitaet *changed to* Strom.
0013-547X Elektrizitaet *see* 0340-7519
0013-5488 Elektrizitaetsverwertung†
0013-5496 Elektrizitaetswirtschaft
0013-550X Elektro
0013-5518 Elektro-Anzeiger
0013-5542 E H - Elektro Handel
0013-5550 Elektro Nachrichten†
0013-5569 Elektropraktiker
0013-5577 Elektromarkt
0013-5585 Biomedizinische Technik
0013-5607 Elektron *see* 0374-3098
0013-5615 Electronaut
0013-5623 Elektronica en Telecommunicatie *changed to* Nederlands Elektronica- en Radiogenootschap. Tijdschrift.
0013-5631 Elektronik *see* 0109-2359
0013-564X Elektronik-Teknik & Marknad *changed to* Elektroniknyheterna.
0013-5658 Elektronik
0013-5666 Elektronik-Anzeiger *see* 0720-101X
0013-5674 Elektronik Journal
0013-5690 Elektronikk
0013-5704 Angewandte Informatik *see* 0937-6429
0013-5712 Elektronische Informationsverarbeitung und Kybernetik *see* 0863-0593
0013-5720 Elektronische Rechenanlagen mit Computer-Praxis *see* 0179-9738
0013-5739 Elektronnaya Obrabotka Materialov
0013-5747 Elektronorm *see* 0722-2912
0013-5755 Elektroprivreda *changed to* Elektroprivreda Jugoslavije.
0013-5763 Elektropromishlenost i Priborostroene
0013-5771 Elektrosvyaz'
0013-578X Elektrotechnicky Casopis
0013-5798 Elektrotechnicky Obzor
0013-581X Elektrotechnik
0013-5828 Elektrotehnicar
0013-5844 Elektrotehnika
0013-5852 Elektrotehniski Vestnik
0013-5860 Elektrotekhnika
0013-5887 Elektrowirtschaft
0013-5895 Elektor Electronics
0013-5909 Elelmezesi Ipar
0013-5917 Elelmiszertudomany *see* 0139-3006
0013-5933 Elementa
0013-5941 Elementary Counselor *see* 0036-6536
0013-595X Elementary Electronics *see* 0279-070X
0013-5968 Elementary English *see* 0360-9170
0013-5976 Elementary School Guidance & Counseling
0013-5984 Elementary School Journal
0013-5992 Elementary Teacher's Ideas and Materials Workshop *changed to* E T Ideas.
0013-600X Elemente
0013-6018 Elemente der Mathematik
0013-6026 Elements, Produits, Services
0013-6042 Elenco dei Quotidiani e Periodici Italiani†
0013-6050 Elenco Ufficiale dei Protesti Cambiari Levati Nella Provincia di Torino
0013-6069 Elepaio
0013-6077 Elet es Tudomany
0013-6085 Eletronica Popular *see* 0101-9112
0013-6093 Elettrificazione
0013-6107 Elettrodomestica
0013-6115 Elettrodomus†
0013-6123 Elettronica e Telecomunicazioni
0013-6131 Elettrotecnica
0013-6158 Elevator World
0013-6166 Eleventh District Dental Society. Bulletin *changed to* Queens County Dental Society. Bulletin.
0013-6182 Elim Evangel *changed to* Direction.
0013-6190 Elinstallatoeren
0013-6204 Eliot Sharp's Tax Exempt Newsletter *changed to* Eliot Sharp.
0013-6212 Elisabethbode
0013-6220 Elisha Mitchell Scientific Society. Journal
0013-6247 Elizabeth†
0013-6255 Elizabethan†
0013-6263 Elks Magazine
0013-6298 Elle (France)
0013-6301 Ellery Queen's Anthology†
0013-631X Ellery Queen's Mystery Magazine. Braille Edition†
0013-6328 Ellery Queen's Mystery Magazine
0013-6336 Ellinika
0013-6352 Eloquenza
0013-6379 Elovilag *see* 0007-7356
0013-6395 Elseviers Magazine *changed to* Elsevier.
0013-6409 Elsevier Select†
0013-6417 Eltat†
0013-6425 Elteknik *see* 0346-6310
0013-6433 Schweizer Zeitschrift fuer die Junge Familie *changed to* Wir Eltern.
0013-6441 Elternblatt
0013-645X Der Elternbrief
0013-6468 Elthetot†
0013-6484 Elvis Monthly
0013-6506 Emajl-Keramika-Staklo
0013-6522 Emantalehti
0013-6530 Embalagem
0013-6549 Emballage *changed to* Transport - Magasinet (Fredensborg).
0013-6557 Emballage Digest
0013-6565 Emballage Moderne *see* 0247-8390
0013-6573 Emballages
0013-6581 Emballering
0013-6603 Embotellador *changed to* Beverage World En Espanol.
0013-6611 Embroidery
0013-662X Ementario da Legislacao do Petroleo
0013-6638 Ementario Forense
0013-6646 Emergency Health Services Newsletter†
0013-6654 Emergency Medicine
0013-6662 Emerita
0013-6697 Emigrato Italiano
0013-6700 Emigrazione†
0013-6719 Emmanuel
0013-6727 Emory Magazine
0013-6743 Forum (Syracuse)
0013-676X Empire State Geogram
0013-6786 Empire State Iris Society Newsletter
0013-6794 Empire State Mason
0013-6808 Employee Benefit Plan Review
0013-6816 Employee Relations Bulletin *see* 0744-7779
0013-6824 Employee Relations in Action
0013-6832 Employers' Review
0013-6840 U.S. Bureau of Labor Statistics. Employment and Earnings
0013-6859 Great Britain. Department of Employment. Employment Gazette
0013-6875 Employment Relations Abstracts *see* 0273-3234
0013-6883 Employment Review
0013-6891 Empoli
0013-6905 Empress Chinchilla Breeder
0013-6913 Emuna†
0013-6921 En Avant
0013-693X En Concreto
0013-6956 En Haat†
0013-6964 En Marche
0013-6972 En Viaje†
0013-6980 Enact
0013-6999 Enamelling Newsletter†
0013-7006 Encephale
0013-7057 Encore: a Quarterly of Verse & Poetic Arts†
0013-7065 Encounter†
0013-7073 Encounter (London, 1953)
0013-7081 Encounter (Indianapolis, 1956)
0013-709X Encounter Today†
0013-7103 Encres Vives
0013-7111 Encuentro†
0013-712X Encyclopaedia Africana. Information Report
0013-7138 Encyclopaedia Moderna†
0013-7146 Encyclopedie Politique Arabe. Documents et Notes
0013-7154 End-Use Markets for Plastics
0013-7170 Endeavour
0013-7200 Endocrinologia Experimentalis *changed to* Endocrine Regulations.
0013-7219 Endocrinologia Japonica
0013-7227 Endocrinology
0013-7235 Endocrinology Index†
0013-7243 Endocrinologya y Terapeutica†
0013-7251 Endokrinologie *see* 0232-7384
0013-726X Endoscopy
0013-7278 Energetik
0013-7286 Energetika
0013-7294 Energetyka
0013-7308 Energia Elettrica
0013-7316 Energia es Atomtechnika
0013-7332 Energia Nucleare†
0013-7340 Energiet†
0013-7359 Energie
0013-7405 Energieanwendung
0013-7421 Energietechnik
0013-7448 Energija
0013-7456 Energomashinostroenie
0013-7464 Energy *changed to* Energy Dialogue.
0013-7472 Energy and Character
0013-7480 Energy Conversion *see* 0196-8904
0013-7502 Energy Developments†
0013-7510 Energy Info†
0013-7529 Energy International *see* 0260-7840
0013-7537 Energy Management Report *issued with* 0031-6466
0013-7537 Energy Management Report *issued with* 0032-0188
0013-7545 Enfance
0013-7553 L'Enfant
0013-7561 Enfant en Milieu Tropical
0013-757X Enfants du Monde

ISSN INDEX 5373

ISSN	Title
0013-7596	Enfys
0013-7618	Engage see 0164-5528
0013-7626	Japanese Society for Horticultural Science. Journal
0013-7634	New Information on Horticulture changed to New Information on Horticulture: Flowers.
0013-7634	New Information on Horticulture changed to New Information on Horticulture: Vegetables.
0013-7642	Engelhard Industries Technical Bulletin†
0013-7669	Engenharia†
0013-7707	Engenharia (Revista) changed to Engenharia Civil.
0013-7723	Engenheiro Moderno†
0013-774X	Engine Data Sheets
0013-7758	Engineer
0013-7766	Engineer of Southern California see 0277-1233
0013-7774	Engineering changed to Engineering Times.
0013-7782	Engineering
0013-7790	Engineering Construction World see 0020-6415
0013-7804	Engineering and Contract Record changed to Construction Record.
0013-7812	Engineering & Science
0013-7839	Engineering Bulletin†
0013-7855	Engineering Capacity Register see 0306-0179
0013-7871	Engineering: Cornell Quarterly
0013-788X	Engineering Cybernetics changed to Soviet Journal of Computer & Systems Sciences.
0013-7898	Engineering Designer†
0013-7901	Engineering Digest
0013-791X	Engineering Economist
0013-7928	Facts from Gatorland†
0013-7936	Engineering Forum
0013-7944	Engineering Fracture Mechanics
0013-7952	Engineering Geology
0013-7960	Engineering Index see 0742-1974
0013-7979	Engineering Index Card-A-Lert†
0013-7987	Engineering Industries & Trade Journal
0013-7995	Engineering Industries Journal changed to Engineering Gazette.
0013-8029	Engineering Journal
0013-8037	Engineering Manpower Bulletin
0013-8053	Engineering Production†
0013-8061	Engineering News
0013-807X	Engineering News-Record see 0891-9526
0013-8088	Engineering Outlook at the University of Illinois at Urbana-Champaign changed to Engineering Outlook.
0013-810X	Engineering Research News†
0013-8118	Engineering Societies of New England. Journal changed to New England Engineering Journal.
0013-8126	Engineering Technician in the News see 0746-6641
0013-8134	Engineering Times
0013-8142	Engineers and Engines Magazine
0013-8150	Engineers' Club of St. Louis. Journal changed to Gateway Engineer.
0013-8169	Engineers' Digest
0013-8177	Coast Guard Engineer's Digest
0013-8185	Englisch
0013-8193	Englisch an Volkshochschulen see 0342-6173
0013-8215	English
0013-8223	English Churchman changed to English Churchman & St. James's Chronicle.
0013-8231	English Dance and Song
0013-824X	English for Immigrants†
0013-8266	English Historical Review
0013-8274	English Journal
0013-8282	English Language Notes
0013-8290	English Language Teaching see 0307-8337
0013-8304	E L H
0013-8312	English Literary Renaissance
0013-8312	English Literary Renaissance Supplements†
0013-8339	English Fiction in Transition see 0364-3549
0013-8355	English Quarterly
0013-8363	English Record
0013-8371	English-Speaking Union News changed to English Speaking Union Today.
0013-838X	English Studies
0013-8398	English Studies in Africa
0013-8401	English Westerners' Brand Book
0013-841X	English Westerners' Tally Sheet
0013-8436	Enigma
0013-8444	Enjiniasu
0013-8460	Enbi to Porima
0013-8479	Enlightenment Essays
0013-8487	Enlite†
0013-8495	Enoch Pratt Free Library. Staff Reporter
0013-8509	Enquiry
0013-8517	Enquiry
0013-8533	Ensanian Physicochemical Institute. Journal
0013-8541	Enjay Magazine changed to Chemsphere Americas.
0013-855X	Ensayot
0013-8576	Techniques Industrielles see 0768-9454
0013-8584	Enseignement Mathematique
0013-8592	Ensemble†
0013-8606	Ensign of the Church of Jesus Christ of Latter-day Saints see 0884-1136
0013-8614	Ensino Secundario
0013-8622	Ente Provinciale per Il Turismo di Nuoro. Notiziario†
0013-8630	Entente Africaine
0013-8657	Enterprise
0013-8665	Enterprise†
0013-8673	Enterprise
0013-8681	Enterprise
0013-8703	Entomologia Experimentalis et Applicata
0013-8711	Entomologica Scandinavica
0013-872X	Entomological News
0013-8738	Entomological Review
0013-8746	Entomological Society of America. Annals
0013-8754	Entomological Society of America. Bulletin see 1046-2821
0013-8762	Entomological Society of India. Bulletin of Entomology
0013-8770	Entomology changed to Japanese Journal of Entomology.
0013-8789	Entomological Society of Southern Africa. Journal
0013-8797	Entomological Society of Washington. Proceedings
0013-8800	Entomologie et Phytopathologie Appliquees
0013-8819	Entomologische Arbeiten aus dem Museum G. Frey, Tutzing-Bei Muenchen†
0013-8827	Entomologische Berichten
0013-8835	Entomologische Blaetter fuer Biologie und Systematik der Kaefer
0013-8843	Entomologische Zeitschrift
0013-8851	Entomologiske Meddelelser
0013-886X	Entomologisk Tidskrift
0013-8886	Entomologiste
0013-8894	Entomologist's Gazette
0013-8908	Entomologist's Monthly Magazine
0013-8916	Entomologist's Record
0013-8924	Entomology Abstracts
0013-8932	Florida. Department of Agriculture and Consumer Services. Entomology Circular
0013-8940	South Africa. Department of Agricultural Technical Services. Entomology Memoirs changed to South Africa. Department of Agriculture. Entomology Memoirs.
0013-8959	Entomophaga
0013-8975	Entr'Acte
0013-8991	Entre - Nous changed to Hydro-Presse.
0013-9033	Entrepreneur en Plomberie-Chauffage see 0032-1591
0013-9084	Entropie
0013-9092	Entscheidung
0013-9106	Entscheidungen des Bundesverwaltungsgerichts
0013-9149	Environment†
0013-9157	Environment (Washington)
0013-9165	Environment and Behavior
0013-9173	Environment and Planning see 0308-518X
0013-9181	Environment Information Access see 0093-3287
0013-919X	Environment Monthly†
0013-9203	Environment Report
0013-9211	Environment Reporter
0013-922X	Environmental Action
0013-9238	Environmental Control News for Southern Industry
0013-9254	Environmental Education see 0095-8964
0013-9262	Environmental Engineering see 0954-5824
0013-9270	Environmental Health
0013-9289	Environmental Health changed to Indian Journal of Environmental Health.
0013-9319	Environmental Mutagen Society Newsletter see 0921-8262
0013-9327	Environmental Pollution see 0269-7491
0013-9343	Environmental Quarterly†
0013-9351	Environmental Research
0013-936X	Environmental Science & Technology
0013-9386	Environmental Spectrum
0013-9394	Envoi
0013-9408	Envoy (Pittsburgh)
0013-9416	Enzymes in Medicine†
0013-9424	Enzymologia see 0300-8177
0013-9432	Enzyme
0013-9440	Eos
0013-9475	Epatologia
0013-9491	Ephemerides Iuris Canonici
0013-9505	Ephemerides Liturgicae
0013-9513	Ephemerides Theologicae Lovanienses
0013-9521	L'Epicier
0013-953X	Epicure†
0013-9548	Epicurean
0013-9556	Epidemiological Review†
0013-9564	Epigraphia Indica
0013-9572	Epigraphica
0013-9580	Epilepsia
0013-9610	Episcopal Recorder
0013-9629	Episcopalian†
0013-9645	Epistemologie Sociologique†
0013-9653	Epistolodidaktika
0013-9661	Epites- Epiteszettudomany
0013-967X	Epitesugyi Szemle
0013-9688	Genike Stratiotike Epitheoresis†
0013-9696	Greek Review of Social Research
0013-970X	Epitoanyag
0013-9718	Epoca
0013-9726	Epoca
0013-9734	Epos, a Quarterly of Poetry†
0013-9742	Epuletgepeszet
0013-9750	Equal Justice†
0013-9777	Equal Opportunity in Federal Government see 1053-4652
0013-9815	Equals One
0013-9831	Equestrian Trails
0013-984X	Equinews changed to Enterprise (New York).
0013-9874	Equipment Industriel†
0013-9882	Equipment Mecanique des Chantiers see 0998-4577
0013-9890	Equity News
0013-9912	Er Ruft
0013-9920	Era changed to Philomel.
0013-9939	E R A
0013-9947	Eranos
0013-9963	Erbe und Auftrag
0013-9971	Ercilla
0013-998X	Erdbau†
0013-9998	Die Erde
0014-0007	Erdkreis
0014-0015	Erdkunde
0014-0031	Az Erdo
0014-004X	Erdoel-Erdgas Zeitschrift see 0179-3187
0014-0058	Erdoel und Kohle, Erdgas, Petrochemie
0014-0066	Erdogazdasag es Faipar
0014-0074	Erevna
0014-0082	Erfahrungsheilkunde
0014-0090	Erfahrungswissenschaftliche Blaetter†
0014-0104	Erfolgs- und Erwerbspost
0014-0112	Ergokratische Schule fuer Dauernden. Frieden (Publication) changed to Die Ergokratische Schule.
0014-0120	Ergonomia
0014-0139	Ergonomics
0014-0147	Erhvervsoekonomisk Tidsskrift see 0902-3704
0014-0155	Erhvervs-Bladet
0014-0163	Eric - Crier Newsletter†
0014-0171	Ericsson Review
0014-018X	Ericsson Technics†
0014-0201	Ermlandbriefe
0014-0228	Ernaehrungsdienst
0014-0252	Eroeffnungen
0014-0260	Erre U
0014-0279	Die Ersatzkasse
0014-0309	Erwerbsobstbau
0014-0317	Dynamic†
0014-0325	Erziehung und Unterricht
0014-0333	Erziehungskunst
0014-0341	Escalpelo
0014-0368	Escort†
0014-0376	El Escribano
0014-0384	Escrow Newsletter†
0014-0392	Escudo†
0014-0422	Universidad de Panama. Escuela de Bibliotecologia. Boletin changed to Universidad de Panama. Departamento de Bibliotecologia. Boletin.
0014-0430	Argentina. Escuela Superior de Guerra. Revista see 0325-0792
0014-0449	Escursionismo
0014-0457	Escutcheon†
0014-0481	Espaces et Societes
0014-049X	Espana Agraria changed to Espana Agricola.
0014-0554	Espansione
0014-0562	Esparavel
0014-0570	Espectaculos†
0014-0597	Espejo†
0014-0600	Esperanta Ligilo
0014-0619	Der Esperantist†
0014-0635	Esperanto
0014-0643	Esperanto en Skotlando
0014-0651	Esperanto-Gazeto†
0014-066X	Esperanto - Lingvo Internacia
0014-0678	Esperienza
0014-0686	Esperienze Amministrative
0014-0694	Espero
0014-0708	Espiral†
0014-0716	Espiritu
0014-0732	L'Espoir du Monde
0014-0740	Esportazione
0014-0759	Esprit
0014-0767	Esprit Createur
0014-0775	Esprit et Vie
0014-0783	Esprit Libre
0014-0791	Esquire see 0194-9535
0014-0805	Esquire's Good Grooming Guide†
0014-0813	Esquiu
0014-0821	N O A A†
0014-083X	Essay and General Literature Index
0014-0848	Essay Proof Journal
0014-0856	Essays in Criticism
0014-0864	Essays in Economics†
0014-0880	Essence (New York)
0014-0902	Essenze-Derivati Agrumari
0014-0910	Essex Countryside
0014-0937	Essex County Medical Society. Bulletin
0014-0945	Essex Farmers Journal changed to Essex Farmer.
0014-0953	Essex Institute Historical Collections
0014-0961	Essex Journal
0014-097X	Esso Agricola†
0014-0988	Esso Air World changed to Exxon Air World.
0014-0996	Esso Aviation News Digest changed to Exxon Aviation News Digest.
0014-1003	Esso Dealer†

ISSN	Title
0014-102X	Esso News *changed to* Esso in Malaysia.
0014-1038	Esso Rivista†
0014-1046	Essobron
0014-1062	Essor du Comminges
0014-1089	Est
0014-1100	Est Sesia
0014-1127	Estacion Experimental. Dr. Mario Cassinoni. Facultad de Agronomia. Boletin Tecnico†
0014-1135	Estadistica
0014-1151	Spain. Instituto Nacional de Estadistica. Estadistica Espanola
0014-1178	Folha Mensal do Estado das Culturas e Previsao de Colheitas *see* 0870-2594
0014-1186	Estafeta Literaria *see* 0210-0835
0014-1194	Estano
0014-1208	Estanzuela - Investigacion Agricola†
0014-1216	Estate Planning
0014-1224	Estate Planning Checklists and Forms
0014-1240	Estates Gazette
0014-1259	Estates Times
0014-1267	Est et Ouest
0014-1283	Esteticka Vychova
0014-1291	Estetika
0014-1313	Estetyka†
0014-1321	Estheticienne
0014-133X	Estilo *see* 0325-0229
0014-1356	Estomatologia†
0014-1364	Estomatologia e Cultura *changed to* Universidade de Sao Paulo. Revista de Odontologia.
0014-1372	Estonian Events *changed to* Baltic Events.
0014-1380	Extra 2200 South
0014-1399	Estrella†
0014-1410	Estudios Americanos†
0014-1429	Estudios Andinos
0014-1437	Estudios Biblicos
0014-1445	Estudios Centro Americanos
0014-1453	Estudios Clasicos
0014-1461	Estudios de Derecho
0014-147X	Estudios de Historia Moderna y Contemporanea de Mexico
0014-1496	Estudios Geograficos
0014-150X	Estudios Historicos sobre San Sebastian. Boletin
0014-1518	Estudios Internacionales†
0014-1542	Estudios Sindicales y Cooperativos†
0014-1550	Estudios sobre el Communismo
0014-1569	Estudios Sobre Hospitales
0014-1577	Estudios Sobre la Union Sovietica†
0014-1585	Estudos Agronomicos†
0014-1607	Estudos Leopoldenses
0014-1623	Estudos Politicos e Sociais
0014-1631	L'Etain et ses Usages
0014-164X	ETC
0014-1658	Eter-Aktuell†
0014-1666	Eterna Sabiduria - Spanish Braille for Theosophists†
0014-1682	Eternity
0014-1690	Ethical Record
0014-1704	Ethics: An International Journal of Social, Political and Legal Philosophy
0014-1712	Ethiopia in the World Press†
0014-1720	Ethiopia Observer†
0014-1739	Ethiopian Geographical Journal†
0014-1747	Ethiopian Library Association. Bulletin
0014-1755	Ethiopian Medical Journal
0014-178X	Ethnie Francaise
0014-1798	Ethnographia
0014-1801	Ethnohistory
0014-181X	Ethnologische Zeitschrift†
0014-1828	Ethnology
0014-1836	Ethnomusicology *changed to* Journal for Ethnomusicology.
0014-1844	Ethnos
0014-1909	Etruscan†
0014-1917	Etude Comparative Benelux sur les Salaires†
0014-1941	Etudes
0014-195X	Etudes Anglaises
0014-1968	Etudes Ardennaises *see* 0035-3272
0014-1976	Etudes Balkaniques
0014-1992	Etudes Cinematographiques
0014-200X	Etudes Classiques
0014-2018	Etudes Dahomeennes
0014-2026	Etudes de Lettres
0014-2034	Etudes Economiques
0014-2042	Banque Francaise et Italienne. Etudes Economiques *changed to* Banque SudAmeris. Etudes Economiques.
0014-2069	Banque des Etats de l'Afrique Centrale. Etudes et Statistiques
0014-2077	Etudes Evangeliques†
0014-2085	Etudes Francaises
0014-2093	Etudes Franciscaines†
0014-2107	Etudes Freudiennes
0014-2115	Etudes Germaniques
0014-2123	Etudes Internationales
0014-2131	Etudes Internationales de Psycho-Sociologie Criminelle†
0014-214X	Etudes Litteraires
0014-2158	Etudes Normandes
0014-2166	Etudes Philosophiques
0014-2182	Etudes Rurales
0014-2204	Etudes Sociales
0014-2212	Etudes Sociales et Syndicales
0014-2220	Etudes Sovietiques
0014-2239	Etudes Theologiques et Religieuses
0014-2247	Etudes Tsiganes
0014-2255	World Student News
0014-2263	Etyka
0014-2271	Eucharist†
0014-2298	Euhemer
0014-2301	E U M I G - Lupe
0014-2328	Euphorion
0014-2336	Euphytica
0014-2352	Euro Abstracts *changed to* Euro Abstracts Section I. Euratom and EEC Research.
0014-2387	Euro Piano
0014-2409	EUROCOM Press Information†
0014-2417	Eurographie
0014-2425	Euromed†
0014-2433	Euromoney
0014-2441	Euromonitor Review *see* 0308-3446
0014-2468	Europa
0014-2476	Europa-Archiv
0014-2484	Europa Chemie
0014-2492	Europa Ethnica
0014-2514	Europa Industrie Revue. Maschinenmarkt und Elektrotechnik *see* 0341-5783
0014-2522	Europa-Korrespondenz
0014-2530	Europa Libera
0014-2549	Europa Medica†
0014-2557	Europa Medica *changed to* Panminerva Medica - Europa Medica.
0014-2565	Revista Clinica Espanola
0014-2573	Europa Medicophysica
0014-259X	Eurosport *see* 0931-5381
0014-2603	Europa Star - International Jewellery Magazine
0014-2611	Europa-Union *changed to* Europaeische Zeitung.
0014-262X	Europa-Verkehrt
0014-2638	Europaeer Diskutierent
0014-2646	Europaeische Begegnung *see* 0014-2468
0014-2670	Europaeische Mode nach Mass†
0014-2697	Europaeische Technische Informationen *changed to* Lagern und Fordern.
0014-2700	Europaeisches Immobilien Journal†
0014-2727	Europastimme
0014-2735	Welthandels Informationen - Europa Technik *changed to* World Trade Information.
0014-2751	Europe
0014-276X	Europe & Oil†
0014-2794	Europe-Echecs
0014-2808	Europe en Formation
0014-2816	Europe France Outremer *changed to* Europe Outremer.
0014-2824	Europe Oil-Telegram
0014-2832	Europe Oriental†
0014-2840	Witchcraft *see* 0085-8250
0014-2859	European Board Markets†
0014-2867	European Business Review†
0014-2875	European Chemical News
0014-2891	European Community *see* 0191-4545
0014-2905	European Documentation - a Survey†
0014-2921	European Economic Review
0014-293X	European Federation for the Protection of Waters. Information Bulletin†
0014-2948	European Grocery Letter
0014-2956	European Journal of Biochemistry
0014-2964	European Journal of Cancer *see* 0964-1947
0014-2972	European Journal of Clinical Investigation
0014-2980	European Journal of Immunology
0014-2999	European Journal of Pharmacology
0014-3006	European Judaism
0014-3014	European Marketing Research Review *see* 0923-5957
0014-3022	European Neurology
0014-3030	European Numismatics
0014-3057	European Polymer Journal
0014-3065	Potato Research
0014-3073	European Railways†
0014-3081	European Review†
0014-309X	European Shipbuilding†
0014-3103	European Studies *changed to* Exploring Europe.
0014-3111	European Studies Review *see* 0265-6914
0014-312X	European Surgical Research
0014-3138	European Taxation
0014-3146	European Teacher†
0014-3154	European Transport Law
0014-3162	European Trends
0014-3170	European University News
0014-3189	Europeo
0014-3197	Europese Documentatie†
0014-3235	Eurosud
0014-3243	Eurotec
0014-3251	Eurotransports Illustrato *changed to* Eurotransports.
0014-326X	Evangelische-Lutherische Kirche in Thueringen. Amtsblatt
0014-3278	Eva†
0014-3286	Eva
0014-3294	Eva†
0014-3308	Eva Express
0014-3316	Evaluation Engineering *see* 0149-0370
0014-3324	Evangelical Baptist
0014-3332	Evangelical Beacon
0014-3340	Evangelical Friend
0014-3359	Evangelical Missions Quarterly
0014-3367	Evangelical Quarterly
0014-3375	Evangelical Truth
0014-3383	Evangelie en Maatschappij *changed to* C N V - Opinie.
0014-3405	Evangelisch-Soziale Warte *changed to* S V A-Zeitung.
0014-3413	Der Evangelische Erzieher
0014-3421	Evangelische Kinderpflege fuer Kindergarten, Hort, Heim und Familie *see* 0342-7145
0014-343X	Evangelische Kirche in Deutschland. Amtsblatt
0014-3472	Evangelische Missionszeitschrift *see* 0342-9423
0014-3480	Der Evangelische Religionslehrer an Beruflichen Schulen†
0014-3502	Evangelische Theologie
0014-3529	Evangelische Landeskirche in Wuerttemberg. Amtsblatt
0014-3553	Evangelischer Nachrichtendienst in der D D R†
0014-3561	Evangelisches Gemeindeblatt Berlin *changed to* Nathanael Evangelisches Gemeindeblatt.
0014-360X	Evangelisches Gemeindeblatt fuer Wuerttemberg
0014-3618	Evangelisches Schulblatt†
0014-3626	Evangelist (Pasadena)
0014-3642	Evanjelicky Hlasnik
0014-3650	Evans-Novak Political Report
0014-3669	Evansville Public Library and Vanderburgh County Public Library. Staff News Bulletin *changed to* Evansville - Vanderburgh County Public Libraries. Staff News Bulletin.
0014-3677	Evansville-Vanderburgh School Corporation. Public Schools Bulletin†
0014-3685	Eve†
0014-3693	Evelyn Waugh Newsletter *changed to* Evelyn Waugh Newsletter and Studies.
0014-3731	Event *changed to* Metropinion.
0014-374X	Event
0014-3804	Everywoman's Daily Horoscope *changed to* Popular Astrology.
0014-3812	Eve's Weekly
0014-3820	Evolution
0014-3839	Panelectronics
0014-3855	Evolution Psychiatrique
0014-3863	Evoluzione Agricola
0014-3871	E W G-Warenhandel
0014-388X	Ex - C B I Roundup
0014-3901	Ex Libris (Lubbock)†
0014-391X	Ex Libris
0014-3928	Ex Ore Infantium
0014-3936	Ex-Serviceman
0014-3952	Exakte Aesthetk†
0014-3960	Examen de la Situacion Economica de Mexico
0014-3979	Examiner
0014-3987	Excalibur
0014-3995	Excavating Contractor
0014-4002	Excavator
0014-4010	Exceptional Child Education Abstracts *see* 0160-4309
0014-4029	Exceptional Children
0014-4037	Excerpta Botanica. Sectio A: Taxonomica et Chorologica
0014-4045	Excerpta Botanica. Sectio B: Sociologica
0014-4053	Excerpta Medica. Section 1: Anatomy, Anthropology, Embryology & Histology
0014-4061	Excerpta Medica. Section 2: Physiology
0014-407X	Excerpta Medica. Section 3: Endocrinology
0014-4088	Microbiology: Bacteriology, Virology, Mycology and Parasitology *see* 0927-2771
0014-4096	Excerpta Medica. Section 5: General Pathology and Pathological Anatomy
0014-410X	Excerpta Medica. Section 6: Internal Medicine
0014-4118	Excerpta Medica. Section 7: Pediatrics *see* 0373-6512
0014-4126	Excerpta Medica. Section 8: Neurology and Neurosurgery
0014-4134	Excerpta Medica. Section 9: Surgery
0014-4142	Excerpta Medica. Section 10: Obstetrics and Gynecology
0014-4150	Excerpta Medica. Section 11: Otorhinolaryngology
0014-4169	Excerpta Medica. Section 12: Ophthalmology
0014-4177	Excerpta Medica. Section 13: Dermatology and Venereology
0014-4185	Excerpta Medica. Section 14: Radiology
0014-4193	Excerpta Medica. Section 15: Chest Diseases, Thoracic Surgery and Tuberculosis
0014-4207	Excerpta Medica. Section 16: Cancer
0014-4215	Excerpta Medica. Section 17: Public Health, Social Medicine and Hygiene *see* 0924-5723
0014-4223	Excerpta Medica. Section 18: Cardiovascular Diseases and Cardiovascular Surgery
0014-4231	Excerpta Medica. Section 19: Rehabilitation and Physical Medicine
0014-424X	Excerpta Medica. Section 20: Gerontology and Geriatrics
0014-4258	Excerpta Medica. Section 21: Developmental Biology and Teratology
0014-4266	Excerpta Medica. Section 22: Human Genetics
0014-4274	Excerpta Medica. Section 23: Nuclear Medicine
0014-4282	Excerpta Medica. Section 24: Anesthesiology

ISSN	Title
0014-4290	Excerpta Medica. Section 25: Hematology
0014-4304	Excerpta Medica. Section 26: Immunology, Serology and Transplantation
0014-4312	Excerpta Medica. Section 27: Biophysics, Bio-Engineering and Medical Instrumentation
0014-4320	Excerpta Medica. Section 28: Urology and Nephrology
0014-4339	Biochemistry see 0927-278X
0014-4347	Excerpta Medica. Section 30: Pharmacology and Toxicology see 0927-2798
0014-4355	Excerpta Medica. Section 31: Arthritis and Rheumatism
0014-4363	Excerpta Medica. Section 32: Psychiatry
0014-4371	Excerpta Medica. Section 33: Orthopedic Surgery
0014-438X	Excerpta Medica. Section 34: Plastic Surgery†
0014-4398	Excerpta Medica. Section 35: Occupational Health and Industrial Medicine
0014-4436	Exchange†
0014-4444	Exchange†
0014-4452	Exchange & Commissary News
0014-4460	Exchange and Mart
0014-4479	Echangiste Universel
0014-4487	Exchangite
0014-4509	Executive see 0145-3963
0014-4525	Executive Fitness Newsletter
0014-4533	Executive Grocer†
0014-455X	Executive Housekeeper†
0014-4568	Executive Life†
0014-4576	Executive Men's Arts Series changed to Executive Men's Advertising Service.
0014-4584	Executive Reading†
0014-4592	Executives Wealth Report†
0014-4622	Exeter University Gazette†
0014-4649	Exhibition Bulletin
0014-4665	Exil et Liberté†
0014-4673	Existential Psychiatry†
0014-4681	Exlibris-Nyt
0014-469X	Expanded Shale Concrete Facts changed to Expanded Shale Lightweight Concrete Facts.
0014-4703	Expansion
0014-4711	Cahiers de l'Expansion Regionale see 0240-9925
0014-472X	Expecting
0014-4738	Expedition
0014-4754	Experientia
0014-4762	Experientiae†
0014-4770	Experiment
0014-4797	Experimental Agriculture
0014-4800	Experimental and Molecular Pathology
0014-4819	Experimental Brain Research
0014-4827	Experimental Cell Research
0014-4835	Experimental Eye Research
0014-4851	Experimental Mechanics
0014-486X	Experimental Medicine and Microbiology†
0014-4878	Experimental Medicine and Surgery†
0014-4886	Experimental Neurology
0014-4894	Experimental Parasitology
0014-4908	Experimentelle Pathologie see 0940-2993
0014-4916	Experimentation Animale†
0014-4924	Experimentelle Technik der Physik
0014-4932	Experiodica
0014-4932	Experiodica issued with 0037-4857
0014-4940	Explicator
0014-4959	Exploration†
0014-4975	Explorations
0014-4983	Explorations in Economic History
0014-4991	Explore†
0014-5009	Explorer (Cleveland)
0014-5017	Explorer (Notre Dame)
0014-5025	Explorers Journal
0014-5033	Exploring
0014-5041	Explosion Hunger-1975
0014-505X	Explosives & Pyrotechnics
0014-5068	Explosivstoffe
0014-5076	Exponent
0014-5084	Export changed to Export Today (London).
0014-5092	Export†
0014-5106	Export Anzeiger†
0014-5122	Export Courier
0014-5130	Export Direction†
0014-5149	Export - Import News
0014-5165	Export Management†
0014-5173	Export Polygraph International (E P I) see 0343-5199
0014-5181	Export Shipping Manual see 1043-5670
0014-519X	Export
0014-5203	Revista Mensal de Exportacao
0014-5211	Exportmarkt†
0014-522X	Expositor Bautista
0014-5238	Expositor Biblico (Teacher Edition)†
0014-5246	Expository Times
0014-5254	Exposvisie
0014-5262	Express†
0014-5270	Express
0014-5289	Express Documents
0014-5327	Expression
0014-5343	Expression†
0014-5351	Expression†
0014-536X	Expression One
0014-5378	Extebank Monthly Economic Report†
0014-5386	Extemporale
0014-5394	Extensao em Minas Gerais
0014-5408	Extension Service Review see 0162-9875
0014-5416	Extensions†
0014-5424	Extensions and Corrections to the U D C
0014-5432	External Affairs see 0381-4874
0014-5440	New Zealand Foreign Affairs Review see 0114-3999
0014-5459	External Studies Gazette changed to Armidale News.
0014-5467	Stamp Digest
0014-5475	American Digest of Foreign Orthopaedic Literature†
0014-5483	Extrapolation
0014-5491	Eye, Ear, Nose and Throat Monthly see 0145-5613
0014-5513	Eyeopener
0014-5521	Eyewitness
0014-553X	F A A Aviation News changed to F A A Aviation News.
0014-5548	F A B I Revue d'Information
0014-5564	F.A.I. Abstract Service
0014-5580	F A O Documentation - Current Index see 0304-582X
0014-5599	F A O Aquaculture Bulletin†
0014-5602	F A O Fisheries Synopsis
0014-5610	F A O Forestry and Forest Industries Bulletin for Latin America†
0014-5629	F A O Information changed to Sekai no Norinsuisan.
0014-5637	F A O Plant Protection Bulletin see 0254-9727
0014-5645	F A P I G
0014-5661	F and S International see 0270-4528
0014-567X	F and S Index of Corporations and Industries see 0270-4544
0014-5688	F B I Law Enforcement Bulletin
0014-570X	F C H News Briefs see 0895-5735
0014-5718	F C I B Bulletin changed to F C I B International Bulletin.
0014-5734	F C N L Washington Newsletter
0014-5742	F C X Patron†
0014-5750	F D A Papers see 0362-1332
0014-5769	Freien Deutschen Gewerkschaftsbundes. Rundschau see 0323-5750
0014-5777	F D I Newsletter see 0965-9986
0014-5785	F E & Z N†
0014-5793	F E B S Letters
0014-5807	F E N: Australian Factory Equipment News see 0728-9413
0014-5815	F F Communications
0014-584X	M F D-Zeitung changed to Schweizer Soldat und M F D.
0014-5874	F I D News Bulletin
0014-5890	F I G A News changed to F I G A.
0014-5904	F I R A Bulletin
0014-5912	F.I.R.O. Quaderni†
0014-5939	F L C Newsletter see 0882-908X
0014-5955	F M G - Fachblatt
0014-5963	F M changed to Vox: Hebdomadaire Militaire.
0014-5971	F M Guide
0014-5998	F.N. Orientering
0014-6013	F O A Orienterar Om
0014-603X	F O I Center Report†
0014-6048	F.O. Licht's Europaeisches Zuckerjournal changed to F.O. Licht's International Sugar and Sweetener Report.
0014-6056	F.O. Licht's International Molasses Report
0014-6072	F.P.A. Journal see 0309-6866
0014-6080	F P C News (U.S. Federal Power Commission) changed to F E R C News.
0014-6102	F R C C changed to B C S Newsletter.
0014-6110	F R E N changed to Florida Rural Electric News.
0014-6137	F R I Monthly Portfolio
0014-6145	Der Sportjournalist
0014-6153	F u Pressedienst Wissenschaft†
0014-6161	F V I†
0014-6196	Fabian News changed to Fabian News.
0014-6226	Fabrieksorganisatie†
0014-6234	Fabriksarbetaren
0014-6242	Fabula
0014-6269	Face au Risque
0014-6277	Face-To-Face†
0014-6285	Facettes
0014-6293	Fachberater
0014-6307	Der Fachberater†
0014-6315	Fachberater fuer das Deutsche Kleingartenwesen
0014-6323	Fachberichte fuer Metallbearbeitung changed to F B M - Fertigungstechnologie.
0014-634X	Fachblatt der Bundesinnung der Metallgiesser, Guertler, Graveure, Metalldrucker†
0014-6366	F F S B changed to Handels-Magazin F S B und Fachblatt fuer Selbstbedienung.
0014-6374	Fachhefte fuer Chemigraphie, Lithographie und Tiefdruck changed to Fachhefte Bulletin Technique.
0014-6382	Fachpresse changed to Schweizer Fachpresse.
0014-6390	Die Fachschule
0014-6412	Fachzeitschrift fuer der Buerofachhandel changed to Fachzeitung fuer den Buerofachhandel.
0014-6420	Facilities for Atmospheric Research see 0091-2026
0014-6447	Die Fackel
0014-6455	Fackfoereningsroerelsen see 0346-895X
0014-6463	Facklaerarent
0014-6471	Fackliga Vaerldsrorelsen†
0014-648X	Universita degli Studi di Perugia. Facolta di Medicina e Chirurgia. Annali
0014-6501	F B; A Fact Book on Higher Education changed to Fact Book for Higher Education.
0014-651X	Fact Finder
0014-6536	De Facto changed to Uni-Press.
0014-6544	Purchasing
0014-6552	Factory Equipment and Materials for Southern Africa changed to Factory Equipment & Materials.
0014-6579	Factory Equipment News
0014-6595	Factory Mutual Record
0014-6617	Facts and Comparisons see 0277-9714
0014-6633	Facts on Dental Health & Smoking†
0014-6641	Facts on File World News Digest With Index
0014-665X	Lisbon. Universidade. Faculdade de Ciencias. Revista. Serie 2. Seccao A. Ciencias Matematicas†
0014-6684	Faculdade de Farmacia e Odontologia de Araraquara. Revista see 0101-1774
0014-6714	Universidad de la Republica. Facultad de Arquitectura. Revista†
0014-6722	Universidad Nacional de Cordoba. Facultad de Ciencias Medicas. Revista
0014-6730	Universidad de Zaragoza. Facultad de Medicina. Archivos†
0014-6749	Universite de Toulouse II (le Mirail). Annales†
0014-679X	Faenza
0014-6803	Fahr mit Uns
0014-6811	Fahr Betriebsleben†
0014-682X	Fahrlehrer†
0014-6838	Fahrschule
0014-6846	Fahrt Frei
0014-6854	Der Fahrzeug- und Metall-Lackierer
0014-6862	Fahrzeug und Karosserie
0014-6870	Der Fahrzeughandel†
0014-6889	Faims et Soifs des Hommes
0014-6897	Faipar
0014-6919	Fair Employment Report
0014-6927	Fair Lady
0014-6943	Fairchild Tropical Garden Bulletin
0014-6951	Faire Face
0014-696X	Fairfield County Economy†
0014-6978	Fairfield County Press†
0014-6986	Fairplay Shipping Journal see 0307-0220
0014-6994	Fait Public†
0014-7001	Faith and Form
0014-701X	Faith and Freedom
0014-7028	Faith and Thought see 0954-4194
0014-7036	Faith and Unity†
0014-7044	Faith for Daily Living
0014-7052	Facts and Tendencies
0014-7079	Falcon†
0014-7087	Faller-Magazin see 0170-0510
0014-7095	Famiglia Cristiana
0014-7109	Familia†
0014-7117	Familia
0014-7125	Familia Crista
0014-7133	Familie Journalen
0014-7141	Familien
0014-715X	Familienblatt
0014-7168	Familienfreund†
0014-7176	Familienverband Avenarius. Familienzeitschrift
0014-7184	Famille Nouvelle
0014-7206	Family Circle
0014-7214	Family Coordinator see 0197-6664
0014-7230	Family Handyman
0014-7257	Family Health Bulletin†
0014-7265	Family History
0014-7273	Family Houseboating see 0006-5374
0014-7281	Family Law
0014-729X	Family Law Quarterly
0014-7303	Family Life
0014-7311	Family Perspective
0014-732X	Family Physician
0014-7338	Family Planning see 0309-1112
0014-7346	Family Planning News changed to Pathways in Population Planning.
0014-7354	Family Planning Perspectives
0014-7362	Family Planning Quarterly†
0014-7370	Family Process
0014-7389	Family Puzzlers
0014-7397	Family Safety see 0749-310X
0014-7435	Famous Artists Magazine†
0014-7443	Famous Monsters of Filmland changed to Famous Monsters.
0014-7451	Famous Photographers†
0014-746X	Famous Writers Magazine†
0014-7478	Fanfare†
0014-7486	Fangst og Fiske changed to Maritime News.
0014-7494	Fant†
0014-7524	Fante di Quadri
0014-7532	Far East see 0048-251X
0014-7540	Far East Architect and Builder see 0264-8164
0014-7559	Far East Engineer†
0014-7567	Far East Medical Journal see 0301-0376
0014-7583	Far East Trade and Development†

ISSN INDEX

ISSN	Title
0014-7591	Far Eastern Economic Review
0014-7605	Far Eastern University Journal†
0014-7613	F A R Horizons Newletter†
0014-7648	Far West News see 0746-4541
0014-7656	Faraday†
0014-7664	Faraday Society. Discussions see 0301-7249
0014-7672	Faraday Society. Transactions see 0956-5000
0014-7680	Die Farbe
0014-7699	Farbe und Lack
0014-7702	Farbe und Raum
0014-7710	Farben-Chemiker see 0931-5985
0014-7737	Farbenkreis, Oesterreichische Malerzeitung
0014-7745	Fare Box
0014-777X	Jern og Farge changed to Jernvarehandleren.
0014-7788	Farhang-e Iran Zamin
0014-7796	Farm†
0014-7818	Big Farm Management changed to Farm Business.
0014-7826	Farm and Dairy
0014-7834	Farm and Power Equipment see 0892-6085
0014-7842	Farm and Ranch Bulletin†
0014-7850	Farm Building Express†
0014-7869	Farm Building News changed to Rural Builder.
0014-7877	Farm Buildings Digest see 0265-5373
0014-7885	Farm Chemicals and Croplife see 0092-0053
0014-7893	Farm City Week Newsletter
0014-7907	Farm Credit Banks of Baltimore. News & Views†
0014-7931	Farm Economist see 0264-5491
0014-7958	Farm Equipment
0014-7974	U.S. Department of Agriculture. Economic Research Service. Farm Income Situation see 0099-1066
0014-7982	Farm Index see 0270-5672
0014-7990	Farm Industry News see 0199-6924
0014-8008	Farm Journal
0014-8016	Farm Labor†
0014-8024	Farm Letter†
0014-8032	Farm Light & Power
0014-8040	Farm Machine Design Engineering†
0014-8059	Farm Management
0014-8075	Farm Policy†
0014-8083	Farm Pond Harvest
0014-8091	Farm Quarterly†
0014-8105	Farm Safety Review†
0014-8113	Farm Service News changed to N J D A Report.
0014-8121	Farm Store
0014-813X	Farm Supplier†
0014-8148	Farm Technology changed to Ag Consultant.
0014-8164	Farmaceuten†
0014-8172	Farmaceuticky Obzor
0014-8199	Farmaceutisk Tidende
0014-8202	Farmaceutski Glasnik
0014-8210	Farmacevtska Revy
0014-8229	Farmacevtski Vestnik
0014-8237	Farmacia
0014-8245	Farmacia Nuova
0014-8253	Farmacista Sociale
0014-8261	Farmacja Polska
0014-827X	Farmaco
0014-8288	Farmacognosia†
0014-8296	Terapeutica Razonada†
0014-8318	Farmakologiya i Toksikologiya
0014-8326	Farmakoterapi
0014-8334	Farmand
0014-8342	Farmatsevtychnyi Zhurnal
0014-8350	Farmer
0014-8369	Farmer and Parliament
0014-8377	Farmer-Labor Press
0014-8393	Farmers Club. Journal
0014-8415	Farmers' Friend
0014-8423	Farmers Guardian
0014-844X	Farmers Newsletter
0014-8458	Farmers Union Herald changed to Harvest States Journal.
0014-8466	Farmers Weekly†
0014-8474	Farmers Weekly
0014-8482	Farmers Weekly
0014-8504	Farming in Zambia†
0014-8512	Foreign Acquisitions Newsletter†
0014-8520	Farmis - Reptilen
0014-8539	Farmland see 0093-5832
0014-8547	Farmweek
0014-8555	Il Faro
0014-8563	Faro Dominical changed to Marchemos.
0014-8571	Farogh-I-Urdu
0014-858X	Farolt
0014-8598	Faarskoetsel
0014-8601	Farumashia
0014-8644	Fashion Accessories
0014-8660	Fashion Calendar
0014-8679	Fashion Forecast
0014-8695	Fashion Week†
0014-8709	Fashionweek see 0312-0325
0014-8725	Fast Food see 0097-8043
0014-8733	Fast Grunn
0014-8741	Fasteners†
0014-875X	Fastline Monthly†
0014-8776	Fate
0014-8784	Res Medicae
0014-8792	Fateh
0014-8814	Fathers of the Church
0014-8822	Fathom
0014-8830	Fatima Findings
0014-8849	Fatos and Fotos changed to Fatos.
0014-8865	U.S. Department of Agriculture. Fats and Oils Situation changed to U.S. Department of Agriculture. Oil Crops Situation and Outlook Report.
0014-8873	Fatti E Notizie
0014-8881	Fauna
0014-8903	Fauna och Flora
0014-892X	Faversham Papers
0014-8938	Fax Forecast
0014-8946	Feasta
0014-8962	Feddes Repertorium
0014-8970	Feder changed to Publizistik und Kunst.
0014-9004	Federal Accountant see 0883-1483
0014-9039	Federal Bar Journal see 0279-4691
0014-9047	Federal Bar News see 0279-4691
0014-9063	Federal Contracts Report
0014-9071	Federal Employee
0014-908X	Federal Fire Council News Letter†
0014-911X	Federal Notes†
0014-9128	Federal Probation
0014-9136	Washington Environmental Protection Report
0014-9144	Federal Reserve Bank of Atlanta. Monthly Review see 0732-1813
0014-9152	Federal Reserve Bank of Kansas City. Monthly Review see 0161-2387
0014-9160	Federal Reserve Bank of New York. Monthly Review see 0147-6580
0014-9179	Federal Reserve Bank of Richmond. Monthly Review see 0094-6893
0014-9187	Federal Reserve Bank of St. Louis. Review
0014-9195	Federal Reserve Bank of San Francisco. Monthly Review see 0363-0021
0014-9209	Federal Reserve Bulletin
0014-9225	Federal Statistics Users' Conference. Newsletter
0014-9233	Federal Times
0014-9241	Federalist changed to World Citizen - Federalist Letter.
0014-9268	Federaliste Europeen
0014-9276	Federation of Industrial, Manufacturing and Engineering Employees. Labor News
0014-9284	Federatie Contact see 0166-7831
0014-9306	Federation of State Medical Boards of the United States. Federation Bulletin
0014-9314	Federation of Synagogues of South Africa. Federation Chronicle changed to Jewish Tradition.
0014-9330	Federation des Entreprises de l'Industrie des Fabrications Metalliques, Mecaniques, Electriques et de la Transformation des Matieres Plastiques. Bulletin d'Information Mensuel changed to Federation des Entreprises de l'Industrie des Fabrications Metalliques, Mecaniques, Electriques et de la Transformation des Matieres Plastiques. Revue Mensuelle.
0014-9349	Federation des Industriels Belges. Bulletin see 0771-2987
0014-9357	Federation des Societes d'Histoire Naturelle de Franche-Comte. Bulletin see 0753-4655
0014-9365	Federation Francaise des Societes de Sciences Naturelles. Revue see 0336-8300
0014-9373	Entreprise Europeenne
0014-9411	Federation News
0014-942X	Federation News
0014-9438	American Beekeeping Federation. Newsletter
0014-9446	Federation of American Societies for Experimental Biology. Federation Proceedings see 0892-6638
0014-9454	Federation of Canadian Archers. Official Bulletin changed to Canadian Archer.
0014-9470	Federation of Indian Chambers of Commerce and Industry. Fortnightly Review changed to Economic Trends.
0014-9489	F. W. I. News
0014-9497	Federazione Italiana Medici Igienisti. Bollettino d'Informazioni Agli Iscritti
0014-9500	Federazione Medica
0014-9519	Federazione Nazionale Stampa Italiana. Bollettino†
0014-9527	Quaerendo
0014-9535	Feed Industry see 0191-9334
0014-9543	Feed Bulletin
0014-9551	Feed - Grain Equipment Times changed to Feed and Grain.
0014-956X	Feed Management
0014-9578	U.S. Department of Agriculture. Feed Situation changed to U.S. Department of Agriculture. Feed Situation and Outlook.
0014-9586	Feed Trade
0014-9594	Feedback changed to Feedback for Improving Vocational-Technical and Career Education.
0014-9608	Feedback†
0014-9616	Feedlot changed to Feedlot Management.
0014-9624	Feedstuffs
0014-9632	Fee†
0014-9640	Fegarbel Revue
0014-9659	Fegato
0014-9667	Fei Ch'ing Yen Chiu see 1015-9355
0014-9675	Fei Ch'ing Yueh Pao - Chinese Communist Affairs Monthly see 1013-2716
0014-9683	Feingeraetetechnik†
0014-9691	Feinkost-Revue†
0014-9713	Feinwerktechnik see 0340-1952
0014-973X	Feju
0014-9748	Feld und Wald changed to Agrar-Praxis.
0014-9756	Feld Wald Wasser
0014-9764	Feldgraut
0014-9772	Fel'dsher i Akusherka
0014-9780	Feldwebel
0014-9799	Feldwirtschaft changed to Neue Landwirtschaft.
0014-9802	Feliciter
0014-9810	Fellowship
0014-9829	Fellowship for Freedom in Medicine. Bulletin see 0305-9324
0014-9837	Fellowship in Prayer
0014-9853	Femina
0014-9861	Femina changed to Femina Maanadens Magasin.
0014-987X	Femina and Woman's Life†
0014-9888	Feminidades†
0014-9896	Femme Chic†
0014-990X	Femme d'Aujourd'hui et Patrie Suisse-Actualites changed to La Femme D'Aujourd'hui.
0014-9918	Femme-Lines
0014-9926	Femme Pratique
0014-9934	Femmes au Village
0014-9942	Femmes Chefs d'Entreprise
0014-9950	Femmes d'Aujourd'hui
0014-9969	Fenarete-Letture d'Italia
0014-9977	Fence Industry - Access Control see 0894-6639
0014-9985	Fendt-Nachrichten†
0015-0002	Fenix
0015-0010	Fennia
0015-0029	Das Fenster
0015-0037	Ferguson-Florissant Schools
0015-007X	Fermettes et Residences Secondaires see 0184-7473
0015-0096	Fernmelde Impuls†
0015-010X	Der Fernmelde-Ingenieur
0015-0118	Fernmelde Praxis changed to Telekom Praxis.
0015-0126	Fernmeldetechnik†
0015-0134	Fernseh-Informationen
0015-0142	Fernseh- und Kino-Technik
0015-0150	Fernsehen und Bildung†
0015-0177	Ferrocarriles changed to Ferrocarriles Mexicanos.
0015-0185	Ferrocarriles y Tranvias
0015-0193	Ferroelectrics
0015-0207	Ferronales
0015-0215	Ferroviere
0015-0223	Ferskvandsfiskeribladet
0015-0231	Fertigteilbau und Industrialisiertes Bauen see 0340-2967
0015-024X	Fertigungstechnik und Betrieb
0015-0258	Feed and Farm Supplies changed to Milling Feed and Farm Supplies.
0015-0266	Fertiliser News
0015-0282	Fertility and Sterility
0015-0290	Fertilizer Abstracts†
0015-0304	Fertilizer International
0015-0312	Fertilizer Solutions see 0199-9869
0015-0320	Der Feste Grund
0015-0339	Feste Prophetische Wort†
0015-0347	Festina Lente
0015-0355	Festiniog Railway Magazine
0015-0363	Festival
0015-0371	Fetes et Saisons
0015-038X	Fette-Seifen-Anstrichmittel see 0931-5985
0015-0401	Feuerungstechnik - Gebaeudetechnik changed to Feuerungstechnik, Energie & Umwelt.
0015-041X	Feuille Anarchiste
0015-0428	Feuille Officielle de la Protection Civile
0015-0452	Feuillets du Praticien
0015-0479	Fiamma†
0015-0495	Fiat Lux
0015-0509	Veckans Stopp changed to Maanadens Stopp.
0015-0517	Fibonacci Quarterly
0015-0525	Fibra†
0015-0533	Fibre and Fabric†
0015-0541	Fibre Chemistry
0015-055X	Fibre e Colori see 0033-9067
0015-0568	Fibre Science and Technology see 0266-3538
0015-0576	Fibula†
0015-0592	Fichero Bibliografico Hispanoamericano
0015-0606	Fichero Medico Terapeutico Purissimus
0015-0614	Fiches Medicales
0015-0630	Fiddlehead
0015-0649	Field
0015-0657	Field
0015-0673	Field & Stream
0015-069X	Field Crop Abstracts
0015-0703	Field Museum of Natural History Bulletin see 1051-4546
0015-0711	Arkansas Archeological Society. Field Notes
0015-072X	Field Notes†
0015-0746	Fieldiana: Botany
0015-0754	Fieldiana: Zoology
0015-0762	Fields see 0744-4052
0015-0770	Fields Within Fields...Within Fields†
0015-0797	Fiere e Mostre
0015-0800	Fifth Estate

ISSN INDEX

ISSN	Title
0015-0819	Fifth Wheel
0015-0827	Fifty Millesimal News Letter
0015-0835	Figaro
0015-0843	Figaro Litteraire†
0015-0851	Figurino Moderno
0015-086X	Figyelo
0015-0878	Fiinta Romaneasca†
0015-0886	Fiji Agricultural Journal
0015-0894	Fiji. Bureau of Statistics. Current Economic Statistics
0015-0908	Fiji Farmer†
0015-0916	Fiji. Government Printing Department. Publications Bulletin
0015-0932	Fikrun Wa Fann
0015-0940	Filatelia Italiana
0015-0959	Filatelie
0015-0967	Filatelija
0015-0975	Filatelista
0015-0983	Filateliya S.S.S.R.
0015-0991	Filipino-American Herald
0015-1009	Filipino Teacher
0015-1017	Film see 0108-5697
0015-1025	Film
0015-1033	Film
0015-1041	Film
0015-105X	Film see 0046-368X
0015-1068	Film a Doba
0015-1076	Schweizer Schmalfilm changed to Film & Foto mit Video.
0015-1084	Film en Televisie changed to Film en Televisie - Video.
0015-1106	F T T and Beta News
0015-1114	Film und Ton-Magazin†
0015-1122	Film Artiste†
0015-1130	Film Bild Ton changed to A V-Praxis.
0015-1149	Film-Echo - Filmwoche
0015-1157	Film Bulletin†
0015-1165	Film Bulletin
0015-1173	Film Canadiana: The Canadian Film Institute Yearbook of Canadian Cinema see 0836-1002
0015-1181	Film Collectors Registry†
0015-119X	Film Comment
0015-1203	Critic
0015-1211	Film Culture
0015-1238	Film Fan Monthly†
0015-1262	Film Francais-Cinematographie Francais see 0397-8702
0015-1270	Film Heritage†
0015-1289	Film Index
0015-1297	Film Information†
0015-1300	Film Italiano†
0015-1319	Film Journal Advertiser†
0015-1327	Film Library Quarterly†
0015-1335	Film-Lyd-Bilde†
0015-1343	Film News changed to Film & Video News (1979).
0015-1351	Film og Kino
0015-136X	Polish Film - Film Polonais changed to Polish Film.
0015-1378	Film-Pop-Telescoop changed to Pop-Telescoop
0015-1386	Film Quarterly
0015-1416	Film, Szinhaz, Muzsika
0015-1424	Fernseh und Film Technikum†
0015-1440	Film und Recht changed to Zeitschrift fuer Urheber- und Medienrecht.
0015-1459	Film User see 0305-2249
0015-1467	Film Weekly†
0015-1475	Film World†
0015-1505	Filmclub Action-Mitteilungen
0015-1513	Filmcritica
0015-1521	Filme e Cultura changed to Filme Cultura.
0015-153X	Filmfacts†
0015-1548	Filmfare
0015-1556	Filmjournalen
0015-1564	Filmkompas changed to Groepsmedia.
0015-1572	Filmkritik
0015-1580	Filmkultura
0015-1599	Filmkunst
0015-1602	Filmlist see 0037-4830
0015-1610	Filmmakers' Newsletter see 0194-4339
0015-1629	Filmograph†
0015-1645	Filmovy Prehled
0015-1653	Filmowy Osrodek Badawczo - Rozwojowy "Techfilm". Przeglad Dokumentacyjny†
0015-1661	Filmrutan
0015-167X	Films & Filming
0015-1688	Films in Review
0015-1696	Filmschau
0015-170X	Filmska Kultura
0015-1734	Filmspiegel
0015-1742	Filmtheater-Praxis changed to Filmtheater-Praxis - Werbung Heute.
0015-1777	Filologia e Letteratura changed to Critica Letteraria.
0015-1785	Filologiai Kozlony
0015-1815	Filomata
0015-1823	Filosofia
0015-1831	Filosoficky Casopis
0015-1858	Filosofskie Nauki (Moscow)
0015-1866	Filozofija see 0351-2274
0015-1874	Filson Club History Quarterly
0015-1882	Filtration & Separation
0015-1890	Filtration Engineering†
0015-1904	Findivert
0015-1912	Finance†
0015-1920	Finance a Uver
0015-1939	Finance & Commerce changed to Finance & Society.
0015-1947	Finance and Development
0015-1955	Finance and Trade Review†
0015-1963	Finance Facts†
0015-1971	Finance Taxation & Company Law
0015-198X	Financial Analysts Journal
0015-1998	Financial Executive see 0895-4186
0015-2005	Financial Express
0015-2013	Financial Mail
0015-2021	Financial Post
0015-203X	Great Britain. Central Statistical Office. Financial Statistics
0015-2064	Financial World
0015-2072	Financieel Overheidsbeheer see 0922-1026
0015-2080	Financiele Flitsen†
0015-2099	Financiele Koerier
0015-2102	Financiero
0015-2110	Financing Agriculture
0015-2129	Financing Foreign Operations: Global Edition
0015-2137	Finansi i Kredit†
0015-2145	Finansije
0015-2153	Finanstidende†
0015-2161	Finansy S.S.S.R.
0015-217X	Finante si Credit†
0015-2188	Finanz-Revue
0015-2196	Finanz-Rundschau see 0176-7771
0015-220X	Finanz und Wirtschaft
0015-2218	Finanzarchiv
0015-2226	Finanzas al Dia
0015-2242	Finanziere changed to Testata: il Finanziere.
0015-2250	Finanzjournal mit Gebuehren- und Verkehrsteuerbeitragen
0015-2269	Finanznachrichten
0015-2277	Finanzrechtliche Erkenntnisse des Verwaltungsgerichtshofes
0015-2285	Findings†
0015-2307	Fine Arts†
0015-2331	Finis Terrae†
0015-234X	Finish†
0015-2358	Finishers' Management
0015-2366	Finite String see 0891-2017
0015-2374	Elbe Wochenblatt fuer Sued Hamburg changed to Elbe Wochenblatt.
0015-2390	Finland. Tilastokeskus. Tilastokatsauksia
0015-2412	Finnfacts†
0015-2420	Finnische Handelsrundschau see 0359-7008
0015-2439	Finnish American Chamber of Commerce Newsletter changed to Finnish American Chamber of Commerce Newsletter.
0015-2447	Finnish Game Research - Riistatieteellisia Julkaisuja see 0783-4365
0015-2455	Finnish Paper and Timber†
0015-2463	Finnish Trade Review
0015-248X	Finsk Tidskrift
0015-2498	Finska Kemistsamfundet. Meddelanden see 0355-1628
0015-2501	Finska Laekaresaellskapet. Handlingar
0015-251X	Finskij Torgovyj Zhurnal
0015-2528	Fiori di S. Antonio
0015-2536	Fiorisce Un Cenacolo
0015-2544	Fire
0015-2552	Fire Chief
0015-2587	Fire Engineering
0015-2595	Fire Fighting in Canada
0015-2609	Fire International
0015-2617	Fire Journal see 1054-8793
0015-2625	Fire News
0015-2641	Fire Protection Review changed to Fire & Security Protection.
0015-2668	Fire Service Information
0015-2684	Fire Technology
0015-2714	Fireside Chats†
0015-2722	Firing Line
0015-2730	Firmenkraftfahrer†
0015-2749	First see 0199-2066
0015-2757	First Hawaiian Bank. Economic Indicators
0015-2773	First National Bank of Chicago. Business and Economic Review†
0015-2781	First National Bank of Chicago. International Economic Review†
0015-279X	Citibank. Monthly Economic Letter†
0015-2803	First to Final†
0015-2811	Fiscaal Tijdschrift voor de Euromarkt changed to Intertax (Dutch Edition).
0015-282X	Fiscalite du Marche Commun see 0165-2826
0015-2838	Fisch und Fang
0015-2846	Fischer Edition News†
0015-2854	Das Fischerblatt
0015-2862	Fischers Tarif Nachrichten fuer Eisenbahn und Kraftwagen
0015-2897	Fish and Game Sportsman see 0709-1532
0015-2900	Fish Boat - Sea Food Merchandising†
0015-2919	Fish Culturist
0015-2927	Fish Friers Review
0015-2943	Fish Trades Gazette changed to Fish Trader.
0015-2951	Fisheries of Canada†
0015-2978	Fisherman†
0015-2986	Fisherman
0015-2994	Fishermen's News
0015-3001	Fishery Technology
0015-301X	Fishing and Hunting News
0015-3028	Fishing Gazette†
0015-3036	Fishing News
0015-3044	Fishing News International
0015-3052	Tackle & Guns
0015-3060	Fishing Tackle Trade News
0015-3079	Fishing World
0015-3087	Fishpaste†
0015-3095	Fiskaren
0015-3109	Fiskehandleren†
0015-3117	Norway. Fiskeridirektoratet. Skrifter. Serie Havundersoekelser
0015-3125	Fiskeritidskrift foer Finland
0015-3133	Fiskets Gang
0015-3141	Fitness and Health†
0015-3176	Five Associated University Libraries. Newsletter†
0015-3184	Five - Six see 0149-7820
0015-3206	Fizika
0015-3214	Fizika i Khimiya Obrabotki Materialov
0015-3222	Fizika i Tekhnika Poluprovodnikov
0015-3230	Fizika Metallov i Metallovedenie
0015-3249	Fizika Tverdogo Tela
0015-3257	Fizikai Szemle
0015-3265	Fiziko-Matematichesko Spisanie
0015-3273	Fiziko-Tekhnicheskie Problemy Razrabotki Poleznykh Iskopaemykh
0015-329X	Fiziologicheskii Zhurnal (Moscow)
0015-3303	Fiziologiya Rastenii
0015-3311	Fiziologichnyi Zhurnal (Ukrainian) see 0201-8489
0015-332X	Fizkul'tura i Sport
0015-3338	Fjaederfae
0015-3346	Fjarmalatidindi
0015-3354	Fjoerfe
0015-3362	Flacara
0015-3370	Flag Bulletin
0015-3389	Flair†
0015-3400	Flakten†
0015-3419	Flama†
0015-3427	Flambeau
0015-3435	Flambeau†
0015-346X	Flame Notes†
0015-3478	Flamingo†
0015-3486	Flammes Vives
0015-3494	Flash
0015-3508	Flash (Seattle)†
0015-3516	Flash Actualite
0015-3524	Flash Art see 0394-1493
0015-3532	Flavour Industry changed to Food Ingredients & Processing International.
0015-3540	De Fleanende Krie
0015-3575	Fleisch
0015-3583	Fleisch und Feinkost†
0015-3605	Fleischer Offerten-Dienst see 0170-0499
0015-3613	Die Fleischerei
0015-363X	Die Fleischwirtschaft
0015-3648	Fleur de Lys
0015-3680	Der Flieger
0015-3699	Luftwaffe
0015-3702	Flight Comment
0015-3710	Flight International
0015-3729	Flight Magazine see 0361-5030
0015-3737	Flight Safety Bulletin
0015-3753	Floor & Wall Covering News†
0015-3761	Floor Covering Weekly
0015-377X	Flooring & Carpet Specifier†
0015-3796	Biochemie und Physiologie der Pflanzen (B P P)
0015-380X	Flora
0015-3818	Flora og Fauna
0015-3826	Floresta
0015-3834	Floricoltura Pesciatina
0015-3842	Florida A A A Motorist see 0277-1403
0015-3850	Florida Academy of Sciences. Quarterly Journal see 0098-4590
0015-3869	Floridagriculture
0015-3877	Florida Alligator see 0889-2423
0015-3885	Florida Sportsman
0015-3893	Florida Anthropologist
0015-3907	Florida Architect†
0015-3915	Florida Bar Journal
0015-3923	Florida Builder Magazine
0015-3931	Florida Cancer News changed to LivingRight.
0015-3958	Florida Cattleman and Livestock Journal
0015-3974	Florida Conservation News†
0015-3982	Florida Contractor and Builder changed to Florida Constructor.
0015-3990	Florida State Dental Society. Journal see 1048-5317
0015-4008	Florida. Department of Agriculture. Division of Plant Industry. News Bulletin changed to Plant Industry News.
0015-4016	Florida Education see 0744-6063
0015-4024	Florida Educational Research and Development Council. Research Bulletin changed to Florida Educational Research Council. Research Bulletin.
0015-4032	Florida Engineering Society. Journal
0015-4040	Florida Entomologist
0015-4059	Florida Explorer†
0015-4067	Florida Family Physician
0015-4075	Florida Field Report see 0015-4091
0015-4091	Florida Grower and Rancher
0015-4105	Florida Health Notes†
0015-4113	Florida Historical Quarterly
0015-4121	Florida Industrial Arts Quarterly Bulletin
0015-413X	Florida Journal of Commerce see 0160-225X
0015-4148	Florida Medical Association. Journal
0015-4164	Florida Municipal Record see 0892-4171
0015-4172	Florida Naturalist

ISSN INDEX

ISSN	Title
0015-4180	Communique (Hollywood)†
0015-4199	Florida Nurse
0015-4202	Florida Pharmaceutical Journal *changed to* Florida Pharmacy Today.
0015-4210	Florida Planning and Development *see* 1044-033X
0015-4229	Florida Police Journal
0015-4237	Florida Prisoner Statistics†
0015-4245	Florida Purchaser
0015-4253	Florida Quarterly†
0015-4261	Florida Reading Quarterly
0015-4288	Florida School Herald
0015-4296	Florida Schools†
0015-430X	Florida State University. Institute for Social Research. Governmental Research Bulletin†
0015-4318	Florida Supplement
0015-4326	Florida Trend
0015-4334	Florida Truck News
0015-4369	Florida Wildlife
0015-4385	Florist
0015-4393	Florist
0015-4407	Florist and Nursery Exchange *see* 0037-0797
0015-4415	Florist Trade Magazine
0015-4423	Florists' Review
0015-4431	Flottans Maen
0015-444X	Flourish†
0015-4458	Flow Line†
0015-4466	Flower and Feather†
0015-4482	Home Garden *see* 0014-7230
0015-4490	Flower News
0015-4504	The Flowering Plants of Africa
0015-4512	Flue Cured Tobacco Farmer
0015-4547	Flug Revue
0015-4563	Der Flugleiter
0015-458X	F M T
0015-4598	Flugsport-Informationen *changed to* Flug-Informationen.
0015-461X	Fluid *changed to* Fluid.
0015-4628	Fluid Dynamics
0015-4636	Fluid Milk and Cream Report†
0015-4644	Fluid Power Abstracts
0015-4660	Fluid Sealing Abstracts
0015-4687	Fluidics Quarterly *see* 8755-8564
0015-4709	Fluorescence News†
0015-4717	Fluoridation Reporter†
0015-4725	Fluoride
0015-4733	Flur und Furche
0015-4741	Fly Fisherman
0015-475X	Flyghorisont
0015-4776	Flygposten
0015-4784	Flygrevyn
0015-4792	FlygvapenNytt
0015-4806	Flying
0015-4822	Flying Angel
0015-4830	Flying Lady
0015-4849	Flying Models
0015-4857	Flying Physician Aerospace Review†
0015-4865	Flying Saucer News
0015-4873	Flying Saucer Review
0015-4881	Flying Saucers *changed to* Search - Flying Saucers.
0015-489X	
0015-4911	Flyleaf†
0015-492X	Flyv
0015-4938	Canadian Journal of Radiography, Radiotherapy, Nucleography *see* 0820-5930
0015-4954	Focus†
0015-4970	Focus (Chicago)†
0015-5004	Focus (New York, 1950)
0015-5012	Bausch and Lomb Focus *changed to* Educational Focus.
0015-5020	National Committee on the Education of Migrant Children. Focus†
0015-5039	Focus (New York, 1964)†
0015-5047	Focus (Columbus, 1967) *see* 0744-1177
0015-5055	South Africa International
0015-5063	Focus on Public Affairs *changed to* Focus on Governmental Affairs.
0015-508X	Focus - Midwest *see* 0036-2972
0015-5098	Focus on Industry and Commerce *changed to* Focus (Stoke-on-Trent).
0015-511X	Focus on Exceptional Children
0015-5128	Focus on Film†
0015-5136	Focus on Guidance *see* 0193-7375
0015-5152	Focus on Indiana Libraries
0015-5160	Focus on Jamaica†
0015-5179	Focus on Saskatchewan Libraries *changed to* Focus (Regina).
0015-5195	Focus: Social and Preventive Medicine
0015-5209	Foden News†
0015-5217	Foer Biblisk Tro *see* 0345-1453
0015-5225	Foerbundet Svenska Finlandsfrivilliga. Tidning
0015-5233	Foerdermittel-Journal
0015-5241	Foerdern und Heben
0015-525X	Foerderungsdienst
0015-5268	F I V Meddelanden
0015-5276	Foeretagaren
0015-5284	Foersamlings- och Pastoratsfoervaltning *changed to* Svenska Kyrkans.
0015-5292	Foerskolan
0015-5306	Foersvarstjaenstemannen
0015-5314	Fogorvosi Szemle
0015-5322	Fogra-Literaturdienst
0015-5330	Fogra-Mitteilungen
0015-5349	F O I Digest†
0015-5357	Foi et Vie
0015-5365	Foi et Vie de l'Eglise au Diocese de Toulouse
0015-5373	Foil
0015-539X	Fold es Eg
0015-5403	Foldrajzi Ertesito
0015-5411	Foldrajzi Kozlemenyek
0015-542X	Foldtani Kozlony
0015-5438	Folger Library Newsletter *changed to* Folger News.
0015-5446	Folha Bancaria
0015-5454	Folha Medica
0015-5470	Folia Allergologica *see* 0303-8432
0015-5489	Folia Biochimica et Biologica Graeca
0015-5497	Folia Biologica
0015-5500	Folia Biologica
0015-5519	Folia Clinica et Biologica†
0015-5527	Folia Clinica Internacional†
0015-5543	Folia Forestalia
0015-5551	Folia Geobotanica et Phytotaxonomica
0015-5578	Folia Hereditaria et Pathologica
0015-5586	Folia Histochemica et Cytochemica *changed to* Folia Histochemica et Cytobiologica.
0015-5594	Folia Humanistica
0015-5608	Folia Medica†
0015-5616	Folia Medica Cracoviensia
0015-5624	Folia Medica Neerlandica *see* 0300-2977
0015-5632	Folia Microbiologica
0015-5640	Folia Morphologica *changed to* Functional and Developmental Morphology.
0015-5659	Folia Morphologica†
0015-5667	Folia Ophthalmologica Japonica
0015-5675	Folia Orientalia
0015-5683	Folia Parasitologica
0015-5691	Folia Pharmacologica Japonica
0015-5705	Folia Phoniatrica
0015-5713	Folia Primatologica
0015-5721	Folia Psychiatrica et Neurologica Japonica *see* 0912-2036
0015-573X	Folia Quaternaria
0015-5748	Folia Veterinaria
0015-5756	Folio (Birmingham)
0015-5764	Folio†
0015-5772	Folio
0015-5780	Folio (Waltham)†
0015-5799	Folio Pharmaceutica
0015-5802	Folium Diocesanum Bauzanense-Brixinense
0015-5810	Folk og Fritid
0015-5829	Folk Style
0015-5837	Folkeskolen
0015-5845	Folkevirke
0015-5853	Folkforsvaret†
0015-5861	Folkets Vael - DKSN *changed to* Drogfritt Liv.
0015-587X	Folklore
0015-5888	Folklore
0015-5896	Folklore
0015-590X	Folklore Brabancon
0015-5918	Folklore de France
0015-5926	Folklore Forum
0015-5950	Folklore Society of Greater Washington Newsletter
0015-6019	Contrary Investor Follow-up Service
0015-6027	Fomento†
0015-6035	Fomento de la Produccion
0015-6043	Revista de Fomento Social
0015-6051	Fondation Eugene Ysaye. Bulletin d'Information
0015-606X	Fondazione Giorgio Ronchi. Atti
0015-6078	Fonderia
0015-6086	Fonderia Italiana†
0015-6108	Fonderie Belge†
0015-6116	Fondeur d'Aujourd'hui *see* 0249-3136
0015-6124	Fondo Nacional de las Artes. Informativo†
0015-6132	Confederacion Espanola de Cajas de Ahorros. Fondo para la Investigacion Economica y Social. Boletin de Documentacion†
0015-6140	FonoForum
0015-6159	Platenwereld†
0015-6167	Foenstret
0015-6175	Fontane-Blaetter
0015-6183	Fontes Archaeologici Pragenses
0015-6191	Fontes Artis Musicae
0015-6213	Food Agriculture and Plantation Journal
0015-6221	Food and Agricultural Legislation
0015-6264	Food and Cosmetics Toxicology *see* 0278-6915
0015-6272	Food and Drug Packaging
0015-6280	Food and Equipment Product News *see* 0199-7696
0015-6302	Hospitality-Food and Lodging *see* 0148-0766
0015-6310	Food & Nutrition News
0015-6329	Food and Nutrition Notes and Reviews *see* 1032-1322
0015-6337	Food Chemical News
0015-6353	Food Distributors News *changed to* Food Distributors Magazine.
0015-6361	Food Drug Cosmetic Law Journal†
0015-637X	Food Engineering *see* 0193-323X
0015-6388	Food Executive *changed to* Hotline Magazine.
0015-6396	Food Farming and Agriculture
0015-640X	Food Fish Situation Outlook *see* 0091-8105
0015-6418	Food from Poland†
0015-6426	Food Hygienic Society of Japan. Journal
0015-6442	Food in Canada
0015-6450	Food Industries of South Africa
0015-6469	Food Ingredients & Equipment *see* 0149-5895
0015-6477	Food Manufacture
0015-6493	Food Merchants Advocate
0015-6507	Food Outlook *changed to* Retail Food Price Report.
0015-6515	Food Plant Equipment *see* 0747-2536
0015-6523	Food Processing (Chicago)
0015-6531	Food Processing Industry *changed to* Food Processing (Bromley).
0015-654X	Food Product Development *see* 0747-2536
0015-6566	Food Research Institute Studies in Agricultural Economics, Trade, and Development *see* 0193-9025
0015-6574	Food Science and Technology Abstracts
0015-6582	Food-Scope†
0015-6604	Food Service Magazine *see* 0894-4466
0015-6639	Food Technology
0015-6647	Food Technology in Australia *see* 1032-5298
0015-6655	Food Technology in New Zealand
0015-6663	Food Trade News
0015-6671	Food Trade Review
0015-668X	Food World *changed to* World Food Review.
0015-6698	Foodpack
0015-6701	Foodpress†
0015-6728	Foodsman
0015-6752	Football Clinic†
0015-6760	Football Digest
0015-6787	Football Pictorial *changed to* Football Monthly.
0015-6795	Football Record
0015-6809	Footplate
0015-6817	Footwear Fashions
0015-6825	Footwear Manufacturers Journal†
0015-6833	Footwear News
0015-6841	Footwear Weekly *see* 0306-3437
0015-685X	For Reference
0015-6868	For Teens Only†
0015-6884	For the Defense
0015-6892	For You from Czechoslovakia
0015-6906	Forage and Grassland Progress†
0015-6914	Forbes
0015-6922	Forbes Magazine's Restaurant Guide†
0015-6930	Forbrukeren†
0015-6949	Foerbundskontakt *changed to* Soedra Skog.
0015-6957	Forces
0015-6981	Ford Estate
0015-699X	Ford Foundation Letter *changed to* Ford Foundation Report.
0015-7007	Ford-Nachrichten
0015-7015	Ford Times
0015-7031	Ford Wereldt
0015-704X	Fordham Law Review
0015-7058	Ford's Freighter Travel Guide *changed to* Ford's Freighter Travel Guide and Waterways of the World.
0015-7066	Ford's International Cruise Guide
0015-7074	Forecast *changed to* Y Seren.
0015-7082	Forecast Data Bank Cumulative Sheets *changed to* Forecast Cumulative Sheets.
0015-7090	Forecast for Home Economics *see* 0890-9849
0015-7104	Advance Weather Forecasts†
0015-7112	Forefront *changed to* Howard University Journal of Science.
0015-7120	Foreign Affairs
0015-7139	Foreign Affairs Bulletin†
0015-7155	Foreign Affairs Reports
0015-7163	Foreign Agriculture
0015-718X	Foreign Language Annals
0015-7198	Foreign Language Beacon *changed to* Beacon (Georgia).
0015-721X	Foreign Chemical Patent News†
0015-7228	Foreign Policy (Washington)
0015-7244	Foreign Projects Newsletter
0015-7260	Foreign Radio Amateur Callbook Magazine *changed to* International Callbook.
0015-7279	Foreign Service Journal
0015-7287	U.S. Department of State. Foreign Service List†
0015-7317	Foreign Trade Bulletin
0015-7325	Foreign Trade Review
0015-7333	Foreman's Letter†
0015-735X	Forensic
0015-7368	Forensic Science Society. Journal
0015-7384	Forest and Bird
0015-7392	Forest and Timber
0015-7406	Forest Farmer
0015-7422	Forest History *see* 1046-7009
0015-7430	Forest Industries
0015-7457	Forest Notes
0015-7473	Forest Products Journal
0015-7481	Forest Research Institute and Colleges, Dehra Dun. Quarterly News Letter
0015-749X	Forest Science
0015-7503	Foresta
0015-7511	Foresters Miscellany
0015-752X	Forestry
0015-7538	Forestry Abstracts
0015-7546	Forestry Chronicle
0015-7546	Forestry Chronicle *issued with* 0068-8991
0015-7570	Forestry Marketing Bulletin *changed to* Sawlog.
0015-7589	Forests & People
0015-7597	Foret

ISSN	Title
0015-7627	Forex Service *changed to* International Business Regulations Report.
0015-7635	Forget
0015-766X	Form
0015-7678	Form
0015-7686	Form & Function
0015-7694	Form und Geist
0015-7708	Forum und Technik *changed to* I G Medien Forum.
0015-7716	Forma et Functio†
0015-7724	Formage des Materiaux *changed to* Travail des Metaux Par Deformation.
0015-7732	Formage et Traitements des Metaux *changed to* Techniques et Equipments de Production.
0015-7740	Format
0015-7759	Format
0015-7767	Formazione e Lavoro
0015-7775	Graveur Flexograf
0015-7791	Formosan Science
0015-7805	Forms of Business Agreements
0015-7813	Fornvaennen
0015-783X	Foro Italiano
0015-7848	Foro Napoletano
0015-7864	Foro Penale
0015-7880	Foersaakringstidningen
0015-7899	Forschung im Ingenieurwesen
0015-7902	Forschungen zur Volks- und Landeskunde
0015-7910	Vierteljahresberichte - Probleme der Entwicklungslaender *changed to* Vierteljahresberichte - Probleme der Internationalen Zusammenarbeit.
0015-7929	Forsikringstidende
0015-7937	Forskning och Framsteg
0015-7945	Norges Almenvitenskapelige Forskiningsraad. Forskningsnytt†
0015-7953	Institutet foer Metallforskning. Forskningsverksamheten
0015-7961	Forst- und Holzwirt *see* 0932-9315
0015-797X	Forstliche Mitteilungen
0015-7988	Forstliche Umschau
0015-7996	Forstpflanzen-Forstsamen
0015-8003	Forstwissenschaftliches Centralblatt
0015-8011	Foersvarsmedicin†
0015-802X	Fort Beaufort Advocate
0015-8038	Fort Dodge Biochemic Review†
0015-8054	Fort Hare Papers
0015-8070	Fort Ticonderoga Museum. Bulletin
0015-8089	Fort Worth
0015-8097	Fort Worth Commercial Recorder
0015-8100	Forth Valley Chamber of Commerce Quarterly Bulletin *changed to* Central Scotland Chamber of Commerce Quarterly Bulletin.
0015-8119	Forthcoming Books
0015-8127	Fortnightly Journal of Industry & Commerce
0015-8135	Fortpflanzung, Besamung und Aufzucht der Haustiere. Biologie, Pathologie und Hygiene†
0015-8151	Fortschritte auf dem Gebiete der Roentgenstrahlen und der Nuklearmedizin *see* 0936-6652
0015-816X	Fortschritte der Kieferorthopaedie
0015-8178	Fortschritte der Medizin
0015-8186	Fortschritte der Mineralogie *see* 0935-1221
0015-8194	Fortschritte der Neurologie, Psychiatrie und Ihrer Grenzgebiete *changed to* Fortschritte der Neurologie, Psychiatrie.
0015-8208	Fortschritte der Physik
0015-8216	Fortschrittliche Betriebs *changed to* Fortschrittliche Betriebsfuehrung und Industrial Engineering.
0015-8224	Der Fortschrittliche Landwirt
0015-8232	Fortuna Italiana
0015-8240	Fortune
0015-8259	Fortune Magazine
0015-8275	Fortune News
0015-8283	Forty Acres and a Mule†
0015-8291	Education Forum†
0015-8305	Forum (Washington, 1963)
0015-8321	Forum†
0015-833X	Forum (London, 1967)
0015-8356	Forum (Chicago, 1965) *see* 0885-856X
0015-8364	Forum†
0015-8372	Forum†
0015-8380	Forum†
0015-8399	Forum (Scranton)
0015-8402	Forum
0015-8410	Forum (Houston)†
0015-8445	Forum
0015-8453	Forum - Revista Invatamintului Superior
0015-847X	Forum Botanicum†
0015-8488	Forum de la Force Terrestre
0015-8496	Forum der Letteren
0015-850X	Forum des Praktischen Arztes
0015-8518	Forum for Modern Language Studies
0015-8526	Forum for the Advancement of Toxicology in Colleges of Pharmacy. Newsletter *changed to* Forum for the Advancement of Toxicology.
0015-8534	Forum Haus Ortlohn. Freundsbrief *changed to* Forum. Berichte aus der Arbeit.
0015-8542	Forum of Education
0015-8550	Forum on Public Affairs†
0015-8577	Forumeler
0015-8585	Foervaltningsraettslig Tidskrift
0015-8593	Forward *see* 0731-3675
0015-8615	Forward *changed to* Civil Aviation in Pakistan: Half-Yearly Newsletter.
0015-8623	Forward in Erie *changed to* Mission Statement.
0015-8631	Forward in Europe *see* 0252-0958
0015-864X	Forward Markets Bulletin
0015-8658	Special Education - Forward Trends *see* 0952-3383
0015-8666	Forza 7
0015-8674	Foss†
0015-8690	Foto-Film-Video-Tip
0015-8704	Foto-Kino Revija
0015-8712	FotoMagazin
0015-8720	Foto-Notiziario
0015-8755	Foto & Film Prisma†
0015-8771	Fotocamara con Popular Photography
0015-8798	Fotografern†
0015-8801	Fotografia *see* 0324-8453
0015-881X	Fotografia Universal
0015-8828	Fotografie *see* 0232-0576
0015-8836	Fotografie†
0015-8844	Fotohaendler *changed to* Fotowirtschaft.
0015-8879	Fotokino-Magazin
0015-8895	Foton
0015-8909	Fotonyheterna
0015-8941	Foundation for Reformation Research. Bulletin of the Library *changed to* Sixteenth Century Bibliography.
0015-895X	Foundation for Reformation Research. Newsletter *changed to* Center for Reformation Research. Newsletter.
0015-8968	Foundation Law Review
0015-8976	Foundation News
0015-8984	Foundation Time
0015-8992	Foundations *changed to* American Baptist Quarterly.
0015-900X	Foundations of Language *see* 0378-4177
0015-9018	Foundations of Physics
0015-9026	F.W.P. Journal *changed to* F W P Materials Engineering Journal.
0015-9034	Foundry *see* 0360-8999
0015-9042	Foundry Trade Journal
0015-9050	Foundry Worker†
0015-9069	Fountainhead†
0015-9077	Four and Five
0015-9093	Peace and Freedom
0015-9107	Four Quarters
0015-9115	Four States Genealogist†
0015-9123	Four Wheeler Magazine
0015-914X	Fourier
0015-9158	La Fournee
0015-9174	Fourrure et Peau en Poil†
0015-9182	Foursquare World Advance
0015-9190	Fourth Estate
0015-9204	Fourth International†
0015-9212	Fox-Report†
0015-9220	Foxfire
0015-9239	Foyers Mixtes
0015-9247	Fra Fysikkens Verden
0015-9255	Fra Haug og Heidni
0015-9271	Fracastoro
0015-928X	Fragen der Freiheit
0015-9298	Fragmenta Balcanica Musei Macedonici Scientiarum Naturalium
0015-9301	Fragmenta Faunistica
0015-931X	Fragmenta Floristica et Geobotanica
0015-9336	Fragments *changed to* Banque Populaire Suisse. Journal.
0015-9344	Fragments
0015-9352	Fraktemann
0015-9379	Franc-Riret
0015-9387	Francais au Nigeria
0015-9395	Francais dans le Monde
0015-9409	Francais Moderne
0015-9417	France - Loisirs†
0015-9425	France-Cuir†
0015-9433	France - Theatre
0015-9441	France a Table†
0015-9476	France-Algerie†
0015-9484	France Alimentaire
0015-9506	France Catholique *changed to* France Catholique - Ecclesia.
0015-9530	France. Commissariat General au Tourisme. Bulletin Mensual de Statistique du Tourisme *see* 0753-311X
0015-9549	France Dimanche
0015-9557	Societe d'Edition de Periodiques Sportifs
0015-9565	France Graphique
0015-9573	France Horlogere
0015-959X	France Informations
0015-9603	France. Institut National de la Sante et de la Recherche Medicale. Bulletin *see* 0755-4168
0015-962X	France Medicale†
0015-9646	France. Ministere de l'Agriculture. Bulletin Technique d'Information (1945) *changed to* France. Ministere de l'Agriculture. Bulletin Technique d'Information.
0015-9654	France. Ministere de l'Economie et des Finances. Statistiques et Etudes Financieres *changed to* France. Ministere de l'Economie et des Finances. Statistiques et Etudes Financieres. Finance Publique. Serie Bleue.
0015-9670	France Mutualite
0015-9689	France Peche *see* 0296-3353
0015-9697	France Pharmacie
0015-9700	France-Pologne, Peuples Amis
0015-9719	France. Ministere de la Defense Nationale. Bulletin d'Information Technique et Scientifique
0015-9727	France. Ministere de la Defense Nationale. Bulletin Officiel
0015-9735	France. Secretariat d'Etat a la Marine. Bulletin d'Information de la Marine Nationale†
0015-9743	Problemes Politiques et Sociaux
0015-9751	France - U.S.A
0015-9778	Franchising Around the World *changed to* Franchising Investments Around the World.
0015-9786	Francis Bolen's Newsletter
0015-9794	Franciskaans Leven
0015-9808	Franciscan *changed to* Inside San Francisco State University.
0015-9816	Franciscan Herald†
0015-9840	Franciscana
0015-9867	Franco-British Trade Review *changed to* Info.
0015-9875	Franco Vida†
0015-9905	Frankenland
0015-9921	Frankford News Gleaner *changed to* NewsGleaner - Frankford - Oxford Circle Edition.
0015-993X	Frankfurter Blaetter fuer Heimatvertriebene
0015-9964	Frankfurter Gastronomie
0015-9972	Frankfurter Handwerk†
0015-9980	Frankfurter Hausfrauen Zeitung†
0015-9999	Frankfurter Hefte
0016-0008	Frankfurter Lehrerblatt†
0016-0024	Frankfurter Wochenschau *changed to* Frankfurter Woche.
0016-0032	Franklin Institute. Journal
0016-0040	Franklin Township Sentinel
0016-0059	Franse Boek *changed to* Rapports Franse Boek.
0016-0067	Franziskanische Studien
0016-0075	Investment Survey of Warrants *changed to* F R A Warrant Service.
0016-0083	Fraser's Circular *changed to* Marketwatch.
0016-0105	Fraternal Monitor
0016-0113	Fraternity Month†
0016-013X	Frau im Beruf
0016-0148	Frau im Leben
0016-0172	Frau und Frieden
0016-0199	Neue Mode - Frau und Mutter
0016-0202	Frau und Politik
0016-0210	Die Frau von Heute
0016-0229	Frauen der Ganzen Welt†
0016-0237	Der Frauenarzt
0016-0245	Frauenkulter *changed to* Frau und Kultur.
0016-0288	Fred och Frihet
0016-0296	Il Freddo
0016-030X	Free China Review
0016-0318	Free China Weekly *see* 0255-9870
0016-0326	Free Church Chronicle†
0016-0334	Free Church of Scotland. Monthly Record
0016-0342	Free Enterprise *changed to* American Patriot (Scottsdale).
0016-0350	Free Labour World
0016-0369	Free Lance
0016-0377	Free-Lance Report†
0016-0385	Free-Lance Writing & Photography
0016-0393	Free News & Feature Service
0016-0423	Boston Free Press†
0016-0431	Free Press Weekly Report on Farming *see* 0317-8552
0016-044X	Free Ranger Inter-Tribal News Service *see* 0730-1766
0016-0458	Free State Libraries
0016-0474	Free Trader†
0016-0482	Free World Horizons
0016-0504	Freedom
0016-0512	Freedom & Union†
0016-0520	Freedom Appeals *changed to* Freedom Review.
0016-0547	Freedom First
0016-0555	Freedom Magazine
0016-0571	Freedom of Vision
0016-061X	Freedomways
0016-0644	Freeland†
0016-0652	Freeman
0016-0679	Freeport Memorial Library. News Bulletin†
0016-0687	Freethinker
0016-0695	Freezer Provisioning and Portion Control *changed to* Meat Business Magazine.
0016-0709	Freiburger Studentenzeitung
0016-0725	Freiburger Zeitschrift fuer Philosophie und Theologie
0016-075X	Freie Lehrerstimme
0016-0768	Freie Presse-Korrespondenz
0016-0776	Freie Religion
0016-0784	Die Freie Wohnungswirtschaft
0016-0792	F D P Informationsdienst†
0016-0806	Freies Bayern
0016-0814	Freies Lebent
0016-0830	Freigeistige Aktion *changed to* Der Humanist.
0016-0849	Freight
0016-0857	Freight *changed to* Commercial Transport.
0016-0865	Freight & Container Transportation†
0016-0873	Freight Management *changed to* Freight Management & Distribution Today.

ISSN	Title
0016-0881	Freight News *changed to* Freight News Weekly.
0016-089X	Freighter Travel News
0016-0903	Freiheitlicher Oberoesterreichischer Landeslehrer Verein. Zeitschrift *changed to* Freiheitlicher Oberoesterreichischer Lehrerverein. Zeitschrift.
0016-0911	Die Freiheitsglocke
0016-092X	Der Freiwillige
0016-0938	Freizeit-Mode *see* 0931-5381
0016-0946	Der Freizeitgaertner
0016-0954	Fremdenverkehr-Reiseland-Oesterreich *changed to* Euro-City.
0016-0962	Fremdenverkehr *changed to* European Tourism & Congress - Der Fremdenverkehr.
0016-0970	Fremdsprachen
0016-0997	Fremonitor
0016-1004	Fremont Schools†
0016-1012	Fremsyn *changed to* Radikal Politik.
0016-1020	Fremtiden *see* 0903-7845
0016-1039	French - American Commerce†
0016-1047	French Canadian and Acadian Genealogical Review
0016-1071	French Historical Studies
0016-108X	French Notes & Queries†
0016-1101	French Railway Techniques†
0016-111X	French Review
0016-1128	French Studies
0016-1136	Frequenz
0016-1144	Freres d'Armes
0016-1152	Fresenius' Zeitschrift fuer Analytische Chemie *changed to* Fresenius' Journal of Analytical Chemistry.
0016-1160	Fresno County Medical Society. Bulletin *changed to* Vital Signs (Fresno).
0016-1187	Freundin
0016-1209	Freyr
0016-1217	Fri Koepenskap
0016-1225	Friar Magazine†
0016-1233	Friday Flash
0016-1268	Friend
0016-1276	Friend of Animals
0016-1284	Friend O'Wildlife
0016-1292	Friendly Companion
0016-1314	Friendly World†
0016-1322	Friends Journal
0016-1330	Friends of the San Bernardino County Library. News Letter†
0016-1349	Friends of Youth Newsletter *changed to* Friends of Youth Newsletter.
0016-1357	Friends' Quarterly
0016-1365	Friends World News
0016-1373	Fries Landbouwblad
0016-1381	Friesch Rundvee-Stamboek. Mededelingen *see* 0168-7565
0016-1403	Friesia *see* 0107-055X
0016-1411	Frigotechnica *changed to* Frigotherma.
0016-142X	Frihet
0016-1438	Frimaerkesamleren
0016-1446	Fripou.net
0016-1454	Friseurhandwerk Friseurspiegel *changed to* Top Hair.
0016-1470	Friseurwelt
0016-1489	Frisur *see* 0323-410X
0016-1500	Fritidsgaardent
0016-1519	Fritt Kjoepmannskap
0016-1527	Fritzsche-D & O Library Bulletin†
0016-1535	Il Friuli Medico
0016-1543	Foersvarsforskningsreferat
0016-156X	Der Froehliche Kreis
0016-1586	From Italy†
0016-1594	From Italy Clothing *see* 0016-1586
0016-1608	From New York†
0016-1616	From Nine to Five
0016-1624	From the California State Librarian†
0016-1632	From the State Capitals. Agricultural and Food Products *changed to* From the State Capitals. Agriculture.
0016-1691	From the State Capitals. General Bulletin *see* 0741-3475
0016-1705	From the State Capitals. Highway Financing and Construction†
0016-1713	From the State Capitals. Housing and Redevelopment *see* 0741-3483
0016-1721	From the State Capitals. Industrial Development *see* 0734-1628
0016-1748	From the State Capitals. Insurance Regulation
0016-1764	From the State Capitals. Juvenile Delinquency and Family Relations *see* 0741-3505
0016-1780	From the State Capitals. Liquor Control *see* 0734-0842
0016-1799	From the State Capitals. Merchandising *see* 0741-3467
0016-1810	From the State Capitals. Motor Vehicle Regulation
0016-1829	From the State Capitals. Off-Street Parking *see* 0749-2774
0016-1845	From the State Capitals. Personnel Management *see* 0741-3521
0016-1888	From the State Capitals. Public Utilities
0016-1896	From the State Capitals. Racial Relations *see* 0741-353X
0016-1926	From the State Capitals. Sewage and Waste Disposal *changed to* From the State Capitals. Waste Disposal and Pollution Control.
0016-1934	From the State Capitals. Small Loans, Sales Finance, Banking *see* 0749-2812
0016-1942	Local Non-Property *see* 0749-2820
0016-2019	Front
0016-2027	Front
0016-2043	Front Page Detective
0016-2078	Frontier†
0016-2086	Frontier†
0016-2094	Frontier
0016-2116	Frontier Nursing Service Quarterly Bulletin
0016-2124	Frontier Times *see* 0041-3615
0016-2132	Frontiera
0016-2159	Frontiers†
0016-2167	Frontiers of Plant Science
0016-2175	Frontlijn
0016-2183	Frontpage
0016-2191	Frozen Food Age
0016-2205	Frozen Foods *changed to* Frozen and Chilled Foods.
0016-2221	Fruechte und Gemuese
0016-2248	Fruit Belge
0016-2256	Fruit Trades Journal *changed to* Fresh Produce Journal.
0016-2264	Fruit of the Vine
0016-2272	Fruit Varieties and Horticultural Digest *see* 0091-3642
0016-2280	Fruit World and Market Grower†
0016-2302	Fruittee†
0016-2310	Frutticoltura
0016-2329	Ftiziologia *changed to* Revista de Igiena, Bacteriologie, Virusologie, Parazitologie, Pneumoftiziologie.
0016-2353	Fuehrungskraefte Foerdern†
0016-2361	Fuel
0016-237X	Ful-, Orr-, Gegegyogyaszat
0016-2388	Fuel Abstracts and Current Titles *see* 0140-6701
0016-2396	Fuel Oil News
0016-240X	Fules
0016-2418	Fueloil and Oil Heat *changed to* Fueloil & Oil Heat.
0016-2426	Fuer Allet
0016-2434	Fuer Arbeit und Besinnung
0016-2442	Fuer Heute
0016-2450	Fuer Sie
0016-2469	Fuerstenfelder Grenzlandecho
0016-2477	Fuerza Nueva
0016-2493	Fuji Bank Bulletin *changed to* Fuji Economic Review.
0016-2507	Keio University. Fujihara Memorial Faculty of Engineering. Proceedings. *see* 0286-4215
0016-2515	Fujitsu
0016-2523	Fujitsu Scientific & Technical Journal
0016-2531	Red Double-Barred Cross
0016-254X	Fukuoka Acta Medica
0016-2558	Fukuoka District Meteorological Observatory. Unusual Meteorological Report
0016-2566	Fukuoka District Meteorological Observatory. Technical Times
0016-2574	Fukuoka Prefecture. Monthly Report of Meteorology
0016-2582	Fukushima Medical Journal
0016-2604	Fukushima Journal of Medical Science
0016-2612	Fulcrum
0016-2612	Fuldaer Geschichtsblaetter
0016-2620	Full Cry
0016-2639	Filmmuseum-Cinematheek *changed to* N F M - Programma.
0016-2655	Fun for Middlers *changed to* Rainbow (Valley Forge).
0016-2663	Functional Analysis and Its Applications
0016-2671	Fund Guide Internationak *changed to* Portfolio and Fund Guide International.
0016-268X	Fund Raising Management
0016-2698	Fundacion Jimenez Diaz. Boletin
0016-2701	Fundacion John Boulton. Boletin Historico†
0016-271X	Fundacion Roux-Ocefa. Archivos†
0016-2728	Fundament
0016-2736	Fundamenta Mathematicae
0016-2744	Fundamentalist
0016-2760	FundScope†
0016-2779	Die Fundstelle
0016-2787	Funeral Forum *see* 1016-7250
0016-2809	Funeral Service Journal
0016-2817	Funk Fachhaendler†
0016-2825	Funk-Technik†
0016-2833	Funk Amateur
0016-2841	Funkschau
0016-285X	Funktsional'nyi Analiz i Ego Prilozheniya
0016-2876	Fuoco
0016-2884	Fur Age Weekly
0016-2892	Fur and Feather, Rabbits and Rabbit Keeping *changed to* Fur & Feather.
0016-2906	Fur & Feathers
0016-2914	Fur Bulletin
0016-2922	Fur - Fish - Game. Harding's Magazine
0016-2930	Fur Market Review *see* 0260-2393
0016-2957	Fur and Leather Review *see* 0260-2393
0016-2965	Fur Taker Journal
0016-2973	Fur Trade Journal *see* 0381-8535
0016-2981	Fur Weekly News
0016-299X	Die Furche
0016-3007	Home Furnishing†
0016-3015	Furnishing World *changed to* Cabinet Maker.
0016-304X	Furniture Design and Manufacturing *see* 0192-8058
0016-3058	Furniture History
0016-3066	Furniture News *see* 0194-360X
0016-3074	Furniture South *changed to* Furniture World.
0016-3082	Furniture Warehouseman *see* 0092-7449
0016-3090	Furniture Workers Press
0016-3104	Furniture World and Furniture Buyer and Decorator
0016-3112	Furrow
0016-3120	The Furrow
0016-3139	Fuersorger *changed to* Suchtprobleme und Sozialarbeit.
0016-3155	Fusion
0016-3171	Fusion Facts†
0016-318X	Fusion Facts†
0016-321X	Fussball-Jugend†
0016-3228	Der Fussballtrainer
0016-3244	Futur†
0016-3252	Futura†
0016-3260	Future *changed to* Jaycees Magazine.
0016-3287	Futures
0016-3295	Futures Market Service
0016-3317	The Futurist
0016-3325	Futuro
0016-3341	Futurum†
0016-335X	4H-Journalen *see* 0281-1278
0016-3376	Fyzika ve Skole *changed to* Matematika a Fyzika ve Skole.
0016-3384	Fysioterapeuten
0016-3392	Fysisk Tidskrift
0016-3406	G A
0016-3414	G A O Review
0016-3422	G A T F Newsletter†
0016-3449	G C A Newsletter *changed to* Voice for Girls.
0016-3457	G D I Information†
0016-3465	G D I Test Universal *see* 0016-3457
0016-3473	G D I Topics *changed to* Brennpunkte.
0016-3481	G D R Peace Council. Information
0016-349X	G D R Review
0016-3503	G E N
0016-3538	G I T
0016-3554	G L C A Newsletter†
0016-3562	G L V Mitteilungen
0016-3570	GmbH-Rundschau
0016-3597	G O†
0016-3600	G P *see* 0002-838X
0016-3619	G R A Reporter
0016-3627	G S N. Gesneriad Saintpaulia News
0016-3635	Grossmont Educator *changed to* G E A Educator.
0016-3651	G W F Gas- und Wasserfach *changed to* Wasser - Abwasser - G W F.
0016-366X	George Washington University Magazine *changed to* G W Magazine.
0016-3678	Gaangsport
0016-3686	Catholic Broadcasters Association. Newsletter *changed to* Unda - U S A Newsletter.
0016-3694	Gabriel
0016-3708	Gabriele *see* 0171-4937
0016-3716	Gaceta
0016-3724	La Gaceta
0016-3759	Gaceta de la Universidad
0016-3767	Gaceta Economica
0016-3775	Gaceta Hipica
0016-3783	Gaceta Ilustrada
0016-3791	Honduras. Corte Suprema de Justicia. Gaceta Judicial
0016-3805	Gaceta Matematica†
0016-3813	Gaceta Medica de Mexico
0016-3821	Gaceta Medica Espanola
0016-383X	Gaceta Militar y Naval†
0016-3848	Gaceta Politecnica
0016-3856	Gaceta Pre Militar†
0016-3864	Gaceta Rural
0016-3880	Gacetilla Agricola de Holanda†
0016-3910	Gaiato
0016-3929	Gairm
0016-3945	Musical Instruments News *changed to* Gakki Shoho.
0016-3953	Gakushuin Economic Papers
0016-397X	Gala *changed to* Gala International.
0016-3988	Galamukani!
0016-3996	Galaxia
0016-4003	Galaxy†
0016-4011	Galencia Acta†
0016-402X	Galeon
0016-4038	Galerie *changed to* Arts-Magazine.
0016-4046	Galerie Raymond Creuze. Bulletin†
0016-4070	Gallagher Report†
0016-4089	Gallaudet Today
0016-4089	Gallaudet Today. Annual Legal Review
0016-4097	Galleria
0016-4100	Galley Sail Review
0016-4119	Gallia
0016-4127	Gallia Prehistoire
0016-4143	Gallneukirchner Bote *changed to* Diakonie.
0016-4151	El Gallo News
0016-416X	Gallo *changed to* Quaderni de il Gallo.
0016-4178	Galloway News
0016-4186	Galloway Times†
0016-4194	Gallup Opinion Index *see* 1051-2616
0016-4216	Galpakabita
0016-4240	Galvanotecnica *changed to* Galvanotecnica e Nuove Finiture.
0016-4259	Gam on Yachting
0016-4275	Gambit†
0016-4283	Gambit
0016-4313	Gamecock
0016-4321	Gamekeeeper and Countryside *see* 0268-9502

0016-433X Gamekeepers' Gazette *changed to* Shooting & Conservation.
0016-4356 Gamesletter *see* 0016-4364
0016-4364 Gamesman†
0016-4380 Gamma
0016-4402 Gan v'Nof
0016-4429 Gandalf's Garden
0016-4437 Gandhi Marg
0016-4445 Gandhian Thought
0016-4453 Gangan
0016-4461 Ganganatha Jha Research Institute. Journal *changed to* Ganganatha Jha Kendriya Sanskrit Vidyapeetha. Journal.
0016-447X Ganigo
0016-4488 Ophthalmology
0016-4496 Ganmitram
0016-450X Gann *see* 0910-5050
0016-4518 Ganterie-Vetements de Peau†
0016-4526 Garage
0016-4542 Garage & Officina
0016-4550 Garage, Tankstelle und Servicestation *changed to* Tankstelle und Garage.
0016-4569 Garcia de Orta†
0016-4585 Garden Journal *see* 0191-3999
0016-4593 Garden News
0016-4607 Garden Path
0016-4615 Garden Stater†
0016-4623 Garden Supplies Retailer†
0016-4631 Garden Writers Bulletin *changed to* Garden Writers Newsletter.
0016-464X Gardener
0016-4682 Gardeners Chronicle - Horticultural Trade Journal *changed to* Horticulture Week.
0016-4712 Garment Worker
0016-4720 Garten und Landschaft
0016-4739 Das Gartenamt
0016-4747 Gartenbau
0016-4755 Gartenbau†
0016-4763 Der Gartenbauingenieur
0016-4771 Gartenbauwirtschaft mit Gartenbau Nachrichten *changed to* Gartenbauwirtschaft.
0016-478X Gartenbauwissenschaft
0016-4798 Gartenwelt *see* 0936-3734
0016-4801 Gary Library Bulletin *changed to* Gary Graphique.
0016-4828 Gas
0016-4844 Gas Abstracts
0016-4852 Gas and Oil Power *see* 0308-4795
0016-4860 Gas & Sanitair Mercuur†
0016-4887 Gas Chromatography Abstracts *see* 0268-6287
0016-4895 Gas Chromatography Literature - Abstracts & Index
0016-4909 Gas - Erdgas - G W F
0016-4925 Gas in Industry and Commerce *changed to* Natural Gas.
0016-4933 Gas in Industry *changed to* Gas Industries Magazine.
0016-495X Gas Liquefatti - le Apparecchiature
0016-4968 Gas Processing - Canada *see* 0319-5759
0016-4976 GaScope
0016-4984 Gas Marketing *see* 0308-7026
0016-4992 Gas Showroom *see* 0308-7026
0016-500X Gas Turbine Magazine *see* 0149-4147
0016-5018 Gas, Wasser, Waerme
0016-5034 Gas-Beispiele†
0016-5042 Gasoline News
0016-5069 Monthly Gasoline Stand
0016-5077 Gastro-Enterologie Quotidienne
0016-5085 Gastroenterology†
0016-5093 Gastroenterology Abstracts and Citations†
0016-5107 Gastrointestinal Endoscopy
0016-5115 Gastronomie *changed to* Plaisirs.
0016-5123 Gastronomie-Rundschau
0016-514X Gastronomo†
0016-5158 Gastwirt
0016-5166 Gastwirt und Hotelier *changed to* D G Deutsche Gaststaette - Deutsche Hotel-Zeitung Gastwirt und Hotelier.
0016-5182 Gasverwendung†
0016-5190 Gateway
0016-5239 Gaudeamus
0016-5247 Gaudeamus
0016-5255 Gauge "O" Guild Gazette
0016-5263 Gaveshana†
0016-5271 Gawein *changed to* Gedrag & Gezondheid.
0016-5298 Gay Scene
0016-5301 Gayana: Botanica
0016-531X Gayana: Zoologica
0016-5328 Gaz d'Aujourd'hui
0016-5352 Gaz, Woda i Technika Sanitarna
0016-5360 Gazdasag
0016-5379 Gazer
0016-5395 Gazeta Cukrownicza
0016-5409 Gazeta da Farmacia†
0016-5433 Gazeta Matematica. Serie A *changed to* Gazeta Matematica.
0016-5441 Gazetta Matematica. Serie B *changed to* Gazeta Matematica.
0016-545X Gazeta Medica da Bahia†
0016-5468 Gazeta Mobil†
0016-5484 Gazette†
0016-5492 Gazette
0016-5506 Gazette Apicole
0016-5514 Gazette de la Region du Nord
0016-5522 Gazette des Archives
0016-5530 Gazette des Beaux Arts
0016-5557 Gazette Medicale de France
0016-5565 Gazette Numismatique Suisse
0016-5573 Gazette Officielle du Tourisme
0016-5581 Gazovaya Promyshlennost'
0016-5603 Gazzetta Chimica Italiana
0016-5611 Gazzetta Commerciale†
0016-562X Gazzetta della Domenica
0016-5638 Gazzetta delle Arti
0016-5646 Gazzetta Farmaceutica†
0016-5654 Gazzetta Filatelica
0016-5662 Gazzetta Internazionale di Medicina e Chirurgia
0016-5670 Gazzetta Medica Italiana *changed to* Gazzetta Medica Italiana Archivio per le Scienze Mediche.
0016-5697 Gazzetta Sanitaria
0016-5700 Rilancio
0016-5719 Gazzettino della Scuola
0016-5727 Gebaeudigereiniger-Handwerk *changed to* Rationell Reinigen.
0016-5735 Gebetsapostolat und Seelsorge
0016-5743 Gebrauchsgraphik *see* 0302-9794
0016-5751 Geburtshilfe und Frauenheilkunde
0016-5778 Gedeeld Domein†
0016-5786 Gedistilleerd, Wijn, Bier en Frisdranken†
0016-5794 Gefaehrdetenhilfe
0016-5808 Gefaehrliche Ladung
0016-5816 Gefiederte Welt
0016-5824 Gefluegel-Boerse
0016-5832 Geflugel und Kleinvieh *changed to* Schweizerische Gefluegelzeitung.
0016-5840 Gegenbaurs Morphologisches Jahrbuch
0016-5859 Gegenwart
0016-5867 Gegenwart
0016-5875 Gegenwartskunde
0016-5883 Gehoert Gelesen (Munich, 1954)
0016-5913 Geisinger Medical Center. Bulletin†
0016-5921 Geist und Leben
0016-593X Surgery
0016-5956 Gekkan Kibbutz *changed to* Cooperative Life.
0016-5964 Monthly Journal of Gasoline Service Stations
0016-5972 Petroleum Monthly
0016-5980 Pharmaceuticals Monthly
0016-5999 Gelatiere Italiano
0016-6006 Die Gelben Hefte
0016-6014 Gelders Oudheidkundig Contactbericht *changed to* Gelders Erfgoed.
0016-6022 Geliotekhnika
0016-6030 Gem†
0016-6049 Gemeenteblad van Amsterdam
0016-6057 Gemeentefinancien *see* 0166-8528
0016-6065 Gemeenteleven
0016-6073 Die Gemeinde (Kassel)
0016-609X Gemeindebote
0016-6103 Gemeindebote *changed to* Kirche in Marburg.
0016-6111 Gemeindebrief
0016-612X Die Gemeindekasse
0016-6146 Gemeindekurier
0016-6154 Evangelische Pfarrgemeinde A.B. Wien-Favoriten-Christuskirche. Gemeindebrief
0016-6170 Gemeindeverwaltung in Rheinland - Pfalz
0016-6200 Gemeinsames Amtsblatt des Landes Baden-Wuerttemberg
0016-6219 Gemeinschaft der Wohnungseigentuemer-Informationen *changed to* G D W Informationen.
0016-6227 Gemeinwirtschaft
0016-6235 Gemengde Branche (1948) *changed to* Gemengde Branche (1978).
0016-6243 Gemischtwarenhandel
0016-6251 Gems†
0016-626X Gems & Gemology
0016-6278 Gems and Minerals *see* 0274-8193
0016-6286 Gemuese
0016-6308 Gemueseproduktion *see* 0138-3280
0016-6316 Prosit
0016-6324 Genadeklanken
0016-6332 Contemporary Library Trends *changed to* Libraries Today.
0016-6359 Genealogical Helper
0016-6367 Genealogical Magazine of New Jersey
0016-6375 Genealogical Quarterly†
0016-6383 Genealogie
0016-6391 Genealogists' Magazine
0016-6405 Geneologist's Post *changed to* Pennsylvania Traveler-Post.
0016-6421 Genealogy Club of America Magazine *see* 0098-7689
0016-643X Geneeskunde
0016-6448 Geneeskunde en Sport
0016-6464 Geneeskundige Gids†
0016-6472 Genen en Phaenen†
0016-6480 General and Comparative Endocrinology
0016-6499 General and Municipal Workers' Union *changed to* G M B Working Together.
0016-6502 General Aviation
0016-6510 General Aviation *see* 1052-9136
0016-6537 General Federation Clubwoman *see* 0745-2209
0016-6545 General Insurance Guide
0016-6553 General Linguistics
0016-657X Strobotactics†
0016-660X General Topology and Its Applications *see* 0166-8641
0016-6634 Genesee Valley Buyer *see* 0192-9607
0016-6642 Genesee Valley Chemunications *changed to* Rochester Chemunications.
0016-6669 Genesis 2
0016-6677 Genetic Psychology Monographs *see* 8756-7547
0016-6685 Genetica Agraria *see* 0394-9257
0016-6693 Genetica Iberica
0016-6707 Genetica
0016-6715 Genetica Polonica
0016-6723 Genetical Research
0016-6731 Genetics
0016-674X Genetics Abstracts
0016-6758 Genetika
0016-6766 Genetika i Selektsiia
0016-6774 Geneva - Africa
0016-6812 Genie Civil
0016-6820 Genie Construction
0016-6839 Genie Medical
0016-6863 Genio Rurale
0016-6871 Genitori†
0016-6898 Genos
0016-6901 Genova†
0016-691X Genova Statistica *changed to* Commune di Genova. Notiziario Statistico Mensile.
0016-6928 Genre (Norman)
0016-6936 Gens Nostra, "Ons Geslacht"
0016-6944 Gente
0016-6952 Gente
0016-6960 Gentes
0016-6979 G Q
0016-6987 Genus
0016-6995 Geobios
0016-7002 Geochemical Journal
0016-7029 Geochemistry International
0016-7037 Geochimica et Cosmochimica Acta
0016-7053 Geocom Bulletin *changed to* Bibliography of Economic Geology.
0016-7061 Geoderma
0016-707X Geodesia
0016-7088 Geodesy and Aerophotography *see* 0749-3878
0016-7096 Geodeticky a Kartograficky Obzor
0016-710X Geodetski List
0016-7118 Geodezia es Kartografia
0016-7126 Geodeziya i Kartografiya
0016-7134 Geodezja i Kartografia
0016-7142 Geoexploration *see* 0926-9851
0016-7169 Geofisica Internacional
0016-7177 Geophysical Transactions
0016-7185 Geoforum
0016-7193 Geograficky Casopis
0016-7207 Geografiya v Shkole
0016-7215 Geografisch Tijdschrift
0016-7223 Geografisk Tidsskrift
0016-7231 Geografiska Annaler *see* 0435-3676
0016-7231 Geografiska Annaler *see* 0435-3684
0016-724X Geografiska Notiser
0016-7266 Geografski Horizont
0016-7274 Geografski Obzornik
0016-7290 Geographica
0016-7312 Geographica Helvetica
0016-7363 Geographical Analysis
0016-7371 Geographical Association of Nigeria. Journal *see* 0029-0084
0016-738X Geographical Association of Tanzania Journal
0016-7398 Geographical Journal
0016-7401 Geographical Knowledge†
0016-741X Geographical Magazine
0016-7428 Geographical Review
0016-7436 Geographical Review of Afghanistan
0016-7444 Geographical Review of Japan. Series A
0016-7452 Geographische Berichte
0016-7460 Geographische Rundschau
0016-7479 Geographische Zeitschrift
0016-7487 Geography
0016-7509 Geography Teacher†
0016-7517 Geography Teacher
0016-7525 Geokhimiya
0016-7533 Geologia y Metalurgia†
0016-7541 Geologic Notes *see* 0272-9873
0016-755X Geologica Bavarica
0016-7568 Geological Magazine
0016-7576 Geological, Mining and Metallurgical Society of India. Bulletin
0016-7584 Geological, Mining and Metallurgical Society of India. Quarterly Journal *see* 0970-1354
0016-7592 Geological Society of America. Abstracts with Programs
0016-7606 Geological Society of America. Bulletin
0016-7614 Geological Society of Australia. Journal *see* 0812-0099
0016-7622 Geological Society of India. Journal
0016-7630 Geological Society of Japan. Journal
0016-7649 Geological Society. Journal
0016-7657 Geological Society of South Africa. Quarterly News Bulletin - Geologiese Vereniging van Suid-Afrika. Kwarataalikse Nuusbulletin *changed to* Geological Society of South Africa. Geobulletin.
0016-7673 Geological Survey of South Australia. Bulletin
0016-7681 Geological Survey of South Australia. Report of Investigations
0016-769X Geologicheskii Zhurnal Armenii
0016-7703 Geologichnii Zhurnal (Ukrainian) *see* 0367-4290
0016-772X Geologicky Pruzkum
0016-7738 Geologicky Zbornik
0016-7746 Geologie en Mijnbouw
0016-7762 Izvestiya Vysshikh Uchebnykh Zavedenii. Seriya Geologiya i Razvedka
0016-7789 Geologija

ISSN

ISSN	Title
0016-7797	Geologische Blaetter fuer Nordost-Bayern und Angrenzende Gebiete
0016-7800	Geologische Bundesanstalt, Vienna. Jahrbuch
0016-7835	Geologische Rundschau
0016-7843	Geologische Gesellschaft, Vienna. Mitteilungen see 0251-7493
0016-7851	Geologisches Jahrbuch see 0341-6429
0016-7851	Geologisches Jahrbuch see 0341-6410
0016-7851	Geologisches Jahrbuch see 0341-6399
0016-7851	Geologisches Jahrbuch see 0341-6402
0016-786X	Geologiska Foereningens i Stockholm. Foerhandlinger
0016-7886	Geologiya i Geofizikat
0016-7894	Geologiya Nefti i Gaza
0016-7908	Geologiya Rudnykh Mestorozhdenii
0016-7924	Geoloski Vjesnik
0016-7932	Geomagnetism and Aeronomy
0016-7940	Geomagnetizm i Aeronomiya
0016-7959	Geometra
0016-7967	Geometre
0016-7975	Geominas
0016-7983	Geophysical Abstracts†
0016-8009	Royal Astronomical Society Geophysical Journal see 0952-4592
0016-8017	Geophysical Magazine
0016-8025	Geophysical Prospecting
0016-8033	Geophysics
0016-8041	Leipzig. Universitaet. Geophysikalisches Institut. Veroeffentlichungen. Zweite Serie see 0138-2357
0016-8076	George Washington Law Review
0016-8084	Georgetown Dental Journal see 0730-0808
0016-8092	Georgetown Law Journal
0016-8106	Georgetown Medical Bulletin
0016-8114	Georgia Journal of Science
0016-8122	Georgia Agricultural Research†
0016-8130	Georgia Alumni Record
0016-8149	Georgia AnchorAge
0016-8157	Georgia Augusta
0016-8173	Georgia Business see 0279-3857
0016-8181	Georgia C. P. A†
0016-819X	Georgia Dental Association. Journal
0016-822X	Georgia Engineer
0016-8254	Georgia Farmer†
0016-8262	Georgia Future Farmer
0016-8270	Georgia Game and Fish see 0147-720X
0016-8289	Georgia Government Review see 0160-323X
0016-8297	Georgia Historical Quarterly
0016-8300	Georgia Law Review
0016-8319	Georgia Librarian
0016-8335	Georgia Nursing
0016-8351	Georgia Professional Engineer
0016-836X	Georgia Progress changed to Georgia.
0016-8378	Georgia Rehabilitation News†
0016-8386	The Georgia Review
0016-8394	Georgia School Boards Bulletin
0016-8416	Georgia State Bar Journal
0016-8424	Georgia State University Signal
0016-8432	Georgia Straight
0016-8440	Georgia Tech Alumnus changed to Tech Topics.
0016-8459	Georgia Tech Engineer changed to Exponent.
0016-8467	Georgian changed to Link (Montreal).
0016-8483	Geoscience Documentation
0016-8491	Geotechnical Abstracts
0016-8505	Geotechnique
0016-8521	Geotectonics
0016-853X	Geotektonika
0016-8548	Geotektonische Forschungen
0016-8556	Geotimes
0016-8564	Geotitles Weekly changed to Geotitles.
0016-8572	Gep
0016-8580	Gepgyartastechnologia
0016-8599	Geraniums around the World
0016-8602	Gereedschap changed to De Vakhandel.
0016-8610	Gereformeerd Theologisch Tijdschrift
0016-8629	Gereformeerde Kerken in Noord-Brabant en Limburg. Kerkblad
0016-8637	Gerencia
0016-867X	Geriatrics
0016-8688	Geriatrics Digest†
0016-8696	Gerlands Beitraege zur Geophysik
0016-870X	Gerling-Informationen fuer Geschaeftsfreunde†
0016-8718	German American Trade News changed to German American Trade.
0016-8726	German Constructions†
0016-8742	German Exporter see 0033-0876
0016-8777	German Life and Letters
0016-8785	German Medical Monthly†
0016-8793	German News
0016-8823	German Postal Specialist
0016-8831	German Quarterly
0016-884X	Philosophy and History†
0016-8858	German Tribune
0016-8866	Germana Esperanto Fervojista Asocio. Bulteno
0016-8874	Germania
0016-8882	Germanic Notes changed to Germanic Notes and Reviews.
0016-8890	Germanic Review
0016-8904	Germanisch-Romanische Monatsschrift
0016-8912	Germanistik
0016-8963	Germany Stamp News†
0016-898X	Gerontologia see 0304-324X
0016-8998	Gerontologia Clinica see 0304-324X
0016-9005	Gerontologie (Year)
0016-9013	Gerontologist
0016-9021	Geschaeftsmann und Christ
0016-903X	Geschaeftsmappe fuer Gemeinden und Standesaemter†
0016-9048	Geschaeftsreisen changed to Verband.
0016-9056	Geschichte in Wissenschaft und Unterricht
0016-9064	Geschichten aus dem Wienerwald changed to W Wintern.
0016-9072	Geschichtsunterricht und Staatsburgerkunde
0016-9080	Gesellschaft fuer Natur- und Voelkerkunde Ostasiens. Nachrichten
0016-9099	Gesellschaft und Politik
0016-9102	Gesellschaftspolitische Kommentare
0016-9129	Gesetz- und Verordnungsblatt fuer Schleswig-Holstein
0016-9145	Gesher
0016-9153	Gesichertes Leben
0016-9161	Gesnerus
0016-920X	Gesta
0016-9218	Gestions Hospitalieres
0016-9226	Gesund durch Sauna†
0016-9234	Gesund Leben
0016-9242	Gesunde Mensch†
0016-9269	Gesundheit
0016-9285	Gesundheitsnachrichten
0016-9293	Gesundheitspolitik†
0016-9307	Gesundheitspolitische Umschau
0016-9315	Gesundheitswesen und Desinfektion see 0340-997X
0016-9323	Getraenkeindustrie
0016-9331	Getraenkehandel
0016-934X	Getroster Tag
0016-9374	Geuzen Penning†
0016-9390	Gewaltfreie Aktion
0016-9412	Gewerbliche Rundschau changed to Chef-Magazin fuer Klein- und Mittelbetriebe.
0016-9420	Gewerblicher Rechtsschutz und Urheberrecht
0016-9439	Gesellen-Mitteilungen see 0343-4052
0016-9447	Gewerkschaftliche Monatshefte
0016-9455	Gewerkschaftliche Rundschau
0016-9463	Gewerkschafts Presse†
0016-948X	Geyer's Dealer Topics changed to Geyer's Office Dealer.
0016-9498	Gezinsblad
0016-9501	Gezond Limburg†
0016-951X	Gezondheid en Ziekenfonds†
0016-9528	Gezondheidszorg†
0016-9536	Ghana Geographical Association. Bulletin
0016-9544	Ghana Journal of Science†
0016-9552	Ghana Library Journal
0016-9579	Ghana News
0016-9587	Ghana Review
0016-9595	Ghana Teacher's Journal changed to Ghana Journal of Education.
0016-9609	Ghana Today changed to New Ghana.
0016-9617	Ghana Workers' Bulletin changed to T U C News.
0016-9633	Ghost Dance
0016-965X	Giardino Fiorito
0016-9668	Gib Acht
0016-9676	Gibbons Stamp Monthly
0016-9706	Gidroliznaya i Lesokhimicheskaya Promyshlennost'
0016-9714	Gidrotekhnicheskoe Stroitel'stvo
0016-9722	Gidrotekhnika i Melioratsiya
0016-9730	Gids
0016-9757	Giervalk-Gerfaut
0016-9765	Giesserei
0016-9773	Giesserei-Erfahrungsaustausch
0016-9781	Giesserei-Praxis
0016-979X	Giesserei Rundschau
0016-9846	Gift and Tableware Reporter see 0163-2175
0016-9854	Gift Buyer International
0016-9889	Gifts & Decorative Accessories
0016-9900	Gigiena i Sanitariya
0016-9919	Gigiena Truda i Professional'nye Zabolevaniya
0016-9935	Technology and Industries†
0016-9943	Gil Vicente†
0016-9951	Gilbert and Sullivan Journal†
0016-9978	Gildenfreund†
0016-9986	Gildenweg
0016-9994	Giligia†
0017-0003	Gimlaoth†
0017-0011	Ginekologia Polska†
0017-002X	Jugoslavenska Ginekologija i Opstetricija see 0352-5562
0017-0046	Ginnasta
0017-0054	Giocattoli
0017-0062	Gioia
0017-0070	Giornale Botanico Italiano
0017-0089	Giornale Critico della Filosofia Italiana
0017-0097	Giornale degli Economisti e Annali di Economia
0017-0100	Giornale degli Uccelli
0017-0119	Giornale dei Distillatori (Nuovo)
0017-0127	Giornale dei Genitori
0017-0135	Giornale degli Allevatori
0017-0143	Giornale del Bieticoltore
0017-0151	Commercio Turismo
0017-016X	Giornale del Genio Civile
0017-0186	Giornale del Mezzogiorno
0017-0208	Giornale della Cogne
0017-0216	Giornale della Libreria
0017-0224	Giornale dell'Arteriosclerosi
0017-0232	Giornale dello Spettacolo
0017-0240	Il Giornale dell'Officina
0017-0259	Giornale di Barga
0017-0267	Giornale di Batteriologia, Virologia ed Immunologia ed Annali dell'Ospedale Maria Vittoria di Torino see 0390-5462
0017-0267	Giornale di Batteriologia, Virologia ed Immunologia ed Annali dell'Ospedale Maria Vittoria di Torino see 0390-5454
0017-0275	Giornale di Clinica Medica
0017-0283	Giornale di Fisica
0017-0291	Giornale di Geologia
0017-0305	Giornale di Gerontologia
0017-0313	Giornale di Igiene e Medicina Preventiva
0017-0321	Giornale di Malattie Infettive e Parassitarie
0017-033X	Giornale di Mathematiche di Battaglini
0017-0364	Giornale di Medicina Militare
0017-0380	Giornale di Microbiologia
0017-0399	Giornale di Psichiatria e di Neuropatologia†
0017-0429	Giornale Economico
0017-0453	Giornale Italiano di Chirurgia
0017-0461	Giornale Italiano di Filologia
0017-047X	Giornale Italiano di Patologia e Scienze Affini†
0017-0496	Giornale Storico della Letteratura Italiana
0017-050X	Giornale Storico della Lunigiana e del Territorio Lucense
0017-0518	Giornalismo Europeo
0017-0526	Giovane Critica
0017-0534	Giovane Montagna
0017-0542	Gioventu Evangelica
0017-0550	Girard Home News
0017-0569	Girl Crusader†
0017-0577	Girl Scout Leader
0017-0615	Gissing Journal
0017-0623	Giurisprudenza Italiana
0017-0631	Giustizia Civile
0017-064X	Giustizia Nuova
0017-0658	Giustizia Penale
0017-0682	Gjuteriet
0017-0690	Glaces et Verrest
0017-0704	Glacier Francais
0017-0712	Glaciological Notes see 0149-1776
0017-0720	Glad Tidings
0017-0739	Glad Tidings of Good Things
0017-0747	Glamour
0017-0755	Glarmestertidende
0017-0763	Glas-Email-Keramo-Technik†
0017-0771	Glas Istre
0017-0798	Glas Omladine
0017-0801	Glas Podravine
0017-081X	Glas Podrinja
0017-0828	Glas Trebinja
0017-0852	Glasforum
0017-0860	Glasgow Chamber of Commerce. Journal
0017-0879	Glasgow Herald Trade Review†
0017-0887	Glasgow Illustrated
0017-0895	Glasgow Mathematical Journal
0017-0917	Glasgow University Guardian
0017-0925	Glasnik
0017-0933	Advokatska Komora Vojvodine. Glasnik
0017-0941	Glasnik Hemijskog Drustva-Societe Chimique, Belgrade. Bulletin see 0352-5139
0017-095X	Glasnik Matematicki
0017-0976	Glasnik Poljoprivredne Proizvodnje, Prerade i Plasmana
0017-0984	Glass (Redhill)
0017-0992	Glass Age
0017-100X	Glass and Ceramics
0017-1018	Glass Digest
0017-1026	Glass Industry
0017-1042	Glass, Potteries and Ceramic Journal changed to Glass, Potteries and Ceramic Annual.
0017-1050	Glass Technology
0017-1069	Glass Workers News†
0017-1077	Glass Workshop
0017-1085	Glastechnische Berichte
0017-1093	Glasteknisk Tidskrift
0017-1107	Glaswelt: Deutsche Glaserzeitung
0017-1123	Glaube und Tat see 0932-0180
0017-1131	Gleaner changed to Rutgers - Camden Gleaner.
0017-114X	Gleanings in Bee Culture
0017-1166	Gledista
0017-1174	Glenbow Newsletter see 0710-3697
0017-1204	Globe and Laurel
0017-1212	Globe and Mail Report on Business
0017-1220	Globent
0017-1239	Glocke
0017-1247	Glocke changed to Zzap.
0017-1263	Glos Nauczycielski
0017-1271	Glossat
0017-1298	Glotta
0017-1301	Gloucester Diocesan Gazette
0017-131X	Gloucestershire Farmer changed to Gloucestershire and North Avon Farmer.
0017-1336	Giovani in Dialogo
0017-1344	Glowna Biblioteka Lekarska. Biuletyn
0017-1352	Gloxinian
0017-1360	Glucose Informatie†

ISSN	Title
0017-1387	Glueckauf-Forschungshefte
0017-1395	Glueckliche Leben-der Stille Weg *changed to* Lebensschutz.
0017-1409	Gnade und Herrlichkeit
0017-1417	Gnomon
0017-1425	Gnosist
0017-1433	Go (Burlingame) *see* 0738-5935
0017-1441	Go (Charlotte)
0017-145X	Go Boating
0017-1476	Go Greyhound†
0017-1484	Goa Today
0017-1506	Gobbles
0017-1522	Goetheana Periodico Literario
0017-1549	Goettingische Gelehrte Anzeigen
0017-1557	Gold Bulletin
0017-1573	Gold und Silber - Uhren und Schmuck
0017-1581	Golden Eye†
0017-159X	Golden Magazine *see* 0009-3971
0017-162X	Golden West Purchasor
0017-1638	Di Goldene Keyt
0017-1646	Der Goldene Pfennig
0017-1654	Die Sphinx
0017-1670	Goldmanns Mitteilungen fuer den Buchhandel
0017-1689	Goldschmiede Zeitung - European Jeweler und Uhrmacherzeitschrift *see* 0932-464X
0017-1697	Goldsmith-Nagan Bond and Money Market Letter *changed to* Washington Bond & Money Market Report.
0017-1700	Goleuad
0017-1727	Golf *changed to* Golf.
0017-1735	Golfmagazin
0017-176X	Golf Digest
0017-1794	Golf Journal
0017-1808	Golf
0017-1816	Golf Monthly
0017-1824	Golf Shop Operations
0017-1832	Golf Singapore Review
0017-1840	Golf Superintendent *see* 0192-3048
0017-1867	Golf/U.S.A†
0017-1883	Golf World
0017-1891	Golf World
0017-1905	Golfdom *see* 0148-3706
0017-1913	Golfer
0017-1948	Golos Radzimy
0017-1956	Goltdammer's Archiv fuer Strafrecht
0017-1964	Gomitolo
0017-1980	Gong
0017-1999	Gong
0017-2014	Gonubie Gazette *changed to* Times of Gonubie.
0017-2022	Good Counsel†
0017-2049	Good Farming†
0017-2065	Good Government†
0017-2073	Good Health *see* 0306-462X
0017-2081	Good Housekeeping
0017-209X	Good Housekeeping
0017-2111	Good Motoring
0017-212X	Good News†
0017-2138	Good News (New York) *changed to* New York Good News.
0017-2146	Good News
0017-2154	Confident Living
0017-2162	Good News Crusades *see* 0164-7253
0017-2170	Good Packaging *see* 1049-3158
0017-2189	Good Reading *changed to* Good Reading for Everyone.
0017-2197	Good Times†
0017-2219	Goodyear Revue†
0017-2227	Gopher Historian *see* 0148-6659
0017-2235	Gopher Music Notes
0017-2243	Gordian
0017-2251	Christian Scholar's Review
0017-226X	Gornik
0017-2278	Gornyi Zhurnal
0017-2286	Gorskostopanska Nauka
0017-2294	Gorteria
0017-2308	Goshen College Bulletin
0017-2332	Gospel Carrier†
0017-2340	Gospel Herald
0017-2359	Gospel Messenger
0017-2367	Gospel Standard
0017-2383	Gospel Truth
0017-2391	Gospel Witness *changed to* Indian Lutheran.
0017-2405	Gospodarka Materialowa
0017-2413	Gospodarka Paliwami i Energia
0017-2421	Gospodarka Planowa
0017-243X	Gospodarka Rybna
0017-2448	Gospodarka Wodna
0017-2456	Gospodarstvo
0017-2472	Gothique
0017-2480	Gottes Wort
0017-2499	Gottesdienst und Kirchenmusik
0017-2510	Gotteskinder *changed to* Regenbogen.
0017-2529	Gouden Sleutels
0017-2537	Gouden Uren
0017-2553	Gourmet
0017-257X	Government and Opposition
0017-2588	Government Business Worldwide *changed to* Defense & Economy World Report.
0017-2596	Government Contractor
0017-260X	Government Employee Relations Report
0017-2618	Government Equipment Reports *changed to* Defense & Economy World Report.
0017-2626	Government Executive
0017-2642	Government Product News
0017-2650	Government Purchasing Digest *see* 0017-2642
0017-2677	Governmental Research Newsletter *see* 0196-7355
0017-2693	Gown
0017-2707	Gownsman†
0017-2715	Goya
0017-2723	Gozdarski Vestnik
0017-2731	Kirjapainotaito - Graafikko
0017-2758	Gracas do Servo de Deus: Padre Cruz
0017-2774	Gradbeni Vestnik
0017-2782	Grade Teacher *see* 1049-5851
0017-2790	Roots
0017-2804	Graduate Careers
0017-2812	Graduate Careers in Science and Technology†
0017-2839	Graduate Research in Education and Related Disciplines *changed to* Graduate Research in Urban Education and Related Disciplines.
0017-2863	Graffitti†
0017-2871	Druk en Papier *changed to* F N V Magazine (Amsterdam).
0017-288X	Grafia
0017-2898	Grafica†
0017-291X	Grafico
0017-2928	Grafico
0017-2936	Graficus
0017-2944	Grafiek
0017-2952	Grafische Literatuur Centrale†
0017-2979	Grafisk Faktorstidning
0017-2987	Grafisk Revy *see* 0017-288X
0017-2995	De Grafiske Fag
0017-3002	Grafiskt Forum
0017-3029	Grain Age
0017-3053	Grain Bulletin†
0017-3061	Grain Market News and Feed Market News *changed to* Grain and Feed Market News.
0017-307X	Revue Technique Automobile
0017-3088	Gralswelt†
0017-310X	Gramophone
0017-3118	Gran Pavese†
0017-3126	Gran Tiramolla
0017-3134	Grana
0017-3142	Grande Hotel
0017-3185	Grani
0017-3207	Granite Cutters Journal†
0017-3231	Granta
0017-324X	Granthagar
0017-3258	Grapevine†
0017-3274	Graphic Antiquarian†
0017-3282	Graphic Arts Abstracts *changed to* G A T F World.
0017-3290	Graphic Arts Bulletin†
0017-3304	Graphic Arts Buyer†
0017-3312	Graphic Arts Monthly and the Printing Industry *see* 1047-9325
0017-3320	Graphic Arts Patent Abstracts†
0017-3339	Graphic Arts Product News†
0017-3347	Graphic Arts Progress *changed to* Institute of Paper Science and Technology. Graphic Arts Bulletin.
0017-3363	Graphic Arts Unionist *see* 0746-3626
0017-341X	Graphic Trends†
0017-3428	Graphics: U S A *see* 0274-7499
0017-3436	Graphicus
0017-3452	Graphis
0017-3479	Graphische Revue Oesterreichs
0017-3487	Graphs and Notes on the Economic Situation in the Community *see* 0379-217X
0017-3495	Grasas y Aceites
0017-3517	Grass Roots Forum†
0017-3525	Grasso Mededelingen *changed to* Grasso Contact.
0017-3541	Grassroots Editor
0017-3568	Gravure *changed to* Package Printing & Converting.
0017-3576	Gravure Technical Association Bulletin *changed to* Gravure Magazine.
0017-3584	Gray and Ductile Iron News *changed to* Metalcaster.
0017-3592	Graybar Outlook
0017-3606	Grazhdanskaya Aviatsiya
0017-3614	Great Basin Naturalist
0017-3630	Great Britain. Central Statistical Office. Statistical News
0017-3665	Great Lakes News Letter†
0017-3673	Great Plains Journal
0017-3681	Great Plains National Instructional Television Library Newsletter *see* 0738-7555
0017-369X	Great Speckled Bird†
0017-3703	Greater Amusements and International Projectionist
0017-3754	Greater Milwaukee Dental Bulletin *see* 0884-6898
0017-3762	Delaware Valley Business Fortnight†
0017-3770	Greater Pittsburgh†
0017-3789	Portland Commerce *changed to* Portland Magazine.
0017-3797	Greater Rochester Commerce†
0017-3819	Grecia de Ayer, de Hoy y de Siempre†
0017-3835	Greece and Rome
0017-3851	Greek Bibliography†
0017-386X	Greek Gazette
0017-3886	Greek Observer
0017-3894	Greek Orthodox Theological Review
0017-3908	Greek Report
0017-3916	Greek, Roman and Byzantine Studies
0017-3924	Green and White
0017-3932	Green Book
0017-3940	Green Cross†
0017-3967	Green Island
0017-3975	Green Pyne Leaf†
0017-3983	Green Revolution
0017-3991	Green River Current
0017-4009	Green River Review
0017-4017	Green Tree†
0017-4041	Greenfield Review†
0017-4068	Greenleaf†
0017-4076	Green's Commodity Market Comments *see* 0146-7190
0017-4084	Greensboro Review
0017-4092	Greensward
0017-4106	Greeting Card Magazine *changed to* Greetings.
0017-4114	Gregorianum
0017-4122	Gregoriusblad†
0017-4149	Grenoble Universite. Faculte des Lettres et Sciences Humaines. Centre de Documentation et de Recherches Bibliographiques. Bulletin d'Information†
0017-4157	Greyhound
0017-4165	Greyhound Owner & Breeder
0017-4181	Grial
0017-419X	Gridley Wave
0017-4203	Griekenland Bulletin *changed to* Internationale Korrespondentie.
0017-422X	Griffin Report of New England *see* 0192-4400
0017-4254	Grille
0017-4289	Grit
0017-4297	Grit and Steel
0017-4300	Grito†
0017-4319	Grits and Grinds†
0017-4327	Grits and Grinds (Swedish edition)†
0017-4335	Grive
0017-4343	Grlica
0017-4351	Grocer
0017-436X	Grocer Management/Western†
0017-4378	Grocers' and Storekeepers' Journal of Western Australia
0017-4386	Grocers Gazette
0017-4394	Grocery Marketing
0017-4416	Grocery Communications
0017-4440	Grocery Review
0017-4459	Groei†
0017-4467	Groei *see* 0169-281X
0017-4483	De Groene Amsterdammer
0017-4491	Groenten en Fruit
0017-4505	Grondboor en Hamer
0017-4521	Groninger Landbouwblad *changed to* Landbode (Groningen).
0017-453X	Gronk
0017-4548	Gronkopings Veckoblad
0017-4556	Groenland (Charlottenlund)
0017-4564	Groote Schrijver-Genesiusblad *see* 0165-8867
0017-4572	Groothandel in Levensmiddelen *changed to* Missets Distrifood.
0017-4599	Gross Wartenberger Heimatblatt
0017-4602	Entschluss
0017-4610	Grosse Pointe Public Library. Newsletter†
0017-4637	Grosseteste Review
0017-4645	Grosswetterlagen Europas
0017-4653	Ground Engineering
0017-467X	Ground Water
0017-4688	Grounds Maintenance
0017-4696	Groundsman
0017-470X	Group Health and Welfare News *see* 1050-9038
0017-4726	Group Practice *see* 0199-5103
0017-4734	Group Psychotherapy *see* 0731-1273
0017-4742	Group Research Report
0017-4750	Group Travel†
0017-4769	Oregon Quality Newsletter *changed to* Oregon Development.
0017-4777	Grower
0017-4785	Grower
0017-4793	Growth *see* 1041-1232
0017-4807	Growth and Acquisition Guide†
0017-4815	Growth and Change
0017-4831	Growth Fund Guide
0017-484X	Growth Stock Digest†
0017-4858	Grubensicherheit *see* 0344-239X
0017-4866	Grudnaya Khirurgiya
0017-4874	Die Waage
0017-4904	Grundfoerbaettring†
0017-4912	Grundig Technische Informationen†
0017-4920	Grundlagen der Landtechnik *changed to* Landtechnik.
0017-4947	Gruppenpsychotherapie und Gruppendynamik
0017-4955	Gruzlica i Choroby Pluc *changed to* Pneumonologia i Alergologia Polska.
0017-4971	Guairat
0017-498X	Guajana
0017-4998	Guanabara Industrial†
0017-5005	Guardia Nacional
0017-5013	Guardian†
0017-5021	Guardian
0017-503X	Guards Magazine
0017-5048	Guatemala. Instituto Nacional de Estadistica. Boletin Estadistico
0017-5056	Guatemala Indigena
0017-5064	Guatemala Pediatrica
0017-5080	Guepes
0017-5110	Guernsey Breeders' Journal
0017-5137	Gueterverkehr
0017-5145	Guia Aeronautico
0017-5153	Guia Guarani
0017-5161	Guia para Maestros de Ninos†

ISSN INDEX

ISSN	Title
0017-5188	Guida allo Spettacolo *changed to* Nuova Guida Cinematografica.
0017-5218	Guidance Report†
0017-5226	Guide (Hagerstown)
0017-5234	Today's Guide *changed to* Guide Patrol.
0017-5242	Guide *see* 0273-3145
0017-5269	Guide Post
0017-5285	Guide to Indian Periodical Literature
0017-5293	Guide to Microforms in Print *see* 0164-0747
0017-5307	Guide to Social Science and Religion in Periodical Literature
0017-5315	Guide to the American Left *see* 8756-0208
0017-5323	Guidepost
0017-5331	Guideposts
0017-534X	Guider *see* 0265-2706
0017-5366	Guild Gardener. Newsletter†
0017-5374	Guild Gazette *changed to* Guild and City Gazette.
0017-5382	Guild Guide *see* 0194-2174
0017-5390	Guild Practitioner *see* 0730-532X
0017-5404	Guild Reporter
0017-5412	Guide du Livre
0017-5439	Guilds of Weavers, Spinners and Dyers. Quarterly Journal *see* 0267-7806
0017-5455	Guion
0017-5463	Guitar Player
0017-5471	Guitar Review
0017-548X	Guitare et Musique Chansons Poesie
0017-5501	Gujarat Labour Gazette
0017-551X	Gujarat Law Reporter
0017-5528	Gujarat Law Times
0017-5536	Gujarat Revenue Tribunal Law Reporter
0017-5544	Guldsmedebladet
0017-5552	Gulf Coast Cattleman
0017-5560	Gulf Coast Lumberman and Building Distributor *see* 0192-4389
0017-5587	Gulf Review†
0017-5609	Gummibereifung
0017-5617	Gun Report
0017-5625	Gun Talk
0017-5633	Gun Week *see* 0195-1599
0017-5641	Gun World
0017-565X	Gunma Journal of Medical Sciences *see* 0386-0760
0017-5668	Gunma Daigaku Kyoikugakubu Kiyo. Shizen Kagaku Hen
0017-5676	Guns
0017-5684	Guns & Ammo
0017-5692	Guns Review
0017-5706	Gurukul Kangri Vishwavidyalaya†
0017-5714	Gurukula Prakashana†
0017-5730	Gustav - Adolf - Blatt
0017-5749	Gut
0017-5765	Gute Fahrt
0017-5781	Gute Nachrichten
0017-579X	Gute Reise†
0017-5803	Die Gute Tat
0017-5811	Le Gutenberg
0017-582X	Guter Rat
0017-5838	Guthrie Clinic Bulletin *see* 0882-696X
0017-5846	Guy†
0017-5854	Guyana Business†
0017-5862	Guyana Information Bulletin *changed to* Guyana Information Bulletin.
0017-5870	Guy's Hospital Gazette
0017-5897	Y Gwyddonydd
0017-5900	Gyermekgyogyaszat
0017-5919	Gymnasieingenjoeren *changed to* T L I - Ingenjoeren.
0017-5927	Gymnasieskolen
0017-5935	Das Gymnasion†
0017-5943	Gymnasium
0017-5951	Gymnasium Helveticum
0017-596X	Gymnastikk og Turn
0017-5978	Gymnastikledaren *see* 0281-5443
0017-5986	Gynecologic Investigation *see* 0378-7346
0017-5994	Der Gynaekologe
0017-6001	Gynaekologische Rundschau
0017-601X	Gynecologie et Obstetrique et Federation des Societes de Gynecologie et d'Obstetrique. Bulletin *see* 0368-2315
0017-6028	Gynecologie Pratique *see* 0301-2204
0017-6036	Gyogyszereszet
0017-6044	Gyogyszereszeti es Gyogyszerterapias Dokumentacios Szemle *see* 0138-9289
0017-6052	Gyorstajekoztato a Magyar Konyvtartudomanyi Irodalomrol *see* 0133-736X
0017-6087	Gypsy Lore Society. Journal
0017-6095	Gypsies for Christ
0017-6109	H A Bulletin†
0017-6117	H & S Reports†
0017-6125	H & W†
0017-6141	H C I Journal *see* 0144-3704
0017-615X	H C R Bulletin *see* 0252-791X
0017-6176	H E A News Flash†
0017-6192	H N O (Berlin)
0017-6206	H. Pt
0017-6214	H R D News *see* 0098-1435
0017-6222	H R I S Abstracts *changed to* Highway Research Abstracts.
0017-6230	H S M A Bulletin and Idea Exchange *changed to* H S M A World.
0017-6249	H S U Brand
0017-6257	H S V - Post *changed to* H S V - Journal.
0017-6265	H T A Contact *changed to* H E A Advocate.
0017-6273	H T A Horizon†
0017-629X	HTS'ert
0017-6303	H U D Challenge Magazine *see* 0196-1969
0017-6311	H U D Newsletter†
0017-632X	Haagse Jazz Club
0017-6346	Habinjan
0017-6362	Habit
0017-6370	Habitatt
0017-6397	Habitatt
0017-6400	Habitation†
0017-6419	Habitation
0017-6443	Haboneh†
0017-6451	Hacettepe Bulletin of Medicine-Surgery - Hacettepe Tip Cerrahi Bulteni *changed to* Hacettepe Medical Journal.
0017-646X	Hinuk̈h†
0017-6478	Hacia la Luz
0017-6486	Hacienda
0017-6508	Hadashot Mehachaim Hadatiyim Beisrael
0017-6516	Hadassah Magazine
0017-6524	Hadoar
0017-6532	Hadorom
0017-6540	Hadtortenelmi Kozlemenyek
0017-6559	Haematologia
0017-6575	Haematologica Latina†
0017-6605	Hagemi
0017-6613	Kir - Ou - Kirk
0017-6621	Hahnemannian
0017-6656	Haiku *see* 0703-1831
0017-6664	Haiku Highlights *see* 0364-359X
0017-6680	Addis Ababa University. College of Technology. Library Bulletin
0017-6699	Hailert
0017-6702	Hair & Beauty
0017-6710	Hair and Makeup Trends†
0017-6729	Hair Beauty Magazine†
0017-6737	Hair Magic†
0017-6753	Hairdressers' Guide
0017-6761	Hairdressers' Journal *changed to* Hairdressers' Journal International.
0017-677X	Hairenik
0017-6788	Haiti. Institut Haitien de Statistique. Bulletin Trimestriel de Statistique
0017-6796	Hakku
0017-680X	Halle aux Cuirs†
0017-6818	I D†
0017-6834	De Halve Maen
0017-6842	Ham Radio *see* 0148-5989
0017-6850	Ha-Maapil
0017-6869	Hamburg Air
0017-6877	Hamburg in Zahlen
0017-6885	Hamburg Journal†
0017-6915	Hamburger Aerzteblatt†
0017-6931	Hamburger Export-Woche
0017-694X	Hamburger Hafen-Nachrichten und Schiffsabfahrten *see* 0341-0862
0017-6966	Hamburger Lehrerzeitung *changed to* H L Z.
0017-6982	Hamburger Sport - Mitteilungen
0017-6990	Hamburger Vorschau
0017-7024	Hamdard Medical Digest *see* 0250-7188
0017-7032	Hamddent
0017-7040	Hamevaser
0017-7059	Ha-Mifal
0017-7067	Hamilton Alumni Review
0017-7075	Hamilton County Pharmacist
0017-7083	Ha-Mizrah Hehadash
0017-7091	Mlonai
0017-7113	Hampshire
0017-7121	Hampshire Farmer
0017-7148	Hand Vol Pluis
0017-7156	Handarbeit
0017-7164	Handasah ve-Adrikhalut *changed to* Handasah.
0017-7172	Handbags and Accessories *changed to* Accessories.
0017-7180	Handbal
0017-7199	Handbook of Basic Economic Statistics
0017-7202	Handbuch des Bauherrn
0017-7210	Handbuch des Hausbesitzers†
0017-7229	Der Handel
0017-7237	Handel en Nywerheid†
0017-7245	Handel Zagraniczny
0017-7253	Handelingen der Staten-Generaal
0017-7261	Agentur *changed to* Agentur.
0017-7288	Handelsbelangen†
0017-7296	Handelsblatt
0017-730X	Handelskammer Hamburg. Mitteilungen *changed to* Hamburger Wirtschaft.
0017-7318	Handelslaget *see* 0781-7347
0017-7326	Handelsnytt
0017-7334	Chambre de Commerce Neerlandaise pour la Belgique et le Luxembourg, S.C. Revue Commerciale
0017-7342	Denmark. Danmarks Statistik. Handelsstatistiske Meddelelser. Maanedsstatistik over Udenrigshandelen *see* 0108-5506
0017-7350	Handelswoche *see* 0863-4084
0017-7369	Handenarbeid *changed to* Beeldpraat.
0017-7377	Handes Amsorya
0017-7385	Handling and Shipping *see* 0895-8548
0017-7393	Handloader
0017-7407	Handweaver and Craftsman†
0017-7415	Handwerken Ariadne *changed to* Ariadne.
0017-7423	Handy Shipping Guide
0017-7431	Hanford Project News *changed to* Hanford News.
0017-744X	Korea Development Bank. Monthly Economic Review
0017-7458	Hannibal Labor Press†
0017-7466	Hannoversche Land- und Forstwirtschaftliche Zeitung
0017-7474	Hannoversches Pferd *changed to* Der Hannoveraner.
0017-7482	Hanover News
0017-7504	Hansa
0017-7520	Animal Reproduction Techniques
0017-7539	Hanson's Latin America Letter
0017-7547	Japanese Journal of Criminal Psychology
0017-7555	Olam Hazeh
0017-7563	Happening in New York†
0017-7571	Praklit
0017-758X	Harangue
0017-761X	Harbinger (Crystal City)
0017-7636	Harbour and Shipping
0017-7644	Hard Fibres†
0017-7652	Hardlines Wholesaling†
0017-7660	Hardware Age *see* 8755-254X
0017-7679	Hardware and Farm Equipment *see* 1044-7768
0017-7687	Hardware Consultant *see* 0361-5294
0017-7709	Hardware Merchandiser†
0017-7717	Hardware Merchandising
0017-7725	Hardware Retailer *changed to* Do-it-Yourself Retailing.
0017-7733	Hardware Review *see* 0266-0539
0017-7741	Hardware Trade Journal *see* 0954-8823
0017-7768	Ha-Refuah
0017-7776	Harian Press *see* 0278-4947
0017-7806	Harmonica Accordeon et Musique
0017-7822	Harmonie *see* 0757-0139
0017-7830	Die Harmonika†
0017-7849	Harmonizer
0017-7857	Harness Horse†
0017-7865	Israel Pharmaceutical Journal
0017-7873	Harper's Bazaar
0017-789X	Harper's Magazine
0017-7903	Harpers Wine and Spirit Gazette
0017-7938	Harris-Report†
0017-7946	Harrison Tape Catalog *changed to* Harrison Tape Guide.
0017-7954	Harry S. Truman Library Institute Research Newsletter *see* 0363-1028
0017-7962	The Hartford Agent
0017-7970	Hartford Hospital Bulletin†
0017-7989	Hartford Studies in Literature *see* 0196-2280
0017-8004	Harvard Advocate
0017-8012	Harvard Business Review
0017-8020	Harvard Business School. Bulletin
0017-8039	Harvard Civil Rights - Civil Liberties Law Review
0017-8047	Harvard Divinity Bulletin
0017-8055	Harvard Educational Review
0017-8063	Harvard International Law Journal
0017-808X	Harvard Journal on Legislation
0017-8098	Harvard Lampoon
0017-8101	Harvard Law Record
0017-811X	Harvard Law Review
0017-8128	Harvard Law School Bulletin *see* 1053-8186
0017-8136	Harvard Library Bulletin
0017-8144	Harvard Project Physics. Newsletter†
0017-8160	Harvard Theological Review
0017-8179	Harvard Today†
0017-8195	Harvest Semi-monthly
0017-8209	Harvest Years *see* 1041-6277
0017-8217	Harvester *changed to* Aware.
0017-8225	Harvester
0017-8233	Haryana Cooperation
0017-8241	Haryana Health Journal
0017-825X	Haryana Journal of Education
0017-8268	Haryou-Act News†
0017-8276	Harzburger Hefte *see* 0302-6671
0017-8284	Ha-Sifrut
0017-8306	Hasler-Mitteilungen
0017-8314	Hassadeh
0017-8322	Hastings Law Journal
0017-8330	Hat Worker†
0017-8349	Hataassiya *changed to* M'lakha V'ta'asiya.
0017-8357	Hatchet *changed to* G W Hatchet.
0017-8381	Hatvertising Weekly
0017-839X	Hauenstein Verlag. Mitteilungsblatt *changed to* Ring-Post.
0017-8403	Haus und Grund
0017-842X	Die Hausfrau
0017-8462	Hauswirtschaftsmeisterin *see* 0341-5295
0017-8470	Der Hautarzt
0017-8497	Havebladet
0017-8500	Haven
0017-8519	Havenloods
0017-8527	Hawadess
0017-8535	Hawaii A F L - C I O News *changed to* Hawaii A F L - C I O Nupepa.
0017-8543	Hawaii Beverage Guide
0017-856X	Business Historical Society. Bulletin *see* 0007-6805
0017-8578	Hawaii Guardsman *changed to* Pupukahi.
0017-8586	Hawaii Library Association Journal *changed to* H L A Journal.

ISSN INDEX 5385

ISSN	Title
0017-8594	Hawaii Medical Journal
0017-8616	Hawaii State Dental Association. Journal *changed to* Hawaii Dental Journal.
0017-8624	Hawaiian Shell News
0017-8632	Hawkeye United Methodist *changed to* Hawkeye (Des Moines).
0017-8640	Hay Guetron
0017-8667	Hayastanyaitz Yegeghetzy *see* 0199-8765
0017-8675	Yahad Digest *changed to* Yahad.
0017-8683	Aiastani Kensabanakan Andes
0017-8691	Yatsiv
0017-8705	Areiniki Dzain *changed to* Hayreniky Dzayn.
0017-8713	Head, Heart, Hands & Health in Virginia†
0017-8721	Head Start Newsletter†
0017-873X	Head Teachers Review
0017-8748	Headache
0017-8756	Headland *changed to* New Headland.
0017-8764	Headlight
0017-8780	Foreign Policy Association. Headline Series
0017-8799	Heads Up†
0017-8829	Healing Hand
0017-8845	Health *see* 0308-602X
0017-8853	Health†
0017-8861	Health
0017-887X	Health
0017-8888	Health and Efficiency
0017-890X	Health and Strength *see* 0266-8963
0017-8926	Ofakim
0017-8950	Health Education *see* 0833-7594
0017-8969	Health Education Journal
0017-8977	Health Foods Retailing†
0017-8985	Health for All *see* 0018-0696
0017-8993	Health Information Digest†
0017-9019	Health Insurance Underwriter
0017-9027	Health Insurance Viewpoints *changed to* Health Care Viewpoint.
0017-9035	Health Laboratory Science†
0017-9043	Health News†
0017-9051	Health-Pac *changed to* Health - P A C Bulletin.
0017-906X	Health, Physical Education, and Recreation Microcard Bulletin *see* 0090-5119
0017-9078	Health Physics
0017-9086	Weekly Government Abstracts. Health Planning *changed to* N T I S Alerts: Health Care.
0017-9116	Health Services Journal *changed to* C O H S E Journal.
0017-9124	Health Services Research
0017-9132	Health Trends
0017-9140	Health Visitor
0017-9159	Healthways Magazine†
0017-9167	Healthy Living
0017-9175	Hear This
0017-9183	Hearing†
0017-9191	Hearing and Speech News *see* 0162-5667
0017-9205	Hearing Dealer *see* 0092-4466
0017-9248	Heart Bulletin†
0017-9256	Heart of America Purchaser
0017-9272	Heartbeat of St. Joseph's Hospital *changed to* Heartbeat of St. Joseph's Medical Center.
0017-9280	Hearth and Home†
0017-9299	Hearthstone†
0017-9302	Hearts of Oak Journal†
0017-9310	International Journal of Heat and Mass Transfer
0017-9329	Heat Engineering
0017-9345	Heat Treating
0017-9353	Heating, Air Conditioning & Refrigeration†
0017-937X	Heating and Ventilating Engineer and Journal of Air Conditioning *changed to* Heating and Ventilating Engineer.
0017-9388	Heating and Ventilating News *changed to* H & V News.
0017-9396	Heating and Ventilating Review
0017-940X	Heating - Piping - Air Conditioning
0017-9418	Heating, Plumbing, Air Conditioning
0017-9426	Heavy Construction News
0017-9434	Heavy Duty Trucking
0017-9442	Hebezeuge und Foerdermittel
0017-9477	Hebrew Christian
0017-9485	Hechos y Dichos†
0017-9493	Hed Hachinuch
0017-9507	Hedeselskabets Tidsskrift
0017-9515	Heemschut
0017-9523	Heer en Mode†
0017-9531	Heerbaan *see* 0165-988X
0017-9566	Heghapoghagan Albom
0017-9590	The Heights
0017-9604	Die Heilberufe
0017-9612	Das Heilige Band
0017-9620	Heiliger Dienst
0017-9639	Heilkunst
0017-9655	Vierteljahresschrift fuer Heilpaedagogik und ihre Nachbargebiete
0017-9671	Heim und Anstalt *changed to* S K A V - Fachblatt.
0017-968X	Heim und Herd *see* 0174-3058
0017-9698	Heima Er Bezt
0017-9701	Die Heimat
0017-9728	Heimat und Kirche†
0017-9736	Heimat und Staat†
0017-9752	Heimat - Zeitung Roemerstaedter Laendchen
0017-9779	Heimatland *changed to* Literatur aus Oesterreich.
0017-9787	Heimatland Lippe
0017-9809	Das Heimatmuseum Alsergrund
0017-9817	Heimatschutz
0017-9833	Heimatwerk *changed to* Schweizer Heimatwerk: Handwerk - Volkskunst - Kunsthandwerk.
0017-9841	Heimen
0017-985X	Heimevernsbladet
0017-9868	Die Heimstatt
0017-9876	Heimtex
0017-9884	Heirs†
0017-9906	H L H, Zeitschrift fuer Heizung, Lueftung, Klimatechnik, Haustechnik *changed to* H L H, Heizung, Lueftung, Klima, Haustechnik.
0017-9914	Hejnal Mariacki
0017-9922	Helan Medical Magazine
0017-9930	Helferbrief *changed to* Bevoelkerungsschutz-Magazin.
0017-9949	Helferin des Artzes *changed to* Die Arzthelferin.
0017-9957	Helgolaender Wissenschaftliche Meeresuntersuchungen *see* 0174-3597
0017-9965	Helicopter World†
0017-9973	Helictite
0017-9981	Helikon
0017-999X	Helikon
0018-0009	Helinium
0018-0025	Hellenic-American Chamber of Commerce. Newsletter
0018-0033	Hellenic Herald *changed to* Greek Herald.
0018-005X	Hellenic Shipping International
0018-0068	Elliniki Ktiniatriki
0018-0076	Hellenicos Erythros Stavros Neotitos
0018-0084	Hellenika
0018-0092	Hellenike Cheirougike
0018-0114	Helmantica
0018-0130	Helminthological Society of Washington. Proceedings *see* 1049-233X
0018-0149	Helse
0018-0157	Helsenytt
0018-0173	Helvetia Archaeologica *see* 0255-9005
0018-0181	Helvetia Chirurgica Acta
0018-019X	Helvetica Chimica Acta
0018-0211	Helvetica Odontologica Acta *see* 1011-4203
0018-022X	Helvetica Paediatrica Acta *see* 0340-6199
0018-0238	Helvetica Physica Acta
0018-0270	Hemecht
0018-0289	Hemel en Dampkring *see* 0165-0211
0018-0297	Hemerocallis Journal *see* 0744-0219
0018-0300	Hemisphere†
0018-0319	Hemispherica†
0018-0327	Hemmets Journal
0018-0335	Hemmets Vaen
0018-0351	Hemvaernet
0018-036X	Hendrik Pierson Vereniging (Publication) *changed to* Hendrik Pierson Stichting (Publication).
0018-0386	Hennepin Reporter†
0018-0394	Hennes†
0018-0408	Henry E. Huntington Library and Art Gallery. Calendar of Exhibitions *changed to* Huntington Library, Art Collections, and Botanical Gardens. Calendar.
0018-0416	Henry Ford Hospital Medical Journal
0018-0424	Henry George News *see* 0734-4031
0018-0432	Hep *changed to* Hip.
0018-0467	Herald
0018-0475	Herald of Christian Science
0018-0483	Herald of Freedom†
0018-0491	Herald of Health
0018-0505	Herald of Health†
0018-0521	Herald of Library Science
0018-053X	Heraldo del Espiritismo *see* 0034-4478
0018-0548	Heraldo Mercantil Internacional
0018-0556	Heraldos del Rey *changed to* Conquistadores (Student Edition).
0018-0572	Herb Grower Magazine†
0018-0580	Herba Hungarica *changed to* Journal of Medicinal and Aromatic Plants.
0018-0599	Herba Polonica
0018-0602	Herbage Abstracts
0018-0629	Hercules Chemist†
0018-0637	Hercynia
0018-0645	Herder - Korrespondenz
0018-0661	Hereditas
0018-067X	Heredity
0018-0688	Herefordshire Farmer
0018-0696	Here's Health
0018-070X	Black Music Review†
0018-0718	Heritage of Vermilion County
0018-0726	Heritage - Southwest Jewish Press
0018-0734	Herkenning (The Hague, 1948)
0018-0742	Hermanus News†
0018-0750	Hermathena
0018-0777	Hermes
0018-0785	Hermes Exchange†
0018-0793	Herold (Berlin)
0018-0807	Herold (Munich)
0018-0815	Herold des Kostbaren Blutes
0018-0823	Heroldo de Esperanto
0018-0831	Herpetologica
0018-084X	Herpetological Review
0018-0858	Der Herr†
0018-0866	Husholdningslaereren (Vaeloese)
0018-0874	Herrenjournal†
0018-0890	Herst
0018-0904	Hertfordshire Countryside Illustrated *see* 0306-672X
0018-0912	Hertha
0018-0920	Hervormd Arnhem
0018-0939	Hervormd Nederland
0018-0947	Hervormd Wageningen
0018-0955	Hervormde Gemeente Musselkanaal. Kerkblad
0018-0971	Herzogia
0018-098X	Hesperia
0018-0998	Hesperide†
0018-1005	Hesperis - Tamuda
0018-1013	Hesperus†
0018-103X	Hessische Blaetter fuer Volksbildung
0018-1056	Hessische Erzieher†
0018-1064	Hessische Familienkunde
0018-1072	Hessischer Gaertner
0018-1080	Hessische Gross- und Aussenhandel *changed to* Grosshandel-Aussenhandel.
0018-1099	Hessische Jugend
0018-1102	Hessische Standesbeamte†
0018-1110	Hestesport
0018-1129	Het Torentje
0018-1137	Heterofonia
0018-1145	Heuristics†
0018-1153	Hewlett-Packard Journal
0018-1188	Hey Lady
0018-1196	Heythrop Journal
0018-120X	HiCall
0018-1218	Hi-Fi - Stereo Buyers' Guide†
0018-1226	Audio Record Review *see* 0142-6230
0018-1242	Hi-Tension News
0018-1269	Hiballer Miner *changed to* Hiballer Contractor Miner.
0018-1277	Hibernia *changed to* Hibernia Weekly.
0018-1285	Hidalguia
0018-1293	Hide and Leather Bulletin
0018-1307	Hides and Skins Quarterly†
0018-1315	Hidro Mecanica en la Construccion Mexicana
0018-1323	Hidrologiai Kozlony
0018-1331	Hydrology and Meteorology
0018-134X	Hidrotehnica, Gospodarirea Apelor, Meteorologia *changed to* Hidrotehnica.
0018-1358	Hidrotehnicka Bibliografija
0018-1382	HiFi Stereophonie *see* 0172-388X
0018-1390	Skin Research
0018-1404	Clinical Dermatology
0018-1412	High Change & Unitholder†
0018-1420	High Country†
0018-1439	High Energy Chemistry
0018-1447	High Energy Physics Index
0018-1455	High Fidelity *see* 0039-1220
0018-1463	High Fidelity - Musical America *see* 0735-777X
0018-1471	High Plains Journal
0018-148X	High Points
0018-1498	High School Journal
0018-1501	High Speed Ground Transportation Journal *see* 0197-6729
0018-151X	High Temperature Physics *changed to* High Temperature.
0018-1536	High Temperature Science
0018-1544	High Temperatures - High Pressures
0018-1552	High Voltage Engineering Corporation Newsletter†
0018-1560	Higher Education
0018-1579	Higher Education and National Affairs
0018-1595	Secondary Education *see* 0951-7855
0018-1609	Higher Education Review
0018-1617	Highland Hotelkeeper & Touristmaker
0018-1625	Highlights
0018-1641	Highlights at B P L *changed to* Bloomfield Public Library Highlights.
0018-165X	Highlights for Children
0018-1668	Highlights of Agricultural Research
0018-1676	Highway
0018-1684	Highway
0018-1692	Highway Builder
0018-1706	Highway Common Carrier Newsletter
0018-1722	Highway Mail
0018-1730	Highway Research Abstracts *see* 0095-2648
0018-1749	Highway Research News *see* 0738-6826
0018-1757	Highway Transport†
0018-1765	Highway User *see* 0094-7393
0018-1773	Highways *changed to* Highways.
0018-1781	Highways. Current Literature *see* 0091-1410
0018-179X	Hika
0018-1803	Leather Technology
0018-1811	Leather Chemistry
0018-182X	Hikone Ronso†
0018-1854	Hillbilly†
0018-1862	Hillel Gate
0018-1889	Himachal Agricultural Newsletter
0018-1897	Himavanta
0018-1900	Himmat
0018-1927	Hinduism
0018-1935	Hindustan Antibiotics Bulletin
0018-1943	Hindustan Chamber Review
0018-1951	Hinshitsu Kanri
0018-1978	Hinterland
0018-1986	Hints to Potato Growers
0018-2001	Hippokrates†
0018-201X	Hippologisk Tidsskrift

5386 ISSN INDEX

0018-2028 Hiradastechnika
0018-2036 Hiram Poetry Review
0018-2044 Hiroshima Medical Association. Journal
0018-2052 Hiroshima Journal of Medical Sciences
0018-2060 Hiroshima University. Faculty of Engineering. Bulletin
0018-2079 Hiroshima Mathematical Journal
0018-2087 Hiroshima Daigaku Igaku Zasshi
0018-2095 His *see* 0743-2399
0018-2117 Hisairdec News†
0018-2125 Hispalis Medica
0018-2133 Hispania
0018-2141 Hispania
0018-215X Hispania Sacra
0018-2168 Hispanic American Historical Review
0018-2176 Hispanic Review
0018-2184 El Hispano
0018-2192 Hispano Americano
0018-2206 Hispanofila
0018-2214 The Histochemical Journal
0018-2222 Histochemie - Histochemistry - Histochimie *see* 0301-5564
0018-2230 Histoire de la Medecine†
0018-2257 Histoire Sociale
0018-2265 Histonium *changed to* Histonium en Su Nueva Dimension.
0018-2273 Historama
0018-229X Historia
0018-2311 Historia
0018-2346 Historia Natural y Pro Natura†
0018-2354 Historia y Vida
0018-2362 Historiallinen Aikakauskirja
0018-2370 The Historian (Tempe)
0018-2389 Historic Aviation†
0018-2397 Historic Kern
0018-2419 Historic Preservation
0018-2427 Historica
0018-2435 Historical Abstracts *see* 0363-2717
0018-2435 Historical Abstracts *see* 0363-2725
0018-2443 Historical Aviation Album
0018-2451 Historical Firearms Society of South Africa. Journal
0018-246X Historical Journal
0018-2478 Historical Journal of Japan
0018-2486 Historical Magazine of the Protestant Episcopal Church *changed to* Anglican and Episcopal History.
0018-2494 Historical Methods Newsletter *see* 0161-5440
0018-2508 Historical New Hampshire
0018-2516 Historical Review
0018-2524 Historical Review of Berks County
0018-2532 Historical Society of Haddonfield. Bulletin
0018-2540 Historical Society of Nigeria. Journal
0018-2559 Historical Studies *see* 1031-461X
0018-2567 Historical Wyoming†
0018-2575 Historicky Casopis
0018-2583 Historie a Vojenstvi
0018-2591 Historiographer†
0018-2605 Das Historisch-Politische Buch
0018-2613 Historische Zeitschrift
0018-2621 Historisches Jahrbuch
0018-263X Historisk Tidsskrift
0018-2648 History
0018-2656 History and Theory
0018-2664 History Book Club Review
0018-2680 History of Education Quarterly
0018-2699 History of Education Society Bulletin
0018-2702 History of Political Economy
0018-2710 History of Religions
0018-2737 History of the Twentieth Century†
0018-2745 History Teacher
0018-2753 History Today
0018-2761 Hit†
0018-277X Hitachi Review
0018-2788 Hitachi Zosen Technical Review
0018-2796 Hitotsubashi Journal of Commerce and Management
0018-280X Hitotsubashi Journal of Economics
0018-2818 Hitotsubashi Review
0018-2842 Hjemmet
0018-2869 Hlas Ludu
0018-2885 Hoard's Dairyman
0018-2893 Hobart Weldworld†
0018-2907 Hobbies, the Magazine for Collectors *changed to* Antiques & Collecting Hobbies.
0018-2931 Hobby Bulletin *see* 0922-2170
0018-2958 Hochfrequenztechnik und Elektroakustik†
0018-2974 Das Hochschulwesen
0018-2982 Hockey Circle
0018-2990 Hockey e Pattinaggio†
0018-3008 Hockey Field *see* 0950-9550
0018-3016 Hockey News
0018-3032 Hockey Sport†
0018-3040 Hodowla Roslin, Aklimatyzacja i Nasiennictwo
0018-3059 Hoechstrichterliche Finanzrechtsprechung
0018-3067 Hoeden & Boetiek†
0018-3075 Tidsskriftet den Hoegre Skolen *see* 0332-7167
0018-3083 Die Hoehere Schule†
0018-3091 Die Hoehle
0018-3105 Hoehlenpost
0018-3113 Hoer Zu
0018-3121 Hoergeschaedigte Kinder
0018-3156 Hoesch *changed to* Estel.
0018-3164 Hoffheimer Nachrichten†
0018-3172 Hofstra Chronicle *changed to* Chronicle (Hempstead).
0018-3180 Hog Farm Management
0018-3199 Hog Guide†
0018-3210 Hogar
0018-3229 Hogar Cristiano
0018-3245 Hohe Bruecke
0018-3253 Hohenzollerische Heimat
0018-327X Hoiku No Tomo
0018-3288 Hoja de Informacion Economica
0018-3296 Hoja del Lunes de Lugo
0018-330X Hoja del Lunes de Orense
0018-3326 Hoja Tisiologica
0018-3334 Hoejskolebladet
0018-3342 Hoken no Kagaku
0018-3350 Health and Physical Education
0018-3369 Hokenfu no Kekkaku Tenbo
0018-3377 Hokkaido Journal of Orthopedic & Traumatic Surgery
0018-3385 Hokkaido Veterinary Medical Association. Journal
0018-3393 Hokkaido Kyoiku Daigaku Kiyo. Dai-2-Bu, B. Seibutsugaku, Chigaku, Nogaku-Hen
0018-3415 Hokkaido Nogyo Shikenjo Kenkyu Hokoku
0018-3431 Hokkaido Toshokan Kenkyukai. Kaiho
0018-344X Hokkaido University. Faculty of Agriculture. Journal
0018-3458 Hokkaido University. Faculty of Fisheries. Bulletin
0018-3466 Hokkaido University. Faculty of Fisheries. Memoirs
0018-3474 Hokkaido University. Faculty of Science. Journal. Series 4: Geology and Mineralogy
0018-3482 Hokkaido University. Faculty of Science. Journal. Series 1: Mathematics *see* 0385-4035
0018-3490 Agriculture in Hokkaido
0018-3504 Hokusuishi Geppo *see* 0914-6849
0018-3512 Holectechniek†
0018-3520 Holiday *changed to* Travel - Holiday.
0018-3539 Holiday Inn *changed to* Holiday Inn Companion.
0018-3555 Holidays in Romania
0018-3563 Holland Herald
0018-3571 Holland Shipbuilding, Marine Engineering and Shipping Herald *see* 0923-666X
0018-358X Holland Shipping and Trading *changed to* Holland's Export Magazine.
0018-3598 Hollandia Variat†
0018-3601 Hollands Maandblad
0018-361X Hollandse Huis†
0018-3628 Hollar†
0018-3636 Hollingsworth Register
0018-3644 Hollins Critic
0018-3652 Hollins Symposium†
0018-3660 Hollywood Reporter
0018-3687 Holstein-Friesian Journal *see* 0710-1309
0018-3695 Holstein-Friesian World *see* 0199-4239
0018-3709 Holsteiner Pferd *changed to* Pferde.
0018-3717 Holt Investment Advisory *see* 1047-9791
0018-3725 Holy Cross. Newsletter
0018-3741 Holy Name Monthly†
0018-375X Holz-Kunststoff *see* 0933-4580
0018-3768 Holz als Roh- und Werkstoff
0018-3776 Holz im Handwerk
0018-3784 Holz - Kurier
0018-3792 Holz-Zentralblatt
0018-3806 Holzarbeiter-Zeitung
0018-3814 Holzbau
0018-3822 H O B - Die Holzbearbeitung
0018-3830 Holzforschung
0018-3849 Holzforschung und Holzverwertung
0018-3857 Holzindustrie†
0018-3865 Die Holzschwelle
0018-3881 Holztechnologie
0018-3911 Home and Auto Retailer *changed to* Aftermarket Business.
0018-392X Home and Building *see* 0110-098X
0018-3938 Home & Country
0018-3946 Home and Family
0018-3954 Home and Garden Supply Merchandiser *see* 0195-1386
0018-3962 Home and Health *changed to* Vitalite.
0018-3970 Home Builder News†
0018-3997 Home Business Digest *changed to* Mail Order Selling & Small Business World.
0018-4039 Home Finders Directory
0018-4047 Home Furnishings Daily *see* 0162-9158
0018-4055 Home Goods Retailing†
0018-4063 Home Improvements *see* 0885-8039
0018-4071 Home Life
0018-408X Home Missions *see* 0279-5345
0018-411X Home Office Report†
0018-4128 Home Rule†
0018-4152 Homecare
0018-4179 Homefront I A D†
0018-4195 Perspectives-In Long Term Care†
0018-4209 Homemakers's Magazine
0018-4217 Homemakers Guide†
0018-4225 Homeopathie Francaise
0018-4233 Homes and Gardens
0018-4241 Homes Overseas
0018-425X Homesewing Trade News
0018-4268 Homiletic and Pastoral Review
0018-4276 Homiletische Monatshefte
0018-4284 Homin Ukrainy
0018-4292 Homine†
0018-4314 Homme Libre
0018-4322 Homme Nouveau
0018-4349 Hommes et Commerce - Horizons et Conjoncture *see* 0223-5846
0018-4357 Hommes et Fonderie
0018-4365 Cahiers Nord Africains *see* 0223-3290
0018-4381 Hommes et Techniques†
0018-439X Hommes et Terres du Nord
0018-4403 Hommes Libres
0018-4411 Hommes Volants
0018-442X Homo
0018-4446 Homeopathic Sandesh†
0018-4454 Homoeopathic Science Quarterly†
0018-4489 Homoeopathisch Maandblad *changed to* Homoeopathisch Tijdschrift.
0018-4500 Hon & Han
0018-4527 Hondenwereld
0018-4535 Honduras Pediatricia
0018-4543 Honest Ulsterman
0018-4551 Honey
0018-456X Honeyguide
0018-4578 Hong Kong Economic Papers
0018-4586 Hong Kong Enterprise
0018-4594 Hong Kong Manager
0018-4616 Hong Kong Travel Bulletin
0018-4632 Honnold Library Record†
0018-4640 Honolulu Magazine *see* 0441-2044
0018-4659 Honolulu Weekly Snooper†
0018-4675 Honourable Company of Master Mariners. Journal
0018-4683 Hoof Beats
0018-4691 Dimensie†
0018-4705 Hoofdlijnen
0018-4721 Hoosharar†
0018-473X Hoosier Banker
0018-4748 Hoosier Farmer
0018-4756 Hoosier Genealogist
0018-4764 Hoosier Independent
0018-4772 Hoosier Legionnaire
0018-4780 Hoosier Outdoors
0018-4799 Hoosier Purchasor
0018-4810 Hoosier Schoolmaster
0018-4829 Hooyce†
0018-4837 Hopeapeili†
0018-4845 Hopfen - Rundschau
0018-4853 Hopital d'Aujourd'hui *see* 0317-3739
0018-4861 Hopital a Paris
0018-487X Hopitaux Civils et Militaires. Gazette†
0018-4888 Hoppe-Seyler's Zeitschrift fuer Physiologische Chemie *changed to* Biological Chemistry Hoppe-Seyler.
0018-4896 Hoppenstedt-Monatskurstabellen *see* 0174-1284
0018-4918 Horatio Alger Newsboy *see* 0028-9396
0018-4934 Hoerelsen
0018-4942 Die Horen
0018-4977 Horizon (Tuscaloosa)
0018-4985 Horizons *changed to* A C A News.
0018-5000 Horizons in Leisure†
0018-5019 Horizons Unlimited
0018-5027 Horizontes
0018-5043 Hormone and Metabolic Research
0018-5051 Hormones *see* 0301-0163
0018-506X Hormones and Behavior
0018-5078 Horn Book Magazine
0018-5086 Hornet
0018-5116 Dell Horoscope
0018-5124 Horoscope Quotidien Eclair
0018-5132 Hors Cote
0018-5140 Horse and Hound
0018-5159 Horse & Rider
0018-5167 Horse and Show Inc†
0018-5175 Horse Lover's Magazine *changed to* Horse Lover's National Magazine.
0018-5191 Horse World
0018-5205 Horsefeathers *see* 0899-5877
0018-5213 Horseless Carriage Gazette
0018-5221 Horseman†
0018-523X Horseman and Fair World
0018-5256 Horsemen's Journal
0018-5264 Horsetrader
0018-5272 Horticultura *see* 0906-7043
0018-5280 Horticultural Abstracts
0018-5299 Horticultural Research *changed to* Crop Research.
0018-5302 Horticultural Society of New York. Bulletin†
0018-5329 Horticulture
0018-5337 Hortikultura
0018-5345 HortScience
0018-5361 Hose & Nozzle†
0018-537X Hosiery Abstracts *see* 0260-8553
0018-5388 Hosiery and Textile Journal
0018-5396 Hosiery and Underwear
0018-540X Hosiery Newsletter *see* 0742-8065
0018-5418 Hosiery *changed to* Hosiery Report Weekly.
0018-5426 British Knitting Industry *see* 0307-2517
0018-5442 Arquivos dos Hospitais e da Faculdade de Ciencias Medicas da Santa Casa de Sao Paulo
0018-5477 Hospital *see* 0953-8534
0018-5485 El Hospital (Cincinnati)
0018-5493 Hospital Abstract Service†
0018-5507 Hospital Abstracts *changed to* Health Service Abstracts.
0018-5515 Hospital and Health Care *changed to* Australian Hospital.
0018-5523 Hospital Administration *see* 8750-3735
0018-5531 Hospital Administration

ISSN

ISSN INDEX 5387

ISSN	Title
0018-554X	Hospital Administration in Canada *see* 0226-5788
0018-5558	Hospital Affairs in New York State†
0018-5566	Health Care Product News *changed to* Health CareSystems.
0018-5574	Hospital Association of New York State. News
0018-5582	Hospital Building and Engineering *see* 0300-5720
0018-5590	Hospital Bureau Market News†
0018-5612	Hospital de Mataro. Anales†
0018-5620	Hospital Equipment & Supplies
0018-5639	Hospital Accounting *see* 0735-0732
0018-5647	Hospital for Joint Diseases Orthopaedic Institute. Bulletin
0018-5655	Hospital Formulary Management *see* 0098-6909
0018-5663	Hospital Forum *see* 0899-9287
0018-568X	Hospital General†
0018-5701	Hospital Highlights *changed to* Hospital Highlights (Year).
0018-571X	Hospital International†
0018-5728	Hospital Law Manual and Quarterly Service *changed to* Hospital Law Manual. Attorneys.
0018-5736	Hospital Literature Index
0018-5760	Hospital Oftalmologico de Nuestra Senora de la Luz. Boletin
0018-5779	Hospital Pharmacy *changed to* White Sheet.
0018-5787	Hospital Pharmacy
0018-5795	Hospital Physician
0018-5817	Hospital Progress *see* 0882-1577
0018-5825	Hospital Purchasing *see* 0300-5461
0018-5833	Hospital R.S.A.
0018-5841	Hospital Supervision *see* 0363-020X
0018-585X	Hospital Supervisor's Bulletin
0018-5868	Hospital Topics
0018-5876	Hospital Tribune†
0018-5884	Hospital Vargas. Archivos
0018-5906	Hospitales y Clinicas
0018-5914	Hospitalia
0018-5922	Hospitalier
0018-5930	Hospitalis
0018-5949	Hospitality *changed to* Hospitality Foodservice.
0018-5973	Hospitals
0018-5981	Hospitals' Association Journal†
0018-599X	Hospodar
0018-6007	Hot Car *see* 0265-6183
0018-6023	Hot Rod Industry News†
0018-6031	Hot Rod
0018-6066	Hotel *changed to* Hotel Voice.
0018-6074	Hotel and Club Voice *changed to* Hotel Voice.
0018-6082	Hotel and Motel Management
0018-6104	Catering and Hotel Management†
0018-6139	Hotel Gazette of South Australia
0018-6147	Hotel Herald†
0018-6171	Hotel Motel and Restaurant†
0018-618X	Hotel, Motel Buyer's Directory†
0018-6201	Hotel og Restaurant *changed to* Hotel Restaurant og Fritid.
0018-621X	Hotel Restaurant
0018-6228	Hotel Review *changed to* Hotel Review of Western Australia.
0018-6279	Hoteles de Colombia
0018-6287	Hotelier
0018-6295	Hotelier & Caterer (Cape Town)
0018-6309	Hotellerie Magazine
0018-6317	Hotelli- ja Ravintolalehti *see* 0357-749X
0018-6333	Hotelnews
0018-6341	Practice in Prosthodontics
0018-6368	Houille Blanche
0018-6384	Hounds and Hunting
0018-6392	House & Bungalow
0018-6406	House and Garden *changed to* H G.
0018-6414	House and Home *see* 0161-0619
0018-6422	House Beautiful
0018-6430	House Beautiful's Building Manual
0018-6457	House Beautiful's Home Decorating *changed to* House Beautiful's Home Remodeling & Decorating.
0018-6465	House Beautiful's Home Remodeling *changed to* House Beautiful's Home Remodeling & Decorating.
0018-6473	House Buyer
0018-6481	House of Tang Family News†
0018-649X	House Physician Reporter†
0018-6503	Housecraft *see* 0264-9683
0018-6554	Housing Affairs Letter
0018-6562	Housing and People†
0018-6570	Housing and Planning References†
0018-6589	Housing and Planning Review *changed to* Housing and Planning Review.
0018-6600	Housing and Urban Affairs†
0018-6619	Housing and Urban Development Trends†
0018-6627	Housing Authority Journal
0018-6635	Housing Finance
0018-6643	Housing Quarterly *changed to* Building Review.
0018-6651	Housing Review
0018-666X	H D A World†
0018-6678	Houston *see* 0745-9807
0018-6686	Houston Geological Society. Bulletin
0018-6694	Houston Law Review
0018-6708	Houston, Texas. Museum of Fine Arts Bulletin
0018-6732	Houtwereld
0018-6740	Houtz†
0018-6767	Hoverfoil News
0018-6775	Hovering Craft and Hydrofoil *see* 0954-3988
0018-6805	Howard Collector†
0018-6813	Howard Law Journal
0018-6856	Hoy Dia
0018-6899	Hromklat
0018-6902	Hrvatska Revija
0018-6910	Hrvatski Katolicki Glasnik
0018-6929	Hsien Tai Hsueh Yuan *see* 1015-8383
0018-6937	Hsin Ju Chia
0018-6945	Hsinhua Selected News Items *changed to* Hsinhua Weekly.
0018-6953	Huaral
0018-6961	Hubbard School System Office of Curriculum and Instruction. Digest Newsletter *changed to* Insight (Hubbard).
0018-6988	Hudba a Zvukt
0018-6996	Hudebni Rozhledy
0018-7003	Hudebni Veda
0018-702X	Hudson Review
0018-7054	Ovum
0018-7070	Huisarts en Wetenschap
0018-7089	Huisgenoot
0018-7097	Huismuziek
0018-7100	Huisvrou
0018-7119	Huizer Kerkblad
0018-7127	Hule Mexicano y Plasticos
0018-7135	Human Side *changed to* Human Side of Supervision.
0018-7143	Human Biology (Detroit)
0018-7151	Human Context†
0018-716X	Human Development
0018-7178	Human Ecology Forum
0018-7194	Human Events
0018-7208	Human Factors
0018-7216	Human Geography
0018-7224	Human Industrial Design
0018-7232	Human Issue *changed to* New Kent Quarterly.
0018-7240	Human Mosaic
0018-7259	Human Organization
0018-7267	Human Relations
0018-7283	Human Relations News of Chicago
0018-7291	Human Relations Training News *changed to* Social Change.
0018-7305	Human Voice *see* 0145-983X
0018-7321	Humanat
0018-733X	Humane Society of the United States. News *see* 1059-1621
0018-7348	Humangenetik *see* 0340-6717
0018-7356	Humanidades
0018-7364	Humanisme
0018-7372	Humanisme et Entreprise
0018-7380	Humanist *see* 0306-512X
0018-7399	Humanist
0018-7402	Humanist in Canada
0018-7410	Humanist News *changed to* Humanist News.
0018-7429	Humanist Outlook
0018-7437	Quest†
0018-7453	Humanitas†
0018-7461	Humanitas
0018-7488	Humanitas†
0018-7496	Humanitas *see* 0193-2748
0018-750X	Humanite Rouge *see* 0754-281X
0018-7518	Humanities Scientific *changed to* Documents et Recherches-Sciences.
0018-7526	Humanities
0018-7534	Humanities. Classes de Lettres. Sections Modernes *changed to* Documents et Recherches.
0018-7542	Humanities Association Review†
0018-7550	Humanities. Classes de Lettres. Section Classiques *changed to* Documents et Recherches.
0018-7569	Humanities. Cycle d'Observation. Classes de 4 et 3 *changed to* Documents et Recherches.
0018-7577	Humanities in the South
0018-7585	Humberside
0018-7615	Humboldt (Spanish Edition)
0018-7623	Humboldt (Portuguese Edition)
0018-7631	Humboldtglocke
0018-7666	Humpty Dumpty's Magazine for Little Children *see* 0273-7590
0018-7682	Die Hundewelt
0018-7690	Hundsport
0018-7712	Hungarian Agricultural Review
0018-7720	Hungarian Building Bulletin†
0018-7739	Hungarian Exporter *see* 0238-602X
0018-7747	Hungarian Foreign Trade†
0018-7755	Hungarian Heavy Industries *see* 0139-035X
0018-7763	Hungarian Review *see* 0209-5386
0018-7771	Hungarian Technical Abstracts *see* 0237-0808
0018-778X	Hungarian Trade Union News
0018-7798	Hungarofilm Bulletin *changed to* Hungarian Cinema.
0018-7801	Hungary. Kozponti Statisztikai Hivatal. Ipari es Epitoipari Statisztikai Ertesito *see* 0239-1589
0018-781X	Hungary. Kozponti Statisztikai Hivatal. Statisztikai Havi Kozlemenyek
0018-7828	Hungary. Kozponti Statisztikai Hivatal. Teruleti Statisztika
0018-7852	Hunterdon Historical Newsletter
0018-7860	Hunter's Horn
0018-7879	Hunting Dog†
0018-7887	Hunting Group Review
0018-7895	Huntington Library Quarterly
0018-7909	Huon News
0018-7917	Huron Church News
0018-7925	Huron Road Hospital. Scientific Bulletin *changed to* Huron Road Hospital. Scientific Bulletin.
0018-7933	Hurra Juventus
0018-795X	Hus og Hjem *changed to* Ugebladet Hus og Hjem.
0018-7968	Husbyggaren
0018-7976	Huset Vaart
0018-7984	Husfreyjan
0018-7992	Hushaallslaerarent
0018-800X	Husipar
0018-8018	Husmandshjemmet *changed to* Landbrugsmagasinet.
0018-8026	Husmodernt
0018-8034	Husmorbladet
0018-8050	Hutmacher-, Modisten- und Schirrmmacher-Zeitung
0018-8069	Hutnicke Listy
0018-8077	Hutnik *changed to* Hutnik - Wiadomosci Hutnicze.
0018-8085	Hutoipar
0018-8093	Hvedekorn
0018-8107	Hvidvare-Nyt
0018-8115	Hydatat
0018-8131	Hydraulic Pneumatic Power *see* 0950-1487
0018-814X	Hydraulics & Pneumatics
0018-8158	Hydrobiologia
0018-8166	Hydrobiological Journal
0018-8182	Hydrocarbon News. *see* 0031-6466
0018-8190	Hydrocarbon Processing
0018-8212	Hydrospace *changed to* Offshore Services & Technology.
0018-8220	Hydrotechnical Construction
0018-8239	Hygien Forum†
0018-8247	Higiena i Zdraveopazvane
0018-8263	Hygienist
0018-8271	Hymn
0018-8298	Hymylehti *see* 0355-4317
0018-831X	Hyperbaric Medicine Newsletter *see* 0889-0242
0018-8328	Hyperion (Austin)
0018-8336	Hyphen
0018-8344	Hypnosis Quarterly *see* 0882-6072
0018-8352	Hypothese†
0018-8360	Hyresgaesten
0018-8387	I A G Journal *see* 0378-7206
0018-8395	T A M†
0018-8409	I A P A News
0018-8425	Institute of Administrative Research. Research Bulletin *changed to* H M L I Research Bulletin.
0018-8441	I A S L I C Bulletin
0018-845X	I A S L I C Newsletter
0018-8468	I A S L News for You (Illinois Association of School Librarians) *changed to* I A M E News for You.
0018-8476	I A T U L Proceedings *see* 0950-4117
0018-8484	I A U News *changed to* Interamericana.
0018-8492	International Association of University Professors & Lecturers. Communication†
0018-8506	Bulletin d'Information de la Region Parisienne *see* 0396-9975
0018-8514	I and N Reporter
0018-8522	I B A Municipal Statistical Bulletin†
0018-8530	I.B.A. News†
0018-8549	I B A Statistical Bulletin†
0018-8557	I B B - Information†
0018-8565	I B B Bulletin *changed to* I B E Bulletin.
0018-8573	I B B R I S *see* 0265-3036
0018-8581	I B E A S
0018-859X	I B E W - A F L - C I O. Local 1470 Journal
0018-8603	I.B. Flash-Edition Batiment†
0018-8611	I B I S (Briefing Service)
0018-862X	I B L A
0018-8638	I B M Iran News Bulletin†
0018-8646	I B M Journal of Research and Development
0018-8654	I B M Kwartaalschrift *changed to* I B M Nieuws.
0018-8662	I B M Nachrichten
0018-8670	I B M Systems Journal
0018-8697	I B Nachrichten
0018-8700	I B P Boletim *changed to* Petroleo e Petroquimica.
0018-8735	I C A Information†
0018-8743	I C A Information Bulletin *changed to* I C A Regional Bulletin.
0018-8751	I C A News†
0018-876X	I C A Newsletter
0018-8778	I C A O Bulletin *changed to* I C A O Journal.
0018-8786	Icare
0018-8794	Instituto Colombiano Agropecuario. Revista I C A
0018-8808	I C A S A L S Newsletter
0018-8816	I C A T U Review
0018-8824	I C B
0018-8832	I C C News *changed to* I C C Information.
0018-8840	I C C Newsletter *changed to* I B I Newsletter.
0018-8859	I C C Practitioners' Journal *see* 8756-9302
0018-8867	I C C W News Bulletin
0018-8875	I C D Letterette

ISSN INDEX

ISSN	Title
0018-8883	Institut Canadien d'Education des Adultes. Bulletin *changed to* I C E A Bulletin de Liaison.
0018-8891	I.C.E.A. Cahiers†
0018-8913	I C F Quarterly
0018-8921	I C F T U Economic & Social Bulletin†
0018-8948	I C I A Information Bulletin†
0018-8972	I C N Calling†
0018-8980	I C O F T News Review
0018-8999	I C O M News
0018-9006	I C P A Quarterly Bulletin *changed to* I C P A Quarterly.
0018-9014	I C P Quarterly *see* 0272-1171
0018-9030	I C S I D Information Bulletin *see* 0145-2118
0018-9049	I C S S R Newsletter
0018-9065	I C V A News†
0018-9073	I D B Newsletter†
0018-9081	I D I A†
0018-909X	I D O C International Documentation on the Contemporary Church *see* 0160-7553
0018-9103	I D O R T†
0018-9111	Probleme de Informare si Documentare
0018-912X	Discover the Bible
0018-9138	I E C Bulletin
0018-9146	I.E.E. - I.E.R.E. Proceedings - India
0018-9154	I E E E Almanack
0018-9162	I E E E Computer *changed to* Computer.
0018-9197	I E E E Journal of Quantum Electronics
0018-9200	I E E E Journal of Solid State Circuits
0018-9219	Institute of Electrical and Electronics Engineers. Proceedings
0018-9235	I E E E Spectrum
0018-9243	I E E E Student Journal†
0018-9251	I E E E Transactions on Aerospace and Electronic Systems
0018-926X	I E E E Transactions on Antennas and Propagation
0018-9278	I E E E Transactions on Audio and Electroacoustics *see* 1053-587X
0018-9286	I E E E Transactions on Automatic Control
0018-9294	I E E E Transactions on Biomedical Engineering
0018-9308	I E E E Transactions on Broadcast and Television Receivers *see* 0098-3063
0018-9316	I E E E Transactions on Broadcasting
0018-9324	I E E E Transactions on Circuit Theory *see* 1057-7122
0018-9324	I E E E Transactions on Circuit Theory *see* 1057-7130
0018-9332	I E E E Transactions on Communication Technology *see* 0090-6778
0018-9340	I E E E Transactions on Computers
0018-9359	I E E E Transactions on Education
0018-9367	I E E E Transactions on Electrical Insulation
0018-9375	I E E E Transactions on Electromagnetic Compatibility
0018-9383	I E E E Transactions on Electron Devices
0018-9391	I E E E Transactions on Engineering Management
0018-9405	I E E E Transactions on Engineering Writing and Speech *see* 0361-1434
0018-9413	I E E E Transactions on Geoscience Electronics *see* 0196-2892
0018-9421	I E E E Transactions on Industrial Electronics and Control Instrumentation *see* 0278-0046
0018-943X	I E E E Transactions on Industry and General Applications *see* 0093-9994
0018-9448	I E E E Transactions on Information Theory
0018-9456	I E E E Transactions on Instrumentation and Measurement
0018-9464	I E E E Transactions on Magnetics
0018-9472	I E E E Transactions on Systems, Man and Cybernetics
0018-9480	I E E E Transactions on Microwave Theory and Techniques
0018-9499	I E E E Transactions on Nuclear Science
0018-9502	I E E E Transactions on Parts, Materials and Packaging *see* 0148-6411
0018-9510	I E E E Transactions on Power Apparatus and Systems *see* 0885-8977
0018-9510	I E E E Transactions on Power Apparatus and Systems *see* 0885-8969
0018-9510	I E E E Transactions on Power Apparatus and Systems *see* 0885-8950
0018-9529	I E E E Transactions on Reliability
0018-9537	I E E E Transactions on Sonics and Ultrasonics *see* 0885-3010
0018-9545	I E E E Transactions on Vehicular Technology
0018-9553	I E E News *changed to* I E E Review.
0018-9561	I E E T E Bulletin *changed to* Electronics and Electrical Engineering.
0018-957X	I E N Pubblicazioni
0018-9596	I E Review
0018-9618	I.E.S. Lighting Review†
0018-9626	I E S P E. Boletim†
0018-9634	I F A N Bulletin. Serie A: Sciences Naturelles
0018-9642	I F A N Bulletin. Serie B: Sciences Humaines
0018-9650	I F A P News - F I P A Nouvelles *changed to* World Agriculture - I F A P News.
0018-9685	I F L A News *see* 0340-0352
0018-9693	I F L - Mitteilungen†
0018-9707	I F L Nieuws
0018-9715	I F M - S E I Bulletin
0018-9723	I F M A News
0018-9731	I F O Studien
0018-974X	I F O Schnelldienst
0018-9758	I.F. Stone's Weekly†
0018-9766	I G A Grocergram
0018-9774	I G C Monthly†
0018-9782	I G F - Journal
0018-9790	I G T - Nieuws†
0018-9804	I G U Bulletin
0018-9820	I H I Engineering Review
0018-9839	I H K Wuppertal. Wirtschaftliche Mitteilungen
0018-9847	I.H.V.E. Journal *changed to* Building Services.
0018-9855	I I C
0018-9863	I I C A. Documentacao
0018-9871	I I E Report†
0018-988X	Insurance Institute for Highway Safety. Status Report
0018-9898	I.I.R.B.†
0018-9936	I K Z *changed to* I K Z - Haustechnik.
0018-9944	I L A Catalyst *see* 0730-711X
0018-9952	I L A Intercambio Latinoamericano†
0018-9960	I L A R News
0018-9979	I L A Reporter
0018-9995	I L P A Reporter *changed to* I L C A Reporter.
0019-0012	I M C Journal
0019-0020	I M M Abstracts *changed to* I M M Abstracts and Index.
0019-0063	I M S Bulletin
0019-0071	I M Z Bulletin *changed to* Music in the Media - I M Z Bulletin.
0019-008X	Imboniselo
0019-0136	I N F O
0019-0144	I N F O Journal
0019-0152	I N P A Advertising Newsletter *see* 0896-1441
0019-0160	International Newspaper Promotion Association Advertising Copy Service Newsletter†
0019-0179	Inpho
0019-0187	I N P S Boletim Informativo *changed to* Informe I N P S.
0019-0195	I N P S Mensario Estatistico *changed to* I N A M P S em Dados.
0019-0209	France. Institut National de la Statistique et des Etudes Economiques. Annales *see* 0769-489X
0019-0217	Inspel
0019-0225	Argentina. Instituto Nacional de Tecnologia Industrial. Boletin I N T I *see* 0325-934X
0019-0233	I N T Informativo
0019-0241	Inqabayokulinda
0019-025X	I P A Forum†
0019-0268	I P A Review *see* 1030-4177
0019-0276	I P A S E Biblioteca Informa
0019-0292	I P E G. Boletim Informativo†
0019-0314	I P I Report
0019-0330	I P M Digest†
0019-0349	Instituut voor Plantenziektenkundig Onderzoek. Mededeling†
0019-0357	I P P F Medical Bulletin
0019-0365	International Philosophical Quarterly
0019-039X	I P S F News Bulletin
0019-0403	I P S S Bulletin
0019-0411	I.P.V.D.F. Boletim Mensal†
0019-042X	I R A L
0019-0446	I R B Revista
0019-0454	I.R. Concepts†
0019-0462	I.R.I. Journal†
0019-0497	I R M P Impact†
0019-0500	I R R A Newsletter
0019-0535	Workers' Power†
0019-0543	I S A C S Bulletin†
0019-0551	Instrumentation Index†
0019-056X	I S A L Abstracts†
0019-0578	I S A Transactions
0019-0586	I S B A Journal
0019-0594	Iscor News
0019-0624	I S E A Communique
0019-0632	Indian Standards Institution Bulletin *see* 0970-2628
0019-0640	Standard and Poor's I S L Daily Stock Price Index. American Stock Exchange. *changed to* Standard & Poor's Daily Stock Price Record. American Exchange.
0019-0659	Standard and Poor's I S L Daily Stock Price Index. New York Stock Exchange *changed to* Standard & Poor's Daily Stock Price Record. New York Stock Exchange.
0019-0691	I S S Letter *changed to* T A I S S A Letter.
0019-0713	I S T A News Bulletin
0019-073X	I T
0019-0748	I T A Bulletin *changed to* Institut du Transport Aerien. Monthly Bulletin.
0019-0756	I T A Bulletin†
0019-0772	I T A - Engenharia†
0019-0780	I T A Studies
0019-0799	I T F Newsletter *changed to* I T F News.
0019-0810	I T L†
0019-0829	I T L Review of Applied Linguistics
0019-0837	I T Novine
0019-0845	I T R
0019-0853	I T U Review
0019-0861	I U E News
0019-087X	I U L A Newsletter *changed to* Local Government Newsletter.
0019-0888	I U S Y Survey *changed to* I U S Y Newsletter.
0019-0896	I V L - Nytt
0019-090X	I.V.-Nieuws *changed to* Vorm.
0019-0918	I V S
0019-0926	I Y F European Bulletin†
0019-0934	Iade
0019-0942	Iatrika Pepragmena
0019-0950	Iatriki
0019-0977	Ibarske Novosti
0019-0993	Ibero-Romania
0019-1000	Ibid
0019-1019	Ibis
0019-1027	Icarus
0019-1035	Icarus
0019-1043	Ice
0019-1051	Ice Cap News
0019-106X	Ice Cream & Frozen Confectionery
0019-1078	Hagtidindi
0019-1094	Iceland Review
0019-1108	Ichthyologica
0019-1140	Iconolatre
0019-1159	Idaho Agricultural Science†
0019-1167	Idaho Business and Economic Review†
0019-1175	Idaho Transportation Department. Highway Information
0019-1183	Idaho Education News *changed to* I E A Reporter (Year).
0019-1205	Idaho Law Review
0019-1213	Idaho Librarian
0019-1221	Idaho Pharmacist
0019-1248	Idaho Wildlife Review *changed to* Idaho Wildlife.
0019-1256	Idaho Woodland Farmer†
0019-1264	Idaho Yesterdays
0019-1272	Idea†
0019-1280	Idea
0019-1299	Idea
0019-1310	Idea Source Guide
0019-1329	Idea Zoofila†
0019-1345	Ideal Companion
0019-1353	Ideal Education
0019-1361	Ideal Home
0019-137X	Ideals
0019-1388	Ideas†
0019-1426	Ideen des Exakten Wissens *see* 0340-0220
0019-1434	Idees pour Tous *changed to* Idees pour Tous - Speciale Hebdo.
0019-1442	Ideggyogyaszati Szemle
0019-1450	Identification News
0019-1485	Idiom†
0019-1507	Idisze Szrift†
0019-1523	Idrijski Razgledi
0019-1531	Iets
0019-154X	If†
0019-1566	Wirtschaftsbilderheft BRD und Ausland *see* 0170-3617
0019-1574	Igaku Hyoron
0019-1582	Igaku to Fukuin
0019-1604	Igaku to Seibutsugaku
0019-1612	Igakushi Kenkyu
0019-1620	Revista de Igiena, Bacteriologie, Virusologie, Parazitologie, Pneumoftiziologie. Igiena
0019-1639	Igiene e Sanita Pubblica
0019-1647	Igiene Mentale
0019-1655	Igiene Moderna
0019-1663	Igitur Revista Literaria
0019-1671	Iglesia Evangelica del Rio de la Plata. Revista Parroquial
0019-168X	Igloos *changed to* Revue Quart Monde.
0019-1698	Ignis *see* 0282-0595
0019-1701	Ihre Brigitte†
0019-171X	Ija Webonere
0019-1728	Ikai Jiho
0019-1736	Ikakikai Gaku Zasshi
0019-1744	Ikont
0019-1752	Ikont
0019-1779	Ilanga
0019-1795	Iliff Review†
0019-1809	Illiana Genealogist
0019-1817	Illiana Research Report†
0019-1825	Illinet Output *changed to* C S O Update.
0019-1833	Illinois Agricultural Economics†
0019-1841	Illinois Alumni News *changed to* Illinois Quarterly.
0019-185X	Illinois Banker
0019-1868	Illinois Baptist
0019-1876	Illinois Bar Journal
0019-1892	Illinois Beverage Journal
0019-1906	Illinois Braille Messenger (Inkprint Edition)
0019-1914	Illinois Building News
0019-1922	Illinois Business Review
0019-1930	Illinois Central Gulf News *changed to* Main Line News.
0019-1949	Illinois County and Township Official
0019-1957	Illinois Courts Bulletin
0019-1973	Illinois Dental Journal
0019-1981	Illinois Business and Economic Development *see* 0161-7885

ISSN INDEX 5389

0019-199X Illinois. Department of Public Health. Division of Disease Control. Weekly Report *changed to* Illinois. Department of Public Health. Division of Disease Control. Monthly Report.
0019-2015 Illinois Engineer
0019-2023 Illinois English Bulletin
0019-2031 Illinois Geographical Society. Bulletin
0019-204X Illinois Health Messenger†
0019-2058 Illinois History
0019-2082 Illinois Journal of Mathematics
0019-2090 Illinois Labor Bulletin†
0019-2104 Illinois Libraries
0019-2112 Illinois Master Plumber Magazine
0019-2120 Illinois Medical Journal *changed to* Illinois Medicine.
0019-2139 Illinois Municipal Review
0019-2147 Illinois Music Educator
0019-2155 Illinois Parks & Recreation
0019-2163 Illinois Pharmacist *see* 0195-2099
0019-2171 Illinois Police Association. Official Journal
0019-2201 Illinois Research
0019-221X Illinois School Board Journal
0019-2228 Illinois School Research *see* 0163-822X
0019-2236 Illinois Schools Journal
0019-2252 Illinois State Academy of Science. Transactions
0019-2260 Illinois State Chamber of Commerce. Current Report *changed to* Voice of Illinois Business.
0019-2287 Illinois State Historical Society. Journal *see* 0748-8149
0019-2295 Illinois Quarterly†
0019-2309 Illinois Truck News
0019-2317 Illinois Wildlife
0019-2325 Illovo Digest†
0019-2333 Illuminating Engineering *see* 0360-6325
0019-2333 Illuminating Engineering *see* 0099-4480
0019-2341 Illuminating Engineering Institute of Japan. Journal
0019-235X Illumination Annual *changed to* Divine Path.
0019-2368 Illuminations *see* 0046-5410
0019-2384 Illuminotecnica
0019-2392 Illustrated Bristol News
0019-2406 Illustrated Carpenter and Builder *see* 0954-0652
0019-2414 Illustrated Life Rhodesia *changed to* Illustrated Life & Talk.
0019-2422 Illustrated London News
0019-2430 Illustrated Weekly of India
0019-2457 Illustration 63
0019-2465 Illustrator
0019-2473 Illustrazione Pubblicitaria†
0019-2481 Illustre Protestant†
0019-249X Illustrerad Motor Sport†
0019-2511 Illustrierte Rundschau der Gendarmerie *changed to* Illustrierte Rundschau der Oesterreichischen Gendarmerie.
0019-252X Ilmailu
0019-2538 Ilocos Review
0019-2546 I L T A M Newsletter
0019-2562 Ilusion y Aventura†
0019-2570 Ilustrovana Politika
0019-2597 Im Lande der Bibel
0019-2651 Image Technology†
0019-2694 Imago†
0019-2708 Imballaggio
0019-2716 Imbongi
0019-2724 Imfama (Inkprint Edition)
0019-2732 Imkerfreund
0019-2740 Immagini/Forma *changed to* Immagini/Technika.
0019-2759 Immanuel's Witness *see* 0308-5252
0019-2767 Immex†
0019-2775 Immigration Bar Bulletin *see* 0884-3244
0019-2783 Immortality Newsletter *see* 0362-0085
0019-2791 Immunochemistry *see* 0161-5890
0019-2805 Immunology
0019-2813 Casting Digest
0019-2821 Impact (Wheaton)
0019-2848 Impact (Valley Forge)†
0019-2856 Impact (Columbia)
0019-2864 Impact - Africa†
0019-2872 Impact of Science on Society
0019-2880 Impacto
0019-2899 Impacts
0019-2902 Imparcial
0019-2910 Imperial Oil Review *see* 0700-5156
0019-2929 Impermeabile Europeo†
0019-2945 Impianti Industriali†
0019-2953 Implement & Tractor
0019-2961 Import†
0019-297X Import Bulletin *changed to* Journal of Commerce Import Bulletin.
0019-3003 Impresa Pubblica
0019-3011 Impressions
0019-302X Imprimerie Nouvelle
0019-3038 Imprint (Bristol)
0019-3046 Imprint
0019-3054 Imprint
0019-3062 Imprint (New York)
0019-3089 Improving College and University Teaching *see* 8756-7555
0019-3097 Impuls†
0019-3100 Int
0019-3127 Animaland†
0019-3135 In Brief†
0019-3143 In Britain
0019-3151 In de Rechte Straat
0019-316X In de Waagschaal
0019-3186 In Famiglia
0019-3194 In Jewish Bookland *changed to* Jewish Books in Review.
0019-3216 In Particular†
0019-3224 Printing Industry†
0019-3232 In-Plant Printer *changed to* In-Plant Printer & Electronic Publisher.
0019-3240 In-Plant Reprographics†
0019-3259 In Review†
0019-3267 In Step *changed to* Lutherans in Step.
0019-3283 In Touch (Pinner)
0019-3291 In Transit
0019-3321 In Your Hands
0019-333X Monthly Newspaper Techniques *changed to* Newspaper Techniques.
0019-3364 Incentive Marketing *changed to* Incentive (Akron).
0019-3399 Inchieste di Urbanistica e Architettura
0019-3402 Co-Incidences *see* 0705-4165
0019-3410 Incidenza
0019-3429 Income Opportunities
0019-3437 Income-Tax Journal†
0019-3453 Income Tax Reports
0019-3461 Incomes Data Report
0019-347X Incontri Culturali†
0019-3488 Incontri Meridionali *changed to* Corrispondenza Meridionale.
0019-3496 L'Incontro
0019-3518 Weekly Law Reports
0019-3526 Incorporated Law Society of Northern Ireland. Gazette†
0019-3534 Incorporated Linguist *see* 0268-5965
0019-3542 Incredible Idaho†
0019-3550 Incunable†
0019-3569 I N D A C
0019-3577 Indagationes Mathematicae
0019-3585 Yogoslavia. Savazni Zavod za Statistiku. Indeks
0019-3593 Indonesian Biological and Agricultural Index *changed to* Indonesian Biological and Agricultural Index.
0019-3631 Independent *changed to* Western Sunday Independent.
0019-3658 Independent Adjuster
0019-3666 Independent American
0019-3674 Independent Banker
0019-3682 Independent Coal Operator *changed to* Coal Operator.
0019-3690 Independent College Funds of America Bulletin†
0019-3712 Independent Film Journal *see* 0199-7300
0019-3720 Independent Formosa†
0019-3747 Independent School†
0019-3755 Independent School Bulletin *see* 0145-9635
0019-3763 Independent Shavian
0019-378X Index Analytique†
0019-3798 Index Bibliographique de Botanique Tropicale†
0019-3801 Index Bibliographique du Vide - Vacuum Index†
0019-3828 Index Chemicus Registry System†
0019-3836 Index de la Litterature Nucleaire Francaise†
0019-3844 Index India
0019-3852 Index Indo-Asiaticus
0019-3860 Index: Industrial Extension for the Forest Products Industry†
0019-3879 Index Medicus
0019-3887 Index Medicus Danicus†
0019-3895 Index of Fungi
0019-3909 Index of Dermatology and Dermapathology *see* 0090-1245
0019-3917 Index of Mathematical Papers
0019-3925 Index of New Products†
0019-3933 Index of Rheumatology *see* 0097-921X
0019-3941 Index of Veterinary Specialities
0019-3968 Index to Australian Book Reviews†
0019-3976 Index to Current E E G Literature *see* 0921-884X
0019-3984 Index to Current Malaysian, Singapore, and Brunei Periodicals†
0019-3992 Index to Dental Literature
0019-400X Index to Foreign Legal Periodicals
0019-4018 Index to Forthcoming Russian Books†
0019-4026 Index to Indian Economic Journals
0019-4034 Index to Indian Legal Periodicals
0019-4069 Index to Latin American Periodicals†
0019-4077 Index to Legal Periodicals
0019-4093 Index to Periodical Articles Related to Law
0019-4107 Index to Religious Periodical Literature *see* 0149-8428
0019-4115 Index to the Literature of Magnetism†
0019-4123 Index Veterinarius
0019-4131 Indexer
0019-414X India Book House News†
0019-4158 India Calling
0019-4166 India Cultures Quarterly *changed to* India Cultures.
0019-4174 India. Central Statistical Organization. Monthly Abstract of Statistics
0019-4182 India in Industries†
0019-4204 India. Ministry of Finance. Finance Library. Weekly Bulletin
0019-4212 India News
0019-4220 India Quarterly
0019-4239 India Today and Tomorrow
0019-4247 Indian Academy of Applied Psychology. Journal
0019-4255 Indian Academy of Dentistry. Journal†
0019-4263 Indian Academy of Medical Sciences. Annals *see* 0379-038X
0019-4271 Indian Academy of Philosophy. Journal
0019-4298 Indian Administrative and Management Review *changed to* Indian Review of Management and Future.
0019-4301 Indian Advocate
0019-4328 Indian Agricultural News Digest†
0019-4336 Indian Agriculturist
0019-4344 Journal of Indian and Buddhist Studies
0019-4352 Indian and Eastern Engineer
0019-4360 Indian & Eastern Pharmacy
0019-4379 Indian and Foreign Review
0019-4387 Indian Anthropological Society. Journal
0019-4395 Indian Antiquary†
0019-4409 Indian Architect
0019-4417 Indian Aviation
0019-4425 Indian Bee Journal
0019-4433 Indian Book Industry
0019-4441 Indian Book Review Supplement
0019-445X Indian Books
0019-4476 Indian Business Review†
0019-4484 Indian Cashew Journal
0019-4492 Indian Ceramics
0019-4506 Indian Chemical Engineer
0019-4514 Indian Chemical Journal†
0019-4522 Indian Chemical Society. Journal
0019-4530 Indian Church History Review
0019-4549 Indian Coffee
0019-4557 Indian Communist†
0019-4565 Indian Concrete Journal
0019-4573 Indian Construction News
0019-4581 Indian Cooperative Review
0019-459X Indian Cotton Mills Federation Journal
0019-4603 Indian Dairyman
0019-4611 Indian Dental Association. Journal
0019-462X Indian Drugs
0019-4638 Indian Drugs and Pharmaceuticals Industry
0019-4646 Indian Economic and Social History Review
0019-4654 Indian Economic Diary
0019-4662 Indian Economic Journal
0019-4670 Indian Economic Review
0019-4689 Indian Education
0019-4697 Indian Education Abstracts
0019-4700 Indian Educational Review
0019-4719 Indian Engineering Exporter
0019-4727 Indian-Eskimo Association of Canada Bulletin *see* 0073-6341
0019-4735 Indian Export Trade Journal
0019-4751 Indian Exporter Quarterly†
0019-4778 Indian Farm Mechanization
0019-4786 Indian Farming
0019-4808 Indian Food Packer
0019-4816 Indian Forester
0019-4824 Indian Geographical Journal
0019-4832 Indian Heart Journal
0019-4840 Indian Historian *see* 0199-9052
0019-4867 Indian Homoeopathic Gazette
0019-4875 Indian Horticulture
0019-4883 Indian Hotelier and Caterer†
0019-4905 Indian Institute of Advanced Study, Simla. Bulletin *changed to* I I A S Newsletter.
0019-4913 Indian Institute of Architects. Journal†
0019-4921 Indian Institute of Bankers. Journal
0019-493X Indian Institute of Metals. Transactions
0019-4948 Indian Institute of Public Opinion. Quarterly Economic Report
0019-4956 Indian Institute of Road Transport. Monthly Bulletin
0019-4964 Indian Institute of Science. Journal
0019-4972 Indian Institute of World Culture. Transactions
0019-4980 I I T C Bulletin
0019-4999 Indian Investment Centre. Monthly Newsletter
0019-5006 Indian Journal of Adult Education
0019-5014 Indian Journal of Agricultural Economics
0019-5022 Indian Journal of Agricultural Sciences
0019-5030 Indian Journal of American Studies
0019-5049 Indian Journal of Anaesthesia
0019-5057 Indian Journal of Animal Health
0019-5065 Indian Journal of Applied Chemistry *see* 0019-4522
0019-5073 Indian Journal of Applied Psychology
0019-5081 Indian Journal of Biochemistry *see* 0301-1208
0019-509X Indian Journal of Cancer
0019-5103 Indian Journal of Chemistry *see* 0376-4710
0019-5103 Indian Journal of Chemistry *see* 0376-4699
0019-512X Indian Journal of Commerce
0019-5138 Journal of Communicable Diseases
0019-5146 Indian Journal of Dairy Science
0019-5154 Indian Journal of Dermatology
0019-5162 Indian Journal of Dermatology and Venereology *see* 0378-6323
0019-5170 Indian Journal of Economics
0019-5189 Indian Journal of Experimental Biology
0019-5197 Indian Journal of Experimental Psychology†
0019-5200 Indian Journal of Genetics and Plant Breeding
0019-5219 Indian Journal of Gerontology
0019-5227 Indian Journal of Helminthology
0019-5235 Indian Journal of History of Science

ISSN

0019-5243 Indian Journal of Homoeopathic Medicine
0019-5251 Indian Journal of Horticulture
0019-526X Indian Journal of Hospital Pharmacy
0019-5278 Indian Journal of Industrial Medicine
0019-5286 Indian Journal of Industrial Relations
0019-5294 Indian Journal of International Law
0019-5308 Indian Journal of Labour Economics
0019-5316 Indian Journal of Marketing
0019-5324 Indian Journal of Mathematics
0019-5340 Indian Journal of Medical Research
0019-5359 Indian Journal of Medical Sciences
0019-5367 Indian Journal of Medicine & Surgery
0019-5375 Indian Journal of Mental Retardation
0019-5383 Indian Journal of Meteorology and Geophysics *see* 0252-9416
0019-5391 Indian Journal of Occupational Health
0019-5413 Indian Journal of Orthopaedics
0019-5421 Indian Journal of Otolaryngology
0019-5448 Indian Journal of Pathology and Bacteriology *changed to* Indian Journal of Pathology & Microbiology.
0019-5456 Indian Journal of Pediatrics
0019-5464 Indian Journal of Pharmaceutical Education
0019-5472 Indian Journal of Pharmacy *see* 0250-474X
0019-5480 Indian Journal of Physics and Proceedings of the Indian Association for the Cultivation of Science
0019-5499 Indian Journal of Physiology and Pharmacology
0019-5502 Indian Journal of Plant Physiology
0019-5510 Indian Journal of Political Science
0019-5529 Indian Journal of Poultry Science
0019-5537 Indian Journal of Power and River Valley Development
0019-5545 Indian Journal of Psychiatry
0019-5553 Indian Journal of Psychology *see* 0253-7176
0019-5561 Indian Journal of Public Administration
0019-557X Indian Journal of Public Health
0019-5588 Indian Journal of Pure and Applied Mathematics
0019-5596 Indian Journal of Pure & Applied Physics
0019-560X Indian Journal of Radiology
0019-5618 Indian Journal of Science and Industry. Section A *see* 0367-8245
0019-5618 Indian Journal of Science and Industry *see* 0367-6722
0019-5634 Indian Journal of Social Work
0019-5642 Indian Journal of Sociology
0019-5650 Indian Journal of Surgery
0019-5669 Indian Journal of Technology
0019-5677 Indian Journal of the History of Medicine *changed to* Indian Institute of History of Medicine. Bulletin (Madras).
0019-5685 Indian Journal of Theology
0019-5693 Indian Journal of Theoretical Physics
0019-5707 Indian Journal of Tuberculosis
0019-5715 Indian Journal of Veterinary Science and Animal Husbandry *changed to* Indian Journal of Animal Sciences.
0019-5723 Indian Labour Journal
0019-5731 Indian Law Institute. Journal
0019-574X Indian Leather
0019-5758 Indian Leather Technologists' Association. Journal
0019-5766 Indian Libertarian†
0019-5782 Indian Library Association. Bulletin
0019-5790 Indian Library Science Abstracts
0019-5804 Indian Literature
0019-5812 Indian Management
0019-5820 Indian Management Abstracts
0019-5839 Indian Mathematical Society. Journal
0019-5847 Indian Medical Association. Journal
0019-5855 Indian Medical Forum
0019-5863 Indian Medical Gazette
0019-5898 Indian Medical Record†
0019-5901 Indian Merchants' Chamber. Journal
0019-591X Indian Military Academy Journal
0019-5928 Indian Mineralogist
0019-5936 Indian Minerals
0019-5944 Indian Mining & Engineering Journal
0019-5952 Indian Modeller
0019-5979 Indian Movie News *changed to* Indian Movie News.
0019-5987 Indian Museum Bulletin
0019-5995 Indian Music Journal
0019-6002 Indian National Bibliography
0019-6029 Indian News†
0019-6037 Indian News Index†
0019-6045 Indian Oil and Soap Journal†
0019-6053 The Indian P.E.N.
0019-6061 Indian Pediatrics
0019-607X Indian Perfumer
0019-6088 Indian Periodicals Record *changed to* Journal of Indexing & Reference Work.
0019-6096 Indian Philosophy & Culture†
0019-610X Indian Plastics Review†
0019-6126 Indian Political Science Review†
0019-6134 Indian Ports
0019-6142 Indian Poultry Gazette *changed to* Avian Research.
0019-6150 Indian Poultry Review
0019-6169 The Indian Practitioner
0019-6177 Indian Press Index
0019-6185 Indian Print & Paper
0019-6193 Indian Progress
0019-6207 Indian Promenade†
0019-6223 Indian Publisher and Bookseller
0019-6231 Indian Pulp and Paper
0019-624X Indian Radio Amateur
0019-6258 Indian Railway Gazette
0019-6266 Indian Railway Technical Bulletin
0019-6274 Indian Railways
0019-6282 Indian Record†
0019-6290 Indian Recorder & Digest†
0019-6304 Indian Review
0019-6312 Indian Rubber & Plastics Age
0019-6320 Indian Rubber Bulletin†
0019-6339 Indian Science Abstracts
0019-6347 Indian Seafoods
0019-6355 Indian Silk
0019-6363 Indian Society of Agricultural Statistics. Journal
0019-6371 Indian Society of Earthquake Technology. Bulletin
0019-638X Indian Society of Soil Science. Journal
0019-6398 International Journal of Contemporary Sociology
0019-6401 Indian Spices
0019-641X Indian Steel Age
0019-6428 Indian Sugar
0019-6436 Indian Textile Journal
0019-6444 Indian Trade Journal
0019-6452 Indian Truth†
0019-6460 Indian Vegetarian Congress Quarterly
0019-6479 Indian Veterinary Journal
0019-6487 Indian Witness
0019-6495 Indian Writing Today†
0019-6509 Indiana
0019-6517 Indiana Alumni Magazine
0019-6525 Indiana Audubon Quarterly
0019-6533 Indiana Business and Industry *see* 0273-7930
0019-6541 Indiana Business Review
0019-655X Indiana Covered Bridge Society. Newsletter
0019-6568 Indiana Dental Association. Journal
0019-6576 Indiana. Department of Public Welfare. Semi-Annual Statistical Series
0019-6584 Indiana English Journal *changed to* Indiana English.
0019-6606 Indiana Family Planner *see* 0146-1117
0019-6614 Indiana Folklore *changed to* Indiana Folklore and Oral History.
0019-6622 Indiana Freemason
0019-6630 Indiana Herald
0019-6649 Indiana History Bulletin†
0019-6665 Indiana Law Journal
0019-6673 Indiana Magazine of History
0019-6681 Indiana Nurse†
0019-6703 Indiana Plumbing - Heating - Cooling Contractor *changed to* Indiana Contractor.
0019-6711 Indiana Publisher
0019-672X Indiana Reading Quarterly
0019-6738 Indiana Slant
0019-6746 Indiana Social Studies Quarterly *see* 0889-0293
0019-6754 Indiana State Board of Health Bulletin
0019-6762 Indiana State Library. Extension Division Bulletin†
0019-6770 Indiana State Medical Association. Journal *see* 0746-8288
0019-6789 Indiana Statesman
0019-6797 Indiana Teacher *changed to* I S T A Advocate.
0019-6800 Indiana University Bookman†
0019-6819 Indiana University. Folklore Institute Journal *see* 0737-7037
0019-6827 Indiana University. Graduate Library School Alumni Newsletter *changed to* Vibrations.
0019-6835 Viewpoints *see* 0160-8398
0019-6851 India's Stamp Journal
0019-686X Indica
0019-6908 Indicateur Universel des P T T
0019-6916 Luxembourg. Service Central de la Statistique et des Etudes Economiques. Indicateurs Rapides
0019-6924 Indicator
0019-6932 Indicator†
0019-6959 Indicatore Cartotecnico†
0019-6967 Indicatore Grafico†
0019-6975 Indice
0019-7009 Indice de Precios al Consumidor para San Salvador, Mejicanos y Villa Delgado *changed to* Indice de Precios al Consumidor.
0019-7017 Indice de Precios al Consumidor para Familias Obreras en Puerto Rico
0019-7025 Indice de Precios al Consumidor
0019-7033 Indice Economico Colombiano†
0019-705X Indice Medico Colombiano†
0019-7068 Indice Medico Espanol
0019-7084 Indice Penale
0019-7114 Indiscret de Paris
0019-7149 Individual Psychologist†
0019-7157 Individual Psychology News Letter
0019-7165 Individualist
0019-7181 Indo-African Trade Journal†
0019-719X Indo-Asia
0019-7203 Indo-Asian Culture *changed to* Indian Horizons.
0019-7211 Indo-British Review
0019-722X Indo-Canadian
0019-7238 Indo-German Review†
0019-7246 Indo-Iranian Journal
0019-7262 Indogermanische Forschungen
0019-7270 Indonesia *changed to* Indochina.
0019-7289 Indonesia (Ithaca)
0019-7297 Indonesia Letter
0019-7319 Indonesian Abstracts *see* 0216-4167
0019-7351 Indonesian Planned Parenthood Association News†
0019-7378 Indus Digest†
0019-7386 Industria
0019-7408 Industria
0019-7416 Industria *changed to* Industria: Rivista di Economia Politica Industriale.
0019-7424 Industria *changed to* Industrie Revu.
0019-7459 Industria Alimenticia
0019-7467 Industria Avicola
0019-7475 Industria Britanica†
0019-7483 Industria Conserve
0019-7491 Industria Cotoniera
0019-7521 Industria del Legno e del Mobile *changed to* L M l'Industria del Legno e del Mobile.
0019-753X Industria del Mobile
0019-7548 Industria della Carta
0019-7556 Industria della Gomma
0019-7564 Industria della Vernice†
0019-7572 Industria do Norte
0019-7602 Industria e Desenvolvimento
0019-7610 Industria Italiana dei Laterizi *changed to* L'Industria dei Laterizi.
0019-7629 Industria Italiana dei Plastici *changed to* Europlast.
0019-7637 Industria Italiana del Cemento
0019-7645 Industria Italiana Elettrotecnica ed Elettronica *see* 0390-6698
0019-7661 Industria Lombarda
0019-767X Industria Meridionale†
0019-7688 Industria Militar
0019-7696 Industria Mineraria *see* 0391-1586
0019-770X Industria Portuguesa†
0019-7718 Industria & Produtividade
0019-7734 Industria Saccarifera Italiana
0019-7742 Industria Textil Sud Americana
0019-7769 Industria Toscana
0019-7777 Industria Turistica
0019-7793 Industrial Accountant
0019-7815 Industrial Advertising & Marketing *changed to* Advertising & Marketing.
0019-7823 Industrial Aerodynamics Abstracts
0019-784X Industrial and Commercial Photographer *changed to* Professional Photographer.
0019-7858 Industrial and Commercial Training
0019-7866 Industrial and Engineering Chemistry†
0019-7912 Industrial and Labor Relations Forum†
0019-7920 Industrial and Labor Relations Report *see* 0736-6396
0019-7939 Industrial and Labor Relations Review
0019-7963 Industrial and Welfare Catering *see* 0306-2538
0019-7971 Industrial Archaeology
0019-8005 Industrial Arts and Vocational Education *see* 0091-8601
0019-8013 Industrial Banker *see* 0097-8345
0019-8021 Industrial Bulletin *changed to* Industrial Product Bulletin.
0019-8056 Industrial Canada†
0019-8064 Industrial Ceylon†
0019-8099 Industrial Courier
0019-8102 Industrial Court Reporter
0019-8110 Industrial Design *see* 0192-3021
0019-8145 Industrial Diamond Review
0019-8153 Industrial Distribution
0019-8161 Industrial Distributor News *changed to* I M P O Distributor News.
0019-817X Industrial Ecology†
0019-8196 Industrial Editor†
0019-820X Industrial Egypt
0019-8226 Engineering Management††
0019-8234 Industrial Engineering
0019-8242 Industrial Engineering and Management
0019-8269 Industrial Enterprise
0019-8277 Industrial Equipment News
0019-8285 I E N: Industrial Equipment News
0019-8307 Industrial Fabric Products Review
0019-8307 Industrial Fabric Products Review Buyer's Guide
0019-8315 Industrial Finishing *see* 0264-2506
0019-8323 Industrial Finishing
0019-834X Industrial Gas†
0019-8358 Industrial Gerontology *see* 0161-2514
0019-8366 Industrial Health
0019-8374 Industrial Heating
0019-8382 Industrial Hygiene Digest
0019-8390 Industrial Hygiene Review†
0019-8412 Industrial India
0019-8439 Industrial Japan *see* 0386-6076
0019-8447 Industrial Laboratory
0019-8455 Industrial Machinery News
0019-8471 Industrial Management
0019-848X Sloan Management Review
0019-8498 Industrial Marketing *see* 0745-5933
0019-8501 Industrial Marketing Management
0019-8528 Industrial Mathematics
0019-8536 Industrial Medicine and Surgery *see* 0362-4064
0019-8544 Industrial Minerals
0019-8552 Industrial Models & Patterns
0019-8579 Industrial Nottinghamshire
0019-8587 Industrial Philippines†
0019-8595 Industrial Photography
0019-8609 Industrial Photography and Commercial Camera *changed to* Commercial Photography.
0019-8617 Industrial Progress
0019-8625 Industrial Property
0019-8633 Industrial Puerto Rico
0019-8641 Industrial Purchasing Agent

ISSN INDEX 5391

0019-8668 Industrial Recovery
0019-8676 Industrial Relations
0019-8684 Industrial Relations *see* 0970-8405
0019-8692 Industrial Relations Journal
0019-8706 Industrial Relations Law Digest†
0019-8714 Industrial Relations News *changed to* Human Resource Management News.
0019-8722 Industrial Research *see* 0746-9179
0019-8757 Industrial Safety *see* 0262-3226
0019-8765 Industrial Safety & Health Bulletin†
0019-8773 Industrial Security *see* 0145-9406
0019-8781 Industrial Society *changed to* I S Magazine.
0019-879X Industrial Supervisor *see* 0734-3302
0019-8803 Industrial Times
0019-8838 Industrial Tribunal Reports†
0019-8846 Industrial Tyneside *changed to* Industrial Tyne & Wear.
0019-8854 Progress Wales
0019-8862 Industrial Water Engineering†
0019-8870 Industrial Worker
0019-8889 Industrial World
0019-8897 Industrialisierung des Bauens†
0019-8927 Industrialization Forum†
0019-8935 Four Hundred and Twenty Five Canadian Weekly Stock Charts *see* 0830-1972
0019-8943 Industrias de la Alimentacion†
0019-8951 Industrias Lacteas *see* 0744-625X
0019-896X Industrie
0019-8978 Industrie†
0019-8986 Industrie- und Handelskammer Frankfurt am Main. Mitteilungen
0019-8994 Ostschwaebische Wirtschaft *changed to* Wirtschaft in Ostwuerttemberg.
0019-901X Industrie Alimentari
0019-9028 Industrie & Nachwuchs†
0019-9036 Industrie-Anzeiger
0019-9044 Societe Francaise de Ceramique. Traductions Brevets. *changed to* Industrie Ceramique.
0019-9060 Industrie du Petrole en Europe-Gaz-Chimie *see* 0220-3294
0019-9095 Industrie Hoteliere de France et d'Outre Mer *changed to* Industrie Hoteliere.
0019-9109 Industrie Lackierbetrieb
0019-9125 Producteur de Lait
0019-9141 Industrie-Post†
0019-9168 Messe Industriespiegel
0019-9176 Industrie Textile
0019-9206 Profit *see* 0721-0477
0019-9214 Der Industrie- und Handelsvertreter
0019-9230 Industriel de Cote d'Ivoire
0019-9249 Industrieel Eigendom
0019-9257 Industriell Teknikt
0019-9265 Industrielle Einkauf *see* 0341-4507
0019-9281 I O Management Zeitschrift
0019-929X Industriemagazin *changed to* Top Business.
0019-9303 Industriemeister Nachrichten
0019-932X Industries Atomiques *see* 0367-6838
0019-9362 Industrie et Travaux d'Outre-Mer *changed to* Industries et Developpement International.
0019-9370 Industries Mecaniques
0019-9389 Industries Nautiques
0019-9397 Proclim *changed to* Promoclim A: Applications Thermiques et Aerauliques.
0019-9397 Proclim *changed to* Promoclim B: Bulletin du Genie Climatique.
0019-9419 Industrijska Istrazivanja
0019-9427 Industritjaenstemannen *changed to* S I F Tidningen.
0019-9435 Industry†
0019-9443 Industry & Finance
0019-9451 Industry & Trade Review
0019-946X Industry of Free China
0019-9494 Industry Today†
0019-9516 Infant and Nursery School Equipment *changed to* Infant and Nursery School Education.
0019-9524 Infanteria
0019-9532 Infantry
0019-9540 Infantry Journal
0019-9559 Infants to Teens Wear Buyers
0019-9567 Infection and Immunity
0019-9591 Infirmiere *see* 0301-0813
0019-9605 Infirmiere Canadienne *changed to* Canadian Nurse - L'Infirmiere Canadienne.
0019-9613 Infirmiere Francaise *changed to* Infirmiere Magazine.
0019-9656 Info
0019-9680 Infor-Austria†
0019-9702 Inform - Letter *changed to* Inform Quarterly Newsletter.
0019-9710 Informa†
0019-9729 Informacao Agricola
0019-9737 Carteria de Comercion Exterior. Informacao Semanal†
0019-9753 Informacio-Elektronika
0019-9761 Informacion Comercial Espanola. Boletin Semanal *changed to* Informacion Comercial Espanola. Boletin Economico.
0019-977X Informacion Comercial Espanola. Revista Mensual *changed to* Informacion Comercial Espanola.
0019-9788 Informacion Educativa *changed to* Argentina. Centro Nacional de Documentacion e Informacion Educativa. Informaciones y Documentos.
0019-9796 Informacion Farmaceutica
0019-9818 Informaciones del Brasil†
0019-9826 Informatsiya o Bibliotechnom Dele i Bibliografii za Rubezhom†
0019-9834 Informacja Ekspresowa *changed to* Instytut Obrobki Skrawaniem. Przeglad Dokumentacyjny.
0019-9869 Informador
0019-9885 Informateur *changed to* Etudes Rwandaises.
0019-9893 Informateur de la Quinzaine
0019-9907 Informatie
0019-9915 Informatik
0019-9923 Informatika
0019-9931 Information about the Oil Industry - for the Oil Industry†
0019-994X Information Agricole
0019-9958 Information and Control *see* 0890-5401
0019-9974 Information Bulletin for the Southern Hemisphere†
0019-9982 Information Bulletin on Isotopic Generators†
0019-9990 Information *see* 0345-5300
0020-000X Information de Sages-Femmes†
0020-0018 Information Dentaire
0020-0026 Information d'Histoire de l'Art†
0020-0034 Information Dietetique
0020-0042 Information Display
0020-0050 Information Economique Africaine
0020-0077 Information fuer auslaendische Studienbewerber an oesterreichischen Hochschulen
0020-0085 Information from the Peace Movement of the German Democratic Republic
0020-0093 Information Geographique
0020-0107 Information Juive
0020-0123 Information Litteraire
0020-0131 Information Los Angeles *changed to* Key Magazine. This Week in Los Angeles and Southern California.
0020-0166 Tajekoztato a Kulfoldi Kozgazdasagi Irodalomrol. Series A, Referatumok - Information on the Foreign Economic Literature, Series A *see* 0237-0840
0020-0174 Information om Rehabilitering
0020-0190 Information Processing Letters
0020-0220 Information Retrieval and Library Automation Newsletter *changed to* Information Retrieval & Library Automation.
0020-0239 Information Science Abstracts
0020-0247 Information Science in Canada†
0020-0255 Information Sciences
0020-0263 Information Scientist *see* 0165-5515
0020-0271 Information Storage and Retrieval *see* 0306-4573
0020-028X Hopital, Information Therapeutique†
0020-0298 Information Transports
0020-0301 Information ueber Aktuelle Probleme der Marxistisch-Leninistischen Philosophie in der U.d.S.S.R. *see* 0138-2055
0020-031X Informationsdienst fuer die Private Krankenversicherung *see* 0343-9321
0020-0328 Informationen aus dem Philosophischen Leben in der D.D.R. *see* 0138-242X
0020-0336 Informationen aus Orthodontie und Kieferorthopaedie
0020-0344 Informationen fuer die Fischwirtschaft
0020-0352 Informationen fuer die Frau
0020-0379 Informationen ueber die Fischwirtschaft des Auslandes
0020-0387 Informationen zur Kernforschung und Kerntechnik *changed to* Fachinformationszentrum Energie, Physik, Mathematik. Kernforschungszentrum. Konferenzberichte. Kernforschung, Kerntechnik.
0020-0395 Informationen zur Soziologische Forschung in der D.D.R.†
0020-0409 Informations Aeronautiques *changed to* Informations Aeronautiques et Spatiales.
0020-0417 Informations & Documents†
0020-0425 Informations Bancaires et Financieres
0020-0433 Informations Canadiennes
0020-0441 Informations Catholiques Internationales *see* 0757-3529
0020-045X Informations - Chimie
0020-0468 Informations du Caoutchouc *see* 0247-3518
0020-0476 Informations Etudes Outre-Mer†
0020-0484 Federation des Comites d'Alliance Ouvriere. Informations Ouvrieres
0020-0492 Informations Rapides de l'Administration Francaise
0020-0506 Statistiques des Enseignements†
0020-0522 Informations Techniques des Directions des Services Veterinaires
0020-0530 Informations Universitaires et Professionnelles Internationales†
0020-0549 Informationsdienst des Deutschen Rates der Europaeischen Bewegung *changed to* Europaeisches Forum.
0020-0581 Informationsdienstkartei (I D K) *changed to* Fachdokumentation Agrargeschichte.
0020-0638 Informativni Bilten Radnickog Sveucilista "Mosa Pijade"†
0020-0654 Informativo Bamerindus
0020-0662 Informatology†
0020-0670 P.I.M.R. Informator Patentowy†
0020-0689 Informatore Agrario
0020-0697 Informatore Botanico Italiano
0020-0700 Informatore del Marmista
0020-0719 Informatore di Ortoflorofrutticoltura†
0020-0727 Informatore Filatelico
0020-0735 Informatore Fitopatologico
0020-0743 Informatore Medico-Sociale
0020-076X Informatore Turistico
0020-0778 Informatore Zootecnico
0020-0786 Informazione Industriale
0020-0794 Informazione Mediterranea
0020-0816 Informazioni Sociali
0020-0832 Estacion Experimental Agropecuaria Pergamino. Informe Tecnico *see* 0325-1799
0020-0840 Informer
0020-0883 Informes de la Construccion
0020-0891 Infrared Physics
0020-0905 Ingegnere
0020-0913 Ingegnere Italiano†
0020-0921 Ingegnere Libero Professionista†
0020-093X Ingegneria Chimica†
0020-0948 Ingegneria Civile
0020-0956 Ingegneria Ferroviaria
0020-0964 Ingegneria Meccanica†
0020-0980 Ingegneria Sanitaria *changed to* Ingegneria Sanitaria Ambientale.
0020-0999 Ingenieria
0020-1022 Ingenieria Civil
0020-1030 Ingenieria e Industria
0020-1049 Ingenieria Electrica y Mecanica†
0020-1057 Recursos Hidraulicos *see* 0186-4076
0020-1065 Ingeneria Internacional Construccion *see* 0020-6415
0020-1073 Ingenieria Naval
0020-1081 Ingenieria Quimica†
0020-109X Ingenieria y Arquitectura†
0020-1103 Ingenieria y Ciencia
0020-1111 Ingeniero Andino†
0020-112X Ingeniero Westinghouse†
0020-1138 L'Ingenieur†
0020-1146 De Ingenieur
0020-1154 Ingenieur-Archiv
0020-1162 Ingenieur Chimiste†
0020-1170 Der Ingenieur der Deutschen Bundespost
0020-1197 Ingenieurs *changed to* Equipement Industriel/Industriele Uitrusting.
0020-1200 Ingenieurs de l'Automobile
0020-1219 Ingenieurs et Cadres de France
0020-1227 Ingenieur et Technicien *changed to* Revue de l'Entreprise.
0020-1243 Ingenioer- og Bygningsvaesen *changed to* Ingenioeren.
0020-126X Ingenioerens Ugeblad *changed to* Ingenioeren.
0020-1278 Ingenjoersvetenskapsakademiens Meddelanden†
0020-1308 Inglewood Public Library Quarterly Report
0020-1324 Respiratory Care *see* 0730-8418
0020-1340 Iniziativa Europea *changed to* Sinistra Europea.
0020-1359 Iniziativa Isontina
0020-1383 Injury
0020-1391 Injury Valuation Reports and Special Research Reports
0020-1405 Inkling (Denver)†
0020-1413 Inkoop *changed to* Bedrijfsvoering.
0020-1421 Inkop†
0020-1448 Inlaendsk Tidningstaxat†
0020-1456 Inland
0020-1464 Inland Africa *changed to* A I M International.
0020-1472 Inland Architect
0020-1502 Inland Printer - American Lithographer *see* 0744-6616
0020-1510 Inland Register
0020-1537 Inland Seas
0020-1553 Inner Space†
0020-1561 Innere Kolonisation *see* 0341-1869
0020-157X Innes Review
0020-1588 Innisfail Canegrower†
0020-1596 Inniu
0020-1618 Innominate
0020-1626 Du Pont Innovation†
0020-1642 Publicum
0020-1650 Inorganic and Nuclear Chemistry Letters *see* 0277-5387
0020-1669 Inorganic Chemistry
0020-1685 Inorganic Materials
0020-1693 Inorganica Chimica Acta
0020-1707 Inpho Oesterreich
0020-1715 Input - Kentucky Quarterly†
0020-1723 Inquirer
0020-1731 Inquiry (Coral Gables)†
0020-174X Inquiry
0020-1766 Insatsukai
0020-1774 Inscape (Phoenix)†
0020-1790 Insect Biochemistry *see* 0965-1748
0020-1804 Insecta Matsumurana
0020-1812 Insectes Sociaux
0020-1820 Insectocutor News†
0020-1839 Insektenboerse *see* 0013-8843
0020-1847 Inside Detective

ISSN

0020-1855 Inside Education†
0020-1863 Inside Kenya Today
0020-1871 Insieme (Rome)
0020-1901 Insight†
0020-191X Insight: Notre Dame†
0020-1928 Insight (Grand Rapids)†
0020-1936 Insight
0020-1944 Insight (Hagerstown)
0020-1960 Insight and Opinion *changed to* Insight Publication.
0020-2002 Insinoorilehti†
0020-2010 Insinooriuutiset *see* 0785-997X
0020-2029 Insite
0020-2045 Netherlands. Inspectie voor het Brandweerwezen. Maandelijkse Mededelingen *changed to* Maandelijkse Mededelingen van de Inspectie voor het Brandweerwezen.
0020-2053 Inspection News *changed to* Equifax Journal.
0020-2061 Inspiration
0020-207X Installateur
0020-2088 Installateur Rhone-Alpes†
0020-2096 Installatie
0020-2118 L'Installatore Italiano
0020-2126 Installment Retailing *changed to* N A I C Reporter.
0020-2134 Instantanes Criminologiques†
0020-2142 Instantanes Medicaux
0020-2150 Instantanes Techniques†
0020-2177 Institut Archeologique du Luxembourg. Bulletins
0020-2185 Institut Royal Belge du Petrole. Annales
0020-2207 Institut d'Amenagement et d'Urbanisme de la Region Parisienne. Cahiers *see* 0153-6184
0020-2223 Institut des Actuaires Francais. Bulletin Trimestriel†
0020-2231 I F R E M E R. Revue des Travaux *see* 0990-7440
0020-2274 Institut Francais du Petrole. Revue et Annales des Liquides Combustibles *changed to* Institut Francais du Petrole. Revue.
0020-2304 Institut fuer Orientforschung. Mitteilungen†
0020-2312 Institut fuer Raumordnung. Informationen *see* 0303-2493
0020-2320 Institut fuer Wissenschaft und Kunst. Mitteilungen
0020-2339 Institut Henri Poincare. Annales. Section A: Physique Theorique
0020-2355 Institut International d'Administration Publique. Bulletin *see* 0152-7401
0020-2363 Institut Maurice Thorez. Cahiers d'Histoire *changed to* Cahiers d'Histoire (Paris).
0020-238X Institut National de la Recherche Agronomique de Tunisie. Documents Techniques
0020-2398 France. Institut National de la Statistique et des Etudes Economiques. Departements et Territoires d'Outre Mer. Bulletin Bibliographique
0020-2401 Institut National des Appellations d'Origine des Vins et Eaux-de-Vie. Bulletin *changed to* Institut National des Appellations d'Origine. Bulletin.
0020-241X Institut National des Industries Extractives. Bulletin Technique "Mines et Carrieres"†
0020-2428 Institut National des Industries Extractives. Fiches de Documentation†
0020-2436 Belgium. Institut National du Logement. Bulletin d'Information/Informatie Bulletin†
0020-2444 Institut Pasteur. Annales *see* 0923-2494
0020-2444 Institut Pasteur. Annales *see* 0923-2508
0020-2452 Institut Pasteur. Bulletin
0020-2460 Institut Pasteur d'Algerie. Archives
0020-2479 Institut Pasteur de la Guyane Francaise. Archives†
0020-2487 Institut Pasteur de Lyon. Revue
0020-2495 Institut Pasteur de Madagascar. Archives
0020-2509 Institut Pasteur de Tunis. Archives
0020-2517 Institut Royal Meteorologique de Belgique Contributions†
0020-2525 Belgium. Institut Royal Meteorologique. Observations Geophysiques
0020-2533 Belgium. Institut Royal Meteorologique. Observations Ionospheriques et du Rayonnement Cosmique
0020-2541 Belgium. Institut Royal Meteorologique. Observations Synoptiques
0020-255X Belgium. Institut Royal Meteorologique. Publications
0020-2568 Institut Technique du Batiment et des Travaux Publics. Annales
0020-2606 Institute for Defence Studies and Analyses. Journal
0020-2614 Pennsylvania State University. Institute for Research on Land and Water Resources. Newsletter *changed to* Pennsylvania State University. Environmental Resources Research Institute. Newsletter.
0020-2622 Institute for Social Research. Newsletter
0020-2630 Institute for the Study of Nonviolence Journal†
0020-2649 Institute for the Study of the U S S R. Bulletin†
0020-2665 Institute for Workers' Control. Bulletin *see* 0306-1892
0020-2673 Young Men's Institute. Institute Journal
0020-2681 Institute of Actuaries. Journal
0020-269X Institute of Actuaries Students' Society. Journal†
0020-2703 University of Ghana. Institute of African Studies. Research Review
0020-2711 Institute of Animal Technicians. Journal *see* 0264-4754
0020-272X Institute of Bankers in Ireland. Journal *see* 0791-1386
0020-2738 Institute of Bankers. Journal†
0020-2746 Motor Management *changed to* Motor Industry Management.
0020-2754 Institute of British Geographers. Transactions
0020-2762 Institute of Burial and Cremation Administration. Journal
0020-2770 Institute of Civil Defence. Journal
0020-2789 Clerk of Works
0020-2800 Institute of Consulting Engineers. Journal
0020-2827 Institute of Developing Economies. Library Bulletin
0020-2835 Institute of Development Studies Bulletin *see* 0265-5012
0020-2843 Institute of Early American History and Culture. News Letter
0020-2851 Institute of Economic Research. Journal
0020-286X Institute of Electrical Communication Engineers of Japan. Journal *see* 0913-5693
0020-2878 Railway Electric Rolling Stocks
0020-2886 Institute of Fuel. Journal *see* 0144-2600
0020-2894 University of London. Institute of Historical Research. Bulletin *see* 0950-3471
0020-2908 Landscape Design
0020-2916 Institute of Management Sciences Bulletin *see* 0092-2102
0020-2924 Institute of Marine Engineers. Transactions *changed to* Marine Management Holdings. Transactions.
0020-2932 Institute of Mathematics and its Applications. Journal *see* 0272-4960
0020-2932 Institute of Mathematics and its Applications. Journal *see* 0272-4979
0020-2940 Measurement and Control
0020-2959 Institute of Medical Laboratory Technology. Gazette *see* 0267-2928
0020-2967 Institute of Metal Finishing. Transactions
0020-2983 Institute of Mine Surveyors of South Africa. Journal
0020-3009 Institute of Navigation. Journal *see* 0373-4633
0020-3017 Institute of Outdoor Drama Newsletter *changed to* U S Outdoor Drama.
0020-3025 Institute of Pacific Research. Journal†
0020-3033 Institute of Paper Chemistry. Abstract Bulletin *changed to* Institute of Paper Science and Technology. Abstract Bulletin.
0020-3041 Institute Paper Chemistry. Keyword Supplement *changed to* Institute of Paper Science and Technology. Keyword Index to Abstract Bulletin.
0020-3076 Petroleum Review
0020-3084 Rikagaku Kenkyujo Hokoku
0020-3092 Institute of Physical and Chemical Research. Scientific Papers
0020-3106 Institute of Public Health. Bulletin
0020-3114 Institute of Rail Transport. Journal
0020-3122 Transport Engineer
0020-3130 Institute of Science Technology. Bulletin
0020-3157 Institute of Statistical Mathematics. Annals
0020-3165 University of Dhaka. Institute of Statistical Research and Training. Bulletin *changed to* Journal of Statistical Research.
0020-3173 Institute of the Motor Industry. Journal *changed to* Motor Industry Management.
0020-3181 Chartered Institute of Transport. Journal *see* 0144-3453
0020-319X Institute of Weights and Measures Administration Monthly Review *see* 0953-8704
0020-322X Institutet Foer Maltdrycksforskning. Meddelande†
0020-3238 Institution of Agricultural Engineers. Journal and Proceedings *see* 0308-5732
0020-3246 Institution of Chemical Engineers. Diary *see* 0302-0797
0020-3254 Institution of Chemists (India). Journal
0020-3270 Institution of Electrical Engineers. Proceedings *changed to* I E E Proceedings Part A: Covering Science, Measurement and Technology.
0020-3270 Institution of Electrical Engineers. Proceedings *see* 0950-107X
0020-3270 Institution of Electrical Engineers. Proceedings *see* 0956-3776
0020-3270 Institution of Electrical Engineers. Proceedings *see* 0143-7038
0020-3270 Institution of Electrical Engineers. Proceedings *see* 0143-7046
0020-3270 Institution of Electrical Engineers. Proceedings *see* 0143-7054
0020-3270 Institution of Electrical Engineers. Proceedings *see* 0143-7062
0020-3270 Institution of Electrical Engineers. Proceedings *see* 0956-3768
0020-3270 Institution of Electrical Engineers. Proceedings *see* 0956-375X
0020-3289 Institution of Engineers and Shipbuilders in Scotland. Transactions
0020-3297 Institutions of Engineers, Australia. Civil Engineering Transactions *see* 0159-2068
0020-3300 Institution of Engineers, Australia. Transactions. Electrical Engineering†
0020-3319 Institution of Engineers, Australia. Journal *changed to* Engineers Australia.
0020-3327 Institution of Engineers, Australia. Mechanical and Chemical Engineering Transactions *see* 0727-7369
0020-3327 Institution of Engineers, Australia. Mechanical and Chemical Engineering Transactions *see* 0157-9762
0020-3335 Institution of Engineers-In-Charge. Transactions
0020-3343 Institution of Engineers (India). Bulletin
0020-3351 Institution of Engineers (India). Chemical Engineering Division. Journal
0020-3378 Institution of Engineers (India). Electronics and Telecommunication Engineering Division. Journal
0020-3386 Institution of Engineers (India). Electrical Engineering Division. Journal
0020-3394 Institution of Engineers (India). Mining and Metallurgy Division. Journal *see* 0257-442X
0020-3408 Institution of Engineers (India). Mechanical Engineering Division. Journal
0020-3416 Institution of Engineers (India). Public Health Engineering Division. Journal *see* 0251-110X
0020-3424 Institution of Fire Engineers Quarterly *changed to* Fire Engineers Journal.
0020-3432 Institution of Gas Engineers. Journal *see* 0306-6444
0020-3475 Institution of Marine Technologists. Journal
0020-3483 Institution of Mechanical Engineers. Proceedings *changed to* Institution of Mechanical Engineers. Proceedings. Part A: Journal of Power and Energy.
0020-3483 Institution of Mechanical Engineers. Proceedings *see* 0954-4054
0020-3483 Institution of Mechanical Engineers. Proceedings *see* 0954-4070
0020-3505 Institution of Municipal Engineers. Journal *see* 0263-788X
0020-3513 Institution of Public Health Engineers. Journal *see* 0300-5925
0020-3521 Institution of Radio and Electronics Engineers Australia. Proceedings *see* 0725-2986
0020-3556 Institution of Water Engineers. Journal *see* 0309-1600
0020-3572 Institutional Distribution
0020-3580 Institutional Investor
0020-3599 Institutional Laundry *changed to* Laundry Cleaning World.
0020-3602 Institutional Management *see* 0144-3704
0020-3610 Institutions - Volume Feeding Management *see* 0273-5520
0020-3629 Instituto Agronomico do Sul. Escola de Agronomia Eliseu Maciel. Arquivos de Entomologia. Serie A & Serie B
0020-3637 Instituto Americano de Estudios Vascos. Boletin
0020-3645 Instituto Barraquer. Anales
0020-3653 Instituto Biologico. Arquivos
0020-3661 Instituto Biologico da Bahia. Boletim
0020-367X Instituto Brasil - Estados Unidos. Boletim
0020-3688 Instituto Brasileiro de Bibliografia e Documentacao. Noticias†
0020-370X Instituto Caro y Cuervo. Noticias Culturales
0020-3718 Instituto Cultural Peruano Norteamericano. Boletin *changed to* Instituto Cultural Peruano Norteamericano. Newsletter.
0020-3726 Instituto de Angola. Boletim *changed to* Lavra & Oficina.
0020-3734 Instituto de Angola. Boletim Analitico *changed to* Uniao dos Escritores Angolanos. Boletim Analitico.
0020-3742 Instituto de Angola. Boletim Bibliografico *changed to* Uniao dos Escritores Angolanos. Boletim Bibliografico.
0020-3750 Universidad Nacional Mayor de San Marcos. Instituto de Biologia Andina. Archivos *changed to* Archivos de Biologia Andina.
0020-3769 Instituto de Biologia Aplicada. Publicaciones†
0020-3777 Lisbon. Instituto de Biologia Maritima. Notas e Estudos *see* 0870-1245
0020-3785 Instituto de Cardiologia de Mexico. Archivos
0020-3807 Instituto de Ciencias Sociales. Revista†
0020-3815 Instituto de Cultura Puertorriquena. Revista

ISSN

ISSN INDEX 5393

0020-3823 Instituto de Derecho Privado. Boletin
0020-3831 Academia de Ciencias de Cuba. Instituto de Documentacion e Informacion Cientifica y Tecnica. Boletin *see* 0138-6107
0020-384X Instituto de Estudios Asturianos. Boletin
0020-3858 Estudios Medicos y Biologicos. Boletin
0020-3866 Instituto de Estudios Politicos. Boletin
0020-3874 Universidade de Sao Paulo. Instituto de Estudos Brasileiros. Revista
0020-3882 Instituto de Fomento Pesquero. Boletin Cientifico *changed to* Serie Investigacion Pesquera.
0020-3890 Instituto de Geografia e Historia Militar do Brasil. Revista
0020-3912 Instituto de Investigacao Cientifica de Angola. Boletim
0020-3939 Chile. Servicio Nacional de Geologia y Mineria. Boletin
0020-3947 Anales de Antropologia
0020-3955 Instituto de Investigaciones Medica. Bulletin†
0020-3963 Instituto de Zoonosis e Investigacion Pecuaria Revista
0020-3971 I M M E Boletin
0020-398X Instituto de Pesquisas e Experimentacao Agropecuarias do Sul. Biblioteca. Boletim Bibliografico. *changed to* Rio Grande do Sul. Unidade Executiva de Pesquisa Agropecuaria Estadual. Boletim Bibliografico.
0020-4005 Instituto de Prevision Social. Boletin
0020-4013 Instituto de Salubridad y Enfermedades Tropicales, Revista *see* 0034-8384
0020-4021 Instituto de Zoologia "Dr. Augusto Nobre". Publicacoes
0020-403X Istituto di Patologia del Libro "Alfonso Gallo." Bollettino *see* 0391-5972
0020-4048 Instituto Ingenieros Civiles de Espana. Boletim Informativo *changed to* Instituto de la Ingenieria de Espana. Hoja Informativa.
0020-4056 Instituto Interamericano del Nino. Boletin
0020-4064 Istituto Italiano di Cultura. Bulletin†
0020-4080 I L P E S Cuadernos
0020-4099 Instituto Latinoamericano de Relaciones Internacionales. Trabajos
0020-4102 Instituto Nacional de Antropologia e Historia. Boletin†
0020-4129 Spain. Instituto Nacional de Investigaciones Agronomicas. Anales *see* 0213-5000
0020-4129 Spain. Instituto Nacional de Investigaciones Agronomicas. Anales *see* 0213-5035
0020-4129 Spain. Instituto Nacional de Investigaciones Agronomicas. Anales *see* 0210-2463
0020-4137 Instituto Nacional de Investigaciones Agronomicas. Boletin†
0020-4145 Instituto Nacional de la Vivienda. Boletin Interior de Informacion†
0020-4153 Instituto Nacional de Pesca del Ecuador. Boletin Cientifico y Tecnico†
0020-4161 Argentina. Instituto Nacional de Tecnologia Agropecuaria. Departamento de Especializacion. Publicacion Didactica†
0020-417X Universidad de Oriente. Instituto Oceanografico. Boletin
0020-4188 Instituto Panamericano de Geografia e Historia. Boletin Aereo
0020-4196 Instituts fuer Landeskunde. Neueingaenge der Bibliothek und Kartensammlung†
0020-4218 Instituto Historico e Geografico de Juiz de Fora
0020-4226 Institutul de Cercetari Piscicole. Buletinul *changed to* Institutul de Cercetari si Proiectari Alimentare. Sectia Cercetare Piscicola. Buletinul de Cercetari Piscicole.
0020-4234 Institutul Geologie si Geofizica. Memoire
0020-4242 Institutul Politehnic "Gheorghe Gheorghiu-Dej". Buletin *changed to* Institutul Politehnic Bucuresti. Buletin Stiintific.
0020-4269 Instructional Materials Intercom†
0020-4277 Instructional Science
0020-4285 Instructor *see* 1049-5851
0020-4293 Instrument and Apparatus News *changed to* Instrumentation & Automation News.
0020-4307 Instrument and Control Engineering†
0020-4323 Instrument Practice for Process Control and Automation†
0020-4331 Instrumentalist
0020-434X Instrumentatiet
0020-4358 Honeywell Instrumentatie Nieuws
0020-4366 Instrumentation†
0020-4382 Instrumentation Technology *see* 0192-303X
0020-4390 Instrumentenbau-Zeitschrift *changed to* Musik International.
0020-4404 Instruments and Control Systems *changed to* Instrumentation and Control Systems.
0020-4412 Instruments and Experimental Techniques
0020-4420 Instruments & Laboratoirest
0020-4447 Instytut Ciezkiej Syntezy Organicznej. Zeszyty Naukowe
0020-4455 Instytut Gospodarstwa Spolecznego. Biuletyn *changed to* Biuletyn I G S.
0020-4463 Instytut Medycyny Morskiej w Gdansku. Biuletyn - Institute of Marine Medicine in Gdansk. Bulletin *changed to* Instytut Medycyny Morskiej i Tropikalnej w Gdyni. Bulletin.
0020-4471 Instytut Metali Niezelaznych. Przeglad Dokumentacyjny†
0020-448X Instytut Ochrony Roslin. Biuletyn
0020-4498 Instytut Urbanistyki i Architektury. Biuletyn†
0020-4501 Instytut Urbanistyki i Architektury. Przeglad Informacyjny†
0020-451X Instytut Lacznosci. Prace†
0020-4528 Instytut Obrobki Skrawaniem. Zeszyty Naukowe
0020-4536 Insula
0020-4544 Insulation - Circuits *see* 0895-3708
0020-4560 Insurance†
0020-4579 Insurance Adjuster *changed to* Claims.
0020-4587 Insurance Advocate
0020-4595 Insurance Agent and Broker in Canada *see* 0008-3879
0020-4609 Insurance and Actuarial Society of Glasgow. Newsletter†
0020-4617 Insurance Broker *see* 0384-5958
0020-4625 Insurance Broker-Aget
0020-4633 Insurance Brokers' Monthly *see* 0260-2385
0020-465X Insurance Counsel Journal *see* 0895-0016
0020-4668 Insurance Economics Surveys†
0020-4676 Insurance Exchange Magazine *changed to* Illinois Underwriter.
0020-4684 Insurance Field
0020-4706 Insurance Index†
0020-4714 Insurance Journal
0020-4722 Insurance Law Journal†
0020-4730 Insurance Law Reports: Fire & Casualty
0020-4757 Insurance Lines
0020-4765 Insurance Literature *changed to* Insurance and Employee Benefits Literature.
0020-4773 Insurance Mail
0020-479X Insurance Record†
0020-4803 Insurance Record
0020-4811 Insurance Review
0020-482X Insurance Salesman *see* 1053-2838
0020-4846 InsuranceWeek
0020-4854 Intanda News
0020-4862 Integrateducation *see* 0894-0681
0020-4870 Integrated Management†
0020-4889 Integrated Personnel Services Index†
0020-4900 Intelligence Digest *changed to* Intelligence Digest - A Review of World Affairs.
0020-4919 Intensive Agriculture
0020-4927 Inter†
0020-4943 Inter-American Economic Affairs
0020-4978 Inter-American Music Bulletin†
0020-4986 Inter-American News†
0020-5001 Inter Auto Ecoles de France - Inter Auto Route
0020-501X Inter-Continental Press Guide
0020-5028 Inter/Ed†
0020-5036 Inter Electronique†
0020-5044 Integre C.H.U†
0020-5079 Inter-Parliamentary Bulletin
0020-5087 Inter-School & Inter-Varsity Christian Fellowship
0020-5095 Inter-State Milk Producers Review *see* 0195-5314
0020-5109 Andy Warhol's Interview *see* 0149-8932
0020-5117 Interaction *changed to* Teacher's Interaction.
0020-5125 Interafrique Presse†
0020-5133 Interamerican†
0020-515X Interauteurs†
0020-5168 Interavia: World Review of Aviation-Astronautics-Avionics *changed to* Interavia: Aerospace Review.
0020-5176 Interavia Air Letter
0020-5184 Intercambio
0020-5192 Inter-Cambio
0020-5206 Interceptor†
0020-5214 Interceram
0020-5222 Interchange†
0020-5249 Intercollegiate Review
0020-5273 Intercom (New York)†
0020-529X Interconair Aviazione e Marina Internazionale Intercontinental Press.
0020-532X Intercultural Education†
0020-5338 Interdisciplinet
0020-5346 Intereconomics
0020-5362 Interesse
0020-5389 Interest and Dividends†
0020-5397 Interet Europeen: Europe et Regions†
0020-5419 Interface (Bethesda)
0020-5451 Interfaith Observer†
0020-5478 Interim†
0020-5494 Interior Design
0020-5508 Interior Design
0020-5516 Interiors *see* 0164-8470
0020-5532 Interline Reporter
0020-5540 Interlingvistika Informa Servo
0020-5559 Interlink
0020-5567 Interlinks†
0020-5575 Interlit
0020-5605 Intermediair
0020-5613 Intermediaire des Chercheurs et Curieux
0020-5621 Intermediaire des Genealogistes
0020-563X Intermediate Teacher†
0020-5656 Intermountain Contractor
0020-5664 Intermountain Economic Review *see* 0195-8550
0020-5672 Intermountain Farmer *changed to* I F A Cooperator.
0020-5680 Intermountain Food Retailer *changed to* Intermountain Retailer.
0020-5699 Intermountain Industry
0020-5702 Transport Management *changed to* Distributie en Transport Management.
0020-5710 Internacia Esperanto-Muzeo en Wien. Informilo *changed to* La Dua Jarcento. Informilo.
0020-5737 Internal *changed to* N Y U Today.
0020-5745 Internal Auditor
0020-5761 Internal Revenue Bulletin
0020-577X Internasjonal Politikk
0020-5796 International Abstract†
0020-580X International Abstracts in Operations Research
0020-5818 International Abstracts of Biological Sciences *see* 0733-4443
0020-5826 International Accountant†
0020-5842 International Aerospace Abstracts
0020-5850 International Affairs
0020-5877 International African Bibliography
0020-5885 International Alliance of Theatrical Stage Employes and Moving Picture Machine Operators of the United States and Canada. Official Bulletin
0020-5893 International and Comparative Law Quarterly
0020-5907 International Anesthesiology Clinics
0020-5915 International Archives of Allergy and Applied Immunology *see* 1018-2438
0020-5923 International Archives of Occupational Health *see* 0340-0131
0020-5931 International Art Market†
0020-594X International Association for Analog Computation. Proceedings *see* 0378-4754
0020-5958 International Association for Mathematical Geology. Journal *see* 0882-8121
0020-5966 International Association of Agricultural Librarians and Documentalists. Quarterly Bulletin *changed to* International Association of Agricultural Information Specialists. Quarterly Bulletin.
0020-5974 I A E I News
0020-6008 International Association of Personnel in Employment Security. News
0020-6016 International Association of Pupil Personnel Workers. Journal
0020-6024 International Association of Scientific Hydrology. Bulletin *see* 0262-6667
0020-6032 International Association of Universities. Bulletin *see* 0952-8733
0020-6059 International Associations *see* 0250-4928
0020-6067 International Atomic Energy Agency. Bulletin
0020-6075 List of Bibliographies on Nuclear Energy†
0020-6091 Audiology
0020-6105 International Aviation Review†
0020-6121 International Bank Note Society Magazine
0020-613X International Behavioural Scientist
0020-6156 International Bibliography of Automatic Control†
0020-6164 International Biodeterioration Bulletin *see* 0265-3036
0020-6172 International Boat Industry
0020-6180 International Bookbinder†
0020-6199 International Beverage News *changed to* International Bottler and Packer.
0020-6202 International Brahman Review†
0020-6229 International Broadcast Engineer
0020-6245 International Bulletin for the Printing and Allied Trades†
0020-627X International Business Contacts†
0020-6288 International Business Equipment†
0020-6296 International Centre for Local Credit. Bulletin *changed to* Local Finance.
0020-630X International Centre for Theoretical Physics. Monthly Bulletin†
0020-6318 International Chemical Engineering
0020-6326 International Chemical Register *changed to* Chemical Trade Magazine.
0020-6334 International Chemical Worker *see* 0162-637X
0020-6342 International Child Welfare Review
0020-6350 International Christian Broadcasters Bulletin†
0020-6369 International Civil Defence *changed to* International Civil Defence Journal.
0020-6377 International Civil Engineering Monthly†
0020-6385 Commerce Today *see* 0190-6275
0020-6393 International Commission of Jurists. Review
0020-6407 International Conciliation†
0020-6415 International Construction
0020-6423 International Construction Reporter
0020-6431 International Consumer†
0020-644X International Cooperative Training Journal *see* 0090-9580

ISSN

0020-6466 International Council for the Exploration of the Sea *see* 1054-3139
0020-6482 International Credit Bank. Quarterly Review†
0020-6490 International Currency Review
0020-6504 International Cycle Sport
0020-6512 International Defense Review
0020-6520 International DeMolay Cordon†
0020-6539 International Dental Journal
0020-6555 International Development Review *see* 1011-6370
0020-6563 International Digest of Health Legislation
0020-6571 International Drug Therapy Newsletter
0020-658X International Dyer, Textile Printer, Bleacher and Finisher
0020-6598 International Economic Review
0020-6601 International Educational and Cultural Exchange†
0020-661X International Egg Commission. Market Review Situation & Outlook Report
0020-6628 International Egg Commission. Six-Monthly Statistical Bulletin
0020-6644 International Electronics†
0020-6652 International Executive
0020-6660 International Federation for Housing and Planning Bulletin *changed to* Prospect.
0020-6687 International Federation of European Contractors of Building and Public Works Review *see* 0014-9373
0020-6695 International Federation of Gynaecology and Obstetrics. Journal *see* 0020-7292
0020-6709 International Federation of Pedestrians. International Bulletin *changed to* Voice of the Pedestrian.
0020-6717 International Financial News Survey *see* 0047-083X
0020-6725 International Financial Statistics
0020-675X International Flying Farmer
0020-6768 International Folk Music Council. Bulletin *see* 0739-1390
0020-6784 International Forum
0020-6792 International Franchise Association. Legal Bulletin *changed to* Franchising World.
0020-6806 International Friendship League. Newsletter *changed to* Friendship News.
0020-6814 International Geology Review
0020-6830 International Grafik
0020-6849 International Guide to Classical Studies†
0020-6857 International Guide to Indic Studies†
0020-6865 International Guide to Medieval Studies
0020-6911 International Hotel Review *see* 1047-2975
0020-692X International Humanism *see* 0925-1375
0020-6938 International Hydrographic Bulletin
0020-6946 International Hydrographic Review
0020-6970 Institut International du Froid. Bulletin
0020-6997 International Insurance Monitor
0020-7004 International Intertrade Index
0020-7020 International Journal
0020-7039 International Journal
0020-7047 International Journal for Philosophy of Religion
0020-7063 International Journal of Accounting Education and Research
0020-7071 International Journal of American Linguistics
0020-708X International Journal of Applied Radiation and Isotopes *see* 0883-2889
0020-7098 International Journal of Arbitration
0020-7101 International Journal of Bio-Medical Computing
0020-711X International Journal of Biochemistry
0020-7128 International Journal of Biometeorology
0020-7136 International Journal of Cancer
0020-7144 International Journal of Clinical and Experimental Hypnosis
0020-7152 International Journal of Comparative Sociology
0020-7160 International Journal of Computer Mathematics
0020-7179 International Journal of Control
0020-7187 International Journal of Early Childhood
0020-7209 International Journal of Electrical Engineering Education
0020-7217 International Journal of Electronics
0020-7225 International Journal of Engineering Science
0020-7233 International Journal of Environmental Studies. Sections A & B
0020-725X International Journal of Fertility
0020-7268 International Journal of Fracture Mechanics *see* 0376-9429
0020-7276 International Journal of Game Theory
0020-7284 International Journal of Group Psychotherapy
0020-7292 International Journal of Gynaecology and Obstetrics
0020-7306 International Journal of Health Education *changed to* Hygie.
0020-7314 International Journal of Health Services
0020-7322 International Journal of Insect Morphology and Embryology
0020-7330 International Journal of Legal Research†
0020-7349 International Journal of Leprosy *see* 0148-916X
0020-7357 International Journal of Machine Tool Design and Research *see* 0890-6955
0020-7365 International Journal of Magnetism†
0020-7373 International Journal of Man-Machine Studies
0020-7381 International Journal of Mass Spectrometry and Ion Physics *see* 0168-1176
0020-739X International Journal of Mathematical Education in Science and Technology
0020-7403 International Journal of Mechanical Sciences
0020-7411 International Journal of Mental Health
0020-7438 International Journal of Middle East Studies
0020-7446 International Journal of Neurology
0020-7454 International Journal of Neuroscience
0020-7462 International Journal of Non-Linear Mechanics
0020-7470 International Journal of Nondestructive Testing *see* 0140-072X
0020-7489 International Journal of Nursing Studies
0020-7497 International Journal of Offender Therapy *see* 0306-624X
0020-7500 International Journal of Orthodontics *see* 0889-5406
0020-7519 International Journal for Parasitology
0020-7527 International Journal of Physical Distribution *see* 0960-0035
0020-7535 International Journal of Powder Metallurgy *see* 0888-7462
0020-7543 International Journal of Production Research
0020-7578 International Journal of Psycho-Analysis
0020-7594 International Journal of Psychology
0020-7608 International Journal of Quantum Chemistry
0020-7616 International Journal of Radiation Biology
0020-7624 International Journal of Rock Mechanics and Mining Sciences *see* 0148-9062
0020-7640 International Journal of Social Psychiatry
0020-7659 International Journal of Sociology
0020-7675 International Journal of Sociometry and Sociatry *changed to* Handbook of International Sociometry.
0020-7683 International Journal of Solids and Structures
0020-7691 International Journal of Speleology†
0020-7705 International Journal of Symbology†
0020-7713 International Journal of Systematic Bacteriology
0020-7721 International Journal of Systems Science
0020-773X International Journal of the Addictions
0020-7748 International Journal of Theoretical Physics
0020-7756 International Labour Documentation
0020-7764 International Labour Office. Legislative Series *see* 1014-7071
0020-7772 International Labour Office. Official Bulletin *see* 0378-5882
0020-7772 International Labour Office. Official Bulletin *see* 0378-5890
0020-7780 International Labour Review
0020-7799 International Language Reporter *changed to* Eco-Logos.
0020-7810 International Lawyer
0020-7829 International Legal Materials
0020-7837 International Library Review *see* 1057-2317
0020-7845 International Licensing
0020-7853 International Lighting Review
0020-7888 International Management
0020-7896 International Management Information Business Digest†
0020-7918 International Marine Science *changed to* I M S Newsletter.
0020-7926 International Mathematical News
0020-7950 International Medieval Bibliography
0020-7969 International Mental Health Research Newsletter *changed to* Transnational Mental Health Research Newsletter.
0020-7977 International Microform Journal of Legal Medicine *changed to* International Microform Journal of Legal Medicine and Forensic Sciences.
0020-7985 International Migration
0020-8000 International Mining Equipment *see* 0010-1281
0020-8019 International Molders' and Allied Workers' Journal†
0020-8027 International Monetary Fund. Staff Papers
0020-8035 International Monetary Issues *changed to* Gold, Money, Commodities.
0020-8051 International Musician
0020-806X International Narcotic Report *see* 0148-4648
0020-8086 International News Items†
0020-8094 International News Letter *changed to* International Report.
0020-8124 International Nursing Index
0020-8132 International Nursing Review
0020-8140 International Odd Fellow†
0020-8159 International Operating Engineer
0020-8167 International Ophthalmology Clinics
0020-8175 International Organization of Good Templars Journal *changed to* The Globe.
0020-8183 International Organization
0020-8191 International Paper Board Industry
0020-8213 International Peace Research Newsletter *changed to* I P R A Newsletter.
0020-823X International P.E.N. Bulletin of Selected Books *changed to* P E N International.
0020-8248 International Perfumer *see* 0305-0319
0020-8256 International Pest Control
0020-8264 International Pharmaceutical Abstracts
0020-8272 International Pharmacopsychiatry *see* 0302-282X
0020-8280 International Photo Technik *changed to* Photo Technik International.
0020-8299 International Photographer
0020-8302 International Piano Library Bulletin†
0020-8337 International Polar Motion Service. Monthly Notes *changed to* International Earth Rotation Service. Monthly Bulletin.
0020-8345 International Political Science Abstracts
0020-8353 Potters Herald†
0020-837X International Press Journal
0020-8396 International Prisoners Aid Association. Newsletter
0020-840X International Problems
0020-8418 International Prospect
0020-8426 International Psychiatry Clinics†
0020-8434 International Public Relations Review *see* 0033-3700
0020-8442 Rail International
0020-8450 International Railway Journal *see* 0744-5326
0020-8477 International Rehabilitation Review
0020-8485 International Relations†
0020-8493 International Reporter
0020-8507 International Reports
0020-8523 International Review of Administrative Sciences
0020-8566 International Review of Education
0020-8574 International Review of History and Political Science†
0020-8582 International Review of Mission
0020-8604 International Review of the Red Cross
0020-8639 Trade and Economic Development†
0020-8647 International Ropeway Review†
0020-8655 International Rubber Digest
0020-8663 International Seed Testing Association. Proceedings *see* 0251-0952
0020-8671 International Seismological Centre. Bulletin
0020-868X International Shipbuilding Progress
0020-8698 International Silk Association. Bulletin *see* 0290-8271
0020-8701 International Social Science Journal
0020-871X International Social Security Review
0020-8728 International Social Work
0020-8736 International Socialism *changed to* International Socialism.
0020-8779 International Statistical Institute Review *see* 0306-7734
0020-8787 Stewardess and Flight Service *see* 0915-2210
0020-8795 International Stock Report *see* 0364-5711
0020-8809 International Student Newsletter *changed to* F.S.S.C. Newsletter.
0020-8817 International Studies
0020-8825 International Studies of Management and Organization
0020-8833 International Studies Quarterly
0020-8841 International Sugar Journal
0020-885X International Sugar Organization Statistical Bulletin
0020-8868 International Surgery
0020-8876 International Swimmer†
0020-8884 World Federation of Teachers' Unions. Information Letter
0020-8892 International Teamster
0020-8930 International Theatre†
0020-8957 International Trade Forum
0020-8981 International Trade Review
0020-899X International Trade Union News†
0020-9007 International Transport Workers' Journal†
0020-9015 International Travel *changed to* Travelweek.
0020-9023 International Trotter and Pacer *changed to* Harness Horsemen International.
0020-9058 I U C N Bulletin
0020-9066 International Union for Vacuum Science, Technique and Applications. News Bulletin
0020-9074 International Union of Food and Allied Workers' Associations. News Bulletin
0020-9090 International Whaling Statistics†
0020-9104 Wheelspin News
0020-9112 International Wildlife
0020-9120 International Women's News
0020-9139 International Woodworker *changed to* Woodworker.
0020-9147 Elektrowaerme International *see* 0340-3521
0020-9147 Elektrowaerme International *see* 0340-3513
0020-9155 International Zoo News
0020-9163 Internationale - A. M. R.
0020-918X I B R
0020-9198 Internationale Bibliographie der Versicherungsliteratur†

ISSN INDEX 5395

0020-9201 Internationale Bibliographie der Zeitschriftenliteratur aus allen Gebieten des Wissens
0020-921X I B N
0020-9236 Internationale Elektronische Rundschau *changed to* Nachrichten - Elektronik und Telematik.
0020-9252 Internationale Kirchliche Zeitschrift
0020-9260 Internationale Luftwaffen Revue *changed to* Luftwaffen Revue.
0020-9309 Internationale Revue der Gesamten Hydrobiologie
0020-9317 Internationale Spectator
0020-9325 Internationale Stiftung Mozarteum. Mitteilungen
0020-9341 Internationale Transport-Zeitschrift
0020-935X Internationale Wirtschaft
0020-9368 Internationale Wirtschafts-Briefe
0020-9376 Internationale Zeitschrift fuer Angewandte Physiologie Einschliesslich Arbeitsphysiologie *see* 0301-5548
0020-9384 Gas Waerme International
0020-9392 Internationale Zeitschrift fuer Klinische Pharmakologie, Therapie und Toxikologie *see* 0174-4879
0020-9406 Internationale Zeitschrift fuer Vitamin-Forschung *see* 0300-9831
0020-9422 Internationaler Holzmarkt
0020-9430 Internationales Afrikaforum
0020-9449 Internationales Asienforum
0020-9457 Internationales Biographisches Archiv *changed to* Internationales Biographisches Archiv - Personen Aktuell.
0020-9465 Internationales Europaforum *see* 0049-7134
0020-9473 Internationales Freies Wort
0020-9481 Internationales Gewerbearchiv
0020-949X Internationales Handbuch *changed to* Internationales Handbuch - Laender Aktuell.
0020-9503 Internationales Recht und Diplomatie†
0020-9511 Internationales Verkehrswesen
0020-952X Internationella Studier
0020-9538 Internit†
0020-9546 Internist *changed to* Internist: Health Policy in Practice.
0020-9554 Der Internist
0020-9562 Internist Observer†
0020-9570 Internistische Praxis
0020-9597 Interplanetary News
0020-9619 Interpressgrafik *changed to* Interpressgraphic.
0020-9635 Interpretation (Flushing)
0020-9643 Interpretation (Richmond)
0020-966X Buffalo and Erie County Public Library Bulletin
0020-9678 Interpreter (Nashville)
0020-9686 Interpreter Releases
0020-9694 Quarterly Report on Public Welfare in Arkansas†
0020-9708 Interracial Books for Children *see* 0146-5562
0020-9716 Interstages†
0020-9724 Interstampa della Capitale†
0020-9732 Interstate Oil Compact Commission. Committee Bulletin *see* 1046-2333
0020-9740 Interstellar Communication *changed to* Huginn and Muninn.
0020-9759 Intervalo†
0020-9783 Interwing Weekly Review
0020-9791 Intimate Apparel *see* 0360-3520
0020-9805 Intimate Confessions
0020-9813 Intimate Story
0020-9848 Intra-Science Chemistry Reports *see* 0276-8585
0020-9864 Intrepid
0020-9872 Inuktitut
0020-9880 Invalidensport *changed to* Behindertensport.
0020-9910 Inventiones Mathematicae
0020-9929 Inverness Courier
0020-9937 Investicni Vystavba
0020-9953 Investigacion Pesquera
0020-9961 Investigaciones en Sociologia
0020-9988 Investigative Ophthalmology *see* 0146-0404
0020-9996 Investigative Radiology
0021-0005 Investigation Urology *see* 0022-5347
0021-0013 Investigator
0021-003X Investing, Licensing & Trading Conditions Abroad: Global Edition
0021-0048 Investment Analyst†
0021-0064 Investment & Marketing
0021-0072 Investment Bulletin *changed to* A I C Investment Bulletin.
0021-0080 Investment Dealers' Digest
0021-0110 Investment Quality Trends
0021-0153 Investor
0021-0161 Investors Chronicle and Stock Exchange Gazette *see* 0261-3115
0021-0218 Investors League Bulletin†
0021-0250 Inward Light†
0021-0269 Inyala News
0021-0277 Inzinierske Stavby
0021-0293 Inzhenernyi Zhurnal *changed to* Inzhenerno-Fizicheskii Zhurnal.
0021-0307 Inzicht
0021-0315 Inzynieria i Budownictwo
0021-0331 Io
0021-034X Ion
0021-0358 Ionian
0021-0374 Ionospheric Data *see* 0111-7122
0021-0382 Ionospheric Data in Japan
0021-0390 Ionospheric Predictions†
0021-0404 Iost
0021-0420 Iowa Adult Education Association. Newsletter *changed to* I A L L Eye-Opener.
0021-0439 Iowa Architect
0021-0447 Iowa Association of School Librarians. Library Lines *changed to* Iowa Media Message.
0021-0455 Iowa Bird Life
0021-0463 Business and Industry
0021-0471 Iowa Conservationist†
0021-0498 Iowa Dental Journal
0021-0501 Iowa Engineer
0021-051X Iowa Farm Bureau Spokesman
0021-0528 Iowa Food Dealer†
0021-0536 Iowa Journal of Social Work *changed to* Social Development Issues.
0021-0552 Iowa Law Review
0021-0560 Iowa Legionnaire
0021-0579 Iowa Library Quarterly†
0021-0587 Iowa Medical Society. Journal *see* 0746-8709
0021-0595 Iowa Municipalities
0021-0609 Iowa Music Educator
0021-0617 Iowa P T A Bulletin
0021-0625 Iowa Plumbing, Heating, Cooling Contractor
0021-0633 Iowa Police Journal
0021-0641 Iowa A E C News *see* 0162-2412
0021-065X Iowa Review
0021-0668 Iowa School Board Dialogue
0021-0676 Iowa Science Teachers Journal
0021-0684 Iowa State Journal of Science *see* 0092-6345
0021-0706 Iowa Transit *changed to* Hawkeye Engineer.
0021-0714 Iowa Veterinarian†
0021-0722 Iowan
0021-0730 Iowa's People†
0021-0749 Ipargazdasag
0021-0757 Ipari Energiagazdalkodas *changed to* Energiagazdalkodas.
0021-0765 Epirotiki Estia
0021-0773 Iqbal Review
0021-0781 Iran News
0021-079X Iran Oil Journal
0021-0803 Iran Trade and Industry
0021-082X Iranian Journal of Dermatology
0021-0846 Iranian Library Association Bulletin†
0021-0854 Iranian Petroleum Institute. Bulletin
0021-0862 Iranian Studies
0021-0870 Iranica Antiqua
0021-0889 Iraq
0021-0897 Iraq Natural History Museum. Bulletin *changed to* Iraq Natural History Museum. Bulletin.
0021-0900 Iraq. Central Statistical Organization. Summary of Foreign Trade Statistics
0021-0919 Iraq. Statistics Bureau. Quarterly Bulletin of Foreign Trade Statistics†
0021-0927 Iraqi Medical Professions' Association. Journal
0021-0935 Ireland *changed to* Ireland Today.
0021-0943 Ireland of the Welcomes
0021-0951 Ireland's Own
0021-096X Ireland's Press and Print†
0021-0978 Irenikon
0021-0986 I R G-M I R Bulletin *changed to* Nonviolence et Societe.
0021-101X Iris an Gharda *changed to* Garda Review.
0021-1028 Irish Accountant and Secretary†
0021-1036 Irish Agricultural and Creamery Review *see* 0790-732X
0021-1052 Irish Astronomical Journal
0021-1060 Irish Banking Review
0021-1079 Irish Bee-Keeper
0021-1087 Irish Builder and Engineer
0021-1095 Irish Catering Review *changed to* Hotel and Catering Review.
0021-1109 Irish Chemist and Druggist *changed to* Irish Pharmacy Journal.
0021-1117 Irish Contracts Weekly
0021-1133 Irish Dental Association. Journal
0021-1141 Irish Electrical Industries Review
0021-115X Irish Engineers *see* 0332-1711
0021-1168 Irish Farmers' Journal
0021-1176 Irish Farming News†
0021-1184 Irish Field
0021-1192 Irish Forestry
0021-1206 Irish Georgian Society. Bulletin
0021-1214 Irish Historical Studies
0021-1249 Irish Journal of Agricultural Economics and Rural Sociology†
0021-1257 Irish Journal of Education
0021-1265 Irish Journal of Medical Sciences
0021-1273 Irish Jurist
0021-1281 Irish Law Times and Solicitors' Journal
0021-129X Irish Medical Association. Journal *see* 0332-3102
0021-1303 Irish Messenger of the Sacred Heart *changed to* Sacred Heart Messenger.
0021-1311 Irish Naturalists' Journal
0021-132X Irish Numismatics†
0021-1338 Irish Nurses' Journal *changed to* World of Irish Nursing.
0021-1354 Irish Nursing News *changed to* Irish Nursing Newsletter.
0021-1362 Irish Plumbing and Heating Engineer *changed to* Irish Heating and Ventilating News.
0021-1370 Irish Statistical Bulletin *see* 0790-8334
0021-1389 Irish Sword
0021-1397 Irish Tatler and Sketch *changed to* I T Magazine.
0021-1400 Irish Theological Quarterly
0021-1419 Irish Travel Trade News†
0021-1427 Irish University Review
0021-1443 Irish World and Gaelic American
0021-1451 Irish Yachting and Motorboating *changed to* Ireland Afloat.
0021-1478 Irodalomtortenet
0021-1486 Irodalomtorteneti Kozlemenyek
0021-1494 Irohin Yoruba
0021-1516 Iron Age Metalworking International *see* 0163-030X
0021-1524 Iron and Steel *see* 0143-7798
0021-1532 Statistical Office of the European Communities. Iron and Steel *see* 0378-7559
0021-1559 Iron and Steel Engineer
0021-1575 Tetsu-to-Hagane
0021-1583 Iron and Steel Institute of Japan. Transactions *see* 0915-1559
0021-1591 Iron and Steel Monthly Statistics *see* 0308-9770
0021-1605 Iron and Steel Translations *changed to* Ferrous and Non-Ferrous Science and Technology Lists-British Industrial and Scientific International Translations.
0021-1613 Iron & Steel Journal of India
0021-1621 Iron Worker†
0021-163X Ironworker
0021-1648 Food Irradiation - Irradiation des Aliments *see* 0301-049X
0021-1656 Irrigation Age†
0021-1664 Irrigation and Power
0021-1672 Irrigation and Power Abstracts
0021-1680 Irrigazione e Drenaggio
0021-1699 Medical Treatment
0021-1710 Iscani†
0021-1737 Isenkraemmerbladet *see* 0107-9263
0021-1753 Isis
0021-1761 Iskra
0021-177X Iskusstvo
0021-1788 Iskusstvo Kino
0021-1796 Isla Literaria†
0021-180X Al-Islaam
0021-1818 Der Islam
0021-1826 Islam and the Modern Age
0021-1834 Islamic Culture
0021-1842 Islamic Quarterly
0021-1850 Islamic Review†
0021-1869 Islander *see* 1051-7898
0021-1885 Isolation et Revetements *see* 0244-2019
0021-1893 Isotope†
0021-1907 Isotope and Radiation Research
0021-1915 Isotopenpraxis
0021-1923 Isotopes and Radiation Technology†
0021-1931 Isotopics†
0021-194X Israel
0021-1958 Israel Annals of Psychiatry and Related Disciplines†
0021-1974 Israel Book World *see* 0333-953X
0021-1982 Israel. Central Bureau of Statistics. Monthly Bulletin of Statistics
0021-1990 Israel. Central Bureau of Statistics. Foreign Trade Statistics Quarterly *changed to* Israel. Central Bureau of Statistics. Annual Foreign Trade Statistics.
0021-2008 Israel. Central Bureau of Statistics. Monthly Price Statistics
0021-2016 Israel Diamonds
0021-2032 Israel Digest of Press and Events in Israel and the Middle East *changed to* Israel Digest.
0021-2040 Israel Economist
0021-2059 Israel Exploration Journal
0021-2067 Israel Export and Trade Journal *changed to* Israel Aussenhandel.
0021-2075 Israel Financial Review
0021-2083 Israel Horizons
0021-2091 Israel Illustrated *see* 0007-7038
0021-2113 Israel Investors' Report *see* 0334-3898
0021-213X Israel Journal of Botany
0021-2148 Israel Journal of Chemistry
0021-2164 Israel Journal of Earth Sciences
0021-2172 Israel Journal of Mathematics
0021-2180 Israel Journal of Medical Sciences
0021-2199 Israel Journal of Physiotherapy
0021-2202 Israel Journal of Technology
0021-2210 Israel Journal of Zoology
0021-2229 Israel Labour Party Bulletin†
0021-2237 Israel Law Review
0021-2245 Israel†
0021-2253 Israel Medical Association. Quarterly Review. *changed to* Israel Medical Association. Quarterly Medical Review.
0021-2261 Israel. Meteorological Service. Series B: Observational Data. Monthly Weather Report
0021-227X Israel Museum News *see* 0333-7499
0021-2288 Israel Numismatic Journal
0021-230X Israel Seaman†
0021-2318 I S L I C Bulletin
0021-2326 Israel. Ministry of Justice. Patent Office. Patents and Designs Journal
0021-2334 Die Gemeinde
0021-2342 Israelitisches Wochenblatt fuer die Schweiz

ISSN

5396 ISSN INDEX

0021-2350 Israel's Oriental Problems *changed to* Merkaz Haribaz.
0021-2369 Issue†
0021-2385 Issues in Criminology *changed to* Social Justice.
0021-2415 Istarski Mozaik
0021-2423 Istina
0021-2431 Istituto Carlo Forlanini. Annali†
0021-244X Istituto Centrale del Restauro. Bollettino†
0021-2458 Istituto di Architettura e Urbanistica. Rassegna
0021-2474 Istituto di Studi Romani. Rassegna d'Informazioni *changed to* Istituto Nazionale di Studi Romani. Rassegna d'Informazioni.
0021-2482 Istituto Italiano degli Attuari. Giornale
0021-2490 Istituto Italiano di Cultura. Newsletter†
0021-2504 Istituto Lombardo Accademia di Scienze e Lettere. Rendiconti. A
0021-2512 Istituto Mobiliare Italiano. Quarterly Economic Review†
0021-2520 Istituto Nazionale della Previdenza Sociale. Atti Ufficiali
0021-2539 I N A I L Notiziario Statistico
0021-2547 Istituto Sieroterapico Milanese. Bollettino
0021-2555 Istituto Storico e di Cultura dell'Arma del Genio. Bollettino
0021-2571 Istituto Superiore di Sanita. Annali
0021-258X Istituto Tecnico
0021-2598 Istituto Vaccinogeno e dei Consorzi Provinciali Antitubercolari. Rivista†
0021-261X Istmo
0021-2644 Istorijski Glasnik
0021-2652 Istorijski Zapisi
0021-2660 Istoriya S.S.S.R.
0021-2679 Istruzione Tecnica *see* 0535-899X
0021-2717 It Starts in the Classroom
0021-2725 It-Torca
0021-2733 Italdoc
0021-2741 Italia (Rome, 1953)†
0021-275X Italia Agricola
0021-2768 Italia che Scrive
0021-2776 Italia Forestale e Montana
0021-2792 Italia Medica *changed to* Italia Medica - Vitalita.
0021-2806 Italia Missionaria
0021-2822 Italia Nostra
0021-2830 Italia Numismatica
0021-2849 L'Italia Scacchistica
0021-2857 Italia sul Mare
0021-2873 Italian American Business
0021-289X Italian Business†
0021-2903 Italian American Chamber of Commerce of Chicago. Bulletin
0021-2911 Italian Economic Survey†
0021-292X Italian General Review of Dermatology
0021-2938 Italian Journal of Biochemistry
0021-2954 Italian Quarterly†
0021-2970 Italiana Stil Maglia
0021-2989 Italian Stock Market†
0021-2997 Italian Trade Topics†
0021-3004 Italian Trends†
0021-3020 Italica (Madison)
0021-3063 Italy - Documents and Notes
0021-3071 Annali della Sanita Pubblica
0021-308X Italy and Nigeria†
0021-3098 Italy Canada Trade
0021-3101 Italy. Centro per la Statistica Aziendale. Index
0021-3128 Italy. Azienda Autonoma delle Ferrovie dello Stato. Informazioni Doc
0021-3136 Italy. Istituto Centrale di Statistica. Bolletino Mensile di Statistica
0021-3144 Italy. Ministero dei Trasporti e dell'Aviazione Civile. Azienda Autonoma delle Ferrovie dello Stato. Bollettino Statistico Mensile
0021-3187 Itineraires
0021-3209 Itinerarium
0021-3225 Acta Biologica Iugoslavica. Serija C: Iugoslavica Physiologica et Pharmacologica Acta
0021-3233 Yunost'
0021-3241 Iura
0021-325X Ius Canonicum
0021-3268 Iustitia
0021-3276 Ivy Leaf
0021-3284 Iwate Igaku Zasshi
0021-3306 Iyyun
0021-3314 Outdoor America
0021-3349 Izmeritel'naya Tekhnika
0021-3357 Izmir Chamber of Commerce Review
0021-3381 Izraz
0021-339X Fountain
0021-3411 Izvestiya Vysshikh Uchebnykh Zavedenii. Seriya Fizika
0021-342X Timiryazevskaya Sel'skokhozyaistvennaya Akademiya. Izvestiya
0021-3438 Izvestiya Vysshikh Uchebnykh Zavedenii. Seriya Chernaya Metallurgiya
0021-3446 Izvestiya Vysshikh Uchebnykh Zavedenii. Seriya Matematika
0021-3454 Izvestiya Vysshikh Uchebnykh Zavedenii. Seriya Priborostroenie
0021-3462 Izvestiya Vysshikh Uchebnykh Zavedenii. Seriya Radiofizika
0021-3470 Izvestiya Vysshikh Uchebnykh Zavedenii. Seriya Radioelektronika
0021-3489 Izvestiya Vysshikh Uchebnykh Zavedenii. Seriya Tekhnologiya Legkoi Promyshlennosti
0021-3497 Izvestiya Vysshikh Uchebnykh Zavedenii. Seriya Tekhnologiya Tekstil'noi Promyshlennosti
0021-3500 J A F News Letter†
0021-3519 J A G Journal *changed to* Naval Law Review.
0021-3527 J A G Bulletin *see* 0094-8381
0021-3551 Japan Agricultural Research Quarterly
0021-356X J.B. Speed Art Museum Bulletin†
0021-3578 J C I World *changed to* J C I News.
0021-3594 B J E Bulletin *changed to* Up-to-Date with B J E.
0021-3608 J E E: Japan Electronic Engineering *see* 0385-4507
0021-3616 J E I: Japan Electronic Industry *see* 0385-4515
0021-3624 J E I
0021-3632 J E M F Newsletter *changed to* American Vernacular Music.
0021-3640 J E T P Letters
0021-3659 J E T S Journal†
0021-3667 Journal of General Education
0021-3675 Japanese Journal of Medical Electronics and Biological Engineering
0021-3691 J M Action *changed to* J-M Future.
0021-3705 J N F Illustrated
0021-3713 J N K V V News
0021-3721 J N K V V Research Journal
0021-3748 J O L A Technical Communications†
0021-3756 J O T (Journal fuer Oberflaechentechnik) *see* 0940-8789
0021-3764 J S M E Bulletin *see* 0913-185X
0021-3772 J T A Daily News Bulletin
0021-3780 J W B Circle *changed to* J C C Circle.
0021-3799 J.W.V.A. Bulletin
0021-3802 Formule 1†
0021-3810 Jacetania
0021-3829 Jack and Jill (Inkprint Edition)
0021-3837 Jack London Newsletter†
0021-3845 Jack-Pine Warbler
0021-3861 Jacksonville Magazine
0021-387X Jacobsen's Fats & Oils Bulletin
0021-3888 Jadeed Science
0021-3896 Jaegerblatt
0021-390X Jag
0021-3918 Jagawani
0021-3926 Jagd und Jaeger in Rheinland-Pfalz
0021-3942 Der Jagdgebrauchshund
0021-3950 Der Jagdspaniel
0021-3969 Jagriti
0021-3977 Jagt og Fiskeri
0021-3985 Jahrbuch der Absatz- und Verbrauchsforschung
0021-3993 Jahrbuch fuer Internationales Recht *see* 0344-3094
0021-4000 Jahrbuch fuer Psychologie, Psychotherapie, und Medizinische Anthropologie *see* 0300-869X
0021-4019 Jahrbuecher fuer Geschichte Osteuropas
0021-4027 Jahrbuecher fuer Nationaloekonomie und Statistik
0021-4035 Jain Jagran
0021-4043 Jain Journal
0021-4051 Jakt-Fiske-Friluftsliv *changed to* Jakt-Fiske.
0021-406X Jaktmaker och Fiskevatten
0021-4078 Jalkine
0021-4094 Jamaica Chamber of Commerce Journal
0021-4108 Jamaica. Department of Statistics. Rural Retail Price Index *changed to* Statistical Institute of Jamaica. Consumer Price Indices Bulletin.
0021-4116 News Review
0021-4124 Jamaica Journal
0021-4132 Jamaica Public Health
0021-4140 Jamaican Nurse
0021-4159 Jamaican Weekly Gleaner
0021-4167 Missionland†
0021-4183 James Joyce Quarterly
0021-4191 Jamia Educational Quarterly†
0021-4205 Jana Sangh Patrika
0021-4213 Janaman
0021-4221 Janata
0021-423X Jantantra
0021-4248 Janus†
0021-4256 Janus†
0021-4264 Janus
0021-4272 Janus & S C T H
0021-4280 Japan Academy. Proceedings *see* 0386-2194
0021-4280 Japan Academy. Proceedings *see* 0386-2208
0021-4299 Japan-America Society of Washington. Bulletin
0021-4302 Japan Architect
0021-4310 Seigyo Kogaku *changed to* Shisutemu to Seigyo.
0021-4329 Japan Automotive News
0021-4337 Japan Book News†
0021-4345 Japan Camera Trade News
0021-4353 Japan Christian Activity News
0021-4361 Japan Christian Quarterly
0021-437X Japan Diabetes Society. Journal
0021-4388 Japan Economic Journal *changed to* The Nikkei Weekly.
0021-4396 Japan Foundrymen's Society. Journal
0021-440X Japan Harvest
0021-4418 Japan Illustrated†
0021-4426 Japan Institute of Metals. Bulletin
0021-4434 Japan Institute of Metals. Transactions *see* 0916-1821
0021-4442 Japan Interior Design
0021-4469 Japan Labour Bulletin
0021-4477 Japan Lumber Journal
0021-4485 Japan. Kaijo Hoan-cho. Suiro-bu. Suiro Yoho
0021-4507 Japan Medical Gazette†
0021-4515 Japan Medical News
0021-4523 Japan Metal Bulletin
0021-4531 Japan Missionary Bulletin
0021-454X Japan Orthodontic Society. Journal
0021-4558 Japan Patent News *changed to* Japan Patent Report.
0021-4574 Japan Plastics†
0021-4582 Japan Plastics Age
0021-4590 Japan Quarterly
0021-4604 Japan Report (New York)
0021-4620 Japan Sea Regional Fisheries Research Laboratory. Bulletin
0021-4639 Japan Sewage Works Association. Journal
0021-4647 Japan Shipbuilding & Marine Engineering
0021-4655 Japan Socialist Review†
0021-4663 Japan Society for Aeronautical and Space Sciences. Journal
0021-4671 Japan Society for Cancer Therapy. Journal
0021-468X Japan Society of Civil Engineers. Journal
0021-4701 Japan Society of London. Bulletin *changed to* Japan Society. Review.
0021-471X Japan Society of Mathematical Education. Journal
0021-4728 J S M E Journal
0021-4736 Japan Stock Journal
0021-4744 Japan Telecommunications Review *see* 0915-2334
0021-4760 Japan Trade Bulletin *see* 0388-0311
0021-4779 Japan Welding News†
0021-4787 Japan Welding Society. Journal
0021-4795 Japan Wood Research Society. Journal
0021-4809 Japanese Archives of Internal Medicine
0021-4817 Japanese Association for Infectious Diseases. Journal
0021-4825 Journal of the Japanese Association of Mineralogists, Petrologists and Economic Geologists. *see* 0914-9783
0021-4833 Economic Survey of Japan†
0021-4841 Japanese Economic Studies
0021-485X Japanese Forestry Society. Journal
0021-4868 Japanese Heart Journal
0021-4876 Japan Institute of Metals. Journal
0021-4884 Japanese Journal of Allergology
0021-4914 Japanese Journal of Applied Entomology and Zoology
0021-4922 Japanese Journal of Applied Physics
0021-4930 Japanese Journal of Bacteriology
0021-4949 Japanese Journal of Cancer Clinics
0021-4957 Japanese Journal of Child Psychiatry *see* 0289-0968
0021-4965 Japanese Journal of Clinical and Experimental Medicine
0021-4973 Japanese Journal of Clinical Dermatology
0021-4981 Japanese Journal of Clinical Electron Microscopy *changed to* Journal of Clinical Electron Microscopy.
0021-499X Japanese Journal of Dermatology: Series A
0021-5007 Japanese Journal of Ecology
0021-5015 Japanese Journal of Educational Psychology
0021-5023 Japanese Journal of Ethnology
0021-5031 Japanese Journal of Experimental Medicine†
0021-504X Japanese Journal of Genetics
0021-5066 Japanese Journal of Geophysics†
0021-5074 Japanese Journal of Human Genetics
0021-5082 Japanese Journal of Hygiene
0021-5090 Japanese Journal of Ichthyology
0021-5104 Japanese Journal of Limnology
0021-5112 Japanese Journal of Medical Science and Biology
0021-5120 Japanese Journal of Medicine
0021-5139 Japanese Journal of Microbiology *see* 0385-5600
0021-5147 Japanese Journal of Nutrition
0021-5155 Japanese Journal of Ophthalmology
0021-5163 Japanese Journal of Oral Surgery
0021-5171 Japanese Journal of Parasitology
0021-5198 Japanese Journal of Pharmacology
0021-5201 Japanese Weekly on Pharmacy and Chemistry
0021-521X Japanese Journal of Physiology
0021-5228 Japanese Journal of Plastic & Reconstructive Surgery
0021-5236 Shinrigaku Kenkyu
0021-5244 Japanese Journal of Studies on Alcohol *changed to* Japanese Journal of Alcohol Studies and Drug Dependence.
0021-5252 Japanese Journal of Thoracic Surgery
0021-5260 Japanese Journal of Tropical Agriculture
0021-5279 Japanese Journal of Tuberculosis and Chest Diseases†
0021-5287 Japanese Journal of Urology
0021-5295 Japanese Journal of Veterinary Science *see* 0916-7250
0021-5309 Japanese Journal of Zootechnical Science *changed to* Animal Science and Technology (Japan).

ISSN

ISSN INDEX 5397

ISSN	Title
0021-5325	Japanese Orthopaedic Association. Journal
0021-5341	Zasshi Kiji Sakuin. Jinbun Shakai Hen
0021-535X	Japanese Poetry in English†
0021-5368	Japanese Psychological Research
0021-5376	Food and Nutrition - Eiyo to Shokuryo see 0287-3516
0021-5384	Japanese Society of Internal Medicine. Journal
0021-5392	Japanese Society of Scientific Fisheries. Bulletin
0021-5406	Japanese Society of Starch Science. Journal
0021-5414	Japanese Sociological Review
0021-5449	Jardin des Arts changed to Arts-Magazine.
0021-5465	Jardin Ouvrier de France see 0240-5024
0021-5481	Jardins de France
0021-5503	Jardin et Logis see 0772-1099
0021-5511	Jarmuvek, Mezogazdasagi Gepek
0021-552X	Jaernhandlaren
0021-5546	Jaernvaegteknik†
0021-5554	La Jaune et la Rouge
0021-5562	Javeriana
0021-5570	Jax
0021-5597	Jazykovedny Casopis
0021-5600	Jazz
0021-5619	Jazz - Rhythm and Blues changed to Jazz.
0021-5627	Jazz & Pop†
0021-5635	Jazz Forum
0021-5643	Jazz Hot
0021-5651	Jazz Journal see 0140-2285
0021-566X	Jazz Magazine
0021-5678	Jazz Monthly†
0021-5686	Jazz Podium
0021-5694	Jazz Report†
0021-5708	Musikrevue†
0021-5716	Jazz Times
0021-5724	Der Jazzfreund
0021-5740	Je Crois
0021-5759	Jeune Garde see 0701-8746
0021-5767	Jean's Journal of Poems changed to Jean's Journal.
0021-5775	Jedinstvo
0021-5783	Jedlesee†
0021-5791	Jednota
0021-5805	Jednotna Skola
0021-5813	Jeevan Jauban
0021-5821	Jefferson Medical College Alumni Bulletin
0021-583X	J.E.M.†
0021-5848	J E N - Bulteno (Junularo Esperantista de Nord-Amerika) changed to Esperanto - U S A.
0021-5856	Jenaer Jahrbuch†
0021-5872	Jenga
0021-5880	Jeopardy
0021-5902	Jernkontorets Annaler see 0284-0448
0021-5910	Jerry Kluttz's Federal Employe Newsletter changed to Mike Causey's Federal Employe Newsletter.
0021-5929	Jersey
0021-5945	Jersey Concrete†
0021-5953	Jersey Journal
0021-5961	Jersey Publisher changed to In Print.
0021-5988	Jesuit†
0021-5996	Jet
0021-6003	Jet Cargo News
0021-602X	Jetline Schedules
0021-6054	Jeugdboekengids
0021-6062	Jeugdnatuurwachter†
0021-6070	J N†
0021-6089	Jeune Afrique
0021-6100	Jeune Revolutionnaire changed to Information Ouvrieres.
0021-6119	Jeune (S)†
0021-6127	Quebec Science
0021-6135	Jeunes
0021-6143	Jeunes Annees
0021-6151	Jeunes Avocats
0021-616X	Jeunes des Auberges
0021-6208	Jeunesse et Orgue†
0021-6224	Jeunesses Numismatiques changed to Vie Numismatique.
0021-6232	Revue Internationale des Jeux et Jouets
0021-6240	Jevrejski Pregled
0021-6267	Jewelers' Circular-Keystone see 0194-2905
0021-6275	Jeweller and Metalworker see 0307-580X
0021-6283	Jewelry Clip Review changed to Costume Jewelry Review.
0021-6291	Jewelry Workers' Bulletin
0021-6305	Jewish Affairs
0021-6313	Jewish Affairs
0021-6321	Jewish Braille Review
0021-633X	Jewish Chronicle
0021-6348	Jewish Civic Press
0021-6364	Jewish Community Bulletin changed to Northern California Jewish Bulletin.
0021-6372	Jewish Community Center Program Aids†
0021-6380	Jewish Current Events
0021-6399	Jewish Currents
0021-6402	Jewish Defense League Newsletter changed to Jewish Defense League Iton.
0021-6410	Jewish Digest††
0021-6429	Jewish Education
0021-6437	Jewish Exponent
0021-6453	Jewish Frontier
0021-6461	Jewish Gazette
0021-647X	Jewish Herald
0021-6488	Jewish Herald-Voice
0021-6534	Jewish Journal of Sociology
0021-6542	Jewish Labor Movement. Bund Archives. Bulletin†
0021-6550	Jewish Ledger
0021-6569	Jewish Liberation Journal†
0021-6577	Jewish Life†
0021-6585	Jewish Memorial Hospital Bulletin†
0021-6615	Jewish Observer
0021-6623	Jewish Observer and Middle East Review†
0021-6631	Jewish Parent††
0021-664X	Jewish Peace Fellowship Newsletter see 0080-9160
0021-6658	Jewish Post and Opinion see 0888-0379
0021-6666	Jewish Press (Omaha)
0021-6674	Jewish Press (Brooklyn)
0021-6682	Jewish Quarterly Review
0021-6690	Jewish Review changed to Jewish Review (1983).
0021-6704	Jewish Social Studies
0021-6712	Jewish Social Work Forum
0021-6720	Jewish Spectator
0021-6739	Jewish Standard
0021-6747	Jewish Standard
0021-6755	Jewish Telegraph
0021-6763	J T A Weekly News Digest
0021-6771	Jewish Times (Boston) see 8750-1961
0021-678X	Jewish Transcript
0021-6801	Jewish Vanguard
0021-681X	Jewish Vegetarian
0021-6828	Jewish Voice
0021-6852	Jewish Week and American Examiner see 0745-5356
0021-6860	Jewish Weekly News
0021-6879	Jewish Western Bulletin
0021-6887	Jewish Youth Monthly changed to Jewish Youth.
0021-6895	Jews and the Jewish People
0021-6909	Jews in Eastern Europe†
0021-6917	Jez
0021-6925	Jezik
0021-6933	Jezik in Slovstvo
0021-6941	Jezyk Polski
0021-695X	Jicarilla Chieftain
0021-6968	Jikeikai Medical Journal
0021-6976	Jiwan Dhara
0021-6984	Free World
0021-700X	Jnanadhara
0021-7042	Jobber and Warehouse Executive see 1047-2312
0021-7050	Jobber News
0021-7069	Jobber Topics changed to Jobber Topics Reports.
0021-7077	Joblinglass†
0021-7093	Jobson's Investment Digest of Australia and New Zealand see 0075-3785
0021-7115	Jockey Club
0021-7131	Joedisk Orientering
0021-714X	Joel†
0021-7158	Joeygram changed to Calliope (Baltimore).
0021-7166	Jogtudomanyi Kozlony
0021-7174	Johann Wilhelm Klein
0021-7182	Johannesburg Stock Exchange Monthly Bulletin
0021-7190	John Herling's Labor Letter†
0021-7204	John Liner Letter
0021-7212	John Marshall Journal of Practice and Procedure see 0270-854X
0021-7220	John Milton Talking Book changed to John Milton Talking Book Magazine.
0021-7239	John Rylands Library. Bulletin see 0301-102X
0021-7255	Johns Hopkins Magazine
0021-7263	Johns Hopkins Medical Journal†
0021-7271	Johnson Drillers Journal†
0021-728X	Johnsonian News Letter
0021-7298	Journal of Information Processing and Managements
0021-7301	Desfile
0021-731X	Joint Acquisitions List of Africana
0021-7336	National Defence College Gazette
0021-7344	Jok†
0021-7379	Jonge Handen changed to Splinter.
0021-7387	Jonge Kampvechter changed to Wyzer.
0021-7395	Jonge Kerk
0021-7409	Jonge Muziek
0021-7417	Stakkato
0021-7441	Jordbrukseкonomiska Meddelanden
0021-745X	Jordbrukskasseroerelsen see 0346-9670
0021-7468	Jordemodern
0021-7476	Jorden Runt†
0021-7484	Jordens Folk - Etnografisk Revy†
0021-7514	Jornal Brasileiro de Neurologia see 0101-8469
0021-7522	Jornal de Estomatologia
0021-7530	Jornal de Letras e Artes
0021-7557	Jornal de Pediatria†
0021-7565	Jornal de Poesia
0021-7573	Jornal do Medico
0021-759X	Josephinum Newsletter
0021-7603	Josephite Harvest
0021-7611	Joslin Diabetes Foundation. Newsletter changed to Joslin Magazine.
0021-762X	Journal Asiatique
0021-7638	Journal Bandeirante†
0021-7654	Journal Belge de Rhumatologie et de Medecine Physique changed to Clinical Rheumatology.
0021-7662	Journal d'Agriculture Tropical et de Botanique Appliquee see 0183-5173
0021-7670	Journal d'Analyse Mathematique
0021-7689	Journal de Chimie Physique et de Physico-Chimie Biologique
0021-7697	Journal de Chirurgie
0021-7719	Journal de Conchyliologie
0021-7735	Journal de France des Appellations d'Origine†
0021-7743	Journal de Genetique Humaine changed to Genetic Counseling.
0021-7751	Journal de Kinesitherapie see 0302-427X
0021-776X	Journal de la Construction de la Suisse Romande
0021-7778	Journal de la Corse Agricole
0021-7786	Journal de la Marine Marchande see 0983-0537
0021-7808	Journal de l'Amateur d'Art
0021-7824	Journal de Mathematiques Pures et Appliquees
0021-7832	Journal de Mecanique see 0997-7538
0021-7832	Journal de Mecanique see 0997-7546
0021-7859	Journal de Medecine de Besancon†
0021-7875	Journal de Medecine de Caen†
0021-7883	Journal de Medecine de Lyon
0021-7891	Journal de Medecine de Montpellier
0021-7905	Journal de Medecine de Strasbourg
0021-7913	Journal de Medecine et de Chirurgie Pratiques
0021-7921	Journal de Microscopie changed to Microscopy Microanalysis Microstrucures.
0021-793X	Journal de Pharmacologie†
0021-7948	Journal de Physiologie
0021-7956	Journal de Psychologie Normale et Pathologique†
0021-7964	Journal de Radiologie d'Electrologie et de Medecine Nucleaire see 0227-9363
0021-7972	Journal de Recherches Atmospheriques see 0169-8095
0021-7980	Journal de Semiologie Medicale†
0021-7999	Journal Dentaire du Quebec see 0845-9320
0021-8006	Journal Historique des Bernier
0021-8014	Journal des Combattants
0021-8022	Journal des Communautes see 0020-0107
0021-8030	Journal des Communes
0021-8049	Journal des Finances
0021-8057	Journal des Horticulteurs et Maraichers. changed to Horticulteurs et Maraichers Romands.
0021-8065	Journal des Ingenieurs
0021-8073	Journal des Instituteurs et des Institutrices
0021-8081	Journal des Medecins du Nord & de l'Est
0021-8111	Journal des Sciences Medicales de Lille
0021-812X	Journal des Tribunaux
0021-8138	Journal d'Hotel
0021-8170	Journal du Droit International
0021-8197	Journal du Textile
0021-8200	Journal d'Urologie et de Nephrologie see 0248-0018
0021-8219	Journal Europeen de Toxicologie changed to European Journal of Toxicology and Environmental Hygiene.
0021-8227	Journal Export
0021-8235	Journal for Anthroposophy
0021-8243	Journal for Geography - Tydskrif vir Aardrykskunde see 0378-5327
0021-8251	Journal for Research in Mathematics Education
0021-8278	Journal for Technical and Vocational Education in South Africa
0021-8286	Journal for the History of Astronomy
0021-8294	Journal for the Scientific Study of Religion
0021-8308	Journal for the Theory of Social Behaviour
0021-8324	Journal Francais de Medecine et Chirurgie Thoracique†
0021-8332	Journal Francais d'Oto-Rhino-Laryngologie et Chirurgie Maxillo-Faciale changed to Journal Francais d'Oto-Rhino-Laryngologie - Audiophonologie - Chirurgie Maxillo-Faciale.
0021-8340	Journal Francais Langenscheidt††
0021-8359	Journal fuer Hirnforschung
0021-8367	Journal fuer Marktforschung†
0021-8375	Journal fuer Ornithologie
0021-8383	Journal fuer Praktische Chemie
0021-8405	Journal Mondial de Pharmacie†
0021-8413	Journal Musical Francais-Musica Disques†
0021-8421	Journal of Abdominal Surgery
0021-843X	Journal of Abnormal Psychology
0021-8448	Journal of Accountancy
0021-8456	Journal of Accounting Research
0021-8464	Journal of Adhesion
0021-8472	Journal of Administration Overseas see 0271-2075
0021-8480	Journal of Adventist Education
0021-8499	Journal of Advertising Research
0021-8502	Journal of Aerosol Science
0021-8510	Journal of Aesthetic Education

5398 ISSN INDEX

0021-8529 Journal of Aesthetics and Art Criticism
0021-8537 Journal of African History
0021-8553 Journal of African Law
0021-8561 Journal of Agricultural and Food Chemistry
0021-857X Journal of Agricultural Economics
0021-8588 Journal of Agricultural Meteorology
0021-8596 Journal of Agricultural Science
0021-860X Journal of Agriculture†
0021-8618 Journal of Agriculture of Western Australia
0021-8626 Journal of Agriculture-South Australia†
0021-8634 Journal of Agricultural Engineering Research
0021-8642 Journal of Air Law and Commerce
0021-8650 Journal of Air Traffic Control
0021-8669 Journal of Aircraft
0021-8677 Journal of Alcohol Education *see* 0090-1482
0021-8685 Journal of Alcoholism; Bulletin of Alcoholism *see* 0735-0414
0021-8693 Journal of Algebra
0021-8707 Journal of Allergy *see* 0091-6749
0021-8715 Journal of American Folklore
0021-8723 Journal of American History
0021-8731 Journal of American Indian Education
0021-874X Journal of American Insurance†
0021-8758 British Association for American Studies. Newsletter *changed to* Journal of American Studies.
0021-8766 Journal of Analytical Chemistry of the U S S R
0021-8782 Journal of Anatomy
0021-8790 Journal of Animal Ecology
0021-8804 Journal of Animal Morphology and Physiology
0021-8812 Journal of Animal Science
0021-8820 Journal of Antibiotics
0021-8839 Journal of Apicultural Research
0021-8847 Journal of Applied Bacteriology
0021-8855 Journal of Applied Behavior Analysis
0021-8863 Journal of Applied Behavioral Science
0021-8871 Journal of Applied Chemistry *see* 0268-2575
0021-888X Journal of Applied Chemistry of the U S S R
0021-8898 Journal of Applied Crystallography
0021-8901 Journal of Applied Ecology
0021-891X Journal of Applied Electrochemistry
0021-8928 Journal of Applied Mathematics and Mechanics
0021-8936 Journal of Applied Mechanics
0021-8944 Journal of Applied Mechanics and Technical Physics
0021-8952 Journal of Applied Meteorology *see* 0733-3021
0021-8960 Journal of Applied Nutrition
0021-8979 Journal of Applied Physics
0021-8987 Journal of Applied Physiology *see* 8750-7587
0021-8995 Journal of Applied Polymer Science
0021-9002 Journal of Applied Probability
0021-9010 Journal of Applied Psychology
0021-9029 Journal of Applied Social Psychology
0021-9037 Journal of Applied Spectroscopy
0021-9045 Journal of Approximation Theory
0021-9053 Journal of Arizona History
0021-9061 Journal of Arkansas Education *see* 0161-7753
0021-907X Journal of Art History
0021-9088 Journal of Art Studies
0021-9096 Journal of Asian and African Studies
0021-910X Journal of Asian History
0021-9118 Journal of Asian Studies
0021-9126 Journal of Asiatic Studies
0021-9134 Journal of Asthma Research *see* 0277-0903
0021-9142 Journal of Astronautical Sciences
0021-9150 Atherosclerosis
0021-9169 Journal of Atmospheric and Terrestrial Physics
0021-9185 Journal of Autism and Childhood Schizophrenia *see* 0162-3257
0021-9193 Journal of Bacteriology
0021-9207 Journal of Band Research
0021-9215 Journal of Bank Research†
0021-9223 Journal of Basic Engineering *see* 0098-2202
0021-9223 Journal of Basic Engineering *see* 0094-4289
0021-9231 Journal of Biblical Literature
0021-924X Journal of Biochemistry
0021-9258 Journal of Biological Chemistry
0021-9266 Journal of Biological Education
0021-9274 Journal of Biological Psychology-Worm Runner's Digest†
0021-9282 Journal of Biological Sciences
0021-9290 Journal of Biomechanics
0021-9304 Journal of Biomedical Materials Research
0021-9320 Journal of Biosocial Science
0021-9339 Journal of Black Poetry *changed to* Kitabu Cha Jua.
0021-9347 Journal of Black Studies
0021-9355 Journal of Bone and Joint Surgery: American Volume
0021-9363 Journal of Botany of the United Arab Republic *see* 1011-3835
0021-9371 Journal of British Studies
0021-938X Journal of Broadcasting *see* 0883-8151
0021-9398 Journal of Business (Chicago)
0021-9401 Journal of Business (South Orange) *see* 0732-9334
0021-941X Journal of Business Administration
0021-9436 Journal of Business Communication
0021-9444 Journal of Business Education *see* 0883-2323
0021-9460 Journal of Business Law
0021-9487 Journal of Canadian Petroleum Technology
0021-9495 Journal of Canadian Studies
0021-9509 Journal of Cardiovascular Surgery
0021-9517 Journal of Catalysis
0021-9525 Journal of Cell Biology
0021-9533 Journal of Cell Science
0021-9541 Journal of Cellular Physiology
0021-955X Journal of Cellular Plastics
0021-9568 Journal of Chemical and Engineering Data
0021-9576 Journal of Chemical Documentation *see* 0095-2338
0021-9584 Journal of Chemical Education
0021-9592 Journal of Chemical Engineering of Japan
0021-9606 Journal of Chemical Physics
0021-9614 Journal of Chemical Thermodynamics
0021-9622 Journal of Chemicals and Allied Industries
0021-9630 Journal of Child Psychology & Psychiatry & Allied Disciplines
0021-9649 Journal of Christian Camping
0021-9657 Journal of Christian Education
0021-9665 Journal of Chromatographic Science
0021-9673 Journal of Chromatography
0021-9681 Journal of Chronic Diseases *see* 0895-4356
0021-969X Journal of Church and State
0021-9703 Journal of Church Music†
0021-9711 Journal of Clinical Chiropractic *see* 0097-4706
0021-972X Journal of Clinical Endocrinology and Metabolism
0021-9738 Journal of Clinical Investigation
0021-9746 Journal of Clinical Pathology
0021-9754 Journal of Clinical Pharmacology and New Drugs *see* 0091-2700
0021-9762 Journal of Clinical Psychology
0021-9770 Journal of College Placement *see* 0884-5352
0021-9789 Journal of College Student Personnel *see* 0897-5264
0021-9797 Journal of Colloid and Interface Science
0021-9800 Journal of Combinatorial Theory *see* 0097-3165
0021-9800 Journal of Combinatorial Theory *see* 0095-8956
0021-9819 Journal of Commerce
0021-9827 Journal of Commerce *see* 0361-5561
0021-9835 Journal of Commerce and Independent Review *see* 0279-4195
0021-9843 Journal of Commerce and Industry *changed to* Journal of Commerce, Industry & Transportation.
0021-9851 Journal of Commerce†
0021-986X Journal of Commercial Bank Lending
0021-9886 Journal of Common Market Studies
0021-9894 Journal of Commonwealth Literature
0021-9908 Journal of Commonwealth Political Studies *see* 0306-3631
0021-9916 Journal of Communication
0021-9924 Journal of Communication Disorders
0021-9932 Journal of Comparative Administration *see* 0095-3997
0021-9940 Journal of Comparative and Physiological Psychology *see* 0735-7044
0021-9940 Journal of Comparative and Physiological Psychology *see* 0735-7036
0021-9967 The Journal of Comparative Neurology
0021-9975 Journal of Comparative Pathology
0021-9983 Journal of Composite Materials
0021-9991 Journal of Computational Physics
0022-0000 Journal of Computer and System Sciences
0022-0019 Journal of Conchology
0022-0027 Journal of Conflict Resolution
0022-0035 Journal of Connoisseurship and Art Technology†
0022-0043 Journal of Constitutional & Parliamentary Studies
0022-0051 Journal of Constitutional Law *see* 0377-0907
0022-006X Journal of Consulting and Clinical Psychology
0022-0078 Journal of Consumer Affairs
0022-0086 Journal of Consumer Credit Management†
0022-0094 Journal of Contemporary History
0022-0116 Journal of Contemporary Psychotherapy
0022-0124 Journal of Continuing Education in Nursing
0022-0132 Journal of Cooperative Education
0022-0140 Journal of Extension
0022-0159 Journal of Correctional Education
0022-0167 Journal of Counseling Psychology
0022-0175 Journal of Creative Behavior
0022-0183 Journal of Criminal Law
0022-0191 Journal of Criminal Law
0022-0205 Journal of Criminal Law, Criminology and Police Science *see* 0091-4169
0022-0213 Journal of Critical Analysis
0022-0221 Journal of Cross-Cultural Psychology
0022-023X Ophthalmic Surgery
0022-0248 Journal of Crystal Growth
0022-0256 Journal of Cuneiform Studies
0022-0264 Journal of Current Laser Abstracts
0022-0272 Journal of Curriculum Studies
0022-0280 Journal of Cybernetics *see* 0196-9722
0022-0299 Journal of Dairy Research
0022-0302 Journal of Dairy Science
0022-0310 Journal of Data Education *see* 0887-4417
0022-0329 Data Management *changed to* Data Management.
0022-0337 Journal of Dental Education
0022-0345 Journal of Dental Research
0022-0353 Journal of Dentistry for Children
0022-0361 Journal of Detergents and Collective Chemistry and Physics *changed to* Journal of Collective Chemistry and Physics.
0022-037X Journal of Developing Areas
0022-0388 Journal of Development Studies
0022-0396 Journal of Differential Equations
0022-040X Journal of Differential Geometry
0022-0418 Journal of Documentation
0022-0426 Journal of Drug Issues
0022-0434 Journal of Dynamic Systems, Measurement and Control
0022-0442 Journal of Earth Sciences
0022-0450 Journal of East Asiatic Studies
0022-0469 Journal of Ecclesiastical History
0022-0477 Journal of Ecology
0022-0485 Journal of Economic Education
0022-0493 Journal of Economic Entomology
0022-0507 Journal of Economic History
0022-0515 Journal of Economic Literature
0022-0531 Journal of Economic Theory
0022-0558 Journal of Ecumenical Studies
0022-0574 Journal of Education (Boston)
0022-0582 Sierra Leone Journal of Education
0022-0590 Journal of Education and Psychology
0022-0604 Journal of Education for Librarianship *see* 0748-5786
0022-0612 Journal of Education for Social Work *changed to* Journal of Social Work Education.
0022-0620 Journal of Educational Administration and History
0022-0639 Journal of Educational Administration
0022-0647 Journal of Educational Data Processing†
0022-0655 Journal of Educational Measurement
0022-0663 Journal of Educational Psychology
0022-0671 Journal of Educational Research
0022-068X Journal of Educational Research and Extension
0022-0698 Journal of Eductional Technology *see* 0007-1013
0022-0701 J E T: Journal of Educational Thought
0022-071X Journal of Elastoplastics. *see* 0095-2443
0022-0728 Journal of Electroanalytical Chemistry and Interfacial Electrochemistry
0022-0736 Journal of Electrocardiology
0022-0744 Journal of Electron Microscopy
0022-0752 Journal of Embryology and Experimental Morphology *see* 0950-1991
0022-0787 Journal of Employment Counseling
0022-0795 Journal of Endocrinology
0022-0809 Engineering Education *changed to* A S E E Prism.
0022-0817 Journal of Engineering for Industry
0022-0825 Journal of Engineering for Power *see* 0889-504X
0022-0833 Journal of Engineering Mathematics
0022-0841 Journal of Engineering Physics
0022-0868 Journal of English and Germanic Philology *see* 0363-6941
0022-0884 Journal of English Teaching Techniques†
0022-0892 Journal of Environmental Health
0022-0906 Journal of Environmental Sciences *see* 1052-2883
0022-0914 Journal of Ethiopian Law†
0022-0922 Journal of Ethiopian Studies
0022-0930 Journal of Evolutionary Biochemistry and Physiology
0022-0949 Journal of Experimental Biology
0022-0957 Journal of Experimental Botany
0022-0965 Journal of Experimental Child Psychology
0022-0973 Journal of Experimental Education
0022-0981 Journal of Experimental Marine Biology and Ecology
0022-099X Journal of Experimental Medical Sciences†
0022-1007 Journal of Experimental Medicine
0022-1015 Journal of Experimental Psychology *see* 0278-7393
0022-1015 Journal of Experimental Psychology *see* 0097-7403
0022-1015 Journal of Experimental Psychology *see* 0096-3445
0022-1015 Journal of Experimental Psychology *see* 0096-1523
0022-1023 Journal of Experimental Research in Personality *see* 0092-6566
0022-1031 Journal of Experimental Social Psychology
0022-104X Journal of Experimental Zoology
0022-1058 Journal of Extra-Corporeal Technology
0022-1066 Journal of Family Law
0022-1074 Journal of Family Welfare
0022-1082 Journal of Finance

ISSN

0022-1090 Journal of Financial and Quantitative Analysis
0022-1104 Journal of Fire & Flammability†
0022-1112 Journal of Fish Biology
0022-1120 Journal of Fluid Mechanics
0022-1139 Journal of Fluorine Chemistry
0022-1147 Journal of Food Science
0022-1155 Journal of Food Science and Technology
0022-1163 Journal of Food Technology *see* 0950-5423
0022-1171 Journal of Forensic Medicine *see* 0379-0738
0022-1198 Journal of Forensic Sciences
0022-1201 Journal of Forestry
0022-121X Journal of Fuel and Heat Technology *see* 0367-1119
0022-1228 Journal of Fukien History
0022-1236 Journal of Functional Analysis
0022-1244 Journal of Gem Industry
0022-1252 Journal of Gemmology and Proceedings of the Gemmological Association of Great Britain *changed to* Journal of Gemmology.
0022-1260 Journal of General and Applied Microbiology
0022-1279 Journal of General Chemistry of the U S S R
0022-1287 Journal of General Microbiology
0022-1295 Journal of General Physiology
0022-1309 Journal of General Psychology
0022-1317 Journal of General Virology
0022-1325 Journal of Genetic Psychology
0022-1333 Journal of Genetics
0022-1341 Journal of Geography
0022-135X Chigaku Zasshi
0022-1368 Journal of Geological Education
0022-1376 Journal of Geology
0022-1384 Journal of Geology of the United Arab Republic *changed to* United Arab Republic Journal of Geology.
0022-1392 Journal of Geomagnetism and Geoelectricity
0022-1406 Journal of Geophysical Research *changed to* J G R: Journal of Geophysical Research: Oceans.
0022-1414 Journal of Geriatric Psychiatry
0022-1422 Journals of Gerontology
0022-1430 Journal of Glaciology
0022-1449 Journal of Graphoanalysis
0022-1457 Journal of Health and Physical Education *changed to* Taiiku no Kagaku.
0022-1465 Journal of Health and Social Behavior
0022-1481 Journal of Heat Transfer
0022-149X Journal of Helminthology
0022-1503 Journal of Heredity
0022-1511 Journal of Herpetology
0022-152X Journal of Heterocyclic Chemistry
0022-152X Journal of Heterocyclic Chemistry *issued with* 0090-2268
0022-1538 Journal of High Temperature Science *see* 0018-1536
0022-1546 Journal of Higher Education
0022-1554 Journal of Histochemistry and Cytochemistry
0022-1562 Journal of Historical Research
0022-1570 Journal of Home Economics
0022-1589 Journal of Horticultural Science
0022-1597 Hospital and Community Psychiatry
0022-1619 Journal of Hospital Pharmacy *see* 0025-7621
0022-1651 Journal of Human Relations†
0022-166X Journal of Human Resources
0022-1678 Journal of Humanistic Psychology
0022-1686 Journal of Hydraulic Research
0022-1694 Journal of Hydrology
0022-1708 Journal of Hydrology
0022-1716 Journal of Hydronautics†
0022-1724 Journal of Hygiene *see* 0950-2688
0022-1732 Journal of Hygiene, Epidemiology, Microbiology and Immunology
0022-1759 Journal of Immunological Methods
0022-1767 Journal of Immunology
0022-1775 Journal of Indian History
0022-1783 Journal of Indian Pharmaceutical Manufacturers
0022-1791 Journal of Indian Philosophy
0022-1805 Journal of Individual Psychology *see* 0277-7010
0022-1813 Man - Society - Technology *see* 0746-3537
0022-1821 Journal of Industrial Economics
0022-183X Journal of Industrial Engineering *see* 0019-8234
0022-1856 Journal of Industrial Relations
0022-1864 Journal of Industrial Teacher Education
0022-1872 Journal of Industry *see* 0818-4674
0022-1880 Journal of Industry and Trade
0022-1899 Journal of Infectious Diseases
0022-1902 Journal of Inorganic and Nuclear Chemistry *see* 0277-5387
0022-1910 Journal of Insect Physiology
0022-1929 Journal of Insurance *see* 0749-8667
0022-1937 Journal of Interamerican Studies and World Affairs
0022-1945 Journal of Interdisciplinary Cycle Research
0022-1953 Journal of Interdisciplinary History
0022-1961 Journal of Internal Medicine *changed to* Internal Medicine.
0022-197X Journal of International Affairs
0022-1988 Journal of International and Comparative Studies *see* 0091-2573
0022-1996 Journal of International Economics
0022-2003 Journal of International Law and Economics *changed to* George Washington Journal of International Law and Economics.
0022-2011 Journal of Invertebrate Pathology
0022-202X Journal of Investigative Dermatology
0022-2038 Journal of Irreproducible Results
0022-2046 Journal of Islamic Studies
0022-2054 Journal of J.J. Group of Hospitals and Grant Medical College
0022-2062 Journal of Japanese Botany
0022-2070 Journal of Japanese Chemistry†
0022-2089 Journal of Jewish Communal Service
0022-2097 Journal of Jewish Studies
0022-2100 Journal of Jinsen Medical Sciences†
0022-2119 Saibokaku Byorigaku Zasshi
0022-2135 Journal of Labelled Compounds *see* 0362-4803
0022-2143 Journal of Laboratory and Clinical Medicine
0022-2151 Journal of Laryngology and Otology
0022-216X Journal of Latin American Studies
0022-2186 Journal of Law and Economics
0022-2194 Journal of Learning Disabilities
0022-2208 Journal of Legal Education
0022-2216 Journal of Leisure Research
0022-2224 Visible Language
0022-2232 Journal of Librarianship *see* 0961-0006
0022-2240 Journal of Library Automation *see* 0730-9295
0022-2267 Journal of Linguistics
0022-2275 Journal of Lipid Research
0022-2283 Journal of Livestock and Agriculture *changed to* St. Joseph Journal of Livestock and Agriculture.
0022-2291 Journal of Low Temperature Physics
0022-2305 Journal of Lubrication Technology *see* 0742-4787
0022-2313 Journal of Luminescence
0022-2321 Journal of Macromolecular Science: Part D - Reviews in Polymer Processing and Technology *see* 0360-2559
0022-233X Journal of Macromolecular Science: Part A - Chemistry *see* 1060-1325
0022-2348 Journal of Macromolecular Science: Part B - Physics
0022-2356 Journal of Macromolecular Science. Part C. Reviews in Macromolecular Chemistry *see* 0736-6574
0022-2364 Journal of Magnetic Resonance
0022-2372 Journal of Mammalogy
0022-2380 Journal of Management Studies
0022-2399 Journal of Management Studies
0022-2402 Journal of Marine Research
0022-2410 Journal of Maritime Law and Commerce
0022-2429 Journal of Marketing
0022-2437 Journal of Marketing Research
0022-2445 Journal of Marriage and the Family
0022-2461 Journal of Materials Science
0022-247X Journal of Mathematical Analysis and Applications
0022-2488 Journal of Mathematical Physics
0022-2496 Journal of Mathematical Psychology
0022-250X Journal of Mathematical Sociology
0022-2518 Indiana University Mathematics Journal
0022-2526 Studies in Applied Mathematics
0022-2542 Journal of Mechanical Engineering Science *changed to* Institution of Mechanical Engineers. Proceedings. Part C: Journal of Mechanical Engineering Science.
0022-2550 Government Mechanical Laboratory of Japan. Journal†
0022-2569 Journal of Mechanisms *see* 0094-114X
0022-2577 Journal of Medical Education *see* 1040-2446
0022-2585 Journal of Medical Entomology
0022-2593 Journal of Medical Genetics
0022-2607 Medical Laboratory Technology *see* 0308-3616
0022-2615 Journal of Medical Microbiology
0022-2623 Journal of Medicinal Chemistry
0022-2631 Journal of Membrane Biology
0022-264X Journal of Mental Deficiency Research *changed to* Journal of Intellectual Disability Research.
0022-2658 Journal of Mental Health†
0022-2666 Journal of Mental Subnormality *see* 0374-633X
0022-2704 Journal of Microbiology of the United Arab Republic *see* 0301-8172
0022-2712 Journal of Micrographics *see* 0892-3876
0022-2720 Journal of Microscopy
0022-2739 Journal of Microwave Power
0022-2747 Journal of Milk and Food Technology *see* 0362-028X
0022-2755 Journal of Mines, Metals and Fuels
0022-2771 Journal of Mississippi History
0022-278X Journal of Modern African Studies
0022-2798 Journal of Modern Education†
0022-2801 Journal of Modern History
0022-2828 Journal of Molecular and Cellular Cardiology
0022-2836 Journal of Molecular Biology
0022-2844 Journal of Molecular Evolution
0022-2852 Journal of Molecular Spectroscopy
0022-2860 Journal of Molecular Structure
0022-2879 Journal of Money, Credit & Banking
0022-2887 Journal of Morphology *see* 0362-2525
0022-2895 Journal of Motor Behavior
0022-2909 Journal of Music Theory
0022-2917 Journal of Music Therapy
0022-2925 Journal of Narrative Technique
0022-2933 Journal of Natural History
0022-2941 Journal of Natural Sciences and Mathematics
0022-295X Journal of Navy Civilian Manpower Management *see* 0364-0426
0022-2968 Journal of Near Eastern Studies
0022-2976 Journal of Necromantic Numismatics†
0022-2984 Journal of Negro Education
0022-2992 Journal of Negro History *see* 0028-2529
0022-300X Journal of Nematology
0022-3018 Journal of Nervous and Mental Disease
0022-3026 Journal of Neuro-Visceral Relations *see* 0300-9564
0022-3034 Journal of Neurobiology
0022-3042 Journal of Neurochemistry
0022-3050 Journal of Neurology, Neurosurgery and Psychiatry
0022-3069 Journal of Neuropathology and Experimental Neurology
0022-3077 Journal of Neurophysiology
0022-3085 Journal of Neurosurgery
0022-3093 Journal of Non-Crystalline Solids
0022-3107 Journal of Nuclear Energy *see* 0306-4549
0022-3115 Journal of Nuclear Materials
0022-3123 Journal of Nuclear Medicine *see* 0161-5505
0022-3131 Journal of Nuclear Science and Technology
0022-314X Journal of Number Theory
0022-3158 Journal of Nursing Education
0022-3166 Journal of Nutrition
0022-3174 Indian Journal of Nutrition and Dietetics
0022-3182 Journal of Nutrition Education
0022-3190 Journal of Obstetrics and Gynaecology of India
0022-3204 Journal of Obstetrics and Gynaecology of the British Commonwealth *see* 0306-5456
0022-3212 J O M: Journal of Occupational Medicine *see* 0096-1736
0022-3239 Journal of Optimization Theory and Applications
0022-3247 Journal of Oral Medicine†
0022-3255 Journal of Oral Surgery *see* 0278-2391
0022-3263 Journal of Organic Chemistry
0022-3271 Journal of Organic Chemistry of the U S S R
0022-328X Journal of Organometallic Chemistry
0022-3298 Journal of Orgonomy
0022-3301 Journal of Oriental Research
0022-331X Journal of Oriental Studies
0022-3336 Journal of Outdoor Education
0022-3344 Journal of Pacific History
0022-3352 J.P.T. Journal of Paint Technology *see* 0361-8773
0022-3360 Journal of Paleontology
0022-3379 Journal of Palynology
0022-3387 Journal of Parapsychology
0022-3395 Journal of Parasitology
0022-3409 Journal of Pastoral Care
0022-3417 Journal of Pathology
0022-3433 Journal of Peace Research
0022-345X Journal of Pediatric Ophthalmology *see* 0191-3913
0022-3468 Journal of Pediatric Surgery
0022-3476 Journal of Pediatrics
0022-3484 Journal of Periodontal Research
0022-3492 Journal of Periodontology
0022-3506 Journal of Personality
0022-3514 Journal of Personality and Social Psychology
0022-3522 Journal of Petroleum Technology *see* 0149-2136
0022-3530 Journal of Petrology
0022-3549 Journal of Pharmaceutical Sciences
0022-3557 Journal of Pharmaceutical Sciences of the United Arab Republic *see* 0301-5068
0022-3565 Journal of Pharmacology and Experimental Therapeutics
0022-3573 Journal of Pharmacy and Pharmacology
0022-3581 Phi Rho Sigma. Journal
0022-359X Journal of Philippine Librarianship
0022-3603 Journal of Philippine Statistics
0022-3611 Journal of Philosophical Logic
0022-362X Journal of Philosophy
0022-3638 Journal of Photographic Science
0022-3646 Journal of Phycology
0022-3654 Journal of Physical Chemistry
0022-3662 Journal of Physical Education *see* 0745-3027
0022-3670 Journal of Physical Oceanography
0022-3689 Journal of Physics *see* 0305-4470
0022-3697 Journal of Physics and Chemistry of Solids
0022-3700 Journal of Physics B: Atomic and Molecular Physics *see* 0953-4075
0022-3719 Solid State Physics *see* 0953-8984
0022-3727 Journal of Physics D: Applied Physics
0022-3735 Journal of Physics E: Scientific Instruments *see* 0957-0233
0022-3743 Journal of Physics of the Earth
0022-3751 Journal of Physiology

5400 ISSN INDEX

0022-376X Journal of Planning and Property Law *see* 0307-4870
0022-3778 Journal of Plasma Physics
0022-3786 D E Journal *changed to* Plumbing, Heating, Piping.
0022-3794 Journal of Podiatric Medicine†
0022-3808 Journal of Political Economy
0022-3816 Journal of Politics
0022-3824 Journal of Polygraph Studies *changed to* Journal of Polygraph Science.
0022-3840 Journal of Popular Culture
0022-3859 Journal of Postgraduate Medicine
0022-3867 Journal of Practical Nursing
0022-3875 Journal of Clinical Orthodontics
0022-3883 Journal of Presbyterian History *see* 0886-5159
0022-3891 Journal of Personality Assessment
0022-3905 Journal of Property Management
0022-3913 Journal of Prosthetic Dentistry
0022-3921 Journal of Protozoology
0022-393X Journal of Psychedelic Drugs *see* 0279-1072
0022-3948 Journal of Psychiatric Nursing *see* 0279-3695
0022-3956 Journal of Psychiatric Research
0022-3964 Journal of Psychoanalysis in Groups *see* 0093-4763
0022-3972 Journal of Psychological Researches
0022-3980 Journal of Psychology
0022-3999 Journal of Psychosomatic Research
0022-4006 Journal of Public Health Dentistry
0022-4014 Journal of Public Law *see* 0094-4076
0022-4030 Journal of Purchasing *changed to* International Journal of Purchasing & Materials Management.
0022-4049 Journal of Pure and Applied Algebra
0022-4057 Journal of Pure and Applied Sciences
0022-4065 Journal of Quality Technology
0022-4073 Journal of Quantitative Spectroscopy and Radiative Transfer
0022-409X Journal of Range Management
0022-4103 Journal of Reading
0022-4111 Journal of Reading Behavior
0022-412X Journal of Recreational Mathematics
0022-4138 Journal of Refrigeration†
0022-4146 Journal of Regional Science
0022-4154 Journal of Rehabilitation
0022-4162 Journal of Rehabilitation in Asia
0022-4170 Journal of Rehabilitation of the Deaf *see* 0899-9228
0022-4189 Journal of Religion
0022-4197 Journal of Religion and Health
0022-4200 Journal of Religion in Africa
0022-4219 Journal of Religious Education *changed to* Journal of Christian Education of the African Methodist Episcopal Church.
0022-4227 Journal of Religious History
0022-4235 Journal of Religious Thought
0022-4243 Journal of Reprints for Antitrust Law & Economics
0022-4251 Journal of Reproduction and Fertility
0022-426X Journal of Research and Development in Education
0022-4278 Journal of Research in Crime and Delinquency
0022-4286 Journal of Research in Indian Medicine *changed to* Journal of Research in Ayurveda and Siddha.
0022-4294 Journal of Research in Music Education
0022-4308 Journal of Research in Science Teaching
0022-4316 U.S. National Bureau of Standards. Journal of Research. Section C: Engineering and Instrumentation†
0022-4324 Journal of Research on the Lepidoptera
0022-4332 U.S. National Bureau of Standards. Journal of Research. Section A. Physics and Chemistry *see* 1044-677X
0022-4359 Journal of Retailing
0022-4367 Journal of Risk and Insurance
0022-4375 Journal of Safety Research
0022-4383 Journal of San Diego History
0022-4391 Journal of School Health
0022-4405 Journal of School Psychology
0022-4413 Journal of Science and Engineering Research†
0022-4421 Journal of Science and Technology *see* 0264-9187
0022-443X Rodo Kagaku (Kawasaki, 1924)
0022-4456 Journal of Scientific and Industrial Research
0022-4464 Journal of Secondary Education *see* 0145-2061
0022-4472 Journal of Sedimentary Petrology
0022-4480 Journal of Semitic Studies
0022-4499 Journal of Sex Research
0022-4502 Journal of Ship Research
0022-4510 Journal of Small Animal Practice
0022-4529 Journal of Social History
0022-4537 Journal of Social Issues
0022-4545 Journal of Social Psychology
0022-4553 Journal of Societal Issues†
0022-4561 Journal of Soil and Water Conservation
0022-457X Journal of Soil and Water Conservation in India
0022-4588 Journal of Soil Science
0022-4596 Journal of Solid State Chemistry
0022-460X Journal of Sound and Vibration
0022-4618 Journal of South African Botany *see* 0254-6299
0022-4634 Journal of Southeast Asian Studies
0022-4642 Journal of Southern History
0022-4650 Journal of Spacecraft and Rockets
0022-4669 Journal of Special Education†
0022-4677 Journal of Speech and Hearing Disorders†
0022-4685 Journal of Speech and Hearing Research
0022-4693 Journal of Spelean History
0022-4707 Journal of Sports Medicine and Physical Fitness
0022-4715 Journal of Statistical Physics
0022-4723 Journal of Steel Castings Research†
0022-4731 Journal of Steroid Biochemistry *see* 0960-0760
0022-474X Journal of Stored Products Research
0022-4758 Journal of Strain Analysis *see* 0309-3247
0022-4766 Journal of Structural Chemistry
0022-4774 Journal of Structural Learning
0022-4790 Journal of Surgical Oncology
0022-4804 Journal of Surgical Research
0022-4812 Journal of Symbolic Logic
0022-4839 Journal of Systems Management†
0022-4847 Journal of Taiwan Agricultural Research *see* 0376-477X
0022-4855 Journal of Tamil Studies
0022-4863 Journal of Taxation
0022-4871 Journal of Teacher Education
0022-4898 Journal of Terramechanics
0022-4901 Journal of Texture Studies
0022-4928 Journal of the Atmospheric Sciences
0022-4936 Journal of the Chemical Society. Chemical Communications
0022-4944 Chemical Society, London. Journal. Section A: Inorganic, Physical and Theoretical Chemistry *see* 0300-9246
0022-4952 Chemical Society, London. Journal. Section C: Organic Chemistry *see* 0300-922X
0022-4979 Karnatak University. College of Education. Journal
0022-4987 Journal of the Dianetic Sciences *changed to* Dianetic Journal Notes.
0022-4995 Journal of the Economic and Social History of the Orient
0022-5002 Journal of the Experimental Analysis of Behavior
0022-5010 Journal of the History of Biology
0022-5029 Journal of the History of Buddhism†
0022-5037 Journal of the History of Ideas
0022-5045 Journal of the History of Medicine and Allied Sciences
0022-5053 Journal of the History of Philosophy
0022-5061 Journal of the History of the Behavioral Sciences
0022-507X Journal of the Indian Medical Profession
0022-5088 Journal of the Less-Common Metals *see* 0925-8388
0022-5096 Journal of the Mechanics and Physics of Solids
0022-510X Journal of the Neurological Sciences
0022-5118 Journal of the New African Literature and the Arts†
0022-5126 Journal of the Reading Specialist *see* 0886-0246
0022-5134 Journal of the Royal Artillery
0022-5142 Journal of the Science of Food and Agriculture
0022-5150 Denison University. Journal of the Scientific Laboratories†
0022-5169 Journal of the West
0022-5177 Journal of the West Australian Nurses†
0022-5185 Journal of Theological Studies
0022-5193 Journal of Theoretical Biology
0022-5207 Journal of Therapy
0022-5223 Journal of Thoracic and Cardiovascular Surgery
0022-5231 Journal of Thought
0022-524X Journal of Transpersonal Psychology
0022-5258 Journal of Transport Economics and Policy
0022-5266 Journal of Transport History
0022-5274 Journal of Transportation Medicine
0022-5282 Journal of Trauma
0022-5290 Journal of Tropical Geography *see* 0129-7619
0022-5304 Journal of Tropical Medicine and Hygiene
0022-5320 Journal of Ultrastructure Research *see* 1047-8477
0022-5339 Journal of Undergraduate Mathematics
0022-5347 Journal of Urology
0022-5355 Journal of Vacuum Science and Technology *see* 0734-2101
0022-5355 Journal of Vacuum Science and Technology *see* 0734-211X
0022-5363 Journal of Value Inquiry
0022-5371 Journal of Verbal Learning and Verbal Behavior *see* 0749-596X
0022-538X Journal of Virology
0022-5398 Journal of Vitaminology *see* 0301-4800
0022-5401 Journal of West African Languages
0022-541X Journal of Wildlife Management
0022-5428 Columbia Journal of World Business
0022-5436 Journal of World History†
0022-5444 Journal of World Trade
0022-5452 Journal of Yugoslav Foreign Trade
0022-5460 Zoological Society of London. Journal of Zoology. Series A *see* 0952-8369
0022-5495 Journal Pratique de Droit Fiscal et Financier *changed to* Journal de Droit Fiscal.
0022-5509 Journalism†
0022-5517 Journalism Educator
0022-5525 Journalism Monographs
0022-5533 Journalism Quarterly *see* 0196-3031
0022-5541 Journalist
0022-555X Journalist
0022-5568 Zhurnalist
0022-5576 Der Journalist
0022-5584 Journalist
0022-5592 Journalisten
0022-5622 Journee des Fruits & Legumes
0022-5630 Journee du Batiment†
0022-5649 Journee Vinicole
0022-5665 Journeyman Barber *see* 0148-2114
0022-569X Joy†
0022-5703 Joy & Light
0022-5711 Jucunda Laudatio
0022-572X Judaica
0022-5738 Judaica Bohemiae
0022-5746 Judaica Book Guide†
0022-5754 Judaica Book News
0022-5762 Judaism
0022-5770 Judean
0022-5800 Judicature
0022-5819 Judo
0022-5827 Judo Echo *changed to* Judo.
0022-5843 Judo Kokokan†
0022-5851 Judy *changed to* Judy and Tracy.
0022-5878 Jugend und Technik *changed to* Vision & Technik.
0022-5886 Jugend Film Fernsehen *see* 0341-6860
0022-5894 Jugend in Arbeit *changed to* Jugend in Schule und Beruf.
0022-5908 Jugend Kurier†
0022-5916 Jugend und Buch†
0022-5924 Jugenddorf-Zeitung *changed to* Klinge.
0022-5932 Jugendherberge
0022-5940 Jugendhilfe
0022-5967 Jugendwacht *changed to* Dafuer.
0022-5975 Jugendwohl
0022-6009 Jugi - Ajiste *changed to* Ticket.
0022-6017 Jugoslavenska Advokatura†
0022-6025 Jugoslavia Fervojisto
0022-6033 Jugoslavija
0022-6041 Yugoslavskie Profsoyuzy
0022-605X Jugoslawische Touristenzeitung
0022-6068 Jugoslovenska i Inostrana Dokumentacija Zastite na Radu
0022-6076 Jugoslovenska Revija za Kriminologiju i Krivicno Pravo
0022-6084 Jugoslovenska Revija za Medjunarodno Pravo
0022-6114 Jugoslovenski Pregled
0022-6130 Jugoslovensko Vinogradarstvo i Vinarstvo
0022-6149 Jugovinil
0022-6157 Juguetes y Juegos de Espana
0022-6165 Juillard†
0022-6173 Juilliard News Bulletin *changed to* Juilliard Journal.
0022-6203 Juncture - Where Ideas Meet†
0022-622X Junge Christliche Arbeitnehmer. Befreiung *changed to* Aktion.
0022-6246 Junge Elektrohandwerk *changed to* Der Junge Elektro-techniker.
0022-6262 Der Junge Florist
0022-6270 Junge Gaertner†
0022-6289 Junge Gemeinde
0022-6297 Junge Generation†
0022-6300 Der Junge Kaufmann
0022-6319 Junge Kirche
0022-6335 Junge Metallhandwerker *changed to* Der Junge Metall-Facharbeiter.
0022-6343 Junge Sammler
0022-636X Junge Stimme†
0022-6378 Junge Textilvekaeufer *changed to* Der Jungkaufmann.
0022-6394 Junger Tischler†
0022-6416 Junge Wirtschaft *changed to* Unternehmer.
0022-6424 Jungfreiheitlichet
0022-6432 Junghandwerker im Kraftfahrzeug Betrieb *changed to* Autofachmann.
0022-6440 Eisenhardt-Post
0022-6467 Jungscharhelfer
0022-6475 Junior
0022-6483 Junior Age†
0022-6505 Junior Bookshelf
0022-6521 Junior Church Paper†
0022-653X Junior College Journal *changed to* Community, Technical, and Junior College Journal.
0022-6548 Junior College Research Review *changed to* Junior College Resource Review.
0022-6556 Junior Dental *see* 0393-0505
0022-6564 Junior Education Equipment *changed to* Primary & Middle School Equipment.
0022-6572 Junior Farmer and 4-H Enthusiast *changed to* Enthusiast.
0022-6602 Texas Historian
0022-6610 Institution of General Technician Engineers Journal *see* 0954-6529
0022-6629 Junior Keynotes
0022-6637 Junior League *changed to* Junior League Review.
0022-6645 Jet Cadet *see* 0162-5217

ISSN

ISSN INDEX 5401

ISSN	Title
0022-6661	Junior Members Round Table. News Notes see 0736-8879
0022-667X	Junior News†
0022-6688	Junior Scholastic
0022-6696	Junior Statesman changed to Junior Statement.
0022-670X	Junior Student†
0022-6718	Junior Trails
0022-6734	Junta Nacional da Cortica Boletim see 0870-1059
0022-6742	Junta Nacional da Marinha Mercante. Boletim changed to Portugal. Direccao Geral de Marinha do Comercio. Boletim.
0022-6769	Juntendo Medical Journal
0022-6777	Juridica†
0022-6785	Juridical Review
0022-6793	Jurimetrics Journal
0022-6807	Juris
0022-6815	Jurisprudence Association. Journal
0022-6823	Jurisprudence Automobile
0022-6831	Jurisprudence du Port d'Anvers
0022-684X	Jurisprudencia e Doutrina
0022-6858	Jurist
0022-6874	Juristen changed to Juristen og Oekonomen.
0022-6882	Juristenzeitung
0022-6890	Juristische Analysen†
0022-6912	Juristische Blaetter
0022-6920	Juristische Rundschau
0022-6939	Juristische Schulung
0022-6947	J U S see 1100-620X
0022-6955	J U S
0022-6963	Jus Gentium
0022-6971	Jussens Venner
0022-698X	Just Between Office Girls see 0273-964X
0022-6998	P L A Newsletter see 0163-5506
0022-7013	Justice
0022-7048	Justice Weekly
0022-7056	Justicia
0022-7064	Justiz-Ministerial-Blatt fuer Hessen
0022-7099	Jute and Jute Fabrics - Pakistan changed to Jute and Jute Fabrics - Bangladesh.
0022-7102	Jute and Synthetics Review†
0022-7129	Jute Markets and Prices
0022-7137	Jutro Polski
0022-7145	Juvenile Braille Monthly†
0022-7153	Juvenile Court Judges Journal see 0161-7109
0022-7161	Juvenile Merchandising
0022-717X	Juvenile Rechabite†
0022-7196	Juventud†
0022-720X	Juventud en Accion†
0022-7218	Juventud Panadera
0022-7226	Juzen Igakkai Zasshi
0022-7234	Jyotish Kalp†
0022-7242	R A C B Royal Auto
0022-7250	K A G P Journal see 0090-5089
0022-7269	K A H P E R Journal changed to K A H P E R D Journal.
0022-7277	K & C
0022-7285	K B S Anvisningar - K B S Directions changed to K B S Tekniska Foereskrifter.
0022-7293	K B S - Rapporter
0022-7307	K E A Publications changed to K E A Research Publications.
0022-7323	K F Z Werkstaette changed to K F Z Wirtschaft.
0022-734X	K L A Bulletin see 0732-5452
0022-7358	K L A Bulletin
0022-7366	K L M Literatuuroverzicht
0022-7374	K L M News
0022-7390	K M U Monthly Newsletter changed to K M U News Report.
0022-7404	K-Rautaviesti see 0786-1443
0022-7412	K U L S A A Newsletter
0022-7439	K V P News
0022-7447	K.W.F. Nieuws changed to Tijdschrift Kanker.
0022-7463	De Kaarsvlam
0022-7471	Kachiku to Eiyo†
0022-748X	Kadima
0022-7498	Kadmos
0022-7501	Kaelte see 0343-2246
0022-751X	Kaelte- und Klima Rundschau changed to Haus Tech.
0022-7528	Kaelte Klima Praktiker see 0172-1984
0022-7552	Kaerntner Gemeindeblatt
0022-7560	Kaerntner Heimatleben
0022-7579	Kaerntner Landes-Zeitung
0022-7587	Kaerntner Museumsschriften
0022-7595	Kaerntner Naturschutzblaetter†
0022-7609	Kaffee und Tee Markt
0022-7625	Kagaku
0022-7633	Kagaku Gijutsu Bunken Sabisu
0022-7641	Kagaku Gijutsu Bunken Sokuho. Doboku, Kenchiku Kogaku Hen
0022-765X	Kagaku Gijutsu Bunken Toyama
0022-7668	Kagaku Kisoron Kenkyu
0022-7676	Kagaku Kogaku
0022-7684	Kagaku to Kogyo (Tokyo)
0022-7692	Kagakushi Kenkyu
0022-7706	Kagoshima-ken Nogyo Kisho Geppo
0022-7714	Kahertaja
0022-7722	Acta Anatomica Nipponica
0022-7730	Kaigai Gijutsu Hairaito
0022-7757	Kairos
0022-7765	Kairos†
0022-779X	Kaiserswerther Mitteilungen
0022-7803	Kaiun
0022-782X	Kajian Ekonomi Malaysia - Malaysian Economic Studies see 0126-5350
0022-7838	Kakao und Zucker
0022-7846	Kakteen und Andere Sukkulenten
0022-7854	Kaku Igaku
0022-7862	Kakyevole
0022-7870	Kalaikathir
0022-7889	Kalakeli
0022-7900	Kalbos Kultura
0022-7919	Kaleidoscope (Springfield)
0022-7927	Kaleidoscope†
0022-7935	Kalendarium†
0022-7943	Kali†
0022-7978	Kalimat Al-Mar'ah†
0022-7994	Kalki
0022-8028	Kalyan
0022-8036	Kalyan Kalpataru†
0022-8052	Kamakoti Vani
0022-8060	Kameradengruss†
0022-8109	Kamera und Schule changed to Medien Aktiv.
0022-8117	Kamerad Tier
0022-8133	Kameralehti
0022-8141	University of Leiden. Kamerlingh Onnes Laboratory. Communications
0022-815X	Japan T A P P I Journal
0022-8168	Kami Parupu Tokei Geppo
0022-8176	Kamm und Schere
0022-8184	Kammer Nachrichten
0022-8192	Kammerspiele Muenchen changed to Muenchner Kammerspiele.
0022-8206	Kampana
0022-8214	Kampanje!
0022-8230	Kampf dem Krieg
0022-8249	Kampf dem Laerm see 0174-1098
0022-8257	Kampftruppen changed to Europaeische Sicherheit. Ausgabe "A".
0022-8265	Kampioen
0022-8273	Kamratposten
0022-8281	Kanadai Magyarsag
0022-829X	Kanaski Srbobran
0022-8311	Kanazawa Irigaku Soshot
0022-832X	Kanazawa Daigaku Kogakubu Kiyo
0022-8338	Kanazawa University. Science Reports
0022-8346	Kandang Kerbau Hospital Bulletin see 0129-3273
0022-8354	Kandelaar
0022-8362	Kango
0022-8370	Kango Kenkyu
0022-8397	Kanot-Nytt
0022-8400	Kansai Medical School. Journal changed to Kansai Medical University. Journal.
0022-8419	Kansallis-Osake-Pankki. Economic Review
0022-8427	Kansantaloudellinen Aikakauskirja
0022-8435	Kansas!
0022-8443	Kansas Academy of Science. Transactions
0022-8451	Kansas Anthropological Association. Newsletter changed to The Kansas Anthropolotist.
0022-8478	Kansas Banker
0022-8486	Kansas Bar Association. Journal
0022-8494	Kansas Beverage News
0022-8516	Kansas City Grocer
0022-8524	Kansas City Jewish Chronicle
0022-8532	Kansas Economic Development Report†
0022-8540	Kansas Electric Farmer see 0091-9586
0022-8559	Kansas Engineer
0022-8567	Kansas Entomological Society. Journal
0022-8575	Kansas Farm Bureau News
0022-8583	Kansas Farmer changed to Kansas Farmer.
0022-8591	Kansas Fish and Game changed to Kansas Wildlife & Parks.
0022-8605	Kansas Food Dealers Bulletin
0022-8613	Kansas Government Journal
0022-8621	Kansas Historical Quarterly see 0149-9114
0022-863X	Kansas Job Opportunities†
0022-8648	Kansas Journal of Sociology see 0732-913X
0022-8656	Kansas Judicial Council Bulletin
0022-8699	Kansas Medical Society. Journal see 8755-0059
0022-8702	Kansas Music Review
0022-8710	Kansas Nurse
0022-8729	Kansas Ornithological Society. Bulletin
0022-8737	Kansas Publisher
0022-8745	Kansas Quarterly
0022-8753	Kansas Restaurant
0022-8761	Kansas School Board Journal†
0022-877X	Kansas School Naturalist†
0022-8788	Kansas Speech and Hearing Association Journal changed to Kansas Speech - Language - Hearing Association Journal.
0022-8796	Kansas State Dental Association. Journal changed to Kansas Dental Association. Journal.
0022-880X	Kansas. State Department of Education. Special Education Section. Typical Report†
0022-8818	Kansas State Teachers College Alumni Association. Alumni News changed to Spotlight (Emporia).
0022-8826	Kansas Stockman
0022-8834	Kansas Teacher
0022-8842	Kansas Transporter changed to Mid-America Transporter.
0022-8850	University of Kansas Science Bulletin
0022-8869	Kansas Water News†
0022-8877	Kant Studien
0022-8885	Kantinen
0022-8893	Kantoor en Efficiency
0022-8907	Kantoor - School - Huis
0022-8923	Kanu Sport
0022-894X	Kappa Delta Epsilon Current changed to The Current of Kappa Delta Epsilon.
0022-8958	Kappa Delta Pi Record
0022-8966	Karachi Commerce Weekly
0022-8974	Karachi University Gazette†
0022-8990	Karamu
0022-9008	Karate and Oriental Arts
0022-9016	Karate Illustrated see 0888-031X
0022-9024	Karayollari Teknik Bulteni
0022-9032	Kardiologia Polska
0022-9040	Kardiologiya
0022-9059	Karlovacki Tjednik
0022-9075	Karma Album Review†
0022-9083	Karnatak Granthalaya
0022-9105	Die Karpatenpost
0022-9113	Kartei der Praktischen Medizin
0022-913X	Karting
0022-9148	Kartofel' i Ovoshchi
0022-9156	Der Kartoffelbau
0022-9164	Kartographische Nachrichten
0022-9172	Karty Dokumentacyjne
0022-9199	Karys
0022-9202	Fossils
0022-9210	Kashmir Affairs
0022-9229	Kasityo ja Teollisuus
0022-9245	Kasseler Sonntagsblatt
0022-9253	Kastner & Oehler Firmen Zeitung
0022-9261	Kasturi
0022-927X	Kasvatus
0022-9288	Katallagete
0022-9296	Katedra
0022-930X	Katera i Yakhty
0022-9318	Katha-Sahitya
0022-9326	Kathakalit
0022-9342	Archief van de Kerken†
0022-9350	Metamedica†
0022-9377	Katholische Frauenbewegung Oesterreichs. Fuehrungsblatt
0022-9385	Katholische Gedanke see 0340-8280
0022-9393	Katholische Hochschuljugend Oesterreichs - Blaetter changed to Wiener Blaetter.
0022-9407	Katholischen Missionen changed to K M - Die Katholischen Missionen.
0022-9415	Katilolehti
0022-9423	Katipo
0022-9431	Katolikus Szemle†
0022-9458	Katsaus
0022-9466	Kauchuk i Rezina
0022-9474	Kaufhaus und Warenhaus
0022-9482	Kaunis Koti see 0355-2950
0022-9490	Kauppa ja Koti see 0789-6093
0022-9504	Kaupparekisteri changed to Kaupparekisterilehti.
0022-9520	Kautschuk und Gummi. Kunststoffe
0022-9539	Kaviamuthu
0022-9547	Kavita
0022-9555	Kayak†
0022-9563	Kayhan-e Bacheha
0022-9571	Kaytannon Maamies
0022-9598	Kazak
0022-961X	Keen Teen
0022-9636	Keeping Posted see 0482-0819
0022-9644	Keeping Posted with N C S Y
0022-9652	Keeping the Record Straight†
0022-9660	Keeping up with Elementary Education changed to Educating Children: Early and Middle Years.
0022-9679	Keesing's Contemporary Archives see 0950-6128
0022-9687	Kehilwenyane
0022-9695	Keidanren Review
0022-9709	Keio Economic Studies
0022-9717	Keio Journal of Medicine
0022-9725	Keizai Kagaku
0022-9733	Keizai Kenkyu
0022-9741	Keizai Shirin
0022-975X	Keizaigaku Kenkyu
0022-9768	Keizaigaku Ronshu
0022-9776	Kekkaku
0022-9784	Kelderblom
0022-9792	Keltia
0022-9806	Keltner Commodity Letter†
0022-9814	Magyar Tudomanyos Akademia. Tudomanyok Osztalya. Kozlemenyek changed to Kemiai Kozlemenyek.
0022-9822	Kemian Teollisuus see 0355-1628
0022-9830	Kemija u Industriji
0022-9857	Kemio Internacia†
0022-9865	Kemisti
0022-9873	Kemixon Reporter
0022-9881	Kemphaan
0022-989X	Kenpo Nyusu
0022-9903	Kempton Park Parade†
0022-992X	Kenko Hoken Shinbun changed to Sukoyaka Kenpo.
0022-9938	Kenko Kyoiku
0022-9946	Kenko na Kurashi
0022-9954	Kenkyuseika Yoshisyu see 0385-6437
0022-9962	Kennel Gazette
0022-9970	K en O changed to K & O voor Jeugdwelzijnswerk.
0022-9997	Kensetsu Kogyo Bukka Chingin Geppo
0023-0014	Kent Archaeological Review
0023-0022	Kent Farmer
0023-0030	Kent Life

ISSN INDEX

ISSN	Title
0023-0049	Kent Messenger
0023-0065	Kentering†
0023-0073	Kentuckiana Purchasor
0023-0081	Kentucky Academy of Science. Transactions
0023-009X	Kentucky Accountant *changed to* Bottom Line (Louisville).
0023-0103	Kentucky Ancestors
0023-0111	Kentucky Banker
0023-012X	Kentucky Beverage Journal
0023-0146	Kentucky Civil War Round Table. Bulletin
0023-0170	Kentucky Education News *see* 0164-3959
0023-0197	Kentucky English Bulletin
0023-0200	Kentucky Farm Bureau News
0023-0219	Kentucky Farmer
0023-0227	Kentucky Folklore Record *see* 0899-594X
0023-0235	Kentucky Happy Hunting Ground *changed to* Kentucky Afield.
0023-0243	Kentucky Historical Society. Register
0023-0251	Kentucky Labor News
0023-026X	Kentucky Law Journal
0023-0294	Kentucky Medical Association. Journal
0023-0316	Kentucky Nurse Association Newsletter *changed to* Kentucky Nurse.
0023-0324	Kentucky Press
0023-0332	Kentucky Foreign Language Quarterly *see* 0883-1157
0023-0359	Kentucky School Journal†
0023-0367	Kentucky State Bar Journal *see* 0164-9345
0023-0413	Kenya Education Journal
0023-0421	Kenya Farmer
0023-043X	Kenya Mirror *changed to* Mambo.
0023-0448	Kenya Police Review
0023-0464	Kenya Teacher Journal
0023-0472	Kenya Weekly News
0023-0480	Kep- es Hangtechnika
0023-0499	Kerala Commerce and Industry *changed to* Vyavasaya Keralam.
0023-0502	Kerala Labour & Industries Review
0023-0510	Kerala Law Journal
0023-0529	Kerala Law Times
0023-0537	Kerala Sree
0023-0553	Keramik-Freunde der Schweiz. Mitteilungsblatt
0023-0561	Keramische Zeitschrift
0023-057X	Kereskedelmi Szervezes†
0023-0588	Kerk en Wereld†
0023-0596	Kerkblad
0023-0618	Kerkbode van Gereformeerde Kerken in Noord en Zuid-Holland *changed to* Kerkbode van Nederlands Gereformeerde Kerken.
0023-0626	Kerknieuws van de Hervormde Gemeente Schoonebeek†
0023-0634	Kern County Dental Society Newsletter *changed to* Kern County Dental Society Occlusal Register.
0023-0642	Kernenergie
0023-0650	Kerngetallen van Europese Effecten†
0023-0669	Kerngetallen van Nederlandse Effecten
0023-0677	Kerteszet es Szolgeszet
0023-0685	Kerugma
0023-0693	Kerygma
0023-0707	Kerygma und Dogma
0023-0715	Keshett
0023-0731	Keuken
0023-074X	Kexue Tongbao
0023-0758	Key (Grand Rapids)†
0023-0766	Key (Philadelphia)
0023-0774	Key Figures to European Securities†
0023-0782	Key Houston
0023-0790	U.S. Department of State. Key Officers of Foreign Service Posts
0023-0804	Key Reporter
0023-0839	Key to Christian Education
0023-0855	Key to the Dayton Scene *changed to* Key Dayton Scene.
0023-0863	Key to Toronto *changed to* Where Toronto.
0023-0952	Keya-the Journal for You†
0023-0987	Keystone Folklore Quarterly *see* 0149-8444
0023-0995	Keystone Motorist *changed to* Keystone A A A Motorist.
0023-1010	Khad Patrika
0023-1029	Khadi Gramodyog
0023-1037	Khadya Vigyan
0023-1045	Khao Kan-Faifa
0023-1053	Khao Setthakit Kan-Kaset
0023-1061	Khartoum†
0023-107X	Khatoon Mashriq
0023-1088	Kheti
0023-1096	Khilauna
0023-110X	Khimicheskaya Promyshlennost'
0023-1118	Khimicheskie Volokna
0023-1126	Khimicheskoe i Neftyanoe Mashinostroenie
0023-1134	Khimiko-farmatsevticheskii Zhurnal
0023-1142	Khimiya i Zhizn'
0023-1150	Khimiya Prirodnykh Soedinenii
0023-1169	Khimiya i Tekhnologiya Topliv i Masel
0023-1177	Khimiya Tverdogo Topliva
0023-1185	Khimiya v Sel'skom Khozyaistve
0023-1193	Khimiya Vysokikh Energii†
0023-1207	Khirurgiya
0023-1215	Khlebopekarnaya i Konditerskaya Promyshlennost' *see* 0235-2508
0023-1223	Khliborob Ukrainy
0023-1231	Khlopkovodstvo
0023-124X	Kholodil'naya Tekhnika
0023-1258	Khudozhnik
0023-1274	Kibernetika
0023-1282	Kick to Corruption
0023-1290	Kicker - Sportmagazin
0023-1304	Kidney
0023-1312	Kids†
0023-1347	Kieler Milchwirtschaftliche Forschungsberichte
0023-1355	Kigyoho Kenkyu†
0023-1363	Kijk op het Noorden
0023-1371	Kikaika Nogyo
0023-138X	Kikan Togyo Shiho
0023-1398	Komuna (Kikinda)
0023-1401	Kilpailunvapauslehti *see* 0356-5092
0023-141X	Kim - Trefle *changed to* Trefle.
0023-1428	Kimya Muhendisligi
0023-1436	Kin
0023-1444	Kind en Zondag
0023-1452	Kindai Chugoku Kenkya Senta Iho†
0023-1460	Kindai Eiga
0023-1479	Kindai Kenchiku
0023-1495	Kinderaerztliche Praxis
0023-1509	S O S Kinderdorfbote
0023-1517	Kindergartner *changed to* Ages 5-6 Church and Home Leaflets.
0023-1541	Kine Weekly†
0023-1568	Kinesis
0023-1576	Kinesitherapie Scientifique
0023-1584	Kinetics and Catalysis
0023-1606	Kingbird
0023-1614	Kingdom Digest
0023-1630	Libya. Census and Statistics Department. Monthly Cost of Living Index for Tripoli Town
0023-1649	Kingsman
0023-1657	Kinki University. Bulletin of Pharmacy
0023-1673	Kino
0023-1681	Kinomekhanik
0023-169X	Kinotechnik
0023-1703	Kinship
0023-1711	Kin'yu Keizai *see* 0916-3158
0023-172X	Kioskejer-Bladet *see* 0903-9287
0023-1738	Kipling Journal
0023-1746	Kiplinger Agriculture Letter
0023-1754	Kiplinger Florida Letter
0023-1762	Kiplinger Tax Letter
0023-1770	Kiplinger Washington Letter
0023-1789	Kirche
0023-1797	Kirchenblatt fuer die Reformierte Schweiz:†
0023-1800	Der Kirchenchor
0023-1819	Der Kirchenmusiker
0023-1827	Kirchliches Amtsblatt fuer das Bistum Essen
0023-1843	Kirjastolehti
0023-1851	Kiryat Sefer
0023-186X	Kirke og Kultur
0023-1878	Kiserletes Orvostudomany
0023-1894	Kitab†
0023-1908	Kitakanto Medical Journal
0023-1916	Kitano Hospital Journal of Medicine
0023-1924	Kitasato Archives of Experimental Medicine
0023-1932	Kitchen Business *see* 0730-2487
0023-1940	Kiva
0023-1959	Kivung
0023-1975	Kizito
0023-1983	Kjemi
0023-1991	Kjoleteknikk og Fryserinaering *see* 0284-0758
0023-2017	Klagenfurt
0023-2025	Klassekampen
0023-2033	Klassieke Nuusbrieg *see* 0303-1896
0023-2041	Klei en Keramiek *changed to* Klei, Glas, Keramiek.
0023-2068	Kleine Chorzeitung†
0023-2076	Kleintier-Praxis
0023-2084	Kleio
0023-2106	Kleuterwereld *see* 0165-4772
0023-2114	Kliatt Paperback Book Guide *see* 0199-2376
0023-2149	Klinicheskaya Meditsina
0023-2157	Klinika Oczna
0023-2165	Klinische Monatsblaetter fuer Augenheilkunde und Augenarztliche Fortbildung
0023-2173	Klinische Wochenschrift *changed to* Clinical Investigation.
0023-2181	Klok en Klepel
0023-219X	Klub *changed to* Klub i Khudozhestvennaya Samodeyatel'nost'
0023-2203	Klub Slowenischer Studenten in Wien. Information
0023-2211	Klueter Blaetter
0023-222X	Die Kluge Hausfrau
0023-2238	Kmecki Glas
0023-2246	Kneipp
0023-2254	Kneipp Blaetter
0023-2262	Knight†
0023-2270	Knight's Industrial Reports *see* 0309-0558
0023-2289	Knip
0023-2297	Knit Directions *changed to* Textile Directions.
0023-2300	Knitting Times
0023-2335	Knitting Industry†
0023-2351	Knitwear and Stockings *see* 0308-9886
0023-2378	Knizhnoe Obozrenie
0023-2386	Knjigovoda
0023-2394	Knjigovodstvo
0023-2408	Knjizevnost
0023-2416	Knjizevne Novine
0023-2424	Knjiznica
0023-2432	Konditor Zeitung
0023-2440	Know Britain
0023-2467	A P S S Know How (Associated Public School Systems) *changed to* H M L I Research Bulletin.
0023-2483	Know Your World *see* 0163-4844
0023-2491	Knowledge Industry Report†
0023-2505	Kobber- og Blikkenslagermesteren
0023-2513	Kobe Journal of Medical Sciences
0023-2521	Kobe Plant Protection and Plant Quarantine Information
0023-2548	Kobieta i Zycie
0023-2556	Kobunshi Kagaku *see* 0386-2186
0023-2564	Polymer Application
0023-2572	Kochniano Anees
0023-2599	Kodai Mathematical Seminar Reports *see* 0386-5991
0023-2602	Kodak Dealer News†
0023-2629	Kodin Kuvalehti
0023-2629	Koebenhavns Havneblad
0023-2637	Koeling†
0023-2653	Koelner Zeitschrift fuer Soziologie und Sozialpsychologie
0023-267X	Koepelt
0023-2688	Koepmannen
0023-2696	Koerpererziehung†
0023-270X	Koers
0023-2718	Kyushu University. Faculty of Engineering. Technology Reports
0023-2726	N A L News
0023-2734	Kogyo Kagaku Zasshi *see* 0369-4577
0023-2742	Kohle und Heizoel
0023-2750	Koinonia†
0023-2777	Kojo Kanri
0023-2785	Kokka
0023-2807	Kokoro to Shakai
0023-2815	Koks i Khimiya
0023-2823	Koks, Smola, Gaz
0023-2831	Koku Eisei Gakkai Zasshi
0023-284X	Koku Gijutsu
0023-2858	Koku Igaku Jikkentai Hokoku
0023-2866	Kokusaiho Gaiko Zasshi
0023-2912	Kolloidnyi Zhurnal
0023-2939	Kolorisztikai Ertesito
0023-2947	Kolpingblatt
0023-2963	Komal Patra
0023-298X	Komfort in Haus und Garten†
0023-3005	Die Kommenden *changed to* Novalis.
0023-3013	Kommentar
0023-3048	Oesterreichische Akademie der Wissenschaften. Kommission fuer Musikforschung. Mitteilungen
0023-3056	Kommunal Litteraturtjaenst *see* 0349-5426
0023-3064	Kommunal Skoltidning *see* 0347-5484
0023-3072	Kommunal Tidskrift *see* 0347-5484
0023-3080	Kommunikation†
0023-3099	Kommunist
0023-3102	Kommunist Belorussii
0023-3110	Kommunist Ukrainy
0023-3129	Kommunisti Tochikiston
0023-3137	Kommunitaet
0023-3161	Komuna (Belgrade)
0023-317X	Komuna Esperanto-Gazeto *see* 0921-2302
0023-3188	Komunikasi
0023-3196	Komunikaty Mazursko-Warminskie
0023-320X	Komunist
0023-3234	Konditorei und Cafe
0023-3250	Der Konditormeister†
0023-3277	Konepajamies
0023-3285	Konevodstvo i Konnyi Sport
0023-3293	Konfeksjon†
0023-3307	Kongelige Danske Videnskabernes Selskab. Historisk - Filosofiske Skrifter
0023-3323	Kongelige Danske Videnskabernes Selskab. Matematisk - Fysiske Meddelelser
0023-3331	Kongelige Danske Videnskabernes Selskab. Matematisk-Fysiske Skrifter†
0023-334X	Kongetsu no Nogyo
0023-3358	Koninklijke Nederlandse Akademie van Wetenschappen. Series A, Mathematical Sciences. Proceedings *see* 0019-3577
0023-3366	Koninklijke Nederlandse Akademie van Wetenschappen. Series B: Physical Sciences. Proceedings *see* 0924-8323
0023-3374	Koninklijke Nederlandse Akademie van Wetenschappen. Series C: Biological and Medical Sciences. Proceedings *see* 0924-8323
0023-3390	Koninklijke Shell-Post *changed to* Shell-Post.
0023-3412	Tractatenblad van het Koninkrijk der Nederlanden
0023-3420	Konjunktur und Kriset
0023-3439	Konjunktur von Morgen
0023-3447	R W I - Konjunkturberichte
0023-3455	Konjunkturdienst *changed to* Konjunktur.
0023-3463	Konjunkturlaget
0023-3471	Konjunkturni Barometar
0023-3498	Konjunkturpolitik
0023-3501	Konkreet
0023-3544	Konkuriito Jaanaru *see* 0387-1061
0023-3552	Konkurs, Treuhand- und Schiedsgerichtswesen *changed to* K T S - Zeitschrift fuer Insolvenzrecht, Konkurs, Treuhand, Sanierung.
0023-3560	Konsertnytt

ISSN INDEX 5403

ISSN	Title
0023-3579	Konservatorium Nuus
0023-3595	Konsonanz
0023-3609	Konsthistorisk Tidskrift
0023-3625	Konstruktion im Maschinen-, Apparate- und Geraetebau *see* 0720-5953
0023-365X	Kontakt
0023-3668	Kontaktt
0023-3676	Kontakt Drei und Zwanzig
0023-3692	Kontakto
0023-3706	Kontinentt
0023-3722	Kontorsvaerlden
0023-3730	Kontorteknikk *see* 0332-8201
0023-3757	Kontur
0023-3765	Kontynenty
0023-3773	Konyvtari Figyelo *changed to* Konyvtari Figyelo. Uj Folyam.
0023-3811	Kooperation *changed to* Agrar-Inform.
0023-382X	Kooperationen
0023-3838	K F F Medlemsblad *see* 0024-015X
0023-3846	Kooperatoeren
0023-3862	Koepmannen
0023-3870	Koppeling
0023-3889	Korea Exchange Bank. Monthly Review
0023-3897	Korea Herald
0023-3900	Korea Journal
0023-3919	Korea Observer
0023-3927	Korea Research Society for Dental Materials. Journal
0023-3935	Korea Times
0023-3943	Korea Trade
0023-396X	Korean Business Journal
0023-3978	Korean Economic Journal
0023-3994	Korean Journal of International Law
0023-4001	Korean Journal of Parasitology
0023-401X	Korean Journal of Public Health
0023-4028	Korean Medical Association. Journal
0023-4036	Korean Nature
0023-4044	Journal of Social Sciences and Humanities
0023-4052	Korean Scientific Abstracts
0023-4079	Koreansk Journal
0023-4087	Korneuburger Kulturnachrichten
0023-4109	Koroth (Haifa)
0023-4117	Korpsblad Rijkspolitie *changed to* Politie Magazine.
0023-4125	Korrespondens /Utbildningskontaktt
0023-4141	Korrosion och Ytskydd *see* 0346-640X
0023-415X	Kortars
0023-4168	Kosmetik-Parfum-Drogen-Rundschau mit Aerosol-Aspectt
0023-4176	Kosmetikerinnen-Fachzeitung - Parfuemerie Journal *see* 0342-2976
0023-4184	Kosmetische Monatschriftt
0023-4192	Kosmicheskaya Biologiya i Meditsina *see* 0321-5040
0023-4206	Kosmicheskie Issledovaniya
0023-4214	Kosmobiologie *changed to* Meridian.
0023-4222	Kosmorama
0023-4230	Kosmos
0023-4249	Kosmos. Series A. Biologia *changed to* Kosmos.
0023-4257	Kosmos Tis Psychis
0023-4265	Kostenrechnungspraxis *see* 0931-9077
0023-4281	Kotiliesi
0023-429X	Kountry Korralt
0023-4303	Kovavet
0023-4311	Kovoexport *changed to* Kovoexport.
0023-432X	Kovove Materialy
0023-4338	Kozarstvi
0023-4346	Kozgazdasagi Szemle
0023-4354	Kozhevenno-Obuvnaya Promyshlennost'
0023-4362	Kozlekedestudomanyi Szemle
0023-4370	Kraaiennestt
0023-4389	Kracht van Omhoog
0023-4397	Kraftfahrzeug und Motorrad-Kurier *changed to* Kraftfahrzeug-Gewerbe Suedbaden.
0023-4400	Kraftfahrzeugvermieter *changed to* Der Autovermieter.
0023-4419	Kraftfahrzeugtechnik
0023-4427	Kraftfutter
0023-4435	Krafthand
0023-446X	Krajina
0023-4478	Krakowskie Studia Prawnicze
0023-4486	Krankendienst
0023-4494	Krankengymnastik
0023-4508	Krankenhaus-Umschau
0023-4516	Krankenhausarzt
0023-4524	Krankenversicherung
0023-4532	Kranti
0023-4567	Kratylos
0023-4583	Kredietbank. Weekly Bulletin *see* 0772-3318
0023-4591	Kredit und Kapital
0023-4605	Kresge Art Center Bulletint
0023-4613	Krestanska Revue
0023-4621	Kridangan
0023-463X	Der Kriegsblinde
0023-4648	Kriegsgraeberfuersorge
0023-4656	Krikost
0023-4664	Krikos Ton Vathmoforon
0023-4672	Krila Armije
0023-4680	Kriminal Journalen
0023-4699	Kriminalistik
0023-4702	Kriminalistik und Forensische Wissenschaften
0023-4710	Krishak Samachar
0023-4729	Krishan
0023-4737	Krishanu
0023-4745	Krishnachura
0023-4753	Kristall und Technik *see* 0232-1300
0023-4761	Kristallografiya
0023-477X	Kristaus Karaliaus Laivast
0023-4788	Kristet Samhaellslivt
0023-4796	Kristliga Esperantofoerbundets Medlemsblad
0023-4818	Kritika
0023-4826	Kritikat
0023-4834	Kritische Justiz
0023-4842	Kritischer Katholizismust
0023-4850	Krmiva
0023-4869	Kroeber Anthropological Society. Papers
0023-4877	Krokodil
0023-4885	Krolikovodstvo i Zverovodstvo
0023-4893	Kroniek van Afrika *changed to* African Perspectives.
0023-4907	Kroniek van het Ambacht
0023-4923	Kronika
0023-494X	Kruidenier *see* 0165-1641
0023-4958	Krul's Maandblad voor Stoom- en Chemische Wasserijen, Ververijen en Wassalons
0023-4982	Ktaadnt
0023-4990	Kudzut
0023-5008	Kuehn Archivt
0023-5016	Kuerbiskernt
0023-5032	Kuki Seijo
0023-5040	Kukuruza
0023-5059	Kulde *see* 0284-0758
0023-5067	Kulfold Mezogazdasagat
0023-5075	Kulfoldi Folyoiratok Tartalomjegyzeket
0023-5083	Kulisy
0023-5091	Kuljetus
0023-5113	Kultur
0023-5121	Kulturberichte aus Niederoesterreich
0023-513X	Kultur un Lebn
0023-5148	Kultura
0023-5156	Kultura
0023-5164	Kultura
0023-5172	Kultura i Spoleczenstwo
0023-5180	Kul'tura i Zhyttya
0023-5199	Kul'tura i Zhizn'
0023-5202	Kultura Slova
0023-5210	Kulturberichte aus Tirol
0023-5229	Kulturgemeinschaft "der Kreis." Mitteilungen
0023-5237	Kulturgeografit
0023-5245	Kulturgeografiske Skrifter
0023-5253	Kulturni Radnik
0023-5261	Kulturni Zivot
0023-5296	Kumamoto University. Faculty of Engineering. Technical Reports
0023-530X	Kumamoto University. Institute of Constitutional Medicine. Bulletin
0023-5318	Kumamoto Journal of Science. Series A: Mathematics, Physics and Chemistry *see* 0914-675X
0023-5326	Kumamoto Medical Journal
0023-5334	Kumamoto University. Faculty of Engineering. Memoirs
0023-5342	Kumar
0023-5350	Kungliga Skogs- och Lantbruksakademiens Tidskrift
0023-5369	Kungliga Krigsvetenskapsakademien. Handlingar och Tidskrift
0023-5377	Kungliga Svenska Vetenskapsademiens. Handlingart
0023-5385	Kunnallistekniikka
0023-5393	Kunst des Orientst
0023-5415	Kunst og Kultur
0023-5423	Kunst und das Schoene Heim *changed to* Die Kunst.
0023-5431	Kunst und Kirche
0023-544X	Kunst und Literaturt
0023-5458	Kunst und Stein
0023-5474	Kunstchronik
0023-5490	Kunstgeschichtliche Anzeigent
0023-5504	Der Kunsthandel
0023-5512	Kunstnachrichten
0023-5539	Kunststoff Dokumentum
0023-5555	Kunststoff Rundschau *see* 0172-6374
0023-5563	Kunststoffe
0023-5571	K I B *see* 0343-3129
0023-558X	Kunststoffe - Plasticos *see* 0303-4011
0023-5598	Kunststoffe - Plastics
0023-5601	Kunststofftechnik *see* 0172-6374
0023-561X	Das Kunstwerk
0023-5628	Kupfer-Mitteilungen *see* 0309-2216
0023-5636	Kurdish Factst
0023-5652	Kursbuch
0023-5660	Kurukshetra
0023-5679	Kurume Medical Journal
0023-5687	Kurz und Buendigt
0023-5695	Kurzauszuege aus dem Schrifttum fuer das Eisenbahnwesen *changed to* Information Eisenbahn.
0023-5717	Kuspi
0023-5725	Kusunoki Noho
0023-5733	Kutlwano
0023-5741	Kuuloviesti
0023-575X	Kuwait al-Youm
0023-5768	Kuwait. Central Statistical Office. Monthly Digest of Statistics *changed to* Kuwait. Central Statistical Office. Annual Statistical Abstract.
0023-5776	Kuwait Medical Association. Journal
0023-5784	Kuwaitt
0023-5792	Kuwaiti
0023-5806	Kuznechno-shtampovochnoe Proizvodstvo
0023-5814	Kvakera Esperantisto
0023-5822	Kvaellsstunden
0023-5830	Kvasny Prumysl
0023-5849	Kvety
0023-5857	Kvinner og Klaer
0023-5865	Kwartalnik Architektury i Urbanistyki
0023-5873	Kwartalnik Geologiczny
0023-5881	Kwartalnik Historii Kultury Materialnej
0023-589X	Kwartalnik Historii Nauki i Techniki
0023-5911	Kwartalnik Neofilologiczny
0023-592X	Kwartalnik Opolski
0023-5938	Kwartalnik Pedagogiczny
0023-5946	Kybernetik *see* 0340-1200
0023-5954	Kybernetika
0023-5962	Kyklos
0023-5970	Kylteknisk Tidskrift *see* 0284-0758
0023-5989	Kymppi
0023-5997	Kyoiku Hyoron
0023-6004	Kyokuchi
0023-6012	Kyoto Prefectural University of Medicine. Medical Society. Journal
0023-6020	Kyoto Shobo
0023-6039	Kyoto University. Bulletin of Stomatologyt
0023-6055	Kyoto University Economic Review
0023-6063	Kyoto University. Faculty of Engineering. Memoirs
0023-6071	Kyoto University. Institute for Chemical Research. Bulletin
0023-608X	Kyoto University. Journal of Mathematics
0023-6101	Kyoto Kyoiku Daigaku Kiyo. B. Shizen Kagaku
0023-611X	Kypros
0023-6128	Kyriost
0023-6136	Kyrkofoerfattningar
0023-6144	Kyushu Neuro-Psychiatry
0023-6152	Kyushu University. Faculty of Agriculture. Journal
0023-6160	Kyushu University. Faculty of Engineering. Memoirs
0023-6179	Kyushu University. Faculty of Science. Memoirs. Series D: Earth and Planetary Sciences
0023-6195	Kyushu University. Research Institute for Applied Mechanics. Reports
0023-6217	L A M Y A Revista Mensual
0023-6225	L A R C Reportst
0023-625X	L B I News
0023-6268	L G A Rundschau
0023-6276	L G M Mededelingent
0023-6292	L I D News Bulletint
0023-6306	L K A B-Tidningent
0023-6314	L K H H Accountant *see* 0147-2208
0023-6322	Laerarinnornas Missionsfoerening. Meddelande till L M F. *see* 0345-7842
0023-6330	L M S - Lingua
0023-6349	L O G A
0023-6365	L S A Bulletin
0023-6373	L S C R R C Newslettert
0023-6381	Laurence Scott Engineering Bulletin
0023-639X	L S E Magazinet
0023-6403	L S U Alumni News *changed to* L S U Magazine.
0023-6411	L S U Engineering News
0023-642X	L V I Teknillingen Aikakaus-Lehti *changed to* L V I.
0023-6438	Food Science and Technology
0023-6446	La-Ya'arant
0023-6454	Lab Worldt
0023-6462	Labeo
0023-6470	Labo-Pharma *see* 1157-1489
0023-6489	Labor
0023-6497	Labort
0023-6500	Labor Arbitration Awards
0023-6519	Labor Chroniclet
0023-6527	Labor Developments Abroadt
0023-6535	Labor Education News *changed to* Workers Education Local 189. Newsletter.
0023-6543	Labor Education Viewpointst
0023-656X	Labor History
0023-6578	Labor in Printt
0023-6586	Labor Law Journal
0023-6594	Labor Leader
0023-6616	Labor Record
0023-6632	Labor Safety Newsletter *changed to* Labor Newsletter.
0023-6640	Labor Today
0023-6667	Labor World
0023-6675	Laboratoire Central des Industries Electriques. Bulletin d'Information *see* 0220-9535
0023-6683	Laboratoires Squibb. Recueil de Nouvellest
0023-6691	Laboratoriot
0023-6705	Laboratorio de Engenharia de Mocambique. Boletim Tecnico de Informacoes *changed to* Laboratorio de Engenharia de Mocambique. Boletin Tecnico.
0023-6713	Soul Illustrated *changed to* Soul.
0023-6721	Laboratoriums-Praxist
0023-6748	Laboratornoe Delo
0023-6764	Laboratory Animal Science
0023-6772	Laboratory Animals
0023-6780	L A C News Letter *see* 0308-9568
0023-6799	Laboratory Digestt
0023-6810	Laboratory Equipment
0023-6829	Laboratory Equipment Digest
0023-6837	Laboratory Investigation
0023-6845	Laboratory Management *changed to* Diagnostics & Clinical Testing.
0023-6853	Laboratory Practice
0023-6888	Laborer
0023-6896	Labour and Employment Gazettet

ISSN INDEX

ISSN	Title
0023-690X	Labour Arbitration Cases
0023-6934	Labour Gazette
0023-6942	Labour History
0023-6969	Labour in Israel
0023-6977	Labour Law Journal
0023-6985	Labour Monthly†
0023-6993	Labour Organisert
0023-7000	Labour Research
0023-7027	Labour Woman†
0023-7035	Labour World
0023-7043	Labris *changed to* Ko-Ko.
0023-7051	Lacerta
0023-706X	Lach-Manoeuvre
0023-7078	Lackawanna Jurist
0023-7086	Lacrossetalk
0023-7094	Lada'at
0023-7108	Ladder†
0023-7116	Laeder och Skor *see* 0040-4845
0023-7124	Ladies Home Journal (Inkprint Edition)
0023-7140	Ladue Public Schools Bulletin
0023-7159	Ladugaardsfoermannen
0023-7167	Lady
0023-7175	Lady *see* 0343-3366
0023-7183	Ladycom - The Military Lifestyle Magazine *changed to* Military Lifestyle.
0023-7191	Lady's Circle
0023-7205	Laekartidningen
0023-7213	Laeknabladid
0023-7256	Lagena†
0023-7272	Lagos Weekend
0023-7280	Lagrimal Trifurca
0023-7299	Lahey Clinic Foundation Bulletin†
0023-7302	Le Lait
0023-7310	Lajpat Bhawan Journal *changed to* Better Life.
0023-7329	Lake Carriers' Association. Bulletin†
0023-7345	Lakeland Boating *see* 0744-9194
0023-7353	Lakimies
0023-7361	Lakimiesuutiset
0023-737X	Lakokrasochnye Materialy i ikh Primenenie
0023-7388	Lal-Baugh
0023-7396	Lalit Kala Contemporary
0023-740X	Lalita *changed to* Priya.
0023-7418	Lamp (New York)
0023-7426	Lamp Journal *see* 0162-9077
0023-7442	Lampetten *see* 0904-7824
0023-7450	Lana Moda
0023-7469	Lancashire Life
0023-7477	Lancaster County Historical Society. Journal
0023-7485	Lancaster Farming
0023-7493	Lance
0023-7515	Lanciana
0023-7523	Land
0023-7531	Land
0023-754X	Landscape Architecture News Digest
0023-7558	Der Land- und Forstwirtschaftliche Betrieb
0023-7574	Land and Liberty
0023-7582	Land en Water†
0023-7590	Land and Water Development *see* 0192-9453
0023-7612	Land and Water Law Review
0023-7639	Land Economics
0023-7655	Land Pollution Reporter
0023-768X	Land Use Digest
0023-7698	Land van Valkenburg
0023-7701	Land Worker *changed to* Landworker.
0023-7728	Landarzt *see* 0341-9835
0023-7736	Landbode (The Hague)
0023-7744	Landbote
0023-7752	Landbouw en Plantenziekten†
0023-7760	Landbouwdocumentatie *see* 0925-2762
0023-7779	Landbouweekblad
0023-7795	Landbouwmechanisatie
0023-7817	Bedrijfsontwikkeling. Editie Akkerbouw *changed to* Agrarische Voorlichting.
0023-7825	Landbouwwereldnieuws†
0023-7833	Landbrukstidende
0023-7841	Koninklijk Instituut voor de Tropen. Afdeling Plattelandsontwikkeling. Landendocumentatie *see* 0922-4939
0023-7868	Schleswig-Holstein. Kulturminister. Nachrichtenblatt *see* 0937-0005
0023-7876	Landesamtsblatt fuer das Burgenland
0023-7884	Landesgesetzblatt fuer das Land Salzburg
0023-7906	Landesmuseum fuer Naturkunde zu Muenster in Westfalen. Abhandlungen *changed to* Westfaelischen Museum fuer Naturkunde. Abhandlungen.
0023-7922	Landesversicherungsanstalt Hessen. Nachrichten
0023-7930	Landfall
0023-7949	Landis und Gyr Mitteilungen†
0023-7957	Landjugend
0023-7965	Landman *changed to* Mielies (Bothaville).
0023-7973	Landmaschinen - Handwerk - Handel
0023-7981	Landmaschinen Markt *changed to* Agrartechnik (Wuerzburg).
0023-799X	Landowning in Scotland
0023-8015	Landsbygdens Folk
0023-8023	Landscape
0023-8031	Landscape Architecture
0023-8058	Landschaft und Stadt *changed to* Naturschutz und Landschaftsplanung.
0023-8066	Landskab
0023-8074	Landstingens Tidskrift *see* 0282-4485
0023-8082	Fachzeitschrift fuer Alle Bereiche der Agrartechnik und Laendliches Bauen *changed to* Landtechnik.
0023-8104	Das Landvolk
0023-8112	Landwirt *changed to* Suedtiroler Landwirt.
0023-8120	V W D - Landwirtschaft und Ernaehrung†
0023-8147	Landwirtschaftliche Forschung *changed to* Agribiological Research.
0023-8163	Landwirtschaftliche Zeitschrift Rheinland
0023-8171	Landwirtschaftliches Jahrbuch der Schweiz†
0023-818X	Landwirtschaftliches Zentralblatt. Abteilung 1: Landtechnik *see* 0233-2655
0023-8198	Landwirtschaftliches Zentralblatt. Abteilung 2: Pflanzliche Produktion *see* 0233-2701
0023-8201	Landwirtschaftliches Zentralblatt. Abteilung 3: Tierzucht, Tierernaehrung, Fischerei *see* 0233-2752
0023-821X	Landwirtschaftliches Zentralblatt. Abteilung 4: Veterinaermedizin *see* 0233-2809
0023-8228	Langage Total
0023-8236	Langenbecks Archiv fuer Chirurgie
0023-8244	Langenscheidt's English Monthly†
0023-8252	Langenscheidts Sprach-Illustrierte
0023-8279	Language-Teaching Abstracts *see* 0261-4448
0023-8287	Language and Automation†
0023-8295	Language and Language Behavior Abstracts *see* 0888-8027
0023-8309	Language and Speech
0023-8317	Language and Style
0023-8325	Language Association of Eastern Africa. Journal†
0023-8333	Language Learning
0023-8341	Language Sciences†
0023-8368	Langue Francaise
0023-8376	Langues Modernes
0023-8384	Lansing Labor News
0023-8406	Lantern
0023-8414	Lantern
0023-8422	Lantern
0023-8430	Lantmaestaren
0023-8449	Lantmannen
0023-8457	Lapidary Journal
0023-8473	Laputa Gazette and Faculty News†
0023-8481	Lara Lamont
0023-849X	Laerartidningen - Svensk Skoltidning *see* 1101-2633
0023-8503	Lares
0023-8511	Larvae du Golden Gate
0023-852X	Laryngoscope
0023-8538	Las Polski
0023-8546	Las Vegas Voice
0023-8554	Laser *see* 0722-9003
0023-8589	Laser Focus *see* 1043-8092
0023-8597	Laser Journal†
0023-8600	Laser Report
0023-8627	Chinese Studies in Philosophy
0023-8635	Last Day Messenger†
0023-8651	Last Post
0023-866X	Lastauto Omnibus
0023-8678	Lastbilen
0023-8686	Lastebilen
0023-8694	Lastechniek
0023-8716	Lather†
0023-8740	Latin American Books Newsletter
0023-8759	Latin American Calendar†
0023-8767	Latin American Digest††
0023-8791	Latin American Research Review
0023-8805	Latin American Studies Association Newsletter *see* 0890-7218
0023-8813	Latin American Theatre Review
0023-8821	Latin Teaching *see* 0268-0181
0023-883X	Latinitas
0023-8856	Latomus
0023-8872	Laettbetong
0023-8899	Latvija
0023-8902	Latvija Amerika
0023-8910	Latvijas P.S.R. Preses Hronika
0023-8937	Laufende Mitteilungen Zum Stand der Politischen Bildung in der Bundesrepublik Deutschland†
0023-8961	Laundry and Cleaning *see* 0142-9442
0023-897X	Laundry and Cleaning International *see* 0261-4421
0023-8988	Laurel Messenger
0023-8996	Laurel of Phi Kappa Tau
0023-9003	Laurel Review (Maryville)
0023-9011	Laurentian University Review†
0023-902X	Laurentianum
0023-9038	Laval Administration
0023-9046	Laval Medical *see* 0315-5153
0023-9054	Laval Theologique et Philosophique
0023-9062	Lavender Band
0023-9070	Lavoro e Medicina†
0023-9089	Lavoro Italiano
0023-9097	Lavoro Neuropsichiatrico
0023-9119	Lavoro Sud†
0023-9135	Lavoura
0023-9143	Lavoura Arrozeira
0023-9151	Lavoura e Cooperativismo *changed to* Agricultura Brasileira.
0023-916X	Law *changed to* A D L Law Report.
0023-9178	Law and Computer Technology *see* 0278-3916
0023-9186	Law and Contemporary Problems
0023-9194	Law and Order
0023-9208	Law and Policy in International Business
0023-9216	Law & Society Review
0023-9224	Law and the Social Order *see* 0164-4297
0023-9232	New South Wales Weekly Notes *see* 0312-1674
0023-9240	Law Books Published
0023-9259	Law Guardian *changed to* Law Society's Guardian Gazette.
0023-9267	Law Institute Journal
0023-9275	Law Librarian
0023-9283	Law Library Journal
0023-9291	Royal National Institute for the Blind. Law Notes. Extracts
0023-9305	Law Notes *see* 0094-5277
0023-9313	Law Office Economics and Management Manual *see* 0458-8630
0023-9321	Law Officer†
0023-933X	Law Quarterly Review
0023-9356	Buffalo Law Review
0023-9364	Law Society Gazette
0023-9372	Law Society Journal
0023-9380	Law Society's Gazette
0023-9399	Law Thesaurus
0023-9402	Lawn Care†
0023-9410	Lawn Equipment Journal *see* 0192-7558
0023-9437	Lawyer
0023-9445	Lawyer of the Americas *changed to* Inter-American Law Review.
0023-9453	Lawyer's Association. Journal
0023-947X	Lawyer's Medical Journal†
0023-9488	Lawyers' Recreation
0023-9518	Laymen's Movement Review *changed to* Catalogue of Conferences, Seminars, Workshop.
0023-9526	Lazio
0023-9534	Havre *changed to* Escale.
0023-9542	An Leabharlann
0023-9550	Lead†
0023-9569	Lead Abstracts *see* 0950-1584
0023-9577	Lead and Zinc Statistics
0023-9585	Leader†
0023-9593	Leader†
0023-9607	Leader
0023-964X	Leaflet (Lexington)
0023-9674	Lealtad
0023-9682	Learn†
0023-9690	Learning and Motivation
0023-9704	Learning for Living *see* 0141-6200
0023-9712	Learning Resources†
0023-9739	Leather
0023-9747	Leather and Shoes†
0023-9755	L I R I Monthly Circular *changed to* L I R I Quarterly Review.
0023-9763	Leather Manufacturer
0023-9771	Leather Science
0023-978X	Leather Titles Service†
0023-9798	Leathergoods *see* 0264-8555
0023-9801	Leathergoods Buyer†
0023-981X	Leatherneck
0023-9828	Leathers
0023-9836	Leaves of Twin Oaks
0023-9852	Lebanese Medical Journal
0023-9860	Lebanon. Direction Centrale de la Statistique. Bulletin Statistique Mensuel
0023-9887	Leben *see* 0303-4283
0023-9895	Leben und Gesundheit *see* 0179-7360
0023-9909	Lebende Sprachen
0023-9917	Lebendige Erde
0023-9925	Lebendige Familie *changed to* Praxis Bilden und Erziehen.
0023-9933	Lebendige Schule†
0023-9941	Lebendiges Zeugnis
0023-995X	Lebenshilfe *see* 0173-9573
0023-9968	Thema Null *changed to* Blaue Feder.
0023-9976	Lebensmittel-Grosshandel - Susswaren-Zeitung *changed to* Food and Nonfood.
0023-9984	Lebensmittelhandel *changed to* Lebensmittel - Revue - Alimentaire.
0023-9992	Lebensmittel Praxis
0024-001X	Lebensmittelhaendler *see* 0047-4282
0024-0028	Lebensmittelindustrie
0024-0036	Lebensmittelpost *see* 0047-4282
0024-0044	Lebensversicherungsmedizin *see* 0933-4548
0024-0052	Lebensweiser†
0024-0060	Lebone la Kgalalelo Isibani Sobu Ngcwele *changed to* Lebone la Kgalalelo.
0024-0079	Lecciones y Ensayos†
0024-0087	Lectura†
0024-0095	Lectura†
0024-0109	Lectura para Todos†
0024-0125	Lecture et Tradition
0024-0133	Lectures Francaises
0024-015X	Ledarforum
0024-0168	Ledarskap och Loensamhet
0024-0176	Das Leder
0024-0184	Leder Echo
0024-0192	L S L
0024-0214	Lederwaren-Report
0024-0222	Ledger†
0024-0230	Lediga Platser
0024-0249	Leeds African Studies Bulletin
0024-0257	Leeds Arts Calendar
0024-0273	Leeds Journal

ISSN	Title
0024-0281	Leeds Philosophical and Literary Society. Proceedings. Literary and Historical Section
0024-029X	Communist News
0024-0303	Left
0024-032X	Lega Navale
0024-0338	Legal Aid Briefcase *changed to* N L A D A Briefcase.
0024-0354	Legal Eagles News *changed to* Lawyer - Pilots Bar Association Journal.
0024-0362	Legal Executive
0024-0370	Legal Record†
0024-0389	Legerkoerier
0024-0400	Leggi
0024-0419	Leggi delle Comunita' Europee†
0024-0427	Legioen van Maria
0024-0435	Legion
0024-0451	Legionair
0024-046X	New Jersey School Boards Association. Legislative Bulletin *changed to* New Jersey School Boards Association. School Leader.
0024-0478	Legislative Conference Reporter *changed to* P S C Clarion.
0024-0486	Legislative Research Checklist *see* 0190-6623
0024-0494	Legislative Roundup†
0024-0508	Legislator
0024-0524	Legislazione Italiana
0024-0532	Legno (Lainate) *changed to* Mondolegno.
0024-0540	Legon Observer†
0024-0567	Lehigh Valley Safety News†
0024-0575	Ligstraal - Lehlasedi
0024-0591	Spark (New York)
0024-0605	Lehrer in Friseurklassen *see* 0723-7928
0024-0613	Leibesuebungen *see* 0344-4023
0024-0621	Leica-Fotografie International
0024-063X	Leica Photography†
0024-0648	Leicester and County Chamber of Commerce Journal *changed to* City and County.
0024-0656	Leicestershire Farmer *see* 0306-0160
0024-0664	Leicestershire Historian
0024-0672	Rijksmuseum van Natuurlijke Historie. Zoologische Mededelingen *changed to* Nationaal Natuurhistorisch Museum. Zoologische Mededelingen.
0024-0699	Leipuri
0024-0702	Leistung†
0024-0710	Leisure Painter
0024-0729	Leisure Time†
0024-0737	Der Leitende Angestellte
0024-0745	Lekarz Wojskowy
0024-0761	Lemouzi
0024-0788	Lenau-Forum
0024-0796	Lenguaje y Ciencias
0024-0818	Leningradskii Universitet. Vestnik. Seriya Ekonomika, Filosofiya i Pravo
0024-0826	Leningradskii Universitet. Vestnik. Seriya Fizika i Khimiya
0024-0834	Leningradskii Universitet. Vestnik. Seriya Geologiya i Geografiya
0024-0842	Leningradskii Universitet. Vestnik. Seriya Istoriya, Yazyk i Literatura
0024-0850	Leningradskii Universitet. Vestnik. Seriya Matematika, Mekhanika i Astronomiya
0024-0877	Lenkurt Demodulator *changed to* G T E Lenkurt Demodulator.
0024-0885	Lentaja†
0024-0893	Lente (Inkprint Edition)†
0024-0907	Lenzinger Berichte
0024-0915	Leo Baeck Institut. Bulletin
0024-0923	Leodiensian
0024-094X	Leonardo: Art Science and Technology
0024-0958	Leone
0024-0966	Lepidopterists' Society. Journal
0024-0974	Lepidopterological Society of Japan. Transactions
0024-1008	Leppro *see* 0386-3980
0024-1016	Leprologia
0024-1024	Leprosy in India *see* 0254-9395
0024-1040	Lerindustrien†
0024-1059	Lernen und Leisten *see* 0340-6040
0024-1067	Les
0024-1075	Leserzeitschrift†
0024-1083	Lesestunde mit dem Grossen Freizeit-Programm
0024-1091	Leshonenu La'am
0024-1105	Lesnictvi
0024-1113	Lesnoe Khozyaistvo
0024-1121	Lesotho-Canada†
0024-1148	Lesovedenie
0024-1156	Letectvi a Kosmonautika
0024-1164	Lethaia
0024-1172	Letopis' Gazetnykh Statei
0024-1180	Letopis na Periodichna Pechat *see* 0324-0398
0024-1180	Letopis na Periodichna Pechat *see* 0324-0347
0024-1199	Letopis' Pechatnykh Proizvedenii Izobrazitel'nogo Iskusstva
0024-1202	Letopis' Zhurnal'nykh Statei
0024-1210	Letras
0024-1229	Letras de Ayer y de Hoy†
0024-1245	Letras Potosinas
0024-1253	Let's Dance
0024-1261	Let's Find Out
0024-1288	Let's Live
0024-1296	Letter to Libraries *changed to* Letter to Libraries.
0024-130X	Letterato
0024-1326	Lettere d'Affari
0024-1334	Lettere Italiane
0024-1350	Lettore di Provincia
0024-1369	Lettres
0024-1377	Lettres et Medecins†
0024-1393	Lettres Francaises†
0024-1407	Lettres Nouvelles†
0024-1415	Les Lettres Romanes
0024-1423	Lettrisme
0024-1431	Lettura Stenografica
0024-144X	Letture
0024-1458	Cineschedario - Letture Drammatiche
0024-1466	Leukemia Abstracts†
0024-1482	Leuvense Bijdragen
0024-1490	Levant Morgenland
0024-1504	Levante
0024-1512	Leveltari Kozlemenyek
0024-1520	Levende Natuur
0024-1539	Levende Talen†
0024-1547	Levend Woord
0024-1555	H L *changed to* Missets Distrifood.
0024-1571	Levnedsmiddelbladet *see* 0105-6654
0024-158X	Legislacao Federal e Marginalia
0024-1598	Lex
0024-161X	Lexington Philharmonic Society Newsletter *changed to* Upbeat.
	Lexington Philharmonic Society Newsletter.
0024-1628	College of the Bible Quarterly *see* 0160-8770
0024-1636	Ley
0024-1652	Rijksmuseum van Natuurlijke Historie. Zoologische Verhandelingen *changed to* Nationaal Natuurlhistorisch Museum. Zoologische Verhandelingen.
0024-1660	Leyland Journal†
0024-1679	Leyte-Samar Studies†
0024-1687	Liaison†
0024-1709	Federation Nationale des Anciens Combattants et Coalets des Transmissions. Liaison des Transmissions
0024-1717	Liaisons
0024-1725	Liaisons Sociales
0024-1733	Al Liamm
0024-1741	Liaudies Balsas†
0024-175X	Libelle
0024-1792	Liberal Catholic
0024-1806	Liberal Context†
0024-1814	Liberal Debatt *see* 0345-3685
0024-1822	Liberal Education
0024-1830	Liberal Opinion†
0024-1849	Liberal Party Organisation. Liberal News *see* 0954-5735
0024-1857	Liberal Ungdom
0024-1865	Liberated Guardian *changed to* City Star.
0024-1873	Liberation
0024-1881	Liberation
0024-189X	Liberation†
0024-1903	Liberation News Service
0024-1911	Liberation News Service
0024-1954	Liberia
0024-1962	Liberian Age
0024-1970	Liberian Law Journal
0024-1989	Liberian Studies Journal
0024-2004	Libertarian *changed to* Common Wealth Journal.
0024-2012	Libertarian Connection *changed to* Connection (Alexandria).
0024-2020	Liberte
0024-2047	Libertijn†
0024-2055	Liberty (Hagerstown)
0024-2063	Liberty *see* 0790-5068
0024-208X	Liberty *see* 0360-3342
0024-2098	Liberty Letter *changed to* Spotlight (Washington).
0024-2101	Libra†
0024-2128	Librairie Ancienne et Moderne. Bulletin *changed to* Bulletin du Bibliophile.
0024-2144	Libraries in International Development. Newsletter†
0024-2152	Librarium
0024-2160	Library
0024-2179	Library & Information Science Abstracts
0024-2187	Library Associate†
0024-2195	Library Association Record
0024-2209	Library Binder *see* 0735-8571
0024-2217	The Library Bookseller
0024-2225	State University of New York. Upstate Medical Center. Library Bulletin†
0024-2233	Library Chronicle (Philadelphia)†
0024-2241	Library Chronicle (Austin)
0024-225X	Library-College Journal *see* 0091-7281
0024-2276	Library Counselor†
0024-2284	Library for the Blind and Physically Handicapped. Newsletter†
0024-2292	Library Herald
0024-2306	Library History
0024-2330	Library Keynotes†
0024-2349	Library Leaves†
0024-2357	Library Lines†
0024-2365	Contra Costa County Library Link†
0024-2373	Library Literature
0024-239X	Library Materials on Africa *see* 0305-862X
0024-2411	Library Notes†
0024-2438	Library Notes†
0024-2446	North Dakota Library Notes†
0024-2454	Library Occurrent *see* 0275-777X
0024-2462	Library Opinion†
0024-2489	Library Periodicals Directory†
0024-2497	Library Progress†
0024-2500	Library Publicity Clippings†
0024-2519	Library Quarterly
0024-2527	Library Resources & Technical Services
0024-2535	Library Review
0024-2543	Library Science with a Slant to Documentation and Information Studies
0024-2551	Library Service News
0024-2578	Library System†
0024-2586	Library Technology Reports
0024-2594	Library Trends
0024-2608	Library World†
0024-2616	Library World *see* 0307-4803
0024-2632	L S A
0024-2640	Libreria
0024-2659	Libreria
0024-2667	Libri
0024-2683	Libri e Riviste d'Italia
0024-273X	Libro Espanol†
0024-2756	Libros†
0024-2764	Licensed Beverage Journal
0024-2772	Licensed Bookmaker & Betting Office Proprietor
0024-2802	Licensee
0024-2810	Lichamelijke Opvoeding
0024-2829	Lichenologist
0024-2845	Lichtbogen
0024-2853	Lichthoeve-Kinderwerk *changed to* Lichthoeve.
0024-2861	Lichttechnik *changed to* Licht.
0024-287X	Licitationen
0024-2888	Licke Novine *see* 0350-2562
0024-2896	Lide a Zeme
0024-290X	Lied und Chor
0024-2918	Lien
0024-2926	Lien Entre Meres et Peres de Pretres
0024-2942	Liens
0024-2950	Lietuviu Dienos
0024-2969	Litovskii Fizicheskii Sbornik
0024-3000	Akademiya Nauk Litovskoi S.S.R. Trudy. Seriya B *see* 0131-3851
0024-3019	Life (New York)
0024-3027	Life and Breath *changed to* Life & Lung.
0024-3035	Life and Health *see* 0749-3509
0024-3043	Life and Health†
0024-306X	Life and Work
0024-3078	Life Association News
0024-3086	Lifeboat
0024-3094	Life Boy Link†
0024-3132	Life Insurance Planning
0024-3140	Life Insurance Selling
0024-3159	Life International†
0024-3167	Life Lines†
0024-3175	Life of Faith *see* 0269-4689
0024-3183	Life Office Management Association. Bulletin *changed to* L.O.M.A. Resource.
0024-3191	Systems and Procedures Review *changed to* L.O.M.A. Resource.
0024-3205	Life Sciences (1973)
0024-3221	Life Underwriters Association of the City of New York. Bulletin *changed to* New York City Association of Life Underwriters.
0024-3264	Ligament *changed to* Aktiviteitensektor. Maandblad.
0024-3272	Die Ligdraer
0024-3299	Light and Life
0024-3302	Light and Lighting†
0024-3329	Light Horse *changed to* Horse & Rider.
0024-3345	Light Metal Age
0024-3353	Light of New York†
0024-3361	Light of the Moon
0024-337X	Light Engineering†
0024-3388	Light Steam Power *changed to* Steam Power.
0024-340X	Lighter†
0024-3418	Lighting Equipment News
0024-3426	Lighting Research and Technology
0024-3434	Ligne de Communication†
0024-3442	Ligstraal - Umsebe - Umtha†
0024-3450	Liguorian
0024-3469	Liiketaloudellinen Aikakauskirja
0024-3477	Lijecnicki Vjesnik†
0024-3485	Lillabuler†
0024-3493	Lille Chirurgical
0024-3507	Lille Medical *see* 0981-1095
0024-3523	Limba Romana
0024-354X	Limen
0024-3558	Limit
0024-3582	Limnological Society of Southern Africa. Newsletter *changed to* Southern Africa Journal of Aquatic Sciences.
0024-3590	Limnology and Oceanography
0024-3604	Limnos *see* 0037-0487
0024-3612	Limonadier de Paris
0024-3620	Limosa
0024-3639	Linacre Quarterly
0024-3647	Linage†
0024-3663	Lincoln Business†
0024-3671	Lincoln Herald
0024-368X	Lincoln Law Review†
0024-3698	Lincoln Library Bulletin
0024-3701	Lincolnian
0024-371X	Lincolnshire Life
0024-3728	Linde Berichte aus Technik und Wissenschaft
0024-3744	Lineagrafica
0024-3752	Linea Italiana†
0024-3760	Linea Maschile e Femminile†
0024-3779	Linea Z

ISSN	Title
0024-3787	Lineamaglia
0024-3795	Linear Algebra and Its Applications
0024-3809	Linear Integrated Circuit D.A.T.A. Book *changed to* Linear I Cs D.A.T.A. Digest.
0024-3817	Lineastruttura
0024-3825	Linen Supply News *see* 0195-0118
0024-3833	Linens, Domestics and Bath Products *see* 0892-743X
0024-3841	Lingua
0024-385X	Lingua e Stile
0024-3868	Lingua Nostra
0024-3876	Lingue del Mondo
0024-3892	Linguistic Inquiry
0024-3906	Linguistic Reporter†
0024-3914	Linguistic Society of Japan. Journal
0024-3922	Linguistica
0024-3930	Linguistische Berichte
0024-3949	Linguistics
0024-3957	Linguistique
0024-3965	Lingvologia Revuo†
0024-3973	Linieofficeren
0024-399X	Link†
0024-4007	Link (New York)
0024-4015	Link-Up†
0024-4023	Linking Ring
0024-404X	Links
0024-4066	Linnean Society. Biological Journal
0024-4074	Linnean Society. Botanical Journal
0024-4082	Linnean Society. Zoological Journal
0024-4090	Linneana Belgica
0024-4104	Linn's Weekly Stamp News *see* 0161-6234
0024-4112	Linoticias†
0024-4139	Linzer Theaterzeitung
0024-4147	Linzer Woche
0024-4155	Legkaya Atletika
0024-4163	The Lion
0024-4171	The Lion en Espanol
0024-418X	Len i Konoplya
0024-4201	Lipids
0024-421X	Liquified Petroleum Gas Report *changed to* Inventories of Natural Gas Liquids & Liquified Refinery Gases.
0024-4228	Liquified Natural Gas†
0024-4236	Liquor Store Magazine *changed to* Beverage Dynamics.
0024-4244	Lira
0024-4260	Lisbon. Instituto Gulbenkian de Cienca. Arquivo. Section A. Estudos Matematicos e Fisico-Matematicos†
0024-4279	Instituto Maternal, Lisbon. Revista Clinica *see* 0302-4326
0024-4309	List-O-Tapes†
0024-4317	List of Accessions to the Science Museum Library *changed to* Science Museum Library Bulletin.
0024-4333	List of Selected Articles on I C A O and Civil Aviation *changed to* International Civil Aviation Organization. Library Information: Recent Accessions and Selected Articles.
0024-4341	List of Technical Studies and Experimental Housing Projects†
0024-435X	Listen
0024-4384	Listen†
0024-4392	Listener†
0024-4406	Listener in T V *changed to* Scene.
0024-4422	Listino della Radio Industria e dell'Elettrodomestica *changed to* Tutto sui Mercati Radio-Televisione-Hi-Fi Elettrodomestici.
0024-4430	Listino Ufficiale della Borsa Valori di Torino
0024-4449	Listy Cukrovarnicke
0024-4457	Listy Filologicke
0024-4465	Listy Sv. Frantiska†
0024-449X	Liteinoe Proizvodstvo
0024-4503	Literacy Discussion†
0024-4511	Literary Cavalcade
0024-452X	Literary Criterion
0024-4538	Preview *see* 0065-9959
0024-4546	Literary Guild Newsletter†
0024-4554	Literary Half-Yearly
0024-4562	Literary Herald†
0024-4570	Literary Quarterly of the Yugoslav Pen-Centre†
0024-4589	Literary Review
0024-4597	Literary Sketches
0024-4600	Literary Studies
0024-4627	Der Literat
0024-4635	Literatur- Eildienst Roche *changed to* Hexagon Roche.
0024-4643	Literatur in Wissenschaft und Unterricht
0024-4651	Literatur-Schnelldienst Kunststoffeund Kautschuk *see* 0932-7754
0024-466X	Literatur & Kritik
0024-4678	Literatur Zum Bibliothekswesen†
0024-4686	Literatura i Mastatstva
0024-4694	Literatura Kajero
0024-4708	Literatura Ludowa
0024-4740	Literature and Ideology *see* 0702-7532
0024-4759	Literature and Psychology
0024-4767	Literature East and West
0024-4775	Literature, Music, Fine Arts†
0024-4783	Literature on Economic Development and Planning - a Select Bibliography†
0024-4791	Literaturen Zbor
0024-4805	Rat fuer Formgebung. Literaturhinweise
0024-4821	Literaturna Ukrayina
0024-483X	Literaturnaya Armeniya
0024-4848	Literaturnaya Gazeta
0024-4856	Literaturnaya Rossiya
0024-4864	Literaturnyi Azerbaidzhan
0024-4872	Literaturrundschaut
0024-4899	Literauur-Overzicht Personeelsaangelegenheden *see* 0921-6154
0024-4902	Lithology and Mineral Resources
0024-4910	Lithopinion†
0024-4929	Lithoprinter Week *see* 0264-732X
0024-4937	Lithos
0024-4953	Litmus
0024-4961	Litografia Oggi
0024-497X	Litologiya i Poleznye Iskopaemye
0024-4988	Litterair Paspoort†
0024-4996	Litterature de Jeunesse†
0024-5011	Little Bronzed Angel†
0024-502X	Little Flower†
0024-5054	Little Review
0024-5062	Little Ship
0024-5070	Little Square Review†
0024-5089	Lituanus
0024-5100	Liturgisches Jahrbuch
0024-5119	Life and Worship *see* 0305-4438
0024-5127	Liv og Helse†
0024-5135	Livarski Vestnik
0024-5143	Live Lines
0024-5151	Liverpool Bulletin†
0024-516X	U.S. Department of Agriculture. Livestock and Meat Situation *changed to* U.S. Department of Agriculture. Livestock and Poultry Situation and Outlook.
0024-5178	Livestock Breeder Journal *changed to* Beefweek.
0024-5208	Livestock Market Digest
0024-5232	Living Blues
0024-5240	Living Church
0024-5259	Living Health Newsletter†
0024-5267	Living Judaism *changed to* Manna.
0024-5275	Living Light
0024-5283	The Living Museum
0024-5291	Living Tapes†
0024-5305	Living Wilderness *see* 0736-6477
0024-5313	Livingston County Agricultural News
0024-5321	Livornocronaca *changed to* Livornocronaca - Il Vernacoliere.
0024-533X	Le Livre et l'Estampe
0024-5348	Livres
0024-5372	Livrustkammaren
0024-5380	Livs
0024-5399	Livsmedelsteknik
0024-5410	Ljusglimtar *changed to* Evangeliska Oestasienmissionen.
0024-5437	Llais Llyfrau
0024-5445	Llan
0024-5453	Llangollen Broadsheet
0024-5461	Lloydia *see* 0163-3864
0024-547X	Lloyds Bank Review Quarterly *see* 0953-5004
0024-5488	Lloyd's Law Reports
0024-550X	Lloyd's Log
0024-5518	Local Government Administration *see* 0727-7342
0024-5526	Local Government Bulletin
0024-5534	Local Government Chronicle
0024-5542	Local Government Finance *see* 0305-9014
0024-5569	Local Government Journal of Western Australia†
0024-5577	Munisipale en Openbare Dienste†
0024-5585	Local Historian
0024-5607	Local Preachers Magazine
0024-5615	Local Self-Government
0024-5623	All India Institute of Local Self Government. Quarterly Journal
0024-5631	Local Taxation†
0024-5658	Locating Gold *changed to* Locating Gold, Gems, & Minerals.
0024-5666	Locations and Ventes *changed to* Semaine Immobiliere.
0024-5674	Locations Vacances
0024-5704	Lockheed Orion Service Digest†
0024-5712	Lockheed Reports *changed to* A S W Log.
0024-5739	Loco-Revue
0024-5747	Locomotive Engineer Newsletter
0024-5755	Lodging and Food Service News *see* 0885-6877
0024-5763	Lodigiano Sudmilano†
0024-5771	Lodzki Numizmatyk
0024-578X	Loefgrenia
0024-5798	Log
0024-5801	Log Analyst
0024-5828	Log of Mystic Seaport
0024-5836	Logique et Analyse
0024-5844	Logistics Review *see* 0047-4991
0024-5852	Logistics Spectrum
0024-5887	Logos
0024-5895	Lohos†
0024-5917	Lok Rajya
0024-5925	Lok Udyog†
0024-5941	Lokomotivtechnik†
0024-595X	Loktantra Samiksha
0024-5976	Lon og Virke *see* 0105-032X
0024-5984	London Archaeological Spokesman *see* 0262-7922
0024-5992	
0024-600X	London Calling
0024-6018	London Clinic Medical Journal†
0024-6026	London Corn Circular
0024-6034	London Diary of Social Events†
0024-6042	London Hilton Magazine *changed to* Hilton International (U.K.) Magazine.
0024-6050	London Hospital Gazette†
0024-6077	London Letter†
0024-6085	London Magazine
0024-6093	London Mathematical Society. Bulletin
0024-6107	London Mathematical Society. Journal
0024-6115	London Mathematical Society. Proceedings
0024-6123	London Mystery Magazine *see* 0307-9112
0024-6131	London Philatelist
0024-614X	London Review
0024-6166	London Times Index†
0024-6174	London Town†
0024-6182	London Weekly Advertiser *see* 0958-9600
0024-6190	London Weekly Diary of Social Events†
0024-6204	Cymro Llundain
0024-6220	Long Cane News Letter
0024-6247	Long Island Builder *changed to* Builder & Remodeler.
0024-6255	Long Island Catholic
0024-6263	Long Island Courant†
0024-628X	Long Island Forum
0024-6298	Long Island University Magazine†
0024-6301	Long Range Planning
0024-631X	Long Room
0024-6328	Longitude
0024-6336	Look†
0024-6344	Look and Learn†
0024-6352	Look & Listen
0024-6360	Look Around†
0024-6379	Look at Finland
0024-6387	Look Fortnightly *changed to* Look Magazine.
0024-6409	Looking Ahead *see* 0747-525X
0024-6417	Looking Back
0024-6425	Lookout (New York)
0024-6433	Lookout
0024-645X	Loon
0024-6476	Looys
0024-6492	Lore
0024-6514	Loris
0024-6522	Los Angeles
0024-6530	Los Angeles Bar Bulletin *see* 0162-2900
0024-6549	Los Angeles Citizen
0024-6557	Los Angeles County Museum of Art. Bulletin†
0024-6565	Los Angeles County Regional Planning Commission. Quarterly Bulletin *see* 0363-3575
0024-6573	Los Angeles Free Press
0024-6581	Image†
0024-6611	Loshen und Leben
0024-662X	Loteria
0024-6638	Lotta Contro la Tubercolosi *changed to* Lotta Contro la Tubercolosi e le Malattie Polmonari Sociali.
0024-6654	Lottery Gazette
0024-6662	Lottoroscopo
0024-6670	Lotus Bleu
0024-6689	Intergroup Relations Newsletter†
0024-6719	Loughborough University of Technology Gazette
0024-6727	Louis Braille
0024-6735	Louisiana Agriculture
0024-6743	Louisiana Baptist Builder
0024-6751	Louisiana Business Review†
0024-6778	Louisiana Conservationist
0024-6786	Louisiana Dental Association. Journal
0024-6794	Louisiana Engineer
0024-6816	Louisiana History
0024-6832	Louisiana Insurer *changed to* Louisiana Avent.
0024-6840	Louisiana L P-Gas News
0024-6859	Louisiana Law Review
0024-6867	L L A Bulletin
0024-6875	Louisiana Methodist†
0024-6891	Louisiana-Revy
0024-6905	Louisiana Schools *see* 0162-2773
0024-6913	Louisiana Senior Citizen†
0024-6921	Louisiana State Medical Society. Journal
0024-693X	Louisiana Studies *see* 0735-8342
0024-6948	Louisville *changed to* Louisville Magazine.
0024-6956	Louvain Medical
0024-6964	Louvain Studies
0024-6980	Lov og Rett
0024-6999	Lovacki Vjesnik
0024-7014	Lovec
0024-7022	Lovejoy's Guidance Digest
0024-7030	Low Bidder
0024-7049	Low Cost Automation Review†
0024-7057	Lowell Observatory Bulletin
0024-7065	Lowry-Cocroft's Review of the Food Service Literature†
0024-7073	Loyola News *changed to* Link (Montreal).
0024-7081	Loyola University of Chicago Law Journal
0024-709X	Liquefied Petroleum Gas
0024-7103	L P - Gas
0024-7111	Lraber Asarakakan Gitutyunneri
0024-7154	Lubrication Engineering
0024-7162	Lubrificazione Industriale e per Autoveicoli *see* 0391-8645
0024-7170	Lucas Engineering Review†
0024-7189	Luce (Milan)
0024-7197	Luce e Immagini *changed to* Vision & Luci Sulla Via†
0024-7200	Luci Sulla Via†
0024-7219	Lucknow Librarian
0024-7235	Lucy Moda†
0024-7243	Lufkin Line†
0024-7251	Luft- und Kaeltetechnik
0024-7286	Luister
0024-7294	Lumber Co-Operator

ISSN INDEX 5407

ISSN	Title
0024-7316	Lumberman changed to Philippine Lumberman.
0024-7332	Lumiere
0024-7340	Lumiere du Monde changed to Solidaires - Lumiere du Monde.
0024-7359	Lumiere et Vie
0024-7375	Luna Monthly changed to Luna.
0024-7383	Luonnon Tutkija
0024-7391	Luscinia
0024-7413	Luso - Brazilian Review
0024-7421	Lustrum
0024-743X	The Lutheran
0024-7448	Lutheran Education
0024-7456	Lutheran Forum
0024-7464	Lutheran Layman
0024-7472	Lutheran Libraries
0024-7480	Lutheran Messenger for the Blind
0024-7499	Lutheran Quarterly†
0024-7502	Lutheran Scholar see 0362-708X
0024-7510	Lutheran Sentinel
0024-7537	Lutheran Spokesman
0024-7545	Lutheran Standard see 0024-743X
0024-7553	Lutheran Theological Journal
0024-7561	Lutheran Welfare in New Jersey changed to Lutheran Times in New Jersey.
0024-757X	Lutheran Witness
0024-7588	Lutheran Witness-Reporter Edition†
0024-7596	Lutheran Woman see 0896-209X
0024-760X	Lutheran World†
0024-7618	Lutherische Monatshefte
0024-7626	Die Lutherkirche
0024-7634	Lutra
0024-7642	Lutte Contre le Cancer changed to Vivre.
0024-7650	Lutte Ouvriere
0024-7669	Lux
0024-7685	Lux Vera
0024-7693	Luz
0024-7715	Luz Apostolica†
0024-7723	Luz del Cosmos†
0024-7731	Luz Y Verdad†
0024-774X	Lyd & Tone†
0024-7758	Journal of Reproductive Medicine
0024-7766	Lymphology†
0024-7774	Lynx
0024-7782	Lyon Chirurgical
0024-7790	Lyon Medical
0024-7804	Lyon Pharmaceutique
0024-7812	Lyons Music News see 0093-0164
0024-7820	Lyric
0024-7839	Lyric Opera News
0024-7847	Lyrica Germanica†
0024-7871	Lyudyna i Svit
0024-788X	M A C Flyer
0024-7898	M A C Gopher
0024-791X	M A S C A Newsletter changed to M A S C A Research Papers in Science and Archaeology.
0024-7944	M & B Laboratory Bulletin†
0024-7952	M B A†
0024-7960	M B A A Technical Quarterly
0024-7995	M C - Nytt
0024-8002	M D en Espanol
0024-8010	Medical Newsmagazine changed to M D Magazine.
0024-8029	M D Moebel Interior Design see 0343-0642
0024-8045	M D S
0024-807X	M D'S Wife see 0163-0512
0024-810X	M F D changed to Medical Electronics.
0024-8118	M E N Economic Weekly
0024-8134	M F C News
0024-8142	M F M - Moderne Fototechnik changed to M F M Fototechnik.
0024-8150	M G A Bulletin changed to Mushroom Journal.
0024-8169	M G Conquest†
0024-8185	N
0024-8207	M I Contact changed to Marconi Instruments Contact.
0024-8215	M L A International Bibliography of Books and Articles on the Modern Languages and Literatures
0024-8231	M L B Log
0024-824X	M' - le Magazine de Madame†
0024-8258	M.M.E.A. Music News see 0147-2550
0024-8266	Astronomical Society of Southern Africa. Monthly Notes
0024-8282	M O N Y News
0024-8320	M R A Information Service see 0959-311X
0024-8347	M R I Quarterly changed to Viewpoint (Kansas City).
0024-8355	M Report†
0024-8363	M S A Monthly Bulletin
0024-8398	M S H A†
0024-8428	M S O A Journal changed to M S O A Bulletin.
0024-8444	M S S C Exchange
0024-8452	M S S P A Bugle†
0024-8460	M S U Business Topics†
0024-8479	M S U Mathematics Letter changed to M S U Mathematics Newsletter.
0024-8487	M T A News†
0024-8495	Weekly Bulletin
0024-8509	M T M Journal of Methods-Time Measurement†
0024-8517	M T T
0024-8525	M T Z
0024-8533	Meridiano Dodici†
0024-8541	Maailma ja Me
0024-855X	Maal og Minne
0024-8568	Maalarilehti
0024-8592	Drenthe
0024-8606	Maandblad Suiker Unie
0024-8614	Maandblad tegen de Kwakzalverij
0024-8622	Maandblad voor Accountancy en Bedrijfshuishoudkunde
0024-8630	Maandblad voor Bedrijfsadministratie en Organisatie
0024-8649	Maandblad voor de Varkensfokkerij changed to Varkens.
0024-8657	Maanblad voor het Land- en Tuinbouwonderwijs changed to Land- en Tuinbouwonderwijs.
0024-8665	Nederduitse Gereformeerde Kerk van Natal Gemeente Vryheid. Maandbrief
0024-8673	Maandschrift Economie
0024-869X	Maandschrift voor Kindergeneeskunde changed to Tijdschrift voor Kindergeneeskunde.
0024-8703	Maandstatistiek Buitenlandse Handel†
0024-8711	Netherlands. Centraal Bureau voor de Statistiek. Maandstatistiek van de Bevolking
0024-872X	Netherlands. Centraal Bureau voor de Statistiek. Maandstatistiek van de Binnenlandse Handel see 0166-9281
0024-8738	Netherlands. Centraal Bureau voor de Statistiek. Maandstatistiek van de Buitenlandse Handel per Goederensoort
0024-8746	Netherlands. Centraal Bureau voor de Statistiek. Maandstatistiek van de Buitenlandse Handel per Land
0024-8754	Netherlands. Centraal Bureau voor de Statistiek. Maandstatistiek van de Landbouw
0024-8762	Maandstatistiek van Het Financiewezen†
0024-8770	Netherlands. Centraal Bureau voor de Statistiek. Maandstatistiek Verkeer en Vervoer
0024-8789	Maanedsskrift for Praktisk Laegegering see 0373-2746
0024-8797	Maanmittausinsinoori see 0356-7869
0024-8819	Maarakennus ja Kuljetus
0024-8827	Maatalous
0024-8835	Scientific Agricultural Society of Finland. Journal see 0782-4386
0024-8843	Maatschappijbelangen
0024-8886	Macabre†
0024-8894	Macaroni Journal†
0024-8908	McCall's
0024-8924	McCall's Needlework & Crafts
0024-8940	McCall's Fabrics Plus†
0024-8959	Macchine
0024-8967	Macchine e Motori Agricoli changed to Macchine e Motori Agricoli - I M A il Trattorista.
0024-8975	McCormick Quarterly†
0024-9009	Macedonian Tribune
0024-9017	Macelleria Italiana
0024-9025	McGill Medical Review
0024-9033	McGill Journal of Education
0024-9041	McGill Law Journal
0024-905X	McGill Medical Journal†
0024-9068	McGill News
0024-9076	McGill University, Montreal. Industrial Relations Centre. Review†
0024-9092	Machine and Machinery
0024-9106	Machine and Tool Blue Book†
0024-9114	Machine Design
0024-9122	Machine Design & Control†
0024-9130	Machine Moderne changed to Techniques et Equipments de Production.
0024-9149	Machine-Outil†
0024-9157	Machine Shop and Engineering Manufacture†
0024-9165	Machine Tool Engineering†
0024-9173	Machine-Tool Review†
0024-919X	Machinery and Production Engineering
0024-9203	Machinery Lloyd see 0266-4070
0024-9211	Machinery Market and the Machinery and Engineering Materials Gazette changed to Machinery Market.
0024-922X	Machines and Tooling see 0144-6622
0024-9238	Machines Francaises†
0024-9246	Machinisme Agricole Tropical†
0024-9254	Maclean's Guide see 0380-9552
0024-9262	Maclean's
0024-9270	McMaster University Library Research News†
0024-9289	Macomb County Legal News
0024-9297	Macromolecules
0024-9300	Mad
0024-9319	Mad
0024-9327	Mad og Gaester†
0024-9335	Mada
0024-9343	Madam
0024-9351	Madam
0024-936X	Madame
0024-9378	Made in Europe changed to Made in Europe. General Merchandise.
0024-9386	Made in Poland†
0024-9394	Mademoiselle
0024-9408	Mademoiselle Gymnast see 0276-1041
0024-9416	Madencilik
0024-9424	Madhumeh see 0970-4035
0024-9432	Madhuri
0024-9459	Madhya Pradesh Law Journal
0024-9467	Madhya Pradesh Medical Journal†
0024-9513	Madison Select changed to Madison Magazine.
0024-9521	Indonesian Journal of Geography
0024-953X	Madjalah Managert
0024-9548	Madjalah Persatuan Dokter Gigi Indonesia
0024-9556	Madjalah Pertanian
0024-9564	Madjalah Kedokteran Surabaja see 0303-7932
0024-9580	Madonna di Barbana†
0024-9599	Madonna di Castelmonte
0024-9602	Madras Agricultural Journal
0024-9610	Madras Labour Gazette. changed to Tamil Nadu Labour Journal.
0024-9629	Spain. Consejo Superior de Investigaciones Cientificas. Instituto de Farmacologia Experimental. Archivos see 0304-8616
0024-9637	Madrono
0024-9645	Danish Dairy Industry
0024-9653	Maelstrom†
0024-9661	Der Maerker
0024-967X	Maerkische Zeitung
0024-9688	Maerklin-Magazin
0024-9696	Maestro
0024-9718	Mafeking Mail and Botswana Guardian changed to The Mail.
0024-9726	Magadh University Journal†
0024-9750	Magazin fuer Fortschrittliche Haustechnik und Wohnkultur†
0024-9769	Magazin fuer Haus und Wohnung
0024-9785	Magazin Vier und Zwanzig changed to Initiative.
0024-9793	Media Industry Newsletter
0024-9807	Magazine Litteraire
0024-9823	Bank Administration changed to Bank Management.
0024-9831	Magazine of Concrete Research
0024-984X	Magazine of Fantasy and Science Fiction
0024-9858	Magazine of Wall Street changed to Wall Street and U S Business News.
0024-9866	Magazyn Polski
0024-9874	Magazzini e Trasporti changed to Logistica.
0024-9890	Maghreb see 0336-6324
0024-9904	Magic Cauldron
0024-9912	"Magische" Welt
0024-9920	The Magistrate
0024-9947	Maglie Calze Industria
0024-9955	Magna Graecia
0024-9963	Magneet-Revue†
0024-9971	Magistrate
0024-998X	Magnetohydrodynamics
0024-9998	Kongresszentralblatt fuer die Gesamte Innere Medizin see 0931-4695
0025-0007	Magnificat
0025-0015	Magnitnaya Gidrodinamika
0025-0023	Magnus see 0165-9677
0025-0031	Magueyt
0025-004X	Magyar Allatorvosok Lapja
0025-0058	Magyar Aluminium
0025-0066	Magyar Belorovosi Archivum see 0133-5464
0025-0074	Magyar Epitoipar
0025-0082	Magyar Epitomuveszet
0025-0090	Magyar Filozofiai Szemle
0025-0104	Magyar Fizikai Folyoirat
0025-0112	Magyar Folyoiratok Repertoriuma see 0133-6894
0025-0120	Magyar Geofizika
0025-0147	Magyar Jog
0025-0155	Magyar Kemiai Folyoirat
0025-0163	Magyar Kemikusok Lapja
0025-0171	Magyar Konyvszemle
0025-018X	Magyar Mezogazdasag
0025-0198	Magyar Mezogazdasagi Bibliografia
0025-021X	Magyar Noorvosok Lapja
0025-0228	Magyar Nyelv
0025-0236	Magyar Nyelvor
0025-0244	Magyar Onkologia
0025-0252	Magyar Orvosi Bibliografia
0025-0260	Magyar Pedagogia
0025-0279	Magyar Pszichologiai Szemle
0025-0287	Magyar Radiologia
0025-0295	Magyar Sebeszet
0025-0309	Magyar Textiltechnika
0025-0317	Magyar Traumatologia, Orthopedia es Helyreallito-Sebeszet
0025-0325	Magyar Tudomany
0025-0333	Magyar Tudomanyos Akademia. Biologiai Tudomanyok Osztalya. Kozlemenyek
0025-035X	Magyar Tudomanyos Akademia. Matematikai es Fizikai Tudomanyok Osztalya. Kozlemenyek see 0133-3399
0025-0368	Magyar Tudomanyos Akademia. Nyelv- es Irodalomtudomanyi Osztaly. Kozlemenyek†
0025-0376	Magyar Tudomanyos Akademia. Filozofiai es Tortenettudomanyi Osztaly. Kozlemenyek
0025-0384	Magyar Zene
0025-0392	Maharashtra
0025-0406	Maha Bodhi
0025-0414	Mahajaneer Lagna
0025-0422	Maharaja Sayajirao University of Baroda. Journal
0025-0430	Maharashtra Co-Operative Quarterly
0025-0449	Maharashtra, India. Directorate of Industries. Industrial Bulletin†
0025-0465	Maharashtra Law Journal
0025-0473	Maharashtra Parichayat

ISSN INDEX

ISSN	Title
0025-0481	Maharashtra Quarterly Bulletin of Economics and Statistics
0025-049X	Mahenjodaro
0025-0503	A Quarterly of South Asian Literature see 0091-5637
0025-0511	Die Mahnung
0025-052X	Maehrisch-Schlesische Heimat†
0025-0538	Maia
0025-0562	Mail Trade
0025-0570	Main Currents in Modern Thought†
0025-0597	Main Roads†
0025-0619	Maine Business Indicators
0025-0643	Maine Fish and Game Magazine see 0360-005X
0025-0651	Maine Law Review
0025-0678	Maine Life Magazine†
0025-0686	Maine Manpower changed to Maine Labor Market Digest.
0025-0694	Maine Medical Association. Journal†
0025-0708	Maine Nature†
0025-0716	Maine Beverage Journal
0025-0732	Maine on the Grow changed to Mark Maine News.
0025-0759	Maine State Labor News changed to Maine Labor News.
0025-0775	Maine Teacher
0025-0783	Maine Times
0025-0791	Maine Townsman
0025-0805	Maine Water Utilities Association. Journal
0025-0813	Mainichi Graphic
0025-083X	Mainliner changed to Vis a Vis.
0025-0848	Mainly
0025-0856	Mainostaja changed to Mark Markkinoinnin Ammattilehti.
0025-0864	Mainosuutiset
0025-0872	Maintenance changed to Maintenance Management.
0025-0880	Maintenance
0025-0899	Maintenance Engineering†
0025-0902	Maintenance Engineering changed to Works and Plane Maintenance.
0025-0910	Maintenance News†
0025-0929	Maintenance Supplies
0025-0937	Maison - Dieu
0025-0945	Maison et Jardin
0025-0953	Maison Francaise
0025-0988	Le Maitre Electricien
0025-0996	Le Maitre Imprimeur
0025-1003	International Phonetic Association. Journal
0025-102X	Majallah†
0025-1038	Diwan al-Tadween al-Qanouni Majallat changed to Adala.
0025-1089	Makedonski Jazik
0025-1119	Makerere Medical Journal
0025-1127	Matekon
0025-1135	Makina Muehendisleri Odasi Haftalik Haberler Gazetesi
0025-1151	Making Music†
0025-116X	Makromolekulare Chemie
0025-116X	Makromolekulare Chemie issued with 0253-5904
0025-1178	Mala Ukrstenica
0025-1186	Malabar Herald†
0025-1208	Maladosts'
0025-1216	Malahat Review
0025-1224	Malamalamat
0025-1232	Maaleri
0025-1240	Malawi Mwezi Uno-Malawi This Month changed to Boma Lathu.
0025-1267	Malawi Patent Journal and Trade Marks Journal
0025-1275	Malayan Forester see 0302-2935
0025-1283	Malayan Law Journal
0025-1291	Malayan Nature Journal
0025-1305	Malaysia†
0025-1313	Quarterly Bulletin of Statistics Relating to the Mining Industry of Malaysia
0025-1321	Malaysian Agricultural Journal
0025-133X	Malaysian Journal of Education changed to South-East Asian Journal of Educational Studies.
0025-1364	Malermesteren see 0905-6440
0025-1380	Mallasjuomat see 0356-3014
0025-1399	Mallige
0025-1402	Malm changed to Graengeskontakten.
0025-1410	Malmoe Museum. Aktuellt†
0025-1429	Studia Historyczne
0025-1437	Malta. Central Office of Statistics. Quarterly Digest of Statistics
0025-1445	Maltechnik-Restauro changed to Restauro.
0025-1453	Malyatko
0025-1461	Mammalia
0025-147X	Mamme e Bimbi
0025-1496	Man
0025-150X	Man and His Music†
0025-1518	Man and Metal†
0025-1526	Man and Society†
0025-1534	Man and World
0025-1542	Man-Environment-Communication Center Report†
0025-1550	Man - Environment Systems
0025-1569	Man in India
0025-1577	Man in New Guinea see 0254-0665
0025-1615	Manab Mon
0025-1623	Manage
0025-1631	Management†
0025-164X	Management
0025-1658	Management
0025-1666	Management Abstracts changed to Management News.
0025-1674	Management Accountant
0025-1682	Management Accounting
0025-1690	Management Accounting
0025-1704	Management & Operations†
0025-1712	Management Australia†
0025-1720	Management Consultant†
0025-1739	Management Controls changed to Management Focus.
0025-1747	Management Decision
0025-1771	Management Ideas
0025-178X	Management in Nigeria
0025-1798	Management Index
0025-1801	Management Industrial see 0374-4795
0025-181X	Management International Review
0025-1828	Management Japan
0025-1836	Management Horizons
0025-1844	Management News changed to Managers' Forum.
0025-1860	Management Quarterly
0025-1895	Management Review
0025-1909	Management Science
0025-1925	Management Today
0025-1933	Management's Bibliographic Data†
0025-1941	Managerial Planning see 0094-064X
0025-195X	Manager's Letter†
0025-1968	Manager's Magazine
0025-1976	Manas†
0025-1984	Manas
0025-200X	Manchester Guardian Weekly
0025-2018	Manchester Medical Gazette see 0261-7099
0025-2026	Manchester Review†
0025-2034	Manchester School of Economic and Social Studies
0025-2042	Manchete changed to Manchete Esportiva.
0025-2077	Manequim
0025-2085	Manhattan Almanac see 1045-5108
0025-2093	Manhattan College Engineer
0025-2107	Manhattan East
0025-2123	Manhattan Review†
0025-2166	Manifold
0025-2174	Manion Forum†
0025-2182	Manitoba changed to Manitoba Business Review.
0025-2190	Manitoba Archaeological Newsletter see 0705-2669
0025-2204	Manitoba Association of School Librarians Newsletter see 0315-9124
0025-2239	Manitoba Co-Operator
0025-2255	Manitoba Medical Review†
0025-2271	Manitoba Professional Engineer
0025-2298	Manitoban
0025-231X	Mankato State Daily Reporter changed to Mankato State Reporter.
0025-2328	Mankind changed to T A J A.
0025-2336	Mankind†
0025-2344	Mankind Quarterly
0025-2352	Mannskapsavisa see 0332-9062
0025-2360	Mannus changed to Volksleben.
0025-2379	Manoir-Express changed to Manoir-Echo.
0025-2387	Manovella
0025-2395	Manpower Magazine changed to Worklife Magazine.
0025-2409	Manpower and Applied Psychology
0025-2433	Manpower Trends changed to Maryland Labor Market Dimensions.
0025-2441	ManRoot†
0025-245X	Man's Conquest†
0025-2468	Man's Illustrated†
0025-2476	Man's Magazine
0025-2484	Manse Mail†
0025-2506	Mantova
0025-2514	Manuelle Medizin
0025-2522	Manufacturers Agent
0025-2530	Manufacturers' Monthly
0025-2557	Manufacturing Chemist and Aerosol News
0025-2565	Manufacturing Clothier
0025-2573	Manufacturing Confectioner
0025-2581	Manufacturing Optics International†
0025-259X	Manufaktur changed to Tekstilforum.
0025-2603	Manuscripta
0025-2611	Manuscripta Mathematica
0025-262X	Manuscripts
0025-2638	Manuskripte
0025-2646	Manutencion y Almacenaje
0025-2654	Manutention-Stockage see 0295-4192
0025-2662	Manutention Mecanique et Automation
0025-2670	Many Smokes see 0889-7867
0025-2689	Mapochot
0025-2697	Die Mappe
0025-2700	Maquinas & Metais
0025-2719	Maquinas y Equipos
0025-2727	Mar see 0102-0382
0025-2735	Mar y Pesca
0025-2751	Marathwada University Journal
0025-2778	Marburger Umschau†
0025-2808	March of Education†
0025-2816	Asahi Evening News International
0025-2824	Marcha
0025-2840	Marche Suisse des Machines
0025-2859	Marches Tropicaux et Mediterraneens
0025-2867	Marcolian
0025-2883	Marconi Review see 0264-9187
0025-2891	Marechal
0025-2905	Maree de France
0025-2913	Marg
0025-2921	Margin
0025-293X	Marginales
0025-2948	Marginalien
0025-2956	Margriet
0025-2972	Maria
0025-2980	Mariages
0025-2999	Mariahilfer Pfarrbote
0025-3006	Mariant
0025-3014	Marianist
0025-3022	Mariannhill
0025-3049	Marie-Claire
0025-3057	Marie-France
0025-3065	Regard de Foi†
0025-3073	Marien Report†
0025-309X	Marina Italiana
0025-3103	Marina Mercantile
0025-312X	Marine & Recreation News
0025-3138	Marine and Air Catering†
0025-3146	Marine Biological Association of India. Journal
0025-3154	Marine Biological Association of the United Kingdom. Journal
0025-3162	Marine Biology
0025-3170	Marine Corps Gazette
0025-3197	Marine Digest changed to Marine Digest and Transportation News.
0025-3219	Marine Engineering - Log see 0897-0491
0025-3227	Marine Geology
0025-3235	Marine Geophysical Researches
0025-3243	Marine News
0025-3251	Marine Observer
0025-326X	Marine Pollution Bulletin
0025-3278	Marine Products changed to Marine Retailer.
0025-3286	Marine Resources Digest/Marine Biology Digest†
0025-3294	Marine-Rundschau
0025-3308	Marine Science Contents Tables
0025-3316	Marine Technology
0025-3324	Marine Technology Society Journal
0025-3332	Marine Equipment News
0025-3340	Marineblad
0025-3359	Mariner's Mirror
0025-3367	Mariners Weather Log
0025-3375	Marinnytt
0025-3383	Marion
0025-3391	Maritime see 0161-9373
0025-3405	Maritime Co-Operator see 0703-5357
0025-3413	Maritime Command Trident
0025-3421	Maritime Exchange Bulletin changed to Maritime Association of the Port of New York - New Jersey. Newsletter.
0025-343X	Maritime Farmer and Co-Operative Dairyman
0025-3448	Maritime Reporter and Engineering News
0025-3464	Maritime Worker
0025-3472	Maritimes
0025-3480	Marjolaine
0025-3499	Mark Twain Journal
0025-3502	Markedsfoering
0025-3510	Markedskommunikasjon†
0025-3529	Marker changed to Arch.
0025-3537	Market
0025-3545	West Virginia. Department of Agriculture. Market Bulletin
0025-3553	Market Frontier News
0025-3561	Market Industries News
0025-357X	Market Place†
0025-3588	Market Research see 0308-3047
0025-3596	Market Research Abstracts
0025-360X	Market Research Facts and Trends†
0025-3618	Market Research Society. Journal
0025-3626	Marketer see 0093-5832
0025-3634	Marketing
0025-3642	Marketing
0025-3650	Marketing
0025-3677	U.S. Department of Agriculture. Economic Research Service. Marketing and Transport Situation see 0099-1066
0025-3685	Marketing/Communications†
0025-3707	Marketing Image
0025-3723	Marketing in Europe
0025-3731	Marketing in Hungary†
0025-374X	Marketing Information Guide†
0025-3774	Marketing Journal
0025-3790	Marketing News
0025-3812	Marketing World†
0025-3820	Markham Review†
0025-3839	Marking Industry
0025-3847	Markkinointi-Myyntimiehet changed to Mark Markkinoinnin Ammattilehti.
0025-3855	Marknaden
0025-3863	Markt
0025-3871	Marktwirtschaft see 0302-6671
0025-388X	Maroc-Medical†
0025-3898	Maroquinerie-Voyage-Parapluie-Chaussure
0025-3901	Maroquinerie, Sellerie et Bagages de France
0025-391X	Marple's Business Roundup see 0279-960X
0025-3928	Marquee
0025-3936	Marques Internationales
0025-3944	Marquetarian
0025-3952	Marquette Business Review†
0025-3960	Marquette Engineer†
0025-3979	Marquette Journal
0025-3987	Marquette Law Review
0025-3995	Marquette Tribune
0025-4002	Marquette University Magazine changed to Marquette.
0025-4010	Marriage see 0276-4512

ISSN INDEX 5409

ISSN	Title
0025-4029	Mars in Cathedra
0025-4037	Mars-Magazine
0025-4053	Marseille Medical
0025-4061	Mart†
0025-407X	Martinella di Milano
0025-4088	Chambre de Commerce et d'Industrie de la Martinique. Bulletin see 0396-2458
0025-4096	Maruee
0025-410X	Marx Memorial Library. Quarterly Bulletin changed to Marx Memorial Library Bulletin.
0025-4118	Marxism Today†
0025-4126	Marxist Studies
0025-4134	Marxist Veekshanam
0025-4142	Maryknoll changed to Maryknoll Fathers and Brothers.
0025-4150	Maryland and Delaware Genealogist†
0025-4169	Baptist True Union
0025-4177	Maryland Bar Journal
0025-4185	Maryland C.P.A. Quarterly†
0025-4193	Maryland Conservationist†
0025-4207	Maryland Crime Report changed to Maryland Crime Control Directory.
0025-4215	Md De D C Press News changed to PressNews.
0025-4223	Maryland Fruit Grower
0025-4231	Maryland Herpetological Society. Bulletin
0025-424X	Maryland Historian
0025-4258	Maryland Historical Magazine
0025-4266	Maryland History Notes changed to Maryland Historical Society. News and Notes.
0025-4274	Maryland Horse
0025-4282	Maryland Law Review
0025-4290	Maryland see 1040-7936
0025-4304	Maryland Municipal News changed to Municipal Maryland.
0025-4312	Maryland Music Educator
0025-4339	Maryland P T A Bulletin
0025-4347	Maryland Pharmacist
0025-4355	Maryland State Dental Association. Journal
0025-4363	Maryland State Medical Journal see 0886-0572
0025-4371	Maryland Teacher†
0025-4398	Maryland Veterinarian†
0025-441X	Mas Chistes†
0025-4428	Masada
0025-4436	Masalah Bangunan†
0025-4452	Maschine und Werkzeug
0025-4460	Maschinen- und Stahlbauindustrie in Oesterreich changed to Maschinen und Stahlbau.
0025-4479	Maschinenbau†
0025-4487	Maschinenbau und Fertigungstechnik der U d S S R
0025-4495	Maschinenbautechnik†
0025-4517	Maschinenschaden
0025-4533	Maschinenwelt - Elektrotechnik
0025-4541	MascuLines
0025-455X	Mashinostroene
0025-4568	Mashinostroitel'
0025-4576	Mashinovedenie
0025-4584	Mashriq
0025-4606	Maske und Kothurn
0025-4614	Maskin changed to Produksion.
0025-4622	Maskinbefaelet
0025-4630	Maskinstationen see 0109-0291
0025-4657	Mason Clinic. Bulletin changed to Virginia Mason Clinic Bulletin.
0025-4665	Masonic Record
0025-4681	Masonry
0025-469X	Masque
0025-4703	Masque
0025-4711	Masque†
0025-472X	Mass Media Ministries. Bi-Weekly Newsletter changed to Mass Media Newsletter.
0025-4738	Mass Spectrometry Bulletin
0025-4762	Massachusetts Bureau of Library Extension. Newsletter changed to Currents (Boston).
0025-4770	Massachusetts C P A Review
0025-4789	Massachusetts College of Pharmacy. Bulletin
0025-4797	Massachusetts Daily Collegian
0025-4800	Massachusetts Dental Society. Journal
0025-4819	Massachusetts Heritage†
0025-4827	Massachusetts Institute of Technology. Research Laboratory of Electronics. Quarterly Progress Report see 0163-9218
0025-4835	Massachusetts Law Quarterly see 0163-1411
0025-4843	Massachusetts Nurses Association. Bulletin see 0163-0784
0025-4851	Massachusetts Physician see 0192-2963
0025-486X	Massachusetts Professional Engineer changed to New England Engineering Journal.
0025-4878	Massachusetts Review
0025-4894	Massachusetts State Labor Council A F L - C I O Newsletter
0025-4908	Massachusetts Teacher†
0025-4916	Massachusetts Trends in Employment and Unemployment changed to Massachusetts Trends, Labor Force, Employment, Unemployment.
0025-4924	Massachusetts Wildlife
0025-4932	Massimario del Foro Italiano
0025-4940	Massimario della Giurisprudenza Italiana
0025-4959	Massimario di Giurisprudenza del Lavoro
0025-4975	Massis
0025-4983	Master Baker, Confectioner & Caterer
0025-4991	Master Builders' Journal
0025-5009	Master Carriers Journal changed to Freight Carriers.
0025-5017	Master Detective
0025-5025	Master Drawings
0025-5041	Master Plumber
0025-505X	Master Plumber and Heating Contractor†
0025-5068	Master Plumber of South Australia
0025-5092	Masterpainter changed to British Decorator.
0025-5106	Masters Abstracts see 0898-9095
0025-5114	Master's Thesis Abstracts Bulletin†
0025-5122	Masthead
0025-5130	Mate changed to Climate.
0025-5149	Matemaattisten Aineiden Aikakauskirja see 0782-6648
0025-5157	Matematicheskii Sbornik
0025-5165	Matematicki Vesnik
0025-5173	Mathematica Slovaca
0025-5181	Matematika v Shkole
0025-519X	Matematikai Lapok
0025-522X	Mater Ecclesiae changed to Ecclesia Mater.
0025-5238	Materia Medica Nordmarkt
0025-5246	Materia Medica Polona
0025-5254	Materiaal, Metodiek, Mededelingen see 0166-3917
0025-5262	Material Handling Engineering
0025-5270	Material und Organismen
0025-5289	Materiale Plastice
0025-5297	Materialehaandtering og Transport Nyt see 0106-1666
0025-5300	Materialpruefung†
0025-5319	Materials Engineering
0025-5327	Materials Evaluation
0025-5335	Materials Handling and Management†
0025-5343	Materials Management & Distribution
0025-5351	Materials Handling News
0025-536X	Materials on Asia and Africa - Accession List and Review see 0913-025X
0025-5378	Materials Protection see 0094-1492
0025-5386	Materials Reclamation Weekly
0025-5394	Materials Research and Standards - MIRS see 0090-1210
0025-5408	Materials Research Bulletin
0025-5416	Material Sciences and Engineering see 0921-5093
0025-5416	Material Sciences and Engineering see 0921-5107
0025-5432	Materials and Structures
0025-5440	Materidouska
0025-5459	Materie Plastiche ed Elastomeri
0025-5467	Materiel d'Enterprise changed to Construction.
0025-5475	Maternal and Child Care†
0025-5491	Maternidade e Infancia†
0025-5505	Mathematica
0025-5513	Mathematica Japonica
0025-5521	Mathematica Scandinavica
0025-553X	Mathematicae Notae
0025-5548	Mathematical Algorithms†
0025-5556	Mathematical Association of India. Bulletin
0025-5564	Mathematical Biosciences
0025-5572	Mathematical Gazette
0025-5580	Mathematical Log
0025-5602	Mathematical Pie
0025-5610	Mathematical Programming
0025-5629	Mathematical Reviews
0025-5637	Mathematical Sciences Employment Register†
0025-5645	Mathematical Society of Japan. Journal
0025-5653	Mathematical Spectrum
0025-5661	Mathematical Systems Theory
0025-567X	Matematicheskie Zametki
0025-570X	Mathematics Magazine
0025-5718	Mathematics of Computation
0025-5726	Mathematics of the U S S R - Izvestiya
0025-5734	Mathematics of the U S S R - Sbornik
0025-5742	Mathematics Student
0025-5750	Mathematics Student Journal see 0095-7089
0025-5769	Mathematics Teacher
0025-5785	Mathematics Teaching
0025-5793	Mathematika
0025-5807	Der Mathematikunterricht
0025-5831	Mathematische Annalen
0025-584X	Mathematische Nachrichten
0025-5858	Universitaet Hamburg. Mathematisches Seminar. Abhandlungen
0025-5866	Der Mathematische und Naturwissenschaftliche Unterricht
0025-5874	Mathematische Zeitschrift
0025-5904	Mathitiki Estia
0025-5912	Mati
0025-5920	Matica see 0353-8052
0025-5939	Letopis Matice Srpske
0025-5955	Matilda Ziegler Magazine for the Blind
0025-5963	Matkailumaailma changed to Matkailu.
0025-598X	Matrix see 0891-1207
0025-5998	Matrix and Tensor Quarterly†
0025-6021	Mature Years
0025-603X	Mature Years-New Directions†
0025-6048	Mauricien Medical
0025-6056	Mauritius. Central Statistical Office. Quarterly Digest of Statistics changed to Mauritius. Central Statistical Office. Bi-Annual Digest of Statistics.
0025-6064	Mauritius Times
0025-6072	Mausolee
0025-6099	Mavoschool changed to Nieuw Zicht.
0025-6102	Max-Planck-Gesellschaft zur Foerderung der Wissenschaften Mitteilungen see 0341-7778
0025-6129	May Day Pictorial News
0025-6137	May Trends
0025-6153	Maydica
0025-6161	Mayfair
0025-617X	Mayfair News changed to NewsGleaner - Mayfair - Northeast Edition.
0025-6188	Mayibuye
0025-6196	Mayo Clinic Proceedings
0025-620X	Mazdaznan - Blatt
0025-6218	Mazputnins
0025-6234	Mbioni
0025-6242	Mvelaphanda see 0250-1910
0025-6269	Me
0025-6277	Me Naiset
0025-6285	Meander
0025-6293	Meanjin Quarterly see 0815-953X
0025-6307	Measurement and Evaluation in Guidance see 0748-1756
0025-6315	National Council on Measurement in Education. Measurement News see 0731-1745
0025-6323	Measurements and Data see 0148-0057
0025-6331	Measuring for Medicine & the Life Sciences†
0025-634X	Meat†
0025-6358	Meat Board Reports
0025-6366	Meat Industry see 0958-5141
0025-6374	Meat Industry
0025-6390	Meat Processing
0025-6412	Meat Trades Journal
0025-6420	Mecanica Popular
0025-6447	M A G see 0531-755X
0025-6455	Meccanica†
0025-6463	Meccano Magazine†
0025-6471	Mech
0025-6501	Mechanical Engineering
0025-651X	Mechanical Engineering News†
0025-6528	Mechanical Handling see 0025-5351
0025-6536	Mechanical Sciences Abstracts changed to Mechanical Sciences.
0025-6544	Mechanics of Solids
0025-6552	Mechanik
0025-6560	Mechanisch Transport en Opslag changed to Bedrijfstransport.
0025-6579	South African Materials Handling News changed to Promat News.
0025-6587	Mechanix Illustrated see 8755-0423
0025-6595	Mechanizaciat
0025-6609	Mecman - Technique
0025-6625	Medailles
0025-6633	Medal Collector changed to Orders and Medals Society of America. Official Journal.
0025-6641	MedBooks†
0025-665X	Medborgaren
0025-6668	Norske Myrselskap. Meddelelser see 0332-5229
0025-6676	Meddelelser om Groenland see 0106-1046
0025-6676	Meddelelser om Groenland see 0106-1054
0025-6676	Meddelelser om Groenland see 0106-1062
0025-6692	Medecin du Quebec
0025-6714	Etudes Medicales
0025-6722	Medecine du Sport
0025-6730	Medecine et Gastronomie†
0025-6749	Medecine et Hygiene
0025-6757	Medecine et Travail
0025-6773	Medecine Infantile
0025-6781	Medecine Interne
0025-6811	Medecine Practicienne†
0025-682X	Medecine Tropicale
0025-6838	Medecins de Groupe
0025-6854	Bedrijfsontwikkeling. Editie Tuinbouw changed to Agrarische Voorlichting.
0025-6870	Medhjalparen see 0349-2559
0025-6889	Media†
0025-6897	Media & Methods
0025-6900	Media Decisions see 1055-176X
0025-6927	Medianite
0025-6943	Medical Abstract Service†
0025-6951	Medical Affairs see 0092-8577
0025-696X	Medical and Biological Engineering see 0140-0118
0025-6978	Medical and Biological Illustration see 0140-511X
0025-6986	Medical Annals of the District of Columbia†
0025-7001	Medical Aspects of Human Sexuality†
0025-701X	Medical Association for Prevention of War. Proceedings see 0748-8009
0025-7028	Medical Association of Georgia. Journal
0025-7036	Medical Association of Thailand. Journal
0025-7044	Medical Association of the State of Alabama. Journal see 0738-4947
0025-7060	Medical Book News
0025-7079	Medical Care
0025-7087	Medical Care Review
0025-7095	Medical Centre Journal
0025-7109	Medical Checklist

ISSN	Title
0025-7117	Medical Chronicle
0025-7125	Medical Clinics of North America
0025-7133	Medical College and Hospital, Calcutta. Bulletin
0025-7141	Medical College of Virginia Quarterly†
0025-715X	Medical Counterpoint†
0025-7168	Medical Digest†
0025-7176	Medical Digest *changed to* Medical Digest (1979) Education in Family Medicine.
0025-7184	Medical Digest
0025-7192	Medical Ecology and Clinical Research†
0025-7206	Medical Economics
0025-7222	Medical Electronics & Communications Abstracts†
0025-7230	Medical Electronics News *changed to* Medical Electronics and Equipment News.
0025-7257	Medical Group Management. Journal
0025-7265	Medical Group News *changed to* Medical Group News & In-Office Testing Advances.
0025-7273	Medical History
0025-729X	Medical Journal of Australia
0025-7303	Medical Journal of Malaya *see* 0300-5283
0025-7311	Medical Lab *changed to* Diagnostics & Clinical Testing.
0025-732X	Medical Letter on Drugs and Therapeutics
0025-7338	Medical Library Association. Bulletin
0025-7346	National Library of Medicine. Current Catalog Proofsheets†
0025-7354	Medical Marketing & Media
0025-7370	Medical Missionary News
0025-7389	Medical Missionary *changed to* Medical Mission Sisters News.
0025-7397	Medical-Moral Newsletter
0025-7400	Medical Officer *see* 0300-8347
0025-7435	Medical Post
0025-7451	Medical Quarterly *see* 0046-9130
0025-746X	Medical Radiography and Photography†
0025-7478	Medical Record *changed to* Journal of Health Information & Medical Records Officers.
0025-7486	Medical Record News *changed to* American Health Information Management Association. Journal.
0025-7494	Medical Research Bulletin†
0025-7508	Medical Research Engineering†
0025-7524	Medical Society of New Jersey. Journal *changed to* New Jersey Medicine.
0025-7532	Medical Society of the County of Kings and Academy of Medicine of Brooklyn. Bulletin *see* 0886-4772
0025-7540	Medical Socioeconomic Research Sources†
0025-7559	Medical Staff in Action†
0025-7567	Medical-Surgical Review†
0025-7583	Medical Times†
0025-7591	Medical Trial Technique Quarterly
0025-7605	Medical Tribune *see* 0279-9340
0025-7613	Medical University of South Carolina. Medical University News *changed to* Medical University of South Carolina. Medical University Review.
0025-7621	Medical World
0025-763X	Medical World News
0025-7648	Medicamenta†
0025-7656	Medicamentos de Actualidad *changed to* Medicamentos de Actualidad - Drugs of Today.
0025-7664	Medicamundi
0025-7672	Medicare Report
0025-7680	Medicina
0025-7699	Medicina
0025-7702	Medicina
0025-7729	Medicina
0025-7753	Medicina Clinica
0025-7761	Medicina Clinica e Sperimentale†
0025-777X	Medicina Contemporanea†
0025-7788	Medicina Cutanea *see* 0210-5187
0025-7796	Medicina Danas
0025-7818	Medicina del Lavoro
0025-7826	Medicina Dello Sport
0025-7834	Medicina e Morale†
0025-7842	Medicina Espanola
0025-7850	Journal of Medicine *changed to* Journal of Medicine (Clinical, Experimental and Theoretical).
0025-7869	Revista de Medicina Interna, Neurologie, Psichiatrie, Neuro-Chirurgie, Dermato-Venerologie. Medicina Interna
0025-7877	Medicina nei Secoli *see* 0394-9001
0025-7893	Medicina Psicosomatica
0025-7907	Medicina Rural†
0025-7915	Rivista Italiana di Medicina Sociale
0025-7923	Medicina Tedesca†
0025-7931	Respiration
0025-794X	Medicina Tropical *changed to* Revista Cubana de Medicina Tropical.
0025-7958	Medicina Tropical†
0025-7966	Medicinar
0025-7974	Medicine (Baltimore)
0025-7982	Medicine and Medicaments Courier
0025-7990	Medicine and Science in Sports *see* 0195-9131
0025-8008	Medicine & Surgery
0025-8016	Medecine Europeene
0025-8032	Medicine Today†
0025-8040	Medicinsk Forum†
0025-8059	Medicinska Foereningernas Tidskrift *see* 0347-0989
0025-8067	Medicinska Revija
0025-8075	Meditsinskaya Tekhnika
0025-8091	Medicinski Glasnik
0025-8105	Medicinski Pregled
0025-8113	Medicinski Radnik
0025-8121	Medicinski Razgledi
0025-813X	Medicot
0025-8148	Medico d'Italia
0025-8164	Medico-Legal Bulletin†
0025-8172	Medico-Legal Journal
0025-8180	Medico Moderno†
0025-8202	Medicost
0025-8210	Medicus†
0025-8229	Medjimurje
0025-8237	Medion†
0025-8245	Medisch Contact
0025-8261	Options Mediterraneennes†
0025-827X	Mediterranean Diplomatic Observer
0025-8296	Mediterranee
0025-830X	Meditsinskii Zhurnal Uzbekistana
0025-8318	Meditsinskaya Gazeta
0025-8326	Meditsinskaya Parazitologiya i Parazitarnye Bolezni
0025-8334	Meditsinskaya Radiologiya
0025-8342	Meditsinskaya Sestra
0025-8350	Medium
0025-8377	Saskatchewan Association of Media Specialists. Medium
0025-8385	Medium Aevum
0025-8393	Medizin in Bild und Ton†
0025-8407	Medizin und Ernaehrung†
0025-8431	Medizinhistorisches Journal
0025-844X	Medizinische Bild†
0025-8466	Das Medizinische Laboratorium†
0025-8474	Medizinische Monatsschrift *see* 0342-9601
0025-8482	Medizinische Neuerscheinungen
0025-8490	Der Medizinische Sachverstaendige
0025-8504	Medizinische Technik *see* 0344-9416
0025-8512	Die Medizinische Welt
0025-8539	Nordisk Numismatisk Union Medlemsblad
0025-8547	Foerfattaren
0025-8555	Medjunarodni Problemi
0025-8571	Medusa *changed to* Agarte.
0025-8601	Medycyna Doswiadczalna i Mikrobiologia
0025-861X	Komunikacyjna *changed to* Lekarz Kolejowy.
0025-8628	Medycyna Weterynaryjna
0025-8636	Medycyna Wiejska
0025-8652	Meetings and Conventions
0025-8679	Megamot
0025-8687	Megaphone (Canton)
0025-8695	Megaphone (Dallas)†
0025-8709	Megaphone (Georgetown)
0025-8717	Meglio
0025-8725	Meharri-Dent†
0025-8741	Meidensha Review *changed to* Meiden Review.
0025-875X	Meie Post
0025-8768	Meie Tee
0025-8776	Meieriposten
0025-8784	Meiklejohn Civil Liberties Library. Acquisitions *changed to* What's Happening to the Law.
0025-8792	Mein Eigenheim
0025-8814	Mein Standpunkt†
0025-8822	Journal fuer Sozialforschung
0025-8830	M E J
0025-8857	Mekeel's Stamp News
0025-8865	Mekhanika Polimerov *see* 0203-1272
0025-8873	Mekhanizatsiya i Avtomatizatsiya Proizvodstva
0025-8881	Mekhanizatsiya i Elektrifikatsiya Sotsialisticheskogo Sel'skogo Khozyaistva *see* 0206-572X
0025-8903	Mekhanizatsiya Stroitel'stva
0025-8911	Melanges de Science Religieuse
0025-892X	Melanges Malraux Miscellany *see* 0839-458X
0025-8938	Melbourne University Law Review
0025-8954	Mele
0025-8970	Melk en Zuivel *changed to* Zuivelkoerier.
0025-8989	Melliand Textilberichte *see* 0341-0781
0025-8997	Melodie
0025-9004	Melodie und Rhythmus
0025-9012	Melody Maker
0025-9020	Melos *see* 0170-8791
0025-9039	Melyepitestudomanyi Szemle
0025-9047	Memeler Dampfboot
0025-9055	Memento General Tequi Quincaillerie *changed to* Essor de la Quincaillerie.
0025-9063	Memisa Nieuws
0025-9071	Memo *see* 0957-5936
0025-908X	Memo from Belgium
0025-9101	Memo Key *see* 0951-1512
0025-911X	Center for Research on Learning and Teaching. Memo to the Faculty†
0025-9128	Revue de Metallurgie. Memoires Scientifiques *see* 0245-8292
0025-9136	Defense Academy. Memoirs
0025-9144	Memon Alam
0025-9152	Mexico. Direccion de Estadistica y Estudios Economicos. Memorandum Tecnico
0025-9160	Memorial de l'Artillerie Francaise
0025-9179	Memorial des Percepteurs et Receveurs des Communes
0025-9195	Memoires C.E.R.E.S.
0025-9209	Memphis State Business Review *see* 0279-8174
0025-9217	Men Only
0025-9225	Menadzer u Privredi *changed to* Privreda i Rukovodjenje.
0025-9233	Menckeniana
0025-9241	Mendel Newsletter†
0025-925X	Mendeleev Chemistry Journal
0025-9268	Mendocino County Historical Society. Newsletter
0025-9284	Menninger Clinic. Bulletin
0025-9292	Menninger Perspective
0025-9314	Mennonitische Rundschau
0025-9322	Mennonit†
0025-9330	Mennonite
0025-9349	Mennonite Brethren Herald
0025-9357	Mennonite Historical Bulletin
0025-9365	Mennonite Life
0025-9373	Mennonite Quarterly Review
0025-9381	Mennonite Research Journal *see* 0148-4036
0025-939X	Menorah
0025-9411	Men's and Boys' Wear Buyers
0025-942X	Men's Art Service
0025-9438	Men's Clip Review *changed to* Menswear Advertising.
0025-9454	Mens en Maatschappij
0025-9462	Mens en Melodie
0025-9470	Mens en Onderneming *see* 0165-1722
0025-9489	Humanist
0025-9497	Men's Fashions†
0025-9500	Men's Hairstylist and Barber's Journal *changed to* Salon Talk.
0025-9519	Men's Wear
0025-9535	Men's Wear of Canada *changed to* Manstyle.
0025-9543	Mensa Bulletin
0025-9586	Mensajero Forestal†
0025-9608	Mensch und Welt†
0025-9616	Das Menschenrecht
0025-9624	Mensucat Meslek Dergisi
0025-9632	Mental Health†
0025-9667	Mental Health in Australia
0025-9683	M H†
0025-9691	Mental Retardation Abstracts *see* 0191-1600
0025-9713	Mentor
0025-9748	Mercado da Borracha no Brasil. Boletim Mensual
0025-9764	Mercados de Grasas y Acietes†
0025-9772	Mercadotecnia
0025-9780	Corriere Mercantile Politico d'Informazioni
0025-9799	Mercantile Gazette of New Zealand *changed to* New Zealand Mercantile Gazette.
0025-9810	Mercantile Law Reporter†
0025-9829	Mercato Metalsiderurgico
0025-9837	Mercator *see* 0533-070X
0025-9845	Mercer Actuarial Bulletin *see* 0714-6914
0025-9853	Mercer Cluster
0025-987X	Mercer Law Review
0025-9888	Merchandising Week *see* 0888-4501
0025-990X	Mercian Geologist
0025-9918	Merck Sharp & Dohme Review†
0025-9926	Mercur
0025-9934	Mercure
0025-9950	Mercurius *changed to* F N V - Magazine (Woerden).
0025-9969	Mercury (Los Angeles)
0025-9985	Finland. Merentutkimuslaitoksen. Julkaisu *see* 0357-1076
0025-9993	Meres es Automatika
0026-0002	Meresugyi Kozlemenyek
0026-0010	Mergers & Acquisitions
0026-0029	Merian
0026-0037	Meridiano
0026-0045	Merino Breeders' Journal
0026-0061	Merkt
0026-007X	Merkenblad Benelux
0026-0088	Merkonomi
0026-0096	Merkur
0026-010X	Merkur Magazin fuer Volksgesundheit
0026-0118	Merkuriusz Polski-Zycie Akademickie†
0026-0126	Merleg
0026-0142	Merova Technika *changed to* Magazin C S N.
0026-0150	Merrill - Palmer Quarterly
0026-0169	Merrimac *changed to* M T I Reporter.
0026-0185	Mesias
0026-0193	Mesures Regulation Automatisme *see* 0755-219X
0026-0215	Message de l'Immaculee†
0026-0223	Message de Verite†
0026-0231	Message (Hagerstown)
0026-024X	Messager
0026-0258	Messager de la Haute Savoie
0026-0266	Messager de l'Exarchat du Patriarche Russe en Europe Occidentale†
0026-0274	Messager Evangelique
0026-0290	Messages du Secours Catholique
0026-0304	Messaggero dei Ragazzi
0026-0312	Messaggero di S. Antonio
0026-0339	Messen und Pruefen *changed to* Messen Pruefen Automatisieren.
0026-0347	Messen - Steuern - Regeln
0026-0355	Messenger (Elgin)
0026-0363	Messenger (Kansas City)
0026-0371	Messenger

ISSN INDEX 5411

0026-0398 Messer und Schere *changed to* Der Buechsenmacher und Messer und Schere.
0026-0401 Messidor
0026-0428 Messtechnische Briefe fuer Elektrisches Messen Mechanischer Groessen *see* 0930-8644
0026-0436 Mester†
0026-0452 Meta
0026-0460 Metaal & Kunststof
0026-0479 Metaal & Techniek
0026-0487 Metaalbewerking *changed to* M B Produktiertechniek.
0026-0495 Metabolism: Clinical and Experimental
0026-0509 Metabolismo†
0026-0517 Metal
0026-0525 Metal Building Review
0026-0533 Metal Bulletin
0026-0541 Metal Construction and British Welding Journal *changed to* Joining and Materials.
0026-055X Metal Fabricating News
0026-0568 Metal Fabricator†
0026-0576 Metal Finishing
0026-0584 Metal Finishing Abstracts *see* 0950-5199
0026-0606 Metal Finishing Plant and Processes *changed to* Surface Treatment Plant and Processes.
0026-0614 Kinzoku Hyomen Gijutsu *see* 0915-1869
0026-0622 Metal Forming *see* 0141-8602
0026-0630 U D S Metal Joining Digest *changed to* Metal Joining Digest.
0026-0649 Metal Polisher, Buffer and Plater†
0026-0657 Metal Powder Report
0026-0665 Metal Progress *see* 0882-7958
0026-0673 Metal Science and Heat Treatment
0026-069X Metal Stamping *see* 1040-967X
0026-0703 Metal Trades Department. Bulletin†
0026-072X Metal Worker†
0026-0738 Metalektro Visie *changed to* Metalektro Profiel.
0026-0746 Metall
0026-0754 Metallarbetaren
0026-0762 Metalle
0026-0789 Metallhandwerk and Metalltechnik *changed to* M & T - Metallhandwerk & Technik.
0026-0797 Metalloberflaeche
0026-0800 Metallography *see* 1044-5803
0026-0819 Metallovedenie i Termicheskaya Obrabotka Metallov
0026-0827 Metallurg
0026-0835 Metallurgia *see* 0141-8602
0026-0843 La Metallurgia Italiana
0026-0851 C R M Metallurgical Reports†
0026-086X Metallurgical Transactions *see* 0360-2133
0026-0878 Metallurgie *see* 0751-588X
0026-0894 Metallurgist
0026-0908 Metallverarbeitung
0026-0924 Metals Abstracts
0026-0932 Metals Abstracts Index
0026-0959 Metals and Minerals Review
0026-0975 Metals Week
0026-0983 Metalurgia A B M *changed to* A B M Metalurgia e Materiais.
0026-1009 Metalworking Digest
0026-1017 Metalworking Economics†
0026-1025 Chilton's Iron Age Management *see* 0891-4036
0026-1033 Metalworking Production
0026-105X Metanoia†
0026-1068 Metaphilosophy
0026-1076 Metapsichica
0026-1084 Metaux
0026-1092 Meteoor†
0026-1114 Meteoritics
0026-1122 Israel. Meteorologia Be-Israel. *changed to* Israel. Meteorological Society. Meteorologia Be-Israel.
0026-1130 Meteorological and Geoastrophysical Abstracts
0026-1149 Meteorological Magazine
0026-1165 Meteorological Society of Japan. Journal
0026-1173 Meteorologicke Zpravy
0026-1181 Meteorologie
0026-1203 Meteorologische Abhandlungen
0026-1211 Meteorologische Rundschau *changed to* Meteorologische Zeitschrift.
0026-1238 Methodist History
0026-1246 Methodist Homes Quarterly *changed to* Horizon (Neptune).
0026-1254 Methodist Message *changed to* Pelita Methodist.
0026-1262 Methodist Recorder
0026-1270 Methods of Information in Medicine
0026-1289 Metiers Graphiques†
0026-1297 Metlfax
0026-1319 Metodiky pro Zavadeni Vysledku Vyzkumu do Praxe†
0026-1327 Metra†
0026-1335 Metrika
0026-1343 Metro†
0026-136X Metro Denver *changed to* Metro Denver Magazine.
0026-1378 Metro Memo†
0026-1386 Metroeconomica
0026-1394 Metrologia
0026-1408 Metrology and Inspection *changed to* Quality Today.
0026-1416 Metron†
0026-1424 Metron
0026-1467 Metropolitan *see* 0162-6221
0026-1475 Metropolitan†
0026-1483 Metropolitan Area Digest†
0026-1491 Metropolitan Computer News†
0026-1505 Metropolitan Council of the Twin Cities Area. Newsletter†
0026-1513 Statistical Bulletin - Metropolitan Life *see* 0741-9767
0026-1521 Metropolitan Museum of Art. Bulletin
0026-153X Metropolitan Nashville Board of Education. News and Views
0026-1556 Metropolitan Pensioner
0026-1564 Metropolitan Restaurant News *changed to* Metro Food Service News.
0026-1580 Metropolitan Star *see* 0745-8509
0026-1599 Metropolitan Washington Board of Trade News *see* 0274-5496
0026-1602 Metsa Ja Puu
0026-1629 Metsastys ja Kalastus
0026-1637 Metterdaad†
0026-1645 Metzger und Wurster
0026-1653 Meubles et Decors *see* 0773-4034
0026-1661 Meunerie Belge†
0026-1688 Mevo†
0026-1696 Mexican-American Review *changed to* Business Mexico.
0026-170X Mexican Life†
0026-1726 Mexico Agricola
0026-1750 Universidad Nacional Autonoma de Mexico. Revista
0026-1769 Mexico. Direccion General de Estadistica. Revista de Estadistica *see* 0186-2707
0026-1785 Mexico Farmaceutico
0026-1793 Mexico Heroico†
0026-1807 Mexico Industrial
0026-1815 Mexico Mercantil
0026-1858 Mexletter
0026-1866 Meyers Modeblatt
0026-1882 Mezhdunarodnyi Sel'skokhozyaistvennyi Zhurnal *changed to* Mezhdunarodnyi Agropromyshlennyi Zhurnal.
0026-1890 Mezogazdasagi Technika
0026-1904 Mezogazdasagi Vilagirodalom†
0026-1912 Eurosud - Il Mezzogiorno e le Comunita' Europee†
0026-1939 Mi Mladi
0026-1947 Miami Business Review†
0026-1955 Miami Valley Dairyman *changed to* Milk Marketer.
0026-1971 Mias†
0026-198X Michel-Rundschau
0026-1998 Michigan A F L - C I O News
0026-2005 Michigan Academician
0026-2013 Michigan Association of Secondary School Principals' Bulletin
0026-2021 Michigan Beverage News
0026-203X Michigan Botanist
0026-2056 Michigan Business Review *see* 0098-1923
0026-2072 Michigan Christian Advocate
0026-2099 Michigan Corrections Association Report
0026-2102 Michigan Dental Association. Journal
0026-2110 Michigan Documents
0026-2129 Teacher's Voice *see* 0883-573X
0026-2137 Michigan Engineer†
0026-2145 Michigan Entomologist *see* 0090-0222
0026-2153 Michigan Farmer
0026-2161 Michigan Farm News *changed to* Michigan Farm News - Rural Living.
0026-217X Michigan Florist
0026-2188 Michigan Heritage *changed to* Family Trails.
0026-2196 Michigan History *changed to* Michigan History Magazine.
0026-2218 Michigan in Books†
0026-2226 Michigan Journal of Secondary Education *changed to* Secondary Education Today.
0026-2234 Michigan Law Review
0026-2242 Michigan Librarian *changed to* Michigan Librarian.
0026-2250 Michigan Magazine Index†
0026-2277 Michigan Manufacturer and Financial Record†
0026-2285 Michigan Mathematical Journal
0026-2293 Michigan Medicine
0026-2315 Michigan Milk Messenger
0026-2323 Michigan Motor Carrier-Folks *changed to* Michigan Trucking Today.
0026-2331 Michigan Municipal Review
0026-234X Michigan Music Educator†
0026-2358 Michigan Natural Resources
0026-2366 Michigan Nurse
0026-2374 Michigan Osteopathic Journal *changed to* Triad (Farmington).
0026-2382 Michigan Out-Of-Doors
0026-2404 Michigan Pharmacist *see* 1045-6481
0026-2412 Michigan Industry
0026-2420 Michigan Quarterly Review
0026-2439 M A S B Journal
0026-2455 Michigan State Economic Record†
0026-2463 Michigan State University Alumni Magazine *see* 0273-6977
0026-2471 Michigan Technic
0026-248X Michigan Tradesman *changed to* Michigan Banker.
0026-251X Michigan's Occupational Health
0026-2528 Micmac News
0026-2536 Micro-Library Bulletin
0026-2544 Micro News Bulletin *see* 0892-3876
0026-2579 Microbial Genetics Bulletin†
0026-2595 Microbiologia Espanola†
0026-2609 Bacteriologia, Virusologia, Parazitologia, Epidemiologia *see* 0301-7338
0026-2617 Microbiology
0026-2633 Microbios
0026-265X Microchemical Journal
0026-2668 Microcosm†
0026-2676 Microcritica
0026-2692 Microelectronics Journal
0026-2706 Microelectronics Abstracts†
0026-2714 Microelectronics and Reliability
0026-2722 Microelectronics Digest†
0026-2730 Microfacts Advertising Reference File†
0026-2749 Microfilm Newsletter *see* 0883-9808
0026-2765 Micrographics News & Views†
0026-2781 Micronesian Reporter†
0026-279X Micronesica
0026-2803 Micropaleontology
0026-2811 Journal of Microphotography *changed to* Journal of Micrographics.
0026-282X Microscope
0026-2838 Microscopy
0026-2846 Microstructures†
0026-2854 Microtecnic
0026-2862 Microvascular Research
0026-2870 University of Utah. Microwave Device and Physical Electronics Laboratory Quarterly Report
0026-2889 Microwave Energy Applications Newsletter *see* 0276-7961
0026-2897 Micorwave Journal *see* 0192-6225
0026-2900 Microwave Tube D.A.T.A. Book *see* 0271-0773
0026-2919 Microwaves *see* 0745-2993
0026-2927 Mid-America
0026-2935 Mid-America Insurance
0026-2943 Mid-Atlantic Apothecary *see* 0003-6560
0026-2986 Mid-Continent Mortician†
0026-3001 Mid East†
0026-301X Mid-East Commerce
0026-3036 Mid-Towner†
0026-3044 Midwest Contractor Magazine
0026-3052 Mid-West Truckman†
0026-3079 American Studies
0026-3095 Middle East Business Digest *changed to* Africa Middle East Business Digest.
0026-3117 Middle East Express
0026-3141 Middle East Journal
0026-315X Middle East Monitor
0026-3176 Middle East Perspective†
0026-3184 Middle East Studies Association Bulletin
0026-3192 Middle East Trade
0026-3206 Middle Eastern Studies
0026-3214 Middle Way
0026-3222 Middlesex Hospital Journal *changed to* Bell - U C M S M Students' Magazine.
0026-3230 MidEast Report
0026-3249 Midland
0026-3257 Midland Bank Review†
0026-3273 Midland Industrialist†
0026-3281 Midland Medical Review†
0026-3311 Midlands Industry and Commerce
0026-332X Midstream
0026-3338 Midwest Automotive News *changed to* Midwest Automotive & Autobody News.
0026-3346 Midwest Chaparral
0026-3354 Midwest Eighty-Eight Manufacturing
0026-3362 Midwest Electrical News†
0026-3370 Midwest Engineer
0026-3397 Midwest Journal of Political Science *see* 0092-5853
0026-3400 Midwest Landscaping *see* 0194-7257
0026-3419 Midwest Modern Language Association. Bulletin *see* 0742-5562
0026-3427 Midwest Motor Transport News
0026-3435 Midwest Motorist
0026-3443 Midwest Museums Conference Quarterly *changed to* Midwest Museums Conference. News Brief.
0026-3451 Midwest Quarterly
0026-346X Midwest Review of Public Administration *see* 0275-0740
0026-3478 Midwestern Dentist
0026-3486 Midwestern Druggist†
0026-3494 Midwestern Nigeria Gazette *changed to* Bendel State Gazette.
0026-3516 Midwife and Health Visitor *see* 0306-9699
0026-3524 Midwives Chronicle
0026-3532 Mie Medical Journal
0026-3540 Miedzynarodowe Czasopismo Rolnicze
0026-3559 Maize News - Mielienuus *changed to* Mielies (Pretoria).
0026-3567 Miesiecznik Literacki
0026-3575 Migrant
0026-3583 Migration News†
0026-3591 Migrations
0026-3605 Mijn Stokpaardje
0026-3613 Mijnwerker†
0026-3621 Mike Shayne Mystery Magazine
0026-363X Mikhtav Lehaver
0026-3648 Mikologiya i Fitopatologiya
0026-3672 Mikrochimica Acta
0026-3680 Mikrokosmos
0026-3702 Mikroskopie†
0026-3710 Mil
0026-3729 Camera di Commercio Industria Artigianato e Agricoltura di Milano. Notiziario Commerciale†
0026-3737 Milap Weekly

ISSN

5412 ISSN INDEX

0026-3745 Milbank Memorial Fund Quarterly *see* 0887-378X
0026-3753 Milch-Praxis *see* 0343-0200
0026-3761 Milch - Fettwaren - Eier - Handel
0026-377X Milchsuppe
0026-3788 Milchwissenschaft
0026-380X Milestones
0026-3826 Militaergeschichtliche Mitteilungen
0026-3842 Militaerpsykologiske Meddelelser
0026-3850 Militaert Tidsskrift
0026-3869 Militaire Spectator
0026-3877 Militant
0026-3885 Militant
0026-3893 Militant Truth *changed to* Independent Voice.
0026-3907 Militaer-Kuechenchef
0026-3915 Militaria†
0026-3923 Militaerwesen†
0026-3931 Military Affairs *see* 0899-3718
0026-394X Military Aircraft and Missile Data Sheets
0026-3958 Military Chaplain
0026-3966 Military Collector & Historian
0026-3974 Military Digest†
0026-3982 Military Engineer
0026-3990 Military Government Journal and Newsletter *see* 0045-7035
0026-4008 Military Historical Society. Bulletin
0026-4016 Military History Journal
0026-4032 Military Journalist *see* 0095-635X
0026-4040 Military Law Review
0026-4067 Military Market
0026-4075 Military Medicine
0026-4083 Military Modelling
0026-4105 Military Police Journal†
0026-4121 Military Record of Atomic C B R Happenings *changed to* Military Record of Atomic C B R Happenings. Armament Data Sheets.
0026-413X Military Research Letter
0026-4148 Military Review
0026-4156 Militia Christi *changed to* Kerk en Vrede.
0026-4164 Miljoespegelen†
0026-4172 Milk Industry
0026-4180 Milk Producer
0026-4199 Milk Producer
0026-4210 Milk Vendor
0026-4229 Milking Shorthorn Journal *see* 0145-8264
0026-4253 Mill News Letter†
0026-427X Millinery and Boutique†
0026-4296 Milling *changed to* Milling Feed and Farm Supplies.
0026-430X Mills Stream *changed to* Mills Weekly.
0026-4318 Milton College Blue and Gold†
0026-4326 Milton Quarterly
0026-4350 Milwaukee Courier
0026-4377 Milwaukee Reader
0026-4385 Mimos
0026-4407 North and South†
0026-4415 Minaret *changed to* Minaret Monthly International.
0026-4423 Mind
0026-4431 Mynd
0026-4458 Mind over Matter†
0026-4474 Mindszenty Report
0026-4490 Mine Medical Officers' Association of South Africa. Proceedings *changed to* Mine Medical Officers' Association of South Africa. Journal.
0026-4504 Mine Ventilation Society of South Africa. Journal
0026-4512 Mined-Land Conservation†
0026-4520 Mineracao Metalurgia
0026-4539 Earth and Mineral Sciences
0026-4547 Mineral Industries Newsletter†
0026-4555 California Geology
0026-4563 Mineral Research and Exploration Institute of Turkey. Bulletin
0026-4571 Mineral Wealth
0026-458X Minerales
0026-4598 Mineralium Deposita
0026-4601 Mineralogical Abstracts
0026-461X Mineralogical Magazine
0026-4628 Mineralogical Record
0026-4652 Minerals Research Laboratory Bulletin *changed to* Minerals Research Laboratory Newsletter.
0026-4660 Minerals Science and Engineering†
0026-4679 Mineria
0026-4687 Miners' International News†
0026-4695 Minerva
0026-4709 Minerva Aerospaziale
0026-4717 Minerva Anestesiologica
0026-4725 Minerva Cardioangiologica
0026-4733 Minerva Chirurgica
0026-4741 Minerva Dermatologica *see* 0533-7712
0026-475X Minerva Dietologica *see* 0391-1993
0026-4776 Minerva Gastroenterologica *see* 0391-1993
0026-4784 Minerva Ginecologica
0026-4806 Minerva Medica
0026-4849 Minerva Medicolegale
0026-4857 Minerva Mediconucleare *changed to* Journal of Nuclear Biology and Medicine.
0026-4873 Minerva Nefrologica *changed to* Minerva Urologica e Nefrologica.
0026-4881 Minerva Neurochirurgica *changed to* Journal of Neurosurgical Sciences.
0026-489X Minerva Nipiologica *see* 0392-4416
0026-4903 Minerva Oftalmologica
0026-4911 Minerva Ortopedica *changed to* Minerva Ortopedica e Traumatologica.
0026-4938 Minerva Otorinolaringologica *changed to* Otorinolaringologica.
0026-4946 Minerva Pediatrica
0026-4954 Minerva Pneumologica
0026-4962 Minerva Radiologica *see* 0033-8362
0026-4970 Minerva Stomatologica
0026-4989 Minerva Urologica *changed to* Minerva Urologica e Nefrologica.
0026-4997 Minervas Kvartalsskrift†
0026-5012 Mines and Factories Journal†
0026-5020 Mines and Minerals†
0026-5039 Mines and Oils; Four Hundred and Fifty Canadian Weekly Stock Charts *see* 0829-3139
0026-5047 Mines et Metallurgie†
0026-5055 Mines Golden *see* 0096-4859
0026-5063 Mineur d'Auvergne *see* 0989-7577
0026-5071 Mineurs de France
0026-508X Mingay's Electrical Supplies Guide†
0026-5098 Mingay's News *see* 0728-9383
0026-5101 Mingay's Price Service *changed to* Mingay's Retail Guide.
0026-5128 Miniature Book News
0026-5152 Mining and Minerals Engineering *see* 0369-1632
0026-5160 Mining Congress Journal *see* 0891-6209
0026-5179 Mining Engineer
0026-5187 Mining Engineering
0026-5209 Mining Geology
0026-5217 Mining Industry and Trade Journal *changed to* Mining Industry & Trade Annual.
0026-5225 Mining Journal
0026-5241 Mining Record
0026-525X Mineral Resources Review *changed to* Mines and Energy Review, South Australia.
0026-5268 Chamber of Mines of South Africa.
Mining Survey
0026-5276 Mining Technology
0026-5284 Belgium. Ministere de l'Education Nationale et de la Culture Francaise. Bulletin d'Information *changed to* Belgium. Ministere de l'Education Nationale. Revue.
0026-5292 Cuba. Ministerio del Commercio Exterior. Revista†
0026-5306 Ministerium
0026-5314 Ministry
0026-5322 Trinidad and Tobago. Ministry of Petroleum and Mines. Monthly Bulletin *changed to* Trinidad and Tobago. Ministry of Energy. Monthly Bulletin.
0026-5330 Ministry Theological Review†
0026-5357 Minkus Stamp Journal *changed to* Minkus Stamp Journal.
0026-5365 Minneapolis District Dental Journal†
0026-5381 Minnesota A. A. A. Motorist†
0026-539X Minnesota Academy of Science. Journal
0026-5403 Minnesota Archaeologist
0026-5411 Minnesota Chemist
0026-542X Minnesota. Department of Agriculture. Agronomy Services Newsletter†
0026-5438 Minnesota. Department of Education. Public Library Newsletter
0026-5446 Minnesota Education News *see* 1053-3362
0026-5454 Minnesota Education Report *changed to* Education Update (St. Paul).
0026-5462 Minnesota Engineer†
0026-5489 Minnesota Food Guide *changed to* Minnesota Grocer.
0026-5497 Minnesota History
0026-5500 Minnesota Horticulturist
0026-5519 Minnesota I R C News *changed to* Insights (Minneapolis).
0026-5527 Minnesota Journal of Education†
0026-5535 Minnesota Law Review
0026-5543 Minnesota Legal Register: Opinions of the Minnesota Attorney General
0026-5551 Minnesota Libraries
0026-5578 Minnesota Municipalities *see* 0148-8546
0026-5586 Minnesota Nursing Accent
0026-5594 Minnesota Optometrist†
0026-5616 Minnesota Pharmacist
0026-5624 Minnesota Police Journal
0026-5632 Minnesota Press†
0026-5659 Minnesota Reading Quarterly†
0026-5667 Minnesota Review
0026-5675 Minnesota Science
0026-5691 Minnesota Technolog
0026-5705 Minnesota Welfare *changed to* People (St. Paul).
0026-5721 Minus One *changed to* The Egoist.
0026-573X Minute *see* 0996-9640
0026-5748 Minuzzolo *changed to* L.G. Argomenti.
0026-5756 Mio Bebe
0026-5764 Mio Lavoro†
0026-5780 Mira
0026-5802 Miraculous Medal
0026-5810 Miroir du Centre
0026-5829 Mirovaya Ekonomika i Mezhdunarodnye Otnosheniya
0026-5837 Sooke Mirror
0026-5845 Mirror
0026-5861 Miscellanea Barcinonensia†
0026-587X Miscellanea Francescana
0026-5888 Miscellanea Storica della Valdelsa
0026-5896 Miscellany
0026-590X Miscellany
0026-5918 Miss Chatelaine *see* 0708-4927
0026-5934 Bakkerswereld
0026-5942 BouwWereld
0026-5950 Missets Horeca
0026-5977 Missi
0026-5993 Missile - Ordinance Letter
0026-6000 Espace†
0026-6019 Missili e Spazio *changed to* Aerotecnica, Missili e Spazio.
0026-6027 Mission *see* 0199-4433
0026-6035 Mission de l'Eglise
0026-6043 Missionary Aviation *changed to* Mission Aviation Life Link.
0026-6051 Missionary News Service†
0026-606X Missionary Research Library. Occasional Bulletin *see* 0272-6122
0026-6078 Missionary Review†
0026-6086 Missionhurst
0026-6094 Mondo e Missione
0026-6108 Missioni Domenicane
0026-6116 Missions-Etrangeres
0026-6124 Mission Messages
0026-6132 Missionsbaneret
0026-6159 Mississippi Banker
0026-6167 Mississippi Business Review†
0026-6175 Mississippi E P A News *see* 1052-2433
0026-6183 Mississippi Educational Advance *see* 0164-8683
0026-6191 Mississippi Educational Journal *see* 0164-8683
0026-6205 Mississippi Farm Bureau News
0026-6213 Mississippi Farm Report†
0026-6221 Mississippi Farm. Research *see* 0091-4460
0026-6248 Mississippi Folklore Register
0026-6256 Mississippi Game and Fish *see* 1041-9306
0026-6264 Mississippi Grocers' Guide
0026-6272 Mississippi Language Crusader
0026-6280 Mississippi Law Journal
0026-6299 Mississippi Legion-Aire
0026-6302 Mississippi Library News *see* 0194-388X
0026-6310 Mississippi Magic†
0026-6329 Mississippi Methodist Advocate *changed to* Mississippi United Methodist Advocate.
0026-6337 Mississippi Municipalities
0026-6353 Mississippi Notes *changed to* Mississippi Music Educator.
0026-637X Mississippi Quarterly
0026-6388 Mississippi R N
0026-6396 Mississippi State Medical Association. Journal
0026-640X Mississippi State University. Forest Products Utilization Laboratory. Research Report
0026-6418 Mississippi Valley Journal of Business and Economics *see* 1058-3300
0026-6434 Mississippi Valley Stockman-Farmer *changed to* Stockman - Grass Farmer.
0026-6442 Mississippi's Business
0026-6477 Missouri Architect†
0026-6493 Missouri Botanical Garden. Annals
0026-6493 Missouri Botanical Gardens. Annals *issued with* 1055-3177
0026-6507 Missouri Botanical Garden Bulletin
0026-6515 Missouri Conservationist
0026-6523 Missouri Dental Association. Journal *changed to* Missouri Dental Journal.
0026-6531 Missouri Disaster Planning and Operations Newsletter *see* 0197-6672
0026-6558 Missouri Engineer
0026-6574 Missouri Farm Bureau News
0026-6582 Missouri Historical Review
0026-6590 Missouri Historical Society. Bulletin *see* 0198-9375
0026-6604 Missouri Law Review
0026-6612 Missouri L P-Gas Talks *changed to* M L P G A News.
0026-6620 Missouri Medicine
0026-6647 Missouri Municipal Review
0026-6655 Missouri Nurse
0026-6663 Missouri Pharmacist
0026-6671 Missouri Press News
0026-668X Missouri Ruralist
0026-6698 Missouri School Board
0026-6701 Missouri School Music
0026-671X Missouri Speleology
0026-6728 Missouri Teamster
0026-6760 Mita Gakkai Zasshi
0026-6779 Die Mitarbeit†
0026-6787 Mithila Institute of Post Graduate Studies and Research in Sanskrit Learning. Bulletin
0026-6809 M E R I's Monthly Circular
0026-6817 Mitsubishi Heavy Industries Technical Review
0026-6825 Mitsui Zosen Giho
0026-6833 Mitteilungen aus Baltischem Leben
0026-6841 Mitteilungen aus der Gebiete der Lebensmitteluntersuchung und Hygiene
0026-6868 Mitteilungen aus der Rheinischen Rinderzucht
0026-6876 Mitteilungen aus Statistik und Verwaltung der Stadt Wien *changed to* Vienna. Statistisches Amt der Stadt Wien. Statistische Mitteilungen.
0026-6884 Mitteilungen der Deutschen Patentanwaelte

ISSN

ISSN	Title
0026-6892	Industrie- und Handelskammer Reutlingen. Mitteilungen *changed to* Wirtschaft - Neckar - Alb.
0026-6906	Wiener Urania. Mitteilungen
0026-6922	Oberoesterreichisches Volksbildungswerk. Mitteilungen *changed to* Bildungsimpuls.
0026-6930	Mitteilungen fuer den Aussenhandel†
0026-6949	Mitteilungen ueber Textilindustrie *changed to* Mittex: Mitteilungen ueber Textilindustrie.
0026-6957	Dokumentation fuer Umweltschutz und Landespflege *changed to* Dokumentation Naturschutz und Landschaft.
0026-6965	Mitteilungsblatt der Genossenschaftlichen Frauenorganisation†
0026-6973	Mitteilungsblatt fuer Dolmetscher und Uebersetzer
0026-6981	Mizan: U S S R-China-Africa-Asia†
0026-699X	Mizrachi Weg†
0026-7007	Mizrachi Woman *see* 0747-0258
0026-7023	Mlad Borec
0026-7031	Mladost
0026-704X	Mljekarstvo
0026-7058	Mlynsko-Pekarensky Prumysl a Technika Skladovani Obili
0026-7066	Mnemonic†
0026-7074	Mnemosyne
0026-7090	Moebelvaerlden *see* 0345-7737
0026-7104	Mobila
0026-7112	Il Mobile
0026-7120	Mobile and Recreational Housing Merchandiser *changed to* Manufactured Home Merchandiser.
0026-7139	Mobile Home *see* 0268-4594
0026-7147	Mobile Home Park Management *changed to* Mobile Home Park Management & Developer.
0026-7163	Mobile Home Reporter and Recreation Vehicle News *changed to* Manufactured Housing Reporter.
0026-7171	Mobile Homes & Recreational Vehicles in Canada *changed to* Canadian Recreational Vehicle Industry.
0026-7198	Mobile Living
0026-7201	Mobile Living in Canada *changed to* Mobile Living in Canada-Manufactured Homes/Canada.
0026-7228	Mobilia†
0026-7244	Moccasin
0026-7252	Moda dei Bimbi
0026-7279	Die Mode†
0026-7295	Model Airplane News
0026-7309	Model Car Science†
0026-7317	Model *see* 0269-834X
0026-7325	Model Engineer
0026-7333	Model Maker and Model Boats *see* 0144-2910
0026-7341	Model Railroader
0026-735X	Model Railway Constructor†
0026-7368	Model Railways *changed to* Model Railways.
0026-7384	Modelbouwer
0026-7392	Modele Magazine
0026-7406	Modele Reduit d'Avion
0026-7414	Modele Reduit de Bateau
0026-7422	Modelleisenbahner
0026-7430	Modena *changed to* Modena Economica.
0026-7449	Moderat Debatt
0026-7457	Modern Age
0026-7473	Modern Applications News for Design and Manufacturing *see* 0277-9951
0026-7481	Modern Asia *changed to* Far East Business.
0026-749X	Modern Asian Studies
0026-7503	Modern Austrian Literature
0026-7511	Modern Beauty Shop *see* 0148-4001
0026-752X	Modern Boating
0026-7538	Modern Brewery Age
0026-7546	Modern Bride
0026-7554	Modern Caravan *see* 0268-0440
0026-7562	Modern Casting
0026-7570	Modern Ceylon Studies†
0026-7597	Modern Churchman
0026-7600	Modern Concepts of Cardiovascular Disease†
0026-7619	Modern Concrete *see* 0899-8671
0026-7635	Modern Converter†
0026-7651	Modern Dairy
0026-766X	Modern Dance and Dancer†
0026-7678	Modern Data *changed to* Systems Integration Business.
0026-7686	Modern Dateteknik†
0026-7694	Modern Drama
0026-7708	Modern English *see* 0306-9346
0026-7716	Modern Farming†
0026-7724	Modern Fiction Studies
0026-7732	Modern Fishing
0026-7759	Modern Franchising†
0026-7775	Modern Geology
0026-7791	Modern Government *see* 0360-7941
0026-7805	Modern Grocer
0026-7813	Modern Gymnast *see* 0276-1041
0026-7821	Modern Haiku
0026-783X	Modern Hospital *see* 0160-7480
0026-7848	Modern Images
0026-7856	Modern International Drama
0026-7864	Modern Jeweler *see* 0193-208X
0026-7872	Modern Kantoor†
0026-7880	Modern Knitting
0026-7899	Modern Knitting Management†
0026-7902	Modern Language Journal
0026-7910	M L N
0026-7929	Modern Language Quarterly
0026-7937	Modern Language Review
0026-7945	Modern Languages *see* 0957-1736
0026-7953	Modern Law and Society†
0026-7961	Modern Law Review
0026-8003	Modern Machine Shop
0026-8011	Modern Man†
0026-802X	Modern Manufacturing *changed to* Factory Management.
0026-8038	Modern Materials Handling
0026-8046	Modern Maturity
0026-8054	Modern Media
0026-8070	Modern Medicine
0026-8089	Modern Medicine of Australia *see* 1030-3782
0026-8097	Modern Medicine of Canada†
0026-8100	Modern Medicine of Great Britain†
0026-8119	Modern Medicine of New Zealand†
0026-8127	Modern Metals
0026-8143	Modern Motor
0026-816X	Modern Needlecraft
0026-8178	Modern Nursing Home *see* 0160-7480
0026-8194	Drug News
0026-8208	Modern Office Procedures *see* 0746-3839
0026-8224	Modern Packaging *see* 0746-3820
0026-8232	Modern Philology
0026-8240	Modern Photography†
0026-8259	Modern Plant Operation and Maintenance†
0026-8267	Modern Plastering *changed to* Specialist Building Finishes.
0026-8275	Modern Plastics
0026-8283	Modern Plastics International
0026-8291	Modern Poetry in Translation *see* 0268-1390
0026-8305	Modern Poetry Studies
0026-8313	Modern Power & Engineering†
0026-833X	Modern Purchasing
0026-8348	Modern Railroads *see* 0033-8826
0026-8356	Modern Railways
0026-8364	Refrigeration Air Conditioning and Heat Recovery *see* 0263-5739
0026-8380	Modern Review
0026-8399	Modern Romances
0026-8402	Modern Schoolman
0026-8410	Modern Schools†
0026-8429	Modern Screen†
0026-8437	Modern Society†
0026-8445	Modern Steel Construction
0026-8453	Modern Stores and Offices†
0026-8461	Modern Sunbathing Quarterly†
0026-847X	Modern Design/Modern Text†ll
0026-8488	Modern Textiles Magazine *see* 0279-5027
0026-8496	Modern Tire Dealer
0026-8496	Modern Tire Dealer Products Catalog *changed to* Modern Tire Dealer: Tire, Tools & Equipment Merchandising Guide.
0026-850X	Modern Tramway and Light Railway Review *see* 0144-1655
0026-8518	Modern Trans†
0026-8526	Modern Treatment††
0026-8534	Modern Utopian *see* 0199-9346
0026-8550	Modern Vocational Trends†
0026-8577	Moderna Spraak
0026-8585	Moderna Transporter†
0026-8593	Moderne Frau *see* 0031-630X
0026-8607	Das Moderne Heim
0026-8623	Moderne Jordflytning *see* 0107-1866
0026-8631	Kontorbladet
0026-864X	Die Moderne Kueche
0026-8666	Moderne Sprachen
0026-8674	Moderne Welt†
0026-8704	Modernes Hotel†
0026-8712	Modernes Wohnen
0026-8720	Moderni Rizeni
0026-8739	Modes et Travaux
0026-8747	Modes de Paris†
0026-8755	Modetelegramm†
0026-8763	Modine Gunch *changed to* Madison Review.
0026-8771	Modische Linie (Ausgabe B)
0026-878X	Modische Maschen
0026-8828	Modus Operandi†
0026-8836	Moebel und Raum†
0026-8844	Moebel und Wohnraum
0026-8852	Moellen
0026-8860	Mofussil
0026-8887	Moissons de l'Esprit†
0026-8895	Moj Pas
0026-8917	Wood Industry
0026-8925	Molecular and General Genetics
0026-8933	Molecular Biology (New York)
0026-8941	Molecular Crystals and Liquid Crystals *see* 1058-725X
0026-8941	Molecular Crystals and Liquid Crystals *see* 1058-7268
0026-895X	Molecular Pharmacology
0026-8968	Molecular Photochemistry†
0026-8976	Molecular Physics
0026-8984	Molekulyarnaya Biologiya
0026-8992	Molennieuws - Windmill News *see* 0169-6459
0026-900X	Molineria y Panaderia
0026-9018	Molini d'Italia
0026-9026	Molochnaya Promyshlennost'
0026-9034	Molochnoe i Myasnoe Skotovodstvo
0026-9042	Moloda Ukraina
0026-9077	Molodoi Kommunist *changed to* Perspektivy.
0026-9093	Molula-Qhooa
0026-9107	Molybdaen-Dienst†
0026-9115	Molykote†
0026-9131	Momento
0026-914X	Catholic School Bulletin *changed to* Momentum (Washington).
0026-9166	Mon Jardin et Ma Maison
0026-9174	Mon Journal Confidences *changed to* Confidences Magazine.
0026-9190	Monastic Studies
0026-9204	Monat†
0026-9212	Interkantonale Kontrollstelle fuer Heilmittel. Monatsbericht
0026-9220	Oesterreichische Landwirtschaft. Monatsberichte
0026-9247	Monatshefte fuer Chemie
0026-9255	Monatshefte fuer Mathematik
0026-9263	Monatshefte fuer Veterinaermedizin
0026-9271	Monatshefte fuer Deutschen Unterricht *changed to* Monatshefte.
0026-9298	Monatsschrift Kinderheilkunde
0026-9301	Monatsschrift fuer Kriminologie und Strafrechtsreform
0026-931X	Monatsschrift fuer Lungenkrankheiten und Tuberkulosebekaempfung†
0026-9328	Monatsschrift fuer Ohrenheilkunde und Laryngo-Rhinologie *see* 0935-8943
0026-9336	Monatsschrift fuer Unfallheilkunde, Versicherungs-, Versorgungs- und Verkehrsmedizin *see* 0177-5537
0026-9344	Mondo Lingvo Problemo *see* 0272-2690
0026-9352	Monday Morning†
0026-9360	Le Monde
0026-9379	Monde de l'Electricite
0026-9387	Monde des Philatelistes
0026-9395	Monde Diplomatique
0026-9417	Monde Gitan†
0026-9425	Monde Juif
0026-9433	Monde Libertaire
0026-9441	Travaux Souterrains†
0026-9468	Mond o†
0026-9476	Mondo Afro-Asiatico
0026-9484	Mondo Agricolo
0026-9492	Mondo Aperto†
0026-9506	Mondo Bancario
0026-9522	Mondo Economico
0026-9530	Mondo Finanziario†
0026-9557	Mondo Occidentale *changed to* Americana.
0026-9565	Mondo Odontostomatologico†
0026-959X	Moneda y Credito
0026-9611	Moneta e Credito
0026-9638	Jamaica. Department of Statistics. Monetary Statistics *changed to* Statistical Institute of Jamaica. Monetary Statistics Report.
0026-9646	Moneysworth
0026-9654	Mongolian Society Bulletin *changed to* Mongolian Studies.
0026-9662	Monist
0026-9670	Moniteur Africain du Commerce et de l'Industrie *changed to* Moniteur Africain.
0026-9689	Moniteur des Pharmacies et des Laboratoires
0026-9700	Moniteur des Travaux Publics et du Batiment
0026-9719	M O C I
0026-9727	Moniteur du Regne de la Justice
0026-9735	Moniteur Professionel de l'Electricite
0026-9743	Monitor *changed to* San Francisco Catholic.
0026-9751	Monitor *see* 0198-7208
0026-976X	Monitor Ecclesiasticus
0026-9786	Monitore Zoologico Italiano - Italian Journal of Zoology *see* 0394-9370
0026-9794	Monkey
0026-9808	Monmouth Educator
0026-9832	Monographien zur Geschichte des Mittelalters
0026-9840	Monroe News Leader *changed to* Monroe Dispatch.
0026-9859	Monsanto Magazine†
0026-9875	Montan-Berichte *see* 0005-8912
0026-9883	Montan-Rundschau *see* 0005-8912
0026-9891	Montana
0026-9905	Montana Agriculture *changed to* Montana Farm Bureau Spokesman.
0026-9913	Montana Beverage News
0026-9921	Montana Business Quarterly
0026-993X	Montana Education *changed to* M E A Today.
0026-9964	Montana Law Forum†
0026-9972	Montana Law Review
0026-9980	Montana League of Cities & Towns. Newsletter
0026-9999	Montana Legionnaire
0027-0016	Montana Outdoors†
0027-0024	Montana Wool Grower
0027-0032	Montaneros de Aragon
0027-0040	Montazhnye i Spetsial'nye Raboty v Stroitel'stve
0027-0059	Montclair Art Museum. Bulletin *changed to* Montclair Art Museum. Bulletin - Newsletter.
0027-0067	Montclair Public Schools†
0027-0075	Montclair Schools†
0027-0105	Montes
0027-0113	Museo Nacional de Historia Natural. Comunicaciones Zoologicas

5414 ISSN INDEX

ISSN	Title
0027-0121	Museo Nacional de Historia Natural. Comunicaciones Botanicas
0027-013X	Universidad de la Republica. Facultad de Ingenieria y Agrimensura. Boletin see 0366-0109
0027-0148	Montfort
0027-0156	Montgomery - Bucks Dental Society. Bulletin
0027-0172	Month
0027-0180	New Zealand. Depar nent of Statistics. Monthly Abstract of Statistics see 0114-2119
0027-0199	Monthly Bank Clearings†
0027-0202	Monthly Bibliography of Medical Reviews†
0027-0210	Monthly Bulletin of African Materials†
0027-0229	F A O Monthly Bulletin of Agricultural Economics and Statistics see 1011-8780
0027-0237	Egypt. Central Agency for Public Mobilisation and Statistics. Monthly Bulletin of Foreign Trade
0027-0245	Iraq. Central Statistical Organization. Monthly Bulletin of Foreign Trade Statistics changed to Iraq. Central Statistical Organization. Quarterly Bulletin of Foreign Trade Statistics.
0027-0253	Monthly Bulletin of Ionospheric Characteristics Recorded at Johannesburg and Capetown changed to Monthly Bulletin of Ionospheric Characteristics Recorded at Johannesburg and Hermanus.
0027-0261	Indian Bureau of Mines. Bulletin of Mineral Information
0027-027X	Monthly Business Failures
0027-0288	U.S. Library of Congress. Monthly Checklist of State Publications
0027-0296	Monthly Climatic Data for the World
0027-030X	Monthly Commentary on Indian Economic Conditions
0027-0318	Monthly Cotton Linters Review
0027-0326	Monthly Cotton Report
0027-0334	Pakistan Central Cotton Committee. Monthly Cotton Review
0027-0342	Ontario. Ministry of Agriculture and Food. Monthly Crop and Livestock Report
0027-0377	Zambia. Central Statistical Office. Monthly Digest of Statistics
0027-0385	Monthly Digest of Tax Articles
0027-0407	Monthly Film Bulletin see 0037-4806
0027-0423	Monthly Guardian
0027-0431	M I M S see 0580-6755
0027-044X	U.S. Bureau of Labor Statistics. Monthly Review see 0098-1818
0027-0458	Monthly Listings of Neuro-Psychiatric Literature†
0027-0466	Monthly Mailer see 0161-8040
0027-0490	Monthly Radiation Values for Bergen, Norway†
0027-0504	Monthly Railway Statistics
0027-0512	International Canada see 0381-4874
0027-0520	Monthly Review
0027-0539	Australia. Bureau of Statistics. Monthly Review of Business Statistics see 0727-1689
0027-0547	Monthly Statistics of Foreign Trade of India
0027-0563	Monthly Statistics of Korea
0027-058X	Monthly Summary of Business Conditions in Southern California
0027-0598	Monthly Summary of Jute and Gunny Statistics
0027-0601	Pakistan Jute Association. Monthly Summary of Jute Goods Statistics changed to Quarterly Summary of Jute Goods Statistics.
0027-061X	Monthly Technical Review†
0027-0628	Jamaica. Department of Statistics. Monthly Trade Bulletin changed to Statistical Institute of Jamaica. External Trade Monthly Bulletin.
0027-0636	Great Britain. Meteorological Office. Monthly Weather Report
0027-0644	Monthly Weather Review
0027-0660	Monti e Boschi changed to Monti e Boschi.
0027-0695	Ecole Publique changed to Trans-Parent.
0027-0709	Montreal General Hospital News changed to Generally Speaking.
0027-0717	Quebec Medical
0027-0725	Montreal. Museum of Fine Arts. Quarterly Review†
0027-0733	Monument in Cantos and Essays†
0027-0741	Monumenta Nipponica
0027-075X	Monumental News-Review see 0160-7243
0027-0776	Monumentum†
0027-0822	Moody's Bond Survey
0027-0830	Moody's Handbook of Common Stocks
0027-0849	Moody's Industrials changed to Moody's Industrial News Reports.
0027-0857	Moody's Municipals and Governments changed to Moody's Municipal and Government News Reports.
0027-0865	Moody's O T C Industrials changed to Moody's O T C Industrial News Reports.
0027-0881	Moody's Stock Survey†
0027-089X	Moody's Transportation changed to Moody's Transportation News Reports.
0027-0903	Moon see 0167-9295
0027-0911	Moon Magazine
0027-0954	Moose
0027-0962	Moottoriviesti see 0041-4468
0027-0970	Moottori see 0359-7636
0027-0989	Mopac News†
0027-1004	Morality in Media Newsletter
0027-1012	North American Moravian see 1041-0961
0027-1020	Moravian Music Foundation. News Bulletin see 0278-0763
0027-1047	Morehouse College Bulletin
0027-1055	Moreland News and Views
0027-1071	Morgagni
0027-1098	The Morgan Horse
0027-1101	Morgonbris
0027-111X	Mormon Americana changed to New Mormon Americana Bibliography.
0027-1136	Mornaricki Glasnik
0027-1144	Morning Rays†
0027-1160	Morocco Tourism
0027-1179	Morokami
0027-1187	Morris Arboretum Bulletin†
0027-1195	Morsingboen
0027-1209	Morsko Ribarstvo
0027-1217	Morskoi Flot
0027-1241	Mortgage Banker see 0730-0212
0027-125X	Morton Arboretum Quarterly
0027-1268	Mortuary Management
0027-1276	Mosaic (Winnipeg, 1967)
0027-1284	Mosaic (Washington)†
0027-1306	Moscow News
0027-1314	Moscow University Chemistry Bulletin
0027-1322	Moscow University Mathematics Bulletin
0027-1330	Moscow University Mechanics Bulletin
0027-1349	Moscow University Physics Bulletin
0027-1357	Moskovskii Universitet. Vestnik. Seriya 12: Pravo
0027-1365	Moskovskii Universitet. Vestnik. Seriya Ekonomika, Filosofiya see 0130-0105
0027-1365	Moskovskii Universitet. Vestnik. Seriya Ekonomika, Filosofiya changed to Moskovskii Universitet. Vestnik. Seriya 8: Filosofiya.
0027-1381	Moskovskii Universitet. Vestnik. Seriya 5: Geografiya
0027-139X	Moskovskii Universitet. Vestnik. Seriya Istoricheskie Nauki see 0130-0083
0027-1403	Moskovskoe Obshchestvo Ispytatelei Prirody. Biologicheskii Otdel. Byulleten
0027-142X	Mosquito News see 8756-971X
0027-1446	Mosul University. College of Medicine. Annals
0027-1454	Mosupa - Tsela
0027-1462	Mot Auto-Kritik changed to Mot.
0027-1470	Mot - Bau
0027-1500	Mother
0027-1527	Mother Cabrini Messenger
0027-1535	Mother Earth News
0027-1543	Mother India
0027-1551	Mothers' Manual changed to Mothers Today.
0027-156X	Mothers-to-Be - American Baby see 0044-7544
0027-1594	Motion Picture Daily†
0027-1616	Motion Picture Herald see 0146-5023
0027-1624	Motion Picture Magazine†
0027-1632	Motion Pictures Technical Bulletin
0027-1667	Motive†
0027-1675	Moto†
0027-1683	Moto Revija†
0027-1691	Motociclismo
0027-1713	Motor
0027-1721	Motor
0027-173X	Motor
0027-1748	Motor
0027-1756	Motor
0027-1764	Motor
0027-1772	Motor Age see 0193-7022
0027-1780	Motor Boat & Yachting
0027-1799	Motor Boating & Sailing
0027-1829	Motor Caravan and Camping changed to Motorcaravan & Motorhome Monthly.
0027-1837	Motor Cycle†
0027-1853	Motor Cycle News
0027-1888	Motor - Dienst und Erdoel - Nachrichten changed to Motor und Erdoel.
0027-190X	Motor in Canada†
0027-1926	Motor Italia
0027-1934	Motor News changed to Michigan Living.
0027-1942	Motor News Analysis changed to Auto Retail Report.
0027-1977	Motor Service
0027-1993	Motor - Service og Autoteknisk Tidsskrift changed to Auto Bladet.
0027-2000	Motor Ship
0027-2019	Motor Sport
0027-2027	Motor Trade Executive changed to Motor Retailer.
0027-2035	Motor Trade Journal
0027-2043	Motor Trader
0027-2051	Motor Trader and Fleet Operator
0027-206X	Motor Transport
0027-2078	Motor Transportation Hi-Lights changed to S C T A Hi-Lights.
0027-2086	Motor Travel see 0890-7471
0027-2094	Motor Trend
0027-2108	Motor Truck
0027-2116	Motor Truck News changed to Iowa Trucking Lifeliner.
0027-2124	Motor West†
0027-2140	Motorbranschen
0027-2159	Motorbranschens Registeringsstatistik see 0027-2140
0027-2167	Enthusiast
0027-2175	Revs Motorcycle News (Revs)
0027-2205	Motorcyclist
0027-2213	Motorfoereren
0027-2221	Motorhome Life see 0744-074X
0027-223X	Motorindia
0027-2248	Motoring
0027-2256	Motoring Life†
0027-2264	Motoring News
0027-2299	Motorist
0027-2302	Motorists Guide to New & Used Car Prices
0027-2310	Motorland
0027-2337	Motorliv
0027-2345	Motorman
0027-2361	Motorpraxist
0027-237X	Das Motorrad
0027-2388	Motortidningen Kart†
0027-2396	Motrix
0027-2485	Mount Allison Record
0027-2493	Mount Holyoke Alumnae Quarterly
0027-2507	Mount Sinai Journal of Medicine
0027-2523	Mount Washington Observatory News Bulletin
0027-254X	Mountain Geologist
0027-2558	Mountain Life and Work†
0027-2566	Mountain†
0027-2574	Mountain Path
0027-2582	Mountain-Plains Library Quarterly see 0145-6180
0027-2590	Mountain States Banker see 0005-5123
0027-2612	Mountain Visitor
0027-2620	Mountaineer (Seattle)
0027-2639	Mousaion
0027-2647	Tele-Moustique
0027-2655	Mouthpiece
0027-2671	Mouvement Social
0027-268X	Movie
0027-2698	Movie Life†
0027-2701	Movie Maker changed to Video Maker.
0027-271X	Movie Mirror
0027-2736	Movie News
0027-2744	Movie Stars†
0027-2779	Movie World†
0027-2787	Movieland and TV Time see 0731-9991
0027-2809	Movimento di Liberazione in Italia see 0392-3568
0027-2817	Movimento Operaio e Socialista
0027-2833	Movoznavstvo
0027-2841	Le Moyen Age
0027-2868	Mozaiek Katholiek Verbond voor Kinderbescherming. Maandblad†
0027-2892	Moznayim
0027-2906	M.S. for Medical Secretaries†
0027-2914	Muanyag es Gumi
0027-2930	El Mueble Actual
0027-2949	Die Muehle und Mischfuttertechnik
0027-2957	Muell und Abfall
0027-2965	Mueller Clipper
0027-299X	Das Muenster
0027-3007	Muenzen und Medaillen
0027-3015	Muszaki Egyetemi Konyvtaros
0027-3023	Muszaki Lapszemle. Anyagmozatas, Csomagolas - Technical Abstracts, Materials Handling, Packaging see 0230-5348
0027-3031	Muhammad Speaks changed to A M Journal.
0027-304X	Muhendis ve Makina
0027-3066	Mujer de America
0027-3104	Mukta
0027-3120	Mulino
0027-3139	Mullard Technical Communications changed to Electronic Components and Applications.
0027-3147	Multi†
0027-3155	Multihull International
0027-3171	Multivariate Behavioral Research
0027-318X	Munca Sanitaria changed to Viata Medicala - Cadre Medii.
0027-3198	Zahnaerztlicher Anzeiger
0027-321X	Office International de Bibliographie. Communications Mundaneum
0027-3228	Mundartfreunde Oesterreichs. Mitteilungen
0027-3244	Mundo Cristao†
0027-3252	Mundo Cristiano
0027-3295	Mundo Eletrico
0027-3309	Mundo Hispanico†
0027-3317	Mundo Hospitalario†
0027-3325	Mundo Madereru
0027-3333	Mundo Nuevo
0027-335X	Mundo Social†
0027-3384	Mundus
0027-3392	Mundus
0027-3406	Mundus Artium†
0027-3414	Munibe
0027-3422	Municipal Administration and Engineering changed to Local Government in Southern Africa.
0027-3430	Municipal and Public Services Journal see 0143-4187
0027-3449	Municipal Attorney
0027-3457	Municipal Engineering see 0143-4187

ISSN INDEX 5415

ISSN	Title
0027-3465	Municipal Engineers Journal
0027-3473	Municipal Finance *changed to* Government Finance Review.
0027-3481	Municipal Finance News Letter *see* 1051-6964
0027-349X	Municipal Journal *see* 0143-4187
0027-3503	Municipal Law Court Decisions *see* 0027-3449
0027-352X	Municipal League of Seattle and King County. Municipal News *changed to* Municipal League of King County. Issue Watch.
0027-3538	Municipal Ordinance Review *see* 0027-3449
0027-3546	Municipal Recreation Pools, Rink & Parks *changed to* Pool Industry Canada.
0027-3554	New York Municipal Reference & Research Center Notes†
0027-3562	Municipal Review *see* 0261-5118
0027-3570	Municipal South†
0027-3589	Municipal World
0027-3597	Municipality
0027-3600	Munka†
0027-3619	Munkavedelem
0027-3627	Munson-Williams-Proctor Institute. Bulletin
0027-3635	Muotisorja *see* 0355-192X
0027-3643	Muoviviesti *see* 0355-7839
0027-366X	Murimi†
0027-3678	Murmesteren
0027-3686	Murray Hill News
0027-3716	Murrelet *see* 1051-1733
0027-3724	Musart *see* 0363-6569
0027-3740	Muscular Dystrophy Journal *changed to* Search (London, 1957).
0027-3759	Muscular Dystrophy News *see* 8750-2321
0027-3767	Musee Carnavalet. Bulletin†
0027-3775	Musee du Soir†
0027-3783	Musee Ingres. Bulletin
0027-3791	Musee National de Varsovie. Bulletin
0027-3813	Museen in Koeln. Bulletin *see* 0933-257X
0027-3821	Musees de Geneve
0027-383X	Musees et Collections Publiques de France
0027-3856	Musees Royaux des Beaux-Arts de Belgique. Bulletin
0027-3872	Musei e Gallerie d'Italia
0027-3880	Museo Argentino de Ciencias Naturales "Bernardino Rivadavia." Instituto Nacional de Investigacion de las Ciencias Naturales. Revista. Geologia
0027-3899	Museo de Ciencias Naturales. Boletin
0027-3902	Museo de Historia Natural de San Rafael. Revista Cientifica de Investigaciones *see* 0375-1155
0027-3910	Museo Nacional de Historia Natural. Boletin
0027-3945	Museo Nacional de Historia Natural. Noticiario Mensual
0027-3953	Museo Nazionale del Cinema. Notiziario†
0027-3961	Museo Trentino del Risorgimento e della Lotta per la Liberta. Bollettino *changed to* Archivio Trentino di Storia Contemporanea. Museo del Risorgimento e della Lotta per la Liberta. Bollettino.
0027-397X	Museologist†
0027-3988	Museu Bocage. Arquivos
0027-3996	Museum
0027-4003	Museum
0027-402X	Museum Alliance Quarterly *see* 0040-3733
0027-4038	Museum Boymans-van Beuningen. Bulletin†
0027-4046	Museum Graphic†
0027-4054	Museum Helveticum
0027-4062	New Brunswick Museum. Memo *see* 0703-0606
0027-4089	Museum News
0027-4100	Museum of Comparative Zoology. Bulletin
0027-4127	Museum of Modern Art. Members Newsletter†
0027-4135	Museum of the Fur Trade Quarterly
0027-4143	Museumjournaal *see* 0924-5251
0027-416X	Museums Journal
0027-4178	Museumskunde
0027-4186	Museumsnytt
0027-4194	Courrier Roumain
0027-4208	Music *see* 0164-3150
0027-4216	Music & Artists†
0027-4224	Music and Letters
0027-4232	Music and Musicians *see* 0952-2697
0027-4240	Music Article Guide
0027-4259	Music at Georgia†
0027-4283	Music Cataloging Bulletin
0027-4291	Music City News
0027-4313	Music Director *see* 0046-4155
0027-4321	Music Educators Journal
0027-433X	Music in Education†
0027-4348	Music Index
0027-4356	Music Industry
0027-4364	Music Journal†
0027-4372	The Music Leader
0027-4380	Music Library Association. Notes
0027-4399	Music Maker†
0027-4402	Music Ministry†
0027-4410	Music News from Prague
0027-4437	Music Now
0027-4445	Music Review
0027-4461	Music Teacher
0027-447X	Music Tempo†
0027-4488	Music Trades
0027-4496	Music World†
0027-450X	Musica
0027-4518	Musica
0027-4526	Musica e Dischi
0027-4534	Musica Iberoamericana *changed to* Latina.
0027-4542	Musica Jazz
0027-4550	Musica Universitat
0027-4569	Musicae Sacrae Ministerium
0027-4577	Musical Box Society. Bulletin *changed to* Mechanical Music.
0027-4585	Musical Denmark
0027-4615	Musical Merchandise Review
0027-4623	Musical Opinion
0027-4631	Musical Quarterly
0027-464X	Musical Salvationist
0027-4658	Musical Show
0027-4666	Musical Times
0027-4674	Musicalbrande
0027-4682	Musicasia†
0027-4690	Impulse
0027-4704	Musik in der Schule
0027-4712	Musik-Informationen *changed to* Musik - Info.
0027-4720	Musik och Ljudteknik
0027-4739	Musik og Handelt
0027-4747	Musik und Bildung
0027-4755	Musik und Gesellschaft
0027-4763	Musik & Gottesdienst
0027-4771	Musik und Kirche
0027-478X	Musikern
0027-4798	Musikerziehung
0027-4801	Die Musikforschung
0027-481X	Musikhandel
0027-4828	Das Musikinstrument
0027-4836	Musiklivet - Vaar Saang
0027-4844	Musikrevy
0027-4860	Muslim Africa
0027-4887	Muslim Digest
0027-4895	Muslim Review
0027-4909	Muslim World
0027-4917	Mustang Review†
0027-4925	Muster *changed to* N.S.W. Farmers News.
0027-4933	Muszaki-Gazdasagi Tajekoztato *changed to* Muszaki-Gazdasagi Magazin.
0027-4941	Muszaki Lapszemle. Uzemszervezes, Ipargazdasag - Technical Abstracts. Business Organization, Industrial Economics *see* 0231-0759
0027-495X	Muszaki Lapszemle. Banyaszat - Technical Abstracts. Mining *see* 0231-0651
0027-4968	Muszaki Lapszemle. Elektrotechnika, Hiradastechnika *see* 0231-0783
0027-4976	Muszaki Lapszemle. Elelmiszeripart
0027-4984	Muszaki Lapszemle. Energia - Technical Abstracts. Energy *see* 0231-0678
0027-4992	Muszaki Lapszemle. Faipar, Papir-es Nyomdaipar - Technical Abstracts. Wood and Paper Industry, Printing *see* 0231-0740
0027-500X	Muszaki Lapszemle. Fizika, Meres- es Muszertechnika, Automatika - Technical Abstracts. Physics, Measurement and Instrument Technology, Automation *see* 0231-0643
0027-5018	Muszaki Lapszemle. Gepeszet *see* 0231-0694
0027-5018	Muszaki Lapszemle. Gepeszet *see* 0231-0686
0027-5026	Muszaki Lapszemle. Kemia Vegyipar - Technical Abstracts. Chemistry, Chemical Industry *see* 0231-0775
0027-5034	Muszaki Lapszemle. Kohaszat, Onteszet - Technical Abstracts. Metallurgy, Foundry *see* 0231-0708
0027-5042	Muszaki Lapszemle. Kozlekedes - Technical Abstracts. Transportation *see* 0231-1941
0027-5042	Muszaki Lapszemle. Kozlekedes - Technical Abstracts. Transportation *see* 0231-0724
0027-5042	Muszaki Lapszemle. Kozlekedes - Technical Abstracts. Transportation *see* 0231-3928
0027-5042	Muszaki Lapszemle. Kozlekedes - Technical Abstracts. Transportation *see* 0231-0767
0027-5050	Muszaki Lapszemle. Melyepites, Vizepites - Technical Abstracts. Civil and Hydraulic Engineering *see* 0231-0732
0027-5069	Muszaki Lapszemle. Textilipar, Eob- es Eorfeldolgozoipar - Technical Abstracts. Textile Industry, Leather and Leatherprocessing Industry *see* 0209-9578
0027-5085	Muszaki Tudomany†
0027-5093	Mut
0027-5115	Mutech Chemical Engineering Journal†
0027-5123	Mutisia
0027-5131	Mutter
0027-514X	Muttersprache
0027-5158	Mutual Benefit Estate and Tax Letter†
0027-5182	Mutual Funds Guide
0027-5204	Mutual Review *see* 0148-8899
0027-5220	Mutualita' Democratica
0027-5239	Mutualite
0027-5247	Muveszettorteneti Ertesito
0027-5255	Muzejni a Vlastivedna Prace
0027-5263	Muzeum
0027-5271	Muzicka Omladina
0027-528X	Muziek Expres
0027-5298	Muziek Mercuur
0027-5301	Muziekhandel
0027-531X	Muzika
0027-5328	Muzilot
0027-5336	Muzsika
0027-5344	Muzyka
0027-5352	Muzykal'naya Zhizn'
0027-5360	Muzzle Blasts
0027-5379	My Baby†
0027-5387	My Devotions
0027-5409	My Home and Family
0027-5417	My i Svit†
0027-5425	My Career
0027-5433	My Magazine of India
0027-545X	My Story
0027-5468	My Volk†
0027-5484	My Weekly Reader (Summer Editions) *see* 0899-6121
0027-5484	My Weekly Reader (Summer Editions) *changed to* Weekly Reader. Summer Edition B. Grades 2-6.
0027-5492	Myasnaya Industriya S.S.S.R
0027-5506	Myastenia Gravis Foundation. Newsletter
0027-5514	Mycologia
0027-5522	Mycological Papers
0027-5530	Mycopathologia et Mycologia - Applicata *see* 0301-486X
0027-5549	Mycophile
0027-5557	Mycoses
0027-5565	Mylpaalt
0027-5573	Mysindia†
0027-5581	Mysl Polska
0027-559X	Mysore Commerce
0027-5611	Mysore Industrial Diary†
0027-562X	Mysore Labour Journal *changed to* Karnataka Labour Journal.
0027-5638	Mysterium
0027-5662	N A A F I News
0027-5670	A D A S Quarterly Review†
0027-5689	N A B A Review
0027-5697	N A B E T News
0027-5700	N A B P Quarterly *changed to* N A B P Newsletter.
0027-5719	N A C†
0027-5727	N A C C Attack *see* 0571-8597
0027-5735	N A C D L Journal *changed to* Trends & Techniques in the Contemporary Dental Laboratory.
0027-5743	N A C O News and Views *see* 0744-9798
0027-5751	N A C U F S Technical Bulletin *changed to* N A C U F S Journal.
0027-576X	N A C W P I Journal
0027-5778	Cars and Trucks *see* 0195-1564
0027-5786	N A D A Auto Auction True Values Guide *changed to* N A D A Official Wholesale Used Car Trade-In Guide.
0027-5824	N A F S A Newsletter
0027-5832	N A H B Journal *see* 0744-1193
0027-5840	N A H B Washington Scope *see* 0744-1193
0027-5859	N A I I News Memo†
0027-5867	N A I I Press Samplings†
0027-5875	N.A.I.L.M. News
0027-5883	N A I S Report†
0027-5891	Two Wheeler Dealer†
0027-5905	N A L L D Journal *see* 0891-2521
0027-5913	N A M M Music Retailer News
0027-5921	N A M Reports *see* 0191-5215
0027-593X	N A N T I S News†
0027-5948	N A O T Notes *changed to* Keyboard Teacher.
0027-5956	Air Pollution Abstracts†
0027-5964	N A P I A Bulletin
0027-5972	N A R D Journal
0027-5980	N A R G U S Bulletin†
0027-5999	N A S C A R Newsletter *changed to* N A S C A R News.
0027-6006	N A S C Quarterly
0027-6014	N A S P A Journal
0027-6022	N A S W News†
0027-6030	N A T E S A Scope *changed to* Professional Electronics.
0027-6049	N A T News
0027-6057	N A T O Letter *see* 0255-3813
0027-6073	N A T S Bulletin *see* 0884-8106
0027-609X	N A V A News *changed to* Communications Industries Report.
0027-6103	N A W G A Management and Controller's Bulletin†
0027-6111	N & M†
0027-612X	N B C News *see* 0848-600X
0027-6138	N B O Abstracts
0027-6146	N.B.O.B. Orgaan *changed to* Unie van Beveiligings- en Bewakingspersoneel. Orgaan.
0027-6162	N B R I Information Sheet
0027-6170	N C A A News
0027-6189	N C A E News Bulletin
0027-6219	N C A Today†
0027-6227	N C A W E News
0027-6235	N C C D News†
0027-6243	N C C-Interface (National Computing Centre) *see* 0957-4611
0027-6251	N C C P A Newsletter *changed to* C M A Newsletter.
0027-6278	N C D C Bulletin
0027-6308	N C E Today *see* 0194-3359
0027-6316	N C I Newsletter†

ISSN INDEX

0027-6332 N C M A Newsletter *changed to* Contract Management.
0027-6340 N C S A W Report *changed to* International Society for Animal Rights Report.
0027-6367 N C W News
0027-6383 Prosecutor
0027-6405 N E A Reporter *see* 0734-7219
0027-6413 N E A Research Bulletin†
0027-6421 N E C News
0027-643X N E D A Journal - Electronic Merchandising†
0027-6448 N E L A Newsletter
0027-6456 N E P P C O News†
0027-6464 N E R B A *changed to* C I M Construction Journal.
0027-6480 N E S D E C News *changed to* N E S D E C Exchange.
0027-6499 N F A Reports†
0027-6502 N F I Bulletin *changed to* Hardware Today.
0027-6510 N F Legal Legislative Reporter News Bulletin (National Foundation of Health, Welfare and Pension Plans) *see* 0458-9599
0027-6529 N G Z *see* 0930-2255
0027-6537 Conservation Commission News
0027-6545 N H D S Newsletter
0027-6553 N H K Gijutsu Kenkyu†
0027-6561 N H K Giken Geppo†
0027-657X N H K Laboratories Note†
0027-6596 N H S C News
0027-660X Granite State School Leader *changed to* Granite State School Leader.
0027-6618 N I A *see* 0165-1439
0027-6634 N I E Journal *changed to* Journal of Indian Education.
0027-6642 N I F Weekly
0027-6669 N I M Abstracts†
0027-6685 N I N
0027-6731 N I T Newsletter *see* 1060-5649
0027-6758 N J E A Review
0027-6766 N K B
0027-6774 N K B Research Monthly *see* 0385-2350
0027-6782 N L G I Spokesman
0027-6790 N L L Review *see* 0264-1615
0027-6804 N L N News *see* 0276-5284
0027-6839 N M L Technical Journal
0027-6855 N M U Pilot†
0027-6871 N O M D A Spokesman
0027-6898 N P L Technical Bulletin
0027-6901 N P N Bulletin†
0027-691X N R A Newsletter *changed to* Renditions.
0027-6928 N R C D Bulletin *see* 0266-6960
0027-6944 N H F A Reports *changed to* Furniture Retailer (Greensboro).
0027-6952 N R I Journal†
0027-6979 N R T A Journal†
0027-6987 N R T A Bulletin
0027-7010 N S S News
0027-7029 New South Wales Contract Reporter†
0027-7037 N T A Journal *changed to* Prism.
0027-7045 N T D R A Dealer News
0027-7053 N T L Institute News and Reports†
0027-707X N T Z
0027-7088 N U B E News *changed to* B I F U Report.
0027-7096 N U E A Spectator *changed to* Continuing Higher Education Review.
0027-710X Centrale Suiker Maatschappij. Voorlichtingsblad *see* 0165-9375
0027-7126 Nya Argus
0027-7134 N Y L A Bulletin
0027-7142 N Y L I C Review
0027-7150 N Y P M A Bulletin
0027-7169 N Y S S A Bulletin *see* 0095-2273
0027-7177 New Zealand Baptist
0027-7185 Electrical Industry
0027-7193 N.Z.H. Maandblad†
0027-7207 New Zealand Institute of Architects Journal *see* 0113-4566
0027-7215 N Z L A Newsletter *see* 0110-4373
0027-7223 N.Z. Licensee
0027-724X New Zealand Shipping Gazette
0027-7266 N Z T C A Journal†
0027-7274 N.Z. Truth
0027-7282 New Zealand Valuer *see* 0113-0315
0027-7304 Na Pua Okika o Hawaii Nei - Orchids of Hawaii *see* 0099-8745
0027-7312 Na Stroikakh Rossii
0027-7320 Na Vijvent
0027-7339 Naaimachine - Nieuws
0027-7347 Naamloos Nieuws *changed to* Milacroniek.
0027-7355 Naar Morgen
0027-7363 Nach der Arbeit
0027-7371 Nachal'naya Shkola
0027-738X Nachrichten aus Chemie und Technik *see* 0341-5163
0027-7398 Nachrichten aus der Aerztlichen Mission
0027-7401 Oesterreichisches Chemiefaser-Institut. Nachrichten†
0027-7428 Nachrichten fuer Die Zivile Luftfahrt, Deutsche Demokratische Republik†
0027-7444 Nachrichten fuer Seefahrer
0027-7460 Deutsche Gesellschaft fuer Geschichte der Medizin, Naturwissenschaft und Technik. Nachrichtenblatt
0027-7479 Nachrichtenblatt des Deutschen Pflanzenschutzdienstes

0027-7487 Nachrichtenblatt fuer die Buersten- und Pinselindustrie *changed to* Brossapress-Nachrichtenblatt fuer die Buersten- und Pinselindustrie.
0027-7495 Nachrichtentechnik *see* 0323-4657
0027-7509 Nacion
0027-7525 Nadel Faden Fingerhut†
0027-7533 Naeringsrevyen
0027-7541 Nafta
0027-755X Nafta
0027-7568 Nagaoka Technical College. Research Reports *changed to* Nagaoka College of Technology. Research Reports.
0027-7576 Nagarjun
0027-7584 Nagarlok
0027-7592 Nagoya Port Statistics Monthly
0027-7606 Nagoya-shiritsu Daigaku Igakkai Zasshi
0027-7614 Japan. Government Industrial Research Institute, Nagoya. Technical News
0027-7622 Nagoya Journal of Medical Science
0027-7630 Nagoya Mathematical Journal
0027-7649 Nagoya Medical Journal
0027-7657 Nagoya University. Faculty of Engineering. Memoirs
0027-7681 Naho†
0027-769X Die Naehrung
0027-7703 Nahrungsmittel
0027-7711 Nailaer Zeitung†
0027-772X Namari to Aen
0027-7738 Names
0027-7746 Namib Times
0027-7754 Namibia
0027-7762 Namrugram†
0027-7770 Nanak Prakash Patrika
0027-7800 Napa-Solano Dental Society. District Six. Newsletter *changed to* Oracle.
0027-7827 Napoleon
0027-7835 Napoli Nobilissima
0027-7843 Napred
0027-7851 Narciso
0027-7886 Narod†
0027-7894 Narod Polski
0027-7908 Narodna Armija
0027-7916 Narodna Odbrana
0027-7932 Narodne Novine
0027-7940 Narodne Noviny
0027-7959 Narodni Borac
0027-7975 Narodni List
0027-7983 Narodni Sumar
0027-8017 Narodno Stvaralastvo - Folklor
0027-8025 Narodno Zdravlje†
0027-8033 Narodnoe Obrazovanie
0027-8041 Narody Azii i Afriki *see* 0130-6995
0027-805X Narragansett Naturalist†
0027-8068 Nas Chov
0027-8076 Revija (Belgrade)
0027-8084 Nas Jezik
0027-8092 Nas Put - Our Way *see* 0702-3855
0027-8106 Nas Svijet
0027-8114 Nas Vesnik†
0027-8122 Nasa Rec
0027-8130 Nasa Rijec
0027-8149 Nasa Stampa
0027-8157 Nasa Strucna Skola
0027-8165 Nasa Zakonitost
0027-819X Nase Planine *see* 0354-0650
0027-8203 Nase Rec
0027-8211 Nase Vojsko†
0027-8246 Nash Swit
0027-8254 Nashe Slovo
0027-8262 Nasi Dani
0027-8270 Nasi Zbori
0027-8319 Nasza Droga†
0027-8327 Nasza Ojczyzna *see* 0137-2955
0027-8335 Natal University News†
0027-8343 Natal Wildlife
0027-8351 Nataller *changed to* Tempo.
0027-836X Nation *see* 0156-8221
0027-8378 Nation
0027-8408 Nation Europa
0027-8416 National Association of College Admissions Counselors. Newsletter *changed to* N A C A C Bulletin.
0027-8424 National Academy of Sciences. Proceedings *changed to* National Academy of Sciences of the United States of America. Proceedings.
0027-8432 National Academy of Sciences. National Academy of Engineering. National Research Council. Institute of Medicine. News Report *changed to* National Research Council. Newsreport.
0027-8459 National Adoptalk *see* 0273-6497
0027-8491 N A C News *changed to* R A S E News.
0027-8505 National Agricultural Library Catalog†
0027-8513 National Alliance (Washington)
0027-8521 National Amateur
0027-853X National AMVET
0027-8548 National and Grindlays Review *changed to* Grindlays Bank Review.
0027-8556 National Antiques Review†
0027-8572 Kukhoe Tosogwanbo
0027-8580 Kukhoebo
0027-8602 National Association of Colleges and Teachers of Agriculture. Journal *see* 0149-4910
0027-8610 National Association of Educational Broadcasters Newsletter *changed to* Current (Washington, 1982).
0027-8629 National Association of Private Psychiatric Hospitals. Journal *changed to* Psychiatric Hospital.

0027-8637 National Association of Private Psychiatric Hospitals. News Letter *changed to* National Association of Private Psychiatric Hospitals. Newsline.
0027-8645 National Association of Regulatory Utility Commissioners. Bulletin
0027-8653 National Association of Secondary School Principals. Bulletin *see* 0192-6365
0027-8661 National Association of Soil and Water Conservation Districts. Tuesday Letter *see* 0047-8733
0027-867X National Association of Summer Sessions. Newsletter *changed to* North American Association of Summer Sessions. Newsletter.
0027-8688 National Association of Watch and Clock Collectors. Bulletin
0027-870X National Association of Women Deans and Counselors. Journal *changed to* Initiatives.
0027-8718 National Athletic Trainers Association. Journal *changed to* Journal of Athletic Training.
0027-8726 National Auricula & Primula Society (Northern) Year Book
0027-8750 National Bank of Ethiopia. Quarterly Bulletin
0027-8769 National Beauty School Journal *see* 1052-4169
0027-8777 National Bibliography of Botswana
0027-8793 National Bowlers Journal and Billiard Revue *see* 0164-9183
0027-8815 National Buildings Organisation. Journal
0027-8823 U.S. National Bureau of Standards. Technical News Buletin *see* 0093-0458
0027-8831 National Business Woman
0027-884X National Button Bulletin
0027-8858 National Cactus and Succulent Journal *see* 0264-3405
0027-8866 Cancer Care and the National Cancer Foundation. Report About the Services Your Contributions Support†
0027-8874 National Cancer Institute. Journal
0027-8882 National Candy Wholesaler *see* 0162-5136
0027-8890 National Capital Pharmacist
0027-8912 National Catholic Guidance Conference Journal *see* 0160-7960
0027-8920 National Catholic Register
0027-8939 National Catholic Reporter
0027-8955 National Chamber of Trade Journal *changed to* Distributor.
0027-8963 National Chinchilla Breeders of Canada. Bulletin
0027-9013 National Civic Review
0027-9021 National Coffee Association News Letter *changed to* National Coffee Association of U.S.A. Newsletter.
0027-9048 American Bankruptcy Law Journal
0027-9064 National Contract Management Journal *changed to* National Contract Management Journal (1980).
0027-9072 National Council for Homemaker Service. News *changed to* National HomeCaring Council. News.
0027-9080 National Cremation *changed to* Cremationist of North America.
0027-9099 National Custodian *see* 1051-5720
0027-9102 National Decency Reporter *changed to* Decency Reporter.
0027-9110 National Defence Academy. Journal†
0027-9129 N.D.A. Quarterly *see* 0097-1901
0027-9145 National Diary
0027-9153 Kokuritsu Kokkai Toshokan Geppo
0027-9161 National Diet Library. Newsletter
0027-917X N.D.T.I. Review†
0027-9188 National Education *see* 0114-8206
0027-9196 National Educational Secretary
0027-920X National Elementary Principal *see* 0271-6062
0027-9218 National Engineer
0027-9226 National Farmers Union Washington Newsletter
0027-9234 National Federation of Housing Societies. Quarterly Bulletin *changed to* Voluntary Housing.
0027-9242 National Federation of Science Abstracting and Indexing Services. Federation Newsletter *see* 0090-0893
0027-9250 National Fisherman
0027-9269 National Fluoridation News
0027-9277 U.S. Department of Agriculture. Economic Research Service. National Food Situation *see* 0161-4274
0027-9293 National Franchise Reports†
0027-9315 National Future Farmer *changed to* F F A New Horizons.
0027-9323 National Gallery of Canada. Bulletin *see* 0711-2866
0027-9331 National Gardener
0027-934X National Genealogical Society Quarterly
0027-9358 National Geographic
0027-9374 National Geographical Journal of India
0027-9382 National Geophysical Research Institute. Bulletin *see* 0378-6307
0027-9390 National Glass Budget *changed to* Glass Factory Directory.
0027-9404 National Guardian *changed to* Scottish Licensed Trade Guardian.
0027-9412 National Guardsman *see* 0163-3945

ISSN INDEX

ISSN	Title
0027-9420	National Health Federation. Bulletin *changed to* Health Freedom News.
0027-9439	National Hearing Aid Journal *see* 0745-7472
0027-9447	National Hog Farmer
0027-9455	National Horseman
0027-9471	Animal Shelter Shoptalk *see* 1040-2225
0027-948X	National Humane Review *see* 1040-2225
0027-9501	National Institute Economic Review
0027-951X	Japan. National Institute of Animal Health Quarterly†
0027-9528	National Institute of Sciences of India. Bulletin *see* 0378-6242
0027-9544	National Jeweler
0027-9552	National Jewish Monthly *see* 0279-3415
0027-9560	National Journal *see* 0360-4217
0027-9587	National Lampoon
0027-9609	National Leaders Magazine†
0027-9617	National League Journal of Insured Savings Associations *see* 0740-5464
0027-9625	National Legal Magazine *see* 0041-2538
0027-9633	National Library News
0027-9641	National Library of Medicine. Current Catalog
0027-965X	National Library of Medicine News
0027-9668	National Live Stock Producer†
0027-9676	National Medical and Dental Association. Bulletin
0027-9684	National Medical Association. Journal
0027-9706	National Merchandiser†
0027-9714	National Messenger *changed to* Upper Case.
0027-9722	National Model Railroad Association. Bulletin
0027-9730	National Museums and Monuments of Rhodesia. Occasional Papers *see* 1011-7881
0027-9730	National Museums and Monuments of Rhodesia. Occasional Papers *changed to* National Museums and Monuments Administration. Occasional Papers. Series A: Human Sciences.
0027-9749	National Music Council Bulletin†
0027-9765	National News†
0027-9773	British Association of Colliery Management. National News Letter
0027-9781	National News of the Blind†
0027-9803	National Observer†
0027-9811	National Oceanographic Data Center. Newsletter†
0027-9838	National P T A Bulletin†
0027-9862	Newsletter - National Parking Association *see* 0031-2193
0027-9870	National Parks and Conservation Magazine *see* 0276-8186
0027-9897	National Pharmaceutical Association. Journal
0027-9900	National Pilots Association News Bulletin *changed to* National Pilots Association News.
0027-9927	National Press Club Record
0027-9935	National Press Photographer *see* 0199-2422
0027-9943	National Program Letter
0027-9951	National Prospector's Gazette & Treasure Hunter's News†
0027-996X	National Provisioner
0027-9978	National Public Accountant
0027-9994	National Real Estate Investor
0027-9994	National Real Estate Investor Directory
0028-0003	National Renaissance Bulletin
0028-0011	National Research Council of Thailand. Journal
0028-0038	National Review
0028-0046	National Review Bulletin†
0028-0054	National Review of Criminal Sciences
0028-0062	National Review of Social Sciences
0028-0089	National Rural Letter Carrier
0028-0097	National Safety
0028-0100	National Safety News *see* 0891-1797
0028-0119	National Science Museum. Bulletin *see* 0385-2431
0028-0119	National Science Museum. Bulletin *see* 0385-244X
0028-0119	National Science Museum. Bulletin *see* 0385-2423
0028-0127	National Sculpture Review *see* 0747-5284
0028-0135	National Service to Regional Councils. Special Reports *changed to* National Association of Regional Councils. Regional Reporter.
0028-0143	National Service to Regional Councils. Newsletter *changed to* National Association of Regional Councils. Regional Focus.
0028-0151	National Service to Regional Councils. Regional Review†
0028-016X	National Sheriff *changed to* Sheriff.
0028-0178	National Shorthand Reporter *changed to* Journal of Court Reporting.
0028-0186	National Society for Medical Research. Bulletin†
0028-0208	National Speed Sport News
0028-0216	National Speleological Society. Bulletin *see* 0146-9517
0028-0232	National Stamp News†
0028-0259	Greece. National Statistical Service. Monthly Statistical Bulletin of Public Finance *see* 0256-3592
0028-0267	National Stock Dog
0028-0275	National Taiwan University. College of Medicine. Memoirs
0028-0283	National Tax Journal
0028-0291	National Technical Report
0028-0305	National Timber Industry *changed to* Western Timber Industry.
0028-0313	National Tuberculosis and Respiratory Disease Association Bulletin *see* 0092-5659
0028-0321	National U. Weekly†
0028-033X	National Underwriter. Life & Health Insurance Edition
0028-0348	National Union Catalog *see* 0734-7650
0028-0356	National Union of the Footwear, Leather and Allied Trades Monthly Journal and Report *changed to* National Union of the Footwear, Leather and Allied Trades Journal and Report.
0028-0364	National Voice of Salesmen
0028-0372	National Voter
0028-0399	National Westminster Bank Quarterly Review
0028-0402	National Wildlife
0028-0410	National Wool Grower
0028-0429	National Writers Club. Bulletin for Professional Members *changed to* Professional Freelance Writers Directory.
0028-0437	Der Nationale Demokratt
0028-0453	Nationaloekonomisk Tidsskrift
0028-047X	Nation's Business
0028-0488	Nation's Cities *see* 0164-5935
0028-0496	Nation's Health
0028-050X	Nations Nouvelles
0028-0518	Nation's Restaurant News
0028-0526	Nation's Schools *see* 0194-2263
0028-0534	Native Nevadan
0028-0542	Native Voice
0028-0550	Natturufraedingurinn
0028-0577	Natur, Kultur und Jagd *see* 0340-4277
0028-0585	Natur og Museum
0028-0593	Natur und Heimat
0028-0607	Natur und Land
0028-0615	Natur und Landschaft
0028-0623	Natur-und Nationalpark†
0028-0631	Natura
0028-064X	Natura
0028-0666	Natura Mosana
0028-0674	Natura
0028-0704	Natural Health World
0028-0712	Natural History
0028-0720	Natural History Society of Northumberland Durham and Newcastle Upon Tyne. Transactions *see* 0144-221X
0028-0739	Natural Resources Journal
0028-0747	Natural Resources Lawyer *see* 0882-3812
0028-0755	Natural Rubber News†
0028-0763	Natural Science in Schools *see* 0263-6107
0028-0771	Naturalist
0028-0798	Naturaliste Canadien
0028-0801	Les Naturalistes Belges
0028-081X	Der Naturarzt
0028-0828	Naturbrunnen *changed to* Der Mineralbrunnen.
0028-0836	Nature
0028-0844	Nature and Resources and Man and Biosphere Programme. Bulletin *see* 0547-9665
0028-0852	Nature Conservancy News *changed to* Nature Conservancy Magazine.
0028-0860	Nature Study
0028-0887	Naturen
0028-0895	Naturens Verden
0028-0909	Nature's Path†
0028-0917	Naturforschende Gesellschaft zu Freiburg. Berichte
0028-0925	Naturfreund
0028-0933	Naturgemaesser Land- und Gartenbau *see* 0170-5385
0028-0941	Naturheilpraxis
0028-095X	Naturhistorisches Museum in Wien. Monatsprogramm
0028-0968	Naturisme
0028-0976	Naturist und Welt†
0028-0984	Naturkautschuk
0028-0992	Naturkunde in Westfalen *see* 0722-7795
0028-100X	Naturopath
0028-1018	Naturschutz- und Naturparke
0028-1026	Naturstein
0028-1034	Die Naturstein-Industrie
0028-1042	Die Naturwissenschaften
0028-1050	Naturwissenschaftliche Rundschau
0028-1077	Natuur en Landschap *changed to* Natuur en Milieu.
0028-1085	Natuur en Museum
0028-1093	Natuur en Techniek
0028-1107	Natuurhistorisch Maandblad
0028-1115	Natya
0028-1123	Nauchen Zhivot
0028-1131	Nauchno-Tekhnicheskaya Informatsiya *see* 0548-0019
0028-1212	Filologicheskie Nauki
0028-1220	Nauncni Skupovi u SFRJ i u Inostranstvu *see* 0350-011X
0028-1239	Nauka i Religiya
0028-1247	Nauka i Suspil'stvo
0028-1255	Nauka i Tekhnika
0028-1263	Nauka i Zhizn'
0028-1271	Nauka Polska
0028-128X	N A U N L U
0028-1298	Naunyn-Schmiedeberg's Archives of Pharmacology
0028-1301	Natur und Museum
0028-131X	Nautakarja
0028-1336	Nautical Magazine
0028-1344	Nautilus (Silver Spring)
0028-1352	Nautilus
0028-1379	Nautisk Tidskrift
0028-1409	Naval Affairs
0028-1417	Naval Aviation News
0028-1425	Naval Engineers Journal
0028-1441	Naval Research Logistics Quarterly *see* 0894-069X
0028-145X	Naval Research Reviews†
0028-1468	Naval Stores Review and Terpene Chemicals *changed to* Naval Stores Review.
0028-1484	Naval War College Review
0028-1492	Navalkathat
0028-1506	Navbharat Times
0028-1514	Navetex *changed to* Modis.
0028-1522	Navigation (Washington)
0028-1530	Navigation
0028-1557	Navigator
0028-1565	Navigatoer *see* 0107-4806
0028-1581	Navioneers
0028-159X	Navires Ports & Chantiers
0028-1603	Navis *changed to* Navigationssaellskapets Medlemsblad.
0028-1611	Navitecnia *changed to* Navitecnia y Comercio Maritimo.
0028-162X	Navnirman
0028-1646	Navy *see* 0144-3194
0028-1654	Navy Chaplains Bulletin
0028-1662	Navy News
0028-1670	Navy News
0028-1689	Navy: the Magazine of Sea Power *see* 0199-1337
0028-1697	Navy Times
0028-1700	Nazareth
0028-1727	Nea Agrotiki Epitheorissis
0028-1735	Nea Hestia
0028-1743	Middle East Council of Churches. News Bulletin†
0028-1751	Near East Foundation News†
0028-176X	Near East Report
0028-1778	Near North News
0028-1786	Nebelspalter
0028-1794	Nebraska Alumnus
0028-1808	Nebraska Beverage Analyst
0028-1816	The Nebraska Bird Review
0028-1832	Nebraska Dental Association. Journal†
0028-1840	Nebraska Education News *changed to* Nebraska Ed News.
0028-1859	Nebraska History
0028-1867	Nebraska Journal of Economics and Business *see* 0747-5535
0028-1875	Nebraska Legionnaire
0028-1883	Nebraska Library Association Quarterly
0028-1891	Nebraska Mortar and Pestle
0028-1905	Nebraska Municipal Review
0028-1913	Nebraska Newspaper
0028-1921	Nebraska Nurse
0028-193X	Nebraska on the March†
0028-1948	Nebraska Retailer
0028-1964	Nebraskaland
0028-1972	Nedelet
0028-1980	Nedeljne Novine
0028-1999	Nedeljne Novosti
0028-2006	Nederduitse Gereformeerde Teologiese Tydskrif
0028-2014	Nederland-Israel
0028-2022	Nederland-U S S R Instituut. Maandberichten
0028-2030	Nederlands Archief voor Kerkgeschiedenis
0028-2049	Nederlands Archievenblad
0028-2057	Nederlands Bosbouw Tijdschrift *changed to* Nederlands Bosbouw Tijdschrift.
0028-2073	Nederlands Korfbalblad
0028-2081	Nederlandsch Maandblad voor Philatelie *see* 0166-3437
0028-209X	Netherlands Milk and Dairy Journal
0028-212X	Nederlands Theologisch Tijdschrift
0028-2138	Nederlands Tijdschrift voor Internationaal Recht - Netherlands International Law Review *see* 0165-070X
0028-2154	Nederlands Tijdschrift voor Criminology *see* 0165-182X
0028-2162	Nederlands Tijdschrift voor Geneeskunde
0028-2170	Nederlands Tijdschrift voor Medische Studenten†
0028-2189	Nederlands Tijdschrift voor Natuurkunde *changed to* Nederlands Tijdschrift voor Natuurkunde A en B.
0028-2197	Nederlands Tijdschrift voor Psychiatrie *see* 0303-7339
0028-2200	Nederlands Tijdschrift voor Tandheelkunde
0028-2227	Nederlands Weekblad voor de Groothandel in Levensmiddelent
0028-2243	European Journal of Obstetrics and Gynecology *see* 0301-2115

5418   ISSN INDEX

ISSN	Title
0028-2251	Nederlandsch-Turksche Vereeniging. Berichten†
0028-226X	De Nederlandsche Leeuw
0028-2278	Nederlandse Gedachten†
0028-2294	Nederlandse Onderneming see 0165-6643
0028-2308	Nederlandse Sport Federatie. Technische Bulletin see 0922-4270
0028-2324	Nederlandse Vereniging van Huisvrouwen Afdeling Amsterdam. Maandbericht†
0028-2332	Nederlandse Vereniging van Vrouwen met Academische Opleiding. Mededelingen
0028-2340	Nederlandse Vereniging voor Zeegeschiedenis. Mededelingen see 0167-9988
0028-2359	Needle's Eye
0028-2375	Neen†
0028-2383	Neerlandia
0028-2391	Neerlands Postduiven Orgaan
0028-2405	Neerlands Volksleven
0028-2421	Neftekhimiya
0028-243X	Neftyanik (Moscow, 1956)
0028-2448	Neftyanoe Khozyaistvo
0028-2456	Negocios y Bancos
0028-2464	Negotiation Research Digest†
0028-2472	Negotiations News changed to New Jersey School Boards Association. School Leader.
0028-2480	Negro American Literature Forum see 0148-6179
0028-2502	Negro Braille Magazine changed to Merrick - Washington Magazine for the Blind.
0028-2510	Negro Heritage changed to Black Heritage.
0028-2529	Negro History Bulletin
0028-2537	Negro Traveler and Conventioneer changed to Traveler & Conventioneer.
0028-2545	Niege et Glace changed to Ski-Flash Magazine.
0028-2553	Neill Letter of Contrary Opinion changed to Fraser Opinion Letter.
0028-2561	Neirofiziologiya
0028-2596	Nematologica
0028-260X	Nemuno Krastas
0028-2626	Nemzetor
0028-2642	Neo Aftokinitot
0028-2677	Neophilologus
0028-2685	Neoplasma
0028-2693	Neos Kosmos
0028-2707	Nepal Gazette Translation Service changed to Nepal Recorder.
0028-2715	Nepal Medical Association. Journal
0028-2723	Nepal Press Digest
0028-2731	Nepal Press Report
0028-274X	Nepal Rastra Bank. Quarterly Economic Bulletin
0028-2758	Nepal Review Monthly†
0028-2766	Nephron
0028-2774	Neprajzi Kozlemenyek
0028-2782	Neptune Nautisme
0028-2790	Neptunus
0028-2804	Der Nervenarzt
0028-2812	Nestor
0028-2820	Net
0028-2847	Netherhall News†
0028-2855	Netherlands - American Trade changed to Holland - U S A (New York).
0028-2871	Amsterdam. Bureau van Statistiek. Maandbericht
0028-2901	Netherlands Economic Bulletin for the Foreign Press changed to Netherlands News.
0028-291X	Statistisch Kwartaaloverzicht Hilversum changed to Statistisch Overzicht Hilversum.
0028-2928	Netherlands Journal of Agricultural Science
0028-2944	Netherlands Journal of Plant Pathology
0028-2960	Netherlands Journal of Zoology
0028-2979	Netherlands. Ministerie van Cultuur, Recreatie en Maatschappelijk Werk. Centrale Afdeling Internationale Betrekkingen. Informatie Bulletin†
0028-2987	Netherlands. Ministerie van Onderwijs en Wetenschappen. Pedagogische Bibliografie
0028-3002	Netherlands. Rijksmuseum. Bulletin see 0569-9665
0028-3029	Netsu Kanri see 0387-1819
0028-3045	Networks: An International Journal
0028-3053	Neue Technik und Wirtschaft
0028-307X	Angestellten see 0935-6592
0028-3088	Neue Betriebswirtschaft†
0028-3096	Neue Blaetter des Theaters in der Josefstadt
0028-310X	Neue Blaetter fuer Taubstummenbildung see 0342-4898
0028-3118	Das Neue Buch
0028-3126	Die Neue Buecherei
0028-3134	Der Neue Bund
0028-3142	Neue Deutsche Heft†
0028-3150	Neue Deutsche Literatur
0028-3169	Das Neue Erlangen
0028-3177	Neue Gesellschaft see 0177-6738
0028-3193	Das Neue Handwerk changed to Das Handwerk.
0028-3207	Neue Huette
0028-3223	Neue Illustrierte Wochenschau
0028-3231	Neue Justiz
0028-324X	Der Neue Kaufmann
0028-3258	Neue Kommentare
0028-3274	Der Neue Mahnruf
0028-3282	Neue Museumskunde
0028-3290	Neue Musikzeitung
0028-3304	Die Neue Ordnung
0028-3320	Neue Politische Literatur
0028-3339	Neue Produkte
0028-3347	Neue Rundschau
0028-3355	Neue Sammlung
0028-3371	Neue Stenographische Praxis
0028-338X	Neue Steuerpraxis
0028-3398	Neue Technik
0028-3401	Neue Technik im Buero†
0028-341X	Neue uhrmacher-Zeitung see 0341-9002
0028-3444	Neue Wege
0028-3452	Neue Werbung
0028-3460	Neue Wirtschafts-Briefe
0028-3479	Zeitschrift fuer Parapsychologie und Grenzgebiete der Psychologie
0028-3495	Neue Zeitschrift fuer Missionswissenschaft
0028-3509	Neue Zeitschrift fuer Musik see 0170-8791
0028-3517	Neue Zeitschrift fuer Systematische Theologie und Religionsphilosophie
0028-3525	Neue Zeitschrift fuer Wehrrecht
0028-3533	Neuen Buecher†
0028-3568	Zions Freund
0028-3584	Neuerer. Ausgaben A-C see 0863-2790
0028-3592	Neues Beginnen changed to Theorie und Praxis der Sozialen Arbeit.
0028-3606	Neues Bei Uns changed to S T E W E A G Rundschau.
0028-3622	Neues Forvm changed to Forvm.
0028-3630	Neues Jahrbuch fuer Geologie und Palaeontologie, Monatshefte
0028-3649	Neues Jahrbuch fuer Mineralogie. Monatshefte
0028-3657	Neues Leben
0028-3665	Neues Leben (Moers)
0028-3681	Neues Polizeiarchiv
0028-3711	Neuheiten und Erfinderdienst changed to Erfinder und Neuheitendienst.
0028-3754	Neuphilologische Mitteilungen
0028-3770	Neuro-Chirurgie
0028-3797	Neuropaediatrie see 0174-304X
0028-3800	Neurobiologia
0028-3819	Neurochirurgia
0028-3827	Neuroendocrine Control Mechanism†
0028-3835	Neuroendocrinology
0028-3843	Neurologia i Neurochirurgia Polska†
0028-386X	Revista de Medicina Interna, Neurologie, Psihiatrie, Neuro-Chirurgie, Dermato-Venerologie
0028-3878	Neurology
0028-3886	Neurology India
0028-3894	Neuropatologia Polska
0028-3908	Neuropharmacology
0028-3916	Neuropsichiatria
0028-3924	Neuropsichiatria Infantile see 0393-361X
0028-3932	Neuropsychologia
0028-3940	Neuroradiology
0028-3959	Neuroscience Translations see 0097-0549
0028-3967	Neurosciences Research Program Bulletin†
0028-3975	Neurospora Newsletter see 0895-1942
0028-3983	Neusprachliche Mitteilungen aus Wissenschaft und Praxis
0028-4009	Neva
0028-4017	Nevada Business Review see 0148-5881
0028-4033	Nevada Education Journal
0028-4041	Nevada Highway News†
0028-405X	Nevada Highways and Parks see 0199-1248
0028-4068	Nevada Libraries changed to High Roller.
0028-4084	Nevada Outdoors and Wildlife Review†
0028-4092	Nevada State Bar Journal see 0092-6086
0028-4106	Nevada State Library. Official Nevada Publications changed to Nevada Official Publications.
0028-4114	Neve International
0028-4122	Nevesport Illustrato
0028-4130	Newt
0028-4149	New Magazine†
0028-4157	New African†
0028-4173	Witches Newsletter see 0049-7754
0028-4181	New Amberola Graphic
0028-419X	New America†
0028-4203	New American & Canadian Poetry†
0028-4211	New American Review changed to American Review.
0028-4238	E A Supplement
0028-4246	New Atlantis†
0028-4254	New Aurora
0028-4262	Green Mountain Post
0028-4270	New Beacon (Inkprint Edition)
0028-4289	New Blackfriars
0028-4297	New Book Review†
0028-4300	New Books†
0028-4319	New Books in Business and Economics changed to Harvard Business School. Baker Library. Recent Additions to Baker Library.
0028-4327	New Books on Family Planning
0028-4335	New Books on World Affairs changed to Council Spotlight Booknotes.
0028-4351	New Brunswick Economic Statistics†
0028-436X	New Building changed to New Building Projects.
0028-4378	New Business Incorporations
0028-4394	New Canadian
0028-4408	New Captain George's Whizzbang†
0028-4424	New Church Messenger changed to Messenger (La Porte).
0028-4459	New Coin changed to New Coin Poetry.
0028-4467	New Collage Magazine
0028-4475	New Commonwealth see 0305-750X
0028-4491	New Construction†
0028-4505	New Cornwall†
0028-4513	New Dawn†
0028-4521	New Dawn changed to U S D A W Today.
0028-453X	The New Day
0028-4548	New Day†
0028-4556	New Day changed to New Century.
0028-4564	Ontario New Democrat
0028-4572	New Democrat†
0028-4599	New Dimensions†
0028-4602	New Dimensions in Education see 0317-0349
0028-4610	New Directions
0028-4629	New Directions changed to Roanoke Regional Chamber of Commerce. Agenda.
0028-4637	New Driver†
0028-4645	New Edinburgh Review see 0267-6672
0028-4653	New England Advertising Week
0028-4661	New England Apparel Retailer changed to Fashion Retailer.
0028-4726	New England Economic Review
0028-4734	New England Electrical News†
0028-4742	New England Furniture News†
0028-4750	New-England Galaxy†
0028-4785	New England Historical and Genealogical Register
0028-4793	New England Journal of Medicine
0028-4807	New England Journal of Optometry
0028-4823	New England Law Review
0028-4831	New England Letter changed to First National Bank of Boston. Economic Review.
0028-484X	New England Printer and Lithographer see 0162-8771
0028-4858	New England Purchaser changed to New England Purchaser.
0028-4866	New England Quarterly
0028-4874	New England Railroad Club. Official Proceedings
0028-4882	New England Reading Association. Journal
0028-4890	New England Real Estate Journal
0028-4912	New England Social Studies Bulletin changed to New England Journal of History.
0028-4920	New England Square Dance Caller changed to Northeast Square Dancer Magazine.
0028-4939	New England Water Works Association. Journal
0028-4947	New Englander see 0164-3533
0028-4955	New Entomologist
0028-4963	New Equipment Digest
0028-4971	New Equipment News
0028-498X	New Equipment News
0028-4998	New Era
0028-5013	New Era†
0028-5021	New Era (Ely)
0028-5048	New Era changed to New Era in Education.
0028-5056	New Era Laundry & Cleaning Lines
0028-5064	New Ethicals see 0311-905X
0028-5072	New Factory Report†
0028-5080	New Forerunner†
0028-5099	New Future changed to News and Views: for Young Workers.
0028-5102	New Generation†
0028-5110	New Geographical Literature and Maps†
0028-5129	New Germany Reports†
0028-5137	New Guard
0028-5145	New Guinea and Australia, the Pacific and South-East Asia†
0028-5153	New Guinea Bulletin†
0028-5161	New Guinea Periodical Index†
0028-517X	New Guinea Psychologist†
0028-5188	New Guinea Research Bulletin†
0028-5196	New Hampshire Alumnus changed to Alumni Companion.
0028-520X	New Hampshire Audubon News see 0162-5284
0028-5234	New Hampshire Educator
0028-5242	New Hampshire Highways
0028-5250	New Hampshire Horizons†
0028-5269	N H L A Newsletter
0028-5277	New Hampshire Motor Transport†
0028-5285	New Hampshire Natural Resources changed to Fish & Game Highlights of New Hampshire.
0028-5293	New Hampshire Polyglot
0028-5307	New Hampshire Profiles
0028-5315	New Hampshire Quarter Notes
0028-5331	New Haven I N F O Magazine
0028-5374	New Horizons (New York)
0028-5382	New Horizons in Education
0028-5390	New Hungarian Quarterly

0028-5412 New Illustrator *changed to* Light on the Word for Adult Teachers.
0028-5420 New in Dentistry†
0028-5439 New Individualist Review†
0028-5455 New Jersey Academy of Science. Bulletin
0028-5463 New Jersey Academy of Science. Newsletter
0028-5498 New Jersey Air, Water and Waste Management Times *changed to* New Jersey Outdoors.
0028-5528 New Jersey Association of Osteopathic Physicians and Surgeons. Journal *see* 0892-0249
0028-5536 New Jersey Banker†
0028-5544 New Jersey Bell†
0028-5552 New Jersey Beverage Journal
0028-5560 New Jersey Business
0028-5579 New Jersey Business Woman *changed to* Voice of Working Women.
0028-5587 New Jersey Club Woman and Even'tide†
0028-5595 New Jersey Correction News†
0028-5617 New Jersey County Government†
0028-5633 New Jersey Days†
0028-5668 New Jersey Division of Veterans Services Information Bulletin. *changed to* New Jersey Bureau of Veterans Services Information Bulletin.
0028-5676 New Jersey Economic Review†
0028-5684 New Jersey Education *see* 0199-4557
0028-5692 New Jersey Elementary School Principals Association. Bulletin *see* 0001-8414
0028-5706 New Jersey Equine Industry News†
0028-5714 New Jersey Federation of Planning Officials. Federation Planner
0028-5722 New Jersey Federation of Planning Officials. Federation Planning Information Reports
0028-5757 New Jersey History
0028-5765 New Jersey Journal of Optometry†
0028-5773 New Jersey Journal of Pharmacy
0028-5781 New Jersey Labor Herald
0028-579X New Jersey Landings†
0028-5803 New Jersey Law Journal
0028-5811 New Jersey Libraries
0028-582X New Jersey Messenger
0028-5838 New Jersey Motor Truck Association. Bulletin
0028-5846 New Jersey Municipalities
0028-5854 New Jersey Music and Arts†
0028-5862 New Jersey Nature News *changed to* N J Audubon.
0028-5870 N J S N A Newsletter *changed to* New Jersey Nurse.
0028-5897 New Jersey Parent Teacher
0028-5900 New Jersey Professional Engineer *changed to* Perspectives in Engineering.
0028-5919 New Jersey Realtor
0028-5927 N J S D C Research Bulletin
0028-5935 New Jersey Speech and Hearing Association. Journal
0028-5951 New Jersey State Bar Journal *see* 0195-0983
0028-6001 New Journal
0028-601X New Journal of Statistics and Operational Research
0028-6044 New Leader
0028-6052 Money Management and Unitholder
0028-6060 New Left Review
0028-6079 New Life (London, 1965)
0028-6087 New Literary History
0028-6125 New Messenger (Braille Edition)†
0028-6141 New Mexico Beverage Journal *see* 0194-813X
0028-6168 New Mexico Business†
0028-6184 New Mexico Extension News†
0028-6192 New Mexico Farm & Ranch
0028-6206 New Mexico Historical Review
0028-6214 New Mexico Law Review
0028-6222 New Mexico Librarian†
0028-6230 New Mexico Lobo
0028-6249 New Mexico Magazine
0028-6257 New Mexico Municipal League. Municipal Reporter
0028-6265 New Mexico Musician
0028-6273 New Mexico Nurse
0028-6281 New Mexico Professional Engineer *changed to* New Mexico Engineering.
0028-6303 New Mexico School Review†
0028-6338 New Mexico Wildlife
0028-6354 New Morality
0028-6362 New Musical Express
0028-6370 New Nation†
0028-6389 New Norfolk *changed to* Tidewater Virginian.
0028-6397 New Orleans Port Record *changed to* Port of New Orleans Record.
0028-6400 New Orleans Review
0028-6419 New Outlook
0028-6427 New Outlook
0028-6435 New Outlook for the Blind *see* 0145-482X
0028-6443 The New Philosophy
0028-6451 New Physician
0028-646X New Phytologist
0028-6478 New Poetry *changed to* Brouhaha.
0028-6486 New Polish Publications *see* 0239-0345
0028-6494 New Politics†
0028-6524 New Product Newsletter *see* 1046-7211
0028-6532 New Race
0028-6540 New Rambler
0028-6559 New Records
0028-6567 New Reference Books at U C L A†
0028-6575 The New Renaissance
0028-6583 New Republic
0028-6591 New Research Centers
0028-6605 New Review *changed to* New Review of East-European History (1981).
0028-6621 New Scholasticism *changed to* American Catholic Philosophical Quarterly.
0028-663X New School Bulletin†
0028-6656 New Schools Exchange Newsletter†
0028-6664 New Scientist
0028-6672 New Scotian *see* 0704-0652
0028-6680 New Serial Titles
0028-6729 New Society *see* 0954-2361
0028-6745 New South *see* 0093-9293
0028-6761 New South Wales Government Publications. Monthly List *changed to* New South Wales Government. Legislation Issued.
0028-677X New South Wales Industrial Gazette
0028-6788 New South Wales Library Bulletin†
0028-6796 New South Wales Official Publications Received in the Library of New South Wales *see* 0729-5464
0028-6818 Journal of Soil Conservation *see* 1032-2426
0028-6826 New South Wales Statistical Bulletin†
0028-6834 New Spotlight
0028-6842 New Statesman *see* 0954-2361
0028-6869 New Technical Books
0028-6877 New Testament Abstracts
0028-6885 New Testament Studies
0028-6907 New Trail
0028-6966 New Window†
0028-6974 New Woman
0028-6990 New World
0028-7008 New World
0028-7016 New World *changed to* The New World.
0028-7032 New World
0028-7067 New World Review *see* 0884-6227
0028-7075 New Worlds
0028-7083 New Writing from Zambia
0028-7091 New York Academy of Medicine. Bulletin
0028-7105 New York Academy of Medicine. News Notes†
0028-7113 New York Academy of Sciences. Transactions
0028-7121 New York Amsterdam News
0028-713X New York Auto Repair News
0028-7164 New York Construction News
0028-7180 New York Column†
0028-7199 New York Entomological Society. Journal
0028-7210 New York Fish and Game Journal†
0028-7229 New York Folklore Quarterly *see* 0361-204X
0028-7237 New York Genealogical and Biographical Record
0028-7245 New York Generator
0028-7253 New York Historical Society Quarterly†
0028-727X New York Holstein Friesian News *see* 0279-8611
0028-7288 New York Convention & Visitors Bureau. Quarterly Calendar of Events
0028-7296 New York Journal of Dentistry
0028-7318 New York Law Forum *see* 0145-448X
0028-7342 New York Letter Carriers' Outlook
0028-7369 New York Magazine
0028-7385 New York Motorist
0028-7431 New York Podiatrist†
0028-7466 New York Public Library. Bulletin *see* 0160-0168
0028-7474 New York Purchasing Review *see* 0192-7973
0028-7482 New York Quarterly
0028-7490 New York Retailer†
0028-7504 New York Review of Books
0028-7512 New York State Archaeological Association. Bulletin *see* 1046-2368
0028-7547 New York State Bar Journal
0028-7555 New York State Bulletin *changed to* New York State Register.
0028-7563 New York State Conference of Mayors and Other Municipal Officials. Legal Bulletin†
0028-7571 New York State Dental Journal
0028-7598 New York State Education†
0028-761X New York State Housing and Community Renewal Reporter†
0028-7628 New York State Journal of Medicine
0028-7644 New York State Nurses Association. Journal
0028-7652 New York State Nurses Association. Report
0028-7660 New York State Pharmacist *see* 0163-1586
0028-7679 New York State Planning News *changed to* New York Planning News.
0028-7687 New York State Psychologist
0028-7709 New York State School Boards Association Journal *changed to* N Y School Boards.
0028-7741 New York State Society of Dentistry for Children. Bulletin
0028-7768 New York State Statistical Reporter†
0028-7776 New York State Taxpayer *changed to* C P E S Taxpayer.
0028-7784 New York Theatre Critics' Reviews
0028-7806 New York Times Book Review
0028-7814 New York Times Large Type Weekly
0028-7830 New York Times School Weekly†
0028-7849 New York Times Student Weekly†
0028-7857 New York University. Center for International Studies. Policy Papers†
0028-7865 New York University Journal of Dentistry†
0028-7873 New York University Journal of International Law and Politics
0028-7881 New York University Law Review
0028-789X New York University Medical Center News†
0028-7903 New York University Medical Quarterly *changed to* N Y U Physician.
0028-792X The New Yorker
0028-7938 Farm Research *changed to* Cornell Focus.
0028-7946 New Yugoslav Law *see* 0350-2252
0028-7962 New Zealand Archaeological Association. Newsletter *see* 0113-7832
0028-7989 New Zealand Camellia Bulletin
0028-7997 New Zealand Christian Pacifist *changed to* Peacemaker.
0028-8004 New Zealand Coal†
0028-8012 New Zealand Commerce†
0028-8020 New Zealand Company Director and Sharemarket Survey *changed to* Company Director & Professional Administrator.
0028-8047 New Zealand Dental Journal
0028-8063 New Zealand Electrical Journal *see* 0111-5839
0028-8071 New Zealand Electrician *see* 0114-8540
0028-808X New Zealand Engineering
0028-8098 New Zealand Farmer
0028-8101 New Zealand Financial Times *see* 0111-8021
0028-811X New Zealand. Forest Service. Forest Research Institute. Research Leaflet†
0028-8128 New Zealand Furnishing and Appliance World†
0028-8136 New Zealand Gardener
0028-8144 New Zealand Geographer
0028-8160 New Zealand Hardware Journal
0028-8179 New Zealand Holiday†
0028-8187 New Zealand Home Journal†
0028-8195 New Zealand Horological Journal *changed to* Jewellery Time.
0028-8209 New Zealand Horse & Pony
0028-8217 New Zealand Hospital *see* 0114-3727
0028-8225 New Zealand Institute of Chemistry. Journal *changed to* Chemistry in New Zealand.
0028-8233 New Zealand Journal of Agricultural Research
0028-8241 New Zealand Journal of Agriculture†
0028-825X New Zealand Journal of Botany
0028-8268 New Zealand Journal of Dairy Technology *see* 0300-1342
0028-8276 New Zealand Journal of Educational Studies
0028-8284 New Zealand Journal of Forestry *see* 0112-9597
0028-8292 New Zealand Journal of Geography
0028-8306 New Zealand Journal of Geology and Geophysics
0028-8314 New Zealand Journal of Health, Physical Education and Recreation
0028-8322 New Zealand Journal of History
0028-8330 New Zealand Journal of Marine and Freshwater Research
0028-8349 New Zealand Journal of Medical Laboratory Technology *see* 1171-0195
0028-8357 New Zealand Journal of Public Administration *see* 0110-5191
0028-8365 New Zealand Journal of Science†
0028-8373 New Zealand Law Journal
0028-8381 New Zealand Libraries
0028-8403 New Zealand Local Government Yearbook
0028-842X New Zealand Marine Sciences Newsletter *see* 0112-8396
0028-8438 New Zealand Meat Producer†
0028-8446 New Zealand Medical Journal
0028-8454 New Zealand Medical Record†
0028-8489 New Zealand Monthly Review
0028-8497 New Zealand National Bibliography
0028-8500 New Zealand News U.K.
0028-8519 New Zealand Newsletter *changed to* Letter from New Zealand.
0028-8527 New Zealand Numismatic Journal
0028-8535 New Zealand Nursing Journal
0028-8543 New Zealand Outdoor
0028-8586 New Zealand Plastics *changed to* Plastics & Packaging.
0028-8594 New Zealand Plumbing Review
0028-8608 New Zealand Potter *see* 0113-583X
0028-8624 New Zealand Railway Observer
0028-8632 New Zealand Rationalist and Humanist
0028-8640 New Zealand Export Review†
0028-8667 New Zealand Science Review
0028-8675 Service Station News *changed to* Motor Trade News.
0028-8683 New Zealand Slavonic Journal
0028-8705 New Zealand Society of Periodontology. Bulletin *see* 0111-1485

5420 ISSN INDEX

0028-8713 New Zealand Speech Therapists Journal *see* 0110-571X
0028-8721 New Zealand Stamp Monthly
0028-873X New Zealand Stock Market Review†
0028-8748 New Zealand Tablet
0028-8756 New Zealand Tenders Gazette
0028-8799 New Zealand Trotting Calendar
0028-8802 New Zealand Wildlife
0028-8829 New Zealand Woman's Weekly
0028-8837 Newark *changed to* Metro Courier.
0028-8845 Newark Beth Israel Medical Center. Journal†
0028-8853 Newark Churchman *see* 0277-2272
0028-887X Newcastle Medical Journal†
0028-8888 Newfoundland Gazette
0028-8918 Newport History
0028-8926 Newport Newstory†
0028-8942 News About Z-39 *see* 1041-0031
0028-8969 News & Letters
0028-9019 News Explorer *see* 0736-0592
0028-9035 News for Farmer Cooperatives *see* 0364-0736
0028-9043 Habitat (London)
0028-9094 News from Pondy
0028-9116 News from Rumania
0028-9132 News from South Africa†
0028-9140 News from the Center†
0028-9159 News from the Gutter
0028-9167 News from the Home Front *changed to* National Asthma Center News.
0028-9175 News from the Library†
0028-9183 News from the Vineyards†
0028-9191 News Front *see* 0194-9225
0028-9205 News in Engineering
0028-9221 News 'n Views†
0028-923X News, Notes, and Quotes
0028-9256 Newark Museum. News Notes *changed to* Newark Museum. Exhibitions & Events.
0028-9264 News of New York
0028-9272 News of Norway
0028-9280 News of the World
0028-9299 News of the World's Children†
0028-9302 News of the Yivo *changed to* Yivo News.
0028-9310 News on Russian Medicine and Biochemistry†
0028-9329 Scholastic News Pilot *see* 0744-916X
0028-9337 News Review†
0028-9353 News Trade Weekly†
0028-9361 News Trails *see* 0736-0576
0028-937X News-View†
0028-9388 Newsagent†
0028-9396 Newsboy
0028-940X Bangkok Standard *changed to* Living in Thailand.
0028-9418 Newsette
0028-9426 Newsletter for Birdwatchers
0028-9434 Newsletter for Research in Psychology *see* 0092-394X
0028-9442 Newsletter from behind the Iron Curtain†
0028-9450 Newsletter of Computer Archaeology†
0028-9469 Newsletter on Comparative Studies of Communism†
0028-9485 Newsletter on Intellectual Freedom
0028-9493 Newsletter on Isotopic Generators and Batteries†
0028-9507 Newsletter on Newsletters
0028-9523 Newsletter on the State of the Culture†
0028-9531 Newsman
0028-954X Newspaper Collector's Gazette†
0028-9558 Newspaper Controller *see* 0889-4590
0028-9566 Trabajador del Periodismo
0028-9574 Newsreel†
0028-9582 Newsseeker†
0028-9590 Newstime *see* 0736-0622
0028-9604 Newsweek
0028-9620 Neydhartinger Moorpost†
0028-9639 Nharireyomurindi
0028-9655 Nia Voceto *changed to* Kalejdoskopo.
0028-9663 Niagara Frontier†
0028-9744 Niederoesterreichische Landes-Landwirtschaftskammer. Amtlicher Marktbericht
0028-9752 Niederrheinische Industrie- und Handelskammer Duisberg Wesel zu Duisberg. Wirtschaftliche Mitteilungen *changed to* NiederrheinKammer.
0028-9779 Niedersaechsische Gemeinde
0028-9787 Niedersaechsischer Staatsanzeiger
0028-9795 Niedersaechsisches Aerzteblatt
0028-9809 Niekas†
0028-9817 Nieman Reports
0028-9825 Nieuw Archief voor Wiskunde
0028-9833 Nieuw Geluid
0028-9841 Nieuw Ruimzicht *see* 0166-4069
0028-9868 Nieuw Vlaams Tijdschrift†
0028-9876 Nieuw Wereld Nieuws
0028-9892 Nieuwe Linie†
0028-9906 Nieuwe Literatuur over Oorlog en Vrede *changed to* Trans-Actie.
0028-9922 Nieuwe Taalgids
0028-9930 Nieuwe West Indische Gids
0028-9949 Nieuws Uit Zuid-Afrika†
0028-9965 Nieuwsblad voor de Boekhandel *see* 0167-4765
0028-999X Verantwoord Levensverkeer
0029-0009 Nigeria English Studies Association Journal
0029-0017 Nigeria. Federal Office of Statistics. Digest of Statistics
0029-0025 Nigeria Lawyers' Quarterly
0029-0033 Nigeria Magazine†
0029-0041 Nigeria Trade Journal
0029-005X Nigerian Christian
0029-0068 Nigerian Commercial Vehicle User
0029-0076 Nigerian Field
0029-0084 Nigerian Geographical Journal
0029-0092 Nigerian Journal of Economic & Social Studies
0029-0106 Nigerian Journal of Islam
0029-0114 Nigerian Journal of Science
0029-0122 Nigerian Libraries
0029-0130 Nigerian Opinion†
0029-0157 Nigerian Schoolmaster
0029-0173 Nigrizia
0029-0181 Butsuri
0029-019X Nihon Gakujutsu Kaigi Geppo
0029-0211 Nihon Gasu Kyokaishi
0029-022X Nihon Gomu Kyokaishi
0029-0238 Nihon Heikatsukin Gakkai Zasshi - Japanese Journal of Smooth Muscle Research *see* 0374-3527
0029-0254 Nihon Kakin Gakkaishi
0029-0262 Nihon Keizai Shihyo
0029-0270 Nihon Kikai Gakkai Ronbunshu
0029-0289 Mycological Society of Japan. Transactions
0029-0297 Nihon Kokuka Gakkai Zasshi
0029-0319 Nihon no Jidosha†
0029-0327 Nihon no Kagaku to Gijutsu
0029-0335 Nihon no Kagakusha
0029-0343 Nihon Onsen Kiko Butsuri Igakkai Zasshi
0029-0351 Nihon Purasuchikkusu Shinpo
0029-036X Nihon Reito Reibo Shinbun
0029-0378 Nihon Rodo Kyokai Zasshi
0029-0386 Nihon Shinseiji Gakkai Zasshi
0029-0394 Nippon Shokuhin Kogyo Gakkaishi
0029-0408 Nihon Terebi
0029-0416 Nihon Tokei Gakkaishi
0029-0424 Nichidai Igaku Zasshi
0029-0432 Nihon University. School of Dentistry. Journal
0029-0440 Niigata Igakkai Zasshi
0029-0459 Nijhoff Information, New Publications from the Netherlands
0029-0467 Nijhoff's Index Op Nederlandse en Vlaamse Periodieken†
0029-0483 Nikkakyo Geppo
0029-0491 Nikkei Business
0029-0505 Nikkyoso Kyoiku Shinbun
0029-0513 Nikon World†
0029-0521 Nillmijmeringen†
0029-053X Nimrod
0029-0556 Nineteen
0029-0564 Nineteenth-Century Fiction *see* 0891-9356
0029-0572 Ningen Igaku
0029-0580 Ninth District Conditions *see* 0271-5287
0029-0602 Japanese Association of Groundwater Hydrology. Journal *see* 0913-4182
0029-0610 Society of the Science of Soil and Manure of Japan. Journal *see* 0911-9973
0029-0629 Nihon Funin Gakkai Zasshi
0029-0645 Nihon Kikan Shokudoka Gakkai Kaiho
0029-0653 Nippon Kikinzoku Tokei Shinbun
0029-067X Musashino Electrical Communication Laboratory. Review of the Electrical Communication Laboratory
0029-0688 Niranjan
0029-0696 Nirmok
0029-070X Nisarg Ane Arogya
0029-0718 Nishi Nihon Kisho Geppo†
0029-0726 Nishinihon Journal of Urology
0029-0734 Nissan Diesel Technical Review
0029-0742 Nissan Graphic
0029-0750 Nisseiken Tayori
0029-0769 Niti†
0029-0777 Nitrogen
0029-0785 Niwatori no Kenkyu
0029-0793 Annales de Physique Biologique and Medicale *see* 0992-3039
0029-0823 No More Hiroshimas†
0029-0831 Brain and Development - No to Hattatsu *changed to* No to Hattatsu.
0029-0831 Brain and Development - No to Hattatsu *see* 0387-7604
0029-084X No Walls Broadsheet†
0029-0858 Nobel Hefte
0029-0874 Nogaku Kenkyu
0029-0882 Nogyo Fumin
0029-0904 Nogyo no Kairyo†
0029-0912 Nogyo to Keizai
0029-0920 Noi Donne
0029-0939 Noi Giovani
0029-0947 Noise & Vibration Bulletin
0029-0963 Magyar Nok Lapja
0029-0971 Noki Shinbun
0029-1013 Canada. Statistics Canada. Non-Ferrous Scrap Metal†
0029-1021 Non-Destructive Testing *see* 0308-9126
0029-103X Non-Foods Merchandising
0029-1056 Non-Manual Worker in the Free Labour World *changed to* International Federation of Commercial Clerical, Professional and Technical Employees. Newsletter.
0029-1080 Noncello
0029-1102 Nonferrous Report†
0029-1137 Noord-Amsterdammer
0029-1145 Noord-Brabant
0029-1161 Nor Or
0029-1188 Nord e Sud
0029-1196 Nordfriesland (Bredstedt)
0029-120X Nord Economique
0029-1226 Norden
0029-1234 Nordens Tidning†
0029-1242 Nordeste
0029-1269 Nordhaeuser Nachrichten
0029-1277 Nordic Hydrology
0029-1285 Nordisk Administrativt Tidsskrift
0029-1307 Nordisk Betong†
0029-1315 Nordisk Domssamling
0029-1323 Nordisk Exlibris Tidsskrift
0029-1331 Nordisk Fagpresse *see* 0106-0120
0029-134X Nordisk Filateli
0029-1374 Nordisk Hygienisk Tidskrift *see* 0355-3140
0029-1382 Nordisk Jaernbane Tidskrift
0029-1390 Nordisk Kriminalteknisk Tidsskrift†
0029-1404 Nordisk Kvaekartidskrift *see* 0345-6005
0029-1412 Nordisk Matematisk Tidskrift *see* 0801-3500
0029-1420 Nordisk Medicin
0029-1439 Nordisk Mejeri-Tidsskrift *changed to* S D I - Scandinavian Dairy Information.
0029-1447 Nordisk Missions Tidsskrift *changed to* Mission.
0029-1455 Nordisk Psykiatrisk Tidsskrift
0029-1463 Nordisk Psykologi
0029-1471 Nordisk Tidskrift foer Doevundervisningen *changed to* Nordisk Tidskrift foer Doevundervisning.
0029-148X Nordisk Tidskrift Foer Bok- och Biblioteksvaesen
0029-1498 Nordisk Tidskrift for Fotografi
0029-1501 Nordisk Tidskrift for Vetenskap, Konst och Industri
0029-151X Nordisk Tidsskrift for International Ret
0029-1544 Nordisk Tidsskrift for Special-Optikere *changed to* Nordisk Tidsskrift for Optikere.
0029-1552 Nordisk Tidsskrift for Tale og Stemme†
0029-1579 Nordisk Veterinaermedicin†
0029-1587 Nordiska Institutet Foer Faergforskning. Litteraturoversigt†
0029-1595 Nordost-Archiv
0029-1609 Nordwestdeutsche Gesellschaft fuer Innere Medizin. Kongressbericht
0029-1617 Nordwestdeutsches Handwerk
0029-1625 Norelco Reporter *changed to* Electron Optics Reporter.
0029-1633 Norfolk and Western *changed to* Norfolk Southern World.
0029-1641 Norfolk Botanical Garden Society Bulletin
0029-165X Norfolk Fair
0029-1676 Norges Bank. Economic Bulletin
0029-1684 Norges Bondeblad *see* 0332-8414
0029-1692 Norges Forsvar
0029-1706 Norges Industri
0029-1722 Norges Utenrikshandel *see* 0800-6733
0029-1730 Norges Vel†
0029-1757 Monthly Statistics on Agriculture, Forestry and Fisheries
0029-1773 Norin Tosho Shiryo Geppo
0029-1781 Normalizace *changed to* Magazin C S N.
0029-179X Normalizacja
0029-1803 Normandie Industrielle
0029-1811 Normandie Protestante *changed to* Nord-Normandie.
0029-182X Norois
0029-1838 Norrlaendsk Tidskrift
0029-1846 Norseman
0029-1854 Norsk Artilleri-Tidsskrift
0029-1862 Norsk Bibliografisk Bibliotek†
0029-1870 Norsk Bokfortegnelse Aarskatalog
0029-1889 Norske Bokhandlertidende *changed to* Bok og Samfunn.
0029-1897 Norwegian Journal of Entomology†
0029-1900 Norsk Fagfoto
0029-1919 Norsk Faktortidende
0029-1927 Norsk Farmaceutisk Selskap. Meddelelser *see* 1100-1801
0029-1935 Norsk Farmaceutisk Tidsskrift
0029-1943 Norsk Filosofisk Tidsskrift
0029-1951 Norsk Geografisk Tidsskrift
0029-196X Norsk Geologisk Tidsskrift
0029-1978 Norsk Grafisk Tidsskrift
0029-1986 Norsk Hagetidend
0029-1994 Norsk Idrett
0029-2001 Norske Laegeforening. Tidsskrift
0029-2028 Norsk Militaert Tidsskrift
0029-2036 Norsk Motorblad
0029-2044 Norsk Musikerblad
0029-2052 Norsk Pedagogisk Tidsskrift
0029-2060 Norsk Retstidende
0029-2079 Norsk Sjoemannsforbund. Medlemsblad
0029-2087 Norsk Skogbruk
0029-2095 Norsk Skogindustri *changed to* Skogindustri.
0029-2109 Norsk Skole†
0029-2117 Norsk Skoleblad
0029-2125 Norsk Skomakertidende†
0029-2133 Norsk Skotoey *changed to* SKO.
0029-2141 Norsk Slektshistorisk Tidsskrift
0029-215X Norsk Styrmansblad *changed to* Norsk Skibsfoerertidende. Maskin-Tidende Styrmansblad.

ISSN

ISSN INDEX 5421

0029-2168 Norsk Tekstiltidende
0029-2176 Norsk Teologisk Tidsskrift
0029-2184 Norsk Tidende for det Industrielle Rettsvern. Del 3: Moenstre
0029-2192 Norsk Tidende for det Industrielle Rettsvern. Del 2: Varemerker *changed to* Norsk Varemerketidende.
0029-2206 Norsk Tidende for det Industrielle Rettsvern. Del 1: Patenter
0029-2214 Norsk Tidsskrift for Misjon
0029-2222 Norsk Tidsskrift for Sjovesen
0029-2249 Norsk Tidsskrift om Alkoholspoersmaalet *see* 0332-5512
0029-2257 Norsk Ukeblad
0029-2265 Norsk V V S
0029-2273 Norsk Veterinaertidsskrift
0029-229X Norske Skogforsoksvesen. Meddelelser†
0029-2303 Norske Tannlegeforenings Tidende
0029-2311 Norske Videnskaps-Akademi. Historisk-Filosofisk Klasse. Avhandlinger
0029-2354 Nortet†
0029-2362 Northt†
0029-2370 North American Gladiolus Council Bulletin
0029-2397 North American Review
0029-2419 North Carolina Anvil
0029-2427 North Carolina Architect†
0029-2435 North Carolina Christian Advocate
0029-2451 North Carolina Education
0029-246X North Carolina Folklore *see* 0090-5844
0029-2478 North Carolina Foreign Language Teacher *changed to* North Carolina Foreign Language Review.
0029-2494 North Carolina Historical Review
0029-2508 North Carolina Journal of Speech *changed to* North Carolina Journal of Speech Communication.
0029-2516 North Carolina Law Enforcement Journal†
0029-2524 North Carolina Law Review
0029-2540 North Carolina Libraries
0029-2559 North Carolina Medical Journal
0029-2567 North Carolina Museum of Art. Bulletin
0029-2575 North Carolina Museum of Art. Calendar of Art Events†
0029-2591 North Carolina Public Schools†
0029-2605 North Carolina Report†
0029-2613 North Carolina School Boards Association Bulletin *see* 0744-4583
0029-2648 North Central Association Quarterly
0029-2672 North Country
0029-2680 North Country Libraries†
0029-2699 North Country Reference and Research Resources Council. Newsletter *changed to* Points North.
0029-2702 North Dakota Employment Trends†
0029-2710 North Dakota History
0029-2729 North Dakota Industrial News *changed to* Network (Bismarck).
0029-2737 North Dakota Journal of Education†
0029-2745 North Dakota Law Review
0029-2753 North Dakota Music Educator
0029-2761 North Dakota Outdoors
0029-277X North Dakota Quarterly
0029-2788 North Dakota Rural Electric Magazine *see* 0885-2499
0029-280X North East Coast Institution of Engineers and Shipbuilders. Transactions
0029-2818 North East Group for the Study of Labour History Bulletin *changed to* North East Labour History Bulletin.
0029-2842 North Jersey Business Review *changed to* Jersey Business Review.
0029-2850 North Jersey Highlander
0029-2877 North Loop News
0029-2885 East Midlands Bibliography
0029-2907 North Texas Retailer *changed to* Retailer and Marketing News.
0029-2923 North West Lancashire Chamber of Commerce Journal *changed to* Chacom.
0029-294X North Wind-Skagway's Newspaper†
0029-2958 North Woods Call
0029-2982 Northeast Business†
0029-2990 Northeast Horseman *see* 8755-3929
0029-3016 N E D C O Producers' Guide *changed to* N E D C O Today.
0029-3032 Northeastern News
0029-3067 Northern Circuit†
0029-3075 Northern District Dental Society. Dental Mirror
0029-3083 Northern Engineer
0029-3091 Northern Illinois University Business Report†
0029-3105 Northern Ireland Legal Quarterly
0029-3113 Northern Ireland Libraries *see* 0023-9542
0029-313X Northern Junket†
0029-3148 Northern Lights (Minneapolis)
0029-3156 Northern Logger and Timber Processer
0029-3164 The Northern Miner
0029-3180 Northern Minnesota Review†
0029-3199 Northern Neighbors†
0029-3202 Northern News *changed to* North Wind.
0029-3210 Northern Railway Newsletter
0029-3253 Northian
0029-3261 Northland
0029-327X Northliner Magazine
0029-3296 Northwest Anthropological Research Notes
0029-330X Northwest Architect *see* 0149-9106
0029-3326 Northwest Association of Secondary and Higher Schools. Committee on Research and Service. Newsletter. *changed to* Northwest Association of Schools and Colleges. Newsletter.
0029-3334 Northwest Community Hospital Medical Bulletin
0029-3350 Northwest Farm Equipment Journal
0029-3369 Northwest Folklore†
0029-3377 Northwest Insurance
0029-3393 Northwest Motor
0029-3407 Northwest Ohio Quarterly
0029-3415 Northwest Passage *changed to* Waves.
0029-3423 Northwest Review
0029-3431 Salmon - Trout Steelheader
0029-344X Northwest Science
0029-3458 Northwest Skier *changed to* Northwest Skier.
0029-3466 Northwest Sportsman†
0029-3474 Northwest Technocrat
0029-3490 Northwestern Jeweler *changed to* Jewelers, Inc.
0029-3512 Northwestern Lutheran
0029-3520 Northwestern Management Reporter†
0029-3539 Northwestern Miller†
0029-3547 Unigard Mutuality†
0029-3555 Northwestern Ontario Timber Operators' Association. Log Book†
0029-3563 Northwestern Report†
0029-3571 Northwestern University Law Review
0029-358X Northwestern University Medical School Magazine *changed to* Northwestern University Medical Center Magazine.
0029-3601 Norveg
0029-361X Norvega Esperantisto
0029-3628 Norway†
0029-3636 Norway. Statistisk Sentralbyraa. Statistisk Maanedshefte
0029-3644 Norwegian American Commerce†
0029-3652 Norwegian Archaeological Review
0029-3660 Norwegian Commercial Banks Financial Review *changed to* Financial Review.
0029-3679 Norwegian Fishing and Maritime News *changed to* Maritime News.
0029-3709 Norwegian Shipping News *changed to* Lloyd's Ship Manager. Shipping News International.
0029-3717 Nos Lettres. Informations *changed to* Nos Lettres.
0029-3725 Nos Oiseaux
0029-3741 Theatre Amateur *see* 0398-0049
0029-3768 Nostra Voce
0029-3784 Nostri Cani
0029-3792 Nostri Ragazzi
0029-3806 Nostro Mondo†
0029-3814 Nostro Tempo
0029-3822 Nota Bene†
0029-3857 Notaro
0029-3865 Centro Brasileiro de Pesquisas. Fisicas. Notas de Fisica†
0029-3881 C.E.P.A.L. Noticias *see* 0257-2168
0029-389X Notatki Plockie
0029-3903 Note di Pastorale Giovanile
0029-392X Note Stiri de Cenaclu
0029-3946 Notes a Tempo
0029-3954 Notes Africaines
0029-3962 Notes and Abstracts in American and International Education
0029-3970 Notes and Queries
0029-3997 France. Commissariat a l'Energie Atomique. Notes d'Information
0029-4004 Notes et Etudes Documentaires
0029-4012 F E E Notes
0029-4020 Notes from the Tarlton Law Library†
0029-4039 Notes from Underground
0029-4047 Notes on Contemporary Literature
0029-4055 Notes on Current Politics *see* 0307-7039
0029-4063 Commercial Bank of Greece. Notes on Foreign Trade *changed to* Commercial Bank of Greece. Notes on Foreign Trade and Main Economic Data.
0029-4071 Notes on Mississippi Writers
0029-408X Notes on Selected Acquisitions†
0029-4098 Notes on Tin
0029-4101 Notes on Water Pollution *see* 0307-6652
0029-411X Nothing Doing in London†
0029-4128 Noticia Geomorfologica†
0029-4136 Noticiarie a Imprensa Falada e Escrita
0029-4144 Noticiario - Odontologia Sanitaria nas Americas†
0029-4152 Noticias. Weekly Digest of Hemisphere Reports *see* 0747-0878
0029-4160 Fundacion Servicio para el Agricultor. Noticias Agricolas
0029-4187 Noticias de Suecia†
0029-4195 Noticias del Trabajo
0029-4225 Noticias Medicas
0029-425X Noticiero de la Fe
0029-4276 Noticioso Perea
0029-4292 Sew Business†
0029-4306 Notitiae
0029-4314 Notiziario Agricolo†
0029-4322 Notiziario d'Arte
0029-4330 Notiziario di Aviazione Civile *changed to* Aviazione Civile.
0029-4349 Notiziario della Lega Italiana per la Lotta Contro i Tumori e dei Centri Oncologici†
0029-4357 Notiziario di Aviazione†
0029-4365 Notiziario di Caccia e Pesca-Tiro a Volo
0029-4373 Notiziario Famiglie Numerose
0029-4381 I S T A T. Notiziario *changed to* Italy. Istituto Centrale di Statistica. Notiziario.
0029-439X Notiziario Medico Farmaceutico
0029-4403 Notiziario Ortofrutticolo dei Prodotti Agricoli-Alimentari *changed to* Esportare.
0029-442X Notiziario Tecnico Worthington *changed to* Ingegneria e Fluidi.
0029-4438 Notizie Olivetti
0029-4446 Notizie per gli Industriali della Provincia di Siena *changed to* Informatore Industriale.
0029-4454 Notizie Rapide *changed to* Information e Technology.
0029-4462 Notnaya Letopis'
0029-4470 Notornis
0029-4489 Notre Bourbonnais
0029-4497 Notre Dame Alumnus *see* 0161-987X
0029-4500 Notre Dame English Journal *changed to* Religion and Literature.
0029-4519 Notre Dame Journal of Education†
0029-4527 Notre Dame Journal of Formal Logic
0029-4535 Notre Dame Lawyer *changed to* Notre Dame Law Review.
0029-4543 Notre Dame Technical Review
0029-4551 Notre Formation *see* 0765-5762
0029-456X Notre Temps
0029-4578 Les Notres
0029-4586 Nottingham French Studies
0029-4594 Notulae Entomologicae *see* 0785-8760
0029-4608 Notulae Naturae
0029-4616 Noturno†
0029-4624 Nous
0029-4632 Nous Deux Presente
0029-4659 Nouveau Cinemonde†
0029-4675 Nouveau Journal de Charpente-Menuiserie-Parquets
0029-4705 A I U Les Nouveaux Cahiers
0029-4713 Nouvel Observateur
0029-473X Nouvelle Etoile
0029-4748 Nouvelle Famille Educatrice
0029-4756 Nouvelle France
0029-4764 Nouvelle Frontiere
0029-4772 Nouvelle Hygiene
0029-4780 Nouvelle Revue d'Optique Appliquee *see* 0150-536X
0029-4799 Nouvelle Revue Franc-Comtoise
0029-4802 Nouvelle Revue Francaise
0029-4810 Journal of Experimental and Clinical Hematology
0029-4837 Nouvelle Revue Pedagogique†
0029-4845 Nouvelle Revue Theologique
0029-4853 Nouvelles Archives Hospitalieres
0029-487X Nouvelles de Chretiente
0029-4888 Nouvelles de l'Estampe
0029-490X Nouvelles Esthetiques
0029-4918 Nouvelles Etudes Marxistes *changed to* Tribune Internationale.
0029-4926 Nouvelles Graphiques
0029-4934 Nouvelles Industrielles et Commerciales et de Midi-Pyrenees
0029-4942 Nouvelles Litteraires, Arts, Sciences, Spectacles *changed to* Autre Journal.
0029-4969 Nova
0029-4977 Nova†
0029-4985 Nova (El Paso)
0029-4993 Nova
0029-5000 Nova Acta Regiae Societatis Scientiarum Upsaliensis *see* 0282-8928
0029-5019 Nova Ecclesia
0029-5027 Nova et Vetera
0029-5035 Nova Hedwiga
0029-5051 Nova Proizvodnja
0029-506X Nova Scotia *changed to* Nova Scotia Times.
0029-5078 Nova Scotia Export Quarterly†
0029-5094 Nova Scotia Medical Bulletin *see* 0838-2638
0029-5108 Nova Scotia Teachers Union Newsletter *see* 0382-408X
0029-5116 Novas de Alegria
0029-5124 Novaya i Noveishaya Istoriya
0029-5132 Novel: A Forum on Fiction
0029-5140 Novena *see* 0308-0617
0029-5159 Novidaded Fotoptica *changed to* Revista Fotoptica.
0029-5167 Novinar†
0029-5175 Novinarstvo
0029-5191 Novinky Literatury: Prehledy Informativni Literatury *see* 0862-1187
0029-5205 Novinky Literatury: Zdravotnictvi
0029-5264 Novitur†
0029-5272 Novosti *changed to* Yu Novosti.
0029-5280 Novoe Vremya
0029-5302 Novy Orient
0029-5310 Novy Shliakh
0029-5329 Novyi Mir
0029-5337 Novyi Zhurnal
0029-5345 Now
0029-5353 Now *see* 0895-1489
0029-537X Nowa Szkola
0029-5396 Nowe Rolnictwo
0029-540X Nowotwory
0029-5426 Ag-Chem Age
0029-5434 Nozzle
0029-5442 Nsanja Ya Olonda
0029-5450 Nuclear Technology
0029-5469 Nuclear Canada

ISSN

ISSN INDEX

ISSN	Title
0029-5477	Nuclear Data see 0092-640X
0029-5477	Nuclear Data see 0090-3752
0029-5485	Nuclear Energy see 0262-5091
0029-5493	Nuclear Engineering and Design
0029-5507	Nuclear Engineering International
0029-5515	Nuclear Fusion
0029-5523	Nuclear India
0029-5531	Nuclear Industry
0029-554X	Nuclear Instruments and Methods see 0168-9002
0029-554X	Nuclear Instruments and Methods see 0168-583X
0029-5558	Nuclear Magnetic Resonance Abstracts Service see 0733-2629
0029-5566	Nuklearmedizin
0029-5574	Nuclear News
0029-5574	Nuclear News Buyers Guide
0029-5582	Nuclear Physics see 0375-9474
0029-5582	Nuclear Physics see 0550-3213
0029-5604	Nuclear Safety
0029-5612	Nuclear Science Abstracts (United States Energy Research and Development Administration) see 0004-7139
0029-5620	Nuclear Science Information of Japan changed to Nuclear Science Information of Japan. Oral Presentation.
0029-5639	Nuclear Science and Engineering
0029-5647	Nuclear Science Journal
0029-5655	Nuclear Standards News
0029-5663	Nuclelect
0029-5671	Recherche
0029-568X	Nucleus
0029-5698	Nucleus
0029-5701	Nuestra Arquitectura
0029-571X	Nuestra Historia†
0029-5728	Nuestra Industria. Revista Economica†
0029-5736	Nuestra Industria. Revista Tecnologia changed to Revista Tecnologica.
0029-5752	Nuestro Amigo
0029-5760	Nuestro Anhelo
0029-5787	Nuestro Holando
0029-5795	Nuestro Tiempo
0029-5809	Nuestros Ninos (Student Edition)†
0029-585X	Nueva Pompeya
0029-5914	Nuklearna Energija see 0351-689X
0029-5922	Nukleonika
0029-5949	Numaga
0029-5965	Number Three St. Jame's Street
0029-5973	Numen
0029-5981	International Journal for Numerical Methods in Engineering
0029-599X	Numerische Mathematik
0029-6007	Numero Economique du Vendredit
0029-6023	Numismatic Circular
0029-6031	Numismatic Literature
0029-604X	Numismatic News
0029-6058	Numismatic Scrapbook see 0010-0447
0029-6066	Numismatic Society of India. Journal
0029-6074	Numismaticke Listy
0029-6090	The Numismatist
0029-6112	Nuntempa Bulgario†
0029-6139	Nuorten Sarka
0029-6155	Nuova Corrente
0029-6163	Nuova Critica
0029-6171	Nuova Economia
0029-618X	Nuova Era†
0029-6198	Nuova Gazzetta di Calabria
0029-6201	Nuova Rassegna
0029-621X	Nuova Rivista Internazionale
0029-6228	Nuova Rivista Musicale Italiana
0029-6236	Nuova Rivista Storica
0029-6244	Nuova Rivista Tributaria
0029-6252	Nuova Tecnica Ospedaliera see 0392-4831
0029-6260	Nuova Venezia
0029-6279	Nuova Veterinaria†
0029-6287	Nuovi Annali di Igiene e Microbiologia
0029-6295	Nuovi Argomenti
0029-6309	Nuovo Agora Omaggio
0029-6317	Nuovo Bollettino Bibliografico Sardo
0029-6325	Il Nuovo Cantiere
0029-6333	Nuovo Chirone
0029-6341	Nuovo Cimento see 0369-3554
0029-6341	Nuovo Cimento see 0369-3546
0029-635X	Nuovo Didaskaleion†
0029-6368	Nuovo Diritto
0029-6376	Nuovo Mezzogiorno
0029-6384	Nuovo Osservatore
0029-6392	Nuovo Pensiero Militare
0029-6406	Nursery Business
0029-6414	Nursery Days see 0275-9667
0029-6422	Nursery World
0029-6430	Nurseryman & Garden Centre
0029-6457	Nursing†
0029-6465	Nursing Clinics of North America
0029-6473	Nursing Forum
0029-649X	Nursing Homes see 0896-6915
0029-6503	Nursing Journal of India
0029-6511	Nursing Mirror changed to Nursing Times.
0029-652X	Nursing News see 0278-4092
0029-6538	Nursing News (Concord)
0029-6546	Nursing News (Brooklyn)
0029-6554	Nursing Outlook
0029-6562	Nursing Research
0029-6570	Nursing Standard
0029-6589	Nursing Times changed to Nursing Times.
0029-6597	Nutida Musik
0029-6619	Nutrition Abstracts and Reviews see 0309-1295
0029-6619	Nutrition Abstracts and Reviews see 0309-135X
0029-6627	Nutrition Information Bulletin see 0309-0531
0029-6635	Nutrition Reports International see 0955-2863
0029-6643	Nutrition Reviews
0029-6651	Nutrition Society. Proceedings
0029-666X	Nutrition Today
0029-6678	Nutrition and Metabolism see 0250-6807
0029-6686	Nutzfahrzeug
0029-6694	Nuus Oor Afrika
0029-6708	Nuwe Protestant
0029-6716	Nux
0029-6724	Ny Boky No Loharanom-Pandrosoana†
0029-6732	Ny Fremtid changed to Paa Flukt.
0029-6775	Den Ny Verden
0029-6783	Nye Bonytt see 0800-1936
0029-6791	Nyelvtudomanyi Kozlemenyek
0029-6813	Nykytekstiili
0029-683X	Nyt for Hospitalslaboranter
0029-6848	Nyt fra Historien
0029-6864	Norwegian Journal of Zoology†
0029-6872	O A C Newsletter changed to Artspace (Columbus).
0029-6910	O A S Chronicle†
0029-6937	O & M
0029-6953	Biologico
0029-6961	O C L A E Revista
0029-702X	O E C D Foreign Trade Statistics. Series A see 0474-5388
0029-7038	O E C D Liaison Bulletin Between Research and Training Institutes
0029-7054	O E C D Observer
0029-7062	Organization for Economic Cooperation and Development. Provisional Oil Statistics - Statistiques Petrolieres Provisoires changed to O E C D Oil and Gas Information.
0029-7070	O E C T A Review changed to O E C T A Reporter.
0029-7089	O G B-Bildungsfunktionaert
0029-7097	O I R T Information†
0029-7127	O I V Bulletin
0029-7135	O L A Bulletin see 1046-4336
0029-7143	OLOGOS
0029-7151	O L W†
0029-716X	O M I Farm News†
0029-7178	O.M.I. Missions†
0029-7194	Oe M V - Zeitschrift changed to Oe M V - Magazin.
0029-7208	O P Z - Dokumentation changed to Betriebswirtschaftliche O P W Z - Dokumentation.
0029-7216	O R M P Newsletter†
0029-7224	Cahiers O R S T O M Serie Entomologie Medicale et Parasitologie†
0029-7232	Cahiers O R S T O M Serie Geologie see 0766-5105
0029-7240	Cahiers O R S T O M Serie Hydrobiologie see 0240-8783
0029-7259	Cahiers O R S T O M Serie Pedologie
0029-7275	O S S T F Bulletin see 0840-9269
0029-7283	O S U Research Review†
0029-7291	O T C Chart Manual changed to Trendline O T C Chart Manual.
0029-7305	O.T.C. Market Chronicle see 0360-1773
0029-7313	O T F Reporter see 0316-3903
0029-7321	O T Kaner
0029-733X	O T O†
0029-7356	Oak Leaf
0029-7372	Oak Ridge Associated Universities. Newsletter†
0029-7380	Oakhamian
0029-7399	Aomori Prefecture. Monthly Report of Meteorology
0029-7402	Die Oase
0029-7410	Expression changed to Oasis (London).
0029-7429	Ob-Gyn Digest see 0198-9197
0029-7437	Ob-Gyn News
0029-7445	Ob-Gyn Observer†
0029-7461	Savez Geodetskih Inzenjera i Geometara Hrvatske. Obavijesti changed to Savez Geodetskih Inzenjera i Geometara Hrvatske. Geodet.
0029-747X	Obcan
0029-7488	Oberflaeche see 0940-8789
0029-7496	Oberfraenkische Wirtschaft
0029-7518	Oberlin Alumni Magazine
0029-7526	Oberlin Review
0029-7534	Oberoesterreichische F P O - Nachrichten fuer Freiheit und Recht
0029-7542	Oberoesterreichische Gemeindezeitung
0029-7550	Oberoesterreichische Heimatblaetter
0029-7569	Oberoesterreichisches Reise Journal changed to Reise-Journal.
0029-7585	Obiter Dicta
0029-7607	Objective: Justice
0029-7615	Objets et Mondes
0029-764X	Andragogija changed to Theleme.
0029-7658	Obrero Ferroviario
0029-7674	Observation, Opinion, Orientation see 0318-9236
0029-7682	Belgium. Institut Royal Meteorologique. Observations Climatologiques
0029-7690	Belgium. Institut Royal Meteorologique. Observations d'Ozone
0029-7704	Observatory
0029-7712	Observer
0029-7720	Observer†
0029-7739	Observer (Rockford)
0029-7763	Obshchestvennye Nauki v Uzbekistane
0029-7771	Obst- und Weinbau changed to Obst - Wein - Garten.
0029-778X	Obst-Gemuese
0029-7798	Obst und Garten
0029-781X	Revista de Pediatrie, Obstetrica, Ginecologie. Obstetrica si Ginecologie
0029-7828	Obstetrical & Gynecological Survey
0029-7844	Obstetrics and Gynecology
0029-7852	Obzor
0029-7860	Obzornik
0029-7879	Occident†
0029-7887	Occult Gazette changed to Royal Cosmic Theology.
0029-7909	Occupational Hazards
0029-7925	Occupational Health Newsletter changed to Environmental Health and Safety News.
0029-7933	Occupational Health Nursing see 0891-0162
0029-7941	Occupational Health Review†
0029-7968	U.S. Bureau of Labor Statistics. Occupational Outlook Quarterly
0029-7976	Occupational Psychology see 0963-1798
0029-7984	Occupational Safety and Health Abstracts see 1010-7053
0029-8018	Ocean Engineering
0029-8026	Ocean Industry
0029-8042	Ocean Oil Weekly Report
0029-8069	Ocean Science News
0029-8077	Oceania
0029-8085	Oceanic Citation Index see 0748-1489
0029-8093	Oceanic Index see 0748-1489
0029-8115	Oceanic Linguistics
0029-8123	Oceanite
0029-8131	Oceanographical Society of Japan. Journal see 0916-8370
0029-814X	Oceanologia et Limnologia Sinica changed to Haiyang yu Huzhao.
0029-8158	Oceanology†
0029-8174	Oceans†
0029-8182	Oceanus
0029-8190	Ochanomizu Joshi Daigaku Shizen Kagaku Hokoku
0029-8204	Ochrana Prirody changed to Pamatky a Priroda.
0029-8220	Ochrona Pracy
0029-8239	Ochrona Roslin
0029-8247	Ochrona Zabytkow
0029-8263	Ocrotirea Naturii si a Mediului Inconjurator
0029-8271	The Octagon
0029-828X	Octobre
0029-8328	Oculus
0029-8336	Odbrana
0029-8344	Odbrana i Zastita
0029-8360	Der Odenwald
0029-8387	Odjek
0029-8395	Odontoiatria
0029-8409	Odontologia see 0120-2855
0029-8417	Odontologia Chilena
0029-8425	Odontologia Uruguaya
0029-8433	Odontological Bulletin changed to Dental Society of Western Pennsylvania. Bulletin.
0029-8441	Odontologisk Revy see 0347-9994
0029-845X	Scandinavian Journal of Dental Research
0029-8468	Odontologiska Foreningens Tidskrift
0029-8476	Odontologiste des Hopitaux†
0029-8484	Shigaku
0029-8492	Odontoprotesti
0029-8506	Odontostomatological Progress
0029-8514	Odrodzenie i Reformacja w Polsce
0029-8522	Odu
0029-8530	Odvjetnik
0029-8549	Oecologia
0029-8565	Der Oeffentliche Dienst
0029-8573	Das Oeffentliche Gesundheitswesen
0029-8581	Das Oeffentliche Haushaltswesen in Oesterreich
0029-859X	Die Oeffentliche Verwaltung
0029-8603	Oeffentliche Wirtschaft changed to Oeffentliche Wirtschaft und Gemeinwirtschaft.
0029-862X	L'Oeil
0029-8638	Oekonomik Gartenbau†
0029-8646	Oekonomisk Kronik
0029-8654	Oekumenische Rundschau
0029-8662	Oel- und Gasfeuerung see 0720-3438
0029-8689	Oel†
0029-8697	Oelhydraulik und Pneumatik
0029-8700	Oil World Weekly
0029-8719	Oertliche Raumheizung†
0029-8727	Oest
0029-8735	Oeste†
0029-8751	Oesterreich-Nederland
0029-876X	Oesterreichische Krankenhaus Zeitung
0029-8786	Oesterreichische Aerztezeitung
0029-8840	Oesterreichischer Alpenverein. Akademische Sektion Graz. Mitteilungen
0029-8859	Oesterreichische Apotheker-Zeitung
0029-8867	Oesterreichische Arbeitsgemeinschaft fuer Rehabilitation. Information†
0029-8875	Der Oesterreichische Arzt
0029-8883	Oesterreichische Autorenzeitung
0029-8891	Oesterreichische Bauzeitung
0029-8905	Oesterreichische Bauernzeitung

0029-8921 Oesterreichische Blaetter fuer Gewerblichen Rechtsschutz und Urheberrecht
0029-8956 Brandverhuetung
0029-8972 Oesterreichische Camping and Caravaning Revue *changed to* Camping Revue.
0029-8980 Oesterreichische Caritas Zeitschrift *changed to* Caritas-Zeitschrift.
0029-8999 Oesterreichische Dachdecker- und Pflasterer-Zeitung *changed to* Dach und Wand Abdichtung.
0029-9006 Oesterreichische Dentistenzeitschrift *see* 0029-9596
0029-9030 Die Oesterreichische Feuerwehr
0029-9057 Der Oesterreichische Filmamateur
0029-9065 Der Oesterreichische Friseur
0029-9073 Der Strassengueterverkehr
0029-9081 Oesterreichische Fussbodenzeitung
0029-909X Oesterreichische Galerie. Mitteilungen
0029-9103 Oesterreichische Gastgewerbe-Zeitung *changed to* Oesterreichische Gastgewerbe- und Hotelzeitung.
0029-9111 Oesterreichische Gefluegelwirtschaft
0029-912X Oesterreichische Gemeinde-Zeitung
0029-9138 Oesterreichische Geographische Gesellschaft. Mitteilungen
0029-9146 Oesterreichische Gesellschaft fuer Filmwissenschaft. Mitteilungen *changed to* Oesterreichische Gesellschaft fuer Filmwissenschaft, Kommunikations- und Medienforschung. Mitteilungen.
0029-9154 Oesterreichische Gesellschaft fuer Holzforschung. Schrifttumskarteidienst - Card Index Service
0029-9162 Oesterreichische Glaserzeitung *changed to* Glas - Oesterreichische Glaserzeitung.
0029-9170 Das Oesterreichische Graphische Gewerbe
0029-9189 Oesterreichische Hausbesitz
0029-9200 Die Oesterreichische Hoehere Schule
0029-9227 Der Oesterreichische Installateur
0029-9235 Oesterreichische Installateurzeitung
0029-9243 Der Oesterreichische Jungarbeiter
0029-9251 Oesterreichische Juristen - Zeitung
0029-926X Oesterreichische Kunststoff Zeitung *changed to* Oesterreichische Kunststoff Zeitschrift.
0029-9278 Laenderbank Boerseninformationen *changed to* Laenderbank Boerse Aktuell.
0029-9286 Oesterreichische Leder- und Haeutewirtschaft
0029-9294 Oesterreichische Mechaniker *changed to* Mechanik.
0029-9308 Oesterreichische Monatshefte
0029-9316 Oesterreichische Musikzeitschrift
0029-9324 Oesterreichische Naehmaschinen- und Fahrrad-Zeitung *changed to* Oesterreichische Naehmaschinen- und Zweirad-Zeitung.
0029-9332 Oesterreichische Nationalbank. Mitteilungen des Direktoriums *changed to* Oesterreichische Nationalbank. Statistisches Monatsheft.
0029-9340 Oesterreichische Notariats-Zeitung
0029-9359 Oesterreichische Numismatische Gesellschaft. Mitteilungen
0029-9367 C W F *changed to* T W F.
0029-9375 Oesterreichische Osthefte
0029-9383 Oesterreichische Paedagogische Warte *changed to* K L O E Impulse.
0029-9391 Oesterreichische Papier-Zeitung *see* 0259-7454
0029-9405 Oesterreichische Raumausstatterzeitung
0029-9421 Oesterreichische Schachzeitung†
0029-943X Oesterreichische Schlosser-und Maschinenbauerzeitung†
0029-9448 Oesterreichische Schmiede-Zeitung†
0029-9456 Oesterreichische Schuhhaendler *changed to* Schuh-Revue.
0029-9464 Oesterreichische Schuhmacher - Zeitung *changed to* Der Oesterreichischer Schuhmarkt.
0029-9499 Der Oesterreichische Spengler und Kupferschmied
0029-9502 Oesterreichische Foerster Zeitung
0029-9510 Oesterreichische Steuer und Wirtschaftskarei *changed to* Steuer und Wirtschaftskartei.
0029-9529 Oesterreichische Steuerzeitung
0029-9537 Austria Tabakwerke A. G. Fachliche Mitteilungen†
0029-9545 Oesterreichische Textil-Mitteilungen
0029-9553 Oesterreichische Textil Zeitschrift *changed to* Mode und Material.
0029-9561 Oesterreichische Trafikanten-Zeitung
0029-957X Der Oesterreichische Volkswirt
0029-9588 Oesterreichische Wasserwirtschaft
0029-9596 Oesterreichische Zahnaerzte - Zeitung
0029-9618 O Z E
0029-9626 Oesterreichische Zeitschrift fuer Kunst und Denkmalpflege
0029-9634 Oesterreichische Zeitschrift fuer Oeffentliches Recht. Neue Folge *see* 0378-3073
0029-9642 Oesterreichische Zeitschrift fuer Stomatologie *see* 0175-7784
0029-9650 Oesterreichische Zeitschrift fuer Vermessungswesen *changed to* Oesterreichische Zeitschrift fuer Vermessungswesen und Photogrammetrie.
0029-9669 Oesterreichische Zeitschrift fuer Volkskunde
0029-9677 Der Oesterreichische Zimmermeister
0029-9685 Oesterreichische Zoll und Steuer Nachrichten
0029-9693 Oesterreichische Arbeitsgemeinschaft fuer Ur- und Fruehgeschichte. Mitteilungen *changed to* Archaeologie Oesterreichs.
0029-9707 Oesterreichisches Institut fuer Raumplanung. Mitteilungen†
0029-9715 Oesterreichischer Alpenverein. Mitteilungen
0029-9723 Oesterreichischer Blindenverband. Mitteilungen
0029-9731 Oesterreichischer Brieftaubensport
0029-974X Kameradschaft der Wiener Panzer-Division. Mitteilungsblatt
0029-9758 Der Oesterreichische Kleingaertner
0029-9766 Oesterreichischer Kleintierzuechter
0029-9774 Oesterreichischer Luftfahrt Pressedienst *changed to* Oesterreichische Luftfahrt Presse.
0029-9782 Oesterreichischer Markenanzeiger
0029-9790 Oesterreichischer Personenverkehr
0029-9804 Oesterreichischer Wohnungs-Geschaefts- und Realitaeten-Anzeiger
0029-9820 Oesterreichisches Archiv fuer Kirchenrecht
0029-9847 Oesterreichisches Cafe Journal
0029-9855 Elektro and Radio *changed to* Elektro Journal.
0029-9863 Berichte und Informationen
0029-988X Oesterreichisches Hotel- und Gastronomie-Journal *changed to* Hotel und Gastronomie.
0029-9898 Oesterreichisches Institut fuer Wirtschaftsforschung. Monatsberichte
0029-9901 Oesterreichisches Jugendrotkreuz. Arbeitsblaetter
0029-991X Oesterreichisches Klerus Blatt†
0029-9928 Oesterreichisches Kolpingblatt
0029-9936 Leben-Wirken *changed to* Mensch und Ziel.
0029-9944 Oesterreichisches Patentblatt
0029-9952 Oesterreichisches Standesamt
0029-9987 Oesterreichs Fischerei
0029-9995 Oesterreichs Paddelsport *changed to* Oesterreichs Kanusport.
0030-0004 Oesterreichs Presse, Werbung, Graphik *changed to* Pressehandbuch (Year).
0030-0012 Oesterreichs Weidwerk
0030-0047 Of Consuming Interest†
0030-0055 Of Sea and Shore
0030-0071 Off Our Backs
0030-0098 Offene Kreis†
0030-0101 Offene Tore
0030-011X Offene Tueren
0030-0128 Office
0030-0136 Office Administration *changed to* Office Product News.
0030-0144 Office Products *changed to* Office Products Dealer Buying Guide and Directory.
0030-0179 Office Equipment and Methods *changed to* Office Systems & Technology.
0030-0187 Office Equipment News
0030-0217 Management in Action *see* 0025-1747
0030-0233 Office Products Dealer†
0030-0241 Office Products News *changed to* Office Technology Management.
0030-025X Office Supervisor's Bulletin *see* 0744-3625
0030-0268 Officer
0030-0284 Official Board Markets
0030-0292 Official Container Directory
0030-0306 Official Detective Stories
0030-0314 Official Gazette of Guyana
0030-0322 Official Guide of the Railways and Steam Navigation Lines of the United States, Puerto Rico, Canada, Mexico and Cuba, Airline Schedules *see* 0190-6704
0030-0330 Official Journal (Patents)
0030-0349 Official Journal of Industrial and Commercial Property
0030-0357 Official Motor Freight Guide
0030-0365 Official Oil in North Dakota *see* 0363-2512
0030-0373 Official Railway Equipment Register
0030-0381 Official Steamship Guide
0030-039X Officiel de la Couleur†
0030-0403 Officiel de la Couture et de la Mode de Paris
0030-0411 Officiel de la Droguerie
0030-042X Officiel de la Librairie†
0030-0438 Officiel de la Photographie et du Cinema
0030-0446 Officiel de l'Ameublement: Ameublement Informations *changed to* Nouvel Officiel de l'Ameublement.
0030-0454 Officiel de l'Automobile
0030-0462 Officiel des Plastiques et du Caoutchouc
0030-0500 Officiel des Spectacles
0030-0519 Officiel du Cycle, du Motocycle et de la Motoculture *see* 0751-994X
0030-0535 Officiel: Magazine des Menagers *see* 0335-9956
0030-0551 Officier de Reserve *changed to* Ares.
0030-056X Officer de Police
0030-0586 Offizieller Salzburger Wochenspiegel
0030-0594 Offsetpraxis
0030-0608 Offshore (Tulsa) *changed to* Offshore Incorporating the Oilman.
0030-0624 Oficina Moderna
0030-0632 Oficina Sanitaria Panamericana. Boletin
0030-0667 Oftalmologia *changed to* Revista de Chirurgie, Oncologie, Radiologie, O.R.L., Oftalmologie, Stomatologie. Oftalmologie.
0030-0675 Oftal'mologicheskii Zhurnal
0030-0683 Ofthalmologika Chronika *changed to* Greek Annals of Ophthalmology.
0030-0691 Ogam
0030-0705 Oggi
0030-0713 Oglas za Pomorce
0030-0721 Ogonek
0030-073X Ogoniok
0030-0756 Ogrodnictwo
0030-0764 Ohio Academy of Science News
0030-0772 Ohio A F L - C I O News and Views
0030-0780 Society of Ohio Archivists Newsletter *see* 1047-5400
0030-0799 Ohio Association of School Librarians' Bulletin *see* 0192-6942
0030-0802 Ohio Banker
0030-0861 Ohio Contractor
0030-087X Ohio Dental Journal
0030-0888 Ohio Family Physician News
0030-0896 Ohio Farmer
0030-090X Ohio Florists Association. Bulletin
0030-0918 Ohio Forestry Association. Bulletin†
0030-0926 Ohio Grange *changed to* Ohio Granger.
0030-0934 Ohio History
0030-0950 Ohio Journal of Science
0030-0977 Ohio Library Trustee *see* 1046-4336
0030-0985 Ohio Motorist
0030-0993 Ohio Nurses Review
0030-1019 Ohio Parent Teacher *see* 0199-0918
0030-1027 Ohio Pharmacist
0030-1035 Ohio Reading Teacher
0030-1043 Ohio Report on Research and Development in Biology, Agriculture and Home Economics *see* 0749-1492
0030-1051 Ohio Researcher†
0030-1078 Ohio School Boards Journal *see* 0893-5289
0030-1086 Ohio Schools
0030-1116 Ohio State Lantern
0030-1124 Ohio State Medical Journal *changed to* Ohio Medicine.
0030-1132 Ohio State University. College of Medicine. Journal
0030-1140 Ohio State University. Institute of Polar Studies. Newsletter†
0030-1159 Ohio State University Libraries Notes†
0030-1167 Ohio State University Monthly *see* 0744-8899
0030-1183 Ohio Tavern News
0030-1191 Ohio Trucking News *changed to* Ohio Government Directory - Ohio Trucking Times.
0030-1205 Ohio University Post *changed to* Post (Athens).
0030-1213 Ohio Veterinarian *changed to* Ohio Veterinary Medical Association. Newsletter.
0030-1221 Ohio Wesleyan Magazine
0030-123X Ohio Woodlands
0030-1248 Ohioana Quarterly
0030-1256 Ohio's Health†
0030-1264 Ohmio†
0030-1272 Ohnicek
0030-1280 Oiga
0030-1299 Oikos
0030-1302 Oikoumenikon†
0030-1310 Lifestream of Progress *changed to* Oil: Lifestream of Progress.
0030-1329 Oil & Chemical Worker
0030-1337 Oil and Colour Chemists' Association. Journal *changed to* Surface Coatings International.
0030-1345 Oil & Gas Discoveries†
0030-1353 Oil, Gas & Petrochem Equipment
0030-1388 Oil & Gas Journal
0030-1396 Oil and Gas Tax Quarterly
0030-1418 Oil Caravan Weekly *changed to* Al-Qafilah.
0030-1426 Oil, Chemical and Atomic Workers International Union. Union News *see* 8756-1727
0030-1434 Oil Daily
0030-1442 Oil Mill Gazetter
0030-1450 Oil News
0030-1469 Oil, Paint and Drug Reporter *see* 0090-0907
0030-1493 Oilgas
0030-1507 Oils and Oilseeds Journal†
0030-1515 Oilweek
0030-1523 Oise Agricole
0030-1531 Oiseau et la Revue Francaise d'Ornithologie
0030-154X Okajima's Folia Anatomica Japonica
0030-1558 Okayama Igakkai Zasshi
0030-1566 Mathematical Journal of Okayama University
0030-1574 Okeanologiya

ISSN

ISSN	Title
0030-1590	Okhrana Truda i Sotsial'noe Strakhovanie
0030-1612	Okki
0030-1620	Oklahoma Union Farmer *changed to* Farm News and Views.
0030-1639	Oklahoma *changed to* O K C Action.
0030-1647	Oklahoma Banker
0030-1655	Oklahoma Bar Association Journal *changed to* Oklahoma Bar Journal.
0030-1663	Oklahoma Beverage News
0030-1671	Oklahoma Business Bulletin
0030-168X	Oklahoma C.P.At
0030-1698	Oklahoma Cowman
0030-1701	Oklahoma Current Farm Economics
0030-171X	Oklahoma Daily
0030-1728	Oklahoma Register (Oklahoma City)
0030-1736	Oklahoma Geology Notes
0030-1744	Oklahoma Labor Markett
0030-1752	Oklahoma Law Review
0030-1760	Oklahoma Librarian
0030-1779	Oklahoma Mason
0030-1787	Oklahoma Nurse
0030-1795	Oklahoma Observer
0030-1809	Oklahoma Odd Fellow
0030-1817	Oklahoma Parent - Teacher
0030-1833	Oklahoma Reader
0030-1841	Oklahoma Retailer
0030-185X	Oklahoma School Board Journal
0030-1868	Oklahoma State Dental Association. Journal *see* 0164-9442
0030-1876	Oklahoma State Medical Association. Journal
0030-1884	Oklahoma Teacher *changed to* O E A Focus.
0030-1892	Oklahoma Today
0030-1906	Oekonomi og Politik
0030-1914	Oekonomisk Revy
0030-1922	Okonomisk Virksomhedsledelse *changed to* Lederskab og Loensomhed.
0030-1949	Oktobar
0030-1957	Oktyabr'
0030-1965	Old Bottle Magazine *changed to* Old Bottle Magazine - Popular Archaeology.
0030-1973	Old English Newsletter
0030-199X	Old Lady of Threadneedle Street
0030-2007	Old Man
0030-2023	Old Motor (London)†
0030-2031	Old-Time New England†
0030-204X	Old Timers' Bulletin†
0030-2058	Old West
0030-2066	Das Oldenburger Sportpferd
0030-2074	Oldenburgische Familienkunde
0030-2082	Oleagineux
0030-2090	Oleario
0030-2104	Oleodinamica - Pneumatica *see* 0391-8645
0030-2112	Olie *changed to* Shell-Venster.
0030-2120	Oljebladet *see* 0006-2367
0030-2139	Olomeinu
0030-2147	Oltre il Cielo
0030-2155	Oltremaret
0030-2163	Olympian (San Francisco)
0030-218X	Oma
0030-2201	Omaha District Dental Society. Chronicle
0030-221X	Omaha Profile *see* 0162-5241
0030-2228	Omega (Amityville)
0030-2244	Omin Kasin *see* 0355-1873
0030-2260	Omnia Medica et Therapeutica
0030-2279	Omnibus-Revue *changed to* Omnibus-Revue und Bus Aktuell.
0030-2287	Omnipraticien Francais
0030-2317	Instytut Metali Niezelaznych. Biuletynt
0030-2325	On Courset
0030-2333	On Dit
0030-2341	On Targett
0030-2368	On the Road (Cape Town)
0030-2376	On the Sound†
0030-2384	On the Track†
0030-2392	On Watch
0030-2406	Oncologia si Radiologia *changed to* Revista de Chirurgie, Oncologie, Radiologie, O.R.L., Oftalmologie, Stomatologie. Oncologie.
0030-2406	Oncologia si Radiologia *see* 0481-6684
0030-2414	Oncology
0030-2430	Onde Electrique
0030-2449	Onder Chevron Vlag *changed to* Chevron Motor.
0030-2457	Onder de Vlam
0030-2465	Onderstepoort Journal of Veterinary Research
0030-2473	Onderwijs en Mediat
0030-2481	Onderwijs en Opvoeding
0030-2503	One Church
0030-2511	One-Design and Offshore Yachtsman *see* 0889-4094
0030-252X	One in Christ
0030-2546	1001 Custom & Rod Ideast
0030-2554	1001 Decorating Ideas *see* 0278-0844
0030-2562	One/Twot
0030-2597	Ongaku Gaku
0030-2600	Ongaku Geijutsu
0030-2619	Onlooker
0030-2627	Onomasticat
0030-2643	Ons Bou *changed to* Tienerkompas.
0030-2651	Ons Erfdeel
0030-266X	Ons Fruitteeltblad *see* 0772-7054
0030-2678	Ons Geestelijk Leven *changed to* Geest en Leven.
0030-2686	Ons Huist
0030-2694	Ons Jeugt
0030-2708	Ons Jonge Platteland(OJP)†
0030-2716	Ons Kompast
0030-2724	Ons Leger *see* 0922-2979
0030-2732	Ons Platteland
0030-2740	Ons Politeuma *changed to* Ons Burgerschap.
0030-2759	Reisiesduif *changed to* Racing Pigeon.
0030-2767	Ons Trekpaardt
0030-2775	Ons Vee
0030-2783	Ons Wapen
0030-2791	Ons Zeewezen *see* 0165-8182
0030-2805	Ons Ziekenhuist
0030-2813	Onsei Gengo Igaku
0030-2821	Science of Hot Springs
0030-283X	Ontario Association of Children's Aid Societies. Journal
0030-2848	Ontario Churchman *see* 1184-6283
0030-2856	Ontario College of Pharmacy. Bulletin†
0030-2864	Ontario Dental Association. Journal *see* 0300-5275
0030-2872	Ontario. Ministry of Agriculture and Food. Monthly Dairy Report.
0030-2902	Ontario Education *changed to* Education Today.
0030-2910	Ontario Film Association. Bulletin *see* 0840-4313
0030-2929	Ontario Fish and Wildlife Review†
0030-2937	Ontario Gazette
0030-2945	Families
0030-2953	Ontario History
0030-297X	Ontario Hydro News *changed to* Hydro News.
0030-2988	Ontario Hydro Research Quarterly†
0030-2996	Ontario Library Review†
0030-3011	Ontario Mathematics Gazette
0030-302X	Ontario Medical Review
0030-3038	Ontario Milk Producer
0030-3054	Ontario Psychologist
0030-3062	O P A L
0030-3070	Ontario Registert
0030-3089	Ontario Reports
0030-3097	Ontario Securities Commission. Monthly Bulletin *see* 0226-9325
0030-3100	Ontario Securities Commission. Weekly Summary *see* 0226-9325
0030-3119	Ontario Showcase *see* 0713-6315
0030-3127	Ontario Statute Citator
0030-3135	Ontladingen
0030-3143	Ontode *see* 0375-9504
0030-3151	Ontological Thought *changed to* Emissary.
0030-316X	Ontwaak!
0030-3186	Onward-Voorwaarts *changed to* Volkstem.
0030-3208	Onze Luchtmacht
0030-3224	Onze Vogels
0030-3232	Onze Wereld
0030-3259	Oomoto
0030-3267	Oorspronkelijk Christendom
0030-3275	Oost en West
0030-3283	Civis Mundi
0030-3291	Oostenrijkse Handelsdelegatie in Nederland *changed to* Oostenrijkse Economische Berichten.
0030-3305	Op Cit
0030-3321	Op de Rails
0030-333X	Op Leeftijd *changed to* Leeftijd.
0030-3348	Opakowanie
0030-3356	Opbouw
0030-3372	Open
0030-3399	Open Deur
0030-3402	Open Deur
0030-3410	Open Doort
0030-3429	Open Forum
0030-3437	Open Road and the Professional Drivert
0030-3445	Open Shelft
0030-3453	Open Venster
0030-3461	Openbaar Vervoer (Amsterdam, 1928)†
0030-3488	Openbare Uitgavent
0030-3496	Public Work, Construction & Transport *changed to* Public Works.
0030-350X	Openingst
0030-3518	Oper und Konzert
0030-3526	Opera
0030-3542	Opera
0030-3577	Opera - Canada
0030-3585	Opera Journal
0030-3593	European Intelligence
0030-3607	Opera News
0030-3615	Operation L A P L†
0030-3623	Operational Research Quarterly *see* 0160-5682
0030-3631	Operations Forestieres et de Scierie
0030-364X	Operations Research
0030-3658	Operations Research - Management Science
0030-3666	Operations Research Society of America. Meeting Bulletin *see* 0161-0295
0030-3674	Opereshonzu Risachi
0030-3690	Opernwelt
0030-3720	Ophthalmic Literature
0030-3739	Ophthalmic Optician *see* 0268-5485
0030-3747	Ophthalmic Research
0030-3755	Ophthalmologica
0030-3763	Ophthalmologistt
0030-3771	Opinie *see* 0167-093X
0030-3798	Opiniont
0030-3836	Klank en Weerklank
0030-3852	Opportunities
0030-3879	Opsaal
0030-3887	Opsearch
0030-3895	Opstina
0030-3909	Optica Acta: International Journal of Optics *see* 0950-0340
0030-3917	Optica Pura y Aplicada
0030-3925	Optical Journal and Review of Optometry *see* 0147-7633
0030-3941	Optical Society of America. Journal *see* 0740-3232
0030-3941	Optical Society of America. Journal *see* 0740-3224
0030-395X	Optical Spectra *see* 0731-1230
0030-3968	Optician
0030-3976	Opticien Belget
0030-3984	Opticien-Lunetier
0030-3992	Optics and Laser Technology
0030-400X	Optics and Spectroscopy
0030-4018	Optics Communications
0030-4026	Optik
0030-4034	Optika i Spektroskopiya
0030-4050	Optima
0030-4069	Optimist
0030-4077	Opto-Electronics *see* 0306-8919
0030-4085	Optometric Management
0030-4093	Optometric Weekly *changed to* International Eyecare.
0030-4107	Optometric World
0030-4115	Optometrie *see* 0988-3525
0030-4123	Optometriet
0030-4131	Opust
0030-414X	Opuscula Medica
0030-4158	Opuscula Zoologicat
0030-4166	Or Hamizracht
0030-4174	Ora et Labora
0030-4182	Orafo Orologiaio
0030-4190	Orafo Valenzano *changed to* Valenza Gioielli.
0030-4204	Oral Health
0030-4212	Oral Research Abstractst
0030-4220	Oral Surgery, Oral Medicine and Oral Pathology
0030-4239	Orang Peladang
0030-4247	Orange County Apartment House News *changed to* Orange County Apartment News.
0030-4255	Orange County Business *changed to* Orange County Business Journal.
0030-4263	Orange County Genealogical Society. Quarterly *changed to* Orange County California Genealogical Society Quarterly.
0030-4271	Orange County Farm News *changed to* Ag Focus.
0030-428X	Orange County Illustratedt
0030-4298	Orange County Jewish Heritage
0030-431X	Orangeburg Historical and Genealogical Record
0030-4328	Oranje-Nassau Postt
0030-4336	Orante
0030-4344	Oratoire
0030-4352	Oratoriana
0030-4360	Orbanismot
0030-4379	Orbis
0030-4387	Orbis (Philadelphia)
0030-4395	Orbis Geographicus
0030-4425	Orbis
0030-4433	Orbit
0030-445X	Orbitat
0030-4468	Das Orchester
0030-4476	Orchid Review
0030-4484	Orchideeen
0030-4492	Ord och Bild
0030-4506	Ordem dos Medicos. Boletim
0030-4514	Order of Scottish Clans Lion Rampantt
0030-4530	Ordine Nuovo *changed to* Linea.
0030-4549	Ordinismot
0030-4557	Ordnance *see* 0092-1491
0030-4565	Ordre National des Medecins. Bulletin
0030-459X	Ore
0030-4603	Oregon Agri-Recordt
0030-4611	Oregon Agriculturet
0030-462X	Oregon Beverage Analystt
0030-4638	Oregon Business Reviewt
0030-4646	Oregon Churchman *changed to* Oregon Episcopal Church News.
0030-4654	Oregon Commercial Fisheries Newsletter *changed to* Oregon Commercial Fisheries.
0030-4662	Oregon Daily Emerald
0030-4670	Oregon Dental Association. Journal
0030-4689	Oregon Education
0030-4697	Oregon Grange Bulletin
0030-4700	Oregon Health Bulletint
0030-4727	Oregon Historical Quarterly
0030-4735	Oregon Library News
0030-4743	Oregon Music Educator
0030-4751	Oregon Nurse
0030-476X	Oregon Optometrist *see* 0274-6549
0030-4778	Oregon Ornamental and Nursery Digest *changed to* Ornamentals NorthWest Newsletter.
0030-4786	Oregon Purchasor
0030-4794	Oregon Science Teacher
0030-4808	Oregon Sportsman and Conservationist *see* 0164-7881
0030-4816	Oregon State Bar Bulletin
0030-4832	Oregon State University. Forest Research Laboratory. Indext
0030-4840	Oregon Teamster
0030-4859	Oregon Voter Digest
0030-4867	Orella
0030-4875	Orfeo
0030-4883	Organ

ISSN INDEX

ISSN	Title
0030-4905	Organi di Trasmissione
0030-4913	Organic Gardening and Farming *see* 0884-3252
0030-4921	O M R - Organic Magnetic Resonance *see* 0749-1581
0030-493X	O M S - Organic Mass Spectrometry
0030-4948	Organic Preparations and Procedures International
0030-4956	Organic Reactivity†
0030-4964	Organisation Gestion des Enterprises
0030-4972	Organisation Internationale pour l'Etude des Langues Anciennes Par Ordinateur. Revue
0030-5006	Organische Land -und Gartenkultur†
0030-5014	Organiser
0030-5022	Organizacija Kadrovska Politika *see* 0350-1531
0030-5049	Organizacion Mercantil *changed to* Noticia Comercial del Oriente.
0030-5057	Organizacja - Metody - Technika *see* 0860-4673
0030-5065	E L N A Newsletter *changed to* Esperanto - U S A.
0030-5073	Organizational Behavior and Human Performance *see* 0749-5978
0030-5081	Organizert
0030-509X	Organizzazione Ferroviaria
0030-5103	Organizzazione Industriale†
0030-5111	Organometallic Chemistry Reviews. Section A: Subject Reviews *see* 0022-328X
0030-512X	Annual Surveys *see* 0022-328X
0030-5138	Organometallic Compounds
0030-5146	Organometallics in Chemical Synthesis†
0030-5154	Organon†
0030-5162	Organorama†
0030-5170	Orgue
0030-5189	Oriens Antiquus
0030-5197	Oriens Extremus
0030-5219	Orient
0030-5227	Orient
0030-5243	South Pacific Travel Trade News *changed to* Thomsons Travel.
0030-5251	Orientacion Docente
0030-526X	Orientacion Economica†
0030-5278	Oriental Art
0030-5294	Oriental Economist *see* 0911-7008
0030-5308	Oriental Geographer
0030-5316	Oriental Insects
0030-5324	Oriental Institute. Journal
0030-5332	Oriental Rug
0030-5340	Oriental Society of Australia. Journal
0030-5359	Oriental Tide
0030-5367	Orientalia
0030-5375	Orientalia Christiana Periodica
0030-5383	Orientalistische Literaturzeitung
0030-5391	Orientamenti Pedagogici
0030-5405	Orientamenti Sociali†
0030-5413	Orientation Professionnelle - Vocational Guidance *see* 0833-0530
0030-543X	Orientations
0030-5448	Orientations
0030-5464	Oriente Europeo†
0030-5472	Oriente Moderno
0030-5480	Orientering *changed to* Ny Tid.
0030-5499	Orientering†
0030-5502	Orientierung
0030-5510	Origin†
0030-5529	The Original Art Report
0030-5537	University of Victoria. Department of Hispanic and Italian Studies. Original Works†
0030-5545	Original Works; Art, Poetry, Fiction†
0030-5553	Oriole
0030-557X	Orion
0030-5588	Orissa Education
0030-5596	Orita
0030-560X	Orizont
0030-5618	Orizzonti Aperti
0030-5634	Orizzonti Professionali
0030-5642	Orkester Journalen
0030-5650	Orkestra
0030-5669	Orleans Parish Medical Society. Bulletin
0030-5677	Ormanci Gazetesi
0030-5685	Ornis Fennica
0030-5693	Ornis Scandinavica
0030-5707	Der Ornithologische Beobachter
0030-5715	Ornithologische Gesellschaft in Bayern. Anzeiger *see* 0940-3256
0030-5723	Ornithologische Mitteilungen
0030-5731	Ornithologische Arbeitsgruppe Mitteilungen *changed to* Lanioturdus
	Ornithologische Arbeitsgruppe Mitteilungen.
0030-5758	Oro y Hora
0030-5774	Orphan's Messenger and Advocate of the Blind *changed to* St. Joseph's Messenger and Advocate of the Blind.
0030-5790	Orpheus
0030-5804	Orphic Lute
0030-5812	Orta Dogut
0030-5839	Orthodox Word
0030-5855	Orthopaedic Medicine Surgery *changed to* Clinical Trials and Meta-Analysis.
0030-5863	Orthopaedics/Oxford†
0030-5871	Orthopaedieschuhmachermeister *see* 0344-6026
0030-588X	Orthopaedische Praxis
0030-5898	Orthopedic Clinics of North America
0030-5901	Orthopedic Surgery
0030-591X	Orthopod
0030-5928	Orthotics and Prosthetics†
0030-5936	Ortodoncia
0030-5944	Ortodontia
0030-5952	Ortodox Kyrkotidning
0030-5979	Ortopedici e Sanitari
0030-5987	Ortopediya, Travmatologiya i Protezirovanie
0030-5995	Ortskrankenkasse *see* 0936-6156
0030-6002	Orvosi Hetilap
0030-6010	Orvosi Konyvtaros
0030-6029	Orvosi Szemle†
0030-6037	Orvoskepzes
0030-6045	Orvostudomany†
0030-6053	Oryx
0030-6061	Orzecznictwo Sadow Polskich i Komisji Arbitrazowych *changed to* Orzecznictwo Sadow Polskich.
0030-607X	Orzel Bialy†
0030-6088	Osaka District Meteorological Observatory. Monthly Report
0030-610X	Osaka University. Economic Review *see* 0473-4548
0030-6118	Osaka Medical College. Journal
0030-6126	Osaka Journal of Mathematics
0030-6134	Osaka Kogyo Daigaku Kiyo. Jinbun Hen
0030-6142	Osaka Medical College. Bulletin
0030-6150	Osaka Odontological Society. Journal
0030-6169	Osaka University. Medical Journal
0030-6185	Osgoode Hall Law Journal
0030-6193	Osiguranje i Privreda
0030-6207	Journal of the Oslo City Hospitals†
0030-6223	Osnovaniya, Fundamenty i Mekhanika Gruntov
0030-6231	Ospedale
0030-624X	Ospedale al Mare. Archivio
0030-6258	Ospedali d'Italia
0030-6266	Ospedali d'Italia-Chirurgia
0030-6274	Ospedali Italiani-Pediatria
0030-6282	Polska Akademia Nauk. Osrodek Dokumentacji i Informacji Naukowej. Biuletyn *see* 0324-8194
0030-6290	Osservatore Legale
0030-6304	Osservatore Politico Letterario
0030-6320	Osservatore Tributario e Rassegna Tributaria†
0030-6339	Ostdeutscher Literatur-Anzeiger†
0030-6355	Ostehandleren *changed to* Maelk & Ost.
0030-6363	Osten
0030-6371	Osteopathic Physician†
0030-638X	Osteroder Zeitung
0030-6398	Oesterreich - Polen, Austria - Polska
0030-6428	Osteuropa
0030-6436	Osteuropa-Naturwissenschaft und Technik†
0030-6444	Osteuropa-Recht
0030-6452	Osteuropaeische Rundschau†
0030-6460	Osteuropa-Wirtschaft
0030-6479	Ostfriesland†
0030-6487	Ostkirchliche Studien
0030-6509	Osto ja Materiaalijohto *see* 0356-7931
0030-6517	Ostomy Quarterly
0030-6525	Ostrich
0030-6533	Osuuskauppalehti *see* 0781-7347
0030-655X	Otazky Miru a Socialismu
0030-6576	Other Voices†
0030-6592	Otot
0030-6614	Oto-Laryngological Society of Australia. Journal *changed to* Journal of Otolaryngology.
0030-6622	Journal of Otolaryngology of Japan
0030-6630	Oto-Rino-Laringologia Italiana†
0030-6649	Oto-Rino Laringologie
0030-6657	Otolaryngologia Polska
0030-6665	Otolaryngologic Clinics of North America
0030-6673	Audio-Digest Otorhinolaryngology *see* 0271-1354
0030-6681	Otrok in Druzina
0030-669X	Otsuka Pharmaceutical Factory. Journal
0030-6703	Ottar
0030-6711	Otto Rank Association. Journal†
0030-672X	Oud-Holland
0030-6738	Oud Utrecht. Maandblad
0030-6746	Oude Paden
0030-6754	Ouest Industriel, Maritime, Agricole et Commercial
0030-6762	Our Age†
0030-6789	Our Animals
0030-6797	Our Boys†
0030-6800	Our Children†
0030-6819	Educating in Faith
0030-6835	Animals
0030-6843	Our Family
0030-6851	Our Fourfooted Friends
0030-686X	Our Generation
0030-6878	Our Lady of the Sacred Heart *changed to* Annals Magazine.
0030-6886	Our Lady's Digest
0030-6894	Our Little Friend
0030-6916	Our Navy†
0030-6924	Our Northland Diocese
0030-6932	Our Paper
0030-6940	Our Public Lands *see* 0732-3581
0030-6959	Our Special
0030-6967	Our Sunday Visitor
0030-6975	Our World
0030-6983	Our World†
0030-6991	Ouranos-Giel-Insolite *see* 0472-2744
0030-7025	Outdoor California
0030-7033	Outdoor Education *changed to* Council on Outdoor Education. Newsletter.
0030-705X	Outdoor Illinois *see* 0148-3390
0030-7068	Outdoor Indiana
0030-7076	Outdoor Life
0030-7092	Outdoor News Bulletin
0030-7106	Outdoor Oklahoma
0030-7122	Outdoor Power Products for Recreational and Garden Merchandising *see* 0381-5528
0030-7130	Outdoor Recreation Action†
0030-7157	Wonderful West Virginia
0030-7165	Outdoor World†
0030-7173	Outdoors Magazine *see* 0004-9905
0030-7181	Outdoors Unlimited
0030-719X	Outlook†
0030-7203	Outlook *see* 0306-7262
0030-7211	Outlook *changed to* Mission Outlook.
0030-7238	Outlook (Wake Forest)
0030-7246	Standard & Poor's Outlook
0030-7254	Outlook
0030-7262	Outlook
0030-7270	Outlook on Agriculture
0030-7289	Outpost
0030-7297	Outposts *see* 0950-7264
0030-7300	Outreach *changed to* Intercom.
0030-7319	Outrider
0030-7335	Over Alle Graenser *see* 0333-2985
0030-7343	Over the Bridge†
0030-7351	Standard and Poor's Over-The-Counter *changed to* Standard & Poor's Daily Stock Price Record. Over the Counter Exchange.
0030-736X	Over-the-Counter Securities Review *changed to* Equities.
0030-7378	Over the Hills†
0030-7386	Overbrook Adviser
0030-7394	Overdrive
0030-7408	Overflow†
0030-7416	Overland
0030-7424	Overseas
0030-7432	Overseas Building Notes
0030-7440	Overseas Development *changed to* British Overseas Development.
0030-7467	Great Britain. British Geological Survey. Overseas Geology and Mineral Resources
0030-7475	Uebersee-Post - Europa-Post
0030-7491	Overseas Review *see* 0307-7039
0030-7505	Trinidad and Tobago. Central Statistical Office. Overseas Trade. Bi-Monthly Report
0030-7513	Overseas Trading
0030-7548	Overtones†
0030-7556	Overture (Los Angeles)
0030-7564	Overview (Chicago)
0030-7572	Ovtsevodstvo
0030-7580	Owl of Minerva
0030-7602	Owlet *changed to* Insight (Akron).
0030-7629	Ox Head†
0030-7645	Oxford
0030-7653	Oxford Economic Papers
0030-7661	Oxford Medical School Gazette
0030-767X	Oxford University. Institute of Statistics. Bulletin *see* 0305-9049
0030-7688	Oxfordshire Farmer *changed to* Berks, Bucks and Oxon Farmer.
0030-7696	Oxidation and Combustion Reviews†
0030-770X	Oxidation of Metals
0030-7718	Afn Shvel
0030-7726	Hokkaido Daigaku Oyo Denki Kenkyujo Hokoku *see* 0286-3189
0030-7734	Kyushu University. Research Institute for Applied Mechanics. Bulletin
0030-7750	Ozarker
0030-7769	Ozarks Mountaineer
0030-7785	R A I Orgaan *see* 0166-1922
0030-7793	P A N S *see* 0143-6147
0030-7807	P.A.R. News Analysis *changed to* P A R Analysis.
0030-7815	P A R D Bulletin
0030-7823	P and I†
0030-7831	P and S Quarterly *changed to* P & S Journal.
0030-784X	P B S Aktuell
0030-7858	P Ch C Journal of Educational Research
0030-7866	P C M - P C E†
0030-7874	P C M R Message†
0030-7904	P E D
0030-7920	P E L: Panorama Economico Latinoamericano
0030-7947	P E P *changed to* P S I: Report Series.
0030-7955	Mundo Policial
0030-7963	P F M†
0030-798X	P H P *see* 0910-4607
0030-7998	P I B Monthly *changed to* Publishers Information Bureau Report.
0030-8005	P I C I C News
0030-8013	P I E F Newsletter *see* 0276-6558
0030-8048	P J G B *see* 0260-6739
0030-8056	Praxis-Kurier *see* 0582-4877
0030-8064	Port of London
0030-8080	P M.†
0030-8099	P M A Newsletter
0030-8102	P M E A News
0030-8110	Photomethods for Industry *see* 1060-4936
0030-8129	P M L A
0030-8145	P M Newsletter (Blackburn) *see* 0141-1241
0030-8153	P.M.O. Notes
0030-817X	P N E U Journal *changed to* W E S Journal.
0030-8188	P N L A Quarterly
0030-8196	P N P A Press
0030-820X	P P G Products

ISSN	Title
0030-8218	P P S T A Herald changed to P P S T A Report.
0030-8226	P R A's Party Line changed to PartyLine.
0030-8242	Profodcil Bulletin
0030-8250	P R S Journal†
0030-8277	P S A Journal
0030-8285	P.S. for Private Secretaries changed to Professional Secretary - Administrative Support Letter.
0030-8315	P.S.: Postscript to Education changed to Alumnews.
0030-8323	P.S. Public Schools in Action†
0030-834X	P T B Mitteilungen changed to P T B - Mitteilungen Forschen und Pruefen.
0030-8358	P T M
0030-8366	P T T Bedrijf†
0030-8374	P T T Informations changed to P T T Info.
0030-8382	Telecommunicatie†
0030-8390	P T T - Zbornik changed to P T T Novice.
0030-8404	P U D O C Bulletin†
0030-8412	P.U.-Kanert
0030-8420	P.U.R. Executive Information Service changed to P.U.R. Letter.
0030-8439	Printing Views changed to Printing News - Midwest.
0030-8447	Paarl Post
0030-8455	Paarlse Padwyser changed to Strooidak.
0030-8471	Pace†
0030-851X	Pacific Affairs
0030-8528	Pacific Bakers News
0030-8536	Pacific Banker and Business see 8750-6718
0030-8544	Pacific Builder and Engineer
0030-8552	Pacific Business News
0030-8560	Pacific Business Magazine†
0030-8579	Pacific Citizen
0030-8587	Pacific Coast Nurseryman and Garden Supply Dealer see 0192-7159
0030-8617	Pacific Coast Society of Orthodontists. Bulletin
0030-8625	Pacific Community†
0030-8633	Pacific Community changed to Asia Pacific Community.
0030-8641	Pacific Discovery
0030-865X	Pacific Factory changed to Western Machining & Metalworking.
0030-8668	Pacific Fruit News
0030-8676	Pacific Historian†
0030-8684	Pacific Historical Review
0030-8692	Pacific Hosteller
0030-8706	Pacific Hotel-Motel News†
0030-8714	Pacific Insects see 0735-6250
0030-8722	Pacific Islands Monthly
0030-8730	Pacific Journal of Mathematics
0030-8757	Pacific Law Journal
0030-8765	P M L - Life changed to Wavelength (Newport Beach).
0030-8781	Pacific Neighbors†
0030-879X	Pacific News changed to Pacific Rail News.
0030-8803	Pacific Northwest Quarterly
0030-8811	Pacific Northwest Underwriter†
0030-882X	Pacific Northwesterner
0030-8838	Pacific Orchid Society of Hawaii. Bulletin see 0099-8745
0030-8846	Pacific Purchasor†
0030-8854	Pacific Research and World Empire Telegrams changed to Pacific Research.
0030-8862	Pacific Review
0030-8870	Pacific Science
0030-8889	Pacific Science Association. Information Bulletin
0030-8900	Pacific Shipper
0030-8919	Pacific Sociological Review see 0731-1214
0030-8943	Pacific Traffic
0030-8951	Pacific Travel News†
0030-896X	Pacific Tribune
0030-8978	Pacific Viewpoint
0030-8986	Pacific Yachting
0030-9001	Pack changed to Pack-Distribution.
0030-901X	Pack-o-Fun
0030-9028	Package Development see 0274-4996
0030-9044	Package Engineering see 0746-3820
0030-9052	Packages & People†
0030-9060	Packaging
0030-9087	Packaging Abstracts see 0260-7409
0030-9095	Packaging Bulletin see 0890-4227
0030-9109	Packaging Design see 0032-8510
0030-9117	Packaging Digest
0030-9125	Packaging India
0030-9133	Packaging News
0030-9141	Packaging Technology changed to Packaging Technology and Management.
0030-9168	Packer
0030-9184	Packung und Transport im Chemiebetrieb see 0343-7183
0030-9192	Padova e la sua Provincia
0030-9206	Padova Economica
0030-9214	Padre Santo
0030-9222	Padres' Trail
0030-9230	Paedagogica Historica
0030-9249	Paedagogik
0030-9257	Paedagogik Heute†
0030-9273	Paedagogische Rundschau
0030-9281	Paedagogisches Institut der Stadt Wien. Mitteilungen changed to Paedagogische Institute. Mitteilungen.
0030-929X	Paedagogisches Institute Salzburg. Mitteilungen changed to Paedagogische Mitteilungen.
0030-9311	Paediatrica Indonesiana
0030-932X	Paediatrie und Grenzgebiete
0030-9338	Paediatrie und Paedologie
0030-9346	Paediatrische Praxis
0030-9362	Page
0030-9389	Pages
0030-9397	Pages†
0030-9400	Pagine di Storia della Medicina see 0394-9001
0030-9427	Pahlavi Medical Journal see 0253-0716
0030-9435	Paideia
0030-9443	Paikallislehdisto
0030-946X	Paint and Resin Patents†
0030-9478	Paint and Varnish Production see 0098-7786
0030-9508	Paint Manufacture see 0261-5746
0030-9516	Paint Oil and Colour Journal see 0370-1158
0030-9524	Paint Technology see 0369-9420
0030-9532	Painter & Allied Trades Journal
0030-9540	Paintindia
0030-9567	Pais e Filhos
0030-9575	Pajara Pinta†
0030-9583	Pajtas
0030-9591	Pak Jamhuriat
0030-9605	Pak-Scout
0030-9613	Pakin
0030-9621	Pakistan Accountant
0030-963X	Pakistan Affairs
0030-9656	Pakistan Army Journal
0030-9664	Pakistan Book News†
0030-9680	Pakistan Chemist & Druggist†
0030-9699	Pakistan Cottons
0030-9702	Pakistan Council for National Integration. Review†
0030-9710	Pakistan Dental Review
0030-9729	Pakistan Development Review
0030-9745	Pakistan Economist see 0253-1941
0030-9753	Pakistan Engineer see 0379-4318
0030-977X	Pakistan Exports
0030-9788	Pakistan Geographical Review†
0030-9796	Pakistan Historical Society. Journal
0030-980X	Pakistan Horizon
0030-9818	Pakistan Journal of Forestry
0030-9826	Pakistan Journal of Geriatrics†
0030-9834	Pakistan Journal of Health
0030-9842	Pakistan Journal of Medical Research
0030-9850	Pakistan Journal of Pharmacy
0030-9869	Pakistan Journal of Psychology†
0030-9877	Pakistan Journal of Science
0030-9885	Pakistan Journal of Scientific and Industrial Research
0030-9893	Pakistan Journal of Soil Science changed to Bangladesh Journal of Soil Science.
0030-9915	Pakistan Journal of Veterinary Science changed to Bangladesh Veterinary Journal.
0030-9923	Pakistan Journal of Zoology
0030-994X	Pakistan Labour Cases
0030-9958	All Pakistan Legal Decisions
0030-9966	Pakistan Library Bulletin
0030-9982	Pakistan Medical Association. Journal
0030-9990	Pakistan Medical Forum†
0031-0026	Pakistan. Ministry of Information & Broadcasting. Progress of the Month†
0031-0034	Pakistan Monitor
0031-0042	Pakistan News Digest changed to Weekly Commentary and Pakistan News Digest.
0031-0050	Pakistan Press Index†
0031-0069	Pakistan Quarterly†
0031-0077	Pakistan Review†
0031-0085	Pakistan Science Abstracts
0031-0093	Pakistan Stamps
0031-0107	Pakistan Studies†
0031-0115	Pakistan Tax Decisions
0031-0131	Pakkaus
0031-0158	El Palacio
0031-0166	Paladijn†
0031-0174	Palaeobotanist
0031-0182	Palaeogeography, Palaeoclimatology, Palaeoecology
0031-0204	Palaeontological Society of Japan. Transactions and Proceedings
0031-0220	Palaeontologische Zeitschrift
0031-0239	Palaeontology
0031-0247	Palaeovertebrata
0031-0255	Palaestra
0031-0263	Palaestra Latina†
0031-0298	PaleoBios
0031-0301	Paleontological Journal
0031-031X	Paleontologicheskii Zhurnal
0031-0328	Palestine Exploration Quarterly
0031-0336	Palestine Refugees Today
0031-0344	Palestra
0031-0360	Palimpsest
0031-0379	Palladio
0031-0387	Pallas
0031-0395	Pallottis Werk
0031-0417	Palm Beach Life
0031-0425	Palm Springs Life
0031-0433	Palmer Writer†
0031-0441	Palmos Tou Geneous†
0031-045X	Palomino Horses
0031-0468	Palontorjunta
0031-0476	Palontorjuntatekniika
0031-0492	Palynological Bulletin see 0022-3379
0031-0506	Pamatky Archeologicke
0031-0514	Pamietnik Literacki
0031-0522	Pamietnik Teatralny
0031-0530	Pamir Monthly changed to Pamir Magazine.
0031-0549	Pammatone see 0393-6414
0031-0557	Pamphleteer Monthly†
0031-0565	Pan-African Journal†
0031-059X	Pan American Review
0031-0603	Pan-Pacific Entomologist
0031-0611	Pan Pipes of Sigma Alpha Iota see 0889-7581
0031-0638	Panadero Latinoamericano - Latin American Baker see 0744-625X
0031-0646	Panama Canal Review†
0031-0662	Pancevac
0031-0697	Pandecte Neon Noman Kediataghmaton
0031-0719	Pandora changed to Pandora: a Washington Women's News Journal.
0031-0735	Panel†
0031-0743	Excerpta Medica. Section 50: Epilepsy Abstracts
0031-076X	Panhandle Magazine
0031-0778	Panidealistische Umschau
0031-0786	Panjab Past and Present
0031-0794	Punjab University Economist changed to Pakistan Economic and Social Review.
0031-0808	Panminerva Medica changed to Panminerva Medica - Europa Medica.
0031-0824	Panorama (Fortitude Valley)
0031-0840	Panorama changed to Colorado Women's College. Bulletin.
0031-0859	Panorama†
0031-0867	Panorama
0031-0875	Panorama†
0031-0883	Panorama
0031-0891	Panorama Ballesterense changed to Reportero.
0031-093X	Panorama Economico†
0031-0948	Panorama Medical†
0031-0964	Panorama Polnocy
0031-0972	Panpere
0031-0980	Panstwo i Prawo
0031-0999	Pantheon see 0720-0056
0031-1006	Panther changed to Advocate (Johnstown).
0031-1014	Pantograph changed to Pantograph.
0031-1022	Pantuflas del Obispo
0031-1049	Papeis Avulsos de Zoologia
0031-1057	Papel
0031-1065	Papeles de Son Armadans†
0031-1081	Paper Age
0031-109X	Printing Abstracts
0031-1103	Paper and Twine Journal
0031-1111	Paper Bulletin changed to Paper and Packaging Analyst.
0031-112X	Paper Facts and Figures
0031-1138	Paper, Film and Foil Converter
0031-1146	Paper Maker†
0031-1154	Paper-Maker see 0306-8234
0031-1162	Paper Money
0031-1170	Paper Sales
0031-1189	Paper Technology changed to Paper Technology.
0031-1197	Paper Trade Journal†
0031-1200	Paper Trends†
0031-1219	Paperbacks in Print see 0262-9763
0031-1227	Paperboard Packaging
0031-1235	Paperbound Books in Print
0031-1243	Paperi ja Puu
0031-1251	Papers in Linguistics: International Journal of Human Communication
0031-126X	Papers in Meteorology and Geophysics
0031-1278	Papers in Psychology†
0031-1286	Papers of Woodrow Wilson
0031-1294	Papers on Language and Literature
0031-1308	Papeterie
0031-1316	Papeterist
0031-1324	Papetier de France
0031-1332	Papetier Libraire
0031-1340	Das Papier
0031-1359	Papier- und Buchgewerbe-rundschau see 0259-7454
0031-1367	Papier Carton et Cellulose
0031-1375	Papier und Druck
0031-1383	Papiergeschichte
0031-1391	Papiershandels-Fachblatt changed to Boss - Oesterreich.
0031-1405	Der Papiermacher
0031-1413	Papierwereld†
0031-1421	Papir a Celuloza
0031-143X	Papirhandleren
0031-1448	Papiripar
0031-1456	Pappershandlaren changed to Papper & Kontor Data.
0031-1464	Papua New Guinea Agricultural Journal changed to Papua New Guinea Journal of Agriculture, Forestry and Fisheries.
0031-1472	Papua New Guinea Journal of Education
0031-1480	Papua New Guinea Medical Journal
0031-1510	Papua New Guinea Overseas Migration see 1017-6551
0031-1529	Papua New Guinea. Bureau of Statistics. Quarterly Retail Price Index see 1017-6500
0031-1537	Papua and New Guinea. Quarterly Summary of Statistics see 0310-5377

ISSN INDEX 5427

ISSN	Title
0031-1545	Para Elite
0031-1553	Parabas
0031-1561	Paraboles
0031-1588	Parachutist
0031-1596	Paradet
0031-160X	Parade
0031-1618	Parade and Foto-Action *changed to* Parade Magazine.
0031-1642	Parag
0031-1650	Paragone
0031-1669	Paragraphs *changed to* Network (Arlington).
0031-1677	Paraguay. Direccion General de Estadistica y Censos. Boletin Estadistico
0031-1685	Paraguay Industrial y Comercial
0031-1715	Parallelo Trentotto
0031-1723	Parameters (Carlisle Barracks)
0031-1731	Parametro
0031-174X	Parana em Paginas
0031-1766	Paraplegia News
0031-1790	Parapsychology Bulletin†
0031-1804	Parapsychology Review†
0031-1812	Parasitica
0031-1820	Parasitology (Cambridge)
0031-1839	Paratus
0031-1847	Parazitologiya
0031-1855	Pardon
0031-1863	Parent Educator†
0031-188X	Parents' Bulletin†
0031-1898	Parents et Instituteurs†
0031-1901	Parents et Maitres†
0031-191X	Parents' Magazine and Better Family Living *see* 0195-0967
0031-1928	Lexington School for the Deaf. Parents' Newsletter. *changed to* Sounds of Lexington.
0031-1936	Parents Voice *changed to* Mencap News.
0031-1952	Parfuemerie und Kosmetik
0031-1979	Parichiti
0031-1987	Paris
0031-2002	Paris District. Journal des Communes†
0031-2010	Paris Gaz Relations *changed to* Gaz Relations.
0031-2029	Paris Match
0031-2037	Paris Review
0031-2045	Paris-Sud
0031-2053	Pariser Kurier†
0031-2061	Parish Councils Review *see* 0308-3594
0031-207X	Parish News†
0031-2088	Parishioner
0031-2096	Pariyal Kalyan
0031-210X	Park
0031-2118	Park Administration
0031-2126	Park East
0031-2134	Park Maintenance *see* 1057-204X
0031-2142	Park News†
0031-2150	Grist
0031-2177	Parkdalian
0031-2193	Parking
0031-2207	Dierenpark Wassenaar Zoo. Parknieuws†
0031-2215	Parks and Recreation
0031-2223	Parks and Recreation *see* 0267-3754
0031-2231	Recreation Canada
0031-224X	Parks and Sports Grounds *changed to* Parks, Golf Courses and Sports Grounds.
0031-2258	Das Parlament
0031-2282	Parliamentarian
0031-2290	Parliamentary Affairs
0031-2312	Parmamedica
0031-2320	Parnasso
0031-2347	Paroisse et Liturgie *changed to* Communautes et Liturgies.
0031-2355	Parola del Passato
0031-2363	Parola del Popolo†
0031-2371	Parola e il Libro
0031-2398	Parole di Vita
0031-2401	Parole e le Idee
0031-2428	Parrocchia
0031-2436	Parson and Parish
0031-2444	U.S. Agency for International Development. Participant Journal†
0031-2460	Particle Accelerators
0031-2479	Particles and Nuclei†
0031-2487	Particulate Matter†
0031-2509	Partiinaya Zhizn'
0031-2517	Activist†
0031-2525	Partisan Review
0031-2533	Partisans†
0031-255X	Partizanov Vesnik
0031-2568	Partners
0031-2576	Parts Line†
0031-2584	Pas a Past
0031-2592	Paseo del Rio Showboat *changed to* Reflexiones.
0031-2606	Pashupalan *see* 0023-1088
0031-2614	Pasicrisie Belge
0031-2630	Pasinomie
0031-2649	Pasque Petals
0031-2657	Pasquino
0031-2665	Passaic County Historical Society. Bulletin†
0031-2673	Passaic County Medical Society. Bulletin†
0031-2681	Passauer Bistumsblatt
0031-2703	Passenger Pigeon
0031-2711	Passerellet
0031-272X	Passport
0031-2738	Password
0031-2746	Past and Present: a Journal of Historical Studies
0031-2754	Pastor Evangelico *changed to* Obrero Cristiano.
0031-2762	Pastoral Life
0031-2789	Pastoral Psychology
0031-2797	Pastoral Review
0031-2800	Pastoralblaetter
0031-2819	Pastoralist and Grazier Newsletter *changed to* Rural Update.
0031-2827	Wissenschaft und Praxis in Kirche und Gesellschaft *see* 0720-6259
0031-2835	Patent and Trademark Review†
0031-286X	Patent Journal Including Trademarks and Models
0031-2878	Patent Licensing Gazette *changed to* World Technology.
0031-2894	Patentblatt
0031-2908	Patentni Glasnik
0031-2916	Finland. Patentti- ja Rekisterihallitus. Patenttilehti
0031-2932	Path of Truth
0031-2940	Pathfinder *changed to* Traveller.
0031-2959	Schweizerische Zeitschrift fuer Allgemeine Pathologie und Bakteriologie *see* 1015-2008
0031-2967	Pathologia Europaea†
0031-2975	Pathologia Veterinaria *see* 0300-9858
0031-2983	Pathologica
0031-2991	Patologicheskaya Fiziologiya i Eksperimental'naya Terapiya
0031-3009	Pathologie Biologie
0031-3017	Pathologist†
0031-3025	Pathology
0031-305X	Patient Care
0031-3068	Patisserie Francaise Illustree
0031-3076	Patissier de l'Ile-De-France†
0031-3084	Patna Journal of Medicine
0031-3092	Patna University Journal
0031-3106	Patologia
0031-3114	Patologia Polska
0031-3122	Patranu
0031-3130	Patria Indipendente
0031-3149	Patrimonium *changed to* Bouw en Beheer.
0031-3165	Patronat Francais *see* 0399-8975
0031-3173	Patronato Genovese Pronatura "A. Anfossi." Notiziario†
0031-3181	Patrys
0031-319X	Pattern Makers' Journal *changed to* Pattern Makers & Allied Crafts Journal.
0031-3203	Pattern Recognition
0031-3211	Patterns *see* 0146-1397
0031-322X	Patterns of Prejudice
0031-3238	Patterson's California Beverage Gazetteer *see* 0895-3872
0031-3246	Paukenslag†
0031-3262	Paunch
0031-3270	Pauzet
0031-3289	Pavliha
0031-3297	Pavo
0031-3300	Paxt
0031-3319	Pax Bulletin *see* 0306-7645
0031-3327	Pax et Libertas
0031-3335	Pax Regis
0031-3351	Pay Planning†
0031-336X	Pay Planning Checklist and Forms†
0031-3386	Pays Bas-Normand
0031-3394	Pays Lorrain
0031-3408	Paz e Terra†
0031-3416	Pcela
0031-3432	Peabody Journal of Education
0031-3440	Peabody Notes *changed to* Peabody News.
0031-3459	Peabody Reflector
0031-3467	Peace
0031-3491	Peace and Freedom
0031-3513	Peace and the Sciences
0031-353X	Peace Monitor
0031-3548	Peace News
0031-3556	Peace Officer *changed to* Police Officers Journal.
0031-3564	Peace Plans
0031-3572	Peace Press†
0031-3580	Excerpta Medica. Section 48: Gastroenterology
0031-3599	Peace Research Abstracts Journal
0031-3602	Peacemaker
0031-3610	Peach-Times
0031-3629	Peak
0031-3637	Peak District Mines Historical Society. Bulletin
0031-3645	Peanut Farmer
0031-3661	Peanut Journal and Nut World
0031-367X	Peat Abstracts
0031-3696	Pebble
0031-370X	Peche au Canada†
0031-3718	Peche et les Poissons
0031-3726	Peche Maritime
0031-3734	Pecheur et Chasseur Suisses *changed to* Pecheur Romand.
0031-3742	Pecheurs d'Hommes†
0031-3750	Pecsi Muszaki Szemle
0031-3777	Pedagogia e Vita
0031-3785	Pedagogiai Szemle
0031-3793	Pedagogic Reporter
0031-3807	Pedagogija
0031-3815	Pedagogika
0031-3823	Pedagogisch Forum *see* 0166-5855
0031-3831	Scandinavian Journal of Educational Research
0031-384X	Pedagoski Rad
0031-3858	Pedagoski Zivot
0031-3866	Pedale d'Oro
0031-3874	Arrive *see* 0144-2694
0031-3882	Pediatria
0031-3890	Pediatria
0031-3904	Revista de Pediatrie, Obstetrica, Ginecologie. Pediatrie
0031-3912	Pediatria e Puericultura
0031-3920	Pediatria Moderna
0031-3939	Pediatria Polska†
0031-3947	Pediatria Pratica
0031-3955	Pediatric Clinics of North America
0031-3963	United Hospitals of Newark. Babies Hospital Unit. Pediatric Conferences *see* 0097-5982
0031-398X	Pediatric News
0031-3998	Pediatric Research
0031-4005	Pediatrics
0031-4013	Pediatrics Digest *see* 0198-6341
0031-4021	Pediatrie
0031-403X	Pediatriya
0031-4048	Pediatriya, Akusherstvo ta Ginekologiya
0031-4056	Pedobiologia
0031-4064	Pedologist
0031-4072	Pegasus *see* 0318-5753
0031-4080	Pegasus Journal
0031-4099	Peiling
0031-4110	Peking Informers
0031-4129	Peking Review *see* 1000-9140
0031-4137	Pelagos
0031-4145	Pelerin du Vingtieme Siecle *see* 0399-5755
0031-4153	Pelicant
0031-4161	Pelican News
0031-417X	Pelitat
0031-4188	Pellervo
0031-4242	The Pen Woman
0031-4250	Pendle Hill Pamphlets
0031-4285	Peninsula
0031-4293	Peninsula Living†
0031-4307	Peninsula Poets
0031-4315	Penmen's News Letter
0031-4331	Penn Dental Journal
0031-434X	Pennsylvania Angler
0031-4366	Pennsylvania. Board of Probation and Parole. Monthly Statistical Report
0031-4374	Pennsylvania. Board of Probation and Parole. Quarterly Statistical Report *see* 0031-4366
0031-4382	Pennsylvania Business Survey
0031-4390	Pennsylvania C P A Spokesman *see* 0746-1062
0031-4404	Pennsylvania Chiefs of Police Association Bulletin
0031-4412	Pennsylvania Contractor
0031-4420	Pennsylvania Dental Association. Newsletter†
0031-4439	Pennsylvania Dental Journal
0031-4455	Pennsylvania Education
0031-4471	Pennsylvania Farmer
0031-448X	Pennsylvania Flower Growers. Bulletin
0031-4498	Pennsylvania Folklife
0031-4501	Pennsylvania Forests
0031-451X	Pennsylvania Game News
0031-4528	Pennsylvania History
0031-4536	Pennsylvania Holstein News†
0031-4544	Pennsylvania Human Relations Report†
0031-4552	Pennsylvania Jewish Life†
0031-4587	Pennsylvania Magazine of History and Biography
0031-4595	Pennsylvania Medicine
0031-4609	Pennsylvania Message
0031-4617	Pennsylvania Nurse
0031-4625	Pennsylvania Optometrist†
0031-4633	Pennsylvania Pharmacist
0031-4641	Pennsylvania Professional Engineer *changed to* Engineer (Pittsburgh).
0031-465X	Pennsylvania Psychiatric Quarterly†
0031-4668	Pennsylvania School Boards Association. Bulletin *see* 0162-3559
0031-4676	Pennsylvania School Journal†
0031-4692	Pennsylvania Traveler *changed to* Pennsylvania Traveler-Post.
0031-4706	Pennsylvania Veterinarian†
0031-4714	Pennsylvanian
0031-4730	Pensadort
0031-4749	Pensamiento
0031-4757	Pensamiento Politico†
0031-4765	Pensamiento y Accion
0031-4781	Pensee Catholique
0031-479X	La Pensee Francaise†
0031-4803	Pensez Plastiques
0031-4811	Pensierot
0031-482X	Pensiero Mazziniano
0031-4838	Pensiero Nazionale
0031-4846	Pensiero Politico
0031-4854	Pensioen Bulletin
0031-4862	Pension and Welfare News *see* 0098-1753
0031-4870	Pentagon
0031-4889	Pentagramma *changed to* Primi Piani.
0031-4897	Pentecostal Evangel
0031-4900	International Pentecostal Holiness Advocate
0031-4919	Pentecostal Messenger
0031-4927	Pentecostal Testimony
0031-4935	Girls of Penthouse
0031-496X	Penzugyi Szemle
0031-4986	People†
0031-4994	People†
0031-5001	People†
0031-501X	People (Kansas City)
0031-5028	People's Action†

ISSN INDEX

ISSN	Title
0031-5036	People's Korea
0031-5044	People's World†
0031-5052	Peoria Labor News *changed to* Labor Paper.
0031-5087	Pepinieristes Horticulteurs Maraichers *see* 0758-1688
0031-5117	Perception & Psychophysics
0031-5125	Perceptual and Motor Skills
0031-5133	Perceptual-Cognitive Development†
0031-5141	Perchtoldsdorfer Pfarrbote
0031-5168	Percussionist and Percussive Notes *see* 0553-6502
0031-5176	Perets
0031-5184	Perfect Home†
0031-5192	Perfekt Kindermode
0031-5206	Perfekt Mode
0031-5214	Performance (Washington, 1977) *changed to* Worklife.
0031-5222	Performing Arts
0031-5230	Performing Arts in Canada
0031-5249	Performing Arts Review *see* 0733-5113
0031-5257	Performing Right *changed to* P R S News.
0031-529X	Periodica de Re Morali Canonica Liturgica
0031-5303	Periodica Mathematica Hungarica
0031-5311	Periodica Polytechnica. Chemical Engineering
0031-532X	Periodica Polytechnica. Electrical Engineering
0031-5338	Periodica Polytechnica. Engineering, Maschinen- und Bauwesen *see* 0324-6051
0031-5346	Periodica Polytechnica. Architecture
0031-5362	Periodicum Biologorum
0031-5397	Periodontology Today
0031-5400	Peripherals Weekly *changed to* Peripherals Digest.
0031-5427	Periscope (Hartsville)†
0031-5435	Perito Industriale†
0031-546X	Perlin et Pinpin *changed to* Perlin et Pinpin.
0031-5478	Permanences
0031-5486	Permanencia
0031-5508	Permanent International Altaistic Conference (PIAC). Newsletter
0031-5516	Permanent Way†
0031-5524	Permanent Way Institution. Journal and Report of Proceedings
0031-5532	P S I†
0031-5540	Perpetual Motion Journal†
0031-5559	Perpustakaan†
0031-5567	Nederlandse Hervormde Kerk. Persbureau. Weekbulletin
0031-5575	Persklaar *changed to* Intercom.
0031-5591	Personal Injury Valuation Handbooks
0031-5605	Personal
0031-5613	Personal Romances
0031-5621	Personalist *see* 0279-0750
0031-563X	Personality†
0031-5648	Personality *changed to* Personality.
0031-5656	Personeelbeleid
0031-5699	Personhistorisk Tidskrift
0031-5702	Personnel *changed to* H R Focus.
0031-5729	Personnel Administrator *changed to* H R Magazine.
0031-5737	Personnel and Guidance Journal *see* 0748-9633
0031-5745	Personnel Journal
0031-5753	Personnel Literature
0031-5761	Personnel Management
0031-577X	Personnel Management Abstracts
0031-5788	International Personnel Management Association. Personnel News *changed to* I P M A News.
0031-580X	Personnel Policies Forum *see* 0361-7467
0031-5818	Australia. Department of Labour and National Service. Personnel Practice Bulletin *see* 0312-455X
0031-5826	Personnel Psychology
0031-5834	Personnel Quarterly *changed to* L.O.M.A. Resource.
0031-5842	Persoon en Gemeenschap†
0031-5850	Persoonia
0031-5869	Persoverzicht
0031-5885	Perspective (Augusta) *changed to* Maine. Arts Commission. Newsletter.
0031-5893	Perpective (St. Louis)†
0031-5915	Perspective†
0031-5923	Perspective
0031-5931	Perspective (Olympia)†
0031-594X	Peace Courier
0031-5958	Perspectives: Journal of General and Liberal Studies *see* 0890-9792
0031-5974	Federation Nationale des Clubs Perspectives et Realities *changed to* Perspectives et Realities.
0031-5982	Perspectives in Biology and Medicine
0031-5990	Perspectives in Psychiatric Care
0031-6016	Perspectives of New Music
0031-6032	Perspectives Psychiatriques
0031-6059	Perspektywy
0031-6067	Biblioteca Nacional del Peru. Boletin
0031-6075	Pesca Italiana
0031-6091	Pescare
0031-6105	Peshawar Times†
0031-6121	Pest Control
0031-613X	Pesticide Science
0031-6148	Pesticides†
0031-6156	Pesticides Monitoring Journal†
0031-6164	Pesum Padam
0031-6180	P S M *see* 0162-8666
0031-6229	Petermanns Geographische Mitteilungen
0031-6245	Petfood Industry
0031-6253	Le Petit Journal du Brasseur
0031-6261	Petit Meunier
0031-627X	Petit Moniteur des Assurances *changed to* Le Moniteur des Assurances.
0031-6296	Petnaest Dana
0031-630X	Petra
0031-6318	Petri-Heil
0031-6326	Petro-Chem Engineer *see* 0031-6466
0031-6334	Petrobrast
0031-6342	PetroChemical News
0031-6350	Petrol si Gaze *changed to* Mine, Petrol si Gaze.
0031-6369	Arab Oil & Gas
0031-6407	Petroleo Interamericano *see* 0093-7851
0031-6415	Petroleo y Mineria de Venezuela
0031-6423	Petroleum Abstracts
0031-6431	Modern Bulk Transporter
0031-644X	Petroleum and TBA Marketer *see* 0362-7799
0031-6458	Petroleum Chemistry U.S.S.R.
0031-6466	Petroleum Engineer International
0031-6490	Petroleum Outlook
0031-6504	Petroleum Press Service *see* 0306-395X
0031-6512	Petroleum Refining Developments†
0031-6539	Petroleum Taxation Report *changed to* Petroleum Taxation & Legislation Report.
0031-6547	Petroleum Times *see* 0141-4437
0031-6555	Petroleum Today†
0031-6563	Petrolieri d'Italia
0031-6571	Petrolio
0031-658X	Petronio
0031-6598	Petrotecnica
0031-661X	Peuple
0031-6644	Pewter Collectors' Club of America. Bulletin
0031-6652	El Pez y la Serpiente
0031-6660	Pfaelzer Bauer
0031-6679	Pfaelzer Heimat
0031-6687	Pfaelzer Saenger
0031-6695	Die Pfalz am Rhein
0031-6709	Pfarrbrief
0031-6725	Pfizer Spectrum†
0031-6733	Pflanzenarzt
0031-6741	Pflanzenernaehrung und Duengung†
0031-675X	Pflanzenschutzberichte
0031-6768	Pfluegers Archiv
0031-6776	Pflugschart
0031-6784	Die Pforte†
0031-6792	Peradarstvo
0031-6806	Phapharna!
0031-6814	Phare
0031-6822	Pharetra
0031-6849	Pharma Times
0031-6857	Pharmaca
0031-6865	Pharmaceutica Acta Helvetiae
0031-6873	Pharmaceutical Journal
0031-689X	Pharmaceutical Research Institute. Bulletin
0031-6903	Pharmaceutical Society of Japan. Journal
0031-692X	Le Pharmacien
0031-6938	Pharmacien de France
0031-6946	Pharmacien de Reserve
0031-6954	Pharmacien Rural
0031-6970	European Journal of Clinical Pharmacology
0031-6989	Pharmacological Research Communications *see* 1043-6618
0031-6997	Pharmacological Reviews
0031-7004	Pharmacologist
0031-7012	Pharmacology
0031-7020	Rational Drug Therapy†
0031-7039	Pharmacotoxicologia et Therapia Clinica†
0031-7047	Pharmacy in History
0031-7063	Pharmacy News
0031-7071	Pharmacy Trade
0031-708X	Pharmakeftikon Deltion†
0031-7098	Pharmakopsychiatrie - Neuro-Psychopharmakologie *see* 0176-3679
0031-7101	Pharmanews†
0031-711X	Die Pharmazeutische Industrie
0031-7128	Pharmazeutische Rundschau
0031-7136	Pharmazeutische Zeitung
0031-7152	Pharmindex
0031-7160	Pharos (St. Petersburg)
0031-7179	Pharos (Menlo Park)
0031-7187	Pharet
0031-7209	Phi Delta Epsilon News & Scientific Journal
0031-7217	Phi Delta Kappan
0031-7233	Philadelphia Magazine
0031-725X	Philadelphia College of Pharmacy and Science Bulletin
0031-7268	Philadelphia County Dental Society. Bulletin
0031-7276	Philadelphia Dental Laboratory Association Journal†
0031-7306	Philadelphia Medicine
0031-7314	Philadelphia Museum of Art. Bulletin
0031-7322	Mid-Atlantic Purchasing *changed to* P M News.
0031-7349	South Africa. Philatelic Services. Philatelic Bulletin *changed to* South Africa. Philatelic Services and Intersapa. Philatelic Bulletin.
0031-7365	Philatelic Trader and Stationer *changed to* Philatelic Trader.
0031-7373	Philatelist *see* 0260-6739
0031-7381	The Philatelic Exporter
0031-739X	Philately *see* 0953-5241
0031-7403	Philately from Australia
0031-7438	Philippine Abstracts *changed to* Philippine Science and Technology Abstracts.
0031-7446	Philippine Agricultural Situation†
0031-7454	Philippine Agriculturist
0031-7462	Philippine Architecture & Building Journal
0031-7470	Philippine Architecture, Engineering & Construction Record
0031-7489	Philippine Business Index *changed to* Philippine Economics and Business Index.
0031-7497	Philippine Dental Association. Journal
0031-7500	Philippine Economic Journal
0031-7527	Philippine Educational Forum
0031-7543	Philippine Fishing Journal
0031-7551	Philippine Geographical Journal
0031-756X	Philippine Geologist *see* 0368-2331
0031-7578	Philippine Health Journal *changed to* Philippine Health Education Journal.
0031-7594	Philippine Journal of Business and Finance
0031-7608	Philippine Journal of Cancer
0031-7616	Philippine Journal of Child-Youth Development
0031-7624	Philippine Journal of Education
0031-7632	Philippine Journal of Leprosy *changed to* Philippine Journal of Dermatology and Leprosy.
0031-7640	Philippine Journal of Nutrition
0031-7659	Philippine Journal of Ophthalmology
0031-7667	Philippine Journal of Pediatrics
0031-7675	Philippine Journal of Public Administration
0031-7683	Philippine Journal of Science
0031-7691	Philippine Journal of Surgical Specialties
0031-7705	Philippine Journal of Veterinary Medicine
0031-7713	Philippine Junior Red Cross Magazine†
0031-7721	Philippine Law Journal
0031-773X	Philippine Manager
0031-7748	Philippine Medical Association. Journal
0031-7764	Philippine Progress†
0031-7780	Philippine Review of Economics and Business
0031-7799	Philippine Scientific Journal
0031-7810	Philippine Sociological Review
0031-7829	Philippine Statistician
0031-7837	Philippine Studies
0031-7845	Philippine Tax Journal
0031-7853	Philippine Women's University Administrative News
0031-787X	Philippines Labor Relations Journal
0031-7888	Philippines Transportation
0031-7896	Philips Cronache *changed to* Cronache.
0031-790X	Philips Music Herald†
0031-7926	Philips Technical Review†
0031-7942	Philips Exeter Bulletin *see* 0195-0207
0031-7969	Philobiblon
0031-7977	Philological Quarterly
0031-7985	Philologus
0031-7993	Philosopher's Index
0031-8000	Philosophia
0031-8019	Philosophia Mathematica
0031-8027	Philosophia Naturalis
0031-8035	Philosophia Reformata
0031-8043	Philosophical Association. Journal†
0031-8051	Philosophical Books
0031-806X	Philosophical Forum
0031-8078	Philosophical Journal†
0031-8086	Philosophical Magazine
0031-8094	Philosophical Quarterly
0031-8108	Philosophical Review
0031-8116	Philosophical Studies
0031-8140	Philosophische Probleme des Sozialistischen Aufbaus und der Technischen Revolution *see* 0232-8798
0031-8159	Philosophische Rundschau
0031-8167	Philosophische Zeitspiegel
0031-8175	Philosophischer Literaturanzeiger
0031-8183	Philosophisches Jahrbuch
0031-8191	Philosophy
0031-8205	Philosophy and Phenomenological Research
0031-8213	Philosophy and Rhetoric
0031-8221	Philosophy East and West
0031-823X	Philosophy Forum *see* 0260-4027
0031-8248	Philosophy of Science
0031-8256	Philosophy Today
0031-8264	Philotelia
0031-8272	Philwomenian
0031-8280	Phlebologie *changed to* Societe Francaise de Phlebologie. Bulletin.
0031-8299	Phoenix (Toronto, 1946)
0031-8310	Phoenix†
0031-8329	Phoenix
0031-8337	Phoenix†
0031-8353	Phoenix Jewish News *see* 0747-444X

0031-837X Phoenix Quarterly *changed to* Phoenix: Voice of the Scrap Recycling Industries.
0031-8388 Phonetica
0031-8396 Phoni Tou Evangeliou
0031-8426 Phosphorus and Potassium
0031-8434 Phosphorus in Agriculture *changed to* Fertilizers and Agriculture.
0031-8442 Photo
0031-8450 Photo-Cine-Expert *changed to* Photo-Cine-Expert (1979).
0031-8469 Photo-Cine-Revue *changed to* Photo-Revue.
0031-8477 Photo-Cinema, Film, Amateur-Son *changed to* Photomagazine.
0031-8485 Photo Dealer†
0031-8515 Photographic Processor†
0031-8523 Photo Interpretation
0031-8531 Photo Marketing Newsline
0031-854X Photo News *changed to* Florida Photo News.
0031-8566 Photo Screen
0031-8574 Photo-Technik und - Wirtschaft†
0031-8590 Photo Trade News *changed to* Photo & Video Retailer.
0031-8604 Photo Trade of Japan†
0031-8612 Photo Trader *changed to* Photo & Video Trader.
0031-8639 Photo Typesetting
0031-8647 Photo Weekly *changed to* Photo Business.
0031-8655 Photochemistry and Photobiology
0031-8663 Photogrammetria *see* 0924-2716
0031-8671 Photogrammetric Engineering *see* 0099-1112
0031-868X Photogrammetric Record
0031-8701 Photographic Abstracts *see* 0896-100X
0031-871X Photographic Applications in Science and Technology *see* 0360-7216
0031-8728 Photographic Business and Product News *changed to* Studio Photography.
0031-8736 Photographic Journal
0031-8744 Photographic Processing
0031-8760 Photographic Science and Engineering *changed to* Journal of Imaging Science.
0031-8779 Photographic Trade News
0031-8809 Photography *see* 0265-7198
0031-8817 Photography and Travel *changed to* Creative Photography.
0031-8833 Photon
0031-8841 Photoplatemakers Bulletin *see* 8750-2224
0031-885X Photoplay (1946)†
0031-8868 Phronesis
0031-8876 Phytiatrie-Phythopharmacie
0031-8884 Phycologia
0031-8892 Phykos
0031-8906 Phylon
0031-8914 Physica *see* 0378-4371
0031-8914 Physica *see* 0921-4534
0031-8914 Physica *see* 0921-4526
0031-8914 Physica *see* 0167-2789
0031-8922 Physica Fennica *see* 0031-8949
0031-8930 Physica Norvegica *see* 0031-8949
0031-8949 Physica Scripta
0031-8965 Physica Status Solidi (A). Applied Research
0031-8973 Physical Education Newsletter†
0031-8981 Physical Educator
0031-899X Physical Review *see* 0556-2791
0031-899X Physical Review *see* 0163-1829
0031-9007 Physical Review Letters
0031-9015 Physical Society of Japan. Journal
0031-9023 Physical Therapy
0031-9031 Physicians' Association of Madras. Journal
0031-904X Physicians' Basic Index†
0031-9058 Physicians' Drug Manual
0031-9066 Physician's Management
0031-9082 Physico-Chemical Biology
0031-9090 Physics and Chemistry of Glasses
0031-9104 Physics and Chemistry of Liquids
0031-9112 Physics Bulletin *see* 0953-8585
0031-9120 Physics Education
0031-9147 Physics in Canada
0031-9155 Physics in Medicine and Biology
0031-9163 Physics Letters *see* 0375-9601
0031-9163 Physics Letters *see* 0370-2693
0031-9171 Physics of Fluids *see* 0899-8221
0031-9171 Physics of Fluids *see* 0899-8213
0031-918X Physics of Metals and Metallography
0031-9198 Physics of Sintering *see* 0350-820X
0031-9201 Physics of the Earth and Planetary Interiors
0031-921X Physics Teacher (College Park)
0031-9228 Physics Today
0031-9236 Physik der Kondensierten Materie - Physique de la Matiere Condensee - Physics of Condensed Matter *see* 0722-3277
0031-9244 Physik in der Schule
0031-9252 Physik in Unserer Zeit
0031-9260 Physikalische Berichte *see* 0170-7434
0031-9279 Physikalische Blaetter
0031-9287 Physikalische Medizin und Rehabilitation *see* 0720-6003
0031-9295 Physikunterricht *changed to* Naturwissenschaften im Unterricht Physik.
0031-9309 Physiologia Bohemoslovencia *changed to* Physiological Research.
0031-9317 Physiologia Plantarum
0031-9325 Physiological Chemistry and Physics *see* 0748-6642
0031-9333 Physiological Reviews
0031-9341 Physiological Society of Japan. Journal
0031-935X Physiological Zoology
0031-9368 Physiologie Vegetale *see* 0981-9428
0031-9376 Physiologist
0031-9384 Physiology and Behavior
0031-9392 Physiotherapie
0031-9406 Physiotherapy
0031-9414 Physis
0031-9422 Phytochemistry
0031-9430 Phytologia
0031-9449 Phytomorphology
0031-9457 Phyton
0031-9465 Phytopathologia Mediterraneat
0031-9473 Phytopathological Society of Japan. Annals
0031-949X Phytopathology
0031-9503 Phytopathology News
0031-9511 Phytoprotection
0031-952X Pi Mu Epsilon Journal
0031-9538 Pianeta
0031-9546 Piano Guild Notes
0031-9554 Piano Quarterly
0031-9562 Piano Technicians Journal
0031-9570 La Pianura
0031-9589 Picchiarello†
0031-9600 Piccolo Missionario *changed to* Piemme.
0031-9619 Picket Post *see* 0734-5712
0031-9627 Pick'n' and Sing'n' Gather'n'. Newsletter
0031-9635 Pictorial†
0031-9643 Pictorial Life *changed to* Florida's Gold Coast.
0031-9651 Pictorial News Review
0031-966X Picturegoer†
0031-9678 Pictures & Prints†
0031-9686 Pictures on Exhibit†
0031-9694 Picturescope†
0031-9708 Pie
0031-9716 Pierian Spring†
0031-9732 Pig Breeders Gazette†
0031-9740 Pig Farmer
0031-9759 Pig Farming
0031-9775 Pig Progress†
0031-9783 Pigeon News†
0031-9791 Piggin String
0031-9805 Pilgrim
0031-9813 Pilgrim Society Notes *see* 0885-4947
0031-983X Pin High†
0031-9856 Pine Cone
0031-9864 Rapt
0031-9872 Pinellas Teacher *changed to* Action (Clearwater).
0031-9880 Pingrin
0031-9899 Pinheiros Farmaceutico†
0031-9902 Pinkster Protestant
0031-9910 Pinpointer
0031-9929 Pins and Needles†
0031-9937 Pinto Horse
0031-9945 Pintores
0031-9953 Pinturas y Acabados Industriales
0031-9961 Rivista degli Infermieri†
0031-997X Pioneer *changed to* Pioneer.
0031-9988 Pioneer†
0032-0005 Pioneer America *see* 0883-3680
0032-0021 Pioneer Woman *see* 0888-191X
0032-003X Pioner
0032-0048 Pionerskaya Pravda
0032-0056 Pionier
0032-0099 Pionir-Kekec
0032-0102 Pioneriya
0032-0110 Pionyrske Noviny *changed to* Sedmicka Pionyru.
0032-0129 Pioppicoltura *see* 0012-9836
0032-0137 Pipeline†
0032-0145 Pipe Line Industry
0032-0153 Pipe Line News *see* 0032-0188
0032-0161 Pipe Smoker's Ephemeris
0032-0188 Pipeline & Gas Journal
0032-0196 Pipeline and Underground Utilities Construction *changed to* Pipeline & Utilities Construction.
0032-020X Pipes and Pipelines International
0032-0226 P I R A Newspaper Information Service *changed to* P I R A Newsbrief.
0032-0234 Piraiki-Patraiki
0032-0242 Pirkka
0032-0250 Pirquet Bulletin of Clinical Medicine *changed to* Virchow-Piquet Medical Society. Proceedings.
0032-0269 Pirsch *see* 0340-7829
0032-0277 Piscator
0032-0285 Piscines *see* 0295-5725
0032-0293 Pit & Quarry
0032-0307 Pitman Journal *changed to* Memo International.
0032-0315 Pittsburgh Business Review†
0032-0323 Pittsburgh Catholic
0032-0331 Pittsburgh Legal Journal
0032-034X Pittsburgh Musician
0032-0358 Pittsburgh Symphony Orchestra Program
0032-0374 Catholic Guild News *changed to* Word for Word.
0032-0382 Pivot (Philadelphia)†
0032-0390 Pix *changed to* People.
0032-0404 Pjichk
0032-0420 Plain Truth
0032-0439 Plain Truth†
0032-0447 Plains Anthropologist
0032-0471 Boum *see* 0957-6215
0032-048X Plaisir de France *see* 0293-9274
0032-0501 Plaisirs de la Peche
0032-051X Plaisirs Equestre†
0032-0528 Plamuk
0032-0536 Plan
0032-0544 Plan *changed to* Plan Canada.
0032-0552 Plan *changed to* Plan for Progress and Liberty.
0032-0560 Plan
0032-0587 Plan Ahead
0032-0595 Plan & Print
0032-0609 Plan og Arbeid
0032-0617 Plane and Pilot
0032-0633 Planetary and Space Science
0032-065X Planned Parenthood Report†
0032-0668 Planned Savings
0032-0676 Planner *changed to* Queensland Planner.
0032-0684 Planning & Changing
0032-0692 Planning and Development in the Netherlands†
0032-0706 Planning Comment†
0032-0714 Planning Outlook *see* 0964-0568
0032-0749 Planovane Hospodarstvi
0032-0757 Planovoe Khozyaistvo
0032-0765 Planseeberichte fuer Pulvermetallurgie†
0032-0773 Plant Administration and Engineering *see* 0845-4213
0032-0781 Plant and Cell Physiology
0032-079X Plant and Soil
0032-0803 Plant Breeding Abstracts
0032-0811 Plant Disease Reporter *see* 0191-2917
0032-082X Plant Engineering
0032-0838 Plant Engineers†
0032-0846 Plant Life *see* 8756-9418
0032-0854 Plant Operating Management†
0032-0862 Plant Pathology
0032-0870 Florida. Department of Agriculture and Consumer Services. Plant Pathology Circular
0032-0889 Plant Physiology
0032-0897 Plant Protection Abstracts†
0032-0919 Plant Science Bulletin
0032-0935 Planta
0032-0943 Planta Medica
0032-096X Planters Bulletin
0032-0978 Planters' Chronicle
0032-0986 Planters Journal and Agriculturist
0032-0994 Plantes Medicinales et Phytotherapie
0032-101X Plants and Gardens *see* 0362-5850
0032-1028 Plasma Physics *see* 0741-3335
0032-1052 Plastic and Reconstructive Surgery
0032-1060 Plastic Industry Notes†
0032-1079 Plastic Laminating†
0032-1087 Plastic-Revue Edition Schweiz†
0032-1095 Plastica *see* 0167-9597
0032-1109 Plasticke Hmoty a Kaucuk *see* 0322-7340
0032-1117 Plasticonstruction *see* 0343-3129
0032-1125 Plasticos *changed to* Plasticos.
0032-1133 Plasticos em Revista
0032-1141 Plasticos y Resinas†
0032-115X Plastics Abstracts†
0032-1168 Plastics and Rubber Weekly
0032-1176 Plastics Design & Processing†
0032-1192 Plastics in Engineering†
0032-1206 Plastics Industry News, Japan
0032-1214 Plastics Industry Notes†
0032-1222 Plastics, Paint and Rubber *changed to* Plastics and Rubber News.
0032-1249 Plastics, Rubber and Leather Industries Journal
0032-1257 Plastics Technology
0032-1265 Plastics Trends†
0032-1273 Plastics World
0032-129X Plastiques Informations *see* 0032-1303
0032-1303 Plastiques Modernes et Elastomeres
0032-1311 Plastnytt *changed to* Plastindustrien.
0032-132X Plastvaerldent
0032-1338 Plastverarbeiter
0032-1346 Plateau
0032-1354 Plateau†
0032-1370 Platform (Manchester)
0032-1389 Platform (Luddendenfoot) *see* 0306-140X
0032-1397 Plating *see* 0360-3164
0032-1400 Platinum Metals Review
0032-1435 Plavi Vjesnik†
0032-1443 Play Schools Newsletter
0032-1451 Playback†
0032-146X Playbill
0032-1478 Playboy
0032-1486 Players Magazine†
0032-1508 Playhour
0032-1516 Playing Fields†
0032-1532 Playmen
0032-1540 Plays
0032-1567 Playthings
0032-1583 Psychologie *changed to* Psychologies.
0032-1591 Plomberie Chauffage et Climatisation
0032-1605 Plomjo
0032-1621 Plug
0032-163X Plumb Line
0032-1656 Plumbing
0032-1672 Plumbing Equipment News and Heating Engineer *changed to* Plumbing and Heating News.
0032-1680 Wholesaler

ISSN INDEX

ISSN	Title
0032-1699	Plumbing and Heating Journal
0032-1702	Plus†
0032-1729	Plutonium-Dokumentation *changed to* Plutonium-Dokumentation/Transplutonium-Elemente.
0032-1737	Plymouth Bulletin
0032-1753	Plymouth Traveler†
0032-1761	Plyn
0032-177X	Plywood and Panel *changed to* Panel World.
0032-1788	Plywood World *changed to* Wood World.
0032-1796	Pobeda
0032-180X	Pochvovedenie
0032-1826	Pocket List of Railroad Officials
0032-1869	Podnikova Organizace
0032-1877	Poe Newsletter *see* 0090-5224
0032-1885	Poem
0032-1893	Poesia de Venezuela
0032-1907	Poesia en la Calle
0032-1915	Poesia-Poesia
0032-194X	Poet
0032-1958	Poet and Critic
0032-1966	Poet Lore
0032-1974	Cahiers de Litterature et de Poesie: Poetes et Leurs Amis†
0032-1982	Poeti della Nuova Italia *changed to* Nuova Rassegna: Rivista Trimestrale.
0032-1990	Poeti Italiani Contemporanei†
0032-2024	Poetique
0032-2032	Poetry (Chicago)
0032-2040	Poetry & Audience
0032-2059	Poetry Australia
0032-2075	Poetry India†
0032-2083	Poetry Market
0032-2105	Poetry Nippon
0032-2113	Poetry Northwest
0032-2148	Poetry Prevue *see* 0190-2253
0032-2156	Poetry Review
0032-2164	Poetry Singapore†
0032-2199	Poetry Venture†
0032-2202	Poetry Wales
0032-2237	Poezja
0032-2245	Pogledi (Skopje)
0032-227X	Poids Lourd†
0032-2288	Poilu Lorrain
0032-230X	Point of View
0032-2318	Point of View
0032-2326	Point 3
0032-2334	Point to Point Communication *see* 0305-3601
0032-2342	Pointer†
0032-2369	Points et Contrepoints
0032-2377	Poirieria
0032-2385	Poissonnier Belge
0032-2393	Pojistny Obzor
0032-2407	Pokret
0032-2415	Pokrof
0032-2423	Pokroky Matematiky, Fyziky a Astronomie
0032-2431	Pola Esperantisto
0032-244X	Poland
0032-2458	Poland and Germany (East & West)†
0032-2466	Poland China World *see* 8750-1880
0032-2474	Polar Record
0032-2482	Polar Times
0032-2490	Polarforschung
0032-2504	Pole et Tropiques
0032-2520	Pole†
0032-2547	Poletarac
0032-2555	Police
0032-2563	Police†
0032-258X	Police Journal
0032-2598	Police Life
0032-2601	Police Times *changed to* Police Times.
0032-2628	Policia Portuguesa Revista Ilustrada†
0032-2636	Policlinico. Sezione Chirurgica
0032-2644	Policlinico. Sezione Pratica
0032-2652	Policy *see* 0263-6700
0032-2660	Policy, Fact and Comment *changed to* P R P Comment.
0032-2679	Policy Holder Insurance Journal *changed to* Policy Holder Insurance News.
0032-2687	Policy Sciences
0032-2709	Poligrafico Italiano
0032-2717	Poligrafiya
0032-2725	Polimery
0032-2733	Polimlje
0032-2741	Polio-France
0032-2768	Poliplasti e Plastici Rinforzati *changed to* Poliplasti.
0032-2776	Polish Academy of Sciences. Review *changed to* Journal of Polish Science.
0032-2784	Polish Affairs
0032-2792	Polish American Journal
0032-2806	Polish American Studies
0032-2814	Polish Building Abstracts†
0032-2822	Polish Co-Operative Review
0032-2873	Polish Facts and Figures†
0032-2881	Polish Foreign Trade
0032-289X	Polish Literature†
0032-2903	Polish Machinery News†
0032-2911	Polish Maritime News†
0032-2938	Polish Medical Journal†
0032-2946	Polish Music
0032-2954	Polish News
0032-2962	Polish Perspectives
0032-2970	Polish Review
0032-2989	Polish Scientific Periodicals-Contents†
0032-2997	Polish Sociological Bulletin
0032-3004	Polish Technical and Economic Abstracts
0032-3012	Polish Technical Review
0032-3020	Polish Weekly†
0032-3039	Polish Western Affairs
0032-3047	Polish Western Association of America. Quarterly
0032-3055	Politecnica
0032-3063	Politica del Diritto
0032-3071	Politica e Mezzogiorno
0032-3101	Politica Internazionale (Florence)
0032-3128	Political Affairs
0032-3152	Political Companion†
0032-3160	Memo from C O P E†
0032-3179	Political Quarterly
0032-3187	Political Science
0032-3195	Political Science Quarterly
0032-3209	Political Scientist
0032-3217	Political Studies
0032-3225	Politicheskoe Samoobrazovanie
0032-3233	Politicka Ekonomie
0032-3241	Politicka Misao
0032-325X	Politico
0032-3268	Politics *see* 1036-1146
0032-3276	Politics
0032-3284	P & M
0032-3292	Politics and Society
0032-3306	Politics†
0032-3322	Politie-Dierenbescherming *changed to* Politie, Dier en Milieu.
0032-3357	Politiidrett
0032-3365	Politiikka
0032-3381	Politika-Ekspres
0032-339X	Politikin Zabavnik
0032-3403	Politikon
0032-342X	Politique Etrangere *changed to* Politique Etrangere de la France.
0032-3438	Politische Dokumentation
0032-3446	Die Politische Meinung
0032-3454	Politische Perspektiven
0032-3470	Politische Vierteljahresschrift
0032-3489	Politisk Tidskrift
0032-3497	Polity
0032-3500	Polityka
0032-3519	Die Polizei
0032-3527	Die Polizei im Lande Berlin
0032-3535	Polizei Technik Verkehr *changed to* Polizeiverkehr und Technik.
0032-3543	Polizeimagazin *changed to* Magazin fuer die Polizei.
0032-3551	Polizeischaut
0032-356X	Polizia Moderna
0032-3578	Polja
0032-3594	Polka
0032-3608	Polled Hereford World
0032-3616	Pollen et Spores
0032-3624	Pollution Abstracts
0032-3632	Pollution Atmospherique
0032-3640	Pollution Engineering
0032-3659	Pollution Equipment News
0032-3667	Il Polo
0032-3675	Pologne et les Affaires Occidentales†
0032-3683	Polonia
0032-3713	Polska Bibliografia Analityczna Mechaniki
0032-3721	Polska Sztuka Ludowa
0032-373X	Polski Przeglad Chirurgiczny†
0032-3756	Polski Tygodnik Lekarski
0032-3764	Polskie Archiwum Hydrobiologii
0032-3772	Polskie Archiwum Medycyny Wewnetrznej
0032-3780	Polskie Pismo Entomologiczne
0032-3799	Annales Societatis Mathematicae Polonae. Seria 1: Commentationes Mathematicae
0032-3802	Polskie Towarzystwo Jezykoznawcze. Biuletyn
0032-3829	Polyclinic Journal†
0032-3837	Polygraph *changed to* Interamericana.
0032-3845	Der Polygraph
0032-3861	Polymer
0032-3888	Polymer Engineering and Science
0032-3896	Polymer Journal
0032-390X	Polymer Mechanics - Mekhanika Polimerov *see* 0191-5665
0032-3918	Polymer News
0032-3926	Polymer Report. Japan†
0032-3934	Polymer Preprints
0032-3942	Polymer Science & Technology Post†
0032-3950	Polymer Science U.S.S.R.
0032-3969	Polymers†
0032-3977	Quarterly Literature Reports. Polymers†
0032-3993	Polymus†
0032-4000	J P S
0032-4019	Polyphonie *see* 0035-3736
0032-4027	Polysar Progress *changed to* Polysar Progress.
0032-4035	Polyscope Automatik und Elektronik *changed to* Polyscope.
0032-4051	Polytechnic *changed to* Rensselaer Polytechnic.
0032-406X	Polytechnic Engineer†
0032-4078	Bouwkunde Wegen- en Waterbouw *changed to* Architectuur - Bouwen.
0032-4086	P T - Elektrotechniek - Elektronica
0032-4094	P T - Procestechniek
0032-4108	Polytechnisch Tijdschrift: Werktuigbouw
0032-4116	Polytechnische Bildung und Erziehung
0032-4124	Polyteknikeren
0032-4140	Pomiary - Automatyka - Kontrola
0032-4159	Pomme de Terre Francaise
0032-4167	Pommern
0032-4175	Pomologie Francaise†
0032-4183	Pomona Today *changed to* Pomona College Today.
0032-4205	Pompebleden
0032-4213	Ponny *see* 0346-4687
0032-4221	Pont†
0032-423X	Ponte
0032-4256	Pony
0032-4272	Pool 'n Patio†
0032-4280	Pool News *see* 0194-5351
0032-4299	Poona Agricultural College Magazine
0032-4302	Poor Richard's Almanack†
0032-4310	Poor Richard's Report *see* 0516-9623
0032-4329	Poor's Investment Advisory Survey *changed to* Standard & Poor's Investment Advisory Survey.
0032-4337	Pootaardappelhandel *see* 0165-6031
0032-4345	Pop-Foto-Tuney Tunes *changed to* Popfoto.
0032-4353	Pope Speaks
0032-4361	El Popola Cinio
0032-437X	Popolo del Friuli-Venezia Giulia
0032-4388	Popayan
0032-440X	Populaer Elektronik og Viden *changed to* Populaer Elektronik og High Fidelity.
0032-4418	Populaer Filateli
0032-4442	Populaer Radio og TV Teknik *see* 0105-4880
0032-4450	Popular Bridge†
0032-4469	Camping *see* 0952-5106
0032-4477	Popular Ceramics
0032-4485	Popular Electronics *see* 0745-1458
0032-4493	Popular Flying
0032-4507	Popular Gardening†
0032-4515	Popular Government
0032-4523	Popular Hot Rodding
0032-4531	Popular Imported Cars *changed to* Small Cars /Magazine.
0032-454X	Popular Mechanics†
0032-4558	Popular Mechanics
0032-4574	Popular Motoring
0032-4582	Popular Photography
0032-4590	Popular Photography's Woman†
0032-4604	Popular Plastics *see* 0253-7303
0032-4620	Popular Rotorcraft Flying *changed to* Rotorcraft.
0032-4639	Popular Science and Technology
0032-4647	Popular Science Monthly *see* 0161-7370
0032-4663	Population
0032-468X	Population Bulletin
0032-4698	Population Chronicle†
0032-4701	Population Index
0032-471X	Population Review
0032-4728	Population Studies
0032-4736	Population Statistics Hilversum *changed to* Statistisch Overzicht Hilversum.
0032-4744	Por Alquimia
0032-4752	Poradnik Bibliotekarza
0032-4779	Polymer Friends for Rubber, Plastics and Fiber
0032-4787	Porodica i Dijete
0032-4795	Poroshkovaya Metallurgiya
0032-4809	Port
0032-4817	Port of Baltimore Bulletin†
0032-4825	Port of Houston Magazine
0032-4833	Port of Karachi†
0032-4841	Port of Norfolk News Letter†
0032-485X	Port of Sydney *see* 0313-4075
0032-4868	Port of Toledo News *changed to* Connections (Toledo, 1956).
0032-4876	Port of Yokohama. Monthly Statistics. *changed to* Port of Yokohama. Annual Statistics.
0032-4884	Portals of Prayer
0032-4892	Portcullis
0032-4906	Porter Library Bulletin *changed to* Kansas State College of Pittsburg. Library Bulletin.
0032-4914	Portico *see* 0956-4241
0032-4922	Presence Orthodoxe
0032-4930	Portland Physician†
0032-4949	Porto di Livorno†
0032-4957	Il Porto di Savona
0032-4965	Porto di Venezia†
0032-4973	Portos e Navios
0032-4981	Portrait *changed to* Maryland Today.
0032-499X	Portraits of Prominent U.S.S.R. Personalities†
0032-5007	International Freighting Weekly
0032-5015	Ports O'Call†
0032-5023	Portsmouth Chamber of Commerce. Newsletter *changed to* Portsmouth Chamber of Commerce. Report.
0032-5031	Portugal-an Information Review†
0032-504X	Portugal. Direccao-Geral dos Servicos Florestais e Aquicolas. Gabinete de Estudos Economicos e Estatisticos. Caderno†
0032-5066	Portugal Evangelico
0032-5082	Portugal. Instituto Nacional de Estatistica. Boletim Mensal *changed to* Portugal. Instituto Nacional de Estatistica. Boletim Mensal de Estatistica: Continente, Acores e Madeira.
0032-5090	Laboratorio Nacional de Engenharia Civil. Boletim Mensal de Informacao *see* 0870-9149

ISSN INDEX

ISSN	Title
0032-5112	Portugal Ministerio da Economia. Comissao Reguladora do Comercio de Arroz. Informacao Bibliografica do Arroz†
0032-5120	Portugal Ministerio da Saude e Assistencia, Direccao-Geral da Assistencia. Informacao Social†
0032-5139	Portugal. Ministerio dos Negocios Estrangeiros. Boletim de Informacao Economica†
0032-5147	Portugaliae Acta Biologica *changed to* Portugaliae Acta Biologica. Serie A. Morfologia, Fisiologia, Genetica e Biologia Geral.
0032-5147	Portugaliae Acta Biologica *see* 0375-0280
0032-5155	Portugaliae Mathematica
0032-5163	Portuguese Journal
0032-5171	Poruka Borca
0032-5198	Poseidon
0032-5201	Possev
0032-521X	Posht
0032-5228	Positions Lutheriennes
0032-5236	Post
0032-5244	Post†
0032-5252	Post Magazine and Insurance Monitor
0032-5260	Post Mark†
0032-5279	Post Mortem
0032-5287	Post Office Electrical Engineers' Journal *see* 0262-401X
0032-5295	Post Office Engineering Union Journal *changed to* National Communications Union Journal.
0032-5309	Post Office Telecommunications Journal†
0032-5317	Postal and Telegraph Herald
0032-5325	Postal Bell†
0032-5341	Postal History Journal
0032-535X	Postal Journal
0032-5368	Postal Life
0032-5376	Postal Record
0032-5384	Postal Supervisor
0032-5392	Postal Worker *changed to* Communications Worker.
0032-5406	Poste e Telecomunicazioni
0032-5414	Postepy Astronomii
0032-5422	Postepy Biochemii
0032-5430	Postepy Fizyki
0032-5449	Postepy Higieny i Medycyny Doswiadczalnej
0032-5457	Postepy Nauk Rolniczych
0032-5473	Postgraduate Medical Journal
0032-5481	Postgraduate Medicine
0032-549X	Posthalter-Kurier†
0032-5503	Postmaennens Tidning
0032-5511	Postmasters Advocate
0032-552X	Postmasters Gazette
0032-5538	Pot-Au-Feu
0032-5546	Potash Review
0032-5554	Potato and Onion World†
0032-5562	Potato Chipper *see* 0896-1670
0032-5570	Potato Councillor *changed to* Maine Potato News.
0032-5589	Potato Grower News†
0032-5600	Potencia
0032-5619	Potentials in Marketing
0032-5635	Potomac Appalachian Trail Club. Bulletin *see* 0092-2226
0032-5643	Potomac View *changed to* Nova Report on Lung Health and Wellness.
0032-566X	Potravinar
0032-5678	Pottery Quarterly *changed to* Real Pottery.
0032-5686	Poty Cuntu
0032-5716	Poultry and Egg Marketing
0032-5724	Poultry Digest
0032-5732	Poultry Farmer†
0032-5740	Poultry Guide
0032-5767	Poultry International
0032-5775	Poultry Market Review
0032-5783	Poultry Press
0032-5791	Poultry Science
0032-5805	Poultry Tribune *changed to* Egg Industry.
0032-5813	Poultry World
0032-5821	Poumon et le Coeur *see* 0761-8417
0032-583X	Pour la Vie
0032-5856	Poverty
0032-5864	Poverty and Human Resources Abstracts *see* 0099-2453
0032-5872	Poverty Law Reports†
0032-5880	Povratak u Zivot
0032-5899	Powder Metallurgy
0032-5910	Powder Technology
0032-5929	Power (New York)
0032-5937	Power and Plant in Southern Africa *changed to* Power & Plant Engineering in South Africa.
0032-5953	Power Engineer†
0032-5961	Power Engineering (Tulsa)
0032-5988	Power Farming
0032-5996	Power Farming and Better Farming Digest *see* 0311-1911
0032-6003	Power for Living
0032-6011	Power for Today
0032-6038	Power Laundry & Cleaning News†
0032-6046	Power Life *changed to* Freeway.
0032-6054	Power Management†
0032-6062	Power Record†
0032-6070	Power Transmission Design
0032-6089	Powerboat
0032-6119	Polytechnic-Window of the Netherlands
0032-6127	Pozarni Ochrana
0032-6135	Pozarni Technika *see* 0032-6127
0032-6151	Poznaj Swoj Kraj
0032-616X	Pozoriste
0032-6178	Prabuddha Bharata
0032-6186	Praca i Zabezpieczenia Spoleczne
0032-6194	Praca Szkolna *changed to* Ogniwo.
0032-6208	Prace a Mzda
0032-6216	Instytut Elektrotechniki. Prace
0032-6232	Instytut Naftowy. Prace *see* 0209-0724
0032-6240	Instytut Technologii Drewna. Prace
0032-6259	Instytut Tele- i Radiotechniczny. Prace
0032-6267	Mineralogia Polonica
0032-6275	Muzeum Ziemi. Prace†
0032-6283	Przemyslowy Instytut Telekomunikacji. Prace
0032-6291	Pracovni Lekarstvi
0032-6305	Practica Oto-Rhino-Laryngologica *see* 0301-1569
0032-6313	Practica Otologica Kyoto
0032-6321	Practical Accountant
0032-633X	Practical Anthropology *see* 0091-8296
0032-6348	Practical Boat Owner
0032-6356	Practical Camper *changed to* Outdoor Action.
0032-6364	Practical Christianity *changed to* Contact (Aldershot).
0032-6372	Practical Electronics
0032-6380	Scholastic Voice
0032-6399	Practical Gardening
0032-6410	Practical Knowledge†
0032-6429	The Practical Lawyer
0032-6437	Practical Motorist *changed to* Motorist.
0032-6445	Practical Photography
0032-6453	Practical Psychology
0032-647X	Television (London, 1934)
0032-6488	Practical Woodworking
0032-6518	Practitioner
0032-6534	Praehistorische Forschungen†
0032-6542	Der Praeparator
0032-6550	Pragati
0032-6569	Prager Volkszeitung
0032-6577	Pragmatist in Art†
0032-6585	Prague Bulletin of Mathematical Linguistics
0032-6593	Praha - Moskva
0032-6607	Prairie Club Bulletin
0032-6615	Prairie Farmer
0032-6623	Prairie Gleaner
0032-664X	Prairie Messenger
0032-6666	Prairie Rose
0032-6674	Prairie School Review†
0032-6682	Prairie Schooner
0032-6690	Prajna†
0032-6704	Praksa
0032-6720	Prakticke Zubni Lekarstvi
0032-6739	Prakticky Lekar
0032-6747	Prakticna Zena
0032-6763	Praktiko†
0032-6771	Praktische Forstwirt fuer die Schweiz *see* 0378-6919
0032-678X	Praktische Metallographie
0032-6798	Praktische Psychologie†
0032-6801	Der Praktische Schaedlingsbekaempfer
0032-681X	Der Praktische Tierarzt
0032-6828	Praline
0032-6836	Pram Retailer†
0032-6844	Pram and Nursery Trader *changed to* Nursery Trader.
0032-6852	Pramo
0032-6879	Prasna
0032-6887	Pratfall†
0032-6895	Materiaux et Techniques
0032-6909	Pratique du Soudage *see* 0035-127X
0032-6917	Pratishruti
0032-6925	Prato - Storia ed Arte
0032-6933	Pratt Cannon *changed to* Pratt Reports.
0032-695X	Pravna Misla
0032-6968	Pravna Misal
0032-6976	Pravnik
0032-6984	Pravny Obzor
0032-6992	Pravoslavnaya Zhyzn'
0032-700X	Pravoslavno Misao
0032-7018	Pravoslavnaya Rus'
0032-7034	Praxis der Kinderpsychologie und Kinderpsychiatrie
0032-7042	Praxis der Mathematik
0032-7069	Praxis der Pneumologie *see* 0934-8387
0032-7077	Praxis der Psychotherapie *see* 0171-791X
0032-7085	Praxis des Neusprachlichen Unterrichts
0032-7093	Pre-Investment News *changed to* Action U N D P.
0032-7093	Pre-Investment News *changed to* Development Business.
0032-7107	Worship and Preaching
0032-7123	Precision†
0032-7131	Precision
0032-714X	Precision Metal†
0032-7166	Predicasts *see* 0278-0135
0032-7174	Predicasts Electronic Trends *changed to* Electronics Trends (Cleveland).
0032-7182	Prediction
0032-7212	Der Prediger und Katechet
0032-7220	Predskolska Vychova
0032-7239	Preet Lari
0032-7247	Prefabbricare
0032-7255	Prefabbricazione
0032-7263	Preface†
0032-7271	Pregled (Sarajevo, 1910)
0032-7298	Pregled Problema Mentalno Retardiranih Osoba
0032-731X	Pregled Zakonodavstva u Stranim Drzavama†
0032-7328	Prehlad Lesnickej, Drevarskej, Celulozovej a Papiernickej Literatury†
0032-7336	Prehled Lesnicke a Myslivecke Literatury†
0032-7344	Novinky Literatury: Prehled Pedagogicke Literatury *see* 0139-9489
0032-7352	Dokumentacni Listkova Sluzba *changed to* Agroindex - Automated Information System.
0032-7379	Prehledy Potravinarske Literatury
0032-7387	Premier Plant
0032-7409	Premio
0032-7425	Prenatal *changed to* Prenatal Gids.
0032-7433	Prensa Confidencial
0032-745X	Prensa Medica Argentina
0032-7468	Prensa Medica Mexicana†
0032-7476	Prent 190
0032-7484	Preparative Biochemistry
0032-7514	Prepravni a Tarifni Vestnik
0032-7522	Presbyterian Guardian *see* 0199-3518
0032-7530	Presbyterian Herald
0032-7549	Presbyterian Journal†
0032-7557	Presbyterian Life *changed to* United Presbyterian A.D.
0032-7565	Presbyterian Outlook
0032-7573	Presbyterian Record
0032-7581	Rush-Presbyterian-St. Luke's Medical Bulletin†
0032-759X	Presbyterian Survey
0032-7611	Prescribers' Journal
0032-762X	Presence†
0032-7638	Presence Africaine
0032-7654	Presence des Lettres des Arts *see* 0336-321X
0032-7662	Presence du Cinema
0032-7689	Presencia
0032-7697	Present
0032-7700	Present Truth and Herald of Christ's Epiphany
0032-7719	Presenter†
0032-7727	Presenza Pastorale
0032-7735	Preservation News
0032-7751	President
0032-7778	Wisconsin Library Association. President's Newsletter *see* 0043-6518
0032-7786	Preslia
0032-7794	Germany (Federal Republic, 1949-) Presse- und Informationsamt. Bulletin†
0032-7808	Press and Public Relations
0032-7816	Press Booklets
0032-7824	Press Woman
0032-7832	Presse Actualite *changed to* Medias Pouvoirs.
0032-7840	Presse der Sowjetunion†
0032-7859	Belgium. Commissariat General au Tourisme. Bulletin†
0032-7867	Presse Medicale *see* 0755-4982
0032-7875	Presse Thermale et Climatique
0032-7883	Pressens Tidning
0032-7891	Presseschau Ostwirtschaft
0032-7905	Pressespiegel Blicknach Drueben *changed to* Pressespiegel aus Zeitungen und Zeitschriften der DDR.
0032-7913	Pressluft *changed to* Drucklufttechnik.
0032-7921	Prestige de l'Hotellerie, de la Restauration et de Tourism *changed to* Resto-Flash.
0032-793X	Prestressed Concrete Institute Journal *see* 0887-9672
0032-7948	South Africa. Weather Bureau. Newsletter
0032-7956	Pretres Diocesains
0032-7964	Pretzel Baker†
0032-7972	Preussenland
0032-7980	Preuves
0032-8006	Prevention
0032-8014	Prevent Blindness News *changed to* National Society to Prevent Blindness. Member News.
0032-8022	Prevention Routiere
0032-8030	Prevention Routiere dans l'Entreprise
0032-8049	Previdencia Social†
0032-8057	Previdenza Agricola
0032-8065	Previdenza Sociale
0032-8081	Previdenza Sociale Nella Stampa Estera†
0032-809X	Previdenza Sociale nell'Artigianato
0032-8103	Preview†
0032-8111	Preview†
0032-812X	Previsoes Ionosfericas M U F
0032-8138	Przeglad Bibliograficzny Pismiennictwa Ekonomicznego†
0032-8146	Priapus†
0032-8154	Pribory i Sistemy Upravleniya
0032-8162	Pribory i Tekhnika Eksperimenta
0032-8170	Price Waterhouse Review
0032-8200	Priest
0032-8219	Landbouw-Economisch Instituut. Prijsstatistiek *see* 0166-8072
0032-8227	Prikazi in Studije
0032-8235	Prikladnaya Matematika i Mekhanika
0032-8243	Prikladnaya Mekhanika
0032-8251	Primalinea
0032-826X	Primary Bookshelf†
0032-8278	Primary Days
0032-8286	Primary Friend†

ISSN	Title
0032-8308	Primary Producer *changed to* Dairyman's Digest and Primary Producer.
0032-8316	Primary Treasure
0032-8324	Primate News
0032-8332	Primates
0032-8340	Primavera
0032-8359	Prime Areas
0032-8367	Primer Acto†
0032-8375	Primera Plana
0032-8383	Primicia
0032-8405	Princeton Engineer
0032-843X	Princeton University. Art Museum. Record
0032-8448	Princeton University Cutaneous Research Project Reports
0032-8456	Princeton University Library Chronicle
0032-8472	Principe de Viana
0032-8480	Principes
0032-8499	Prinsejagt†
0032-8502	Prinses†
0032-8510	Print
0032-8529	Print
0032-8537	Print Collector's Newsletter
0032-8553	Print Project Amerika†
0032-8561	Print Room†
0032-857X	Printindia
0032-8588	Printing and Publishing†
0032-8596	Printing Equipment and Materials *see* 0032-8715
0032-860X	Printing Impressions
0032-8618	Printing†
0032-8626	Printing News *see* 1046-8595
0032-8634	Printing Plates†
0032-8642	Printing Product Information Cards
0032-8650	Printing Management *see* 0032-860X
0032-8685	Printing Technology *see* 0308-4205
0032-8707	Printing Trades Journal†
0032-8715	Printing World
0032-8731	Priroda
0032-874X	Priroda
0032-8758	Ceskoslovenska Akademie Ved. Brnenska Zakladna. Prace *changed to* Ceskoslovenska Acedemie Ved. Ustav v Brne. Prirodovedne Prace.
0032-8766	Prirodni Vedy ve Skole
0032-8774	Prirucka Casopisu Zena a Moda *see* 0231-6471
0032-8790	Prism International
0032-8812	Prismat
0032-8847	Prismet
0032-8855	Prison Journal
0032-8863	Prison Officers Magazine *changed to* Gatelodge.
0032-8871	Private Carrier
0032-888X	Private Eye
0032-8898	Private Library
0032-8901	Private Pilot
0032-891X	Private Practice
0032-8928	Private Practice News†
0032-8936	Private Printer & Private Press†
0032-8944	Private Wirtschaft†
0032-8960	Privreda Kotara Osijek *see* 0350-9427
0032-8979	Privredna Izgradnja
0032-8995	Privredni Vjesnik
0032-9002	Privredno Pravni Prirucnik
0032-9010	Prizewinner *changed to* Enter-Prizes.
0032-9037	Pro Magazin†
0032-9045	Pro
0032-9053	Pro Football Weekly
0032-907X	Pro Medico†
0032-9088	Pro Medico
0032-9096	Pro Metal†
0032-910X	Pro Patria
0032-9118	Pro Senectute *changed to* Zeitlupe.
0032-9126	Pro-Sports†
0032-9134	Pro Tem
0032-9142	Pro Veritate
0032-9150	Proa
0032-9177	Probe (Santa Barbara)
0032-9185	Probe
0032-9193	Probe (Rockville Centre) *see* 0024-3078
0032-9215	Probe (Memphis) *changed to* Pioneer (Memphis).
0032-9223	Problemas
0032-9231	Probleme Agricole†
0032-9258	Probleme des Friedens und des Sozialismus†
0032-9266	Probleme Economice†
0032-9290	Problemes d'Outre-Mer†
0032-9304	Problemes Economiques
0032-9312	Problemes Sociaux Congolais *changed to* Problemes Sociaux Zairois.
0032-9320	Problemes Sovietiques†
0032-9339	Problemi
0032-9347	Problemi della Pedagogia
0032-9355	Problemi della Sicurezza Sociale†
0032-9363	Problemi di Gestione
0032-9371	Problemi na Izkustvoto
0032-938X	Problemi Spoljne Trgovine i Konjunkture†
0032-9398	Problemist
0032-941X	Problems of Communism
0032-9428	Problemy Osvoeniya Pustyn'
0032-9436	Problems in Economics *changed to* Problems in Economic Transition.
0032-9444	Problems of Forensic Medicine & Criminalistics†
0032-9452	Journal of Ichthyology
0032-9460	Problems of Information Transmission
0032-9479	Problems of the Peoples of the USSR†
0032-9487	Problemy
0032-9495	Problemy Alkoholizmu
0032-9509	Problemy Endokrinologii i Gormonoterapii *see* 0375-9660
0032-9517	Problemy Inwestowania i Rozwoju *changed to* Problemy Rozwoju Budownictwa.
0032-9525	Problemy Transportu Samochodowego†
0032-9533	Problemy Tuberkuleza
0032-9541	Problemy Uczelni i Instytutow Medycznych *see* 0137-7183
0032-955X	Procedes et Equipements Electroniques†
0032-9568	Proceedings in Print
0032-9576	Journal of Technical Physics
0032-9592	Process Biochemistry
0032-9606	Process Engineering, Plant and Control *see* 0370-1859
0032-9614	Process Journal *see* 0032-8529
0032-9622	Proche-Orient Chretien
0032-9649	Proche-Orient Etudes Juridiques
0032-9665	Prodotti di Marca
0032-9681	Produccion†
0032-969X	Produce News
0032-9703	Producers Guild of America. Journal†
0032-972X	Producers Review†
0032-9738	Product Design and Development *changed to* Chilton's Product Design and Development.
0032-9746	Product Design Engineering†
0032-9762	Product Finishing
0032-9770	Product Licensing Index *changed to* P L I Know How.
0032-9789	American Hotel and Motel Association. Product News. *changed to* American Hotel and Motel Association. Buyers Guide for Hotels & Motels.
0032-9797	European Plant Equipment News†
0032-9819	Production
0032-9827	Weekly Production and Drilling Statistics *changed to* Alberta Drilling Progress Weekly Report.
0032-9843	Production and Inventory Management
0032-9851	Production Engineer *changed to* Manufacturing Engineer.
0032-9878	Production Journal
0032-9908	Productividad
0032-9924	Productivity
0032-9932	Productivity Letter†
0032-9940	Products Finishing
0032-9967	Produktion
0032-9975	Produktivnost
0032-9983	Produrre†
0033-0000	Produzione Animale
0033-0019	Proefstation voor de Groenten- en Fruitteelt onder Glas. Mededelingen *changed to* Proefstation voor Tuinbouw onder Glas.
0033-0043	Professional Builder *changed to* Professional Builder & Remodeler.
0033-0051	Professional Engineer (Washington)†
0033-006X	Professional Engineer
0033-0078	Professional Engineer
0033-0086	Professional Engineer in Nova Scotia *changed to* Engineer.
0033-0094	Professional Fisherman's Association of Tasmania Magazine *see* 0156-3548
0033-0108	Professional Flashes†
0033-0116	Professional Gardener *changed to* Grounds Management Forum.
0033-0124	Professional Geographer
0033-0132	Professional Golfer *see* 0161-1259
0033-0140	Professional Medical Assistant
0033-0159	Professional Nutritionist†
0033-0167	Professional Photographer
0033-0175	Professional Psychology *see* 0735-7028
0033-0183	Professional Public Service *changed to* Professional Institute of the Public Service of Canada. Journal.
0033-0191	Professional Sanitation Management *changed to* Environmental Management.
0033-0205	Professioni Infermieristiche†
0033-0213	Professions et Entreprises
0033-0221	Professor *changed to* Professor an A H S & B H S.
0033-023X	Profile†
0033-0248	Profile (Kansas City)†
0033-0256	Profile *changed to* Harbinger (Detroit).
0033-0280	Profit Sharing
0033-0299	Profitable Hobby Merchandising *changed to* Profitable Craft Merchandising.
0033-0329	Profoto
0033-0337	Program
0033-0353	Norsk Rikskringkastning. Programbladet
0033-037X	Programme Communiste
0033-0396	Programmed Learning *see* 0954-7304
0033-0434	Progres
0033-0442	Progres Islamique†
0033-0450	Progres Medical
0033-0469	Progres Scientifique†
0033-0477	Progresele Stintei†
0033-0485	Progreso
0033-0507	Progresos de Patologia y Clinica†
0033-0515	Progresos de Pediatria y Puericultura†
0033-0523	Progresos de Terapeutica Clinica†
0033-054X	Progress
0033-0566	Progress
0033-0574	Progress
0033-0582	Deurbraak *changed to* Democrat.
0033-0590	Progress†
0033-0604	Progress Against Cancer
0033-0612	Progress & Care
0033-0620	Progress in Cardiovascular Diseases
0033-0639	Progress in Dermatology
0033-0655	Progress in Organic Coatings
0033-0663	Progress of Education
0033-068X	Progress of Theoretical Physics
0033-0698	Progres Social†
0033-0701	Progressi in Patologia Cardiovascolare
0033-071X	Progressi in Radiologia *changed to* Progressi in Radiologia.
0033-0728	Progressio
0033-0736	Progressive (Madison)
0033-0744	Progressive Agriculture in Arizona *see* 0744-5474
0033-0752	Progressive Architecture
0033-0760	Progressive Farmer
0033-0779	Progressive Fish-Culturist
0033-0787	Progressive Grocer
0033-0809	Progressive Plastics†
0033-0817	Progressive Railroading
0033-0825	Progressive Teacher
0033-0833	Progressive Woman†
0033-0841	Progressive Worker
0033-085X	Progressive World†
0033-0868	Progresso Fotografico
0033-0876	Technic International†
0033-0884	Projet
0033-0892	Project - Guidelines to Equal Opportunity *see* 0006-4122
0033-0906	Project Concern News *changed to* Concern News.
0033-0914	Project†
0033-0922	Project on Linguistics Analysis Reports†
0033-0957	Projekt
0033-0981	Proletaire
0033-099X	Prolipsis Ton Atychimaton
0033-1007	Prologue (Medford)
0033-1023	National Arts Centre. Calendar of Events *changed to* N A C Calendar of Events.
0033-1031	Prologue (Washington)
0033-1066	Promesses†
0033-1082	Promethee
0033-1090	Promien
0033-1112	Promoting Church Music *see* 0307-6334
0033-1120	Promotion des Affaires
0033-1139	Promotor de Educacion Cristiana
0033-1147	Prompt
0033-1155	Promyshlennaya Energetika
0033-1163	Promyshlennost' Armenii
0033-1171	Promyshlennost' Belorussii
0033-118X	Promyshlennoe Stroitel'stvo
0033-1201	Pronab
0033-121X	Proof
0033-1228	Proof Sheet *changed to* S A L S in Brief.
0033-1236	Proofs
0033-1244	Propaganda
0033-1260	Propane - Canada
0033-1279	Propel
0033-1287	Properties
0033-1295	Property and Compensation Reports *changed to* Property, Planning and Compensation Reports.
0033-1309	Property Journal
0033-1317	Property Mail†
0033-1325	Property Survey†
0033-1333	Prophetic News and Israel's Watchman *changed to* Your Tomorrow.
0033-1341	Prophetic Newsletter
0033-135X	Prophetic Witness *changed to* Your Tomorrow.
0033-1368	Prophylaxe (Heidelberg) *see* 0340-7047
0033-1376	Propiedad Intelectual†
0033-1384	Propos en l'Air *changed to* A P a la Une.
0033-1392	Propos Utiles aux Medecins
0033-1414	Propria Cures (PC)
0033-1422	Proprieta Edilizia Lombarda
0033-1430	Propriete Industrielle
0033-1449	Propriete Industrielle Nucleaire†
0033-1465	Proscopos
0033-1481	Prospect
0033-1503	Prospectives *see* 0337-307X
0033-1511	Prospectives†
0033-1538	Prospects in Education *changed to* Prospects.
0033-1546	University of Michigan Journal of Law Reform
0033-1554	Prosperite
0033-1562	Prospetti†
0033-1570	Nuove Prospettive†
0033-1600	Prostor in Cast
0033-1619	Prosveta
0033-1627	Prosveten Glasnik
0033-1635	Prosvetni Rabotnik
0033-1643	Prosvetni Delavec
0033-1651	Prosvetni Pregled
0033-166X	Prosvjeta†
0033-1678	Prosvjetni List
0033-1686	Prosvjetni Rad
0033-1716	Protection†
0033-1724	Protection Civile et Securite Industrielle *see* 0222-559X
0033-1732	Protection of Metals
0033-1759	Protestant en de Weg *changed to* Tenminste.
0033-1767	Protestantesimo

0033-1783 Protetyka Stomatologiczna
0033-1791 Proteus
0033-1805 Proteus
0033-1821 Protistologica *see* 0932-4739
0033-183X Protoplasma
0033-1848 Prove di Letteratura†
0033-1856 Provence Historique
0033-1864 Providence Hospital of Southfield. Medical Bulletin†
0033-1872 Province de Liege-Tourisme†
0033-1880 Province du Maine
0033-1902 Provincia di Forli in Cifre
0033-1910 Provincia di Padova in Cifre†
0033-1929 Provincia Social
0033-1937 Provokert
0033-1945 Provost Parade
0033-1953 Proyecto Hidrometeorologico Centroamericano. Boletin Informativo†
0033-1988 Prumysl Potravin
0033-2003 Przeglad Antropologiczny
0033-2011 Przeglad Artystyczny *see* 0324-8232
0033-202X Przeglad Biblioteczny
0033-2038 Przeglad Budowlany
0033-2046 Przeglad Dokumentacyjny Materialow Ogniotrwalych
0033-2054 Przeglad Dokumentacyjny Maszyn Rolniczych
0033-2062 Przeglad Dokumentacyjny Elektrotechniki
0033-2089 Elektronika
0033-2097 Przeglad Elektrotechniczny
0033-2100 Przeglad Epidemiologiczny
0033-2119 Przeglad Gastronomiczny
0033-2127 Przeglad Geodezyjny
0033-2135 Przeglad Geofizyczny
0033-2143 Przeglad Geograficzny
0033-2151 Przeglad Geologiczny
0033-216X Przeglad Gorniczy
0033-2178 Przeglad Historyczno-Oswiatowy†
0033-2186 Przeglad Historyczny
0033-2208 Przeglad Kolejowy Drogowy *see* 0137-284X
0033-2216 Przeglad Kolejowy Elektrotechniczny *see* 0137-2858
0033-2224 Przeglad Kolejowy Mechaniczny *see* 0137-2963
0033-2232 Przeglad Komunikacyjny
0033-2240 Przeglad Lekarski
0033-2259 Przeglad Mechaniczny
0033-2275 Przeglad Odlewnictwa
0033-2291 Przeglad Papierniczy
0033-2313 Przeglad Piekarski i Cukierniczy
0033-2321 I.B. Informacja Biezaca
0033-233X Bibliografia Analityczna Bibliotekoznawstwa i Informacji Naukowej
0033-2348 Przeglad Pismiennictwa Zagadnien Informacji *changed to* Przeglad Dokumentacyjny Informacji Naukowej.
0033-2356 Przeglad Socjologiczny
0033-2364 Przeglad Spawalnictwa
0033-2372 Przeglad Statystyczny
0033-2380 Przeglad Techniczny *see* 0137-8783
0033-2399 Przeglad Telekomunikacyjny
0033-2402 Przeglad Ustawodawstwa i Czasopism Prawniczych Socjalistycznych Krajow Europy†
0033-2410 Przeglad Wlokienniczy *changed to* Przeglad Wlokienniczy plus Technik Wlokienniczy.
0033-2429 Przeglad Wybranych Czasopism Prawniczych Krajow Zachodnich†
0033-2437 Przeglad Zachodni
0033-2445 Przeglad Zachodnich Czasopism Ekonomicznych†
0033-2453 Przeglad Zagranicznej Literatury Naukowej z Zakresu Genetyki i Hodowli Roslin
0033-2461 Przeglad Zbozowo - Mlynarski
0033-247X Przeglad Zoologiczny
0033-2488 Przekroj
0033-2496 Przemysl Chemiczny
0033-250X Przemysl Spozywczy
0033-2518 Przewodnik Bibliograficzny
0033-2526 Przeglad Dermatologiczny
0033-2534 Przyjaciolka
0033-2542 Psallitet†
0033-2569 Psi Chi Newsletter
0033-2585 Psionic Medicine
0033-2615 Psyche
0033-2623 Psyche
0033-264X Psychiatria Clinica *see* 0254-4962
0033-2658 Psychiatria et Neurologia Japonica (Tokyo, 1899)
0033-2666 Psychiatria, Neurologia, Neurochirurgia†
0033-2674 Psychiatria Polska†
0033-2682 Psychiatric Communications†
0033-2690 Psychiatric Forum
0033-2704 Psychiatric News
0033-2712 O P. Psychiatric Opinion *see* 0163-2655
0033-2720 Psychiatric Quarterly
0033-2739 Psychiatrie, Neurologie und Medizinische Psychologie†
0033-2747 Psychiatry
0033-2755 Psychiatry and Medical Practice Bulletin†
0033-2771 Psychiatry Digest *see* 0278-4602
0033-278X Psychiatry in Medicine *see* 0091-2174
0033-2798 Psychic *see* 0147-7625
0033-2801 Psychic News
0033-2828 Psychoanalytic Quarterly
0033-2836 Psychoanalytic Review
0033-2844 Physchogram†
0033-2852 Psychologia
0033-2860 Psychologia Wychowawcza
0033-2879 Psychologica Belgica
0033-2887 Psychological Abstracts
0033-2895 Psychological Association of Trinidad and Tobago. Journal
0033-2909 Psychological Bulletin
0033-2917 Psychological Medicine
0033-2925 Psychological Perspectives
0033-2933 Psychological Record
0033-2941 Psychological Reports
0033-295X Psychological Review
0033-2968 Psychological Studies
0033-2984 Psychologie Francaise
0033-2992 Psychologie und Praxis *see* 0932-4089
0033-300X Psychologie v Ekonomicke Praxi
0033-3018 Psychologische Beitraege
0033-3034 Psychologische Menschenkenntnis *changed to* Psychologie im Gespraech.
0033-3042 Psychologische Rundschau
0033-3050 Psychologist Magazine
0033-3077 Psychology
0033-3085 Psychology in the Schools
0033-3093 Psychology Quarterly
0033-3107 Psychology Today
0033-3115 De Psycholoog
0033-3123 Psychometrika
0033-3131 Psychonomic Science†
0033-314X Psychopathologie Africaine
0033-3158 Psychopharmacology
0033-3166 Psychopharmacology Abstracts†
0033-3174 Psychosomatic Medicine
0033-3182 Psychosomatics
0033-3190 Psychotherapy and Psychosomatics
0033-3204 Psychotherapy: Theory, Research and Practice *changed to* Psychotherapy.
0033-3212 Psykisk Haelsa
0033-3239 Ptitsevodstvo
0033-3263 Pubdisco News
0033-3271 Public Address Engineers Journal *changed to* Public Address.
0033-328X Public Administration *see* 0313-6647
0033-3298 Public Administration
0033-3301 Public Administration†
0033-331X Public Administration Abstracts and Index of Articles *changed to* Documentation in Public Administration.
0033-3328 Public Administration News and Views *see* 0149-8797
0033-3336 Public Administration Recruiter *see* 0149-8797
0033-3344 Public Administration Review
0033-3352 Public Administration Review
0033-3360 Public Administration Survey
0033-3387 Public Affairs Bulletin†
0033-3395 Public Affairs Comment
0033-3409 Public Affairs Information Service. Bulletin *see* 1051-4015
0033-3417 Public Affairs Report
0033-3425 Public Aid in Illinois†
0033-3433 Public Cleansing *changed to* Wastes Management.
0033-3441 Public Contract Law Journal
0033-345X Public Employee Press
0033-3468 Public Enterprise Recorder
0033-3476 Public Finance
0033-3484 Public Health†
0033-3492 Public Health†
0033-3506 Public Health
0033-3522 Public Health Laboratory†
0033-3530 Public Health News†
0033-3549 Public Health Reports *see* 0090-2918
0033-3557 Public Interest
0033-3565 Public Law
0033-3573 Public Library of Youngstown and Mahoning County. Staff Bulletin *changed to* At the Library.
0033-3581 Public Library Trustee†
0033-3603 Public Lighting *see* 0950-4559
0033-3611 Public Management
0033-362X Public Opinion Quarterly
0033-3638 Public Personnel Review *see* 0091-0260
0033-3646 Public Policy (Cambridge) *see* 0276-8739
0033-3654 Public Power
0033-3662 Public Relations *see* 0307-9252
0033-3689 Public Relations Journal of India
0033-3697 Public Relations News
0033-3700 Public Relations Quarterly
0033-3719 Public Relations Reporter†
0033-3727 P R Revue
0033-3735 Public Roads
0033-3743 Public Safety Systems†
0033-3751 Public Schools of New York City. Staff Bulletin *changed to* Learning in New York.
0033-376X Public Servant
0033-3786 Public Service Review
0033-3794 Public Undertakings
0033-3808 Public Utilities Fortnightly
0033-3816 Public Welfare
0033-3840 Public Works
0033-3867 Publicaciones Cientificas Alter†
0033-3875 Publication Management†
0033-3913 Media News Keys
0033-3921 Publicity Review
0033-3948 Publieke Werken *see* 0046-5577
0033-3956 Publik†
0033-3972 Publisher†
0033-3999 Publitransport
0033-4006 Publizistik
0033-4014 Pueblo†
0033-4030 Puerto Rico Libre†
0033-4049 Puerto Rico Living
0033-4073 Pneumonologie - Pneumonology *see* 0341-2040
0033-4081 Pulp and Paper
0033-409X Pulp & Paper International
0033-4103 Pulp and Paper Magazine of Canada *see* 0316-4004
0033-4111 Pulp Era†
0033-4138 The Christian Ministry
0033-4146 Pulpit Digest *see* 0160-838X
0033-4154 Pulpwood Production *see* 0160-6433
0033-4162 Pulse†
0033-4170 Pulse (Lafayette)†
0033-4197 Pulse (Tulsa)†
0033-4200 Pulse Beat
0033-4219 Pulse of Public School Adult Education *changed to* Online with Adult and Continuing Educators.
0033-4227 Pulse of Youth
0033-4251 Pult†
0033-426X Pumps - Pompes - Pumpen *see* 0262-1762
0033-4278 Punch†
0033-4286 Pungolo del Sud
0033-4294 Pungolo Verde
0033-4308 Punjab Educational Journal†
0033-4316 Punjab Fruit Journal
0033-4324 Punjab Horticultural Journal
0033-4332 Punjab Law Reporter
0033-4340 Punjab Medical Journal
0033-4359 Haryana Veterinarian
0033-4367 Punto de Partida
0033-4375 Punto de Vista†
0033-4391 Punto Omega
0033-4405 Puppenspiel und Puppenspieler
0033-4421 Puppet Post†
0033-443X Puppetry Journal
0033-4448 Purchasing (Newton)
0033-4456 Purchasing Bulletin *see* 0306-1922
0033-4472 Purchasing Journal *see* 0265-2072
0033-4480 Purchasing Week *see* 0093-1659
0033-4502 Purdue Alumnus
0033-4510 Purdue Engineer
0033-4529 Purdue Pharmacist
0033-4537 Purdue University. School of Electrical Engineering. Annual Research Summary
0033-4545 Pure and Applied Chemistry
0033-4553 Pure and Applied Geophysics
0033-4561 Pure-Bred Dogs, American Kennel Gazette
0033-4588 Pure Verite
0033-4596 Pure Water†
0033-4642 Purple Thumb†
0033-4669 Purpose†
0033-4677 Pursuit & Symposium†
0033-4685 Pursuit *changed to* Pursuit - S I T U.
0033-4693 Pustakalaya
0033-4707 Pustakalaya Sandesh
0033-4715 Put' i Putevoe Khozyaistvo
0033-474X Pyrenees
0033-4758 Pythagoras†
0033-4766 Pythagoras†
0033-4774 Q B Beam
0033-4782 A F C I Q Bulletin *changed to* Qualite en Mouvement.
0033-4790 Q I M P Quarterly
0033-4804 Q L†
0033-4812 Q S T
0033-4820 Q T C
0033-4839 Kadmoniot
0033-4863 Quaderni del Conoscitore di Stampe *changed to* Conoscitore di Stampe.
0033-4898 Quaderni dello Sport†
0033-491X Quaderni di Clinica Ostetrica e Ginecologica
0033-4928 Quaderni di Criminologia Clinica *changed to* Rassegna Penitenziaria e Criminologica.
0033-4952 Quaderni di Sociologia
0033-4960 Quaderni Ibero-Americani
0033-4979 Quaderni Sclavo di Diagnostica Clinica e di Laboratorio†
0033-4987 Quaderni Urbinati di Cultura Classica
0033-4995 Quadrangle†
0033-5002 Quadrant
0033-5010 Quadrant
0033-5029 Quadrante Sardo†
0033-5037 Quaestiones Entomologicae†
0033-5045 Quaker Campus
0033-5053 Quaker History
0033-5061 Quaker Life
0033-507X Quaker Monthly
0033-5088 Quaker Religious Thought
0033-5096 Quaker Service Bulletin
0033-510X Bulletin (Philadelphia) *see* 0033-5096
0033-5118 Electrical Contractor
0033-5126 Qualitaet und Zuverlaessigkeit (1969) *changed to* Qualitaet und Zuverlaessigkeit (1980).
0033-5134 Qualitas Plantarum et Materiae Vegetabiles *see* 0921-9668
0033-5142 Qualite *see* 0766-5210
0033-5169 Quality
0033-5177 Quality and Quantity

5434 ISSN INDEX

0033-5193 Quality Control
0033-5207 Quality Control and Applied Statistics
0033-5215 Quality Engineer *see* 0959-3268
0033-5231 Quality of Sheffield *changed to* Quality of Sheffield and South Yorkshire.
0033-524X Quality Progress
0033-5266 Quarry
0033-5274 Quarry Managers' Journal *changed to* Quarry Management.
0033-5290 Quarterly Analysis of Failures *changed to* Quarterly Business Failures.
0033-5304 Quarterly Bibliography of Economics†
0033-5312 Quarterly Blue Book on Joint Stock Companies in India
0033-5320 Canada. Statistics Canada. Quarterly Bulletin of Agricultural Statistics†
0033-5339 Building *see* 0479-4826
0033-5347 Quarterly Check -List of Ethnology & Sociology†
0033-5355 Quarterly Check-List of Biblical Studies *see* 0033-5428
0033-5363 Quarterly Check-List of Classical Studies
0033-5371 Quarterly Check-List of Economics & Political Science†
0033-538X Quarterly Check-List of Linguistics
0033-5398 Quarterly Check-List of Literary History: English, French, German†
0033-5401 Quarterly Check-List of Medievalia
0033-541X Quarterly Check-List of Musicology
0033-5428 Quarterly Check-List of Oriental Studies
0033-5436 Quarterly Check-List of Psychology
0033-5444 Quarterly Check-List of Renaissance Studies *see* 0033-5401
0033-5452 Quarterly Construction Statistics
0033-5479 Quarterly Dental Review *see* 0300-5712
0033-5487 Quarterly Digest of Urban and Regional Research†
0033-5495 Quarterly Economic Reviews *changed to* Country Reports.
0033-5509 U.S. Federal Trade Commission. Quarterly Financial Report: United States Manufacturing Corporations *see* 0098-681X
0033-5517 Quarterly Inventory of Economic Research on New England†
0033-5525 Quarterly Journal of Crude Drug Research *see* 0925-1618
0033-5533 Quarterly Journal of Economics
0033-555X Quarterly Journal of Experimental Psychology *see* 0272-4987
0033-555X Quarterly Journal of Experimental Psychology *see* 0272-4995
0033-5568 Quarterly Journal of Forestry
0033-5576 Quarterly Journal of Indian Studies in Sciences†
0033-5584 Quarterly Journal of Indian Studies in Social Sciences *changed to* Asian Economic and Social Review.
0033-5592 Quarterly Journal of Indian Studies in Technical Knowledge†
0033-5606 Quarterly Journal of Mathematics
0033-5614 Quarterly Journal of Mechanics and Applied Mathematics
0033-5622 Quarterly Journal of Medicine
0033-5630 Quarterly Journal of Speech
0033-5649 Quarterly Journal of Studies on Alcohol *see* 0096-882X
0033-5657 Quarterly Journal of Surgical Sciences
0033-5665 Quarterly Journal of Taiwan Land Credit
0033-5673 Psychiatria et Neurologia Japonica (Tokyo, 1949)
0033-569X Quarterly of Applied Mathematics
0033-5711 Quarterly Predictions of National Income and Expenditure
0033-572X Quarterly Report to Investors in Puerto Rican Securities†
0033-5754 Quarterly Review of Agricultural Economics *see* 1032-9722
0033-5762 Quarterly Review of Australian Education. *see* 0311-6875
0033-5770 Quarterly Review of Biology
0033-5789 Quarterly Review of Drilling Statistics *changed to* American Petroleum Institute. Quarterly Completion Report.
0033-5797 Quarterly Review of Economics and Business *changed to* Quarterly Review of Economics and Finance.
0033-5800 Quarterly Review of Historical Studies
0033-5819 Quarterly Review of Literature *see* 0748-0873
0033-5835 Quarterly Reviews of Biophysics
0033-5843 Australia. Bureau of Statistics. Quarterly Summary of Australian Statistics.†
0033-5851 Quarterly Summary of Business Statistics, New York State
0033-586X Quartet *see* 0011-9210
0033-5878 Quatre Verites
0033-5894 Quaternary Research
0033-5908 Quatro Rodas
0033-5916 Quattroruote
0033-5924 Quattrosoldi†
0033-5940 Que Tal
0033-5967 Quebec Home & School News
0033-5975 Quebec Industriel†
0033-5983 Quebec Official Gazette
0033-5991 Quebec/Travail†
0033-6009 Queen *see* 0141-0547
0033-6017 Queen of All Hearts
0033-6025 Queen's Highway†
0033-6033 Queens Medical Magazine
0033-6041 Queen's Quarterly
0033-6068 Queensborough
0033-6084 Queensland Country Life
0033-6092 Queensland Country Woman
0033-6106 Queensland Dairyfarmer
0033-6114 Queensland Electrical Contractor
0033-6122 Queensland Fruit and Vegetable News
0033-6149 Queensland Government Mining Journal
0033-6157 Queensland Heritage†
0033-6165 Q. Industry†
0033-6181 Queensland Justice of the Peace and Reports *see* 0312-1658
0033-6203 Queensland Motor Industry *changed to* Motor Trader.
0033-6211 Queensland Nurses Journal†
0033-622X Queensland Shopkeeper *see* 0034-6144
0033-6238 Queensland Teachers' Journal
0033-6246 Die Quelle
0033-6262 Querce
0033-6270 Query
0033-6289 Quest *changed to* New Quest.
0033-6297 Quest (Champaign)
0033-6300 Little Magazine†
0033-6319 Quest (Chardon)†
0033-6327 Quest (Pullman)†
0033-6335 Questa Sicilia
0033-6343 Question†
0033-6351 Questions Actuelles du Socialisme
0033-636X Questions Internat *changed to* Nouvelles Questions.
0033-6378 Questitalia
0033-6386 Quetta Times
0033-6408 Quick Frozen Foods†
0033-6416 Quick Frozen Foods International
0033-6432 Quid
0033-6440 Quiet Please *changed to* Noise News Digest.
0033-6459 Quilates
0033-6467 Quill†
0033-6483 Quill (Wood Ridge)
0033-6491 Quill and Quire
0033-6505 Quill and Scroll
0033-6521 Quimica e Industria
0033-653X Quimica Iberoamericana†
0033-6548 Quincailliers de France *changed to* Quincailliers de France-l'Argus Menager.
0033-6556 Quincy College Bulletin
0033-6572 Quintessence International
0033-6599 Quintessenz Journal
0033-6602 Quinto Lingo
0033-6610 Quis Custodiet *changed to* Law & Justice.
0033-6629 Quixote
0033-6637 Quo Vadis
0033-6661 Quondam Magazine
0033-667X Quote Magazine *see* 0273-6705
0033-6688 Quotes Ending†
0033-6696 R.A.C.S. Newsletter†
0033-670X R A E C Gazette *changed to* Torch (London).
0033-6718 R A E News†
0033-6734 R A News
0033-6742 R A P
0033-6750 R A P R A Abstracts
0033-6769 R A S
0033-6777 R A S Kennel Control Journal *changed to* Victorian Canine Association Journal.
0033-6785 R A U - Rapport
0033-6793 R & D Contracts Monthly
0033-6807 R & D Management
0033-6815 R & L News
0033-6823 R and R Magazine *changed to* Sales Builder Magazine.
0033-6831 R C A Review†
0033-684X R C M Magazine
0033-6858 R C M P Quarterly
0033-6866 R-C Modeler
0033-6874 R E F A Nachrichten
0033-6882 R E L C Journal
0033-6890 R E S. Reticuloendothelial Society. Journal *see* 0741-5400
0033-6904 R E S News Exchange *changed to* R E C News Exchange.
0033-6912 R I B A Library Bulletin *see* 0266-4380
0033-6939 R I C S Abstracts and Reviews *changed to* R I C S Library Information Service Abstracts and Reviews.
0033-6947 R I C S Technical Information Service. Weekly Briefing *changed to* R I C S Library Information Service. Weekly Briefing.
0033-6955 R I L M Abstracts of Music Literature
0033-6963 R I O Newsletter†
0033-6971 R J
0033-698X R L A
0033-7021 R N
0033-703X R O C†
0033-7048 R O S C†
0033-7056 R P A Bulletin
0033-7064 R P M Weekly
0033-7072 R Q
0033-7099 R S A World†
0033-7129 R S I
0033-7137 R.T.A. Journal *changed to* N.T.A. Journal.
0033-7145 R T E Guide
0033-7153 R T N D A Communicator
0033-7161 R T T Y Journal
0033-7196 R W D S U Record
0033-720X R X Sports and Travel†
0033-7218 R Z - Illustrierte Romanzeitung
0033-7226 Raadgevend-Ingenieur†
0033-7234 Raam†
0033-7242 Rabbits in Canada
0033-7250 Rabels Zeitschrift fuer auslaendisches und internationales Privatrecht
0033-7269 Raccolto *see* 0040-3776
0033-7277 Race *see* 0306-3968
0033-7285 Race News
0033-7293 Race Relations†
0033-7323 Race Relations Bulletin *changed to* Runnymede Bulletin.
0033-7331 Race Relations Law Survey†
0033-734X Race Relations News
0033-7358 Race Today
0033-7366 Racing & Football Outlook
0033-7374 Racing Car News
0033-7390 Racing Pigeon
0033-7404 Racing Pigeon Pictorial
0033-7412 Racing Report†
0033-7420 Racing Specialist
0033-7439 Racing Star Weekly
0033-7447 Racquette
0033-7455 Das Rad
0033-7463 Rad
0033-748X Denmark. Statens Husholdningsraad. Raad og Resultater *changed to* Denmark. Forbrugerstyrelsen. Raad og Resultater.
0033-7501 Radar
0033-751X Radar and Electronics *changed to* I. P. R. E. Review.
0033-7528 Radcliffe Quarterly
0033-7536 Informacije Rade Koncar *see* 0350-5537
0033-7544 Radford Review†
0033-7552 Radiaesthesie - Geopathie - Strahlenbiologie *changed to* Radiaesthesie.
0033-7560 Radiation Botany *see* 0098-8472
0033-7579 Radiation Effects
0033-7587 Radiation Research
0033-7617 Radical America
0033-7625 Radical Humanist
0033-7641 Radical Therapist†
0033-765X Radio
0033-7668 Radio - Plans
0033-7676 Radio - Television†
0033-7684 Radio Active *see* 0811-9929
0033-7692 Radio Aids to Marine Navigation
0033-7706 U S Listings *changed to* North American Callbook.
0033-7722 Radio and Electronic Engineer *see* 0954-0695
0033-7730 Radio & Electronics
0033-7749 Radio & Television
0033-7757 Radio und Television *changed to* R T V.
0033-7781 Radio Chassis Television
0033-779X Radio Club of America. Proceedings
0033-7803 Radio Communication
0033-7811 Techniques Electroniques et Audiovisuelles *see* 0397-6424
0033-782X Radio Constructor *see* 0374-4361
0033-7838 Radio Control Models & Electronics
0033-7846 Radio, Electrical & Furniture Merchandiser†
0033-7854 Radio Electronica *see* 0168-7840
0033-7862 Radio-Electronics
0033-7870 Radioelectronics and Communications Systems
0033-7889 Radio Engineering and Electronic Physics *see* 8756-6648
0033-7897 Radio Fernseh Phono Praxis†
0033-7900 Radio Fernsehen Elektronik
0033-7919 Radio Industria *changed to* Radioindustria-Elettronica-Televisione.
0033-7927 Radio Japan News
0033-7935 Radio Mentor Electronic†
0033-7943 Radio Mozambique†
0033-7951 Radio Nederland *changed to* Radio Nederland Programme Schedule.
0033-796X Radio Portugal Listeners Magazine†
0033-7986 Radio Propagation Predictions for Southern Africa
0033-7994 Radio R E F
0033-8001 Radio Research Laboratory. Journal *see* 0914-9260
0033-801X Denpa Kenkyujo Kiho - Radio Research Laboratory. Review *see* 0914-9279
0033-8028 Radio Revue TV-Electronique Industrielle
0033-8036 Radio Rivista†
0033-8052 Radio Tecnica
0033-8060 Radio Times
0033-8079 Radio Times of India†
0033-8087 R T H†
0033-8095 Radio - TV - Electronic Service *changed to* R T E.
0033-8109 Radio-TV Wereld *see* 0027-5298
0033-8133 Radio y Television†
0033-8141 Radio y Television Practica *changed to* Radio Electronica Practica.
0033-815X Radio Z S
0033-8168 Radio-Amater
0033-8176 Radiobiologia, Radioterapia e Fisica Medica *see* 0003-4673
0033-8184 Radiobiologia - Radiotherapia†
0033-8192 Radiobiologiya
0033-8206 Radiobiology†
0033-8214 Radiobote
0033-8222 Radiocarbon
0033-8249 Radiochimie†
0033-8257 Radiocorriere - T V

ISSN

0033-8273 Radiographer
0033-8281 Radiography
0033-829X Radioisotope Report *changed to* Radiation Report.
0033-8303 Radioisotopes
0033-8311 Radiokhimiya
0033-832X Der Radiologe
0033-8338 Radiologia
0033-8346 Radiologia Clinica et Biologica *see* 0254-881X
0033-8362 Radiologia Medica
0033-8370 Radiologia y Medicina Nuclear
0033-8389 Radiologic Clinics of North America
0033-8397 Radiologic Technology†
0033-8400 Radiological Health Data and Reports. *see* 0091-6722
0033-8419 Radiology
0033-8427 Radiology/Today & Tomorrow†
0033-8443 Radiophysics and Quantum Electronics
0033-8451 Radioprotection
0033-846X Radioschau *see* 0254-4318
0033-8478 Radiotechnika
0033-8486 Radiotekhnika (Moscow)
0033-8494 Radiotekhnika i Elektronika
0033-8516 Radiovy Konstrukter *changed to* Amaterske Radio B.
0033-8532 Radius†
0033-8540 Radmarkt
0033-8559 Imunoloski Zavod. Radovi
0033-8575 Sveuciliste u Zagrebu. Medicinski Fakultet. Radovi
0033-8583 Univerzitet u Sarajevu. Poljoprivredni Fakultet. Radovi
0033-8605 Radyans'ka Osvita
0033-8621 Rag
0033-8648 Ragguaglio Librario
0033-8656 Ragione
0033-8672 Ragtimer
0033-8680 Rehabilitacia
0033-8699 Rahnema-Ye Ketab†
0033-8702 Raiffeisenblatt fuer Niederoesterreich und Wien†
0033-8710 Raiffeisenbotet†
0033-8737 R M F
0033-8745 Railnews
0033-8761 Railroad Magazine *see* 0163-7266
0033-877X Railroad Model Craftsman
0033-8788 U.S. Railroad Retirement Board. Quarterly Review†
0033-8796 Railroad Yardmaster†
0033-880X Railroading *changed to* Railroading Series.
0033-8818 Railway Advocate
0033-8826 Railway Age
0033-8834 Railway and Canal Historical Society Journal
0033-8842 Railway and Locomotive Historical Society. Bulletin *see* 0090-7847
0033-8850 Railway Carmen's Journal†
0033-8869 Railway Clerk - Interchange *changed to* Interchange (Rockville).
0033-8885 S.A. Railway Engineering *changed to* Railways in Southern Africa.
0033-8893 Railway Forum†
0033-8907 Railway Gazette *see* 0373-5346
0033-8923 Railway Magazine
0033-8931 Railway Modeller
0033-894X Railway Research & Engineering News. Section A†
0033-8958 Railway Research & Engineering News. Section B†
0033-8966 Railway Research & Engineering News. Sections D,E,F and G†
0033-8974 Railway Review *changed to* Transport Review.
0033-8990 Railway Steel Topics†
0033-9008 Railway Technical Research Institute. Quarterly Report
0033-9016 Railway Track & Structures
0033-9032 Railway World
0033-9040 Railways Institute Magazine
0033-9067 Textilia
0033-9075 Raison Presente
0033-9083 Rajasthan Board Journal of Education
0033-9105 Rajasthan Srama Patrika†
0033-9113 Rakam
0033-9121 Rakennuslehti
0033-913X Rakennustekniikka
0033-9148 Rallye Racing
0033-9156 Ramakrishna Mission Institute of Culture. Bulletin
0033-9164 Ramparts†
0033-9172 Ranch Romances†
0033-9180 Randolph-Macon Alumni Bulletin *changed to* Randolph-Macon College. Bulletin.
0033-9199 Range†
0033-9202 Rangefinder
0033-9229 Ranger Rick's Nature Magazine *see* 0738-6656
0033-9237 Ranger *see* 0751-5731
0033-9245 Ransomer
0033-9261 Rapid Handler†
0033-9296 Rapport†
0033-930X Racquet (La Crosse)
0033-9318 Rasprostranenie Pechati
0033-9334 Rassegna Chimica
0033-9342 Rassegna Cinofila†
0033-9350 Camera di Commercio della Spezia. Rassegna Commerciale *see* 0391-7983
0033-9369 Associazione Nazionale Commercianti, Gas Liquefatti. Bollettino Informativo
0033-9377 Rassegna dei Lavori Pubblici
0033-9385 Rassegna del Lavoro†
0033-9407 Rassegna del Mercato
0033-9415 Rassegna dell'Arbitrato
0033-9423 Rassegna della Letteratura Italiana
0033-9431 Rassegna della Letteratura Odontoiatrica
0033-944X Rassegna della Letteratura Sui Cicli Economici
0033-9458 Rassegna della Stampa
0033-9466 Rassegna dell'Istruzione Secondaria *changed to* Rassegna dell'Istruzione.
0033-9482 Rassegna di Cultura e Vita Scolastica
0033-9490 Rassegna di Dermatologia e Sifilografia
0033-9504 Rassegna di Diritto Cinematografico, Teatrale e della Radiotelevisione
0033-9512 Rassegna di Diritto Pubblico
0033-9547 Rassegna di Legislazione Italiana Nei Rapporti Internazionali†
0033-9555 Rassegna di Medicina Sperimentale
0033-9563 Rassegna di Patologia dell'Apparato Respiratorio
0033-9571 Rassegna di Pedagogia
0033-958X Rassegna di Politica e di Storia
0033-9601 Rassegna di Servizio Sociale
0033-9628 Rassegna di Studi Penitenziari *changed to* Rassegna Penitenziaria e Criminologica.
0033-9636 Rassegna di Studi Psichiatrici
0033-9644 Rassegna di Teologia
0033-9652 Rassegna ed Archivio di Chirurgia†
0033-9679 Rassegna Giuridica Ed Economica sui Danni di Guerra
0033-9687 Rassegna Grafica
0033-9695 Rassegna Internazionale di Clinica e Terapia
0033-9709 Rassegna Internazionale di Meccanica *changed to* Rassegna di Meccanica.
0033-9725 Rassegna Italiana di Linguistica Applicata
0033-9733 Rassegna Italiana di Ricerca Psichica
0033-975X Rassegna Lucchese†
0033-9768 Rassegna Medica e Culturale†
0033-9776 Rassegna Medica Sarda
0033-9784 Rassegna Melodrammatica
0033-9792 Rassegna Mensile di Israel
0033-9806 Rassegna Musicale Curci
0033-9814 I S L E Rassegna Parlamentare Schedario Legislativo *changed to* Rassegna Parlamentare.
0033-9822 Rassegna Petrolifera
0033-9830 Rassegna Quindicinale dell'Agricoltura *changed to* Ecomese.
0033-9849 Rassegna Sindacale
0033-9857 Rassegna Sovietica
0033-9865 Rassegna Speleologica Italiana†
0033-9873 Rassegna Storica del Risorgimento
0033-9881 Rassegna Storica Toscana
0033-9903 Rassegna Tecnica Enel *changed to* Rassegna Tecnica di Problemi dell'Energia Elettrica.
0033-9911 Rassegna Trimestrale di Odontoiatria
0033-992X Rassegna di Urologia e Nefrologia
0033-9938 Raster†
0033-9946 Rastitel'nye Resursy
0033-9962 Rateko
0033-9970 Rateksa *see* 0108-6626
0033-9989 Der Ratgeber
0033-9997 Ratgeber fuer Kranke und Gesunde *changed to* Ratgeber aus der Apotheke.
0034-0006 Ratio
0034-0014 Ratio *see* 0035-6816
0034-0030 Individualist
0034-0049 Rational Living *see* 0894-9085
0034-0065 Rationalist *see* 1036-8191
0034-009X Raumausstattung Report†
0034-0103 Raumfahrtforschung *see* 0342-068X
0034-0111 Raumforschung und Raumordnung
0034-0138 Rave†
0034-0146 Raven (Lynchburg)
0034-0162 Ray Palmer's Forum†
0034-0170 Rayito (Counselor's Edition)†
0034-0197 Rayons
0034-0200 Rays of Sunshine *see* 0039-5412
0034-0227 Razgledi
0034-0235 Razon y Fe
0034-0243 Razonoda Miliona
0034-0251 Razprave in Gradivo - Treatises and Documents *changed to* Razprave in Gradivo.
0034-026X Razvedka i Okhrana Nedr
0034-0286 Re: Arts and Letters *see* 1054-5212
0034-0294 Re: Search†
0034-0308 Reach *see* 0745-1172
0034-0316 Reach Out†
0034-0324 Reaching Out *changed to* Feelings.
0034-0332 Reactor Technology†
0034-0359 Read Magazine
0034-0367 Readaption *see* 0823-9436
0034-0375 Reader's Digest
0034-0383 Reader's Digest (Asia Edition)
0034-0391 Reader's Digest (Australian Edition)
0034-0405 Reader's Digest (British Edition)
0034-0413 Reader's Digest (Canadian-English Edition)
0034-0421 Reader's Digest (Indian Edition)
0034-043X Reader's Digest (Japanese Edition)†
0034-0448 Reader's Digest (New Zealand Edition)
0034-0456 Reader's Digest (South African Edition)
0034-0464 Readers' Guide to Periodical Literature
0034-0472 Reading
0034-0502 Reading Horizons
0034-0510 Reading Improvement
0034-0537 Reading Newsreport†
0034-0545 Reading Quarterly†
0034-0553 Reading Research Quarterly
0034-0561 Reading Teacher
0034-057X Reaktorn†
0034-0588 Real†
0034-0596 Real Academia de Ciencias Exactas, Fisicas y Naturales. Revista
0034-060X Real Academia de Cordoba de Ciencias, Bellas Letras y Nobles Artes. Boletin
0034-0618 Real Academia de Farmacia. Anales
0034-0626 Real Academia de la Historia. Boletin
0034-0634 Real Academia Nacional de Medicina. Anales
0034-0642 Real Confessions Magazine
0034-0669 Real Estate and Stock Journal *changed to* Victorian Real Estate Journal.
0034-0677 Real Estate Appraiser *changed to* Real Estate Appraiser.
0034-0693 Real Estate Investment Planning Checklist and Forms
0034-0707 Real Estate Forum
0034-0715 Real Estate Insider
0034-0723 Real Estate Investment Ideas
0034-0731 Real Estate Investment Planning
0034-074X Real Estate Journal (Sydney South)
0034-0758 Real Estate Law Brief Case†
0034-0766 Real Estate News (New York)†
0034-0774 Real Estate Record and Builder's Guide
0034-0790 Real Estate Review
0034-0804 Real Estate Today
0034-0839 Real Life Confessions
0034-0847 Real Living
0034-0855 Real Property, Probate and Trust Journal
0034-0863 Real Sociedad Arqueologica. Boletin Arqueologico
0034-0871 Fisica *changed to* Real Sociedad Espanola de Fisica. Anales de Fisica.
0034-088X Quimica *changed to* Real Sociedad Espanola de Quimica. Anales de Quimica.
0034-0898 Real West†
0034-091X The Realist
0034-0960 Reality
0034-0979 Reality
0034-0987 Reality
0034-0995 Realta
0034-1029 Realta Sovietica†
0034-1037 Realtor Headlines†
0034-1045 Realty and Building
0034-1053 Realty and Chain Store Renting Leads *changed to* Realty.
0034-1061 Realty Review†
0034-107X Reaper
0034-1096 Reassurance *see* 0153-3614
0034-1118 Rebe und Wein
0034-1142 Rec Naroda
0034-1150 Recall†
0034-1169 C L R Recent Developments *see* 0892-0605
0034-1185 Recent Publications on Governmental Problems
0034-1193 Recenti Progressi in Medicina
0034-1207 Recenzija†
0034-1215 Rechabite
0034-1223 Recherche Aerospatiale
0034-1231 C A R D A N. Bulletin d'Information et de Liaison†
0034-124X Recherche Sociale
0034-1258 Recherches de Science Religieuse
0034-1266 Recherches de Theologie Ancienne et Medievale
0034-1282 Recherches Sociographiques
0034-1290 Rechnoi Transport
0034-1312 Recht der Jugend und des Bildungswesens
0034-1320 Recht der Schiffahrt
0034-1339 Recht im Amt
0034-1355 Rechtsarchiv der Wirtschaft *changed to* Das Recht der Wirtschaft.
0034-1363 Rechtspflegerblatt
0034-1371 Rechtsprechung der Bau-Ausfuehrung *changed to* Rechtsprechung Zum Privaten Baurecht.
0034-138X Rechtsprechung in Strafsachen
0034-1398 Rechtstheorie
0034-141X Reclamation Era *see* 0733-6446
0034-1436 Reclamation Safety News *see* 0270-4447
0034-1452 Recommend: Florida *changed to* Recommend: Magazine.
0034-1479 Reconciliation Quarterly
0034-1487 Reconstruction
0034-1495 Reconstructionist
0034-1509 Rencontre Orient Occident†
0034-1517 Record†
0034-1525 Lancashire Authors' Association. Record
0034-1541 Record (New York, 1940)
0034-155X Record Collector (Leicester)
0034-1568 Record Collector (Broomfield)
0034-1592 Record Research
0034-1606 Record Retailer *see* 0265-1548
0034-1614 Record Stockman
0034-1622 Record World
0034-1630 Recorded Sound†
0034-1649 Recorder
0034-1657 Recorder†
0034-1665 Recorder and Music *see* 0961-3544
0034-1673 Recording Engineer Producer *changed to* Recording Engineering Production.
0034-1703 Records and Statistics†

ISSN

0034-1711 Records Management Journal†
0034-1738 Records of Huntingdonshire
0034-1746 Records of the Month†
0034-1770 Recreation Management *see* 0744-3676
0034-1827 Recruiting Trends
0034-1835 Recueil Dalloz-Sirey
0034-1843 Recueil de Medecine Veterinaire d'Alfort
0034-1851 Recueil des Brevets d'Invention
0034-1878 Recueil Juridique de l'Est Securite Sociale
0034-1886 Recueil Officiel des Marques de Fabrique et de Commerce†
0034-1916 Recuperatie *changed to* Magazine Recycling Benelux.
0034-1924 Recuperation *see* 1156-962X
0034-1932 Recusant History
0034-1940 Red and Black (Washington)
0034-1959 Red and Green
0034-1967 Red Cedar Review
0034-1975 Red Clay Reader†
0034-1983 Red Cross Newsletter *changed to* Good Neighbor.
0034-1991 Panorama†
0034-2009 Red Hill Press *see* 0147-4936
0034-2017 Red Mole *see* 0142-6575
0034-2025 Red Notes
0034-2033 Red Poll News
0034-2041 Red Shield *changed to* Red Shield News.
0034-2068 Red Star Weekly
0034-2076 Red Tape
0034-2092 Redaktions-Archiv
0034-2106 Redbook
0034-2114 Reddingwezen *changed to* Nederlands Tijdschrift voor E H B O en Reddingwngwezen.
0034-2122 Redeemer's Voice†
0034-2130 Redlands Bulldog *changed to* Bulldog Weekly.
0034-2165 Redstart
0034-2181 Redwood Rancher *changed to* Redwood Rancher Country.
0034-219X Reed's Aircraft & Equipment News†
0034-2203 Reed's Marine Equipment News *see* 0140-8046
0034-2211 Reeducation
0034-222X Reeducation Orthophonique
0034-2238 Reel
0034-2246 Referateblatt zur Raumordnung *see* 0341-2512
0034-2254 Referatekartei Korrosion-Korrosionsschutz†
0034-2262 Bibliographie Philosophie†
0034-2297 Referativnyi Zhurnal. Avtomobil'nyi i Gorodskoi Transport
0034-2300 Referativnyi Zhurnal. Biologiya
0034-2327 Referativny Zhurnal. Elektrotekhnika i Energetika *see* 0203-5316
0034-2343 Referativnyi Zhurnal. Fizika
0034-2351 Referativnyi Zhurnal. Geodeziya *see* 0375-9717
0034-236X Referativnyi Zhurnal. Geofizika
0034-2378 Referativnyi Zhurnal. Geografiya
0034-2386 Referativnyi Zhurnal. Gornoe Delo
0034-2394 Gornye Mashiny *see* 0373-6415
0034-2408 Referativnyi Zhurnal. Issledovanie Kosmicheskogo Prostranstva
0034-2416 Referativnyi Zhurnal. Khimicheskoe i Kholodil'noe Mashinostroenie *see* 0370-8098
0034-2424 Referativnyi Zhurnal. Kotlostroenie
0034-2432 Referativnyi Zhurnal. Legkaya Promyshlennost'
0034-2440 Referativnyi Zhurnal. Lesovedenie i Lesovodstvo
0034-2459 Referativnyi Zhurnal. Mashinostroitel'nye Materialy, Konstruktsii i Raschet Detali Mashin. Gidroprivod
0034-2467 Referativnyi Zhurnal. Matematika
0034-2475 Referativnyi Zhurnal. Meditsinskaya Geografiya
0034-2483 Referativnyi Zhurnal. Mekhanika
0034-2491 Referativnyi Zhurnal. Metallurgiya
0034-2505 Referativnyi Zhurnal. Metrologiya i Izmeritel'naya Tekhnika
0034-2513 Referativnyi Zhurnal. Nasosostroenie i Kompressorstroenie *changed to* Referativnyi Zhurnal. Nasosostroenie i Kompressorostroenie. Kholodil'noe Mashinostroenie.
0034-2521 Referativnyi Zhurnal. Oborudovanie Pishchevoi Promyshlennosti
0034-253X Referativnyi Zhurnal. Organizatsiya Upravleniya Promyshlennost'yu *see* 0132-5639
0034-2548 Referativnyi Zhurnal. Pochvovedenie i Agrokhimiya
0034-2556 Referativnyi Zhurnal. Promyshlennyi Transport
0034-2580 Referativnyi Zhurnal. Tekhnologiya i Oborudovanie Tsellyulozno-vumazhnogo i Poligraficheskogo Proizvodstva†
0034-2599 Referativnyi Zhurnal. Tekhnologiya Mashinostroeniya
0034-2602 Referativnyi Zhurnal. Traktory i Sel'skokhozyaistvennye Mashiny i Orudiya
0034-2610 Referativnyi Zhurnal. Truboprovodnyi Transport
0034-2629 Referativnyi Zhurnal. Turbostroenie
0034-2637 Referativnyi Zhurnal. Voprosy Tekhnicheskogo Progressa i Organizatsii Proizvodstva v Mashinostroenii
0034-2645 Referativnyi Zhurnal. Vzaimodeistvie Raznykh Vidov Transporta i Konteinernye Perevozki
0034-2653 Referativnyi Zhurnal. Yadernye Reaktory
0034-2661 Referativnyi Zhurnal. Zhivotnovodstvo i Veterinariya *see* 0206-5525
0034-267X Referativnyi Zhurnal. Radiotekhnika
0034-2688 Referatovy Vyber z Anestesiologie a Resuscitace
0034-2696 Referatovy Vyber z Chirurgie
0034-270X Referatovy Vyber z Chorob Infekcnich
0034-2718 Referatovy Vyber z Dermatovenerologie
0034-2726 Referatovy Vyber z Endokrinologie†
0034-2734 Referatovy Vyber z Fysiologie†
0034-2742 Referatovy Vyber z Gastroenterologie
0034-2750 Referatovy Vyber z Gerontologie a Geriatrie†
0034-2769 Referatovy Vyber z Kardiologie, Fysiologie a Patologie Obehoveho Ustroji
0034-2777 Referatovy Vyber z Lekarenstvi
0034-2785 Referatovy Vyber z Lekarskeho Tisku o Vychove a Doskolovani Zdravotnickych Pracovniku†
0034-2793 Referatovy Vyber z Neurologie
0034-2807 Referatovy Vyber z Oftalmologie
0034-2815 Referatovy Vyber z Onkologie†
0034-2823 Referatovy Vyber z Ortopedie, Traumatologie a Pribuznych Oboru
0034-2831 Referatovy Vyber z Otorhinolaryngologie a Foniatrie†
0034-284X Referatovy Vyber z Patologicke Anatomie†
0034-2858 Referatovy Vyber z Pediatrie
0034-2866 Referatovy Vyber z Porodnictvi a Gynekologie
0034-2874 Referatovy Vyber z Rentgenologie
0034-2882 Referatovy Vyber z Revmatologie
0034-2890 Referatovy Vyber z Pneumologie a Tuberkulosy
0034-2904 Referatovy Vyber ze Sportovni Mediciny - Abstracts of Sports Medicine *changed to* Referatovy Vyber ze Sportovni Mediciny a Lecebne Rehabilitace.
0034-2912 National Diet Library. Reference
0034-2947 Reflector
0034-2963 Reflector Newsletter
0034-2971 Reflets et Perspectives de la Vie Economique
0034-298X Reflets Guildiens†
0034-3005 Reflexion *see* 0384-8167
0034-3013 Kontakt und Reflexionen *changed to* Kontakt.
0034-3021 Reformatio *changed to* ZeitSchrift fuer Kultur Politik Kirche.
0034-303X Reformation Review
0034-3048 Reformation Today
0034-3056 Reformed World
0034-3064 Reformed Review
0034-3072 Reformed Theological Review
0034-3080 Reformer
0034-3102 Refractories
0034-3110 Refractories Journal *see* 0959-6127
0034-3129 Refrigerated Transporter
0034-3153 Refuah Veterinarith *see* 0334-9152
0034-3161 Refuat Hape Vehashinaim
0034-317X Regan Report on Hospital Law
0034-3188 Regan Report on Medical Law
0034-3196 Regan Report on Nursing Law
0034-320X Regards sur le Comite d'Etablissement d'Orly Sud
0034-3218 Regelrecht
0034-3250 Regensburger Bistumsblatt
0034-3269 Der Reggeboge
0034-3285 T V Panorama *changed to* Panorama - De Post.
0034-3293 Regio Basiliensis
0034-3315 Region Six Sentinel
0034-3323 Regional Action†
0034-3331 Regional and Urban Economics - Operational Methods *see* 0166-0462
0034-334X International Seismological Centre. Regional Catalogue of Earthquakes
0034-3358 Regional Cultural Institute. Journal
0034-3366 Regional Development Newsletter *see* 0310-5946
0034-3374 Regional Plan News *changed to* Regional Plan News.
0034-3382 Regional Review Quarterly *changed to* National Association of Regional Councils. Regional Reporter.
0034-3390 Regional Spotlight
0034-3404 Regional Studies
0034-3412 Regione e Potere Locale
0034-3420 Region's Agenda
0034-3439 Regionwide†
0034-3471 Regmaker
0034-348X Regmi Research Series
0034-3498 Regno - Attualita
0034-3501 Rehabilitation in South Africa
0034-351X Rihabiriteshon Igaku
0034-3528 Rehabilitation†
0034-3536 Die Rehabilitation
0034-3552 Rehabilitation Counseling Bulletin
0034-3579 Rehabilitation Literature†
0034-3587 Rehabilitation Record *changed to* U.S. Health Care Financing Administration Forum.
0034-3609 Rehovot
0034-3617 Reinforced Plastics
0034-3625 Reiniger und Waescher
0034-3633 Reino
0034-3641 Reinsurance Reporter
0034-365X Reinwardtia
0034-3668 Deutsche Reisebuero-Zeitung†
0034-3676 Reiseliv i Norge *changed to* Reiseliv.
0034-3684 Reiss-Davis Clinic Bulletin†
0034-3692 Reiter Revue International
0034-3714 Refrigeration
0034-3722 Refrigeration and Air Conditioning Technology *see* 0034-3714
0034-3749 Rekenschap
0034-3765 Relacoes Humanas†
0034-3773 Relais
0034-3781 Relations
0034-379X Relations Industrielles
0034-3803 Relations Latines
0034-3811 Relations Publiques Informations
0034-382X Relay Association Journal *changed to* Cablevision News.
0034-3838 Relazioni†
0034-3846 Relazioni Internazionali
0034-3854 Etocomunicazione *changed to* Etocom (1980).
0034-3862 Relazioni Sociali†
0034-3897 Relics
0034-3900 Relics†
0034-3935 Religioese Graphik
0034-3943 Religion and Church in the Communist Orbit†
0034-3951 Religion and Society
0034-396X Religion and Society *see* 0093-2582
0034-3978 R C D A - Religion in Communist Dominated Areas *changed to* R C D A.
0034-3986 Religion in Life *see* 0270-9287
0034-401X Religion Teacher's Journal
0034-4036 Religiose nell'Apostolato Diretto†
0034-4044 Religious & Theological Abstracts
0034-4052 Religious and Theological Resources†
0034-4060 Religious Book Review Index
0034-4079 Religious Broadcasting
0034-4087 Religious Education
0034-4095 Religious Humanism
0034-4109 R N A Newsletter
0034-4117 Religious Periodicals Index†
0034-4125 Religious Studies
0034-4141 Reluire *see* 0758-413X
0034-4168 Remag
0034-4176 Remainders' Book Italiano
0034-4184 Remanso
0034-4192 Remarques Africaines *changed to* Remarques Arabo-Africaines.
0034-4206 Remedes des Corps et des Ames *see* 0048-7228
0034-4214 Remedial Education *see* 0268-2141
0034-4230 Reminder†
0034-4249 Remodeling Contractor (Arlington)†
0034-4257 Remote Sensing of Environment
0034-4265 Removals and Storage
0034-4273 Rempart
0034-4281 Renaissance *changed to* New Reformation.
0034-429X Renaissance and Reformation
0034-4311 Renaissance Deux-Mille *changed to* Tribune Gaulliste.
0034-4338 Renaissance Quarterly
0034-4346 Renascence
0034-4362 Renderer *see* 0090-8932
0034-4370 Rendez-Vous†
0034-4389 Rendez Vous
0034-4400 Rendezvous
0034-4419 Rendiconti†
0034-4427 Rendiconti di Matematica
0034-4451 Renfro Valley Bugle
0034-446X Renovacion
0034-4478 Renovacion
0034-4486 Renovatio
0034-4494 Renovation *see* 0041-5103
0034-4508 Rensselaer Engineer
0034-4516 Rent-All Magazine†
0034-4524 Rental Equipment Register
0034-4532 Rental Laundry Management *changed to* Laundry Cleaning World.
0034-4567 Repertoire Bibliographique de la Philosophie
0034-4575 Repertoire des Voyages
0034-4583 Repertoire Permanent des Groupes Financiers et Industriels *changed to* Repertoire des Groupes d'Entreprises.
0034-4591 Repertorio Analitico della Stampa Italiana. Quotidiani e Periodici†
0034-4613 Repertorio Centroamericano†
0034-463X Repertorium Verpakte Geneesmiddelen Periodiek Overzicht voor Artsen *changed to* Repertorium.
0034-4648 Repertuar Khudozhestvennoi Samodeyatel'nosti
0034-4664 Report from Germany†
0034-4672 Report of Ionosphere and Space Research in Japan *see* 0386-5444
0034-4680 Report on Education of the Disadvantaged
0034-4699 Report on Education Research
0034-4702 Report on Preschool Education *changed to* Report on Preschool Programs.
0034-4737 Report on World Affairs
0034-4745 Reportage
0034-4753 Reporter
0034-4788 Reporter
0034-4796 Reporter for Conscience' Sake

0034-480X Reporter of Construction Equipment *see* 0891-141X
0034-4818 Reportero Industrial
0034-4826 I A B C Notebook†
0034-4834 Reporting on Governments
0034-4842 Union of Japanese Scientists and Engineers. Reports of Statistical Application Research
0034-4869 Reports on Higher Education *see* 0511-7666
0034-4877 Reports on Mathematical Physics
0034-4885 Reports on Progress in Physics
0034-4893 Representation
0034-4907 Representative Research in Social Psychology
0034-4923 Reprint Expediting Service Bulletin *see* 0275-682X
0034-4931 Reprints from the Soviet Press
0034-4958 Reproduction
0034-4966 Reproduction Paper News Bulletin *changed to* Reproduction Bulletin.
0034-4982 Reprographics
0034-5016 China, Republic. National Central Library. Newsletter
0034-5024 South Africa. Department of Statistics. Bulletin of Statistics *changed to* South Africa. Central Statistical Service. Bulletin of Statistics.
0034-5032 Republic Weekly with Newsday
0034-5040 Republica Argentina. Transporte Aereo. Noticiero
0034-5059 Republicant
0034-5067 Republican Battle Line *see* 0145-1677
0034-5075 Republican Journal
0034-5091 Res Gestaet
0034-5105 Resale Weekly
0034-5113 Research†
0034-5121 Research and Farming *see* 0732-4766
0034-513X Research and Industry
0034-5148 Office of the Provost at Notre Dame *changed to* Notre Dame Report.
0034-5156 Research Association of Powder Technology, Japan. Journal *see* 0386-6157
0034-5164 Research Communications in Chemical Pathology and Pharmacology
0034-5172 Alberta Research Council. Bulletins
0034-5180 Alberta Research Council. Information Series
0034-5199 Research - Development *see* 0746-9179
0034-5202 Research Film†
0034-5210 Research in African Literatures
0034-5229 Research in Education *see* 0098-0897
0034-5237 Research in Education
0034-5245 Research in Librarianship†
0034-5253 Research in Reproduction†
0034-5261 Research in the Life Sciences†
0034-527X Research in the Teaching of English
0034-5288 Research in Veterinary Science
0034-5296 Research Index
0034-530X Hokkaido University. Research Institute for Catalysis. Journal†
0034-5318 Research Institute for Mathematical Sciences. Publications
0034-5326 Research into Higher Education Abstracts
0034-5334 Research Management *see* 0895-6308
0034-5342 Research News†
0034-5350 Research Papers in Physical Education *changed to* Carnegie Research Papers.
0034-5369 University of North Carolina. Institute for Research in Social Science. Research Reviews.†
0034-5377 American Alliance for Health, Physical Education and Recreation. Research Quarterly *see* 0270-1367
0034-5393 California University Center for Research and Development in Higher Education. Research Reporter†
0034-5407 American Institute for Economic Research. Research Reports
0034-5415 Research Reports in Social Science†
0034-5431 Research Society of Pakistan. Journal
0034-5458 Researcher†
0034-5466 Researches on Population Ecology
0034-5474 Resena de Hispanoamerica†
0034-5490 Reservbefal
0034-5504 Reserve Bank of Australia. Statistical Bulletin *see* 0725-0320
0034-5512 Reserve Bank of India. Bulletin
0034-5520 Reserve Bank of Malawi. Economic and Financial Review *see* 0376-5725
0034-5539 Reserve Bank of New Zealand. Bulletin *see* 0112-871X
0034-5547 Reserve Marine
0034-5555 Resident and Staff Physician
0034-5571 Resin Review
0034-5598 Resistenza†
0034-5636 Resort Management *see* 0886-9863
0034-5652 Resource†
0034-5660 Resources for Youth Ministry *changed to* Youth Ministry Quarterly (St. Louis).
0034-5687 Respiration Physiology
0034-5695 Respond†
0034-5709 Response (New York, 1967)
0034-5725 Response (New York, 1969)
0034-575X Ressorgiment†
0034-5792 Restaurante
0034-5806 Restaurator
0034-5814 Restauratoeren
0034-5822 Restoration & Eighteenth Century Theatre Research
0034-5830 Restoration Herald
0034-5857 Results of the Business Survey Carried out Among Heads of Enterprises in the Community *changed to* Results of the Business Survey Carried out Among Management in the Community.
0034-5865 Resument†
0034-5873 Resumenes Analiticos sobre Defensa y Seguridad Nacional - Abstracts of Military Bibliography *changed to* Abstracts of Military Bibliography.
0034-5881 Resumenes de Articulos Cientificos y Tecnicos. Serie A: Quimica Industrial *changed to* Alerta Informativa. Serie A: Quimica Industrial.
0034-589X Resumenes de Articulos Cientfficos y Tecnicos. Serie B: Fisica Aplicada *see* 0210-6825
0034-5903 Resumenes de Articulos Cientificos y Tecnicos. Serie C: Ciencia y Tecnica de los Metales *changed to* Alerta Informativa. Serie C: Ciencia y Tecnica de los Metales.
0034-5911 Resumenes de Articulos Cientificos y Tecnicos. Serie D: Ingenieria y Tecnologia Varias *see* 0210-7007
0034-592X Resumenes de Articulos Cientificos y Tecnicos. Serie E: Economia de la Empresa *see* 0210-7023
0034-5946 Mozambique. Servico Meteorologico. Resumos Meteorologicas para a Aeronautica†
0034-5970 Resurgence
0034-5989 Retail Ad News†
0034-5997 Retail Advertising Week
0034-6012 Retail Business
0034-6020 Retail Chemist *see* 0009-3033
0034-6039 Retail Clerks Advocate†
0034-6047 Retail Control
0034-6055 Retail Food Price Bulletin *see* 0028-6168
0034-6063 Retail Jeweller
0034-6071 Retail Labor Report *see* 0891-4141
0034-6098 Retail Newsagent, Bookseller and Stationer *see* 0961-5202
0034-6136 Retail World
0034-6144 Retailer of Queensland
0034-6152 Retarded
0034-6160 The Retired Officer
0034-6179 Retirement Life (Washington)
0034-6187 Rettens Gang
0034-6195 Rjettur
0034-6209 Reuma
0034-6217 Reuma Bulletin
0034-6233 Reumatologia
0034-6241 Reus Avicola y Agricola†
0034-625X Revealing Confession
0034-6268 Revealing Romances†
0034-6276 Reveil de Djibouti *changed to* Nation Djibouti.
0034-6284 Reveil Missionnaire
0034-6292 Reveil Socialiste de Lannemezan
0034-6306 Reveille
0034-6314 Revetements Sols et Murs†
0034-6322 American Logistics Association Review *see* 0273-7485
0034-6330 Review†
0034-6349 Review: Worldwide Reinsurance
0034-6357 Review
0034-6373 Review and Expositor
0034-6381 Review and Herald *see* 0161-1119
0034-639X Review for Religious
0034-6403 Review of Agricultural Economics Malaysia†
0034-6438 Review of Plant Pathology
0034-6446 Review of Black Political Economy
0034-6454 Review of Business
0034-6462 Alaska Review of Business and Economic Conditions *see* 0162-5403
0034-6489 Review of Communist Scientific and Political Publications (Soviet Union)†
0034-6497 Review of Czechoslovak Medicine *changed to* Czechoslovak Medicine.
0034-6500 Turkiye Is Bankasi. Review of Economic Conditions
0034-6519 Bank Leumi Economic Review *see* 0334-9160
0034-6527 Review of Economic Studies
0034-6535 Review of Economics and Statistics
0034-6543 Review of Educational Research
0034-6551 Review of English Studies
0034-6578 Review of Ghana Law
0034-6586 Review of Income and Wealth
0034-6594 Review of Indonesian and Malayan Affairs *changed to* R I M A: Review of Indonesian and Malaysian Affairs.
0034-6608 Review of International Cooperation
0034-6616 Review of Marketing and Agricultural Economics
0034-6624 Review of Medical and Veterinary Mycology
0034-6632 Review of Metaphysics
0034-6640 Review of National Literatures
0034-6659 Nutrition and Food Science
0034-6667 Review of Palaeobotany and Palynology
0034-6675 Review of Physical Chemistry of Japan†
0034-6691 Review of Polarography
0034-6705 Review of Politics
0034-6713 Review of Popular Astronomy†
0034-6721 Review of Religions
0034-673X Review of Religious Research
0034-6748 Review of Scientific Instruments
0034-6756 Standard and Poor's Review of Securities Regulation *changed to* Standard & Poor's Review of Securities, Commodities Regulation.
0034-6764 Review of Social Economy
0034-6772 Review of Soviet Medical Sciences†
0034-6780 Review of Surgery *see* 0149-7944
0034-6802 Review of the News *changed to* New American (Appleton).
0034-6810 Review of the River Plate
0034-6829 Magyar Jog es Kulfoldi Jogi Szemle *see* 0025-0147
0034-6853 Reviews of Geophysics and Space Physics *see* 8755-1209
0034-6861 Reviews of Modern Physics
0034-687X Reviews of Pure and Applied Chemistry†
0034-6888 Revija (Osijek)
0034-6896 Revija Skolstva i Prosvetna Dokumentacija *see* 0351-0697
0034-690X Revija za Kriminalistiko in Kriminologijo
0034-6918 Revision & Regnskabsvaesen
0034-6926 Revista A P H
0034-6934 Revista Aerea Latinoamericana *see* 0279-4519
0034-6942 Revista Aeronautica
0034-6950 Revista Aguas e Energia Eletrica de Sao Paulo†
0034-6969 Revista Alamar†
0034-6977 Revista Alentejana
0034-6985 Anales de Legislacion Argentina
0034-6993 Revista Argentina de Angiologia
0034-7019 Revista Argentina de Ciencia Politica
0034-7027 Revista Argentina de Psicologia†
0034-7043 Revista Arhivelor
0034-706X Revista Bancaria Brasileira
0034-7078 Revista Biblica
0034-7086 Revista Bibliotecilor†
0034-7094 Revista Brasileira de Anestesiologia
0034-7094 Atlas de Tecnicas de Bloqueios Regionais†
0034-7108 Revista Brasileira de Biologia
0034-7116 Revista Brasileira de Cancerologia
0034-7124 Revista Brasileira de Cirurgia
0034-7140 Revista Brasileira de Economia
0034-7159 Revista Brasileira de Energia Eletrica†
0034-7167 Revista Brasileira de Enfermagem
0034-7175 Revista Brasileira de Estatistica
0034-7183 Revista Brasileira de Estudos Pedagogicos
0034-7191 Revista Brasileira de Estudos Politicos
0034-7205 Revista Brasileira de Filosofia†
0034-7213 Revista Brasileira de Folclore†
0034-723X Revista Brasileira de Geografia
0034-7256 Revista Brasileira de Malariologia e Doencas Tropicais
0034-7264 Revista Brasileira de Medicina
0034-7272 Revista Brasileira de Odontologia
0034-7280 Revista Brasileira de Oftalmologia
0034-7299 Revista Brasileira de Oto-Rino-Laringologia
0034-7302 Revista Brasileira de Patologia Clinica
0034-7329 Revista Brasileira de Politica Internacional
0034-7337 Revista Brasileira de Saude Mental†
0034-7353 Revista Campinense de Cultura
0034-7361 C E C Revista
0034-737X Ceres *changed to* Revista Ceres.
0034-7388 Revista Chilena de Neuropsiquiatria
0034-7396 Revista Chilena de Pediatria†
0034-740X Revista Chilena de Entomologia
0034-7418 Revista Colombiana de Ciencias Quimico Farmaceuticas
0034-7426 Revista Colombiana de Matematicas
0034-7434 Revista Colombiana de Obstetricia y Ginecologia
0034-7442 Revista Colombiana de Pediatria y Puericultura
0034-7450 Revista Colombiana de Psiquiatria
0034-7469 Revista Comercial de Nicaragua
0034-7477 Revista Conservadora del Pensamiento Centroamericano *see* 0378-3340
0034-7485 Revista Cubana de Ciencia Agricola
0034-7493 Revista Cubana de Cirugia
0034-7507 Revista Cubana de Estomatologia
0034-7515 Revista Cubana de Farmacia
0034-7523 Revista Cubana de Medicina
0034-7531 Revista Cubana de Pediatria
0034-754X Revista Cultului Mozaic
0034-7558 Bolsa de Valores de Sao Paulo. Revista†
0034-7566 Revista da Construcao Civil
0034-7582 Revista da Madeira
0034-7590 Revista de Administracao de Empresas
0034-7604 Revista de Administracao Municipal
0034-7612 Revista de Administracao Publica
0034-7620 Revista de Administracion Publica
0034-7639 Revista de Administracion Publica
0034-7647 Revista de Aeronautica y Astronautica
0034-7655 Revista de Agricultura
0034-7671 Revista de Agricultura *see* 0138-7251
0034-7698 Revista de Agroquimica y Tecnologia de Alimentos *see* 1131-799X
0034-7701 Revista de Antropologia
0034-771X Revista de Archivos, Bibliotecas y Museos†
0034-7728 Revista de Bellas Artes†
0034-7736 Revista de Biologia

ISSN

5438 ISSN INDEX

0034-7744 Revista de Biologia Tropical
0034-7752 Revista de Chimie
0034-7779 Revista de Ciencias Economicas *changed to* Administracion.
0034-7779 Revista de Ciencias Economicas *see* 0325-0830
0034-7787 Revista de Ciencias Juridicas†
0034-7817 Revista de Ciencias Sociales
0034-7825 Revista de Compendios de Articulos de Economia
0034-7833 Revista de Conservatorio†
0034-7841 Revista de Criminalistica do Rio Grande do Sul†
0034-785X Revista de Cultura Brasilena†
0034-7868 Revista de Derecho
0034-7876 Revista de Derecho Comercial *changed to* Revista de Derecho Comercial y de la Empresa.
0034-7884 Revista de Derecho Deportivo
0034-7892 Revista de Derecho Internacional y Ciencias Diplomaticas
0034-7906 Revista de Derecho, Jurisprudencia y Administracion
0034-7914 Revista de Derecho Penal y Criminologia†
0034-7922 Revista de Derecho Privado
0034-7930 Revista de Derecho Puertorriqueno
0034-7949 Revista de Derecho y Ciencias Politicas
0034-7957 Revista de Derecho y Ciencias Sociales *see* 0303-9986
0034-7965 Revista de Derecho y Legislacion†
0034-7973 Revista de Diagnostico Biologico
0034-7981 Revista de Dialectologia y Tradiciones Populares
0034-8007 Revista de Direito Administrativo†
0034-8015 Revista de Direito Publico
0034-8023 Revista de Direito Publico e Ciencia Politica *see* 0716-1417
0034-804X Revista de Economia Latinoamericana *changed to* Banco Central de Venezuela. Revista.
0034-8066 Revista de Economia y Estadistica
0034-8074 Revista de Educacion
0034-8082 Revista de Educacion (Madrid)
0034-8090 Revista de Enfermagem†
0034-8104 Revista de Engenharia do Estado da Guanabara
0034-8112 Revista de Engenharia Mackenzie
0034-8139 Revista de Entomologia de Mocambique†
0034-8147 Revista de Espiritualidad
0034-8155 Revista de Estudios Agro-Sociales
0034-8163 Revista de Estudios de la Vida Local *see* 0213-4675
0034-8171 Revista de Estudios de Teatro *changed to* Instituto Nacional de Estudios de Teatro. Boletin.
0034-818X Revista de Estudios Hispanicos
0034-8198 Revista de Etnografie si Folclor
0034-8201 Revista de Farmacia e Odontologia *changed to* Especialidades Odontologicas.
0034-8228 Revista de Filosofia†
0034-8236 Revista de Filosofia
0034-8244 Revista de Filosofia†
0034-8252 Revista de Filosofia
0034-8260 Revista de Filosofie
0034-8279 Revista de Geofisica
0034-8287 Revista de Ginecologia e d'Obstetricia†
0034-8295 Revista de Guimaraes
0034-8309 Revista de Historia
0034-8317 Revista de Historia†
0034-8325 Revista de Historia de America
0034-8333 Revista de Ideas Esteticas†
0034-8341 Revista de Indias
0034-835X Revista de Informacao Legislativa
0034-8368 Revista de Intendencia
0034-8376 Revista de Investigacion Clinica
0034-8384 Revista de Investigacion en Salud Publica†
0034-8406 Revista de la Defensa Nacional†
0034-8422 Revista de la Integracion *see* 0325-1675
0034-8430 Revista de la Sanidad de Policia *changed to* Peru. Policia Nacional. Revista de la Sanidad.
0034-8457 Revista de las Fuerzas Armadas
0034-8473 Revista de las Fuerzas Armadas
0034-8481 Revista de Legislacion Argentina
0034-8511 Revista de Marina
0034-852X Revista de Marina
0034-8538 Revista de Marina del Peru
0034-8546 Revista de Marinha
0034-8554 Revista de Medicina
0034-8562 Revista de Medicina Social y del Trabajo
0034-8570 Revista de Metalurgia
0034-8589 Revista de Neumologia y Cirugia de Torax
0034-8597 Revista de Neuro-Psiquiatria
0034-8600 Revista de Nutricion y Aterosclerosis
0034-8619 Revista de Obras Publicas
0034-8627 Revista de Obras Sanitarias de la Nacion
0034-8635 Revista de Occidente
0034-8643 Revista de Otorrinolaringologia *see* 0716-4084
0034-8651 Revista de Pedagogia†
0034-866X Revista de Tecnologia Educativa
0034-8678 Revista de Pedagogie
0034-8686 Revista de Planeacion y Desarrollo
0034-8694 Revista de Planificacion†
0034-8708 Revista de Plasticos Modernos
0034-8732 Revista de Prevencion
0034-8740 Revista de Psicoanalisis
0034-8759 Revista de Psihologie
0034-8767 Revista de Psiquiatria Dinamica†
0034-8775 Revista de Publicaciones Navales
0034-8783 Revista de Referate in Bibliologie *see* 1220-3076
0034-8791 Filosofie-Logica; Revista de Referate, Recenzii si Sinteze†
0034-8805 Istorie- Etnografie Revista de Referate, Recenzii si Sinteze†
0034-8813 Lingvistica-Filologie; Revista de Referate, Recenzii si Sinzeze†
0034-8821 Psihologie; Revista de Referate Recenzii si Sinteze†
0034-883X Sociologie; Revista de Referate Recenzii si Sinteze†
0034-8848 Stiinte Economice; Revista de Referate, Recenzii si Sinteze†
0034-8856 Stiinte Juridice; Revista de Referate, Recenzii si Sinteze†
0034-8864 Teoria si Istoria Literaturii si Artei; Revista de Referate, Recenzii si Sinteze†
0034-8872 Revista de Resumenes†
0034-8880 Revista de Revistas
0034-8899 Revista de Sanidad e Higiene Publica
0034-8902 Revista de Santander
0034-8910 Revista de Saude Publica
0034-8937 Revista de Servicio Social
0034-8961 Revista de Telecomunicacion
0034-897X Revista de Trabajo
0034-8988 Revista de Trabajo
0034-8996 Revista de Urologia†
0034-9003 Costa Rica. Archivo Nacional. Revista
0034-902X Circulo Odontologico del Sur. Revista†
0034-9046 Revista del Ejercito
0034-9054 Revista del Ejercito y Armada
0034-9070 Revista del Hogar
0034-9089 I D I E M Revista†
0034-9100 Revista del Pacifico†
0034-9119 Revista del Suboficial
0034-9127 Czechoslovak Glass Review *changed to* Glass Review.
0034-9135 Rivista dell'Informazione†
0034-9143 Revista Dental de Chile
0034-9178 Revista Diesel†
0034-9186 Diners
0034-9194 Revista Diplomatica e Internacional
0034-9208 Revista do Ar
0034-9216 Sao Paulo (City) Arquivo Municipal. Revista
0034-9224 Revista do Comercio de Cafe
0034-9240 Revista do Servico Publico
0034-9259 Revista dos Criadores
0034-9267 Revista dos Transportes†
0034-9275 Revista dos Tribunais
0034-9283 I I E. Revista
0034-9291 Revista Economica†
0034-9305 Revista Ecuatoriana de Educacion†
0034-9313 Revista Ecuatoriana de Medicina y Ciencias Biologicas
0034-933X El Sol
0034-9356 Revista Espanola de Anestesiologia y Reanimacion
0034-9372 Revista Espanola de Derecho Canonico
0034-9380 Revista Espanola de Derecho Internacional
0034-9399 Revista Espanola de Derecho Militar
0034-9402 Revista Espanola de Fisiologia
0034-9410 Revista Espanola de Gerontologia *see* 0211-139X
0034-9429 Revista Espanola de la Opinion Publica *see* 0210-5233
0034-9437 Revista Espanola de las Enfermedades del Aparato Digestivo *see* 1130-4588
0034-9445 Revista Espanola de Obstetricia y Ginecologia
0034-9453 Revista Espanola de Oto-Neuro-Oftalmologia y Neurocirugia†
0034-9461 Revista Espanola de Pedagogia
0034-947X Revista Espanola de Pediatria
0034-9496 Revista Farmaceutica
0034-950X Revista Ferroviaria
0034-9526 Revista Finlay†
0034-9534 Revista Fiscal e de Legislacao de Fazenda†
0034-9542 Revista Gaucha de Odontologia
0034-9569 Revista General de Marina
0034-9577 Revista Geografica de Valparaiso
0034-9585 Revista Goiana de Medicina
0034-9593 Revista Hispanica Moderna
0034-9607 Revista I M C Y C *see* 0187-7895
0034-9615 Revista Iberica de Endocrinologia†
0034-9623 Revista Iberica de Parasitologia
0034-9631 Revista Iberoamericana
0034-964X Revista Iberoamericana de Seguridad Social†
0034-9658 Revista I B Y S†
0034-9666 Revista Imposto Fiscal
0034-9690 Revista Interamericana de Psicologia
0034-9704 Revista Interamericana de Radiologia†
0034-9712 Revista Internacional de Sociologia
0034-9720 Revista Internacional y Diplomatica
0034-9739 Revista Juridica
0034-9747 Revista Juridica de Buenos Aires†
0034-9771 Revista Latinoamericana de Microbiologia
0034-9798 Revista Latinoamericana de Siderurgia *changed to* Siderurgia Latinoamericana.
0034-9801 Revista Latinoamericana de Sociologia†
0034-981X Revista Literaria Azor
0034-9828 Cenit
0034-9844 Manana
0034-9852 Revista Manizales
0034-9860 Revista Maritima Brasileira
0034-9887 Revista Medica de Chile
0034-9909 Revista Medica de Costa Rica
0034-9917 Revista Medica de Valparaiso
0034-9925 Revista Medica del Hospital General de Mexico S.S.A.
0034-9933 Revista Medica del Paraguay
0034-9941 Revista Medica do Estado da Guanabara *see* 0100-0195
0034-995X Revista Medicala - Medical Review *changed to* Revista de Medicina si Farmacie.
0034-9976 Revista Mexicana de Ciencia Politica *see* 0185-1918
0034-9984 Revista Mexicana de Cirugia, Ginecologia y Cancer
0035-001X Revista Mexicana de Fisica
0035-0028 Revista Mexicana de Ingenieria y Arquitectura†
0035-0044 Revista Mexicana de la Propiedad Industrial y Artistica
0035-0079 Revista Mexicana de Psicologia†
0035-0109 Revista Militar†
0035-0117 Revista Militar
0035-0125 Revista Militar Brasileira *see* 0101-7284
0035-0133 Revista Militar
0035-0141 Revista Militar del Peru
0035-015X Revista Militar y Naval†
0035-0168 Revista Minelor *changed to* Mine, Petrol si Gaze.
0035-0176 Revista Mineria, Geologia y Mineralogia
0035-0184 Revista Municipal†
0035-0206 Revista Muzeelor *changed to* Revista Muzeelor.
0035-0214 Revista Nacional da Pesca
0035-0222 Revista Nacional de Agricultura
0035-0257 Revista Odontologica *see* 0325-1071
0035-0265 Revista Odontologica de Concepcion†
0035-0273 Revista Odontologica de Merida *changed to* Universidad de Los Andes. Facultad de Odontologia. Revista.
0035-0281 Revista Odontologica de Puerto Rico
0035-029X Revista Padurilor-Industria Lemnului-Celuloza si Hirtie *changed to* Industria Lemnului.
0035-029X Revista Padurilor-Industria Lemnului-Celuloza si Hirtie *see* 0008-879X
0035-029X Revista Padurilor-Industria Lemnului-Celuloza si Hirtie *changed to* Revista Padurilor.
0035-0303 Revista para Parvulos y Principiantes†
0035-0311 Revista para Uniones de Adultos *changed to* Accion.
0035-032X Revista para Uniones de Intermedios *changed to* Ahora.
0035-0338 Revista para Jovenes *changed to* Adelante.
0035-0346 Revista para Uniones de Primarios†
0035-0354 Revista Paraguaya de Sociologia
0035-0362 Revista Paulista de Medicina
0035-0370 Revista Peruana de Derecho Internacional
0035-0389 Revista Portuguesa de Ciencias Veterinarias
0035-0397 Revista Portuguesa de Estomatologia e Cirurgia Maxilo-Facial
0035-0419 Revista Portuguesa de Quimica
0035-0427 Revista Referativo de la Construccion *changed to* Servicio Referativo de la Construccion.
0035-0435 Revista Romana de Drept
0035-0443 Revista Rotaria†
0035-0451 Revista Signos de Valparaiso
0035-046X Revista Sindical de Estadistica
0035-0478 Sur
0035-0486 Revista Tamaulipas
0035-0516 Revista Telegrafica Electronica
0035-0524 Revista Textil
0035-0532 Revista Transporturilor *changed to* Revista Transporturi Auto, Navale si Aeriene.
0035-0567 Rivista Veneta†
0035-0575 Revista Venezolana de Folklore†
0035-0583 Revista Venezolana de Sanidad y Asistencia Social
0035-0591 Revista Venezolana de Urologia
0035-0605 Revista do Livro (Rio de Janeiro)†
0035-0621 Revolution Africaine
0035-0672 Revue Administrative
0035-0699 Revue Algerienne des Sciences Juridiques, Politiques et Economiques *changed to* Revue Algerienne des Sciences Juridiques.
0035-0702 Revue Algologiqusе *see* 0181-1568
0035-0710 Revue Analytique d'Education Physique et de Sport†
0035-0729 Revue
0035-0737 Revue Archeologique
0035-0745 Revue Archeologique de l'Est et du Centre-Est
0035-0753 Revue Archeologique du Centre *see* 0220-6617
0035-077X Revue Belge d'Archeologie et d'Histoire de l'Art
0035-0788 Revue Belge de Droit International
0035-0818 Revue Belge de Philologie et d'Histoire
0035-0826 Revue Belge de Psychologie et de Pedagogie
0035-0834 Revue Belge de Securite Sociale
0035-0850 Revue Belge des Vins & Spiritueux

ISSN

0035-0869 Revue Belge d'Histoire Contemporaine
0035-0877 Revue Belge d'Histoire Militaire
0035-0885 Revue Belge d'Homoeopathie
0035-0893 Revue Benedictine
0035-0907 Revue Biblique
0035-0915 Revue Canadienne de Biologie *changed to* Experimental Biology.
0035-0931 Revue Congolaise des Sciences Humaines†
0035-0958 Revue Critique de Droit International Prive
0035-0966 Revue Critique de Jurisprudence Belge
0035-0974 Revue d'Allemagne *changed to* Revue d'Allemagne et des Pays de Langue Allemande.
0035-0990 Revue d'Ascetique et de Mystique *changed to* Revue d'Histoire de la Spiritualite.
0035-1008 Revue d'Auvergne
0035-1016 La Revue de Belles-Lettres
0035-1024 Revue de Bio-Mathematique
0035-1032 Revue de Chimie Minerale - Inorganic Chemistry Review - Revue fuer Anorganische Chemie *see* 0992-4361
0035-1040 Revue de Chirurgie Orthopedique et Reparatrice de l'Appareil Moteur
0035-1059 Revue de Comminges
0035-1067 Revue de Cytologie et de Biologie Vegetales *see* 0181-7582
0035-1075 Revue de Defense Nationale *see* 0336-1489
0035-1083 Revue de Droit Intellectuel l'Ingenieur-Conseil
0035-1091 Revue de Droit International de Sciences Diplomatiques et Politiques
0035-1105 Revue de Droit International et de Droit Compare
0035-1113 Revue de Droit Social
0035-1121 Revue de Geographie Alpine
0035-113X Revue de Geographie de Lyon
0035-1148 Revue de Geographie de Montreal *see* 0705-7199
0035-1156 Revue de Geographie du Maroc
0035-1172 Revue de Kinesitherapie *see* 0302-427X
0035-1199 Revue de la Cooperation Scolaire†
0035-1210 Revue de la France Libre
0035-1237 Revue de la Police Nationale
0035-1245 Revue de la Presse Arabe
0035-1253 Revue de la Protection†
0035-1261 Revue de la Securite
0035-127X Revue de la Soudure
0035-1288 Revue de l'Agenais
0035-130X Revue de l'Alcoolisme†
0035-1318 Revue de l'Aluminium†
0035-1326 Revue de l'Art
0035-1334 Revue de Laryngologie - Otologie - Rhinologie
0035-1342 Revue de l'Avranchin et du Pays de Granville
0035-1350 Revue de l'Economie du Centre-Est
0035-1369 Revue de l'Economie Meridionale
0035-1377 Revue de l'Education Physique
0035-1385 Revue de l'Embouteillage et des Industries Connexes *changed to* Conditionnement des Liquides-Embouteillage.
0035-1393 Revue de l'Enseignement Philosophique *see* 0986-1653
0035-1407 Revue de l'Enseignement Superieur *changed to* Revue de l'Enseignement Superieur et de la Recherche Scientifique.
0035-1415 Revue de l'Est *changed to* Revue d'Etudes Comparatives Est-Ouest.
0035-1423 Revue de l'Histoire des Religions
0035-1431 Revue de l'Industrie Minerale *changed to* Industrie Minerale Mines et Carrieres.
0035-144X Revue de l'Infirmiere et de l'Assistante Sociale *see* 0397-7900
0035-1458 Revue de Linguistique Romane
0035-1466 Revue de Litterature Comparee
0035-1474 Revue de l'Occident Musulman et de la Mediterranee
0035-1482 Revue de Madagascar†
0035-1490 Flair
0035-1504 Revue de Mathematiques Speciales
0035-1512 Revue de Medecine†
0035-1520 Revue de Medecine Aeronautique et Spatiale *see* 0294-0817
0035-1539 Revue de Medecine Moderne *see* 0292-384X
0035-1547 Revue de Medecine Psychosomatique
0035-1555 Revue de Medecine Veterinaire
0035-1563 Revue de Metallurgie *changed to* Revue de Metallurgie. Cahiers d'Information Techniques.
0035-1571 Revue de Metaphysique et de Morale
0035-1598 Revue de Micropaleontologie
0035-1601 Revue de Musicologie
0035-161X Revue de Neuropsychiatrie de l'Ouest
0035-1628 Revue de Neuropsychiatrie Infantile et d'Hygiene Mentale de l'Enfance *see* 0222-9617
0035-1636 Revue de Pathologie Comparee†
0035-1644 Revue de Pediatrie
0035-1652 Revue de Philologie, de Litterature et d'Histoire Anciennes
0035-1660 Revue de Phonetique Appliquee
0035-1679 Revue de Physiologie Subaquatique et Medecine Hyperbare†
0035-1687 Revue de Physique Appliquee *changed to* Journal de Physique III.
0035-1709 Revue de Psychologie Appliquee *changed to* Revue Europeene de Psychologie Appliquee.
0035-1725 Revue de Qumran
0035-1733 Revue de Science Criminelle et de Droit Penal Compare
0035-1741 Revue de Science Financiere†
0035-175X Revue de Statistique Appliquee
0035-1768 Revue de Stomatologie et de Chirurgie Maxillo-Faciale
0035-1776 Revue de Synthese
0035-1784 Revue de Theologie et de Philosophie
0035-1792 Revue de Tuberculose et de Pneumologie *see* 0761-8425
0035-1806 Revue de Zoologie Agricole et de Pathologie Vegetale†
0035-1822 Revue d'Ecologie et de Biologie du Sol *changed to* European Journal of Soil Biology.
0035-1849 Revue d'Egyptologie
0035-1865 Revue d'Elevage et de Medecine Veterinaire des Pays Tropicaux
0035-1873 Lebanese Dental Journal†
0035-1881 Revue der Reclame *changed to* Kontekst.
0035-1903 Revue des Agents de Police *changed to* Flute.
0035-1911 Revue des Applications de l'Electricite *see* 0035-2926
0035-1938 Revue des Caisses d'Epargne
0035-1954 Revue des Corps de Sante des Armees *see* 0300-4937
0035-1962 Revue des Deux Mondes *see* 0750-9278
0035-1970 Revue des Disques et de la Haute Fidelite *changed to* Hifi Musique. Revue des Disques et de la Haute Fidelite.
0035-1989 Revue des Droits de l'Homme†
0035-1997 Revue des Ecoles
0035-2004 Revue des Etudes Anciennes
0035-2012 Revue des Etudes Augustiniennes
0035-2020 Revue des Etudes Cooperatives *changed to* Revue des Etudes Cooperatives, Mutualistes et Associatives.
0035-2039 Revue des Etudes Grecques
0035-2047 Revue des Etudes Italiennes
0035-2055 Revue des Etudes Juives
0035-2063 Revue des Etudes Sud-Est Europeennes
0035-208X Revue des Finances Communales *see* 0042-5400
0035-2098 Revue des Hotesses†
0035-2101 Offrir *changed to* Offrir International.
0035-211X Revue des Langues Vivantes†
0035-2128 Revue des Lettres *changed to* Journal des Lettres et de l'Audiovisuel.
0035-2136 Revue des Lettres Modernes
0035-2144 Revue des Materiaux de Construction et de Travaux Publics *see* 0397-006X
0035-2152 Revue des P T T de France *changed to* Revue des Postes et Telecommunications de France.
0035-2160 Revue des Questions Scientifiques
0035-2179 Cahiers des Ingenieurs Agronomes *changed to* Ingenieurs de la Vie.
0035-2187 Revue des Sciences Economiques†
0035-2209 Revue des Sciences Philosophiques et Theologiques
0035-2217 Revue des Sciences Religieuses
0035-2241 Revue des Societes Savantes de Haute Normandie
0035-225X Revue des Tabacs
0035-2284 Revue Desjardins
0035-2292 Revue d'Esthetique
0035-2306 Revue d'Etudes Militaires, Aeriennes et Navales
0035-2314 Revues d'Histoire de la Deuxieme Guerre Mondiale *see* 0984-2292
0035-2322 Revue d'Histoire de la Gaspesie *see* 0227-1370
0035-2330 Revue d'Histoire de la Medecine Hebraique
0035-2349 Revue d'Histoire de la Pharmacie
0035-2357 Revue d'Histoire de l'Amerique Francaise
0035-2365 Revue d'Histoire Diplomatique
0035-2373 Revue d'Histoire du Theatre
0035-2381 Revue d'Histoire Ecclesiastique
0035-239X Revue d'Histoire Economique et Sociale *see* 0752-5702
0035-2403 Revue d'Histoire et de Philosophie Religieuses
0035-2411 Revue d'Histoire Litteraire de la France
0035-242X Revue d'Hygiene du Travail†
0035-2438 Revue d'Epidemiologie, Medecine Sociale et Sante Publique *see* 0398-7620
0035-2446 Revue d'Hygiene et Medecine Scolaire et Universitaire†
0035-2462 Revue d'Informatique Medicale†
0035-2470 Revue d'Odonto-Stomatologie du Midi de la France
0035-2497 Revue d'Oto-Neuro-Ophtalmologie†
0035-2500 Revue du Bois Detail†
0035-2519 Revue du Bois et de ses Applications
0035-2527 Revue du Bouton†
0035-2535 Revue du Cethedec *see* 0765-0019
0035-2543 Revue du Cinema International & TV†
0035-2551 Revue du Clerge Africain†
0035-256X Revue du Droit du Travail†
0035-2578 Revue du Droit Public et de la Science Politique en France et a l'Etranger
0035-2594 Revue du Jouet
0035-2608 Revue du Louvre et des Musees de France
0035-2616 Revue du Marche Commun
0035-2624 Revue du Nord
0035-2632 Revue du Notariat
0035-2640 Revue du Praticien
0035-2659 Revue du Rhumatisme et des Maladies Osteoarticulaires
0035-2667 Revue du Rouergue
0035-2675 Revue du Son *changed to* Nouvelle Revue du Son.
0035-2683 Asia Quarterly†
0035-2705 Revue du Travail
0035-2713 Revue du Tresor
0035-273X Revue du Vin de France
0035-2748 Revue du Vivarais
0035-2756 Acta Technica Belgica. Revue E: Electricite Courants Forts. Electrotechnique Generale et ses Applications
0035-2764 Revue Economique
0035-2772 Revue Economique et Sociale
0035-2780 Revue Economique Francaise
0035-2799 Revue Economique Franco Suisse
0035-2802 Revue Europeenne des Papiers Cartons-Complexes†
0035-2810 Revue Fiscale *changed to* Journal de Droit Fiscal.
0035-2829 Revue Forestiere Francaise
0035-2845 Revue Francaise d'Allergologie *see* 0335-7457
0035-2861 Revue Francaise de Bridge
0035-287X Revue Francaise de Droit Aerien
0035-2888 Revue Francaise de Gastro Enterologie
0035-2896 Revue Francaise de Gerontologie *changed to* Revue de Geriatrie.
0035-290X Revue Francaise de Gynecologie et d'Obstetrique
0035-2918 Revue Francaise de l'Agriculture†
0035-2926 Revue Francaise de l'Electricite†
0035-2934 Revue Francaise de l'Energie *see* 0303-240X
0035-2942 Revue Francaise de Psychanalyse
0035-2950 Revue Francaise de Science Politique
0035-2969 Revue Francaise de Sociologie
0035-2977 Revue Francaise de Transfusion *see* 0338-4535
0035-2985 Revue Francaise des Affaires Sociales
0035-2993 Revue Francaise des Bijoutiers Horlogers *changed to* Bijoutier.
0035-3000 Revue Francaise des Corps Gras
0035-3019 Revue Europeenne d'Etudes Cliniques et Biologiques *see* 0753-3322
0035-3027 Revue Francaise d'Etudes Politiques Africaines
0035-3035 Revue Francaise d'Informatique et de Recherche Operationnelle *see* 0399-0559
0035-3035 Revue Francaise d'Informatique et de Recherche Operationnelle *see* 0752-4072
0035-3035 Revue Francaise d'Informatique et de Recherche Operationnelle *see* 0988-3754
0035-3043 Revue Francaise d'Odonto-Stomatologie *see* 0300-9815
0035-3078 Revue Generale Belge *see* 0770-8602
0035-3094 Revue Generale de Droit International Public
0035-3108 Revue Generale de l'Air et de l'Espace†
0035-3116 Revue Generale de l'Electricite
0035-3124 Revue Generale de l'Enseignement des Deficients Auditifs†
0035-3132 Revue Generale de l'Etancheite et de l'Isolation
0035-3140 Revue Generale de l'Hotellerie, de la Gastronomie et du Tourisme
0035-3159 Revue Generale de Thermique
0035-3167 Revue Generale des Assurances Terrestres
0035-3175 Caoutchoucs et Plastiques
0035-3183 Revue Generale des Chemins de Fer
0035-3191 Revue Generale des Routes et des Aerodromes
0035-3205 Revue Generale du Froid
0035-3213 Revue Geographique de l'Est
0035-3221 Revue Geographique des Pyrenees et du Sud-Ouest
0035-323X Revue Graphique-Imprivaria
0035-3248 Acta Technica Belgica. Revue H F: Electricite Courants Faibles. Electronique Telecommunications
0035-3256 Revue Hellenique de Droit International
0035-3264 Revue Historique
0035-3272 Revue Historique Ardennaise
0035-3280 Revue Historique de Droit Francais et Etranger
0035-3299 Revue Historique des Armees
0035-3302 Revue Horticole *see* 0758-1688
0035-3310 Revue Independante
0035-3329 Revue Internationale de Criminologie et de Police Technique†
0035-3337 Revue Internationale de Droit Compare
0035-337X Revue Internationale de la Propriete Industrielle et Artistique
0035-3396 Revue Internationale de Police Criminelle
0035-340X Revue Internationale de Psychologie Appliquee†

0035-3418 Comptabilite Economique Universelle-Scientifique
0035-3434 Revue Internationale des Hautes Temperatures et des Refractaires
0035-3442 Revue Internationale des Industries Agricoles. Bulletin Analytique†
0035-3450 Revue Internationale des Produits Tropicaux
0035-3477 Revue Internationale des Tabacs
0035-3485 Revue Internationale d'Ethnopsychologie Normale et Pathologique†
0035-3493 Revue Internationale d'Oceanographie Medicale
0035-3515 Revue Internationale du Droit d'Auteur
0035-3531 Revue Internationale du Trachome et des Maladies Oculaires des Pays Tropicaux et Sub Tropicaux *see* 0301-5017
0035-354X International Review for Business Education
0035-3566 Revue Juridique et Economique du Sud-Quest *changed to* Revue Economique du Sud-Ouest.
0035-3582 Revue de l'Air Liquide†
0035-3590 Revue Laitiere Francaise
0035-3604 Revue Legale
0035-3612 Revue "M" Mecanique *see* 0777-2734
0035-3620 Revue Mabillon
0035-3639 Revue Medicale de Bruxelles
0035-3655 Revue Medicale de la Suisse Romande
0035-3663 Revue Medicale de Liege
0035-368X Revue Militaire Suisse
0035-3698 Revue Moderne
0035-371X Revue-Moteur *changed to* Moteur et Equipement.
0035-3728 Revue Municipale
0035-3736 Revue Musicale
0035-3744 Revue Musicale de Suisse Romande
0035-3752 Revue Nationale de la Chasse
0035-3779 Revue Neuchateloise *changed to* Nouvelle Revue Neuchateloise.
0035-3787 Revue Neurologique
0035-3795 R N D
0035-3825 Revue Penitentiaire et de Droit Penal
0035-3833 Revue Philosophique de la France et de l'Etranger
0035-3841 Revue Philosophique de Louvain
0035-385X Revue Politique et Parlementaire
0035-3868 Revue Pratique du Froid *changed to* R P F.
0035-3876 Revue Pratique des Questions Commerciales et Economiques†
0035-3884 Societe Calviniste de France. Revue Reformee
0035-3892 Revue Romaine des Sciences Sociales. Serie de Psychologie *changed to* Revue Roumaine de Psychologie.
0035-3906 Revue Romane
0035-3914 Revue Roumaine de Biologie. Serie Botanique *changed to* Revue Roumaine de Biologie. Serie Biologie Vegetale.
0035-3922 Revue Roumaine de Biologie. Serie Zoologie *changed to* Revue Roumaine de Biologie. Serie Biologie Animale.
0035-3930 Revue Roumaine de Chimie
0035-3957 Revue Roumaine de Linguistique
0035-3965 Revue Roumaine de Mathematiques Pures et Appliquees
0035-3973 Revue Roumaine de Medecine Interne *changed to* Revue Roumaine de Medecine Interne.
0035-3981 Revue Roumaine de Neurologie et Psychiatrie *changed to* Revue Roumaine de Neurologie et Psychiatrie.
0035-399X Revue Roumaine de Physiologie *changed to* Revue Roumaine de Physiologie.
0035-4007 Revue Roumaine de Morphologie, d'Embryologie et de Physiologie. Serie Morphologie et Embryologie *changed to* Revue Roumaine de Morphologie et d'Embryologie.
0035-4015 Revue Roumaine d'Endocrinologie *changed to* Revue Roumaine d'Endocrinologie.
0035-4023 Revue Roumaine des Sciences Sociales. Serie de Sciences Juridiques *changed to* Revue Roumaine de Sciences Juridiques.
0035-4031 Revue Roumaine des Sciences Sociales. Serie de Philosophie et Logique *changed to* Revue de Philosophie.
0035-404X Revue Roumaine des Sciences Sociales. Serie de Sciences Economiques *changed to* Revue Roumaine de Sciences Economiques.
0035-4066 Revue Roumaine des Sciences Techniques. Serie Electrotechnique et Energetique
0035-4074 Revue Roumaine des Sciences Techniques. Serie de Mecanique Appliquee
0035-4082 Revue Roumaine d'Inframicrobiologie *changed to* Revue Roumaine de Virologie.
0035-4090 Revue Roumaine de Physique
0035-4104 Revue Scolaire†
0035-4112 Revue Senegalaise de Droit
0035-4120 Servir
0035-4139 Revue Socialiste
0035-4147 Revue Stomato-Odontologique du Nord de la France
0035-4163 Revue Suisse de Numismatique
0035-4171 Revue Suisse de Viticulture et Arboriculture *changed to* Revue Suisse de Viticulture, Arboriculture et Horticulture.
0035-418X Revue Suisse de Zoologie
0035-4198 Revue Suisse des Marches Agricoles *changed to* Schweizerischer Bauernverband. Information.
0035-4201 Revue Suisse du Trafic Routier†
0035-421X Revue Syndicale Suisse
0035-4228 Revue Technique des Hotels, Restaurants, Bars, Brasseries, Limonadiers, Tabacs, Habitats Collectifs
0035-4252 Revue de la Technique Europeenne *changed to* Indicateur Industriel.
0035-4260 Revue Technique Luxembourgeoise
0035-4279 Revue Technique Thomson - C S F
0035-4287 Revue Textile Melliand†
0035-4295 Revue Thomiste
0035-4317 Revue Trimestrielle de Droit Europeen
0035-4325 Revue Trimestrielle de Droit Sanitaire et Social *changed to* Revue de Droit Sanitaire et Social.
0035-4333 Revue Tunisienne des Sciences Sociales
0035-4341 Revue Universelle des Mines, de la Metallurgie, de la Mecanique, des Travaux Publics, des Sciences et des Arts Appliques a l'Industrie†
0035-435X Revue Universitaire de Science Morale *see* 0773-1213
0035-4376 Revues Medicales Normandes†
0035-4384 Revue de Droit Penal et de Criminologie
0035-4406 La Revuo Orienta
0035-4422 Rexevents
0035-4449 Rheinhessische Wirtschaft
0035-4457 Rheinisch-Westfaelische Boerse zu Duesseldorf. Amtliches Kursblatt
0035-4465 Rheinisch-Westfaelisches Institut fuer Wirtschaftsforschung. Mitteilungen
0035-4473 Rheinische Vierteljahrsblaetter
0035-4481 Rheinisches Aerzteblatt
0035-449X Rheinisches Museum fuer Philologie
0035-4511 Rheologica Acta
0035-452X Rheology Abstracts
0035-4538 Rheology Bulletin
0035-4546 Rheumatism
0035-4554 Rheumatologia, Balneologia, Allergologia
0035-4562 Rhode Island Beverage Journal
0035-4570 Rhode Island Business Quarterly *changed to* Journal of Business and Economic Studies.
0035-4589 Rhode Island College Alumni Association. Review *changed to* Perspectives (Providence).
0035-4597 Rhode Island. Department of State Library Services. Newsletter
0035-4600 Rhode Island. Department of Labor and Employment Security. Employment Bulletin *changed to* Rhode Island. Department of Employment and Training. Employment Bulletin.
0035-4619 Rhode Island History
0035-4635 Rhode Island Resources†
0035-4643 Rhode Island State Dental Society. Journal *changed to* Rhode Island Dental Association. Journal.
0035-466X Rhodeo
0035-4678 Rhodes Newsletter *changed to* Rhodes Review.
0035-4686 Rhodesia Agricultural Journal *changed to* Zimbabwe Agricultural Journal.
0035-4694 Rhodesia and World Report
0035-4708 Rhodesia Calls *changed to* Africa Calls Worldwide.
0035-4716 Zimbabwe. National Archives. Occasional Papers
0035-4724 Zimbabwe Railways Magazine *changed to* Railroader.
0035-4732 Rhodesia Science News *changed to* Zimbabwe Science News.
0035-4759 Rhodesian Commentary *changed to* Spotlight on Zimbabwe.
0035-4775 Rhodesian Farmer *see* 1011-0488
0035-4791 Rhodesian Industrialist
0035-4805 Rhodesian Insurance Review *changed to* Insurance Review.
0035-4813 Rhodesia, Zambia and Malawi Journal of Agricultural Research *changed to* Zimbabwe Journal of Agricultural Research.
0035-4821 Rhodesian Journal of Economics
0035-483X Rhodesia Law Journal *changed to* Zimbabwe Law Journal.
0035-4848 Rhodesian Librarian *changed to* Zimbabwe Librarian.
0035-4864 Rhodesian Property & Finance
0035-4872 Rhodesian Railway Review *changed to* Railway Review.
0035-4880 Rhodesian Tobacco Journal *changed to* Zimbabwe Tobacco Today.
0035-4899 Rhodesian Viewpoint†
0035-4902 Rhodora
0035-4929 Rhumatologie†
0035-4953 Ribarski List
0035-4961 Rice Journal
0035-497X Rice Review *changed to* Farmer.
0035-4988 Rice University Review†
0035-4996 Rice University Studies†
0035-5011 Ricerca Scientifica
0035-502X Ricerche Bibliche e Religiose†
0035-5038 Ricerche di Matematica
0035-5046 Ricerche Didattiche
0035-5054 Ricerche Economiche
0035-5062 Ricerche Filosofiche†
0035-5070 Ricerche Storiche (Reggio Emilia)
0035-5089 Richard Cotten's Conservative Viewpoint
0035-5097 Richesses de France
0035-5100 Greater Richmond Chamber of Commerce. Research Bulletin†
0035-5119 Richmond County History†
0035-5135 Richting *changed to* R S G Richting - Sport-Gericht.
0035-5143 Ridge News†
0035-516X Riding
0035-5186 Ridotto
0035-5194 Riechstoffe, Aromen, Koerperpflegemittel *see* 0341-440X
0035-5216 Rifle Magazine *see* 0162-3583
0035-5224 Rifleman
0035-5240 Riforma della Scuola
0035-5259 La Riforma Medica
0035-5267 Rig
0035-5275 Right of Way
0035-5283 Rights
0035-5291 Rights & Reviews†
0035-5305 Rihabiriteshon
0035-5313 Het Rijk der Vrouw
0035-533X Rijksuniversiteit te Gent. Faculteit Landbouwwetenschappen. Mededelingen
0035-5348 Rijksuniversiteit te Groningen. Mededelingenblad *changed to* Universiteitskrant Groningen.
0035-5356 St. Paul's Economic Review
0035-5364 Sweden.Kungliga Biblioteket. Notiser Fraan Riksbibliotekarien†
0035-5372 Rimba Indonesia
0035-5380 Rinascita
0035-5402 Rinderproduktion *see* 0138-3337
0035-5410 Ring
0035-5429 Ring
0035-5437 Ring-Rund†
0035-5453 Ringing World
0035-5461 Ringling Museums Newsletter *changed to* John & Mable Ringling Museum of Art.
0035-5488 Rinsho Shika
0035-550X Journal of Clinical Pediatrics
0035-5518 Ripley's Believe It or Not
0035-5526 Ripon Forum
0035-5534 Ripresa Nazionale
0035-5550 Rise Hvezd
0035-5569 Risiko *see* 0922-2472
0035-5585 Risk†
0035-5593 Risk Management
0035-5607 Risorgimento
0035-5615 Risparmio
0035-5623 Risveglio del Molise e del Mezzogiorno
0035-5631 Ritenour School District News *changed to* Ritenour News.
0035-564X Intercom (Overland) *changed to* Ritenour Reporter.
0035-5666 Rivarol *changed to* Rivarol and Political.
0035-5682 Riverlander *changed to* Riverlander Notes.
0035-5690 Riverside County Farm and Agricultural Business News *changed to* Riverside County Agriculture.
0035-5720 Riviere
0035-5739 Rivista Abruzzese
0035-5747 Rivista Aeronautica - Missilistica *see* 0391-6162
0035-5755 Rivista Agricola dell'O C D E†
0035-5763 Rivista Amministrativa della Repubblica Italiana
0035-5771 Rivista Araldica
0035-5801 Rivista Chirurgia Pediatrica†
0035-581X Rivista Critica di Storia della Filosofia *changed to* Rivista di Storia della Filosofia.
0035-5836 Rivista degli Infortuni e delle Malattie Professionali
0035-5852 La Rivista dei Combustibili
0035-5860 Rivista del Catasto e dei Servizi Tecnici Erariali
0035-5879 Rivista del Cinematografo†
0035-5887 Rivista del Diritto Commerciale e del Diritto Generale delle Obbligazioni
0035-5895 Rivista del Diritto della Navigazione†
0035-5917 Rivista del Nuovo Cimento *see* 0393-697X
0035-5925 Rivista del Porto di Napoli
0035-595X Rivista della Guardia di Finanza *changed to* Testata: Rivista della Guardia di Finanza.
0035-5968 Rivista della Ortoflorofrutticoltura Italiana *see* 0394-6169
0035-5976 Rivista della Proprieta' Industriale e della Concorrenza†
0035-5984 Rivista della Proprieta Intellettuale Ed Industriale†
0035-5992 Rivista della Strada *see* 0393-8077
0035-600X Consacrazione e Servizio
0035-6018 Rivista delle Societa
0035-6026 Rivista di Agricoltura Subtropicale e Tropicale
0035-6034 Rivista di Agronomia
0035-6042 Rivista di Archeologia Cristiana

0035-6050 Rivista di Biologia
0035-6069 Rivista di Chirurgia Pediatrica†
0035-6077 Rivista di Clinica Pediatrica *see* 0026-4946
0035-6085 Rivista di Cultura Classica e Medioevale
0035-6093 Rivista di Diritto Civile
0035-6107 Rivista di Diritto del Lavoro *see* 0393-2494
0035-6115 Rivista di Diritto Economia e Tecnica della Pesca
0035-6123 Rivista di Diritto Europeo
0035-6131 Rivista di Diritto Finanziario e Scienza delle Finanze
0035-614X Rivista di Diritto Industriale
0035-6158 Rivista di Diritto Internazionale
0035-6166 Rivista di Diritto Internazionale e Comparato del Lavoro
0035-6174 Rivista di Diritto Internazionale Privato e Processuale
0035-6182 Rivista di Diritto Processuale
0035-6190 Rivista di Economia Agraria
0035-6212 Rivista di Estetica
0035-6220 Rivista di Filologia Classica
0035-6239 Rivista di Filosofia
0035-6247 Rivista di Filosofia Neoscolastica
0035-6255 Rivista di Gastroenterologia
0035-6263 Ingegneria†
0035-6271 Rivista di Legislazione Scolastica Comparata†
0035-628X Rivista di Lugano
0035-6298 Universita degli Studi di Parma. Rivista di Matematica
0035-6301 Rivista di Meccanica
0035-631X Rivista di Medicina Aeronautica e Spaziale
0035-6328 Rivista di Meteorologia Aeronautica
0035-6336 Rivista di Neurobiologia
0035-6344 Rivista di Neurologia *changed to* Nuova Rivista di Neurologia.
0035-6352 Rivista di Neuropsichiatria e Scienze Affini
0035-6360 Rivista di Organizzazione Aziendale†
0035-6379 Rivista di Ostetricia e Ginecologia†
0035-6387 Rivista di Parassitologia
0035-6395 Rivista di Pastorale Liturgica
0035-6409 Rivista di Patologia Clinica e Sperimentale *see* 0394-4549
0035-6417 Rivista di Patologia e Clinica
0035-6425 Rivista di Patologia e Clinica della Tubercolosi *see* 0302-4717
0035-6433 Rivista di Patologia Nervosa e Mentale†
0035-6441 Rivista di Patologia Vegetale
0035-645X Rivista di Politica Agraria
0035-6468 Rivista di Politica Economica
0035-6476 Rivista di Polizia
0035-6484 Rivista di Psichiatria
0035-6492 Rivista di Psicoanalisi
0035-6506 Rivista di Psicologia
0035-6514 Rivista di Scienze Preistoriche
0035-6522 Rivista di Servizio Sociale
0035-6530 Rivista di Sociologia†
0035-6549 Rivista di Statistica Applicata†
0035-6557 Rivista di Storia della Chiesa in Italia
0035-6565 Rivista di Storia della Medicina†
0035-6573 Rivista di Storia e Letteratura Religiosa
0035-6581 Rivista di Studi Classici
0035-659X Rivista di Studi Crociani
0035-6603 Rivista di Studi Liguri
0035-6611 Rivista di Studi Politici Internazionali
0035-662X Rivista di Suinicoltura
0035-6638 Rivista di Vita Spirituale
0035-6646 Rivista di Zootecnia *changed to* Rivista di Zootecnia e Veterinaria.
0035-6654 Rivista Diocesana del Patriarcato di Venezia
0035-6662 Rivista Diocesana Riminit†
0035-6689 Rivista Generale Italiana di Chirurgia
0035-6697 Rivista Geografica Italiana
0035-6700 Rivista Giuridica della Circolazione e dei Trasporti
0035-6719 Rivista Internazionale di Dialogo†
0035-6727 Rivista Internazionale di Filosofia del Diritto
0035-6735 Rivista Internazionale di Filosofia Politica e Sociale e Diritto Comparato†
0035-6743 Rivista Internazionale di Psicologia e Ipnosi†
0035-6751 Rivista Internazionale di Scienze Economiche e Commerciali
0035-676X Rivista Internazionale di Scienze Sociali
0035-6778 Rivista Italiana del Petrolio†
0035-6786 Rivista Italiana del Tracoma e di Patologia Oculare Virale Ed Esotica†
0035-6794 Rivista Italiana della Saldatura
0035-6808 Rivista Italiana delle Sostanze Grasse
0035-6816 Impresa
0035-6824 Rivista Italiana di Diritto Sociale
0035-6832 Rivista Italiana di Economia Demografia e Statistica
0035-6840 Rivista Italiana di Ginecologia†
0035-6867 Rivista Italiana di Musicologia
0035-6875 Rivista Italiana di Ornitologia
0035-6883 Rivista Italiana di Paleontologia e Stratigrafia
0035-6905 Rivista Italiana di Stomatologia
0035-6913 Rivista Italiana di Studi Napoleonici
0035-6921 Rivista Italiana d'Igiene
0035-6948 Rivista Italiana Essenze Profumi, Piante Officianali, Aromi, Saponi, Cosmetici, Aerosol†
0035-6956 Rivista Liturgica
0035-6964 Rivista Marittima
0035-6972 Rivista della Citta di Trieste
0035-6980 Rivista Militare
0035-6999 Rivista Militare della Svizzera Italiana
0035-7022 Rivista Penale
0035-7030 Rivista Rosminiana di Filosofia e di Cultura
0035-7049 Rivista Siciliana della Tubercolosi e delle Malattie Respiratorie†
0035-7057 Rivista Sperimentale di Freniatria
0035-7065 Rivista Storica del Mezzogiorno
0035-7073 Rivista Storica Italiana
0035-7081 Rivista Tecnica di Cinematografia
0035-709X Rivista Tributaria
0035-7103 Rivista Trimestrale†
0035-7138 Riv'on l'Inyanei Misim - Quarterly Tax Journal *see* 0334-3065
0035-7146 Rizeni Ekonomiky v Socialistickych Zemich *changed to* Rizeni Ekonomiky.
0035-7154 R.L.C.'s Museum Gazette
0035-7162 Australia. Bureau of Statistics. Road Accident Fatalities *see* 1031-1084
0035-7170 Road Ahead
0035-7189 Road & Track
0035-7200 Road Apple Review
0035-7219 Road International†
0035-7227 Road Maps of Industry *see* 0884-4887
0035-7235 Raad och Roen
0035-7243 Road Rider
0035-7251 Road Tar†
0035-726X Road Test/Dune Buggy†
0035-7294 Road Transport and Contracting
0035-7308 Road Transporter *changed to* Road Transporter of Australia.
0035-7316 Road Way
0035-7324 Roadrunner *changed to* Wow.
0035-7332 Roads and Road Construction
0035-7340 Roads and Streets *changed to* Highway & Heavy Construction Products.
0035-7367 Roanoke Review
0035-7375 Roaring Twenties (Seabrook) *see* 0147-6165
0035-7383 Robert Dumm Piano Review†
0035-7391 Robot
0035-7405 Rochester Engineer
0035-7413 Rochester History
0035-743X Rock and Roll Songs *see* 8756-3487
0035-7448 Rock Mechanics *see* 0723-2632
0035-7456 Rock Mechanics Abstracts *see* 0148-9062
0035-7464 Rock Products
0035-7480 Rocket†
0035-7510 Rockhurst Hawk
0035-7529 Rocks and Minerals
0035-7537 Rocks & Minerals in Canada
0035-757X Rocky Mountain Druggist *see* 0191-6394
0035-7588 Rocky Mountain Food Dealer
0035-7596 Rocky Mountain Journal of Mathematics
0035-760X Rocky Mountain Medical Journal *see* 0199-7343
0035-7618 Rocky Mountain Mineral Law Review *see* 0148-6489
0035-7626 Rocky Mountain Modern Language Association. Bulletin *see* 0361-1299
0035-7634 Rocky Mountain Social Science Journal *changed to* Social Science Journal.
0035-7642 Western Association of Africanists. Newsletter†
0035-7650 Rocky Mountain Union Farmer
0035-7669 Rocznik Historii Czasopismiennictwa Polskiego *see* 0137-2998
0035-7677 Roczniki Chemii *see* 0137-5083
0035-7685 Roczniki Filozoficzne
0035-7715 Panstwowy Zaklad Higieny. Roczniki
0035-7723 Roczniki Teologiczno-Kanoniczne
0035-7758 Rodeo Sports News *see* 0161-5815
0035-7766 Rodina a Skola
0035-7774 Rodo no Kagaku (Kawasaki, 1946)
0035-7782 Roedovre Avis†
0035-7790 Roeh Hacheshbon
0035-7812 Roemische Quartalschrift fuer Christliche Altertumskunde und Kirchengeschichte
0035-7820 Roentgenpraxis
0035-7839 Roester i Radio-TV
0035-7847 Rohm and Haas Reporter
0035-7855 Rohre-Rohrleitungsbau-Rohrleitungstransport *changed to* 3 R - International.
0035-7863 Rohstoff Rundschau
0035-7871 Rolandino†
0035-788X Roll Call
0035-7898 Roll Sign
0035-7901 Roller *see* 0959-5740
0035-791X Rolling Stone
0035-7928 Rolling Stone of Tampa†
0035-7936 Rollins Sandspur
0035-7944 Rolls-Royce News†
0035-7952 Rolls Royce Owner
0035-7960 Roma e Provincia Attraverso la Statistica
0035-7979 Roman-Zeitung†
0035-7995 Romance Notes
0035-8002 Romance Philology
0035-8029 Romania
0035-8037 Revista de Statistica
0035-8045 Romanian Books
0035-8053 Romanian Bulletin†
0035-8061 Romanian Engineering
0035-807X Romanian Foreign Trade
0035-8088 Romanian Review
0035-8096 Romanian Scientific Abstracts
0035-810X Romanian Scientific Abstracts. Social Sciences†
0035-8118 Romanic Review
0035-8126 Romanische Forschungen
0035-8142 Romantikk
0035-8150 Rome Report of Business Publication Advertising *changed to* Media Records Report of Business Publication Advertising.
0035-8169 Rond de Tafel
0035-8177 Rondom het Boek†
0035-8185 Ronzatore
0035-8193 Roofing Contractor
0035-8207 Rooi Rose
0035-8215 Roopa-Lekha
0035-8231 Ropa a Uhlie
0035-824X Rope News *changed to* Rope Links.
0035-8266 Rosacruz
0035-8274 Rosario de Maria
0035-8282 Il Rosario e la Nuova Pompei
0035-8290 Rosebank Record†
0035-8304 Roseburg Woodsman†
0035-8312 Rosenberg Library Bulletin†
0035-8320 Roses and Gold from Our Lady of the Ozarks†
0035-8339 Rosicrucian Digest
0035-8355 Ross Reports Television
0035-8363 Rossica Society of Russian Philately Journal
0035-838X The Rotarian
0035-8401 Rotary
0035-8428 Rote Revue *changed to* Rote Revue.
0035-8444 Rothwell Advertiser
0035-8452 Rotor and Wing *see* 0191-6408
0035-8487 Rotterdam Europoort Delta *see* 0922-7148
0035-8495 Rotunda
0035-8525 Rough Notes
0035-8533 The Round Table
0035-8541 Round-up - Children's Services†
0035-855X Roundup (El Paso)
0035-8568 Route
0035-8584 Rowing Magazine *changed to* Rowing Magazine Monthly.
0035-8606 Royal Air Force College Journal
0035-8614 Royal Air Force News
0035-8630 Royal Air Forces Quarterly†
0035-8649 Royal Arch Mason
0035-8657 Royal Army Chaplains Department. Quarterly Journal *changed to* Great Britain. Royal Army Chaplains' Department. Journal.
0035-8673 Royal Army Pay Corps Journal†
0035-8681 Royal Army Veterinary Corps. Journal†
0035-869X Royal Asiatic Society of Great Britain and Ireland. Journal
0035-8711 Royal Astronomical Society. Monthly Notices
0035-872X Royal Astronomical Society of Canada. Journal
0035-8738 Royal Astronomical Society. Quarterly Journal
0035-8746 Royal Australian Chemical Institute. Proceedings *see* 0314-4240
0035-8762 Royal Australian Historical Society. Journal
0035-8770 Royal Bank of Canada. Monthly Letter *see* 0229-0243
0035-8789 Royal Central Asian Society. Journal *see* 0306-8374
0035-8797 Royal College of General Practitioners. Journal. *see* 0960-1643
0035-8800 Royal College of Physicians and Surgeons of Canada. Annals
0035-8827 Royal College of Surgeons in Ireland. Journal *see* 0374-8405
0035-8835 Royal College of Surgeons of Edinburgh. Journal
0035-8843 Royal College of Surgeons of England. Annals
0035-8851 Royal Commonwealth Society Library Notes†
0035-886X Royal Commonwealth Society. Newsletter *changed to* Commonwealth Outlook.
0035-8878 Royal Engineers Journal
0035-8894 Royal Entomological Society of London. Transactions *see* 0307-6946
0035-8908 Royal Gazette
0035-8916 Royal Historical Society of Queensland Bulletin
0035-8924 Royal Horticultural Society Journal *changed to* The Garden.
0035-8932 R I B A Journal *see* 0953-6973
0035-8940 Royal Institute of Chemistry Reviews *see* 0306-0012
0035-8967 Royal Institution of Naval Architects. Transactions
0035-8975 Royal Irish Academy. Proceedings. Section A: Mathematical, Astronomical and Physical Science *changed to* Royal Irish Academy. Proceedings. Section A: Mathematical and Physical Sciences.
0035-8983 Royal Irish Academy. Proceedings. Section B: Biological, Geological and Chemical Sciences
0035-8991 Royal Irish Academy. Proceedings. Section C: Archaeology, Celtic Studies, History, Linguistics and Literature

5442 ISSN INDEX

0035-9009 Royal Meteorological Society. Quarterly Journal
0035-9017 Royal Microscopical Society. Proceedings
0035-9025 Royal Military Police Journal
0035-9033 Royal Naval Medical Service. Journal
0035-9041 Royal Naval Sailing Association Journal
0035-905X Royal Neighbor
0035-9068 Royal Nepal Economist†
0035-9076 Royal Pioneer
0035-9084 Royal Service
0035-9092 Royal Society International Scientific Information Services. Bulletin†
0035-9106 Royal Society of Antiquaries of Ireland. Journal
0035-9114 Royal Society of Arts. Journal *see* 0958-0433
0035-9122 Royal Society of Canada. Transactions
0035-9149 Royal Society of London. Notes and Records
0035-9157 Royal Society of Medicine. Proceedings *see* 0141-0768
0035-9165 Royal Society of Medicine. Section of Odontology Proceedings†
0035-9173 Royal Society of New South Wales. Journal and Proceedings
0035-9181 Royal Society of New Zealand. Transactions *see* 0303-6758
0035-919X Royal Society of South Africa. Transactions
0035-9203 Royal Society of Tropical Medicine and Hygiene Transactions
0035-9211 Royal Society of Victoria. Proceedings
0035-922X Royal Society of Western Australia. Journal
0035-9238 Royal Statistical Society. Journal. Series A: General *changed to* Royal Statistical Society. Journal. Series A: Statistics in Society.
0035-9246 Royal Statistical Society. Journal. Series B: Methodological
0035-9254 Royal Statistical Society. Journal. Series C: Applied Statistics
0035-9262 Royal Tehran Hilton
0035-9270 Royal Television Society. Journal *see* 0308-454X
0035-9289 Royal United Service Institution. Journal *see* 0307-1847
0035-9297 University of Malta. Faculty of Arts. Journal†
0035-9300 Royalauto
0035-9319 Royale Federation Colombophile Belge. Bulletin Federal *changed to* Royale Federation Colombophile Belge. Bulletin National.
0035-9327 Rozhl'ady†
0035-9335 Rozhlasova Prace
0035-9343 Rozhledy Matematicko-Fyzikalni
0035-9351 Rozhledy v Chirurgii
0035-9378 Narodni Technicke Muzeum. Rozpravy
0035-9386 Rozprawy Elektrotechniczne *changed to* Rozprawy Elektroniki i Telekomunikacji. Kwartalnik.
0035-9394 Rozprawy Hydrotechniczne
0035-9416 Rozvoj Mistniho Hospodarstvi
0035-9424 Rtam
0035-9432 Rub-Off†
0035-9440 Rubber Age *see* 0146-0706
0035-9467 Rubber Chem Lines†
0035-9475 Rubber Chemistry and Technology
0035-9491 Rubber India
0035-9513 Rubber News
0035-9521 Rubber Research Institute of Sri Lanka. Quarterly Journal *see* 0379-1130
0035-953X Rubber Research Institute of Malaysia. Journal *see* 0127-7065
0035-9548 Rubber Statistical Bulletin
0035-9556 Rubber Statistical News Sheet†
0035-9564 Rubber Trends
0035-9572 Rubber World
0035-9580 Ruby Magazine
0035-9599 Ruch Filozoficzny
0035-9602 Ruch Literacki
0035-9610 Ruch Muzyczny
0035-9629 Ruch Prawniczy, Ekonomiczny i Socjologiczny
0035-9637 Rudarski Glasnik
0035-9645 Rudarsko-Metalurski Zbornik
0035-9661 Ruedo
0035-9688 Rudy
0035-9696 Rudy i Metale Niezelazne
0035-970X La Rue
0035-9726 Rugby
0035-9742 Rugby League Week
0035-9750 Rugby News *changed to* Rugby (Year).
0035-9777 Rugby World *changed to* Rugby World and Post.
0035-9793 Rukovet
0035-9815 Romania Today *see* 1220-5028
0035-9823 Ruminskii Biulleten Naucinoi Informatii. Estestvennie Nauki *changed to* Ruminskii Biulleten Naucinoi Informatii. Estestvennie Nauki. Meditinskie Nauki.
0035-9831 Ruminskii Biuleten Naucinoi Informatii. Obscestvennie Nauki†
0035-9866 Rundfunk- Fernseh- Grosshandel *changed to* Rundfunk - Fernseh - Wirtschaft.
0035-9874 Rundfunk und Fernsehen
0035-9882 Rundfunkjournalistik in Theorie und Praxis†
0035-9890 Rundfunktechnische Mitteilungen
0035-9904 Rundschau fuer den Deutschen Einzelhaendler
0035-9912 Rundschau fuer Internationale Damenmode
0035-9920 Hotel und Gastgewerbe
0035-9939 Runner's World *see* 0897-1706
0035-9955 Ruota Diorama
0035-9963 Rupambara
0035-998X Ruperto-Carola
0035-9998 Rural and Urban Roads *see* 8750-9229
0036-0007 Rural Councillor
0036-0023 National Rural Education News
0036-0058 Rural India
0036-0066 Rural Kentuckian *changed to* Kentucky Living.
0036-0074 Rural Life†
0036-0082 Rural Missions *changed to* T N T.
0036-0090 C S I R O Rural Research
0036-0104 Rural Roundup
0036-0112 Rural Sociology
0036-0120 Rural Youth
0036-0139 Ruralista
0036-0147 Ruritan
0036-0155 Rusky Jazyk *changed to* Rusky Jazyk ve Skole.
0036-0163 Russell: The Journal of the Bertrand Russell Archives
0036-0171 Russell's Official National Motor Coach Guide
0036-018X Russia Cristiana *changed to* L'Altra Europa.
0036-0201 Russian Castings Production†
0036-021X Russian Chemical Reviews
0036-0228 Russian Engineering Journal *see* 0144-6622
0036-0236 Russian Journal of Inorganic Chemistry
0036-0244 Russian Journal of Physical Chemistry
0036-0252 Russian Language Journal
0036-0260 Russian Language Monthly†
0036-0279 Russian Mathematical Surveys
0036-0287 Russian Messenger - Russkij Vistnik *changed to* U R O B A Messenger.
0036-0295 Russian Metallurgy
0036-0309 Russian Oil and Gas Bulletin†
0036-0317 Russian Orthodox Journal
0036-0325 Russian Pharmacology and Toxicology
0036-0341 Russian Review
0036-035X Russisch *see* 0173-9522
0036-0368 Russkaya Rech'
0036-0384 Russkii Yazyk za Rubezhom
0036-0406 Russky Golos
0036-0414 Russland und Wir
0036-0422 Ruta Dominicana
0036-0430 Rutas de Pasion
0036-0449 Rutgers-Camden Law Journal *see* 0277-318X
0036-0457 Rutgers Alumni Magazine *changed to* Rutgers Magazine.
0036-0465 Rutgers Law Review
0036-0473 Rutgers University. Libraries. Journal
0036-0481 Rwanda-Carrefour d'Afrique *changed to* Releve.
0036-049X Rybnoe Khozyaistvo
0036-0511 Rydge's *see* 0727-758X
0036-052X Rynki Zagraniczne
0036-0538 Ryoiku
0036-0546 Rythmes du Monde†
0036-0570 South African Banking†
0036-0597 S A C O Tidningen *see* 0347-0342
0036-0600 South African Cerebral Palsy Journal
0036-0627 South African Chemical Processing *changed to* Power & Plant Engineering in South Africa.
0036-0643 South African Draughtsman
0036-0651 S A E - Australasia
0036-0678 Transactions S A E S T
0036-0708 S A F E - Nachrichten
0036-0716 S A F T O Exporter
0036-0724 South African Friesland Journal
0036-0740 Swiss-American Historical Society. Newsletter *changed to* Swiss-American Historical Society. Review.
0036-0759 S.A. Hairdressing and Beauty Culture
0036-0767 S A I P A
0036-0775 S A I S Review
0036-0783 S A L A Newsletter - S A B V Nuusbrief *see* 0256-6710
0036-0791 Southern African Museums Association. Publication *see* 0370-8314
0036-0805 Advanced Management Journal
0036-0813 S A M P E Journal†
0036-0821 S A M P E Quarterly
0036-083X S A M *changed to* Adweek: Midwest.
0036-0848 South African Machine Tool Review
0036-0856 South Africa Motoring Mirror *changed to* South Africa Motor.
0036-0864 South African National Bibliography
0036-0872 S A N T A. T B News
0036-0880 S A N T A Bantu *changed to* S A N T A Health Magazine.
0036-0899 S. A. News for the Deaf†
0036-0929 S.A.R. and H. Employees' Review *changed to* Emplo Review/Tydskrif.
0036-0945 S.A. Road Transport *changed to* S.A. Road Transport Journal.
0036-0953 SASSAR†
0036-097X S A T I S†
0036-0988 S A U K-S A B C Bulletin *changed to* Personality.
0036-1003 Texnews
0036-1011 S.A. Worker
0036-102X S B
0036-1038 S-B Gazette/Sutters Bourgeoisie Gazette *see* 0038-9900
0036-1046 S B I C - Venture Capital *changed to* Venture Capital Journal.
0036-1062 Bibliotheque de Travail avec Supplement†
0036-1070 S B Z - Sanitaer-Technik, Heizungs-, und Lueftungsbau *see* 0342-8184
0036-1089 S C A A Viewpoint†
0036-1119 S C A - Tidningen *see* 1101-1939
0036-1127 S.C.E.T.A. Bulletin de Documentation *changed to* S C E T A Documentation.
0036-1135 S C J
0036-1143 S C L A Data†
0036-116X Santa Casa di Loreto. Messaggio
0036-1178 S D C Bulletin
0036-1186 S D L Newsletter†
0036-1194 S D R-Kontakt
0036-1224 S E A G Boletin del Algodon *changed to* E A G Publicaciones.
0036-1232 S E A G Boletin del Maiz *changed to* E A G Publicaciones.
0036-1240 S E A G Boletin del Trigo *changed to* E A G Publicaciones.
0036-1267 S E D O C
0036-1275 S E H A Newsletter and Proceedings
0036-1291 S E M Newsletter *changed to* Ethnomusicology Newsletter.
0036-1313 S E S A Proceedings *changed to* S E M Proceedings.
0036-1321 S E V Bulletin *changed to* Bulletin S E V - V S E.
0036-1364 S F W A Bulletin
0036-1372 Slovenska Akademia Vied. Geologicky Ustav D. Stura: Zbornik: Zapadne Karpaty†
0036-1380 S H E N†
0036-1399 S I A M Journal on Applied Mathematics
0036-1402 S I A M Journal on Control *see* 0363-0129
0036-1410 S I A M Journal on Mathematical Analysis
0036-1429 S I A M Journal on Numerical Analysis
0036-1437 S I A M Newsletter *changed to* S I A M News.
0036-1445 S I A M Review
0036-147X S I C A S H Newsletter *changed to* S I G L A S H Newsletter.
0036-1488 Sida; Contributions to Botany
0036-1496 S.I.D. Proceedings
0036-150X S I E C U S Newsletter *see* 0091-3995
0036-1518 S I E T Studies *changed to* S E D M E.
0036-1526 S I G S P A C†
0036-1534 S I I - Socialist International Information *see* 0049-0946
0036-1542 S I L B I Bollettino
0036-1550 S I L News *changed to* Individual Liberty.
0036-1569 S J M Bulletin/Scandinavian Steel and Metal News *changed to* Skrot och Miljoteknik.
0036-1585 S Z
0036-1607 Special Libraries Association. Geography and Map Division. Bulletin
0036-1615 S L F Tidningen†
0036-1631 S L R Camera *changed to* Photo Answers.
0036-164X S M E A Maskin - Industrien *changed to* Maskin - Aktuelt.
0036-1666 S.M.M.B. Bulletin *see* 0309-0809
0036-1682 S M P T E Journal
0036-1704 S. M. U. H. Bulletin *see* 0399-0966
0036-1720 S N E C M A *see* 0750-7569
0036-1755 New York State School Nurse-Teachers Association. Journal *changed to* N Y S S N T A Journal.
0036-1763 S Nine Two Way Radio *see* 0145-4560
0036-1771 S. O. L. A. I. A. T
0036-178X S O S Messenger *changed to* S O S Kinderdorf International.
0036-1798 S. O. S. Soviet Jewry†
0036-181X S P A Journal†
0036-1836 Student Personnel Association for Teacher Education. Journal *see* 0735-6846
0036-1844 S P E Journal *see* 0091-9578
0036-1852 S P I C
0036-1860 S P I E Journal *see* 0091-3286
0036-1879 Sweden. Sjukvaardens och Socialvaardens Planerings- och Rationaliseringsinstitut. S P R I Litteraturtjaenst
0036-1887 S R F Resume *changed to* Resume.
0036-1925 S S S Newsletter (Simulation in the Service of Society) *see* 0037-5497
0036-1933 S & T A-Scienza e Tecnologia degli Alimenti†
0036-1941 S T A Educator†
0036-1976 S T E L C O - Scope†
0036-1984 S U C Bulletin
0036-200X S U D E NE. Boletim da Biblioteca†
0036-2018 S U H A F - Tidningen *changed to* Universitetslaeraren.
0036-2034 Society of St. Vincent de Paul. Bulletin for Southern Africa†

ISSN

ISSN INDEX 5443

ISSN	Title
0036-2069	South West Africa Scientific Society. Newsletter - S W A Wetenskaplike Vereniging. Nuusbrief - S W A Wissenschaftliche Gesellschaft. Mitteilungen *changed to* Namibia Scientific Society. Newsletter.
0036-2085	S.W.L.A. Newsletter†
0036-2093	S Y R-Information med Fruktodlaren *see* 0348-7032
0036-2107	Commercial Transport *changed to* Commercial Transport.
0036-2115	Saarbruecker Hefte
0036-2123	Saastopankki
0036-2131	Sabah Society. Journal
0036-214X	Sabbath Recorder
0036-2158	Sabena Revue
0036-2174	Sabouraudia: Journal of Medical and Veterinary Mycology *see* 0268-1218
0036-2182	Saco-Lowell Bulletin *changed to* Platt Saco Lowell Bulletin.
0036-2190	Sacra Doctrina
0036-2204	Sacramento Business†
0036-2212	Sacramento Observer
0036-2239	Sacramento Teacher†
0036-2247	Sacramento Valley Union Labor Bulletin
0036-2255	Sacred Music
0036-2263	Sacred Organ Journal
0036-2271	Saddle and Bridle
0036-228X	Sadelmager-og Tapetserer Tidende
0036-231X	Holzindustrie†
0036-2328	Saenger- und Musikantenzeitung
0036-2336	Saenger-Zeitung
0036-2344	Saeugetierkundliche Mitteilungen
0036-2352	Safari
0036-2360	Safe and Security News
0036-2379	Safe Deposit Bulletin
0036-2387	Safe Driver
0036-2395	Safe Engineering†
0036-2409	SAFECO Agent
0036-2417	Safer (Volkswagen) Motoring *see* 0953-6167
0036-2425	Safer Oregon *changed to* Update (Salem).
0036-2433	Safety†
0036-2441	Safety at Sea International *see* 0142-0666
0036-245X	Safety Briefs
0036-2468	Safety Digest *see* 0377-8592
0036-2476	Safety Energizer†
0036-2484	Safety in Industry *see* 0377-8592
0036-2492	Safety in Mines Abstracts *see* 0141-9803
0036-2514	Environmental Control & Safety Management†
0036-2549	Safety Review†
0036-2557	Safety Standards *see* 0090-4589
0036-2565	Saga†
0036-2573	Sagan-Sprottauer Heimatbriefe
0036-259X	Saagverken
0036-2603	Sahakar *changed to* Satyachar.
0036-2611	Sahakari Jagat
0036-262X	Sahamies†
0036-2638	Sahara
0036-2646	Saharien
0036-2654	Sahifat Al-Tarbiya
0036-2670	Sahko-Elektriciten i Finland - Sahko-Elektricity in Finland *changed to* Sahko - Tele.
0036-2689	Journal of Accidental Medicine *see* 0387-4095
0036-2700	Sail
0036-2719	Sailing
0036-2727	Sailing Industry News†
0036-2735	Sailplane and Gliding
0036-2743	Sainik Samachar
0036-2751	St. Andrews Review
0036-276X	St. Anthony Messenger
0036-2778	St. Bartholomew's Hospital Journal *changed to* Barts Journal.
0036-2794	Triomphe Saint-Cyr
0036-2808	St. Dunstan's Review
0036-2824	St. Francis Xavier University Contemporary and Alumni News *changed to* St. Francis Xavier University Alumni News.
0036-2832	St. Gallen
0036-2840	Saint George's Hospital Gazette
0036-2859	St. Hallvard
0036-2867	Saint Hubert
0036-2883	St. John Review *changed to* St. John World.
0036-2891	St. John's Hospital Dermatological Society. Transactions *see* 0307-6938
0036-2905	St. John's Law Review
0036-2921	St. Jude's Magazine†
0036-293X	St. Louis Commerce
0036-2948	St. Louis Countian
0036-2956	St. Louis Genealogical Society Quarterly
0036-2964	St. Louis Jewish Light
0036-2972	St. Louis Journalism Review
0036-2980	St. Louis Park Medical Center. Bulletin *changed to* Park-Nicollet Medical Foundation Bulletin.
0036-3006	St. Louis Purchaser
0036-3014	Saint Louis University Research Journal
0036-3022	St. Louis Review
0036-3030	Saint Louis University Law Journal
0036-3057	Saint-Luc Medical
0036-3065	St. Lucas Allgemeine Glaserzeitung *see* 0342-5142
0036-3081	St. Luke's Hospital Gazette†
0036-309X	St. Luke's Journal *changed to* St. Luke's Journal of Theology.
0036-3103	St. Mark's Review
0036-3111	St. Martin's Review
0036-312X	St. Mary's Hospital Gazette
0036-3138	Saint Mary's University Journal
0036-3146	Saint Paul Area Chamber of Commerce Action†
0036-3154	St. Paul News
0036-3162	St. Poeltner Dioezesanblatt
0036-3189	St. Regis News, Southern Edition *changed to* St. Regis News.
0036-3197	Saint Thomas More Political Science Journal
0036-3200	St. Thomas's Hospital Gazette *changed to* St. Thomas's Hospital Gazette.
0036-3219	Saint Vincent de Paul Record
0036-3227	St. Vladimir's Theological Quarterly
0036-3243	Sainte Therese de Lisieux. Annales
0036-3251	Saints' Herald
0036-326X	Sairaala
0036-3278	Sairaanhoitaja - Sjukskoterskan *see* 0358-4038
0036-3286	Collecting and Breeding
0036-3294	Saison†
0036-3316	Saiva Siddhanta
0036-3324	Saivite Light *changed to* Gracious Light.
0036-3340	Sakharnaya Promyshlennost'†
0036-3359	Sakharnaya Svekla Proizvodstvo i Pererabotka
0036-3367	Salt
0036-3375	Salamandra
0036-3383	Salem County Historical Society Newsletter
0036-3391	Sales†
0036-3405	Sales Executive
0036-3413	Sales Management *changed to* Sales & Marketing Management.
0036-3421	Sales Manager's Bulletin
0036-3448	Sales - Promotion *changed to* Sales & Marketing Manager Canada.
0036-3456	Sales Prospector
0036-3464	Sales/Slants†
0036-3472	Sales Tax Advices
0036-3480	Salesian
0036-3502	Salesianum
0036-3510	Salesman's Opportunity Magazine *see* 0741-3750
0036-3529	Salmagundi
0036-3537	Salmanticensis
0036-3545	Salmon and Trout Magazine
0036-3553	Salon Owner *changed to* American Salon.
0036-357X	Salpisma
0036-360X	Salt Lick
0036-3618	Salt Water Sportsman
0036-3634	Salud Publica de Mexico
0036-3642	Salus Militiae
0036-3650	Salut les Copains *changed to* Salut.
0036-3669	Salvage Bids
0036-3677	Salzburger Wirtschaft
0036-3693	Samaj Kalyan
0036-3715	Samarbete
0036-3723	Samaritano *changed to* La San Vincenzo in Italia.
0036-3731	Samaru Agricultural Newsletter *see* 0331-6742
0036-374X	Samatat Prakashan
0036-3782	Samhaellsgemenskap *see* 0284-9941
0036-3804	Sammelwerk Bauzentrumring†
0036-3820	Sammler Express
0036-3839	Samoa Times
0036-3847	Samostiina Ukrayina†
0036-3855	Samouprava Zavarovancev†
0036-3871	Sampada
0036-388X	Samphire†
0036-3898	Sample Case
0036-391X	Samson Technology Trends†
0036-3928	Samtiden
0036-3944	Samvirke
0036-3952	San Antonian *see* 0279-0785
0036-3960	San Antonio Monthly
0036-3979	San Antonio District Dental Society. Journal *changed to* San Antonio District Dental Society Newsletter.
0036-3987	San Beda Review
0036-3995	San Bernardino County Library Newsletter†
0036-4002	San Diego Business†
0036-4010	San Diego County Dental Society. Bulletin *changed to* Facets (San Diego).
0036-4029	Door
0036-4037	San Diego Law Review
0036-4045	San Diego
0036-4053	San Diego Numismatic Society. Bulletin
0036-4061	San Diego Physician
0036-407X	American Federation of Musicians Local 325
0036-4096	San Francisco Bay Guardian
0036-410X	San Francisco Business
0036-4118	San Francisco Camera
0036-4126	San Francisco Earthquake†
0036-4134	San Francisco Labor *changed to* Northern California Labor.
0036-4142	San Francisco Medical Society. Bulletin *changed to* San Francisco Medicine.
0036-4169	San Francisco Unified School District Newsletter†
0036-4185	San Jose Post-Record
0036-4215	San Luis Valley Historian
0036-4223	San Marino (Repubblica) Bollettino Ufficiale
0036-424X	San Salvatore da Horta
0036-4258	Sanatorio Sao Lucas. Boletim
0036-4266	Sand Castles†
0036-4282	Sandal Prints†
0036-4290	Sandlapper *see* 0195-282X
0036-4304	SANE World - Freeze Focus *changed to* SANE - Freeze News.
0036-4312	Saneamento
0036-4320	Sangeet Kala Vihar *see* 0251-012X
0036-4339	Sangeet Natak
0036-4355	Sangre
0036-4363	Sangue della Redenzione†
0036-4371	Sangyo Gijutsu Joho Yokkaichi
0036-438X	Industrial Training
0036-4398	Sangyo Sharyo
0036-4401	Sanitaer- und Heizungstechnik
0036-4428	University of California. Sanitary Engineering and Environmental Health Research Laboratory. News Quarterly†
0036-4436	Sanitary Maintenance
0036-4444	Sanity†
0036-4460	Sannio Elegante
0036-4479	Sanomalehtimies
0036-4487	Sanop Kwa Kyongyong
0036-4495	Sanshi Kenkyu†
0036-4517	Santa Clara County Historical and Genealogical Quarterly *see* 0895-6103
0036-4525	Santa Clara County in Action†
0036-4541	Santa Fe Magazine†
0036-455X	Santa Gertrudis Journal
0036-4568	La Sante de l'Abeille
0036-4576	Sante et Sport
0036-4584	Sante, Liberte et Vaccinations†
0036-4606	Santo dei Voli
0036-4614	Santuario de Aparecida
0036-4622	Santuario della Madonna delle Rocche
0036-4630	Santuario di N.S.D. Grazie e di S. Maria Goretti *changed to* La Stella del Mare.
0036-4649	Sanyo Kasei News
0036-4657	Sao Paulo
0036-4665	Instituto de Medicina Tropical de Sao Paulo. Revista
0036-4681	Sapere
0036-469X	Sapeur-Pompier
0036-4703	Sapientia
0036-4711	Sapienza
0036-472X	Sapporo Igaku Zasshi
0036-4738	Sarah Lawrence Journal†
0036-4746	S.L. Literary Review *changed to* Sarah Lawrence Review.
0036-4754	Sarasvat
0036-4762	Sarawak Gazette
0036-4770	Sardegna Economica
0036-4789	Sardegna Informazioni
0036-4797	Sarika
0036-4819	S A R P *changed to* Servamus.
0036-4827	Sarsia
0036-4835	Sarvodaya
0036-4843	Sash
0036-4851	SaskTel News
0036-4878	Saskatchewan Archaeology Newsletter *see* 0227-7514
0036-4886	Saskatchewan Bulletin
0036-4894	Saskatchewan Gazette
0036-4908	Saskatchewan History
0036-4916	Saskatchewan Law Review
0036-4924	Saskatchewan Library†
0036-4940	Saskatchewan Motorist *changed to* Westworld Saskatchewan.
0036-4975	Saturday Night
0036-4983	Saturday Review *see* 0091-620X
0036-4991	Satya Prakash
0036-5009	Sau og Geit
0036-5025	Saucers, Space & Science†
0036-5033	Sauna Nachrichten mit Sauna Archiv *see* 0178-7764
0036-5041	Sauvegarde de l'Enfance
0036-505X	Sauvegarde des Chantiers
0036-5068	Savacou
0036-5084	Savant *see* 0822-7896
0036-5092	Savez Omladine†
0036-5106	Saving Health
0036-5114	Savings and Loan News *see* 0746-1321
0036-5122	Savings Association News *changed to* New York League News.
0036-5130	Savings Bank Journal *see* 0740-5464
0036-5157	Savoia
0036-5165	Savoir et Beaute *changed to* Cahiers du C A C E F.
0036-5173	Savremena Praksa
0036-519X	Savremenik
0036-5203	Savremeno Domacinstvo
0036-522X	Sbirka Soudnich Rozhodnuti a Stanovisek
0036-5238	Sbirka Zlepsovacich Navrhu a Pokrokovych Vyrobnich Zkusenosti *see* 0322-9564
0036-5246	Sbornik Archivnich Praci
0036-5254	Ceskoslovenska Spolecnost Zemepisna. Sbornik *see* 0231-5300
0036-5270	Sbornik Geologickych Ved: Antropozoikum
0036-5289	Sbornik Geologickych Ved: Hydrogeologie, Inzenyrska Geologie
0036-5297	Sbornik Geologickych Ved: Paleontologie
0036-5300	Sbornik Geologickych Ved: Technologie, Geochemie
0036-5319	Sbornik Geologickych Ved: Uzita Geofyzika

0036-5327 Sbornik Lekarsky
0036-5335 Narodni Muzeum v Praze. Sbornik. Rada A: Historie
0036-5343 Narodni Muzeum v Praze. Sbornik. Rada B: Prirodni Vedy
0036-5351 Narodni Muzeum v Praze. Sbornik. Rada C: Literarni Historie
0036-536X V S D a V u D Sobornik Pracit
0036-5378 Sbornik U V T I Z - Genetika a Slechteni *changed to* Genetika a Slechteni.
0036-5386 Sbornik U V T I Z - Meliorace *changed to* Meliorace.
0036-5394 Sbornik U V T I Z - Ochrana Rostlin *changed to* Ochrana Rostlin.
0036-5408 Scabbard and Blade Journal
0036-5416 Scala International
0036-5424 Scale Modeler
0036-5432 Scale Models *see* 0269-834X
0036-5467 Scan (New York)
0036-5475 Scan *changed to* Newscan.
0036-5483 Scandia
0036-5491 Scandinavian Economic History Review
0036-5505 Scandinavian Journal of Rehabilitation Medicine
0036-5513 Scandinavian Journal of Clinical & Laboratory Investigation
0036-5521 Scandinavian Journal of Gastroenterology
0036-553X Scandinavian Journal of Haematology *see* 0902-4441
0036-5548 Scandinavian Journal of Infectious Diseases
0036-5556 Scandinavian Journal of Plastic and Reconstructive Surgery
0036-5564 Scandinavian Journal of Psychology
0036-5580 Scandinavian Journal of Thoracic and Cardiovascular Surgery
0036-5599 Scandinavian Journal of Urology and Nephrology
0036-5602 Scandinavian Public Library Quarterly
0036-5610 Scandinavian Research Information Notes†
0036-5629 Scandinavian Shipping Gazette
0036-5637 Scandinavian Studies (Eugene)
0036-5653 Scandinavica
0036-5661 Scanlan's Monthly†
0036-567X Scarabee
0036-5696 Scautismo
0036-570X Scelte del Consumatore†
0036-5718 Scen och Salong†
0036-5726 Scena
0036-5734 Scena
0036-5742 Scena Illustrata
0036-5777 Scene from Oceana†
0036-5793 Scenes et Pistes
0036-5831 Schach-Echo *changed to* Schachmagazin 64 - Schach-Echo.
0036-584X Schacklub Hietzing Nachrichtenblatt *changed to* Schachklub Hietzing Memphis Nachrichtenblatt.
0036-5882 Schakels†
0036-5890 Schakend Nederland
0036-5904 Schakt-Bladet
0036-5920 Scharnhorst Auslese
0036-5939 Schaufenster *see* 0933-016X
0036-5947 Die Schaulade
0036-5955 Schedario
0036-5971 Scheepspraat *changed to* Fama.
0036-5998 Scheppend Ambacht
0036-6005 Scherma
0036-6013 Schiedamse Gemeenschap†
0036-6021 Schienenfahrzeuge *see* 0013-2810
0036-603X Schiff und Hafen *changed to* Schiff und Hafen - Kommandobruecke.
0036-6048 Schiffbau-Normung *see* 0722-2912
0036-6056 Schiffbauforschung
0036-6064 Schiffstechnik
0036-6072 Schilder *see* 0169-0930
0036-6080 Norda Schimmel Briefs *see* 0090-1903
0036-6099 Schip en Werf
0036-6102 Schippersblad†
0036-6110 Schism, a Journal of Divergent American Opinion†
0036-6129 Schizophrenia *changed to* Journal of Orthomolecular Medicine.
0036-6137 Schlager fuer Dich
0036-6145 Schlern
0036-6153 Schlesien
0036-617X Der Schluessel†
0036-6188 Der Schluessel†
0036-6196 Schmalenbachs Zeitschrift fuer Betriebswirtschaftliche Forschung *changed to* Z F B F.
0036-6218 Schmiertechnik *see* 0724-3472
0036-6226 Schmierungstechnik†
0036-6234 Schmollers Jahrbuch fuer Wirtschafts- und Sozialwissenschaften *see* 0342-1783
0036-6250 Schoeffe
0036-6269 Schoen - Visie
0036-6307 Schoenwereld
0036-6331 Scholarly Books in America†
0036-634X Scholarly Publishing
0036-6358 Scholars' Choice
0036-6366 Scholarships, Fellowships, Loans News Service *changed to* Student Aid Newsletter: Fellowships, Grants, Loans, Awards and Scholarships.
0036-6374 Scholarships for Foreign Students and Postgraduates at Austrian Universities and Art Academies†
0036-6382 Scholastic Coach
0036-6390 Scholastic Editor Graphics - Communications *changed to* Trends in College Media.
0036-6404 Scholastic News Ranger *see* 0736-055X
0036-6412 Scholastic Scope
0036-6439 School Administrator
0036-6447 School and Community
0036-6455 School and Society *see* 0161-7389
0036-6463 School Arts
0036-6471 School Board†
0036-648X School Boards Newsletter *see* 0039-0070
0036-6498 School Buildings Equipment and Supplies *changed to* School Buildings Equipment and Supplies and School Government Chronicle.
0036-6501 School Bus Fleet
0036-651X School Business Affairs
0036-6528 School Community Observer *changed to* Daybreak.
0036-6536 School Counselor
0036-6544 School en Godsdienst
0036-6552 School Food Services Bulletin *changed to* School Lunch Newsletter.
0036-6552 School Food Services Bulletin *changed to* School Breakfast Newsletter.
0036-6560 School Government Chronicle *changed to* School Buildings Equipment and Supplies and School Government Chronicle.
0036-6587 School Law Review†
0036-6595 School Librarian
0036-6609 School Libraries *see* 0278-4823
0036-6617 School Library *see* 1016-8206
0036-6641 School Lunch Journal *see* 0160-6271
0036-6668 School Music News
0036-6676 School Musician Director and Teacher†
0036-6684 School News†
0036-6692 School News *changed to* EdNews.
0036-6706 Michigan State University. School of Labor and Industrial Relations. Newsletter
0036-6730 School Press Review
0036-6749 School Product News *see* 1045-3970
0036-6765 School Research Information Service Quarterly *see* 0147-9741
0036-6773 School Review *see* 0195-6744
0036-6781 School Safety *changed to* School Safety World.
0036-679X School Science
0036-6803 School Science and Mathematics
0036-6811 School Science Review
0036-682X School Shop *see* 1050-3749
0036-6838 School Tie *changed to* Education News.
0036-6846 School Times†
0036-6854 School Trustee
0036-6862 School Yarn Magazine
0036-6889 Schoolblad
0036-6897 Schoolgirl Story Magazine
0036-6900 Schools in Action†
0036-6919 Schott-Kurier *changed to* Schott Aktuell.
0036-6927 De Schouw *changed to* Gawalo - V K L Journaal.
0036-6943 Evangelischer Bund in Oesterreich. Schriftenreihe
0036-696X Schriftenreihe fuer die Evangelische Frau
0036-6978 Geschichte der Naturwissenschaften, Technik und Medizin. Schriftenreihe *changed to* N T M Geschichte der Naturwissenschaften, Technik und Medizin. Schriftenreihe.
0036-6986 Das Schrifttum der Agrarwirtschaft
0036-6994 Schrifttumkartei Bauwesen *see* 0722-060X
0036-7001 Schrifttumkartei Beton *see* 0722-060X
0036-701X Schrifttumsuebersicht Laermminderung *see* 0344-7758
0036-7044 Schuh-Kurier
0036-7060 Schuh-Zeitung
0036-7079 Schuhmarkt
0036-7087 Schuhwirtschaft†
0036-7095 Schul- und Sportstaettenbau *changed to* Schule- und Sportstaette.
0036-7109 Schule und Europa†
0036-7117 Schule und Gesellschaft†
0036-7125 Schulfernsehen (Munich)
0036-7133 Schutz und Wehr†
0036-715X Schwann Record and Tape Guide *see* 1047-2355
0036-7168 Schweineproduktion *see* 0138-3388
0036-7176 Schweinezucht und Schweinemast
0036-7184 Schweissen und Schneiden
0036-7192 Schweisstechnik *see* 0036-7184
0036-7206 Schweisstechnik
0036-7214 Schweizerische Arbeitslehrerinnen-Zeitung
0036-7230 Schweiz, Suisse, Svizzera, Switzerland *changed to* Revue Schweiz Suisse Svizzera.
0036-7257 Schweizer Aluminium Rundschau†
0036-7273 Schweizer Archiv fuer Neurologie, Neurochirurgie und Psychiatrie
0036-7281 Schweizer Archiv fuer Tierheilkunde
0036-729X Schweizer Auto-Verkehr†
0036-7303 Schweizer Baublatt
0036-7311 Schweizer Brauerei-Rundschau *changed to* Brauerei und Getraenke-Rundschau.
0036-732X Schweizer Buch
0036-7338 Schweizer Buchhandel
0036-7346 Schweizer Frauenblatt
0036-7354 Schweizer Hundesport *changed to* Hunde Haltung Zucht Sport.
0036-7370 Schweizer Journal
0036-7389 Schweizer Kavallerist
0036-7397 Schweizer Maschinenmarkt
0036-7400 Schweizer Monatshefte
0036-7419 Schweizer Musiker-Revue
0036-7427 Schweizer Naturschutz
0036-7435 Schweizer Pedicure
0036-7443 Schweizer Schule
0036-746X Der Schweizer Treuhaender
0036-7478 Schweizer Uhr *see* 0255-6944
0036-7486 Schweizerische Aerztezeitung
0036-7508 Schweizerische Apotheker-Zeitung
0036-7516 Schweizerische Arbeitgeber-Zeitung
0036-7524 Schweizerische Bauzeitung *changed to* Schweizer Ingenieur und Architekt.
0036-7532 Schweizerische Beobachter
0036-7540 Schweizerische Bienen-Zeitung
0036-7559 Schweizerische Blatter fuer Heizung und Lueftung - Revue Suisse du Chauffage et de la Ventilation *changed to* Heizung und Lueftung.
0036-7567 Schweizerische Drogistenzeitung
0036-7575 Schweizerische Entomologische Gesellschaft. Mitteilungen
0036-7583 Schweizerische Fachschrift fuer Buchbindereien *changed to* Bindetechnik.
0036-7591 Schweizerische Gesellschaft der Offiziere des Munitionsdienstes. Bulletin
0036-7613 Schweizerische Juristen-Zeitung
0036-763X Schweizerische Landwirtschaftliche Forschung
0036-7648 Schweizerische Landwirtschaftliche Monatshefte†
0036-7656 Schweizerische Lehrerzeitung
0036-7672 Schweizerische Medizinische Wochenschrift
0036-7680 Schweizerische Metzger-Zeitung
0036-7699 Schweizerische Mineralogische und Petrographische Mitteilungen
0036-7702 Schweizerische Monatsschrift fuer Zahnheilkunde *see* 1011-4203
0036-7710 Schweizerische Musikzeitung†
0036-7729 Schweizerische Nationalbank. Monatsbericht
0036-7737 Schweizerische Photorundschau
0036-7745 Schweizerische Schachzeitung
0036-7753 Schweizerische Schreinerzeitung
0036-7761 Schweizerische Uhrmacher Zeitung *changed to* Schweizerische Uhrmacher- und Goldschmiede-Zeitung.
0036-777X Schweizerische Vereinigung fuer Atomenergie. Bulletin
0036-7788 Schweizerische Vereinigung fuer Klinische Chemie. Bulletin *see* 0253-035X
0036-7796 Schweizerische Weinzeitung
0036-780X Schweizerische Wirte-Zeitung *changed to* Schweizer Gastronomie.
0036-7818 Schweizerische Zeitschrift fuer Forstwesen
0036-7826 Schweizerische Zeitschrift fuer Gemeinnuetzigkeit
0036-7834 Schweizerische Zeitschrift fuer Geschichte
0036-7842 Swiss Journal of Hydrology *see* 1015-1621
0036-7869 Schweizerische Zeitschrift fuer Psychologie *changed to* Schweizerische Zeitschrift fuer Psychologie.
0036-7877 Schweizerische Zeitschrift fuer Sozialversicherung *changed to* Schweizerische Zeitschrift fuer Sozialversicherung und Berufliche Vorsorge.
0036-7885 Schweizerische Zeitschrift fuer Sportmedizin
0036-7893 Schweizerische Zeitschrift fuer Strafrecht
0036-7907 Schweizerische Zeitschrift fuer Vermessung, Photogrammetrie und Kulturtechnik *changed to* Mensuration, Photogrammetrie, Genie Rural.
0036-7923 Schweizerischer Zeitungsverleger-Verband. Bulletin *changed to* Schweizerischer Verband der Zeitungs- und Zeitschriftenverleger. Bulletin.
0036-7931 Schweizerisches Archiv fuer Verkehrswissenschaft und Verkehrs-Politik *changed to* Schweizerische Zeitschrift fuer Verkehrswirtschaft.
0036-794X Schweizerisches Archiv fuer Volkskunde
0036-7958 Schweizerisches Gutenbergmuseum†
0036-7966 Schweizerisches Kaufmaennisches Zentralblatt *changed to* Schweizerische Kaufmaennische Zeitung.
0036-7974 Schweizerisches Patent-, Muster- und Markenblatt
0036-7982 Schweizerisches Rotes Kreuz *changed to* Actio.
0036-7990 Schweizerisches Zentralblatt fuer Staats- und Gemeindeverwaltung

ISSN	Title
0036-8008	G W A - Gas Wasser Abwasser changed to G.W.A.
0036-8016	Schweizer Jaeger
0036-8024	Schweizerische Zeitschrift fuer Militaermedizin see 0377-8347
0036-8032	Schwenkfeldian
0036-8040	Sci
0036-8059	Sci-Tech News
0036-8067	Sci/Tech Quarterly Index†
0036-8075	Science
0036-8091	Physics Abstracts
0036-8105	Electrical & Electronics Abstracts
0036-8113	Computer & Control Abstracts
0036-8121	Science Activities
0036-813X	Science Affairs†
0036-8148	Science and Children
0036-8156	Science and Culture
0036-8164	Science and Engineering
0036-8172	Doshisha Daigaku Rikogaku Kenkyu Hokoku
0036-8180	Science and Industry†
0036-8237	Science and Society
0036-8245	Science and Technology (New York)†
0036-8253	Science Books see 0098-342X
0036-8261	Science Bulletin
0036-827X	Science Citation Index
0036-8288	Science Curriculum Improvement Study Newsletter†
0036-8296	Science Digest changed to Breakthroughs in Health & Science.
0036-830X	Science Dimension changed to Science and Technology Dimensions.
0036-8318	Science du Sol see 0335-1653
0036-8326	Science Education
0036-8334	Science Education News†
0036-8342	Science et Nature
0036-8350	Science et Peche see 0765-5320
0036-8369	Science et Vie
0036-8377	Science Fiction Review†
0036-8385	Science for Schools
0036-8407	Science in Parliament
0036-8423	Science News
0036-8458	Science of Mind Magazine
0036-8466	Science of the Soul
0036-8474	Science on the March see 0160-0664
0036-8482	Science Policy Reviews†
0036-8504	Science Progress
0036-8520	Science Review†
0036-8539	Science Studies changed to Us.
0036-8555	The Science Teacher
0036-858X	Science Today
0036-8598	Science Tools†
0036-8601	Science World
0036-861X	Sciences
0036-8628	Sciences & l'Enseignement des Sciences†
0036-8636	Sciences et Avenir
0036-8652	Science et Techniques changed to Sciences et Technologies.
0036-8679	Scientia
0036-8687	Scientia†
0036-8695	Scientia Electrica†
0036-8709	Scientia Pharmaceutica
0036-8717	Scientiae see 1017-4966
0036-8725	Scientiarum Historia†
0036-8733	Scientific American
0036-8741	S T A R
0036-875X	Science and Australian Technology see 0310-9100
0036-8768	Scientific, Engineering, Technical Manpower Comments
0036-8776	Information-Part 1-News, Sources, Profiles see 0360-5817
0036-8784	Scientific Information Notes changed to Science Technology: Information.
0036-8792	Industrial Lubrication & Tribology
0036-8814	Scientific Progress - Wetenskaplike Vordering see 0038-2353
0036-8822	Scientific Research Council of Jamaica. Journal see 1016-2054
0036-8830	Scientific Researches changed to Bangladesh Journal of Scientific and Industrial Research.
0036-8857	Scientific World
0036-8865	Scienza dell'Alimentazione see 0391-4887
0036-8873	Scienza e la Tecnica della Organizzazione Nella Pubblicac Amministrazione changed to Rivista Trimestrale di Scienza dell'Amministrazione.
0036-8881	Scienza e Tecnica Agraria
0036-889X	Scienza e Tecnica Lattiero-Casearia
0036-8903	Scienze ed il Loro Insegnamento changed to Scienze, la Matematica e Il Loro Insegnamento.
0036-892X	Scierie & Charpente†
0036-8962	Scopcraeft†
0036-8970	Scope†
0036-8989	Scope changed to Health Student.
0036-8997	Scope see 0896-209X
0036-9012	Scope
0036-9020	Scopus
0036-9039	Scoret
0036-9055	Scotland changed to Business Scotland.
0036-9063	Scotland's Magazine†
0036-9071	Scots Independent
0036-908X	Scots Law Times
0036-911X	Scottish Art Review
0036-9128	Scottish Bankers Magazine changed to Scottish Banker.
0036-9136	Scottish Baptist Magazine
0036-9144	Scottish Birds
0036-9152	Scottish Clubman changed to Motorscot.
0036-9160	Scottish Curler
0036-9195	Scottish Farmer
0036-9209	Scottish Field
0036-9217	Scottish Forestry
0036-9225	Scottish Geographical Magazine
0036-9233	Scottish Grocer
0036-9241	Scottish Historical Review
0036-925X	Scottish Home and Country
0036-9284	Scottish Journal of Occupational Therapy†
0036-9292	Scottish Journal of Political Economy
0036-9314	Scottish Law Gazette
0036-9322	Scottish Licensed Trade News
0036-9357	Scottish Pharmacist†
0036-9365	Scottish Plumbing and Heating Monthly changed to Plumb and Heat.
0036-9373	Scottish Primary Quarterly†
0036-939X	Scottish Schoolmaster†
0036-9411	Scottish Studies
0036-942X	Scottish Sunday School Teacher†
0036-9446	Scottish Women's Temperance News
0036-9454	Scott's Monthly Journal changed to Scott Stamp Monthly.
0036-9470	Scout Pionnier see 0751-5723
0036-9489	Scouting
0036-9500	Scouting Magazine
0036-9519	Scoutledaren
0036-9527	Scrap Age see 0898-0756
0036-9535	Scraper†
0036-9543	Screen
0036-9551	Screen
0036-956X	Screen Actor
0036-9586	Point of Sale and Screenprinting changed to Screen Process.
0036-9594	Screen Printing
0036-9608	Screen Stories†
0036-9616	Screenland†
0036-9624	Screw
0036-9632	Scribblings†
0036-9640	Scriblerian see 0190-731X
0036-9640	Scriblerian see 0190-731X
0036-9721	Scripta Medica
0036-973X	Scripta Mercaturae
0036-9748	Scripta Metallurgica see 0956-716X
0036-9764	Scripta Theologica
0036-9772	Scriptorium
0036-9780	Scripture Bulletin
0036-9799	Scroll of Phi Delta Theta
0036-9802	Scugnizzo
0036-9810	Scuola Cattolica
0036-9837	Scuola di Base
0036-9845	Italy. Scuola di Guerra. Biblioteca. Bollettino
0036-9853	Scuola e Citta
0036-9861	Scuola e Didattica
0036-987X	Scuola e l'Uomo
0036-9888	Scuola Italiana Moderna
0036-9896	Scuola Media†
0036-990X	Scuola Normale Superiore di Pisa. Annali. Lettere, Storia e Filosofia changed to Scuola Normale Superiore di Pisa. Annali. Classe di Lettere e Filosofia.
0036-9918	Scuola Normale Superiore di Pisa. Annali. Scienze, Fisiche e Matematiche changed to Scuola Normale Superiore di Pisa. Annali. Classe di Scienze.
0036-9926	Scuola Viva
0036-9942	Sdelovaci Technika
0036-9950	Se Vuoi
0036-9969	Sea and Pacific Motor Boat see 0746-8601
0036-9977	Sea Breezes
0036-9985	Sea Cadet changed to Navy News. Sea Cadet Edition.
0037-0010	San Francisco Maritime Museum. Sea Letter see 0732-6882
0037-0029	Sea Secrets see 0897-2249
0037-0037	Sea Spray
0037-0045	Maryland-Washington-Delaware Beverage Journal changed to Maryland-Washington Beverage Journal.
0037-0053	Seaby's Coin and Medal Bulletin changed to Classical Numismatic Review.
0037-0061	Seacraft see 0005-0237
0037-007X	Seafarer
0037-0096	Seafarer's Log changed to Seafarers Log.
0037-010X	Seafood Export Journal
0037-0118	Seahorse†
0037-0126	Sea†
0037-0142	Seaman
0037-0150	Seaports and the Shipping World
0037-0169	Seara Medica Neurocirurgica
0037-0177	Seara Nova (Lisbon, 1921)
0037-0193	Search and Seizure Bulletin
0037-0207	Search: Chemical Materials & Products Division†
0037-0215	Search: Coal, Coke & Mineral Tars Division†
0037-0223	Search: CPI Marketing & Statistics Division†
0037-0231	Search: Drugs Division†
0037-024X	Search: Dyes, Pigments & Coatings Division†
0037-0258	Search: Essential Oils, Soaps & Toiletries Division†
0037-0266	Search: Fertilizers Division†
0037-0274	Search: Foodstuffs Division†
0037-0282	Search: Inorganic Chemicals Division†
0037-0290	Search (Amherst) changed to Search - Flying Saucers.
0037-0304	Search: Metals Division†
0037-0312	Search: Non-Metallic Minerals Division†
0037-0320	Search: Oils, Fats & Waxes Division†
0037-0339	Search: Organic Chemicals Division†
0037-0347	Search: Pesticides Division†
0037-0355	Search: Petroleum Division†
0037-0363	Search: Plastics & Resins Division†
0037-0371	Search: Pulp & Paper Division†
0037-038X	Search: Rubber Division†
0037-0398	Search: Textiles Division†
0037-0401	Searcher
0037-041X	Searcher
0037-0428	Seatrade changed to Seatrade Review.
0037-0436	Seattle Audubon Society Notes changed to Earthcare Northwest.
0037-0444	Seattle Business†
0037-0452	Seattle - King County Dental Society. Journal
0037-0460	Seattle Folklore Society Newsletter
0037-0479	Seattle University Spectator changed to Spectator (Seattle).
0037-0487	Seaway Review
0037-0495	Adhesion and Adhesives
0037-0509	Sechaba
0037-0517	Secoul 20
0037-0576	Second Line
0037-0584	Secondary Raw Materials see 1051-1091
0037-0592	Secret Confessions
0037-0606	Secret Place
0037-0622	The Secretary
0037-0649	Secrets
0037-0657	Securitas
0037-0665	Securities Regulation & Law Report
0037-069X	Security Systems Digest†
0037-0703	Security World changed to Security.
0037-0711	Sedia e Il Mobile†
0037-0738	Sedimentary Geology
0037-0746	Sedimentology
0037-0754	See
0037-0762	See India
0037-0770	Seed and Nursery Trader changed to Australian Horticulture.
0037-0789	Seed Trade News
0037-0797	Seed World
0037-0819	Seeing Eye Guide
0037-0827	Seek†
0037-0843	Schiffahrt International - Seekiste see 0342-491X
0037-0851	Seer (Inkprint Edition)†
0037-086X	Seeverkehr†
0037-0878	Der Seewart†
0037-0886	Seewirtschaft
0037-0894	Sefarad
0037-0916	Seglarbladet
0037-0924	Segnalatore Musicale delle Edizioni Carrara changed to Carrara.
0037-0932	Segnalazioni Cinematografiche
0037-0940	Camera di Commercio Italiana per la Gran Bretagna e il Commonwealth. Segnalazioni
0037-0959	Segnalazioni Stradali see 0391-2019
0037-0967	Segretario del Comune e della Provincia†
0037-0975	Sehen und Hoeren changed to Sehen - Hoeren - Bilden.
0037-0991	Seihin News†
0037-1009	Seihonkai
0037-1017	Seikagaku
0037-1025	Seikatsu to Kankyo
0037-1033	Seikei Geka to Saigai Geka
0037-1041	Seine et Paris†
0037-105X	Seisan Kenkyu
0037-1068	Seisan to Unpan
0037-1076	Seishin Bunseki†
0037-1084	Seishin Studies
0037-1092	Seishonen Sekijuji
0037-1106	Seismological Society of America. Bulletin
0037-1114	Seismological Society of Japan. Journal
0037-1122	Seiva
0037-1130	Sejl og Motor
0037-1149	Sekretarska Praxe
0037-1157	Selbst Ist der Mann changed to Selbst mit 1000 Tips.
0037-1173	Sele Arte†
0037-1181	Selecciones de Libros see 0211-4143
0037-119X	Selecciones de Teologia
0037-1203	Selecciones del Reader's Digest (Chilean Edition)
0037-1246	Selecciones del Reader's Digest (Iberian Edition)
0037-1262	Selecoes Zootecnicas†
0037-1297	Selected Abstracts of Non-U.S. Literature on Production and Industrial Uses of Radioisotopes†
0037-1300	University of California, Berkeley. Library School Library. Selected Additions to the Library School Library Collection.
0037-1327	Crime and Delinquency Literature see 0146-9177
0037-1335	Selected Philippine Periodical Index†
0037-1343	Selected Rand Abstracts
0037-1351	Princeton University. Industrial Relations Sections Selected References
0037-136X	Selected Water Resources Abstracts
0037-1378	Selection du Reader's Digest (Canadian-French Edition)

ISSN	Title
0037-1386	Selection du Reader's Digest (French Edition)
0037-1394	Selection du Reader's Digest (Swiss-French Edition)
0037-1408	Selection du Reader's Digest (Belgian - French Edition)
0037-1416	Belgium. Office Belge du Commerce Exterieur. Informations du Commerce Exterieur see 0770-3058
0037-1424	Selection of International Railway Documentation†
0037-1432	Selective Abstracting Service: Welding and Allied Processes see 0340-4749
0037-1459	Selektsiya i Semenovodstvo
0037-1467	Selenium and Tellurium Abstracts see 0749-7350
0037-1483	Selezione Dal Reader's Digest (Italian Edition)
0037-1491	Selezione di Picchiariello changed to Top Mix.
0037-1505	Selezione per l'Avicoltore
0037-1521	Selezione Veterinaria
0037-153X	Self
0037-1556	Self-Knowledge
0037-1564	Self-Realization
0037-1572	Self Service and Supermarketing see 0261-4251
0037-1599	Selling see 0263-4503
0037-1602	Selling Christmas Decorations†
0037-1610	Selling Sporting Goods see 1045-2087
0037-1629	Selling Today
0037-1637	Selmer Bandwagon†
0037-1688	Sel'skokhozyaistvennaya Literatura S.S.S.R.
0037-1718	Selskostopanska Tekhnika
0037-1734	Semailles†
0037-1750	Semaine Commerciale
0037-1769	Annales de Pediatrie
0037-1793	Semana
0037-1807	Semana Medica†
0037-1815	Semana Medica de Centroamerica y Panama
0037-1823	Semana Medica de Mexico
0037-184X	Semana Vitivinicola
0037-1858	Semanario Israelita
0037-1866	Sembrador
0037-1874	Semeador Baptista
0037-1882	Gemengo Textiel†
0037-1890	Sementi Elette
0037-1904	Semiconductor Diode and S C R D.A.T.A. Book see 1040-0249
0037-1912	Semigroup Forum
0037-1939	Seminar
0037-1947	Seminar†
0037-1963	Seminars in Hematology
0037-198X	Seminars in Roentgenology
0037-1998	Semiotica
0037-2005	Seemat
0037-2013	Semper Floreat changed to Semper.
0037-203X	Sempre Pronto
0037-2064	Sen-i Kogyo Zasshi
0037-2072	Sen'i Seihin Shohi Kagaku
0037-2080	S E R Tidningen changed to Maskinentreprenoeren.
0037-2099	Senales
0037-2102	Senckenbergiana Biologica
0037-2110	Senckenbergiana Lethaea
0037-2129	Sendbote des Herzens Jesu
0037-2145	Seneca Review
0037-2153	Senegal. Direction de la Statistique. Bulletin Statistique et Economique Mensuel changed to Senegal. Ministere de l'Economie et des Finances. Bulletin Statistiques et Economique.
0037-2161	Senftenegger Monatsblatt fuer Genealogie und Heraldik†
0037-217X	Sen'i Kako
0037-2188	Sen'i to Kogyo†
0037-2196	Senior Citizens News changed to S R S News.
0037-2218	The Senior Golfer
0037-2234	Senior News
0037-2242	Senior Scholastic see 0745-7065
0037-2250	Seniorscope†
0037-2269	Sent changed to Share.
0037-2277	Sentai Chii Zappo†
0037-2285	Senten Ijo see 0914-3505
0037-2315	Sentinel (Ottawa)
0037-234X	Sentinella Agricola
0037-2366	Separation Science see 0149-6395
0037-2374	Sepia†
0037-2390	Sept Jours de l'Economie Britannique changed to Semaine Economique et Financiere en Grande Bretagne.
0037-2404	Sept Jours de l'Economie Francaise†
0037-2412	Sequences
0037-2420	Sequoia (Stanford)
0037-2439	Serafico Vessillo
0037-2447	Serials Bulletin†
0037-2455	Journal of Sericultural Science of Japan
0037-2463	Series Haematologica†
0037-248X	Sermon Builder
0037-2498	Serpe
0037-2501	Serra d'Or
0037-251X	Serra-Post†
0037-2536	Serviam
0037-2544	Service†
0037-2560	Service de la Carte Geologique d'Alsace et de Lorraine. Bulletin see 0302-2692
0037-2579	Revue Technique Diesel
0037-2595	Service Economique & Financier "Secofi"
0037-2609	Service Employees changed to Service Employees Union.
0037-2617	Service News (Elkhart) changed to Harvest News.
0037-2625	Service Protestant Francais de Presse et d'Information changed to Bulletin d'Information Protestant.
0037-2633	Service Social
0037-2641	Service Social dans le Monde
0037-265X	Service Station
0037-2668	Service Station & Garage Management
0037-2676	Service Station Management and Merchandising see 0037-2668
0037-2684	Service World Reports changed to I/V 400 Chain Report.
0037-2692	Servicio Nacional Tecnico del Carton Ondulado. Revista†
0037-2706	Servicios Publicos see 0099-1694
0037-2714	Portugal. Servico de Administracao Militar. Revista Mensal changed to Portugal. Servico de Administracao Militar. Revista Bimestral.
0037-2722	Servico de Odontologia Sanitaria. Boletim changed to Equipe de Odontologia Sanitaria. Boletim.
0037-2730	Portugal. Servicos Geologicos. Comunicacoes
0037-2757	Servir Mieux
0037-2765	Servire
0037-2773	Servizio della Parola
0037-2781	Rassegna degli Archivi di Stato
0037-279X	Servizio Informazioni Avio
0037-2803	Servizio Migranti
0037-2811	Sesenta
0037-282X	Session Cases
0037-2838	Sessuologia changed to Rivista di Sessuologia.
0037-2846	Sestina Sveta v Obraze†
0037-2862	Setimo Ceu
0037-2870	Seto Marine Biological Laboratory. Publications
0037-2889	Square Dancing†
0037-2897	Settanta Anni di Calcio†
0037-2900	Settegiorni
0037-2919	Settimana del Sordomuto changed to Settimana del Sordo.
0037-2927	Settimana Medica†
0037-2935	Settimanale di Diritto e Legislazione del Lavoro†
0037-2943	Seura changed to Seura (1979).
0037-2951	Seva-Bharati
0037-2986	Seven Arts†
0037-2994	Seven Arts Digest†
0037-3001	Seven Arts Guide†
0037-301X	Seventeen
0037-3028	Seventeenth - Century News
0037-3036	73 Amateur Radio see 1052-2522
0037-3044	The Sewanee News
0037-3052	Sewanee Review
0037-3060	Sexology see 0199-7149
0037-3087	Sekstant
0037-3095	Sexual Behavior†
0037-3117	S-Gravenhage changed to Den Haag.
0037-3125	Shabistan Urdu Digest
0037-3133	Shade Tree
0037-3168	Shaftesbury Review
0037-3176	Shaheen
0037-3184	Shahpart
0037-3214	Shakespeare Newsletter
0037-3222	Shakespeare Quarterly
0037-3230	Shakhmatnyi Byulleten' changed to Express - Shakhmaty.
0037-3249	Shakhmaty v S.S.S.R.
0037-3257	Shale Shaker
0037-3265	Shalom
0037-3273	Shama
0037-3281	Shankar's Weekly†
0037-329X	Shantih†
0037-3311	Shareholder†
0037-332X	Sharkara
0037-3346	Shavian
0037-3354	Shaw Review see 0741-5842
0037-3362	Shawcover†
0037-3370	She
0037-3389	Shet
0037-3400	Sheep Breeder and Sheepman
0037-3419	Sheera Udyog†
0037-3435	Sheet Metal Industries
0037-3494	Shelfmark
0037-3508	Shell Aviation News†
0037-3516	Shell Bitumen Review
0037-3524	Shell Chronicle changed to Nutshell.
0037-3532	Shell Dealer News changed to Go!
0037-3540	Shell Hausnachrichten changed to Hausnachrichten.
0037-3559	Shell Revue†
0037-3567	Shell Erdoel-Informationen changed to Erdoel.
0037-3575	Shellfish Situation and Outlook see 0098-8014
0037-3583	Shenandoah: The Washington and Lee University Review
0037-3605	Shepherd's Call†
0037-3621	Sherlock Holmes Journal
0037-3648	Shetkari
0037-3656	Sheviley Hahinuch†
0037-3664	Shichokaku Kyoiku
0037-3672	Shield
0037-3680	Shikoku Entomological Society. Transactions
0037-3699	Shikoku Igaku Zasshi
0037-3702	Shikoku National Agricultural Experiment Station. Bulletin
0037-3710	Shika Gakuho
0037-3729	Shilo Stag
0037-3737	Shin Kaki
0037-3745	Shin Nippon Denki Gihot
0037-3788	Shinkan News for Readers
0037-3796	Shinkei Kagaku
0037-3818	Shinshu University. Faculty of Engineering. Journal
0037-3826	Shinshu Medical Journal
0037-3842	Ship-Shape†
0037-3850	Shipbuilding and Shipping Record see 0306-347X
0037-3885	Shipping and Port Review†
0037-3893	Shipping Digest
0037-3907	Shipping Executive
0037-3915	Shipping Gazette
0037-3923	Shipping Register and Shipbuilder
0037-3931	Shipping World & Shipbuilder
0037-394X	Ships Monthly
0037-3958	Shipyard Review
0037-3966	Shire & Municipal Record†
0037-3982	Shiryo Gaido†
0037-3990	Shitai Fujiyu Kyoiku
0037-4008	Shituf
0037-4024	Shkola i Proizvodstvo
0037-4032	Shoe and Leather Journal see 0705-1433
0037-4040	Shoe and Leather News
0037-4067	Shoe Service Wholesaler†
0037-4075	Shoe Workers' Journal†
0037-4083	Shoes on Parade
0037-4091	Shokubutsu Boeki
0037-4105	Shokuhin To Kagaku
0037-4113	Shoni Hoken Kenkyu
0037-4121	Shonika
0037-413X	Shurote
0037-4148	Shooting Industry
0037-4156	Shooting Sport-Tir Sportif-Tiro Deportivo-Schiess-Sport changed to U I T Journal.
0037-4164	Shooting Times and Country Magazine
0037-4172	Shop Equipment & Shopfitting News
0037-4180	Shop Fitting and Equipment Monitor†
0037-4199	Shop Property†
0037-4202	Shopfitting International†
0037-4210	Shopping Center Directory
0037-4229	Shopping Guide changed to Home Services.
0037-4237	Shore and Beach
0037-4245	Short's Story
0037-4253	Short-Term Economic Survey of Principal Enterprises in Japan see 0387-0642
0037-4261	Short Wave Magazine
0037-427X	Shorthorn News
0037-4288	Shorthorn World†
0037-430X	Show-Business†
0037-4318	Show Business
0037-4326	Show-Me Libraries
0037-4334	Show-Me Missouri Legionnaire
0037-4342	Showa Medical Association. Journal
0037-4350	Showcase
0037-4377	Shoyakugaku Zasshi
0037-4385	Shreveport Magazine see 0744-3064
0037-4393	Shropshire Magazine
0037-4407	Shubyo to Engei
0037-4415	Shui Hsing Tsa Chih
0037-4423	Shujutsu
0037-4431	Shveinaya Promyshlennost'
0037-444X	Si De Ka Magazine
0037-4466	Siberian Mathematical Journal
0037-4474	Sibirskii Matematicheskii Zhurnal
0037-4482	Sibylle
0037-4504	Sicher ist Sicher
0037-4512	Sichere Arbeit
0037-4520	Sicherheit Bergbau, Energiewirtschaft, Metallurgie changed to Sicherheit Bergbau, Energiewirtschaft, Geologie, Metallurgie.
0037-4539	Sicherheit Zuerst
0037-4547	Sicherheitstechniker-Korrespondenz†
0037-4563	Sicilia
0037-4571	Sicilia Archeologica
0037-458X	Siculorum Gymnasium
0037-4598	Sicurezza Sociale†
0037-4601	Sidemount Reporter
0037-461X	7 Tage
0037-4628	Siecle a Mains
0037-4652	Siemens Data Report changed to Siemens-Magazin COM.
0037-4660	Siemens Electromedica see 0340-5389
0037-4679	Siemens Electronic Components Bulletin see 0173-1726
0037-4687	Elektrodienst†
0037-4695	Siemens Informationen Fernsprech-Vermittlungstechnik see 0344-4724
0037-4725	Sierra Club Bulletin see 0161-7362
0037-4733	Sierra Leone
0037-4741	Sierra Leone. Central Statistics Office. Quarterly Statistical Bulletin†
0037-475X	Sierra Leone Studies†
0037-4768	Sierra Leone Trade Journal
0037-4784	Siete Dias Ilustrados
0037-4792	Sifriya Laam
0037-4806	Sight and Sound
0037-4814	Sight & Sound Marketing
0037-4822	Sightsaving Review see 0735-5688
0037-4830	Sightlines (Niles)
0037-4849	Sigma†
0037-4857	Sigma issued with 0014-4932

ISSN INDEX 5447

ISSN	Title
0037-4857	Sigma
0037-4865	Sigma-T *changed to* Metamorph.
0037-4873	Sign (Union City)†
0037-4903	Signat
0037-4911	Signal†
0037-492X	Signal
0037-4938	Signal (Fairfax)
0037-4946	Signal (Upminster)†
0037-4954	Signal
0037-4970	Signal International
0037-4997	Signal und Draht
0037-5004	Signal und Schiene *see* 0037-4997
0037-5012	Signal 8-2
0037-5020	Signalman's Journal
0037-5039	Signature *changed to* Conde Nast Traveler.
0037-5055	Signs of the Times
0037-5063	Signs of the Times (Cincinnati)
0037-5071	Signs of the Times†
0037-508X	Sigurnost u Pogonu *see* 0350-6886
0037-5098	Siipikarja
0037-5101	Sika
0037-511X	Sikh Courier *changed to* Sikh Courier International.
0037-5128	Sikh Review
0037-5136	Sikio *changed to* Kenrail.
0037-5136	Sikio *changed to* Tanzania Railways Corporation. Habari za Reli.
0037-5144	Sikkimt
0037-5152	Sikorsky News
0037-5160	Siksha - O - Sahitya
0037-5179	Silarus
0037-5187	Silent Advocate
0037-5195	Silent Messenger
0037-5209	Silent Picture†
0037-5217	Silhouette
0037-5225	Silicates Industriels
0037-5233	Silikattechnik
0037-5241	Silikaty
0037-525X	Silk and Rayon Industries of India *see* 0377-7537
0037-5268	Silk Screen
0037-5276	Silliman Christian Leader†
0037-5284	Silliman Journal
0037-5292	Silnicni Doprava *see* 0322-7154
0037-5306	Silo†
0037-5314	Silpakon
0037-5322	Sil's'ke Budivnytstvo
0037-5330	Silva Fennica
0037-5349	Silvae Genetica
0037-5357	Silver-Rama *see* 0899-6105
0037-5365	Silver Screen†
0037-5373	Silvicultura†
0037-539X	Simian
0037-5403	Simiente
0037-5411	Simiolus
0037-542X	Simmenthal Club†
0037-5446	Simon Fraser University. Library. Information Bulletin†
0037-5454	Simon Stevin
0037-5462	Simon van der Stel Foundation. Bulletin *changed to* Restorica.
0037-5470	Simon's Town Historical Society Bulletin
0037-5497	Simulation (San Diego)
0037-5500	Simulation and Games *see* 1046-8781
0037-5519	Simulation Councils Proceedings *see* 0735-9276
0037-5527	Sin Nombre†
0037-5535	Sinai Hospital of Detroit. Bulletin
0037-5543	Sindacato Moderno
0037-556X	Sindicato Nacional de la Pesca Boletin de Informacion
0037-5578	Sindicato Nacional Textil. Boletin de Informacion
0037-5594	Sinfonian Newsletter *see* 8750-5347
0037-5608	Sinfonie Scacchistiche
0037-5616	Sinformation
0037-5624	Sing Out!
0037-5632	Singabout; Journal of Australian Folksong *see* 0157-3381
0037-5640	Singapore. Department of Statistics. Monthly Digest of Statistics.
0037-5659	Singapore International Chamber of Commerce. Economic Bulletin
0037-5675	Singapore Medical Journal
0037-5683	Singapore Paediatric Society. Journal†
0037-5705	Singapore Trade and Industry *see* 0129-2951
0037-5713	Singapore Travel News *see* 0129-5020
0037-5721	Singende Kirche
0037-573X	Singer Showcase *see* 0026-816X
0037-5748	Single Parent
0037-5756	Sinn und Form
0037-5764	Sino Azul
0037-5772	Sintese Politica, Economica e Social *see* 0103-4332
0037-5780	Sintesi Economica†
0037-5799	Sintesis Informativa Economica y Financiera
0037-5802	Sintesis *changed to* Sintesis - A L A D I.
0037-5810	Sion
0037-5829	Sioux City Journal Farm Weekly†
0037-5837	Sipapu
0037-5853	Siren†
0037-5861	Standard *changed to* Maanadens Standard.
0037-5888	Sistematica
0037-5896	Sistemi e Automazione *changed to* Sistemi e Impresa.
0037-590X	Sisters Today
0037-5926	Situation Economique *see* 0242-5815
0037-5934	Situation in Argentina†
0037-5942	Gesellschaft Naturforschender Freunde zu Berlin. Sitzungsberichte. Neue Folge
0037-5950	Sivam
0037-5969	Seventies *changed to* Eighties.
0037-5985	S J-Nytt
0037-5993	Sjaloom *changed to* Achtergrond.
0037-6000	Sjoesport
0037-6019	Sjukgymnasten
0037-6027	Tidskrift foer Sveriges Sjukskoeterskort
0037-6035	Skagerak
0037-6043	Skakbladet
0037-6051	Skakelblad *see* 0259-1871
0037-606X	Skandinavisk Aktuarientidskrift *see* 0346-1238
0037-6086	Skandinavisk Motor Journal *changed to* Motor-Journalen Bilen.
0037-6094	Faerg och Lack Scandinavia
0037-6108	Skandinaviska Banken. Quarterly Review *see* 0347-3139
0037-6124	Skate†
0037-6132	Skating
0037-6140	Skeet Shooting Review
0037-6159	Ski
0037-6167	Ski
0037-6175	Ski Area Management
0037-6191	Ski Business†
0037-6205	Helice *see* 0762-7378
0037-6213	Ski Racing
0037-6221	Ski Runner
0037-623X	Ski - Schweizer Skisport
0037-6248	Skier (Brattleboro)†
0037-6256	Skiers Gazette *changed to* Mountain Gazette.
0037-6264	Skiing
0037-6299	Skiing Trade News
0037-6310	Ringspoot
0037-6329	Skillings' Mining Review
0037-6337	Skin & Allergy News
0037-6345	Skin Diver Magazine
0037-6361	Skipsteknikk *changed to* Skipsrevyen.
0037-637X	Sklar a Keramik
0037-6388	Sko-Magasinet *see* 0901-0114
0037-6396	Skogeieren
0037-640X	Skogen
0037-6418	S L A-Tidskriften†
0037-6426	Skogsaegaren†
0037-6442	Skol Vreizh- l'Ecole Bretonne *see* 0755-8848
0037-6450	Skola Danas
0037-6469	Skolans Artikelservice
0037-6477	Barn och Kultur
0037-6485	Skolefilm†
0037-6493	Skolepsychologi *see* 0906-219X
0037-6515	Skolledaren
0037-6523	Skolska Televizija
0037-6531	Skolske Novine
0037-654X	Skolski Vjesnik
0037-6558	Skolta Mondo†
0037-6566	Skolvaerlden
0037-6574	Skotoidetaljisten *changed to* SKO.
0037-6582	Skov og So
0037-6590	Skraeddarmaestaren *see* 0346-1386
0037-6604	Sky and Telescope
0037-6620	Skylights†
0037-6647	Skyscraper Management *see* 0892-7847
0037-6663	Skytte-bladet
0037-6671	Skyways
0037-668X	Slaboproudy Obzor
0037-6698	De Slager
0037-6701	Slagerij *changed to* Misset's Vlees en Vleeswaren.
0037-671X	Slagersambacht *changed to* Ambacht & Industrie.
0037-6736	Slavia
0037-6744	Slavia Orientalis
0037-6752	Slavic and East European Journal
0037-6779	Slavic Review
0037-6787	Slavica Slovaca
0037-6795	Slavonic and East European Review
0037-6809	Sleep Bulletin *changed to* Sleep Bulletin (1978).
0037-6817	Sleep-Learning Association. Journal
0037-6825	Slevarenstvi
0037-6833	Slezsky Sbornik
0037-6841	Drinks
0037-685X	Slingervel
0037-6868	Sloboda
0037-6876	Sloboda
0037-6884	Slobodna Rec
0037-6892	Sloejd och Ton†
0037-6906	Slovenska Chemicka Spolocnost. Chemicke Zvesti
0037-6914	Slovak Press Digest
0037-6922	Slovansky Prehled
0037-6930	Slovenska Akademia Vied. Biologicke Prace
0037-6949	Slovenska Archeologia
0037-6957	Slovenska Drzava
0037-6965	Slovenska Hudba†
0037-6973	Slovenska Literatura
0037-6981	Slovenska Rec
0037-699X	Slovenske Divadlo
0037-7007	Slovenske Pohlady na Literaturu a Umenie
0037-7015	Slovensky Hlast
0037-7023	Slovensky Narodopis
0037-7031	Slovo a Slovesnost
0037-704X	Slow Learning Child *changed to* International Journal of Disability, Development and Education.
0037-7058	Slowakei
0037-7074	Sluzba Bozja
0037-7082	Sluzba Lidu
0037-7104	Sluzbene Novine Opcine Karlovac
0037-7112	Opcina Podravska Slatina. Sluzbeni Glasnik
0037-7120	Sluzbeni Glasnik Opcine Rovinj
0037-7147	Sluzben Vesnik na Socijalisticka Republika Makedonija
0037-7155	Sluzbeni Vjesnik Opcine Buje, Novigrad i Umag
0037-7163	Sluzbeni Vjesnik Opcine Krizevci
0037-7171	Smaaskipfart *changed to* Skipsrevyen.
0037-718X	Small Boat *changed to* Yacht and Boat Owner.
0037-7198	Voice of Small Business *changed to* Small Business U S A.
0037-7201	Small Offset Printing *see* 0263-4384
0037-721X	Small Pond Magazine of Literature
0037-7228	Small Press Review
0037-7252	Small Trader and Wholesaler *changed to* Trader.
0037-7260	Small World
0037-7279	Volkswagen's World *changed to* Volkswagen.
0037-7287	Smit-las *changed to* Smitweld Reportage.
0037-7295	Holecpost
0037-7317	Smith College Studies in Social Work
0037-7325	Smith's Trade News *changed to* C T N.
0037-7333	Smithsonian
0037-7341	Smithsonian Torch *changed to* Torch (Washington).
0037-735X	Smog
0037-7368	Smokeless Air *see* 0300-5143
0037-7376	Smuffeltjet
0037-7406	Snack Food
0037-7414	Snack Foods Merchandiser *see* 0026-7805
0037-7449	Sneha Sandesh†
0037-7457	Snips
0037-7473	Snowy Egret
0037-7481	Soap and Chemical Specialties *see* 0091-1372
0037-749X	Soap, Perfumery and Cosmetics
0037-7503	Soaring
0037-7511	Slaski Kwartalnik Historyczny "Sobotka"
0037-752X	Sobre Educacion Superior†
0037-7538	Soccer News†
0037-7546	Soccer Start
0037-7554	Soccer World
0037-7562	Soccorso Perpetuo di Maria
0037-7589	Sociaal-Economische Raad. Informatie-en Documentatie Bulletin *see* 0920-4849
0037-7597	Sociaal-Economische Wetgeving *changed to* Tijdschrift voor Europees en Economisch Recht.
0037-7600	Sociaal Maandblad Arbeid
0037-7619	Socialnytt *changed to* Vael & Ve.
0037-7627	Social Action
0037-7635	Social Action *see* 0164-5528
0037-7643	Social and Economic Administration *see* 0144-5596
0037-7651	Social and Economic Studies
0037-766X	Social Biology
0037-7678	Social Casework *see* 1044-3894
0037-7686	Social Compass
0037-7694	Social Crediter
0037-7708	Social Debatt i Tidningar och Tidskrifter *see* 0349-9375
0037-7716	Social Defence
0037-7724	Social Education
0037-7732	Social Forces
0037-7740	Social Health News *changed to* V D News.
0037-7759	Social Horizon *changed to* Journal of Social Development.
0037-7767	Social Justice Review
0037-7775	Washington Bulletin *see* 0149-2578
0037-7783	Social Policy
0037-7791	Social Problems
0037-7805	Church and Society
0037-7813	Social Psychiatry *see* 0933-7954
0037-783X	Social Research
0037-7848	Social Science *see* 0278-2308
0037-7864	Social Sciences Information - Information sur les Sciences Sociales *see* 0539-0184
0037-7872	Social Science Record
0037-7880	Social Science Reporter and Public Relations Research Review†
0037-7899	Social Sciences and Humanities Index *see* 0094-4920
0037-7899	Social Sciences and Humanities Index *see* 0095-5981
0037-7902	Social Security Abstracts†
0037-7910	Social Security Bulletin
0037-7929	Social Security Rulings on Federal Old-Age, Survivors, Disability and Health Insurance, Supplemental Security Income and Miners Benefits *changed to* Social Security Rulings, Acquiescence Rulings on Federal Old-Age, Survivors, Disability, Supplemental Security Income and Black Lung Benefits.
0037-7937	Social Service†
0037-7945	Social Service Outlook†
0037-7953	Social Service Quarterly†
0037-7961	Social Service Review

5448 ISSN INDEX

0037-797X Social Services in Wisconsin†

0037-7996 Social Studies

0037-8003 Social Studies Teacher†

0037-8011 Social Survey

0037-802X Social Theory and Practice

0037-8038 Social Welfare

0037-8046 Social Work

0037-8054 Social Work

0037-8062 Social Work Education Reporter

0037-8070 Social Work Today

0037-8089 Social Worker

0037-8097 Sociale Wetenschappen

0037-8100 Socialfoerfattningar

0037-8127 Socialisme

0037-8135 Socialisme en Democratie *changed to* Christen Democratische Verkenningen.

0037-8143 Socialismo Democratico *changed to* Umanita.

0037-8151 Socialismo Settanta†

0037-816X Socialist Action†

0037-8178 Socialist Commentary†

0037-8186 Socialist Digest

0037-8194 Socialist Forum

0037-8208 Socialist India

0037-8216 Sotsialisticheskii Trud

0037-8224 Socialist Leader *see* 0951-2187

0037-8232 Socialist Monitor†

0037-8240 Socialist Revolution *see* 0161-1801

0037-8259 Socialist Standard

0037-8275 Socialista *changed to* Pensare Faenza.

0037-8283 Socialista†

0037-8291 Socialisticka Skola

0037-8305 Socialisticka Zakonnost *changed to* Pravo a Zakonnost.

0037-8313 Socialisticke Zemedelstvi

0037-8321 Socialisticky Obchod

0037-833X Socialmedicinsk Tidskrift

0037-8364 Sociedad Americana de Oftalmologia y Optometria. Archivos

0037-8372 Sociedad Antioquena de Ingenieros. Boletin *changed to* Noti S A I.

0037-8380 Sociedad Argentina de Biologia. Revista†

0037-8402 Sociedad Bolivariana de Venezuela. Revista

0037-8410 Sociedad Canaria de Pediatria. Boletin†

0037-8429 Sociedad Castellano-Astur-Leonosa de Pediatria. Boletin *changed to* Pediatria. Boletin.

0037-8437 Sociedad Cientifica Argentina. Anales

0037-8453 Sociedad Colombiana de Ortodoncia. Revista

0037-8461 Sociedad Colombiana de Quimicos Farmaceuticos. Boletin

0037-847X Sociedad Cubana de Historia de la Medicina. Revista†

0037-8488 Sociedad Cubana de Ingenieros. Revista†

0037-8496 Sociedad de Bibliotecarios de Puerto Rico. Boletin†

0037-850X Sociedad de Biologiá de Concepcion. Boletin

0037-8518 Sociedad de Ciencias Naturales la Salle. Memoria

0037-8526 Sociedad de Cirugia de Rosario. Boletines†

0037-8534 Sociedad de Medicina Veterinaria de Chile. Revista

0037-8550 Sociedad Espanola de Ceramica. Boletin *changed to* Sociedad Espanola de Ceramica y Vidrio. Boletin.

0037-8569 Sociedad Espanola de Socorros Mutuos y Beneficencia. Boletin

0037-8577 Sociedad Geografica de Colombia. Boletin

0037-8585 Sociedad Geografica de Lima, Peru. Boletin

0037-8607 Gazeta de Baixada

0037-8615 Sociedad Matematica Mexicana. Boletin

0037-8623 Sociedad Quimica del Peru. Boletin

0037-8631 Sociedad Rural Argentina. Anales

0037-864X Sociedad Rural Argentina. Boletin

0037-8658 Sociedad Vasco-Navarra de Pediatria. Boletin

0037-8666 Sociedade Brasileira de Estudos sobre Discos Voadores. Boletim

0037-8674 Sociedade Brasileira de Geografia. Boletim

0037-8682 Sociedade Brasileira de Medicina Tropical. Revista

0037-8712 Sociedade Paranaense de Matematica. Boletim

0037-8720 Societa Astronomica Italiana. Memorie

0037-8739 Societa di Studi Valdesi. Bollettino

0037-8747 Societa Entomologica Italiana. Bollettino e Memorie *see* 0373-3491

0037-8755 Societa Geografica Italiana. Bollettino

0037-8763 Societa Geologica Italiana. Bollettino e Memorie *changed to* Societa Geologica Italiana. Bollettino, Memorie e Rendiconti.

0037-8771 Societa Italiana di Biologia Sperimentale. Bollettino

0037-878X Societa Italiana di Cardiologia. Bollettino *changed to* Cardiologia.

0037-8801 Societa Italiana di Fisica. Bollettino *see* 0393-4578

0037-8828 Rendiconti della Societa Italiana di Mineralogie e Petrologia *see* 0935-1221

0037-8844 Societa Italiana di Scienze Naturali e del Museo Civico di Storia Naturale. Atti

0037-8852 Societa Medica Chirurgica, Cremona. Bollettino

0037-8879 Societas†

0037-8887 Archivum Historicum Societatis Iesu

0037-8895 Societe Archeologique, Historique, Litteraire & Scientifique du Gers. Bulletin

0037-8909 Societe Belge de Geologie, de Paleontologie et d'Hydrologie. Bulletin *see* 0772-9464

0037-8917 Societe Belge de Photogrammetrie. Bulletin Trimestriel *see* 0771-7873

0037-8925 Societe Belge d'Etudes Geographiques. Bulletin/Belgische Vereniging voor Aardrijkskundige Studies. Tijdschrift

0037-8933 Societe Belge d'Etudes Napoleoniennes. Bulletin†

0037-8941 Societe Botanique de France. Bulletin *see* 0181-1797

0037-895X Societe Centrale d'Education et d'Assistance pour les Sourds-Muets en France. Bulletin d'Information†

0037-8968 Societe Chimique de France. Bulletin

0037-8984 Societe d'Anthropologie de Paris. Bulletins & Memoires

0037-8992 Bulletin d'Archeologie et de Statistique de la Drome *see* 0398-0022

0037-900X Societe d'Astronomie Populaire de Toulouse. Bulletin Mensuel *see* 0154-4101

0037-9018 Societe de Biogeographie. Compte Rendu *changed to* Societe de Biogeographie. Compte Rendu des Seances.

0037-9026 Societe de Biologie et de ses Filiales. Comptes Rendus des Seances

0037-9034 Societe de Botanique du Nord de la France. Bulletin

0037-9042 Societe de Chimie Biologique. Bulletin *see* 0300-9084

0037-9050 Societe de l'Histoire du Protestantisme Francais. Bulletin

0037-9069 Societe de Linguistique de Paris. Bulletin

0037-9077 Societe de Mythologie Francaise Bulletin

0037-9085 Societe de Pathologie Exotique et de ses Filiales. Bulletin

0037-9093 Societe de Pharmacie de Bordeaux. Bulletin

0037-9107 Societe de Pharmacie de Lyon. Bulletin des Travaux

0037-9115 Societe de Pharmacie de Montpellier. Travaux†

0037-9123 Societe de Pharmacie de Nancy. Bulletin *see* 0301-0635

0037-9131 Societe de Pharmacie de Strasbourg. Bulletin

0037-914X Societe de Statistique de Paris. Journal *changed to* Societe de Statistique de Paris. Journal.

0037-9158 Societe d'Emulation du Bourbonnais. Bulletin

0037-9166 Societe des Africanistes. Journal *see* 0399-0346

0037-9174 Societe des Americanistes. Journal

0037-9182 Societe des Amis de Montaigne. Bulletin

0037-9190 Societe des Antiquaires de l'Ouest. Bulletin

0037-9204 Societe des Antiquaires de Picardie. Quarterly Bulletin

0037-9212 Revue Francaise d'Histoire du Livre

0037-9220 Societe des Chirurgiens de Paris. Bulletin et Memoires†

0037-9247 Societe des Sciences Medicales du Grand-Duche de Luxembourg. Bulletin

0037-9255 Societe des Sciences Naturelles et Physiques du Maroc. Bulletin

0037-9263 Etudes et Expansion *see* 0773-0543

0037-9271 Societe Entomologique de France. Annales

0037-9301 Societe Entomologique du Quebec. Annales *see* 0825-1215

0037-931X Societe Francaise de Ceramique. Bulletin. *changed to* Industrie Ceramique.

0037-9336 Societe Francaise de Mycologie Medicale. Bulletin

0037-9344 Societe Francaise de Numismatique. Bulletin

0037-9352 Societe Francaise de Philosophie. Bulletin

0037-9360 Societe Francaise de Physique. Bulletin

0037-9379 Societe Francaise d'Egyptologie. Bulletin

0037-9387 Societe Genealogique Canadienne-Francaise. Memoires

0037-9395 Societe Geologique de Belgique. Annales

0037-9409 Societe Geologique de France. Bulletin

0037-9417 Societe Geologique de France. Compte Rendu Sommaire des Seances *see* 0037-9409

0037-9425 Societe Historique et Archeologique du Perigord. Bulletin

0037-9441 Societe Industrielle de Mulhouse. Bulletin

0037-945X Societe Internationale de Chirurgie. Bulletin *see* 0364-2313

0037-9468 Societe Internationale de Psycho-Prophylaxie Obstetricale. Bulletin Officiel *changed to* Societe Francaise de Psycho-Prophylaxie Obstetricale. Bulletin Officiel.

0037-9476 Societe Mathematique de Belgique. Bulletin

0037-9484 Societe de Mathematique de France. Bulletin *changed to* Societe Mathematique de France. Bulletin et Memoires.

0037-9492 Societe Medico-Chirurgicale des Hopitaux et Formations Sanitaires des Armees. Bulletin

0037-9506 Societe Paul Claudel. Bulletin

0037-9514 Societe Prehistorique Francaise. Bulletin

0037-9522 Societe Royale Belge de Gynecologie et d'Obstetrique. Bulletin

0037-9530 Societe Royale Belge des Electriciens. Bulletin

0037-9549 Societe Royale Belge des Ingenieurs et des Industriels. Revue†

0037-9557 Societe Royale de Botanique de Belgique. Bulletin

0037-9565 Societe Royale des Sciences de Liege. Bulletin

0037-9573 Societe Royale Forestiere de Belgique. Bulletin - Koninklijke Belgische Bosbouwmaatschappij. Tydschrift *changed to* Silva Belgica.

0037-9581 Societe Scientifique de Bretagne. Bulletin

0037-959X Societe Scientifique de Bruxelles. Annales. Sciences Mathematiques, Astronomiques et Physiques†

0037-9603 Societe Vaudoise des Sciences Naturelles. Bulletin

0037-9611 Societe Vaudoise des Sciences Naturelles. Memoires

0037-962X Societe Zoologique de France. Bulletin.

0037-9646 Bulletin des Societes Chimiques Belges

0037-9662 Society and Culture

0037-9670 Society and Leisure†

0037-9689 Current Titles in Electrochemistry

0037-9697 Society for Analytical Chemistry. Proceedings *see* 0144-557X

0037-9700 Society for Army Historical Research. Journal

0037-9719 S C U P News and Journal *see* 0736-0983

0037-9727 Society for Experimental Biology and Medicine. Proceedings

0037-9735 Society for Historical Archaeology Newsletter

0037-9743 Society for Italic Handwriting. Journal

0037-9751 Society for Psychical Research. Journal

0037-976X Society for Research in Child Development. Monographs

0037-9778 Society for the Bibliography of Natural History. Journal *see* 0260-9541

0037-9786 Society for the Study of State Governments. Journal

0037-9794 Society of Actuaries. Transactions (General)

0037-9808 Society of Architectural Historians. Journal

0037-9816 Society of Archivists. Journal

0037-9824 Society of Chartered Property and Casualty Underwriters. Annals *see* 0162-2706

0037-9832 Society of Cosmetic Chemists. Journal

0037-9840 Society of Dairy Technology. Journal

0037-9859 Society of Dyers and Colourists. Journal

0037-9867 Society of Engineers. Journal and Transactions *changed to* Engineering World.

0037-9875 Society of Fiber Science and Technology, Japan. Journal

0037-9883 Society of Film & Television Arts. Journal†

0037-9905 Society of Health of Nigeria. Journal

0037-9913 Society of Independent Professional Earth Scientists. Newsletter

0037-9921 Society of Leather Trades' Chemists. Journal *see* 0144-0322

0037-993X Society of Malawi Journal

0037-9948 Society of Medalists. News Bulletin†

0037-9956 Society of Medical Friends of Wine. Bulletin

0037-9964 Society of Mining Engineers of A I M E. Transactions†

0037-9972 Society of Occupational Medicine Transactions *changed to* Occupational Medicine.

0038-0008 Society of Professional Investigators. Bulletin

0038-0016 Society of Public Teachers of Law Journal *see* 0261-3875

0038-0024 Society of Research Administrators. Journal

0038-0032 Society of Rheology. Transactions *see* 0148-6055

0038-0059 Society of Photographic Science and Technology of Japan. Bulletin *changed to* Society of Photographic Science and Technology of Japan. Journal.

0038-0067 Society of Women Engineers. Newsletter *see* 0272-7838

0038-0075 Society Page

0038-0091 Socijalna Politika

0038-0105 Socijalni Rad

0038-0113 Socio-Economic History

ISSN

0038-0121 Socio-Economic Planning Sciences
0038-013X Sociocom Directory of Positions†
0038-0148 Sociologia†
0038-0156 Sociologia (Rome)
0038-0164 Sociologia Internationalis
0038-0172 Sociologia Neerlandica *changed to* Netherlands Journal of Social Sciences.
0038-0180 Sociologia Religiosa†
0038-0199 Sociologia Ruralis
0038-0202 Sociological Abstracts
0038-0210 S A
0038-0229 Sociological Bulletin
0038-0237 Sociological Focus
0038-0245 Sociological Inquiry
0038-0253 Sociological Quarterly
0038-0261 Sociological Review
0038-027X Sociological Symposium *see* 0273-2173
0038-0288 Sociologicky Casopis
0038-0296 Sociologie du Travail
0038-030X Sociologie et Societes
0038-0318 Sociologija
0038-0326 Sociologija Sela
0038-0334 Sociologische Gids
0038-0342 Sociologisk Forskning
0038-0350 Sociologiske Meddelelser *see* 0901-0025
0038-0369 Sociologist
0038-0377 Sociologus
0038-0385 Sociology
0038-0393 Sociology and Social Research
0038-0407 Sociology of Education
0038-0415 Sociology of Education Abstracts
0038-0431 Sociometry *see* 0190-2725
0038-044X Socionomen *see* 0283-1910
0038-0458 Socioscoop *changed to* De Bijstaander.
0038-0466 Socker Handlingar†
0038-0474 Sodobna Pedagogika
0038-0482 Sodobnost
0038-0490 Soedra Afrika. Informations Bulletin *see* 0346-9158
0038-0504 Soekaren
0038-0512 Soendags - B.T. *changed to* Ugemagasinet Soendag.
0038-0520 Soefart
0038-0547 Soft Drink Industry *see* 0148-6187
0038-0555 Soft Drink "Insider" Newsletter *see* 1040-3736
0038-0571 Soft Drinks *see* 0098-2318
0038-058X Soft Drinks Trade Journal *changed to* Soft Drinks Managment International.
0038-0598 Soft Serve & Drive-in Field†
0038-061X Software Age†
0038-0628 Software Central†
0038-0636 Software Digest (Annandale) *changed to* Software Industry Report.
0038-0644 Software: Practice & Experience
0038-0652 Software World
0038-0660 Sogo Kango
0038-0687 Soil & Health Journal
0038-0695 Soil and Water†
0038-0709 Soil Association. Journal *see* 0954-1098
0038-0717 Soil Biology & Biochemistry
0038-0741 Soil Mechanics and Foundation Engineering
0038-075X Soil Science
0038-0768 Soil Science and Plant Nutrition
0038-0776 Soil Science Society of America. Proceedings *see* 0361-5995
0038-0784 Soil Sense†
0038-0792 Soils and Fertilizers
0038-0806 Soils & Foundations
0038-0814 Soins
0038-0822 Sokol Polski
0038-0830 Sokuchi Gakkaishi
0038-0849 El Sol
0038-0857 Sol de Uruapan
0038-0865 Sol Institiae *changed to* Utrechts Universiteitsblad.
0038-0881 Solaire Reflexen *changed to* Utrechts Universiteitsblad.
0038-0903 Solanus
0038-092X Solar Energy
0038-0938 Solar Physics
0038-0946 Solar System Research
0038-0954 Soldado Argentino
0038-0962 Der Soldat
0038-0989 Soldat und Technik
0038-0997 Soldaten Kurier†
0038-1012 Soleil
0038-1039 Solia
0038-1047 Solicitors' Journal
0038-1055 Solid Fuel
0038-1063 Solid-Liquid Flow Abstracts
0038-108X Solid State Abstracts *see* 0896-5900
0038-1098 Solid State Communications
0038-1101 Solid-State Electronics
0038-111X Solid State Technology
0038-1128 Solid Waste Report
0038-1136 Solid Wastes Management-Refuse Removal Journal *see* 0745-6921
0038-1152 Solidarity (Hicksville)
0038-1160 Solidarity
0038-1187 Solon
0038-1217 Sols-Soils†
0038-1241 Solution *changed to* Amplifier.
0038-125X Solvent Extraction Reviews†
0038-1268 Somali National Bank. Bulletin *changed to* Central Bank of Somalia. Bulletin.
0038-1276 Somborske Novine
0038-1284 Some/Thing†
0038-1292 Somenit
0038-1314 Somerset Farmer
0038-1322 Somerset Gazette†
0038-1349 Something Else Newsletter†
0038-1357 Sonderschule
0038-1365 Song Hits *changed to* Song Hits' Heartbreakers.
0038-1373 Songwriter's Review†
0038-1381 Sonjog
0038-139X Sonntagspost
0038-1411 Sonntag
0038-1438 Sonorum Speculum *changed to* Key Notes.
0038-1446 Sons of Italy News
0038-1454 Sons of Italy Times
0038-1462 Sons of Norway Viking
0038-1489 Gosudarstvennyi Astronomicheskii Institut im. P.K. Shternberga. Soobshcheniya
0038-1500 Sooner L P G Times
0038-1519 Sooner State Press†
0038-1527 Sophia
0038-1551 Sorby Natural History Society Newsletter
0038-156X Sorrisi e Canzoni T V (Milan)
0038-1578 Japanese Society of Phycology. Bulletin *changed to* Japanese Journal of Phycology.
0038-1586 Japan Society for Technology of Plasticity. Journal
0038-1594 Sosiaalinen Aikakauskirja
0038-1608 Sosial Trygd
0038-1616 Sosialistinen Aikakauslehti
0038-1624 Sosialoekonomen
0038-1632 Sosialt Arbeid *changed to* Helse og Sosial Forum.
0038-1659 Sot la Nape
0038-1667 Soteria
0038-1675 Sotilasaikakauslehti
0038-1691 Sotsialisticheskaya Zakonnost'
0038-1705 Sotsialistychna Kul'tura
0038-1713 Sotsial'noe Obespechenie
0038-173X Soudage et Techniques Connexes
0038-1748 Souder
0038-1756 Soul
0038-1764 Soul Force†
0038-1799 Sound *see* 0300-5364
0038-1802 Sound & Image†
0038-1810 Sound and Vibration
0038-1829 Sound and Vision *see* 0305-3601
0038-1837 Sound Ideas *see* 0888-0387
0038-1845 Sound & Communications
0038-1853 Soundings (Santa Barbara)
0038-1861 Soundings (Knoxville)
0038-187X Sounds of Truth and Tradition
0038-1896 Source
0038-190X SourceBook for Interior Planning and Design
0038-1934 South Africa. Department of Agricultural Technical Services. Science Bulletins *changed to* South Africa. Department of Agriculture. Science Bulletins.
0038-1942 South Africa. Weather Bureau. Monthly Weather Report
0038-1969 South African Archaeological Bulletin
0038-1977 South African Architectural Record *changed to* Architecture S.A. (Johannesburg).
0038-1985 South African Association for the Advancement of Science. Newsletter†
0038-1993 South African Bakery and Confectionery Review
0038-2000 South African Banker
0038-2019 South African Bee Journal
0038-2027 South African Builder
0038-2035 S.A. Building and Decorating Materials *changed to* Building Products News.
0038-2043 South African Cancer Bulletin†
0038-206X South African Chartered Accountant - Suid-Afrikaanse Geoktrooieerde Rekenmeester *see* 0258-7254
0038-2078 South African Chemical Institute. Journal *see* 0379-4350
0038-2094 South African Chessplayer†
0038-2116 South African Citrus Journal *see* 0257-2095
0038-2132 South African Digest†
0038-2140 South African Engineer *changed to* Current.
0038-2159 South African Fire Services Institute. Quarterly
0038-2167 South African Forestry Journal
0038-2175 South African Garage and Motor Engineer *changed to* Motor World.
0038-2183 South African Garden & Home
0038-2205 S.A. Medical Equipment News *changed to* S.A. Hospital Supplies.
0038-2213 South African Institute of Assayers and Analysts. Journal
0038-2221 South African Institute of Electrical Engineers. Transactions
0038-223X South African Institute of Mining and Metallurgy. Journal
0038-2256 South African Insurance Magazine†
0038-2264 South African Jersey†
0038-2272 S. A. Jewellery & Gifts†
0038-2280 South African Journal of Economics
0038-2299 South African Journal of Laboratory and Clinical Medicine†
0038-2302 South African Journal of Medical Laboratory Technology†
0038-2310 South African Journal of Medical Sciences†
0038-2329 South African Journal of Obstetrics and Gynecology *see* 0038-2469
0038-2337 South African Journal of Occupational Therapy
0038-2353 South African Journal of Science
0038-2361 South African Journal of Surgery
0038-237X South African Lapidary Magazine
0038-2388 South African Law Journal
0038-2396 South African Law Reports
0038-240X South African Libraries - Suid-Afrikaanse Biblioteke *see* 0256-8861
0038-2418 South African Library. Quarterly Bulletin
0038-2442 South African Mechanical Engineer
0038-2450 S.A. Mechanised Handling Equipment *changed to* Promat News.
0038-2469 South African Medical Journal
0038-2477 South African Mining Equipment *changed to* South African Mining, Coal, Gold and Base Minerals.
0038-2485 South African Motor-Cyclist
0038-2493 South African Music Teacher
0038-2507 South African Nursing Journal *changed to* Nursing News.
0038-2523 South African Observer
0038-2531 S.A. Packaging *changed to* Pack & Print.
0038-254X South African Panorama (English Edition)
0038-2558 South African Pharmaceutical Journal
0038-2566 South African Philatelist
0038-2574 South African Press Review *see* 0015-5055
0038-2582 S.A. Printer *changed to* Pack & Print.
0038-2590 South African Racehorse *changed to* South African Racehorse.
0038-2604 South African Red Cross News Digest *changed to* South African Red Cross Society (Cape Region). Newsletter.
0038-2612 South African Refractionist
0038-2620 South African Reserve Bank. Quarterly Bulletin
0038-2639 South African Retail Chemist
0038-2647 South African Review†
0038-2655 South African Rider
0038-2671 South African Shipping News and Fishing Industry Review†
0038-2698 South African Bureau of Standards. Bulletin
0038-2701 South African Stationery Trades Journal *changed to* Office Products S A.
0038-271X South African Statistical Journal
0038-2728 South African Sugar Journal
0038-2736 South African Survey Journal - Suid-Afrikaanse Opmetings Tydskrif *changed to* South African Journal of Surveying and Mapping.
0038-2744 South African Table Tennis News
0038-2752 South African Tax Cases Reports *changed to* Juta's Tax Service.
0038-2760 South African Transport
0038-2779 South African Treasurer
0038-2787 South African Typographical Journal
0038-2795 South African Union Lantern *changed to* Maranatha.
0038-2809 South African Veterinary Medical Association. Journal *changed to* South African Veterinary Association. Scientific Journal.
0038-2817 South African Yachting, Powerboats, Sailing, Waterski *changed to* South African Yachting.
0038-2841 South Asian Review†
0038-285X South Asian Studies
0038-2876 S A Q: The South Atlantic Quarterly
0038-2892 South Australian Electrical Contractor
0038-2906 South Australian Government Gazette
0038-2922 South Australian Institute of Architects' Monthly Bulletin
0038-2949 Central Times *changed to* New Times.
0038-2957 South Australian Motor
0038-2965 South Australian Naturalist
0038-2981 South Australian Racing Calendar
0038-3015 South Australian Teachers Journal *changed to* S A I T Journal.
0038-3023 South Australiana†
0038-3031 South Bay Economic Review *changed to* Daily Breeze Economic Review.
0038-304X South Carolina Economic Indicators
0038-3058 South Carolina Education Journal†
0038-3066 South Carolina Education News Emphasis *changed to* S C E A Emphasis.
0038-3074 South Carolina Farmer-Grower†
0038-3082 South Carolina Historical Magazine
0038-3090 South Carolina History Illustrated†
0038-3104 South Carolina Law Review
0038-3120 South Carolina Magazine†
0038-3139 South Carolina Medical Association. Journal
0038-3147 South Carolina Methodist Advocate *changed to* South Carolina United Methodist Advocate.
0038-3155 South Carolina Nursing†
0038-3163 South Carolina Review
0038-3171 South Carolina Schools
0038-318X South Carolina. State Department of Education. Office of General Education Media Services Newsletter†
0038-3198 South Carolina Wildlife
0038-3201 South Carolina Young Farmer and Future Farmer

5450 ISSN INDEX

0038-321X South Central Bulletin *see* 0743-6831
0038-3228 South Coast Herald
0038-3252 South Dakota Bird Notes
0038-3260 South Dakota Business Review
0038-3279 South Dakota Conservation Digest
0038-3287 South Dakota Dental Association. Newsletter
0038-3295 Farm and Home Research
0038-3309 South Dakota High Liner
0038-3317 South Dakota Journal of Medicine
0038-3325 South Dakota Law Review
0038-3341 South Dakota Musician
0038-3368 South Dakota Review
0038-3376 South Dakota State Library Commission Bulletin†
0038-3384 South Dakota Stockgrower
0038-3406 South East Asia Journal of Theology†
0038-3414 South-East Asia Treaty Organization. Economic Bulletin†
0038-3422 South East London & Kentish Mercury
0038-3430 The South End
0038-3465 South India Churchman
0038-3473 South Indian Horticulture
0038-3481 South Indian Teacher
0038-349X South Pacific Bulletin†
0038-352X South Shore Record
0038-3538 South Street Reporter *see* 0743-6246
0038-3546 South Texas Law Journal *changed to* South Texas Law Review.
0038-3562 South Wales Institute of Architects. Journal†
0038-3597 Southam Building Guide *changed to* Building Homes & Renovation.
0038-3600 Southeast Asia Quarterly *changed to* Southeast Asia Journal.
0038-3619 Southeast Asian Journal of Tropical Medicine and Public Health
0038-3627 Southeast Furniture & Appliance News†
0038-3643 Southeastern Dairy Review
0038-3651 Southeastern Drug Journal *see* 0192-5792
0038-366X Southeastern Geographer
0038-3678 Southeastern Geology
0038-3686 Southeastern Librarian
0038-3694 Southeastern Peanut Farmer
0038-3708 Southeastern Poultry Times *see* 0885-3371
0038-3716 Southeasterner
0038-3724 Southend-on-Sea and District Chamber of Trade and Industry. Monthly Journal *changed to* South Essex Chamber of Commerce, Trade & Industry. Southend. Monthly Journal.
0038-3732 Southerly
0038-3775 Southern Africa†
0038-3791 Southern Africa Textiles†
0038-3805 Southern and Southwestern Railway Club. Proceedings
0038-3813 Southern Association of Colleges and Schools. Proceedings
0038-3821 Southern Automotive Journal†
0038-383X Southern Banker†
0038-3848 Southern Baptist Educator
0038-3856 Southern Bell Views
0038-3864 Southern Building
0038-3872 Southern California Academy of Sciences. Bulletin
0038-3902 Southern California Guide
0038-3910 Southern California Law Review
0038-3929 Southern California Quarterly
0038-3937 Southern California Rancher†
0038-3945 Southern California Dental Laboratory Association. Bulletin
0038-3953 Southern California Teamster
0038-3988 Southern Connecticut Business Journal *see* 0887-2252
0038-4003 Southern Cooperator
0038-4011 Southern Cross
0038-402X Southern Dairy Products Journal†
0038-4038 Southern Economic Journal
0038-4046 Southern Economist
0038-4054 Southern Engineer
0038-4070 Southern Exposure (Talladega)
0038-4089 Southern Exposure Library Staff Bulletin *changed to* Southern Exposure (Carbondale).
0038-4097 Southern Farm Equipment *changed to* National Farm Equipment and Supply.
0038-4119 Southern Florist and Nurseryman *changed to* Nursery Manager.
0038-4127 Southern Folklore Quarterly *see* 0899-594X
0038-4143 Southern Gardens
0038-4151 Southern Garment Manufacturer *changed to* Southern Garment.
0038-416X Southern Hardware†
0038-4186 Southern Humanities Review
0038-4208 Southern Industrial Supplier
0038-4224 Southern Israelite *see* 0892-3345
0038-4232 Southern Jeweler *see* 0274-7456
0038-4240 Southern Jewish Weekly
0038-4259 Southern Journal of Business *see* 0148-2963
0038-4267 Southern Journal of Education Research *see* 0279-0688
0038-4275 Southern Journal of Optometry
0038-4283 Southern Journal of Philosophy
0038-4291 Southern Literary Journal
0038-4305 Southern Living
0038-4313 Southern Lumberman
0038-433X Southern Medical Bulletin *see* 0097-5419
0038-4348 Southern Medical Journal
0038-4364 Southern Methodist University. Industrial Information Services. Newsletter†
0038-4372 Southern Motor Cargo
0038-4380 Southern News and Views
0038-4399 Southern Outdoors - Gulf Coast Fisherman *see* 0199-3372
0038-4402 Southern Patriot *see* 0199-8668
0038-4410 Southern Pharmaceutical Journal *see* 0192-5792
0038-4461 Southern Plumbing, Heating, Cooling
0038-447X Southern Poetry Review
0038-4488 Southern Pulp and Paper Manufacturer *see* 0270-5222
0038-4496 Southern Quarterly
0038-450X Southern Railways
0038-4518 Southern Research Institute Bulletin†
0038-4526 Southern Review
0038-4534 Southern Review
0038-4542 Southern Sawdust†
0038-4577 Southern Sociologist
0038-4585 Southern Speech Journal *changed to* Southern Communication Journal.
0038-4593 Southern Stationer and Office Outfitter *changed to* Southern Office Dealer.
0038-4607 Southern Textile News
0038-464X Southern Wings
0038-4658 Southwest Advertising and Marketing *changed to* Adweek: Southwest.
0038-4666 Southwest Furniture News *changed to* Home Furnishings Review.
0038-4674 Southwest Jewish Chronicle
0038-4690 Southwest Kansas Register
0038-4704 Southwest News-Herald
0038-4712 Southwest Review
0038-4720 Southwest Water Works Journal *see* 0196-0717
0038-4739 Southwestern Art *changed to* Art Insight Southwest.
0038-4747 Southwestern Association on Indian Affairs. Quarterly†
0038-4763 Southwestern Collegian†
0038-478X Southwestern Historical Quarterly
0038-4798 Independent Jeweler *changed to* Independent Jeweler (1978).
0038-4801 Southwestern Journal of Anthropology *see* 0091-7710
0038-481X Southwestern Journal of Philosophy *see* 0276-2080
0038-4828 Southwestern Journal of Theology
0038-4836 Southwestern Law Journal
0038-4844 Southwestern Lore
0038-4852 Southwestern (Georgetown)
0038-4860 Southwestern Medicine†
0038-4879 Southwestern Miller *see* 0091-4843
0038-4887 Southwestern Minnesota Education Association Bulletin†
0038-4895 Southwestern Musician *see* 0162-380X
0038-4909 Southwestern Naturalist
0038-4917 Southwestern News
0038-4925 Southwestern Philosophical Society. Newsletter *changed to* Southwest Philosophy Review. Journal.
0038-4941 Social Science Quarterly
0038-495X Southwestern Veterinarian†
0038-4968 Souvenirs and Novelties
0038-4984 Sou'wester (South Bend)
0038-500X Sovetakan Arvest
0038-5018 Sovetakan Grakanutiun
0038-5026 Sovetakan Mankavarzh
0038-5034 Sovetskaya Arkheologiya
0038-5050 Sovetskaya Etnografiya
0038-5069 Sovetskaya Geologiya
0038-5077 Sovetskaya Meditsina
0038-5085 Sovetskaya Muzyka
0038-5093 Sovetskaya Pedagogika
0038-5107 Sovetskaya Torgovlya *changed to* Torgovaya Gazeta.
0038-5115 Sovetskaya Yustitsiya
0038-5123 Sovetskii Ekran *changed to* Ekran.
0038-5158 Sovetskii Shakhter
0038-5166 Sovetskie Arkhivy
0038-5174 Sovetskie Profsoyuzy
0038-5182 Sovetskoe Finnougrovedenie *changed to* Linguistica Uralica.
0038-5190 Sovetskoe Foto
0038-5204 Sovetskoe Gosudarstvo i Pravo
0038-5220 Soviet Military Review
0038-5239 Sovetskoe Zdravookhranenie
0038-5247 Sovety Deputatov Trudyashchikhsya *changed to* Sovety Narodnykh Deputatov.
0038-5263 Soviet and Eastern European Foreign Trade *changed to* Russian and East European Finance and Trade.
0038-5271 Soviet Antarctic Expedition Information Bulletin†
0038-528X Soviet Anthropology and Archeology *changed to* Anthropology and Archeology of Eurasia.
0038-5298 Soviet Applied Mechanics
0038-5301 Soviet Astronomy A.J. *changed to* Soviet Astronomy.
0038-531X Soviet Atomic Energy
0038-5328 Soviet Automatic Control - Avtomatyka *see* 0882-570X
0038-5336 Soviet-Bloc Research in Geophysics, Astronomy, and Space *changed to* U S S R Report: Space.
0038-5344 Soviet Chemical Industry
0038-5360 Soviet Education *changed to* Russian Education and Society.
0038-5379 Soviet Electrical Engineering
0038-5387 Soviet Electrochemistry
0038-5395 Soviet Film
0038-5409 Soviet Genetics
0038-5417 Soviet Geography - Review and Translation *changed to* Soviet Geography.
0038-5425 Soviet Hydrology: Selected Papers†
0038-545X Soviet Jewish Affairs
0038-5468 Soviet Jewry Action Newsletter†
0038-5484 Soviet Journal of Non-Ferrous Metals
0038-5492 Soviet Journal of Nondestructive Testing
0038-5506 Soviet Journal of Nuclear Physics
0038-5514 Soviet Journal of Optical Technology
0038-5522 Soviet Land
0038-5530 Soviet Law and Government *changed to* Russian Politics.
0038-5549 Soviet Life†
0038-5565 Soviet Materials Science
0038-5581 Soviet Mining Science
0038-559X Soviet Neurology and Psychiatry *changed to* Journal of Russian and East European Psychiatry.
0038-5603 Soviet News†
0038-5611 Soviet Panorama *see* 0038-5549
0038-562X Soviet Physics - Acoustics
0038-5638 Soviet Physics - Crystallography
0038-5646 Soviet Physics - J E T P
0038-5654 Soviet Physics - Solid State
0038-5662 Soviet Physics - Technical Physics
0038-5670 Soviet Physics - Achievements *changed to* Soviet Physics - Uspekhi.
0038-5689 Soviet Physics - Doklady
0038-5697 Soviet Physics Journal
0038-5700 Soviet Physics - Semiconductors
0038-5719 Soviet Plant Physiology
0038-5727 Soviet Plastics†
0038-5735 Soviet Powder Metallurgy and Metal Ceramics
0038-5743 Soviet Progress in Chemistry
0038-5751 Soviet Psychology *changed to* Journal of Russian and East European Psychology.
0038-576X Soviet Radiochemistry
0038-5786 Soviet Review
0038-5816 Soviet Science Review†
0038-5824 Soviet Sociology *changed to* Sociological Record.
0038-5832 Soviet Soil Science
0038-5840 Soviet Statutes and Decisions *changed to* Statutes and Decisions.
0038-5859 Soviet Studies
0038-5867 Soviet Studies in History *changed to* Russian Studies in History.
0038-5875 Soviet Studies in Literature *changed to* Russian Studies in Literature.
0038-5883 Soviet Studies in Philosophy *changed to* Russian Studies in Philosophy.
0038-5891 Soviet Technology Bulletin†
0038-5905 Soviet Weekly†
0038-5913 Sovetskaya Zhenshchina
0038-5921 Sovietica†
0038-5948 Sovremennik†
0038-5956 Sovremennoe Polskoe Pravo
0038-5964 Sovremeno Pretprijatie
0038-5972 Sovremenost
0038-5980 The Sower
0038-5999 Sowjetstudien†
0038-6006 Sowjetwissenschaft†
0038-6014 Soybean Digest
0038-6030 Der Sozialdemokrat
0038-6049 Soziale Berufe
0038-6057 Soziale Selbstverwaltung
0038-6065 Soziale Sicherheit
0038-6073 Soziale Welt
0038-609X Sozialer Fortschritt
0038-6103 Der Sozialistische Akademiker†
0038-6111 Sozialistische Arbeitswissenschaft†
0038-6138 Sozialistische Demokratie†
0038-6146 Sozialistische Erziehung
0038-6154 Sozialistische Forstwirtschaft *see* 0863-4807
0038-6162 Der Sozialistische Kaempfer
0038-6170 Sozialkunde Heute†
0038-6189 Sozialpaedagogik
0038-6197 Sozialpolitik und Arbeitsrecht
0038-6200 Sozial Versicherung - Arbeitsschutz†
0038-6219 Space (London)
0038-6227 Space†
0038-6235 Space Age Market Research
0038-6243 Space Business Daily News Service *see* 0889-0404
0038-6251 Space Business Week†
0038-6278 Space Letter
0038-6286 Space Life Sciences *see* 0169-6149
0038-6294 Space Propulsion *see* 0363-8219
0038-6308 Space Science Reviews
0038-6324 Space-Wise
0038-6332 Space World (Amherst)†
0038-6340 Spaceflight
0038-6367 Spafaswap†
0038-6375 Spain. Departamento de Fomento y Difusion Internacional. Documentacion†
0038-6391 Spain. Instituto Nacional de Estadistica. Boletin de Estadistica *changed to* Spain. Instituto Nacional de Estadistica. Boletin Mensual de Estadistica.
0038-6413 Boletin Oficial de la Propiedad Industrial *see* 0211-0105
0038-6413 Boletin Oficial de la Propiedad Industrial *see* 0211-0121
0038-6413 Boletin Oficial de la Propiedad Industrial *see* 0211-013X

ISSN

ISSN	Title
0038-6448	Span (Stowmarket)†
0038-6456	Spanish Cultural Index
0038-6464	Spanish Newsletter†
0038-6499	Spare Time
0038-6502	Sparebankbladet
0038-6510	Der Sparefroh
0038-6537	Sparer Magazin†
0038-6545	Sparfraemjaren see 0346-1602
0038-6553	Spark
0038-6561	Sparkasset
0038-657X	Sparkling Gems†
0038-6588	Sparrow changed to Sparrow (West Lafayette).
0038-6596	Spartacist
0038-6618	Frosch†
0038-6626	Speaking of "Columbias"
0038-6634	Spear
0038-6650	Spearhead†
0038-6677	Spear's Special Situation Reports†
0038-6685	Specchio del Libro per Ragazzi†
0038-6693	Special
0038-6715	Special Events in Georgia†
0038-6723	Special Libraries
0038-6731	Special Libraries Association. Biological Sciences Division. Reminder†
0038-6782	Special Libraries Association. Publishing Division. Bulletin†
0038-6855	Specialities†
0038-6863	Specializzazione
0038-6871	Specialty Advertising Report changed to Ideasworth.
0038-688X	Specialty Baker's Voice
0038-6898	Specialty Foods Magazine†
0038-6901	Specialty Salesman and Franchise Opportunities see 0738-4211
0038-6936	Specijalna Skola
0038-6944	Spectacle du Monde changed to Spectacle du Monde - Realites - Perspectives.
0038-6952	Spectator
0038-6960	Spectator†
0038-6995	Spectroscopia Molecular†
0038-7002	Spectroscopical Society of Japan. Journal
0038-7010	Spectroscopy Letters
0038-7029	Spectrovision changed to S C A N.
0038-7037	Unity-in-Diversity Centers Bulletin changed to Spectrum Magazine (Los Angeles).
0038-7061	Spectrum (Amherst)
0038-7088	Spectrum†
0038-7096	Spectrum der Herenmode changed to Mannenmode.
0038-7126	Speculator†
0038-7134	Speculum
0038-7142	Speech and Drama
0038-7150	Speech and Hearing Association of Virginia. Journal
0038-7169	Speech Monographs see 0363-7751
0038-7177	Speech Teacher see 0363-4523
0038-7185	Speed Age†
0038-7193	Speed and Custom Dealer changed to S C & O: Specialty & Custom Dealer.
0038-7207	Speed and Custom Equipment News see 0018-6023
0038-7215	Speed and Super†
0038-7223	Speed Mechanics†
0038-7231	Speedway Post†
0038-724X	Speedway Star
0038-7258	D O E
0038-7266	Spej†
0038-7274	Spektrum
0038-7282	S P E L D Information
0038-7290	Speleologia Emiliana
0038-7304	Speleologist
0038-7312	Speleweit
0038-7320	Speling
0038-7339	Spelling Progress Bulletin†
0038-7347	Spenser Newsletter
0038-7355	Sperimentale
0038-738X	Spettacolo
0038-7398	Spettatore Internazionale†
0038-7401	Spettatore Musicale
0038-741X	Sphincter
0038-7428	Sphinx
0038-7436	Sphinx-Magazin
0038-7444	Spica
0038-7452	Der Spiegel
0038-7460	Spiegel der Historie†
0038-7479	Spiegel der Letteren
0038-7487	Spiegel Historiael
0038-7495	Spiegelreflex - Praxis Reflex changed to Reflex.
0038-7509	Spiel und Theater
0038-7517	Der Spielplan
0038-7525	Das Spielzeug
0038-7533	Spint
0038-755X	Spinning Wheel†
0038-7584	Spirit (South Orange)
0038-7592	Spirit & Life
0038-7606	Spiritual Book News
0038-7614	Spiritual Frontiers†
0038-7622	The Spiritual Healer
0038-7630	Spiritual Life
0038-7649	Spiritualita
0038-7657	Spirituosen- und Weinhandel
0038-7665	Spiritus
0038-7681	Spokane Affairs
0038-7711	Spokane, Washington. Official Gazette
0038-772X	Spoken English
0038-7738	Spokeswoman
0038-7746	Spolem
0038-7754	Spoljnopoliticka Dokumentacija†
0038-7770	Sport
0038-7789	International Union of Students. Sport Bulletin
0038-7797	Sport
0038-7800	Sport Age†
0038-7819	Sport and Recreation see 0144-7181
0038-7827	Sport-Auto
0038-7835	Sport Aviation
0038-7851	Sport en Spel
0038-786X	Sport Fishery Abstracts changed to Fisheries Review.
0038-7878	Sport Flying†
0038-7916	Sport Italia
0038-7924	Sport- und Baederbauten see 0344-6492
0038-7932	Sport und Technik
0038-7940	Sport World†
0038-7959	Sportartikel-Sportmode changed to Spiel-Sport-Freizeit-Mode.
0038-7967	Sportdykaren
0038-7991	Sportimes
0038-8017	Sporting Goods Dealer
0038-805X	Sporting News
0038-8076	Sporting Shooter†
0038-8084	Shooting Times
0038-8092	Sportivnaya Zhizn' Rossii
0038-8106	Sportivnye Igry
0038-8114	Sportovni a Umelecka Gymnastika changed to Sportovni a Moderni Gymnastika.
0038-8122	Sportowiec
0038-8130	Sportparade
0038-8149	Sports Afield
0038-8165	Sports Car Graphic see 0027-2094
0038-8173	Sports Car World†
0038-8181	Sports and Recreation Equipment†
0038-8211	Sportsfiskeren
0038-822X	Sports Illustrated
0038-8238	Sports Loisirs, Education Physique†
0038-8254	Sports Trader changed to Sports Retailing.
0038-8270	Sportshelf News†
0038-8289	Sportski Ribolov see 0350-6789
0038-8297	Sportswear on Parade
0038-8300	Sportyvna Gazeta
0038-8319	Sposa
0038-8343	Spot News from Abroad†
0038-8351	Spotlight†
0038-8386	Spotlight: trade journal on the book, stationery, magazine, greeting cards, games and toy trade in New Zealand changed to Spotlight.
0038-8408	Spotlight on South Africa†
0038-8416	P D C A 74 see 0735-9713
0038-8424	Spots and Stripes see 0163-416X
0038-8432	Spotted News
0038-8440	Spraakvaard
0038-8459	Sprachdienst
0038-8467	Die Sprache
0038-8475	Sprache im Technischen Zeitalter
0038-8483	Sprachkunst
0038-8491	Sprachlabor†
0038-8505	Der Sprachmittler
0038-8513	Sprachspiegel
0038-8521	Spraak og Spraakundervisning†
0038-853X	Sprawy Miedzynarodowe
0038-8548	Sprechsaal fuer Keramik, Glas, Email, Silikate see 0341-0676
0038-8556	Sprig of Shillelagh†
0038-8564	Spring Arbor College Bulletin changed to Spring Arbor College Journal.
0038-8572	Spring Thirty-One Hundred†
0038-8580	Springfield-Illinois-Review of Business & Economic Conditions†
0038-8599	Springfield. Massachusetts. City Library Bulletin
0038-8602	Springfield Public Schools. News and Views
0038-8610	Springfielder changed to Concordia Theological Quarterly.
0038-8629	Springs & Brakpan Advertiser
0038-8637	Sprinkler Bulletin
0038-8645	Sprog og Kultur†
0038-8661	Spudman
0038-867X	Spur changed to Young Country.
0038-8688	Spur of Virginia see 0098-5422
0038-8696	Spurk
0038-870X	Der Spurkranz
0038-8726	Sputnik Junior
0038-8734	Square Dance see 0091-3383
0038-8750	Squilla
0038-8769	Squilla di S. Gerardo
0038-8777	Srecanja
0038-8785	Srednee Spetsial'noe Obrazovanie
0038-8793	Srpska Akademija Nauka i Umetnosti. Glasnik†
0038-8807	Sruth†
0038-8815	St. Paul's Printer
0038-8823	Staal†
0038-884X	Der Staat
0038-8858	Staat und Recht
0038-8866	Staatsbibliothek Preussischer Kulturbesitz. Mitteilungen
0038-8874	Der Staatsbuerger
0038-8882	Staatspensioenen
0038-8890	Stackst
0038-8904	Stad Gods
0038-8912	Stadio Club†
0038-8920	Stadion
0038-8939	Stadlinger Post
0038-8947	Stads og Havneingenioeren
0038-8963	Stadsbyggnad
0038-8971	Amtsblatt der Landeshauptstadt Linz
0038-898X	Stadt- und Gebaeudetechnik
0038-8998	Stadtbau-Informationen
0038-9013	Stadtverkehr
0038-9021	S I N Information†
0038-903X	Staedtebund changed to Stadt und Gemeinde.
0038-9048	Der Staedtetag
0038-9056	Starch
0038-9064	Staff and Line changed to Inforcadre.
0038-9072	Staff Spectator†
0038-9080	Stage and Cinema changed to Cinema & T V.
0038-9099	Stage and Television Today
0038-9110	Stage in Canada†
0038-9129	Stagioni changed to Quattro Stagioni.
0038-9145	Stahlbau
0038-9153	Stain Technology see 1052-0295
0038-917X	Stainless Steel
0038-9188	Stakker changed to Elvas-Krant.
0038-9196	Stalt
0038-920X	Stal'
0038-9218	Steel in the U S S R
0038-9226	Stalactite
0038-9234	Stamboeker changed to Veeverbetering.
0038-9269	Stamp Collecting see 0953-5241
0038-9277	Stamp Lover
0038-9293	Stamp News changed to Stamp News.
0038-9307	Stamp Weekly†
0038-9315	Stamp Wholesaler
0038-9323	Stampa Medica
0038-934X	Stamping/Diemaking†
0038-9358	Stamps
0038-9366	Stand Magazine
0038-9374	Standard
0038-9382	Standard (Arlington Heights)
0038-9390	Standard (Quincy)
0038-9404	Standard see 0740-9680
0038-9412	Standard and Poor's Security Owner's Stock Guide see 0737-4135
0038-9420	Standard & Poor's Stock Summary
0038-9439	Standard Bank Review see 0305-9553
0038-9447	Standard Bearer (Sacramento)
0038-9455	Standard Rate and Data Service. Print Media Production Data
0038-948X	Standard Rate and Data Service. Business Publication Rates and Data
0038-9498	Standard Rate and Data Service. Canadian Advertising Rates and Data changed to Canadian Advertising Rates and Data.
0038-9501	Dati e Tariffe Pubblicitarie
0038-951X	Media Daten see 0931-3265
0038-9528	Medios Publicitarios Mexicanos changed to Directorio M P M - Medios Impresos.
0038-9536	Standard Rate and Data Service. Network Rates and Data†
0038-9544	Standard Rate and Data Service. Newspaper Rates and Data
0038-9552	Standard Rate and Data Service. Spot Television Rates and Data
0038-9560	Standard Rate and Data Service. Spot Radio Rates and Data
0038-9579	Tarif Media
0038-9587	Standard Rate and Data Service. Weekly Newspaper Rates and Data see 0162-8887
0038-9595	Standard Rate and Data Service. Consumer Magazine and Farm Publication Rates and Data changed to Standard Rate and Data Service. Consumer Magazine and Agri-Media Rates and Data.
0038-9609	Standard Rate and Data Service. Transit Advertising Rates and Data†
0038-9617	Standard-Serie changed to Record-Serie.
0038-9625	Standardisering
0038-9633	Standards Action
0038-9641	Standards and Specifications Information Bulletin
0038-965X	Standards - Canada changed to Focus.
0038-9668	Standards Engineering
0038-9676	A N S I Reporter
0038-9684	Standards: Monthly Additions
0038-9692	Standarty i Kachestvo
0038-9706	Stander
0038-9714	Standing Conferences of Women's Organisations. Newsletter changed to Newsletter of Women's Forum and the Standing Conferences of Women's Organisations.
0038-9730	Standpunte
0038-9749	Stanford Alumni Almanac†
0038-9757	Stanford Chaparral
0038-9765	Stanford Law Review
0038-9781	Stanford M.D.†
0038-9803	Stanford University. Graduate School of Business. Bulletin see 0883-265X
0038-9811	Stanki i Instrumenty
0038-982X	Stanovnistvo
0038-9838	Staple Cotton Review changed to StaplReview.
0038-9846	Star and Garter Magazine
0038-9854	Star & Lamp of Pi Kappa Phi
0038-9862	Star & Style
0038-9870	Star of Zion
0038-9889	Star Serviceman
0038-9900	Star West
0038-9919	Stardock
0038-9927	Starlights

0038-9935 Start
0038-9943 Start & Speed†
0038-9951 Start und Aufstieg
0038-996X Startling Detective
0038-9978 Stash Capsules†
0038-9986 Stat (Madison)
0038-9994 The State
0039-0003 State Bank of India. Monthly Review
0039-0011 State Bank of Pakistan. Bulletin
0039-002X State Bar of California. Journal *see* 0279-4063
0039-0038 State Bar of New Mexico. Bar Bulletin and Advance Opinions *changed to* State Bar of New Mexico. Bar Bulletin.
0039-0046 State Education Journal Index
0039-0054 State Engineer†
0039-0070 New Jersey School Boards Association. School Board Notes
0039-0089 State Geologists Journal
0039-0097 Journal of State Government
0039-0119 State Government News
0039-0143 State Principals Association. Bulletin *changed to* Maine Principal.
0039-0151 State Service *see* 0958-5222
0039-016X State Transport News *see* 0970-4736
0039-0178 State Underwriter *see* 0198-683X
0039-0186 State University of New York. College at Buffalo. Record *changed to* Buffalo State Record.
0039-0194 State University College of Arts and Science at Geneseo. School of Library Science. Newsletter *changed to* State University College of Arts & Science at Geneseo. School of Library and Information Science. Newsletter.
0039-0208 State University of New York. Downstate Medical Center. Faculty Briefs *changed to* Focus (New York, 1978).
0039-0232 Staten Island Historian
0039-0240 Staten Island Institute of Arts & Sciences. Proceedings
0039-0259 Sweden. Statens Naturvaardsverk. Publikationer†
0039-0267 Sweden. Statens Planverk. Statens Planverk Aktuellt *see* 0280-4131
0039-0275 Statens Vaextskyddsanstalt. Meddelanden†
0039-0291 States†
0039-0305 Statesman
0039-0313 Statesman
0039-0321 Statesman Weekly
0039-0348 Stati Uniti d'Europa
0039-0356 Station Seismographique de Lisboa. Bulletin Seismique
0039-0364 Stationer's
0039-0372 Stationery Trade Review
0039-0380 Statistica
0039-0399 Statistica del Turismo†
0039-0402 Statistica Neerlandica
0039-0410 U.S. Securities and Exchange Commission. Statistical Bulletin *see* 0272-7846
0039-0437 Statistical Methods in Linguistics *changed to* Linguistic Calculation.
0039-0445 Statistical News Summary†
0039-0453 Statistical Office of the European Communities. Foreign Trade - Monthly Statistics *changed to* Statistical Office of the European Communities. Monthly External Trade Bulletin.
0039-0461 Statistical Office of the European Communities. General Statistical Bulletin†
0039-047X Statistical Office of the European Communities. Industrial Statistics†
0039-0488 Statistical Office of the European Communities. Social Statistics†
0039-050X Statistical Reporter†
0039-0518 Statistical Theory and Method Abstracts
0039-0526 The Statistician
0039-0534 Yugoslavia. Savezni Zavod za Statistiku. Statisticka Revija
0039-0542 Statisticki Pregled Socijalisticke Republike Bosne i Hercegovine
0039-0550 Revue Statistique du Quebec *see* 0227-0668
0039-0569 State Bank of Pakistan. Statistics on Co-Operative Banks
0039-0577 State Bank of Pakistan. Statistics on Scheduled Banks
0039-0585 Austria. Bundeskammer der Gewerblichen Wirtschaft. Statistik und Dokumnentation. Information *changed to* Austria. Bundeskammer der Gewerblichen Wirtschaft. Fremdenverkehr in Zahlen.
0039-0593 Statistika
0039-0607 Bank of Israel. Banking Statistics *changed to* Bank of Israel. Current Banking Statistics.
0039-0615 Belgium. Institut National de Statistique. Statistique de la Navigation Maritime†
0039-0623 Bourse de Paris. Statistiques Mensuelles
0039-0631 Statistische Hefte *see* 0932-5026
0039-064X Statistische Praxis†
0039-0658 Denmark. Danmarks Statistik. Statistisk Tabelvaerk†
0039-0682 Denmark. Danmarks Statistik. Statistiske Undersogelser
0039-0690 Hungary. Kozponti Statisztikai Hivatal. Statisztikai Szemle
0039-0704 Statni Statky
0039-0712 Statsanstaelld
0039-0720 Statsoekonomisk Tidsskrift
0039-0747 Statsvetenskaplig Tidskrift
0039-0755 Status of Your Vestal Schools *changed to* V C S Newsletter.
0039-0763 Statutes and Notifications
0039-0771 Staub, Reinhaltung der Luft†
0039-078X Stavebnicky Casopis
0039-0798 Stavebnik
0039-0801 Stavivo
0039-081X Stazione Zoologica di Napoli. Pubblicazioni *see* 0391-9714
0039-081X Stazione Zoologica di Napoli. Pubblicazioni *see* 0173-9565
0039-0828 Steam & Fuel Users' Journal
0039-0836 Steam and Heating Engineer *see* 0307-7950
0039-0844 Steamboat Bill
0039-0852 Steaua
0039-0879 Stedebouw en Volkshuisvesting
0039-0887 Stedfast Magazine†
0039-0895 Industry Week
0039-0909 Steel Castings Abstracts†
0039-0917 Steel Facts *changed to* Steel (Year).
0039-0925 Steel Horizons *see* 0149-1997
0039-0941 Steel Labor *changed to* Steelabor.
0039-095X Steel Times
0039-0968 Steel Trade
0039-0976 Steelwork in South Africa *see* 0010-6690
0039-0984 Steering Wheel *changed to* Cab Driver.
0039-0992 Steiermark, das Land der Vielfalt
0039-100X Steinbeck Quarterly
0039-1018 Steinbruch und Sandgrube
0039-1026 Steine Sprechen
0039-1034 Steinmetz und Bildhauer *changed to* Stein.
0039-1042 Steirische Berichte
0039-1050 Steirische Gemeinde-Nachrichten
0039-1077 Steirische Handelszeitung
0039-1085 Steirische Kriegsopfer Zeitung
0039-1093 Steirische Statistiken
0039-1107 Steirische Wirtschaft
0039-1115 Steklo i Keramika
0039-1131 Stelutis Alpinis
0039-1158 Stendhal Club. Quarterly
0039-1166 Stenografisk Tidsskrift
0039-1174 Der Stenopraktiker *see* 0863-4912
0039-1182 Stephen Crane Newsletter†
0039-1190 Stephenson Locomotive Society Journal
0039-1204 Ster
0039-1212 Stereo Headphones
0039-1220 Stereo Review
0039-1239 Stern *changed to* Stern Magazin.
0039-1247 Sterna†
0039-1255 Sterne
0039-1263 Sterne und Weltraum
0039-1271 Der Sternenbote
0039-128X Steroids: Structure, Function and Regulation
0039-1298 Steering Wheel
0039-1328 Stevens Indicator
0039-1344 Steward Anthropological Society. Journal
0039-1387 Paardesport in Ren en Draf
0039-1395 Welzijn in Stadt
0039-1409 Wirtschaft und Wissenschaft†
0039-1417 Stiinta si Tehnica
0039-1425 Stijl *changed to* Women.
0039-1433 Stil Novo
0039-1441 Stile Casa *changed to* Casa Stile.
0039-1484 Stimme und Weg†
0039-1492 Stimmen der Zeit
0039-1514 Stimulus†
0039-1522 Stirpes
0039-1557 Stock and Crops *changed to* Zimbabwe Tobacco Today.
0039-1565 Stock and Land
0039-1573 Stock Car-Hot Rod Journal†
0039-1581 Stock Exchange Journal†
0039-1611 Stock Exchange of New Zealand *changed to* Stock Exchange Journal of New Zealand.
0039-162X Stock Journal
0039-1638 Stock Market Magazine
0039-1654 Stockholms Handelskammare. Meddelanden *see* 0345-4495
0039-1662 Stockton-San Joaquin County Public Library Newsletter†
0039-1670 Stokvis Expres *changed to* Inzicht.
0039-1689 Stolica
0039-1697 Stoma *see* 0044-166X
0039-1700 Stomatologia
0039-1719 Stomatologia *changed to* Revista de Chirurgie, Oncologie, Radiologie, O.R.L., Oftalmologie, Stomatologie. Stomatologie.
0039-1727 Stomatologica *changed to* Parodontologia e Stomatologia Nuova.
0039-1735 Stomatologiya
0039-1743 Stomatoloski Glasnik Srbije
0039-1778 Stone Industries
0039-1786 Stonehenge†
0039-1794 Stony Brook†
0039-1808 Stop
0039-1816 Stopanski Pregled
0039-1824 Stoperitidende
0039-1832 Storage Handling Distribution
0039-1859 Store Planning Service
0039-1867 Stores
0039-1875 Storia Contemporanea
0039-1891 Storia e Nobilta
0039-1905 Storia e Politica†
0039-1913 Storia Illustrata
0039-1921 Storie di Cucciolo†
0039-193X Storie di Tiramolla *changed to* Racolta Storie di Tiramolla.
0039-1948 Storie e Fiabe†
0039-1956 Storkjoekken
0039-1964 Storkoek *see* 0282-0390
0039-1972 Storm Data
0039-1980 Stormklockan
0039-1999 Story Art
0039-2006 Story Friends
0039-2014 Story of Life†
0039-2022 Discovery (Winona Lake) *see* 0273-3145
0039-2030 Storyville
0039-2049 Strad
0039-2057 Strade Aperte
0039-2065 Strade e Traffico†
0039-2073 Strahlentherapie; Zeitschrift fuer Radiologie und Onkologie *see* 0179-7158
0039-2081 Formerly (until 1977) Straight *changed to* Straight.
0039-2103 Strain
0039-2111 Radio-Electronica
0039-212X Strandjaegeren
0039-2138 Strani Pravni Zivot. Serija D: Teorija, Zakonodavstvo, Praksa
0039-2146 Die Strasse†
0039-2162 Strasse und Autobahn
0039-2170 Strasse und Nuechternheit *changed to* Freie Fahrt.
0039-2189 Strasse und Verkehr
0039-2197 Strassen- und Tiefbau *changed to* Strassen- und Tiefbau Vereinigt mit Strasse-Bruecke-Tunnel, Bitumen-Teere-Asphalts-Peche.
0039-2200 Strassenbau-Technik *see* 0005-6634
0039-2219 Strassenverkehrstechnik
0039-2235 Strategie†
0039-2243 Strathclyde Telegraph
0039-2251 Straub Clinic Proceedings *changed to* Proceedings of the Straub Pacific Health Foundation.
0039-226X Street and Highway Lighting†
0039-2278 Streiflichter†
0039-2294 Stremez
0039-2308 Strength & Health Magazine†
0039-2316 Strength of Materials
0039-2324 Strevent
0039-2340 Stride
0039-2359 Igaku no Ayumi
0039-2375 Stroitel'
0039-2383 Stroitel'naya Mekhanika i Raschet Sooruzhenii
0039-2391 Stroitel'nye i Dorozhnye Mashiny
0039-2405 Stroitel'stvo i Arkhitektura
0039-2413 Stroitel'stvo i Arkhitektura Leningrada *changed to* Leningradskaya Panorama.
0039-2421 Stroitel'stvo i Arkhitektura Moskvy
0039-243X Stroitel'stvo i Arkhitektura Uzbekistana
0039-2448 Stroitel'stvo Truboprovodov
0039-2456 Strojirenska Vyroba
0039-2464 Strojirenstvi
0039-2472 Strojnicky Casopis
0039-2480 Strojniski Vestnik
0039-2499 Stroke
0039-2502 Association of Lunar and Planetary Observers. Journal
0039-2510 Strom & See
0039-2537 Strophes
0039-2545 Strout World
0039-2553 Structural Engineer *changed to* Structural Engineer.
0039-2561 Structural Mechanics *see* 0890-5452
0039-257X Structure
0039-2588 Struggle
0039-260X Strumenti & Musica
0039-2618 Strumenti Critici
0039-2634 Stud. Med.
0039-2669 Student†
0039-2677 Student (Lincoln)
0039-2685 The Student (Nashville)
0039-2693 Student
0039-2715 Student Advocate†
0039-2723 Student Federalist *changed to* World Citizen - Federalist Letter.
0039-2731 Student Impact *see* 0195-153X
0039-274X Student Lawyer (Chicago)
0039-2758 Student Life (St. Louis)
0039-2766 Student Life Highlights *changed to* Leadership (Reston).
0039-2790 Student Times International
0039-2804 Student Voice
0039-2839 Danske Studerendes Faellesraad. Studenterbladet
0039-2847 Studentische Politik†
0039-2855 Studentravel Magazine
0039-2863 Students' Digest†
0039-2871 Students Quarterly Journal *changed to* I E E Review.
0039-288X S L
0039-2898 Studi Biblici
0039-2901 Studi Cattolici
0039-291X Studi di Sociologia
0039-2928 Studi Economici
0039-2936 Studi Emigrazione
0039-2944 Studi Francesi
0039-2952 Studi Germanici

ISSN

ISSN	Title
0039-2960	Studi Grafici
0039-2979	Studi Internazionali di Filosofia see 0270-5664
0039-2987	Studi Italiani di Filologia Classica
0039-2995	Studi Romani
0039-3002	Studi Salentini
0039-3010	Studi Senesi
0039-3037	Studi Storici
0039-3045	Studi Storici dell'Ordine dei Servi di Maria
0039-3053	Studi Sul Lavoro†
0039-3061	Studi Teatrali†
0039-307X	Studi Urbinati. Serie A: Diritto
0039-3088	Studi Urbinati. Serie B: Letteratura, Storia, Filsofia changed to Studi Urbinati. Serie B: Scienze Umane e Sociali.
0039-310X	Studia Canonica
0039-3126	Studia Cywilistyczne
0039-3134	Studia Demograficzne
0039-3142	Studia Filozoficzne
0039-3150	Studia Forestalia Suecica
0039-3169	Studia Geophysica et Geodaetica
0039-3177	Instytut Przemyslu Drobnego i Rzemiosla Studia i Informacje changed to Instytut Ekonomiki Uslug i Drobnej Wytworczosci. Studia i Informacje.
0039-3185	Studia Leibnitiana
0039-3193	Studia Linguistica
0039-3207	Studia Liturgica
0039-3215	Studia Logica
0039-3223	Studia Mathematica
0039-3231	Studia Mediewistyczne
0039-324X	Studia Metodologiczne. Dissertationes Methodologicae
0039-3258	Studia Monastica
0039-3266	Studia Musicologica Academiae Scientiarum Hungaricae
0039-3274	Studia Neophilologica
0039-3282	Studia Orientalia
0039-3290	Studia Papyrologica†
0039-3304	Studia Patavina
0039-3312	Studia Prawnicze
0039-3320	Studia Psychologica
0039-3339	Studia Romanica et Anglica Zagrabiensia
0039-3347	Studia Rosenthaliana
0039-3355	Studia Slaskie
0039-3363	Studia Slavica Academiae Scientiarum Hungaricae
0039-3371	Studia Socjologiczne
0039-338X	Studia Theologica
0039-3398	Studia Universitatis "Babes-Bolyai". Biologia
0039-3401	Studia Universitatis "Babes-Bolyai". Chemia
0039-3428	Studia Universitatis "Babes-Bolyai". Historia
0039-3436	Studia Universitatis "Babes-Bolyai". Series Mathematica - Physica changed to Studia Universitatis "Babes-Bolyai". Mathematica.
0039-3444	Studia Universitatis "Babes-Bolyai". Philologia
0039-3460	Studiemappen†
0039-3495	Studies
0039-3525	Studies in Adult Education see 0266-0830
0039-3533	Studies in African Linguistics
0039-3541	Studies in Art Education
0039-3568	Studies in Bibliography and Booklore
0039-3576	Studies in Black Literature†
0039-3584	Studies in Burke and His Time see 0193-5380
0039-3592	Studies in Comparative Communism
0039-3606	Studies in Comparative International Development
0039-3622	Studies in Comparative Religion
0039-3630	Studies in Conservation
0039-3649	Studies in English Literature
0039-3657	Studies in English Literature 1500-1900
0039-3665	Studies in Family Planning
0039-3673	Studies in Germanicst
0039-3681	Studies in History and Philosophy of Science
0039-369X	Studies in History and Society†
0039-3703	Studies in Iowa History†
0039-3711	Studies in Islam
0039-3738	Studies in Philology
0039-3746	Studies in Philosophy and Education
0039-3754	Studies in Race and Nations†
0039-3762	Studies in Romanticism
0039-3770	Studies in Scottish Literature†
0039-3789	Studies in Short Fiction
0039-3797	Studies in Soviet Thought
0039-3800	Studies in the Humanities (Indiana)
0039-3819	Studies in the Literary Imagination
0039-3827	Studies in the Novel
0039-3835	Studies in the Twentieth Century†
0039-3851	Studies on Oriental Music
0039-386X	Studies on the Soviet Union†
0039-3886	Studii si Cercetari de Antropologie
0039-3940	Studii si Cercetari de Fizica
0039-3959	Studii si Cercetari de Fiziologie†
0039-3967	Studii si Cercetari de Geologie, Geofizica si Geografie. Geografie changed to Studii si Cercetari de Geografie.
0039-3983	Studii si Cercetari de Istoria Artei. Seria Arta Plastica
0039-3991	Studii si Cercetari de Istoria Artei. Seria Teatru, Muzica, Cinematografie
0039-4009	Studii si Cercetari de Istorie Veche changed to Studii si Cercetari de Istorie Veche si Arheologie.
0039-4017	Studii si Cercetari de Mecanica Aplicata
0039-4041	Studii si Cercetari Juridice changed to Studii de Drept Romanesc.
0039-405X	Studii si Cercetari Lingvistice
0039-4068	Studii si Cercetari Matematice
0039-4084	Studio
0039-4092	Studio†
0039-4106	Studio
0039-4114	Studio International†
0039-4122	Studio Light
0039-4130	Studium
0039-4149	Studium Generale†
0039-4157	Study Encounter†
0039-4165	Stuekulturer
0039-4181	Stuff†
0039-419X	Stukadoorspatroon changed to N A V A S.
0039-4203	Stuurwiel
0039-4211	Stuwing changed to Toorts.
0039-422X	Stvaranje
0039-4238	Style (DeKalb)
0039-4254	Style Auto
0039-4262	Style for Men
0039-4289	Stylus (Brockport)
0039-4319	Styret changed to Cykelbranchen.
0039-4335	Sub-Postmaster
0039-4351	Subject Index to Children's Magazines see 0743-9873
0039-436X	Suboticke Novine
0039-4378	Subsidia Medica†
0039-4386	Subsidia Pataphysica changed to Organographes du Cymbalum Pataphysicum.
0039-4394	Subterranean Sociology Newsletter
0039-4424	Success Unlimited see 0745-2489
0039-4432	Successful Farming
0039-4440	Success†
0039-4459	Succhi di Frutta e Bevande Gassate†
0039-4467	Succulenta
0039-4491	Sucrerie Francaise
0039-4505	Sud Africa - Ieri, Oggi, Domani changed to Realta Sudafricana.
0039-4521	Sudebnomeditsinskaya Ekspertiza
0039-453X	Sudene Informa†
0039-4556	Sudetenpost
0039-4564	Sudhoffs Archiv
0039-4572	Suedost-Gesellschaft. Mitteilungen see 0340-174X
0039-4580	Sudostroenie
0039-4599	Suecana Extranea
0039-4610	Suedamerika
0039-4629	Suedtirol in Wort und Bild
0039-4637	Suedwestfaelische Wirtschaft
0039-4645	Suenos
0039-4653	Suesswaren
0039-4661	Suffolk Cooperative Library System. Newsletter†
0039-467X	Suffolk County Agricultural News
0039-4688	Suffolk County Dental Society. Bulletin changed to Suffolk Dentistry.
0039-4696	Suffolk University Law Review
0039-470X	Sugaku
0039-4726	Sugar Bulletin
0039-4734	Sugar Journal
0039-4742	Sugar y Azucar
0039-4750	Sugarbeet Grower
0039-4777	Sugarland
0039-4793	Suggestion Systems Quarterly changed to Performance (Chicago).
0039-4807	Suid-Afrikaanse Akademie vir Wetenskap en Kuns. Nuusbrief
0039-4823	Suiker-Facetten changed to Kwartaalblad Suiker.
0039-484X	Suion no Kenkyu
0039-4858	Suiri Kagaku
0039-4866	Suisan Kai
0039-4874	Suisse Horlogere et Revue Internationale de l'Horlogerie changed to Suisse Horlogere et Revue Europeenne de l'Horlogerie-Bijouterie.
0039-4882	Sukh Datta
0039-4890	Sulphur
0039-4904	Sulphur Institute Journal see 0160-0680
0039-4912	Sulzer Technical Review
0039-4947	Sumarios de Odontologia†
0039-4963	Sumitomo Keikinzoku Giho
0039-4971	Summa†
0039-498X	Summa Brasiliensis Mathematicae†
0039-4998	Summary of Available Applicants and Summary of Academic, Industrial, and Government Openings†
0039-5005	Summary of Labor Arbitration Awards
0039-5021	Summer Texan changed to Daily Texan.
0039-5056	Summit: The Mountain Journal
0039-5072	Summons
0039-5080	Sun
0039-5099	Sun Dance changed to Detroit Sun.
0039-5102	Sun
0039-5110	Sun & Health†
0039-5137	Sun Seeker†
0039-5145	Sunbelt Dairyman
0039-5153	Sunday†
0039-5161	Sunday
0039-517X	Sunday Companion†
0039-5188	Sunday Digest
0039-5196	Sunday Express
0039-520X	Sunday Gleaner
0039-5218	Sunday Independent
0039-5226	Sunday Mail
0039-5234	Sunday Mainichi
0039-5242	Sunday Mercury
0039-5250	Bible-in-Life Pix
0039-5277	Sunday Post
0039-5285	Sunday School Counselor
0039-5315	Sunday Sun
0039-5323	Sunday Times changed to Dominion Sunday Times.
0039-5358	Sunday Truth changed to Sunday Sun.
0039-5366	Sundhedsbladet
0039-5374	Sun (New York)
0039-5382	Sunflower (Manhattan)
0039-5390	Sunlore
0039-5404	Sunset
0039-5412	Sunshine Magazine
0039-5420	Sunshine†
0039-5439	Sunshine & Health
0039-5447	Sunshine State Agricultural Research Report changed to Florida Agricultural Research.
0039-5455	Sunt Foernuft
0039-5471	Suo
0039-548X	Suomalainen†
0039-5498	Suomalaiset B-Referaatit see 0781-8904
0039-5501	Suomen Elainlaakarilehti
0039-551X	Finnish Dental Society. Proceedings
0039-5528	Suomen Kalastuslehti
0039-5544	Suomen Kunnallislehti
0039-5552	Suomen Kuvalehti
0039-5560	Suomen Laakarilehti
0039-5579	Laakintavoimistelija changed to Fysioterapia.
0039-5587	Suomen Lehdisto
0039-5595	Suomen Maataloustieteellisen Seuran Julkaisuja†
0039-5609	Osuustoimintalehti
0039-5617	Suomen Puutalous see 0781-6758
0039-5625	Suomen Silta
0039-565X	Super Omnia Caritas†
0039-5676	Super Service Station see 0896-0437
0039-5684	Super Sports†
0039-5692	Super Stock & Drag Illustrated
0039-5706	Superba
0039-5714	Superconducting Devices and Materials†
0039-5765	Superlove†
0039-5773	Supermachos†
0039-5781	Supermarket
0039-579X	Supermarket Management†
0039-5803	Supermarket News
0039-5811	Supermarketing see 0196-5700
0039-582X	Supernovelas changed to Supernovelas Capricho.
0039-5846	Supertiendas†
0039-5854	Supervision
0039-5862	Supervisor changed to Modern Management.
0039-5870	Supervisor Nurse see 0744-6314
0039-5889	Supervisor's Bulletin
0039-5897	Supervisors Quarterly changed to Teacher Educator.
0039-5919	Supervisory Management (New York) changed to Supervisory Management (New York).
0039-5927	Supplementary Service to European Taxation
0039-5935	Supply House Times
0039-5951	Supreme Court Cases
0039-596X	Supreme Court Notes
0039-5994	Sur l'Eau†
0039-6001	Industrial Finishing and Surface Coatings see 0264-2506
0039-6028	Surface Science
0039-6036	Surfer
0039-6052	Surfing East††
0039-6060	Surgery
0039-6087	Surgery, Gynecology & Obstetrics
0039-6095	Surgical Business see 0745-4678
0039-6109	Surgical Clinics of North America
0039-6125	Surgo
0039-6133	Surinaamse Landbouw
0039-6141	Suriname Zending changed to Hernhutter Suriname Zending.
0039-615X	Surplus Record
0039-6176	Surrey N.F.U. Journal changed to Central Southern Farmer.
0039-6184	Sursum Corda
0039-6206	Survey of Anesthesiology
0039-6214	Survey of Current Affairs
0039-6222	Survey of Current Business
0039-6230	Survey of International Development†
0039-6249	Quarterly Survey of Japanese Finance and Industry changed to Japanese Finance and Industry: Quarterly Survey.
0039-6257	Survey of Ophthalmology
0039-6265	Great Britain. Directorate of Overseas Surveys. Survey Review changed to Great Britain. Commonwealth Association of Surveying and Land Economy. Survey Review.

ISSN	Title
0039-6273	Surveying and Mapping *changed to* Surveying and Land Information Systems.
0039-6303	Surveyor - Local Government Technology *changed to* Surveyor.
0039-6311	Survey of the Work of British Writers *changed to* Writers & Their Work.
0039-6338	Survival
0039-6354	Survive *see* 0740-5537
0039-6362	Sus Hijost
0039-6370	Sushama
0039-6397	Sussex Life
0039-6427	Sveiseteknikk
0039-6435	Svensk Bergs- och Brukstidning
0039-6443	Svensk Bokfoerteckning
0039-6451	Svensk Bokhandel
0039-646X	Svensk Botanisk Tidskrift
0039-6478	Svensk Bridge
0039-6494	Nord-Emballage
0039-6508	Svensk Export
0039-6516	Svensk Faerghandel
0039-6524	Svensk Farmaceutisk Tidskrift
0039-6532	Svensk Filatelistisk Tidskrift
0039-6540	Svensk Fotografisk Tidskrift *see* 0284-7035
0039-6559	Svensk Guldsmeds Tidning *see* 0282-4175
0039-6575	Svensk Handelstidning Justita
0039-6583	Svensk Jakt
0039-6591	Svensk Juristtidning
0039-6605	Kemisk Tidskrift
0039-6613	Svensk Lantmaeteritidskrift
0039-6621	Svensk Leksaksrevy
0039-663X	Svensk Litteraturtidskriftt
0039-6648	Svensk Lokaltrafik
0039-6664	S M T *see* 0027-1764
0039-6672	Svensk Omnibustidning *see* 0282-7654
0039-6680	Svensk Papperstidning *see* 0283-6831
0039-6699	Svensk Pastoral Tidskrift
0039-6702	Svensk Sjoefarts Tidning
0039-6729	Svensk Snickeritidskrift *see* 0346-2846
0039-6737	Svensk Sparbankstidskrift *see* 0346-1602
0039-6745	Svensk Tandlaekare-Tidskrift *see* 0347-9994
0039-6761	Svensk Teologisk Kvartalskrift
0039-677X	Svensk Tidskrift
0039-6788	Svensk Tidskrift for Industriellt Rattsskydd
0039-6796	Svensk Traevaru- och Pappersmassetidningt
0039-680X	Svensk Ur- Optik Tidning *changed to* Svensk Urmakartidning.
0039-6818	Svensk Valltidskriftt
0039-6826	Svensk Veckotidning
0039-6834	Gasnytt
0039-6842	Svenska Litteratursaellskapet i Finland. Skrifter
0039-6869	Svenska Mejeriernas Riksfoerening. Meddelandet
0039-6877	Svenska Mejeritidningen *see* 1101-8399
0039-6885	Svenska Museer
0039-6893	Meddelanden fraan Svenska Riksarkivett
0039-6907	Svenska Tidningsartiklar
0039-6915	Svenska Tidskriftsartiklar
0039-6923	Svenska Vaegfoereningens Tidskrift *changed to* Svensk Vaegtidning.
0039-6931	Svenska Kraftverksfoereningens Publikationert
0039-694X	Svenskt Fiske *changed to* Sportfiskaren.
0039-6958	Sverige-Nytt
0039-6966	Sveriges Flotta *changed to* Under Svensk Flagg.
0039-6982	Tandlaekartidningent
0039-6990	Sveriges Utsaedesfoerenings Tidskrift
0039-7008	Svett
0039-7016	Svet Motoru
0039-7024	Svet Sovetu *changed to* Svet Socialismu.
0039-7059	Svetlost
0039-7067	Svetotekhnika
0039-7075	Svetova Literatura
0039-7083	Svetsaren
0039-7091	Svetsen
0039-7105	Zvezda
0039-7113	Svijet (Zagreb)
0039-7121	Svijet (Sarajevo)
0039-713X	Svinovodstvo
0039-7148	Svisa Espero *changed to* Svisa Esperanto Revuo.
0039-7156	Svit
0039-7180	Swap Shop *changed to* Administrator's Swap Shop Newsletter.
0039-7199	Swarajya
0039-7202	Swatantra in Parliamentt
0039-7210	Swatantra Newslettert
0039-7229	Swaziland Recordert
0039-7245	Sweden Now
0039-7253	Sweden. Statistiska Centralbyraan. Allmaan Maanadsstatistik
0039-7261	Sweden. Statistiska Centralbyraan. Statistik Tidskrif *see* 0282-423X
0039-727X	Sweden. Statistiska Centralbyraan. Utrikeshandel. Kvartalsstatistik
0039-7288	Sweden. Statistiska Centralbyraan. Utrikeshandel. Maanadsstatistik *see* 1100-9381
0039-7296	Swedish Economy
0039-730X	Skogsvaardsfoereningens Tidskrift *see* 0371-2907
0039-7318	Swedish Journal of Economics *see* 0347-0520
0039-7326	Swedish Pioneer Historical Quarterly *see* 0730-028X
0039-7342	Sweet Briar College. Alumnae Magazine *changed to* Sweet Briar Alumnae Magazine.
0039-7377	Swiat *see* 0031-6059
0039-7385	Swimming Pool Review *changed to* Swimming Pool.
0039-7393	Swimming Pool Weekly and Swimming Pool Age *see* 0899-1022
0039-7393	Swimming Pool Weekly - Age - Data and Reference Annual *see* 0899-1022
0039-7415	Swimming Technique
0039-7423	Swimming Times
0039-7431	Swimming World
0039-744X	Swing Journal
0039-7458	Swing Through the Air *see* 0921-8017
0039-7466	Swiss Bank Corporation. Bulletin *see* 0304-2162
0039-7474	Swiss Journal
0039-7482	Swiss Observert
0039-7490	Swiss Review of World Affairs
0039-7504	Swiss Technicst
0039-7512	Swiss Watcht
0039-7520	Swiss Watch and Jewelry Journal
0039-7547	Sword of the Lord
0039-7563	Sybarite Review
0039-7571	Sydan
0039-758X	Sydney Jewish News *changed to* Australian Jewish News (Darlinghurst).
0039-7598	Sydney Stock Exchange Limited Gazette *see* 0045-0901
0039-761X	Sydney Water Board Journalt
0039-7628	Sykepleien *see* 0802-9776
0039-7628	Sykepleien *changed to* Fagtidsskriftet Sykepleien.
0039-7636	S Y L F Nytt *changed to* Tidskrift foer Yngre Laekare.
0039-7652	Sylvaply News *changed to* MacMillan Bloedel Building Materials News.
0039-7660	Sylwan
0039-7679	Symbolae Osloenses
0039-7695	Symposium
0039-7709	Symposium
0039-7717	Syn og Segn
0039-7725	Synagogue School *changed to* Impact! (New York).
0039-7733	Synagogue Servicet
0039-7741	Syndicalisme Hebdo *changed to* Syndicalisme Hebdo.
0039-775X	Syndicalisme C F T C
0039-7776	Syndicat des Critiques Litteraires. Bulletin
0039-7784	Syndicat National des Officers de la Marine Marchande C.F.D.T. Bulletin de Liaison
0039-7830	Synopsis Revuet
0039-7849	Synpunkt
0039-7857	Synthese
0039-7873	Who Put the Bomp *changed to* Bomp.
0039-7881	Synthesis
0039-789X	Synthesis in Inorganic and Metalorganic Chemistry *see* 0094-5714
0039-7903	Synthesis Microbiologicat
0039-7911	Synthetic Communications
0039-792X	Syracuse Chemist
0039-7938	Syracuse Law Review
0039-7946	Syria
0039-7954	Syria. Central Bureau of Statistics. Summary of Foreign Trade Statistics *changed to* Syria. Central Bureau of Statistics. Summary of Foreign Trade.
0039-7962	Syrie et Monde Arabe
0039-7989	Systematic Zoology *changed to* Systematic Biology.
0039-8004	Systemation Service *see* 0563-0355
0039-8012	Systeme D
0039-8020	Systems & Communications
0039-8039	Systems Education Forumt
0039-8047	Systems Technologyt
0039-8055	Systems, Technology and Science for Law Enforcement and Security Newsletter *see* 0271-7565
0039-8071	Szabadalmi Kozlony es Vedjegyertesito
0039-808X	Szamvitel es Ugyviteltechnika
0039-8098	Szazadok
0039-8101	Szemeszet
0039-811X	Szene
0039-8128	Szigma
0039-8136	Szinhaz
0039-8144	Szklo i Ceramika
0039-8152	Szpilki
0039-8160	T.I.T. Journal of Life Sciences
0039-8179	T At
0039-8187	T A C Quarterly Circular
0039-8209	T A I C H Newst
0039-8217	T.A. Informations
0039-8225	T A L B Talkst
0039-8233	T A M S Journal
0039-8241	T A P P I *see* 0734-1415
0039-8268	T A V R *changed to* Territorial Army Magazine.
0039-8292	T E A News
0039-8306	T E A Newsletter
0039-8314	T E C Report
0039-8322	T E S O L Quarterly
0039-8330	T F C Nieuws
0039-8349	T G A Cosmetic Journal *see* 0090-0591
0039-8357	Textile Institute and Industry *see* 0260-6518
0039-839X	T. I. P. Informatiet
0039-8403	T I P R O Reporter
0039-8411	T I S C O Technical Journal
0039-842X	T N A News
0039-8438	T N C - Aktuellt
0039-8446	T N O Nieuws *changed to* T N O Project.
0039-8454	T.P.A. Travelers
0039-8462	T P Annales
0039-8470	T.P.L. News
0039-8497	T T A
0039-8500	T T G International *changed to* Travel Trade Gazette Europa.
0039-8519	T V Communications *see* 0745-2802
0039-8527	T V Comict
0039-8535	I V At
0039-8543	T V Guide
0039-8551	T V Hebdo
0039-856X	T V Picture Life *changed to* T V Picture Life - Metal Edge.
0039-8578	T V Radio Mirror *changed to* T V Mirror.
0039-8608	T V Timest
0039-8624	T V Times
0039-8632	T W A Ambassador
0039-8640	T W A U News
0039-8659	T W U Express
0039-8667	T Z fuer Praktische Metallbearbeitung *see* 0170-9577
0039-8675	Ta Kung Pao
0039-8683	Taag
0039-8691	Taal en Tongval
0039-8705	Taalgenoot
0039-8721	Tabak
0039-873X	Tabakt
0039-8748	Tabak Journal International
0039-8756	Der Tabakpflanzer Oesterreichst
0039-8772	Tabakverschleisser Oesterreichs *changed to* Trafik-Journal.
0039-8780	Table et Cadeau
0039-8799	Table Tennis News
0039-8802	Tableaux de l'Economie Francaise
0039-8829	Tables of Redemption Values for U.S. Savings Bonds, Series A-E *changed to* Tables of Redemption Values for U.S. Savings Bonds, Series E and Tables of Redemption Values for U.S. Savings Bonds, Series EE.
0039-8837	Tablet
0039-8845	Tablet
0039-8853	Tableware International and Pottery Gazette *see* 0143-7755
0039-8888	Tachydromos
0039-8896	Tacticst
0039-890X	Facultad de Medicina de Sevilla. Revistat
0039-8926	Taeglicher Wetterbericht *see* 0341-2970
0039-8934	Wiener Tagebucht
0039-8942	Tageszeitung fuer Brauerei *see* 0179-2466
0039-8950	Tagus
0039-8969	Tahqiqat e Eqtesadi
0039-8977	Taide
0039-8993	Taikabutsu
0039-9000	Japan Society of Air Pollution. Journal
0039-9019	Air Pollution Newst
0039-9027	Tail-Wagger and Family Magazinet
0039-9043	Tailor and Men's Wear *changed to* Menswear Magazine.
0039-9051	Taipei Pictorial
0039-906X	Japanese Journal of Physical Fitness and Sports Medicine
0039-9078	Taiwant
0039-9086	Taiwan *changed to* Taiwan Pictorial.
0039-9094	Taiwan Chenglian
0039-9108	Taiwan Industrial Panorama
0039-9116	Taiwan Museum. Quarterly Journal *see* 0256-257X
0039-9124	Taiwan Trade Monthlyt
0039-9140	Talanta
0039-9159	Talespinnert
0039-9175	Talim-O-Tarbiat
0039-9183	Talking Book Topics (Large Print Edition)
0039-9191	Talking Machine Review *changed to* Talking Machine Review, International.
0039-9213	Talks and Tales
0039-9221	Taller
0039-9248	Talont
0039-9256	Tamarack Reviewt
0039-9264	Tamarind Fact Sheetst
0039-9280	Tamil Arasu
0039-9299	Tamil Culture
0039-9310	Tamil Nadu Information
0039-9329	Tamil Nadu Police Journal
0039-9345	Tan *see* 0163-3007
0039-9353	Tandlaegebladet
0039-937X	Tanecni Listy
0039-9388	Tangentt
0039-940X	Tangerine
0039-9418	Tank
0039-9434	Report of Coal Mine Safetyt
0039-9442	Tanner
0039-9469	Tanpakushitsu Kakusan Koso
0039-9477	Tanzania. Bureau of Statistics. Quarterly Statistical Bulletin
0039-9485	Tanzania Education Journal
0039-9507	Tanzania Notes & Records
	Tanzania Zamani

ISSN INDEX 5455

0039-9531 Tape Record *changed to* Soundings.
0039-954X Studio Sound *see* 0144-5944
0039-9566 Tapetenzeitung Tapete und Bodenbelag *changed to* B T H - Tapetenzeitung.
0039-9574 Tapetsererent†
0039-9582 Tapissier Decorateur
0039-9590 Taproots†
0039-9604 Taptoe
0039-9612 Tar Heel Economist *changed to* N C State Economist.
0039-9620 Tar Heel Nurse
0039-9639 Tar River Poetry
0039-9655 Lengo
0039-9663 Tarheel Banker
0039-968X Tarheel Wheels
0039-9698 Tarikh†
0039-971X Tarsadalmi Szemle
0039-9728 Tartarino
0039-9736 Wijk en Speeltuinvereniging Tarwewijk. Mededelingenblad
0039-9760 Tasmanian Eudcation Gazette *see* 1037-2040
0039-9787 Tasmanian Fruitgrower & Farmer
0039-9795 Tasmanian Government Gazette
0039-9809 Tasmanian Historical Research Association. Papers and Proceedings
0039-9817 Tasmanian Journal of Agriculture†
0039-9825 Tasmanian Journal of Education *see* 0314-2531
0039-9833 Australia. Bureau of Statistics. Tasmanian Office. Monthly Summary of Statistics *changed to* Australia. Bureau of Statistics. Tasmanian Office. Tasmanian Statistical Indicators.
0039-9841 Tasmanian Motor News *see* 0818-5549
0039-985X Tasmanian Motor Trader
0039-9892 Tatka
0039-9906 Tatler & Bystander
0039-9914 Tatrzanski Orzel
0039-9922 Finland. Patentti- ja Rekisterihallitus. Tavaramerkkilehti
0039-9930 Tawow†
0039-9949 Tax Administrators News
0039-9957 Tax Adviser
0039-9965 Tax Affairs
0039-9973 Tax Alert†
0039-999X Tax Coordinator *see* 0738-8632
0040-0017 United States Tax Court Reports
0040-0025 Tax Executive
0040-0041 Tax Law Review
0040-005X Tax Lawyer
0040-0068 Philippines. National Tax Research Center. Tax Monthly†
0040-0076 Tax News Service
0040-0084 Tax Planning†
0040-0092 Tax Planning Ideas
0040-0106 Tax Policy†
0040-0114 Tax Foundation's Tax Review *see* 0737-3481
0040-0122 Tax Times
0040-0130 Taxa Droske Tidende *changed to* Dansk Taxi Tidende.
0040-0149 Taxation
0040-0157 Taxation
0040-0165 Taxation for Accountants
0040-0173 Taxation Record Journal
0040-0181 Taxes
0040-0203 Taxes Interpreted†
0040-0211 Taxi News Digest†
0040-022X Taxitrafiken
0040-0238 Taxia Fungorum *changed to* Mycological Flora.
0040-0246 Taxicab Management†
0040-0254 Taxinews
0040-0262 Taxon
0040-0270 Taxpayer
0040-0289 Taxpayer
0040-0297 Tchahert
0040-0300 Te Ao Hou†
0040-0319 Te Maori *changed to* Te Awatea.
0040-0327 Te-ve Guia
0040-0343 Tea and Coffee Trade Journal
0040-036X Tea Quarterly *see* 1010-4208
0040-0378 Tea Research Foundation of Central Africa. Quarterly Newsletter *changed to* Tea Research Foundation. Quarterly Newsletter.
0040-0386 Tea Room, Restaurant and Catering Journal†
0040-0394 Teach†
0040-0408 Teacher†
0040-0416 Teacher
0040-0424 Teacher Education in New Countries†
0040-0440 Teacher of the Blind *see* 0264-6196
0040-0459 Teacher of the Deaf *changed to* British Association of Teachers of the Deaf. Journal.
0040-0467 Teacher Paper†
0040-0483 Teachers'Journal *see* 1036-3904
0040-0505 Message of the Teacher
0040-0521 Teacher's World
0040-053X Teaching†
0040-0556 T A D *see* 0046-1482
0040-0564 Teaching All Nations *changed to* East Asian Pastoral Review.
0040-0572 Teaching & Training
0040-0580 Teaching Beginners *changed to* Teaching Under 5's.
0040-0599 Teaching Exceptional Children
0040-0602 Teaching History
0040-0610 Teaching History
0040-0629 Teaching Juniors *changed to* Learning Together with 7-11's.
0040-0645 Teaching Pictures for Bible Searchers†
0040-0653 Teaching Primaries *changed to* Learning Together with 5-7's.
0040-0661 Milwaukee Public Schools Superintendent's Bulletin *changed to* Milwaukee Public Schools Staff Bulletin.
0040-067X Teaching Teenagers *see* 0308-356X
0040-0688 Teaching Tools for Consumer Ed *changed to* Teaching Tools for Consumer Reports.
0040-0696 Team
0040-0718 Teamwork in Industry *changed to* Worklife.
0040-0734 Teashi no Fujiyuuna Kodomotachi
0040-0750 Teatern
0040-0769 Teatr
0040-0777 Teatr
0040-0785 Teatral'naya Zhizn'
0040-0793 Teatro
0040-0807 Teatro e Cinema†
0040-0815 Teatrul *changed to* Teatrulazi.
0040-0823 Tebiwa *changed to* Tebiwa.
0040-0831 Tech Air *see* 0305-0831
0040-0858 Tech Talk (Herndon) *see* 0002-242X
0040-0866 Technica
0040-0874 Technical Association of Graphic Arts of Japan. Bulletin *changed to* Japanese Society of Printing Science and Technology. Bulletin.
0040-0882 Technical Association of Malaysia. Journal *see* 0127-6441
0040-0890 Technical Book Review Index†
0040-0904 Technical Co-operation†
0040-0912 Education and Training
0040-0920 Technical Education Abstracts
0040-0939 Technical Education Newsletter *see* 0889-6488
0040-0947 Technical Film International Bulletin *see* 0138-9157
0040-0955 T.I.
0040-0963 National Association of Teachers in Further and Higher Education. Technical Journal *see* 0308-1907
0040-0971 Technical Photography†
0040-098X Technical Progress in Israel†
0040-0998 Manila. Department of Public Works. Communications Technical Statistical Review *changed to* M P W Bulletin.
0040-1005 Technical Survey†
0040-1013 Technicar *see* 0008-5995
0040-1021 Technicien Belge en Prothese Dentaire
0040-103X Technicien du Film *changed to* Technicien du Film et de la Video.
0040-1056 Technicka Praca
0040-1064 Technicky Tydenik
0040-1072 Technicuir†
0040-1099 Die Technik†
0040-1102 Technik und Betrieb†
0040-1110 Technika
0040-1137 Technika i Gospodarka Morska
0040-1145 Technika Lotnicza i Astronautyczna
0040-1153 Technika Motoryzacyjna *changed to* Auto-Technika Motoryzacyjna.
0040-1161 Technika Poszukiwan *changed to* Technika Poszukiwan Geologicznych, Geosynoptyka i Goetermia.
0040-117X Technikgeschichte†
0040-1188 Technion *see* 0792-3244
0040-1196 Technique Chaussure
0040-1226 Technique et Pratique Agricoles *changed to* Lettre des I T P A.
0040-1242 Technique Laitiere *changed to* Process Magazine.
0040-1250 Technique Moderne
0040-1269 Technique Pharmaceutique *changed to* Sciences et Technique Pharmaceutiques.
0040-1277 Technique Routiere
0040-1285 Techniques†
0040-1293 Techniques C E M
0040-1307 Techniques de l'Air Comprime†
0040-1315 Techniques de l'Habillement
0040-1323 Techniques du Petrole *changed to* Techniques Petrole Petrochimie.
0040-1331 Techniques Economiques *see* 0987-710X
0040-1358 Techniques for Teachers of Adults *see* 1045-1595
0040-1374 Techniques Hospitalieres, Medico-Sociales et Sanitaires
0040-1382 Techniques Nouvelles†
0040-1390 Technisch Gemeenteblad†
0040-1420 Technische Information Armaturen†
0040-1439 Technische Mitteilungen
0040-1455 R F Z. Technische Mitteilungen†
0040-1463 Technische Mitteilungen Krupp. Werksberichte *see* 0494-9390
0040-1471 P T T Technische Mitteilungen
0040-148X Technische Rundschau
0040-1498 T U Technische Ueberwachung *changed to* T U - Technische Ueberwachung. Sicherheit Zuverlaessigheit und Umweltschutz in Wirtschaft und Verkehr.
0040-1501 Technische Universitaet Clausthal. Mitteilungsblatt
0040-151X Schweizerische Technische Zeitschrift
0040-1536 Technischer Ansporn†
0040-1552 Technischer Handel
0040-1560 Technisches Journal†
0040-1587 Technocracy Digest
0040-1595 Technocrat†
0040-1609 Technocrat *changed to* Techno Japan.
0040-1617 Technocratic Trendevents†
0040-1625 Technological Forecasting and Social Change
0040-1641 Technology *changed to* Fertiliser Technology.
0040-165X Technology and Culture
0040-1676 Technology Ireland
0040-1692 Technology Review
0040-1706 Technometrics
0040-1714 Tecnica
0040-1722 Tecnica de la Regulacion y Mando Automatico *see* 0213-3113
0040-1730 Tecnica del Frio y del Calor
0040-1757 Tecnica dell'Aria Compressa†
0040-1765 Tecnica dell'Arte
0040-1773 Tecnica e Circolazione Autostradale
0040-1781 Tecnica e Industria
0040-179X Tecnica e Invencion
0040-1803 Tecnica e Ricostruzione
0040-1811 Tecnica e Uomo
0040-182X Tecnica Hospitalaria
0040-1838 Tecnica Industrial†
0040-1846 Tecnica Italiana
0040-1854 Tecnica Mecanica†
0040-1862 Tecnica Molitoria
0040-1889 Tecnica Pecuaria en Mexico
0040-1897 Tecnica Sanitaria
0040-1900 Tecnica Textil Internacional
0040-1919 Tecnicas Financieras†
0040-1927 Tecniche dell'Automazione e Robotica
0040-1943 Tecnologia Alimentaria
0040-1951 Tectonophysics
0040-196X Tedenska Tribuna *see* 0350-7564
0040-1978 Tednik
0040-1986 Teen Guide†
0040-1994 Teen Life†
0040-2001 Teen
0040-201X Teen Pin-Ups†
0040-2044 Teen World†
0040-2060 Teens' and Boys' Outfitter *see* 0195-2137
0040-2087 Teenways†
0040-2109 Teg och Teknik†
0040-2125 Tegen de Tuberculose
0040-2133 Tegenwoordig
0040-2141 Tegl
0040-215X Tegnikon†
0040-2168 Tekhniceska Misal
0040-2176 Tehnika *see* 0350-2597
0040-2184 Teilhard Review *changed to* Teilhard Review and Journal of Cosmic Convergence.
0040-2192 Teintex *see* 0019-9176
0040-2222 Tekenen des Tijds†
0040-2230 Tekhnicheskaya Estetika
0040-2249 Tekhnika Kino i Televideniya
0040-2257 Tekhnika Molodezhi
0040-2273 Tekko Rodo Eisei
0040-2303 Tekniikka *see* 0785-997X
0040-2311 Teknisk Information†
0040-232X Teknisk Nyt
0040-2338 Teknisk Skoletidende *changed to* D T L - Nyt.
0040-2346 Teknisk Tidskrift *see* 0550-8754
0040-2354 Teknisk Ukeblad-Teknikk *changed to* Teknisk Ukeblad.
0040-2362 Tekniskt Forum *see* 0533-070X
0040-2370 Tekstiililehti
0040-2389 Tekstilna Industrija
0040-2397 Tekstil'naya Promyshlennost'
0040-2400 Tel Hashomer Hospital Proceeding†
0040-2419 Tel Quel
0040-2427 Tele (Swedish Edition)
0040-2451 Tele-Scout†
0040-2486 Telecommunication Journal of Australia
0040-2494 Telecommunications (Norwood)
0040-2508 Telecommunications and Radio Engineering
0040-2524 Teledyne Ryan Aeronautical Reporter†
0040-2532 Teleflora Spirit *changed to* Flowers&
0040-2567 Telegrama Politico
0040-2575 Telegraph
0040-2583 Telegraph Worker Journal†
0040-2591 Telekomunikace
0040-2605 Telekomunikacije
0040-2621 Telemetry Journal†
0040-263X Telephone Engineer and Management
0040-2648 Telephone Review Magazine†
0040-2656 Telephony
0040-2664 Telepro
0040-2672 Teleprograma
0040-2680 Telepulestudomanyi Kozlemenyek
0040-2699 Telerama
0040-2702 Telescope (Detroit)
0040-2710 Telesis (Ottawa)
0040-2729 Telesna Vychova Mladeze
0040-2737 Telespazio
0040-2745 Telespiegel *changed to* Der Oesterreichische Schulfunk mit Telespiegel.
0040-2753 Teleteknik.
0040-277X Television - Radio Age
0040-2788 Broadcast
0040-2796 Television Quarterly
0040-2818 Telhan Patrika
0040-2826 Tellus *see* 0280-6495
0040-2826 Tellus *see* 0280-6509
0040-2834 Telonde *changed to* Thomson Magazine.
0040-2850 Telovychovny Pracovnik
0040-2869 Temas
0040-2877 Temas Administrativos *see* 0120-341X
0040-2885 Temas Contemporaneos
0040-2915 Temas Sociales

ISSN

ISSN	Title
0040-2958	Temple Apothecary
0040-2966	Temple David Bulletin
0040-2974	Temple Law Quarterly see 0899-8086
0040-2982	Tempo (London, 1939)
0040-2990	Tempo†
0040-3008	Tempo (New York)
0040-3016	Tempo (New York, 1955)†
0040-3024	Tempo
0040-3040	Tempo Economico
0040-3067	Temps Libre Informations changed to Enjeu.
0040-3075	Temps Modernes
0040-3083	Tenant
0040-3113	Tenders see 0812-2288
0040-3121	Tennecot
0040-313X	Tennessee Academy of Science. Journal
0040-3148	Tennessee Agricultural Experiment Station. Bulletin
0040-3156	Tennessee Alumnus
0040-3180	Tennessee Archaeologist
0040-3199	Tennessee Banker
0040-3202	Tennessee Conservationist
0040-3229	Tennessee Farm and Home Science
0040-3245	Tennessee Farmer
0040-3253	Tennessee Folklore Society Bulletin
0040-3261	Tennessee Historical Quarterly
0040-327X	Tennessee Law Enforcement Journal
0040-3288	Tennessee Law Review
0040-3296	T L - Tennessee Librarian see 0162-1564
0040-330X	Tennessee Life Insurance News see 0194-4312
0040-3318	Tennessee Medical Association. Journal
0040-3334	Tennessee Musician
0040-3342	Tennessee Nurses Association. Bulletin
0040-3350	Tennessee Planner†
0040-3369	Tennessee Poetry Journal†
0040-3377	Tennessee Public Welfare Record see 0360-4608
0040-3385	Tennessee Dental Association. Journal
0040-3393	Tennessee Survey of Business see 0099-0973
0040-3407	Tennessee Teacher
0040-3415	Tennessee Town and City
0040-3423	Tennis
0040-3431	Tennis Tidningen†
0040-344X	Tennis de France
0040-3458	Golf Europeen
0040-3466	Tennis U.S.A.†
0040-3474	Tennis World
0040-3482	Tenrikyo
0040-3490	Tenside - Detergents see 0932-3414
0040-3504	Tensor
0040-3520	Tentoonstellingsagenda see 0920-7430
0040-3539	Teollisuuslehti see 0358-7673
0040-3547	Teollisuustekniikka
0040-3555	Teologinen Aikakauskirja
0040-3563	Teoresi†
0040-3571	Teoreticheskie Osnovy Khimicheskoi Tekhnologii
0040-358X	Teorie a Praxe Telesne Vychovy†
0040-3598	Teorija in Praksa
0040-3601	Teoriya i Praktika Fizicheskoi Kul'tury
0040-361X	Teoriya Veroyatnostei i ee Primenenie
0040-3628	Teosofi i Norden changed to Tidlos Visdom.
0040-3636	Teploenergetika
0040-3644	Teplofizika Vysokikh Temperatur
0040-3652	Teramo
0040-3660	Terapevticheskii Arkhiv
0040-3679	Terapia†
0040-3687	Terapia†
0040-3695	Terapia Moderna
0040-3709	Teratology
0040-3717	Termeszet Vilaga
0040-3725	Termotecnica
0040-3733	Terra
0040-3741	Terra
0040-375X	Terra Ameriga
0040-3768	Terra e Sole
0040-3776	Terra e Vita
0040-3784	Terra Santa
0040-3792	Terra Umbra†
0040-3806	Terrazzo Topics
0040-3814	Terre
0040-3822	Terre Cuite†
0040-3830	Terre de Chez Nous
0040-3865	Terre et Vie see 0249-7395
0040-389X	Terres Australes et Antarctiques Francaises†
0040-3903	Terveydenhoitolehti see 0355-1903
0040-3911	Terveys
0040-392X	Terzo Mondo
0040-3938	Tesoro Eucaristico
0040-3946	Test
0040-3962	Testigo†
0040-3970	Textil & Beklaedningst†
0040-3989	Testimonianze
0040-3997	Testing, Instruments, and Controls see 0157-6461
0040-4004	Tete†
0040-4012	Tethys†
0040-4020	Tetrahedron
0040-4039	Tetrahedron Letters
0040-4047	Tetsudo Pikutoriaru
0040-4055	Monthly Statistics of Actual Production of Railway Cars changed to Tetsudo Sharyoto Seisan Dotai Tokei Geppo.
0040-4071	Tevyne
0040-4101	Texaco Tempo†
0040-4128	Texas A & M University. College of Liberal Arts. Review†
0040-4136	Texas A & M University Library Notes
0040-4144	Texas Academy of Science. Newsletter†
0040-4152	Texas Agriculture changed to Texas Agriculture.
0040-4160	Texas and Southwest Hotel-Motel Review see 8750-4634
0040-4179	Texas Architect
0040-4187	Texas Bar Journal
0040-4195	Financial Trend†
0040-4209	Texas Business Review
0040-4241	Texas Coach
0040-425X	Texas Concho Register changed to West Texas Angelus.
0040-4284	Texas Dental Journal
0040-4314	Texas Fashions†
0040-4322	Texas Food Merchant
0040-4330	Texas F F A Magazine
0040-4349	Texas Highways
0040-4357	Texas Hospitals changed to Health Texas.
0040-4365	Texas Industrial Expansion
0040-4373	Texas Industry changed to T. A. B. Quarterly.
0040-4381	Texas International Law Forum see 0163-7479
0040-439X	Texas Jewish Post
0040-4403	Texas Journal of Science
0040-4411	Texas Law Review
0040-442X	Texas Lawman
0040-4438	Texas Libraries
0040-4446	Texas Library Journal
0040-4454	Texas L P - Gas News
0040-4462	Texas Manpower Trends changed to Texas Labor Market Review.
0040-4470	Texas Medicine
0040-4489	Texas Methodist changed to United Methodist Reporter.
0040-4519	Texas Observer
0040-4527	Texas Oil Jobber see 0896-8969
0040-4535	Texas Oil Journal†
0040-4543	Texas Ornithological Society. Bulletin
0040-4551	Texas Outlook
0040-456X	Texas Parade see 0164-7628
0040-4578	Texas Parent-Teacher changed to P T A Communicator.
0040-4586	Texas Parks and Wildlife Magazine
0040-4608	Texas Poultry and Egg News see 0885-3371
0040-4616	Texas Presbyterian changed to Presbyterian.
0040-4624	Texas Press Messenger changed to T P A Messenger.
0040-4632	Texas Professional Engineer
0040-4640	Texas Public Employee
0040-4659	Texas Quarterly†
0040-4675	Texas Reports on Biology and Medicine†
0040-4683	Texas Schools changed to T S T A Texas Schools.
0040-4691	Texas Studies in Literature and Language
0040-4705	Texas Study of Secondary Education Research Bulletin
0040-4721	Texas Techsan
0040-473X	Texas Town & City
0040-4748	Texas Transportation Researcher
0040-4756	Texas Veterinary Medical Journal
0040-4764	Technika Chronika
0040-4772	Texpress
0040-4780	Text†
0040-4799	France. Institut National de Recherche et de Documentation Pedagogiques. Textes et Documents pour la Classe see 0395-6601
0040-4810	Textiel-Visie - Weekly (Amsterdam) changed to TextielVisie.
0040-4829	Textil
0040-4837	Textil
0040-4845	Textil och Konfektion
0040-4853	Textil Praxis International
0040-4861	Textil-Revue
0040-487X	Textil-Wirtschaft
0040-4888	Textilbranschen see 0284-6152
0040-4896	Textile Bulletin†
0040-490X	Textile Chemist and Colorist
0040-490X	American Association of Textile Chemists and Colorists. Buyer's Guide
0040-4926	Textile Dyer and Printer
0040-4934	Textile Engineer changed to Ramifications.
0040-4969	Textile History†
0040-4977	Textile India changed to Textile India Progress.
0040-4993	Textile Industry & Trade Journal
0040-5000	Textile Institute. Journal
0040-5019	Textile Journal of Australia see 0816-3588
0040-5027	Textile Labor see 0271-5848
0040-5035	Textile Machinery
0040-5043	Textile Machinery Society of Japan. Journal
0040-5078	Textile Magazine
0040-5086	Textile Magazine
0040-5094	Textile Maintenance Reporter changed to Texas Textile Maintenance Reporter.
0040-5116	Textile Month
0040-5124	Textile News
0040-5132	Textile Organon changed to Fiber Organon.
0040-5140	Textiles Panamericanos
0040-5159	Textile Production changed to World Fibre News.
0040-5167	Textile Progress
0040-5175	Textile Research Journal
0040-5191	Textile Technology Digest
0040-5205	Textile Trends
0040-5213	Textile World
0040-5221	Officiel du Pret a Porter
0040-523X	Textiles of Ireland and Linen Trade Circular changed to Textile Times International.
0040-5248	Textiles Suisses
0040-5264	Textilia
0040-5280	Textilis changed to Tex-Textilis.
0040-5299	Textilmesteren†
0040-5302	Textilreinigung†
0040-5329	Text und Kritik
0040-5353	Thai Journal of Development Administration
0040-5361	Thai Junior Red Cross Magazine
0040-537X	Thailand Illustrated†
0040-5418	Theater der Zeit
0040-5442	Theater-Rundschau
0040-5450	Theaternachrichten changed to Theater in Graz.
0040-5469	Theatre Crafts
0040-5477	Theatre Design and Technology
0040-5485	Theatre Documentation†
0040-5493	Theatre en Pologne
0040-5507	Theater Heute
0040-5515	Theatre Information Bulletin
0040-5523	Theatre Notebook
0040-5531	Theatre Organ
0040-5558	Theatre Organ Review
0040-5566	Theatre Research see 0307-8833
0040-5574	Theatre Survey
0040-5604	Theatron
0040-5612	Theologia Reformata
0040-5620	Theological Education
0040-5639	Theological Studies
0040-5655	Theologie und Philosophie
0040-5663	Theologisch-Praktische Quartalschrift
0040-5671	Theologische Literaturzeitung
0040-568X	Theologische Revue
0040-5698	Theologische Rundschau
0040-5701	Theologische Zeitschrift
0040-571X	Theology
0040-5728	Theology Digest
0040-5736	Theology Today
0040-5744	Theoretica Chimica Acta
0040-5752	Theoretical and Applied Genetics
0040-5760	Theoretical and Experimental Chemistry
0040-5779	Theoretical and Mathematical Physics
0040-5787	Theoretical Chemical Engineering Abstracts
0040-5795	Theoretical Foundations of Chemical Engineering
0040-5809	Theoretical Population Biology
0040-5817	Theoria
0040-5825	Theoria
0040-5833	Theory and Decision
0040-5841	Theory Into Practice
0040-585X	Theory of Probability and Its Applications
0040-5868	Theosofia
0040-5876	Theosophical Journal
0040-5884	Theosophical Movement
0040-5892	Theosophist
0040-5906	Theosophy
0040-5914	Therapeutic Recreation Journal
0040-5922	Therapeutique†
0040-5930	Therapeutische Umschau
0040-5949	Therapia Hungarica
0040-5957	Therapie
0040-5965	Therapie der Gegenwart
0040-5973	Therapiewoche
0040-599X	Thermal Abstracts see 0140-4237
0040-6007	Thermal Analysis Review see 0956-2265
0040-6015	Thermal Engineering
0040-6023	Thermiek
0040-6031	Thermochimica Acta
0040-604X	Thesaurus
0040-6058	These Times†
0040-6066	Theta (Carrollton)
0040-6074	Theta (New York)
0040-6082	Thin Films see 0305-3091
0040-6090	Thin Solid Films
0040-6112	Think†
0040-6120	Third Branch
0040-6139	Third Degree (New York)
0040-6155	Magazine of Metals Producing see 0149-1210
0040-6171	This England
0040-6198	This is London
0040-6228	This Magazine Is About Schools see 0381-3746
0040-6244	This Month in London†
0040-6252	This Month in Your Library changed to Spotlight on Your Library.
0040-6260	This Paper Belongs to the People
0040-6279	Key Magazine. This Week in Chicago
0040-6295	This Week in Rome
0040-6309	This Week changed to This Week in Western North Carolina.
0040-6317	This Week in the Nation's Capital
0040-6325	Thomist
0040-6341	Revue Technique Thomson - C S F. Electronique
0040-6368	Thoracic Medicine and Surgery
0040-6376	Thorax
0040-6384	Thoraxchirurgie - Vaskulaere Chirurgie see 0171-6425

ISSN INDEX

0040-6392 Thoreau Journal Quarterly see 0730-868X
0040-6406 Thoreau Society Bulletin
0040-6414 Thoroughbred Record and the Racing Calendar changed to Thoroughbred Record.
0040-6430 Thoth†
0040-6449 Thought†
0040-6457 Thought
0040-6465 Thought†
0040-649X Three Banks Review see 0267-1190
0040-6511 Three Crafts Journal†
0040-652X Three Crowns
0040-6538 Three/Four changed to Vine.
0040-6546 Three Hundred Thirty-Eight News
0040-6562 Threshold
0040-6589 Throb
0040-6597 Thrombosis et Diathesis Haemorrhagica see 0340-6245
0040-6600 Through to Victory†
0040-6619 Thru the Garden Gate
0040-6635 Thunder
0040-6643 Thunderbolt changed to The Truth at Last.
0040-6651 Thursday†
0040-666X Thyssenforschung see 0340-5060
0040-6686 Ti Saluto, Fratello!
0040-6694 Tibet im Exil†
0040-6708 Tibetan Review
0040-6716 Tic†
0040-6732 Tici†
0040-6759 Tiden
0040-6767 Tidens Ekko†
0040-6775 Tidens Kvinder†
0040-6791 Tidings (Los Angeles)
0040-6805 Tidnings Nytt†
0040-6821 Tidskrift foer Kriminalvaard
0040-683X Tidskrift foer Kustartilleriet
0040-6848 Tidskrift foer Schack
0040-6856 Tidskrift foer Yrkesutbildning
0040-6872 Tidskrift foer Dokumentation
0040-6880 Tidsskrift for Groenlands Retsvaesen
0040-6899 Tidskrift foer Svenska Folkhoegskolan see 0348-4769
0040-6902 Sveriges Advokatsamfund. Tidskrift see 0281-3505
0040-6937 Tidskrift i Fortifikation
0040-6945 Tidskrift i Sjovasendet
0040-6953 Juridiska Foereningen i Finland. Tidskrift
0040-6961 Tidskriften Bostadsnaemnden
0040-6988 Tidskriften Heimdal
0040-7003 Tidskriften Landsstaten
0040-7011 Tidskriften Taxeringsnaemden
0040-702X Tidsskrift for Danske Sygehuse
0040-7038 Tidsskrift for Faareavl changed to Tidsskrift for Dansk Faareavl.
0040-7046 Tidsskrift for Fjerkraeavl see 0045-9607
0040-7062 Tidsskrift for Hermetikkindustri see 0040-7127
0040-7089 Tidsskrift for Jordmoedre
0040-7100 Tidsskrift for Kortboelge Radio changed to OZ.
0040-7119 Tidsskrift for Landoekonomi
0040-7127 Naeringsmiddelindustrien
0040-7135 Tidsskrift for Planteavl
0040-7143 Tidsskrift for Rettsvitenskap
0040-7151 Tidsskrift for Revisjon og Regnskapsvesen see 0332-7795
0040-716X Tidsskrift for Samfunnsforskning
0040-7178 Tidsskrift for Skogbrukt
0040-7186 Tidsskrift for Soevaesen
0040-7194 Tidsskrift for Teologi og Kirke
0040-7208 Tidsskrift for Textilteknik see 0107-5373
0040-7216 Tidsskrift for Voksenopplaering changed to Nordisk Tidskrift foer Folkbildning och Vuxenundervisning.
0040-7224 Tidsskriftet Ny Tid og Vit
0040-7232 Tie
0040-7259 Tiefkuehl Praxis International changed to G V - Praxis.
0040-7267 Tielehti see 0355-7855
0040-7275 Tiempo
0040-7283 Tiempo de Cine
0040-7291 Das Tier
0040-7313 Tierfreund changed to Schweizer Tierschutz.
0040-733X Tierra
0040-7348 Tierra y dos Mares†
0040-7356 Tiers Monde
0040-7364 Der Tierzuechter
0040-7372 Tiesa
0040-7380 Tiger Beat (Teaneck)
0040-7402 Tiili
0040-7410 Vereniging Koninklijke Nederlandsche Heide Maatschappij. Tijdschrift changed to Vereniging Koninklijke Nederlandsche Heide Maatschappij. Heidemijtijdschrift.
0040-7429 Tijdschrift voor Architectuur en Beeldende Kunsten†
0040-7437 Tijdschrift voor Bestuurswetenschappen en Publiekrecht
0040-7445 Tijdschrift voor Chemie & Instrument changed to Chemie & Instrument.
0040-7453 Tijdschrift voor Diergeneeskunde
0040-7461 Tijdschrift voor Economie see 0772-7674
0040-747X Tijdschrift voor Economische en Sociale Geografie
0040-7488 Tijdschrift voor Effectief Directiebeleid†
0040-7496 Tijdschrift voor Entomologie

0040-750X Tijdschrift voor Filosofie
0040-7518 Tijdschrift voor Geschiedenis
0040-7550 Tijdschrift voor Nederlandse Taal- en Letterkunde
0040-7569 Tijdschrift voor Oppervlaktetechnieken van Materialen see 0923-1722
0040-7577 Tijdschrift voor Opvoedkunde see 0166-5855
0040-7585 Tijdschrift voor Rechtsgeschiedenis
0040-7593 Tijdschrift voor Revalidatie changed to Revalidatie.
0040-7607 Tijdschrift voor Sociale Geneeskunde see 0920-0517
0040-7615 Tijdschrift voor Sociale Wetenschappen
0040-7623 Tijdschrift voor Vervoerswetenschap
0040-764X Tijdspiegel
0040-7658 Tilastollisia Kuukaustitietoja Helsingista see 0357-3362
0040-7666 Tile and Architectural Ceramics see 0192-9550
0040-7674 Tile and Till†
0040-7682 Till Rors (Med Segel och Motor) changed to Paa Kryss och till Rors.
0040-7704 Tim changed to Maky.
0040-7712 T I M
0040-7720 Timber changed to Timber and Timber Products.
0040-7739 Timber and Plywood see 0262-6071
0040-7755 Timber Development Association of India. Journal
0040-7763 Timber Grower
0040-7771 Timber Journal†
0040-778X Timber Supply Review changed to Quarterly Timber Statistics.
0040-7798 Timber Trades Journal and Woodworking Machinery see 0262-6071
0040-781X Time
0040-7828 Time and Tide†
0040-7836 Time & Tide
0040-7852 Time Machine
0040-7879 Times and Challenge
0040-7887 Times Educational Supplement
0040-7895 Times Literary Supplement
0040-7909 Times of Israel
0040-7917 The Times of the Americas
0040-7933 Timmerfabrikant
0040-7941 Tin and Its Uses
0040-795X Tin International
0040-7968 Tin News
0040-7976 Tin Printer and Box Maker see 0040-795X
0040-7984 Tinctoria (Milan)
0040-8018 Tip
0040-8026 Tip-O-Texan†
0040-8034 Tipperary Star
0040-8042 Tips and Topics in Home Economics†
0040-8050 Welsh Farmer
0040-8069 Tir Sportif en France†
0040-8077 Tiramolla
0040-8085 Tire Review
0040-8093 Federacion Nacional del Tiro Olimpico Espanol. Revista Informativa changed to Federacion Nacional del Tiro Olimpico Espanol. Boletin Informativo.
0040-8107 Tirol†
0040-8115 Tiroler Heimatblaetter
0040-8123 Tisch und Kueche changed to T U K Inform.
0040-8131 Der Tischler
0040-814X Tischtennis-Schau
0040-8158 Tish
0040-8166 Tissue & Cell
0040-8174 Tissue Culture Abstracts†
0040-8182 Titanic Commutator
0040-8190 Title News
0040-8204 Titogradska Tribina
0040-8212 Titular
0040-8239 Tlalocan
0040-8247 To Free Mankind changed to World Citizen - Federalist Letter.
0040-8255 Nisaki Mas i Kea
0040-8263 Toastmaster
0040-8271 Tobacco
0040-828X Tobacco†
0040-8298 Tobacco Abstracts
0040-8301 Tobacco Intelligence†
0040-8328 Tobacco Reporter changed to Tobacco Reporter.
0040-8336 Tobacco Retailers Journal changed to Retail Tobacconist.
0040-8344 U.S. Department of Agriculture. Tobacco Situation changed to U.S. Department of Agriculture. Tobacco Situation and Outlook Report.
0040-8352 Dialogue (Birmingham)†
0040-8360 Today (Kent)
0040-8379 Today†
0040-8387 Today changed to Today in Africa.
0040-8409 Today in Anaheim/Orange County†
0040-8417 Today in France
0040-8433 Today in San Diego
0040-8441 Today's Catholic Teacher
0040-845X Today's Chef changed to Today's Chef-Food Service Executive.
0040-8468 Today's Child Newsmagazine†
0040-8476 Today's Children†
0040-8484 Today's Education see 0734-7219
0040-8484 Today's Education see 0272-359X
0040-8484 Today's Education see 0272-3581
0040-8492 Todays Family†
0040-8522 Today's Housing Briefs†
0040-8549 Today's Parish
0040-8565 Today's Secretary†

0040-8573 Today's Speech see 0146-3373
0040-8581 Today's Teens†
0040-859X Today's Transport International†
0040-8603 Todo
0040-8611 Todo es Historia†
0040-862X Tudomanyszervezesi Tajekoztato see 0866-5192
0040-8638 Toerist see 0005-1772
0040-8646 Wudd
0040-8654 Toga Calabrese
0040-8670 Toho University Medical Society. Journal
0040-8689 Tohoku Daigaku Kagaku Keisoku Kenkyujo Hokoku
0040-8697 Tohoku Daigaku Nogaku Kenkyujo Hokoku†
0040-8700 Tohoku Medical Journal
0040-8719 Tohoku Journal of Agricultural Research
0040-8727 Tohoku Journal of Experimental Medicine
0040-8735 Tohoku Mathematical Journal
0040-8743 Tohoku Psychologica Folia
0040-8751 Tohoku Archivo por Orthopedia Kej Akcidenta Hirurgio changed to Tohoku Archives of Orthopaedic Surgery and Traumatology.
0040-876X Tohoku Daigaku Senko Seiren Kenkyujo Iho
0040-8778 Tohoku University. Science Reports. Series 1: Physics, Chemistry, Astronomy see 0388-5607
0040-8786 Tohoku University. Science Reports. Series 4: Biology†
0040-8794 Tohoku Geophysical Journal
0040-8808 Tohoku University. Science Reports of the Research Institutes. Series A: Physics, Chemistry, and Metallurgy
0040-8816 Tohoku University. Faculty of Engineering. Technology Reports†
0040-8824 Toilers of the Deep
0040-8832 Toison d'Or
0040-8859 Tokai Regional Fisheries Research Laboratory (Report) changed to Chuo Suisan Kenkyujo Kenkyu Hokoku.
0040-8867 Toko-Ginecologia Practica
0040-8875 Tokushima Journal of Experimental Medicine
0040-8883 University of Tokushima. Faculty of Engineering. Bulletin
0040-8891 Tokyo Dental College. Bulletin
0040-8905 Tokyo Medical College. Journal
0040-8913 Tokyo Journal of Climatology
0040-8921 Tokyo Medical and Dental University. Bulletin
0040-893X Tokyo Municipal News changed to Tokyo Metropolitan News.
0040-8948 Japan. National Museum News
0040-8964 University of Tokyo. College of General Education. Scientific Papers see 0289-7520
0040-8972 University of Tokyo. Earthquake Research Institute. Bulletin
0040-8980 University of Tokyo. Faculty of Science. Journal. Section 1A: Mathematics
0040-9006 Tokyo Daigaku Seisan Gijutsu Kenkyujo Hokoku
0040-9014 Tokyo University of Fisheries. Journal
0040-9022 Tokyo Joshi Ika Daigaku Zasshi
0040-9030 Tolar Creek Syndicate†
0040-9049 Toldbladet
0040-9057 Toledo Business News changed to Chamber Insider.
0040-9065 Toledo City Journal
0040-9081 Toledo Jewish News
0040-909X Tolkien Journal see 0146-9339
0040-9103 Tolpolski's Chronicle†
0040-9111 Tolvmansbladet changed to Erhvervs-Jordbruget.
0040-912X Tom Thumb
0040-9146 Tomorrow Through Research changed to Technology Today.
0040-9154 Tomorrow's Man†
0040-9170 Toneel Teatraal
0040-9189 Tong-Tong see 0165-6546
0040-9200 Tonindustrie-Zeitung und Keramische Rundschau changed to T I Z International.
0040-9219 Manufacturing Engineering and Management see 0361-0853
0040-9227 Tooling†
0040-9243 Tooling & Production
0040-9251 Toonzaalt
0040-926X Top Gear†
0040-9286 Top of the News see 0894-2498
0040-9308 Topcu Dergisi†
0040-9316 Topic News Weekly
0040-9324 Topical Dates & Facts Newsletter†
0040-9332 Topical Time
0040-9340 Topicator
0040-9367 Topics (Boston)
0040-9375 Topique - Revue Freudienne
0040-9383 Topology
0040-9391 Tora Ya Tebelo
0040-9405 Torah Umesorah Report†
0040-9413 Toranjisuta Gijutsu
0040-9448 Torch (Chicago)
0040-9456 Torch of Knowledge†
0040-9472 Torfyanaya Promyshlennost'
0040-9499 Tornado†
0040-9502 Foro Universitario
0040-9510 Metropolitan Toronto Board of Trade. Journal changed to Metropolitan Toronto Business Journal.

ISSN INDEX

ISSN	Title
0040-9529	Toronto Boys and Girls House Subscription Reviews†
0040-9537	Toronto Calendar Magazine
0040-9553	Toronto Railway Club. Official Proceedings
0040-957X	Torque†
0040-9588	La Torre
0040-9596	Torre Civica†
0040-960X	Torre Davidica
0040-9618	Torrey Botanical Club. Bulletin
0040-9626	Illinois State Bar Association. Tort Trends *changed to* Tort Trends Newsletter.
0040-9634	Tortenelmi Szemle
0040-9650	Japan Society of Library Science. Annals
0040-9669	Library World
0040-9677	Tot 'n Teen Fashions
0040-9693	Total Comfort Dealer†
0040-9723	Totem
0040-9731	Tour de Feu *see* 0294-4030
0040-974X	Tourama *changed to* Hotel Tourama of Rhodesia.
0040-9758	Touring
0040-9766	Touring Freizeit *changed to* Freizeit.
0040-9782	Tourisme Informations†
0040-9804	Tourist Time†
0040-9839	Tout-Rouen
0040-9855	Toute l'Electronique
0040-9863	Toutou - Journal
0040-9898	Toward Freedom
0040-9901	Tower†
0040-991X	Tower Smiling *see* 0190-3284
0040-9928	Towers
0040-9952	Town and Country
0040-9960	Town and Country Planning
0040-9979	Town & Village
0040-9995	Town Planning and Local Government Guide
0041-0012	New Zealand Planning Institute. Town Planning Quarterly *see* 0111-9435
0041-0020	Town Planning Review
0041-0039	Town Talk about Toronto†
0041-0047	Towns & Cities Magazines†
0041-0063	Towson State Journal of International Affairs
0041-0071	Toxicity Bibliography†
0041-008X	Toxicology and Applied Pharmacology
0041-0101	Toxicon
0041-011X	Toy & Hobby World
0041-0128	Toy Trader†
0041-0136	Toy Trader
0041-0144	Toyo Soda Manufacturing Company. Scientific Report *see* 0914-3106
0041-0152	Toyoda Technical Review *changed to* Toyoda Machine Works Technical Review.
0041-0160	Toys†
0041-0179	Toys *see* 0160-8010
0041-0195	Toys International *see* 0260-4760
0041-0209	Tozhil Udayam *changed to* Tozhil Uravu.
0041-0233	Fomento del Trabajo Nacional. Economia Nacional, Internacional de la Empresa *see* 0212-0607
0041-0241	Trabajos de Estadistica e Investigacion Operativa
0041-025X	Trabajos de Hematologia y Hemoterapia†
0041-0276	Traces
0041-0284	Track & Field News
0041-0292	Track and Field Quarterly Review
0041-0306	Track Newsletter
0041-0314	Track Technique *see* 0742-3918
0041-0330	Tracker
0041-0349	Tracks
0041-0357	Tract Messenger
0041-0365	Trade-A-Plane
0041-0373	Trade and Industry
0041-0381	Trade and Industry of Japan *see* 0388-0311
0041-039X	Trade and Tours†
0041-0403	Trade Channel *changed to* Export Channel (Technical Products Edition).
0041-0411	Trade Chronicle
0041-042X	Trade Digest *changed to* World Fairs Guide.
0041-0438	Trade Marks Journal
0041-0446	Trade Marks Journal
0041-0454	Trade Marks Journal
0041-0462	Trade of the Maltese Islands *changed to* Malta Trade Statistics.
0041-0470	Trade Review of the Week†
0041-0489	Trade Trends†
0041-0497	Trade Union Courier
0041-0500	Trade Union Information†
0041-0519	Trade Union News Bulletin from Norway†
0041-0527	Trade Union Press *changed to* Flashes from the Trade Unions.
0041-0535	Trade Union Record
0041-0543	Trade with Greece
0041-0551	Trade with Italy
0041-056X	Trademark Reporter
0041-0586	Trading Post (Greenville)
0041-0594	Tradition
0041-0608	Tradition (New York)
0041-0624	Trae Nyt
0041-0632	Traeindustrien *see* 0105-8738
0041-0659	Traffic Bulletin†
0041-0675	Traffic Engineering *see* 0162-8178
0041-0683	Traffic Engineering & Control
0041-0691	Traffic Management
0041-0705	Traffic Manager
0041-0713	Traffic Quarterly *see* 0278-9434
0041-0721	Traffic Safety (Chicago)
0041-073X	Traffic World
0041-0748	Trail and Landscape
0041-0756	Trail and Timberline
0041-0764	Trailblazer†
0041-0772	Trailer-Body Builders
0041-0780	Trailer Life
0041-0799	Trailer Topics Magazine†
0041-0802	Trailer Travel Magazine *see* 0160-3000
0041-0829	Train Collectors Quarterly
0041-0837	Train Dispatcher
0041-0845	Trainsheet
0041-0853	Trained Men *changed to* Training Digest.
0041-0861	Training and Development Journal *see* 1055-9760
0041-087X	Training Briefs†
0041-0888	Training Directors Newsletter†
0041-0896	Training in Business and Industry *see* 0095-5892
0041-090X	Training Officer
0041-0918	Training School Bulletin†
0041-0926	Trainmaster
0041-0934	Trains
0041-0950	Traitement Thermique
0041-0969	Traktoeren
0041-0977	Traktor- og Landbrugsbladet
0041-0985	Traktor Aktuell
0041-1000	Tramontane
0041-1027	Tranciatura Stampaggio *changed to* Tecnologia della Deformazione.
0041-1035	Trans-Action-Social Science and Modern Society *see* 0147-2011
0041-1043	Transair *changed to* Australian Way.
0041-1051	Transactional Analysis Bulletin *see* 0362-1537
0041-106X	Transafrican Journal of History
0041-1078	Transatlantic Review†
0041-1086	Transatom Bulletin *see* 0259-8264
0041-1108	Transcultural Psychiatric Research Review
0041-1116	Transdex Index
0041-1124	Transformacion
0041-1132	Transfusion
0041-1140	Transistor
0041-1167	Transit of Chi Epsilon
0041-1175	Transit Postmark Collector
0041-1183	Transit Record†
0041-1191	Transition *changed to* Transition (New York).
0041-1205	Transition
0041-1213	Transitrends†
0041-1221	Translation *changed to* In Other Words.
0041-123X	Translation Talk†
0041-1256	Translations Register-Index†
0041-1264	Translatoeren
0041-1272	Transmisiones
0041-1280	Transmission and Distribution
0041-1302	Transparent†
0041-1310	Transpatent
0041-1337	Transplantation
0041-1345	Transplantation Proceedings
0041-1361	Transport (Fredensborg) *changed to* Transport - Magasinet (Fredensborg).
0041-137X	Transport
0041-1388	Transport and Communications
0041-1396	Transport and Communications Bulletin for Asia and the Far East *see* 0252-4392
0041-140X	Transport Commercial *changed to* Moteur et Equipement.
0041-1418	Transport-Communications Monthly Review *see* 0376-7256
0041-1426	Transport-Dienst *changed to* Transport-Dienst & Wirtschaftscorrespondent.
0041-1434	Transport Economics†
0041-1442	Transport et Tourisme
0041-1450	Transport Theory and Statistical Physics
0041-1469	Transport History
0041-1477	Transport Industry and Trade Journal *changed to* Transport Industry and Trade Annual.
0041-1485	Transport Journal
0041-1493	Transport Journal of Australia
0041-1523	Transport-Nytt
0041-1531	Transport Salaried Staff Journal
0041-154X	Transport Teknik *changed to* Transport i Dag.
0041-1558	Transport Topics
0041-1566	Transport und Lager *changed to* Euro Transport Journal.
0041-1574	Transport und Lagertechnik *changed to* Transport, Foerder- und Lagertechnik.
0041-1582	Transport und Schiffahrt†
0041-1590	Transportation Ad Views†
0041-1604	Transportation Engineer *changed to* Lifting & Transportation International.
0041-1612	Transportation Journal
0041-1639	Translog
0041-1647	Transportation Research *see* 0191-2607
0041-1647	Transportation Research *see* 0191-2615
0041-1655	Transportation Science
0041-1663	Standard and Poor's Transportation Securities Weekly Outlook *changed to* Standard & Poor's Transportation Securities.
0041-1671	Transportation Technology *see* 0308-1060
0041-168X	Transporte
0041-1698	Transporte Moderno†
0041-1701	Transportnoe Stroitel'stvo
0041-171X	Transvaal Education Bulletin†
0041-1728	Transvaal Educational News
0041-1736	Transvaal Farmer†
0041-1744	Transvaal Gardener
0041-1752	Transvaal Museum. Annals
0041-1760	Trap & Field
0041-1779	Trapani Nuova *changed to* Terza Pagina.
0041-1787	La Trasfusione del Sangue
0041-1795	Trasporti Aerei
0041-1809	Trasporti Industriali *changed to* Trasporti Industriali e Movimentazione.
0041-1817	Trasporti Pubblici†
0041-1825	Trattamenti dei Metalli†
0041-1833	Trattamenti e Finitura - Superfici *changed to* Trattamenti e Finiture.
0041-1841	I M A Trattorista *changed to* Macchine e Motori Agricoli - I M A il Trattorista.
0041-185X	Travail et Methodes
0041-1868	Travail Humain
0041-1876	Travailleur du Livre
0041-1892	Saagverken - Traevarunindustrin *see* 0036-259X
0041-1906	Travaux
0041-1914	Travaux de Peinture†
0041-1930	Travaux et Jours†
0041-1965	Travel *changed to* Travel - Holiday.
0041-1973	TravelAge West
0041-1981	Travel Agency
0041-199X	Travel Agent
0041-2007	Travel & Leisure
0041-2015	Travel Management Daily
0041-2023	Travel Marketing Newsletter†
0041-2031	Travel Times†
0041-204X	Travel Times
0041-2058	Travel Trade Magazine *see* 0311-2179
0041-2066	Travel Trade
0041-2074	Travel Trade Directory
0041-2082	Travel Weekly
0041-2090	Travel World†
0041-2104	TravelAge East
0041-2112	Traveler†
0041-2120	Travelling†
0041-2139	Treasure
0041-2155	U.S. Treasury Department. Treasury Bulletin
0041-2163	Treasury Information Bulletin†
0041-2171	Tree†
0041-2198	Tree - Ring Bulletin
0041-2201	Tree Talks
0041-221X	Trees
0041-2228	Trees†
0041-2236	Trees in South Africa
0041-2244	Trefoil
0041-2260	Trekker *changed to* Trekkerskrant.
0041-2279	Tremplin
0041-2287	Trend†
0041-2295	Trend†
0041-2317	Trend in Engineering
0041-2325	Trenden
0041-2333	Standard & Poor's Trendline Current Market Perspectives *changed to* Trendline Current Market Perspectives.
0041-2341	Trends *see* 0729-6509
0041-2368	Bauma-Trends
0041-2376	Trends (Arlington)†
0041-2384	Trends in Adjusting
0041-2406	Trends in Management - Stockholder Relations *changed to* Georgeson Report.
0041-2414	Trends in Parks and Recreation *changed to* Trends (Alexandria).
0041-2449	Trenton *see* 0194-9101
0041-2457	Trgovinski Glasnik
0041-2481	Tri-Ology Technical Report
0041-249X	Tri-State Food News
0041-2503	Tri-State Trader *changed to* AntiqueWeek - Central.
0041-2511	Triad (Wooster)
0041-252X	Triades
0041-2538	Trial
0041-2546	Trial Lawyer's Guide
0041-2554	Trial Lawyers Quarterly
0041-2562	Inklusief
0041-2570	Triangle (Lakeland)
0041-2597	Triangle
0041-2600	Triangle of Mu Phi Epsilon
0041-2619	Triangle Pointer
0041-2643	Tribal Spokesman†
0041-266X	Tribina
0041-2678	Tribology *see* 0301-679X
0041-2694	Tribos - Tribology Abstracts
0041-2708	Tribritta
0041-2716	Tribuene
0041-2732	Tribuna Alemana
0041-2767	Tribuna Musical
0041-2775	Tribuna Odontologica†
0041-2783	Tribuna Politica
0041-2791	Tribuna Postale *changed to* Tribuna Postale e delle Telecomunicazioni.
0041-2805	Tribunal de Justica do Estado do Rio Grande do Sul. Revista de Jurisprudencia
0041-2813	Tribunal Federal de Recursos. Revista *changed to* Revista Trimestral de Jurisprudencia.
0041-2821	Tribune

ISSN INDEX

ISSN	Title
0041-2848	Tribune des Nations
0041-2864	Tribune Graphologique
0041-2872	Tribune Libre
0041-2899	Tributi Sugli Affari
0041-2902	Tricolor
0041-2910	Tricontinental - Edition Francaist
0041-2929	Tridentt
0041-2945	Trierer Theologische Zeitschrift
0041-2953	Trierer Zeitschrift fuer Geschichte und Kunst des Trierer Landes und seiner Nachbargebiete
0041-2961	Trieste
0041-297X	Trilce de Poesia
0041-3003	Trim U Fitt
0041-3011	Trimestre Economico
0041-302X	Trinaesti Maj
0041-3046	Trinidad and Tobago. Central Statistical Office. Quarterly Economic Report
0041-3062	Trinity News
0041-3097	TriQuarterly
0041-3119	Triton *changed to* Diver.
0041-3127	Triumpht
0041-3135	Triveni
0041-3143	Trivselt
0041-316X	Trompie *changed to* Student.
0041-3178	Trons Segrar
0041-3186	Tropenlandwirt
0041-3208	Tropical Abstracts *see* 0304-5951
0041-3216	Tropical Agriculture
0041-3224	Tropical Agriculturist
0041-3232	Tropical and Geographical Medicine
0041-3240	Tropical Diseases Bulletin
0041-3259	Tropical Fish Hobbyist
0041-3267	Tropical Medicine
0041-3275	Tropical Medicine and Hygiene News
0041-3283	Tropical Products Quarterlyt
0041-3291	Tropical Science
0041-3321	Tros-Kompas
0041-333X	Trottingbredt
0041-3348	Trotwaer
0041-3356	Trotzdem
0041-3364	Trout
0041-3372	Trout and Salmon
0041-3380	Truck and Bus Transportation
0041-3399	Truck Insider Newsletter *see* 0148-6721
0041-3410	Trucking Business *changed to* Heavy Truck Business.
0041-3429	Trucking Newst
0041-3437	Trudbenik
0041-3445	Trudov Invalid
0041-3453	Gosudarstvennyi Astronomicheskii Institut im. P.K. Shternberga. Trudy
0041-3461	Truet
0041-347X	True Confessionst
0041-3488	True Confessions
0041-3496	True Confidential Confessions
0041-350X	True Detective
0041-3518	True Experiencet
0041-3534	True Life Secrets
0041-3542	True Lovet
0041-3550	True Love
0041-3569	True Modern Romances
0041-3585	True Romancet
0041-3593	True Storyt
0041-3607	Treasure World *see* 0195-2692
0041-3615	True West
0041-3658	Truppendienst
0041-3666	Truppenpraxis
0041-3674	Trustee
0041-3682	Trusts and Estates
0041-3690	Truth (Mogadore)
0041-3704	Truth about Communismt
0041-3712	Truth Seeker
0041-3720	Trybuna Spoldzielcza
0041-3739	Tryckluftt
0041-3747	Trziste Povrca i Vocat
0041-3755	Trziste Stoke i Stocnih Proizoda
0041-3763	T M P M - Tschermaks Mineralogische und Petrographische Mitteilungen *see* 0930-0708
0041-3771	Tsitologiya
0041-378X	Tsopano News
0041-3798	Soil Mechanics and Foundation Engineering
0041-3801	Tsukumo Earth Sciencet
0041-381X	Communication Industries
0041-3836	Tu Cher Wen Cher Reader's Digest (Chinese Edition)
0041-3844	Tu Sei Me
0041-3852	Tuatarat
0041-3860	Tuatara
0041-3879	Tubercle *see* 0962-8479
0041-3887	Tuberkulozis es Tudobetegsegek *changed to* Pneumonologia Hungarica.
0041-3895	Tuberkulozis es Tudogyogyaszat Referalo Szemlet
0041-3909	Tubular Structures
0041-3917	Tudomanyos es Muszaki Tajekoztatas
0041-3925	Turk Idare Dergisi
0041-3933	Tuesday
0041-3941	Tufts Dental Outlookt
0041-3968	Tuiles et Briques *changed to* Connaissance des Ceramiques.
0041-3976	Tuinbouwberichten *see* 0772-7054
0041-3984	Tuinderij
0041-3992	Tulane Law Review
0041-400X	Tulane Medicine: Faculty and Alumni *changed to* Tulane Medicine.
0041-4018	Tulane Studies in Geology and Paleontology
0041-4026	Tulanian
0041-4034	Tulimuld
0041-4042	Tulsat
0041-4050	Tulsa Law Journal
0041-4069	Tulsa Lawyer
0041-4085	Tummelplatz
0041-4093	Tumor Research: Experimental and Clinical
0041-4107	Tungsram Technische Mitteilungen
0041-4115	Tunisia. Institut National de la Statistique. Bulletin Mensuel de Statistique
0041-4123	Tunisie Economique
0041-4131	La Tunisie Medicale
0041-414X	Tunnels & Tunnelling
0041-4182	Turist *see* 0868-9547
0041-4190	Turist
0041-4204	Turisticke Novine
0041-4212	Turisticni Vestnikt
0041-4220	Turk Dili
0041-4239	Turk Kulturu
0041-4247	Turk Tarih Kurumu. Belgeler
0041-4255	Turk Tarih Kurumu. Belleten
0041-4263	Turkey. Devlet Istatistik Enstitusu. Aylik Istatistik Bulteni
0041-4271	Turkey World
0041-4298	Turkish Digestt
0041-4301	Turkish Journal of Pediatrics
0041-431X	Turkish Medical Association. Journal - Turk Tip Cemiyeti Mecmuasi *changed to* Turk Tip Dernegi Dergisi.
0041-4328	Turkish National Bibliography
0041-4336	Turkiye Cumhuriyet Merkez Bankasi. Aylik Bulten
0041-4344	Bibliography of Articles in Turkish Periodicals
0041-4352	Tumori
0041-4360	Turrialba
0041-4379	Tussen de Rails
0041-4395	Tutti Fotografi
0041-4409	Tuttitaliat
0041-4417	Tutto Cucciolo
0041-4441	Tuttosport
0041-445X	Tuttoville
0041-4468	Tuulilasi
0041-4476	T.V. *see* 0773-3429
0041-4484	T V and Movie Playt
0041-4492	T V and Movie Screen
0041-4506	T V Digest *changed to* T V Times (St. Paul).
0041-4514	T V Publicity Outlets - Nationwide *see* 1054-4259
0041-4522	T V Sorrisi e Canzoni (Rome)
0041-4530	T V Star Paradet
0041-4549	Tvai
0041-4565	Tvorchestvo
0041-4573	Twainian
0041-4581	Twee N
0041-459X	Twentieth Centuryt
0041-4611	Twentieth Century Fund. Newsletter *changed to* Twentieth Century Fund. Newsletter.
0041-462X	Twentieth Century Literature
0041-4638	Twentieth Century Studiest
0041-4646	Twigs *see* 0163-1209
0041-4654	Twin Circle *changed to* Catholic Twin Circle.
0041-4662	Two Bridges Newst
0041-4670	Two Rivers
0041-4697	Two Wheelert
0041-4700	Two Wheels
0041-4727	Tworczosc
0041-4751	Tydskrif vir Geesteswetenskappe
0041-476X	Tydskrif vir Letterkunde
0041-4778	Journal for Secondary Educationt
0041-4786	Tydskrif vir Natuurwetenskappet
0041-4794	Tydskrif vir Rasse - Aangeleenthede
0041-4808	Tygodnik Powszechny
0041-4816	Tyo - Terveys - Turvallisuus
0041-4824	Typetalks Magazinet
0041-4832	Typographical Journal
0041-4840	Typografische Monatsblaetter
0041-4859	Tyres and Accessories
0041-4867	Tsement
0041-4891	Tsvetnye Metally
0041-4905	Tsvetovodstvo
0041-4921	U. A. L. Economic and Financial Reviewt
0041-493X	U A M P Tt
0041-4948	Egypt. Ministry of Tourism. Statistical Bulletin
0041-4972	U A W Fair Practices Fact Sheett
0041-4980	U A W Washington Report
0041-4999	Alumni U B C Chronicle
0041-5006	U B Nt
0041-5014	U C L A Graduate Journalt
0041-5030	U E C Journalt
0041-5049	U E News *changed to* U E News Magazine.
0041-5057	U E G Boletim *changed to* Boletim U E R J.
0041-5065	U E News
0041-5073	U F O Investigatort
0041-5081	U F O - Nachrichtent
0041-509X	U H S Bulletin *changed to* H I A S Reporter.
0041-5103	U.I.A.M.S. Informations
0041-5111	U I C C Bulletin *changed to* U I C C Magazine.
0041-512X	U I R Research Newsletter *changed to* Touchstone Magazine.
0041-5146	U I T P Biblio-Index *changed to* U I T P Biblio-Express.
0041-5154	U I T P Revue *changed to* Public Transport International.
0041-5162	U.I.U. Journalt
0041-5170	U K Press Gazette
0041-5189	U L L I C O Bulletin
0041-5200	U M Profiles *changed to* Montanan.
0041-5219	U N A F. Bulletin de Liaison *see* 0220-9926
0041-5227	U N C T A D Guide to Publications *see* 0255-9358
0041-5243	Unesco Bulletin for Libraries *see* 0379-122X
0041-5251	Unesco. Oficina Regional de Educacon para America Latina y el Caribe. Boletin de Educaciont
0041-5278	Unesco Courier *changed to* Courier (Paris).
0041-5294	Unesco Philippines
0041-5308	U N H C R Report *see* 1014-1235
0041-5324	U N I A P A C *changed to* U N I A P A C. International.
0041-5340	U N I C E F Newst
0041-5359	U N I S A English Studies
0041-5367	U N Monthly Chronicle *see* 0251-7329
0041-5375	U N U C I
0041-5383	U.P.A. Journalt
0041-5405	U P E N
0041-5421	University Reviewt
0041-543X	U R S I Information Bulletin
0041-5456	U S A F Instructors Journalt
0041-5464	U S A Record
0041-5472	U S B W A Tip-Off
0041-5480	U S C O L D Newsletter
0041-5502	U S G A Green Section Record
0041-5537	U S News & World Report
0041-5545	U S S R and Third World
0041-5553	U S S R Computational Mathematics and Mathematical Physics
0041-5561	U S U Staff News
0041-557X	U T
0041-5588	U. T. Ct
0041-5642	Ubulumt
0041-5650	U C L A Law Review
0041-5669	Ude og Hjemme
0041-5677	Udenrigs Handel og Industri Information
0041-5685	Udenrigsministeriets Tidsskrift *changed to* Eksport.
0041-5693	Udenrigspolitiske Skrifter
0041-5707	Uebersee Rundschau
0041-5731	Ufficio Moderno - Pubblicita
0041-574X	Uganda Journal
0041-5758	Uganda. Ministry of Planning and Economic Development. Statistics Division. Quarterly Economic and Statistical Bulletin
0041-5766	Uganda Teachert
0041-5774	Ugeskrift for Agronomer *see* 0906-7043
0041-5782	Ugeskrift for Laeger
0041-5790	Ugol'
0041-5804	Ugol' Ukrainy
0041-5812	Uhli
0041-5820	Uhr *changed to* Uhren - Juwelen - Schmuck.
0041-5839	Uhren Juwelen
0041-5847	Uhren und Schmuck *see* 0017-1573
0041-5855	Uhrenjournel *changed to* Uhren und Schmuck Journel.
0041-5863	Uit de Pluimveepers *see* 0168-1168
0041-5871	Uit de Verf *changed to* Bouwvaria.
0041-588X	Uit Europoortkringen
0041-5901	Uit Ons Werkt
0041-591X	Uitgelezen
0041-5936	Uitlotings-Archief
0041-5944	Uitzicht
0041-5952	Uj Iras
0041-5979	Ukiyo-e Art
0041-5987	Ukrainian Bulletint
0041-5995	Ukrainian Mathematical Journal
0041-6002	Ukrainian News
0041-6010	Ukrainian Quarterly
0041-6029	Ukrainian Review
0041-6037	Ukrainian Voice
0041-6045	Ukrainskii Khimicheskii Zhurnal
0041-6053	Ukrainskii Matematicheskii Zhurnal
0041-6061	Ukrains'kyi Istoryk
0041-607X	Ukrainian Medical Association of North America. Journal
0041-6088	Ukraina
0041-6096	Ukrains'ka Mova i Literatura v Shkoli
0041-6142	Ukrains'kyi Samostijnykt
0041-6150	Ukulima Wa Kisasa
0041-6177	Finland. Tullihallituksen Tilastotoimisto. Ulkomaankauppa-Kuukausijulkaisu/ Foreign Trade Monthly Bulletin *changed to* Finland. Tullihallitus. Ulkomaankauppa/Utrikeshandel/ Foreign Trade.
0041-6185	Ulster Commentaryt
0041-6193	Ulster Medical Journal
0041-6207	Ulster Motorist
0041-6215	Ulster Young Farmer
0041-6223	Ultima Moda
0041-624X	Ultrasonics
0041-6258	Ultreya
0041-6266	Ulysses S. Grant Association. Newslettert
0041-6274	Umafrika
0041-6282	Umanat
0041-6290	Umanesimot
0041-6320	Umetnost
0041-6339	Umpqua Trapper
0041-6347	Weltraumfahrt - Raketentechnik *see* 0722-8562
0041-6355	Umwelt

0041-6371 Economic Bulletin for Asia and the Far East *see* 0378-455X
0041-638X Economic Bulletin for Europe (Quarterly) *changed to* Economic Bulletin for Europe (Annual).
0041-638X Economic Bulletin for Europe (Quarterly) *changed to* Economic Studies.
0041-638X Economic Bulletin for Europe (Quarterly) *changed to* United Nations Economic Commission for Europe. Occasional Studies.
0041-6398 Economic Bulletin for Latin America *see* 0251-2920
0041-641X U N A Nursing Journal†
0041-6428 Una Sancta†
0041-6436 Unasylva†
0041-6444 Unausforschlicher Reichtum
0041-6452 Unauthorized Practice News†
0041-6460 Under Glass†
0041-6479 Under the Sign of Pisces: Anais Nin and Her Circle†
0041-6487 Undergraduate Journal of Philosophy†
0041-6533 Undersea Technology *see* 0093-3651
0041-6541 Underseas Cable World†
0041-655X Understanding
0041-6576 Understanding Japan
0041-6584 Undervisning og Velferd
0041-6592 Underwater Letter
0041-6606 Underwater Naturalist
0041-6614 Underwater Journal and Information Bulletin *see* 0302-3478
0041-6622 Underwriters' Report
0041-6649 Unzer Weg†
0041-6657 Unga Oernar *see* 0284-4524
0041-6665 Jornal dos Espectaculos *changed to* Associacao Portuguesa de Empresas Cinematograficas. Jornal.
0041-6681 Unicorn Folio†
0041-6703 Unidad†
0041-6711 Unidad Cristiana-Oriente Cristiano†
0041-672X Uniform Commercial Code Law Journal *changed to* Quinn's Uniform Commercial Code Law Journal.
0041-6738 Uniforms and Accessories Review
0041-6746 Cinema Francais *changed to* Presence du Cinema Francais.
0041-6754 Unijapan Film Quarterly†
0041-6762 Unilit
0041-6770 Union
0041-6800 Union Agricultural Cooperative of Syra. Bulletin†
0041-6819 Union Agriculture
0041-6827 Assembly of Western European Union. Monthly Information Bulletin†
0041-6835 Union Democracy in Action *changed to* Union Democracy Review.
0041-6843 Union des Aveugles de Guerre. Bulletin Mensuel
0041-6851 Union Douaniere et Economique de l'Afrique Centrale. Bulletin des Statistiques Generales *changed to* Division d'Aide et de Cooperation Francaise. Bulletin Trimestriel de Statistique.
0041-686X Electrical Union World
0041-6878 Union Farmer
0041-6908 Union Industrial Uruguaya. Guia de Socios y de Productos *changed to* Products of Uruguay.
0041-6916 U I A Information *changed to* U I A Newsletter.
0041-6924 Union Labor News
0041-6932 Union Matematica Argentina. Revista
0041-6940 Union Medicale Balkanique. Archives
0041-6959 Union Medicale du Canada
0041-6975 Leeds Student
0041-6991 Union Postal Clerk and Postal Transport Journal *see* 0044-7811
0041-7009 Union Postale
0041-7017 Union Recorder
0041-7025 Union Seminary Quarterly Review
0041-7033 Union Signal
0041-7041 Union Sociale
0041-705X Union Technique de l'Automobile du Motocycle et du Cycle. Bulletin Mensuel de Documentation *changed to* U T A C Bulletin de Documentation.
0041-7068 Union-Tribune Index of San Diego Business Activity
0041-7076 Unione degli Industriali della Provincia di Imperia. Notiziario†
0041-7084 Unione Matematica Italiana. Bollettino
0041-7092 Unionist
0041-7106 Unitholder *see* 0028-6052
0041-7122 Unitarian Universalist World *changed to* World (Boston).
0041-7130 Unitas
0041-7149 Unitas
0041-7157 Unite Stenographique
0041-7165 United Arab Republic Journal of Veterinary Science *see* 1110-0222
0041-7173 United Asia†
0041-7181 United Association Journal
0041-719X United Bible Societies. Bulletin
0041-7203 United Business Service *changed to* United & Babson Investment Report.
0041-7211 Journal of Current Social Issues†
0041-722X United Church Herald *changed to* United Church of Christ A.D.
0041-7238 United Church Observer
0041-7246 United Church Review†
0041-7262 United Evangelical *changed to* E.C. Doors and Windows.
0041-7270 United Evangelical Action
0041-7289 United Kingdom Atomic Energy Authority. List of Publications Available to the Public
0041-7300 United Lutheran
0041-7319 United Methodist Periodical Index†
0041-7327 United Mine Workers Journal
0041-7335 Asian Development Institute. Newsletter *changed to* A D I Quarterly News Letter.
0041-7343 United Nations. Dag Hammarskjold Library. Current Bibliographical Information
0041-7351 U N D E X *see* 0250-5584
0041-736X Economic Bulletin for Africa†
0041-7378 Quarterly Bulletin of Steel Statistics for Europe†
0041-7386 International Social Development Review†
0041-7394 United Nations Library. Monthly List of Books Catalogued in the Library of the United Nations. *see* 0251-6616
0041-7408 United Nations Library. Monthly List of Selected Articles *see* 0251-6624
0041-7416 United Nations. Population and Vital Statistics Report
0041-7424 U N Quarterly Housing Construction Summary for Europe *see* 0066-3840
0041-7432 United Nations Statistical Office. Monthly Bulletin of Statistics
0041-7440 United Neighborhood Houses. News†
0041-7459 United Paper *see* 0363-6437
0041-7483 U S A (New York)†
0041-7491 United States Air Force Medical Service Digest
0041-7505 U.S. Army Natick Laboratories. Activities Report *see* 0099-6335
0041-7513 U.S. Army Recruiting and Career Counseling Journal *changed to* Recruiter Journal.
0041-753X United States Book Exchange Newsletter *see* 0364-5215
0041-7548 U S Catholic
0041-7556 U. S. Chemical Patents†
0041-7564 U.S. Coast Guard. Merchant Marine Council. Proceedings *see* 0364-0981
0041-7572 U.S. Consumer *changed to* Consumer Newsweekly.
0041-7580 United States: Cotton Quality Reports for Ginnings
0041-7610 U.S. Department of State. Bulletin†
0041-7629 U.S. Department of State. Newsletter *see* 0278-1859
0041-7637 U S Farm News
0041-7645 U.S. Federal Home Loan Bank Board. Journal†
0041-7653 U S Fur Rancher *see* 0744-7701
0041-7661 U S Glass, Metal & Glazing
0041-7688 G R I (U.S. Government Reports Index) *see* 0097-9007
0041-770X U S I Journal
0041-7718 United States Investor *see* 0148-8848
0041-7726 L C Card Number Index to the National Union Catalog
0041-7734 U.S. Library of Congress. Accessions List: India†
0041-7742 U.S. Library of Congress. Accessions List: Indonesia, Malaysia, Singapore and Brunei *see* 0096-2341
0041-7769 U.S. Library of Congress. Accessions List: Middle East
0041-7785 U.S. Library of Congress. Books: Subjects *see* 0096-8803
0041-7793 U.S. Library of Congress Catalog - Music and Phonorecords *see* 0092-2838
0041-7807 Library of Congress Catalog. Motion Pictures and Filmstrips *changed to* National Union Catalog. Audiovisual Materials.
0041-7815 U.S. Copyright Office. Catalog of Copyright Entries. Third Series. Part 1. Books and Pamphlets *see* 0163-7290
0041-7815 U.S. Copyright Office. Catalog of Copyright Entries. Third Series. Part 1. Books and Pamphlets, Including Serials and Contributions to Periodicals *see* 0163-7304
0041-784X U.S. Copyright Office. Catalog of Copyright Entries. Third Series. Part 2. Periodicals *see* 0163-7304
0041-7858 U.S. Copyright Office. Catalog of Copyright Entries. Third Series. Parts 3-4. Drama and Works Prepared for Oral Delivery *see* 0163-7312
0041-7866 U.S. Copyright Office Catalog of Copyright Entries. Third Series. Part 5. Music *see* 0163-7312
0041-7874 U.S. Copyright Office. Catalog of Copyright Entries. Third Series. Part 6. Maps and Atlases *see* 0163-7347
0041-7882 U.S. Copyright Office. Catalog of Copyright Entries. Third Series. Parts 7-11A: Works of Art *see* 0163-7339
0041-7890 U.S. Library of Congress. Cataloging Service *see* 0160-8029
0041-7904 U.S. Library of Congress. Information Bulletin
0041-7912 U.S. Library of Congress. L.C. Classification - Additions and Changes
0041-7920 U.S. Library of Congress Pl-480 Newlsetter *see* 0095-0629
0041-7939 U.S. Library of Congress. Quarterly Journal†
0041-7947 U.S. Library of Congress. Subject Headings Used in the Dictionary Catalogs of the Library of Congress *changed to* U.S. Library of Congress Subject Headings Supplement.
0041-7955 United States Municipal News *see* 1049-2119
0041-7971 United States National Student Association Newsletter *see* 0098-5570
0041-798X U S Naval Institute. Proceedings
0041-7998 U.S. Navy Medical Newsletter *changed to* Navy Medicine.
0041-8013 U S P Boletim Informativo†
0041-8021 U.S. Patent Office. Official Gazette *see* 0098-1133
0041-8021 U.S. Patent Office. Official Gazette *see* 0360-5132
0041-803X United States Patents Quarterly
0041-8048 U S Piper
0041-8056 United States Review†
0041-8072 Gosudarstvennaya Biblioteka S.S.S.R. im. V.I. Lenina. Informatsionnyi Byulleten' Novykh Inostrannykh Knig, Postupivshikh v Biblioteku. Seriya 1: Fiziko-Matematicheskie i Khimicheskie Nauki; Nauki o Zemle; Tekhnika i Tekhnicheskie Nauk
0041-8080 Gosudarstvennaya Biblioteka S.S.S.R. im. V.I. Lenina. Informatsionnyi Byulleten' Novykh Inostrannykh Knig, Postupivshikh v Biblioteku. Seriya 3: Obshchestvennye Nauki; Khudozhestvennaya Literatura; Iskusstvo
0041-8099 United States Ski News†
0041-8129 U S Tax Week
0041-8137 United States Tobacco and Candy Journal *changed to* United States Distribution Journal.
0041-8153 United Synagogue Review
0041-8161 United Teacher *changed to* New York Teacher.
0041-817X Uniter
0041-8188 Unity Daily Word *see* 0011-5525
0041-820X Universal News *see* 0197-1506
0041-8218 Universalist
0041-8226 Universe
0041-8234 Universidad
0041-8250 Universidad Argentina de la Empresa. Revista†
0041-8277 Universidad Autonoma de Santo Domingo. Biblioteca Central. Boletin de Adquisiciones
0041-8285 Universidad Central de Venezuela. Facultad de Agronomia. Revista
0041-8293 Universidad Central de Venezuela. Facultad de Derecho. Revista *changed to* Universidad Central de Venezuela. Facultad de Ciencias Juridicas y Politicas. Revista.
0041-8307 Universidad Central de Venezuela. Facultad de Farmacia. Revista
0041-8323 Universidad de Antioquia. Instituto de Antropologia. Boletin de Antropologia *see* 0120-2510
0041-8331 Universidad de Buenos Aires. Facultad de Filosofia y Letras. Gaceta†
0041-834X Universidad de Buenos Aires. Instituto Bibliotecologico. Boletin Informativo†
0041-8358 Universidad de Chile. Anales†
0041-8366 Universidad de Chile. Biblioteca. Instituto de Economia. Boletin *changed to* Universidad de Chile. Facultad de Ciencias Economicas y Adinistrativas. Biblioteca. Lista de Memorias y Libros Seleccionados.
0041-8374 Universidad de Chile. Boletin
0041-8390 Universidad de Cuenca. Anales
0041-8404 Universidad de Guadalajara. Instituto de Astronomia y Meteorologia. Informacion
0041-8412 Universidad de Guayaquil. Facultad de Ciencias Medicas. Revista
0041-8420 Universidad de la Habana. Departmento de Actividades Culturales. Revista
0041-8439 Universidad de la Republica. Facultad de Ciencias Economicas y Administracion. Instituto de Estadistica. Indice de Precios al Consumidor
0041-8447 Universidad de la Republica. Facultad de Humanidades y Ciencias. Publicaciones†
0041-8455 Universidad de la Republica. Hospital de Clinicas. Informe Estatistico
0041-848X Universidad de Narino. Biblioteca Central. Boletin Informativo y Bibliograficas†
0041-8498 Universidad Autonoma de Nuevo Leon. Centro de Investigaciones Economicas. Boletin Bimestral
0041-851X Universidad de Puerto Rico. Escuela de Derecho. Revista Juridica *changed to* Universidad de Puerto Rico. Revista Juridica.
0041-8528 Universidad de Puerto Rico. Servicio de Extension Agricola. Boletin Ganadero†

0041-8536 Universidad de Yucatan. Revista *see* 0186-7180
0041-8544 Universidad Externado de Colombia. Revista *changed to* Externado.
0041-8552 Universidad Hispalense. Anales. Series: Filosofia y Letras, Derecho, Medicina, Ciencias y Veterinaria *changed to* Universidad de Sevilla. Serie: Filosofia y Letras.
0041-8579 Universidad Industrial de Santander. Boletin Informativo†
0041-8587 Universidad Industrial de Santander. Revista *see* 0120-0852
0041-8587 Which superseded in part (in 1969); Universidad Industrial de Santander. Revista *see* 0121-0807
0041-8609 Universidad Mayor de San Andres. Gaceta Universitaria†
0041-8617 Universidad Boliviana Mayor de San Simon. Instituto de Estudios Sociales y Economicos. Revista
0041-8625 Universidad Nacional de la Plata. Revista
0041-8633 Boletin Mexicano de Derecho Comparado
0041-8641 Noticias de la Biblioteca†
0041-865X Universidad Nacional de Cordoba. Instituto de Administracion. Revista *changed to* Revista de Ciencias Administrativas.
0041-8668 Universidad Nacional de Cuyo. Facultad de Ciencias Economicas. Revista
0041-8676 Universidad Nacional de la Plata. Facultad de Agronomia. Revista
0041-8714 Universidad Nacional Mayor de San Marcos. Boletin Universitario†
0041-8730 Universidad Pontificia Bolivariana†
0041-8749 Universidad Tecnica Federico Santa Maria. Boletin Informativo†
0041-8765 Universidade de Coimbra. Museum Zoologico. Memorias e Estudos *see* 0378-875X
0041-8781 Universidade de Sao Paulo. Hospital das Clinicas. Revista
0041-8803 Universidade de Sao Paulo. Museu de Arte Contemporanea. Boletim Informativo
0041-8811 Universidad del Zulia. Revistas
0041-8838 Universidade Federal de Minas Gerais. Escola de Engenharia. Revista†
0041-8846 Universidade Federal de Santa Maria. Faculdade de Farmacia e Bioquimica. Revista
0041-8870 Universidade Federal do Ceara. Departamento de Ciencias Sociais e Filosofia. Documentos
0041-8889 Universidade Federal do Ceara. Faculdade de Medicina. Revista *see* 0100-1302
0041-8900 Universidade do Parana. Departamento do Botanica e Farmacognosia. Boletim *see* 0301-2123
0041-8919 Universidade Federal do Rio de Janeiro. Faculdade de Odontologia. Anais
0041-8927 Universidade Federal do Rio Grande do Norte. Instituto de Biologia Marinha. Boletim *see* 0100-7068
0041-8935 Universidades
0041-8943 Universita degli Studi Perugia. Istituto di Anatomia e Istologia. Lavori†
0041-8951 Universita degli Studi di Cagliari. Seminario della Facolta di Scienza. Rendiconti
0041-896X Universita degli Studi di Firenze. Istituto di Statistica. Documentazione
0041-8978 Universita degli Studi di Genova. Istituto di Geologia. Atti
0041-8986 Universita degli Studi di Modena. Seminario Matematico e Fisico. Atti
0041-8994 Universita di Padova. Seminario Matematico. Rendiconti
0041-9001 Universita Urbinate. Notiziario Mensile†
0041-9036 Etudes Scientifiques
0041-9044 Universitario
0041-9052 Universitas
0041-9060 Universitas
0041-9079 Universitas (German Edition)
0041-9087 Universitas Comeniana. Acta Facultatis Pharmaceuticae
0041-9095 Universitas Medica
0041-9109 Universitatea "Al. I. Cuza" din Iasi. Analele Stiintifice. Sectiunea 1a: Matematica
0041-9117 Universitatea "Al. I. Cuza" din Iasi. Analele Stiintifice. Sectiunea 1c: Chimie†
0041-9125 Universitatea "Al. I. Cuza" din Iasi. Analele Stiintifice. Sectiunea 3a: Istorie
0041-9133 Universitatea "Al. I. Cuza" din Iasi. Analele Stiintifice. Sectiunea 2a: Biologie
0041-9141 Universitatea "Al. I. Cuza" din Iasi. Analele Stiintifice. Sectiunea 1b: Fizica
0041-915X Universite de Lausanne. Faculte des Lettres. Publications
0041-9168 Universite de Montreal. Institute Botanique. Contributions†
0041-9176 Universite de Paris. Annales†
0041-9184 Universite de Paris VI (Pierre et Marie Curie). Institut de Statistique. Publications
0041-9192 Universite de Tehran. Faculte des Lettres et des Sciences Humaines. Revue
0041-9206 Universite d'Ottawa. Revue†
0041-9214 Universite Laval. Fonds de Recherches Forestieres. Bulletin†
0041-9230 Universities Quarterly *see* 0951-5224
0041-9249 University†
0041-9257 University Affairs
0041-9265 University Bookman
0041-9273 University College Hospital Magazine *changed to* Too Much - University College Hospital Magazine.
0041-9281 University College Quarterly†
0041-929X University Engineer†
0041-9303 University Equipment†
0041-9311 University Film Association. Journal *see* 0742-4671
0041-932X University Jewish Voice†
0041-9346 University of Alabama in Birmingham. Medical Center Bulletin *changed to* University of Alabama, Birmingham. Medical Center.
0041-9354 University of Alaska. Anthropological Papers
0041-9362 University of Alaska. Geophysical Institute. Report Series
0041-9370 University of Alberta. Department of Chemistry. Division of Theoretical Chemistry. Technical Report†
0041-9389 University of Arizona. Agricultural Experiment Station. Technical Bulletin†
0041-9397 University of Auckland Gazette *changed to* University of Auckland News.
0041-9400 University of Auckland. Fine Arts Library Bulletin†
0041-9419 University of Baghdad. Faculty of Medicine. Journal
0041-9427 University of British Columbia Library. Asian Studies Division. List of Catalogued Books†
0041-9435 University of California U C News Clip Sheet *see* 0745-3213
0041-9443 University of California. Institute of Governmental Studies Library. Accessions List
0041-946X University of California. Seismographic Stations. Bulletin
0041-9486 University of Chicago. Department & Graduate School of Education. Newsletter *changed to* Education on the Midway.
0041-9494 University of Chicago Law Review
0041-9508 University of Chicago Magazine
0041-9516 University of Colorado Law Review
0041-9524 University of Dayton Review
0041-9532 University of Denver Alumni News *changed to* University of Denver News.
0041-9559 Journal of Urban Law *changed to* University of Detroit Law Review.
0041-9567 University of Edinburgh Journal
0041-9583 University of Florida Law Review *changed to* Florida Law Review.
0041-9605 University of Ghana Law Journal
0041-9613 University of Ibadan. Department of Linguistics and Nigerian Languages. Research Notes
0041-963X University of Illinois Law Forum *see* 0276-9948
0041-9648 University of Iowa. School of Library Science. Newsletter *changed to* University of Iowa. School of Library and Information Science. Newsletter.
0041-9656 University of Iowa Studies in Natural History†
0041-9672 University of Kansas. Museum of Art. Register *see* 0733-866X
0041-9680 University of Kansas Newsletter†
0041-9737 University of Leeds Review
0041-9745 University of Liberia Journal
0041-977X University of London. School of Oriental and African Studies. Bulletin
0041-9788 Library Review
0041-9796 University of Manila Law Gazette
0041-9818 University of Miami Law Review
0041-9826 University of Michigan Medical Center Journal†
0041-9834 University of Michigan. Museum of Paleontology. Contributions
0041-9842 University of Michigan. Division of Research Development and Administration. Research News
0041-9850 Michigan Today
0041-9869 University of Minnesota Alumni News *changed to* Minnesota (Minneapolis).
0041-9877 University of Montana Law School News†
0041-9907 University of Pennsylvania Law Review
0041-9915 University of Pittsburgh Law Review
0041-9923 University of Portland Review
0041-9931 University of Puerto Rico Dental School Newsletter†
0041-994X University of Puerto Rico. Journal of Agriculture
0041-9958 University of Queensland. Computer Centre. Computer Centre Bulletin†
0041-9974 University of Rochester Library Bulletin
0041-9990 University of San Carlos. University Bulletin
0042-000X University of San Fernando Valley Law Review *changed to* San Fernando Valley Law Review.
0042-0018 University of San Francisco Law Review
0042-0026 University of Saskatchewan. University News†
0042-0034 University of Sheffield. Diary of Events *changed to* University of Sheffield. Diary of Events.
0042-0042 University of South Carolina Education Report
0042-0050 University of South Carolina Governmental Review *changed to* Public Affairs Bulletin.
0042-0077 University of South Florida Language Quarterly *changed to* Language Quarterly.
0042-0085 Trojan Family *see* 8750-7927
0042-0093 University of Sydney. Australian Language Research Centre. Occasional Papers†
0042-0107 University of Sydney. Gazette
0042-0115 University of Sydney. Postgraduate Committee in Medicine. Bulletin†
0042-0123 University of Teheran. Faculty of Veterinary Medicine. Journal†
0042-0131 University of Teheran. Faculty of Science. Quarterly Bulletin
0042-014X University Medical†
0042-0158 U E Business Review
0042-0174 University of the State of New York Bulletin†
0042-0182 University of the Witwatersrand, Johannesburg. University Gazette†
0042-0190 University of Toledo Law Review
0042-0212 University of Toronto News *see* 0840-562X
0042-0220 University of Toronto Law Journal
0042-0239 University of Toronto Medical Journal
0042-0247 University of Toronto Quarterly
0042-0255 University of Toronto Undergraduate Dental Journal
0042-0271 University of Virginia News Letter
0042-0298 University of Washington Business Review *see* 0194-0430
0042-0301 University of Washington. College of Education Record†
0042-031X University of Waterloo. Gazette
0042-0328 University of Western Australia Law Review
0042-0336 University of Western Ontario Medical Journal
0042-0344 University of Western Ontario. Alumni Gazette
0042-0352 University of Windsor Review
0042-0360 University (Philippines)
0042-0379 University Review *see* 0146-4930
0042-0387 University Seminar Directory†
0042-0395 University Vision†
0042-0409 L'Universo
0042-0417 Universum†
0042-0425 Univerzitet Danas
0042-0433 Uniwersytet Warszawski. Instytut Geograficzny. Katedra Klimatologii. Biuletyn†
0042-0441 Unlisted Drugs
0042-0468 Unscheduled Events
0042-0476 Unsearchable Riches
0042-0484 Unser Neustadt
0042-0492 Unser Schaffen
0042-0506 Unser Tsait
0042-0549 Unsere Wirtschaft
0042-0565 Unterhaltungskunst *see* 0863-1611
0042-0573 Unternehmensforschung - Operations Research - Recherche Operationelle *changed to* Z O R - Methods and Models of Operations Research.
0042-0581 Unternehmer
0042-059X Die Unternehmung
0042-0603 Unterricht Heute†
0042-0611 Unterrichtsblaetter fuer die Bundeswehrverwaltung
0042-062X Unterrichtspraxis
0042-0638 Die Unterstufe
0042-0646 Uomini e Idee
0042-0654 Uomini e Libri
0042-0700 Upholstering Industry *see* 0744-138X
0042-0735 Upper Room
0042-0778 Uradni Vestnik Obcin Ormoz in Ptuj
0042-0786 Ural-Altaische Jahrbuecher
0042-0794 Urania
0042-0816 Urban Affairs Quarterly
0042-0824 Urban and Rural Planning Thought
0042-0832 Urban and Social Change Review
0042-0840 Urban Crisis Monitor†
0042-0859 Urban Education
0042-0867 Urban Employment†
0042-0875 Urban Georgia *changed to* Georgia's Cities.
0042-0883 Urban History Newsletter†
0042-0891 Urban Land
0042-0905 Urban Lawyer
0042-0913 Urban Memo†
0042-0921 Urban Renewal and Low-Income Housing *see* 0383-3003
0042-0948 Urban Reporter†
0042-0956 Urban Research Bulletin/Bulletin de Recherches Urbaines *see* 0318-8140
0042-0964 Urban Research News†
0042-0972 The Urban Review
0042-0980 Urban Studies
0042-1006 Urban World†
0042-1014 Urbanisme
0042-1030 Urbe
0042-1057 Adhuna

ISSN

ISSN INDEX

ISSN	Title
0042-1065	Urdu Namah
0042-1081	Urmager-Tidende *changed to* Ure & Optik.
0042-1103	Urologe-Ausgabe A *see* 0340-2592
0042-1111	Urologe-Ausgabe B *changed to* Der Urologe. Section B.
0042-112X	Urologia
0042-1138	Urologia Internationalis
0042-1146	Urological Survey *see* 0022-5347
0042-1154	Urologiya i Nefrologiya
0042-1162	Urology and Nephrology *see* 0301-1623
0042-1170	Urology Digest *see* 0197-7709
0042-1189	Uruguay Filatelico
0042-1197	Urval
0042-1200	Urzica *changed to* Moftul Roman.
0042-1219	U.S. Federal Register. (Microfiche Edition)
0042-1235	Us Wurk
0042-1243	Use of English
0042-1251	Usine Automation†
0042-126X	Usine Nouvelle
0042-1286	Usines et Industries
0042-1294	Uspekhi Fizicheskikh Nauk
0042-1308	Uspekhi Khimii
0042-1316	Uspekhi Matematicheskikh Nauk
0042-1324	Uspekhi Sovremennoi Biologii
0042-1340	Eko-Index
0042-1359	Statni Ustav Geologicky. Vestnik *see* 0042-4730
0042-1367	Ut de Smidte fan de Fryske Akademy
0042-1375	Utah Cattleman
0042-1383	Utah Construction Report
0042-1391	Utah Eagle†
0042-1405	Utah Economic and Business Review
0042-1413	U E A Action
0042-1421	Utah. Geological and Mineral Survey. Quarterly Review *changed to* Utah Geological Survey. Survey Notes.
0042-143X	Utah Historical Quarterly
0042-1448	Utah Law Review
0042-1456	Utah Libraries†
0042-1464	Utah Medical Bulletin†
0042-1472	Utah P T A Bulletin *changed to* Sound-off.
0042-1499	Utah Publisher and Printer†
0042-1529	Utah State Historical Society Newsletter
0042-1537	Utan Grans
0042-1553	Ute och Hemma
0042-157X	Uthon
0042-1588	Utility Purchasing & Stores†
0042-1618	Uttar Bharat Bhoogol Patrika
0042-1626	Uttar Pradesh. State Planning Institute. Quarterly Bulletin of Statistics
0042-1642	Uusi Maailma *see* 0355-3043
0042-1650	Uw Koninkrijk Kome: Zendingsblad
0042-1669	Uw Rijk Komet
0042-1685	Uzbekskii Biologicheskii Zhurnal
0042-1693	Uzbekskii Geologicheskii Zhurnal
0042-1707	Uzbekskii Khimicheskii Zhurnal
0042-1715	V A M Mededelingen
0042-1723	V A S L A†
0042-174X	V D I - Forschungsheft†
0042-1758	V D I - Nachrichten
0042-1766	V D I - Z
0042-1774	V D K - Mitteilungen *changed to* Sozialrecht & Praxis.
0042-1782	V D M A-Wirtschaftsbild†
0042-1790	V E A News
0042-1804	V F D B: Zeitschrift fuer Forschung und Technik im Brandschutz
0042-1820	V F W Magazine
0042-1839	V I C A *see* 1044-0151
0042-1847	V I P: The Playboy Club Magazine
0042-1863	V I T A Newsletter *see* 0882-0937
0042-1871	V-Illustriert
0042-188X	V Mire Knig
0042-1898	V. G. R. O-Mededelingen†
0042-1901	Vereinigung Schweizerischer Petroleum-Geologen und -Ingenieure. Bulletin
0042-191X	V S S D A Newsletter *changed to* From the Board Room.
0042-1928	V S T Revue *changed to* T T - Revue.
0042-1944	V V S
0042-1952	V W *changed to* Auto Toeruit.
0042-1960	V W D-Kaffee-Spezialdienst†
0042-1979	V W D-Kaffee Uebersee Sonderdienst†
0042-1987	V W D-Kakao-Spezialdienst†
0042-1995	Va-Nytt
0042-2002	Vaar Bostad
0042-2010	Vaar Fana
0042-2029	Vaar Skole†
0042-2037	Vaart Vern
0042-2053	Vacature
0042-207X	Vacuum
0042-2118	Vaeddelobsbladet
0042-2126	Vaerksteds Nyt *see* 0106-0104
0042-2134	Vaerldshorisont
0042-2142	Vaerldsmarknad†
0042-2150	Vaestgoetalitteratur
0042-2169	Vaextskyddsnotiser
0042-2177	Vaeg- och Vattenbyggaren
0042-2185	Vaegnytt
0042-2193	Vagabond†
0042-2215	Vakblad voor Biologen *changed to* BioNieuws.
0042-2223	Vakblad voor de Bloemisterij
0042-2231	Vakblad voor de Meubelindustrie *see* 0165-4543
0042-224X	Vakblad voor Textielreiniging *changed to* Textielverzorging.
0042-2266	Vakuum-Technik *see* 0934-9758
0042-2274	Vale do Rio dos Sinos *see* 0100-039X
0042-2290	Valitut Palat
0042-2304	Valle Santa di Rieti
0042-2312	Vallecchi Informa†
0042-2339	Valley Views†
0042-2347	Enforcement Journal
0042-2363	Valparaiso University Law Review
0042-2371	Valsalva
0042-238X	Valuation Magazine
0042-2398	Value Line Convertible Survey *changed to* Value Line Options.
0042-2401	Value Line Investment Survey
0042-241X	Valuer *changed to* Valuer and Land Economist.
0042-2428	Valuer
0042-2436	Valve Information Report *see* 1056-1544
0042-2444	Nav-Chitrapat
0042-2479	Vancouver Art Gallery. Bulletin *see* 0315-5226
0042-2495	Vancouver Public Aquarium Newsletter *see* 0700-9275
0042-2509	Vand†
0042-2517	Vanderbilt Hustler
0042-2525	Vanderbilt International *see* 0090-2594
0042-2533	Vanderbilt Law Review
0042-2541	Vanfoerebladet *see* 0904-8081
0042-255X	Vanguard (San Francisco) *changed to* Young Ideas.
0042-2568	Vanguard (Milwaukee)
0042-2584	Vanity Fair *see* 0018-4551
0042-2614	Vantaggio
0042-2622	Vanyajati
0042-2630	Vapor Trail's Competition News and Manufacturing Report *changed to* Vapor Trail's Boating News & International Yachting & Cruiser and Manufacturers Report.
0042-2649	Vaar Faagelvaerld
0042-2657	Vaar Foeda
0042-2665	Var Konst
0042-2673	Vaar Kyrka†
0042-2681	Vaar Naering
0042-269X	Vaara Hundar
0042-2703	Vaara Paelsdjur
0042-2711	Varazdinske Vijesti
0042-272X	Variator
0042-2738	Variety
0042-2754	Vaerldspolitikens Dagsfragor
0042-2762	Varlik
0042-2770	Varme og Sanitets Nyt
0042-2789	Varsity
0042-2797	Varsity
0042-2800	Vaart Foersvar
0042-2819	Apropaa Roeda Korset *see* 1101-413X
0042-2827	Vartavaha†
0042-2835	Vascular Surgery
0042-2843	Vaskeri-Tidende *changed to* Vask-Rens-Rengoering.
0042-2851	Vassar Quarterly
0042-286X	Vaste Goederen *changed to* Vastgoed.
0042-2878	Vasudha Monthly
0042-2886	Vatten
0042-2894	Vaugirard-Grenelle *see* 0031-2045
0042-2908	Vauxhall Motorist†
0042-2924	Vcelarstvi
0042-2932	Ve Venezuela *changed to* Caracas.
0042-2940	Veckojournalen *changed to* Maanadsjournalen.
0042-2959	Vector†
0042-2983	Vedanta Kesari
0042-2991	Vedecky Svet†
0042-3009	Vedetta†
0042-3017	Verkhovnyi Sovet S.S.S.R. Vedomosti
0042-3025	Vee-en Vleeshandelt
0042-3033	Bedrijfsontwikkeling. Editie Veehouderij *changed to* Agrarische Voorlichting.
0042-3041	Veevoeding *changed to* Veehouden Nu.
0042-305X	Vega
0042-3092	Vegetables Newsletter *changed to* Vegetables Specialist.
0042-3106	Vegetatio
0042-3114	Vehicle System Dynamics
0042-3122	Veilig Vliegen
0042-3130	Veilig Werken *changed to* Uoorkomen.
0042-3149	De Veiligheid - Safety *changed to* Arbeidsomstandigheden.
0042-3157	Veilingberichten†
0042-3165	Veja
0042-3173	Vejen Frem
0042-3181	Vela e Motore
0042-3203	Veld & Flora
0042-3211	Veliger
0042-322X	Velikogoricki List
0042-3238	Velki
0042-3246	Vellez Music News
0042-3254	Veltro
0042-3262	Veluws Kerkblad
0042-3297	Vend *see* 0042-3327
0042-3319	Vending Engineer†
0042-3327	Vending Times
0042-3343	Vene
0042-3351	Veneficus
0042-336X	Turismo in Italia *changed to* Italia Turistica.
0042-3378	Venezuela. Archivo General de la Nacion. Boletin
0042-3394	Venezuela. Ministerio de Minas e Hidrocarburos. Carta Semanal *changed to* Venezuela. Ministerio de Energia y Minas. Carta Semanal.
0042-3408	Venezuela. Ministerio de Minas e Hidrocarburos. Informations *changed to* Venezuela. Ministerio de Energia y Minas. Informations.
0042-3416	Venezuela. Ministerio de Minas e Hidrocarburos. Monthly Bulletin *changed to* Venezuela. Ministerio de Energia y Minas. Quarterly Bulletin.
0042-3424	Venezuela Odontologia
0042-3432	Venezuela Up-to-Date†
0042-3440	Vent - Art
0042-3459	Ventana
0042-3483	Venture
0042-3491	Ventura County Historical Society Quarterly
0042-3548	Venture *changed to* Fast Forward.
0042-3556	Venture-the Traveler's World†
0042-3564	Venture†
0042-3572	Venturi
0042-3580	Venus: Japanese Journal of Malacology
0042-3599	Vera Giustizia Sociale
0042-3610	Anzeiger des Verbandes der Antiquare Oesterreichs
0042-3637	Verband Oesterreichischer Landsmannschaften Nachrichten-und Mitteilungsblatt
0042-3645	Verband Schweizerischer Verkehrsvereine und der Verband Schweizerischer Kur- und Verkehrsdirektoren. Bulletin†
0042-3653	Verbraucher Politische Korrespondenz
0042-3661	Verbraucher Rundschau
0042-3688	Verbum†
0042-3696	Verbum
0042-370X	Communion†
0042-3718	Verdad y Vida
0042-3726	Vysoka Skola Banska. Sbornik Vedeckych Praci: Rada Hutnicka
0042-3734	Verdi
0042-3750	Verein der Freunde Carnuntums. Mitteilungen
0042-3769	S.W.A. Scientific Society. Verein fuer Hochlenforschung. Arbeitsberichte†
0042-3777	Verein fuer Krebsforschung. Mitteilungen†
0042-3785	V G B Mitteilungen *see* 0372-5715
0042-3793	Vereinigung Oesterreichischer Bibliothekare. Mitteilungen
0042-3807	Nachrichten V S B - S V D *see* 0258-0764
0042-3815	Schweizerische Vereinigung der Versicherungsmathematiker. Mitteilungen
0042-3831	Verein Schweizerischer Lithographiebesitzer. Mitteilungen†
0042-384X	Vereinte Nationen
0042-3858	Vereniging van Vrienden van de Nederlandse Ceramiek. Mededelingenblad *see* 0920-1009
0042-3866	Vereniging voor Naamkunde. Mededelingen *see* 0167-5257
0042-3874	Vereniging voor Nederlandse Muziekgeschiedenis. Tijdschrift
0042-3882	Vereniging voor Oppervlaktetechnieken van Metalen. Documentatieservice *changed to* Vereniging voor Oppervlaktetechnieken van Materialen. Documentatieservice.
0042-3890	Verfahrenstechnische Berichte
0042-3904	Verfkroniek
0042-3912	Verget
0042-3920	Vergleichende Paedagogik
0042-3939	Verhuetet Unfaelle
0042-3947	Veritas
0042-3955	Veritas
0042-3963	Veritas *changed to* Veritas Forum.
0042-3971	Verite *changed to* Magnificat - la Verite.
0042-398X	Verkeersrecht
0042-3998	Verkeerstechniek *changed to* Verkeerskunde.
0042-4013	Verkehrsblatt
0042-4021	Verkehrsmedizin und ihre Grenzgebiete†
0042-4048	Verkehrspsychologischer Informationsdienst
0042-4056	Verkstaederna
0042-4064	Verladent
0042-4099	Der Vermessungsingenieur
0042-4102	Vermessungstechnik
0042-4110	Vermessungstechnische Rundschau (VR) *see* 0340-5141
0042-4129	Vermissa Herald
0042-4137	Vermont Blackboard *changed to* Vermont - N E A Today.
0042-4145	Vermont Catholic Tribune
0042-4161	Vermont History
0042-417X	Vermont Life
0042-420X	Vero Dialogo
0042-4234	Verona Fathers Missions *see* 0279-3652
0042-4242	Verona Fedele
0042-4250	Wiener Boersekammer. Verordnungsblatt
0042-4269	Verpackung
0042-4277	Die Verpackung
0042-4293	Verpackungs Berater
0042-4307	Verpackungs-Rundschau
0042-4315	Verpakken

ISSN INDEX 5463

ISSN	Title
0042-4323	Verre Naasten Naderbij *changed to* Culturen.
0042-4331	Verres et Refractaires *see* 0984-7979
0042-434X	Vers Demain
0042-4358	Versicherungswirtschaft
0042-4366	Versiones†
0042-4374	Verso l'Azzurro
0042-4382	Versorgungswirtschaft
0042-4390	Versuchsstation fuer das Gaerungsgewerbe in Wien. Mitteilungen *changed to* Oesterreichisches Getraenke Institut. Mitteilungen.
0042-4412	Vertegenwoordiger
0042-4420	Vertex
0042-4439	Vertical File Index
0042-4447	Vertice
0042-4455	Vertiflite
0042-4463	Vertragssystem *changed to* Wirtschaftsrecht.
0042-4471	Vertriko Visie†
0042-448X	Vervoer *changed to* Vervoer en Transporttechniek.
0042-4498	Die Verwaltung
0042-4501	Verwaltungsarchiv
0042-451X	Verwarming en Ventilatie
0042-4528	Verzekerings-Archief
0042-4536	Veseli Svet
0042-4544	Vesmir
0042-4552	Udruzenje Pravoslavnog Svestenstva S.F.R. Jugoslavije. Glavni Savez. Vesnik
0042-4560	Vestes *see* 0818-8068
0042-4579	Vestire *changed to* Vestire Uomo.
0042-4587	Vestnik
0042-4595	Ceskoslovenska Spolecnost Zoologicka. Vestnik
0042-4609	Vestnik Dermatologii i Venerologii
0042-4617	Vestnik Drevnei Istorii
0042-4625	Vestnik Khirurgii im. I.I. Grekova
0042-4633	Vestnik Mashinostroeniya
0042-4641	Federalni Ministerstvo Financi. Vestnik *see* 0322-9653
0042-465X	Vestnik Oftal'mologii
0042-4668	Vestnik Otorinolaringologii
0042-4676	Vestnik Rentgenologii i Radiologii
0042-4684	Vestnik Sel'skokhozyaistvennoi Nauki Kazakhstana
0042-4692	Vestnik Statistiki
0042-4706	Vestnik Svyazi
0042-4714	Czechoslovakia. Federalni Urad pro Normalizaci a Mereni. Vestnik
0042-4722	Ustredni Sprava Spoju. Vestnik *changed to* Federalni Ministerstvo Spoju. Vestnik.
0042-4730	Ustredni Ustav Geologicky. Vestnik
0042-4749	Vsesoyuznyi Nauchno-Issledovatel'skii Institut Zheleznodorozhnogo Transporta. Vestnik
0042-4757	Vestnik Vysshei Shkoly
0042-4765	Veteran
0042-4773	Veteran and Vintage *changed to* Collector's Car.
0042-4781	Veteran Car
0042-4811	Veterantics
0042-482X	Veterinaria Mocambicana†
0042-4838	Veterinario y la Industria†
0042-4846	Veterinariya
0042-4854	Veterinary Bulletin
0042-4862	Veterinary Economics
0042-4870	Veterinary Institute, Pulawy. Bulletin
0042-4889	Veterinary Medicine - Small Animal Clinician *see* 8750-7943
0042-4897	Veterinary Practice
0042-4900	Veterinary Record
0042-4919	Pionyr
0042-4935	Vetus Testamentum
0042-4943	Vi Bilaegare med Hem och Hobby *changed to* Vi Bilaegare.
0042-4951	Vi Menn
0042-4978	Via
0042-4986	Via Libera
0042-4994	Via Migliore
0042-5001	Via Port of New York *changed to* Via Port of New York - New Jersey.
0042-5028	Vialidad†
0042-5036	Viata Medicala - Pentru Cadre Superioare *changed to* Viata Medicala - Pentru Medici.
0042-5044	Viata Militara *see* 1018-0400
0042-5052	Viata Romineasca
0042-5060	Vibrations†
0042-5079	Vichiana
0042-5087	Vickers Voice
0042-5095	Victoria Government Gazette
0042-5109	Victoria Reports†
0042-5117	Victoria University of Wellington Law Review
0042-5125	Victorian
0042-5141	Victorian Dry Cleaner†
0042-515X	Victoria Farmer *changed to* Victorian Farmer.
0042-5184	Victorian Naturalist
0042-5192	Victorian Newsletter
0042-5206	Victorian Poetry
0042-5214	Victorian Reports
0042-5222	Victorian Studies
0042-5230	Victoria's Resources *see* 0814-4680
0042-5265	Vida Pastoral *see* 0507-7184
0042-5281	Vide
0042-529X	Vidici
0042-5303	Vidura
0042-5311	Vidya *changed to* Oriente e Occidente.
0042-532X	Vidyodaya *changed to* Vidyodaya Journal of Social Science.
0042-532X	Vidyodaya *changed to* Viyodaya Journal of Science.
0042-5338	Vie Asistenziali *changed to* Promozione Sociale.
0042-5346	Vie Canine†
0042-5362	Vie Catholique du Berry
0042-5370	Vie Collective
0042-5400	Vie Communale et Departementale
0042-5419	Vie de la Douane
0042-5427	Vie de la Recherche Scientifique
0042-5435	Vie des Arts
0042-5451	Vie des Transports
0042-546X	Qui Touring
0042-5478	Vie du Rail
0042-5486	Vie et Bonte *see* 0301-0260
0042-5524	Vie et Sante
0042-5567	Vie Judiciaire
0042-5583	Vie Medicale
0042-5591	Vie Musicale†
0042-5605	Vie Sociale
0042-5613	Vie Spirituelle
0042-5621	Vie Theresienne
0042-563X	Vie Urbaine
0042-5656	Vient de Paraitre†
0042-5672	Naturforschende Gesellschaft in Zuerich. Vierteljahresschrift
0042-5680	Vierteljahresschrift Wirtschaft und Verwaltung†
0042-5702	Vierteljahrshefte fuer Zeitgeschichte
0042-5710	Vietnam
0042-5745	Vietnam International Information Bulletin *changed to* Vietnam - South East Asia International.
0042-5788	Vietnambulletinen
0042-5796	Vieux Jardinier *see* 0772-1099
0042-580X	View from the Bottom†
0042-5818	Viewpoints
0042-5834	Viewpoint (London, 1965)
0042-5842	Viewpoint (London)
0042-5850	Viewpoint†
0042-5869	Viewpoint (Indianapolis)†
0042-5877	Viewpoints *changed to* Humanist Viewpoints.
0042-5893	Views†
0042-5907	Views and Ideas on Mankind†
0042-5915	Views & Reviews (New York, 1937)
0042-5931	Viga en el Ojo
0042-594X	Vigencia
0042-5958	Vigilance
0042-5966	Vigilance†
0042-5974	Vigilancia
0042-6024	Vigilia
0042-6032	Vigiliae Christianae
0042-6040	Vignes & Raisins
0042-6059	Vigo County Public Library Staff Bulletin
0042-6075	Vigyan Pragati
0042-6083	Vijesti Muzealaca i Konzervatora Hrvatske
0042-6105	Vikan
0042-6113	Viikkosanomat†
0042-6121	Vikram
0042-613X	Vikrant
0042-6156	Villa & Hem i Sverige†
0042-6164	Villa de Madrid
0042-6172	Village *see* 0264-4002
0042-6180	Village Voice
0042-6199	Villager (Bronxville)
0042-6202	Villager (New York)
0042-6210	Villamossag
0042-6229	Villanova Law Review
0042-6237	Ville-Giardini
0042-6253	Viltis
0042-6288	Vinduet
0042-6296	Vingehjulet *see* 0900-3665
0042-630X	Vini d'Italia
0042-6326	Vinohrad
0042-6334	Vins d'Alsace
0042-6350	Vintage Ford
0042-6369	Vintage Jazz Mart
0042-6385	Vinyl Technology Newsletter†
0042-6393	Vinzenzbote *changed to* Dienen und Helfen.
0042-6415	Viomichaniki Epitheorissis
0042-6423	Pathologische Anatomie *see* 0174-7398
0042-6431	Virchows Archiv. Abt. B. Zellpathologie-Cell Pathology *see* 0340-6075
0042-644X	Virginia Accountant *changed to* Disclosures.
0042-6458	Virginia Advocate *changed to* Virginia United Methodist Advocate.
0042-6466	Virginia Agricultural Economics
0042-6474	Virginia Cavalcade
0042-6482	Virginia. Department of Agriculture and Consumer Services. Bulletin
0042-6490	Virginia Economic Indicators
0042-6504	Virginia Forward†
0042-6512	Virginia Geographer
0042-6547	Virginia Highway Bulletin *changed to* Virginia Department of Transportation Bulletin.
0042-6555	Virginia Historical Society. Occasional Bulletin *changed to* Virginia Historical Society. Historical Notes.
0042-6563	Virginia Journal of Education†
0042-6571	Virginia Journal of International Law
0042-658X	Virginia Journal of Science
0042-6598	Kirkus Reviews
0042-6601	Virginia Law Review
0042-661X	Virginia Law Weekly
0042-6636	Virginia Magazine of History and Biography
0042-6652	Virginia Minerals
0042-6660	Virginia Municipal Review *changed to* Virginia Review.
0042-6687	Virginia Museum Bulletin *see* 0363-3519
0042-6695	Virginia Nurse Quarterly *see* 0270-7780
0042-6709	Virginia P T A Bulletin
0042-6717	Virginia Pharmacist
0042-6725	Virginia Polytechnic Institute and State University. Extension News
0042-6733	Virginia Poultryman
0042-6741	Virginia Publisher and Printer *see* 0887-5227
0042-675X	Virginia Quarterly Review
0042-6768	Virginia Record
0042-6776	Virginia School Boards Association Newsletter
0042-6784	Virginia Town & City
0042-6792	Virginia Wildlife
0042-6806	Virittaajaa
0042-6822	Virology
0042-6830	Virology Abstracts *see* 0896-5919
0042-6849	Viroviticki List
0042-6857	Virus
0042-6865	Visages de l'Ain†
0042-6873	Visao
0042-6881	Vishwakarma
0042-6911	Vision
0042-692X	Vision Magazine
0042-6938	Weyerhaeuser World *changed to* Weyerhaeuser Today.
0042-6946	Vision and Voice†
0042-6954	Vision - Europe†
0042-6962	Vision Letter
0042-6970	Vision of India†
0042-6989	Vision Research
0042-7004	Visnyk
0042-7020	Visnyk Sil's'kogospodar'skoi Nauki
0042-7039	Vispera†
0042-7047	Visserij†
0042-7101	Vista†
0042-711X	Vista *see* 0094-5072
0042-7128	Vistazo
0042-7136	Visti Ukrayins'kykh Inzheneriv
0042-7152	Visual Education†
0042-7160	Visual Medicine†
0042-7179	Visva - Bharati Patrika
0042-7187	Visva - Bharati Journal of Philosophy
0042-7195	Visva - Bharati Quarterly
0042-7209	Viswa Rachana
0042-7217	Viswasilpi
0042-7233	Vita Cattolica
0042-7241	Vita dell'Infanzia
0042-725X	Vita e Pensiero
0042-7268	Vita e Salute
0042-7276	Vita Giuseppina
0042-7284	La Vita in Cristo e nella Chiesa
0042-7292	Vida Italiana
0042-7306	Vita Latina
0042-7330	Vita Consacrata
0042-7349	Vita Scolastica
0042-7357	Vita Sindacale Bergamasca
0042-7365	Vita Sociale
0042-7381	Vital Christianity
0042-739X	Vital Issues
0042-7411	Vital Notes on Medical Periodicals†
0042-742X	Vital Speeches of the Day
0042-7438	Vital Statistics Monthly Report†
0042-7446	Vitalita *changed to* Italia Medica - Vitalita.
0042-7470	Vitchyzna
0042-7489	Vitesse - Speed
0042-7497	Vitezna Kridla
0042-7500	Vitis
0042-7519	Vitreous Enameller
0042-7527	Vivant Univers
0042-7543	Vivarium
0042-7551	Viviamo
0042-756X	Vivienda
0042-7578	Vivir
0042-7586	Rivista del Clero Italiano
0042-7594	Vivliothiki Ghoneon
0042-7608	Vivre en Harmonie
0042-7616	Vizugyi Kozlemenyek
0042-7624	Vjesnik Komune *changed to* Daruvarski List.
0042-7632	Vjesnik Rada
0042-7640	Vjesnik U Srijedu†
0042-7659	Vjesnik Nadbiskupije Splitsko-Makarske
0042-7667	Vlaamse Chemische Vereniging. Mededelingen†
0042-7675	Vlaamse Gids
0042-7683	Vlaanderen
0042-7691	Vleesdistributie en Vleestechnologie
0042-7705	Vliegende Hollander
0042-7713	Voz de Mocambique
0042-7721	Foreign Trade
0042-773X	Vnitrni Lekarstvi
0042-7756	Vocation†
0042-7764	Vocational Guidance Quarterly *see* 0889-4019
0042-7772	Vocations for Social Change *changed to* Workforce.
0042-7780	Voce
0042-7802	Voce Bruzia
0042-7810	Voce degli Italiani
0042-7829	La Voce del Tabaccaio
0042-7837	Voce della Fiera
0042-7845	Voce della Madonna delle Grazie
0042-7861	Voce di Siracusa
0042-787X	Voce Nuova *changed to* Voce della Regione.
0042-7888	Voci Fraterne
0042-790X	Vodohospodarsky Casopis

ISSN	Title
0042-7918	Vodosnabzhenie i Sanitarnaya Tekhnika
0042-7926	Voeding
0042-7934	Voedingsmiddelentechnologie
0042-7942	Voeest-Alpine Betriebskurier
0042-7950	Voegel der Heimat *changed to* Ornis.
0042-7977	Voetbal International
0042-7985	Vogeljaar
0042-7993	Die Vogelwelt
0042-8000	Vogue
0042-8019	Vogue Australia
0042-8027	Vogue Italia
0042-8035	Vogue Living
0042-8043	Vogue Pattern Book International *see* 0095-2788
0042-8051	Queens Voice *changed to* New York Voice.
0042-806X	National Institute of Rug Cleaning Voice *see* 0886-9901
0042-8086	Voice of Ahinsa
0042-8094	Voice of Buddhism
0042-8108	Voice of Business†
0042-8116	Voice of Freedom†
0042-8132	Voice of Islam
0042-8140	Voice of Jamaica
0042-8159	Voice of Liberty
0042-8167	Voice of Methodism
0042-8175	Voice of Missions
0042-8183	Voice of the Black Community
0042-8191	Voice of the Cement, Lime, Gypsum and Allied Workers†
0042-8213	Voice of the Nazarene
0042-8221	Voice of the People
0042-8248	Voice of the Union†
0042-8256	Voice of Youth
0042-8264	Full Gospel Business Men's Voice
0042-8272	Voices
0042-8280	Voices International
0042-8299	Voicespondent
0042-8302	Phase Zero†
0042-8329	Voie de la Paix
0042-8337	Volk auf dem Weg
0042-8345	Voix de l'Edition de la Presse et de l'Audiovision
0042-837X	Voix des Enseignants *see* 0293-8286
0042-8388	Voix du Silence *changed to* Voice of Silence Newsletter.
0042-8396	Voix et Visages
0042-840X	Vojni Glasnik
0042-8418	Vojnik
0042-8426	Vojno Delo
0042-8442	Vojnoistorijski Glasnik
0042-8450	Vojnosanitetski Pregled
0042-8469	Vojnotehnicki Glasnik
0042-8493	Volksgesundheit
0042-8507	Volkshochschule Brigittenau. Mitteilungsblatt†
0042-8515	Volkshochschule im Westen *changed to* Volkshochschule.
0042-8523	Volkskunde, Driemaandelijks Tijdschrift voor de Studie van het Volksleven
0042-8531	Volkskunde in Oesterreich
0042-854X	Volksmacht
0042-8558	Volksmusik *see* 0323-5106
0042-8574	Volkstuin
0042-8582	Wirtschaftswoche: Volkswirt *changed to* Wirtschaftswoche.
0042-8590	Switzerland. Bundesamt fuer Industrie, Gewerbe und Arbeit. Volkswirtschaft
0042-8612	Volonte du Commerce et de l'Industrie *changed to* Volonte du Commerce, de l'Industrie et des Prestataires de Services.
0042-8620	Volt
0042-8639	Volta Review
0042-8671	Volunteer
0042-868X	Volunteer Views *see* 1041-1542
0042-8698	Volunteer World *changed to* News from C C I V S.
0042-8701	Volunteer's Digest†
0042-871X	Vom S I H fuer Sie *changed to* S I H Magazin.
0042-8728	Die Voorligter
0042-8736	Voprosy Ekonomiki
0042-8744	Voprosy Filosofii
0042-8752	Voprosy Ikhtiologii
0042-8779	Voprosy Istorii
0042-8787	Voprosy Kurortologii, Fizioterapii i Lechebnoi Fizicheskoi Kul'tury
0042-8795	Voprosy Literatury
0042-8809	Voprosy Meditsinskoi Khimii
0042-8817	Voprosy Neirokhirurgii
0042-8825	Voprosy Okhrany Materinstva i Detstva
0042-8833	Voprosy Pitaniya
0042-8841	Voprosy Psikhologii
0042-885X	Voprosy Revmatizma *see* 0233-7029
0042-8868	Voprosy Yazykoznaniya
0042-8884	Vorarlbergs Gewerbliche Wirtschaft *changed to* Vorarlbergs Wirtschaft Aktuell.
0042-8892	Vorschau Europa *see* 0342-1716
0042-8914	Vorschau-Tabelle *changed to* Messe- und Kongress-Vorschau.
0042-8922	Vorschriften fuer die Veterinaerverwaltung†
0042-8930	Vorwaerts
0042-8949	Vorwaerts
0042-8957	Vospitanie Shkol'nikov
0042-8965	Votre Beaute
0042-8973	Votre Maison
0042-8981	Vout
0042-899X	Vox Romanica
0042-9007	Vox Sanguinis
0042-9015	Vox Theologica†
0042-9031	Voyagest
0042-9058	Voenno-Istoricheskii Zhurnal
0042-9066	Voennyi Vestnik
0042-9074	Voennye Znaniya
0042-9082	Voz de la Biblioteca Universitaria†
0042-9090	Voz del Pueblo
0042-9104	Vozhatyi *see* 0321-0642
0042-9112	Vredesactie†
0042-9120	Vredesopbouw *changed to* Vrede.
0042-9139	Vriend
0042-9147	Vriend der Kinderen†
0042-9155	Vriend van Oud en Jong
0042-9171	Vriendenkring van Het Rembrandthuis. Kroniek†
0042-9198	Vrishchik
0042-921X	Vrouw in Middenstand en Burgerij *changed to* Vrouw.
0042-9228	Free State Educational News
0042-9236	Vsemirnoe Profsoyuznoe Dvizhenie
0042-9244	Vsezoyuznaya Akademiya Sel'skokhozyaistvennykh Nauk im. V.I. Lenina. Doklady
0042-9287	Vu Par les Belges†
0042-9317	Vuoriteollisus
0042-9325	Vyapar (Gujarati Edition)
0042-935X	Vynalezy *changed to* Vynalezy a Zlepsovaci Navrhy.
0042-9368	Vysokomolekulyarnye Soedineniya
0042-9376	Vystavba a Architektura
0042-9384	Vytis
0042-9392	Vytvarnictvo, Fotografia, Film
0042-9406	Vyziva a Zdravie
0042-9414	Vyziva Lidu *changed to* Vyziva.
0042-9422	Vyzvol'nyi Shlyakh
0042-9430	W A A C C S Motor Industry (Western Australian Automobile Chamber of Commerce) *changed to* Motor Trade Association of Western Australia. Journal.
0042-9449	W A C L Bulletin *changed to* Freedom Digest.
0042-949X	W.A. Teachers' Journal *changed to* Western Teacher.
0042-9503	W A V A E News *changed to* W V A Views & Visions.
0042-9511	W A W Newsletter
0042-952X	W & L Magazine
0042-9538	W & V
0042-9562	W B F O
0042-9589	W D†
0042-9635	W E M Newsletter†
0042-9643	W F L N Philadelphia Guide *changed to* W F L N Philadelphia Guide to Events and Places.
0042-9651	Chicago Guide *see* 0362-4595
0042-966X	W G A Geschaeftsbericht
0042-9678	W G O - Monatshefte fuer Osteuropaeisches Recht
0042-9686	World Health Organization. Bulletin
0042-9694	W H O Chronicle†
0042-9716	W I N†
0042-9732	W I Z O Review
0042-9740	Indo-Iran Journal
0042-9767	W M O Bulletin
0042-9775	W N Y F
0042-9783	W P M Newsletter (World Presbyterian Missions) *changed to* Network (Atlanta).
0042-9791	W R L News†
0042-9805	Washington Recreation and Park Society. News *changed to* Washington Recreation and Park Association. Syllabus.
0042-983X	W S D A News
0042-9864	Women Strike for Peace†
0042-9872	W W I Mitteilungen *see* 0342-300X
0042-9899	W Z E Wissenschaftliche Zeitschrift der Elektrotechnik†
0042-9902	Wacht te Kooi
0042-9929	Waerme- und Stoffuebertragung
0042-9937	Waescherei- und Reinigungs-Praxis
0042-9945	Waffen- und Kostumkunde†
0042-9953	Wagenbouwnieuws†
0042-9961	Waggoner
0042-997X	Karosseriebauer und Wagner†
0042-9988	Wagtail
0042-9996	Die Wahrheit
0043-0005	Waiblinger Anzeigenblatt†
0043-0013	Wakayama Medicine
0043-0021	Wakayama Prefecture. Monthly Report of Meteorology
0043-003X	Wake Forest Law Review
0043-0048	Die Waldarbeit
0043-0056	Wales
0043-0064	Walkabout†
0043-0072	Walker Watchword†
0043-0102	Wall Street Transcript
0043-0129	Wallaces Farmer
0043-0137	Wallerstein Laboratories Communications†
0043-0145	Wallpaper and Wallcoverings *see* 1055-4394
0043-0153	Wallpaper, Paint and Wallcovering *changed to* Home Decor.
0043-0161	Walls & Ceilings
0043-017X	Walt Whitman Review *see* 0737-0679
0043-0188	Walters Art Gallery Bulletin
0043-0196	Wanasan
0043-020X	War Communiques
0043-0218	War Cry
0043-0226	War Cry
0043-0234	War Cry
0043-0242	War Cry
0043-0250	War Cry
0043-0269	War on Hunger *see* 0735-1755
0043-0277	War - Peace Report *see* 0305-0629
0043-0307	Waratah†
0043-0315	Ward's Auto World
0043-0323	Ward's Bulletin
0043-0331	Warenzeichenblatt. Teil 1: Angemeldete Zeichen
0043-034X	Warenzeichenblatt. Teil 2: Eingetragene Zeichen
0043-0358	Warmte†
0043-0374	Warship International
0043-0382	Balai Penyelidikan Perusahaan Perkebunan Gula. Warta Bulanan
0043-0390	Warwickshire and Worcestershire Life
0043-0404	Was Tun
0043-0412	Wascana Review
0043-0420	Washburn Law Journal
0043-0439	Washington Academy of Sciences. Journal
0043-0447	Washington Afro-American
0043-0455	Washington and Jefferson Literary Journal†
0043-0463	Washington & Lee Law Review
0043-0471	Washington Atomic Energy Report and Guideletter *changed to* Washington Atomic Energy Report.
0043-0501	Washington Coach
0043-051X	Washington County Education News
0043-0536	Washington Dental Service Newsletter
0043-0544	Washington Diocese
0043-0552	Washington Education†
0043-0560	Washington Food Dealer Magazine
0043-0587	Washington Grange News *changed to* Grange News.
0043-0609	Washington International Arts Letter
0043-0617	Washington Law Review
0043-0633	Washington Monthly
0043-0641	Washington Motorist *see* 0899-7578
0043-065X	Washington Music Educator *see* 0147-4367
0043-0684	Washington Newspaper
0043-0692	Washington Plumbing and Heating Contractor
0043-0706	Washington Purchaser†
0043-0714	Washington Report (Washington, 1979) *changed to* Business Counsel.
0043-0730	Washington Report on Medicine and Health *see* 1047-8922
0043-0749	Science Trends
0043-0757	Washington Sounds *see* 0162-5667
0043-0773	Washington State Entomological Society Proceedings
0043-0781	Washington State Journal of Nursing†
0043-0803	Washington State Research Council Monthly Report *changed to* Washington Research Council. Notebook.
0043-0811	Washington State School Directors Association Newsletter *changed to* Signal (Olympia).
0043-082X	Washington State University. Mathematics Notes
0043-0838	Washington State University. Research Studies†
0043-0846	Washington State Voter
0043-0862	Washington University Law Quarterly
0043-0897	Washingtonian
0043-0927	Wasmann Journal of Biology
0043-0951	Wasser und Boden
0043-096X	Wasser und Energiewirtschaft *changed to* Wasser, Energie, Luft.
0043-0978	Wasserwirtschaft
0043-0986	Wasserwirtschaft - Wassertechnik (W W T)
0043-0994	Wasserwirtschaftliche Mitteilungen
0043-1001	Waste Age
0043-1028	Wastewater Works News
0043-1036	Wat Kan Ons Opvoer'
0043-1079	Watchmaker, Jeweller & Silversmith
0043-1087	Watchtower
0043-1117	Water and Pollution Control *changed to* Municipal and Industrial Water and Pollution Control.
0043-1125	Water and Sewage Works *see* 0273-2238
0043-1133	Water and Waste Treatment
0043-1141	Water and Wastes Digest
0043-115X	Water and Wastes Engineering *see* 0273-2238
0043-1168	Water and Water Engineering *see* 0301-7028
0043-1176	Water Bodem Lucht†
0043-1184	Water Conditioning *see* 0746-4029
0043-1192	Water Conditions in Wisconsin†
0043-1206	Water Desalination Report
0043-1222	Water in the News†
0043-1249	Water Law Newsletter
0043-1257	Water Management Bulletin†
0043-1265	Water News
0043-1273	Water Newsletter
0043-1281	Water Pollution Abstracts *see* 0748-2531
0043-129X	Water Pollution Control†
0043-1303	Water Pollution Control Federation. Journal *changed to* Water Pollution Control Federation. Research Journal.
0043-1311	Water Polo Scoreboard†
0043-1338	Water Power *see* 0306-400X
0043-1346	U D S Water Quality Control Digest *changed to* Water Quality Control Digest.
0043-1354	Water Research

ISSN INDEX 5465

0043-1362 Water Resources Abstracts *see* 0731-6445
0043-1370 Water Resources Bulletin
0043-1397 Water Resources Research
0043-1435 Water Spectrum†
0043-1443 Water Well Journal
0043-1451 Waterkampioen
0043-146X Waterloo Campus *see* 0700-5105
0043-1486 Waterschapsbelangen
0043-1494 Watershed News
0043-1508 Watersheds†
0043-1516 Watersport†
0043-1524 Waterways Journal
0043-1532 Watsonia
0043-1559 Wave Hill News†
0043-1567 Wavriensia
0043-1575 Way
0043-1583 Shlach *changed to* Way - Ukrainian Catholic Bi-Weekly.
0043-1591 Way-Catholic Viewpoints *changed to* Way of St. Francis.
0043-1605 Way of Life
0043-1613 Wayne County Farm and Home News *changed to* Extension (Alton).
0043-1621 Wayne Law Review
0043-163X Wayne State University Alumni News
0043-1648 Wear
0043-1656 Weather
0043-1664 Weather Vane
0043-1672 Weatherwise
0043-1680 Webb Society Quarterly Journal
0043-1699 Webe Mit
0043-1710 Wee Wisdom†
0043-1729 Weed Abstracts
0043-1737 Weed Research
0043-1745 Weed Science
0043-1753 Weeds, Trees and Turf *changed to* Landscape Management.
0043-1761 Week-End
0043-177X Weekblad Cinema
0043-1788 Weekblad voor Bloembollencultuur *changed to* Bloembollencultuur.
0043-180X Weekend *changed to* Weekend News.
0043-1818 Weekend†
0043-1826 Weekend Magazine†
0043-1834 Weekly Letter Commentary†
0043-1842 Weekly Livestock Reporter
0043-1850 Weekly Market Bulletin
0043-1869 National Braille Press. Weekly News†
0043-1877 Weekly News *changed to* Sunday Herald.
0043-1885 Weekly People *see* 0199-350X
0043-1893 Weekly Pharmacy Reports: The Green Sheet
0043-1907 National Promotion Audit†
0043-1923 Weekly Statistical Sugar Trade Journal
0043-194X Weekly Times
0043-1966 Weekly Underwriter†
0043-1974 Weekly Weather and Crop Bulletin, National Summary†
0043-2008 Weekly Wool Chart *changed to* Wool Record Weekly Market Report.
0043-2016 Weg en Waterbouw†
0043-2024 Weg und Ziel
0043-2032 Weg zur Gesundheit
0043-2040 Wege zum Menschen
0043-2059 Wege zur Sozialversicherung
0043-2067 Wegen
0043-2075 Gornictwo Odkrywkowe†
0043-2113 Wehr und Wirtschaft *changed to* Wehrtechnik, Vereinigt mit Wehr und Wirtschaft.
0043-2121 Wehrausbildung in Wort und Bild *changed to* Wehrausbildung.
0043-2156 Wehrmedizinische Monatsschrift
0043-2180 Weight Watchers Magazine
0043-2199 Weimarer Beitraege
0043-2202 Weiss - Blaue Rundschau
0043-2210 Welcome to Czechoslovakia
0043-2229 Welcome to Singapore†
0043-2237 Welder
0043-2245 Welding and Metal Fabrication
0043-2253 Welding Design and Fabrication
0043-227X Welding Engineer *see* 0043-2253
0043-2288 Welding in the World
0043-2296 Welding Journal
0043-230X Welding Production†
0043-2318 Welding Research Abroad
0043-2326 Welding Research Council Bulletin
0043-2342 Welfare in Review *changed to* Human Needs.
0043-2369 Welfare Reporter†
0043-2385 Welfarer†
0043-2407 Welldoer
0043-2415 Wells Fargo Bank Business Review†
0043-2431 Welsh History Review
0043-244X Welsh Music
0043-2458 Welsh Nation
0043-2466 Welsh Rugby
0043-2474 Welsh Secondary Schools Review†
0043-2482 Welt der Arbeit†
0043-2490 Die Welt der Buecher†
0043-2512 Die Molkerei-Zeitung Welt der Milch
0043-2520 Die Welt der Slaven
0043-2539 Die Welt des Islams
0043-2555 Welt Agni *changed to* Welt Spirale und Agni Yoga.
0043-2563 Welt und Sport†
0043-258X Weltblick†
0043-2598 Die Weltbuehne
0043-2601 Weltgewerkschaftsbewegung†
0043-261X Weltkunst
0043-2636 Weltwirtschaftliches Archiv
0043-2644 Weltweite Hilfe
0043-2652 Die Weltwirtschaft
0043-2679 Die Wende†
0043-2687 Wendepunkt†
0043-2695 Wending
0043-2709 Werbegeschenk - Berater *see* 0341-5600
0043-2725 Werbung in Oesterreich
0043-2741 Wereldmarkt†
0043-275X Wereldwijzer†
0043-2776 Werkmeister und Techniche Arbeitsleiter - Contremaitre et Agent de Maitrise *changed to* Werkmeister.
0043-2784 Werkpaedagogische Hefte†
0043-2792 Werkstatt und Betrieb
0043-2806 Werkstattstechnik *see* 0340-4544
0043-2814 Werkstoffe *changed to* Werkstoffe - in der Fertigung.
0043-2822 Werkstoffe und Korrosion
0043-2830 Werkzeitung des Schweizerischen Industrie *changed to* W Z : Wirtschaftszeitung fuer Alle.
0043-2849 Die Weser
0043-2857 Weserlotse
0043-2865 Wesfarmers News *changed to* Western Farmer and Grazier.
0043-2873 Wesley Historical Society. Proceedings
0043-289X Wesleyan Advocate
0043-2911 Wesleyan News†
0043-292X Wessex Life†
0043-2954 West-Ost-Journal
0043-2962 West Africa
0043-2970 West African Builder and Architect
0043-2989 West African Journal of Biological and Applied Chemistry
0043-2997 West African Journal of Education
0043-3004 West African Medical Journal
0043-3020 West African Science Association. Journal
0043-3039 West African Technical Review ABC *see* 0954-6782
0043-3047 West & East
0043-3055 West Australian Craftsman
0043-3071 West Bengal Labour Gazette
0043-3098 West Cameroon Monthly Digest of Statistics†
0043-3101 West Coast Druggist *see* 0191-6394
0043-311X West Coast Review *changed to* West Coast Line.
0043-3136 West Georgia College Review
0043-3144 West Indian Medical Journal
0043-3152 West Indies Chronicle *see* 0142-4742
0043-3179 West Pakistan Journal of Agricultural Research *see* 0251-0480
0043-3187 West Texas Register *changed to* West Texas Catholic.
0043-3195 West Virginia Agriculture & Forestry†
0043-3209 West Virginia Archaeologist†
0043-3217 West Virginia C.P.A.
0043-3225 West Virginia Dental Journal
0043-3241 West Virginia Hillbilly *see* 0887-4743
0043-325X West Virginia History
0043-3268 West Virginia Law Review
0043-3276 West Virginia Libraries
0043-3284 West Virginia Medical Journal
0043-3292 West Virginia Pharmacist†
0043-3306 West Virginia Progress†
0043-3314 West Virginia School Boards Association. Bulletin. *changed to* Communicator (Charleston).
0043-3322 West Virginia School Journal *see* 0274-8606
0043-3330 West Virginia. State Department of Health. Weekly Morbidity Report *changed to* State of the State's Health.
0043-3349 West Virginia University Magazine *changed to* West Virginia University Alumni Magazine.
0043-3357 WestArt
0043-3373 Westchester County Press
0043-339X Westchester Realtor
0043-342X Westerly
0043-3438 Westermanns Monatshefte *see* 0931-9360
0043-3454 Western†
0043-3462 Western American Literature
0043-3470 Western Apparel Industry *see* 0192-1878
0043-3489 Western Australia. Government Gazette
0043-3527 Western Buddhist†
0043-3535 Western Builder
0043-3551 Western Carolina University Journal of Education†
0043-3578 Western Collector *changed to* Western World Avon Collectors Marketplace.
0043-3594 Western Confectioner and Tobacconist *changed to* Candy World Illustrated.
0043-3624 Western Commerce & Industry Magazine
0043-3640 Western Economic Journal *see* 0095-2583
0043-3659 Western Electric Engineer *changed to* Engineer.
0043-3675 Western European Education *changed to* European Education.
0043-3691 Western Farm Equipment
0043-3705 Western Fire Journal *changed to* American Fire Journal.
0043-3721 Western Fisheries†
0043-373X Western Folklore
0043-3764 Western Fruit Grower
0043-3780 Western Grocer and Food Store Manager *see* 0705-906X
0043-3799 Western Grower and Shipper
0043-3802 Western Heart
0043-3810 Western Historical Quarterly
0043-3829 Western Horizons
0043-3837 Western Horseman
0043-3845 Western Humanities Review
0043-3853 Western Illinois University Bulletin†
0043-387X Western Livestock Journal *see* 0192-2815
0043-3888 Western Lumber and Building Materials Merchant *see* 0739-9723
0043-390X Western Manufacturing *changed to* Western Plant Operation.
0043-3918 Western Meat Industry *see* 0892-6077
0043-3934 Western Miner†
0043-3942 Western Mobile News
0043-3950 Western Motor Fleet†
0043-3977 Western New York Motorist
0043-3985 Western Oil Reporter *changed to* Western Oil World.
0043-3993 Western Ontario History Nuggets†
0043-4000 Western Outdoors
0043-4019 Western Pacific Orthopaedic Association. Journal
0043-4027 Western Paint Review *see* 0884-3848
0043-4035 Western Pennsylvania Historical Magazine *changed to* Pittsburgh History.
0043-4051 Western Plains Library System Newsletter
0043-4086 Western Printer & Lithographer†
0043-4094 Western Producer
0043-4108 Western Railroader *changed to* Western Railroader.
0043-4124 Western Real Estate News
0043-4132 Western Recorder
0043-4140 Case Western Reserve University. School of Dentistry. Dental Alumni Bulletin *changed to* Case Western Reserve University School of Dentistry: Alumni Magazine.
0043-4175 Western School Law Review†
0043-4191 Western Socialist†
0043-4205 Western Speech *see* 1057-0314
0043-4213 Western Stamp Collector *see* 0277-3899
0043-4221 Western States Jewish Historical Quarterly *changed to* Western States Jewish History.
0043-423X Western Sun *changed to* Labor Voice.
0043-4256 Western Underwriter†
0043-4280 Western Wear and Equipment *changed to* Equine Business Journal.
0043-4299 Western World Review†
0043-4310 Westernews *see* 0191-5959
0043-4329 Western's World†
0043-4345 Westhoek†
0043-4361 Westinghouse Engineer†
0043-437X Westminster Review *changed to* Westminster.
0043-4388 Westminster Theological Journal
0043-440X Westport Historical Quarterly†
0043-4418 Der Westpreusse
0043-4426 Westsider *see* 0148-0146
0043-4434 Westways
0043-4442 Wetenschap & Samenleving
0043-4450 Wetter und Leben
0043-4477 Whaley-Eaton Foreign Letter†
0043-4485 Wharton Quarterly†
0043-4493 What†
0043-4507 What Goes on in Medicine *changed to* What Goes on in Continuing Medical Education.
0043-4523 What's Happening†
0043-454X What's New at Colgate *changed to* Colgate Scene.
0043-4558 What's New in Advertising and Marketing
0043-4574 What's New in Co-Op Information†
0043-4582 What's New in Food and Drug Research†
0043-4612 What's News in Reinsurance†
0043-4620 What's on for Young People†
0043-4639 What's on in Aberdeen *changed to* What's On in Aberdeen.
0043-4647 What's on in Calcutta
0043-4655 What's on in Glasgow
0043-4663 What's on in Jersey
0043-4671 What's on in London (London, 1935)
0043-468X What's On in Ottawa - Voici Ottawa *see* 1187-1350
0043-4698 Australia. Bureau of Statistics. Wheat Industry *changed to* Australia. Bureau of Statistics. Wheat, Australia.
0043-4701 Wheat Life
0043-471X Wheat Review†
0043-4728 Wheat Scoop†
0043-4736 Wheat Situation *see* 0310-9917
0043-4744 Wheel Clicks
0043-4752 Wheel of Delta Omicron
0043-4760 Wheeled Sportsman†
0043-4779 Wheels
0043-4787 Wheels Afield *see* 0027-2094
0043-4795 Whenever Whatever *changed to* Rainbow (Valley Forge).
0043-4809 Where *see* 0266-6278
0043-4817 Where to Go in London and Around *changed to* What's on in London (London, 1966).
0043-4825 Whereas†
0043-4841 Which?

ISSN

0043-485X Whip *changed to* National Union for Civil and Public Servants. Journal.

0043-4868 Whitaker's Books of the Month and Books to Come

0043-4876 White Collar

0043-4884 White Collar Management *changed to* Management Policies & Personnel Law.

0043-4892 White Collar Report *see* 0891-4141

0043-4906 White County Heritage

0043-4922 White Fathers†

0043-4930 White Horse and Fleur de Lys *see* 0140-0991

0043-4965 White Ribbon Bulletin

0043-4973 The White Ribbon

0043-499X White Tops

0043-5007 White Wing Messenger

0043-5015 Whiteshell Echo

0043-5023 Whitley Bulletin *see* 0261-3824

0043-5031 Whole Earth Catalog *see* 0749-5056

0043-504X Wholesale Commodity Prices†

0043-5058 Wholesale Food Prices†

0043-5066 Industrial Engineering Management Science *see* 0833-1146

0043-5074 Wiadomosci

0043-5082 Wiadomosci Archeologiczne

0043-5090 Wiadomosci Botaniczne

0043-5104 Wiadomosci Chemiczne

0043-5112 Wiadomosci Elektrotechniczne

0043-5120 Wiadomosci Gornicze

0043-5139 Wiadomosci Hutnicze

0043-5147 Wiadomosci Lekarskie

0043-5155 Wiadomosci Numizmatyczne

0043-5171 Wiadomosci Sluzby Hydrologicznej i Meteorologicznej *see* 0208-6263

0043-518X Poland. Glowny Urzad Statystyczny. Wiadomosci Statystyczne

0043-5198 Wiadomosci Telekomunikacyjne

0043-5201 Poland. Urzad Patentowy. Wiadomosci

0043-521X Wiadomosci Warsztatowe

0043-5228 Wichita *changed to* Wichita Business.

0043-5236 Wichtigste fuer den Chef *changed to* Das Recht der Wirtschaft.

0043-5244 Widnokregi

0043-5252 Wiederbelebung-Organersatz-Intensivmedizin *see* 0175-3851

0043-5260 De Wielewaal

0043-5309 Wiener Entomologische Gesellschaft. Zeitschrift

0043-5317 Wiener Geschichtsblaetter

0043-5325 Wiener klinische Wochenschrift

0043-5333 Wiener Library Bulletin†

0043-5341 Wiener Medizinische Wochenschrift

0043-535X Wiener Tieraerztliche Monatsschrift

0043-5376 Wiener Zeitschrift fuer Innere Medizin und ihre Grenzgebiete. *see* 0303-8173

0043-5406 Wigs & Hairpieces†

0043-5414 Wijsgerig Perspectief op Maatschappij en Wetenschap

0043-5422 Wild und Hund

0043-5430 Wilderness Camping *see* 0277-867X

0043-5449 Wilderness Travel Magazine†

0043-5457 Wildlife Crusader

0043-5473 Wildlife Disease Association. Journal *see* 0090-3558

0043-5481 Wildlife Australia

0043-549X Wildlife in North Carolina

0043-5503 Wildlife News *changed to* International Wildlife (Canadian Edition) .

0043-5511 Wildlife Review (Fort Collins)

0043-552X Wildlife Society News *see* 0091-7648

0043-5538 Wildlife Views†

0043-5546 Roux' Archiv fuer Entwicklungsmechanik der Organismen *see* 0930-035X

0043-5554 Willamette Bridge†

0043-5562 Willamette Law Journal *see* 0191-9822

0043-5589 William & Mary Law Review

0043-5597 William and Mary Quarterly

0043-5600 William and Mary Review

0043-5619 Comments on Current World Affairs *see* 0274-5852

0043-5627 Williams' Family Bulletin†

0043-5635 Wilmington Public Schools, Profile†

0043-5643 Wilson Bulletin

0043-5651 Wilson Library Bulletin

0043-566X Wiltshire Farmer

0043-5678 Wimpel†

0043-5686 Win Magazine *changed to* Wind.

0043-5694 W I N B A N News†

0043-5708 Wind Bell

0043-5716 Windless Orchard

0043-5724 Window†

0043-5759 House & Garden (London)

0043-5775 Off Licence News

0043-5791 Wine Magazine†

0043-5805 Wine Review†

0043-5813 Wine, Spirit & Malt†

0043-5821 Wineletter†

0043-583X Wines and Vines

0043-5848 Winged Arrow†

0043-5856 Winged Foot

0043-5864 Winged Head

0043-5880 Wings

0043-5899 Wings *see* 0110-1471

0043-5902 Wings at Home *see* 0704-6804

0043-5910 Wings Over Africa *see* 0261-2399

0043-5929 Wingspan *changed to* B C A L News.

0043-5937 Winner (Hagerstown)

0043-5953 Der Winzer

0043-5961 Wir Blenden Auf†

0043-597X Wir Herbergs Freunde *changed to* Jugendherbergswerk.

0043-5988 Wir und Unsere Welt *changed to* Wir Lehrlinge.

0043-5996 Wire

0043-6011 Wire Industry

0043-602X Wire Journal *see* 0277-4275

0043-6046 Wire World International *see* 0934-5906

0043-6062 Wireless World *see* 0266-3244

0043-6089 Wirkendes Wort

0043-6097 Wirkerei - und Strickerei - Technik

0043-6100 Die Wirtschaft *changed to* Die Neue Wirtschaft.

0043-6119 Wirtschaft: Ausgabe A *see* 0232-4768

0043-6135 Wirtschaft und Recht

0043-6143 Wirtschaft und Statistik

0043-6151 Wirtschaft und Wettbewerb

0043-616X Wirtschaft und Wissen *see* 0341-017X

0043-6186 Wirtschaftliche Mitteilungen - Informations Economiques *changed to* L'Exportation en Pratique.

0043-6194 Wirtschaft und Investment

0043-6208 Wirtschaftsblaetter *changed to* B F G: Wirtschaftsblaetter.

0043-6240 Wirtschaftsbericht ueber die Lateinamerikanischen Laender sowie Spanien und Portugal *changed to* Wirtschaftsbericht Lateinamerika.

0043-6259 Wirtschaftsberichte *changed to* Trends.

0043-6275 Wirtschaftsdienst

0043-6283 Wirtschaftskonjunktur

0043-6291 Wirtschaftspolitische Blaetter

0043-6305 Wirtschaftspolitische Chronik *see* 0721-3808

0043-633X Wirtschaftswissenschaft†

0043-6348 Wisconsin A A A Motor News *see* 0277-1004

0043-6356 Wisconsin Agriculturist

0043-6364 Wisconsin Archeologist

0043-6380 Wisconsin Bar Bulletin *changed to* Wisconsin Lawyer.

0043-6399 Wisconsin Beverage Journal

0043-6402 Wisconsin C P A

0043-6410 Wisconsin Conservation Bulletin *see* 0736-2277

0043-6453 Wisconsin Engineer

0043-6488 Wisconsin Jewish Chronicle

0043-6496 Wisconsin Journal of Education†

0043-650X Wisconsin Law Review

0043-6518 W L A Newsletter

0043-6526 Wisconsin Library Bulletin†

0043-6534 Wisconsin Magazine of History

0043-6542 Wisconsin Medical Journal

0043-6550 Wisconsin Mental Hygiene Review†

0043-6569 Wisconsin Newsletter†

0043-6577 Wisconsin Parent Teacher Bulletin *changed to* Wisconsin Parent Teacher.

0043-6585 Wisconsin Pharmacist

0043-6593 Wisconsin Pharmacy Extension Bulletin†

0043-6615 Wisconsin Professional Engineer

0043-6623 Wisconsin Rehabilitation†

0043-6631 Wisconsin Review

0043-664X Wisconsin School Board News *changed to* Wisconsin School News.

0043-6658 Wisconsin School Musician

0043-6666 Wisconsin Sociologist

0043-6674 Wisconsin State Dental Society. Journal *see* 0091-4185

0043-6682 Wisconsin State Laboratory of Hygiene. Laboratory Newsletter†

0043-6690 Wisconsin State Universities Report†

0043-6704 Wisconsinsuror *changed to* Wisconsin Insuror.

0043-6712 Wisconsin Tales and Trails *see* 0095-4314

0043-6739 Wisconsin Then and Now *see* 0196-1306

0043-6747 Wisconsin's Health *see* 0146-2768

0043-6755 Wise Owl News *changed to* National Society to Prevent Blindness. Member News.

0043-6763 Mitteilungen aus dem Wissenschaftlichen Bibliothekswesen der DDR†

0043-678X Wissenschaft und Weisheit†

0043-6798 Wissenschaft und Weltbild

0043-6801 A E G-Telefunken. Wissenschaftliche Berichte†

0043-6828 Deutsche Gesellschaft fuer Ernaehrung. Wissenschaftliche Veroeffentlichungen†

0043-6836 Friedrich-Schiller-Universitaet Jena. Mathematisch-Naturwissenschaftliche Reihe. Wissenschaftliche Zeitschrift†

0043-6844 Hochschule fuer Verkehrswesen "Friedrich List". Wissenschaftliche Zeitschrift *changed to* Hochschule fuer Verkehrswesen "Friedrich List". Verkehrswissenschaft Aktuell - Wissenschaftliche Zeitschrift.

0043-6879 Karl Marx Universitaet, Leipzig. Wissenschaftliche Zeitung *changed to* Karl Marx Universitaet, Leipzig. Wissenschaftliche Zeitschrift.

0043-6895 Paedagogischen Hochschule, Potsdam. Gesellschafts und Sprachwissenschaftliche u. Math. Nat. Reihe. Wissenschaftliche Zeitschrift†

0043-6917 Technische Hochschule Ilmenau. Wissenschaftliche Zeitschrift†

0043-6925 Technische Universitaet Dresden. Wissenschaftliche Zeitschrift

0043-6933 Rostock Universitaet. Wissenschaftliche Zeitschrift. Gesellschafts- und Sprachwissenschaftliche Reihe *see* 0323-4630

0043-6941 Wissenschaftlicher Dienst fuer Ostmitteleuropa *see* 0340-3297

0043-695X Wissenschaftlicher Dienst Suedosteuropa *see* 0722-480X

0043-6976 Wissenschaftsrecht, Wissenschaftsverwaltung, Wissenschaftsfoerderung

0043-6992 Within Our Gates *changed to* Open House.

0043-7018 Without the Camp *changed to* New Day.

0043-7050 Witte Krant†

0043-7069 Witte Museum Quarterly†

0043-7077 Witterung in Oesterreich. Monatsuebersicht

0043-7085 Witterung in Uebersee

0043-7093 Wittgenstein

0043-7107 Wivenhoe Park Review

0043-7123 Woche in Australien

0043-7131 Wochenblatt fuer Papierfabrikation

0043-714X Wofford Bibliopolist†

0043-7158 Wohnen und Siedeln *changed to* Wohnen Plus.

0043-7166 Wohnungseigentum

0043-7174 Wojsko Ludowe *changed to* Wojsko Ludowe.

0043-7182 Wojskowy Przeglad Historyczny

0043-7190 Wojskowy Przeglad Lotniczy†

0043-7212 Wolkenridder

0043-7220 Woman

0043-7239 Woman†

0043-7255 Woman Bowler

0043-7263 Woman, Bride and Home†

0043-7271 Woman C P A†

0043-728X Woman Constitutionalist†

0043-7298 Woman Engineer

0043-7301 Woman Golfer†

0043-7328 Woman's Day

0043-7336 Woman's Day

0043-7344 Woman's Journal

0043-7352 Woman's National Magazine *changed to* Woman's National Farm & Garden Magazine.

0043-7360 Woman's Own

0043-7379 Woman's Pulpit†

0043-7387 Woman's Realm

0043-7395 Woman's Realm Home Sewing and Knitting *changed to* Sewing & Knitting.

0043-7409 Woman's Way Weekly *changed to* Woman's Way.

0043-7417 Woman's Weekly

0043-7425 Woman's World†

0043-7433 Women: A Journal of Liberation†

0043-7441 Women in Business

0043-745X Women in Council†

0043-7468 Women Lawyers Journal

0043-7476 Women of the Whole World†

0043-7492 Women-To-By-Of-and About†

0043-7506 Women Today

0043-7514 Women's American O R T Reporter *changed to* The Reporter (New York).

0043-7522 Women's Dress Buyers *changed to* Women's, Misses & Jr. Ready to Wear Buyers.

0043-7530 Women's Employment

0043-7549 Women's Intimate Apparel Buyers

0043-7557 Women's League Outlook

0043-7565 Women's Sportswear Buyers *changed to* Women's, Misses & Jr. Sportswear Buyers.

0043-7573 Women's Track and Field World *see* 0193-8312

0043-7581 Women's Wear Daily *changed to* Women's Wear Daily.

0043-759X Women's World

0043-7603 Women's Zionist Council of South Africa. News and Views *changed to* Women's Zionist Organization of South Africa. News and Views.

0043-762X Wood *see* 0262-6071

0043-7646 Wood & Equipment News

0043-7654 Wood and Fiber *see* 0735-6161

0043-7662 Wood & Wood Products

0043-7670 Wood Construction and Building Materialist†

0043-7689 Wood Heat Quarterly†

0043-7697 Wood Preserving *see* 0099-1716

0043-7700 Wood Science†

0043-7719 Wood Science and Technology

0043-7727 Woodall's Trailer Travel *see* 0160-3000

0043-7743 Pulp and Paper Research Institute of Canada. Woodlands Papers†

0043-7751 Woodmen of the World Magazine

0043-776X Woodworker

0043-7778 Woodworking & Furniture Digest†

0043-7786 Woodworking Industry†

0043-7808 Wool and Woolens of India

0043-7816 Wool Intelligence (and Fibres Supplement)†

0043-7824 Wool News

0043-7832 Wool Record and Textile World *changed to* Wool Record.

0043-7840 Wool Sack

0043-7859 Wool Science Review

ISSN	Title
0043-7867	U.S. Department of Agriculture. Economic Research Service. Wool Situation changed to U.S. Department of Agriculture. Cotton and Wool Situation and Outlook.
0043-7875	Wool Technology and Sheep Breeding
0043-7883	Woollens & Worsteds of India
0043-7891	Worcester Art Museum. News Bulletin and Calendar see 0193-9564
0043-7905	Worcester Medical News changed to Worcester Medicine.
0043-7913	Worcester Polytechnic Institute. Journal see 0148-6128
0043-7921	Worcester Punch†
0043-7948	Word
0043-7956	Word
0043-7980	Word Ways
0043-7999	On the Line (Scottdale)
0043-8006	Wordsworth Circle
0043-8014	WorkBoat
0043-8022	Work Study
0043-8030	Work Study and Management Services see 0307-6768
0043-8057	Workbench
0043-8065	Queensland Worker see 0045-0979
0043-809X	Workers World
0043-8103	Working for Boys†
0043-8111	Workmen's Circle Call
0043-812X	Works†
0043-8146	Workshop see 0308-6283
0043-8154	The World (New York)
0043-8162	World†
0043-8170	Canada & the World
0043-8189	World Affairs
0043-8200	World Affairs
0043-8219	World Agricultural Economics and Rural Sociology Abstracts
0043-8227	World Agriculture - Agriculture dans le Monde changed to World Agriculture - I F A P News.
0043-8235	World and the School
0043-8243	World Archaeology
0043-826X	World Aviation Directory
0043-8278	World Bowls Magazine
0043-8286	World Buddhism†
0043-8294	World Calendar of Forthcoming Meetings: Metallurgical and Related Fields see 0263-7987
0043-8308	World Call see 0092-8372
0043-8324	World Christian Digest†
0043-8332	World Christian Education†
0043-8340	World Coffee & Tea
0043-8359	World Coins†
0043-8375	World Construction see 0020-6415
0043-8383	World Convention Dates see 1042-3141
0043-8391	World Crops see 0269-2457
0043-8405	World Dredging and Marine Construction see 1045-0343
0043-8413	World Encounter†
0043-8421	World Farming changed to Agribusiness Worldwide.
0043-843X	World Federalist see 0252-9505
0043-8448	World Federation
0043-8464	World Fellowship of Buddhists. Review
0043-8472	World Fisheries Abstracts†
0043-8480	World Fishing
0043-8502	World Health
0043-8510	World Health Statistics Report see 0379-8070
0043-8529	World Highways
0043-8537	World Hunger changed to Action for Development.
0043-8561	World Industrial Reporter
0043-857X	World Informo
0043-8588	World Irrigation†
0043-8596	World Jewry†
0043-860X	World Journal of Psychosynthesis
0043-8634	World Leprosy News†
0043-8642	World Marxist Review†
0043-8669	World Medicine†
0043-8677	World Meetings: Outside United States and Canada
0043-8685	World Meetings: Social and Behavioral Sciences, Education and Management see 0194-6161
0043-8693	World Meetings: United States and Canada
0043-8707	World Mining see 0746-729X
0043-874X	World News of the Week changed to World Newsmap of the Week - Headline Focus.
0043-8758	World Metal Statistics
0043-8774	The World of Music
0043-8782	World of Pretzels†
0043-8790	World Oil
0043-8804	World Order
0043-8812	New World Outlook
0043-8820	World Overt
0043-8839	World Parish
0043-8847	World Petroleum†
0043-8855	International Oil News changed to International Oil News: Management Edition.
0043-8871	World Politics (Baltimore)
0043-888X	World Ports changed to W W S - World Wide Shipping.
0043-8898	World-Product-Casts see 0163-6723
0043-8901	World Progress
0043-891X	World Radio Bulletin†
0043-8928	World Refrigeration and Air Conditioning†
0043-8936	World-Regional Casts see 0163-6731
0043-8944	World Report on Technical Advancement
0043-8952	Credit Union World Reporter
0043-8979	World Review of Animal Production
0043-8987	World Revolution†
0043-8995	World Scouting†
0043-9002	World Scouting Newsletter changed to World Scouting News.
0043-9010	World Ships on Order changed to Newbuildings.
0043-9029	World Shopping changed to World Shopping Encyclopedia.
0043-9037	World Soccer
0043-9045	World Space Directory Including Oceanology†
0043-9053	World Sports changed to Sportsworld.
0043-9061	World Stamps
0043-907X	W S C F Newsletter†
0043-9088	World Surface Coating Abstracts
0043-9096	World Survey
0043-910X	World Tennis†
0043-9118	World Textile Abstracts
0043-9126	World Tobacco
0043-9134	World Today
0043-9142	World Trade
0043-9150	World Trade Bulletin see 0884-495X
0043-9169	World Travel†
0043-9177	World Traveler†
0043-9185	World Union
0043-9215	World Vision
0043-9223	World War II Historical Association. Newsletter changed to World War Enthusiast 1939-1945.
0043-9231	World Week see 0745-7065
0043-9258	World Wood
0043-9274	World Youth
0043-9282	Worldmission†
0043-9290	World's Children
0043-9304	World's Fair
0043-9312	Worlds of If†
0043-9320	World's Paper Trade Review see 0306-8234
0043-9339	World's Poultry Science Journal
0043-9355	Worldwide Art Book Bibliography†
0043-9363	Worldwide Art Catalogue Bulletin†
0043-9371	Worldwide Marketing Horizons†
0043-9398	Worldwide Projects and Installation Planning see 0091-4800
0043-9401	Wormwood Review
0043-941X	Worship
0043-9428	Das Wort fuer Heute†
0043-9444	Wort und Weg
0043-9452	Wrangler's Roost
0043-9460	Wrecking & Salvage Journal
0043-9479	Wrestler†
0043-9495	Wretched Mess News†
0043-9509	Wright's Advisory Report changed to Wright Investment Advice and Analysis.
0043-9517	Writer (Boston)
0043-9525	Writer's Digest
0043-9533	Writers Guild of America, West. Newsletter see 1055-1948
0043-9541	Writers Newsletter changed to J R G Newsletter.
0043-9568	Writer's Review see 0260-2776
0043-9576	Writers' World
0043-9592	Wszechswiat
0043-9606	Wuerttembergisches Wochenblatt fuer Landwirtschaft†
0043-9614	Wuerzburg-Heute
0043-9622	Wuestenrot-Heim changed to Wuestenrot Magazin.
0043-9630	Wychowanie Fizyczne i Sport. Studia i Materialy
0043-9649	Temat - Wynalazczosc i Racjonalizacja changed to Nowator.
0043-9657	Wynboer
0043-9665	Wyoming Archaeologist
0043-9673	Wyoming Beverage Analyst†
0043-9681	Wyoming Education News
0043-969X	Wyoming Educator
0043-9703	Wyoming Employment Outlook†
0043-9711	Wyoming Future Farmer†
0043-972X	Wyoming History News
0043-9738	Wyoming Library Roundup†
0043-9754	Wyoming P T A News†
0043-9762	Big Wyoming Progress Reports changed to Wyoming Progress Report.
0043-9770	Wyoming Rural Electric News Pulse changed to Wyoming Physicians Newsletter.
0043-9797	
0043-9800	Wyoming Stockman Farmer
0043-9819	Wyoming Wildlife
0043-9827	Wyoming Wool Grower
0043-9851	X-Ray Fluorescence Spectrometry Abstracts
0043-986X	Xaloc
0043-9878	Xaverian†
0043-9886	Xaverian Weekly
0043-9916	Y.M.H.A. Bulletin changed to Y Bulletin.
0043-9924	Y W C A Magazine†
0043-9932	Yacht
0043-9940	Yachting
0043-9959	Yachting changed to Yachting News.
0043-9975	Yachting Italiano-Atomare changed to Yachting Italiano.
0043-9983	Yachting Monthly
0043-9991	Yachting World
0044-0000	Yachts and Yachting
0044-0019	Yachtsman's Wife†
0044-0027	Yadernaya Fizika
0044-0035	Practical Pharmacy
0044-0043	Pharmacy Companion
0044-0051	Yale Alumni Magazine
0044-006X	Yale Economic Essays†
0044-0078	Yale French Studies
0044-0086	Yale Journal of Biology and Medicine
0044-0094	Yale Law Journal
0044-0108	Yale Literary Magazine see 0148-4605
0044-0124	Yale Review
0044-0132	Yale Review of Law and Social Action†
0044-0140	Yale Scientific Magazine see 0091-0287
0044-0167	Yale - Theatre see 0161-0775
0044-0175	Yale University Library Gazette
0044-0183	Yamashina Institute for Ornithology. Miscellaneous Reports changed to Yamashina Institute for Ornithology. Journal.
0044-0191	Yankee
0044-0205	Yankee Oilman
0044-0213	Yaqeen International
0044-023X	Y A R N
0044-0280	Rashut ha-Nemalim be-Yisrael, Yedion changed to Nemalim be-Israel. Berashut.
0044-0310	Yememhiran Dimts
0044-0329	Yememhiran Melkt
0044-0337	Yeni Sinema
0044-0345	Yeon-Gu Weolbo
0044-0353	Yes see 0315-467X
0044-0361	Yesodot†
0044-037X	Yesteryears
0044-0388	Yevanhelskyj Ranok
0044-0396	Yhteishyva
0044-040X	Der Yid
0044-0418	Yiddishe Heim
0044-0426	Yiddishe Kultur
0044-0434	Yiddisher Kemfer
0044-0442	Yidishe Shprakh
0044-0469	Yleiselektroniikka changed to Elektroniikkauutiset.
0044-0485	Yoga
0044-0493	Yoga Institute. Journal see 0970-1737
0044-0507	Yoga - Mimamsa
0044-0515	Yojana
0044-0523	Yokohama Mathematical Journal
0044-0531	Yokohama Medical Bulletin
0044-054X	Yontev Bleter
0044-0558	Yonago Medical Association. Journal
0044-0574	Yorker News see 0883-1513
0044-0590	Yorkshire Bulletin of Economic and Social Research see 0307-3378
0044-0612	Yorkshire Journal
0044-0620	Yorkshire Life
0044-0639	Yorkshire Ridings Magazine
0044-0647	Yorkshire Terrier Quarterly†
0044-0663	Monthly Statistics of Paper Distribution
0044-0671	Fish Culture
0044-068X	You and Your World†
0044-0698	Welcome to Cyprus
0044-0701	You†
0044-071X	T Q
0044-0728	Young Children
0044-0736	Young Citizen
0044-0744	Young Citizen changed to Scholastic News: Citizen.
0044-0752	Young Engineer & Scientist†
0044-0760	Young Folk†
0044-0787	Young Ideas
0044-0795	Young India
0044-0809	Young Israel Viewpoint
0044-0817	Young Judaean
0044-0833	Young Miss see 0888-5842
0044-0841	Young Musicians
0044-0876	Young Scotland†
0044-0884	Young Socialist
0044-0892	Young Socialist - The Organizer see 0360-0157
0044-0906	Young Soldier
0044-0914	Young Sower changed to Search (London, 1924).
0044-0922	Young Teen Power changed to Teen Power (1979).
0044-0957	Young Writer
0044-0973	Youngstown Jewish Times†
0044-0981	Your Astrology†
0044-099X	Your Business†
0044-1007	Your Child
0044-1015	Your Edmundite Missions News Letter
0044-1031	Your Garden
0044-104X	Your Health
0044-1058	Your Library Presents†
0044-1074	Your New Baby†
0044-1082	Your Personal Astrology Magazine
0044-1090	International Rider and Driver see 0094-3355
0044-1104	Your Public Schools changed to Education News.
0044-1112	Your Schools
0044-1139	You're the Critic
0044-1155	Youth Aliyah Review
0044-1171	Youth and Nation
0044-118X	Youth & Society
0044-1201	Youth Chronicle
0044-121X	Youth Happiness changed to Young & Alive (Large Print Edition).
0044-1228	Youth Hosteller changed to Triangle.
0044-1236	Youth in Action†
0044-1244	Youth Life changed to Union of Yugoslav Youth. Newsletter.
0044-1252	Youth Program Service changed to Emmaus Letter.
0044-1260	Youth Review
0044-1309	Yritystalous see 0358-4208

0044-1317 Yrkesopplaering *see* 0332-5814
0044-1333 Yugoslav Life
0044-1341 Yugoslav Survey
0044-135X Yugoslav Trade Unions
0044-1368 Yugoslavia Export†
0044-1376 Yukon News
0044-1384 Yunak
0044-1414 Yuvak
0044-1422 Z
0044-1449 Zeitschrift fuer Dialektologie und Linguistik
0044-1457 Informationsdienst Bibliothekswesen *see* 0176-781X
0044-1465 Z I S Mitteilungen *see* 0863-2162
0044-1473 Z Naszej Oficyny†
0044-1481 Z Otchlani Wiekow
0044-149X Z Pola Walki
0044-1503 Z Prac Zakladu Nauk Ekonomicznych PAN†
0044-1511 Z V und Z V (Zeitungsverleger und Zeitschriftenverleger) *changed to* Copy.
0044-152X Za Domovinu
0044-1538 Za i Przeciw
0044-1554 Za Rubezhom
0044-1562 Zaaiert
0044-1570 Zacchia†
0044-1589 Zadarska Revija
0044-1600 Zagadnienia Ekonomiki Rolnej
0044-1619 Zagadnienia Naukoznawstwa
0044-1627 Zagaglia
0044-1651 Zahnaerztliche Praxis
0044-166X Z W R
0044-1678 Der Zahnarzt *see* 0044-166X
0044-1686 Zahntechnik
0044-1694 Zahradnicke Listy *changed to* Zahradnictvo.
0044-1708 Zabrana Skod
0044-1716 Zajednica
0044-1724 Zambia Library Service Bulletin†
0044-1732 Zambia Mail *changed to* Zambia Daily Mail.
0044-1783 Zapatos y Zapaterias
0044-1791 Zapiski Historyczne
0044-1805 Vsesoyuznoe Mineralogicheskoe Obshchestvo. Zapiski
0044-1813 Zapowiedzi Wydawnicze
0044-1821 Zaragoza†
0044-183X Zaranie Slaskie
0044-1848 Zarja
0044-1856 Zashchita Metallov
0044-1864 Zashchita Rastenii
0044-1872 Zastita
0044-1880 Zastita Rada
0044-1899 Zastosowania Matematyki
0044-1902 Zavarivanje
0044-1910 Zavodskaya Laboratoriya
0044-1929 Zbior Dokumentow
0044-1937 Zbornik za Drustvene Nauke
0044-1945 Zdorov'e
0044-1953 Zdravie
0044-1961 Zdravookhranenie Belorussii
0044-197X Zdravookhranenie Rossiiskoi Federatsii
0044-1988 Zdravotni Technika a Vzduchotechnika
0044-1996 Zdravotnicke Noviny
0044-2011 Zdrowie Publiczne
0044-202X Zealandia *changed to* New Zealandia.
0044-2038 Zeichen der Zeit
0044-2046 Zeichnen in Technik, Architektur, Vermessung *see* 0932-7509
0044-2054 Zeiss Information
0044-2062 Zeiss-Mitteilungen ueber Fortschritte der Technischen Optik†
0044-2070 Die Zeit
0044-2089 Die Zeit im Buch
0044-2097 Zeit- und Kulturarchiv *changed to* Internationales Handbuch - Zeitarchiv.
0044-2100 ZeitBild
0044-2119 Zeitgeist†
0044-2127 Zeitschrift des Bernischen Juristenvereins
0044-2135 Deutscher Verein fuer Kunstwissenschaft. Zeitschrift
0044-216X Zeitschrift fuer Aegyptische Sprache und Altertumskunde
0044-2178 Zeitschrift fuer Aerztliche Fortbildung
0044-2186 Zeitschrift fuer Aesthetik und Allgemeine Kunstwissenschaft
0044-2194 Zeitschrift fuer Agrargeschichte und Agrarsoziologie
0044-2208 Zeitschrift fuer Allgemeine Mikrobiologie *see* 0233-111X
0044-2216 Zeitschrift fuer Allgemeine Wissenschaftstheorie *see* 0925-4560
0044-2224 Zeitschrift fuer Alternsforschung†
0044-2232 Zeitschrift fuer Anatomie und Entwicklungsgeschichte *see* 0340-2061
0044-2240 Journal of Applied Entomology
0044-2259 Zeitschrift fuer Angewandte Geologie
0044-2267 Zeitschrift fuer Angewandte Mathematik und Mechanik
0044-2275 Zeitschrift fuer Angewandte Mathematik und Physik
0044-2283 Zeitschrift fuer Angewandte Physik *see* 0721-7250
0044-2291 Zeitschrift fuer Angewandte Zoologie
0044-2305 Zeitschrift fuer Anglistik und Amerikanistik
0044-2313 Zeitschrift fuer Anorganische und Allgemeine Chemie
0044-2321 Zeitschrift fuer Arbeitsrecht und Sozialrecht
0044-233X Zeitschrift fuer Archaeologie
0044-2348 Zeitschrift fuer Auslaendisches Oeffentliches Recht und Voelkerrecht
0044-2356 Zeitschrift fuer Balkanologie
0044-2364 Zeitschrift fuer Bayerische Landesgeschichte
0044-2372 Z f B
0044-2380 Zeitschrift fuer Bibliothekswesen und Bibliographie
0044-2399 Zeitschrift fuer Bienenforschung *see* 0044-8435
0044-2410 Zeitschrift fuer das Gesamte Familienrecht
0044-2429 Zeitschrift fuer das Gesamte Genossenschaftswesen
0044-2437 Zeitschrift fuer das Gesamte Handelsrecht und Wirtschaftsrecht
0044-2461 Zeitschrift fuer den Erdkundeunterricht
0044-247X Zeitschrift fuer den Lastenausgleich
0044-2496 Zeitschrift fuer Deutsche Philologie
0044-2518 Zeitschrift fuer Deutsches Altertum und Deutsche Literatur
0044-2526 Zeitschrift fuer die Alttestamentliche Wissenschaft
0044-2534 Zeitschrift fuer die Gesamte Experimentelle Medizin Einschliesslich Experimenteller Chirurgie *see* 0300-9130
0044-2542 Zeitschrift fuer die Gesamte Innere Medizin und Ihre Grenzgebiete
0044-2585 Zeitschrift fuer die Gesamte Versicherungswissenschaft
0044-2593 Zeitschrift fuer die Geschichte der Juden†
0044-2607 Zeitschrift fuer die Geschichte des Oberrheins
0044-2615 Zeitschrift fuer die Neutestamentliche Wissenschaft und die Kunde der Aelteren Kirche
0044-2623 Zeitschrift fuer die Zuckerindustrie *see* 0344-8657
0044-264X Zeitschrift fuer Ernaehrungswissenschaft
0044-2658 Erzmetall
0044-2666 Zeitschrift fuer Ethnologie
0044-2674 Zeitschrift fuer Evangelische Ethik
0044-2682 Zeitschrift fuer Evangelische Rundfunk- und Fernseharbeit Medium *see* 0025-8350
0044-2690 Zeitschrift fuer Evangelisches Kirchenrecht
0044-2712 Zeitschrift fuer Experimentelle und Angewandte Psychologie
0044-2720 Zeitschrift fuer Fischerei und deren Hilfswissenschaften†
0044-2739 Zeitschrift fuer Flugwissenschaften *see* 0342-068X
0044-2747 Zeitschrift fuer Franzoesische Sprache und Literatur
0044-2755 Zeitschrift fuer Fremdenverkehr
0044-2763 Zeitschrift fuer Ganzheitsforschung
0044-2771 Zeitschrift fuer Gastroenterologie
0044-278X Zeitschrift fuer Geburtshilfe und Gynaekologie *see* 0300-967X
0044-2801 Zeitschrift fuer Geophysik *see* 0340-062X
0044-281X Zeitschrift fuer Gerontologie
0044-2828 Zeitschrift fuer Geschichtswissenschaft
0044-2836 Zeitschrift fuer Gletscherkunde und Glazialgeologie
0044-2844 Zeitschrift fuer Haut- und Geschlechtskrankheiten *see* 0301-0481
0044-2852 Zeitschrift fuer Heereskunde
0044-2860 Zeitschrift fuer Hoergeraete Akustik *see* 0172-8261
0044-2887 Zeitschrift fuer Jagdwissenschaft
0044-2895 Zeitschrift fuer Katholische Theologie
0044-2909 Zeitschrift fuer Kinderchirurgie und Grenzgebiete *see* 0174-3082
0044-2925 Zeitschrift fuer Kirchengeschichte
0044-2941 Zeitschrift fuer Krankenpflege - Revue Suisse des Infirmieres *changed to* Krankenpflege.
0044-295X Zeitschrift fuer Kreislaufforschung *see* 0300-5860
0044-2968 Zeitschrift fuer Kristallographie
0044-2976 Zeitschrift fuer Kulturaustausch
0044-2984 Zeitschrift fuer Kulturtechnik und Flurbereinigung *see* 0934-666X
0044-2992 Zeitschrift fuer Kunstgeschichte
0044-300X Zeitschrift fuer Landeskultur†
0044-3018 Zeitschrift fuer Laryngologie, Rhinologie, Otologie und ihre Grenzgebiete *see* 0935-8943
0044-3026 Zeitschrift fuer Lebensmittel-Untersuchung und -Forschung
0044-3034 Zeitschrift fuer Luftrecht und Weltraumrechtsfragen *see* 0340-8329
0044-3042 Zeitschrift fuer Markt, Meinungs- und Zukunftsforschung
0044-3050 Zeitschrift fuer Mathematische Logik und Grundlagen der Mathematik. Zeitschrift
0044-3069 Zeitschrift fuer Medizinische Labortechnik *see* 0323-5637
0044-3077 Zeitschrift fuer Medizinische Mikrobiologie und Immunologie *see* 0300-8584
0044-3085 Zeitschrift fuer Menschenkunde und Zentralblatt fuer Graphologie, Ausdruckswissenschaft und Charakterkunde *changed to* Zeitschrift fuer Menschenkunde. Zentralblatt fuer Schriftpsychologie und Schriftvergleichung.
0044-3093 Zeitschrift fuer Metallkunde
0044-3107 Zeitschrift fuer Mikroskopisch-Anatomische Forschung
0044-3115 Zeitschrift fuer Militaergeschichte *see* 0323-5254
0044-3123 Zeitschrift fuer Missionswissenschaft und Religionswissenschaft
0044-3131 Zeitschrift fuer Morphologie der Tiere *see* 0720-213X
0044-314X Zeitschrift fuer Morphologie und Anthropologie
0044-3158 Journal of Economics (New York) *see* 0931-8658
0044-3166 Zeitschrift fuer Naturforschung. Ausgabe A *see* 0932-0784
0044-3174 Zeitschrift fuer Naturforschung. Ausgabe B. *see* 0932-0776
0044-3182 Zeitschrift fuer Naturheilkunde
0044-3190 Zeitschrift fuer Niederdeutsche Familienkunde *changed to* Nordeutsche Familienkunde in Verbindung mit der Zeitschrift fuer Niederdeutsche Familienkunde.
0044-3204 Zeitschrift fuer Oeffentliche Fuersorge
0044-3220 Zeitschrift fuer Orthopaedie und Ihre Grenzgebiete
0044-3239 Zeitschrift fuer Ostforschung
0044-3247 Zeitschrift fuer Paedagogik
0044-3255 Zeitschrift fuer Parasitenkunde *see* 0932-0113
0044-3263 Zeitschrift fuer Pflanzenernaehrung und Bodenkunde
0044-3271 Zeitschrift fuer Pflanzenkrankheiten und Pflanzenschutz
0044-328X Zeitschrift fuer Pflanzenphysiologie *see* 0176-1617
0044-3298 Zeitschrift fuer Pflanzenzuechtung *see* 0179-9541
0044-3301 Zeitschrift fuer Philosophische Forschung
0044-331X Zeitschrift fuer Phonetik, Sprachwissenschaft und Kommunikationsforschung
0044-3328 Zeitschrift fuer Physik *see* 0930-1151
0044-3336 Zeitschrift fuer Physikalische Chemie
0044-3344 Zeitschrift fuer Physikalische Medizin†
0044-3360 Zeitschrift fuer Politik
0044-3379 Zeitschrift fuer Praeventivmedizin *changed to* Sozial- und Praeventivmedizin.
0044-3387 Zeitschrift fuer Praktische Anaesthesie, Wiederbelebung und Intensivtherapie *see* 0939-2661
0044-3395 Zeitschrift fuer Psycho-Somatische Medizin *see* 0340-5613
0044-3409 Zeitschrift fuer Psychologie
0044-3417 Zeitschrift fuer Psychotherapie und Medizinische Psychologie *see* 0173-7937
0044-3425 Zeitschrift fuer Radiaesthesie *changed to* Zeitschrift fuer Radiaesthesie und Harmoniefindung.
0044-3433 Zeitschrift fuer Rechtsmedizin - Journal of Legal Medicine *see* 0937-9827
0044-3441 Zeitschrift fuer Religions- und Geistesgeschichte
0044-345X Zeitschrift fuer Rheumaforschung *see* 0340-1855
0044-3468 Zeitschrift fuer Saeugetierkunde
0044-3476 Zeitschrift fuer Schweizerische Archaeologie und Kunstgeschichte
0044-3484 Zeitschrift fuer Schweizerische Kirchengeschichte
0044-3492 Zeitschrift fuer Slavische Philologie
0044-3506 Zeitschrift fuer Slawistik
0044-3522 Zeitschrift fuer Sozialberatung†
0044-3557 Zeitschrift fuer Therapie†
0044-3565 Journal of Animal Physiology and Animal Nutrition
0044-3573 Zeitschrift fuer Tierpsychologie *see* 0179-1613
0044-3581 Journal of Animal Breeding and Genetics
0044-359X Zeitschrift fuer Tropenmedizin und Parasitologie *see* 0177-2392
0044-3611 Zeitschrift fuer Urologie und Nephrologie *see* 0001-7868
0044-362X Zeitschrift fuer Vergleichende Physiologie *see* 0340-7594
0044-362X Zeitschrift fuer Vergleichende Physiologie *see* 0174-1578
0044-3638 Zeitschrift fuer Vergleichende Rechtswissenschaft
0044-3646 Zeitschrift fuer Vergleichende Sprachforschung *see* 0935-3518
0044-3654 Zeitschrift fuer Verkehrssicherheit
0044-3662 Zeitschrift fuer Verkehrsrecht
0044-3670 Zeitschrift fuer Verkehrswissenschaft
0044-3697 Journal of Experimental Animal Science
0044-3700 Zeitschrift fuer Volkskunde
0044-3719 Zeitschrift fuer Wahrscheinlichkeitstheorie und Verwandte Gebiete *see* 0178-8051
0044-3727 Zeitschrift fuer Wasser- und Abwasserforschung
0044-3743 Z W F - C I M

ISSN	Title
0044-3751	Zeitschrift fuer Wirtschaftsgeographie
0044-376X	Microscopica Acta†
0044-3778	Zeitschrift fuer Wissenschaftliche Zoologie. Abteilung A†
0044-3786	Zeitschrift fuer Wuerttembergische Landesgeschichte
0044-3794	Zeitschrift fuer Zellforschung und Mikroskopische Anatomie see 0302-766X
0044-3808	Zeitschrift fuer Zoologische Systematik und Evolutionsforschung
0044-3816	Zeitschrift Interne Revision
0044-3824	Zeitschriftendienst Musik
0044-3832	Zeitungs- und Zeitschriftenhandel see 0341-8073
0044-3840	Zeitwende/Die Neue Furche changed to Zeitwende.
0044-3867	Zellstoff und Papier
0044-3883	Zemedelska Technika
0044-3891	Zemedelsky a Lesni Zamestnanec changed to Socialisticky Zemedelec.
0044-3905	Zement - Kalk - Gips see 0722-4397
0044-3905	Zement - Kalk - Gips see 0722-4400
0044-3913	Zemledelie
0044-3921	Zemlja Sovjeta†
0044-3948	Zemlya i Vselennaya
0044-3956	Zen Bow changed to Zen Bow Newsletter.
0044-3972	Zending changed to Vandaar.
0044-3980	Zenit
0044-3999	Zenit†
0044-4006	Zenken Journal
0044-4022	Zentralblatt fuer Aero- und Astronautik†
0044-4030	Zentralblatt fuer Allgemeine Pathologie und Pathologische Anatomie see 0863-4106
0044-4049	Zentralblatt fuer Arbeitsmedizin und Arbeitsschutz see 0340-7047
0044-4073	Zentralblatt fuer Bakteriologie, Parasitenkunde, Infektionskrankheiten und Hygiene see 0177-3100
0044-4081	Zentralblatt fuer Bibliothekswesen see 0044-2380
0044-409X	Zentralblatt fuer Chirurgie
0044-4103	Zentralblatt fuer Didaktik der Mathematik
0044-4111	Zentralblatt fuer die Gesamte Kinderheilkunde see 0722-8953
0044-412X	Zentralblatt fuer die Gesamte Neurologie und Psychiatrie see 0722-3064
0044-4138	Zentralblatt fuer die Gesamte Ophthalmologie und ihre Grenzgebiete see 0722-9933
0044-4146	Zentralblatt fuer die Gesamte Radiologie see 0722-3072
0044-4154	Zentralblatt fuer die Gesamte Rechtsmedizin und ihre Grenzgebiete see 0722-3056
0044-4189	Zentralblatt fuer Geologie und Palaeontologie. Teil II: Palaeontologie
0044-4197	Zentralblatt fuer Gynaekologie
0044-4200	Zentralblatt fuer Hals-, Nasen- und Ohrenheilkunde Sowie Deren Grenzgebiete see 0340-5214
0044-4219	Zentralblatt fuer Haut- und Geschlechtskrankheiten Sowie Deren Grenzgebiete see 0343-3048
0044-4227	Zentralblatt fuer Industriebau see 0935-2023
0044-4235	Zentralblatt fuer Mathematik und ihre Grenzgebiete
0044-4251	Zentralblatt fuer Neurochirurgie
0044-426X	Zentralblatt fuer Phlebologie see 0301-1526
0044-4278	Zentralblatt fuer Sozialversicherung, Sozialhilfe und Versorgung
0044-4286	Zentralblatt fuer Verkehrs-Medizin, Verkehrs-Psychologie, Luft- und Raumfahrt-Medizin†
0044-4294	Zentralblatt fuer Veterinaermedizin see 0931-184X
0044-4294	Zentralblatt fuer Veterinaermedizin see 0931-1793
0044-4308	Zentralorgan fuer die Gesamte Chirurgie und ihre Grenzgebiete see 0722-6985
0044-4316	Zentralsparkasse der Gemeinde Wien. Information changed to Informationen aus der Wirtschaft.
0044-4324	Zentralverein der Wiener Lehrerschaft. Mitteilungen
0044-4340	Zero One
0044-4383	Zeszyty Problemowe Gornictwa†
0044-4391	Zeszyty Historyczne
0044-4405	Katolicki Uniwersytet Lubelski. Zeszyty Naukowe
0044-4413	Fasciculi Mathematici
0044-443X	Zeszyty Teoretyczno-Polityczne see 0137-3609
0044-4448	Zheleznodorozhnyi Transport
0044-4456	Zhenshchiny Mira
0044-4464	Zhilishchnoi i Kommunal'noe Khozyaistvo
0044-4472	Zhilishchnoe Stroitel'stvo
0044-4480	Zhivotnovodstvo changed to Zootekhniia.
0044-4499	Zhovten' changed to Dzvin.
0044-4502	Zhurnal Analiticheskoi Khimii
0044-4510	Zhurnal Eksperimental'noi i Teoreticheskoi Fiziki
0044-4529	Zhurnal Evolyutsionnoi Biokhimii i Fiziologii
0044-4537	Zhurnal Fizicheskoi Khimii
0044-4553	Russkaya Pravoslavnaya Tserkov'. Moskovskaya Patriarkhiya. Zhurnal
0044-4561	Zhurnal Nauchnoi i Prikladnoi Fotografii i Kinematografii
0044-457X	Zhurnal Neorganicheskoi Khimii
0044-4588	Zhurnal Nevropatologii i Psikhiatrii im. S.S. Korsakova
0044-4596	Zhurnal Obshchei Biologii
0044-460X	Zhurnal Obshchei Khimii
0044-4618	Zhurnal Prikladnoi Khimii
0044-4626	Zhurnal Prikladnoi Mekhaniki i Tekhnicheskoi Fiziki
0044-4634	Zhurnal Strukturnoi Khimii
0044-4642	Zhurnal Tekhnicheskoi Fiziki
0044-4650	Zhurnal Ushnykh, Nosovykh i Gorlovykh Boleznei
0044-4669	Zhurnal Vychislitel'noi Matematiki i Matematicheskoi Fiziki
0044-4677	Zhurnal Vysshei Nervnoi Deyatel'nosti
0044-4693	Ziegelindustrie see 0341-0552
0044-4707	Ziekenfondsgids†
0044-4715	Ziekenhuis
0044-4723	Zimbabwe Review changed to Revolution.
0044-4731	Zinc Abstracts see 0950-1592
0044-474X	Alte und Neue Zinnfiguren
0044-4758	Zion
0044-4766	Zionist Collegiate†
0044-4774	Zionist Literature
0044-4782	Zionist Record and S.A. Jewish Chronicle
0044-4790	Zion's Herald see 0098-9282
0044-4812	Ziva
0044-4820	Ziviler Bevoelkerungsschutz. ZB†
0044-4839	Zivilverteidigung see 0938-7390
0044-4847	Zivocisna Vyroba
0044-4855	Zivot i Skola
0044-4863	Zivotne Prostredie
0044-4871	Zlaty Maj
0044-488X	Znak
0044-4898	Znamya
0044-4928	Zobozdravstveni Vestnik
0044-4936	Zodiac (Italian Edition)
0044-4944	Zodiac changed to Helix.
0044-4952	Zodiaque
0044-4979	Zolnierz Polski
0044-4995	Zona: Revista de Comercio Latino-Americana
0044-5002	Zondagsmis
0044-5010	Zone
0044-5029	Zoo Anvers
0044-5037	Zoot
0044-5045	Zoolog see 0315-5064
0044-5053	Zoologia see 0301-2123
0044-5061	Ricerche di Zoologia Applicata alla Caccia see 0375-0736
0044-5088	Zoologica
0044-5096	Zoologica Africana see 0254-1858
0044-510X	Zoologica Poloniae
0044-5118	Zoological Magazine†
0044-5126	Zoological Society of Southern Africa. News Bulletin changed to Zoological Society of Southern Africa. Occasional Bulletin.
0044-5134	Zoologicheskii Zhurnal
0044-5142	Zoologicke a Entomologicke Listy (Folia Zoologica et Entomologica) see 0139-7893
0044-5150	Zoologische Beitraege
0044-5169	Der Zoologische Garten
0044-5177	Zoologische Jahrbuecher. Abteilung fuer Anatomie und Ontogenie der Tiere
0044-5185	Zoologische Jahrbuecher. Abteilung fuer Allgemeine Zoologie und Physiologie der Tiere
0044-5193	Zoologische Jahrbuecher. Abteilung fuer Systematik, Oekologie und Geographie der Tiere
0044-5223	Zoologisches Museum Hamburg. Entomologische Mitteilungen
0044-5231	Zoologischer Anzeiger
0044-5258	Zoologisk Revy
0044-5274	Zoon†
0044-5282	Zoonooz
0044-5290	Zooprofilassi†
0044-5304	Zoo's Letter changed to Zoosletter.
0044-5320	Brazil. Instituto de Zootecnia. Zootecnia
0044-5339	Zorgenkind see 0166-4298
0044-5347	Japan Shipping and Shipbuilding changed to Zosen.
0044-5355	V Z L U Zpravodaj
0044-5371	Zuchthygiene see 0936-6768
0044-538X	Zucker see 0344-8657
0044-5398	Die Zuckerruebe
0044-5401	Zuechtungskunde
0044-5428	Zuid - Afrika
0044-5436	Zuivelnieuws
0044-5452	Zukunft
0044-5460	Zukunft
0044-5479	Zulqarnain
0044-5487	Zum Nachdenken
0044-5509	Zur Geschichte der Pharmazie see 0939-334X
0044-5517	Revista de Historia Jeronimo Zurita
0044-5525	Zvaranie
0044-5533	Zvezdna Revija
0044-555X	Zvuk
0044-5576	Zwingli
0044-5584	Zycie i Mysl
0044-5592	A - Rivista Anarchica
0044-5606	A B C Decor
0044-5622	A B S E E S
0044-5649	A D P Newsletter†
0044-5657	A F - Architekturforum
0044-5681	A I M
0044-569X	A Is A Newsletter changed to A Is A.
0044-5711	A R I S
0044-5746	Aboriginal Quarterly†
0044-5762	Revista del Frio
0044-5800	Abstracts of Hungarian Economic Literature
0044-5819	Abstracts on Health Effects of Environmental Pollutants†
0044-5827	Abundance
0044-5835	Academy of Parish Clergy. Journal†
0044-5843	Acadia Bulletin
0044-5851	Acadiensis: Journal of the History of the Atlantic Region
0044-586X	Acarologia
0044-5878	Accident Prevention
0044-5894	Accion Empresarial
0044-5908	Accion Indigenista see 0185-058X
0044-5916	Accountants and Secretaries Educational Journal
0044-5924	Accountants" Washington Taxletter†
0044-5932	A C E
0044-5940	Acoma†
0044-5967	Acta Amazonica
0044-5975	Academia Scientiarum Hungarica. Acta Antiqua
0044-5983	Acta Botanica Neerlandica
0044-5991	Acta Histochemica et Cytochemica
0044-6009	Acta Hospitalia
0044-6017	Acta Medica del Valle changed to Colombia Medica.
0044-6025	Acta Medica Iranica
0044-6033	Acta Physiologica Polonica†
0044-6041	Acta Socio-Medica Scandinavica see 0300-8037
0044-605X	Acta Veterinaria Scandinavica
0044-6068	Action
0044-6092	Action Era Vehicle
0044-6106	Action Populaire
0044-6130	Actualidade Universitaria†
0044-6149	Actualite de la Medecine Officielle et Medecine Naturelle
0044-6157	Actualite Fiduciaire
0044-6165	Actualites Industrielles Lorraines
0044-6173	Aktuelle Traumatologie
0044-6181	Adam and Eve
0044-6203	Alcoholism and Drug Addiction Research Foundation. Journal changed to Addiction Research Foundation. Journal.
0044-6211	Adelaide. National Gallery of South Australia see 0004-3206
0044-622X	Adelaide. Stock Exchange. Official Record†
0044-6238	Adelante (Orlando)
0044-6254	Adhesifs changed to Assemblages Adhesifs.
0044-6262	Administracion, Desarrollo, Integracion†
0044-6300	Administrative Scene
0044-6319	Administrator†
0044-6327	Administrator†
0044-6335	Adolescent Medicine (Washington)
0044-6343	Adult & Child see 0092-4032
0044-636X	Advanced Technology Libraries
0044-6378	Advances in Urethane Science and Technology
0044-6386	Adventures in Experimental Physics see 0893-8067
0044-6394	Adverse Drug Reaction Bulletin
0044-6408	Ad. Activities†
0044-6416	Advocate (West Vancouver)
0044-6432	Aero News†
0044-6459	Affaires see 0229-3404
0044-6467	Affirm
0044-6475	Africa (London)
0044-6483	Africa Confidential
0044-6491	Africa Letter
0044-6513	Africa Now see 0711-6683
0044-653X	African Crescent
0044-6556	African Jewish Newspaper
0044-6564	African Journal of Pharmacy and Pharmaceutical Sciences
0044-6580	African Missionary changed to S M A - the African Missionary.
0044-6602	African Religious Research
0044-6610	African Studies Association of the West Indies. Bulletin
0044-6629	African Urban Notes changed to African Urban Studies.
0044-6645	Africana i Nordiska Vetenskapliga. Bibliotek see 0348-8691
0044-6661	Afrique et Parole†
0044-6696	After School
0044-670X	Afterthought
0044-6718	Agency Sales - With Agent and Representative see 0749-2332
0044-6726	Agora
0044-6734	Agra University. Bulletin
0044-6742	Agregation
0044-6750	Agri Sept changed to Le Nouvel Agriculteur.
0044-6769	Agrichemical Age†
0044-6785	Agricultura†
0044-6793	Agricultura em Sao Paulo
0044-6807	Agricultural Engineering Australia
0044-6823	Agriculture and Farming†
0044-6831	Agrifack
0044-684X	Agrologist see 0840-8289
0044-6858	Agronomia Mocambicana
0044-6866	Agronomist†
0044-6882	Agrosintesis
0044-6890	Agua

ISSN INDEX

ISSN	Title
0044-6904	Ahead: Australian Health Advisory Digest†
0044-6912	Aichi-Gakuin Journal of Dental Science
0044-6920	Aikamerkki‡
0044-6963	Air Enthusiast see 0306-5634
0044-6971	Air et Cosmos
0044-698X	Air over Arizona†
0044-7005	Airfair Interline
0044-7013	Airline Passengers Association News changed to A P A Holiday.
0044-7021	Airport Report
0044-703X	Laisvė†
0044-7048	Akron Business and Economic Review†
0044-7064	Alaluz
0044-7080	Alberta Bowhunter and Archer
0044-7099	Alberta Builder†
0044-7102	Alberta Certified Nursing Aide Association. Newsletter see 0706-2192
0044-7129	Alberta Education Council. Newsletter†
0044-7137	A H E A Newsletter see 0834-213X
0044-7145	Alberta Landrace Association. Newsletter
0044-7153	Alberta, Lands, Forests, Parks, Wildlife†
0044-7161	A M T A News Bulletin changed to Truxpress.
0044-7218	Alcheringa†
0044-7226	Alcoholism and Alcohol Education see 0744-2823
0044-7234	Alert (Wahroonga)†
0044-7242	Alert (Crows Nest) changed to Wormald Journal.
0044-7250	Alexandria Journal of Agricultural Research
0044-7277	Alianza Federal de Pueblos Libres. Vox de la Alianza
0044-7293	All India Institute of Medical Sciences, New Delhi. Bulletin†
0044-7307	All India Ophthalmological Society. Journal see 0301-4738
0044-734X	Alliance changed to Alliance News.
0044-7358	Allo Dix-Huit
0044-7374	Alm und Weide changed to Alm und Bergbauer.
0044-7382	Alternative see 0148-8414
0044-7390	Alternatives Journal changed to Guide to Self-Directed Living Bulletin.
0044-7412	Amanuensis†
0044-7439	Ambassador†
0044-7447	Ambio
0044-7455	Ambulance changed to Ambulance Service Journal.
0044-7463	Amenagement et Nature
0044-7471	Amerasia Journal
0044-748X	Latinskaya Amerika changed to Evropa i Amerika.
0044-7501	American Alumni Council Commentary†
0044-751X	American Antiquarian Society. Proceedings
0044-7528	American-Arab Association of Commerce and Industry. Bulletin changed to American Mideast Business Association. Bulletin.
0044-7536	A A M Bulletin changed to Aviso.
0044-7544	American Baby
0044-7552	A B A Bulletin see 0045-1312
0044-7560	A L I - A B A - C L E Review
0044-7579	AmCham Journal see 0116-452X
0044-7587	A C S Single Article Announcement†
0044-7595	S C A L A C S
0044-7609	A C A Journal of Chiropractic see 0744-9984
0044-7617	American Chronicle†
0044-7625	American Cinemeditor changed to On Production.
0044-7633	American Classical Review
0044-7641	Nurses Association of the American College of Obstetricians and Gynecologists. Bulletin News see 0884-2175
0044-765X	American Cotton Grower see 0194-9772
0044-7676	American Federation of Television and Radio Artists. A F T R A changed to A F T R A.
0044-7684	American Film Institute Report†
0044-7692	American Fisheries Society. Newsletter see 0363-2415
0044-7714	American Indian Crafts and Culture see 0099-0361
0044-7722	A S†
0044-7749	American Laboratory
0044-7757	A L A Zurnals†
0044-7765	A M A Update†
0044-7773	American Notary
0044-7714	Nursing Research Report†
0044-779X	American Philological Association. Directory of Members
0044-7803	American Politics Quarterly
0044-7811	American Postal Worker
0044-782X	A P W A Washington Report see 0160-001X
0044-7838	American Revolution†
0044-7854	A S E A Newsletter†
0044-7870	American Society for Information Science. Proceedings see 0160-0044
0044-7889	A S M News (Materials Park)
0044-7897	A S M News (Washington)
0044-7900	American Society for Neo-Hellenic Studies. Newsletter
0044-7919	A S P R Newsletter
0044-7927	A S T R Newsletter
0044-7935	American Society of Architectural Hardware Consultants. News and Views see 0361-5294
0044-7943	American Society of Cartographers. Bulletin
0044-7951	American Society of Civil Engineers. Engineering Mechanics Division. Journal see 0733-9399
0044-796X	American Society of Civil Engineers. Hydraulics Division. Journal see 0733-9429
0044-7978	American Society of Civil Engineers. Irrigation and Drainage Division. Journal see 0733-9437
0044-7986	American Society of Civil Engineers. Sanitary Engineering Division. Journal see 0733-9372
0044-7994	American Society of Civil Engineers. Soil Mechanics and Foundation Division. Journal see 0733-9410
0044-8001	American Society of Civil Engineers. Structural Division. Journal see 0733-9445
0044-801X	American Society of Civil Engineers. Transportation Engineering Division. Journal see 0733-947X
0044-8028	American Society of Civil Engineers. Waterways, Harbors, and Coastal Engineering Division. Journal see 0733-950X
0044-8044	American Society of Planning Officials. A S P O Planning Advisory Service see 0160-8266
0044-8052	A S D A Newsletter see 0277-3627
0044-8060	American Studies in Scandinavia
0044-8079	American Zionist Federation. News and Views†
0044-8087	Ami de la Boulangerie changed to Nouvelles de la Boulangerie.
0044-8095	Ami des Jardins et de la Maison
0044-8117	Ami du Charcutier, du Boucher et du Salaisonnier see 0296-8746
0044-8125	Amino-Acids, Peptide and Protein Abstracts see 8756-7520
0044-8133	Amis d'Andre Gide. Bulletin
0044-8141	Amministrare
0044-815X	Ampute de Guerre
0044-8168	Amrat
0044-8176	Analecta Linguistica
0044-8184	Anales de Ortopedia y Traumatologia
0044-8192	Analysen und Prognosen ueber die Welt von Morgen
0044-8206	Anapress
0044-8214	Anasthesiologische Praxis see 0303-6200
0044-8222	Ancestor
0044-8249	Angewandte Chemie
0044-8257	A.C.A. Review
0044-8265	Anglo-Soviet Journal
0044-8273	Anglo-Ukranian News†
0044-8281	Angola Bulletin see 0166-0373
0044-829X	Animal Defence League of Canada. News Bulletin
0044-832X	Annals of Economic and Social Measurement†
0044-8338	Annals of Immunology see 0324-8534
0044-8370	Anthropological Society of Oxford. Journal
0044-8389	Antioquia Medica
0044-8400	Apartment News changed to Apartment Owner - Builder.
0044-8419	Apero†
0044-8427	Apiculture in Western Australia†
0044-8435	Apidologie
0044-8451	Applied Radiology see 0160-9963
0044-8486	Aquaculture
0044-8508	Aquarium Society of New South Wales. Monthly Journal
0044-8516	Aquatic Sciences and Fisheries Abstracts see 0140-5373
0044-8516	Aquatic Sciences and Fisheries Abstracts see 0140-5381
0044-8524	Aqui
0044-8540	Arab-Canada Newsletter see 0703-9018
0044-8559	Arab News†
0044-8567	Arbetsgivaren see 0349-6740
0044-8575	West Virginia University. Department of Biology. Arboretum Newsletter changed to West Virginia University. Department of Biology. Core Arboretum Bulletin.
0044-8591	Archaeology in Montana
0044-8613	Archipel
0044-8621	De Architect
0044-863X	Architectura
0044-8648	A A Notes†
0044-8672	Architekt
0044-8680	Architektura a Urbanizmus
0044-8699	Archiv Orientalni
0044-8702	Archives Medicales de Normandie†
0044-8710	Archives of Child Health
0044-8729	Archives of Labor History and Urban Affairs Newsletter changed to Archives of Labor and Urban Affairs Newsletter.
0044-8737	Archivio Storico Siracusano
0044-8745	Archivium Hibernicum
0044-8753	Archivum Mathematicum
0044-8761	Archiwum Procesow Spalania - Archives of Combustion Processes see 0208-4198
0044-877X	Arctic Frontiers†
0044-8788	Areas of Concern
0044-8796	Arecanut and Spices Bulletin changed to Indian Cocoa, Arecanut & Spices Journal.
0044-8818	Argosy Weekly
0044-8826	Argus (College Park) changed to Argus Magazine.
0044-8850	A S D M Newsletter changed to Sonorensis.
0044-8869	Arizona Safety Sad-Istics see 0147-3743
0044-8877	University of Arizona Library. Bibliographic Bulletin†
0044-8885	Ark River Review
0044-8893	Arkansas L P News changed to Arkansas Propane Gas News.
0044-8907	Arkansas Poultry Times
0044-8915	Arkkitehtiuutiset
0044-8931	Armed Citizen News
0044-894X	Armenian Observer
0044-8958	Armidale, New South Wales. Teachers' College. Bulletin changed to Armidale College of Advanced Education. Bulletin.
0044-8966	Armor
0044-8974	Armstrong Logic
0044-8982	Arquivos Fluminenses de Odontologia†
0044-9008	Ars
0044-9016	Art Gallery of Greater Victoria. Bulletin see 0317-2031
0044-9024	Art Gallery of Ontario. Coming Events see 0829-4437
0044-9032	A R L I S Newsletter see 0307-4722
0044-9059	Art Teachers Association of Victoria. Journal changed to Interacta.
0044-9067	Arte Nuova Oggi changed to Arte Nuova.
0044-9075	Artefact
0044-9091	Arthur
0044-9105	Artificial Rainfall Newsletter†
0044-913X	Artistic Pakistan†
0044-9148	Asahi Camera
0044-9164	Asia Focus†
0044-9172	Asia Research Bulletin†
0044-9199	Asian Development Bank. Newsletter changed to A D B Quarterly Review.
0044-9202	Asian Music
0044-9210	Asian Periodicals changed to Periodicals of Asia and the Pacific.
0044-9229	A P O News
0044-9245	Asian Studies Professional Review†
0044-9253	Revista Astronomica
0044-9261	A I T I M Boletin de Informacion Tecnica
0044-9288	A N A B A Boletin see 0210-4164
0044-930X	A N E C
0044-9318	Asociacion Peruana de Astronomia. Boletin
0044-9326	Asociacion Rural del Uruguay. Revista
0044-9369	Associacao Brasileira de Educacao Agricola Superior. A B E A S Informa
0044-9393	A C A Reports see 0748-6723
0044-9407	Association Canadienne des Bibliothecaires de Langue Francaise. Nouvelles de l'ACBLF see 0316-0963
0044-9415	Association des Architects de la Province de Quebec. Bulletin see 0316-9200
0044-9423	Archives
0044-9458	A.F.E.A.S. Bulletin see 0705-3851
0044-9466	Association for Preservation Technology. Bulletin changed to Association for Preservation Technology International. Bulletin.
0044-9482	Association for the Advancement of Agricultural Sciences in Africa. Journal changed to African Journal of Agricultural Sciences.
0044-9490	A I L A Bulletin
0044-9504	A I O S P Bulletin changed to Educational and Vocational Guidance - Bulletin A I O S P, I A E V G, I V S B B.
0044-9539	Association of British Columbia Librarians. Newsletter†
0044-9547	A C D Bulletin†
0044-9555	Association of Canadian Faculties of Dentistry. Newsletter see 0820-5949
0044-9563	A C U Bulletin of Current Documentation (ABCD)
0044-958X	A E N Bulletin see 0270-6881
0044-9598	Association of Engineers, India. Journal
0044-9601	A G B Notes
0044-961X	A G B Reports
0044-9628	Association of Law Teachers. Journal see 0306-9400
0044-9636	Association of New Jersey Conservation Commissions Newsletter changed to A N J E C Report.
0044-9652	A R L Minutes
0044-9660	A S L A President's Newsletter†
0044-9687	A T S S Bulletin
0044-9695	A U A Newsletter†
0044-9709	Association pour l'Histoire de Belle-Ile-En-Mer. Bulletin Trimestriel
0044-9725	Association Senegalaise pour l'Etude du Quaternaire de l'Ouest African. Bulletin de Liaison changed to Association Senegalaise pour l'Etude du Quaternaire Africain. Bulletin de Liaison.
0044-9733	Associazione Italiana di Cartografia. A I C Bollettino
0044-9741	A P A C Inform
0044-975X	A I S C A T Informazioni

ISSN INDEX 5471

0044-9768 Astarte†
0044-9776 Asthma Welfarer
0044-9784 Astrological Review
0044-9792 Astrology and Athrishta
0044-9806 Astronomical Society of South Australia. Bulletin
0044-9814 Astronomical Society of Victoria. Journal†
0044-9822 Astronomy & Space†
0044-9830 At Home and Abroad *changed to* Junkanoo.
0044-9849 Atenea
0044-9865 Athenes-Presse Libre†
0044-9873 Athletic Administration
0044-9881 Atlantic Control States Beverage Journal
0044-989X Atlantic Provinces Economic Council. Newsletter
0044-9903 Atlantic Provinces Numismatic Association. Newsletter
0044-9911 Atlantic Review (St. Johns)
0044-992X Atlantic Salmon Journal
0044-9954 Atomic Absorption Newsletter *see* 0195-5373
0044-9962 Attak *see* 0167-5303
0044-9970 W R R I News Report
0044-9989 Audience and Programme Research
0045-0006 Auditor's Computer Update Digest†
0045-0014 Audubon Leader
0045-0030 Auris
0045-0049 Ausbildung und Beratung in Land- und Hauswirtschaft
0045-0073 Australasian Insurance Journal†
0045-0081 Australasian Kennel Review and Dog News†
0045-009X Australian Model Railroad Magazine *changed to* Australian Model Railway Magazine.
0045-0103 A S E Journal
0045-0111 Australia. Bureau of Statistics. Balance of Payments (Canberra, 1963) *changed to* Australia. Bureau of Statistics. Balance of Payments, Australia (Annual).
0045-012X Industrial Information Bulletin†
0045-0138 Australia. Department of National Development. Nat/Devt†
0045-0146 Australia. Department of the Northern Territory. Northern Territory Affairs†
0045-0170 A N Z A News
0045-0189 Australia. Northern Territory Division. Northern Newsletter *changed to* Australia. Northern Territory Protocol and Public Relations Branch. Territory Digest.
0045-0197 Australia Now
0045-0200 Australia. Bureau of Agricultural Economics. Fibres Other Than Wool *see* 0311-2950
0045-0219 Australian and New Zealand Association for Medieval and Renaissance Studies. Bulletin†
0045-0235 Australian Angler *see* 0158-572X
0045-0243 Australian Apprenticeship Advisory Committee. Apprenticeship News†
0045-026X Australian Author
0045-0286 Australian Bankruptcy Bulletin *changed to* Australian Insolvency Bulletin.
0045-0294 Australian Bee Journal
0045-0308 Australian Biblical Review
0045-0316 Australian Birdwatcher
0045-0324 Australian Boating Industry†
0045-0332 Australian Bridge
0045-0340 Australian Chemical Industry Directory†
0045-0359 Australian Chiropractors Association. Journal *see* 1036-0913
0045-0383 Australian Computer Society. Canberra Branch. Bulletin *changed to* Canberra Computer Bulletin.
0045-0391 A C O S S Quarterly *changed to* Impact (Sydney).
0045-0391 A C O S S Quarterly *see* 0004-9557
0045-0405 Australian Current Law *changed to* Australian Current Law Legislation.
0045-0405 Australian Current Law *changed to* Australian Current Law Reporter.
0045-0413 Australian Current Law Review†
0045-0421 Australian Dental Journal
0045-043X Australian Environmental Report *see* 0311-0931
0045-0448 Australian Films†
0045-0456 Australian Furnishing Trade Journal
0045-0472 Australian Goat World
0045-0480 Australian Government News†
0045-0537 Australian Home Gardener†
0045-0545 Australian Institute of Agricultural Science. Journal†
0045-0553 Australian Institute of Dairy Factory Managers and Secretaries. Butter Fats and Solids
0045-057X Management Diary *see* 0313-0835
0045-0588 Australian Jersey Journal
0045-0596 Australian Journal of Advanced Education *changed to* Journal of Advanced Education.
0045-060X Australian Journal of Experimental Agriculture and Animal Husbandry *see* 0816-1089
0045-0618 Australian Journal of Forensic Sciences
0045-0626 Australian Journal of Instrumentation and Control
0045-0634 Australian Journal of Mental Retardation *see* 0726-3864
0045-0642 Australian Journal of Optometry *see* 0816-4622
0045-0650 Australian Journal of Sports Medicine *see* 0813-6289
0045-0669 Australian Labor Party. A.L.P. *see* 0819-9825
0045-0677 Australian Maps
0045-0693 Australian Meat Board. Meat Producer and Exporter *changed to* A M L C News.
0045-0707 A M D E L Bulletin
0045-0715 A M R A Journal
0045-0731 A N C O L D Bulletin
0045-074X Australian National Drycleaner
0045-0758 Australian Nurses' Journal
0045-0766 Australian Occupational Therapy Journal
0045-0774 Australian O.C.C.A. Proceedings and News *see* 0815-709X
0045-0782 Australian Orchid Review
0045-0820 Australian Retail Tobacconist
0045-0847 Australian Roads†
0045-0855 27stralian Science Teachers' Journal
0045-0863 Australian Sea Spray Weekly *see* 0311-7839
0045-0898 Australia Stevedoring Industry Authority. Monthly Statistics
0045-0901 Australian Stock Exchange Journal
0045-091X Australian Teacher *changed to* Teachers Guild of New South Wales. Proceedings.
0045-0928 Australian Technical Teacher *see* 0815-3701
0045-0936 Australian Tobacco Journal†
0045-0944 Australian Trader
0045-0960 Australian Welding Research†
0045-0979 Australian Worker
0045-1002 Auto-Neige†
0045-1010 Auto und Reise
0045-1053 Automobile & Tractor
0045-1061 Automobile Connoisseur
0045-107X Automotive Marketing *see* 0193-3264
0045-1088 Automotive Messenger
0045-110X Automotive Transport Labour Relations Association. Monthly Labour Bulletin†
0045-1118 Autonomi
0045-1126 Autotouring *changed to* Touring Club Magazine.
0045-1142 Auvergne Economique
0045-1150 Avant-Scene Cinema
0045-1169 Avant Scene Theatre
0045-1177 Aviacion y Astronautica
0045-1185 Aviation Historical Society of Australia. Journal *see* 0815-4392
0045-1193 Aviation Mechanics Journal *changed to* General Aviation Mechanics Journal.
0045-1207 Aviation Safety Digest†
0045-1223 Aware†
0045-1231 Awareness†
0045-124X Ayn Rand Letter†
0045-1258 Azor *see* 0572-2969
0045-1266 B E E - Bulletin of Environmental Education *see* 0957-6517
0045-1274 B P Shield International *changed to* Shield.
0045-1282 Ba Shirut
0045-1290 Background to South African and World News†
0045-1304 Badger Herald
0045-1312 Badminton U.S.A.†
0045-1320 Baha'i World
0045-1347 Ballet-Hoo
0045-1355 Balloon *changed to* Atkinsonian.
0045-1363 Baltimore Health News *changed to* Perspectives (Baltimore).
0045-138X Bamah
0045-1398 Banana Bulletin *changed to* B G F Bulletin.
0045-1401 Banco de Guatemala. Informe Economico
0045-1428 Bangladesh Journal of Biological and Agricultural Sciences *changed to* Bangladesh Journal of Biological Sciences.
0045-1436 Bank Directory of Canada *changed to* Canadian Payments Directories.
0045-1444 Bank Melli Iran. Bulletin
0045-1460 Bank of Canada. Review
0045-1487 Bank Operations Report
0045-1495 Bank Pembangunan Indonesia. Newsletter
0045-1509 Bank Street Reporting *changed to* Street Scenes.
0045-1533 Banque Canadienne Nationale. Bulletin Mensuel†
0045-1541 Bar Executive Key Handbook†
0045-155X Barnet Marksman
0045-1576 Battle Line *see* 0145-1677
0045-1584 Beat Instrumental and International Recording Studio *changed to* Beat Instrumental Songwriting & Recording Magazine.
0045-1592 Beaverbrook Art Gallery *see* 0845-8081
0045-1606 Bedriftsoekonomisk Informasjon *changed to* Oekonomisk Rapport.
0045-1614 Bedryfsleiding - Business Management *see* 0378-9098
0045-1622 Beef & You†
0045-1649 Beer in Canada†
0045-1657 Beermat *see* 0306-7912
0045-1673 B R S Monthly Index†
0045-169X Beitraege zur Konfliktforschung†
0045-1703 Belgium. Institut National de Statistique. Bulletin de Statistique
0045-172X Benefits International *see* 0268-764X
0045-1738 Bensiini Uutiset
0045-1746 Bergens Privatbanks Kvartalsskrift *see* 0332-6756
0045-1762 Berliner Bauwirtschaft
0045-1789 Erziehung *changed to* Paedagogik Heute - Paedagogische Beitraege.
0045-1797 Better Boating†
0045-1800 Better Business Bureau of Metropolitan New York. News Review†
0045-1819 Better Business Bureau of Metropolitan New York. Report to Business *changed to* Report to Business.
0045-1835 Bias
0045-186X Bibliografie van de Nederlandse Taal- en Literatuur Wetenschap
0045-1878 Bibliographic Society of Canada. Index Committee. Newsletter†
0045-1886 Bibliographie Nationale de la Tunisie†
0045-1894 Bibliographie Selective des Publications Officielles Francaise†
0045-1908 Bibliographies of Chemists†
0045-1916 Bibliographische Informationen aus der Technik und Ihren Grundlagenwissenschaften†
0045-1924 Bibliography of Articles on Physical and Health Education, Sport and Allied Subjects *changed to* Bibliographical Index on Physical and Health Education, Sport and Allied Subjects.
0045-1932 Bibliography on High Pressure Research
0045-1959 Biblioteca Teatrale
0045-1967 Bibliotheque Nationale. Bulletin *see* 0825-1746
0045-1975 Big Bike Magazine *see* 0194-9888
0045-1983 Big Book of Metalworking Machinery
0045-2009 Bil-Nyt *changed to* Motor-Journalen Bilen.
0045-2025 Biochemical Systematics *see* 0305-1978
0045-2033 Biological Science
0045-205X Biologie in Unserer Zeit
0045-2068 Bioorganic Chemistry
0045-2076 Bird Keeping in Australia
0045-2084 Black Bag
0045-2114 Black Books Bulletin†
0045-2157 Black Flag
0045-2165 Black Graphics International
0045-219X Black Lechwe
0045-2203 Black Lines: a Journal of Black Studies†
0045-222X Black Maria
0045-2238 Black News Digest
0045-2246 Black Oracle *see* 0198-1064
0045-2270 Blackfish
0045-2289 Bleu et Rouge
0045-2297 Blues & Soul Music Review
0045-2300 Boardroom Reports
0045-2319 Bodyshop
0045-2351 Boian News Service†
0045-236X BolaffiArte *changed to* Arte.
0045-2378 Boletim de Materiais Dentarios
0045-2386 Boletim de Vulgarizacao Veterinaria†
0045-2394 Boletin de Ciencias Politicas y Sociales *changed to* Anales Ciencias Politicas y Sociales.
0045-2424 Bollettino di Magistratura Democratica
0045-2432 Bollettino Bibliografico Sardo e Archivio Tradizioni Popolari
0045-2467 Bolsa de Cereales. Revista Institucional†
0045-2483 Bonsai in Australia†
0045-2505 Book Anglest
0045-2513 Book Trolley *see* 0305-9340
0045-2521 Bookplates in the News
0045-253X Books *see* 0266-4208
0045-2556 Books for Young People *see* 0033-6491
0045-2564 Books in Canada
0045-2572 Books in English
0045-2580 Border Business Digest *changed to* Cumbria Weekly Digest.
0045-2599 Bosch Kurier†
0045-2602 Boston After Dark *see* 0163-3015
0045-2629 Botanica
0045-2637 Botaniste *see* 0181-7582
0045-2688 Boys Village Report *changed to* Dellcrest News.
0045-2696 Brannmannen
0045-270X Brasil Florestal†
0045-2718 Brauer und Maelzer *see* 0341-7115
0045-2726 M A N (Mensario de Arquivo Nacional) *see* 0102-700X
0045-2742 Brazil. Superintendencia do Desenvolvimento da Amazonia. S U D A M Documenta
0045-2750 Bread Manufacturer and Pastrycook of Western Australia
0045-2769 Break Throught
0045-2777 Breakthrough†
0045-2785 Breves Nouvelles de France *see* 0398-9682
0045-2793 Brian Bex Report *changed to* American Record.
0045-2823 Bridge (New York) *changed to* Bridge: Asian American Perspectives.
0045-2831 Church Lads' and Church Girls' Brigade. Annual Report
0045-2858 Bristol Diocesan Gazette *changed to* Bristol Diocesan News.
0045-2866 Britain and Overseas

ISSN

ISSN INDEX

ISSN	Title
0045-2874	British Advent Messenger see 0309-3654
0045-2890	British Caribbean Philatelic Journal
0045-2904	British Columbia Art Teachers' Association. Newsletter see 0316-1544
0045-2912	B.C. Association of Teachers of Classics. Newsletter see 0316-2508
0045-2947	British Columbia Counsellors' Association. Newsletter see 0705-8802
0045-2955	British Columbia English Teacher see 0316-0173
0045-2963	British Columbia Historical News
0045-2971	British Columbia Hotelman†
0045-2998	British Columbia Mountaineer
0045-3005	British Columbia Museums Association. Museum Round Up
0045-3013	B C Outdoors
0045-303X	British Columbia Snow Survey Bulletin
0045-3048	British Columbia Social Studies Teachers' Association. Newsletter see 0315-8527
0045-3056	British Columbia Tax Reports
0045-3064	British Columbia Thoroughbred
0045-3072	Phycological Newsletter
0045-3080	B.C. Voice
0045-3099	British Iron and Steel Research Association. Open Report List changed to British Steel Corporation. Corporate Development Laboratory. Open Report List.
0045-3102	British Journal of Social Work
0045-3110	British Naturopathic Journal and Osteopathic Review†
0045-3129	B N A Topics
0045-3137	British Racing News
0045-3145	British Society of Rheology. Bulletin
0045-3153	British Speleological Association. Bulletin see 0142-1832
0045-317X	B M I: The Many Worlds of Music changed to B M I: Music World.
0045-3188	Broadcasting Bibliophile's Booknotes see 0748-657X
0045-3226	Broken Spoke
0045-3242	B A C A Calendar of Cultural Events
0045-3250	Bruce County Historical Notes see 0084-8115
0045-3269	Brush
0045-3277	Belgium. Institut Royal Meteorologique. Bulletin Mensuel: Pollution Atmospherique. Fumee et So Deux†
0045-3285	Buckeye Review
0045-3293	Buck's Safety Management AID†
0045-3315	Buddhist Quarterly see 0265-2900
0045-3323	Budgerigar Bulletin
0045-3331	Museo Social Argentino. Boletin changed to Conceptos Boletin.
0045-334X	Buffalo
0045-3366	Milwaukee Bugle
0045-3374	Buhiti†
0045-3382	Builder changed to LifeLine (Kingston).
0045-3412	Building Ideas†
0045-3420	Building News see 1030-1925
0045-3447	University of Stellenbosch. Bureau for Economic Research. Building Survey see 0586-4941
0045-348X	Bullet
0045-3498	Bulletin Bibliographique de la Prevention see 1010-7061
0045-3501	Bulletin de l'Afrique Noire
0045-351X	Bulletin Jugend und Literatur
0045-3536	Bulwark
0045-3544	Bureaucrat see 1061-7639
0045-3552	Burning Spear†
0045-3587	Business and Professional Woman (Canada)
0045-3595	Business and Professional Woman (England)
0045-3609	Business and Society Review
0045-3617	Business Aviation changed to Business Aviation Weekly.
0045-3625	Business Dynamics see 0361-7653
0045-3633	Business Ideas and Facts†
0045-3641	Business Venezuela
0045-3668	Businessman's Law
0045-3676	Bust†
0045-3684	Buyers' Market
0045-3692	Buzz changed to Alpha (New Malden)
0045-3706	C I D X Messenger
0045-3714	Cable
0045-3730	Cahiers Bibliographiques des Lettres Quebecoise†
0045-3749	Cahiers de Litterature et de Linguistique Appliqué†
0045-3765	Cahiers d'Outre-Mer
0045-3773	Cahiers du Bilinguisme
0045-3781	Cahiers du Travailleur Intellectuel
0045-379X	Cahiers Spartacus
0045-3803	University of Cairo. Faculty of Medicine. Medical Journal
0045-3811	Caisses et Emballages en Bois†
0045-3838	Calcutta Gazette
0045-3846	Calcutta Review
0045-3854	Calcutta Weekly Notes
0045-3862	Calcuttan
0045-3889	Calgary Livestock Market Journal†
0045-3900	California Builder and Engineer
0045-3919	C C A C Review
0045-3935	California Grocers Advocate†
0045-3943	California Institute of Technology. Division of Geological and Planetary Sciences. Report on Geological and Planetary Sciences for the Year
0045-3951	California News Index†
0045-396X	California News Reporter†
0045-3978	California Quarterly
0045-3986	University of California, Los Angeles. Chicano Studies Center. Creative Series†
0045-3994	University of California, Los Angeles. Chicano Studies Center. Monographs changed to University of California, Los Angeles. Chicano Studies Research Center. Monographs.
0045-4001	Caliper
0045-401X	Call
0045-4036	Call and Post
0045-4044	Callboard
0045-4052	Calquarium
0045-4087	Cameroun Litteraire†
0045-4095	CAMmuniqué†
0045-4109	Campaigner
0045-4125	Camping
0045-4133	Campus (Toronto) see 0383-2406
0045-4168	Canada. Department of Agriculture. Forage Notes changed to Canada. Agriculture Canada. Forage Notes.
0045-4176	Canada. Department of Energy, Mines, and Resources. Departmental Map Library. Acquisitions of Maps, Atlases and Gazeteers†
0045-4192	Canada Gazette: Part 1: Government, Divorce, Bankruptcy Notices, Etc
0045-4206	Canada Gazette: Part 2: Statutory Orders and Regulations changed to Canada Gazette: Part 2: Statutory Instruments.
0045-4214	Canada Japan Trade Council. Newsletter
0045-4249	Canada-Svensken
0045-4257	Canada Today
0045-4265	Canada Travel Digest†
0045-4273	Canada Trust Bulletin†
0045-4281	Canada - U.K. Trade News changed to Can - U.K. Link.
0045-429X	Canada. Western Forest Products Laboratory. Information Reports see 0708-6172
0045-4303	Canada's Business Climate
0045-432X	Canadian Agricultural Engineering
0045-4338	Canadian Air Comments changed to Atlas Copco Comments.
0045-4354	Canadian Association for Laboratory Animal Science Newsletter
0045-4389	Canadian Association of Medical Clinics. Bulletin changed to Group Practice in Canada.
0045-4397	Canadian Association of Medical Record Librarians. Bulletin changed to C H R A Progress Notes.
0045-4419	Canadian Association of Social Workers. Newsletter†
0045-4427	Canadian Athletic Director and Coach
0045-4435	C. B. A. Bulletin†
0045-4451	Canadian Barber and Men's Hairstylists changed to Canadian Men's Hairstylist and Barber.
0045-446X	Canadian Bee Journal†
0045-4486	Canadian Biographical Studies†
0045-4494	Canadian Boating
0045-4508	Canadian Building News†
0045-4524	Canadian Chamber of Commerce. Newsletter†
0045-4540	Canadian Chess Chat
0045-4559	Transit Canada†
0045-4567	Canadian Coach†
0045-4575	Canadian Coin Box
0045-4583	Canadian Community Publisher see 0380-8025
0045-4605	Canadian Council of Churches. Council Communicator changed to Entre - Nous.
0045-4613	Canadian Journal of English Language Arts†
0045-4621	Canadian Courses and Seminars see 0318-6237
0045-463X	Canadian Criminology and Corrections Association. Bulletin see 0823-9436
0045-4648	Canadian Curling News
0045-4656	Canadian Daily Stock Charts changed to Dailies.
0045-4702	C E M A Newsletter changed to Scanner.
0045-4729	C.F.C.F. News for the Canadian Camper see 0316-280X
0045-4737	Canadian Far Eastern Newsletter
0045-4745	Canadian Farmer see 0041-6037
0045-477X	Canadian Fiction
0045-4788	Canadian Field Hockey News†
0045-480X	Canadian Film Institute. Bulletin changed to Images.
0045-4834	Canadian Football News
0045-4850	Canadian Forces Dental Services Quarterly†
0045-4869	C F A News†
0045-4877	Canadian Forwarder†
0045-4885	Canadian Fruitgrower
0045-4893	Canadian Government Programs and Services
0045-4907	Canadian Guernsey Breeders' Journal changed to Canadian Guernsey Journal.
0045-4915	Canadian Handgun
0045-4931	Canadian Imperial Bank of Commerce. Foreign Trade News†
0045-494X	Importweek
0045-4958	Canadian India Times
0045-4966	Canadian Industrial Relations and Personnel Developments
0045-4974	Canadian Industrial Traffic League. Traffic Notes see 0826-8770
0045-4982	C I C A Dialogue
0045-4990	Canadian Insurance Law Reporter
0045-5008	Canadian Interline News†
0045-5024	Canadian Ionospheric Data
0045-5059	Canadian Jewish Outlook see 0834-0242
0045-5067	Canadian Journal of Forest Research
0045-5075	Canadian Journal of Optometry
0045-5083	Canadian Journal of Otolaryngology see 0381-6605
0045-5091	Canadian Journal of Philosophy
0045-5105	Canadian Journal of Spectroscopy changed to Canadian Journal of Applied Spectroscopy.
0045-5121	Canadian Leathercraft
0045-5156	Canadian Manager
0045-5164	Canadian Mathematical Congress. Notes, News and Comments changed to C M S Notes.
0045-5172	Canadian Music Educators Association. Newsletter
0045-5202	Canadian Numismatic Research Society. Transactions
0045-5229	Canadian Opera Guild. Guild News changed to Overtures (Toronto).
0045-5237	Canadian Paper Money Journal
0045-5245	Canadian Parachutist see 0319-3896
0045-5253	Canadian Philatelist
0045-527X	Canadian Red Book
0045-530X	Canadian Risk Management and Business Insurance see 0821-6916
0045-5318	Canadian Sales and Credit Law Guide changed to Canadian Commercial Law Guide.
0045-5326	Canadian Sales Tax Reports changed to Canadian Sales Tax Reporter.
0045-5334	Canadian Scene
0045-5342	Canadian Securities Law Reporter
0045-5369	Canadian Society for Education Through Art. Newsletter
0045-5385	Canadian Sports Digest
0045-5393	Canadian Steam
0045-5407	Canadian Stock Market Point and Figure Summary†
0045-5423	Canadian Swine
0045-5431	Canadian Teacher of the Deaf see 0382-7976
0045-544X	Canadian Theosophist
0045-5458	Canadian Training Methods see 0225-6320
0045-5466	Canadian Transport
0045-5482	Canadian Travel News see 0319-7093
0045-5490	Canadian Travel Press see 0831-9138
0045-5504	Canadian Trot Canadien see 0704-0733
0045-5512	Canadian Union of Public Employees. Journal changed to Canadian Union of Public Employees. The Public Employee.
0045-5520	Canadian Vocational Journal
0045-5539	Canadian Warehousing Association. C W A Reporter†
0045-5571	Canadian Wildlife and Fisheries Newsletter Bulletin see 0318-5133
0045-5598	Canadian Wool Grower and Sheep Breeder see 0829-075X
0045-5601	Canberra and District Historical Society. Journal see 0313-5977
0045-561X	Canberra Comment see 0817-4830
0045-5628	Canberra Survey
0045-5636	Candido
0045-5660	Capella†
0045-5687	Capitol Studies see 0734-3469
0045-5695	Caps and Flints
0045-5709	Car Buyer†
0045-5717	Car Tips†
0045-5725	Caravan Industry and Park Operator see 0268-5558
0045-5733	Carbide Journal see 0192-8333
0045-5741	Cardiac Rehabilitation†
0045-575X	Cardiovascular & Metabolic Diseases†
0045-5776	Career Development†
0045-5792	Caribbean Business News
0045-5830	Carleton Education Bulletin†
0045-5857	Carolina Centerscope†
0045-5865	Carolina Tips
0045-5873	Carolinian
0045-5881	Cartologica
0045-5903	Cash & Carry
0045-5911	Cashew News Teller see 0970-2423
0045-592X	Castle Street Circular see 0266-8750
0045-5938	J S A S (Journal Supplement Abstract Service) changed to Psychological Documents.
0045-5946	Catalogue of Replacement Books for Children's Library Collections†
0045-5954	Catalyst changed to Book Marks.
0045-5962	Catalyst for the Scottish Viewpoint
0045-5970	Catholic Agitator
0045-5989	Catholic Citizen
0045-5997	Cavalletto e Tavolozza

0045-6004 Caveat Emptor *changed to* Caveat Emptor Consumers Bulletin.
0045-6020 Celebrity Bulletin
0045-6039 Cell Differentiation *see* 0925-4773
0045-6047 Cent Blagues
0045-6055 C R R I Road Abstracts
0045-6063 Centre Canadien International de Recherches et d'Information sur l'Economie Publique et Cooperative. Revue du Canadien *see* 0384-8744
0045-608X Centre de Recherche en Civilisation Canadienne-Francaise. Bulletin *see* 0825-2777
0045-6098 C H I S S Cahiers†
0045-6101 Centre International pour le Credit Communal *changed to* Local Finance.
0045-611X Ecuador. Centro de Desarrollo Industrial. Boletin Industrial *changed to* Ecuador. Centro de Desarrollo Industrial. Boletin Estadisticas. Economicas.
0045-6128 Centro de Estudios Educativos. Revista *see* 0185-1284
0045-6152 Ceramurgia
0045-6179 Cercles des Jeunes Naturalistes. Feuillets du Club *see* 0827-1356
0045-6187 Ceskoslovensky Casopis Historicky
0045-6195 Ceylon Forester *changed to* Sri Lanka Forester.
0045-6209 Ceylon Trade Journal†
0045-6217 Congress News
0045-6225 Chakra†
0045-6233 Challenge (Washington) *changed to* Republican Woman.
0045-6268 Challenger†
0045-6276 Chambre de Commerce, d'Agriculture, d'Industrie et des Mines du Gabon. Bulletin
0045-6292 Chambre de Commerce du Sud de la Tunisie. Bulletin Economique *changed to* Chambre de Commerce et d'Industrie du Sud. Bulletin.
0045-6306 Chambre de Commerce Francaise au Canada. Revue *see* 0318-7306
0045-6314 Champion†
0045-6330 Channel (Wellesley)†
0045-6349 Chaplin
0045-6365 Chat†
0045-6381 Chelsea Spelaeological Society. Newsletter
0045-639X Chemical Industry Notes
0045-6403 Chemical Insight
0045-6411 C R C Critical Reviews in Biochemistry *see* 1040-9238
0045-642X C R C Critical Reviews in Bioengineering *changed to* Critical Reviews in Biomedical Engineering.
0045-6446 C R C Critical Reviews in Toxicology *see* 1040-8444
0045-6454 C R C Critical Reviews in Microbiology *see* 1040-841X
0045-6470 Chemical Society, London. Journal. Section B: Physical Organic Chemistry *see* 0300-9580
0045-6497 Chemical Take-Off
0045-6500 Chemical Weekly
0045-6519 Chemische Technik
0045-6527 Chemists' Quarterly *see* 0115-2130
0045-6535 Chemosphere
0045-656X Chesapeake Bay Magazine
0045-6578 Chess Canada
0045-6594 Chess Player†
0045-6608 Chevre
0045-6616 C A G L A Newsletter *changed to* Chicago Area Group on Latin America. Occasional Papers.
0045-6624 Chicagoland Development†
0045-6632 Child Care Quarterly *see* 1053-1890
0045-6640 Child Education Quarterly *see* 0269-9524
0045-6659 Child Welfare League Newsletter *see* 1057-736X
0045-6667 Children's Aid Society News *changed to* Children's Aid Society News.
0045-6675 C.A.S. Record *see* 0319-7468
0045-6691 Children's Apparel Merchandising Aids *changed to* C A M A Parade.
0045-6705 Children's Libraries Newsletter *changed to* Orana.
0045-6713 Children's Literature in Education
0045-6721 Chilton's Truck Repair Manual *changed to* Chilton's Truck and Van Repair Manual.
0045-6756 China Monthly†
0045-6764 China Now
0045-6780 Christian Brothers of the Australian and New Zealand Provinces. Our Studies *changed to* Catholic School Studies.
0045-6799 Christian Communications Journal in Africa†
0045-6802 Christian Graduate *see* 0264-598X
0045-6810 Christian Institute for Ethnic Studies in Asia. Bulletin
0045-6829 Christian Patriot†
0045-6845 Christian Research Institute. Newsletter *changed to* Christian Research Journal.
0045-6861 Church and Clergy Finance†
0045-6888 Ciencia Agronomica
0045-6896 Ciervo
0045-6918 Cine-Revue
0045-6926 Cinema (Year)
0045-6942 Circulo Odontologico de Cordoba. Revista
0045-6969 C L News†
0045-6977 Citta Futura
0045-6985 City and Suburban Travel
0045-6993 City College Alumnus
0045-7019 City of Ottawa Coin Club. Monthly Bulletin
0045-7027 Civic Affairs
0045-7035 Civil Affairs Journal & Newsletter
0045-7043 Civil & Military Law Journal
0045-7051 Civil Liberties (Seattle) *changed to* Civil Liberties of Washington.
0045-706X Civil Rights Newsletter
0045-7116 Clave
0045-7159 Climbing
0045-7175 Clinical Trends in Anesthesiology†
0045-7183 Clio Medica
0045-7205 Club Management in Australia†
0045-7213 Club Mirror
0045-723X Coastal Zone Management
0045-7248 Cocina y Hogar
0045-7256 Cocoa Growers Bulletin
0045-7272 Coin Launderer and Cleaner
0045-7280 Coin Wholesaler
0045-7310 C O D I A
0045-7329 Colegio Nacional de Enfermeras. Revista
0045-7337 Coleopterists Newsletter *see* 0010-065X
0045-7345 Collective Bargaining Settlements in New York State
0045-7361 College Canada†
0045-737X College Law Digest
0045-7388 College of Physicians and Surgeons of Ontario. Interim Report†
0045-740X Colony *changed to* Question Mark.
0045-7426 Colorado Journal of Educational Research†
0045-7434 C T R C Newsletter†
0045-7469 Combat pour l'Homme *see* 0244-7878
0045-7523 Comfort Engineering *changed to* Environmental Design.
0045-754X Commerce *changed to* Australian-American Dialog.
0045-7558 Commerce et Distribution†
0045-7566 Commercial Bank of Australia. Economic Review†
0045-7574 Commercial Bank of Ethiopia. Market Report
0045-7620 Commonwealth and Colonial History Newsletter
0045-7639 Commonwealth Professional
0045-7647 Commonwealth Scientific and Industrial Research Organization. Industrial Research News†
0045-7663 Communication (London, 1967)
0045-7671 Communicator (Ann Arbor) *changed to* Great Lakes Communicator.
0045-768X Communicator of Technical Information *see* 0953-3699
0045-7698 Communika
0045-7701 Communitarian *see* 0199-9346
0045-771X Community *changed to* Community (Alexandria).
0045-7728 Community College Social Science Quarterly *changed to* Community College Social Science Newsletter.
0045-7736 Community Education Journal†
0045-7787 Company Law Institute of India. Reports of Company Cases Including Banking & Insurance
0045-7809 Compass
0045-7817 Compulsory Military Service and the Objector†
0045-7825 Computer Methods in Applied Mechanics and Engineering
0045-7833 Computer Operations†
0045-7841 Computer Price Guide
0045-785X Computer Program Abstracts†
0045-7868 Computer Programs in Science and Technology†
0045-7892 Computer Society of India. Journal
0045-7906 Computers & Electrical Engineering
0045-7930 Computers & Fluids
0045-7949 Computers & Structures
0045-7957 Computing Newsletter for Community Colleges *see* 0045-7965
0045-7965 Computing Newsletter for Instructors of Data Processing
0045-7981 Comunita Mediterranea
0045-799X Concerns
0045-8007 Concrete Abstracts
0045-8015 Concrete Pipe News
0045-8023 Confederation Nationale de la Construction. Annuaire†
0045-804X Conference Board of the Mathematical Sciences. Newsletter†
0045-8058 Conference on Great Lakes Research. Proceedings *see* 0380-1330
0045-8066 Conflux†
0045-8082 Congiuntura Economica Lombarda
0045-8120 Connecticut Nutmegger
0045-8139 I P S Local Government Newsletter†
0045-8147 Conquest *changed to* Diabetes Conquest.
0045-8155 Conservation Council of Ontario. Bulletin†
0045-8171 Consoliere†
0045-8198 Construction Metallique *changed to* C T I C M-Construction Metallique.
0045-8201 Consultants News
0045-8236 Consumer Comment
0045-8252 Consumer Interest†
0045-8260 Consumer News†
0045-8279 Consumerism-New Developments for Business†
0045-8309 Contact in Urban and Regional Affairs *see* 0711-6780
0045-8317 Contacto *changed to* Contacto.
0045-8325 Contacts
0045-8333 Contemporary Indian Literature†
0045-835X Content
0045-8368 Contents of Recent Economics Journals
0045-8376 Continental Franchise Review
0045-8384 Continuing Education Directory for Metropolitan Toronto†
0045-8406 Contractspeler
0045-8414 Contrasts
0045-8422 Convenience Store News
0045-8430 C A I D Newsletter (Convention of American Instructors of the Deaf) *changed to* Advocate for Education of the Deaf.
0045-8449 Conventions, Meetings, Incentive World†
0045-8457 Cooperateur de France†
0045-8465 C E I R (Cooperative Economic Insect Report) *see* 0363-0889
0045-8473 Cooperative Educational Abstracting Service *changed to* International Bureau of Education. Bulletin.
0045-849X Cooperator†
0045-8503 Cooperator's Bulletin†
0045-8511 Copeia
0045-8538 Core Teacher
0045-8546 Cormorant *see* 0362-9368
0045-8554 Cormorant News Bulletin
0045-8562 Cornell University. Libraries. Bulletin†
0045-8570 Cornish Nation
0045-8635 Correctional Process *see* 0823-9436
0045-8643 Correio Portugues
0045-8651 Correo Hispano-Americano
0045-866X Corriere Canadese
0045-8678 Corrosion y Proteccion *see* 0210-6604
0045-8686 Corse Mediterranee Medicale *see* 0302-9263
0045-8716 Cosmorama
0045-8732 C O S P A R Information Bulletin
0045-8740 Costa Rica. Instituto Geografico Nacional. Informe Semestral†
0045-8759 Cotton Development†
0045-8775 Council for Planning & Conservation. Newsletter†
0045-8791 C P L Newsletter
0045-8813 Countdown (Wichita)†
0045-8848 Country Bizarre
0045-8856 Country Life
0045-8864 Courier *changed to* B.C. Corrections Courier.
0045-8872 C F B Cold Lake Courier
0045-8902 Courrier du Vietnam
0045-8910 Courrier Pedagogigue *changed to* Courrier du Francais-Cadre.
0045-8929 Coursing News *changed to* Greyhound Review.
0045-8937 Cowan Investment Survey. Weekly Market Digest *changed to* Cowan Investment Survey. Midas.
0045-897X Creative Moment *changed to* Creative Moment World Poetry and Criticism.
0045-8988 Creative Teacher†
0045-8996 Creative Urge†
0045-9003 Credit Union National Association. Research and Economics Department. R E Statistical Bulletin *changed to* Credit Union National Association. Research Division. Research Bulletin.
0045-9011 Creditalk†
0045-902X Crime and Delinquency Abstracts†
0045-9038 Criminal Justice Newsletter
0045-9046 Crisis Intervention†
0045-9054 Cristiani nel Mondo
0045-9062 Critic†
0045-9070 Critical Digest
0045-9089 Critique Socialiste
0045-9097 Critiques de l'Economie Politique
0045-9100 Cross Reference *see* 0740-9982
0045-9119 Crossroads (Le Mars)
0045-9127 Crown
0045-9135 Crucible
0045-9151 Cryptogram†
0045-9178 Cuadernos de Historia de la Salud Publica
0045-9186 Cuadernos de Historia Economica de Cataluna†
0045-9194 Cuadernos de Informacion Cientifica†
0045-9208 Cuisine Collective
0045-9232 Cultura Antiqua
0045-9240 Culture and Education *changed to* Education for the Disadvantaged Child.
0045-9259 Cultured Dairy Products Journal
0045-9267 Cultuurtechnisch Tijdschrift *changed to* Tijdschrift Landinrichting.
0045-9275 Cumberland-Samford Law Review *see* 0360-8298
0045-9283 Current Citations on Communication Disorders *changed to* Current Citations on Communication Disorders: Hearing and Balance.
0045-9283 Current Citations on Communication Disorders *changed to* Current Citations on Communications Disorders: Language, Speech, and Voice.

ISSN

ISSN	Title
0045-9291	Current Engineering Practice
0045-933X	Current Physics Advance Abstracts: Solid State†
0045-9348	Current Physics Microform
0045-9380	Current Problems in Pediatrics
0045-9399	Current Problems in Radiology see 0363-0188
0045-9429	Cyprus To-day
0045-9445	Czas
0045-9453	Czasopismo Geograficzne
0045-9461	Czechoslovak Economic Digest†
0045-947X	Czechoslovak Science & Technology Digest†
0045-9488	Czechoslovak Scientific and Technical Periodicals Contents†
0045-9496	Dafnit
0045-9534	Dalhousie University. University News changed to Dalhousie University. University News This Week.
0045-9534	Dalhousie University. University News changed to Dalhousie University. University News This Month.
0045-9542	Dalka
0045-9550	Dallas. Methodist Hospital. Bulletin of the Medical Staff†
0045-9569	Dallas News changed to Iconoclast.
0045-9577	Dance - America†
0045-9585	Danmarks Handels Tidende†
0045-9593	Dansk Bygge Journal†
0045-9607	Dansk Erhvervsfjerkrae
0045-9615	Dansk Handelsblad
0045-9623	Dansk Industri
0045-9631	Dansk Ungdom og Idraet changed to Ungdom og Idraet.
0045-9658	Darshak
0045-9666	Data†
0045-9674	Data-Canada†
0045-9704	Datapro 70†
0045-9739	Davidsonia†
0045-9747	De Nos Mains
0045-9755	De Rebus Procuratoriis see 0250-0329
0045-9771	Deacon
0045-9801	Deccan College. Postgraduate & Research Institute. Bulletin
0045-981X	Decennie 2†
0045-9836	Defending All Outdoors†
0045-9844	Delaware Basin Bulletin†
0045-9852	Delaware Conservationist
0045-9879	Delikt en Delinkwent
0045-9887	Delinquiency Prevention Reporter see 0092-5438
0045-9895	Delta del Parana
0045-9909	Democratic Commitment
0045-9917	Dental Association of Thailand. Journal
0045-9933	Dental Hygienist changed to C D H A Journal.
0045-9941	Dental Radiography and Photography†
0045-995X	Dental Student News†
0045-9968	Dentoscope†
0045-9984	Departements et Communes
0045-9992	Derecho Penal Contemporaneo
0046-0001	Dermatology in Practice†
0046-001X	Desarrollo Economico
0046-0028	Desarrollo Rural en las Americas†
0046-0036	Descent
0046-0044	Desert Rancher
0046-0060	Designer & Builder in Asia†
0046-0079	Despatch
0046-0087	Despatch see 0227-034X
0046-0095	Detective†
0046-0117	Deutsche Baecker Zeitung
0046-0141	Deutsche Vereinigung von Winnipeg. Mitteilungen
0046-015X	Deutsches Wirtschafts Institut, Berlin. D W I Forschungshefte see 0323-3901
0046-0168	Deux-Tiers†
0046-0184	Devonport News
0046-0192	Diabetes
0046-0206	Dialogo Social
0046-0222	Diana's Bimonthly
0046-0249	Digest of Executive Opportunities†
0046-0265	Dimension
0046-029X	Dinny's Digest
0046-0303	Dio e Popolo
0046-032X	Dire
0046-0338	Direct from Cuba
0046-0346	Discussion changed to American Film.
0046-0362	Disposable Soft Goods see 0163-4429
0046-0370	Disposables International†
0046-0389	Dissonance†
0046-0435	Dixie Logger and Lumberman see 0192-7124
0046-0443	Djassin'foue
0046-0451	Doctor
0046-0478	Documentation par l'Image
0046-0486	Documentos de Educacion Cooperativa see 0210-7295
0046-0494	Doings†
0046-0508	Dokita
0046-0516	S I C C Dolphin changed to College Voice (Staten Island).
0046-0540	Domestic Heating Engineer changed to Comfort Engineering.
0046-0559	Dominion Companies Law Reports changed to Canada Corporations Law Reporter.
0046-0567	Dominion Tax Cases
0046-0583	Domino changed to Schweizer Buch-Spiegel.
0046-0591	Donna di Casa
0046-0605	Donnybrook Report: Photography†
0046-0621	Dorset
0046-063X	Doshisha Literature
0046-0648	Down Under†
0046-0656	Downtown Athletic Club Journal
0046-0664	Downtown Developments†
0046-0672	Dravo Review†
0046-0680	Dressage see 0147-796X
0046-0702	Drilling Contractor
0046-0710	Drive changed to Drive.
0046-0729	Driveway Reporter
0046-0737	Druckindustrie
0046-0745	Drug Education Report see 0091-2395
0046-0753	Drug Forum†
0046-0788	Duckological changed to From Duck Country.
0046-0796	Duesseldorf Magazin
0046-080X	Duitse Boek see 0167-2185
0046-0818	DukEngineer
0046-0826	Duodecimal Bulletin
0046-0834	Du Pont Magazine
0046-0842	Dutch Quarterly Review of Anglo American Letters changed to D Q R.
0046-0869	E E (Epargne Europe) changed to E U F I - Journal.
0046-0877	E F B†
0046-0885	E I
0046-0915	Eagle's Eye
0046-0958	East Anglian Bibliography
0046-0966	East St. Louis Monitor
0046-0974	Eastern Film†
0046-0990	Easyriders
0046-1016	Eau Vive changed to L'Eau Vive.
0046-1024	Eburnea
0046-1032	Ecclaire
0046-1059	Echo (Huntsville)
0046-1067	Echo (Skokie)
0046-1083	Echo des Vieux de France see 0243-0738
0046-1091	Echoes of History†
0046-1105	Eclectic Theosophist
0046-1121	Ecology Law Quarterly
0046-113X	Economia
0046-1148	Economia Cafetera
0046-1180	Economic Research Corporation. Research Review†
0046-1199	Economic Analysis and Policy
0046-1245	EdCentric
0046-1253	Edge
0046-1261	Editing Technology see 0736-7260
0046-127X	Editor's Newsletter†
0046-1288	Edmonton Livestock Market News changed to Western Beef Producers News.
0046-1296	Edmonton Native News
0046-1318	Edmonton Stamp Club Bulletin
0046-1326	Edseletter
0046-1334	Educacaot
0046-1369	Education†
0046-1377	Education and Culture†
0046-1385	Education and Psychology Review
0046-1407	Education Commission of the States Bulletin†
0046-1415	Education Equipment Selector
0046-1423	Education in Eastern Africa†
0046-1431	Education Mathematique†
0046-144X	Education News from Metrologic changed to Laser Quest.
0046-1474	Educational Broadcasting changed to Instructional Broadcasting.
0046-1482	Educational Digest
0046-1490	Education Exchange changed to Educational International.
0046-1504	Educational Forum†
0046-1520	Educational Psychologist
0046-1539	Educational Reporter
0046-1547	E T S Developments
0046-1555	Educator changed to National Educator.
0046-1571	Educators Negotiating Service changed to Employers Negotiating Service.
0046-158X	Educator's Purchasing Guide†
0046-1598	Effective Teaching with Programmed Instruction†
0046-1601	Eglise de Quebec changed to Pastorale-Quebec.
0046-161X	Egyptian Journal of Genetics and Cytology
0046-1628	Eirene
0046-1636	Eisenhower College Newsletter changed to Eisenhower.
0046-1644	Election Archives changed to Election Archives and International Politics.
0046-1660	Electrical Contractor (Jolimont)†
0046-1679	Electrical Equipment Selector see 0013-4317
0046-1695	Electrical Week changed to Electric Utility Week.
0046-1709	Electromagnetic Metrology Current Awareness Service†
0046-1717	Electronic Equipment Monitor
0046-1725	Electronic Products see 0046-1717
0046-1733	Electronics Communicator
0046-1741	Electronics of America
0046-175X	Electronique et Microelectronique Industrielles see 0398-1851
0046-1776	Elektro-Handel
0046-1784	Elektromonteur changed to Elektrotechnik.
0046-1792	Elements†
0046-1806	Elements of Technology
0046-1814	Eletronica em Foco
0046-1822	Eleveur Maine Anjou
0046-1830	Ellipse
0046-1849	Eltern
0046-1857	Embassy
0046-1865	Embassy of Switzerland Bulletin
0046-1881	Emily Dickinson Bulletin see 0164-1492
0046-1903	Employer
0046-1946	Enchantment
0046-1954	Encore (New York) see 0161-6536
0046-1962	Enfance et la Mode
0046-1970	Enfant Exceptionnel changed to Apprentissage et Socialisation.
0046-1997	Engineer in Education Newsletter†
0046-2004	Engineering and Construction†
0046-2012	Engineering Design Graphics Journal
0046-2020	Engineering Horizons†
0046-2039	Engineering in Medicine see 0954-4119
0046-2055	Engineering News of India changed to Engineering & Metals Review.
0046-2063	Engineering Opportunities changed to Factory & Industrial Equipment.
0046-208X	English in Australia
0046-2098	English Usage in Southern Africa
0046-2101	Enseignants
0046-211X	Enseignement see 0710-5568
0046-2144	Entre-Nous
0046-2152	Enterprises Agricoles†
0046-2160	L'Entreprise et l'Homme
0046-2187	Envers et l'Endroit†
0046-2217	Environment Improvement Case History Report Service†
0046-2225	Environmental Affairs see 0190-7034
0046-2241	G A T F Environmental Control Report changed to G A T F World.
0046-225X	Environmental Entomology
0046-2268	Excerpta Medica. Section 46: Environmental Health see 0300-5194
0046-2276	Environmental Law (Portland)
0046-2284	Environmental Law Reporter
0046-2306	Indexed Article Titles changed to Environmental Periodicals Bibliography.
0046-2314	Environmental Quality Report†
0046-2330	Environmental Technology and Economics†
0046-2349	Envoy†
0046-2357	Kruidenier
0046-2365	Epidemiology Notes and Communicable Disease Morbidity Report see 0095-313X
0046-2373	Eprouvette changed to Defisicence.
0046-2381	Saint John Viewpoint changed to Baron.
0046-239X	Equipet
0046-2403	Era
0046-2411	Erasmus Review†
0046-242X	Erdoel-Dienst
0046-2438	Ergo (Cambridge)
0046-2446	Ergonomics Abstracts
0046-2454	Ergot
0046-2489	Escutcheon
0046-2497	Espace Geographique
0046-2500	Esperanto - Interlangue Universelle
0046-2519	Esperanto Contact†
0046-2527	Esperanto Teacher
0046-2535	Espoir de la Nation Togolaise†
0046-256X	Est - Ovest
0046-2578	Estrategia
0046-2586	Et la Lumiere Fut
0046-2608	Ethnopsychologie see 0761-9871
0046-2616	Ethnologie Francaise
0046-2632	Etnia
0046-2640	Etudes Polemologiques†
0046-2659	Etudes Renaniennes Bulletin
0046-2667	Eureka
0046-2683	Europaeisches Bau-Forum†
0046-2697	Europe Left
0046-2705	European Civil Engineering Abstracts see 0332-4095
0046-273X	European Demographic Information Bulletin see 0168-6577
0046-2756	European Journal of Social Psychology
0046-2772	European Studies Newsletter
0046-2802	Translation News†
0046-2837	Evangelical Magazine†
0046-2853	Events
0046-2861	Executive Review†
0046-2896	Experimental Study of Politics
0046-2926	Expression
0046-2977	Eye†
0046-2985	F T Abstracts in Science & Technology†
0046-3000	F Y I (Washington)†
0046-3019	Fabbrica e Stato
0046-3027	Fabricator
0046-3035	Facets of Freshwater
0046-306X	Factory and Office Selector†
0046-3086	Facts and Reports changed to Komitee Zuidelijk Afrika. Facts and Reports.
0046-3116	Facts on Fish†
0046-3140	F A C C C Bulletin
0046-3159	Fag Rag
0046-3167	Family Service Highlights†
0046-323X	Fanfare see 0217-765X
0046-3248	Fanfares
0046-3256	Far East Week by Week
0046-3264	Far Eastern Law Review
0046-3272	Farbenhaendler changed to Heim und Farbe.
0046-3280	Farm and Country
0046-3299	Farm and Food Research changed to Farm and Food.
0046-3302	Farm Supply Store†
0046-3329	

ISSN	Title
0046-3337	Farmer's Digest
0046-337X	Fauna†
0046-3388	Fauna & Flora
0046-3396	Features and News from Behind the Iron Curtain *changed to* Freedom Communications International News Agency.
0046-3418	Federal Labor - Management Consultant *changed to* Federal Labor - Management and Employee Relations Consultant.
0046-3426	Federal Librarian†
0046-3434	Federal Linguist†
0046-3442	Federal Program Monitor†
0046-3450	Federal Reserve Bank of Chicago. Banking Briefs†
0046-3469	Federal Reserve Bank of Chicago. International Letter†
0046-3477	F E W's News and Views *see* 0895-3619
0046-3523	Federation des Travaux Publics et des Transports. Revue *changed to* Infos Federales.
0046-3531	F I E J Bulletin†
0046-354X	Federacion Odontologica Colombiana. Revista
0046-3558	F A H Review *see* 1055-7466
0046-3566	Federation of British Columbia Naturalists. Newsletter *changed to* B.C. Naturalist.
0046-3582	Federation of Victorian Film Societies. Federation News *see* 0158-3778
0046-3604	Feed and Farm Supply Dealer†
0046-3620	Feldpost
0046-3639	Companion Animal Practice *see* 1057-6614
0046-3647	Feltornitologen *see* 0107-3729
0046-3655	Femeia
0046-3663	Feminist Studies
0046-368X	Fernsehen und Film†
0046-3698	Ferrocarriles Argentinos
0046-3701	Fettesian
0046-3728	Fibre Market News
0046-3736	Fiction
0046-3760	Fighting Back†
0046-3787	Film Journal†
0046-3809	Film Review Index *see* 0094-6818
0046-3817	Films - Learning Corporation of America†
0046-3825	Films a l'Ecran
0046-3841	Revista Filologia Moderna *changed to* Filologia Moderna.
0046-385X	Filozofia
0046-3876	Financial Daily *see* 0279-0734
0046-3892	Financial Management
0046-3906	Financne Studie†
0046-3922	Finishing Highlights†
0046-3957	First-Fleeters
0046-3965	Fish Trades Review
0046-3973	Fisheries Council of Canada. Bulletin
0046-399X	Fitofilo†
0046-4031	Flame and Flavour
0046-404X	Flap Internacional
0046-4058	Flashpoint *see* 0308-1230
0046-4082	Florafacts
0046-4112	Florida Contractor
0046-4120	Florida. Department of Agriculture and Consumer Services. Market Bulletin *changed to* Florida Market Bulletin.
0046-4139	Florida. Department of State. Division of Archives. Archives and History News†
0046-4147	Florida Libraries†
0046-4155	Florida Music Director
0046-4171	F P *changed to* Florida Psychologist.
0046-4201	Flow†
0046-421X	Flower Arranger
0046-4228	Flyfishers Journal
0046-4236	Flyer International
0046-4244	Flying Fish Newsletter†
0046-4260	Focus
0046-4287	Focus *changed to* Tell.
0046-4295	Focus on Asian Studies†
0046-4317	Focus on Mental Health†
0046-4325	Focus on Pakistan†
0046-4333	Folio (Stamford)
0046-435X	Fontes Linguae Vasconum
0046-4368	Food Aid Bulletin†
0046-4384	Food and Nutrition
0046-4414	Food Industry Futures: a Strategy Service
0046-4422	Foodcorp Quarterly
0046-4449	Football Association News *see* 0306-1132
0046-4457	Football News†
0046-4473	For Adults Only *changed to* Adult and Continuing Education Newsletter.
0046-4481	Forages
0046-449X	Forbruker-Rapporten
0046-4511	Force Ouvriere Hebdo†
0046-4538	Ford World
0046-4546	Foreign Agricultural Trade of the United States
0046-4554	Foreign Investment News†
0046-4570	Forensic Science Gazette†
0046-4597	Forestdale News *changed to* Bangladesh Journal of Forest Science.
0046-4600	Foret Privee *see* 0153-0216
0046-4619	Forets de France et Action Forestiere
0046-4627	Formation Premilitaire et Physique†
0046-4643	Foersvar i Nutid
0046-4651	Fort Concho Report *changed to* Fort Concho and the South Plains Journal.
0046-466X	Fort Worth Como Monitor
0046-4678	Universidade do Ceara. Boletim†
0046-4686	Forthcoming International Scientific and Technical Conferences
0046-4708	Forum for the Discussion of New Trends in Education *see* 0963-8253
0046-4716	Forum Internationale†
0046-4732	Lutheran Forum. Forum Letter
0046-4759	Forward Atlanta *changed to* Forward Metro Atlanta.
0046-4767	Foster Parent Nourricier *see* 0705-1123
0046-4775	Foto-Avisen
0046-4783	Foto und Film Rundschau†
0046-4791	Fotoarte
0046-4813	Journal of Thanatology *see* 0196-1934
0046-4848	Fourth Estate†
0046-4856	Fox†
0046-4864	Fra Ribe Amt
0046-4872	Francaise Frisonne Pied Noire *changed to* La Prim Holstein.
0046-4899	France Agricole
0046-4910	France Forum
0046-4937	Annales d'Hydrobiologie†
0046-4945	France Pays-Bas Informations Rapides
0046-4961	Franklin County Historical Review
0046-497X	Frau im Spiegel
0046-4988	Fredonia Statement *changed to* Statement (Fredonia).
0046-5003	Free Market†
0046-5011	Free Press†
0046-502X	Freedom from Hunger Campaign/Ideas and Action Bulletin *changed to* Freedom from Hunger Campaign/Action for Development.
0046-5038	Freedom to Read Foundation News
0046-5046	World Freight
0046-5054	Freighter Travel-Letter
0046-5062	Frendz
0046-5070	Freshwater Biology
0046-5097	Friday Report
0046-5100	Friend International
0046-5119	Friendly Way†
0046-5135	Friidrott
0046-5143	Frivakt
0046-5151	Froid et la Climatisation
0046-5178	Mibifnim
0046-5186	Front and Center†
0046-5208	Front Rouge
0046-5216	Frontiersman
0046-5224	Frugt, Groent og Blomster
0046-5240	Fruit Intelligence†
0046-5259	Fulbright Newsletter
0046-5267	Full Tide
0046-5275	Fulton County (Illinois) Historical Society Newsletter *changed to* Fulton County (Illinois) Historical & Genealogical Society Newsletter.
0046-5291	Fur, Feathers and Fins†
0046-5305	Furies†
0046-5313	Furniture and Furnishings†
0046-5321	Furniture Index†
0046-5364	Gaceta Textil
0046-5372	Galvano Teknisk Tidsskrift *see* 0801-9606
0046-5380	Gambia News Bulletin
0046-5399	Ganagrinco
0046-5402	Ganita
0046-5410	Gar
0046-5429	Garage and Transport Equipment *see* 0264-0163
0046-5437	Gartneryrket
0046-5445	Garuda†
0046-5453	Garuda Indonesia Airways Magazine *changed to* Garuda Magazine.
0046-5461	Gas Chromatography - Mass Spectrometry Abstracts
0046-547X	Gastgewerbe *changed to* D G Deutsche Gaststaette - Deutsche Hotel-Zeitung Gastwirt und Hotelier.
0046-5496	Gay Liberator†
0046-550X	Gay Sunshine†
0046-5518	Gazdalkodas
0046-5526	Gazette des Hopitaux†
0046-5542	Gazette Officielle de la Peche
0046-5569	Gee Report†
0046-5577	Gemeentewerken
0046-5593	G E C Telecommunications Journal†
0046-5607	General Practitioner
0046-5615	Generazione Zero†
0046-5623	Genhinen†
0046-5658	Geodex Retrieval System for Geotechnical Abstracts
0046-5666	Geographer
0046-5690	Geographical Review of India
0046-5704	Geographical Society of New South Wales. Geography Bulletin *see* 0156-9236
0046-5712	Geographical View Point
0046-5720	Geologi
0046-5755	Geometriae Dedicata
0046-5763	Geophysical Surveys *see* 0169-3298
0046-578X	Georgia Journal of International and Comparative Law
0046-5798	Georgia Music News
0046-5801	Geoscience Information Society. Newsletter *changed to* G I S Newsletter.
0046-581X	Geoscope
0046-5828	Geotechnical Engineering
0046-5836	German - American Studies *changed to* Yearbook of German - American Studies.
0046-5879	Getreide und Mehl *see* 0367-4177
0046-5895	Ghala†
0046-5909	Ghana Bulletin of Theology†
0046-5917	Ghana Farmer
0046-5925	Ghana Social Science Journal
0046-5933	Giessereiforschung
0046-5941	Ginecologia Brasileira†
0046-5968	Giornale Italiano di Cardiologia
0046-5984	Giorni
0046-5992	Glas Kanadskin Srba
0046-600X	Glasgow Dental Journal†
0046-6018	Glassposten *see* 0802-5428
0046-6034	Glos Polski-Gazeta Polska
0046-6042	Go
0046-6050	Goeteborgs - Koepmannen
0046-6069	Golden Gate North†
0046-6077	Golden Legacy
0046-6085	Golden Spike†
0046-6093	Das Goldene Blatt
0046-6107	Gondolier *changed to* Boat/America.
0046-6115	Gonzaga Law Review
0046-6123	Good Gardening†
0046-6131	Good Healthkeeping†
0046-614X	Good News†
0046-6158	Good Old Days
0046-6174	Good Fruit Grower
0046-6182	Goodfruit Grower. Supplement *changed to* Goodgrape Grower.
0046-6190	Gooolt
0046-6212	Government Data Systems†
0046-6220	Government Purchasing Guide
0046-6239	Grace
0046-6247	Graduado†
0046-6263	Grains *changed to* Negoce et Agriculture.
0046-6271	Grande Sinal
0046-628X	Grands-Musees†
0046-6298	Granite *see* 0741-5028
0046-6301	Granite State Libraries
0046-631X	Graphoscope
0046-6328	Grassroots (Carbondale) *see* 0017-3541
0046-6344	Great Lakes Sportsman†
0046-6352	Greater World *see* 0957-8935
0046-6379	Greek - American Trade
0046-6395	Green Egg†
0046-6409	Green Sheet†
0046-6417	Green 'unt
0046-6433	Gridweek *changed to* Gridweek (1979).
0046-6441	Grosshandelskaufmann *changed to* Handel.
0046-645X	Ground Water Age
0046-6468	Group Process†
0046-6476	Grower†
0046-6484	Growing Minds
0046-6492	Growing Older *see* 0726-4240
0046-6506	Growing Point
0046-6514	Gruppendynamik
0046-6522	Guam Recorder†
0046-6549	Guatemala Filatelica
0046-6557	Guayacan
0046-6565	Guest and Host†
0046-659X	Gulf Coast Plumbing - Heating - Cooling News
0046-6603	Gullsmedkunst
0046-6638	Guppy Digest
0046-6646	Guyana Development Corporation. Industrial Review†
0046-6654	Guyana Journal
0046-6662	Guynews†
0046-6670	Gymnast *see* 0276-1041
0046-6689	Habit†
0046-6697	Hablemos de Cine†
0046-6700	Hackney Journal
0046-6719	Haiku Byways *changed to* Byways.
0046-6735	Halifax Board of Trade. Commercial News
0046-6743	Halifax Wildlife Association. The Four Seasons
0046-6751	Royal Botanical Gardens, Hamilton, Ont. Gardens' Bulletin
0046-676X	Hamore
0046-6778	Handball
0046-6786	Handbook of Environmental Management Series†
0046-6794	Handchirurgie
0046-6808	Handelsvertreter und Handelsmakler *see* 0936-9856
0046-6816	Haandverk og Industri†
0046-6832	Happiness Holding Tank
0046-6840	Hardsyssels Aarbog
0046-6859	Harian's the Traveler's Newsletter†
0046-6875	Harris Survey Column Subscription *see* 0273-1037
0046-6891	Harvard Dental Alumni Bulletin
0046-6905	Harvard University. Graduate School of Education. Bulletin
0046-6913	Haryana Electricity
0046-6921	Haryana Labour Journal
0046-693X	Haustechnischer Anzeiger *see* 0341-4817
0046-6948	Hawaii Farm Science†
0046-6980	Headmasters Association Review *changed to* Secondary Heads Association Review.
0046-6999	Headpiece†
0046-7006	Health†
0046-7014	Health and Vision
0046-7022	Health Devices
0046-7049	Health Food Trader *changed to* Natural Food Trader.
0046-7057	Health for Life†

0046-7065 Health in New Brunswick *changed to* New Brunswick. Department of Health. Happenings in Health /Actualites Sante.
0046-7073 Health in New South Wales†
0046-709X Health Planning in Illinois†
0046-7103 Health Sciences TV Bulletin†
0046-7111 Heart Care
0046-7146 Heat Pipe Technology†
0046-7154 Hebdo de la Blanchisserie - Teinturerie *changed to* Hebdo-Tex.
0046-7170 Hedmark Slektshistorielags Tidsskrift
0046-7197 Helderberg Review†
0046-7227 Hemelspleet
0046-7235 Hemicrania†
0046-7243 Hemingway Notes *see* 0276-3362
0046-7251 Hemophilia Today
0046-7278 Her World
0046-7286 Heraldo del Cine
0046-7294 Here Now†
0046-7316 Heron
0046-7324 Herz Kreislauf
0046-7332 Hi-Fidelity & Video Review†
0046-7340 Hi-Fi Newsletter†
0046-7359 Hibueras
0046-7367 High Fidelity Trade News *see* 0739-8123
0046-7375 Higher Education in the States†
0046-7383 Highway†
0046-7391 Highway Engineering in Australia
0046-7405 Highway Users Federation. Federation Reporter†
0046-7413 Hikobia
0046-7421 Hill Monitor†
0046-7448 Him†
0046-7456 Himalayan Observer
0046-7472 Hiroshima University Dental Society. Journal
0046-7480 Hispania
0046-7499 Histoire au Pays de Matane *see* 0836-3102
0046-7502 Histoire d'Aujourd'hui
0046-7510 Histoire en Savoie
0046-7537 Historian†
0046-7545 Historical Journal of Barmera and District†
0046-7553 Historical Musings†
0046-7561 Historie
0046-757X Historiens et Geographes
0046-7596 Historisk Tidskrift foer Finland
0046-760X History of Education
0046-7618 History of Medicine†
0046-7626 Hjemmet
0046-7634 Hjukrunarfelag Islands. Timarit *see* 0250-4731
0046-7642 Hobart and William Smith Colleges Official Publication *changed to* Hobart and William Smith Colleges Bulletin.
0046-7650 Hobby
0046-7677 Hoch und Tiefbau *changed to* Schweizer Bauwirtschaft.
0046-7693 Hockey Digest
0046-7707 Hockey World *changed to* Hockey Pictorial World.
0046-7715 Hoefslag
0046-7723 Hogar y Moda
0046-774X Holly Letter *see* 0738-2421
0046-7758 Home Beer and Winemaking
0046-7766 Home Economics and Domestic Subjects *see* 0265-6930
0046-7774 Home Economics Research Journal
0046-7812 Homoeopathic World
0046-7820 Homoeopathy
0046-7839 Hon: a Book-Bin for Scholars†
0046-7855 Honneur et Fidelite
0046-7863 Honourable Artillery Company Journal
0046-7901 Horizons du Fantastique
0046-791X Horizont (Berlin)†
0046-7928 Horn Call
0046-7936 Horses
0046-7995 Hospital Indicators†
0046-8010 Hospital Medical Practice
0046-8037 Hospitais Civis de Lisboa. Boletim Clinico
0046-8045 Hot Bike
0046-8088 Houses for Sale *changed to* New Homes and Apartment Guide.
0046-8096 Housing Australia *changed to* Housing Victoria - Tasmania.
0046-8134 Human Behavior†
0046-8150 Human Design
0046-8169 Human Ecology (Park Ridge)
0046-8177 Human Pathology
0046-8185 Human Rights
0046-8207 H R W Newsletter†
0046-8215 Human Rights in U.S.S.R†
0046-8223 Human Rights News and Views *changed to* Human Rights News.
0046-8231 Human Settlements *see* 0255-271X
0046-824X Humanistische Union. Mitteilungen
0046-8258 Humanitas†
0046-8266 Humanities Journal *see* 0882-5475
0046-8274 Humbard Christian Report
0046-8304 Hungarian Library and Information Science Abstracts
0046-8312 Hunter Natural History†
0046-8339 Husdjur
0046-8347 Husholdningslaereren (Copenhagen)
0046-8371 I E E E Publications Bulletin
0046-838X I E E E Transactions on Manufacturing Technology *see* 0148-6411
0046-8398 I E T: Zeitschrift fuer Elektrische Informations- und Energietechnik†
0046-8401 I S L A
0046-841X I S M†
0046-8428 I W K
0046-8436 University of Ibadan. Library. Library Record
0046-8444 Ibero-Americana *changed to* Nordic Journal on Latin American Studies.
0046-8452 Icelandic Canadian
0046-8495 I E A Reporter *changed to* I E A Reporter (Year).
0046-8517 Ide
0046-8541 Idealistic Studies
0046-855X Identity *changed to* Aboriginal and Islander Identity.
0046-8568 Idiom
0046-8576 Idoles†
0046-8592 Ikorok†
0046-8606 Illinois Education News *changed to* State of Education.
0046-8622 Illinois State Genealogical Society Quarterly
0046-8630 Illinois University. Department of Urban and Regional Planning. Research Bureau. Newsletter *changed to* Planning and Public Policy.
0046-8665 Images du Transport *changed to* Magazine du Transport Routier.
0046-869X Impact (Ottawa)†
0046-8703 Impact (London)
0046-8711 Impegno Settanta
0046-872X Impianti Manutenzione Trasporti†
0046-8754 In Re *changed to* San Francisco Attorney Magazine.
0046-8762 In-Short
0046-8770 In Step with the Visiting Nurse Association of Brooklyn *changed to* V N A B Newsletter.
0046-8797 Inbavan Tanah Air
0046-8819 Inchiesta
0046-8827 Incorporated Swimming Teacher *see* 0306-0403
0046-8843 Independent Republic Quarterly
0046-8851 Independent Weekly
0046-8886 Index to Chinese Periodicals - Humanities and Social Sciences *see* 0378-0112
0046-8894 Index to Chinese Periodicals - Science and Technology *see* 0378-0112
0046-8908 Index to Current Urban Documents
0046-8916 Index to the American Banker *changed to* Index to the American Banker.
0046-8924 Index to the Times *changed to* Times Index.
0046-8932 India Abroad
0046-8940 India. Directorate of Jute Development. Jute Bulletin *see* 0970-3497
0046-8959 India Weekly
0046-8967 Indian Affairs
0046-8975 Indian Archives
0046-8983 Indian Geotechnical Journal
0046-9009 Indian Journal of Psychometry and Education
0046-9017 Indian Journal of Regional Science
0046-9025 Indian Manager
0046-9033 I P I R I Journal
0046-9068 Indian Tourist
0046-9076 Indian Trader, Inc.
0046-9092 Indian Welding Journal
0046-9106 Indiana Law Review
0046-9114 Indiana University Libraries. Library Newsletter†
0046-9122 M E R P Memo
0046-9130 Indiana University. School of Medicine. Review†
0046-9149 Indien
0046-9157 Exceptional Parent
0046-9165 Indonesian Current Affairs Translation Bulletin†
0046-9173 Indonesian Review of International Affairs
0046-9181 Industria Lechera
0046-919X Industrial Bookshelf *changed to* Business/Management Book Review.
0046-9211 Industrial Launderer
0046-9246 Industrial Relations Review and Report
0046-9254 Industrial Sewing Machine Times *see* 0305-7046
0046-9262 Industrial Wastes†
0046-9270 Industrialist†
0046-9319 Brewers Association of Canada. Industry Notes†
0046-9327 Informateur des Chefs d'Entreprises Libres
0046-9343 Information G†
0046-9351 Information Historique
0046-936X Information Immobiliere
0046-9378 Information-Part 2-Reports - Bibliographies *see* 0360-0971
0046-9386 Comite Belge de la Distribution. Information Specialisee *changed to* Comite Belge de la Distribution. Editions Speciales.
0046-9394 Informationen der Afrika-Studienstelle *changed to* I F O Mitteilungen der Abteilung Entwicklungslaender.
0046-9408 Informationen zur Politischen Bildung
0046-9416 Informations Aerauliques et Thermiques†
0046-9432 Informations Laitieres
0046-9459 Informations Sociales
0046-9483 Informatologia Yugoslavica *changed to* Informatologia.
0046-9491 Informazioni di Parapsicologia *changed to* Quaderni Gnosis.
0046-9505 Informer *changed to* Tourist Talks.
0046-9513 Ingenieur-Constructeur†
0046-9521 Ingenieur et le Technicien de l'Enseignement Technique *changed to* Technologies et Formations.
0046-9556 Innenrikske Blad og Tidsskrifter *see* 0333-0451
0046-9564 Innovation World
0046-9572 Innovator (Ann Arbor)
0046-9580 Inquiry (Chicago)
0046-9599 Inquisitor
0046-9629 Inside Canberra
0046-9653 Insight (St. Paul)†
0046-9661 Insita *changed to* Ars Populi.
0046-967X Instant Research on Peace and Violence *see* 0356-7893
0046-9688 I F E P P Informations
0046-9696 Institut fuer Gesellschaftspolitik. Mitteilungen†
0046-970X I P W Berichte
0046-9718 I I E E Bulletin†
0046-9726 Belgium. Institut National d'Assurance Maladie Invalidite. I.N.A.M.I. Bulletin d'Information
0046-9734 Institut Panafricain pour le Developpement. Annuaire des Anciens Etudiants *changed to* Institut Panafricain pour le Developpement. Travaux d'Etudiants. Bulletin Analytique.
0046-9742 I.A.P. Professional Photography in Australia *see* 0159-8880
0046-9750 Institute of Brewing. Journal (London)
0046-9769 I C B Review (Institute of Canadian Bankers) *see* 0822-6830
0046-9777 C F A Digest
0046-9785 Institute of Club Managers and Secretaries. Club Guide
0046-9793 Institute of Commerce, London. Magazine *changed to* Business Education International.
0046-9807 Institute of Electrical Inspectors. I.E.I. Journal
0046-984X Institute of Southeast Asian Studies. Library. Accessions List
0046-9858 Institution of Chemical Engineers. Transactions *see* 0302-0797
0046-9858 Institution of Chemical Engineers. Transactions *see* 0263-8762
0046-9858 Institution of Chemical Engineers. Transactions *see* 0957-5820
0046-9866 Institution of Engineers, Australia. Brisbane Division. Technical Papers *changed to* Institution of Engineers, Australia. Queensland Division. Technical Papers.
0046-9874 Institution of Engineers Australia. South Australian Division. Bulletin†
0046-9882 Institution of Engineers, Jamaica. Journal
0046-9890 Instituto Agricola Catalan de San Isidro. Revista†
0046-9912 Instituto Brasileiro de Mercado de Capitais. Boletim de Documentacao†
0046-9920 I C A Informa
0046-9939 Instituto de Pesca, Sao Paulo. Boletim
0046-9947 Instituto de Pesquisa Agropecuaria do l'Este. Pesquisa e Experimentos. Comunicado Tecnico†
0046-9955 Instituto de Soldadura. Boletim†
0046-9963 Instituto Estadual de Hematologia Arthur de Siqueira Cavalcanti. Boletim *see* 0103-3263
0046-9971 Instituto Forestal Latinoamericano de Investigacion y Capacitacion. Boletin Bibliografico. *see* 0798-1945
0046-9998 Pan American Institute of Geography and History. Commission on Cartography. Cartografia†
0047-0007 Boletin de la Integracion *see* 0325-1675
0047-0015 Institutul Central de Documentare Tehnica. Revista de Titluri: Aspecte Ale Economiei Mondiale *changed to* Institutul National de Informare si Documentare Stiintifica si Tehnica Revista de Titluri: Economia Mondiala si Nationala.
0047-0023 Institutul National de Informare si Documentare Stiintifica si Tehnica Revista de Titluri: Arhitectura. Sistematizare. Constructii†
0047-0031 Institutul Central de Documentare Tehnica. Revista de Titluri: Cibernetica. Automatizarea *changed to* Institutul National de Informare si Documentare Stiintifica si Tehnica Revista de Titluri: Automatica.
0047-0031 Institutul Central de Documentare Tehnica. Revista de Titluri: Cibernetica. Automatizarea *changed to* Institutul National de Informare si Documentare Stiintifica si Tehnica Revista de Titluri: Cibernetica.
0047-004X Institutul Central de Documentare Tehnica. Revista de Titluri: Cresterea Animalel *changed to* Institutul National de Informare si Documentare Stiintifica si Tehnica. Revista de Titluri: Agricultura. Cresterea Animalelor.
0047-0058 Institutul National de Informare si Documentare Stiintifica si Tehnica Revista de Titluri: Constructii de Masini†

ISSN

ISSN INDEX

0047-0066 Institutul Central of Documentare Tehnica. Revista de Titluri: Cultura Plantelor *changed to* Institutul National de Informare si Documentare Stiintifica si Tehnica Revista de Titluri: Agricultura. Cultura Plantelor.
0047-0074 Institutul National de Informare si Documentare Stiintifica si Tehnica. Revista de Titluri: Coroziune. Protectia Suprafetelor†
0047-0082 Institutul National de Informare si Documentare Stiintifica si Tehnica Revista de Titluri: Conducerea si Organizarea Intreprinderilor†
0047-0090 Institutul Central de Documentare Tehnica. Revista de Titluri: Energetica. Electrotehnica *changed to* Institutul National de Informare si Documentare Stiintifica si Tehnica. Revista de Titluri: Energetica.
0047-0090 Institutul Central de Documentare Tehnica. Revista de Titluri: Energetica. Electrotehnica *changed to* Institutul National de Informare si Documentare Stiintifica si Tehnica. Revista de Titluri: Electrotehnica.
0047-0104 Institutul National de Informare si Documentare Stiintifica si Tehnica Revista de Titluri: Eficienta Economica. Pret de Cost. Evidenta Contabila si Statistica†
0047-0112 Institutul Central de Documentare Tehnica. Revista de Titluri: Electronica. Telecomunicatii *changed to* Institutul National de Informare si Documentare Stiintifica si Tehnica. Revista de Titluri: Telecomunicatii.
0047-0120 Institutul National de Informare si Documentare Stiintifica si Tehnica Revista de Titluri: Frecare. Uzura. Ungere. Intretinerea si Repararea Utilajelor†
0047-0139 Institutul Central de Documentare Tehnica. Revista de Titluri: Gospodarirea Apelor *changed to* Institutul National de Informare si Documentare Stiintifica si Tehnica Revista de Titluri: Gospodarirea Apelor. Hidrotehnica.
0047-0147 Institutul National de Informare si Documentare Stiintifica si Tehnica Revista de Titluri: Industria Alimentara†
0047-0155 Institutul Central Documentare Tehnica. Revista de Titluri: Industria Chimica *changed to* Institutul National de Informare si Documentare Stiintifica si Tehnica Revista de Titluri: Chimie.
0047-0163 Institutul National de Informare si Documentare Stiintifica si Tehnica Revista de Titluri: Informare Documentare†
0047-0171 Institutul Central de Documentare Tehnica. Revista de Titluri: Industria Lemnului *changed to* Institutul National de Informare si Documentare Stiintifica si Tehnica Revista de Titluri: Lemn. Celuloza. Hirtie.
0047-018X Institutul National de Informare si Documentare Stiintifica si Tehnica Revista de Titluri: Industria Miniera†
0047-0198 Institutul Central de Documentare Tehnica. Revista de Titluri: Industria Petrolului si a Gazelor Naturale *changed to* Institutul National de Informare si Documentare Stiintifica si Tehnica Revista de Titluri: Petrol si Gaze.
0047-0201 Institutul National de Informare si Documentare Stiintifica si Tehnica Revista de Titluri: Industria Usoara†
0047-021X Institutul National de Informare si Documentare Stiintifica si Tehnica Revista de Titluri: Metalurgie†
0047-0228 Institutul Central de Documentare Tehnica. Rivista de Titluri: Mecanizarea Agriculturii *changed to* Institutul National de Informare si Documentare Stiintifica si Tehnica Revista de Titluri: Agricultura. Mecanizarea Agriculturii.
0047-0236 Institutul Central de Documentare Tehnica. Revista de Titluri: Marketing. Organizarea Desfacerii Produselor si a Activitatii de Servicii *changed to* Institutul National de Informare si Documentare Stiintifica si Tehnica Revista de Titluri: Marketing. Organizarea Desfacerii si a Prestarilor de Servicii.
0047-0244 Institutul National de Informare si Documentare Stiintifica si Tehnica, Revista de Titluri: Mecanica. Rezistenta Materialelor. Mecanisme†
0047-0260 Institutul National de Informare si Documentare Stiintifica si Tehnica Revista de Titluri Organizarea Productiei si a Muncii†
0047-0279 Institutul Central de Documentare Tehnica. Revista de Titluri: Poluarea Aerului si Apei. Tratarea Deseurilor *changed to* Institutul National de Informare si Documentare Stiintifica si Tehnica Revista de Titluri: "Poluarea si Protectia Mediului Inconjurator".

0047-0287 Institutul National de Informare si Documentare Stiintifica si Technica. Revista de Titluri: Protectia Muncii†
0047-0295 Institutul Central de Documentare Tehnica. Revista de Titluri: Poligrafie. Reprografie *changed to* Institutul National de Informare si Documentare Stiintifica si Tehnica. Revista de Titluri: Poligrafie.
0047-0295 Institutul Central de Documentare Tehnica. Revista de Titluri: Poligrafie. Reprografie *changed to* Institutul National de Informare si Documentare Stiintifica si Tehnica. Revista de Titluri: Reprografie.
0047-0309 Institutul Central de Documentare Tehnica. Revista de Titluri: Silvicultura. Expoatare Forestiera *changed to* Institutul National de Informare si Documentare Stiintifica si Tehnica Revista de Titluri: Silvicultura.
0047-0317 Institutul Central de Documentare Tehnica. Revista de Titluri: Sistemul Informational Economic. Masini si Echipamet de Birou *changed to* Institutul National de Informare si Documentare Stiintifica si Tehnica Revista de Titluri: Teoria Informatiei. Informatica.
0047-0325 Institutul National de Informare si Documentare Stiintifica si Tehnica Revista de Titluri: Tehnica Fotografica si Cinematografica†
0047-0333 Institutul National de Informare si Documentare Stiintifica si Technica. Revista de Titluri: Transport Intern. Ambalare. Depozitare.†
0047-0341 Institutul National de Informare si Documentare Stiintifica si Tehnica Revista de Titluri: Tehnica Masurarii. Controlul Calitatii†
0047-035X Institutul National de Informare si Documentare Stiintifica si Tehnica Revista de Titluri: Transporturi Cai de Comuncatie†
0047-0368 Institutul National de Informare si Documentare Stiintifica si Tehnica. Revista de Titluri: Scientica. Cercetare. Proiectare. Estetica Indusriala†
0047-0376 Instruments India
0047-0384 Insurgent Sociologist *see* 0896-9205
0047-0392 Integration
0047-0406 Intelligence Survey
0047-0414 Intercom (Washington, 1971)
0047-0422 I M C O Bulletin *changed to* I M O News.
0047-0430 Interchange
0047-0449 Interchange†
0047-0457 Interchange (Portland)
0047-0465 Interchange *changed to* Population Education Interchange.
0047-0473 Intercom†
0047-049X Interior†
0047-0503 Intermode
0047-0511 Intermountain Jewish News
0047-0538 International Afro-American Museum. Newsletter *changed to* Museum of African-American History. Newsletter.
0047-0554 I A C P Law Enforcement Legislation and Litigation Report†
0047-0562 I A C P Law Enforcement Legislative Research Digest†
0047-0570 International Bank for Reconstruction and Development. Statement of Loans†
0047-0589 International Bar Journal *see* 0143-7453
0047-0597 International Barbed Wire Gazette†
0047-0619 International Book Year Newsletter *changed to* Book Promotion News.
0047-0627 International Business Digest†
0047-0635 International Cataloguing *see* 1011-8829
0047-0651 I C M A Newsletter
0047-0678 International Commission of Jurists. Journal *see* 0020-6393
0047-0686 International Dostoevsky Society Bulletin *changed to* Dostoevsky Studies.
0047-0716 International Institute for Population Studies. Newsletter *changed to* I I P S Newsletter.
0047-0724 International Journal of Government Auditing
0047-0732 International Journal of Group Tensions
0047-0740 International Journal of Nuclear Medicine and Biology *see* 0883-2897
0047-0759 International Journal of Radiation Engineering†
0047-0767 International Journal of Sport Psychology
0047-0783 Co-operative Information†
0047-0791 International Labour Office. Minutes of the Governing Body†
0047-0813 International Law News
0047-083X I M F Survey
0047-0856 I N I S Newsletter
0047-0864 International Oil Scouts Association. Official Newsletter *see* 0277-6812
0047-0880 International Planned Parenthood Federation. Library Bulletin *see* 0309-6904
0047-0899 International Press Cutting Service: Modern Plastics and Engineering

0047-0902 International Press Cutting Service: Ceramics - Porcelain - Refractory - Cement - Glass
0047-0910 International Press Cutting Service: Chemical Process Engineering. Drugs - Pharmaceuticals
0047-0929 International Press Cutting Service: Dyestuff Industry and Chemicals
0047-0937 International Press Cutting Service: Electronics and Electricals Industry
0047-0945 International Press Cutting Service: Fermented Wines, Liqueurs, Brandy, Gin, Rum, Whisky, Beer and Alcoholic Drinks
0047-0953 International Press Cutting Service: Import - Export - Licenses
0047-0961 International Press Cutting Service: Jute, Gunny, Hessian, Burlap, Coir
0047-097X International Press Cutting Service: Labour Welfare - Industrial Legislation and Personnel Management
0047-0988 International Press Cutting Service: Leather - Hides - Skin - Footwear
0047-0996 International Press Cutting Service: Machine Tool and Iron Steel Industry
0047-1003 International Press Cutting Service: Mines & Minerals (Coal and Ores)
0047-1011 International Press Cutting Service: Non-Ferrous Metals - Aluminium
0047-102X International Press Cutting Service: Oils (Vegetable) Fats - Soap - Animalfeed
0047-1038 International Press Cutting Service: Paper - Pulp - Board - Straw
0047-1046 International Press Cutting Service: Petroleum - Petrochemicals - Fertilisers - Agricultural Chemistry
0047-1054 International Press Cutting Service: Plywood - Timber - Particle Board
0047-1062 International Press Cutting Service: Rubber and Rubber Technology
0047-1070 International Press Cutting Service: Scientific Instruments, Laboratory Equipment & Chemicals
0047-1089 International Press Cutting Service: Sugar - Gur - Khandasari
0047-1097 International Press Cutting Service: Taxation - Finance - Company Law
0047-1100 International Press Cutting Service: Tea and Coffee News
0047-1119 International Press Cutting Service: Textile News
0047-1127 International Press Cutting Service: Tender Notifications (Indian & Global)
0047-1135 International Press Cutting Service: Tobacco News
0047-1143 International Press Cutting Service: Wheat & Wheat Products (Rice - Food Grains)
0047-1151 International Press Cutting Service: Processed Food Products - Spices
0047-116X International Psychologist
0047-1178 International Relations
0047-1208 International Review of Music Aesthetics and Sociology *see* 0351-5796
0047-1216 I T C C Review†
0047-1224 International Telecommunication Union. Operational Bulletin
0047-1240 International Understanding at School
0047-1259 I U G G Chronicle
0047-1267 International Union of Geological Sciences. Geological Newsletter *see* 0705-3797
0047-1275 International Wealth Success Newsletter
0047-1291 Interprete
0047-1305 I F C O News
0047-1321 Intervention
0047-1348 Investa *changed to* Kovoexport.
0047-1356 Investor's Digest of Canada
0047-1372 Invitation to Snowmobiling†
0047-1380 Involvement *see* 0319-1443
0047-1399 Iowa Geographer *see* 0199-994X
0047-1402 University of Iowa. Libraries. Newsletter
0047-1410 Iran Family Planning Bulletin†
0047-1429 Iraq News Bulletin
0047-1437 Irish Ancestor
0047-1445 Irish Bacon News
0047-1453 Irish Equipment News
0047-1461 Irish Hardware and Allied Trader
0047-147X Irish Medical Times
0047-1488 Irish Pulset
0047-1496 IronMan
0047-150X Ironwood†
0047-1518 Irrigation Journal (Van Nuys)
0047-1542 Islas
0047-1550 Isotype Titles *changed to* Zidis.
0047-1569 Israel. Department of Antiquities and Museums. Archaeological News *changed to* Hadashot Arkheologiyot.
0047-1577 Israel Gerontological Society. Information Bulletin
0047-1585 Israel Oil News†
0047-1593 Israel Shipping Research Institute. Journal *see* 0334-2751
0047-1607 Issue
0047-1623 Istanbul Universitesi. Tip Fakultesi. Tip Fakultesi Mecmuasi *see* 0374-1656
0047-1631 I A I Informat
0047-164X It Ain't Me Babe†
0047-1658 Italian-Australian Bulletin of Commerce
0047-1666 Italix†
0047-1674 Ivoire Dimanche

5478 ISSN INDEX

0047-1690 Jack O'Dwyer's Newsletter *changed to* Jack O'Dwyer's Newsletter.
0047-1712 Jakemate
0047-1720 Jamaica Churchman
0047-1739 Janus†
0047-1755 Japan Chemical Week
0047-1763 Japan Dental Association. Journal
0047-1771 Japan Foreign Trade Journal†
0047-1798 Japan Society of Civil Engineers. Transactions†
0047-181X Japanese Business Journal†
0047-1828 Japanese Circulation Journal
0047-1836 Josanpu Zasshi
0047-1844 Hokenfu Zasshi
0047-1852 Japanese Journal of Clinical Medicine
0047-1860 Japanese Journal of Clinical Pathology
0047-1879 Japanese Journal of Industrial Health
0047-1887 Japanese Journal of Legal Medicine
0047-1895 Kango Kyoiku
0047-1917 Japanese Journal of Veterinary Research
0047-1925 J N R Bulletin
0047-1933 Jasmin†
0047-1941 Javelin *changed to* Scrapie.
0047-1968 Jeremiad†
0047-1976 Jeugd en Samenleving
0047-1984 Jeunesse Ouvriere
0047-1992 Jeunesse Ouvriere Chretienne *changed to* Equipe Ouvriere.
0047-200X Jewish Radical
0047-2018 Jewish Veteran
0047-2034 Jobs in Social Work†
0047-2042 Johnstown Motorist *changed to* A A A Traveler (York).
0047-2050 Joka Poika *see* 0781-7177
0047-2077 Jornal Brasileiro de Medicina
0047-2085 Jornal Brasileiro de Psiquiatria
0047-2093 Jornal de Letras
0047-2123 Journal de la Navigation
0047-2131 Journal de la Police Nationale†
0047-214X Journal de la Publicite et des Techniques de la Promotion et Publi-Magazine
0047-2158 Journal de Mathematiques Elementaires†
0047-2166 Journal de Pharmacie de Belgique
0047-2174 Journal de Tanger
0047-2182 Journal des Caisses d'Epargne
0047-2212 Journal for the Study of Judaism in the Persian, Hellenistic and Roman Period
0047-2220 Journal of Applied Rehabilitation Counseling
0047-2255 Journal of Canadian Fiction
0047-2263 Journal of Caribbean History
0047-228X Journal of Clinical Child Psychology
0047-2298 Journal of Coated Fibrous Materials *see* 0093-4658
0047-2301 Journal of Collective Negotiations in the Public Sector
0047-231X Journal of College Science Teaching
0047-2328 Journal of Comparative Family Studies
0047-2336 Journal of Contemporary Asia
0047-2352 Journal of Criminal Justice
0047-2360 Journal of Development Administration
0047-2379 Journal of Drug Education
0047-2395 Journal of Educational Technology Systems
0047-2409 Journal of Entomology (A) *see* 0307-6962
0047-2417 Journal of Entomology (B) *see* 0307-6970
0047-2425 Journal of Environmental Quality
0047-2433 Journal of Environmental Systems
0047-2441 Journal of European Studies
0047-245X Journal of Food Distribution Research
0047-2468 Journal of Geometry
0047-2476 Journal of Geriatrics†
0047-2484 Journal of Human Evolution
0047-2492 Journal of Intergroup Relations
0047-2506 Journal of International Business Studies
0047-2514 Journal of Irish Literature
0047-2522 Journal of Korean Affairs†
0047-2530 Journal of Legal Studies
0047-2549 Journal of Marketing and Economic Research
0047-2557 Journal of Mathematical and Physical Sciences
0047-2565 Journal of Medical Primatology
0047-2573 Journal of Medieval and Renaissance Studies
0047-2581 Journal of Mexican American History
0047-259X Journal of Multivariate Analysis
0047-2603 Journal of Neurosurgical Nursing *see* 0888-0395
0047-262X Journal of Nursing
0047-2638 Journal of Operational Psychiatry†
0047-2646 Journal of Organizational Communication†
0047-2662 Journal of Phenomenological Psychology
0047-2670 Journal of Photochemistry *see* 1010-6030
0047-2689 Journal of Physical and Chemical Reference Data
0047-2697 Journal of Political and Military Sociology†
0047-2700 Journal of Political Studies
0047-2719 Journal of Popular Film *see* 0195-6051
0047-2727 Journal of Public Economics
0047-2735 The Journal of Religious Studies
0047-2743 Journal of Remote Sensing†
0047-2751 Journal of Rural Development and Administration (PARD)
0047-276X Journal of Russian Studies *see* 0957-1760
0047-2778 Journal of Small Business Management
0047-2786 Journal of Social Philosophy
0047-2794 Journal of Social Policy
0047-2816 Journal of Technical Writing and Communication
0047-2824 Journal of Technology
0047-2840 Journal of the New Harbinger *see* 0190-2741
0047-2867 Journal of Theology for Southern Africa
0047-2875 Journal of Travel Research
0047-2883 Journal of Value Engineering†
0047-2891 Journal of Youth and Adolescence
0047-2905 Journal on the Handicapped Child†
0047-2913 Journal Pakistan†
0047-293X Journalistes Francais
0047-2956 Juco Review
0047-2972 Judges' Journal
0047-2980 Judo-Koerier *changed to* Budo Koerier.
0047-2999 Jungle
0047-3014 Juris Doctor†
0047-3030 K: Revista de Poesia
0047-3049 K F Z Betrieb und Automarkt *changed to* K F Z Betrieb Unternehmermagazin.
0047-3057 K-Kauppa Ja Myyja *see* 0783-5167
0047-3065 K-3 Bulletin of Teaching Ideas and Materials†
0047-3073 Kaeltetechnik Klimatisierung *see* 0172-1984
0047-3081 Kainai News
0047-309X Kajian Veterinar *see* 0126-9437
0047-3103 Kalakalpam
0047-3111 Kalakshetra *changed to* Kalakshetra Quarterly.
0047-312X Kalori
0047-3138 Makerere University. Library. Library Bulletin and Accessions List
0047-3146 Kanadai Fuggetlen Hirlap *changed to* Magyar Naplo (Toronto, 1966).
0047-3154 Kanadsky Slovak
0047-3170 Kansas Professional Engineer
0047-3189 Kansas State Engineer
0047-3197 Karachi. Chamber of Commerce and Industry. Trade Journal†
0047-3200 Karakit†
0047-3219 Karavana†
0047-3235 Karibu Tanzania†
0047-3243 Karjantuote *see* 0784-1736
0047-3251 Karjatalous†
0047-326X Karnatak University, Dharwad, India. Bulletin†
0047-3278 Kart og Plan
0047-3286 Kasari†
0047-3308 Kauneus ja Terveys
0047-3316 Kauppateknikko
0047-3340 Kenya Journal of Adult Education†
0047-3359 Kerala Industry
0047-3367 Kerala Sabha
0047-3375 Keretapi
0047-3383 Kesatuan Bulletin
0047-3391 Keste Damena
0047-3405 Kettenwirk-Praxis
0047-3413 Keynote *see* 0272-6513
0047-343X Kirjakauppalehti
0047-3456 Kirkens Verdent†
0047-3472 Kneipp-Bademeister†
0047-3499 Knox Alumnus *changed to* Knox Alumnus.
0047-3510 Koettbranschen
0047-3537 Kommunalt Tidsskrift†
0047-3545 Konditormestrenes Medlemsblad *changed to* Bager-Konditor.
0047-3553 Konfekturehandleren
0047-3561 Koninklijke Officiers Schermbond. Kos-Gebeuren
0047-3588 Korea Focus†
0047-3596 Korea Today
0047-360X Korean Medical Abstracts
0047-3618 Korean Nurse
0047-3626 Korps Komando *changed to* Mari Jo.
0047-3650 Kosmos
0047-3677 Kotiseutu
0047-3685 Kotitalous
0047-3693 Krishnamurti Foundation. Bulletin
0047-3715 Kryds-Avisent†
0047-3731 Kulturen Zivot
0047-3766 Kunststoff Journal
0047-3774 L A S I E
0047-3839 Labor Arbitration in Government
0047-3855 Laboratory Product News
0047-3863 Labores del Hogar
0047-3871 Labor *changed to* Labor Press and Information.
0047-388X Labour Research Department. Fact Service
0047-3898 Lago
0047-3901 Lagos Librarian
0047-391X Lakaskultura
0047-3928 Lambda Alpha Journal of Man
0047-3936 Lamp
0047-3944 Lamp in the Spine†
0047-3952 Land Reform, Land Settlement and Cooperatives
0047-3960 Landbonyt
0047-3979 Landesverband der Tonkuenstler und Musiklehrer. Mitteilungsblatt
0047-3995 Landmaschinen Rundschau
0047-4002 Landwirt im Ausland *see* 0343-6462
0047-4010 Die Landwirtschaft
0047-4029 Landwirtschaftsblatt Weser-Ems
0047-4037 Language and Literature†
0047-4045 Language in Society
0047-4053 Lantern's Core
0047-4061 Lanzadera†
0047-407X Lapsi Ja Nuoriso *see* 0786-0188
0047-4088 Lariat
0047-410X Laser Raman Spectroscopy Abstracts *see* 0309-5320
0047-4126 Lastebileieren
0047-4134 Latin American Literary Review
0047-4142 Literacy Advance
0047-4169 Law and Society Newsletter *changed to* Law and Society Quarterly.
0047-4177 Law Council of Australia. Law Council Newsletter *see* 0159-7531
0047-4185 Law Report News†
0047-4193 Law Review Digest†
0047-4207 Lawasia
0047-4215 LawLab Journal *changed to* Expert Witness Journal.
0047-4231 Lazio Ieri e Oggi
0047-424X Leadership
0047-4258 League of Pity Paper *changed to* Wake Up (London).
0047-4274 Leben und Erziehen
0047-4282 Der Lebensmittelkaufmann
0047-4290 Lebensmitteltechnik
0047-4304 Lecturas
0047-4312 Lederwaren-Zeitung *see* 0178-5052
0047-4320 Leeds and West Riding Topic *changed to* Yorkshire Topic.
0047-4339 Leeds Weekly Citizen *changed to* Leeds Citizen.
0047-4355 Leichtathletik
0047-4363 Leisure
0047-438X Leka Nuhout
0047-4401 Ragioni Critiche
0047-441X Letras da Provincia
0047-4428 Letras de Hoje
0047-4436 Lettres Mensuelles; Revue Philosophique et Sociale
0047-4444 Levende Gedachten *changed to* Theosofisch Forum.
0047-4452 Lex
0047-4460 Liberal
0047-4479 Liberalt Perspektiv *changed to* Populist.
0047-4495 Liberation War
0047-4509 Libertarian Analysis†
0047-4517 Libertarian Forum
0047-4525 Library Action
0047-4533 Library Association of Australia. University and College Libraries Section. News Sheet†
0047-4541 Library Trustees Foundation of New York State. Newsletter
0047-4568 Libros Nuevos†
0047-4576 L E S Nouvelles
0047-4584 Licht und Leben
0047-4592 Life Threatening Behavior *see* 0363-0234
0047-4614 Life in America†
0047-4630 Lifeliner (Riverside)
0047-4649 Light (London, 1881)
0047-4657 Light (London, 1969)
0047-4665 Lilit†
0047-4681 Lincolnshire Agricultural and Industrial Sales and Wants
0047-469X Linde Distributor Progress†
0047-4703 Lingua e Cultura
0047-4711 Lingua e Literatura
0047-472X Sprache und Literatur in Wissenschaft
0047-4746 Linnean Society of New South Wales. Proceedings
0047-4754 Liquified Petroleum Gas *changed to* L.P. Gas News.
0047-4762 Listening Index *changed to* A M P S White - Coloured - Asian Radio Diary.
0047-4770 Literacy: a Newsletter *changed to* Adult Education Information Notes.
0047-4789 Literacy Documentation†
0047-4797 Literary Repository†
0047-4800 Litterature
0047-4819 Little Flower Monthly†
0047-4827 Liverpool Newsletter
0047-4835 Living City†
0047-4843 Living Earth†
0047-4851 Living Historical Farms Bulletin
0047-486X Living in South Carolina
0047-4878 Living Music
0047-4894 Llewellyn *see* 0145-885X
0047-4908 Lloyd's Weekly Casualty Reports
0047-4916 Lo Gai Saber *changed to* Lo Gai Saber.
0047-4924 Local Government in South Australia†
0047-4959 Locus (Oakland)
0047-4967 Logberg-Heimskringla
0047-4975 Logger†
0047-4983 Loggers World
0047-4991 Logistics and Transportation Review
0047-5009 Logistik Technik und Versorgung†
0047-5017 Loisirs Nautiques
0047-5025 London City Mission Magazine *changed to* Span (London).
0047-5033 London Collector
0047-505X Lost
0047-5068 W C N Commercial News
0047-5076 Los Angeles County Medical Association. Bulletin *see* 0162-7163
0047-5084 Los Angeles County Museum of Art. Graphic Arts Council. Newsletter†
0047-5106 Louisiana Researcher†
0047-5149 Loyalist Gazette
0047-5157 Ludd's Mill†

ISSN

ISSN INDEX

ISSN	Title
0047-5165	Lugha Yetu
0047-5173	Lument
0047-522X	Luton Commerce and Trade Journal *changed to* Chiltern Enterprise.
0047-5246	M D of Canada†
0047-5254	M H Builders News *changed to* M H - R V Builders News.
0047-5262	M I S Reports
0047-5270	M S News
0047-5289	M S T English Quarterly
0047-5297	M T A Journal
0047-5300	M U M
0047-5319	Maanmittaus
0047-5327	Maansiirto
0047-5335	MacDonald Journal
0047-5351	Machinery & Machine Tool Journal
0047-536X	Machines Production
0047-5378	Machinist
0047-5386	McKee-Pedersen Instruments. M P I Applications Notes†
0047-5394	McKinsey Quarterly
0047-5416	Madagascar; Revue de Geographie
0047-5424	Made in Europe. Technical Equipment Catalog *changed to* Made in Europe. Technical and Industrial Supply Guide.
0047-5432	Madrona†
0047-5467	Magic and Spells Quarterly†
0047-5475	Magic Carpet
0047-5491	Magnesium Monthly Review
0047-5513	Magyar Elet
0047-5521	Magyar Hirlap†
0047-5548	Maine Trails
0047-5572	Mak†
0047-5599	Malayan Economic Review *see* 0217-5908
0047-5610	Malaysia in History†
0047-5629	Malaysian Digest
0047-5637	Mallee Horticulture Digest†
0047-5653	Management†
0047-567X	Management Development Centre, Dacca. Quarterly Bulletin *see* 0378-7532
0047-5688	Management Education & Development
0047-570X	Management in Government
0047-5718	Management-Scope *see* 0895-4844
0047-5726	Manager Magazin
0047-5734	University of Santo Tomas. Faculty of Civil Law. Law Review
0047-5742	University of Santo Tomas. Graduate School. Journal of Graduate Research
0047-5750	U.S.T. Library Bulletin†
0047-5769	Manitoba Journal of Education†
0047-5785	Manpower and Vocational Education Weekly *changed to* Vocational Training News.
0047-5793	Manpower Documentation
0047-5815	Manufacturing Engineer *changed to* Industrial Technology and Machine Tools.
0047-5823	Manx Star
0047-5858	Maquettes-Plastiques *changed to* Maquettes Plastique Magazine.
0047-5866	Mar
0047-5874	Marathon
0047-5904	Marelli *changed to* Ercole Marelli.
0047-5912	Marga
0047-5920	Mariemou
0047-5939	Marine and Outdoor Trades *see* 0705-8993
0047-5947	Marine Aquarist
0047-5955	Marine Engineers Review
0047-5963	Maritime Express†
0047-5971	Maritimes Tax Reports
0047-598X	Market Research in Benelux *see* 0308-3446
0047-5998	Market Research in Germany *see* 0308-3446
0047-6005	Market Research in Italy *see* 0308-3446
0047-603X	Marmi Graniti Pietre
0047-6048	Marquette University Education Review†
0047-6056	Marriage Counseling Quarterly *changed to* Marriage and Family Counselors Quarterly.
0047-6064	Marturion
0047-6072	Marxistiskt Forum
0047-6080	Maryland Nurse
0047-6099	Maryland Reacher†
0047-6102	Maskinmesteren
0047-6110	Road of the Party
0047-6129	Massachusetts Correctional Association. Correctional Research Bulletin†
0047-6137	Massachusetts Journal of Mental Health†
0047-6153	Massachusetts Researcher†
0047-6161	Massachusetts Studies in English
0047-6188	Master Indicator of the Stock Market
0047-6196	Master Photographer *see* 0956-2745
0047-6218	Material Management Journal and Review *changed to* Focus (Lansing).
0047-6234	Materials Handling and Storage *changed to* Materials Handling & Distribution.
0047-6242	Mathematical Association of South Australia. S.A. Mathematics Teacher *changed to* Mobius.
0047-6250	Mathematical Association of Tanzania. Bulletin *see* 0856-065X
0047-6269	The Mathematics Education
0047-6277	Mathematische Operationsforschung und Statistik *changed to* Statistics.
0047-6277	Mathematische Operationsforschung und Statistik *changed to* Optimization.
0047-6285	Matthew Bender Tax Letter *changed to* Washington Tax and Business Report.
0047-6293	Mawazo
0047-6315	Me Jane
0047-6323	Measurement in Education†
0047-6331	Meat and Allied Trades Federation of Australia. Western Australian Division. Meat Industry†
0047-634X	Meat and Livestock Commission, Bucks, England. International Market Survey *see* 0263-2217
0047-6358	Meat Packers Council of Canada. Facts, Figures, Comment *changed to* Canadian Meat Council. Facts, Figures, Comment.
0047-6366	Meat Trades Journal of Australia *see* 0156-2681
0047-6374	Mechanisms of Ageing and Development
0047-6390	Medaille Militaire
0047-6404	Medecine d'Afrique Noire
0047-6412	Medecine et Chirurgie Digestives
0047-6439	Media and Consumer *see* 0010-194X
0047-6447	Media Mix Newsletter *changed to* Media Mix.
0047-6455	Medical Assistance†
0047-6463	Medical Chronicle Monthly†
0047-6471	M C G Today
0047-648X	Medical Dimensions†
0047-651X	Medical Journal of Zambia
0047-6536	Medical News, Medicine and Law
0047-6552	Medical Progress Through Technology
0047-6560	Medical Research Council Newsletter
0047-6587	Medico-Legal Society of New South Wales. Proceedings
0047-6595	Medico-Legal Society of Victoria. Proceedings
0047-6609	Mediterraneo†
0047-6641	Meetings on Atomic Energy
0047-665X	Meie Elu
0047-6668	Mekong Monthly Bulletin *see* 0252-5348
0047-6676	Melbourne. Royal Melbourne Hospital. Quarterly†
0047-6692	Memo: To the President
0047-6706	Memorial-Sloan Kettering Cancer Center. Clinical Bulletin†
0047-6714	Memphis State University Law Review
0047-6730	Men's Week†
0047-6749	Mental Health News†
0047-6757	Mental Hygiene News†
0047-6765	Mental Retardation (Washington)
0047-6773	Mercury (San Francisco)
0047-6781	Merseyside Business News†
0047-679X	Message (Bronx)
0047-6803	Message of Life†
0047-6838	Metal and Engineering†
0047-6854	M T I A News Bulletin *changed to* M T I A Input.
0047-6862	Metal Trades Journal *see* 0047-6838
0047-6870	Metaletter
0047-6889	Metallbericht†
0047-6897	Metals Australia *see* 0818-3597
0047-6919	Methodist Church Music Society Bulletin
0047-6927	Metier d'Art du Quebec
0047-6935	Metro Guide. Halifax-Dartmouth Current Events
0047-6943	Metro Teen Scene†
0047-696X	Metropolitan Area Planning Council Regional Report†
0047-6978	M A U D E P Newsletter
0047-6986	Metsastaja
0047-6994	Mexican Newsletter†
0047-701X	C I A B Circular†
0047-7028	Mexico Forestal
0047-7036	Mexico Ganadero
0047-7052	Michigan Academy of Science, Arts, and Letters. Academy Letter
0047-7060	Michigan Society for Respiratory Therapy. Journal
0047-7087	Michigan Civil Rights Commission Newsletter
0047-7095	Michigan Dental Hygienist Association. Bulletin
0047-7109	Michigan. Department of Commerce. Corporation and Securities Bureau. Securities Bulletin *changed to* Update (Lansing).
0047-7117	Michigan Food News
0047-7125	Michigan Reading Journal
0047-7133	Michigan Researcher†
0047-7141	Michigan State University. Center for International Programs. International Report†
0047-715X	Michigan State University. Latin American Studies Center. Newsletter†
0047-7168	Summation†
0047-7184	Microfilm Techniques†
0047-7192	Microinfo Microfilm News *changed to* O M N I.
0047-7206	Micron *see* 0739-6260
0047-7214	Microwave Systems News *changed to* Microwave Systems News.
0047-7222	The Midden
0047-7230	Middle East Economic Digest
0047-7249	Middle East International
0047-7257	Middle East Observer
0047-7265	M E R I P Reports *see* 0899-2851
0047-7273	Midi-Minuit Fantastique†
0047-7281	Midland Cooperator†
0047-729X	Midland History
0047-7311	Midwest Purchasing
0047-732X	Midwest Racing News
0047-7338	Migrant Echo†
0047-7346	Militaertechnik
0047-7354	Militaer Teknisk Tidskrift
0047-7362	Militaerseelsorge
0047-7370	Military Collectors News
0047-7389	Military History of Texas and the Southwest *see* 0898-8064
0047-7397	Voenno-Meditsinskii Zhurnal
0047-7400	Milk News
0047-7419	Milk Topics
0047-7427	Mill Trade Journal *changed to* M T J Recycling Markets.
0047-7443	Mineria y Metalurgia, Plasticos y Electricidad
0047-7478	Miniaturbahnen *see* 0723-3841
0047-7494	Mining in Canada *see* 0008-4492
0047-7508	M L N Bulletin *changed to* M L N New Directions.
0047-7524	Mirror of the Month†
0047-7540	Mississippi Housing Newsletter†
0047-7559	Mississippi Review
0047-7567	Missouri Highways†
0047-7575	U M K C Law Review
0047-7583	Mlezi
0047-7605	Mobile Home and Trailer News *changed to* Manufactured Home News.
0047-7648	Modelisme
0047-7664	Modern Astronomy†
0047-7672	Modern Athlete and Coach
0047-7699	Modern Farmer *see* 0267-4637
0047-7702	Modern Greek Studies Association Bulletin
0047-7710	Modern Kemit
0047-7729	Modern Language Studies
0047-7737	Modern Office *see* 0810-9451
0047-7753	Modern Unionist
0047-7761	Modern Woman
0047-777X	Moderna Organizacija *see* 0350-1531
0047-7788	Modersmaalet
0047-7796	Moebel-Kultur
0047-780X	Der Moebelspediteur
0047-7826	Molecular Sieve Abstracts†
0047-7834	Monarchist *changed to* Monarchist League Newsletter.
0047-7842	Monatschrift Deutscher Zahnaerzte *see* 0340-1766
0047-7850	Monde Arabe†
0047-7869	Mondo Occulto *changed to* Nuovo Mondo Occulto.
0047-7877	Monete e Medaglie
0047-7885	Monika
0047-7893	Moniteurs *changed to* M.A.
0047-7907	Monographs for Teachers of French *see* 0815-7138
0047-7915	Monster Times†
0047-7923	Montagne et Alpinisme
0047-7931	Montana Food Distributor
0047-794X	Montana Oil Journal
0047-7958	Montana Post
0047-7966	Montana Public Affairs Report†
0047-7974	Montana Rural Electric News *changed to* Rural Montana.
0047-7982	Montana. State University. Library. Recent Acquisitions†
0047-7990	Montana Stockgrower
0047-8008	Montana's Treasure Acres†
0047-8016	Montevecchio†
0047-8032	Australia. Bureau of Statistics. South Australian Office. Monthly Summary of Statistics, South Australia.
0047-8040	Monthly Tax Features *see* 0883-1335
0047-8059	Montreal Children's Hospital. Children's News *changed to* Fax Plus.
0047-8075	Montreal. Stock Exchange. Monthly Review *changed to* Montreal Exchange. Monthly Review.
0047-8083	Moon Rainbow
0047-8091	MORE
0047-8105	Moreana
0047-813X	Mortgage and Real Estate Executives Report
0047-8148	Mosca Profana
0047-8164	Mosella
0047-8172	Mother & Baby
0047-8180	Moto Revue
0047-8199	Motor
0047-8210	Motor Manual *changed to* Australian Motor Manual.
0047-8261	Mountain and Plain History Notes *see* 0895-0083
0047-8288	Movie - T V Marketing
0047-830X	Moving Out
0047-8318	Ms
0047-8326	Mufulira Mirror *changed to* Mining Mirror.
0047-8342	Mundo Taquigrafico†
0047-8350	Munger Africana Library Notes†
0047-8369	Municipal Engineer
0047-8377	Munnplein
0047-8385	Murmur
0047-8407	Muscle Training Illustrated
0047-8415	Muscular Development
0047-8423	Music & Arts†
0047-8431	Music and the Teacher

ISSN INDEX

ISSN	Title
0047-844X	Music Educators National Conference. Contemporary Music Project. C M P Newsletter†
0047-8466	Musical Newsletter†
0047-8474	Der Musikmarkt
0047-8482	Mutter und Kind
0047-8490	Mutual Fund Performance Monthly†
0047-8504	Mutual Funds Forum†
0047-8512	Mylord†
0047-8539	Mysore Journal of Agricultural Sciences
0047-8555	Mythic Society. Quarterly Journal
0047-8563	N P†
0047-8601	Naering i Nord
0047-861X	Naftika Chronika
0047-8628	Nairang Da'ijist
0047-8636	Nairobi Handbook†
0047-8644	Nande†
0047-8660	Nashotah Review†
0047-8679	Nashville, Tennessee. Children's Museum. Museum Notes†
0047-8687	N C P C Newsletter†
0047-8695	Nassau Lawyer
0047-8717	N A R D A News
0047-8733	National Association of Conservation Districts. Tuesday Letter
0047-8741	N A J E Educator see 0730-9791
0047-8784	National Congress of American Indians. Bulletin changed to Sentinel: Bulletin - N C A I News.
0047-8792	National Council of Women of Australia. Quarterly Bulletin
0047-8806	National Council on Alcoholism. Friday Letter†
0047-8822	National C F News Bulletin†
0047-8830	National Democrat†
0047-8857	National Electronics Council. Review see 0305-2257
0047-8865	National Folk†
0047-8881	N I C A Outlook changed to Outlook (Alexandria, 1953).
0047-8903	National League of Cities. Congressional Report changed to N L C Washington Report to the Nations Cities.
0047-8938	N L F A Feed-Lines changed to Beef Business Bulletin.
0047-8946	National Maritime S A R Review see 0093-2124
0047-8962	British Israel World Federation. National Message changed to Wake-up! (Ayrshire).
0047-8989	N O L P E School Law Journal†
0047-8997	N O L P E Notes
0047-9012	National Parks Journal
0047-9020	N.P.A. Journal
0047-9047	National Police Journal†
0047-9055	National Research Council, Canada. Division of Mechanical Engineering and National Aeronautical Establishment. Quarterly Bulletin†
0047-9063	National Saver see 0047-9071
0047-9071	National Savings Newsletter†
0047-908X	N S S F N S News
0047-911X	National Time†
0047-9128	National Trust of Australia (New South Wales) National Trust Bulletin see 1036-9880
0047-9136	N T I Newsletter
0047-9144	Native People†
0047-9152	Natural Health Bulletin†
0047-9160	Natural Life Styles†
0047-9195	Nebraska Art Association Quarterly changed to Nebraska Art Association Newsletter.
0047-9209	Nebraska Law Review
0047-9217	Nebraska Resources
0047-9233	Nederlands Tijdschrift voor Vacuumtechniek - Dutch Journal of Vacuum Technology see 0169-9431
0047-925X	Needle Arts
0047-9276	Neerlandica Extra Muros†
0047-9284	Nederlands Voetbal changed to Voetbal Totaal.
0047-9292	Negotiations Management changed to Inside Negotiations.
0047-9306	Negro Lawmaker Journal†
0047-9314	Neighbors - Interracial Living
0047-9322	Nelson Gallery and Atkins Museum. Gallery Events changed to Nelson-Atkins Museum of Art. Calendar of Events.
0047-9330	Nepal Digest
0047-9349	Nepalese Perspective†
0047-9357	Nepriklausoma Lietuva
0047-9365	Netherlands Journal of Veterinary Science†
0047-9373	Network - Urban Coalition†
0047-939X	Neue Barke changed to Lektuere.
0047-9403	Neue Bergbautechnik
0047-9411	Neurocirugia†
0047-942X	Neuroelectric News
0047-9438	Neuropsihijatrija see 0353-8842
0047-9446	Neutron Activation Analysis Abstracts
0047-9454	Nevada Engineer†
0047-9462	Nevada Historical Society Quarterly
0047-9470	Nevada Livestock and Agriculture Journal†
0047-9489	Nevada Rancher
0047-9497	R C U Report†
0047-9500	New Age
0047-9519	New American Electronics Literature and Technical Data
0047-9527	New Banner†
0047-9543	New Brunswick Historical Society. Historical Review†
0047-9551	N.B. Naturalist
0047-956X	New Chislehurst Announcer
0047-9578	New Church Herald†
0047-9594	New Critic changed to Saturday Review Book Club News.
0047-9608	New Diffusionist†
0047-9616	New Directions (Washington)
0047-9624	New Electronics
0047-9632	New Engineer†
0047-9640	N E A P Q News†
0047-9659	New England Marine Resources Information changed to Rhode Island Coastline.
0047-9683	New Focus see 0890-538X
0047-9691	New French Books†
0047-9705	New Frontiers in Education
0047-9721	New Hellas
0047-973X	New Human Services Newsletter see 0094-5129
0047-9756	New Jersey Environmental Times changed to New Jersey Outdoors.
0047-9772	New Jersey Historical Commission Newsletter
0047-9810	New Mexico Transporter†
0047-9829	New Patriot
0047-9837	New Priorities see 0305-0629
0047-9845	New Products Medical - Surgical changed to Clinical Trials and Meta-Analysis.
0047-9853	New Promotions and Competitions
0047-987X	New Shetlander
0047-9888	Bush Fire Bulletin†
0047-9918	New South Wales Journal of Optometry see 0816-4622
0047-9926	New South Wales Pastoral Conditions see 0034-6616
0047-9942	New Times (Phoenix) see 0273-9836
0047-9950	New Unity†
0047-9969	New Wave
0047-9977	New Ways†
0047-9985	New Writing†
0047-9993	New York (City) Economic Development Administration. Office of Public Affairs. Economic and Other Indicators†
0048-0002	New York Denik†
0048-0037	New York Liberty Dispatch†
0048-0045	New York State Migrant Center. Newsletter†
0048-0053	New York State Environment†
0048-0061	New York (State) Office of Planning Coordination. O P C News Summary†
0048-0118	New Zealand Camera see 0114-264X
0048-0134	New Zealand Journal of Forestry Science
0048-0142	New Zealand Sanitarian see 0112-0212
0048-0150	New Zealand Surveyor
0048-0169	New Zealand Veterinary Journal
0048-0177	Newfoundland Amateur†
0048-0185	Newfoundland. Department of Education. Newsletter changed to School World.
0048-0193	Newfoundland Medical Association. Newsletter see 0705-6702
0048-0215	News and Farmer
0048-0223	News from Zambia†
0048-0231	News of the New World
0048-024X	Newscope - Current Events Edition changed to Newscope - Middle-Intermediate-Junior High School Edition.
0048-0258	Newscope - Science Edition changed to Newscope - Science Edition.
0048-0266	Newscope - Secondary Current Events Edition changed to Newscope - High School-College Edition.
0048-0274	Newshunter changed to Hunter Magazine.
0048-0282	Newsletter of Biomedical Safety & Standards
0048-0304	Newspeace changed to Peacelinks.
0048-0320	Niagara Frontier Purchaser changed to Empire Niagara Purchaser.
0048-0339	Niedersaechsischer Jaeger
0048-0355	Nieuwe Pockets en Paperbacks
0048-0363	Nigeria Confidential
0048-0371	Nigerian Accountant
0048-038X	Nigerian Business Digest
0048-0398	Nigerian Insurance Monitor
0048-0401	Nigerian Journal of Contemporary Law
0048-041X	Nile Gazette
0048-0428	Nippon Acta Radiologica
0048-0444	Nippon Medical School. Journal
0048-0452	Nippon Steel News
0048-0460	Niv Hamidrashia
0048-0479	Noir et Rouge†
0048-0495	Nordisk Jordbruksforskning
0048-0509	Nordisk Tidsskrift for Spesialpedagogikk
0048-0541	Norkontakt changed to Utvikling.
0048-0568	Norronat
0048-0576	Norsk Dampkjelforening. Meddelelser see 0800-7896
0048-0584	Norsk Drosjeeierblad changed to Taxi.
0048-0592	Norsk Husflid
0048-0606	Norsk Skibsfoerertidende
0048-0614	Norsk Tidsskrift for Sjakk
0048-0630	N A C L A News see 1058-5397
0048-0657	North Carolina Bar see 0164-6850
0048-0665	North Carolina Researcher†
0048-0673	N C I Catalyst
0048-0681	North Dakota Education News
0048-069X	North Dakota Society of Medical Technologists. Newsletter
0048-0711	Northampton and County Independent changed to Northamptonshire Image.
0048-0746	Northeastern Regional Antipollution Conference. Proceedings†
0048-0754	Northern Air
0048-0770	Northern Ireland. Ministry of Education. Education Statistics
0048-0797	Northern Teacher†
0048-0800	Special Schools Bulletin see 0310-5709
0048-0835	Nos Chasses
0048-0843	Nos Maisons Familiales de Vacances
0048-0886	Noticias da Africa do Sul changed to S.A. Panorama.
0048-0908	Noticiero Quimico
0048-0916	Notizie dall'Albania
0048-0924	Notre Comte
0048-0932	Notre Dame Journal
0048-0940	Nottingham Topic
0048-0967	Nouvelle Ecole
0048-0975	Nouvelle Revue Internationale
0048-0983	Nova Scotia Reports
0048-1009	Novum Testamentum
0048-1017	Nowi Dni
0048-1025	Nuclear Active†
0048-1033	Nuclear Magnetic Resonance Spectrometry Abstracts
0048-1041	Nucleic Acids Abstracts see 8756-7512
0048-105X	Nucleonics Week
0048-1076	Nueva Cultura see 0011-2755
0048-1084	Nueva Narrativa Hispanoamericana†
0048-1106	Nuggets
0048-1114	Numismatic Messenger†
0048-1122	Nuova Tradotta
0048-1165	Ha-Achote be-Yisrael
0048-119X	Midland News
0048-1203	Ny Jord see 0332-5229
0048-1211	Nya Cyklisten
0048-122X	Det Nye
0048-1246	O A G Travel Planner see 1053-0002
0048-1254	O.R.L. Digest see 0198-7038
0048-1262	Oak Ridge National Laboratory Review
0048-1270	Oberflaeche
0048-1289	Objectif Monde Uni†
0048-1297	Obra de Cooperacion Sacerdotal Hispanoamericana. Mensaje Iberoamericano changed to Comision Episcopal de Misiones y Cooperacion Entre las Iglesias. Mensaje Iberoamericano.
0048-1319	Observateur Africain
0048-1335	Observations from the Treadmill
0048-1378	Occupational Health New Zealand see 0301-0384
0048-1386	Ocean Soundings see 0025-3324
0048-1394	Ochrana Fauny†
0048-1408	Odd Fellow
0048-1416	Oesterreichische Bau-Wirtschaft
0048-1424	Oesterreichische Buergermeister Zeitung
0048-1440	Oesterreichische Militaerische Zeitschrift
0048-1459	Oesterreichische Foto-Zeitung
0048-1467	Oesterreichische Schulfunk changed to Der Oesterreichische Schulfunk mit Telespiegel.
0048-1475	Oesterreichische Tieraerztezeitung
0048-1483	Oesterreichische Touristenzeitung
0048-1505	Official Karate†
0048-1513	Official Organ Blue Book changed to Official Electronic Keyboard Bluebook.
0048-1521	Pan-American Coffee Bureau. Boletin Mensual†
0048-153X	Ohio Archaeologist
0048-1548	Ohio Insect Information†
0048-1556	Ohio Jersey News
0048-1564	Ohio Researcher†
0048-1572	Ohio State Law Journal
0048-1580	Oil Palm News see 0041-3216
0048-1599	Oklahoma Farm Bureau Farmer changed to Oklahoma Farm Bureau Journal.
0048-1602	Oklahoma Highwayman†
0048-1610	Oklahoma Rural News
0048-1629	Okyeame†
0048-1637	Old Cars changed to Old Cars Weekly.
0048-1645	Old Contemptible
0048-1653	Old Time Music
0048-1661	Omicron Nu changed to Omicron Nu Newsletter.
0048-1696	Onderwatersport
0048-170X	One-Ten see 0092-5667
0048-1734	Ontario Amateur
0048-1742	Ontario Archaeological Society. Arch Notes
0048-1750	Ontario Companies Law Guide changed to Ontario Corporations Law Guide.
0048-1769	Ontario Education Review changed to O E A Review.
0048-1785	Ontario Forests†
0048-1793	Ontario Geography Teachers Association Monograph changed to Ontario Association for Geographic & Environmental Education. Monograph.
0048-1807	Ontario Journal and Tax Sale Register
0048-1815	Ontario Numismatist

ISSN	Title
0048-1823	Ontario Plumbing Inspectors Association. Bulletin
0048-1831	Ontario Research Foundation. Newsletter see 0712-9467
0048-1858	Urban Forest
0048-1866	Ontario Tax Reports
0048-1882	Onward†
0048-1890	Op Safari
0048-1904	Open Access
0048-1912	Open Court Newsletter changed to Educator: Open Court Newsletter.
0048-1920	Open Home†
0048-1939	Open Letter
0048-1947	Open Road
0048-1955	Ophthalmology Digest (1979)†
0048-2013	Optics changed to Scottish Optometrist.
0048-2021	Optikko
0048-203X	Optometry Today
0048-2064	Oral Implantology see 0160-6972
0048-2080	Orben Comedy Letter†
0048-2099	Orben's Comedy Fillers†
0048-2102	Orben's Current Comedy changed to Current Comedy for Speakers.
0048-2110	Orbit Weekly†
0048-2129	Ordo
0048-2137	Oregon A S C D Curriculum Bulletin changed to Curriculum Bulletin.
0048-2145	Oregon Environmental Council Newsletter changed to Earthwatch Oregon.
0048-2153	Research and Development Perspectives changed to Center (Eugene).
0048-2161	Organists' Review
0048-217X	Organizacija i Kadrovi
0048-2196	Organized Farmer see 0383-2244
0048-220X	Orient
0048-2242	Orissa Homoeopathic Bulletin
0048-2269	Orthodox Church
0048-2277	Volund
0048-2285	Ospedale Psichiatrico
0048-2293	Osteopathic Hospital changed to A O H A Today.
0048-2331	Ottawa Law Review
0048-234X	University of Ottawa. Aesculapian Society. Medical Review†
0048-2358	A P M Bulletin
0048-2366	Ouest Medical†
0048-2382	Our Children see 1030-7451
0048-2390	Our Local Sixty Six
0048-2420	Outdoor Guide†
0048-2447	Outdoorman†
0048-2455	Outdoorsman†
0048-2463	Outlook†
0048-2471	Outlook†
0048-2498	Ouvrier Senegalais
0048-251X	Overseas Advertising
0048-2528	Overseas Books
0048-2536	Overseas Hindustan Times†
0048-2544	Overseas Press Bulletin changed to Overseas Press Club Bulletin.
0048-2579	Oxford Mission
0048-2587	P D & D International†
0048-2595	P G - Prisonniers de Guerre see 0154-7313
0048-2609	P R Reporter
0048-2617	Pacific Alert see 0882-0929
0048-2625	P A T A Indonesia
0048-2633	Pacific Marketer
0048-2641	Pacific Sun
0048-265X	Pacifist
0048-2668	Package
0048-2676	Packaging News
0048-2684	Packaging Review changed to Packaging Week.
0048-2692	Pakistan Educational Review†
0048-2706	Pakistan Heart Journal
0048-2714	P L A Newsletter
0048-2722	Pakistan Pediatric Journal
0048-2749	Pakistan Survey changed to Dakshinesia.
0048-2757	Pakistan Textile Journal
0048-2765	Palabra†
0048-2773	Palette†
0048-2781	Palmetto Piper
0048-282X	Panorama (Boston)
0048-2838	Panorama Aujourd'hui see 0299-6898
0048-2846	Panorama des Entreprises†
0048-2854	Papel Impreso
0048-2862	Paperprintpack India
0048-2870	Papers on Far Eastern History
0048-2889	Papetier
0048-2897	Papier und Kunststoff Verarbeiter
0048-2919	Papua and New Guinea Education Gazette
0048-2935	Paragraphic
0048-2951	Parassitologia
0048-296X	Paratracks changed to Son of Paratracks.
0048-2978	Parent Cooperative Preschools International changed to Co-operatively Speaking.
0048-2986	Parenteral Drug Association. Bulletin see 0279-7976
0048-2994	Parliamentary Journal
0048-3001	Parliamentary Studies see 0301-9047
0048-301X	Parnassos
0048-3028	Parnassus: Poetry in Review
0048-3036	Parsiana
0048-3044	Partisan
0048-3079	National Asphalt Pavement Association. Paving Forum changed to H M A T.
0048-3087	Pax
0048-3095	Pazifische Rundschau
0048-3109	Pearl Gazette†
0048-3117	Pecan Quarterly see 8750-5797
0048-3133	Pediatric Clinics of India
0048-315X	Pedra e Cal
0048-3176	L P T Journal
0048-3176	Pelzwirtschaft see 0048-3176
0048-3192	The Pennant
0048-3206	Pennsylvania Academy of Ophthalmology and Otolaryngology. Transactions
0048-3214	Pennsylvania Geology
0048-3230	Pennsylvania News changed to P M H A News.
0048-3249	Pennsylvania Researcher†
0048-3257	Pennsylvania Road Builder
0048-3273	Penny Wise Motoring
0048-3281	Pensioners Voice
0048-329X	People
0048-3303	People
0048-3311	People for Progress†
0048-332X	People United to Save Humanity. P.U.S.H.-Operation Push
0048-3338	People Watching†
0048-3354	New Zealand People's Voice
0048-3362	People's Voice†
0048-3370	Periodista
0048-3389	Western Society of Periodontology. Journal. Periodontal Abstracts
0048-3397	Periscoop†
0048-3400	Periscope
0048-3419	Faculdade de Odontologia de Pernambuco. Revista
0048-3435	Personal Injury Researcher†
0048-3443	Personal Report for the Executive†
0048-3451	Personnel Guide to Canada's Travel Industry
0048-346X	Personnel Management see 1032-3627
0048-3478	Personnel News for School Systems changed to Wages and Benefits.
0048-3486	Personnel Review
0048-3494	Perspective (Washington) see 1045-7097
0048-3508	Perspectives (Washington, 1971)
0048-3516	Perspectives Euro Africaines
0048-3524	Perspectives in Defense Management††
0048-3532	Perspectives Syndicalistes changed to Pense et Lutte.
0048-3540	Royal Perth Hospital. Journal†
0048-3559	Perth. Stock Exchange. Official Record†
0048-3567	Pesquisa Medica
0048-3575	Pesticide Biochemistry and Physiology
0048-3583	Petersen's PhotoGraphic Magazine see 0199-4913
0048-3591	Petroleum Gazette
0048-3605	Petts Wood Post
0048-3613	P.G. Football Newsletter
0048-3621	Pharmaceutical Salesman see 0161-8415
0048-363X	Pharmacognosy Titles†
0048-3648	Pharmascope
0048-3664	Pharmazie in Unserer Zeit
0048-3672	Pharos changed to Pharos International.
0048-3699	Phi Sigma Iota Newsletter changed to Phi Sigma Iota Forum.
0048-3702	Philadelphia Tribune
0048-3710	Philatelic Journalist†
0048-3729	P T S Journal changed to P T S News.
0048-3737	Philatopic Magazine†
0048-3745	Philippine Economy and Industrial Journal
0048-3753	The Philippine Entomologist
0048-3761	Philippine Journal of Animal Industry†
0048-377X	Philippine Journal of Fisheries
0048-3796	Philippine Journal of Linguistics
0048-380X	Philippine Journal of Mental Health
0048-3818	Philippine Journal of Nursing
0048-3826	Philippine Journal of Plant Industry
0048-3834	Philippine Journal of Soils
0048-3842	Philippine Mining & Engineering Journal
0048-3850	Philippine Planning Journal
0048-3869	Philippine Sugar Institute Quarterly changed to Philippine Sugar Commission. Quarterly.
0048-3885	Philologica Pragensia changed to Linguistica Pragensia.
0048-3885	Philologica Pragensia changed to Litteraria Pragensia.
0048-3893	Philosophia
0048-3907	Philosophic Research and Analysis see 0732-4944
0048-3915	Philosophy and Public Affairs
0048-3923	Philosophy of Education Society of Great Britain. Proceedings see 0309-8249
0048-3931	Philosophy of the Social Sciences
0048-3966	Der Foto-Markt††
0048-3974	Photo-Memo
0048-3982	Photo Reporter†
0048-3990	Photographe Professionnel†
0048-4008	Photographic Journal of the Sun†
0048-4016	Photography North
0048-4024	Physical Review Abstracts
0048-4059	Physiological Plant Pathology see 0885-5765
0048-4083	Physiotherapists' Quarterly
0048-4091	Phytoma
0048-4105	Piano-Tuners Quarterly
0048-4113	Pick's World Currency Report†
0048-4121	Pictorial Education see 0309-3484
0048-413X	Pictorial Education Quarterly see 0269-9532
0048-4148	Pielegniarka i Polozna
0048-4156	Pig Breeders Gazette
0048-4164	Pigeon Racing News and Gazette changed to Pigeon Racing Gazette.
0048-4172	Piltdown Newsletter†
0048-4180	Pink Sheet on the Left see 0278-0585
0048-4199	Pioneer
0048-4202	Pioneer†
0048-4229	Pirogue
0048-4237	Pisciculture Francaise
0048-4245	Pitture e Vernici
0048-4253	Place†
0048-4261	Placedart†
0048-427X	Plaisirs de la Chasse
0048-4288	Planet
0048-4296	Planner's Notebook see 0001-2610
0048-430X	Planning Advisory Service Reports see 0160-8266
0048-4318	Planning in Northeastern Illinois
0048-4326	P I B C News
0048-4334	Plant Genetic Resources Newsletter
0048-4342	Plant Varieties and Seeds Gazette
0048-4350	Plaste und Kautschuk
0048-4369	Plastforum see 0347-8262
0048-4385	Plastics Southern Africa
0048-4415	Playboard
0048-4423	Playfair Cricket Monthly†
0048-444X	Plebeian†
0048-4466	P L E R U S
0048-4474	Ploughshares
0048-4482	Plural Societies
0048-4490	Plymothian
0048-4504	Pneumatik Digest und Druckluftpraxis changed to Drucklufttechnik.
0048-4512	Poder Politico
0048-4547	Poesia Hispanica†
0048-4563	Poesie Presente
0048-458X	Poetry
0048-4598	Poetry Information see 0260-9339
0048-4601	Poetry Miscellany
0048-461X	Poetry of Our Times†
0048-4636	Point and Figure Digest††
0048-4695	Police Nationale
0048-4709	Policia Espanola see 0213-4012
0048-4717	Policlinico. Sezione Medica
0048-4725	Poliisimies
0048-4733	Polska Akademia Nauk. Wydzial Nauk Medycznych. Annals see 0001-608X
0048-4741	Polish Institute of Arts and Sciences in America. Information Bulletin†
0048-475X	Politieke Dokumentatie
0048-4768	Polizeiblatt fuer das Land Baden-Wuerttemberg†
0048-4776	Polizei und Verkehrsjournal changed to Polizei Journal.
0048-4784	Pollution
0048-4806	Polymer India†
0048-4822	Popular Culture Association Newsletter changed to Popular Culture Association. Newsletter and Popular Culture Methods.
0048-4830	Popular Dogs†
0048-4849	Population Newsletter changed to Population.
0048-4857	Porfeydd†
0048-4865	Port of Melbourne Quarterly see 0814-9089
0048-489X	Portside
0048-4903	Portugaliae Physica
0048-4911	Positif
0048-492X	Posta si Telecomunicatii†
0048-4946	Postgraduate Medicine Quarterly Abstracts†
0048-4954	Pottery in Australia
0048-4962	Poultry Fancier
0048-5004	Pourquoi
0048-5012	P M I - Powder Metallurgy International
0048-5020	Powder Metallurgy Science & Technology†
0048-5039	Power
0048-5047	Power & Industry in Asia†
0048-5071	Practical Education and School Crafts see 0943-612X
0048-508X	Practical Forms and Precedents
0048-511X	Prairies Tax Reports†
0048-5128	Der Praktische Arzt
0048-5136	Praxis der Beregnungswirtschaft†
0048-5144	Precision Shooting
0048-5160	Premisa
0048-5179	Prensa Chilena y Sus Comentarios
0048-5187	Presbyterian Leader see 0010-5848
0048-5195	Presence Francophone
0048-5209	Press Forum changed to Depthnews.
0048-5233	Prevention
0048-5241	Prevention changed to Prevoyance.
0048-525X	Preview Abstracts in Physics and Astronomy†
0048-5268	Preview Bermuda
0048-5276	Prim-Aid†
0048-5284	Primary Education
0048-5306	Principality of Liechtenstein - A Documentary Handbook†
0048-5314	Print-Equip News
0048-5322	Printers News†
0048-5330	Printers News
0048-5349	Prism changed to Pratt Reports.
0048-5357	Prisma
0048-5365	Prison Law Reporter†

0048-5373 Prisoners Rights Newsletter *see* 0048-5365
0048-5381 Pro Motion
0048-539X Probation *see* 0264-5505
0048-5411 Problemi di Ulisse†
0048-5438 Professional Engineer *changed to* Professional Engineer.
0048-5446 Professional Engineer in Industry Newsletter†
0048-5454 Professional Officer
0048-5489 Progreso
0048-5497 Progress in Fire Retardancy†
0048-5500 Progress in Materials Science†
0048-5519 Progress in Physical Therapy†
0048-5543 Promise M/R†
0048-5551 Propeller Club Quarterly
0048-5578 Prophetic Expositor
0048-5608 Prosperity
0048-5616 Protection†
0048-5624 Protection Management *see* 1040-4201
0048-5632 Proud
0048-5640 Proud Black Images†
0048-5659 Proust Research Association Newsletter
0048-5667 Proverbium†
0048-5675 Przeglad Psychologiczny
0048-5683 PSI *changed to* I Am.
0048-5691 Psicologia e Lavoro
0048-5713 Psychiatric Annals
0048-5721 Psychiatric Outpatient Services in Los Angeles County†
0048-573X Psychic Observer†
0048-5748 Psychological Issues
0048-5756 Psychologie Medicale
0048-5764 Psychopharmacology Bulletin
0048-5772 Psychophysiology
0048-5799 Public Administration *changed to* Public Administration and Finance Newsletter.
0048-5802 Public Affairs†
0048-5810 Public Affairs Information Service Foreign Language Index *see* 1051-4015
0048-5829 Public Choice
0048-5853 Public Finance Quarterly
0048-5888 Public Ledger
0048-5896 Public Relations Australia†
0048-5926 Public Service *changed to* Public Service-Staff Vacancies Weekly.
0048-5942 Publishers' Auxiliary
0048-5950 Publius
0048-5977 Puhelin
0048-6000 Pulse
0048-6019 Punjab Agricultural University. Journal of Research
0048-6027 Punjab Punch
0048-6035 Purchasing Management Newsletter†
0048-6043 Pyrethrum Post
0048-6051 O and M Bulletin *changed to* Management in Government.
0048-606X Q E D Renaissance *see* 0194-8431
0048-6078 Q I M A
0048-6094 Quaderni Piacentini†
0048-6108 Quantity Surveyor *see* 0007-3431
0048-6116 Quarry Mine and Pit *see* 1032-0776
0048-6124 Quarter Racing World *changed to* Speedhorse - Racing Report.
0048-6132 Quarterly Bibliography of Computers and Data Processing *see* 0270-4846
0048-6159 Quarterly Bulletin of Statistics for Asia and the Far East *see* 0125-0019
0048-6167 Quarterly Bulletin on Solar Activity
0048-6175 Quarterly Journal of Management Development *changed to* Organization & Administrative Sciences.
0048-6183 Quarterly Market Projection†
0048-6191 Quarterly Statistical Bulletin for Africa†
0048-6205 Quarto Mondo
0048-6213 Quasi
0048-6221 Que Pasa†
0048-623X Que Pasa in Puerto Rico *changed to* Que Pasa.
0048-6248 Quebec Aujourd' Hui†
0048-6256 Quebec-Histoire†
0048-6299 Quebec Tax Reports
0048-6302 Queens Bar Bulletin
0048-6310 Queen's Intramural Law Journal *changed to* Queen's Law Journal.
0048-6337 Queensland. Guidance and Special Education Branch. Special Schools Bulletin for Teachers of Exceptional Children *see* 0313-6728
0048-6345 Q H A Review
0048-6353 Queensland Littoral Society. Newsletter *changed to* Operculum.
0048-6361 Queensland Master Builder
0048-637X Queensland Master Plumber
0048-6388 Queensland Roads†
0048-6396 Australia. Bureau of Statistics. Queensland Office. Monthly Summary of Statistics, Queensland
0048-6418 Administrators' Bulletin†
0048-6426 Quest for Higher Productivity *changed to* Productivity Australia.
0048-6434 Quest in Education
0048-6442 Questo Nostro Ambiente†
0048-6450 Queyras
0048-6477 Journal de la Quincaillerie†
0048-6493 Quinzaine Litteraire
0048-6507 R E
0048-6523 Racehorse *changed to* Raceform Handicap Book.
0048-654X Radharc†
0048-6582 R C A Plain Talk and Technical Tips *changed to* Communicator (Indianapolis).
0048-6590 RadioFernseh-Haendler *see* 0343-4206
0048-6604 Radio Science
0048-6612 Rail Engineering International
0048-6639 Railroad Modeler†
0048-6647 Railway Digest International
0048-6663 Rakennustaito
0048-668X Rally
0048-671X Ramus
0048-6744 Rassegna di Medicina del Traffico†
0048-6760 Rassegna di Neuropsichiatria e Scienze Affini†
0048-6779 Rassegna Internazionale di Logica
0048-6787 Rassegna Odontotecnica
0048-6809 Ratcliffian
0048-6817 Rating and Valuation Reporter
0048-6825 Raum und Siedlung *changed to* Structur.
0048-6833 Rautatieliikenne
0048-6841 Razon y Fabula†
0048-685X Real Estate Journal (Brisbane)
0048-6868 Real Estate Law Journal
0048-6884 Realist†
0048-6892 Realites Malgaches *changed to* Zava Misy.
0048-6906 Reason
0048-6914 Receptarius
0048-6930 Recherche Spatiale†
0048-6949 Rechte Lijn
0048-6957 Record - Dossier *changed to* Phosphore.
0048-6965 Records Management Report†
0048-6973 Recreation Property Ontario *changed to* Ontario Cottager.
0048-6981 Recursos Hidricos
0048-7023 Red Cross Quarterly
0048-7031 Red Cross Senior *changed to* Link-up.
0048-7066 Reeves Journal
0048-7090 Regione Toscana†
0048-7104 R N A B C News *see* 1185-3638
0048-7112 R N A O News†
0048-7120 Rehabilitacion
0048-7139 Rehabilitation Digest
0048-7155 Reign of the Sacred Heart
0048-7163 Universite de Reims. Institut de Geographie. Travaux
0048-7171 Reinsurance
0048-718X Relay Engineer *changed to* International Cable.
0048-7198 Relazioni Clinico Scientifiche
0048-7201 Relevo†
0048-721X Religion
0048-7228 Remedes
0048-7236 Remedial Education *see* 0311-1954
0048-7260 Report on Indian Legislation†
0048-7279 Reports on Rheumatic Diseases
0048-7287 Die Republik†
0048-7325 Research Journal of Philosophy
0048-7333 Research Policy
0048-7341 Researcher
0048-7368 Reserve Bank of Australia. Currency†
0048-7376 Resources (Washington, 1959)
0048-7392 Respiratory Therapy *see* 0892-9289
0048-7406 Restaurant News
0048-7422 Retail Operations News Bulletin†
0048-7430 Rettung
0048-7449 Reumatismo
0048-7457 Reuse - Recycle
0048-7465 Review of Books and Religion *see* 0890-0841
0048-7473 International Review of Contemporary Law
0048-7481 Review of Law & Social Change
0048-749X Review of Regional Studies
0048-7511 Reviews in American History
0048-752X Reviews in Analytical Chemistry
0048-7538 Reviews on Coatings and Corrosion *changed to* Corrosion Reviews.
0048-7546 Reviews on Drug Interactions *changed to* Drug Metabolism and Drug Interactions.
0048-7554 Reviews on Environmental Health
0048-7562 Reviews on Reactive Species in Chemical Reactions *see* 0922-6168
0048-7570 Reviews on Silicon, Germanium, Tin and Lead Compounds *see* 0334-7575
0048-7589 Reviews on Deformation Behaviour of Materials *see* 0334-8938
0048-7597 Revista Agropecuaria
0048-7600 Revista Argentina de Cirurgia
0048-7619 Revista Argentina de Radiologia
0048-7627 Revista Argentina de Urologia y Nefrologia
0048-7643 Revista Brasileira de Tecnologia
0048-7651 Revista Chilena de Literatura
0048-766X Revista Chilena de Obstetricia y Ginecologia
0048-7678 Revista Cubana de Ciencias Veterinarias
0048-7694 Revista de Estudios Politicos
0048-7708 Revista de Geografia
0048-7716 Revista de la Sanidad Militar Argentina
0048-7724 Revista de Medicina Veterinaria y Parasitologia *changed to* Universidad Central de Venezuela. Facultad de Ciencias Veterinarias. Revista.
0048-7732 Revista de Obstetricia y Ginecologia de Venezuela
0048-7740 Revista de Psicologia Normal e Patologica
0048-7759 Revista de Soldadura
0048-7767 Revista Dental
0048-7775 Revista Ecuatoriana de Higiene y Medicina Tropical
0048-7783 Revista Educativa†
0048-7791 Revista Espanola de Reumatismo y Enfermedades Osteoarticulares
0048-7848 Revista Medico-Chirurgicala
0048-7856 Revista Odonto-Estomatologica
0048-7864 Revista Paulista de Hospitais
0048-7880 Revista Portuguesa de Pediatria e Puericultura
0048-7902 Revue Avicole
0048-7929 Revue de Droit et d'Economie Immobiliere *see* 0556-7297
0048-7937 Revue de Jurisprudence Commerciale
0048-7945 Revue de l'Atherosclerose†
0048-7953 Revue de l'Habitat Francais
0048-7996 Revue d'Histoire des Sciences et de leurs Applications
0048-8003 Revue d'Histoire Moderne et Contemporaine
0048-8062 Revue Francaise d'Endocrinologie Clinique, Nutrition et Metabolisme
0048-8097 Revue Generale de Botanique
0048-8100 Revue Generale des Transmissions *changed to* Entrainements.
0048-8143 Revue Internationale de Philosophie
0048-8151 Revue Internationale d'Onomastique
0048-816X Revue Ivoirienne de Droit
0048-8178 Revue Roumaine d'Etudes Internationales
0048-8186 Revue Technique du Batiment et des Constructions Industrielles
0048-8208 Revue Trimestrielle de Droit Commercial *see* 0244-9358
0048-8216 Rhode Island. University. U. R. I. Commercial Fisheries Newsletter†
0048-8224 Rhodes Report†
0048-8232 Rhodesian Caravaner and Outdoor Life *changed to* Caravaner and Outdoor Life.
0048-8267 Ricardian
0048-8275 Ricemill News *changed to* R C L Magazine.
0048-8291 Ricerche di Automatica†
0048-8305 Right On!
0048-8321 Risques du Metier *changed to* Prevenir les Risques du Metier.
0048-8348 Rivista del Colore
0048-8364 Rivista di Anatomia Patologica e di Oncologia
0048-8372 Rivista di Diritto Sportivo
0048-8399 Rivista di Idrobiologia
0048-8402 Rivista Italiana di Scienza Politica
0048-8410 Rivista Oto-Neuro-Oftalmologica
0048-8429 Rivista Tributaria Ticinese†
0048-8437 Roan Antelope *changed to* Mining Mirror.
0048-8445 Rock & Folk
0048-8453 Rock & Gem
0048-8461 Rocket
0048-847X Rockhound†
0048-8496 Rod & Line†
0048-850X Rodale's Environment Action Bulletin *see* 0013-922X
0048-8518 Roeien
0048-8526 Roerfag
0048-8534 Rogue Digger
0048-8542 Rolling Along
0048-8550 Romania Literara
0048-8577 Rumanian Journal of Chemistry
0048-8593 Romantisme
0048-8631 Rotary Down Under
0048-8658 Romania: Documents-Events
0048-8666 Roundabout
0048-8674 Rountree Report†
0048-8690 Royal Canadian Legion's Coaching Review†
0048-8704 Royal Life Saving Society - U.K. Quarterly Journal *changed to* The Royal Life Saving Society. Lifesaver U.K.
0048-8712 Royal National Institute for the Blind. School Magazine *changed to* Fizz.
0048-8720 R S P C A Today *changed to* Animal Life.
0048-8739 Royal Town Planning Institute Journal *see* 0309-1384
0048-8747 Rubber, Plastic and Cable Industries Journal *changed to* National Allied Store Talk.
0048-8755 Rund Um den Pelz International *changed to* Pelz International.
0048-8771 Running Board
0048-878X Rural Arkansas
0048-8798 Rural Education Review†
0048-8801 Rural Electric Missourian *see* 0164-8578
0048-881X Russian Literature Triquarterly†
0048-8828 Russian Ultrasonics
0048-8836 Rutebiltidende *changed to* Transportforum-Kollektivtrafikk.
0048-8844 Rutgers Journal of Computers and the Law *see* 0735-8938
0048-8852 Rutland Historical Society Newsletter *see* 0748-2493
0048-8860 Rx Bulletin†
0048-8879 Ryde Recorder
0048-8887 Rydge's Construction, Civil Engineering and Mining Review *changed to* Rydge's C C E M - Construction, Civil Engineering and Mining.
0048-8895 S F Greats†

ISSN

ISSN INDEX 5483

ISSN	Title
0048-8917	S M - Sales Meetings see 0148-4052
0048-8933	Sabretache
0048-8941	Sackbutt
0048-895X	Saddle and Striker
0048-8968	Safety Canada
0048-8976	Sage Professional Papers in International Studies†
0048-8984	Sahkourakoitsija changed to Sahkoala.
0048-8992	Saint Louis Chronicle
0048-900X	St. Paul Dispatch and Pioneer Press Newspaper Index changed to Index to the St. Paul Pioneer Press.
0048-9018	Saisons d'Alsace
0048-9026	Salary and Merit changed to Wages and Benefits.
0048-9034	Sales and Marketing in Australia†
0048-9050	Salvage Locator changed to Locator (Whiting).
0048-9069	S A E
0048-9077	San Bernardino County Museum Association. Newsletter†
0048-9107	Sante Publique
0048-9115	Santiago
0048-9123	Santo Tomas Nursing Journal
0048-914X	Saskatchewan Administrator see 0709-8146
0048-9166	Saskatchewan Care changed to S A S C H Newsletter.
0048-9174	Saskatchewan Farm Science see 0707-7793
0048-9182	Saskatchewan Genealogical Society. Bulletin
0048-9190	Saskatchewan Guidance and Counseling Association. Guidelines
0048-9204	Saskatchewan Indian
0048-9212	Saskatchewan Journal of Educational Research and Development†
0048-9220	Saskatchewan Medical Quarterly†
0048-9239	Saturday Evening Post
0048-9247	Savings Banks Institute. Journal
0048-9255	Scalpel and Tongs
0048-9263	Scandinavian - American Bulletin
0048-9271	Scandinavian Audiology
0048-928X	Scandinavian Canadian Businessman†
0048-9301	Scandinavian Refrigeration see 0284-0758
0048-931X	Scene (Northridge)
0048-9328	Schach
0048-9336	Scheideweget
0048-9344	Schietsport
0048-9352	Schiltrom†
0048-9360	Schizophrenics Anonymous International. Bulletin see 0831-8530
0048-9387	School Bell
0048-9409	School Guidance Worker changed to Guidance & Counselling.
0048-9417	School Health Bulletin changed to H E A P Journal.
0048-9425	School Library Association of Queensland. Journal†
0048-9433	School Library Newsletter†
0048-9441	S M S G Newsletter
0048-9476	School Services Curriculum Perspectives†
0048-9484	Schulverwaltungsblatt fuer Niedersachsen
0048-9492	Schuss
0048-9514	Schweizer Hotel Journal
0048-9522	Schweizer Volkskunde
0048-9530	Schweizerische Zeitschrift fuer Nachwuchs und Ausbildung†
0048-9549	Schwestern Revue
0048-9581	Science and Government Report
0048-9603	Science Education News
0048-962X	Science Fantasy†
0048-9646	Science Fiction Research Association Newsletter
0048-9654	Science Fiction Times
0048-9662	Science for the People
0048-9670	Science in Agriculture†
0048-9689	Science of Man†
0048-9697	Science of the Total Environment
0048-9700	Science Policy see 0302-3427
0048-9719	S T A News see 0834-2466
0048-9727	Sciences Medicales
0048-9735	Scope
0048-9743	Scope: Recreational Vehicle and Camping News changed to Scope Camping News.
0048-9751	Scots Magazine
0048-976X	Scottish Cooperator see 0009-9821
0048-9778	Scottish Institute of Missionary Studies Bulletin
0048-9786	S L A News see 0950-0189
0048-9794	Scottish Literary News see 0305-0785
0048-9808	Scottish Transport
0048-9816	Scout Leader changed to The Leader.
0048-9824	Scrap and Waste Reclamation and Disposal†
0048-9832	Screenings
0048-9859	S G M News Digest changed to S G M News.
0048-9867	Sea Classics†
0048-9875	Sea Grant Seventies see 0197-3460
0048-9883	Sealandair
0048-9891	Seaposter
0048-9905	Sear
0048-9913	Search (Nashville)
0048-9921	Search (Washington, D.C.) see 0741-8485
0048-9948	Seattle Centerstage
0048-9956	Second Coming†
0048-9964	Second Order
0048-9972	Second Souffle
0048-9980	Second Wave
0048-9999	Secondary Curriculum Letter changed to Curriculum Letter.
0049-0008	Secularist
0049-0016	Security Distributing & Marketing
0049-0024	Security Gazette
0049-0032	Seed Producers Review changed to Australian Seed Producers Review.
0049-0040	Seed Scoop
0049-0059	Seguranca
0049-0067	Selecciones Municipales
0049-0075	Selecoes Odontologicas
0049-0083	Select†
0049-0091	Select Bibliography on Higher Education†
0049-0105	Selected References on Environmental Quality as It Relates to Health†
0049-0113	Selective Service Law Reporter see 0193-3906
0049-0156	Semaine Juridique
0049-0164	Semina
0049-0172	Seminars in Arthritis & Rheumatism
0049-0199	Senior Citizens Today
0049-0202	Sentinel (Willowdale)
0049-0210	Srpski Arhiv za Celokupno Lekarstvo
0049-0229	Service to Business and Industry - B P L
0049-0237	Service World International see 1047-2975
0049-0253	Sesame Street
0049-027X	Seventeen's Make It!†
0049-0296	Severn and Wye Review†
0049-030X	Sewing Machine Times changed to Knitting and Sewing Machine Times.
0049-0326	Sexologie†
0049-0334	Shareholder and New Investor†
0049-0342	Shawensis†
0049-0369	Ship Repair and Maintenance changed to Shipcare & Maritime Management.
0049-0385	Sh'ma
0049-0393	Shopping Center World
0049-0415	Shotgun News
0049-0423	Shuttle, Spindle & Dyepot
0049-0431	Sic†
0049-044X	Sierra Club. National News Report
0049-0466	Sign World
0049-0474	N B F A A Signal see 0199-6835
0049-0490	Silent News
0049-0504	Sillon†
0049-0512	Simmons Review
0049-0520	S I A Journal
0049-0547	Singapore Undergrad
0049-0555	Singles-Mingles
0049-0563	Sinnets Helse
0049-0571	Sinopse de Cardiologia changed to Sinopse de Medicina Interna.
0049-058X	Sinopse de Gastroenterologia changed to Sinopse de Medicina Interna.
0049-0598	Sintesis
0049-0601	Sinteza
0049-061X	Sioniste
0049-0628	Sirjana
0049-0636	Sistema Nervoso†
0049-0652	Ski Scene†
0049-0660	Skolnytt see 0356-7842
0049-0679	Skotoey changed to SKO.
0049-0687	Skylook see 0270-6822
0049-0709	Slavic Gospel News changed to Breakthrough (Wheaton).
0049-0725	Sleutelaar changed to N O W Nieuws.
0049-0733	Slice of Pizza†
0049-075X	Slimming and Nutrition see 0144-8129
0049-0776	Smoke Signals
0049-0806	Sno-Fari News Events changed to Colorado Outfitter.
0049-0822	SnoTrack see 0274-8363
0049-0849	Sobre los Derivados de la Cana de Azucar
0049-0857	Social Change
0049-0865	Social Dimension Newsletter†
0049-089X	Social Science Research Items
0049-0903	Social Sciences
0049-0911	Social Sciences
0049-092X	Social Sciences in Canada†
0049-0946	Socialist Affairs
0049-0954	Socialist Press Bulletin
0049-0962	Socialni Politika
0049-0970	Socialt Forum see 0347-5484
0049-0989	Boletin S A C M†
0049-0997	Sociedad Dominicana de Geografia Boletin†
0049-1004	Sociedad Mexicana de Geografia y Estadistica. Boletin
0049-1039	Sociedade de Lingua Portuguesa. Boletim
0049-1055	Societe des Ecrivains Canadiens. Bulletin†
0049-1063	Societe d'Etudes. Revue d'Etudes
0049-108X	Societe Francaise de Photogrammetrie. Bulletin see 0244-6014
0049-1098	Societe Historique Acadienne. Cahiers
0049-1101	Societe Medicale d'Afrique Noire de Langue Francaise. Bulletin changed to Dakar Medical.
0049-111X	Etudes Prehistoriques†
0049-1128	Societe Royale Belge d'Entomologie. Bulletin et Annales†
0049-1136	Societe Royale Zoologique de Belgique. Annales see 0777-6276
0049-1144	S A M News International changed to S A M Management Journal.
0049-1152	Society for Ancient Numismatics. S A N Journal
0049-1160	S A A D Digest
0049-1179	Society for the Study of Labour History. Bulletin see 0961-5652
0049-1187	Society of Archer-Antiquaries. Newsletter see 0144-7424
0049-1195	Society of Architectural Historians. Newsletter
0049-1209	Society of Manufacturing Engineers. Technical Digest
0049-1217	Sociolinguistics†
0049-1225	Sociologia
0049-1233	Sociological Analysis see 0306-2481
0049-1241	Sociological Methods & Research
0049-125X	Soenderjysk Maanedsskrift
0049-1276	Sol
0049-1292	Solidarite Ouvriere
0049-1306	Somerset and Dorset Notes and Queries
0049-1330	Sosialistisk Perspektiv changed to Aktuelt Perspektiv.
0049-1349	Sotainvalidi
0049-1381	S A Athlete
0049-1403	South African Financial Gazette
0049-1411	South African Metrication News†
0049-142X	South African Studies†
0049-1438	South Australia. Department of Education. Education Gazette
0049-1446	South Australian Dairymen's Journal see 0818-7169
0049-1454	South Australian Garden Guide†
0049-1470	South Australian State Reports
0049-1489	South Carolina Dental Journal†
0049-1497	Medical University of South Carolina. Bulletin changed to Auctus.
0049-1519	South Coast Sun
0049-1527	South Eastern Latin Americanist
0049-1543	S.W.A. Boer†
0049-1551	Southeast Asia†
0049-156X	Southern California Dental Association. Journal see 0008-0977
0049-1616	Southern MotoRacing
0049-1624	Southern Purchasor
0049-1640	Southern Stars
0049-1659	Southern Utah News
0049-1667	Southwest Skier changed to Skier.
0049-1683	Southwestern Journal of Social Education†
0049-1691	S P R P C Reports changed to Omnibus (Pittsburgh).
0049-1705	Sou'wester
0049-1713	Soviet Analyst
0049-173X	Soviet Journal of Developmental Biology
0049-1748	Soviet Journal of Quantum Electronics
0049-1756	Soviet Power Engineering†
0049-1764	Soviet Progress in Polyurethanes†
0049-1772	Sower changed to Sower.
0049-1780	Space Adventures†
0049-1802	Spanish Today
0049-1810	Spastics News changed to Disability Now.
0049-1829	Spear†
0049-1837	Special Education Newsletter†
0049-1845	Special Interest Autos
0049-1861	Spektrum see 0170-2971
0049-187X	Spoke Wheels†
0049-1888	Spokesman
0049-190X	Sport Heroes changed to Hockey Illustrated.
0049-1926	Sport und Mode
0049-1934	Sporting Investor Method Magazine†
0049-1942	Sporting Press
0049-1950	Sporting Start
0049-1985	Sports Merchandiser see 0890-8745
0049-1993	Sportshandleren changed to Sport.
0049-2000	Spotlight (Bath)
0049-2019	Sprachpflege changed to Sprachpflege and Sprachkultur.
0049-2027	Squadron†
0049-2035	Stagione delle Arti, del Libro, e del Turismo†
0049-2051	Stampa Sud
0049-206X	Standard-Bearer (New York)†
0049-2078	Standpunkte und Dokumente
0049-2108	Stanford University Campus Report
0049-2116	Star (Carville)†
0049-2140	State of the Nation†
0049-2159	State Supplies
0049-2167	Statement of the Assets and Liabilities of the Chartered Banks of Canada†
0049-2175	Statistical Indicators in E C A F E Countries see 0252-4457
0049-2183	Switzerland. Directorate General of Customs. Monthly Statistics
0049-2205	Steel Construction
0049-2213	Steel Pipe News†
0049-2221	Steroidologica see 0301-0163
0049-223X	Der Steuerberater
0049-2248	Sti og Varde
0049-2272	Stock Car
0049-2280	Stockowners' Digest
0049-2329	Street Chopper changed to Custom Cycle.
0049-2337	Street Level†
0049-2345	Strobet
0049-2353	Stromata
0049-2361	Studi e Problemi di Critica Testuale
0049-237X	Studies in Logic and the Foundations of Mathematics

ISSN INDEX

ISSN	Title
0049-2388	University of Illinois. Department of Linguistics. Working Papers *changed to* Studies in the Linguistic Sciences.
0049-2396	Studii si Cercetari de Biochimie
0049-2418	Sub-Normal Children's Welfare Association. Welfare News *changed to* Challenge Advocate.
0049-2426	Sub-Stance
0049-2434	S F M A Bulletin *changed to* F M A Bulletin.
0049-2442	Success (Peterborough)†
0049-2450	Sud
0049-2469	Sudan Engineering Society. Journal
0049-2531	Sundet Rundt
0049-254X	Bulletin of Sung-Yuan Studies *changed to* Journal of Sung-Yuan Studies.
0049-2558	Sunstone Review (Santa Fe)†
0049-2566	Suomen Invalidi *see* 0356-7249
0049-2574	Super-8 Filmaker *see* 0276-3494
0049-2590	Supermarket and Retailer
0049-2612	Supreme Court Researcher†
0049-2620	Sur les Sentiers de l'Ecole Active†
0049-2639	Surface Wave Abstracts
0049-2647	Surgelation
0049-2655	Survie de l'Ame Humaine *see* 0151-4016
0049-2663	Svensk Idrott
0049-2671	Svensk Skidsport
0049-268X	Svensk Socialvardstidning *see* 0346-5365
0049-2698	Svensk Ishockeymagasin *see* 0345-4347
0049-2701	Swedish Journal of Agricultural Research
0049-271X	Swinton Journal
0049-2728	Swiss Canadian News
0049-2736	Syndicats de Roumanie†
0049-2744	Syndicats Vietnamiens
0049-2752	Synergist†
0049-2787	Terveystyo *see* 0356-3081
0049-2795	Systems/Stelsels *changed to* Computer Systems in S.A.
0049-2817	Taamuli
0049-2825	Die Tabak Zeitung
0049-2833	Tactile†
0049-2868	Take Over
0049-2876	Talent News and Views *changed to* Whitmark Magazine.
0049-2884	Taliesin
0049-2906	Talk
0049-2914	Tallow Light†
0049-2922	Tambor
0049-2930	Tamkang Journal of Mathematics
0049-2949	Tamkang Review
0049-2957	Tangley Oaks Reading Guide†
0049-2973	Tanzania. Bureau of Statistics. Employment and Earnings *changed to* Tanzania. Bureau of Statistics. Survey of Employment.
0049-2981	Tanzania Police Journal
0049-3007	Tasmanian Association for the Teaching of English. Journal *see* 0311-1784
0049-3015	Tasmanian Fisheries Research
0049-3023	Tasmanian Hotel Review†
0049-304X	Taxi
0049-3058	Taxi Drivers Voice†
0049-3066	Tchad et Culture
0049-3074	Teacher *changed to* M T A Association A E M.
0049-3082	Teacher in Wales†
0049-3090	Teacher and Librarian
0049-3112	Teacher Today†
0049-3139	Teachers World *see* 0309-3484
0049-3147	Teaching of English
0049-3155	Technical Communication
0049-3171	Technicka Knihovna *see* 0862-9382
0049-3198	Technology Mart†
0049-3201	I I T Tecnologia†
0049-3228	Teen's Start
0049-3252	Tele Presse
0049-3287	Telecine†
0049-3295	Teleguide†
0049-3317	Television Sponsors Directory
0049-3325	TeleVizier
0049-3333	Temas de Orientacion Agropecuaria
0049-335X	Tempo
0049-3368	Tempus†
0049-3376	Tenants Outlook†
0049-3392	Tennessee Parent - Teacher *changed to* Tennessee Parent - Teacher Bulletin.
0049-3406	Tennessee School Board Bulletin
0049-3422	Tennessee Vo-Tech News†
0049-3430	Tent h†
0049-3449	Teologia y Vida
0049-3473	Terre Africaine
0049-3481	Teton
0049-349X	Texas Agricultural Progress†
0049-3503	Texas Dental Assistants Association. Bulletin *changed to* Texas Dental Assistants Association. Bulletin.
0049-3511	Texas Farm and Ranch News
0049-352X	Texas Metro†
0049-3538	C R W R News *see* 0894-511X
0049-3546	Textil
0049-3554	Textile Asia
0049-3562	Textile Labour - Canadian Edition *see* 0271-5848
0049-3589	Thai Journal of Agricultural Science
0049-3597	Theatre Enfance et Jeunesse
0049-3600	Theatre Quarterly *see* 0266-464X
0049-3619	Theatre-Quebec†
0049-3635	Theologia
0049-3643	Theologia Practica
0049-3651	Theological Times
0049-366X	Theologie und Glaube
0049-3686	Theoria to Theory†
0049-3694	Theosophy in Australia
0049-3708	Theosophy in New Zealand
0049-3716	Therapeutica Nova *changed to* Probatum Est.
0049-3724	Thin-Layer Chromatography Abstracts
0049-3740	Third World Reports
0049-3759	This Fortnight in Pakistan†
0049-3767	This Is Calgary *changed to* Calgary.
0049-3783	This Week†
0049-3805	Thomas
0049-3813	T P S Bulletin *changed to* T P S Bulletin.
0049-3821	Thoroughbred of California
0049-3848	Thrombosis Research
0049-3856	Sygeplejersken
0049-3864	Tieraerztliche Umschau
0049-3880	Tijdschrift voor Bejaarden-, Kraam- en Ziekenverzorging *changed to* Tijdschrift voor Verzorgenden.
0049-3899	Tijdschrift voor Gastro-Enterologie†
0049-3910	Time Out
0049-3929	Times Higher Education Supplement
0049-3937	Tips
0049-3945	Tobacco International
0049-3953	Tobacco Review†
0049-3961	Tobakk - Frukt - Sjokolade
0049-397X	Tocher
0049-3988	Today in Mining†
0049-4003	Today's Girl†
0049-402X	Tohoku Regional Fisheries Research Laboratory. Bulletin
0049-4038	Toike Oike
0049-4046	Tokyo Book Development Centre. Newsletter *changed to* Asian - Pacific Book Development.
0049-4054	Freshwater Fisheries Research Laboratory, Tokyo. Bulletin *see* 0389-5858
0049-4062	Toledo Museum News†
0049-4070	Tomorrow's Newspaper†
0049-4089	Tonnage Club Farm News†
0049-4100	Top Management Abstracts
0049-4119	Top of the News with Fulton Lewis†
0049-4127	Topic (Washington)
0049-4135	Topical Stamp Handbooks
0049-4143	Torax
0049-416X	Torch *changed to* Torchlight.
0049-4178	Torch of Homoeopathy†
0049-4186	Toronto Jewish Press
0049-4194	Toronto Life
0049-4216	Toronto Stock Exchange Review
0049-4224	Toronto Symphony News *changed to* Toronto Symphony Magazine.
0049-4232	Toronto Vegetarian Association. Newsletter *see* 0834-3543
0049-4240	Torontoer Zeitung
0049-4283	Touristik Aktuell
0049-4291	Town and Countryside†
0049-4313	T P I C News *see* 0708-5397
0049-4321	Trade and Commerce
0049-433X	Trade Unions International of Workers in Commerce. Bulletin
0049-4348	Trade Winds from Japan†
0049-4356	Traedgaardsnytt
0049-4372	Tramway Museum Society. Journal
0049-4380	Trans Tasman
0049-4402	Transit News†
0049-4410	Transit - Times (Oakland)
0049-4429	Transition
0049-4445	Transition *changed to* Perspective (Boston).
0049-4461	Transport
0049-4488	Transportation
0049-4496	Transportation and Distribution Management†
0049-450X	Transportation Law Journal
0049-4518	Transportation Safety Association of Ontario. Bulletin
0049-4526	Transportation Safety Association of Ontario. Drivers' News Letter
0049-4542	Travel and Camera *see* 0041-2007
0049-4577	Travel News *see* 0041-2082
0049-4585	TravLtips Freighter Bulletin *see* 0162-9816
0049-4593	Treasure
0049-4623	Trend
0049-4631	Tribuna Farmaceutica
0049-464X	Tribuna Italiana
0049-4658	Sackville Tribune-Post
0049-4666	Tribune Psychique
0049-4674	Tribune Socialiste†
0049-4682	Revista Tricontinental
0049-4690	Trident
0049-4704	Universita degli Studi di Trieste. Istituto di Matematica. Rendi Conti. *changed to* Universita degli Studi di Trieste. Dipartimento di Scienze Matematiche. Rendiconti.
0049-4712	Trinitarian Bible Society. Quarterly Record
0049-4720	Tripura Review†
0049-4739	Troisieme Civilisation
0049-4755	Tropical Doctor
0049-4763	Tropical Grasslands
0049-477X	Truck Trends
0049-4801	Tundra Times
0049-481X	Tungsten News†
0049-4828	Tungsten Statistics
0049-4836	Tupart Monthly Reports on the Underground Press†
0049-4844	Turkish Bulletin of Hygiene and Experimental Biology
0049-4852	Turkiye Muhendislik Haberleri
0049-4887	Tvaettnytt *changed to* Rent.
0049-4917	Two Tone
0049-4925	Two-Year College Mathematics Journal *see* 0746-8342
0049-4933	Tydskrif vir Volkskunde en Volkstaal
0049-495X	Typog†
0049-4968	New York Typographical Union Number Six. Bulletin
0049-4976	U F O - Nyt
0049-4984	U N I C E F Information Bulletin†
0049-500X	Ubiquet
0049-5026	Uganda Schools Newsletter
0049-5034	Ugens Politik†
0049-5042	Uhrenfachgeschaeft
0049-5069	Uj Konyvek
0049-5107	Ulster Tatler
0049-5123	Umeni
0049-5131	Umweltschutz
0049-514X	Unabashed Librarian
0049-5166	U E C A Publication *changed to* E C A Publication.
0049-5174	Underground Lamp Post
0049-5190	Une Semaine de Paris-Pariscope
0049-5204	Unesco. Centro de Documentacion Cultural, Havana. Informaciones Trimestrales
0049-5212	Unesco. Regional Centre for Book Development in Asia, Karachi. Newsletter *changed to* Asia Pacific Book News.
0049-5220	Unidad Latina†
0049-5239	Unifier†
0049-528X	Union Herald
0049-5298	Manhattan-Bronx Postal Union. Union Mail *changed to* New York Metro Area Postal Union. Union Mail.
0049-5301	Union Research Service†
0049-531X	Unitarian
0049-5328	U C O News *changed to* Co-Op Cornerstone.
0049-5344	United Florists News *changed to* United Flowers-by-Wire Canada Journal.
0049-5379	U N I D O Documents Checklist†
0049-5387	U N I D O Newsletter
0049-5433	United Reformed Church History Society. Journal
0049-5441	United Senior Citizens of Ontario. Bulletin *see* 0382-0068
0049-5468	B N D D Bulletin *see* 0098-3470
0049-5484	U.S. National Clearinghouse for Poison Control Centers. Bulletin†
0049-5506	Universe
0049-5514	Universita Karlova. Fakulta Vseobecneho Lekarstvi. Pobocka v Hradci Kralove. Sbornik Vedeckych Praci
0049-5522	Universita Karlova. Fakulta Vseobecneho Lekarstvi. Pobocka v Hradci Kralove. Sbornik Vedeckych Praci: Supplementum
0049-5530	Universitas
0049-5557	Unmuzzled Ox
0049-5581	Unser Kleeblatt *changed to* Fragezeichen.
0049-559X	Unspeakable Visions of the Individual†
0049-562X	Urania†
0049-5638	Urban Affairs Today†
0049-5654	Urban Data Service Report *see* 0739-6279
0049-5662	Urban Life and Culture *see* 0891-2416
0049-5689	Urban Rights†
0049-5697	Urbat *see* 0241-6794
0049-5700	Urethane Plastics and Products
0049-5719	Urogallot
0049-5735	Utbildningstidningen
0049-576X	V E News *see* 0318-0867
0049-5778	V E 6
0049-5794	Valeurs Actuelles
0049-5808	Valiseesti
0049-5816	Vancouver Calendar Magazine
0049-5824	Vancouver Numismatic Society. News Bulletin
0049-5832	Vancouver Stock Exchange Review
0049-5867	Vaar Industri†
0049-5883	Vasama
0049-5891	Vasculum
0049-5905	Vegetarian Courier
0049-5913	Velocidad
0049-5921	Verbindungstechnik†
0049-5948	Verfahrenstechnik *see* 0255-2701
0049-5956	Vermont Libraries†
0049-5964	Vern og Velferd *see* 0332-9127
0049-5972	La Vernice†
0049-5980	Vers la Vie Nouvelle
0049-5999	Der Versandhausberater
0049-6006	Versicherungskaufmann
0049-6014	Versicherungsvermittlung
0049-6022	Vertical
0049-6030	Vesey Street Letter *changed to* N.Y. County Lawyer.
0049-6057	Die Veterinaermedizin†
0049-6065	Veterinary Doctor and Veterinary Digest†
0049-6073	Vibration
0049-6081	Vibrations *changed to* Preview (Tempe).
0049-609X	Vickers News†
0049-6103	Victoria. Department of Agriculture. Dairyfarming Digest†

ISSN INDEX 5485

0049-6111 Victoria, Australia. Education Department. Curriculum and Research Bulletin†
0049-6138 Victorian Computer Bulletin *changed to* A C S Victorian Bulletin.
0049-6146 Victorian Horticulture Digest†
0049-6154 V I E R Bulletin
0049-6162 Australia. Bureau of Statistics. Victorian Office. Victorian Monthly Statistical Review *see* 0158-202X
0049-6170 Victorian Municipal Directory
0049-6189 Victorian Periodicals Newsletter *see* 0709-4698
0049-6197 Vic Rail News *see* 0814-7078
0049-6200 Victorian Tobacco Grower†
0049-6227 Vida Nostra *changed to* Vida Nostra Revolum.
0049-6278 Vie du Rail Outremer *changed to* Le Rail.
0049-6286 Vie Mutualiste
0049-6294 Vie Publique
0049-6308 Viehhandel *changed to* Oesterreichische Fleischer-Zeitung.
0049-6316 Vieilles Maisons Francaises
0049-6340 Vietnam Digest
0049-6359 Vietnam Economic Report†
0049-6367 Vietnam: Yesterday and Today†
0049-6375 Vietnam Youth
0049-6383 View from Ottawa *see* 0702-8210
0049-6405 Viewpoint†
0049-6421 Vigilante *changed to* Hotel and Catering.
0049-643X Vigneron Champenois
0049-6448 Viking
0049-6464 V I N A Quarterly
0049-6472 Virginia Dental Journal
0049-6480 Virginia Gazette
0049-6499 Virginia Researcher†
0049-6510 Vision Index†
0049-6529 Visite†
0049-6537 Visor
0049-6545 Vista Femenina Centroamericana
0049-657X Vivre†
0049-660X Vivres-Voeding *changed to* Federation Belge des Enterprises de Distribution. Courrier Hebdomadaire.
0049-6618 V F I Information Bulletin†
0049-6626 Voce dell'Africa†
0049-6650 Vogelwarte
0049-6669 Voice (Grandville)
0049-6677 Voix de la Construction†
0049-6685 Voix de la Resistance
0049-6693 Voix des Parents
0049-6707 Voix du Retraite
0049-6715 Volare Necesse Est
0049-6723 Volkswagen Greats *changed to* European Car.
0049-6731 Volley Kroniek *see* 0167-0247
0049-674X Volume Retail Merchandising†
0049-6804 Vrachebnoe Delo
0049-6812 Vrije Pers†
0049-6820 Wirtschaft und Technik im Transport *changed to* Foerdertechnik.
0049-6847 A Wake Newslitter†
0049-6871 Wallonie Art et Histoire†
0049-688X War Cry
0049-6898 War Cry
0049-6901 Warrior
0049-691X Washington International Business Report
0049-6928 Washington Researcher†
0049-6952 Washington Wildlife†
0049-6979 Water, Air and Soil Pollution
0049-6987 Federation Highlights
0049-6995 Water Rights and Quality News and Views *changed to* California Waterscape.
0049-7002 Water Skier
0049-7010 Water Talk†
0049-7037 Wayne Engineer
0049-7045 Wealth of Nations
0049-7061 Weekly Nation
0049-707X Weekly Unity†
0049-7088 Weewish Tree†
0049-710X Weimaraner *see* 0162-315X
0049-7126 Weltbild
0049-7134 Weltgeschehen
0049-7142 Werk und Leben *changed to* Magazin fuer Mitarbeiter - Werk und Leben.
0049-7150 Werk und Zeit
0049-7169 Wertpapier
0049-7177 West†
0049-7185 West Australian Gardener
0049-7193 West Bengal
0049-7215 West Coast Poetry Review†
0049-7223 West End
0049-7231 West Indian Sportsman
0049-724X West Texas Livestock Weekly *see* 0162-5047
0049-7258 West Virginia Economic Indicators†
0049-7266 Westchester Historian
0049-7274 Westchester Law Journal
0049-7282 Western Association of Map Libraries. Information Bulletin
0049-7312 Western Australia. Education Department. Education Circular *changed to* Western Australia. Ministry of Education. Education Circular.
0049-7320 Western Australia. Forest Department. Forest Focus *see* 0815-4465
0049-7347 Western Australian Institute of Technology Gazette†
0049-7371 Western Canadian Lumber Worker
0049-7398 Western Floors
0049-741X Western Cleaner and Launderer
0049-7436 W I D News
0049-7444 Western Living
0049-7460 Western Ontario Farmer *changed to* Ontario Farmer (Western Edition).
0049-7479 Western Outdoor News
0049-7487 Western Outfitter†
0049-7495 Western Potter†
0049-7517 Western Temperance Herald *changed to* The Herald.
0049-7525 Western Weekly Reports
0049-7533 What's New†
0049-7541 Wheel
0049-755X The Wheel Extended
0049-7568 Wheelchair Competitor *changed to* Achievement.
0049-7584 White Pelican
0049-7592 Whooper *changed to* S W F News.
0049-7614 Widening Horizons
0049-7622 Wiesbadener Leben
0049-7630 Wilcox Report *changed to* Wilcox Report Newsletter.
0049-7649 Wilmington Journal
0049-7657 Wind Rose†
0049-7673 Window†
0049-7681 Windsor Sportsmen's News
0049-7703 Wirtschaft Zwischen Nord- und Ostsee
0049-7711 Das Wirtschaftseigene Futter
0049-772X W A V A Dispatch†
0049-7746 Wisconsin Researcher†
0049-7754 Witches International Craft Associates. W I C A Newsletter
0049-7762 Wloptoonakun†
0049-7770 Woman Activist
0049-7797 Women and Film†
0049-7800 Women in Kenya†
0049-7819 Women in Struggle†
0049-7827 Women Speaking†
0049-7835 Women Studies Abstracts
0049-7843 Women's Army Corps Journal†
0049-786X Womyn's Press
0049-7878 Women's Studies (New York)
0049-7886 Wood Duck
0049-7908 Wood Products Industry Abstracts Bulletin *see* 0360-3083
0049-7916 Wood Research
0049-7924 Wood World†
0049-7940 Woodworkers and Painters Journal *see* 0042-5842
0049-7959 Word and Way
0049-7967 Word Processing Report *changed to* Office Automation Report.
0049-7975 Workers Action
0049-8017 World Agricultural Report†
0049-8025 World Animal Review†
0049-8033 W A Y Forum
0049-805X World Ecology Two Thousand†
0049-8068 W F P A News *see* 0254-3923
0049-8076 W F D Y News
0049-8084 World Food Programme News *see* 1010-9099
0049-8092 World Future Society Bulletin *see* 8755-3317
0049-8106 World Gift Review Monthly Newsletter
0049-8114 Weekly Epidemiological Record
0049-8122 World Medical Journal
0049-8130 World Peace News
0049-8149 World Sugar News
0049-8157 World Tanker Fleet Review
0049-8165 World Tribune
0049-8211 Writing Published *see* 0957-3577
0049-822X Wyoming Valley Motorist *changed to* Valley Motorist.
0049-8238 X-Ray on Current Affairs in Southern Africa
0049-8246 X R S - X-Ray Spectrometry
0049-8254 Xenobiotica
0049-8262 Xi Psi Phi Quarterly
0049-8289 Yatri
0049-8319 Yoga Life International†
0049-8327 Yoga Quarterly Review
0049-8335 Yokohama Plant Protection News
0049-8343 Yout†
0049-8351 Young Age
0049-836X Young Alliance†
0049-8432 Your Region in Action *changed to* Your Region.
0049-8440 Youth Action†
0049-8459 Youth Mirror
0049-8467 Youth Report *see* 0160-9696
0049-8475 Yrke
0049-8483 Yugoslavia
0049-8505 Zahir
0049-8513 Zaire - Afrique
0049-8521 Zambia Farmer†
0049-853X Zambia Library Association. Journal
0049-8572 Zdravotnicka Pracovnice
0049-8580 Zeitschrift fuer Analytische Psychologie und ihre Grenzgebiete *see* 0301-3006
0049-8599 Zeitschrift fuer Auslaendische Landwirtschaft
0049-8602 Zeitschrift fuer Bewaesserungswirtschaft
0049-8610 Zeitschrift fuer die Gesamte Hygiene und Ihre Grenzgebiete†
0049-8629 Zeitschrift fuer Eigenheimfreunde *changed to* Domus Magazin.
0049-8637 Zeitschrift fuer Entwicklungspsychologie und Paedagogische Psychologie
0049-8645 Zeitschrift fuer Lateinamerika Wien
0049-8653 LiLi
0049-8661 Zeitschrift fuer Romanische Philologie
0049-867X Zeitschrift fuer Sozialpsychologie
0049-8688 Zeitschrift fuer Werkstofftechnik *see* 0933-5137
0049-8696 Zentralblatt fuer Pharmazie, Pharmakotherapie und Laboratoriumsdiagnostik†
0049-8718 Z P G National Reporter *see* 0199-0071
0049-8750 Zonneland
0049-8769 Zoological Society of India. Journal
0049-8777 Zootecnia e Veterinaria *see* 0020-0735
0049-8785 Zuidafrikaanse Koerier†
0052-2678 World Council of Young Men's Service Clubs. Minutes of the General Meeting *changed to* World Council of Service Clubs. Minutes of the General Meeting.
0065-0005 A B Bookman's Yearbook
0065-0013 A B C British Columbia Lumber Trade Directory and Year Book†
0065-003X A B C Europ Production - Europex
0065-0048 A B C of Book Trade†
0065-0072 Ag Engineers Notebook
0065-0099 Voeikov Main Geophysical Observatory. Leningrad. Results of Ground Observations of Atmospheric Electricity. The World Network. Additional Issue
0065-0102 A V E in Japan
0065-0129 A.W. Mellon Lectures in the Fine Arts
0065-0137 Aachener Geschichtsverein. Zeitschrift
0065-0145 Dansk Skolehistorie. Aarbog *changed to* Uddannelshistorie. Selskabet for Dansk Skolehistorie. Aarbog.
0065-017X Aarhus Universitet. Matematisk Institut. Lecture Notes Series
0065-0188 Aarhus Universitet. Matematisk Institut. Various Publications Series
0065-0196 Aarsbok foer Skolan
0065-020X Aarsbok foer Sveriges Kommuner
0065-0218 Norges Landbrukshoegskole. Institutt for Bygningsteknikk. Byggekostnadsindeks for Driftsbygninger i Jordbruket. Prisutviklingen†
0065-0226 Norges Landbrukshoegskole. Institutt for Bygningsteknikk. Aarsmelding†
0065-0234 Norges Landbrukshoegskole. Institutt for Bygningsteknikk. Melding†
0065-0242 Norges Landbrukshoegskole. Institutt for Jordskifte og Eiendomsutforming. Melding *see* 0801-2334
0065-0269 Hong Kong. Fisheries Research Station. Bulletin†
0065-0277 University of Aberdeen. Department of Forestry. Economic Survey of Private Forestry†
0065-0285 Aberystwyth Memoranda in Agricultural, Applied and Biometeorology†
0065-0293 Wales. National Library. Handlist of Manuscripts in the National Library of Wales†
0065-0315 Abhandlungen Moderner Medizin†
0065-0323 Abhandlungen und Materialen zur Publizistik
0065-0358 Abhandlungen zur Handels- und Sozialgeschichte
0065-0366 Abhandlungen zur Philosophie, Psychologie und Paedagogik
0065-0374 About Zambia†
0065-0382 Abr-Nahrain
0065-0390 Abr-Nahrain. Supplements†
0065-0412 Absorption Spectra in the Ultraviolet and Visible Region†
0065-0420 Abstracts of Belgian Geology and Physical Geography†
0065-0439 Abstracts of Gothenburg Dissertations in Science†
0065-0447 Academia Campinense de Letras. Publicacoes
0065-0455 Academia Espanola, Madrid. Anejos del Boletin
0065-0463 Academia Guatemalteca de Estudios Genealogicos, Heraldicos e Historicos. Revista
0065-0471 Academia Hondurena de la Lengua. Boletin
0065-048X Institutul de Istorie si Arheologie - Cluj-Napoca. Anuarul *changed to* Institutul de Arheologie - Cluj-Napoca. Anuarul.
0065-0498 Institut de Speologie Emil Racovitza. Travaux
0065-0501 Academia Scientiarum Fennica. Proceedings - Sitzungsberichte *see* 0356-6927
0065-051X Academic Underachiever†
0065-0544 Academie des Inscriptions et Belles-Lettres. Etudes et Commentaires
0065-0552 Academie des Sciences. Annuaire
0065-0560 Academie des Sciences. Index Biographique des Membres et Correspondants
0065-0579 Academie des Sports, Paris. Annuaire
0065-0587 Academie Francaise. Annuaire
0065-0595 Academie Royale de Medecine de Belgique. Memoires. *see* 0377-8231
0065-0609 Academie Royale des Sciences, des Lettres et des Beaux Arts de Belgique. Index Biographique des Membres, Correspondants et Associes
0065-0625 Academy for Educational Development. Academy Papers†
0065-0633 Academy of American Franciscan History. Documentary Series

ISSN

5486 ISSN INDEX

0065-0641 Academy of American Franciscan History. Monograph Series

0065-065X Academy of American Franciscan History. Propaganda Fide Series

0065-0668 Academy of Management. Proceedings

0065-0676 A N P H I Papers

0065-0684 Academy of Political Science. Proceedings

0065-0692 Academy of the Hebrew Language. Specialized Dictionaries

0065-0714 Accademia Musicale Chigiana. Quaderni *see* 0069-3391

0065-0722 Accademia dei Fisiocritici, Siena. Sezione Medico-Fisica *see* 0390-7783

0065-0730 Accademia Etrusca di Cortona. Annuario

0065-0757 Accademia Nazionale Italiana di Entomologia. Rendiconti

0065-0765 Accademia Patavina di Scienze Lettere ed Arti. Collana Accademica

0065-0781 Accademia Toscana di Scienze e Lettere La Colombaria. Studi

0065-079X Accepted Dental Therapeutics†

0065-082X Accidents in North American Mountaineering

0065-0846 Accounting Research Studies†

0065-0862 Accredited Institutions of Higher Education *see* 0270-1715

0065-0870 Acoustical Holography *changed to* Acoustical Imaging.

0065-0889 Acronyms and Initialisms Dictionary *see* 0270-4404

0065-0897 Acta Academiae Regiae Gustavi Adolphi

0065-0900 Acta Ad Archaeologiam et Artium Historiam Pertinentia (Monograph)

0065-0919 Acta Agraria et Silvestria. Series Agraria

0065-0927 Acta Agraria et Silvestria. Seria Lesna *see* 0860-4053

0065-0935 Acta Agraria et Silvestria. Series Zootechnica

0065-0943 Acta Agriculturae Scandinavica. Supplementum *issued with* 0001-5121

0065-0951 Acta Agrobotanica

0065-096X Acta Allergologica. Supplementum *see* 0108-1675

0065-0986 Acta Archaeologica Lodziensia

0065-0994 Acta Archaelogica Lundensia: Monographs of Lunds Universitets Historiska Museum. Series in 8

0065-1001 Acta Archaelogica Lundensia: Monographs of Lunds Universitets Historiska Museum. Series in 4

0065-101X Acta Archaeologica

0065-1028 Acta Arctica

0065-1036 Acta Arithmetica

0065-1044 Acta Baltico - Slavica

0065-1052 Acta Bernensia: Beitraege zur Praehistorischen, Klassischen und Juengeren Archaeologie

0065-1060 Acta Bibliothecae Regiae Stockholmiensis

0065-1079 Acta Bibliothecae Universitatis Gothoburgensis

0065-1095 Acta Biologica Hellenica *see* 0750-7321

0065-1109 Acta Borealia A. Scientia†

0065-1133 Acta Chemica Scandinavica. Supplementum†

0065-1141 Acta Classica

0065-115X Acta Concilium Ophthalmologicum

0065-1168 Acta Criminologica *see* 0316-0041

0065-1176 Acta Dermatologica

0065-1184 Acta Embryologiae Experimentalis *changed to* Animal Biology.

0065-1192 Acta Endocrinologica Panamericana

0065-1206 Acta Facultatis Medicae Fluminensis

0065-1214 Medicinska Misla

0065-1222 Acta Geobotanica Barcinonensia *see* 0210-7597

0065-1230 Acta Geographica†

0065-1249 Acta Geographica Lodziensia

0065-1257 Acta Geographica Lovaniensia

0065-1265 Acta Geologica Taiwanica

0065-1273 Acta Germanica

0065-1281 Acta Histochemica

0065-1303 Acta Historica

0065-1311 Acta Historica Scientiarum Naturalium et Medicinalium

0065-132X Acta Hydrobiologica

0065-1338 Acta Hydrophysica

0065-1346 Acta Juridica

0065-1362 Acta Leidensia†

0065-1370 Acta Manilana

0065-1389 Acta Medicae Historiae Patavina

0065-1397 Acta Medicinae Legalis et Socialis

0065-1400 Acta Neurobiologiae Experimentalis

0065-1419 Acta Neurochirurgica. Supplement *see* 0001-6268

0065-1427 Acta Neurologica Scandinavica. Supplementum

0065-1435 Acta Neuropathologica. Supplement

0065-1443 Acta Nuntiaturae Gallicae

0065-1451 Acta Ophthalmologica. Supplementum

0065-146X Acta Pacis Westphalicae

0065-1478 Acta Parasitologica Polonica

0065-1508 Acta Pharmacologica et Toxicologica. Supplementum *see* 0901-9936

0065-1516 Acta Philologica

0065-1524 Acta Philologica

0065-1532 Acta Philologica Aenipontana

0065-1540 Acta Philosophica et Theologica

0065-1559 Acta Physica Austriaca. Supplement

0065-1567 Acta Phytomedica

0065-1575 Acta Phytotaxonomica Barcinonensia†

0065-1583 Acta Protozoologica

0065-1591 Acta Psychiatrica Scandinavica. Supplementum

0065-1605 Acta Psychologica - Gothoburgensia†

0065-1613 Acta Psychologica Taiwanica *see* 1013-9656

0065-1621 Acta Radiobotanica et Genetica

0065-1656 Acta Scientiarum Socialium

0065-1672 Acta Theologica Danica

0065-1699 Acta Veterinaria Scandinavica. Supplementum

0065-1702 Acta Visbyensia

0065-1710 Acta Zoologica Cracoviensia

0065-1729 Acta Zoologica Lilloana

0065-1737 Acta Zoologica Mexicana†

0065-1753 Action in Pharmacy†

0065-177X Action Universitaire

0065-1796 Actrascope *see* 0315-484X

0065-180X Actua. Special Enfants

0065-1818 Actualite Rhumatologique Presentee au Praticien

0065-1826 Actualites Endocrinologiques†

0065-1850 Adan E. Treganza Anthropology Museum. Papers†

0065-1869 Adansonia. Memoires†

0065-1877 Adaptations Series

0065-1885 Addiction Research Foundation of Ontario. Bibliographic Series†

0065-1907 Adelaide. Institute of Medical and Veterinary Science. Annual Report of the Council

0065-1915 Adelaide Law Review

0065-1923 Aden Magazine†

0065-1931 Adhesives Red Book *see* 0001-821X

0065-194X Adlai Stevenson Institute of International Affairs. Annual Report†

0065-1966 Kenya Institute of Administration. Journal†

0065-1974 Administrator

0065-1982 Administrators in Action†

0065-1990 Admission Requirements of American Dental Schools *see* 0091-729X

0065-2008 Adolescent Psychiatry

0065-2024 Zuerl's Adressbuch der Deutschen Luft- und Raumfahrt

0065-2032 Adressbuch fuer den Deutschsprachigen Buchhandel

0065-2067 Advance of Christianity through the Centuries†

0065-2075 Advanced Accountancy Seminar. Proceedings†

0065-2091 Advances in Activation Analysis†

0065-2113 Advances in Agronomy

0065-2121 Advances in Alicyclic Chemistry†

0065-213X Advances in Alicyclic Chemistry. Supplement†

0065-2148 Advances in Analytical Chemistry and Instrumentation†

0065-2156 Advances in Applied Mechanics

0065-2164 Advances in Applied Microbiology

0065-2180 Advances in Astronomy and Astrophysics†

0065-2199 Advances in Atomic and Molecular Physics *changed to* Advances in Atomic, Molecular and Optical Physics.

0065-2210 Advances in Biochemical Engineering *see* 0724-6145

0065-2229 Advances in Biochemical Psychopharmacology

0065-2245 Advances in Biological and Medical Physics†

0065-2253 Advances in Biology of Skin†

0065-2261 Advances in Biomedical Engineering and Medical Physics†

0065-227X Advances in Biophysics

0065-2288 Advances in Blood Grouping†

0065-2296 Advances in Botanical Research

0065-230X Advances in Cancer Research

0065-2318 Advances in Carbohydrate Chemistry and Biochemistry

0065-2326 Advances in Cardiology

0065-2334 Advances in Cardiopulmonary Diseases†

0065-2342 Advances in Catalysis and Related Subjects *see* 0360-0564

0065-2350 Advances in Cell and Molecular Biology†

0065-2377 Advances in Chemical Engineering

0065-2385 Advances in Chemical Physics

0065-2393 Advances in Chemistry Series

0065-2407 Advances in Child Development and Behavior

0065-2415 Advances in Chromatography

0065-2423 Advances in Clinical Chemistry

0065-2431 Advances in Communication Systems†

0065-244X Advances in Comparative Physiology and Biochemistry†

0065-2458 Advances in Computers

0065-2466 Advances in Control Systems *see* 0090-5267

0065-2474 Advances in Corrosion Science and Technology†

0065-2482 Advances in Cryogenic Engineering

0065-2490 Advances in Drug Research

0065-2504 Advances in Ecological Research

0065-2539 Advances in Electronics and Electron Physics

0065-2555 Advances in Engineering

0065-2563 Advances in Environmental Science and Technology†

0065-2571 Advances in Enzyme Regulation

0065-258X Advances in Enzymology and Related Areas of Molecular Biology

0065-2598 Advances in Experimental Medicine and Biology

0065-2601 Advances in Experimental Social Psychology

0065-261X Advances in Fluorine Research and Dental Caries Prevention†

0065-2628 Advances in Food Research *changed to* Advances in Food and Nutrition Research.

0065-2644 Advances in Free Radical Chemistry†

0065-2652 Advances in Gas Chromatography†

0065-2660 Advances in Genetics

0065-2687 Advances in Geophysics

0065-2709 Advances in Gerontological Research†

0065-2717 Advances in Heat Transfer

0065-2725 Advances in Heterocyclic Chemistry

0065-2733 Advances in High Pressure Research†

0065-2741 Advances in High Temperature Chemistry†

0065-275X Advances in Human Genetics

0065-2768 Advances in Hydroscience†

0065-2776 Advances in Immunology

0065-2784 Advances in Information Systems Science†

0065-2792 Advances in Inorganic Chemistry and Radiochemistry

0065-2806 Advances in Insect Physiology

0065-2814 Advances in Instrumentation

0065-2822 Advances in Internal Medicine

0065-2830 Advances in Librarianship

0065-2849 Advances in Lipid Research

0065-2857 Advances in Machine Tool Design and Research *see* 0890-6955

0065-2865 Advances in Macromolecular Chemistry†

0065-2873 Advances in Magnetic Resonance

0065-2881 Advances in Marine Biology

0065-2903 Advances in Metabolic Disorders

0065-2911 Advances in Microbial Physiology

0065-292X Advances in Microbiology of the Sea *see* 0161-8954

0065-2938 Advances in Microcirculation

0065-2946 Advances in Microwaves

0065-2954 Advances in Molten Salt Chemistry

0065-2962 Advances in Morphogenesis†

0065-2970 Advances in Nuclear Physics

0065-2989 Advances in Nuclear Science and Technology

0065-2997 Advances in Obstetrics and Gynaecology *see* 0304-4246

0065-3004 Advances in Ophthalmology *see* 0250-3751

0065-3012 Advances in Optical and Electron Microscopy

0065-3020 Advances in Oral Biology†

0065-3039 Advances in Oral Surgery *changed to* Update in Oral Surgery.

0065-3047 Advances in Organic Chemistry†

0065-3055 Advances in Organometallic Chemistry

0065-3063 Advances in Orthodontics *changed to* Update in Orthodontics.

0065-3071 Advances in Oto-Rhino-Laryngology

0065-308X Advances in Parasitology

0065-3098 Advances in Particle Physics†

0065-3101 Advances in Pediatrics

0065-311X Advances in Pedodontics†

0065-3128 Advances in Periodontics *changed to* Update in Periodontics.

0065-3136 Advances in Pharmaceutical Sciences

0065-3144 Advances in Pharmacology and Chemotherapy *changed to* Advances in Pharmacology.

0065-3152 Advances in Photochemistry

0065-3160 Advances in Physical Organic Chemistry

0065-3187 Advances in Plasma Physics†

0065-3195 Advances in Polymer Science

0065-3217 Advances in Probability *changed to* Advances in Probability and Related Topics.

0065-3225 Advances in Prosthodontics†

0065-3233 Advances in Protein Chemistry

0065-3241 Advances in Psychobiology†

0065-325X Advances in Psychological Assessment†

0065-3268 Advances in Psychosomatic Medicine

0065-3276 Advances in Quantum Chemistry

0065-3284 Advances in Quantum Electronics†

0065-3292 Advances in Radiation Biology

0065-3306 Advances in Radiation Chemistry†

0065-3322 Advances in Reproductive Physiology†

0065-3357 Advances in Solid State Physics†

0065-3365 Advances in Space Science and Technology†

0065-3373 Advances in Space Science and Technology†

0065-339X Advances in Steroid Biochemistry and Pharmacology *changed to* Advances in Steroid Biochemistry and Pharmacology (Year).

0065-3403 Advances in Structure Research by Diffraction Methods†

0065-3411 Advances in Surgery

0065-342X Advances in Teratology *see* 0306-2090

0065-3438 Advances in the Astronautical Sciences

0065-3446 Advances in the Biosciences

0065-3454 Advances in the Study of Behavior

0065-3500 Advances in Tuberculosis Research†

0065-3519 Advances in Veterinary Science and Comparative Medicine

ISSN

0065-3527 Advances in Virus Research
0065-3535 Advances in Water Pollution Research†
0065-3543 Advancing Frontiers of Plant Sciences†
0065-3578 Advertiser's Annual
0065-3586 Ad Guide: An Advertiser's Guide to Scholarly Periodicals *changed to* Advertising and Publicity Resources for Scholarly Books.
0065-3594 Advertising and Press Annual of Africa *changed to* Promadata.
0065-3640 Advertising Statistical Review†
0065-3667 Aeldre Danske Tingboeger
0065-3683 Aeromedical Reviews *changed to* U.S. Air Force. School of Aerospace Medicine. Standard Technical Report Series.
0065-3691 Aeromodeller Annual†
0065-3713 Aeronomica Acta
0065-3721 Aeroports de Paris. Rapport du Conseil d'Administration
0065-373X National Aerospace and Electronics Conference. Record *see* 0547-3578
0065-3756 Aerospace Materials Buyers Guide†
0065-3764 Aerospace Medical Association. Annual Scientific Meeting; Preprints†
0065-3772 Aerospace Safety Buyers Guide†
0065-3780 Revue Aerospatiale
0065-3799 Affaires et Gens d'Affaires
0065-3802 Africa Annual†
0065-3810 Africa Annual
0065-3829 Africa at a Glance: A Quick Reference of Facts and Figures on Africa†
0065-3845 Africa Contemporary Record. Annual Survey and Documents
0065-3853 Africa Institute. Annual Report *changed to* Africa Institute. Chairman's Report.
0065-3861 Africa Institute. Communications†
0065-3896 Africa South of the Sahara (Year)
0065-3918 African Bibliographic Center, Washington, D.C. Biblioresearch Series†
0065-3926 African Bibliographic Center, Washington, D.C. Current Reading List Series†
0065-3934 African Bibliographic Center, Washington D.C. Special Bibliographic Series *see* 0749-2308
0065-3942 African Bibliographic Center, Washington, D.C. Special Bibliographic Series: Labor in Africa†
0065-3985 African Language Studies†
0065-4000 African Literature Today†
0065-4019 African Music
0065-4027 African Regional Trade Union Conference. Report
0065-4043 African Social Security Series *see* 0379-7074
0065-4051 Indiana University. Research Center for the Language Sciences. African Studies *see* 0073-7062
0065-406X African Studies Series
0065-4086 African Wildlife News *see* 0270-0360
0065-4116 Africana Collectanea Series†
0065-4140 Journal of African Studies
0065-4159 Afrika-Studiecentrum. Communications†
0065-4191 Afro-Asian Peoples' Conference. Proceedings
0065-4248 Agence pour la Securite de la Navigation Aerienne en Afrique et a Madagascar. Direction de l'Exploitation Meteorologique. Publications. Serie 1
0065-4256 Agenda de la Quincaillerie
0065-4264 Agenda del Dirigente di Azienda
0065-4272 Agent's and Buyer's Guide *changed to* Shortcut.
0065-4299 Agents and Actions
0065-4337 Agrarian Development Studies
0065-4345 Agrarmarkt-Studien
0065-4353 Agrarpolitik und Marktwesen†
0065-4361 A S G Eingliederung Heimatvertriebener Landwirte auf Vollbauernstellen†
0065-437X Agrarsoziale Gesellschaft. Geschaefts- und Arbeitsbericht
0065-4388 Agrarsoziale Gesellschaft. Rundbriefe *see* 0179-7603
0065-440X Agricultura Espanola en (Year)
0065-4418 North Carolina Agricultural Chemicals Manual
0065-4426 Agricultural Development Bank of Pakistan. Annual Report and Statement of Accounts
0065-4434 Agricultural Economics Bulletin for Africa†
0065-4442 Michigan State University. Agricultural Economics Report
0065-4469 Agricultural Economist
0065-4477 Agricultural Engineers Yearbook of Standards *see* 8755-1187
0065-4485 Agricultural Pesticide Society. Annual Meeting. Proceedings *see* 0227-7980
0065-4493 Agricultural Progress
0065-4507 Great Britain. Institute of Animal Physiology. Report *changed to* Great Britain. Institute of Animal Physiology and Genetics Research. Report.
0065-4515 Agricultural Research Council of Malawi. Annual Report *changed to* Malawi. Department of Agricultural Research. Annual Report.
0065-4523 Agricultural Research Guyana
0065-4531 Agricultural Research Index *changed to* Agricultural Research Centres.
0065-454X Agricultural Society of Nigeria. Proceedings
0065-4558 Agricultural Statistics, England and Wales *see* 0262-2394
0065-4566 Agricultural Statistics of Bangladesh *changed to* Yearbook of Agricultural Statistics of Bangladesh.
0065-4574 Agricultural Statistics of Greece
0065-4582 Agricultural Statistics, Scotland *changed to* Economic Report on Scottish Agriculture.
0065-4604 Cornell Agricultural Waste Management Conference. Proceedings†
0065-4612 U.S. Department of Agriculture. Agriculture Handbook
0065-4639 U.S. Department of Agriculture. Agriculture Information Bulletin
0065-4647 Agro-Ecological Atlas of Cereal Growing in Europe†
0065-4655 Agro-Nouvelles
0065-4663 Agronomy: a Series of Monographs
0065-4671 Agronomy Abstracts
0065-468X Ahmadu Bello University. Centre of Islamic Legal Studies. Journal
0065-4698 Ahmadu Bello University. Department of Geography. Occasional Paper
0065-471X Ahmadu Bello University. Institute for Agricultural Research. Annual Report
0065-4728 Ahmadu Bello University. Institute for Agricultural Research. Soil Survey Bulletin
0065-4744 Ahmadu Bello University. Institute of Administration. Traditional Land Tenure Surveys†
0065-4752 Ahmadu Bello University. Institute of Education. Paper *see* 0189-2916
0065-4760 Ahmadu Bello University. Northern History Research Scheme. Papers *changed to* Ahmadu Bello University. Northern History Research Scheme. Interim Report.
0065-4779 Ahmedabad Textile Industry's Research Association. Proceedings of the Management Conference†
0065-4787 Ailleurs et Demain; Classiques
0065-4809 Air Conditioning, Ventilating and Heating Equipment *changed to* H V A C Red Book of Heating, Ventilating and Air Conditioning Equipment.
0065-4817 Air New Zealand. Annual Report
0065-4841 Air Safety Forum†
0065-485X Air Transport Association of Canada. Annual Report
0065-4876 Aircraft Accident Digest
0065-4892 Aircraft Engines of the World†
0065-4906 A O P A Airport Directory *see* 1056-7704
0065-4914 Airline Guide to Stewardess and Stewards Career *changed to* Official Guide to Flight Attendants Careers.
0065-4949 Universite d'Aix-Marseille I. Centre d'Etudes des Societes Mediterraneennes. Cahiers
0065-4965 Universite d'Aix-Marseille 3. Centre des Hautes Etudes Touristiques. Etudes et Memoires
0065-4973 Universite d'Aix-Marseille I. Faculte des Lettres et Sciences Humaines. Annales†
0065-4981 Universite d'Aix-Marseille I. Centre d'Etudes et de Recherches Helleniques. Publications
0065-499X Universite d'Aix-Marseille. Faculte des Lettres et Sciences Humaines. Travaux et Memoires†
0065-5007 Universite d'Aix-Marseille I. Institut d'Histoire des Pays d'Outre-Mer. Etudes et Documents
0065-5015 Akademie der Wissenschaften der D.D.R. Geodaetisches Institut. Veroeffentlichungen *see* 0514-8790
0065-5023 Zentralinstitut fuer Physik der Erde. Seismologischer Dienst Jena. Seismologische Bulletin†
0065-5066 Akademie der Wissenschaften. Berlin. Jahrbuch *see* 0304-2154
0065-5198 Akademie der Wissenschaften, Berlin. Sektion fuer Vor- und Fruehgeschichte. Schriften *see* 0138-3361
0065-5228 Akademie der Wissenschaften, Berlin. Volkskundliche Veroeffentlichungen *see* 0138-3167
0065-5260 Akademie der Wissenschaften, Berlin. Zentralinstitut fuer Sprachwissenschaft. Schriften *see* 0138-5852
0065-5287 Akademie der Wissenschaften in Goettingen. Nachrichten 1. Philologisch-Historische Klasse
0065-5295 Akademie der Wissenschaften in Goettingen. Nachrichten 2. Mathematisch-Physikalische Klasse
0065-5317 Deutsche Geodaetische Kommission. Veroeffentlichungen: Reihe B. Angewandte Geodaesie
0065-5325 Deutsche Geodaetische Kommission. Veroeffentlichungen: Reihe C. Dissertationen
0065-5333 Deutsche Geodaetische Kommission. Veroeffentlichungen: Reihe D. Tafelwerke
0065-5341 Deutsche Geodaetische Kommission. Veroeffentlichungen: Reihe E. Geschichte und Entwicklung der Geodaesie
0065-535X Oesterreichische Akademie der Wissenschaften, Vienna. Mathematisch-Naturwissenschaftliche Klasse. Anzeiger *see* 0379-0207
0065-5376 Oesterreichische Akademie der Wissenschaften. Praehistorische Kommission. Mitteilungen
0065-5384 Akademie fuer Fuehrungskraefte der Wirtschaft. Taschenbuecher zur Betriebspraxis
0065-5392 Akademie fuer Staatsmedizin, Duesseldorf. Jahrbuch *see* 0172-2131
0065-5511 Koninklijke Nederlandse Akademie van Wetenschappen. Afdeling Letterkunde. Verhandelingen. Nieuwe Reeks
0065-552X Koninklijke Nederlandse Akademie van Wetenschappen. Afdeling Natuurkunde. Verhandelingen. Tweede Reeks
0065-5538 Akademische Vortraege und Abhandlungen
0065-5554 Akiyoshi-dai Science Museum. Bulletin *changed to* Akiyoshidai Kagaku Hakubutsukan Hokoku.
0065-5562 Aktion fuer Kultur und Politik *see* 0002-3760
0065-5589 Aktuelle Probleme in der Chirurgie *changed to* Aktuelle Probleme in Chirurgie und Orthopadie.
0065-5597 Aktuelle Probleme in der Klinischen Biochemie *see* 0300-1725
0065-5600 Aktuelle Probleme in der Psychiatrie, Neurologie, Neurochirurgie†
0065-5619 Aktuellt och Historiskt *see* 0283-8400
0065-5627 Al-Hikma†
0065-5635 Alabama Geological Society. Guidebook for the Annual Field Trip
0065-5643 A P A Newspaper Directory *changed to* Alabama Press Association. Rate and Data Guide.
0065-5686 Selected Sites for Caravanning and Camping in Europe *changed to* Good Camps Guide Europe (Year).
0065-5694 Alaska. Agricultural Statistics Service. Agricultural Statistics
0065-5708 Alaska. Department of Fish and Game. Annual Report†
0065-5724 Alaska. Division of Geological and Geophysical Surveys. Annual Report†
0065-5732 Alaska. Division of Geological and Geophysical Surveys. Geochemical Report†
0065-5759 Alaska. Division of Geological and Geophysical Surveys. Information Circular
0065-5767 Alaska. Division of Geological and Geophysical Surveys. Laboratory Note *changed to* Alaska. Division of Geological and Geophysical Surveys. Report of Investigations.
0065-5775 Alaska. Division of Geological and Geophysical Surveys. Laboratory Report *changed to* Alaska. Division of Geological and Geophysical Surveys. Geologic - Professional Report.
0065-5783 Alaska. Division of Geological and Geophysical Surveys. Miscellaneous Paper†
0065-5805 Alaska. Employment Security Division. Workforce Estimates, by Industry and Area *see* 0362-4196
0065-5813 Alaska Petroleum and Industrial Directory†
0065-5821 Annual Report of the Public Libraries of Alaska†
0065-583X Alaska State Plan for the Construction of Hospitals and Medical Facilities†
0065-5848 Alaska Travel Guide *see* 1054-5034
0065-5864 University of Alaska. Geophysical Institute. Contributions. Series A†
0065-5872 University of Alaska. Geophysical Institute. Contributions. Series B†
0065-5929 University of Alaska. Institute of Marine Science. Technical Report
0065-5937 Institute of Social, Economic and Government Research. Reports *changed to* Institute of Social and Economic Research. Reports.
0065-5945 I S E G R Research Notes *changed to* I S E R Research Notes.
0065-5953 University of Alaska. Institute of Water Resources. Annual Report *changed to* University of Alaska. Institute of Northern Engineering.
0065-597X Alberta. Department of Agriculture. Annual Report *changed to* Alberta Agriculture. Annual Report.
0065-5996 Alberta Poetry Yearbook†
0065-6003 Alberta Society of Petroleum Geologists. Geological Guide *changed to* Canadian Society of Petroleum Geologists. Bulletin.
0065-6046 University of Alberta. Department of Agricultural Economics and Rural Sociology. Research Bulletin *changed to* University of Alberta. Department of Rural Economy. Bulletin.

5488 ISSN INDEX

0065-6062 University of Alberta. Department of Computing Science. Publication *see* 0316-4683
0065-6070 University of Alberta. Faculty of Business Administration and Commerce. Research Studies in Business†
0065-6089 Alberta Writers Speak Overland to the Klondike
0065-6097 Albertan Geographer†
0065-6100 Albrecht von Graefes Archiv fuer Klinische und Experimentelle Ophthalmologie *see* 0721-832X
0065-6119 Alcoholism and Drug Addiction Research Foundation. Annual Report *changed to* Addiction Research Foundation of Ontario. Annual Report.
0065-6127 Alcoy; Fiesta de Moros y Cristianos
0065-6143 Aldrich Entomology Club. Newsletter
0065-6151 Quaderni Ce D R E S
0065-616X Alexander Lectures
0065-6232 Observatoire Astronomique d'Alger. Annales
0065-6240 Algorytmy†
0065-6259 Aligarh Muslim University, Aligarh, India. Department of History. Publication
0065-6267 Alimentation et la Vie *changed to* Alimentation et la Vie - Nouvelle Presentation.
0065-6275 Aliso
0065-6283 All India Crime Prevention Society. Annual Report and Audited Statement of Accounts
0065-6291 All India Government Travellers Bungalows Annual Recorder
0065-6305 All India Leather Directory†
0065-6313 All-Pakistan Income-Tax Reports and Returns and Income-Tax Revenue Statistics†
0065-6321 All Pakistan Women's Association. Annual Report†
0065-633X All-Time Favorite Poetry†
0065-6348 Allam es Jogtudomany Uttoroi†
0065-6364 Allan Hancock Monographs in Marine Biology†
0065-6372 Allergologicum; Transactions of the Collegium Internationale
0065-6410 Allied Artists of America. Exhibition Catalog
0065-6429 Allionia
0065-6461 Almanac of the Pacific *changed to* Thrum's All About Hawaii.
0065-647X Almanac of World Military Power†
0065-650X Almanach du Peuple
0065-6526 Almanach Sceny Polskiej
0065-6542 Alpha Annual†
0065-6569 Alpine Journal
0065-6585 Alt-Thueringen
0065-6593 Altbabylonische Briefe im Umschrift und Uebersetzung
0065-6607 Altdeutsche Textbibliothek. Ergaenzungsreihe
0065-6623 Altech
0065-6631 Naturkindliches Museum "Mauritianum" Altenburg. Abhandlungen und Berichte *see* 0233-173X
0065-6658 Aluminum Standards and Data
0065-6666 Aluminum Statistical Review
0065-6674 Amakusa Marine Biological Laboratory. Contributions†
0065-6682 Amakusa Marine Biological Laboratory. Publications
0065-6690 Amateur Athletic Association. Handbook
0065-6704 Amateur Chamber Music Players. Directory
0065-6712 Percy Thrower's Guide to Modern Gardening *changed to* Amateur Gardening Guide.
0065-6739 Amateur Softball Association of America. Official Guide and Rule Book
0065-6747 Amateur Trapshooting Association. Official Trapshooting Rules
0065-6755 Amazoniana; Limnologia et Oecologia Regionalis Systemae Fluminis Amazonas
0065-6763 America - Problema
0065-6771 America en Cifras†
0065-678X America Votes
0065-6798 American Academy for Jewish Research. Proceedings of the A A J R
0065-6801 American Academy in Rome. Memoirs
0065-681X American Academy in Rome. Papers and Monographs
0065-6836 American Academy of Arts and Letters. Proceedings *see* 0145-8493
0065-6852 American Academy of Child Psychiatry. Journal. Monograph†
0065-6860 American Academy of Environmental Engineers. Roster *changed to* Who's Who in Environmental Engineering.
0065-6879 A A M A Executive *changed to* Medical Administration Executive.
0065-6887 American Academy of Optometry Series†
0065-6909 American Academy of Pediatrics. Committee on Infectious Diseases. Report (Year)
0065-6917 American Academy of Political and Social Science. Monographs†
0065-6925 American Alpine Journal
0065-6933 American Anthropological Association. Annual Report and Directory†
0065-6941 American Anthropologist. Special Publication
0065-6968 American Art Directory
0065-6976 American Assembly (Background Papers and Final Report) *see* 0569-2245
0065-6984 American Association for Conservation Information. Yearbook†
0065-700X A A H P E R Archery-Riding Guide *changed to* N A G W S Guide. Archery-Fencing.
0065-7018 Basketball Guide, with Official Rules and Standards *see* 0362-3254
0065-7026 Field Hockey-Lacrosse Guide *changed to* N A G W S Guide. Field Hockey.
0065-7026 Field Hockey-Lacrosse Guide *changed to* N A G W S Guide. Lacrosse.
0065-7034 Soccer-Speedball Guide *see* 0190-9363
0065-7042 Tennis - Badminton - Squash Guide *see* 0272-863X
0065-7050 N A G W S Guide. Volleyball
0065-7085 American Association for the Advancement of Science. Publications†
0065-7107 American Association of Cereal Chemists. Monograph Series
0065-7115 Standard Methods of Clinical Chemistry†
0065-7123 A A C T E Yearbook†
0065-7158 American Association of Cost Engineers. Transactions of the Annual Meeting
0065-7182 American Association of Equine Practitioners. Proceedings of the Annual Convention
0065-7190 American Association of Foot Specialists. Program Journal *changed to* American College of Foot Specialists. Annual Yearbook.
0065-7204 American Association of Genito-Urinary Surgeons. Transactions
0065-7239 American Association of Community and Junior Colleges. Governmental Affairs Special†
0065-7255 A A L L Publications Series
0065-7263 American Association of Medical Milk Commissions. Methods and Standards for the Production of Certified Milk
0065-7271 American Association of Motor Vehicle Administrators. Annual Conference. Proceedings
0065-728X American Association of Obstetricians and Gynecologists. Transactions
0065-7298 American Association of Pathologists and Bacteriologists. Symposium. Monographs†
0065-731X American Association of Petroleum Geologists. Memoir
0065-7328 A A S A Convention Reporter†
0065-7344 A A S C U Studies *changed to* A A S C U Issues.
0065-7352 American Association of Textile Chemists and Colorists. Products Buyer's Guide *see* 0040-490X
0065-7360 American Association of Theological Schools in the United States and Canada. Bulletin *see* 0362-1472
0065-7379 American Association of Theological Schools in the United States and Canada. Directory *changed to* Association of Theological Schools in the United States and Canada. Directory.
0065-7395 American Association of Workers for the Blind. Proceedings *changed to* American Association of Workers for the Blind. Annual Report.
0065-7417 A A S Microfiche Series
0065-7433 A A S Photo-Bulletin†
0065-7441 American Bankers Association. National Automation Conference. Proceedings *see* 0095-5396
0065-745X American Bantam Association. Yearbook
0065-7468 American Baptist Education Association. Report†
0065-7476 Federal Government Legal Career Opportunities *changed to* Now Hiring.
0065-7492 American Bar Association. Section of Labor-Relations Law. Report *see* 0270-4889
0065-7522 American Bar Association. Standing Committee on Legal Assistance for Servicemen. Occasional Newsletter *see* 1044-8756
0065-7549 American Bar Foundation. Research Contributions†
0065-7565 American Blue Book of Funeral Directors
0065-759X American Book Trade Directory
0065-7603 American Broncho-Esophagological Association. Transactions
0065-7611 American Bureau of Metal Statistics. Year Book *see* 0360-9553
0065-762X American Camellia Yearbook
0065-7638 American Catholic Philosophical Association. Proceedings
0065-7646 American Cement Directory
0065-7654 American Ceramic Society. Special Publications†
0065-7662 American Chamber of Commerce for Brazil. Annual Directory
0065-7670 American Chamber of Commerce in France. Directory
0065-7689 AmCham Morocco
0065-7697 American Chamber of Commerce of Venezuela. Yearbook and Membership Directory *changed to* Venezuelan - American Chamber of Commerce and Industry. Yearbook and Membership Directory.
0065-7700 A C S Laboratory Guide *changed to* Analytical Chemistry. Labguide (Year).
0065-7719 A C S Monographs
0065-7727 American Chemical Society. Abstracts of Papers (at the National Meeting)
0065-7735 American Chemical Society. Abstracts of Papers (at the Regional Meetings)
0065-7743 Annual Reports in Medicinal Chemistry
0065-7778 American Clinical and Climatological Association. Transactions
0065-7786 American College of Apothecaries. Proceedings†
0065-7794 American College of Hospital Administrators. Directory *changed to* American College of Healthcare Executives. Directory.
0065-7832 A C T Monograph Series†
0065-7840 A C T Research Service Report *see* 0569-3993
0065-7875 A C I Manual of Concrete Practice
0065-7883 A C I Monograph†
0065-7891 American Concrete Institute. Special Publication
0065-7905 American Conference of Academic Deans. Proceedings
0065-7913 American Congress on Surveying and Mapping. Papers from the Annual Meetings *see* 0277-2876
0065-793X American Cooperation Yearbook
0065-7948 American Correctional Association. Annual Congress of Correction. Proceedings *changed to* American Correctional Association. The State of Corrections. Proceedings.
0065-7956 State and Federal Correctional Institutions *see* 0190-2555
0065-7964 American Council of Independent Laboratories. Directory
0065-7972 A C L S Annual Report
0065-7980 Accredited Colleges of Pharmacy *changed to* Accredited Professional Programs of Colleges and Schools of Pharmacy.
0065-7999 American Country Life Association. Proceedings of the Annual Conference†
0065-8006 American Crystallographic Association. Transactions
0065-8014 American Culture†
0065-8022 American Dance Therapy Association. Proceedings of the Annual Conference†
0065-8030 Annual Report on Dental Education
0065-8049 Dental Students' Register *see* 0065-8030
0065-8057 American Dental Association. Council on Dental Education. Requirements and Registration Data: State Dental Examining Boards†
0065-8073 American Dental Directory
0065-8081 American Dexter Cattle Association. Herd Book
0065-809X American Doctoral Dissertations
0065-8103 American Drop-Shippers Directory
0065-8111 American Drug Index
0065-8146 American Enterprise Institute for Public Policy Research. Legislative and Special Analyses *changed to* American Enterprise Institute for Public Policy Research. Legislative Analyses.
0065-8154 American Enterprise Institute for Public Policy Research. Long-Range Studies *see* 0732-4308
0065-8162 American Entomological Institute. Memoirs
0065-8170 American Entomological Society. Memoirs
0065-8189 American Ephemeris and Nautical Almanac *changed to* Astronomical Almanac.
0065-8197 American Ethnological Society. Monographs†
0065-8200 American Ethnological Society. Proceedings of Spring Meeting†
0065-8219 American Exploration and Travel
0065-8308 American Film Review *changed to* American Film & Video Review.
0065-8316 American Folk Music Occasional†
0065-8324 American Folklore Society. Bibliographical and Special Series†
0065-8332 American Folklore Society. Memoirs†
0065-8359 American Foundation for the Blind. Annual Report
0065-8367 A F B Research Bulletin *see* 0145-482X
0065-8375 American Foundrymen's Society. Transactions
0065-8391 Gas Utility and Pipeline Industry Projections†
0065-8413 American Geographical Society of New York. Occasional Publication†
0065-8421 American Geographical Society of New York. Research Series†
0065-843X American Geographical Society of New York. Special Publication†
0065-8448 American Geophysical Union. Geophysical Monograph *changed to* American Geophysical Union. Geophysical Monograph Book Series.

ISSN

ISSN INDEX 5489

0065-8456 American Goat Society. Year Book
0065-8480 American Gynecological Society. Transactions of the A G S *changed to* American Gynecological and Obstetrical Society. Transactions of the A G O S.
0065-8499 American Heart Association. Monographs *changed to* American Heart Association. Supplements.
0065-8502 American Heart Association. Scientific Sessions. Abstracts
0065-8510 American Helicopter Society. National Forum. Proceedings *changed to* American Helicopter Society. Annual Forum. Proceedings.
0065-8529 American-Hellenic Chamber of Greece. Business Directory
0065-8537 American - Hellenic Chamber of Commerce. Business Directory. Special Issue
0065-8545 American Histadrut Cultural Exchange Institute. Annual Arden House Conference. Proceedings†
0065-8553 American Histadrut Cultural Exchange Institute. Round Table Pamphlet Series†
0065-8561 American Historical Association. Annual Report
0065-8588 American Home Economics Association. Textiles and Clothing Section. Textile Handbook†
0065-860X American Imago
0065-8618 American Industrial Arts Association. Addresses and Proceedings of the Annual Convention†
0065-8634 American Industrial Arts Association. Yearbook *changed to* Council on Technology Teacher Education. Yearbook.
0065-8642 American Industrial Real Estate Association. Journal†
0065-8669 American Institute for Marxist Studies. Historical Series†
0065-8677 American Institute for Marxist Studies. Monograph Series†
0065-8685 American Institute of Aeronautics and Astronautics. A I A A Los Angeles Section. Monographs†
0065-8693 A I A A Roster
0065-8715 American Institute of Aeronautics and Astronautics. Selected Reprint Series†
0065-8723 A I A Building Construction Legal Citator. Supplement†
0065-874X American Institute of Certified Public Accountants. Division of Federal Taxation. Statements on Responsibilities in Tax Practice†
0065-8758 American Institute of Certified Public Accountants. Committee on Practice Review. Practice Review Bulletin†
0065-8766 American Institute of Certified Public Accountants. Management Advisory Services. Guideline Series†
0065-8774 American Institute of Certified Public Accountants. Practical Accounting and Auditing Problems†
0065-8782 American Institute of Certified Public Accountants. Statements on Auditing Procedure†
0065-8790 A I Ch E Continuing Education Series†
0065-8804 A I Ch E Monograph Series
0065-8812 A I Ch E Symposium Series†
0065-8820 American Institute of Graphic Arts. Journal†
0065-8847 American Institute of Islamic Studies. Bibliographic Series
0065-8855 American Institute of Musicology. Miscellanea
0065-8871 American Institute of Ultrasound in Medicine. Annual Scientific Conference. Program *changed to* American Institute of Ultrasound in Medicine. Annual Scientific Conference. Proceedings.
0065-891X American Institutes for Research. Seminar Series†
0065-8928 American Jewish Committee. Institute of Human Relations. Pamphlet Series. *changed to* American Jewish Committee. Institute of Human Relations. Paperback Series.
0065-8936 American Jewish Communal History
0065-8944 American Jewish Historical Society. News *see* 0732-0914
0065-8987 American Jewish Year Book
0065-8995 American Journal of Jurisprudence
0065-9010 A J S Information Report Series†
0065-9029 American Junior College†
0065-9037 American Laryngological, Rhinological and Otological Society Transactions†
0065-9045 American Law Institute. Annual Meeting. Proceedings
0065-9053 Official Lawn Bowls Handbook *changed to* Official Lawn Bowls Almanac.
0065-907X A L A Studies in Librarianship†
0065-9088 L T P Publications†
0065-9096 A L A Social Responsibilities Round Table Newsletter *see* 0749-1670
0065-910X American Library Directory
0065-9118 American Life Collector's Annual†
0065-9142 American Literary Scholarship
0065-9150 American Littoral Society. Special Publications
0065-9185 American Management Association. Research Reports
0065-9193 American Management Association. Seminar Program
0065-9215 A M A Abstracts of Papers of the Conferences *changed to* American Marketing Association. Annual Marketing Educators' Conference. Proceedings.
0065-9231 American Marketing Association. Proceedings *changed to* American Marketing Association. Annual Marketing Educators' Conference. Proceedings.
0065-924X American Marketing Association. Reprint Series†
0065-9258 American Mathematical Society. Colloquium Publications
0065-9266 American Mathematical Society. Memoirs
0065-9274 Selected Translations in Mathematical Statistics and Probability
0065-9282 Translations of Mathematical Monographs
0065-9290 American Mathematical Society. Translations. Series 2
0065-9304 A M A Drug Evaluations†
0065-9312 Current Procedural Terminology *see* 0276-8283
0065-9320 Medical and Surgical Motion Pictures†
0065-9339 American Medical Directory *changed to* American Medical Directory.
0065-938X American Merchant Marine Library Association. Report *changed to* American Merchant Marine Library Association. Annual Report.
0065-9401 American Meteorological Society. Meteorological Monographs
0065-9452 American Museum of Natural History. Anthropological Papers
0065-9479 American Neurological Association. Transactions†
0065-9495 A N A Clinical Sessions†
0065-9517 American Nurses' Association. House of Delegates. Reports†
0065-9533 American Ophthalmological Society. Transactions
0065-9541 American Oriental Series
0065-955X American Orthoptic Journal
0065-9576 American Osteopathic College of Radiology. Newsletter. *changed to* Viewbox.
0065-9630 Tables of Selected Values of Physical and Thermodynamic Properties of Hydrocarbons *changed to* T R C Thermodynamic Tables - Hydrocarbons.
0065-9649 Selected Infrared Spectral Data *changed to* T R C Spectral Data - Infared.
0065-9657 Selected Ultraviolet Spectral Data *changed to* T R C Spectral Data - Ultraviolet.
0065-9665 A P I Research Project 44. Selected Values of Properties of Hydrocarbons and Related Compounds. Category D: Selected Raman Spectral Data *changed to* T R C Spectral Data - Raman.
0065-9673 A P I Research Project 44. Selected Values of Properties of Hydrocarbons and Related Compounds. Category E: Selected Mass Spectral Data *changed to* T R C Spectral Data - Mass.
0065-9681 Selected Nuclear Magnetic Resonanance Data *changed to* T R C Spectral Data - 1 H Nuclear Magnetic Resonance.
0065-9711 American Philological Association. Transactions and Proceedings *see* 0362-9945
0065-9711 American Philological Association. Transactions and Proceedings *see* 0360-5949
0065-972X American Philosophical Association. Proceedings and Addresses
0065-9738 American Philosophical Society. Memoirs
0065-9746 American Philosophical Society. Transactions
0065-9762 American Philosophical Society. Yearbook
0065-9797 American Power Boat Association. A P B A Rule Book *changed to* American Power Boat Association. A P B A Rule - Reference Book.
0065-9800 American Printing House for the Blind. Department of Educational Research. Annual Report. *changed to* American Printing House for the Blind. Department of Educational and Technical Research. Report of Research and Development Activities.
0065-9819 A P I C S Annual Conference Proceedings *changed to* American Production and Inventory Control Society. Annual International Conference Proceedings.
0065-9827 American Psychiatric Association. Biographical Directory†
0065-9843 American Psychoanalytic Association. Journal. Monograph
0065-9886 American Psychopathological Association. Publications†
0065-9894 American Public Gas Association. Memorandum Bulletins *changed to* American Public Gas Association. Newsletter.
0065-9932 American Public Works Association. Research Foundation. Special Reports
0065-9940 American Railway Bridge and Building Association. Proceedings
0065-9959 American Reference Books Annual
0065-9967 American Register of Exporters and Importers *see* 0272-1163
0065-9975 American Register of Inter-Corporate Ownership *changed to* Directory of Inter-Corporate Ownership.
0065-9991 American Research Center in Egypt. Journal
0066-0000 American Rose Annual
0066-0027 American School of Prehistoric Research. Bulletins
0066-0035 American Schools of Oriental Research. Annual
0066-0043 American Science Manpower†
0066-0051 American Series of Foreign Penal Codes
0066-006X American Society for Abrasive Methods. Technical Conference. Proceedings *see* 0363-8065
0066-0086 American Society for Cybernetics. Proceedings of the Annual Symposium
0066-0116 American Society for Horticultural Science. Caribbean Region. Proceedings of the Annual Meeting *see* 0254-2528
0066-0124 A S I S Handbook and Directory
0066-0132 American Society for Neurochemistry. Transactions
0066-0159 American Society for Quality Control. Transactions of Annual Technical Conferences *see* 0360-6929
0066-0183 Annual Book of A S T M Standards. Volume 01.01. Steel-Piping, Tubing, Fittings
0066-0191 Annual Book of A S T M Standards. Part 2. Ferrous Castings, Ferro Alloys *changed to* Annual Book of A S T M Standards. Volume 01.02. Ferrous Castings, Ferro Alloys.
0066-0205 Annual Book of A S T M Standards. Part 3. Steel Strip, Bar, Rod, Wire, Chain, and Spring; Wrought Iron; Metallic Coated Products; Ferrous Surgical Implants *changed to* Annual Book of A S T M Standards. Volume 01.03. Steel Plate, Sheet, Strip Wire.
0066-0213 Annual Book of A S T M Standards. Part 4. Structural Steel; Concrete Reinforcing Steel; Pressure Vessel Plate; Steel Rails; Wheels, and Tires; Bearing Steel; Steel Forgings *changed to* Annual Book of A S T M Standards. Volume 01.04. Steel-Structural, Reinforcing, Pressure Vessel; Railway.
0066-0221 Annual Book of A S T M Standards. Part 6. Copper and Copper Alloys (Including Electrical Conductors) *changed to* Annual Book of A S T M Standards. Volume 02.01. Copper and Copper Alloys.
0066-0221 Annual Book of A S T M Standards. Part 6. Copper and Copper Alloys (Including Electrical Conductors) *changed to* Annual Book of A S T M Standards. Volume 02.03. Electrical Conductors.
0066-023X Annual Book of A S T M Standards. Part 7. Die-Cast Metals; Light Metals and Alloys (Including Electrical Conductors) *changed to* Annual Book of A S T M Standards. Volume 02.02. Die-Cast Metals; Aluminum and Magnesium Alloys.
0066-023X Annual Book of A S T M Standards. Part 7. Die-Cast Metals; Light Metals and Alloys (Including Electrical Conductors) *changed to* Annual Book of A S T M Standards. Volume 02.03. Electrical Conductors.
0066-0248 Annual Book of A S T M Standards. Part 8. Nonferrous Metals and Alloys (Including Corrosion Tests); Electrodeposited Metallic Coatings; Metal Powders; Surgical Implants. *changed to* Annual Book of A S T M Standards. Volume 02.04. Nonferrous Metals-Nickel, Lead, Tin Alloys, Precious, Primary, Reactive Metals.
0066-0256 Annual Book of A S T M Standards. Part 9. Cement; Lime; Gypsum *changed to* Annual Book of A S T M Standards. Volume 04.01. Cement; Lime; Gypsum.
0066-0264 Annual Book of A S T M Standards. Part 14. Concrete and Mineral Aggregates (Including Manual of Concrete Testing) *changed to* Annual Book of A S T M Standards. Volume 04.02. Concrete and Aggregates (Including Manual of Aggregate and Concrete Testing).
0066-0272 Soil and Rock; Skid Resistance *changed to* Annual Book of A S T M Standards. Volume 04.03. Road and Paving Materials; Pavement Management Technologies.

ISSN

0066-0280 Annual Book of A S T M Standards. Part 12. Chemical-Resistant Nonmetallic Materials; Clay and Concrete Pipe and Tile; Masonry Mortars and Units; Asbestos-Cement Products; Natural Building Stones *changed to* Annual Book of A S T M Standards. Volume 04.05. Chemical-Resistant Materials; Vitrified Clay, Concrete; Fiber-Cement Products; Masonry; Mortars.
0066-0299 Annual Book of A S T M Standards. Part 17. Refractories, Glass and Other Ceramic Materials; Manufactured Carbon and Graphite Products *changed to* Annual Book of A S T M Standards. Volume 15.01. Refractories, Manufactured Carbon and Graphite Products; Activated Carbon.
0066-0299 Annual Book of A S T M Standards. Part 17. Refractories, Glass and Other Ceramic Materials; Manufactured Carbon and Graphite Products *changed to* Annual Book of A S T M Standards. Volume 15.02. Glass; Ceramic Whitewares.
0066-0302 Annual Book of A S T M Standards. Part 18. Thermal and Cryogenic Insulating Materials; Building Seals and Sealants; Fire Tests; Building Constructions; Environmental Acoustics *changed to* Annual Book of A S T M Standards. Volume 04.06. Thermal Insulation; Environmental Acoustics.
0066-0310 Annual Book of A S T M Standards. Part 15. Paper; Packaging; Cellulose; Casein; Flexible Barrier Materials; Carbon Paper; Leather *changed to* Annual Book of A S T M Standards. Volume 15.09. Paper; Packaging; Flexible Barrier Materials; Business Copy Products.
0066-0329 Annual Book of A S T M Standards. Part 22. Wood; Adhesives *changed to* Annual Book of A S T M Standards. Volume 04.09. Wood.
0066-0329 Annual Book of A S T M Standards. Part 22. Wood; Adhesives *changed to* Annual Book of A S T M Standards. Volume 15.06. Adhesives.
0066-0337 Annual Book of A S T M Standards. Part 17. Petroleum Products - Fuels, Solvents, Burner Fuel Oils, Lubricating Greases, Hydraulic Fluids *changed to* Annual Book of A S T M Standards. Volume 05.01. Petroleum Products and Lubricants (1).
0066-0345 Annual Book of A S T M Standards. Part 18. Petroleum Products - Measurement and Sampling; Liquefied Petroleum Gases; Light Hydrocarbons; Plant Spray Oils; Aerospace Materials; Sulfonates; Crude Petroleum; Petroleum; Wax; Graphite *changed to* Annual Book of A S T M Standards. Volume 05.02. Petroleum Products and Lubricants (2).
0066-0353 Annual Book of A S T M Standards. Part 26. Gaseous Fuels; Coal and Coke *changed to* Annual Book of A S T M Standards. Volume 05.05. Gaseous Fuels; Coal and Coke.
0066-037X Annual Book of A S T M Standards. Volume 06.01. Paint - Tests for Formulated Products and Applied Coatings
0066-0388 Annual Book of A S T M Standards. Part 30. Soap; Engine Coolants; Polishes; Halogenated Organic Solvents; Activated Carbon *changed to* Annual Book of A S T M Standards. Volume 15.05. Engine Coolants; Halogenated Organic Solvents; Industrial Chemicals.
0066-0388 Annual Book of A S T M Standards. Part 30. Soap; Engine Coolants; Polishes; Halogenated Organic Solvents; Activated Carbon *changed to* Annual Book of A S T M Standards. Volume 15.04. Soaps; Polishes; Cellulose; Leather; Resilient Floor Covering.
0066-0396 Annual Book of A S T M Standards. Part 23. Water; Atmospheric Analysis *changed to* Annual Book of A S T M Standards. Volume 11.01. Water (1).
0066-040X Annual Book of A S T M Standards. Volume 07.01. Textiles - Yarn, Fabrics, and General Test Methods
0066-0418 Annual Book of A S T M Standards. Part 33. Textiles - Fibers, Zippers; High Modulus Fibers *changed to* Annual Book of A S T M Standards. Volume 07.02. Textiles - Fibers, Zippers.
0066-0426 Annual Book of A S T M Standards. Part 26. Plastics - Specifications; Methods of Testing Pipe, Film, Reinforced and Cellular Plastics *changed to* Annual Book of A S T M Standards. Volume 08.02. Plastics (2): D 1601 to D 3099.
0066-0434 Annual Book of A S T M Standards. Part 35. Plastics - General Test Methods; Nomenclature *changed to* Annual Book of A S T M Standards. Volume 08.01. Plastics (1): C 177 to D 1600.
0066-0442 Annual Book of A S T M Standards. Part 28. Rubber; Carbon Black; Gaskets *changed to* Annual Book of A S T M Standards. Volume 09.02. Rubber Products, Industrial - Specifications and Related Test Methods; Gaskets; Tires.
0066-0450 Annual Book of A S T M Standards. Part 39. Electrical Insulating Materials - Test Methods *changed to* Annual Book of A S T M Standards. Volume 10.01. Electrical Insulation, Composites, and Coatings - Solids.
0066-0469 Annual Book of A S T M Standards. Part 41. General Test Methods (Nonmetal); Statistical Methods; Space Simulation; Particle Size Measurement; Deterioration of Nonmetallic Materials *changed to* Annual Book of A S T M Standards. Volume 14.02. General Test Methods, Nonmetal; Laboratory Apparatus; Statistical Methods; Appearance of Materials; Durability of Nonmetallic Materials.
0066-0477 Which was formerly; Annual Book of A S T M Standards. Part 31. Metals--Physical, Mechanical, Nondestructive, and Corrosion Tests, Metallography, Fatigue, Effect of Temperature *changed to* Annual Book of A S T M Standards. Volume 03.01. Metals - Mechanical Testing; Elevated and Low-Temperature Tests Metallography.
0066-0485 Annual Book of A S T M Standards. Volume 03.05. Chemical Analysis of Metals; Metal Bearing Ores
0066-0493 Annual Book of A S T M Standards. Volume 00.01. Index
0066-0507 Annual Book of A S T M Standards. Part 8. Magnetic Properties; Metallic Materials for Thermostats and Contacts; Materials for Electron Devices and Microelectronics *changed to* Annual Book of A S T M Standards. Volume 03.04. Magnetic Properties; Metallic Materials for Thermostats, Electrical Resistance, Heating Contacts.
0066-0523 American Society for Testing and Materials. Compilation of A S T M Standards in Building Codes
0066-0531 American Society for Testing and Materials. Data Series Publications
0066-054X American Society for Testing and Materials. Five-Year Index to A S T M Technical Papers and Reports
0066-0558 American Society for Testing and Materials. Special Technical Publications
0066-0566 A S A Special Publication
0066-0582 American Society of Bakery Engineers. Proceedings of the Annual Meeting
0066-0590 C L U Forum Report†
0066-0604 American Society of Civil Engineers. Transactions
0066-0620 A S H R A E Handbook and Product Directory *see* 1041-2344
0066-0639 American Society of International Law. Newsletter
0066-0647 American Society of International Law. Proceedings *see* 0272-5045
0066-0655 American Society of Ophthalmologic and Otolaryngologic Allergy. Transactions†
0066-068X American Society of Sanitary Engineering. Year Book
0066-0698 American Society of Traffic and Transportation, Ohio Chapter. Proceedings of the Annual Seminar†
0066-0701 American Society of University Composers. Proceedings†
0066-071X A S H A Monographs†
0066-0736 American Statistical Association. Business and Economic Statistics Section. Proceedings
0066-0752 American Statistical Association. Social Statistics Section. Proceedings
0066-0760 American Stock Exchange. AMEX Databook *changed to* American Stock Exchange. AMEX Fact Book.
0066-0779 American Stock Exchange. Annual Report
0066-0795 American Studies Research Centre. Newsletter
0066-0809 American Studies Series†
0066-0868 American Theological Library Association. Conference. Summary of Proceedings
0066-0884 American Trail Series
0066-0892 American Trucking Associations Report *changed to* American Trucking Trends (Year).
0066-0922 American Universities and Colleges
0066-0930 American Universities Field Staff. Reports. Central and Southern Africa Series *changed to* Fieldstaff Reports. Central and Southern Africa Series.
0066-0949 American Universities Field Staff. Reports. East Africa Series *changed to* Fieldstaff Reports. East Africa Series.
0066-0973 American Universities Field Staff. Reports. Mexico and Caribbean Area *changed to* Fieldstaff Reports. North America Series.
0066-0981 American Universities Field Staff. Reports. North Africa Series *changed to* Fieldstaff Reports. North Africa Series.
0066-104X American Universities Field Staff. Reports. Southeast Europe Series *changed to* Fieldstaff Reports. Southeast Europe Series.
0066-1058 American Universities Field Staff. Reports. West Africa Series *changed to* Fieldstaff Reports. West Africa Series.
0066-1082 American Universities Field Staff. Annual Report of the Executive Director†
0066-1104 American Universities Field Staff. List of Publications†
0066-1112 American Universities Field Staff. Select Bibliography: Asia, Africa, Eastern Europe, Latin America. Supplement†
0066-1147 American Veterinary Medical Association. Directory
0066-1155 American Veterinary Radiology Society. Journal *see* 1058-8183
0066-1171 American Water Resources Conferences. Annual Proceedings *changed to* American Water Resources Symposia. Annual Proceedings.
0066-118X American Waterways Series†
0066-1201 American Youth Hostels Guide and Handbook *changed to* Hostelling North America.
0066-121X Americans Before Columbus
0066-1228 A C A Index
0066-1236 Americans for Constitutional Action. Report
0066-1244 Amino Acides, Peptides, Proteines. Cahier†
0066-1252 Amities Philosophiques Internationales. Bulletin
0066-1260 Amli Studies in Music Bibliography†
0066-1287 Netherlands. Rijksinstituut voor Oorlogsdocumentatie. Documenten
0066-1295 Rijksinstituut voor Oorlogsdocumentatie. Monografieen
0066-1309 Amsterdam-Rotterdam Bank. Annual Report
0066-1317 Universiteit van Amsterdam. Fysisch Geografisch en Bodemkundig Laboratorium. Publikaties
0066-1325 Universiteit van Amsterdam. Zoologisch Museum. Bulletin
0066-1333 Anadolu Sanati Arastirmalari
0066-1341 Anaesthesiology and Resuscitation *see* 0171-1814
0066-135X Analecta Biblica
0066-1368 Analecta Boerhaaviana†
0066-1376 Analecta Gregoriana
0066-1392 Analecta Romana Instituti Danici
0066-1406 Analecta Romana Instituti Danici. Supplementum
0066-1414 Analecta Vaticano-Belgica. Deuxieme Serie. Section A: Nonciature de Flandre
0066-1422 Analecta Vaticano-Belgica. Deuxieme Serie. Section B: Nonciature de Cologne
0066-1430 Analecta Vaticano-Belgica. Deuxieme Serie. Section C: Nonciature de Bruxelles
0066-1449 Analecta Vaticano-Belgica. Premiere Serie: Documents Relatifs aux Anciens Dioceses de Cambrai, Liege, Therouanne et Tournai
0066-1465 Anales de Cirugia
0066-1473 Anales de Moral Social y Economica
0066-1481 Analog: Stories Selected from Analog Science Fact and Science Fiction†
0066-149X Analyses of Natural Gases of the United States *changed to* Analyses of Natural Gases.
0066-152X Analyst†
0066-1538 Analytical Calorimetry†
0066-1546 Anatolian Studies
0066-1554 Anatolica
0066-1562 Anatomische Gesellschaft. Verhandlungen
0066-1589 Anciens Pays et Assemblees d'Etats
0066-1600 Ancient Pakistan†
0066-1619 Ancient Society
0066-1635 M.D. Anderson Hospital and Tumor Institute. Research Report *changed to* M.D. Anderson Cancer Center. Research Report.
0066-1651 Andhra Pradesh, India. Department of Archaeology. Epigraphy Series *changed to* Andhra Pradesh, India. Department of Archaeology and Museums. Epigraphy Series.
0066-166X Andhra Pradesh, India. Department of Archaeology. Museum Series *changed to* Andhra Pradesh, India. Department of Archaeology and Museums. Museum Series.
0066-1678 Andhra University Humanities and Sciences Series†
0066-1686 Andhra University Memoirs in Oceanography

ISSN

ISSN INDEX 5491

0066-1694 Andrew W. Mellon Foundation. Report
0066-1708 Andrews University. Monographs
0066-1724 Anesthesiologie Europeenne et Mediterraneenne. Annuaire†
0066-1732 Anesthesiologie Francaise. Annuaire†
0066-1759 Angewandte Botanik
0066-1767 Angewandte Forschung in der Bundesrepublik Deutschland†
0066-1783 Anglers' Annual *changed to* Fishing Waters.
0066-1791 Anglica Germanica. British Studies in Germanic Languages and Literatures†
0066-1805 Anglistica
0066-1848 Angola. Direccao dos Servicos de Estatistica. Estatisticas do Comercio Externo
0066-1872 Animal Health Yearbook
0066-1899 Canada. Agriculture Canada. Animal Research Institute. Research Report *changed to* Canada. Agriculture Canada. Animal Research Centre. Research Report.
0066-1910 Anleitung fuer die Chemische Laboratoriumspraxis *changed to* Anleitung fuer die Chemische Laboratoriumspraxis - Chemical Laboratory Practice.
0066-1937 Annales Academiae Medicae Cracoviensis. Index Dissertationum Editarum
0066-1945 Annales Academiae Medicae Stetinensis
0066-1953 Annales Academiae Scientiarum Fennicae. Series A, I: Mathematica
0066-1961 Annales Academiae Scientiarum Fennicae. Series A, II: Chemica
0066-197X Annales Academiae Scientiarum Fennicae. Series A, III: Geologica-Geographica
0066-1988 Annales Academiae Scientiarum Fennicae. Series A, 4: Biologica†
0066-1996 Annales Academiae Scientiarum Fennicae. Series A, V: Medica
0066-2003 Annales Academiae Scientiarum Fennicae. Series A, VI: Physica
0066-2011 Annales Academiae Scientiarum Fennicae. Series B
0066-2054 Annales de Chirurgie Thoracique et Cardio-Vasculaire
0066-2062 Annales de Demographie Historique
0066-2070 Annales de Gastroenterologie et d'Hepatologie
0066-2119 Annales d'Esthetique
0066-2127 Annales d'Ethiopie†
0066-2135 Annales d'Etudes Internationales†
0066-2143 Annales Francaises de Chronometrie et de Micromecanique *see* 0294-1228
0066-216X Annales Malgaches. Series Lettres et Sciences Humaines *changed to* Universite de Madagascar. Annales. Serie Lettres et Sciences Humaines.
0066-2186 Annales Moreau de Tours†
0066-2194 Annales Odonto-Stomatologiques†
0066-2216 Annales Polonici Mathematici
0066-2224 Annales Silesiae
0066-2232 Annales Universitatis Mariae Curie-Sklodowska. Sectio C. Biologia
0066-2240 Annales Universitatis Mariae Curie-Sklodowska. Sectio D. Medicina
0066-2259 Annali del Mezzogiorno†
0066-2275 Annali di Sociologia
0066-2283 Quaderni Internazionali di Storia Economica e Sociale
0066-2291 Annals of Clinical Research. Supplement *changed to* Annals of Medicine.
0066-2348 Annee Epigraphique; Revue des Publications Epigraphiques Relatives a l'Antiquite Romaine
0066-2356 Annee Politique *see* 0764-8138
0066-2364 Annee Politique Africaine
0066-2372 Annee Politique Suisse
0066-2380 Universite Libre de Bruxelles. Institut de Sociologie. Annee Sociale
0066-2399 Annee Sociologique
0066-2402 Annee Therapeutique en Ophtalmologie *see* 0301-4495
0066-2410 Annotated Bibliography and Index of the Geology of Zambia
0066-2445 Annotated Guide to Taiwan Periodical Literature†
0066-2453 Annuaire Administratif de la Republique du Mali
0066-2461 Annuaire Administratif et Judiciaire de Belgique
0066-247X Annuaire Biographique du Cinema et de la Television en France et en Belgique
0066-2488 Annuaire Catholique de France
0066-2518 Annuaire de la Chapellerie et de la Mode†
0066-2526 Annuaire de la Chaussure et des Cuirs
0066-2534 Annuaire de la France Rurale dans le Marche Commun *changed to* Annuaire de la France Rurale et de l'Agro-Alimentaire dans le Marche Commun.
0066-2542 Annuaire de la Maree *changed to* Annuaire de la Maree et de l'Aquaculture.
0066-2550 Annuaire de la Marine Marchande
0066-2569 Annuaire de la Noblesse de France et d'Europe
0066-2577 Annuaire de la Papeterie Francaise *changed to* Annuaire de la Papeterie.
0066-2585 Annuaire de la Presse et de la Publicite
0066-2593 Directory of the French Nuclear Industry
0066-2615 Annuaire de l'Ameublement et des Industries s'y Rattachant *changed to* Annuaire de l'Ameublement.
0066-2623 Annuaire de l'Armement a la Peche
0066-264X Annuaire de l'Eclairage
0066-2658 Annuaire de Legislation Francaise et Etrangere
0066-2674 Annuaire de l'Industrie du Caoutchouc et de ses Derives
0066-2690 Annuaire de l'Industrie et du Commerce France-Afrique
0066-2704 Annuaire de l'U.R.S.S. *see* 0397-8249
0066-2712 Annuaire Dentaire
0066-2720 Annuaire des Annuaires *changed to* Repertoire des Annuaires.
0066-2747 Annuaire des Architectes†
0066-2763 Annuaire des Boissons et des Liquides Alimentaires†
0066-2771 Annuaire des Chercheurs Francais du Fonds de Bourses de Recherche Scientifique et Technique de l'Organisation du Traite de l'Atlantique Nord
0066-278X Annuaire des Caisses d'Epargne; France et Outre-Mer *changed to* Annuaire du Reseau Ecureuil.
0066-2798 Annuaire des Chambres de Commerce et d'Industrie
0066-281X Annuaire des Docteurs (Lettres) de l'Universite de Paris et Autres Universites Francaises
0066-2828 Annuaire des Entreprises d'Afrique Noire, des Organismes Officiels et Professionels d'Outre-Mer, des Organismes de Cooperation Francais, Etrangers et Internationaux *changed to* Annuaire des Entreprises et Organismes d'Outre-Mer.
0066-2844 Annuaire des Geographes de la France et de l'Afrique Francophone *changed to* Repertoire des Geographes Francais.
0066-2860 Annuaire des Instituts de Religieuses en France
0066-2895 Annuaire des Mouvement de Jeunesse†
0066-2909 Annuaire des Negociants en Combustibles†
0066-2917 Annuaire des Organismes d'Habitat Rural *changed to* Guide de l'Habitat et du Developpement Local.
0066-2933 Groupement des Societes Immobilieres d'Investissement. Annuaire
0066-2941 Annuaire des Stations Hydro-Minerales, Climatiques, et Balneaires de France et des Etablissements Medicaux *changed to* Annuaire des Stations Thermales et Climatiques et des Etablissements Medicaux Francais.
0066-295X Annuaire Diplomatique et Consulaire de la Republique Francaise
0066-2968 Annuaire du Cinema et Television *changed to* Annuaire du Cinema, Television, Video.
0066-2976 Annuaire du Corps Interministeriel des Ingenieurs des Telecommunications
0066-300X Annuaire du Marketing
0066-3018 Annuaire du Quebec *changed to* Annuaire du Quebec Statistiques.
0066-3026 Annuaire du Spectacle
0066-3042 Annuaire Economique de la Tunisie
0066-3069 Guide Europeen de l'Amateur d'Art, de l'Antiquaire et du Bibliophile
0066-3077 Annuaire Europeen des Directeurs Commerciaux et de Marketing
0066-3085 Annuaire Francais de Droit International
0066-3107 Annuaire Franco-Asiatique†
0066-3115 Annuaire Franco-Italien
0066-3123 Annuaire Franco-Suisse†
0066-3131 Annuaire Fructidor
0066-3158 Annuaire General de la Pharmacie Francaise
0066-3174 Jaarboek der Schone Kunsten
0066-3182 Annuaire General des Cooperatives Francaises et de leurs Fournisseurs: France, Afrique et Marche Commun *changed to* Annuaire General des Cooperatives et de leurs Fournisseurs: France, Outre-Mer et Marche Europeen.
0066-3204 Guide de l'Organisation et de la Modernisation des Industries et Collectives *changed to* Guide de l'Organisation de l'Informatique et de la Formation.
0066-3212 Annuaire-Guide International de l'Energie Atomique et des Autres Energies *changed to* Guide International de l'Energie Nucleare.
0066-3255 Annuaire International des Jus de Fruits
0066-3263 Annuaire International des Ventes
0066-328X Annuaire Luxembourgeois; Annuaire LUX pour l'Industrie, le Commerce et l'Artisant†
0066-3298 Annuaire Medical de l'Hospitalisation Francaise
0066-3301 Annuaire National de la Kinesitherapie†
0066-331X Annuaire National de la Musique†
0066-3328 Annuaire National de l'Aviculture *changed to* Annuaire des Industries Avicoles.
0066-3352 Annuaire National des Beaux-Arts
0066-3379 Annuaire National des Fournisseurs des Administrations Francaises
0066-3387 Annuaire National des Lettres
0066-3395 Annuaire National des Specialistes en Gynecologie-Obstetrique et des Competents Exlusifs en Gynecologie et Obstetrique
0066-3417 Annuaire National des Specialistes Qualifies en Chirurgie
0066-3425 Annuaire National des Specialistes Qualifies Exclusifs des Maladies de l'Appareil Digestif
0066-345X Annuaire National des Specialistes Qualifies Exclusifs en Dermatologie et Venereologie
0066-3468 Annuaire National des Specialistes Qualifies Exclusifs en Electroradiologie
0066-3476 Annuaire National des Specialistes Qualifies Exclusifs en Neuropsychiatrie
0066-3514 Annuaire National des Specialistes Qualifies Exclusifs en Pediatrie
0066-3522 Annuaire National des Specialistes Qualifies Exclusifs en Rhumatologie
0066-3549 Annuaire National des Transports
0066-3557 Annuaire National du Verre†
0066-3565 Annuaire O.G.M.
0066-3581 Annuaire Paris: Bijoux
0066-362X Annuaire Protestant: la France Protestante et les Eglises de Langue Francaise *changed to* France Protestante et les Eglises de Langue Francaise.
0066-3638 Quatre Mille Imprimeries Francaises
0066-3654 Annuaire Statistique de la France
0066-3689 Annuaire Statistique de la Tunisie
0066-3697 Annuaire Statistique de l'Industrie Francaise du Jute†
0066-3727 Annuaire Suisse de Science Politique
0066-3743 Annuaires Francais et Listes d'Adresses Susceptibles d'Interesser le Commerce et l'Industrie *changed to* Repertoire d'Annuaires Francais.
0066-376X Annual Banff Regional Conference for School Administrators. Report†
0066-3778 Annual Basic Hobby Industry Trade Directory *changed to* Hobby Merchandiser Annual Trade Directory.
0066-3786 Annual Bibliography of English Language and Literature
0066-3794 Annual Bibliography of Indian Archaeology†
0066-3808 Annual Bulletin of Coal Statistics for Europe
0066-3816 Annual Bulletin of Electric Energy Statistics for Europe
0066-3824 Annual Bulletin of Gas Statistics for Europe
0066-3832 Annual Bulletin of Historical Literature
0066-3840 Annual Bulletin of Housing and Building Statistics for Europe
0066-3859 Annual Bulletin of Transport Statistics for Europe
0066-3875 Annual Coffee Statistics *changed to* Mercadeo de Cafe nos Estados Unidos e no Canada.
0066-3883 Annual Conference of Model Reporting Area for Blindness Statistics. Proceedings†
0066-3891 Annual Development Plan of Madhya Pradesh
0066-3913 Annual Directory of Booksellers in the British Isles Specialising in Antiquarian and Out-Of-Print Books†
0066-3921 Annual Dog Watch *changed to* Dog Watch.
0066-3964 Annual Estimates of the Population of Scotland
0066-3972 N U T Guide to Careers Work†
0066-3999 Annual Industry Survey of Computer and Software and Services Industry†
0066-4014 Annual of Advertising, Editorial and Television Art and Design *see* 0735-2026
0066-4030 Annual Progress in Child Psychiatry and Child Development
0066-4049 Annual Register of Grant Support
0066-4057 Annual Register World Events
0066-4065 Oklahoma. Department of Libraries. Annual Report and Directory of Libraries in Oklahoma *changed to* Oklahoma Department of Libraries. Annual Report.
0066-4065 Oklahoma. Department of Libraries. Annual Report and Directory of Libraries in Oklahoma *changed to* Annual Directory of Oklahoma Libraries.
0066-409X Annual Reports in Organic Synthesis
0066-4103 Annual Reports on N M R Spectroscopy
0066-412X Hawaii Visitors Bureau. Annual Research Report
0066-4138 Annual Review in Automatic Programming
0066-4146 Annual Review of Astronomy and Astrophysics
0066-4154 Annual Review of Biochemistry
0066-4162 Annual Review of Ecology and Systematics
0066-4170 Annual Review of Entomology
0066-4189 Annual Review of Fluid Mechanics

ISSN

0066-4197 Annual Review of Genetics
0066-4200 Annual Review of Information Science and Technology
0066-4219 Annual Review of Medicine: Selected Topics in the Clinical Sciences
0066-4227 Annual Review of Microbiology
0066-4235 Annual Review of N M R Spectroscopy *see* 0066-4103
0066-4243 Annual Review of Nuclear Science *see* 0163-8998
0066-4251 Annual Review of Pharmacology *see* 0362-1642
0066-426X Annual Review of Physical Chemistry
0066-4278 Annual Review of Physiology
0066-4286 Annual Review of Phytopathology
0066-4294 Annual Review of Plant Physiology *see* 1040-2519
0066-4308 Annual Review of Psychology
0066-4332 Silver Market
0066-4340 Annual Review of United Nations Affairs
0066-4359 Annual Safety Education Review†
0066-4367 Annual Statistical Review: The Distilled Spirits Industry†
0066-4375 Annual Summary of Business Statistics, New York State
0066-4383 Annual Summary of Information on Natural Disasters†
0066-4391 Annual Summary of Merchant Ships Launched in the World *see* 0261-2720
0066-4405 Annual Survey of African Law
0066-4413 Annual Survey of American Law
0066-443X Annual Survey of Psychoanalysis†
0066-4456 Annuale Mediaevale†
0066-4464 Annuario Cattolico d'Italia
0066-4472 Annuario Ceramica
0066-4480 Annuario della Comunita Lombarda†
0066-4499 Annuario dell'Industria Italiana della Gomma *changed to* Guida all'Industria Italiana della Gomma.
0066-4510 Annuario Politecnico Italiano†
0066-4545 Annuario Statistico Italiano
0066-4553 Anorganische und Allgemeine Chemie in Einzeldarstellungen *see* 0172-7966
0066-4596 Anschriften Deutscher Verlage und Auslaendischer Verlage mit Deutschen Auslieferungen *changed to* Deutschsprachige Verlage.
0066-460X Anschriften Deutschsprachiger Zeitschriften *changed to* Deutschsprachige Zeitschriften.
0066-4618 Anson G. Phelps Lectureship on Early American History†
0066-4626 Antarctic Bibliography
0066-4634 Antarctic Research Series *changed to* Antarctic Research Book Series.
0066-4642 Antemurale†
0066-4677 Anthropological Forum
0066-4685 Anthropologie
0066-4693 Anthropologische Gesellschaft, Vienna. Mitteilungen
0066-4715 Anthropology of the North. Translations from Russian Sources†
0066-4723 Anthropos
0066-4758 Antibiotics and Chemotherapy
0066-4766 Antichita Classica e Cristiana
0066-4774 Antichthon
0066-4782 Antike Kunst. Beihefte
0066-4804 Antimicrobial Agents and Chemotherapy
0066-4812 Antipode
0066-4839 Antiquitas. Reihe 1. Abhandlungen zur Alten Geschichte
0066-4847 Antiquitas. Reihe 2. Abhandlungen aus dem Gebiete der Vor- und Fruehgeschichte
0066-4855 Antiquitas. Reihe 3. Abhandlungen zur Vor- und Fruehgeschichte, zur Klassischen und Provinzial-Roemischen Archaeologie und zur Geschichte des Altertums
0066-4863 Antiquitas. Reihe 4. Beitraege zur Historia-Augusta-Forschung
0066-4871 Antiquites Africaines
0066-488X Israel. Ministry of Education and Culture. Department of Antiquities and Museums. Atiqot (English Series) *changed to* Israel. Antiquities Authority. Atiqot (English Series).
0066-4898 Antiquites Nationales
0066-4928 Antologia del Folklore Musical Chileno†
0066-4936 Antologias del Pensamiento Politico†
0066-4979 Kunsthistorische Musea, Antwerp. Schone Kunsten†
0066-5010 Anuario Bibliografico Costarricense
0066-5045 Anuario Colombiano de Historia Social y de la Cultura
0066-5053 Anuario de Cinema†
0066-5061 Anuario de Estudios Medievales
0066-507X Anuario de Filologia†
0066-5088 Anuario de Historia Economica y Social
0066-5096 Anuario de la Mineria de Chile
0066-510X Anuario de Relojeria y Arte en Metal para Espana e Hispanoamerica
0066-5118 Anuario del Comercio Exterior Latino-Americano†
0066-5126 Anuario de Psicologia
0066-5169 Mexico. Direccion General de Estadistica. Anuario Estadistico Compendiado†
0066-5177 Spain. Instituto Nacional de Estadistica. Anuario Estadistico: Edicion Extensa
0066-5185 Anuario Estadistico de los Andes: Venezuela†
0066-5193 Angola. Direccao dos Servicos de Estatistica. Anuario Estatistico
0066-5207 Anuario F.H.I. Argentina: Frutas y Hortalizas Industriarizadas y Frescas
0066-5215 Anuario Filosofico
0066-5223 Anuario Geografico del Peru
0066-5231 Anuario Industrial de Minas Gerais *changed to* Guia Economico e Industrial do Estado de Minas Gerais.
0066-524X Anuario Martiano *changed to* Centro de Estudios Martianos. Anuario.
0066-5274 Yearbook for Inter-American Musical Research†
0066-5282 Anzeiger fuer Slavische Philologie
0066-5304 Aphidologists' Newsletter†
0066-5320 Apocrypha Novi Testamenti†
0066-5339 Apollonia†
0066-5347 Apotheker - Jahrbuch
0066-5363 Financial Review (Kingston)
0066-5371 Appalachian Gas Measurement Short Course, West Virginia University. Proceedings†
0066-538X Appalachian Underground Corrosion Short Course, West Virginia University. Proceedings†
0066-5398 Appel Service; Repertoire d'Adresses Utiles pour le Commerce et l'Industrie
0066-5401 Appliance Technical Conference. Preprints†
0066-541X Applied Chemistry Series†
0066-5436 A F R I Miscellaneous Report†
0066-5444 Applied Forestry Research Institute. Research Report†
0066-5452 Applied Mathematical Sciences
0066-5460 North-Holland Series in Applied Mathematics and Mechanics
0066-5479 Applied Mathematics and Mechanics
0066-5487 Applied Mineralogy - Technische Minerologie
0066-5495 Applied Optics. Supplement
0066-5509 Applied Physics and Engineering
0066-5517 Applied Polymer Symposium. Papers†
0066-5533 Applied Solid State Science
0066-5592 Aquatica†
0066-5606 Aqui
0066-5614 Aquinas Lecture Series
0066-5622 Arab and Afro-Asian Monograph Series *changed to* Institute for Arab Studies. Publications and Studies.
0066-5630 Al-Kitab al-Arabi Fi Aam
0066-5657 Arabidopsis Information Service. Newsletter
0066-5673 Arbeiten zur Angewandten Statistik
0066-569X Arbeiten zur Paedagogik
0066-5711 Arbeiten zur Theologie. Reihe 1
0066-572X Arbeiten zur Theologie. Reihe 2†
0066-5738 Arbeitsblaetter fuer Restauratoren
0066-5746 A R D - Jahrbuch
0066-5754 Rheinisch-Westfaelische Akademie der Wissenschaften. Veroeffentlichungen *changed to* Rheinisch-Westfaelische Akademie der Wissenschaften. Vortraege Natur- Ingenieur-und Wirtschaftswissenschaften.
0066-5770 Arbeitsgemeinschaft zur Verbesserung der Agrarstruktur in Hessen. A V A-Beratungsunterlagen†
0066-5789 Arbeitsgemeinschaft zur Verbesserung der Agrarstruktur in Hessen. A V A-Hefte†
0066-5797 Arbeitsgemeinschaft zur Verbesserung der Agrarstruktur in Hessen. A V A-Materialsammlungen†
0066-5800 Arbeitsgemeinschaft zur Verbesserung der Agrarstruktur in Hessen. A V A-Sonderhefte†
0066-5819 Arbeitsgemeinschaft zur Verbesserung der Agrarstruktur in Hessen. A V A Bezugshefte†
0066-5843 Arbeitsmedizin†
0066-5851 Arbeitsmedizinische Fragen in der Ophthalmologie†
0066-586X Arbeitsrecht der Gegenwart
0066-5878 Arboretum Kornickie
0066-5886 Archaeo-Physika
0066-5894 Archaeologia Cantiana
0066-5908 Archaeologia Geographica
0066-5924 Archaeologia Polona
0066-5967 Archaeological Bibliography for Great Britain and Ireland†
0066-5975 Archaeological Exploration of Sardis. Monographs
0066-5983 Archaeological Journal
0066-6009 Archaeologische Funde und Denkmaeler des Rheinlandes
0066-6017 Archaeologische Gesellschaft Koeln. Schriftenreihe†
0066-6025 Archeologische Kaarten van Belgie†
0066-6033 Archaeologische Mitteilungen aus Iran. Neue Folge
0066-6041 Archeion
0066-605X Archeologia (Wroclaw)
0066-6068 Archeologie et Civilisation†
0066-6084 Archeologie Mediterraneenne
0066-6092 Archigram†
0066-6114 Architect and Contractors Yearbook
0066-6122 Architectes *see* 1147-7105
0066-6149 Architects, Builders and Contractors Pocket Book†
0066-6157 Architects, Contractors & Engineers Guide to Construction Costs
0066-6165 Architect's Detail Library†
0066-6173 Architect's Handbook of Professional Practice
0066-6181 Architects Standard Catalogues *changed to* A S C Mini-File.
0066-619X Architects' Year Book†
0066-6203 Architectural and Archaeological Society of Durham and Northumberland. Transactions. New Series *changed to* Durham Archaeological Journal.
0066-6211 A A Papers†
0066-622X Architectural History
0066-6238 Architecture at Rice University†
0066-6262 Architecture in Greece
0066-6270 Architectura
0066-6297 Archiv fuer Diplomatik, Schriftgeschichte, Siegel- und Wappenkunde
0066-6327 Archiv fuer Geschichte des Buchwesens
0066-6335 Archiv fuer Geschichte von Oberfranken
0066-636X Archiv fuer Hessische Geschichte und Altertumskunde
0066-6378 Archiv fuer Kinderheilkunde. Beihefte *see* 0373-3165
0066-6386 Archiv fuer Liturgiewissenschaft
0066-6416 Archives for Meteorology, Geophysics, and Bioclimatology. Series A: Meteorology and Geophysics - Archiv Fuer Meteorologie, Geophysik und Bioklimatologie. Series A. *see* 0177-7971
0066-6424 Archives for Meteorology, Geophysics, and Bioclimatology. Series B: Climatology, Environmental Meteorology, Radiation Research - Archiv fuer Meteorologie, Geophysik und Bioklimatologie. Series B *see* 0177-798X
0066-6432 Archiv fuer Mittelrheinische Kirchengeschichte
0066-6440 Archiv fuer Orientforschung
0066-6459 Archiv fuer Papyrusforschung und Verwandte Gebiete
0066-6475 Archiv fuer Psychologie
0066-6491 Archiv fuer Schlesische Kirchengeschichte
0066-6505 Archiv fuer Sozialgeschichte
0066-6513 Archiv fuer Voelkerkunde
0066-6521 Archivalia Medica†
0066-653X Archives and the User
0066-6548 Archives Bakounine
0066-6556 Archives Claudeliennes
0066-6564 Archives de Philosophie du Droit
0066-6572 Archives des Lettres Canadiennes
0066-6580 Archives d'Ethnologie Francaise *see* 0046-2616
0066-6599 Archives in Trade Union History and Theory Series†
0066-6602 Archives Internationales de Finances Publiques†
0066-6610 Archives Internationales d'Histoire des Idees
0066-6629 Archives of Archaeology†
0066-6637 Archives of Asian Art
0066-6645 Archives of Maryland†
0066-6653 Archives Suisses d'Anthropologie Generale†
0066-6661 Archivio del Teatro Italiano
0066-667X Archivio di Oceanografia e Limonologia
0066-6688 Archivio Italiano per la Storia della Pieta
0066-6696 Archivio Linguistico Veneto. Quaderni
0066-670X Archivio Putti di Chirurgia degli Organi di Movimento
0066-6718 Archivio Storico Italiano. Biblioteca
0066-6734 Archivo Epistolar Colombiano
0066-6742 Archivo Espanol de Arqueologia
0066-6750 Archivos Argentinos de Dermatologia
0066-6769 Archivos de Investigacion Medica
0066-6777 Archivos de Oftalmologia de Buenos Aires
0066-6785 Archivum Historiae Pontificae
0066-6793 Archivum
0066-6807 Archivum Romanicum. Biblioteca. Serie 1: Storia Letteratura Paleografia
0066-6815 Archivum Romanicum. Biblioteca. Serie 2: Linguistica
0066-6823 Archiwum Akustyki†
0066-6831 Archiwum Dziejow Oswiaty
0066-684X Archiwum Energetyki
0066-6858 Archiwum Etnograficzne†
0066-6866 Archiwum Filologiczne
0066-6874 Archiwum Historii Filozofii i Mysli Spolecznej
0066-6882 Archivum Iuridicum Cracoviense
0066-6890 Archiwum Kryminologii
0066-6904 Archiwum Literackie
0066-6912 Archiwum Mineralogiczne
0066-6939 Arctic Anthropology
0066-6947 Arctic Bibliography†
0066-6955 Arctic Institute of North America. Annual Report†
0066-6963 Arctic Institute of North America. Newsletter *see* 0315-2561
0066-6971 Arctic Institute of North America. Research Paper†
0066-698X Arctic Institute of North America. Technical Paper†
0066-6998 Arctos; Acta Philologica Fennica. Supplementum†
0066-7005 Argentina. Consejo Federal de Inversiones. Bibliografia Sobre el Desarrollo Economico Nacional†

0066-7021 Argentina. Departamento de Estadistica Educativa. Boletin Informativo.
0066-703X Argentina. Departamento de Estudios Historicos Navales. Serie A: Cultura Nautica
0066-7048 Argentina. Departamento de Estudios Historicos Navales. Serie B: Historia Naval Argentina
0066-7056 Argentina. Departamento de Estudios Historicos Navales. Serie C: Biografias Navales Argentinas
0066-7080 Argentina. Departamento de Estudios Historicos Navales. Serie J: Libros y Impresos Raros
0066-7099 Argentina. Direccion de Investigaciones Forestales. Misceleneas Forestales†
0066-7102 Argentina. Direccion de Investigaciones Forestales. Notas Silvicolas†
0066-7110 Argentina. Direccion de Investigaciones Forestales. Notas Tecnologicas Forestales *see* 0325-9781
0066-7129 Argentina. Direccion de Investigaciones Forestales. Planificacion del Desarrollo Forestal†
0066-7145 Argentina. Servicio Nacional Minero Geologico. Anales
0066-7153 Argentina. Servicio Nacional Minero Geologico. Boletin
0066-7161 Argentina. Servicio Nacional Minero Geologico. Estadistica Minera
0066-717X Argentina. Servicio Nacional Minero Geologico. Revista
0066-7188 Argentina. Instituto Nacional de Derecho Aeronautico y Espacial†
0066-7196 Argentina. Instituto Nacional de Estadistica y Censos. Informe Serie E: Edificacione†
0066-7242 Argentina. Estacion Experimental Agropecuaria Manfredi. Serie Informacion Tecnica†
0066-7269 Argentina. Junta Nacional de Carnes. Sintesis Estadistica
0066-7277 Combustible. *changed to* Argentina. Direccion General de Evaluacion Energetica. Anuario de Combustibles.
0066-7285 Argentina. Oficina Sectorial de Desarrollo de Energia. Anuarios Estadisticos. Energia Electrica *changed to* Argentina. Direccion General de Evaluacion Energetica. Anuario Energia Electrica.
0066-7293 Argentina. Secretaria de Guerra. Direccion de Estudios Historicos. Boletin Bibliografico
0066-7331 Argentina. Servicio de Inteligencia Naval. Bibliotecas de la Armada. Boletin Bibliografico.
0066-734X Argus de la Poesie Francaise
0066-7358 Arheologia Moldovei
0066-7366 Arid Zone Research†
0066-7374 Aristotelian Society. Proceedings
0066-7382 Arizona. Department of Public Safety. Annual Report†
0066-7390 Arizona. Department of Public Safety. Statistical Reviews *see* 0066-7382
0066-7404 Arizona Forestry Notes
0066-7412 Arizona Geological Society Digest
0066-7447 Arizona Model United Nations†
0066-7455 Arizona State University. Bureau of Educational Research and Services. Educational Services Bulletin.†
0066-7463 Arizona State University. Bureau of Educational Research and Services. Research and Services Bulletin.†
0066-748X Arizona State University, Tempe. Institute of Public Administration. Monograph. *changed to* Arizona State University. Center for Public Affairs. Monograph.
0066-751X University of Arizona. College of Education. Monograph Series†
0066-7536 University of Arizona. Department of English. Graduate English Papers *see* 0275-5203
0066-7560 E E S Series Report†
0066-7587 University of Arizona. Laboratory of Tree-Ring Research. Papers†
0066-7609 University of Arizona. Optical Sciences Center. Newsletter†
0066-7617 University of Arizona. Optical Sciences Center. Technical Report†
0066-7641 Continuing Education in Business Administration†
0066-7668 Arkiv for Nordisk Filologi
0066-7684 Arlington Historical Magazine
0066-7706 University of New England. Department of Geography. Monograph Series in Geography†
0066-7714 University of New England. Department of Geography and Planning. Research Series in Applied Geography
0066-7730 University of New England. Exploration Society. Report†
0066-7749 Armorial†
0066-7765 Arnamagnaean Institute. Bulletin *see* 0107-1475
0066-7781 Arnoldia Rhodesia *see* 0250-6386
0066-7803 Arqueologicas†
0066-7811 Arquivo de Anatomia e Antropologia
0066-782X Arquivos Brasileiros de Cardiologia
0066-7846 Arquivos de Cirurgia Clinica e Experimental
0066-7854 Arquivos de Patologia Geral e Anatomia Patologica
0066-7862 Arquivos de Tisiologia†
0066-7870 Arquivos de Zoologia
0066-7900 Ars Quatuor Coronatorum
0066-7919 Ars Suecica
0066-7927 Art and Artists of the Monterey Peninsula
0066-7935 Art Bulletin of Victoria
0066-7943 Art Directors Club Milano†
0066-7951 Art et les Grandes Civilisations *changed to* Art et les Grandes Civilisations.
0066-796X Art Gallery of South Australia. Special Exhibitions†
0066-7978 Art in Its Context: Studies in Ethno-Aesthetics. Field Reports†
0066-7986 Art in Its Context: Studies in Ethno-Aesthetics. Museum Series†
0066-8036 Arthropods of Florida and Neighboring Land Areas
0066-8044 Arthur Holmes Society. Journal
0066-8079 Universidade de Lisboa. Faculdade de Ciencias. Instituto Botanico. Artigo de Divulgacao
0066-8095 Arts
0066-8133 Arts Council of Great Britain. Annual Report and Accounts
0066-815X Arts of Mankind†
0066-8168 Arts Patronage Series
0066-8176 Arv
0066-8184 Arvernia Biologica: Botanique
0066-8192 Arznei-Telegramm
0066-8214 Handbook of Asbestos Textiles†
0066-8222 Ascidian News
0066-8230 Asia - Africa World Trade Register
0066-8249 Centro de Estudios Orientales. Anuario
0066-8265 Asia Monograph Series
0066-8281 Asian and African Studies
0066-8303 Asian and Pacific Council. Cultural and Social Centre. Annual Report†
0066-8311 A S P A C Seminar on Audio-Visual Education. Proceedings†
0066-8346 Asian and Pacific Marketing Conference. Proceedings†
0066-8354 Asian Annual
0066-8362 Asian Book Trade Directory†
0066-8370 Asian Development Bank. Annual Report
0066-8389 Asian Development Bank. Board of Governors. Summary of Proceedings.
0066-8397 Asian Development Bank. Occasional Papers†
0066-8419 Asian Journal of Pharmacy
0066-8435 Asian Perspectives
0066-8443 Asian Philosophical Studies†
0066-8451 United Nations. Economic and Social Commission for Asia and the Pacific. Asian Population Studies Series
0066-846X A P O Annual Report
0066-8508 Asien - Afrika - Lateinamerika *see* 0232-8410
0066-8532 Aslib Occasional Publications†
0066-8540 Asociacion Espanola Contra el Cancer. Memoria de la Assemblea General *changed to* Asociacion Espanola Contra el Cancer. Memoria Tecnico-Administrativa.
0066-8567 Asociacion Nacional del Cafe. Departamento de Asuntos Agricolas. Informe Anual
0066-8591 Asociacion Venezolana de Archiveros. Coleccion Doctrina
0066-8613 Asociacion Venezolana de Enfermeras Profesionales. Boletin
0066-8656 Aspects of Adhesion
0066-8672 Aspects of Education
0066-8699 Assembly Directory and Handbook *changed to* Assembly Technology Buyer's Guide.
0066-8702 Assembly Engineering Master Catalog *changed to* Assembly Technology Buyer's Guide.
0066-8710 Associated Church Press. Directory
0066-8729 Associated Colleges of Illinois. Report
0066-8753 Associated Public Schools Systems. Yearbook
0066-8761 Bibliography of Publications of University Bureaus of Business and Economic Research *see* 0738-3215
0066-877X Associated Western Universities. Annual Report *changed to* Associated Western Universities. Program Guide.
0066-8796 Association Belge pour l'Etude, l'Essai et l'Emploi des Materiaux. Publication A.B.E.M
0066-880X Association Belge pour l'Etude, l'Essai et l'Emploi des Materiaux. Publication Groupement†
0066-8818 Association Belge pour l'Etude, l'Essai et l'Emploi des Materiaux. Proces Verbal de l'Assemblee Generale Ordinaire
0066-8826 Association Canadienne des Bibliothecaires de Langue Francaise. Rapport *see* 0316-0955
0066-8842 Association Canadienne-Francaise pour l'Avancement des Sciences. Annales
0066-8850 Association Canadienne-Francaise pour l'Avancement des Sciences. Bulletin *see* 0826-4864
0066-8877 Association de l'Ecole Nationale Superieure des Bibliothecaires. Annuaire
0066-8893 Association des Amis d'Alfred de Vigny. Bulletin
0066-8907 Association des Amis de Pierre Teilhard de Chardin. Bulletin
0066-8915 Association des Anatomistes. Bulletin
0066-8923 Association of Attenders and Alumni of the Hague Academy of International Law. Yearbook
0066-8931 Association des Bibliothecaires Francais. Annuaire†
0066-894X Documents A B F†
0066-8958 Association des Bibliotheques Ecclesiastiques de France. Bulletin de Liaison
0066-8982 I C A M Annuaire
0066-8990 Association des Institutions d'Enseignement Secondaire. Annuaire
0066-9008 Association des Societes et Fonds Francais d'Investissement. Annuaire
0066-9016 Association des Traducteurs et Interpretes de l'Ontario. Repertoire
0066-9024 Association des Universites Partiellement Ou Entierement de Langue Francaise. Cahiers†
0066-9032 Association des Universites Partiellement Ou Entierement de Langue Francaise. Colloques et Congres. Comptes Rendus†
0066-9040 Association Euratom-Ital. Annual Report *changed to* Centre for Plant Breeding and Reproduction Research. Annual Report.
0066-9075 Association for Childhood Education International. Yearbook†
0066-9083 Association for Commonwealth Literature and Language Studies. Bulletin
0066-9091 Association for Computing Machinery. Proceedings of National Conference†
0066-9105 Association for Education of the Visually Handicapped. Selected Papers from A E V H Biennial Conferences†
0066-9156 A S C U S Annual - Teaching Opportunities for You *changed to* A S C U S Annual - A Job Search Handbook for Educators.
0066-9164 A S C U S Directory of Membership and Subject Field Index
0066-9172 Association for Social Anthropology in Oceania. Monograph Series
0066-9199 Association for Supervision and Curriculum Development. Yearbook
0066-9210 A D B S Annuaire†
0066-9229 Association Francaise des Ingenieurs du Caoutchouc et des Plastiques. Annuaire *changed to* Association Francaise des Ingenieurs et Cadres du Caoutchouc et des Plastiques. Annuaire.
0066-9245 Association Francaise des Ingenieures et Techniciens de l'Aeronautique et de l'Espace. Annuaire *see* 0001-9275
0066-9253 Union des Association Francaises de Relations Publiques. Annuaire
0066-927X Association Francaise des Techniciens et Ingenieurs de Securite et des Medecins du Travail. Annuaire
0066-9288 Association Francaise des Experts de la Cooperation Technique Internationale. Annuaire
0066-9296 Association Francaise d'Informatique et de Recherche Operationnelle. Annuaire *changed to* Association Francaise pour la Cybernetique Economique et Technique. Annuaire.
0066-9318 Association Nationale de la Recherche Technique. Information et Documentation†
0066-9350 Association of American Geographers. Commission on College Geography. General Series Publications†
0066-9369 Association of American Geographers. Resource Papers *changed to* Resource Publications in Geography.
0066-9393 Association of American Geographers. Monograph Series†
0066-9407 Association of American Law Schools. Proceedings
0066-9423 Medical School Admission Requirements, United States and Canada
0066-9431 Association of American Pesticide Control Officials. Official Publication
0066-944X Association of American Pesticide Control Officials. Pesticide Chemicals Official Compendium†
0066-9458 Association of American Physicians. Transactions
0066-9466 Association of Asphalt Paving Technologists. Proceedings
0066-9474 Association of Canadian Map Libraries. Annual Conference Proceedings *see* 0840-9331
0066-9482 Association of Canadian Map Libraries. Newsletter *see* 0840-9331
0066-9490 Association of Canadian Schools of Business. Proceedings of the Annual Conference *changed to* Administrative Sciences Association of Canada. Proceedings, Annual Conference.
0066-9539 Association of Colleges for Further and Higher Education. Year Book *changed to* Association of Colleges for Further and Higher Education. Handbook.

0066-9547 Association of European Paediatric Cardiologists. Proceedings *see* 0167-5273
0066-9555 Association of Faculties of Pharmacy of Canada. Proceedings
0066-9563 Association of Graduate Schools in Association of American Universities. Journal of Proceedings and Addresses†
0066-9571 Association of Island Marine Laboratories of the Caribbean. Proceedings *changed to* Association of Marine Laboratories of the Caribbean. Proceedings.
0066-958X Association of Japanese Geographers. Special Publication
0066-9598 Association of Life Insurance Medical Directors of America. Transactions
0066-9601 Association of Midwest Fish and Game Commissioners. Proceedings *changed to* Association of Midwest Fish and Wildlife Agencies. Proceedings.
0066-961X Association of Official Analytical Chemists. Official Methods of Analysis *changed to* A O A C International. Official Methods of Analysis.
0066-9628 Association of Pacific Coast Geographers. Yearbook
0066-9652 A R L Newsletter *see* 1050-6098
0066-9679 A S A Monographs (San Diego) *changed to* A S A Research Methods in Social Anthropology.
0066-9687 Association of Southeast Asian Institutions of Higher Learning. Handbook: Southeast Asian Institutions of Higher Learning
0066-9695 A S A I H L Seminar Reports
0066-9717 Association of Russian - American Scholars in the U S A. Transactions
0066-9725 Association of Universities and Colleges of Canada. Annual Meeting. Proceedings†
0066-9741 Association of University Evening Colleges. Proceedings *changed to* Association for Continuing Higher Education. Proceedings.
0066-975X Association of University Summer Sessions. Summary Report
0066-9768 A V S Journal *changed to* Pegasus.
0066-9776 T A Documents
0066-9784 A.E.T.F.A.T. Index
0066-9792 Association Scientifique de la Precontrainte. Sessions d'Etudes
0066-9806 Association Technique de l'Industrie du Gaz en France. Compte Rendu du Congres†
0066-9814 Association Technique Maritime et Aeronautique, Paris. Bulletin
0066-9822 Associazione Elettrotecnica Ed Elettronica Italiana. Rendiconti della Riunione Annuale
0066-9830 Associazione Genetica Italiana. Atti
0066-9857 Associazione Internazionale della Stampa Medica. Bollettino Bibliografico†
0066-9865 Associazione Italiana Laringectomizzati. Atti (del) Convegno Nazionale
0066-9873 Associazione Medica Chirurgica di Tivoli e della Val d'Aniene. Atti e Memorie
0066-989X Assurances Generales de France. Informations *see* 0761-7593
0066-9903 Assyriological Studies
0066-9911 Asterisks†
0066-992X Asticou
0066-9938 Astrology and Horse Racing†
0066-9946 Astronautics Year†
0066-9962 Astronomical Ephemeris *changed to* Astronomical Almanac.
0066-9970 Astronomical Ephemeris of Geocentric Places of Planets
0066-9997 Astronomical Society of Australia. Proceedings
0067-0006 Astronomical Society of Victoria. Astronomical Yearbook
0067-0014 Astronomische Grundlagen fuer den Kalender
0067-0022 Astronomy and Astrophysics Abstracts
0067-0030 Astrophysica Norvegica†
0067-0049 Astrophysical Journal. Supplement Series
0067-0057 Astrophysics and Space Science Library
0067-0073 Athens Center of Ekistics. Research Report
0067-009X Scuola Archeologica di Atene e delle Missioni Italiane in Oriente. Monografie
0067-0103 Centre des Sciences Sociales d'Athenes. Publications†
0067-012X Athletisme Francais *changed to* Athlerama.
0067-0138 Israel. Ministry of Education and Culture. Department of Antiquities and Museums. Atiqot (Hebrew Series) *changed to* Israel. Antiquities Authority. Atiqot (Hebrew Series).
0067-0162 Atlantic Provinces Economic Council. Annual Report
0067-0197 Atlantic Provinces Inter-University Committee on the Sciences. Annual Report
0067-0200 Atlantic Provinces Studies†
0067-0219 Atlantic Yearbook†
0067-0227 Atlantide Report. Scientific Results of the Danish Expedition to the Coasts of Tropical West Africa
0067-0235 Atlantische Tijdingen *see* 0167-1847
0067-0243 Atlas Arqueologico de la Republica Mexicana†
0067-0251 Atlas de la Economia Colombiana†
0067-026X Atlas d'Attraction Urbaine.†
0067-0286 Atlas des Structures Agraires au Sud du Sahara†
0067-0294 Atlas Flory Polskiej i Ziem Osciennych
0067-0308 Atlas of External Diseases of the Eye†
0067-0316 Atlas Polskich Strojow Ludowych
0067-0324 Atlas Rozmieszczenia Drzew i Krzewow w Polsce†
0067-0332 Atlas Rozmieszczenia Roslin Zarodnikowych w Polsce. Seria Iv. Watrobowce. Hepaticae†
0067-0340 Colorado State University. Atmospheric Science Paper
0067-0367 A E C L Report Series
0067-0383 Atomic Energy of Canada. Annual Report
0067-0405 Atomic Energy of Canada. List of Publications
0067-0421 Auburn Forestry Forum†
0067-043X Auburn University. Water Resources Research Institute. Annual Report
0067-0456 Auckland Institute and Museum. Bulletin
0067-0464 Auckland Institute and Museum. Records
0067-0480 University of Auckland Historical Society. Annual
0067-0499 University of Auckland. Library. Bibliographical Bulletin
0067-0510 Auckland University Law Review
0067-0537 Audarena Stadium Guide and International Directory *changed to* AudArena Stadium International Guide.
0067-0545 Audio Annual *changed to* Hi Fi News & Record Review Annual.
0067-0553 Audiovisual Market Place *see* 1044-0445
0067-057X Augustana Library Publications
0067-0588 Augustana Historical Society, Rock Island, Illinois. Publications
0067-0618 Aus dem Schweizerischen Landesmuseum†
0067-0634 Buecher fuer Sie *changed to* Buecher (Year).
0067-0642 Aus Forschung und Kunst
0067-0685 Ausruestung in Luft- und Raumfahrt†
0067-0707 University of Texas, Austin. Center for Neo-Hellenic Studies. Bulletin†
0067-0715 Australasian Corrosion Directory†
0067-0731 Australia. Bureau of Statistics. Banking and Currency Bulletin†
0067-074X Australia. Bureau of Statistics. Building and Construction Bulletin†
0067-0758 Australia. Bureau of Statistics. Commonwealth Finance†
0067-0766 Australia. Bureau of Statistics. Causes of Death (Canberra) *see* 1031-2005
0067-0774 Australia. Bureau of Statistics. Commonwealth Taxation Assessment Bulletin†
0067-0782 Australia. Bureau of Statistics. Demography (Population and Vital) Bulletin†
0067-0790 Australia. Bureau of Statistics. Insurance and Other Private Finance Bulletin†
0067-0804 Australia. Bureau of Statistics. Imports Cleared for Home Consumption, Australia†
0067-0812 Australia. Bureau of Statistics. Labour Report *see* 0314-2779
0067-0820 Australia. Bureau of Statistics. Manufacturing Commodities Bulletin†
0067-0839 Australia. Bureau of Statistics. Manufacturing Industry Bulletin†
0067-0847 Australia. Bureau of Statistics. Non-Rural Primary Industries†
0067-0855 Australia. Bureau of Statistics. Northern Territory Statistical Summary
0067-0871 Australia. Bureau of Statistics. Rural Industries Bulletin†
0067-088X Australia. Bureau of Statistics. South Australian Office. Births, South Australia *changed to* Australia. Bureau of Statistics. South Australian Office. Demography, South Australia.
0067-0898 Australia. Bureau of Statistics. South Australian Office. Deaths, South Australia
0067-0901 Australia. Bureau of Statistics. South Australian Office. Divorces, South Australia
0067-0928 Australia. Bureau of Census and Statistics. South Australian Office. Factories *changed to* Australia. Bureau of Statistics. South Australian Office. Manufacturing Establishments: Details of Operations by Industry.
0067-0936 Australia. Bureau of Statistics. South Australian Office. General Insurance†
0067-0979 Australia. Bureau of Statistics. South Australian Office. Projections of Population†
0067-0987 Australia. Bureau of Statistics. South Australian Office. Agriculture: General Summary-South Australia†
0067-1002 Australia. Bureau of Statistics. Transport and Communication Bulletin†
0067-1029 Australia. Bureau of Statistics. Tasmanian Office. Demography†
0067-1037 Australia. Bureau of Statistics. Tasmanian Office. Finance *changed to* Australia. Bureau of Statistics. Tasmanian Office. Government Finance Statistics.
0067-1045 Australia. Bureau of Statistics. Tasmanian Office. Labour, Wages and Prices *see* 0814-9593
0067-1053 Australia. Bureau of Statistics. Tasmanian Office. Primary Industries (Excluding Mining) *changed to* Australia. Bureau of Statistics. Tasmanian Office. Agriculture, Tasmania.
0067-1061 Australia. Bureau of Statistics. Tasmanian Office. Social *see* 0314-1705
0067-107X Australia. Bureau of Statistics. Tasmanian Office. Trade and Shipping *changed to* Australia. Bureau of Statistics. Tasmanian Office. Interstate Trade.
0067-1096 Australia. Bureau of Statistics. Victorian Office. Demography, Victoria *changed to* Australia. Bureau of Statistics. Victorian Office. Demography Summary Statement, Victoria.
0067-1126 Australia. Bureau of Statistics. Victorian Office. Hospital Morbidity†
0067-1134 Australia. Bureau of Statistics. Victorian Office Industrial Accidents and Workers Compensation. Statistics *changed to* Australia. Bureau of Statistics. Victorian Office. Industrial Accidents and Workers Compensation.
0067-1142 Australia. Bureau of Statistics. Victorian Office. Government Finance *see* 1030-0724
0067-1150 Australia. Bureau of Statistics. Victorian Office. Primary and Secondary Education, Victoria *see* 1031-7767
0067-1169 Australia. Bureau of Statistics. Value of Production Bulletin†
0067-1193 Australia. Bureau of Statistics. Victorian Office. Tertiary Education†
0067-1207 Victorian Pocket Yearbook *see* 1033-3665
0067-1223 Australia. Bureau of Statistics. Victorian Office. Victorian Yearbook
0067-124X Australia. Bureau of Statistics. Western Australian Office. Abstract of Statistics of Local Government Areas. *see* 0312-6072
0067-1266 Australia. Bureau of Statistics. Western Australian Office. Industrial Accidents, Western Australia *changed to* Western Australia. Department of Occupational Health, Safety and Welfare. Industrial Accidents.
0067-1282 Australia. Bureau of Statistics. Western Australian Office. Local Government Revenue and Expenditure: Budget Estimates†
0067-1290 Australia. Bureau of Statistics. Western Australian Office. Population, Dwellings and Vital Statistics†
0067-1312 Australia. Bureau of Meteorology. Bulletin
0067-1320 Australia. Bureau of Meteorology. Meteorological Study
0067-1339 Australia. Bureau of Mineral Resources, Geology and Geophysics. Pictorial Index of Activities†
0067-1347 Australia. Department of Industry and Commerce. Annual Report *see* 0728-6856
0067-1355 Australia. Department of Education. A.C.T. Education Directory†
0067-1436 Australia. Operation of the Fishing Industry, A.C.T. Annual Report
0067-1444 Australia. Department of the Treasury. Income Tax Statistics
0067-1452 Australia. Forestry and Timber Bureau. Bulletins *changed to* Commonwealth Scientific and Industrial Research Organization. Division of Forest Research. Bulletins.
0067-1460 Australia. Forestry and Timber Bureau. Forest Resources Newsletter *see* 0314-1438
0067-1479 Australia. Forestry and Timber Bureau. Leaflets *changed to* Commonwealth Scientific and Industrial Research Organization. Division of Forest Research. Leaflets.
0067-1495 Australia Handbook†
0067-1509 Australia Mineral Industry Review *see* 0084-7488
0067-1517 Australia. National Capital Development Commission. Annual Report†
0067-155X Australian Academy of Science. Records *changed to* Historical Records of Australian Science.
0067-1568 Australian Academy of Science. Reports *changed to* Australian Academy of Science. Annual General Meeting Symposium.
0067-1576 Australian Academy of Science. Science and Industry Forum Reports
0067-1584 Australian Academy of Science. Year Book
0067-1592 Australian Academy of the Humanities. Proceedings

ISSN INDEX 5495

0067-1606 Australian Advertising Rate and Data Service
0067-1622 Australian and New Zealand Law List and Legal Compendium *changed to* Australian and New Zealand Law List.
0067-1630 Australian Association of Adult Education. Monograph†
0067-1649 Australian Association of Adult Education. Proceedings of the National Conference†
0067-1657 Australia. Atomic Energy Commission. Research Establishment. A A E C - E *see* 1030-7745
0067-1665 Australia. Atomic Energy Commission. Research Establishment. A A E C - M *changed to* Australia. Nuclear Science and Technology Organisation. A N S T O - M.
0067-1703 Australian Biochemical Society. Proceedings
0067-172X Australian Books in Print
0067-1738 Australian Books
0067-1754 Australian Capital Territory Statistical Summary
0067-1762 Australian Coal Industry Research Laboratories. Annual Report
0067-1789 Australian College of Ophthalmologists Transactions. *see* 0814-9763
0067-1819 Australian Computer Society. Council. Report†
0067-1835 Australian Council for Educational Research. Occasional Papers†
0067-1843 Australian Digest
0067-186X Australia. Bureau of Statistics. Australian Exports Bulletin *see* 0705-0534
0067-1878 Australian Government Publications
0067-1886 Australian Hereford Annual *see* 0814-7663
0067-1894 Australian Honey Board. Annual Report
0067-1916 Australia. Bureau of Statistics. Australian Imports Bulletin *see* 0705-0542
0067-1924 Australian Journal of Botany
0067-1940 Australian Journal of Marine and Freshwater Research
0067-1959 Australian Market Guide
0067-1967 Australian Museum, Sydney. Memoirs *see* 0812-7387
0067-1975 Australian Museum, Sydney. Records
0067-1983 Australian National Accounts: National Income and Expenditure (Annual)
0067-2017 Australian National University, Canberra. Department of International Relations. Documents and Data Paper†
0067-2025 Australian National University, Canberra. Department of International Relations. Workpaper†
0067-2033 Australian National University, Canberra. Department of Political Science. Occasional Paper. *changed to* Australian National University, Canberra. Research School of Social Sciences. Department of Political Science. Occasional Papers.
0067-2041 Australian National University, Canberra. Faculty of Asian Studies. Occasional Papers†
0067-2076 Australian Photography Directory *changed to* Australian Photography Photo-Directory.
0067-2084 Australian Physiological and Pharmacological Society. Proceedings
0067-2106 Australian Agriculture, Fisheries and Forestry Directory *see* 0812-1729
0067-2130 Australian Society for Medical Research Proceedings *see* 0305-1870
0067-2149 Australian Society of Animal Production. Proceedings *see* 0728-5965
0067-2165 Australian Studies in Health Service Administration
0067-2173 Australian Sugar Year Book
0067-2181 Australian Telecommunication Monographs
0067-219X Australia. Australian Water Resources Council. Hydrological Series†
0067-222X Australian Wool *see* 0311-9882
0067-2238 Australian Zoologist
0067-2246 Australiana Facsimile Editions†
0067-2262 Austria. Bundesministerium fuer Land- und Forstwirtschaft. Taetigkeitsbericht
0067-2270 Austria. Bundesministerium fuer Unterricht und Kunst. Erziehung, Wissenschaft, Forschung *changed to* Austria. Bundesministerium fuer Unterricht und Kunst. Schriftenreihe.
0067-2289 Austria. Bundesministerium fuer Unterricht und Kunst. Jahresbericht†
0067-2297 Oesterreichisches Staatsarchiv. Mitteilungen
0067-2300 Austria. Statistisches Zentralamt. Die Wohnbautaetigkeit *changed to* Austria. Statistisches Zentralamt. Wohnungsdaten.
0067-2319 Beitraege zur Oesterreichischen Statistik
0067-2327 Austria. Statistisches Zentralamt. Ergebnisse der Landwirtschaftlichen Statistik
0067-2335 Austria. Statistisches Zentralamt. Die Natuerliche Bevoelkerungsbewegung *changed to* Austria. Statistisches Zentralamt. Demographisches Jahrbuch Oesterreiches.
0067-2343 Oesterreichische Hochschulstatistik
0067-2351 Austria. Zentralanstalt fuer Meteorologie und Geodynamik. Jahrbuch
0067-2378 Austrian History Yearbook
0067-2386 Author's and Writer's Who's Who *see* 0143-8263
0067-2408 Auto Racing Guide†
0067-2416 Auto-Universum
0067-2424 Autocatalogue
0067-2432 Autocourse†
0067-2491 Automatic Support Systems Symposium for Advanced Maintainability. Proceedings *changed to* Autotestcon.
0067-2521 Automobile Buyers' Guide†
0067-253X Automobile Facts and Figures *see* 0146-9932
0067-2548 Automobile News Annual
0067-2572 Automotive Mass Marketer *see* 0702-8318
0067-2580 Automotive News Almanac *changed to* Automotive News Market Data Book.
0067-2610 Avant-Siecle
0067-2629 Aventure des Civilisations†
0067-2637 Aves del Arca
0067-2645 Aviation Directory of Asia†
0067-2653 Aviation et Astronautique†
0067-2661 Aviation Medical Education Series
0067-2696 Ayer Directory of Newspapers, Magazines, and Trade Publications *see* 1048-7972
0067-270X Azania
0067-2734 B B A Library†
0067-2742 B.G. Rudolph Lectures in Judaic Studies
0067-2777 Bacteriological Proceedings *changed to* American Society for Microbiology. Abstracts of the General Meeting.
0067-2793 Badania z Dziejow Spolecznych i Gospodarczych
0067-2807 Badania Fizjograficzne nad Polska Zachodnia. Seria A. Geografia Fizyczna
0067-2815 Badania Fizjograficzne nad Polska Zachodnia. Seria B. Biologia *changed to* Badania Fizjograficzne nad Polska Zachodnia. Seria B. Botanika.
0067-2823 Badania Nad Dziejami Przemyslu i Klasy Robotniczej W Polsce†
0067-2831 Kommission fuer Geschichtliche Landeskunde in Baden-Wuerttemberg. Veroeffentlichungen. Reihe A. Quellen
0067-284X Staatliche Kunstsammlungen in Baden-Wuerttemberg. Jahrbuch
0067-2858 Badischer Landesverein fuer Naturkunde und Naturschutz, Freiburg. Mitteilungen. Neue Folge
0067-2866 Badlands Natural History Association. Bulletin†
0067-2874 Badman†
0067-2882 Badminton Association of England. Official Handbook *see* 0262-1940
0067-2890 Scientific Research Council of Iraq. Biological Science Research Centre. Journal *see* 1012-344X
0067-2904 University of Baghdad. College of Science. Bulletin *changed to* Iraqi Journal of Science.
0067-2912 Bahamas Handbook and Businessman's Annual
0067-2947 Baily's Hunting Directory
0067-2955 Baja California Travels Series†
0067-2963 Baker and Bakery Management Handbook and Buyers Guide†
0067-298X Balance of Payments of Japan†
0067-2998 Balance of Payments of Sierra Leone
0067-3005 Balance of Payments of Trinidad and Tobago
0067-3013 Balanza de Pagos de Chile†
0067-3021 Balanza de Pagos de Espana
0067-303X Baldwin Lectures in Teacher Education *changed to* Baldwin Lectures.
0067-3048 Bale Catalogue of Israel Stamps *changed to* Bale Catalogue of Israel Postage Stamps.
0067-3064 Baltica†
0067-3072 Baltimore College of Dental Surgery, Journal†
0067-3080 Baltimore Museum of Art. Annual†
0067-3099 Baltische Studien
0067-3102 Baltisches Recht; das Recht Estlands, Lettlands und Litauens in Vergangenheit und Gegenwart†
0067-3110 Chambre de Commerce et d'Industrie du Mali. Precis Fiscal, Commercial, des Changes et des Echanges
0067-3129 Bampton Lectures in America
0067-3161 Banca d'Italia. Assemblea Generale Ordinaria dei Partecipanti.
0067-3188 Somali National Bank. Report and Balance Sheet *changed to* Central Bank of Somalia. Annual Report and Statement of Accounts.
0067-320X Banco Central de Costa Rica. Memoria Anual
0067-3218 Banco Central de Honduras. Memoria *changed to* Banco Central de Honduras. Memoria (Year).
0067-3226 Banco Central de Nicaragua. Informe Anual
0067-3234 El Salvador. Superintendencia de Bancos y Otras Instituciones Financieras. Estadisticas: Seguros, Finanzas, Capitalization *changed to* El Salvador. Superintendencia del Sistema Financiero. Junta Monetaria. Anuario Estadistico: Seguros, Fianzas, Bancos.
0067-3250 Banco Central de Venezuela. Informe Economico
0067-3269 Banco Central de Venezuela. Memoria
0067-3277 Banco Central del Ecuador. Memoria del Gerente General
0067-3285 Banco Central del Paraguay. Memoria
0067-3315 Banco de Espana. Informe Anual
0067-3323 Banco de la Republica Cuentas Nacionales†
0067-3331 Banco de la Republica Disposiciones†
0067-334X Guia para el Inversionista.†
0067-3366 Banco de la Republica Series Estadisticas y Graficos.†
0067-3374 Banco de Mexico. Informe Anual
0067-3390 Banco Nacional de Fomento, Tegucigalpa. Memoria Anual *changed to* Banco Nacional de Desarrollo Agricola. Memoria Anual.
0067-3412 Bancroftiana
0067-3439 Indian Statistical Institute. Documentation Research and Training Centre. D R T C Annual Seminar
0067-3455 University of Agricultural Sciences, Bangalore. Annual Report
0067-3463 University of Agricultural Sciences, Bangalore. Research Series†
0067-3471 U A S Extension Series
0067-348X U A S Miscellaneous Series
0067-3498 Bangkok, Thailand. College of Education. Thesis Abstract Series
0067-3501 Bank Administration Institute. Accounting Bulletins†
0067-351X Bank Administration Institute. Annual Report†
0067-3528 Bank Officer Salary Survey *see* 0525-4620
0067-3536 Bank Administration Institute. Personnel Policies and Practices *changed to* Biennial Survey of Bank Personnel Policies and Practices.
0067-3544 Bank Administration Institute. Security Bulletins†
0067-3560 Bank for International Settlements. Annual Report
0067-3587 Bank of Canada. Annual Report
0067-3595 Bank of Canada. Staff Research Studies *see* 0713-7931
0067-3617 Central Bank of Ceylon. Report and Accounts *changed to* Bank of Ceylon. Annual Report and Accounts.
0067-3625 Bank of England. Report *see* 0308-5279
0067-3633 Hawaii Annual Economic Review *see* 1043-6685
0067-3641 Bank of Israel. Main Points of the Annual Report†
0067-365X Bank of Israel. Annual Report
0067-3668 Bank of Jamaica. Report and Statement of Accounts
0067-3676 Bank of Japan. Annual Report of the Policy Board *changed to* Bank of Japan. Annual Report.
0067-3684 Bank of Japan. Business Report†
0067-3714 Bank of Libya. Annual Report of the Board of Directors
0067-3722 Bank of Mauritius. Annual Report
0067-3730 Bank of Sierra Leone. Annual Report *changed to* Bank of Sierra Leone. Annual Report and Statement of Accounts.
0067-3749 Bank of Sudan. Report
0067-3757 Bank of Tanzania. Economic and Operations Report (Year)
0067-3765 Bank of Tanzania. Economic Report *see* 0067-3757
0067-379X Bankers Almanac and Year Book
0067-3803 Bankers' Who's Who
0067-3811 Banking Statistics of Pakistan
0067-382X Bankwirtschaftliche Forschungen
0067-3846 Banque Centrale de Syrie. Bulletin Periodique *changed to* Central Bank of Syria. Quarterly Bulletin.
0067-3854 Banque Centrale de Tunisie. Bulletin
0067-3862 Banque Centrale de Tunisie. Rapport d'Activite
0067-3889 Banque Centrale des Etats de l'Afrique de l'Ouest. Rapport Annuel
0067-3897 Banque Centrale des Etats de l'Afrique de l'Ouest. Rapport d'Activite
0067-3900 Banque des Etats de l'Afrique Centrale. Rapport d'Activite
0067-3919 Banque de Bruxelles. Rapport Annuel *changed to* Banque de Bruxelles Lambert. Rapports de l'Exercice.
0067-3927 Banque de France. Compte-Rendu
0067-3943 Banque de l'Union Europeenne. Informations Economiques et Financieres. *see* 0245-761X
0067-3951 Banque des Mots
0067-396X Banque du Maroc. Rapport Annuel *changed to* Bank Al-Maghrib. Rapport Annuel.
0067-3978 Banque Nationale de Belgique. Rapport sur les Operations

ISSN

0067-4001 Banque Nationale du Congo. Rapport Annuel *see* 0300-1172
0067-401X Banque Nationale Malagasy de Developpement. Rapport d'Activite *changed to* Bankin'Ny Indostria. Rapport Annuel.
0067-4028 Banque Populaire Suisse. Information
0067-4036 Banque Togolaise de Developpement. Rapport Annuel *changed to* Banque Togolaise de Developpement. Rapport d'Activites.
0067-4044 Bantu Treasury *changed to* Black Writers Series.
0067-4052 Baptist Handbook†
0067-4060 Baptist Missionary Society, Didcot. Annual Report
0067-4079 Baptist Missionary Society, London. Official Report and Directory of Missionaries
0067-4087 Baptist Union of Western Canada. Yearbook
0067-4095 Baptist World Alliance. Congress Reports
0067-4109 Bar-Ilan: Annual of Bar-Ilan University
0067-4125 Barbados. Statistical Service. Overseas Trade Report
0067-4141 Universidad de Barcelona. Biblioteca Central. Catalogos de la Production Editorial Barcelona *see* 0210-6833
0067-4168 Patronato Municipal de la Vivienda de Barcelona. Memoria
0067-4176 Universidad de Barcelona. Facultad de Farmacia. Memoria
0067-4184 Universidad de Barcelona. Instituto de Arqueologia y Prehistoria. Publicaciones Eventuales
0067-4206 Die Barke
0067-4222 Baroque
0067-4230 Barque's Pakistan Trade Directory and Who's Who
0067-4249 Barsoomian
0067-4265 Baseball Dope Book *see* 0162-5411
0067-4273 Baseball Guide
0067-4281 Baseball Register *see* 0162-542X
0067-4303 Gewerbemuseum Basel. Schriften†
0067-4311 Oeffentliche Kunstsammlung. Jahresbericht *changed to* Oeffentliche Kunstsammlung. Museum fuer Gegenwart. Jahresbericht.
0067-4338 Basic Auto Repair Manual†
0067-4362 Basic Bodywork and Painting†
0067-4370 Basic Cams, Valves and Exhaust Systems†
0067-4389 Basic Carburetion and Fuel Systems†
0067-4397 Basic Chassis, Suspension and Brakes†
0067-4400 Basic Clutches and Transmissions†
0067-4419 Basic Facts about the United Nations
0067-4427 Basic Ignition and Electrical Systems†
0067-4443 Basic Science Symposium Series†
0067-446X Basis†
0067-4478 Basler Beitraege zur Ethnologie
0067-4486 Basler Beitraege zur Geographie
0067-4494 Basler Drucke†
0067-4508 Basler Studien zur Deutschen Sprache und Literatur
0067-4524 Basler Veroeffentlichungen zur Geschichte der Medizin und der Biologie
0067-4532 Basler Wirtschaftswissenschaftliche Vortraege†
0067-4540 Basler Zeitschrift fuer Geschichte und Altertumskunde
0067-4575 Bau und Baustoff Handbuch†
0067-4583 Baubeschlag-Taschenbuch
0067-4591 Bauernhaeuser der Schweiz
0067-4605 Bauhinia
0067-463X Bausteine zur Geschichte des Neuhochdeutschen *changed to* Bausteine zur Sprachgeschichte des Neuhochdeutschen.
0067-4648 Instituto Nacional de la Pesca de Cuba. Centro de Investigaciones Pesqueras. Boletin de Divulgacion Tecnica†
0067-4656 Centro de Investigaciones Pesqueras. Contribuciones *changed to* Revista Cubana de Investigaciones Pesqueras. Boletines Bibliograficos.
0067-4664 Bauwelt Katalog *changed to* Bertelsmann Baukatalog.
0067-4672 Bayer-Symposien
0067-4710 Bayerisches Forstdienst-Taschenbuch
0067-4729 Bayerisches Jahrbuch fuer Volkskunde
0067-4745 Beaufortia
0067-4761 Bed and Breakfast in South and Southwest England *see* 0267-3436
0067-477X Bed and Breakfast in Wales, Northern England and Scotland *see* 0267-3436
0067-4788 Bedford Institute of Oceanography. A O L Data Series *changed to* Bedford Institute of Oceanography. Data Report.
0067-4796 Atlantic Oceanographic Laboratory. A O L Report *changed to* Bedford Institute of Oceanography. Report.
0067-480X Bedford Institute of Oceanography. Biennial Review *changed to* Bedford Institute of Oceanography. Science Review.
0067-4826 Bedfordshire Historical Record Society. Publications
0067-4834 Bedrijfschap voor de Lederwarenindustrie. Jaarverslag
0067-4893 Beihefte der Bonner Jahrbuecher
0067-4907 Sonderbaende zur Theologischen Zeitschrift
0067-4915 Beilsteins Handbuch der Organischen Chemie. Supplement
0067-4931 Beiruter Texte und Studien
0067-4974 Technische Beitraege zur Archaeologie†
0067-5008 Beitraege zur Geologie von Thueringen†
0067-5016 Beitraege zur Gerichtlichen Medizin
0067-5024 Beitraege zur Geschichte der Philosophie und Theologie des Mittelalters. Neue Folge
0067-5059 Beitraege zur Geschichte des Religioesen und Wissenschaftlichen Denkens†
0067-5067 Beitraege zur Harmonikalen Grundlagenforschung
0067-5075 Beitraege zur Heilpaedagogik und Heilpaedagogischen Psychologie†
0067-5091 Beitraege zur Inkunabelkunde. Dritte Folge
0067-5105 Beitraege zur Kinderpsychotherapie
0067-5113 Krebsforschung. Beitraege†
0067-5121 Beitraege zur Kunst des Christlichen Ostens
0067-5148 Beitraege zur Meereskunde
0067-5164 Beitraege zur Oberpfalzforschung
0067-5172 Beitraege zur Oekumenischen Theologie
0067-5180 Beitraege zur Praktischen Medizin†
0067-5202 Beitraege zur Romanischen Philologie des Mittelalters
0067-5210 Beitraege zur Sexualforschung
0067-5237 Beitraege zur Strafvollzugswissenschaft
0067-5245 Beitraege zur Ur- und Fruehgeschichtlichen Archaeologie des Mittelmeerkulturraumes
0067-5253 Beitraege zur Wehrforschung†
0067-5261 Beitraege zur Westfaelischen Familienforschung
0067-527X Brazil. Instituto de Pesquisas Agropecuarias do Norte. Boletim Tecnico†
0067-5288 Instituto de Pesquisas Agropecuarias do Norte. Circular†
0067-5296 Instituto de Pesquisas Agropecurarias do Norte. Communicado Tecnico†
0067-5342 Belfast and Northern Ireland Directory
0067-5350 Belfast History and Philosophical Society. Proceedings and Reports
0067-5369 Belgium. Administration des Eaux et Forets. Station de Recherche des Eaux et Forets. Travaux. Serie D. Hydrobiologie *changed to* Belgium. Station de Recherches Forestieres et Hydrobiologiques. Travaux. Serie D. Hydrobiologie.
0067-5385 Belgium. Conseil National du Travail. Rapport du Secretaire sur l'Activite du Conseil†
0067-5393 Belgium. Conseil Superieur des Classes Moyennes. Rapport Annuel du Secretaire General
0067-5407 Belgium. Nationaal Fonds voor Wetenschappelijk Onderzoek. Jaarverslag
0067-5415 Activities des Aerodromes Belges *see* 0773-4255
0067-5423 Belgium. Institut National de Statistique. Annuaire Statistique de l'Enseignement *see* 0773-5820
0067-5431 Belgium. Institut National de Statistique. Annuaire Statistique de Poche
0067-544X Belgium. Institut National de Statistique. Batiments et Logements *see* 0772-7720
0067-5458 Belgium. Institut National de Statistique. Mouvement de la Population des Communes†
0067-5466 Belgium. Institut National de Statistique. Statistiques Agricoles
0067-5482 Belgium. Institut National de Statistique. Statistique Annuelle du Trafic International des Ports *see* 0772-7739
0067-5490 Belgium. Institut National de Statistique. Statistiques Demographiques
0067-5512 Belgium. Institut National de Statistique. Statistique des Accidents de Roulage *see* 0770-237X
0067-5520 Belgium. Institut National de Statistique. Statistique de la Navigation du Rhin *see* 0773-2805
0067-5547 Belgium. Institut National de Statistique. Statistique du Tourisme et de l'Hotellerie
0067-5563 Belgium. Institut National de Statistique. Statistiques Sociales
0067-5571 Belgium. Ministere de la Prevoyance Sociale. Annuaire Statistique de la Securite Sociale/Statistisch Jaarboek van de Sociale Zeherheid†
0067-558X Belgium. Ministere de la Prevoyance Sociale. Rapport General sur la Securite Sociale
0067-5598 Belgium. Ministere de l'Education Nationale et de la Culture Francaise. Rapport Annuel *changed to* Belgium. Ministere de l'Education Nationale. Rapport Annuel.
0067-5601 Bibliotheque Africaine. Catalogue des Acquisitions. Catologus van de Aanwinsten†
0067-5644 Belgium. Office National de l'Emploi. Rapport Annuel *changed to* Belgium. Office National de l'Emploi. Etudes Economiques et Sociales.
0067-5652 Societe National du Logement. Rapport Annuel
0067-5660 Vojni Muzej, Belgrade. Vesnik
0067-5687 Universidade Federal de Minas Gerais. Instituto de Pesquisas Radioativas. Relatorios Anuais†
0067-5695 Beloit Poetry Journal. Chapbook
0067-5709 B E M A Engineering Directory
0067-5717 Benjamin F. Fairless Lectures
0067-5725 Benn's Hardware Directory *see* 0954-8548
0067-5733 Bent
0067-5768 Berg- und Huettenmaennische Monatshefte. Supplement†
0067-5792 Bergischer Geschichtsverein. Zeitschrift
0067-5806 Berichte des Vereins Natur und Heimat und des Naturhistorischen Museums zu Luebeck
0067-5814 Nursing Journal of Singapore
0067-5822 Berkeley Analyses of Molecular Spectra†
0067-5830 Berkeley Journal of Sociology
0067-5849 Biologische Bundesanstalt fuer Land- und Forstwirtschaft, Berlin-Dahlem. Mitteilungen
0067-5857 Historische Kommission zu Berlin. Einzelveroeffentlichungen
0067-5865 Berlin. Freie Universitaet. Institut fuer Statistik und Versicherungsmathematik. Berichte *see* 0066-5673
0067-5881 Freie Universitaet Berlin. Osteuropa-Institut. Bibliographische Mitteilungen
0067-589X Freie Universitaet Berlin. Osteuropa-Institut. Erziehungswissenschaftliche Veroeffentlichungen
0067-5903 Freie Universitaet Berlin. Osteuropa-Institut. Historische Veroeffentlichungen
0067-5911 Freie Universitaet Berlin. Osteuropa-Institut. Philosophische und Soziologische Veroeffentlichungen
0067-592X Freie Universitaet Berlin. Osteuropa-Institut. Slavistische Veroeffentlichungen
0067-5938 Freie Universitaet Berlin. Osteuropa-Institut. Wirtschaftswissenschaftliche Veroeffentlichungen
0067-5954 Hochschule fuer Oekonomie "Bruno Leuschner" Berlin. Wissenschaftliche Zeitschrift†
0067-5962 Museum fuer Voelkerkunde, Berlin. Veroeffentlichungen. Neue Folge. Abteilung: Afrika
0067-5989 Museum fuer Voelkerkunde, Berlin. Veroeffentlichungen. Neue Folge. Abteilung: Suedsee
0067-5997 R I A S-Funkuniversitaet, Berlin. Forschung und Information *changed to* R I A S-Funkuniversitaet, Berlin. Schriftenreihe. Forschung und Information.
0067-6004 Staatliche Museen zu Berlin. Jahrbuch. Forschungen und Berichte
0067-6039 Technische Universitaet. Institut fuer Sozialoekonomie der Agrarentwicklung. Taetigkeitsbericht *see* 0177-6673
0067-6047 Berlin, Theater und Drama†
0067-6055 Berliner Byzantinistische Arbeiten
0067-6063 Berliner Handelsregister Verzeichnis
0067-6098 Berliner Tierpark-Buch
0067-611X Berlinische Reminiszenzen
0067-6128 Berner Beitraege zur Nationaloekonomie
0067-6136 Berner Beitraege zur Soziologie†
0067-6144 Berner Kriminologische Untersuchungen†
0067-6152 Berner Studien zum Fremdenverkehr†
0067-6160 Bernice Pauahi Bishop Museum, Honolulu. Occasional Papers
0067-6179 Bernice Pauahi Bishop Museum, Honolulu. Special Publications
0067-6195 Berytus Archeological Studies
0067-6233 Best American Short Stories
0067-6276 Borestone Mountain Poetry Awards†
0067-6284 Best Short Plays
0067-6292 Best Sports Stories
0067-6306 Bestands-Statistik der Kraftfahrzeuge in Oesterreich
0067-6314 Bestimmungsbuecher zur Bodenfauna Europas†
0067-6330 Bestsellers du Monde Entier†
0067-6357 Beta Phi Mu Chapbook†
0067-6365 Beton- und Fertigteil-Jahrbuch
0067-6381 Schriftenreihe Betriebswirtschaftiche Beitraege zur Organisation und Automation†
0067-639X Betriebswirtschaftliche Mitteilungen *changed to* Management Praxis.
0067-642X Better Building Bulletin†
0067-6454 Bharat Krishak Samaj. Year Book†
0067-6462 Basic Road Statistics of India
0067-6470 Bialostockie Towarzystwo Naukowe. Prace
0067-6489 Akademia Medyczna w Bialymstoku. Roczniki
0067-6535 Biblical Research
0067-6543 Bibliografi over Danmarks Offentlige Publikationer

0067-6551 Bibliografia Analitica a Periodicelor Romanesti†
0067-656X Bibliografia Bibliotecologica Argentina
0067-6578 Bibliografia Boliviana *changed to* Bio-Bibliografia Boliviana.
0067-6586 Bibliografia Brasileira de Botanica†
0067-6594 Bibliografia Brasileira de Ciencias Agricolas *changed to* Bibliografia Brasileira de Agricultura (Year).
0067-6608 Bibliografia Brasileira de Ciencias Sociais†
0067-6616 Bibliografia Brasileira de Direito†
0067-6624 Bibliografia Brasileira de Documentacao†
0067-6632 Bibliografia Brasileira de Educacao
0067-6640 Bibliografia Brasileira de Fisica†
0067-6659 Bibliografia Brasileira de Livros Infantis†
0067-6667 Bibliografia Brasileira de Matematica†
0067-6675 Bibliografia Brasileira de Medicina†
0067-6683 Bibliografia Brasileira de Quimica *see* 0100-0756
0067-6691 Bibliografia Brasileira de Zoologia†
0067-6721 Bibliografia Historii Polskiej
0067-6748 Bibliografia Oficial Colombiana†
0067-6756 Bibliografia Portuguesa de Construcao Civil *changed to* Bibliografia Portuguesa de Engenharia Civil.
0067-6764 Bibliografia Sobre a Economia Portuguesa†
0067-6772 Bibliografia Ticinese†
0067-6780 Bibliograficky Zbornik
0067-6799 Bibliografija Medicinske Periodike Jugoslavije
0067-6802 Bibliographia Medica Cechoslovaca
0067-6829 Bibliographia Scientiae Naturalis Helvetica
0067-6837 Bibliographic Annual in Speech Communication†
0067-6853 Bibliographica Judaica
0067-6861 Bibliographical Selection of Museological Literature *changed to* Selected Bibliography of Museological Literature.
0067-687X Bibliographical Society of Canada. Facsimile Series
0067-6888 Bibliographical Society of Canada. Monographs
0067-6896 Bibliographical Society of Canada. Papers
0067-6918 Bibliographie Annuelle de l'Histoire de France
0067-6926 Bibliographie Annuelle de Madagascar
0067-6934 Bibliographie Cartographique Internationale†
0067-6942 Bibliographie de la Litterature Francaise du Moyen Age a Nos Jours†
0067-6950 Bibliographie der Chemisch-Archaeologischen Literatur†
0067-6969 Bibliographie der Paedagogischen Veroeffentlichungen in der Deutschen Demokratischen Republik
0067-6977 Bibliographie der Sozialethik†
0067-6985 Bibliographie en la Langue Francaise d'Histoire du Droit de 987 a 1875 *changed to* Bibliographie en Langue Francaise d'Histoire du Droit de 987 a 1914.
0067-6993 Bibliographie Geographique Internationale
0067-7000 Bibliographie Internationale de l'Humanisme et de la Renaissance
0067-7027 Bibliographie Programmierter Unterricht *see* 0523-2678
0067-7043 Bibliographie d'Histoire Luxembourgeoise
0067-706X Bibliographie zur Symbolik, Ikonographie und Mythologie
0067-7094 Bibliographies in Paint Technology†
0067-7116 Bibliographies on the Near East†
0067-7132 Bibliography and Reference Series†
0067-7159 Bibliography of Asian Studies
0067-7183 Bibliography of Developmental Medicine and Child Neurology. Books and Articles Received
0067-7191 Bibliography of Historical Works Issued in the United Kingdom†
0067-7205 Bibliography of Interlingual Scientific and Technical Dictionaries†
0067-7213 Bibliography of Old Norse-Icelandic Studies
0067-7256 Bibliography of South African Government Publications†
0067-7264 Bibliography of Surgery of the Hand†
0067-7272 Bibliography of the Geology of Missouri
0067-7280 Bibliography of the History of Medicine
0067-7302 Bibliography of the Middle East
0067-7310 Bibliography of Works by Polish Scholars and Scientists Published Outside Poland in Languages Other Than Polish
0067-7329 Bibliography on Foreign and Comparative Law: Books and Articles in English.
0067-7353 Bibliography on Satellite Geodesy and Related Subjects *changed to* International Association of Geodesy. Central Bureau for Satellite Geodesy. Bibliography.
0067-7361 Bibliography on Smoking and Health
0067-737X Bibliohrafichnyi Pokazhchyk Ukrains'koi Presy Poza Mezhamy Ukrainy†
0067-7388 Biblioteca de Arheologie
0067-7396 Biblioteca de Cultura Vasca†
0067-740X Biblioteca de Teologia
0067-7418 Biblioteca di Bibliografia Italiana
0067-7434 Biblioteca di Labeo
0067-7442 Biblioteca di Storia Toscana Moderna e Contemporanea. Studi e Documenti
0067-7450 Biblioteca di Studi Etruschi
0067-7469 Biblioteca do Educador Profissional
0067-7477 Bibliotheca Germanica. Handbuecher, Texte und Monographien aus dem Gebiete der Germanischen Philologie
0067-7493 Biblioteca Istorica
0067-7507 Biblioteca Prehistorica Hispana†
0067-7515 Bibliotheca Romanica
0067-7523 Biblioteca Storica Toscana *changed to* Biblioteca Storica Toscana. Serie I.
0067-7531 Biblioteconomia e Bibliografia. Saggi e Studi
0067-754X Biblioteczka Ateisty
0067-7558 Biblioteczka Kopernikanska†
0067-7582 Biblioteczka Wiedzy O Slasku. Seria Archeologiczna†
0067-7590 Biblioteczka Wiedzy O Slasku. Seria Etnograficzna†
0067-7604 Biblioteczka Wiedzy O Slasku. Seria Historyczna†
0067-7612 Biblioteczka Wiedzy O Slasku. Seria Literatura Ludowa†
0067-7620 Biblioteczka Wiedzy O Slasku. Seria Przyrodnicza†
0067-7639 Biblioteka Archeologiczna
0067-7655 Biblioteka Etnografii Polskiej
0067-7671 Biblioteka Klasykow Pedagogiki†
0067-7698 Biblioteka Krakowska
0067-7701 Biblioteka Mechaniki Stosowanej
0067-7728 Biblioteka Nawigatora†
0067-7736 Biblioteka Pisarzow Polskich *see* 0519-8631
0067-7760 Biblioteka Popularnonaukowa†
0067-7779 Biblioteka Sluchacza Koncertowego. Seria Wprowadzajaca
0067-7787 Towarzystwo Literackie im. A. Mickiewicza. Biblioteka
0067-7795 Biblioteka Wiadomosci Statystycznych
0067-7809 Biblioteka Zagadnien Gospodarczych Polski†
0067-7817 Bibliotheca Aegyptiaca
0067-7825 Bibliotheca Africana Droz†
0067-7833 Bibliotheca Anatomica
0067-7841 Bibliotheca Arnamagnaeana
0067-785X Bibliotheca Arnamagnaeana. Supplementum
0067-7868 Bibliotheca Athena
0067-7876 Bibliotheca Australiana
0067-7884 Bibliotheca Bibliographica Aureliana
0067-7892 Bibliotheca Botanica
0067-7906 Bibliotheca Cardiologica
0067-7914 Bibliotheca Celtica *changed to* Bibliography of Wales.
0067-7922 Bibliotheca del Planeamiento Educativo
0067-7930 Bibliotheca Emblematica†
0067-7965 Bibliotheca Helvetica Romana
0067-7981 Bibliotheca Historica Romaniae. Studies
0067-799X Bibliotheca Historica Romaniae. Monographies
0067-8007 Bibliotheca Hungarica Antiqua
0067-8015 Bibliotheca Ibero-Americana
0067-8023 Bibliotheca Indonesica
0067-8031 Bibliotheca Latina Medii et Recentiori Aevi
0067-8058 Bibliotheca Microbiologia *see* 0301-3081
0067-8066 Bibliotheca Mycologica
0067-8082 Bibliotheca Oeconomica
0067-8090 Bibliotheca Ophthalmologica *see* 0250-3751
0067-8104 Bibliotheca Orientalis Hungarica
0067-8112 Bibliotheca Phycologica
0067-8120 Bibliotheca Phonetica†
0067-8139 Bibliotheca Primatologica *see* 0301-4231
0067-8147 Bibliotheca Psychiatrica
0067-8163 Bibliotheca Seraphico-Capuccina. Sectio Historica
0067-8198 Bibliotheca Nutritio et Dieta
0067-8201 Bibliothek der Klassischen Altertumswissenschaften. Neue Folge
0067-821X Bilder aus Deutscher Vergangenheit†
0067-8228 Bibliothek fuer das Gesamtgebiet der Lungenkrankheiten†
0067-8236 Bibliothek und Wissenschaft
0067-8244 Bibliotheque Arctique et Antarctique†
0067-8260 Bibliotheque de la Mer
0067-8279 Bibliotheque de la Revue d'Histoire Ecclesiastique
0067-8295 Bibliotheque de Sciences Religieuses†
0067-8309 Bibliotheque des Cahiers Archeologiques *see* 0068-4945
0067-8325 Bibliotheque d'Etudes Balkaniques
0067-8333 Bibliotheque Europeenne†
0067-8341 Bibliotheque Francaise et Romane. Serie A: Manuels et Etudes Linguistiques
0067-835X Bibliotheque Francaise et Romane. Serie B: Editions Critiques de Textes
0067-8368 Bibliotheque Francaise et Romane. Serie C: Etudes Litteraires
0067-8376 Bibliotheque Francaise et Romane. Serie D: Initiation, Textes et Documents
0067-8384 Bibliotheque Francaise et Romane. Serie E: Langue et Litterature Francaises au Canada
0067-8406 Bibliotheque Historique Vaudoise
0067-8414 Bibliotheque Ideale†
0067-8422 Bibliotheque Introuvable
0067-8430 Bibliotheque Philosophique de Louvain†
0067-8457 Bibliotheque Rencontre des Lettres Anciennes et Modernes†
0067-8473 Bidrag til H. C. Andersens Bibliografi†
0067-8481 Bidrag till Kaennedom av Finlands Natur och Folk
0067-849X Biennale Internationale de la Tapisserie *changed to* Catalogue Biennale Internationale de Lausanne.
0067-8538 Bijdragen tot de Bibliotheekwetenschap
0067-8546 Bijdragen tot de Dierkunde
0067-8554 Bijdragen tot de Geschiedenis van Arnhem
0067-8562 Bilateral Studies in Private International Law†
0067-8570 Bild des Menschen in der Wissenschaft†
0067-8589 Bildungsplanung in Oesterreich†
0067-8597 Campus Attractions *see* 0732-0124
0067-8600 Billboard's International Buyer's Guide of the Music-Record-Tape Industry
0067-8627 International Directory of Recording Studios *changed to* Billboard's International Recording Studio and Equipment Directory.
0067-8643 Die Binnengewaesser
0067-8651 Binsted's Directory of Food Trade Marks and Brand Names
0067-8678 Biochemistry of Disease
0067-8686 Biochemical Preparations†
0067-8708 Biofeedback and Self-Control†
0067-8716 Biogeographical Society of Japan. Bulletin
0067-8724 Biograficke Studie
0067-8732 Biographical Encyclopedia of Pakistan
0067-8740 Biographies de Personnalites Francaises Vivantes†
0067-8767 Biologia Pesquera
0067-8775 Biological Macromolecules Series†
0067-8783 B S C S Bulletin Series†
0067-8791 B S C S Special Publication†
0067-8805 Biologie du Sol *see* 0378-181X
0067-8821 Biomathematics
0067-8848 Biomedical Engineering Series of Monographs *changed to* Biomedical Engineering and Health Systems: A Wiley-Interscience Series.
0067-8856 Biomedical Sciences Instrumentation
0067-8864 Biomembranes
0067-8872 Biometeorological Research Centre. Monograph Series
0067-8880 Biometeorological Research Centre. Special Monograph Series
0067-8899 Verzeichnis Lieferbarer Buecher
0067-8902 Biometeorology; Proceedings
0067-8910 Biophysical Society. Abstracts
0067-8929 Biophysics Series†
0067-8937 List of Serials *see* 0162-2048
0067-8945 Bird Control Seminar. Proceedings†
0067-8953 University of Birmingham. Centre for Urban and Regional Studies. Occasional Papers
0067-8961 University of Birmingham. Centre for Urban and Regional Studies. Urban and Regional Studies
0067-897X Bituminous Coal Data *see* 0145-417X
0067-8988 Bituminous Coal Facts *changed to* Coal Facts.
0067-8996 Biuletyn Fonograficzny†
0067-9003 Uniwersytet Warszawski. Wydzial Geologii. Biuletyn Geologiczny
0067-902X Biuletyn Polonistyczny
0067-9038 Biuletyn Peryglacjalny
0067-9070 Black Experience in Children's Books
0067-9100 Black Orpheus
0067-9119 Black Review†
0067-9127 Blaetter fuer Technikgeschichte
0067-9178 Blick hinter die Fassade
0067-9186 Association for Education and Rehabilitation of the Blind and Visually Impaired. Yearbook†
0067-9208 National Museum, Bloemfontein. Research
0067-9216 University of the Orange Free State. Opsommings van Proefskrifte en Verhandelinge. Abstracts of Dissertations and Theses
0067-9224 Bloodstock Breeders' Review
0067-9232 Bloomsbury Geographer
0067-9240 Blue Book: Leaders of the English-Speaking World†
0067-9267 Blue Book of Europe; European Export Directory
0067-9275 Blue Book of Occupational Education *see* 0360-5434
0067-9283 Blue Book of Optometrists
0067-9321 Boat Owners Buyers Guide *changed to* Yachting's Boat Buyers Guide.
0067-933X Boat World†
0067-9399 Boating Guide†
0067-9402 B I A Certification Handbook *changed to* N M M A Certification Handbook.
0067-9437 Bochum. Amt fuer Statistik, Stadtforschung und Wahlen. Statistical Yearbook
0067-9453 Bochumer Universitaetsreden†
0067-9461 Bodendenkmalpflege in Mecklenburg
0067-947X Bydgoskie Towarzystwo Naukowe. Wydzial Nauk Humanistycznych. Prace. Seria D: (Sztuka)
0067-9488 Bodleian Library Record
0067-9496 Boersen- und Wirtschaftshandbuch†

ISSN

0067-9518 Colombia. Observatorio Astronomico Nacional. Publicaciones

0067-9534 Universidad Nacional de Colombia. Centro de Estudios Folkloricos. Monografias

0067-9542 Bois-Chantiers†

0067-9550 Bol og By *changed to* Landbohistorisk Tidsskrift.

0067-9585 Boletim Climatologico

0067-9593 Boletim de Ciencias do Mar

0067-9607 Boletim de Engenharia de Producao†

0067-9615 Boletim de Industria Animal

0067-9623 Boletim de Zoologia e Biologia Marinha. Nova Serie *see* 0101-3580

0067-9631 Boletim Oficial de Angola

0067-964X Boletim Paranaense de Geociencias†

0067-9666 Boletin de Estudios Medicos y Biologicos

0067-9674 Boletin de Filologia

0067-9690 Boletin de Literatura Argentina e Iberoamericana†

0067-9720 Boletin Genetico

0067-9747 Boletin Hidrologico

0067-9828 Bolivia. Servicio Geologico. Boletin

0067-9836 Bolivia. Servicio Geologico. Circulare

0067-9844 Bolivia. Servicio Geologico. Informe

0067-9852 Bolivia. Servicio Geologico. Serie Mineralogica. Contribucione

0067-9860 B R A D S

0067-9887 Universita degli Studi di Bologna. Osservatorio Astronomico. Notizie e Rassegne†

0067-9895 Universita degli Studi di Bologna. Osservatorio Astronomico. Pubblicazioni†

0067-9909 Bolsilibros

0067-9917 Bombay Labour Journal

0067-9925 Bombay Technologist

0067-9941 Institut "Finanzen und Steuern." Gruene Briefe

0067-995X Institut "Finanzen und Steuern." Schriftenreihe

0067-9968 Rheinisches Landesmuseum, Bonn. Schriften

0067-9976 Bonner Jahrbuecher

0068-001X Bonner Arbeiten zur Deutschen Literatur

0068-0028 Bonner Beitraege zur Bibliotheks- und Buecherkunde

0068-0036 Bonner Beitraege zur Kunstwissenschaft

0068-0044 Bonner Beitraege zur Soziologie†

0068-0052 Bonner Geschichtsblaetter

0068-0087 Station Biologique de Bonnevaux (Doubs). Section de Biologie et d'Ecologie Animales. Publications†

0068-0095 Book Auction Records

0068-0109 Bookdealers in North America *see* 0269-1469

0068-0117 Book of Bantams

0068-0125 Book of the States

0068-0133 Bookman's Guide to Americana

0068-0141 Bookman's Price Index

0068-0168 Books about Canada†

0068-0176 Books about Singapore

0068-0192 Books for the Teen Age

0068-0206 Books from Pakistan

0068-0214 Books in Print

0068-0222 Books of the Theatre Series†

0068-0249 Booksellers Association of Great Britain and Ireland. List of Members *see* 0952-1666

0068-0273 Universite de Bordeaux. Collection Sinologique

0068-0281 Boreal Institute, Edmonton. Annual Report *changed to* Canadian Circumpolar Library. Report of Activities.

0068-029X Boreal Institute, Edmonton. Miscellaneous Publications *changed to* Canadian Circumpolar Library. Miscellaneous Publications.

0068-0303 Boreal Institute, Edmonton. Occasional Publications *changed to* Canadian Circumpolar Library. Occasional Publications Series.

0068-0338 Boston College. Bureau of Public Affairs. Community Analysis and Action Series. Monograph†

0068-0346 Boston Studies in the Philosophy of Science

0068-0354 Bostwick Paper

0068-0370 Botanica Gothoburgensia

0068-0397 Botany as a Profession *changed to* Careers in Botany.

0068-0419 Botanical Society of South Africa. Journal *see* 0042-3203

0068-0427 Botanische Studien†

0068-0443 Botschaft des Alten Testaments

0068-0451 Botswana. Annual Statements of Accounts

0068-046X Botswana. Commissioner of the Police. Annual Report

0068-0478 Botswana. Ministry of Agriculture. Annual Report

0068-0486 Botswana. Forest Department. Report

0068-0494 Bottin International†

0068-0508 Bottlers Year Book

0068-0524 Boundary Historical Society. Report

0068-0532 Boutique†

0068-0540 The Bowker Annual Library and Book Trade Almanac

0068-0567 Bowling Guide†

0068-0575 Boys Baseball. Blue Book *changed to* Pony Baseball. Blue Book.

0068-0605 Boys' Brigade, London. Annual Report

0068-0613 Svenska Riksbyggen. Byggteknisk Information

0068-0621 Braby's Transvaal Directory

0068-063X Bradford's Directory of Marketing Research Agencies and Management Consultants in the United States and the World

0068-0672 Brandeis University. Society of Bibliophiles. Publications

0068-0699 Brasil Industrial *see* 0005-4585

0068-0702 Brassey's Annual - the Armed Forces Year-Book *see* 0305-6155

0068-0710 Brauereien und Maelzereien in Europa

0068-0729 Technische Universitaet Braunschweig. Pharmaziegeschichtlichen Seminar. Veroeffentlichungen *see* 0722-7159

0068-0745 Braunschweigisches Jahrbuch

0068-0761 Technion-Israel Institute of Technology. Braverman Memorial Lecture†

0068-0788 Brazil. Diretoria do Patrimonio Historico e Artistico Nacional. Revista *changed to* Brazil. Patrimonio Historico e Artistico Nacional. Revista.

0068-0796 Brazil. Divisao de Pesquisas Ictiologicas. Serie Circular *see* 0374-6658

0068-080X Brazil. Instituto Nacional de Estudos e Pesquisas Educacionais. Conferencia Nacional de Educacao. Anais†

0068-0834 Brazil. Ministerio das Relacoes Exteriores. Biblioteca. Bibliografia Anual *changed to* Brazil. Ministerio das Relacoes Exteriores. Biblioteca. Aquisicoes Bibliograficas.

0068-0850 Brazil. Servico de Piscicultura. Publicacao

0068-0877 Breifne

0068-0885 Uebersee-Museum, Bremen. Veroeffentlichungen. Reihe A: Naturwissenschaften

0068-0893 Uebersee-Museum, Bremen. Veroeffentlichungen. Reihe B: Voelkerkunde†

0068-0907 Bremer Archaeologische Blaetter†

0068-0915 Institut fuer Meeresforschung, Bremerhaven. Veroeffentlichungen†

0068-0931 Brewery Manual *see* 0305-8123

0068-094X Brewing and Malting Barley Research Institute. Annual Report

0068-0958 Brewing Industry Survey†

0068-0982 Bridge†

0068-1008 Brigham Young University. College of Engineering Sciences and Technology. Annual Engineering Symposium. Abstracts†

0068-1016 Brigham Young University. Department of Geology. Geology Studies *changed to* Brigham Young University Geology Studies.

0068-1032 Bristol and Gloucestershire Archaeological Society, Bristol, England. Transactions

0068-1040 Bristol Naturalists' Society. Proceedings

0068-1075 Britain: An Official Handbook

0068-1105 Britain in the World Today†

0068-113X Britannia

0068-1148 Britannica Atlas

0068-1156 Britannica Book of the Year

0068-1180 A C T F L Annual Review of Foreign Language Education *see* 0147-1236

0068-1199 Britannica Yearbook of Science and the Future *see* 0096-3291

0068-1210 British Aid Statistics; Statistics of U.K. Economic Aid to Developing Countries

0068-1229 Great Britain. British Airports Authority. Annual Report and Accounts *changed to* Great Britain. B A A Annual Report and Accounts.

0068-1245 British and Foreign State Papers†

0068-1261 British Antarctic Survey. Scientific Reports†

0068-1288 British Archaeological Association. Journal

0068-1296 Who's Who in Industrial Editing *changed to* B A I E Membership and Services Directory (Year).

0068-130X British Astronomical Association. Handbook

0068-1318 British Astronomical Association. Memoirs†

0068-1326 British Athletics *see* 0267-0267

0068-1334 British Authors Series *changed to* British and Irish Authors: Introductory Critical Studies.

0068-1342 British Aviation Year Book†

0068-1350 British Books in Print *see* 0953-0398

0068-1377 B B C Annual Report and Handbook†

0068-1385 British Bryological Society. Transactions *see* 0373-6687

0068-1407 British Catalogue of Music

0068-1415 British Chamber of Commerce in France. Year Book *changed to* Franco - British Chamber of Commerce and Industry. Year Book.

0068-1423 British Columbia. Cancer Foundation. Annual Report *changed to* British Columbia Cancer Research Centre. Annual Report.

0068-1431 University of British Columbia. Department of Geophysics and Astronomy. Publications†

0068-144X British Columbia. Ministry of Energy, Mines and Petroleum Resources. Bulletin

0068-1458 British Columbia. Department of Recreation and Conservation. Annual Report†

0068-1466 British Columbia. Department of Human Resources. Annual Report *changed to* British Columbia. Ministry of Social Services and Housing. Services for People. Annual Report (Year).

0068-1490 British Columbia. Forest Service. Annual Report *changed to* British Columbia. Ministry of Forests. Annual Report.

0068-1520 British Columbia. Forest Service. Research Notes *see* 0226-9368

0068-1539 British Columbia. Forest Service. Research Review *changed to* British Columbia. Ministry of Forests and Lands. Forest Research Review.

0068-1555 British Columbia Fruit Growers Association. Horticultural Conference Proceedings *changed to* British Columbia Fruit Growers Association. Horticultural Forum Proceedings.

0068-1563 British Columbia Fruit Growers Association. Minutes of the Proceedings of the Annual Convention

0068-1571 British Columbia Geographical Series: Occasional Papers in Geography

0068-158X British Columbia Hospitals' Association. Proceedings of the Annual Conference *changed to* B. C. Health Association. Proceedings of the Annual Conference.

0068-1598 British Columbia Insurance Directory. Insurance Companies, Agents and Adjusters

0068-1601 British Columbia Lumberman's Greenbook†

0068-161X British Columbia Municipal Yearbook

0068-1628 Natural History Handbook Series†

0068-1636 Royal British Columbia Museum. Occasional Papers Series†

0068-1652 British Columbia Research Council. Annual Report *changed to* B.C. Research. Annual Report & Brochure.

0068-1687 University of British Columbia Library. Asian Studies Division. List of Catalogued Books. Supplement†

0068-1695 University of British Columbia. Center for Continuing Education. Occasional Papers in Continuing Education

0068-1709 University of British Columbia. Department of Civil Engineering. Soil Mechanics Series

0068-1725 University of British Columbia. Department of Geophysics and Astronomy. Annual Report

0068-1733 University of British Columbia. Department of Geology. Report *changed to* University of British Columbia. Department of Geological Sciences. Report.

0068-1768 University of British Columbia. Faculty of Education. Journal of Education†

0068-1776 University of British Columbia. Faculty of Forestry. Foresty Bulletin *see* 0318-9171

0068-1784 University of British Columbia. Faculty of Forestry. Research Notes†

0068-1792 University of British Columbia. Faculty of Forestry. Research Papers†

0068-1806 University of British Columbia. Faculty of Forestry. Translations†

0068-1849 University of British Columbia Law Review

0068-1857 University of British Columbia Library. Reference Publication†

0068-1873 British Columbia. Department of Lands, Forests and Water Resources. Water Resources Service. Report *see* 1181-8336

0068-1938 British Cycling Federation. Handbook

0068-1970 British Exports *changed to* British Exports.

0068-1989 British Federation of Master Printers. Master Printers Annual *changed to* Printers Yearbook.

0068-1997 British Film and T.V. Yearbook *changed to* Screen International Film and T.V. Yearbook.

0068-2004 British Film Fund Agency. Annual Report

0068-2020 British Glass Industry Research Association. Annual Report *changed to* British Glass Manufacturers Confederation. Annual Review.

0068-2039 British Goat Society. Herd Book

0068-2047 British Goat Society. Year Book

0068-208X British Hospitals Contributory Schemes Association. Directory of Convalescent Homes Serving the Provinces.

0068-2098 British Hospitals Contributory Schemes Association. Directory of Hospitals Contributory Scheme Benefits

0068-211X British Hospitals Home and Overseas†

0068-2128 B H R C A Guide to Hotels and Restaurants *changed to* Hotels and Restaurants of Britain.

0068-2144 British Initials and Abbreviations†
0068-2152 British Institute in Eastern Africa. Annual Report
0068-2195 British International Law Cases *changed to* Commonwealth International Law Cases.
0068-2217 British Journal of Photography Annual
0068-2268 British Middle Market Directory *changed to* Guide to Key British Enterprises I and II.
0068-2292 British Museum (Natural History) Bulletin. Botany
0068-2306 British Museum (Natural History) Bulletin. Historical†
0068-2314 British Orthoptic Journal
0068-2322 British Paper and Board Industry Federation. Technical Association. Fundamental Research International Symposia *changed to* Paper Industry Technical Association. Fundamental Research International Symposia.
0068-2330 British Paper and Board Industry Federation. Technical Association. Technical Papers
0068-2349 British Paper and Board Industry Federation. Technical Section. Yearbook†
0068-2365 British Petroleum Equipment and Services
0068-2381 Europlastics Year Book *see* 0306-5502
0068-239X British Printer Specification Manual *changed to* British Printer Dataguide.
0068-2403 British Pteridological Society. Newsletter *see* 0301-9195
0068-242X British Railways Board. Report and Statement of Accounts *see* 0305-1420
0068-2446 British Rowing Almanack *changed to* British Rowing Almanack. A R A Yearbook.
0068-2454 British School at Athens. Annual
0068-2462 British School at Rome. Papers. Archeology *changed to* British School at Rome. Papers. Archaeology, History, History of Art.
0068-2519 British Society for the History of Pharmacy. Transactions
0068-2578 British Standards Year Book *changed to* B S I Catalogue.
0068-2586 British Steel Corporation. Annual Report and Accounts *changed to* British Steel Plc. Annual Report and Accounts.
0068-2616 British Tourist Authority. Digest of Tourist Statistics
0068-2624 B T H A Directory†
0068-2632 British Trades Alphabet *changed to* B T A Studycards.
0068-2640 British Transport Commission. Annual Report and Accounts†
0068-2659 British Transport Docks Board. Annual Report and Accounts *changed to* Associated British Ports Holdings PLC. Annual Report and Accounts.
0068-2667 British Tourist Authority. Annual Report†
0068-2675 British Trust for Ornithology. Annual Report
0068-2683 British Waterways Board. Annual Report and Accounts
0068-2691 British Year Book of International Law
0068-2705 Univerzita J.E. Purkyne. Filozoficka Fakulta. Sbornik Praci. I: Rada Pedagogicka - Psychologicka *changed to* Masarykova Univerzita. Filozoficka Fakulta. Sbornik Praci. I: Rada Pedagogicka - Psychologicka.
0068-2713 Broadcasting C A T V Sourcebook (also known as Broadcasting Cable Sourcebook; Cable T V Sourcebook) *changed to* Broadcasting & Cable Market Place (Year).
0068-2721 Broadman Comments; International Sunday School Lessons
0068-273X Broads Book†
0068-2748 Broadside (New York, 1940)
0068-2780 Brookfield Bandarlog
0068-2799 Brookhaven Symposia in Biology
0068-2810 Brookings Institution. Reprint *changed to* Brookings Reprint Series.
0068-2829 Brookings Research Report Series *changed to* Brookings Reprint Series.
0068-2853 Brookside Monographs†
0068-2861 Brown and Haley Lecture Series†
0068-2888 Brown's Directory of North American Gas Companies *see* 0197-8098
0068-290X Brown's Nautical Almanac
0068-2918 Brunei Museum Journal
0068-2926 Bibliotheque Royale Albert 1er. Catalogue Collectif des Periodiques Etrangers†
0068-2934 Discotheque Nationale de Belgique. Catalogue General
0068-2942 Annuaire et Statistique de l'Enseignement Catholique†
0068-2985 Universite Libre de Bruxelles. Institut de Sociologie. Cahiers†
0068-2993 Universite Libre de Bruxelles. Institut d'Etudes Europeennes. Enseignement Complementaire. Nouvelle Serie†
0068-3000 Universite Libre de Bruxelles. Institut d'Etudes Europeennes. Theses et Travaux Economiques†
0068-3019 Universite Libre de Bruxelles. Institut d'Etudes Europeennes. Theses et Travaux Juridiques†
0068-3035 Bryn Mawr-Haverford Review†
0068-3043 Das Buch der Jugend
0068-3051 Buch und Buchhandel in Zahlen
0068-306X Institutul de Geologie si Geofizica. Dari de Seama ale Sedintelor
0068-3078 Muzeul de Istorie Naturala "Grigore Antipa." Travaux *changed to* Travaux du Museum d'Histoire Naturelle "Grigore Antipa".
0068-3086 Institutul Astronomic din Bucuresti. Anuarul *changed to* Centrul de Astronomie si Stiinte Spatiale. Anuarul Astronomic.
0068-3094 Institutul Astronomic din Bucuresti. Observations Solaires *changed to* Centre de l'Astronomie et des Sciences Spatiales. Observations Solaires.
0068-3108 Analele Universitatii Bucuresti. Fizica†
0068-3116 Universitatea Bucuresti. Analelf. Acta Logica†
0068-3124 Analele Universitatii Bucuresti. Biologie Animala†
0068-3132 Analele Universitatii Bucuresti. Biologie Vegetala†
0068-3140 Analele Universitatii Bucuresti. Chimie†
0068-3159 Analele Universitatii Bucuresti. Estetica†
0068-3167 Analele Universitatii Bucuresti. Filologie†
0068-3175 Analele Universitatii Bucuresti. Filozofie†
0068-3183 Analele Universitatii Bucuresti. Geologie†
0068-3191 Analele Universitatii Bucuresti. Geografie†
0068-3205 Analele Universitatii Bucuresti. Istorie†
0068-3213 Analele Universitatii Bucuresti. Limbi Clasice†
0068-3221 Analele Universitatii Bucuresti. Limbi Germanice†
0068-323X Analele Universitatii Bucuresti. Limbi Romanice†
0068-3248 Analele Universitatii Bucuresti. Limbi Slave†
0068-3256 Analele Universitatii Bucuresti. Limba si Literatura Romana†
0068-3264 Analele Universitatii Bucuresti. Literatura Universala si Comparata†
0068-3272 Analele Universitatii Bucuresti. Matematica-Mecanica†
0068-3280 Analele Universitatii Bucuresti. Pedagogie†
0068-3299 Analele Universitatii Bucuresti. Psihologie†
0068-3302 Analele Universitatii Bucuresti. Sociologie†
0068-3310 Analele Universitatii Bucuresti. Stiinte Juridice†
0068-3329 Acta Botanica Horti Bucurestiensis
0068-3345 Buddhist Publication Society. Report†
0068-3361 Buecherei des Augenarztes
0068-337X Buecherei des Frauenarztes
0068-3388 Buecherei des Orthopaeden
0068-340X Buenos Aires. Centro de Investigacion de Biologia Marina. Contribucion Cientifica†
0068-3418 Buenos Aires. Instituto de Fitotecnia. Boletin Informativo†
0068-3485 Universidad del Salvador. Anales†
0068-3493 Universidad de Buenos Aires. Instituto Bibliotecologico. Publicacion†
0068-3507 B and C J Directory†
0068-3523 Building Board Directory†
0068-3531 Building Construction Cost Data (Year)
0068-354X Great Britain. Building Research Establishment. Annual Report *changed to* Great Britain. Building Research Establishment. Annual Review.
0068-3566 Building Societies. Year Book
0068-3612 National Free Library of Rhodesia. Annual Report *changed to* National Library and Documentation Service. Annual Report.
0068-3620 Bulgarska Akademiia na Naukite. Arkheologicheski Institut Izvestiia
0068-3639 Astronomicheski Kalendar na Observatoriiata v Sofia
0068-3655 Bulgarska Akademiia na Naukite. Botanicheski Institut. Izvestiia†
0068-3671 Bulgarska Akademiia na Naukite. Tsentralna Biblioteka. Izvestiia†
0068-371X Bulgarska Akademiia na Naukite. Tsentralna Khelmintologichna Laboratoriia. Izvestiia†
0068-3736 Bulgarska Akademiia na Naukite. Geofizichni Institut. Izvestiia *changed to* Balgarskoto Geofizichno Spisanije.
0068-3744 Bulgarska Akademiia na Naukite. Geografski Institut. Izvestiia *changed to* Problemi na Geografijata.
0068-3787 Bulgarska Akademiia na Naukite. Institut za Bulgarski Ezik. Izvestiia
0068-3817 Bulgarska Akademiia na Naukite. Institut po Morfologiia. Izvestiia†
0068-3841 Bulgarska Akademiia na Naukite. Institut po Obshta i Sravnitelna Patalogiia. Izvestiia†
0068-385X Bulgarska Akademiia na Naukite. Institut po Tekhnicheska Kibernetika. Izvestiia†
0068-3876 Bulgarska Akademiia na Naukite. Institut po Khidrologiia i Meteorologiia. Izvestiia *see* 0018-1331
0068-3884 Bulgarska Akademiia na Naukite. Institut za Pravni Nauki. Izvestiia†
0068-3949 Bulgarian Academy of Sciences, Sofia. Mathematical Institute. Bulletin†
0068-3957 Bulgarska Akademiia na Naukite. Mikrobiologichni Institut. Izvestiia†
0068-3965 Bulgarska Akademiia na Naukite. Institut za Muzikoznanie. Izvestiia†
0068-3973 Bulgarska Akademiia na Naukite. Institut po Filosofiia. Izvestiia†
0068-3981 Bulgarska Akademiia na Naukite, Sofia. Zoologicheski Institut S Muzei. Izvestiia *see* 0324-0770
0068-4007 Institut de Recherches Agronomiques Tropicales et des Cultures Vivrieres. Bulletin Agronomique†
0068-4015 Bulletin d'Archeologie Marocaine
0068-4023 Bulletin de Philosophie Medievale
0068-4031 Bulletin des Jeunes Romanistes†
0068-4058 Bulletin d'Histoire Economique et Sociale de la Revolution Francaise *see* 0766-4516
0068-4066 Bulletin Linguistique et Ethnologique
0068-4090 Bulletin of Sugar Beet Research. Supplement
0068-4104 Bulletin of Suicidology†
0068-4112 Bulletin of Suicidology. Supplements†
0068-4120 Bulletin of the European Communities and Supplements
0068-4139 Bulletin of Thermodynamics and Thermochemistry *see* 0149-2268
0068-4155 Bulletin Socialiste *changed to* Le Poing et la Rose.
0068-4171 Institut National des Industries Extractives. Bulletin Technique: Securite et Salubrite†
0068-4198 Bulletins of Marine Ecology†
0068-4201 Bullinger's Postal and Shippers Guide for the United States and Canada
0068-421X Bundesanstalt fuer Pflanzenbau und Samenpruefung, Vienna. Jahrbuch *changed to* Bundesanstalt fuer Pflanzenbau, Vienna. Jahrbuch.
0068-4376 Buses Annual *changed to* Buses Yearbook.
0068-4392 West Virginia University. Business and Economic Studies†
0068-4406 Business Blue-Book of Southern Africa *changed to* Business Blue Book of S.A.
0068-4414 Business Education Index
0068-4430 University of New Mexico. Bureau of Business and Economic Research. Business Information Series†
0068-4449 Business Monitor: Miscellaneous Series. M2 Cinemas
0068-4457 Business Monitor: Miscellaneous Series. M3 Company Finance
0068-4465 Business Monitor: Miscellaneous Series. M4 Overseas Transactions
0068-4503 The Business Who's Who of Australia
0068-452X Butterworths Tax Handbook *see* 0141-3856
0068-4562 Buying and Selling United States Coins†
0068-4570 Bydgoskie Towarzystwo Naukowe. Wydzial Nauk Humanistycznych. Prace. Seria B (Jezyk i Literatura)
0068 4589 Bydgoskie Towarzystwo Naukowe. Wydzial Nauk Humanistycznych. Prace. Seria C (Historia i Archeologia)
0068-4597 Bydgoskie Towarzystwo Naukowe. Wydzial Nauk Technicznych. Prace. Seria Z: (Prace Zbiorowe)
0068-4600 Byers National Industrial Directory
0068-4635 Muzeum Gornoslaskie w Bytomiu. Rocznik. Seria Archeologia
0068-4643 Muzeum Gornoslaskie w Bytomiu. Rocznik. Seria Etnografia
0068-4651 Muzeum Gornoslaskie w Bytomiu. Rocznik. Seria Historia
0068-466X Muzeum Gornoslaskie w Bytomiu. Rocznik. Seria Przyroda
0068-4678 Muzeum Gornoslaskie w Bytomiu. Rocznik. Seria Sztuka
0068-4686 Byzantinobulgarica
0068-4694 C A T V and Station Coverage Atlas and 35-Mile Zone Maps *changed to* Cable and Station Coverage Atlas.
0068-4708 C. C. Williamson Memorial Lecture†
0068-4716 C E Cost Guide for General Building Construction *see* 0270-1626
0068-4759 C A T V Buyer's Guide†
0068-4767 C A T V Systems Directory and Map Service *see* 0091-1984
0068-4775 Cadastro Brasileiro de Materias-Primas Farmaceuticas, Por Produto, Por Fabricante†
0068-4791 Centre de Geomorphologie, Caen. Bulletin
0068-4805 Universita degli Studi di Cagliari. Istituto di Storia Medioevale. Publicazioni
0068-4813 Economies et Societes. Serie F. Developpement, Croissance, Progres des Pays en Voie de Developpement
0068-4821 Economies et Societes. Serie AB. Economie du Travail
0068-483X Economies et Societes. Serie G. Economie Planifiee
0068-4848 Economies et Societes. Serie L. Economie Regionale†

5500 ISSN INDEX

0068-4856 Economies et Societes. Serie S. Etudes de Marxologie
0068-4864 Economies et Societes. Serie AF. Histoire Quantitative de l'Economie Francaise
0068-4872 Economies et Societies. Serie T. Information - Recherche Innovation
0068-4880 Economies et Societes. Serie M. Philosophie - Sciences Sociales Economie
0068-4899 Economies et Societes. Serie AG. Progres et Agriculture
0068-4902 Economies et Societes. Serie P. Relations Economiques Internationales
0068-4945 Cahiers Archeologiques
0068-4953 Cahiers Bretons
0068-4961 Cahiers Canadiens Claudel†
0068-4996 Cahiers d'Allemand; Revue de Linguistique et de Pedagogie†
0068-5011 Cahiers de Civilisation Medievale. Supplement
0068-502X Cahiers de Droit d'Auteur†
0068-5038 Cahiers de la Quatrieme Internationale
0068-5046 Cahiers de l'Homme
0068-5054 Cahiers de Micropaleontologie
0068-5070 Cahiers de Psychomecanique de Langage
0068-5089 Cahiers de Saint-Michel de Cuxa
0068-5097 Cahiers de Sciences Sociales†
0068-5143 Cahiers du Pacifique *see* 0180-9954
0068-5151 Cahiers du Tourisme. Serie A: France
0068-516X Cahiers Ferdinand de Saussure
0068-5194 Cahiers Nepalais
0068-5208 Cahiers O.R.S.T.O.M. Serie Biologie†
0068-5224 Cahiers Rouge. Nouvelle Serie Internationale
0068-5232 Cahiers-Theatre *see* 0771-4653
0068-5267 Cairngorm Club Journal
0068-5275 Egyptian National Museum. Library. Catalogue *changed to* Egyptian Museum. Library. Catalogue.
0068-5283 Societe d'Archeologie Copte. Bibliotheque de Manuscrits
0068-5291 Societe d'Archeologie Copte. Bulletin
0068-5305 Societe d'Archeologie Copte. Textes et Documents
0068-5313 University of Cairo. Herbarium. Publications
0068-5356 Calcutta Management Association. Annual Report
0068-5364 Calcutta Research Series†
0068-5372 School of Tropical Medicine, Calcutta. Bulletin†
0068-5380 University of Calcutta. Centre of Advanced Study in Ancient Indian History and Culture. Lectures
0068-5399 University of Calcutta. Centre of Advanced Study in Ancient Indian History and Culture. Proceedings of Seminars
0068-5402 Calendar of International Film and Television Events *changed to* World Screen Bulletin and Calendar.
0068-5410 Calendars of American Literary Manuscripts†
0068-5437 University of Calgary. Archaeological Association. Paleo-Environmental Workshop. Proceedings *changed to* University of Calgary. Archaeological Association. Archaeological Conference. Proceedings.
0068-5453 Universidad del Valle Biblioteca. Publicaciones *changed to* Universidad del Valle. Departamento de Biliotecas. Boletin de Adquisiciones.
0068-5461 California Academy of Sciences. Occasional Papers
0068-547X California Academy of Sciences. Proceedings
0068-5488 California. Administrative Office of the Courts. Annual Report *changed to* Judicial Council Report to the Governor and Legislature.
0068-5496 California. Air Resources Board. Annual Report
0068-5518 Preservation, Organization and Display of State of California's Historic Documents: Report to the California State Legislature†
0068-5526 Annotated Bibliography of Research in Economically Important Species of California Fish and Game. Supplement†
0068-5550 California. Department of Parks and Recreation. Archaeological Report *changed to* California Archeological Reports.
0068-5569 California. Department of Forestry. Range Improvement Studies†
0068-5577 California. Department of Forestry. State Forest Notes *changed to* California Forestry Note.
0068-5585 California Environmental Law: A Guide†
0068-5607 California Government Notes†
0068-5615 California Handbook
0068-5631 California Insect Survey. Bulletin
0068-564X California Institute of International Studies. Report *see* 0090-7103
0068-5658 California Institute of Technology. Division of Engineering and Applied Science. Report of Research and Other Activities *changed to* California Institute of Technology. Division of Engineering and Applied Science. Research Report.
0068-5682 U.S. National Aeronautics and Space Administration. Jet Propulsion Laboratory. Technical Memorandum†
0068-5720 California Macadamia Society. Yearbook
0068-5739 California Manufacturers Register
0068-5755 California Natural History Guides
0068-5763 California Newspaper Directory *changed to* California Newspaper Publishers Association. Directory and Rate Book.
0068-5771 California Public School Directory
0068-5798 California Slavic Studies†
0068-5801 California. State Board of Equalization. Annual Report
0068-5836 San Diego State University. Bureau of Business and Economic Research. Monographs
0068-5844 San Diego State University. Bureau of Business and Economic Research. Research Studies and Position Papers
0068-5879 California County Law Library Basic List
0068-5887 California Transportation and Public Works Conference. Proceedings *see* 0192-4117
0068-5895 California Studies in Classical Antiquity *see* 0278-6656
0068-5909 California Studies in the History of Art
0068-5917 California Studies in Urbanization and Environmental Design†
0068-5933 University of California, Berkeley. Archaeological Research Facility. Contributions
0068-5968 University of California, Berkeley. Center for Real Estate and Urban Economics. Reprint Series
0068-5976 University of California, Berkeley. Center for Real Estate and Urban Economics. Research Report *changed to* University of California, Berkeley. Center for Real Estate and Urban Economics. Working Paper.
0068-600X University of California. Center for South and Southeast Asia Studies. Occasional Papers
0068-6018 University of California. Center for South and Southeast Asia Studies. Research Monograph Series
0068-6077 University of California. Institute of Business and Economic Research. Publications†
0068-6093 University of California, Berkeley. Institute of International Studies. Research Series
0068-6115 University of California, Berkeley. Institute of Transportation Studies. Library References
0068-6123 University of California, Berkeley. Institute of Transportation Studies. Selected List of Recent Acquisitions of the Transportation Library†
0068-6166 University of California, Santa Barbara. Library. Annual Report†
0068-6182 University of California, Los Angeles. Institute of Archaeology. Archaeological Survey. Annual Report†
0068-6190 University of California, Los Angeles. African Studies Center. Occasional Paper†
0068-6204 University of California, Los Angeles. Institute of Archaeology. Archaeological Survey. Special Monograph Series *changed to* University of California, Los Angeles. Institute of Archaeology. Monograph Series.
0068-6212 University of California, Los Angeles. Biotechnology Laboratory. Progress Report†
0068-6220 University of California, Los Angeles. Center for Medieval and Renaissance Studies. Publications
0068-6239 University of California, Los Angeles. Center for Medieval and Renaissance Studies. Contributions
0068-6247 University of California, Los Angeles. Center for the Study of Comparative Folklore and Mythology. Publications
0068-6255 University of California, Los Angeles. Institute of Industrial Relations. Monograph Series *see* 0739-439X
0068-6263 University of California, Los Angeles. Latin American Center. Reference Series
0068-628X University of California, Los Angeles. Museum of Cultural History. Occasional Papers *changed to* University of California, Los Angeles. Fowler Museum of Cultural History. Occasional Papers.
0068-6301 University of California, Davis. Water Resources Center. Contributions
0068-631X University of California Engineering and Physical Sciences Extension Series†
0068-6336 University of California Publications. Anthropological Records
0068-6344 University of California Publications. Classical Studies
0068-6352 University of California Publications. English Studies†
0068-6360 University of California Publications. Folklore Studies *changed to* University of California Publications. Folklore & Mythology Studies.
0068-6379 University of California Publications in Anthropology
0068-6387 University of California Publications in Automatic Computation†
0068-6395 University of California Publications in Botany
0068-6409 University of California Publications in Contemporary Music†
0068-6417 University of California Publications in Entomology
0068-6433 University of California Publications in Egyptian Archaeology†
0068-6441 University of California Publications in Geography
0068-645X University of California Publications in Geological Sciences
0068-6468 University of California Publications in History†
0068-6476 University of California Publications in Librarianship†
0068-6484 University of California Publications in Linguistics
0068-6492 University of California Publications in Modern Philology
0068-6506 University of California Publications in Zoology
0068-6514 University of California Publications. Near Eastern Studies
0068-6522 University of California Publications. Occasional Papers†
0068-6530 Californians in Congress
0068-6549 Calwer Hefte†
0068-6557 Calwer Predigthilfen *changed to* Neue Calwer Predigthilfen.
0068-659X Cambridge Air Surveys
0068-6603 Cambridge Authors' and Printers' Guides *changed to* Cambridge Authors' and Publishers' Guides.
0068-6611 Cambridge Bibliographical Society. Transactions
0068-662X Cambridge Bibliographical Society. Transactions. Monograph Supplements
0068-6638 Cambridge Classical Texts and Commentaries
0068-6654 Cambridge Geographical Studies
0068-6689 Cambridge Latin American Studies
0068-6697 Cambridge Monographs in Experimental Biology
0068-6719 Cambridge Papers in Social Anthropology
0068-6727 Cambridge Papers in Sociology
0068-6735 Cambridge Philological Society. Proceedings
0068-6743 Cambridge Philological Society. Proceedings. Supplement
0068-6751 Cambridge Studies in International and Comparative Law *changed to* Cambridge Studies in International and Comparative Law: New Series.
0068-676X Cambridge Studies in Linguistics
0068-6786 Cambridge Studies in Medieval Life and Thought. Third Series *changed to* Cambridge Studies in Medieval Life and Thought. Fourth Series.
0068-6794 Cambridge Studies in Social Anthropology
0068-6808 Cambridge Studies in Sociology
0068-6824 Cambridge Tracts in Mathematics and Mathematical Physics *changed to* Cambridge Tracts in Mathematics.
0068-6832 Cambridge University. Department of Applied Economics. Monographs
0068-6840 Cambridge University. Department of Applied Economics. Occasional Papers
0068-6883 Cambridge University. Institute of Criminology. Bibliographical Series
0068-6891 Cambridge University. Oriental Publications
0068-6905 Camden Fourth Series
0068-693X Campground Guide for Tent and Trailer Tourists†
0068-6948 Camping Caravanning and Sports Equipment Trades Directory
0068-6956 Camping Club of Great Britain and Ireland. Year Book with List of Camp Sites *changed to* Your Big Sites List: Camping and Caravanning Club Sites List.
0068-6956 Camping Club of Great Britain and Ireland. Year Book with List of Camp Sites *changed to* Your Place in the Country: A Guide to Camping and Caravanning Club Sites.
0068-6964 Camping Guide†
0068-6980 Camping Sites in Britain and France *see* 0957-7327
0068-7014 Can Manufacturers Institute. Annual Metal Can Shipments Report *changed to* Annual Can Shipments Report.
0068-7057 Canada. Statistics Canada. Aviation Statistics Centre. Service Bulletin
0068-7065 Canada. Grain Commission. Marketings, Distribution and Visible Carry-over of Canadian Grain in and Through Licensed Elevators *see* 0380-8718
0068-7073 Canada. Statistics Canada. Aggregate Productivity Trends - Tendances de la Productivite des Agregats *see* 0317-7882
0068-7103 Canada. Statistics Canada. Crude Petroleum and Natural Gas Industry
0068-7111 Canada. Statistics Canada. Dairy Statistics/Statistique Laitiere†

ISSN

ISSN INDEX 5501

0068-712X Canada. Statistics Canada. Farm Net Income†
0068-7138 Canada. Statistics Canada. Placer Gold Mines, Gold Quartz Mines and Copper-Gold-Silver Mines/Placers d'Or Mines de Quartz Aurifere et Mines de Cuivre-Or-Argent see 0380-4968
0068-7146 Canada. Statistics Canada. Index of Farm Production†
0068-7154 Canada. Statistics Canada. Livestock and Animal Products Statistics
0068-7162 Canada. Statistics Canada. Petroleum Refineries/Raffineries de Petrole†
0068-7189 Canada. Statistics Canada. Production of Poultry and Eggs
0068-7227 Canada. Statistics Canada. System of National Accounts, Domestic Product by Industry-Systeme de Comptabilite Nationale. Produit Interieur par Industrie: Releve de la Production see 0712-8762
0068-7278 Canada. Department of Agriculture. Analytical Chemistry Research Service. Research Report†
0068-7286 Canada. Agriculture Canada. Policy Branch. Trade in Agricultural Products see 0317-7483
0068-7294 Canada. Department of Agriculture. Engineering Research Service, Ottawa. Research Report changed to Canada. Agriculture Canada. Engineering & Statistical Research Institute, Ottawa. Research Report.
0068-7308 Canada. Agriculture Canada. Food Research Institute, Ottawa. Research Report
0068-7316 Canada. Agriculture Canada. Health of Animals Branch. Bovine Tuberculosis and Brucellosis†
0068-7324 Canada. Agriculture Canada. Livestock Market Review
0068-7375 Canada. Fisheries and Environment Canada. Annual Report see 0711-0782
0068-7383 Canada. Department of Insurance. Report. Co-Operative Credit Associations
0068-7391 Canada. Department of Insurance. Report. Trust and Loan Companies
0068-7405 Canada. Department of Insurance. Report of the Superintendent of Insurance
0068-7413 Canada. Department of Insurance. Report. Small Loans Companies and Money-Lenders
0068-743X Canada. Labour Canada. Wage Rates, Salaries and Hours of Labour changed to Canada. Labour Canada. Wages and Working Conditions in Canada.
0068-7448 Canada. Women's Bureau. Women in the Labour Force: Facts and Figures changed to Canada. Women's Bureau. Women in the Labour Force.
0068-7456 Canada. Department of National Health and Welfare. Annual Report
0068-7472 Canada. Agriculture Canada. Research Station, Melfort, Saskatchewan. Research Highlights. Annual Publications changed to Canada. Agriculture Canada. Research Station, Melfort, Saskatchewan. Highlights.
0068-7499 Canada. Fisheries & Marine Service Annual. changed to Canada. Fisheries Research Board Annual Report.
0068-7510 Canada. Fisheries and Marine Service. Biological Station, St. Andrews, New Brunswick. General Series Circular†
0068-7537 Canada. Fisheries Research Board. Bulletin see 0706-6503
0068-7545 Canada. Fisheries and Marine Service Review.†
0068-7553 Canada. Fisheries and Marine Service. Technical Report Series see 0706-6457
0068-7588 Canada. Department of the Environment. Forest Insect and Disease Survey. Annual Report changed to Canada. Forestry Canada. Insect and Disease Conditions in Canada.
0068-7626 Canada. Geological Survey. Bulletin
0068-7634 Canada. Geological Survey. Memoir
0068-7642 Canada. Geological Survey. Miscellaneous Report
0068-7650 Canada. Geological Survey. Paper
0068-7669 Canada. Hydrographic Service. Water Levels see 0706-2354
0068-7669 Canada. Hydrographic Service. Water Levels see 0706-2346
0068-7677 Canada in the Atlantic Economy†
0068-7685 Canada in World Affairs†
0068-7693 Canada Land Inventory. Report††
0068-7723 Canada. Atmospheric Environment Service. Ice Observations: Canadian Arctic†
0068-7731 Canada. Atmospheric Environment Service. Ice Observations: Canadian Inland Waterways†
0068-774X Canada. Atmospheric Environment Service. Ice Observations: Eastern Canadian Seaboard†
0068-7758 Canada. Atmospheric Environment Service. Ice Summary and Analysis, Canadian Arctic†
0068-7766 Canada. Atmospheric Environment Service. Ice Summary and Analysis, Eastern Canadian Seaboard†
0068-7774 Canada. Atmospheric Environment Service. Ice Summary and Analysis, Hudson Bay and Approaches†
0068-7812 Canada. Mineral Resources Branch. Mineral Information Bulletin changed to Canada. Mineral Policy Sector. Mineral Bulletins.
0068-7839 Canada. Mineral Resources Branch. Mineral Survey see 0229-8325
0068-7847 Canada. Centre for Mineral and Energy Technology. Information Circular†
0068-7863 Canada. Department of Energy, Mines and Resources. Monographs†
0068-7871 Canada. Mines Branch. Research Report changed to Canada. Centre for Mineral and Energy Technology. Technology Series Reports.
0068-7898 Canada. Expert Committee on Pesticide Use in Agriculture. Pesticide Research Report
0068-7901 Canada. National Energy Board. Annual Report
0068-7928 Canada. National Harbours Board. Annual Report changed to Canada. National Harbours Board. Port Directory.
0068-7987 Canada. National Museums, Ottawa. Publications in Botany†
0068-7995 Canada. National Museums, Ottawa. Publications in Biological Oceanography†
0068-8002 Canada. National Museums, Ottawa. Publications in Ethnology†
0068-8010 Canada. National Museums, Ottawa. Publications in History†
0068-8037 Canada. National Museums, Ottawa. Publications in Zoology†
0068-8061 Canada. Oceanographic Data Centre. Data Record Series†
0068-8088 Canada. Public Archives. Register of Post Graduate Dissertations in Progress in History and Related Subjects changed to Canada. Register of Post Graduate Dissertations in Progress in History and Related Subjects.
0068-8134 Canada Who's Who of the Poultry Industry
0068-8142 Canada Yearbook†
0068-8185 Canadian Agricultural Insect Pest Review
0068-8193 Canadian Almanac and Directory
0068-8207 Canadian Alpine Journal
0068-8215 Canadian Annual Review see 0315-1433
0068-8231 Canadian Architecture Yearbook changed to Canadian Architect Yearbook.
0068-824X Canadian Archivist see 0318-6954
0068-8258 C.A.R. Scope see 0820-9006
0068-8274 C A A E Annual Report††
0068-8312 Canadian Association of Geographers. Newsletter see 0707-3844
0068-8320 Canadian Association of Management Consultants. Annual Report†
0068-8347 Canadian Bankruptcy Reports. (3rd Series)
0068-8398 Canadian Books in Print
0068-8401 C B C Engineering Review
0068-841X Canadian Building Series†
0068-8428 Canadian Bureau for International Education. Bulletin see 0827-0678
0068-8436 Canadian Cancer Research Conference. Proceedings†
0068-8444 Canadian Ceramic Society. Journal
0068-8452 Canadian Chemical, Pharmaceutical and Product Directory
0068-8487 Canadian Conference of the Arts. Miscellaneous Reports see 0843-9583
0068-8495 Canadian Conference on Research in the Rheumatic Diseases. Proceedings†
0068-8509 Canadian Conference on Social Welfare. Proceedings/Compte Rendu changed to Canadian Conference on Social Development. Proceedings/ Compte Rendu.
0068-8517 Canadian Conference on Uranium and Atomic Energy. Proceedings changed to Canadian Nuclear Association. Annual International Conference Proceedings.
0068-855X Canadian Correspondence Courses for University Credit changed to Canadian University Distance Education Directory.
0068-8584 Canadian Council on Social Development. Annual Report - Rapport Annuel
0068-8622 Canadian Dental Association. Directory†
0068-8649 Canadian Depreciation Guide†
0068-8657 C E A Handbook
0068-8665 Canadian Engineering & Industrial Year Book
0068-8681 Canadian Federation of Biological Societies. Newsletter
0068-869X Canadian Federation of Biological Societies. Proceedings changed to Canadian Federation of Biological Societies. Programme and Proceedings of the Annual Meeting.
0068-8703 Canadian Federation of Biological Societies. Programme of the Annual Meeting changed to Canadian Federation of Biological Societies. Programme and Proceedings of the Annual Meeting.
0068-8711 Canadian Federation and Municipalities. Annual Conference and Proceedings see 0708-9511
0068-872X Canadian Filmography Series†
0068-8746 Canadian Folk Music Journal
0068-8754 Canadian Food and Packaging Directory
0068-8762 Canadian Footwear & Leather Directory
0068-8770 Canadian Fruit Wholesalers' Association. Yearbook†
0068-8789 Canadian Furniture & Furnishings Directory
0068-8797 Canadian Gas Association. Manufacturers' Section. Manufacturers Directory†
0068-8800 Canadian Gas Association. Statistical Summary of the Canadian Gas Industry†
0068-8819 Canadian Geophysical Bulletin†
0068-8827 Canadian Good Roads Associations. Annual Conference see 0826-8193
0068-8835 Canadian Government Series†
0068-8843 Canadian Gunner
0068-8851 Canadian Heart Foundation. Annual Report changed to Heart and Stroke Foundation of Canada. Annual Report.
0068-886X Canadian Historical Association. Historical Booklets - Brochures Historiques
0068-8878 Canadian Historical Association. Historical Papers
0068-8886 Canadian Historical Readings†
0068-8908 Canadian Horticultural Council. Annual Meeting Reports
0068-8916 Canadian Horticultural Council. Committee on Horticultural Research. Annual Reports
0068-8932 Canadian Hospital Directory
0068-8940 Canadian Housing Statistics
0068-8967 Canadian Industry Shows and Exhibitions
0068-8975 Canadian Institute of Actuaries. Yearbook
0068-8983 C I C A Handbook
0068-8991 Canadian Institute of Forestry. Annual Report
0068-9009 C I M Directory
0068-9025 Canadian Insurance. Annual Statistical Issue
0068-9033 Canadian Insurance Law Bulletin Service
0068-9041 Canadian Jewellery & Giftware Directory
0068-905X Canadian Labour Terms
0068-9068 Canadian Library Association. Annual Reports†
0068-9092 Canadian Library Association. Occasional Papers†
0068-9106 Canadian Library Association. Proceedings†
0068-9130 C L A Organization Handbook and Membership List changed to C L A Directory.
0068-9157 Canadian Life and Health Insurance Facts
0068-919X Canadian Mathematical Congress. Proceedings†
0068-9203 Canadian Medical Directory
0068-9211 Canadian Mental Health Association. Annual Report
0068-9254 Canadian Meteorological Society. Annual Congress changed to Canadian Meteorological and Oceanographic Society. Annual Congress.
0068-9270 Canadian Minerals Yearbook
0068-9289 Canadian Mines Handbook
0068-9297 Canadian Mines Register of Dormant and Defunct Companies†
0068-9300 Canadian Mines Register of Dormant and Defunct Companies. Supplement†
0068-9319 Canadian Mining Manual see 0315-9140
0068-9335 Canadian Music Industry Directory†
0068-9378 Canadian National Institute for the Blind. National Annual Report
0068-9386 Canadian Nurses Association. Biennial Meeting. Folio of Reports†
0068-9424 Canadian Paraplegic Association. Annual Report
0068-9440 Canadian Phytopathological Society. Proceedings†
0068-9459 Canadian Plastics Directory and Buyer's Guide
0068-9467 Canadian Ports and Seaways Directory†
0068-9505 Canadian Pulp and Paper Association. Pulp and Paper Report changed to Canadian Pulp and Paper Association. Annual Report.
0068-9556 Canada. Radio-Television Commission. Annual Report changed to Canada. Canadian Radio - Television and Telecommunications Commission. Annual Report.
0068-9572 Canadian Red Cross Society. Annual Report

ISSN INDEX

ISSN	Title
0068-9580	Canadian Rehabilitation Council for the Disabled. Annual Report *changed to* Canadian Rehabilitation Council. Annual Report.
0068-9602	Canadian Rose Annual
0068-9610	Canadian Seed Growers Association. Annual Report
0068-9629	Automotive Service Data Book†
0068-9637	Canadian Skater†
0068-9645	Canadian Society for Education Through Art. Annual Journal *changed to* Canadian Society for Education Through Art. Journal.
0068-9653	Canadian Society for Immunology. Bulletin
0068-9688	Canadian Society of Agronomy. Annual Meeting. Proceedings†
0068-9696	Canadian Society of Animal Production. Proceedings†
0068-970X	Canadian Society of Biblical Studies. Bulletin
0068-9718	Canadian Society of Rural Extension. Meeting and Convention. Proceedings†
0068-9734	Canadian Special Truck Equipment Manual†
0068-9793	Canadian Studies in History and Government††
0068-9807	Canadian Studies in Sociology†
0068-9815	Canadian Tax Foundation. Annual Report†
0068-9823	Canadian Tax Foundation. Provincial Finances *see* 0317-946X
0068-984X	Canadian Technical Asphalt Association. Proceedings of the Annual Conference
0068-9858	Canadian Textile Directory
0068-9874	Canadian Theses
0068-9882	Canadian Tide and Current Tables
0068-9890	Canadian Toy Fair. Trade Show Directory *see* 0317-9443
0068-9904	Canadian Trade Index
0068-9912	Canada. Transport Commission. Annual Report *changed to* Canada. National Transportation Agency. Annual Report.
0068-9939	Canadian Tuberculosis and Respiratory Disease Association. Annual Report *changed to* Canadian Lung Association. Bulletin.
0068-9955	Canadian Variety Merchandise Directory
0068-9963	Canadian Who's Who
0069-0007	Federal - Provincial Wildlife Conference. Transactions†
0069-0015	Canadian Wildlife Service. Monograph Series†
0069-0023	Canadian Wildlife Service. Progress Notes
0069-0031	Canadian Wildlife Service. Report Series
0069-0058	Canadian Yearbook of International Law
0069-0066	Canals Book†
0069-0082	National Library of Australia. Annual Report of the Council *see* 0313-1971
0069-0104	Canberra Papers on Strategy and Defense†
0069-0147	Cancer Facts and Figures
0069-0155	Cancer Incidence in Sweden
0069-0163	Cancer Institute, Tokyo. Selected Papers†
0069-0171	Cancer Seminar Proceedings
0069-018X	Canned Food Pack Statistics†
0069-0198	Canterbury Archaeological Society. Occasional Papers
0069-0201	Canterbury Engineering Journal†
0069-021X	Cape Cod Compass *see* 1045-7771
0069-0228	University of Cape Town. Department of Gynaecology. Annual Report *changed to* University of Cape Town. Department of Obstetrics and Gynaecology. Annual Report.
0069-0244	Capuchin Annual†
0069-0260	Car and Driver Yearbook *changed to* Car and Driver Buyers Guide.
0069-0309	Caravan Sites and Mobile Home Parks *changed to* Caravan Sites.
0069-0317	Caravan and Chalet Sites Guide *see* 0269-8730
0069-035X	Cardiff Medical Society. Scientific Proceedings†
0069-0368	Cardinal O'Hara Series†
0069-0384	Cardiovascular Clinics
0069-0392	Cardiovascular Review; a Medical World News Publication†
0069-0406	Cardiovascular Surgery
0069-0422	Careers for School Leavers *changed to* Careers.
0069-0430	Careers in Banking, Insurance, Finance†
0069-0449	Careers in Depth
0069-0457	Caribbean Conference Series†
0069-0465	Caribbean Bibliography†
0069-0473	Caribbean Documents†
0069-0481	Caribbean Economic Almanac†
0069-0503	Caribbean Islands Research Institute. Annual Report *changed to* Caribbean Research Institute. Report.
0069-0511	Caribbean Monograph Series
0069-052X	Caribbean Scholars' Conference. Proceedings†
0069-0538	Caribbean Series†
0069-0546	Caridad, Ciencia y Arte *changed to* Nueva Enfermeria.
0069-0554	Caritas Internationalis. International Yearbooks†
0069-0570	Caritas; Jahrbuch des Deutschen Caritasverbandes
0069-0597	Carl X Gustaf-Studier†
0069-0600	Carleton Mathematical Series *changed to* Mathematical Preprints.
0069-0619	Carleton University, Ottawa. Department of Geology. Geological Papers†
0069-0635	Carnegie Corporation of New York. Annual Report *changed to* Carnegie Corporation of New York. Grants and Appropriations.
0069-0643	Carnegie Endowment for International Peace Report *changed to* Carnegie Endowment for International Peace in the 1970's.
0069-0651	Carnegie Foundation for the Advancement of Teaching. Annual Report
0069-066X	Carnegie Institution of Washington. Year Book
0069-0694	Carnet des Arts†
0069-0724	Carolina Population Center. Monograph†
0069-0732	Carotenoids Other Than Vitamin A
0069-0740	Carpet and Rug Institute. Directory and Report *changed to* Carpet and Rug Institute. Directory.
0069-0767	Carpet Annual
0069-0783	Carson - Newman College, Jefferson City, Tennessee. Faculty Studies
0069-0805	Cartography
0069-0821	Institut des Peches Maritimes. Bulletin†
0069-0848	Case Studies in Library Science†
0069-0872	Cases Decided in the Court of Claims of the United States†
0069-0880	Cass Library of African Studies. Africana Modern Library
0069-0899	Cass Library of African Studies. General Studies
0069-0902	Cass Library of African Studies. Researches and Travels
0069-0910	Cass Library of African Studies. South African Studies
0069-0929	Cass Library of African Studies. Travels and Narratives
0069-0937	Cass Library of Industrial Classics
0069-0945	Cass Library of Science Classics
0069-0961	Cassal Bequest Lectures
0069-097X	Cassell's Directory of Publishing in Great Britain, The Commonwealth, Ireland and South Africa *changed to* Cassell and Publishers Association Directory of Publishing in the United Kingdom, Commonwealth and Overseas.
0069-0988	Castle's Guide to the Fruit, Flower, Vegetable and Allied Trades
0069-0996	Castle's Town and County Trades Directory
0069-1011	Catalog for College Stores: General Merchandise Buyer's Guide for College Store Managers and Buyers†
0069-102X	Catalog of Modern World Coins†
0069-1038	Catalog of Selected Films for Mental Health Education *changed to* Mental Health Media Center Film Catalog.
0069-1046	Catalogo de Publicaciones Latinoamericanas Sobre Formacion Profesional
0069-1054	Catalogo dei Libri Italiani in Commercio *changed to* Catalogo dei Libri in Commercio.
0069-1062	Catalog of Reprints in Series†
0069-1089	Catalogue de l'Edition Francaise *changed to* Livres Disponibles.
0069-1097	Catalogue des Catalogues Automobile
0069-1100	Catalogue des Produits Agrees Par Qualite-France
0069-1135	Catalogue of Reproductions of Paintings Prior to 1860†
0069-1143	Catalogue of Reproductions of Paintings, 1860-1979
0069-1151	Catalogue of Indian Chemical Plants *changed to* Guide to Indian Chemical Plants and Equipment.
0069-116X	Catalogus Musicus
0069-1178	Cataluna Exporta
0069-1186	Universita degli Studi di Catania. Istituto di Storia delle Tradizioni Popolari. Studi e Testi
0069-1194	Catering & Hotel Management Year Book & Diary†
0069-1208	Catholic Almanac
0069-1216	Catholic Central Union of America. Proceedings†
0069-1232	Catholic Directory for the Clergy and Laity in Scotland *see* 0306-5677
0069-1267	Catholic Theological Society of America. Proceedings
0069-1291	Cavalcade and Directory of Fairs *see* 0361-4255
0069-1305	Cave Research Group of Great Britain. Transactions *see* 0263-760X
0069-1313	Cave Studies†
0069-1321	University of San Carlos. Series A: Humanities *changed to* San Carlos Publications. Series A: Humanities.
0069-133X	University of San Carlos. San Carlos Publications. Series B: Natural Sciences†
0069-1348	University of San Carlos. San Carlos Publications. Series C: Religion†
0069-1356	University of San Carlos. Series D: Occasional Monographs†
0069-1372	Celebrity Service International Contact Book
0069-1399	Celtica
0069-1402	Cement Industry Technical Conference. Record *changed to* I E E E Cement Industry Technical Conference. Record.
0069-1429	Census of Industrial Production in Zambia
0069-1437	Census of U.S. Civil Aircraft
0069-1461	Centers of Civilization Series
0069-147X	Central African Power Corporation. Annual Report and Accounts
0069-1488	Central Asiatic Studies†
0069-1496	Central Bank of Ceylon. Annual Report *changed to* Central Bank of Sri Lanka. Annual Report.
0069-150X	Central Bank of China. Annual Report
0069-1518	Central Bank of Cyprus. Annual Report
0069-1526	Central Bank of Egypt. Board of Directors. Report *changed to* Central Bank of Egypt. Annual Report.
0069-1534	Central Bank of Iraq, Baghdad. Report
0069-1542	Central Bank of Ireland. Quarterly Bulletin
0069-1542	Central Bank of Ireland. Annual Report
0069-1550	Central Bank of Jordan. Annual Report
0069-1569	Central Bank of Kenya. Annual Report *changed to* Central Bank of Kenya. Annual Economic Report.
0069-1577	Central Bank of Nigeria. Annual Report and Statement of Accounts
0069-1593	Central Bank of Trinidad and Tobago. Annual Report
0069-1607	Central Conference of American Rabbis. Yearbook
0069-1615	Central Conference of Teamsters. Officers' Report
0069-1623	Central Electric Railfans' Association. Bulletin
0069-1631	Central Institute of Research and Training in Public Cooperation, New Delhi. Publications
0069-164X	Central Literary Magazine
0069-1674	Central Naugatuck Valley Regional Planning Agency. Annual Report†
0069-1690	Central Road Research Institute, New Delhi. Road Research Paper
0069-1712	Scandinavian Institute of Asian Studies. Monograph Series
0069-1720	Centre Culturel Francais, Alger. Rencontres Culturelles
0069-1739	Centre Culturel International de Cerisy-La-Salle. Decades. Nouvelle Serie†
0069-1747	Centre de Cartographie Phytosociologique. Communications *changed to* Centre d'Ecologie Forestiere et Rurale. Communications.
0069-1755	Centre International de Documentation et Sociale Africaine. Enquetes Bibliographiques
0069-1763	Centre International de Documentation Economique et Sociale Africaine. Monographies Documentaires
0069-1771	French - Canadian Civilization Research Center. Cahiers
0069-1798	France. Centre de Recherches sur les Zones Arides. Publications. Serie Geologie *changed to* Centre Geologique et Geophysique de Montpellier. Publications. Serie Geologie.
0069-1801	Centre d'Ecologie Forestiere. Notes Techniques *changed to* Centre de Recherches sur l'Elevage et les Productions Fourrageres en Haute Belgique. Notes Techniques. B: Herbageres.
0069-1801	Centre d'Ecologie Forestiere. Notes Techniques *see* 0775-3446
0069-1836	Centre d'Etude du Sud-Est Asiatique et de l'Extreme-Orient. International Working Sessions. Proceedings†
0069-1844	Centre d'Etudes et de Documentation Europeennes. Cahiers. Annals†
0069-1852	Centre d'Etudes Pratiques d'Informatique et d'Automatique. Collection†
0069-1860	Arts du Spectacle en Belgique†
0069-1879	Centre d'Information des Services Medicaux d'Entreprises et Interentreprises. Annuaire†
0069-1895	Centre Europeen d'Etudes Bourguignonnes (XIVe-XVIe S.). Publication
0069-1909	C E L O S Bulletins†
0069-1917	Centre for Environmental Studies, London. Conference Paper†
0069-1925	Centre for Environmental Studies, London. Information Paper†
0069-1968	Centre National de Documentation Scientifique et Technique. Rapport d'Activite
0069-1976	Centre National de la Recherche Scientifique. Colloques Internationaux. Sciences Humaines *changed to* Centre National de la Recherche Scientifique. Colloques Internationaux.
0069-1984	Centre National d'Archeologie et d'Histoire du Livre. Publication†

ISSN INDEX 5503

0069-1992 Centre National de Recherches Archeologiques en Belgique. Repertoires Archeologiques. Serie A: Repertoires Bibliographiques†
0069-200X Centre National de Recherches Archeologiques en Belgique. Repertoires Archeologiques. Serie B: Repertoires des Collections†
0069-2018 Centre National de Recherches Archeologiques en Belgique. Repertoires Archeologiques. Serie C: Repertoires Divers†
0069-2026 Centre National de Recherches Scientifiques et Techniques pour l'Industrie Cimentiere. Brussels. C R I C Rapport de Recherche *see* 0770-0725
0069-2034 Centre National d'Etudes Spatiales. Rapport d'Activite
0069-2050 Centre Regional de Recherche et de Documentation Pedagogiques de Lyon. Annales
0069-2069 Centre Regional de Documentation Pedagogique de Toulouse. Annales
0069-2077 Centres of Art and Civilization†
0069-2093 Centro Brasileiro de Pesquisas Fisicas. Notas Tecnicas†
0069-2107 Tropical Science Center, Costa Rica. Occasional Paper
0069-214X Centro de Investigaciones en Administracion Publica. Documentos de Trabajo *changed to* Centro de Estudios de Estado y Sociedad. Documentos de Trabajo.
0069-2166 Centro de Salud "Max Arias Schreiber", Lima. Congreso Nacional de Tuberculosis y Enfermedades Respiratorias
0069-2204 Centro Studi per la Magna Grecia, Naples. Pubblicazioni Proprie
0069-2212 Center for Agricultural Publishing and Documentation. Agricultural Research Reports†
0069-2220 Ceramic Plants in Canada†
0069-2239 Ceramics and Glass Series *changed to* Ceramics and Glass: Science and Technology Series.
0069-2247 Cercle d'Etudes Numismatiques. Travaux
0069-2255 Cerebral Vascular Diseases. Conference *changed to* Princeton Research Conferences on Cerebrovascular Diseases.
0069-2263 Ceredigion
0069-228X Ceskoslovenska Akademie Ved. Rozpravy. M P V: Rada Matematickych a Prirodnich Ved
0069-2298 Ceskoslovenska Akademie Ved. Rozpravy. S V: Rada Spolecenskych Ved
0069-2301 Ceskoslovenska Akademie Ved. Rozpravy. T V: Rada Technickych Ved
0069-2328 Ceskoslovenska Pediatrie
0069-2336 Ceskoslovenska Psychiatrie
0069-2344 Ceskoslovenska Radiologie
0069-2352 Sri Lanka. Department of National Museums. Translations Series†
0069-2360 Sri Lanka Export Directory
0069-2379 Ceylon Journal of Science. Biological Sciences
0069-2387 Chain Shoe Stores and Leased Shoe Department Operators†
0069-2395 Chain Store Age Supermarket Sales Manual†
0069-2417 Chalmers Tekniska Hoegskola. Handlingar†
0069-2441 Survey of Local Chambers of Commerce
0069-245X Chamber of Mines of South Africa. Research Review†
0069-2476 Chambers Trades Register. Lancashire, Cheshire, and North Wales *see* 0309-5649
0069-2484 Chambers Trades Register. Midlands†
0069-2492 Chambers Trades Register of Scotland *see* 0309-5630
0069-2506 Chambers Trades Register. South Wales and South West England†
0069-2514 Chambers Trades Register. Yorkshire Northumberland and Durham†
0069-2522 Chambre de Commerce d'Agriculture et d'Industrie de Bamako, Mali. Annuaire Statistique *changed to* Mali. Direction Nationale de la Statistique et de l'Informatique. Annuaire Statistique.
0069-2530 Chambre de Commerce, d'Industrie et des Mines du Cameroun. Rapport Annuel
0069-2549 Chambre de Commerce et d'Industrie d'Alger. Centre d'Etudes Economiques. Publication†
0069-2557 Chambre de Commerce Franco-Asiatique. Annuaire des Membres
0069-2565 Chambre de Commerce Japonaise en France. Annuaire
0069-2581 Chambre Officielle Franco Allemande de Commerce et d'Industrie. Liste des Membres *changed to* Chambre Franco Allemande de Commerce et d'Industrie. Liste des Membres.
0069-259X Chambre Syndicale des Mines de Fer de France. Rapport d'Activite†
0069-2603 Chambre Syndicale Nationale des Entreprises et Industries de l'Hygiene Publique. Annuaire
0069-2611 Chambre des Ingenieurs-Conseils de France. Annuaire
0069-2646 Champlain Society, Toronto. Report
0069-2654 Chanakya Defence Annual
0069-2662 Chandler and Boatbuilder Trade Directory *changed to* Boat Equipment Buyers' Guide.
0069-2697 Charbonnages de France. Rapport *changed to* Charbonnages de France. Rapport d'Activite.
0069-2727 Charles E. Merrill Monograph Series in the Humanities and Social Sciences†
0069-2735 Charles F. Kettering Foundation. Annual Report *changed to* Connections (Dayton).
0069-2751 Charles W. Hunt Lecture†
0069-276X Charles Warren Center for Studies in American History. Annual Report†
0069-2778 Chart
0069-2786 Charter
0069-2808 Chartered Insurance Institute, London. Yearbook *see* 0957-4883
0069-2824 Checklists in the Humanities and Education†
0069-2840 Chefs-d'Oeuvre de la Science-Fiction†
0069-2859 Chefs-d'Oeuvre Interdits†
0069-2867 Chelates in Analytical Chemistry: A Collection of Monographs†
0069-2875 ChemBooks†
0069-2883 Chemical Analysis
0069-2891 Chemical Buyers Guide
0069-2921 Chemical Engineering Progress. Reprint Manuals†
0069-293X Chemical Engineering Progress. Safety in Air and Ammonia Plants *see* 0360-7011
0069-2948 Chemical Engineering Progress Symposium Series *see* 0065-8812
0069-2956 Chemical Engineering Progress. Technical Manuals *see* 0149-3701
0069-2964 Chemical Guide to Europe†
0069-2972 Chemical Guide to the United States
0069-2980 Chemical Industry Directory *changed to* Chemical Industry Europe.
0069-2999 Chemical Peddler
0069-3022 Chemical Society, London. Annual Reports on the Progress of Chemistry. Section A: General, Physical and Inorganic Chemistry *see* 0260-1818
0069-3030 Royal Society of Chemistry. Annual Reports on the Progress of Chemistry. Section B: Organic Chemistry
0069-3073 Chemie, Physik und Technologie der Kunststoffe in Einzeldarstellungen *see* 0171-709X
0069-3111 Chemistry and Biochemistry of Amino Acids, Peptides, and Proteins
0069-312X Chemistry and Industry Buyers' Guide†
0069-3138 Chemistry and Physics of Carbon: A Series of Advances
0069-3146 Chemistry of Functional Groups
0069-3154 Chemistry of Heterocyclic Compounds (New York, 1951)
0069-3162 Chemistry of Natural Products
0069-3197 Chess Book List *changed to* Maxwell Macmillan Chess Books.
0069-3219 Chiba University. Faculty of Horticulture. Transactions†
0069-3227 Chiba University. Faculty of Horticulture. Technical Bulletin
0069-3235 Art Institute of Chicago. Museum Studies
0069-3243 Chicago Buyer's Guide *changed to* Buyers' Guide and Industrial Directory of Chicago.
0069-3251 Chicago, Cook County and Illinois Industrial Directory†
0069-326X Chicago Crime Commission. Annual Report†
0069-3278 Chicago History of American Civilization
0069-3286 Chicago Lectures in Mathematics
0069-3294 Chicago Lectures in Physics
0069-3316 University of Chicago. Center for Health Administration Studies. Research Series†
0069-3324 University of Chicago. Center for Middle Eastern Studies. Publications†
0069-3340 University of Chicago. Department of Geography. Research Papers. *changed to* University of Chicago. Geography Research Papers.
0069-3367 University of Chicago Oriental Institute. Publications
0069-3375 University of Chicago Studies in Library Science
0069-3391 Chigiana
0069-3405 C A D U Publications *changed to* A R D U Publication.
0069-3413 Child Health in Israel
0069-3456 Children Welcome *changed to* Children Welcome! Family Holiday Guide.
0069-3472 Children's Books: Awards and Prizes
0069-3480 Children's Books in Print
0069-3499 Children's Books of the Year†
0069-3502 Suggested as Holiday Gifts *changed to* Children's Books: One Hundred Titles for Reading and Sharing.
0069-3510 Chile. Comision de Planeamiento Integral de la Educacion. Bibliografia de Investigaciones y Estudios en Educacion†
0069-3529 Chile. Comision de Planeamiento Integral de la Educacion. Publicacion†
0069-3537 Chile. Servicio Agricola y Ganadero. Division Proteccion Pesquera. Anuario Estadistico *see* 0716-0976
0069-3545 Chile. Superintendencia de Educacion Publica. Cuadernos†
0069-3553 Universidad de Chile. Departamento de Astronomia. Publicaciones
0069-357X Universidad de Chile. Departamento de Geologia. Serie Comunicaciones
0069-3588 Universidad de Chile. Departamento de Geologia. Serie Publicaciones†
0069-3596 Universidad Catolica de Chile. Facultad de Teologia. Anales
0069-3634 Chilton's Auto Repair Manual
0069-3642 Chimes
0069-3677 China Glass and Tableware Red Book Directory
0069-3685 China Medical Board of New York. Annual Report
0069-3715 Chiron
0069-3723 Chittagong Port Trust. Yearbook of Information *changed to* Chittagong Port Authority. Yearbook.
0069-3758 Chord and Discord
0069-3774 University of Canterbury. Department of Psychology and Sociology. Research Projects
0069-3790 Lincoln College. Agricultural Economics Research Unit. Research Report *see* 1170-7682
0069-3804 Lincoln College. Agricultural Economics Research Unit. Technical Paper†
0069-3820 Lincoln College. Department of Horticulture. Bulletin
0069-3839 Lincoln College. Farmers' Conference. Proceedings†
0069-3855 Christian Camping International Directory *changed to* Official Guide to Christian Camps & Conference Centers.
0069-3863 Christian Endeavour Year Book *changed to* Christian Endeavour Programme Book.
0069-3871 Christian Periodical Index
0069-3898 Christian Service Training Series†
0069-391X Handbook for Christian Writers *changed to* Successful Writers and Editors Guidebook.
0069-3928 Christmas: An American Annual of Christmas Literature and Art *changed to* Christmas: The Annual of Christmas Literature and Art.
0069-3936 Chromatographic Science Series
0069-3944 Chromosomes Today†
0069-3952 Chronologie des Communautes Europeennest
0069-3960 Chronology of the United Nations†
0069-3979 Church and Society Series†
0069-3987 Church of England Yearbook
0069-3995 Church of Scotland. Yearbook
0069-4002 Church Pulpit Year Book
0069-4029 Churchman's Pocket Book and Diary *changed to* Church Pocket Book and Diary.
0069-4037 CIBA Foundation. Study Groups†
0069-4045 CIBA Zeitschriften†
0069-4053 Ciencia e Sociedade: Temas e Debates†
0069-4061 Cincinnati Art Museum. Bulletin *changed to* Cincinnati Art Museum. Annual Report.
0069-4088 Cincinnati Classical Studies. Supplementary Monograph†
0069-410X Excavations of the University of Cincinnati: Guide Book†
0069-4118 Cine Club del Uruguay. Cuadernos
0069-4134 Cineguia
0069-4177 Circe
0069-4215 Circum-Spice
0069-4231 C R F Listing of Contributions of National Level Political Committees to Incumbents and Candidates for Public Offices†
0069-424X C R F Listing of Political Contributors of Five Hundred Dollars or More†
0069-4258 Civic Municipal Reference Manual and Purchasing Guide *changed to* Civic Public Works Reference Manual and Buyer's Guide.
0069-4266 University of Illinois at Urbana-Champaign. Civil Engineering Studies. Construction Research†
0069-4290 Civilisations et Societes
0069-4304 Civilization of the American Indian
0069-4312 Civilta Asiatiche
0069-4339 Civilta Veneziana. Dizionari Dialettali e Studi Linguistici
0069-4347 Civilta Veneziana. Fonti e Testi. Serie Terza
0069-4355 Civilta Veneziana. Fonti e Testi. Serie Prima: Fonti e Testi per la Storia dell'Arte Veneta
0069-4371 Civilta Veneziana. Saggi
0069-438X Civilta Veneziana. Studi
0069-4401 Clark Guidebooks†
0069-4444 Clasicos Colombianos
0069-4452 Classic European Historians†
0069-4460 Classical Association. Proceedings
0069-4495 Classics in Education†

ISSN

5504 ISSN INDEX

0069-4509 Classics of British Historical Literature

0069-4525 Classified Directory of Wisconsin Manufacturers

0069-4533 Classiques de la Pensee Politique

0069-4541 Classiques de la Renaissance en France. Premiere Serie†

0069-4592 Clay Resources Bulletin†

0069-4606 Clean Air Year Book *changed to* N.S.C.A. Pollution Handbook.

0069-4614 Clegg's International Directory of the World's Book Trade†

0069-4630 Poultry Health and Management Short Course. Proceedings†

0069-4649 Clemson University Review of Industrial Management and Textile Science†

0069-4657 Clemson University. Water Resources Research Institute. Report

0069-4665 Catalogue des Theses de Pharmacie Soutenues en France *see* 1157-1489

0069-4681 Universite de Clermont-Ferrand II. Annales Scientifiques. Serie Biologie Animale†

0069-469X Universite de Clermont-Ferrand II. Annales Scientifiques. Serie Biologie Vegetale†

0069-4703 Universite de Clermont-Ferrand II. Annales Scientifiques. Serie Chemie†

0069-4711 Universite de Clermont-Ferrand II. Annales Scientifiques. Serie Geologie et Mineralogie†

0069-472X Universite de Clermont-Ferrand II. Annales Scientifiques. Serie Mathematique

0069-4738 Universite de Clermont-Ferrand II. Annales Scientifiques. Serie Physique†

0069-4746 Universite de Clermont-Ferrand II. Annales Scientifiques. Serie Physiologie Animale†

0069-4754 Cles de l'Entreprise†

0069-4770 Clin-Alert

0069-4789 University of Illinois at Urbana-Champaign. Clinic on Library Applications of Data Processing. Proceedings

0069-4797 Clinical Approaches to the Problems of Childhood: The Langley Porter Child Psychiatry Series†

0069-4800 Clinical Conference on Cancer. Papers†

0069-4819 Clinical Endocrinology†

0069-4827 Clinical Neurosurgery: Proceedings

0069-4835 Clinics in Developmental Medicine

0069-4843 Closed-Circuit Television and Educational Television; Bibliographical References

0069-4851 Co-Operation†

0069-4886 Coach Tours in Britain and Ireland *changed to* Luxury Coach Tours in Britain & Europe.

0069-4894 Coal Mines in Canada†

0069-4916 Coal Traffic Annual

0069-4924 Coates's Herd Book (Beef)

0069-4932 Coates's Herd Book (Dairy)

0069-4967 Coffee Drinking in the United States†

0069-4983 Coins Market Values

0069-4991 Coke Oven Managers' Association. Year Book

0069-5009 Cold Spring Harbor Laboratory. Annual Report

0069-5017 Colecao Filosofia†

0069-5025 Coleccion Aberri ta Azkatasuna†

0069-5033 Coleccion "Aniversarios Culturales"

0069-505X Coleccion Canonica

0069-5068 Coleccion Ciencia Urbanistica

0069-5076 Coleccion Filosofica

0069-5084 Coleccion "Foros y Seminarios." Serie Foros

0069-5092 Coleccion "Foros y Seminarios." Serie Seminarios

0069-5106 Coleccion Historica

0069-5114 Coleccion "Humanism y Ciencia"

0069-5122 Coleccion Juridica

0069-5130 Coleccion Monografica Africana†

0069-5149 Coleccion Pensamiento Argentino†

0069-5165 Collana di Cultura

0069-5203 Collana di Studi e Saggi

0069-5254 Collana Ricciana. Fonti

0069-5262 Collect British Stamps

0069-5270 Collectanea Historiae Musicae†

0069-5319 Collected Works on Cardio-Pulmonary Disease†

0069-5335 Collection de Sociologie Generale et de Philosophie Sociale†

0069-5351 Collection Dictionnaires des Idees dans les Litteratures Occidentales. Litterature Francaise†

0069-5378 Collection Etudes et Travaux de la Revue "Mediterranee"†

0069-5386 Figures de Wallonie

0069-5416 Collection "Pilotes"†

0069-5513 Collections: Les Idees du Jour

0069-553X College and Adult Reading *changed to* Journal of College and Adult Reading.

0069-5548 Football Guide

0069-5572 College Blue Book

0069-5580 College de France. Annuaire

0069-5599 College des Medecins et Chirurgiens de la Province de Quebec. Bulletin *see* 0315-2979

0069-5602 Baccalaureate Education in Nursing: Key to a Professional Career in Nursing

0069-5688 College Facts Chart

0069-5696 College Music Symposium

0069-570X College of Dairy Agriculture, Hokkaido. Journal *see* 0388-001X

0069-570X College of Dairy Agriculture, Hokkaido. Journal *see* 0388-0028

0069-5718 College of Insurance. General Bulletin *changed to* College of Insurance. Academic Bulletin.

0069-5726 College of Physicians and Surgeons of British Columbia. Medical Directory

0069-5734 College Placement Annual *see* 0749-7474

0069-5777 Collezione di Filosofia

0069-5815 Colloques Internationaux d'Histoire Maritime. Travaux

0069-5823 Colloquium on Scottish Studies. Proceedings *changed to* Scottish Tradition.

0069-5831 Colloquium on the Law of Outer Space. Proceedings

0069-584X Colloquium Series on Transportation. Proceedings *see* 0076-3993

0069-5858 Bibliothekar-Lehrinstitut des Landes Nordrhein-Westfalen. Arbeiten aus dem B L I *see* 0721-7587

0069-5866 Bibliothekar-Lehrinstitut des Landes Nordrhein-Westfalen. Bibliographische Hefte *see* 0721-7587

0069-5874 Universitaet zu Koeln. Geologisches Institut. Sonderveroeffentlichungen

0069-5882 Universitaet zu Koeln. Institut fuer Geophysik und Meteorologie. Mitteilungen

0069-5890 Universitaet Zu Koeln. Jahrbuch

0069-5904 Banco de la Republica Estadisticas Basicas.†

0069-5920 Universidad Nacional de Colombia. Centro de Bibliografia y Documentacion. Boletin Informativo *changed to* Universidad Nacional de Colombia. Biblioteca Central. Boletin de Adquisiciones.

0069-5939 Colombo Law Review

0069-5947 Colombo Plan Bureau. Technical Cooperation under the Colombo Plan. Report *changed to* Colombo Plan Bureau. The Colombo Plan Council Report.

0069-5963 Colombo Plan for Co-operative Economic Development in South and South-East Asia. Report of the Consultative Committee *changed to* Colombo Plan for Co-operative Economic and Social Development in Asia and the Pacific. Consultative Committee. Proceedings and Conclusions.

0069-5971 Colonial Williamsburg Archaeological Series

0069-598X Coloquio de Estudos Luso Brasileiros. Anais

0069-5998 Color Photography†

0069-6005 Colorado. Cooperative Wildlife Research Unit. Special Scientific Reports. Technical Papers†

0069-6013 Colorado. Department of Highways. Traffic Volume Study *changed to* Colorado State Highway Condition and Volume Report.

0069-6048 Colorado Rail Annual

0069-6056 Colorado School of Mines. Professional Contributions

0069-6099 Colorado State University. Fluid Mechanics Papers†

0069-6110 Colorado State University. Hydrology Papers†

0069-6129 Colorado State University. Sanitary Engineering Papers†

0069-6145 University of Colorado. Institute of Arctic and Alpine Research. Occasional Papers

0069-6161 University of Colorado Libraries. Report†

0069-6285 Columbia Biological Series

0069-6293 Columbia County History (Oregon)

0069-6307 Columbia Essays in International Affairs. The Dean's Papers†

0069-6315 Columbia Essays on Modern Writers†

0069-6323 Columbia Essays on the Great Economists†

0069-6331 Columbia Studies in Economics

0069-634X Columbia University - Presbyterian Hospital School of Nursing. Alumnae Association. Magazine

0069-6358 Columbia University Studies in International Organization†

0069-6366 Columbia University Studies in Jewish History, Culture, and Institutions†

0069-6412 Comitatus

0069-6439 Marine Marchand: Etudes et Statistiques *changed to* Transport Maritime: Etudes et Statistiques.

0069-6447 Comite International des Poids et Mesures. Comite Consultatif de Photometrie. Travaux *changed to* Comite International des Poids et Mesures. Comite Consultatif de Photometrie et Radiometrie. (Rapport et Annexes).

0069-6455 Comite International des Poids et Mesures. Comite Consultatif d'Electricite. (Rapport et Annexes)

0069-6463 Comite International des Poids et Mesures. Comite Consultatif de Thermometrie. Rapports et Annexes

0069-6498 Comite International des Poids er Mesures. Comite Consultatif pour la Definition du Metre. Travaux *changed to* Bureau International des Poids et Mesures. Recueil de Travaux.

0069-651X Comite National de l'Organisation Francaise. Annuaire

0069-6528 Comite National Francais de Geodesie et Geophysique. Comptes-Rendus†

0069-6536 Comite National Francais de Geodesie et Geophysique. Rapport National Francais a l'U G G I†

0069-6552 Petrole (Year)

0069-6579 Commentationes Biologicae†

0069-6587 Commentationes Humanarum Litterarum

0069-6609 Commentationes Physico-Mathematicae *see* 0788-5717

0069-6617 Commerce Exterieur de la Republique du Chad

0069-6625 Annuaire du Commerce Franco-Italien

0069-6633 Commerce in Nigeria *see* 0189-5036

0069-6676 Commercial Transport Handbook and Buyer's Guide for S A *changed to* Transport Manager's Handbook and Trucker's Guide.

0069-6692 Commission of the European Communities. Etudes: Serie Aide au Developpement *changed to* Commission of the European Communities. Studies: Development Series.

0069-6706 Commission of the European Communities. Etudes: Serie Concurrence-Rapprochement des Legislations *changed to* Commission of the European Communities. Studies: Competition-Approximation of Legislation.

0069-6714 Commission of the European Communities. Etudes: Serie Energie *changed to* Commission of the European Communities. Studies: Energy Series.

0069-6730 Commission of the European Communities. Etudes: Serie Politique Sociale *changed to* Commission of the European Communities. Studies: Social Policy Series.

0069-6749 General Report on the Activities of the European Communities

0069-6765 Commission of the European Communities. Studies: Agricultural Series†

0069-6773 Commission of the European Communities. Studies: Economic and Financial Series†

0069-679X Commission of the European Communities. Studies: Transport Series†

0069-6811 Commissione Italiana per la Geofisica. Pubblicazioni. Serie I Q S Y†

0069-682X C E D Newsletter†

0069-6838 Committee for International Cooperation in Information Retrieval Among Patent Offices. Bulletin.†

0069-6846 Committee for International Cooperation in Information Retrieval Among Patent Offices. Proceedings of Annual Meetings†

0069-6854 Committee on Institutional Cooperation. Annual Report

0069-6862 Commodity Year Book

0069-6870 Commonwealth Acoustic Laboratories, Sydney. Annual Report *see* 0311-8983

0069-6897 Commonwealth Agricultural Bureaux. List of Research Workers†

0069-6919 Commonwealth Bureau of Animal Breeding and Genetics. Technical Communications *changed to* C.A.B. International. Bureau of Animal Breeding and Genetics. Technical Communications.

0069-6927 Commonwealth Bureau of Animal Health. Review Series†

0069-6935 Commonwealth Bureau of Nutrition. Annotated Bibliographies *changed to* C.A.B. International. Bureau of Nutrition. Annotated Bibliographies.

0069-6943 Commonwealth Bureau of Nutrition. Technical Communications *changed to* C.A.B. International. Bureau of Nutrition. Technical Communications.

0069-6986 Commonwealth Bureau of Horticulture and Plantation Crops. Horticultural Review†

0069-6994 Commonwealth Bureau of Horticulture and Plantation Crops. Research Reviews†

0069-7001 Commonwealth Bureau of Horticulture and Plantation Crops. Technical Communications†

0069-701X Commonwealth Bureau of Pastures and Field Crops. Bulletin *changed to* C.A.B. International. Bureau of Pastures and Field Crops. Bulletin.

0069-7036 Commonwealth Bureau of Soils. Technical Communications *changed to* C.A.B. International. Bureau of Soils. Technical Communications.

ISSN

ISSN INDEX 5505

0069-7052 Commonwealth Forestry Bureau Annotated Bibliographies *changed to* C.A.B. International. Forestry Bureau. Annotated Bibliographies.
0069-7060 Commonwealth Forestry Bureau. Technical Communications *changed to* C.A.B. International. Forestry Bureau. Technical Communications.
0069-7087 Commonwealth Foundation Occasional Paper (No.)
0069-7109 Commonwealth Institute, London. Annual Report
0069-7125 Commonwealth Institute of Biological Control. Technical Communications *changed to* C.A.B. International. Institute of Biological Control. Technical Communications.
0069-7133 Commonwealth Law Reports
0069-7141 Commonwealth Mycological Institute. Phytopathological Papers *changed to* C.A.B. International. Mycological Institute. Phytopathological Papers.
0069-7168 Commonwealth Press Union. Book of Quinquennial Conference†
0069-7184 Commonwealth Scientific and Industrial Research Organization. Annual Report
0069-7192 C S I R O Film Catalogue†
0069-7222 Commonwealth Scientific and Industrial Research Organization. Division of Applied Geomechanics. Report†
0069-7249 Commonwealth Scientific and Industrial Research Organization. Division of Geomechanics. Technical Report
0069-7257 Commonwealth Scientific and Industrial Research Organization. Division of Geomechanics. Technical Paper†
0069-7265 Commonwealth Scientific and Industrial Research Organization. Division of Applied Geomechanics. Technical Memorandum†
0069-7273 Commonwealth Scientific and Industrial Research Organization. Division of Animal Health. Annual Report *see* 1031-1580
0069-7281 Commonwealth Scientific and Industrial Research Organization. Division of Animal Physiology. Report. *see* 0155-7742
0069-729X Commonwealth Scientific and Industrial Research Organization. Division of Building Research. Building Study†
0069-732X Commonwealth Scientific and Industrial Research Organization. Division of Entomology. Report
0069-7338 Commonwealth Scientific and Industrial Research Organization. Division of Entomology. Technical Paper†
0069-7346 Commonwealth Scientific and Industrial Research Organization. Division of Fisheries and Oceanography. Fisheries Synopsis†
0069-7370 Commonwealth Scientific and Industrial Research Organization. Division of Fisheries and Oceanography. Report *see* 0725-4598
0069-7397 Commonwealth Scientific Industrial Research Organization. Division of Fisheries and Oceanography. Report *see* 1031-9964
0069-7397 Commonwealth Scientific Industrial Research Organization. Division of Fisheries and Oceanography. Report *see* 1031-9956
0069-7419 Commonwealth Scientific and Industrial Research Organization. Division of Food Research. Report of Research *changed to* Commonwealth Scientific and Industrial Research Organization. Division of Food Processing. Report of Research.
0069-7427 Commonwealth Scientific and Industrial Research Organization. Division of Food Research. Technical Paper *changed to* Commonwealth Scientific and Industrial Research Organization. Division of Food Processing. Technical Paper.
0069-7435 Commonwealth Scientific and Industrial Research Organization. Division of Horticultural Research. Report *changed to* Commonwealth Scientific and Industrial Research Organization. Division of Horticulture. Report.
0069-7443 Commonwealth Scientific and Industrial Research Organization. Division of Irrigation Research. Report†
0069-746X Commonwealth Scientific and Industrial Research Organization. Division of Land Use Research. Technical Paper *see* 0813-474X
0069-7486 Commonwealth Scientific and Industrial Research Organization. Division of Mechanical Engineering. Circular†
0069-7494 Commonwealth Scientific and Industrial Research Organization. Division of Mechanical Engineering. Engineering Development Reports *changed to* Commonwealth Scientific and Industrial Research Organization. Division of Mechanical Engineering. Technical Reports.
0069-7508 Commonwealth Scientific and Industrial Research Organization. Division of Mechanical Engineering. Report†
0069-7524 Commonwealth Scientific and Industrial Research Organization. Division of Mathematical Statistics. Technical Paper†
0069-7540 Commonwealth Scientific and Industrial Research Organization. Division of Plant Industry. Annual Report *changed to* Commonwealth Scientific and Industrial Research Organization. Division of Plant Industry. Report.
0069-7575 Commonwealth Scientific and Industrial Research Organization. Division of Radiophysics. Report *changed to* Commonwealth Scientific and Industrial Research Organization. Division of Radiophysics. Research Activities.
0069-7583 Commonwealth Scientific and Industrial Research Organization. Division of Soils. Biennial Report *see* 1032-5441
0069-7591 Commonwealth Scientific and Industrial Research Organization. Division of Soils. Soil Publications†
0069-7613 Commonwealth Scientific and Industrial Research Organization. Division of Tropical Pastures. Technical Paper *changed to* Commonwealth Scientific and Industrial Research Organization. Division of Tropical Crops and Pastures. Technical Paper.
0069-7648 Commonwealth Scientific and Industrial Research Organization. Land Research Series†
0069-7680 Commonwealth Scientific and Industrial Research Organization. Wheat Research Unit. Report†
0069-7699 Commonwealth Secretariat. Commodities Division. Dairy Produce†
0069-7702 Commonwealth Secretariat. Commodities Division. Fruit†
0069-7710 Commonwealth Secretariat. Commodities Division. Meat†
0069-7729 Commonwealth Secretariat. Commodities Division. Plantation Crops†
0069-7737 Commonwealth Secretariat. Commodities Division. Vegetable Oils and Oilseeds†
0069-7745 Commonwealth Universities Yearbook
0069-7761 Annuaire des Communautes d'Enfants
0069-777X Communications Handbook
0069-7788 Communist China Problem Research Series
0069-7796 Communist China Yearbook Series
0069-7818 Community Council of Greater New York. Budget Standard Service. Annual Price Survey and Family Budget Costs†
0069-7842 Community Improvement Corporation. Annual Report *changed to* Regional Development Corporation. Annual Report.
0069-7850 Community Mental Health Journal Monograph Series†
0069-7893 Comparative Juridical Review
0069-794X Comparazione dei Salari e del Costo del Lavoro in Europa†
0069-7958 Compendio Statistico Italiano (Year)
0069-7966 Compendium of Pharmaceuticals and Specialties
0069-7974 Complete Book of Engines†
0069-7982 Complete Chevrolet Book†
0069-7990 Complete Ford Book†
0069-8008 Complete Volkswagen Book†
0069-8016 Composers of the Americas
0069-8024 Wilson and Wilson's Comprehensive Analytical Chemistry *changed to* Comprehensive Analytical Chemistry.
0069-8032 Comprehensive Biochemistry *changed to* New Comprehensive Biochemistry.
0069-8040 Comprehensive Chemical Kinetics
0069-8067 Comprehensive Media Guide: Korea†
0069-8075 Belgium. Institut National de Statistique. Etudes Statistiques *issued with* 0772-1838
0069-8075 Belgium. Institut National de Statistique. Etudes Statistiques
0069-8091 Compton Yearbook *changed to* Compton's Yearbook.
0069-8105 Computer Applications in the Natural and Social Sciences *see* 0308-4221
0069-8121 Computer Index†
0069-8148 Association for Computing Machinery. Annual Computer Personnel Research Conference Proceedings†
0069-8164 Computer Service Buyers Guide†
0069-8180 Computer Yearbook
0069-8202 Comunidad Latinoamericana de Escritores. Boletin *changed to* Comunidad Latinoamericana de Escritores. Revista.
0069-8210 Comunidad. Suplementos†
0069-8245 Concise Statistical Yearbook of Greece
0069-8288 The Concrete Yearbook
0069-8296 Condon Lectures†
0069-830X Confederation des Industries Ceramiques de France. Annuaire
0069-8326 Confederation Nationale des Groupes Folkloriques Francais. Annuaire†
0069-8350 Conference Board Cumulative Index
0069-8369 Conference Board. Report on Company Contributions *see* 0146-0986
0069-8393 Conference in Reading. Proceedings†
0069-8407 Conference in the Study of Twentieth-Century Literature, Michigan State University. Proceedings†
0069-8415 Conference of Chief Justices. Proceedings†
0069-8474 Conference of State Sanitary Engineers. Report of Proceedings
0069-8490 Advances in X-Ray Analysis
0069-8512 Conference on Biological Sonar and Diving Mammals. Proceedings†
0069-8520 Perugia Quadrennial International Conferences on Cancer. Proceedings
0069-8547 Conference on Frontiers in Education. Digest *see* 0190-5848
0069-8555 Conference on Human Relations in Industry. Proceedings†
0069-8563 Conference on Labor, New York University. Proceedings *see* 0193-3418
0069-8571 Conference on Land Surveying, Purdue University. Proceedings†
0069-8598 Conference on Latin American History. Publications†
0069-8601 Conference on United Nations Procedures. Report *see* 0743-9180
0069-8644 Conference on Remote Systems Technology. Proceedings
0069-8652 Conference on Research in Income and Wealth *changed to* Studies in Income and Wealth.
0069-8687 National Tax Association - Tax Institute of America. Proceedings of the Annual Conference
0069-8695 Conference on Teacher Education in the Eastern Caribbean. Report *changed to* Eastern Caribbean Standing Conference on Teacher Education. Report.
0069-8741 Conference on Trace Substances in Environmental Health. Proceedings *see* 0361-5162
0069-8784 Conferencias de Bioquimica
0069-8792 Conflict Studies
0069-8814 Confluence. Etats des Recherches en Sciences Sociales: Surveys of Research in the Social Sciences†
0069-8830 Zaire. Direction de la Statistique et des Etudes Economiques. Annuaire des Statistiques du Commerce Exterieur *see* 0304-5692
0069-8849 Congregational Church in England and Wales. Congregational Year book *changed to* United Reformed Church in the United Kingdom. United Reformed Church Year Book.
0069-8857 Congregational Council for World Mission. Annual Report *changed to* C W M Report.
0069-8881 Congres Archeologique de France (Publication)
0069-889X Congres National des Peches et Industries Maritimes. Compte Rendu
0069-8903 Congress for Recreation and Parks. Proceedings *changed to* Congress for Recreation and Parks. Symposium for Leisure Research. Abstracts.
0069-8911 Congres National de Speleologie. Actes
0069-892X Congressional Record Digest and Tally of Roll Call Votes
0069-8938 Congressional Staff Directory
0069-8946 Coniectanea Biblica. New Testament Series
0069-8954 Coniectanea Biblica. Old Testament Series
0069-8970 Connecticut Academy of Arts and Sciences. Memoirs
0069-8989 Connecticut Academy of Arts and Sciences. Transactions
0069-8997 Storrs Agricultural Experiment Station. Research Report
0069-9012 Connecticut College Monograph†
0069-9020 Connecticut. Department of Community Affairs Division of Research and Program Evaluation. Construction Activity Authorized by Building Permits. Summary *changed to* Connecticut Housing Production and Permit Authorized Construction.
0069-9039 Connecticut Master Transportation Plan
0069-9047 University of Connecticut. Center for Real Estate and Urban Economic Studies. General Series
0069-9055 Connecticut Urban Research Report†
0069-9063 University of Connecticut. Institute of Water Resources. Report Series
0069-908X Connolly's Suppressed Writings
0069-9101 U.S. Department of the Interior. Conservation Bulletins†
0069-911X Conservation Directory
0069-9128 Fish and Wildlife Facts†
0069-9136 Conservation of Library Materials
0069-9144 Conservation of Nature and Natural Resources *changed to* Nature and Environment Series.
0069-9152 U.S. Department of the Interior. Conservation Yearbook.†
0069-9160 Consortium for the Study of Nigerian Rural Development†
0069-9179 Consortium for the Study of Nigerian Rural Development. C S N R D Working Paper†
0069-9187 Construction in Hawaii

ISSN

5506 ISSN INDEX

0069-9195 Israel. Central Bureau of Statistics. Construction in Israel
0069-9209 C I R I A. Bulletin *see* 0305-4047
0069-9217 Construction Writers Association. Newsletter
0069-9233 U. S. Federal Trade Commission. Consumer Bulletins†
0069-9241 Consumers' Research Magazine Handbook of Buying†
0069-9276 U.S. National Bureau of Standards. Consumer Information Series†
0069-9284 Consumers Directory *changed to* International Consumer Directory.
0069-9292 Contabilidad Nacional de Espana
0069-9306 Contact†
0069-9322 Contamination Control Directory†
0069-9330 Contemporary African Monographs
0069-9357 Contemporary American History Series
0069-9381 Contemporary Drama Series
0069-942X Contemporary Issues Series
0069-9446 Contemporary Neurology Series
0069-9454 Contemporary Neurology Symposia†
0069-9527 Continental Camping & Caravan Sites†
0069-9535 Continental Research Series
0069-956X Continuing Engineering Studies Series *changed to* College-Industry Education Conference. Proceedings.
0069-9578 Contract Carpeting†
0069-9616 Contributii Botanice
0069-9624 Contributions in Afro-American and African Studies
0069-9640 Texas A & M University. College of Geosciences. Contributions in Oceanography
0069-9667 Contributions to Indian Sociology
0069-9683 Contributions to Library Literature†
0069-9691 Contributions to Marine Science†
0069-9705 Contributions to Sensory Physiology†
0069-9713 Contributions to the History of Science and Technology in Baltics. *see* 0130-3252
0069-973X Control Magazine
0069-9748 Convegno di Studi Sulla Magna Grecia. Atti†
0069-9764 Convegno Nazionale dei Commercianti de Mobili. Atti e Relazioni†
0069-9772 Convegno Nazionale per la Civilta del Lavoro. Atti.†
0069-9780 Cooper Monographs on English and American Language and Literature†
0069-9799 Cooperador Dental
0069-9810 Cooperative Education Association Membership Directory
0069-9829 C I C R I S Directory and Guide to Resources *changed to* C I C R I S Directory.
0069-9837 Cooperative Trade Directory for Southeast Asia
0069-9845 Coordination Chemistry
0069-9861 Danmarks Biblioteksskole. Skrifter
0069-987X Geoteknisk Institut, Copenhagen. Bulletin
0069-9896 Denmark. Kongelige Bibliotek. Fund og Forskning
0069-9918 Koebenhavns Universitet. Filosofiska Fakultet. Extracts†
0069-9950 Copyright Law Symposium
0069-9969 Copyright Laws and Treaties of the World. Supplement
0069-9977 Coral Gables Conference on Fundamental Interactions at High Energy. (Proceedings)†
0069-9993 Corn Annual
0070-0002 Cornell Biennial Electrical Engineering Conference
0070-0010 Cornell International Agricultural Development Mimeographs *changed to* Cornell International Agriculture Mimeographs.
0070-0029 Cornell International Industrial and Labor Relations Reports
0070-0053 Cornell Studies in Industrial and Labor Relations
0070-0061 Cornell University. Center for Housing and Environmental Studies. Research Reports *changed to* Cornell University. Department of City and Regional Planning. Research Reports.
0070-0096 Cornell University. Modern Indonesia Project. Bibliography Series†
0070-0118 Tree-Fruit Production Recommendations *changed to* Pest Management Recommendations for Commercial Tree-Fruit Production.
0070-0126 Cornell University. New York State School of Industrial and Labor Relations. Annual Institute for Training Specialists. (Publication)†
0070-0134 New York State School of Industrial and Labor Relations. Bulletin
0070-0142 Industrial and Labor Relations Bibliography Series
0070-0177 I L R Paperbacks
0070-0185 New York State School of Industrial and Labor Relations. Key Issues Series
0070-0207 Cornell University. New York State School of Industrial and Labor Relations. Technical Monograph Series†
0070-0215 Cornell University. Southeast Asia Program. Data Papers†
0070-0223 Cornell University. Thailand Project. Interim Reports Series†
0070-024X Cornish Archaeology
0070-0282 Corporate Management Tax Conference
0070-0290 Corporate Pension Fund Seminar. Proceedings†
0070-0304 Corporation des Ingenieurs Forestiers du Quebec. Congres Annuel. Texte des Conferences *changed to* Ordre des Ingenieurs Forestiers du Quebec. Congres Annuel. Texte des Conferences.
0070-0312 Corpus Antiquitatum Americanensium†
0070-0320 Corpus Catholicorum
0070-0339 Corpus der Romanischen Kunst im Saechsisch-Thueringischen Gebiet†
0070-0347 Corpus Medicorum Graecorum
0070-0355 Corpus Medicorum Latinorum†
0070-0363 Corpus Mensurabilis Musicae
0070-038X Corpus Palladianum†
0070-0398 Corpus Scriptorum Christianorum Orientalium: Aethiopica
0070-0401 Corpus Scriptorum Christianorum Orientalium: Arabica
0070-041X Corpus Scriptorum Christianorum Orientalium: Armeniaca
0070-0428 Corpus Scriptorum Christianorum Orientalium: Coptica
0070-0436 Corpus Scriptorum Christianorum Orientalium: Iberica
0070-0444 Corpus Scriptorum Christianorum Orientalium: Subsidia
0070-0452 Corpus Scriptorum Christianorum Orientalium: Syriaca
0070-0460 Corpus Scriptorum de Musica
0070-0479 Corpus Vasorum Antiquorum. Italia
0070-0495 Corpus Vasorum Antiquorum. Poland†
0070-0509 Correctional Literature Published in Canada†
0070-0517 Correspondance d'Orient†
0070-0533 Cosmetic Formulary†
0070-0576 Costa Rica. Ministerio de Hacienda Oficina del Presupesto. Informe
0070-0584 Universidad de Costa Rica. Serie Agronomia†
0070-0592 Universidad de Costa Rica. Serie Bibliotecologia†
0070-0606 Universidad de Costa Rica. Series Ciencias Juridicas y Sociales†
0070-0614 Universidad de Costa Rica. Serie de Filosofia†
0070-0622 Universidad de Costa Rica. Serie Educacion†
0070-0630 Universidad de Costa Rica. Serie Economia y Estadistica†
0070-0649 Universidad de Costa Rica. Serie Economia y Estadistica. Estadistica Universitaria†
0070-0657 Universidad de Costa Rica. Serie Historia y Geografia†
0070-0665 Universidad de Costa Rica. Serie Textos Universitarios†
0070-0673 Cotton International
0070-069X Council for Basic Education. Occasional Papers
0070-072X Council for Old World Archaeology: C O W A Surveys and Bibliographies. Area 1: British Isle†
0070-0738 Council for Old World Archaeology: C O W A Surveys and Bibliographies. Area 2: Scandinavia†
0070-0746 Council for Old World Archaeology: C O W A Surveys and Bibliographies. Area 3: Western Europe: Part 1†
0070-0754 Council for Old World Archaeology: C O W A Surveys and Bibliographies. Area 3: Western Europe: Part 2†
0070-0762 Council for Old World Archaeology: C O W A Surveys and Bibliographies. Area 4: Western Mediterranean†
0070-0770 Council for Old World Archaeology: C O W A Surveys and Bibliographies. Area 5: Central Europe†
0070-0789 Council for Old World Archaeology: C O W A Surveys and Bibliographies. Area 6: Balkans†
0070-0797 Council for Old World Archaeology: C O W A Surveys and Bibliographies. Area 7: Eastern Mediterranean†
0070-0800 Council for Old World Archaeology: C O W A Surveys and Bibliographies. Area 8: European Russia†
0070-0819 Council for Old World Archaeology: C O W A Surveys and Bibliographies. Area 9: Northeast Africa†
0070-0827 Council for Old World Archaeology: C O W A Surveys and Bibliographies. Area 10. Northwest Africa†
0070-0835 Council for Old World Archaeology: C O W A Surveys and Bibliographies. Area 11. West Africa†
0070-0843 Council for Old World Archaeology: C O W A Surveys and Bibliographies. Area 12. Equatorial Africa†
0070-0851 Council for Old World Archaeology: C O W A Surveys and Bibliographies. Area 13. South Africa†
0070-086X Council for Old World Archaeology: C O W A Surveys and Bibliographies. Area 14. East Africa†
0070-0878 Council for Old World Archaeology: C O W A Surveys and Bibliographies. Area 15. Western Asia†
0070-0886 Council for Old World Archaeology: C O W A Surveys and Bibliographies. Area 16. Southern Asia†
0070-0894 Council for Old World Archaeology: C O W A Surveys and Bibliographies. Area 17. Far East†
0070-0916 Council for Old World Archaeology: C O W A Surveys and Bibliographies. Area 18. Northern Asia†
0070-0924 Council for Old World Archaeology: C O W A Surveys and Bibliographies. Area 19. Southeast Asia†
0070-0932 Council for Old World Archaeology: C O W A Surveys and Bibliographies. Area 20. Indonesia†
0070-0940 Council for Old World Archaeology: C O W A Surveys and Bibliographies. Area 21. Pacific Islands†
0070-0959 Council for Old World Archaeology: C O W A Surveys and Bibliographies. Area 22. Australia†
0070-1009 Council of Europe. Consultative Assembly. Documents: Working Papers *see* 0252-0656
0070-1017 Council of Europe. Consultative Assembly. Orders of the Day, Minutes of Proceedings *see* 0377-1962
0070-1033 Council of Europe. Consultative Assembly. Texts Adopted by the Assembly *see* 0377-6093
0070-105X Council of Europe. European Treaty Series
0070-1076 Council of Graduate Schools in the United States. Proceedings of the Annual Meeting
0070-1106 Council of Organizations Serving the Deaf. Annual Forum Proceedings†
0070-1114 Council of Organizations Serving the Deaf. Council Membership Directory†
0070-1157 Suggested State Legislation
0070-1173 Council on Legal Education for Professional Responsibility. Newsletter†
0070-1181 Council on Library Resources Report *changed to* Council on Library Resources Annual Report.
0070-119X C R I A Special Studies†
0070-1211 Councils, Committees and Boards
0070-1238 Countdown: Canadian Nursing Statistics†
0070-1262 Country Dance and Song
0070-1270 Country Life Annual†
0070-1300 County and Municipal Year Book for Scotland *see* 0305-6562
0070-1327 County Louth Archaeological and Historical Journal
0070-136X Course Guide for High School Theatre *changed to* Secondary School Theatre Association Course Guide.
0070-1386 Court of Justice of the European Communities. Recueil de la Jurisprudence *changed to* Court of Justice of the European Communities. Report of Cases of the Court.
0070-1394 Courtenay Library of Reformation Classics
0070-1408 Courtenay Studies in Reformation Theology
0070-1416 Cranbrook Institute of Science, Bloomfield Hills, Michigan. Bulletin
0070-1424 Cranfield Fluidics Conference. Proceedings†
0070-1467 Credit Manual of Commercial Laws
0070-1475 Cremation Society of Great Britain. Conference Report†
0070-1483 Cri du Peuple
0070-1505 Crime and Delinquency Issues: Monographic Series *changed to* Crime and Delinquency Topics: Monograph Series.
0070-1521 Criminal Appeal Reports
0070-153X Critical Essays in Modern Literature†
0070-1548 Critical Review Melbourne *changed to* Critical Review.
0070-1556 Critiques de Notre Temps Et...
0070-1572 Croissance Urbaine et Progres des Nations
0070-1580 Croner's Reference Book for Employers
0070-1599 Croner's Reference Book for Exporters
0070-1602 Croner's Reference Book for Importers
0070-1610 Croner's Road Transport Operation
0070-1629 Croner's World Directory of Freight Conferences
0070-167X Crystal Structures†
0070-1688 Cuadernos de Historia del Arte
0070-1696 Cuadernos de Historia del Islam. Serie Monografica Islamica Occidentalia *changed to* Cuadernos de Historia del Islam.
0070-170X Cuadernos de Orientacion†
0070-1718 Cuadernos de Pedagogia†
0070-1726 Cuadernos de Sintesis†
0070-1734 Cuadernos de Sociologia†
0070-1750 Cuadernos del Mexico Prehispanico†
0070-1785 Cuadernos para Estudiantes: Los Poetas
0070-1793 Cumulative Index to Nursing Literature, Nursing Subject Headings *see* 0146-5554
0070-1815 Universidade do Parana. Departamento de Historia. Boletim *changed to* Universidade do Parana. Setor de Ciencias Humanas, Letras e Artes. Departamento de Historia. Boletim.
0070-184X Current Australian Serials†
0070-1858 Current British Directories
0070-1866 Current Caribbean Bibliography
0070-1882 Current Coins of the World†

ISSN

0070-1904 Current Concerns in Clinical Psychology†
0070-1947 Index of Current Equine Research†
0070-1955 Current European Directories†
0070-1971 Current Issues in Higher Education
0070-198X Current Issues in Music Education
0070-2005 Current Medical Information and Terminology†
0070-203X Current Practice in Orthopaedic Surgery†
0070-2064 Current Problems in Dermatology
0070-2080 Current Psychiatric Therapies†
0070-2099 Nebraska Symposium on Motivation (Publication)
0070-2110 Current Therapy in Dentistry†
0070-2129 Current Topics in Bioenergetics
0070-2137 Current Topics in Cellular Regulation
0070-2145 Current Topics in Clinical and Community Psychology†
0070-2153 Current Topics in Developmental Biology
0070-2161 Current Topics in Membranes and Transport
0070-217X Current Topics in Microbiology and Immunology
0070-2188 Current Topics in Pathology
0070-2196 Current Topics in Surgical Research†
0070-2234 Cusanus-Gesellschaft. Buchreihe
0070-2242 Cushman Foundation for Foraminiferal Research. Special Publication
0070-2250 U S Custom House Guide
0070-2277 Cycle Buyers Guide
0070-2307 Cyprus. Agricultural Research Institute. Annual Report *changed to* Cyprus. Agricultural Research Institute. Annual Review.
0070-2315 Cyprus. Agricultural Research Institute. Technical Bulletin
0070-2323 Cyprus. Budget: Estimates of Revenue and Expenditure
0070-2331 Cyprus Chamber of Commerce and Industry Directory
0070-234X Cyprus. Department of Agriculture. Soils and Plant Nutrition Section. Report *changed to* Cyprus. Department of Agriculture. Land Use Section. Annual Report.
0070-2366 Cyprus. Department of Antiquities. Monographs
0070-2374 Cyprus. Department of Antiquities. Annual Report
0070-2390 Cyprus. Ministry of Labour and Social Insurance. Annual Report
0070-2404 Cyprus. Department of Social Welfare Services. Annual Report†
0070-2412 Cyprus. Department of Statistics and Research. Economic Report
0070-2420 Cyprus. Department of Statistics and Research. Statistics of Imports and Exports
0070-2439 Cyprus. Department of Statistics and Research. Shipping Statistics†
0070-2447 Cystic Fibrosis: A Bibliography†
0070-2455 Cystic Fibrosis Club Abstracts†
0070-2463 Cytobiologie *see* 0171-9335
0070-248X Czechoslovakia. Federalni Statisticky Urad. Statisticka Rocenka
0070-2498 D.A.T.A. Book of Discontinued Transistors *see* 0730-4846
0070-251X Dacia; Revue d'Archeologie et d'Histoire Ancienne
0070-2528 Daedalus
0070-2544 Daffodils
0070-2595 Dairy Products and Sugar in Coffee in the United States *changed to* How do Americans Drink Their Coffee?
0070-2617 Institut Fondamental d'Afrique Noire. Catalogues et Documents
0070-2625 Institut Fondamental d'Afrique Noire. Initiations et Etudes Africaines
0070-2633 Institut Fondamental d'Afrique Noire. Memoires†
0070-2668 Dana-Report
0070-2676 Dance Directory (Year)
0070-2684 Dance Magazine Annual *see* 0896-3193
0070-2692 Dance World†
0070-2714 Dania Polyglotta
0070-2749 Danish Yearbook of Philosophy
0070-2765 Danmarks Folkeminder†
0070-2781 Danmarks Vareindfoersel og- Udfoersel
0070-279X Dans le Fantastique†
0070-2803 Dansk Elvaerksstatistik *see* 0106-4711
0070-282X Danske Forlaeggerforening. Faelleslagerkatalog
0070-2846 Danske Magazin
0070-2854 Oplagstal og Markedstal
0070-2862 Dante Studies
0070-2889 Data Processing in Medicine†
0070-2897 Datos y Cifras de la Ensenanza en Espana
0070-2900 David Davies Memorial Institute of International Studies, London. Annual Memorial Lecture
0070-2927 University of Toronto. David Dunlap Observatory. Publications†
0070-2943 Davison's Knit Goods Trade†
0070-2951 Davison's Textile Blue Book
0070-2986 Davy's Devon Herd Book
0070-3001 Dawn Song and All Day
0070-3028 Dayton Art Institute. Annual Report *changed to* Dayton Art Institute. Annual Report.
0070-3044 University of Dayton. School of Education. Abstracts of Research Projects
0070-3052 University of Dayton. School of Education. Workshop Proceedings
0070-3109 Dealers in Coins
0070-3141 December
0070-315X Dechema Monographien
0070-3176 Decisions of the United States Courts Involving Copyrights
0070-3192 Decorating Contractor Annual Directory
0070-3206 Decorative Art and Modern Interiors†
0070-3222 Deems Lectureship†
0070-3230 Defects in Crystalline Solids *changed to* Defects in Solids.
0070-3249 Deiches Fund Studies of Public Library Service†
0070-3257 Dein Kind†
0070-3273 Delaware Geological Survey Bulletins
0070-3281 Delaware Nurse *changed to* Delaware Nurses' Association Reporter.
0070-329X Delaware. Department of Highways and Transportation. Traffic Summary
0070-3303 Delegations to the United Nations†
0070-3311 Institute of Economic Growth, Delhi. Census Studies
0070-3338 Delphica†
0070-3346 Democrat
0070-3354 Demographie et Sciences Humaines *see* 0032-4663
0070-3362 Demographie et Societes
0070-3370 Demography
0070-3389 Demokratische Existenz Heute†
0070-3419 Denken, Schauen, Sinnen†
0070-3427 Denkmaeler des Rheinlandes†
0070-3435 Denmark. Danmarks Fiskeri- og Havundersoegelser. Meddelelser *see* 0106-553X
0070-346X Denmark. Danmarks Statistik. Arbejdsloesheden†
0070-3478 Denmark. Danmarks Statistik. Befolkningens Bevaegelser
0070-3486 Danmarks Skibe og Skibsfart
0070-3508 Denmark. Danmarks Statistik. Ejendomssalg†
0070-3516 Denmark. Danmarks Statistik. Faerdselsuheld
0070-3524 Denmark. Danmarks Statistik. Indkomstansaettelser til Staten *see* 0107-105X
0070-3532 Denmark. Danmarks Statistik. Industristatistik
0070-3540 Denmark. Danmarks Statistik. Kriminalstatistik
0070-3559 Denmark. Danmarks Statistik. Landbrugsstatistik. Herunder Gartneri og Skovbrug *changed to* Denmark. Danmarks Statistik. Landbrugsstatistik.
0070-3567 Denmark. Danmarks Statistik. Statistisk Aarbog
0070-3583 Denmark. Danmarks Statistik. Statistisk Tiars-Oversigt
0070-3605 Denmark. Fiskeriministeriet. Forsoegslaboratorium. Aarsberetning
0070-3621 Denmark. Statens Filmcentral. S F C Film and Video Catalogue *changed to* Denmark. Statens Filmcentral. S F C Film og Video Catalogue.
0070-3648 Dental Delineator
0070-3656 Dental Guide
0070-3664 Dental Images
0070-3672 Dental Laboratorie Bladet
0070-3702 Dental Products Annual Report *see* 0011-8737
0070-3729 Tenth District Dental Society of the State of New York. Bulletin *changed to* Nassau County Dental Society. Newsletter.
0070-3737 Dentistry in Japan
0070-3745 Denver Museum of Natural History. Museum Pictorial†
0070-3753 Denver Museum of Natural History. Proceedings†
0070-3788 Derbyshire Archaeological Journal
0070-3834 Design and Industries Association. Year Book and Membership List *changed to* D I A Yearbook.
0070-3869 Dessinateurs, Peintres et Sculpteurs de Belgique *see* 0066-3174
0070-3885 Detroit Studies in Music Bibliography
0070-3893 Deutsch-Slawische Forschungen zur Namenkunde und Siedlungsgeschichte
0070-3907 Deutsche Akademie der Landwirtschaftswissenschaften, Berlin. Jahrbuch†
0070-3915 Akademie fuer Aerztliche Fortbildung der DDR. Bibliographie†
0070-3923 Deutsche Akademie fuer Sprache und Dichtung. Jahrbuch
0070-3931 Bibliographischer Informationsdienst der Deutschen Buecherei†
0070-394X Deutsche Bundesbank. Geschaeftsbericht
0070-3958 Deutsche Dendrologische Gesellschaft. Mitteilungen
0070-3966 D F V L R Jahresbericht *see* 0938-2194
0070-3974 Deutsche Forschungsgemeinschaft. Denkschriften zur Lage der Deutschen Wissenschaft
0070-3982 Deutsche Forschungsgemeinschaft. Forschungsberichte
0070-3990 Deutsche Forschungsgemeinschaft. Kommissionenmitteilungen
0070-4016 Deutsche Gaue
0070-4040 Deutsche Gesellschaft fuer Chronometrie. Jahrbuch
0070-4067 Deutsche Gesellschaft fuer Innere Medizin. Verhandlungen
0070-4083 D G L R Jahrbuecher
0070-4091 Deutsche Gesellschaft fuer Orthopaedie und ihre Grenzgebiete. Verhandlungen *see* 0044-3220
0070-4105 Deutsche Gesellschaft fuer Ostasienkunde. Koordinierungstelle fuer Gegenwartsbezogene Ostasienforschung Mitteilungen *changed to* Deutsche Gesellschaft fuer Ostasienkunde. Koordinierungsstelle fuer Gegenwartsbezogene Ost- und Suedostasienforschung. Mitteilungen.
0070-4113 Deutsche Gesellschaft fuer Pathologie. Verhandlungen
0070-4121 Deutsche Gesellschaft fuer Rheumatologie. Verhandlungen *changed to* Deutsche Gesellschaft fuer Rheumatologie. Fortschritte der Rheumatologie. Verhandlungen.
0070-413X Deutsche Gesellschaft fuer Urologie. Verhandlungsbericht *changed to* Deutsche Gesellschaft fuer Urologie. Verhandlungen.
0070-4148 German Merchant Fleet
0070-4164 Deutsche Hydrographische Zeitschrift. Ergaenzungsheft. Reihe A
0070-4172 Deutsche Hydrographische Zeitschrift. Ergaenzungsheft. Reihe B
0070-4210 Deutsche Kraftfahrtforschung und Strassenverkehrstechnik†
0070-4229 Deutsches Krebsforschungszentrum. Veroeffentlichungen
0070-4237 Die Deutsche Lebensversicherung. Jahrbuch
0070-4245 Deutsche Luft- und Raumfahrt Forschungsberichte *changed to* D L R - Forschungsberichte.
0070-4253 Deutsche Luft- und Raumfahrt. Mitteilungen†
0070-427X Deutsche Ophthalmologische Gesellschaft. Zusammenkunft. Bericht†
0070-4296 Deutsche Papierwirtschaft
0070-430X Deutsche Physikalische Gesellschaft. D P G - Nachrichten†
0070-4318 Deutsche Schiller-Gesellschaft. Jahrbuch
0070-4326 Deutsche Shakespeare-Gesellschaft West. Jahrbuch
0070-4334 Deutsche Texte des Mittelalters
0070-4342 Deutsche Zoologische Gesellschaft. Verhandlungen
0070-4377 Deutscher Kuesten-Almanach
0070-4431 Deutsches Buehnen-Jahrbuch
0070-444X Deutsches Dante-Jahrbuch
0070-4458 Deutsches Hydrographisches Institut. Jahresbericht
0070-4490 Deutsches Institut fuer Puppenspiel. Forschung und Lehre†
0070-4504 Deutsches Jahrbuch der Musikwissenschaft *see* 0323-8105
0070-4512 Deutsches Universitaets-Handbuch†
0070-4563 Developments in Industrial Microbiology
0070-4571 Developments in Sedimentology
0070-458X Developments in Solid Earth Geophysics
0070-4598 Developments in Theoretical and Applied Mechanics†
0070-4628 Central Mining Research Station, Dhanbad. Progress Research *changed to* C M R S Annual Report.
0070-4660 Diagnostische Informationen fuer die aerztliche Praxis *see* 0300-8096
0070-4695 Dichter und Zeichner
0070-4709 Dictionary of African Biography†
0070-4717 Dictionary of Canadian Biography
0070-4725 Dictionary of Dairying. Supplement†
0070-4733 Dictionary of Latin American and Caribbean Biography†
0070-475X Dictionnaire des Parfums de France et des Lignes pour Hommes
0070-4768 Dictionnaire des Produits de Beaute et de Cosmetologie *changed to* Dictionnaire des Produits de Soins de Beaute.
0070-4776 Dictionnaire des Valeurs des Meubles et Objets d'Art
0070-4792 Didactica Classica Gandensia
0070-4806 Diderot Studies
0070-4814 Diebeners Goldschmiede- und Uhrmacher-Jahrbuch *changed to* Goldschmiede- und Uhrmacher-Jahrbuch.
0070-4822 Diesel and Gas Turbine World Wide Catalog *changed to* Diesel and Gas Turbine Catalog.
0070-4830 Diesel Locomotive Question & Answer Manual
0070-4849 Digest of Health Statistics for England and Wales *changed to* Health and Personal Social Services Statistics.
0070-4857 Digest of Legal Activities of International Organizations and Other Institutions
0070-4865 Digest of Literature on Dielectrics *see* 0018-9367
0070-4873 Digest of World Events
0070-4881 Dimension: Languages (Year)
0070-4903 Dine Israel
0070-4938 Diplomatarium Danicum†

ISSN

5508 ISSN INDEX

0070-4946 Diplomatic Corps of Belgrade†
0070-4962 Diplomat's Annual†
0070-4970 Direct Selling: Association Membership Roster Listing Major Companies and Commodities *changed to* Who's Who in Direct Selling.
0070-4997 Directories of Science Information Sources, International Bibliography†
0070-5012 Directory for Exceptional Children
0070-5020 Directory for the Nonwoven Fabrics and Disposable Soft Goods Industries *see* 0095-683X
0070-5039 Directory Iron and Steel Plants
0070-5047 Directory of Accredited Camps for Boys and Girls *changed to* Parents' Guide to Accredited Camps. West Edition.
0070-5047 Directory of Accredited Camps for Boys and Girls *changed to* Parents' Guide to Accredited Camps. South Edition.
0070-5055 Directory of Accredited Private Home Study Schools *changed to* Directory of Accredited Home Study Schools.
0070-5063 Directory of American College Theatre†
0070-5071 Directory of American Firms Operating in Foreign Countries
0070-508X Directory of American Philosophers
0070-5098 Directory of American Savings and Loan Associations
0070-5101 Directory of American Scholars
0070-5152 Directory of British Associations
0070-5160 Directory of British Recruitment Services
0070-5179 Directory of Brush and Allied Trades *changed to* Brush and Allied Trades Directory.
0070-5187 Directory of Business Schools *changed to* Directory of Educational Institutions.
0070-5195 Directory of Buying Offices and Accounts
0070-5217 Directory of Canadian Map Collections
0070-5233 Directory of Catholic Schools and Colleges *see* 0952-083X
0070-525X Directory of Chemical Engineering Research in Canada
0070-5268 Directory of Church of England Social Services *changed to* Social Responsibility.
0070-5276 Directory of College and University Libraries in New York State
0070-5284 Directory of College Placement Offices *changed to* Directory of Career Planning and Placement Offices.
0070-5292 Directory of Communication Organizations *see* 0094-2588
0070-5306 Directory of Community Services in Maryland†
0070-5314 Directory of Companies and Their Subsidiaries in the Wine, Spirit and Brewing Trades *changed to* Off Licence News Directory.
0070-5322 Directory of Company Secretaries
0070-5330 Directory of Computerized Information in Science and Technology†
0070-5365 Directory of Corporate Affiliations
0070-5373 Directory of Correctional Institutions and Agencies of the United States of America, Canada, and Great Britain *see* 0190-2555
0070-5381 Directory of Correctional Services in Canada - Repertoire des Services de Correction du Canada *see* 0225-4115
0070-539X Directory of Current Research in Israel: Physical and Life Sciences *see* 0301-4657
0070-5403 Directory of Current Scientific Research Projects in Pakistan†
0070-5411 Directory of Dealers in Secondhand and Antiquarian Books in the British Isles *see* 0950-0715
0070-542X Directory of Directors
0070-5438 Directory of Directors
0070-5446 Directory of Discount Centers *see* 0897-5442
0070-5454 Directory of Education Studies in Canada†
0070-5462 Directory of Engineering College Research and Graduate Study *changed to* Engineering College Research and Graduate Study.
0070-5470 Directory of Engineering Societies and Related Organizations
0070-5489 Directory of Engineers *changed to* Institution of Engineers of Ireland. Register of Chartered Engineers and Members.
0070-5500 Directory of European Associations. Part 1: National Industrial Trade and Professional Associations *changed to* Directory of European Industrial & Trade Associations.
0070-5543 Directory of Foreign Firms Operating in the United States
0070-556X Directory of Franchising Organizations
0070-5586 Directory of Government Agencies Safeguarding Consumer and Environment†
0070-5594 Directory of Government Production Prime Contractors *see* 0887-4107
0070-5616 Directory of Graduate Programs in the Speech Communication Arts and Sciences *see* 0732-2755
0070-5624 Directory of Grant-Making Trusts
0070-5632 Hawaii's Scientific Resources Directory†
0070-5640 Directory of Health, Welfare and Recreation Services of Greater Montreal *see* 0319-258X
0070-5659 Directory of Historical Societies and Agencies in the United States and Canada *changed to* Directory of Historical Organizations in the United States and Canada.
0070-5675 Directory of Institutions of Higher Education in Missouri
0070-5691 Directory of Insurance Companies Licensed in New York State
0070-5705 Directory of Israeli Merchants and Manufacturers *changed to* Directory of Israel.
0070-5721 Directory of Kansas Manufacturers and Products
0070-573X Directory of Law Teachers
0070-5756 Directory of Lawyer Referral Services, Legal Aid and Defender Offices and Legal Assistance Offices of the Armed Forces†
0070-5772 Directory of Machine Tools and Related Products *changed to* U S Machine Tool Directory.
0070-5780 Directory of Magazine Editorial Shopping Sections
0070-5799 Directory of Maryland Exporters-Importers†
0070-5802 Harris Maryland Industrial Directory (Year)
0070-5810 Directory of Medical Libraries in New York State
0070-5829 Directory of Medical Specialists
0070-5837 Directory of Mental Health Resources in Florida†
0070-5845 Directory of Michigan Manufacturers *see* 0736-2889
0070-5861 Directory of Mineral Producers in Oklahoma†
0070-5888 Directory of Municipal Officials of New Mexico *changed to* Directory of New Mexico Municipal Officials.
0070-5896 Directory of National and International Labor Unions in the United States *see* 0090-4163
0070-5918 Directory of National Trade and Professional Associations of the United States *changed to* National Trade and Professional Associations of the United States and Labor Unions.
0070-5926 Directory of Nebraska Manufacturers
0070-5934 Directory of New Mexico Manufacturing and Mining *changed to* New Mexico Directory of Manufacturers.
0070-5950 Directory of New York State Public Library Systems *changed to* Directory of Library Systems in New York State.
0070-5969 Directory of Oceanographers in the United States *changed to* U S Directory of Marine Scientists.
0070-5977 Directory of Official Architects and Planners *changed to* Directory of Official Architecture and Planning.
0070-5985 Directory of Ohio Manufacturers *see* 0888-8140
0070-5993 Directory of Oil Marketing and Wholesale Distributors *changed to* Oil Marketing Industry.
0070-6000 Directory of On-Going Research in Smoking and Health†
0070-6019 Directory of Opportunities for Graduates†
0070-6027 Directory of Oregon Manufacturers
0070-6035 Directory of Organizations and Personnel in Educational Management *changed to* Directory of Organizations in Educational Management.
0070-6051 Directory of Overseas Summer Jobs
0070-606X Directory of Pakistani Scholars Abroad
0070-6078 Directory of Pakistan's Periodicals in Social Sciences†
0070-6086 Directory of Pathology Training Programs (Year)
0070-6094 Directory of Periodicals Publishing Articles on English and American Literature and Language
0070-6124 Directory of Premium and Incentive Buyers *see* 0196-8262
0070-6167 Directory of Public Refrigerated Warehouses. *changed to* International Directory of Public Refrigerated Warehouses.
0070-6175 Directory of Quarries and Pits†
0070-6183 Directory of Reference and Research Library Resource Systems in New York State *changed to* Directory of Library Systems in New York State.
0070-6205 Directory of Regional Councils *changed to* Directory of Regional Councils.
0070-6213 Directory of Research Reports Relating to Produce Packaging and Marketing†
0070-623X Directory of Scholarly and Research Publishing Opportunities *see* 0275-3820
0070-6256 Directory of Science Resources for Maryland *changed to* Maryland High-Tech Directory (Year).
0070-6264 Directory of Scientific and Technical Associations and Institutes in Israel *see* 0334-2824
0070-6272 Directory of Scientific Directories *changed to* Directory of Technical and Scientific Directories.
0070-6280 Directory of Scientific Research in Nigeria
0070-6302 Directory of Serials in Pure and Applied Science and Economics Published in Israel†
0070-6310 Directory of Shipowners, Shipbuilders and Marine Engineers *changed to* Directory of Shipowners and Shipbuilding.
0070-6337 Directory of Singapore Manufacturers *see* 0217-7447
0070-6345 Directory of Service Organizations.†
0070-637X Directory of Special Libraries in Israel
0070-6396 Directory of Special Libraries in Montreal *see* 0319-2563
0070-640X Directory of State and Federal Funds Available for Business Development†
0070-6418 Directory of State Arts Councils†
0070-6426 Directory of Steel Foundries in the United States, Canada and Mexico
0070-6442 Tennessee Directory of Manufacturers *see* 0360-5477
0070-6450 Directory of Texas Manufacturers
0070-6477 Directory of the Forest Products Industry
0070-6515 World Directory of Travel Agencies†
0070-6523 Directory of United Funds and Community Health and Welfare Councils *changed to* United Way of America. International Directory.
0070-6531 Directory of United States Importers
0070-654X Directory of U.S. Institutions of Higher Education *changed to* Directory of Postsecondary Institutions.
0070-6558 Directory of United States Standardization Activities *changed to* Standards Activities of Organizations in the U S.
0070-6566 Directory of Utah Manufacturers *see* 8755-2841
0070-6574 Directory of Virginia Manufacturing and Mining *changed to* Virginia Industrial Directory.
0070-6582 Directory of Visiting Scholars in the United States Awarded Grants Under the Mutual Educational and Cultural Exchange Act (the Fulbright-Hays Act) *changed to* Directory of Visiting Fulbright Scholars and Occasional Lecturers.
0070-6604 Directory to the Furnishing Trade
0070-6612 Diretorio Brasileiro da Industria Farmaceutica
0070-6639 D I S A Information. Measurement and Analysis *see* 0900-5579
0070-6655 Disc Collector's Newsletter *see* 0731-843X
0070-6663 Discourse Units in Human Communication for Librarians
0070-668X Discoveries in the Judaean Desert of Jordan
0070-6698 Discovery Reports†
0070-6701 Dispersion and Unity *see* 0334-2506
0070-671X Disquisitiones Mathematicae Hungaricae
0070-6728 Dissertationes Botanicae
0070-6736 U S C Annual Distinguished Lecture Series Monographs in Special Education and Rehabilitation
0070-6760 Dix-Huitieme Siecle
0070-6779 Do-It-Yourself. Annual†
0070-6787 Do-It-Yourself Gardening Annual†
0070-6795 Doblingers Verlagsnachrichtent†
0070-6817 Documentologie†
0070-6825 Documenta Romaniae Historica. Serie A: La Moldavie
0070-6833 Documenta Romaniae Historica. Serie B: La Valachie
0070-6841 Documentacion Bibliotecologica†
0070-6868 Documentation du Batiment†
0070-6884 Documente Istorice†
0070-6892 Documente si Manuscrise Literare†
0070-6906 Documenti Sulle Arti del Libro
0070-6922 Documentos Latino Americanos†
0070-6957 Documents et Recherches sur le Monde Byzantins, Neohellenique et Balkanique
0070-6973 Documents on American Foreign Relations *see* 0362-3653
0070-7007 Dod's Parliamentary Companion
0070-7015 Dog World Annual
0070-7023 Dokumentation Verschleiss, Reibung und Schmierung *see* 0340-3475
0070-7031 Dokumente zur Deutschlandpolitik
0070-704X Dollars and Cents of Shopping Centers
0070-7058 Domestic Oceanborne and Great Lakes Commerce of the United States *changed to* Domestic Waterborne Trade of the United States.
0070-7066 Dominican Republic. Secretaria de Obras Publicas y Comunicaciones. Estadistica *changed to* Dominican Republic Secretaria de Estado de Obras Publicas y Comunicaciones. OPC.
0070-7074 Donauschwaebisches Schrifttum†
0070-7112 Dorset Natural History and Archaeological Society. Proceedings
0070-7120 Dorset Worthies
0070-7139 Revue Pedagogique et Litteraire *changed to* Ecoles des Lettres.

ISSN

ISSN INDEX 5509

0070-7155 Dossiers du Cinema†

0070-7171 Downdraft

0070-718X Downhill Only Journal

0070-7198 Dramascripts Series

0070-7201 Landesmuseum fuer Vorgeschichte, Dresden. Veroeffentlichungen

0070-721X Medizinische Akademie "Carl Gustav Carus" Dresden. Schriften

0070-7228 Staatliches Museum fuer Mineralogie und Geologie, Dresden. Abhandlungen†

0070-7260 Staatliches Museum fuer Tierkunde Dresden. Malakologische Abhandlungen

0070-7279 Reichenbachia

0070-7295 Staatliches Museum fuer Voelkerkunde Dresden. Abhandlungen und Berichte

0070-7325 Droit Polonais Contemporain

0070-7333 Drosophila Information Service

0070-7341 Drug Abuse Law Review†

0070-735X Drug Abuse Papers†

0070-7368 Drug Dependence†

0070-7376 Drug Topics Red Book

0070-7392 Drugs in Current Use and New Drugs *changed to* Modell's Drugs in Current Use and New Drugs.

0070-7414 Dublin Institute for Advanced Studies. Communications. Series A

0070-7422 Dublin Institute for Advanced Studies. School of Cosmic Physics. Geophysical Bulletin

0070-7430 Dudley, England (West Midlands) Public Libraries. Archives Department. Transcripts†

0070-7457 Universitaet Duesseldorf. Jahrbuch

0070-7473 Duke University. Commonwealth-Studies Center. Publications *changed to* Duke University. Center for International Studies. Publications.

0070-7481 Duke University. Cooperative Oceanographic Program. Progress Report†

0070-7546 Dumbarton Oaks Papers

0070-7554 Dumbarton Oaks Studies

0070-7562 Dumbarton Oaks Texts

0070-7589 Electronic Marketing Directory

0070-7597 Dun and Bradstreet Metalworking Directory *see* 0278-8799

0070-7600 Dun and Bradstreet Middle Market Directory *changed to* Million Dollar Directory Series.

0070-7627 Dun and Bradstreet Reference Book of Corporate Managements *changed to* Reference Book of Corporate Managements.

0070-7635 Dun and Bradstreet Register *changed to* Dun & Bradstreet Standard Register.

0070-7643 Dunsink Observatory. Publications

0070-7694 Duquesne Studies. Philological Series *changed to* Duquesne Studies. Language and Literature Series.

0070-7708 Duquesne Studies. Philosophical Series†

0070-7716 Duquesne Studies. Psychological Series†

0070-7732 Duquesne Studies. Theological Series†

0070-7740 University of Durban-Westville. Journal

0070-7759 University of Natal. Institute for Social Research. Annual Report *changed to* University of Natal. Centre for Social and Development Studies. Annual Report.

0070-7767 Durch Stipendien Studieren

0070-7783 Dutch Studies in Russian Literature†

0070-7791 Dzieje Polskiej Granicy Zachodniej

0070-7805 E D P Conference for Retailers†

0070-7821 E I A Guide *changed to* Hi-Tech Buyers Guide.

0070-7902 Earth and Extraterrestrial Sciences *see* 0146-2970

0070-7910 Earth Sciences Series

0070-7945 East African Academy. Proceedings *changed to* Kenya National Academy for Advancement of Arts and Sciences. Proceedings.

0070-7953 East African Freshwater Fisheries Research Organization. Annual Report *changed to* Uganda Freshwater Fisheries Research Organization. Annual Report.

0070-7961 East African Geographical Review

0070-7988 Maktaba

0070-8003 East African Railways. Annual Report†

0070-8011 East African Research Information Centre. E A R I C Information Circular *changed to* Kenya National Academy for Advancement of Arts and Sciences. Research Information Circulars.

0070-8038 East African Wildlife Journal *see* 0141-6707

0070-8062 University of Kansas. Center for East Asian Studies. International Studies: East Asian Series. Research Series

0070-8070 University of Kansas. Center for East Asian Studies. International Studies: East Asian Series. Reference Series

0070-8089 East Carolina University Publications in History

0070-8097 East Europe in German Books

0070-8100 East Europe Monographs

0070-8127 East Lakes Geographer

0070-8135 Bangladesh. Education Directorate. Report on Pilot Project on Adult Education

0070-8143 Bangladesh. Directorate of Agricultural Marketing. Agricultural Marketing Series

0070-8151 Bangladesh. Directorate of Agriculture. Season and Crop Report

0070-8178 Bangladesh Research and Evaluation Centre. Report

0070-8186 Bangladesh University of Engineering and Technology, Dhaka. Technical Journal

0070-8208 East Yorkshire Local History Series

0070-8224 Eastern Hemisphere Petroleum Directory *see* 0275-3871

0070-8224 Eastern Hemisphere Petroleum Directory *see* 0748-4089

0070-8232 Eastern New Mexico University. Contributions in Anthropology

0070-8259 University of Eastern Philippines. Research Center. Report

0070-8275 Eaton Electronics Research Laboratories. Technical Report†

0070-8305 Echos des Charites de St. Vincent de Paul *see* 0763-5184

0070-8321 Ecole Francaise des Attaches de Presse. Association des Anciens Eleves. Annuaire

0070-833X Tall Timbers Conference on Ecological Animal Control by Habitat Management. Proceedings†

0070-8348 Ecological Society of Australia. Proceedings

0070-8356 Ecological Studies; Analysis and Synthesis

0070-8364 Ecologie Marina†

0070-8372 Ecology and Conservation Series†

0070-8399 Economia *changed to* Revista Economia.

0070-8402 Economia e Storia (Rome)

0070-8437 Economic and Scientific Research Foundation. Annual Report

0070-8453 National Institute of Economic and Social Research, London. Economic and Social Studies

0070-847X Economic Council of Canada. Annual Report

0070-8488 Economic Council of Canada. Annual Review

0070-8518 Economic Development Programme for the Republic of South Africa†

0070-8550 Economic Handbook of the Machine Tool Industry

0070-8593 Economic Picture of Japan†

0070-8615 Economic Questions for Illinois Agriculture†

0070-8623 Economic Research Studies†

0070-8631 Economic Review

0070-864X Economic Review of World Tourism†

0070-8674 Economic Studies†

0070-8690 Economic Survey of Asia and the Far East *see* 0252-5704

0070-8704 Bangladesh Economic Survey *changed to* Bangladesh Arthanaitika Jarip.

0070-8712 Economic Survey of Europe

0070-8720 Economic Survey of Latin America *see* 0257-2184

0070-8747 Economic Yearbook of Tunisia

0070-8755 Economic and Social Research Institute. Publications Series. Paper *changed to* Economic and Social Research Institute. General Research Series.

0070-8763 Economics of Fruit Farming†

0070-8771 Economie Belge et Internationale†

0070-878X Economie de la Tunisie en Chiffres

0070-8798 Economie et Finances Agricoles

0070-8801 Economie et Societe

0070-881X Luxembourg. Service Central de la Statistique et des Etudes Economiques. Cahiers Economiques. Serie A: Economie Luxembourgeoise

0070-8836 Economisch Instituut voor Het Midden-en Kleinbedrijf. Year Report

0070-8852 Economy and History†

0070-8860 Ecrits Libres

0070-8879 Ecriture

0070-8887 Ecuador. Centro de Desarrollo Industrial. Informe de Labores

0070-8895 Ecuador. Instituto Nacional de Estadistica y Censos. Anuario de Estadisticas Hospitalarias†

0070-8909 Ecuador. Instituto Nacional de Estadistica y Censos. Anuario de Estadisticas Vitales†

0070-8917 Ecuador. Instituto Nacional de Estadistica y Censos. Estadistica del Trabajo

0070-8925 Ecuador Economico

0070-8933 Ecuador. Servicio Nacional de Meteorologia e Hidrologia. Anuario Hidrologico *changed to* Ecuador. Instituto Nacional de Meteorologia e Hidrologia. Anuario Hidrologico.

0070-8941 Ecuador. Servicio Nacional de Meteorologia e Hidrologia. Anuario Meteorologico *changed to* Ecuador. Instituto Nacional de Meteorologia e Hidrologia. Anuario Meteorologico.

0070-8976 Edgar Brookes Academic and Human Freedom Lecture

0070-8992 University of Edinburgh. Architecture Research Unit. Report

0070-9018 University of Edinburgh. Publications. Language and Literature†

0070-9034 University of Edinburgh. Publications. Science†

0070-9069 Editiones Arnamagnaeanae. Series A

0070-9077 Editiones Arnamagnaeanae. Series B

0070-9085 Editiones Arnamagnaeanae. Supplementum

0070-9093 Editori Librai Cartolibrai e Biblioteche d'Italia†

0070-9107 Editorial Offices in the West†

0070-9115 Education and Science *changed to* Great Britain. Department of Education and Science. Annual Report.

0070-9131 Education Authorities' Directory and Annual

0070-9158 Education Committees Year Book *see* 0143-5469

0070-9166 Education for Nursing: The Diploma Way

0070-9182 Education in Europe. Section 1: Higher Education and Research

0070-9204 Education in Europe. Section 3: Out-of-School Education *changed to* Education and Culture. Section 3: Out-of-School Education.

0070-9212 Education in Europe. Section 4 (General)†

0070-9220 Education in Japan; A Graphic Presentation

0070-9239 Education in Large Cities Series†

0070-9263 Educational and Psychological Interactions

0070-931X Educational/Instructional Broadcasting Buyers Guide†

0070-9344 Educational Studies and Documents

0070-9352 Educational Technology Bibliography Series†

0070-9360 Educational Theatre Journal. Supplement†

0070-9379 Educational Therapy†

0070-9387 Educators Grade Guide to Free Teaching Aids

0070-9395 Educators Guide to Free Films

0070-9409 Educators Guide to Free Filmstrips *changed to* Educators Guide to Free Filmstrips and Slides.

0070-9417 Educators Guide to Free Guidance Materials

0070-9425 Educators Guide to Free Science Materials

0070-9433 Educators Guide to Free Social Studies Materials

0070-9441 Educators Guide to Free Tapes, Scripts, and Transcriptions *see* 0160-1296

0070-945X Edward Shann Memorial Lecture in Economics†

0070-9468 Egon Ronay's Dunlop Guide to Hotels and Restaurants in the British Isles *changed to* Egon Ronay's Lucas Guide to Hotels, Restaurants and Inns in Great Britain and Ireland.

0070-9484 Egyptian Dental Journal

0070-9492 Egyptian Religious Texts and Representation†

0070-9506 Egyptian Society of Endocrinology and Metabolism. Journal

0070-9522 Einfuehrung in die Information und Dokumentation†

0070-9530 Einkaufsfuehrer durch die Pelz- und Ledermode

0070-9557 Ekologia Polska

0070-9565 El-Hi Textbooks in Print *see* 0000-0825

0070-9573 El Paso Archaeological Society. Special Reports

0070-959X Eldridge Reeves Johnson Foundation for Medical Physics. Colloquium. Proceedings

0070-9603 Electeur†

0070-962X Electric Power in Canada

0070-9638 Electrical and Electronic Trader Year Book†

0070-9654 Electrical Contractors' Year Book *changed to* E C A Year Book Desk Diary.

0070-9662 Electrical Engineering Research Abstracts. Canadian Universities†

0070-9670 Electrical Engineer's Pocket Book†

0070-9689 Electrical Equipment Representatives Association. Directory

0070-9697 Electrical - Electronics Insulation Conference. Record

0070-9719 Electrical Process Heating in Industry. Technical Conference. Record†

0070-9735 Electricite de France. Rapport d'Activite

0070-9751 Electricite de France. Statistiques de la Production et de la Consommation

0070-976X Electricity Supply Handbook

0070-9778 Electroanalytical Chemistry: A Series of Advances

0070-9816 Electron Technology

0070-9840 Electronic Connection Techniques and Equipment†

0070-9859 Electronic Engineering Association. Annual Report *changed to* E E A. Association of the Electronics, Telecommunications & Business Equipment Industries. Annual Report.

0070-9867 Electronic Market Data Book

0070-9875 Electronic News Financial Fact Book and Directory

0070-9956 Elektro-Jahr *changed to* Super Electronics. Jahrbuch.

0070-9964 Elektryfikacja i Mechanizacja Gornictwa i Hutnictwa *see* 0239-5320

ISSN

5510 ISSN INDEX

0070-9964 Elektryfikacja i Mechanizacja Gornictwa i Hutnictwa *see* 0239-5312
0070-9972 Elementa Ad Fontium Editiones
0070-9980 Elementary Teachers Guide to Free Curriculum Materials
0070-9999 Elements de Mathematique†
0071-0008 Elements du Bilan Economique
0071-0016 Elizabethan Bibliographies Supplements
0071-0024 Elizabethan Stamp Catalogue *changed to* Elizabethan Catalogue of Modern Commonwealth Stamps.
0071-0032 Elizabethan Theatre†
0071-0067 Elsner: Handbuch fuer Strassenbau und Strassenverkehrstechnik *changed to* Elsners Handbuch fuer Strassenwesen.
0071-0075 Elsners Taschenbuch der Eisenbahntechnik *see* 0934-5930
0071-0113 E R E A C Directory *see* 0160-9629
0071-013X Employment and Earnings Statistics for the United States *see* 0271-4787
0071-0148 Employment Opportunities for Advanced Post-Graduate Scientists and Engineers
0071-0156 En Direct Avec l'Histoire
0071-0164 Encore (Blacksburg)
0071-0180 Encyclopaedia Chimica Internationalis†
0071-0199 Encyclopaedic Dictionary of Physics. Supplement†
0071-0202 Encyclopedia of Associations
0071-0210 Encyclopedia of Business Information Sources
0071-0229 Encyclopedia of Materials Handling. Supplement†
0071-0237 Encyclopedia of Social Work
0071-0288 Engineer Buyers Guide
0071-0318 Engineering Geology and Soils Engineering Symposium. Proceedings *changed to* Engineering Geology & Geotechnical Engineering Symposium. Proceedings.
0071-0326 Engineering Geology Case Histories†
0071-0334 Engineering in Medicine and Biology Conference. Record *changed to* Conference on Engineering in Medicine and Biology. Record.
0071-0342 Engineering Industries Association. Classified Directory and Buyers Guide
0071-0350 Engineering Laboratories Series†
0071-0369 Tennessee Valley Authority. Engineering Laboratory. Research in the Fields of Civil Engineering, Mechanical Engineering, Instrumentation†
0071-0377 Engineering Sciences Data Index *changed to* Validated Engineering Data Index.
0071-0385 Engineers Joint Council. Engineering Manpower Commission. Demand for Engineers and Technicians *changed to* Engineers Joint Council. Engineering Manpower Commission. Demand for Engineers.
0071-0393 American Association of Engineering Societies. Engineering Manpower Commission. Engineering and Technology Degrees
0071-0407 American Association of Engineering Societies. Engineering Manpower Commission. Engineering and Technology Enrollments (Year)
0071-0415 American Association of Engineering Societies. Engineering Manpower Commission. Engineers' Salaries: Special Industry Report (Year)
0071-0423 American Association of Engineering Societies. Engineering Manpower Commission. Professional Income of Engineers (Year)
0071-0431 Prospects of Engineering and Technology Graduates *changed to* American Association of Engineering Societies. Engineering Manpower Commission. Placement of Engineering and Technology Graduates.
0071-0474 Salaries of Engineering Technicians *changed to* American Association of Engineering Societies. Engineering Manpower Commission. Salaries of Engineering Technicians and Technologists.
0071-0490 English and American Studies in German
0071-0547 English Ceramic Circle. Transactions
0071-0555 English Church Music *changed to* World of Church Music.
0071-0571 English Guernsey Herd Book
0071-058X English Historical Documents
0071-0601 English Language and Orientation Programs in the United States
0071-061X English Little Magazines
0071-0628 English Monarch Series
0071-0636 English Place-Name Society
0071-0660 English Translations of German Standards *see* 0174-3805
0071-0679 Ensayo y Testimonio
0071-0687 Ente Nazionale Idrocarburi. Report and Statement of Accounts
0071-0695 Entertainment Industry Series
0071-0709 Entomological Society of Alberta. Proceedings
0071-0717 Entomological Society of America. Miscellaneous Publications
0071-0725 Entomological Society of Australia (N.S.W.) Journal *see* 0158-0760
0071-0733 Entomological Society of British Columbia. Journal
0071-0741 Entomological Society of Canada. Bulletin
0071-075X Entomological Society of Canada. Memoirs
0071-0768 Entomological Society of Ontario. Proceedings
0071-0776 Entomological Society of Pennsylvania. Newsletter
0071-0784 Societe Entomologique du Quebec. Memoires
0071-0792 Entomologicke Problemy
0071-0822 Entretiens sur l'Antiquite Classique
0071-0830 Environment Law Review *see* 0192-8309
0071-0857 Vermont Geological Survey. Evironmental Geology *changed to* Vermont Division of Geology and Mineral Resources. Environmental Geology.
0071-0873 Environmental Health Engineering Series†
0071-092X Environmental Hygiene for the Public Health Inspector *see* 0316-0661
0071-0946 Environmental Wastes Control Manual *see* 0163-9730
0071-0954 Kentron Epistemonikon Ereunon. Epeteris
0071-0962 Ephemeris of the Sun, Polaris and Other Selected Stars with Companion Data and Tables†
0071-0989 Epigraphische Studien
0071-1004 Epimeleia: Beitraege zur Philosophie†
0071-1039 Equal Opportunity: The Minority Student Magazine *changed to* Equal Opportunity.
0071-1055 Eranos Yearbook. Papers†
0071-1063 Erasmus in English
0071-108X Eretz-Israel. Archaeological, Historical and Geographical Studies
0071-111X Ergebnisse der Inneren Medizin und Kinderheilkunde. New Series
0071-1128 Ergebnisse der Limnologie
0071-1136 Ergebnisse der Mathematik und Ihrer Grenzgebiete. Neue Folge
0071-1160 Erlanger Geologische Abhandlungen
0071-1179 Ernaehrungsforschung
0071-1187 Ernest Bloch Lectures
0071-1195 Ernest Bloch Society. Bulletin *changed to* Ernest Bloch Society. Bulletin.
0071-1217 Ernst-Mach-Institut, Freiburg. Wissenschaftlicher Bericht *see* 0340-8833
0071-1233 Ertekezesek a Torteneti Tudomanyok Korebol
0071-125X Erziehung und Unterricht
0071-1268 Esakia
0071-1276 Escola Superior de Agricultura "Luiz de Queiroz". Anais
0071-1284 Universidade de Sao Paulo. Escola Superior de Agricultura "Luis de Queiroz." Boletim Didactico†
0071-1292 Escola Superior de Agricultura "Luiz de Queiroz". Boletim de Divulgacao†
0071-1306 Universidade de Sao Paulo. Escola Superior de Agricultura "Luis de Queiroz." Boletim Tecnico-Cientifico†
0071-1314 Escuela Interamericana de Bibliotecologia. Estadisticas†
0071-1330 Esprit et Liberte *changed to* Esquisse d'Une Philosophie de la Religion.
0071-1349 Essais Philosophiques
0071-1357 Essays and Studies
0071-1365 Essays in Biochemistry
0071-1373 Essays in Chemistry
0071-139X Essays in French Literature†
0071-1411 Essays in History
0071-142X Essays in International Finance
0071-1438 Essays in Physics†
0071-1446 Essays in Toxicology†
0071-1462 Essener Bibliographie *changed to* Essen.
0071-1470 Essential Articles
0071-1489 Essex Naturalist
0071-1497 Estadistica de la Ensenanza Media en Espana *changed to* Estadistica de la Ensenanza en Espana.
0071-1500 Estadistica de la Primaria y de las Escuelas Magisterio en Espana *changed to* Estadistica de la Ensenanza en Espana.
0071-1519 Estadistica de la Ensenanza Superior en Espana *changed to* Estadistica de la Ensenanza en Espana.
0071-1527 Estadistica del Comercio Exterior de Espana
0071-1543 Mexico. Direccion General de Estadistica. Estadistica Industrial Anual
0071-156X Estadisticas Minera y Metalurgica de Espana *changed to* Estadisticas Minera de Espana.
0071-1578 Estate Planning, Quick Reference Outline†
0071-1586 Estates Gazette Digest of Land and Property Cases *changed to* Estates Gazette Law Reports.
0071-1594 Mid-Year Estimates of Population of New Mexico Counties†
0071-1616 Current Population Reports: Population Estimates and Projections. Estimates of the Population of the United States and Components of Population Change *changed to* Current Population Reports: Population Estimates and Projections. United States Population Estimates and Components of Change.
0071-1624 Population Estimates and Projections. Estimates of the Population of the United States by Age, Color and Sex *changed to* Current Population Reports: Population Estimates and Projections. United States Population Estimates by Age, Sex, Race and Hispanic Origin.
0071-1632 Coleccion Estructuras y Formas
0071-1640 Estudios de Arte Moderno†
0071-1659 Estudios de Arte y Estetica
0071-1667 Estudios de Cultura Maya
0071-1675 Universidad Nacional Autonoma de Mexico. Instituto de Investigaciones Historicas. Serie de Cultura Nahuatl. Estudios de Cultura Nahuatl
0071-1683 Estudios de Folklore
0071-1691 Estudios de Literatura
0071-1705 Estudios de Literatura Contemporanea
0071-1713 Estudios Filologicos
0071-1721 Estudios Filologicos. Anejo†
0071-173X Estudios Oceanologicos
0071-1748 Estudios y Fuentes del Arte en Mexico
0071-1772 Ethiopian Publications: Books, Pamphlets, Annuals and Periodical Articles
0071-1780 Ethnic Chronology Series
0071-1845 Ethnologia†
0071-1853 Ethnomedizin†
0071-1861 Etnografia Polska
0071-187X Etudes Africaines†
0071-1896 Etudes de Cas de Conflits Internationaux†
0071-190X Etudes de Linguistique Appliquee
0071-1918 Etudes de Litterature Etrangere et Comparee *see* 0035-1466
0071-1926 Etudes de Philologie, d'Archeologie et d'Histoire Ancienne
0071-1934 Etudes de Philologie et d'Histoire
0071-1942 Etudes de Pollution Atmospherique a Paris et dans les Departments Peripheriques
0071-1969 Etudes d'Histoire de l'Art
0071-1977 Etudes d'Histoire Economique et Sociale
0071-1993 Etudes d'Histoire Africaine
0071-2027 Etudes et Travaux d'Archeologie Marocaine
0071-2035 Etudes Ethnologiques†
0071-2043 Etudes Europeennes†
0071-2051 Etudes Finno-Ougriennes
0071-206X Etudes Foreziennes
0071-2078 Etudes Gobiniennes†
0071-2086 Etudes Gregoriennes
0071-2108 Etudes Historiques
0071-2116 Etudes Juives†
0071-2124 Etudes Linguistiques
0071-2140 Etudes Picardes†
0071-2175 Cahiers des Etudes Rurales†
0071-2191 Studies on Taxation and Economic Development†
0071-2205 Etudes sur l'Histoire, l'Economie et la Sociologie des Pays Slaves†
0071-2213 Etudes Universitaires sur l'Integration Europeenne
0071-2221 Eucarpia
0071-223X Eugenics Society Symposia†
0071-2248 Eureka: the Archimedean's Journal
0071-2264 European Company for the Financing of Railway Rolling Stock. Annual Report
0071-2272 Europa Camping und Caravaning. Internationaler Fuehrer
0071-2299 Europa. Revue de Presse Europeenne
0071-2302 Europa Year Book: A World Survey *see* 0956-2273
0071-2329 Europaeische Schriften
0071-2396 European and Mediterranean Plant Protection Organization. Publications. Series B: Plant Health Newsletter†
0071-240X European and Mediterranean Plant Protection Organization. Publications. Series C; Reports of Working Parties *see* 0250-8052
0071-2418 European and Mediterranean Plant Protection Organization. Publications. Series D: Miscellaneous†
0071-2426 European Art Exhibitions. Catalog
0071-2477 European Association for Animal Production. Publications
0071-2485 European Association for Animal Production. Symposia on Energy Metabolism†
0071-2493 European Association for Personnel Management. Congress Reports
0071-2507 European Association for Potato Research. Proceedings of the Triennial Conference *changed to* E A P R Abstracts of Conference Papers.
0071-2523 European Bookdealers *see* 0963-0171
0071-2531 European Brewery Convention. Proceedings of the International Congress
0071-2558 European Civil Aviation Conference (Report of Session)

ISSN

ISSN INDEX 5511

0071-2574 Comite Europeen du Beton. Bulletin d'Information *changed to* Comite Euro-International du Beton. Bulletin d'Information.
0071-2582 European Companies†
0071-2612 European Conference of Local Authorities. Documents *changed to* European Conference of Local and Regional Authorities. Documents.
0071-2620 European Conference of Local Authorities. Official Reports of Debates *changed to* Standing Conference of Local and Regional Authorities of Europe. Official Reports of Debates.
0071-2639 European Conference of Local Authorities. Texts Adopted *changed to* Standing Conference of Local and Regional Authorities of Europe. Texts Adopted.
0071-2647 European Congress on Electron Microscopy
0071-2671 European Congress of Anaesthesiology. Proceedings
0071-2701 European Convention on Human Rights. Yearbook
0071-2728 European Curriculum Studies†
0071-2787 European Federation of Finance House Associations. Annual Report
0071-2795 European Federation of Finance House Associations. Conference Proceedings†
0071-2817 Confederation Europeenne pour la Therapie Physique. Congress Reports
0071-2825 European Grassland Federation. Proceedings of the General Meeting
0071-2868 European Investment Bank. Annual Report
0071-2884 European League for Economic Cooperation. Publications
0071-2892 European League for Economic Cooperation. Reports of the International Congress
0071-2906 European Leather Guide *see* 0955-5080
0071-2930 European Marketing Data and Statistics
0071-2957 European Monetary Agreement. Report of the Board of Management†
0071-2981 European Organization for Quality Control. Conference Proceedings *changed to* European Organization for Quality. Conference Proceedings.
0071-3015 Debates of the European Parliament
0071-3023 European Parliament. Documents de Seance *changed to* European Parliament. Working Documents.
0071-3074 E S O M A R Handbook
0071-3082 E S O M A R Congress. Proceedings
0071-3104 European Southern Observatory. Bulletin†
0071-3112 International Symposium on Chemical Reaction Engineering. Proceedings
0071-3139 European Yearbook
0071-3171 E T S Bulletin *see* 0360-8808
0071-321X Evasion†
0071-3236 Everyman's Income Tax†
0071-3244 Everyman's United Nations *see* 0251-690X
0071-3252 Evolution de l'Economie des Pays Sud-Americains
0071-3260 Evolutionary Biology
0071-3279 Excavaciones Arqueologicas en Espana
0071-3287 Excavations at Dura-Europos
0071-3295 Exceptional Infant†
0071-3309 Executive Directory of the U.S. Pharmaceutical Industry†
0071-3333 Experiences in Faith†
0071-335X Experientia. Supplementum
0071-3376 Experiment in International Living. President's Report *changed to* Experiment in International Living. Annual Report.
0071-3384 Experimental Biology and Medicine *see* 1010-8408
0071-3392 Experimental Botany; An International Series of Monographs
0071-3430 Experimentelle Medizin, Pathologie und Klinik†
0071-3473 Exploration Geophysics†
0071-3481 Explorations in Education
0071-3503 Export-Import Bank of Japan. Annual Report
0071-3511 Export-Import Bank of the United States. Summary of Operations *see* 0270-5109
0071-3546 Exporters' Encyclopaedia-World Marketing Guide *see* 0732-0159
0071-3554 Export Data Exporters Year Book *changed to* Export Data.
0071-3570 Fabian Society. Annual Report
0071-3597 Facet Books. Biblical Series†
0071-3600 Facet Books. Historical Series†
0071-3619 Facet Books. Social Ethics Series†
0071-3627 Fachliteratur zum Buch- und Bibliothekswesen
0071-3635 Facts About Israel
0071-3651 Facts about Nursing†
0071-3678 Facts and Figures on Government Finance
0071-3686 Faculty of Actuaries in Scotland. Transactions
0071-3716 Fairchild's Financial Manual of Retail Stores
0071-3724 Fallout in Norway†
0071-3740 Family Holiday Guide *changed to* Children Welcome! Family Holiday Guide.
0071-3759 Family Planning Association of Pakistan. Annual Report *changed to* F P A P Biennial Report.
0071-3791 Far East and Australasia (Year)
0071-3821 Far Eastern Economic Review. Yearbook *changed to* Asia Yearbook.
0071-3864 Farm Credit Corporation Canada. Annual Report
0071-3872 Farm Credit Corporation Canada. Federal Farm Credit Statistics/ Statistiques du Credit Agricole Federal
0071-3880 Farm and Garden Equipment Guide†
0071-3899 Farm Equipment Directory/Annuaire†
0071-3910 Farm Incomes in England and Wales *changed to* Farm Incomes in England.
0071-3937 Nogyo Kikai Nenkan
0071-3945 Farm Management *see* 1035-1914
0071-3961 Farming in the East Midlands
0071-397X Lincoln College. Department of Farm Management and Rural Valuation. Farm Management Papers†
0071-3988 Lincoln College. Department of Farm Management and Rural Valuation. Farm Management Studies†
0071-4003 Farm Real Estate Taxes *changed to* Farm Real Estate Taxes. Recent Trends and Developments.
0071-402X Farnborough Air Show (Public Programme)
0071-4038 Fasciculi Historici
0071-4046 Fastener Standards
0071-4054 Fauna Fennica *see* 0001-7299
0071-4062 Fauna of the Clyde Sea Area†
0071-4070 Fauna Republicii Socialiste Romania†
0071-4089 Fauna Slodkowodna Polski
0071-4097 Fawley Foundation Lectures
0071-4119 Federacion Espanola Galguera. Anuario y Memoria Deportiva†
0071-4127 Federal Employees' Almanac
0071-4135 Federal Graduated Withholding Tax Tables
0071-4143 Federal Tax Return Manual *changed to* Federal Tax Manual with Monthly Reports.
0071-4151 Federatie van Bedrijfsverenigingen. Jaarverslag
0071-416X Federation d'Associations de Techniciens des Industries des Peintures, Vernis, Emaux et Encres d'Imprimerie de l'Europe Continentale. Annuaire Officiel. Official Yearbook. Amtliches Jahrbuch
0071-4178 Federation des Industries Belges. Rapport Annuel *changed to* Federation des Entreprises de Belgique. Rapport Annuel.
0071-4194 Federation Francaise de Natation. Annuaire
0071-4232 Federation Francaise des Sports Equestres. Annuaire Officiel *changed to* Federation Equestre Francaise. Guide Officiel du Cavalier.
0071-4240 Federation Francaise et Europeenne du Commerce, de l'Industrie et de l'Epargne. Revue
0071-4259 Federation Horlogere Suisse. Annual Report *changed to* Federation de l'Industrie Horlogere Suisse. Annual Report.
0071-4267 Federation Internationale de Rugby Amateur. Annuaire
0071-4283 Federation Internationale Motocycliste. Annuaire
0071-4348 Federation Nationale des Conseils Juridiques et Fiscaux. Cahiers
0071-4356 Annuaire de la Cooperation F.N.C.C.
0071-4364 Federation Nationale des Foyers Ruraux de France. Informations et Liaisons *changed to* Animer.
0071-4380 Federation Nationale du Credit Agricole. Annuaire du Credit Agricole Mutuel
0071-4399 Federation of American Societies for Experimental Biology. Council on Biological Sciences Information. Working Documents†
0071-4402 Federation of European Biochemical Societies. (Proceedings of Meeting)†
0071-4410 Federation of Migros Cooperatives. Annual Report *changed to* Federation of Migros Cooperatives. Documentation and Information.
0071-4429 Federation of Pakistan Chambers of Commerce and Industry. Brief Report of Activities
0071-4445 Federation Professionnelle des Producteurs et Distributeurs d'Electricite de Belgique. Consommation d'Electricite par Provinces et par Regions /Electricitets Verbruik per Provincie en per Streek *changed to* Federation Professionnelle des Producteurs et Distributeurs d'Electricite de Belgique. Consommation d'Electricite par Provinces et par Regions/ Elektriciteitsverbruik per Provincie en per Gewest.
0071-4453 Federation Professionnelle des Producteurs et Distributeurs d'Electricite de Belgique. Rapport Annuel. Jaarverslag
0071-4461 Federation Professionnelle des Producteurs et Distributeurs d'Electricite de Belgique. Repertoire des Enterprises de Production d'Electricite *see* 0778-631X
0071-447X Federation Professionnelle des Producteurs et Distributeurs d'Electricite de Belgique. Statistiques Provisoires. Voorlopige Statistieken
0071-4488 Federation Professionnelle des Producteurs et Distributeurs d'Electricite de Belgique. Secteurs de Distribution *see* 0778-6336
0071-450X Feed Additive Compendium
0071-4518 Feed Industry Red Book
0071-4542 Universita degli Studi di Ferrara. Istituto di Geologia, Paleontologia e Paleontologia Umana. Annali. Sezione 15. Paleontologia Umana e Paleontologia *changed to* Universita degli Studi di Ferrara. Istituto di Geologia. Annali. Sezione 15. Paleontologia Umana e Paletnologia.
0071-4550 Universite degli Studi di Ferrara. Istituto di Geologia, Paleontologia e Paleontologia Umana. Annali. Sezione 9. Scienze Geologiche *changed to* Universita degli Studi di Ferrara. Dipartimento di Scienze Geologiche e Paleontologiche. Annali. Sezione: Scienze della Terra.
0071-4569 Universita degli Studi di Ferrara. Istituto di Geologia, Paleontologia e Paleontologia Umana. Memorie Geopaleontologiche†
0071-4577 Universita degli Studi di Ferrara. Istituto di Geologia, Paleontologia e Paleontologia Umana. Pubblicazioni *changed to* Universita degli Studi di Ferrara. Istituto di Geologia. Pubblicazioni.
0071-4615 Fertilizer Industry Series†
0071-4623 Fertilizer Science and Technology Series
0071-4631 Fertilizer Trends†
0071-464X An Annual Review of World Production, Consumption and Trade *see* 0251-1525
0071-4658 Festival Film Guide *changed to* American Film and Video Festival Guide.
0071-4674 Feuerwehr-Jahrbuch
0071-4682 Fiber Science Series
0071-4690 Fibrinolysis, Thrombolysis, and Blood Clotting; a Bibliography *see* 0360-7607
0071-4704 Fiches Analytiques de la Presse Technique Francaise†
0071-4712 Fiches Typologiques Africaines†
0071-4739 Fieldiana: Anthropology
0071-4763 Fielding's Quick Currency Guide for Europe†
0071-4771 Fielding's Quick Currency Guide for Far, Near and Middle East Including Russia and China†
0071-478X Fielding's Selective Shopping Guide to Europe
0071-4801 Fielding's Travel Guide to Europe *see* 0192-5326
0071-481X Figura. Nova Series
0071-4828 Fiji. Bureau of Statistics. Annual Statistical Abstract†
0071-4844 Fiji. Ministry of Agriculture & Fisheries. Annual Report
0071-4852 Filipiniana Book Guild. Publications†
0071-4860 Film: An Anthology by the National Society of Film Critics†
0071-4879 Film-Echo Filmwoche. Verleih-Katalog
0071-4895 Film Product Association of Great Britain. Annual Report
0071-4917 Film Review (London, 1970)†
0071-4925 Filmarsboken
0071-4933 Spielfilmliste
0071-4941 Filmstatistisches Taschenbuch
0071-495X Filologia
0071-4968 Filologia e Critica†
0071-4976 Filologos Colombianos
0071-4992 Filozofiai Tanulmanyok†
0071-5042 Financial Post Directory of Directors
0071-5050 Financial Post Survey of Industrials
0071-5077 Financial Post Survey of Markets *see* 0227-6038
0071-5085 Financial Post Survey of Mines *see* 0227-1656
0071-5115 Financial Reporting in Canada
0071-5131 Financial Times of Canada. Economic Forecast and Top Hundred *changed to* Top Hundred.
0071-5166 Financing Higher Education in Canada.†
0071-5182 Finishing Handbook and Directory
0071-5190 Ilmatieteen Laitoksen Toimituksia - Finnish Meteorological Institute Contributions *see* 0782-6117
0071-5204 Finland. Ilmatieteen Laitos. Tiedonantoja†
0071-5212 Magnetic Results from Nurmijarvi Geophysical Observatory†
0071-5220 Finnish Meteorological Institute. Observations of Radioactivity†

ISSN

5512 ISSN INDEX

0071-5239 Finnish Meteorological Institute. Soil Temperature Measurements†
0071-5247 Finland. Kansanelakelaitos. Tilastollinen Vuosikirja
0071-5255 Finland. Kansantalousosasto. Kansantalouden Kehitysarvio. Summary: National Budget for Finland
0071-5271 Finland. Kansantalousosasto. Taloudellinen Katsaus. Economic Survey
0071-528X Finland. Ulkoasiainministerio. Ulkapoliittisia Lausuntoja ja Asiakirjoja
0071-5298 Finland. Posti-ja Lennatinlaitos. Kotimaisten Sanomalehtien Hinnasto. Inhemsk Tidningstaxa
0071-5301 Finland. Posti-ja Lennatinlaitos. Ulkomaisten Sanomalehtien Hinnasto. Utlandsk Tidningstaxa
0071-531X Finland. Rakennushallitus. Tiedotuksia *changed to* Finland. Rakennushallitus. Tutkimus-ja Kehitystoiminnan. Tiedote.
0071-5328 Finland. Sosiaalihallitus. Sosiaalihuoltotilaston Vuosikirja
0071-5336 Finland. Sosiaali- ja Terveysministerio. Tukimusosasto. Sosiaalisia Erikoistutkimuksia†
0071-5344 Finland. Tilastokeskus. Teollisuustilasto
0071-5360 Finland. Valtakunnansuunnittelutoimisto. Julkaisuja. Sarja A *see* 0355-8878
0071-5379 Great Britain. Department of the Environment. Fire Research Station. Fire Notes *changed to* Great Britain. Building Research Establishment. Reports.
0071-5387 Crime and Fire Prevention *see* 0049-0024
0071-5395 Fire Prevention News†
0071-5409 Fire Protection Directory
0071-5417 Fire Protection Handbook
0071-5425 Fire Protection Handbook Study Guide†
0071-5433 Fire Research Annual Reports *changed to* Great Britain. Building Research Establishment. Annual Review.
0071-545X Great Britain. Department of the Environment. Fire Research Station. Technical Papers *changed to* Great Britain. Building Research Establishment. Reports.
0071-5468 Fire Yearbook†
0071-5484 National Bureau of Economic Research. Fiscal Studies†
0071-5492 Fish Disease Leaflets
0071-5522 Fisheries and Wildlife Paper. Victoria†
0071-5530 Fisheries Circular, Victoria†
0071-5549 Fisheries Contribution, Victoria†
0071-5581 Fisheries Statistics of Japan
0071-5603 Fishery Statistics of the United States *changed to* Fisheries of the United States.
0071-5611 Fresh Water Fishing Guide†
0071-5638 Fisken og Havet
0071-5654 Fitzgerald - Hemingway Annual†
0071-5662 British Librarianship and Information Science *changed to* British Librarianship & Information Work.
0071-5670 Fix Your Chevrolet†
0071-5689 Fix Your Ford†
0071-5697 Fix Your Volkswagen†
0071-5735 Flood Damage Prevention; an Indexed Bibliography†
0071-5751 Flora Ecologica de Restingas do Sudeste do Brasil
0071-576X Flora et Vegetatio Mundi
0071-5778 Flora Malesiana Bulletin
0071-5786 Flora Malesiana. Series 2: Pteridophyta
0071-5794 Flora Neotropica
0071-5808 Flora of Texas†
0071-5824 Flora Polska: Rosliny Zarodnikowe Polski i Ziem Osciennych
0071-5840 Flora Slodkowodna Polski
0071-5867 Flore du Cambodge, du Laos et du Vietnam
0071-5875 Flore du Cameroun
0071-5883 Flore du Gabon
0071-5948 Florida. Division of Plant Industry. Biennial Report
0071-5999 Florida Requirements for Teacher Certification
0071-6006 Florida Speleological Society. Special Papers
0071-6014 Florida State Documents *see* 0430-7801
0071-6022 Florida Statistical Abstract
0071-6030 University of Florida. Bureau of Economic and Business Research. Population Studies
0071-6065 University of Florida. Department of Accounting. Accounting Series
0071-609X University of Florida. Institute of Food and Agricultural Sciences. Annual Research Report†
0071-6103 University of Florida. Center for Gerontology. Studies and Programs†
0071-6111 Southern Conference on Gerontology Report†
0071-6138 University of Florida. Libraries. Technical Processes Department. Caribbean Acquisitions†
0071-6146 University of Florida. School of Forestry. Cooperative Forest Genetics Research Program. Progress Report *changed to* University of Florida. School of Forest Resources & Conservation. Cooperative Forest Genetics Research Program. Progress Report.
0071-6154 Florida State Museum. Bulletin. Biological Series *changed to* Florida Museum Natural History. Bulletin. Biological Sciences.
0071-6162 Florida State Museum. Contributions. Social Sciences *changed to* Florida State Museum. Contributions. Anthropology and History.
0071-6189 University of Florida Monographs. Humanities
0071-6197 University of Florida Monographs. Social Sciences
0071-6243 Flour Milling and Baking Research Association. Annual Report and Accounts
0071-6286 Flying Annual and Pilots' Guide *see* 0163-1144
0071-6294 Focus on Dance
0071-6308 Focus (Drink and Gambling) *see* 0260-6429
0071-6316 Focus Series†
0071-6340 Fodor's Austria
0071-6359 Fodor's Belgium and Luxembourg
0071-6367 Fodor's Czechoslovakia
0071-6375 Fodor's Guide to Europe *see* 0362-0204
0071-6383 Fodor's France
0071-6391 Fodor's Germany *changed to* Fodor's Germany.
0071-6405 Fodor's Great Britain
0071-6413 Fodor's Greece
0071-6421 Fodor's Hawaii
0071-643X Fodor's Holland
0071-6456 Fodor's Guide to India *changed to* Fodor's India.
0071-6464 Fodor's Ireland
0071-6472 Fodor's Italy
0071-6480 Fodor's Japan and East Asia *changed to* Fodor's Japan.
0071-6480 Fodor's Japan and East Asia *see* 0160-8991
0071-6480 Fodor's Japan and East Asia *changed to* Fodor's Korea.
0071-6499 Fodor's Mexico
0071-6510 Fodor's Portugal
0071-6529 Fodor's Scandinavia
0071-6537 Fodor's South America
0071-6545 Fodor's Spain
0071-6553 Fodor's Switzerland
0071-6561 Fodor's Guide to the Caribbean, Bahamas and Bermuda *changed to* Fodor's Caribbean.
0071-657X Fodor's Yugoslavia
0071-6588 Fodor's Israel
0071-6596 Fodor's London
0071-660X Fodor's Rome: A Companion Guide†
0071-6618 Fodor's Turkey
0071-6634 Foerderungsgemeinschaft fuer Absatz- und Werbeforschung. Schriften *changed to* Aus dem Schrifttum ueber Werbung.
0071-6650 Foldrajzi Tanulmanyok
0071-6677 Folia Forestalia Polonica. Series A. Lesnictwo
0071-6685 Folia Forestalia Polonica. Series B. Drzewnictwo
0071-6693 Folia Geographica Danica
0071-6707 Folia Geographica. Geographica-Oeconomica
0071-6715 Folia Geographica. Geographica-Physica
0071-6723 Folia Historiae Artium
0071-6731 Folia Medica Lodziensia†
0071-674X Folia Oeconomica Cracoviensia
0071-6766 Folklivsskildringar och Bygdestudier
0071-6774 Folklore Americano
0071-6782 Folklore Annual *changed to* University Folklore Association. Collectanea.
0071-6804 Folktales of the World
0071-6847 Fonds de Developpement Economique et Social. Conseil de Direction. Rapport
0071-6855 Fonetica si Dialectologie†
0071-6863 Fontes Archaeologici Posnanienses
0071-6898 Fontes Rerum Austriacarum. Reihe 3. Fontes Juris
0071-6901 Fonti Sui Comuni Rurali Toscani
0071-6928 Food and Agriculture Organization of the United Nations. Commodity Policy Studies†
0071-6944 Food and Agriculture Organization of the United Nations Conference. Report
0071-6952 Food and Agriculture Organization of the United Nations. Commodity Reference Series†
0071-6960 F A O Agricultural Development Paper†
0071-6979 F A O Atomic Energy Series†
0071-6987 F A O Agricultural Studies *see* 1010-9021
0071-7002 F A O Commodity Review and Outlook
0071-7010 F A O Food Additive Control Series†
0071-7029 F A O Forestry Development Papers†
0071-7037 F A O Fisheries Studies *see* 0259-2509
0071-7045 F A O Legislative Series *changed to* F A O Legislative Studies.
0071-7061 F A O Manuals in Fisheries Science†
0071-707X F A O Nutrition Meetings Report Series†
0071-7088 F A O Nutritional Study *see* 1014-3181
0071-7096 F A O Rice Report†
0071-710X Food and Agriculture Organization of the United Nations. National Grain Policies†
0071-7118 Food and Agriculture Organization of the United Nations. Production Yearbook
0071-7126 Food and Agriculture Organization of the United Nations. Trade Yearbook
0071-7142 Philippines. Food and Nutrition Research Center. Annual Report *changed to* Philippines. Food and Nutrition Research Institute. Annual Report.
0071-7150 Kansas State University. Food and Feed Grain Institute. Technical Assistance in Food Grain Drying, Storage, Handling and Transportation *changed to* Kansas State University. Food and Feed Grain Institute. Technical Assistance in Grain Storage, Processing and Marketing, and Agribusiness Development.
0071-7177 Food Industries Manual
0071-7185 Food Industries of S.A. Buyers' Guide *changed to* Food Industries Yearbook and Buyers' Guide.
0071-7193 Food Industry Studies†
0071-7215 Food Processing Review *see* 0093-0075
0071-7223 Food Science Series
0071-724X Football Association Year Book
0071-7258 Football Register
0071-7274 Ford Foundation Annual Report
0071-7282 Forecast (Los Angeles)
0071-7312 Foreign Area Studies Series†
0071-7320 Foreign Consular Offices in the United States
0071-7339 Foreign Liabilities, Assets and Foreign Investments in Pakistan
0071-7355 Foreign Relations of the United States
0071-7371 Annual Foreign Trade Statistics of Bangladesh *changed to* Foreign Trade Statistics of Bangladesh.
0071-738X Foreign Trade of Greece *changed to* Commerce Exterieur de la Grece.
0071-7398 Foreign Trade Statistics of Africa. Series A: Direction of Trade
0071-7401 Foreign Trade Statistics of Africa. Series B: Trade by Commodity†
0071-7436 Foreningen til Norske Fortidsminnesmerkers Bevaring. Aarbok
0071-7444 Forest Engineering Symposium. Proceedings†
0071-7452 Forest Farmer. Manual Edition
0071-7479 U.S. Forest Service. Forest Insect Conditions in the Northern Region *changed to* U.S. Forest Service. Forest Insect and Disease Conditions in the Northern Region.
0071-7495 Canada. Forest Management Institute. Program Review *see* 0710-4251
0071-7533 Forest Research in India†
0071-7541 Forest Research News for the South *changed to* U.S. Forest Service. Southern Forest Experiment Station. Recent Publications.
0071-7568 Forest Science Monographs
0071-7584 Forestry Abstracts. Leading Article Reprint Series
0071-7614 Etudes Mathematiques en Vue des Applications: Formulaire de Mathematiques a l'Usage des Physiciens et des Ingenieurs†
0071-7622 Formulaire Thera†
0071-7630 Forretnings- og Bedriftslederen†
0071-7649 Forschung und Konstruktion im Stahlbau†
0071-7657 Forschungen aus Staat und Recht
0071-7665 Forschungen zur Antiken Sklaverei
0071-7673 Forschungen zur Mittelalterlichen Geschichte
0071-7681 Forschungen zur Romanischen Philologie†
0071-769X F I W - Schriftenreihe
0071-7703 Forschungsprobleme der Vergleichenden Literaturgeschichte†
0071-7711 Forschungsstelle fuer Jagdkunde und Wildschadenverhuetung. Schriftenreihe
0071-772X Forstwissenschaftliche Forschungen
0071-7738 Fort Belknap Genealogical Association. Bulletin
0071-7754 Fort Burgwin Research Center. Publications
0071-7762 Fort Hays Studies. New Series. Art†
0071-7770 Fort Hays Studies. New Series. Bibliography†
0071-7789 Fort Hays Studies. New Series. Economics†
0071-7800 Fort Hays Studies. New Series. Literature†
0071-7819 Fort Hays Studies. New Series. Music†
0071-7827 Fort Hays Studies. New Series. Science†
0071-7835 Fortbildung und Praxis
0071-7843 Gastroenterologische Fortbildungskurse fuer die Praxis†
0071-7851 Fortbildungskurse fuer Rheumatologie
0071-786X Fortschritte der Arzneimittelforschung

ISSN

0071-7878 Fortschritte der Botanik *see* 0340-4773
0071-7886 Fortschritte der Chemie Organischer Naturstoffe
0071-7894 Fortschritte der Chemischen Forschung *see* 0340-1022
0071-7908 Immunology Reports and Reviews†
0071-7924 Fortschritte der Physikalischen Chemie†
0071-7932 Fortschritte der Praktischen Dermatologie und Venerologie
0071-7940 Fortschritte der Psychoanalyse†
0071-7991 Fortschritte der Zoologie
0071-8009 Fortschritte in der Geologie von Rheinland und Westfalen
0071-8025 Forum der Psychiatrie
0071-8033 Forum des Transports Publics *see* 0397-6521
0071-8041 Forum on Fundamental Surgical Problems
0071-805X Forum on Homemaker-Home Health Aide Service. Report†
0071-8068 Fotogrammetriska Meddelanden
0071-8076 Uniwersytet Slaski w Katowicach. Prace Naukowe. Fotointerpretacja w Geografii
0071-8084 Foulsham's Original Old Moore's Almanack
0071-8092 Foundation Directory
0071-8106 Foundation for the Study of Cycles. Research Bulletin†
0071-8122 Foundations of Language Supplementary Series†
0071-8130 Foundry Directory and Register of Forges
0071-8157 Fowler's Mechanical Engineers Pocket Book†
0071-8165 Fowler's Mechanics and Machinists Pocket Book†
0071-8173 Fraenkische Geographische Gesellschaft. Mitteilungen
0071-8181 France - Allemagne
0071-819X France. Archives Nationales. Centre d'Information de la Recherche Historique en France. Bulletin†
0071-8211 France. Service du Traitement de l'Information et des Statistiques Industrielles. Annuaire de Statistique Industrielle *changed to* France. Service d'Etude des Strategies et des Statistiques Industrielles. Annuaire de Statistique Industrielle.
0071-822X Annuaire de l'Administration et du Corps des Mines *see* 1140-7123
0071-8246 France. Bureau de Recherches Geologiques et Minieres. Memoires
0071-8254 France. Caisse Nationale de Credit Agricole. Rapport sur le Credit Agricole Mutuel
0071-8270 Centre National de la Recherche Scientifique. Seminaire d'Econometrie. Monographies *changed to* Centre National de la Recherche Scientifique. Monographies d'Econometrie.
0071-8289 Centre d'Etudes Sociologiques. Travaux et Documents†
0071-8297 France. Centre National de Coordination des Etudes et Recherches sur la Nutrition et l'Alimentation. Cahiers Techniques†
0071-8319 France. Centre National de la Recherche Scientifique. Colloques Nationaux†
0071-8335 Centre National de la Recherche Scientifique. Rapport National de Conjoncture Scientifique†
0071-8351 Centre National de la Recherche Scientifique. Annuaire des Chercheurs†
0071-836X Centre National du Commerce Exterieur. Annuaire†
0071-8378 Chambre Syndicale des Commissionaires pour le Commerce Exterieur. Annuaire Officiel†
0071-8394 France. Comite des Travaux Historiques et Scientifiques. Bulletin Archeologique.
0071-8416 France. Comite des Travaux Historiques et Scientifiques. Section d'Archeologie. Actes du Congres National des Societes Savantes
0071-8424 Comite des Travaux Historiques et Scientifiques. Section de Geographie. Actes du Congres National des Societes Savantes
0071-8432 France. Comite des Travaux Historiques et Scientifiques. Section de Geographie. Bulletin†
0071-8440 France. Comite des Travaux Historiques et Scientifiques. Section d'Histoire Moderne et Contemporaine. Actes du Congres National des Societes Savantes
0071-8459 France. Comite des Travaux Historiques et Scientifiques. Section d'Histoire Moderne et Contemporaine. Bulletin†
0071-8467 France. Commissariat a l'Energie Atomique. Annual Report
0071-8483 France. Commission Centrale des Marches. Guide du Fournisseur de l'Etat et des Collectivites Locales
0071-8491 France. Commission Nationale de l'Amenagement du Territoire. Rapport†
0071-8505 France. Commission de la Concurrence. Rapports Economiques
0071-8513 France. Conseil National de la Comptabilite. Rapport d'Activite
0071-853X France. Delegation Generale a la Recherche Scientifique et Technique. Recherche dans le Domaine de l'Eau: Repertoire des Laboratoires†
0071-8548 France. Delegation Generale a la Recherche Scientifique et Technique. Repertoire National des Laboratoires; la Recherche Universitaire; Sciences Exactes et Naturelles. Tome 2: Biologie *changed to* France. Ministere de l'Industrie et de la Recherche. Repertoire National des Laboratoires; la Recherche Universitaire. Tome 2: Sciences de la Vie.
0071-8556 France. Delegation Generale a la Recherche Scientifique et Technique. Repertoire National des Laboratoires; la Recherche Universitaire; Sciences Exactes et Naturelles. Tome 3: Chimie *changed to* France. Ministere de l'Industrie et de la Recherche. Repertoire National des Laboratoires; la Recherche Universitaire. Tome 3: Sciences Humaines et Sociales.
0071-8564 France. Delegation Generale a la Recherche Scientifique et Technique. Repertoire National des Laboratoires; la Recherche Universitaire; Sciences Exactes et Naturelles. Tome 4: Mathematiques, Sciences de l'Espace et de la Terre *changed to* France. Ministere de la Recherche et de l'Industrie. Repertoire National des Laboratoires; la Recherche Universitaire; Sciences Exactes et Naturelles. Tome 4: Mathematiques, Sciences de l'Espace et de la Terre.
0071-8572 France. Delegation Generale a la Recherche Scientifique et Technique. Repertoire National des Laboratoires; la Recherche Universitaire; Sciences Exactes et Naturelles. Tome 1: Physique *changed to* France. Ministere de l'Industrie et de la Recherche. Repertoire National des Laboratoires; la Recherche Universitaire. Tome 1: Sciences de la Matiere.
0071-8629 France. Direction Generale des Douanes et Droits Indirects. Annuaire†
0071-8637 France. Direction Generale des Douanes et Droits Indirects. Annuaire Abrege de Statistiques
0071-8645 France. Direction Generale des Douanes et Droits Indirects. Commentaires Annuels des Statistiques du Commerce Exterieur
0071-8653 France. Direction Generale des Douanes et Droits Indirects. Navigation Maritime Internationale de la France (Tableaux Generaux)†
0071-8661 France. Direction Generale des Douanes et Droits Indirects. Statistiques du Commerce Exterieur. Transit Direct†
0071-8688 France. Direction Generale des Douanes et Droits Indirects. Statistiques du Commerce Exterieur: Importations - Exportations. Nomenclature: N.G.P. (Nomenclature Generale des Produits)
0071-8696 France. Direction Generale des Douanes et Droits Indirects. Statistiques du Commerce Exterieur: Importations-Exportations. Nomenclature C.T.C.I. (Classification Type pour le Commerce International)†
0071-870X France. Direction Generale de la Concurrence et des Prix. Bulletin Officiel des Services des Prix *changed to* France. Direction Generale de la Concurrence et de la Consommation. Bulletin Officiel - Service des Prix.
0071-8718 France. Direction Nationale des Douanes et Droits Indirects. Transport du Commerce Exterieur
0071-8726 France. Direction Nationale des Douanes et Droits Indirects. Tableau General des Transports
0071-8734 France en Poche. Total Guide
0071-8742 France. Inspection Generale des Finances. Annuaire
0071-8793 Annuaire Statistique des Territoires d'Outre Mer†
0071-8823 France. Institut National d'Etudes Demographiques. Cahiers de Travaux et Documents
0071-884X France. Institut Pedagogique National. Dossiers Pedagogiques de la Radio-Television Scolaire†
0071-8866 France. Ministere de la Sante Publique et de la Securite Sociale. Annuaire Statistique de la Sante et de l'Action Sociale *changed to* France. Ministere de la Sante et de la Securite Sociale. Annuaire des Statistiques Sanitaires et Sociales.
0071-8882 France. Ministere de la Sante. Note d'Information *changed to* France. Ministere de la Sante et de la Securite Sociale. Notes d'Information.
0071-8890 France. Ministere de l'Economie et des Finances. Balance des Paiements Entre la France et l'Exterieur *changed to* France. Ministere de l'Economie, des Finances et du Budget. Balance des Paiements de la France.
0071-8904 France. Ministere du Budget. Budget *see* 0244-1179
0071-8912 France. Ministere de l'Economie et des Finances. Rapport du President de la Republique Francaise sur les Operations des Caisses d'Epargne Ordinaires. *changed to* France. Ministere de l'Economie et des Finances. Statistiques et Etudes Financieres. Finance Publique. Serie Bleue.
0071-8920 France. Ministere de l'Economie. Rapport du Conseil de Direction du Fonds de Developpement Economique et Social *changed to* France. Conseil de Direction du Fonds de Developpement Economique et Social. Projet de Loi de Finances.
0071-8963 France. Institut National de Recherche et de Documentation Pedagogiques. Repertoire d'Etablissements Publics d'Enseignement et de Services†
0071-8971 France. Secretariat d'Etat aux Affaires Etrangeres Charge de la Cooperation. Recueil des Traites et Accords de la France
0071-8998 O.R.S.T.O.M. Annales Hydrologiques†
0071-9005 Memoires O.R.S.T.O.M.†
0071-9013 O R S T O M Institut Francais de Recherche pour le Developement en Cooperation. Rapport d'Activite
0071-9021 O.R.S.T.O.M. Initiations Documentations Techniques†
0071-903X France. Office National d'Immigration. Statistiques de l'Immigration *changed to* France. Office des Migrations Internationales. OMISTATS.
0071-9048 France - Peinture
0071-9056 France Plastiques
0071-9064 France Protestante *changed to* Federation Protestante de France. Annuaire.
0071-9072 France. Direction Generale de l'Aviation Civile. Annuaire†
0071-9102 France - Sports
0071-9129 Tribunal de Commerce, Paris. Annuaire
0071-917X Franco-British Trade Directory
0071-9188 Archiv Ungedruckter Wissenschaftlicher Schriften†
0071-9196 Institut fuer Angewandte Geodaesie. Mitteilungen
0071-920X Nachrichten aus dem Karten- und Vermessungswesen *see* 0469-4236
0071-920X Nachrichten aus dem Karten- und Vermessungswesen *see* 0469-4244
0071-9218 Frankfurt am Main. Statistisches Amt und Wahlamt. Statistisches Jahrbuch *changed to* Frankfurt am Main. Amt fuer Statistik, Wahlen und Einwohnerwesen. Statistisches Jahrbuch.
0071-9226 Frankfurter Beitraege zur Germanistik
0071-9234 Frankfurter Geographische Hefte†
0071-9277 Fraser's Canadian Trade Directory
0071-9285 Frater of Psi Omega
0071-9293 Fraternal Actuarial Association. Proceedings†
0071-9307 Free and Inexpensive Learning Materials†
0071-9315 Free China *see* 0304-1204
0071-9331 Free-World Trends in Passenger-Car Production and Engines *changed to* World Trends in Passenger-Car Production and Engines.
0071-934X Freedom from Hunger Campaign. Basic Studies†
0071-9366 Freedom of Speech Yearbook *changed to* S C A Free Speech Yearbook.
0071-9374 Freelance Photo Journalist. Yearbook
0071-9382 Freer Gallery of Art, Washington, D.C. Occasional Papers
0071-9390 Freiberger Forschungshefte. Montanwissenschaften: Reihe A. Bergbau und Geotechnik, Arbeitsschutz und Sicherheitstechnik, Grundstoff-Verfahrenstechnik, Maschinen- und Energietechnik
0071-9404 Freiberger Forschungshefte. Montanwissenschaften: Reihe C. Geowissenschaften
0071-9412 Freiberger Forschungshefte. Montanwissenschaften. Reihe D: Economic Sciences.†
0071-9420 Freiberger Forschungshefte. Montanwissenschaften: Reihe B. Metallurgie *changed to* Freiberger Forschungshefte. Montanwissenschaften: Reihe B. Metallurgie und Werstofftechnik.
0071-9439 Freiburger Geographische Arbeiten†
0071-9447 Freiburger Geographische Hefte
0071-9463 Freies Deutsches Hochstift, Frankfurt am Main. Jahrbuch
0071-9471 Freight Industry Yearbook
0071-948X Fremdenverkehr in Oesterreich
0071-9498 Fremdenverkehrswissenschaftliche Reihe†

5514 ISSN INDEX

ISSN	Title
0071-9536	Fresh Water and Salmon Fisheries Research (Scotland)†
0071-9544	Fifth District Dental Society. Bulletin *changed to* Thirtieth District Dental Society, Fresno, California. Bulletin.
0071-9552	Universite de Fribourg. Paedagogisches Institut. Studien und Forschungsberichte†
0071-9560	F C L Action Alerts
0071-9587	Friends Historical Society. Journal
0071-9609	Friends Service Council. Annual Report *see* 0260-9584
0071-9617	American Friends Service Committee. Annual Report
0071-9625	Fringe Benefit Costs in Canada *see* 0701-1539
0071-9641	Frontier Military Series
0071-965X	Frontiers of Biology†
0071-9676	Frontiers of Radiation Therapy and Oncology
0071-9684	Frozen Food Factbook and Directory *changed to* National Frozen Food Association Directory.
0071-9692	Frozen Foods Year Book *changed to* Frozen and Chilled Foods Year Book.
0071-9706	Fruehmittelalterliche Studien
0071-9730	Fuchsia Annual
0071-9749	Fuehrer durch die technische Literatur
0071-9757	Fuehrer zu Archaeologischen Denkmaelern in Deutschland
0071-9765	Fuehrung und Organisation der Unternehmung
0071-9773	Fuentes Indigenas de la Cultura Nahuatl
0071-9781	Fukui Daigaku Kyoikugakubu Kiyo. Dai 2-bu. Shizen Kagaku
0071-979X	Fulcrum
0071-982X	Fundacion Bariloche. Boletin *changed to* Universitaet Zuerich. Soziologisches Institut. Bulletin.
0071-9838	Fundacion Bariloche. Departamento de Sociologia. Documentos de Trabajo *changed to* Fundacion Bariloche. Desarrollos Humano Social Publicaciones.
0071-9846	Fundacion Bariloche. Programa de Recursos Naturales y Energia. Publicaciones *changed to* Fundacion Bariloche. Instituto de Economia de la Energia. Publicaciones.
0071-9862	Fundamentals of Educational Planning
0071-9870	Fundamentals of Educational Planning. Lecture-Discussion Series†
0071-9889	Fundberichte aus Hessen
0071-9897	Fundberichte aus Schwaben, Neue Folge *changed to* Fundberichte aus Baden-Wuerttemberg.
0071-9900	Fundheft fuer Arbeitsrecht *see* 0173-1688
0071-9919	Fundheft fuer Oeffentliches Recht
0071-9927	Fundheft fuer Zivilrecht
0071-9943	Funnyworld
0071-9951	Funspots Directory *changed to* Directory of Funparks & Attractions.
0071-9994	Furniture Forum†
0072-0003	Further Aspects of Piaget's Work†
0072-0038	Fysiatricky a Reumatologicky Vestnik
0072-0046	G; Documentation Technique et Commerciale des Vendeurs de Gaz
0072-0062	G Q, Guide to Fashion Sources†
0072-0070	Gabinetto Disegni e Stampe degli Uffizi. Cataloghi.
0072-0089	Galerie Nierendorf, Berlin. Kunstblaetter
0072-0100	Gallia Prehistoire. Supplement
0072-0119	Gallia. Supplement
0072-0127	Galpin Society Journal
0072-0143	Gandhi Memorial Lectures†
0072-0151	Gann Monographs *changed to* Gann Monographs on Cancer Research.
0072-016X	Ganterie Francaise†
0072-0178	Gardens' Bulletin, Singapore
0072-0186	Gardens of England and Wales Open to the Public *changed to* Gardens of England and Wales.
0072-0208	Gas and Fuel Corporation of Victoria. Annual Report
0072-0216	British Gas Corporation. Report and Accounts *changed to* British Gas. Annual Report and Accounts.
0072-0232	Gas Industry Directory *see* 0954-853X
0072-0240	Gas Journal Directory *see* 0954-853X
0072-0267	Gas Turbine Catalog *see* 0748-0903
0072-0291	Gaster; l'Annuaire de Gastro-Enterologie
0072-0313	Gaz de France. Rapport Annuel†
0072-0321	Gaz de France. Secretariat General. Schema d'Organisation Profor
0072-033X	Gazdasagtorteneti Ertekezesek†
0072-0348	Gazeteer of India
0072-0356	Gazeto
0072-0364	Politechnika Gdanska. Zeszyty Naukowe. Fizyka
0072-0372	Politechnika Gdanska. Zeszyty Naukowe. Matematyka
5072-0380	Politechnika Gdanska. Zeszyty Naukowe. Mechanika
0072-0402	Uniwersytet Gdanski. Wydzial Matematyki, Fizyki i Chemii. Zeszyty Naukowe. Matematyka
0072-0410	Gdanskie Towarzystwo Naukowe. Wydzial 1. Nauk Spolecznych i Humanistycznych. Komisja Archeologiczna. Prace
0072-0429	Gdanskie Towarzystwo Naukowe. Wydzial 1. Nauk Spolecznych i Humanistycznych. Seria Popularnonaukowa "Pomorze Gdanskie"
0072-0437	Gdanskie Towarzystwo Naukowe. Wydzial 1. Nauk Spolecznych i Humanistycznych. Seria Zrodel
0072-0445	Gdanskie Towarzystwo Naukowe. Wydzial 3. Nauk Matematyczno-Przyrodniczych. Rozprawy *changed to* Gdanskie Towarzystwo Naukowe. Wydzial 3. Nauk Matematyczno-Fizyczno-Chemicznych. Prace.
0072-0453	Uniwersytet Gdanski. Wydzial Humanistyczny. Zeszyty Naukowe. Filozofia i Socjologia
0072-0461	Uniwersytet Gdanski. Wydzial Humanistyczny. Zeszyty Naukowe. Historia
0072-047X	Uniwersytet Gdanski. Wydzial Humanistyczny. Zeszyty Naukowe. Pedagogika, Historia Wychowania
0072-0488	Uniwersytet Gdanski. Wydzial Humanistyczny. Zeszyty Naukowe. Prace Historyczno-Literackie
0072-0496	Morski Instytut Rybacki, Gdynia. Prace. Seria A: Oceanograficzno - Ichtiologiczna†
0072-050X	Morski Instytut Rybacki, Gdynia. Prace. Seria B: Technika Rybacka i Technologia Ryb†
0072-0518	Morski Instytut Rybacki, Gdynia. Prace. Seria C: Ekonomika Rybacka†
0072-0526	Gebbie House Magazine Directory *changed to* Internal Publications Directory.
0072-0542	Geiriadur Prifysgol Cymru
0072-0550	Geistige Begegnung†
0072-0569	Gem State R.N. *see* 0192-298X
0072-0577	Gemeinschaft der Selbst-Verwirklichung. Jahresheft *changed to* Selbst-Verwirklichung: Jahresheft.
0072-0585	Genava
0072-0623	General Agreement on Tariffs and Trade. Basic Instruments and Selected Documents Series. Supplement
0072-064X	General Agreement on Tariffs and Trade. International Trade
0072-0658	General Catalogue of Unesco and Unesco-Sponsored Publications†
0072-0666	General Conference of the New Church. Yearbook
0072-0674	General Dental Council. Dentists Register
0072-0682	General Dental Council. Minutes of the Proceedings
0072-0690	General Directory of the Press and Periodicals in Jordan and Kuwait
0072-0704	General Directory of the Press and Periodicals in Syria
0072-0720	General Education Reading Material Series
0072-0747	General Fisheries Council for the Mediterranean. Proceedings and Technical Papers†
0072-0755	General Fisheries Council for the Mediterranean. Reports of the Sessions
0072-0763	General Medical Council. Medical Register
0072-0771	General Semantics Bulletin
0072-078X	General Stud Book
0072-0798	General Systems Yearbook
0072-0801	Geneseo Studies in Library and Information Science†
0072-081X	Genetics Lectures†
0072-0828	Musee d'Ethnographie de la Ville de Geneve. Bulletin Annuel†
0072-0836	Universite de Geneve. Section d'Histoire. Documents
0072-0844	Genie Industriel; Catalogue de l'Ingenierie
0072-0852	Universita degli Studi di Genova. Istituto di Filologia Classica e Medievale. Pubblicazioni
0072-0860	Universita degli Studi di Genova. Istituto di Paleografia e Storia Medievale. Collana. Storica di Fonti e Studi *changed to* Universita degli Studi di Genova. Istituto di Medievistica. Collana. Storica di Fonti e Studi.
0072-0879	Gentes Herbarum
0072-0887	Genuine Irish Old Moore's Almanac
0072-0909	Geographer
0072-0917	Geografinis Metrastis
0072-0925	Geographical Observer
0072-0941	Geographische Gesellschaft, Munich. Mitteilungen
0072-0968	Geographisches Taschenbuch
0072-0984	Geography of New Zealand†
0072-0992	Geologia Colombiana
0072-100X	Geologia Sudetica
0072-1018	Geologica et Palaeontologica
0072-1026	Geologica Ultraiectina
0072-1042	Geological Association of Canada. Special Paper
0072-1050	Geological Journal
0072-1069	Geological Society of America. Memoirs
0072-1077	Geological Society of America. Special Papers
0072-1085	Geological Society of Australia. Special Publication
0072-1107	Geologie des Aires Oceaniques†
0072-1115	Universitaet Hamburg. Geologisch-Palaeontologisches Institut. Mitteilungen
0072-1174	Geophysica Norvegica†
0072-1182	Geofizicheskii Byulleten' *see* 0016-7886
0072-1190	George Ernest Morrison Lectures in Ethnology
0072-1204	Georgetown University. Center for Strategic and International Studies. Special Report Series†
0072-1212	Georgetown University. Institute of Languages and Linguistics. Report of the Annual Round Table Meeting on Linguistics and Language Studies *see* 0196-7207
0072-1220	Georgia Congress of Parents and Teachers. Annual Summer Institute. Handbook for P T A Leaders *changed to* Georgia Congress of Parents and Teachers. Annual Leadership Training Conference. Workshop for P T A Leaders.
0072-1247	Georgia State University. Hospital Administration Program. Occasional Publication *see* 0093-8041
0072-1255	University of Georgia. Anthropology Curriculum Project. Occasional Paper Series†
0072-1263	University of Georgia. College of Business Administration. Travel Research Series†
0072-1271	University of Georgia. College of Agriculture Experiment Stations. Bulletin
0072-128X	University of Georgia. College of Agriculture Experiment Stations. Research Reports
0072-131X	University of Georgia Libraries. Miscellanea†
0072-1379	Georgia Vital Morbidity Statistics *changed to* Georgia Vital Statistics Report.
0072-1395	Geoscience and Man *see* 0191-6122
0072-1409	Geoscience Information Society. Proceedings
0072-1417	Geoserials *see* 0952-2700
0072-1433	German Arab Trade
0072-145X	German Motor Tribune
0072-1476	German Research Service
0072-1484	Germanica†
0072-1492	Germanistische Linguistik
0072-1549	D B Report
0072-1573	Germany (Federal Republic, 1949-). Bundesministerium fuer Ernaehrung, Landwirtschaft und Forsten. Jahresbericht. Forschung im Bereich des Bundesministers. *see* 0343-7477
0072-1581	Statistisches Jahrbuch ueber Ernaehrung, Landwirtschaft und Forsten der Bundesrepublik Deutschland
0072-159X	Germany (Federal Republic, 1949-). Sachverstaendigenrat zur Begutachtung der Gesamtwirtschaftlichen Entwicklung. Jahresgutachten
0072-1603	Deutscher Wetterdienst. Seewetteramt. Einzelveroeffentlichungen
0072-1611	Germany (Federal Republic, 1949-). Statistisches Bundesamt Arbeiten *changed to* Survey of German Federal Statistics.
0072-162X	Das Arbeitsgebiet der Bundesstatistik
0072-1638	Germany (Federal Republic, 1949-). Statistisches Bundesamt. Alphabetisches Laenderverzeichnis fuer die Aussenhandelsstatistik
0072-1646	Germany (Federal Republic, 1949-) Statistisches Bundesamt. Fachserie 7, Aussenhandel, Reihe 1: Zusammenfassende Uebersichten fuer den Aussenhandel
0072-1654	Germany (Federal Republic, 1949-). Statistisches Bundesamt. Fachserie 7, Aussenhandel, Reihe 2: Aussenhandel nach Waren und Laendern (Spezialhandel)
0072-1662	Germany (Federal Republic, 1949-). Statistisches Bundesamt. Fachserie 7, Aussenhandel, Reihe 3: Aussenhandel Nach Laendern und Warengruppen (Spezialhandel)
0072-1697	Germany (Federal Republic, 1949-). Statistisches Bundesamt. Fachserie 7, Aussenhandel, Reihe 6: Durchfuhr im Seeverkehr und Seeumschlag
0072-1700	Germany (Federal Republic, 1949-). Statistiches Bundesamt. Fachserie 7, Aussenhandel, Reihe 7: Sonderbeitraege *changed to* Germany (Federal Republic, 1949-). Statistisches Bundesamt. Fachserie 7, Aussenhandel, Reihe 7: Aussenhandel nach Laendern und Guetergruppen der Produktionsstatistiken (Spezialhandel)
0072-1719	Germany (Federal Republic, 1949-) Statistisches Bundesamt. Ausgewaehlte Zahlen fuer die Bauwirtschaft

ISSN INDEX 5515

0072-1727 Germany (Federal Republic, 1949-) Statistisches Bundesamt. Fachserie 4, Reihe 5: Beschaeftigung, Umsatz, Investitionen und Kosten Struktur im Baugewerbe *changed to* Germany (Federal Republic, 1949-). Statistisches Bundesamt. Fachserie 4, Produzierendes Gewerbe, Reihe 5: Bauwerbe.

0072-1735 Germany (Federal Republic, 1949-). Statistisches Bundesamt. Fachserie 5, Bautaetigkeit und Wohnungen, Reihe 1: Bautaetigkeit

0072-1743 Germany (Federal Republic, 1949-) Statistisches Bundesamt. Fachserie 5, Bautaetigkeit und Wohnungen, Reihe 2: Bewilligungen im Sozialen Wohnungsbau

0072-1751 Germany (Federal Republic, 1949-) Statistisches Bundesamt. Fachserie 5, Bautaetigkeit und Wohnungen, Reihe 3: Bestand an Wohnungen

0072-1778 Germany (Federal Republic, 1949-). Statistisches Bundesamt. Fachserie 11: Bildung und Kultur

0072-1786 Germany (Federal Republic, 1949) Statistisches Bundesamt. Bevoelkering und Kultur. Reihe 1: Bevoelkerungsstand und Entwicklung *changed to* Germany (Federal Republic, 1949-) Statistisches Bundesamt. Bevoelkering und Erwerbstaetigkeit. Reihe 1: Gebiet und Bevoelkerung.

0072-1794 Germany (Federal Republic, 1949-). Statistisches Bundesamt. Fachserie 1, Bevoelkerung und Erwerbstaetigkeit, Reihe 1: Gebiet und Bevoelkerung

0072-1808 Germany (Federal Republic, 1949-) Statistisches Bundesamt. Fachserie 1, Reihe 2.3: Wanderungent

0072-1832 Germany (Federal Republic, 1949-). Statistisches Bundesamt. Fachserie 1, Bevoelkerung und Erwerbstaetigkeit, Reihe 4: Erwerbetaetigkeit

0072-1840 Germany (Federal Republic, 1949-). Statistisches Bundesamt. Fachserie 12, Gesundheitswesen, Reihe 1: Ausgewaehlte Zahlen fuer das Gesundheitswesen

0072-1859 Germany (Federal Republic, 1949-). Statistisches Bundesamt. Fachserie 10. Rechtspflege

0072-1867 Bevoelkerungsstruktur und Wirtschaftskraft der Bundeslaender

0072-1964 Germany (Federal Republic, 1949-). Statistisches Bundesamt. Fachserie 6, Handel, Gastgewerbe, Reiseverkehr; Reihe 1: Grosshandel

0072-1972 Germany (Federal Republic, 1949-). Statistisches Bundesamt. Fachserie 6, Handel, Gastgewerbe, Reiseverkehr; Reihe 3: Einzelhandel

0072-1980 Germany (Federal Republic, 1949-). Statistisches Bundesamt. Fachserie 6, Handel, Gastgewerbe, Reiseverkhr; Reihe 6: Wahrenverkehr mit der Deutschen Demokratischen Republik und Berlin (Ost)

0072-1999 Germany (Federal Republic, 1949-). Statistisches Bundesamt. Fachserie 6, Handel, Gastgewerbe, Reiseverkehr; Reihe 7: Reiseverkehr

0072-2014 Germany (Federal Republic, 1949-). Statistisches Bundesamt. Fachserie 9, Reihe 1: Boden- und Kommunalkreditinstitutet

0072-2022 Germany (Federal Republic, 1949-) Statistisches Bundesamt. Geld und Kredit. Reihe 2: Aktienkurse *changed to* Germany (Federal Republic, 1949-) Statistisches Bundesamt. Fachserie 9, Geld und Kredit, Reihe 2: Aktienmaerkte.

0072-2030 Germany (Federal Republic, 1949-) Statistisches Bundesamt. Fachserie 2, Unternehmen und Arbeitsstaetten, Reihe 4: Zahlungsschwierigkeiten

0072-209X Germany (Federal Republic, 1949-) Statistisches Bundesamt. Fachserie 4, Reihe 2: Indices des Auftragseingangs in Ausgewaehlten Industriezweigen und im Bauhauptgewerbe *changed to* Germany (Federal Republic, 1949-) Statistisches Bundesamt. Fachserie 4, Produzierendes Gewerbe, Reihe 2.2: Indices des Auftragseingangs, des Umsatzes und des Auftragsbestands fuer das Verarbeitende Gewerbe und fuer das Bauhaupt Gewerbe.

0072-2103 Germany (Federal Republic, 1949-). Statistisches Bundesamt. Fachserie 4, Produzierende Gastgewerbe, Reihe 7.1: Handwerk. Beschaeftigte um Umsatz im Handwerk

0072-3673 Germany (Federal Republic, 1949-). Statistisches Bundesamt. Fachserie 3, Land- und Fortstwirtschaft, Fischerei; Reihe 4.5: Fischerei

0072-3681 Germany (Federal Republic, 1949-). Statistisches Bundesamt. Fachserie 3, Land- und Fortstwirtschaft, Fischerei; Reihe 2: Betriebs-, Arbeits- und Einkommensverhaeltnisse

0072-3754 Germany (Federal Republic, 1949-). Statistisches Bundesamt. Fachserie 13, Reihe 2: Sozialhilfe; Reihe 3: Kriegsopferfuersorge

0072-3762 Germany (Federal Republic, 1949-). Statistisches Bundesamt. Fachserie 13, Sozialleistungen, Reihe 6: Jugendhilfe

0072-3789 Germany (Federal Republic, 1949-) Statistisches Bundesamt. Fachserie 16, Reihe 2: Angestelltenverdienste in Industrie und Handel *changed to* Germany (Federal Republic, 1949-) Statistisches Bundesamt. Fachserie 16, Loehne und Gehaelter, Reihe 2.1: Arbeiterverdienste in der Industrie.

0072-3797 Germany (Federal Republic, 1949-) Statistisches Bundesamt. Fachserie 16, Loehne und Gehaelter, Reihe 3: Arbeitverdienste im Handwerk

0072-3827 Germany (Federal Republic, 1949-) Statistisches Bundesamt. Fachserie 17, Preise, Reihe 10: Internationaler Vergleich der Preise fuer die Lebenserhaltung

0072-3843 Germany (Federal Republic, 1949-) Statistisches Bundesamt. Fachserie 16, Loehne und Gehaelter, Reihe 4: Tarifloehne und Tarifgehaelter

0072-386X Germany (Federal Republic, 1949-) Statistisches Bundesamt. Fachserie 15, Reihe 1: Wirtschaftsrechnungen *changed to* Germany (Federal Republic, 1949-) Statistisches Bundesamt. Fachserie 15, Wirtschaftsrechnungen, Reihe 1: Einnahmen und Ausgaben Ausgewaehlter Privater Haushalte.

0072-3878 Germany (Federal Republic, 1949-) Statistisches Bundesamt. Fachserie 17, Preise, Reihe 3: Index der Grundstoffrpreise

0072-3886 Germany (Federal Republic, 1949-) Statistisches Bundesamt. Fachserie 17, Reihe 2: Preise und Preisindizes fuer Industrielle Produkte. Erzeugerpreise *changed to* Germany (Federal Republic, 1949-) Statistisches Bundesamt. Fachserie 17, Preise, Reihe 2: Preise und Preisindizes fuer Gewerbliche Produkte. Erzeugerpreise.

0072-3894 Germany (Federal Republic, 1949-). Statistisches Bundesamt. Fachserie 17, Preise, Reihe 1: Preise und Preisindizes fuer die Land- und Forstwirtschaft

0072-3908 Germany (Federal Republic, 1949-) Statistisches Bundesamt. Preise, Loehne, Wirtschaftsrechnungen. Reihe 5: Preise und Preisindices fuer Bauwerke und Bauland *changed to* Germany (Federal Republic 1949-) Statistisches Bundesamt. Fachserie 17, Preise, Reihe 5: Kaufwerte fuer Bauland.

0072-3916 Germany (Federal Republic, 1949-). Statistisches Bundesamt. Fachserie 17, Preise, Reihe 7: Preise und Preisindices der Lebenshaltung

0072-3924 Germany (Federal Republic, 1949-). Statistisches Bundesamt. Fachserie 17, Preise, Reihe 9: Preise fuer Verkehrsleistungen

0072-3940 Germany (Federal Republic, 1949-) Statistisches Bundesamt. Fachserie 17, Preise, Reihe 11: Preise und Preisindizes im Ausland

0072-3967 Studies on Statistics

0072-3975 Germany (Federal Republic, 1949-) Statistisches Bundesamt. Unternehmen und Arbeitsstaetten. Reihe 1: Die Kostenstruktur in der Wirtschaftt

0072-4009 Germany (Federal Republic, 1949-). Statistisches Bundesamt. Fachserie 18, Volkswirtschaftliche Gesamtrechnungen, Reihe 1: Konten und Standardtabellen

0072-4017 Germany (Federal Republic, 1949-) Statistisches Bundesamt. Fachserie 8, Verkehr, Reihe 4: Binnenschiffahrt

0072-4025 Germany (Federal Republic, 1949-) Statistisches Bundesamt. Fachserie 8, Verkehr, Reihe 5: Seeschiffahrt

0072-4033 Germany (Federal Republic, 1949-) Statistisches Bundesamt. Fachserie 8, Verkehr, Reihe 6: Luftverkehr

0072-4041 Germany (Federal Republic, 1949-) Statistisches Bundesamt. Fachserie 8, Verkehr, Reihe 2: Eisenbahnverkehr

0072-405X Germany (Federal Republic, 1949-). Statistisches Bundesamt. Fachserie 8, Verkehr, Reihe 3: Strassenverkehr

0072-4068 Germany (Federal Republic, 1949-). Statistisches Bundesamt. Fachserie 8, Verkehr, Reihe 3.3.: Haushaelte und Familien *changed to* Germany (Federal Republic, 1949-). Statistisches Bundesamt. Fachserie 8, Verkehr, Reihe 3.3: Strassenverkehrsunfaelle.

0072-4092 Germany (Federal Republic, 1949-) Statistisches Bundesamt. Fachserie 8, Verkehr, Reihe 1: Gueterverkehr der Verkehrszweige

0072-4106 Germany (Federal Republic, 1949-) Statistisches Bundesamt. Warenverzeichnis fuer die Aussenhandelsstatistik

0072-4114 Germany (Federal Republic, 1949-) Statistisches Bundesamt. Zahlenkompass

0072-4122 Annalen der Meteorologie. Neue Folge
0072-4130 Deutscher Wetterdienst. Berichte
0072-4149 Deutscher Wetterdienst. Bibliographien
0072-4157 Geront
0072-4165 Gesamtverzeichnis Oesterreichischer Dissertationent

0072-4173 Geschichte der Ethikt
0072-4203 Geschichtliche Landeskunde
0072-4211 Geselecteerde Agrarische Cijfers van de E E C *changed to* E E G Vademecum.

0072-422X Gesellschaft fuer die Geschichte und Bibliographie des Brauwesens. Jahrbuch

0072-4238 Gesellschaft fuer Niedersaechsische Kirchengeschichte. Jahrbuch

0072-4246 Gesellschaft fuer Physiologische Chemie, Mosbach. Colloquium *see* 0366-5887

0072-4254 Gesellschaft fuer Schleswig-Holsteinische Geschichte. Zeitschrift
0072-4270 Gesellschaft pro Vindonissa. Jahresbericht
0072-4289 Gesellschaft pro Vindonissa. Veroeffentlichungen

0072-4327 Geyer's Who Makes It Directory
0072-4335 Ghana. Central Bureau of Statistics. Economic Survey *changed to* Ghana. Statistical Service. Economic Survey.

0072-436X Ghana Law Reports
0072-4378 Ghana National Bibliography
0072-4408 Ghana. Railway and Ports Administration. Reportt

0072-4416 University of Ghana. Institute of Statistical, Social and Economic Research. Technical Research Monographs *changed to* University of Ghana. Institute of Statistical, Social and Economic Research. Technical Publication Series.

0072-4432 Rijksuniversiteit te Gent. Sterrenkundig Observatorium. Mededelingen

0072-4440 Rijksuniversiteit te Gent. Sterrenkundig Observatorium. Mededelingen: Meteorologie en Geofysica

0072-4459 Giannini Foundation of Agricultural Economics. Research Report

0072-4475 Gids van de Nederlandse Gasindustrie *changed to* Gids van Produkten en Materialen Voorzien van Het GIVEG-Merk.

0072-4483 Universitaetsbibliothek Giessen. Berichte und Arbeiten
0072-4491 Universitaetsbibliothek Giessen. Kurzberichte aus den Papyrus-Sammlungen

0072-4505 Gift and Decorative Accessories Buyers Directory
0072-4513 Gifu Daigaku Nogakubu Kenkyu Hokoku
0072-4521 Gifu University. School of Medicine. Archives
0072-4548 Gioventu Passionista
0072-4556 Girios Aidast
0072-4564 Girls School Year Book *changed to* Independent Schools Yearbook: Girls Schools.

0072-4610 University of Glasgow. Social and Economic Studies. Occasional Paperst
0072-4629 University of Glasgow. Social and Economic Research Studiest
0072-4637 Glass Containers *changed to* Glass Packaging Institute. Annual Report.
0072-4645 Glass-Metal Catalog *see* 0147-300X
0072-4661 Glaxo Volume; an Occasional Contribution to the Science and Art of Medicinet

0072-467X Glenbow - Alberta Institute. Occasional Papers

0072-4688 Politechnika Slaska. Zeszyty Naukowe. Elektryka
0072-4696 Politechnika Slaska. Zeszyty Naukowe. Inzynieria Sanitarna *see* 0867-6038
0072-470X Politechnika Slaska. Zeszyty Naukowe. Matematyka - Fizyka
0072-4718 Politechnika Slaska. Zeszyty Naukowe. Nauki Spoleczne

0072-4742 Global Focus Seriest
0072-4750 Glossaria Interpretumt
0072-4769 Glottodidactica
0072-4777 Glove News
0072-4793 Goeteborger Germanistische Forschungen
0072-4807 Acta Regiae Societatis Scientiarum et Litterarum Gothoburgensis. Zoologica
0072-4815 Acta Regiae Societatis Scientiarum et Litterarum Gothoburgensis. Geophysica
0072-4823 Acta Regiae Societatis Scientiarum et Litterarum Gothoburgensis. Humaniora
0072-4831 Goteborgs Tandlaekare Saellskap. Aarsbokt
0072-484X Goethe-Gesellschaft. Jahrbuch *see* 0323-4207

ISSN INDEX

0072-4858 Goethe-Institut zur Pflege Deutscher Sprache und Kultur im Ausland. Jahrbuch changed to Goethe-Institut zur Pflege der Deutschen Sprache im Ausland und zur Foerderung der Internationalen Kulturellen Zusammenarbeit. Jahrbuch.
0072-4866 Niedersaechsische Staats- und Universitaetsbibliothek, Goettingen. Arbeiten
0072-4890 Goff's Guide to Motels in Great Britain and Europe changed to Goff's Guide to Motels and Motorways in Great Britain and Ireland.
0072-4904 Going-To-College Handbook
0072-4912 Gokhale Institute of Politics and Economics. Studies
0072-4920 Gold†
0072-4939 All-Asia Guide
0072-4947 Golf Course Superintendents Association of America. Proceedings of the International Golf Course Conference and Show
0072-4955 Golf Guide
0072-4963 Golf Rules Illustrated
0072-498X Golfer's Handbook
0072-4998 Gondwana Newsletter
0072-5005 Good Food Guide
0072-5013 Gornoslaskie Studia Socjologiczne
0072-503X Gothenburg Studies in English
0072-5048 Gothenburg Studies in Philosophy†
0072-5056 Gothenburg Studies in Physics†
0072-5064 Demografiska Forskargruppen, Goeteborg. Reports†
0072-5072 Oceanografiska Institutet, Goeteborg. Meddelanden changed to Goeteborgs Universitet. Oceanografiska Institutionen. Reports.
0072-5080 Goeteborgs Universitet. Ekonomisk-Historiska Institutionen. Meddelanden
0072-5099 Goeteborgs Universitet. Sociologiska Institutionen. Forsknings-Rapport
0072-5102 Goeteborgs Universitet. Sociologiska Institutionen. Monografier
0072-5110 Goeteborgs Universitet. Statistiska Institutionen. Skriftserie. Publications
0072-5129 Sell's Government and Municipal Contractors Register see 0140-5764
0072-5137 Government Contracts Directory
0072-5145 Government Contracts Guide†
0072-5153 Government Contracts Monographs
0072-5161 Government Finance Brief. New Series†
0072-517X Government in Hawaii
0072-5188 Government Reference Books
0072-5196 Arizona State University. Governmental Finance Institute. Proceedings see 0078-9151
0072-520X Governmental Research Association Directory
0072-5250 Graduate Fellowship Awards Announced by National Science Foundation
0072-5277 Graduate Study in Psychology changed to Graduate Study in Psychology and Associated Fields.
0072-5285 Graduate Texts in Mathematics
0072-5315 Grafton Fashions for Men†
0072-534X Grain Crops†
0072-5358 Grain Trade of Canada†
0072-5382 Universidad de Granada. Coleccion Monografica
0072-5404 Grandes Figures de la Charite
0072-5439 Grandes Todos
0072-5455 Grands Courants de la Pensee Mondiale Contemporaine†
0072-548X Japan Graphic Arts
0072-5498 Graphic Arts Trade Directory and Register see 1044-8535
0072-5501 Graphic Directory†
0072-551X Graphic Guide to Consumer Markets see 0072-8314
0072-5528 Graphis Annual changed to Graphis Design.
0072-5536 Graphis Packaging†
0072-5544 Grass†
0072-5552 Grassland Research Institute, Hurley, England (Berkshire) Technical Reports see 0961-6071
0072-5560 Grassland Society of Southern Africa. Proceedings of the Annual Congresses see 0256-6702
0072-5579 Great Black Athletes†
0072-5587 Great Britain. Admiralty Advisory Committee Reports: Structural Steel†
0072-5617 Great Britain. Air Transport Licensing Board. Report see 0306-3569
0072-5625 Ancient Monuments Board for England. Annual Report
0072-5633 Great Britain. Department of Trade. Bankruptcy: General Annual Report changed to Great Britain. Department of Trade. Insolvency: General Annual Report.
0072-5641 Great Britain. Civil Aviation Authority. Civil Aviation Publications†
0072-565X Great Britain. Department of Trade. Companies: General Annual Report
0072-5684 Great Britain. Board of Trade. Insurance Business: Annual Report see 0308-499X
0072-5692 Great Britain. Department of Trade. Particulars of Dealers in Securities and of Trust Units changed to Great Britain. Department of Trade. Dealers in Securities and Authorised Unit Trust Schemes.
0072-5706 Great Britain. Department of Trade. Patents, Design and Trade Marks (Annual Report)
0072-5714 Great Britain. Central Health Services Council. Report†
0072-5722 Great Britain. Central Office of Information. Overseas Publications Division. Reference Pamphlets Series
0072-5730 Great Britain. Central Statistical Office. Annual Abstract of Statistics
0072-5749 Great Britain. Central Statistical Office Abstracts of Regional Statistics see 0261-1783
0072-5757 Great Britain. Central Statistical Office. Research Series
0072-5765 Great Britain. Central Statistical Office. Social Trends
0072-579X Great Britain. Commission on Industrial Relations. Reports†
0072-5803 Great Britain. Department of the Environment. Committee on Synthetic Detergents. Progress Report†
0072-5811 Great Britain. Committee on Tribology. Report†
0072-582X Great Britain. Department of Education and Science. Computer Board for Universities and Research Councils. Report
0072-5838 Great Britain. Consumer Council. Report†
0072-5846 Annual Statement of the Overseas Trade of the United Kingdom†
0072-5870 Great Britain. Department of Education and Science. Building Bulletins
0072-5889 Great Britain. Department of Education and Science. Education Planning Paper†
0072-5897 Great Britain. Department of Education and Science. Education Surveys
0072-5900 Great Britain. Department of Education and Science. Statistics of Education
0072-5927 Great Britain. Department of Employment. Family Expenditure Survey
0072-5935 Great Britain. Department of Employment and Productivity. Safety, Health and Welfare. New Series Booklets†
0072-5943 Great Britain. Department of Employment. Training Information Papers†
0072-5994 Great Britain. Department of Health and Social Security. Hospital Building Bulletins†
0072-6001 Great Britain. Department of Health and Social Security. Hospital Building, England and Wales: Progress Report†
0072-601X Great Britain. Department of Health and Social Security. Hospital Building Notes changed to Great Britain. Department of Health and Social Security. Health Building Notes.
0072-6028 Great Britain. Department of Health and Social Security. Hospital Equipment Notes see 0141-1403
0072-6036 Great Britain. Department of Health and Social Security. Hospital In-Patient Inquiry
0072-6044 Great Britain. Department of Health and Social Security. Hospital Organization and Methods Service Reports†
0072-6052 Great Britain. Department of Health and Social Security. Health Service Design Notes†
0072-6060 Great Britain. Department of Health and Social Security. Hospital Technical Memoranda†
0072-6087 Great Britain. Department of Health and Social Security. On the State of the Public Health
0072-6141 Scotland. Directorate of Fisheries Research. Annual Report changed to Scotland. Department of Agriculture and Fisheries. Marine Laboratory Aberdeen Annual Review.
0072-615X General Agreement on Tariffs and Trade. G A T T Activities in (Year)
0072-6168 Great Britain. Foreign and Commonwealth Office. Antigua. Report†
0072-6184 Great Britain. Foreign and Commonwealth Office. Bahamas. Report†
0072-6192 Great Britain. Foreign and Commonwealth Office. Bermuda. Report†
0072-6230 Great Britain. Foreign and Commonwealth Office. Colonial Numbered Series†
0072-6249 Great Britain. Foreign and Commonwealth Office. Dominica. Report†
0072-6257 Great Britain. Foreign and Commonwealth Office. Falkland Islands. Report†
0072-6303 Great Britain. Foreign and Commonwealth Office. Montserrat. Report†
0072-632X Great Britain. Foreign and Commonwealth Office. Overseas Research Publications†
0072-6338 Great Britain. Foreign and Commonwealth Office. St. Christopher-Nevis-Anguilla. Report†
0072-6354 Great Britain. Foreign and Commonwealth Office. St. Lucia. Report†
0072-6362 Great Britain. Foreign and Commonwealth Office. Seychelles. Report†
0072-6370 Great Britain. Foreign and Commonwealth Office. St. Vincent. Report†
0072-6397 Great Britain. Foreign and Commonwealth Office. Treaty Series
0072-6400 Great Britain. General Register Office. Studies on Medical and Population Subjects
0072-6419 Great Britain. Herring Industry Board. Annual Report changed to Great Britain. Sea Fish Industry Authority. Annual Report and Accounts.
0072-6435 Great Britain. Home Office. Research Studies
0072-6478 Great Britain. Industrial Reorganization Corporation. Report and Accounts†
0072-6494 Great Britain. Institute of Geological Sciences. Memoirs of the Geological Survey of Great Britain changed to Great Britain. British Geological Survey. Memoirs.
0072-6508 Great Britain. Iron and Steel Consumers' Council. Report†
0072-6524 Great Britain. Laboratory of the Government Chemist. Annual Report of the Government Chemist
0072-6559 Great Britain. Medical Research Council. Monitoring Report Series. Assay of Strontium - 90 in Human Bone in the United Kingdom changed to Great Britain. Medical Research Council. Special Report Series.
0072-6567 Great Britain. Medical Research Council. Report see 0141-2256
0072-6575 Great Britain. Medical Research Council. Special Report Series†
0072-6583 Great Britain. Medical Research Council. Memoranda†
0072-6605 Great Britain. Meteorological Office. Annual Report
0072-6664 Great Britain. Ministry of Agriculture, Fisheries and Food. Animal Disease Surveys†
0072-6680 Great Britain. Ministry of Agriculture, Fisheries and Food. Fishery Investigations. Series II: Sea Fisheries†
0072-6729 Great Britain. Ministry of Agriculture, Fisheries and Food. Technical Bulletin
0072-677X Great Britain. Ministry of Housing and Local Government. Handbook of Statistics†
0072-6796 Great Britain. Ministry of Housing and Local Government. Planning Bulletin changed to Great Britain. Department of the Environment. Housing and Construction. Planning Bulletin.
0072-680X Great Britain. Ministry of Housing and Local Government. Report†
0072-6893 Great Britain. Department of the Environment. Highway Statistics changed to Transport Statistics Great Britain.
0072-6907 Great Britain. National Advisory Council on Art Education. Report†
0072-6923 Great Britain. National Agricultural Advisory Service. Experimental Husbandry Farms and Experimental Horticulture Stations. Progress Report†
0072-694X Great Britain. National Economic Development Office. Monographs†
0072-6958 Great Britain. National Film Finance Corporation. Annual Report
0072-6966 Great Britain National Health Service. Hospital Costing Returns changed to England and Wales National Health Service. Health Services Costing Returns.
0072-6990 Great Britain. National Savings Committee. Report
0072-7008 Great Britain. Natural Environment Research Council. Report changed to Great Britain. Natural Environment Research Council. Institute of Terrestrial Ecology. Annual Report.
0072-7032 Great Britain. Public Works Loan Board. Report
0072-7059 Great Britain. Road Research Laboratory. Technical Papers†
0072-7067 Great Britain. Royal Commission on the Ancient and Historical Monuments and Constructions of England. Interim Report changed to Great Britain. Royal Commission on the Historical Monuments of England. Interim Report.

ISSN INDEX 5517

0072-7075 Great Britain. Royal Commission on the Ancient and Historical Monuments and Constructions in Wales and Monmouthshire. Interim Report *changed to* Great Britain. Royal Commission on Ancient and Historical Monuments in Wales. Interim Report.
0072-7105 Great Britain. Royal Mint. Annual Report
0072-7113 Great Britain. Schools Council Publications. Curriculum Bulletins
0072-7121 Great Britain. Schools Council Publications. Examinations Bulletins
0072-713X Great Britain. Schools Council Publications. Working Papers
0072-7148 Great Britain. Science Research Council. Report *see* 0261-7005
0072-7172 Great Britain. Soil Survey of England and Wales. Memoirs†
0072-7180 Great Britain. Soil Survey of England and Wales. Records
0072-7199 Great Britain. Soil Survey of England and Wales. Report†
0072-7202 Great Britain. Soil Survey of England and Wales. Special Surveys
0072-7210 Great Britain. Soil Survey of England and Wales. Technical Monographs
0072-7229 Great Britain Specialised Stamp Catalogue
0072-7237 Great Britain. University Grants Committee. Annual Survey†
0072-7253 Great Britain. Water Resources Board. Report
0072-7261 Great Britain. White Fish Authority. Annual Report and Accounts *changed to* Great Britain. Sea Fish Industry Authority. Annual Report and Accounts.
0072-727X Great Decisions
0072-7288 Great Ideas Today
0072-7296 Great Lakes Fishery Commission (United States and Canada) Annual Report
0072-730X Great Lakes Fishery Commission (United States and Canada) Technical Report Series
0072-7318 Great Lakes Red Book
0072-7326 Great Lakes Research Checklist
0072-7334 Great Ormond Street Gazette†
0072-7342 Great West and Indian Series
0072-7350 Greater London Papers
0072-7385 Greek National Committee for Astronomy. Annual Reports of the Astronomical Institutes of Greece
0072-7393 Greece. National Statistical Service. Annual Industrial Survey
0072-7407 Greece. National Statistical Service. Annuaire Statistique de l'Enseignement *changed to* Greece. National Statistical Service. Education Statistics.
0072-7415 Greece. National Statistical Service. Annual Statistical Survey on Mines, Quarries and Salterns
0072-7423 Greece. National Statistical Service. Shipping Statistics
0072-7431 Greece. National Statistical Service. Statistical Yearbook of Public Finance *see* 0256-3568
0072-744X Greek Coins in North American Collections *see* 0271-4019
0072-7458 State of Greek Industry in (Year)
0072-7466 Greek Mathematical Society. Bulletin
0072-7474 Greek, Roman and Byzantine Monographs
0072-7482 Greek, Roman, and Byzantine Studies. Scholarly Aids
0072-7490 Greenwood's Guide to Great Lakes Shipping
0072-7504 Greifswald. Universitaet. Wissenschaftliche Zeitschrift. Gesellschafts- und Sprachwissenschaftliche Reihe *see* 0138-1016
0072-7520 Bibliotheque Universitaire, Grenoble. Publications†
0072-7539 Universite des Sciences Sociales de Grenoble. Centre de Recherche d'Histoire Economique, Sociale et Institutionnelle. Collection. Serie Histoire Institutionnelle†
0072-7547 Universite des Sciences Sociales de Grenoble. Centre de Recherche d'Histoire Economique, Sociale et Institutionnelle. Collection. Serie Histoire Sociale†
0072-7555 Universite des Sciences Sociales de Grenoble. Centre de Recherche Economique et Sociale. Collection. Serie Agriculture et Devenir Social†
0072-7563 Universite des Sciences Sociales de Grenoble. Centre de Recherche Economique et Sociale. Collection. Serie Economie du Financement†
0072-7571 Universite des Sciences Sociales de Grenoble. Centre de Recherche Economique et Sociale. Collection. Serie Etudes d'Economie de l'Energie†
0072-758X Universite des Sciences Sociales de Grenoble. Centre de Recherche Economique et Sociale. Collection. Serie Economie du Developpement†
0072-7598 Universite des Sciences Sociales de Grenoble. Centre de Recherche Juridique. Collection. Serie Droit de la Propriete Industrielle†
0072-7601 Universite des Sciences Sociales de Grenoble. Centre de Recherche Juridique. Collection. Serie Droit du Tourisme†
0072-761X Universite des Sciences Sociales de Grenoble. Centre de Recherche Juridique. Collection. Serie Droits Etrangers et Droit Compare†
0072-7628 Universite des Sciences Sociales de Grenoble. Collection Generale†
0072-7636 Universite des Sciences Sociales de Grenoble. Institut d'Etudes Politiques. Serie Essais et Travaux†
0072-7644 Universite des Sciences Sociales de Grenoble. Institut d'Etudes Politiques. Serie Textes et Documents†
0072-7687 Gripper†
0072-7695 Grocer Directory of Multiples and Co-Operatives *changed to* Grocer Marketing Directory.
0072-7725 Grosse Heimatbuecher
0072-7741 Grosse Naturforscher
0072-775X Group for the Advancement of Psychiatry. Report *changed to* Group for the Advancement of Psychiatry. Publication.
0072-7792 Groupement des Directeurs Publicitaires de France. Annuaire *see* 0751-6649
0072-7806 Groupement des Entreprises Francaises dans la Lutte Contre le Cancer. Bulletin National de Liaison
0072-7814 Growth of Crystals
0072-7830 Grundlehren der Mathematischen Wissenschaften in Einzeldarstellungen *changed to* Grundlehren der Mathematischen Wissenschaften.
0072-7873 Guam. Department of Revenue and Taxation. Report
0072-7903 Guia de Editores y de Libreros de Espana
0072-7911 Guia Judicial de Lima
0072-792X Guida Camping d'Italia
0072-7954 Guide Analytique du Pharmacien d'Officine†
0072-7970 Guide de la Papeterie†
0072-7989 Guide de la Parfumerie
0072-8012 Guide des Ports: France, Maghreb, Algerie, Tunisie, Maroc, Afrique Noire
0072-8020 Guide des Prix Litteraires†
0072-8039 Guide des Sports†
0072-8047 Guide du Feu et de la Protection Civile *see* 0337-5781
0072-8055 Guide du Petrole, Gaz, Chimie *changed to* Guide du Petrole, Gaz, Petrochimie.
0072-8063 Guide du Show-Business; Guide Professionnel du Spectacle
0072-8071 Guide du Slaviste†
0072-808X Guide Europeen de l'Immobilier†
0072-8098 Guide for Laboratory Animal Facilities and Care *changed to* Guide for the Care and Use of Laboratory Animals.
0072-8101 Guide for Planning Educational Facilities
0072-8128 Guide International de l'Energie Atomique et des Etudes Spatiales *changed to* Guide International de l'Energie Nucleare.
0072-8136 Guide International des Machines, Appareils, Outils†
0072-8144 Guide Medical et Hospitalier
0072-8209 Guide Rosenwald: Annuaire Medical et Pharmaceutique *changed to* Guide Rosenwald: Annuaire Medical.
0072-8217 Guide Sommaire des Ouvrages de Reference en Sciences Sociales†
0072-8284 Guide to College Courses in Film and Television
0072-8314 Guide to Consumer Markets†
0072-8322 Guide to Correspondence Studies in Colleges and Universities *see* 0733-6020
0072-8330 Guide to Europe†
0072-8403 Guide to Fluorescence Literature†
0072-8411 Guide to Foreign Government-Loan Film (16 MM) *changed to* Guide to Free Loan Films About Foreign Lands.
0072-842X Guide to Foreign Legal Materials Series†
0072-8438 Guide to Free-Loan Training Films (16 MM)†
0072-8446 Guide to Gas Chromatography Literature†
0072-8454 Guide to Government in Hawaii
0072-8462 Guide to Government-Loan Films Volume 1: the Civilian Agencies
0072-8497 Guide to Graduate Departments of Geography in the United States and Canada *changed to* Guide to Departments of Geography in the United States and Canada - A A G Membership Directory.
0072-8500 Guide to Graduate Study in Botany for the United States and Canada
0072-8519 Guide to Graduate Study: Programs Leading to the Ph.D. Degree†
0072-8551 Guide to Japanese Taxes
0072-8586 Guide to Military-Loan Films *changed to* Guide to Government-Loan Films.
0072-8608 Guide to National Bibliographical Information Centres
0072-8616 Guide to New Zealand Income Tax Practice *see* 0111-9370
0072-8624 Guide to Reference Books
0072-8632 Guide to Reference Books. Supplement†
0072-8640 Guide to Reference Material *changed to* Walford's Guide to Reference Material.
0072-8659 Guide to Refinery Operating Costs†
0072-8667 Guide to Reprints
0072-8705 Guide to Summer Camps and Summer Schools
0072-8713 Guide to the Coalfields
0072-873X Guide to the Performing Arts†
0072-8748 Guide to the Press of the World *changed to* Guide to International Journals & Periodicals.
0072-8756 Guide to the Social Services
0072-8764 Guide to the World's Training Facilities in Documentation and Information Work.†
0072-8772 Travel Routes Around the World: Guide to Traveling Around the World by Passenger-Carrying Freighters†
0072-8802 Guidebook of English Coins, Nineteenth and Twentieth Centuries†
0072-8810 Guidebook of Modern United States Currency†
0072-8829 Guidebook of United States Coins
0072-8837 Guidebook to California Taxes
0072-8845 Guidebook to Illinois Taxes
0072-8853 Guidebook to Labor Relations
0072-8861 Guidebook to Massachusetts Taxes
0072-887X Guidebook to Michigan Taxes
0072-8888 Guidebook to New Jersey Taxes
0072-8896 Guidebook to New York Taxes
0072-890X Guidebook to Pennsylvania Taxes
0072-8918 Guidelines for Teachers
0072-8934 Guides to Information Sources in Science and Technology†
0072-8950 Guid'Ouest Africain†
0072-8977 Guild of Prescription Opticians of America. Reference List†
0072-8985 Guildhall Miscellany *changed to* Guildhall Studies in London History.
0072-9019 Gulf and Caribbean Fisheries Institute. Annual Proceedings
0072-9027 Gulf Research Reports†
0072-906X Guns and Ammo Annual†
0072-9086 Perspectives in Virology†
0072-9094 Gutenberg - Jahrbuch
0072-9108 Guyana. Geological Survey Department. Annual Reports *changed to* Guyana. Geology & Mines Commission. Annual Report.
0072-9124 Guyana. Geological Survey Department. Mineral Resources Pamphlet *changed to* Guyana. Geology & Mines Commission. Mineral Resources Pamphlet.
0072-9140 H.R. Macmillan Lectureship in Forestry
0072-9159 H. Rowan Gaither Lectures in Systems Science†
0072-9167 H.S.M.A. Hotel-Motel Directory and Facilities Guide *changed to* H.S.M.A. Hotel Facilities Digest.
0072-9175 Habelts Dissertationsdrucke. Reihe Alte Geschichte
0072-9183 Habelts Dissertationsdrucke. Reihe Klassische Archaeologie
0072-9191 Habelts Dissertationsdrucke. Reihe Klassische Philologie
0072-9205 Habelts Dissertationsdrucke. Reihe Kunstgeschichte
0072-9213 Habelts Dissertationsdrucke. Reihe Mittelalterliche Geschichte
0072-9221 Hacettepe Fen ve Muhendislik Bilimleri Dergisi
0072-9248 Hadassah Vocational Guidance Institute. Report *changed to* Hadassah Career Counseling Institute. Annual Report for the Year.
0072-9272 Hague Conference on Private International Law. Actes et Documents
0072-9280 Hahn-Meitner-Institut fuer Kernforschung Berlin. Bericht *changed to* Hahn-Meitner-Institut fuer Kernforschung Berlin. Jahresbericht.
0072-9302 T.A.E. Report
0072-9310 M E D Report†
0072-9329 Israel Institute of Technology. President's Report and Reports of Other Officers *changed to* Technion - Israel Institute of Technology. President's Report.
0072-9345 Addis Ababa University. Geophysical Observatory. Contributions†
0072-9361 Addis Ababa University. Institute of Ethiopian Studies. Qene Collections†
0072-9388 Addis Ababa University. University Testing Center. Technical Report
0072-9396 Hakluyt Society. Works in the Ordinary Series. Second Series
0072-940X Landesmuseum fuer Vorgeschichte, Halle. Veroeffentlichungen
0072-9418 Hals-, Nasen- und Ohrenheilkunde†
0072-9426 Analysen†
0072-9469 Hamburgisches Museum fuer Voelkerkunde. Mitteilungen
0072-9493 Forschungstelle fuer Voelkerrecht und Auslaendisches Oeffentliches Recht. Werkhefte *see* 0341-3241
0072-9507 Hamburger Abhandlungen
0072-9515 Hamburger Beitraege fuer Russischlehrer
0072-9523 Hamburger Beitraege zur Numismatik

ISSN

0072-954X Hamburger Hafen Handbuch†
0072-9558 Hamburger Historische Studien
0072-9566 Hamburger Jahrbuch fuer Wirtschafts- und Gesellschaftspolitik
0072-9574 Hamburger Oeffentlich-Rechtliche Nebenstunden
0072-9582 Hamburger Philologische Studien
0072-9604 Hamburger Studien zur Philosophie
0072-9612 Hamburgisches Zoologisches Museum und Institut. Mitteilungen
0072-9639 Art Gallery of Hamilton. Annual Exhibition *changed to* Art Gallery of Hamilton. Annual Winter Exhibition.
0072-9647 Royal Botanical Gardens, Hamilton, Ont. Special Bulletin
0072-9655 Royal Botanical Gardens, Hamilton, Ont. Technical Bulletin
0072-9663 Hammarskjold Forum. Working Paper and Proceedings†
0072-9671 Hampstead Clinic Psychoanalytic Library†
0072-968X Hand *see* 0266-7681
0072-9698 Handball und Faustball in Oesterreich
0072-9728 Handbook of Basic Statistics of Maharashtra State
0072-9736 Handbook of Biochemistry *changed to* C R C Handbook of Biochemistry and Molecular Biology.
0072-9760 Handbook of Colleges and Departments of Education *changed to* Handbook of Institutions.
0072-9787 Handbook of Denominations in the U.S.
0072-9795 Handbook of Electronic Materials†
0072-9817 Handbook of Geochemistry†
0072-9825 Official Handbook of Ghana
0072-9833 Handbook of Latin American Studies: A Selected and Annotated Guide to Recent Publications
0072-9841 Handbook of Medical Treatment
0072-985X Handbook of Ocular Therapeutics and Pharmacology *changed to* Ocular Therapeutics and Pharmacology.
0072-9868 Handbook of Papua and New Guinea *changed to* Papua New Guinea Handbook.
0072-9876 Handbooks of Physiology
0072-9884 Handbook of Private Schools
0072-9892 Handbook of Securities of the United States Government and Federal Agencies and Related Money Market Instruments *changed to* Handbook of United States Government and Federal Agency and Related Money Market Instruments.
0072-9906 Handbook of Sensory Physiology
0072-9914 Handbook of Servicemen's and Veterans' Benefits *changed to* Handbook of Service Members' and Veterans' Benefits.
0072-9922 Handbook of the Northern Wood Industries
0072-9930 Handbook of the Universities of Pakistan†
0072-9949 Handbook of United States Coins
0072-9965 Handbook on International Study *see* 0364-1449
0072-9965 Handbook on International Study *changed to* Handbook on U.S. Study for Foreign Nationals.
0072-9981 Handbook on U S Luminescent Stamps
0073-0009 Handbuch der Analytischen Chemie. Part 2: Qualitative Nachweisverfahren†
0073-0017 Handbuch der Analytischen Chemie. Part 3: Quantitative Bestimmungs- und Trennungsmethoden†
0073-0025 Europaeische Volksmusikinstrumente. Handbuch†
0073-0068 Handbuch der Grossunternehmen
0073-0076 Handbuch der Internationalen Kautschukindustrie
0073-0084 Handbuch der Internationalen Kunststoffindustrie
0073-0106 Handbuch der Klassifikation†
0073-0149 Handbuch der Sudetendeutschen Kulturgeschichte
0073-0165 Handbuch fuer den Werbenden Buch- und Zeitschriftenhandel
0073-0173 Handbuch fuer die Druckindustrie Berlin
0073-0181 Handbuch fuer die Sanitaetsberufe Oesterreich
0073-019X Handbuch Oeffentlicher Verkehrsbetriebe
0073-0203 Statistik des Hamburgischen Staates
0073-022X Haney Foundation Series†
0073-0238 Hank Seale Oil Directory - Central United States *see* 0273-5229
0073-0254 Armstrong Oil Directories - Louisiana, Texas Gulf Coast, East Texas, Arkansas and Mississippi *see* 0273-4931
0073-0262 Hank Seale Oil Directory - Texas Including Southeast New Mexico *see* 0277-2280
0073-0270 Voelkerkundliche Abhandlungen
0073-0289 Technische Universitaet Hannover. Lehrstuhl fuer Stahlbau. Schriftenreihe *changed to* Universitaet Hannover. Institut fuer Stahlbau. Schriftenreihe.
0073-0300 Technische Universitaet Hannover. Institut fuer Statik. Mitteilungen *changed to* Universitaet Hannover. Institut fuer Statik. Mitteilungen.
0073-0319 Technische Universitaet Hannover. Institut fuer Siedlungswasserwirtschaft. Veroeffentlichungen *changed to* Universitaet Hannover. Institut fuer Siedlungswasserwirtschaft. Veroeffentlichungen.
0073-0327 Hansische Geschichtsblaetter
0073-036X Hardware Merchandising's Hardware Handbook *changed to* Hardware Merchandising's Canadian Hardware Handbook.
0073-0408 Harpers Directory and Manual of the Wine and Spirit Trade *changed to* Harpers Wine and Spirit Annual.
0073-0416 Harpers Guide to Sports Trade
0073-0424 Harry S. Truman Research Institute, Jerusalem. Publications†
0073-0432 Hartford Studies in Linguistics†
0073-0459 Harvard Armenian Texts and Studies
0073-0467 Harvard Books in Biology†
0073-0475 Harvard Books in Biophysics
0073-0483 Harvard East Asian Monographs
0073-0491 Harvard East Asian Series
0073-0505 Harvard Economic Studies
0073-0513 Harvard English Studies
0073-0521 Harvard Historical Monographs
0073-053X Harvard Historical Studies
0073-0548 Harvard Journal of Asiatic Studies
0073-0564 Harvard Librarian
0073-0572 Harvard Middle Eastern Monographs†
0073-0580 Harvard Middle Eastern Studies
0073-0599 Harvard Oriental Series†
0073-0610 Harvard Papers in Theoretical Geography†
0073-0629 Harvard Publications in Music
0073-0637 Harvard Semitic Monographs
0073-0645 Harvard Semitic Series *changed to* Harvard Semitic Studies.
0073-067X Harvard Studies in Business History
0073-0688 Harvard Studies in Classical Philology
0073-0696 Harvard Studies in Comparative Literature
0073-070X Harvard Studies in East Asian Law *changed to* Studies in East Asian Law, Harvard University.
0073-0718 Harvard Studies in Romance Languages
0073-0726 Harvard Theological Studies
0073-0734 Harvard University. Center for International Affairs. Annual Report
0073-0742 Harvard University. Center for Studies in Education and Development. Annual Report†
0073-0750 Harvard University. Computation Laboratory. Annals†
0073-0769 Harvard University. Computation Laboratory. Mathematical Linguistics and Automatic Translation; Report to National Science Foundation
0073-0777 Harvard University. Graduate School of Business Administration. Baker Library. Kress Library of Business and Economics. Publications *changed to* Harvard Business School. Baker Library. Kress Library of Business and Economics. Publications.
0073-0785 Harvard University. Graduate School of Business Administration. Program for Management Development. Publication
0073-0793 Harvard University. Law School. Library. Annual Legal Bibliography†
0073-0807 Harvard University. Museum of Comparative Zoology. Department of Mollusks. Occasional Papers on Mollusks
0073-0815 Harvard University. Program on Regional and Urban Economics. Discussion Paper†
0073-0831 Harvard University. Russian Research Center. Studies
0073-084X Harvard - Yenching Institute. Monograph Series
0073-0858 Harvard - Yenching Institute. Studies
0073-0874 Harvey Lectures
0073-0882 Harz - Zeitschrift
0073-0904 American Hatter *changed to* Hat Life Yearbook & Directory.
0073-0912 Hattori Botanical Laboratory. Journal
0073-0920 Haute Coiffure Francaise
0073-0939 Hautes Etudes du Monde Greco-Romain
0073-0947 Hautes Etudes Islamiques et Orientales d'Histoire Comparee
0073-0955 Hautes Etudes Medievales et Modernes
0073-0963 Hautes Etudes Numismatiques
0073-0971 Hautes Etudes Orientales
0073-1021 Hawaii Dental Association. Transactions
0073-1048 Hawaii. Department of Health. Mental Health Statistical Section Psychiatric Outpatient Program *changed to* Hawaii. Department of Health. Mental Health Statistical Section. Psychiatric Outpatient, Inpatient and Community Programs.
0073-1056 Hawaii. Department of Health Research and Planning Statistical Office. (Report on) Waimano Training School and Hospital *changed to* Hawaii. Department of Health. Waimano Training School and Hospital Division (Report).
0073-1072 Hawaii. Department of Planning and Economic Development. Annual Report *changed to* Hawaii. Department of Business and Economic Development. Annual Report.
0073-1080 State of Hawaii Data Book
0073-1102 Hawaii Economic Review. Market Annual†
0073-1110 Hawaii. Insurance Division. Report of the Insurance Commissioner of Hawaii
0073-1129 Hawaii International Conference on System Sciences. Proceedings
0073-1137 Hawaii. Office of the Ombudsman. Report
0073-1153 Hawaii Topical Conference in Particle Physics. Proceedings *changed to* Hawaii Conference on High Energy Physics.
0073-1226 University of Hawaii. Industrial Relations Center. Occasional Publications
0073-1234 Hawaii Institute of Geophysics. Contributions *changed to* School of Ocean and Earth Science and Technology. Yearbook.
0073-1277 Hawaii. Legislative Reference Bureau. Report
0073-1293 University of Hawaii. Water Resources Research Center. Collected Reprints
0073-1307 University of Hawaii. Water Resources Research Center. Technical Report
0073-1315 Meteorological Monographs†
0073-1331 Hawaii Institute of Marine Biology. Technical Reports
0073-134X Hawaiian Entomological Society. Proceedings
0073-1358 Hawaiian Planters' Record
0073-1366 Hawaiian Sugar Planters' Association Experiment Station. Annual Report
0073-1382 Nathaniel Hawthorne Journal
0073-1404 Hayes Directory of Dental Supply Houses
0073-1412 Hayes Directory of Physician and Hospital Supply Houses *changed to* Hayes Directory of Medical Supply Houses.
0073-1420 Hayes Druggist Directory
0073-1439 University of Iowa. Graduate Program in Hospital and Health Administration. Health Care Research Series†
0073-1455 Health Education Monographs *see* 0195-8402
0073-1471 List of Worthwhile Life and Health Insurance Books†
0073-148X Source Book of Health Insurance Data
0073-1498 Health Physics Society. Newsletter
0073-1501 Health Statistics of India†
0073-151X Heat Bibliography†
0073-1552 Heating and Ventilating Year Book *changed to* The Specifier's Guide to Heating, Ventilating, Air Conditioning, and Refrigeration.
0073-1560 Hebbel - Jahrbuecher
0073-1579 Hegel-Jahrbuch†
0073-1587 Hegel - Studien
0073-1595 Heidelberg Science Library
0073-1633 Heidelberger Arbeitsbuecher
0073-1641 Heidelberger Jahrbuecher
0073-165X Heidelberger Rechtswissenschaftliche Abhandlungen. Neue Folge
0073-1676 Heidelberger Sociologica
0073-1684 Heidelberger Taschenbuecher
0073-1692 Heine-Jahrbuch
0073-1714 Helps for Students of History
0073-1730 Helsingin Yliopisto Keskussairaala. Psykiatrian Klinikka. Julkaisusarja *changed to* Psychiatria Fennica. Reports.
0073-179X University of Helsinki. Department of Education. Research Bulletin
0073-1803 Helvetica Odontologica Acta. Supplementum *see* 1011-4203
0073-182X Helvetia Politica†
0073-1846 Henrietta Szold Institute. Report on Activities†
0073-1897 Heraldisch - Genealogische Gesellschaft Adler. Jahrbuch
0073-1900 Heraldo Dental
0073-1927 Herbert Read Series
0073-1943 Herd Book of Hereford Cattle
0073-1951 Hereford Breed Journal
0073-196X Herforder Jahrbuch; Beitraege zur Geschichte der Stadt und des Stiftes Herford *changed to* Herforder Jahrbuch; Beitraege zur Geschichte der Stadt des Kreises und des Stiftes Herford.
0073-1978 Heritage†
0073-1986 Heritage of Sociology†
0073-1994 University of Queensland. Great Barrier Reef Committee: Heron Island Research Station. Papers†
0073-2001 Hessisches Jahrbuch fuer Landesgeschichte
0073-201X Heutiges Deutsch. Reihe I: Linguistische Grundlagen†
0073-2060 Hi-Fi Year Book†
0073-2095 High Fidelity. Records in Review†
0073-2109 High Polymers†
0073-2141 Highlights of V A Medical Research *changed to* Medical Research in the V.A.
0073-215X Nation on the Move†
0073-2176 Highway Planning Notes

0073-2184 U.S. Federal Highway Administration. Highway Planning Technical Reports
0073-2206 Highway Research Record *see* 0361-1981
0073-2214 Highway Safety Literature Annual Cumulations†
0073-2222 Highway Safety Literature Indexes†
0073-2230 Hilgardia
0073-2273 Hind Mazdoor Sabha. Report of the Annual Convention
0073-2281 Hindu Astronomical and Mathematical Text Series
0073-229X Hirosaki University. Faculty of Agriculture. Bulletin
0073-2303 Hiroshima University. Department of Geology. Geological Report
0073-2311 Hiroshima University. Faculty of Engineering. Memoirs
0073-232X Hiroshima University. Research Institute for Nuclear Medicine and Biology. Proceedings
0073-2338 Histochemische-Methoden†
0073-2354 Histoire de l'Europe†
0073-2362 Histoire de la Pensee
0073-2370 Histoire de la Philosophie Europeenne†
0073-2389 Histoire des Personnages Mysterieux et des Societes Secretes†
0073-2397 Histoire des Idees et Critique Litteraire
0073-2400 Histoire et Civilisation Arabe
0073-2419 Histoire et Civilisation du Livre
0073-2435 Historia
0073-2443 Historia†
0073-2451 Historia del Arte en Mexico†
0073-2486 Historia y Cultura
0073-2494 Historia y Filosofia de la Ciencia. Serie Mayor. Encuadernada
0073-2508 Historia y Filosofia de la Ciencia. Serie Menor. Rustica
0073-2516 Historiae Musicae Cultores Biblioteca
0073-2524 Historiae Naturalis Classica†
0073-2532 Historiae Scientiarum Elementa
0073-2540 Historiallinen Arkisto
0073-2559 Historiallisia Tutkimuksia
0073-2567 Historic Houses, Castles and Gardens *changed to* Historic Houses, Castles and Gardens in Great Britain and Ireland.
0073-2591 Historical Association, London. Aids for Teachers†
0073-2605 Teaching of History
0073-2613 Historical Conservation Society. Publications
0073-2621 Historical Problems: Studies and Documents†
0073-2648 Historical Society of Ghana. Transactions
0073-2656 Historical Statistics of the Gas Industry
0073-2664 Historical Statistics of the United States
0073-2672 Historical Studies in the Physical Sciences *see* 0890-9997
0073-2680 Historischer Verein der Pfalz. Mitteilungen
0073-2699 Historischer Verein Dillingen an der Donau. Jahrbuch
0073-2702 Historiska och Litteraturhistoriska Studier
0073-2737 History of Menshevism†
0073-2745 Chicago History of Science and Medicine
0073-2753 History of Science
0073-277X Historyka; Studia Metodologiczne
0073-2788 Hitotsubashi Journal of Arts and Sciences
0073-2796 Hitotsubashi Journal of Law and Politics
0073-280X Hitotsubashi Journal of Social Studies
0073-2818 Hobart Papers
0073-2842 Hochschulbuecher fuer Mathematik
0073-2850 Hochschulbuecher fuer Physik
0073-2877 Hoehnea
0073-2885 E.T.A. Hoffmann-Gesellschaft. Mitteilungen
0073-2893 United States & Canadian Mailing Lists
0073-2907 Hofstra University Yearbook of Business
0073-2915 Hokkaido Dental Association. Journal
0073-2923 Hokkaido Nogyo Shikenjo Dojo Chosa Hokoku†
0073-2931 Hokkaido University. Institute of Low Temperature Science. Series A. Physical Science *see* 0439-3538
0073-294X Hokkaido University. Institute of Low Temperature Science. Series B. Biological Science *see* 0439-3546
0073-2958 Holiday Book†
0073-2966 Holiday Camps Directory and Magazine *changed to* Holiday Centres, Chalet and Caravan Parks.
0073-2982 Holiday Chalets and Caravans Directory Magazine *changed to* Holiday Centres, Chalet and Caravan Parks.
0073-3016 Holiday Haunts in Great Britain
0073-3024 Holidays in Britain
0073-3032 Holland Exports
0073-3059 Hollis Press & Public Relations Annual
0073-3075 U.S. Department of Agriculture. Home and Garden Bulletin
0073-3091 Home Economics Education Association. Bulletin *changed to* Home Economics Educator.
0073-3105 Home Economics in Institutions Granting Bachelors or Higher Degrees†
0073-3113 U.S. Department of Agriculture. Home Economics Research Report
0073-3148 Home University Library†
0073-3164 Homing World Stud Book
0073-3180 Homme Face a la Nature†
0073-3199 Hommes et Civilisations
0073-3202 Hommes et la Terre
0073-3210 Hong Kong Catholic Church Directory
0073-3229 Hong Kong. Census and Statistics Department. Annual Departmental Reports†
0073-3237 Hong Kong Library Association. Journal
0073-3245 Hong Kong Manufacturers and Exporters Register
0073-3253 Hong Kong Nursing Journal
0073-3261 Hong Kong Trade Directory†
0073-327X Hontanar
0073-3288 Hood College, Frederick, Maryland. Monograph†
0073-3326 Actualites Nephrologiques
0073-3342 Hoppenstedt Vademecum der Investmentfonds
0073-3350 Hoppenstedt Versicherungs-Jahrbuch
0073-3369 Horace M. Albright Conservation Lectureship
0073-3385 Horizon
0073-3407 Hornero
0073-3415 Horse and Hound Year Book†
0073-3431 Hoseasons Holiday Boats and Bungalows Hire *changed to* Hoseasons Boating Holidays.
0073-3458 Sell's Hospital and Surgical Supplies *see* 0140-5748
0073-3466 Hospital Statistics of New Zealand *see* 0110-1900
0073-3474 Hospitals & Health Services Year Book and Directory of Hospital Suppliers†
0073-3482 Hot Rod Yearbook†
0073-3490 Hotel and Motel Red Book
0073-3504 Sell's Hotel, Restaurant and Canteen Supplies *see* 0142-1824
0073-3512 Hotels and Restaurants in Britain†
0073-3539 Hotels de la France et d'Outre-Mer *changed to* Hotels de la France.
0073-3563 House Beautiful's Gardening and Outdoor Living†
0073-3571 House Beautiful's Houses and Plans
0073-3601 Households with Television Sets in the United States†
0073-361X House's Guide to the Building Industry *changed to* House's Guide to the Construction Industry.
0073-3644 Housing and Planning Year Book *changed to* National Housing and Town Planning Council. Handbook and Year Book.
0073-3741 Howard Journal of Penology and Crime Prevention *see* 0265-5527
0073-375X Hsin-Ya Hsueh Pao†
0073-3768 Atlas of Mammalian Chromosomes†
0073-3776 Hudson Institute. Report to the Members *changed to* Hudson Institute Report.
0073-3792 Hueber Hochschulreihe†
0073-3806 University of Hull. Institute of Education. Aids to Research†
0073-3814 University of Hull. Institute of Education. Research Monographs†
0073-3865 Human Resources Research Organization. Bibliography of Publications†
0073-3873 Human Resources Research Organization. Professional Papers
0073-389X Human Resources Research Organization. Technical Report†
0073-3903 European Court of Human Rights. Publications. Series A: Judgments and Decisions
0073-3911 European Court of Human Rights. Publications. Series B: Pleadings, Oral Arguments and Documents
0073-3938 Humanities, Christianity and Culture
0073-3946 Humanities Research Council of Canada. Report *see* 0225-6932
0073-4004 Egeszsegneueles
0073-4012 Egeszsegneveles Szakkonyvtara
0073-4020 Hungary. Kozponti Statisztikai Hivatal. Demografiai Evkonyv
0073-4039 Hungary. Kozponti Statisztikai Hivatal. Statisztikai Evkonyv
0073-4055 Magyar Orszagos Leveltar Kiadvanyai. 2. Forraskiadvanyok†
0073-4063 Orszagos Muemleki Felugyeloseg. Kiadvanyok
0073-4071 Huntia
0073-411X Hurricane Annual†
0073-4128 Hvalraadets Skrifter†
0073-4136 Hybrid Microelectronics Symposium. (Papers)
0073-4144 National Geophysical Research Institute. Publications
0073-4160 Hydraulic Research in the United States *see* 0094-1832
0073-4179 Hydraulics Conference. Proceedings†
0073-4187 Great Britain. Hydraulics Research Station. Reports†
0073-4217 Hydrological Yearbook of Israel
0073-4268 I F O Institut fuer Wirtschaftsforschung. Studien zu Handelsfragen *see* 0170-5695
0073-4284 I N F A Press and Advertisers Year Book
0073-4292 I N U F A: Internationaler Nutzfahrzeug-Katalog - International Catalogue for Commercial Vehicles *changed to* I N U F A Katalog.
0073-4314 University of Ibadan. Institute of Education. Occasional Publications
0073-4322 University of Ibadan. Library. Annual Report
0073-4349 Ibero-Americana†
0073-4365 Ibsenaarboken *changed to* Contemporary Approaches to Ibsen.
0073-4373 Icefield Ranges Research Project Scientific Results†
0073-4381 J L B Smith Institute of Ichthyology. Ichthyological Bulletin
0073-439X Icones Fungorium Maris†
0073-4403 Icones Plantarum Africanarum
0073-4411 Iconographia Mycologia†
0073-442X Idaho. Bureau of Mines and Geology. Bulletin *see* 0734-3825
0073-4446 Idaho. Bureau of Mines and Geology. Information Circular *changed to* Idaho. Geological Survey. Information Circular.
0073-4462 Idaho. Bureau of Mines and Geology. Pamphlet†
0073-4497 Idaho Education Association. Proceedings
0073-4527 Idaho. Department of Fish and Game. Federal Aid Investigation Projects. Progress Reports and Publications
0073-4551 Idaho State University Museum. Occasional Papers *see* 0196-7703
0073-456X Idaho Statistical Abstract†
0073-4586 University of Idaho. Forest, Wildlife and Range Experiment Station, Moscow. Station Bulletin
0073-4594 University of Idaho. Forest, Wildlife and Range Experiment Station, Moscow. Station Note
0073-4608 University of Idaho. Forest, Wildlife and Range Experiment Station, Moscow. Station Paper†
0073-4616 University of Idaho. Water Resources Research Institute. Annual Report
0073-4624 Ideas for Management†
0073-4640 Dictionnaires du Savoir Moderne
0073-4667 Ethnies†
0073-4675 Idesia
0073-4691 Iheringia. Serie Antropologia
0073-4705 Iheringia. Serie Botanica
0073-4713 Iheringia. Serie Geologia
0073-4721 Iheringia. Serie Zoologia
0073-4748 Illinois Biological Monographs
0073-4756 Illinois. Board of Higher Education. Report†
0073-4799 Illinois Directory and Suppliers Listing *changed to* Illinois Dealer Directory and Buyer's Guide.
0073-4810 Illinois. Department of Conservation. Technical Bulletin†
0073-4837 Illinois Government. *see* 0195-7783
0073-4853 Illinois. State Geological Survey. Industrial Mineral Notes *changed to* Illinois Minerals.
0073-487X Illinois Law Enforcement Commission. Annual Report†
0073-490X Illinois. Natural History Survey. Biological Notes
0073-4918 Illinois. Natural History Survey. Bulletin
0073-4926 Illinois. Natural History Survey. Circular
0073-4934 Northern Illinois University. Center for Southeast Asian Studies. Special Report Series
0073-4950 Southern Illinois University, Carbondale. Department of Geography. Discussion Paper
0073-4969 Southern Illinois University, Carbondale. Occasional Paper Series in Geography
0073-4977 Southern Illinois University, Carbondale. University Libraries. Bibliographic Contributions *changed to* Southern Illinois University at Carbondale. Library. Bibliographic Contributions.
0073-4985 Southern Illinois University. University Museum Studies
0073-4993 Southern Illinois University, Edwardsville. Center For Urban and Environmental Research and Services. C U E R S Report *changed to* Southern Illinois University, Edwardsville. Regional Research and Development Services. Report: Private Sector Investments.
0073-5051 Illinois. State Geological Survey. Bulletins
0073-506X Illinois. State Geological Survey. Circulars
0073-5078 Illinois. State Geological Survey. Educational Series
0073-5086 Illinois. State Geological Survey. Environmental Geology Notes *changed to* Illinois. State Geological Survey. Environmental Geology.
0073-5094 Illinois. State Geological Survey. Guidebook Series
0073-5108 Progress (Springfield) *changed to* Environmental Progress (Springfield).
0073-5116 Illinois. State Geological Survey. Mineral Economic Briefs *changed to* Illinois Minerals.
0073-5124 Illinois. State Geological Survey. Reports of Investigations†
0073-5167 Illinois Studies in Anthropology

0073-5191 University of Illinois at Urbana-Champaign. Center for International Education and Research in Accounting. Monographs
0073-5205 University of Illinois at Urbana-Champaign. College of Agriculture. Special Publication†
0073-5213 University of Illinois at Urbana-Champaign. Department of Agricultural Economics. Agricultural Finance Program Report
0073-5221 University of Illinois at Urbana-Champaign. Department of Agriculturеal Economics. Bulletin†
0073-523X University of Illinois at Urbana-Champaign. Department of Agricultural Economics. Research Report†
0073-5256 University of Illinois at Urbana-Champaign. Department of Art. Newsletter *changed to* University of Illinois at Urbana-Champaign. School of Art and Design. Newsletter.
0073-5264 T & A M Report
0073-5272 University of Illinois at Urbana - Champaign. Engineering Experiment Station. Bulletin†
0073-5280 University of Illinois at Urbana-Champaign. Engineering Experiment Station. Summary of Engineering Research
0073-5299 University of Illinois at Urbana-Champaign. College of Agriculture. Agricultural Communications Research Report†
0073-5302 University of Illinois at Urbana-Champaign. Graduate School of Library Science. Monograph Series. *changed to* University of Illinois at Urbana-Champaign. Graduate School of Library and Information Science. Monograph Series.
0073-5353 University of Illinois at Urbana-Champaign. Institute of Labor and Industrial Relations. Reprint Series
0073-5396 University of Illinois. Small Homes Council. Building Research Council. Circulars *changed to* University of Illinois. Small Homes Council. Building Research Council. Council Notes.
0073-540X University of Illinois. Small Homes Council. Building Research Council. Research Report
0073-5426 University of Illinois. Small Homes Council. Building Research Council. Technical Notes
0073-5434 University of Illinois at Urbana-Champaign. Water Resources Center. Annual Report
0073-5442 University of Illinois at Urbana-Champaign. Water Resources Center. Research Report
0073-5469 I E S Lighting Handbook
0073-5477 Illustrators: The Annual of American Illustration
0073-5507 Image and Sound in Teaching; Bibliographical References
0073-5515 Image; Illustrierte Zeitschrift fuer Aerzte und Apotheken†
0073-5531 Immunopathology†
0073-5566 Implement & Tractor Product File
0073-5574 Implement & Tractor Red Book
0073-5582 Import Car Buyer's Guide†
0073-5604 Importers and Exporters Trade Promotion Guide†
0073-5612 Imports into Pakistan under U.S. Economic Aid†
0073-5620 Imprimatur. Jahrbuch fuer Buecherfreunde. Neue Folge *changed to* Imprimatur. Neue Folge.
0073-5639 InFact Medical School Information System
0073-5655 In Vitro *changed to* In Vitro Cellular & Developmental Biology - Animal.
0073-5655 In Vitro *see* 1054-5476
0073-5671 Income, Estate and Gift Tax Provisions: Internal Revenue Code *changed to* Income, Employment, Estate and Gift Tax Provisions: Internal Revenue Code.
0073-5698 Money Income in (Year) of Families, Unrelated Individuals and Persons in the United States *changed to* Current Population Reports: Consumer Income. Money Income of Households, Families and Persons in the United States (Year).
0073-5701 Incontri e Testimonianze†
0073-571X Restrictive Practices Reports *see* 0306-2163
0073-5728 Incorporated Law Society of Sri Lanka. Annual Report
0073-5736 Incorporated Law Society of Sri Lanka. Journal
0073-5744 Incorporated Society of Organ Builders. Journal
0073-5752 Incunabula Graeca
0073-5779 Independent Schools Association of the Southwest. Membership List
0073-5787 Index Hepaticarum
0073-5817 Index of Articles on Jewish Studies
0073-5825 Index of Graduate Theses in Baptist Theological Seminaries†
0073-5884 Index of Psychoanalytic Writings†
0073-5892 Index to Book Reviews in the Humanities†
0073-5914 Index to Early American Periodical Literature, 1728-1870†
0073-5930 Index to How to Do It Information
0073-5949 Index to Little Magazines†
0073-5957 Index to New Zealand Periodicals *see* 0113-6526
0073-5965 Index to Nigeriana in Selected Periodicals
0073-5973 Index to Selected Periodicals *changed to* Index to Black Periodicals.
0073-5981 Index to Periodicals of the Church of Jesus Christ of Latter-Day Saints
0073-599X Index to Philippine Periodicals
0073-6007 Index to Plant Chromosome Numbers
0073-6023 Index to Reviews, Symposia Volumes and Monographs in Organic Chemistry†
0073-6031 U.S. Bureau of Outdoor Recreation. Index to Selected Outdoor Recreation Literature†
0073-6066 Index to Theses Accepted for Higher Degrees in the Universities of Great Britain and Ireland
0073-6074 Index Translationum
0073-6082 Indexes of Output per Person Employed and per Man-Hour in Canada, Commercial Industries *see* 0317-7882
0073-6090 India: a Reference Annual
0073-6120 India. Central Board of Revenue. Central Excise Manual
0073-6139 India. Central Statistical Organization. Annual Survey of Industries
0073-6147 India. Central Statistical Organization. Estimates of National Income *changed to* India. Central Statistical Organization. National Accounts Statistics.
0073-6155 India. Central Statistical Organization. Statistical Abstract
0073-6163 India. Central Statistical Organization. Sample Surveys of Current Interest in India. Report *changed to* India. Central Statistical Organization. Annual Report.
0073-6171 India. Central Vigilance Commission. Report
0073-618X India. Department of Atomic Energy. Annual Report
0073-6198 India. Khadi and Village Industries Commission. Report *changed to* K V I C Annual Report.
0073-6201 India. Ministry of Education and Social Welfare. Department of Education. Report *changed to* India. Ministry of Human Resource Development. Department of Education. Report.
0073-6236 India. Union Public Service Commission Report
0073-6244 India Who's Who
0073-6252 Indian Adult Education Association. National Seminar. Report†
0073-6260 I A S L I C Technical Pamphlets
0073-6279 I A S L I C Special Publication
0073-6287 Indian Books; Bibliography of Indian Books Published or Reprinted in the English Language *changed to* B E P I.
0073-6295 Indian Chemical Directory *issued with* Guide to Indian Chemical Plants and Equipment.
0073-6295 Indian Chemical Directory
0073-6309 Indian Council of Medical Research. Annual Report
0073-6317 Indian Council of Medical Research. Report of the Advisory Committees†
0073-6325 Indian Council of Medical Research. Special Report Series†
0073-6333 Indian Engineering Association. Handbook of Statistics *changed to* Confederation of Indian Industry. Handbook of Statistics.
0073-6341 C. A. S. N. P. Bulletin†
0073-635X Indian Forest Bulletin (New Series)
0073-6368 Indian Forest Leaflets (New Series)
0073-6376 Indian Forest Records (New Series) Botany
0073-6384 Indian Forest Records (New Series) Composite Wood
0073-6392 Indian Forest Records (New Series) Entomology
0073-6406 Indian Forest Records (New Series) Forest Pathology
0073-6414 Indian Forest Records (New Series) Logging
0073-6422 Indian Forest Records (New Series) Silviculture
0073-6430 Indian Forest Records (New Series) Statistical
0073-6449 Indian Forest Records (New Series) Timber Mechanics
0073-6465 Indian Institute of Advanced Study. Transactions and Monographs
0073-6473 Indian Institute of Foreign Trade. Report
0073-649X Indian Institute of Sugarcane Research, Lucknow. Annual Report
0073-6503 Indian Institute of Technology, Bombay. Series†
0073-6511 Indian Institute of Technology, Madras. Annual Report
0073-652X Indian Institute of Technology, Madras. Technical Communications†
0073-6546 I I T C Directory
0073-6554 Indian Journal of Engineers. Annual Foundry Number
0073-6562 Indian Jute Mills Association. Annual Summary of Jute and Gunny Statistics
0073-6570 Indian Jute Mills Association. Loom and Spindle Statistics
0073-6589 Indian Linguistics Monograph Series
0073-6597 I M E Directory: Mines, Minerals, Equipment†
0073-6600 Indian National Science Academy. Proceedings
0073-6619 Indian National Science Academy. Year Book
0073-6627 I N S D O C Union Catalogue Series
0073-6635 Indian Pharmaceutical Guide
0073-6651 Indian Rubber Statistics
0073-666X Indian School of International Studies *see* 0075-3548
0073-6678 Indian Society of International Law. Publications
0073-6686 Indian Statistical Institute. Annual Report
0073-6694 Indian Statistical Institute. Econometric and Social Sciences Series. Research Monographs
0073-6708 Indian Statistical Institute. Library. Bibliographic Series
0073-6716 Indian Statistical Institute. Statistics and Probability Series. Research Monographs
0073-6724 Indian Statistical Series
0073-6732 Indian Voice
0073-6759 Indiana Academy of Science. Monograph
0073-6767 Indiana Academy of Science. Proceedings
0073-6775 Indiana. Aeronautics Commission. Annual Report†
0073-6783 Indiana. Agricultural Experiment Station. Inspection Report
0073-6791 Indiana. Agricultural Experiment Station. Research Bulletin
0073-6821 Ball State Monographs†
0073-6856 Indiana. Civil Rights Commission. Annual Report *changed to* Indiana. Civil Rights Commission. Triennial Report.
0073-6880 Indiana Historical Collections
0073-6899 Indiana Historical Society. Prehistory Research Series
0073-6902 Indiana Historical Society. Publications
0073-6910 Indiana Industrial Directory *see* 0888-8175
0073-6937 Indiana State University. Department of Geography and Geology. Professional Paper
0073-6945 Indiana Studies in Prediction *changed to* Indiana Studies in Higher Education.
0073-6953 Indiana University. Department of Geography. Geographic Monograph Series
0073-6961 Indiana University. Department of Geography. Occasional Publication.
0073-6996 Indiana University. Folklore Institute. Monograph Series†
0073-702X Indiana University Monograph Series in Adult Education†
0073-7038 Indiana University Art Museum. Publications†
0073-7062 Indiana University. Research Center for Language and Semiotic Studies. African Series†
0073-7097 Indiana University. Research Institute for Inner Asian Studies. Uralic and Altaic Series.
0073-7135 Indianapolis District Dental Society. Journal *changed to* Indianapolis District Dental Society. Newsletter.
0073-7151 Indice Agricola Colombiano
0073-7178 Indice General de Publicaciones Periodicas Latinoamericanas. Humanidades y Ciencias Sociales†
0073-7186 Indices of Urban Land Prices and Construction Cost of Wooden Houses in Japan
0073-7194 Indices Verborum Linguae Mongoliae Monumentis Traditorum
0073-7208 Indices zur Deutschen Literatur†
0073-7224 Indo-Iranian Monographs†
0073-7240 Indo-Pacific Mollusca†
0073-7275 Industria del Petrolio in Italia
0073-7283 Industria International *see* 0039-7245
0073-7291 Industria Italiana del Ciclo e del Motociclo. Annuario
0073-7305 Industrial Accident Prevention Association. Annual Report
0073-7313 Industrial Accident Prevention Association. Guide to Safety†
0073-7321 Industrial Alabama *changed to* Alabama Industrial Directory.
0073-733X Industrial and Commercial Power Systems and Electrical Space Heating and Air Conditioning Joint Technical Conference. Record *changed to* Industrial and Commercial Power Systems Technical Conference.
0073-7356 Industrial Bank of Sudan. Board of Directors. Annual Report
0073-7364 Industrial Catering†
0073-7372 Industrial Development Bank of India. Annual Report
0073-7402 Industrial Development Bank of Turkey. Annual Statement
0073-7410 Foundation for Business Responsibilities. Discussion Paper

ISSN INDEX 5521

0073-7429 Foundation for Business Responsibilities. Occasional Papers
0073-7437 Foundation for Business Responsibilities. Research Paper
0073-7445 Industrial Engineering Conference. Proceedings†
0073-7453 Industrial Fibres†
0073-7488 Chemical-Toxicological Series. Bulletins
0073-7496 Industrial Health Foundation. Engineering Series. Bulletins
0073-750X Industrial Health Foundation. Legal Series Bulletins
0073-7518 Industrial Health Foundation. Medical Series. Bulletins
0073-7526 Industrial Health Foundation. Nursing Series. Bulletins
0073-7542 Industrial Hygiene Highlights *changed to* Industrial Environmental Health.
0073-7550 Industrial Intelligence; Industrial Yearbook†
0073-7569 Industrial Locations in Canada
0073-7577 Industrial Planning and Programming Series†
0073-7593 Industrial Relations Research in Canada†
0073-7623 Industrial Research Laboratories of the United States *see* 0886-0076
0073-7658 Industrial South Africa
0073-7666 Industrial Structure of Rajasthan
0073-7682 Industrial Waste Conference, Purdue University, Lafayette, Indiana. Proceedings
0073-7704 Industrie-Adresboek voor Zuid-Holland *changed to* Adreslijst van de Zuid-Hollandse Industrie.
0073-7712 Industrie-Compass Oesterreich
0073-7720 Industrie de la Manutention dans les Ports Francais
0073-7747 Industrie Francaise des Moteurs a Combustion Interne
0073-7755 Industrieabwaesser
0073-7763 Industries Directory, Capitals
0073-7771 Industries Directory, Delhi
0073-7798 Industries Directory, Northern India
0073-7801 Industry-Engineering Education Series *changed to* College-Industry Education Conference. Proceedings.
0073-781X Industry in East Africa
0073-7828 Inedits Russes
0073-7844 Information Display Buyers Guide†
0073-7879 Information Processing Association of Israel. National Conference on Data Processing. Proceedings
0073-7887 Information Series on Agricultural Economics *changed to* Giannini Foundation of Agricultural Economics. Information Series.
0073-7895 Information Service of the European Communities. Newsletter on the Common Agricultural Policy
0073-7909 Information Service of the European Communities. Trade Union News
0073-7917 Informations Annuelles de Caryosystematique et Cytogenetique
0073-7925 Informations et Etudes Socialistes
0073-7941 Informatique *see* 0398-1169
0073-7984 Informatore Farmaceutico
0073-7992 Ingenieria. Boletin Informativo. *see* 0120-5609
0073-800X Inglis Lecture†
0073-8018 Initiation a la Linguistique. Serie A. Lectures
0073-8026 Initiation a la Linguistique. Serie B. Problemes et Methodes
0073-8034 Initiation. Serie Textes, Bibliographies
0073-8042 Inland Printer/American Lithographer Buyer's Guide†
0073-8077 Inorganic Syntheses Series
0073-8085 Chimica Acta Reviews *see* 0020-1693
0073-8093 Canada. Insect Pathology Research Institute. Program Review†
0073-8115 Insects of Micronesia
0073-8123 Insights
0073-8131 Institut Belge de Science Politique. Bibliotheque. Nouvelle Serie *changed to* Institut de Science Politique. Bibliotheque. Nouvelle Serie.
0073-814X Institut Belge de Science Politique. Bibliotheque. Serie Documents *changed to* Institut de Science Politique. Bibliotheque. Serie Documents.
0073-8158 Institut Belge de Science Politique. Documents *changed to* Institut de Science Politique. Documents.
0073-8174 Institute Collegial Europeen. Bulletin *changed to* Institut Collegial Europeen. Actes des Colloques de Loches.
0073-8212 Institut de Recherche et d'Histoire des Textes, Paris. Documents, Etudes et Repertoires
0073-8220 Institut Armoricain de Recherches Historiques, Rennes. (Publication) *changed to* Universite de Rennes. Institut Armoricain de Recherches Economiques et Humaines. (Publication).
0073-8239 Institut de Science Economique Appliquee. Rapport d'Activite *changed to* Institut de Sciences Mathematiques et Economiques Appliquees. Rapport d'Activite.
0073-8247 Institut d'Emission d'Outre Mer, Paris. Rapport d'Activite
0073-8255 Institut d'Emission Malgache. Rapport d'Activite *changed to* Banque Centrale de la Republique Malgache. Rapport d'Activite.
0073-8263 Institut des Etudes Occitanes. Publications†
0073-8271 Institut des Hautes Etudes de l'Amerique Latine. Cahiers†
0073-828X Institut des Hautes Etudes de l'Amerique Latine. Centre d'Etudes Politiques, Economiques et Sociales. Publications Multigraphiees.†
0073-8298 Institut des Hautes Etudes de l'Amerique Latine. Travaux et Memoires *see* 0993-5878
0073-8301 Institut des Hautes Etudes Scientifiques, Paris. Publications Mathematiques
0073-8336 Institut Francais de Pondichery. Section Scientifique et Technique. Travaux. *changed to* Institut Francais de Pondichery. Publications du Departement d'Ecologie.
0073-8344 Institut Francais de Pondichery. Section Scientifique et Technique. Travaux. Hors Serie *changed to* Institut Francais de Pondichery. Publications du Departement d'Ecologie.
0073-8352 Institut Francais de Pondichery. Departement d'Indologie. Publications
0073-8360 Institut Francais du Petrole. Collection Colloques et Seminaires
0073-8379 Institut Francais du Petrole. Rapport Annuel
0073-8387 Institut fuer Asienkunde. Schriften
0073-8417 Institut fuer den Wissenschaftlichen Film. Publikationen zu Wissenschaftlichen Filmen. Sektion Biologie
0073-8433 Publikationen zu Wissenschaftlichen Filmen. Sektion Technische Wissenschaften, Naturwissenschaften
0073-8441 Publikationen zu Wissenschaftlichen Filmen. Sektion Geschichte, Paedagogik *see* 0341-5937
0073-8468 Institut fuer Gewerbeforschung, Vienna. Taetigkeitsbericht
0073-8484 Institut fuer Oesterreichische Geschichtsforschung. Mitteilungen
0073-8492 Institut fuer Ostrecht. Studien
0073-8522 Institut Historique Belge de Rome. Bibliotheque
0073-8530 Institut Historique Belge de Rome. Bulletin
0073-8549 Institut Historique et Archeologique Neerlandais de Stamboul. Publications
0073-8557 Institut Jules Destree. Etudes et Documents
0073-8565 Institut Michel Pacha. Annales
0073-8573 Institut Pasteur de Lille. Annales†
0073-859X Universite de Geneve. Institut Universitaire de Hautes Etudes Internationales. Etudes et Travaux†
0073-8603 Universite de Geneve. Institut Universitaire de Hautes Etudes Internationales. Publication†
0073-8611 Instituta et Monumenta. Serie I: Monumenta
0073-862X Institute for Balkan Studies. Publications
0073-8638 Institute for Clinical Science. Proficiency Test Service. Report *changed to* Check Sample.
0073-8654 Institute for Defense Analyses. Papers
0073-8697 I D E A Monographs†
0073-8700 I D E A Occasional Papers†
0073-8751 Institute for Fermentation, Osaka. Research Communications
0073-8778 Institute for Monetary Research. Monographs†
0073-8786 Institute for Palestine Studies. Anthology Series†
0073-8794 Institute for Palestine Studies. Basic Documents Series *changed to* Institute for Palestine Studies. United Nations Resolutions on Palestine and the Arab-Israeli Conflict Series.
0073-8808 Institute for Palestine Studies. International Annual Documentary Series†
0073-8816 Institute for Palestine Studies. Monograph Series
0073-8832 Institute for Petroleum Research and Geophysics, Holon, Israel. Report
0073-8875 Institute for Psychoanalysis. Report *changed to* Institute for Psychoanalysis. Newsletter.
0073-8921 I S M A Papers
0073-893X I S M A Occasional Papers
0073-8948 Institut fuer Iberoamerika-Kunde. Schriftenreihe†
0073-8999 Institute of Bankers in Pakistan. Council. Report and Accounts
0073-9014 Chartered Institute of Building. Year Book and Directory of Members *changed to* Chartered Institute of Building. Handbook.
0073-9030 Institute of Chartered Accountants in England and Wales. Management Information Series†
0073-9049 Institute of Chartered Accountants in England and Wales. Practice Administration Series, Exposure Drafts and Statements of Standard Accounting Practice *changed to* Institute of Chartered Accountants in England and Wales. Exposure Drafts and Financial Reporting Standards.
0073-9057 Institute of Chartered Accountants of Scotland. Official Directory
0073-9065 C F A Monograph Series†
0073-9073 Institute of Clerk of Works of Great Britain Incorporated. Year Book
0073-909X Institute of Economic Affairs. Occasional Papers
0073-9103 Institute of Economic Affairs. Research Monographs
0073-9154 I E E E Power Engineering Society. Winter Meeting. Preprints
0073-9170 I E E E Region 3 Technical Convention. Record *changed to* I E E E Southeastcon (Region 3 Conference) Record.
0073-9189 I E E E Region 6. Technical Conference. Record *changed to* I E E E Region 6. Conference (Publication).
0073-9197 I E E E Region 5 Conference. Record
0073-9200 Institution of Engineers. Technical Journal
0073-9219 Institution of Engineers. Year Book
0073-9227 Institute of Environmental Sciences. Annual Meeting. Proceedings
0073-9251 Institute of Environmental Sciences. Tutorial Series
0073-9286 I F T World Directory and Buyers' Guide†
0073-9294 Institute of Forest Genetics, Suwon, Korea. Research Report
0073-9316 Great Britain. Institute of Geological Sciences. Geomagnetic Bulletin *changed to* Great Britain. British Geological Survey. Geomagnetic Bulletin.
0073-9324 Great Britain. Institute of Geological Sciences. Geophysical Papers†
0073-9332 Great Britain. Institute of Geological Sciences. Overseas Geology and Mineral Resources *see* 0030-7467
0073-9340 Institute of Geological Sciences, London. Overseas Geology and Mineral Resources. Supplement Series†
0073-9359 Great Britain. Institute of Geological Sciences. Report *changed to* Great Britain. British Geological Survey. Report.
0073-9367 Institute of Geological Sciences, London. Statistical Summary of the Mineral Industry *changed to* World Mineral Statistics.
0073-9375 Great Britain. Institute of Geological Sciences. Water Supply Papers†
0073-9383 Great Britain. Institute of Geological Sciences. Water Supply Papers. Research Reports†
0073-9391 Great Britain. Institute of Geological Sciences. Water Supply Papers. Technical Communications†
0073-9413 Institute of Judicial Administration. Calendar Status Study†
0073-9421 Institute of Labor and Industrial Relations. Policy Papers in Human Resources and Industrial Relations†
0073-943X Institute of Labor and Industrial Relations. Reprint Series
0073-9448 Institute of Medical Laboratory Technology. London. Annual Report *changed to* Institute of Medical Laboratory Sciences, London. Annual Report.
0073-9456 Institute of Mennonite Studies Series
0073-9464 Institute of Metals. Monograph and Report Series†
0073-9472 Institute of Nuclear Materials Management. Proceedings of Annual Meeting
0073-9480 Institute of Paper Chemistry. Bibliographic Series *changed to* Institute of Paper Science and Technology. Bibliographic Series.
0073-9502 Institute of Pastoral Psychology. Proceedings *see* 0079-0141
0073-9529 Institute of Petroleum, London. Report of the Summer Meeting†
0073-9537 I P C Monographs
0073-9545 I P C Papers
0073-9561 Institute of Psychophysical Research. Proceedings
0073-957X Institute of Public Administration, Dublin. Administrative Procedure Series†
0073-9588 Institute of Public Administration, Dublin. Annual Report
0073-9596 Institute of Public Administration, Dublin. Administration Yearbook and Diary
0073-960X Institute of Public Administration, Dublin. Research Series†
0073-9618 Institute of Public Administration, Khartoum. Occasional Papers
0073-9626 Institute of Public Administration, Khartoum. Proceedings of the Annual Round Table Conference
0073-9650 Institute of Purchasing and Supply. Yearbook†

ISSN

0073-9677 Institute of Refrigeration, London. Proceedings†
0073-9693 Institute of Social Studies, The Hague. Publications. Paperback Series†
0073-9707 Institute of Social Studies, The Hague. Publications. Series Major†
0073-9731 Institute of Southeast Asian Studies. Occasional Paper
0073-9766 I E E Monograph Series†
0073-9782 Institution of Engineers (India). Directory†
0073-9790 Institution of Engineers of Ireland. Transactions
0073-9804 Institution of Municipal Engineers, London. Annual Conference. Proceedings†
0073-9812 Institution of Nuclear Engineers. Year Book†
0073-9839 Institution of Railway Signal Engineers. Proceedings
0073-9847 Institution of Structural Engineers. Yearbook *changed to* Institution of Structural Engineers. Sessional Yearbook and Directory of Members.
0073-9855 Instituto Adolfo Lutz. Revista
0073-9863 Instituto Antartico Chileno. Boletin *see* 0716-0763
0073-9871 Instituto Antartico Chileno. Contribution. Serie Cientifica
0073-988X Instituto Brasileiro do Cafe. Departamento Economico. Anuario Estatistico do Cafe. *changed to* Instituto Brasileiro do Cafe. Departamento Economico. Anuario Estatistico do Cafe.
0073-9901 Instituto Butantan. Memorias
0073-991X Instituto Caro y Cuervo. Serie Bibliografica
0073-9928 Instituto Caro y Cuervo. Serie Minor
0073-9936 Instituto Centro Americano de Investigacion y Tecnologia Industrial. Publicaciones Geologicas†
0073-9944 Instituto Centroamericano de Administracion Publica. Serie 100. Aspectos Humanos de la Administracion
0073-9952 Instituto Centroamericano de Administracion Publica. Serie 200. Ciencia de la Administracion
0073-9960 Instituto Centroamericano de Administracion Publica. Serie 300: Investigacion
0073-9979 Instituto Centroamericano de Administracion Publica. Serie 400: Economia y Finanzas
0073-9995 Instituto Centroamericano de Administracion Publica. Serie 600: Informes de Seminarios
0074-0004 Instituto Centroamericano de Administracion Publica. Serie 700: Materiales de Informacion
0074-0012 Instituto Centroamericano de Administracion Publica. Serie 800: Metodologia de la Administracion
0074-0020 Instituto Centroamericano de Administracion Publica. Serie 900: Miscelaneas
0074-0039 Instituto Costarricense de Cultura Hispanica. Publicacion†
0074-0047 Informe de Operacion de las Principales Empresas Productoras y Distribuidoras de Energia Electrica de Costa Rica
0074-0063 Instituto de Ciencia Politica Rafael Bielsa. Anuario
0074-008X Instituto de Investigacao Cientifica de Angola. Bibliograficas Tematicas
0074-0098 Instituto de Investigacao Cientifica de Angola. Memorias e Trabalhos
0074-0144 Instituto de Tecnologia de Alimentos. Instrucoes Praticas
0074-0152 Instituto de Tecnologia de Alimentos. Instrucoes Tecnicas
0074-0195 Instituto Espanol de Oceanografia. Boletin
0074-0209 Instituto Espanol de Oceanografia. Trabajos *see* 0214-1949
0074-0233 Instituto Hondureno de Seguridad Social. Departamento de Estadistica y Procesamiento de Datos. Anuario Estadistico
0074-025X Fundacion Miguel Lillo. Miscelanea
0074-0268 Instituto Nacional de Seguros. Informe Anual *changed to* Instituto Nacional de Seguros Memoria Anual.
0074-0276 Instituto Oswaldo Cruz, Rio de Janeiro. Memorias
0074-0284 Instituto Paranaense de Botanica. Revista. Serie: Flora do Parana
0074-0292 I T A Humanidades†
0074-0306 Instituto Tecnologico y de Estudios Superiores. Publicaciones. Serie: Catalogos de Biblioteca†
0074-0330 Instituto Torcuato di Tella. Centro de Estudios Urbanos Regionales. Documentos de Trabajo†
0074-0349 Instituto Torcuato di Tella. Centro de Investigaciones Economicas. Documentos de Trabajo†
0074-0357 Instituto Torcuato di Tella. Centro de Investigaciones Sociales. Documentos de Trabajo†
0074-0373 Institutul de Cercetari Pentru Cultura Cartofului si Sfeclei de Zahar, Brasov. Anale. Cartoful *changed to* Institutul de Cercetare si Productie Pentru Cultura si Industrializarea Sfeclei de Zahar si a Substantelor Dulci-Fundulea. Lucrari Stiintifice. Sfecla si Zahar.
0074-0381 Institutul de Cercetari pentru Cultura Cartofului si Sfeclei de Zahar, Brasov. Anale. Sflecla de Zahar *changed to* Institutul de Cercetari pentru Cereale si Plante Tehnice. Laborator Sfecla de Zahar. Anale. Lucrari Stiintifice.
0074-039X Institutul de Istorie si Arheologie "A.D. Xenopol" - Iasi. Anuarul *changed to* Institutul de Arheologie - Iasi. Anuarul.
0074-0411 Instituut voor Cultuurtechniek en Waterhuishouding. Mededeling *changed to* Instituut voor Cultuurtechniek en Waterhuishouding. Mededeling. Nieuwe Serie.
0074-042X Instituut voor Cultuurtechniek en Waterhuishouding. Technical Bulletin *changed to* Instituut voor Cultuurtechniek en Waterhuishouding. Technical Bulletins. New Series.
0074-0438 Instituut voor Cultuurtechniek en Waterhuishouding. Verspreide Overdrukken *changed to* Instituut voor Cultuurtechniek en Waterhuishouding. Mededeling. Nieuwe Serie.
0074-0446 Instituut voor Planteziektenkundig Onderzoek. Jaarverslag
0074-0462 Koninklijk Instituut voor Taal-, Land- en Volkenkunde. Bibliographical Series
0074-0470 Koninklijk Instituut voor Taal-, Land- en Volkenkunde. Translation Series
0074-0489 Instituut voor Veevoedingsonderzoek "Hoorn". Jaarverslag *changed to* Instituut voor Veevoedingsonderzoek. Jaarverslag.
0074-0527 Standards and Practices for Instrumentation
0074-0551 Instrumentation in the Chemical and Petroleum Industries
0074-056X Instrumentation in the Power Industry
0074-0578 Instruments, Electronics and Automation Purchasing Directory *changed to* Electronics & Instruments Directory.
0074-0586 Instytut Gospodarki Wodnej. Prace†
0074-0616 Instytut Slaski. Kommunikaty. Seria Niemcoznawcza†
0074-0632 Instytut Slaski. Wydawnictwa†
0074-0640 Instytut Badan Jadrowych. Zaklad Radiobiologii i Ochrony Zdrowia. Prace Doswiadczalne
0074-0659 Insulation - Circuits Directory - Encyclopedia *changed to* Electronic Manufacturing Desk Manual.
0074-0675 Insurance Almanac; Who, What, When and Where in Insurance
0074-0683 Insurance Casebook†
0074-0691 Insurance Directory and Year Book
0074-0705 Israel. Central Bureau of Statistics. Insurance in Israel
0074-0713 Insurance Facts
0074-0721 Insurance Institute of Canada. Report *changed to* Insurance Institute of Canada. Perspectives.
0074-073X Insurance Periodicals Index
0074-0748 Asociacion Interamericana de Bibliotecarios y Documentalistas Agricolas. Boletin Especial
0074-0756 Asociacion Interamericana de Bibliotecarios y Documentalistas Agricolas. Boletin Tecnico†
0074-0764 Inter-American Commission of Women. Special Assembly. Final Act
0074-0780 Inter-American Commission on Human Rights. Report on the Work Accomplished During Its Special Sessions†
0074-0799 Inter-American Conference of Ministers of Labor on the Alliance for Progress. Final Act†
0074-0802 Inter-American Conference on Community Development. Final Act†
0074-0810 Congresos Indigenistas Interamericanos. Actas
0074-0829 Inter-American Council for Education, Science, and Culture. Final Report
0074-0837 Work Accomplished by the Inter-American Juridical Committee during its Meeting
0074-0861 Inter-American Development Bank. Board of Governors. Proceedings of the Meeting
0074-087X Inter-American Development Bank. Report *changed to* Inter-American Development Bank. Annual Report.
0074-0888 Socio-Economic Progress in Latin America; Annual Report *see* 0095-2850
0074-0918 Inter-American Economic and Social Council. Final Report of the Annual Meeting at the Ministerial Level
0074-0926 Inter-American Institute of Agricultural Sciences. Center for Training and Research. Bibliotecologia y Documentacion *see* 0301-438X
0074-0934 Inter-American Music Monograph Series†
0074-0950 Inter-American Port and Harbor Conferences. Final Act†
0074-0969 Inter-American Statistical Conferences. Final Report†
0074-0985 Inter-American Travel Congresses. Final Act†
0074-0993 Inter-American Tropical Tuna Commission. Bulletin
0074-1000 Inter-American Tropical Tuna Commission. Annual Report
0074-1019 Inter-Documentation Company. Newsletter†
0074-1043 Chronicle of Parliamentary Elections *changed to* Chronicle of Parliamentary Elections and Developments.
0074-1051 Inter-Parliamentary Union. Conference Proceedings *changed to* Inter-Parliamentary Union. Summary Records of the Inter-Parliamentary Conferences.
0074-106X Inter-University Case Program. Case Study
0074-1078 Inter-University Consortium for Political and Social Research. Annual Report
0074-1086 Interamerican Conference on Materials Technology. (Proceedings)†
0074-1116 Interavia A B C *changed to* International A B C Aerospace Directory.
0074-1132 Interdisciplinary Topics in Gerontology
0074-1140 Interferences, Arts, Lettres
0074-1175 Intergovernmental Oceanographic Commission. Technical Series
0074-1191 Design in Greece *changed to* Design & Art in Greece.
0074-1205 Internal Revenue Guide to Your Federal Income Tax†
0074-1213 Internal Trade of Iran
0074-123X International Academy of Indian Culture. Satapitaka Series
0074-1248 International Academy of Legal Medicine and of Social Medicine. (Congress Reports)
0074-1256 International Academy of Oral Pathology. Proceedings†
0074-1264 International Actuarial Congress. Transactions†
0074-1272 Biennial Survey of Advertising Expenditures Around the World *see* 0568-0301
0074-1329 International Air Transport Association. Bulletin *changed to* International Air Transport Association. Annual General Meeting. Reports and Proceedings.
0074-1337 International Air Transport Association. Symposium Papers from the Annual General Meeting†
0074-1353 International Anatomical Congress. Proceedings
0074-137X International Archery Federation. Bulletin Officiel
0074-1388 International Arthurian Society. Bibliographical Bulletin
0074-1396 International Arthurian Society. Report on Congress *see* 0074-1388
0074-140X International Association for Bridge and Structural Engineering. Bulletin/Mitteilungen†
0074-1418 International Association for Bridge and Structural Engineering. Final Report (of Congress) *changed to* I A B S E Congress Report.
0074-1434 International Association for Bridge and Structural Engineering. Preliminary Report (of Congress)†
0074-1442 International Association for Bridge and Structural Engineering. Reports of the Working Commissions *changed to* I A B S E Report.
0074-1450 International Association for Cereal Chemistry. Congress Proceedings *changed to* International Association for Cereal Science and Technology. Congress Proceedings.
0074-1469 International Association for Classical Archaeology. Proceedings of Congress
0074-1477 International Association for Hydraulic Research. Congress Proceedings
0074-1507 International Association for Statistics in Physical Sciences. Proceedings (of Meetings)†
0074-1515 I A A E E (International Association for the Advancement of Ethnology and Eugenics). Reprint *changed to* White Paper on Human Ecology.
0074-1523 I A A E E (International Association for the Advancement of Ethnology and Eugenics). Monographs *changed to* I C H E International Commission on Human Ecology.
0074-154X International Association for the Advancement of Educational Research. Congress Reports *changed to* World Association for Educational Research. Congress Reports.
0074-1582 International Association of Chain Stores. Report of Plenary Session *changed to* International Center for Companies of the Food Trade and Industry. Congress Report.
0074-1604 International Association of Democratic Lawyers. Congress Report
0074-1612 International Association of Engineering Geology. Bulletin

ISSN

0074-1620 International Association of Gerontology. European Clinical Section Proceedings
0074-1647 International Association of Hail Insurers. Congress Report
0074-1655 International Association of Logopedics and Phoniatrics. Reports of Congress
0074-1663 International Association of Meteorology and Atmospheric Physics. Report of Proceedings of General Assembly
0074-1671 International Association of Milk Control Agencies. Proceedings of Annual Meetings
0074-168X International Association of Museums of Arms and Military History. Congress Reports
0074-1728 International Association of Physical Education and Sports for Girls and Women. Proceedings of the International Congress
0074-1744 International Association of State Lotteries. (Reports of Congress)
0074-1760 International Association of Thalassotherapy. Congress Reports
0074-1787 International Association of Workers for Maladjusted Children. Congress Report *changed to* International Association of Workers for Troubled Children and Youth. Congress Reports.
0074-1795 International Astronautical Congress. Proceedings *see* 0304-8705
0074-1809 International Astronomical Union. Proceedings of Symposia
0074-1833 International Atomic Energy Agency. Bibliographical Series†
0074-1841 I A E A Laboratory Activities†
0074-185X I A E A Research Contracts†
0074-1868 International Atomic Energy Agency. Legal Series
0074-1876 International Atomic Energy Agency. Panel Proceedings Series
0074-1884 International Atomic Energy Agency. Proceedings Series
0074-1892 International Atomic Energy Agency. Safety Series
0074-1906 International Atomic Energy Agency. Technical Directories
0074-1914 International Atomic Energy Agency. Technical Report Series
0074-1922 International Auction Records
0074-1930 International Audio-Visual Technical Centre. Bibliographical References
0074-1949 International Audio-Visual Technical Centre. Studies and Reports
0074-1973 International Baccalaureate Office. Annual Bulletin *changed to* International Baccalaureate Organisation. Annual Bulletin.
0074-1981 International Badminton Federation. Annual Handbook *see* 0255-4437
0074-199X World Bank Staff Occasional Papers†
0074-2007 International Beekeeping Congress. Reports
0074-2015 International Bibliography of Historical Sciences
0074-2031 International Bibliography of Rice Research
0074-204X International Bibliography of Studies on Alcohol
0074-2066 International Biennial Exhibition of Prints in Tokyo†
0074-2074 I B P Handbooks†
0074-2082 International Biometeorological Congress. Summaries and Reports Presented to the Congress
0074-2104 International Bureau of Fiscal Documentation. Annual Report
0074-2147 International Catalogue of Occupational Safety and Health Films
0074-2155 International Cemetery Directory *changed to* American Cemetery Association. Membership Directory.
0074-2163 International Centre for Settlement of Investment Disputes. Annual Report
0074-2171 International Centre of Fertilizers. World Congress. Acts
0074-218X International Ceramic Congress. Proceedings
0074-221X International Civil Aviation Organization. Aeronautical Agreements and Arrangements. Annual Supplement
0074-2228 International Civil Aviation Organization. (Panel On) Application of Space Techniques Relating to Aviation. Report of Meeting†
0074-2244 International Civil Aviation Organization. Airworthiness Committee. Report of Meeting
0074-2252 International Civil Aviation Organization. Automated Data Interchange Systems Panel. Report of Meeting
0074-2287 International Civil Aviation Organization. Air Navigation Plan. Africa - Indian Ocean Region
0074-2295 International Civil Aviation Organization. Air Navigation Plan. Caribbean and South American Regions
0074-2309 International Civil Aviation Organization. Air Navigation Plan. European Region†
0074-2317 International Civil Aviation Organization. Air Navigation Plan. Middle East and South East Asia Regions *see* 1014-0034
0074-2325 International Civil Aviation Organization. Air Navigation Plan. North Atlantic, North American and Pacific Regions
0074-2333 International Civil Aviation Organization. All-Weather Operations Panel. Report of Meeting
0074-235X International Civil Aviation Organization. Assembly. Resolutions
0074-2368 International Civil Aviation Organization. Assembly. Report and Minutes of the Legal Commission
0074-2376 International Civil Aviation Organization. Assembly. Report of the Economic Commission
0074-2384 International Civil Aviation Organization. Assembly. Report of the Technical Commission
0074-2422 International Civil Aviation Organization. Digests of Statistics. Series AT. Airport Traffic
0074-2430 International Civil Aviation Organization. Digests of Statistics. Series F. Financial Data
0074-2449 International Civil Aviation Organization. Digests of Statistics. Series FP. Fleet, Personnel *changed to* International Civil Aviation Organization. Digests of Statistics. Series FP. Fleet, Personnel, Commercial Air Carriers.
0074-2457 International Civil Aviation Organization. Digests of Statistics. Series R. Civil Aircraft on Register
0074-2465 International Civil Aviation Organization. Digests of Statistics. Series T. Traffic *see* 1014-0077
0074-2473 International Civil Aviation Organization. Digests of Statistics. Series TF. Traffic Flow *see* 1014-0093
0074-2481 I C A O Circulars
0074-249X International Civil Aviation Organization. Index of I C A O Publications. Annual Cumulation
0074-2503 International Civil Aviation Organization. Legal Committee. Minutes and Documents (of Sessions)
0074-252X International Civil Aviation Organization. Obstacle Clearance Panel. Report of Meeting†
0074-2546 International Civil Aviation Organization. Report of the Air Navigation Conference†
0074-2562 International Civil Aviation Organization. Sonic Boom Panel. Report of the Meeting *changed to* International Civil Aviation Organization. Sonic Boom Committee. Report of the Meeting.
0074-2589 International Civil Aviation Organization. Visual Aids Panel. Report of Meeting†
0074-2597 International Clay Conference. Proceedings†
0074-2600 International College of Dentists. India Section. Newsletter
0074-2627 International Commission for the Northwest Atlantic Fisheries. Annual Proceedings *see* 0704-4798
0074-2635 International Commission for the Northwest Atlantic Fisheries. List of Fishing Vessels *see* 0250-7811
0074-2643 International Commission for the Northwest Atlantic Fisheries. Redbook *see* 0250-6416
0074-2651 International Commission for the Northwest Atlantic Fisheries. Research Bulletin *see* 0250-6408
0074-266X International Commission for the Northwest Atlantic Fisheries. Statistical Bulletin *see* 0250-6394
0074-2708 International Commission of Sugar Technology. Proceedings of the General Assembly
0074-2732 International Commission on Irrigation and Drainage. Congress Reports
0074-2775 International Organizing Committee of World Mining Congresses. Report *changed to* World Mining Congress. Report.
0074-2783 International Committee for Historical Science. Bulletin d'Information
0074-2791 International Committee of Onomastic Sciences. Congress Proceedings
0074-2805 International Committee on Laboratory Animals. Proceedings of Symposium *changed to* International Council for Laboratory Animal Science. Proceedings of the Symposium.
0074-283X International Computer Bibliography†
0074-2856 International Confederation for Agricultural Credit. Assembly and Congress Reports
0074-2872 International Confederation of Free Trade Unions. World Congress Reports
0074-2880 International Confederation of Midwives. Congress Reports
0074-2899 International Confederation of Societies of Authors and Composers
0074-2902 International Conference of Agricultural Economists. Proceedings
0074-2937 International Conference of Educators of Blind Youth. Proceedings *changed to* I C E V H Educator.
0074-2945 International Conference of Ethiopian Studies. Proceedings
0074-2961 International Conference of Social Work. Conference Proceedings
0074-297X International Conference for the Sociology of Religion *changed to* International Society for the Sociology of Religion.
0074-3011 International Conference on Cloud Physics. Proceedings
0074-3038 International Conference on Congenital Malformations. Proceedings†
0074-3046 International Conference on Cosmic Rays. (Proceedings)
0074-3054 International Conference on Endodontics. Transactions†
0074-3062 International Conference on Engineering in the Ocean Environment. Digest *see* 0197-7385
0074-3089 International Conference on Fluid Sealing. Proceedings
0074-3100 International Conference on Health and Health Education. Proceedings†
0074-3143 International Conference on Phenomena in Ionized Gases. Proceedings†
0074-3151 International Conference on Large High Voltage Electric Systems. Proceedings
0074-316X International Conference on Lead. Proceedings
0074-3178 International Conference on Low Temperature Physics. Reports
0074-3216 International Conference on Oral Biology. Proceedings
0074-3240 International Conference on Physics of Semiconductors. Proceedings *changed to* Physics of Semiconductors.
0074-3259 International Conference on Planned Parenthood. Proceedings†
0074-3267 International Conference on Protozoology. Proceedings *changed to* Progress in Protozoology.
0074-3275 International Conference on Education. Proceedings *changed to* International Conference on Education. Final Report.
0074-3305 International Conference on Social Welfare. Proceedings
0074-3313 International Society for Soil Mechanics and Foundation Engineering. Proceedings
0074-333X International Conference on the Physics of Electronic and Atomic Collisions. Papers *changed to* International Conference on the Physics of Electronic and Atomic Collisions. Abstracts of Contributed Papers and Invited Papers.
0074-3348 International Conference on the Structural Design of Asphalt Pavements. Proceedings
0074-3356 International Commission on Trichinellosis. Proceedings
0074-3364 International Congress for Analytical Psychology. Proceedings
0074-3380 International Congress for Cybernetics. Proceedings. Actes
0074-3429 International Congress for Papyrology. Proceedings
0074-3437 International Congress for Stereology. Proceedings
0074-347X International Congress of Angiology. Proceedings
0074-3488 International Congress of Animal Production. Proceedings†
0074-3496 International Union of Anthropological and Ethnological Sciences Newsletter
0074-3534 International Congress of Biochemistry. Proceedings†
0074-3542 International Congress for Byzantine Studies. Acts
0074-3577 International Congress of Chemotherapy. Proceedings†
0074-3615 International Congress of Cybernetic Medicine. Proceedings
0074-364X International Congress of Entomology
0074-3682 International Congress of Hematology. Proceedings
0074-3690 International Congress of Histochemistry and Cytochemistry. Proceedings
0074-3704 International Congress of History of Medicine. Proceedings†
0074-3712 International Congress of Home Economics. Report
0074-3755 International Congress of Linguists. Proceedings
0074-3771 International Congress of Nephrology. Abstracts of Reports and Communications
0074-378X International Congress of Nephrology. Proceedings†
0074-3828 International Congress of Occupational Therapy. Proceedings
0074-3844 International Congress of Orthoptists. Transactions
0074-3860 International Congress of Parasitology. Proceedings
0074-3879 International Congress of Pharmaceutical Sciences. Proceedings
0074-3895 International Congress of Primatology. Proceedings
0074-3933 International Congress of Radiology. (Reports)
0074-3968 International Congress of Sugarcane Technologists. Proceedings
0074-3984 Transplantation Today†

0074-3992 International Congress of University Adult Education. Journal *changed to* International Journal of University Adult Education.
0074-400X International Conference on Acoustics. Reports
0074-4026 International Congress on Animal Reproduction and Artificial Insemination. Proceedings *changed to* International Congress on Animal Reproduction. Proceedings.
0074-4042 International Congress on Clinical Chemistry. Abstracts
0074-4050 International Congress on Clinical Chemistry. Proceedings†
0074-4069 International Congress on Clinical Chemistry. Papers
0074-4077 International Congress on Combustion Engines. Proceedings
0074-4115 International Commission on Large Dams. Transactions
0074-4123 International Congress on Metallic Corrosion. (Proceedings)
0074-4131 International Congress on Occupational Health. Proceedings†
0074-414X International Congress on Phonetic Sciences. Proceedings†
0074-4190 International Congress on the History of Art. Proceedings
0074-4204 International Congress on Underground Techniques and Town-Planning. Reports
0074-4212 International Congresses on Tropical Medicine and Malaria. (Proceedings)
0074-4220 International Convocation on Immunology. Papers†
0074-4247 International Cooperative Alliance. Congress Report†
0074-4255 International Cooperative Alliance. Cooperative Series
0074-4263 International Council for Bird Preservation. British Section. Report
0074-4271 International Council for Bird Preservation. Proceedings of Conferences
0074-428X International Council for Building Research, Studies and Documentation. Congress Reports†
0074-4328 I C E S Oceanographic Data Lists *see* 0106-6935
0074-4336 International Council for the Exploration of the Sea. Rapports et Proces-Verbaux des Reunions *see* 0906-060X
0074-4360 International Council of Homehelp Services. Reports of Congress
0074-4387 International Council of Scientific Unions. Year Book
0074-4395 International Council of Voluntary Agencies. Documents Series†
0074-4409 International Council of Voluntary Agencies. General Conference. Record of Proceedings†
0074-4417 I C H P E R Congress Reports *changed to* I C H P E R Congress Proceedings.
0074-4425 International Council on Social Welfare. European Symposium. Proceedings
0074-445X International Court of Justice. Yearbook
0074-4468 Credit Union Yearbook†
0074-4476 International Customs Journal
0074-4522 International Diabetes Federation. Proceedings of Congress *changed to* International Diabetes Federation. Triennial Report.
0074-4557 S D C E International Die Casting Congress. Transactions *changed to* N A D C A International Die Casting Congress. Transactions.
0074-4565 International Directory of Arts
0074-4573 International Directory of Biological Deterioration Research†
0074-4581 International Directory of Computer and Information System Services†
0074-4603 International Directory of Philosophy and Philosophers
0074-4611 International Directory of Programs in Business and Commerce†
0074-462X International Directory of 16MM Film Collectors
0074-4638 International District Heating Association. Proceedings
0074-4646 International Economic Association. Proceedings of the Conferences and Congresses
0074-4670 International Electron Devices Meeting. Abstracts *see* 0163-1918
0074-4697 International Electrotechnical Commission. Yearbook - Annuaire
0074-4700 International Encyclopedia of Food and Nutrition *see* 0306-0632
0074-5774 International Engineering Directory
0074-5782 International Eucharist Congress. Proceedings
0074-5790 International Falcon Movement. Conference Reports
0074-5804 F I D - C R Report Series†
0074-5812 International Federation for Documentation. Proceedings of Congress *changed to* International Federation for Information and Documentation. Proceedings of Congress.
0074-5820 F I D Annual Report†
0074-5839 F I D Yearbook *see* 0379-3680
0074-5847 International Federation for Medical Psychotherapy. Congress Reports
0074-5863 International Federation of Agricultural Producers. General Conference Proceedings
0074-588X International Federation of Asian and Western Pacific Contractors' Associations. Proceedings of the Annual Convention
0074-5898 International Federation of Associations of Textile Chemists and Colorists. Reports of Congress
0074-5952 International Federation of Fruit Juice Producers. Proceedings of Congress. Compte-Rendu du Congres
0074-5960 I F I Information†
0074-5979 International Federation of Journalists and Travel Writers. Official List/ Repertoire Officiel
0074-5987 I F L A Annual
0074-6002 I F L A Directory
0074-6037 International Federation of Medical Students' Associations. Minutes and Reports of the General Assembly
0074-6045 International Federation of Prestressing. Congress Proceedings
0074-6053 International Film Guide
0074-6061 International Finance Corporation. Report
0074-6096 International Folk Music Council Journal *see* 0740-1558
0074-610X International Football Book
0074-6118 International Foundry Congress. Papers and Communications
0074-6126 International Gas Union. Proceedings of Conferences *changed to* International Gas Union. Proceedings of World Gas Conferences.
0074-6142 International Geophysics Series
0074-6169 International Graphical Federation. Conference. Proceedings *see* 0018-9782
0074-6177 International Graphical Federation. Report of Activities
0074-6185 International Grassland Congress. Proceedings
0074-6193 International Green Book
0074-6215 International Handbook of Universities and Other Institutions of Higher Education
0074-6223 International Hop Growers Convention. Report of Congress
0074-6231 International Horticultural Congress. Proceedings
0074-624X International Hotel Guide
0074-6258 International Humanist and Ethical Union. Proceedings of the Congress
0074-6274 International Hydrographic Conference. Reports of Proceedings
0074-6282 International Hydrographic Bureau. Yearbook *changed to* International Hydrographic Organization. Yearbook.
0074-6320 International Indian Ocean Expedition. Collected Reprints†
0074-6401 I I E P Occasional Papers
0074-641X International Institute for Labour Studies. International Educational Materials Exchange. List of Available Materials†
0074-6428 International Institute for Land Reclamation and Improvement. Annual Report
0074-6436 International Institute for Land Reclamation and Improvement. Bibliography
0074-6444 International Institute for Land Reclamation and Improvement. Bulletin†
0074-6452 International Institute for Land Reclamation and Improvement. Publication
0074-6460 International Institute for Sugar Beet Research. Reports of the Winter Congress
0074-6479 International Institute of Administrative Sciences. Reports of the International Congress
0074-6495 International Institute of Ibero-American Literature. Congress Proceedings. Memoria
0074-6509 International Institute for Labour Studies. Publications†
0074-6525 International Institute of Philosophy. Actes
0074-6533 International Institute of Public Finance. Papers and Proceedings
0074-6541 Institut International du Froid. Comptes Rendus de Reunions de Commissions
0074-655X International Institute of Seismology and Earthquake Engineering. Bulletin
0074-6568 International Institute of Seismology and Earthquake Engineering. Earthquake Report†
0074-6584 International Institute of Seismology and Earthquake Engineering. Lecture Note†
0074-6592 International Institute of Seismology and Earthquake Engineering. Progress Report†
0074-6606 International Institute of Seismology and Earthquake Engineering. Report of Individual Study by Participants to I S E E *changed to* International Institute of Seismology and Earthquake Engineering. Individual Studies by Participants at I I S E E.
0074-6614 International Institute of Seismology and Earthquake Engineering. Year Book
0074-6630 International Iron and Steel Institute. Report of Conference Proceedings
0074-6657 International Labor Studies†
0074-6665 International Labour and Industrial Film Triennial. Catalogue of the Participating Films
0074-6681 International Labour Conference. Reports to the Conference and Record of Proceedings
0074-6703 Management Development Series
0074-6738 International Law Association. Reports of Conferences
0074-6746 International League of Liberal Christian Women. Newsletter *changed to* International Association of Liberal Religious Women. Newsletter.
0074-6754 International League of Societies for the Mentally Handicapped. World Congress Proceedings. *changed to* I L S M H News.
0074-6762 International Leprosy Congress. Abstracts and Papers *changed to* International Leprosy Congress. Transactions.
0074-6797 International Linguistic Association. Monograph
0074-6800 International Linguistic Association. Special Publications
0074-6819 International Literary and Artistic Association. Proceedings and Reports of Congress
0074-6827 International Literary Market Place
0074-6835 International Machine Tool Design and Research Conference. Proceedings†
0074-6843 International Magnetics Conference. Digest *changed to* International Magnetics Conference. Digests of the Intermag Conference.
0074-6878 International Maize and Wheat Improvement Center. Research Bulletin†
0074-6908 International Market Guide - Continental Europe *see* 0278-6524
0074-6916 International Measurement Conference. Proceedings. Acta IMEKO *see* 0237-028X
0074-6959 International Meeting of Animal Nutrition Experts. Proceedings
0074-6975 International Meeting on Cattle Diseases. Reports. *changed to* World Buiatrics Congress.
0074-6983 International Metalworkers' Congress. Reports
0074-7009 International Microwave Symposium Digest *see* 0149-645X
0074-7017 International Mineralogical Association. Proceedings of Meetings
0074-7025 International Monetary Fund. Summary Proceedings of the Annual Meeting of the Board of Governors
0074-7033 International Monographs on Advanced Biology and Biophysics
0074-7041 International Monographs on Advanced Chemistry
0074-705X International Monographs on Advanced Mathematics and Physics
0074-7068 International Monographs on Studies in Indian Economics
0074-7084 International Motion Picture Almanac
0074-7114 International Narcotic Conference. Report: Proceedings of Annual Conference *see* 0148-4648
0074-7122 International Naturist Guide
0074-7157 International North Pacific Fisheries Commission. Bulletin†
0074-7165 International North Pacific Fisheries Commission. Annual Report†
0074-7173 International Olive Growers Federation. Congress Reports†
0074-7181 International Olympic Academy. Report of the Sessions
0074-7203 International Organization of Citrus Virologists. Proceedings of the Conference†
0074-722X International P.E.N. Congress. Report
0074-7238 International Pacific Halibut Commission (U.S. and Canada). Annual Report
0074-7246 International Pacific Halibut Commission (U.S. and Canada). Scientific Reports
0074-7254 International Pacific Salmon Fisheries Commission. Annual Report†
0074-7262 International Pacific Salmon Fisheries Commission. Bulletin†
0074-7270 International Pacific Salmon Fisheries Commission. Progress Report†
0074-7289 I P R A Studies in Peace Research†
0074-7297 International Peace Research Association. Proceedings of the Conference†
0074-7300 International Pediatric Association. Proceedings of Congress

ISSN INDEX 5525

0074-7343 International Philatelic Federation. General Assembly. Proces-Verbal
0074-7351 International Photobiological Congress. Proceedings†
0074-7386 International Planned Parenthood Federation. Proceedings of the Conference of the Europe and near East Region†
0074-7394 International Planned Parenthood Federation. Working Papers†
0074-7408 International Association of Plant Breeders for the Protection of Plant Varieties. Congress Reports
0074-7432 Bureau International de l'Heure . Rapport Annuel *changed to* International Earth Rotation Service. Annual Report.
0074-7459 International Political Science Association. Circular *see* 0709-6941
0074-7467 International Political Science Association. World Conference. Proceedings *changed to* International Political Science Association. World Congress.
0074-7475 International Poplar Commission. Session Reports†
0074-7483 International Poster Annual†
0074-7491 International Potash Institute. Colloquium. Proceedings
0074-7505 International Potash Institute. Congress Report *changed to* International Potash Institute. Congress Proceedings.
0074-7513 International Powder Metallurgy Conference. Proceedings - Modern Developments in Powder Metallurgy *changed to* Modern Developments in Powder Metallurgy.
0074-7521 International Pressure Die Casting Conferences. Report *changed to* International Pressure Die Casting Conferences. Proceedings.
0074-753X International Psycho-Analytical Association. Bulletin *issued with* 0020-7578
0074-7556 International Publishers Association. Proceedings of Congress
0074-7564 I R T S Gold Medal Annual *changed to* I R T S Gold Medal Journal.
0074-7572 International Railway Progress *see* 0309-1465
0074-7580 International Railway Statistics. Statistics of Individual Railways
0074-7599 International Rayon and Synthetic Fibres Committee. Statistical Yearbook
0074-7602 International Rayon and Synthetic Fibres Committee. Technical Conference. Reports†
0074-7610 International Rayon and Synthetic Fibres Committee. World Congress. Report†
0074-7637 International Real Estate Federation. Reports of Congress†
0074-7645 International Reference Annual for Building and Equipment of Sports, Tourism, Recreation Installations
0074-7653 International Reference Handbook of Services, Organizations, Diplomatic Representation, Marketing and Advertising Channels *changed to* International Reference Handbook of Marketing, Management and Advertising Organizations.
0074-7661 International Reinforced Plastics Conference. Papers and Proceedings. *changed to* Reinforced Plastics. Composite Papers.
0074-767X International Review of Connective Tissue Research†
0074-7688 International Review of Criminal Policy
0074-7696 International Review of Cytology
0074-7718 International Review of Experimental Pathology
0074-7726 International Review of Forestry Research†
0074-7734 International Review of General and Experimental Zoology†
0074-7742 International Review of Neurobiology
0074-7750 International Review of Research in Mental Retardation
0074-7769 International Review of Sport Sociology *changed to* International Review for the Sociology of Sport.
0074-7777 International Review of Tropical Medicine†
0074-7785 International Reviews in Aerosol Physics and Chemistry†
0074-7793 I R R I Annual Report *changed to* I R R I Program Report.
0074-7815 International Road Congresses. Proceedings
0074-7823 International Rubber Study Group. Summary of Proceedings of the Group Meetings and Assemblies
0074-784X International School of Physics "Enrico Fermi". Proceedings *changed to* International School of Physics "Enrico Fermi". Italian Physical Society. Proceedings.
0074-7858 International School of Physics "Ettore Majorana". Proceedings *changed to* International School of Physics "Enrico Fermi". Italian Physical Society. Proceedings.
0074-7866 International Science Review Series†
0074-7874 International Seaweed Symposium. Proceedings
0074-7882 International Society for Performing Arts Libraries and Museums. Congress Proceedings *changed to* International Association of Performing Arts Libraries and Museums. Congress Proceedings.
0074-7890 International Security Directory
0074-7904 International Sedimentological Congress. Guidebook
0074-7947 International Series of Monographs in Aeronautics and Astronautics. Division 1. Solid and Structural Mechanics *changed to* International Series in Aeronautics and Astronautics. Division 1. Solid and Structural Mechanics.
0074-7955 International Series of Monographs in Aeronautics and Astronautics. Division 2. Aerodynamics *changed to* International Series in Aeronautics and Astronautics. Division 2. Aerodynamics and Astronautics.
0074-7963 International Series of Monographs in Aeronautics and Astronautics. Division 3. Propulsion Systems Including Fuels *changed to* International Series in Aeronautics and Astronautics. Division 3. Propulsion Systems Including Fuels.
0074-7998 International Series of Monographs in Aeronautics and Astronautics. Division 7. Astronautics *changed to* International Series in Aeronautics and Astronautics. Division 7. Astronautics.
0074-8005 International Series of Monographs in Aeronautics and Astronautics. Division 9. Symposia *changed to* International Series in Aeronautics and Astronautics. Division 9. Symposia.
0074-8021 International Series on Chemical Engineering†
0074-8056 International Series of Monographs in Mechanical Engineering†
0074-8064 International Series in Natural Philosophy†
0074-8080 International Series on Automation and Automatic Control†
0074-8099 International Series on Analytical Chemistry†
0074-8129 International Series on Electronics and Instrumentation†
0074-820X International Series in Library and Information Sciences†
0074-8234 International Series on Oral Biology†
0074-8242 International Series on Organic Chemistry†
0074-8269 International Series of Monographs on Pure and Applied Biology. Division: Biochemistry *changed to* International Series on Pure and Applied Biology. Biochemistry Division.
0074-8277 International Series of Monographs on Pure and Applied Biology. Division: Botany *changed to* International Series on Pure and Applied Biology. Botany Division.
0074-8285 International Series of Monographs on Pure and Applied Biology. Division: Modern Trends in Physiological Sciences *changed to* International Series on Pure and Applied Biology. Modern Trends in Physiological Science Division.
0074-8293 International Series of Monographs on Pure and Applied Biology. Division: Plant Physiology *changed to* International Series on Pure and Applied Biology. Plant Physiology Division.
0074-8307 International Series of Monographs on Pure and Applied Biology. Division: Zoology *changed to* International Series on Pure and Applied Biology. Zoology Division.
0074-8315 International Series on Semiconductors†
0074-834X International Shade Tree Conference. Proceedings *see* 0278-5226
0074-8358 International Shipping and Shipbuilding Directory†
0074-8439 International Social Security Association. Technical Reports of Assemblies *see* 0251-1339
0074-8447 International Society for Cell Biology. Symposia†
0074-8455 International Society for Labour Law and Social Legislation. Proceedings of Congress
0074-848X International Society for Rock Mechanics. Congress. Proceedings
0074-8528 International Society of Blood Transfusion. Proceedings of the Congress
0074-8536 International Society of Geographical Pathology. Proceedings of the Conference†
0074-8544 International Society of Internal Medicine. Congress Proceedings†
0074-8552 International Society of Orthopaedic Surgery and Traumatology. Proceedings of Congresses *see* 0341-2695
0074-8560 International Society of Surgery. Comptes-Rendus†
0074-8579 International Society of Urology. Reports of Congress
0074-8587 International Solid State Circuits Conference. Digest *see* 0193-6530
0074-8595 International Spectroscopy Colloquium. Proceedings†
0074-8609 International Statistical Institute. Bulletin. Proceedings of the Biennial Sessions
0074-8617 International Statistical Yearbook of Large Towns†
0074-8684 International Studies in Sociology and Social Anthropology
0074-8692 International Study Week in Traffic Engineering and International Road Safety Congress
0074-8706 International Sugar Organization. Annual Report†
0074-8722 International Symposia on Comparative Law. Proceedings†
0074-8765 International Symposium on Atherosclerosis. Proceedings
0074-8781 International Symposium on Chromatography and Electrophoresis. Proceedings†
0074-8811 I E E E International Electromagnetic Compatibility Symposium. Record *see* 0190-1494
0074-882X International Symposium on Fault-Tolerant Computing. Digest *see* 0731-3071
0074-8897 International Symposium on Regional Development. Papers and Proceedings
0074-8935 International Symposium on the Reactivity of Solids. Proceedings†
0074-8951 International T N O Conference. (Proceedings)†
0074-9001 List of Cables Forming the World Submarine Network
0074-901X List of Destination Indicators and Telex Identification Codes *changed to* Indicators for the Telegram Retransmission System (TRS) - Telex Identification Codes.
0074-9028 List of International Telephone Routes
0074-9044 International Telecommunication Union. List of Telegraph Offices Open for International Service
0074-9052 Table of International Telex Relations and Traffic
0074-9087 International Textile Machinery†
0074-9095 International Thyroid Conference. Proceedings†
0074-9109 International Tin Council. Statistical Supplement. Tin, Tinplate Canning *changed to* Tin Statistics.
0074-9117 International Tin Council. Statistical Yearbook *changed to* Tin Statistics.
0074-9125 International Tin Research Council. Annual Report *changed to* International Tin Research Institute. Annual Report.
0074-9141 International Tracts in Computer Science and Technology and Their Application†
0074-915X I T C - Publications. Series A (Photogrammetry)†
0074-9184 International Travel Statistics *changed to* Yearbook of Tourism Statistics.
0074-9192 International Union Against Cancer. Manual†
0074-9214 International Union against Cancer. U I C C Monograph Series†
0074-9222 U I C C Technical Report Series†
0074-9230 International Union Against the Venereal Diseases and the Treponematoses. Proceedings of Assemblies *changed to* Genitourinary Medicine: The Journal of Sexual Health, STDs and HIV.
0074-9249 International Union against Tuberculosis and Lung Disease. Bulletin *see* 0962-8479
0074-9265 I U C N Yearbook *changed to* I U C N Annual Report.
0074-9273 I U C N Publications. New Series†
0074-9281 International Union for Conservation of Nature and Natural Resources. Proceedings and Papers of the Technical Meeting†
0074-929X International Union for Conservation of Nature and Natural Resources. Proceedings of the General Assembly
0074-9311 International Union for Inland Navigation. Annual Report
0074-9338 International Population Conference. Proceedings
0074-9346 Union Academique Internationale. Compte Rendu de la Session Annuelle du Comite
0074-9362 International Union of Biological Sciences. Reports of General Assemblies *see* 0445-1333
0074-9370 International Union of Building Societies and Savings Associations. Congress Proceedings *changed to* International Union of Housing Finance Institutions. Congress Proceedings.
0074-9389 International Union of Crystallography. Abstracts of the Triennial Congress

5526 ISSN INDEX

0074-9400 International Union of Forestry Research Organizations. Congress Proceedings
0074-9419 International Union of Geodesy and Geophysics. Proceedings of the General Assembly
0074-9427 Commission for the Geological Map of the World. Bulletin
0074-9435 International Union of Latin Notaries. Proceedings of Congress
0074-9443 International Union of Local Authorities. Reports of Congress†
0074-9451 International Union of Official Travel Organizations. Minutes of the IUOTO General Assemblies†
0074-946X International Union of Physiological Sciences. Proceedings of Congress†
0074-9486 International Union of Producers and Distributors of Electrical Energy. (Congress Proceedings)
0074-9508 International Union of Pure and Applied Chemistry. Comptes Rendus of IUPAC Conference†
0074-9516 International Union of Radio Science. Proceedings of General Assemblies
0074-9524 International Union of School and University Health and Medicine. Congress Reports
0074-9532 International Union of Students. Congress Resolutions *changed to* International Union of Students. Congress and Executive Committee Meetings Resolutions.
0074-9540 Congres International d'Histoire des Sciences. Actes
0074-9575 International Water Conference. Proceedings
0074-9583 International Water Supply Congress. Proceedings *see* 0735-1917
0074-9591 International Whaling Commission. Report *see* 0143-8700
0074-9613 International Who's Who
0074-9621 International Year Book and Statesmen's Who's Who
0074-963X International Association for Child Psychiatry and Allied Professions. Yearbook *changed to* International Association of Child and Adolescent Psychiatry and Allied Professions. Yearbook.
0074-9648 International Yearbook of the Underwater World†
0074-9664 International Zoo Yearbook
0074-9672 Internationale Bibliographie der Fachadressbuecher
0074-9729 Der Internationalen Gesellschaft fuer Geschichte der Pharmazie. Veroeffentlichungen. Neue Folge
0074-9737 Internationale Volkskundliche Bibliographie
0074-9745 Internationale Zeitschriftenschau fuer Bibelwissenschaft und Grenzgebiete†
0074-9753 Internationaler Campingfuehrer *see* 0179-6089
0074-977X Internationaler Spitalbedarf *changed to* Internationaler Arzt- und Spitalbedarf.
0074-9796 International Brewer's Directory
0074-980X Internationales Forschungszentrum fuer Grundfragen der Wissenschaften, Salzburg. Forschungsgespraeche†
0074-9818 Internationales Jahrbuch der Erwachsenenbildung
0074-9834 Internationales Jahrbuch fuer Geschichts und Geographieunterricht *see* 0172-8237
0074-9850 Internationales Jahrbuch fuer Religionssoziologie†
0074-9877 Internationales Verlagsadressbuch mit I S B N - Register *changed to* Publishers' International I S B N Directory.
0074-9907 Internationales Zucker-Jahrbuch
0074-9931 Interscience Monographs and Texts in Physics and Astronomy†
0074-994X Interscience Tracts in Pure and Applied Mathematics *changed to* Pure and Applied Mathematics: A Wiley Interscience Series of Texts, Monographs and Tracts.
0074-9958 Interscience Tracts on Physics and Astronomy†
0074-9966 Interstate Commission on the Potomac River Basin. Technical Bulletin *changed to* Interstate Commission on the Potomac River Basin. Technical Reports.
0074-9974 North American Conference on Labor Statistics. Selected Papers†
0075-0018 Inventaire General des Monuments et des Richesses Artistiques de la France
0075-0026 Inventari dei Manoscritti delle Biblioteche d'Italia
0075-0034 Inventaria Archaeologica Belgique
0075-0042 Inventaria Archaeologica Ceskoslovensko
0075-0050 Inventaria Archaeologica Denmark
0075-0069 Inventaria Archaeologica Deutschland
0075-0077 Inventaria Archaeologica Espana
0075-0085 Inventaria Archaeologica France
0075-0093 Inventaria Archaeologica Great Britain
0075-0107 Inventaria Archaeologica Italia
0075-0115 Inventaria Archaeologica Jugoslavija
0075-0123 Inventaria Archaeologica Norway
0075-0131 Inventaria Archaeologica Oesterreich
0075-014X Inventaria Archaeologica Pologne
0075-0158 Inventaria Archaeologica Ungarn
0075-0166 Inventaris van Het Kunstpatrimonium van Oost-Vlaanderen
0075-0174 Inventory of Programs in Maryland's Private and Public Universities and Colleges†
0075-0220 Investigations in Physics†
0075-0247 Investissements Etrangers en Belgique *changed to* Belgium. Ministere des Affaires Economiques. Rapport Annuel sur les Investissements Etrangers en Belique.
0075-0255 I B A Occasional Paper†
0075-0263 Securities Industry Association. State and Local Pension Funds†
0075-0271 Investment Companies†
0075-028X Investment Dealers' Association of Canada. Canada and Canadian Provinces: Funded Debts Outstanding *see* 0317-607X
0075-0301 Invitation to Photography†
0075-0328 Ion Exchange: A Series of Advances *see* 0092-0193
0075-0336 Ionenaustauscher in Einzeldarstellungen†
0075-0344 I A S Bulletin
0075-0352 Iowa English Yearbook *see* 0444-4663
0075-0360 Iowa Development Commission. Digest†
0075-0387 Iowa Nurses' Association. Bulletin†
0075-0409 Iowa State Engineering Research *see* 0149-0605
0075-0425 Iowa State University. Library. Annual Report†
0075-0433 Iowa State University. Engineering Research Institute. Engineering Research Report
0075-045X University of Iowa. Center for Labor and Management. Monograph Series *see* 0578-6371
0075-0468 I P E K†
0075-0476 Iran Almanac and Book of Facts
0075-0484 Iran. Geological Survey. Report
0075-0492 Foreign Trade Statistics of Iran. Yearbook
0075-0506 Iranian Industrial Statistics
0075-0514 Iranian Mineral Statistics
0075-0522 Iranian National Bibliography
0075-0549 Ireland (Eire) Central Statistics Office. Crops and Livestock Numbers. *see* 0791-3524
0075-0557 Ireland (Eire) Central Statistics Office. Estimates of the Quantity and Value of Agricultural Output *see* 0791-3001
0075-0565 Ireland (Eire) Central Statistics Office. External Trade Statistics *see* 0790-9381
0075-0573 Ireland (Eire) Central Statistics Office. Hire - Purchase and Credit Sales *see* 0791-3389
0075-0581 Ireland (Eire) Central Statistics Office. Inquiry into Advertising Agencies Activities *see* 0791-3516
0075-059X Ireland (Eire) Central Statistics Office. Livestock Numbers *see* 0791-3133
0075-0603 Ireland (Eire) Central Statistics Office. National Income and Expenditure
0075-0611 Ireland (Eire) Central Statistics Office. Statistics of Wages, Earnings and Hours of Work†
0075-062X Ireland (Eire) Central Statistics Office. Tuarascail Ar Staidreamh Beatha - Report on Vital Statistics
0075-0638 Ireland (Eire) Central Statistics Office. Trend of Employment and Unemployment
0075-0646 Ireland. Department of Agriculture and Fisheries. Annual Report *changed to* Ireland. Department of Agriculture. Annual Report.
0075-0654 Ireland (Eire) Department of Agriculture and Fisheries. Journal†
0075-0662 Ireland Department of Education. Liosta de Iar-Bhunscoileanna Aitheanta - List of Recognised Post-Primary Schools
0075-0670 Ireland (Eire) Department of Finance. Financial Statement of the Minister for Finance
0075-0697 Ireland (Eire) National Industrial Economic Council. Report†
0075-0700 Iris Year Book
0075-0719 Irish Agricultural Organization Society. Annual Report *see* 0790-4568
0075-0727 Irish Baptist Historical Society. Journal
0075-0735 Irish Catholic Directory
0075-0743 Historical Studies
0075-0751 Irish Creamery Managers' Association. Creamery Yearbook and Diary *changed to* Dairy Executive. Directory and Diary.
0075-076X Irish Drama Series†
0075-0778 Irish Geography
0075-0816 Irish Play Series
0075-0824 Irodalom - Szocializmus
0075-0832 Irodalomelmelet Klasszikusai
0075-0840 Irodalomtorteneti Fuzetek
0075-0859 Irodalomtorteneti Konyvtar
0075-0867 Iron and Steel. Annual Statistics for the United Kingdom *see* 0952-5505
0075-0875 Iron and Steel Works of the World
0075-0921 Islam in Paperback
0075-0948 Islamic World†
0075-0964 Israel. Agricultural and Settlement Planning and Development Center. Statistical Series for the Agricultural Year *changed to* Israel. Rural Planning and Development Authority. Agricultural and Rural Economic Report.
0075-0972 Israel Annual Conference on Aviation and Astronautics. Proceedings
0075-0980 Israel. Atomic Energy Commission. I A - Reports
0075-0999 Israel. Central Bureau of Statistics. Causes of Death
0075-1006 Israel. Central Bureau of Statistics. Criminal Statistics
0075-1014 Israel. Central Bureau of Statistics. Diagnostic Statistics of Hospitalized Patients
0075-1022 Israel. Central Bureau of Statistics. Juvenile Delinquency†
0075-1030 Israel. Central Bureau of Statistics. Judicial Statistics
0075-1049 Israel. Central Bureau of Statistics. Labour Force Surveys
0075-1057 Israel. Central Bureau of Statistics. Motor Vehicles
0075-1065 Israel. Central Bureau of Statistics. Schools and Kindergartens
0075-1081 Israel. Central Bureau of Statistics. Students in Academic Institutions *changed to* Israel. Central Bureau of Statistics. Students in Universities.
0075-109X Israel. Central Bureau of Statistics. Survey of Housing Conditions
0075-1111 Israel. Central Bureau of Statistics. Vital Statistics
0075-1138 Israel. Department of Surveys. Geodetic Papers
0075-1154 Israel Export Directory
0075-1162 Israel Film-Making Plus *changed to* Filmmaking in Israel.
0075-1189 Israel. Ministry of Agriculture. Department of Fisheries. Israel Fisheries in Figures†
0075-1200 Israel. Geological Survey. Bulletin
0075-1219 Israel. Hydrological Service. Hydrological Paper†
0075-1227 Israel Institute of Applied Social Research. Research Report†
0075-1235 Israel Institute of Productivity. Report of Activities†
0075-1243 Israel Journal of Entomology
0075-1251 Israel Medical Bibliography†
0075-126X Israel. Meteorological Service. Series B: Observational Data. Annual Rainfall Summary
0075-1278 Israel. Meteorological Service. Series A (Meteorological Notes)†
0075-1286 Israel. Meteorological Service. Series B: Observational Data. Annual Weather Report
0075-1294 Israel. Agricultural and Settlement Planning and Development Center. Statistical Series of the Budgetary Year *changed to* Israel. Rural Planning and Development Authority. Agricultural and Rural Economic Report.
0075-1308 Israel. Ministry of Communications. Statistics
0075-1324 National Insurance Institute, Jerusalem. Full Actuarial Report
0075-1383 Israel Society for Rehabilitation of the Disabled. Annual
0075-1405 Israel Tourist Statistics
0075-1413 Israel Yearbook *changed to* Israel Yearbook and Almanac (Year).
0075-1421 Israel. Central Bureau of Statistics. Israel's Foreign Trade
0075-143X Issues†
0075-1472 Studi Etruschi†
0075-1499 Istituto e Museo di Storia della Scienza. Biblioteca
0075-1502 Istituto Ellenico di Studi Bizantini e Postbizantini, Venice. Biblioteca
0075-1529 Istituto Mobiliare Italiano. Annual Report
0075-1537 Istituto Nazionale per l'Assicurazione Contro le Malattie, Rome. Bilancio Consuntivo†
0075-1545 Istituto Siciliano di Studi Bizantini e Neoellenici. Quaderni
0075-1553 Istituto Siciliano di Studi Bizantini e Neoellenici. Testi e Monumenti. Testi
0075-1561 Istituto Storico della Resistenza in Modena e Provincia. Quaderni†
0075-157X Istituto Storico della Resistenza in Modena e Provincia. Rassegna Annuale†
0075-160X Istoria Limbii Romane†
0075-1626 Istorie si Civilizatie
0075-1634 Italian Studies
0075-1642 Italy: An Economic Profile†
0075-1650 Italy. Direzione Generale delle Fonti di Energia e delle Industrie di Base. Bilanci Energetici
0075-1669 Italy. Istituto Centrale di Statistica. Annuario di Statistica Agraria *changed to* Italy. Istituto Centrale di Statistica. Statistiche dell'Agricoltura, Zootecnia e Mezzi di Produzione. Annuario.
0075-1677 Italy. Istituto Centrale di Statistica. Annuario delle Statistiche Culturali *changed to* Italy. Istituto Centrale di Statistica. Statistiche Culturali.

ISSN

ISSN INDEX 5527

0075-1685 Italy. Istituto Centrale di Statistica. Annuario di Statistiche Demografiche *changed to* Italy. Istituto Centrale di Statistica. Statistiche Demografiche.
0075-1693 Italy. Istituto Centrale di Statistica. Annuario di Statistiche del Lavoro e dell'Emigrazione *changed to* Italy. Istituto Centrale di Statistica. Statistiche del Lavoro.
0075-1707 Italy. Istituto Centrale di Statistica. Annuario di Statistica Forestale *changed to* Italy. Istituto Centrale di Statistica. Statistiche Forestali.
0075-1715 Italy. Istituto Centrale di Statistica. Annuario di Statistiche Giudiziario *changed to* Italy. Istituto Centrale di Statistica. Statistiche Giudiziarie.
0075-1723 Italy. Istituto Centrale di Statistica. Annuario di Statistiche Industriali *changed to* Italy. Istituto Centrale di Statistica. Statistiche Industriali.
0075-1731 Italy. Istituto Centrale di Statistica. Annuario di Statistiche Meteorologiche *changed to* Italy. Istituto Centrale di Statistica. Statistiche Meteorologiche.
0075-1758 Italy. Istituto Centrale di Statistica. Annuario di Statistiche Sanitarie *changed to* Italy. Istituto Centrale di Statistica. Statistiche Sanitarie.
0075-1774 Italy. Istituto Centrale di Statistica. Annuario Statistiche Zootecniche *changed to* Italy. Istituto Centrale di Statistica. Statistiche della Zootecnia, della Pesca e della Caccia.
0075-1782 Italy. Istituto Centrale di Statistica. Annuario Statistico del Commercio Interno *changed to* Italy. Istituto Centrale di Statistica. Statistiche del Commercio Interno.
0075-1790 Italy. Istituto Centrale di Statistica. Annuario Statistico dell' Assistenza e della Previdenza Sociale *changed to* Italy. Istituto Centrale di Statistica. Statistiche dell' Assistenza e della Previdenza Sociale.
0075-1804 Annuario Statistico dell'Attivita Edilizia e delle Opere Pubbliche
0075-1820 Statistiche dei Bilanci delle Amministrazioni Regionali, Provinciali e Comunali
0075-1871 Italy. Istituto Centrale di Statistica. Statistica Annuale del Commercio con l'Estero *see* 0390-6558
0075-1871 Italy. Istituto Centrale di Statistica. Statistica Annuale del Commercio con l'Estero *see* 0390-6566
0075-188X Statistica degli Incidenti Stradali
0075-1898 Italy. Istituto Centrale di Statistica. Annuario Statistico della Navigazione Marittima *changed to* Italy. Istituto Centrale di Statistica. Statistiche della Navigazione Marittima.
0075-1901 Istituto di Fisica dell'Atmosfera, Rome. Bibliografia Generale
0075-191X Istituto di Fisica dell'Atmosfera, Rome. Contributi Scientifici: Pubblicazioni di Fisica dell'Atmosfera e di Meteorologia
0075-1928 Istituto di Fisica dell'Atmosfera, Rome. Pubblicazioni Didattiche
0075-1936 Istituto di Fisica dell'Atmosfera, Rome. Pubblicazioni Scientifiche
0075-1944 Istituto di Fisica dell'Atmosfera, Rome. Pubblicazioni Varie.
0075-1952 Istituto di Fisica dell'Atmosfera, Rome. Rapporti Interni Provvisori Adiffusione Limitata
0075-1960 Istituto di Fisica dell'Atmosfera, Rome. Rapporti Scientifici
0075-1979 Istituto di Fisica dell'Atmosfera, Rome. Rapporti Tecnici
0075-1987 Italy. Istituto Nazionale per lo Studio della Congiuntura. Quaderni Analitici
0075-1995 Italy. Ministero del Bilancio e della Programmazione Economica. Relazione Generale Sulla Situazione Economica del Paese
0075-2002 Itinera Romana†
0075-2010 Itsuu Laboratory, Tokyo. Annual Report
0075-2029 Ius Romanum in Helvetia†
0075-2037 Ius Romanum Medii Aevi
0075-2045 J. Anderson Fitzgerald Lecture†
0075-2053 Miller's Sporting Annual and Athletic Record†
0075-2061 J.K. Lasser's Your Income Tax, Professional Edition
0075-207X J. L. B. Smith Institute of Ichthyology. Occasional Paper†
0075-2088 J L B Smith Institute of Ichthyology. Special Publication
0075-2118 Vooraziatisch-Egyptish Genootschap "Ex Oriente Lux". Jaarbericht
0075-2142 Jacob Blaustein Lectures in International Affairs
0075-2150 Jaeger's Intertravel
0075-2193 Jahrbuch der Auktionspreise *changed to* Jahrbuch der Auktionspreise fuer Buecher, Handschriften und Autographen.
0075-2207 Jahrbuch der Berliner Museen
0075-2215 Jahrbuch der Bibliotheken, Archive und Informationseinrichtungen der Deutschen Demokratischen Republik
0075-2223 Jahrbuch der Deutschen Bibliotheken
0075-224X Jahrbuch der Export- und Versandtleiter
0075-2266 Graphische Unternehmungen Oesterreichs. Jahrbuch
0075-2274 Jahrbuch der Hamburger Kunstsammlungen†
0075-2282 Jahrbuch des Heeres†
0075-2312 Kunsthistorische Sammlungen in Wien. Jahrbuch
0075-2320 Jahrbuch der Luftwaffe†
0075-2347 Jahrbuch der Oeffentlichen Meinung *see* 0175-9191
0075-2363 Jahrbuch der Psychoanalyse
0075-2371 Raabe-Gesellschaft. Jahrbuch
0075-238X Jahrbuch der Schiffart†
0075-2398 Jahrbuch der Schleiff-, Hon-, Laepp- und Poliertechnik *changed to* Jahrbuch Schleiffen, Honen, Laeppen und Polieren, Verfahren und Maschinen.
0075-2401 Deutscher Turner-Bund. Jahrbuch der Turnkunst
0075-241X Jahrbuch der Wehrmedizin†
0075-2428 Jahrbuch der Wehrtechnik
0075-2436 Jahrbuch des Baltischen Deutschtums
0075-2479 Jahrbuch des Eisenbahnwesens
0075-2487 Jahrbuch des Elektrischen Fernmeldewesens†
0075-2509 Jahrbuch des Kameramanns
0075-2517 Jahrbuch des Oeffentlichen Rechts der Gegenwart
0075-2533 Jahrbuch fuer Amerikastudien *see* 0340-2827
0075-2541 Jahrbuch fuer Antike und Christentum
0075-2568 Jahrbuch fuer Berlin-Brandenburgische Kirchengeschichte
0075-2584 Jahrbuch fuer Christliche Sozialwissenschaften
0075-2592 Jahrbuch fuer das Textil-Reinigungs-Gewerbe: Waescherei und Chemischreinigung†
0075-2606 Jahrbuch fuer den Oesterreichischen Tierarzt
0075-2622 Erziehungs- und Schulgeschichte Jahrbuch
0075-2630 Exlibriskunst und Graphik *see* 0172-2859
0075-2649 Jahrbuch fuer Fremdenverkehr
0075-2665 Geschichte der Sozialistischen Laender Europas. Jahrbuch
0075-2673 Jahrbuch fuer Geschichte von Staat, Wirtschaft und Gesellschaft Lateinamerikas
0075-2681 Jahrbuch fuer Liturgik und Hymnologie
0075-269X Jahrbuch der Luftfahrt und Raumfahrt *changed to* Reuss Jahrbuch der Luft- und Raumfahrt.
0075-2703 Jahrbuch fuer Musikalische Volks- und Voelkerkunde
0075-2711 Jahrbuch fuer Numismatik und Geldgeschichte
0075-272X Jahrbuch fuer Optik und Feinmechanik
0075-2738 Jahrbuch fuer Ostdeutsche Volkskunde
0075-2746 Jahrbuch fuer Ostrecht
0075-2754 Jahrbuch fuer Salesianische Studien
0075-2762 Jahrbuch fuer Schlesische Kirchengeschichte
0075-2770 Jahrbuch fuer Sozialwissenschaft
0075-2789 Jahrbuch fuer Volksliedforschung
0075-2800 Jahrbuch fuer Wirtschaftsgeschichte
0075-2819 Jahrbuch Oberflaechentechnik (Year)
0075-2827 Jahrbuch zur Alkohol- und Tabakfrage *changed to* Jahrbuch Sucht.
0075-2835 Jahresbericht der Bayerischen Bodendenkmalpflege
0075-2851 Jahresbericht ueber die Deutsche Fischwirtschaft
0075-286X Deutsche Geschichte. Jahresberichte
0075-2878 Jahresberichte ueber Holzschutz†
0075-2894 Jahreshefte fuer Karst- und Hoehlenkunde *see* 0342-2062
0075-2908 Jahreskatalog Kybernetik, Automation, Informatik *changed to* Kybernetik Jahreskatalog.
0075-2932 Jahresschrift fuer Mitteldeutsche Vorgeschichte
0075-2940 Jahresverzeichnis der Deutschen Hochschulschriften *see* 0323-455X
0075-2959 Jahresverzeichnis der Musikalien und Musikschriften
0075-2967 Jahresverzeichnis des Deutschen Schrifttums *see* 0300-8436
0075-2983 Jamaica. Department of Statistics. Annual Abstract of Statistics *changed to* Statistical Institute of Jamaica. Statistical Abstract.
0075-2991 Jamaican National Bibliography
0075-3009 James Terry Duce Memorial Series†
0075-3017 Jane's All the World Aircraft
0075-3025 Jane's Fighting Ships
0075-3033 Jane's Freight Containers *changed to* Jane's Containerisation Directory.
0075-305X Jane's Surface Skimmers *changed to* Jane's High-Speed Marine Craft.
0075-3068 Jane's Weapon Systems *changed to* Jane's Battlefield Surveillance.
0075-3068 Jane's Weapon Systems *changed to* Jane's C 3 I Systems.
0075-3084 Jane's World Railways
0075-3157 Japan Annual of Law and Politics†
0075-3165 Japan Anti-Tuberculosis Association. Reports on Medical Research Problems†
0075-3173 Japan. Statistics Bureau. Annual Report on Family Income and Expenditures *changed to* Japan. Statistics Bureau. Annual Report on Family Income and Expenditure Survey.
0075-319X Japan Chemical Annual
0075-3203 Japan Chemical Directory (Tokyo, 1963)
0075-3211 Japan Company Directory (Tokyo, 1974) *see* 0288-9307
0075-322X Japan Directory
0075-3238 Japan Center for Economic Research. Center Paper Series
0075-3246 Japan Economic Year Book†
0075-3270 Japan. Ministry of Health and Welfare. Statistics and Information Department. Vital Statistics
0075-3289 Japan Census of Manufactures: Report by Commodities
0075-3300 Japan P.E.N. News *changed to* Japanese Literature Today.
0075-3319 Japan Road Association. Annual Report of Roads
0075-3327 Japan Society for Cancer Therapy. Proceedings of the Congress
0075-3343 Japanese Antarctic Research Expedition Data Reports
0075-336X Japanese Antarctic Research Expedition, 1956-1962. Scientific Reports. Series B: Meteorology *see* 0386-5525
0075-3378 Japanese Antarctic Research Expedition, 1956-1962. Scientific Reports. Series C: Earth Sciences. *see* 0386-5533
0075-3386 Japanese Antarctic Research Expedition, 1956-1962. Scientific Reports. Series D: Oceanography *changed to* National Institute of Polar Research. Memoirs. Series D: Oceanography.
0075-3394 Japanese Antarctic Research Expedition, 1956-1962. Scientific Reports. Series E. Biology *see* 0386-5541
0075-3408 Japanese Antarctic Research Expedition, 1956-1962. Scientific Reports. Series F: Logistic *see* 0386-555X
0075-3424 Japanese Journal of Botany†
0075-3440 Japanese Miniature Electronic Components Data†
0075-3467 Japanese Progress in Climatology
0075-3475 Japan's Iron and Steel Industry
0075-3491 Jarlibro
0075-3505 Institutul Agronomic Ion Ionescu de la Brad. Lucrari Stiintifice. Seria Agronomie-Horticultura *see* 0379-8364
0075-3505 Institutul Agronomic Ion Ionescu de la Brad. Lucrari Stiintifice. Seria Agronomie-Horticultura *see* 0379-8372
0075-3513 Institutul Agronomic Ion Ionescu de la Brad. Lucrari Stiintifice, Seria Zootechnie - Medicina Veterinaria
0075-353X Universitatea "Al. I. Cuza" din Iasi. Analele Stiintifice. Sectiunea 3b: Stiinte Filozofice *see* 0379-7856
0075-3548 Jawaharlal Nehru University. School of International Studies Series
0075-3556 Jazz Catalogue†
0075-3572 Jazzforschung
0075-3580 Jean-Paul-Gesellschaft. Jahrbuch
0075-3599 Jefferson Memorial Lecture Series†
0075-3602 Jehovah's Witnesses Yearbook
0075-3610 Jerome Lectures
0075-3629 Jersey Herd Book and Directory of the U.K. *changed to* Jersey Herd Book and Members Directory.
0075-3637 Hebrew University of Jerusalem. Authority for Research Report. Medicine, Pharmacy, Dental Medicine *see* 0333-6964
0075-3645 Hebrew University of Jerusalem. Authority for Research and Development. Research Report: Humanities, Social Sciences, Law, Education, Social Work, Library *see* 0333-6964
0075-3653 Hebrew University of Jerusalem. Authority for Research and Development. Research Report. Science and Agriculture *see* 0333-6964
0075-3661 Hebrew University of Jerusalem. Folklore Research Center. Studies
0075-3696 Jerusalem Symposia on Quantum Chemistry and Biochemistry
0075-3726 Jewish Book Annual
0075-3734 Jewish Federations, Welfare Funds and Community Councils Directory *see* 0161-2638
0075-3742 Jewish Social Service Yearbook†
0075-3750 Jewish Travel Guide
0075-3769 Jewish Year Book
0075-3777 Jobson's Mining Year Book
0075-3785 Jobson's Year Book of Public Companies
0075-3793 Johannesburg Stock Exchange. Handbook *changed to* The J S E Handbook.

ISSN

5528 ISSN INDEX

0075-3807 University of the Witwatersrand, Johannesburg. Library. Annual Report of the University Librarian
0075-3815 John Alexander Monograph Series on Various Phases of Thoracic Surgery†
0075-384X John E. Owens Memorial Foundation. Publications†
0075-3858 Johns Hopkins Oceanographic Studies
0075-3866 Johns Hopkins Series in Integration and Community Building in Eastern Europe†
0075-3874 Johns Hopkins Symposia in Comparative History
0075-3890 Johns Hopkins University Studies in Geology
0075-3904 Johns Hopkins University Studies in Historical and Political Science
0075-3912 Johnson Photographic Year Book
0075-3920 Johnsonia
0075-3939 Joint Automatic Control Conference. Record *changed to* American Control Conference. Conference Proceedings.
0075-3947 Joint Center for Urban Studies. Publications
0075-3963 Joint F A O - W H O Expert Committee on Food Additives Report†
0075-3971 Joint F A O/W H O Expert Committee on Nutrition. Report†
0075-4005 Ahmedabad Textile Industry's Research Association. Joint Technological Conferences. Proceedings
0075-4013 Jordan. Department of Statistics. Annual Statistical Yearbook
0075-4021 Jordan. Department of Statistics. External Trade Statistics
0075-403X Sweden. Sveriges Geologiska Undersoekning. Jordmagnetiska Publikationer
0075-4056 Jouets et Jeux
0075-4072 Journal de Biologie et de Medicine Nucleaires†
0075-4080 Journal des Oiseaux *changed to* Journal des Oiseaux.
0075-4099 Journal for the Protection of All Beings†
0075-4102 Journal fuer die Reine und Angewandte Mathematik
0075-4110 Journal of Ancient Indian History
0075-4129 Journal of Animal Science. Supplement *changed to* Journal of Animal Science. Supplement. Biennial Symposium on Animal Reproduction.
0075-4145 Journal of Behavioural Science *see* 0081-2463
0075-4161 Journal of Byelorussian Studies†
0075-417X Journal of Child Psychotherapy
0075-4188 Journal of Civil Procedure
0075-4196 Journal of Commerce Annual Review†
0075-4218 Journal of Croatian Studies
0075-4242 Journal of English Linguistics
0075-4250 Journal of Glass Studies
0075-4269 Journal of Hellenic Studies
0075-4277 Journal of Juristic Papyrology
0075-4285 Journal of Maltese Studies
0075-4293 Journal of Mathematics
0075-4307 Journal of Natural Science
0075-4315 Journal of Nuclear Medicine. Supplement†
0075-4323 Journal of Neuro-Visceral Relations. Supplement *see* 0303-6995
0075-4331 Journal of Periodontal Research. Supplementum†
0075-434X Journal of Rhodesian History *changed to* Zimbabwean History.
0075-4358 Journal of Roman Studies
0075-4366 Hiroshima University. Journal of Science. Series B. Division 2. Botany
0075-4374 Hiroshima University. Journal of Science. Series C. Geology and Mineralogy
0075-4390 Journal of the Warburg and Courtauld Institutes
0075-4412 Journalism Abstracts
0075-4420 Journee de Reeducation *see* 0755-3951
0075-4439 Journees Annuelles de Diabetologie de l'Hotel Dieu
0075-4447 Journees Biochimiques Latines. Rapports
0075-4455 Journees de Physiologie Appliquee au Travail Humain
0075-4463 Acquisitions Medicales Recentes.†
0075-4501 Judean Desert Studies
0075-4528 Jugendherbergs-Verzeichnis
0075-4536 Yugoslovenska Investiciona Banka. Annual Report *changed to* Investbanka. Annual Report.
0075-4544 Sir Moses Montefiore Collections des Juifs Celebres†
0075-4552 Junior College Directory *changed to* A A C J C Statistical Yearbook.
0075-4579 Juntendo University. Medical Ultrasonics Research Center. Annual Report
0075-4587 An Interlibrary Loan Service Newsletter *changed to* Just B'twx Us: An Interlibrary Loan Information Bulletin.
0075-4609 Universitaet Giessen. Ergebnisse Landwirtschaftlicher Forschung
0075-4617 Justus Liebigs Annalen der Chemie *see* 0170-2041
0075-4625 Jyvaskyla Studies in Education, Psychology and Social Research
0075-4633 Jyvaskyla Studies in the Arts
0075-4641 Jyvaskylan Yliopisto. Matematiikan Laitos. Report
0075-465X Jyvaskylan Yliopisto. Department of Physics. Research Report *changed to* University of Jyvaskyla. Department of Physics. Preprints.
0075-4684 Kalastuspaikkaopas *changed to* Suomen Kalapaikkaopas.
0075-4722 Makerere University. Department of Geography. Occasional Paper
0075-4730 Makerere University. Faculty of Agriculture. Handbook
0075-4773 Makerere University. Faculty of Agriculture. Technical Bulletin
0075-4781 Makerere University. Faculty of Law. Handbook
0075-4854 Makerere University. Library. Makerere Library Publications
0075-4900 Kansainvalinen Automatkailu *see* 0355-2896
0075-4919 Kansas Linguistics Conference. Papers *changed to* Mid-America Linguistics Conference. Papers.
0075-4927 Kansas Geological Survey. Computer Contribution†
0075-4935 Kansas Geological Survey. Short Papers in Research†
0075-4951 Kansas State University. Library Bibliography Series
0075-4986 University of Kansas. Center for Latin American Studies. Graduate Studies on Latin America†
0075-4994 University of Kansas. Department of Geology. Special Publications†
0075-5001 University of Kansas Libraries. Library Series.
0075-501X University of Kansas. Museum of Art. Miscellaneous Publications *changed to* University of Kansas. Spencer Museum of Art. Miscellaneous Publications.
0075-5028 University of Kansas. Museum of Natural History. Miscellaneous Publications
0075-5036 University of Kansas. Museum of Natural History. Publications. *changed to* University of Kansas. Museum of Natural History. Museum Series Publications.
0075-5044 University of Kansas. Paleontological Contributions. Articles *see* 1046-8390
0075-5052 University of Kansas. Paleontological Contributions. Papers. *see* 1046-8390
0075-5060 Kappa Tau Alpha Yearbook†
0075-5079 Karachi. Chamber of Commerce and Industry. Annual Report
0075-5095 Karachi Law Journal†
0075-5109 Karachi Port Trust. Year Book of Information, Port of Karachi, Pakistan
0075-5125 Wyzsza Szkola Ekonomiczna. Zeszyty Naukowe *see* 0208-7944
0075-5133 Staatliche Kunsthalle Karlsruhe. Bildhefte
0075-5141 Staatliche Kunsthalle Karlsruhe. Graphik-Schriftenreihe
0075-515X Karnatak University, Dharwad, India. Journal. Humanities
0075-5168 Karnatak University, Dharwad, India. Journal. Science
0075-5176 Karnatak University, Dharwad, India. Journal. Social Sciences
0075-5184 Kathargo. Collection Epigraphique *see* 0453-3429
0075-5192 Kasetsart Journal
0075-5222 Kasmera
0075-5230 Katalog Fauny Pasozytniczej Polski
0075-5257 Katalog Zabytkow Sztuki w Polsce
0075-5265 Katherine Asher Engel Lectures
0075-5281 Wyzsza Szkola Pedagogiczna, Katowice. Zeszyty Naukowe. Sekcja Jezykoznawstwa†
0075-529X Kazakhskii Nauchno-Issledovatel'skii Institut Onkologii i Radiologii. Trudy
0075-5303 Keeping Track, Current News from the Department of Agricultural Economics at Purdue†
0075-5311 Keepsake (Davis)
0075-532X Keilschrifturkunden aus Boghazkoei
0075-5346 Keio Monographs of Business and Commerce
0075-5354 Kekkaku No Kenkyu *changed to* Hokkaido University. Institute of Immunological Science. Bulletin.
0075-5370 Kelly's Manufacturers and Merchants Directory *see* 0269-9265
0075-5389 Kelly's Post Office London Directory *see* 0266-3791
0075-5397 A Kemia Ujabb Eredmenyei
0075-5400 Kempe's Engineers Year-Book
0075-5419 Kemps Directory†
0075-5427 Kemps Film and Television Year Book (International) *changed to* Kemps International Film and Television Year Book.
0075-5443 Kemp's Jersey Holiday Guide†
0075-5451 Kemps Music and Record Industry Year Book *changed to* Kemps International Music Book.
0075-546X Kent Studies in Anthropology and Archaeology†
0075-5494 Kentucky Directory of Manufacturers
0075-5508 Kentucky Folklore Series†
0075-5516 Kentucky Industrial Directory *see* 0075-5494
0075-5524 Kentucky Nature Studies†
0075-5532 Kentucky Personal Income *changed to* Kentucky Personal Income Report.
0075-5559 Kentucky Geological Survey. Series 11. Bulletin
0075-5567 Kentucky Geological Survey. Series 11. County Report
0075-5575 Kentucky Geological Survey. Guidebook to Geological Field Trips
0075-5583 Kentucky Geological Survey. Series 11. Information Circular
0075-5591 Kentucky Geological Survey. Series 11. Report of Investigations
0075-5605 Kentucky Geological Survey. Series 11. Reprints
0075-5613 Kentucky Geological Survey. Series 11. Special Publication
0075-5621 Kentucky Geological Survey. Series 11. Thesis Series
0075-5761 K I A Occasional Papers
0075-580X Kenya. Mines and Geological Department. Annual Report†
0075-5818 Kenya. Ministry of Economic Planning and Development. Statistics Division. Development Estimates *changed to* Kenya. Central Bureau of Statistics. Development Estimates.
0075-5826 Kenya. Ministry of Economic Planning and Development. Estimates of Revenue Expenditures *changed to* Kenya. Central Bureau of Statistics. Estimates of Revenue Expenditures.
0075-5834 Kenya. Ministry of Economic Planning and Development. Statistics Division. Estimates of Recurrent Expenditures *changed to* Kenya. Central Bureau of Statistics. Estimates of Recurrent Expenditures.
0075-5842 Kenya. Ministry of Economic Planning and Development. Economic Survey *changed to* Kenya. Central Bureau of Statistics. Economic Survey.
0075-5850 Kenya. Ministry of Economic Planning and Development. Statistics Division. Statistical Abstract *changed to* Kenya. Central Bureau of Statistics. Statistical Abstract.
0075-5869 Kenya. Ministry of Education. Annual Report
0075-5877 Kenya. Ministry of Health and Housing. Annual Report *changed to* Kenya. Ministry of Housing. Annual Report.
0075-5885 Kenya. Ministry of Information. Annual Report *changed to* Kenya. Ministry of Information and Broadcasting. Annual Report.
0075-5915 Kenya. National Irrigation Board. Reports and Accounts
0075-5923 Kenya. National Library Service Board. Annual and Audit Report
0075-5931 Kenya. Public Accounts Committee. Annual Report
0075-594X Kenya. Public Service Commission. Annual Report
0075-5966 Keswick Week†
0075-5974 Kew Bulletin
0075-5982 Kew Bulletin. Additional Series
0075-5990 Canadian Electronics Engineering Annual Buyers' Guide and Catalog Directory *see* 0008-3461
0075-6008 Keys to Music Bibliography†
0075-6016 Khosla's Industrial and Commercial Directory of India, Afghanistan, Burma, Ceylon, Japan and Foreign
0075-6032 Kierkegaardiana
0075-6040 Kime's International Law Directory
0075-6067 Kinetics and Mechanisms of Polymerization†
0075-6083 Kings of Tomorrow Series
0075-6091 Queen's University at Kingston. Department of Electrical Engineering. Research Report
0075-6113 Queen's University at Kingston. Douglas Library. Occasional Papers
0075-6121 Queen's University. Engineering Society. Proceedings†
0075-613X Queen's University at Kingston. Industrial Relations Centre. Bibliography Series
0075-6148 Queen's University at Kingston. Industrial Relations Centre. Report of Activities†
0075-6156 Queen's University at Kingston. Industrial Relations Centre. Reprint Series†
0075-6164 Queen's University. Industrial Relations Centre. Research Series *see* 0317-2546
0075-6199 Kirchenmusikalisches Jahrbuch
0075-6202 Kirchenreform†
0075-6210 Kirchliches Jahrbuch fuer die Evangelische Kirche in Deutschland
0075-6229 Kirin Brewery Company, Tokyo. Research Laboratory. Report *changed to* Technical Report of Kirin.
0075-6245 Kirtlandia
0075-6261 Kjelberg och S A B Schriften *see* 0039-7083
0075-627X Klasings Bootsmarkt International; Yachten und Boote Zubehoer, Ausruestung, Motoren
0075-6288 Klassieken Nederlandse Letterkunde†

ISSN

ISSN INDEX 5529

0075-6318 Kleine Deutsche Prosadenkmaeler des Mittelalters
0075-6326 Kleine Museumshefte
0075-6334 Klio
0075-6342 Klucze do Oznaczania Kregowcow Polski†
0075-6350 Klucze do Oznaczania Owadow Polski
0075-6369 Kniznicny Zbornik
0075-6385 Knotty Problems of Baseball
0075-6407 Kobe Economic and Business Review
0075-6415 Kobe Economic and Business Research Series
0075-6423 Kobe University Law Review. International Edition
0075-6431 Kobe Daigaku Igakubu Kiyo
0075-6458 Koedoe
0075-6466 Koedoe. Monographs
0075-6474 Koehlers Flottenkalender. Jahrbuch fuer Schiffahrt und Haefen
0075-6482 Koeln
0075-6490 Koelner Ethnologische Mitteilungen†
0075-6512 Koelner Jahrbuch fuer Vor- und Fruehgeschichte
0075-6520 Koelner Romanistische Arbeiten
0075-6547 Koleopterologische Rundschau
0075-6555 Kolloid-Gesellschaft. Verhandlungsberichtet†
0075-6563 Kolloquium ueber Spaetantike und Fruehmittelalterliche Skulptur
0075-6601 Kommunikation und Kybernetik in Einzeldarstellungen *see* 0340-0034
0075-661X Kompass Danmark
0075-6628 Kompass Australia *changed to* Kompass Australia.
0075-6636 Kompass Belgium - Luxembourg *changed to* Kompass Belgium.
0075-6652 Annuaire Industriel. Repertoire General de la Production Francaise *changed to* La France de l'Industrie et ses Services.
0075-6660 Kompass Holland
0075-6679 Kompass Hong Kong†
0075-6687 Kompass Italia
0075-6695 Kompass Maroc
0075-6709 Kompass Norge
0075-6717 Kompass Schweiz - Liechtenstein
0075-6725 Kompass Sverige
0075-6733 Kompass United Kingdom - C B I *changed to* Kompass United Kingdom.
0075-6741 Koninklijk Nederlands Geologisch Mijnbouwkundig Genootschap. Verhandelingen
0075-675X Konjunkturberichte ueber das Handwerk *see* 0341-0978
0075-6768 Konstruktionsbuecher
0075-6776 Kontrollraadet foer Betongvaror. Meddelandet
0075-6784 Konyvtartudomanyi Tanulmanyok†
0075-6792 Koranyi Sandor Tarsasag. Tudomanyos Ulesek
0075-6806 Korea Development Bank: Its Functions and Activities
0075-6814 Korea Directory
0075-6822 Korea (Republic). National Bureau of Statistics. Annual Report on the Family Income and Expenditure Survey *changed to* Korea (Republic). National Statistical Office. Annual Report on the Family Income and Expenditure Survey.
0075-6830 Korea (Republic). National Bureau of Statistics. Annual Report on the Price Survey *changed to* Korea (Republic). National Statistical Office. Annual Report on the Price Survey.
0075-6849 Korea (Republic). National Bureau of Statistics. Report on Mining and Manufacturing Survey *changed to* Korea (Republic). National Statistical Office. Report on Mining and Manufacturing Survey.
0075-6857 Korea (Republic). National Bureau of Statistics. Wholesale and Retail Trade Census Report†
0075-6865 Korea (Republic). Office of Rural Development. Agricultural Research Report *changed to* Korea (Republic). Office of Rural Development. Research Report.
0075-6873 Korea Statistical Yearbook
0075-6881 Korean Publications Yearbook
0075-6911 Korosi Csoma Kiskonyvtar
0075-6938 Korrosion†
0075-6946 Korunk Tudomanya
0075-6954 Kosten en Financiering van de Gezondheidzorg in Nederland
0075-6962 Koszen es Koolaj Anyagismereti Monografiak†
0075-6970 Kothari's World of Reference Works
0075-6989 Kozgazdasagi Ertekezesek
0075-7004 Akademia Gorniczo-Hutnicza im. Stanislawa Staszica. Zeszyty Naukowe. Hutnictwo†
0075-7012 Akademia Gorniczo-Hutnicza im. Stanislawa Staszica. Instytut Ceramiki Specjalnej i Ogniotrwalej. Prace Naukowe *changed to* Akademia Gorniczo-Hutnicza im. Stanislawa Staszica. Zeszyty Naukowe. Ceramika.
0075-7020 Krakow Dawniej i Dzis
0075-7039 Muzeum Archeologiczne, Krakow. Materialy Archeologiczne†
0075-7047 Obserwatorium Krakowskie. Rocznik Astronomiczny. Dodatek Miedzynarodowy
0075-7055 Politechnika Krakowska. Zeszyty Naukowe. Chemia *changed to* Politechnika Krakowska. Zeszyty Naukowe. Inzynieria i Technologia Chemiczna.
0075-7071 Krankenhaus-Apotheke *see* 0173-7597
0075-708X Krankenhaus-Probleme der Gegenwart†
0075-7098 Krebsforschung und Krebsbekaempfung†
0075-7101 Beitraege zur Kardiologie und Angiologie†
0075-7136 Kriminologische Gegenwartsfragen
0075-7144 Kriminologie. Abhandlungen ueber abwegiges Sozialverhalten
0075-7152 Kriminologische Abhandlungen†
0075-7160 Kryptadia: Journal of Erotic Folklore
0075-7179 Ksiazka w Dawnej Kulturze Polskiej
0075-7209 Kulturpflanze
0075-7217 Kumamoto University. Institute of Constitutional Medicine. Bulletin. Supplement
0075-7225 University of Science and Technology. Journal
0075-7233 Kungliga Skogs- och Lantbruksakademiens Tidskrift. Supplement *issued with* 0023-5350
0075-7241 Kunst-Katalog: Auktionen
0075-725X Kunst und Altertum am Rhein
0075-7268 Kunstdenkmaeler des Rheinlandes. Beiheft†
0075-7276 Kunststoff Industrie und ihre Helfer
0075-7292 Kunststoffe im Lebensmittelverkehr
0075-7306 Kuratorium fuer Verkehrssicherheit. Kleine Fachbuchreihe
0075-7314 Kurtziana
0075-7322 Kurzauszuege Oesterreichischer Dissertationen: Geistes- und Sozialwissenschaften†
0075-7330 Kurzuaszuege Oesterreichischer Dissertationen: Naturwissenschaften und Technik†
0075-7349 Kush
0075-7357 Kyoto University. Institute for Virus Research. Annual Report
0075-7365 Kyoto University. Research Activities in Civil Engineering and Related Fields
0075-7373 Kyoto Prefectural University. Scientific Reports: Agriculture
0075-7381 Kyoto-furitsu Daigaku Gakujutsu Hokoku: Jinbun
0075-739X Kyoto Prefectural University. Scientific Reports: Natural Science, Domestic Science and Social Welfare *changed to* Kyoto-furitsu Daigaku Gakujutsu Hokoku. Rigaku Seikatsu Kagaku.
0075-7403 Universidad Nacional Agraria. Programa Cooperativo de Investigaciones en Maiz. Boletin†
0075-742X Universidad Nacional de la Plata. Instituto de Estudios Sociales y del Pensamiento Argentino. Cuadernos de Extension Universitaria†
0075-7446 Lab World. Labstracts. Annual Reference Guide†
0075-7470 University of Pennsylvania. Wharton School of Finance and Commerce. Labor Relations and Public Policy Series. Reports *changed to* Labor Relations and Public Policy Series.
0075-7489 Labor Relations Yearbook†
0075-7500 Laboratory Guide†
0075-7535 Laboratory Techniques in Biochemistry and Molecular Biology
0075-756X Labour Literature: A Bibliography†
0075-7578 Directory of Labour Organizations in Canada
0075-7586 Labour Standards in Canada - Normes du Travail au Canada *changed to* Employment Standards Legislation in Canada.
0075-7608 Lafayette Clinic Handbooks in Psychiatry†
0075-7616 Lafayette Clinic Monographs in Psychiatry†
0075-7624 National Library of Nigeria. Annual Report
0075-7632 National Library of Nigeria. National Library Occasional Publication
0075-7640 Lagos Notes and Records†
0075-7659 University of Lagos. Inaugural Lecture Series
0075-7667 University of Lagos. Continuing Education Centre. Occasional Papers†
0075-7675 University of Lagos. Humanities Series
0075-7691 University of Lagos. Law Series†
0075-7705 University of Lagos. Library. Annual Report
0075-7713 University of Lagos. Scientific Monograph Series
0075-7721 Universidad de la Laguna. Facultad de Ciencias. Anales
0075-773X Universidad de la Laguna. Facultad de Derecho. Anales
0075-7748 Lake Carriers' Association. Annual Report
0075-7772 Lamar Lecture Series
0075-7780 Lammergeyer
0075-7799 Lancashire Dialect Society. Journal
0075-7810 University of Lancaster. Library. Occasional Papers†
0075-7837 Land Economics Monographs
0075-7853 Landbrukets Aarbok. Jordbruk, Hagebruk, Skogbruk
0075-7861 Landbrukets Aarbok. Skogbruk *see* 0075-7853
0075-787X Landolt-Boernstein, Zahlenwerte und Funktionen aus Naturwissenschaften und Technik. Neue Serie. Group 3: Crystal Physics
0075-7888 Landolt-Boernstein, Zahlenwerte und Funktionen aus Naturwissenschaften und Technik. Neue Serie. Group 1: Nuclear Physics
0075-7896 Landolt-Boernstein, Zahlenwerte und Funktionen aus Naturwissenschaften und Technik. Neue Serie. Group 6: Astronomy
0075-790X Landolt-Boernstein, Zahlenwerte und Funktionen aus Naturwissenschaften und Technik. Neue Serie. Group 5: Geophysics
0075-7918 Landolt-Boernstein, Zahlenwerte und Funktionen aus Naturwissenschaften und Technik. Neue Serie. Group 2: Atomic Physics
0075-7926 Landolt-Boernstein, Zahlenwerte und Funktionen aus Naturwissenschaften und Technik. Neue Serie. Group 4: Macroscopic and Technical Properties of Matter
0075-7942 Landschaftsverband Westfalen-Lippe. Volkskundliche Kommission. Schriften *changed to* Volkskuendlichen Kommission fuer Westfalen. Schriften.
0075-7950 Language Monographs†
0075-7969 Leading Science Monographs†
0075-7993 Langues et Litteratures de l'Afrique Noire†
0075-8019 Lares. Biblioteca
0075-8027 Laser Focus Buyers' Guide *changed to* Laser Focus World Buyers' Guide.
0075-8035 Lasers: A Series of Advances†
0075-8108 Latin American Monographs
0075-8124 Latin American Political Guide†
0075-8132 University of California, Los Angeles. Latin American Center. Latin American Studies Series
0075-8140 University of Pittsburgh. Center for International Studies: Latin American Studies. Occasional Papers *changed to* University of Pittsburgh. Center for International Studies. Latin American Reprint Series.
0075-8159 Latin American Travel and Pan American Highway Guide *changed to* Latin American Travel Guide & Pan American Highway Guide (Mexico-Central-South America).
0075-8167 Latin American Urban Research†
0075-8175 Latin Language Mathematicians Group. Actes et Travaux du Congres†
0075-8191 Universite de Lausanne. Ecole des Sciences Sociales et Politiques. Publications†
0075-8213 World Legal Directory†
0075-8221 Law Books in Print
0075-823X Law in Eastern Europe
0075-8256 Law Reprints. Trade Regulation Series *changed to* Law Reprints: Trade Regulation Series.
0075-8264 Prelaw Handbook. Official Law School Guide *see* 0886-3342
0075-8272 Lazy Man's Guide to Holidays Afloat
0075-8310 Leading Advertisers in Business Publications†
0075-8329 Leahy's Hotel-Motel Guide and Travel Atlas†
0075-8337 Learning Disorders†
0075-8345 Leather Buyers Guide and Leather Trade Marks†
0075-8353 Lebanese Industrial and Commercial Directory
0075-8361 Year-Book of the Lebanese Joint-Stock Companies
0075-837X Lebanon. Direction Centrale de la Statistique. Comptes Economiques
0075-8388 Lebanon. Direction Centrale de la Statistique. Recueil de Statistiques Libanaises
0075-8396 LeBaron Russell Briggs Prize Honors Essays in English
0075-8418 Lebensdarstellungen Deutscher Naturforscher†
0075-8434 Lecture Notes in Mathematics
0075-8442 Lecture Notes in Economics and Mathematical Systems
0075-8450 Lecture Notes in Physics
0075-8469 Lecture Notes in Pure and Applied Mathematics
0075-8485 Lectures in Applied Mathematics
0075-8493 Lectures in Biblical Studies†
0075-8523 Lectures on Mathematics in the Life Sciences
0075-8531 Lectures on the History of Religions. New Series
0075-854X University of Leeds. Institute of Education. Papers†
0075-8558 University of Leeds. Research Institute of African Geology. Annual Report†
0075-8566 Leeds Studies in English
0075-8574 Leeds Texts and Monographs. New Series
0075-8582 Legal Almanac Series *changed to* Oceana's Legal Almanacs, Second Series.

ISSN

5530 ISSN INDEX

ISSN

0075-8590 Legal Medicine Annual *see* 0197-9981

0075-8612 Lehrer-Briefe zur Verkehrserziehung *changed to* Praxis Verkehrserziehung.

0075-8620 Leicester University Geographical Journal *changed to* Confluence.

0075-8639 Leidse Geologische Mededelingen†

0075-8655 Sportmedizinische Schriftenreihe

0075-8663 Museum fuer Voelkerkunde, Leipzig. Jahrbuch

0075-8671 Museum fuer Voelkerkunde, Leipzig. Veroeffentlichungen

0075-871X Leitende Maenner der Wirtschaft *changed to* Leitende Maenner und Frauen der Wirtschaft.

0075-8728 Stamm Leitfaden Durch Presse und Werbung

0075-8736 Lekarske Prace

0075-8744 Leo Baeck Institute. Year Book

0075-8760 Leonardo

0075-8779 Lepetit Colloquia on Biology and Medicine. Proceedings†

0075-8787 Lepidoptera

0075-8795 Lepidopterists' Society. Memoirs

0075-8809 Leprosy Mission, London. Annual Report

0075-8817 Lesotho. Treasury. Report on the Finances and Accounts

0075-8825 Lessico Intellettuale Europeo

0075-8833 Lessing Yearbook

0075-8841 Letopis Pamatnika Slovenskej Literatury *changed to* Literarno - Muzejny Letopis.

0075-8868 Let's Go: The Student Guide to Europe *see* 0163-4585

0075-8892 Lettere Italiane. Biblioteca

0075-8906 La Lettre†

0075-8914 Levant

0075-8922 Lewis Henry Morgan Lectures†

0075-8949 Leybold-Kontakt *changed to* Contact.

0075-8957 Liaisons Financieres en France *changed to* Les Liaisons Financieres.

0075-8973 Librarians, Censorship and Intellectual Freedom†

0075-8981 Libraries in Nigeria: A Directory

0075-899X Libraries, Museums and Art Galleries Year Book *changed to* Libraries Directory.

0075-9007 Library and Documentation Journals†

0075-9031 Library Association. Library History Group. Occasional Publication†

0075-904X Library Association of Alberta. Occasional Papers *changed to* Library Association of Alberta. Newsletter.

0075-9058 Library Association. Reference, Special and Information Section. North Western Group. Occasional Papers†

0075-9066 Library Association. Yearbook

0075-9074 Library Buildings *see* 0307-9767

0075-9082 Library Journal Book Review†

0075-9104 Library of Exact Philosophy

0075-9120 Library of Law and Contemporary Problems

0075-9201 Libros y Material de Ensenanza

0075-921X Bank of Libya. Balance of Payments

0075-9228 Libya. Census and Statistics Department. External Trade Statistics

0075-9236 Libya. Census and Statistics Department. General Population Census

0075-9244 Libya. Census and Statistics Department. Industrial Census

0075-9252 Libya. Census and Statistics Department. Report of the Annual Survey of Large Manufacturing Establishments

0075-9260 Libya. Census and Statistics Department. Report of the Annual Survey of Petroleum Mining Industry

0075-9279 Libya. Census and Statistics Department. Report of the Survey of Licensed Construction Units

0075-9287 Libya. Census and Statistics Department. Statistical Abstract

0075-9295 Libya. Census and Statistics Department. Wholesale Prices in Tripoli Town

0075-9309 Libyan Travel Series *changed to* Libya Past and Present Series.

0075-9325 Lick Observatory. Publications

0075-9333 Universite de Liege. Faculte des Sciences Appliquees. Collection des Publications

0075-9341 Universite de Liege. Institut de Pharmacie. Recueil des Conferences Organisees Par le Cercle A. Gilkinet *changed to* Journee Scientifique de Mars. Conferences et Communications.

0075-935X Universite de Liege. Institut de Pharmacie. Travaux Publies†

0075-9368 Universite de Liege. Laboratoire d'Analyse Statistique des Langues Anciennes. Travaux Publies†

0075-9376 Lieux et les Dieux†

0075-9384 Life around Us: A Commercial Directory†

0075-9406 Life Insurance Fact Book

0075-9414 Life Insurers Conference. Annual Meeting. Proceedings†

0075-9422 Life Sciences and Space Research *see* 0273-1177

0075-9457 Lightweight Concrete Information Sheets

0075-9465 Ligue Antituberculeuse de Quebec. Rapport

0075-9473 Institut de Medecine Legale et de Medecine Sociale. Archives†

0075-9481 Lilloa

0075-949X Lilies and Other Liliaceae†

0075-9511 Limnologica

0075-9554 Lindley Lecture

0075-9597 Linguistic Circle of Manitoba and North Dakota. Proceedings

0075-9600 Linguistic Society of America. Meeting Handbooks

0075-9627 Linguistic Society of India. Bulletin

0075-9635 Linguistic Structures†

0075-9643 Academy of the Hebrew Language. Linguistic Studies *changed to* Academy of the Hebrew Language. Texts & Studies.

0075-9651 Linguistics in Documentation; Current Abstracts†

0075-9686 Linguistische Reihe†

0075-9724 Linzer Hochschulschriften *changed to* Linzer Universitaetsschriften.

0075-9732 Linzer Jahrbuch fuer Kunstgeschichte *changed to* Kunstjahrbuch der Stadt Linz.

0075-9740 Hebrew University of Jerusalem. Lionel Cohen Lectures

0075-9759 L P - Gas Market Facts *changed to* Propane Industry Profile.

0075-9767 Lisbon. Escola Nacional de Saude de Medicina Tropical. Anais *see* 0303-7762

0075-9775 Lisbon. Universidade. Faculdade de Ciencias. Revista. Serie 2. Seccao B. Ciencias Fisicq-Quimicas†

0075-9813 List Bio-Med; Biomedical Serials in Scandinavian Libraries

0075-9821 L I S T†

0075-983X List of Grants and Awards Available to American Writers *see* 0092-5268

0075-9872 Literarny Archiv

0075-9880 Literary and Library Prizes†

0075-9899 Names and Numbers *see* 0161-2905

0075-9902 Literary Monographs

0075-9929 Literary Prizes in Pakistan

0075-9937 Literatur und Wirklichkeit

0075-9945 Literatura Piekna. Adnotowany Rocznik Bibliograficzny

0075-9961 Literatures of the World in English Translation: A Bibliography†

0075-997X Literaturwissenschaftliches Jahrbuch. Neue Folge

0075-9988 Litomericko

0075-9996 Litterature. Science. Ideologie. *see* 0335-9190

0076-0013 Little Red Book, Classified to All Public Transport Fleet Owners and Operators and Vehicle Manufacturers

0076-003X University of Notre Dame. Department of Theology. Liturgical Studies

0076-0048 Liturgiewissenschaftliche Quellen und Forschungen

0076-0072 Living History of the World†

0076-0080 Living Word Commentary†

0076-0102 Livre Contemporain et les Bibliophiles Francosuisses†

0076-0110 Livre de Langue Francaise - Repertoire des Editeurs *changed to* Repertoire International des Editeurs et Diffuseurs de Langue Francaise.

0076-0129 Livre et Societes†

0076-0137 Bulletin Bibliographique Thematique

0076-0145 Livres de l'Annee/BIBLIO†

0076-0153 Livres et Auteurs Quebecois†

0076-0188 Llen Cymru

0076-0196 Lloyd's Calendar and Nautical Yearbook *see* 0952-5394

0076-020X Lloyd's Maritime Atlas

0076-0226 Lloyd's Register of American Yachts *see* 0163-285X

0076-0234 Lloyd's Register of Shipping. Statistical Tables

0076-0242 Local Government Reports of Australia

0076-0269 Locations of Industries in Gujarat State

0076-0277 Lockwood's Directory of the Paper and Allied Trades *changed to* Lockwood - Post's Directory of the Pulp, Paper and Allied Trades.

0076-0285 Locomotive Maintenance Officers Association. Annual Proceedings

0076-0293 Locomotive Maintenance Officers Association. Preconvention Report

0076-0315 Muzeum Archeologiczne i Etnograficzne, Lodz. Prace i Materialy. Seria Etnograficzna

0076-0323 Politechnika Lodzka. Zeszyty Naukowe. Budownictwo

0076-0331 Politechnika Lodzka. Zeszyty Naukowe. Wlokiennictwo

0076-034X Uniwersytet Lodzki. Prace

0076-0358 Uniwersytet Lodzki. Zeszyty Naukowe. Seria 1: Nauki Humanistyczno-Spoleczne *see* 0208-6093

0076-0358 Uniwersytet Lodzki. Zeszyty Naukowe. Seria 1: Nauki Humanistyczno-Spoleczne *see* 0208-6069

0076-0358 Uniwersytet Lodzki. Zeszyty Naukowe. Seria 1: Nauki Humanistyczno-Spoleczne *see* 0208-6050

0076-0358 Uniwersytet Lodzki. Zeszyty Naukowe. Seria 1: Nauki Humanistyczno-Spoleczne *see* 0208-6107

0076-0358 Uniwersytet Lodzki. Zeszyty Naukowe. Seria 1: Nauki Humanistyczno-Spoleczne *see* 0208-6034

0076-0358 Uniwersytet Lodzki. Zeszyty Naukowe. Seria 1: Nauki Humanistyczno-Spoleczne *see* 0208-6077

0076-0358 Uniwersytet Lodzki. Zeszyty Naukowe. Seria 1: Nauki Humanistyczno-Spoleczne *see* 0208-6085

0076-0366 Uniwersytet Lodzki. Zeszyty Naukowe. Seria 2: Nauki Matematyczno-Przyrodnicze *see* 0208-6204

0076-0366 Uniwersytet Lodzki. Zeszyty Naukowe. Seria 2: Nauki Matematyczno-Przyrodnicze *see* 0208-6190

0076-0366 Uniwersytet Lodzki. Zeszyty Naukowe. Seria 2: Nauki Matematyczno-Przyrodnicze *see* 0208-6182

0076-0366 Uniwersytet Lodzki. Zeszyty Naukowe. Seria 2: Nauki Matematyczno-Przyrodnicze *see* 0208-6174

0076-0366 Uniwersytet Lodzki. Zeszyty Naukowe. Seria 2: Nauki Matematyczno-Przyrodnicze *see* 0208-6166

0076-0366 Uniwersytet Lodzki. Zeszyty Naukowe. Seria 2: Nauki Matematyczno-Przyrodnicze *see* 0208-614X

0076-0366 Uniwersytet Lodzki. Zeszyty Naukowe. Seria 2: Nauki Matematyczno-Przyrodnicze *see* 0208-6158

0076-0366 Uniwersytet Lodzki. Zeszyty Naukowe. Seria 2: Nauki Matematyczno-Przyrodnicze *see* 0208-6123

0076-0366 Uniwersytet Lodzki. Zeszyty Naukowe. Seria 2: Nauki Matematyczno-Przyrodnicze *see* 0208-6131

0076-0366 Uniwersytet Lodzki. Zeszyty Naukowe. Seria 2: Nauki Matematyczno-Przyrodnicze *see* 0860-3111

0076-0374 Uniwersytet Lodzki. Zeszyty Naukowe. Seria 3: Nauki Ekonomiczne i Socjologiczne *see* 0208-6018

0076-0374 Uniwersytet Lodzki. Zeszyty Naukowe. Seria 3: Nauki Ekonomiczne i Socjologiczne *see* 0208-600X

0076-0382 Lodzkie Studia Etnograficzne†

0076-0390 Lodzkie Towarzystwo Naukowe. Rozprawy Komisji Jezykowej

0076-0404 Lodzkie Towarzystwo Naukowe. Prace Wydzialu Jezykoznawstwa, Nauki o Literaturze i Filozofii

0076-0412 Lodzkie Towarzystwo Naukowe. Wydzial III Nauk Matematyczno-Przyrodniczych. Prace†

0076-0420 Lodzkie Towarzystwo Naukowe. Wydzial IV. Nauk Lekarskich. Prace†

0076-0439 Lodzkie Towarzystwo Naukowe. Wydzial V. Nauk Technicznych. Prace†

0076-0447 Log (Long Beach)

0076-0455 Log of the Star Class

0076-0471 Logos†

0076-048X Loi de l'Impot sur le Revenu Canadien *changed to* Loi de l'Impot sur le Revenu du Canada et Reglements.

0076-0501 London and Middlesex Archaeological Society. Transactions

0076-051X London Bibliography of the Social Sciences†

0076-0528 London Chamber of Commerce and Industry. Annual Report and Annual Directory *see* 0142-9728

0076-0536 London Divinity Series. New Testament†

0076-0544 London History Studies

0076-0552 London Mathematical Society. Lecture Note Series

0076-0560 L M S Monographs *changed to* London Mathematical Society. Monographs.

0076-0579 London Naturalist

0076-0587 University of Western Ontario. Centre for Radio Science. Annual Report†

0076-0595 University of Western Ontario. D.B. Weldon Library. Library Bulletin

0076-0609 University of Western Ontario. Museums. Museum Bulletin†

0076-0633 London Papers in Regional Science *see* 0960-6130

0076-0641 London School of Economics and Political Science. Department of Geography. Geographical Papers†

0076-0668 L S E Research Monographs

0076-0684 Stock Exchange Official Year Book

0076-0692 University of London Historical Studies†

0076-0714 University of London Legal Series†

0076-0722 University of London. Institute of Archaeology. Bulletin *changed to* University College London. Institute of Archaeology. Bulletin.

0076-0730 University of London. Institute of Classical Studies. Bulletin

0076-0749 University of London. Institute of Classical Studies. Bulletin Supplement

0076-0765 University of London. Institute of Commonwealth Studies. Commonwealth Papers†

0076-0773 University of London. Institute of Commonwealth Studies. Collected Seminar Papers

0076-0781 University of London. Institute of Commonwealth Studies. Annual Report

0076-079X Education Libraries Bulletin Supplements

ISSN INDEX 5531

0076-0803 University of London. Institute of Germanic Studies. Library Publications
0076-0811 University of London. Institute of Germanic Studies. Publications
0076-0846 University of London. Institute of Latin American Studies. Monographs
0076-0854 University of London. Royal Postgraduate Medical School. Annual Report
0076-0862 Looking for Leisure†
0076-0870 Looking Forward†
0076-0889 Looking into Leadership Series
0076-0897 Lorentzia
0076-0900 Natural History Museum of Los Angeles County. Contributions in Science *see* 0459-8113
0076-0927 Natural History Museum of Los Angeles County. Contributions in History†
0076-0935 Science Bulletin *see* 0459-8113
0076-0943 Natural History Museum of Los Angeles County. Science Series
0076-101X Lotus
0076-1028 Louisiana Directory of Manufacturers *see* 0275-1089
0076-1044 Louisiana Tech University. Division of Life Sciences Research. Research Bulletin
0076-1052 Livestock Producer's Day Report *changed to* Animal Science Research Report.
0076-1087 Louisiana State University. Law School. Institute on Mineral Law. Proceedings
0076-1095 Louisiana State University. School of Forestry and Wildlife Management. Annual Forestry Symposium. Proceedings. *changed to* Louisiana State University. School of Forestry, Wildlife, and Fisheries. Annual Forestry Symposium. Proceedings.
0076-1109 L S U Wood Utilization Notes
0076-1168 Instituto de Investigacao Cientifica de Mocambique. Memorias. Series A (Ciencias Biologicas)†
0076-1176 Instituto de Investigacao Cientifica de Mocambique. Memorias. Serie B (Ciencias Geograficas-Geologicas)†
0076-1184 Instituto de Investigacao Cientifica de Mocambique. Memorias. Serie C (Ciencias Humanas)†
0076-1192 Centre Belge d'Histoire Rurale. Publications
0076-1206 Universite Catholique de Louvain. Centre d'Etudes Politiques. Working Group "American Foreign Policy." Cahier
0076-1214 Universite Catholique de Louvain. Ecole des Sciences Politiques et Sociales. Collection.
0076-1222 Universite Catholique de Louvain. Faculte de Philosophie et Lettres. Travaux
0076-1230 Universite Catholique de Louvain. Faculte de Theologie et de Droit Canonique. Travaux de Doctorat en Theologie et en Droit Canonique. Nouvelle Serie
0076-1249 Universite Catholique de Louvain. Institut des Langues Vivantes. Cahiers
0076-1265 Universite Catholique de Louvain. Institut Orientaliste. Publications
0076-1273 Universite Catholique de Louvain. Institut Superieur de Philosophie. Cours Publies
0076-1281 Universite Catholique de Louvain. Laboratoire de Pedagogie Experimentale. Cahiers de Recherches†
0076-129X Universite Catholique de Louvain. Section de Philologie Germanique. Serie Microfiches†
0076-1303 Universite Catholique de Louvain. Institut de Recherches Economiques, Politiques et Sociales. Publications†
0076-1311 Universite Catholique de Louvain. Recueil de Travaux d'Histoire et de Philologie
0076-132X Lovejoy's College Guide
0076-1354 Lovoe Geomagnetic Observatory Yearbook
0076-1370 International Symposium on Atomic, Molecular and Solid-State Theory and Quantum Biology. Proceedings *changed to* International Symposium on Atomic, Molecular and Solid-State Theory, Collision Phenomena and Computational Methods. Proceedings.
0076-1389 Lower Paleozoic Rocks of the New World†
0076-1400 National Botanic Gardens, Lucknow. Annual Report *changed to* National Botanic Research Institute, Lucknow. Progress Report.
0076-1419 National Botanical Research Institute, Lucknow. Bulletin†
0076-1427 Lucknow Law Journal†
0076-1435 Lud
0076-1443 Lueneburger Blaetter†
0076-1451 Lund Studies in English
0076-146X Lund Studies in Geography. Series A. Physical Geography
0076-1478 Lund Studies in Geography. Series B. Human Geography
0076-1486 Lund Studies in Geography. Series C. General and Mathematical Geography *changed to* Lund Studies in Geography. Series C. General, Mathematical and Regional Geography.
0076-1494 Lund Studies in International History
0076-1508 Lusitania Sacra
0076-1516 Lustracje Dobr Krolewskich XVI-XVIII Wieku
0076-1524 Lute Society of America. Journal
0076-1532 L E A Yearbook†
0076-1540 Lutheran World Federation. Proceedings of the Assembly†
0076-1559 Luxembourg. Ministere des Finances. Budget de l'Etat
0076-1567 Luxembourg. Office National du Travail. Rapport Annuel *changed to* Luxembourg. Administration de l'Emploi. Rapport Annuel.
0076-1575 Luxembourg. Service Central de la Statistique et des Etudes Economiques. Annuaire Statistique
0076-1583 Luxembourg. Service Central de la Statistique et des Etudes Economiques. Bulletin du STATEC
0076-1591 Luxembourg. Service Central de la Statistique et des Etudes Economiques. Collection D et M: Definitions et Methodes
0076-1613 Luxembourg. Service Central de la Statistique et des Etudes Economiques. Collection RP: Recensement de la Population *changed to* Luxembourg. Service Central de la Statistique et des Etudes Economiques. Collection RP: Recensement de la Population et Mouvement de la Population.
0076-163X Lychnos-Bibliotek. Studies och Kaellskrifter Udgivna av Laerdomshistoriska Samfundet. Studies and Sources Published by the Swedish History of Science Society
0076-1648 Lychnos-Laerdomshistoriska Samfundets Aarsbok. Annual of the Swedish History of Science Society
0076-1656 Universite Claude Bernard. Departement de Mathematiques. Publications
0076-1664 Universite de Lyon. Faculte de Droit et des Sciences Economiques. Annales *changed to* Universite Jean Moulin. Annales.
0076-1699 Lyrical Iowa
0076-1710 Sweden. Institute of Marine Research. Series Biology. Reports *see* 0346-8666
0076-1729 M L Seidman Memorial Town Hall Lecture Series
0076-1745 Asta-Press
0076-1818 Universita degli Studi di Macerata. Facolta di Lettere e Filosofia. Annali
0076-1842 McGill University, Montreal. Department of Meteorology. Publication in Meteorology†
0076-1850 McGill University, Montreal. Axel Heiberg Island Research Reports
0076-1893 McGill University, Montreal. Centre for Developing-Area Studies. Annual Report
0076-1907 McGill University, Montreal. Centre for Developing-Area Studies. Occasional Paper Series *see* 0702-8431
0076-1915 McGill University, Montreal. Centre for Developing-Area Studies. Reprint Series†
0076-1931 McGill University, Montreal. Department of Geography. Climatological Research Series
0076-1966 McGill University, Montreal. Mechanical Engineering Research Laboratories. Report
0076-1974 McGill University, Montreal. Mechanical Engineering Research Laboratories. Technical Note
0076-1982 McGill Sub-Arctic Research Papers
0076-1990 McGoldrick's Handbook of Canadian Customs Tariff and Excise Duties *see* 1183-3246
0076-2016 McGraw-Hill Yearbook of Science and Technology
0076-2032 Machine Intelligence Workshop
0076-2040 Machinery's Annual Buyer's Guide *see* 0305-3121
0076-2059 McMaster University, Hamilton, Ontario. Institute for Materials Research. Annual Report
0076-2067 MacRae's Blue Book *changed to* MacRae's Blue Book.
0076-2075 Macromolecular Chemistry (Oxford)
0076-2083 Macromolecular Reviews†
0076-2091 Macromolecular Syntheses†
0076-2105 Made in Austria
0076-213X Madison Avenue Europe†
0076-2148 Madison Avenue Handbook
0076-2156 Madison Avenue London†
0076-2164 Madison Avenue Paris†
0076-2180 Madison Avenue West Germany†
0076-2202 University of Madras. Archaeological Series
0076-2210 University of Madras. Endowment Lectures
0076-2229 University of Madras. Historical Series
0076-2237 University of Madras. Kannada Series
0076-2245 University of Madras. Malayalam Series
0076-2253 University of Madras. Philosophical Series
0076-2261 University of Madras. Sanskrit Series
0076-227X University of Madras. Tamil Series
0076-2288 University of Madras. Telugu Series
0076-2296 University of Madras. Urdu Series
0076-230X Casa de Velasquez, Madrid. Melanges
0076-2318 Real Conservatorio Superior de Musica. Anuario†
0076-2326 Maerchen der Europaeischen Voelker†
0076-2342 Magazine of Albemarle County History
0076-2350 Magenta Frog†
0076-2369 Magon. Serie Scientifique
0076-2377 Magon. Serie Technique
0076-2385 Magyar Irodalomtortenetiras Forrasai
0076-2393 Magyar Konyv†
0076-2407 Magyar Kozlony
0076-2415 Magyar Munkasmozgalmi Muzeum. Evkonyv†
0076-2423 Magyar Tudomanyos Akademia. Agrartudomanyok Osztalya. Monografiasorozat
0076-2431 Magyar Tudomanyos Akademia. Mikrobiologiai Kutato Intezet. Proceedings
0076-244X Studia Biologica Academiae Scientiarum Hungaricae
0076-2458 Studia Historica Academiae Scientiarum Hungaricae
0076-2466 Studia Philosophica Academiae Scientiarum Hungaricae†
0076-2474 Magyarorszag Allatvilaga
0076-2482 Magyarorszag Kulturfloraja
0076-2490 Magyarorszag Muemleki Topografiaja
0076-2504 Magyarorszag Regeszeti Topografiaja
0076-2512 Magyarorszag Tajfoldrajza
0076-2520 Maharaja Sayajirao University of Baroda. Department of Archaeology and Ancient History. Archaeology Series
0076-2539 An Economic Review *changed to* Economic Survey of Maharashtra.
0076-2555 Maharashtra State Budget in Brief
0076-2563 Maharashtra State Financial Corporation. Annual Report
0076-2571 Mahratta
0076-258X Maia†
0076-2636 Maine. Department of Sea and Shore Fisheries. General Bulletin *changed to* Maine. Department of Marine Resources. Fisheries Circulars.
0076-2679 Maine Pocket Data Book *see* 0093-724X
0076-2695 Maine Recreation Authority. Annual Report *changed to* Maine Guarantee Authority. Annual Report.
0076-2709 Maine That Was Series†
0076-2717 Maine Writers' Conference Chapbook†
0076-2725 Mainfraenkisches Jahrbuch fuer Geschichte und Kunst
0076-2733 Roemisch-Germanisches Zentralmuseum, Mainz. Ausstellungskataloge†
0076-2741 Roemisch-Germanisches Zentralmuseum, Mainz. Jahrbuch
0076-275X Roemisch-Germanisches Zentralmuseum, Mainz. Kataloge Vor- und Fruehgeschichtlicher Altertuemer
0076-2776 Mainzer Philosophische Forschungen
0076-2784 Mainzer Reihe
0076-2792 Mainzer Zeitschrift
0076-2806 Maison des Sciences de l'Homme. Collection de Reeditions†
0076-2814 Maisons d'Enfants et d'Adolescents de France. Album-Annuaire National
0076-289X Makedonika
0076-2989 Mala Biblioteka Baletowa
0076-2997 Malacologia
0076-3004 Malacological Review
0076-3012 Malawi Yearbook *changed to* Malawi Handbook.
0076-3020 Malawi. Accountant General. Report
0076-3047 Malawi. Department of Agriculture. Annual Report *changed to* Malawi. Department of Agricultural Research. Annual Report.
0076-3055 Malawi. Department of Civil Aviation. Annual Report
0076-3063 Malawi. Department of Customs and Excise. Annual Report†
0076-3071 Malawi. Department of Forestry and Game. Report
0076-308X Malawi. Police Force. Annual Report
0076-3101 Malawi Economic Report
0076-311X Malawi. Geological Survey Department. Annual Report
0076-3128 Malawi. Geological Survey. Bulletin†
0076-3136 Malawi. Geological Survey. Memoir†
0076-3144 Malawi. Geological Survey. Records†
0076-3152 Malawi. Judicial Department. Annual Report†
0076-3160 Malawi. Ministry of Justice. Annual Report
0076-3179 Malawi. Lands Department. Annual Report†
0076-3195 Malawi. Ministry of Finance. Budget Statement
0076-3225 Malawi. Ministry of Local Government. Annual Report
0076-3233 Malawi. Ministry of Works and Supplies. Annual Report†
0076-3241 Malawi. National Statistical Office. Annual Survey of Economic Activities

0076-325X Malawi. National Statistical Office. Annual Statement of External Trade
0076-3268 Malawi. National Statistical Office. Compendium of Statistics *changed to* Malawi Statistical Yearbook.
0076-3276 Malawi. National Statistical Office. Household Income and Expenditure Survey
0076-3284 Malawi. National Statistical Office. National Accounts Report
0076-3292 Malawi. National Statistical Office. National Sample Survey of Agriculture
0076-3306 Malawi. National Statistical Office. Population Census Final Report
0076-3314 Malawi. Office of the Auditor General. Report
0076-3322 Malawi. Post Office Savings Bank. Annual Report
0076-3330 Malawi Railways. Annual Reports and Accounts
0076-3349 Malawi. Registrar of Insurance. Report
0076-3357 Malawi Treaty Series
0076-3365 Malawi. Department of Veterinary Services and Animal Industry. Annual Report
0076-3381 National Archives of Malaysia. Annual Report
0076-339X Malaysia Year Book *changed to* Information Malaysia.
0076-3411 Mali. Service de la Statistique Generale, de la Comptabilite Nationale et de la Mecanographie. Annuaire Statistique *changed to* Mali. Direction Nationale de la Statistique et de l'Informatique. Annuaire Statistique.
0076-342X Malignant Intrigue
0076-3438 University of Lund. School of Dentistry. Faculty of Odontology. Annual Publications
0076-3446 Malta Trade Directory *changed to* Malta Trade Directory (Year).
0076-3454 Malta. Office of Statistics. Census of Agriculture *changed to* Malta. Central Office of Statistics. Census of Agriculture and Fisheries.
0076-3462 Malta. Central Office of Statistics. Census of Industrial Production Report
0076-3470 Malta. Central Office of Statistics. Demographic Review
0076-3489 Malta. Central Office of Statistics. Education Statistics
0076-3519 Mammalian Species
0076-356X Management Aids Annuals†
0076-3578 Management Aids for Small Manufacturers *see* 0190-3225
0076-3586 Management and Labor Studies. English Series†
0076-3616 Management, Fonctions, Methodes, Experiences†
0076-3624 Management Guide to N C†
0076-3640 Management Monographs *changed to* L R I Guides to Management. Monographs.
0076-3667 Management Advisory Services Technical Study†
0076-3705 Manchester Association of Engineers. Transactions†
0076-3713 Manchester Guardian Society for the Protection of Trade. Annual Report†
0076-3721 Manchester Literary and Philosophical Society. Memoirs and Proceedings *changed to* Manchester Memoirs.
0076-3748 La Mandragore Qui Chante
0076-3756 National Museum of the Philippines. Annual Report
0076-3764 National Museum of the Philippines. Museum Publications (Pamphlet Series)†
0076-3772 National Museum of the Philippines. Monograph Series†
0076-3780 Philippine Normal College. Language Study Center. Occasional Paper†
0076-3802 Manitoba Cancer Treatment and Research Foundation. Report
0076-3810 Manitoba Entomologist†
0076-3829 Manitoba Historical Society. Transactions†
0076-3853 Manitoba Labour - Management Review Committee. Annual Report
0076-3861 Manitoba Law Journal
0076-387X Manitoba. Mineral Resources Division. Geological Paper *changed to* Manitoba Energy and Mines. Geological Paper.
0076-3888 Manitoba Museum of Man and Nature. Biennial Report *changed to* Manitoba Museum of Man and Nature. Annual Report.
0076-3896 Manitoba Record Society. Publications
0076-390X Manitoba Trade Directory†
0076-3918 University of Manitoba. Center for Settlement Studies. Publication Series†
0076-3926 University of Manitoba. Center for Settlement Studies. Series 1. Annual Reports†
0076-3934 University of Manitoba. Center for Settlement Studies. Series 2. Research Report†
0076-3942 University of Manitoba. Center for Settlement Studies. Series 3. Bibliography and Information†
0076-3950 University of Manitoba. Center for Settlement Studies. Series 4. Proceedings†
0076-3969 University of Manitoba. Center for Settlement Studies. Series 5. Occasional Papers†
0076-3977 University of Manitoba. Center for Transportation Studies. Occasional Paper. *changed to* University of Manitoba. Transport Institute. Occasional Paper.
0076-3993 University of Manitoba. Center for Transportation Studies. Seminar Series on Transportation. Proceedings†
0076-4035 University of Manitoba. Department of Slavic Studies. Readings in Slavic Literature†
0076-4051 University of Manitoba. Faculty of Agriculture. Progress Report on Agricultural Research and Experimentation *changed to* University of Manitoba. Faculty of Agriculture. Annual Progress Review: Agricultural Research, Teaching and Extension.
0076-4108 University of Manitoba. Medical Journal *see* 0832-6096
0076-4116 Mankind Quarterly Monograph Series
0076-4124 Manna†
0076-4140 Manpower/Automation Research Notices†
0076-4167 Manual of Materials Handling and Ancilliary Equipment *see* 0142-114X
0076-4175 Mutual Funds Almanac
0076-4205 Manuels Pratiques d'Economie†
0076-4213 MacRae's Manufacturers' Agents Guide *see* 0749-1093
0076-423X Manufacturing Chemists Association. Statistical Summary†
0076-4248 Canada. Statistics Canada. Manufacturing Industries of Canada: Type of Organization and Size of Establishment/Industries Manufacturieres du Canada: Forme d'Organisation et Taille des Etablissements†
0076-4256 Manufacturing Management Series†
0076-4264 Manx Museum, Douglas, Isle of Man. Journal†
0076-4280 Maori Education Foundation. Annual Report
0076-4299 Instituto de Biologia Marina. Boletin†
0076-4302 Instituto de Biologia Marina. Serie Contribuciones *see* 0325-6790
0076-4310 Instituto de Biologia Marina. Memoria Anual†
0076-4337 Universidad Nacional del Zulia. Facultad de Humanidades y Educacion. Artes y Letras†
0076-4345 Universidad Nacional del Zulia. Facultad de Humanidades y Educacion. Conferencias y Coloquios†
0076-4353 Universidad Nacional del Zulia. Facultad de Humanidades y Educacion. Fuera de Serie†
0076-4361 Universidad Nacional del Zulia. Facultad de Humanidades y Educacion. Manuales de la Escuela de Educacion†
0076-437X Universidad Nacional del Zulia. Facultad de Humanidades y Educacion. Monografias y Ensayos†
0076-4418 Marconi's International Register
0076-4434 Marian Library Studies. New Series
0076-4442 Marine Biology; Proceedings of the Interdisciplinary Conference†
0076-4477 Morskaya Geologiya i Geofizika
0076-4493 Marine Research†
0076-4507 Marine Science Affairs *changed to* Reports on Marine Science Affairs.
0076-4515 Maritime Bank of Israel. Annual Report
0076-4523 Market Research Society. Yearbook
0076-4531 Market Statistics Key Plant Directory *see* 0098-1397
0076-4582 Marketing Guide to the Chemical Industry *changed to* Kline Guide to the Chemical Industry.
0076-4590 Marketing Guide to the Packaging Industries *changed to* Kline Guide to the Packaging Industry.
0076-4604 Marketing Guide to the Paint Industry *changed to* Kline Guide to the Paint Industry.
0076-4612 Marketing Guide to the Paper and Pulp Industry *changed to* Kline Guide to the Paper and Pulp Industry.
0076-4620 Marketing Research Techniques Series†
0076-4647 Markets Year Book
0076-4655 Le Maroc en Chiffres
0076-4671 Marquette Slavic Studies†
0076-4701 Marsyas†
0076-471X Martin Classical Lectures
0076-4728 Mary C. Richardson Lecture†
0076-4736 Maryland. Council for Higher Education. Annual Report *see* 0361-140X
0076-4752 Maryland. Department of State Planning. Activities Report†
0076-4779 Maryland. Geological Survey. Bulletin
0076-4787 Maryland. Geological Survey. Educational Series
0076-4795 Maryland. Geological Survey. Information Circular
0076-4809 Maryland. Geological Survey. Report of Investigations
0076-4817 Maryland. Geological Survey. Water Resources Basic Data Report
0076-4833 University of Maryland. College of Library and Information Services. Conference Proceedings†
0076-4841 University of Maryland. College of Library and Information Services. Student Contribution Series
0076-4892 Massachusetts Audubon Newsletter *see* 0272-8966
0076-4906 Massachusetts. Department of Mental Health. Newsletter†
0076-4922 Massachusetts. Division of Employment Security. Employment and Wages in Establishments Subject to the Massachusetts Employment Security Law. State Summary *changed to* Massachusetts. Department of Employment and Training. Employment and Wages State Summary.
0076-4930 Massachusetts. Division of Employment Security. Annual Planning Report†
0076-4949 Massachusetts. Division of Employment Security. Statistical Digest†
0076-4957 Massachusetts. Division of Fisheries and Game. Annual Report *changed to* Massachusetts. Division of Fisheries and Wildlife. Annual Report.
0076-4981 Massachusetts Historical Society. Proceedings
0076-499X Massachusetts Housing Finance Agency. Annual Report
0076-5066 University of Massachusetts. Department of Anthropology. Research Reports
0076-5104 Master's Education: Route to Opportunities in Modern Nursing *changed to* Master's Education: Route to Opportunities in Contemporary Nursing.
0076-5112 Master's Theses in Education
0076-5139 Material Culture Monographs (American Indian) *changed to* Material Culture Notes (American Indian).
0076-5147 Materiale si Cercetari Arheologice†
0076-5163 Materiali per Una Storia della Cultura Giuridica
0076-5171 Materialien zur Roemisch-Germanischen Keramik
0076-5201 Materials Science Research
0076-521X Materialy i Prace Antropologiczne
0076-5228 Materialy i Studia do Historii Prasy i Czasopismiennictwa Polskiego†
0076-5236 Materialy Zachodnio-Pomorskie
0076-5244 Materialy Zrodlowe do Dziejow Kosciola W Polsce
0076-5252 Materiaux pour l'Etude de l'Extreme-Orient Moderne et Contemporain. Etudes Linguistiques†
0076-5260 Materiaux pour l'Etude de l'Extreme-Orient Moderne et Contemporain. Textes†
0076-5279 Materiaux pour l'Etude de l'Extreme-Orient Moderne et Contemporain. Travaux†
0076-5287 Materiaux pour l'Histoire du Socialisme International. Serie 2. Essais Bibliographiques†
0076-5295 Materiaux pour l'Histoire du Socialisme International. Serie 1. Textes et Documents†
0076-5333 Mathematical Expositions†
0076-5341 University of Notre Dame. Department of Mathematics. Mathematical Lectures
0076-5376 Mathematical Surveys *changed to* Mathematical Surveys & Monographs.
0076-5384 Mathematical Table Series†
0076-5392 Mathematics in Science and Engineering
0076-5406 Mathematiques et Sciences de l'Homme
0076-5414 Mathematische Forschungsberichte†
0076-5422 Mathematische Lehrbuecher und Monographien. Abteilung 1: Mathematische Lehrbuecher
0076-5430 Mathematische Lehrbuecher und Monographien. Abteilung 2: Mathematische Monographien
0076-5449 Mathematische Schuelerbuecherei
0076-5473 Maurice Falk Center for Economic Research in Israel. Report. *see* 0333-7839
0076-5481 Mauritius. Archives Department. Annual Report
0076-549X Mauritius. Customs and Excise Department. Annual Report
0076-5503 Mauritius. Legislative Assembly. Sessional Paper
0076-5511 Mauritius. Meteorological Services. Report
0076-552X Mauritius. Ministry of Housing, Lands and Town and Country Planning. Annual Reports
0076-5538 Mauritius. Ministry of Social Security. Annual Report *changed to* Mauritius. Ministry of Social Security. National Solidarity and Reform Institutions.
0076-5554 Mauritius. Ministry of Works and Internal Communications. Report
0076-5562 Mauritius. Public Accounts Committee. Report
0076-5589 Max C. Fleischmann College of Agriculture. Publications. B (Series)†
0076-5597 Max C. Fleischmann College of Agriculture. Publications. C (Series)†

0076-5600 Max C. Fleischmann College of Agriculture. Publications. R (Series)†
0076-5619 Max C. Fleischmann College of Agriculture. Publications. T (Series)†
0076-5627 Studien und Berichte
0076-5635 Max-Planck-Gesellschaft zur Foerderung der Wissenschaften. Jahrbuch
0076-5643 Max-Planck-Institut fuer Aeronomie. Mitteilungen†
0076-5651 Max-Planck-Institut fuer Auslaendisches Oeffentliches Recht und Voelkerrecht. Fontes *changed to* Max-Planck-Institut fuer Auslaendisches Oeffentliches Recht und Voelkerrecht. Fontes Iuris Gentium.
0076-566X Max-Planck-Institut fuer Silikatforschung, Wuerzburg. Veroeffentlichungen†
0076-5678 Mitteilungen aus dem Max-Planck-Institut fuer Stroenmungsforschung und der Aerodynamischen Versuchsansalt *see* 0374-1257
0076-5694 Max-Reger-Institut, Bonn. Mitteilungen†
0076-5716 Meat and Livestock Commission, Bucks, England. Index of Research†
0076-5732 Mechanical Engineering Monographs†
0076-5783 Mechanics
0076-5791 Mechanisms of Molecular Migrations†
0076-5805 Politechnika Poznanska. Zeszyty Naukowe. Mechanizacja i Elektryfikacja Rolnictwa *see* 0137-6918
0076-5813 Electro-Radiologiste Qualifie de France. Annuaire *changed to* Medecin Electro-Radiologiste Qualifie de France.
0076-5821 Media Scandinavia
0076-583X Medieval Academy of America. Publications *changed to* Medieval Academy Books.
0076-5856 Mediaeval Philosophical Texts in Translation
0076-5864 Mediaeval Scandinavia
0076-5872 Mediaeval Studies
0076-5880 Mediaevalia Philosophica Polonorum
0076-5902 Medical Art *see* 0094-2499
0076-5929 Medical Books in Print *see* 0000-085X
0076-5945 Medical Library Association. Publication†
0076-5953 Medical Physics Series
0076-5961 Medical Protection Society. Annual Report
0076-5988 Medical Research Centre, Nairobi. Annual Report
0076-5996 Medical Research Council (Ireland). Report†
0076-6003 Medical Research Index *changed to* Medical Research Centres.
0076-6011 Medical Society of London. Transactions
0076-6038 Medical Ultrasonics†
0076-6046 Medicina
0076-6054 Medicinal Chemistry†
0076-6062 Medicinal Research: A Series of Monographs *changed to* Medicinal Research Series.
0076-6070 Medicine and Sport *see* 0254-5020
0076-6097 Medieval Archaeology
0076-6100 Medieval Iberian Peninsula
0076-6127 Medievalia et Humanistica
0076-6135 Medium Aevum Monographs†
0076-6143 Medium Industry Bank, Seoul. Report *changed to* Industrial Bank of Korea, Seoul. Annual Report (Year).
0076-6151 Medizinische Laenderkunde. Geomedical Monograph Series
0076-616X Medizinische Praxis†
0076-6178 Medizinische Radiographie und Photographie†
0076-6194 Meet the U. S. A†
0076-6208 Meier-Dudy
0076-6216 Meister des Puppenspiels
0076-6224 Melanderia
0076-6232 Melbourne Historical Journal†
0076-6259 Melbourne Monographs in Germanic Studies†
0076-6267 Melbourne Slavonic Studies *see* 0818-8149
0076-6275 Melbourne Studies in Education
0076-6283 University of Melbourne. Institute of Applied Economic and Social Research. Monographs†
0076-6291 University of Melbourne. Institute of Applied Economic and Social Research. Technical Papers†
0076-6321 Melsheimer Entomological Series
0076-633X Melville Society Newsletter *see* 0193-8991
0076-6348 Melville Society. Special Publication *see* 0193-8991
0076-6356 Membranes: a Series of Advances†
0076-6364 Memoires de Photo-Interpretation
0076-6372 Memorabilia Zoologica
0076-6380 Junta de Estudios Historicos de Mendoza. Revista
0076-6399 Universidad Nacional de Cuyo. Biblioteca Central. Boletin Bibliografico†
0076-6402 Universidad Nacional de Cuyo. Biblioteca Central. Cuadernos de la Biblioteca†
0076-6429 Mennonite History Series
0076-6437 Men's Wear Year Book and Diary†
0076-6453 Mental Health Statistics for Illinois
0076-6461 Mental Measurements Yearbook
0076-6518 Merck Index: An Encyclopedia of Chemicals and Drugs
0076-6526 Merck Manual: A Handbook of Diagnosis and Therapy
0076-6542 Merck Veterinary Manual: A Handbook of Diagnosis and Therapy for the Veterinarian
0076-6550 Universidad de Los Andes. Facultad de Derecho. Anuario
0076-6569 Universidad de Los Andes. Instituto de Geografia y Conservacion de Recursos Naturales. Cuadernos Geograficos
0076-6607 Mesoamerican Studies†
0076-6615 Mesopotamia
0076-6658 Metal Statistics
0076-6690 Metallurgical Reviews *see* 0950-6608
0076-6704 Metallurgical Works in Canada, Nonferrous and Precious Metals†
0076-6712 Metallurgical Works in Canada, Primary Iron and Steel†
0076-6720 Metaphysische Rundschau
0076-6739 Meteorological Yearbook of Finland. Part 1B: Climatological Data from Jokioinen and Sodankyla Observatories†
0076-6747 Meteorological Yearbook of Finland. Part 1: Climatological Data
0076-6755 Meteorological Yearbook of Finland. Part 2: Precipitation and Snow Cover Data
0076-6763 Meteorological Yearbook of Finland. Part 4: Measurements of Radiation and Bright Sunshine *see* 0783-103X
0076-6763 Meteorological Yearbook of Finland. Part 4: Measurements of Radiation and Bright Sunshine *see* 0783-0556
0076-6771 Methodensammlung der Elektronenmikroskopie
0076-678X Methodes de la Sociologie†
0076-681X Methods and Achievements in Experimental Pathology
0076-6836 Methods and Techniques in Geophysics†
0076-6860 Methods in Computational Physics: Advances in Research and Applications†
0076-6879 Methods in Enzymology
0076-6887 Methods in Free-Radical Chemistry†
0076-6895 Methods in Geochemistry and Geophysics
0076-6909 Methods in Hydroscience *see* 0065-2768
0076-6925 Methods in Neurochemistry†
0076-6933 Methods in Virology†
0076-6941 Methods of Biochemical Analysis
0076-695X Methods of Experimental Physics
0076-6984 Metodicke Prirucky Experimentalni Botaniky
0076-700X Metro Building Industry Directory†
0076-7018 METRO; New York Metropolitan Reference and Research Library Agency. METRO Miscellaneous Publications Series
0076-7050 Metropolitan Library Service Agency. Annual Report†
0076-7069 Metropolitan Milwaukee Association of Commerce. Trends in Selected Economic Indicators *changed to* Milwaukee Commerce Hot-line.
0076-7077 Metropolitan Milwaukee Association of Commerce. Economic Studies *changed to* Metropolitan Milwaukee Economic Fact Book.
0076-7085 Metropolitan Politics†
0076-7093 Metropolitan Toronto
0076-7107 Metropolitan Washington Council of Governments. Annual Report†
0076-7131 Instituto Nacional de Cancerologia de Mexico. Revista
0076-7158 Museu Nacional de Antropologia. Cuadernos
0076-7166 Universidad Nacional Autonoma de Mexico. Centro de Estudios Mayas. Cuadernos
0076-7174 Universidad Nacional Autonoma de Mexico. Instituto de Biologia. Anales *see* 0368-8720
0076-7174 Universidad Nacional Autonoma de Mexico. Instituto de Biologia. Anales *see* 0374-5511
0076-7182 Universidad Nacional Autonoma de Mexico. Instituto de Geofisica. Anales†
0076-7204 Universidad Nacional Autonoma de Mexico. Instituto de Geofisica. Monografias
0076-7212 Universidad Nacional Autonoma de Mexico. Instituto de Investigaciones Historicas. Serie de Cultura Nahuatl. Fuentes
0076-7247 Universidad Nacional Autonoma de Mexico. Instituto de Investigaciones Esteticas. Anales. Suplemento†
0076-7255 Universidad Nacional Autonoma de Mexico. Instituto de Investigaciones Esteticas. Publicaciones Especiales†
0076-7263 Universidad Nacional Autonoma de Mexico. Instituto de Investigaciones Antropologicas. Cuadernos Serie Antropologica *see* 0076-7298
0076-7271 Universidad Nacional Autonoma de Mexico. Instituto de Investigaciones Historicas. Cuadernos Serie Documental
0076-7298 Universidad Nacional Autonoma de Mexico. Instituto de Investigaciones Antropologicas. Serie Antropologica
0076-7301 Universidad Nacional Autonoma de Mexico. Instituto de Investigaciones Historicas. Serie Bibliografica
0076-731X Universidad Nacional Autonoma de Mexico. Instituto de Investigaciones Historicas. Serie Documental
0076-7328 Universidad Nacional Autonoma de Mexico. Instituto de Investigaciones Historicas. Serie de Culturas Mesoamericanas
0076-7344 Universidad Nacional Autonoma de Mexico. Instituto de Investigaciones Historicas. Serie de Cultura Nahuatl. Monografias
0076-7352 Universidad Nacional Autonoma de Mexico. Instituto de Investigaciones Historicas. Serie de Historia General
0076-7379 Universidad Nacional Autonoma de Mexico. Instituto de Investigaciones Historicas. Serie de Historia Novohispana *see* 0185-2523
0076-7387 Universidad Nacional Autonoma de Mexico. Instituto de Investigaciones Historicas. Serie de Historiadores y Cronistas
0076-7468 Universidad Nacional Autonoma de Mexico. Seminario de Investigaciones Bibliotecologica. Publicaciones. Serie B. Bibliografia
0076-7476 Instituto Nacional de Energia Nuclear. Publication†
0076-7492 Mexico. Secretaria de Programacion y Presupuesto†
0076-7506 Instituto Nacional de Antropologia e Historia. Departamento de Monumentos Coloniales. (Publicaciones)†
0076-7514 Instituto Nacional de Antropologia e Historia. Departamento de Monumentos Prehispanicos. (Publicaciones)†
0076-7557 Instituto Nacional de Antropologia e Historia. Anales†
0076-7565 Instituto Nacional de Antropologia e Historia. Coleccion Breve†
0076-7573 Instituto Nacional de Antropologia e Historia. Investigaciones†
0076-759X Instituto Nacional de Antropologia e Historia. Memorias†
0076-7611 Instituto Nacional de Antropologia e Historia. Coleccion Cientifica
0076-762X Instituto Nacional de Antropologia e Historia. Serie Culturas del Mundo†
0076-7670 Meyers Grosses Jahreslexikon†
0076-7689 Meyniana
0076-7697 Miami Linguistic Series†
0076-7719 University of Miami Hispanic-American Studies†
0076-7727 Michel-Briefmarken-Kataloge
0076-7735 Camping, Caravaning in France *changed to* Michelin Red Guide Series: Camping, France.
0076-7743 Michelin Red Guide Series: Benelux
0076-7751 Michelin Red Guide Series: Germany *changed to* Michelin Red Guide Series: Deutschland.
0076-776X Michelin Red Guide Series: Espana & Portugal
0076-7778 Michelin Red Guide Series: France
0076-7786 Michelin Red Guide Series: Italy
0076-7794 Michelin Red Guide Series: Paris
0076-7808 Michigan Abstracts of Chinese and Japanese Works on Chinese History *changed to* Michigan Monographs in Chinese Studies.
0076-7824 Michigan Beef Cattle Day Report†
0076-7832 Michigan Business Cases†
0076-7840 Michigan Business Papers†
0076-7859 Michigan Business Reports†
0076-7867 Michigan Business Studies†
0076-7875 Michigan. Civil Rights Commission. Report *changed to* Michigan. Civil Rights Commission. Annual Report.
0076-7905 Michigan. Department of Natural Resources. Institute for Fisheries Research. Miscellaneous Publication
0076-7913 Michigan. Division of Vocational Education. Report†
0076-7948 Michigan Geographical Publications†
0076-7956 Michigan Governmental Studies†
0076-7964 Michigan. Department of Natural Resources. Institute for Fisheries Research. Lake Inventory Summary†
0076-7972 Michigan International Business Studies†
0076-7999 Michigan International Labor Studies†
0076-8014 Michigan Municipal League. Municipal Legal Briefs
0076-8057 Michigan Natural Resources Council. Scientific Advisory Committee. Annual Report†
0076-8065 Michigan Papers in Chinese Studies *changed to* Michigan Monographs in Chinese Studies.
0076-8073 Michigan. Plant Industry Division. Plant Pest Control Programs†
0076-8081 Michigan Library Directory and Statistics *changed to* Michigan Library Directory.
0076-809X Michigan Science in Action *changed to* Futures (East Lansing).

0076-8103 Michigan Slavic Contributions
0076-8111 Michigan State Plan for Construction of Community Mental Health Facilities†
0076-812X Michigan State University. Asian Studies Center. Occasional Papers: East Asia Series
0076-8138 Michigan State University. Asian Studies Center. Occasional Papers: South Asia Series
0076-8146 Michigan State University. Department of Physics. Cyclotron Project (Publication) *changed to* Michigan State University. National Superconducting Cyclotron Laboratory (Publication).
0076-8189 Michigan State University. Latin American Studies Center. Monograph Series
0076-8197 Michigan State University. Latin American Studies Center. Occasional Papers†
0076-8200 Michigan State University. Latin American Studies Center. Research Reports
0076-8227 Michigan State University. Museum Publications. Biological Series
0076-8235 Michigan State University. Museum Publications. Cultural Series
0076-8243 Michigan State University. Public Administration Program. Research Report†
0076-8251 Michigan State University. Rural Manpower Center. R M C Mimeograph *changed to* Michigan State University. Center for Rural Manpower & Public Affairs. Mimeograph.
0076-826X Michigan State University. Rural Manpower Center. R M C Report *changed to* Michigan State University. Center for Rural Manpower & Public Affairs. Report.
0076-8278 Michigan State University. Rural Manpower Center. R M C Special Paper *changed to* Michigan State University. Center for Rural Manpower & Public Affairs. Special Paper.
0076-8308 Michigan Statistical Abstract†
0076-8332 University of Michigan. Graduate School of Business Administration. Leadership Award Lecture†
0076-8340 University of Michigan. Center for Japanese Studies. Bibliographical Series†
0076-8359 University of Michigan. Center for Japanese Studies. Occasional Papers†
0076-8367 University of Michigan. Museum of Anthropology. Anthropological Papers.
0076-8375 University of Michigan. Museum of Anthropology. Memoirs
0076-8391 University of Michigan. Museum of Art. Bulletin *see* 0270-1642
0076-8405 University of Michigan. Museum of Zoology. Miscellaneous Publications
0076-8413 University of Michigan. Museum of Zoology. Occasional Papers
0076-8421 University of Michigan Observatories. Publications†
0076-843X University of Michigan. School of Dentistry. Alumni Bulletin
0076-8480 Microfiche Foundation. Newsletter
0076-8502 Middle East and North Africa (Year)
0076-8510 Middle East Economic Papers†
0076-8529 Middle East Record
0076-8537 Middle Eastern Monographs†
0076-8561 Middle States Association of Colleges and Secondary Schools. Proceedings *changed to* Middle States Association of Colleges and Schools. Proceedings of the Annual Convention.
0076-857X University of Chicago. Midwest Administration Center. Monograph Series†
0076-8588 Midwest Electrical Buyers' Guide†
0076-8596 Midwest Monographs. Series 1 (Drama)†
0076-860X Midwest Monographs. Series 2 (Poetry)†
0076-8618 Midwest Monographs. Series 3 (Graphic Works)†
0076-8626 Midwest Monographs. Series 4 (Translation)†
0076-8634 Midwest Monographs. Series 5 (Culture and Criticism)†
0076-8642 Mikrochimica Acta. Supplement
0076-8650 Istituto di Ricerche Agrarie, Milan. Contributi†
0076-8669 Universita Cattolica del Sacro Cuore, Milan. Contributi. Serie Terza. Scienze Storiche†
0076-8677 Universita Cattolica del Sacro Cuore, Milan. Contributi. Serie Terza. Scienze Filosofiche†
0076-8685 Universita Cattolica del Sacro Cuore, Milan. Contributi. Serie Terza. Scienze Filologiche e Letteratura†
0076-8693 Universita Cattolica del Sacro Cuore, Milan. Contributi. Serie Terza. Scienze Psicologiche†
0076-8707 Universita Cattolica del Sacro Cuore, Milan. Istituto di Archeologia. Contributi†
0076-8715 Universita Cattolica del Sacro Cuore, Milan. Saggi e Ricerche. Serie Terza. Scienze Filologiche e Letteratura†
0076-8723 Universita Cattolica del Sacro Cuore, Milan. Saggi e Ricerche. Serie Terza. Scienze Filosofiche†
0076-8731 Universita Cattolica del Sacro Cuore, Milan. Saggi e Ricerche. Serie Terza. Scienze Geografiche†
0076-874X Universita Cattolica del Sacro Cuore, Milan. Saggi e Ricerche. Serie Terza. Scienze Psicologiche†
0076-8758 Universita Cattolica del Sacro Cuore, Milan. Saggi e Ricerche. Serie Terza. Scienze Storiche†
0076-8766 Mildex Motor Book†
0076-8774 Military Research Series†
0076-8782 Military Year Book
0076-8790 Milla Wa-Milla†
0076-8812 Millesime
0076-8820 Milton Studies
0076-8839 Milu: Wissenschaftliche und Kulturelle Mitteilungen aus dem Tierpark Berlin
0076-8847 M I M S Desk Reference
0076-8855 Brazil. Tribunal Regional do Trabalho. Tercera Regiao. Revista
0076-8863 Universidade Federal de Minas Gerais. Escola de Veterinaria. Arquivos *see* 0102-0935
0076-8871 Universidade Federal de Minas Gerais. Revista†
0076-8901 Mindolo News Letter *changed to* Mindolo World.
0076-891X M W V Jahresbericht
0076-8944 Minerals, Rocks and Inorganic Materials *see* 0343-2181
0076-8952 U.S. Bureau of Mines. Minerals Yearbook
0076-8987 Mining in Rhodesia *changed to* Mining in Zimbabwe.
0076-8995 Mining Annual Review
0076-9010 Zambia Mining Yearbook
0076-9029 Minkus Austria, Switzerland, Lichtenstein Stamp Catalog†
0076-9037 Minkus British Commonwealth Stamp Catalog†
0076-9045 Minkus Germany and Colonies Stamp Catalog†
0076-9053 Minkus Italy, San Marino and Vatican Stamp Catalog†
0076-9061 Minkus New American Stamp Catalog *changed to* Minkus (Year) Specialized American Stamp Catalog.
0076-907X Minkus New World Wide Stamp Catalog†
0076-9088 Minkus Russia, Poland, Hungary, Romania, Czechoslovakia Stamp Catalog†
0076-9096 Minneapolis Institute of Arts. Annual Report
0076-910X Minneapolis Institute of Arts. Bulletin
0076-9118 Minnesota. Department of Human Rights. Biennial Report
0076-9126 Minnesota. Department of Manpower Services. Annual Report *changed to* Minnesota. Department of Jobs and Training. Annual Report.
0076-9134 Minnesota. Division of Game and Fish. Technical Bulletin *changed to* Minnesota Wildlife Reports.
0076-9142 Minnesota Drama Editions†
0076-9150 Minnesota Fisheries Investigations *changed to* Minnesota Fisheries Investigational Reports.
0076-9169 Minnesota. Geological Survey. Bulletin
0076-9177 Minnesota. Geological Survey. Report of Investigations
0076-9185 Minnesota. Geological Survey. Special Publication Series†
0076-9215 Minnesota Monographs in the Humanities†
0076-9258 Minnesota Studies in the Philosophy of Science
0076-9266 Minnesota Symposia on Child Psychology Series
0076-9274 University of Minnesota. Audio-Visual Library Service. Educational Resources Bulletin
0076-9282 University of Minnesota. Center for Research in Human Learning. Report *changed to* University of Minnesota. Center for Research in Learning, Perception & Cognition. Report and Fellowship Offerings.
0076-9290 University of Minnesota. Graduate School Research Center. Inventory of Faculty Research†
0076-9312 University of Minnesota Studies in Economics and Business.†
0076-9347 Miscellanea Byzantina Monacensia
0076-9355 Miscellanea Musicologica†
0076-9371 Mision Arqueologica Espanola en Nubia. Memorias†
0076-9401 Missions to Seamen Handbook *changed to* Missions to Seamen Annual Report.
0076-941X Missionswissenschaftliche Abhandlungen und Texte†
0076-9428 Missionswissenschaftliche Forschungen
0076-9436 Mississippi Academy of Science. Journal
0076-9460 Mississippi Congress of Parents and Teachers. Proceedings
0076-9479 Mississippi Congress of Parents and Teachers. Yearbook
0076-9509 Mississippi State University. Forest Products Utilization Laboratory. Information Series
0076-9517 Mississippi State University. Christian Student Center. Annual Lectureship
0076-9525 M V C Bulletin†
0076-9533 Mississippi Water Resources Conference. Proceedings†
0076-9541 Missouri Archaeological Society. Memoir Series†
0076-955X Missouri Archaeological Society. Newsletter *see* 0743-7641
0076-9568 Missouri Archaeological Society. Research Series†
0076-9576 Missouri Archaeologist
0076-9584 Missouri Directory of Manufacturing and Mining *see* 0895-2469
0076-9606 Missouri. Division of Geological Survey and Water Resources. Engineering Geology Series
0076-9614 Missouri. Division of Geological Survey and Water Resources. Water Resources Report
0076-9630 Missouri Handbook Series†
0076-9649 Missouri Literary Frontiers Series†
0076-9657 University of Missouri, St. Louis. Center for International Studies. Monograph†
0076-969X University of Missouri. College of Business and Public Administration. Office of Research, Annual Report†
0076-9703 University of Missouri Studies†
0076-9711 University of Missouri, Columbia. Veterinary Medical Diagnostic Laboratory. Annual Report
0076-9754 Mittellateinische Studien und Texte
0076-9762 Mittellateinisches Jahrbuch
0076-9770 Moana: Estudios de Antropologia Oceanica
0076-986X Current Population Reports: Population Characteristics. Mobility of the Population of the United States *changed to* Current Population Reports: Population Characteristics. Geographical Mobility.
0076-9878 Moccasin Telegraph *see* 0227-3780
0076-9894 Modern America†
0076-9908 Modern Analytic and Computational Methods in Science and Mathematics†
0076-9916 Modern Approaches to the Diagnosis and Instruction of Multi-Handicapped Children†
0076-9924 Modern Aspects of Electrochemistry
0076-9932 Modern Brewery Age Blue Book
0076-9959 Modern Drug Encyclopedia and Therapeutic Index†
0076-9967 Modern Filologiai Fuzetek
0076-9983 Modern Humanities Research Association. Monograph *changed to* Modern Humanities Research Association. Publications.
0076-9991 Modern Machine Shop N C Guidebook and Directory *changed to* N C - C I M Guidebook.
0077-0000 Modern Materials. Advances in Development and Applications†
0077-0027 Modern Middle East Series
0077-0043 Modern Perspectives in Psychiatry†
0077-0078 Modern Problems in Ophthalmology *see* 0250-3751
0077-0086 Modern Problems in Paediatrics *see* 1017-5989
0077-0094 Modern Problems of Pharmacopsychiatry
0077-0108 Modern Publicity *changed to* World Advertising Review.
0077-0167 Modern Vocational Trends Reference Handbook†
0077-0205 Moebel-Industrie und Ihre Helfer
0077-0221 Molecular Biology, Biochemistry and Biophysics
0077-023X Molecular Biology; Proceedings of the International Conference†
0077-0264 University of the West Indies, Jamaica. Department of Geography. Occasional Publications Series†
0077-0272 University of the West Indies, Jamaica. Department of Geography. Research Notes Series†
0077-0280 Monarchist Book Review
0077-0299 Monarchist Press Association. Historical Series
0077-0310 Monde d'Outre-Mer, Passe et Present. 1 Serie: Etudes†
0077-0329 Monde d'Outre-Mer, Passe et Present. 2 Serie: Documents†
0077-0337 Monde d'Outre-Mer, Passe et Present. 3 Serie: Essais†
0077-0345 Monde d'Outre-Mer, Passe et Present. 4 Serie: Bibliographies et Instruments de Travail†
0077-0353 Centre pour l'Etude des Problemes de Monde Musulman Contemporain. Initiations†
0077-0361 Mondo†
0077-0388 Money Market Directory *see* 0736-6051
0077-0396 Mongolia Society. Occasional Papers
0077-040X Monitor (Albany)†
0077-0418 Monks Wood Experimental Station. Report *see* 0308-1125
0077-0434 Monnaies, Prix, Conjoncture
0077-0442 Monografias de Filosofia Juridica y Social

ISSN INDEX 5535
ISSN

0077-0469 Monografias de Psicologia, Normal y Patologica
0077-0485 Monografie Biochemiczne
0077-0493 Monografie di Archeologia Libica
0077-0507 Monografie Matematyczne
0077-0515 Monografie Psychologiczne
0077-0523 Monografie Slaskie Ossolineum
0077-0531 Monografie Slawistyczne
0077-054X Monografie z Dziejow Nauki i Techniki
0077-0558 Monografie z Dziejow Oswiaty
0077-0574 Monograph Series in Probability and Statistics†
0077-0582 G S I S Monograph Series in World Affairs
0077-0612 Monograph Series on Languages and Linguistics *see* 0196-7207
0077-0620 Monograph Series on Schizophrenia
0077-0639 Monographiae Biologicae
0077-0647 Monographiae Biologicae Canarienses†
0077-0671 Monographien aus dem Gesamtgebiete der Psychiatrie - Psychiatry Series
0077-0698 Monographs to Applied Entomology
0077-0701 Monographies de l'Industrie et du Commerce en France
0077-0728 Monographies Juridiques†
0077-0744 Monographs and Textbooks in Material Science†
0077-0752 Monographs and Texts in the Behavioral Sciences†
0077-0760 Monographs in Allergy
0077-0809 Monographs in Clinical Cytology
0077-0825 Monographs in Developmental Biology
0077-0833 Monographs in Electroanalytical Chemistry and Electrochemistry Series
0077-085X Monographs in Geology and Paleontology†
0077-0868 Monographs in Hormone Research *see* 0301-3073
0077-0876 Monographs in Human Genetics
0077-0884 Monographs in Macromolecular Chemistry†
0077-0892 Monographs in Oral Science
0077-0906 Monographs in Organic Functional Group Analysis *changed to* Analysis of Organic Materials: an International Series of Monographs.
0077-0914 Monographs in Paediatrics *see* 1017-5989
0077-0930 Monographs in Population Biology
0077-0949 Monographs in Statistical Physics and Thermodynamics†
0077-0965 Monographs in Virology
0077-099X Monographs on Atherosclerosis
0077-1007 Monographs on Education†
0077-1015 Monographs on Endocrinology
0077-1023 Monographs on Immunology *see* 0092-6019
0077-1031 Monographs on Linguistic Analysis†
0077-104X Monographs on Oceanographic Methodology
0077-1074 London School of Economics Monographs on Social Anthropology
0077-1090 Montana. Bureau of Mines and Geology. Bulletin
0077-1104 Montana. Bureau of Mines and Geology. Directory of Mining Enterprises
0077-1112 Montana. Bureau of Mines and Geology. Ground Water Reports *see* 0077-1090
0077-1120 Montana. Bureau of Mines and Geology. Memoir
0077-1139 Montana. Bureau of Mines and Geology. Special Publications
0077-1147 Montana Journalism Review†
0077-1155 University of Montana. Forest and Conservation Experiment Station, Missoula. Bulletin *changed to* University of Montana. Forest and Conservation Experiment Station, Missoula. Miscellaneous Publications.
0077-1163 University of Montana. Forest and Conservation Experiment Station, Missoula. Research Notes.
0077-1198 Montana Vital Statistics
0077-1201 Montana. Water Resources Board. Inventory Series†
0077-1228 Instituto Tecnologico y de Estudios Superiores. Publicaciones. Serie Historia†
0077-1236 Instituto Tecnologico y de Estudios Superiores. Publicaciones. Serie Letras†
0077-1244 Museo Nacional de Historia Natural. Comunicaciones Antropologicas
0077-1252 Universidad de Uruguay. Departamento de Literatura Iberoamericana Publicaciones
0077-1260 Universidad de Uruguay. Facultad de Agronomia. Boletin
0077-1279 Universidad de la Republica. Facultad de Agronomia. Publicacion Miscelanea†
0077-1287 Universidad de la Republica. Instituto de Administracion. Cuaderno
0077-1295 Universidad de Uruguay. Instituto de Mathematica y Estadistica. Publicaciones Didacticas†
0077-1317 Jardin Botanique de Montreal. Annuelles et Legumes†
0077-1325 Jardin Botanique de Montreal. Memoire†
0077-1341 Universite de Montreal. Ecole de Bibliotheconomie. Publications†
0077-1368 Montreal Women's Liberation Newsletter
0077-1376 Monumenta Aegyptiaca
0077-1384 Monumenta Americana
0077-1392 Monumenta Antiquitatis Extra Fines Hungariae Reperta Quae in Museo Artium Hungarico Aliisque Museis et Collectionibus Hungaricis Conservantur†
0077-1406 Monumenta Artis Romanae
0077-1414 Monumenta Chartae Papyraceae Historiam Illustrantia
0077-1430 Monumenta Historica Budapestinensia†
0077-1449 Monumenta Historica Ordinis Minorum Capuccinorum
0077-1457 Monumenta Iuris Canonici
0077-1465 Monumenta Musicae in Polonia *changed to* Monumenta Musicae in Polonia. Series A: Works by Polish Composers.
0077-1465 Monumenta Musicae in Polonia *changed to* Monumenta Musicae in Polonia. Series B: Collectanea Musicae Artis.
0077-1465 Monumenta Musicae in Polonia *changed to* Monumenta Musicae in Polonia. Series C: Tractatus de Musica.
0077-1465 Monumenta Musicae in Polonia *changed to* Monumenta Musicae in Polonia. Series D: Bibliotheca Antiqua.
0077-1473 Monumenta Musicae Suecicae
0077-1481 Monumenta Paedagogica
0077-1503 Monuments of Renaissance Music
0077-152X Moravskie Numismaticke Zpravy *see* 0862-1195
0077-1546 Trends, Financial Statements and Operating Ratios *see* 0278-6567
0077-1554 Moscow Mathematical Society. Transactions
0077-1562 Gosudarstvennyi Muzei Izobrazitel'nykh Iskusstv im. Pushkina. Soobshcheniya
0077-1570 Motocyclo Catalogue
0077-1589 Motor Cycle Diary†
0077-1597 Motor Industry of Great Britain *changed to* Motor Industry of Great Britain (Year) World Automotive Statistics.
0077-1600 Motor Manual†
0077-1619 Motor Traffic in Sweden
0077-1643 Motor Truck Facts *see* 0146-9932
0077-166X Motorboote und Yachten
0077-1678 Motorcycle Buyer's Guide *see* 0027-2205
0077-1694 Motoring in Malaya
0077-1716 Motor Parts & Time Guide
0077-1724 Motor Truck and Diesel Repair Manual *changed to* Motor Light Truck & Van Repair Manual.
0077-1732 Motorsporten i Tekst og Billeder *changed to* Motorsporten.
0077-1740 Mount Zion Hospital and Medical Center, San Francisco. Bulletin†
0077-1759 Mountain World†
0077-1767 Movimiento Natural de la Poblacion de Espana
0077-1775 Moyens de la Recherche Scientifique et Technique en Haute-Normandie.†
0077-1791 Instituto de Investigacao Agronomica de Mocambique. Centro de Documentacas Agraria. Memorias
0077-1805 Mozart - Jahrbuch
0077-1813 Muelleria
0077-1864 Muenchener Entomologische Gesellschaft. Mitteilungen
0077-1872 Muenchner Germanistische Beitraege
0077-1880 Muenchener Indologische Studien
0077-1899 Muenchener Jahrbuch der Bildenden Kunst
0077-1902 Muenchener Studien zur Sozial- und Wirtschaftsgeographie
0077-1910 Muenchener Studien zur Sprachwissenschaft
0077-1929 Universitaet Muenster. Astronomisches Institut. Mitteilungen†
0077-1937 Universitaet Muenster. Astronomisches Institut. Sonderdruck†
0077-1945 Universitaet Muenster. Institut fuer Christliche Sozialwissenschaften. Schriften†
0077-1953 Fontes et Commentationes†
0077-197X Universitaet Muenster. Institut fuer Missionswissenschaft. Veroeffentlichungen†
0077-1996 Muenstersche Beitraege zur Deutschen Literaturwissenschaft†
0077-2003 Muenstersche Beitraege zur Vor- und Fruehgeschichte
0077-2011 Muensterschwarzacher Studien
0077-202X Multihull International Catalogue Annual†
0077-2054 Coleccion Mundo Antiguo
0077-2062 Statistisches Jahrbuch Muenchen
0077-2070 Bayerische Staatssammlung fuer Palaeontologie und Historische Geologie. Mitteilungen
0077-2089 Technische Universitaet Muenchen. Jahrbuch
0077-2100 Universitaet Muenchen. Geophysikalisches Observatorium, Fuerstenfeldbruck. Veroeffentlichungen. Serie B
0077-2119 Westfaelische Wilhelms-Universitaet Muenster. Institut fuer Kreditwesen. Schriftenreihe†
0077-2127 Universitaet Muenchen. Wirtschaftsgeographisches Institut. "W G I"-Berichte zur Regionalforschung
0077-2143 Municipal Association of Victoria. Minutes of Proceedings of Annual Session
0077-2151 American City & County Municipal Index
0077-2186 Municipal Year Book
0077-2194 Muse (Columbia)
0077-2208 Museion
0077-2216 Museu Paraense Emilio Goeldi. Boletim. Nova Serie: Botanica *changed to* Museu Paraense Emilio Goeldi. Boletim. Serie Botanica.
0077-2224 Museu Paraense Emilio Goeldi. Boletim. Nova Serie: Geologia
0077-2232 Museu Paraense Emilio Goeldi. Boletim. Nova Serie: Zoologia *changed to* Museu Paraense Emilio Goeldi. Boletim. Serie Zoologia.
0077-2240 Museu Paraense Emilio Goeldi. Publicacoes Avulsas†
0077-2267 Museums and Galleries *see* 0141-6723
0077-2275 Museum Boymans-van Beuningen. Agenda - Diary
0077-2313 Museum Publications†
0077-233X Museums and Monuments Series
0077-2356 Insects†
0077-2364 Mushroom Science
0077-2372 Music Handbook†
0077-2402 Music Educators National Conference. Selective Music Lists: Vocal Solos and Ensembles†
0077-2410 Music in Higher Education†
0077-2429 Music Indexes and Bibliographies†
0077-2445 Music Library Association. Index Series *see* 0094-6478
0077-2453 Music World Year Book
0077-2461 Musica Disciplina
0077-247X Musica Medii Aevi
0077-2488 Musicologica Hungarica *changed to* Studies in Central and Eastern European Music.
0077-2496 Musicological Studies and Documents
0077-250X Musicology *see* 0814-5857
0077-2518 Musik i Sverige
0077-2526 Musikalische Denkmaeler
0077-2542 Musk - Ox
0077-2550 Mutual Fund Fact Book
0077-2577 Muzea Walki
0077-2615 Mystic Seaport Manuscripts Inventory†
0077-2623 N A S A - University Conference on Manual Control (Papers)
0077-2631 N H K Technical Monograph†
0077-264X Nagoya University. Research Institute of Atmospherics. Proceedings - Nagoya Daigaku Kuden Kenkyujo Hokoku *changed to* Nagoya University. Solar-Terrestrial Environment Laboratory. Proceedings.
0077-2658 Nagyuzemi Gazdalkodas Kerdesei
0077-2666 Nairobi Airport. Annual Report
0077-2690 Names in South Carolina†
0077-2704 Namn och Bygd
0077-2712 Universite de Nancy II. Centre de Recherches et d'Applications Pedagogiques en Langues. Melanges
0077-2720 Universite de Nancy II. Centre Europeen Universitaire. Memoires†
0077-2739 Nanta Mathematica†
0077-2747 Nanyang University Journal†
0077-2755 Napao: A Saskatchewan Anthropology Journal *see* 0829-0547
0077-2763 Istituto Universitario Orientale di Napoli. Annali. Sezione Germanica†
0077-2771 Istituto Universitario Orientale di Napoli. Annali. Sezione Slava†
0077-2801 Narradores de Arca
0077-281X University of Rhode Island. Narragansett Marine Laboratory. Collected Reprints *changed to* University of Rhode Island. Graduate School of Oceanography. Collected Reprints.
0077-2828 University of Rhode Island. Narragansett Marine Laboratory. Occasional Publication†
0077-2836 Narragansett Marine Laboratory. Technical Reports *changed to* University of Rhode Island. Graduate School of Oceanography. Marine Technical Reports.
0077-2844 Narrativa Latinoamericana
0077-2879 Nassau Review
0077-2887 Nassauische Annalen
0077-2895 Natal Regional Survey. Additional Report†
0077-2925 National Academy of Sciences. Annual Report†
0077-2933 National Academy of Sciences. Biographical Memoirs
0077-295X National Accounts of the Maltese Islands
0077-2968 Catalogue of N A L Technical Translations†
0077-2976 National Aeronautical Laboratory. Annual Report
0077-300X National Aeronautical Laboratory. Technical Note
0077-3085 U.S. National Aeronautics and Space Administration. N A S A Factbook†
0077-3093 N A S A Facts

0077-3115 U.S. National Aeronautics and Space Administration. Research and Technology Program Digest. Flash Index *changed to* U.S. National Aeronautics and Space Administration. Research and Technology Operating Plan (RTOP) Summary.
0077-3131 U.S. National Aeronautics and Space Administration. Technical Notes
0077-314X U.S. National Aeronautics and Space Administration. Technical Reports
0077-3158 U.S. National Aeronautics and Space Administration. Technical Translations
0077-3166 List of Accredited Schools of Architecture *changed to* Accredited Programs in Architecture.
0077-3174 National Art Education Association. Research Monograph†
0077-3190 National Association for Foreign Student Affairs N A F S A Directory *see* 0736-4660
0077-3204 National Association for Physical Education of College Women. Biennial Record†
0077-3212 N A A C P Annual Report
0077-3220 National Association for the Care and Resettlement of Offenders. Papers and Reprints†
0077-3255 National Association of Animal Breeders. Annual Proceedings
0077-3263 National Association of Boards of Pharmacy. Proceedings
0077-3298 N A E S P Convention Reporter†
0077-3336 N A I A Handbook
0077-3344 N A I A Official Records Book *changed to* N A I A Official Records Book and Championship Summaries.
0077-3352 National Association of Jewish Center Workers. Conference Papers†
0077-3360 N A M F Accounting Manual†
0077-3379 N A M F Management Manual
0077-3387 National Association of Regulatory Utility Commissioners. Proceedings
0077-3409 National Association of Schools of Music. Proceedings of the Annual Meeting
0077-3417 N A S S P Convention Reporter†
0077-3425 National Association of State Universities and Land-Grant Colleges. Appropriations of State Tax Funds for Higher Education
0077-3433 National Association of State Universities and Land-Grant Colleges. Proceedings
0077-3441 National Association of Suggestion Systems. Statistical Report
0077-345X National Association of Teachers' Agencies. List of the Accredited Members
0077-3468 Coordinator (New York)†
0077-3476 National Association of Training Schools and Juvenile Agencies. Proceedings
0077-3506 National Bank of Ethiopia. Local Prices†
0077-3514 National Bank of Greece. Annual Report
0077-3522 National Bank of Pakistan. Report and Statement of Accounts
0077-3557 National Bible Society of Scotland. Annual Report
0077-3573 National Budget of Norway *changed to* Norway. Royal Norwegian Ministry of Finance. The Revised National Budget. (Year).
0077-3573 National Budget of Norway *changed to* Norway. Royal Norwegian Ministry of Finance. The National Budget. (Year).
0077-3581 National Building Research Institute. Complete List of N B R I Publications
0077-359X National Building Studies (Great Britain) Research Papers†
0077-3603 National Building Studies (Great Britain) Special Reports†
0077-3611 National Bureau of Economic Research. Annual Report†
0077-3638 National Bureau of Economic Research. General Series†
0077-3654 National Bureau of Economic Research. Technical Papers†
0077-3662 National Cancer Center Research Institute. Collected Papers
0077-3670 National Cancer Conference. Proceedings
0077-3689 National Cancer Institute of Canada. Annual Report
0077-3719 National Center for Audio Tapes. Catalog *changed to* National Center for Audio Tapes Archive. Catalog.
0077-3735 National Civil Service League. Annual Report†
0077-376X National Coal Board (Great Britain). Annual Report and Accounts. Vol. 2, Accounts and Statistical Tables *see* 0307-7691
0077-3794 National Collegiate Athletic Association. Annual Reports.
0077-3808 National Collegiate Athletic Association. Convention Proceedings
0077-3816 National Collegiate Athletic Association. Manual
0077-3840 National Committee for Audio-Visual Aids in Education. Experimental Development Unit. Report†
0077-3859 National Committee for Audio-Visual Aids in Education. Occasional Paper†
0077-3964 National Conference on Weights and Measures. Report
0077-3980 National Congress of Parents and Teachers. Proceedings of Annual Convention *changed to* National Congress of Parents and Teachers. Convention Digest.
0077-4006 National Consumer Credit Counseling Service. Proceedings†
0077-4014 Selected and Annotated Bibliography of Reference Materials in Consumer Credit†
0077-4022 National Cottonseed Products Association. Trading Rules
0077-4030 National Council for Geographic Education. Yearbook *changed to* National Council for Geographic Education. Pacesetter Series.
0077-4049 National Council for the Social Studies. Bulletins
0077-4057 National Council for the Social Studies. Social Studies Readings†
0077-4065 N C A E R Occasional Papers†
0077-4073 National Council of Churches. Division of Education and Ministry. Audio-Visual Resource Guide†
0077-4081 National Council of Engineering Examiners. Proceedings *changed to* National Council of Examiners for Engineering and Surveying. Proceedings.
0077-409X National Council of Social Service. Annual Report *changed to* National Council for Voluntary Organizations. Annual Report.
0077-4103 National Council of Teachers of Mathematics. Yearbook
0077-4111 National Council of the Churches of Christ in the U.S.A. Triennial Report *changed to* National Council of the Churches of Christ in the U.S.A. Biennial Report.
0077-4162 National Council on Family Relations. Annual Meeting Proceedings†
0077-4189 National Dahlia Society Annual
0077-4219 National Distribution Directory *changed to* M C D's Warehousing Distribution Directory.
0077-4235 U.S. Food and Drug Administration. National Drug Code Directory
0077-4243 National Education Association of the United States. Addresses and Proceedings *changed to* National Education Association of the United States. Proceedings of the Representative Assembly.
0077-4413 National Electronics Conference. Proceedings *see* 0886-229X
0077-4421 National Electronics Conference. Record†
0077-443X National Engineering Laboratory, East Kilbridge, Scotland. Annual Report†
0077-4448 National Equine (and Smaller Animals) Defence League. Annual Report
0077-4456 N A L G O Annual Report
0077-4472 National Faculty Directory
0077-4480 National Federation of Plastering Contractors. Year Book
0077-4499 National Federation of Retail Newsagents. National Federation Yearbook†
0077-4510 National Fertilizer Development Center. Annual Report *see* 0730-7322
0077-4529 National Finances: An Analysis of the Revenues and Expenditures of the Government of Canada
0077-4537 National Fire Prevention Gazette†
0077-4545 National Fire Protection Association. National Fire Codes
0077-4553 N F P A Technical Committee. Report
0077-4588 National Football League. Record Manual†
0077-4596 National Foundation for Education Research in England and Wales. Occasional Publication Series†
0077-4618 National Geographic Books (Series)
0077-4626 National Geographic Society. Research Reports *see* 1056-800X
0077-4634 National Governors' Conference. Proceedings of the Annual Meeting *see* 0191-3441
0077-4642 National Guild of Piano Teachers. Guild Syllabus
0077-4685 National Heart Foundation of Australia. Research in Progress
0077-4707 National Housing and Town Planning Council. Handbook and Year Book *changed to* National Housing and Town Planning Council. Conference and Exhibition Guide.
0077-4723 National Income Statistics of Thailand *changed to* National Income of Thailand.
0077-4731 National Industrial Fuel Efficiency Service, London Progress Survey with Report and Accounts
0077-474X National Institute for Architectural Education. Yearbook†
0077-4758 National Institute for Personnel Research. Annual Report†
0077-4766 National Institute for Personnel Research. List of N I P R Publications†
0077-4774 National Institute Social Services Library†
0077-4782 National Institute of Agricultural Botany, Cambridge, England. Annual Report of the Council and Accounts *changed to* National Institute of Agricultural Botany, Cambridge, England. Annual Report and Accounts.
0077-4790 National Institute of Agricultural Botany, Cambridge, England. Journal *see* 0952-3863
0077-4820 National Institute of Agricultural Sciences, Tokyo. Bulletin. Series A (Physics and Statistics)†
0077-4839 National Institute of Agricultural Sciences, Tokyo. Bulletin. Series B (Soils and Fertilizers)†
0077-4847 National Institute of Agricultural Sciences, Tokyo. Bulletin. Series C (Plant Pathology and Entomology)†
0077-4855 National Institute of Agricultural Sciences, Tokyo. Bulletin. Series D (Physiology and Genetics)†
0077-4863 National Institute of Agricultural Sciences, Tokyo. Bulletin. Series H (Farm Management, Land Utilization, Rural Life)†
0077-4871 National Institute of Agricultural Sciences, Tokyo. Miscellaneous Publication†
0077-488X Japan. Chiba National Institute of Animal Industry. Bulletin *changed to* Japan. Ibaraki National Institute of Animal Industry. Bulletin.
0077-491X National Institute of Economic and Social Research. Annual Report
0077-4928 National Institute of Economic and Social Research, London. Occasional Papers
0077-4936 National Institute of Economic and Social Research, London. Regional Studies *changed to* National Institute of Economic and Social Research, London. Regional Papers.
0077-4944 N I F P General Series
0077-4952 N I F P Manual Series
0077-4960 N I F P Monograph Series
0077-4979 N I F P Report Series
0077-4987 N I F P Technical Paper Series
0077-4995 Japan. National Institute of Genetics, Mishima. Annual Report
0077-5002 National Institute of Hygienic Sciences. Bulletin
0077-5010 N I I P Bulletin†
0077-5037 Israeli Life Table†
0077-5053 Jamaica. National Insurance Scheme. Annual Reports *changed to* Jamaica. Ministry of Social Security. Report.
0077-5061 National Investment Bank, Ghana. Report of the Directors *changed to* National Investment Bank, Ghana. Annual Report.
0077-5088 National Junior Horticultural Association. Newsletter
0077-5096 National Kidney Foundation. Annual Report
0077-5118 National League for Nursing. Associate Degree Education for Nursing *changed to* Associate Degree Education for Nursing.
0077-5134 National League for Nursing. League Exchange†
0077-5177 National List of Advertisers
0077-5185 National Maritime Board. (Great Britain) Year Book
0077-5193 Sefunim
0077-5223 National Microfilm Association. Proceedings of the Annual Convention *changed to* National Micrographics Association. Proceedings of the Annual Conference.
0077-5231 National Minority Business Directory *changed to* Try Us.
0077-524X National Observer Index†
0077-5258 N O R C Monographs in Social Research†
0077-5266 National Opinion Research Center. Newsletter *see* 0147-0124
0077-5274 National Opinion Research Center. Report *changed to* N O R C Report.
0077-5282 National Party Platforms. Supplement
0077-5290 National Physical Laboratory, Teddington, England. Annual Report†
0077-5312 National Pig Breeders' Association Herd Book *changed to* British Pig Association Herd Book.
0077-5320 National Planning Association Center for Development Planning. Planning Methods Series†
0077-5339 National Psychological Association for Psychoanalysis. Bulletin
0077-5347 National Publishing Directory
0077-5355 N R M C A Publication
0077-5371 National Register of Prominent Americans and International Notables
0077-538X National Register of Scholarships and Fellowships†
0077-5401 National Relay Conference. Proceedings

ISSN INDEX

0077-541X National Reprographic Centre for Documentation, Hertford, England. Technical Evaluation Reports *changed to* National Centre for Information Media & Technology (CIMITECH). Technical Evaluation Reports.
0077-5428 National Research Council, Canada. Associate Committee on Geotechnical Research. Technical Memorandum
0077-5452 National Research Council, Canada. Division of Building Research. Bulletin†
0077-5460 National Research Council, Canada. Division of Building Research. Building Research Note†
0077-5479 National Research Council, Canada. Division of Building Research. Computer Program†
0077-5487 National Research Council, Canada. Division of Building Research. Fire Research Note†
0077-5495 National Research Council, Canada. Division of Building Research. Fire Study†
0077-5509 National Research Council, Canada. Division of Building Research. Housing Note†
0077-5517 National Research Council, Canada. Division of Building Research. Research Program *changed to* National Research Council, Canada. Institute for Research in Construction. Research Program.
0077-5525 National Research Council, Canada. Division of Building Research. Research Paper†
0077-5533 National Research Council, Canada. Division of Building Research. Technical Paper†
0077-5541 National Research Council, Canada. National Aeronautical Establishment. Aeronautical Report (L R Series) *changed to* National Research Council, Canada. Institute for Aerospace Research. Aeronautical Report (A N Series).
0077-555X National Research Council, Canada. National Aeronautical Establishment. Mechanical Engineering Reports *changed to* National Research Council, Canada. Institute for Mechanical Engineering. Mechanical Engineering Reports.
0077-5568 National Research Council, Canada. National Aeronautical Establishment. Publications List and Supplements *changed to* National Research Council, Canada. Institute for Aerospace Research. Publications List and Supplements.
0077-5576 National Science Library of Canada. Annual Report *see* 0703-0320
0077-5592 National Research Council, Canada. Space Research Facilities Branch. Report. (SRFB Series)†
0077-5606 National Research Council, Canada. Technical Translation†
0077-5614 National Cooperative Highway Research Program Reports
0077-5622 Highway Research Board Special Publication *see* 0360-859X
0077-5657 National Rural Electric Cooperative Association. Government Relations Department. Research Division. Research Papers and Circulars.
0077-5673 N S G A Circular
0077-5703 National Securities and Research Corporation. Annual Forecast†
0077-5711 National Shellfisheries Association. Proceedings *see* 0730-8000
0077-572X National Shorthand Reporters Association. Proceedings of the Annual Convention *changed to* National Court Reporters Association. Proceedings of the Annual Convention.
0077-5738 National Skeet Shooting Association. Records Annual
0077-5754 National Society for Prevention of Cruelty to Children. Annual Report
0077-5762 National Society for the Study of Education. Yearbook
0077-5770 National Society of Public Accountants. Proceedings of the Annual Professional Institute†
0077-5789 National Soybean Processors Association. Yearbook *changed to* National Oilseed Processors Association. Yearbook and Trading Rules.
0077-5819 National Taiwan University. College of Agriculture. Memoirs
0077-5827 National Taiwan University. College of Engineering. Memoirs†
0077-5835 National Taiwan University. College of Law. Journal of Social Science
0077-5843 National Taiwan University. Department of Archaeology and Anthropology. Bulletin *changed to* National Taiwan University. Department of Anthropology. Bulletin.
0077-5851 National Taiwan University Journal of Sociology
0077-586X National Tank Truck Carrier Directory
0077-5886 Tire Dealers Survey *see* 0027-7045
0077-5894 National Trade-Index of Southern Africa
0077-5916 National Trust for Scotland Yearbook *see* 0269-0934
0077-5932 N U S Yearbook *changed to* N U S Action.
0077-5940 National Union of Teachers. Annual Report
0077-5959 National University Extension Association. Proceedings†
0077-5975 Nationale-Nederlanden. Annual Report
0077-5983 Nationwide Directory of Men's and Boys' Wear Buyers (Exclusive of New York Metropolitan Area)
0077-5991 Nationwide Directory of Women's and Children's Wear Buyers (Exclusive of New York Metropolitan Area)
0077-6009 Nationwide Major Mass Market Merchandisers (Exclusive of New York Metropolitan Area)
0077-6017 Native American Arts†
0077-6025 Natur und Mensch: Jahresmitteilungen der Naturhistorischen Gesellschaft Nuernberg
0077-6033 Natura Jutlandica
0077-6041 Natural Gas Processing Plants in Canada†
0077-6084 Natural Resources Law Newsletter
0077-6092 Natural Resources Research
0077-6106 Naturegraph Ocean Guidebooks†
0077-6114 Mouvement Naturel de la Population de la Grece
0077-6122 Naturforschende Gesellschaft in Basel. Verhandlungen
0077-6130 Naturforschende Gesellschaft in Bern. Mitteilungen
0077-6149 Naturhistorische Gesellschaft Nuernberg. Abhandlungen
0077-6157 Naturwissenschaftliche Rundschau. Buecher der Zeitschrift
0077-6165 Naturwissenschaftlicher Verein fuer Schleswig-Holstein. Schriften
0077-6173 Nauheimer Fortbildungs-Lehrgaenge†
0077-6181 Nauka dla Wszystkich
0077-619X Nautical Almanac
0077-6211 Nautisches Jahrbuch, oder Ephemeriden und Tafeln
0077-6238 Naval Review
0077-6262 Navigation
0077-6270 Navis
0077-6289 Maritime Survey†
0077-6297 Nawpa Pacha
0077-6343 Nebraska Academy of Sciences. Proceedings
0077-6351 Nebraska Academy of Sciences. Transactions
0077-636X Nebraska. Equal Opportunity Commission. Annual Report†
0077-6378 University of Nebraska. School of Journalism. Depth Report
0077-6386 University of Nebraska Studies. New Series
0077-6394 Nebraska Water Resources Research Institute. University of Nebraska. Annual Report of Activities *changed to* University of Nebraska. Water Center. Annual Report of Activities.
0077-6408 Nebula Award Stories *see* 0162-3818
0077-6416 Nederlands-Zuidafrikaanse Vereniging. Jaarverslag
0077-6432 Nederlandse Malacologische Vereniging. Correspondentieblad
0077-6467 Negev Institute for Arid Zone Research, Beer-Sheva, Israel. Report for Year *changed to* Ben-Gurion University of the Negev. Institutes for Applied Research. Scientific Activities.
0077-6483 Negro in the Congressional Record†
0077-6513 Nelson Gallery and Atkins Museum. Bulletin *changed to* Nelson-Atkins Museum of Art. Bulletin.
0077-6521 Neo-Hellenika
0077-653X Neodidagmata
0077-6548 Nepal Industrial Development Corporation. Annual Report
0077-6556 Nepal Industrial Development Corporation. Industrial Digest
0077-6564 Nepal Industrial Development Corporation. Statistical Abstracts
0077-6572 Nepal Law Translation Series *changed to* Nepal Miscellaneous Series.
0077-6580 Nepal Rastra Bank. Report of the Board of Directors *changed to* Nepal Rastra Bank. Annual Report.
0077-6599 Neprajzi Ertesito
0077-6602 Neprajzi Tanulmanyok
0077-6610 Nerthus†
0077-6637 Nether Press Miscellaneous Series
0077-6645 Jaarstatistiek de in-en Uitvoer per Land van de Nederlandse Antillen
0077-6653 Jaarstatistiek van de in-en Uitvoer per Goederensoort van de Nederlandse Antillen
0077-6661 Netherlands Antilles. Bureau voor de Statistiek. Statistisch Jaarboek
0077-667X Netherlands Antilles. Bureau voor de Statistiek. Statistiek van de Meteorologische Waarnemingen in de Nederlandse Antillen
0077-6688 Netherlands. Centraal Bureau voor de Statistiek. Bezoek aan Vermakelijkheidsinstellingen. Attendance at Public Entertainments†
0077-670X Belastingdruk in Nederland†
0077-6777 Sportaccommodatie in Nederland
0077-6785 Netherlands. Centraal Bureau voor de Statistiek. Voorziening in de Behoefte aan Onderwijzers Bij het Lager Onderwijs. Supplying the Need for Teachers in Elementary Education†
0077-6793 Netherlands. Centraal Bureau voor de Statistiek. Faillissementsstatistiek. Bankruptcies
0077-6815 Netherlands. Centraal Bureau voor de Statistiek. Gevangenisstatistiek
0077-6823 Netherlands. Centraal Bureau voor de Statistiek. Hypotheken en Hypotheekbanken. Statistics of Mortgages *see* 0168-4590
0077-6904 Omvang der Vakbeweging in Nederland *see* 0168-4035
0077-6912 Netherlands. Centraal Bureau voor de Statistiek. Produktiestatistieken. Production Statistics of Individual Industries†
0077-6955 Netherlands. Centraal Bureau voor de Statistiek. Statistiek der Branden
0077-6963 Netherlands. Centraal Bureau voor de Statistiek. Statistiek der Lonen in de Landbouw. Statistics of Wages in Agriculture†
0077-698X Netherlands. Centraal Bureau voor de Statistiek. Statistiek der Motorrijtuigen *see* 0168-4973
0077-7005 Netherlands. Centraal Bureau voor de Statistiek. Statistiek der Spaarbanken. Statistical View of the Savings Banks†
0077-7048 Netherlands. Centraal Bureau voor de Statistiek. Statistische en Econometrische Onderzoekingen *changed to* Netherlands. Centraal Bureau voor de Statistiek. Statistische Onderzoekingen.
0077-7110 Netherlands. Centraal Bureau voor de Statistiek. Statistiek van de Investeringen in Vaste Activa in de Industrie *see* 0168-7956
0077-7196 Netherlands. Centraal Bureau voor de Statistiek. Statistiek van de Uitgaven der Overheid voor Cultuur en Recreatie *see* 0168-4248
0077-720X Netherlands. Centraal Bureau voor de Statistiek. Statistiek van de Uitgaven der Overheid voor Onderwijs, Wetenschap en Cultuur. Statistics of the Expenditure of the State, the Provinces and the Municipalities on Education, Science and Culture†
0077-7218 Netherlands. Centraal Bureau voor de Statistiek. Statistiek van de Voorlichting Bij Beroepskeuze *see* 0168-423X
0077-7226 Netherlands. Centraal Bureau voor de Statistiek. Statistiek van de Gemeentewege per Leerling Beschikbaar Gestelde Bedragenter Bestrijding van de Materiele Exploitatiekosten der Lagere Scholen. *see* 0168-5244
0077-7285 Netherlands. Centraal Bureau voor de Statistiek. Statistiek van het Beroepsonderwijs *see* 0168-5457
0077-7293 Netherlands. Centraal Bureau voor de Statistiek. Statistiek van het Internationaal Goederenvervoer *see* 0168-4876
0077-7307 Netherlands. Centraal Bureau voor de Statistiek. Statistiek van het Kunstonderwijs. Statistics on Art Colleges *see* 0168-5503
0077-7315 Netherlands. Centraal Bureau voor de Statistiek. Statistiek van Het Kleuteronderwijs. Statistics of Nursery Schools†
0077-7323 Netherlands. Centraal Bureau voor de Statistiek. Statistiek van het Kweekschoolonderwijs. Statistics on Teacher Training Colleges *changed to* Netherlands. Centraal Bureau voor de Statistiek. Statistiek van het Beroepsonderwijs: Opleidingsscholen Kleuterleidsters en Pedagogische Academies.
0077-7331 Netherlands. Centraal Bureau voor de Statistiek. Statistiek van het Land- en Tuinbouwonderwijs. Statistics Concerning Agricultural and Horticultural Education *changed to* Netherlands. Centraal Bureau voor de Statistiek. Statistiek van het Hoger Beroepsonderwijs: Agrarisch Onderwijs.
0077-734X Netherlands. Centraal Bureau voor de Statistiek. Statistiek van het Nijverheidsonderwijs *see* 0168-5406
0077-7366 Netherlands. Centraal Bureau voor de Statistiek. Statistiek van het Schriftelijk Onderwijs *see* 0168-4906
0077-7374 Netherlands. Centraal Bureau voor de Statistiek. Statistiek van het Sociaal-Pedagogisch Onderwijs *see* 0168-5600
0077-7382 Netherlands. Centraal Bureau voor de Statistiek. Statistiek van Het Toneel. Statistics on Theatre Performances†
0077-7390 Netherlands. Centraal Bureau voor de Statistiek. Statistiek van Het Uitgebreid Lager Onderwijs. Statistics of Continued Elementary Education†
0077-7404 Leraren - Statistics of Secondary Education: Teachers *see* 0168-5856

5538 ISSN INDEX

0077-7471 Netherlands. Centraal Bureau voor de Statistiek. Toepassing der Kinderwetten *changed to* Netherlands. Centraal Bureau voor de Statistiek. Justiciele Kinderbescherming.
0077-7501 Vakantiebesteding van de Nederlandse Bevolking *see* 0168-3411
0077-751X Netherlands. Centraal Bureau voor de Statistiek. Winststatistiek der Grotere Naamloze Vennootschappen†
0077-7528 Netherlands. Centraal Bureau voor de Statistiek. Zuivelstatistiek *see* 0168-518X
0077-7536 Netherlands. Centraal Planbureau. Centraal Economisch Plan
0077-7552 Netherlands. Commissie Zeehavenoverleg. Jaarverslag *changed to* Nationale Havenraad. Jaarverslag (Year).
0077-7560 Netherlands Investment Bank for Developing Countries. Annual Report *changed to* Netherlands Investment Bank for Developing Countries. Report.
0077-7579 Netherlands Journal of Sea Research
0077-7587 Yearbook Geomagnetism: Paramaribo, Surinam†
0077-7595 Netherlands Nitrogen Technical Bulletin *see* 0169-2313
0077-7609 Produktschap voor Siergewassen. Jaarverslag *changed to* Produktschap voor Siergewassen. Jaarverslag - Statistiek.
0077-7617 Netherlands. Rijks Geologische Dienst. Jaarverslag
0077-7625 Netherlands. Rijkscommissie voor Geodesie. Publications on Geodesy. New Series *changed to* Netherlands. Commissie voor Geodesie. Publications on Geodesy. New Series.
0077-7633 Universite de Neuchatel. Faculte des Lettres. Recueil de Travaux
0077-7641 Universite de Neuchatel. Seminaire de Geometrie. Publications. Serie 1. Courtes Publications *changed to* Centre de Recherches en Mathematiques Pures. P 1.
0077-765X Universite de Neuchatel. Seminaire de Geometrie. Publications. Serie 2. Monographies *changed to* Centre de Recherches en Mathematiques Pures. Publications. Serie 2. Monographies.
0077-7668 Neudrucke Deutscher Literaturwerke
0077-7676 Neudrucke Deutscher Literaturwerke. Sonderreihe
0077-7684 Neue Beitraege zur Englischen Philologie†
0077-7706 Neue Muenstersche Beitraege zur Geschichtsforschung†
0077-7714 Neue Musikgeschichtliche Forschungen
0077-7730 Neues aus der Mariahilfer Strasse†
0077-7749 Neues Jahrbuch fuer Geologie und Palaeontologie. Abhandlungen
0077-7757 Neues Jahrbuch fuer Mineralogie. Abhandlungen
0077-7765 Neues Trierisches Jahrbuch *changed to* Neues Trierisches Jahrbuch fuer Heimatpflege und Heimatgeschichte.
0077-7773 Neumanns Jahrbuch der Deutschen Versicherungswirtschaft. Teil 1: Personenversicherung (Lebens- und Krankenversicherung)†
0077-7781 Neumanns Jahrbuch der Deutschen Versicherungswirtschaft. Teil 2: Schaden- und Rueckversicherung†
0077-779X Neumanns Jahrbuch der Deutschen Versicherungswirtschaft. Teil 3: Institutionen, Uebersichten und Anschriften†
0077-7803 Neuro-Ophthalmology†
0077-7838 Neuroradiology Workshop†
0077-7846 Neurosciences Research†
0077-7862 Neusser Jahrbuch fuer Kunst, Kulturgeschichte und Heimatkunde
0077-7889 Nevada. Division of Personnel. Biennial Report†
0077-7897 Nevada. State Museum, Carson City. Anthropological Papers
0077-7900 Nevada. State Museum, Carson City. Natural History Publications
0077-7919 Nevada. State Museum, Carson City. Occasional Papers
0077-7927 Nevada. State Museum, Carson City. Popular Series
0077-7935 Nevada Studies in History and Political Science *changed to* Wilbur S. Shepperson Series in History and Humanities.
0077-7943 University of Nevada. Bureau of Business and Economic Research. Research Report
0077-7951 Nevada. University System. Western Studies Center. Desert Research Institute Publications in the Social Sciences *see* 0271-1001
0077-7986 New Acronyms and Initialisms *see* 0148-866X
0077-7994 New African Literature and the Arts†
0077-8036 New Brunswick. Department of Fisheries. Annual Report *changed to* New Brunswick. Department of Fisheries and Aquaculture. Annual Report.
0077-8052 New Brunswick. Department of Labour. Annual Report *changed to* New Brunswick. Department of Labour. Annual Report.
0077-8060 New Brunswick. Department of Municipal Affairs. Report†
0077-8079 New Brunswick. Department of Youth. Report
0077-8087 New Brunswick. Liquor Control Commission. Report†
0077-8109 New Brunswick. Mineral Resources Branch. Report of Investigations
0077-8117 New Brunswick. Research and Productivity Council. Report *changed to* New Brunswick. Research and Productivity Council. Annual Report.
0077-8168 New Campus†
0077-8206 N D T†
0077-8222 New England Guide *see* 0734-4066
0077-8230 New England Papers on Education†
0077-832X New Hampshire. Agricultural Experiment Station, Durham. Research Reports
0077-8338 New Hampshire. Agricultural Experiment Station, Durham. Station Bulletins
0077-8346 New Hampshire Archeologist
0077-8362 New Hampshire. Fish and Game Department. Biennial Report
0077-8370 New Hampshire. Fish and Game Department. Game Management and Research Division. Biological Survey Series
0077-8389 New Hampshire. Fish and Game Department. Game Management and Research Division. Technical Circular Series.
0077-8397 New Hampshire. Fish and Game Department. Game Management and Research Division. Biological Survey Bulletin
0077-8427 New Hampshire Winter Holidays†
0077-8435 New Hebrides. Anglo-French Condominium Geological Survey. Annual Reports *changed to* Vanuatu. Geological Survey. Annual Reports.
0077-8443 Vanuatu. Geological Survey. Reports
0077-8451 New Jersey Clean Air Council. Report
0077-846X New Jersey. Department of Agriculture. Highlights of the Annual Report *changed to* New Jersey Agriculture.
0077-8478 New Jersey. Economic Policy Council. Annual Report of Economic Policy Council and Office of Economic Policy†
0077-8508 New Jersey Public Employer-Employee Relations†
0077-8516 New Jersey Speech and Hearing Association. Newsletter
0077-8540 New Mexico Agricultural Statistics
0077-8559 New Mexico. Employment Security Commission. Annual Rural Manpower Service Report *changed to* New Mexico. Employment Services Department. Annual Rural Manpower Service Report.
0077-8567 New Mexico Geological Society. Guidebook, Field Conference
0077-8575 New Mexico Statistical Abstract
0077-8583 University of New Mexico Art Museum. Bulletin
0077-8591 New Official Guide: Japan
0077-8605 New Orleans Academy of Ophthalmology. Transactions
0077-8613 New Perspectives in Political Science†
0077-8621 New Poetry
0077-8672 New South Wales. Department of Mines. Chemical Laboratory. Report†
0077-8680 New South Wales. Department of Mines. Coalfields Branch. Reports†
0077-8699 New South Wales. Department of Mines. Memoirs: Palaeontology *changed to* New South Wales. Geological Survey. Memoirs: Palaeontology.
0077-8710 New South Wales. Geological Survey. Memoirs: Geology
0077-8729 New South Wales. Geological Survey. Mineral Industry Series
0077-8737 New South Wales. Geological Survey. Mineral Resources Series
0077-8753 New South Wales National Herbarium. Contributions *see* 0312-9764
0077-8788 New South Wales. State Fisheries. Research Bulletin†
0077-8796 University of New South Wales. School of Civil Engineering. U N I C I V Reports. Series I
0077-880X University of New South Wales. School of Civil Engineering. U N I C I V Reports. Series R
0077-8818 University of New South Wales. Water Research Laboratory, Manly Vale. Laboratory Research Reports
0077-8826 New Teacher
0077-8842 New Testament Tools and Studies
0077-8869 New Trade Names in the Rubber and Plastics Industries *see* 0747-4954
0077-8877 New Trends in Biology Teaching
0077-8885 New Trends in Chemistry Teaching
0077-8893 New Trends in Mathematics Teaching
0077-8907 New Trends in Physics Teaching
0077-8923 New York Academy of Sciences. Annals
0077-8931 New York Botanical Garden. Memoirs
0077-894X City College Papers†
0077-8958 Metropolitan Museum Journal
0077-8974 New York Crop Reporting Service. Statistics Relative to the Dairy Industry in New York State *see* 0732-9121
0077-9008 New York Psychoanalytic Institute. Kris Study Group. Monographs
0077-9016 New York Public Library. Films†
0077-9024 New York Publicity Outlets
0077-9059 New York State Archeological Association. Occasional Papers†
0077-9067 New York State Archeological Association. Researches and Transactions†
0077-9083 New York State Business Fact Book. Part 1: Business and Manufacturing†
0077-9091 New York State Business Fact Book. Part 2: Population and Housing†
0077-9105 New York State Business Fact Book. Supplement
0077-9113 A F R I Research Note†
0077-9148 New York (State) Crime Victims Compensation Board. Report *changed to* New York (State). Crime Victims Board. Report.
0077-9156 New York (State). Department of Commerce. Research Bulletin *changed to* New York (State) Department of Economic Development. Research Bulletin.
0077-9172 College and University Degrees Conferred, New York State
0077-9180 College and University Enrollment in New York State *see* 0147-5894
0077-9210 Distribution of High School Graduates and College Going Rate, New York State
0077-9229 Public School Professional Personnel Report, New York State
0077-9245 New York (State) Education Department. Public School Professional Personnel Report *see* 0077-9229
0077-9253 Nonpublic School Enrollment and Staff, New York State
0077-927X New York (State) Interdepartmental Committee on Indian Affairs. Report†
0077-9296 Checklist of Official Publications of the State of New York
0077-930X New York State Library, Albany. Library Development. Excerpts from New York State Education Law, Rules of the Board of Regents, and Regulations of the Commissioner of Education Pertaining to Public and Free Association Libraries, Library Systems, Trustees and Librarians
0077-9318 New York State Library, Albany. Library Development. Institution Libraries Statistics
0077-9326 New York State Library, Albany. Library Development. Public and Association Libraries Statistics
0077-9334 New York (State) Division of the Budget. New York State Statistical Yearbook *changed to* New York (State). Rockefeller Institute of Government. New York State Statistical Yearbook.
0077-9342 Analysis of School Finances, New York State School Districts
0077-9385 State University of New York, College at Buffalo. Program in Soviet and East Central European Studies. Publications *changed to* State University of New York. College at Buffalo's Program in East European and Slavic Studies. Publications.
0077-9407 New York (State) Upstate Medical Center, Syracuse. Library. Faculty Bibliography†
0077-9415 New York (State) Upstate Medical Center, Syracuse. Library. Library Guide†
0077-9423 New York State Urban Development Corporation. Annual Report
0077-944X New York University. Comparative Criminal Law Project. Publications *changed to* Wayne State University Law School. Comparative Criminal Law Project. Publications Series.
0077-9490 New York University. Libraries. Bulletin of the Tamiment Library *changed to* New York University. Bulletin of the Tamiment Institute - Ben Josephson Library.
0077-9504 New York University Studies in Comparative Literature†
0077-9520 New Zealand Agricultural Engineering Institute. Annual Report†
0077-9539 Lincoln College. New Zealand Agricultural Engineering Institute. Extension Bulletin†
0077-9563 Lincoln College. New Zealand Agricultural Engineering Institute. Research Publication†
0077-9571 New Zealand Business Who's Who
0077-958X New Zealand. Central Advisory Committee on the Appointments and Promotion of Primary Teachers. Report to the Minister of Education
0077-9601 New Zealand. Department of Scientific and Industrial Research. Annual Report
0077-961X New Zealand. Department of Scientific and Industrial Research. Bulletin†

ISSN

0077-9628 New Zealand. Department of Scientific and Industrial Research. Geological Survey. Bulletin *changed to* New Zealand Geological Survey. Bulletin.

0077-9636 New Zealand. Department of Scientific and Industrial Research. Information Series†

0077-9644 New Zealand. Soil Bureau. Bulletin†

0077-9652 New Zealand. Department of Statistics. Annual Report of the Government Statistician†

0077-9687 New Zealand. Department of Statistics. Population Census: Ages and Marital Status *changed to* New Zealand. Department of Statistics. Population Census: Ages, Marital Status and Fertility.

0077-9695 New Zealand. Department of Statistics. Population Census: Dwellings

0077-9709 New Zealand. Department of Statistics. Population Census: Education *changed to* New Zealand. Department of Statistics. Population Census: Education and Training.

0077-9717 New Zealand. Department of Statistics. Population Census: General Report *see* 0110-8700

0077-9725 Households *changed to* New Zealand. Department of Statistics. Population Census: Families.

0077-9733 Incomes *changed to* New Zealand. Department of Statistics. Population Census: Incomes and Welfare Payments.

0077-9741 New Zealand. Department of Statistics. Population Census: Industries and Occupations *changed to* New Zealand. Department of Statistics. Population Census: Labour Force.

0077-9776 New Zealand. Department of Statistics. Population Census: Race *changed to* New Zealand. Department of Statistics. Population Census: Birthplaces and Ethnic Origin.

0077-9784 New Zealand. Department of Statistics. Population Census: Religious Professions

0077-9792 New Zealand. Department of Statistics. Population Census. Increase and Location of Population *changed to* New Zealand. Department of Statistics. Population Census: Total Population Statistics.

0077-9806 New Zealand. Department of Statistics. Report and Analysis of External Trade *see* 0114-2607

0077-9822 New Zealand. Department of Statistics. Statistical Report of Farm Production *see* 0110-4624

0077-9865 New Zealand. Department of Statistics. Industrial Production†

0077-9903 New Zealand. Department of Statistics. Statistical Report of Population, Migration and Building. *see* 0113-3667

0077-9911 New Zealand. Department of Statistics. Prices, Wages and Labour *see* 0112-6598

0077-9946 New Zealand Ecological Society. Proceedings *see* 0110-6465

0077-9954 New Zealand Economic Papers

0077-9962 New Zealand Entomologist

0077-9997 New Zealand. Forest Research Institute. Report

0078-0006 New Zealand. Forest Research Institute. Technical Paper†

0078-0022 New Zealand Geographical Society. Miscellaneous Series

0078-0030 New Zealand Geography Conference Proceedings Series

0078-0049 New Zealand Institute of Economic Research. Discussion Paper

0078-0057 New Zealand Institute of Economic Research. Annual Report

0078-0065 New Zealand Institute of Economic Research. Research Paper *see* 0113-1877

0078-0073 New Zealand Institute of Economic Research. Technical Memorandum†

0078-0081 New Zealand Law Register

0078-009X New Zealand Library School, Wellington. Bibliographical Series†

0078-0103 New Zealand Library School, Wellington. Occasional Papers†

0078-0111 New Zealand. Marine Department. Annual Report on Fisheries†

0078-0138 New Zealand. Meat and Wool Boards' Economic Service. Annual Review of the Sheep Industry *changed to* New Zealand. Meat and Wool Boards' Economic Service. Annual Review of the New Zealand Sheep & Beef Industry.

0078-0146 New Zealand Medical Records Officers' Association. Conference Proceedings†

0078-0154 New Zealand. National Research Advisory Council. Senior and Post Doctoral Research Fellowship Awards for Research in New Zealand Government Departments†

0078-0170 New Zealand Official Year-Book

0078-0189 New Zealand Pottery and Ceramics Research Association. Technical Report†

0078-0219 New Zealand Wheat Review†

0078-0243 Newcastle History Monographs

0078-0251 University of Newcastle-Upon-Tyne. Philosophical Society. Proceedings

0078-026X University of Newcastle-Upon-Tyne. Department of Geography. Research Series

0078-0278 Newfoundland and Labrador. Department of Education. Statistical Supplement to the Annual Report†

0078-0286 Newfoundland and Labrador Who's Who†

0078-0294 Newfoundland. Department of Social Services. Annual Report

0078-0308 Newfoundland. Mineral Development Division. Geological Survey. Bulletin. *changed to* Newfoundland. Geological Survey Branch. Bulletin.

0078-0316 Newfoundland Medical Directory

0078-0340 Newfoundland. Mineral Development Division. Information *changed to* Newfoundland. Geological Survey Branch. Information.

0078-0359 Newfoundland. Mineral Development Division. Information Circular *changed to* Newfoundland. Geological Survey Branch. Information Circular.

0078-0367 Newfoundland. Mines Branch. Annual Report Series

0078-0383 Newfoundland. Mines Branch. Geological Survey of Newfoundland. Report Series

0078-0421 Newsletters on Stratigraphy

0078-043X Newspaper Press Directory *changed to* Benn's Media Directory. U.K. Edition.

0078-0448 Israel. Government Press Office. Newspapers and Periodicals Appearing in Israel†

0078-0502 Niagara Parks Commission. Annual Report

0078-0510 Nicaragua. Direccion General de Aduanas. Memoria

0078-0537 Niederdeutsche Beitraege zur Kunstgeschichte

0078-0545 Niederdeutsches Wort

0078-0561 Niedersaechsisches Jahrbuch fuer Landesgeschichte *changed to* Niedersachsisches Jahrbuch.

0078-057X Nigeria Annual and Trading Directory

0078-0588 Nigeria Assistance Programs of U.S. Non-Profit Organizations†

0078-0596 Nigeria Business Directory

0078-0626 Nigeria. Federal Office of Statistics. Annual Abstract of Statistics

0078-0634 Nigeria. Federal Office of Statistics. Review of External Trade

0078-0642 Nigeria. Federal Office of Statistics. Trade Report†

0078-0650 Nigeria Trade Summary

0078-0677 University of Nigeria. Report on Research†

0078-0685 Nigeria Year Book

0078-0693 Nigerian Books in Print

0078-0707 Nigerian Chamber of Mines. Annual Review

0078-0715 Nigerian Institute for Oil Palm Research. Journal *changed to* Nigerian Journal of Palms and Oil Seeds.

0078-0723 Nigerian Institute of International Affairs. Digest of Selected Articles on International Questions†

0078-074X Nigerian Institute of Social and Economic Research. Annual Report

0078-0758 Nigerian Institute of Social and Economic Research. Information Bulletin†

0078-0766 Nigerian Institute of Social and Economic Research. Library. List of Accessions

0078-0774 Nigerian Law Journal†

0078-0782 Nigerian Medical Directory

0078-0812 Current National Bibliography *see* 0331-0019

0078-0820 Nigerian Tobacco Company. Report *changed to* Nigerian Tobacco Company. Annual Report and Accounts.

0078-0839 Nippon Jui Chikusan Daigaku Kiyo *see* 0373-8361

0078-0847 N I B S Bulletin of Biological Research†

0078-0855 Nityanand Universal Series

0078-0863 Nivel de la Economia Argentina

0078-088X N M R Basic Principles and Progress *see* 0170-5989

0078-0898 NMR Data Table for Organic Compounds†

0078-0901 Nobel Symposium Series

0078-091X Noble Official Catalog of Canada Precancels

0078-0928 Noble Official Catalog of United States Bureau Precancels

0078-0936 Noctes Romanae

0078-0944 Noda Institute for Scientific Research. Report

0078-0952 Nomenclator Zoologicus

0078-0960 Nomenclature des Entreprises Nationales a Caractere Industriel ou Commercial et des Societies d'Economie Mixte d'Interet National

0078-0979 Nomos

0078-0987 Non-Ferrous Metal Works of the World

0078-0995 Non-Metallic Solids†

0078-1029 Nord-Norge Naeringsliv og Oekonomi

0078-1037 Nordelbingen

0078-1045 Nordfriesisches Jahrbuch

0078-1053 Nordicana

0078-1061 Nordisk Medicinhistorisk Aarsbok

0078-107X Nordisk Numismatisk Aarsskrift†

0078-1088 Nordisk Statistisk Aarsbok

0078-1096 Nordisk Statistisk Skriftserie

0078-110X Nordiska Afrikainstitutet. Skriftserie†

0078-1118 Nordic Association for American Studies. Publications†

0078-1126 N K B Skriftserie

0078-1134 Nordistica Gothoburgensia

0078-1150 Norfolk Holiday Handbook *changed to* Holiday Hints Handbook.

0078-1169 Norfolk Record Society. Publications

0078-1185 Norges Bank. Report and Accounts

0078-1193 Norges Geotekniske Institutt. Publikasjon

0078-1207 Norwegian Geotechnical Institute. Technical Report†

0078-1215 Norges Handels-Kalender

0078-1223 Norges Landbruksoekonomiske Institutt. Driftsgranskinger i Jordbruket *see* 0333-2500

0078-1231 Norges Teknisk-Naturvitenskapelige Forskningsraad. Aarsberetning

0078-124X Norges Teknisk-Naturvitenskapelige Forskningsraad. Transportoekonomisk Institutt. Aarsberetning *changed to* Transportoekonomisk Institutt. Aarsberetning.

0078-1266 Norsk Litteraer Aarbok

0078-1274 North American Association of Alcoholism Programs. Meeting. Selected Papers *changed to* A D P A Selected Papers of Annual Meetings.

0078-1282 North American Association of Alcoholism Programs. N A A P Facilities Directory *see* 0092-3826

0078-1304 North American Fauna

0078-1312 North American Flora

0078-1320 North American Forest Soils Conference. Proceedings†

0078-1339 North American Protestant Ministries Overseas *changed to* Mission Handbook: U S A - Canada Protestant Ministries Overseas.

0078-1347 North American Radio-T V Guide†

0078-1355 North American Wildlife and Natural Resources Conference. Transactions

0078-1371 North Carolina. Division of Health Services. Public Health Statistics Branch. North Carolina Vital Statistics *changed to* North Carolina. Department of Environment, Health and Natural Resources. State Center for Health and Environmental Statistics. North Carolina Vital Statistics.

0078-138X North Carolina. Department of Revenue. Franchise Tax and Corporate Income Tax Bulletins for Taxable Years *changed to* North Carolina. Department of Revenue. Franchise Tax and Corporate Income Tax Rules and Regulations.

0078-1398 North Carolina. Division of Mineral Resources. Special Publication *changed to* North Carolina. Department of Natural Resources and Community Development. Division of Land Resources. Special Publication.

0078-141X North Carolina. State Commission on Higher Education Facilities. Facilities Inventory and Utilization Study, for the State of North Carolina

0078-1428 North Carolina State University. Development Council. Report *changed to* North Carolina State University. Chancellor's Report.

0078-1444 North Carolina State University. School of Design. (Student Publication Magazine)

0078-1452 University of North Carolina, Chapel Hill. Graduate School of Business Administration. Technical Papers†

0078-1460 University of North Carolina, Greensboro. Faculty Publications†

0078-1495 University of North Carolina, Chapel Hill. Institute of Statistics. Mimeo Series

0078-1525 North Carolina State University. Water Resources Research Institute. Report *see* 0549-799X

0078-1541 North Dakota Crop and Livestock Statistics *changed to* North Dakota Agricultural Statistics.

0078-155X North Dakota. Employment Security Bureau. Annual Report *changed to* Job Service North Dakota. Annual Report.

0078-1568 North Dakota. Employment Security Bureau. Biennial Report to the Governor *changed to* Job Service North Dakota. Biennial Report to the Governor.

0078-1576 North Dakota. Geological Survey. Miscellaneous Series

0078-1592 North-Holland Linguistic Series

0078-1622 North Pacific Fur Seal Commission. Proceedings of the Annual Meeting†

0078-1630 North Queensland Naturalist

0078-1649 North Staffordshire Journal of Field Studies *see* 0950-1630

0078-1681 Northeast Folklore

5540 ISSN INDEX

0078-169X Northeastern University Studies in Rehabilitation†
0078-1703 Northeastern Weed Science Society. Proceedings
0078-1711 Northern Cavern and Mine Research Society. Occasional Publications *changed to* Northern Mine Research Society. Occasional Publications.
0078-172X Northern History
0078-1738 Northern House Pamphlet Poets
0078-1746 Northern Ireland. Department of Agriculture. Annual Report on Research, Development and Technical Work *changed to* Northern Ireland. Department of Agriculture. Annual Report on Research and Development.
0078-1754 Northern Ireland. Department of Agriculture. Record of Agricultural Research†
0078-1762 North-Central State. Ministry of Works. Report *changed to* Kaduna State. Ministry of Works. Report.
0078-1770 Northern Virginia Planning District Commission. Annual Report†
0078-1789 Northwest Historical Series
0078-1797 Northwest Wood Products Clinic. Proceedings†
0078-1800 Northwestern-Iowa Dealer Reference Manual *changed to* Northwestern Lumbermens Association Dealer Reference Manual.
0078-1843 Norway. Fiskeridirektoratet. Skrifter. Serie Fiskeri†
0078-186X Norway. Fiskeridirektoratet. Skrifter. Serie Teknologiske Undersoekelser†
0078-1878 Norway. Statistisk Sentralbyraa. Arbeidsmarkedstatistikk - Labour Market Statistics
0078-1886 Norway. Statistisk Sentralbyraa. Industristatistikk *see* 0800-580X
0078-1886 Norway. Statistisk Sentralbyraa. Industristatistikk *see* 0800-5818
0078-1894 Norway. Statistisk Sentralbyraa. Jordbruksstatistikk
0078-1908 Norway. Statistisk Sentralbyraa. Kredittmarked Statistikk
0078-1916 Norway. Statistisk Sentralbyraa. Loennsstatistikk
0078-1924 Norway. Statistisk Sentralbyraa. Oekonomisk Utsyn†
0078-1940 Norway. Statistisk Sentralbyraa. Utenrikshandel
0078-1959 Norway. Statistisk Sentralbyraa. Varehandelsstatistikk
0078-1967 Norwegian-American Historical Association. Newsletter
0078-1975 Norwegian-American Historical Association. Travel and Description Series
0078-1983 Norwegian-American Studies
0078-1991 Norwegian Studies in English†
0078-2009 Notas de Algebra y Analisis
0078-2017 Notas de Logica Matematica
0078-2025 Notes for Medical Catalogers *see* 0027-9641
0078-2041 Notes in Anthropology†
0078-205X Noticiario Arqueologico Hispanico *see* 0211-1748
0078-2076 University of Notre Dame. Department of Economics. Union-Management Conference. Proceeding†
0078-2084 Geographical Field Group (Nottingham). Regional Studies
0078-2106 University of Nottingham. School of Agriculture. Report†
0078-2114 Town and Country Planning Summer School: Report of Proceedings
0078-2122 Nottingham Medieval Studies
0078-2130 O.R.S.T.O.M. Recueils des Travaux. Oceanographie *changed to* O.R.S.T.O.M. Resumes des Travaux. Oceanographie.
0078-2157 Nouveautes Techniques Maritimes†
0078-2165 Nouvelle Bibliotheque Nervalienne
0078-2211 Nouvelles Economiques
0078-2238 Nova Hedwiga, Beihefte
0078-2246 Nova Kepleriana. Neue Folge
0078-2254 Instituto de Investigacao Agronomica de Angola. Relatorio
0078-2262 Instituto de Investigacao Agronomica de Angola. Serie Cientifica
0078-2270 Instituto de Investigacao Agronomica de Angola. Serie Tecnica
0078-2300 Nova Scotia Community Planning Conference Proceedings†
0078-2319 Nova Scotia. Department of Bacteriology. Annual Report†
0078-2351 Nova Scotia. Department of Pathology. Annual Report†
0078-236X Nova Scotia. Department of Health. Nutrition Division. Annual Report
0078-2378 Nova Scotia. Emergency Measures Organization. Report†
0078-2386 Nova Scotia Fruit Growers Association. Annual Report and Proceedings
0078-2459 Nova Scotia Power Corporation. Annual Report
0078-2483 Nova Scotia Research Foundation. Bulletin†
0078-2491 Nova Scotia Technical College. School of Architecture. Report Series *changed to* Technical University of Nova Scotia. School of Architecture. Report Series.
0078-2521 Nova Scotian Institute of Science. Proceedings
0078-253X Novarien
0078-2564 Novos Taxa Entomologicos†
0078-2602 Nuclear Medicine Seminar†
0078-2653 Nuernberger Forschungen
0078-2696 Numismatic Chronicle and Journal
0078-270X Numismatic Literature. Supplement†
0078-2718 Numismatic Notes and Monographs
0078-2726 Numismatica Moravica
0078-2734 Numismatiska Meddelanden
0078-2742 Nuntiaturberichte aus Deutschland Nebst Ergaenzenden Aktenstuecken
0078-2769 Nuovi Saggi
0078-2777 Stadtbibliothek Nuernberg. Ausstellungskatalog
0078-2785 Beitraege zur Geschichte und Kultur der Stadt Nuernberg
0078-2807 S I N - Staedtebauinstitut. Schriftenreihe
0078-2815 S I N - Staedtebauinstitut. Studienhefte
0078-2823 S I N - Staedtebauinstitut. Werkberichte
0078-2831 Nursing Education Monographs†
0078-284X Nutrition News in Zambia
0078-2858 Nyelveszeti Tanulmanyok
0078-2866 Nyelvtudomanyi Ertekezesek
0078-2874 O.I.G.G.†
0078-2882 O.P. Market
0078-2890 Oak Ridge Institute for Nuclear Studies. Medical Division. Research Report *changed to* Oak Ridge Associated Universities. Medical Sciences Division. Research Report.
0078-2904 Oak Ridge Institute for Nuclear Studies. Report *changed to* Oak Ridge Associated Universities. Annual Report.
0078-2920 Oberhessische Gesellschaft fuer Natur- und Heilkunde, Giessen. Berichte
0078-2939 Oberrheinische Geologische Abhandlungen†
0078-2947 Oberrheinischer Geologischer Verein. Jahresberichte und Mitteilungen
0078-2955 Objecta
0078-2963 Obraz Literatury Polskiej
0078-3005 Occasional Papers in Anthropology
0078-3013 Occasional Papers in Economic and Social History *changed to* Monographs in Economic and Social History.
0078-303X Occasional Papers in English Local History
0078-3048 Occasional Papers in Estate Management
0078-3056 Occasional Papers in Geography *changed to* Monographs in Geography.
0078-3064 Occasional Papers in Industrial Relations†
0078-3072 Occasional Papers in International Affairs *changed to* Harvard Studies in International Affairs.
0078-3080 Occasional Papers in Librarianship†
0078-3099 Occasional Papers in Modern Languages *changed to* Monographs in Modern Languages.
0078-3129 Occupational Safety and Health Series
0078-3137 Ocean Engineering Information Series
0078-3153 Ocean Technology†
0078-3161 Oceana Docket Classics†
0078-317X Oceana Docket Series†
0078-3188 Oceanic Linguistics. Special Publications
0078-320X Oceanographic Research Institute. Investigational Report
0078-3218 Oceanography and Marine Biology: an Annual Review
0078-3226 Elsevier Oceanography Series
0078-3234 Oceanologia
0078-3250 Ochrona Przyrody
0078-3269 Octagon Lectures†
0078-3277 Odense University Slavic Studies
0078-3285 Odense University Studies in Art History
0078-3293 Odense University Studies in English
0078-3307 Odense University Studies in History and Social Sciences
0078-3315 Odense University Studies in Linguistics
0078-3323 Odense University Studies in Literature
0078-3331 Odense University Studies in Scandinavian Languages and Literatures
0078-3358 Odontologiska Samfundet i Finland. Aarsbok
0078-3366 Odrodzenie w Polsce†
0078-3374 O'Dwyer's Directory of Public Relations Firms
0078-3390 Oekonometrie und Unternehmensforschung
0078-3404 Oekonomische Studientexte *see* 0233-0946
0078-3412 Oenologie Pratique†
0078-3420 Oerlikon Schweissmitteilungen
0078-3439 Oesterreichisches Ost- und Suedosteuropa Institut. Schriftenreihe
0078-3455 Das Oesterreichische Buch
0078-3463 Oesterreichische Gesellschaft fuer Aussenpolitik und Internationale Beziehungen. Schriftenreihe†
0078-3471 Oesterreichische Gesellschaft fuer Musik. Beitraege
0078-3501 Oesterreichische Komponisten des 20. Jahrhunderts
0078-351X Oesterreichische Moorforschung†
0078-3528 Oesterreichische Nationalbank, Bericht ueber das Geschaeftsjahr mit Rechnungsabschluss - Annual Report *changed to* Oesterreichische Nationalbank. Geschaeftsbericht ueber das Geschaeftsjahr mit Jahresabschluss - Annual Report.
0078-3536 Oesterreichische Schriften zur Entwicklungshilfe
0078-3544 Oesterreichische Schul-Statistik†
0078-3552 Oesterreichische Zeitschrift fuer Oeffentliches Recht. Supplement *see* 0173-1718
0078-3560 Oesterreichischer Buchklub der Jugend. Jahrbuch
0078-3579 Oesterreichisches Archaeologisches Institut. Jahreshefte: Grabungen *changed to* Oesterreichisches Archaeologisches Institut. Jahreshefte.
0078-3595 Oesterreichisches Wirtschaftsinstitut fuer Strukturforschung und Strukturpolitik. Schriftenreihe†
0078-3617 Oesterreichisches Institut fuer Raumplanung. Taetigkeitsbericht†
0078-3625 Oesterreichisches Institut fuer Raumplanung. Veroeffentlichungen *changed to* Oesterreichisches Institut fuer Raumplanung. Oe I R - Forum.
0078-3692 Offshore Europe†
0078-3706 Off-Shore Technology Conference. Record
0078-3714 Offa-Jahrbuch; Vor- und Fruehgeschichte
0078-3722 Office des Communications Sociales, Montreal. Cahiers d'Etudes et de Recherches
0078-3730 Office des Communications Sociales, Montreal. Selection de Films pour Cine Clubs. *changed to* Office des Communications Sociales, Montreal. Selection de Films en 16 MM.
0078-3749 Rydge's Office Equipment Buyers Guide†
0078-3773 France. Office National d'Etudes et de Recherches Aerospatiales. Activities
0078-3781 France. Office National d'Etudes et de Recherches Aerospatiales. Notes Techniques
0078-379X France. Office National d'Etudes et de Recherches Aerospatiales. Publications
0078-3803 Office Universitaire de Recherche Socialiste. Cahiers
0078-382X Official American Basketball Association Guide†
0078-3838 Official Baseball Guide
0078-3846 Official Baseball Rules
0078-3854 Official Catholic Directory
0078-3862 Official N B A Guide
0078-3897 Official Touring Guide to East Africa *changed to* A A Guide to Motoring in Kenya.
0078-3900 Official World Series Records†
0078-3919 Official Directory of the Catholic Church of Australia and Papua-New Guinea, New Zealand and the Pacific Islands *changed to* Official Directory of the Catholic Church of Australia and New Zealand.
0078-3927 Official Year Book of the Commonwealth of Australia *see* 0810-8633
0078-3943 D C C - Camping Fuehrer Europa
0078-3951 Ohio Agricultural Research and Development Center, Wooster. Research Bulletin
0078-396X Ohio Agricultural Research and Development Center, Wooster. Research Circular
0078-3978 Ohio Agricultural Research and Development Center, Wooster. Research Summary†
0078-3986 Ohio Biological Survey. Biological Notes
0078-3994 Ohio Biological Survey. Bulletin. New Series
0078-4001 Ohio. Division of State Personnel. Annual Report
0078-401X Ohio. Division of Mines. Report *changed to* Report on Ohio Mineral Industries.
0078-4028 Ohio Fish Monographs *see* 0085-4468
0078-4036 Ohio Game Monographs *see* 0085-4468
0078-4044 Ohio Valley Philosophy of Education Society. Proceedings of the Annual Meetings *see* 0160-7561
0078-4052 Ohio Speech Journal
0078-4087 Ohio State University. College of Administrative Science. Monograph†
0078-4095 Ohio State University. College of Law. Law Forum Series†
0078-4109 Ohio State University. Disaster Research Center. D R C - T R *see* 0164-1875
0078-4133 Ohio State University. Disaster Research Center. Report Series *changed to* University of Delaware. Disaster Research Center. Report Series.
0078-415X Ohio State University. Institute of Polar Studies. Report Series *see* 0896-2472

ISSN

ISSN	Title
0078-4184	Kent State University. Center for Business and Economic Research. Comparative Administration Research Institute Series†
0078-4192	Kent State University. Center for Business and Economic Research. Labor and Industrial Relations Series†
0078-4206	Kent State University. Center for Business and Economic Research. Printed Series†
0078-4214	Kent State University. Center for Business and Economic Research. Research Papers†
0078-4222	Kent State University. Libraries. Occasional Paper†
0078-4265	Oikos. Supplementum†
0078-429X	Okayama University. Faculty of Science. Research Laboratory for Surface Science. Reports
0078-4303	Oklahoma Academy of Science. Proceedings
0078-4311	Oklahoma Academy of Science. Annals†
0078-432X	Oklahoma Anthropological Society. Bulletin
0078-4338	Oklahoma Anthropological Society. Newsletter
0078-4362	Oklahoma. Department of Institutions, Social and Rehabilitative Services. Annual Report see 0277-8289
0078-4370	Oklahoma. Fishery Research Laboratory, Norman. Bulletin†
0078-4389	Oklahoma Geological Survey. Bulletin
0078-4397	Oklahoma Geological Survey. Circular
0078-4400	Oklahoma Geological Survey. Guidebook
0078-4427	Oklahoma State University. College of Business Administration. Extension Service. Business Papers changed to Oklahoma State University. College of Business Administration. Working Papers.
0078-4435	University of Oklahoma. Center for Economic and Management Research. Monograph Series†
0078-4508	Oklahoma. Grand River Dam Authority. Annual Report
0078-4516	Old Farmer's Almanac
0078-4540	Old Salem Gleaner†
0078-4559	Old Sturbridge Village Booklet Series†
0078-4583	Wyzsza Szkola Rolnicza, Olsztyn. Zeszyty Naukowe see 0860-2832
0078-4591	Ombres de l'Histoire
0078-4605	Official Baseball Record Book changed to Complete Baseball Record Book.
0078-463X	Onoma
0078-4648	Onomastica
0078-4656	Onomastica Canadiana
0078-4664	Ontario. Agricultural Research Institute. Report see 0706-425X
0078-4672	Ontario Archaeology
0078-4680	Ontario Association for Curriculum Development. Annual Conference (Report)
0078-4699	Ontario Cancer Treatment and Research Foundation. Annual Report see 0315-9884
0078-4702	Ontario Catholic Directory
0078-4745	Ontario. Ministry of Transportation and Communications. Research and Development Division. Research Report†
0078-4753	Ontario. Division of Forests. Research Library. Research Report see 0381-3924
0078-4826	Ontario Federation of Labour. Report of Proceedings†
0078-4834	Ontario Field Biologist
0078-4850	Ontario Geography
0078-4885	Ontario. Ministry of Municipal Affairs and Housing. Annual Report see 0835-0213
0078-4893	Ontario. Ministry of the Environment. Industrial Waste Conference. Proceedings
0078-5032	Ontario Joint Highway Research Programme. Report see 0078-4745
0078-5067	Ontario Planning changed to Community Ontario.
0078-5083	Ontario Research Foundation. Annual Report changed to ORTECH International. Annual Report.
0078-5105	Ontario Speech and Hearing Association. Journal†
0078-5113	Ontario Statistical Review see 0319-7751
0078-5148	Ontario. Ministry of the Environment. Pollution Control Branch. Research Publication
0078-5156	Ontario. Ministry of the Environment. Ground Water Bulletin
0078-5164	Open Door International for the Emancipation of the Woman Worker. Report of Congress
0078-5172	Open Doors
0078-5237	Opera Botanica
0078-5245	Opera Lilloana
0078-5261	C O R S I Bulletin
0078-5318	Operations Research - Verfahren
0078-5326	Ophelia
0078-5334	Ophthalmological Societies of the United Kingdom. Transactions
0078-5342	Ophthalmological Society of Egypt. Bulletin
0078-5385	Wyzsza Szkola Pedagogiczna, Opole. Zeszyty Naukowe. Seria A. Fizyka
0078-5393	Wyzsza Szkola Pedagogiczna, Opole. Zeszyty Naukowe. Seria A. Historia
0078-5407	Wyzsza Szkola Pedagogiczna, Opole. Zeszyty Naukowe. Seria A. Historia Literatury see 0324-9050
0078-5415	Wyzsza Szkola Pedagogiczna, Opole. Zeszyty Naukowe. Seria A. Historia Slaska†
0078-5423	Wyzsza Szkola Pedagogiczna, Opole. Zeszyty Naukowe. Seria A. Jezykoznawstwo
0078-5431	Wyzsza Szkola Pedagogiczna, Opole. Zeszyty Naukowe. Seria A. Matematyka
0078-544X	Wyzsza Szkola Pedagogiczna, Opole. Zeszyty Naukowe. Seria B. Studia i Monografie
0078-5458	Opportunities Abroad for Teachers changed to U.S. Department of Education. Opportunities for Teachers Abroad.
0078-5466	Optica Applicata
0078-5474	Optical Industry and Systems Directory see 1044-1425
0078-5482	Optical Physics and Engineering
0078-5504	Optics and Spectroscopy. Supplement
0078-5512	Optik und Feinmechanik in Einzeldarstellungen†
0078-5520	Opuscula Atheniensia
0078-5539	Opuscula - aus Wissenschaft und Dichtung
0078-5547	Orange Free State. Director of Hospital Services. Report
0078-5555	Orbis Antiquus
0078-5563	Orbis Artium†
0078-5571	Orbis Pictus†
0078-5598	Dictionnaire National des Architectes
0078-5601	Ordre des Geometres-Experts. Annuaire
0078-5644	Oregon Research Institute. Research Bulletins†
0078-5652	Oregon Research Institute. Research Monographs†
0078-5679	Oregon School Directory
0078-5709	Oregon. Department of Geology and Mineral Industries. Bulletin
0078-5717	Oregon. State Department of Geology and Mineral Industries. G M I Short Papers†
0078-5725	Oregon. State Department of Geology and Mineral Industries. Miscellaneous Papers†
0078-5733	Oregon. State Department of Geology and Mineral Industries. Miscellaneous Publications†
0078-5741	Oregon. State Department of Geology and Mineral Industries. Oil and Gas Investigations
0078-575X	Oregon State Plan for the Construction and Modernization of Hospitals, Public Health Centers and Medical Facilities†
0078-5768	Oregon State Monographs. Bibliographic Series
0078-5776	Oregon State Monographs. Studies in Botany†
0078-5784	Oregon State Monographs. Studies in Economics†
0078-5792	Oregon State Monographs. Studies in Education and Guidance†
0078-5806	Oregon State Monographs. Studies in Entomology†
0078-5814	Oregon State Monographs. Studies in Geology†
0078-5822	Oregon State Monographs. Studies in History†
0078-5830	Oregon State Monographs. Studies in Zoology†
0078-5849	Oregon State University. Water Resources Research Institute. Water Research Summary†
0078-5865	Oregon State University. Forest Research Laboratory. Annual Report changed to Oregon State University. Forest Research Laboratory. Biennial Report.
0078-5903	Oregon State University. Forest Research Laboratory. Research Bulletin
0078-5911	Oregon State University. Forest Research Laboratory. Research Note
0078-592X	Oregon State University. Forest Research Laboratory. Research Paper
0078-5938	Oregon State University. School of Engineering. Graduate Research and Education†
0078-5946	Oregon State University. School of Engineering. Research Activities†
0078-5962	University of Oregon. Bureau of Business Research. Research Studies†
0078-5970	University of Oregon. Bureau of Governmental Research and Service. Information Bulletin†
0078-5989	University of Oregon. Bureau of Governmental Research and Service. Legal Bulletin†
0078-5997	University of Oregon. Bureau of Governmental Research and Service. Local Government Notes and Information: Policy and Practice Series†
0078-6004	University of Oregon. Center for the Advanced Study of Educationl Administration. Monographs changed to University of Oregon. Center for Educational Policy and Management. Monographs.
0078-6012	University of Oregon. Center for the Advanced Study of Educational Administration. Occasional Papers changed to University of Oregon. Center for Educational Policy and Management. Occasional Papers.
0078-6020	University of Oregon. Center for Educational Policy and Management. Technical Reports†
0078-6039	University of Oregon. Library. Occasional Paper†
0078-6047	University of Oregon. Museum of Natural History. Bulletin†
0078-6063	University of Oregon. Bureau of Business Research. Business Publications†
0078-6071	University of Oregon Anthropological Papers
0078-608X	Orestes Brownson Series on Contemporary Thought and Affairs†
0078-6098	Organ Yearbook
0078-611X	Organic Chemistry
0078-6128	Organic Directory†
0078-6136	Organic Electronic Spectral Data
0078-6144	Organic Photochemical Syntheses†
0078-6152	Organic Photochemistry: A Series of Advances
0078-6160	Organic Reaction Mechanisms. Annual Survey
0078-6179	Organic Reactions
0078-6187	Organic Substances of Natural Origin†
0078-6209	Organic Syntheses
0078-6217	Organic Syntheses Collective Volumes
0078-6225	Organische Chemie in Einzeldarstellungen
0078-6233	Afro-Asian Peoples' Solidarity Organization. Council. Documents of the Session
0078-6241	Review of Fisheries in O E C D Member Countries
0078-625X	O E C D. Nuclear Energy Agency. Activity Report changed to O E C D Nuclear Energy Agency Activities in (Year).
0078-6276	O E C D High Temperature Reactor Project Dragon†
0078-6284	O E C D Halden Reactor Project††
0078-6292	List of Research Institutes and Scientists in O E C D Member Countries†
0078-6306	O A U Review†
0078-6322	Organization of American States. Department of Scientific Affairs. Serie de Fisica: Monografias
0078-6330	Organization of American States. Department of Scientific Affairs. Serie de Matematica: Monografias
0078-6357	Organization of American States. Department of Cultural Affairs. Cuadernos Bibliotecologicos†
0078-6373	Organization of American States. Department of Cultural Affairs. Estudios Bibliotecarios†
0078-6381	Organization of American States. Department of Cultural Affairs. Manuales del Bibliotecario
0078-6403	O A S. General Secretariat. Annual Report
0078-642X	Organization of American States. Official Records. Indice y Lista General
0078-6438	Organization of American States. Permanent Council. Decisions Taken at Meetings (Cumulated Edition)
0078-6489	Organometallic Compounds of the Group IV Elements†
0078-6497	Organometallic Reactions Series changed to Organometallic Reactions and Syntheses.
0078-6500	Organon
0078-6527	Oriens
0078-6543	Oriental Notes and Studies
0078-6551	Oriental Studies
0078-656X	Orientalia Gothoburgensia
0078-6578	Orientalia Suecana
0078-6586	Original Manuscript Music for Wind and Percussion Instruments†
0078-6594	Ornithological Monographs
0078-6608	Orthodontie Francaise
0078-6624	Orton Society. Bulletin. see 0474-7534
0078-6632	Center for Adult Diseases, Osaka. Annual Report
0078-6640	Osaka City University Economic Review
0078-6659	Osaka City University. Faculty of Engineering. Memoirs
0078-6667	Osaka Medical School, Takatsuki. Bulletin. Supplement†
0078-6675	Osaka-shiritsu Shizenshi Hakubutsukan Kenkyu Hokoku
0078-6683	Shizenshi Kenkyu
0078-6705	Osaka University. Institute for Protein Research. Memoirs
0078-6713	Norges Veterinaerhoegskole. Aarsberetning†
0078-6721	Norges Veterinaerhoegskole. Publikasjoner
0078-673X	Norway. Statens Institutt for Alkoholforskning. Skrifter

0078-6748 Universitetet i Oslo. Etnografiske Museum. Aarbok†
0078-6764 Universitetet i Oslo. Institutt for Bibelvitenskap. Smaarskrifter†
0078-6772 Universitetet i Oslo. Institutett for Statsvitenskap. Skrifter†
0078-6780 Physica Mathematica Universitatis Osloensis†
0078-6799 Osram-Gesellschaft. Technisch-Wissenschaftliche Abhandlungen†
0078-6810 Ost-West Paedagogik†
0078-6845 Ostbairische Grenzmarken
0078-687X Osteuropa Institut, Munich. Veroeffentlichungen. Reihe Geschichte
0078-6888 Osteuropastudien der Hochschulen des Landes Hessen. Reihe 1. Giessener Abhandlungen zur Agrar- und Wirtschaftsforschung des Europaeischen Ostens†
0078-6896 Ostpanorama
0078-690X Otago Geographer
0078-6918 Otago Law Review
0078-6926 Other Lands, Other Peoples†
0078-6950 Dominion Astrophysical Observatory, Victoria. Publications
0078-6977 National Gallery of Canada. Annual Review *see* 0711-2866
0078-6985 National Gallery of Canada. Library. Canadiana in the Library of the National Gallery of Canada: Supplement†
0078-6993 National Gallery of Canada. Library. Checklist of Canadian Artists Files *changed to* Artists in Canada: A Union List of Artists Files.
0078-7000 National Library of Canada. Annual Report
0078-7035 Ou Monter a Cheval *changed to* Guide du Cheval Arabe en France.
0078-7094 Outline of Japanese Tax
0078-7108 Overseas Development Council. Monograph Series†
0078-7116 O D I Review *see* 0950-6764
0078-7124 Overseas Directories, Who's Who, Press Guides, Year Books and Overseas Periodical Subscriptions
0078-7132 Overseas Media Guide *changed to* O P M A Overseas Media Guide.
0078-7159 Overseas Newspapers and Periodicals
0078-7167 Owen's Commerce and Travel and International Register *changed to* Owen's Africa Business Directory.
0078-7175 Oxford Bibliographical Society. Occasional Publications
0078-7183 Oxford Bibliographical Society. Publications. New Series
0078-7191 Oxford German Studies
0078-7256 Oxford Slavonic Papers
0078-7264 Oxford Studies of Composers
0078-7272 Oxford Theological Monographs
0078-7353 P A S Reporter†
0078-7388 P I - L T; Occasional Papers on Programmed Instruction and Language Teaching†
0078-740X Pacific Anthropological Records
0078-7418 Pacific Anthropologists†
0078-7426 Pacific Botanists†
0078-7442 Pacific Coast Obstetrical and Gynecological Society. Transactions
0078-7469 Pacific Coast Philology
0078-7507 Pacific History Series†
0078-7515 Pacific Insects Monographs†
0078-7523 Pacific Islands Year Book
0078-7531 Pacific Linguistics. Series A: Occasional Papers
0078-754X Pacific Linguistics. Series B: Monographs
0078-7558 Pacific Linguistics. Series C: Books
0078-7566 Pacific Linguistics. Series D: Special Publications
0078-7574 Pacific Marine Fisheries Commission. Annual Report *changed to* Pacific States Marine Fisheries Commission. Annual Report.
0078-7582 Pacific Marine Fisheries Commission. Bulletin†
0078-7590 Pacific Marine Fisheries Commision. Newsletter *changed to* Pacific States Marine Fisheries Commission. Newsletter.
0078-7612 Pacific Northwest Conference on Foreign Languages. Proceedings *see* 0277-0598
0078-7620 Pacific Northwest Conference on Higher Education. Proceedings†
0078-7647 Pacific Science Association. Congress Proceedings *changed to* Pacific Science Association. Congress and Inter-Congress Proceedings.
0078-7663 Pacific Trollers Association Newsletter
0078-7698 Packaging Machinery Manufacturers Institute. Official Packaging Machinery Directory
0078-7701 Papua New Guinea. National Statistical Office. Rural Industries
0078-771X Universita degli Studi di Padova. Centro per la Storia della Tradizione Artistotelica nel Veneto. Saggi e Testi
0078-7728 Universita degli Studi di Padova. Facolta di Lettere e Filosofia. Opuscoli Accademici
0078-7736 Universita degli Studi di Padova. Facolta di Lettere e Filosofia. Pubblicazioni
0078-7744 Universita degli Studi di Padova. Istituto di Storia Antica. Pubblicazioni
0078-7752 Universita degli Studi di Padova. Istituto per la Storia. Contributi
0078-7760 Universita degli Studi di Padova. Istituto per la Storia. Quaderni
0078-7779 Universita degli Studi di Padova. Scuola di Perfezionamento in Filosofia. Pubblicazioni
0078-7787 Paedagogica Europaea *see* 0141-8211
0078-7795 Paediatrische Fortbildungskurse fuer die Praxis†
0078-7809 Paideuma
0078-7817 Polymers Paint and Colour Year Book
0078-785X Pakistan Annual Law Digest
0078-7868 Pakistan Archaeology
0078-7884 Pakistan Banking Directory
0078-7892 Pakistan Basic Facts
0078-7914 Pakistan. Central Bureau of Education. Educational Statistics Bulletin Series
0078-7922 Pakistan. Central Bureau of Education. Yearbook *see* 0078-8287
0078-7930 Pakistan Central Cotton Committee. Agricultural Survey Report
0078-7949 Pakistan Central Cotton Committee. Technological Bulletin. Series A
0078-7957 Pakistan Central Cotton Committee. Technological Bulletin. Series B
0078-7965 Pakistan. Central Statistical Office. Census of Electricity Undertakings†
0078-7973 Pakistan. Central Statistical Office. Consumer Price Index Numbers for Industrial Workers†
0078-8015 Pakistan. Central Statistical Office. Some Socio-Economic Trends†
0078-804X Pakistan Council of Scientific and Industrial Research. Report†
0078-8058 Pakistan Customs Tariff
0078-8082 Pakistan Economic Survey
0078-8090 Pakistan Export Directory *changed to* Directory of Exporters (Year).
0078-8104 Pakistan. Export Promotion Bureau. Export Guide Series†
0078-8112 Pakistan. Export Promotion Bureau. Fresh Fruits†
0078-8139 Pakistan. Food and Agricultural Division. Yearbook of Agricultural Statistics *changed to* Pakistan. Food and Agriculture Division. Agricultural Statistics of Pakistan.
0078-8147 Pakistan Forest Institute, Peshawar. Annual Progress Report
0078-8155 Pakistan. Geological Survey. Memoirs; Paleontologia Pakistanica
0078-8163 Pakistan. Geological Survey. Records
0078-8171 Pakistan Historical Society. Memoir
0078-818X Pakistan Historical Society. Proceedings of the Pakistan History Conference
0078-8198 P I C I C. Annual Report
0078-8201 Pakistan Industrial Development Corporation. Report
0078-821X Pakistan Institute of Development Economics. Report
0078-8228 Pakistan Institute of Development Economics. Research Reports
0078-8244 Pakistan Journal of Biological and Agricultural Sciences *changed to* Bangladesh Journal of Biological Sciences.
0078-8252 Pakistan Leather Year Book†
0078-8287 Pakistan. Ministry of Education. Yearbook
0078-8295 Pakistan. Ministry of Finance. Basic Facts About the Budget *see* 0078-7892
0078-8309 Pakistan. Ministry of Finance. Budget in Brief *changed to* Pakistan. Finance Division. Budget in Brief.
0078-8317 Pakistan. Ministry of Finance. Budget of the Central Government *changed to* Budget of the Government of Pakistan. Demands for Grants and Appropriations.
0078-8325 Pakistan. Ministry of Finance. Economic Analysis of the Central Government *changed to* Pakistan. Finance Division. Economic Analysis of the Budget.
0078-8333 Pakistan. National Assembly. Debates. Official Report
0078-8341 Pakistan National Bibliography
0078-835X Lists of P A N S Doc Bibliographies *changed to* Lists of P A S T I C Bibliographies.
0078-8368 P A N S D O C Translations *changed to* P A S T I C Translations.
0078-8376 Pakistan Nursing and Health Review
0078-8392 Pakistan. Office of the Economic Adviser. Government Sponsored Corporations and Other Institutions
0078-8406 Pakistan Philosophical Congress. Proceedings
0078-8414 Pakistan. Planning and Development Division. Development Programme
0078-8422 Pakistan Postage Stamps
0078-8430 Pakistan Science Conference. Proceedings
0078-8457 Pakistan Standards Institution. Report†
0078-8473 Pakistan Statistical Association. Proceedings
0078-8481 Pakistan. Survey of Pakistan. General Report
0078-849X Bangladesh Tea Board. Annual Review†
0078-852X Pakistan's Balance of Payments
0078-8538 Palaeoecology of Africa and the Surrounding Islands and Antarctica *see* 0168-6208
0078-8546 Palaeontographica Americana
0078-8554 Palaeontologia Africana
0078-8562 Palaeontologia Polonica
0078-8570 Paleoecologia†
0078-8589 New Zealand. Department of Scientific and Industrial Research. Paleontological Bulletin *see* 0114-2283
0078-8597 Paleontological Society. Memoir
0078-8600 Zentrales Geologisches Institut. Palaeontologische Abhandlungen†
0078-8619 Universita degli Studi di Palermo. Istituto di Entomologia Agraria. Bollettino *see* 0393-8131
0078-8627 Universita degli Studi di Palermo. Istituto di Filologia Greca. Quaderni†
0078-866X Pamietnik Slowianski
0078-8686 Universidad de Navarra. Instituto de Ciencias de la Educacion. Coleccion I C E *changed to* Universidad de Navarra. Facultad de Ciencias de la Educacion. Coleccion.
0078-8708 Universidad de Navarra. Instituto de Estudios Superiores de la Empresa. Coleccion I E S E. Serie L *changed to* Coleccion la Empresa y Su Entorno. Serie L.
0078-8716 Universidad de Navarra. Instituto de Estudios Superiores de la Empresas. Coleccion I E S E. Serie A C *changed to* Coleccion la Empresa y Su Entorno. Serie A C.
0078-8732 Universidad de Navarra. Escuela de Arquitectura. Coleccion de Arquitectura
0078-8740 Universidad de Navarra. Escuela de Bibliotecarias. Coleccion Bibliotecarias
0078-8759 Universidad de Navarra. Facultad de Derecho Canonico. Manuales: Derecho Canonico
0078-8767 Universidad de Navarra. Manuales: Derecho Notarial Espanol *changed to* Universidad de Navarra. Coleccion Manuales de Derecho.
0078-8783 Universidad de Navarra. Facultad de Ciencias de la Informacion. Manuales: Periodismo
0078-8791 Pan American Federation of Engineering Societies. Bulletin
0078-8805 Pan American Highway Congresses. Final Acts†
0078-8821 Pan American Institute of Geography and History. Commission on History. Guias†
0078-8899 Panama Canal Company. Meteorological and Hydrographic Branch. Climatological Data: Canal Zone and Panama†
0078-8902 Estadistica Panamena. Seccion 221. Movimento de Poblacion *see* 0378-6749
0078-8937 Panama. Direccion de Estadistica y Censo. Estadistica Panamena. Serie F. Industrias-Encuestas *see* 0378-2557
0078-897X Estadistica Panamena. Estadistica Electoral *changed to* Estadistica Panamena. Situacion Politica, Administrativa y Justicia. Seccion 611. Estadistica Electoral.
0078-8996 Panama en Cifras
0078-9038 Papermakers' and Merchants' Directory of All Nations *see* 0954-8521
0078-9054 Papers in Anthropology†
0078-9062 Papers in Australian Linguistics
0078-9070 Papers in Borneo Linguistics†
0078-9100 Papers in International Studies: Africa Series *changed to* Monographs in International Studies: Africa Series.
0078-9119 Papers in International Studies: Southeast Asia Series *changed to* Monographs in International Studies: Southeast Asia Series.
0078-9127 Papers in Linguistics of Melanesia†
0078-9135 Papers in New Guinea Linguistics†
0078-9143 Papers in Philippine Linguistics†
0078-9151 Papers in Public Administration
0078-916X Papers in Public Administration (Ann Arbor)†
0078-9178 Papers in South East Asian Linguistics
0078-9216 Papers on Modern Japan†
0078-9224 London School of Economics Papers in Soviet and East European Law, Economics and Politics†
0078-9232 Papiermusterheft†
0078-9259 Papua New Guinea. National Statistical Office. Statistical Bulletin: Capital Expenditure by Private Businesses
0078-9267 Papua New Guinea. Bureau of Statistics. Workers' Compensation Statistics *changed to* Papua New Guinea. Department of Labour and Employment. Worker's Compensation Claims.
0078-9283 Papua New Guinea. Bureau of Statistics. Private Overseas Investment†

ISSN INDEX 5543

0078-9291 Papua New Guinea. Bureau of Statistics. Overseas Trade Statistics *changed to* Papua New Guinea. National Statistical Office. International Trade Statistics.
0078-9313 Papua New Guinea. National Statistical Office. Secondary Industries (Factories and Works). Preliminary Statement *changed to* Papua New Guinea. National Statistical Office. Secondary Industries (Preliminary Statement).
0078-9321 Papua New Guinea. National Statistical Office. Rural Industries. Preliminary Statement *changed to* Papua New Guinea. National Statistical Office. Rural Industries. Agriculture Largeholdings (Preliminary).
0078-933X Papua New Guinea. National Statistical Office. Secondary Industries
0078-9356 Papua New Guinea. Bureau of Statistics. Statistics of Religious Organisations†
0078-9372 Papua New Guinea. National Statistical Office. Taxation Statistics. Preliminary Bulletin
0078-9399 Papua New Guinea. Public Service Board. Report *changed to* Papua New Guinea. Public Service Commission. Report.
0078-9402 Papyrologica Bruxellensia
0078-9410 Papyrologica Coloniensia
0078-9429 Paralogue
0078-9437 Parapsychological Monographs
0078-947X Aeroports de Paris. Service Statistique. Statistique de Trafic
0078-9496 Paris - Bijoux Exportation
0078-950X Bureau Universitaire de Recherche Operationnelle. Cahiers
0078-9518 Societe de l'Ecole des Chartes. Memoires et Documents
0078-9534 Ecole Pratique des Hautes Etudes, Paris. Centre des Etudes Arctiques et Finno-Scandinaves. Contributions *changed to* Ecole des Hautes Etudes en Science Sociales. Centre des Etudes Arctiques et Finno-Scandinaves. Contributions.
0078-9577 Sciences Humaines Africanistes
0078-9585 Ecole Pratique des Hautes Etudes, Paris. Centre d'Etudes des Techniques Economiques Modernes. Etudes et Memoires *changed to* Ecole des Hautes Etudes en Sciences Sociales. Centre des Techniques Economiques Modernes. Etudes et Memoires.
0078-9593 Ecole Pratique des Hautes Etudes, Paris. Centre de Psychiatrie Sociale. Publications†
0078-9615 Ecole Pratique des Hautes Etudes, Paris. Centre de Sociologie Europeenne. Cahiers†
0078-9631 Ecole Pratique des Hautes Etudes, Paris. Division des Aires Culturelles. Congres et Colloques†
0078-964X Ecole Pratique des Hautes Etudes. Quatrieme Section. Historiques et Philologiques. Annuaire *changed to* Livret de la Quatrieme Section, Ecole Pratique Hautes Etudes.
0078-9666 France. Imprimerie Nationale. Annuaire.
0078-9674 Institut de Recherches Agronomiques Tropicales et des Cultures Vivrieres. Bulletin Scientifique.†
0078-9682 Institut Oceanographique. Annales
0078-9720 Museum National d'Histoire Naturelle, Paris. Annuaire†
0078-9739 Museum National d'Histoire Naturelle, Paris. Archives†
0078-9747 Museum National d'Histoire Naturelle, Paris. Memoires. Nouvelle Serie. Serie A. Zoologie
0078-9755 Museum National d'Histoire Naturelle. Memoires. Nouvelle Serie. Serie B. Botanique
0078-9771 Museum National d'Histoire Naturelle, Paris. Memoires. Nouvelle Serie. Serie D. Sciences Physico-Chimiques†
0078-9909 Universite de Paris VI (Pierre et Marie Curie). Institut Henri Poincare. Seminaire Choquet. Initiation a l'Analyse†
0078-995X Institut d'Etudes Politiques de Paris. Livret†
0078-9968 Institut d'Etudes Slaves, Paris. Annuaire†
0078-9976 Institut d'Etudes Slaves, Paris. Bibliotheque Russe
0078-9984 Institut d'Etudes Slaves, Paris. Collection de Grammaires
0078-9992 Institut d'Etudes Slaves, Paris. Collection de Manuels
0079-0001 Institut d'Etudes Slaves, Paris. Collection Historique
0079-001X Institut d'Etudes Slaves, Paris. Textes
0079-0028 Institut d'Etudes Slaves, Paris. Travaux
0079-0036 Universite de Paris VI (Pierre et Marie Curie). Institut Henri Poincare. Seminaire Lions†
0079-0044 Parker Directory of Attorneys *see* 0196-6138
0079-0052 Parkes Library Pamphlets†
0079-0060 Parkinson's Disease and Related Disorders. Cumulative Bibliography†
0079-0079 Parkinson's Disease and Related Disorders: Citations from the Literature†
0079-0095 Parliament House Book
0079-0117 Partners in Learning
0079-0125 Passaic County Dental Society. Bulletin *changed to* Passaic County Dental Society Newsletter.
0079-0133 Passenger Transport in Great Britain *changed to* Transport Statistics Great Britain.
0079-0141 Pastoral Psychology Series†
0079-015X Patent and Trademark Institute of Canada. Annual Proceedings
0079-0168 Patent Law Review *see* 0193-4864
0079-0184 Pathology Annual
0079-0206 Patterns of Literary Criticism†
0079-0214 Patterns of Religious Commitment†
0079-0230 Patterson's American Education
0079-0249 Paul Anthony Brick Lectures
0079-0257 Paul Carus Lectures
0079-0265 Universita degli Studi di Pavia. Istituto Botanico. Atti
0079-0273 Paving Conference. Proceedings. *changed to* Paving and Transportation Conference. Proceedings.
0079-0281 Pax Romana†
0079-029X Peabody Museum of Archaeology and Ethnology. Memoirs
0079-0303 Peabody Museum of Archaeology and Ethnology. Papers
0079-032X Peabody Museum of Natural History. Bulletin
0079-0338 Peabody Museum of Natural History. Special Publication
0079-0354 Pearce-Sellards Series
0079-0362 Pears Cyclopaedia
0079-0370 Paedagogica Belgica Academica†
0079-0400 Pediatrics; a Medical World News Publication†
0079-0435 Marine Research in Indonesia
0079-0451 Penn State Studies†
0079-046X Pennsylvania. Agricultural Statistics Service. Crop and Livestock Annual Summary
0079-0478 Pennsylvania Crop Reporting Service. C.R.S. *see* 0079-046X
0079-0486 P.E.L. State Bulletin†
0079-0494 Indiana University of Pennsylvania. Annual Research Bulletin†
0079-0508 Pennsylvania School Study Council. Reports
0079-0524 Millersville State College. Contributions to Research: Faculty and Student Publications†
0079-0540 Pennsylvania State University. College of Business Administration. Center for Research. Occasional Papers†
0079-0567 Pennsylvania State University. College of Engineering. Engineering Research Bulletin†
0079-0583 Pennsylvania State University. Council on Research. Research Publications and Other Contributions *see* 0093-7568
0079-0591 Pennsylvania State University. Earth and Mineral Sciences Experiment Station. Bulletin†
0079-0605 Pennsylvania State University. Earth and Mineral Sciences Experiment Station. Bulletin. Mineral Conservation Series. Paper *changed to* Pennsylvania State University. Earth and Mineral Sciences Experiment Station. Technical Papers.
0079-0613 Pennsylvania State University. Earth and Mineral Sciences Experiment Station. Circular†
0079-0621 Pennsylvania State University. Institute for Research on Land and Water Resources. Information Reports†
0079-063X Pennsylvania State University. Institute for Research on Land and Water Resources. Research Publication†
0079-0656 Pennsylvania State University. Libraries. Bibliographical Series
0079-0710 Penrose Annual†
0079-0729 People from the Past Series
0079-0737 Peoples' Appalachia†
0079-0745 Peoria Academy of Science. Proceedings†
0079-0753 Peptides†
0079-0761 Per Jacobsson Foundation. Proceedings *changed to* Per Jacobsson Foundation. Lectures.
0079-077X Per Jacobsson Memorial Lecture *changed to* Per Jacobsson Foundation. Lectures.
0079-0788 Performance Data on Architectural Acoustical Materials *changed to* Acoustical and Board Products. Bulletin.
0079-0826 Pergamon Mathematical Tables Series†
0079-0834 Pergamon Series of Monographs in Laboratory Techniques†
0079-0842 Pergamon Series of Monographs on Furniture and Timber†
0079-0877 Periodicals in East African Libraries: a Union List *changed to* Periodicals in Eastern African Libraries: a Union List.
0079-0885 Periscope 2000†
0079-0893 Persica
0079-0907 Personal Income in Counties of New York State *changed to* Personal Income in Areas and Counties of New York State.
0079-0931 Personality, Psychopathology and Psychotherapy
0079-0958 Perspecta
0079-0966 Perspective†
0079-0982 Perspectives de l'Economique. Serie 1. Fondateurs de l'Economie
0079-0990 Perspectives in American History *see* 0266-1322
0079-1008 Perspectives in Criticism†
0079-1016 Perspectives in Jewish Learning *see* 0196-2183
0079-1032 Perspectives in Powder Metallurgy *see* 0146-9711
0079-1040 Perspectives in Social Work†
0079-1059 Perspectives in Structural Chemistry†
0079-1067 Perth Observatory. Communications
0079-1075 Peru - Problema
0079-1083 Instituto Nacional de Enfermedades Neoplasicas. Trabajos de Investigacion Clinica y Experimental†
0079-1091 Sociedad Geologica del Peru. Boletin
0079-1148 Pesticide Review†
0079-1156 Petersen's Pro Football Annual *see* 0079-5526
0079-1288 Petroleum and Chemical Industry Technical Conference. Record *see* 0090-3507
0079-1296 Petroleum Refineries in Canada†
0079-130X Pets Welcome
0079-1334 Pflanzenschuetzer†
0079-1350 Phaenomenologica
0079-1369 Phanerogamarum Monographiae
0079-1393 Pharmaceutical Historian
0079-1407 Pharmacopeia of the United States of America *see* 0195-7996
0079-1423 Philippine Education Abstracts†
0079-1458 Philippine Men of Science†
0079-1466 Philippine Scientist
0079-1490 Philippines Nuclear Journal
0079-1504 Philippines. Board of Investments. Annual Report
0079-1512 Philippines. Bureau of Agricultural Economics. Crop, Livestock and Natural Resources Statistics *changed to* Philippines. Bureau of Agricultural Economics. Crop and Livestock Statistics.
0079-1520 Philippines. Bureau of Agricultural Economics. Report†
0079-1539 Philippines. Department of Commerce and Industry. Annual Report *changed to* Philippines. Department of Trade and Industry. Annual Report.
0079-158X Phillips' Paper Trade Directory - Europe-Mills of the World *see* 0954-8521
0079-1598 Philologen-Jahrbuch
0079-1628 Philological Monographs
0079-1636 Philological Society Transactions
0079-1644 Philologische Beitraege zur Suedost- und Osteuropaforschung†
0079-1660 Philosophes Contemporains
0079-1679 Philosophes Medievaux
0079-1687 Philosophia Antiqua
0079-1695 Philosophical Society of the Sudan. Proceedings of the Annual Conference
0079-1717 Philosophische Studientexte *see* 0233-089X
0079-1733 Philosophy of Education Society. Proceedings of the Annual Meetings *see* 8756-6575
0079-1768 Phineas L. Windsor Lecture in Librarianship†
0079-1776 Phoenix†
0079-1784 Phoenix. Supplementary Volumes
0079-1806 Photochemistry (Oxford)
0079-1814 Photoelectric Spectrometry Group Bulletin *see* 0144-2317
0079-1830 Photographis *changed to* Graphis Photo.
0079-1849 Photography Annual†
0079-1857 Photography Directory and Buying Guide *changed to* Photography Buyers Guide.
0079-1865 Photography Year Book
0079-1873 Physical Acoustics: Principles and Methods
0079-1881 Physical Chemistry†
0079-189X Physical Education Around the World. Monograph
0079-1903 Physical Education Association of Great Britain and Northern Ireland. Report†
0079-1911 Physical Education Year Book†
0079-192X Physician's Handbook
0079-1938 Physics and Chemistry in Space
0079-1946 Physics and Chemistry of the Earth
0079-1954 Physics and Chemistry of the Organic Solid State†
0079-1970 Physics of Thin Films; Advances in Research and Development
0079-1989 Physik und Technik†
0079-1997 Physikalisch-Chemische Trenn- und Messmethoden
0079-2004 Physikalisch-Medizinische Sozietaet Erlangen. Sitzungsberichte
0079-2012 Physiologia Plantarum. Supplementum†
0079-2020 Physiological Society, London. Monographs
0079-2047 Phyton. Annales Rei Botanicae

ISSN

ISSN INDEX

ISSN	Title
0079-2055	Pianeta Fresco
0079-2063	Pick's Currency Yearbook see 0743-5363
0079-2071	Pilot Studies Approved for State Aid in Public School Systems in Virginia†
0079-208X	Pion Applied Physics Series†
0079-211X	Pisarze Slascy 19 i 20 Wieku
0079-2128	Pit and Quarry Handbook and Purchasing Guide changed to Pit & Quarry Handbook and Buyers Guide.
0079-2144	Pittsburgh Studies in Library and Information Sciences†
0079-2179	L R D C News†
0079-2225	Plant Breeding Institute, Cambridge. Annual Report†
0079-2233	Plant Monograph: Reprints†
0079-2241	Plant Physiology. Supplement Abstracts of Annual Meeting
0079-225X	Plant Protection Abstracts. Supplement†
0079-2268	Plante et l'Homme
0079-2276	Planung und Kontrolle in der Unternehmung
0079-2284	Planungsstudien
0079-2306	Plastics, Paint and Rubber Buyers' Guide for S.A. changed to Plastics and Rubber Yearbook and Buyers' Guide of S.A.
0079-2314	Playfair Cricket Annual
0079-2322	Playfair Football Annual
0079-2349	Playthings Directory
0079-2373	Poche-Couleurs Larousse†
0079-2381	Pocket Book of Transport Statistics of India
0079-239X	Pocket Compendium of Australian Statistics see 0727-145X
0079-2403	Pocket Data Book, USA†
0079-2411	Pocket Digest of New Zealand Statistics
0079-242X	Pocket Library of Studies in Art
0079-2438	Pocket Poets Series
0079-2446	Pocket Year Book of South Australia
0079-2462	Poesia
0079-2470	Poetes et Prosateurs du Portugal
0079-2500	Poeti e Prosatori Tedeschi
0079-2519	Poetry Eastwest†
0079-2527	Poetyka. Zarys Encyklopedyczny
0079-2535	Points. Films
0079-2543	Points for Emphasis; International Sunday School Lessons in Pocket Size
0079-256X	Universite de Poitiers. Centre d'Etudes Superieures de Civilisation Medievale. Publications
0079-2594	Poland. Glowny Urzad Statystyczny. Budzet Panstwa
0079-2608	Poland. Glowny Urzad Statystyczny. Maly Rocznik Statystyczny
0079-2616	Poland. Glowny Urzad Statystyczny. Rocznik Demograficzny
0079-2632	Poland. Glowny Urzad Statystyczny. Rocznik Statystyczny Budownictwa
0079-2640	Poland. Glowny Urzad Statystyczny. Rocznik Statystyczny Finansow
0079-2659	Poland. Glowny Urzad Statystyczny. Rocznik Statystyczny Gospodarki Mieszkaniowej i Komunalnej
0079-2667	Poland. Glowny Urzad Statystyczny. Rocznik Statystyczny Gospodarki Morskiej
0079-2675	Poland. Glowny Urzad Statystyczny. Rocznik Statystyczny Gornictwa†
0079-2683	Poland. Glowny Urzad Statystyczny. Rocznik Statystyczny Handlu Wewnetrznego†
0079-2691	Poland. Glowny Urzad Statystyczny. Rocznik Statystyki. Handel Zagraniczny (Year)
0079-2705	Poland. Glowny Urzad Statystyczny. Rocznik Statystyczny Inwestycji i Srodkow Trwalych
0079-2713	Poland. Glowny Urzad Statystyczny. Kultura changed to Poland. Glowny Urzad Statystyczny. Rocznik Statystyczny Kultury.
0079-2721	Poland. Glowny Urzad Statystyczny. Rocznik Statystyczny Lesnictwa changed to Poland. Glowny Urzad Statystyczny. Rocznik Statystyczny Lesnictwa i Gospodarki Drewnem.
0079-273X	Poland. Glowny Urzad Statystyczny. Rocznik Statystyki Miedzynarodowej
0079-2748	Poland. Glowny Urzad Statystyczny. Rocznik Statystyczny Ochrony Zdrowia
0079-2756	Poland. Glowny Urzad Statystyczny. Rocznik Statystyczny Powiatow†
0079-2764	Poland. Glowny Urzad Statystyczny. Rocznik Statystyczny Przemyslu
0079-2772	Poland. Glowny Urzad Statystyczny. Rocznik Statystyczny Pracy
0079-2780	Poland. Glowny Urzad Statystyczny. Rocznik Statystyczny
0079-2799	Poland. Glowny Urzad Statystyczny. Rocznik Statystyczny Szkolnictwa
0079-2802	Poland. Glowny Urzad Statystyczny. Rocznik Statystyczny Transportu
0079-2810	Poland. Glowny Urzad Statystyczny. Rolniczy Rocznik Statystyczny - Poland. Central Statistics Office. Yearbook of Agricultural Statistics changed to Poland. Glowny Urzad Statystyczny. Rocznik Statystyczny Rolnictwa i Gospodarki Zywnosciowej.
0079-2829	Poland. Glowny Urzad Statystyczny. Zeszyty Metodyczne
0079-2837	Poland. Glowny Urzad Statystyczny. Statystyka Zeglugi Srodladowej i Drog Wodnych Srodladowych
0079-2845	Poland. Glowny Urzad Statystyczny. Studia i Prace Statystyczne changed to Poland. Glowny Urzad Statystyczny. Statystyka Polski. Studia i Prace Statystyczne.
0079-2853	Poland. Glowny Urzad Statystyczny. Ubezpieczenia Majatkowe i Osobowe
0079-2861	Poland. Glowny Urzad Statystyczny. Uzytkowanie Gruntow i Powierzchnia Zasiewow oraz Zwierzeta Gospodarskie changed to Poland. Glowny Urzad Statystyczny. Wyniki Spisu Rolniczego. Uzytkowanie Gruntow i Powierzchnia Zasiewow, oraz Zwierzeta Gospodarskie.
0079-287X	Poland. Glowny Urzad Statystyczny. Wypadki Drogowe
0079-2888	Poland. Glowny Urzad Statystyczny. Wypadki przy Pracy
0079-2896	Poland. Glowny Urzad Statystyczny. Zatrudnienie w Gospodarce Narodowej
0079-290X	Poland. Glowny Urzad Statystyczny. Zwierzeta Gospodarskie†
0079-2918	Polar Notes†
0079-2926	Polemologische Studien†
0079-2950	Police Yearbook†
0079-2985	Polish Journal of Soil Science
0079-2993	Polish Psychological Bulletin
0079-3000	Polish Round Table see 0208-7375
0079-3027	Politica
0079-3035	Political Handbook and Atlas of the World see 0193-175X
0079-3043	Political Science Annual†
0079-3051	Maharaja Sayajirao University of Baroda. Political Science Series†
0079-3078	Politics†
0079-3094	Politics of Modernization Series†
0079-3108	Politique Belge†
0079-3116	Pollution Control Review see 0090-516X
0079-3124	K-W Probe†
0079-3132	Polonia Typographica Saeculi Sedecimi
0079-3140	Polska Akademia Nauk. Biblioteka, Krakow. Rocznik
0079-3159	Academie Polonaise des Sciences. Centre Scientifique, Paris. Conferences†
0079-3167	Accademia Polacca delle Scienze. Conferenze see 0239-8605
0079-3175	Polska Akademia Nauk. Centrum Obliczeniowe. Prace changed to Polish Academy of Sciences. Institute of Computer Science. Reports.
0079-3183	Sredniowiecze. Studia o Kulturze†
0079-3205	Polska Akademia Nauk. Instytut Maszyn Przeplywowych. Prace
0079-3256	Polska Akademia Nauk. Oddzial w Krakowie. Komisja Archeologiczna. Prace
0079-3264	Polska Akademia Nauk. Oddzial w Krakowie. Komisja Ceramiczna. Prace: Ceramika
0079-3272	Polska Akademia Nauk. Oddzial w Krakowie. Komisja Filologii Klasycznej. Prace
0079-3280	Polska Akademia Nauk. Oddzial w Krakowie. Komisja Gorniczo-Geodezyjna. Prace: Gornictwo
0079-3299	Polska Akademia Nauk. Oddzial w Krakowie. Komisja Gorniczo-Geodezyjna. Prace: Geodezja
0079-3310	Polska Akademia Nauk. Oddzial w Krakowie. Komisja Jezykoznawstwa. Prace
0079-3329	Polska Akademia Nauk. Oddzial w Krakowie. Komisja Jezykoznawstwa. Wydawnictwa Zrodlowe
0079-3337	Polska Akademia Nauk. Oddzial w Krakowie. Komisja Mechaniki Stosowanej. Prace: Mechanika
0079-3345	Polska Akademia Nauk. Oddzial w Krakowie. Komisja Metalurgiczno-Odlewnicza. Prace: Metalurgia
0079-3353	Polska Akademia Nauk. Oddzial w Krakowie. Komisja Nauk Ekonomicznych. Prace
0079-3361	Prace Geologiczne
0079-337X	Polska Akademia Nauk. Oddzial w Krakowie. Komisja Historycznoliteracka. Rocznik
0079-3388	Polska Akademia Nauk. Oddzial w Krakowie. Komisja Nauk Historycznych. Prace
0079-3396	Polska Akademia Nauk. Oddzial w Krakowie. Komisja Nauk Mineralogicznych. Prace Mineralogiczne
0079-340X	Polska Akademia Nauk. Oddzial w Krakowie. Komisja Nauk Pedagogicznych. Prace
0079-3418	Polska Akademia Nauk. Oddzial w Krakowie. Komisja Nauk Pedagogicznych. Rocznik
0079-3426	Polska Akademia Nauk. Oddzial w Krakowie. Komisja Orientalistyczna. Prace
0079-3434	Polska Akademia Nauk. Oddzial w Krakowie. Komisja Slowianoznawstwa. Prace
0079-3442	Polska Akademia Nauk. Oddzial w Krakowie. Komisja Socjologiczna. Prace
0079-3450	Polska Akademia Nauk. Oddzial w Krakowie. Komisja Urbanistyki i Architektury. Teka
0079-3477	Polska Akademia Nauk. Komitet Gospodarki Wodnej. Prace i Studia
0079-3485	Prace Jezykoznawcze
0079-3493	Polska Akademia Nauk. Komitet Przestrzennego Zagospodarowania Kraju. Biuletyn
0079-3507	Polska Akademia Nauk. Komitet Przestrzennego Zagospodarowania Kraju. Studia
0079-3531	Polska Akademia Nauk. Oddzial w Krakowie. Rocznik
0079-354X	Polska Akademia Nauk. Oddzial w Krakowie. Komisje Naukowe. Sprawozdania z Posiedzen
0079-3558	Polska Akademia Nauk. Wydzial Nauk Medycznych. Rozprawy
0079-3566	Academie Polonaise des Sciences. Centre d'Archeologie Mediterraneenne. Etudes et Travaux
0079-3574	Polska Akademia Nauk. Instytut Geofizyki. Materialy i Prace see 0137-2440
0079-3574	Polska Akademia Nauk. Instytut Geofizyki. Materialy i Prace see 0138-0109
0079-3574	Polska Akademia Nauk. Instytut Geofizyki. Materialy i Prace see 0138-0117
0079-3574	Polska Akademia Nauk. Instytut Geofizyki. Materialy i Prace see 0138-0125
0079-3574	Polska Akademia Nauk. Instytut Geofizyki. Materialy i Prace see 0138-0141
0079-3574	Polska Akademia Nauk. Instytut Geofizyki. Materialy i Prace see 0208-8061
0079-3574	Polska Akademia Nauk. Instytut Geofizyki. Materialy i Prace see 0138-015X
0079-3582	Polska Akademia Nauk. Centrum Badan Naukowych w Wojewodztwie Katowickim. Prace i Studia changed to Polska Akademia Nauk. Instytut Podstaw Inzynierii Srodowiska. Prace i Studia.
0079-3590	Polska Bibliografia Literacka
0079-3612	Polska Piesn i Muzyka Ludowa. Zrodla i Materialy
0079-3620	Polska 2000
0079-3647	Polskie Archiwum Weterynaryjne
0079-3655	Polskie Towarzystwo Cybernetyczne. Biuletyn see 0137-3595
0079-3663	Polskie Towarzystwo Geologiczne. Rocznik
0079-3698	Polskie Towarzystwo Matematyczne. Roczniki. Seria 2: Wiadomosci Matematyczne
0079-3701	Mechanika Teoretyczna i Stosowana
0079-371X	Polskie Towarzystwo Naukowe na Obczyznie. Rocznik
0079-3728	Polymer Engineering and Technology Series†
0079-3736	Polymer Reviews†
0079-3795	Pomologia Republicii Socialiste Romania†
0079-3809	University of Poona. Centre of Advanced Study in Sanskrit. Publications
0079-3825	Poor's Register of Corporations, Directors and Executives changed to Standard & Poor's Register of Corporations, Directors and Executives.
0079-3833	Popes through History†
0079-3841	Popular Lectures in Mathematics Series†
0079-3868	Population Census of Papua New Guinea. Population Characteristics Bulletin Series
0079-3876	Population Council, New York. Country Profiles†
0079-3892	Population Council, New York. Reports on Population/Family Planning†
0079-3906	Population Estimates of Arizona changed to Demographic Guide to Arizona (Year).
0079-3914	Population Health Survey Research Bulletin†
0079-3922	University of California, Berkeley. Institute of International Studies. Population Monograph Series†
0079-3957	University of Port Elizabeth. Publications. General Series
0079-3965	University of Port Elizabeth. Publications. Research Papers
0079-3973	University of Port Elizabeth. Publications. Symposia and Seminars changed to University of Port Elizabeth. Publications. Symposia, Seminars, and Lectures.
0079-3981	Port of Baltimore Handbook changed to Port of Baltimore Magazine.
0079-399X	Port of Piraeus Authority. Statistical Bulletin changed to Port of Piraeus Authority. Statistical Report.
0079-4007	Port Phillip Authority. Annual Report
0079-4058	Universidade do Rio Grande do Sul. Instituto de Ciencias Naturais. Boletim see 0102-597X
0079-4066	Ports of the World†
0079-4074	Ports - Routes - Trafics

0079-4082 Portugal. Instituto Nacional de Estatistica. Centro de Estudos Demograficos. Revista *see* 0871-875X
0079-4104 Portugal. Instituto Nacional de Estatistica. Anuario Demografico. *changed to* Portugal. Instituto Nacional de Estatistica. Estatisticas Demograficas. Continente, Acores e Madeira.
0079-4112 Portugal. Instituto Nacional de Estatistica. Anuario Estatistico *see* 0871-8741
0079-4120 Portugal. Instituto Nacional de Estatistica. Estatisticas das Contribuicoes e Impostos *changed to* Portugal. Instituto Nacional de Estatistica. Estatisticas das Contribuicoes e Impostos. Continente, Acores e Madiera.
0079-4139 Portugal. Instituto Nacional de Estatistica. Estatisticas Agricolas. Continente, Acores e Madeira
0079-4147 Portugal. Instituto Nacional de Estatistica. Estatisticas do Comercio Externo *changed to* Portugal. Instituto Nacional de Estatistica. Estatisticas do Comercio Externo. Continente, Acores e Madeira.
0079-4155 Portugal. Instituto Nacional de Estatistica. Estatisticas de Educacao *changed to* Portugal. Instituto Nacional de Estatistica. Estatisticas da Educacao. Continente, Acores e Madeira.
0079-4163 Portugal. Instituto Nacional de Estatistica. Estatisticas das Organizacoes Sindicais *see* 0870-4406
0079-418X Portugal. Estatisticas Industriais: Continente, Acores e Madeira. Volume 2: Industrias Transformadoras
0079-4201 Portugal. Ministerio das Financas. Relatorio do Orcamento Geral do Estado
0079-421X Portugiesische Forschungen der Goerresgesellschaft. Reihe 1: Aufsaetze zur Portugiesischen Kulturgeschichte
0079-4228 Portugiesische Forschungen der Goerresgesellschaft. Reihe 2: Monographien
0079-4236 Post-Medieval Archaeology
0079-4244 Postage Stamps of the United States *changed to* Postal Service Guide to U S Stamps.
0079-4252 Postepy Mikrobiologii
0079-4260 Postepy Napedu Elektrycznego
0079-4279 Postepy Pediatrii
0079-4295 Postilla
0079-4309 Potato Marketing Board, London. Annual Report and Accounts
0079-4317 Abstracts of Theses and Dissertations Accepted for Higher Degrees in the Potchefstroom University for Christian Higher Education†
0079-4325 Union Catalogue of Theses and Dissertations of the South African Universities†
0079-4333 Potchefstroom University for Christian Higher Education. Wetenskaplike Bydraes. Reeks A: Geesteswetenskappe
0079-4341 Potchefstroom University for Christian Higher Education. Wetenskaplike Bydraes. Reeks B: Natuurwetenskappe. Series
0079-4376 Museum fuer Ur- und Fruehgeschichte der Bezirke Potsdam, Frankfurt - Oder und Cottbus. Veroeffentlichungen
0079-4414 Power Conditioning Specialists Conference. Record *see* 0275-9306
0079-4422 Power Farming Technical Annual *changed to* Power Farming Annual.
0079-4457 Power Sources Symposium. Proceedings†
0079-4465 Powstanie Styczniowe. Materialy i Dokumenty
0079-4473 Politechnika Poznanska. Zeszyty Naukowe. Chemia *changed to* Politechnika Poznanska. Zeszyty Naukowe. Chemia i Inzynieria Chemiczna.
0079-4481 Politechnika Poznanska. Materialy Historyczno-Metodyczne. Studia Filozoficzne *changed to* Materialy Historyczno-Metodyczne.
0079-449X Politechnika Poznanska. Zeszyty Naukowe. Budownictwo Ladowe *changed to* Politechnika Poznanska. Zeszyty Naukowe. Budownictwo Ladowe.
0079-4503 Politechnika Poznanska. Zeszyty Naukowe. Elektryka
0079-4511 Politechnika Poznanska. Zeszyty Naukowe. Fizyka†
0079-452X Politechnika Poznanska. Zeszyty Naukowe. Matematyka *see* 0044-4413
0079-4538 Politechnika Poznanska. Zeszyty Naukowe. Mechanika
0079-4546 Akademia Ekonomiczna, Poznan. Zeszyty Naukowe. Seria 1
0079-4554 Akademia Ekonomiczna, Poznan. Zeszyty Naukowe. Seria 2. Prace Habilitacyjne i Doktorskie
0079-4570 Societe des Amis des Sciences et des Lettres de Poznan. Bulletin. Serie D: Sciences Biologiques
0079-4589 Poznanskie Towarzystwo Przyjaciol Nauk. Komisja Automatyki. Prace *changed to* Studia z Automatyki.
0079-4597 Poznanskie Towarzystwo Przyjaciol Nauk. Komisja Budownictwa i Architektury. Prace†
0079-4619 Poznanskie Towarzystwo Przyjaciol Nauk. Komisja Biologiczna. Prace
0079-4627 Poznanskie Towarzystwo Przyjaciol Nauk. Komisja Elektrotechniki. Prace†
0079-4635 Poznanskie Towarzystwo Przyjaciol Nauk. Komisja Filozoficzna. Prace
0079-4651 Poznanskie Towarzystwo Przyjaciol Nauk. Komisja Historyczna. Prace
0079-466X Poznanskie Towarzystwo Przyjaciol Nauk. Komisja Historii Sztuki. Prace
0079-4678 Poznanskie Towarzystwo Przyjaciol Nauk. Komisja Jezykoznawcza. Prace
0079-4708 Poznanskie Towarzystwo Przyjaciol Nauk. Komisja Nauk Rolniczych i Komisja Nauk Lesnych. Prace
0079-4716 Poznanskie Towarzystwo Przyjaciol Nauk. Komisja Nauk Spolecznych. Prace
0079-4724 Poznanskie Towarzystwo Przyjaciol Nauk. Komisja Technologii Drewna. Prace
0079-4740 Lingua Posnaniensis
0079-4759 Prace i Materialy Etnograficzne†
0079-4767 Prace Literackie†
0079-4775 Prace Onomastyczne
0079-4783 Polska Akademia Nauk. Komitet Nauk Orientalistycznych. Prace Orientalistyczne
0079-4791 Prace Polonistyczne
0079-4805 Towarzystwo Naukowe w Toruniu. Prace Popularnonaukowe
0079-4821 Practical Table Series†
0079-4848 Praehistorische Zeitschrift
0079-4856 Prague Studies in Mathematical Linguistics†
0079-4872 Prakseologia
0079-4880 Praktische Betriebswirtschaft
0079-4899 Praktische Chirurgie
0079-4902 Prameny Ceske a Slovenske Lingvistiky. Rada Ceska
0079-4929 Pravnehistoricke Studie
0079-4937 Pravoslavny Theologicky Sbornik
0079-4945 Praxis der Klinischen Psychologie†
0079-4953 Prediction Annual
0079-4961 Predigtstudien
0079-497X Prehistoric Society, London. Proceedings
0079-4988 Preparative Inorganic Reactions†
0079-4996 Presbyterian Church in Canada. General Assembly. Acts and Proceedings
0079-502X Press Braille, Adult *see* 0277-5247
0079-5046 Press Radio and T.V. Guide†
0079-5062 Pretoria College for Advanced Technical Education. Annual/Jaarblad†
0079-5089 Primary Socialization, Language, and Education†
0079-5100 Primates†
0079-5127 Primatologia†
0079-5143 Prince Edward Island. Department of Fisheries. Annual Report *changed to* Prince Edward Island. Department of Fisheries and Aquaculture. Annual Report.
0079-5151 Prince Edward Island. Public Utilities Commission. Annual Report
0079-5186 Princeton Essays in Literature.
0079-5194 Princeton Mathematical Series
0079-5208 Princeton Monographs in Art and Archaeology
0079-5216 Princeton Series in Physics
0079-5240 Princeton Studies in Mathematical Economics†
0079-5259 Princeton Studies in Music†
0079-5267 Princeton University. Center of International Studies. Policy Memorandum Series†
0079-5275 Princeton University. Committee for the Excavation of Antioch. Publications†
0079-5283 Princeton University. Computer Sciences Laboratory. Technical Report *changed to* Princeton University. Department of Computer Science. Technical Reports.
0079-5291 Princeton University. Econometric Research Program. Research Memorandum
0079-5305 Princeton University. Industrial Relations Section. Research Report
0079-5313 Prindle, Weber and Schmidt Complementary Series in Mathematics†
0079-5321 Printing Historical Society. Journal
0079-533X Printing Magazine Purchasing Guide†
0079-5348 Printing Trades Blue Book. New York Edition *see* 1044-8527
0079-5356 Printing Trades Blue Book. Northeastern Edition *see* 1044-646X
0079-5364 Printing Trades Blue Book. Southeastern Edition *see* 1044-7989
0079-5372 Printing Trades Directory
0079-5399 Private Independent Schools (Year)
0079-5402 Private Press Books
0079-5453 Prize Stories: The O. Henry Awards
0079-550X Pro and Senior Hockey Guide *see* 0278-4955
0079-5518 Pro Basketball Guide *changed to* Basketball Guide.
0079-5526 Pro Football (Los Angeles)
0079-5550 Pro Helvetia†
0079-5569 N.H.L. Pro Hockey†
0079-5577 Pro Hockey Guide†
0079-5593 Pro Mundi Vita. Special Notes *see* 1012-4543
0079-5607 Probability and Mathematical Statistics
0079-5615 Probation and Parole *see* 0278-1042
0079-5623 Probau
0079-5631 Probe
0079-564X Probleme der Festkoerperelektronik†
0079-5666 Problemes Actuels d'Endocrinologie et de Nutrition†
0079-5682 Problemi e Ricerche di Storia Antica
0079-5690 Problemi Economici d'Oggi†
0079-5704 Problems behind the Iron Curtain Series†
0079-5739 Problems in Mathematical Analysis Report†
0079-5763 Problems of the Contemporary World
0079-5771 Problems of the North†
0079-578X Problemy Ekonomiczne
0079-5798 Problemy Polonii Zagranicznej *see* 0138-094X
0079-5801 Problemy Rad Narodowych. Studia i Materialy
0079-5836 Prodei
0079-5852 Produccion Rural Argentina†
0079-5860 Produce Marketing Association. Yearbook *changed to* Produce Marketing Association Membership Directory & Buyer's Guide.
0079-5879 Production et la Consommation de l'Electricite en Belgique. Annuaire Statistique. Statistisch Jaarboek
0079-5925 Professional and Trade Organisations in India
0079-5933 Professional School Psychology *see* 1045-3830
0079-595X Profitability of Cotton Growing in Israel
0079-5968 Profitability of Poultry Farming in Israel
0079-5976 Profitability of Sugarbeet Growing in Israel†
0079-5984 Profits†
0079-600X Programmed Learning and Teaching Machines; Bibliographical References
0079-6026 Progress in Aeronautical Sciences *see* 0376-0421
0079-6034 Progress in Allergy *see* 1015-0145
0079-6042 Progress in Analytical Chemistry†
0079-6050 Progress in Astronautics and Aeronautics Series
0079-6077 Progress in Bio-Organic Chemistry†
0079-6085 Progress in Biochemical Pharmacology
0079-6107 Progress in Biophysics & Molecular Biology
0079-6115 Progress in Boron Chemistry†
0079-6123 Progress in Brain Research
0079-614X Progress in Ceramic Science†
0079-6158 Progress in Chemical Toxicology†
0079-6166 Progress in Clinical Cancer†
0079-6174 Progress in Clinical Pathology†
0079-6182 Progress in Clinical Psychology†
0079-6212 Progress in Control Engineering†
0079-6247 Progress in Elementary Particle and Cosmic Ray Physics†
0079-6255 Progress in Experimental Personality Research†
0079-6263 Progress in Experimental Tumor Research
0079-6271 Progress in Gastroenterology†
0079-628X Progress in Geophysics†
0079-6298 Progress in Gynecology†
0079-6301 Progress in Hematology
0079-631X Progress in Heat and Mass Transfer†
0079-6328 Progress in High Temperature Physics and Chemistry†
0079-6336 Progress in Histochemistry and Cytochemistry
0079-6344 Progress in Immunobiological Standardization *see* 0301-5149
0079-6379 Progress in Inorganic Chemistry
0079-6387 Progress in Learning Disabilities†
0079-6409 Progress in Liver Diseases†
0079-6417 Progress in Low Temperature Physics
0079-6425 Progress in Materials Science
0079-645X Progress in Medical Virology
0079-6468 Progress in Medicinal Chemistry
0079-6484 Progress in Molecular and Subcellular Biology
0079-6492 Progress in Neurological Surgery
0079-6506 Progress in Neurology and Psychiatry†
0079-6514 Progress in Nuclear Energy. Series 3 - Process Chemistry *see* 0149-1970
0079-6530 Progress in Nuclear Energy. Series 9 - Analytical Chemistry *see* 0149-1970
0079-6565 Progress in Nuclear Magnetic Resonance Spectroscopy
0079-6581 Progress in Nuclear Medicine *see* 0163-6170
0079-659X Progress in Nuclear Physics *see* 0146-6410
0079-6603 Progress in Nucleic Acid Research and Molecular Biology
0079-6611 Progress in Oceanography
0079-6638 Progress in Optics
0079-6654 Progress in Pediatric Surgery

0079-6662 Progress in Physical Organic Chemistry
0079-6670 Progress in Physiological Psychology *changed to* Progress in Psychobiology and Physiological Psychology.
0079-6689 Progress in Phytochemistry†
0079-6697 Progress in Polarography†
0079-6700 Progress in Polymer Science
0079-6719 Progress in Powder Metallurgy†
0079-6727 Progress in Quantum Electronics
0079-6735 Progress in Radiation Therapy†
0079-6743 Progress in Reaction Kinetics
0079-6751 Progress in Respiration Research
0079-6786 Progress in Solid State Chemistry
0079-6794 U.S. Fish and Wildlife Service. Progress in Sport Fishery Research *changed to* Fisheries and Wildlife Research.
0079-6808 Progress in Stereochemistry†
0079-6816 Progress in Surface Science
0079-6824 Progress in Surgery
0079-6832 Progress in the Chemistry of Fats and Other Lipids *see* 0163-7827
0079-6840 Progress in the Science and Technology of the Rare Earths†
0079-6859 Progress in Theoretical Biology†
0079-6883 Progress Polimernoi Khimii
0079-6891 Progress of Public Education in the United States *changed to* Progress of Education in the United States of America.
0079-6913 Progress Report on Clays and Shales of Montana†
0079-6921 Progressive Grocer's Marketing Guidebook
0079-6956 Project Skywater. Annual Report†
0079-6980 Proof: The Yearbook of American Bibliographical and Textual Studies†
0079-6999 Proportions†
0079-7014 Prospects for America†
0079-7022 Prospezioni Archeologiche†
0079-7049 Protein Synthesis: a Series of Advances†
0079-7065 Protides of the Biological Fluids
0079-7073 Protoplasmologia: Handbuch der Protoplasmaforschung *see* 0172-4665
0079-7111 Pruefen und Entscheiden
0079-7138 Przeglad Archeologiczny
0079-7154 Przeglad Naukowej Literatury Rolniczej i Lesnej
0079-7170 Przeglad Zagranicznej Literatury Geograficznej
0079-7189 Przeszlosc Demograficzna Polski
0079-7197 Pseudepigrapha Veteris Testamenti Graece
0079-7227 Psychiatria Fennica
0079-726X Psychiatrie de l'Enfant
0079-7278 Psychiatry; a Medical World News Publication†
0079-7286 Psychiatry and Art†
0079-7294 Psychoanalytic Study of Society
0079-7308 Psychoanalytic Study of the Child
0079-7324 Psychologen Adresboek
0079-7332 Psychologia Africana *see* 0081-2463
0079-7340 Psychologia Africana. Monograph Supplement†
0079-7359 Psychological Issues. Monograph *see* 0048-5748
0079-7383 Psychological Studies. Major Series *changed to* Psychological Studies.
0079-7391 Psychological Studies. Minor Series†
0079-7405 Psychologie und Person
0079-7421 Psychology of Learning and Motivation: Advances in Research and Theory
0079-743X Psychopharmacology Handbook: Animal Research in Psychopharmacology†
0079-7448 Psychotheque
0079-7456 Pszichologia a Gyakorlatban
0079-7464 Pszichologiai Tanulmanyok
0079-7472 Pubblicita in Italia
0079-7499 Public Administration in Israel and Abroad†
0079-7537 Public and Preparatory Schools. Yearbook *changed to* Independent Schools Yearbook: Boys & Co-Ed.
0079-7561 Sweden. Riksrevisionsverket. Statens Finanser†
0079-7588 Public Health Conference on Records and Statistics. Proceedings
0079-7596 Public Health Monograph
0079-7618 University of Kansas Libraries. Annual Public Lecture on Books and Bibliography†
0079-7626 Public Papers of the Presidents of the United States
0079-7634 Public Policy Issues in Resource Management
0079-7642 Public Affairs Manual for the Bench and Bar of California†
0079-7650 Public Schools Careers Guide†
0079-7669 S I L Publications on Linguistics and Related Fields *changed to* Summer Institute of Linguistics and The University of Texas at Arlington Publications in Linguistics.
0079-7677 Publications in Medieval Studies
0079-7685 Publications in Medieval Science
0079-7731 Publications in Psychology
0079-774X Publications in Seismology
0079-7758 Publications in Tropical Geography Savanna Research Series *changed to* McGill University Savanna Research Project - Savanna Research Series.
0079-7782 Publications on Asia *changed to* School of International Studies. Publications on Asia.
0079-7790 Publications on Russia and Eastern Europe *changed to* School of International Studies. Publications on Russia and Eastern Europe.
0079-7804 Publications on Social History†
0079-7812 Publications Romanes et Francaises
0079-7820 A Select List *see* 0333-6018
0079-7839 Publishers in the United Kingdom and Their Addresses
0079-7847 Publishers International Yearbook†
0079-7855 Publishers' Trade List Annual
0079-7863 Puerto Rico. Negociado del Presupuesto. Resoluciones Conjuntas del Presupuesto General y de Presupuestos Especiales *changed to* Puerto Rico. Oficina de Presupuesto y Gerencia. Resoluciones Conjuntas del Presupuesto General y de Presupuestos Especiales.
0079-788X Universidad de Puerto Rico. Institute of Caribbean Studies. Special Studies *see* 0069-0511
0079-7936 Canada's Pulp and Paper Business Directory *see* 0708-501X
0079-7944 Pulp and Paper Industry Technical Conference. Record *see* 0190-2172
0079-7952 Pulp and Paper Magazine of Canada's Reference Manual and Buyers' Guide *see* 0709-2563
0079-7960 Pulp and Paper Research Institute of Canada. Annual Report
0079-8029 University of the Punjab. Arabic and Persian Society. Journal
0079-8045 University of the Punjab. Department of Zoology. Bulletin. New Series *changed to* Punjab University Journal of Zoology.
0079-8061 Pupila: Libros de Nuestro Tiempo
0079-807X Purdue Opinion Panel, Lafayette, Indiana. Report†
0079-810X Purdue University. Engineering Experiment Station. Joint Highway Research Project. Research Reports†
0079-8126 Materials Research in Science and Engineering at Purdue University. Progress Report†
0079-8134 Purdue University. Office of Manpower Studies. Manpower Report *changed to* Purdue University. Office of Manpower Studies. Manpower & Technical Education Requirements Reports.
0079-8142 Purdue University. Road School. Proceedings of Annual Road School
0079-8150 Pure and Applied Cryogenics†
0079-8169 Pure and Applied Mathematics
0079-8177 Pure and Applied Mathematics Series
0079-8185 Pure and Applied Mathematics; a Series of Texts and Monographs *changed to* Pure and Applied Mathematics: A Wiley Interscience Series of Texts, Monographs and Tracts.
0079-8193 Pure and Applied Physics†
0079-8215 Pyrenae: Cronica Arqueologica
0079-8223 Pyttersen's Nederlandse Almanak
0079-824X Quaderni dei Padri Benedettini di San Giorgio Maggiore†
0079-8258 Quaderni di Archeologia della Libia
0079-8274 Quaderni di Poesia Neogreca
0079-8282 Quaderni e Guide di Archeologia†
0079-8304 Quality of Surface Waters of the United States†
0079-8312 Quarterly Journal of Studies on Alcohol. Supplement *see* 0363-468X
0079-8347 Universite Laval. Centre d'Etudes Nordiques. Travaux et Documents†
0079-8355 Universite Laval. Departement d'Exploitation et Utilisation des Bois. Note de Recherches
0079-8363 Universite Laval. Departement d'Exploitation et Utilisation des Bois. Note Technique
0079-838X Universite Laval. Fonds de Recherches Forestieres. Contribution†
0079-8398 Universite Laval. Institut d'Histoire. Cahiers *changed to* Universite Laval. Les Cahiers d'Histoire.
0079-8738 Quebec (Province). Department of Natural Resources. Geological Reports *changed to* Quebec (Province) Department of Energy and Resources. Geological Reports.
0079-8746 Quebec (Province). Ministere des Richesses Naturelles. Travaux sur le Terrain *changed to* Quebec (Province) . Departement d'Energie et Resources. Rapport des Representants Regionaux.
0079-8754 Quebec (Province) Marine Biological Station, Grande-Riviere. Rapport *changed to* Quebec (Province) Direction de la Recherche Scientifique et Technique. Activites (Year).
0079-8762 Quebec (Province). Marine Biological Station, Grande-Riviere. Cahiers d'Information *changed to* Quebec (Province). Direction de la Recherche Scientifique et Technique Cahier d'Information.
0079-8770 Quebec (Province) Office de la Langue Francaise. Cahiers *changed to* Vocabulaire des Imprimes Administratifs.
0079-8789 Queen's Medical Review
0079-8797 Queen's Papers in Pure and Applied Mathematics
0079-8800 Geological Survey of Queensland Publications†
0079-8819 Geological Survey of Queensland. Report†
0079-8827 Queensland Law Almanac *changed to* Queensland Legal Directory.
0079-8835 Queensland Museum, Brisbane. Memoirs
0079-8843 Queensland Naturalist
0079-8851 Queensland Society of Sugar Cane Technologists. Proceedings *see* 0726-0822
0079-886X University of Queensland. Computer Centre. Papers†
0079-8878 University of Queensland. Department of Agriculture. Papers†
0079-8886 University of Queensland. Department of Architecture. Papers†
0079-8894 University of Queensland. Department of Accountancy. Papers *changed to* University of Queensland. Department of Commerce. Papers.
0079-8908 University of Queensland. Department of Botany. Papers†
0079-8916 University of Queensland. Department of Entomology. Papers†
0079-8924 University of Queensland. Departments of Government and History. Paper†
0079-8932 University of Queensland. Department of Geology. Papers†
0079-8940 University of Queensland. Department of Social Sciences. Papers†
0079-8959 University of Queensland. Department of Zoology. Papers†
0079-8975 University of Queensland. Faculty of Arts. Papers†
0079-8983 University of Queensland. Faculty of Education. Papers†
0079-8991 University of Queensland. Faculty of Law. Papers†
0079-9009 University of Queensland. Faculty of Medicine. Papers†
0079-9017 University of Queensland. Faculty of Veterinary Science. Papers†
0079-9033 University of Queensland Inaugural Lectures†
0079-9041 Queensland'S Health†
0079-905X Quellenkataloge zur Musikgeschichte
0079-9068 Quellen und Forschungen aus Italienischen Archiven und Bibliotheken
0079-9076 Quellen und Forschungen zur Basler Geschichte
0079-9084 Quellen und Forschungen zur Wuerttembergischen Kirchengeschichte
0079-9114 Quellen und Studien zur Geschichte Osteuropas
0079-9130 Quellen und Untersuchungen zur Geschichte der Deutschen und Oesterreichischen Arbeiterbewegung. Neue Folge†
0079-9149 Quellenschriften zur Westdeutschen Vor- und Fruehgeschichte
0079-9157 Quellenwerke zur Alten Geschichte Amerikas
0079-919X Question†
0079-9211 Quetico-Superior Wilderness Research Center, Ely, Minnesota. Annual Report
0079-922X Quetico-Superior Wilderness Research Center, Ely, Minnesota. Technical Notes
0079-9238 University of the Philippines. Asian Center. Monograph Series
0079-9246 University of the Philippines. Community Development Research Council. Study Series
0079-9254 University of the Philippines. College of Public Administration. (Publication) *see* 0031-7675
0079-9262 Qui Represente Qui
0079-9270 Qui Vend et Achete Quoi?
0079-9289 Quick Frozen Foods Directory of Frozen Food Processors†
0079-9300 R I C
0079-9327 Universidade Federal de Minas Gerais. Corpo Discente. Revista Literaria.
0079-9335 R L S: Regional Language Studies - Newfoundland *changed to* Regional Language Studies - Newfoundland.
0079-9343 R.M. Bucke Memorial Society for the Study of Religious Experience. Newsletter-Review†
0079-9351 R.M. Bucke Memorial Society for the Study of Religious Experience. Proceedings of the Conference†
0079-936X Rabbinical Assembly, New York. Proceedings
0079-9386 Rabindranath Tagore Memorial Lectureship†
0079-9394 Raceform Up-to-Date *changed to* Raceform Weekly.
0079-9408 Racehorses
0079-9416 Racial Policies of American Industry. Reports†
0079-9424 Racing and Football Outlook: Racing Annual
0079-9440 Radio Amateur's Handbook
0079-9467 Radio Handbook

ISSN

0079-9483 Radiochemical and Radioanalytical Letters *changed to* Journal of Radioanalytical and Nuclear Chemistry. Articles.
0079-9483 Radiochemical and Radioanalytical Letters *changed to* Journal of Radioanalytical and Nuclear Chemistry. Letters.
0079-9491 Radner Lectures
0079-9513 Railway Directory and Yearbook
0079-9521 Railway Fuel and Operating Officers Association. Proceedings
0079-9548 Railway Technical Review
0079-9556 Rajasthan, India. Directorate of Economics and Statistics. Budget Study
0079-9564 Rajasthan, India. Directorate of Economics and Statistics. Basic Statistics
0079-9572 Rajasthan Year Book and Who's Who
0079-9580 Incidenca Raka v Sloveniji
0079-9599 Rampenlicht
0079-9602 Ranchi University Mathematical Journal
0079-9610 Rand McNally Campground and Trailer Park Guide *see* 0733-8309
0079-9629 Rand McNally National Park Guide *changed to* National Park Guide.
0079-9637 Rand McNally Discover Historic America†
0079-9645 Rand McNally Travel Trailer Guide *see* 0733-8309
0079-967X Ranganathan Series in Library Science†
0079-9688 Rapport Annuel sur l'Economie Arabe†
0079-9696 Rapport Annuel sur l'Economie Syrienne
0079-9726 Rassegna Internazionale del Film Scientifico - Didattico†
0079-9815 Raymond Dart Lectures
0079-9831 Reader's Digest Almanac and Yearbook†
0079-984X Readex Microprint Publications *changed to* United Nations Documents and Publications.
0079-9866 Reading University Studies on Contemporary Europe
0079-9874 Readings in Political Economy *see* 0305-814X
0079-9890 Real Estate Reports
0079-9904 Reanimation et Organes Artificiels. Revue Internationale de Physiologie, Medecine, Chirugie et des Techniques Appliquees aux Sciences Biologiques
0079-9912 Recent Advances in Food Science†
0079-9939 Recent Advances in Plasma Diagnostics†
0079-9947 Recent Developments in the Chemistry of Natural Carbon Compounds
0079-9955 Recent Developments of Neurobiology in Hungary
0079-9963 Recent Progress in Hormone Research. Proceedings of the Laurentian Hormone Conference
0079-9971 Recent Progress in Surface Science *changed to* Recent Progress in Surface Membrane Science.
0079-998X Recent Publications in the Social and Behavioral Sciences. A B S Guide Supplement††
0080-0015 Recent Results in Cancer Research
0080-0023 Recent Sociology†
0080-0031 Recherches Africaines†
0080-004X Recherches Cooperatives†
0080-0058 Recherches de Psychologie Experimentale et Comparee†
0080-0066 Recherches de Psychopedagogie et de Pedagogie Experimentale†
0080-0090 Recherches Mediterraneennes. Bibliographies†
0080-0104 Recherches Mediterraneennes. Serie 1. Etudes†
0080-0112 Recherches Mediterraneennes. Serie 2 Documents†
0080-0120 Recherches Mediterraneennes. Serie 3: Textes et Etudes Linguistiques†
0080-0139 Vie Musicale en France Sous les Rois Bourbons. Serie 2: Recherches sur la Musique Francaise Classique
0080-0155 Recht und Wettbewerb†
0080-0163 Rechts- und Staatswissenschaften
0080-018X Rechtspflege Jahrbuch
0080-0228 Universidade Federal de Pernambuco. Instituto de Antibioticos. Revista
0080-0236 Universidade Federal de Pernambuco. Instituto Oceanografico. Trabalhos *see* 0374-0412
0080-0244 Universidade Federal de Pernambuco. Instituto de Geosciencias. Serie B: Estudos e Pesquisas *changed to* Universidade Federal de Pernambuco. Departamento de Geologia. Serie B. Estudos e Pesquisas.
0080-0252 Recommended Wayside Inns of Britain
0080-0260 Reconstruction Surgery and Traumatology
0080-0287 Records of Civilization. Sources and Studies
0080-0295 Records of Oceanographic Works in Japan. New Series†
0080-0309 Recueil Complet des Budgets de la Syrie
0080-0333 Recueil des Instructions Donnees aux Ambassadeurs et Ministres de France
0080-0341 Recurring Bibliography, Education in the Allied Health Professions†
0080-0384 American National Red Cross. Annual Report *changed to* American Red Cross. Annual Report.
0080-0392 New Zealand Red Cross Society. Report
0080-0414 Reducing Your Income Tax†
0080-0422 Reed's Nautical Almanac
0080-0449 Reference Book - Argentina
0080-0457 Reference Book - Republic of South Africa
0080-0481 Reformed Church of America. Historical Series
0080-049X Refractory Materials†
0080-0503 Refrigeration and Air Conditioning Directory *see* 0305-0777
0080-0511 Refrigeration Annual†
0080-0538 Regency International Directory
0080-0562 Regi Magyar Dallamok Tara
0080-0570 Regi Magyar Prozai Emlekek
0080-0589 Regional Conference on Water Resources Development in Asia and the Far East. Proceedings†
0080-0619 Regional Science Research Institute. Bibliography Series†
0080-0627 Regional Science Research Institute. Monograph Series†
0080-0643 Regions
0080-066X Registre Aeronautique International
0080-0678 Registre International de Classification de Navires et d'Aeronefs *changed to* Registre Maritime.
0080-0686 Registry of Accredited Facilities and Certified Individuals in Orthotics and Prosthetics†
0080-0694 Regnum Vegetabile
0080-0708 Rehabilitation der Entwicklungsgehemmten
0080-0724 Rehabilitation Industries Corporation. Annual Report
0080-0759 Rehovot Conference on Science in the Advancement of New States. (Proceedings)†
0080-0783 Reilly-Lake Shore Graphics. R O P Color Requirements Report *changed to* Newspaper Requirements.
0080-0791 Reine und Angewandte Metallkunde in Einzeldarstellungen *changed to* Materials Research and Engineering.
0080-0813 Reliability and Maintainability†
0080-0821 Reliability Physics Symposium Abstracts *see* 0735-0791
0080-0864 Religion et Sciences de l'Homme
0080-0872 Religion, Wissenschaft, Kultur. Jahrbuch *changed to* Religion, Wissenschaft, Kultur. Schriftenreihe.
0080-0880 Chetham Society Publications - Remains, Historical and Literary, Connected with the Palatine Countries of Lancaster and Chester
0080-0899 Remedia Hoechst††
0080-0910 Renderers' Yearbook *changed to* Spectrum.
0080-0929 Universite de Haute Bretagne. Centre d'Etudes Hispaniques, Hispano-Americaines et Luso-Bresiliennes. Travaux *changed to* Etudes sur les Mondes Hispanophones.
0080-0937 Commission Belge de Bibliographie, Repertoire des Comptes-Rendus de Congres Scientifiques†
0080-0945 Repertoire Complementaire Alphabetique des Valeurs Mobilieres Francaises et Etrangeres Non Cotees en France
0080-0953 Bulletin Signaletique. Part 530: R A A (Repertoire d'Art et d'Archeologie. Nouvelle Serie) *see* 1150-1588
0080-097X Repertoire des Cooperatives du Quebec†
0080-0988 Annuaire des Entreprises du Mali
0080-1003 Repertoire des Livres de Langue Francaise Disponibles *changed to* Livres Disponibles.
0080-1011 Repertoire des Principaux Textes Legislatifs et Reglementaires Promulgues en Republique du Mali
0080-102X Repertoire des Productions de l'Industrie Cotonniere Francaise†
0080-1038 France. Delegation Generale a la Recherche Scientifique et Technique. Repertoire des Scientifiques Francais. Tome 3: Biologie†
0080-1046 France. Delegation Generale a la Recherche Scientifique et Technique. Repertoire des Scientifiques Francais. Tome 4: Chimie†
0080-1062 France. Delegation Generale a la Recherche Scientifique et Technique. Repertoire des Scientifiques Francais. Tome 5: Physique†
0080-1070 Repertoire des Societes de Commerce Exterieur Francaises
0080-1089 Repertoire Dictionnaire Industriel
0080-1097 Repertoire du Marketing et du Management
0080-1100 Syndicat National de la Librairie Ancienne et Moderne. Repertoire *changed to* Syndicat National de la Librairie Ancienne et Moderne. Repertoire des Membres.
0080-1119 Repertoire Francais du Commerce Exterieur *changed to* Essor Francais du Commerce Exterieur.
0080-1127 Repertoire General Alphabetique des Valeurs Cotees en France et des Valeurs Non Cotees
0080-1151 Repertoire International des Medievistes
0080-116X France. Delegation Generale a la Recherche Scientifique et Technique. Repertoire National des Chercheurs: Sciences Sociales et Humaines. Tome 1: Ethnologie, Linguistique, Psychologie, Psychologie Sociale, Sociologie†
0080-1186 France. Delegation Generale a la Recherche Scientifique et Technique. Repertoire Permanent de l'Administration Publique *changed to* Repertoire Permanent de l'Administration Francaise.
0080-1216 Repertorio delle Industrie Siderurgiche Italiane†
0080-1240 Report and Studies in the History of Art *see* 0091-7338
0080-1267 Report of Milk Utilization in Montana *changed to* Recap of Milk Receipts and Utilization in Montana.
0080-1283 Fisheries of Scotland Report
0080-1305 Zambia. Central Statistical Office. Agricultural and Pastoral Production *changed to* Zambia. Central Statistical Office. Agricultural and Pastoral Production (Commercial and Non-Commercial).
0080-1305 Zambia. Central Statistical Office. Agricultural and Pastoral Production *changed to* Zambia. Central Statistical Office. Agricultural and Pastoral Production (Non-Commercial).
0080-1305 Zambia. Central Statistical Office. Agricultural and Pastoral Production *changed to* Zambia. Central Statistical Office. Agricultural and Pastoral Production (Commercial Farms).
0080-1313 Israel. Ministry of Labour. Registrar of Cooperative Societies. Report on the Cooperative Movement in Israel
0080-1321 Development of Education in Pakistan
0080-133X Reportages Fantastiques
0080-1348 Reports and Papers in the Social Sciences
0080-1364 Reports of Patent, Design, Trade Mark and Other Cases
0080-1372 International Astronomical Union. Transactions
0080-1380 Reprints in International Finance
0080-1429 Requirements for Certification of Teachers, Counselors, Librarians, Administrators for Elementary Schools, Secondary Schools, Junior Colleges
0080-1437 Requirements for Teaching Certificates in Canada
0080-1453 Research and Clinical Studies in Headache *see* 0255-3910
0080-1461 Research and Development Directory
0080-147X Register of Research and Investigation in Adult Education†
0080-1488 Research and Publications in New York State History†
0080-1518 Research Centers Directory
0080-1526 Alberta Research Council. Annual Report
0080-1534 Alberta Research Council. Contribution Series
0080-1542 Alberta Research Council. Hail Studies Reports *changed to* Alberta Research Council. Atmospheric Sciences Reports.
0080-1550 Alberta Research. Highways and River Engineering Reports *changed to* Alberta Research Council. River Engineering and Surface Hydrology Reports.
0080-1569 Alberta Research Council. List of Publications
0080-1577 Alberta Research Council. Memoirs†
0080-1593 Alberta Research Council. Preliminary Reports. Soil Surveys†
0080-1607 Research Council of Alberta. Report *changed to* Alberta Research Council. Reports.
0080-1623 Research Group for European Migration Problems. Publications
0080-1631 Research in Economics/Business Administration†
0080-1658 Research in Protozoology†
0080-1666 Research in Surface Forces†
0080-1674 Research in the History of Education: A List of Theses for Higher Degrees in the Universities of England and Wales
0080-1704 Research Relating to Children. Bulletins
0080-1739 Research Studies in Library Science†
0080-1763 Resena de Literatura, Arte y Espectaculos
0080-1771 Reserve Bank of Australia. Annual Report
0080-178X Reserve Bank of Australia. Occasional Papers
0080-1801 Reserve Bank of India. Annual Report
0080-181X Residue Reviews
0080-1828 Resources of Music *changed to* Resources of Music Series.
0080-1836 Restaurator. Supplement††
0080-1844 Results and Problems in Cell Differentiation

5548 ISSN INDEX

0080-1852 Retail Credit Federation Membership Directory *changed to* Consumer Credit Association of the United Kingdom. Membership Directory.
0080-1933 Review of Accidents on Indian Government Railways *changed to* Indian Railways Safety Performance - A Review.
0080-1992 Review of the Economy of Rhodesia *changed to* Annual Economic Review.
0080-2018 Reviews in Engineering Geology
0080-2026 U.S. National Science Foundation. Reviews of Data on Science Resources†
0080-2050 Reviews of Plasma Physics
0080-2069 Revista Agronomica del Noroeste Argentino
0080-2085 Revista Cartografica
0080-2093 Revista Chilena de Historia y Geografia
0080-2107 Revista de Administracao
0080-2115 Revista de Biologia Marina
0080-2123 Revista de Ciencias Agronomicas. Serie A†
0080-2131 Revista de Ciencias Agronomicas. Serie B†
0080-214X Revista de Ciencias Biologicas. Serie A†
0080-2158 Revista de Ciencias Biologicas. Serie B†
0080-2166 Revista de Ciencias do Homem. Serie A†
0080-2174 Revista de Ciencias do Homen. Serie B†
0080-2182 Revista de Ciencias Geologicas. Serie A†
0080-2190 Revista de Ciencias Geologicas. Serie B†
0080-2204 Revista de Ciencias Matematicas. Serie A†
0080-2212 Revista de Ciencias Matematicas. Serie B†
0080-2220 Revista de Ciencias Medicas. Serie A†
0080-2239 Revista de Ciencias Medicas. Serie B†
0080-2247 Revista de Ciencias Veterinarias. Serie A†
0080-2255 Revista de Ciencias Veterinarias. Serie B†
0080-2263 Revista de Fisica, Quimica e Engenharia. Serie A†
0080-2271 Revista de Fisica, Quimica e Engenharia. Serie B†
0080-228X Revista de Humanidades†
0080-2360 Revista de Matematica y Fisica Teorica. Serie A
0080-2387 Revista Humanidades†
0080-2425 Revista Peruana de Entomologia
0080-2433 Revista Portuguesa de Filologia
0080-2441 Revista Scriitorilor Romani
0080-2476 Revolutionary Cuba: A Bibliographical Guide†
0080-2484 Revue Bibliographique de Sinologie
0080-2492 Revue Canadienne de Psycho-Education
0080-2506 Revue Francaise de Cooperation Economique Avec Israel
0080-2530 Revue des Archeologues et Historiens d'Art de Louvain
0080-2549 Revue des Etudes Armeniennes Nouvelle Serie
0080-2557 Revue des Etudes Slaves
0080-2581 Revue Economique de Madagascar†
0080-259X Egyptian Review of International Law
0080-2603 Revue Hittite et Asiatique†
0080-2611 Revue Internationale d'Histoire de la Banque†
0080-262X Revue Roumaine d'Histoire de l'Art. Serie Beaux-Arts
0080-2638 Revue Roumaine d'Histoire de l'Art. Serie Theatre, Musique, Cinematographie
0080-2646 Revue Roumaine des Sciences Sociales. Serie de Sociologie *changed to* Roumanian Journal of Sociology.
0080-2654 Revue Theologique de Louvain
0080-2662 Rhein-Mainische Forschungen†
0080-2670 Rheinische Lebensbilder
0080-2689 Rheinische Schriften†
0080-2697 Rheinisches Jahrbuch fuer Volkskunde
0080-2700 Rheumatism Review†
0080-2719 Rheumatismus†
0080-2727 Rheumatology
0080-2743 Rhode Island Directory of Manufacturers and List of Commercial Establishments *changed to* Rhode Island Directory of Manufacturers.
0080-2751 National Education Association. Journal *see* 0886-9979
0080-2778 University of Rhode Island. Bureau of Government Research. Information Series†
0080-2786 University of Rhode Island. Bureau of Government Research. Metropolitan Series†
0080-2794 University of Rhode Island. Bureau of Government Research. Research Series†
0080-2808 University of Rhode Island. Law of the Sea Institute. Occasional Paper Series†
0080-2832 Zimbabwe. Ministry of Water Resources and Development. Hydrological Summaries *changed to* Zimbabwe. Ministry of Energy and Water Resources and Development. Hydrological Summaries.
0080-2840 Zimbabwe. Ministry of Water Resources and Development. Hydrological Year Book†
0080-2859 Zimbabwe. Ministry of Education. African Education Report
0080-2875 Zimbabwe - Rhodesia. Tobacco Research Board. Annual Report and Accounts *changed to* Zimbabwe. Tobacco Research Board. Annual Report and Accounts.
0080-2883 Rhodesian Nurse†
0080-2891 Rhododendrons, with Camellias and Magnolias
0080-2905 Rhododendron Information†
0080-293X Ricerche di Storia della Lingua Latina
0080-2948 Ricerche Filosofiche†
0080-2964 Ricerche Sulle Dimore Rurali in Italia
0080-2972 Richard J. Gonzalez Lecture†
0080-3006 University of Richmond. Institute for Business and Community Development. Newsletter†
0080-3014 Rickia *see* 0073-2877
0080-3022 Rickia. Suplemento†
0080-3065 Instituut voor Rassenonderzoek van Landbouwgewassen. Mededelingen *changed to* Centrum voor Rassenonderzoek en Zaadtechnologie. Mededelingen.
0080-3073 Rinascimento
0080-309X A List of Ring Systems Used in Organic Chemistry. Supplement *see* 0742-5996
0080-3103 Colegio Militar do Rio de Janeiro. Revista Didactica
0080-3111 Museu Nacional, Rio de Janeiro. Arquivos
0080-312X Museu Nacional, Rio de Janeiro. Boletim. Nova Serie. Zoologia
0080-3138 Observatorio Nacional, Rio de Janeiro. Relatorios Preliminares†
0080-3146 Observatorio Nacional, Rio de Janeiro. Servico Astronomico. Publicacoes†
0080-3154 Observatorio Nacional, Rio de Janeiro. Servico Gravimetrico. Publicacoes†
0080-3162 Observatorio Nacional, Rio de Janerio. Servico Magnetico. Publicacoes†
0080-3189 Museu Nacional, Rio de Janeiro. Boletim. Nova Serie. Antropologia
0080-3197 Museu Nacional, Rio de Janeiro. Boletim. Nova Serie. Botanica
0080-3200 Museu Nacional, Rio de Janeiro. Boletim. Nova Serie. Geologie
0080-3227 River Bend Library System. Report of the Director
0080-3235 Rivista Archeologica dell'Antica Provincia e Diocesi di Como
0080-3243 Rivista di Chirurgia della Mano
0080-3251 Rivista di Cultura Classica e Medioevale. Quaderni
0080-3278 Road Builder's Clinic. Proceedings
0080-3286 Road Facts India†
0080-3294 Road Notes *changed to* Transport and Road Research Laboratory. Research Reports.
0080-3308 Road Research *changed to* Transport and Road Research Laboratory. Research Reports.
0080-3316 Roadmasters and Maintenance of Way Association of America. Proceedings†
0080-3324 Roads and Transportation Association of Canada. Proceedings *see* 0826-8193
0080-3340 R M A Annual Statement Studies
0080-3375 Rock Mechanics - Felsmechanik - Mechanique des Roches. Supplement
0080-3383 Rockbridge Historical Society, Lexington, Virginia. Proceedings
0080-3405 Rockefeller University, New York. Annual Report *changed to* Rockefeller University, New York. Scientific and Educational Programs.
0080-3413 Rocket and Space Science Series†
0080-3421 Rocznik Bialostocki
0080-343X Rocznik Ekonomiczny
0080-3448 Rocznik Elektrycznosci Atmosferycznej i Meteorologii†
0080-3456 Rocznik Gdanski
0080-3464 Rocznik Grudziadzki
0080-3472 Rocznik Historii Sztuki
0080-3480 Rocznik Jeleniogorski
0080-3499 Rocznik Krakowski
0080-3510 Rocznik Lubelski
0080-3537 Rocznik Olsztynski
0080-3545 Rocznik Orientalistyczny
0080-3561 Rocznik Sadecki
0080-3588 Rocznik Slawistyczny
0080-3618 Rocznik Wroclawskit
0080-3626 Roczniki Biblioteczne
0080-3634 Roczniki Dziejow Spolecznych i Gospodarczych
0080-3642 Roczniki Gleboznawcze
0080-3650 Roczniki Nauk Rolniczych. Seria A. Produkcja Roslinna
0080-3669 Roczniki Nauk Rolniczych. Seria B. Zootechniczna
0080-3677 Roczniki Nauk Rolniczych. Seria C. Technika Rolnicza
0080-3685 Roczniki Nauk Rolniczych. Seria D. Monografie
0080-3693 Roczniki Nauk Rolniczych. Seria E. Ochrona Roslin
0080-3707 Roczniki Nauk Rolniczych. Seria F. Melioracji i Uzytkow Zielonych
0080-3715 Roczniki Nauk Rolniczych. Seria G. Ekonomika Rolnictwa
0080-3723 Roczniki Nauk Rolniczych. Seria H. Rybactwo
0080-3731 Roczniki Socjologii Wsi. Studia i Materialy
0080-374X Roczniki Technologii i Chemii Zywnosci *see* 0137-1495
0080-3758 Rodd's Chemistry of Carbon Compounds
0080-3782 Roemische Bronzen aus Deutschland
0080-3790 Roemische Historische Mitteilungen
0080-3820 Romance Languages and Their Structures. First Series. F: (French)†
0080-3839 Romance Languages and Their Structures. First Series. R: (Rumanian)†
0080-3847 Romance Languages and Their Structures. First Series. S: (Spanish)†
0080-3855 Romanica Gandensia
0080-3863 Romanica Gothoburgensia
0080-3871 Romanica Helvetica
0080-388X Romanische Bibliographie
0080-3898 Romanistisches Jahrbuch
0080-391X Istituto Giapponese di Cultura, Rome. Annuario.
0080-3928 Istituto Giapponese di Cultura, Rome. Notiziario.
0080-3936 Museo dell'Impero Romano. Studi e Materiali *changed to* Museo della Civilta Romana. Studi e Materiali.
0080-3960 Pontificia Universita Gregoriana. Istituto di Scienze Sociali Studia Socialia.
0080-3979 Pontificia Universita Gregoriana. Miscellanea Historiae Pontificiae
0080-3987 Pontificia Universita Gregoriana. Studia Missionalia
0080-4010 Universita degli Studi di Roma. Istituto di Economia Politica. Collana di Studi†
0080-4045 U P Irrigation Research Institute. General Annual Report
0080-4053 U P Irrigation Research Institute. Technical Memorandum
0080-4088 Rothmans Football Yearbook
0080-4134 Royal Agricultural Society of England. Journal
0080-4185 Royal Architectural Institute of Canada. Allied Arts Catalogue. Catalogue des Arts Connexes†
0080-4193 Royal Astronomical Society of Canada. Observer's Handbook
0080-4274 Notes from the Royal Botanic Garden, Edinburgh
0080-4282 Royal Caledonian Curling Club. Annual
0080-4290 Royal Canadian Academy of Arts. Annual Exhibition. Catalogue†
0080-4304 Royal Canadian Institute. Proceedings†
0080-4312 Royal Canadian Institute. Transactions†
0080-4320 Royal College of Organists. Year Book
0080-4339 Royal Dublin Society. Scientific Proceedings Series A†
0080-4347 Royal Dublin Society. Scientific Proceedings. Series B†
0080-4355 Royal Entomological Society of London. Proceedings *see* 0140-1890
0080-4363 Royal Entomological Society of London. Symposia
0080-4371 Great Britain. Royal Greenwich Observatory. Annals†
0080-4398 Royal Historical Society. Guides and Handbooks
0080-4401 Royal Historical Society. Transactions. Sixth Series
0080-441X R.H.S. Gardener's Diary
0080-4428 Royal Society of Chemistry. Monographs for Teachers *changed to* R S C Paperback Series. Monographs for Teachers.
0080-4444 Royal Institute of the Architects of Ireland. Yearbook *changed to* R I A I Architects Yearbook.
0080-4452 Royal Musical Association, London. Proceedings *see* 0269-0403
0080-4460 Royal Musical Association. R.M.A. Research Chronicle
0080-4487 Royal Numismatic Society. Special Publications
0080-4495 Royal School of Mines, London. Journal
0080-4509 R S P B Annual Report and Accounts *see* 0006-3665
0080-4517 Royal Society of Canada. Proceedings
0080-4541 Royal Society of Edinburgh. Proceedings. Section A. Mathematical and Physical Sciences *see* 0308-2105
0080-455X Royal Society of Edinburgh. Proceedings. Section B. Biology *changed to* Royal Society of Edinburgh. Proceedings. Section B (Biological Sciences).
0080-4576 Royal Society of Edinburgh. Year Book
0080-4606 Royal Society of London. Biographical Memoirs of Fellows of the Royal Society
0080-4614 Royal Society of London. Philosophical Transactions. Series A. Mathematical and Physical Sciences *see* 0962-8428
0080-4622 Royal Society of London. Philosophical Transactions. Series B. Biological Sciences

ISSN

0080-4630 Royal Society of London. Proceedings. Series A. Mathematical and Physical Sciences
0080-4649 Royal Society of London. Proceedings. Series B. Biological Sciences
0080-4673 Royal Society of London. Year Book
0080-469X Royal Society of Queensland, St. Lucia. Proceedings
0080-4703 Royal Society of Tasmania, Hobart. Papers and Proceedings
0080-4711 Royal Society of Tropical Medicine and Hygiene, London. Yearbook
0080-472X Royal Society of Ulster Architects. Year Book
0080-4738 Early Days
0080-4746 Rozell'S Complete Lessons†
0080-4754 Rozprawy z Dziejow Oswiaty
0080-4762 Rubber and Plastics Industry Technical Conference. Record *see* 0272-4685
0080-4789 Rudolf Steiner Publications
0080-4797 Rudolf Virchow Medical Society in the City of New York. Proceedings
0080-4800 Ruestungsbeschraenkung und Sicherheit†
0080-4819 Ruff's Guide to the Turf and the Sporting Life Annual
0080-4827 Rugby Football League Official Guide
0080-4835 Rumanian Journal of Sociology†
0080-4843 Runa: Archivo para las Ciencias del Hombre†
0080-4851 Rural Development Research Paper
0080-4878 Russian and East European Series†
0080-4886 Russian and East European Studies†
0080-4916 Russian Series on Social History
0080-4924 Rutgers Banking Series†
0080-4940 Rutgers Series on Systems for the Intellectual Organization of Information†
0080-4967 Rutgers University. Bureau of Biological Research. Research Conference. Research Conferences of the Bureau of Biological Research (Proceedings)†
0080-4983 Rutgers University. Center of Alcohol Studies. Monograph *changed to* Rutgers Center of Alcohol Studies. Monograph.
0080-5009 Rutherglen, Australia. Research Station. Digest of Recent Research *see* 0814-4990
0080-5033 Rwanda. Direction Generale de la Documentation et de la Statistique. Rapport Annuel *changed to* Rwanda. Direction Generale de la Statistique. Rapport Annuel.
0080-505X Ryland's Directory
0080-5084 S I A M - A M S Proceedings
0080-5092 S.J. Hall Lectureship in Industrial Forestry
0080-5122 S W A T H†
0080-5130 S.A. Mechanised Handling Equipment Buyer's Guide†
0080-5149 Saab Technical Notes
0080-5165 Annales Universitatis Saraviensis. Reihe: Mathematisch-Naturwissenschaftliche Fakultaet†
0080-5173 Universitaet des Saarlandes. Jahresbibliographie
0080-5181 Saarbruecker Beitraege zur Altertumskunde
0080-519X Saarbruecker Studien zur Musikwissenschaft
0080-5203 Malaysia. Department of Statistics. Annual Bulletin of Statistics Sabah
0080-5211 Sabah. Forest Department. Annual Report
0080-522X Sabah. Marine Department. Annual Report
0080-5246 Sacred Books of the East†
0080-5262 Saechsische Akademie der Wissenschaften, Leipzig. Jahrbuch
0080-5297 Saechsische Akademie der Wissenschaften, Leipzig. Philologisch-Historische Klasse. Abhandlungen
0080-5319 Saeculum
0080-5335 Sagamore Army Materials Research Conference. Proceedings
0080-5343 Sage Professional Papers in Comparative Politics†
0080-5351 Sage Readers in Cross-National Research†
0080-536X Sage Research Progress Series on War, Revolution and Peacekeeping†
0080-5378 Sage Series on Armed Forces and Society†
0080-5386 Sage Series on Politics and the Legal Order†
0080-5394 Saggi e Memorie di Storia dell'Arte
0080-5408 Sagittarius *see* 0174-2345
0080-5416 Sahitya Akademi, New Delhi. Report
0080-5432 Saint Bonaventure University. Franciscan Institute. Philosophy Series
0080-5440 Saint Bonaventure University. Franciscan Institute. Text Series
0080-5459 Franciscan Studies
0080-5467 Saint Bonaventure University. Science Studies†
0080-5483 St. Louis University. Pius XII Library. Publications†
0080-5513 Science Museum of Minnesota. Museum Observer†
0080-5521 Science Museum of Minnesota. Scientific Publications *see* 0161-4452
0080-5548 Salaries, Wages, and Fringe Benefits in Michigan Municipalities over 4,000 Population *changed to* Salaries and Wages for Michigan Municipalities over 1,000 Population.
0080-5572 Saling Aktienfuehrer
0080-5661 El Salvador. Direccion General de Estadistica y Censos. Anuario Estadistico
0080-567X Salvation Army Year Book
0080-5696 Salzburger Jahrbuch fuer Philosophie
0080-570X Salzburger Patristische Studien†
0080-5718 Salzburger Studien zur Anglistik und Amerikanistik†
0080-5726 Salzburger Studien zur Philosophie
0080-5769 Samaru Miscellaneous Papers
0080-5777 Samaru Research Bulletin
0080-5793 Sammlung Chemischer und Chemisch-Technischer Beitraege. Neue Folge†
0080-5807 Sammlung Dalp†
0080-5815 Sammlung Dialog†
0080-5823 Sammlung Geltender Staatsangehoerigkeitsgesetze
0080-5831 Sammlung Lebensmittelrechtlicher Entscheidungen
0080-584X Sammlung Meusser†
0080-5858 Sammlung Wissenschaft und Gegenwart†
0080-5866 Samos
0080-5882 San Diego Business Survey†
0080-5890 San Diego Museum of Man. Ethnic Technology Notes
0080-5904 San Diego Museum of Man. Papers
0080-5920 San Diego Society of Natural History. Memoirs†
0080-5939 San Diego Society of Natural History. Occasional Papers *see* 0080-5947
0080-5947 San Diego Society of Natural History. Transactions†
0080-5955 Instituto y Observatorio de Marina. Observaciones Meteorologicas, Magneticas y Sismicas. Anales *changed to* Real Instituto y Observatorio de la Armada. Observaciones Meteorologicas, Magneticas y Sismicas. Anales.
0080-5971 Instituto y Observatorio de Marina. Efemerides Astronomicas *changed to* Real Instituto y Observatorio de la Armada. Efemerides Astronomicas.
0080-598X San Mateo County Dental Society. Bulletin *changed to* Mouthpiece (San Mateo).
0080-6013 Water Quality Conference. Proceedings *changed to* Public Water Supply Engineers Conference (Proceedings).
0080-603X Hochschule St. Gallen fuer Wirtschafts- und Sozialwissenschaften. Forschungsinstitut fuer Absatz und Handel. Schriftenreihe *changed to* Forschungsinstitut fuer Absatz und Handel. Schriftenreihe.
0080-6048 Sankt Galler Beitraege zum Fremdenverkehr und zur Verkehrswirtschaft: Reihe Verkehrswirtschaft
0080-6056 Sankt Gallische Naturwissenschaftliche Gesellschaft. Bericht ueber die Taetigkeit *changed to* Sankt Gallische Naturwissenschaftliche Gesellschaft. Berichte.
0080-6064 Sankyo Kenkyusho Nempo
0080-6099 Santa Fe. Centro de Documentacion e Informacion Educativa. Boletin de Informacion Educativa†
0080-6137 Santakuti Vedic Research Series
0080-6145 Universidad Internacional Menendez Pelayo. Publicaciones
0080-6153 Santiago de Chile. Instituto de Fomento Pesquero Publicacion *changed to* Instituto de Fomento Pesquero. Informes Pesquero.
0080-6234 Universidade de Sao Paulo. Escola de Enfermagem. Revista
0080-6250 Universidade de Sao Paulo. Faculdade de Direito. Revista
0080-6374 Universidade de Sao Paulo. Museu Paulista. Anais
0080-6382 Museu Paulista. Colecao *changed to* Universidade de Sao Paulo. Museu Paulista. Colecao. Serie de Etnologia.
0080-6382 Museu Paulista. Colecao *changed to* Universidade de Sao Paulo. Museu Paulista. Colecao. Serie de Historia.
0080-6382 Museu Paulista. Colecao *changed to* Universidade de Sao Paulo. Museu Paulista. Colecao. Serie de Numismatica.
0080-6382 Museu Paulista. Colecao *changed to* Universidade de Sao Paulo. Museu Paulista. Colecao. Serie de Mobiliario.
0080-6382 Museu Paulista. Colecao *changed to* Universidade de Sao Paulo. Museu Paulista. Colecao. Serie de Geografia.
0080-6382 Museu Paulista. Colecao *changed to* Universidade de Sao Paulo. Museu Paulista. Colecao. Serie de Arqueologia.
0080-6390 Universidade de Sao Paulo. Museu Paulista. Revista
0080-6404 Sao Paulo. Coordenadoria de Saude Mental. Arquivos *see* 0103-0809
0080-6412 Sao Paulo, Brazil (State). Observatorio. Anuario Astronomico *changed to* Universidade de Sao Paulo. Instituto Astronomico e Geofisico. Anuario Astronomico.
0080-6420 Sarawak. Department of Agriculture. Research Branch. Annual Report
0080-6455 Sarawak External Trade Statistics *see* 0127-0451
0080-6471 Sarvadanand Universal Series
0080-6498 Saskatchewan. Department of Industry and Commerce. Report for the Fiscal Year
0080-6501 Saskatchewan. Department of Mineral Resources. Core Index†
0080-6536 Saskatchewan Manufacturers Guide
0080-6544 Saskatchewan. Medical Care Insurance Commission. Annual Report *changed to* Saskatchewan Health. Annual Report.
0080-6552 Saskatchewan Natural History Society. Special Publications
0080-6560 Saskatchewan Poetry Book
0080-6579 Saskatchewan Professional Engineer *changed to* Professional Edge.
0080-6587 Saskatchewan Research Council. Annual Report
0080-6595 Saskatchewan Research Council. Geology Division. Circular†
0080-6609 Saskatchewan. Research Council. Geology Division. Report†
0080-6633 Saskatchewan Telecommunications. Annual Report
0080-665X University of Saskatchewan. Institute for Northern Studies. Annual Report†
0080-6676 Saskatchewan Economic and Finance Position *changed to* Economic and Fiscal Policy.
0080-6684 Sather Classical Lectures
0080-6706 Scandinavian Institute of African Studies. Annual Seminar Proceedings *see* 0281-0018
0080-6714 Scandinavian Institute of African Studies. Research Report
0080-6722 Scandinavian Journal of Haematology. Supplementum *see* 0902-4506
0080-6730 Scandinavian Journal of Respiratory Diseases. Supplementum *see* 0106-4347
0080-6757 Scandinavian Political Studies
0080-6765 Scando-Slavica
0080-6773 Scavi di Spina. *changed to* Scavi di Luni.
0080-679X Schiffahrtmedizinisches Institut der Marine, Kiel. Veroeffentlichungen
0080-6811 Embroidery Directory
0080-6838 Schoenste Schweizer Buecher
0080-6854 Scholae Adriani de Buck Memoriae Dicatae†
0080-6897 Schools *see* 0952-083X
0080-6900 Schools Abroad
0080-6919 Schools of England, Wales, Scotland and Ireland *changed to* Independent Schools of the United Kingdom.
0080-6927 Schools of English in Great Britain *see* 0143-2214
0080-6935 Schopenhauer-Jahrbuch
0080-6943 Schowalter Memorial Lecture Series†
0080-6951 Monumenta Germaniae Historica. Schriften
0080-696X Schriften und Quellen der Alten Welt
0080-6994 Schriften zur Geschichte und Kultur des Alten Orients
0080-7001 Schriften zur Handelsforschung
0080-7028 Schriften zur Kooperationsforschung. Berichte
0080-7036 Schriften zur Kooperationsforschung. Studien
0080-7044 Schriften zur Kooperationsforschung. Vortraege
0080-7052 Schriften zur Kunstgeschichte†
0080-7060 Schriften zur Rechtslehre und Politik†
0080-7079 Schriften zur Sozialpsychologie†
0080-7087 Schriftenreihe zur Theoretischen und Angewandten Betriebswirtschlaftslehre†
0080-7117 Schriftenreihe des Buchklubs der Jugend†
0080-7125 Deutsch-Auslaendische Beziehungen. Schriftenreihe†
0080-7133 Schriftenreihe fuer Laendliche Sozialfragen
0080-7141 Schriftenreihe fuer Sportwissenschaft und Sportpraxis *see* 0342-457X
0080-715X Schriftenreihe Neurologie - Neurology Series
0080-7176 Schrifttum zur Deutschen Kunst
0080-7192 Schrijvers Prentenboek
0080-7214 Schweizer Anglistische Arbeiten
0080-7230 Schweizer Buchhandels-Adressbuch
0080-7249 Publicus
0080-7257 Switzerland. Schweizerische Anstalt fuer das Forstliche Versuchswesen. Mitteilungen *see* 0251-4133
0080-7273 Schweizerische Beitraege zur Altertumswissenschaft
0080-7281 Schweizerische Botanische Gesellschaft. Berichte *see* 0253-1453
0080-729X Schweizerische Geisteswissenschaftliche Gesellschaft. Schriften†
0080-732X Schweizerische Gesellschaft fuer Volkskunde. Schriften

0080-7346 Schweizerische Meterologische Zentralanstalt. Veroeffentlichungen *changed to* Schweizerische Meteorologische Anstalt. Veroeffentlichungen.

0080-7354 Schweizerische Musikforschende Gesellschaft. Publikationen. Serie 2

0080-7389 Schweizerische Palaeontologische Abhandlungen

0080-7400 Schweizerisches Medizinisches Jahrbuch

0080-7419 Schweizerisches Sozialarchiv

0080-7427 T.M.

0080-7451 Science and Technology (San Diego) *see* 0278-4017

0080-746X Science and Technology (Pittsburgh)

0080-7478 Science Council of Canada. Annual Report *see* 0228-6246

0080-7540 Science Nouvelle

0080-7559 Science of Advanced Material and Process Engineering Series

0080-7591 Science Policy Studies and Documents

0080-7605 Science Record†

0080-7613 Science Surveys†

0080-7621 Science Year

0080-763X Sciences

0080-7648 Sciences de l'Education†

0080-7672 Sciences Secretes†

0080-7680 Scientific and Learned Societies of Great Britain†

0080-7702 Scientific and Technical Periodicals Published in South Africa†

0080-7710 Scintific and Technical Societies in South Africa *changed to* Directory of South African Associations.

0080-7737 Scientific Horticulture *see* 0950-0928

0080-7745 Scientific Research in British Universities and Colleges†

0080-7761 Scientific Research Organisations in South Africa *changed to* Directory of Research Organisations and Facilities in South Africa.

0080-7788 Scotland by Road†

0080-7796 Great Britain. Department of Agriculture and Fisheries for Scotland. Advisory Bulletins†

0080-7826 Scotland for Coarse Fishing *changed to* Angler's Guide to Scottish Waters.

0080-7834 Scotland for Fishing *changed to* Angler's Guide to Scottish Waters.

0080-7842 Scotland-Home of Golf†

0080-7850 Scotland. Red Deer Commission. Annual Report

0080-7869 Scotland. Registrar General. Annual Report

0080-7877 Great Britain. Scottish Health Services Planning Council. Annual Report†

0080-7885 Scotland. Scottish Home and Health Department. Hospital Design in Use†

0080-7915 Great Britain. Scottish Law Commission. Annual Report

0080-7923 Scotland Tomorrow *see* 0266-5441

0080-7931 Scottish Castles and Historic Houses *changed to* Scotland: 1001 Things to See.

0080-7966 Scottish Agricultural Economics; Some Studies of Current Economic Conditions in Scottish Farming *changed to* Economic Report on Scottish Agriculture.

0080-7974 Scottish Bakers' Year Book

0080-8008 Scottish Council for Research in Education. Publications

0080-8024 Scottish Gaelic Studies†

0080-8075 Scottish Journal of Science

0080-8083 Scottish Law Directory

0080-8105 Scottish Licensed Trade Association. Annual Handbook†

0080-8113 Scottish Licensed Trade Directory†

0080-8121 S.M.B.A. Collected Reprints†

0080-813X Scottish Mountaineering Club. Journal

0080-8148 Scottish National Register of Classified Trades *changed to* Sell's Scottish Directory.

0080-8164 Scottish Postmark Group. Handbook

0080-8202 Scottish Sea Fisheries Statistical Tables

0080-8210 Scottish Society for Prevention of Vivisection. Annual Pictorial Review *changed to* Advocates for Animals. Annual Pictorial Review.

0080-8229 Scottish Sports Holidays *changed to* Scotland for Youth.

0080-8245 Scottish Typographical Annual Report†

0080-8288 Screen World

0080-830X Scripps Clinic and Research Foundation. Annual Report

0080-8318 Scripps Institution of Oceanography. Bulletin

0080-8326 Scripps Institution of Oceanography. Contributions *changed to* Scripps Institution of Oceanography. Contributions. New Series.

0080-8334 Scripps Institution of Oceanography. Deep Sea Drilling Project. Initial Reports.

0080-8350 Scripta Artis Monographia

0080-8369 Scripta Hierosolymitana

0080-8377 Scripta Mongolica†

0080-8385 Scriptores Byzantini†

0080-8393 Scriptores Latini

0080-8415 Seabird Report *see* 0267-9310

0080-8423 Seaports and the Shipping World. Annual Issue

0080-8474 Securities Law Review

0080-8482 Sediment Data for Selected Canadian Rivers

0080-8504 Seed Trade Buyer's Guide

0080-8512 Seeker's Guide

0080-8539 Kihara Seibutsugaku Kenkyujo. Seiken Jiho

0080-8547 Seishin Igaku Kenkyujo, Tokyo. Gyosekishu

0080-858X Selected Documents of the International Petroleum Industry†

0080-8628 Selected Studies on Indonesia†

0080-8636 Selected Topics in Solid State Physics

0080-8644 Selected Trade and Professional Associations in Texas *changed to* Texas Trade and Professional Associations and Other Selected Organizations.

0080-8660 Selective Organic Transformations†

0080-8695 Sell's British Aviation *changed to* Aerospace Europe.

0080-8709 Sell's British Exporters *changed to* Sell's British Exporters.

0080-8717 Sell's Building Index

0080-8725 Sell's Directory of Products and Services *see* 0261-5584

0080-875X Selysia

0080-8768 Semainier Beaux Pays de France

0080-8792 Seminaire Belge de Perfectionnement aux Affaires. Exposes

0080-8806 Seminar de Fizica Teoretica†

0080-8814 Seminar on Canadian-American Relations (Papers) *see* 0384-1103

0080-8830 Seminar on Integrated Surveys of Environment. Proceedings *changed to* I T C-U N E S C O International Seminar. Proceedings.

0080-8849 Seminar on the Acquisition of Latin American Library Materials. Final Report and Working Papers *changed to* Seminar on the Acquisition of Latin American Library Materials. Papers.

0080-8857 Seminar on the Acquisition of Latin American Library Materials. Microfilming Projects Newsletter

0080-8881 Semitic Texts with Translations†

0080-889X Senckenbergiana Maritima. Zeitschrift fuer Meeresgeologie und Meeresbiologie

0080-8903 Sennacieca Revuo

0080-8938 Serie Afrique Noire

0080-8946 Universidad de Costa Rica Serie Ciencias Naturales†

0080-8954 Series Entomologica

0080-8962 Series in Decision and Control†

0080-8997 Series on Company Approaches to Industrial Relations†

0080-9004 Series on Rock and Soil Mechanics

0080-9012 Series Paedopsychiatrica†

0080-9020 Service de la Carte Geologique d'Alsace et de Lorraine. Memoires *see* 0302-2684

0080-9039 Service d'Echange d'Informations Scientifiques. Serie A: Bibliographies†

0080-9047 Service d'Echange d'Informations Scientifiques. Serie B: Guides et Repertoires†

0080-9055 Service d'Echange d'Informations Scientifiques. Serie C: Catalogues et Inventaires†

0080-9063 Service d'Echange d'Informations Scientifiques. Serie D: Methodes et Techniques†

0080-9071 Servitor di Piazza†

0080-9098 Seto Marine Biological Laboratory. Special Publications *see* 0389-6609

0080-9101 Universidad de Sevilla. Seminario de Antropologia Americana. Publicaciones

0080-911X Seyd's Commercial Lists *changed to* Dun & Bradstreet Standard Register.

0080-9128 Shakespeare - Jahrbuch

0080-9152 Shakespeare Survey

0080-9160 Shalom

0080-9209 University of Sheffield. Metallurgical Society. Journal†

0080-9233 Shepard's Acts and Cases by Popular Names, Federal and State *changed to* Acts and Cases by Popular Names, Federal and State.

0080-9241 Sherborn Fund Facsimiles

0080-9268 Shipping and Aviation Statistics of the Maltese Islands

0080-9284 Shipping Marks on Timber†

0080-9292 Ships and Aircraft of the United States Fleet

0080-9314 Shivaji University, Kolhapur, India. Journal. Humanities and Sciences

0080-9322 Shri Chhatrapati Shivaji University. Report

0080-9330 Shoe Buyers Guide†

0080-9349 Shoe Trades Directory

0080-9365 Shooter's Bible

0080-9381 Shop Equipment and Shopfitting Directory *see* 0143-0971

0080-9403 Short Play Series

0080-9411 Short Studies in Political Science†

0080-9446 Shuttle Craft Guild. Monographs

0080-9497 Siemens-Entwicklungsberichte *see* 0370-9736

0080-9519 Sierra Club Exhibit Format Series†

0080-9527 Chamber of Commerce of Sierra Leone. Journal

0080-9535 Sierra Leone in Figures

0080-9551 Sierra Leone. Ministry of Education. Report

0080-956X Sigma†

0080-9578 Sigma Zetan

0080-9594 Silesia Antiqua

0080-9608 Sinclair Lewis Newsletter†

0080-9616 University of Sind. Research Journal. Arts Series: Humanities and Social Sciences

0080-9624 University of Sind. Research Journal. Science Series

0080-9640 Singapore Accountant

0080-9659 Singapore Book World

0080-9667 University of Singapore. Chinese Society. Journal†

0080-9675 Singapore. Economic Development Board. Report on the Census of Industrial Production

0080-9683 Singapore. Economic Development Board. Annual Report

0080-9691 Singapore Law Review

0080-973X Singapore. National Library. Board Report†

0080-9748 Sinologica†

0080-9756 Sinopsis Dun - Brazil

0080-9772 Sintesis Bibliografica

0080-9780 Sir George Earle Memorial Lecture on Industry and Government

0080-9829 Situation Economique de Cote d'Ivoire

0080-9837 Situation Economique de l'Algerie†

0080-9845 Situation Economique du Maroc†

0080-9853 Situation Economique du Senegal

0080-9888 Sjoefartshistorisk Aarbok

0080-9918 Skier's Guide†

0080-9950 Skolens Aarbok†

0080-9985 S L A M: Trade Year Book of Africa†

0080-9993 Slavia Antiqua

0081-0002 Slavia Occidentalis

0081-0010 Slavica Gothoburgensia

0081-0045 Sloan-Kettering Institute for Cancer Research. Progress Report *changed to* Sloan-Kettering Institute: Research and Educational Programs.

0081-0053 Slog-Europa†

0081-0061 Slovaci v Zahranici

0081-007X Slovanske Historicke Studie

0081-0088 Slovenska Numizmatika

0081-0118 Small Business Management Series†

0081-0126 Small Business Research Series†

0081-0142 Family Hotel and Guest House†

0081-0169 Small Marketers Aids†

0081-0177 Small Marketers Aids Annuals†

0081-0193 Smith College Studies in History

0081-0207 Smithsonian Annals of Flight†

0081-0223 Smithsonian Contributions to Anthropology

0081-0231 Smithsonian Contributions to Astrophysics†

0081-024X Smithsonian Contributions to Botany

0081-0258 Smithsonian Studies in History and Technology

0081-0266 Smithsonian Contributions to Paleobiology

0081-0274 Smithsonian Contributions to the Earth Sciences

0081-0282 Smithsonian Contributions to Zoology

0081-0304 International Astronomical Union. Central Bureau for Astronomical Telegrams. Circular

0081-0312 International Association of Geodesy. Central Bureau for Satellite Geodesy. Information Bulletin

0081-0320 Smithsonian Institution. Astrophysical Observatory. S A O Special Report†

0081-0339 Smithsonian Opportunities for Research and Study in History Art Science

0081-0355 Smoker's Handbook *changed to* Tobacco Trade Directory and Diary.

0081-0363 Smoking and Health Bulletin

0081-038X Soccer Year Book for Northern Ireland

0081-0398 Sociaal-Geografische Studien†

0081-0401 Sociaal-Historische Studien

0081-041X Social and Economic Studies. New Series†

0081-0444 Great Britain. Social Science Research Council. Report *see* 0266-2043

0081-0452 Social Science Research Council of Canada. Report *changed to* Social Science Federation of Canada. Annual Report.

0081-0460 Social Science Studies†

0081-0487 Social Scientist

0081-0495 Social Security Handbook†

0081-0533 Zambia. Department of Social Welfare. Social Welfare Research Monographs *changed to* Zambia. Department of Social Development. Social Welfare Research Monographs.

0081-055X Social Work and Social Issues

0081-0568 Social Work Practice†

0081-0606 Socialist Register

0081-0630 Sociedad Rural Argentina. Memoria

0081-0649 Sociedad Uruguaya

0081-0657 Sociedade Broteriana. Boletim

0081-0665 Sociedade Broteriana. Memorias

0081-0681 Societa di Studi Romagnoli. Guide

0081-0703 S.I.S.F. Documenti

0081-0711 Societatis Scientiarum Lodziensis. Acta Chimica†

0081-072X Societe Academique des Arts Liberaux de Paris. Anthologie des Societaires *changed to* Societe Academique des Arts Liberaux de Paris. Collection.

0081-0738 Societe Astronomique de Bordeaux. Bulletin
0081-0746 Societe Belge d'Ophtalmologie. Bulletin
0081-0754 Societe Chateaubriand. Bulletin. Nouvelle Serie
0081-0770 Societe de Chimie Physique. Annuaire†
0081-0789 Societe de Geographie de Marseille. Bulletin
0081-0797 Societe de l'Industrie Minerale. Annuaire *changed to* Societe de l'Industrie Minerale Guide des Mines et Carrieres.
0081-0819 Societe d'Emulation Historique et Litteraire d'Abbeville. Bulletin
0081-0835 Societe d'Ergonomie de Langue Francaise. Actes du Congres
0081-0843 Societe des Auteurs, Compositeurs, Editeurs pour la Gerance des Droits de Reproduction Mecanique. Bulletin
0081-086X Societe des Explorateurs et des Voyageurs Francais. Annuaire General
0081-0878 Societe des Francs-Bibliophiles. Annuaire
0081-0886 Societe des Ingenieurs Civils de France. Annuaire *changed to* Societe des Ingenieurs et Scientifiques de France. Annuaire.
0081-0894 Societe des Oceanistes. Publications
0081-0908 Societe des Poetes Francais. Annuaire
0081-0916 Societe des Professeurs Francais en Amerique. Bulletin Annuel
0081-0924 Bulletin S.E.D.E.I.S†
0081-0940 Societe d'Histoire de France. Annuaire
0081-0959 Societe d'Histoire et d'Archaeologie de Geneve. Bulletin
0081-0967 Societe d'Histoire et d'Archeologie de la Goele. Bulletin d'Information
0081-0975 Societe d'Histoire Moderne. Annuaire
0081-0983 Societe Entomologique d'Egypte. Bulletin
0081-0991 Societe Entomologique d'Egypte. Bulletin. Economic Series
0081-1033 Societe Francaise de Chirurgie Orthopedique et Traumatologique. Conferences d'Enseignement
0081-1068 Societe Francaise de Microbiologie. Annuaire
0081-1076 Societe Francaise de Physique. Annuaire
0081-1084 Societe Francaise des Ingenieurs d'Outre-Mer. Annuaire†
0081-1106 Societe Franco-Japonaise de Biologie. Bulletin†
0081-1114 Societe Generale de Belgique. Rapport - Report
0081-1122 Bulgarsko Istoricheskо Druzhestvo. Izvestiiat
0081-1130 Societe Historique de Quebec. Textes†
0081-1157 Societe Mouvements Sociaux et Ideologies. 1 Serie: Etudes†
0081-1165 Societe Mouvements Sociaux et Ideologies. 2 Serie: Documents et Temoignages†
0081-1173 Societe Mouvements Sociaux et Ideologies. 3 Serie: Bibliographies†
0081-1181 Societe Nationale des Antiquaires de France. Bulletin
0081-119X Societe Nationale des Chemins de Fer Belges. Rapport Annuel
0081-1203 Societe Odonto-Stomatologique du Nord-Est. Revue Annuelle
0081-1211 Mededelingen "Ex Oriente Lux" *changed to* Vooraziatisch-Egyptisch Genootschap "Ex Oriente Lux". Mededelingen en Verhandelingen.
0081-122X Societe Phycologique de France. Bulletin *see* 0181-1568
0081-1238 Bibliotheque de la S E L A F
0081-1262 Federation Nationale des Societes d'Economie Mixte de Construction, d'Amenagement et de Renovation. Annuaire
0081-1270 Societe d'Ophtalmologie de France. Bulletin
0081-1297 Society for African Church History. Bulletin†
0081-1300 Society for American Archaeology. Memoirs†
0081-1319 Asian Music Publications. Series A: Bibliographic and Research Aids
0081-1327 Asian Music Publications. Series B. Translations
0081-1335 Asian Music Publications. Series C: Reprints
0081-1343 Asian Music Publications. Series D: Monographs
0081-1394 Society for General Microbiology. Symposium
0081-1416 Society for International Development. World Conference Proceedings†
0081-1424 Society for Italian Historical Studies. Newsletter
0081-1432 Society for New Testament Studies. Monograph Series
0081-1440 Society for Old Testament Study. Book List
0081-1459 Society for Pediatric Research. Program and Abstracts *changed to* American Pediatric Society and Society for Pediatric Research. Program and Abstracts.
0081-1475 Society for Psychical Research. Proceedings
0081-1483 Society for the Advancement of Food Service Research. Proceedings
0081-1491 Society for the History of Technology. Monograph Series†
0081-1513 Society for the Promotion of Nature Reserves. Technical Publications *see* 0261-7358
0081-153X Society for the Study of Human Biology. Symposia†
0081-1556 National S A M P E Technical Conference Series. N S T C Preprint Series *changed to* International S A M P E Technical Conference Series. I S T C Preprint Series.
0081-1564 Society of Antiquaries of Scotland. Proceedings
0081-1572 Society of Chemical Industry, London. Reports on the Progress of Applied Chemistry *see* 0263-5917
0081-1580 Society of Cypriot Studies. Bulletin
0081-1599 Society of Exploration Geophysicists. Yearbook†
0081-1602 Society of Glass Decorators. Papers Presented at Annual Seminar *changed to* Society of Glass and Ceramic Decorators. Seminar Proceeding.
0081-1637 Society of Manufacturing Engineers. Collected Papers and Technical Papers Presented at Southeastern Engineering and Tool Exposition†
0081-1645 Society of Manufacturing Engineers. Collected Papers and Technical Papers Presented at Western Metal and Tool Exposition and Conference†
0081-1653 Society of Manufacturing Engineers. Technical Papers
0081-1661 Society of Naval Architects and Marine Engineers. Transactions
0081-1688 Society of Petroleum Engineers of American Institute of Mining, Metallurgical and Petroleum Engineers. Petroleum Transactions Reprint Series *changed to* Society of Petroleum Engineers. Reprint Series.
0081-1696 Society of Petroleum Engineers. Transactions
0081-1718 Society of Professional Well Log Analysts. S P W L A Annual Logging Symposium Transactions
0081-1734 Sociologia I†
0081-1742 Sociologia II†
0081-1750 Sociological Methodology
0081-1777 Sociological Yearbook of Religion in Britain†
0081-1807 Sociologist
0081-1823 Sofiiski Universitet. Biologicheski Fakultet. Godishnik
0081-1831 Sofiiski Universitet. Fakultet po Slavianska Filologiia. Godishnik
0081-184X Sofiiski Universitet. Filosofski Fakultet. Godisnik
0081-1858 Sofiiski Universitet. Fakultet po Matematika i Mekhanika. Godishnik
0081-1866 Sofiiski Universitet. Juridiheski Fakultet. Godisnik
0081-1882 Soil Conservation Society of America. Proceedings of the Annual Meeting†
0081-1890 Books in Soils and the Environment Series
0081-1904 S S S A Special Publication Series
0081-1912 Soils and Land Use Series
0081-1939 Preparation and Properties of Solid State Materials†
0081-1947 Solid State Physics: Advances in Research and Applications
0081-1963 Solid State Physics Literature Guides†
0081-1971 Solid State Surface Science†
0081-203X Some Statistics on Baccalaureate and Higher Degree Programs in Nursing *changed to* N L N Nursing Data Review.
0081-2048 Somerset Birds
0081-2056 Somerset Archaeology and Natural History
0081-2080 Soundings: A Music Journal†
0081-2110 Sources in Ancient History†
0081-2129 Sources of Supply - Buyers Guide
0081-2137 S A B S Yearbook *see* 1018-4295
0081-2145 Department of Agricultural Technical Services. Agricultural Research *changed to* South Africa. Department of Agriculture. Agricultural Research.
0081-2153 South Africa. Department of Agricultural Technical Services. Report of the Secretary for Agricultural Technical Services *changed to* South Africa. Department of Agricultural Development. Annual Report of the Chief for Agricultural Development.
0081-2161 South Africa. Department of Agricultural Technical Services. Special Publication *changed to* South Africa. Department of Agriculture. Special Publications.
0081-217X South Africa. Department of Agricultural Technical Services. Technical Communication *changed to* South Africa. Department of Agriculture. Technical Communication.
0081-2188 South Africa. Department of Bantu Education. Annual Report *changed to* South Africa. Department of Education and Training. Annual Report.
0081-2196 South Africa. Department of Customs and Excise. Foreign Trade Statistics *changed to* South Africa. Commissioner for Customs and Excise. Foreign Trade Statistics.
0081-220X South Africa. Department of Higher Education. Annual Report†
0081-2218 South Africa. Division of Sea Fisheries. Annual Report *changed to* South Africa. Sea Fisheries Research Institute. Chief Directorate Sea Fisheries. Annual Report.
0081-2234 South Africa. Sea Fisheries Institute. Investigational Report *changed to* South Africa. Sea Fisheries Research Institute. Investigational Report.
0081-2250 University of South Africa. Communications†
0081-2307 South Africa. Weather Bureau. Notos†
0081-2315 South Africa. Weather Bureau. Radiosonde Rawin Data†
0081-2323 South Africa. Weather Bureau. Report on Meteorological Data of the Year/ Verslag Oor Weerkundige Data van die Jaar†
0081-2331 South Africa. Weather Bureau. W.B. Series
0081-234X South African Association for Marine Biological Research. Bulletin†
0081-2390 C S I R Organisation and Activities†
0081-2412 Report to S C A R on South African Antarctic Research Activities
0081-2420 S.A. Engineer and Electrical Review *changed to* Current.
0081-2439 South African Institute of International Affairs. Annual Report *changed to* South African Institute of International Affairs. Biennial Report of the National Chairman.
0081-2455 South African Journal of Antarctic Research
0081-2463 South African Journal of Psychology
0081-2471 South African Speech and Hearing Association. Journal *changed to* South African Journal of Communication Disorders.
0081-248X South African Medical Research Council. Research Report *see* 1015-2377
0081-248X South African Medical Research Council. Research Report *see* 0375-1880
0081-2498 South African Mining and Engineering Yearbook†
0081-2501 S A N T A Annual Report
0081-251X South African Pollen Grains and Spores†
0081-2528 South African Reserve Bank. Annual Economic Report
0081-2536 South African Society of Animal Production. Proceedings. Handelinge *see* 0375-1589
0081-2544 South African Statistics
0081-2552 S A F T O Annual Report
0081-2560 S A W T R I Technical Report *changed to* TexReport.
0081-2587 South and Southeast Asia Urban Affairs Bi-Annuals†
0081-2595 South Asia Church Aid Newsletter *changed to* South Asia Church Aid Association. Annual.
0081-2633 South Australia. Libraries Board. Annual Report
0081-2641 South Australia. Libraries Board. Books for Young People†
0081-2676 South Australian Museum, Adelaide. Records
0081-2684 South Carolina Arts Commission. Annual Report
0081-2714 University of South Carolina. School of Education. Proceedings of the Reading Conference†
0081-2722 South Central Research Library Council. Library Directory *changed to* Directory of Libraries and Library Systems in the South Central Research Library Council Region.
0081-2773 South Dakota State Historical Society. Collections *changed to* South Dakota Historical Collections.
0081-2803 South London Field Studies Society. Journal
0081-2811 South Pacific Commission. Handbook
0081-2838 South Pacific Commission. Information Document
0081-2846 South Pacific Commission. Report of S P C Fisheries Technical Meetings *see* 0377-452X
0081-2854 South Pacific Commission. South Pacific Report *changed to* South Pacific Commission. Annual Report.
0081-2862 South Pacific Commission. Technical Paper
0081-2889 South Seas Society. Journal
0081-2897 South Seas Society. Monograph
0081-2935 University of Southampton. Library. Automation Project Report†
0081-2943 Southeastern Association of Game and Fish Commissioners. Proceedings of the Annual Conference *changed to* Southeastern Association of Fish and Wildlife Agencies. Proceedings.
0081-2951 S E C O L A S Annals

5552 ISSN INDEX

0081-296X Southeastern Geology. Special Publication†
0081-2986 Southern Angler's and Hunter's Guide†
0081-2994 Southern Anthropological Society. Proceedings
0081-3001 Southern Baptist Convention. Annual
0081-301X Southern Baptist Convention. Historical Commission. Microfilm Catalogue
0081-3028 Southern Baptist Periodical Index†
0081-3036 Southern Historical Publications†
0081-3044 Southern Illinois Studies†
0081-3052 Southern Journal of Agricultural Economics
0081-3060 Southern Regional Education Board. Annual Report
0081-3079 S R E B Research Monograph Series†
0081-3087 Southern Regional Education Board. State Legislation Affecting Higher Education in the South *changed to* Southern Higher Education Legislative Report.
0081-3109 Southern Water Resources and Pollution Control Conference. Proceedings†
0081-3141 Southwestern Profiles†
0081-315X Southwestern Studies. Monographs
0081-3192 Sovietica. Monographs *changed to* Sovietica. Publications and Monographs.
0081-3206 Sovietica. Publication *changed to* Sovietica. Publications and Monographs.
0081-3222 Soybean Digest Blue Book *see* 0275-4509
0081-3249 Soziale Sicherheit†
0081-3257 Textausgaben zur Fruehen Sozialistischen Literatur in Deutschland
0081-3265 Soziologische Gegenwartsfragen. Neue Folge
0081-3338 Spain. Instituto Nacional de Estadistica. Estadistica del Movimento de Viajeros en Alojamientos Hoteleros y Acampamentos Turisticos *changed to* Estadisticas de Turismo.
0081-3346 Spain. Instituto Nacional de Estadistica. Estadistica de Transporte†
0081-3354 Spain. Instituto Nacional de Estadistica. Estadistica Industrial *changed to* Spain. Instituto Nacional de Estadistica. Encuesta Industrial.
0081-3362 Spain. Instituto Nacional de Estadistica. Industrias Derivadas de la Pesca†
0081-3370 Spain. Instituto Nacional de Estadistica. Informe sobre la Distribucion de las Rentas *changed to* Spain. Instituto Nacional de Estadistica. La Renta Nacional en (Year) y Su Distribution.
0081-3389 Spain. Instituto Nacional de Estadistica. Poblacion Activa *see* 0212-6532
0081-3435 Spain. Ministerio de Hacienda. Informacion Estadistica *changed to* Spain. Ministerio de Economia y Hacienda. Estadisticas Presupuestarias y Fiscales.
0081-3451 Spain. Instituto de Credito Oficial. Memoria del Credito Oficial *changed to* Memoria del Grupo I C O.
0081-346X Spain. Ministerio de Informacion y Turismo. Estadisticas de Turismo *see* 0212-5773
0081-3478 Spain. Servicio de Extension Agraria. Serie Tecnica†
0081-3494 Spanische Forschungen der Goerresgesellschaft. Reihe 2: Monographien
0081-3532 Special Education and Rehabilitation Monograph Series *changed to* Syracuse Special Education and Rehabilitation Monograph Series.
0081-3559 Special Papers in International Economics
0081-3567 Specification
0081-3575 Specola Astronomica Vaticana, Castel Gandolfo, Italy. Annual Report†
0081-3583 Specola Astronomica Vaticana, Castel Gandolfo, Italy. Miscellanea Astronomica†
0081-3591 Specola Astronomica Vaticana, Castel Gandolfo, Italy. Ricerche Astronomiche†
0081-3605 Specola Astronomica Vaticana, Castel Gandolfo, Italy. Ricerche Spettroscopiche†
0081-3648 Speech Communication Association. Directory *see* 0190-2075
0081-3656 Speech Index
0081-3680 Spezialbibliographien zu Fragen des Staates und des Rechts
0081-3699 Spezielle Pathologische Anatomie
0081-3702 Spiegel Deutscher Buchkunst *changed to* Die Schoensten Buecher der Deutschen Demokratischen Republik.
0081-3729 Spirituosen-Jahrbuch
0081-3745 Spolia Zeylanica
0081-3761 Raceform "Horses in Training"
0081-377X Raceform Up-to-Date Form Book Annual *changed to* Raceform Flat Annual.
0081-3788 Sporting News' National Football Guide *see* 0732-1902
0081-3818 Sprache und Denken; Finnische Beitrage zur Philosophie und Sprachwissenschaft†
0081-3826 Sprache und Dichtung. Neue Folge
0081-3834 Sprawozdania Archeologiczne
0081-3842 Sprechplatten Katalog†
0081-3850 Sprenger Instituut. Jaarverslag†
0081-3869 Springer Tracts in Modern Physics
0081-3877 Springer Tracts in Natural Philosophy
0081-3885 Squash Rackets Association. Handbook *changed to* Squash Rackets Association. Annual.
0081-3907 Sri Venkateswara University. Oriental Journal
0081-3915 Sri Venkateswara University. Department of Sanskrit. Symposium
0081-394X Srpska Akademija Nauka i Umetnosti. Odeljenje Drustvenih Nauka. Glas
0081-3958 Srpska Akademija Nauka i Umetnosti. Odeljenje Jezika i Knjizevnosti. Glas
0081-3966 Srpska Akademija Nauka i Umetnosti. Odeljenje Medicinskih Nauka. Glas
0081-3974 Srpska Akademija Nauka i Umetnosti. Odeljenje Tehnickih Nauka. Glas
0081-3982 Srpska Akademija Nauka i Umetnosti. Odeljenje Drustvenih Nauka. Posebna Izdanja
0081-3990 Srpska Akademija Nauka i Umetnosti. Odeljenje Jezika i Knjizevnosti. Posebna Izdanja
0081-4008 Srpska Akademija Nauka i Umetnosti. Odeljenje Likovne i Muzicke Umetnosti. Posebna Izdanja
0081-4016 Srpska Akademija Nauka i Umetnosti. Odeljenje Medicinskih Nauka. Posebna Izdanja
0081-4024 Srpska Akademija Nauka i Umetnosti. Odeljenje Prirodno-Matematickih Nauka. Posebna Izdanja
0081-4032 Srpska Akademija Nauka i Umetnosti Spomenica
0081-4040 Srpska Akademija Nauka i Umetnosti. Odeljenje Tehnickih Nauka. Posebna Izdanja
0081-4059 Srpska Akademija Nauka i Umetnosti. Odeljenje Drustvenih Nauka. Spomenik
0081-4067 Srpski Etnografski Zbornik. Naselja i Poreklo Stanovnistva
0081-4075 Srpski Etnografski Zbornik. Rasprave i Gradja
0081-4083 Srpski Etnografski Zbornik. Srpske Narodne Umotvorine
0081-4091 Srpski Etnografski Zbornik. Zivot i Obicaji Narodni
0081-4105 Staat und Politik
0081-4113 Staatliche Mathematisch-Physikalische Salons, Dresden. Veroeffentlichungen
0081-4148 Stadler Genetics Symposium. Proceedings
0081-4172 Stahl und Form†
0081-4180 Stahleisen Kalender *see* 0724-8482
0081-4210 Stanley Gibbons Simplified Catalogue. Stamps of the World
0081-4229 Standard Directory of Advertisers
0081-4237 Standard Education Almanac†
0081-4245 Standard Lesson Commentary
0081-427X Standard Nomenclature of Athletic Injuries†
0081-430X Standards Engineering Society. Proceedings of Annual Meeting
0081-4318 National Conference of Standards Laboratories. Proceedings *changed to* National Conference of Standards Laboratories. Newsletter.
0081-4326 Stanford Journal of International Studies *see* 0731-5082
0081-4342 Stanford Studies in Germanics and Slavics†
0081-4350 Stanford University. Publications. Geological Sciences†
0081-4369 Stanstead County Historical Society. Journal *changed to* Stanstead Historical Society. Journal.
0081-4377 Star Almanac for Land Surveyors
0081-4407 Stars and Stellar Systems†
0081-4423 State-Approved Schools of Nursing - L.P.N. - L.V.N.
0081-4431 State-Approved Schools of Nursing - R.N.
0081-444X State Bank of Pakistan. Annual Report
0081-4458 State Bank of Pakistan. Department of Research. Report on Currency and Finance†
0081-4466 State Bank of Pakistan. Index Numbers of Stock Exchange Securities
0081-4474 State Constitutional Convention Studies†
0081-4482 State Court Systems†
0081-4504 State Government Undertakings in Gujarat†
0081-4520 State of British Agriculture†
0081-4539 State of Food and Agriculture
0081-4563 State of Nevada Wage Report *changed to* Nevada Wage Survey.
0081-4571 State of the Air Transport Industry *changed to* I A T A Annual Report.
0081-4598 State Tax Handbook
0081-4601 The Statesman's Year - Book
0081-461X Stationery Trade Reference Book and Buyers Guide
0081-4636 Statistical Abstract of Ceylon *changed to* Statistical Abstract of the Democratic Socialist Republic of Sri Lanka.
0081-4644 Statistical Abstract of Higher Education in North Carolina
0081-4660 Statistical Abstract of Ireland *see* 0790-8970
0081-4679 Israel. Central Bureau of Statistics. Statistical Abstract of Israel
0081-4687 Statistical Abstract of Latin America
0081-4695 Statistical Abstract of Louisiana
0081-4709 Statistical Abstract of Maharashtra State
0081-4717 Statistical Abstract of Rajasthan
0081-4725 Syria. Central Bureau of Statistics. Statistical Abstract
0081-4733 Malta. Central Office of Statistics. Annual Abstract of Statistics
0081-4741 Statistical Abstract of the United States
0081-475X Statistical Abstract of Virginia†
0081-4768 Statistical Analysis of World's Merchant Fleets Showing Age, Size, Speed and Draft by Frequency Groupings†
0081-4776 Statistical and Social Inquiry Society of Ireland. Journal
0081-4784 Statistical Guides in Educational Research†
0081-4792 Statistical Handbook of Japan
0081-4806 Korea Statistical Korea†
0081-4814 Statistical Handbook of Sarawak†
0081-4857 Statistical Office of the European Communities. Associes Statistique du Commerce Exterieur. Annuaire†
0081-4865 Statistical Office of the European Communities. Balances of Payments Yearbook *changed to* Statistical Office of the European Communities. Balances of Payments. Quarterly Data.
0081-4873 Statistical Office of the European Communities. Basic Statistics *changed to* Basic Statistics of the European Community.
0081-4881 Statistical Office of the European Communities. Commerce Exterieur: Products C E C A
0081-489X Statistical Office of the European Communities. Energy Statistics. Yearbook
0081-4903 Statistical Office of the European Communities. Foreign Trade: Standard Country Classification
0081-4911 Statistical Office of the European Communities. National Accounts Yearbook
0081-492X Statistical Office of the European Communities. Overseas Associates. Annuaire Statistiques des Etats Africains et Malgache†
0081-4938 Statistical Office of the European Communities. Recettes Fiscales. Annuaire†
0081-4946 Statistical Office of the European Communities. Statistique Agricole *changed to* Statistical Office of the European Communities. Statistical Yearbook. Agriculture.
0081-4954 Statistical Office of the European Communities. Siderurgie Annuaire†
0081-4962 Statistical Office of the European Communities. Statistiques des Tranports. Annuaire *changed to* Statistical Office of the European Communities. Transport, Communications, Tourisme - Annuaire Statistique.
0081-4970 Statistical Office of the European Communities. Statistiques Industrielles Annuaire†
0081-4989 Statistical Office of the European Communities. Statistiques Sociales. Annuaire†
0081-4997 Statistical Office of the European Communities. Yearbook of Regional Statistics
0081-5012 Statistical Pocket Book: India
0081-5020 Statistical Research Monographs†
0081-5039 Statistical Review of the World Oil Industry *changed to* B P Statistical Review of World Energy.
0081-5063 Suomen Tilastollinen Vuosikirja
0081-5071 Statistical Yearbook of Greece
0081-508X Statisticians and Others in Allied Professions *see* 0278-405X
0081-5098 Statistics - Africa†
0081-5101 Statistics - Europe
0081-511X Statistics for Iron and Steel Industry in India
0081-5128 Statistics of Farmer Cooperatives
0081-5136 Statistics of Foreign Trade of Syria
0081-5144 India (Republic) Ministry of Shipping and Transport. Statistics of Water Transport Industries *changed to* Water Transport Statistics of India.
0081-5152 Statistics of Indiana Libraries
0081-5160 Statistics of Road Traffic Accidents in Europe
0081-5179 Statistics of the Communications Industry in the United States
0081-5209 Statistics on Japanese Industries
0081-5217 Statistics on Social Work Education *see* 0091-7192
0081-5225 Statistiek van de Gasvoorziening in Nederland
0081-5233 Austria. Statistisches Zentralamt. Statistik der Aktiengesellschaften in Oesterreich
0081-5241 Statistik der Kommunalen Oeffentlichen Bibliotheken der Bundesrepublik†
0081-525X Switzerland. Directorate General of Customs. Annual Statistics

ISSN

ISSN INDEX 5553

0081-5268 Statistique Judiciaire de la Belgique *changed to* Belgium. Institut National de Statistique. Statistiques Judiciaires.
0081-5276 Statistiques du Commerce Exterieur de Cote d'Ivoire
0081-5292 Statistiques du Commerce Exterieur de la Tunisie
0081-5306 Statistiques du Commerce Exterieur de Madagascar†
0081-5314 Statistisches Handbuch fuer die Republik Oesterreich
0081-5322 Statistisches Jahrbuch Berlin
0081-5330 Statistisches Jahrbuch der Schweiz
0081-5357 Statistisches Jahrbuch fuer die Bundesrepublik Deutschland
0081-5365 Statistisches Jahrbuch der Eisen- und Stahlindustrie
0081-5381 Statistisk Aarsbok foer Sverige
0081-539X Statni Banka Ceskoslovenska. Bulletin
0081-5403 Statsvetenskapliga Foereningen i Uppsala. Skrifter†
0081-5411 Steam - Electric Plant Factors *changed to* Steam - Electric Plant Factors (1978).
0081-542X Steam Passenger Service Directory
0081-5438 Steklov Institute of Mathematics. Proceedings
0081-5446 Stellenbosch, South Africa. University. Bureau for Economic Research. Economic Prospects. Ekonomiese Vooruitsigte†
0081-5454 University of Stellenbosch. Bureau for Economic Research. Survey of Contemporary Economic Conditions and Prospects *see* 0259-4862
0081-5462 Steppenwolf†
0081-5470 Stereo Hi-Fi Directory *changed to* Stereo Review's Stereo Buyers' Guide.
0081-5519 Steuerberater-Jahrbuch
0081-5535 Der Stickstoff
0081-5551 Stifterverband fuer die Deutsche Wissenschaft. Jahrbuch *changed to* Stifterverband fuer die Deutsche Wissenschaft. Taetigkeitsbericht.
0081-5586 Still: Yale Photography Annual
0081-5594 Stille Schar
0081-5608 Stimmen Indianischer Voelker†
0081-5624 Stock Values and Dividends for Tax Purposes
0081-5632 Ethnographical Museum of Sweden. Monograph Series *changed to* Folkens Museum - National Museum of Ethnography.
0081-5640 Flygtekniska Foersoeksanstalten. Meddelande - Report
0081-5659 Ingenioersvetenskapsakademien. Transportforskningskommissionen. Meddelanden†
0081-5667 Ingenioersvetenskapsakademien. Transportforskningskommissionen. Utredningsrapporter†
0081-5675 Musikhistoriska Museets. Skrifter *see* 0282-8952
0081-5683 Sweden. Nationalmuseum. Skriftserie *changed to* Sweden. Nationalmusei Skriftserie.
0081-5691 Museum of Far Eastern Antiquities. Bulletin
0081-5705 Statens Geotekniska Institut. Proceedings *see* 0348-0755
0081-5772 Stone and Cox General Insurance Year Book *see* 0380-223X
0081-5799 Stones of Pittsburgh†
0081-5802 Storage Battery Manufacturing Industry Yearbook†
0081-5810 Stores and Shops Retail Directory *changed to* Retail Directory.
0081-5829 Stores of the World Directory *changed to* Directory of European Retailers & International Buying Agents.
0081-5837 Storia, Costumi e Tradizioni†
0081-5845 Storia della Miniatura. Studi e Documenti
0081-5861 Stories from the Hills
0081-5896 Strahovska Knihovna
0081-590X Observatoire de Strasbourg. Publication *changed to* Journees de Strasbourg.
0081-5918 Universite de Strasbourg II. Centre de Philologie et Litteratures Romanes. Actes et Colloques
0081-5926 Universite de Strasbourg. Centre de Recherche et de Documentation des Institutions Chretiennes. Bulletin du CERDIC†
0081-5934 Universite de Strasbourg II. Institut de Phonetique. Travaux
0081-5942 Strategy for Peace Conference. Report *see* 0748-9641
0081-5950 Stratford International Film Festival†
0081-5977 Street and Highway Manual *see* 0163-9730
0081-5985 Strikes and Lockouts in Canada†
0081-5993 Structure and Bonding
0081-6027 Structurist
0081-6043 Stubbs Buyers Guide *changed to* Stubbs Directory.
0081-6051 Stubs (Metro NY)
0081-606X Student Guide: North America†
0081-6086 Student London†
0081-6116 Studi Albanesi. Studi e Testi
0081-6124 Studi Classici e Orientali
0081-6140 Studi d'Architettura Antica
0081-6159 Studi di Metrica Classica
0081-6175 Studi e Materiali di Storia delle Religioni. Quaderni†
0081-6205 Studi Romagnoli
0081-6213 Studi Romagnoli. Estratti di Sezione
0081-6221 Studi Romagnoli. Quaderni
0081-6248 Studi Secenteschi
0081-6256 Studi Tassiani
0081-6264 Studi Veneziani†
0081-6272 Studia Anglica Posnaniensia
0081-6280 Studia Archaeologica
0081-6299 Studia Archaeologica
0081-6302 Studia Archeologiczne
0081-6310 Studia Aristotelica
0081-6337 Studia Biophysica
0081-6345 Studia Caucasica
0081-6353 Studia Celtica
0081-637X Studia Estetyczne
0081-6388 Studia et Documenta Historiae Musicae: Bibliotheca
0081-6396 Studia Francisci Scholten Memoriae Dicata
0081-640X Studia Geograficzne
0081-6418 Studia Geograficzno-Fizyczne z Obszaru Opolszczyzny†
0081-6426 Studia Geologica Polonica
0081-6434 Studia Geomorphologica Carpatho-Balcanica
0081-6442 Studia Germanica Gandensia
0081-6450 Studia Graeca et Latina Gothoburgensia
0081-6469 Studia Grammatica
0081-6477 Studia Hibernica
0081-6485 Studia Historiae Oeconomicae
0081-6493 Studia Historica
0081-6507 Studia Historica
0081-6515 Studia Historica Gothoburgensia†
0081-6523 Studia Historica Jyvaskylaensia
0081-6531 Studia Historica Upsaliensia
0081-654X Studia i Materialy do Dziejow Wielkopolski i Pomorza
0081-6566 Studia i Materialy do Teorii i Historii Architektury i Urbanistyki
0081-6574 Studia i Materialy z Dziejow Nauki Polskiej. Seria A. Historia Nauk Spolecznych
0081-6582 Studia i Materialy z Dziejow Nauki Polskiej. Seria B. Historia Nauk Biologicznych i Medycznych
0081-6590 Studia i Materialy z Dziejow Nauki Polskiej. Seria C. Historia Nauk Matematycznych, Fizyko-Chemicznych i Geologiczno-Geograficznych
0081-6604 Studia i Materialy z Dziejow Nauki Polskiej. Seria D. Historia Techniki i Nauk Technicznych
0081-6612 Studia i Materialy z Dziejow Nauki Polskiej. Seria E. Zagadnienia Ogolne
0081-6620 Studia i Materialy z Dziejow Polski w Okresie Oswiecenia†
0081-6647 Studia i Materialy z Dziejow Teatru Polskiego *see* 0208-404X
0081-6663 Studia Irenica
0081-6671 Studia Iuridica
0081-668X Studia Judaica†
0081-6698 Studia Juridica
0081-6701 Studia Copernicana
0081-6736 Studia Moralia
0081-6744 Studia Musicologica Upsaliensia. Nova Series
0081-6752 Studia nad Zagadnieniami Gospodarczymi i Spolecznymi Ziem Zachodnich
0081-6760 Studia Naturae *changed to* Studia Naturae. Seria A. Wydawnictwa Naukowe.
0081-6760 Studia Naturae *see* 0551-4193
0081-6779 Studia Numismatica et Medailistica
0081-6787 Studia Palmyrenskie
0081-6795 Studia Pedagogiczne
0081-6809 Studia Philologiae Scandinavicae Upsaliensia
0081-6817 Studia Philologica†
0081-6825 Studia Philosophica†
0081-6833 Studia Philosophica Gandensia *see* 0379-8402
0081-6841 Studia Prawno-Ekonomiczne
0081-685X Studia Psychologiczne
0081-6884 Studia Rossica Posnaniensia
0081-6892 Studia Scientiae Paedagogicae Upsaliensia *see* 0347-1314
0081-6906 Studia Scientiarum Mathematicarum Hungarica
0081-6914 Studia Semitica Neerlandica
0081-6922 Studia Slovenica. Special Series
0081-6930 Studia Spoleczno-Ekonomiczne
0081-6949 Studia Staropolskie
0081-6957 Studia Theodisca
0081-7015 Studia Uralica et Altaica Upsaliensia
0081-7023 Studia Warszawskie†
0081-704X Studia z Dziejow Gornictwa i Hutnictwa†
0081-7058 Studia z Dziejow Osadnictwa†
0081-7082 Studia z Dziejow Z S R R i Europy Srodkowej
0081-7090 Studia z Filologii Polskiej i Slowianskiej
0081-7104 Studia z Historii Sztuki
0081-7112 Studia z Okresu Oswiecenia
0081-7120 Studia z Teorii Filmu†
0081-7139 Studia z Zakresu Budownictwa *see* 0137-5393
0081-7155 Studiecentrum voor Kernenergie. Annual Scientific Report *changed to* S C K Annual Report.
0081-7163 Centre d'Etude de l'Energie Nucleaire. Index of S.C.K. /C.E.N. Papers†
0081-718X Studien zu Religion, Geschichte und Geisteswissenschaften†
0081-7198 Studien zur Agrarwirtschaft
0081-721X Studien zur Begabungsforschung und Bildungsfoerderung†
0081-7228 Studien zur Deutschen Kunstgeschichte
0081-7236 Studien zur Deutschen Literatur
0081-7244 Studien zur Englischen Philologie, Neue Folge
0081-7252 Studien zur Europaeischen Geschichte
0081-7260 Studien zur Evangelischen Ethik†
0081-7279 Studien zur Finanzpolitik
0081-7287 Studien zur Geschichte Asiens, Afrikas und Lateinamerikas. *see* 0138-5550
0081-7295 Studien zur Geschichte der Katholischen Moraltheologie
0081-7309 Studien zur Geschichte des Neunzehnten Jahrhunderts
0081-7317 Studien zur Geschichte Osteuropas†
0081-7325 Studien zur Kunst des Neunzehnten Jahrhunderts†
0081-7333 Studien zur Medizingeschichte des Neunzehnten Jahrhunderts
0081-7341 Studien zur Musikgeschichte des Neunzehnten Jahrhunderts
0081-735X Studien zur Philosophie und Literatur des Neunzehnten Jahrhunderts†
0081-7368 Studien zur Rhetorik des Neunzehnten Jahrhunderts†
0081-7376 Studien zur Wissenschaftstheorie im Neunzehnten Jahrhundert†
0081-7384 Studienbuecherei
0081-7392 Studienhefte Psychologie in Erziehung und Unterricht
0081-7406 Studientage fuer Die Pfarrer†
0081-7414 Studier i Nordisk Arkeologi
0081-7449 Studies and Reports in Hydrology Series
0081-7465 University of Texas, Austin. Bureau of Business Research. Studies in Accounting†
0081-7481 Studies in African History†
0081-749X Studies in African History, Anthropology, and Ethnology†
0081-7503 Studies in American History†
0081-7511 Studies in American Jewish History
0081-752X Studies in American Literature†
0081-7538 Studies in Anabaptist and Mennonite History
0081-7554 Studies in Ancient Oriental Civilization
0081-7562 Studies in Art†
0081-7570 University of Texas, Austin. Bureau of Business Research. Studies in Banking and Finance†
0081-7589 Studies in Biblical Theology†
0081-7597 Studies in Biblical Theology. Second Series†
0081-7600 Studies in Bibliography
0081-7619 Studies in British History and Culture†
0081-7627 University of New Mexico. Bureau of Business and Economic Research. Studies in Business and Economics†
0081-7635 Studies in Business and Society
0081-7643 Studies in Business Cycles†
0081-766X Studies in Capital Formation and Financing†
0081-7694 Studies in Chinese Government and Politics†
0081-7708 University of Notre Dame. Department of Theology. Studies in Christian Democracy†
0081-7732 Studies in Communism, Revisionism and Revolution†
0081-7767 Studies in Comparative Literature (Los Angeles)†
0081-7775 Studies in Comparative Literature (Chapel Hill)
0081-7783 Studies in Compulsory Education†
0081-7791 Studies in Consumer Instalment Financing†
0081-7805 Studies in Corporate Bond Financing†
0081-7813 Studies in Development Progress†
0081-7821 Studies in Early English History *changed to* Studies in the Early History of Britain.
0081-783X Finnish Meteorological Institute. Studies on Earth Magnetism†
0081-7848 Studies in Economic Growth
0081-7856 Studies in Economics†
0081-7872 Studies in Economics and Business Administration†
0081-7899 Studies in English Literature†
0081-7902 Studies in Ethnomusicology†
0081-7961 Studies in Geography in Hungary
0081-797X Studies in German Literature†
0081-7988 Studies in Higher Education in Canada†
0081-7996 Studies in Historical and Political Science. Extra Volumes
0081-8011 Studies in Industrial Economics†
0081-802X Studies in International Affairs (Baltimore)
0081-8054 Studies in International Communism†
0081-8062 Studies in International Economic Relations†
0081-8070 Studies in International Finance
0081-8097 Studies in Irish History†
0081-8100 Studies in Irish History. Second Series†
0081-8127 Studies in Japanese Culture†
0081-8135 University of Texas, Austin. Bureau of Business Research. Studies in Latin American Business†

ISSN

5554 ISSN INDEX

0081-8143 Studies in Latin Literature and Its Influence *changed to* Greek and Latin Studies Series.
0081-8151 Studies in Librarianship†
0081-8186 University of Texas, Austin. Bureau of Business Research. Studies in Marketing†
0081-8194 Studies in Mathematical and Managerial Economics
0081-8208 Studies in Mathematics (Washington)
0081-8224 Studies in Medieval and Renaissance History
0081-8232 Studies in Mediterranean Archaeology. Monograph Series
0081-8240 Studies in Money in Politics†
0081-8259 Studies in Museology
0081-8267 Studies in Music
0081-8275 Studies in Mycenaean Inscriptions and Dialect†
0081-8291 New York University. Studies in Near Eastern Civilization
0081-8305 Studies in Neuro-Anatomy†
0081-8313 Great Britain. Central Statistical Office. Studies in Official Statistics
0081-8321 Studies in Oriental Culture
0081-8348 University of Texas, Austin. Bureau of Business Research. Studies in Personnel and Management†
0081-8364 Studies in Personnel Psychology†
0081-8402 Studies in Political Development†
0081-8437 University of Pennsylvania. Wharton School of Finance and Commerce. Studies in Quantitative Economics
0081-8453 Studies in Rural Land Use†
0081-8461 Studies in Semitic Languages and Linguistics
0081-850X Studies in Social History†
0081-8518 Studies in Social Life†
0081-8534 Studies in Spanish Literature†
0081-8542 Studies in Statistical Mechanics
0081-8569 Studies in the Economic Development of India†
0081-8577 Studies in the Foundations, Methodology and Philosophy of Science
0081-8585 Michkarim Begeografiyah Shel Eretz Yisrael
0081-8593 Studies in the Germanic Languages and Literatures
0081-8607 Studies in the History of Christian Thought
0081-8615 Studies in the History of Discoveries†
0081-8623 Studies in the Humanities†
0081-864X Studies in the National Income and Expenditure of the United Kingdom
0081-8658 Studies in the Renaissance *see* 0034-4338
0081-8666 Studies in the Romance Languages and Literatures *changed to* North Carolina Studies in the Romance Languages and Literatures.
0081-8682 West Georgia College Studies in the Social Sciences
0081-8690 Studies in the Structure of Power: Decision Making in Canada
0081-8704 Studies in the Theory of Science†
0081-8720 Studies in Tropical Oceanography†
0081-8747 Studies in Vermont Geology
0081-8771 Studies of Developing Countries
0081-878X Studies of Negro Employment†
0081-8798 Studies of Northern Peoples†
0081-8844 Studii Clasice
0081-8852 Studii de Literatura Universala si Comparata†
0081-8860 Studii de Slavistica†
0081-8879 Studii si Cercetari de Bibliologie. Serie Noua†
0081-8887 Studii si Cercetari de Numismatica
0081-8909 Studium Biblicum Franciscanum. Analecta
0081-8917 Studium Biblicum Franciscanum. Collectio Maior
0081-8925 Studium Biblicum Franciscanum. Collectio Minor
0081-8933 Studium Biblicum Franciscanum. Liber Annuus
0081-895X Study Abroad
0081-8992 Bibliothek fuer Zeitgeschichte, Stuttgart. Jahresbibliographie
0081-900X Bibliothek fuer Zeitgeschichte, Stuttgart. Schriften
0081-9050 Sudan. National Planning Commission. Economic Survey *changed to* Sudan. Ministry of Finance and National Economy. Economic and Financial Research Section. Economic Survey.
0081-9077 Suedost-Forschungen
0081-9085 Suedostdeutsches Archiv
0081-9093 Suedostdeutsches Kulturwerk, Munich. Kleine Suedostreihe *changed to* Suedostdeutsches Kulturwerk. Veroeffentlichungen. Reihe D: Kleine Suedostreihe.
0081-9107 Suedostdeutsches Kulturwerk, Munich. Schriftenreihen. Reihe A: Kultur und Dichtung *changed to* Suedostdeutsches Kulturwerk. Veroeffentlichungen. Reihe A: Kultur und Dichtung.
0081-9115 Suedostdeutsches Kulturwerk, Munich. Schriftenreihen. Reihe B: Wissenschaftliche Arbeiten *changed to* Suedostdeutsches Kulturwerk. Veroeffentlichungen. Reihe B: Wissenschaftliche Arbeiten.
0081-9123 Suedostdeutsches Kulturwerk, Munich. Schriftenreihen. Reihe C. Erinnerungen und Quellen *changed to* Suedostdeutsches Kulturwerk. Veroeffentlichungen. Reihe C: Erinnerungen und Quellen.
0081-9131 Suedosteuropa - Bibliographie
0081-914X Suedosteuropa - Jahrbuch
0081-9158 Suedosteuropa-Schriften†
0081-9166 Suedosteuropa - Studien
0081-9174 Suesswaren Jahrbuch
0081-9204 Sugar Technology Reviews†
0081-9212 Sugar y Azucar Yearbook
0081-9255 Sulphur Institute. Technical Bulletin†
0081-9271 Sumer
0081-928X Sumitomo Sangyo Eisei
0081-9301 Summary of Floods in the United States†
0081-931X Summary of State Laws and Regulations Relating to Distilled Spirits
0081-9352 Summer Employment Directory of the United States
0081-9379 Summer Study Abroad *changed to* Vacation Study Abroad.
0081-9387 Summer Theatre Directory†
0081-9395 Suomen Aikakauslehti-Indeksi†
0081-9417 Suomen Historiallinen Seura. Kasikirjoja
0081-9425 Suomen Historian Laehteitae
0081-9433 Suomen Naishammaslaakarit Ryhma. Julkaisu
0081-9441 Suomen Osallistuminen Yhdistyneiden Kansakuntien Toimintaan *see* 0781-2442
0081-945X Bank of Finland. Annual Statement *see* 0081-9468
0081-9468 Bank of Finland. Yearbook
0081-9476 Suomen Pankki. Taloustieteellinen Tutkimuslaitos. Julkaisuja. Series A: Taloudellisia Selvityksia *see* 0355-6034
0081-9484 Suomen Pankki. Taloustieteellinen Tutkimuslaitos. Julkaisuja. Series B *see* 0357-4776
0081-9492 Suomen Pankki. Julkaisuja. Sarja C
0081-9506 Suomen Pankki. Taloustieteellinen Tutkimuslaitos. Series D. Mimeographed Series *see* 0355-6042
0081-9514 Suomen Pankki. Taloustieteellinen Tutkimuslaitos. Julkaisuja. Series Kasvututkimuksia *see* 0355-6050
0081-9522 Facts About New Supermarkets *see* 0732-233X
0081-9530 Supermarket Industry Speaks *see* 0190-3349
0081-9557 Supreme Court Review
0081-9573 Surface and Colloid Science†
0081-9581 Surface Water Supply of the United States†
0081-959X Surface Water Year Book of Great Britain
0081-9603 Surfactant Science Series
0081-9611 Surfboard Builder's Yearbook *see* 0276-6582
0081-9638 Surgery Annual
0081-9654 Surgical Trade Buyers Guide *changed to* Health Industry Buyers Guide.
0081-9662 Surplus Dealers Directory†
0081-9670 Surrey Papers in Economics
0081-9697 Survey of Biological Progress†
0081-9727 Survey of Consumer Finances *see* 0085-3410
0081-9743 Surveys and Development Plans of Industry in Israel
0081-9751 Survey of London
0081-976X Survey of Progress in Chemistry†
0081-9778 Survey of Race Relations in South Africa *see* 0258-7246
0081-9794 Svensk Foersaekrings-Aarsbok
0081-9808 Svensk Geografisk Aarsbok
0081-9816 Svensk Tidskrift foer Musikforskning
0081-9867 Svenska Filminstitutet. Dokumentationsavdelningen. Skrifter†
0081-9905 Cement- och Betonginstitutet. Utredningar. Applied Studies†
0081-9913 Svenska Handelsbanken. Annual Report
0081-9921 Svenska Institutet i Athen. Skrifter
0081-993X Svenska Institutet i Rom. Skrifter. Acta Series Prima
0081-9956 Kungliga Vetenskapsakademien. Bidrag till Kungliga Vetenskapsakademiens Historia
0081-9964 Sveriges Jaernvaegar
0081-9980 Swansea Geographer
0081-9999 Swaziland. Geological Survey and Mines Department. Annual Report
0082-0008 Swaziland. Geological Survey and Mines Department. Bulletin
0082-0016 Sweden. Sveriges Geologiska Undersoekning. Serie Ca. Avhandlingar och Uppsatser i Kvarto
0082-0024 Sweden. Sveriges Geologiska Undersoekning. Serie C. Avhandlingar och Uppsatser
0082-0032 Institute of Freshwater Research, Drottningholm. Report *see* 1100-4096
0082-0040 Kungliga Skogshoegskolan. Institutionen foer Virkeslaera. Rapporter *see* 0348-4599
0082-0059 Kungliga Skogshoegskolan. Institutionen foer Virkeslaera. Uppsatser *changed to* Sveriges Lantbruksuniversitet. Institutionen foer Virkeslaera. Uppsatser.
0082-0067 Sweden. Konjunkturinstitutet. Occasional Paper
0082-0075 Sweden. Riksfoersaekringsverket. Allmaen Foersaekring
0082-0083 Swedish Social Security Scheme†
0082-0091 Riksgaeldskontoret. Aarsbok *see* 0280-4182
0082-0121 Sweden. Statens Institut foer Konsumentfraagor. Meddelar *see* 0035-7235
0082-0156 Sweden. Statistiska Centralbyraan. Befolkningsfoeraendringar
0082-0180 Sweden. Statistiska Centralbyraan. Information i Prognosfragor/ Forecasting Information†
0082-0199 Sweden. Statistiska Centralbyraan. Jordbruksstatistisk Aarsbok
0082-0210 Sweden. Statistiska Centralbyraan. Loener†
0082-0229 Sweden. Statistiska Centralbyraan. Meddelanden i Samordningsfraagor
0082-0237 Sweden. Statistiska Centralbyraan. Statistiska Meddelanden. Subgroup Am (Labor Market)
0082-0245 Sweden. Statistiska Centralbyraan. Statistiska Meddelanden. Subgroup Be (Population & Living Conditions)
0082-0261 Sweden. Statistiska Centralbyraan. Statistiska Meddelanden. Subgroup H (Trade) *see* 1100-9373
0082-027X Sweden. Statistiska Centralbyraan. Statistiska Meddelanden. Subgroup I (Manufacturing)
0082-0288 Sweden. Statistiska Centralbyraan. Statistiska Meddelanden. Subgroup J (Agriculture)
0082-0296 Sweden. Statistiska Centralbyraan. Statistiska Meddelanden. Subgroup N (National Accounts and Finance)
0082-030X Sweden. Statistiska Centralbyraan. Statistiska Meddelanden. Subgroup P (Prices and Price Indices)
0082-0318 Sweden. Statistiska Centralbyraan. Statistiska Meddelanden. Subgroup R (Judicial Statistics. Law and Social Welfare)
0082-0326 Sweden. Statistiska Centralbyraan. Statistiska Meddelanden. Subgroup S (Social Welfare Statistics)
0082-0334 Sweden. Statistiska Centralbyraan. Statistiska Meddelanden. Subgroup T (Transport and Other Forms of Communication)
0082-0342 Sweden. Statistiska Centralbyraan. Statistiska Meddelanden. Subgroup U (Education and Research)
0082-0350 Sweden. Statistiska Centralbyraan. Urval Skriftseries - Selection Series
0082-0369 Sweden. Statistiska Centralbyraan. Foreign Trade: Import-Export. Distribution by Country - Commodity according to the S I T C
0082-0377 Sweden. Universitetskanslersaembetet. *see* 0283-7692
0082-0393 Swedish Budget
0082-0415 Swedish Nutrition Foundation. Symposia
0082-0423 Swedish Theological Institute, Jerusalem. Annual†
0082-0431 Sweet's Canadian Construction Catalogue File
0082-044X Swiatowit
0082-0458 Rocznik Magnetyczny†
0082-0490 Switching and Automata Theory Conference. Record *see* 0272-5428
0082-0504 Switzerland. Bundesamt fuer Sozialversicherung. Spezialitaetenliste - Liste des Specialites - Elenco delle Specialita
0082-0512 Sydney Law Review
0082-0520 Sydney Studies in Literature†
0082-0547 University of Sydney. Basser Department of Computer Science. Technical Report
0082-0555 University of Sydney. Department of Agricultural Economics. Mimeographed Report. *see* 0817-8771
0082-0563 University of Sydney. Department of Agricultural Economics. Research Bulletin†
0082-0571 University of Sydney. Department of Architectural Science. Reports†
0082-0598 Sydowia: Annales Mycologici
0082-0601 Syesis *see* 0832-8609
0082-0601 Syesis *see* 0829-609X
0082-0601 Syesis *changed to* Contributions to Museum Studies.
0082-061X Sylloge Nummorum Graecorum Deutschland *changed to* Sylloge Nummorum Graecorum Deutschland. Staatliche Muenzsammlung Muenchen.
0082-0644 Symbolae Botanicae Upsalienses
0082-0660 Symbolon†

ISSN

ISSN INDEX 5555

0082-0695 Symposia Biologica Hungarica
0082-0717 American Mathematical Society. Proceedings of Symposia in Pure Mathematics
0082-0725 Symposia Mathematica
0082-0733 Symposia on Fundamental Cancer Research. Papers
0082-0741 Symposia on Naval Structural Mechanics. Proceedings†
0082-075X Symposia on Theoretical Physics and Mathematics changed to Institute of Mathematical Sciences, Madras. Reports.
0082-0768 Symposia Series in Immunobiological Standardization see 0301-5149
0082-0776 International Television Symposium and Technical Exhibition, Montreux. Symposium Record
0082-0784 Symposium (International) on Combustion
0082-0806 Symposium on Advanced Propulsion Concepts. Proceedings†
0082-0830 Symposium on Information Display. Digest of Technical Papers see 0097-966X
0082-0849 Symposium on Naval Hydrodynamics. Proceedings
0082-0857 Symposium on Nondestructive Evaluation of Components and Materials in Aerospace, Weapons Systems and Nuclear Applications changed to Symposium on Nondestructive Evaluation.
0082-0865 Symposium on Nondestructive Testing of Aircraft and Missile Components changed to Symposium on Nondestructive Evaluation.
0082-0873 Symposium on Ocular Therapy†
0082-089X Symposium on Particleboard. Proceedings
0082-0911 Institute of Management Sciences. Symposium on Planning. Proceedings†
0082-092X Symposium on Reliability. Proceedings see 0149-144X
0082-0954 Symposium on Special Ceramics, Stoke-On-Trent, England. Special Ceramics, Proceedings
0082-0970 Symposium on the Nondestructive Testing of Wood. Proceedings†
0082-1012 Symposium on Water Resources Research. Proceedings†
0082-1020 Syndicat des Industries de Materiel Professionnel Electronique et Radioelectrique. Annuaire changed to S P E R Annuaire.
0082-1055 Syndicat General des Impots. Guide National de l'Enregistrement et des Domaines changed to Syndicat General des Impots. Guide Foncier.
0082-1098 Syndromes de la Douleur†
0082-1101 Synopses of the British Fauna†
0082-111X Synthese Historical Library
0082-1128 Synthese Library
0082-1144 Synthetic Organic Chemicals, United States Production and Sales
0082-1152 Synthetic Procedures in Nucleic Acid Chemistry†
0082-1160 Syracuse Geographical Series†
0082-1179 Syracuse University Publications in Continuing Education. Occasional Papers
0082-1217 Systems Engineering of Education Series
0082-1241 Szczecinskie Towarzystwo Naukowe. Sprawozdania
0082-125X Szczecinskie Towarzystwo Naukowe. Wydzial Nauk Lekarskich. Prace
0082-1268 Szczecinskie Towarzystwo Naukowe. Wydzial Nauk Matematyczno Technicznych. Prace†
0082-1276 Szczecinskie Towarzystwo Naukowe. Wydzial Nauk Przyrodniczo-Rolniczych. Prace
0082-1306 Szilikatkemiai Monografiak
0082-1322 Szociologiai Tanulmanyok
0082-1330 T.B. Davie Memorial Lecture
0082-1365 T V - Film Filebook
0082-1381 T V "Free" Film Source Book†
0082-139X T V in Psychiatry Newsletter
0082-1411 Tables of Constants and Numerical Data†
0082-1438 Tableware and Pottery Gazette Reference Book changed to European Tableware Buyers Guide.
0082-1446 Taccuino dell'Azionista
0082-1454 Tagore Studies†
0082-1470 Taiwan Buyers' Guide
0082-1497 Taiwan. Fisheries Research Institute, Keelung. Laboratory of Fishery Biology. Report††
0082-1519 Talking Books, Adult (Large Print Edition)†
0082-1527 Tall Timbers Fire Ecology Conference. Proceedings changed to Tall Timbers Fire Ecology Conference. Proceedings.
0082-156X Tamagawa University. Faculty of Agriculture. Bulletin
0082-1578 Tamil Nadu. Department of Statistics. Annual Statistical Abstract
0082-1586 Tamil Nadu. Department of Statistics. Season and Crop Report
0082-1594 Tamil Nadu. Legislative Council. Quinquennial Review†
0082-1608 Tamworth Annual

0082-1624 Universite de Madagascar. Annales. Serie Sciences de la Nature et Mathematiques†
0082-1632 Tanulmanyok a Nevelestudomany Korebol
0082-1659 Review of the Mineral Industry in Tanzania
0082-1675 National Museum of Tanzania. Annual Report
0082-1705 Tappert
0082-1713 Tarbell's Teacher's Guide
0082-173X Tariff Schedules of the United States Annotated
0082-1748 Tarsadalomtudomanyi Kismonografiakt
0082-1764 Taschenbuch der Fernmelde-Praxis changed to Taschenbuch der Telekom Praxis.
0082-1772 Taschenbuch der Giesserei-Praxis
0082-1799 Taschenbuch der Pflanzenarztes
0082-1802 Taschenbuch der Werbung changed to Deutscher Werbekalender.
0082-1829 Taschenbuch des Oeffentlichen Lebens
0082-1837 Taschenbuch des Textileinzelhandels
0082-1845 Taschenbuch fuer Agrarjournalisten
0082-1853 Taschenbuch fuer den Buchhalter changed to Jahrbuch fuer Fuehrungs Kraefte des Rechnungswesens.
0082-1861 Taschenbuch fuer den Fernmeldedienst†
0082-187X Taschenbuch fuer Liturgie und Kirchenmusik see 0344-1407
0082-1896 Taschenbuch fuer die Textil-Industrie
0082-190X Taschenbuch der Post- und Fernmelde-Verwaltung see 0939-4400
0082-1918 Taschenbuch fuer Ingenieure und Techniker im Industrie und Wirtschaft†
0082-1926 Taschenbuch fuer Ingenieure und Techniker im Oeffentlichen Dienst†
0082-1934 Taschenbuch fuer Kriminalisten
0082-1942 Taschenbuch fuer Logistik†
0082-1950 Taschenbuch Geschichte
0082-1969 Taschenbuecher zur Musikwissenschaft
0082-1985 Information about Investment in Tasmania†
0082-1993 Tasmania. Department of Agriculture. Annual Report changed to Tasmania. Department of Primary Industry. Annual Report.
0082-2043 Tasmania. Department of Mines. Geological Survey Bulletins changed to Tasmania. Department of Resources and Energy. Division of Mines and Mineral Resources. Geological Survey Bulletins.
0082-2051 Tasmania. Department of Mines. Geological Survey Record†
0082-206X Tasmania. Department of Mines. Geological Survey Reports†
0082-2078 Tasmania. Department of Mines. Technical Reports†
0082-2086 Tasmania. Department of Mines. Underground Water Supply Papers†
0082-2094 Tasmania. Metropolitan Water Board. Report. changed to Tasmania. Hobart Regional Water Board. Annual Report.
0082-2108 University of Tasmania Law Review
0082-2116 Australia. Bureau of Statistics. Tasmanian Office. Tasmanian Year Book
0082-2124 Tatura, Australia. Horticultural Research Station. Annual Research Report changed to Tatura, Australia. Irrigation Research Institute. Biennial Report.
0082-2132 Tatzlilt
0082-2159 Tax Foundation. Research Publications. New Series†
0082-2167 Taxation in Western Europe†
0082-2175 Taxation Tables
0082-2183 Taylor's Encyclopedia of Government Officials. Federal and State
0082-2191 Tbilisskii Universitet. Institut Prikladnoi Matematiki. Seminar. Annotatsii Dokladov see 0320-9512
0082-2205 Teacher Education†
0082-2213 Teachers' Associations. Associations d'Enseignants. Asociaciones de Personal Docente†
0082-223X Teaching
0082-2256 Teatro Clasico de Mexico. Boletin. Notas y Comentarios†
0082-2264 Technical Aids for Small Manufacturers†
0082-2272 Technical and Scientific Books in Print††
0082-2299 T A G A Proceedings
0082-2310 Technical Papers in Hydrology Series
0082-2329 Technical Service Data (Automotive) changed to Technical Service Data (Cars).
0082-2353 Technician Education Yearbook changed to Technician Education Directory.
0082-2361 Technikgeschichte in Einzeldarstellungen†
0082-240X Technique of Organic Chemistry see 0082-2531
0082-2418 Techniques and Applications in Organic Synthesis Series
0082-2434 Techniques and Methods of Polymer Evaluation†
0082-2450 Techniques Avancees†
0082-2469 Techniques d'Aujourd'Hui
0082-2477 Techniques Economiques Modernes. Analyse Economique

0082-2485 Techniques Economiques Modernes. Espace Economique†
0082-2493 Techniques Economiques Modernes. Histoire et Pensee Economique†
0082-2507 Techniques Economiques Modernes. Production et Marches†
0082-2515 Techniques in Pure and Applied Microbiology†
0082-2523 Techniques of Biochemical and Biophysical Morphology†
0082-2531 Techniques of Chemistry
0082-254X Techniques of Electrochemistry†
0082-2558 Techniques of Metals Research†
0082-2566 Technische Fortschrittsberichte†
0082-2590 Technische Physik in Einzeldarstellungen
0082-2604 Technology and Democratic Society changed to Organisations, People, Society/O P S.
0082-2612 Etudes Teilhardiennes
0082-2620 Museum of Antiquities of Tel-Aviv-Yafo. Publications
0082-2639 Tel Aviv - Yafo. Research and Statistical Department. Special Surveys see 0792-0601
0082-2647 Telemetry Journal Buyers Guide†
0082-2655 Telephone Engineer & Management Directory
0082-2663 Telephone Tickler for Insurance Men and Women changed to New York Telephone Tickler for Insurance Men and Women.
0082-2671 Telephony's Directory of the Telephone Industry changed to Telephony's Directory & Buyers Guide for the Telecommunications Industry.
0082-268X Television Factbook see 0732-8648
0082-2698 Television for the Family†
0082-2701 Coleccion Temas de Arquitectura Actual
0082-2744 East Tennessee State University. Research Development Committee. Publications†
0082-2752 Tennessee. State Planning Office. State Planning Office Publication†
0082-2760 Tennessee Statistical Abstract
0082-2779 Tennessee Tech Journal†
0082-2809 Tennessee Valley Authority. Technical Monographs†
0082-2817 Tennessee Valley Authority. Technical Reports†
0082-2825 Tennis for Travelers†
0082-2833 Tennis Guide†
0082-2841 Tennyson Research Bulletin
0082-285X Tennyson Society, Lincoln, England. Monographs
0082-2868 Tennyson Society, Lincoln, England. Report
0082-2884 Terrae Incognitae
0082-2930 Texas Archeological Society. Bulletin
0082-2949 Texas Archeology
0082-2957 Texas Archeology Salvage Project. Papers†
0082-2973 Texas Christian University Monographs in History and Culture†
0082-2981 Texas. Coordinating Board. Texas College and University System. C B Annual Report changed to Texas Higher Education Coordinating Board. Annual Status Report and Statistical Report.
0082-299X Texas College and University System. Coordinating Board. C B Policy Paper changed to Texas Higher Education Coordinating Board. C B Policy Paper.
0082-3007 Texas Coordinating Board. Texas College and University System. C B Study Paper changed to Texas Higher Education Coordinating Board. C B Study Paper.
0082-3015 Texas Folklore Society. Paisano Series†
0082-3023 Texas Folklore Society. Publications
0082-304X Texas Forestry Papers†
0082-3058 Texas. Governor's Committee on Aging. Biennial Report changed to Texas. Department on Aging. Annual Report.
0082-3066 Texas Industry Series†
0082-3074 Texas Memorial Museum. Bulletin
0082-3082 Texas Memorial Museum. Miscellaneous Papers
0082-3090 Texas Memorial Museum. Notes Series†
0082-3104 Texas Mineral Producers†
0082-3120 Texas Public Library Statistics
0082-3139 Texas Research Foundation, Renner. Contributions†
0082-3163 Texas Special Libraries Directory†
0082-318X Stephen F. Austin State University. School of Forestry. Bulletin†
0082-3198 Texas Tech University. Graduate Studies
0082-3201 University of Texas. African and Afro-American Research Institute. Occasional Publication changed to African and Afro-American Studies and Research Center. Occasional Publication.
0082-3228 University of Texas, Austin. Bureau of Business Research. Area Economic Survey†
0082-3236 University of Texas, Austin. Bureau of Business Research. Bibliography†
0082-3244 University of Texas, Austin. Bureau of Business Research. Business Guide†

ISSN INDEX

0082-3279 University of Texas, Austin. Bureau of Business Research. Research Monograph changed to University of Texas, Austin. Bureau of Business Research. Research Monograph Series.
0082-3287 University of Texas at Austin. Bureau of Economic Geology. Annual Report
0082-3295 University of Texas. Bureau of Economic Geology. Guidebook see 0363-4132
0082-3309 University of Texas at Austin. Bureau of Economic Geology. Geological Circular
0082-3333 University of Texas at Austin. Bureau of Economic Geology. Mineral Resource Circulars
0082-335X University of Texas at Austin. Bureau of Economic Geology. Report of Investigations
0082-3384 University of Texas, Austin. Natural Fibers Economic Research. Research Report†
0082-3392 Texas Cotton Review†
0082-3406 University of Texas, Austin. County Auditors' Institute. Proceedings†
0082-3414 University of Texas, Austin. Department of Anthropology. Anthropology Series‡
0082-3422 University of Texas, Austin. Governmental Accounting and Finance Institute. Proceedings†
0082-3430 University of Texas, Austin. Institute for Tax Assessors. Proceedings†
0082-3449 University of Texas. Institute of Marine Science. Contributions changed to Contributions in Marine Science - Monographic Series.
0082-3554 Texas. Water Development Board. Biennial Report†
0082-3562 Texas. Water Development Board. Report changed to Texas. Water Development Board. Report.
0082-3570 Texas. Water Quality Board. Biennial Report†
0082-3589 Texte und Untersuchungen zur Geschichte der Altchristlichen Literatur
0082-3597 Texte zur Kirchen- und Theologiegeschichte†
0082-3600 Textes Sociologiques changed to Textes de Sciences Sociales.
0082-3627 Textil-Industrie und ihre Helfer
0082-3635 Textile Chemistry†
0082-3651 Textile Industry Technical Conference. Record see 0094-9884
0082-366X Textile Japan
0082-3708 Textiles Suisses: Interieur
0082-3759 Texts from Cuneiform Sources
0082-3767 Textus
0082-3775 Textus Patristici et Liturgici
0082-3783 Thai Investment Review†
0082-3805 Thames Book
0082-3821 Theatre Annual
0082-3848 Theatre Student Series†
0082-3856 Theatre World
0082-3880 Theodor-Storm-Gesellschaft. Schriften
0082-3902 Theologische Dissertationen
0082-3945 Theoretical and Experimental Biology
0082-3953 Theoretical and Experimental Biophysics: A Series of Advances†
0082-3961 Theoretical Chemistry
0082-3988 Theorie de la Production
0082-3996 Theory, Technique and Functional Use of Film; Bibliographical References
0082-4003 Theriaca
0082-4011 Thermal Analysis Series†
0082-402X Thermodynamics Research Center. Data Project. Selected Values of Properties of Chemical Compounds. Category B. Selected Infrared Spectral Data†
0082-4038 Thermodynamics Research Center. Data Project. Selected Values of Properties of Chemical Compounds. Category D. Selected Raman Spectral Data changed to T R C Spectral Data - Raman.
0082-4046 Thermodynamics Research Center. Data Project. Selected Values of Properties of Chemical Compounds. Category A. Tables of Selected Values of Physical and Thermodynamic Properties of Chemical Compounds changed to T R C Thermodynamic Tables - Non-Hydrocarbons.
0082-4054 Thermodynamics Research Center Data Project. Selected Values of Properties of Chemical Compounds. Category C. Selected Ultraviolet Spectral Data†
0082-4062 Thermodynamics Research Center Data Project. Selected Values of Properties of Chemical Compounds. Category E. Selected Mass Spectral Data†
0082-4070 Thermodynamics Research Center Data Project. Selected Values of Properties of Chemical Compounds. Category F. Selected Nuclear Magnetic Resonance Spectral Data changed to Thermodynamics Research Center. Data Project. Selected Values of Properties of Chemical Compounds. Category F. Selected 1H Nuclear Magnetic Resonance Spectral Data.
0082-4089 Silumine Fizika
0082-4097 Thesaurismata
0082-4100 Theses and Dissertations Accepted for Higher Degrees in Nigerian Universities
0082-4119 Theses in Germanic Studies†
0082-4127 University of London. Institute of Germanic Studies. Theses in Progress at British Universities see 0260-5929
0082-4151 Thomas Grocery Register changed to Thomas Food Industry Register.
0082-416X Thomas Hardy Year Book
0082-4178 Thomas Jefferson Center for Political Economy. Research Monographs.†
0082-4186 Thomas Mann Gesellschaft. Blaetter
0082-4208 St. Thomas More Lectures†
0082-4216 Thomas Register of American Manufacturers see 0362-7721
0082-4224 Thom's Commercial Directory
0082-4232 Thoresby Society, Leeds, England. Publications
0082-4240 Thoroughbred Racing Associations. Directory and Record Book
0082-4283 Thunder Bay Historical Museum Society. Papers and Records
0082-4305 Tierwelt Deutschlands
0082-4313 Tijdschrift voor Privaatrecht
0082-433X Timber and Plywood. Board News Annual
0082-4364 Timber Trades Journal. Annual Special Issue
0082-4372 Timber Trades Directory†
0082-4399 Times Guide to the House of Commons
0082-4429 Times 1000
0082-4453 Universitatea din Timisoara. Analele. Stiinte Fizico-Chimice changed to Universitatea din Timisoara. Analele. Stiinte Fizice.
0082-4461 Universitatea din Timisoara. Analele. Stiinte Filologice
0082-4496 Tire and Rim Association. Standards Year Book
0082-450X Tiryns
0082-4518 Tissue Culture Studies in Japan: The Annual Bibliography†
0082-4526 Titles in Series†
0082-4534 Titles of Dissertationa and Theses Completed in Home Economics see 0046-7774
0082-4542 Tjaenstemaennens Central Organisation. Aarsrapport changed to Aaret som Gaatt.
0082-4550 Tlatoani†
0082-4569 Tlatoani. Suplemento†
0082-4585 Sources of Contemporary Jewish Thought
0082-4593 Tobacco Associates. Annual Report
0082-4607 Tobacco Research Council. Research Papers†
0082-4615 Tobacco Research Council. Review of Activities†
0082-4623 Tobacco Science Yearbook
0082-4631 Tobacco Trade Year Book and Diary changed to Tobacco Trade Directory and Diary.
0082-464X Tohoku University. Faculty of Science. Institute of Geology and Paleontology. Science Reports. Second Series
0082-4658 Tohoku Daigaku Rigakubu Chishitsugaku Koseibutsugaku Kyoshitsu Kenkyu Hobun Hokoku
0082-4666 Tohoku University. Research Institutes. Science Reports. Series D: Agriculture changed to Tohoku University. Institute for Agricultural Research. Reports.
0082-4674 Tokai-Kinki National Agricultural Experiment Station, Tsu, Japan. Bulletin†
0082-4690 Tokyo Astronomical Bulletin changed to National Astronomical Bulletin.
0082-4704 Tokyo Astronomical Observatory. Annals see 0915-3640
0082-4712 Tokyo Astronomical Observatory. Reprints see 0915-0021
0082-4720 Tokyo Metropolitan Agricultural Experiment Station, Itsukaichi Office. Forestry Experimental Bulletin
0082-4739 Tokyo Medical and Dental University. Institute for Medical and Dental Engineering. Reports
0082-4747 Tokyo Metropolitan University. Faculty of Technology. Memoirs
0082-4755 Kokuritsu Kagaku Hakubutsukan Senpo
0082-4763 Snow Brand Milk Products Company. Research Laboratory. Reports
0082-4771 Tokyo-toritsu Eisei Kenkyujo Kenkyu Nenpo
0082-478X University of Tokyo. Department of Geography. Bulletin
0082-4798 University of Tokyo. Institute for Solid State Physics. Technical Report. Series A
0082-4801 University of Tokyo. Institute for Solid State Physics. Technical Report. Series B
0082-481X University of Tokyo. Institute of Applied Microbiology. Reports
0082-4836 Tokyo University of Fisheries Journal. Special Edition†
0082-4844 Tokyo University of Foreign Studies. Summary see 0493-4342
0082-4895 Tonga. Minister of Health. Report
0082-495X Topics in Inorganic and General Chemistry
0082-4968 Topics in Lipid Chemistry†
0082-4992 Topics in Phosphorous Chemistry†
0082-500X Topics in Stereochemistry
0082-5018 Art Gallery of Ontario. Annual Report
0082-5034 Hospital for Sick Children, Toronto. Research Institute. Annual Report
0082-5042 Toronto Medieval Bibliographies
0082-5050 Toronto Mediaeval Latin Texts
0082-5077 Royal Ontario Museum. Art and Archaeology. Occasional Papers changed to Royal Ontario Museum. Archaeology Occasional Papers.
0082-5093 Royal Ontario Museum. Life Sciences. Miscellaneous Publications
0082-5107 Royal Ontario Museum. Life Sciences. Occasional Papers
0082-5115 Royal Ontario Museum. Annual Report
0082-5123 Toronto Semitic Texts and Studies†
0082-514X University of Toronto. Department of Electrical Engineering. Research Report†
0082-5158 University of Toronto. Department of English. Studies and Texts†
0082-5166 Natural Hazard Research Working Papers
0082-5174 University of Toronto. Department of Geography. Research Publications†
0082-5182 University of Toronto. Department of Mechanical Engineering. Technical Publication Series
0082-5190 University of Toronto. Faculty of Forestry. Technical Reports†
0082-5239 University of Toronto. Institute for Aerospace Studies. Annual Progress Report
0082-5247 University of Toronto. Institute for Aerospace Studies. Review
0082-5255 University of Toronto. Institute for Aerospace Studies. Report
0082-5263 University of Toronto. Institute for Aerospace Studies. Technical Note
0082-5271 University of Toronto. Institute for the Quantitative Analysis of Social and Economic Policy. News Letter changed to University of Toronto. Institute for Policy Analysis. Annual Report.
0082-5298 University of Toronto. Institute for the Quantitative Analysis of Social and Economic Policy. Reprint Series changed to University of Toronto. Institute for Policy Analysis. Reprint Series.
0082-5301 University of Toronto. Institute for the Quantitative Analysis of Social and Economic Policy. Working Paper Series see 0829-4909
0082-531X University of Toronto. Library. Annual Report†
0082-5328 Pontifical Institute of Mediaeval Studies. Studies and Texts
0082-5336 University of Toronto Romance Series
0082-5344 Torquay Natural History Society. Transactions and Proceedings
0082-5352 Torry Research Station, Aberdeen, Scotland. Annual Report†
0082-5360 Tottori University. Faculty of Agriculture. Journal
0082-5379 Tottori Daigaku Nogakubu Fuzoku Enshurin Hokoku
0082-5395 Universite de Toulouse-le Mirail. Faculte des Sciences. Annales†
0082-5409 France - Iberie Recherche. Etudes et Documents
0082-5417 France - Iberie Recherche. Theses et Documents changed to France - Iberie Recherche. Theses et Recherches.
0082-5433 T'oung Pao
0082-5441 Touring with Towser
0082-545X Tourism in Greece†
0082-5468 Tourist Bibliography changed to Tourism Compendium.
0082-5484 Toute la Boisson. International
0082-5506 Towarzystwo Naukowe w Toruniu. Fontes
0082-5514 Towarzystwo Naukowe w Toruniu. Komisja Historii Sztuki. Teka
0082-5522 Towarzystwo Naukowe w Toruniu. Roczniki
0082-5530 Studia Societatis Scientiarum Torunensis. Sectio B. Chemia†
0082-5549 Studia Societatis Scientiarum Torunensis. Sectio C. Geografia et Geologia
0082-5557 Studia Societatis Scientiarum Torunensis. Sectio D. Botanica
0082-5565 Studia Societatis Scientiarum Torunensis. Sectio E. Zoologia
0082-5573 Studia Societatis Scientiarum Torunensis. Sectio F. Astronomia
0082-5581 Studia Societatis Scientiarum Torunensis. Sectio G. Physiologia†
0082-5611 Toy Trader Year Book changed to Toy Directory.
0082-562X Oriental Library. Research Department. Memoirs
0082-5638 Trabajos de Prehistoria. Nueva Serie
0082-5662 Tractocatalogue
0082-5689 Trade Associations and Professional Bodies of the United Kingdom
0082-5697 Trade Directory of Malta†
0082-5735 Trade Directory of the Republic of the Sudan

0082-5743 Trade Directory Wine and Spirit *changed to* Off Licence News Directory.
0082-5778 Trade of China†
0082-5786 Trademark Register of the United States
0082-5808 Trades Register of London *changed to* London Directory of Industry and Commerce.
0082-5824 Trado: Asian - African Directory of Exporters, Importers and Manufacturers
0082-5859 Traffic Laws Commentary
0082-5867 Traffic Report of the St. Lawrence Seaway
0082-5891 Railway World Annual *changed to* Railway World Yearbook.
0082-5913 Transit Fact Book *see* 0821-2996
0082-5921 Transition Metal Chemistry: A Series of Advances†
0082-593X Translations and Reprints from the Original Sources of European History *changed to* Middle Ages.
0082-5948 Transplantation Reviews *see* 0105-2896
0082-5956 Transportation Statistics in the United States
0082-5964 Transportieren Umschlagen Lagern†
0082-5980 Transtelel: Transmissions, Telecommunications, Electronique en France
0082-6006 Trattati di Architettura
0082-6022 Travaux de Droit, d'Economique de Sociologie et de Sciences Politiques
0082-6049 Travaux de Linguistique
0082-6057 Travaux de Linguistique et de Litterature
0082-6073 Travaux d'Histoire Ethico-Politique
0082-6081 Travaux d'Humanisme et Renaissance
0082-609X Travaux sur les Pecheries du Quebec†
0082-6103 Travel Abroad: Frontier Formalities†
0082-612X Canadian Tourist Association. Proceedings *changed to* Tourism Industry Association of Canada. Convention Report.
0082-6146 Travel Industry Personnel Directory
0082-6197 Travel Research Journal†
0082-6200 Travel Trends in the United States and Canadian Provinces *changed to* Travel Trends in the United States and Canada.
0082-6219 Travel World Year Book and Diary†
0082-6243 Treatise on Analytical Chemistry. Part 1: Theory and Practice of Analytical Chemistry†
0082-6251 Treatise on Analytical Chemistry. Part 2: Analytical Chemistry of the Elements; Analytical Chemistry of Inorganic and Organic Compounds†
0082-626X Treatise on Analytical Chemistry. Part 3: Analytical Chemistry in Industry†
0082-6278 Treatise on Coatings†
0082-6286 Trends in Developing Countries†
0082-6316 Trends in Southeast Asia
0082-6324 Trends in the International Petroleum-Refining Industry†
0082-6340 Treubia
0082-6367 T R I U M F Annual Report *changed to* T R I U M F Annual Report Scientific Activities.
0082-6391 Tribolium Information Bulletin
0082-6405 Tribology Convention. Proceedings†
0082-6413 Tribus
0082-643X Trierer Grabungen und Forschungen
0082-6448 Istituto Sperimentale Talassografico, Trieste. Annuario.†
0082-6456 Istituto Sperimentale Talassografico di Trieste. Pubblicazione
0082-6464 Universita di Trieste. Istituto di Chimica Biologica. Publicazioni†
0082-6472 Universita degli Studi di Trieste. Istituto di Chimica Farmaceutica. Pubblicazioni†
0082-6480 Universita degli Studi di Trieste. Istituto di Pedagogia. Quaderni
0082-6502 Trinidad and Tobago. Central Statistical Office. Annual Statistical Digest
0082-6510 Trinidad and Tobago. Central Statistical Office. Digest of Statistics on Education†
0082-6529 Trinidad and Tobago. Central Statistical Office. Financial Statistics
0082-6537 Trinidad and Tobago. Central Statistical Office. International Travel Report
0082-6545 Trinidad and Tobago. Central Statistical Office. Overseas Trade. Annual Report
0082-6553 Trinidad and Tobago. Central Statistical Office. Population and Vital Statistics; Report
0082-6561 Trinidad and Tobago Today†
0082-657X Trinidad and Tobago Trade Directory
0082-6596 Trinity University Studies in Religion†
0082-6618 Universitet i Trondheim. Norges Tekniske Hoegskole. Vassdrags-og Havnelaboratoriet. Meddlelelse *changed to* Norwegian Hydrotechnical Laboratory. Bulletin.
0082-6642 Tropical Pesticides Research Institute. Annual Report
0082-6669 Tuberkulose-Jahrbuch†
0082-6677 Tuberkulose und ihre Grenzgebiete in Einzel-Arstellungen†
0082-6693 Universidad Nacional de Tucuman. Instituto de Ingenieria Electrica. Revista
0082-6707 Tudomanyszervezesi Fuzetek
0082-6715 Tudomanytorteneti Tanulmanyok†
0082-6731 Tuebinger Rechtswissenschaftliche Abhandlungen
0082-674X Tufting Year Book *changed to* Carpet Manufacturer International.
0082-6758 Tulane Studies in English *changed to* T S E: Tulane Studies in English.
0082-6774 Tulane Studies in Political Science
0082-6782 Tulane Studies in Zoology and Botany
0082-6790 Howard-Tilton Memorial Library. Report†
0082-6812 University of Tulsa. Department of English. Monograph Series *changed to* University of Tulsa. Monograph Series.
0082-6820 Tunisia. Ministere du Plan. Budget Economique
0082-6839 Tunisia. Institut National de la Statistique. Statistiques Industrielles *changed to* Tunisia. Institut National de la Statistique. Recensement des Activites Industrielles.
0082-6847 Turcica; Revue d'Etudes Turques
0082-6855 Institut Universitaire d'Etudes Europeennes de Turin. Annuaire†
0082-6871 Universita di Torino. Facolta di Agraria. Annali *changed to* Universita di Torino. Facolta di Scienze Agrarie. Annali.
0082-688X Universita degli Studi di Torino. Istituto di Storia. Collana†
0082-6898 Turkish Review of Ethnography
0082-6901 Turkey. Devlet Istatistik Enstitusu. Dis Ticaret Yillik Istatistik
0082-691X Turkiye Istatistik Yilligi
0082-6928 Turkey. Devlet Istatistik Enstitusu. Tarim Istatistikleri Ozeti
0082-6936 Turkey. Devlet Istatistik Enstitusu. Tarimsal Yapi ve Uretim
0082-6944 Turkey. Devlet Planama Teskilati. Yili Programi Ucuncu Bes Yil
0082-6952 Turkish Trade Directory & Telex Index
0082-6979 Turun Yliopisto. Julkaisuja. Sarja A. II. Biologica - Geographica - Geologica
0082-6987 Turun Yliopisto. Julkaisuja. Sarja B. Humaniora
0082-6995 Turun Yliopisto. Julkaisuja. Sarja C. Scripta Lingua Fennica Edita
0082-7002 Turun Yliopisto. Julkaisuja. Sarja A. I. Astronomica - Chemica - Physica - Mathematica
0082-7010 Turun Yliopisto. Kirjasto. Julkaisuja
0082-7029 Turun Yliopisto. Klassillisen Filologian Laitos. Opera Ex Instituto Philologiae Classicae Universitatis Turkuensis Edita†
0082-7037 Turun Yliopisto. Psykologian Laitos. Reports *see* 0359-0216
0082-7037 Turun Yliopisto. Psykologian Laitos. Reports *see* 0356-8741
0082-7088 Twentieth Century Legal Philosophy Series†
0082-710X St. Paul, Minnesota. Metropolitan Transit Commission. Annual Report *changed to* St. Paul, Minnesota. Twin Cities Area Metropolitan Transit Commission. Annual Report.
0082-7118 Tyndale Bulletin
0082-7126 U C L A Business Forecast for the Nation and California *changed to* U C L A Business Forecast for California.
0082-7126 U C L A Business Forecast for the Nation and California *changed to* U C L A National Business Forecast.
0082-7134 U C L A Forum in Medical Sciences
0082-7142 U K Trade Names *changed to* U K Industrial Trade Names.
0082-7150 Ub'†
0082-7169 Uganda. Geological Survey and Mines Department. Memoirs†
0082-7177 Uganda. Forestry Department. Annual Report
0082-7185 Uganda. Forestry Department. Bulletins†
0082-7193 Uganda. Forestry Department. Technical Notes
0082-7215 Uganda. Geological Survey and Mines Department. Annual Report *changed to* Records of Geological Survey and Mines.
0082-724X Uganda. Ministry of Planning and Economic Development. Statistics Division. Enumeration of Employees
0082-7282 Uhrmacher-Jahrbuch†
0082-7290 Uhrmacher - Jahrbuch fuer Handwerk und Handel†
0082-7312 Uj Magyar Nepkoltesi Gyujtemeny
0082-7347 Ulster Folklife
0082-7355 Ulster Journal of Archaeology
0082-7363 Ulster-Scot Historical Series†
0082-7371 Ulster Year Book
0082-7444 Underwater Acoustics†
0082-7452 Underwriting Results in Canada†
0082-7460 Unesco Bibliographical Handbooks *changed to* Documentation, Libraries and Archives: Bibliographies and Reference Works.
0082-7487 Unesco Handbook of International Exchanges†
0082-7495 Unesco Manuals for Libraries *changed to* Documentation, Libraries and Archives: Studies and Research.
0082-7509 Unesco. Records of the General Conference. Proceedings
0082-7517 Unesco. Records of the General Conference. Resolutions
0082-7525 Unesco. Report of the Director-General on the Activities of the Organization
0082-7533 Unesco Statistical Reports and Studies
0082-7541 Unesco Statistical Yearbook
0082-755X Ungarn - Jahrbuch†
0082-7568 Uniatec Congress. Records
0082-7576 Uniespana-Cine Espanol
0082-7584 International Conference of Building Officials. Uniform Building Code
0082-7592 Uniform Crime Reports for the United States
0082-7630 Union List of Publications in Opaque Microforms†
0082-7649 Union List of Scientific and Technical Periodicals Held in the Principal Libraries of East Africa†
0082-7657 Union List of Scientific Serials in Canadian Libraries
0082-7665 Union List of Serials in Israel Libraries
0082-7681 Union List of Serials in the Wayne State University Libraries *changed to* Union List of Selected Serials of Michigan.
0082-7711 Union Nationale de l'Enseignement Agricole Prive. Annuaire
0082-7738 Union Nationale des Oenologues. Annuaire
0082-7762 Union of Nova Scotia Municipalities. Proceedings of the Annual Convention†
0082-7770 Union Professionnelle Feminine. Annuaire
0082-7789 Index to Titles of English News Releases of Hsinhua News Agency
0082-7797 Unitarian and Free Christian Churches. Yearbook of the General Assembly *changed to* Unitarian and Free Christian Churches. Handbook and Directory of the General Assembly.
0082-7800 Unitarian Historical Society, London. Transactions
0082-7819 Unitarian Historical Society. Proceedings *changed to* Unitarian Universalist Historical Society. Proceedings.
0082-7827 Unitarian Universalist Directory
0082-7835 Egypt. Service des Antiquites. Annales
0082-7843 United Baptist Convention of the Atlantic Provinces. Yearbook
0082-786X United Church of Canada. Committee on Archives. Bulletin. Records and Proceedings†
0082-7878 United Church of Canada. General Council. Record of Proceedings
0082-7886 United Church of Canada. Year Book *changed to* United Church of Canada. Year Book and Directory.
0082-7894 United Community Funds and Councils of America. Addresses Delivered at the United Way Staff Conference†
0082-7908 United Free Church of Scotland. Handbook
0082-7916 United Graphic Guide *changed to* United & Babson Graphic Guide.
0082-7932 Travel Trade Directory, U K and Ireland
0082-7940 United Kingdom Atomic Energy Authority. Annual Report
0082-7959 United Kingdom Fire and Loss Statistics *see* 0260-3098
0082-7983 United Methodist Church (United States) Division of Education. Adult Planbook *see* 0149-998X
0082-8009 United Nations and What You Should Know about It†
0082-8025 United Nations Congress on the Prevention of Crime and the Treatment of Offenders. Report
0082-8041 Demographic Yearbook
0082-805X Population Studies
0082-8076 United Nations. Disarmament Commission. Official Records *see* 0252-5607
0082-8084 United Nations. Economic and Social Council. Index to Proceedings
0082-8092 United Nations. Economic and Social Council. Official Records
0082-8106 United Nations. Economic and Social Commission for Asia and the Pacific. Development Programming Techniques Series†
0082-8114 United Nations. Economic and Social Commission for Asia and the Pacific. Mineral Resources Development Series
0082-8122 United Nations Economic and Social Commission for Asia and the Pacific. Regional Economic Cooperation Series†
0082-8130 United Nations. Economic and Social Commission for Asia and the Pacific. Water Resources Development Series *changed to* United Nations. Economic and Social Commission for Asia and the Pacific. Water Resources Series.
0082-8157 United Nations. General Assembly. Index to Proceedings
0082-8211 Resolutions of the General Assembly of the United Nations *see* 0082-8157
0082-8289 United Nations. International Law Commission Yearbook
0082-8297 United Nations Juridical Yearbook
0082-8319 United Nations. Multilateral Treaties in Respect of Which the Secretary-General Performs Depository Functions *see* 0255-724X

5558 ISSN INDEX

0082-8327 Estimated World Requirements of Narcotic Drugs. Supplement†
0082-8335 Estimated World Requirements of Narcotic Drugs *see* 1013-3453
0082-8343 United Nations. Permanent Central Opium Board. Report to the Economic and Social Council on the Work of the Permanent Central Narcotics (Opium) Board *see* 0257-3717
0082-836X United Nations Regional Cartographic Conference for Asia and the Far East. Proceedings of the Conference and Technical Papers *changed to* United Nations Regional Cartographic Conference for Asia and the Pacific. Report of the Conference.
0082-8408 United Nations. Security Council. Index to Proceedings
0082-8416 United Nations. Security Council. Official Records
0082-8459 United Nations. Statistical Yearbook
0082-8475 United Nations. Trade and Development Board. Official Records *see* 0503-4108
0082-8483 United Nations. Trade and Development Board. Official Records. Supplements *changed to* United Nations. Conference on Trade and Development. Trade and Development Board. Official Records. Supplements.
0082-8491 United Nations. Trusteeship Council. Index to Proceedings
0082-8505 United Nations. Trusteeship Council. Official Records
0082-8513 United Nations. Trusteeship Council. Official Records. Supplements
0082-8521 United Nations. Yearbook
0082-8548 United Presbyterian Church in the United States of America. Minutes of the General Assembly
0082-8556 U S O Annual Report
0082-8564 United Society for Christian Literature. Annual Report *changed to* U S C L Bulletin.
0082-8599 U S A Oil Industry Directory
0082-8602 U S College-Sponsored Programs Abroad. Academic Year *changed to* Academic Year Abroad.
0082-8637 U.S. Agency for International Development. Proposed Foreign Aid Program, Summary Presentation to Congress†
0082-8661 Tables on Hatchery and Flock Participation in the National Poultry Improvement Plan
0082-867X U.S. Agricultural Research Service. Animal Science Research Division. Tables on Hatchery and Flock Participation in the National Turkey Improvement Plan *see* 0082-8661
0082-870X U.S. Air Force Cambridge Research Laboratories. A F C R L (Series) *changed to* U.S. Air Force Geophysics Laboratory. A F G L (Series).
0082-8742 United States and Canadian Publications on Africa†
0082-8750 United States Animal Health Association. Proceedings of the Annual Meeting
0082-8769 U.S. Arms Control and Disarmament Agency. Annual Report to Congress
0082-8793 World Military Expenditures and Related Data *see* 0897-4667
0082-8815 U. S. Atomic Energy Commission. Annual Report to Congress†
0082-8823 U. S. Atomic Energy Commission. Annual Report to Congress. Supplement. Atomic Energy Research Reports†
0082-8831 U. S. Atomic Energy Commission. Division of Plans and Reports. Fundamental Nuclear Energy Research†
0082-884X U. S. Atomic Energy Commission. Safety and Fire Protection Technical Bulletins†
0082-8904 U.S Bureau of Commercial Fisheries. Special Scientific Report *changed to* U.S. National Marine Fisheries Service. Technical Report.
0082-8939 U.S. Bureau of International Commerce. Annual Reports
0082-8963 U.S. Bureau of International Commerce. Trade Lists *changed to* U.S. Department of Commerce. Trade Lists.
0082-9013 U.S. Bureau of Labor Statistics. Analysis of Work Stoppages†
0082-9021 U.S. Bureau of Labor Statistics. Bulletins
0082-903X U.S. Bureau of Labor Statistics. B L S Staff Paper†
0082-9048 U.S. Bureau of Labor Statistics. Employment and Earnings Statistics for States and Areas *changed to* U.S. Bureau of Labor Statistics. Employment and Earnings: States and Areas.
0082-9056 U.S. Bureau of Labor Statistics. Handbook of Labor Statistics
0082-9064 U.S. Bureau of Labor Statistics. Industry Wage Surveys
0082-9099 U.S. Bureau of Labor Statistics. Union Wages and Hours Surveys†
0082-9102 U.S. Bureau of Labor Statistics. Wage Chronologies†
0082-9110 U.S. Bureau of Land Management. Public Land Statistics
0082-9129 U.S. Bureau of Mines. Bulletin
0082-9137 U.S. Bureau of Mines. Commodity Data Summaries *see* 0160-5151
0082-9250 U. S. Bureau of Radiological Health. Seminar Paper Series†
0082-9307 U.S. Bureau of the Census. Annual Survey of Manufactures
0082-9315 U.S. Bureau of the Census. Census of Agriculture
0082-9323 U.S. Bureau of the Census. Census of Business *changed to* U.S. Bureau of the Census. Census of Retail Trade.
0082-9323 U.S. Bureau of the Census. Census of Business *changed to* U.S. Bureau of the Census. Census of Wholesale Trade.
0082-9323 U.S. Bureau of the Census. Census of Business *changed to* U.S. Bureau of the Census. Census of Service Industries.
0082-934X U.S. Bureau of the Census. Census of Construction Industries
0082-9358 U.S. Bureau of the Census. Census of Governments
0082-9366 U.S. Bureau of the Census. Census of Housing
0082-9374 U.S. Bureau of the Census. Census of Manufactures
0082-9382 U.S. Bureau of the Census. Census of Mineral Industries
0082-9390 U.S. Bureau of the Census. Census of Population
0082-9404 U.S. Bureau of the Census. Census of Transportation
0082-9412 U.S. Bureau of the Census. Census Tract Manual†
0082-9420 U.S. Bureau of the Census. Recurrent Reports on Governments. Chart Book on Government Finances and Employment *see* 0360-2508
0082-9439 Current Governments Reports: City Government Finances
0082-9455 U.S. Bureau of the Census. County and City Data Book
0082-9463 U.S. Bureau of the Census. County Business Patterns
0082-9471 Current Population Reports
0082-9498 International Population Reports *changed to* International Population Data.
0082-9501 Current Population Reports: Population Characteristics. Marital Status and Family Status *changed to* Current Population Reports: Population Characteristics. Marital Status and Living Arrangements.
0082-951X U.S. Bureau of the Census. Current Population Reports: Negro Population *changed to* Current Population Reports: Population Characteristics. Social and Economic Characteristics of the Black Population.
0082-9528 U.S. Bureau of the Census. Current Population Reports: School Enrollment: October (Year) *changed to* Current Population Reports: Population Characteristics. School Enrollment: Social and Economic Characteristics of Students.
0082-9536 U.S. Bureau of the Census. Technical Notes†
0082-9544 U.S. Bureau of the Census. Technical Papers
0082-9552 U.S. Bureau of the Census. Working Papers
0082-9560 United States Catholic Missionary Personnel Overseas *changed to* Mission Handbook.
0082-9609 U.S. Civil Aeronautics Board. Aircraft Operating Cost and Performance Report†
0082-9625 U.S. Coast Guard. Oceanographic Reports (CG-373 Series)†
0082-9641 U.S. Commission on Civil Rights. Clearinghouse Publications
0082-965X World Refugee Report†
0082-9706 United States Cross-Country and Distance Running Coaches Association. Proceedings *changed to* United States Cross-Country Coaches Association. Annual Business Meeting. Minutes.
0082-9714 U.S. Department of Agriculture. Agricultural Statistics
0082-9722 Hatcheries and Dealers Participating in the National Poultry Improvement Plan
0082-9765 U.S. Department of Agriculture. Farmer Cooperative Service. Information (Series) *changed to* U.S. Department of Agriculture. Agricultural Cooperative Service. Cooperative Information Report Series.
0082-9781 U.S. Department of Agriculture. Marketing Research Report
0082-979X U.S. Department of Agriculture. Production Research Reports
0082-9803 U.S. Department of Agriculture. Report of the Secretary of Agriculture
0082-9811 U.S. Department of Agriculture. Technical Bulletin
0082-9846 U.S. Bureau of Domestic and International Business Administration. Overseas Business Reports
0082-9862 U.S. Department of Defense. Defense Program and Defense Budget
0082-9889 U.S. Department of Health, Education, and Welfare. Catalog of H E W Assistance Providing Financial Support and Service to States, Communities, Organizations, Individuals†
0082-9897 U.S. Department of Health, Education and Welfare. Health, Education and Welfare Trends†
0082-9900 U.S. National Center for Juvenile Justice. Juvenile Court Statistics†
0082-9935 U.S. Department of Health, Education and Welfare. Statistics on Public Institutions for Delinquent Children *see* 0147-9881
0082-9943 U.S. Department of Justice. Annual Report of the Attorney General of the United States
0082-9951 U.S. Department of Justice. Opinions of Attorney General
0083-0003 U.S. Department of State. African Series†
0083-002X U.S. Department of State. Commercial Policy Series
0083-0038 U.S. Department of State. Department and Foreign Service Series†
0083-0054 U.S. Department of State. East Asian and Pacific Series†
0083-0062 U.S. Department of State. Economic Cooperation Series
0083-0070 U.S. Department of State. European and British Commonwealth Series†
0083-0089 Far Eastern Series *see* 0083-0054
0083-0097 U.S. Department of State. General Foreign Policy Series†
0083-0100 U.S. Department of State. Geographic Bulletins†
0083-0119 U.S. Department of State. International Information and Cultural Series†
0083-0127 U.S. Department of State. International Organization and Conference Series†
0083-0135 U.S. Department of State. International Organization Series†
0083-0143 U.S. Department of State. Inter-American Series†
0083-0151 U.S. Department of State. Near and Middle Eastern Series *changed to* U.S. Department of State. Near East and South Asian Series.
0083-016X U.S. Department of State. Office of the Geographer. Geographic Notes
0083-0186 U.S. Department of State. Treaties and Other International Acts Series
0083-0194 U.S. Department of State. Treaties in Force
0083-0208 United States Participation in the United Nations
0083-0321 U.S. Department of the Interior.Annual Report *see* 0069-9152
0083-0364 U. S. Department of the Interior. Safety Conference Guides†
0083-0380 U.S. Department of Transportation. Bibliographic Lists
0083-0399 U.S. Department of Transportation. Annual Report on High Speed Ground Transportaion Act *changed to* U.S. Department of Transportation. Report on the High Speed Ground Transportation Act of 1965.
0083-0429 United States Dispensatory and Physicians Pharmacology *changed to* United States Dispensatory.
0083-0445 U.S. Department of Agriculture. Agricultural Economic Reports
0083-050X Sewage Facilities Construction†
0083-0518 U.S. Environmental Protection Agency. Pesticides Enforcement Division. Notices of Judgement under Federal Insecticide, Fungicide, and Rodenticide Act
0083-0526 U.S. Equal Employment Opportunity Commission. Annual Report
0083-0534 U S Excise Tax Guide
0083-0542 U.S. Farm Credit Administration. Annual Report of the Farm Credit Administration on the Work of the Cooperative Farm Credit System *changed to* Farm Credit Administration. Annual Report.
0083-0607 U.S. Federal Communications Commission. I N F Bulletins
0083-0631 U. S. Federal Council for Science and Technology. Interdepartmental Committee for Atmospheric Sciences. I C A S Reports†
0083-0658 U.S. Federal Deposit Insurance Corporation. Annual Report
0083-0666 U.S. Federal Deposit Insurance Corporation. Bank Operating Statistics
0083-0674 U.S. Federal Deposit Insurance Corporation. Changes Among Operating Banks and Branches
0083-0682 U.S. Federal Fire Council. Federal Fire Experience for Fiscal Year†
0083-0690 U.S. Federal Fire Council. Minutes of Annual Meeting†
0083-0704 U.S. Federal Fire Council. Recommended Practices†
0083-0720 U.S. Federal Home Loan Bank Board. Report

ISSN

0083-0747 U.S. Federal Home Loan Bank Board. Trends in the Savings and Loan Field
0083-0755 U.S. Federal Maritime Commission. Annual Report
0083-0771 U.S. Federal Mediation and Conciliation Service. Annual Report
0083-078X U.S. Federal Power Commission. Annual Report†
0083-0828 Statistics of Electric Utilities in the United States. Classes A and B Privately Owned Companies *changed to* Financial Statistics of Selected Electric Utilities.
0083-0852 Steam Electric Plant Construction Cost and Annual Production Expenses *changed to* Electric Plant Costs & Power Production Expenses.
0083-0887 U.S. Federal Reserve System. Annual Report
0083-0917 U.S. Federal Trade Commission. Annual Report
0083-0925 U.S. Federal Trade Commission. Federal Trade Commission Decisions, Findings, Orders and Stipulations
0083-0933 U.S. Federal Trade Commission. Statutes and Court Decisions Pertaining to the Federal Trade Commission. Supplements *changed to* U.S. Federal Trade Commission. Court Decisions Pertaining to the Federal Trade Commission.
0083-0941 U.S. Fish and Wildlife Service. Research Reports
0083-0968 United States Foamed Plastic Markets and Directory *changed to* U S Foamed Plastics Markets and Directory.
0083-0976 U.S. Foreign Agricultural Service. Food and Agricultural Export Directory
0083-0984 Foreign Agriculture Reports†
0083-0992 U.S. Foreign Agricultural Service. Miscellaneous Reports†
0083-1018 U.S. Forest Service. Forest Products Laboratory, Madison, Wisconsin. Report of Research at the Forest Products Laboratory.†
0083-1166 U.S. Government Films for Public Educational Use†
0083-1174 United States Government Organization Manual *see* 0092-1904
0083-1220 U.S. Immigration and Naturalization Service. Administrative Decisions Under Immigration and Nationality Laws
0083-1239 U.S. Immigration and Naturalization Service. Administrative Decisions Under Immigration and Nationality Laws. Interim Decisions of the Department of Justice
0083-1247 U.S. Immigration and Naturalization Service. Annual Report
0083-1263 United States Import Duties Annotated†
0083-128X United States in World Affairs *see* 0362-3653
0083-1298 United States Independent Telephone Association. Annual Statistical Volume *changed to* United States Telephone Association. Annual Statistical Volume.
0083-1328 U.S. Industrial College of the Armed Forces. Monographs. R Series
0083-1344 U.S. Industrial Outlook *changed to* U.S. Industrial Outlook (Year).
0083-1425 U.S. Institute of Tropical Forestry. Annual Report†
0083-1468 U.S. Forest Service. Annual Report *changed to* U.S. Forest Service. Intermountain Research Station. Recent Reports.
0083-1476 U.S. Internal Revenue Service. Annual Report
0083-1484 U.S. Internal Revenue Service. Tax Guide for Small Business
0083-1506 U.S. Interstate Commerce Commission. Advance Bulletin of Interstate Commerce Acts Annotated†
0083-1514 U.S. Interstate Commerce Commission. Annual Report
0083-1522 U.S. Interstate Commerce Commission. Interstate Commerce Acts Annotated†
0083-1530 U.S. Interstate Commerce Commission. Interstate Commerce Commission Reports. Decisions of the Interstate Commerce Commission of the United States
0083-1557 United States Lawn Tennis Association. Yearbook *changed to* United States Tennis Association. Yearbook.
0083-1565 U.S. Library of Congress. Annual Report of the Librarian of Congress
0083-1573 Dewey Decimal Classification Additions, Notes and Decisions
0083-1603 U.S. Library of Congress. Library of Congress Publications in Print
0083-1611 U.S. Library of Congress. Manuscript Division. Registers of Papers
0083-1646 Newspapers Currently Received and Permanently Retained in the Library of Congress *changed to* U.S. Library of Congress. Newspapers Received Currently.
0083-1670 U.S. Maritime Administration. Annual Report *changed to* M A R A D (Year).
0083-1697 U.S. Maritime Administration. Technical Report Index, Maritime Administration Research and Development†
0083-1700 U S Master Tax Guide
0083-1794 U.S. National Bureau of Standards. Building Science Series *see* 1049-7579
0083-1816 U.S. National Bureau of Standards. Federal Information Processing Standards *changed to* Federal Information Processing Standards Publication.
0083-1824 N B S Handbook *changed to* N I S T Handbook.
0083-1832 U.S. National Bureau of Standards. Monograph *changed to* N I S T Monograph.
0083-1840 U.S. National Bureau of Standards. National Standard Reference Data Series *see* 0097-0395
0083-1883 N B S Special Publication *see* 1048-776X
0083-1913 U.S. National Bureau of Standards. Technical Notes *see* 1054-013X
0083-1921 National Cancer Institute. Monographs *see* 1052-6773
0083-1956 U.S. National Center for Health Statistics. Health Resources Statistics†
0083-1964 U.S. National Center for Health Care Statistics. Vital and Health Statistics. Series 12. Data from the Institutional Population Surveys *changed to* U.S. National Center for Health Statistics. Vital and Health Statistics. Series 13. Data on Health Resources Utilization.
0083-1972 U.S. National Center for Health Statistics. Vital and Health Statistics. Series 10. Data from the Health Interview Survey
0083-1980 U.S. National Center for Health Statistics. Vital and Health Statistics. Series 11. Data from the Health Examination Survey *changed to* U.S. National Center for Health Statistics. Vital and Health Statistics. Series 11. Data from the Health and Nutrition Examination Survey.
0083-1999 U.S. National Center for Health Statistics. Vital and Health Statistics. Series 14. Data on Health Resources: Manpower and Facilities *changed to* U.S. National Center for Health Statistics. Vital and Health Statistics. Series 14. Data on Health Resources.
0083-2006 U.S. National Center for Health Care Statistics. Vital and Health Statistics. Series 13. Data from the Hospital Discharge Survey *changed to* U.S. National Center for Health Statistics. Vital and Health Statistics. Series 13. Data on Health Resources Utilization.
0083-2014 U.S. National Center for Health Statistics. Vital and Health Statistics. Series 1. Programs and Collection Procedures
0083-2022 U.S. National Center for Health Statistics. Vital and Health Statistics. Series 20. Data on Mortality
0083-2030 U.S. National Center for Health Statistics. Vital and Health Statistics. Series 21. Data on Natality, Marriage, and Divorce
0083-2049 U.S. National Center for Health Statistics. Vital and Health Statistics. Series 22. Data on Natality and Mortality Surveys *see* 0083-2022
0083-2049 U.S. National Center for Health Statistics. Vital and Health Statistics. Series 22. Data on Natality and Mortality Surveys *see* 0083-2030
0083-2057 U.S. National Center for Health Statistics. Vital and Health Statistics. Series 2. Data Evaluation and Methods Research
0083-2065 U.S. National Center for Health Statistics. Vital and Health Statistics. Series 3. Analytical Studies
0083-2073 U.S. National Center for Health Statistics. Vital and Health Statistics. Series 4. Documents and Committee Report
0083-209X N C R P Report
0083-2103 U.S. National Endowment for the Arts. Annual Report
0083-2111 National Endowment for the Humanities. Annual Report
0083-2162 U.S. National Institute of Neurological Diseases and Stroke. N I N D S Research Profiles: Summary of Research†
0083-2200 U.S. National Labor Relations Board. Annual Report
0083-2219 U.S. National Labor Relations Board. Court Decisions Relating to the National Labor Relations Act
0083-2243 U.S. National Library of Medicine. Annual Report *see* 0093-0393
0083-2251 National Library of Medicine. Literature Search Series *changed to* National Library of Medicine. Current Bibliographies in Medicine.
0083-2278 U.S. National Mediation Board. (Reports of Emergency Boards)
0083-2286 U.S. National Mediation Board. Annual Report
0083-2294 National Medical Audiovisual Center. Catalog†
0083-2308 U.S. National Park Service. Archaeological Research Series *see* 0270-1308
0083-2316 U.S. National Park Service. Historical Handbook Series
0083-2324 U.S. National Park Service. Source Books Series†
0083-2332 U.S. National Science Foundation. Annual Report *changed to* U.S. National Science Foundation. Fiscal Year Awards.
0083-2359 U.S. National Science Foundation. Federal Funds for Science *changed to* U.S. National Science Foundation. Federal Funds for Research Development.
0083-2375 U.S. National Science Foundation. N S F Factbook†
0083-2383 U.S. National Science Foundation. Research and Development in Industry
0083-2421 Astronomical Phenomena
0083-243X U.S. Naval Observatory. Astronomical Papers Prepared for Use of American Ephemeris and Nautical Almanac†
0083-2448 U.S. Naval Observatory. Publications. Second Series†
0083-2472 U.S. Forest Service. North Central Forest Experiment Station, St. Paul. Annual Report *changed to* U.S. Forest Service. North Central Forest Experiment Station. List of Publications.
0083-2480 U.S. Forest Service. General Technical Report N E
0083-2618 U.S. Office of Education. Accredited Higher Institutions†
0083-2634 U.S. National Center for Education Statistics. Digest of Educational Statistics *changed to* U.S. Department of Education. National Center for Education Statistics. Digest of Education Statistics.
0083-2677 Education Directory. Public Schools Systems *changed to* Directory of Public Elementary and Secondary Education Agencies.
0083-2715 U.S. Office of Education. Guide to Organized Occupational Curriculums in Higher Education†
0083-2723 U.S. Office of Education. International Teacher Development Program. Annual Report to Bureau of Education and Cultural Affairr, Department of State†
0083-2758 Opening Fall Enrollment in Higher Education *see* 0362-5036
0083-2774 U.S. Office of Education. Public School Finance Program†
0083-2790 U.S. Office of Education. Residence and Migration of College Students, Analytic Report†
0083-2855 U.S. Office of Education. Studies in Comparative Education. Education in (Country)†
0083-288X U.S. Office of Education. Title VII: New Educational Media News and Reports†
0083-2898 U. S. Office of Education. Vocational and Technical Education, Annual Report†
0083-2901 U. S. Office of Saline Water. Desalting Plants Inventory Report†
0083-291X U.S. Office of Saline Water. Saline Water Conversion Report†
0083-2987 U.S. Forest Service. Pacific Northwest Forest and Range Experiment Station. Annual Report†
0083-2995 U.S. Forest Service. Pacific Southwest Forest and Range Experiment Station. Annual Report†
0083-3002 U.S. Patent and Trademark Office. Annual Report of the Commissioner of Patents
0083-3010 U.S. Patent and Trademark Office. Classification Bulletins
0083-3029 General Information Concerning Trademarks
0083-3037 U.S. Patent Office. Index of Patents Issued from the United States Patent Office *see* 0362-0719
0083-3045 Index of Trademarks Issued from the United States Patent Office *see* 0099-0809
0083-3088 U.S. Peace Corps. Annual Report
0083-3118 United States Polo Association. Yearbook
0083-3134 U.S. Renewal Assistance Administration. Technical Guides†
0083-3142 U.S. Renewal Assistance Administration. Urban Renewal Project Characteristics†
0083-3150 U.S. Renewal Assistance Administration. Urban Renewal Service Bulletins†
0083-3169 U.S. Rocky Mountain Forest and Range Experiment Station. Annual Report of Research at the Station†
0083-3177 U.S. Rural Electrification Administration. Annual Statistical Report. Rural Electrification Borrowers
0083-3185 U.S. Rural Electrification Administration. Annual Statistical Report. Rural Telephone Program *changed to* U.S. Rural Electrification Administration. Annual Statistical Report. Rural Telephone Borrowers.

5560 ISSN INDEX

0083-3193 U.S. Rural Electrification Administration. Report of the Administrator of the Rural Electrification Administration
0083-3207 U.S. Saint Lawrence Seaway Development Corporation. Annual Report
0083-3215 U.S. Securities and Exchange Commission. Annual Report
0083-3223 U.S. Securities and Exchange Commission. Decisions and Reports
0083-3231 U.S. Securities and Exchange Commission. Judicial Decisions
0083-3258 United States Ski Association. Directory
0083-3274 U.S. Small Business Administration. Annual Report
0083-3282 S B I C Industry Review *see* 0149-2500
0083-3304 U.S. Soil Conservation Service. National Engineering Handbook
0083-3320 U.S. Soil Conservation Service. Soil Survey Investigation Reports
0083-3339 U.S. Soil Conservation Service. Technical Publications
0083-3398 United States Squash Racquets Association. Official Year Book
0083-3401 United States Statutes at Large
0083-3428 U.S. Tariff Commission. Annual Report *changed to* U.S. International Trade Commission. Annual Report.
0083-3436 U.S. International Trade Commission. Imports of Benzenoid Chemicals and Products†
0083-3444 U.S. International Trade Commission. Operation of the Trade Agreements Program
0083-3479 United States Tobacco and Candy Journal Supplier Directory *changed to* United States Distribution Journal Supplier Directory.
0083-3487 United States Treaties and Other International Agreements
0083-3495 Sires and Dams *changed to* U S T A Sires and Dams.
0083-3509 Trotting and Pacing Guide
0083-3517 U S T A Year Book
0083-3533 U.S. Veterans Administration. Annual Report
0083-355X U.S. Veterans Administration. Medical Research Program.
0083-3576 U.S. Veterans Administration. V A Fact Sheets *changed to* Federal Benefits for Veterans and Dependents, IS-1 Fact Sheet.
0083-3592 United States Volleyball Association. Official Volleyball Guide *changed to* United States Volleyball Association. Official Volleyball Rule Book.
0083-3622 Handbook of Women Workers *changed to* Time of Change: Handbook on Women Workers.
0083-3665 United Way of America. Directory *changed to* United Way of America. International Directory.
0083-3673 Univers Historique
0083-369X Universal Business Directories, Brisbane and Suburban Business and Trade Directory *changed to* Universal Business Directories. Brisbane Business to Business Directory.
0083-3703 Universal Business Directories Combined Central and Southern New South Wales Business and Trade Directory†
0083-3746 Universal Business Directories, Melbourne and Suburban Business and Trade Directory *changed to* Universal Business Directories. Melbourne Business to Business Directory.
0083-3754 Universal Business Directories North Territory Business and Trade Directory†
0083-3789 Universal Business Directories, Perth and Fremantle and Suburbs Business and Trade Directory *changed to* Universal Business Directories. Perth Business to Business Directory.
0083-3797 Universal Business Directories, Adelaide and South Australia Country Trade and Business Directory *changed to* Universal Business Directories. Adelaide Business to Business Directory.
0083-3819 Universal Business Directories, Sydney and Suburban Business and Trade Directory *changed to* Universal Business Directories. Sydney Business to Business Directory.
0083-3827 Universal Business Directories, Tasmania Business and Trade Directory *changed to* Universal Business Directories. Tasmania Business to Business Directory.
0083-3835 Universal Business Directories West Victoria Country Business and Trade Directory†
0083-3843 Universal Business Directories, Western Australia Country Business and Trade Directory†
0083-3851 Kongresa Libro
0083-3878 Universal Postal Union. Documents du Congres *changed to* Union Postale Universelle. Actes.
0083-3886 Universalist Historical Society. Journal†
0083-3932 Universities and Colleges of Canada *see* 0706-2338
0083-3940 Universities-National Bureau Conference Series†
0083-3967 U C E A Case Series in Educational Administration†
0083-3975 University Geographer
0083-4025 University of Kansas Law Review
0083-4041 University of Queensland Law Journal
0083-405X University of Singapore Science Journal†
0083-4068 University of West Los Angeles Law Review *see* 0899-7446
0083-4106 Univerzita Komenskeho. Filozoficka Fakulta. Zbornik: Ethnologia Slavica
0083-4114 Univerzita Komenskeho. Filozoficka Fakulta. Zbornik: Graecolatina et Orientalia
0083-4122 Univerzita Komenskeho. Filozoficka Fakulta. Zbornik: Historica
0083-4130 Univerzita Komenskeho. Filozoficka Fakulta. Zbornik: Musaica
0083-4165 Univerzita Komenskeho. Filozoficka Fakulta. Zbornik: Paedagogica
0083-4173 Univerzita Komenskeho. Filozoficka Fakulta. Zbornik: Philologica
0083-4181 Univerzita Komenskeho. Filozoficka Fakulta. Zbornik: Philosophica
0083-419X Univerzita Komenskeho. Filozoficka Fakulta. Zbornik: Psychologica
0083-4211 Univerzita Komeskeho. Oddelenie Liecebnej a Specialnej Pedagogiky. Zbornik. Paedagogica Specialis *changed to* Univerzita Komenskeho. Pedagogicka Fakulta. Katedra Specialnej Pedagogiky. Zbornik. Paedagogica Specialis.
0083-422X Univerzita Komenskeho. Filozoficka Fakulta. Zbornik: Zurnalistika
0083-4238 Uniwersytet im. Adama Mickiewicza w Poznaniu. Wydzial Biologii i Nauk of Ziemi. Prace. Seria Geologia *changed to* Geologia.
0083-4246 Uniwersytet im. Adama Mickiewicza w Poznaniu. Wydzial Filozoficzno-Historyczny. Prace. Seria Filozofia-Logika *changed to* Filozofia-Logika.
0083-4254 Uniwersytet im. Adama Mickiewicza w Poznaniu. Wydzial Historyczny. Prace. Seria Psychologia-Pedagogika *changed to* Psychologia-Pedagogika.
0083-4262 Uniwersytet im. Adama Mickiewicza w Poznaniu. Wydzial Prawa. Prace *changed to* Prawo.
0083-4270 Historia Sztuki
0083-4289 Uniwersytet Jagiellonski. Zeszyty Naukowe. Prace Geograficzne. Prace z Geografii Ekonomicznej†
0083-4300 Uniwersytet Jagiellonski. Zeszyty Naukowe. Prace Archeologiczne
0083-4319 Uniwersytet Jagiellonski. Zeszyty Naukowe. Prace Chemiczne
0083-4327 Uniwersytet Jagiellonski. Zeszyty Naukowe. Prace Etnograficzne
0083-4335 Uniwersytet Jagiellonski. Zeszyty Naukowe. Prace Fizyczne
0083-4343 Uniwersytet Jagiellonski. Zeszyty Naukowe. Prace Geograficzne
0083-4351 Uniwersytet Jagiellonski. Zeszyty Naukowe. Prace Historyczne
0083-436X Uniwersytet Jagiellonski. Zeszyty Naukowe. Prace Historycznoliterackie
0083-4378 Uniwersytet Jagiellonski. Zeszyty Naukowe. Prace Jezykoznawcze
0083-4386 Uniwersytet Jagiellonski. Zeszyty Naukowe. Prace Matematyczne *changed to* Uniwersytet Jagiellonski. Zeszyty Naukowe. Acta Matematica.
0083-4394 Uniwersytet Jagiellonski. Zeszyty Naukowe. Prace Prawnicze
0083-4408 Uniwersytet Jagiellonski. Zeszyty Naukowe. Prace Psychologiczno-Pedagogiczne
0083-4416 Uniwersytet Jagiellonski. Zeszyty Naukowe. Prace Zoologiczne
0083-4424 Uniwersytet Jagiellonski. Zeszyty Naukowe. Prace z Historii Sztuki
0083-4432 Uniwersytet Jagiellonski, Krakow. Zeszyty Naukowe. Prace z Logiki *see* 0137-2904
0083-4467 Uniwersytet Mikolaja Kopernika, Torun. Nauki Humanistyczno-Spoleczne. Archeologia *see* 0137-6616
0083-4475 Uniwersytet Mikolaja Kopernika, Torun. Nauki Humanistyczno-Spoleczne. Filozofia *see* 0208-564X
0083-4483 Uniwersytet Mikolaja Kopernika, Torun. Nauki Humanistyczno-Spoleczne. Filologia Polska *see* 0208-5321
0083-4491 Uniwersytet Mikolaja Kopernika, Torun. Nauki Humanistyczno-Spoleczne. Historia *see* 0137-5830
0083-4513 Uniwersytet Mikolaja Kopernika, Torun. Nauki Humanistyczno-Spoleczne. Prawo *see* 0208-5283
0083-4521 Uniwersytet Mikolaja Kopernika, Torun. Nauki Matematyczno-Przyrodnicze. Biologia *see* 0208-4449
0083-453X Unternehmensforschung fuer die Wirtschaftspraxis†
0083-4548 Unternehmung und Unternehmungsfuehrung
0083-4564 Untersuchungen zur Deutschen Literaturgeschichte
0083-4572 Untersuchungen zur Deutschen Staats- und Rechtsgeschichte. Neue Folge†
0083-4580 Untersuchungen zur Sprach- und Literaturgeschichte der Romanischen Voelker
0083-4610 Upper Midwest Economic Study. Progress Report *changed to* Upper Midwest Council. (Reports).
0083-4637 Upper Midwest Economic Study. Technical Paper *changed to* Upper Midwest Council. (Reports).
0083-4645 Upper Midwest Economic Study. Urban Report *changed to* Upper Midwest Council. (Reports).
0083-4661 Uppsala Universitet. Institutionen foer Nordiska Spraak. Skrifter†
0083-4688 Urban Affairs Annual Reviews
0083-4696 Urban Environment†
0083-470X Urban Land Institute. Research Report†
0083-4718 Urban Land Institute. Technical Bulletin†
0083-4726 Urban Planning - Development Series *changed to* University of Washington. College of Architecture and Urban Planning. Development Series.
0083-4769 Uro-Nephro: Annuaire de l'Urologie et de la Nephrologie†
0083-4785 Universidad de la Republica. Facultad de Odontologia. Anales
0083-4793 Uruk-Warka: Abhandlungen der Deutschen Orient-Gesellschaft *changed to* Deutsche Orient-Gesellschaft. Abhandlung.
0083-4807 Used Book Price Guide *see* 1045-5388
0083-4823 Utah Academy of Sciences, Arts, and Letters. Proceedings *see* 0196-9110
0083-484X Utah Geological Association. Annual Guidebook
0083-4858 Utah State University of Agriculture and Applied Science. Monograph Series†
0083-4947 University of Utah Anthropological Papers
0083-4963 Utrecht Micropaleontological Bulletins
0083-4998 Disputationes Rheno-Trajectinae†
0083-5013 Uttar Pradesh, India. Scientific Research Committee Monograph Series
0083-5021 V W Z
0083-5072 Vade-Mecum
0083-5080 Vademecum Deutscher Lehr- und Forschungsstaetten. Staetten der Forschung
0083-5102 Vaikunth Mehta National Institute of Cooperative Management. Publications
0083-5137 Value Engineering Association. Proceedings†
0083-5145 Van Nostrand Mathematical Studies†
0083-5161 Vancouver Art Gallery. Annual Report
0083-517X Vancouver Board of Trade. Annual Report
0083-5196 Vancouver Neurological Centre. Annual Reports
0083-520X Vancouver Stock Exchange. Annual Report
0083-5218 Vanderbilt Rubber Handbook
0083-5226 Vanderbilt Sociology Conference. Proceedings†
0083-5242 Varia†
0083-5250 VARTA - Fuehrer durch Deutschland, Westlicher Teil und Berlin *changed to* VARTA - Fuehrer.
0083-5277 Vaskohaszati Enciklopedia†
0083-5293 Vatican Observatory Publications
0083-5307 Vegetable Growers Association of Manitoba. Technical and Scientific Papers Presented at the Annual Meeting *changed to* Vegetable Growers Association of Manitoba. Technical and Scientific Papers Presented at Horticultural Industry Days.
0083-5315 Vegetarian Handbook *changed to* Vegetarian Handbook.
0083-5323 Die Vegetation Ungarischer Landschaften†
0083-5331 Vehicle Builders and Repairers Association. Yearbook *changed to* Vehicle Builders & Repairers Association. Industry Yearbook.
0083-534X Veiligheidsjaarboek *changed to* Arbo Jaarboek.
0083-5358 Vejtransporten i Tal og Tekst
0083-5366 Venezuela. Ministerio de Agricultura y Cria. Direccion de Economica y Estadistica Agropecuaria. Anuario Estadistico Agropecuario
0083-5374 Venezuela. Ministerio de Minas e Hidrocarburos. Memoria y Cuenta *changed to* Venezuela. Ministerio de Energia y Minas. Memoria y Cuenta.
0083-5382 Venezuela. Ministerio de Minas e Hidrocarburos. Oficina de Economia Minera. Hierro y Otros Datos Estadisticos *changed to* Venezuela. Ministerio de Energia y Minas. Anuario Estadistico Minero.
0083-5390 Venezuela. Ministerio de Minas e Hidrocarburos. Oficina de Economia Petrolera. Petroleo y Otros Datos Estadisticos *changed to* Venezuela. Ministerio de Energia y Minas. Petroleo y Otros Datos Estadisticos.

ISSN

ISSN INDEX 5561

0083-5412 Universidad Central de Venezuela. Facultad de Derecho. Coleccion Tesis de Doctorado†
0083-5420 Universidad Central de Venezuela. Instituto de Estudios Politicos. Cuadernos†
0083-5439 Universidad Central de Venezuela. Consejo de Desarrollo Cientifico y Humanistico. Bibliografia de Humanidades y Ciencias Sociales y Bibliografia de Ciencia y Tecnologia del Profesorado
0083-5447 Musei Civici Veneziani. Bollettino
0083-5455 Venture Capital†
0083-5471 Verband der Automobilindustrie. Taetigkeitsbericht *changed to* Verband der Automobilindustrie. Jahresbericht.
0083-548X Tatsachen und Zahlen aus der Kraftverkehrswirtschaft
0083-5501 Verband der Versicherungsunternehmungen Oesterreichs. Bericht ueber das Geschaeftsjahr *changed to* Verband der Versicherungsunternehmungen Oesterreichs. Geschaeftsbericht.
0083-5536 Varbergs Museum. Aarsbok
0083-5544 Verdensmarkedet og Danmark†
0083-5560 V D I - Berichte
0083-5579 Verein fuer Geschichte der Stadt Nuernberg. Mitteilungen
0083-5587 Verein fuer Hamburgische Geschichte. Zeitschrift
0083-5609 Verein fuer Luebeckische Geschichte und Altertumskunde. Zeitschrift
0083-5617 Jahrbuch des Vereins fuer Niederdeutsche Sprachforschung
0083-5625 Verein zum Schutze der Alpenpflanzen und Tiere. Jahrbuch *changed to* Verein zum Schutz der Bergwelt. Jahrbuch.
0083-5633 Vereinigte Evangelisch-Lutherische Kirche Deutschlands. Amtsblatt†
0083-5641 Vereinigung Pro Sihltal. Blaetter
0083-565X Vereinigung Freunde der Universitaet Mainz. Jahrbuch†
0083-5676 Verfassung und Verfassungswirklichkeit
0083-5684 Verhandlungen des Deutschen Geographentages
0083-5692 Verified Directory of Manufacturers' Representatives *changed to* MacRae's Verified Directory of Manufacturers' Representatives.
0083-5706 Vermont. Agricultural Experiment Station, Burlington. Research Report
0083-5714 Vermont. Agricultural Experiment Station, Burlington. Station Bulletin Series
0083-5722 Vermont. Agricultural Experiment Station, Burlington. Station Pamphlet Series
0083-5730 Vermont. Commissioner of Banking and Insurance. Annual Reports of the Bank Commissioner *changed to* Vermont. Commissioner of Banking Insurance and Securities. Annual Report of the Bank Commissioner.
0083-5757 Vermont Geological Survey. Bulletin *changed to* Vermont Division of Geology and Mineral Resources. Bulletin.
0083-5765 Vermont Geological Survey. Special Publications *changed to* Vermont Geological Survey. Special Publication.
0083-5781 Vermont Year Book
0083-579X Vermont's Game Annual†
0083-5803 Verpackungs-Magazin†
0083-5811 Verpackungsfolien - Verpackungspapiere†
0083-582X Verse Speaking Anthology†
0083-5846 Verstaendliche Wissenschaft
0083-5862 Veterinaer-Medizinische Nachrichten
0083-5870 Veterinary Annual
0083-5889 Vetus Testamentum. Supplements
0083-5897 Viator
0083-5900 Great Britain. Victoria and Albert Museum. Illustrated Booklets *changed to* Great Britain. Victoria and Albert Museum. Illustrated Books.
0083-5919 Great Britain. Victoria and Albert Museum. Monographs†
0083-5927 Victoria and Albert Museum, South Kensington. Yearbook†
0083-5935 Victoria, Australia. Department of Agriculture. Agricultural Economics Branch. Contract Rates†
0083-5943 Victoria, Australia. Department of Agriculture. Agricultural Economics Branch. Farm Credit (Sources and Terms)†
0083-5951 Victoria, Australia. Department of Agriculture. Pig Industry Branch. Pig Farm Management Study†
0083-596X Victoria, Australia. Department of Agriculture. Poultry Branch. Poultry Farm Management Study†
0083-5978 Victoria, Australia. Forests Commission. Forestry Technical Papers†
0083-5986 National Museum of Victoria. Memoirs *see* 0814-1827
0083-601X Victoria League for Commonwealth Friendship. Annual Report
0083-6036 Victoria University of Wellington. Awards Handbook
0083-6079 Victorian Society. Annual
0083-6087 Victorian Society. Conference Reports†
0083-6095 Vie des Affaires
0083-6109 Vie Musicale en France Sous les Rois Bourbons. Serie 1: Etudes
0083-6125 Informationen zu Aktuellen Fragen der Sozial- und Wirtschaftpolitik
0083-6133 Naturhistorisches Museum in Wien. Annalen
0083-6141 Naturhistorisches Museum in Wien. Flugblatt†
0083-6168 Universitaet Wien. Institut fuer Statistik. Schriftenreihe. Neue Folge†
0083-6176 Vienna. Universitaet. Institut fuer Theaterwissenschaft. Wissenschaftliche Reihe *changed to* Wiener Forschungen zur Theater und Medienwissenschaft.
0083-6184 Assemblees de Dieu de France. Annuaire
0083-6230 Viewpoints in Biology†
0083-6249 Viking Fund Publications in Anthropology†
0083-6265 Vilagtortenet
0083-6273 Villa Guide
0083-6281 Vincentian Studies†
0083-629X Virgil Society. Proceedings
0083-6311 Virginia Baptist Register
0083-632X Virginia. Division of Mineral Resources. Information Circular *changed to* Virginia. Division of Mineral Resources. Publications.
0083-6338 Virginia. Division of Mineral Resources. Mineral Resources Report *changed to* Virginia. Division of Mineral Resources. Publications.
0083-6346 Virginia. Division of Mineral Resources. Report of Investigations *changed to* Virginia. Division of Mineral Resources. Publications.
0083-6354 Virginia Educational Directory
0083-6370 Virginia Highway Conference. Proceedings *changed to* Virginia Highway and Transportation Conference. Proceedings.
0083-6389 Virginia Historical Society. Documents
0083-6397 Virginia Institute of Marine Science, Gloucester Point. Translation Series.†
0083-6427 Virginia Institute of Marine Science, Gloucester Point. Educational Series
0083-6435 Virginia Institute of Marine Science, Gloucester Point. Marine Resources Advisory Series
0083-6443 Virginia Institute of Marine Science, Gloucester Point. Special Scientific Report
0083-6451 Virginia Military Institute, Lexington. Publications, Theses, and Dissertations of the Staff and Faculty†
0083-6508 Virginia Polytechnic Institute and State University. Wood Research and Wood Construction Laboratory. Special Report *changed to* Virginia Polytechnic Institute and State University. Sardo Pallet and Container Research Laboratory. Laboratory Report.
0083-6516 Virginia Port Authority. Foreign Trade Annual Report: The Ports of Virginia†
0083-6524 Virginia. State Library. Publications†
0083-6532 Virginia Port Authority. Board of Commissioners. Annual Report†
0083-6575 Virginia's Supply of Public School Instructional Personnel†
0083-6591 Virology Monographs
0083-6613 Vishveshvaranand Indological Paper Series
0083-6621 Vishveshvaranand Indological Series
0083-6656 Vistas in Astronomy
0083-6672 Visti Iz Sarseliu
0083-6680 Visual Education Yearbook†
0083-6710 Vital Statistics of the United States
0083-6729 Vitamins and Hormones: Advances in Research and Applications
0083-6737 Kungliga Vitterhets Historie och Antikvitets Akademien. Antikvariskt Arkiv
0083-6745 Kungliga Vitterhets Historie och Antikvitets Akademien. Filologiskt Arkiv
0083-6753 Kungliga Vitterhets Historie och Antikvitets Akademien. Historiskt Arkiv
0083-6761 Kungliga Vitterhets Historie och Antikvitets Akademien. Handlingar. Antikvariska Serien
0083-677X Kungliga Vitterhets Historie och Antikvitets Akademien. Handlingar. Filologisk-Filosofiska Serien
0083-6788 Kungliga Vitterhets Historie och Antikvitets Akademien. Handlingar. Historiska Serien
0083-6796 Kungliga Vitterhets Historie och Antikvitets Akademien. Aarsbok
0083-6826 Voix dans le Monde
0083-6842 Agricultural Research Organization, Rehovot. Bulletin *changed to* Agricultural Research Organization. Pamphlet.
0083-6877 Volkstum der Schweiz
0083-6893 Vollschlank†
0083-6907 Voluntary Social Services *changed to* Voluntary Agencies Directory.
0083-6915 Vom Wasser
0083-6923 Vorreformationsgeschichtliche Forschungen
0083-6931 Vortraege aus der Praktischen Chirurgie *see* 0079-4899
0083-694X Vulkaniseur - Jahrbuch *changed to* Service - Jahrbuch.
0083-6982 Waermelehre und Waermewirtschaft in Einzeldarstellungen†
0083-6990 Landbouwhogeschool, Wageningen. Miscellaneous Papers
0083-7016 Tasmanian Almanac†
0083-7024 Walden's A B C Guide and Paper Production Yearbook
0083-7059 Walia
0083-7067 Walker's Old Moore's Almanac
0083-7075 Wall Street Journal Index
0083-7091 Wallace Wurth Memorial Lecture†
0083-7105 Wallraf-Richartz-Jahrbuch; Westdeutsches Jahrbuch fuer Kunstgeschichte *changed to* Wallraf-Richartz-Jahrbuch; Westdeutsches Jahrbuch fuer Kunstgeschichte. Neue Folge.
0083-7113 Wirtschaftswissenschaftliche und Wirtschaftsrechtliche Untersuchungen
0083-7121 Walter Lynwood Fleming Lectures in Southern History
0083-7148 Walter W.S. Cook Alumni Lecture
0083-7156 Journal of the Walters Art Gallery
0083-7172 Wanderlust†
0083-7199 Warburg Institute. Studies
0083-7202 Warburg Institute. Surveys *see* 0266-1772
0083-7210 Ward - Phillips Lectures in English Language and Literature
0083-7229 Ward's Automotive Yearbook
0083-7261 Rocznik Biblioteki Narodowej
0083-7288 Akademia Rolnicza, Warsaw. Zeszyty Naukowe. Ogrodnictwo *changed to* Warsaw Agricultural University. S G G W. Annals. Horticulture.
0083-7296 Akademia Rolnicza, Warsaw. Zeszyty Naukowe. Seria Historyczna†
0083-730X Szkola Glowna Planowania i Statystyki. Zeszyty Naukowe†
0083-7326 Uniwersytet Warszawski. Instytut Geograficzny. Prace i Studia.†
0083-7334 Uniwersytet Warszawski. Katedra Klimatologii. Prace i Studia†
0083-7342 Uniwersytet Warszawski. Rocznik†
0083-7350 Warwick Economic Research Papers†
0083-7369 Warwick Research Industrial and Business Studies *changed to* Warwick Business School Research Papers.
0083-7393 Washington (Year)
0083-7407 Textile Museum Journal
0083-744X Washington (State). Department of Fisheries. Fisheries Research Papers†
0083-7466 Washington (State). Department of Fisheries. Research Bulletin†
0083-7474 Washington (State) Department of Fisheries. Technical Report†
0083-7482 Washington (State) Office of Program Planning and Fiscal Management. Population and Enrollment Section. Population Trends *changed to* Washington (State) Office of Financial Management Forecasting. Population Trends.
0083-7512 Washington State University. College of Engineering. Annual Report *see* 0033-6327
0083-7520 University of Washington. Department of Oceanography. Contribution†
0083-7539 University of Washington. Department of Oceanography. Fishery Report†
0083-7547 University of Washington. Department of Oceanography. Special Report†
0083-7555 Research in Fisheries
0083-7563 Washington State University, Pullman. Library Staff Association. L S A Open Stacks†
0083-7571 University of Washington Publications in Biology†
0083-758X Washington (State) Utilities and Transportation Commission. Transportation Report†
0083-761X Waste Management Research Abstracts
0083-7628 Watchmaker, Jeweller and Silversmith Directory of Trade Names and Punch Marks *changed to* Jewellers' Reference Book.
0083-7636 Water†
0083-7644 Water Engineer's Handbook *changed to* Water Services Year Book.
0083-7652 Water in Biological Systems†
0083-7660 Water Pollution Research†
0083-7679 Water Pollution Research Laboratory, Stevenage, England. Technical Papers†
0083-7717 Water Works Manual *see* 0163-9730
0083-7725 Waterborne Commerce of the United States
0083-7733 Waterloo Historical Society. Report *changed to* Waterloo Historical Society. Annual Volume.
0083-775X Wayne State University. Medical Library. Report *changed to* Wayne State University, Detroit. Medical School Library. Report.
0083-7776 Wealth and Welfare of Andhra Pradesh Series *changed to* Social Sciences Research Series.
0083-7822 Wehrwissenschaftliche Berichte *changed to* Bernard und Graefe Aktuell.

ISSN

5562 ISSN INDEX

0083-7849 Weizmann Institute of Science, Rehovot, Israel. Scientific Activities
0083-789X New Zealand Oceanographic Institute. Collected Reprints†
0083-7903 New Zealand Oceanographic Institute. Memoir
0083-7911 Welsh Bibliographical Society. Journal†
0083-7938 Welsh Soils Discussion Group. Report
0083-7946 Welsh Studies in Education Series†
0083-7954 Weltstaedte der Kunst. Edition Leipzig†
0083-7989 Wenner Gren Center International Symposium Series
0083-7997 Wenner - Gren Foundation for Anthropological Research. Report *changed to* Wenner - Gren Foundation for Anthropological Research. Annual Report.
0083-8012 Werbung in Deutschland *see* 0932-6251
0083-8047 Werken und Wohnen
0083-8055 Werkstattbuecher fuer Betriebsfachleute Konstrukteure und Studenten *see* 0171-5062
0083-811X Wessex Cave Club Occasional Publication *changed to* Wessex Cave Club Journal.
0083-8136 Wessex Geographical Year
0083-8144 West Africa Annual
0083-8160 West African Journal of Archaeology
0083-8187 West African Religion
0083-8217 West Coast Reliability Symposium
0083-8241 West Midland Bird Report
0083-8292 Pakistan. Directorate of Livestock Farms. Report
0083-8306 Pakistan. Directorate of Rural Works Programme. Evaluation Report
0083-8322 Pakistan. Official Language Committee. Urdu Translation of Official Terms and Phraseology
0083-8349 Pakistan. Water and Power Development Authority. Report
0083-8381 West Virginia. Agricultural Experiment Station, Morgantown. Current Report *changed to* West Virginia. Agricultural and Forestry Experiment Station. Current Report.
0083-8403 West Virginia University. Center for Appalachian Studies and Development. Information Series†
0083-8411 West Virginia University. Center for Appalachian Studies and Development. Research Series *changed to* West Virginia University. Center for Extension and Continuing Education. Research Series.
0083-842X West Virginia Coal Mining Institute. Proceedings
0083-8438 West Virginia. Commission on Aging. Annual Progress Report
0083-8446 West Virginia. Commission on Mental Retardation. Annual Report†
0083-8462 West Virginia. Department of Mines. Directory of Mines *changed to* West Virginia. Office of Miner's Health, Safety & Training. Report & Digest Directory.
0083-8470 West Virginia Geological Survey Newsletter *see* 0163-2825
0083-8489 West Virginia Geological Survey. Archaeological Series†
0083-8497 West Virginia Geological Survey. Basic Data Reports *changed to* West Virginia River Basin Basic Data Reports.
0083-8500 West Virginia Geological Survey. Bulletin†
0083-8519 West Virginia Geological Survey. Circulars†
0083-8527 West Virginia Geological Survey. Geological Publications. Volumes†
0083-8535 West Vigînia Geological Survey. Archaeological Investigations *changed to* West Virginia Reports of Archaeological Investigations.
0083-8543 West Virginia Geological Survey. Reports of Investigations *changed to* West Virginia Reports of Geologic Investigations.
0083-856X West Virginia Geological Survey. River Basin Bulletins *changed to* West Virginia River Basin Bulletins.
0083-8578 West Virginia Geological Survey. State Park Bulletins *changed to* West Virginia State Park Geology Bulletins.
0083-8586 West Virginia Government†
0083-8594 West Virginia. Human Rights Commission. Report
0083-8608 West Virginia University. Bureau for Government Research. Publications†
0083-8640 West Virginia University. Engineering Experiment Station. Bulletin†
0083-8659 West Virginia University. Engineering Experiment Station. Report†
0083-8675 Western Australia. Department of Agriculture. Technical Bulletin
0083-8683 Western Australia. Fisheries and Fauna Department. Bulletin *changed to* Western Australia. Fisheries Department. Fisheries Research Bulletin.
0083-8691 Western Australia. Office of Director General of Transport. Annual Report†
0083-8705 University of Western Australia. Institute of Agriculture. Research Report: Agricultural Economics†
0083-8713 University of Western Australia. Library. Report on the Library†
0083-8721 Western Australia Museum, Perth. Report of the Museum Board *changed to* Western Australian Museum, Perth. Annual Report.
0083-873X Western Australian Museum, Perth. Special Publication†
0083-8748 Western Australian Naturalists' Club, Perth. Handbook *changed to* Western Australian Naturalist.
0083-8756 Western Australian Pocket Yearbook *changed to* Western Australia: Facts and Figures.
0083-8764 Western Australian Reports *see* 0158-1996
0083-8772 Western Australian Yearbook
0083-8799 Western Canada Water and Sewage Conference. Papers Presented at Annual Convention *changed to* Western Canada Water and Waste Water Association. Bulletin.
0083-8810 Western Canadian Society for Horticulture. Reports of Proceedings of Annual Meeting
0083-8829 Western Canadian Studies in Modern Languages and Literature†
0083-8853 Assembly of Western European Union. Proceedings
0083-887X Western Frontier Library
0083-8888 Western Frontiersmen Series
0083-8918 Western Highway Institute. Research Committee. Report
0083-8934 Western Lands and Waters Series
0083-8942 Western Market Almanac†
0083-8950 Western Ontario Law Review *see* 0703-900X
0083-8969 Western Pharmacology Society. Proceedings
0083-8977 W P S Professional Handbook Series
0083-8985 Western Reserve Historical Society, Cleveland. Publications *see* 0882-3154
0083-9000 Western Thoroughbred
0083-9019 Westernlore Ghost Town Series
0083-9027 Westfaelische Forschungen
0083-9043 Westfaelische Zeitschrift
0083-906X Westminster Series†
0083-9078 Weyers Flottentaschenbuch
0083-9086 Whales Research Institute, Tokyo, Japan. Scientific Reports *see* 0917-0537
0083-9094 University of Pennsylvania. Wharton School of Finance and Commerce. Industrial Research Unit Studies *changed to* Major Industrial Research Unit Studies.
0083-9108 What Every Veteran Should Know
0083-9116 What Research Says to the Teacher Series
0083-9167 Where America's Large Foundations Make Their Grants†
0083-9175 Where To Buy *changed to* Where to Buy: Chemicals & Chemical Plant (Year).
0083-9213 Where to Golf in Europe *see* 0017-1735
0083-9221 Where to Stay in Scotland *changed to* Scotland: Hotels and Guest Houses.
0083-9221 Where to Stay in Scotland *changed to* Scotland: Bed and Breakfast.
0083-923X Which University *changed to* Which Degree.
0083-9256 Whitaker's Almanack
0083-9272 White Paper on Japan's Forest Industries *changed to* Japan's Timber Consuming Industries.
0083-9299 Wer Baut Maschinen *changed to* Wer Baut Maschinen und Anlagen.
0083-9302 Who Owns Whom. Continental Europe
0083-9310 Who Owns Whom. North America
0083-9329 Who Owns Whom. United Kingdom *see* 0140-4040
0083-9337 Who Represents Whom†
0083-937X Who's Who
0083-9396 Who's Who in America
0083-9477 Who's Who in Communist China
0083-9485 Who's Who in Consulting†
0083-9493 Who's Who in East Africa†
0083-9515 Who's Who in Europe
0083-9523 Who's Who in Finance and Industry
0083-9531 Who's Who in France
0083-9558 Who's Who in Indian Engineering and Industry
0083-9566 Who's Who in Indian Science
0083-9574 Who's Who in Insurance
0083-9590 Who's Who in Israel
0083-9612 Who's Who in Lebanon
0083-9620 Who's Who in Malaysia and Singapore
0083-9639 Who's Who in Movies†
0083-9647 Who's Who in Music and Musicians' International Directory *see* 0307-2894
0083-9655 Who's Who in New Zealand†
0083-9671 Who's Who in Pakistan
0083-9701 Who's Who in Soviet Science and Technology†
0083-971X Who's Who in Soviet Social Sciences, Humanities, Art and Government†
0083-9728 Who's Who in Space†
0083-9736 Who's Who in Switzerland
0083-9752 Who's Who in the Arab World
0083-9760 Who's Who in the East
0083-9779 Who's Who in the Gas Industry *see* 0954-853X
0083-9787 Who's Who in the Midwest
0083-9809 Who's Who in the South and Southwest
0083-9817 Who's Who in the West
0083-9825 Who's Who in the World
0083-9833 Who's Who in the Theatre *see* 0749-064X
0083-9841 Who's Who of American Women
0083-985X Who's Who of British Engineers†
0083-9868 Who's Who of Rhodesia, Mauritius, Central and East Africa *changed to* Who's Who of Southern Africa Including Mauritius, Namibia, Zimbabwe, Botswana, Swaziland and Neighboring Countries.
0083-9876 Who's Who of Southern Africa *changed to* Who's Who of Southern Africa Including Mauritius, Namibia, Zimbabwe, Botswana, Swaziland and Neighboring Countries.
0083-9892 Widener Library Shelflist†
0083-9906 Wiener Arbeiten zur Deutschen Literatur
0083-9914 Wiener Beitraege zur Englischen Philologie
0083-9922 Wiener Beitraege zur Kulturgeschichte und Linguistik
0083-9930 Wiener Beitraege zur Theologie†
0083-9973 W I S T-Informationen
0083-9981 Wiener Jahrbuch fuer Kunstgeschichte
0083-999X Wiener Jahrbuch fuer Philosophie
0084-0009 Wiener Katholische Akademie. Studien†
0084-0017 Wiener Musikhochschule. Publikationen
0084-0025 Wiener Rechtswissenschaftliche Studien
0084-0033 Wiener Romanistische Arbeiten
0084-0041 Wiener Slavistisches Jahrbuch
0084-005X Wiener Studien. Zeitschrift fuer Klassische Philologie und Patristik
0084-0068 Wiener Voelkerkundliche Mitteilungen
0084-0076 Wiener Zeitschrift fuer die Kunde des Morgenlandes
0084-0084 Wiener Zeitschrift fuer die Kunde Suedasiens und Archiv fuer Indische Philosphie
0084-0092 Wiener Zeitschrift fuer Nervenheilkunde und deren Grenzgebiete. Supplement†
0084-0106 Wijsgerige Teksten en Studies
0084-0114 Wilderness Report†
0084-0122 Wildlife Behavior and Ecology
0084-0130 Alaska. Department of Fish and Game. Wildlife Booklet Series *changed to* Alaska. Department of Fish and Game. Wildlife Notebook Series.
0084-0149 Wildlife Circular, Victoria†
0084-0157 Victoria, Australia. Fisheries and Game Department. Wildlife Contributions *changed to* Wildlife Contribution, Victoria.
0084-0165 U.S. Fish and Wildlife Service. Wildlife Leaflets
0084-0173 Wildlife Monographs
0084-0181 Wiley American Republic Series†
0084-019X Wiley Series on Systems Engineering and Analysis†
0084-0203 Wiley Series on the Science and Technology of Materials†
0084-0238 William-Frederick Poets Series†
0084-0246 William K. McInally Lecture
0084-0254 William Morris Society. Journal
0084-0300 Williamsburg Research Studies†
0084-0327 Wilmington Society of the Fine Arts. Report *changed to* Delaware Art Museum. Annual Report.
0084-0335 Wiltshire Archaeological and Natural History Magazine *changed to* Wiltshire Archaeological and Natural History Magazine (1982).
0084-0343 Wine and Spirit Trade Review Directory *changed to* Off Licence News Directory.
0084-0351 Wines and Vines - Annual Directory of the Wine Industry *changed to* Wines and Vines: Directory of the Wine Industry in North America.
0084-036X Child Guidance Clinic of Winnipeg. Annual Report†
0084-0386 Winter Sports in Scotland†
0084-0408 Winterthur Conference Report *see* 0084-0416
0084-0416 Winterthur Portfolio: A Journal of American Material Culture
0084-0424 Wire Industry Yearbook
0084-0432 Wire Review *changed to* Wire Industry Machinery Guide.
0084-0440 Wireless Pioneer *changed to* Sparks (Santa Rosa).
0084-0459 Wireless World Diary†
0084-0467 Wirkung der Literatur†
0084-0483 Wirtschaft im Ostseeraum *see* 0720-4868
0084-0505 Wisconsin Academy of Sciences, Arts and Letters. Transactions†
0084-0513 Wisconsin Business Monographs
0084-0521 Wisconsin Business Papers†
0084-053X Wisconsin China Series
0084-0548 Wisconsin. Commissioner of Securities. Annual Report *changed to* Wisconsin. Commissioner of Securities. Biennial Report.
0084-0564 Wisconsin. Department of Natural Resources. Technical Bulletin

ISSN

0084-0572 Wisconsin. Department of Transportation. Division of Planning and Budget. Highway Mileage Data
0084-0580 Wisconsin. Department of Transportation. Division of Planning. Highway Traffic
0084-0599 Wisconsin Economy Studies
0084-0602 Wisconsin. Governor's Advocacy Committee on Children and Youth Annual Report†
0084-0610 Wisconsin Project Reports†
0084-0629 Wisconsin Research and Development Center for Cognitive Learning. Practical Papers *changed to* Wisconsin Research and Development Center for Individualized Schooling. Practical Papers.
0084-0637 Wisconsin Research and Development Center for Cognitive Learning. Theoretical Papers *changed to* Wisconsin Research and Development Center for Individualized Schooling. Theoretical Papers.
0084-0645 Wisconsin Research and Development Center for Cognitive Learning. Technical Reports *changed to* Wisconsin Research and Development Center for Individualized Schooling. Technical Reports.
0084-067X Wisconsin State Historical Society. Urban History Group. Newsletter†
0084-0734 University of Wisconsin, Madison. Applied Population Laboratory. Population Notes
0084-0742 University of Wisconsin, Madison. Applied Population Laboratory. Population Series
0084-0769 University of Wisconsin, Madison. Institute for Research on Poverty. Reprint Series
0084-0785 Land Tenure Center. Newsletter†
0084-0793 Land Tenure Center. Paper
0084-0807 University of Wisconsin, Madison. Land Tenure Center. Reprint†
0084-0815 Land Tenure Center. Research Paper
0084-0823 University of Wisconsin, Madison. Land Tenure Center. Training and Methods Series†
0084-0831 University of Wisconsin-Milwaukee. Center for Latin America. Discussion Paper Series
0084-084X University of Wisconsin-Milwaukee. Center for Latin America. Essay Series
0084-0858 University of Wisconsin-Milwaukee. Center for Latin America. Special Studies Series *changed to* University of Wisconsin-Milwaukee. Center for Latin America. Bibliographic Series.
0084-0904 Wisdom†
0084-0912 Wissenschaftliche Alpenvereinshefte
0084-0939 Wissenschaftliche Gesellschaft fuer Personenstandswesen und Verwandte Gebiete. Schriftenreihe. Neue Folge
0084-0947 Wissenschaftliche Normung†
0084-0955 Die Wissenschaftliche Redaktion†
0084-0963 Wissenschaftliche Taschenbuecher. Reihe Biologie
0084-0971 Wissenschaftliche Taschenbuecher. Reihe Chemie
0084-098X Wissenschaftliche Taschenbuecher. Reihe Mathematik - Physik
0084-1005 Wissenschaftliche Vereinigung der Augenoptiker. Fachvortraege der Jahrestagungen *changed to* Wissenschaftliche Vereinigung fuer Augenoptik und Optometrie. Fachvortraege des W V A O Jahreskongresses.
0084-1013 Wistar Institute Symposium Monograph†
0084-103X Wolfman Report on the Photographic Industry in the United States
0084-1056 Women's Accessories Directory - New York Metropolitan Area *changed to* Women's Accessories Buyers - New York Metropolitan Area.
0084-1064 Women's Coats and Suits Directory - New York Metropolitan Area *changed to* Metro New York Ready-to-Wear.
0084-1072 Woningbouwstudies *changed to* R.I.W. Publicaties.
0084-1080 Wood & Wood Products Reference Data - Buying Guide *changed to* Wood & Wood Products Reference Buying Guide.
0084-1102 Woodall's Mobile-Modular Living *see* 0731-6526
0084-1110 Woodall's Trailering Parks and Campgrounds *changed to* Woodall's Campground Directory. North American Edition.
0084-1110 Woodall's Trailering Parks and Campgrounds *see* 0162-7414
0084-1110 Woodall's Trailering Parks and Campgrounds *see* 0162-7406
0084-1137 Woodrow Wilson National Fellowship Foundation. Newsletter
0084-1145 Woodrow Wilson National Fellowship Foundation. Annual Report
0084-117X Woodstock Papers: Occasional Essays for Theology†
0084-1188 Woodworker *changed to* Woodworker Projects & Techniques.
0084-1196 Woodworker Annual *see* 0043-776X
0084-120X Woodworking Industry - Directory *changed to* Woodworking Industry - Buyers' Guide.
0084-1218 Wool Review
0084-1226 Woolhope Naturalists' Field Club, Herefordshire. Transactions
0084-1234 Knitovations
0084-1242 Woolner Indological Series
0084-1250 Words: Wai-Te-Ata Studies in Literature†
0084-1285 Work of Aslib: Annual Report *changed to* Aslib Annual Report.
0084-1307 Canada. Labour Canada. Working Conditions in Canadian Industry *changed to* Canada. Labour Canada. Wages and Working Conditions in Canada.
0084-1323 Working Press of the Nation
0084-1358 World Agricultural Situation
0084-1366 World Air Transport Statistics
0084-1374 World Airline Record
0084-1382 World Almanac and Book of Facts
0084-1404 World Association for the Advancement of Veterinary Parasitology. Proceedings of Conference†
0084-1439 World Book Year Book
0084-1455 WorldBusiness Perspectives†
0084-1463 World Cars†
0084-1471 World Cartography
0084-148X World Coal Trade *changed to* International Coal.
0084-1498 World Collectors Annuary
0084-1501 World Commerce Annual
0084-151X World Confederation for Physical Therapy. Proceedings of the Congress
0084-1528 W C O T P Annual Report *changed to* W C O T P Biennial Report.
0084-1544 Trade Unions International of Chemical, Oil and Allied Workers. International Trade Conference. Documents
0084-1552 World Conference on Animal Production. Proceedings
0084-1560 World Conference on Earthquake Engineering. Proceedings†
0084-1609 World Congress of Psychiatry. Proceedings
0084-1625 World Congress of the Deaf. Lectures and Papers *changed to* World Congress of the W F D. Proceedings.
0084-1641 World Congress on Fertility and Sterility. Proceedings
0084-165X World Congress on the Prevention of Occupational Accidents and Diseases. Proceedings
0084-1668 World Council of Churches. Commission on World Mission and Evangelism. Research Pamphlets†
0084-1676 World Council of Churches. General Assembly. Assembly - Reports
0084-1684 World Council of Churches. Minutes and Reports of the Central Committee Meeting
0084-1692 World Council of Churches. World Council Studies†
0084-1714 World Economic Survey
0084-1722 World Energy Conference. Plenary Conferences. Transactions
0084-1730 World Energy Conference. Survey of Energy Resources
0084-1749 World Energy Supplies *see* 0256-6400
0084-1781 World Fellowship of Buddhists. Book Series
0084-179X World Food Problems†
0084-1811 World Forestry Congress. Proceedings†
0084-182X World Grain Trade Statistics†
0084-1854 World Jersey Cattle Bureau. Conference Reports
0084-1862 World Jute Directory
0084-1870 World List of Social Science Periodicals
0084-1889 World List of Universities, Other Institutions of Higher Education and University Organizations
0084-1897 World Medical Association. General Assembly. Proceedings†
0084-1919 World Meteorological Association. Technical Commissions Abridged Final Reports *changed to* World Meteorological Organization. Abridged Final Reports of Sessions of Technical Commissions.
0084-1927 World Meteorological Organization. Congress. Abridged Report with Resolutions
0084-1935 World Meteorological Congress. Proceedings
0084-1943 World Meteorological Organization. Basic Documents, Records and Reports *changed to* World Meteorological Organization. Basic Documents.
0084-1951 World Meteorological Organization. Commission for Maritime Meteorology. Abridged Final Report of the (No.) Session *see* 1011-3207
0084-196X Abridged Reports with Resolutions *see* 1011-3231
0084-1978 Global Atmospheric Research Programme. Publication Series†
0084-1986 Global Atmospheric Research Programme. G A R P Special Reports†
0084-1994 World Meteorological Organization. Annual Reports
0084-2001 World Meteorological Organization. Reports on Marine Science Affairs
0084-201X World Meteorological Organization. Technical Notes
0084-2028 World Money Guide†
0084-2036 World Motor Vehicle Production and Registration†
0084-2044 World Movement of Mothers. Reports of Meetings
0084-2052 World Muslim Conference. Proceedings
0084-2060 World Muslim Gazetteer
0084-2117 World of Learning
0084-2141 World Peace through Law Center. Pamphlet Series†
0084-2206 World Psychiatric Association. Bulletin†
0084-2214 World Record Marine Fishes *see* 0194-3340
0084-2230 World Review of Nutrition and Dietetics
0084-2257 U.S. Department of State. World Strength of the Communist Party Organizations. Annual Report.†
0084-2273 World Tobacco Directory
0084-2281 World Today Series: Africa
0084-229X World Today Series: Far East and Southwest Pacific *changed to* World Today Series: East Asia and the Western Pacific.
0084-2311 World Today Series: Middle East and South Asia
0084-2338 World Today Series: Western Europe
0084-2346 World Touring and Automobile Organization. Documentation for Traffic Engineering and Safety Study Weeks
0084-2370 World Trade Union Congress. Reports†
0084-2400 World Union of Organizations for the Safeguard of Youth *changed to* World Union for the Safeguard of Youth. Conference Proceedings.
0084-2419 World University Service. Annual Report†
0084-2427 World University Service. Programme of Action†
0084-2443 World Veterinary Congress. Proceedings
0084-2451 World Weather Watch Planning Reports
0084-2486 Worldwide Register of Adult Education
0084-2494 World Wildlife Series†
0084-2508 World Yearbook of Education
0084-2516 World Zionist Organization. General Council. Addresses, Debates, Resolutions
0084-2532 World's Poultry Science Association. Report of the Proceedings of International Congress *changed to* World's Poultry Science Association. Proceedings of World's Poultry Congress.
0084-2540 World's Woman's Christian Temperance Union. Convention Report *changed to* World's Woman's Christian Temperance Union. Triennial Report.
0084-2559 Worldview†
0084-2567 Worldwide Directory of National Technical Information Services†
0084-2575 Worldwide Offshore Contractors Directory *changed to* Offshore Contractors and Equipment Worldwide Directory.
0084-2583 Worldwide Petrochemical Directory
0084-2605 Wormley, England (Surrey) National Institute of Oceanography. Collected Reprints *see* 0309-7463
0084-2613 Der Wormsgau
0084-2621 Wormsloe Foundation. Publications
0084-263X Woytinsky Lectures†
0084-2648 Wrightia†
0084-2664 Writers' and Artists' Yearbook
0084-2680 Writers' and Photographers' Marketing Guide; Directory of Australian and New Zealand Literary and Photo Markets
0084-2699 Writers Directory
0084-2702 Writer's Guide
0084-2710 Writer's Handbook
0084-2729 Writer's Market
0084-2737 Writer's Yearbook
0084-2745 Writing (San Francisco)
0084-2753 Writings on British History *see* 0308-4558
0084-277X Akademia Medyczna we Wroclawiu. Prace Naukowe†
0084-2788 Instytut Automatyki Systemow Energetycznych. Prace
0084-2796 Muzeum Etnograficzne, Wroclaw. Zeszyty Etnograficzne
0084-280X Politechnika Wroclawska. Instytut Technologii Elektronowej. Prace Naukowe. Monografie
0084-2818 Politechnika Wroclawska. Instytut Chemii i Technologii Nafty i Wegla. Prace Naukowe. Studia i Materialy
0084-2826 Politechnika Wroclawska. Instytut Energoelektryki. Prace Naukowe. Studia i Materialy
0084-2834 Politechnika Wroclawska. Instytut Geotechniki. Prace Naukowe. Monografie *changed to* Politechnika Wroclawska. Instytut Geotechniki i Hydrotechniki. Prace Naukowe. Monografie.
0084-2842 Politechnika Wroclawska. Instytut Geotechniki. Prace Naukowe. Studia i Materialy

ISSN

0084-2850 Politechnika Wroclawska. Instytut Inzynierii Chemicznej i Urzadzen Cieplnych. Prace Naukowe. Monografie
0084-2869 Politechnika Wroclawska. Instytut Inzynierii Ochrony Srodowska. Prace Naukowe. Monografie
0084-2877 Politechnika Wroclawska. Instytut Inzynierii Ochrony Srodowiska. Prace Naukowe. Studia i Materialy
0084-2885 Politechnika Wroclawska. Instytut Technologii Elektronowej. Prace Naukowe. Studia i Materialy
0084-2893 Politechnika Wroclawska. Instytut Technologii Nieorganicznej i Nawozow Mineralnych. Prace Naukowe. Konferencje
0084-2907 Politechnika Wroclawska. Instytut Technologii Nieorganicznej i Nawozow Mineralnych. Prace Naukowe. Monografie
0084-2915 Politechnika Wroclawska. Instytut Technologii Nierorganicznej i Nawozow Mineralnych. Prace Naukowe. Studia i Materialy
0084-294X Politechnika Wroclawska. Instytut Ukladow Elektromaszynowych. Prace Naukowe. Studia i Materialy
0084-2958 Politechnika Wroclawska. Instytut Metrologii Elektrycznej. Prace Naukowe. Studia i Materialy
0084-2974 Wroclawski Rocznik Ekonomiczny
0084-2982 Wroclawskie Towarzystwo Naukowe. Komisja Historii Sztuki. Rozprawy
0084-2990 Wroclawskie Towarzystwo Naukowe. Komisja Jezykowa. Rozprawy
0084-3008 Litteraria
0084-3016 Wroclawskie Towarzystwo Naukowe. Prace. Seria A. Humanistyka
0084-3024 Wroclawskie Towarzystwo Naukowe. Prace. Seria B. Nauki Scisle
0084-3032 Wspolczesne Malarstwo Wroclawskie†
0084-3040 Wuerttembergischer Pferdeuchtverband. Mitteilungen†
0084-3067 Wuerttembergisch Franken
0084-3083 Wuerzburger Wehrwissenschaftliche Abhandlungen
0084-3091 Technische Akademie Wuppertal. Berichte†
0084-3113 Wykeham Science Series†
0084-3121 Wykeham Technological Series†
0084-3164 Wyoming Nurses Newsletter *changed to* Wyoming Nurse.
0084-3180 University of Wyoming. Natural Resources Research Institute. Information Circular†
0084-3210 University of Wyoming. Water Resources Research Institute. Water Resources Series†
0084-3229 Xavier University. Museum and Archives Publications†
0084-3237 Yachting Belge†
0084-3253 Yachting World Handbook†
0084-3261 Yachtsman's Guide to the Caribbean
0084-327X Yachtsman's Guide to the Great Lakes
0084-3288 Yad Vashem News†
0084-3296 Yad Vashem Studies on the European Jewish Catastrophe and Resistance *changed to* Yad Vashem Studies.
0084-330X Yale Classical Studies
0084-3318 Yale College Series
0084-3326 Yale Fastbacks
0084-3334 Yale Germanic Studies†
0084-3342 Yale Historical Publications (Manuscripts and Edited Texts)†
0084-3350 Yale Historical Publications
0084-3369 Yale Judaica Series
0084-3377 Yale Mathematical Monographs†
0084-3385 Yale Near Eastern Researches
0084-3393 Yale Publications in American Studies†
0084-3407 Yale Publications in Religion†
0084-3415 Yale Publications in the History of Art
0084-3423 Yale Romanic Studies. Second Series†
0084-3431 Yale Russian and East European Studies†
0084-344X Yale Scene; University Series
0084-3458 Yale Series of Younger Poets
0084-3482 Yale Studies in English
0084-3490 Yale Studies in Political Science†
0084-3504 Yale Studies in the History of Music†
0084-3512 Yale Studies in the History of Science and Medicine†
0084-3539 Yale University Art Gallery Bulletin
0084-3555 Yale Western Americana Paperbounds†
0084-3563 Yale Western Americana Series
0084-358X Yearbook and Directory of Osteopathic Physicians *changed to* A O A Yearbook and Directory of Osteopathic Physicians.
0084-3601 Yearbook of Adult Education *see* 0265-1726
0084-3628 U.S. Department of Agriculture. Yearbook of Agriculture
0084-3644 Yearbook of American and Canadian Churches
0084-3652 Year Book of Anesthesia
0084-3679 Year Book of Cancer *see* 1040-1741
0084-3687 Yearbook of Cardiovascular Medicine and Surgery *see* 0145-4145
0084-3695 Yearbook of Comparative and General Literature
0084-3717 Year Book of Dentistry
0084-3733 Year Book of Drug Therapy
0084-3741 Year Book of Endocrinology
0084-375X Yearbook of Fishery Statistics *see* 0259-2509
0084-3768 Yearbook of Forest Products
0084-3784 Yearbook of Higher Education†
0084-3806 Yearbook of International Congress Proceedings
0084-3814 Yearbook of International Organizations
0084-3822 United Nations. Yearbook of International Trade Statistics *see* 1010-447X
0084-3830 Yearbook of Israel Ports Statistics
0084-3857 Year Book of Labour Statistics
0084-3865 Manitoba Agriculture Yearbook
0084-3873 Year Book of Medicine
0084-3881 Yearbook of National Account Statistics *see* 0259-3017
0084-3881 Yearbook of National Account Statistics *see* 0259-3009
0084-3881 Yearbook of National Account Statistics *see* 0259-3025
0084-3903 Year Book of Nuclear Medicine
0084-3911 Year Book of Obstetrics and Gynecology
0084-392X Year Book of Ophthalmology
0084-3938 Year Book of Orthopedics and Traumatic Surgery *see* 0276-1092
0084-3946 Year Book of Pathology and Clinical Pathology
0084-3954 Year Book of Pediatrics
0084-3962 Year Book of Plastic and Reconstructive Surgery *see* 1040-175X
0084-3970 Year Book of Psychiatry and Applied Mental Health
0084-3989 Year Book of Radiology *see* 0098-1672
0084-4020 Yearbook of Technical Education and Training for Industry *see* 0309-5290
0084-4047 Yearbook of the Commonwealth
0084-4055 Year Book of the Ear, Nose and Throat *see* 1041-892X
0084-4071 Year Book of Urology
0084-408X Yearbook of World Affairs†
0084-4098 Yearbook on Human Rights
0084-4101 Yearbook on International Communist Affairs†
0084-411X Yearbook on Jute
0084-4128 Yearbooks in Christian Education†
0084-4144 Year's Work in English Studies
0084-4152 Year's Work in Modern Language Studies
0084-4160 Yeats Centenary Papers *changed to* New Yeats Papers.
0084-4179 Yerkes Regional Primate Research Center. Newsletter†
0084-4195 Yeshiva University. Belfer Graduate School of Science. Monographs†
0084-4209 Yivo Annual of Jewish Social Science *changed to* Yivo Annual.
0084-4217 Yivo Bleter
0084-4225 Finnish Broadcasting Company. Section for Long-Range Planning. Research Reports *changed to* Finnish Broadcasting Company. Planning and Research Department. Research Reports.
0084-4241 York University. Toronto. Institute of Behavioural Research. Bulletin *changed to* York University, Toronto. Institute for Behavioural Research. Newsletter.
0084-4268 York University, Toronto. Molecular Psycho-Biology Laboratory. Report†
0084-4276 Yorkshire Archaeological Journal
0084-4292 Y M C A Yearbook and Official Roster
0084-4314 J.K. Lasser's Your Income Tax
0084-4322 Your United Nations
0084-4349 Yugoslav Export - Import Directory
0084-4357 Yugoslavia. Savazni Zavod za Statistiku. Demografska Statistika
0084-4365 Yugoslavia. Savezni Zavod za Statistiku. Statisticki Bilten
0084-4373 Statistika Spoljne Trgovine S F R Jugoslavije
0084-439X Yuval
0084-4411 Z Dziejow Form Artystycznych w Literaturze Polskiej
0084-442X Z Dziejow Muzyki Polskiej
0084-4438 Z Dziejow Stosunkow Polsko-Radzieckich *see* 0137-6381
0084-4446 Zagadnienia Rodzajow Literackich
0084-4454 Zagadnienia Eksploatacji Maszyn
0084-4462 Zahnaerztliche Fortbildung†
0084-4489 Zambia. Central Statistical Office. Annual Statement of External Trade
0084-4497 Zambia. Office of the Auditor-General. Report of the Auditor-General
0084-4500 Zambia. Central Statistical Office. Employment and Earnings
0084-4519 Zambia. Central Statistical Office. Financial Statistics of Public Corporations
0084-4527 Zambia. Central Statistical Office. Government Sector Accounts (Economic and Functional Analysis) *changed to* Zambia. Central Statistical Office. Financial Statistics of Government Sector (Economic and Functional Analysis).
0084-4535 Zambia. Central Statistical Office. Insurance Statistics†
0084-4543 Zambia. Central Statistical Office. Migration Statistics
0084-4551 Zambia. Central Statistical Office. Statistical Year Book
0084-456X Zambia. Central Statistical Office. Vital Statistics
0084-4586 Zambia. Commission for the Preservation of Natural and Historical Monuments and Relics. Annual Report
0084-4608 Zambia. Department of Community Development. Report *changed to* Zambia. Department of Social Development. Report.
0084-4616 Zambia. Department of Forestry. Report
0084-4632 Zambia. Department of Labour. Report
0084-4659 Zambia. Prisons Department. Report
0084-4667 Zambia. Department of Social Welfare. Report *changed to* Zambia. Department of Social Development. Report.
0084-4675 Zambia. Department of Taxes. Annual Report of the Commissioner of Taxes
0084-4683 Zambia. Department of the Administrator-General and Official Receiver. Report
0084-4705 Zambia. Department of Water Affairs. Report
0084-4713 Fisheries Research Bulletin of Zambia *changed to* Department of Fisheries. Research Division. Annual Report.
0084-473X Zambia. Geological Survey. Annual Reports
0084-4748 Zambia. Geological Survey. Economic Reports
0084-4756 Zambia. Geological Survey. Occasional Papers
0084-4764 Zambia. Geological Survey. Reports
0084-4802 Zambia. Immigration Department. Report
0084-4810 Zambia. Information Services. Annual Report
0084-4853 Ministry of Agriculture. Annual Report *changed to* Zambia. Ministry of Agriculture and Water Development. Annual Report.
0084-487X Zambia. Ministry of Education. Annual Report
0084-4896 Zambia. Ministry of Finance. Annual Report *changed to* Zambia. Ministry of Planning and Finance. Annual Report.
0084-4942 National Archives of Zambia. Annual Report
0084-4950 Zambia. National Council for Scientific Research. Annual Report
0084-4969 Zambia. National Food and Nutrition Commission. Annual Report
0084-4977 Zambia. National Museums Board. Report
0084-4993 Zambia. Natural Resources Board. Annual Report *changed to* Zambia. Natural Resources Department. Annual Report.
0084-5000 Zambia. Pneumoconiosis Medical and Research Bureau and Pneumoconiosis Compensation Board. Annual Reports
0084-5019 Zambia. General Post Office. Annual Report of the Postmaster-General *changed to* Zambia. Posts and Telecommunications Corporation. Annual Report.
0084-5035 Zambia. Public Service Commission. Report
0084-506X Zambia. Sports Directorate. Report *changed to* Zambia. Ministry of Youth and Sport. Report.
0084-5078 Zambia. Survey Department. Report
0084-5086 Zambia. Teaching Service Commission. Annual Report
0084-5108 University of Zambia. Institute for African Studies. Communication†
0084-5116 Zambian Industrial Directory.†
0084-5124 Zambian Papers
0084-5132 Escuela de Gerentes de Cooperativas. Cartillas de Cooperacion
0084-5159 Escuela de Gerentes de Cooperativas. Coleccion Textos
0084-5167 Escuela de Gerentes de Cooperativas. Cuadernos de Practicas
0084-5175 Escuela de Gerentes de Cooperativas. Serie Especial
0084-5183 Zbornik Istorije Knjizevnosti
0084-5191 Zbornik za Istoriju, Jezik i Knjizevnost Srpskog Naroda. Fontes Rerum Slavorum Meridionalium
0084-5205 Zbornik za Istoriju, Jezik i Knjizevnost Srpskog Naroda. Spomenici na Srpskom Jeziku
0084-5213 Zbornik za Istoriju, Jezik i Knjizevnost Srpskog Naroda. Spomenici na Tudjim Jezicima
0084-5221 Ze Skarbca Kultury
0084-523X Zeichenwerk *see* 0932-7959
0084-5280 Zeitschrift fuer Angewandte Baeder- und Klimaheilkunde†
0084-5299 Zeitschrift fuer Assyriologie und Vorderasiatische Archaeologie
0084-5302 Zeitschrift fuer Celtische Philologie
0084-5310 Zeitschrift fuer die Gesamte Strafrechtswissenschaft
0084-5337 Zeitschrift fuer Ernaehrungswissenschaft. Supplementa†
0084-5345 Zeitschrift fuer Klinische Psychologie - Forschung und Praxis

ISSN

ISSN INDEX 5565

0084-5353 Zeitschrift fuer Krebsforschung und Klinische Onkologie *see* 0171-5216
0084-5361 Zeitschrift fuer Meteorologie
0084-5388 Zeitschrift fuer Papyrologie und Epigraphik
0084-5396 Zeitschrift fuer Romanische Philologie. Beihefte
0084-5442 Zenith *changed to* Zenith Science Magazine.
0084-5477 Zeszyty Problemowe Postepow Nauk Rolniczych
0084-5485 Ziegeleitechnisches Jahrbuch
0084-5493 Ziema Kozielska. Studia i Materialy†
0084-5507 Ziemie Zachodnie. Studia i Materialy
0084-5515 Jinbun *changed to* Zinbvn.
0084-5523 Zionism: Studies in the History of the Zionist Movement and of the Jews in Palestine - Ha-Tsiyonut *see* 0334-1771
0084-5531 Zionist Year Book†
0084-554X Zonaridat
0084-5558 Zondervan Pastor's Annual
0084-5566 Zoning Digest *see* 0094-7598
0084-5574 ZooBooks†
0084-5582 Zoologia†
0084-5590 Zoologica Gothoburgensia†
0084-5604 Vestnik Zoologii
0084-5612 Zoological Society of London. Symposia
0084-5620 Zoological Society of London. Transactions *see* 0952-8369
0084-5639 Zoologisch - Botanische Gesellschaft, Vienna. Abhandlungen
0084-5647 Zoologisch - Botanische Gesellschaft, Vienna. Verhandlungen
0084-5655 Zoology of Iceland†
0084-5663 Zoophysiology and Ecology *see* 0720-1842
0084-5671 Shipbuilding Yearbook†
0084-568X Zrodla do Dziejow Bydgoszczy
0084-5698 Zrodla do Dziejow Mysli Pedagogicznej†
0084-5701 Zrodla do Dziejow Nauki i Technikit
0084-5736 Zuckerwirtschaftliches Taschenbuch *changed to* Zuckerwirtschaft.
0084-5744 Eidgenoessische Technische Hochschule Zuerich. Mitteilungen. Aerodynamik
0084-5752 Eidgenoessische Technische Hochschule Zuerich. Mitteilungen. Photoelastizitaet
0084-5779 Eidgenoessische Technische Hochschule Zuerich. Institut fuer Geophysik. Schweizerische Erdbebendienst. Jahresbericht†
0084-5809 Zur Lage der Schweiz
0084-5817 Zweisprachige Reihe†
0084-5825 Zwierzeta Laboratoryjne†
0084-5833 A D C A: American Directory of Collection Agencies and Attorneys†
0084-5841 A M A - Agricultural Mechanization in Asia, Africa and Latin America
0084-585X Aarboeger for Nordisk Oldkyndighed og Historie
0084-5876 Academie d'Architecture, Paris. Annuaire
0084-5884 Accountancy Research Foundation, Melbourne. Accounting and Auditing Research Committee. Research Studies *changed to* Australian Accounting Research Foundation. Research Studies.
0084-5892 Achter het Boek
0084-5906 Acta Botanica Venezuelica
0084-5914 Acta Phytogeographica Suecica
0084-5922 Adelaide City Council Municipal Yearbook *changed to* Adelaide City Council Municipal Reference Book.
0084-5930 Advances in Cyclic Nucleotide Research *changed to* Advances in Second Messenger and Phosphoprotein Research.
0084-5949 Advances in Cytopharmacology†
0084-5957 Advances in Nephrology from the Necker Hospital *changed to* Advances in Nephrology.
0084-5965 Adventure Trip Guide *changed to* Adventure Travel North America.
0084-5981 African and Oriental Holiday *changed to* African, Mediterranean and Oriental Travel.
0084-6015 Agence pour la Securite de la Navigation Aerienne en Afrique et a Madagascar. Direction de l'Exploitation Meteorologique. Publications. Serie 2
0084-6023 Agenda Memento des Cadres et Maitrises de l'Imprimerie, de l'Edition et des Industries Graphiques *changed to* Agenda Memento des Protes.
0084-6031 Agricultural Technologist†
0084-6066 Agricultural Wages in India
0084-6082 Akademie der Wissenschaften in Goettingen. Jahrbuch
0084-6090 Bayerische Akademie der Wissenschaften. Jahrbuch
0084-6104 Akademie der Wissenschaften und der Literatur, Mainz. Jahrbuch
0084-6112 Alabama Linguistic and Philological Series†
0084-6120 Alaska Science Conference. Proceedings *changed to* Arctic Science Conference. Proceedings.
0084-6147 University of Alaska. Institute of Marine Science. Occasional Publication
0084-6163 Alberta. Department of Health and Social Development. Annual Report *changed to* Alberta. Department of Family and Social Services. Annual Report.
0084-618X University of Alberta. Department of Animal Science. Annual Feeders' Day Report
0084-6198 ALGOL Bulletin†
0084-6201 All Sports International
0084-621X University of Allahabad. Education Department. Researches and Studies
0084-6236 Almanaque Salvadoreno
0084-6244 Aloha Aina†
0084-6252 Altern und Entwicklung†
0084-6260 Alternatives Newsmagazine *see* 0199-9346
0084-6287 A A R Studies in Religion
0084-6317 A B F Research Reporter *changed to* American Bar Foundation Research Reporter.
0084-6325 A C I Bibliography
0084-6333 American Council on Industrial Arts Teacher Education. Yearbook *changed to* Council on Technology Teacher Education. Yearbook.
0084-6341 American Educational Research Association. Annual Meeting Paper and Symposia Abstracts†
0084-635X American Frozen Food Institute. Membership Directory *see* 0361-0888
0084-6376 American Institute of Chemists. Membership Directory *changed to* American Institute of Chemists. Professional Directory.
0084-6384 A I G A Children's Books Show†
0084-6406 A L A Handbook of Organization
0084-6414 National Formulary *see* 0195-7996
0084-6422 American Philosophical Quarterly. Monograph Series†
0084-6430 American Philosophical Society. Library Publications†
0084-6449 American Society of Hospital Pharmacists. Membership Directory†
0084-6465 Andersenana
0084-6473 Annee Balzacienne
0084-6481 Annuaire de la Photographie Professionnelle
0084-6511 Annuaire des Institutions d'Enseignement Secondaire *see* 0066-8990
0084-652X Annuaire National des Industries de la Conserve *changed to* Annuaire des Industries de la Conserve.
0084-6538 Annuaire National du Lait *changed to* Annuaire des Industries Laitieres.
0084-6546 Annual Fertilizer Review *see* 0251-1525
0084-6554 Annual Report on Dental Auxillary Education *changed to* Annual Report on Allied Dental Health Education.
0084-6570 Annual Review of Anthropology
0084-6589 Annual Review of Biophysics and Bioengineering *see* 1056-8700
0084-6597 Annual Review of Earth and Planetary Sciences
0084-6600 Annual Review of Materials Science
0084-6619 Annuario Amministrativo Italiano
0084-6627 Annuario Generale Italiano
0084-6635 Annuario Italiano delle Imprese Assicuratrici
0084-6651 Apartment Building Income - Expense Analysis *see* 0194-1941
0084-666X Apocalypse†
0084-6678 Apparel Plant Wages and Personnel Policies *see* 0275-8873
0084-6678 Apparel Plant Wages and Personnel Policies *changed to* Personnel Policies and Benefits for the Apparel Industry.
0084-6708 Architects, Builders, and Contractors Blue-Book†
0084-6716 Buildings of the Year
0084-6724 Archiv fuer Religionspsychologie
0084-6732 Armidale and District Historical Society. Journal and Proceedings
0084-6740 University of New England. Bulletin *see* 0156-1006
0084-6759 University of New England. Faculty of Agricultural Economics. Farm Case Study†
0084-6767 University of New England. Faculty of Agricultural Economics. Farm Management Report *see* 0156-0913
0084-6775 Arquivos Brasileiros de Nutricao
0084-6783 Art at Auction: the Year at Sotheby's and Parke-Bernet
0084-6805 Asia in the Modern World Series†
0084-6813 Asian Institute Translations†
0084-6821 Asian Population Programme News *see* 0252-3639
0084-683X A T A V E Boletin Informativo
0084-6848 Asociacion Venezolano Britanica de Comercio e Industria. Anuario *changed to* Camara Venezolano Britanica de Comercio e Industria. Anuario.
0084-6864 Association for Supervision and Curriculum Development. Curriculum Materials *changed to* Association for Supervision and Curriculum Development. Curriculum Materials Digest.
0084-6899 Association of Consulting Engineers of Canada. Specialization Typical Projects *changed to* Association of Consulting Engineers of Canada. Directory of Member Firms and Their Services.
0084-6902 Center for Chinese Research Materials. Bibliographical Series
0084-6929 Revista del Ateneo Paraguayo†
0084-6953 Australasian Bandsman
0084-6961 Australasian Commercial Teachers' Association. Journal
0084-697X A.I.J. Manual of Australasian Life Assurance†
0084-6988 Australasian Methodist Historical Society. Journal and Proceedings *changed to* Church Heritage.
0084-7011 Australia. Bureau of Agricultural Economics. Beef Situation *see* 0311-0885
0084-702X Australia. Bureau of Agricultural Economics. Coarse Grains and Oilseeds Situation *see* 0311-0788
0084-702X Australia. Bureau of Agricultural Economics. Coarse Grains and Oilseeds Situation *see* 0311-8789
0084-7038 Australia. Bureau of Agricultural Economics. Dairy Situation *see* 0311-8843
0084-7046 Australia. Bureau of Agricultural Economics. Egg Situation *changed to* Australia. Bureau of Agricultural Economics. Eggs: Situation and Outlook.
0084-7054 Australia. Bureau of Agricultural Economics. Mutton and Lamb Situation *see* 0311-0885
0084-7089 Australia. Bureau of Mineral Resources, Geology and Geophysics. Bulletin
0084-7097 Australia. Bureau of Mineral Resources, Geology and Geophysics. Petroleum Search Subsidy Acts. Publications†
0084-7100 Australia. Bureau of Mineral Resources, Geology and Geophysics. Reports
0084-7135 Australia. Department of Foreign Affairs. International Treaties and Conventions *changed to* Australia. Department of Foreign Affairs and Trade. Select Documents on International Affairs.
0084-7208 Australian and New Zealand Hospitals and Health Services Yearbook *see* 0312-5599
0084-7216 A.A.T.E. Guide to English Books *changed to* A.A.T.E. Guide to English Books and Resources.
0084-7224 Australian Association of Neurologists Proceedings *see* 0158-1597
0084-7232 Australian Aviation Yearbook†
0084-7259 Australian Catholic Historical Society. Journal
0084-7267 Australian Coin Catalogue†
0084-7275 Australian Communist
0084-7283 A C F Newsletter *changed to* Conservation News.
0084-7291 Australian Cricket Yearbook *changed to* Australian Cricket Tour Guide.
0084-7305 Australian Directory of Exports *see* 1032-2116
0084-7356 Australian Fisheries Paper†
0084-7364 Australian Gliding Yearbook
0084-7402 Australian Horse Racing Annual
0084-7410 Australian Hospital Newsletter *see* 0817-5675
0084-7429 Australian House and Garden Annual†
0084-7453 Australian Insurance Institute Journal *see* 0314-8580
0084-747X Australian Journal of Biblical Archaeology†
0084-7488 Australian Mineral Industry. Annual Review†
0084-7496 Australian National University, Canberra. Department of Engineering Physics. Publication Ep-Rr
0084-750X Australian National University, Canberra. Geology Department. Publication *changed to* Australian National University, Canberra. Geology Department. Annual Report.
0084-7518 Australian National University, Canberra. Research School of Physical Sciences. Research Paper
0084-7526 Australian Packaging and Materials Handling Yearbook and Buyers Guide *changed to* Australian Packaging Buyers Guide.
0084-7534 A.P.E.A. Journal
0084-7550 Australian Poetry†
0084-7585 Australian Science Fiction Association. Journal *see* 0156-6342
0084-7593 Australian Ski Yearbook
0084-7607 Australian Society for Limnology. Bulletin†
0084-7623 Australian Welder *changed to* Australian and New Zealand Welder.
0084-7631 Australian Welding Research Association. Bulletin *changed to* Welding Technology Institute of Australia. Bulletin.
0084-764X Australian Wool Corporation. Statistical Analysis *see* 0311-9882
0084-7658 Australian Yearbook of International Law†
0084-7674 Automobile Year
0084-7682 Bach-Jahrbuch

ISSN

ISSN INDEX

ISSN	Title
0084-7690	Forststatistisches Jahrbuch *changed to* Jahresbericht der Landesforstverwaltung.
0084-7704	Band Music Guide
0084-7712	Battelle Memorial Institute. Published Papers and Articles
0084-7720	Baurat
0084-7739	Baustatistisches Jahrbuch
0084-7747	Bean Improvement Cooperative. Annual Report
0084-7763	Beecham Society Bulletin *changed to* Le Petit Baton.
0084-7771	Belgica Selecta; Nouveau Livres Belges†
0084-778X	University of Bergen. Department of Applied Mathematics. Report
0084-7798	Musikwissenschaftliche Arbeiten in der DDR. Bericht†
0084-7801	Beyond the Age Barrier: Newsletter for Adult Students at Iowa State University *changed to* Adult Students.
0084-781X	Indian Agriculture in Brief
0084-7828	Bibliografia Internationala Cinema†
0084-7836	Bibliographia Internationalis Spiritualitatis
0084-7844	Bibliographia Musicologica
0084-7852	Bibliographical Society of Australia and New Zealand. Bulletin
0084-7860	Bibliographie de la Cote d'Ivoire
0084-7879	Bibliography of Electrical Recordings in the CNS and Related Literature†
0084-7887	Bibliography on the Hypothalamic-Pituitary-Gonadal System†
0084-7909	Black Position†
0084-7925	Blantyre Water Board. Annual Report and Statement of Accounts
0084-7941	Federacion Nacional de Cafeteros de Colombia. Boletin de Informacion Estadistica Sobre Cafe
0084-7968	Bolsa de Cereales. Revista Institucional. Numero Estadistico
0084-7976	Bornholmske Samlinger
0084-7984	Borough of Twickenham Local History Society. Papers
0084-7992	Bowdoin College. Museum of Art. Occasional Papers
0084-800X	Bradea
0084-8018	B B C Music Guides†
0084-8034	British Columbia. Library Development Commission. Public Libraries, Statistics *changed to* British Columbia Public Libraries, Statistics.
0084-8050	University of British Columbia Library. Serial Holdings†
0084-8069	University of British Columbia. Research Forest Annual Report†
0084-8085	Checklist of British Official Serial Publications
0084-8093	Broadcasting and Television Year Book *see* 0810-669X
0084-8107	Bromeliads
0084-8115	Bruce County Historical Society. Year Book
0084-8123	Brunei Annual Report†
0084-8131	Brunei Museum. Special Publication
0084-814X	Building and Engineering Review†
0084-8174	Statistics on World Trade in Engineering Products. Bulletin
0084-8182	Bulletin of Zoo Management
0084-8204	Buyer's Guide to Microfilm Equipment, Products, and Services *see* 0362-0131
0084-8212	By og Bygd
0084-8239	Cahiers Paul-Louis Courier
0084-8263	California. Department of Water Resources. Bulletin
0084-8271	California Government & Politics Annual
0084-828X	California Savings and Loan Data Book†
0084-8298	University of California, Davis. Institute of Governmental Affairs. Environmental Quality Series†
0084-8328	Cambrian Law Review
0084-8336	Cambridge Studies in Early Modern History
0084-8352	Camena†
0084-8379	Canada. Department of Agriculture. Library. Current Periodicals. Periodiques en Cours†
0084-8387	Canada. Earth Physics Branch. Seismological Series *see* 0068-7650
0084-8425	Canadian Catholic Conference. National Bulletin on Liturgy *changed to* Canadian Conference of Catholic Bishops. National Bulletin on Liturgy.
0084-8565	Canadian Ladies' Golf Association. Year Book
0084-8573	Canadian Law List
0084-859X	Caracterologie†
0084-8603	Cardiologisches Bulletin *see* 0179-7166
0084-862X	Catalog of Dealers' Prices for Marine Shells
0084-8638	Catholic International Education Office. Bulletin Trimestriel *see* 0770-1683
0084-8646	Universidade Federal do Ceara. Escola de Agronomia. Departamento de Fitotecnia. Relatoria Tecnico
0084-8654	Center for Consumer Education Services. Monographs†
0084-8662	Central Valley Project (California) Annual Report *see* 0148-3811
0084-8689	Circular C I A T
0084-8697	Centro de Investigaciones Agricolas de Tamaulipas. Informe Anual de Labores
0084-8700	Channel Islands Annual Anthology *changed to* Channel Islands Anthology.
0084-8719	Chapel Hill Conference on Combinatorial Mathematics and Its Applications. Proceedings†
0084-8727	Charles C. Moskowitz Lectures *changed to* Joseph I. Lubin Memorial Lectures.
0084-8735	Chiasma *see* 0819-2995
0084-8743	Chilton's Import Car Repair Manual *changed to* Chilton's Import Car Repair Manual.
0084-8751	Chitty's Ontario Annual Practice *changed to* Ontario Annual Practice.
0084-8786	Ciba Collection of Medical Illustrations
0084-8794	Ciencia
0084-8808	Coburger Landesstiftung. Jahrbuch
0084-8816	Cold-Drill
0084-8824	Cold Spring Harbor Laboratory. Abstracts of Papers Presented at Meetings
0084-8859	C.T.T.S. Annual
0084-8875	Colorado. Division of Wildlife. Special Report
0084-8883	Colorado. Division of Wildlife. Technical Publication
0084-8891	Colorado Ski and Winter Recreation Statistics
0084-8905	Colorado State University Libraries. Publication
0084-893X	Anuario - C B A - Yearbook
0084-8948	Comitato Glaciologico Italiano. Bollettino†
0084-8956	Commentary
0084-8964	Committee for Economic Development. Supplementary Paper†
0084-8972	Council of Ontario Universities Biennial Review *changed to* Council of Ontario Universities Quadrennial Review.
0084-8999	Commonwealth Scientific and Industrial Research Organization. Minerals Research Laboratories. Investigation Report *see* 0726-1780
0084-9014	Commonwealth Scientific and Industrial Research Organization. Division of Animal Physiology. Technical Report *changed to* Commonwealth Scientific and Industrial Research Organization. Division of Animal Production. Technical Report.
0084-9073	Commonwealth Scientific and Industrial Research Organization. Division of Wildlife Research. Technical Memorandum *changed to* Commonwealth Scientific and Industrial Research Organization. Division of Wildlife and Ecology. Technical Memorandum.
0084-909X	Company of Master Mariners of Australia. Journal
0084-9103	Texas Tech University. Interdepartmental Committee on Comparative Literature. Proceedings of the Comparative Literature Symposium *see* 0899-2193
0084-9138	Conference for College and University Leaders in Continuing Education. Proceedings†
0084-9146	Conference on Artifical Insemination of Beef Cattle. Proceedings *changed to* Conference on Artificial Insemination and Embryo Transfer of Beef Cattle. Proceedings.
0084-9154	Conference on Bank Structure and Competition. Proceedings
0084-9162	Conference on Electrical Insulation and Dielectric Phenomena. Annual Report
0084-9189	Conimbriga
0084-9197	Conseil Superieur du Livre. Annuaire *changed to* Societe de Developpement du Livre et du Periodique. Annuaire.
0084-9219	Contributions in American History
0084-9227	Contributions in American Studies
0084-9235	Contributions in Economics and Economic History
0084-9243	Contributions in Librarianship and Information Science
0084-9251	Contributions in Military History *see* 0883-6884
0084-926X	Contributions in Philosophy
0084-9278	Contributions in Sociology
0084-9294	Convenience Store Industry Report *changed to* Convenience Store News Industry Report.
0084-9308	Denmark. Nationalmuseet. Arbejdsmark
0084-9324	Cosmetics Handbook†
0084-9332	COSPAR Technique Manual†
0084-9340	C O S P A R Transactions†
0084-9359	Costs and Curves†
0084-9405	Cover
0084-9413	Cowles Foundation for Research in Economics at Yale University. Monographs *changed to* Cowles Foundation Monographs.
0084-943X	Criminal Justice Review†
0084-9456	Bikoret Veparshanut
0084-9499	Current Biography Yearbook
0084-9502	Curtain, Drapery and Bedspread National Buyers Guide *changed to* Linens, Domestics & Bath - Interior Textile Annual Directory.
0084-9510	Cyprus. Development Estimates
0084-9529	Dacotah Territory†
0084-9537	Dada - Surrealism
0084-9553	Danforth News and Notes†
0084-957X	Biblioteksaarbog
0084-9588	Dansk Medicinhistorisk Aarbog
0084-9596	Dansk Periodicafortegnelse. Supplement†
0084-960X	University of Dar es Salaam. Bureau of Resource Assessment and Land Use Planning. Annual Report
0084-9626	University of Dar es Salaam. Bureau of Resource Assessment and Land Use Planning. Research Paper
0084-9634	University of Dar es Salaam. Bureau of Resource Assessment and Land Use Planning. Research Report
0084-9642	Delaware. Department of Natural Resources and Environmental Control. Annual Report
0084-9650	Delaware Museum of Natural History. Monograph Series
0084-9669	Delaware Museum of Natural History. Reproduction Series
0084-9677	Delaware Museum of Natural History. Special Publications†
0084-9685	Delaware. State Treasurer. Annual Report
0084-9693	Denmark Exports†
0084-9715	Denmark. Rigsbibliotekarembedet. Accessionskatalog *changed to* Denmark. Statens Bibliotekstjeneste. ALBA - Accessionskatalogen.
0084-9731	Descent
0084-974X	Designers in Britain†
0084-9758	Deutsche Gesellschaft fuer Hygiene und Mikrobiologie. Berichte ueber Tagungen†
0084-9766	Deutsche Messen und Ausstellungen - Ein Zahlenspiegel *see* 0933-6206
0084-9774	Gezeitentafeln
0084-9782	Institut der Deutschen Wirtschaft. Gewerkschaftsreport
0084-9790	Deutschlandfunk. Jahrbuch *changed to* Deutschlandfunk. Geschaeftsbericht.
0084-9804	Dialectic
0084-9812	Dickens Studies Annual *changed to* Dickens Studies Annual: Essays on Victorian Fiction.
0084-9820	Dimensions of Radio†
0084-9839	Dimensions of Television†
0084-9855	Bankers Schools Directory (Year)†
0084-9863	Directory of Canadian Community Funds and Councils *changed to* United Way of Canada. Directory of Members.
0084-988X	Directory of College Stores
0084-9898	Directory of Colorado Manufacturers
0084-9901	Directory of Data Processing Service Organizations *changed to* I T A A Membership Directory.
0084-991X	Directory of Educational Institutions in New Mexico
0084-9936	Directory of Fulbright Alumni
0084-9944	Directory of Governments in Metropolitan Toronto†
0084-9952	Directory of Incorporated (Registered) Companies in Nigeria†
0084-9960	Directory of Iranian Periodicals *see* 0378-7443
0084-9979	Directory of Little Magazines, Small Presses and Underground Newspapers *see* 0092-3974
0084-9987	Directory of National Organizations Concerned with Land Pollution Control
0084-9995	Directory of Pakistan Commerce and Industry†
0085-0004	Directory of Registered Dentists and Registered Dental Hygienists in Connecticut†
0085-0012	Directory of Social and Health Agencies of New York City
0085-0020	Directory of the College Student Press in America *see* 1046-4255
0085-0039	Directory of the Public Aquaria of the World†
0085-0071	Drexel Research Conference. Summary Report *changed to* Drexel Faculty Publication.
0085-008X	Drexel University Research Review†
0085-0128	Earth's Wild Places†
0085-0144	Economic Aspects of Public Education in Pennsylvania†
0085-0160	Economic Survey of Indian Agriculture *changed to* India. Ministry of Agriculture. Bulletin on Commercial Crops Statistics.
0085-0187	Edubba
0085-0225	Elizabethan Club Series
0085-025X	English around the World†
0085-0268	Enterprise (Kensington)
0085-0276	Enzyklopaedie der Rechts- und Staatswissenschaft. New Series. Staatswissenschaft†
0085-0284	Universidade Federal do Espirito Santo. Comissao de Planejamento. Documentario Estatistico sobre a Situacao Educacional†
0085-0292	Universidade Federal do Espirito Santo. Comissao de Planejamento. Documentario Estatistico sobre a Situacao Educacional. Supplemento†

ISSN INDEX 5567

0085-0306 Universidade Federal do Espirito Santo. Comissao de Planejamento. Vestibulandos†
0085-0314 Estimates of Area and Production of Principal Crops in India. Summary Tables *changed to* Area and Production of Principal Crops in India. Summary Tables.
0085-0322 Etudes Haguenoviennes†
0085-0330 Eurail Guide
0085-0349 Europa Handbuch der Werbegesellschaften
0085-0365 Excerpta Historica Nordica *see* 0346-8755
0085-0373 Explore Canada *changed to* Guide to Canada.
0085-039X Expression
0085-042X Universidade Federal do Rio Grande do Sul. Faculdade de Medicina. Anais†
0085-0438 Farm and Ranch Vacation Guide *see* 0195-8437
0085-0462 Federal Law Reports
0085-0489 Federation des Industries Chimiques de Belgique. Rapport Annuel
0085-0497 Federation Nationale des Chambres de Commerce, d'Industrie et d'Agriculture de la Republique du Zaire. Circulaire d'Information *changed to* Association Nationale des Entreprises du Zaire. Circulaire d'Information.
0085-0500 Felix Ravenna; Rivista di Antichita Ravennati, Cristiane e Bizantine
0085-0519 Fer-Blanc en France et dans le Monde
0085-0527 Ferdinand Roten Galleries. Catalog of Original Graphic Art
0085-0535 Film and TV Festival Directory†
0085-0543 Financial Aids to Illinois Students
0085-0551 Financial Stock Guide Service. Directory of Obsolete Securities *changed to* Directory of Obsolete Securities.
0085-0586 Flinders Asian Studies Lecture
0085-0608 Florida. Bureau of Geology. Geological Bulletins
0085-0616 Florida. Bureau of Geology. Information Circulars
0085-0624 Florida. Bureau of Geology. Map Series
0085-0640 Florida. Bureau of Geology. Special Publications
0085-0659 Florida. Bureau of Historic Sites and Properties. Bulletin†
0085-0683 Memoirs of the Hourglass Cruises
0085-0748 Acta Musei Moraviae. Supplementum: Folia Mendeliana
0085-0756 Folk; Dansk Etnografisk Tidsskrift
0085-0764 Folklivsstudier
0085-0802 Foreign Investment Opportunities in the Philippines *changed to* Investment Opportunities in the Philippines.
0085-0829 Foreign Medical School Catalogue†
0085-0845 Fra Als og Sundeved
0085-0853 Fra Viborg Amt. Aarbog
0085-0861 Frantsia
0085-0888 French 20 Bibliography
0085-0896 Frodskaparrit; Annales Societatis Scientiarum Faeroensis
0085-090X Fruit World Annual and Orchardists Guide†
0085-0918 Fynske Aarboeger
0085-0934 Genealogisches Handbuch des Bayerischen Adels
0085-0942 Observatoire de Geneve. Publications. Serie A
0085-0950 Universita degli Studi di Genova. Bollettino dei Musei e degli Istituti Biologici
0085-0969 Geographical Education
0085-0977 Geography Teachers Association of Queensland. Journal *see* 0314-3457
0085-0985 Geological Survey of Ireland. Bulletin
0085-0993 Geological Survey of Ireland. Information Circulars
0085-1000 Geological Survey of Ireland. Memoirs†
0085-1019 Geological Survey of Ireland. Special Papers
0085-1027 Geology, Exploration, and Mining in British Columbia *see* 0823-2059
0085-1027 Geology, Exploration and Mining in British Columbia *see* 0823-1257
0085-1027 Geology, Exploration and Mining *changed to* Engineering and Inspection Annual Report.
0085-1043 Georgia Statistical Abstract
0085-106X Gesellschaft zur Foerderung Tiefenpsychologischer und Psychotherapeutischer Forschung und Weiterbildung, Munich. Beitraege und Berichte†
0085-1078 Rijksuniversiteit te Gent. Laboratorium voor Experimentele, Differentiele en Genetische Psychologie. Mededelingen en Werkdocumenten†
0085-1108 Goettinger Universitaetsreden
0085-1124 Good Health†
0085-1132 Graduate Careers Directory *see* 0311-4201
0085-1140 Grain†
0085-1167 Great Britain. Commission of Inquiry on Small Firms. Research Report†
0085-1191 Great Britain. Ministry of Housing and Local Government. Design Bulletin *changed to* Great Britain. Department of the Environment. Housing and Construction. Design Bulletin.
0085-1205 University of Northern Colorado. Museum of Anthropology. Occasional Publications in Anthropology. Ethnology Series
0085-1213 University of Northern Colorado. Museum of Anthropology. Occasional Publications in Anthropology. Miscellaneous Series
0085-1221 University of Northern Colorado. Museum of Anthropology. Occasional Publications in Anthropology. Archaeology Series
0085-123X University of Northern Colorado. Museum of Anthropology. Occasional Publications in Anthropology. Linguistics Series
0085-1264 Universite de Grenoble. Institut de Phonetique. Manuels. Serie A *changed to* Universite de Grenoble III. Institut de Phonetique. Travaux. Serie A: Manuels.
0085-1272 Universite de Grenoble III. Institut de Phonetique. Travaux. Serie B: Etudes Linguistiques
0085-1280 Growth
0085-1299 Grundbegriffe der Modernen Biologie†
0085-1302 Gruppenpsychotherapie und Gruppendynamik. Beihefte
0085-1310 Guam Statistical Annual Report
0085-1329 University of Guelph. Department of Land Resource Science. Progress Report
0085-1337 Guia de los Caballos Verificados en Espana
0085-1361 Hafnia: Copenhagen Papers in the History of Art
0085-140X Handbuch der Physik†
0085-1418 Handels- og Soefartsmuseet paa Kronborg. Aarbog
0085-1442 Harris Survey Yearbook of Public Opinion†
0085-1450 Health Physics Research Abstracts
0085-1469 Hefte zur Unfallheilkunde
0085-1477 Herald Caravanning Guide
0085-1485 Herald Motel Guide
0085-1493 Here and Now
0085-1523 Higher Education Monograph Series†
0085-1531 California Senior Citizen News *changed to* California Senior Citizen.
0085-154X History Teacher
0085-1558 History Teachers Association of New South Wales. Newsletter
0085-1566 Hockey Association. Official Handbook
0085-1574 Home Appliance Blue Book *changed to* Home Appliance Trade-in Blue Book.
0085-1647 How to Avoid Financial Tangles: Section C. The Harvest Years Financial Plan†
0085-1663 Hunter Valley Research Foundation. Monographs
0085-1671 Hypomnemata
0085-1698 Icographic†
0085-1728 Illinois Labor History Society Reporter
0085-1736 Illustrated Human Embryology†
0085-1760 Index of Art in the Pacific Northwest†
0085-1779 India. Department of Science & Technology. Annual Report
0085-1787 Indian Agricultural Statistics†
0085-1795 F M U Occasional Lectures
0085-1809 Indian Livestock Census†
0085-1817 Indian Science Congress Association. Proceedings
0085-1876 Informator Archeologiczny
0085-1884 Inlet
0085-1892 Institut Royal du Patrimoine Artistique. Bulletin
0085-1914 Instituto Boliviano del Petroleo. Boletin†
0085-1922 Instituto de la Patagonia. Anales *see* 0716-6478
0085-1930 Insurance - Non-Life Annual Statistics *see* 0910-5719
0085-1930 Insurance - Non-Life Annual Statistics *see* 0910-5727
0085-1949 Inter-American Institute of Agricultural Sciences. Bibliografias *see* 0301-438X
0085-1965 S T P Notes†
0085-1981 Intergovermental Council for Automatic Data Processing. Proceedings of Conference *changed to* International Council for Automatic Data Processing in Government Administration. Proceedings of Conference.
0085-199X I A T A News Review *see* 0376-642X
0085-2007 International Association for Scientific Study of Mental Deficiency. Proceedings of International Congress
0085-2015 I A S L Newsletter
0085-2023 International Atomic Energy Agency. Annual Report
0085-204X International Bibliography of the Social Sciences. Economics
0085-2058 International Bibliography of the Social Sciences. Political Science
0085-2066 International Bibliography of the Social Sciences. Sociology
0085-2074 International Bibliography of the Social Sciences. Social and Cultural Anthropology
0085-2082 I B M Research Symposia Series†
0085-2090 International Clean Air Congress. Proceedings
0085-2104 International Conference on Chemical Vapor Deposition. Proceedings†
0085-2112 International Congress of Psychology. Proceedings
0085-2147 International Court of Justice. Bulletin†
0085-2163 International Monetary Fund. Annual Report on Exchange Restrictions *see* 0250-7366
0085-2171 International Monetary Fund. Annual Report of the Executive Directors *see* 0250-7498
0085-218X International Percussion Reference Library. Catalog†
0085-2198 International Press Institute. Survey *changed to* World Press Freedom Review.
0085-2201 International Telecommunication Union. Report on the Activities
0085-221X Memento de l'O.I.V.†
0085-2236 Iowa Academy of Science. Proceedings *see* 0896-8381
0085-2252 Iowa State Archaeologist. Report
0085-2260 Iraq Natural History Museum. Publication *changed to* Iraq Natural History Museum. Publication.
0085-2295 L'Italia Dialettale
0085-2309 Italy. Consiglio Nazionale delle Ricerce. Nota di Bibliografia e di Documentazione Scientifica *changed to* Italy. Istituto di Studi sulla Ricerca e Documentazione Scientifica. Note di Bibliografia e Documentazione Scientifica.
0085-2325 Iwate University. Faculty of Engineering. Technology Reports
0085-2341 Jahrbuch fuer Regionalgeschichte
0085-2368 Jewish Boston
0085-2376 Journal of Arabic Literature
0085-2384 Journal of Astrological Studies
0085-2406 Journal of Drug Research of Egypt
0085-2414 Journal of Northwest Semitic Languages†
0085-2430 Juvenile Court Digest *see* 0279-2257
0085-2449 Kalamies
0085-2457 University of Kansas. Department of Anthropology. Publications in Anthropology
0085-2465 University of Kansas. Museum of Natural History. Monographs
0085-2473 University of Kansas Humanistic Studies
0085-2481 Karate International Anniversary *changed to* Karate Budokan International Anniversary.
0085-249X Kariba Studies†
0085-2503 Kerry Archaeological and Historical Society. Journal
0085-2511 Key to Finland†
0085-2538 Kidney International
0085-2546 King's Gazette
0085-2554 Kirkon Nuoriso-Pistis *see* 0356-794X
0085-2562 Knitting Times Yearbook†
0085-2570 Kobe University. School of Business Administration. Annals
0085-2589 Kongelig Dansk Hof- og Statskalender; Statshaandbog for Kongeriget Danmark
0085-2597 Kontrast
0085-2600 Kultaseppien Lehti
0085-2619 Kyrkohistorisk Aarsskrift
0085-2627 Kyushu University. Faculty of Science. Memoirs Series B: Physics†
0085-2635 Kyushu University. Faculty of Science. Memoirs. Series C: Chemistry
0085-2643 France. Laboratoire des Ponts et Chaussees. Rapport de Recherche *see* 0222-8394
0085-266X Land Laws Service†
0085-2678 Langue et Cultures
0085-2686 Langue Internationale†
0085-2694 Latin American Studies in the Universities of the United Kingdom *see* 0956-9006
0085-2708 Staff Research in Progress or Recently Completed in the Humanities and the Social Sciences *changed to* Research on Latin America in the Humanities and Social Sciences in the Universities and Polytechnics of the United Kingdom.
0085-2724 L I R I Research Bulletin
0085-2740 Report by the Auditor General on the Accounts of Lesotho
0085-2759 Louisiana State University. Library Lectures
0085-2767 Library Lit
0085-2775 Light Age Directory; The Buyers Guide to Lamps. Lighting Fixtures, Accessories and Shades†
0085-2805 Livestock and Poultry in Latin America. Annual Conference *changed to* International Conference on Livestock and Poultry in the Tropics (Proceedings).
0085-2813 Lloyds Australian and New Zealand Trade Register
0085-2821 Local Government Finances in Maryland
0085-283X London Record Society. Occasional Publications†
0085-2848 London Record Society. Publications
0085-2856 Contemporary China Institute Publications
0085-2899 Lozania
0085-2902 Luksave†

ISSN

5568 ISSN INDEX

0085-2910	Lyman's Canada-British North America Standard Postage Stamp Retail Catalogue *see* 0227-1699
0085-2945	Madras. Government Museum. Bulletin. New Series
0085-2953	Mail Order Business Directory
0085-297X	Maine. Soil and Water Conservation Commission. Biennial Report†
0085-2988	Malacological Society of Australia. Journal
0085-3003	Malawi. National Statistical Office. Balance of Payments
0085-3011	Malawi. National Statistical Office. Compendium of Agricultural Statistics *see* 0076-3292
0085-302X	Malawi. National Statistical Office. Tourist Report *changed to* Malawi Tourism Report.
0085-3038	University of Malawi Libraries. Report to the Senate on the University Libraries
0085-3046	Malaysia. Department of Statistics. Survey of Construction Industries: Peninsular Malaysia†
0085-3054	Management Monographs (New York)†
0085-3070	Manitoba. Mines Branch. Publication *changed to* Manitoba Energy and Mines. Geological Report.
0085-3100	Mario Negri Institute for Pharmacological Research. Monographs
0085-3119	Marken-Handbuch der Werbung und Etatbetreuung
0085-3135	Maryland. Police Training Commission. Annual Report *changed to* Maryland. Police and Correctional Training Commissions. Report to the Governor, the Secretary of Public Safety and Correctional Services, and Members of the General Assembly.
0085-3186	Matrix (North Hollywood)†
0085-3194	Mauritius Directory of the Diplomatic Corps
0085-3208	Ny Carlsberg Glyptotek. Meddelelser
0085-3224	Melbourne Journal of Politics
0085-3232	Melbourne Notes on Agricultural Extension†
0085-3240	University of Melbourne. Department of Civil and Agricultural Engineering. Departmental Report†
0085-3259	University of Melbourne. Department of Electrical Engineering. Research Report
0085-3267	University of Melbourne. Faculty of Agriculture and Forestry. Agricultural Economics Report†
0085-3275	University of Melbourne. Gazette
0085-3283	Melbourne University Magazine†
0085-3291	Memo of Current Books in the Brain Sciences†
0085-3321	M T I A Annual Report *see* 0314-1586
0085-3356	Michigan. Department of Education. Bulletin†
0085-3364	Michigan. Geological Survey Division. Miscellany†
0085-3372	Michigan Mineral Producers Annual Directory:†
0085-3380	Michigan Police Journal *changed to* Michigan Police Chiefs Newsletter.
0085-3410	Surveys of Consumers†
0085-3429	Michigan's Oil and Gas Fields: Annual Statistical Summary
0085-3445	Mineral Industry of Michigan Annual Statistical Summary†
0085-3453	Mine and Quarry Mechanisation†
0085-3461	Ministerialtidende for Kongeriget Danmark
0085-3488	Minority Student Opportunities in United States Medical Schools
0085-3496	Missouri. Department of Conservation. Annual Report
0085-350X	Missouri Journal of Research in Music Education
0085-3518	Modern Plastics Encyclopedia
0085-3526	Modern Teaching†
0085-3534	Monmouth Reviews: Journal of the Literary Arts *changed to* Monmouth Review.
0085-3542	Monographs in Modern Concepts of Philosophy†
0085-3550	Montana. Governor's Annual Report†
0085-3577	Movie - T V Marketing Global Motion Picture Year Book
0085-3585	Municipal Association of Tasmania. Session. Minutes of Proceedings
0085-3607	Music and Life
0085-3623	Musikalier i Danske Biblioteker (Annual)
0085-364X	N U M U S Numismatica, Medalhistica, Arqueologia *changed to* N U M M U S.
0085-3658	NADA†
0085-3674	Natalia
0085-3690	National Council for the Social Studies. Curriculum Series†
0085-3704	National Council for the Social Studies. Crisis Series†
0085-3712	National Council for the Social Studies. How to Do It Series†
0085-3720	National Council for the Social Studies. Yearbook†
0085-378X	National Institute for Educational Research. Research Bulletin
0085-3798	National Institute for Research in Dairying. Biennial Report *see* 0302-0851
0085-3801	National Institute for Research in Dairying. Biennial Reviews†
0085-3828	National Research Council, Canada. Division of Building Research. Bibliography *changed to* National Research Council, Canada. Institute for Research in Construction. Bibliography.
0085-3836	National Science Council (Ireland). Register of Scientific Research Personnel
0085-3860	Nature - Science Annual†
0085-3887	Nemouria: Occasional Papers of the Delaware Museum of Natural History
0085-3909	Network (New York, 1970)†
0085-3917	Neue Hefte fuer Philosophie
0085-3925	University of Nevada. Anthropology Department. Student Papers in Anthropology†
0085-3933	N E H T A Newsletter *changed to* New England Journal of History.
0085-395X	New Jersey. Department of Transportation. Report of Operations *changed to* New Jersey. Department of Transportation. Annual Report.
0085-3968	University of New Mexico. Institute of Meteoritics. Special Publication
0085-3976	New South Wales. Department of Education. School Management Bulletin†
0085-3984	New South Wales. Forestry Commission. Research Notes
0085-400X	New South Wales. Law Reform Commission. Report
0085-4026	New South Wales Veterinary Proceedings†
0085-4042	New York Pro Musica Instrumental Series†
0085-4077	Annual Educational Summary, New York State
0085-4093	Racial - Ethnic Distribution of Public School Students and Staff, New York State
0085-414X	New Zealand. Water and Soil Division. Hydrological Research Annual Report & Series†
0085-4158	University of Newcastle. Department of Electrical Engineering. Technical Report EE *changed to* University of Newcastle. Department of Electrical and Computer Engineering. Technical Report EE.
0085-4166	News from the Rare Book Room
0085-4174	Newsletter on Contemporary Japanese Prints
0085-4190	Nigerian Office and Quarters Directory *see* 0331-0973
0085-4204	Nimrod†
0085-4212	Nordisk Ekumenisk Aarsbok†
0085-4220	Nordiske Domme i Sjofartsanliggender
0085-4247	Universitetet i Trondheim. Norges Tekniske Hoegskole. Biblioteket. Literaturliste†
0085-4263	Norsk Institutt for By- og Regionforskning. Rapport *see* 0801-1699
0085-4271	Norsk Polarinstitutt. Aarbok
0085-428X	North Carolina Communicable Disease Morbidity Statistics
0085-4301	Norway. Forsvaret Forskningsinstitutt. N D R E Report *see* 0800-4412
0085-431X	Norway. Statistisk Sentralbyraa. Artikler - Articles†
0085-4344	Norway. Statistisk Sentralbyraa. Social and Economic Studies
0085-4352	Norwegian-American Historical Association. Topical Studies
0085-4387	Noticiero Tuberosas
0085-4395	Nova Scotia. Fire Marshal. Annual Report
0085-4409	Nucleus†
0085-4417	Nuytsia
0085-4433	Oesterreichs Volkseinkommen
0085-4441	Official Year Book of New South Wales *see* 0810-9338
0085-445X	Oficina
0085-4468	Ohio Fish and Wildlife Report
0085-4484	Oklahoma Art Center. Annual Eight State Exhibition of Painting and Sculpture Catalog†
0085-4506	Oondoona†
0085-4514	Opera Slavica *changed to* Opera Slavica. Neue Folge.
0085-4522	Orientalia Lovaniensia Periodica
0085-4530	Der Orthopaede
0085-4557	Osler Library Newsletter
0085-4565	Oslo Boers. Beretning
0085-4573	Ostracodologist†
0085-4581	P I E
0085-459X	Pacific Islands Studies and Notes
0085-4603	Paedagogica†
0085-4611	Palaeontographica. Supplementbaende
0085-4638	Pan American Health Organization. Bulletin
0085-4662	Papers on Islamic History†
0085-4670	Papers on the History of Bourke
0085-4689	Papua and New Guinea Law Reports
0085-4697	Papua New Guinea Scientific Society. Annual Report and Proceedings *see* 0310-4303
0085-4700	Papua and New Guinea Scientific Society. Transactions†
0085-4719	Papua New Guinea. Department of Labour. Industrial Review.†
0085-4735	University of Papua New Guinea. Department of Physics. Technical Paper
0085-4743	Paraguay. Ministerio de Industria y Comercio. Division de Registro y Estadistica Industrial. Encuesta Industrial
0085-476X	Museum National d'Histoire Naturelle, Paris. Bibliotheque Centrale. Liste des Periodiques Francais et Etrangers. Supplement†
0085-4778	Cartes Synoptiques de la Chromosphere Solaire *changed to* Cartes Synoptiques de la Chromosphere Solaire et Catalogues des Filaments et des Centres d'Activite.
0085-4786	Documents de Linguistique Quantitative
0085-4794	Partiojohtaja
0085-4816	Pennsylvania. Department of Education. Our Colleges and Universities Today†
0085-4840	Peru. Oficina Regional de Desarrollo del Norte. Analisis General de Situacion de la Region Norte
0085-4859	Petroleum Search in Australia†
0085-4867	Phi Sigma Iota News Notes *changed to* Phi Sigma Iota Forum.
0085-4875	Philippine Mining and Engineering Journal. Mining Annual and Directory
0085-4883	Philippines Today†
0085-4905	Plumbers Friend
0085-4956	Teki Historyczne
0085-4980	Politique de la Science
0085-4999	Polk's World Bank Directory. International Edition *see* 1058-0603
0085-5006	Population Profile *see* 0146-7646
0085-5014	P R B Selection *see* 0146-7646
0085-5022	University of Port Elizabeth. Publications. Inaugural and Emeritus Addresses
0085-5030	Port of New Orleans Annual Directory
0085-5065	Practical Welder
0085-5073	Praxis der Kinderpsychologie und Kinderpsychiatrie. Beihefte
0085-5103	Prescriber's Journal *see* 0312-8008
0085-512X	Prince Edward Island. Department of Labour. Annual Report
0085-5138	Prince Edward Island. Department of the Environment Annual Report *changed to* Prince Edward Island. Department of Community and Cultural Affairs. Annual Report.
0085-5154	Privates Bausparwesen
0085-5170	Progress and Growth of Papua New Guinea†
0085-5189	Progress in Atomic Medicine *see* 0163-6170
0085-5219	International Personnel Management Association. Annual Report†
0085-5227	Publications in the American West
0085-5235	Quaternaria†
0085-5243	Universite Laval. Archives de Folklore
0085-526X	Queen Alexandra Solarium for Crippled Children Annual Report *changed to* Arbutus Society for Children. Annual Report.
0085-5278	Queen Victoria Museum and Art Gallery, Launceston, Tasmania. Records
0085-5286	Queensland. Bureau of Sugar Experiment Stations. Technical Communication†
0085-5308	Queensland Historical Review†
0085-5316	Queensland Pocket Year Book
0085-5324	Queensland Police Journal
0085-5332	Queensland Primary Producers' Co-Operative Association. Primary Producers' Guide†
0085-5359	Queensland Government Statistician. Queensland Year Book *see* 1030-7389
0085-5367	Quellen und Studien zur Geschichte der Pharmazie†
0085-5375	Quirindi and District Historical Notes†
0085-5383	Randschriften; a Newsletter for the Guild of Carillonneurs *see* 0730-5001
0085-5391	Readings in Literary Criticism†
0085-5405	Real Estate Trends in Metropolitan Vancouver *changed to* MetroTrends.
0085-5413	Notas e Comunicacoes de Matematica
0085-5421	Record Houses†
0085-543X	Recueil des Films
0085-5456	Register of Companies in New South Wales†
0085-5499	Repertoire Bibliographique des Livres Imprimes en France
0085-5510	Report on Australian Universities†
0085-5529	Report on the World Health Situation
0085-5545	Research and Development in Ireland
0085-5553	Research in Phenomenology
0085-5561	Respiratory Therapy Buyers Guide and Ordering Catalog *see* 0892-9289
0085-5596	Review of Economic Situation of Air Transport *changed to* Economic Situation of Air Transport. Review and Outlook (Years).
0085-560X	Review of Maritime Transport
0085-5626	Revista Brasileira de Entomologia
0085-5642	Revistero
0085-5650	Revolver/Tijdschrift voor Hedendragse Poezie

ISSN

ISSN INDEX 5569

ISSN	Title
0085-5677	Rhodesia National Bibliography *changed to* Zimbabwe National Bibliography.
0085-5693	Zimbabwe. Department of Meteorological Services. Rainfall Report†
0085-5707	Zimbabwe. Department of Meteorological Services. Report of the Director
0085-5715	Riddell's Australian Purchasing Yearbook *changed to* The Business Who's Who Australian Products and Trade Names Guide.
0085-5723	Rivista di Antropologia
0085-5731	Rivista di Etnografia
0085-5774	Royal Asiatic Society. Hong Kong Branch. Journal
0085-5782	Royal Automobile Association of South Australia. Accommodation Guide *changed to* Australian Accommodation Guide.
0085-5790	Royal Geographical Society of Australasia. South Australian Branch. Proceedings *see* 1030-0481
0085-5804	Royal Historical Society of Queensland. Journal
0085-5812	Royal Society of South Australia. Transactions
0085-5820	Royal Zoological Society of New South Wales. Proceedings *changed to* Koolewong.
0085-5839	Rural Africana
0085-5855	St. John's University, Collegeville, Minnesota. Monastic Manuscript Microfilm Library. Project Progress Report†
0085-588X	Sammlung Musikwissenschaftlicher Abhandlungen
0085-5898	San Francisco Bay Conservation and Development Commission. Annual Report
0085-5901	Universidade Federal de Santa Maria. Centro de Ciencias Rurais. Revista
0085-591X	Scandinavian Journal of Clinical and Laboratory Investigation. Supplement
0085-5928	Scandinavian Journal of Gastroenterology. Supplement
0085-5936	Scandinavian Studies in Criminology
0085-5944	Scandinavian Studies in Law
0085-5952	Schmankerl†
0085-5960	Schriftenreihe fuer Vegetationskunde
0085-5979	Science Fiction Book Review Index
0085-5995	Scientific, Technical and Related Societies of the United States†
0085-6002	Scottish Building & Civil Engineering Year Book
0085-6010	Search†
0085-6029	Seminario Matematico Garcia de Galdeano. Publicaciones†
0085-6037	Semitica
0085-6045	Setting National Priorities. the (Year) Budget†
0085-6053	Seychelles. Labour Department. Annual Report†
0085-6061	Shaw's Directory of Courts in England and Wales *see* 0264-312X
0085-607X	Sheller's Directory of Clubs, Books, Periodicals and Dealers
0085-6118	Singapore Libraries
0085-6126	Skandinavisk Tidskrift for Faerg och Lack. Aarsbok
0085-6142	Center for Short Lived Phenomena. Annual Report†
0085-6169	Snoeck's Almanach
0085-6177	Snoeck's: Literatuur Kunst Film Toneel Mode Reizen
0085-6193	Social, Economic and Political Studies of the Middle East
0085-6207	Social History of Canada
0085-6223	Sociedad Mexicana de Micologia. Boletin *see* 0187-3180
0085-6231	Societa Storica Valtellinese. Bollettino
0085-624X	Societe d'Etude du Vingtieme Siecle. Bulletin†
0085-6266	Societe Historique et Archeologique dans le Limbourg. Publications
0085-6282	Societe Royale des Sciences de Liege. Memoires in 8†
0085-6304	Society for the Study of Midwestern Literature. Newsletter
0085-6312	Real Estate Agents & Valuers Society. Land and Planning
0085-6320	Socioloski Pregled
0085-6339	Soelleroedbogen
0085-6347	Source (Ann Arbor)†
0085-6355	Investment Sources and Ideas *changed to* S I E (Year) Guide to Investment Services.
0085-6363	South African Biographical and Historical Studies
0085-6371	South African Jewish Frontier†
0085-638X	South African Journal of African Affairs *see* 0256-2804
0085-6398	South African Journal of Photogrammetry *changed to* South African Journal of Photogrammetry, Remote Sensing and Cartography.
0085-6401	South Asia: Journal of South Asian Studies
0085-641X	South Australian Road Transport Year Book
0085-6428	South Australian Yearbook
0085-6436	South Carolina. Alcoholic Beverage Control Commission. Annual Report *changed to* South Carolina. Commission on Alcoholism and Drug Abuse. Annual Report.
0085-6452	University of South Carolina. Institute of International Studies. Essay Series
0085-6460	South Dakota. Department of Revenue. Annual Statistical Report
0085-6479	South Dakota Geological Survey. Bulletin
0085-6487	South Dakota Geological Survey. Circular
0085-6495	South Dakota Geological Survey. Reports of Investigation
0085-6509	Southeast Asian Archives
0085-6517	Southeast Asian Seminar on Parasitology and Tropical Medicine. Proceedings *changed to* TropMed Seminars on Tropical Medicine. Proceedings.
0085-6525	Southern Indian Studies
0085-6533	Soviet Affairs Symposium†
0085-6541	Spain. Direccion General de Capacitacion y Extension Agrarias Resumen de Actividades†
0085-655X	Spain. Ministerio del Interior. Direccion General de Trafico. Boletin Informativo: Accidentes
0085-6592	S F I Bulletin
0085-6606	Standard Australian Coin Catalogue†
0085-6614	Standard Directory of Advertising Agencies
0085-6622	Standard Directory of Newsletters†
0085-6630	Standard Periodical Directory
0085-6665	Stanford Museum
0085-6673	Stanford Occasional Papers in Linguistics†
0085-6703	New South Wales State Reports *see* 0312-1674
0085-6711	Statistical Yearbook for Asia and the Far East *see* 0252-3655
0085-672X	Statistics on the Developing South *changed to* Southeastern Historical Statistics.
0085-6738	Status
0085-6746	Steinbeck Monograph Series
0085-6770	Stratford Festival
0085-6800	Student Mathematics
0085-6819	Studi Americani†
0085-6827	Studi e Saggi Linguistici
0085-6835	Studia Fennica
0085-6843	Studies in Anthropology†
0085-6851	University of Texas, Austin. Bureau of Business Research. Studies in Insurance and Actuarial Science†
0085-686X	Studies in Jewish Jurisprudence†
0085-6878	Studies in Medieval Culture
0085-6886	Studies in Polish Civilization†
0085-6894	Studies in Romance Languages *changed to* Studies in Romance Languages & Literatures.
0085-6908	Studies on Selected Development Problems in Various Countries in the Middle East
0085-6916	Universitaet Stuttgart. Institut fuer Steuerungstechnik der Werkzeugmaschinen und Fertigungseinrichtungen. i S W Berichte
0085-6932	Suomen Geodeettisen Laitoksen. Julkaisuja
0085-6940	Suomen Kalatalous
0085-6967	Cement- och Betonginstitutet. Handlingar. Proceedings†
0085-6975	Cement- och Betonginstitutet. Meddelanden. Bulletins†
0085-6983	Svenska Traeforskningsinstitutet. Meddelande. Series A *see* 0348-2650
0085-6991	Sweden. Statistiska Centralbyraan. Statistiska Meddelanden. Subgroup Bo (Housing and Construction)
0085-7009	Sydney Observatory Papers†
0085-7017	Sydney Speleological Society. Communications *changed to* Sydney Speleological Society. Occasional Paper.
0085-7025	University of Sydney. Economics Society. Economic Review†
0085-7033	University of Sydney. Institute of Criminology. Proceedings *see* 1034-5329
0085-7041	University of Sydney Medical Journal†
0085-7068	Symposium on Coal Mine Drainage Research. Papers†
0085-7076	Symposium on the Physiology and Pathology of Human Reproduction *changed to* Harold C. Mack Symposium. Proceedings.
0085-7092	University of Texas, Austin. Tarlton Law Library. Legal Bibliography Series
0085-7106	Tasmanian Reports
0085-7114	Teachers of History in the Universities of the United Kingdom *see* 0268-6732
0085-7130	Telektronikk
0085-7149	Television Blue Book *changed to* Television Trade-in Blue Book.
0085-7157	Television News Index and Abstracts
0085-7165	Tennessee Civilian Work Force Estimates *changed to* Labor Force and Nonagricultural Employment Estimates.
0085-7246	Thailand. Division of Agricultural Chemistry. Report on Fertilizer Experiments and Soil Fertility Research
0085-7262	Thorvaldsens Museum. Meddelelser
0085-7270	Today's House
0085-7289	Nankyoku Shiryo
0085-7297	Topics in Ocean Engineering†
0085-7327	Transport och Hanteringsekonomi *see* 0346-2773
0085-7335	Travaux Linguistiques de Prague†
0085-7351	Better Homes and Gardens Travel Ideas†
0085-7378	Treewell
0085-7386	Trilobite News
0085-7408	True to Life†
0085-7416	TRUK-PACT *changed to* TRU K PACT Info.
0085-7432	Turkiyat Mecmuasi
0085-7440	Turun Historiallinen Arkisto
0085-7467	Annuaire U N I T†
0085-7475	United Nations Association of Australia. K U R U N A†
0085-7491	United Nations. Division of Narcotic Drugs. Information Letter
0085-7513	United Nations Economic and Social Commission for Asia and the Pacific. Social Development Division. Social Work Training and Teaching Materials Newsletter *see* 0252-452X
0085-7580	Dairy Herd Improvement *changed to* Dairy Herd Improvement Letter.
0085-7602	Union Postale Universelle. Statistique des Services Postaux
0085-7629	University of Newcastle Historical Journal†
0085-7645	Vendsyssel Aarbog
0085-7653	Venezuela. Ministerio de Agricultura y Cria. Direccion de Economia y Estadistica Agropecuaria. Division de Estadistica. Plan de Trabajo
0085-7661	Verbaende, Behoerden, Organisationen der Wirtschaft
0085-767X	Museo Civico di Storia Naturale, Verona. Memorie *see* 0392-0062
0085-770X	Victoria, Australia. Department of Agriculture. Technical Bulletin†
0085-7718	Vegetable Growers Digest†
0085-7726	Victoria, Australia. Education Department. Curriculum and Research Branch. Research Reports†
0085-7742	Victoria, Australia. Forest Commission. Bulletin *changed to* Victoria, Australia. Department of Conservation, Forests and Lands. Lands and Forests Bulletin.
0085-7750	Victoria, Australia. Geological Survey. Bulletin
0085-7769	Victoria, Australia. Geological Survey. Memoirs
0085-7823	Vietnamese Studies
0085-7831	Viridian Starfire *changed to* Square Balloon.
0085-784X	Vocational Training in New York City: Where to Find It†
0085-7858	Wagga Wagga and District Historical Society. Journal
0085-7866	Waigani Seminar. Papers
0085-7882	W R I Newsletter *see* 0031-3548
0085-7904	Washington Center for Metropolitan Studies. Metropolitan Bulletin†
0085-7920	University of Washington Publications in Anthropology†
0085-7939	University of Washington Publications in Fisheries†
0085-7947	University of Washington Publications on Language and Literature†
0085-798X	Washington University. Institute for Urban and Regional Studies. Working Paper†
0085-8013	Water Research Foundation of Australia. Bulletin *see* 0085-8021
0085-8021	Water Research Foundation of Australia. Research Report
0085-803X	Weed Society of New South Wales. Proceedings†
0085-8048	Welcome to Finland
0085-8056	Welcome to Greenland *changed to* North Atlantic.
0085-8064	Welcome to Iceland *changed to* North Atlantic.
0085-8072	Welcome to the Faroes *changed to* North Atlantic.
0085-8080	West Malaysia Annual Statistics of External Trade *see* 0127-8533
0085-8099	West Virginia Education Directory
0085-8102	Western Association of State Game and Fish Commissioners. Proceedings *changed to* Western Association of Fish and Wildlife Agencies. Proceedings.
0085-8110	Western Australia. Aboriginal Affairs Planning Authority. Newsletter *changed to* Western Australia. Department of Aboriginal Affairs. Newsletter.
0085-8129	Western Australia. Forest Department. Bulletin *see* 1032-8106
0085-8137	Western Australia. Geological Survey. Bulletin
0085-8145	Western Australia. Geological Survey. Report

0085-8153 Western Australia. Government Chemical Laboratories. Report of Investigations *changed to* Western Australia. Chemistry Centre. Report of Investigations.
0085-8161 Western Australia Law Almanac
0085-8188 Western Canadian Steam Locomotive Directory
0085-8196 Wheat Australia
0085-820X Whiteacre
0085-8226 Wisconsin. Department of Administration. Annual Fiscal Report
0085-8242 Wisconsin Women Newsletter *changed to* Wisconsin Women and Public Policy.
0085-8250 Witchcraft Digest *issued with* 0049-7754
0085-8250 Witchcraft Digest
0085-8285 World Health Organization. Work of W H O
0085-8307 World Motor Vehicle Data
0085-8315 World Population Data Sheet
0085-8331 Wyoming Work Injury Report *see* 0093-1241
0085-834X Yamagata Daigaku Kiyo
0085-8366 Yokohama National University. Science Reports. Section 1: Mathematics, Physics, Chemistry
0085-8374 York Journal of Convocation
0085-8382 Your Australian Garden
0085-8412 Zeitschrift fuer Psychosomatische Medizin und Psychoanalyse. Beihefte
0085-8420 Eidgenoessische Sternwarte, Zurich. Astronomische Mitteilungen†
0088-7714 Materiali e Documenti Ticinesi
0090-0036 American Journal of Public Health
0090-0044 National Union Catalog of Manuscript Collections
0090-0079 MEDI-KWOC Index†
0090-0087 Monthly List of State Publications *see* 0027-0288
0090-0117 U.S. Library of Congress. Legislative Reference Service. Digest of Public General Bills *changed to* U.S. Library of Congress. Congressional Research Service. Digest of Public General Bills and Resolutions.
0090-0125 U.S. Library of Congress. Legislative Reference Service. Digest of Public General Bills and Selected Resolutions *changed to* U.S. Library of Congress. Congressional Research Service. Digest of Public General Bills and Resolutions.
0090-0141 Directory of Dental Educators *changed to* Directory of Dental Educators.
0090-0176 Japanese Studies in the History of Science *see* 0285-4821
0090-0214 Nuclear Data Tables *see* 0092-640X
0090-0222 Great Lakes Entomologist
0090-0311 J O G N Nursing *see* 0884-2175
0090-0443 Current Concepts in Nutrition†
0090-046X Medical Communications *changed to* A M W A Journal.
0090-0486 Environment Film Review†
0090-0494 Obesity & Bariatric Medicine†
0090-0508 Current Contents: Agriculture, Biology & Environmental Sciences
0090-0559 Clinical Trends in Family Practice†
0090-0575 International Bibliography on Burns
0090-0591 C T F A Cosmetic Journal†
0090-0613 N O A A National Weather Service. Climate Analysis Center. Average Monthly Weather Outlook *changed to* N O A A National Weather Service. Climate Analysis Center. Monthly and Seasonal Weather Outlook.
0090-0656 Fishery Bulletin
0090-0664 North Carolina State University. School of Forest Resources. Technical Report *changed to* North Carolina State University. College of Forest Resources. Technical Report.
0090-0672 Union Catalog of Medical Periodicals *see* 0276-7570
0090-0702 Maternal - Child Nursing Journal
0090-0710 Hospital Medical Staff *changed to* Medical Staff Leader.
0090-0737 Pennsylvania Crop Reporting Service. Pennsylvania Orchard and Vineyard Survey†
0090-0753 Index of Tissue Culture†
0090-077X New Jersey. Developmental Disabilities Council. Annual Report
0090-0818 Pro and Amateur Hockey Guide *see* 0278-4955
0090-0834 Optical Management†
0090-0842 Consensus†
0090-0869 O A G Travel Planner and Hotel-Motel Guide *see* 1053-0002
0090-0877 Immunological Communications *see* 0882-0139
0090-0893 N F A I S Newsletter
0090-0907 Chemical Marketing Reporter
0090-0923 Family Planning - Population Reporter†
0090-0931 New Mexico. State Records Center and Archives. Publications Filed *changed to* New Mexico. State Records Center & Archives. Annual Publications List.
0090-0958 Institute for the Development of Indian Law. Education Journal *see* 0145-7993
0090-1032 Harvard Political Review
0090-1059 Oregon. Department of Education. Racial and Ethnic Survey†
0090-1083 Annual Review of Allergy *see* 0278-9566
0090-1091 Journal of Clinical Computing
0090-1156 U.S. Centers for Disease Control. Brucellosis Surveillance: Annual Summary
0090-1164 Current Citations on Strabismus, Amblyopia, and Other Diseases of Ocular Motility
0090-1180 Administration in Mental Health *see* 0894-587X
0090-1210 A S T M Standardization News
0090-1229 Clinical Immunology and Immunopathology
0090-1237 Claudel Studies
0090-1245 Index of Dermatology†
0090-1326 Recurring Bibliography of Hypertension†
0090-1377 Cumulated Abridged Index Medicus
0090-1407 Cerebrovascular Bibliography†
0090-1423 Cumulated Index Medicus
0090-144X Psychotherapy *changed to* Psychotherapy.
0090-1482 Journal of Alcohol and Drug Education
0090-1520 Florida. Legislature. Joint Legislative Management Committee. Summary of General Legislation
0090-161X Bio-Medical Insight†
0090-1652 Biology of Brain Dysfunction†
0090-1660 Committee of Interns and Residents Bulletin *changed to* C I R News.
0090-1741 National Roster of Realtors
0090-1830 Marine Fisheries Review
0090-1881 American Psychiatric Association. Scientific Proceedings in Summary Form
0090-1903 Norda Briefs†
0090-1911 Vibrational Spectra and Structure
0090-192X Key Systems Guide†
0090-1938 Journal of Erie Studies
0090-1954 Symposium on Creation†
0090-1989 Directory: North Dakota City Officials
0090-1997 Florida Symposium on Automata and Semigroups†
0090-2020 Penthouse
0090-2047 Oui
0090-2055 U.S. Environmental Protection Agency. Office of Research and Development. Bibliography of Water Quality Research Reports *changed to* U.S. Environmental Protection Agency. Office of Research and Development. Indexed Bibliography.
0090-2063 Photographica *changed to* Photographica.
0090-2071 Proteus†
0090-208X Official Associated Press Almanac *changed to* Hammond Almanac: One-Volume Encyclopedia of a Million Facts & Records (year).
0090-2136 Q P Herald *see* 0146-5023
0090-2209 Newspaper Guild. Annual T.N.G. Convention Officers' Report
0090-2225 In-Service Training and Education *see* 0160-7006
0090-2233 Hawaii. Commission on Aging. Report of Achievements of Programs for the Aging
0090-225X Foreign Newspaper Report *see* 0190-9819
0090-2268 Lectures in Heterocyclic Chemistry
0090-2292 Hockey Register
0090-2381 I E E E Power Processing and Electronics Specialists Conference. Record *see* 0275-9306
0090-2411 A E Legal Newsletter
0090-2446 Field and Stream Camping on Wheels *changed to* Field & Stream Guide to Camping on Wheels.
0090-2454 Product Management *see* 0278-1530
0090-2500 Adit†
0090-2519 Contamination Control/Biomedical Environments†
0090-2535 Guidebook of Catholic Hospitals *changed to* Catholic Health Association of the United States. Guidebook.
0090-2578 Sunset Christmas Ideas and Answers†
0090-2586 Journal for the Study of Consciousness
0090-2594 Vanderbilt Journal of Transnational Law
0090-2616 Organizational Dynamics
0090-2756 Connecticut. Department of Correction. Publications
0090-2810 World Currency Charts
0090-2845 U.S. Copyright Office. Annual Report of the Register of Copyrights
0090-2861 Microfilm Source Book *changed to* International Imaging Source Book.
0090-287X Annual Review of the Schizophrenic Syndrome†
0090-2918 Public Health Reports
0090-2934 Dialysis & Transplantation
0090-2942 American Journal of Chinese Medicine *see* 0192-415X
0090-2969 Alcohol and Health Notes *see* 0364-0531
0090-2977 Neurophysiology
0090-2985 Carnival & Circus Booking Guide†
0090-2993 Cavalcade and Directory of Acts and Attractions *changed to* Cavalcade of Acts & Attractions.
0090-3000 Cinemagic†
0090-3019 Surgical Neurology
0090-3116 Association of Hospital and Institution Libraries. Quarterly *see* 0270-6717
0090-3159 Contemporary Ob-Gyn
0090-3167 Learning (Year)
0090-3191 United Way of America. Information Center. Digest of Current Reports *changed to* United Way of America. Information Center. Digest of Selected Reports.
0090-3213 Planetarian
0090-3221 State of Nebraska Uniform Crime Report
0090-3248 Illinois. Housing Development Authority. Annual Report
0090-3256 Good Sam Club's Recreational Vehicle Owners Directory *changed to* Trailer Life's Recreational Vehicle Campground and Services Directory.
0090-3272 Communications in Statistics *see* 0361-0926
0090-3272 Communications in Statistics *see* 0361-0918
0090-3280 Non-G P O Imprints Received in the Library of Congress†
0090-3299 National Register of Microform Masters *see* 0028-6680
0090-3329 American Dental Association. Annual Reports and Resolutions *changed to* American Dental Association. Transaction Series: Annual Reports and Resolutions, Supplements One and Two, Transactions.
0090-3353 Rock Scene
0090-3361 Keyboard Arts
0090-3477 Journal of Non-Metals *see* 0309-5991
0090-3485 Engage - Social Action *see* 0164-5528
0090-3493 Critical Care Medicine
0090-3507 Petroleum and Chemical Industry Conference. Record of Conference Papers
0090-3515 A R L I S - N A Newsletter *see* 0730-7187
0090-3531 Minority Group Employment in the Federal Government *changed to* Affirmative Employment Statistics.
0090-3558 Journal of Wildlife Diseases
0090-3604 American Academy of Psychoanalysis. Journal
0090-3612 Puerto Rico Official Industrial Directory
0090-3647 American Bar Association. Section of Administrative Law. Annual Reports of Committees†
0090-3655 Semiconductor Application Notes D.A.T.A. Book *changed to* Application Notes Reference D.A.T.A. Digest.
0090-3663 Music World Magazine†
0090-3671 Year Book of Surgery
0090-371X U.S. Library of Congress. Accessions List: Eastern Africa
0090-3736 U.S. Library of Congress. Accessions List: Sri Lanka†
0090-3744 U.S. Library of Congress. Accessions List: Nepal†
0090-3752 Nuclear Data Sheets
0090-3779 Appalachian Journal
0090-3809 Montana State Plan for Alcohol Abuse and Alcoholism Prevention, Treatment and Rehabilitation *changed to* Montana Comprehensive Chemical Dependency Plan.
0090-3817 Lutheran Historical Conference. Essays and Reports
0090-3825 Management World†
0090-3833 Destination: Philadelphia†
0090-3841 Recreational Vehicle Retailer *changed to* R V Business.
0090-3868 World Today Series: Soviet Union and Eastern Europe
0090-3884 Steam Electric Fuels *changed to* Steam - Electric Plant Factors (1978).
0090-3906 Oregon. Mass Transit Division. Annual Report *changed to* Public Transportation in Oregon.
0090-3914 American Society of Civil Engineers. Environmental Engineering Division. Journal *see* 0733-9372
0090-3949 Cross-Talk†
0090-3957 Group Therapy *see* 0276-5594
0090-3965 National Association of College Admissions Counselors. Membership Directory
0090-3973 Journal of Testing and Evaluation
0090-3981 High Fidelity's Test Reports†
0090-399X Realty Bluebook
0090-4023 Successful Ventures in Contemporary Education in Oklahoma†
0090-4058 Franklin Mint. Numismatic Issues *changed to* Franklin Mint. Limited Editions.
0090-4066 Directory of Corporate Urban Affairs Officers†
0090-4074 National Directory of Providers of Psychiatric Services to Religious Institutions†
0090-4082 Outstanding Elementary Teachers of America†
0090-4104 Journal of Soviet Mathematics
0090-4112 Critique†
0090-4155 Behaviorism *changed to* Behavior and Philosophy.
0090-4163 Directory of National Unions and Employee Associations†

ISSN

ISSN INDEX 5571

0090-4171 Stations†
0090-418X Who's Who in the Securities Industry
0090-4201 Journal of Sports Medicine *see* 0363-5465
0090-4236 Annual Editions: Readings in Sociology *see* 0277-9315
0090-4244 Mountain Plains Journal of Adult Education
0090-4260 Literature - Film Quarterly
0090-4295 Urology
0090-4309 Annual Editions: Business and Management†
0090-4325 Montana. Office of the Legislative Auditor. Department of Institutions Reimbursements Program; Report on Audit†
0090-4341 Archives of Environmental Contamination and Toxicology
0090-4368 G H S Foot - Notes
0090-4376 Cable Tech†
0090-4384 Annual Editions: Readings in Biology *changed to* Annual Editions: Biology.
0090-4392 Journal of Community Psychology
0090-4406 Photography Year†
0090-4414 Amateur Athletic Union of the United States. Official A A U Basketball Handbook†
0090-4422 Economics: Encyclopedia *changed to* Encyclopedic Dictionary of Economics.
0090-4430 Annual Editions: Readings in Economics *changed to* Annual Editions: Economics.
0090-4449 Evaluation and Change†
0090-4473 American Association of Zoological Parks and Aquariums. Proceedings. A A Z P A Annual Conference
0090-4481 Pediatric Annals
0090-449X Clark County History
0090-4511 Annual Editions: American History
0090-452X Catskills†
0090-4546 Virginia Woolf Quarterly†
0090-4570 Rag Times
0090-4589 Job Safety and Health†
0090-4600 Tax Management International Journal
0090-466X Journal of Pharmacokinetics and Biopharmaceutics
0090-4716 New York (State) Department of Social Services. Bureau of Data Management and Analysis. Program Analysis Report
0090-4759 Soviet Journal of Particles and Nuclei
0090-4848 Human Resource Management
0090-4872 Directory - Juvenile Adult Correctional Institutions and Agencies of the United States of America, Canada, and Great Britain *see* 0190-2555
0090-4910 Retirement Living *see* 1041-6277
0090-4937 Junior American Modeler *changed to* Sport Modeler.
0090-4945 Directory of Consulting Specialists†
0090-4961 Sunday Clothes†
0090-4996 Animal Learning & Behavior
0090-502X Memory and Cognition
0090-5038 National Trade and Professional Associations of the United States and Labor Unions *changed to* National Trade and Professional Associations of the United States and Labor Unions.
0090-5046 Physiological Psychology *see* 0889-6313
0090-5054 Psychonomic Society. Bulletin
0090-5070 The Groundwater Newsletter
0090-5089 K A F P Journal
0090-5119 Health, Physical Education and Recreation Microform Publications Bulletin
0090-5143 Iowa Summary of Vital Statistics *see* 0161-8695
0090-5151 Woodall's Campground Directory. Florida Campgrounds Edition *changed to* Woodall's Campground Directory. Florida Edition.
0090-516X Pollution Technology Review
0090-5178 Heavy Duty Equipment Maintenance-Management *see* 0733-3056
0090-5224 Poe Studies - Dark Romanticism
0090-5232 L C Science Tracer Bullet
0090-5259 Scene†
0090-5267 Control and Dynamic Systems: Advances in Theory and Applications
0090-5291 Electronics Buyers' Guide†
0090-5305 Pocket Playboy†
0090-5313 Fire Marshals Association of North America. Directory
0090-5348 Annual Editions: Human Development
0090-5364 Annals of Statistics
0090-5380 Symphony News *see* 0271-2687
0090-5402 Modern Paint & Coatings Paint Red Book
0090-5461 Journal of Non-White Concerns in Personnel and Guidance *see* 0883-8534
0090-547X Annual Editions: Readings in American Government *changed to* Annual Editions: American Government.
0090-5496 Oregon. State Board of Education. ESEA Title III State Plan†
0090-5526 Small Group Behavior *see* 1046-4964
0090-5542 Basic Life Sciences
0090-5550 Rehabilitation Psychology
0090-5569 Selected Abstracts on Animal Models for Biomedical Research†
0090-5577 Directory of North Dakota Manufacturers *changed to* Directory of North Dakota Manufacturers and Food Processors.
0090-5593 California. Teachers Retirement Board. State Teacher's Retirement System; Annual Report to the Governor and the Legislature
0090-5607 Ultrasonics Symposium. Proceedings
0090-5631 Meat Science Institute. Proceedings
0090-5674 Paideuma
0090-5720 Journal of Behavioral Economics
0090-5747 Sage Urban Studies Abstracts
0090-5771 Chrysanthemum
0090-5844 North Carolina Folklore Journal
0090-5895 Current Governments Reports: State Government Finances
0090-5917 Political Theory
0090-5968 Management of the California State Water Project
0090-5992 Nationalities Papers
0090-600X Wheelers Trailer Resort and Campground Guide *changed to* Wheelers R V Resort and Campground Guide: North American Edition.
0090-6034 Cricket
0090-6077 Connecticut. Department on Aging. Report to the Governor and General Assembly
0090-6093 Cowan Clan United. Newsletter
0090-6107 Maine. Law Enforcement Planning & Assistance Agency. Progress Report *changed to* Maine. Criminal Justice Planning & Assistance Agency. Progress Report.
0090-6263 Annual Report of Federal Civilian Employment by Geographic Area *changed to* Federal Civilian Workforce Statistics. Biennial Report of Employment by Geographic Area.
0090-628X Nebraska. Accounting Division. Annual Report of Receipts and Disbursements *changed to* Nebraska. Department of Administrative Services. Annual Fiscal Report.
0090-6352 Assessment and Valuation Legal Reporter†
0090-6360 Atomic Physics†
0090-6425 Minnesota. State Board of Health. Biennial Report†
0090-6433 Better Homes and Gardens Hundreds of Ideas†
0090-645X Billboard International Tape Directory *changed to* Billboard's Tape - Disc Directory.
0090-6514 Telos
0090-6549 Infectious Disease Reviews†
0090-6557 Tennessee Pocket Data Book†
0090-6581 Cosmetics and Perfumery *see* 0361-4387
0090-6611 Popular Computing (Calabasas)†
0090-662X Yearbook of Drug Abuse *see* 0273-3722
0090-6638 American Druggist Merchandising *see* 0190-5279
0090-6662 Hospital Statistics; Data from American Hospital Association Annual Survey *changed to* A H A Hospital Statistics (Year).
0090-6689 Medical Instrumentation *see* 0899-8205
0090-6700 Official Museum Directory
0090-6735 Oregon. State Board of Accountancy. Certified Public Accountants, Public Accountants, Professional Corporations, and Accountants Authorized to Conduct Municipal Audits in Oregon *changed to* Oregon. State Board of Accountancy. Certified Public Accountants, Public Accountants, and Accountants Authorized to Conduct Municipal Audits in Oregon.
0090-6743 Montana. Department of Public Instruction. Descriptive Report of Program Activities for Vocational Education†
0090-6778 I E E E Transactions on Communications
0090-6786 Stereo Directory and Buying Guide *changed to* Stereo Review's Stereo Buyers' Guide.
0090-6808 U.S. Environmental Protection Agency. Office of Research and Development. Selected Irrigation Return Flow Quality Abstracts†
0090-6816 U S A N and the U S P Dictionary of Drug Names
0090-6883 Synthesis (Cambridge)
0090-6905 Journal of Psycholinguistic Research
0090-6913 Letters in Applied and Engineering Sciences *see* 0020-7225
0090-693X Community-Clinical Psychology Series†
0090-6964 Annals of Biomedical Engineering
0090-6980 Prostaglandins
0090-7103 World Affairs Report
0090-7111 Census of Maine Manufactures
0090-7227 Federal Civilian Manpower Statistics. Monthly Release *changed to* Federal Civilian Workforce Statistics. Employment and Trends.
0090-7235 L O M A Literature on Modern Art *see* 0300-466X
0090-7286 Topical New Issues†
0090-7324 R S R
0090-7383 Conference on Data Systems Languages. Data Base Task Group. Report
0090-7421 Journal of Allied Health
0090-7480 Best's Safety Directory
0090-760X Missouri Life *changed to* Missouri Magazine.
0090-7618 U.S. National Center for Education Statistics. Expenditures and Revenues for Public Elementary and Secondary Education *changed to* U.S. Department of Education. National Center for Education Statistics. Public Elementary and Secondary State Aggregate Data, by State.
0090-7634 B and P - Brass & Percussion *changed to* Woodwind, Brass & Percussion.
0090-7782 A H M E Journal†
0090-7790 Black Perspective in Music†
0090-7812 Directory of Missouri's Regional Planning System *changed to* Directory of Missouri's Regional Planning Commissions.
0090-7820 Bonnes Feuilles†
0090-7847 Railroad History
0090-7855 P A A B S Revista†
0090-7863 U.S. National Credit Union Administration. N C U A Quarterly†
0090-788X Let's Go: The Student Guide to the United States and Canada *changed to* Let's Go: U S A.
0090-791X Environment Index *see* 0000-1198
0090-7944 Columbia Human Rights Law Review
0090-7987 Children's Book Review Service
0090-7995 Rhodes Directory of Black Dentists Registered in the United States *changed to* Who's Who in Black Dentistry in America.
0090-8002 U.S. Emergency Loan Guarantee Board. Annual Report†
0090-8029 Auto Racing Digest
0090-8142 Western Society of Weed Science. Research Progress Report
0090-8177 Minnesota. Department of Natural Resources. Biennial Report
0090-8185 Dirt Bike Buyer's Guide†
0090-8207 Graphic Arts Literature Abstracts *changed to* Institute of Paper Science and Technology. Graphic Arts Bulletin.
0090-8223 Urban Mass Transportation Abstracts
0090-8258 Gynecologic Oncology
0090-8266 Graduate & Professional School Opportunities for Minority Students†
0090-8274 Hawaii Literary Review *see* 0093-9625
0090-8282 Insect World Digest†
0090-8304 U.S. Library of Congress. Accessions List. Bangladesh†
0090-8312 Energy Sources
0090-8320 Ocean Development and International Law
0090-8339 Coastal Zone Management Journal *see* 0892-0753
0090-8347 Energy Systems and Policy
0090-8363 Chemical Abstracts - Applied Chemistry and Chemical Engineering Sections
0090-8371 U.S. Copyright Office. Catalog of Copyright Entries. Third Series. Parts 12-13. Motion Pictures and Filmstrips *see* 0163-7320
0090-838X Alcohol Health & Research World
0090-8401 Michigan. Employment Security Commission. Labor Market Analysis Section. Annual Manpower Planning Report: Detroit Labor Market Area *changed to* Michigan. Employment Security Commission. Annual Planning Report.
0090-8479 Venereal Disease Bibliography†
0090-8517 Connecticut River Valley Covered Bridge Society. Bulletin†
0090-8584 Current Topics in Comparative Pathobiology†
0090-8592 Behavior of Nonhuman Primates: Modern Research Trends†
0090-8614 A L A Sights to See Book†
0090-8630 Family Circle's Home Decorating Guide *changed to* Decorating Remodeling.
0090-8649 Southern Regional Education Board. State and Local Revenue Potential *changed to* Southern Regional Education Board. State and Local Tax Performance.
0090-8649 Southern Regional Education Board. State and Local Revenue Potential *changed to* Financing Higher Education.
0090-8657 Tire Science and Technology†
0090-8673 Ohio College Library Center. Annual Report *see* 0730-5125
0090-8711 Cuttin' Hoss Chatter
0090-8738 Bromeliad Society. Journal
0090-8746 Library Scene *see* 0735-8571
0090-8762 Practical Horseman
0090-8800 Contemporary Topics in Molecular Immunology
0090-8843 Alabama Marine Resources Bulletin†
0090-8878 Household & Personal Products Industry
0090-8886 Infectious Diseases
0090-8932 Render
0090-8967 Illinois Institute for Environmental Quality. Annual Report†

ISSN

5572 ISSN INDEX

ISSN

0090-8991 New York Mercantile Exchange Statistical Yearbook†
0090-9033 Buyer's Guide to the World of Tape *see* 0161-4371
0090-905X Iowa Genealogical Society. Surname Index
0090-9076 American Psychological Association. Biographical Directory *see* 0196-6545
0090-9084 Journal of Police Science and Administration
0090-9092 Art Psychotherapy *see* 0197-4556
0090-9106 A I A W Handbook of Policies and Operating Procedures *see* 0361-5898
0090-9114 Americana
0090-9130 Index of American Periodical Verse
0090-919X Corporation Finance and New Issue Weekly *changed to* Corporate Financing Week.
0090-9203 H I S S News-Journal†
0090-9211 Art Investment Report *see* 0161-1232
0090-9300 Maryland Geographer†
0090-9319 Woman's Day 101 Gardening & Outdoor Ideas†
0090-9327 Penny Stock Handbook
0090-9386 Maine. Criminal Justice Planning & Assistance Agency. Criminal Justice Internship Program. Report and Evaluation
0090-9416 Latin American Index
0090-9440 Hawaii. Department of Education. Office of Business Services. Report on Federally Connected Pupils: Hawaii Public Schools†
0090-9467 Foreign Economic Trends and Their Implications for the United States†
0090-9475 Exporter's Encyclopedia-United States Marketing Guide†
0090-9491 Stochastics *see* 1045-1129
0090-9521 Architecture Plus†
0090-9556 Drug Metabolism and Disposition
0090-9580 International Journal of Cooperative Development†
0090-9599 R F Illustrated *changed to* R F.
0090-9661 F L I R T Newsletter *see* 0273-1061
0090-9688 U.S. Department of Agriculture. Food and Home Notes†
0090-9718 Focus: Technical Cooperation†
0090-9742 Private Investments Abroad
0090-9785 M R I S Bulletin *see* 0147-572X
0090-9815 North Dakota Crop and Livestock Reporting Service. Wheat Varieties, North Dakota†
0090-9866 Clergy's Federal Income Tax Guide *see* 0163-1241
0090-9882 Journal of Applied Communication Research
0090-9912 Montana. Office of the Legislative Auditor. State of Montana Board of Investments. Report on Examination of Financial Statements
0090-9955 Directory of Polish Officials
0090-9963 Maryland. Correctional Training Commission. Annual Report *changed to* Maryland. Police and Correctional Training Commissions. Report to the Governor, the Secretary of Public Safety and Correctional Services, and Members of the General Assembly.
0090-9971 Executive Compensation Service. Reports on International Compensation. Puerto Rico†
0090-998X Audio Journal Review: General Surgery†
0091-0031 U.S. National Communicable Disease Center. Morbidity and Mortality *see* 0149-2195
0091-004X Pediatric Conferences with Sydney Gellis†
0091-0155 Enzyme Technology Digest†
0091-018X Food Management
0091-0198 Grain and Farm Service Centers *changed to* Grain & Feed Journals.
0091-0260 Public Personnel Management
0091-0279 Veterinary Clinics of North America *see* 0195-5616
0091-0279 Veterinary Clinics of North America *see* 0196-9846
0091-0287 Yale Scientific
0091-0376 Prairie Naturalist
0091-0392 Bank Protection Bulletin *changed to* Banking Insurance and Protection Bulletin.
0091-0406 Nebraska State Publications Checklist†
0091-0430 Lawyer-to-Lawyer Consultation Panel†
0091-0449 D M G - D R S Journal: Design Research and Methods *see* 0147-1147
0091-0457 Montana. Environmental Quality Council. Annual Report *changed to* Montana. Environmental Quality Council. Biennial Report.
0091-0465 Annual Guide to Undergraduate Study *see* 0894-9336
0091-0538 A P L A Quarterly Journal (American Patent Law Association) *see* 0883-6078
0091-0546 Oregon Public Utility Commissioner. Statistics of Electric, Gas, Steam Heat, Telephone, Telegraph and Water Companies *changed to* Oregon. Public Utility Commissioner. Oregon Utility Statistics.
0091-0554 Space Age News†
0091-0562 American Journal of Community Psychology
0091-0600 International Journal of Psychoanalytic Psychotherapy†
0091-0627 Journal of Abnormal Child Psychology
0091-0651 Field & Stream Sportsman†
0091-0678 Maine. State Planning Office. Annual Report†
0091-0716 Guide to Nebraska State Agencies
0091-0724 Annual Causes and Conditions of Poverty in South Dakota *changed to* Poverty in South Dakota.
0091-0759 Maine. State Library. Special Subject Resources in Maine
0091-0775 Kentucky School Directory
0091-0791 Public Continuing and Adult Education Almanac†
0091-0848 Texas. Water Quality Board. Agency Publication†
0091-0864 American Fabrics & Fashions†
0091-0899 Dairy Scope†
0091-0988 Western Economic Indicators†
0091-0996 Montana. Department of Social and Rehabilitation Services. Annual Report†
0091-1003 Directory. Diocesan Agencies of Catholic Charities. United States, Puerto Rico and Canada *changed to* Directory of Catholic Charities, Diocesan Agencies and Organizations. United States, Puerto Rico and Canada (Year).
0091-1054 Oklahoma Pontotoc County Quarterly
0091-1062 S A M P E Journal
0091-1097 Missouri Annual Highway Safety Work Program *changed to* Missouri. Division of Highway Safety. Highway Safety Plan.
0091-1143 Montana. Department of Social and Rehabilitation Services. Statistical Report
0091-1186 Guidebook to North Carolina Taxes
0091-1305 FarmFutures
0091-1372 Soap, Cosmetics, Chemical Specialties
0091-1402 Statehouse Observer
0091-1410 Transportation. Current Literature
0091-1461 Ski Racing Redbook
0091-1488 Bachy†
0091-150X Pharmaceutical Chemistry Journal
0091-1518 S I O: A Report on the Work and Programs of Scripps Institution of Oceanography *see* 1046-9443
0091-1526 Wall Street Review of Books *see* 1045-7798
0091-1550 Texas Livestock Statistics
0091-1607 The-A-KiKi
0091-1615 Working Papers for a New Society *changed to* Modern Times.
0091-1658 American Statistics Index
0091-1666 Chicago Dental Society Review
0091-1674 Clinical Social Work Journal
0091-1682 Clinical Trends in Urology†
0091-1704 Current Contents: Clinical Pratice *changed to* Current Contents: Clinical Medicine.
0091-1712 Environmental Education Report *see* 0840-5662
0091-1720 Public Science Newsletter†
0091-1747 Syndrome Identification†
0091-1798 Annals of Probability
0091-181X Marine Behaviour and Physiology. Sections A & B
0091-1860 University of Michigan. Herbarium. Contributions
0091-1887 Underwater Photographer†
0091-1909 Journal of Urban Analysis *changed to* Journal of Urban Analysis and Public Management.
0091-1984 C A T V Systems Directory, Map Service and Handbook†
0091-2026 Atmospheric Technology†
0091-2085 Documents to the People
0091-2131 Ethos (Washington)
0091-2166 Hearing Aid Journal *see* 0745-7472
0091-2174 International Journal of Psychiatry in Medicine
0091-2182 Journal of Nurse-Midwifery
0091-2220 Best Editorial Cartoons of the Year
0091-2263 Population and the Population Explosion: a Bibliography†
0091-2271 U.S. Army Infantry Center. History; Annual Supplement *changed to* U.S. Army Infantry School. History; Annual Supplement.
0091-231X Missouri. Division of Mental Health. Annual Report *changed to* Missouri. Department of Mental Health. Progress Notes.
0091-2328 Investment Adviser Directory†
0091-2360 Today's Chiropractic
0091-2379 Nursing Care *changed to* Licensed Practical Nurse.
0091-2387 National Spokesman
0091-2395 National Drug Reporter†
0091-2468 Transportation Research Forum. Proceedings: Annual Meeting†
0091-2476 A C T F L Review of Foreign Languages Education *see* 0147-1236
0091-2484 News Citizen *changed to* Scholastic News: Citizen.
0091-2492 U.S. Executive Office of the President. International Economic Report of the President†
0091-2573 Potomac Review†
0091-2611 Corrective and Social Psychiatry and Journal of Applied Behavior Therapy *see* 0093-1551
0091-262X Iowa. Department of Job Service. Research and Statistics Division. Annual Manpower Planning Report†
0091-2646 U.S. Labor - Management Services Administration. Decisions and Reports on Rulings of the Assistant Secretary of Labor for Labor - Management Relations†
0091-2662 Drug Abuse Council. Public Policy†
0091-2700 Journal of Clinical Pharmacology
0091-2743 Baptist Missionary Association of America. Directory and Handbook
0091-2751 Journal of Clinical Ultrasound
0091-2786 American Gas Association. Research and Development†
0091-2859 Regional Institute of Social Welfare Research. Annual Report
0091-2921 Perspectives in Pediatric Pathology
0091-2948 Lost Generation Journal
0091-3057 Pharmacology, Biochemistry and Behavior
0091-3065 Review of Child Development Research
0091-3154 Who's Who in Ecology†
0091-3219 Journal of Ethnic Studies†
0091-3235 Directory of Latin Americanists *changed to* Directory of A S U Latin Americanists.
0091-3243 Directory of Secondary Schools with Occupational Curriculums, Public and Nonpublic *changed to* Occupational Education: Enrollments and Programs in Noncollegiate Postsecondary Schools.
0091-3251 New York (State). Department of Audit and Control. Index to the Public Schools†
0091-3286 Optical Engineering
0091-3294 Films and Other Materials for Projection *changed to* National Union Catalog. Audiovisual Materials.
0091-3367 Journal of Advertising
0091-3383 American SquareDance
0091-3391 Amateur Athletic Union of the United States. Athletic Library. Official A A U Gymnastics Handbook†
0091-3405 Amateur Athletic Union of the United States. Official Handbook of the A A U Code
0091-3421 Contemporary Literary Criticism Series
0091-3448 Georgia. State Economic Opportunity Office. Annual Report†
0091-3464 Georgia Manpower Trends *changed to* Georgia Labor Market Trends.
0091-3472 Robert Wood Johnson Foundation. Annual Report
0091-3499 Building Cost File *changed to* Berger Building & Design Cost File. Unit Prices. Vol. 1: General Construction Trades.
0091-3499 Building Cost File *changed to* Berger Building & Design Cost File. Unit Prices. Vol. 2: Mechanical and Electrical Trades.
0091-3502 U.S. Department of Agriculture. Economics, Statistics, and Cooperatives Service. Agricultural Finance Statistics†
0091-3553 U.S. Community Services Administration. Federal Outlays in Summary
0091-3588 State of Iowa Scholarships, Tuition Grants. Biennium Report *changed to* Iowa. College Student Aid Commission. Annual Data Digest Report.
0091-360X A V Guide
0091-3634 Deeds and Data†
0091-3642 Fruit Varieties Journal
0091-3669 Mosquito Systematics
0091-3685 National Journal Reports *see* 0360-4217
0091-3707 Social Sciences Citation Index
0091-3715 Political Science Reviewer
0091-3723 Journal of Chinese Linguistics
0091-3731 Print Review†
0091-3774 Motorcycle Blue Book
0091-3782 Northwest Missouri State University Studies†
0091-3804 American Bankers Association. Committee on Uniform Security Identification Procedures. C U S I P Directory: Corporate Directory *changed to* C U S I P Corporate Directory.
0091-3839 U S P Guide to Select Drugs†
0091-3847 Physician and Sportsmedicine
0091-3855 Cost of Personal Borrowing in the United States.
0091-3901 Illustrated Digest of Baseball†
0091-391X International Symposium on Silicon Materials Science and Technology. Proceedings†
0091-3952 Advances in Neurology
0091-3960 American Journal of Acupuncture
0091-3979 Dental Hygiene *see* 1043-254X
0091-3995 S I E C U S Report
0091-4010 Guidebook to Ohio Taxes

0091-4029 Hofstra Law Review
0091-4037 International Journal of Polymeric Materials
0091-4045 Nutritional Update *changed to* Your Good Health.
0091-4061 S E C Docket
0091-407X U S - Japan Outlook†
0091-4118 Pennsylvania. Crime Commission. Report
0091-4150 International Journal of Aging & Human Development
0091-4169 Journal of Criminal Law & Criminology
0091-4185 Wisconsin Dental Association. Journal
0091-4266 History of Childhood Quarterly *see* 0145-3378
0091-4347 Lietuviu Tautos Praeitis
0091-4371 American Horseman
0091-4428 Cutter and Chariot Racing World *see* 0194-8814
0091-4452 Journal of Color and Appearance†
0091-4460 M A F E S Research Highlights
0091-4479 Association of Research Libraries. University Library Management Studies Office. Occasional Paper *changed to* Association of Research Libraries. Office of Management Studies. Occasional Paper.
0091-4487 Western Society of Weed Science. Proceedings
0091-4509 Contemporary Drug Problems
0091-4576 Consumer Guide Photographic Equipment Test Reports Quarterly *changed to* Consumer Guide Photo Annual.
0091-4630 U.S. Office of Minority Business Enterprise. Minority Enterprise Progress Report†
0091-4665 Lawn & Garden Marketing†
0091-4673 Texas Small Grains Statistics
0091-4711 Louisiana Labor Market *changed to* Louisiana Labor Market Information.
0091-4738 C V P: Journal of Cardiovascular and Pulmonary Technology *see* 0892-9327
0091-4789 Colorado County and City Retail Sales by Standard Industrial Classification *see* 0732-071X
0091-4800 Worldwide Projects†
0091-4835 Governmental Finance *changed to* Government Finance Review.
0091-4843 Milling & Baking News
0091-4916 Journal of Nuclear Medicine Technology
0091-4924 Flannery O'Connor Bulletin
0091-4932 U.S. Federal Housing Administration. F H A Homes
0091-4975 Corporate Reports on File†
0091-5041 Geological Society of America. Memorials
0091-5122 American Association of State Highway and Transportation Officials. Sub-Committee on Computer Technology. National Conference. Proceedings
0091-5173 Health Care Engineering *see* 0098-8219
0091-519X Criminal Justice News†
0091-5203 Gravure Environmental and O S H A Newsletter *see* 0271-1699
0091-5254 Wisconsin Population Projections
0091-5270 C A L L
0091-5300 Veterinary Toxicology *see* 0145-6296
0091-536X Conservation Foundation Letter *changed to* W W F & C F Letter.
0091-5440 University of Baltimore Law Review
0091-5459 Union Labor Report
0091-5513 West Virginia Coal Facts
0091-5521 Community College Review
0091-553X A D & D: Tax Interpretations†
0091-5564 Delaware Reporter
0091-5572 Railroad Car Journal
0091-5599 Survey of Salaries and Employee Benefits of Private and Public Employers in Arizona. *changed to* Joint Governmental Salary and Benefits Survey: Arizona.
0091-5610 American Universities Field Staff. Population: Perspective†
0091-5629 Illinois. Governor's Office of Human Resources. Annual Report†
0091-5637 Journal of South Asian Literature
0091-5645 Coda: Poets and Writers Newsletter *see* 0891-6136
0091-5653 Monthly Checklist of Kentucky State Publications *see* 1054-2841
0091-5661 Personal Income Tax in Oregon†
0091-5688 Access (Washington)†
0091-5696 Quality of Life in Iowa†
0091-5793 Motorcycle Facts†
0091-5823 Colorado. Department of Social Services. Research and Statistics Section. Research Report AFDC†
0091-584X University of Alaska. State Wide Bulletin†
0091-5858 Multi Media Reviews Index *see* 0363-7778
0091-5882 Idaho. State Board for Vocational Education. Annual Descriptive Report of Program Activities for Vocational Education *changed to* Idaho. State Division of Vocational Education. Annual Performance Report.
0091-5939 Housing and Development Reporter
0091-6080 Wisconsin. Department of Transportation. Traffic Planning Section. Automatic Recorder Station Traffic Data *see* 0098-0323
0091-6129 Pennsylvania Manufacturing Exporters *see* 0360-8859
0091-6137 Magazine of New York Business *see* 0148-0146
0091-6145 Progress in Extractive Metallurgy†
0091-6188 Delaware. Department of Public Instruction. Educational Personnel Directory
0091-6196 West Virginia's State System of Higher Education; Annual Report, Current Operating Revenues and Expenditures†
0091-620X Saturday Review†
0091-6242 U.S. General Services Administration. Management Report
0091-6269 A O A Newsbriefs†
0091-6277 Surgical Team *see* 0161-9721
0091-6315 Mental Retardation and Developmental Disabilities
0091-6323 Soul Journey†
0091-6331 Exercise and Sport Sciences Reviews
0091-634X American Academy of Psychiatry and the Law. Bulletin
0091-6358 Astronomy
0091-6439 Midwest Genealogical Society. Surname Index *see* 0271-8685
0091-6471 Journal of Psychology and Theology
0091-6501 California Mosquito Control Association. Proceedings and Papers of the Annual Meeting *changed to* California Mosquito and Vector Control Association. Proceedings and Papers of the Annual Meeting.
0091-6528 Society for Neuroscience. Annual Meeting. Conference Report†
0091-6536 C R C Critical Reviews in Clinical Radiology and Nuclear Medicine *see* 1040-8371
0091-6544 Family Therapy
0091-6579 Methods in Cell Physiology *see* 0091-679X
0091-6595 Annual Review of Behavior Therapy: Theory and Practice *changed to* Review of Behavior Therapy: Theory & Practice.
0091-6633 Missouri State Government Publications
0091-6641 Studio Potter
0091-6676 Irvine Humanities Review†
0091-6684 Navajo Historical Publications. Biographical Series†
0091-6706 Wood - Woods Family Magazine
0091-6722 Radiation Data and Reports†
0091-6730 Nebraska Medical Journal
0091-6749 Journal of Allergy and Clinical Immunology
0091-6765 E H P
0091-6773 Behavioral Biology *see* 0163-1047
0091-679X Methods in Cell Biology
0091-6811 Research Futures†
0091-6846 Strategic Review
0091-6854 Spectrum One: Stock Holdings Survey *changed to* Spectrum 1: U S and European Investment Company Stock Holdings Survey.
0091-6862 Spectrum Two: Investment Company Portfolios *changed to* Spectrum 2: U S and European Investment Company Portfolios.
0091-6900 Kansas Agriculture Report *changed to* Kansas. State Board of Agriculture. Annual Report with Farm Facts.
0091-6919 U.S. Department of Defense. Defense Department Report
0091-6943 Vintage Airplane
0091-6978 New Jersey Airport Directory
0091-7036 International Journal of Computer and Information Sciences *see* 0885-7458
0091-7052 Guide to Graduate Departments of Sociology
0091-7176 Ancient Times
0091-7192 Statistics on Social Work Education in the United States
0091-7206 E D P Performance Review *see* 1049-2194
0091-7214 Mathematics International†
0091-7222 National Gallery of Art. Annual Report
0091-7257 Vertex (Los Angeles)†
0091-7265 Washington (State). Department of Social and Health Services. Jail Inspection Report†
0091-7281 Learning Today†
0091-729X Admission Requirements of U S and Canadian Dental Schools
0091-7311 Washington Report on Long Term Care *changed to* Long Term Care Management.
0091-732X Review of Research in Education
0091-7338 Studies in the History of Art
0091-7346 Index to Literature on the American Indian†
0091-7354 U.S. Department of Transportation. Office of Policy Review. Working Paper†
0091-7370 Annals of Clinical and Laboratory Science
0091-7389 American Psychopathological Association. Proceedings of the Annual Meeting
0091-7397 Current Topics in Experimental Endocrinology
0091-7419 Journal of Supramolecular Structure *see* 0730-2312
0091-7435 Preventive Medicine
0091-7443 Association for Research in Nervous and Mental Disease. Research Publications
0091-7451 Cold Spring Harbor Laboratory. Symposia on Quantitative Biology
0091-746X Institute of Medicine of Chicago. Proceedings
0091-7516 Quarter Racing Record
0091-7605 Food Purity Perspectives
0091-7613 Geology (Boulder)
0091-7648 Wildlife Society Bulletin
0091-7664 Whiskey, Women, And...†
0091-7699 Instrument Society of America. I S A Final Control Elements Symposium. Final Control Elements; Proceedings†
0091-7710 Journal of Anthropological Research
0091-7729 Science-Fiction Studies
0091-780X Colorado. Department of Social Services. Research and Statistics Section. Research Report W P M†
0091-7818 Colorado. Department of Social Services. Research and Statistics Section. Research Report W I N†
0091-7842 Colorado. Department of Social Services. Research and Statistics Section. Research Report A D M†
0091-7885 Technology Book Guide *see* 0360-2761
0091-7907 Conference Publications Guide *see* 0360-2729
0091-7915 Government Publications Guide *see* 0360-2796
0091-7958 University of Kansas. Museum of Natural History. Occasional Papers
0091-8059 Headlights
0091-8075 Statistical Profile of the U.S. Exchange Program†
0091-8083 Studies in American Fiction
0091-8105 Food Fish Market Review and Outlook†
0091-8172 Psychotherapy and Behavior Change *see* 0360-0696
0091-8180 Colorado. Department of Social Services. Research and Statistics Section. Report A D C†
0091-8245 Guidelines for Improving Practice. Architects and Engineers Professional Liability
0091-8253 Washington (State) Legislature. Pictorial Directory
0091-8261 U.S. Bureau of Labor Statistics. Employee Compensation in the Private Nonfarm Economy†
0091-8296 Missiology
0091-830X Best's Recommended Independent Insurance Adjusters *changed to* Best's Directory of Recommended Insurance Adjusters.
0091-8369 Journal of Homosexuality
0091-8377 Industrial Machinery and Equipment Pricing Guide
0091-8385 Techniques of Marriage and Family Counseling†
0091-8393 U S Medical Directory
0091-8415 Fixed Income Investor *see* 0731-1974
0091-844X Nebraska. Department of Roads. Traffic Analysis Unit. Continuous Traffic Count Data and Traffic Characteristics on Nebraska Streets and Highways
0091-8512 U.S. National Oceanic and Atmospheric Administration. National Climatic Center. Marine Climatological Summaries†
0091-8601 Industrial Education
0091-861X Cooking for Profit
0091-8644 U.S. Department of Transportation. Climatic Impact Assessment Program Office. Technical Abstract Report†
0091-8660 Ebony Jr†
0091-8695 Report on Federal Funds Received in Iowa†
0091-8725 U.S. National Weather Service. Data Acquisition Division. Marine Surface Observations†
0091-8733 Muleskinner News *see* 0161-1747
0091-8784 Oregon Education Biennial Report†
0091-8792 Arizona. State Advisory Council for Vocational Education. Annual Report *changed to* Arizona. State Council for Vocational Education. Biennial Report.
0091-8806 Cincinnati. Division of Police. Annual Report
0091-8822 Motor Sport Yearbook†
0091-8830 Southwest Art Magazine *see* 0192-4214
0091-8857 Watauga Association of Genealogists. Upper East Tennessee. Bulletin
0091-8873 Alaska State Chamber of Commerce. Membership Directory†
0091-8938 Student Enrollment Report; West Virginia Institutions of Higher Education†
0091-8954 Product Safety Up To Date
0091-8962 Iowa. Department of Public Instruction. Summary of Federal Programs†
0091-8970 Indiana. State Advisory Council for Vocational Technical Education. Annual Report *changed to* Indiana. Indiana Commission on Vocational and Technical Education.

5574 ISSN INDEX

0091-8989 Educational Testing Service Annual Report
0091-9004 North Dakota. Geological Survey. Educational Series
0091-9039 U.S. Department of Commerce. Publications; a Catalog and Index Supplement *see* 0277-7207
0091-9047 Michigan Business and Economic Research Bibliography†
0091-908X K-Bar-T Country Roundup *changed to* Country Music Roundup.
0091-9101 Election Laws of Hawaii *changed to* Election Laws of Hawaii Handbook.
0091-9128 Nebraska. Commission on Law Enforcement and Criminal Justice. Criminal Justice Comprehensive Plan†
0091-9144 Centrum†
0091-9152 Chain Store Guide Directory: Food Service Distributors *see* 0271-7662
0091-9187 New Jersey. Office of Demographic and Economic Analysis. Population Estimates for New Jersey *changed to* New Jersey. Division of Labor Market and Demographic Research. Population Estimates for New Jersey.
0091-9195 Nebraska. Commission on Law Enforcement and Criminal Justice. Criminal Justice Action Plan†
0091-9209 Current Governments Reports: City Employment
0091-9217 Best Science Fiction†
0091-9225 Air Defense Trends *changed to* Air Defense Artillery.
0091-9233 Puerto Rico. Department of Labor. Bureau of Labor Statistics. Employment Hours and Earnings in the Manufacturing Establishments Promoted by the Economic Development Administration of the Puerto Rican Industrial Development Company
0091-9276 Johns Hopkins University. Population Information Program. Population Reports. Series G. Prostaglandins†
0091-9284 Johns Hopkins University. Population Information Program. Population Reports. Series F. Pregnancy Termination†
0091-9322 Temperature: Its Measurement and Control in Science and Industry
0091-9357 American Book Prices Current
0091-9381 American Baptist Churches in the U S A Directory
0091-9403 U.S. Bureau of Labor Statistics. Employment and Wages.†
0091-9446 North Dakota. Milk Stabilization Board. Annual Report of Administrative Activities
0091-9489 Lawrence Berkeley Laboratory. Research Highlights *changed to* Lawrence Berkeley Laboratory. Catalog of Research Projects.
0091-9500 U.S. National Oceanographic Data Center. Key to Oceanographic Records Documentation
0091-9519 Electronic Industries Association. Trade Directory and Membership List
0091-9527 Catholic Schools in the United States *see* 0147-8044
0091-956X Report from N J D A†
0091-9578 Plastics Engineering
0091-9586 Kansas Country Living
0091-9632 Guide to Graduate Study in Political Science
0091-9659 Northwest Journal of African and Black American Studies†
0091-9675 Semiconductor Diode D.A.T.A. Book *see* 1040-0249
0091-9683 To the World's Oboists *see* 0741-7659
0091-9748 U.S. Advisory Council on Historic Preservation. Newsletter *see* 0098-4035
0091-9756 Metropolitan Atlanta Business Directory *changed to* Terminus Business Directory.
0091-9772 Journal of Primal Therapy *see* 0164-5056
0091-9780 Art Dealer and Framer *see* 0273-5652
0091-9837 Environmental Defense Fund. Annual Report
0091-9845 Hawaii Observer†
0091-9918 Conference Board. Monthly Business Review *see* 0362-5435
0091-9942 Florida. Governor. Annual Report on State Housing Goals†
0091-9977 Street & Smith's College Football
0091-9993 No-Till Farmer
0092-0002 International Decade of Ocean Exploration. Progress Report†
0092-0037 Ag Chem and Commercial Fertilizer *see* 0092-0053
0092-0053 Farm Chemicals
0092-0150 Modern Pharmacology *see* 0098-6925
0092-0177 Florida. Division of Motor Vehicles. Tags and Revenue
0092-0193 Ion Exchange and Solvent Extraction
0092-0258 Stanford Review†
0092-0290 University of California, Berkeley. Office of Institutional Research. Campus Statistics *changed to* University of California, Berkeley. Campus Statistics.
0092-0320 U.S. Coast Guard. Polluting Incidents in and Around U.S. Waters†
0092-0371 A A M C Curriculum Directory
0092-038X Current Business Reports: Monthly Selected Services Receipts†
0092-0436 Disc and That
0092-0444 Apartment Life *see* 0273-2858
0092-0479 Powder Coating Conference†
0092-0487 Faxon Librarians' Guide to Periodicals *changed to* Faxon Guide to Serials.
0092-0495 Carpet and Rug Institute. Review-State of the Industry *changed to* Carpet and Rug Industry Review.
0092-0509 Powder Diffraction File Search Manual. Alphabetical Listing. Inorganic
0092-0517 Journal of Country Music
0092-0525 Jazz Digest
0092-0541 Solid Waste Management: Abstracts from the Literature†
0092-055X Teaching Sociology
0092-0576 Powder Diffraction File Search Manual. Organic
0092-0606 Journal of Biological Physics
0092-0614 Directory of Louisiana Cities, Towns and Villages
0092-0622 Aqueduct
0092-0673 Louisiana Annual Rural Manpower Report†
0092-0703 Academy of Marketing Science. Journal
0092-0711 A.D. United Church Herald Edition *changed to* United Church of Christ A.D.
0092-072X Christian Association for Psychological Studies. Proceedings *see* 0733-4273
0092-0827 International Double Reed Society Journal *see* 0741-7659
0092-0908 World Directory of Environmental Organizations
0092-0940 A E L E Law Enforcement Legal Liability Reporter *see* 0271-5481
0092-0959 Baldwin's Ohio Legislative Service
0092-1009 Air Pollution Effects Surveillance Network Data Report *changed to* Air Quality Data for Arizona.
0092-1025 Outstanding Secondary Educators of America†
0092-105X Soviet Aerospace *changed to* Soviet Aerospace & Technology.
0092-1068 American Hunter
0092-1084 Nevada. Commission on Crime, Delinquency and Corrections. Comprehensive Law Enforcement Plan†
0092-1122 Battelle Memorial Institute. Research Outlook *see* 0145-8477
0092-1157 Journal of Biological Standardization *see* 1045-1056
0092-1270 Virgin Islands Register
0092-1289 Camp Fire Leadership†
0092-1297 Commercial Directory of Puerto Rico-Virgin Islands *changed to* Commercial Buyer's Guide Puerto Rico-Virgin Islands.
0092-1300 Powder Diffraction File Search Manual. Fink Method. Inorganic†
0092-1319 Powder Diffraction File Search Manual. Hanawalt Method. Inorganic
0092-1335 Annual Reports in Inorganic and General Syntheses†
0092-1343 California Environmental Yearbook and Directory *see* 0148-0324
0092-1386 Current World Leaders - Speeches, Reports and Position Papers *see* 0192-6802
0092-1416 Directory of Women Attorneys in the United States *changed to* Directory of Women Law Graduates and Attorneys in the U.S.A.
0092-1424 M A T Y C Journal *see* 0730-8639
0092-1459 New Jersey Covered Employment Trends by Geographical Areas of the State *changed to* Trends in Employment and Wages.
0092-1483 Directory-Hardware and Home Improvement Center Chains, Auto Supply Chains *see* 0736-0452
0092-1491 National Defense
0092-1505 Nebraska. Commission on Law Enforcement and Criminal Justice. Legislative Reporter†
0092-153X Texas Field Crop Statistics†
0092-1548 Brookhaven Highlights
0092-1599 U.S. National Credit Union Administration. Research Report†
0092-1602 New Jersey. Division of Water Resources. Special Report†
0092-1645 U.S. Federal Railroad Administration. Office of Safety. Accident Bulletin *see* 0163-4674
0092-1661 Symposium on Incremental Motion Control Systems and Devices. Proceedings
0092-1696 Nebraska. Fisheries Division. Annual Report
0092-1726 North Carolina. Secretary of State. North Carolina Elections†
0092-1734 New Fishing
0092-1777 Hawaii. Department of Education. Educational Directory: State & District Office
0092-1785 U.S. Agricultural Research Service. A R S - N C
0092-1793 Fremontia
0092-1807 Twentieth Century *see* 0272-1635
0092-1815 International Journal of Instructional Media
0092-184X Psychotherapy Economics *see* 0163-1543
0092-1858 Alaska Blue Book
0092-1866 Intercultural Studies Information Service†
0092-1874 Directory of Registered Federal and State Lobbyists *see* 0146-0323
0092-1904 United States Government Manual
0092-1912 Fiction International
0092-1920 Incentive Travel Manager *see* 0892-8193
0092-1939 U.S. Agricultural Research Service. A R S-S†
0092-198X South Dakota. Department of History. Report and Historical Collections *changed to* South Dakota Historical Collections.
0092-2013 Teaching Political Science *see* 1045-7097
0092-2056 U.S. National Oceanic and Atmospheric Administration. Interdepartmental Committee for Meteorological Services and Supporting Research. National Hurricane Operations Plan
0092-2102 Interfaces
0092-2145 California and Western States Grape Grower *see* 1049-670X
0092-2226 Potomac Appalachian
0092-2242 University of California, Los Angeles. Latin American Center. Latin American Activities and Resources†
0092-2293 Verdict Reports *changed to* Verdict Review.
0092-2307 H I S S Titles and Review†
0092-2315 American Journal of Criminal Law
0092-2323 Journal of Indo-European Studies
0092-2358 Tri-State Regional Planning Commission. Annual Regional Report *changed to* Tri-State Planning Commission. Annual Report.
0092-2374 Utah Export Directory†
0092-2382 Journal of World Education *changed to* Association for World Education. Journal.
0092-2463 New Times (New York)†
0092-2471 Chicagoan†
0092-2498 Criminal Justice (Washington, 1973)†
0092-2528 Oklahoma Water Resources Research Institute. Annual Report
0092-2552 A.E.L.E. Law Enforcement Legal Defense Manual *see* 0191-877X
0092-2560 Weekly California Citator
0092-2633 National Peach Council. Proceedings
0092-2684 Colorado Water Resources Circulars†
0092-2765 U.S. Postal Service. Support Group. Revenue and Cost Analysis *changed to* U.S. Postal Service. Revenue and Cost Analysis Report.
0092-2803 Rand Paper Series *changed to* The Rand Corporation's Research Publications.
0092-2811 American Coin-Op
0092-282X Pickup, Van and 4WD *see* 0747-1971
0092-2838 Music, Books on Music and Sound Recordings
0092-2846 Review of Public Data Use *see* 0747-9662
0092-2870 Air Freight Directory
0092-2889 Arkansas Average Covered Employment and Earnings by County and Industry *changed to* Arkansas Covered Employment and Earnings.
0092-2900 Perspectives in Nephrology and Hypertension†
0092-2935 National Roster of Black Elected Officials *see* 0882-1593
0092-2986 Midwest History of Education Society. Journal
0092-3052 Homosexual Counseling Journal†
0092-3060 Oregon. Office of Community Health Services. Local Health Services Annual Summary†
0092-3079 New Jersey. Violent Crimes Compensation Board. Annual Report†
0092-3117 U.S. Department of Transportation. Fiscal Year Budget in Brief
0092-315X Science Indicators
0092-3168 Guide to U S Government Publications
0092-3206 U.S. Bureau of East-West Trade. Office of Export Administration. Export Administration Report *changed to* U.S. International Trade Administration. Export Administration Annual Report.
0092-3214 Street & Smith's Pro Football
0092-3257 Directory of Facilities for the Learning Disabled *changed to* Directory of Services and Facilities for the Learning Disabled.
0092-3281 Illinois Air Sampling Network Report *changed to* Illinois. Division of Air Pollution Control. Annual Air Quality Report.
0092-3311 New Jersey. Department of Environmental Protection. Annual Report
0092-3362 Massachusetts. Division of Mineral Resources. Annual Report†
0092-3419 Native American Rights Fund. Catalogue *changed to* National Indian Law Library. Catalogue.
0092-3427 Tennessee Thrust†

ISSN

0092-3435 Occupational Safety and Health Decisions
0092-346X N A S A Report to Educators
0092-3478 American Baptist Churches in the U S A Yearbook
0092-3486 Annual Index to Popular Music Record Reviews†
0092-3524 Iustitia (Bloomington)†
0092-3540 Texscope: U S A Textile Industry Overview
0092-3559 Texas Southern University Law Review *changed to* Thurgood Marshall Law Review.
0092-3591 Overview of the F A A Engineering & Development Programs
0092-380X Washington State†
0092-3818 Illinois Services Directory
0092-3826 Alcoholism Treatment Facilities Directory: United States and Canada†
0092-3850 Woman's Day Gifts You Can Make for Christmas *changed to* Woman's Day Best Ideas for Christmas.
0092-3877 Bar†
0092-394X Newsletter for Research in Mental Health & Behavioral Sciences†
0092-3974 International Directory of Little Magazines and Small Presses
0092-4032 Medical Challenge†
0092-4067 Directory of Missouri Libraries
0092-4091 Present Tense†
0092-4113 W P A S Museletter
0092-4148 World Today Series: Latin America
0092-4164 Where the Trails Cross
0092-4180 Better Homes and Gardens Crafts & Sewing†
0092-4199 Day Care and Early Education
0092-4202 Directory of Private Business Correspondence Schools *changed to* Directory of Private Vocational Schools.
0092-4229 Speed†
0092-4245 Wesleyan Theological Journal
0092-4261 Woodrow Wilson International Center for Scholars. Annual Report
0092-427X Arctic Bulletin†
0092-4288 University of Nevada. Seismological Laboratory. Bulletin
0092-430X Pepperdine Law Review
0092-4318 Platte Valley Review
0092-4326 American Society for Engineering Education. Review and Directory *changed to* A S E E Profile.
0092-4334 B I S Conference Report†
0092-4407 Managers†
0092-4415 Primitive Baptist Yearbook
0092-4423 Resource Guide to Reading & Language Arts Programs & Materials†
0092-444X Intercom (Washington) *see* 0749-2448
0092-4466 Hearing Instruments
0092-4555 U.S. Federal Aviation Administration. National Aviation System Policy Summary *changed to* U.S. Federal Aviation Administration. National Aviation System: Development and Capital Needs.
0092-4563 Syntax and Semantics
0092-4571 Border States
0092-4598 Who's Who in Training and Development
0092-4601 N A D A Recreation Vehicle Appraisal Guide
0092-461X Facts About Maryland Public Education *changed to* Fact Book.
0092-4652 Criminal Justice Plan for New Jersey *changed to* New Jersey. State Law Enforcement Planning Agency. Applicants Guide.
0092-4679 National Security Traders Association. Traders' Annual
0092-4725 Browning Institute Studies†
0092-4733 Michigan State University. Institute for Community Development and Services. Population Report. Community Development Series†
0092-4768 American Institute of Certified Public Accountants. Committee on Minority Recruitment and Equal Opportunity. Report†
0092-4857 M E I Marketing Economics Guide
0092-4865 R E I T Handbook of Member Trusts†
0092-489X Artes Visuales
0092-4962 Classified Index of National Labor Relations Board Decisions and Related Court Decisions *changed to* Classified Index of N.L.R.B. and Related Court Decisions.
0092-4970 Directory of Electric Light and Power Companies *changed to* Directory of Electric Utility Industry.
0092-4989 International Directory of Executive Recruiters†
0092-5039 Franklin Mint Almanac
0092-5055 Annual of Psychoanalysis†
0092-5071 Colorado Business
0092-508X D.A.T.A. Book of Discontinued Thyristors *changed to* Thyristor Discontinued Devices D.A.T.A. Book.
0092-511X Street and Smith's College and Pro Official Basketball Yearbook *see* 0149-7103
0092-5144 Vermont Facts and Figures†
0092-5187 N E M A Bulletin
0092-5268 Grants and Awards Available to American Writers
0092-5322 Fusilier (La Puente)†
0092-5349 Michigan. State Library Services. Catalog of Books on Magnetic Tape†
0092-542X Safety Science Abstracts *see* 0892-9351
0092-5438 Youth Reporter†
0092-5462 Data Resources Review *changed to* D R I - McGraw-Hill Review of the U.S. Economy.
0092-5470 Developments in Human Services Series†
0092-5489 National Directory of Women's Athletics *see* 0739-1226
0092-5535 Panjandrum Poetry Journal
0092-5543 Washington (State). Vocational Rehabilitation Services Division. State Facilities Plan *changed to* Washington (State). Division of Vocational Rehabilitation. State Facilities Development Plan.
0092-5594 U.S. Centers for Disease Control. Congenital Malformations Surveillance
0092-5632 American Journal of Roentgenology and Radium Therapy *see* 0361-803X
0092-5659 American Lung Association. Bulletin†
0092-5667 Healthnews†
0092-5675 Academy Awards Oscar Annual
0092-5756 Bibliography of Noise†
0092-5764 Connecticut Walk Book
0092-5799 O S H A Compliance Letter *changed to* Safety Compliance Letter.
0092-5810 Vermont's Fisheries Annual†
0092-5845 Food Service Marketing *see* 0894-4466
0092-5853 American Journal of Political Science
0092-5896 U.S. Department of Agriculture. Bimonthly List of Publications and Visuals *changed to* U.S. Department of Agriculture. Quarterly List of Publications.
0092-590X American History and Culture†
0092-5934 Attorneys and Agents Registered to Practice Before the U.S. Patent Office *see* 0361-3844
0092-5950 N M R I Compensation in Mass Retailing, Salaries and Incentives
0092-5969 Popular Sports Face-off†
0092-6000 Current Literature in Family Planning
0092-6019 Immunology: An International Series of Monographs and Treatises†
0092-606X Degrees Conferred by West Virginia Institutions of Higher Education†
0092-6086 Inter Alia
0092-6108 Title Varies†
0092-6132 Directory of the Mutual Savings Banks of the United States *changed to* National Council of Savings Institutions Directory.
0092-6175 Transportation and Products Legal Directory
0092-6213 Circulatory Shock
0092-6221 High School Behavioral Science†
0092-623X Journal of Sex & Marital Therapy
0092-6248 Lawrence Berkeley Laboratory. Inorganic Materials Research Division. Annual Report *changed to* Lawrence Berkeley Laboratory. Materials and Chemical Sciences Division. Annual Report.
0092-6256 Aurora A F X Road Racing Handbook
0092-6280 Association for Educational Data Systems. Handbook and Directory†
0092-6299 Iowa. Bureau of Labor. Occupational Injuries and Illnesses Survey *changed to* Iowa. Division of Labor. Occupational Injuries and Illnesses Survey.
0092-6302 Semiconductor Heat Sink, Socket & Associated Hardware D.A.T.A. Book†
0092-6345 Iowa State Journal of Research†
0092-6353 HorsePlay
0092-6361 Current Contents: Social & Behavioral Sciences
0092-640X Atomic Data and Nuclear Data Tables
0092-6426 Limits in the Seas
0092-6442 Nebraska. Natural Resources Commission. State Water Plan Publication (Lincoln) *changed to* Nebraska. Natural Resources Commission. State Water Planning and Review Process.
0092-6485 American Medical Technologists. Official Journal *see* 0741-5397
0092-6507 Auerbach Annual: Best Computer Papers†
0092-6531 Federal Estate and Gift Taxes Explained, Including Estate Planning
0092-654X Illustrated Digest of Pro Football†
0092-6558 Interdenominational Theological Center, Atlanta. Journal
0092-6566 Journal of Research in Personality
0092-6639 Women's Organizations & Leaders Directory
0092-6647 Foreign Newspaper and Gazette Report *see* 0190-9819
0092-6655 Personal Income Tax Analysis *changed to* Oregon Personal Income Tax Statistics.
0092-6736 Alaska. Department of Revenue. State Investment Portfolio
0092-6752 Pesticides (Sacramento)
0092-6841 Nevada. Office of Fiscal Analyst. Annual Report *changed to* Nevada. Office of Legislative Auditor. Biennial Report.
0092-6868 Aspen Leaves *changed to* Aspen Journal of the Arts.
0092-6876 Automatic Taxfinder and Tax Preparer's Handbook†
0092-6884 Daily Tax Report
0092-7023 Journal of Physical and Colloid Chemistry *see* 0022-3654
0092-7082 Sports Afield Almanac *see* 0190-1249
0092-7147 Daily Bread
0092-718X Letters & Papers on the Social Sciences: an Undergraduate Review†
0092-7201 Linear Integrated Circuits and M.O.S. Devices†
0092-721X R C A Corporation. Solid State Division. R. F. Power Devices†
0092-7228 Thyristors, Rectifiers, and Diacs†
0092-7287 U.S. National Center for Health Statistics. Current Listing and Topical Index to the Vital and Health Statistics Series *see* 0278-4912
0092-735X Continuing Education for the Family Physician†
0092-7384 I A B C Journal *see* 0744-7612
0092-7392 Index to the Contemporary Scene†
0092-7422 American Defense Preparedness Association. Annual Directory. *see* 0092-1491
0092-7449 Direction (Alexandria)
0092-7473 Tennis Trade *changed to* Tennis/Racquet Trade.
0092-7481 Urban Institute. Annual Report
0092-749X Walker's Manual of Western Corporations and Securities *see* 0894-153X
0092-7643 Overseas Development Council. Annual Report
0092-7651 Archives of Podiatric Medicine and Foot Surgery†
0092-7678 Asian Affairs: An American Review
0092-7686 Booklegger
0092-7694 Cason Quarterly
0092-7708 Conch Review of Books
0092-7724 Past and Likely Future of 58 Research Libraries, 1951-1980: a Statistical Study of Growth and Change†
0092-7732 Product Safety & Liability Reporter
0092-7759 Social and Rehabilitation Record *changed to* U.S. Health Care Financing Administration Forum.
0092-7767 Predicasts Source Directory
0092-7783 Illinois. Junior College Board. Annual Report *changed to* Illinois. Community College Board. Annual Report.
0092-7813 Children's Hospital National Medical Center. Clinical Proceedings†
0092-7821 World Association for Christian Communication. Journal *changed to* Media Development.
0092-7856 Guide to Architecture Schools in North America
0092-7872 Communications in Algebra
0092-7899 Mississippi Educational Directory
0092-7929 Annual of New Art and Artists†
0092-7937 Pennsylvania. Citizens Advisory Council to the Department of Environmental Resources. Annual Report
0092-7945 Missouri River Basin Commission. Annual Report *changed to* Missouri Basin States Association. Annual Report.
0092-7953 Genealogical Society of Old Tryon County. Bulletin
0092-7961 Better Homes and Gardens Furnishings and Decorating Ideas *changed to* Better Homes and Gardens Decorating.
0092-797X Keeping Up with Orff Schulwerk in the Classroom†
0092-7996 Texas Yearbook†
0092-8003 Save On Shopping *see* 0276-6701
0092-8089 Adsorption and Adsorbents†
0092-8208 Children's Literature (New Haven)
0092-8216 Cord Sportfacts: Hunting†
0092-8240 Bulletin of Mathematical Biology
0092-8313 Prairie Scout
0092-833X Libraries of Maine; Directory and Statistics
0092-8364 District of Columbia. City Council. Annual Report†
0092-8372 Disciple (St. Louis)
0092-8380 Encyclopedia of Governmental Advisory Organizations
0092-8410 N.A.C.D.S. Lilly Digest†
0092-8437 Physics *changed to* Physics News.
0092-847X University of Wisconsin, Madison. Institute for Research on Poverty. Research Report†
0092-8526 Directory Listing Curriculums Offered in the Community Colleges of Pennsylvania†
0092-8550 U.S. General Accounting Office. Office of the General Counsel. Quarterly Digest of Unpublished Decisions of the Comptroller General of the United States; Procurement Law†
0092-8577 Health Affairs†
0092-8593 A P C D Digest
0092-8607 Biomedical Communications†
0092-8615 Drug Information Journal

ISSN

0092-8623 Journal of Mental Health Administration
0092-8631 St. Luke's Hospital. Medical Staff Journal
0092-8658 A P S A Directory of Department Chairmen *changed to* A P S A Directory of Department Chairpersons.
0092-8666 Bell Tower
0092-8674 Cell
0092-8682 Current Medical Diagnosis and Treatment
0092-8704 Jacksonville Genealogical Society. Magazine. *see* 0149-6867
0092-881X College Football Modern Record Book *see* 0735-5475
0092-8828 P B X Systems Guide
0092-8836 Reference Data on Socioeconomic Issues of Health *see* 0198-7399
0092-8887 Creative Guitar International†
0092-8917 U.S. National Oceanic and Atmospheric Administration. Manned Undersea Science and Technology Program; Report
0092-8933 Police and Law Enforcement
0092-9018 Inspiration Three†
0092-9158 California. Department of Water Resources. Inventory of Waste Water Production and Waste Water Reclamation Practices in California†
0092-9166 Creation Research Society Quarterly
0092-9174 Directory of San Francisco Attorneys
0092-9190 Hawaii. State Commission on the Status of Women. Annual Report
0092-9212 Michigan State Employees' Retirement System Financial and Statistical Report
0092-9301 Memory and Learning - Neural Correlates in Animals *changed to* Memory and Learning - Research in the Nervous System.
0092-9336 Osteopathic Annals
0092-9395 G P S A Journal *see* 0730-2177
0092-9425 Schist†
0092-9433 U.S. Environmental Protection Agency. Clean Water: Report to Congress
0092-9441 Urban Telecommunications Forum†
0092-945X C & P Warrant Analysis†
0092-9476 Maryland. Department of Human Resources. Information Pamphlet†
0092-9492 U.S. Department of State. Foreign Affairs Research Documentation Center. Foreign Affairs Research Papers Available†
0092-9506 Fielding's Selected Favorites: Hotels and Inns, Europe *see* 0191-0329
0092-9522 Abortion Bibliography
0092-9530 U.S. Department of Agriculture. Economics, Statistics and Cooperatives Service. Cost of Storing and Handling Cotton at Public Storage Facilities†
0092-9549 Oswego County Historical Society. Journal†
0092-9565 Current Geological and Geophysical Studies in Montana
0092-9638 Utah. Forestry and Fire Control. R C and D Release†
0092-9654 U.S. Forest Service. General Technical Report I N T
0092-9662 U.S. Forest Service. General Technical Report PSW *see* 0196-2094
0092-9670 National Air Monitoring Program Air Quality and Emissions Trends. Report *changed to* National Air Quality and Emissions Trends Report.
0092-9727 Popular Periodical Index
0092-9751 Nuclear Industry Status *changed to* Worldwide Uranium Producer Profiles.
0092-9778 National Issues Outlook *see* 0360-4217
0092-9794 Massachusetts Agricultural Statistics *changed to* Massachusetts Agriculture (Year) Annual Report.
0092-9824 F A S Public Interest Report
0092-9832 Bergen County Dental Society. Newsletter
0092-9867 Toxicological and Environmental Chemistry Reviews *see* 0277-2248
0092-993X Nuclear Fuel Status and Forecast *changed to* N A C - Focus.
0092-9948 Nuclear Powerplant Performance†
0093-0040 Utah. State Office of Education. Opinions of the Utah State Superintendent of Public Instruction
0093-0075 Food Technology Review†
0093-0083 Clemson University. Department of Forestry. Forestry Bulletin *changed to* Clemson University. Department of Forest Resources. Forestry Bulletin.
0093-0164 Lyons Teacher-News
0093-0237 American Association of Psychiatric Services for Children. Newsletter *see* 0027-6022
0093-0245 Business Radio - Action *see* 0746-8911
0093-0261 Energy Users Report *see* 0888-8183
0093-0288 N U Quarter Notes
0093-0296 R C A Corporation. Solid State Division. Power Transistors and Power Hybrid Circuits†
0093-0334 Hastings Center Report
0093-0393 National Library of Medicine. Programs and Services
0093-0407 Sleep Research
0093-0415 Western Journal of Medicine
0093-0431 Children's Literary Almanac *changed to* International Directory of Children's Literature.
0093-044X Crime Prevention Review†
0093-0458 Dimensions (Washington)†
0093-0466 Automobile Insurance Losses, Collision Coverages, Variations by Make and Series
0093-0482 Meetings & Expositions†
0093-0512 Energy Pipelines and Systems *changed to* Chilton's Oil & Gas Energy.
0093-0520 Maryland. State Department of Legislative Reference. Synopsis of Laws Enacted by the State of Maryland
0093-0539 Summary of Ground Water Data for Tennessee†
0093-0563 U.S. Library of Congress. Library of Congress Name Headings with References†
0093-0571 Monographic Series†
0093-061X Government Publications Review *see* 0277-9390
0093-0679 Landslide (Eureka)
0093-0709 Syracuse Journal of International Law & Commerce
0093-0717 Arizona Business
0093-0741 Missouri. Public Service Commission. Regulated Electric Study†
0093-0776 Something Else Yearbook†
0093-0938 Better Homes and Gardens Building Ideas
0093-1004 Biological Psychology Bulletin†
0093-1039 Alaska Bar Brief *changed to* Alaska Bar Rag.
0093-1047 Harris Auction Galleries. Collectors' Auction
0093-1063 Florida Law Revision Commission. Annual Report *changed to* Florida Law Revision Council. Annual Report.
0093-1071 Florida. State Board of Independent Colleges and Universities. Report
0093-1098 New Jersey Public Libraries. Statistics *changed to* New Jersey Public Library Statistics For (Year).
0093-111X Pretrial Justice Quarterly†
0093-1160 Association of Trial Lawyers of America. Newsletter *see* 0364-8125
0093-1179 Atlanta Constitution: a Georgia Index†
0093-1241 Wyoming. Department of Labor and Statistics. Survey of Occupational Injuries and Illnesses†
0093-125X Marketing Guide†
0093-1284 American Annals of the Deaf and Dumb *see* 0002-726X
0093-1314 Medical Meetings
0093-1330 American Bell Association. Directory
0093-1365 Photo Information Almanac†
0093-1454 American Marketing Association. Directory of Marketing Services and Membership Roster *changed to* American Marketing Association. International Membership Directory and Marketing Services Guide.
0093-1535 Employment Safety and Health Guide
0093-1551 Corrective and Social Psychiatry and Journal of Behavioral Technology Methods and Therapy
0093-156X Journal of Numerical Control *see* 0886-1463
0093-1659 Purchasing World†
0093-1713 Excited States†
0093-173X Hospital Topics and Buyer's Guide *see* 0018-5868
0093-1799 Official Port of Detroit World Handbook
0093-1853 Journal of Psychiatry and Law
0093-1861 American Artist Business Letter†
0093-1888 Librarians' Handbook
0093-1896 Critical Inquiry
0093-190X Babson's Investment Digest†
0093-1918 Classic Collector†
0093-1926 I.R.C.A. Foreign Log†
0093-2094 American Indian Media Directory†
0093-2124 On Scene
0093-2132 Product Digest *see* 0146-5023
0093-2205 International Journal of Occupational Health and Safety *see* 0362-4064
0093-2213 Pavlovian Journal of Biological Science *changed to* Integrative Physiological and Behavioral Science.
0093-2302 Minicomputer Review†
0093-2310 Serials Updating Service†
0093-2329 Serials Updating Service Quarterly†
0093-2337 Terminals Review *see* 0093-416X
0093-2388 U.S. Federal Railroad Administration. Bibliography of Published Research Reports *see* 0097-0042
0093-2485 Economic Books: Current Selections†
0093-2515 Drug Abuse Bibliography
0093-2531 McLean Guide to Kennels of America†
0093-2558 Minnesota Alcohol Programs for Highway Safety†
0093-2574 Consortium on Revolutionary Europe Proceedings
0093-2582 St. Croix Review
0093-2825 For Younger Readers, Braille and Talking Books (Large Print Edition)
0093-2914 Applied Anthropology *see* 0018-7259
0093-304X Columbia Law Alumni Observer
0093-3058 Duquesne Law Review
0093-3066 American Chemical Society. Division of Environmental Chemistry. Preprints of Papers.
0093-3074 U.S. National Park Service. Public Use of the National Park System: Fiscal Year Report
0093-3082 Montana. Animal Health Division. Statistical Data *changed to* Montana. Animal Health Division. Statistical Summary.
0093-3090 Southern California Business Directory and Buyers Guide
0093-3104 Theory and Research in Social Education
0093-3139 College Literature
0093-3155 Forest H. Belt's Yearbook of Consumer Electronics†
0093-3163 Grants and Awards Available to Foreign Writers†
0093-3171 Journal of Family Counseling *see* 0192-6187
0093-318X Monday *see* 0145-1677
0093-3236 E C & M's Electrical Products Yearbook
0093-3252 Hastings Center Studies *see* 0093-0334
0093-3279 Alcoholism Digest Annual
0093-3287 Environment Abstracts
0093-3295 Pesticides Abstracts
0093-3317 Studies on the Development of Behavior and the Nervous System†
0093-3414 College and University Employees, New York State
0093-3430 U.S. Department of Health, Education and Welfare. Annual Report to the Congress of the United States on Services to Handicapped Children in Project Head Start *changed to* U.S. Department of Health and Human Services. Annual Report to the Congress of the United States on Services Provided to Handicapped Children in Project Head Start.
0093-3465 Opportunities in Iowa's Area Schools†
0093-3481 Hawaii. Department of Health. Research and Statistics Office. R & S Report
0093-3503 Your Business and the Law *changed to* You and the Law.
0093-3546 Cardiovascular Diseases *see* 0730-2347
0093-3589 Industrial Pharmacology†
0093-3619 Year Book of Dermatology
0093-3627 Yearbook of Dermatology and Syphilology *see* 0093-3619
0093-3643 N E C Newsletter *changed to* Campus Activities Programming.
0093-3651 Sea Technology
0093-366X U.S. Civil Service Commission. Personnel Research and Development Center. Technical Study†
0093-3686 Studies in Jazz Discography *see* 0731-0641
0093-3708 Metric News†
0093-3716 U. S. Department of the Interior. Office of Personnel Management. Annual Manpower Personnel Statistics†
0093-3813 I E E E Transactions on Plasma Science
0093-3821 List of Journals Indexed in Index Medicus
0093-3864 Land Use Planning Report *changed to* Land Use Law Report.
0093-3929 Southern Horseman
0093-3945 U. S. Office of Saline Water. Catalog of Research Projects†
0093-3961 Journal of Financial Education
0093-397X Legal Notes for Education
0093-3996 Pacific Tropical Botanical Garden. Bulletin *changed to* National Tropical Botanical Garden. Bulletin.
0093-4038 California and Western Medicine *see* 0093-0415
0093-4054 Contemporary Topics in Immunobiology
0093-4062 American Automobile Association. Digest of Motor Laws
0093-4089 Florida Senate
0093-416X Computer Review
0093-4240 New School for Social Research. Philosophy Department. Graduate Faculty Philosophy Journal
0093-4267 Battelle Memorial Institute. Columbus Laboratories. Report on National Survey of Compensation Paid Scientists and Engineers Engaged in Research and Development Activities†
0093-4283 Trailer Life's Recreational Vehicle Campground and Services Guide *changed to* Trailer Life's Recreational Vehicle Campground and Services Directory.
0093-433X Cotton Ginnings in the United States *changed to* Cotton Ginnings by States.
0093-4429 Peanut Market News
0093-4437 Anesthesiology Review
0093-4445 Journal of Long-Term Care Administration
0093-4461 Physicians' Desk Reference
0093-447X Physicians' Desk Reference to Pharmaceutical Specialties and Biologicals *see* 0093-4461
0093-4518 American Society for Preventive Dentistry Journal†
0093-4526 Journal of Zoo Animal Medicine *see* 1042-7260
0093-4585 Guide to the Recommended Country Inns of New England

ISSN	Title
0093-4593	Leisure Home Living†
0093-4615	Council on Foreign Relations. President's Report see 0192-236X
0093-4623	University of Michigan. Graduate School of Business Administration. Proceedings of the Annual Business Conference†
0093-4631	U.S. Fish and Wildlife Service. Selected List of Federal Laws and Treaties Relating to Sport Fish and Wildlife
0093-4658	Journal of Coated Fabrics
0093-4666	Mycotaxon
0093-4674	Criminal Law Commentator (New York) †
0093-4682	Family Law Commentator (New York)†
0093-4690	Journal of Field Archaeology
0093-4712	American Journal of Pharmacy see 0730-7780
0093-4720	Benchmark Papers in Animal Behavior changed to Benchmark Papers in Behavior.
0093-4755	Evolutionary Theory changed to Evolutionary Theory and Review.
0093-4763	Groups: a Journal of Group Dynamics and Psychotherapy†
0093-4771	Methods in Membrane Biology changed to Cell Membranes, Methods and Reviews.
0093-4909	Lackawanna - Wayne - Pike - Susquehanna Farm & Home News
0093-4992	Energy Resources Report see 0278-5099
0093-500X	Energy Today
0093-5018	Basic Oil Laws & Concession Contracts: Europe
0093-5026	Good News of Tomorrow's World see 0032-0420
0093-5034	New York (State) Department of Labor. Division of Research and Statistics. Labor Research Report
0093-5050	Skeptic see 0160-4929
0093-5069	U.S. Division of Wildlife Services. Annual Report†
0093-5107	Journal of Real Estate Taxation
0093-5166	Contemporary Problems in Cardiology†
0093-5220	Insiders' Guide to the Colleges†
0093-5239	U. S. Bureau of Sport Fisheries and Wildlife. Report to the Fish Farmer†
0093-5255	Business Week Letter changed to Personal Finance Letter.
0093-5263	Creativity in Action
0093-5271	Doane's Agricultural Report
0093-5301	Journal of Consumer Research
0093-531X	Perspectives in Religious Studies
0093-5328	Phi Kappa Phi Newsletter
0093-5336	Recon
0093-5352	Retirement Letter
0093-5387	Undersea Biomedical Research
0093-5417	Budd Gore Media Mix Newsletter
0093-5530	Wyoming. Division of Planning, Evaluation and Information Services. Statistical Report Series
0093-5557	Benchmark Papers in Human Physiology†
0093-5603	Population Analysis of the Illinois Adult Prison System†
0093-5654	U.S. Bureau of Radiological Health. Research Grants Program†
0093-5700	Geothermal Energy Magazine changed to Renewable Energy News Digest.
0093-5778	Montclair Journal of Social Science and Humanities changed to Montclair Journal of Social and Behavorial Sciences.
0093-5794	Word Processing World see 0279-7992
0093-5816	Directory of Published Proceedings. Series P C E : Pollution Control & Ecology
0093-5832	Farmland News
0093-5891	Toxic Materials News
0093-6049	Foresight (Washington)†
0093-609X	Origins, N C Documentary Service changed to Origins, C N S Documentary Service.
0093-6138	Florida Speech Communication Journal changed to Florida Communication Journal.
0093-6235	North American Society for Sport History. Proceedings
0093-6332	Vanderbilt University. Department of Environmental and Water Resources Engineering. Technical Reports
0093-6383	Civil Liberties Review†
0093-6391	Endocrine Research Communications see 0743-5800
0093-6405	American Society of Civil Engineers. Geotechnical Engineering Division. Journal see 0733-9410
0093-6413	Mechanics Research Communications
0093-6472	Montana Advisory Council for Vocational Education. Annual Report changed to Montana Council on Vocational Education. Annual Report.
0093-6502	Communication Research
0093-6510	Findings and Forecasts†
0093-6553	Cost of Picking and Hauling Florida Citrus Fruits
0093-6626	Biography News†
0093-6642	Monographs on Music in Higher Education†
0093-6693	Washington (State). Attorney General's Office. Directory of Charitable Organizations and Trusts Registered with the Office of Attorney General changed to Washington (State). Attorney General's Office. Charitable Trust Directory.
0093-6715	Florida. Division of Family Services. Annual Statistical Report changed to Florida. Department of Health and Rehabilitative Services. Annual Statistical Report.
0093-674X	Federal Telephone Directory†
0093-6758	Film Literature Index
0093-6766	International Bonds changed to International Bond Guide.
0093-6774	Michigan. Department of Social Services. Public Assistance Statistics see 0093-7835
0093-6782	Motorboat see 0006-5374
0093-6804	B.C.D. Business Cycle Development see 0146-7735
0093-691X	Theriogenology
0093-6960	Kinesiology†
0093-6987	Ridge Runners†
0093-6995	Tax Management Executive Compensation Journal see 0747-8607
0093-7002	American Journal of Optometry and Physiological Optics see 1040-5488
0093-7053	Modern Healthcare (Long-Term Care) see 0160-7480
0093-7061	Modern Healthcare (Short-Term Care) see 0160-7480
0093-707X	Persimmon Hill
0093-7134	Idaho's Comprehensive Plan for Criminal Justice†
0093-7142	Montana Manual of State and Local Government†
0093-7215	Catalog of Captioned Films for the Deaf
0093-7223	Idaho. State Superintendent of Public Instruction. Annual Report. State of Idaho Johnson-O'Malley Program
0093-7231	Juvenile Justice see 0161-7109
0093-724X	Maine Economic Data Book†
0093-7274	Woodall's Directory of Mobile Home Communities see 0731-6526
0093-7282	Audio Journal of Podiatric Medicine†
0093-7290	Data Channels
0093-7312	Investor-Owned Hospital Review see 1055-7466
0093-7347	New Jersey Dental Association. Journal
0093-7355	Lab Animal
0093-7363	National Medical Audiovisual Center Motion Picture and Videotape Catalog see 0083-2294
0093-7398	Population Sciences: Index of Biomedical Research†
0093-7436	University of Alaska Museum. Annual Report
0093-7487	Multinational Executive Travel Companion
0093-7495	Origins (Loma Linda)
0093-7525	California. Department of Industrial Relations. Division of Labor Statistics and Research. Building Trades Wage Rates†
0093-7568	Pennsylvania State University. Research Publications and Professional Activities†
0093-7630	F E P Guidelines
0093-7657	Energy Report
0093-7673	People (New York) changed to People Weekly.
0093-7703	Directory of Educational Facilities for the Learning Disabled changed to Directory of Services and Facilities for the Learning Disabled.
0093-7711	Immunogenetics
0093-7754	Seminars in Oncology
0093-7797	American Bar Association. Special Committee on Environmental Law. Quarterly Newsletter see 0748-8769
0093-7800	Compliance and Legal Seminar. Proceedings†
0093-7835	Michigan. Department of Social Services. Program Statistics
0093-7843	North Dakota State Plan for Rehabilitation Facilities and Workshops
0093-7851	Petroleo Internacional
0093-786X	Deseret News Church Almanac
0093-7886	Maine. Bureau of Labor and Industry of Labor and Industry. Occupational Wage Survey changed to Maine. Department of Labor. Occupational Wage Survey.
0093-7924	U.S. National Advisory Council on Indian Education. Annual Report to the Congress of the United States
0093-8041	Georgia State University. Institute of Health Administration. Occasional Publication†
0093-8076	C L R
0093-8130	Mission Handbook: North American Protestant Ministries Overseas changed to Mission Handbook: U S A - Canada Protestant Ministries Overseas.
0093-8149	Public Telecommunications Review (PTR)†
0093-8157	Reviews in Anthropology
0093-8203	North Dakota. Department of Agriculture. Annual Report changed to North Dakota. Department of Agriculture. Biennial Report.
0093-8246	Montana. Department of Business Regulation. Annual Report changed to Montana. Department of Commerce. Professional and Occupational Licensing Bureau. Public Safety Division. Biennial Report.
0093-8262	Federal Reserve Bank of San Francisco. Business Review see 0363-0021
0093-8270	C O S - M O S Digital Integrated Circuits†
0093-8297	E S Q
0093-8327	Industrial Fishery Products; Market Review and Outlook†
0093-8343	Engineering Issues see 1052-3928
0093-8394	Energy Conservation Abstracts†
0093-8408	Energy Abstracts
0093-8416	Energy Conversion Abstracts see 0093-8408
0093-8440	Soldiers
0093-8475	Folklore Feminists Communication†
0093-8505	Railway History Monograph
0093-8548	Criminal Justice & Behavior
0093-8572	Funds and Manpower in the United States changed to National Patterns of R & D Resources.
0093-8599	U.S. National Clearinghouse for Drug Abuse Information. Report Series changed to U.S. National Institute on Drug Abuse. Report Series.
0093-8610	Criminal Defense†
0093-8637	Guidebook to Florida Taxes
0093-8645	Guidebook to Wisconsin Taxes
0093-8653	Annual Public Defenders' Workshop. Handbook†
0093-8688	Journal of College and University Law
0093-8696	Learning and the Law†
0093-870X	Minnesota. Department of Education. Biennial Report†
0093-8726	Industrial Fishery Products. Annual Summary†
0093-8742	Educational Research Service. Salaries Scheduled for Administrative and Supervisory Personnel in Public Schools†
0093-8750	Executive Compensation Servive. Technician Report changed to Technical & Skilled Trade Personnel Report.
0093-8769	Clinical Dentistry†
0093-8785	U.S. Health Resources Administration. Health Resources News†
0093-8823	Direct Levies on Gaming in Nevada†
0093-8831	Fact Book and Report of the West Virginia State System of Higher Education†
0093-884X	Physical Facilities at Institutions of Higher Education in West Virginia†
0093-8858	Pro Set
0093-8874	Teaching English to the Deaf changed to Teaching English to Deaf and Second Language Students.
0093-8912	California. Council on Criminal Justice. Comprehensive Plan for Criminal Justice†
0093-8920	Latvija Sodien
0093-8939	Illinois. Judicial Inquiry Board. Report
0093-8955	Utah. State Archives and Records Service. Administrative Rule Making Bulletin see 0882-4738
0093-9021	National Environmental Research Center. Annual Report†
0093-9048	Montana Law Enforcement Academy. Annual Report to the Governor of Montana†
0093-9102	Missouri. Air Conservation Commission. Annual Report†
0093-9137	Michigan Council on Vocational Eduation. Biennial Evaluation Report (Year)
0093-9161	Public Sector Arbitration Awards
0093-9188	Alternatives in Print†
0093-9277	Education Bulletin (Missoula)†
0093-9285	Sociology of Work and Occupations see 0730-8884
0093-9293	Southern Voices†
0093-9307	Translation (New York, 1972)
0093-934X	Brain and Language
0093-9374	Leica Manual†
0093-9382	United Methodists Today†
0093-9390	Michigan. Office of Criminal Justice. Comprehensive Law Enforcement and Criminal Justice Plan†
0093-9404	Overview of Blood†
0093-9447	Media Guide International. Newspapers-Newsmagazines Edition changed to International Media Guide. Newspapers Worldwide.
0093-9501	Directory of Special Programs for Minority Group Members; Career Information Services, Employment Skills, Banks, Financial Aid Sources
0093-951X	Directory of Trust Institutions of United States and Canada changed to Directory of Trust Institutions.
0093-9552	Illinois State and Regional Economic Data Book
0093-9579	Semiotext(e)

5578 ISSN INDEX

0093-9595 Nevada. Advisory Council for Manpower Training and Career Education. Annual Evaluation Report *changed to* Nevada. Advisory Council for Vocational-Technical Education. Annual Evaluation Report.
0093-9625 Hawaii Review
0093-9633 U S Export Weekly *see* 0748-0172
0093-9692 U.S. Department of Commerce. Effects of Pollution Abatement on International Trade†
0093-9706 Guide to Dental Materials and Devices *changed to* Dentist's Desk Reference.
0093-9714 Research Advances in Alcohol & Drug Problems
0093-9722 Urology Times
0093-9730 North Carolina. Council on State Goals and Policy. Annual Report *changed to* North Carolina. State Goals and Policy Board. Annual Report.
0093-9811 Parrott Talk
0093-982X E M Bibliography for Consumers†
0093-9854 Heart of Texas Records
0093-9889 Tennessee. State Board for Vocational Education. Information Series
0093-9897 U.S. Department of Transportation. Year-End Report†
0093-9951 Roster of Black Elected Officials in the South
0093-996X Tape Recording and Buying Guide *changed to* Stereo Review's Tape Recording & Buying Guide.
0093-9978 Noise Control Engineering *see* 0736-2501
0093-9986 New Jersey. Legislature. Office of Fiscal Affairs. Annual Report†
0093-9994 I E E E Transactions on Industry Applications
0094-0003 Physical Review - Index
0094-002X American Indian Law Review
0094-0089 U S China Business Review *see* 0163-7169
0094-0100 Advanced Biomedical Technology *see* 0147-2682
0094-0119 Biomedical Inventions Reporter *see* 0147-2682
0094-0127 Government Documents Review *see* 0147-2682
0094-0135 Health Care Statistics Report *see* 0147-2682
0094-0143 Urologic Clinics of North America
0094-0151 Reference Guide and Comprehensive Catalog of International Serials *see* 0742-3985
0094-0178 Old-House Journal
0094-0186 Off-Lead
0094-0194 New York Culture Review
0094-0208 N A E P Newsletter
0094-0216 Library Security Newsletter *see* 0196-0075
0094-0224 Lawyer's Newsletter *changed to* Law Office Management Digest.
0094-0232 Imprint: Oregon†
0094-0240 First Friday
0094-0259 Alfantics
0094-0267 Addictive Diseases *see* 0276-5608
0094-0283 Genealogy†
0094-0291 Hiking (Highland Park)†
0094-0305 McCall's Cooking School†
0094-033X New German Critique
0094-0348 Population Mobility in Hawaii *see* 0145-9643
0094-0364 Multitype Library Cooperative News
0094-0372 Cockshaw's Construction Labor News & Opinion
0094-0399 Your School and the Law
0094-0402 Biennial Report of the Arts Activities in Alabama *see* 0096-1388
0094-0488 Arkansas Nurse†
0094-0496 American Ethnologist
0094-050X S C A G Annual Report†
0094-0526 Blair and Ketchum's Country Journal *changed to* Country Journal.
0094-0534 Consumers Index
0094-0585 Journal of Carbohydrates, Nucleosides, Nucleotides *see* 0732-8311
0094-0585 Journal of Carbohydrates, Nucleosides, Nucleotides *see* 0732-8303
0094-0593 Journal of Corporate Taxation
0094-0615 Law & Liberty†
0094-0623 Legal Notes for Insurance
0094-064X Planning Review (Oxford)
0094-0658 Sage International Yearbook of Foreign Policy Studies†
0094-0712 Arizona. Department of Economic Security. Annual Report *changed to* D E S Activities Report.
0094-0763 Huber Law Survey†
0094-0771 Middle School Journal
0094-078X Northwestern Tour Book *see* 0363-2695
0094-0798 Oral History Review
0094-0801 University of Florida. Growth Conference. Prepared Papers†
0094-0836 Student Advocate *changed to* Leadership (Reston).
0094-0844 Thorny Trail
0094-0852 Explorations in Economic Research†
0094-0887 Far-Western Forum†
0094-0895 Biofeedback Society of America. Proceedings of the Annual Meeting *changed to* Association for Applied Psychophysiology and Biofeedback. Proceedings of the Annual Meeting.
0094-0968 University of Chicago. Law School. Law Alumni Journal†
0094-100X Directory of Municipal Bond Dealers of the United States
0094-1093 Administrative Law Newsletter†
0094-1115 Basic Economic Data for Idaho
0094-1123 Nevada State Plan for Vocational Education *changed to* Nevada State Plan for Occupational Education (Year).
0094-114X Mechanism and Machine Theory
0094-1182 Civil War Collectors' Dealer Directory
0094-1190 Journal of Urban Economics
0094-1204 National Investor Relations Institute. Proceedings of the Annual National Conference *changed to* National Investor Relations Institute. Executive Summary of the Annual National Conference.
0094-1220 Social Sciences in North Dakota *changed to* North Dakota Human Services.
0094-1247 Nebraska. State Patrol. Annual Report
0094-1255 Book of Names†
0094-1271 Idaho Agricultural Statistics
0094-128X Northeast Pacific Pink and Chum Salmon Workshop. Proceedings
0094-1298 Clinics in Plastic Surgery
0094-1344 Country Music World
0094-1352 IndustriScope†
0094-1360 Jeffersonian Review†
0094-1409 Minnesota. Office of Ombudsman for Corrections. Annual Report
0094-1417 Astrograph
0094-1468 Florida. Department of Education. Florida Statewide Assessment Program: Capsule Report *changed to* Florida. Department of Education. Florida Statewide Assessment Program: State, District and Regional Report of Statewide Assessment Results.
0094-1476 Philadelphia Association for Psychoanalysis. Journal†
0094-1484 Magyar Evkonyv
0094-1492 Materials Performance
0094-1506 Michigan State Plan for Vocational Education
0094-1514 Motor Handbook†
0094-1522 N.C.F.A. Office Manual *see* 0276-783X
0094-1557 Georgia. Department of Education. Statistical Report†
0094-1565 University of Toledo. Business Research Center. Working Papers in Operations Analysis *changed to* University of Toledo. Business Research Center. Working Papers.
0094-162X Tenth Muse†
0094-1638 Sociology: Reviews of New Books†
0094-1646 Industrial Energy *changed to* Gas Industries Magazine.
0094-1670 Conservation in Kansas
0094-1689 American Cartographer *changed to* Cartography and Geographic Information Systems.
0094-1697 Minnesota. Governor. Annual Report on the Quality of the Environment *changed to* Minnesota. Governor. Governor's Report on Environmental Quality.
0094-1700 Journal of Sport History
0094-1719 Academy of Sciences of the Lithuanian S.S.R. Mathematical Transactions *see* 0363-1672
0094-1727 Minnesota Statutes. Supplement
0094-1735 International Monetary Fund. Selected Decisions of the International Monetary Fund and Selected Documents
0094-176X W V E A School Journal *see* 0274-8606
0094-1786 Alaska. State Board of Registration for Architects, Engineers and Land Surveyors. Directory of Architects, Engineers and Land Surveyors
0094-1794 Estate Planning
0094-1824 Society of Pharmacological and Environmental Pathologists. Bulletin *see* 0192-6233
0094-1832 Hydraulic Research in the United States and Canada†
0094-1840 International Contact Lens Clinic *changed to* International Eyecare.
0094-1859 Journal of Afro-American Issues†
0094-1875 National Traffic Law News
0094-1891 Woodall's Mobile Home Park Directory *see* 0731-6526
0094-1948 Forum (Baltimore) *changed to* The Law Forum.
0094-1956 Journal of Instructional Psychology
0094-1964 Paintbrush
0094-1972 Review of Applied Urban Research†
0094-2006 University of Washington Medicine†
0094-2057 California School Law Digest
0094-2065 Communio
0094-2073 Minnesota. Governor's Commission on Crime Prevention and Control. Comprehensive Plan *changed to* Minnesota. Crime Control Planning Board. Comprehensive Plan.
0094-209X Directories of Hawaii†
0094-2200 South Dakota. Department of Labor. Research and Statistics. Annual Report on State and Area Occupational Requirements for Vocational Education†
0094-2227 American College Testing Program. Handbook for Financial Aid Administrators *changed to* American College Testing. Handbook for Financial Aid Administrators.
0094-2235 Illinois Student Lawyer†
0094-2243 Cincinnati Bar Association. Journal†
0094-2251 Virginia State Bar. Younger Members Conference. Newsletter *changed to* Docket Call (Richmond).
0094-226X Newsletter & Digest of Selected Opinions of State Attorneys General†
0094-2278 Railway Passenger Car Annual
0094-2294 Florida. Mental Health Program Office. Statistical Report of Hospitals†
0094-2308 Supply and Demand: Educational Personnel in Delaware
0094-2316 World of Politics
0094-2332 Criminal Justice Digest†
0094-2367 Everyman†
0094-2375 Fantasiae (Los Angeles)
0094-2383 Journal of Abstracts in International Education
0094-2391 Journal of Agronomic Education
0094-2405 Medical Physics
0094-2413 Juvenile Justice Digest
0094-2421 Celebration: a Creative Worship Service
0094-243X A I P Conference Proceedings
0094-2448 Bead Journal *see* 0148-3897
0094-2464 Small Businessman's Clinic†
0094-2499 Journal of Biocommunication
0094-2502 Business Regulation Law Report†
0094-2510 Marketing California Dried Fruits: Prunes, Raisins, Dried Apricots & Peaches†
0094-2553 United States Judicial Reporter
0094-2561 Disclosure Record
0094-257X Weekly Record†
0094-2588 Communication Directory†
0094-260X A A B C Newsletter
0094-2626 Library Statistics of Illinois Colleges and Universities: Institutional Data†
0094-2634 Index to Foreign Market Reports†
0094-2677 Ohio Juvenile Court Statistics†
0094-2715 Inscape (Pasadena)
0094-2758 South Dakota Manufacturers & Processors Directory
0094-2766 Monthly Summary of Texas Natural Gas
0094-2782 New Mexico Forest Products Directory *changed to* Wood Industries of New Mexico.
0094-2790 Movement of California Fruits and Vegetables by Rail, Truck, and Air *see* 0270-384X
0094-2820 Washington Geologic Newsletter *see* 1058-2134
0094-2855 Southwestern Camping *see* 0731-8103
0094-2871 U.S. Environmental Protection Agency. Office of Air Quality Planning and Standards. State Air Pollution Implementation Plan Progress Report†
0094-2898 Southeastern Symposium on System Theory. Proceedings
0094-2987 Illinois. Department of Public Instruction. Publications Resource Manual†
0094-3002 Broker-Dealer Directory†
0094-3029 Carnegie Endowment for International Peace. Financial Report
0094-3061 Contemporary Sociology
0094-3096 American Metric Journal *changed to* A M J - S I Metricpac.
0094-310X Barrister Bulletin *see* 0162-2900
0094-3134 Probe Directory of Foreign Direct Investment in the United States
0094-3142 U.S. Environmental Protection Agency. Summaries of Foreign Government Environmental Reports†
0094-3231 Environmental Information Systems Directory†
0094-324X International Academy of Preventive Medicine. Journal *see* 0021-8960
0094-3320 13th Moon
0094-3339 East-West Markets†
0094-3347 Eutrophication†
0094-3355 Horse and Horseman
0094-3452 Places†
0094-3460 National Association for Women Deans, Administrators and Counselors. Journal *changed to* Initiatives.
0094-3479 Michigan. Department of Commerce. Annual Report Summary *changed to* Michigan. Department of Commerce. Annual Report.
0094-3495 Journal of Social Welfare†
0094-3509 Journal of Family Practice
0094-3517 I C T A Roster *changed to* I C T A Directory.
0094-3568 Arts in Alaska *changed to* Alaska. State Council on the Arts. Bulletin.
0094-3576 Arkansas. Bureau of Vital Statistics. Annual Report of Births, Deaths, Marriages and Divorces as Reported to the Bureau of Vital Statistics
0094-3584 American Bar - The Canadian Bar - The International Bar

ISSN

ISSN INDEX 5579

0094-3614 Southern Europe Travel Guide *changed to* Travel Guide to Europe.
0094-3622 New Orleans Business
0094-3630 Missouri. Division of Fisheries. Abstracts of Fishery Research Reports†
0094-3649 Drum Corps Review *see* 0012-8902
0094-3657 Central Europe and Scandinavia Travel Guide *changed to* Travel Guide to Europe.
0094-3673 Behavior Science Research
0094-3681 Chem Sources - Europe†
0094-372X South Dakota Indian Recipients of Social Welfare†
0094-3738 Journal of Peace Science *see* 0738-8942
0094-3746 Glass Dealer *see* 0747-4261
0094-3754 Michigan. Department of Education. College Admissions and Financial Assistance Handbook *changed to* Michigan Postsecondary Admissions & Financial Assistance Handbook.
0094-3770 American Bibliography of Slavic and East European Studies
0094-3800 California Plant Pathology
0094-3894 Recipe Index Series†
0094-3924 Wyoming. State of Wyoming Annual Report
0094-3932 Advances in Fire Retardants†
0094-3975 Fundamentals of Aerospace Instrumentation *see* 0277-7576
0094-3983 Minnesota Pocket Data Book†
0094-3991 Narcotics and Drug Abuse A to Z
0094-4033 Union Catalog of Maps†
0094-4076 Emory Law Journal
0094-4084 International Directory of Behavior and Design Research†
0094-4114 Nantucket Review
0094-422X American Society of Pension Actuaries. Transcribings. Annual Conference†
0094-4246 Arizona Legislative Service
0094-4262 Facts About South Dakota†
0094-4270 I.C.C. Supplemental Reports†
0094-4289 Journal of Engineering Materials and Technology
0094-4327 California. State Board of Cosmetology. Rules and Regulations.
0094-4335 Statistics for Water Utilities Including Water Authorities in Pennsylvania†
0094-4424 U.S. Centers for Disease Control. Family Planning Services: Annual Summary
0094-4459 National Collegiate Athletic Association. Proceedings of the Special Convention
0094-4491 Maryland Manual
0094-4505 Guide to American Scientific and Technical Directories
0094-4548 Letters in Heat and Mass Transfer *see* 0735-1933
0094-4610 Visual Merchandising *see* 0745-4295
0094-4629 Maryland. Bureau of Air Quality Control. State-Local Cooperative Air Sampling Program Yearly Data Report. *changed to* Maryland Air Management Administration. Data Report.
0094-4742 World Environmental Directory†
0094-4831 Bibliography of Society, Ethics and the Life Sciences†
0094-484X Dental Research in the United States, Canada, and Great Britain *see* 0147-264X
0094-4858 Fresh Fruit and Vegetable Market News: Weekly Summary, Shipments, Unloads *changed to* Fresh Fruit and Vegetable Market News: Weekly Summary, Shipments-Arrivals.
0094-4904 Companion to Animal Pratice *see* 1057-6622
0094-4920 Social Sciences Index
0094-5048 Maine. Department of Transportation. Annual Report†
0094-5056 Eastern Economic Journal
0094-5072 InterDependent
0094-5080 Journal of Forest History *see* 1046-7009
0094-5099 Music Library Association. Technical Reports
0094-5102 Journal of Marriage and Family Counseling *see* 0194-472X
0094-5129 New Human Services Review†
0094-5145 Journal of Community Health
0094-5196 U.S. National Oceanic and Atmospheric Administration. Report to the Congress on Ocean Dumping and Other Man-Induced Changes to Ocean Ecosystems *see* 0098-4922
0094-5218 Official Railway Guide. North American Passenger Travel Edition *see* 0273-9658
0094-5226 Official National Collegiate Athletic Association Football Rules and Interpretations *see* 0736-5160
0094-5234 Official National Collegiate Athletic Association Basketball Rules *changed to* N C A A Men's and Women's Basketball Rules and Interpretations.
0094-5242 Official Meeting Facilities Guide
0094-5277 Barrister (Chicago)
0094-5307 Advances in Satellite Meteorology†
0094-5323 Augustinian Studies
0094-534X Ohio Northern University Law Review
0094-5358 Solid Waste Systems *see* 0190-7808
0094-5366 Bilingual Review
0094-5404 Essays in Literature
0094-5420 Judicial Education News†
0094-5439 Maine Prosecutor Bulletin†
0094-5447 Metallurgy - Materials Education Yearbook
0094-5455 North Dakota Academic Library Statistics. *changed to* North Dakota Library Statistics.
0094-5463 Product Safety & the Law†
0094-5471 Directory of Women Physicians in the U.S.†
0094-5498 Journal of Altered States of Consciousness *see* 0276-2366
0094-5528 Agricultural Situation in Africa and West Asia *changed to* World Agriculture Regional Supplement: Middle East and North Africa.
0094-5587 Community Leaders and Noteworthy Americans *changed to* Community Leaders of America.
0094-5617 Hastings Constitutional Law Quarterly
0094-5633 Measuring Mormonism†
0094-5641 Minnesota Health Statistics
0094-5668 Ohio Journal of Religious Studies *see* 0193-3604
0094-5676 Oppositions†
0094-5714 Synthesis and Reactivity in Inorganic and Metalorganic Chemistry
0094-5749 Indiana. Environmental Management Board. Annual Report *changed to* Indiana. Department of Environmental Management. Annual Report.
0094-5765 Acta Astronautica
0094-579X Stone Soup
0094-5803 University of Wisconsin, Madison. Bureau of Business Research and Service. Research in the School of Business†
0094-582X Latin American Perspectives
0094-5846 Fundamentals of Cosmic Physics
0094-5870 Dine Bizaad Manil'iih
0094-5897 Arnold Newsletter *changed to* Nineteenth-Century Prose.
0094-5900 Syracuse University. Libraries. Annual Report†
0094-5978 Illinois. Cities and Villages Municipal Problems Commission. Annual Report to the Session of the General Assembly *changed to* Illinois. Cities and Villages Municipal Problems Commission. Biennial Report to the Session of the General Assembly.
0094-6028 Computer Medicine†
0094-6109 Ohio Higher Education. Basic Data Series
0094-615X L A C U N Y Journal *see* 0276-9298
0094-6176 Seminars in Thrombosis and Hemostasis
0094-6184 Serial Handbook of Modern Psychiatry†
0094-6192 Continuing Education in Nursing Home Administration *see* 0160-6980
0094-6206 Origins of Behavior Series†
0094-6230 Oklahoma. Department of Highways. Sufficiency Rating Report and Needs Study: Oklahoma State Highways *changed to* Oklahoma. Department of Transportation. Sufficiency Rating Report and Needs Study: Oklahoma State Transportation.
0094-6265 Maryland. State Highway Administration. Traffic Trends
0094-6281 Energy Index *see* 0739-3679
0094-6303 Global Directory of Gas Companies†
0094-6338 South Carolina Vital and Morbidity Statistics
0094-6354 A A N A Journal
0094-6427 Susquehanna River Basin Commission. Annual Report
0094-6435 Florida. Division of Corrections. Financial Report *changed to* Florida. Department of Corrections. Annual Report.
0094-6451 Economics Working Papers
0094-6478 Music Library Association. Index and Bibliography Series
0094-6494 Illinois. Department of Public Health. Poison Control Program Report†
0094-6516 Legal Bibliographic Data Service Weekly Subject Listing *see* 0360-7151
0094-6532 Early Years *changed to* Teaching K-8.
0094-6575 Emergency Medical Services
0094-6591 Orthopaedic Review
0094-6648 Graduate School Programs in Public Affairs and Public Administration *changed to* Graduate Programs in Public Affairs and Public Administration.
0094-6745 Institutions - Volume Feeding *see* 0273-5520
0094-6761 Current Topics in Molecular Endocrinology†
0094-6818 International Index to Multi Media Information†
0094-6842 Systems and Management Annual†
0094-6893 Federal Reserve Bank of Richmond. Economic Review
0094-6907 Cantwell Tapestry
0094-6915 Backtracker
0094-6923 International Telex Book. Americas Edition
0094-6958 Sage Public Administration Abstracts
0094-7008 U.S. National Marine Fisheries Service. Grant-in-Aid for Fisheries: Program Activities
0094-7024 S S I E Science Newsletter†
0094-7032 Advances in Image Pickup and Display†
0094-7040 Aldine Crime and Justice Annual†
0094-7091 Geokhimiya Translations†
0094-7148 Report of Cases Determined in the Supreme Court and Court of Appeals of the State of New Mexico
0094-7156 Federal Home Loan Mortgage Corporation. Report
0094-7172 Research in Parapsychology
0094-7202 Nassau County Medical Center. Proceedings *changed to* N C M C Proceedings.
0094-727X Connecticut. Commission to Study and Investigate the Problems of Deaf and Hearing-Impaired Persons. Annual Report *changed to* Connecticut. Commission on the Deaf and Hearing-Impaired. Annual Report.
0094-7288 Engineering and Society Series†
0094-7296 Federal Aid Fact Book†
0094-730X Journal of Fluency Disorders
0094-7326 New Mexico. Veterans' Service Commission. Report
0094-7342 Journal of Mormon History
0094-7393 Highway User Quarterly†
0094-7466 International Symposium on Transport and Handling of Minerals. Proceedings†
0094-7474 Summer Computer Simulation Conference. Proceedings
0094-7482 Status of the Market Nuclear Fuel Fabrication†
0094-7504 Annual Statistical Report of the Colorado Judiciary
0094-7512 Directory of Counseling Services†
0094-7520 Foreign Trade Reports. General Imports of Cotton Manufactures *changed to* Foreign Trade Reports. General Imports of Cotton, Wool and Manmade Fiber Manufacturers.
0094-7547 New York (City). Schedules Supporting the Executive Budget.
0094-7555 Banking Legislation in the Congress†
0094-7571 Crime and Social Justice *changed to* Social Justice.
0094-7598 Land Use Law and Zoning Digest
0094-7628 New Hampshire Comprehensive Law Enforcement Plan *changed to* New Hampshire Comprehensive Criminal Justice Plan.
0094-7660 Illinois Insurance
0094-7679 Journalism History
0094-7687 New Hampshire Annual Rural Manpower Report†
0094-7695 National Federation of Independent Business. Quarterly Economic Report *see* 0362-3548
0094-7733 Society of General Physiologists Series†
0094-775X Folk Mass and Modern Liturgy *see* 0363-504X
0094-7768 International Studies Notes
0094-7776 U.S. Occupational Safety and Health Review Commission. Administrative Law Judge and Commission Decisions
0094-7814 Inventory of Marriage and Family Literature
0094-7822 Theatre - Drama and Speech Index *changed to* Theatre - Drama Abstracts.
0094-7857 U.S. National Science Foundation. Division of Environmental Systems and Resources. Summary of Awards†
0094-7881 U.S. National Science Foundation. Selected Data on Students and Postdoctorals in Science & Engineering
0094-789X Executive Compensation Journal *see* 0747-8607
0094-792X C P A Letter
0094-7954 A P S A Departmental Services Program Survey of Departments
0094-7962 University of California, Davis. Food Protection and Toxicology Center. Summary Report†
0094-7989 Bergen County History†
0094-8012 Firelands Arts Review *changed to* Firelands Review.
0094-8039 Journal of Muscle Shoals History
0094-8055 Peace Science Society (International). Papers†
0094-8063 Energy Review (Santa Barbara)
0094-8071 Flammability Institute. News Bulletin *changed to* Flammability News Bulletin.
0094-8101 Outboard Boating Handbook†
0094-8128 Combustion Toxicology *see* 0362-1669
0094-8136 Yachting Year Book of Northern California
0094-8187 Surgery Update†
0094-8233 Alloys Index
0094-8268 Summary of Expenditure Data for Michigan Public Schools
0094-8276 Geophysical Research Letters
0094-8284 National Trade and Professional Associations of the United States and Canada and Labor Unions *changed to* National Trade and Professional Associations of the United States and Labor Unions.

ISSN

5580 ISSN INDEX

0094-8306 North Dakota. State Advisory Council for Vocational Education. Annual Evaluation Report *changed to* North Dakota. Council on Vocational Education. Biennial Evaluation Report.
0094-8314 Utah. State Office of Education. Annual Report of the State Superintendent of Public Instruction
0094-8322 Illinois. Board of Higher Education. Directory of Higher Education
0094-8373 Paleobiology
0094-8381 Air Force Law Review
0094-8403 Directory of Colorado Libraries *changed to* Colorado Education & Library Directory.
0094-8454 Official Southern California Ports Maritime Directory and Guide
0094-8470 Progress in Radiation Protection†
0094-8500 Enzyme Engineering
0094-8519 American Society for Microbiology. Abstracts of the Annual Meeting *changed to* American Society for Microbiology. Abstracts of the General Meeting.
0094-8543 American Arabic Speaking Community Almanac†
0094-8551 Florida. Department of Banking & Finance. Annual Local Government Financial Report
0094-8594 Journal of Purchasing and Materials Management *changed to* International Journal of Purchasing & Materials Management.
0094-8616 U.S. Bureau of Labor Statistics. Consumer Price Index *see* 0095-926X
0094-8632 Eastern Europe Travel Guide *changed to* Travel Guide to Europe.
0094-8667 Directory: Home Centers and Hardware Chains, Auto Supply Chains *see* 0736-0452
0094-8667 Directory: Home Centers and Hardware Chains, Auto Supply Chains *see* 0272-0167
0094-8675 Homeowners Handbook *see* 0195-2196
0094-8705 Journal of the Philosophy of Sport
0094-873X Montana Library Directory, with Statistics of Montana Public Libraries *changed to* Montana Library Directory.
0094-8764 Association of American Plant Food Control Officials. Official Publication
0094-8837 Selected Tables in Mathematical Statistics
0094-8845 St. Lawrence University. Conference on the Adirondack Park (Proceedings)†
0094-8853 Council of Better Business Bureaus. Annual Report *changed to* Council of Better Business Bureaus. Business Advisory Series.
0094-890X New Jersey. State Library. Union List of Serials†
0094-8934 Folk Harp Journal
0094-8950 Monographs in Lipid Research†
0094-8969 American Hospital Association Guide to the Health Care Field
0094-8985 Los Angeles Institute of Contemporary Art. Journal *changed to* Journal: A Contemporary Art Magazine.
0094-9000 Theory of Probability and Mathematical Statistics
0094-9019 Wyoming. Department of Revenue and Taxation. Annual Report
0094-9027 Young Students Encyclopedia Yearbook†
0094-9043 Ohio Geographers: Recent Research Themes†
0094-9086 Hopkins Quarterly
0094-9108 Physical Fitness Research Digest†
0094-9183 Annual Editions: Readings in Social Problems *see* 0272-4464
0094-9191 A P C A Directory and Resource Book *changed to* A P C A Government Agencies Directory.
0094-9205 University of Georgia. Institute of Ecology. Annual Report
0094-9264 Principles and Techniques of Human Research and Therapeutics†
0094-9302 Concise Clinical Neurology Review†
0094-9329 Modern Sawmill Techniques†
0094-9337 International Journal of Sulfur Chemistry. Part A. Original Articles, Notes and Communications *see* 1042-6507
0094-9345 International Journal of Sulfur Chemistry. Part B. Quarterly Reports *see* 1042-6507
0094-9353 International Journal of Sulfur Chemistry. Part C. Mechanisms of Reactions of Sulfur Compound *see* 1042-6507
0094-9426 Book Forum
0094-9442 Illinois Minerals Notes *changed to* Illinois Minerals.
0094-9477 Previews of Heat and Mass Transfer
0094-9515 Joint Federal-State Land Use Planning Commission for Alaska. Annual Report *changed to* Alaska's Land.
0094-9531 Shepard's Federal Law Citations in Selected Law Reviews
0094-9582 U.S. National Institute of Neurological Diseases and Stroke. Research Program Reports†
0094-9604 Medical Group Management Association. International Directory *see* 1040-2330
0094-9620 American Optometric Association News
0094-9655 Journal of Statistical Computation and Simulation
0094-9671 Conference on Ground Water. Proceedings
0094-9701 Ha-Mesivta
0094-9744 Basenji
0094-9779 Geothermal World Directory†
0094-9787 Olympian (Colorado Springs)
0094-9841 Chemical Engineering. Equipment Buyer's Guide Issue *see* 0272-4057
0094-9884 Textile Industry Technical Conference (Publication)
0094-9914 Your Highway Department, Arkansas†
0094-9922 Transportation U S A
0094-9930 Journal of Pressure Vessel Technology
0094-9973 Best's Agents Guide to Life Insurance Companies
0095-0025 Job Corps Happenings†
0095-0033 Database (New York)
0095-0084 Business Digest†
0095-0092 Business Monthly *changed to* Managing (New York).
0095-0106 Communique (Boston)†
0095-0149 Environmental Quality Abstracts *see* 0095-2958
0095-0157 Florida Marine Research Publications
0095-0165 Homegrown†
0095-019X Osiris (Deerfield)
0095-0203 Personal Finance Letter†
0095-0211 Real Estate Investor *see* 0734-5860
0095-036X Texas Nursing
0095-0386 Mort's Guide to Low-Cost Vacations & Lodgings on College Campuses†
0095-0475 Practical Psychology for Physicians *see* 0162-6957
0095-0491 Catfish Farmer and World Aquaculture News *see* 0199-1388
0095-053X National Library Reporter†
0095-0556 Car Classics *see* 0164-5552
0095-0564 Wisconsin. Division of Corrections. Bureau of Planning, Development and Research. Work Release-Study Release Program *changed to* Wisconsin. Division of Corrections. Office of Information Management. Work Release-Study Release Program.
0095-0580 Hospital - Health Care Training Media Profiles *see* 0740-1892
0095-0629 L C Foreign Acquisitions Newsletter†
0095-0637 Fact Book. Alabama Institutions of Higher Education, Universities and Colleges *changed to* Directory of Higher Education in Alabama.
0095-0645 Minnesota. Department of Revenue. Biennial Report
0095-0653 Collegiate Woman's Career Magazine *see* 8755-9218
0095-067X WoodenBoat
0095-0688 Manhattan Directory of Commercial & Industrial Properties†
0095-0696 Journal of Environmental Economics and Management
0095-0726 Commerce Reporter†
0095-0777 Instrumentation in the Food Industry *changed to* Instrumentation in the Food and Pharmaceutical Industries.
0095-084X Electrical Installation & Repair Projects†
0095-0858 Social Psychiatry†
0095-0866 Western Pennsylvania Genealogical Quarterly *see* 0278-7431
0095-0874 Symbols of American Libraries
0095-0890 Foreign Trade Reports. U.S. Waterborne Exports and General Imports
0095-0963 Automedica
0095-0971 Bio-Medical Scoreboard†
0095-0998 Medical School Rounds†
0095-1005 Search and Seizure Law Report
0095-1013 Lifestyle†
0095-1021 I.F.T. Journal†
0095-1048 Footwear Manual
0095-1072 U.S. Library of Congress. Chinese Cooperative Catalog†
0095-1080 Africana Journal *changed to* Africana Journal.
0095-1102 New Hampshire Occupational Outlook†
0095-1137 Journal of Clinical Microbiology
0095-1145 Psychology†
0095-1188 Women Law Reporter†
0095-1250 Water Resources Research in Virginia, Annual Report†
0095-1269 Alabama World Trade Directory *changed to* Alabama International Trade Directory.
0095-1285 Alabama. Commission on Higher Education. Biennial Report to the Governor and the Legislature *changed to* Alabama. Commission on Higher Education. Annual Report.
0095-134X CoEvolution Quarterly *see* 0749-5056
0095-1358 Fodor's Soviet Union *changed to* Fodor's Commonwealth of Independent States and the Baltic Countries.
0095-1374 R.E.I.T. Fact Book
0095-1382 Vermont. Department of Employment Security. Statistical Tables. *changed to* Vermont. Department of Employment & Training Security. Statistical Tables.
0095-1390 Albion
0095-1404 American Hairdresser - Salon Owner *changed to* American Salon.
0095-1420 Artbibliographies Current Titles
0095-1439 Central Kentucky Researcher
0095-1447 Cinefan†
0095-1455 National Association of Regional Councils. Directory *changed to* Directory of Regional Councils.
0095-148X American Venereal Disease Association. Journal *see* 0148-5717
0095-1498 Kentucky Local Debt Report
0095-1528 Urban Planning Quarterly†
0095-1536 Women (Washington)†
0095-1544 Journal of Cyclic Nucleotide Research *see* 0895-7479
0095-1579 British Isles and Ireland Travel Guide *changed to* Travel Guide to Europe.
0095-1587 Foster Natural Gas Report
0095-1625 Rider
0095-1633 North Dakota. Social Service Board. Statistics†
0095-165X El Dorado
0095-1684 American Poetry and Poetics
0095-1692 Civil Engineering Report Series *changed to* Water Resources Report Series.
0095-1714 Imprint†
0095-1730 Seems
0095-1811 American Clean Car
0095-182X American Indian Quarterly
0095-1846 Virginia. Law Enforcement Officers Training Standards Commission. Biennial Report *changed to* Virginia. Criminal Justice Services Commission. Annual Report.
0095-1870 Industrial Contact List for North Carolina Communities†
0095-1897 Monthly Energy Indicators *see* 0095-7356
0095-1900 Texas. Department of Corrections. Research and Development Division. Research Report
0095-1978 Virginia. State Water Control Board. Annual Report†
0095-1994 Tennessee. Department of Safety. Annual Report
0095-2060 Florida. Department of Transportation. Annual Report†
0095-2087 I M P Directory *see* 0148-6942
0095-2109 U.S. Office of Technology Assessment Annual Report to the Congress
0095-2117 Comptroller General's Procurement Decisions
0095-2125 Energy: a Continuing Bibliography with Indexes†
0095-2141 U.S. Bureau of Health Resources Development. Division of Nursing. Special Project Grants and Contracts Awarded for Improvement in Nurse Training†
0095-2184 Integrity: Gay Episcopal Forum *changed to* Integrity Forum.
0095-2214 Chromatography Newsletter†
0095-2222 Consumers' Research *changed to* Consumer's Research Magazine.
0095-2257 Russian Orthodox Greek-Catholic Church of America. Yearbook *see* 0145-7950
0095-2265 New York State Society of Anesthesiologists. Bulletin *see* 0095-2273
0095-2273 N Y S S A Sphere
0095-2338 Journal of Chemical Information and Computer Sciences
0095-2354 Southeastern Drug - Southern Pharmaceutical Journal *see* 0192-5792
0095-2397 Advent Review and Sabbath Herald *see* 0161-1119
0095-2427 Harvard Magazine
0095-2443 Journal of Elastomers and Plastics
0095-2583 Economic Inquiry
0095-2591 International Netsuke Collectors Society Journal†
0095-2605 Keeping up with Experimental Music in the Schools†
0095-2613 Orff Echo
0095-263X Rare Coin Review
0095-2648 Transportation Research Abstracts†
0095-2656 Transportation Research News *see* 0738-6826
0095-2664 Tunneling Technology Newsletter
0095-2699 Agricultural Libraries Information Notes
0095-2702 Serials Updating Service Annual†
0095-2737 Computers & Society
0095-2788 Vogue Patterns
0095-280X Studies in American Humor
0095-2826 American Society for Personnel Administration. Personnel and Industrial Relations Colleges†
0095-2850 Economic and Social Progress in Latin America; Annual Report
0095-2869 Directory of American Book Specialists†
0095-2893 Illinois. State Museum. Inventory of the Collections
0095-2907 Dickson Mounds Museum Anthropological Studies†
0095-2915 Illinois. State Museum. Research Series. Papers in Anthropology
0095-2923 Insurance Forum
0095-2931 Alan Shawn Feinstein Insiders Report
0095-294X Forecaster
0095-2958 Biology Digest

ISSN

ISSN INDEX 5581

0095-2966 Resources†
0095-2974 New World Communications†
0095-2982 Nurses Association of A.C.O.G. Bulletin *see* 0884-2175
0095-2990 American Journal of Drug and Alcohol Abuse
0095-3024 Minnesota. Department of Revenue. Petroleum Division. Annual Report
0095-3075 Virginia. Employment Commission. Manpower Research Division. Economic Assumptions†
0095-3105 Nebraska Statistical Report of Abortions
0095-3113 National Directory of State Agencies†
0095-3121 Family Planning Programs in Oklahoma
0095-313X Epidemiologic Notes and Communicable Disease Morbidity Report†
0095-3237 Occupational Safety & Health Reporter
0095-3245 Fleet Maintenance and Specifying *see* 0747-2544
0095-327X Armed Forces and Society
0095-3318 Alaska. Department of Health and Social Services. Office of Alcoholism. Report *changed to* Alaska. Department of Health and Social Services. Division of Alcoholism and Drug Abuse. Report.
0095-3326 Nation's Schools and Colleges *see* 0194-2263
0095-3342 Federal Funding Guide for Elementary and Secondary Education *see* 0275-8393
0095-3369 Digest of the United States Practice in International Law†
0095-3415 Alaska. Violent Crimes Compensation Board. Annual Report
0095-3423 Commerce Business Daily
0095-3431 Alabama's Vital Events
0095-3482 Summary and Analysis of International Travel in the U.S.
0095-3490 Statistics of Virginia Public Libraries *see* 0731-8464
0095-3555 Books - 100 Reviews
0095-3563 Vinifera Wine Growers Journal
0095-3601 Cal-Neva Wildlife; Transactions
0095-361X Alabama. Public Library Service. Basic State Plan and Annual Program *changed to* Alabama. Public Library Service. Annual Report.
0095-3628 Microbial Ecology
0095-3679 Peanut Science
0095-3741 Current Governments Reports: Government Finances
0095-3784 Abstracts of Instructional and Research Materials in Vocational and Technical Education *see* 0160-2004
0095-3814 Topics in Health Care Financing
0095-3830 Economic Outlook U.S.A.†
0095-3865 Alaska. Legislature. Budget and Audit Committee. Annual Report.
0095-389X Wyoming. Employment Security Commission. Research and Analysis Section. Farm Labor Report†
0095-3903 Foreign Trade Annual Report. Virginia Ports *see* 0083-6516
0095-3911 St. Clair County Historical Society. Journal
0095-392X State University of New York at Buffalo. Law Library. Law Library Periodicals†
0095-3962 Sales Training & Development *see* 0193-2136
0095-3997 Administration and Society
0095-4004 Wisconsin. Division of Corrections. Bureau of Planning, Development, and Research. Adult Probation Admissions†
0095-4012 American Journal of I.V. Therapy *changed to* Intravenous Therapy News.
0095-4020 Massachusetts. Department of Public Welfare. State Advisory Board. Annual Report†
0095-4047 New York (State). Division of Criminal Justice Service. Annual Report
0095-4063 Communications World†
0095-4101 Popular Music Periodicals Index†
0095-411X Production and Marketing California Grapes, Raisins and Wine *see* 0527-2181
0095-4144 Executive Compensation Service. Reports on International Compensation. Argentina†
0095-4152 State Tax Collections *changed to* Current Governments Reports: State Government Tax Collections.
0095-4209 Hawaii. State Law Enforcement and Juvenile Delinquency Planning Agency. Annual Action Program†
0095-4225 Power Semiconductors *see* 1040-0214
0095-4241 S M - Successful Meetings *see* 0148-4052
0095-425X Christianity Applied†
0095-4306 Wisconsin. Division of Corrections. Office of Information Management. Juvenile Probation Admissions†
0095-4314 Wisconsin Trails
0095-4322 World Mines Register†
0095-4330 Washington Agricultural Statistics
0095-4365 U.S. National Climatic Center. Climatological Data; National Summary†
0095-4403 American Society for Information Science. Bulletin
0095-4411 Northwestern Camping *changed to* Northwestern Campbook.
0095-442X Oklahoma. Conservation Commission. Biennial Report
0095-4438 Columban Mission
0095-4470 Journal of Phonetics
0095-4489 Studies in Browning and His Circle
0095-4519 Innovations†
0095-4527 Cytology and Genetics
0095-4535 Advances in Environmental Sciences *see* 0065-2563
0095-4543 Primary Care: Clinics in Office Practice
0095-4551 International Bibliography of Research in Marriage and the Family *see* 0094-7814
0095-4594 Corrections Magazine†
0095-4608 Byzantine Studies
0095-4616 Applied Mathematics and Optimization
0095-4624 Connecticut. Council on Environmental Quality. Annual Report
0095-4632 Alaska. Department of Fish and Game. Technical Data Report *changed to* Alaska. Department of Fish and Game. Technical Fishery Report.
0095-4640 Benchmark Papers in Ecology†
0095-4659 West Virginia. Department of Natural Resources. Annual Report on the Comprehensive Water Resources Plan†
0095-4667 Alaska Medicaid Status Report†
0095-4675 Alaska. Division of Medical Assistance. Medicaid Annual Status Report *see* 0095-4667
0095-4683 Airline Handbook
0095-4721 Hawaii. State Public Library System. L S C A Annual Program†
0095-4748 National Treasury Employees Union. Bulletin *see* 0279-540X
0095-4772 Pensions and Investments *see* 1050-4974
0095-4829 Advances and Technical Standards in Neurosurgery
0095-4837 U.S. Bureau of Labor Statistics. Chartbook on Prices, Wages, and Productivity†
0095-4861 Clinical and Biochemical Analysis
0095-4888 Directory of Minnesota's Area Mental Health, Mental Retardation, Inebriety Programs†
0095-490X Intercollegiate Bibliography. New Cases in Administration *see* 1042-654X
0095-4918 Journal of Portfolio Management
0095-4942 North Carolina. Department of Human Resources. Annual Plan of Work†
0095-4977 Curriculum Materials Clearinghouse. Index and Curriculum Briefs†
0095-4993 Journal of African Studies†
0095-5086 Public Utilities Law Anthology
0095-5108 Clinics in Perinatology
0095-5183 Drug Development Communications *see* 0363-9045
0095-5191 Directory of Investor-Owned Hospitals and Hospital Management Companies *changed to* Directory of Investor-Owned Hospitals, Residential Treatment Facilities and Centers, Hospital Management Companies and Health Systems.
0095-5213 Kaleidoscope (Boston)†
0095-5221 Interest-Adjusted Index†
0095-5248 New Frontiers (Seattle)†
0095-5264 Nevada. Bureau of Mines and Geology. Report
0095-5299 U S Auto Reports *see* 0148-9410
0095-5310 Arizona. Department of Education. Annual Report of the Superintendent of Public Instruction
0095-5329 Consolidated Report on Elementary and Secondary Education in Colorado†
0095-537X Weighing & Measurement
0095-5388 Voyages to the Inland Sea
0095-5396 American Bankers Association. National Operations & Automation Conference. Proceedings
0095-5418 Strictly U.S.†
0095-5434 World Bank Publications. Index *changed to* World Bank. Publications Update.
0095-5493 Foreign Trade Reports. U.S. Exports - Schedule A - Commodity by Country *see* 1057-9680
0095-5523 New Hampshire Vital Statistics
0095-5558 Country Place *see* 0147-4928
0095-5574 Kentucky Manpower Development. Annual Report
0095-5582 Annual Editions: Readings in Anthropology *changed to* Annual Editions: Anthropology.
0095-5590 New York (State) Consumer Protection Board. Annual Report
0095-5655 Gallaudet Almanac†
0095-5663 New York Times School Microfilm Collection Index by Reels *changed to* New York Times School Microfilm Collection Index.
0095-5698 Access: The Supplementary Index to Periodicals
0095-571X Semeia
0095-5744 Viking
0095-5760 Alaska Hunting Guide†
0095-5787 Annual Editions: Education
0095-5809 Arion
0095-5833 Criminal Victimization in the United States
0095-585X Montana Federal Grants-in-Aid Report†
0095-5876 San Diego Biomedical Symposium. Proceedings
0095-5884 Louisiana. State Board of Nurse Examiners. Report *changed to* Louisiana. State Board of Nursing. Report (Calendar Year).
0095-5892 Training
0095-5930 N A C L A's Latin America and Empire Report *see* 1058-5397
0095-5981 Humanities Index
0095-599X Drug Interactions†
0095-6120 North Dakota. Judicial Council. Statistical Compilation and Report *changed to* North Dakota. Judicial System. Annual Report.
0095-6139 Ethnicity†
0095-6155 Annual Editions: Readings in Marriage and Family *see* 0272-7897
0095-6201 Georgia Archive *see* 0739-4241
0095-6236 Rangeman's Journal *see* 0190-0528
0095-6317 Technical Education Reporter†
0095-635X Military Media Review
0095-6384 Kentucky Law Enforcement Council. Annual Report†
0095-6406 Fielding's Low-Cost Europe *changed to* Fielding's Budget Europe.
0095-6414 Directory of Small Magazine - Press Editors and Publishers
0095-6430 State of Florida Comprehensive Manpower Plan
0095-6449 Computer Design's Data Sheet
0095-6457 Directory of Digital Electronics†
0095-6457 Carpet Specifier's Handbook
0095-6465 California Historical Courier†
0095-6481 National Conference on Power Transmission. Proceedings†
0095-6538 N.A.D.A. Mobile Home Appraisal Guide *changed to* N.A.D.A. Mobile - Manufactured Housing Appraisal Guide.
0095-6562 Aviation, Space, and Environmental Medicine
0095-6570 State-Approved Schools of Practical and Vocational Nursing *see* 0081-4423
0095-6619 Hawaii. Legislative Reference Bureau. Digest and Index of Laws Enacted†
0095-6627 Pet Mass Marketing *see* 0162-8666
0095-6694 O S S C Bulletin
0095-6708 Impact (Ann Arbor)†
0095-6716 U.S. National Center for Education Statistics. Financial Statistics of Institutions of Higher Education *changed to* U.S. Department of Education. National Center for Education Statistics. State Higher Education Profiles.
0095-6740 Blue Cross Association. Research Series†
0095-6775 Damon Runyon - Walter Winchell Cancer Research Fund. Annual Report
0095-6783 Mississippi Marine Resources Council. Annual Report
0095-683X International Directory of the Nonwoven Fabrics Industry
0095-6848 Journal of Japanese Studies
0095-6880 National Computer Conference and Exposition (Proceedings) *changed to* National Computer Conference (Proceedings).
0095-6910 Homegrown†
0095-6937 V.D. Fact Sheet *changed to* S T D Fact Sheet.
0095-6945 Intersections
0095-6953 N.A.D.A. Motorcycle Appraisal Guide *changed to* N.A.D.A. Motorcycle - Snowmobile - A T V - Personal Watercraft Appraisal Guide.
0095-697X Juvenile Law Newsletter†
0095-702X Rendezvous of Western Art†
0095-7089 Mathematics Student†
0095-7100 B N A Pension Reporter
0095-7119 Best Science Fiction of the Year
0095-7151 Convenience Store Merchandiser *changed to* Convenience Store Management.
0095-7186 Election Index†
0095-7216 Hip†
0095-7232 Reviews in European History†
0095-7240 World Almanac Guide to Pro Hockey
0095-7267 California. Office of Criminal Justice Planning. Bulletin
0095-7275 Electronics and Equipment Market Abstracts *see* 0161-8032
0095-7291 Foreign Tax Law Bi-Weekly Bulletin
0095-733X Michigan. Department of Management and Budget. Annual Report†
0095-7348 Minnesota and Environs Weather Almanac *changed to* Minnesota Weather Guide Calendar.
0095-7356 Monthly Energy Review
0095-7364 New England Journal on Prison Law *see* 0740-8994
0095-7437 Alaska. Division of Geological Survey. Miscellaneous Paper *see* 0065-5783
0095-7526 Electric Vehicle News *see* 0739-5388
0095-7550 Reviews of Neuroscience†
0095-7577 Journal of Space Law
0095-7607 European Parliament Digest†
0095-7615 Grumman Aerospace Horizons *changed to* Grumman Horizons.

ISSN

ISSN INDEX

ISSN	Title
0095-7755	Software Briefs†
0095-7771	Foreign Trade Reports. U.S. Airborne Exports and General Imports†
0095-781X	National Savings and Loan League Journal see 0740-5464
0095-7895	Cancer Therapy Abstracts†
0095-7917	Current Contents: Engineering, Technology & Applied Sciences
0095-7925	Directory of Health Sciences Libraries in the United States†
0095-795X	U.S. Library of Congress. Accessions List: Brazil see 1041-1763
0095-7976	Materials Performance Buyer's Guide changed to Corrosion Engineer's Source Book.
0095-7984	Journal of Black Psychology
0095-8034	California Union List of Periodicals
0095-8107	New Harbinger; a Journal of the Cooperative Movement see 0190-2741
0095-8115	Discography Series
0095-8123	Interface Journal†
0095-8131	Information Times changed to Information Times.
0095-8174	Virginia. Department of Labor and Industry. Division of Research and Statistics. Occupational Injuries and Illnesses by Industry†
0095-8247	Illinois. Fire Protection Personnel Standards and Education Commission. Annual Report††
0095-8301	Diabetes Forecast
0095-8387	Del-Chem Bulletin
0095-8514	Earth Science Digest see 0012-8228
0095-8522	Journal of Colloid Science see 0021-9797
0095-8891	Journal of Consulting Psychology see 0022-006X
0095-8948	Engineering & Mining Journal
0095-8956	Journal of Combinatorial Theory. Series B.
0095-8964	Journal of Environmental Education
0095-8972	Journal of Coordination Chemistry. Sections A & B
0095-9006	Journal of Health and Human Behavior see 0022-1465
0095-9057	Journal of Mathematics and Mechanics see 0022-2518
0095-9065	Journal of Medicinal and Pharmaceutical Chemistry see 0022-2623
0095-9154	Dissertation Abstracts. Section A: Humanities and Social Sciences see 0419-4209
0095-9197	Electrical Engineering see 0018-9235
0095-926X	U.S. Bureau of Labor Statistics. C P I Detailed Report
0095-9286	New Silver Technology†
0095-9294	National Center for the Study of Collective Bargaining in Higher Education. Annual Conference Proceedings see 0742-3667
0095-9308	Mortgage Banking: Financial Statements and Operating Ratios see 0278-6567
0095-9618	Journal of Oral Surgery, Anesthesia and Hospital Dental Service see 0278-2391
0095-9626	Journal of Morphology and Physiology see 0362-2525
0095-9650	American Society of Agronomy. Journal see 0002-1962
0095-9669	C O M S A T Technical Review
0095-9782	Journal of Solution Chemistry
0095-9820	Journal of the Aerospace Sciences see 0001-1452
0095-9952	Cement - Mill and Quarry see 0032-0293
0095-9960	Ceramic Abstracts
0096-0179	Connecticut State Medical Journal see 0010-6178
0096-025X	American Public Works Association. Yearbook see 0360-6899
0096-0284	Journal of New Drugs see 0091-2700
0096-0322	American Physics Teacher see 0002-9505
0096-0349	American Professional Pharmacist see 0003-0627
0096-0365	American Rabbit Journal
0096-0381	American Review of Tuberculosis see 0003-0805
0096-039X	American Review of Tuberculosis and Pulmonary Diseases see 0003-0805
0096-0489	Florida. Bureau of Geology. Report of Investigations
0096-0551	Computer Languages
0096-0586	Group Psychotherapy and Psychodrama see 0731-1273
0096-0640	Journal of Engineering Education (Washington) changed to A S E E Prism.
0096-0764	Fluid Mechanics - Soviet Research
0096-0772	Foote Prints†
0096-0799	Government Reports Announcements see 0097-9007
0096-0802	Heat Transfer - Japanese Research
0096-0810	I S A Journal see 0192-303X
0096-0845	American Society of Brewing Chemists. Proceedings see 0361-0470
0096-0896	American Perfumer see 0361-4387
0096-090X	American Paper Converter see 0031-1138
0096-0918	American Painter and Decorator see 0003-0325
0096-1043	Reviews of Modern Physics see 8755-1209
0096-1159	Graphic Arts Technical Foundation. Research Project Report††
0096-1191	Journal of Foraminiferal Research
0096-1221	International Pacific Halibut Commission. Report see 0579-3920
0096-1248	Tennessee Valley Authority. Division of Land and Forest Resources. Technical Note changed to Tennessee Valley Authority. Division of Land Resources. Technical Note.
0096-1337	Journal of Undergraduate Psychological Research†
0096-1345	Index and Cumulative List of Papers on Radiation Chemistry see 0164-5315
0096-1353	Ford's Deck Plan Guide
0096-1388	Annual Report of the Arts Activities in Alabama†
0096-140X	Aggressive Behavior
0096-1442	Journal of Urban History
0096-1469	Ashleys of America Quarterly changed to Ashleys Addenda Annual.
0096-1507	A I D Research and Development Abstracts
0096-1515	Journal of Experimental Psychology: Human Learning and Memory see 0278-7393
0096-1523	Journal of Experimental Psychology: Human Perception and Performance
0096-1736	Journal of Occupational Medicine
0096-1868	Henry Ford Hospital Medical Bulletin see 0018-0416
0096-2023	Ice Cream Review see 0198-9995
0096-2031	Ice Cream Trade Journal see 0198-9995
0096-221X	Eastman Organic Chemical Bulletin changed to Eastman Fine Chemicals News.
0096-2279	Colorado-Wyoming Academy of Sciences. Journal
0096-2333	Rubber Age and Tire News see 0146-0706
0096-2341	U.S. Library of Congress. Accessions List: Southeast Asia
0096-2546	Ice Cream Field see 0198-9995
0096-2651	Fieldiana: Geology
0096-2686	Journal of Gas Chromatography see 0021-9665
0096-2708	Horizons in Biochemistry and Biophysics†
0096-2716	Contact Lens Journal†
0096-2732	Journal of Preventive Dentistry see 0163-9633
0096-2740	Perspective on Aging
0096-3003	Applied Mathematics and Computation
0096-3070	Florida State University Law Review
0096-3135	Politeia†
0096-3143	Orange County Bar Journal†
0096-3216	Karter News
0096-3224	Current Governments Reports: Finances of Employee Retirement Systems of State and Local Governments
0096-3259	Translator Referral Directory†
0096-3291	Yearbook of Science and the Future
0096-3364	Current Aviation Statistics†
0096-3380	American Baptist Convention. Directory see 0091-9381
0096-3402	Bulletin of the Atomic Scientists
0096-3445	Journal of Experimental Psychology: General
0096-3518	I E E E Transactions on Acoustics, Speech and Signal Processing see 1053-587X
0096-378X	South Dakota Academy of Science. Proceedings
0096-3917	Cancer Letter
0096-3925	Moscow University Biological Sciences Bulletin
0096-3933	Applied Hydraulics see 0018-814X
0096-3941	Eos
0096-3984	Operations Research Society of America. Journal see 0030-364X
0096-4077	Tulane Studies in Geology see 0041-4018
0096-4131	Buffalo Society of Natural Sciences. Bulletin
0096-414X	South Carolina Academy of Science. Bulletin
0096-4158	Maryland Naturalist
0096-4417	American Horticulturist
0096-4484	Industrial and Analytical Chemistry. Analytical Edition see 0003-2700
0096-4859	Mines Magazine
0096-5022	Michigan. Department of Conservation. Geological Survey Division. Progress Report changed to Michigan. Geological Survey Division. Report of Investigation.
0096-5154	American Machinist - Metalworking Manufacturing see 1041-7958
0096-5278	American Manufacturer see 0019-8889
0096-5294	Journal of Hygiene see 0002-9262
0096-5332	Advances in Carbohydrate Chemistry see 0065-2318
0096-5502	Mental Hospitals see 0022-1597
0096-591X	Textile Colorist and Converter see 0002-8266
0096-6088	Virginia Polytechnic Institute and State University. Virginia Agricultural Experiment Station. Bulletin
0096-6320	Water Works and Wastes Engineering see 0273-2238
0096-6347	American Journal of Orthodontics see 0889-5406
0096-6746	American Journal of Tropical Medicine see 0002-9637
0096-686X	American Therapeutic Society. Transactions see 0002-8614
0096-6894	A.M.A. Archives of Otolaryngology see 0886-4470
0096-7033	Lying-in see 0024-7758
0096-7238	Instrumentation in the Aerospace Industry see 0277-7576
0096-736X	S A E Transactions
0096-7394	American Ceramic Society. Transactions see 0002-7820
0096-7408	American Institute of Chemical Engineers. Transactions see 0360-7275
0096-7688	Michigan State Horticultural Society. Annual Report
0096-7750	Academy of Natural Sciences of Philadelphia. Monographs
0096-7807	Soviet Journal of Ecology
0096-7955	Nondestructive Testing (Chicago) see 0025-5327
0096-820X	American Industrial Hygiene Association Quarterly see 0002-8894
0096-8293	Pipeline Engineer see 0032-0188
0096-848X	Yearbook of Physical Anthropology
0096-8684	Begonian
0096-8692	Bell Telephone Magazine†
0096-8765	Systems, Computers, Control see 0882-1666
0096-8803	U.S. Library of Congress. Subject Catalog†
0096-882X	Journal of Studies on Alcohol
0096-8846	Italian Americana
0096-8870	Gas Processors Association. Annual Convention. Proceedings
0096-8994	A M A American Journal of Diseases of Children see 0002-922X
0096-9117	Society of Vertebrate Paleontology. News Bulletin
0096-9168	Plastics Industry see 0032-1273
0096-9192	Louisiana Academy of Sciences. Proceedings
0096-9222	Pennsylvania Academy of Science. Proceedings see 1044-6753
0096-9419	Navy Civil Engineer
0096-9842	Wyoming Mineral Yearbook
0096-9877	U.S. Bureau of the Census. Data User News changed to U.S. Bureau of the Census. Census and You.
0096-9907	International Economic Indicators and Competitive Trends changed to International Economic Indicators.
0097-0042	Railroad Research Bulletin†
0097-0050	School Health Review see 1055-6699
0097-0085	Medicolegal News see 0277-8459
0097-0247	Journal of Fire & Flammability/Fire Retardant Chemistry see 0362-1693
0097-0255	National University Extension Association. Handbook and Directory changed to National University Continuing Education Association. Directory.
0097-0263	H I A S Bulletin changed to H I A S Reporter.
0097-0395	N S R D S - N B S: National Standard Reference Data Series
0097-0492	Sport Fishing Institute. Bulletin see 0085-6592
0097-0549	Neuroscience and Behavioral Physiology
0097-0638	American Fisheries Society. Special Publication
0097-0883	Mount Desert Island Biological Laboratory. Bulletin
0097-0905	Connecticut. Agricultural Experiment Station, New Haven. Bulletin
0097-109X	Progress in Cardiology
0097-1138	Absolute Sound
0097-1146	Anima
0097-1154	Indian Law Reporter
0097-1162	Journal of Fire and Flammability - Consumer Product Flammability Supplement see 0362-1677
0097-1170	Journal of Physical Education and Recreation see 0730-3084
0097-1189	State O'Maine Facts†
0097-1197	Regional Science Perspectives
0097-1324	Association of Official Seed Analysts. Proceedings see 0146-3071
0097-1510	Virginia Polytechnic Institute and State University Research Division. Report see 0096-6088
0097-1901	National Dental Association. Journal†
0097-1936	Air Quality Instrumentation†
0097-2126	American Power Conference. Proceedings.
0097-2509	International Pulp & Paper Directory
0097-2533	Modern Hi-Fi & Music
0097-2762	Eugenics Quarterly see 0037-766X
0097-3157	Academy of Natural Sciences of Philadelphia. Proceedings
0097-3165	Journal of Combinatorial Theory. Series A

ISSN INDEX 5583

0097-3254 Academy of Natural Sciences of Philadelphia. Special Publications
0097-3289 Milk Dealer *see* 0198-9995
0097-3297 American Photo-Engraver *see* 0746-3626
0097-3416 Iowa Agriculture and Home Economics Experiment Station. Research Bulletin
0097-3491 Arkansas. Agricultural Experiment Station. Bulletins
0097-3599 Journal of Medical Research *see* 0002-9440
0097-4056 A R S Journal *see* 0001-1452
0097-4080 Converter *see* 0031-1138
0097-4145 American Concrete Institute. Proceedings†
0097-4153 A S T M Proceedings†
0097-4382 Gulf Coast Research Laboratory. Publications of the Museum†
0097-4455 Conference Board of the Mathematical Sciences. Regional Conference Series in Applied Mathematics *see* 0163-9439
0097-4463 Carnegie Museum of Natural History. Annals of Carnegie Museum
0097-4536 Crossties
0097-4706 J.C.C.: Journal of Clinical Chiropractic†
0097-4714 Journal of Clinical Chiropractic. Archives *see* 0097-4706
0097-4730 Statistics of Paper and Paperboard *see* 0731-8863
0097-4773 Chilton's Motor-Age Service Handbook *see* 0363-2393
0097-4854 Dental Research in the United States and Canada *see* 0147-264X
0097-4862 From the State Capitals. Drug Abuse Control Report *see* 0734-0877
0097-4943 Computers & Mathematics with Applications *see* 0898-1221
0097-496X Pembroke Magazine
0097-5125 Iowa Agriculture and Home Economics Experiment Station. Special Report
0097-5184 Nineteenth Century (Philadelphia)†
0097-5192 Official Airline Guide. International Edition *see* 0364-3875
0097-5206 Randax Education Guide
0097-5222 Shale Country†
0097-5230 Cold Spring Harbor Conferences on Cell Proliferation†
0097-5257 Pediatric Nephrology†
0097-5370 Arkansas. Agricultural Experiment Station. Report Series
0097-5397 S I A M Journal on Computing
0097-5419 Southern Medicine†
0097-5427 Wadley Medical Bulletin *see* 0162-9360
0097-5478 Ohio. Division of Geological Survey. Bulletin
0097-5877 Photoengravers Bulletin *see* 8750-2224
0097-5982 Pediatric Conferences†
0097-6008 Sonix†
0097-6024 Middle East Newsletter
0097-6059 California Historical Quarterly *see* 0162-2897
0097-6075 Creativity
0097-6083 Directory of Law Enforcement and Criminal Justice Education *changed to* Law Enforcement and Criminal Justice Education Directory.
0097-6156 A C S Symposium Series
0097-6164 Advocate (Springfield) *changed to* I E A - N E A Advocate.
0097-6172 America: History and Life. Part B: Index to Book Reviews *changed to* America: History and Life. Articles Abstract and Citations of Reviews and Dissertations Covering the United States and Canada.
0097-6180 A C S M Bulletin
0097-6199 Current Awareness in Real Estate and Planning†
0097-6237 Florida Journal of Commerce - American Shipper *see* 0160-225X
0097-627X American Dance Therapy Association. Monographs†
0097-6288 Principal International Businesses
0097-6326 Federal Register
0097-6482 Analog Sounds†
0097-6512 National Braille Club. Bulletin *see* 0550-5666
0097-6539 Hype†
0097-6555 Issues in Ego Psychology
0097-6563 Sigma Phi Epsilon Journal
0097-6687 Railway Engineering and Maintenance *see* 0033-9016
0097-6830 North American Wildlife Conference. Transactions *see* 0078-1355
0097-7004 Modern China
0097-7039 Amtrak Annual Report
0097-711X S A E Journal of Automotive Engineering *see* 0098-2571
0097-7136 Directory of Nature Centers and Related Environmental Education Facilities†
0097-7144 Audubon Field Notes *see* 0004-7686
0097-7209 Crystal Mirror
0097-7268 North Cal-Neva Resource Conservation and Development Project. Annual Work Plan *changed to* North Cal-Neva Resource Conservation and Development Area. Annual Work Plan.
0097-7314 International Tax Journal
0097-7330 Magnetic Resonance Review
0097-7357 Pulpwood Production and Timber Harvesting *see* 0160-6433
0097-7373 Ski Magazine's Guide to Cross Country Skiing *changed to* Cross Country Ski Magazine.
0097-739X Wyoming Area Manpower Review†
0097-7403 Journal of Experimental Psychology: Animal Behavior Processes
0097-7519 Water Quality Monitoring Data for Georgia Streams†
0097-7721 G T E Journal of Research and Development†
0097-7764 Study of Employment of Women in the Federal Government *changed to* Affirmative Employment Statistics.
0097-7799 U.S. Office of Management and Budget. Catalog of Federal Domestic Assistance *changed to* U.S. General Services Administration. Catalog of Federal Domestic Assistance.
0097-7829 Copper *see* 0163-4186
0097-7977 U.S. Administrative Office of the United States Courts. Report on Applications for Orders Authorizing or Approving the Interception of Wire or Oral Communications
0097-7985 U.S. Library of Congress. Accessions List: Pakistan†
0097-8035 Paid My Dues†
0097-8043 Restaurant Business
0097-8051 San Jose Studies
0097-8078 Water Resources
0097-8124 Babe Ruth Baseball's Athletes of the Year†
0097-8132 Broadcasting Cable Yearbook *changed to* Broadcasting & Cable Market Place (Year).
0097-8140 Creative Computing†
0097-8159 Energy Communications†
0097-8167 Washington Post. Newspaper Index *see* 0195-6361
0097-8175 Gebbie Press All-in-One Directory
0097-8213 New Settler's Guide for Washington, D.C. and Communities in Nearby Maryland and Virginia
0097-8221 Occasional Review†
0097-8256 Record and Tape Reviews Index†
0097-8299 Transit Journal†
0097-8329 Consumer Electronics Product News
0097-8337 Consumer Guide Magazine
0097-8345 Credit (Washington)
0097-8388 I and S M *changed to* Iron & Steelmaker.
0097-8396 I C P Software Directory *see* 0272-1171
0097-840X Journal of Human Stress *changed to* Behavioral Medicine.
0097-8418 S I G C S E Bulletin
0097-8442 Ancient Interface†
0097-8485 Computers & Chemistry
0097-8493 Computers & Graphics
0097-8507 Language (Baltimore)
0097-8515 Transportation Research Circular
0097-8523 European Labor and Working Class History Newsletter *see* 0147-5479
0097-8620 Current Prescribing†
0097-8663 Estreno
0097-8779 O A G Worldwide Cruise & Shipline Guide
0097-8884 Bittersweet†
0097-8892 Journal of Developmental Disabilities†
0097-8930 Computer Graphics (New York)
0097-8949 American Blade *see* 0744-6179
0097-8957 Consumer Guide Magazine: Stereo & Tape Equipment Test Reports†
0097-8965 International Studies Newsletter *see* 0020-8817
0097-899X American Medical Association. Directory of Residency Training Programs *changed to* Directory of Graduate Medical Education.
0097-9007 Government Reports Announcements and Index Journal
0097-9015 Government Reports Index *see* 0097-9007
0097-9031 J N M *see* 0161-5505
0097-9112 Montana State Board of Health. Annual Statistical Supplement *see* 0077-1198
0097-9120 Montana. State Department of Health. Annual Statistical Supplement *see* 0077-1198
0097-9171 Wisconsin. Employment Relations Commission. Reporter
0097-921X Annual Index of Rheumatology†
0097-9325 Nebraska Statistical Handbook
0097-9376 U.S. Mining Enforcement and Safety Administration. Informational Report *changed to* U.S. Mine Safety and Health Administration. Informational Report.
0097-9473 Ohio. Division of Geological Survey. Guidebook
0097-952X Cultural Information Service
0097-9546 Orchid Advocate
0097-9554 Securities Regulation Law Journal
0097-9562 Soroptimist
0097-9627 Newspapers in Microform†
0097-9643 National District Attorneys Association. Economic Crime Project. Annual Report†
0097-966X S I D International Symposium. Digest of Technical Papers
0097-9708 Tennessee Valley Historial Review *changed to* Historical Review & Antique Digest.
0097-9716 Journal of Dermatologic Surgery *see* 0148-0812
0097-9732 Medoc: Index to U S Government Publications in the Medical and Health Sciences
0097-9740 Signs: Journal of Women in Culture and Society
0097-9759 Cooperative Housing Bulletin
0097-9783 Human Life Review
0097-9805 Pediatric Nursing
0097-9813 Litigation
0097-9937 Journal of Contemporary Law
0097-9953 Arizona. Governor's Commission on Arizona Environment. Annual Report *changed to* Arizona. Commission on the Arizona Environment. Annual Report.
0098-0005 List of Legal Investments for Savings Banks in Connecticut†
0098-0110 Missouri. State Board of Training Schools. Annual Report *changed to* Missouri. Division of Youth Services. Annual Report.
0098-0129 Transportation Focus†
0098-0137 Advances in Sex Hormone Research†
0098-0269 Illinois. Department of Public Instruction. Annual State of Education Message *see* 0147-2860
0098-0285 New Jersey. Department of Labor and Industry. Division of Planning and Research. Commercial and Industrial Construction Plans Approved; Annual Summary†
0098-0307 Michigan Labor Market Review
0098-0323 Wisconsin Traffic Data - Automatic Traffic Recorder
0098-0331 Journal of Chemical Ecology
0098-0366 Somatic Cell Genetics *changed to* Somatic Cell and Molecular Genetics.
0098-0404 Air Carrier Traffic Statistics *see* 0731-3411
0098-0471 Film Review Digest†
0098-051X North Carolina. Division of Social Services. Statistical Journal†
0098-0579 Human Rights Organizations & Periodicals Directory
0098-0668 Keeping up with Kodaly Concepts in Music Education†
0098-0714 Railfan (Newton) *see* 0163-7266
0098-0722 Remote Computing Directory†
0098-0757 Alcohol, Tobacco and Firearms Bulletin
0098-079X Maine Prosecutor, Criminal Legislation Manual†
0098-0846 Wyoming. Water Quality Division. Wyoming State Plan *changed to* Wyoming. Water Quality Division. State - E P A Agreement.
0098-0889 Radioassay News *changed to* Radioassay - Ligand Assay News.
0098-0897 Resources in Education
0098-0900 Center for Hermeneutical Studies in Hellenistic and Modern Culture. Protocol Series of the Colloquies
0098-0919 H U L Notes *see* 1050-2408
0098-096X Directory of Occupational Education Programs in New York State†
0098-1109 Directory of U.S. Government Audiovisual Personnel†
0098-1133 Official Gazette of the United States Patent and Trademark Office. Patents
0098-115X Utah. Geological and Mineral Survey. Special Studies *changed to* Utah Geological Survey. Special Studies.
0098-1176 Chicago Tribune. Newspaper Index *see* 0195-6353
0098-1184 Index to the Christian Science Monitor *see* 0893-245X
0098-1192 Los Angeles Times. Newspaper Index *see* 0742-4817
0098-1206 New Orleans Times-Picayune. Newspaper Index *see* 0893-2484
0098-1214 The Asia Society. Annual Report
0098-1222 Insects of Virginia
0098-1230 Bicycle Bibliography *see* 0193-8584
0098-1273 Journal of Polymer Science. Polymer Physics Edition *see* 0887-6266
0098-1354 Computers & Chemical Engineering
0098-1389 Social Work in Health Care
0098-1397 Marketing Economics Key Plants
0098-1435 California Employer
0098-1451 National Directory of Summer Internships for Undergraduate Students†
0098-1486 The American Nurse
0098-1508 Directory of Visiting Fulbright Scholars in the United States *changed to* Directory of Visiting Fulbright Scholars and Occasional Lecturers.
0098-1516 Emergency Nurse Legal Bulletin
0098-1524 Emergency Physician Legal Bulletin
0098-1532 Medical and Pediatric Oncology
0098-1540 Microbiology (Washington)†
0098-1575 Practical Guide to Individual Income Tax Return Preparation *changed to* 1040 Preparation.
0098-1605 Anthropology Newsletter
0098-1613 Fodor's Japan and Korea *changed to* Fodor's Japan.
0098-1613 Fodor's Japan and Korea *changed to* Fodor's Korea.

ISSN

0098-1648 Library of Congress Professional Association. Newsletter *changed to* Insights (Washington, 1988).
0098-1664 Student Activities Programming *changed to* Campus Activities Programming.
0098-1672 Year Book of Diagnostic Radiology
0098-1702 B O C A Basic Plumbing Code *changed to* B O C A National Plumbing Code.
0098-1745 Motor's Auto Repair Manual *changed to* Motor Auto Repair Manual.
0098-1753 Pension World
0098-1761 Pickin' *see* 0162-0401
0098-180X Hospital Infection Control
0098-1818 U.S. Bureau of Labor Statistics. Monthly Labor Review
0098-1850 Abstracts of Doctoral Dissertations in Anthropology†
0098-1923 University of Michigan Business Review†
0098-1974 Missouri Vital Statistics
0098-2067 Policy Analysis *see* 0276-8739
0098-2091 National Basic Intelligence Factbook *see* 0277-1527
0098-2113 Currents in Theology and Mission
0098-2121 De-Acquisitions Librarian *see* 0146-2679
0098-213X Forecast (Bridgewater)
0098-2164 Academy of Sciences of the U S S R. Biology Bulletin
0098-2180 Emergency Product News *see* 0162-5942
0098-2199 John Berryman Studies†
0098-2202 Journal of Fluids Engineering
0098-2210 Metal Distribution
0098-2245 F and O S *see* 0160-4570
0098-2318 Beverage World (English Edition)
0098-2326 Hebert's Catalogue of Used Plate Number Singles *changed to* Hebert's Catalogue of Plate Number Singles.
0098-2342 American Journal of Therapeutics & Clinical Reports - Cases & Comments†
0098-2377 American Group Practice Association Directory
0098-2393 International Bibliography of the Forensic Sciences
0098-2423 Sexual Law Reporter†
0098-2431 Institute for the Certification of Computer Professionals. Annual Report
0098-2466 Dun & Bradstreet's Guide to Your Investments
0098-2474 Explorations in Renaissance Culture
0098-2512 Washington Report on Health Legislation *see* 0899-8965
0098-2520 F A S - F A X: Canadian Newspapers. Daily Newspapers
0098-2547 Fodor's Caribbean, Bahamas and Bermuda *changed to* Fodor's Caribbean.
0098-2571 Automotive Engineering Magazine
0098-2601 Eighteenth Century Life
0098-261X Justice System Journal
0098-2644 Yearbook of Herpetology†
0098-2741 M G World *changed to* M G International.
0098-275X Studies in Modern European History and Culture
0098-2784 Bibliography and Index of Geology
0098-2806 Fate of Drugs in the Organism; a Bibliographic Survey†
0098-2814 A-Ph-Armacy Weekly *see* 1042-0991
0098-2822 Art and Architecture Book Guide *see* 0360-2699
0098-2830 Federal Home Loan Bank of San Francisco. Annual Report.
0098-2857 National Bar Examination Digest
0098-2865 N A H B Journal-Scope *see* 0744-1193
0098-2873 Estate Planning Review
0098-2881 Council on Anthropology and Education Quarterly *see* 0161-7761
0098-2997 Molecular Aspects of Medicine
0098-3004 Computers & Geosciences
0098-3039 Urban Life *see* 0891-2416
0098-3063 I E E E Transactions on Consumer Electronics
0098-308X National Capital Planning Commission. Quarterly Review of Commission Proceedings
0098-311X Health Consequences of Smoking
0098-3209 Annual Report on Highway Safety Improvement Programs *see* 0277-2310
0098-3217 North Carolina Reported Abortions *changed to* North Carolina Reported Pregnancies.
0098-3276 Fire Independent
0098-3292 Hospitality, Restaurant *see* 0147-9989
0098-3322 Yellow Book of Funeral Directors and Services *changed to* Yellow Book of Funeral Directors.
0098-3365 Phaedrus†
0098-3381 New England Musician's Guide *see* 0362-2959
0098-342X Science Books & Films
0098-3446 Medical Electronics and Data *changed to* Medical Electronics.
0098-3462 Health and Rehabilitative Library Services News *see* 0270-6717
0098-3470 Drug Enforcement
0098-3497 Current Governments Reports: Local Government Employment in Selected Metropolitan Areas and Large Counties†
0098-3500 A C M Transactions on Mathematical Software
0098-3519 Cruising World
0098-3527 Dulcimer Players News
0098-3543 American Association of Veterinary Laboratory Diagnosticians. Proceedings of Annual Meeting†
0098-3551 I E E E Vehicular Technology Conference. Record
0098-356X Schwann-1, Records and Tapes *see* 1047-2355
0098-3608 Labor Rates for the Construction Industry *changed to* Means Labor Rates for the Construction Industry.
0098-3616 Medicaid Recipient Characteristics and Units of Selected Medical Services
0098-3624 Motor Truck Repair Manual *changed to* Motor Light Truck & Van Repair Manual.
0098-3675 Urban Anthropology Newsletter†
0098-3721 American College of Nurse-Midwifery. Bulletin *see* 0091-2182
0098-3748 American Medical Association Auxiliary. Bulletin *see* 0163-0512
0098-3772 Allegheny County Medical Society. Bulletin
0098-3780 A A A M Bulletin *changed to* A A A M Quarterly Journal.
0098-3810 Academy of General Dentistry. Bulletin *see* 0363-6771
0098-3888 U.S. Department of Defense. Report of Secretary of Defense to the Congress
0098-3896 U.S. Treasury Department. Bureau of Government Financial Operations. Report on Foreign Currencies Held by the U.S. Government†
0098-3942 Federal Communications Commission Reports
0098-4000 Agricultural Situation in Eastern Europe *changed to* World Agriculture Regional Supplement: Eastern Europe.
0098-4027 United States. Defense Property Disposal Service. Annual Historical Summary†
0098-4035 U.S. Advisory Council on Historic Preservation. Report†
0098-4094 I E E E Transactions on Circuits and Systems *see* 1057-7122
0098-4094 I E E E Transactions on Circuits and Systems *see* 1057-7130
0098-4108 Journal of Toxicology and Environmental Health
0098-4132 State Directory of Higher Education Institutions and Agencies in Maryland†
0098-4485 Doctoral Dissertations on Asia
0098-4507 Sav-on-Hotels (Year)
0098-4558 JOM *see* 1047-4838
0098-4574 Woodwind World-Brass and Percussion *changed to* Woodwind, Brass & Percussion.
0098-4582 Columbia Journal of Environmental Law
0098-4590 Florida Scientist
0098-4604 Index to U.S. Government Periodicals
0098-4612 Journal of Political Science (Clemson)
0098-4752 Condition of Education
0098-4760 Old Fort Log
0098-4779 Equipment Market Abstracts *see* 0161-8032
0098-4825 Utah. Geological and Mineral Survey. Bulletin *changed to* Utah Geological Survey. Bulletin.
0098-4833 Medical Law Letter for Physicians, Surgeons & Health Professionals
0098-4841 Copper State Bulletin
0098-4922 U.S. National Oceanic and Atmospheric Administration. Report to the Congress on Ocean Pollution, Overfishing, and Offshore Development
0098-4981 American Portuguese Society. Journal
0098-499X Sou'wester (Edwardsville)
0098-5058 Wyoming. Governor's Office of Highway Safety. Annual Report†
0098-5104 Energy Abstracts for Policy Analysis†
0098-5139 Ohio. Council on Vocational Education. Annual Report
0098-5147 California Private School Directory
0098-5244 Joint Center for Urban Studies of M I T and Harvard University. Review *changed to* Joint Center for Housing Studies of M I T and Harvard University. Joint Center Review.
0098-5252 Medical Bulletin (New York)†
0098-5279 Data Book on Illinois Higher Education
0098-5368 Pennsylvania Chamber of Commerce. Directory of State, Regional and Commercial Organizations *changed to* Pennsylvania Chamber of Business and Industry. State & Regional Directory.
0098-5376 Equipment & Technology International†
0098-5406 Pet Age
0098-5422 Spur
0098-5430 American Paint & Coatings Journal
0098-5449 Faith & Reason (Front Royal)
0098-5481 Backstage T V Film - Tape & Syndication Directory†
0098-5554 Current Christian Books. Authors and Titles *see* 0270-2347
0098-5562 Current Christian Books. Titles, Authors, and Publishers *see* 0270-2347
0098-5570 United States National Student Association. N S A Magazine†
0098-5589 I E E E Transactions on Software Engineering
0098-5597 Review of Education
0098-5619 A S T D Consultant Directory *changed to* A S T D Buyers Guide and Consultants Directory.
0098-5651 Oklahoma Health Statistics
0098-5708 Hawaii. Criminal Injuries Compensation Commission. Annual Report.
0098-5716 Idaho. Department of Agriculture. Annual Report†
0098-5805 Medical College of South Carolina Bulletin *changed to* Auctus.
0098-5910 Society of Wireless Pioneers. Yearbook†
0098-5929 Working Papers on Language Universals†
0098-5961 Law and Psychology Review
0098-597X Journal of Computer-Based Instruction
0098-5988 Basketball Digest
0098-6054 Romanian Sources
0098-6062 Index to St. Louis Newspapers†
0098-6070 A C R Bulletin
0098-6089 Advances in Neurochemistry
0098-6097 American Association of Industrial Nurses Journal *see* 0891-0162
0098-6127 Artery
0098-6151 J A O A: Journal of the American Osteopathic Association
0098-616X Psychopharmacology Communications†
0098-6186 Connecticut State Industrial Directory *see* 0740-2937
0098-6194 Maine State Industrial Directory *see* 0740-2945
0098-6216 New Hampshire State Industrial Directory *see* 0740-2945
0098-6224 New Jersey State Industrial Directory *see* 0733-3684
0098-6232 Delaware Valley Regional Planning Commission. Biennial Report *changed to* Delaware Valley Regional Planning Commission. Annual Report.
0098-6240 Medical Tribune and Medical News *see* 0279-9340
0098-6267 A W I S Newsletter *changed to* A W I S Magazine.
0098-6275 S A L A L M Newsletter
0098-6283 Teaching of Psychology
0098-6291 Teaching English in the Two-Year College
0098-6305 E N R Directory of Design Firms
0098-6399 New Jersey. Department of Human Services. Community Mental Health Projects Summary Statistics†
0098-6445 Chemical Engineering Communications
0098-6453 E N R Directory of Contractors
0098-6461 Mideast Markets
0098-647X Research Opportunities in Renaissance Drama
0098-6569 Catheterization and Cardiovascular Diagnosis
0098-6577 Kidney International. Supplement
0098-6615 Ecology U S A
0098-6623 U.S. Centers for Disease Control. Foodborne & Waterborne Disease Outbreaks. Annual Summary
0098-6631 Golden Gate Law Review *see* 0363-0307
0098-664X Directory of Music Faculties in Colleges & Universities U S and Canada
0098-6658 Microelectronics *see* 0363-8529
0098-6739 Kentucky Vital Statistics *changed to* Kentucky. Cabinet for Human Resources. Vital Statistics Report.
0098-6755 Delaware State Minority Business Directory†
0098-678X Current Governments Reports: County Government Finances
0098-681X U.S. Federal Trade Commission. Quarterly Financial Report for Manufacturing, Mining and Trade Corporations†
0098-6909 Hospital Formulary
0098-6917 Journal of Optometric Education *changed to* Optometric Education.
0098-6925 Modern Pharmacology - Toxicology Series
0098-6976 Wisconsin Journal of Public Instruction†
0098-6984 Wyoming. Department of Health and Social Services. Annual Report *changed to* Wyoming. Department of Health. Annual Report.
0098-7077 New Mexico. Bureau of Mines and Mineral Resources. Progress Report
0098-7093 Coldspring Journal†
0098-7107 Michigan State Dental Association *see* 0026-2102
0098-7115 Southern California State Dental Association. Journal *see* 0008-0977
0098-7174 Pennsylvania Police Criminal Law Bulletin
0098-7182 Flight Safety Facts and Reports *see* 0898-5715
0098-7239 Issues in Media Management†
0098-7298 Journal of Applied Photographic Engineering *see* 0747-3583
0098-7301 Perspectives on Contemporary Literature†
0098-7336 Bankruptcy Court Decisions
0098-7387 Arizona Commission on the Arts. Report to the Governor

ISSN INDEX 5585

0098-7409 New Jersey. Division of Banking. Annual Report *changed to* New Jersey. Department of Banking. Annual Report.
0098-7484 J A M A: The Journal of the American Medical Association
0098-7522 Michigan State Medical Society. Journal *see* 0026-2293
0098-7530 Product Safety Letter
0098-7549 It's Happening
0098-7557 Downtown Malls *see* 0364-586X
0098-7565 Creative Child and Adult Quarterly
0098-7573 Devices & Diagnostics Letter
0098-7611 B A R - B R I Bar Review. Torts
0098-762X B A R - B R I Bar Review. Contracts
0098-7638 B A R - B R I Bar Review. Constitutional Law
0098-7689 Genealogy Digest
0098-7700 International Juridical Association. Monthly Bulletin *see* 0730-532X
0098-7719 International Trade Perspective *changed to* International Law and Trade Perspective.
0098-7735 National Urban League Progress Report *changed to* National Urban League Annual Report.
0098-7778 Package Printing and Diecutting *changed to* Package Printing & Converting.
0098-7786 Modern Paint and Coatings
0098-7840 Mississippi. State Game and Fish Commission. Annual Report to the Regular Session of the Mississippi Legislature *see* 0733-2017
0098-7875 Michigan. State Court Administrator. Annual Report.
0098-7913 Serials Review
0098-7921 Population and Development Review
0098-793X Allied Landscape Industry Member Directory *changed to* American Association of Nurserymen Who's Who in the Nursery Industry Member Directory.
0098-7956 Historical Evaluation and Research Organization. Combat Data Subscription Service†
0098-7972 L A D Newsletter (Library Administration Division) *see* 0888-4463
0098-7980 Bay Area Review Course. Legal Ethics *changed to* B A R - B R I Bar Review. Professional Responsibility.
0098-7999 B A R - B R I Bar Review. Remedies
0098-8014 Shellfish Market Review and Outlook†
0098-8030 Michigan Germanic Studies
0098-8049 B A R - B R I Bar Review. Criminal Law
0098-8073 New Jersey. Division of Savings and Loan Associations. Annual Report *changed to* New Jersey. Department of Banking. Annual Report.
0098-809X Center for the Study of the Presidency. Center House Bulletin *see* 0360-4918
0098-8111 U.S. President's Committee on Mental Retardation. Mental Retardation and the Law†
0098-8138 Connecticut. Judicial Department. Report
0098-8162 N C C C Chronicles†
0098-8219 Health Care Facilities†
0098-8227 Photographic Applications in Science, Technology and Medicine *see* 0360-7216
0098-8235 World Environment Report *changed to* Greenhouse Effect Report.
0098-8243 Comprehensive Therapy
0098-826X Nebraska. Governor's Conference on Human Resource Development Report†
0098-8278 I A S S W Directory; Member Schools and Associations
0098-8332 California. Employment Data and Research Division. Taxable and Total Wages, Regular Benefits Paid, Employer Contributions Earned, and Average Covered Employment, by Industry†
0098-8340 Canto Libre†
0098-8359 Export-Import Bank of the United States. Cumulative Records†
0098-8383 Marine Science Communications *see* 0890-5460
0098-8421 American Medical Women's Association. Journal
0098-8448 Association for Physical and Mental Rehabilitation. Journal *changed to* Clinical Kinesiology.
0098-8472 Environmental and Experimental Botany
0098-8510 Pennsylvania. Department of Public Welfare. Public Welfare Annual Statistics†
0098-8529 Rental Age *changed to* Rental Management.
0098-8537 Homicide in California
0098-8553 Multidisciplinary Research
0098-8561 Idaho. Department of Health and Welfare. Bureau of Research and Statistics. Research Report *changed to* Idaho. Department of Health and Welfare. Research and Statistics Section. Quarterly Welfare Statistical Bulletin.
0098-857X Scandinavian Review
0098-8588 American Journal of Law & Medicine
0098-8596 Biocharacterist *see* 0098-8618
0098-860X Birth and the Family Journal *see* 0730-7659
0098-8618 Health Evaluation Review†
0098-8642 Aquatic World†
0098-8650 Bike World†
0098-8669 Down River *see* 0161-052X
0098-8677 Gymnastics World†
0098-8685 Nordic World *see* 0273-642X
0098-8693 Self-Defense World†
0098-8707 Soccer World†
0098-8731 North Carolina Review of Business and Economics†
0098-874X Florida Administrative Weekly
0098-8847 Earthquake Engineering and Structural Dynamics
0098-8855 Alternatives†
0098-8863 Exposure (Boulder)
0098-8871 Court Crier *changed to* Court Manager.
0098-8898 Employee Relations Law Journal
0098-8901 Land Use Planning Abstracts†
0098-891X Lending Law Forum
0098-8928 Marketing California Pears for Fresh Market
0098-8936 Real Estate Directory of Manhattan
0098-8944 Savings Association Annals†
0098-8952 School Student and the Courts *see* 0164-3851
0098-8960 Upshaw Family Journal†
0098-8979 U.S. National Bureau of Standards. Journal of Research. Section B. Mathematical Sciences *see* 1044-677X
0098-9010 73 Magazine for Radio Amateurs *see* 1052-2522
0098-9037 Country Music News
0098-9053 Linguistic Analysis
0098-9061 Quarterly Survey of Judicial Salaries in State Court Systems *changed to* Survey of Judicial Salaries.
0098-907X Optics News *see* 1047-6938
0098-910X U.S. International Trade Commission. Quarterly Report to the Congress and the East-West Foreign Trade Board on Trade Between the United States and the Nonmarket Economy Countries
0098-9134 Journal of Gerontological Nursing
0098-9142 R C Respiratory Care *see* 0730-8418
0098-9169 Assets Protection
0098-9207 Qualified Remodeler
0098-9215 Radio Control Buyers Guide†
0098-924X Centerpoint†
0098-9258 Advances in Consumer Research
0098-9266 Journal of Early Southern Decorative Arts
0098-9282 Zion's Herald (1976)
0098-9355 French Forum
0098-9363 Ascent†
0098-9371 Children's Book Showcase. Catalog†
0098-9398 Media Guide International. Business Publications Edition *changed to* International Media Guides. Business - Professional Publications Edition.
0098-9444 Biblical Archaeology Review
0098-9452 Chariton Review
0098-9487 I A J R C Journal
0098-9495 Journal of Education Finance
0098-9509 Marxism and the Mass Media
0098-9517 Sabbath Watchman
0098-9533 National Journal of Criminal Defense†
0098-9541 New Jersey Orchard and Vineyard Survey
0098-955X Quest (Washington)
0098-9568 Real Estate Valuation Cost File†
0098-9576 Washington Energy Directory†
0098-9584 Journal of School Social Work†
0098-9665 Index to Scientific Reviews. Guide and Journal Lists†
0098-9673 Special Project Grants Awarded for Improvement in Nurse Training *see* 0095-2141
0098-972X U.S. National Institute of Mental Health. Mental Health Statistical Notes†
0098-9738 Aha'llono
0098-9770 Kentucky. Council on Public Higher Education. Origin of Enrollments, Accredited Colleges and Universities *changed to* Kentucky College and University Origin of Enrollments.
0098-9819 Current Physics Index
0098-9827 Educational opportunity Program Notes†
0098-9835 Guide to Professional Development Opportunities for College and University Administrators: Seminars, Workshops, Conferences, and Internships *see* 0197-128X
0098-9886 International Journal of Circuit Theory & Applications
0098-9983 California State Plan for Hospital and Health Center Construction *changed to* California State Health Plan.
0099-0027 Professional Safety
0099-0035 National Bluegrass News
0099-0043 Engravers Journal
0099-0051 Bowling-Fencing Guide *changed to* N A G W S Guide. Bowling - Golf.
0099-006X Council of State Governments. Southern Legislative Conference. Summary, Annual Meeting†
0099-0086 College & Research Libraries News
0099-0094 Environmental Geology *changed to* Environmental Geology and Water Sciences.
0099-0116 Child Study Journal Monograph†
0099-0159 Goldenseal
0099-0167 Schwann-2, Records and Tapes *see* 1047-2371
0099-0205 N A A Where to Stay Book
0099-0213 Grant Information System†
0099-0248 C R C Critical Reviews in Food Science and Nutrition *see* 1040-8398
0099-0256 Accreditation
0099-0264 Moons and Lion Tailes†
0099-0280 Moment
0099-0299 Nebraska Library Commission. Annual Report *changed to* Nebraska Libraries: A Directory.
0099-0302 Pennsylvania. Department of Education. Special Education Programs-Services†
0099-0310 Professional Decorating and Coating Action *see* 0735-9713
0099-0329 Western Society for French History. Proceedings of the Annual Meeting
0099-0353 Commercial Fish Farmer and Aquaculture News *see* 0199-1388
0099-0361 Indian America†
0099-037X Progress in Behavior Modification
0099-0418 Bay Area Review Course. Conflicts of Law†
0099-0442 State and Local Construction Mileage *changed to* Nebraska. Department of Roads. Nebraska Selected Statistics.
0099-0450 Plastics Manufacturing Capabilities in Mississippi†
0099-0604 Harmony (Harmony)†
0099-0612 Guide to Occupational Safety Literature†
0099-0809 Index of Trademarks Issued from the U.S. Patent and Trademark Office
0099-085X Southeastern Library Network. Annual Report *changed to* Solinet. Annual Report.
0099-0868 Common Ground (Hanover)†
0099-0876 Index to Pravda†
0099-0914 P I M S Monthly Petroleum Report *see* 0095-7356
0099-0957 Declassified Documents Quarterly Catalog *see* 1046-4239
0099-0973 Survey of Business†
0099-1015 County Year Book†
0099-1023 Indiana Public Management *changed to* Indiana University. School of Public and Environmental Affairs. Review.
0099-1031 Bar Leader
0099-1058 State Bar of Arizona. Newsletter *see* 0745-4384
0099-1066 U.S. Department of Agriculture. Agricultural Outlook
0099-1090 I F P A Communicator *changed to* A V C Visions.
0099-1112 Photogrammetric Engineering and Remote Sensing
0099-1147 Advances in Pathobiology†
0099-118X Public Health Statistics, State of Oklahoma *see* 0098-5651
0099-1236 B A R - B R I Bar Review. Corporations
0099-1244 B A R - B R I Bar Review. Civil Procedure
0099-1260 Oregon. Employment Division. Annual Report†
0099-1279 Wyoming. Department of Environmental Quality. Annual Report
0099-1333 Journal of Academic Librarianship
0099-135X Detroit College of Law Review
0099-1414 Sage Annual Reviews of Communication Research
0099-1465 Southern University Law Review
0099-152X Internal Medicine News *see* 0274-5542
0099-1546 Progress in Anesthesiology
0099-1554 Training Directory of the Rehabilitation Research and Training Centers†
0099-166X Defense Reference Reports
0099-1694 Desarrollo Nacional
0099-1708 Journal of Design Automation and Fault-Tolerant Computing *see* 0888-224X
0099-1716 A-E Concepts in Wood Design†
0099-1759 Faith for the Family†
0099-1767 J E N
0099-1791 Luptonian
0099-1821 N C R R Bulletin *see* 0745-6999
0099-183X Social Thought
0099-1848 Collier Bankruptcy Cases
0099-1864 Martin Family Quarterly†
0099-1872 Industrial Growth in Tennessee, Annual Report *changed to* Economic Growth in Tennessee, Annual Report.
0099-1929 Louisiana. Department of Agriculture. Analysis of Official Pesticide Samples. Annual Report
0099-2011 Meat Industry *see* 0892-6077
0099-2224 Management Research (Amherst)†
0099-2232 Lutheran New Yorker†
0099-2240 Applied and Environmental Microbiology
0099-2267 U.S. Department of Transportation. Office of University Research. Awards to Academic Institutions by the Department of Transportation

ISSN

0099-2305 South Dakota. State Department of Public Welfare. Research and Statistical Annual Report *changed to* South Dakota. State Department of Social Services. Annual Statistical Report.
0099-2313 Sunset Ideas for Improving Your Home†
0099-2356 Mid-South Folklore *see* 0275-6013
0099-2364 Applied Radiology and Nuclear Medicine *see* 0160-9963
0099-2372 Cancer News Journal *see* 0891-0766
0099-2399 Journal of Endodontics
0099-2410 Public Documents - State of Louisiana *changed to* State of Louisiana Public Documents.
0099-2445 Financial Analysis of the Motor Carrier Industry†
0099-2453 Human Resources Abstracts
0099-4294 N P N Factbook
0099-4480 Illuminating Engineering Society. Journal
0099-5010 Arkansas Agricultural Experiment Station. Mimeograph Series *changed to* Arkansas. Agricultural Experiment Station. Research Series.
0099-5355 Lancet (North American Edition)
0099-5428 Analytical Profiles of Drug Substances
0099-5851 Iowa State University Veterinarian
0099-6335 Research & Development Associates for Military Food and Packaging Systems. Activities Report
0099-8281 Construction Directory *changed to* Construction Industries of Massachusetts Directory.
0099-8400 McIlvainea
0099-8729 Water *see* 0196-0717
0099-8745 Na Okika O Hawaii
0099-9059 Raptor Research *see* 0892-1016
0099-9660 Wall Street Journal (Eastern Edition)
0099-9857 F A O Forestry and Forest Products Studies *see* 0532-0283
0100-0039 Cientifica
0100-0195 Revista Medica do Estado do Rio de Janeiro
0100-0217 Revista Pernambucana de Desenvolvimento
0100-0233 Revista Baiana de Saude Publica
0100-039X Perspectiva Economica
0100-0551 Pesquisa e Planejamento Economico
0100-0705 Bibliografia Brasileira de Engenharia†
0100-0756 Bibliografia Brasileira de Quimica e Quimica Tecnologica†
0100-0829 U F M G. Escola de Biblioteconomia. Revista
0100-0845 Centro de Pesquisas do Cacau. Boletim Tecnico
0100-0888 Revista Letras
0100-0977 Amazonia - Bibliografia†
0100-123X Brazil. Servico Nacional de Levantamento e Conservacao de Solos. Boletim Tecnico†
0100-1248 Navigator
0100-1299 Anuario Estatistico do Brasil
0100-1302 Universidade Federal do Ceara. Centro de Ciencias da Saude. Revista de Medicina
0100-1345 Sinopse Estatistica do Brasil†
0100-1574 Cadernos de Pesquisa
0100-1671 Construcao Rio de Janeiro
0100-1876 Biblioteca Nacional de Brasil. Boletim Bibliografico *changed to* Bibliografia Brasileira.
0100-1922 Biblioteca Nacional de Brasil. Anais
0100-1949 Bahia, Brazil (State). Centro de Pesquisas e Desenvolvimento. Boletim Tecnico†
0100-1965 Ciencia da Informacao
0100-204X Pesquisa Agropecuaria Brasileira
0100-2139 Anais de Historia *see* 0101-9074
0100-2228 Sistemas†
0100-2538 Estudos Juridicos
0100-2546 Instituto de Pesquisas Zootecnicas "Francisco Osorio". Anuario Tecnico
0100-2635 Estudos Brasileiros†
0100-2694 Faculdade de Ciencias Agrarias do Para. Boletim
0100-2716 Periodicos Brasileiros de Cultura *see* 0100-2767
0100-2767 Periodicos Brasileiros de Ciencias e Tecnologia†
0100-2910 Brazilian Economic Studies†
0100-3143 Educacao e Realidade
0100-3151 Instituto Florestal. Boletim Tecnico†
0100-3232 Revista Brasileira de Clinica e Terapeutica
0100-3283 Hansenologia Internationalis
0100-3364 Informe Agropecuario
0100-3399 Calendario de Eventos Tecnico-Cientificos Realizados no Brazil *changed to* Eventos em Politica Cientifica e Tecnologica.
0100-350X Instituto de Tecnologia de Alimentos. Coletanea
0100-3593 Energia Nuclear e Agricultura
0100-3941 Rede Ferroviaria Federal. Lista de Artigos Selecionados†
0100-3984 Radiologia Brasileira
0100-4158 Fitopatologia Brasileira
0100-4204 Fitossanidade
0100-4298 Agroanalysis†
0100-4409 Sao Paulo, Brazil (State). Instituto de Economia Agricola. Informacoes Economicas *changed to* Informacoes Economicas.
0100-4557 I P E F Journal
0100-4670 Ecletica Quimica
0100-4700 Natureza em Revista
0100-4743 Index Medicus Latinoamericano
0100-4859 Sociedade Brasileira de Zootecnia. Revista
0100-4948 Sao Paulo. Biblioteca Mario de Andrade. Boletim Bibliografico *changed to* Sao Paulo. Biblioteca Mario de Andrade. Revista.
0100-4956 Revista Economica do Nordeste
0100-4964 Instituto de Tecnologia de Alimentos. Estudos Economicos. Alimentos Processados
0100-5065 Centro de Pesquisas do Cacau. Informe Tecnico *changed to* Centro de Pesquisas do Cacau. Informe de Pesquisas.
0100-5146 Universidade de Sao Paulo. Instituto Oceanografico. Publicacao Especial
0100-5162 Precos Medios do Boi Gordo e La†
0100-5197 Universidade de Sao Paulo. Instituto Oceanografico. Relatorio de Cruzeiros
0100-5219 Precos Recebidos Pelos Agricultores
0100-5243 Universidade de Sao Paulo. Instituto Oceanografico. Relatorio Interno
0100-526X Prognostico
0100-5316 Prognostico Regiao Centro-Sul†
0100-5405 Summa Phytopathologica
0100-560X Acompanhamento da Situacao Agropecuaria do Parana
0100-5790 Instituto de Resseguros do Brasil. Secretaria Geral da Presidencia. Relatorio do Exercicio†
0100-6045 Manuscrito
0100-607X Revista do Setor de Ciencias Agrarias
0100-6142 Data News
0100-6266 Bibliografia Brasileira de Odontologia
0100-655X Literatura Economica
0100-6800 Bibliografia Brasileira de Agricultura *changed to* Bibliografia Brasileira de Agricultura (Year).
0100-6916 Engenharia Agricola
0100-7025 Novos Estudos C E B R A P
0100-705X Revista Paulista de Odontologia
0100-7068 Universidade Federal do Rio Grande do Norte. Centro de Biociencias. Departamento de Oceanografia e Limnologia. Boletim
0100-7076 Revista de Cultura Vozes
0100-7157 Revista de Biblioteconomia de Brasilia
0100-7173 Informe Demografico
0100-722X Bibliografia de Publicacoes Oficiais Brasileiras†
0100-7238 Brazil. Fundacao Nacional do Livro Infantil e Juvenil. Boletim Informativo†
0100-7475 Brazil. Museu do Indio. Boletim. Etno-Historia
0100-7912 Geografia
0100-8064 Brazil. Centro Nacional de Pesquisa de Mandioca e Fruticultura. Circular Tecnica
0100-8102 Centro de Pesquisa Agropecuaria do Tropico Umido. Boletim de Pesquisa
0100-8153 Africa
0100-8161 Pesquisa em Andamento
0100-8226 Hanseniasis Letter†
0100-8404 Revista Brasileira de Botanica
0100-8455 Brazilian Journal of Genetics
0100-8501 Pesquisa Agropecuaria Pernambucana
0100-8633 Annuario Brasileiro de Ceramica
0100-8692 Arquivos Brasileiros de Psicologia†
0100-8730 Anuario Estatistico do Estado de Sao Paulo
0100-879X Revista Brasileira de Pesquisas Medicas e Biologicas
0100-8854 Brazil. Centro Nacional de Pesquisa de Mandioca e Fruticultura. Comunicado Tecnico
0100-9354 Revista UniMar
0100-9591 Forum Educacional†
0100-9761 Boletim de Geografia Teoretica
0100-9974 Ministerio de Educacao. Faculdade de Ciencias Agrarias do Para. Informe Tecnico
0101-0352 Universidade Federal do Parana. Centro de Estudos Portugueses. Arquivos†
0101-0433 Brazil. Museu do Indio. Boletim. Antropologia
0101-0484 Brazil. Museu do Indio. Boletim. Documentacao
0101-0530 Brazil. Museu do Indio. Boletim. Linguistica
0101-059X Didatica
0101-0646 Banco do Brasil. Annual Report
0101-0697 Banco de Bibliografias†
0101-0794 C & I
0101-0972 Universidade Federal do Rio Grande do Sul. Instituto Central de Biociencias. Boletim *see* 0102-597X
0101-1049 Laudo
0101-1138 Tecnicouro
0101-1480 Rio Grande do Sul, Brazil. Procuradoria Geral do Estado. Revista
0101-1774 Universidade Estadual Paulista. Revista de Odontologia
0101-1944 Naturalia
0101-2223 Nordeste: Analise Conjuntural
0101-2304 Som†
0101-2711 Central Nacional de Pesquisa de Mandioca e Fruticultura. Relatorio Tecnico Anual
0101-3157 Revista Economia Politica
0101-3173 Trans - Form - Acao
0101-322X Revista de Ciencias Biomedicas
0101-3289 Revista Brasileira de Ciencias do Esporte
0101-3300 Estudos C E B R A P *see* 0100-7025
0101-3459 Perspectivas
0101-3505 Revista de Letras
0101-3580 Boletim de Zoologia
0101-3645 Brazil Comercio e Industria
0101-3793 Revista de Ciencias Farmaceuticas
0101-4064 Estudos Ibero-Americanos *changed to* Revista de Estudos Ibero-Americanos.
0101-4110 Estudos Economicos *see* 0101-4161
0101-4161 Revista Estudos Economicos
0101-4315 Confederacao Nacional do Comercio. Conselho Tecnico Consultivo. Carta Mensal
0101-4331 Informacao Psiquiatrica
0101-4366 Instituto Historico e Geografico Brasileiro. Revista
0101-465X Pontificia Universidade Catolica do Rio Grande do Sul. Educacao
0101-4781 Revista do Medico†
0101-4854 Documentacao Amazonica
0101-5117 Boletim de Pesquisa
0101-5303 Estudos Tecnologicos
0101-5354 Acta Biologica Leopoldensia
0101-5400 Universidade Federal do Rio Grande do Norte. Departamento de Geologia. Boletim
0101-546X Estudos Afro-Asiaticos
0101-563X Revista Brasileira de Mandioca
0101-5680 Brazil. Departamento Nacional de Obras Contra as Secas. Relatorio
0101-6261 Micro Mundo
0101-630X C T A A. Boletim de Pesquisa
0101-6377 Informe Conjuntural
0101-6547 Clube Militar. Revista
0101-658X Destaques†
0101-6636 Balanco Energetico Nacional
0101-6903 Camara Brasileira do Livro. Centro de Catalogacao na Fonte. Oficina de Livros: Novidades Catalogadas na Fonte
0101-7136 Inter-Acao
0101-7217 Revista DocPop
0101-7284 Revista do Exercito Brasileiro
0101-7616 Roessleria
0101-8205 Matematica Aplicada e Computacional
0101-8248 Revista Brasileira de Lingua e Literatura†
0101-8353 Indicadores I B G E†
0101-837X Estudos Germanicos
0101-8469 Revista Brasileiro de Neurologia
0101-9074 Historia
0101-9082 Geociencias
0101-9112 Antenna - Eletronica Popular
0101-9236 Centro Brasileiro de Pesquisas Fisicas. Monografias†
0101-9457 Revista de Geografia
0101-9635 Leopoldianum
0101-9708 Reuniao Geral de Cultura do Arroz. Anais
0102-0145 Mundo Mecanico
0102-0218 Mensario Estatistico Sul-Rio-Grandense
0102-0226 Anuario Estatistico do Rio Grande do Sul
0102-0382 Clube Naval Revista
0102-0471 Associacao Mineira de Acao Educacional. Revista
0102-0501 Construcao Minas Centro Oeste
0102-051X Construcao Norte Nordeste
0102-0528 Construcao Regiao Sul
0102-0617 Ensayos E C I E L
0102-0692 Bahia, Brazil (State). Centro de Planejamento. Comercio Exterior da Bahia: Exportacao Segundo as Firmas e Mercadorias
0102-0811 Revista de Matematica e Estatistica
0102-0935 Arquivo Brasileiro de Medicina Veterinaria e Zootecnia
0102-129X Faculdade de Odontologia de Ribeirao Preto. Revista *changed to* Universidade de Sao Paulo. Revista de Odontologia.
0102-1397 Universidade Federal de Uberlandia. Curso de Direito. Revista
0102-1931 Plastico Moderno
0102-2253 Congresso Brasileiro de Economia e Sociologia Rural. Anais
0102-2555 Universidade de Sao Paulo. Faculdade de Educacao. Revista
0102-2636 Convivium
0102-3225 Guia Panrotas
0102-3292 Sociedade Paranaense de Matematica. Monografias
0102-3306 Congresso Nacional de Botanica. Anais
0102-3314 Iheringia. Serie Miscelanea
0102-3357 Art
0102-3500 Bibliografia Brasileira de Energia Nuclear
0102-3519 Energia: Bibliografia Seletiva
0102-3586 Jornal de Pneumologia
0102-3772 Psicologia: Teoria e Pesquisa
0102-4264 Acta Semiotica et Linguistica
0102-4450 Documentacao de Estudos em Linguistica Teorica e Aplicada
0102-4930 R F F S A. Anuario Estatistico
0102-5694 Sintese Ferroviaria Brasileira

ISSN INDEX

0102-5716 Veterinaria e Zootecnia
0102-5767 Cadernos de Estudos Linguisticos
0102-597X Universidade Federal do Rio Grande do Sul. Instituto de Biociencias. Boletim
0102-6275 Boletim I G - U S P. Publicacao Especial
0102-6283 Boletim I G - U S P. Serie Cientifica
0102-6291 Boletim I G - U S P. Serie Didatica
0102-6380 Ars Veterinaria
0102-6445 Lua Nova
0102-6526 Summer Institute of Linguistics. Serie Linguistica
0102-6550 Arte U N E S P
0102-6887 Paulo-Coutiana
0102-6992 Sociedade e Estado
0102-700X Acervo
0102-7077 Especialist
0102-7085 Revista Analise e Conjuntura
0102-7336 Revista de Teatro
0102-7646 Associacao Brasileira de Psiquiatria e Asociacion Psiquiatrica de la America Latina. Revista
0102-8839 Revista Sao Paulo em Perspectiva
0102-8979 Arquitetura e Urbanismo
0102-9053 Instituto Historico, Geografico e Ethnografico do Brasil. Revista Trimensal see 0101-4366
0102-9304 Boletim de Geociencias da Petrobras
0102-9460 Pontificia Universidade Catolica do Rio Grande do Sul. Odontociencia. Revista
0102-9479 Humanidades
0103-0809 Arquivos de Saude Mental do Estado de Sao Paulo
0103-1414 Verso e Reverso
0103-1813 Trabalhos em Linguistica Aplicada
0103-1821 Estudos Portugueses e Africanos
0103-2038 Bibliografia de Politica Industrial
0103-2070 Tempo Social
0103-2550 Jardim Botanico do Rio de Janeiro. Arquivos
0103-2690 Medicina da Pontificia Universidade Catolica do Rio Grande do Sul. Revista
0103-2909 Ciencias em Museus
0103-3131 Revista Brasileira de Fisiologia Vegetal
0103-314X Teocomunicacao
0103-3263 Instituto Estadual de Hematologia Arthur de Siqueira Cavalcanti. Revista
0103-3816 Agrotropica
0103-4235 Alimentos e Nutricao
0103-4278 Museu Paraense Emilio Goeldi. Boletim. Serie Ciencias da Terra
0103-4332 Sintese
0103-443X Levantamento Sistematico da Producao Agricola
0103-5525 Revista Musica
0103-6076 Goeldiana Zoologia
0103-7021 Solos e Rochas
0103-8834 Sindicato Nacional dos Editores de Livros. Informativo Bibliografico
0103-913X Meio Ambiente
0105-001X Acta Linguistica see 0374-0463
0105-0141 Odontologi
0105-0168 Automatik
0105-0192 Arv og Eje
0105-0257 Kopenhagener Beitraege zur Germanistischen Linguistikt
0105-0281 Stambog over Kvaeg af Roed Dansk Malkeracet
0105-032X L O Bladet
0105-0370 Dansk Psoriasis Tidsskrift
0105-0516 Veterinaermedicinsk Tidsskrift Informationt
0105-0532 I E F Information
0105-0583 Cras
0105-0621 Odense University Studies in Psychiatry and Medical Psychology
0105-063X Danmarks Geologiske Undersoegelse. Aarbogt
0105-0648 Danske Fysioterapeuter
0105-0656 Acta Pathologica et Microbiologica Scandinavica. Section B: Microbiology. Supplementum see 0108-0199
0105-0788 Denmark. Danmarks Statistik. Arbejdsmarkedsstatistik: Kvartalsvis Regionalstatistikt
0105-0826 Mark og Montre
0105-0834 Dansk Pelsdyrblad see 0011-6424
0105-0877 Denmark. Danmarks Statistik. Maanedlig Ordre- og Omsaetningsstatistik for Industri
0105-0885 Groenlands Befolkning
0105-0907 Danmarks Tekniske Hoejskole. Fysisk Laboratorium 1. Report
0105-0982 Kontakt (Copenhagen, 1948)
0105-1024 Folk og Kulturt
0105-1040 Dansk Geologisk Forening. Meddelelser see 0011-6297
0105-1083 Denmark. Danmarks Statistik. Maanedlig Beskaeftigelses- og Loenstatistik for Industri
0105-1113 Rajneesh see 0107-7996
0105-1121 Retfaerd
0105-1164 Denmark. Danmarks Statistik. Skatter og Afgifter
0105-1245 Dansk Dragesport see 0109-5595
0105-1377 Boernefilmkataloget
0105-1385 Nordicom
0105-1393 Psykologisk Litteratur i Danske Forskningsbibliotekert
0105-1423 Historia Medicinae Veterinariae
0105-1466 Convivium (Copenhagen)†
0105-1504 Alrune
0105-1660 Harja
0105-1830 Almindelige Danske Laegeforening changed to Laegeforeningens Vejviser.
0105-1873 Contact Dermatitis
0105-189X Odont changed to Det Ny Infodont.
0105-1903 Kommunistisk Tidsskrift see 0109-890X
0105-192X Teknisk Videnskabelig Forskning
0105-1938 Carlsberg Research Communicationst
0105-2071 Blixenianat
0105-208X D S L's Praesentationshaefte
0105-2233 Arbejderbevaegelsen i Danmark. Historisk og Aktuelt. Tilvaekst
0105-2373 Aktuel Elektronik
0105-2454 Welcome to Norwayt
0105-2543 Denmark. Kg. Veterinaer- og Landbohoejskole. Meddelelser see 0905-8478
0105-2608 Vendsyssel Nu og Da
0105-2616 Information for Forskningsbiblioteker see 0903-6342
0105-2691 Udkast
0105-2853 Danmarks Tekniske Hoejskole. Laboratoriet for Akustik. Publikation
0105-287X Laegemiddelkataloget
0105-2896 Immunological Reviews
0105-3027 Technical University of Denmark. Acoustics Laboratory Report
0105-3035 Bidragt
0105-3051 Kritiske Historikere
0105-3094 Miljoe-Projekter changed to Miljoeprojekt.
0105-3167 Kongelige Bibliotek. Publikumsorienteringer
0105-3191 Dansk Teologisk Tidsskrift
0105-3213 International Council for the Exploration of the Sea. Cooperative Research Report see 1017-6195
0105-3507 Groenlands Geologiske Undersoegelse. Bulletin
0105-3531 Sociologisk Litteratur i Danske Forskningsbibliotekert
0105-3639 Alfred Benzon Symposium. Proceedings
0105-3647 Denmark. Danmarks Statistik. Kvartalsvis Konjunkturbarometer for Industrit
0105-4058 Handelshoejskolen i Aarhus. Institut for Finansiering og Kreditvaesen. Kompendium D
0105-4066 Denmark. Statens Planteavlsforsoeg. Sorter af Groensagert
0105-4090 Tidsskriftindeks for Skolebiblioteker
0105-4112 Aarhus Universitet. Slavisk Institut. Arbejdspapirer
0105-4120 Forest Tree Improvement
0105-4139 Koebenhavns Universitet. Institut for Social Medicin. Publikationer
0105-4201 V og S Priser. Husbygning
0105-421X V og S Priser changed to V og S Priser. Anlaeg.
0105-4236 Aarhus University. Botanical Institute. Reports
0105-4244 Landbrugets Samraad for Forskning og Forsoeg. Kortlaegning see 0906-1770
0105-4260 Forsikring
0105-4503 I W G I A Documents
0105-452X Denmark. Planlaegningsraadet for Forskningen - Dandok - Statens 6 Forskningsraad. Beretningt
0105-4538 Allergy
0105-4554 Danske Statslaan see 0902-6681
0105-4570 Landinspektoeren
0105-4821 Koebenhavns Universitet. Institut for Religionshistorie. Skrifter
0105-4856 Danmarks Laererhoejskole. Geografisk Institut. Skrifter
0105-4880 Ny Elektronikt
0105-4899 O O A - Saertryk
0105-5003 S T S Information see 0108-2655
0105-5046 Kongelige Bibliotek. Fagbibliografer
0105-5070 Denmark. Statens Filmcentral. Statistik over Udlejning af 16 MM Film i Finansaaret changed to Denmark. Statens Filmcentral. Statistik over Udlejning og Deponering af 16 MM Film og Video i Finansaaret.
0105-5100 Nordisk Kulturelt Samarbejdet
0105-5119 Technical University of Denmark. Institute of Roads, Transport and Town Planning. Papers and Reports
0105-5194 Danmarks Tekniske Hoejskole. Instituttet for Landmaaling og Fotogrammetri. Meddelelse
0105-5216 Humaniorat
0105-533X Handelshoejskolen i Aarhus. Institut for Markedsoekonomi. Skriftserie Et
0105-5399 Socialpaedagogen
0105-5526 Denmark. Statens Filmcentral. S F C, 16mm Filmt
0105-564X Roskilde Universitetsbibliotek. Skriftserie
0105-5801 Forteana
0105-5836 Denmark. Nyt fra Miljoestyrelsen see 0903-5907
0105-5933 Fajabefa Nyt changed to Evelyn Booster.
0105-5992 Erhvervfremmende og Forbrugerpolitiske Foranstaltningert
0105-6077 Folkebiblioteksstatistik, Budgetter, Virksomhedt
0105-614X Lydteknisk Institut. Rapport
0105-6239 Pas Paa see 0905-5010
0105-6255 Acta Campanologica
0105-6263 International Journal of Andrology
0105-6336 Hvide Lotus see 0108-9145
0105-6387 I W G I A Newsletter
0105-6433 Byhornet
0105-6441 Modelflyve Nyt
0105-6492 N A A
0105-6514 Statens Planteavlsforsoeg. Meddelelse see 0903-0727
0105-6603 D P A
0105-6611 Nordisk Tidsskrift for Rensning og Vask
0105-6654 Levnedsmiddelbladet - Supermarkedet
0105-6662 Erhvervsnoeglen
0105-6867 Episkopet see 0900-1433
0105-6883 Denmark. Statens Husdyrbrugsforsoeg. Beretning
0105-6956 Rapport fra S T I K K
0105-709X Boernebladets Jul changed to Jul i Familien.
0105-7154 Historiske Studier fra Fynt
0105-7162 Haandbog for Provinsens Distriksblade
0105-7340 Asien-Studier i Skandinavien see 0904-4337
0105-7405 Serie om Videnskabsforskningt
0105-7456 Kommunal Litteraturt
0105-7480 Danske Laegemiddelstandarder
0105-7502 Forskning i Groenland-Tusaat
0105-7510 Orbis Litterarum
0105-7618 Sfinx
0105-7669 Contact with Denmark
0105-7723 Doeves Jul
0105-7855 Flygtning Bladet see 0108-1837
0105-7871 Danmarks Ingenioerakademi. Bygningsafdelningen. Dialogt
0105-7936 Panda-Nyt see 0108-7991
0105-8010 Nordisk Kunst og Designt
0105-8045 Dansk Musikfortegnelse
0105-8118 Hikuin
0105-8126 Pulso
0105-8134 Goer det Selv Indeks
0105-8215 Kongelige Bibliotek. Specialhjaelpemidler
0105-824X Aarhus Universitet. Geologisk Institut. Geoskrifter
0105-8258 Aarhus Universitet. Geologisk Institut. Geokompendier
0105-8266 Aarhus Universitet. Geologisk Institut. Georapporter
0105-8282 Ergoterapeuten
0105-8347 Jeg Arbejder Med
0105-8355 Zise
0105-8509 Oekonomisk Oversigt for Amtskommunerne see 0109-7822
0105-8517 Aarhus Universitet. Matematisk Institut. Datalogisk Afdeling. DAIMI PB
0105-8525 Aarhus Universitet. Matematisk Institut. Datalogisk Afdeling. DAIMI MD
0105-8533 Aarhus Universitet. Matematisk Institut. Datalogisk Afdeling. DAIMI FN
0105-8541 Danmarks Tekniske Hoejskole. Instituttet for Teleteknik. Rapport I T
0105-8630 Zoneterapeut Forening af 28. Februar 1976 see 0109-0895
0105-8738 Trae og Industri
0105-8819 Nyt fra Nationalmuseet
0105-8827 Roskilde Universitetscenter. Institut for Samfundsoekonomi og Planlaegning. Research Report
0105-8924 Lovbibliotek
0105-9033 Fiskeri og Fiskeriundersoegelser ved Groenland see 0905-5193
0105-9041 Grafiske Funktionaerers Landesforening. Medlemsblad see 0109-0879
0105-9068 Kvindestudiert
0105-9106 Nordisk Julemaerke Katalog
0105-9122 Forbrugerindeks
0105-9173 Register over Autoriserede Laboratorier
0105-9211 Fisk og Hav
0105-9254 Koebstadmuseet Den Gamle By
0105-9289 Dansk Paediatrisk Selskab. Aarbog
0105-9327 Holarctic Ecology see 0906-7590
0105-936X Koebenhavns Bymuseumt
0105-9386 Kemisk Analyse af Mineraler og Bjergarter
0105-9416 Haandvaerket and Maskinen
0105-9459 Urban and Regional Research in Denmarkt
0105-9475 Select Bibliography of Danish Works on the History of Towns Published
0105-9483 D U E Notatt
0105-9556 Skolebiblioteket
0105-9602 Denmark. Planstyrelsen. Regionplanorienteringt
0105-9629 Installations Nyt
0105-9645 Universitetets Statistiske Institut. Research Report
0105-9750 Denmark. Danmarks Statistik. Statistike Efterreningert
0105-9785 Hjerteforeningen
0105-9807 Denmark. Statens Husdyrbrugsforsoeg. Indeks
0105-9815 Dansk Amatoer Astronomi see 0905-8958
0105-9858 Frederiksborgmuseet. Aarskrift changed to Carlsbergfondet Aarsskrift.
0105-9882 Landsudvalget for Fjerkrae. Meddelelse
0105-9963 Anglica et Americana
0105-9998 New Religious Movements Up-Date see 1011-8101
0106-0031 Danske Hedeselskab. Forsoegsvirksomheden. Beretning see 0903-5664
0106-004X Frugtavleren

5588 ISSN INDEX

ISSN	Title
0106-0090	Danmarks Deltagelse i det Internationale Udviklingssamarbejde. Aarsrapport
0106-0104	Produktions Nyt
0106-0120	Dansk Fagpresse
0106-0147	Danmarks Tekniske Hoejskole. Afdelingen for Baerende Konstruktioner. Forelaesningsnotat F†
0106-0279	Hjemkundskab
0106-035X	Novelleregister
0106-0392	Haandbog i Dansk Politik†
0106-0406	Dansk Betonforening. Publikation†
0106-0430	Loegumkloster-Studier
0106-0449	Filosofiske Studier
0106-0465	Aarbog for Folkeskolen
0106-0473	Auto Nytt
0106-0481	Kongelige Danske Videnskabernes Selskab. Historisk - Filosofiske Meddelelser
0106-0546	Ugeskrift for Jordbrug see 0906-7043
0106-0627	1066 Tidsskrift for Historisk Forskning
0106-0724	Danmarks Transport-Tidende
0106-0791	Aalborg Universitetscenter. Institut for Elektroniske Systemer. Rapport
0106-0805	C D R Project Paper
0106-0821	Roskilde Universitetscenter. Lingvistgruppen. Rolig-Papir
0106-0864	Denmark. Jordbrugsoekonomisk Institut. Undersoegelse†
0106-0872	G I P
0106-0899	Groenland i Tal†
0106-0937	Acta Jutlandica
0106-0953	Paedagogik†
0106-1003	International Council for the Exploration of the Sea. Annales Biologiques†
0106-102X	Mediaeval Scandinavia Supplements
0106-1046	Meddelelser om Groenland, Geoscience
0106-1054	Meddelelser om Groenland, Bioscience
0106-1062	Meddelelser om Groenland, Man & Society
0106-1100	Kompass Select Export. Business Services
0106-1119	Kompass Select Export. Chemical Industry
0106-1135	Kompass Select Export. Building Construction, Contractors
0106-1143	Kompass Select Export. Electrical and Electronic Equipment
0106-1151	Kompass Select Export. Food Industry
0106-116X	Kompass Select Export. Furniture
0106-1178	Kompass Select Export. Scientific and Industrial Instruments, Watch Industry
0106-1186	Kompass Select Export. Machine Industry
0106-1194	Kompass Select Export. Metal Products
0106-1208	Kompass Select Export. Paper Industry, Graphic Arts
0106-1216	Kompass Select Export. Rubber Industry, Plastics Industry
0106-1224	Kompass Select Export. Textiles, Clothing and Footwear
0106-1232	Kompass Select Export. Transport Equipment
0106-1240	Kompass Select Export. Wood Industry
0106-1275	Laegeforeningens Medicinfortegnelse
0106-1283	Varnaes Birk
0106-1291	Denmark. Jordbrugsoekonomiske Institut. Landbrugets Oekonomi
0106-1313	Slavica Othiniensia
0106-1348	I C O - Iconographisk Post
0106-1356	Ny Korea see 0108-8467
0106-1372	Commission for Scientific Research in Greenland. Newsletter changed to Danish Polar Center. Newsletter.
0106-147X	Dansk Artikelindeks: Aviser og Tidsskrifter
0106-1488	Dansk Anmeldelsesindeks
0106-1585	Plast Nytt
0106-1607	International Journal of Andrology. Supplement
0106-164X	Elektronik Nyt
0106-1658	Agro Nyt†
0106-1666	Virksomheds Nyt
0106-1720	Plast Emballage Scandinavia
0106-1763	Reproduction & Emancipation changed to Gloder.
0106-1852	Trafikoekonomiske Enhedspriser
0106-1860	Antikvariske Studier
0106-1887	Denmark. Statens Husholdningsraad. Pjecer changed to Denmark. Forbrugerstyrelsen. Pjecer.
0106-1895	Denmark. Statens Husholdningsraad. Tekniske Meddelelser changed to Denmark. Forbrugerstyrelsen. Tekniske Meddelelser.
0106-1917	Moelposen
0106-1925	Touring Nyt
0106-1933	Hyologisk Tidsskrift Svinet
0106-1941	Danske Byggemarkedert
0106-1968	Tropical Bands Survey
0106-1992	Serie om Fremmedsprog see 0902-9958
0106-2034	Denmark. Danmarks Statistik. Landbrugets Produktions- og Prisforhold Maanedlig Statistik†
0106-2085	Fortegnelse over Danske Aktieselskaber, Anpartsselskaber, Filialer af Udenlandske Selskaber samt over Foreninger
0106-2093	Forsvar: Militaer Kritisk Magasin†
0106-2107	Information om Skolen i Norden see 0109-8985
0106-214X	Romansk Filmklub. Medlemsblad see 0109-0631
0106-2212	Odense Universitet. Laboratorium for Folkesproglig Middelalderlitteratur. Mindre Skrifter
0106-2220	Aarbog for Svendborg & Omegns Museum
0106-228X	Groenland (Copenhagen)
0106-2301	Scandinavian Psychoanalytic Review
0106-2328	Forbrugerombudsmanden. Beretning changed to Forbrugerstyrelsen. Beretning.
0106-2344	Statistik for Hovedstadsregionen
0106-2484	Sekvens
0106-2530	Folkeskolen i de Enkelte Kommuner see 0905-1449
0106-2557	Forsoegsanlaeg Risoe. Aarsberetning changed to Forskningscenter Risoe. Aarsberetning.
0106-2573	Forskningslaboratoriet for Frugt og Groentindustri. Aarsberetning†
0106-259X	Denmark. Statens Planteavlsudvalg. Sorter af Landbrugsplanter†
0106-2689	Denmark. Jordbrugsoekonomisk Institut. Meddelelset
0106-2697	Skive-egnens Jul
0106-2735	Dansk Forsikrings Aarbog
0106-2778	Roskilde Universitetscenter. Department of Geography, Social Economics and Computer Science. Meddelelser
0106-2808	Entomonograph
0106-2840	Denmark. Forsoegsanlaeg Risoe. Risoe-R changed to Denmark. Forskningscenter Risoe. Risoe-R.
0106-2875	Greenland in Figures†
0106-2891	Denmark. Ministeriet for Groenland. Statistisk Kontor. Meddelelser changed to Groenlandsdepartementet. Statistike Meddelelser.
0106-2905	Statens og Kommunernes Budgetter
0106-2956	Krigsplan†
0106-3006	Denmark. Finansministeriet. Budgetdepartementet. Budgetredegoerelse changed to Denmark. Finansministeriet. Redegoerelse om den Offentlige Sektor.
0106-3014	U Vejviser
0106-3022	Guide i Jylland
0106-3030	Architectura
0106-3081	Atomkraft†
0106-3111	S V Leveringsbetingelser og Proevningsmetoder
0106-312X	Denmark. Statens Vejlaboratorium. Laboratorierapport
0106-3197	Handicap Idraet
0106-3278	Film†
0106-3324	Fabrik og Bolig
0106-343X	M S T Luft changed to D M U Luft. A.
0106-3537	Roskilde Universitetscenter. Department of Geography, Social Economics and Computer Science. Research Reports
0106-3545	Roskilde Universitetscenter. Department of Geography, Social Economics and Computer Science. Kompendium
0106-357X	Combined Simulation
0106-3618	Koebenhavns Universitet. Geografisk Centralinstitut. Laboratorium for Geomorfologi†
0106-3626	Denmark. Bibliotekstilsynet Informerert
0106-3642	Denmark. Jordbrugsoekonomisk Institut. Memorandum†
0106-3677	Vandteknik
0106-3715	Bygningsstatiske Meddelelser
0106-3812	Landbrugseksporten
0106-3839	Kobenhavns Statistiske Aarbog
0106-3871	Scandinavian Institute of Asian Studies. Annual Newsletter see 0904-597X
0106-3952	U T changed to Eksport.
0106-4002	Korrosionscentralen. Rapport†
0106-407X	Environmental Radioactivity in Denmark
0106-4177	Hvem, Hvad, Hvor
0106-4339	European Journal of Respiratory Diseases see 0903-1936
0106-4347	European Journal of Respiratory Diseases. Supplementum†
0106-4355	Gas-Teknik
0106-4363	Handelshoejskolen i Aarhus. Institut for Erhvervs- og Samfundsbeskrivelse. Skriftserie C
0106-441X	A R K
0106-4428	Biophon†
0106-4452	Soenderjyske Aarboeger
0106-4479	Moeldrup Kommunes Lokalhistoriske Arkiv. Aarsskrift
0106-4487	Dolphin
0106-4517	Faerdselsorientering†
0106-4622	Dansk Udsyn
0106-4711	Dansk Elforsyning
0106-4762	Denmark. Forskningsafdelingen. Forskning og Samfund see 0906-5822
0106-4797	Fortid og Nutid
0106-4819	Actualitates see 0901-2273
0106-4878	Kroghs Register see 0108-7878
0106-4908	Denmark. Statsskattedirektoratet og Ligningsraadet. Meddelelser 1. Haefte: Indkomst- og Formueansaettelser†
0106-4932	Forbrugerklagenaevnet. Aarsberetning changed to Forbrugerstyrelsen. Juridisk Aarbog.
0106-4940	Hymnologiske Meddelelser
0106-4959	Hug!
0106-4967	Denmark. Jordbrugsoekonomisk Institut. Aarsberetning see 0108-7479
0106-4991	Historisk Tidsskrift (Copenhagen)
0106-5017	Souvenir Normand changed to Annuaire Souvenir Normand.
0106-5076	Is- og Beseijlingsforholdene i de Danske Farvande i Vinteren
0106-5114	Herefordbladet see 0108-9692
0106-5122	Marinehistorisk Tidsskrift
0106-519X	Denmark. Jordbrugsoekonomisk Institut. Beretning†
0106-5327	Rougsoe Lokalhistoriske Forening. Aarsskrift
0106-5343	Dansk Presse
0106-5351	Lokalhistorisk Journal see 0906-1614
0106-5440	Helsingoer som Fotografen saa det
0106-553X	Dana
0106-5726	Dansk Natur - Dansk Skole
0106-5815	Classica et Mediaevalia
0106-5823	Undervisningsmidler for Folkeskolen. Oversigtskatalog
0106-5866	Kulturgeografiske Haefter
0106-5912	Aarbog for Arbejderbevaegelsens Historie
0106-5920	Roskilde Universitetscenter. Department of Geography, Social Economics and Computer Science. Working Papers
0106-5955	Undervisningsmidler for Gymnasiet og Hf
0106-5963	Undervisningsmidler for Erhvervsuddannelserne
0106-5971	Undervisningsmidler for Ungdoms- og Voksenundervisning
0106-6072	Brandvaern
0106-6137	Fra Vestsjaellands Museer†
0106-6145	Noerre-Alslev Kommune. Lokalhistorisk Arkiv. Aarsskrift
0106-6218	Praesteforeningens Blad
0106-6234	Fjernvarmen
0106-6242	Tekster fra I M F U F A
0106-6366	D C A M M Report
0106-6439	Denmark. Danmarks Statistik. Statistiske Meddelelser
0106-6463	Meteorologisk Aarbog†
0106-6579	Pressens Aarbog
0106-6641	Udenlandsk Litteratur i Danske Folkebiblioteker. Skoenlitteratur changed to Udenlandsk Litteratur i Danske Folkebiblioteker.
0106-665X	Skuespilregister
0106-6668	Filosofi og Videnskabsteori paa Roskilde Universitetscenter
0106-6706	D S I Notat
0106-6714	Opdraettervejviseren
0106-6838	Denmark. Arbejdstilsynet. Rapport
0106-6854	Dansk Veterinaertidsskrift
0106-6927	Sporvejsmuseet Skjoldenaesholm. Aarsberetning
0106-6935	I C E S Oceanographic Data Lists and Inventories
0106-7052	Beretning over Arbejdsmiljoefondets Virksomhed
0106-7125	Orienting om Skoleaaret
0106-7222	University of Copenhagen. Physics Laboratory. Report
0106-7265	Nordeuropaeisk Mejeri-Tidsskrift changed to S D I - Scandinavian Dairy Information.
0106-729X	Boernebibliotekskatalog. Grammofonplader, Kassettebaand
0106-7338	Svineavl og Produktion i Danmark changed to Svineavl og Produktion i Danmark. Aarsberetning (Year).
0106-7354	Fortegnelse over Autoriserede Laeger, Tandlaeger, Dyrlaeger i Danmark changed to Autoriserede Laeger i Danmark.
0106-7362	Kommuneplanorientering†
0106-7389	Denmark. Vejdirektoratet. Trafikrapport changed to Denmark. Vejdirektoratet. Oekonomisk-Statistisk Afdeling. Trafikrapport.
0106-7451	Svampe
0106-7478	Askov Laerlinge
0106-7508	Fred og Sikkerhed see 0109-2855
0106-7540	Stopinterviewanalyse
0106-7575	Katalog for Skolebiblioteker. Forfatterkatalog changed to Katalog for Skolebiblioteker. Skolebibliotekarens.
0106-7583	Katalog for Skolebiblioteker. Titelkatalog
0106-7591	Katalog for Skolebiblioteker. Emnekatalog changed to Katalog for Skolebiblioteker. Skolebibliotekarens.
0106-7699	Gallup Media & Marketing Index. Konsumentvaremarkedet changed to Gallup Media & Marketing Index.
0106-7729	Statistik om Praevention og Aborter
0106-7737	Landscentralen for Undervisningsmidler. Baandcentralen. Baandkatalog†
0106-7745	Undervisningsmidler til Specialundervisning
0106-7753	A V Katalog
0106-7826	Arbejdsmarkedsoversigt†

ISSN INDEX

0106-7990 Boernefilmkataloget. Supplement
0106-8024 Skatten
0106-8113 Planteavlsarbejdet i de Landoekonomiske Foreninger
0106-8172 Anmeldelser i Paedagogiske Tidsskrifter†
0106-8180 Filmregistret
0106-8199 Boernebogsserier Tegneserier
0106-8229 Fra Bov Museum
0106-8237 Kongelige Veterinaer- og Landbohoejskole. Jordbrugsteknisk Institut. Meddelelse
0106-8253 Romanserier og Selvbiografiske Serier
0106-8261 Kongelige Veterinaer og Landbohoejskole. Skovbruginstituttet. Meddelelser
0106-8334 Tidevandstabeller for Danmark
0106-8342 Tidevandstabeller for Faeroerne
0106-8377 Fauna Entomologica Scandinavica
0106-8393 Gartner Tidende
0106-8458 Lovtidende A for Kongeriget Danmark
0106-8466 Lovtidende B for Kongeriget Danmark
0106-8474 Lovtidende C for Kongeriget Danmark
0106-8490 Handelshoejskolen i Aarhus. Skriftserie
0106-8539 Skoven
0106-8563 Koebenhavns Universitet. Institut for Anvendt og Matematisk Lingvistik. Skrifter
0106-8598 Statsfroekontrollen. Beretning
0106-8628 Institut for Graenseregionsforskning. Arbejdspapir
0106-8709 Odense Universitet. Erhvervoekonomisk Institut. Skrifter†
0106-8725 Brandmanden
0106-8822 Faaborg-Aarbogen
0106-8857 Statens Husdyrbrugsforsoeg. Meddelelse
0106-8881 V V S Installatoeren see 0902-5456
0106-8911 Roskilde Universitetscenter. Institut for Socialvidenskab. Instituttets Skriftserie†
0106-8989 Liber Academiae Kierkegaardiensis Annuarius
0106-8997 Aarhus Universitet. Matematisk Institut. Elementaerafdeling
0106-9039 Nordisk Statistisk Sekretariat. Tekniske Rapporter
0106-9047 Aarhus Universitet. Geografisk Institut. Notat†
0106-9128 Dansk Biavl see 0108-3139
0106-9136 Toget see 0107-6310
0106-925X Dans
0106-9276 Kartoffel Nyt
0106-9306 Danmarks Tekniske Hoejskole. Matematisk Institut. Mat - P R
0106-9403 In-Pak
0106-9411 Deruda see 0109-3851
0106-9446 Tvaerfagligt Forum for Sundhedspaedagogik og -Politik. Nyhedsbrev see 0107-3575
0106-9535 Driftsoekonomi
0106-9543 Liver
0106-9586 Gospel Time
0106-9608 Sloejd
0106-9616 Raethinge-Posten
0106-9683 Arbejdsulykker. Aarsstatistik
0106-9691 Boernebibliotekskatalog. Boeger & Tidsskrifter. Forfatterkatalog
0106-9705 Boernebibliotekskatalog. Boeger & Tidsskrifter. Titelkatalog
0106-9713 Boernebibliotekskatalog. Boeger & Tidsskrifter. Emnekatalog
0106-9748 Lokalhistorisk Forening for Sejlflod Kommune
0106-9780 Denmark. Danmarks Statistik. Kvartalsstatistik over Udenrigshandelen see 0109-5420
0106-9802 Denmark. Danmarks Statistik. Kommunale Finanser
0106-9969 Aarhus Universitet. Matematisk Institut. Datalogisk Afdeling. DAIMI IR
0106-9977 Danmarks 200 Stoerste Virksomheder
0106-9985 Danmarks 2000 Stoerste Virksomheder changed to Danmarks 15000 Stoerste Virksomheder.
0107-0061 Endelig Betaekning over Statsregnskabet for Finansaaret
0107-007X Ide-Nyt: Til Villa og Raekkehuse see 0906-0952
0107-0134 Danmarks Tekniske Hoejskole. Institutet for Veje, Trafik og Byplan. Notat
0107-0258 U F O Aspekt see 0108-3503
0107-0304 Aarsskrift for Toender Landbrugsskole
0107-0363 Selskabet for Dansk Fotografi. Aarskatalog†
0107-0371 Denmark. Danmarks Statistik. Valgene til de Kommunale og Amtskommunale Raad†
0107-0398 Tidevandstabeller for Groenland
0107-0436 Dansk Historisk Aarsbibliografi
0107-0452 Copenhagen Political Studies Abstracts
0107-0479 Blickpunkt Daenemark†
0107-0487 Dansk Udenrigspolitisk Aarbog
0107-0517 Denmark. Levnedsmiddelstyrelsen. Publikation
0107-0525 M T M (Meddelelser til Medlemmerne) changed to Folkeminder.
0107-0533 Data Center - Nyt see 0109-4157
0107-055X Nordic Journal of Botany
0107-0606 M C Revyen
0107-0614 Vejdatalaboratoriet. Rapport
0107-0665 Civilforsvar
0107-072X Bjerg-Posten. Medlemsblad

0107-0851 Dansk Arbejdsgiverforening. Statistikken
0107-0886 D I F Flyaarbog
0107-0908 D D Bulletin see 0900-3517
0107-0916 Litteraturtolkninger
0107-0924 Bil-Revyen
0107-0932 Denmark. Jordfordelingssekretariatet. Aarsberetning†
0107-0940 Filmatiserede Boeger
0107-0967 Denmark. Danmarks Statistik. Varestatistik for Industri. Series A
0107-0975 Denmark. Danmarks Statistik. Varestatistik for Industri. Series B
0107-0983 Denmark. Danmarks Statistik. Varestatistik for Industri. Series C
0107-0991 Denmark. Danmarks Statistik. Varestatistik for Industri. Series D
0107-1033 Filmsaesonen: Dansk Filmfortegnelse
0107-105X Denmark. Danmarks Statistik. Indkomster og Formuer
0107-1076 Social Aarbog†
0107-1165 Laegestillinger og Sengepladser paa Institutioner
0107-1173 Personale- og Oekonomiatistik for Sygehusvaesenet
0107-1181 Tal og Data, Medicin og Sundhedsvaesen
0107-119X Bygge- og Boligpolitiske Oversigt
0107-1211 Psyke & Logos
0107-1238 Lyboen
0107-1270 Take Off
0107-1300 Landboforeningernes Driftsoekonomiske Virksomhed, Regnskabresultater, Kalenderaar changed to Regnskabsstatistik-Landbrug.
0107-136X Vore Kunstnere†
0107-1378 Odense University Classical Studies
0107-1475 Arnamagnaean Institute and Dictionary. Bulletin
0107-1491 Forlagsseriekatalog for Boerne- og Skolebiblioteker
0107-1572 Almennyttige Boligselskabers Regnskaber changed to Almennyttige Boligafdelingers Regnskaber.
0107-1629 Uddannelse Institutioner over Grundskoleniveau†
0107-1637 Danmarks Laererhoeskole. Institut for Paedagogik og Psykologi. Testsamling
0107-1742 Odense Universitetsbibliotek. Specialer og Prisopgaver
0107-1769 Haandarbejdets Fremme
0107-1777 Kaelvningsstatistik†
0107-1815 Denmark. Miljoestyrelsen. Oversigt over Godkendte Bekaempelsesmidler see 0107-2722
0107-184X Soemaendenes Idraets Klub
0107-1866 Byggeri
0107-2013 Vedroerende Udviklingen i de Europaeiske Faellesskaber. Beretning
0107-2064 Organisatoriske Fragmenter
0107-2072 Spansk Skandinavisk Forening. Medlemsinformation
0107-2188 Nordschleswig†
0107-2242 Dansk Squash
0107-2366 Romanske Stenarbejder
0107-2390 Modersmaal Selskabet. Aarbog
0107-2412 Oversaettelser af Dansk Lovgivning med Alfabetisk Register. Fortegnelse†
0107-2455 Havneguide for Fritidssejlere
0107-248X Teaterraadets Indstilling
0107-2560 A S F-Dansk Folkehjaelp. Aarsskrift
0107-2587 Internationalen
0107-2668 Epilepsi
0107-2676 Themata
0107-2692 K M D Plannyt†
0107-2722 Denmark. Orientering fra Miljoestyrelsen
0107-2757 Fra Bjerringbro Kommune
0107-2854 Jysk Arkaeologisk Selskabs. Skrifter
0107-2862 Astronomi og Rumfart see 0905-8958
0107-2870 Standardnyt
0107-2900 Skeptika see 0901-201X
0107-2951 Denmark. Statens Kunstfond. Beretning
0107-301X D S - Kontakt
0107-3028 Skolestart
0107-3052 Race Walking World Statistics
0107-3060 Psykologisk Laboratorium. Forskningsrapport
0107-3095 Denmark. Danmarks Statistik. Kreditmarkedsstatistik. see 0108-5476
0107-3109 Kontaktudvalget for Dansk Maritim Historie- og Samfundsforskning. Aarsbibliografi
0107-3117 Faellesraadet Vedroerende Mineraliske Raastoffer i Groenland. Beretning changed to Joint Committee on Mineral Resources in Greenland. Annual Report.
0107-3168 Dags Data
0107-3265 Koebenhavns Universitets Slaviske Institut. Rapporter
0107-3362 Fodplejeren
0107-3435 Uddannelsesnoeglen
0107-3532 Projekt†
0107-3575 Helt
0107-3591 Kultur og Samfund
0107-363X Arken
0107-3680 Profil
0107-3699 K G Orientering see 0107-3680
0107-3702 Jernbanen
0107-3729 Fugle

0107-3737 Emballageinstituttets Leverandoerhaandbog changed to Leverandoerhaandbogen (Skovlunde).
0107-3761 Teknologi og Effektivitet
0107-377X Undervisningsmaterialer til Begynder- og Specialundervisning
0107-3796 Vandrerhjem
0107-380X Oplagsbulletin
0107-3818 Stambog
0107-3826 Technical University of Denmark. Institute of Mathematical Statistics and Operations Research. Research Reports
0107-3885 Skatten. Erhverv
0107-3893 Politihistorisk Selskab. Aarsskrift
0107-3931 El & Energi
0107-3982 Luftskibet†
0107-4083 Vaard i Norden
0107-4148 Fodspecialisten see 0107-3362
0107-4156 Befolkningens Forbrug af Psykiatriske Sengepladser†
0107-4172 Broken Strings see 0906-1061
0107-4202 O - Posten
0107-4229 Dansk Massekommunikationsforskning†
0107-4237 Shan
0107-4296 Undervisningsmidler for Folkeskolen. Nyhedskatalog
0107-430X Specifications of Mineral Concessions and Licenses in Greenland
0107-4350 Adresseloese Postforsendelser
0107-4369 Adresserede Brevforsendelser
0107-4377 Denmark. Socialforskningsinstituttet. Beretning om Socialforskningsinstituttets Virksomhed
0107-4393 Danskerne
0107-4415 Bio-Nyt
0107-4431 Dansk Digtregister
0107-444X Arbejdsformidlingsstatistik for Erhvervshaemmede†
0107-4458 Handelshoejskolen i Koebenhavn. Institut for Organisation og Arbejdssociologi. H D Studiet i Organisation
0107-4466 D E K Haandbog
0107-4504 Folkehoejskoler
0107-4520 Arken-Tryk
0107-4539 Danske Vinselskab see 0109-5684
0107-4547 D A F i Tal
0107-4598 Kursuskoordineringsudvalgets Oversigt over Kurser for Medarbejdere i den Sociale Sektor†
0107-4601 Small Investors' Newsletter
0107-461X Landbrugets Maskinoversigt
0107-4628 Arbejderbevaegelsens Bibliotek og Arkiv. Bibliografisk Serie
0107-4636 Laes om
0107-4652 Denmark. Statens Paedagogiske Forsoegscenter. Arbejdsbeskrivelse
0107-4687 Nyt fra Danmark
0107-4733 Specialarbejderkurser
0107-4806 Navigatoer
0107-4849 Fra Bornholms Museum
0107-4857 Dansk Orgelaarbog
0107-4911 Skulptur Veksoelund
0107-492X Monopoltilsynets Aarsberetning
0107-4946 Matieres see 0109-2820
0107-4954 Sygehusvaesenet changed to Sygehusstatistik.
0107-4989 Paedagogisk Bibliograf
0107-4997 Oversigt over Rapporter m.m. Vedroerende Vandkraftundersoegelser i Groenland†
0107-5047 Sociale Ydelser, Hvem, Hvad, og Hvornaar
0107-5071 Befolkningen i Koebenhavn i Januar
0107-508X Sygehusklassifikation og Kommunekoder
0107-5098 Kommunal Budgetredegoerelse†
0107-511X Denmark. Direktoratet for Kriminalforsorgen. Kriminalforsorgen see 0904-1990
0107-5144 Biologiske Udvikling i Uttersley Mose, Koebenhavn ned Henblik Specielt paa Fuglebestandene†
0107-5152 Denmark. Statens Uddannelsesstoette. Regelsamling for Stoetteaaret changed to Denmark. Statens Uddannelsesstoette. Haandbog.
0107-5179 Sikkerhedsmaessig Vurdering og Prioritering af Mindre Anlaegsarbejder paa Hovedlandeveje
0107-5187 Bog og Baand
0107-5209 Gode Lydboeger
0107-5217 Computerworld
0107-5225 Nye Verdener
0107-5233 Institutet for Matematisk Statistik og Operationsanalyse. Working Paper see 0107-3826
0107-5276 Ikkevold
0107-5330 Modelbanen
0107-5357 Denmark. Jordbrugsoekonomiske Institut. Rapport
0107-5373 Teknisk Tidsskrift for Textil og Beklaedning†
0107-539X Slaegt og Stavn
0107-5403 D D V - Analysen†
0107-5411 Effektiv Kontoradministration
0107-5446 Jul i Frederikssund
0107-5462 Odense Universitetsbibliotek. Tidsskriftkatalog†
0107-556X I W G I A Boletin
0107-5586 Casesamling†

ISSN INDEX

ISSN	Title
0107-5608	D P B's Litteratur om Boerns og Unges Laesning
0107-5624	Euro Laerer Nyt
0107-5675	Denmark. Statens Jordbrugsoekonomiske Institut. Serie A: Landbrugets Regnskabsstatistik
0107-5683	Denmark. Statens Jordbrugsoekonomiske Institut. Serie B: Oekonomien i Landbrugets Driftsgrenet
0107-5691	Denmark. Jordbrugsoekonomiske Institut. Serie C: Landbrugets Prisforhold
0107-5705	Denmark. Jordbrugsoekonomisk Institut. Serie D: Gartneri-Regnskabsstatistik
0107-590X	Register over Danske Patenter Udstedt
0107-5993	Margrethe og Vi Andret
0107-6094	Blicheregnens Museumsforening. Aarsskrift
0107-6108	Jordbrug Oestjylland (Midt): Samtlige Landbrug, Skovbrug og Gartnerier
0107-6116	Twist
0107-6167	Plant Diseases and Pests in Denmark changed to Plant Diseases, Pests and Weeds in Denmark.
0107-6183	Factsheet Denmark
0107-6264	Danmarks Eksportmarkedert
0107-6280	Rytme
0107-6299	Patient
0107-6310	Modeltoget
0107-6329	Objektiv
0107-6345	Daginstitutionen
0107-6353	Vore Daginstitutioner see 0107-6345
0107-6396	Dansk Japansk Venskabsforenings Blad
0107-6418	Dansk Joedisk Historie
0107-6531	Aarhus Universitet. Romansk Institut. Spansk Afdelingen. Information
0107-6582	Stikordt
0107-6612	Folkefronten
0107-6663	Zoneterapi og Sundhed
0107-6701	Krejl
0107-6744	Statistisk Tiaars-Oversigt for Koebenhavns Kommune
0107-6752	Holstebro Museum. Aarsskrift
0107-6760	Peru Information
0107-6779	B T B
0107-6787	Skibstilsynets Godkendelsesbog
0107-6795	Kaleidoscope
0107-6841	Kunst i Dagt
0107-6868	Historisk Samfund for Praesto Amt. Aarbog
0107-6876	Goer det Selv see 0901-4241
0107-6922	Fortegnelse over Anerkendte Avlscentre, Aspirantbesaetninger, Opformeringsbesaetninger
0107-6930	Hitchcock's Krimi Magasin
0107-6949	Paa Jobbett
0107-6957	Kunstavisen
0107-7031	Denmark. Danmarks Statistik. Varestatistik for Industri
0107-7074	Folkemusikhusringen
0107-7090	Recipientundersoegelser ved Marmorilik changed to Miljoeundersoegelser ved Marmorilik.
0107-7104	F L's Medlevsavis changed to Medlemsavisen.
0107-7112	Dansk Grafia
0107-7120	Aarhus Kommunes Statistiske Kontor. Information
0107-7139	Danmark i Tal
0107-7163	Landoekonomisk Oversigt
0107-721X	Historisk Aarbog for Skive og Omegn
0107-7279	Lyrikt
0107-7295	Ud med Kirken
0107-7325	Slaa Igent
0107-7333	Joedisk Revyt
0107-7384	Odense University Studies in Philosophy
0107-7392	Universite d'Odense. Etudes Romanes
0107-7430	Denmark. Miljoestyrelsen. Havforureningslaboratorium. Report of the Marine Pollution Laboratory
0107-7449	Kulturkampen
0107-7481	Display
0107-749X	Sundhedsstyrelsen Vitalstatistik
0107-752X	Nippon Nytt
0107-7546	Avisteknisk Informationt
0107-7554	Motor - Bladet
0107-7597	Medicinsk Foedselsstatistik see 0904-1966
0107-7619	Aktiviteten i Sygehusvaesenett
0107-7627	Forbruget af Somatiske Sengepladsert
0107-7716	Fagligt Forsvar
0107-7724	Harvard Boersent
0107-7767	Boernenes Aarbogt
0107-7783	Ungdomskalender
0107-7805	Cykle-Jul
0107-7848	Lyngby - Bogen
0107-7902	Kosmos
0107-7988	Maelkeproducenten
0107-7996	Rajneesh Buddhafelt Dansk Newslettert
0107-8003	Denmark Bibliotekstilsynet. Beretningt
0107-8011	Dansk Illustreret Skibsliste
0107-8054	Connaisseur
0107-8097	Infodont changed to Det Ny Infodont.
0107-8119	Smalfilm og Video
0107-8135	Voksenuddannelse
0107-8216	D.M.C. Informatiom changed to Netvaerkstedet.
0107-8224	Den Danske Bank. Orientering
0107-8224	Danske Bank af 1871. Orientering see 0107-8224
0107-8232	Naar Lampen Taendes. Fortaellinger see 0905-1678
0107-8275	E G V Information
0107-8283	Koebenhavns Universitet. Datalogisk Institut. Rapport
0107-8305	Markeds-bog
0107-8313	I Byen's Spiseguide
0107-833X	Scandinavian Journal of Primary Health Care
0107-8348	Denmark. Forsoeganslaeg Risoe. Fysikafdelingen. Annual Progress Report changed to Denmark. Risoe National Laboratory. Physics Department. Annual Progress Report.
0107-8356	Folk i Fuglebjergt
0107-8372	Grenaa og Noerre Djurs Foer og Nu
0107-8380	Sygdomsmoensteret ved Somatiske Sygehusafdelinger changed to Sygdomsmoensteret for Indlagte Patienter.
0107-8399	Fyens Stiftsbog
0107-8437	Sygesikringsstatistik
0107-8453	Skole- og Laereboeger
0107-8496	Feltbiologen
0107-8518	Arbejderbladet Deruda see 0109-3851
0107-8534	Fremtiden i Vore Haender. Nyhedsbrev see 0107-8542
0107-8542	F I V H-Nyt
0107-8550	Miljoevaernt
0107-8585	Langhaars-Nyt
0107-8623	Radio Denmark see 0109-3088
0107-8631	Aarhus Universitet. Institut for Litteraturhistorie. Skrifter see 0901-8883
0107-8666	Rapport om Kontrollen med Konsummaelkprodukter
0107-8720	Deutscher Volkskalender Nordschleswig
0107-8747	Rasp
0107-8771	Denmark. Danmarks Statistik. Loen- og Indkomstatistik
0107-878X	Fra Holback Amt: Historiske Aarboeger
0107-8798	Lolland-Falsters Historiske Samfund. Aarbog
0107-8801	Oversigt over de Meteorologiske Forhold paa Forsoegsstationernet
0107-8860	Kristelig Fagforening og K F O see 0109-2057
0107-8860	Kristelig Fagforening og K F O see 0109-1131
0107-8879	Hippokratent
0107-8887	Julehilsen
0107-8917	Uddannelse og Arbejde i Udlandet
0107-8925	Viborg Stifts Aarbog
0107-8933	Kunstmuseets Aarsskrift
0107-8941	Novelle Magasinett
0107-895X	Fra Kvangaard til Humlekule
0107-8976	Motionsgang
0107-8984	D M C see 0109-3649
0107-900X	S B I Aarsberetning
0107-9018	Arbejderbevaegelsens Bibliotek og Arkiv. Liste over Loebende Tidsskrifter og Aarboeger paa A B A
0107-9042	Discinform
0107-9069	Environmental Radioactivity in the Faroes
0107-9077	Forsoegsanlaeg Risoe. changed to Forskningscenter Risoe. Energi Systems Gruppen. Annual Progress Report.
0107-9085	Kulturpolitisk Redegoerelset
0107-9101	Effektiv Butiksdrift
0107-9123	Kirkegaardslederen
0107-9131	Jagt
0107-9166	Erhvenrssprog
0107-9190	Manuel Medicin
0107-9263	Isenkram-Goer-det-Selv - Byggemarkedet
0107-928X	Romu
0107-931X	Koege Museum
0107-9328	M I V: Museerne i Viborg Amt
0107-9336	Nordslesvigske Museer
0107-9352	Universitetet Statistiske Institut. Computer Programmes
0107-9387	D F 3 Formning
0107-9395	Historisk Arbog for Thy, Mors og Vester Hanherred see 0904-6267
0107-9417	Aulisarnermit Nutarsiagssat
0107-9476	Frederiksvaerkegnens Museumsforening. Aarsskriftt
0107-9522	Film U V see 0904-4159
0107-9573	Humanist
0107-959X	Inspirationt
0107-9611	Haandarbejdets Fremme. Aarets Korssting
0107-962X	Elnyt
0107-9646	Dansk Windsurfing
0107-9670	Folketingets Haandbog
0107-9735	Arbejdsmarkedet og Arbejdsmarkedspolotikt
0107-9743	Arbejdsmarkedets Regelsamlingt
0107-976X	Koebenhavnerliv Foer og Nu
0107-9794	Corner
0107-9816	Dansk Lydfortegnelse
0107-9824	Kirkefondets Aarbog
0107-9840	Grenzland
0107-9948	Greenland Newslettert
0107-9980	Datajournalen
0107-9999	Plovfuren
0108-0016	Foto-Revyent
0108-0024	Nyt om Arbejdsmiljoet
0108-0032	Galten Egnsarkiv. Annales
0108-0040	Musikbranchens Aarbog
0108-0075	Arusia. Historiske Skrifter
0108-0105	Ny Torsdag
0108-0164	Acta Pathologica, Microbiologica et Immunologica Scandinavica. Section A: Pathology see 0903-4641
0108-0172	Acta Pathologica, Microbiologica et Immunologica Scandinavica. Section A: Pathology. Supplementumt
0108-0180	Microbiology see 0903-4641
0108-0199	Acta Pathologica, Microbiologica et Immunologica Scandinavica. Section B: Microbiology. Supplementumt
0108-0202	Immunology see 0903-4641
0108-0210	Acta Pathologica, Microbiologica et Immunologica Scandinavica. Section C: Immunology. Supplementumt
0108-0229	V og S Priser. Bygningsdele
0108-0253	A S E A N Business Club of Denmark. Newslettert
0108-0261	Artikler i Boeger
0108-027X	Nyt om Euro-Forskning
0108-0296	Filatelistisk Katalog-Noegle
0108-0326	Bryozoa
0108-0342	Skanderborg Museum. Aarsskrift see 0903-3424
0108-0385	V D L Nyt
0108-0393	Helsingoer Kommunes Museer. Aarbog
0108-0458	Serigrafen
0108-0466	Spildevandsteknisk Tidsskrift
0108-0504	Denmark. Geografisk Magasint
0108-0571	Danmarks Tekniske Hoejskole. Afdelingen for Baerende Konstruktioner. Serie F
0108-058X	Danmarks Tekniske Hoejskole. Afdelingen for Baerende Konstruktioner. Serie I
0108-061X	Billedterapi
0108-0687	Laegemiddelforbruget i Danmark
0108-0695	Design from Scandinavia
0108-0717	D S A M Orientering see 0109-2235
0108-0768	Danmarks Tekniske Hoejskole. Afdelingen for Baerende Konstruktioner. Serie R.
0108-0806	Ribe Stiftsbog
0108-0814	Danske Reklamefotografert
0108-0822	Profiler i Dansk Erhvervslivt
0108-0830	H S G's Aarbog
0108-0849	Lovnoegle
0108-0857	Plejehjemshaandbogen changed to Haandbog for Social og Sundhedssektor.
0108-0903	Stambog over Koeer af Roed Dansk Malkeracet
0108-0962	Environmental Radioactivity in Greenland
0108-1012	Stofskifte changed to Tidsskriftet Antropologi.
0108-1020	Studenterhaandbogen
0108-1098	Trav & Galop Journalen
0108-1101	Studenteravisen
0108-1195	Nyt fra Dansk P E Nt
0108-1217	D A L Forumt
0108-1225	D S T S - Nyt
0108-1233	Rugby Nytt
0108-1306	Detailforskrifter for Koeretoejer
0108-1349	Lyrikbogklubbent
0108-1357	Gamle Evangelium er Lige Nyt i Dag
0108-142X	Faeroesk Lovregister
0108-1489	Institut for Afsaetningsoekonomi. Nytt
0108-1497	New Products from Denmarkt
0108-1527	Lev Bedre
0108-1594	Prima Vistat
0108-1608	Print
0108-1632	Philosophia
0108-1675	Allergy. Supplementum
0108-1683	Meddelelser fra Sortsafproevningen
0108-1756	Blaa Kors Familieaarbog see 0108-1764
0108-1764	Blaa Kors' Aarbogt
0108-1780	Zinx
0108-1810	Aarets Bogarbejde
0108-1829	New United Nations Publications
0108-1837	Flygtninget
0108-1845	Nyt om Flygtninge see 0900-2537
0108-1888	Kvinder, Kvinder
0108-190X	D T Forum see 0904-1796
0108-1969	I F U's Participation in Joint Ventures see 0901-6171
0108-1993	Religionsvidenskabeligt Tidsskrift
0108-2019	Boghvedegryn
0108-2027	Fagpressenoeglen
0108-2051	Videofilm
0108-2078	Women and the Labour Market
0108-2086	Pesticidrester i Danske Levnedsmidler
0108-2108	Chef-Nyt
0108-2124	Ascolta see 0900-6354
0108-2132	Socialpaedagogernes Landsforbund. T R Information
0108-2191	Annoncoerforenings Bureaufortegnelse
0108-2205	Roskilde Universitetscenter. Institut for Samfundsoekonomi og Planlaegning. Arbejdspapir.
0108-2272	Dansk Sangindeks
0108-2299	Dansk Literaturhistorisk Bibliografit
0108-2302	Vore Kirkegaarde
0108-2329	Investering i Produktion changed to National Agency of Industry and Trade. Annual Reports (Year).
0108-2388	Nyrenyt
0108-2396	Akvariebladet
0108-240X	Fredsmeddelelser fra Samarbejdskomiteen see 0109-2855
0108-2418	F I C E Information
0108-2426	Ungdomsskolen i Talt

ISSN INDEX 5591

ISSN	Title
0108-2442	Russisklaererforeningen. Meddelelser
0108-2450	Trigon
0108-2469	Studies in Labor Market Dynamics see 0905-6955
0108-2477	O S - Information see 0108-2485
0108-2485	O S - Nyt
0108-2515	Danske Tegneserier Ekstra
0108-2531	Redningshistorisk Forening. Information see 0108-254X
0108-254X	Redningshistorisk Forenings Information
0108-2558	Selskabet for Dansk Fotografi. Kontaktblad changed to Dansk Fotografi.
0108-2604	A F I D-Dialog
0108-2612	Kina Information
0108-2655	S T S Debat
0108-2671	Skole and Landbrug
0108-2698	Ejendomsinformation
0108-2701	Acta Crystallographica. Section C: Crystal Structure Communications.
0108-271X	Nordisk Sexologi
0108-2736	Samojeden
0108-2744	Landbrug Fyn
0108-2779	Dialyse og Transplantation see 0108-2388
0108-2787	Aarsskrift for Sottrup Sogn
0108-2795	Zibaldone
0108-2833	Stemmer fra Oldtiden
0108-285X	Danmarks Journalisthoejskoles Aarskrift
0108-2868	Mariager Aarbog
0108-2922	Occurrences of the Polar Slant E Condition, SEC at Narssarssuag, Godhavn, Thule†
0108-2957	Nyt fra Tyrkiet
0108-2965	Jul i Lejre
0108-3023	Nemalah
0108-3082	Danmarks Folkehoejskoler
0108-3104	International Kierkegaard Newsletter
0108-3139	Dansk-Biavl og Miljoe
0108-321X	Gymnasiemusik
0108-3236	Libyen Bulletin
0108-3244	Lokalhistorien for Torslunde Ishoej og Tranegilde
0108-3279	Forum
0108-3309	Forskellighed
0108-3333	Nouvelles Scientifiques Franco-Danoises†
0108-3376	Politiets Aarsberetning
0108-3422	Naturgas Nyt
0108-3430	Specialarbejderskolen
0108-3449	Dansk i Dag†
0108-3457	L V S Bladet see 0108-3430
0108-3503	Nyt Aspekt
0108-3511	Omkring et Kunstvaerk
0108-3562	Teknik-Samfund
0108-3570	Oestjysk Hjemstavn
0108-3589	Arilds Lokaltidende
0108-3627	D J OE F - Haandbogen
0108-3643	F R A M
0108-366X	Vidar see 0108-3678
0108-3678	Gymnastik
0108-3708	Datalogi O
0108-3759	Semajna Bulteno
0108-3775	Erhvervslederen (Frederiksberg, 1981)
0108-3783	Israelske Ambassade. Information
0108-3791	Gamle Loejt
0108-3805	Thorslunde Ishoej Lokalhistoriske Forening see 0108-3244
0108-3813	Power
0108-3821	Race Walking World Statistics - Women
0108-3856	S L F Information
0108-3864	Alt om Video†
0108-3872	Skole og Fremtid†
0108-3880	Slaegten Fisker
0108-3910	Danmark Export: Food & Beverages
0108-3945	Kulturgeografiske Haefters Skriftserie
0108-3953	Supplement til Skattelovsamling†
0108-3961	Kvindestudier ved A U C. Aarbog
0108-397X	Skaeppen
0108-4003	Landbrugets Organisationshaandbog
0108-4011	Denmark. Energiministeriet. Energiforskningsprogram
0108-402X	Uddrag af Energilitteratur paa Danmarks Tekniske bibliotek, Soenderborg Tekniske Bibliotek, Aarhus Tekniske Bibliotek changed to Danmarks Tekniske Bibliotek. Uddrag.
0108-4054	Gymnasieskolernes Musiklaererforening Medlemsorientering see 0108-321X
0108-4089	Frimaerkens Verden
0108-4100	Historisk Aarbog fra Randers Amt
0108-4135	Living Architecture
0108-4151	Oversigt over By- og Regionforskning†
0108-4232	V S R Kommunikation see 0108-3279
0108-4259	Friskoler og Private Grundskoler†
0108-4267	Denmark. Undervisningsministeriet. Datakontoret. Statistik for de Videregaaende Uddannelser
0108-4291	Kontaktkalender
0108-433X	Sprog og Samfund
0108-4380	Oestnyt†
0108-4402	Skolemusikhaandbogen†
0108-4429	Dansk Isolering z Energihaandbog
0108-4453	Chaos
0108-4496	Gralen
0108-450X	Centra Bulteno see 0108-3759
0108-4518	Landbrugets Samraad for Forskning og Forsoeg. Rammeplaner see 0906-1894
0108-4550	Luft og Rumfartsaarbogen
0108-4577	Energi Information
0108-4585	D A B Information
0108-4593	Skole-Bladet
0108-4615	Varmeforsyningsplanlaegning: Status†
0108-4631	Bridgeaarbogen†
0108-464X	Journal of Danish Archaeology
0108-4658	Hi-Fi and Video Revyen
0108-4666	Focus Damefodbold
0108-4690	Lokal Historie i Skoerping Kommune
0108-4712	Tidsskrift for Oplysningens Tidsalder†
0108-4739	Autoriserede Laeger, Tandlaeger, Dyrlaeger i Danmark changed to Autoriserede Laeger i Danmark.
0108-4755	Groent Miljoe
0108-4763	Denmark. Statens Levnedsmiddelinstitut. Centrallaboratoriet. Arbejdsprogrammer†
0108-4844	Danmarks Fiskeri- og Havundersoegelser. Ferskvandsfiskerilaboratoriet. Meddelelser. changed to Meddelelser fra Ferskvandsfiskerilaboratoriet.
0108-4887	Plantebeskyttelsemidler
0108-4925	C B N
0108-4968	Sejlsport
0108-4976	B U M
0108-4992	Toyo Spiseguide
0108-5018	Bilens Aarsrevy†
0108-5077	Fodboldens Aarsrevy†
0108-5115	Sportens Aarsrevy†
0108-5174	Barbara Cartland's Verden af Romantik
0108-5190	Kontakt (Copenhagen, 1977)†
0108-5212	Nyt fra Brasilien
0108-5220	Visuelt
0108-5255	Discountbutikker changed to Supermarkeder og Andre Store Dagligvarebutikker (Year).
0108-528X	Uddrag af Energilitteratur paa Danmarks Tekniske Bibliotek changed to Danmarks Tekniske Bibliotek. Uddrag.
0108-5328	Music Management & International Promotion
0108-5344	Oftalmolog
0108-5409	Hej see 0901-4500
0108-5417	S D A - Nyt see 0905-9539
0108-5476	Denmark. Danmarks Statistik. Penge og Kapitalmarked.
0108-5506	Denmark. Danmarks Statistik. Udenrigshandel
0108-5557	Faroerne og Groenland†
0108-562X	Human Settlements Situation and Related Trends and Policies
0108-5646	Doedsaarsagerne
0108-5697	Levende Billeder
0108-5727	Markedsdata†
0108-5883	Produktion
0108-6022	Skattelove see 0905-4367
0108-6049	Skattepolitisk Oversigt
0108-6103	Socialraadgiveren
0108-6251	Teater, Film og T V see 0900-0119
0108-6391	Vestfynsk Hjemstavn
0108-6464	Oekonomiske Udvikling paa Faeroerne
0108-6510	El Salvador Nyt see 0904-6089
0108-6596	C D R Research Reports
0108-6618	Boernetandplejen i Danmark changed to Boerne- og Ungdomstandplejen i Danmark.
0108-6626	Radiobranchen
0108-6634	Nyt om Naturgas†
0108-6650	Sikkerhed
0108-6669	Aktuelt om Byggelitteratur†
0108-6707	Driftsteknikerbogen
0108-6715	Forum Fabulatorum
0108-6758	Trailer
0108-6804	Historisk Forening for Vaerloese Kommune. Arsskrift
0108-6812	Rejsebogen (Year)
0108-6898	Inuit see 0906-5504
0108-6901	Denmark. Miljoeministeriet. Miljoeministerens Redegoerelse om Landsplanlaegning
0108-691X	Vulkanen: Ren L A V A
0108-6944	Studie- og Erhvervsvalget
0108-6952	Unge Laeser Om
0108-6979	Danmarks Nationalbank. Beretning og Regnskab (Dansk Udgave)
0108-6987	Handleren
0108-6995	Danmarks Nationalbank. Report and Accounts for the Year (Year)
0108-7029	Update (Aarhus) see 1011-8101
0108-707X	Vaabenhistoriske Aarboeger
0108-7142	Allesoe, Broby, Naesby Lokalarkiv
0108-7150	Arbejdsretligt Tidsskrift
0108-7169	Anklagemyndighedens Aarsberetning
0108-7193	Denmark. Forsvarsministeriet. Forsvarsministerens Aarlige Redegoerelse see 0109-5757
0108-7207	P P P changed to Stamme-Bladet.
0108-7215	Litteratur paa Indvandrersprog i Danske Folkebiblioteker
0108-7231	Landshavneplanbidrag†
0108-724X	Social Revy
0108-7258	U K - Modelinformation see 0900-470X
0108-7266	Sikkerhed og Nedrustning
0108-7274	Normtal for Koebmaend†
0108-7282	Fugle i Nordjylland see 0903-1731
0108-7290	Aktiv Islam
0108-7320	D I M S Bulletin
0108-7355	Camping Danmark
0108-7371	Polen-Nytt
0108-738X	Denmark. Danmarks Statistik. Regnskabsstatistik for Industrien
0108-7460	Philosophus see 0109-4831
0108-7479	Denmark. Statens Jordbrugsoekonomiske Institut. Aarsberetning
0108-7487	Denmark. Miljoekreditraadet. Beretning†
0108-7495	Denmark. Energistyrelsen. Nyt fra Energistyrelsen
0108-7509	Eksportkredit, Eksportfremme: Aarsberetninger
0108-7517	Dansk E D B Bibliografi
0108-7568	Denmark. Danmarks Statistik. Bygningsopgoerelsen†
0108-7584	Sail Surfing
0108-7606	Dandoknotater
0108-7622	Andelsbanken Boersoversigt†
0108-7630	Andelsbanken Erhvervsorientering changed to Konsekvens.
0108-7649	Andelsbanken Handelskontakter†
0108-7673	Acta Crystallographica. Section A: Foundations of Crystallography
0108-7681	Acta Crystallographica. Section B: Structural Science
0108-7711	L A N A Nyt
0108-772X	Film Magasinet
0108-7738	Fjordhesten
0108-7746	Focus paa Undervisning†
0108-7754	Reportage†
0108-7789	Nordisk Tidsskrift for Fagsprog og Terminologi†
0108-7800	Psykisk Forum see 0108-3503
0108-7819	Beretning for Psykiatriske Institutioner i Danmark†
0108-7843	Mer om Koenssygdomme see 0901-9685
0108-7851	Mer om Sex og Sikkerhed see 0901-9685
0108-786X	Husholdningsarbejdet
0108-7878	Kroghs Lovinformation
0108-7886	Udviklingstendenserne paa de Langvarigt Uddannedes Arbejdsmarked
0108-7908	Socialistisk Folkeparti. Status see 0902-1612
0108-7924	Nyt fra S S F see 0903-7543
0108-7991	Levende Natur
0108-8017	Herning - Bogen
0108-8025	Ord & Sag
0108-805X	Landsdelslaboratoriernet
0108-8068	Dansk Energi Tidsskrift
0108-8076	Befolkningen i Kommunerne
0108-8149	Elektronik Indkoebsbogen
0108-8157	Transport (Aarlig)†
0108-8165	Odense Universitet. Institut for Virksomhedsledelse. Skrifter
0108-8173	Denmark. Danmarks Statistik. Nationalregnskabsstatistik
0108-8203	Miljoeundersoegelser ved Ivigtut
0108-822X	Selskab for Nordisk Filologi. Aarsberetning
0108-8238	Biblioteksvejviser over Storkoebenhavns Folkebiblioteker
0108-8262	Efterskoler. Fortegnelse
0108-8297	Nye Aar
0108-8300	Gartneriets Informationstjeneste. Planteskoleinfo changed to Groensagsinfo.
0108-8335	Kraks TransportKatalog
0108-8343	Dansen's Blad†
0108-8351	Bistandshaandbogen changed to Haandbog for Social og Sundhedssektor.
0108-8378	Eleven
0108-8416	N O W E L E
0108-8440	Horisont see 0901-2605
0108-8459	Agrologisk Tidsskrift Marken
0108-8467	Korea Bulletin
0108-8491	Radisen†
0108-8513	Teledata Nyt†
0108-853X	Rakettidende
0108-8572	Dansk Kunstnerraad†
0108-8580	Dayanisma
0108-8599	Risoe International Symposium on Metallurgy and Materials Science. Proceedings
0108-8602	Murerhaandbog
0108-8629	Fiskeriet ved Groenland og Groenlands Fiskeriundersoegelsers Aktivitet see 0905-5193
0108-8645	Aulisarneq Ama Aulisagkanik Misigssuineq Kalatdlit Nunane see 0905-5215
0108-867X	Vendsyssel Historiske Museum†
0108-8688	Commercial Times
0108-8718	D M U - Nyt
0108-8734	Turistfoerer
0108-8777	Frederiksberg Gennem Tiderne
0108-8793	Familieplanlaegning
0108-8815	F S Bulletin
0108-884X	Jordbrug
0108-8858	Museumsavisen
0108-8866	Standpunkt see 0905-1503
0108-8874	Liberal Debat see 0905-1503
0108-8904	Hjertenyt
0108-8912	Shipping-Bladet
0108-8920	Groenne Fag
0108-8939	T F Nyhedsbrev see 0109-3169
0108-8963	B U K S
0108-898X	Nyt fra Bibelselskabet
0108-8998	Dansk Atlet Union, Landdsorganisation for Brydning see 0903-5524
0108-9013	D A U Bladet see 0903-5524
0108-9048	F A T - Bladet
0108-9072	Huset Ude og Inde changed to Interieur.

ISSN INDEX

ISSN	Title
0108-9102	Love og Bekendtgoerelser m.v.
0108-9129	Denmark. Finanstilsynet. Banker of Sparekasser see 0905-0965
0108-9145	Factum Humanum
0108-9161	Westcoast Offshore Guide changed to Danish Offshore Guide and Yearbook.
0108-917X	Museet for Holbaek og Omegn. Aarsberetning
0108-9188	D M P F Medlemmer
0108-9196	Revisor Posten
0108-9218	Tracking
0108-9307	Lokomotivet
0108-9315	Sandeviften
0108-934X	Helses Boerneblad†
0108-9358	E S O Foelgeforskning
0108-9412	Kommunernes Institutions. Haandbog
0108-9439	Ren Energi
0108-9463	Skat
0108-948X	Undersoegelse over Apotekernes Driftsforhold
0108-9625	Arbejderbevaegelsens Erhvervsraad. Beretning
0108-9668	Three Year Art Book
0108-9684	Photodermatology see 0905-4383
0108-9692	Hereford
0108-9714	Statistik om Sundhedsplejerskernes Virksomhed
0108-9722	Opgavesamling i Skat 1
0108-9730	Opgavesamling i Skat 2 og Erhvervsjura
0108-9773	E K-Bladet
0108-979X	Denmark. Indenrigsministeriet. Indenrigsministeriets Afgoerelser og Udtalelser om Kommunale Forhold
0108-9811	Koebenhavns Universitet. Retsvidenskabeligt Institut B. Studier
0108-982X	Danish Contract changed to Nordic Contract.
0108-9846	Alle Tiders Odsherred
0108-9862	Vinyl
0108-9870	Facet
0108-9900	E D B - Kursuskatalog†
0108-9935	Piranesi
0108-996X	Facts om Danmark†
0109-0003	Treklang
0109-002X	Lokalhistorie: Hadsund Kommune
0109-0054	Niels Bohr International Gold Medal†
0109-0062	Verden Rundt
0109-0070	Denmark. Teknologistyrelsen. Nyhedsbrev
0109-0089	T I
0109-0097	Gaffa
0109-0100	Vaernskontakt
0109-0119	Druiden see 0903-9295
0109-0135	Avis 81
0109-0178	Langaa
0109-0194	Egnshistorisk Forening i Grundsoe. Aarsskrift
0109-0208	Nyt for Bogvenner
0109-0259	Sund og Rask†
0109-0291	Maskinstationen og Landbrugslederen
0109-0321	Denmark. Statens Byggeforskningsinstitut. Program Resumeer see 0904-2253
0109-033X	Andels-Boligen
0109-0356	Kvinder paa Tinder†
0109-0364	Musikalier i Danske Biblioteker (Quarterly)
0109-0372	Fructus
0109-0402	Amazoner net†
0109-0429	Samspil
0109-0453	Vesttyskland i Bevaegelse
0109-0461	Gryden
0109-047X	Kerteminde Museum. Aarsskrift changed to Cartha.
0109-050X	Alle Boerns Jul changed to Jul i Familien.
0109-0518	Nyt fra D U K
0109-0526	D F L†
0109-0534	D U K
0109-0550	New Foundland Information
0109-0631	R F Medlemsblad
0109-064X	Landskomiteen Sydafrika-Aktion. Nyhedsbrev†
0109-0690	Historisk Arkiv for Broerup og Omegn. Aarsskrift
0109-0690	Motionsbladet
0109-0704	Hjerteforeningens Motionsblad see 0109-0690
0109-0712	Ledoeje-Smoerum Historisk Forening og Arkiv
0109-0720	Focus paa Mellemoesten†
0109-0747	Lokalhistorisk Orientering Hvidovre see 0902-3046
0109-0755	Buteo see 0109-257X
0109-0763	Hurtigmetode-nyt changed to Mikrobiologi-Nyt.
0109-0828	P & I
0109-0852	Stoft
0109-0860	Grafiske Funktionaerers Landsforening. Orientering see 0109-0879
0109-0879	Grafiske Funktionaerer
0109-0895	Fagblad for Zoneterapeuter
0109-0917	Fremtider
0109-0925	F A K E Nyt changed to K C Nyt.
0109-095X	Bios
0109-0968	Dansk Fagpressekatalog
0109-0976	Odense Universitet. Institut for Offentlig Oekonomi og Politik. Occasional Paper see 0903-5079
0109-0984	Rue-Revue
0109-100X	Retspolitik
0109-1026	D O N G Orientering changed to Dansk Olie & Naturgas. Orientering.
0109-1107	Ankenaevnet for Arbejdsloeshedsforsikringen. Beretning
0109-1115	E S A Foelgeforskning
0109-1131	Kristelig Funktionaer-Organisation. Medlemsblad
0109-1158	Arbejdermuseet. Aarbog†
0109-1174	Film Premiere r†
0109-1190	Dyr i Natur og Museum
0109-1212	Liste over Rytmiske Spillesteder i Danmark
0109-1239	Vaabenkaploeb og Vaabenkontrol†
0109-1247	Opgavesaet til Dansk Skr. Fremstilling, Folkeskolens Udvidede Afgangsproeve see 0109-1255
0109-1255	Opgavesaet til Dansk Skriftlig Fremstilling, Folkeskolens Afgangsproeve
0109-1271	Denmark. Danmarks Statistik. Konjunkturtendenser i Udvalgte Lande
0109-128X	Transportnyt
0109-1328	Uddelerbladet
0109-1417	Engelsk Fodbold
0109-1425	Fortvivl
0109-1441	Fynboer og Arkaeologi
0109-145X	Danske Assurandoerer see 0109-1875
0109-1468	Tidsskrift for Danske Assurandoerer see 0109-1875
0109-1476	D K K F - Nyt
0109-1492	Kvindeliv†
0109-1514	Arbejdsdirektoratet Beretning om Arbejdsformidlingen og Arbejdsloeshedsforsikringen†
0109-1549	P S
0109-1565	Arbejdsmiljoe og Samfund
0109-1581	Fisk & Fri
0109-159X	Sport paa Bornholm†
0109-1646	T V Aarbogen†
0109-1700	Rambukken
0109-1743	Advance
0109-1751	Detail-Bladet
0109-176X	Folkets Roest
0109-1816	Gamle Maane
0109-1875	Assurandoeren
0109-1913	Denmark. Miljoeministeriet. Miljoeministeriets Lovregister
0109-193X	Boernebibliotekskatalog. Lydboeger, Bog & Baand
0109-2049	Vind - Nyt see 0905-3549
0109-2057	Kristelig Fagforening. Medlemsblad
0109-2073	Groenlands Geologiske Undersoegelse. Gletscher-hydrologiske Meddelelser†
0109-2111	Gyden
0109-2138	Historisk Aarbog for Felsted Sogn
0109-2146	Sport
0109-2162	Lokalhistorisk Arkiv Stubbekoebing. Aarsskrift
0109-2170	Brorfelde Magnetic Results see 0901-9413
0109-2235	Practicus
0109-2251	Loevens Gab
0109-2278	Europa†
0109-2294	Kliniske Tandteknikere
0109-2308	Travsport for Fagfolk
0109-2316	Thomson Nytt
0109-2324	Gartneren
0109-2359	Elteknik
0109-2367	D G U Information
0109-2375	Soendagskolekontakt
0109-2383	Tidsskrift for Skatteret
0109-2391	S & P
0109-2405	Denmark. Vejdirektoratet. Aarsberetning
0109-2421	Indvandreren
0109-2464	Illustreret Videnskab
0109-2472	Vadehavsrapport
0109-2480	Lydhullet see 0906-1061
0109-2499	Antikvitetsudstilling, Odd-Fellow Palaeet
0109-2502	Endodontics & Dental Traumatology
0109-2510	I C E S Identification Leaflets for Diseases and Parasites of Fish and Shellfish
0109-2529	I C E S Identification Leaflets for Plankton
0109-257X	Bladsmutten
0109-2588	Start
0109-2596	U F O Forskning†
0109-260X	Schultz Medicinalbibliotek. Publikation†
0109-2618	Musikhistorisk Museum og Carl Claudius' Samling. Meddelelser
0109-2669	Dansk-Fransk Handelsunion. Bulletin
0109-2707	Skolernes Indkoebshaandbog
0109-274X	Stigsnaes
0109-2766	Folk og Liv paa Roendeegnen-Dengang
0109-2774	Film Aarbogen
0109-2820	Poetica et Analytica
0109-2839	Lokalhistorisk Forening for Hoerup Sogn. Aarsskrift
0109-2847	Alt om Data
0109-2855	Fredsavisen†
0109-2863	Soenderjyllands Erhvervsorientering: Produktion, Handel, Kontakt
0109-2936	Kristelig Fagforening, Kristelig Funktionaer-Organisation. Medlemsblad see 0109-2057
0109-2936	Kristelig Fagforening, Kristelig Funktionaer-Organisation. Medlemsblad see 0109-1131
0109-2944	Historisk Samfund for Hoeje-Taastrup Kommune. Meddelelser
0109-2952	Roeddernet
0109-2979	C C Orientering
0109-2987	I P Information
0109-2995	Naturligvis
0109-3002	Statistik om Hjemmessygeplejerkevirksomheden
0109-3010	Fiskeri- og Miljoeundersoegelser i Groenland. Serie 1. Aarsberetning see 0905-5193
0109-3061	Heraldiske Studier
0109-307X	Spansklaererforeningen. Informationer
0109-3088	Baereboelgen†
0109-3118	Grafisk Kontakt†
0109-3142	Danske Plantevaernskonference
0109-3169	Nyhedsbrev
0109-3177	Apotekett
0109-3207	North European Dairy Journal changed to S D I - Scandinavian Dairy Information.
0109-3290	Ernaeringsnyt
0109-3304	Eftersyn
0109-3312	Plantevaern i Landbruget
0109-3339	Danske Illustratorer see 0903-6962
0109-3347	Munksgaards Social Aarbog†
0109-3363	Teaterseminar
0109-3371	D K
0109-3401	Copenhagen School of Economics and Business Administration. Marketing Institute. Working Papers
0109-3460	Samlernyt
0109-3479	Charlottenborg Foraarsudstillingen
0109-3487	Informationskatalog for Social- og Sundhedssektor changed to Nyhedsinformation for Social-, Sygehus- og Sundhedssektor.
0109-3509	Traeets Arbejdsgivere
0109-3525	Jaeger-Nytt
0109-3533	Konsulentordningen
0109-355X	Firezfirs
0109-3592	D B D Bat
0109-3649	D M C - Bladet
0109-3762	Aksel see 0905-975X
0109-3797	Serie Kureren
0109-3800	Kalveproducenten
0109-3835	Idraetsliv
0109-3851	Arbejderbladet
0109-3878	Komiteen mod Dyreforsoeg, Fonden til Sygdomsbekaempelse uden Dyreforsoeg changed to Dyrenes Ret.
0109-3886	K S Bulletin
0109-3916	Olieberetning
0109-3967	Nordica
0109-3975	Nordafrika
0109-3983	Vi Med Hus og Have see 0906-0952
0109-4017	Lokalhistorisk Forening for Soenderhald Kommune. Aarsskrift
0109-4033	D M V Nyt
0109-405X	Forlagsvejviser
0109-4076	Denmark. Statens Filmcentral. Information og Beretning
0109-4106	Child Care International†
0109-4130	Vand og Miljoe
0109-4157	A U D - Nyt
0109-4165	Dansk Kunst†
0109-4203	C I N A - Nytt see 0904-4337
0109-4211	Cyklen
0109-4262	Organisationer og Tal i Gartneriet
0109-4289	Rude Skov Magnetic Results†
0109-4300	Godhavn Magnetic Results
0109-4319	Indsatsen mod Ungdomsarbejdsloesheden
0109-4378	Afghanistan Bulletin
0109-4432	D F H - Rapport
0109-4440	Aarets Pressefoto
0109-4475	D Bat see 0109-3592
0109-4505	Ide-nyt: Til Lejligheder i Etagebebyggelse
0109-4513	Ide-Nyt: Til Jordbrugere see 0906-0952
0109-4564	Haandvaerkshistorisk Tidsskrift
0109-4599	Muldvarpen
0109-4718	Ask
0109-4777	Horse Holidays in W. Europe
0109-4831	P S
0109-4939	Tennis Jul
0109-4955	Fortegnelse over Dansk Udviklingsforskning
0109-4998	Kongelige Veterinaer- og Landbohoejskole. Haandbog
0109-5013	Data om Markedet
0109-5021	Doeveforsorgens Historiske Selskab changed to Doevehistorisk Tidsskrift.
0109-503X	Raastofproduktionsopgoerelse see 0109-7474
0109-5072	Nu changed to Magasinet Nu.
0109-5110	Danish Hydraulics
0109-5129	Fravaer ved Anmeldte Arbejdsulykker
0109-5196	R F Avisen
0109-5234	Danske Statsskoves Udbytte af Ved og Penge changed to Skov og Natur.
0109-5250	A S - Bogen
0109-5277	Kvartalsvis Statistik for Koebenhavnsomraadet†
0109-5315	Denmark. Statens Vejlaboratorium. Notat
0109-534X	Pladeanmeldelser, Rytmisk Musik
0109-5358	Dansk-Tjekkoslovakisk Selskab. Kvartalsnyt
0109-5366	I F L A Communications
0109-5390	L Ae S
0109-5420	Udenrigshandelen Fordelt paa Varer og Lande
0109-5439	Laegekredsforeningen Fyns Amt changed to Fynske Laeger.
0109-548X	R D F Bulletin†

ISSN INDEX 5593

0109-5498 Fortegnelse over Fabrikanter og Importoerer af Goedninger og Grundforbedringsmidler *changed to* Producenter og Importoerer af Goedninger og Jordforbedringsmidler.
0109-5536 Dansk Idraet
0109-5544 Ny Abstraktion†
0109-5579 Penge
0109-5587 Handelshoejskolen i Koebenhavn. Center for Uddannelsesfrosknning. Rapport *see* 0109-6257
0109-5595 Dragesport
0109-5641 Dental Materials
0109-565X Gerodontics†
0109-5668 Cancer Reviews†
0109-5684 Danske Vinblad
0109-5692 Bygningskonstruktoerernes Medlemsorientering *changed to* Bygningskonstruktoerernes Fagblad.
0109-5757 Denmark. Forsvarsministeriet. Aarlige Redegoerelse
0109-5781 Hele Fyns Erhvervsliv
0109-5811 Farvandvaesenets Trafikanalyset†
0109-582X Odense Universitet. Arabisk Informationscenter. Nyhedsbrev *changed to* Mellemoest Information. Maanedsoversigt.
0109-5846 Danske Bibelselskabs Aarbog
0109-5854 Museumsforeningen for Laesoe. Litterature
0109-5994 Dansk Golfhaandbog
0109-6044 Laengden af Offentlige Veje
0109-6060 T L Aarbog
0109-6109 Edb Nyt†
0109-6125 Danmarks Turist Vejviser
0109-6222 Nyt om Moebler†
0109-6257 Center of Educational Research. Copenhagen Business School. Report
0109-6311 Politikens Computer Aarbog†
0109-6389 D S U -Nyt *see* 0905-5525
0109-6397 En Tern. Informations og Debatblad *see* 0905-5525
0109-6486 Dansk Faellesrejse Forening. Medlemsblad
0109-6605 Dansk Rumforskninginstitut. Publikationer
0109-6656 Gilleleje Museum
0109-6664 Fysiktips
0109-6672 Denmark. Direktoratet for Toldvaesenet. Toldvaesenets Aarsberetning†
0109-6699 Lokalhistorisk Arkiv, Aalestrup. Aarsskrift
0109-6761 Bordtennis Aarbogen
0109-6796 Dannebrog Comics†
0109-6966 Alt om Mad†
0109-7172 Vaern om Danmark
0109-7202 Pulsen†
0109-7318 Windpower Monthly
0109-7334 Service- og Varevogne†
0109-7458 Raastofproduktionen, Landomraadet. Produktionsmaengden af Geologiske Raastoffer Fordelt paa Amtskommuner og Kommuner
0109-7466 Raastofproduktionen, Havomraadet
0109-7474 Raastofproduktionen, Landomraadet. Handelsvarer og Anvendelse, Gravforhold, Arealforhold
0109-7598 Managements Erhvervspolitiske Forum. Rapport
0109-7644 Dagens Danmark
0109-7679 Landscentralen for Undervisningsmidler. Teknisk Information†
0109-7687 Cielo dei Vichinghi
0109-7709 Barn og Kultur i Norden†
0109-7717 Video. Vaerd at Se†
0109-7725 Oekonomisk Analyse, Sommerregnskaber
0109-7814 Vision
0109-7822 Amstkommunernes Oekonomi
0109-792X Erhvervslederen (Frederiksberg, 1984)
0109-8047 Aktuell Nordisk Statistik
0109-8071 Telex Danmark
0109-8314 Denmark. Danmarks Statistik. Vejviser i Statistiken
0109-8330 Veteranfly Klubben
0109-8365 Folk Fortaeller
0109-8411 Dansk Artist Forbund. Show Guide
0109-8438 Samfundet til Udgivelse af Dansk Musik. Bulletin
0109-8489 Bangsbomuseet. Aarbog
0109-8551 Lokalhistorisk Arkiv, Roedby. Aarsskrift
0109-856X Feltundersoegelse†
0109-8586 Dansk Textil Exportguide - Danish Textile Export Guide *changed to* Export Guide - Dansk Textil og Beklaedning.
0109-8608 Du-Bladet *see* 0906-1592
0109-8640 Bibliotek og Uddannelse
0109-8667 Hele Aarhus Amts Erhvervsliv
0109-8691 Dansk Karate Forbund *see* 0109-8705
0109-8705 Dansk Karate Forbund. Medlemsblad
0109-8845 V F *see* 0109-8861
0109-8853 Folkebibliotekernes Udenlanske Boernebogssamling. Katalog†
0109-8861 Vegetarisk Tidsskrift
0109-887X Q - Avisen
0109-890X K T†
0109-8985 Skolen i Norden
0109-9019 Videofilm der er og for Boern†
0109-9035 Aarhus Universitet. Center for Latinamerikastudier. Nyhedsbrev†
0109-9043 Exportoeren
0109-9051 Grusavisen
0109-906X Lyrik & Prosa
0109-9078 Fuglelivet ved Roskilde Fjord
0109-9108 Freinet Nyt
0109-9140 Homeservice Stations Outside the Tropical Bands
0109-9167 A - Kasse Information
0109-923X Bibliotekshistorie
0109-9256 Denmark. Rigsbibliotekarembedet. ALBA - Accessionskatalogen *changed to* Denmark. Statens Bibliotekstjeneste. ALBA - Accessionskatalogen.
0109-9264 Historisk Samfund for Soenderjylland. Skrifter
0109-9280 Jyske Historiker
0109-9299 Leder. Kursuskatalog
0109-9310 Erhvervs-Orientering Stat Amt, Kommune
0109-9418 Amt- og Kommune Bladet
0109-9426 Denmark. Finanstilsynet. Investeringsforeninger *see* 0905-0965
0109-9442 G L B
0109-9485 Om Gymnasiet, Studenterkursus og Hoejre Forberedelseseksamen
0109-9531 Soft†
0109-9639 Ingenioer *changed to* Ingenioer - Hvorfor, Hvordan.
0109-9779 Datalogiske Skrifter
0109-9787 Sporten
0109-9876 Fodbold, Danske Kampe
0109-9892 Fodbold, Udenlandse Kampe
0109-9914 Om Laerlinge og Efg Uddannelserne
0109-9930 Denmark. Sundhetsstyrelsen. Laegemiddelafdelningen. Aarsberetning
0109-9957 Operationsmoensteret paa Danske Sygehuse
0109-9973 Aarhus Universitet. Socialmedicinsk Institut. Rapport†
0110-0068 Miorita
0110-0076 New Quarterly Cave *changed to* Crosscurrent.
0110-0084 Outrigger†
0110-022X N Z Family Physician
0110-0238 New Zealand Gay News *see* 0110-4454
0110-0246 New Zealand Tax Reports
0110-0262 New Zealand International Review
0110-0297 New Zealand Gymnast
0110-036X Noumenon
0110-0483 Country Side of Music
0110-0637 New Zealand Journal of Industrial Relations
0110-070X Butterworths Current Law
0110-0793 Property *see* 0113-4620
0110-0831 New Zealand Annual *changed to* Weekly News Annual.
0110-084X Farming Statistics†
0110-0858 Islands
0110-0890 New Zealand Nursing Forum
0110-098X New Zealand Home and Building
0110-1048 What's New in Forest Research
0110-1102 Art New Zealand
0110-1145 Spiral
0110-1153 Horticulture in N.Z. (Wellington) *see* 0114-1481
0110-1242 New Zealand Wool Board. Statistical Handbook
0110-1277 New Zealand Administrative Reports
0110-1390 New Zealand Town Planning Appeals
0110-1447 National Museum of New Zealand. Miscellaneous Series
0110-1471 New Zealand Wings
0110-148X New Zealand Law Reports
0110-1625 Turnbull Library Record
0110-165X New Zealand. Soil Bureau. Bibliographic Report†
0110-1668 New Zealand Energy Journal *see* 0111-5839
0110-1749 New Zealand. Ministry of Agriculture and Fisheries. Fisheries Research Division. Bulletin *see* 0113-2261
0110-1765 New Zealand. Ministry of Agriculture and Fisheries. Fisheries Research Division Occasional Publication *see* 0113-227X
0110-1900 New Zealand. Health Statistical Services. Hospital Management Data†
0110-1951 United Nations Handbook
0110-2079 New Zealand. Soil Bureau. Soil Survey Reports†
0110-2184 New Zealand. Department of Statistics. Exports *see* 0114-2607
0110-2192 University of Waikato. Antarctic Research Unit. Report
0110-3458 New Zealand. Department of Statistics. Transport Statistics†
0110-3466 New Zealand. Department of Statistics. Local Authority Statistics†
0110-3474 New Zealand. Department of Statistics. Insurance Statistics†
0110-3482 New Zealand. Department of Statistics. Justice Statistics *see* 0112-4447
0110-3482 New Zealand. Department of Statistics. Justice Statistics *see* 0112-4501
0110-3490 New Zealand. Department of Statistics. Building Statistics†
0110-3563 Engineering Management & Equipment Digest
0110-3741 New Zealand. Department of Statistics. Imports *see* 0114-2607
0110-375X Population *see* 0113-3667
0110-3768 New Zealand. Department of Statistics. Population and Migration. Part B: External Migration *see* 0112-6709
0110-392X New Zealand Household Survey *see* 1170-747X
0110-392X New Zealand Household Survey *see* 1170-8271
0110-3970 Pacific Quarterly Moana *changed to* Crosscurrent.
0110-3989 Camera *see* 0114-264X
0110-4004 Whakatane & District Historical Society. Monographs
0110-4012 New Zealand Genealogist
0110-4152 University of Auckland. Department of Mathematics and Statistics. Report Series
0110-4233 New Zealand Tax Planning Report
0110-4373 Library Life
0110-4454 Out !
0110-4470 New Zealand Institute of Economic Research. Quarterly Survey of Business Opinion
0110-4519 New Zealand. Ministry of Agriculture and Fisheries. Fisheries Research Division: Information Leaflet *see* 0113-2180
0110-4527 Entomological Society of New Zealand. Bulletin
0110-4586 New Zealand. Department of Statistics. Vital Statistics†
0110-4616 New Zealand. Department of Statistics. Balance of Payments *see* 0112-5117
0110-4624 New Zealand. Department of Statistics. Agricultural Statistics
0110-4640 New Zealand. Department of Statistics. Census of Building and Construction†
0110-4748 Delta Research Monograph
0110-4772 New Zealand Economist *see* 0111-8021
0110-4802 New Zealand. Ministry of Foreign Affairs. Development
0110-487X Prudentia
0110-4888 Bulletin of New Zealand Art History
0110-4896 Onslow Historian
0110-4969 New Zealand Environmental Health Inspector *see* 0112-0212
0110-5019 New Zealand. Department of Statistics. Part A: Prices *see* 0112-6598
0110-5027 New Zealand. Department of Statistics. Part B: Wages and Labour†
0110-5124 New Zealand Antarctic Record
0110-5132 Book Trade Monthly *see* 0111-8781
0110-5191 Public Sector
0110-5205 N Z O I Oceanographic Field Report†
0110-5221 D S I R Discussion Paper†
0110-523X Reserve Bank of New Zealand. Research Papers
0110-5264 New Zealand Health Statistics Report†
0110-5337 N.Z.A.R.T. Amateur Radio Callbook
0110-540X New Zealand Journal of Archaeology
0110-5493 Aviation Historical Society of New Zealand. Journal
0110-5558 Massey University. Centre for Agricultural Policy Studies. Agricultural Policy Paper
0110-5698 New Zealand. Department of Statistics. Shipping and Cargo *see* 0114-2607
0110-571X New Zealand Speech-Language Therapists Journal
0110-5760 Royal New Zealand Institute of Horticulture. Annual Journal *see* 1170-1803
0110-5787 New Zealand Listener
0110-585X English in New Zealand
0110-5892 Canterbury Botanical Society. Journal
0110-5949 Consumer
0110-6007 New Zealand Cartographic Journal *changed to* New Zealand Cartography and Geographic Information Systems.
0110-604X Wildlife - a Review†
0110-6112 New Zealand. Department of Scientific and Industrial Research. Geophysics Division. Report *see* 0113-2903
0110-6155 Rails
0110-618X N Z O I Records†
0110-6236 Transport News of New Zealand
0110-6260 Orchardist of New Zealand
0110-6287 New Zealand Environment
0110-6295 Automation and Control
0110-6376 S E T: Research Information for Teachers
0110-6392 New Zealand Operational Research *changed to* Asia Pacific Journal of Operational Research.
0110-6465 New Zealand Journal of Ecology
0110-6589 Agronomy Society of New Zealand. Proceedings
0110-6619 Continuing Education in New Zealand *see* 0112-224X
0110-6635 New Zealand Justices' Quarterly
0110-666X Directory of Australian Associations
0110-6813 National Business Review
0110-6872 New Zealand. Ministry of Transport. Traffic Research Report†
0110-6902 Contacts in Agriculture
0110-6945 Public Service Association Journal
0110-7011 Blue Water *changed to* Boating Safety.
0110-7089 New Zealand. Department of Scientific and Industrial Research. Geophysics Division. Technical Note *see* 0113-3055

ISSN

0110-7321 Inter - Industry Study of the New Zealand Economy
0110-7380 New Zealand Journal of French Studies
0110-7720 Lincoln College. Agricultural Economics Research Unit. Discussion Paper *see* 1170-7607
0110-7844 Forest Industries Review *see* 0113-3128
0110-7992 Deer Farmer
0110-8034 New Electronics
0110-8085 Celluloid Strip
0110-8247 People & Planning†
0110-8603 Broadsheet
0110-8700 New Zealand. Department of Statistics. Population Census: General Information
0110-943X National Museum of New Zealand Records
0110-9464 National Museum of New Zealand. Bulletin
0110-9510 New Ethicals Catalogue
0110-9944 New Zealand. Department of Health. National Radiation Laboratory. Environmental Radioactivity Annual Report
0111-0225 New Zealand. Department of Statistics. New Zealand Life Tables
0111-0489 Youth Studies in New Zealand†
0111-0756 New Zealand. Road Research Unit. Occasional Paper†
0111-0829 New Zealand Agricultural Engineering Institute. Current Publications†
0111-0950 Technical Papers on New Zealand Wool *see* 0112-2932
0111-1108 Economic Review of New Zealand Agriculture†
0111-1302 N Z O I Oceanographic Summary†
0111-1485 New Zealand Society of Periodontology. Journal
0111-1957 Alpha
0111-2473 Agricultural Economist†
0111-2805 Roll Back the Years†
0111-2821 N Z C E R Newsletter
0111-3364 New Zealand Pottery and Ceramics Research Association. Annual Report†
0111-378X N.Z.A.E.I. Newsletter†
0111-3895 Royal Society of New Zealand. Miscellaneous Series
0111-395X Nat Ed Newsletter *see* 0114-8206
0111-4123 Planning Research Index†
0111-4239 New Zealand District Court Reports *changed to* Butterworths District Court Reports.
0111-431X New Zealand Pharmacy
0111-5251 New Zealand. Ministry of Foreign Affairs. Project Profiles
0111-5308 Centrepoint†
0111-5383 Fauna of New Zealand
0111-5499 Weather and Climate
0111-5774 Pacific Arts Newsletter *see* 1018-4252
0111-5782 New Zealand Times *changed to* Dominion Sunday Times.
0111-5839 Energy Journal†
0111-6142 New Zealand Diplomatic Corps and Consular and Other Representatives *changed to* Diplomatic List - Diplomatic and Consular Representatives in New Zealand.
0111-6207 New Zealand Asian Studies Society. Newsletter
0111-6339 Massey University. Centre for Agricultural Policy Studies. Agricultural Policy Proceedings
0111-6355 New Zealand School Journal
0111-6606 Food Technologist
0111-672X New Zealand Science Abstracts†
0111-6770 Mazengarb's Industrial Law Bulletin
0111-686X New Zealand. Nature Conservation Council. Newsletter†
0111-7122 Ionospheric Data, New Zealand†
0111-7343 Russell Review
0111-7351 New Zealand Social Work
0111-7416 Quality Assurance New Zealand *changed to* Quality New Zealand.
0111-7653 Auckland-Waikato Historical Journal
0111-7874 Massey University. Department of Accounting and Finance. Discussion Paper Series *see* 0114-5932
0111-8021 New Zealand Financial Review
0111-8129 New Zealand. F R I Bulletin
0111-834X New Zealand Publishing News
0111-8358 New Zealand Family Law Reports *changed to* Butterworths Family Law Reports.
0111-8587 D S I R Industrial Information Series†
0111-8617 New Zealand. National Health Statistics Centre. Fetal and Infant Deaths *changed to* New Zealand. Health Statistical Services. Fetal and Infant Deaths.
0111-8676 Parallax†
0111-8781 New Zealand Bookseller & Publisher
0111-8854 Mentalities
0111-9044 Marketing
0111-915X New Zealand Dairy Exporter
0111-9176 New Zealand Statistician
0111-9370 Staples' Guide to New Zealand Income Tax Practice
0111-9435 New Zealand Planning Institute. Planning Quarterly
0111-946X Institution of Professional Engineers. Transactions. Electrical, Mechanical and Chemical Engineering Section
0111-9508 Institution of Professional Engineers. Transactions. Civil Engineering Section
0111-9656 Butterworths Conveyancing Bulletin
0112-0212 New Zealand Journal of Environmental Health
0112-0395 N Z O I Hydrology Station Data†
0112-0433 N Z Micro
0112-0603 Massey University. Centre for Agricultural Policy Studies. Discussion Paper *changed to* Massey University. Centre for Agricultural Policy Studies. Agricultural Discussion Paper.
0112-0743 Historic Places in New Zealand *see* 0114-9172
0112-0808 More
0112-109X New Zealand Journal of Psychology
0112-1170 New Zealand Institute of Economic Research. Medium Term Review *see* 0033-5711
0112-1227 Journal of New Zealand Literature
0112-1545 University of Auckland. Department of Geography. Occasional Publication
0112-1642 Sports Medicine
0112-2061 New Zealand Planning Council. Monitoring Reports†
0112-224X New Zealand Journal of Adult Learning†
0112-2290 N Z Agrichemical and Plant Protection Manual
0112-2320 AgLink Index and Catalogue
0112-2339 New Zealand. Department of Scientific and Industrial Research. Social Science Series†
0112-2479 Collected Papers from the Journal of the Royal Society of New Zealand
0112-2541 Journal of General Practice *see* 0114-2550
0112-255X Hospital Therapeutics†
0112-2584 New Zealand. Ministry of Energy. Annual Returns of Production from Quarries and Mineral Production Statistics *changed to* New Zealand Annual Mining Review.
0112-2754 Wool Research Organisation of New Zealand. Special Publications
0112-2851 Wool Research Organisation of New Zealand Reports
0112-2908 Wool Research Organisation of New Zealand Communications
0112-2932 Wool Research Organisation of New Zealand. Technical Papers†
0112-3629 New Zealand. Department of Statistics. Census of Transport, Storage & Communication†
0112-3718 New Zealand Census of Agricultural Contracting Services†
0112-3823 New Zealand Tax Cases
0112-3890 New Zealand Journal of Technology†
0112-3939 New Zealand. Department of Statistics. Statistics of Incomes and Income Tax of Persons†
0112-3998 New Zealand. Department of Statistics. Statistics of Incomes and Income Tax of Companies†
0112-4048 New Zealand Dairy Research Institute. Annual Report *changed to* New Zealand Dairy Research Institute. Report.
0112-4412 New Zealand Powerboat
0112-4447 New Zealand. Department of Statistics. Justice Statistics: Part A†
0112-4501 New Zealand. Department of Statistics. Justice Statistics: Part B†
0112-4951 Dance News
0112-5117 New Zealand. Department of Statistics. Overseas Balance of Payments†
0112-5443 New Zealand Stamp Collector
0112-5842 Business Keynote†
0112-6261 New Zealand Family Law Bulletin *changed to* Butterworths Family Law Bulletin.
0112-6598 New Zealand. Department of Statistics. Consumers Price Index†
0112-6601 New Zealand Household Expenditure and Income Survey *see* 1170-747X
0112-6601 New Zealand Household Expenditure and Income Survey *see* 1170-8271
0112-6709 New Zealand. Department of Statistics. External Migration Statistics†
0112-6997 Ad Media
0112-8094 Motor World *changed to* Directions.
0112-8388 C.P. Newsletter Monthly
0112-8396 New Zealand Marine Sciences Society Newsletter
0112-871X Reserve Bank Bulletin
0112-8949 New Zealand Flight Safety
0112-9058 Directory of Technology
0112-9155 New Zealand. Department of Statistics. Demographic Trends Bulletin *see* 0113-3667
0112-949X Supermarketing
0112-9589 N Z T P Product Research Series *changed to* New Zealand Tourism Department. Product Research Series.
0112-9597 New Zealand Forestry
0112-9686 N Z T P Tourism Incentives Series *changed to* New Zealand Tourism Department. Tourism Incentives Series.
0112-9724 N Z T P Overseas Market Research Series
0112-9732 N Z T P Visitor Statistics Research Series *changed to* New Zealand Tourism Department. Visitor Statistics Research Series.
0112-9740 N Z T P Social Research Series *changed to* New Zealand Tourism Department. Social Research Series.
0112-9767 N Z T P Domestic Research Series *changed to* New Zealand Tourism Department. Domestic Research Series.
0112-9783 N Z T P Regional Research Series *changed to* New Zealand Tourism Department. Regional Research Series.
0112-9821 N Z T P Committee - Departmental Report Series *changed to* N Z T Committee - Departmental Report Series.
0112-983X N Z T P International Visitors Research Series *changed to* New Zealand Tourism Department. International Visitors Research Series.
0112-9864 N Z T P Economic Research Series *changed to* New Zealand Tourism Department. Economic Research Series.
0112-9880 N Z T P Marketing Series *changed to* New Zealand Tourism Department. Marketing Series.
0113-0161 N Z T P Catalogue Series *changed to* New Zealand Tourism Department. Catalogue Series.
0113-0196 New Zealand Car
0113-0315 New Zealand Valuers' Journal
0113-0374 Matangi Tonga
0113-0498 New Zealand Manufacturer *see* 0113-9320
0113-0501 N Z Petroleum Exploration News
0113-115X New Zealand Conveyancing Bulletin *see* 0111-9656
0113-1222 New Zealand Labour Force
0113-1877 New Zealand Institute of Economic Research. Research Monographs
0113-2024 Crosslink
0113-2180 New Zealand Fisheries Technical Report
0113-2261 New Zealand Fisheries Research Bulletin
0113-227X New Zealand Fisheries Occasional Publication
0113-2644 Cornucopia Magazine†
0113-2792 New Zealand Wool Market Review
0113-2903 New Zealand. Department of Scientific and Industrial Research. Geophysics Division. Research Report†
0113-3055 New Zealand. Department of Scientific and Industrial Research. Geophysics Division. Technical Report†
0113-3128 New Zealand Forest Industries
0113-3292 Contraband
0113-3462 Interface†
0113-3667 New Zealand. Department of Statistics. Demographic Trends
0113-4566 Architecture New Zealand
0113-4620 New Zealand Property
0113-468X Merchant
0113-4957 New Zealand Business
0113-5090 Motoring Today *changed to* Directions.
0113-583X Potter (Auckland)
0113-6526 Index New Zealand
0113-6739 Consumer Home and Garden
0113-7492 New Zealand Natural Sciences
0113-7832 Archaeology in New Zealand
0113-8901 Food Industry News
0113-9320 Manufacturer
0113-9371 Industrial Equipment News
0113-9495 American Chamber of Commerce in New Zealand. Annual Directory
0113-9606 New Zealand Fisherman
0114-0353 N Z T P Implications of Tourism Growth Series *changed to* New Zealand Tourism Department. Implications of Tourism Growth Series.
0114-0671 New Zealand Journal of Crop and Horticultural Science
0114-0892 Clinical Pharmacokinetics Drug Data Handbook (Year)
0114-1090 Te Puna Matauranga
0114-1481 Royal New Zealand Institute of Horticulture. Newsletter
0114-2119 New Zealand. Department of Statistics. Key Statistics
0114-2283 New Zealand Geological Survey. Paleontological Bulletin
0114-2550 New Zealand General Practice
0114-2607 New Zealand. Department of Statistics. Overseas Trade
0114-264X Camera New Zealand
0114-3727 New Zealand Health & Hospital
0114-3999 New Zealand External Relations Review
0114-4138 Takahe
0114-541X Consumer Voice†
0114-5436 Consumer Food and Health†
0114-5932 Massey University. Division of Accountancy. Discussion Paper Series
0114-8206 N Z E I Rourou
0114-8540 N Z Electrical Focus
0114-8818 D S I R Plant Protection Report
0114-9172 New Zealand Historic Places
0115-0022 Sylvatrop
0115-0243 Philippine Quarterly of Culture and Society
0115-0405 C L S U Journal of the Arts†
0115-0456 Forpride Digest *changed to* F P R D I Journal.
0115-0464 Private Development Corporation of the Philippines. Monthly Economic Letter†

ISSN INDEX 5595

0115-0529 Philippine Council for Agriculture, Forestry, and Natural Resources Research & Development. Monitor
0115-0553 Kalikasan
0115-0804 Philippine Phytopathology
0115-0820 Araneta Research Journal
0115-0944 International Rice Research Newsletter
0115-0960 Canopy *changed to* Canopy International.
0115-1126 Santo Tomas Journal of Medicine
0115-1142 I R R I Research Highlights
0115-1169 P S S C Social Science Information
0115-1207 Philippine Astronomical Handbook
0115-1266 University of the Philippines at Los Banos. College of Forestry. Conservation Circular†
0115-1304 N R C P Research Bulletin
0115-1312 Construction & Engineering
0115-138X Integrated Bar of the Philippines. Journal
0115-1401 C B Review
0115-1541 P C A Coconut Farmers Bulletin†
0115-1746 Philippine Business Review†
0115-1843 Builder of Progress†
0115-1851 Philippines. Labor Statistics Service. Yearbook of Labor Statistics *changed to* Philippines. Bureau of Labor and Employment Statistics. Yearbook of Labor Statistics.
0115-2092 N S O Monthly Bulletin of Statistics
0115-2106 Philippine Biota
0115-2130 Kimika
0115-2157 Trends in Technology
0115-2173 Philippine Journal of Veterinary and Animal Sciences
0115-2351 Philippine Textile Digest†
0115-2394 Trade Post†
0115-2408 Journal of Northern Luzon
0115-2467 I R R I Reporter
0115-2521 University of Baguio Journal†
0115-2661 Social Development News†
0115-2742 Mindanao Journal
0115-2777 D O S T Technology Journal *see* 0116-7294
0115-2971 Homelife
0115-3110 Graduate School Journal
0115-3307 Table of Sunrise, Sunset, Twilight, Moonrise and Moonset
0115-3676 Evergreen *see* 0115-9259
0115-3757 Atomedia†
0115-3773 S M A R C Monitor *changed to* U S M A R C Monitor.
0115-3862 I R R I Research Paper Series
0115-3994 Balikatanews
0115-4141 I C L A R M Translations
0115-4192 Philippine Business and Industry Index
0115-4389 I C L A R M Studies and Reviews
0115-4419 Private Development Corporation of the Philippines. Industry Digest
0115-4435 I C L A R M Conference Proceedings.
0115-4575 I C L A R M Newsletter *changed to* N A G A: I C L A R M Quarterly.
0115-4729 Abstract Bibliography on Coconut†
0115-4842 World Executive's Digest
0115-4931 C M U Journal of Agriculture, Food and Nutrition *see* 0116-7847
0115-4990 Habitat Philippines†
0115-5032 Ang Tagamasid
0115-5490 P F N P Newsletter†
0115-5547 I C L A R M Technical Reports
0115-5679 Agham
0115-5814 Ang Tala
0115-5997 I C L A R M Bibliographies
0115-6012 Kinaadman
0115-6144 Likha
0115-6195 Malay
0115-625X Scientia Filipinas†
0115-6276 De La Salle University. Department of History and Area Studies. Anuaryo - Annales
0115-6292 Kaya Tao
0115-6349 Religious Studies Journal
0115-6373 Philippine Journal of Industrial Relations *changed to* Philippine Journal of Labor and Industrial Relations.
0115-6403 P B S Bulletin
0115-6594 D L S U Dialogue
0115-6608 Philippines Footwear Leathergoods & Accesories Journal
0115-6640 D L S U Graduate Journal
0115-6853 Mindanao Art & Culture
0115-690X Journal of Fisheries & Aquaculture
0115-6950 Arts & Sciences Journal
0115-7000 Development Administration Journal
0115-7167 Philippines. National Library. T N L News
0115-7205 Philippine Law Report
0115-7213 Philippines. National Library. T N L Research Guide Series
0115-7329 Mindanao State University. U R C Professional Papers
0115-7809 Science Diliman
0115-8341 S L U - E I S S I F Newsletter
0115-835X Likas-Yaman
0115-8473 N F E - W I D Exchange - Asia. Occasional Paper†
0115-852X N F E - W I D Exchange - Asia. Newsletter
0115-8686 Computer Issues
0115-8724 Philippine Science and Technology Abstracts Bibliography *changed to* Philippine Science and Technology Abstracts.
0115-8988 Sophia
0115-9097 Development Research News
0115-9143 Journal of Philippine Development
0115-9194 P I D S Monograph Series
0115-9259 Bagong Sibol†
0116-0109 Philippine Journal of Volcanology†
0116-0516 Studies in Philippine Linguistics
0116-0710 Annals of Tropical Research
0116-1105 Asian Development Review
0116-1520 Philippine Yearbook
0116-1822 Foreign Trade Statistics of the Philippines
0116-2624 Philippines. National Statistics Office. Integrated Survey of Households Bulletin.
0116-2659 Philippines. National Statistics Office. Annual Survey of Establishments
0116-2675 Philippines. National Statistics Office. Vital Statistics Report
0116-2993 Asian Environment
0116-3426 Philippine Revenue Journal
0116-3590 Business Eye
0116-452X Business Journal
0116-4856 Landas
0116-4864 P I C News
0116-5461 W C C I Forum
0116-6417 Graduate Forum
0116-6514 Asian Fisheries Science
0116-7073 Karunungan
0116-7081 Philippine-American Studies Journal
0116-709X Praxis
0116-7103 D L S U Engineering Journal
0116-7111 D L S U Business & Economics Review
0116-7294 Philippine Technology Journal
0116-7847 C M U Journal of Science
0116-7979 Sambahayan
0116-8037 Teaching English for Specific Purposes Journal
0116-9688 Exhibits Asia
0117-0686 Philippines. Republic. National Museum Papers
0120-0011 Universidad Nacional de Colombia. Facultad de Medicina. Revista
0120-0062 Ideas y Valores *changed to* Revista Ideas y Valores.
0120-0216 Aleph
0120-0283 Universidad Industrial de Santander. Boletin de Geologia
0120-033X Revista E A F I T - Temas Administrativos *see* 0120-341X
0120-0534 Revista Latinoamericana de Psicologia
0120-0631 Revista de las Fuerzas Armadas
0120-0682 Revista COMALFI
0120-0747 Estudios Rurales Latinoamericanos†
0120-0798 Revista Acodal
0120-0852 Universidad Industrial de Santander. Revista - Investigaciones
0120-0887 C E R L A L C: Noticias sobre el Libro y Bibliografia *see* 0121-1242
0120-0909 Universidad Industrial de Santander. Revista - Medicina *see* 0121-0807
0120-0933 Universidad de Antioquia. Facultad de Ciencias Economicas. Administracion de Empresas. Tecnologia Administrativa
0120-095X Universidad Industrial de Santander. Revista - Humanidades
0120-0976 Revista Interamericana de Bibliotecologia
0120-0992 Universidad de los Andes. Cuadernos de Filosofia y Letras
0120-100X Revista Ion
0120-1034 Neurologia Colombia
0120-1085 Museo de Arte Moderno. Boletin Informativo†
0120-1131 Resumenes de la Literatura Medica Colombiana†
0120-1182 Sociedad Colombiana de Endocrinologia. Revista
0120-1204 Boletin Bibliografico C E R L A L *see* 0121-1242
0120-1263 Escritos
0120-1344 Memorias Martes del Paraninfo†
0120-1425 Boletin Geologico
0120-1468 Franciscanum
0120-1484 Pastos Tropicales. Boletin Informativo *see* 1012-7410
0120-1492 Universidad de Caldas. Facultad de Filosofia. Revista
0120-1557 Revista de Egresados
0120-1573 Ciencia Tecnologia y Desarrollo
0120-1603 Revista Universidad Tecnologica
0120-162X Educar
0120-1794 Revista Temas Economicos *see* 0120-2596
0120-1824 Yuca Boletin Informativo
0120-1875 Informativo Juridico
0120-1921 Informativo Fasecolda *changed to* Informativo Tecnico.
0120-1972 Revista Fasecolda
0120-2073 Instituto Colombiano para el Fomento de la Educacion Superior. Boletin Bibliografico†
0120-2235 Internation Center for Tropical Agriculture. Bean Program Annual Report *changed to* Bean Program Annual Report.
0120-2278 Revista Cafetera de Colombia
0120-2367 Universidad de Antioquia. Revista
0120-2391 Informe Anual del Programa de Pastos Tropicales
0120-2480 Hojas de Frijol para America Latina *changed to* Hojas de Frijol.
0120-2499 Centro Interamericano de Fotointerpretacion. Revista
0120-2510 Universidad de Antioquia. Departamento de Antropologia. Boletin de Antropologia
0120-2561 Universidad Nacional de Colombia. Facultad Nacional de Minas. Anales†
0120-2596 Lecturas de Economia
0120-2669 Universidad Nacional de Colombia. Facultad de Arquitectura. Revista
0120-2758 Colombia. Observatorio Astronomico Nacional. Anuario
0120-2812 Acta Agronomica
0120-2839 Universidad Pedagogica Nacional. Centro de Investigaciones. Boletin Informativo†
0120-2855 Revista Odontologia
0120-288X Abstracts on Cassava
0120-2928 Abstracts on Field Beans
0120-2944 Resumenes Analiticos sobre Pastos Tropicales
0120-3045 Maguare
0120-3053 Universidad Pedagogica y Tecnologica de Colombia. Centro de Estudios Economicos. Apuntes del C E N E S
0120-3169 C I A T Report
0120-3215 Familia y Sociedad
0120-324X Revista Comercio Exterior de Colombia
0120-3347 Revista Colombiana de Anestesiologia
0120-338X Forma y Funcion
0120-341X Revista Universidad E A F I T
0120-3479 Lenguaje
0120-3576 Coyuntura Economica
0120-3584 Desarrollo y Sociedad
0120-3649 Theologica Xaveriana
0120-3754 Administracion y Desarrollo
0120-3797 Avances en Psicologia Clinica Latinoamericana
0120-3819 Educacion Superior y Desarrollo†
0120-3878 Perspectivas en Psicologia
0120-4009 Nuestra America
0120-4017 Colombia. Superintendencia Bancaria. Revista
0120-4084 C I A T International
0120-4092 C I A T Internacional
0120-4114 Revista Veterinaria y Zootecnica de Caldas
0120-4165 Controversia
0120-422X Semillas
0120-4289 Camara de Comercio de Bogota. Revista
0120-4351 Flora de Colombia
0120-4416 Paginas de Contenido. Fisiologia Vegetal
0120-4424 Paginas de Contenido. Proteccion de Plantas
0120-4440 Paginas de Contenido. Pastos, Produccion Animal y Nutricion
0120-4467 Paginas de Contenido. Economia Agricola y Desarrollo Rural
0120-4483 Ensayos Sobre Politica Economica
0120-4564 Catalogo Colectivo de Libros y Monografias Economicas
0120-5056 Directorio de la Educacion Superior en Colombia
0120-5102 C A M A C O L. Revista
0120-5226 Bancos y Bancarios de Colombia
0120-5307 Investigacion y Educacion en Enfermeria
0120-5455 Texto e Contexto
0120-5587 Linguistica y Literatura
0120-5595 Colombia: Ciencia y Tecnologia
0120-5609 Ingenieria e Investigacion
0120-5692 Universidad de Medellin. Revista
0120-5862 Revista S A I
0120-5986 Carta de Colciencias
0120-6281 Colombia. Departamento Administrativo Nacional de Estadistica. Boletin de Estadistica
0120-6311 Revista Internacional de Pediatria
0120-6613 Revista de Antropologia *changed to* Revista de Antropologia y Arqueologia.
0120-6745 Colombia. Departamento Administrativo Nacional de Estadistica. Choco Estadistico
0120-677X Educacion Fisica y Deporte
0120-6907 Colombia: sus Gentes y Regiones
0120-713X Art Nexus
0120-727X Colombia Exporta
0120-7296 Museo del Oro. Boletin
0120-7601 Industria Grafica *see* 1054-2434
0120-7644 Tecnologia del Plastico
0120-8993 Ecotropica. Ecosistemas Tropicales. Boletin
0120-9515 Asociacion Nacional de Industriales. Revista Bimestral
0121-0203 Revista de Ascolbi
0121-0807 Universidad Industrial de Santander. Revista - Salud
0121-0890 Universidad Nacional de Colombia. Revista
0121-1242 C E R L A L C: El Libro en America Latina y el Caribe
0121-1390 Correo Editorial
0121-1870 Colombia. Corporacion Nacional de Turismo. Catalogo Nacional de Tesis de Turismo y Hoteleria
0121-1889 Colombia. Corporacion Nacional de Turismo. Catalogo Turistico
0121-2400 Boletin Bibliografico I S B N
0121-3776 Kinetoscopio
0121-4977 Revue Francaise de Service Social
0125-0000 Thai Abstracts, Series A. Science and Technology

ISSN

0125-0019 Quarterly Bulletin of Statistics for Asia and the Pacific†
0125-0027 Sample Surveys in the ESCAP Region
0125-0140 Business in Thailand
0125-0191 Thai-American Business
0125-0477 Business Review
0125-0566 Journal of Commerce
0125-0981 Thailand Business
0125-1074 Bank of Thailand. Monthly Report
0125-1090 Thailand Airline Timetable
0125-1759 Journal of Ferrocement
0125-1767 A G E News
0125-1775 R E R I C News
0125-1783 E N F O Newsletter
0125-2186 Environmental Sanitation Abstracts - Low Cost Options
0125-2488 P A S A A Journal
0125-3719 Renewable Energy Review Journal *see* 0857-6173
0125-4529 Scientific Serials in Thai Libraries
0125-4537 List of Scientific and Technical Literature Relating to Thailand
0125-5088 Environmental Sanitation Reviews
0125-5606 N I D A Bulletin
0125-5827 Index to Thai Periodical Literature
0125-5983 Chiang Mai Medical Bulletin
0125-605X Bank of Thailand. Quarterly Bulletin
0125-6440 Population Newsletter
0125-6459 Thailand. Ministry of Foreign Affairs. Foreign Affairs Newsletter
0125-7978 Kasetsart University, Bangkok, Thailand. Faculty of Fisheries. Notes
0125-9008 Baca
0125-9156 Berita Ilmu Pengetahuan den Teknologi
0125-9229 Warta Ekonomi Maritim Review for Entrepreneurs
0125-9318 Menara Perkebunan
0125-9555 Indonesia. Badan Tenaga Atom Nasional. Majalah B A T A N *see* 0303-2876
0125-9652 Majalah Administrasi Negara
0125-9679 Warta Demografi
0125-9687 Hukum dan Pembangunan
0125-9830 Oseanologi di Indonesia
0125-9997 Pusat Penelitian Perkebunan Gula Indonesia. Bulletin
0126-0057 Trubus
0126-0251 Journal of Indonesian Demography
0126-0561 Badan Meteorologi dan Geofisika. Laporan Evaluasi Hujan dan Perkiraan Hujan
0126-057X Foto Indonesia†
0126-0758 BioIndonesia†
0126-0812 Indonesia. National Scientific Documentation Center. Annual Report *changed to* Indonesia. Centre for Scientific Documentation and Information. Annual Report.
0126-1282 Indeks Berita Surat Kabar†
0126-1312 Journal of the Medical Sciences
0126-1568 Atom Indonesia
0126-1584 Atma Jaya Research Centre. Newsletter
0126-1630 Atma Jaya Research Centre. Library Bulletin
0126-1924 Brackishwater Aquaculture Development Centre. Bulletin
0126-2319 Indonesia. Central Bureau of Statistics. Economic Indicator Bulletin
0126-270X Prisma
0126-2874 Nusa
0126-2912 Statistical Year Book of Indonesia
0126-3595 Statistical Pocketbook of Indonesia
0126-3714 Indonesia. Export by Commodity, Country of Destination and Port of Export
0126-4273 Tempo
0126-4419 Indonesia. Import by Commodity and Country of Origin
0126-5024 Masalah Pendidikan
0126-5040 Malaysian Periodicals Index
0126-5105 Development Forum
0126-5156 Foram Pembangunan
0126-5210 Malaysian National Bibliography
0126-527X Malaysian Panorama
0126-5350 Malaysian Journal of Economic Studies
0126-5393 Wings of Gold
0126-5415 Pemberita†
0126-5520 U M B C Economic Review†
0126-5539 Geological Society of Malaysia Newsletter *changed to* Warta Geologi.
0126-5547 Timah Malaysia†
0126-5636 Islamiyyat
0126-5652 Malaysian Veterinary Journal†
0126-5709 M A R D I Research Bulletin *see* 0128-0686
0126-575X Planter
0126-5806 Siaran Pekebun
0126-5849 Rubber Research Institute of Malaysia. Planters Conference Proceedings *see* 0127-9785
0126-5865 Malaysian Rubber Producers' Council. Monthly Statistical Bulletin
0126-6020 Journal of Educational Research
0126-6039 Sains Malaysiana: Jernal Sains Alam Semula
0126-6098 Malaysia Official Year Book
0126-6128 Pertanika
0126-6136 Jurnal Sains Institut Penyelidikan Getah Malaysia†
0126-6187 Geological Society of Malaysia. Bulletin
0126-6209 A B U Technical Review
0126-625X Accounting Journal
0126-6322 Journal of Malaysian and Comparative Law
0126-6330 Malaysia. Directory of Timber Trade
0126-6403 Asian Defence Journal
0126-6705 Malaysian Mathematical Society. Bulletin
0126-690X Foreign Affairs Malaysia
0126-7000 Ilmu Alam
0126-7191 Suara Buruh
0126-7558 Kuala Lumpur Stock Exchange. Companies Handbook
0126-7590 Southeast Asian Ministers of Education Organisation. Regional Centre for Education in Science and Mathematics. Library Accession List
0126-7612 R E C S A M News
0126-7663 Journal of Science and Mathematics Education in Southeast Asia
0126-771X Maskayu
0126-7809 Majallah Perpustakaan Malaysia
0126-8031 Concern†
0126-8104 Malaysia. National Population and Family Development Board. Buletin Keluarga
0126-8155 Southeast Asian-Ministers of Education Organisation. Regional Centre for Education in Science and Mathematics. Governing Board Meeting. Final Report
0126-818X Malaysia. Department of Mines. Statistics Relating to the Mining Industry of Malaysia
0126-8198 Forest Research Institute: Research Pamphlet
0126-8279 Rubber Research Institute of Malaysia. Annual Report
0126-8309 Malaysian Rubber Producers' Council. Annual Report
0126-8392 National Productivity Centre, Malaysia. Annual Report *changed to* National Productivity Corporation, Malaysia. Annual Report.
0126-8635 Malaysian Journal of Pathology
0126-8856 Malaysia. Ministry of Agriculture. Fisheries Division. Annual Fisheries Statistics
0126-8864 Malaysia. Meteorological Service. Summary of Observations for Malaysia *changed to* Malaysia. Meteorological Service. Annual Summary of Meteorological Observations.
0126-8872 Monthly Abstract of Meteorological Observations of Malaysia
0126-8937 Usahaluan
0126-9003 Menemui Matematik
0126-9046 District Memoir
0126-9062 Indeks Suratkhabar Malaysia
0126-9267 Malaysia. Department of Statistics. Vital Statistics Sarawak
0126-9410 Rubber Research Institute of Malaysia. Technology Bulletin
0126-9437 Kajian Veterinar Malaysia†
0126-9518 Jurnal Antropologi dan Sosiologi
0127-0001 Business Conditions Malaysia
0127-0451 Malaysia. Department of Statistics. Statistics of External Trade Sarawak
0127-0559 Malaysia. Geological Survey. Annual Report
0127-1075 Jurnal Perubatan U K M
0127-144X Sarawak Electricity Supply Corporation. Annual Report
0127-1474 Malaysian Journal of Tropical Geography
0127-1555 Current Malaysian Serials (Non-Government)
0127-1962 Jurnal Ekonomi Malaysia
0127-2012 Infofish International
0127-2624 Malaysia. Department of Statistics. Yearbook of Statistics
0127-2713 Jurnal Pengurusan
0127-2721 Sari
0127-3337 Asian and Pacific Development Centre Newsletter
0127-4007 M A R D I Report
0127-466X Malaysia. Department of Statistics. Vital Statistics, Peninsular Malaysia
0127-4732 Malaysia. Department of Statistics. Annual Statistical Bulletin Sarawak
0127-4880 Index to Malaysian Conferences
0127-4937 Surveyor
0127-6409 Suara Sam
0127-6441 Malaysian Technologist
0127-6948 Warta Nuklear Malaysia
0127-7065 Journal of Natural Rubber Research
0127-7162 Environmental News Digest
0127-7170 Asian-Pacific Environment
0127-8029 Jurnal Psikologi Malaysia
0127-8533 Malaysia External Trade Statistics
0127-9068 Pofam
0127-9785 Rubber Research Institute of Malaysia. Rubber Growers' Conference - Proceedings
0128-0333 Jurnal Fizik Malaysia
0128-0686 M A R D I Research Journal
0128-1186 Malay Literature
0128-1232 Malaysian Journal of Family Studies
0128-1283 Journal of Tropical Forest Science
0128-3022 Malaysian Tatler
0128-4134 Third World Economics
0129-0533 International Journal of High Speed Computing
0129-0541 International Journal of Foundations of Computer Science
0129-055X Reviews in Mathematical Physics
0129-0568 Concepts in Neuroscience
0129-0657 International Journal of Neural Systems
0129-0789 I T Singapore
0129-0835 International Journal of P I X E
0129-0967 Coin Digest†
0129-1262 South East Asian Printer Magazine
0129-1564 International Journal of High Speed Electronics
0129-167X International Journal of Mathematics
0129-1831 International Journal of Modern Physics C: Physics and Computers
0129-2056 Asian Mass Communications Bulletin
0129-279X Singapore. National Statistical Commission. Statistical News†
0129-2900 A S E A N Business Quarterly
0129-2935 Catering and Hotel News *changed to* Catering and Hotel News International.
0129-2951 Singapore Business
0129-3109 Singapore Government Directory
0129-3117 Singapore Literature
0129-315X Singapore National Bibliography
0129-3184 Planews
0129-3214 Shaonian Yuekan†
0129-3273 Singapore Journal of Obstetrics & Gynaecology
0129-3281 Journal of Numerical Linear Algebra with Applications
0129-3389 Characters - Singapore and Malaysia Editions
0129-3621 Singapore Banking & Finance
0129-4172 Asian Journal of Pharmaceutical Sciences
0129-4202 Business Opportunities
0129-4776 Singapore Journal of Education
0129-4822 Lion City *changed to* This Week Singapore.
0129-5020 Singapore Travel
0129-508X Students' Literature†
0129-511X Southeast Asia Microfilms Newsletter
0129-5276 Investors' Guide to the Economic Climate of Singapore
0129-5411 Asia-Pacific Engineering Journal
0129-5519 Asia Pacific Metalworking Equipment News
0129-5721 S E A I S I Quarterly Journal
0129-5780 Singapore Chinese Chamber of Commerce and Industry. Economic Quarterly
0129-5896 Asia Computer Weekly
0129-606X Silver Kris
0129-6256 Singapore Standards Catalogue
0129-6264 Parallel Processing Letters
0129-6310 Singapore. Ministry of Labour. Annual Report
0129-6477 Singapore. Department of Statistics. Shipping and Cargo Statistics *changed to* Singapore Shipping & Cargo Statistics.
0129-6485 Singapore Journal of Primary Industries
0129-6531 Engineering Journal of Singapore
0129-6612 Media Asia
0129-6639 Young Generation
0129-6736 Harapan†
0129-6760 Singapore. Department of Statistics. Report on the Census of Wholesale, Retail Trades, Restaurants and Hotels *changed to* Singapore. Department of Statistics. Report on the Survey of Wholesale Trade, Retail Trade, Restaurants & Hotels (Year).
0129-6787 New Worker†
0129-6884 Singapore Arts†
0129-7414 Singapore Monthly Trade Statistics: Imports & Exports
0129-7457 Singapore Community Health Bulletin†
0129-7619 Singapore Journal of Tropical Geography
0129-766X Singapore
0129-7716 R E L C Annual Report
0129-7767 R E L C Guidelines
0129-797X Contemporary Southeast Asia
0129-8194 Decor Guide *changed to* Home & Decor.
0129-8372 Mimar
0129-8828 Institute of Southeast Asian Studies. Research Notes and Discussion Series
0129-8844 R E L C Occasional Papers
0129-8895 S E A M E O Regional Language Centre. Anthology Series
0129-9239 N B D C S News
0129-9786 Singapore. Department of Statistics. Report on the Survey of Services (Year)
0129-9867 Singapore Manufacturers' Association Directory *see* 0217-7447
0129-9913 Aircraft Engineer *changed to* Asia - Pacific Aviation and Engineering.
0129-9972 Asian Aviation
0130-0083 Moskovskii Universitet. Vestnik. Seriya 9: Istoriya
0130-0105 Moskovskii Universitet. Vestnik. Seriya 7: Ekonomika
0130-0172 Lietuviu Kalbotyros Klausimai
0130-1128 Geokhimiya i Rudoobrazovanie
0130-1152 Gidravlicheskie Mashiny
0130-1519 Zashchitnye Pokrytiya na Metallakh
0130-1608 Prapor *changed to* Berezil.
0130-1802 Izobretatel' i Ratsionalizator
0130-2469 Komsomol'skaya Zhizn'
0130-2663 Kriobiologiya i Kriomeditsina†
0130-2701 Kryl'ya Rodiny
0130-2906 Meteorologiya i Gidrologiya
0130-3104 Detskaya Literatura

ISSN INDEX 5597

0130-3252 Contributions to the History of Natural Sciences and Technology in the Baltic
0130-3414 Literatura v Shkole
0130-3686 Materialy Glyatsiologicheskikh Issledovanii
0130-5247 Ukrains'kyi Istorychnyi Zhurnal
0130-5395 Upravlyayushchie Sistemy i Mashiny
0130-5719 Filosofska Dumka *changed to* Filosofskaya i Sotsiologicheskaya Mysl'
0130-6634 Iskatel
0130-6774 Itogi Nauki i Tekhniki: Tekhnicheskaya Kibernetika
0130-6782 Itogi Nauki i Tekhniki: Tekhnologiya i Oborudovanie Mekhanosborochnogo Proizvodstva†
0130-6804 Itogi Nauki i Tekhniki: Elektrosvyaz'
0130-6936 Narodna Tvorchist' ta Etnografiya
0130-6995 Narody Azii i Afriki: Istoriya, Ekonomika, Kul'tura
0130-7517 Neman
0130-8068 Polymya
0130-8114 Leninyan Ugiov
0130-9218 Letopis' Pechati B.S.S.R.
0130-9404 Matematicheskie Metody v Ekonomike
0130-9420 Matematicheskie Metody i Fiziko-mekhanicheskie Polya
0130-9641 International Affairs
0131-0194 Radyans'ke Literaturoznavstvo
0131-0208 Ekspress-Informatsiya. Kvantovaya Radiotekhnika
0131-0224 Ekspress-Informatsiya. Kontrol'no-Izmeritel'naya Tekhnika
0131-0232 Ekspress-Informatsiya. Korroziya i Zashchita Metallov
0131-0275 Ekspress-Informatsiya. Nadezhnost' i Kontrol' Kachestva
0131-0321 Ekspress-Informatsiya. Podvodno-Tekhnicheskie, Vodolaznye i Sudopod'emnye Raboty. *changed to* Ekspress-Informatsiya. Podvodno-Tekhnicheskie, Vodolaznye i Sudopod'emnye Raboty. Gidrotekhnicheskie Sooruzheniya.
0131-0356 Ekspress-Informatsiya. Porshnevye i Gazoturbinnye Dvigateli
0131-0380 Ekspress-Informatsiya. Pribory i Elementy Avtomatiki i Vychislitel'noi Tekhniki
0131-0402 Ekspress-Informatsiya. Promyshlennyi Transport
0131-0437 Ekspress-Informatsiya. Radiotekhnika Sverkhvysokikh Chastot
0131-0445 Ekspress-Informatsiya. Rezhushchie Instrumenty†
0131-047X Ekspress-Informatsiya. Sinteticheskie Vysokopolimernye Materialy
0131-0488 Ekspress-Informatsiya. Sistemy Avtomaticheskogo Upravleniya
0131-0526 Ekspress-Informatsiya. Tara i Upakovka. Konteinery
0131-0577 Ekspress-Informatsiya. Tekhnicheskaya Kibernetika
0131-0593 Ekspress-Informatsiya. Tekhnologiya i Oborudovanie Liteinogo Proizvodstva†
0131-0607 Ekspress-Informatsiya. Tekhnologiya i Oborudovanie Mekhanosborochnogo Proizvodstva†
0131-0615 Ekspress-Informatsiya. Tekhnologiya i Oborudovanie Kuznechno-Shtampovochnogo Proizvodstva†
0131-0747 Ekspress-Informatsiya. Elektronika
0131-1417 Yunyi Tekhnik
0131-1441 Keel ja Kirjandus
0131-1611 Problemy Spetsial'noi Elektrometallurgii†
0131-1719 Litologiya i Paleogeografiya
0131-176X Fizika Molekul *see* 0206-3638
0131-2243 Modelist - Konstruktor
0131-2251 Molodaya Gvardiya
0131-2332 Moskva
0131-2413 Mukomolno-elevatornaya i Kombikormovaya Promyshlennost' *see* 0235-2508
0131-2596 Okhota i Okhotnich'e Khozyaistvo
0131-2669 Pomniki Histor'ii Kul'tury Belarusi
0131-2928 Problemy Mashinostroeniya
0131-3010 Problemy Poles'ya
0131-3525 Referativnyi Zhurnal. Svarka
0131-3533 Referativnyi Zhurnal. Korroziya i Zashchita ot Korrozii
0131-3541 Referativnyi Zhurnal. Biofizika†
0131-355X Referativnyi Zhurnal. Radiatsionnaya Biologiya
0131-3568 Sadovodstvo *changed to* Sadovodstvo i Vinogradarstvo.
0131-3843 Akademiya Nauk Litovskoi S.S.R. Trudy. Seriya A. Obshchestvennye Nauki†
0131-3851 Akademiya Nauk Litovskoi S.S.R. Trudy. Seriya C. Biologicheskie Nauki†
0131-5560 Promyshlennyi Transport *see* 0235-5116
0131-5587 Prostor
0131-5862 Eesti Loodus
0131-5994 Rovesnik
0131-6133 Russkii Yazyk v Natsional'noi Shkole *changed to* Russkii Yazyk v S.S.S.R.
0131-6141 Russkii Yazyk v Shkole
0131-6265 Sovetskaya Bibliografiya
0131-6311 Khozyain (Minsk)
0131-6397 Sel'skokhozyaistvennaya Biologiya
0131-6451 Signal'naya Informatsiya. Avtomatika i Telemekhanika†
0131-646X Signal'naya Informatsiya. Vychislitel'naya Tekhnika†
0131-6478 Signal'naya Informatsiya. Poluprovodnikovye Pribory†
0131-6508 Signal'naya Informatsiya. Teoreticheskaya Radiotekhnika - Radiosvyaz' - Radioizmereniya†
0131-6516 Signal'naya Informatsiya. Tekhnicheskaya Kibernatika†
0131-6532 Signal'naya Informatsiya. Virusologiya†
0131-6540 Signal'naya Informatsiya. Neirofiziologiya - Vysshaya Nervnaya Deyatel'nost' - Obshchaya i Eksperimental'naya Psikhologiya - Nervnomyshechnaya Sistema†
0131-6559 Signal'naya Informatsiya. Fiziologiya Cheloveka i Zhivotnykh: Krov' i Limfa *see* 0233-6618
0131-6567 Signal'naya Informatsiya. Fiziologiya Endokrinnoi Sistemy: Razmnozhenie - Laktatsiya†
0131-6656 Smena
0131-6672 Rybovodstvo i Rybolovstvo
0131-7105 Tekhnika v Sel'skom Khozyaistve
0131-7377 Sem'ya i Shkola
0131-7393 Sel'skii Mekhanizator
0131-7741 Ekonomika Sovetskoi Ukrainy
0131-775X Ekonomika Radyanskoi Ukrainy
0131-7962 Ekspress-Informatsiya. Gorodskoi Transport
0131-7970 Ekspress-Informatsiya. Detali Mashin
0131-7997 Ekspress-Informatsiya. Ispytatel'nye Pribory i Stendy
0131-8136 Raduga
0131-8748 Sputnik
0132-0696 Prepodavanie Istorii v Shkole
0132-0793 Model's Season
0132-1226 Sovetskii Krasnyi Krest
0132-1331 Radyans'ke Pravo
0132-1390 Sovremennaya Khudozhestvennaya Literatura za Rubezhom *changed to* Diapason.
0132-165X Ekspress-Informatsiya. Avtomaticheskie Linii i Metallorezhushchie Stanki†
0132-1668 Ekspress-Informatsiya. Astronavtika i Raketodinamika
0132-1943 Murzilka
0132-1986 Literaturnaya Osetiya. Literaturno-Khudozhestvennyi i Obshchestvenno-Politicheskii Zhurnal
0132-2729 Akademiya Nauk Litovskoi S.S.R. Trudy. Seriya B. Khimiya, Tekhnika, Fizicheskaya Geografiya†
0132-2818 Litovskii Matematicheskii Sbornik
0132-3458 Akademiya Nauk S.S.S.R. Obshchestvennye Nauki *changed to* Obshchestvennye Nauki i Sovremennost'
0132-4160 Avtomatika i Vychislitel'naya Tekhnika (Riga)
0132-5639 Referativnyi Zhurnal. Organizatsiya Upravleniya
0132-6058 Sak'art'velos S.S.R. Mec'nierebat'a Akademiis Mac'ne. Istoriis Ark'eologiis, Et'nograp'iisa da Xelovnebis Istoriis Seria
0132-6074 Akademiya Nauk Gruzinskoi S.S.R. Izvestiya. Seriya Khimicheskaya
0132-6414 Fizika Nizkikh Temperatur
0132-6422 Akademiya Nauk Latviiskoi S.S.R. Izvestiya
0132-6457 Darzs un Drava
0132-6503 Baltistica
0132-6562 Jaunimo Gretos
0132-6732 Signal'naya Informatsiya. Plazma†
0132-7348 Obshchestvennye Nauki za Rubezhom. Vostokovedenie i Afrikanistika
0132-7356 Obshchestvennye Nauki za Rubezhom. Filosofiya i Sotsiologiya *changed to* Obshchestvennye Nauki za Rubezhom. Filosofiya.
0132-7356 Obshchestvennye Nauki za Rubezhom. Filosofiya i Sotsiologiya *see* 0868-4448
0132-7372 Obshchestvennye Nauki za Rubezhom. Ekonomika
0132-8816 Molodezhnaya Estrada
0132-9030 Signal'naya Informatsiya. Zoologiya Nazemnykh Pozvonochnykh†
0133-0047 Egyhazi Kronika
0133-011X Baromfitenyesztes es Feldolgozas
0133-0152 Magyar Kozgazdasagi Irodalom
0133-0276 Hungarian Journal of Industrial Chemistry
0133-0314 Varosi Kozlekedes
0133-0365 Hungarian Economy
0133-0373 Muszaki Lapszemle. Elektrotechnika - Technical Abstracts. Electrical Engineering *see* 0231-0783
0133-0381 Tarsadalomtudomanyi Kozlemenyek
0133-0438 Kulfoldi Magyar Nyelvu Folyoiratok Repertoriuma *see* 0133-333X
0133-056X Forras
0133-0616 Kulpolitika
0133-0748 Soproni Szemle
0133-0829 Novenyvedelem
0133-090X Uj Magyar Hirek
0133-0918 Gabonaipar
0133-0950 Szabad Fold
0133-1167 Tiszataj
0133-1353 Uj Elet
0133-1531 Ars Hungarica
0133-1620 Automatizalas
0133-1655 Tajekoztato a Kulfoldi Kozgazdasagi Irodalomrol. Series B, Bibliografia *see* 0237-0859
0133-168X Filateliai Szemle
0133-1736 Reaction Kinetics and Catalysis Letters
0133-1779 Teologia
0133-1922 Halaszat
0133-1949 Magyar Konyvtarosok Egyesuletenek Evkonyve†
0133-2074 Szociologiai Informacio
0133-2368 Literatura
0133-2449 Budapesti Statisztikai Tajekoztato
0133-2465 Szabolcs - Szatmari Szemle
0133-2546 Korrozios Figyelo
0133-2929 Publications of the Technical University for Heavy Industry. Series D: Natural Sciences
0133-297X Publications of the Technical University for Heavy Industry. Series C, Mechanical Engineering
0133-3046 Studia Comitatensia
0133-3321 Hungarian Building Marketing
0133-333X Kulfoldi Magyar Nyelvu Kiadvanyok†
0133-3356 Alkohologia
0133-3399 Alkalmazott Matematikai Lapok
0133-3410 Kertgazdasag
0133-3461 Szociologia
0133-3496 Magyar Konyveszet (Budapest, 1961)
0133-3720 Cereal Research Communications
0133-3755 Kincskereso
0133-381X Szoleszet es Boraszat *see* 0023-0677
0133-3844 Biologia
0133-3852 Analysis Mathematica
0133-4239 Studia Uralo-Altaica
0133-4387 Vizminosegi es Viztechnologiai Kutatasi Eredmenyek†
0133-4611 Magyar Konyveszet. Tankonyvek†
0133-4751 Eletunk
0133-4875 Mezogazdasagi es Elelmiszeripari Konyvtarosok Tajekoztatoja
0133-5162 Marx Karoly Kozgazdasagtudomanyi Egyetem Oktatoinak Szakirodalmi Munkassaga *changed to* Budapesti Kozgazdasagtudomanyi Egyetem Oktatoinak Szakirodalmi Munkassaga.
0133-543X Hungary. Kozponti Statisztikai Hivatal. Foglalkoztatottsag es Kereseti Aranyok
0133-5464 Magyar Belorvosi Archivum
0133-5499 Zalai Gyujtemeny
0133-5502 Hungarian Academy of Sciences. Central Research Institute for Physics. Yearbook
0133-5545 Bulletin du Musee Hongrois des Beaux-Arts
0133-5707 Muszaki es Gazdasagi Fejlodes Fo Iranyai†
0133-5782 Magyar Nemzeti Bibliografia. Zenemuvek Bibliografiaja
0133-5847 Magyar Statisztikai Zsebkonyv
0133-6193 Keleti Tanulmanyok
0133-6436 Epitesugyi Ertesito
0133-6452 Ipargazdasagi Szemle
0133-6622 Folia Historica
0133-6673 Ars Decorativa
0133-6843 Magyar Nemzeti Bibliografia. Konyvek Bibliografiaja
0133-6894 Magyar Nemzeti Bibliografia. Idoszaki Kiadvanyok Repertoriuma
0133-6924 Ungarische Akademie der Wissenschaften. Archaelogisches Institut. Mitteilungen *see* 0238-0218
0133-7319 Vengerskaja Literatura po Bibliotekovedeniju i Informatike†
0133-7351 Vas Megyei Konyvtarak Ertesitoje
0133-736X Magyar Konyvtari Szakirodalom Bibliografiaja
0133-7505 Hungarika Irodalmi Szemle†
0133-7564 Hevesi Szemle
0133-7599 Theologiai Szemle
0133-7769 Trends in World Economy
0133-7890 Szovosz Tajekoztato
0133-8358 Tolnai Konyvtaros
0133-8684 Hungary. Kozponti Statisztikai Hivatal. Ipari Zsebkonyv
0133-8862 Magyar Tudomanyos Akademia Konyvtaranak Kiadvanyai *changed to* Magyar Tudomanyos Akademia Konyvtaranak Kozlemenyei.
0133-9060 Debreceni Orvostudomanyi Egyetem Evkonyve†
0133-9133 Hungary. Kozponti Statisztikai Hivatal. Kozlekedesi es Hirkozlesi Evkonyv *see* 0237-8280
0133-9214 Ludas Matyi Evkonyve
0133-9559 Szamitastechnikai Evkonyv *changed to* Hungary. Kozponti Statisztikai Hivatal. Szamitastechnikai Statisztikai Zsebkonyv.
0133-9680 Made in Hungary Special
0133-9966 Gyorsindex - Szamitastechnika, Automatizalas†
0134-0050 Historisch-Demographische Mitteilungen
0134-0247 Kurrens Idoszaki Kiadvanyok *see* 0231-4592
0134-0719 Journal of Radioanalytical Chemistry *changed to* Journal of Radioanalytical and Nuclear Chemistry. Articles.
0134-0719 Journal of Radioanalytical Chemistry *changed to* Journal of Radioanalytical and Nuclear Chemistry. Letters.
0134-1103 Nemzetkozi Szemle†

ISSN

ISSN INDEX

ISSN	Title
0134-1138	Hungary. Kozponti Statisztikai Hivatal. Belkereskedelmi Evkonyv see 0866-1146
0134-1464	Magyar Irodalom es Irodalomtudomany Bibliografiaja
0134-1510	Informacio a Konyvtari es Informacios Munka Eszkozeirol es Berendezeseirol† Taheke
0134-2266	Taheke
0134-2304	Noorus
0134-2673	Itogi Nauki i Tekhniki: Fiziologiya Cheloveka i Zhivotnykh
0134-272X	Novaya Sovetskaya Literatura po Obshchestvennym Naukam. Ekonomika
0134-2738	Novaya Sovetskaya Literatura po Obshchestvennym Naukam. Gosudarstvo i Pravo
0134-2746	Novaya Sovetskaya Literatura po Obshchestvennym Naukam. Istoriya - Arkheologiya - Etnografiya
0134-2754	Novaya Sovetskaya Literatura po Obshchestvennym Naukam. Naukovedenie
0134-2762	Novaya Sovetskaya Literatura po Obshchestvennym Naukam. Yazykoznanie
0134-2770	Novaya Sovetskaya Literatura po Obshchestvennym Naukam. Literaturovedenie
0134-2789	Novaya Sovetskaya Literatura po Obshchestvennym Naukam. Filosofskie Nauki
0134-2797	Novaya Inostrannaya Literatura po Obshchestvennym Naukam. Literaturovedenie
0134-2800	Novaya Inostrannaya Literatura po Obshchestvennym Naukam. Naukovedenie
0134-2819	Novaya Inostrannaya Literatura po Obshchestvennym Naukam. Yazykoznanie
0134-2827	Novaya Inostrannaya Literatura po Obshchestvennym Naukam. Istoriya - Arkheologiya - Etnografiya
0134-2835	Novaya Inostrannaya Literatura po Obshchestvennym Naukam. Ekonomika
0134-2843	Novaya Inostrannaya Literatura po Obshchestvennym Naukam. Gosudarstvo i Pravo
0134-2851	Novaya Inostrannaya Literatura po Obshchestvennym Naukam. Filosofiya i Sotsiologiya
0134-2916	Novaya Sovetskaya i Inostrannaya Literatura po Obshchestvennym Naukam. Blizhnii i Srednii Vostok - Afrika
0134-2924	Novaya Sovetskaya i Inostrannaya Literatura po Obshchestvennym Naukam. Pol'skaya Narodnaya Respublika changed to Novaya Sovetskaya i Inostrannaya Literatura po Obshchestvennym Naukam. Pol'sha.
0134-2932	Novaya Sovetskaya i Inostrannaya Literatura po Obshchestvennym Naukam. Problemy Ateizma i Religii
0134-2940	Novaya Sovetskaya i Inostrannaya Literatura po Obshchestvennym Naukam. Mezhdunarodnoe Rabochee Dvizhenie
0134-2959	Novaya Sovetskaya i Inostrannaya Literatura po Obshchestvennym Naukam. Yuzhnaya i Yugo-Vostochnaya Aziya - Dal'nii Vostok
0134-2967	Novaya Sovetskaya i Inostrannaya Literatura po Obshchestvennym Naukam. Chekhoslovatskaya Sotsialisticheskaya Respublika changed to Novaya Sovetskaya i Inostrannaya Literatura po Obshchestvennym Naukam. Chekhoslovakiya.
0134-2975	Novaya Sovetskaya i Inostrannaya Literatura po Obshchestvennym Naukam. Germanskaya Demokraticheskaya Respublika
0134-2983	Novaya Sovetskaya i Inostrannaya Literatura po Obshchestvennym Naukam. Evropeiskie Sotsialisticheskie Strany. Obshchie Problemy changed to Novaya Sovetskaya i Inostrannaya Literatura po Obshchestvennym Naukam. Strany Vostochnoi Evropy. Obshchie Problemy.
0134-2991	Novaya Sovetskaya i Inostrannaya Literatura po Obshchestvennym Naukam. Narodnaya Respublika Bolgariya changed to Novaya Sovetskaya i Inostrannaya Literatura po Obshchestvennym Naukam. Bolgariya.
0134-3009	Novaya Sovetskaya i Inostrannaya Literatura po Obshchestvennym Naukam. Sotsialisticheskaya Federativnaya Respublika Yugoslaviya changed to Novaya Sovetskaya i Inostrannaya Literatura po Obshchestvennym Naukam. Yugoslaviya.
0134-3017	Novaya Sovetskaya i Inostrannaya Literatura po Obshchestvennym Naukam. Vengerskaya Narodnaya Respublika changed to Novaya Sovetskaya i Inostrannaya Literatura po Obshchestvennym Naukam. Vengriya.
0134-3033	Novaya Sovetskaya i Inostrannaya Literatura po Obshchestvennym Naukam. Strany Azii i Afriki. Obshchie Problemy
0134-3041	Novaya Sovetskaya i Inostrannaya Literatura po Obshchestvennym Naukam. Problemy Slavyanovedeniya i Balkanistiki
0134-3270	Kehakultuur changed to Spordiilm.
0134-3475	Biologiya Morya
0134-3815	Polutehniline Instituut Tallinn. Gibkie Avtomatizirovannye Proizvodstvennye Sistemy i ikh Elemenly dlya Liteinogo Proizvodstva see 0868-426X
0134-3823	Polutehniline Instituut Tallinn. Raschet i Proektirovanie Priborov, Ustroistv i Sistem Tekhnicheskoi Kibernetiki changed to Tallinna Tehnikaulikool. Modelirovanie i Upravlenie v Sistemakh Tekhnicheskoi Kibernetiki.
0134-4536	Looming
0134-5605	Kultuur ja Elu
0134-580X	Referativnyi Zhurnal. Farmakologiya. Obshchaya Farmakologiya Nervnoi Sistemy
0134-7683	Ekspress-Informatsiya. Put' i Stroitel'stvo Zheleznykh Dorog. Problemy B.A.M.†
0134-7772	Referativnyi Zhurnal. Elektrosvyaz'†
0134-7799	Itogi Nauki i Tekhniki: Organizatsiya Upravleniya Transportom
0134-9236	Morskoi Sbornik
0135-0536	Patma-Banasirakan Handes
0135-0609	Voprosy Informatsionnoi Teorii i Praktiki†
0135-0617	Vsesoyuznyi Institut Nauchno-Tekhnicheskoi Informatsii. Deponirovannye Nauchnye Raboty
0135-0633	Signal'naya Informatsiya. Radiofizika i Fizicheskie Osnovy Elektroniki
0135-0870	Signal'naya Informatsiya. Atomy i Molekuly
0135-0889	Signal'naya Informatsiya. Gazy i Zhidkosti. Termodinamika i Statisticheskaya Fizika
0135-0897	Signal'naya Informatsiya. Optika
0135-0919	Signal'naya Informatsiya. Tekhnicheskii Analiz v Metallurgii†
0135-0927	Signal'naya Informatsiya. Teoriya Metallurgicheskikh Protsessov†
0135-0935	Signal'naya Informatsiya. Kompozitsionnye Materialy
0135-0986	Signal'naya Informatsiya. Metallurgiya Poluprovodnikov†
0135-1281	Analogo-Diskretnye Preobrazovaniya Signalov
0135-1419	Atmosferos Fizika
0135-2164	Geologiya i Geokhimiya Goryuchikh Iskopaemykh
0135-2202	Istorychni Doslidzhennya. Istoriya Zarubizhnykh Krayin
0135-2210	Istorychni Doslidzhennya. Vitchyznyana Istoriya
0135-2253	Problemy Kontrolya i Zashchita Atmosfery ot Zagryazneniya
0135-3071	Otbor i Obrabotka Informatsii
0135-8375	Signal'naya Informatsiya. Struktura i Svoistva Chuguna, Stali, Splavov i Kompozitsionnykh Materialov na Osnove Zheleza†
0135-8383	Signal'naya Informatsiya. Poroshkovaya Metallurgiya†
0135-8405	Signal'naya Informatsiya. Fizicheskie Svoistva. Prochnost' i Plastichnost' Metallov i Splavov†
0135-8537	Semiotika i Informatika†
0135-857X	Signal'naya Informatsiya. Svarka†
0136-0612	Signal'naya Informatsiya. Magnitnye Svoistva Tverdykh Tel
0136-1732	Adgeziya Rasplavov i Paika Materialov
0136-3549	Polutehniline Instituut Tallinn. Avtomatizatsiya Tekhnologicheskogo Proektirovaniya Protsessov Mekhanicheskoi Obrabotki see 0868-4375
0136-3557	Polutehniline Instituut Tallinn. Svoistva i Tekhnologiya Izgotovleniya Iznosostoikikh Materialov†
0136-3581	Polutehniline Instituut Tallinn. Fizicheskaya Khimiya Soedinenii A2B6 i A4B6 see 0868-4308
0136-4863	Voeikov Main Geophysical Observatory, Leningrad. Results of Ground Observations of Atmospheric Electricity. The World Network
0136-9377	Biokhimiya Zhivotnykh i Cheloveka
0137-0251	Itogi Nauki i Tekhniki: Organicheskaya Khimiya
0137-1088	Uniwersytet Wroclawski. Instytut Geograficzny. Prace. Seria B: Geografia Spoleczna i Ekonomiczna
0137-1096	Acta Universitatis Wratislaviensis. Prace Pedagogiczne
0137-1126	Studies on Fascism and Hitlerite Crimes
0137-1142	Results of Investigations of the Polish Scientific Spitsbergen Expeditions
0137-1215	Politechnika Wroclawska. Prace Naukowczne i Prognostyczne
0137-1223	Systems Science
0137-1339	Materials Science
0137-1363	Politechnika Krakowska. Zeszyty Naukowe. Budownictwo Wodne i Inzynieria Sanitarna changed to Politechnika Krakowska. Zeszyty Naukowe. Inzynieria Sanitarna i Wodna.
0137-1371	Politechnika Krakowska. Zeszyty Naukowe. Architektura
0137-138X	Politechnika Krakowska. Zeszyty Naukowe. Podstawowe Nauki Techniczne
0137-1398	Politechnika Wroclawska. Instytut Technologii Organicznej i Tworzyw Sztucznych. Prace Naukowe. Konferencje
0137-141X	Nauki Polityczne
0137-1428	Nauki Ekonomiczne
0137-1444	Jezykoznawstwo Stosowane
0137-1460	Antropologia
0137-1479	Fruit Science Reports
0137-1495	Acta Alimentaria Polonica
0137-1592	Acta Ichthyologica et Piscatoria
0137-1657	Instytut Zootechniki. Roczniki Naukowe Zootechniki
0137-169X	Akademia Rolnicza, Poznan. Roczniki. Algorytmy Biometryczne i Statystyczne
0137-1703	Akademia Rolnicza, Poznan. Roczniki. Archeozoologia
0137-1711	Akademia Rolnicza, Poznan. Roczniki. Ekonomika i Organizacja Rolnictwa
0137-172X	Akademia Rolnicza, Poznan. Roczniki. Lesnictwo
0137-1738	Akademia Rolnicza, Poznan. Roczniki. Ogrodnictwo
0137-1746	Akademia Rolnicza, Poznan. Roczniki. Ornitologia Stosowana
0137-1754	Akademia Rolnicza, Poznan. Roczniki. Rolnictwo
0137-1762	Akademia Rolnicza, Poznan. Roczniki. Technologia Rolno-Spozywcza changed to Akademia Rolnicza, Poznan. Roczniki. Technologia Zywnosci.
0137-1770	Akademia Rolnicza, Poznan. Roczniki. Zootechnika
0137-1797	Akademia Rolnicza, Poznan. Roczniki. Technologia Drewna changed to Akademia Rolnicza, Poznan. Roczniki. Chemiczna Technologia Drewna.
0137-1800	Akademia Rolnicza, Poznan. Roczniki. Mechaniczna Technologia Drewna
0137-1819	Annales Universitatis Mariae Curie-Sklodowska. Section AA. Physica et Chemica see 0137-6861
0137-1924	Akademia Rolnicza w Szczecinie. Zeszyty Naukowe. Rolnictwo
0137-1940	Akademia Rolnicza w Szczecinie. Zeszyty Naukowe. Zootechnika
0137-1983	Annales Universitatis Mariae Curie-Sklodowska. Sectio B. Geographia, Geologia, Mineralogia et Petrographia
0137-2025	Annales Universitatis Mariae Curie-Sklodowska. Sectio I. Philosophia-Sociologia
0137-2033	Annales Universitatis Mariae Curie-Sklodowska. Sectio F. Humaniora see 0239-4251
0137-2149	Akademia Rolnicza w Szczecinie. Informatory
0137-219X	Eksploatacja Kolei†
0137-2351	Uniwersytet Jagiellonski. Zeszyty Naukowe. Prace z Biologii Molekularnej
0137-2378	Uniwersytet Jagiellonski. Zeszyty Naukowe. Prace z Nauk Politycznych
0137-2440	Polish Academy of Sciences. Institute of Geophysics. Publications. Series A: Physics of the Earth's Interior
0137-2459	Papers and Studies in Contrastive Linguistics
0137-2467	Studia Germanica Posnaniensia
0137-2564	Politechnika Lodzka. Zeszyty Naukowe. Fizyka
0137-2572	Politechnika Lodzka. Zeszyty Naukowe. Matematyka
0137-2599	Politechnika Lodzka. Zeszyty Naukowe. Organizacja i Zarzadzanie
0137-2602	Politechnika Lodzka. Zeszyty Naukowe. Inzynieria Chemiczna
0137-2645	Przemysl Fermentacyjny i Owocowo Warzywny
0137-2661	Politechnika Lodzka. Zeszyty Naukowe. Cieplne Maszyny Przeplywowe
0137-2696	Biuletyn Informacyjny o Budownictwie see 0867-4485
0137-284X	Drogi Kolejowe†
0137-2858	Automatyka Kolejowa†
0137-2904	Reports on Mathematical Logic
0137-2939	Polska Akademia Nauk. Oddzial w Krakowie. Osrodek Dokumentacji Fizjograficznej. Studia
0137-2955	Panorama Polska (Nasza Ojczyzna)
0137-2963	Trakcja i Wagony†
0137-2998	Kwartalnik Historii Prasy Polskiej
0137-3013	Humanizacja Pracy
0137-303X	Przeglad Polonijny
0137-3056	Uniwersytet Warszawski. Wydzial Nauk Ekonomicznych. Ekonomia
0137-3080	Estudios Latinoamericanos
0137-3102	Kronika Wielkopolski
0137-3218	Nasza Przeszlosc
0137-3234	Pamietnikarstwo Polskie
0137-3250	Poznanskie Towarzystwo Przyjaciol Nauk. Komisja Archeologiczna. Prace
0137-3277	Uniwersytet Slaski w Katowicach. Prace Naukowe. Historia i Wspolczesnosc
0137-3390	Studia Historyczne (Bydgoszcz)†

ISSN INDEX

ISSN	Title
0137-3404	Studia o Ksiazce
0137-3471	Wolnosc i Lud
0137-3501	Rocznik Kaliski
0137-3536	American Studies
0137-3544	Polska Akademia Nauk. Instytut Krajow Socjalistycznych. Biuletyn Informacyjny
0137-3587	Studia Maritima
0137-3595	Postepy Cybernetyki
0137-3609	Prezentacje
0137-3935	Pagine
0137-3943	Paideia
0137-4079	Ethnologia Polona
0137-4354	Studia Kieleckie
0137-4370	Studia Polonistyczne
0137-4389	Studia Polono-Slavica Orientalia. Acta Litteraria
0137-4435	Transport Museums
0137-4761	Przeglad Lubuski
0137-477X	Quaestiones Geographicae
0137-4885	Polish Archaeological Abstracts
0137-4990	Ergonomia
0137-5059	Biblioteka Fizyki
0137-5075	Archives of Acoustics
0137-5083	Polish Journal of Chemistry
0137-5156	Radomskie Towarzystwo Naukowe. Biuletyn Kwartalny
0137-5164	Zeszyty Gorzowskie†
0137-5172	Z Badan nad Polskimi Ksiegozbiorami Historycznymi
0137-5253	Instytut Baltycki Gdansk. Komunikaty
0137-530X	Studia i Materialy do Dziejow Zup Solnych w Polsce
0137-5326	Szkice Legnickie
0137-5377	Stutthof Muzeum. Zeszyty
0137-5393	Studia z Zakresu Inzynierii
0137-5415	Przestepczosc na Swiecie
0137-544X	Przeglad Glottodydaktyczny
0137-5482	Uniwersytet Slaski w Katowicach. Prace Naukowe. Kras i Speleologia
0137-5695	Muzeum Narodowe w Krakowie. Rozprawy i Sprawozdania†
0137-5733	Studia do Dziejow Dawnego Uzbrojenia i Ubioru Wojskowego
0137-5806	Oeconomica Polona†
0137-5822	Uniwersytet Warszawski. Instytut Nauk Politycznych. Zeszyty Naukowe
0137-5830	Acta Universitatis Nicolai Copernici. Historia
0137-5873	Wyzsza Szkola Pedagogiczna im. Komisji Edukacji Narodowej w Krakowie. Rocznik Naukowo-Dydaktyczny. Prace Historyczne
0137-5881	Acta Physiologiae Plantarum
0137-589X	Instytut Metali Niezelaznych. Prace†
0137-5911	Czasopismo Techniczne. Series B: Budownictwo
0137-592X	Czasopismo Techniczne. Series M: Mechanika
0137-6217	Politechnika Wroclawska. Biblioteka Glowna i Osrodek Informacji Naukowo-Technicznej. Prace Naukowe. Konferencje†
0137-6225	Politechnika Wroclawska. Biblioteka Glowna i Osrodek Informacji Naukowo-Technicznej. Prace Naukowe. Studia i Materialy
0137-6233	Politechnika Wroclawska. Instytut Architektury i Urbanistyki. Prace Naukowe. Konferencje
0137-6241	Politechnika Wroclawska. Instytut Budownictwa. Prace Naukowe. Studia i Materialy
0137-625X	Politechnika Wroclawska. Instytut Fizyki. Prace Naukowe. Konferencje
0137-6268	Politechnika Wroclawska. Instytut Matematyki. Prace Naukowe. Konferencje
0137-6276	Politechnika Wroclawska. Instytut Podstaw Elektrotechniki i Elektrotechnologii. Prace Naukowe. Wspolpraca
0137-6284	Politechnika Wroclawska. Instytut Ukladow Elektromaszynowych. Prace Naukowe. Monografie
0137-6292	Politechnika Wroclawska. Instytut Ukladow Elektromaszynowych. Prace Naukowe. Przemysl†
0137-6306	Politechnika Wroclawska. Osrodek Badan Prognostycznych. Prace Naukowe. Konferencje†
0137-6314	Politechnika Wroclawska. Osrodek Badan Prognostycznych. Prace Naukowe. Monografie†
0137-6322	Politechnika Wroclawska. Osrodek Badan Prognostycznych. Prace Naukowe. Studia i Materialy†
0137-6330	Politechnika Wroclawska. Osrodek Badan Prognostycznych. Prace Naukowe. Wspolpraca.†
0137-6349	Politechnika Wroclawska. Studium Praktycznej Nauki Jezykow Obcych. Prace Naukowe. Studia i Materialy
0137-6365	Studia Geotechnica et Mechanica
0137-6381	Z Dziejow Stosunkow Polsko-Radzieckich i Rozwoju Wspolnoty Panstw Socjalistycznych†
0137-6462	Fluid Dynamics Transactions
0137-6535	Akademia Gorniczo-Hutnicza im. Stanislawa Staszica. Zeszyty Naukowe. Metalurgia i Odlewnictwo. Kwartalnik
0137-6586	Problemy Agrofizyki
0137-6608	Studia Semiotyczne
0137-6616	Acta Universitatis Nicolai Copernici. Archeologia
0137-6667	Acta Universitatis Nicolai Copernici. Nauki Polityczne
0137-6683	Badania Fizjograficzne nad Polska Zachodnia. Seria C. Zoologia
0137-6780	Poradnik Gospodarski
0137-6853	Annales Universitatis Mariae Curie-Sklodowska. Sectio AA. Chemia
0137-6861	Annales Universitatis Mariae Curie-Sklodowska. Sectio AAA. Physica
0137-6896	Politechnika Poznanska. Zeszyty Naukowe. Chemia Techniki Zastosowan changed to Politechnika Poznanska. Zeszyty Naukowe. Chemia i Inzynieria Chemiczna.
0137-690X	Politechnika Poznanska. Zeszyty Naukowe. Ekonomika i Organizacja Przemyslu see 0239-9415
0137-6918	Politechnika Poznanska. Zeszyty Naukowe. Maszyny Robocze i Pojazdy
0137-6934	Polish Academy of Sciences. Mathematical Institute. Banach Center Publications
0137-6969	Politechnika Czestochowska. Zeszyty Naukowe. Nauki Techniczne. Mechanika
0137-6977	Politechnika Czestochowska. Zeszyty Naukowe. Nauki Techniczne. Elektrotechnika
0137-7175	Nowy Medyk see 0867-3055
0137-7183	Problemy Szkolnictwa i Nauk Medycznych†
0137-7310	Zycie Szkoly
0137-7426	Szkola Glowna Gospodarstwa Wiejskiego w Warszawie. Zeszyty Naukowe. Technologia Rolno-Spozywcza changed to Warsaw Agricultural University. S G G W. Annals. Food Technology and Nutrition.
0137-7566	Geografia w Szkole
0137-7612	Hotelarz
0137-7647	Jezyk Rosyjski see 0446-7965
0137-8015	Poland. Urzad Patentowy. Biuletyn
0137-8031	Biologia w Szkole
0137-8082	Wychowanie w Przedszkolu
0137-8120	Wiadomosci Produkcyjne: Wlokno, Odziez, Skora
0137-8171	Szkola Zawodowa
0137-818X	Szkola Specjalna
0137-8198	Szachyt
0137-8465	Postepy Fizyki Medycznej
0137-8651	Problemy Jakosci
0137-8708	Przekazy i Opinie
0137-8783	Przeglad Techniczny, Innowacje
0137-8813	Horyzonty Techniki
0137-8848	Matematyka (Warsaw)
0137-8856	Kalejdoskop Technikit
0137-8996	Poznanskie Towarzystwo Przyjaciol Nauk. Komisja Matematyczno-Przyrodnicza. Prace
0137-9585	Rocznik Pedagogiczny
0137-9666	Humanitas
0137-9704	Studia Ubezpieczeniowe
0137-9712	Polonica
0137-9771	Poznanskie Towarzystwo Przyjaciol Nauk. Komisja Geograficzno-Geologiczna. Prace
0137-9860	Studies on the Developing Countries†
0137-9941	Instytut Metalurgii Zelaza. Prace
0138-0109	Polish Academy of Sciences. Institute of Geophysics. Publications. Series B: Seismology
0138-0117	Polish Academy of Sciences. Institute of Geophysics. Publications. Series C: Geomagnetism
0138-0125	Polish Academy of Sciences. Institute of Geophysics. Publications. Series D: Physics of the Atmosphere
0138-0141	Polish Academy of Sciences. Institute of Geophysics. Publications. Series F: Planetary Geodesy
0138-015X	Polish Academy of Sciences. Institute of Geophysics. Publications. Series M: Miscellanea
0138-032X	Archiwum Nauki o Materialach
0138-0389	Instytut Geologiczny. Biuletyn. Geology of Poland
0138-0508	Prace Popularnonaukowe. Biblioteczka Prawnicza
0138-0516	Prace Popularnonaukowe. Zabytki Polski Polnocnej
0138-0532	Science of Science
0138-063X	Uniwersytet Gdanski. Wydzial Humanistyczny. Zeszyty Naukowe. Studia Scandinavica
0138-0702	Bibliografia Pomorza Zachodniego - Pismiennictwo Zagraniczne
0138-0796	Instytut Techniki Budowlanej. Prace changed to Prace Instytutu Techniki Budowlanej. Kwartalnik
0138-0923	Akademia Gorniczo-Hutnicza im. Stanislawa Staszica. Zeszyty Naukowe. Sozologia i Sozotechnika
0138-094X	Biblioteka Polonijna
0138-0974	Akademia Gorniczo-Hutnicza im. Stanislawa Staszica. Zeszyty Naukowe. Geologia. Kwartalnik
0138-0990	Akademia Gorniczo-Hutnicza im. Stanislawa Staszica. Zeszyty Naukowe. Gornictwo. Kwartalnik
0138-1016	Ernst-Moritz-Arndt-Universitaet Greifswald. Wissenschaftliche Zeitschrift. Gesellschaftswissenschaftliche Reihe†
0138-1059	Akademie der Wissenschaften der D.D.R. Abhandlungen. Abteilung Mathematik, Naturwissenschaften, Technik
0138-1067	Ernst-Moritz-Arndt-Universitaet Greifswald. Wissenschaftliche Zeitschrift. Medizinische Reihe†
0138-1091	Hallesche Studien zur Geschichte der Sozialdemokratie
0138-1105	Meteorologischen Dienstes der D D R. Veroeffentlichungen
0138-113X	Beitraege zur Geschichte des Rundfunks†
0138-1245	Boxring†
0138-127X	Wissenschaftliche Taschenbuecher. Reihe Texte und Studien
0138-1296	Handball (Raugsdorf)
0138-1334	Bibliographie Voelkerrecht und Internationale Beziehungen changed to Bibliographie Politikwissenschaft und Voelkerrecht.
0138-1342	Pferd und Sport†
0138-1377	Paedagogische Hochschule Liselotte Herrmann Guestrow. Philosophische Fakultaet. Wissenschaftliche Zeitschrift
0138-1385	Rechtswissenschaftliche Dokumentation changed to Bibliographie Rechtswissenschaft.
0138-1393	Radsportler
0138-144X	Sportkeglert
0138-1482	Tanz
0138-1520	Paedagogische Hochschule Karl Friedrich Wilhelm Wander. Wissenschaftliche Zeitschrift changed to Paedagogische Hochschule Karl Friedrich Wilhelm Wander. Wissenschaftliche Zeitschrift. Paedogogische Reihe.
0138-1520	Paedagogische Hochschule Karl Friedrich Wilhelm Wander. Wissenschaftliche Zeitschrift changed to Paedagogische Hochschule Karl Friedrich Wilhelm Wander. Wissenschaftliche Zeitschrift. Gesellschaftswissenschaftliche Reihe.
0138-1520	Paedagogische Hochschule Karl Friedrich Wilhelm Wander. Wissenschaftliche Zeitschrift changed to Paedagogische Hochschule Karl Friedrich Wilhelm Wander. Wissenschaftliche Zeitschrift. Mathematisch-naturwissenschaftliche Reihe.
0138-1539	Zauberkunst
0138-1555	Arbeitsschutz, Arbeitshygiene†
0138-1563	Paedagogische Hochschule Liselotte Herrmann Guestrow. Wissenschaftliche Zeitschrift see 0138-1377
0138-1563	Paedagogische Hochschule Liselotte Herrmann Guestrow. Wissenschaftliche Zeitschrift see 0138-1768
0138-1601	Visier
0138-1644	Deutsche Demokratische Republik. Gesetzblatt
0138-1652	Friedrich-Schiller-Universitaet Jena. Wissenschaftliche Zeitschrift†
0138-1687	Super Knobel Knifflig
0138-1768	Paedagogische Hochschule Liselotte Herrmann Guestrow. Paedagogische Fakultaet. Wissenschaftliche Zeitschrift†
0138-1989	Informationen fuer die Museen in der DDR
0138-2004	Fundgrube
0138-2055	Informationsbulletin. Aktuelle Probleme der Philosophie der U.d.S.S.R.
0138-208X	Bibliographie "Nahrung und Ernaehrung der Menschen": Ernaehrung changed to Bibliographie Nutris, Series: Ernaehrungswissenschaft.
0138-2098	Hochschule fuer Bauwesen Cottbus. Wissenschaftliche Zeitschrift†
0138-2101	Betontechnik
0138-2136	Bibliographie "Nahrung und Ernaehrung der Menschen": Lebensmittelwissenschaft changed to Bibliographie Nutris, Series: Lebensmittelwissenschaft.
0138-2144	Thematische Information Philosophie†
0138-2225	Bibliographie Aktuell†
0138-2233	Zeitschriftenschau Keramik†
0138-2357	Geophysik und Geologie
0138-242X	Informationsbulletin aus dem Philosophischen Leben der D.D.R.
0138-2543	Katolski Posol
0138-2578	Referateblatt Philosophie. Reihe A: Dialektischer un Historischer Materialismus, Philosophie Probleme des Sozialismus see 0232-8798
0138-2586	Gemeinsamt
0138-2691	Gewerkschaftsleben
0138-2721	Referateblatt Philosophie. Reihe E. Aktuelle Probleme und Kritik der Buergerlichen Philosophie†
0138-2764	Wohnen im Gruenent
0138-2802	Nordeuropa Studien
0138-2810	Wohnen†
0138-2845	Leitung und Planung von Wissenschaft und Technik†
0138-2853	Ernst-Moritz-Arndt-Universitaet Greifswald. Wissenschaftliche Zeitschrift. Mathematisch-Naturwissenschaftliche Reihe†

5600 ISSN INDEX

0138-290X Paedagogische Hochschule "Karl Liebknecht" Potsdam. Wissenschaftliche Zeitschrift *see* 0939-3986
0138-3019 Mathematische Forschung. Schriftenreihe *changed to* Mathematische Forschung.
0138-3027 Literaturschau Polymere und Chemiefaserstoffe†
0138-3116 Quartaerpalaeontologie
0138-3167 Veroeffentlichungen zur Volkskunde und Kulturgeschichte
0138-3213 Werte Unserer Heimat
0138-3280 Industriemaessige Gemueseproduktion†
0138-3337 Industriemaessige Rinderproduktion†
0138-3361 Schriften zur Ur- und Fruehgeschichte
0138-3388 Industriemaessige Schweineproduktion†
0138-340X Referatedienst zur Literaturwissenschaft
0138-3418 Schriften zur Philosophie und ihrer Geschichte
0138-3469 Akademie der Wissenschaften der D.D.R. Zentralinstitut fuer Wirtschaftswissenschaften. Schriften
0138-3566 Akademie der Wissenschaften der D.D.R. Zentralinstitut fuer Geschichte. Schriften
0138-3604 Jenaer Beitraege zur Parteigeschichte†
0138-3612 Kritik der Buergerlichen Ideologie†
0138-3655 Referatedienst Jugendforschung†
0138-3663 Meroitica
0138-3914 Zentralinstituts fuer Alte Geschichte und Archaeologie. Veroeffentlichungen
0138-3957 Saechsische Akademie der Wissenschaften, Leipzig. Philologisch-Historische Klasse. Sitzungsberichte
0138-3973 Der Tourist†
0138-4074 Common Name - Kartei Pflanzenschutz- und Schaedlingsbekaempfungsmittel†
0138-4112 Akademie der Wissenschaften der D.D.R. Studien zur Geschichte
0138-4228 Berliner Turfantexte
0138-4279 Beitraege zur Ur- und Fruehgeschichte der Bezirke Rostock, Schwerin und Neubrandenburg
0138-435X Jahrbuch fuer Soziologie und Sozialpolitik
0138-4414 Schuetzen und Helfen
0138-4422 Beitraege zur Geographie
0138-4449 Vorderasiatische Schriftdenkmaler der Staatlichen Mussen zu Berlin
0138-4503 Jahrbuch fuer Volkskunde und Kulturgeschichte. Neue Folge
0138-4600 Forschungsbereichs Geo- und Kosmoswissenschaften. Veroeffentlichungen
0138-4821 Beitraege zur Algebra und Geometrie
0138-4856 Jahrbuch fuer Geschichte des Feudalismus
0138-4988 Acta Biotechnologica
0138-5003 Erkrankungen der Zootiere
0138-5011 Neue Zeit
0138-502X Teubner-Texte zur Mathematik
0138-5038 Bibliographie Soziologie†
0138-5100 Forschungen zur Wirtschaftsgeschichte
0138-5208 Staats- und Rechtstheoretische Studien
0138-5410 German Democratic Republic. Consumer Co-operative Societies. Magazine†
0138-547X Biene†
0138-550X Sammlung Akademie-Verlag: Sprache†
0138-5518 Der Lustige Grillenfaenger†
0138-5550 Studien ueber Asien, Afrika und Lateinamerika
0138-5569 Kunterbunt†
0138-5658 Germany (Democratic Republic, 1949-). Meteorologischer Dienst. Abhandlungen
0138-5666 Steckenpferd†
0138-5739 Information und Dokumentation: Annotierte Titelliste†
0138-5755 Wissenschaft und Gesellschaft
0138-5836 Referatblatt Soziologie†
0138-5852 Sprache und Gesellschaft
0138-595X Schriften zur Geschichte und Kultur der Antike
0138-600X Revista Cubana de Obstetricia y Ginecologia
0138-6093 Ciencia y Tecnica en la Agricultura. Serie: Cafe y Cacao
0138-6107 Revista de Informacion Cientifica y Tecnica Cubana
0138-614X Cuba. Ministerio de la Agricultura. Centro de Informacion y Documentacion Agropecuario. Extranjeras
0138-614X Cuba. Ministerio de la Agricultura. Centro de Informacion y Documentacion Agropecuario. Noticiero Agropecuario
0138-6190 Cuba. Ministerio de la Agricultura. Centro de Informacion y Documentacion Agropecuario. Noticiero Agropecuario. Suplemento Agrometeorologico
0138-6212 Teoria y Practica de Precios†
0138-631X Filatelia Cubana
0138-6328 Academia de Ciencias de Cuba. Instituto de Oceanologia. Reporte de Investigacion
0138-6352 Revista Cubana de Ciencia Avicola
0138-6409 Revista Avicultura
0138-6441 Revista Forestal Baracoa
0138-6492 Revista Plantas Medicinales
0138-6611 Deporte-Derecho del Pueblo
0138-6700 Revista Cubana de Reproduccion Animal
0138-6735 Informacion Express. Serie: Forestales
0138-6786 Informacion Express. Serie: Pastos y Forrajes
0138-6824 Acta Botanica Cubana
0138-6832 Informacion Express. Serie: Genetica y Reproduccion
0138-6921 Revista Referativa. Organizacion de la Direccion†
0138-6948 Revista de Literatura Cubana
0138-7014 Ciencia y Tecnica en la Agricultura. Serie: Canera
0138-7030 Informacion Express. Serie: Suelos y Agroquimica
0138-7049 Cuba. Ministerio de la Industria Ligera. Revista Ciencia y Tecnica
0138-7081 Informacion Express. Serie: Rumiantes
0138-7103 Hospital Psiquiatrico de la Habana. Revista
0138-7138 Informacion Express. Serie: Tabaco
0138-7154 Ciencias Biologicas
0138-7170 Problemas de Organizacion de la Ciencia
0138-7189 Informacion Express. Serie: Viandas, Hortalizas y Granos
0138-7235 Informacion Express. Serie: Veterinaria
0138-7251 Ciencias de la Agricultura
0138-7286 Informacion Express. Serie: Proteccion de Plantas
0138-7324 Academia de Ciencias de Cuba. Instituto de Documentacion e Informacion Cientifica y Tecnica. Actualidades de la Informacion Cientifica y Tecnica
0138-7332 Informacion Express. Serie: Mechanizacion Agropecuaria
0138-7383 Informacion Express. Serie: Avicultura
0138-743X Informacion Express. Serie: Citricos y Otros Frutales
0138-7480 Informacion Express. Serie: Economia y Organizacion del Trabajo Agropecuario
0138-7537 Informacion Express. Serie: Ganado Equino
0138-7588 Informacion Express. Serie: Ganado Porcino
0138-7634 Informacion Express. Serie: Cafe y Cacao
0138-7685 Informacion Express. Serie: Apicultura
0138-7731 Informacion Express. Serie: Arroz
0138-7766 Cuba Quarterly Economic Report
0138-7782 Cuba. Centro de Informacion y Documentacion Agropecuario. Boletin de Resenas. Serie: Forestales
0138-7839 Cuba. Centro de Informacion y Documentacion Agropecuario. Boletin de Resenas. Serie: Pastos y Forrajes
0138-788X Cuba. Centro de Informacion y Documentacion Agropecuario. Boletin de Resenas. Serie: Riego y Drenaje
0138-7936 Cuba. Centro de Informacion y Documentacion Agropecuario. Boletin de Resenas. Serie: Suelos y Agroquimica
0138-8037 Cuba. Centro de Informacion y Documentacion Agropecuario. Boletin de Resenas. Serie: Plantas Medicinales
0138-8088 Cuba. Centro de Informacion y Documentacion Agropecuario. Boletin de Resenas. Serie: Proteccion de Plantas
0138-8118 Revista de Normalizacion
0138-8134 Cuba. Centro de Informacion y Documentacion Agropecuario. Boletin de Resenas. Serie: Veterinaria
0138-8185 Ciencia y Tecnica en la Agricultura. Serie: Tabaco
0138-8207 Revista de Historia
0138-8231 Cuba. Centro de Informacion y Documentacion Agropecuario. Boletin de Resenas. Serie: Hortalizas, Papas, Granos y Fibras
0138-8339 Cuba. Centro de Informacion y Documentation Agropecuario. Boletin de Resenas. Serie: Citricos
0138-838X Cuba. Centro de Informacion y Documentacion Agropecuario. Boletin de Resenas. Serie: Arroz
0138-8436 Cuba. Centro de Informacion y Documentacion Agropecuario. Boletin de Resenas. Serie: Cafe y Cacao
0138-8452 Revista Cubana de Investigaciones Pesqueras *changed to* Revista Cubana de Investigaciones Pesqueras. Boletines Bibliograficos.
0138-8487 Ciencia y Tecnica en la Agricultura. Serie: Riego y Drenaje
0138-8533 Ciencia y Tecnica en la Agricultura. Serie: Pastos y Forrajes
0138-8584 Ciencia y Tecnica en la Agricultura. Serie: Economia Agropecuaria
0138-8630 Ciencia y Tecnica en la Agricultura. Serie: Hortalizas, Papas, Granos y Fibras
0138-8681 Ciencia y Tecnica en la Agricultura. Serie: Mecanizacion de la Agricultura
0138-8738 Ciencia y Tecnica en la Agricultura. Serie: Ganado Porcino
0138-8789 Ciencia y Tecnica en la Agricultura. Serie: Arroz
0138-8800 Tecnica Popular
0138-8835 Ciencia y Tecnica en la Agricultura. Serie: Citricos y Otros Frutales
0138-8886 Ciencia y Tecnica en la Agricultura. Serie: Viandas Tropicales
0138-8932 Ciencia y Tecnica en la Agricultura. Serie: Proteccion de Plantas
0138-8940 Boletin Tecnico Pulpa y Papel
0138-8983 Ciencia y Tecnica en la Agricultura. Serie: Suelos y Agroquimica
0138-9130 Scientometrics
0138-9157 Technical Film Cards - International Selection†
0138-9238 Spectrum Pharmaceuticum†
0138-9289 Gyogyszerterapias Dokumentacios Szemle†
0139-035X Hungarian Machinery†
0139-1305 Konyv es Konyvtar
0139-1380 Horizont
0139-1682 Heti Vilaggazdasag
0139-2026 Revue de Droit Hongrois†
0139-2115 Fejer Megyei Konyvtaros
0139-2409 Historia (Budapest)
0139-2751 Opuscula Byzantina *see* 0567-7246
0139-3006 Acta Alimentaria Hungarica
0139-3286 Hungary. Kozponti Statisztikai Hivatal. Szamitastechnikai Statisztikai Evkonyv *changed to* Hungary. Kozponti Statisztikai Hivatal. Szamitastechnikai Statisztikai Zsebkonyv.
0139-3510 Hungary. Kozponti Statisztikai Hivatal. Beruhazasi, Epitoipari, Lakasepitesi Zsebkonyv
0139-3634 Hungary. Kozponti Statisztikai Hivatal. Kulkereskedelmi Statisztikai Evkonyv
0139-3669 E C S S I D Bulletin
0139-4045 Marx Karoly Kozgazdasagtudomanyi Egyetem Folyoirata. Egyetemi Szemle *changed to* Budapesti Kozgazdasagtudomanyi Egyetem Folyoirata. Aula.
0139-4533 Hungary. Kozponti Statisztikai Hivatal. Belkereskedelmi es Idegenforgalmi Adatok†
0139-4614 Budapesti Oriental Reprints, Series A-2
0139-4649 Artes Populares
0139-4932 International Basketball
0139-5009 Heraldika
0139-5106 Novinky Literatury: Biologie†
0139-5203 Novinky Literatury: Ekonomie†
0139-5335 Knihovna
0139-5351 Novinky Literatury: Chemie†
0139-5378 Slovenske Narodne Muzeum. Zbornik Etnografia
0139-5408 Novinky Literatury: Matematika. Fyzika†
0139-5459 Novinky Literatury: Novinky Knihovnicke Literatury
0139-5505 Novinky Literatury. Spolecenske Vedy. Politika *see* 0862-1179
0139-5548 Univerzita Komenskeho Trnave. Pedagogicke Fakulta. Zbornik. Spolocenske Vedy. Historia
0139-5602 Novinky Literatury: Umeni†
0139-570X Zemedelska Ekonomika
0139-6129 Statni Knihovna C S R. Zpravodaj *see* 0862-7487
0139-617X Krajske Vlastivedne Muzeum v Olomouci. Zpravy *changed to* Vlastivedne Muzeum v Olomouci. Zpravy.
0139-6587 Zdravotnicka Dokumentace†
0139-6595 Pedagogicka Fakulta v Ostrave. Sbornik Praci. Radi C: Dejepis-Zemepis
0139-6765 Vodni Sporty†
0139-7346 Pedagogicka Fakulta v Plzni. Sbornik. Dejepis
0139-7605 Tesinsko
0139-7893 Folia Zoologica
0139-7915 Zakladni a Rekreacni Telesna Vychova *changed to* Pohyb a My.
0139-8539 Bibliografie Ceskeho Knihovnictvi, Bibliografie a V T I
0139-8571 Biologizace a Chemizace Zivocisne Vyroby - Veterinaria
0139-8741 Geneologicka a Heraldicka Spolecnost Prague. Zpravodaj. Acta Geneologica ac Heraldica
0139-9322 Referatovy Vyber z Urologie
0139-9349 Slovak Seismological Stations: Bratislava, Srobarova, Hurbanovo and Skalnate Pleso for the Year. Bulletin
0139-9446 Novinky Literatury: Marxismus-Leninismus. Spolecenske Vedy†
0139-9462 Vlastivedny Sbornik Okresu Novy Jicin
0139-9489 Prehled Pedagogicke Literatury
0140-0053 Emergency Services News†
0140-0061 Economic and Social History Surveys
0140-0096 The Conservator
0140-0118 Medical & Biological Engineering & Computing
0140-0142 Chartered Institute of Public Finance and Accountancy. Waste Disposal Statistics. Estimates
0140-0150 Chartered Institute of Public Finance and Accountancy. Waste Disposal Statistics. Actuals
0140-0304 Houseleeks *changed to* Sempervivum Society. Newsletter.
0140-038X Staffordshire Guide Industry and Commerce
0140-041X R A P R A News
0140-0428 Educational Administration and History Monographs
0140-0525 Hazards Bulletin *see* 0267-7296

0140-0649 International Communist†
0140-0673 Creativity Network *see* 0953-4199
0140-0711 Felix
0140-072X International Advances in Nondestructive Testing
0140-0789 Royal College of Psychiatrists. Bulletin *changed to* Psychiatric Bulletin.
0140-0835 Topics in Enzyme and Fermentation Biotechnology
0140-0991 Kingsman
0140-1017 Local Government Manpower *see* 0957-5111
0140-1149 Coin Hoards
0140-1165 Sepia
0140-1270 Labour Review†
0140-1319 Traveller's Guide to the Middle East
0140-1378 New African Yearbook
0140-1599 Acoustics Letters
0140-170X Great Britain. Department of the Environment and Department of Transport. Library. Library Bulletin.†
0140-1769 International Symposium on Dredging Technology. Proceedings†
0140-1785 British Hydromechanics Research Association. Proceedings of Pneumotransport
0140-1874 Arab Business Yearbook†
0140-1890 Antenna
0140-1939 Clover Information Index
0140-1963 Journal of Arid Environments
0140-1971 Journal of Adolescence
0140-2080 International Conference on Pressure Surges. Proceedings
0140-2099 Fluid Power Symposium. Proceedings
0140-2129 European Conference on Mixing and Centrifugal Separation. Proceedings
0140-2145 British Pump Manufacturers Association. Technical Conference Proceedings†
0140-2188 C B I News
0140-2285 Jazz Journal International
0140-2382 West European Politics
0140-2390 Journal of Strategic Studies
0140-2447 New Literature on Old Age
0140-2498 Marine Stores International†
0140-2722 British Medicine†
0140-2773 Interlending Review: Journal of the British Library Lending Division *see* 0264-1615
0140-2889 B A P I P Bulletin
0140-2935 Envoy International†
0140-2986 Health and Hygiene
0140-3028 Medical Laboratory World
0140-315X Concetto
0140-3206 London Shop Surveys *changed to* Retail Directory.
0140-3230 Education Equipment, Primary and Middle School Edition *changed to* Primary & Middle School Equipment.
0140-3273 Health Education Index
0140-3281 Knight's Local Government Reports
0140-332X Historic Society of Lancashire and Cheshire. Transactions
0140-3397 Quinquereme
0140-3435 Which Computer?
0140-3494 Browne Records
0140-3664 Computer Communications
0140-3826 Zero†
0140-3990 Leicestershire Archaeological and Historical Society. Transactions
0140-4040 Who Owns Whom. United Kingdom and Republic of Ireland
0140-4059 Milling Feed and Fertiliser *changed to* Milling Feed and Farm Supplies.
0140-4067 Nuclear Energy
0140-4113 British Library of Political and Economic Science. Quarterly List of Additions in Russian and East European Languages†
0140-413X Leather Guide *see* 0955-5080
0140-4156 R A P R A Recent Literature on Hazardous Environments in Industry†
0140-4199 National Institute of Agricultural Botany, Cambridge, England. Technical Leaflets†
0140-4202 Birmingham & Warwickshire Archaeological Society. Transactions
0140-4229 Whitaker's Cumulative Book List *see* 0953-041X
0140-4237 International Building Services Abstracts
0140-4253 C R U S News *changed to* Information Research News.
0140-427X Map Collector
0140-4288 IMS Pharmaceutical Marketletter *changed to* Marketletter.
0140-4415 M I M S Africa
0140-4474 Technical Export News
0140-4539 Treasure Hunting
0140-4547 Bike
0140-4563 Association of National Health Service Supplies Officers. Reference Book & Buyer's Guide
0140-458X Climate Monitor
0140-4636 Commonwealth Mycological Institute. Annual Review *changed to* C A B's Annual Report.
0140-4741 IMS Monitor Report: Europe *changed to* Marketletter.
0140-4768 Rural Development Abstracts
0140-4776 Rural Extension, Education and Training Abstracts†
0140-4784 Forest Products Abstracts
0140-4822 Agricultural Supply Industry
0140-4857 Bio-Medical Applications of Polymers†
0140-489X Economic Outlook
0140-4903 Library Management News†
0140-492X European Bibliography of Soviet, East European and Slavonic Studies
0140-4962 People's Dispensary for Sick Animals. Guild News†
0140-4989 Sheffield and North Derbyshire Topic *changed to* South Yorkshire Topic.
0140-5004 Freshwater Fisheries Laboratory Pitlochry. Triennial Review of Research *see* 0951-3752
0140-5012 Scotland. Department of Agriculture and Fisheries. Marine Laboratory. Triennial Review of Research *changed to* Scotland. Department of Agriculture and Fisheries. Marine Laboratory Aberdeen Annual Review.
0140-5039 E A R
0140-5047 Fairplay World Shipping Directory
0140-5098 Middle East Water & Sewage†
0140-511X Journal of Audiovisual Media in Medicine
0140-5136 Alembic
0140-5179 Sales Management *see* 0264-3200
0140-525X Behavioral and Brain Sciences
0140-5268 Offshore Petroleum Exploration Service *changed to* Petroleum Services. Weekly Service.
0140-5284 European Journal of Science Education *see* 0950-0693
0140-5365 Toxicology Abstracts
0140-5373 Aquatic Sciences & Fisheries Abstracts. Part 1: Biological Sciences and Living Resources
0140-5381 Aquatic Sciences & Fisheries Abstracts. Part 2: Ocean Technology, Policy and Non-Living Resources
0140-542X Rally Sport
0140-5500 International Accounting and Financial Report†
0140-5578 Shoe Retailers Manual *see* 0080-9349
0140-5721 Country Music Round up
0140-5748 Health Service Buyers Guide
0140-5764 Government and Municipal Contractors
0140-5772 British Exporters *changed to* Sell's British Exporters.
0140-5810 Scottish Women's Liberation Journal
0140-5845 New City
0140-5977 Gem Craft *see* 0144-2937
0140-6000 Darts World
0140-6078 Musica Asiatica
0140-6116 Afrique†
0140-6337 British Furniture for the World†
0140-6450 World Airline Fleets Monthly *see* 0951-8673
0140-654X Stonehenge Viewpoint
0140-6566 M C L C Letters
0140-6647 Pension Funds & Their Advisers
0140-668X International Monograph Series on Early Child Care†
0140-6701 Fuel and Energy Abstracts
0140-671X Journal of Sources in Educational History
0140-6728 Westminster Studies in Education
0140-6736 Lancet
0140-6787 N.S.C.A. Members Handbook
0140-6795 N.S.C.A. Reference Book *changed to* N.S.C.A. Pollution Handbook.
0140-6981 Leicester Topic
0140-7007 International Journal of Refrigeration
0140-7082 Edinburgh Bibliographical Society Transactions
0140-7260 University of London. School of Slavonic and East European Studies. Library. Bibliographical Guides
0140-7430 National Gallery, London. Technical Bulletin
0140-7503 Essex Family Historian
0140-7554 International Association of Orientalist Librarians. Newsletter *see* 0161-7397
0140-7562 Kevren
0140-7570 The Great Outdoors
0140-7597 Iron
0140-7635 Economics Selections *see* 0884-8335
0140-766X British Electrotechnical Approvals Board. Annual List of Approved Electrotechnical Equipment
0140-7694 Gay Christian
0140-7724 Postgraduate Doctor: Middle East
0140-7732 School Technology†
0140-7740 Animations
0140-7767 Pellison's Researcher
0140-7775 Journal of Fish Diseases
0140-7783 Journal of Veterinary Pharmacology and Therapeutics
0140-7791 Plant, Cell and Environment
0140-7805 Books in the Earth Sciences
0140-7813 British Geological Literature
0140-7821 Zapis†
0140-7880 Archaeology Abroad Bulletin
0140-7953 Middle East Living Costs†
0140-7961 Matter of Degree
0140-797X Future Studies Centre Newsletter *changed to* Common Futures.
0140-8003 Private Post
0140-8011 Arab Business
0140-8046 Reed's Special Ships†
0140-8089 Leeds Medieval Studies†
0140-8186 Coventry Chamber of Commerce & Industry Directory†
0140-8291 Chartered Institute of Public Finance and Accountancy. Probation Statistics. Actuals
0140-8313 Middle East Transport *changed to* Middle East Transport.
0140-8321 Middle East Travel
0140-833X New African Development *see* 0142-9345
0140-8399 Minor Metals Survey†
0140-8402 Iron & Manganese Ores Survey†
0140-8410 Revealer Cassettes†
0140-8429 Flintshire Historical Society. Publications, Journal and Record Series
0140-8453 Chief Executive†
0140-8461 Maritime Management *changed to* Shipcare & Maritime Management.
0140-8488 Building with Steel†
0140-8623 Banyan Tree
0140-8720 Eurofish Report
0140-8763 British Art and Antiques Yearbook *changed to* British Art & Antiques Directory.
0140-878X Plastics in Retail Packaging Bulletin *see* 0951-4554
0140-895X Irish Literary Studies
0140-9050 World Water
0140-9069 Rabies Magazine†
0140-9115 Annual Reports on Fermentation Processes†
0140-9131 Northamptonshire Past and Present
0140-9158 Medicine Digest
0140-9174 Management Research News
0140-9220 Aerial Archaeology
0140-9247 Forecasts of Exchange Rate Movements (Dollar Edition) *see* 0143-0769
0140-9255 Forecasts of Exchange Rate Movements (Overseas Edition) *see* 0143-0769
0140-9301 Leicestershire Family History Circle. Newsletter *see* 0262-7574
0140-9352 Aggie Weston's
0140-9360 Machine Tool Enterprise
0140-9506 New Equals†
0140-9719 Henley Centre for Forecasting. Director's Guide *see* 0952-5467
0140-9727 Modern Chess Theory†
0140-9743 General Review of the World Coal Industry. Progress Report†
0140-9883 Energy Economics
0140-9948 Clothing Research Journal†
0141-0008 University of Nottingham. Department of Adult Education. Bulletin of Local History, East Midlands Region
0141-0121 Aquarian Arrow
0141-0156 Collected Papers on South Asia
0141-0164 Rice Abstracts
0141-0172 Soyabean Abstracts
0141-0180 Seed Abstracts
0141-0229 Enzyme and Microbial Technology
0141-0288 National Association of Plumbing, Heating and Mechanical Services Contractors Yearbook†
0141-0296 Engineering Structures
0141-030X Studies in Welsh History
0141-0342 Midland Macromolecular Monographs†
0141-0423 Journal of Research in Reading
0141-0547 Harpers & Queen
0141-0555 Cosmopolitan (British Edition)
0141-0571 Current Literature on Health Services *changed to* Health Service Abstracts.
0141-061X Electronic Technology†
0141-0644 Medicine in Society†
0141-0660 W E A Southern District Journal†
0141-0687 Cargo Handling Abstracts *changed to* I C H C A Quarterly Bulletin.
0141-0741 Financial Times World Tax Report
0141-0768 Royal Society of Medicine. Journal
0141-0784 Building Refurbishment and Maintenance *changed to* Building Refurbishment.
0141-0792 Liszt Society. Journal
0141-0806 World Stainless Steel Statistics
0141-0814 Society for Underwater Technology. Journal *changed to* Underwater Technology.
0141-0822 Veterinary Review†
0141-0857 Practical Wireless
0141-0962 Forensic Photography
0141-1004 Studies in Operations Research
0141-1012 Library of Anthropology
0141-1020 American Business Overseas†
0141-1039 Overseas American
0141-1047 European and Middle East Tax Report†
0141-1063 Tax Haven & Shelter Report *changed to* Tax Haven & Investment Report.
0141-108X Durham and Newcastle Research Review *see* 0950-0790
0141-1128 Monographs on Astronomical Subjects
0141-1136 Marine Environmental Research
0141-1144 Company
0141-1152 Oxford Theatre Texts
0141-1179 Dramau'r Byd
0141-1187 Applied Ocean Research
0141-1195 Advances in Engineering Software *see* 0965-9978
0141-1241 Global Tapestry Journal
0141-1268 National Maritime Museum. Occasional Lectures Series†
0141-1314 I D S Research Reports
0141-1381 Diesel Engines for the World†

0141-1403 Great Britain. Department of Health and Social Security. Health Equipment Notes
0141-142X Harpers Sports and Camping *see* 0263-8134
0141-1500 Butterworths Orange Tax Handbook
0141-1594 Phase Transitions. Sections A & B
0141-1667 State Research
0141-1772 Benn's Press Directory *changed to* Benn's Media Directory. U.K. Edition.
0141-1780 Queen's Award Magazine
0141-187X Chartered Institute of Public Finance and Accountancy. Leisure and Recreation Statistics. Estimates
0141-1896 Journal of Musicological Research
0141-190X Bentham Newsletter *see* 0953-8208
0141-1918 International Power Generation
0141-1926 British Educational Research Journal
0141-2116 National Institute for Medical Research. Report
0141-2140 General and Synthetic Methods
0141-2159 Direction Line†
0141-2175 Planned Innovation
0141-2183 Publications Review-Management & Technology Policy *changed to* Publications Review-Innovation & Management.
0141-2213 Green Europe
0141-2221 Potato Markets
0141-223X Preserved Milk
0141-2256 Great Britain. Medical Research Council. Annual Report (Year)
0141-2264 Kent Monograph Series
0141-2361 Gardens Open to the Public in England and Wales *changed to* Gardens of England and Wales.
0141-2442 Socialist Review *changed to* International Socialism.
0141-2604 Great Britain. Department of the Environment and Department of Transport. Library Services. Annual List of Publications
0141-2698 Stanley Link in Design and Craft Education *changed to* Stanley Link in Design and Technology.
0141-2701 Thomas Cook International Timetable *see* 0952-620X
0141-2701 Thomas Cook International Timetable *see* 0144-7475
0141-2728 Education Journal†
0141-2760 Journal of Clinical & Laboratory Immunology
0141-2779 Planning for Social Change
0141-2817 C I R I A News
0141-2876 British Tax Report†
0141-2930 B C I R A Abstracts of International Foundry Literature *see* 0268-3393
0141-2949 Police Studies
0141-299X Cell Nucleus
0141-3228 Financial Times International Year Books: Oil and Gas
0141-3236 Financial Times International Year Books: Who's Who in World Oil and Gas
0141-3244 Financial Times International Year Books: Mining
0141-3279 Great Britain. Warren Spring Laboratory. Annual Review
0141-3287 Natural Energy & Living
0141-3325 British Antarctic Survey. Annual Report
0141-3376 Prospecting in Areas of Glaciated Terrain
0141-3406 Information Privacy *see* 0960-3395
0141-3473 Behavioural Psychotherapy
0141-3511 Leicester Literary & Philosophical Society. Transactions
0141-3589 Talbotania
0141-3619 Open Earth†
0141-3635 Factotum
0141-3856 Butterworths Yellow Tax Handbook
0141-3899 Nursing Research Abstracts
0141-3910 Polymer Degradation and Stability
0141-3929 African Business
0141-4100 Scan
0141-4143 Register of Offshore Units, Submersibles and Diving Systems *changed to* Register of Offshore Units, Submersibles and Underwater Systems.
0141-4151 Seatrade Guide to Arab Shipping *changed to* Seatrade Arab Shipping Guide.
0141-4305 Know More About Oil World Statistics
0141-4348 London Bird Report
0141-4437 Petroleum Times (1981)†
0141-447X Free!
0141-4690 Ferro Alloys: A World Survey†
0141-4704 Falmer
0141-4739 British Review of Economic Issues
0141-4836 International Environment and Safety
0141-4852 Corporate Legal Letter
0141-4909 Lloyd's Register of Ships
0141-4925 Development Research Digest†
0141-5050 Writers of Wales
0141-5085 Grainger Society Journal
0141-5107 Clocks *changed to* Antique Clocks.
0141-5204 Kennington News†
0141-5263 Industrial Minerals Directory *see* 0269-1701
0141-5298 Stainless Steel World Guide†
0141-531X Aluminum World Survey†
0141-5352 Quaker Peace and Service *see* 0265-7848
0141-5387 European Journal of Orthodontics
0141-5425 Journal of Biomedical Engineering
0141-5433 Practical Computing
0141-5492 Biotechnology Letters
0141-5530 International Journal of Materials in Engineering Applications *see* 0264-1275
0141-559X Charles Rennie Mackintosh Society Newsletter
0141-5689 Great Britain. Department of Energy. Publications in Print *see* 0951-855X
0141-5735 T T J Timber Telephone Address Book
0141-5859 Justice of the Peace
0141-5867 Law Notes
0141-5875 Building Law Reports
0141-5956 Aspects of Educational Technology Series *changed to* Aspects of Educational and Training Technology Series.
0141-5972 British Qualifications
0141-5999 Construction Today
0141-6014 Decanter
0141-6022 Primary Education Review *see* 0951-7855
0141-6197 British Insurance Broker *changed to* Broker.
0141-6200 British Journal of Religious Education
0141-6251 A B C Hotel Guide *changed to* Hotel & Travel Index - A B C International Edition.
0141-6278 A B C Guide to International Travel
0141-6340 Nomina
0141-6359 Precision Engineering
0141-6383 A.S.L.G. Newsletter *see* 0265-3389
0141-6391 The Hermetic Journal
0141-6405 Scoltock Family Bulletin†
0141-6413 B A S R A Journal
0141-6421 Journal of Petroleum Geology
0141-6456 Bibliofem†
0141-6529 A B C Air Cargo Guide
0141-6561 Library and Information Research News
0141-6707 African Journal of Ecology
0141-6723 Museums and Galleries in Great Britain and Ireland
0141-6782 Plastics Today†
0141-6790 Art History
0141-6936 B Q S F Review†
0141-6952 New Ecologist *see* 0261-3131
0141-7258 Commercial Laws of Europe
0141-7266 European Commercial Cases
0141-7282 Educare
0141-7436 Quest (London)†
0141-7533 Monitor (London, 1976)
0141-7568 Occupational Hygiene Monographs
0141-7584 Intellectual Property Decisions
0141-7592 Engineering Employers' Federation Directory
0141-7681 Journal of Epidemiology & Community Health
0141-769X Competition Law in the European Communities
0141-7711 C S A Neurosciences Abstracts
0141-772X Pharmacology Abstracts†
0141-7762 Fortnight
0141-7789 Feminist Review
0141-7835 Chartered Institute of Public Finance and Accountancy. Water Services Charges Statistics *changed to* Chartered Institute of Public Finance and Accountancy. Charges for Water Services.
0141-7835 Chartered Institute of Public Finance and Accountancy. Water Services Charges Statistics *changed to* Chartered Institute of Public Finance and Accountancy. Costs of Water Services.
0141-8009 Glasgow & West of Scotland Family History Society. Newsletter
0141-8017 International Security Review
0141-8033 Journal of Social Welfare Law *changed to* Journal of Social Welfare and Family Law.
0141-8092 Quarterly Economic Review of Madagascar, Mauritius, Seychelles, Comoros *see* 0269-5154
0141-8106 Advances in Environmental Science and Engineering
0141-8130 International Journal of Biological Macromolecules
0141-8149 Oxford German Studies Book Supplement†
0141-8181 C F I Occasional Papers *see* 0269-5790
0141-8211 European Journal of Education
0141-8327 Extel Dividend & Interest Record
0141-8335 Extel Capital Gains Tax Service
0141-8416 Quarterly Economic Review of United Arab Emirates *see* 0269-5162
0141-8505 University of London. Institute of Archaeology. Occasional Publication *changed to* University College London. Institute of Archaeology. Occasional Publication.
0141-8513 Commonwealth Currents
0141-8602 Metallurgia: The Journal of Metals Technology, Metal Forming and Thermal Processing
0141-8688 Rank & File Teacher
0141-8696 Cheshire History
0141-8734 Combustion Research Digest†
0141-8912 Association of Clinical Biochemists. News Sheet
0141-8955 Journal of Inherited Metabolic Disease
0141-8963 Laboratory Equipment Directory
0141-8971 Archaeological Reports
0141-898X Rural Technology Guide
0141-9056 British Theatrelog†
0141-9072 Scottish Educational Review
0141-917X Booksellers Association of Great Britain and Ireland. Charter Group. Economic Survey
0141-9307 Social Work Service†
0141-9331 Microprocessors & Microsystems
0141-9382 Displays
0141-9412 International Theatrelog†
0141-9471 Broadcast Engineering Notes†
0141-948X M - F†
0141-9498 Great Britain. Civil Aviation Authority. Library Bulletin
0141-9501 International Distribution & Handling Review
0141-9536 Africa Health
0141-9544 North Middlesex Family History Society. Journal
0141-9684 B N F Nutrition Bulletin
0141-9749 Intellectual Property Newsletter
0141-9803 H S L Abstracts†
0141-9811 Electric Vehicle Developments
0141-982X Teaching Statistics
0141-9838 Parasite Immunology
0141-9846 Journal of Developmental Physiology
0141-9854 Clinical and Laboratory Haematology
0141-9862 Fisheries Management *see* 0266-996X
0141-9870 Ethnic and Racial Studies
0141-9889 Sociology of Health and Illness
0141-9927 Buses Extra
0141-9935 Trains Illustrated - Express Trains *changed to* Steam Days.
0141-9943 Sequel†
0142-0011 Motor Caravan World
0142-0097 Craft and Hobby Trade Directory
0142-0100 Rural Wales *changed to* Rural Wales - Cymru Wledig.
0142-0232 Personal Computer World
0142-0313 Gay Scotland
0142-0356 Journal of Chemical Technology and Biotechnology *see* 0268-2575
0142-0364 Command
0142-0399 Ecologist Quarterly *see* 0261-3131
0142-0453 Journal of Automatic Chemistry
0142-0461 E I P R: European Intellectual Property Review
0142-0496 Computer Fraud and Security Bulletin
0142-050X Product Liability Bulletin *see* 0143-1587
0142-0534 Clothing and Footwear Journal *see* 0263-1008
0142-0569 Agrospray†
0142-0615 Electrical Power and Energy Systems†
0142-064X Journal for the Study of the New Testament
0142-0666 Safety at Sea
0142-0674 B E C A N†
0142-0755 Publican
0142-0798 Hali
0142-095X International Journal of Cement Composites *changed to* Cement and Concrete Composites.
0142-0968 International Journal of Lightweight Concrete *changed to* Cement and Concrete Composites.
0142-0976 International Journal of Wood Preservation†
0142-1042 Click
0142-1050 Current
0142-1085 Light Hovercraft†
0142-1123 International Journal of Fatigue
0142-114X Materials Handling Buyers Guide
0142-128X Urbane Gorilla
0142-1468 Chartered Institute of Public Finance and Accountancy. Water and Sewage Treatment and Disposal Statistics. Actuals†
0142-1484 Chartered Institute of Public Finance and Accountancy. Charges for Leisure Services. Actuals
0142-1557 I C L Technical Journal
0142-1581 Pharmaceutical Medicine (Worthing)
0142-159X Medical Teacher
0142-162X Financial Times World Business Weekly†
0142-1670 Outcome†
0142-1794 Sports Documentation Monthly Bulletin
0142-1824 Hotel, Restaurant and Catering Supplies
0142-1832 Caves & Caving
0142-1875 University of London. Institute of Latin American Studies. Working Papers *see* 0957-7947
0142-1883 Fruit and Tropical Products
0142-1891 Hides and Skins
0142-193X Tsetse and Trypanosomiasis Information Quarterly
0142-1972 C H E C Points
0142-2049 L'Eylah
0142-2081 Fashion Index†
0142-209X British Airports World†
0142-2146 N H R National Newsletter *see* 0952-5335
0142-2154 General Teaching Council for Scotland. Bulletin
0142-2197 Employment Report†
0142-2324 Earth Science Conservation
0142-2367 Royal Society of Medicine. International Congress and Symposium Series
0142-2383 Network†
0142-2391 Resource Management and Optimization

ISSN INDEX 5603

0142-2405 Radioactive Waste Management *see* 0739-5876
0142-2413 Surveys in High Energy Physics
0142-2421 S I A - Surface and Interface Analysis
0142-2448 Radiation Effects Letters *see* 0888-448X
0142-2456 Community Medicine *see* 0957-4832
0142-2464 I U C C Bulletin *see* 0265-4385
0142-2472 Research in British Universities Polytechnics and Colleges. Vol.1: Physical Sciences *see* 0267-1948
0142-2499 Great Britain. Ministry of Agriculture, Fisheries and Food. Directorate of Fisheries Research. Aquatic Environment Monitoring Report
0142-2529 Industrial Relations News†
0142-2545 Food Books Review
0142-2693 C C E T S W News *changed to* Central Council for Education and Training in Social Work. Report of Council Meeting.
0142-2774 Journal of Occupational Behaviour *see* 0894-3796
0142-2782 Biopharmaceutics & Drug Disposition
0142-3134 Assistant Masters & Mistresses Association. Report
0142-3215 Metal Detecting *see* 0140-4539
0142-3304 Historical Metallurgy
0142-3312 Institute of Measurement and Control. Transactions
0142-3363 Board of Celtic Studies. Bulletin
0142-3371 Efrydiau Athronyddol
0142-3401 Chemical Physics of Solids and Their Surfaces†
0142-3460 Family History Newsletter *changed to* Lincolnshire Family Historian.
0142-3479 Msprint
0142-3517 Public Health Laboratory Service Board. Biennial Report
0142-3525 Czechout
0142-3630 Building Services Journal *changed to* Building Services.
0142-3711 Quarterly Economic Review of Austria *see* 0269-5170
0142-372X Quarterly Economic Review of Belgium, Luxembourg *see* 0269-4158
0142-3754 Quarterly Economic Review of Thailand, Burma *see* 0269-5189
0142-3762 Quarterly Economic Review of Canada *see* 0269-4166
0142-3770 Quarterly Economic Review of Sri Lanka *see* 0269-4174
0142-3789 Quarterly Economic Review of Chile *see* 0269-5197
0142-3819 Quarterly Economic Review of Cuba, Dominican Republic, Haiti, Puerto Rico *see* 0269-5251
0142-3827 Quarterly Economic Review of Egypt *see* 0269-526X
0142-3835 Quarterly Economic Review of Ireland *see* 0269-5278
0142-3843 Quarterly Economic Review of France *see* 0269-5286
0142-3851 Quarterly Economic Review of India, Nepal *see* 0269-5294
0142-3878 Quarterly Economic Review of Indonesia *see* 0269-5413
0142-3886 Quarterly Economic Review of Italy *see* 0269-5421
0142-3908 Quarterly Economic Review of Norway *see* 0269-4182
0142-3916 Quarterly Economic Review of Peru, Bolivia *see* 0269-543X
0142-3924 Quarterly Economic Review of Iran *see* 0269-5448
0142-3932 Quarterly Economic Review of Portugal *see* 0269-5456
0142-3959 Quarterly Economic Review of United Kingdom *see* 0269-5472
0142-3967 Quarterly Economic Review of U S S R *changed to* Country Report. Commonwealth of Independent States.
0142-3975 Quarterly Economic Review of Germany *changed to* Country Report. Germany.
0142-3983 Quarterly Economic Review of Yugoslavia *see* 0269-4190
0142-4009 Quarterly Economic Review of Iraq *see* 0269-4395
0142-4025 Quarterly Economic Review of Zaire, Rwanda, Burundi *see* 0269-5510
0142-4033 Quarterly Economic Review of Nigeria *see* 0269-4204
0142-4068 Quarterly Economic Review of Romania, Bulgaria, Albania *see* 0269-5669
0142-4076 Quarterly Economic Review of Indochina - Vietnam, Laos, Cambodia *see* 0269-5677
0142-4092 Quarterly Economic Review of Uganda, Ethiopia, Somalia, Djibouti *see* 0269-5685
0142-4106 Quarterly Economic Review of Lebanon, Cyprus *see* 0269-5693
0142-4114 Quarterly Economic Review of Bahrain, Qatar, Oman, Yemen *see* 0269-7335
0142-4130 Quarterly Economic Review of Algeria *see* 0269-5723
0142-4149 Quarterly Economic Review of Argentina *see* 0269-4468
0142-4165 Quarterly Economic Review of Brazil *see* 0269-5731
0142-4181 Quarterly Economic Review of Denmark, Iceland *see* 0269-574X
0142-419X Quarterly Economic Review of Finland *see* 0269-5901
0142-4203 Quarterly Economic Review of Greece *see* 0269-591X
0142-4211 Quarterly Economic Review of Guatemala, El Salvador, Honduras *see* 0269-4220
0142-422X Agra Europe (London). Special Report
0142-4238 Quarterly Economic Review of Israel *see* 0269-5928
0142-4254 Quarterly Economic Review of Kenya *see* 0269-4239
0142-4270 Quarterly Economic Review of Mexico *see* 0269-5596
0142-4289 Quarterly Economic Review of Morocco *see* 0269-6126
0142-4297 Quarterly Economic Review of Netherlands *see* 0269-6134
0142-4300 Quarterly Economic Review of Nicaragua, Costa Rica, Panama *see* 0269-4247
0142-4319 Journal of Muscle Research and Cell Motility
0142-4394 Quarterly Economic Review of Spain *see* 0269-4263
0142-4408 Quarterly Economic Review of Sudan *see* 0269-6150
0142-4416 Quarterly Economic Review of Sweden *see* 0269-6142
0142-4424 Quarterly Economic Review of Switzerland *see* 0269-6169
0142-4440 Quarterly Economic Review of Uruguay, Paraguay *see* 0269-6177
0142-4467 Quarterly Economic Review of Zambia *see* 0269-4271
0142-4491 Quarterly Economic Review of Saudia Arabia *see* 0269-6215
0142-4505 Quarterly Economic Review of Tanzania, Mozambique *see* 0269-6223
0142-4602 Great Britain. Department of Employment. Work Research Unit. Information System Abstract *see* 0960-2615
0142-4645 Language for Learning†
0142-4688 Southern History
0142-4696 Armed Forces†
0142-4742 Caribbean Insight
0142-4769 Directory of Export Buyers in the U.K.
0142-4807 Studies in Design, Education Craft and Technology *see* 0958-3017
0142-4823 Currency Forecasting Service *see* 0955-5323
0142-4866 E O C Research Bulletin†
0142-4874 International Education Newsletter†
0142-4904 Ciba-Geigy Technical Notes†
0142-4963 Pictorial Education Special *see* 0269-9532
0142-498X Year Book of Agricultural Co-Operation *see* 0952-5556
0142-5005 Plunkett Foundation for Co-Operative Studies. Study Series
0142-5021 Health & Safety Newsline
0142-5048 Key British Enterprises
0142-5056 Seatrade U.S. Yearbook *changed to* Seatrade U.S. Shipping Guide.
0142-5064 Seatrade Guide to Latin American Shipping *changed to* Seatrade Turkish Shipping Guide.
0142-5072 City of London Directory & Livery Companies Guide
0142-5080 Society for Seventeenth Century French Studies. Newsletter *see* 0265-1068
0142-5145 A S R A Journal
0142-5196 Chartered Quantity Surveyor
0142-5218 British Alternative Theatre Directory
0142-5242 Grass and Forage Science
0142-5285 World Alcohol Project
0142-5307 Paper and Packaging Bulletin *changed to* Paper and Packaging Analyst.
0142-5374 A B C Nordic Air Guide†
0142-5382 Actions (London)†
0142-5455 Employee Relations
0142-5463 International Journal of Cosmetic Science
0142-5471 Information Design Journal
0142-5498 Arena†
0142-5595 Narrow Gauge News
0142-5625 Channel Islands Specialised Catalogue
0142-5633 C A P Monitor
0142-5641 Coins and Medals†
0142-5692 British Journal of Sociology of Education
0142-5854 Communication Technology Impact *see* 0961-7612
0142-5862 Hazards Review†
0142-5889 Advances in Desert and Arid Land Technology and Development Series
0142-5897 Annual Accounting Review
0142-5900 Economic Perspectives: An Annual Survey of Economics
0142-5919 International Journal of Solar Energy
0142-5927 Practical Approach to Patents, Trademarks and Copyrights†
0142-5935 Go Teach Primaries
0142-5943 Teen-Search
0142-5951 Journal Contents in Quantitative Methods
0142-596X African Construction†
0142-5978 Good Camps Guide Britain (Year)
0142-6001 Applied Linguistics
0142-601X London Studies on South Asia
0142-6028 Studies on Asian Topics
0142-6044 Exchange Rate Outlook
0142-6168 Highways and Public Works *changed to* Highways.
0142-6184 Defence
0142-6222 Warship
0142-6230 Hi-Fi News and Record Review
0142-6265 Insurance Age
0142-6338 Journal of Tropical Pediatrics
0142-6354 Investment - U S A *see* 0958-3076
0142-6397 Landscape Research
0142-6419 C B I Members Bulletin *see* 0140-2188
0142-6427 C B I Education and Training Bulletin†
0142-6435 C B I Industrial Trends Survey *changed to* C B I Quarterly Industrial Trends Survey.
0142-646X West European Living Costs†
0142-6494 Dragon's Teeth
0142-6540 Oxford Art Journal
0142-6575 Socialist Challenge†
0142-6591 Animal Health Trust. Annual Report
0142-6699 Air Cushion Review†
0142-6702 Art Monthly
0142-6761 Scottish Sports Council. Bulletin *changed to* Arena (Edinburgh).
0142-6796 Buyer
0142-694X Design Studies
0142-7024 Atlantic Review (London) *see* 0264-6773
0142-7067 I P R A Review *see* 0269-0357
0142-7113 C A A T Newsletter
0142-7164 Applied Psycholinguistics
0142-7210 Computing Today†
0142-7229 Electronics Today International *see* 0957-0438
0142-7237 First Language
0142-7245 Minerals and the Environment *changed to* Environmental Geochemistry and Health.
0142-7253 Archaeoastronomy
0142-727X International Journal of Heat and Fluid Flow
0142-7318 Aliphatic and Related Natural Product Chemistry†
0142-7326 Live Rail
0142-7377 Hull Papers in Politics
0142-7466 T V World
0142-7490 Lawyer's Remembrancer
0142-7547 Society for General Microbiology Quarterly
0142-7555 Welsh Medieval Pottery Research Group. Bulletin
0142-761X Fast Food *see* 0955-2979
0142-7628 Book Report *changed to* The Euromonitor Book Report (Year).
0142-7660 Bonny Moor Hen
0142-7830 Commonwealth Catalogue of Queen Elizabeth Stamps†
0142-7849 Third World Planning Review
0142-7865 Photography - Politics†
0142-7873 Journal of Plankton Research
0142-7946 Postgraduate Doctor: Africa
0142-7954 U H Stamp Digest†
0142-8004 Biological Rhythms
0142-8012 Cardiovascular Physiology
0142-8020 Cell Calcium (Sheffield)
0142-8039 Cell Contact Phenomena
0142-8047 Cell Membranes
0142-8055 Cyclic Amp *see* 0964-7589
0142-8071 Enzyme Regulation
0142-8098 Gastric Secretion
0142-8101 Gastrointestinal Hormones
0142-811X Human Sexuality
0142-8128 Immunoassay
0142-8136 Immunohistochemistry
0142-8144 Insulin and Glucagon
0142-8152 Iron Metabolism
0142-8160 Leucocytes
0142-8179 Lymphocytes
0142-8187 Lysosomes
0142-8195 Macrophages
0142-8209 Microfilaments and Microtubules *see* 0268-1625
0142-8217 Mitochondria
0142-8225 Nerve Cell Biology
0142-8233 Neuropeptides (Sheffield)
0142-8241 Neurophysiology
0142-825X Pancreatic and Salivary Secretion
0142-8268 Platelets (Sheffield)
0142-8276 Prolactin
0142-8284 Prostaglandins - Biology
0142-8292 Protein Phosphorylation *see* 0952-0406
0142-8306 Protein Synthesis†
0142-8314 Releasing Hormones
0142-8322 Ribosomes *see* 0952-0414
0142-8330 Steroid Receptors
0142-8349 Thyroid Hormones
0142-8357 Renal Transplantation and Dialysis
0142-8365 Autoimmune Diseases
0142-8373 Demyelinating Diseases†
0142-8381 Drug Addiction†
0142-8403 Neurochemistry
0142-8411 Psychopharmacology†
0142-8446 Transplantation Immunology†
0142-8462 Antigen Antibody Reactions†
0142-8470 Carbohydrate Metabolism†
0142-8497 Hypersensitivity†
0142-8500 Neoplasm Immunology†
0142-8519 Phagocytes†
0142-8527 Steroidogenesis†
0142-8535 Toxins†
0142-8543 Vision (Sheffield)
0142-8551 Adrenal Glands†
0142-856X Autonomic Nervous System†

ISSN

0142-8586 Blood Coagulation†
0142-8594 Blood Proteins†
0142-8624 Diet†
0142-8640 D N A
0142-8659 Environmental Physiology†
0142-8683 Hypothalamus†
0142-8691 Inborn Errors of Metabolism†
0142-8705 Kidney Diseases†
0142-873X Mineralocorticoids and Glucocorticoids†
0142-8748 Mucopolysaccharides†
0142-8780 Respiratory System
0142-8799 R N A†
0142-8802 Receptors (Sensory)†
0142-8810 Tissue Culture
0142-8829 Toxoplasmosis†
0142-8853 Graphics World
0142-887X Association of Independent Museums Bulletin
0142-8934 @Bookselllers Association of Great Britain. List of Charter Members *see* 0952-1666
0142-8950 Hampshire Field Club and Archaeological Society Proceedings
0142-8977 Royal Observatory, Edinburgh. Communications†
0142-9086 Health and Safety Information Bulletin *changed to* Health, Safety Environment Bulletin.
0142-9094 What's New in Building
0142-9124 South West Review†
0142-9132 Arts Alert†
0142-9191 Committee of Vice-Chancellors and Principals of the Universities of the United Kingdom. Newsletter†
0142-9256 Quantitative Sociology Newsletter†
0142-9272 Nigeria Newsletter†
0142-9310 Egypt Newsletter†
0142-9345 New African
0142-9353 Rubber and Plastics Fire and Flammability Bulletin *see* 0952-2727
0142-9361 Simulation - Games for Learning *changed to* Aspects of Educational and Training Technology Series.
0142-9361 Simulation - Games for Learning
0142-937X Great Britain. Sea Fish Industry Authority. European Supplies Bulletin
0142-9388 Parley Papers
0142-9418 Polymer Testing
0142-9442 Laundry and Cleaning News
0142-9469 Rolls-Royce Magazine
0142-9523 Book Dealers' and Collectors' Year-Book and Diary†
0142-9612 Biomaterials
0142-9663 Ten.8 International Photography Magazine *changed to* Ten.8 Photo Paperback.
0142-9671 Mackintosh European Electronics Companies File *see* 0951-5747
0142-968X Journal of Plant Foods *changed to* Food Science.
0142-971X Runnymede Trust Bulletin *changed to* Runnymede Bulletin.
0142-9728 London Chamber of Commerce and Industry. Directory
0142-9752 Stanley Gibbons Stamp Catalogue. Part 1: British Commonwealth
0142-9760 Austria & Hungary Stamp Catalogue
0142-9779 Balkans Stamp Catalogue
0142-9787 Benelux Stamp Catalogue
0142-9795 Czechoslovakia & Poland Stamp Catalogue
0142-9809 France Stamp Catalogue
0142-9817 Germany Stamp Catalogue
0142-9825 Italy & Switzerland Stamp Catalogue
0142-9833 Portugal & Spain Stamp Catalogue
0142-9841 Russia Stamp Catalogue
0142-985X Scandinavia Stamp Catalogue
0142-9868 Africa Since Independence Stamp Catalogue
0142-9876 Central America Stamp Catalogue
0142-9884 Central Asia Stamp Catalogue
0142-9892 China Stamp Catalogue
0142-9906 Japan & Korea Stamp Catalogue
0142-9914 Middle East Stamp Catalogue
0142-9922 South America Stamp Catalogue
0142-9930 South-East Asia Stamp Catalogue
0142-9949 United States Stamp Catalogue
0142-9981 Journal of Morphanalysis†
0143-0009 University of St. Andrews. Library. Current Serials
0143-0076 Y Cylchgrawn Efengylaidd
0143-0084 Res Mechanica *see* 0951-8320
0143-0092 Ysgrifau Diwinyddol
0143-0106 The Plantsman
0143-0122 Reality Studios†
0143-0149 Pope Teaches
0143-0181 Revelation†
0143-0211 O P T: One Parent Times
0143-0238 Cycling World
0143-0246 Argo (Oxford)†
0143-0262 Popular Archaeology *see* 0952-1240
0143-0270 Bookdealers in India, Pakistan and Sri Lanka *changed to* Sheppard's Book Dealers in India and the Orient.
0143-0289 British Institute of Mental Handicap. Current Awareness Service
0143-0297 Nottinghamshire Industrial Archaeological Society Journal
0143-0343 School Psychology International
0143-036X New Magic Lantern Journal
0143-0378 Nature Conservancy Council. Chief Scientist Team Reports *changed to* Nature Conservancy Council. Chief Scientist Directorate Reports.
0143-0386 Research Reports Digest†
0143-0394 Soviet Scientific Reviews. Section A: Physics Reviews
0143-0408 Soviet Scientific Reviews. Section B: Chemistry Reviews
0143-0416 Soviet Scientific Reviews. Section C: Mathematical Physics Reviews
0143-0424 Soviet Scientific Reviews. Section D: Biological Reviews *see* 0734-9351
0143-0432 Soviet Scientific Reviews. Section E: Astrophysics & Space Physics Reviews
0143-053X U K S T U Newsletter†
0143-0599 U K I R T Newsletter *see* 0963-2700
0143-0602 International Journal of Masonry Construction†
0143-0645 Far East Health
0143-0661 Archaeolog†
0143-067X Auto Export†
0143-0688 Annual Art Sales Index (Year) *changed to* Art Sales Index: Oil Paintings, Drawings, Water Colours and Sculpture.
0143-0696 Mackintosh European Electronics Companies Bulletin *see* 0951-5747
0143-0734 Research in British Universities Polytechnics and Colleges. Vol.2: Biological Sciences *see* 0267-1956
0143-0742 Research in British Universities Polytechnics and Colleges. Vol.3: Social Sciences *see* 0267-1964
0143-0750 International Journal of Ambient Energy
0143-0769 Currency Profiles
0143-0793 Journal of Advertising History *see* 0309-0566
0143-0807 European Journal of Physics
0143-0815 Clinical Physics and Physiological Measurement
0143-084X Journal of Industrial Affairs
0143-0955 Oral History
0143-0963 Cleaning Maintenance and Big Buildings Management *changed to* Cleaning Maintenance.
0143-0971 Shop Equipment Display & Shopfitting Directory
0143-1005 Helicopter Magazine *changed to* Helicopter International Magazine.
0143-103X Return of Outstanding Debt *see* 0263-2985
0143-1064 Syzygy†
0143-1080 European Medical Ultrasonics†
0143-1102 D P International†
0143-1145 Aviation Europe *changed to* Aerospace Europe.
0143-1153 Sell's Marine Market
0143-1161 International Journal of Remote Sensing
0143-117X Hypertension
0143-120X Vitamin D†
0143-1218 Journal of Biodynamic Psychology
0143-1234 Scottish Wildlife
0143-1250 Transactions of the Monumental Brass Society
0143-1269 Elgar Society. Journal
0143-1285 Books in Scotland
0143-1307 West African Farming and Food Processing *see* 0266-8017
0143-1366 Ur
0143-1374 Mind Your Own Business
0143-1404 Biocontrol News and Information
0143-1412 Slow Dancer
0143-1455 Process Engineering Directory
0143-1471 Environmental Pollution. Series A. Ecological and Biological *see* 0269-7491
0143-148X Environmental Pollution. Series B. Chemical and Physical *see* 0269-7491
0143-1536 N P L News
0143-1587 Product Liability International
0143-1722 N C C Information and Library Services. Bibliography Series†
0143-1749 Secondary Education Journal *see* 0951-7855
0143-1927 Ambassador†
0143-1935 British Alternative Press Index†
0143-1951 University of Bristol. Newsletter
0143-2028 Cosmos Newsletter†
0143-2044 Cryo-Letters
0143-2060 Environmental Technology Letters *changed to* Environmental Technology.
0143-2087 Optimal Control Applications and Methods
0143-2095 Strategic Management Journal
0143-2192 Labels and Labelling International
0143-2214 Where to Learn English in Great Britain†
0143-2257 Airfinance Journal
0143-2389 Worcestershire Archaeological Society. Transactions
0143-2443 Water Research Centre. Annual Report *changed to* Water Research Centre. Annual Review.
0143-2478 Where (London, 1975)
0143-2532 Cambridge Economic Policy Review†
0143-263X Industrial Minerals Merchants, Agents and Processors *see* 0269-1701
0143-2680 Bargaining Report
0143-2729 Ireland Socialist Review
0143-2745 Worker Writer
0143-2796 Architectural Association Annual Review *changed to* Construction and Architectural Specifiers Guide. Annual Review.
0143-280X Rowland's Tax Guide *see* 0267-8829
0143-2885 International Endodontic Journal
0143-294X Tolley's Practical Tax Newsletter
0143-2958 European Electronic Component Distributor Directory
0143-2974 Local Population Studies
0143-3083 Research and Clinical Forums
0143-3105 Latin American Newsletters. Book News†
0143-3164 Directory of Crematoria
0143-3180 Journal of Clinical and Hospital Pharmacy *see* 0269-4727
0143-3199 Poetry Nottingham
0143-3237 Home Office List of Publications
0143-3245 Block
0143-3253 Action Newsletter
0143-3296 Ecology Abstracts
0143-330X Biochemistry Abstracts: Part 1. Biological Membranes *see* 8756-7504
0143-3318 Biochemistry Abstracts: Part 2. Nucleic Acids *see* 8756-7512
0143-3326 Biochemistry Abstracts. Part 3: Amino-Acids, Peptides and Proteins *see* 8756-7520
0143-3334 Carcinogenesis
0143-3369 International Journal of Vehicle Design
0143-3385 A L L C Journal *see* 0951-1474
0143-3415 Quarterly Review of South African Gold Shares *changed to* International Quarterly.
0143-3490 Directory of Summer Jobs in Britain
0143-3512 Business Matters
0143-3555 L R D G Bulletin *see* 0268-2125
0143-3563 Nova Hrvatska
0143-3571 Cyclamen Journal
0143-3598 Fouling Prevention Research Digest *changed to* Heat Transfer & Fluid Flow Service Digest.
0143-3601 Footprints (Northampton)
0143-3628 Geriatric Medicine†
0143-3636 Nuclear Medicine Communications
0143-3679 Habitat Europe†
0143-3709 Marine Propulsion International
0143-3725 Science Fiction Media News *see* 0307-3335
0143-3768 Landscape History
0143-3784 Medieval English Theatre
0143-3857 Ergodic Theory and Dynamical Systems
0143-389X Adventure Holidays
0143-4004 Placenta
0143-4020 Measurement and Inspection Technology *changed to* Quality Today.
0143-4128 International Society for the Study of Church Monuments. Bulletin *see* 0268-7518
0143-4136 National Association for the Teaching of English. Newsletter
0143-4144 Conserver
0143-4160 Cell Calcium (Edinburgh)
0143-4179 Neuropeptides (Edinburgh)
0143-4187 Municipal Journal
0143-4209 Histamine Receptors†
0143-4217 Lectins
0143-4225 Polypeptides
0143-4233 Membrane Proteins
0143-4241 Transmitters, Receptors & Synapses
0143-425X Gonadotrophins†
0143-4268 Growth Promoting Hormones
0143-4276 Neurohypophysial Hormones
0143-4284 Renin, Angiotensin & Kinins
0143-4314 Glycoproteins†
0143-4330 Medical Computing†
0143-4381 Vending International Manual
0143-4500 Aberdeen and North East Scotland Family History Society. Newsletter *changed to* Aberdeen and North East Scotland Family History Society. Journal.
0143-4519 Arts Council of Great Britain. Education Bulletin†
0143-4632 Journal of Multilingual & Multicultural Development
0143-4659 Worcestershire Archaeology and Local History Newsletter
0143-4748 Youth Service Scene†
0143-4780 Smaller Business Management Abstracts†
0143-4861 R L J: Roskill's Letter from Japan
0143-4918 Plainsong & Mediaeval Music Society. Journal
0143-4977 British Journal of Acupuncture
0143-5000 Drydock
0143-5019 Current Affairs Bibliographies†
0143-5051 Social Biology and Human Affairs
0143-5094 European Monographs in Health Education Research†
0143-5108 Journal for the Study of the New Testament. Supplement Series
0143-5124 Library Management
0143-5140 International Labmate
0143-5205 Institute of Chartered Accountants in England and Wales. Quarterly Taxation Bulletin†
0143-5221 Clinical Science
0143-523X Latin America Regional Reports - Caribbean
0143-5248 Latin American Regional Reports - Andean Group
0143-5256 Latin American Regional Reports - Southern Cone
0143-5264 Latin America Regional Reports - Mexico & Central America

ISSN INDEX 5605

0143-5272 Latin America Regional Reports - Brazil
0143-5280 Latin America Weekly Report
0143-5329 Credit Control
0143-537X Aspects
0143-5418 Sut Anubis
0143-5426 Fight Racism! Fight Imperialism!
0143-5442 Stainless Steel: An International Directory *see* 0953-7228
0143-5469 Education Year Book
0143-5485 Coin *changed to* Coin Monthly (1980).
0143-554X Home Miniaturist
0143-5590 Torquay Pottery Collectors Society. Newsletter *see* 0951-6751
0143-5663 International Index to Television Periodicals
0143-5671 Fiscal Studies
0143-5698 International Tree Crops Journal
0143-5744 Voluntary Action *see* 0955-2170
0143-5795 Chatham House Papers†
0143-5833 B A R B S†
0143-5906 Hereford's North America *changed to* Hereford's Americas.
0143-5922 King's Theological Review†
0143-5949 Street Machine
0143-6058 Educational Computing†
0143-6112 Contraceptive Delivery Systems *changed to* Advances in Contraceptive Delivery Systems.
0143-6147 Tropical Pest Management
0143-6228 Applied Geography
0143-6236 Social Science Information Studies *see* 0268-4012
0143-6244 Building Services Engineering Research & Technology
0143-6260 Popular Technology
0143-6287 Coal Calendar
0143-6295 Business Law Review
0143-6333 James Joyce Broadsheet
0143-6368 Arid Land Abstracts†
0143-6392 Which World Processor? *see* 0265-6965
0143-6473 Investors Chronicle Hillier Parker Rent Index
0143-6481 Noise and Vibration Contro - Worldwide *see* 0957-4565
0143-6503 Oxford Journal of Legal Studies
0143-652X Commercial Fishing
0143-6538 Tibet News Review
0143-6554 Sudan Texts Bulletin
0143-6570 M D E - Managerial and Decision Economics
0143-6597 Third World Quarterly
0143-6619 WestIndian Digest
0143-6643 Air Infiltration Review
0143-6694 Oilman *changed to* Offshore Incorporating the Oilman.
0143-683X Historical Geography Research Series
0143-6864 Hazardous Cargo Bulletin
0143-6945 Motor *see* 0955-5889
0143-6996 Peatain Family History Newsletter†
0143-7011 Stamps *changed to* Stamps and Foreign Stamps.
0143-702X I E E Proceedings Part A: Covering Reviews, Physical Science, Measurement and Instrumentation, Management and Education *changed to* I E E Proceedings Part A: Covering Science, Measurement and Technology.
0143-7038 I E E Proceedings Part B: Electric Power Applications
0143-7046 I E E Proceedings Part C: Generation, Transmission and Distribution
0143-7054 I E E Proceedings Part D: Control Theory and Applications
0143-7062 I E E Proceedings Part E: Computers and Digital Techniques
0143-7070 I E E Proceedings Part F: Communications, Radar and Signal Processing *see* 0956-375X
0143-7089 I E E Proceedings Part G: Electronic Circuits and Systems *see* 0956-3768
0143-7097 I E E Proceedings Part H: Microwaves, Optics and Antennas *see* 0950-107X
0143-7100 I E E Proceedings I - Solid-State and Electronics *see* 0956-3776
0143-7127 Journal of Oil and Petrochemical Pollution *see* 0141-1136
0143-7208 Dyes and Pigments
0143-7216 Anglo-Japanese Economic Institute. Bulletin *see* 0951-5860
0143-7240 Aeroplane Monthly
0143-7267 Thoroughbred and Classic Cars *changed to* Thoroughbred and Classic Cars.
0143-7283 University of Strathclyde. Department of Architecture & Building Science. Research Bulletin
0143-7364 C I E News *changed to* C I T E News.
0143-7380 Labour Party. Economic Review†
0143-7402 British Music Society. Journal *see* 0958-5664
0143-7410 Reports Index
0143-7429 Glasgow Directory of Voluntary Organizations
0143-7453 International Bar News
0143-7488 Academus Poetry Magazine
0143-7496 International Journal of Adhesion and Adhesives
0143-7518 Christian Fellowship†
0143-7526 Sensory Perception and Information Processing
0143-7534 Learning and Memory
0143-7550 Mental Retardation†
0143-7585 Reactive Personal Distress†
0143-7593 Psychotherapy†
0143-7607 Metal Traders of the World
0143-7690 Scrip - World Pharmaceutical News
0143-7704 Community Studies Series
0143-7720 International Journal of Manpower
0143-7739 Leadership and Organization Development Journal
0143-7755 Tableware International
0143-7798 Steel Times International
0143-781X History of Political Thought
0143-7844 Sheet Metal Industries International†
0143-7852 Bulk Systems International *see* 0269-381X
0143-7895 Conference World
0143-7917 Family Life
0143-7925 Focus (Grantham)
0143-7941 Tax Management International Forum
0143-795X Hereford's Air Cargo
0143-7984 Wellcome Unit for the History of Medicine. Research Publications
0143-800X Abstracts: Histopathology, Cytopathology *see* 0268-4993
0143-8018 Great Britain. Ministry of Agriculture, Fisheries and Food. Directorate of Fisheries Research. Laboratory Leaflet
0143-8115 Numerical Engineering
0143-8123 Comments on Molecular and Cellular Biophysics
0143-814X Journal of Public Policy
0143-8158 West Midlands Archives Newsletter†
0143-8166 Optics and Lasers in Engineering
0143-8174 Reliability Engineering *see* 0951-8320
0143-8190 Countryside Planning Yearbook *changed to* International Yearbook of Rural Planning.
0143-8247 One Earth†
0143-8263 International Authors and Writers Who's Who
0143-8301 Scottish Journal of Religious Studies
0143-831X Economic and Industrial Democracy
0143-8328 Pay and Benefits Bulletin
0143-8352 F R A M E Technical News *see* 0268-4306
0143-8425 Drawing Paper
0143-8441 Food: Flavouring Ingredients Processing and Packaging *changed to* Food Ingredients & Processing International.
0143-8484 Plunkett Development Series
0143-8514 Thinking Mission
0143-8557 Solids Handling
0143-8565 Yesteryear Transport†
0143-859X N I M L A
0143-8611 Electronics Engineer†
0143-8654 School of Agriculture, Aberdeen. Annual Report†
0143-8689 Curriculum
0143-8697 Kent Review *changed to* Process Instrumentation Review.
0143-8700 International Whaling Commission. Annual Reports
0143-8743 Miniature Book World *see* 0142-9523
0143-8751 Target Gun
0143-8786 Outlook (Milton Keynes)†
0143-8859 Strays
0143-8875 Platform (Sutton-on-Craven)
0143-8883 Prospect (Edinburgh)
0143-8972 Scottish Planning Appeal Decisions
0143-8999 Planning Exchange Information Bulletin†
0143-9014 Pig News & Information
0143-9030 N C V O Information Service†
0143-9073 Ecos
0143-909X Books for Keeps
0143-9111 British Business†
0143-912X Interim (Birmingham)
0143-9138 Waifarers
0143-9162 Bus Fayre
0143-9170 Fare Stage *see* 0143-9162
0143-926X Cosmatom
0143-9308 War on Wants Outlook†
0143-9359 Administrative Accounting *see* 0953-2579
0143-9405 China Business Report†
0143-9553 Keyword Index to Serial Titles
0143-9561 Communications Engineering International *changed to* C E I - Communications Engineering International.
0143-9596 What's New in Farming
0143-960X I W P C Newsletter *changed to* Institution of Water and Environmental Management. Newsletter.
0143-9634 Nature in Devon
0143-9642 Computer Performance†
0143-9669 Re Report†
0143-9677 Tax Haven & Shelter Report-North American Edition†
0143-9685 Historical Journal of Film, Radio and Television
0143-9693 Sussex Genealogist and Local Historian
0143-9715 European Muslims and Christian-Muslim Relations. Abstracts†
0143-974X Journal of Constructional Steel Research
0143-9758 Institute of Chartered Accountants in England and Wales. Technical Bulletin *changed to* Institute of Chartered Accountants in England and Wales. Update.
0143-9782 Journal of Time Series Analysis
0143-9855 Multiracial School *see* 0260-0226
0143-9863 Ramp†
0143-9871 Inklings
0143-991X Industrial Robot
0143-9952 Jane's Armour and Artillery
0143-9995 Medisport
0144-0004 Jane's Military Communications
0144-0063 British Geologist *see* 0961-5628
0144-0101 Scottish Business Education Council. Business Education Guide *changed to* On Course.
0144-025X Online Notes
0144-0292 Modern Railways Pictorial *changed to* Motive Power Monthly.
0144-0322 Society of Leather Technologists and Chemists. Journal
0144-0357 Prose Studies
0144-0365 Journal of Legal History
0144-0373 Journal of Media Law and Practice
0144-0381 Arms Control
0144-039X Slavery & Abolition
0144-0403 Medicine International. U K Edition
0144-0411 Medicine International. Quarterly Edition
0144-042X Medicine International. Irish Edition†
0144-0438 Medicine International. Middle Eastern Edition
0144-0462 Scope (Belfast)
0144-0470 Jane's Defence Review *see* 0265-3818
0144-0497 Middle Thames Naturalist
0144-0543 Franchise World
0144-056X Library Association. University, College and Research Section. Newsletter
0144-0586 Northamptonshire Natural History Society and Field Club Journal
0144-0640 Social Services Research Group. Journal *see* 0264-519X
0144-0675 Farm Contractor
0144-0683 Nottinghamshire Link
0144-0713 Radio Modeller
0144-073X Christian Statesman *changed to* Christian Today.
0144-0764 Stirling Technical Reports in Education†
0144-0810 Netball
0144-0888 British Journal of Language Teaching *see* 0957-1736
0144-0918 Politics and Power†
0144-0969 Social Work Information Bulletin
0144-1019 Seaways
0144-1027 Company Lawyer *changed to* Company Lawyer and Company Lawyer Digest.
0144-1078 Recent Advances in Infection†
0144-123X Northern Bibliography†
0144-1248 Camera *changed to* Photo Answers.
0144-1302 Scottish Pottery Historical Review
0144-1396 A Y R S Airs
0144-1647 Transport Reviews
0144-1655 Modern Tramway and Light Rail Transit
0144-1671 European Digest†
0144-1752 Socialist Librarians Journal†
0144-1779 Radical Bookseller
0144-1795 Journal of Autonomic Pharmacology
0144-1825 Ceramic Review
0144-1973 Societe Guernesiaise. Report and Transactions
0144-2015 Hambro Company Guide
0144-2066 Word Processing Now *changed to* Word & Information Processing.
0144-2147 British Ceramic Research. Special Publications
0144-221X Natural History Society of Northumbria. Transactions
0144-2317 U.V. Spectrometry Group. Bulletin†
0144-235X International Reviews in Physical Chemistry
0144-2368 Beacon House Bulletin *changed to* Mental Health Matters.
0144-2376 Felt and Damaging Earthquakes
0144-2384 Refer
0144-2406 Food Legislation Surveys
0144-2449 Zeolites
0144-2457 Logos
0144-2481 Great Britain. Civil Aviation Authority. General Aviation Airmisses *changed to* Great Britain. Civil Aviation Authority. General Aviation Airmiss Bulletin.
0144-249X Stanley Gibbons Postcard Catalogue
0144-252X Magnetic Fluids†
0144-2570 U K C I S Newsletter *changed to* Royal Society of Chemistry. Database Newsletter.
0144-2600 Institute of Energy. Journal
0144-2694 Walk
0144-2708 Tiddly Dyke
0144-2740 Major Companies of Nigeria†
0144-2767 Business Yearbook of Brazil, Mexico & Venezuela†
0144-2791 History Journal
0144-2813 Business Education *see* 0309-0582
0144-2821 Scottish Arts Council. Bulletin†
0144-2848 T O P S: The Old Police Station†
0144-2872 Policy Studies
0144-2880 Polymer Photochemistry *see* 0141-3910
0144-2902 Christian Jewish Relations
0144-2910 Model Boats
0144-2937 Popular Crafts
0144-2988 Macromolecular Chemistry (London)†

ISSN

0144-2996 Croydon Chamber of Commerce and Industry Directory *changed to* Croydon Chamber of Commerce Directory.
0144-3054 E C L R: European Competition Law Review
0144-3070 Occasional Papers in Modern Dutch Studies *changed to* Monographs in Modern Dutch Studies.
0144-3194 Navy International
0144-3313 University of Edinburgh. Department of Archaeology. Occasional Papers
0144-333X International Journal of Sociology and Social Policy
0144-3356 School of Agriculture, Aberdeen. Research Investigations and Field Trials†
0144-3399 Context (Leeds)†
0144-3410 Educational Psychology
0144-3453 Transport (London)
0144-3461 Caprice†
0144-3488 Interchange
0144-3569 Action *see* 0954-6693
0144-3577 International Journal of Operations and Production Management
0144-3585 Journal of Economic Studies
0144-3593 Statute Law Review
0144-3607 Zoological Record
0144-3631 British Ceramic Research Limited. Technical Notes†
0144-364X Birdwatcher's Yearbook *changed to* Birdwatcher's Yearbook and Diary.
0144-3674 Computer Age (London)
0144-3690 Auction Prices of American Artists
0144-3704 Hospitality
0144-3720 Management Confidential *changed to* Management Success.
0144-3755 Hovercraft Bulletin
0144-378X Foundations
0144-3828 Gardening World†
0144-3879 Animal Disease Occurrence - Data Tables†
0144-3879 Animal Disease Occurrence
0144-3968 Haverhill and District Archaeological Group. Journal
0144-3976 Aviation Postcard Collector
0144-4018 Kent Recusant History
0144-4034 Boat Technology International†
0144-4077 Journal of Local Studies *changed to* Journal of Regional and Local Studies.
0144-4212 P S L G
0144-4220 Annual Monetary Review *see* 0266-7339
0144-4247 Energy R & D Summary and Sources
0144-4271 Medeconomics
0144-4298 World Studies Journal *changed to* Annual Review of Global Education.
0144-4301 S P A I D News
0144-4360 Literary Review and Quarto
0144-4425 Paint Titles
0144-4476 I C B P Newsletter *changed to* World Birdwatch.
0144-4484 Co-Operative Fishermen's Bulletin†
0144-4492 Solar System Today
0144-4514 Chartered Institute of Public Finance and Accountancy. Homelessness Statistics
0144-4549 Lloyd's Shipping Index
0144-4557 Lloyd's Voyage Record
0144-4565 Biomass *see* 0960-8524
0144-4581 State Enterprise
0144-459X Doncaster Ancestor
0144-4611 Awards for Commonwealth University Academic Staff *see* 0964-2706
0144-462X Grants for Study Visits by University Administrators and Librarians *see* 0964-2714
0144-4646 Communication Research Trends
0144-4751 Venezuela
0144-4778 Midlands Homoeopathy Research Group. Research Letter *changed to* British Homoeopathy Research Group. Communications.
0144-4816 Essex Review of Children's Literature
0144-4948 Health Now
0144-5014 B I P Plastics Review†
0144-5073 University of Bath. Centre for Catalogue Research. Newsletter *changed to* University of Bath. Centre for Bibliographic Management. Newsletter.
0144-5081 Community Service Statistics: Scotland
0144-5138 History of Universities
0144-5154 Assembly Automation
0144-5170 Journal of Garden History
0144-5243 Miltronics
0144-5251 Dairyman's Yearbook†
0144-5324 International Investment Guide *changed to* Global Trends.
0144-5340 History and Philosophy of Logic
0144-5359 Wessex Studies in Special Education
0144-557X Analytical Proceedings
0144-5596 Social Policy and Administration
0144-5618 Royal Society of Medicine. Forum Series *see* 0268-3091
0144-574X About Books for Children *changed to* Pick of the Year.
0144-5774 Sounds
0144-5804 Record Mirror *changed to* R M.
0144-5847 Other Poetry†
0144-5863 Anglo-Catalan Society. Occasional Publications
0144-5871 High Performance Textiles
0144-5898 Lookback†
0144-5944 Studio Sound & Broadcast Engineering
0144-5952 Human Toxicology *changed to* Human & Experimental Toxicology.
0144-5960 Wolff's Guide to the London Metal Exchange
0144-5979 Clinical Physiology
0144-5987 Energy Exploration and Exploitation
0144-5995 Termite Abstracts
0144-6002 Orbit (London)†
0144-6010 Video Today
0144-6037 Sound International *see* 0144-5944
0144-6045 Plastics and Rubber Processing and Applications *see* 0959-8111
0144-6053 Great Britain. Harwell Laboratory. Harwell Information Bulletin
0144-6088 Cue Technical Theatre Review *changed to* Theatre Crafts International.
0144-610X Chartered Institute of Public Finance and Accountancy. Personal Social Services Statistics. Estimates
0144-6126 B R A D Advertiser and Agency List *changed to* Advertiser & Agency List.
0144-6169 Farm Animal Welfare Co-ordinating Executive. Newsletter
0144-6193 Journal of Construction Industry Economics and Management *changed to* Construction Management and Economics.
0144-624X Recreation Management Handbook†
0144-6258 Ecology & Conservation Studies
0144-6266 Recent Advances in Crosslinking & Curing
0144-6274 Grow Together†
0144-6282 Surgery Today
0144-6304 Insurance Index
0144-6320 What Camera Weekly *changed to* Camera Weekly.
0144-6339 Arthritis News
0144-6347 B S H S Newsletter
0144-6355 G D R Monitor
0144-6363 Heritage and Destiny†
0144-6371 Quest (Cardiff)†
0144-6398 A R V A C Pamphlet†
0144-6401 Crystal Palace Matters
0144-6428 Slade Magazine†
0144-6436 Loot†
0144-6487 English Magazine *changed to* English and Media Magazine.
0144-6517 Property Law Bulletin
0144-6525 R I P A Report
0144-6533 Legion
0144-655X Dine Out
0144-6576 B A R G Review *see* 0263-1091
0144-6592 Recent Advances in Nursing†
0144-6622 Soviet Engineering Research
0144-6630 New Age†
0144-6649 Computerworld UK†
0144-6657 British Journal of Clinical Psychology
0144-6665 British Journal of Social Psychology
0144-6673 Lloyd's Shipping Economist
0144-6681 Lloyd's Loading List
0144-672X Brentford and Chiswick Local History Society. Journal
0144-6738 Warwick Statistics Service. Occasional Review *changed to* University of Warwick Business Information Service. Occasional Review.
0144-6800 I C O Library Monthly Entries - Coffeeline
0144-6827 L A Trade Union News *see* 0963-5548
0144-6835 Retail Review
0144-6843 National Council for Educational Standards. Bulletin†
0144-686X Ageing and Society
0144-6878 Sussex Yesterdays†
0144-6894 Timepiece *changed to* Timepiece Register.
0144-6916 Midland Bonsai Society Journal
0144-6924 Child's Play
0144-6967 N A C C Newsletter
0144-6991 National College of Agricultural Engineering News *changed to* C R I News.
0144-7076 P N Review
0144-7106 Trade Union Studies Journal
0144-7114 Music and Video *see* 0261-4200
0144-7122 Assyrian Observer
0144-7130 Textile News†
0144-7149 Chronicle (London)
0144-7165 YF: Yours Financially *changed to* Stockmarket Confidential.
0144-7181 Sport and Leisure (London)
0144-719X N A M E *see* 0260-0226
0144-7203 British Equestrian Directory
0144-7211 Inquisition *changed to* North West Societies. Combined Register of Members' Interests.
0144-7238 Wood Based Panels International
0144-7262 Rock Drill
0144-7327 Youth Exchange News
0144-7394 Teaching Public Administration
0144-7416 Ritz Newspaper
0144-7424 Arrowhead
0144-7440 Political Studies Association of the United Kingdom. Newsletter *see* 0955-6281
0144-7467 Thomas Cook Continental Timetable *see* 0952-620X
0144-7475 Thomas Cook Overseas Timetable
0144-7505 Printing Historical Society Bulletin
0144-7521 African Textiles
0144-7548 Republican Englishman
0144-7564 Comparative Criticism
0144-7572 Heatline†
0144-7580 H C I M A Quarterly Bibliography of Hotel and Catering Management
0144-7602 British Plant Growth Regulator Group. News Bulletin *see* 0963-6749
0144-7637 Traveller's Guide to North Africa
0144-7645 Traveller's Guide to West Africa
0144-7653 Traveller's Guide to East Africa and the Indian Ocean
0144-7661 Traveller's Guide to Central and Southern Africa
0144-7750 World Radio T V Handbook
0144-7777 Clinica
0144-7823 High-Speed Surface Craft *see* 0954-3988
0144-7831 Res Mechanica Letters†
0144-784X Bucks Advertiser
0144-7866 London Drinker
0144-8005 New Celtic Review†
0144-8072 Early Music Record Services. Monthly Review
0144-8099 Tourism†
0144-8129 Slimming
0144-8153 Evangelical Review of Theology
0144-817X Information Technology: R & D†
0144-8188 International Review of Law and Economics
0144-8196 Scottish Planning Law & Practice
0144-8218 Far Eastern Technical Review *see* 0956-3784
0144-8234 Africa Economic Digest
0144-8242 British Shipbuilder†
0144-8250 Car Parts & Accessories†
0144-8285 Catholic Commission for Racial Justice. Notes & Reports†
0144-8315 Staffordshire Post
0144-8331 Organ Player and Keyboard Review *see* 0269-3836
0144-8374 Baking Today†
0144-8382 County Trades Finder. Section 3: Southern
0144-8390 County Trades Finder. Section 1: Northern
0144-8404 Spon's Landscape Pricebook *see* 0267-4181
0144-8412 Artery
0144-8420 Radiation Protection Dosimetry
0144-8439 Conduit
0144-8447 Science for People†
0144-8455 Postgraduate Doctor: Asia†
0144-8463 Bioscience Reports
0144-8471 Insight (London, 1978)†
0144-8498 Quarterly Energy Review: Far East & Australasia†
0144-8560 Running
0144-8579 Hampshire Field Club and Archaeological Society. Local History Newsletter *see* 0265-9190
0144-8587 Chartered Institute of Building. Construction Papers†
0144-8609 Aquacultural Engineering
0144-8617 Carbohydrate Polymers
0144-8625 British Journal of Family Planning
0144-8676 Royal Society of Medicine. Annual Report of the Council
0144-8722 Sobornost
0144-8757 Quarterly Journal of Experimental Physiology and Cognate Medical Sciences *see* 0958-0670
0144-8765 Biological Agriculture and Horticulture
0144-8773 Heterocyclic Chemistry†
0144-8781 Far East Shipping†
0144-879X British Journal of Intravenous Therapy *see* 0264-7494
0144-8803 British Journal of Pharmaceutical Practice†
0144-8854 Quarterly Economic Review of China, North Korea *see* 0269-6231
0144-8870 Quarterly Economic Review of Poland *see* 0269-6193
0144-8889 Quarterly Economic Review of East Germany *changed to* Country Report. Germany.
0144-8897 Quarterly Economic Review of Japan *see* 0269-5405
0144-8900 Quarterly Economic Review of South Korea *see* 0269-669X
0144-8919 Quarterly Economic Review of Malaysia, Brunei *see* 0269-6703
0144-8927 Quarterly Economic Review of Singapore *see* 0269-6711
0144-8935 Quarterly Economic Review of Philippines *see* 0269-428X
0144-8943 Quarterly Economic Review of Taiwan *see* 0269-672X
0144-8951 Quarterly Economic Review of South Africa *see* 0269-6738
0144-896X Quarterly Economic Review of Namibia, Botswana, Lesotho, Swaziland *see* 0269-6746
0144-8978 Quarterly Economic Review of Czechoslovakia *see* 0269-4298
0144-8986 Quarterly Economic Review of Hungary *see* 0269-4301
0144-8994 Quarterly Energy Review: Middle East†
0144-901X Chartered Institute of Public Finance and Accountancy. Planning and Development Statistics. Estimates
0144-9036 B M P Monthly Statistical Bulletin
0144-9052 B M P Information
0144-9060 B M P Forecasts
0144-9117 O R C Notes

ISSN INDEX 5607

0144-9206 Quarterly Energy Review: North America†
0144-9214 Quarterly Energy Review: Latin America & the Caribbean†
0144-9222 Quarterly Energy Review: Western Europe†
0144-9230 Quarterly Energy Review: U.S.S.R. & Eastern Europe†
0144-9249 Quarterly Energy Review: Africa†
0144-9281 Environmental Education and Information
0144-929X Behavior and Information Technology
0144-9311 Transmission
0144-932X Liverpool Law Review
0144-9346 Tried & Tested†
0144-9451 Liverpool Latin Texts *see* 0951-7391
0144-946X Purvadesh
0144-9478 Butterworths International Medical Reviews: Obstetrics and Gynecology†
0144-9486 University College of Swansea. Centre for Development Studies. Monograph Series†
0144-9494 University College of Swansea. Centre for Development Studies. Occasional Papers Series†
0144-9508 United Society for the Propagation of the Gospel. Annual Report - Review *changed to* United Society for the Propagation of the Gospel. Yearbook.
0144-9524 Production Management and Control
0144-9613 Association Management†
0144-9621 B A S C A News
0144-9745 A R C News†
0144-9753 Asian Digest *changed to* Asian Times.
0144-9761 British Naturalist
0144-9818 Western Buddhist
0144-9826 Conchological Society Special Publication
0144-9842 Not Poetry†
0144-9850 University of London. Institute of Germanic Studies. Bithell Memorial Lectures
0144-9877 Chelmer Working Papers in Environmental Planning
0144-9885 Chartered Institute of Public Finance and Accountancy. Police Statistics. Estimates
0144-9893 Corporate Crime *changed to* Corporate Crime & Security.
0144-9907 Security Report *changed to* Corporate Crime & Security.
0144-9915 Chartered Institute of Public Finance and Accountancy. Police Statistics. Actuals†
0144-9931 Catalyst (London)
0144-9958 British Library. Reference Division Newspaper Library. Newsletter *changed to* British Library. Newspaper Library. Newsletter.
0144-9966 Bibliography in Socio-Legal Studies†
0144-9974 Pippin in Playland *changed to* Pippin.
0145-0034 Abstract Newsletter: Behavior and Society *changed to* N T I S Alerts: Behavior and Society.
0145-0085 Electronic Connector Study Group. Annual Connector Symposium. Proceedings *changed to* International Institute of Connector and Interconnection Technology. Annual Connector Symposium. Proceedings.
0145-0093 Kansas State University. Center for Energy Studies. Report†
0145-0344 Weekly Government Abstracts. Civil and Structural Engineering *changed to* N T I S Alerts: Civil Engineering.
0145-0379 Berkeley Papers in History of Science
0145-062X Public Documents Highlights†
0145-0689 River Currents
0145-0743 American Society of Civil Engineers. Water Resources Planning and Management Division. Journal *see* 0733-9496
0145-1014 Aviation Monthly
0145-1022 Real Estate Investing Letter
0145-1030 Money Management Digest†
0145-1065 U.S. National Institute on Drug Abuse. Statistical Series D. Client Oriented Data Acquisition Process. Quarterly Report *see* 0161-603X
0145-1073 Surface Warfare
0145-109X Boating Safety Newsletter *see* 0198-1501
0145-112X Profile (Norfolk)
0145-1146 Vessel Safety Review†
0145-1227 Fireword†
0145-1391 Epoch (Ithaca)
0145-1405 Atlanta Historical Bulletin *see* 0896-3975
0145-1413 Museum Notes (New York) *changed to* American Journal of Numismatics. Series 2.
0145-1421 East-West Technology Digest
0145-1456 Soviet Journal of Marine Biology
0145-1472 College Student and the Courts
0145-1499 Authors in the News†
0145-1502 U.S. General Accounting Office. Office of the General Counsel. Digests of Unpublished Decisions of the Comptroller General of the United States
0145-160X Washington Spectator - Between the Lines *see* 0887-428X
0145-1642 Ayer Directory of Publications *see* 1048-7972
0145-1677 First Monday
0145-1715 Downtown Planning & Development Annual†
0145-1731 Caligrafree Scribe *changed to* Calligranews.
0145-1847 Tax Facts on Life Insurance *changed to* Tax Facts 1.
0145-188X Industrial Relations Law Journal
0145-191X Guide to Catholic Literature *see* 0008-8285
0145-2029 And It Is Divine *changed to* Elan Vital.
0145-2037 Educational Commission for Foreign Medical Graduates. Annual Report
0145-2061 Thrust (Sacramento)
0145-207X Engineering Index. Notes and Comment *changed to* Notes & Comment.
0145-2096 Diplomatic History
0145-210X Songsmith's Journal†
0145-2118 Design Abstracts International†
0145-2126 Leukemia Research
0145-2134 Child Abuse & Neglect
0145-224X Nuclear Track Detection *changed to* International Journal of Radiation Applications and Instrumentation. Part D: Nuclear Tracks and Radiation Measurements.
0145-2258 African Economic History
0145-2355 Sources: A Guide to Print and Nonprint Materials Available from Organizations, Industry, Government Agencies, and Specialized Publishers *see* 0738-1522
0145-2363 Anales de la Novela de Posguerra *see* 0272-1635
0145-2371 Alpine Information†
0145-2517 Music & Musicians: Instructional Disc Recordings Catalog (Large Print Edition)
0145-2525 Music & Musicians: Instructional Cassette Recordings Catalog (Large Print Edition)
0145-2584 International Countermeasures Handbook
0145-2681 De Colores
0145-2711 Society of Biblical Literature. Seminar Papers (Year)
0145-3017 Corporate Buyers of Design Services/U S A
0145-3041 Social Services U.S.A.†
0145-305X Developmental and Comparative Immunology
0145-3068 Journal of Bioengineering *see* 0090-6964
0145-3076 State Court Journal
0145-3084 Bibliography Newsletter
0145-3130 Music & Musicians: Braille Scores Catalog - Piano (Large Print Edition)
0145-3149 Music & Musicians: Braille Scores Catalog - Organ (Large Print Edition)
0145-3157 Music and Musicians: Braille Scores Catalog - Voice *changed to* Music & Musicians: Braille Scores Catalog Vocal Part I: Classical (Large Print Edition).
0145-3157 Music and Musicians: Braille Scores Catalog - Voice *changed to* Music & Musicians: Braille Scores Catalog Vocal Part II: Popular (Large Print Edition).
0145-3165 Music & Musicians: Braille Scores Catalog - Instrumental (Large Print Edition)
0145-3173 Music & Musicians: Braille Scores Catalog - Choral (Large Print Edition)
0145-319X N A S A Tech Briefs *see* 0889-8464
0145-3351 Association for the Care of Children in Hospitals. Journal *see* 0273-9615
0145-3378 Journal of Psychohistory
0145-3416 Immigration Newsletter
0145-3432 Southern Illinois University Law Journal
0145-3483 Cinegram
0145-3505 Professional Liability Reporter
0145-3513 International Trombone Association. Journal
0145-370X International Ophthalmological Reporter
0145-3718 Advances in Modern Nutrition†
0145-3726 Progress in Cancer Research and Therapy
0145-3793 National New Health Practitioner Program Profile *see* 1051-600X
0145-3815 Environmental Periodicals Bibliography: Indexed Article Titles *changed to* Environmental Periodicals Bibliography.
0145-3831 Swimming and Diving Case Book *changed to* Swimming and Diving and Water Polo Rulebook.
0145-3939 Extra!
0145-3963 Cornell Executive†
0145-4013 Visual Arts Program *changed to* N E A Grantmaking Programs: Visual Arts.
0145-403X Cardiovascular Medicine *see* 0363-5104
0145-4048 Alabama Directory of Mining and Manufacturing *changed to* Alabama Industrial Directory.
0145-4064 Firehouse
0145-4072 Exchange (Columbia)†
0145-4129 Health Lawyers News Report *changed to* Health Lawyers News Report.
0145-4145 Year Book of Cardiology
0145-417X Coal Data
0145-4250 American Handgunner
0145-4455 Behavior Modification
0145-4471 Powder
0145-448X New York Law School Law Review
0145-4498 Current Concepts in Emergency Medicine†
0145-4560 C B Radio - S 9
0145-4692 Evaluation Quarterly *see* 0193-841X
0145-479X Journal of Bioenergetics and Biomembranes
0145-482X Journal of Visual Impairment & Blindness
0145-4927 Current Industrial Reports: Manufacturers' Export Sales and Orders of Durable Goods†
0145-5028 Woven Fabrics. Production, Inventories, and Unfilled Orders *changed to* Current Industrial Reports: Broadwoven Fabrics (Gray).
0145-5125 Radio Free Jazz *see* 0272-572X
0145-5168 Current Industrial Reports: Fats and Oils. Oilseed Crushings
0145-5176 Current Industrial Reports: Fats and Oils. Production, Consumption, and Factory and Warehouse Stocks *changed to* Current Industrial Reports: Fats and Oils. Production, Consumption, and Stocks.
0145-5273 Package Development and Systems *see* 0274-4996
0145-5281 Circus Maximus†
0145-529X Milton and the Romantics *see* 0733-6519
0145-5303 Phantasm†
0145-5311 Recently Published Articles†
0145-5338 Benchmark Papers in Analytical Chemistry†
0145-5397 Library Developments
0145-5400 G.P.U. News
0145-5419 Music America *see* 0733-5253
0145-546X Mountain Review†
0145-5508 Journal of Pedodontics *see* 1053-4628
0145-5532 Social Science History
0145-5575 Thorndyke File
0145-5605 Earth Resources: A Continuing Bibliography with Indexes†
0145-5613 Ear, Nose and Throat Journal
0145-5664 Current Business Reports: Canned Food†
0145-5672 I U P A C Information Bulletin *see* 0193-6484
0145-5680 Cellular & Molecular Biology
0145-5699 Communications in Psychopharmacology†
0145-5702 Mazingira
0145-5753 Rohmer Review
0145-5761 Working Woman
0145-5788 Teaching Philosophy
0145-5818 Criminal Justice Periodical Index
0145-5869 Foodservice Distributor Salesman†
0145-5885 Florida Environmental and Urban Issues *see* 1044-033X
0145-5958 Symposium on Engineering Problems of Fusion Research. Proceedings *changed to* Symposium on Fusion Engineering. Proceedings.
0145-5982 R I L A (Repertoire International de la Litterature de l'Art) *see* 1150-1588
0145-5990 Kentucky. Department for Human Resources. Selected Vital Statistics and Planning Data *changed to* Kentucky. Cabinet for Human Resources. Vital Statistics Report.
0145-6008 Alcoholism: Clinical and Experimental Research
0145-6016 Hobby Artist News†
0145-6024 Country Messenger†
0145-6032 Cinefantastique
0145-6075 White Book of U S Ski Areas *see* 0163-9684
0145-6105 American Historical Society of Germans from Russia. Work Paper *see* 0162-8283
0145-613X Daiwa Fishing Annual†
0145-6180 M P L A Newsletter
0145-6202 Federal Yellow Book
0145-6210 Body Forum†
0145-6237 Guitar Foundation of America Soundboard *changed to* Soundboard.
0145-6261 Feed-Back (San Francisco)†
0145-627X Book Talk
0145-6288 International Plant Protection Center. Infoletter
0145-6296 Veterinary and Human Toxicology
0145-6318 China Exchange Newsletter *see* 0272-0086
0145-6334 Assur
0145-6342 A L I - A B A Course Materials Journal
0145-6431 Orlando-Land *see* 0279-1323
0145-644X Washington Watch†
0145-6466 Indian Opinion†
0145-6571 Law Officer's Bulletin
0145-6601 N A G W S Guide. Soccer, Speedball, Flag Football *see* 0163-4747
0145-6636 Pastoral Music Notebook
0145-6644 Fund Sources in Health and Allied Fields†
0145-6776 Auto Index
0145-6784 Soldier of Fortune
0145-6792 Glassworks†
0145-6822 A C T News *see* 0163-7908
0145-6830 Society for Slovene Studies Newsletter *see* 0193-1075
0145-6857 Alabama's Health
0145-6873 C N L - Quarterly World Report *changed to* C N L - World Report.

ISSN

ISSN	Title
0145-692X	Corporate Profiles for Executives & Investors†
0145-7055	McCutcheon's Emulsifiers and Detergents - North American Edition
0145-7071	Business People in the News†
0145-7217	Diabetes Educator
0145-7233	Concordia Journal
0145-7241	Artnewsletter
0145-7322	Criminal Law Outline
0145-7365	Christian Science Quarterly (Inkprint Edition)
0145-7616	Computed Axial Tomography see 0899-7071
0145-7624	Death Education see 0748-1187
0145-7632	Heat Transfer Engineering
0145-7659	Privacy Journal
0145-7667	Liberty Bell
0145-7675	The Other Side (Philadelphia)
0145-7683	Significant Advances in Science†
0145-7780	Graham House Review
0145-7861	Society for South India Studies. Newsletter changed to South Asia News.
0145-7888	Studies in Twentieth Century Literature
0145-7918	Blaisdell Institute. Journal.†
0145-7950	Orthodox Church in America. Yearbook and Church Directory
0145-7969	New Pulpit Digest see 0160-838X
0145-7985	W I N News
0145-7993	American Indian Journal
0145-8035	Guide to Graduate and Professional Study†
0145-8043	Student Aid Manual changed to Chronicle Financial Aid Guide.
0145-8116	International Review of African American Art
0145-8124	Election Administration Reports
0145-8213	Scale Cabinetmaker
0145-8256	Needlepoint News see 1040-5518
0145-8264	Journal of the Milking Shorthorn and Illawarra Breeds
0145-8302	Grantechs
0145-8310	Cathartic
0145-8361	Seeker Newsletter see 0890-538X
0145-837X	Pharmaceutical Trends†
0145-8388	New Laurel Review
0145-8396	Institute for Studies in American Music. Newsletter
0145-840X	Korean Studies
0145-8418	Eastern Electrical Buyers' Guide†
0145-8426	Southern Electrical Buyers' Guide†
0145-8442	Customer Service Newsletter
0145-8477	Battelle Today
0145-8493	American Academy and Institute of Arts and Letters. Proceedings
0145-8515	Ranch Magazine
0145-871X	Consultant's Coin Report changed to Consultant's Certified Coin Report.
0145-8752	Moscow University Geology Bulletin
0145-8779	Marianne Moore Newsletter†
0145-8787	Pulp†
0145-8795	Joint Conference†
0145-8809	Astrology Now†
0145-8825	Greater Llano Estacado Southwest Heritage†
0145-8833	Vantage Conference Report see 0748-0571
0145-8841	Stanley Foundation. Policy Paper†
0145-885X	Gnostica†
0145-8868	Llewellyn's Astrological Calendar
0145-8876	Journal of Food Process Engineering
0145-8884	Journal of Food Biochemistry
0145-8892	Journal of Food Processing and Preservation
0145-8930	Hospital Libraries†
0145-8973	Chasqui
0145-899X	Combinations
0145-9007	Maine Marketing Directory changed to Maine Manufacturing Directory.
0145-9031	Carnegie Museum of Natural History. Special Publications
0145-904X	Racing Cars†
0145-9058	Carnegie Museum of Natural History. Bulletin
0145-9074	Business Law Review†
0145-9090	World Coin News
0145-9104	Gaysweek
0145-9112	Northeast Improver†
0145-918X	Ski Competition East†
0145-9198	American Oil & Gas Reporter
0145-9244	Materials and Components in Fossil Energy Applications and E R D A Newsletter changed to Materials and Components in Fossil Energy Applications.
0145-9317	Near East and North Africa Report changed to Near East - South Asia Report.
0145-935X	Child & Youth Services
0145-9376	Florida Vocational Journal
0145-9392	Oklahoma Farmer-Stockman
0145-9406	Security Management
0145-9457	B P Report
0145-9473	Joyer Travel Report see 0741-5826
0145-9481	Sahel Bibliographic Bulletin/Bulletin Bibliographique.†
0145-949X	Chairman's Chat see 0163-0253
0145-952X	U.S. Social Security Administration. Office of Research and Statistics. Public Assistance Statistics changed to Quarterly Public Assistance Statistics.
0145-9546	Horological Times
0145-9570	Coach: Women's Athletics see 0160-2624
0145-9635	Independent School
0145-9643	Population Reports
0145-9651	Media Report to Women
0145-9678	Clements' International Report
0145-9678	Clements' Encyclopedia of World Governments
0145-9740	Medical Anthropology
0145-9759	Film - Psychology changed to Film - Psychology Review.
0145-9767	N A G W S Guide. Team Handball, Racquetball, Orienteering changed to N A G W S Guide. Team Handball, Orienteering.
0145-9783	Man and Medicine
0145-9791	Horse Illustrated
0145-983X	Weid: the Sensibility Revue†
0145-997X	Bulletin: Open Court Newsletter changed to Educator: Open Court Newsletter.
0146-0005	Seminars in Perinatology
0146-0013	Quarterly Review of Film Studies see 1050-9208
0146-0021	Sundance Community Dream Journal†
0146-0072	Pay T V Newsletter
0146-0080	Cablecast see 0731-0250
0146-0099	Multicast
0146-0102	Cable TV Regulation see 0731-0269
0146-0110	Broadcast Investor
0146-0129	In a Nutshell†
0146-0137	Technical Education News
0146-0145	International Flash†
0146-0153	Photomethods see 1060-4936
0146-0196	South Carolina Baptist Historical Society Journal
0146-020X	Agenda (Washington)
0146-0234	International Society for Labor Law and Social Legislation. United States National Committee. Bulletin see 0147-9202
0146-0269	Graves Family Newsletter
0146-0315	Santa Clara Law Review
0146-0323	Directory of Registered Lobbyists and Lobbyist Legislation†
0146-0382	Legal Research Journal
0146-0404	Investigative Ophthalmology & Visual Science
0146-0412	Journal of Energy†
0146-0463	Xanadu
0146-0471	Ear (San Francisco)
0146-0498	Indiana Speech Journal†
0146-0501	Pesticide & Toxic Chemical News
0146-0595	Real Estate Issues
0146-0609	New Review of Books and Religion see 0890-0841
0146-0625	B M W E Railway Journal see 1049-3921
0146-0641	Journal of Solid-Phase Biochemistry see 0273-2289
0146-0706	Elastomerics
0146-0722	Advances in Pain Research and Therapy
0146-0749	Microbiological Reviews
0146-0781	American Motor Carrier Directory: Illinois-Missouri Edition†
0146-079X	American Motor Carrier Directory: Southeastern Edition†
0146-0803	American Motor Carrier Directory: Middle Atlantic Edition†
0146-0811	American Motor Carrier Directory: New England Edition†
0146-0838	Checklist of Official New Jersey Publications
0146-0862	Issues in Comprehensive Pediatric Nursing
0146-0889	Sporting Goods Business
0146-0897	Catalog Showroom Business changed to C S M.
0146-0900	Bank Systems & Technology
0146-0919	Multi Housing News†
0146-0935	Trademark Design Register†
0146-0951	National Purchasing Review†
0146-0986	Conservative Digest†
0146-0986	Conference Board. Survey of Corporate Contributions
0146-0994	Japanese Philately
0146-1001	Alternative Sources of Energy see 1043-7320
0146-1044	Sexuality and Disability
0146-1052	Journal of Population see 0199-0039
0146-1060	U.S. Library of Congress. Accessions List: Brazil. Annual List of Serials see 1042-1734
0146-1079	Biblical Theology Bulletin
0146-1087	New Jersey Poetry Monthly changed to New Jersey Poetry.
0146-1095	Channel D L S
0146-1109	Midcontinental Journal of Archaeology
0146-1117	Council Notes†
0146-1133	Women's Coaching Clinic see 0009-9880
0146-1141	International Foundation of Employee Benefit Plans. Digest
0146-115X	Career Education Workshop†
0146-1168	Guidance Clinic†
0146-1176	Reading Clinic†
0146-1184	Slow Learner Workshop†
0146-1214	Technology and Conservation
0146-132X	North American Metalworking Research Conference. Proceedings changed to Transactions of the North American Manufacturing Research Conference. Proceedings.
0146-1362	Woodall's Campground Directory. North American - Canadian Edition changed to Woodall's Campground Directory. North American Edition.
0146-1397	Stone Country†
0146-1559	Tox-Tips†
0146-1672	Personality and Social Psychology Bulletin
0146-1710	Yale Italian Studies†
0146-1737	Production Engineering changed to Controls and Systems.
0146-1745	International Review of Natural Family Planning changed to International Review.
0146-1788	Educom Networking†
0146-1842	News for South Carolina Libraries
0146-1869	Rio Grande History†
0146-1885	Rockingchair: The Review Newsletter for Librarians and Popular Music Fans Who Buy Records see 0160-4201
0146-1907	Summary of Rate Schedules of Natural Gas Pipeline Companies as Filed with the Federal Power Commission changed to Summary of Rate Schedules of Natural Gas Pipeline Companies.
0146-194X	Geothermal Energy Update changed to Geothermal Energy.
0146-1958	Flagstaff Institute. Journal
0146-1990	Bryant Backtrails†
0146-2059	Structural Mechanics Software Series†
0146-2067	Stony Hills
0146-2075	Pimienta†
0146-2083	Tuumba†
0146-2091	Media Digest
0146-2105	Star-Web Paper
0146-2113	Affirmative Action Register
0146-2156	Summary of Congress
0146-2199	Cape Rock
0146-2202	J'adoube!†
0146-2229	Utah Genealogical Association. Genealogical Journal
0146-2237	P L A Report†
0146-2334	Lilith
0146-2350	E D C News†
0146-2377	Konglomerati†
0146-2520	In Situ
0146-2539	Senior World changed to Senior World of Los Angeles County.
0146-2547	Second Republic Newsletter changed to Rangel's Reports.
0146-2555	G S M Quarterly†
0146-2571	University of California, Los Angeles. Graduate School of Management. Annual Report†
0146-2598	University of Wisconsin-Milwaukee. Center for Latin America. Special Papers Series changed to University of Wisconsin-Milwaukee. Center for Latin America. Community Resources Series.
0146-2628	Super Chevy
0146-2644	1001 Truck and Van Ideas see 0195-0509
0146-2660	Faxon Librarians' Guide changed to Faxon Guide to Serials.
0146-2679	Collection Management
0146-2725	L B L Newsmagazine†
0146-275X	Long-Term Care Administrator
0146-2768	Health in Wisconsin
0146-2806	Current Problems in Cardiology
0146-2857	Factory Outlet Newsletter†
0146-2962	Journal of Cherokee Studies
0146-2970	Comments on Astrophysics
0146-2989	Bulletin of Medieval Canon Law. New Series
0146-2997	Arizona Mining and Manufacturing†
0146-3071	Journal of Seed Technology
0146-308X	Audio Journal Review: Ophthalmology†
0146-3128	PharmChem Newsletter
0146-3136	Poets On:
0146-3160	Mystery Fancier†
0146-3225	Chowder Review†
0146-3284	Soccer Corner†
0146-3292	Motocross Action
0146-3349	Worldwide Pipelines and Contractors Directory†
0146-3365	C A O Times changed to C A O.
0146-3373	Communication Quarterly
0146-3381	Teachers & Writers Magazine
0146-339X	Off Belay†
0146-3403	Optical Index
0146-3411	Heresies
0146-3489	Relix
0146-3527	Pulp, Paper and Board see 0164-095X
0146-3535	Progress in Crystal Growth and Characterization see 0960-8974
0146-3586	Studies in Human Rights
0146-3608	Contributions in Labor History see 0886-8239
0146-3640	Older Americans Report
0146-3659	Plants Alive
0146-3667	Electro-Technology Newsletter
0146-3675	Geothermal Energy changed to Renewable Energy News Digest.
0146-3721	American Journal of Dance Therapy
0146-3764	L.S.B. Leakey Foundation News changed to Anthroquest.

0146-3772 Hang Glider Weekly see 0164-3452
0146-3810 Advances in General and Cellular Pharmacology†
0146-3861 Law Book Guide see 0360-2745
0146-390X World Issues†
0146-3934 College Student Journal
0146-3942 Institute of Mathematical Statistics. Bulletin
0146-3977 International Institute of Synthetic Rubber Producers. Annual Meeting Proceedings
0146-4094 Hebrew Studies
0146-4108 Soviet Meteorology and Hydrology
0146-4116 Automatic Control and Computer Sciences
0146-4124 Topology Proceedings
0146-4132 Aramco World Magazine see 1044-1891
0146-4140 Journal of Ballistics
0146-4167 Colloquia in Anthropology
0146-423X Columbia Today see 0162-3893
0146-4299 Fossil Energy Update†
0146-4329 School Universe Data Book see 0162-9646
0146-437X New York History
0146-4396 C A Selects. Catalysis (Organic Reactions)
0146-440X C A Selects. Catalysis (Applied & Physical Aspects)
0146-4426 C A Selects. Coal Science and Process Chemistry
0146-4434 C A Selects. Corrosion
0146-4442 C A Selects. Electrochemical Reactions
0146-4450 C A Selects. Electron & Auger Spectroscopy
0146-4469 C A Selects. Electron Spin Resonance (Chemical Aspects)
0146-4477 C A Selects. Gas Chromatography
0146-4485 C A Selects. Gel Permeation Chromatography
0146-4493 C A Selects. Ion Exchange
0146-4515 C A Selects. Paper & Thin-Layer Chromatography
0146-4523 C A Selects. Radiation Chemistry
0146-4531 C A Selects. Solvent Extraction
0146-454X C A Selects. Surface Chemistry (Physicochemical Aspects)
0146-4558 Distribution of Physicians in the U S see 0731-0315
0146-4566 International Solar Energy Society. American Section. Annual Meeting. Proceedings changed to American Solar Energy Society. Annual Meeting.
0146-4574 Polo
0146-4582 Red Book of Ophthalmology
0146-4604 Radiation Curing see 1057-5715
0146-4639 Product Safety Watchdog Service see 0275-0902
0146-4647 I T A News Digest†
0146-4671 Petersen's Hunting
0146-4701 Audio Critic
0146-4744 Business Assistance Monograph Series†
0146-4752 High Solids Coatings†
0146-4760 Journal of Analytical Toxicology
0146-4779 Journal of Environmental Pathology and Toxicology see 0731-8898
0146-4817 Noise Control Report see 1043-5565
0146-4825 D.A.T.A. Book of Discontinued Integrated Circuits changed to Digital & Audio-Video Discontinued Devices D.A.T.A. Book.
0146-4833 Computer Communications Review
0146-485X S E C Accounting Report
0146-4906 Federal Civilian Workforce Statistics. Occupations of Federal White-Collar Workers changed to Federal Civilian Workforce Statistics. Occupations of Federal White-Collar and Blue-Collar Workers.
0146-4922 Milton Newsletter see 0026-4326
0146-4930 New Letters
0146-4965 African Literature Association Newsletter changed to African Literature Association. Bulletin.
0146-4981 International Journal of Fusion Energy
0146-5007 Basketball Clinic see 0009-9880
0146-5015 Salaries of Scientists, Engineers and Technicians
0146-5023 Motion Picture Product Digest†
0146-5031 U V Curing Buyer's Guide see 0197-8039
0146-5090 Journal of Cybernetics and Information Science†
0146-5104 Handbook for Recruiting at the Historically Black Colleges changed to C C D M Minority Student Recruitment Guide.
0146-521X Regional Anesthesia
0146-5376 Contemporary China†
0146-5414 Harvest Book Series
0146-5422 Online (Weston)
0146-5449 Analyzer see 0893-2972
0146-5473 Public Works News
0146-5481 N A I C Malpractice Claims†
0146-5511 American Jewish Historical Society. Publications see 0164-0178
0146-5546 Jump Cut
0146-5554 Cumulative Index to Nursing & Allied Health Literature
0146-5562 Interracial Books for Children Bulletin
0146-5643 Idaho Heritage†
0146-5678 Nonferrous Castings
0146-5716 New Periodicals Index†
0146-5724 Radiation Physics and Chemistry changed to International Journal of Radiation Applications and Instrumentation. Part C: Radiation Physics and Chemistry.
0146-5759 Crime in Virginia
0146-5783 Association for Gravestone Studies. Newsletter
0146-5813 C B Report
0146-5856 Arnold Schoenberg Institute. Journal
0146-5864 Solar Thermal Energy Utilization changed to Solar Energy Utilization: a Bibliography. Vol. 1. Solar Power Generation.
0146-5864 Solar Thermal Energy Utilization see 0148-4397
0146-5864 Solar Thermal Energy Utilization see 0160-368X
0146-5872 American Board of Medical Specialties. Annual Report see 0272-9741
0146-5945 Policy Review
0146-5996 Home Improvement Contractor see 0885-8039
0146-6119 E M S A Bulletin
0146-6143 Dixie Gun Works Muzzleloaders' Annual†
0146-6178 Group Psychotherapy, Psychodrama and Sociometry see 0731-1273
0146-6216 Applied Psychological Measurement
0146-6283 Cereal Foods World
0146-6291 Deep-Sea Research see 0198-0149
0146-6291 Deep-Sea Research see 0198-0254
0146-6305 Oceanographic Abstracts and Bibliography see 0198-0149
0146-6305 Oceanographic Abstracts and Bibliography see 0198-0254
0146-6321 A H C A Weekly Notes changed to A H C A Notes.
0146-6364 Chinese Astronomy see 0275-1062
0146-6372 Journal of Enterprise Management†
0146-6380 Organic Geochemistry
0146-6399 Materials and Society†
0146-6402 Advances in Behaviour Research and Therapy
0146-6410 Progress in Particle and Nuclear Physics
0146-6429 Society of Vector Ecologists. Bulletin changed to Society for Vector Ecology. Bulletin.
0146-6453 International Commission on Radiological Protection. Annals
0146-6518 International Journal for Housing Science and Its Applications
0146-6534 Dow Jones-Irwin Business Almanac changed to Business One Irwin Business and Investment Almanac.
0146-6607 Crafts 'n Things
0146-6615 Journal of Medical Virology
0146-6623 Journal of Aquatic Plant Management
0146-6631 Journal of Medical Entomology. Supplement†
0146-664X Computer Graphics and Image Processing see 1049-9652
0146-678X Oriental Institute Communications
0146-6798 Materials and Studies for Kassite History
0146-6801 Toll Free Business
0146-6887 Linn's World Stamp Almanac
0146-6917 Princeton Conference on Cerebrovascular Diseases changed to Princeton Research Conferences on Cerebrovascular Diseases.
0146-6941 Northwest Chess
0146-695X Monthly Poetry Anthology changed to Realities.
0146-7042 Big Deal†
0146-7085 Directory Information Service†
0146-7123 Design Automation Conference. Proceedings see 0738-100X
0146-7158 California. Division of Mines and Geology. Preliminary Report†
0146-7166 Christian Science Bible Lessons (Braille Edition)
0146-7190 Powell Monetary Analyst
0146-7204 Powell Gold Industry Guide & International Mining Analyst
0146-7220 Eudora Welty Newsletter
0146-7239 Motivation and Emotion
0146-7247 Year Book of Otolaryngology see 1041-892X
0146-728X Washington Drug Review see 0744-2823
0146-7336 Directory of Research Grants
0146-7352 Administration of the Employee Retirement Income Security Act see 0271-1567
0146-7581 Value Line Option and Convertible Survey changed to Value Line Options.
0146-7611 Investigative and Cell Pathology see 0022-3417
0146-7638 Keeping Abreast Journal see 0164-7083
0146-7646 P R B Report†
0146-7662 Eyepiece
0146-7735 Business Conditions Digest†
0146-7743 Insight (New York)
0146-7751 Minnesota State Register
0146-776X Sea Grant Law Journal see 0197-9906
0146-7824 Well-Being
0146-7832 New Thought (Mesa)
0146-7883 Music-in-Print Series
0146-7891 Nineteenth Century French Studies
0146-7921 Christopher Street
0146-7980 I L Z R O Lead Research Digest†
0146-7999 I L Z R O Zinc Research Digest changed to I L Z R O Zinc Cadmium Research Digest.
0146-8006 Struggle changed to Practice (New York).
0146-8022 Medical and Healthcare Marketplace Guide
0146-8030 Fiber and Integrated Optics
0146-809X Southern Exposure (Durham)
0146-8170 New Thought Bulletin see 0146-7832
0146-8197 International Series on Biomechanics†
0146-8227 Developmental Neurobiology†
0146-8251 Southern Golf - Landscape and Turf Industry changed to Southern Golf - Landscape & Resort Management.
0146-8286 National Federation of State High School Associations. Softball Rules see 0732-2844
0146-8294 Artist's and Photographer's Market see 0161-0546
0146-8383 Racing Pigeon Bulletin
0146-8510 Uroboros
0146-8537 Comentarios Sobre el Desarrollo Internacional†
0146-8545 H S R I Research Review see 0739-7100
0146-8588 Advances in Modern Toxicology†
0146-860X Video Bluebook see 0731-454X
0146-860X Video Bluebook changed to General Interest and Education Videolog.
0146-8677 Queens College Studies in Librarianship†
0146-8685 Rhode Island Library Association. Bulletin
0146-8693 Journal of Pediatric Psychology
0146-8790 Advances in the Management of Clinical Heart Disease†
0146-8812 Fighting Woman News
0146-8901 C O M P Newsletter changed to Local Government Performance.
0146-8936 L C Acquisition Trends†
0146-8995 Canto†
0146-9061 Universitas
0146-9096 Kettering Abstracts of Available Literature on the Biological and Related Aspects of Lead and Its Compounds
0146-9126 Ocean Resources Engineering†
0146-9177 Criminal Justice Abstracts
0146-9223 Progressive Grocer's Market Scope
0146-924X Vestnik Leningrad University: Mathematics
0146-9282 Educational Considerations
0146-9290 Coatings Adlibra see 0891-1886
0146-9304 Foods Adlibra
0146-9312 Sea History
0146-9339 Mythlore
0146-9347 Mythprint
0146-9398 Ala-Arts changed to Alabama Arts.
0146-9428 Journal of Food Quality
0146-9436 M A S K C Komondor News
0146-9487 Homemaker†
0146-9517 N S S Bulletin
0146-9568 Toledo†
0146-9576 San Francisco Theatre Magazine
0146-9584 Journal of Legislation
0146-9592 Optics Letters
0146-9606 American Artist Directory of Art Schools & Workshops
0146-9657 Korea Newsreview
0146-9673 Employment and Training Reporter
0146-9711 New Perspectives in Powder Metallurgy
0146-9738 Dental Lab Products
0146-9770 A I C P A Washington Report†
0146-9819 Auditing Research Monographs
0146-9924 Circuit Rider (Nashville)
0146-9932 M V M A Motor Vehicle Facts and Figures
0146-9959 Meteor News
0146-9967 Longest Revolution†
0146-9975 N S O A Bulletin
0146-9983 Postal History U.S.A†
0146-9991 Colorado Express
0147-0019 Brown Family changed to Brown Family News & Geneological Society.
0147-0035 Data Entry Digest and Distributed Processing changed to Data Entry Digest.
0147-0051 Fire & Movement
0147-006X Annual Review of Neuroscience
0147-0078 Recent Researches in American Music
0147-0086 Recent Researches in the Music of the Classical Era
0147-0108 Collegium Musicum: Yale University
0147-0124 N O R C Reporter
0147-0272 Current Problems in Cancer
0147-0302 Motor Skills: Theory into Practice†
0147-0310 Association of American Publishers. Exhibits Directory
0147-0353 Health Values
0147-037X Ming Studies
0147-0396 Rebis Chapbook Series
0147-0418 Journal of Interior Design Education and Research
0147-0493 C C L P: Contents of Current Legal Periodicals see 0279-5787
0147-0515 N I A A A - R U C A S Alcoholism Treatment Series
0147-0590 Regulation (Washington, 1977)†

5610 ISSN INDEX

0147-0604 Michigan State University. Library. Africana: Select Recent Acquisitions
0147-0612 Michigan State University. Library. Latin America: Select Recent Acquisitions†
0147-0620 Michigan State University. Library. Asia: Select Recent Acquisitions†
0147-0639 Maine Antique Digest
0147-0655 Human Sexuality *changed to* Annual Editions: Human Sexuality.
0147-0671 International Progress in Urethanes
0147-071X Advances in Behavioral Pharmacology†
0147-0728 Gay Community News (Boston)
0147-0779 Modern Greek Society: A Social Science Newsletter
0147-0787 Books at Brown
0147-0833 Journal of Equine Medicine and Surgery *see* 0162-8941
0147-0906 Linguistics in Literature *see* 1057-6037
0147-0981 Fletcher Forum *see* 1046-1868
0147-1015 Ukrainian Orthodox Word. English Edition
0147-1023 Contributions in Family Studies
0147-1031 Contributions in Intercultural and Comparative Studies
0147-104X Contributions in Women's Studies
0147-1058 Contributions in Medical History *see* 0886-8220
0147-1066 Contributions in Political Science
0147-1074 Contributions in Legal Studies
0147-1082 Contemporary Problems of Childhood
0147-1090 New Directions in Librarianship *see* 0887-3844
0147-1104 Studies in Population and Urban Demography
0147-1112 Dax Money-Maker Newsletter
0147-1120 Association of College Unions - International. Proceedings of the Annual Conference
0147-1139 Dignity - U S A
0147-1147 Design Methods and Theories
0147-1155 Cancer Focus *changed to* Northwestern University. Robert H. Lurie Cancer Center. Journal.
0147-1201 M A I N
0147-121X Light†
0147-1228 Hoosier Journal of Ancestry
0147-1236 A C T F L Foreign Language Education Series
0147-1260 Child Protection Report
0147-1465 Washington Review of Strategic and International Studies *see* 0163-660X
0147-1481 Offshore Rig Newsletter
0147-149X Cottonwood Review *changed to* Cottonwood.
0147-1503 Thermodynamics Research Center. International Data Series. Selected Data on Mixtures. Series A. Thermodynamic Properties on Non-reacting Binary Systems of Organic Substances *changed to* International Data Series. Selected Data on Mixtures. Series A. Thermodynamic Properties of Non-reacting Binary Systems of Organic Substances.
0147-152X Offshore Construction Report *see* 1058-5842
0147-1554 Across the Board
0147-1570 CompFlash
0147-1597 Opus Two
0147-1627 Calyx
0147-1635 Journal of Basic Writing
0147-1651 Graphic Arts Green Book *see* 1044-8535
0147-1678 Directory of Fee-Based Information Services *changed to* Burwell Directory of Information Brokers.
0147-1686 Floating Island
0147-1694 Contemporary Jewry†
0147-1724 Southwestern Entomologist
0147-1740 Urban League Review
0147-1759 Women & Literature
0147-1767 International Journal of Intercultural Relations
0147-1775 International Journal of Family Counseling *see* 0192-6187
0147-1783 Washington (State). Department of Natural Resources. Division of Geology and Earth Resources. Information Circular
0147-1821 Graduate Programs: Physics, Astronomy, and Related Fields (Year)
0147-1902 Georgia Museum of Art. Bulletin
0147-1937 Real Analysis Exchange
0147-1961 Banking Today *changed to* Florida Banking.
0147-197X Current Problems in Anesthesia and Critical Care Medicine†
0147-1988 Current Problems in Obstetrics and Gynecology *see* 8756-0410
0147-1996 Year Book of Family Practice
0147-2003 Southwest Regional Conference for Astronomy and Astrophysics. Proceedings†
0147-2011 Society
0147-2135 A R L Statistics
0147-216X Directory of Washington Representatives of American Associations and Industry *see* 0192-060X
0147-2208 Laventhol and Horwath Perspective†
0147-2275 Seriatim
0147-2313 Screen Achievement Records Bulletin *see* 0163-5123
0147-2399 Travel Research Bulletin *see* 0047-2875
0147-2410 Western Investor†
0147-2429 Plastics in Building Construction
0147-2453 Curriculum Review
0147-2461 Art and Crafts Market *see* 0161-0554
0147-2461 Art and Crafts Market *see* 0161-0546
0147-247X Photographer's Market
0147-2488 Richardson Family Researcher and Historical News
0147-2496 Environmental Review *changed to* Environmental History Review.
0147-250X Bibliography of Books for Children†
0147-2526 Dance Chronicle
0147-2542 Ohio Documents
0147-2550 Massachusetts Music News
0147-2569 Chess Horizons
0147-2593 Lion & the Unicorn
0147-2615 Abstracts of Popular Culture†
0147-2631 Hollow Spring Review of Poetry
0147-264X Dental Research in the United States and Other Countries†
0147-2682 Biomedical Technology Information Service
0147-2704 Seventh Ray
0147-2747 N S P I Journal (Year) *see* 0884-1985
0147-281X West Point Museum Bulletin†
0147-2828 Black Press Information Handbook†
0147-2860 Illinois. State Board of Education. Annual Report
0147-2917 Comparative Medicine East and West *see* 0192-415X
0147-2968 Running Times
0147-2992 Interface Age *changed to* Computing for Business.
0147-300X International Glass-Metal Catalog
0147-3077 Periodical Guide for Computerists†
0147-3085 Celestinesca
0147-3158 R G L in (Year) *see* 0196-173X
0147-3158 Research Libraries Group. Newsletter *see* 0196-173X
0147-3166 Winesburg Eagle
0147-3204 I E E E Transactions on Cable Television†
0147-3247 Nuestro
0147-328X Liquid Chromatography Literature - Abstracts and Index
0147-3301 Cablelines
0147-3328 G T E Automatic Electric Technical Journal *see* 0273-141X
0147-3379 Product Marketing *see* 0278-1530
0147-345X Eastman Notes
0147-3522 Ocean Engineering *see* 0146-9126
0147-3565 Porsche Panorama
0147-3646 A.P.S. Writers Unit Number Thirty News Bulletin *changed to* Philatelic Communicator.
0147-3654 Scienceland
0147-3700 Mental Disability Law Reporter *see* 0883-7902
0147-3735 Presbyterian Historical Society Journal *see* 0886-5159
0147-3743 Safety Sadistics†
0147-3751 Americans Abroad†
0147-3786 Quest (Year)†
0147-3867 Country Vacations U.S.A. *see* 0195-8437
0147-3964 Multivariate Experimental Clinical Research
0147-4006 Carcinogenesis
0147-4022 Journal of Divorce *see* 1050-2556
0147-4030 How to Fly for Less†
0147-4049 Bright Lights†
0147-4057 Newsounds
0147-409X Export Grafics U S A *changed to* Printing Product International.
0147-4189 Year in Metabolism *see* 0193-340X
0147-4243 Economic Analysis of North American Ski Areas
0147-4308 Israel Securities Review Monthly Magazine *see* 0147-4316
0147-4316 Israel Securities Review†
0147-4367 Voice of Washington Music Educators
0147-4375 A A E S P H Review (American Association for the Education of the Severely-Profoundly Handicapped) *changed to* Association for Persons with Severe Handicaps. Journal.
0147-4391 B I A Education Research Bulletin†
0147-4413 American Liszt Society. Journal *changed to* J A L S.
0147-4502 West Coast Plays†
0147-4529 Government-Supported Research on Foreign Affairs *see* 0194-8660
0147-4650 Checklist of Official Publications of the State of Oregon†
0147-4685 National Doll World *changed to* International Doll World.
0147-4693 On the Line Magazine (New York)
0147-4707 Chicago Library System Communicator *see* 0277-8955
0147-4804 World Wide Printer
0147-4820 A A S H T O Quarterly Magazine
0147-4863 Advances in Microbial Ecology
0147-4871 Feedback
0147-4928 Country Gentleman
0147-4936 Invisible City
0147-507X First World
0147-510X Us (New York, 1977)
0147-5118 Toxic Substances Sourcebook†
0147-5185 American Journal of Surgical Pathology
0147-5207 Mon-Khmer Studies
0147-5231 Somatics
0147-5363 Project Management Quarterly *see* 8756-9728
0147-538X New York Times Index
0147-5401 Industrial Hygiene News
0147-5428 West Coast Writer's Conspiracy
0147-5436 Aloha
0147-5452 Telephone†
0147-5460 Journal of Hispanic Philology
0147-5479 International Labor and Working Class History
0147-5533 Billboard's International Disco Sourcebook *changed to* Billboard's International Club and Disco Equipment Sourcebook.
0147-5622 Psychosocial Rehabilitation Journal
0147-5630 Index to Free Periodicals
0147-5681 Children's Book Review Index
0147-572X M R I S Abstracts†
0147-5754 Intermedia Magazine†
0147-5762 Alive & Kicking†
0147-5770 Finders International Newsletter
0147-5789 Scintillation *see* 0162-0126
0147-5851 E M T Journal†
0147-5894 College and University Admissions and Enrollment, New York State
0147-5916 Cognitive Therapy and Research
0147-5924 Info Franchise Newsletter
0147-5967 Journal of Comparative Economics
0147-5975 Experimental Mycology
0147-6041 State Legislatures
0147-6165 Roaring Twenties, Gay Nineties†
0147-619X Plasmid
0147-6203 Scripps Institution of Oceanography. Annual Report *see* 1046-9443
0147-6254 Bedside Care†
0147-6297 Contemporary Art - Southeast *see* 0278-1441
0147-6335 Korean Studies Forum
0147-6491 Bibliographic Guide to North American History
0147-6513 Ecotoxicology and Environmental Safety
0147-6521 Energy Information Abstracts
0147-6521 Energy Information Abstracts Annual *see* 0739-3679
0147-6548 New Atlantean Journal†
0147-6580 Federal Reserve Bank of New York. Quarterly Review
0147-6580 Federal Reserve Bank of New York. Annual Report
0147-6629 Seattle Review
0147-6726 Journal for Medicaid Management *changed to* Perspectives on Medicaid and Medicare Management.
0147-6742 Medical Ultrasound†
0147-6750 C R C Critical Reviews in Diagnostic Imaging *see* 1040-8371
0147-6793 Orthopaedic Survey *see* 0738-2278
0147-6874 Moscow University Soil Science Bulletin
0147-6882 Scientific and Technical Information Processing
0147-6890 Fiscal Observer†
0147-6939 Fatal Accident Reporting System. Annual Report *see* 0732-9792
0147-698X Journal of Powder & Bulk Solids Technology
0147-6998 D E - Domestic Engineering *changed to* Plumbing, Heating, Piping.
0147-7013 Moravian Music Foundation. Bulletin *see* 0278-0763
0147-7129 Attic Press†
0147-7137 Urban Futures Idea Exchange *see* 0732-8265
0147-7188 Managing the Leisure Facility†
0147-720X Outdoors in Georgia†
0147-7218 Law and Behavior†
0147-7226 Hope Reports Perspective†
0147-7285 Mideastern Camping *see* 0734-2705
0147-7307 Law and Human Behavior
0147-7366 International Review of Biochemistry†
0147-7439 Satellite Communications
0147-7447 Orthopedics (Thorofare)
0147-7463 Human Nature†
0147-7471 Adventure Travel (Seattle)†
0147-7536 Musica Judaica
0147-7544 Dialogue in Instrumental Music Education
0147-7625 New Realities†
0147-7633 Chilton's Review of Optometry
0147-7668 Aerophile
0147-7676 High Fidelity's Buying Guide to Speaker Systems *see* 0278-1387
0147-7684 Car Care Handbook†
0147-7706 Short Story International
0147-782X International Psychic Register†
0147-7862 Hart Crane Newsletter *changed to* Visionary Company: A Magazine of the Twenties.
0147-7870 U.S. Department of Housing and Urban Development. Statistical Yearbook†
0147-7889 A S C Newsletter (Washington)
0147-7927 Perinatology - Neonatology†
0147-7927 Perinatology - Neonatology Buyer's Guide *changed to* Perinatology - Neonatology Directory.
0147-7943 District Lawyer *changed to* Washington Lawyer.
0147-7951 Dressage and Combined Training *see* 0147-796X
0147-796X Dressage & C T

ISSN

ISSN INDEX 5611

0147-8001 Urban Systems *see* 0198-9715
0147-8044 N C E A Ganley's Catholic Schools in America
0147-8087 Pharmaceutical Technology
0147-8168 Southern Review of Public Administration *see* 0734-9149
0147-8176 Fodor's Egypt
0147-8222 Illinois Journal of Pharmacy *see* 0195-2099
0147-8257 Harvard Environmental Law Review
0147-8265 Who's Who in Chiropractic, International
0147-829X Social Psychology *see* 0190-2725
0147-8311 Conditions
0147-832X Kitchens & Baths *see* 0270-305X
0147-8354 Adult Literacy and Basic Education *changed to* Adult Basic Education Journal.
0147-8389 P A C E
0147-8451 Peterson's Annual Guide to Undergraduate Study *see* 0894-9336
0147-8451 Peterson's Annual Guide to Undergraduate Study *see* 0894-9328
0147-8591 Gardens *see* 0270-3041
0147-8613 North Central Campbook
0147-8648 Update on Law-Related Education
0147-8656 Fodor's Southwest†
0147-8680 Fodor's the South
0147-8745 Fodor's U S A
0147-877X Business Officer
0147-8818 Ham Radio Horizons *see* 0148-5989
0147-8869 Cuba Review *changed to* Cubatimes.
0147-8885 Journal of Histotechnology
0147-8893 Diagnostic Medicine†
0147-8907 Video (New York) *see* 1044-7288
0147-8923 Marine Business *see* 0006-5404
0147-9024 Journal of New World Archaeology†
0147-9156 Contemporary French Civilization
0147-9202 Comparative Labor Law Journal
0147-9245 Digital Design *see* 0893-2565
0147-9253 Intermedia Arts and Communication Resource Newsletter†
0147-9288 American Alpine News
0147-9296 Association for Educational Data Systems. Annual Convention Proceedings†
0147-9415 Computer Terminals Review *see* 0093-416X
0147-9466 Directory of African and Afro-American Studies in the United States *changed to* Directory of Third World Studies in the United States.
0147-9512 Global Political Assessment†
0147-9563 Heart and Lung
0147-9571 Comparative Immunology, Microbiology and Infectious Diseases
0147-958X Clinical and Investigative Medicine
0147-9695 Vintage Triumph
0147-9725 Maryland Birdlife
0147-9733 Colorado Libraries
0147-9741 Center on Evaluation, Development and Research. Quarterly†
0147-9881 Children in Custody
0147-9911 The Aviation Consumer
0147-992X McElroy Family Newsletter†
0147-9970 Litigation News
0147-9989 Restaurant Hospitality
0148-0057 Measurements and Control
0148-0065 Directory of East Asian Collections in North American Libraries *changed to* C E A L Directory.
0148-012X Contract Interiors *see* 0164-8470
0148-0146 Manhattan Business†
0148-0162 Raccoon
0148-0170 Transportation Engineering *see* 0162-8178
0148-0227 J G R: Journal of Geophysical Research *changed to* J G R: Journal of Geophysical Research: Oceans.
0148-0227 J G R: Journal of Geophysical Research *see* 0196-6928
0148-0227 J G R: Journal of Geophysical Research *changed to* J G R: Journal of Geophysical Research: Solid Earth.
0148-0227 J G R: Journal of Geophysical Research
0148-0243 American Go Journal
0148-0324 California Environmental Directory
0148-0375 International Petroleum Encyclopedia
0148-0537 Fusion (New York)
0148-0545 Drug and Chemical Toxicology
0148-0561 Kxe6s Verein Newsletter
0148-057X Kxe6s Verein Chess Society. Advisory Board Record
0148-0588 National Lawyers Guild. Guild Notes
0148-0650 Illinois Health Sciences Libraries Serials Holdings List†
0148-0685 Women's Studies (Oxford) *see* 0277-5395
0148-0731 Journal of Biomechanical Engineering
0148-0766 Lodging Hospitality
0148-0812 Journal of Dermatologic Surgery and Oncology
0148-0847 Social Work Research and Abstracts
0148-0863 Public Revenues from Alcohol Beverages†
0148-1037 Minority Voices†
0148-1045 Media Law Reporter
0148-1061 Education Libraries
0148-107X Employment Discrimination Digest
0148-1096 Zetetic *see* 0194-6730
0148-1150 N A G W S Rules. Skiing†
0148-1177 Pacific Almanac. Pacific Northwest and Alaska *see* 0276-8771
0148-1789 Thomas Wolfe Newsletter *see* 0276-5683
0148-1827 Ore Bin *see* 0164-3304
0148-186X Administration of the Marine Mammal Protection Act of 1972 *see* 0196-4690
0148-1878 Moody's Bond Record and Annual Bond Record Service
0148-1886 Massachusetts Archaeological Society. Bulletin
0148-1940 I R S Letter Rulings
0148-1959 Interdisciplinary Perspectives *see* 0890-9792
0148-2009 Lonergan Workshop
0148-2033 Specialty Advertiser†
0148-2041 Event
0148-2076 19th Century Music
0148-2092 Freebies
0148-2114 Journeyman Barber and Beauty Culture†
0148-2122 Narrow Gauge & Short Line Gazette
0148-2165 Lifelong Learning: The Adult Years *see* 1045-1595
0148-2181 Journal of Pension Planning and Compliance
0148-2203 Spinoff
0148-2327 C A Selects. Flavors & Fragrances
0148-2335 C A Selects. Photobiochemistry
0148-2343 C A Selects. Prostaglandins
0148-2351 C A Selects. Liquid Crystals
0148-236X C A Selects. Solar Energy
0148-2378 C A Selects. Atherosclerosis & Heart Disease
0148-2386 C A Selects. Antitumor Agents
0148-2394 C A Selects. Anti-Inflammatory Agents and Arthritis
0148-2408 C A Selects. Carcinogens, Mutagens & Teratogens
0148-2416 C A Selects. New Books in Chemistry
0148-2432 C A Selects. Raman Spectroscopy
0148-2440 C A Selects. Silver Chemistry
0148-2459 C A Selects. Beta-Lactam Antibiotics
0148-2548 Radio Liberty Research Bulletins *changed to* Report on the U S S R.
0148-2963 Journal of Business Research
0148-3102 Chevron World
0148-3161 Homeowners How-To Handbook *see* 0195-2196
0148-3218 Best's Insurance Report: Property - Casualty
0148-3250 Louisville Review
0148-3277 Directory of Women in Philosophy†
0148-3331 Christianity and Literature
0148-3390 Illinois Magazine
0148-3471 Surgical Techniques Illustrated†
0148-3641 Directory of Washington Manufacturers *see* 0148-5687
0148-3706 Golf Business†
0148-3730 Road-House
0148-3811 U.S. Bureau of Reclamation. Mid-Pacific Region. Report†
0148-382X Refrigeration Service and Contracting (Troy)
0148-3838 University of Michigan. Museum of Paleontology. Papers on Paleontology
0148-3846 Journal of Rehabilitation Administration
0148-3897 Ornament
0148-3900 Journal of Interdisciplinary Modeling and Simulation†
0148-3919 Journal of Liquid Chromatography
0148-3927 Clinical and Experimental Hypertension *see* 0730-0077
0148-3927 Clinical and Experimental Hypertension *see* 0730-0085
0148-396X Neurosurgery (Baltimore)
0148-3994 Parke Society News Letter
0148-4001 Modern Salon
0148-4036 Pennsylvania Mennonite Heritage
0148-4052 Successful Meetings
0148-4079 Job Safety and Health (Silver Spring) *see* 0196-058X
0148-4087 Public Transit Report *changed to* Urban Transport News.
0148-4095 Solar Energy Intelligence Report *changed to* International Solar Energy Intelligence Report.
0148-4109 Federal Research Report
0148-4125 Sludge Newsletter
0148-415X New International Review
0148-4184 Accounting Historians Journal
0148-4214 Missouri Area Labor Trends
0148-4265 Current Nephrology
0148-432X American Educator
0148-4397 Solar Energy Utilization: a Bibliography. Vol. 2. Solar Thermal Components†
0148-4419 Southern Journal of Applied Forestry
0148-4427 Physiological Society of Philadelphia. Monographs†
0148-4443 Pipeline (Houston) *see* 0032-0188
0148-4451 Serials in Transition†
0148-446X Abstract Newsletter: Energy *changed to* N T I S Alerts: Energy.
0148-4478 Chilton's Food Engineering International
0148-4508 National Directory of Educational Programs in Gerontology *changed to* National Directory of Educational Programs in Gerontology and Geriatrics.
0148-4532 Yale Lit *see* 0148-4605
0148-4605 Yale Literary Magazine
0148-4648 International Drug Report
0148-4761 Health Labor Relations Reports
0148-477X Special Education Report†
0148-4818 U S Pharmacist
0148-4834 J N E: Journal of Nursing Education *see* 0022-3158
0148-4958 Foodservice Equipment Specialist *changed to* Foodservice Equipment & Supplies Specialist.
0148-5008 Inquiry (Washington)†
0148-5016 Archives of Andrology
0148-5032 Mayflower Quarterly
0148-5040 Wisconsin. Department of Public Instruction. Newsletter *changed to* Education Forward.
0148-5059 Wisconsin Public School Directory *changed to* Wisconsin Public - Private School Directory.
0148-5113 Geographical Survey†
0148-5121 International File of Micrographics Equipment and Accessories. *changed to* Micrographics and Optical Storage Equipment Review.
0148-5164 Journal of Continuing Education in Obstetrics and Gynecology *see* 0198-9197
0148-5172 Journal of Continuing Education in Urology *see* 0197-7709
0148-5180 Journal of Continuing Education in O.R.L. & Allergy *see* 0198-7038
0148-5199 Journal of Continuing Education in Cardiology *changed to* Cardiology Digest (1979).
0148-530X U.S. Bureau of Labor Statistics. Publications†
0148-5407 Disabled U S A *changed to* Worklife.
0148-5431 D M: Data Management *changed to* Data Management.
0148-5482 Mandolin Notebook *see* 0270-9325
0148-5512 Federal Index Monthly *changed to* C S I Federal Index.
0148-558X Journal of Accounting, Auditing & Finance
0148-5598 Journal of Medical Systems
0148-561X Degre Second: Studies in French Literature
0148-5628 Climatological Data for Amundsen-Scott, Antarctica†
0148-5644 U.S. Library of Congress. Accessions List: Afghanistan†
0148-5652 Delaware State Industrial Directory *changed to* MacRae's State Industrial Directory: Maryland - District of Columbia - Delaware.
0148-5660 Maryland State Industrial Directory *changed to* MacRae's State Industrial Directory: Maryland - District of Columbia - Delaware.
0148-5679 Rhode Island State Industrial Directory *see* 0740-4689
0148-5687 Washington Manufacturers Register
0148-5717 Sexually Transmitted Diseases
0148-5733 Pacific Information Service on Street-Drugs†
0148-5741 Yale Forest School News
0148-5784 N A B T E Review
0148-5792 Jobber Retailer
0148-5806 Educational Communications and Technology Journal *see* 1042-1629
0148-5865 Arabesque
0148-5881 Nevada Review of Business and Economics
0148-5903 American Bookseller
0148-5989 Ham Radio Magazine†
0148-6039 Accident Facts
0148-6055 Journal of Rheology
0148-6071 J P E N: Journal of Parenteral and Enteral Nutrition
0148-611X Journal of Asian-Pacific & World Perspectives
0148-6128 W P I Journal
0148-6179 Black American Literature Forum
0148-6187 Beverage Industry
0148-6195 Journal of Economics and Business
0148-6225 Association for Asian Studies. Committee on East Asian Libraries. Bulletin
0148-6373 Electronic, Electro-Optic and Infrared Countermeasures *see* 0164-4076
0148-6381 Who's Who Among Vocational and Technical Students in America†
0148-639X Muscle & Nerve
0148-6403 Head and Neck Surgery *see* 1043-3074
0148-6411 I E E E Transactions on Components, Hybrids and Manufacturing Technology
0148-642X Catalog of Fossil Spores and Pollen†
0148-6489 Public Land & Resources Law Digest
0148-6543 Studies in History and Philosophy. Pamphlet Series†
0148-6551 Studies in Law†
0148-656X Studies in Social Theory†
0148-6578 Teacher *see* 1049-5851
0148-6586 Index to Mormonism in Periodical Literature†
0148-6608 Journal of Metals *see* 1047-4838
0148-6616 Genealogical Society of Okaloosa County, Florida. Journal
0148-6659 Roots
0148-6675 Fire Technology Abstracts†
0148-6705 Funeral Service Insider
0148-6721 Car Dealer Insider Newsletter
0148-673X Trumpeter
0148-6748 Europe Today (Augusta)
0148-6802 Invest Yourself *changed to* Volunteer! (Newton, 1944).

ISSN

5612 ISSN INDEX

0148-6845 Violin Society of America. Journal
0148-690X Compensation Planning Journal *see* 0747-8607
0148-6934 E E O Review
0148-6942 Mime Directory†
0148-6985 State of Black America
0148-7043 Annals of Plastic Surgery
0148-7078 Motel - Hotel Insider†
0148-7094 Africa and West Asia Agricultural Situation *changed to* World Agriculture Regional Supplement: Middle East and North Africa.
0148-7132 Wallace Stevens Journal
0148-7175 Afro-American Journal†
0148-7191 S A E Technical Papers
0148-7280 Gamete Research†
0148-7299 American Journal of Medical Genetics
0148-7442 Directory of Michigan Municipal Officials
0148-7469 Air Cargo Magazine *see* 0745-5100
0148-7558 Massachusetts State Industrial Directory *see* 0740-4689
0148-7566 Get Ready Sheet
0148-7604 D.A.T.A. Book of Discontinued Semiconductor Diodes *changed to* Diode Discontinued Devices D.A.T.A. Book.
0148-7639 A D F L Bulletin
0148-7655 Louisiana Genealogical Register
0148-7671 Polar Geography *see* 0273-8457
0148-771X Grass Roots Perspectives on American History
0148-7736 Texas Monthly
0148-7760 U S S R Facts & Figures Annual
0148-7795 Panhandle-Plains Historical Review
0148-7868 Africana Libraries Newsletter *changed to* Africana Libraries Newsletter.
0148-7876 Texas. Department of Water Resources. Library. Bulletin *changed to* Texas. Water Commission. Library. Bulletin.
0148-7922 Family Law Reporter
0148-7930 Retail - Services Labor Report *see* 0891-4141
0148-7949 Government Manager
0148-7957 Noise Regulation Reporter
0148-7965 B N A's Patent, Trademark & Copyright Journal
0148-7973 Chemical Regulation Reporter
0148-7981 B N A Labor Relations Reporter
0148-799X Dynamic Years†
0148-8066 Association of Departments of Foreign Languages. Bulletin *see* 0148-7639
0148-8139 United States Law Week
0148-8147 Affirmative Action Compliance Manual for Federal Contractors
0148-8155 Daily Report for Executives
0148-8279 Lithuanian Mathematical Transactions *see* 0363-1672
0148-8287 Journal of Thermal Insulation
0148-8295 Tax Management Memorandum
0148-8309 Stack Sampling News *changed to* Source Sampling News.
0148-8317 Environmental Impact News†
0148-8325 South Dakota. Department of Social Services. Annual Medical Report†
0148-8376 Journal of Social Service Research
0148-8384 International Journal of Family Therapy *see* 0892-2764
0148-8414 American Spectator
0148-8430 Press
0148-8465 M R I S Current Awareness Service†
0148-849X National Research Council. Transportation Research Board. Bibliography
0148-8546 Minnesota Cities
0148-8597 Federal Civilian Workforce Statistics. Annual Report of Employment by Geographic Area *changed to* Federal Civilian Workforce Statistics. Biennial Report of Employment by Geographic Area.
0148-8619 U S Journal of Drug and Alcohol Dependence†
0148-8627 Ensayistas†
0148-866X New Acronyms, Initialisms and Abbreviations
0148-8732 Sailboat & Equipment Directory
0148-8740 Motorboat & Equipment Directory†
0148-8821 Marriage and Divorce Today *see* 0005-7924
0148-883X Sexuality Today *see* 0005-7924
0148-8848 United States Banker
0148-8899 Professional Agent
0148-8996 Biblioscan Q-Z
0148-9011 Biblioscan H-L
0148-902X Plainswoman†
0148-9038 Fungicide and Nematicide Tests
0148-9062 International Journal of Rock Mechanics and Mining Sciences & Geomechanics Abstracts
0148-9100 American Art and Antiques *see* 0195-8208
0148-9119 Plastics Compounding
0148-9127 Crafts
0148-9143 Florida Monthly†
0148-9151 Jackson Magazine *see* 0164-6699
0148-916X International Journal of Leprosy and Other Mycobacterial Diseases
0148-9232 Indiana. Office of Community Services Administration. Annual Report†
0148-9267 Computer Music Journal
0148-9364 Fanfare
0148-9410 Auto Reports†
0148-9437 Gift and Tableware Reporter. Gift Guide *changed to* Gift & Stationery Business.
0148-9496 Federation of American Hospitals. Review *see* 1055-7466
0148-9526 Outlook for U.S. Agricultural Exports
0148-9542 Jax Fax *see* 0279-7984
0148-9585 Higher Education Review *see* 0162-5748
0148-9607 The Tech
0148-9615 I E E E Communications Society Magazine *see* 0163-6804
0148-9666 Driftwood East *see* 0190-2253
0148-9798 National Collegiate Championships Record Book *see* 0190-4329
0148-9801 Fueloil and Oil Heat and Solar Systems *changed to* Fueloil & Oil Heat.
0148-9836 Northeast Gulf Science
0148-9895 American Society of Civil Engineers. Waterway, Port, Coastal and Ocean Division. Journal *see* 0733-950X
0148-9909 American Society of Civil Engineers. Technical Councils. Journal *see* 0733-9461
0148-9917 Journal of Ambulatory Care Management
0149-015X Studies in the American Renaissance
0149-0214 Gambling Times *see* 1047-854X
0149-0257 Holiday Homes International *changed to* Homes International.
0149-0265 Journal of Continuing Education in Psychiatry *see* 0278-4602
0149-0273 Journal of Continuing Education in Family Medicine *changed to* Medical Digest (1979) Education in Family Medicine.
0149-0281 Who Audits America
0149-0354 Barataria
0149-0370 E E: Evaluation Engineering
0149-0389 Terrorism (Bristol) *changed to* Studies in Conflict and Terrorism.
0149-0397 Marine Mining
0149-0400 Leisure Sciences
0149-0419 Marine Geodesy
0149-0427 Acoustical Imaging and Holography *see* 0732-6726
0149-0451 Geomicrobiology Journal
0149-046X Membrane Biochemistry
0149-0478 Expenditure and Employment Data for the Criminal Justice Systems *changed to* Justice Expenditure and Employment in the U.S.
0149-0508 Peace & Change
0149-0516 Pequod
0149-0532 Women's Agenda†
0149-0605 Engineering Research Highlights†
0149-0672 Equus
0149-0680 Sports Wise: New York
0149-0699 Self
0149-0729 Mahogany
0149-0737 News Media and the Law
0149-0796 African Index
0149-080X Manpower and Human Resources Studies
0149-0818 Multinational Industrial Relations Series
0149-0907 Bioresearch Today: Pesticides†
0149-0915 Bioresearch Today: Population, Fertility & Birth Control†
0149-0923 Bioresearch Today: Industrial Health & Toxicology†
0149-0931 Bioresearch Today: Human Ecology†
0149-094X Bioresearch Today: Human and Animal Parasitology†
0149-0958 Bioresearch Today: Food Additives & Residues†
0149-0966 Bioresearch Today: Human & Animal Aging†
0149-0974 Bioresearch Today: Food Microbiology†
0149-0982 Bioresearch Today: Birth Defects†
0149-0990 Bioresearch Today: Bio Engineering & Instrumentation†
0149-1008 Bioresearch Today: Addiction†
0149-1016 Bioresearch Today: Cancer A - Carcinogenesis†
0149-1024 Bioresearch Today: Cancer B - Anticancer Agents†
0149-1032 Bioresearch Today: Cancer C - Immunology†
0149-1040 New York Literary Forum†
0149-1083 Guide to Independent Study Through Correspondence Instruction *see* 0733-6020
0149-1091 O'Dwyer's Directory of Corporate Communications
0149-1148 Comprehensive Immunology
0149-1199 A C M Guide to Computing Literature
0149-1202 Bibliography and Subject Index of Current Computing Literature *see* 0149-1199
0149-1210 33 Metal Producing
0149-1237 Kastlemusick Exchange *see* 0276-0606
0149-1288 Fodor's Paris
0149-1342 Urethane Abstracts
0149-1423 A A P G Bulletin
0149-144X Reliability and Maintainability Symposium. Proceedings
0149-1482 Reading Today International†
0149-1547 Peasant Studies
0149-1563 Russian & East European Studies Indexed Journal Reference Guide†
0149-1598 N A C L A Report on the Americas *see* 1058-5397
0149-1644 Organizational Communication†
0149-1695 Legal Briefs for Editors, Publishers and Writers†
0149-1717 Pharmacy Law Digest
0149-175X Texas Tech University. Museum. Occasional Papers
0149-1768 Texas Tech University. Museum. Special Publications
0149-1776 Glaciological Data
0149-1784 Journal of South Asian and Middle Eastern Studies
0149-1830 Velvet Light Trap
0149-1911 Avanti Owners Association Newsletter
0149-192X Quantitative Applications in the Social Sciences
0149-1946 Off P'tree
0149-1970 Progress in Nuclear Energy
0149-1997 Allegheny Ludlum Horizons†
0149-2004 Aletheia
0149-2047 Community Health Studies *see* 1035-7319
0149-2063 Journal of Management
0149-2136 J P T: Journal of Petroleum Technology
0149-2195 U.S. Centers for Disease Control. Morbidity and Mortality Weekly Report
0149-2268 Bulletin of Chemical Thermodynamics (1977)†
0149-2276 Competitivedge *changed to* Furniture Retailer (Greensboro).
0149-2357 Modern Electronics
0149-2365 Soccer Digest
0149-2373 Strike
0149-2381 Chemical Times & Trends
0149-2438 Tufts Kinsmen
0149-2446 A C S A News
0149-2462 Georgia. Water Resources Survey. Hydrologic Report†
0149-2489 A F L - C I O American Federationist†
0149-2497 U.S. National Center for Education Statistics. Revenues and Expenditures for Public Elementary and Secondary Education *changed to* U.S. Department of Education. National Center for Education Statistics. Public Elementary and Secondary State Aggregate Data, by State.
0149-2500 U.S. Small Business Administration. S B I C Digest
0149-2551 New England Antiquities Research Association Journal
0149-2578 Washington Social Legislation Bulletin
0149-2616 U.S. Centers for Disease Control. Tuberculosis in the United States *changed to* U.S. Centers for Disease Control. Tuberculosis Statistics in the United States.
0149-2632 Hospital Peer Review
0149-2675 B N A Policy and Practice Series. Personnel Management
0149-2683 B N A Policy and Practice Series. Fair Employment Practices
0149-2691 B N A Policy and Practice Series. Wages and Hours
0149-2705 Payroll Compensation *see* 0279-5418
0149-2713 B N A Policy and Practice Series. Labor Relations
0149-2918 Clinical Therapeutics
0149-2926 Sexual Medicine Today†
0149-2993 Journal of Architectural Education
0149-3361 Indiana Writes *see* 0738-386X
0149-337X American City & County
0149-3442 Tack 'n Togs Merchandising
0149-3450 ElHi Funding Sources Newsletter†
0149-3574 NuclearFuel
0149-3582 Securities Week
0149-3639 Hotel & Resort Industry
0149-3701 C E P Technical Manuals†
0149-3752 Illinois Issues Annual†
0149-3922 Powder Metallurgy in Defense Technology†
0149-399X Asia Mail†
0149-4147 Turbomachinery International
0149-4228 Grub Street†
0149-4236 Chaplaincy†
0149-4244 New Oxford Review
0149-4252 Chaplaincy Letter†
0149-4260 Journal of Continuing Education in Ophthalmology *see* 0048-1955
0149-435X Michigan Librarian Newsletter *changed to* Michigan Librarian.
0149-4465 Diesel and Gas Turbine Progress Worldwide *see* 0278-5994
0149-4473 Viva†
0149-449X Iowa. Department of Job Service. Annual Report
0149-4511 American Transportation Builder *see* 1043-4054
0149-4635 Hustler
0149-466X Players
0149-4694 Register of Indexers
0149-4732 Advances in Clinical Child Psychology
0149-4740 National N O W Times
0149-4880 Papers in International Studies: Latin American Series *changed to* Monographs in International Studies: Latin America Series.
0149-4899 Plastics Machinery and Equipment
0149-4902 M O T A
0149-4910 N A C T A Journal
0149-4929 Marriage & Family Review
0149-4953 Money

ISSN

0149-4996 Western Railroader and Western Railfan *changed to* Western Railroader.
0149-5011 Overtones
0149-5046 Heard Heritage
0149-5054 Computer Peripherals Review *see* 0093-416X
0149-5070 Western New York Magazine
0149-5135 Sufi Times *see* 0161-6331
0149-516X Southern Accents
0149-5240 Equipment Guide News *see* 0891-141X
0149-5267 National Petroleum News
0149-5283 Mine Productivity Report *see* 0149-578X
0149-5348 Current Bibliography of Plastic & Reconstructive Surgery
0149-5364 Federal Reserve Bank of Dallas. Economic Review
0149-5372 Checklist of Human Rights Documents†
0149-5380 W W D *changed to* Women's Wear Daily.
0149-5437 Olson†
0149-5534 Industry Mart†
0149-5585 International Construction Week†
0149-5682 Textile Booklist†
0149-5712 Maarav
0149-5720 Numerical Heat Transfer *see* 1040-7782
0149-5720 Numerical Heat Transfer *see* 1040-7790
0149-5739 Journal of Thermal Stresses
0149-5747 Advanced Lighter-Than-Air Review†
0149-5771 Electrical Marketing Newsletter
0149-578X Coal Week
0149-5879 Sewage Treatment Construction Grants Manual†
0149-5887 Tiger Report†
0149-5895 Food, Drug & Cosmetic Manufacturing†
0149-5917 Inspiration (Los Angeles)†
0149-5925 Vans & Pickups†
0149-5933 Comparative Strategy
0149-5941 Conflict *changed to* Studies in Conflict and Terrorism.
0149-5968 Drug Abuse and Alcoholism Review *see* 1055-0887
0149-5976 Detroit Monthly
0149-5992 Diabetes Care
0149-5992 Clinical Practice Recommendations
0149-6018 Routes
0149-6026 Inner Paths
0149-6085 Journal of Food Safety
0149-6093 Good Ideas for Decorating *changed to* Good Ideas.
0149-6115 Geotechnical Testing Journal
0149-6123 Cement, Concrete, and Aggregates
0149-614X Together (New York) *see* 0199-7149
0149-6158 Together Sexology *see* 0199-7149
0149-6166 Index to Federal Tax Articles (Supplement)
0149-6212 S G A Journal *see* 1042-895X
0149-6352 Hospital Week†
0149-6395 Separation Science and Technology
0149-6425 Rodeo News
0149-6441 West Branch
0149-645X I E E E - M T T - S International Microwave Symposium. Digest
0149-6492 Voluntary Action Leadership
0149-6540 Health Practitioner *changed to* Physician Assistant.
0149-6573 Environmental Comment†
0149-6581 Directory of Companies Required to File Annual Reports with the Securities and Exchange Commission Under the Securities Exchange Act of 1934†
0149-6646 Alaska. Department of Natural Resources. Annual Report†
0149-6700 Studies in History of Biology
0149-6719 Cardiopulmonary Medicine†
0149-6727 Medical Imaging†
0149-6743 Nutrition Planning†
0149-676X American Wine Society Manual
0149-6778 American Wine Society. Bulletin
0149-6840 Folklife Center News
0149-6859 Cross Reference†
0149-6867 Jacksonville Genealogical Society Quarterly
0149-6891 Unearth†
0149-6913 George D. Hall's Directory of Massachusetts Manufacturers
0149-6948 Case Analysis
0149-6956 Crain's Chicago Business
0149-6964 International Review of Food and Wine *see* 0279-6740
0149-6972 Far West†
0149-6980 Media & Values
0149-7014 On Location Magazine
0149-7081 Women Artists News
0149-709X R F D
0149-7103 Street & Smith's Pro Basketball
0149-7111 Symposium on Computer Architecture. Conference Proceedings *changed to* International Symposium on Computer Architecture. Conference Proceedings.
0149-712X Journal of Reform Judaism *changed to* C C A R Journal.
0149-7189 Evaluation and Program Planning
0149-7197 Retired Military Almanac
0149-7219 Yearbook of Romanian Studies
0149-7308 A S B C Newsletter
0149-7316 Runner *see* 0897-1706
0149-7324 Impresario†
0149-7332 Somos
0149-7421 Developments in Marketing Science
0149-7448 Regulators†
0149-7499 Floral Underawl & Gazette Times
0149-7510 Job Safety & Health (Washington)
0149-7537 Who's Who in Engineering
0149-7545 Engineers of Distinction *see* 0149-7537
0149-7634 Neuroscience and Biobehavioral Reviews
0149-7642 Red Book of Housing Manufacturers
0149-7677 Dance Research Journal
0149-7790 Mariah *see* 0278-1433
0149-7820 Beehive†
0149-7847 Directory of Conservative and Libertarian Serials, Publishers, and Freelance Markets
0149-7863 Pushcart Prize: Best of the Small Presses
0149-7898 Silicon Gulch Gazette†
0149-7901 Journal of Applied Management†
0149-791X New Mexico Studies in the Fine Arts†
0149-7936 Washington Dossier *see* 0891-5741
0149-7944 Current Surgery
0149-7952 German Studies Review
0149-7995 Arizona Manpower Review†
0149-8029 OpFlow
0149-8037 Willing Water (Denver) *see* 0273-3218
0149-8045 Quilt World
0149-8061 Humane Education *changed to* Children and Animals.
0149-8088 Index to Scientific & Technical Proceedings
0149-810X Subject Guide to Reprints†
0149-8118 Dun and Bradstreet Exporters' Encyclopaedia - World Marketing Guide *see* 0732-0159
0149-8142 Dunsworld Marketing Management†
0149-8231 New York Business Change Service†
0149-824X New Jersey Business Change Service†
0149-8274 U.S. Federal Deposit Insurance Corporation. Trust Assets of Insured Commercial Banks *see* 0278-5692
0149-8347 Adult Bible Studies
0149-838X A E I Defense Review *see* 0163-9927
0149-8398 Ecolibrium†
0149-8428 Religion Index One: Periodicals
0149-8436 Religion Index Two: Multi-Author Works
0149-8444 Keystone Folklore†
0149-8452 New York (City). Commission on the Status of Women. Status Report
0149-8487 Gratz College Annual of Jewish Studies†
0149-8606 Encyclopedia of Food Technology and Food Science Series†
0149-8681 Marxist Perspectives†
0149-8711 Omni
0149-8738 International Environment Reporter
0149-8797 Public Administration Times
0149-8851 River Styx
0149-886X Journal of Optometric Vision Development
0149-8886 Academy of Rehabilitative Audiology. Journal
0149-8924 Sourcebook of Equal Educational Opportunity†
0149-8932 Interview (New York)
0149-8991 Geothermal Resources Council. Special Report
0149-9017 A T Q
0149-9106 Architecture Minnesota
0149-9114 Kansas History
0149-9130 Contemporary Economic Problems *see* 0732-4308
0149-9157 Public Opinion (Washington) *see* 1047-3572
0149-922X A E I Studies on Contemporary Economic Problems *see* 0732-4308
0149-9246 Hastings International and Comparative Law Review
0149-9262 Access (Washington, 1975)†
0149-9270 Princeton Alumni Weekly
0149-9289 Ningas-Cogon *changed to* Ningas.
0149-9300 Micrographics Today *see* 0892-3876
0149-9319 Shorthorn Country
0149-936X C T: The Journal of Computed Tomography *see* 0899-7071
0149-9386 Energy Magazine
0149-9408 American Book Review
0149-9483 Advances in Nutritional Research
0149-953X Prana Yoga Life
0149-9572 Minority Group Media Guide *see* 0730-5141
0149-9580 Disciplinary Law and Procedure Advance Sheets *see* 0273-2122
0149-9602 Health Foods Business
0149-9688 Journal of Multivariate Experimental Personality and Clinical Psychology *see* 0147-3964
0149-970X Chicago Catholic *changed to* The New World.
0149-9785 A E I Economist†
0149-9807 Immigration and Nationality Law Review
0149-9815 Inland Shores†
0149-9858 Slavic and European Education Review *changed to* East-West Education.
0149-9912 Physician's Guide to Practical Gastroenterology *see* 0277-4208
0149-9939 National Library of Medicine. Audiovisuals Catalog
0149-9963 American Statistical Association. Statistical Computing Section. Proceedings (of the Annual Meeting)
0149-9971 Review of International Broadcasting
0149-998X Adult Planbook†
0150-0112 Dossiers de l'Elevage†
0150-1399 Bibliographie de la France. Supplement 1: Publications en Serie
0150-1402 Bulletin du Livre et Connaissance et Formation *see* 0294-0000
0150-2441 Confluent†
0150-4428 Lys Rouge
0150-536X Journal of Optics
0150-5467 Feuillet Rapide Fiscal Social
0150-5505 Geostandards Newsletter
0150-5602 Medica Gestion
0150-5955 Bibliographie de la France. Publications Officielles
0150-5971 Bibliographie de la France. Supplement 3: Musique
0150-5998 Bibliographie de la France. Supplement 4: Atlas, Cartes et Plans
0150-6404 Foret - Entreprise
0150-6463 Petrole Informations *see* 0755-561X
0150-6471 Petrole Informations, la Revue Petroliere *see* 0755-561X
0150-651X Maille Informations *see* 0750-4764
0150-6617 Industries et Techniques *see* 0537-5819
0150-7206 Revue Technique Carrosserie
0150-7214 Revue Moto Technique
0150-7230 Auto Expertise
0150-7516 Revue des Ingenieurs
0150-7540 Toutes les Nouvelles de l'Hotellerie et du Tourisme
0150-8695 Bulletin Signaletique. Part 528: Bibliographie Internationale de Science Administrative
0150-9861 Journal of Neuroradiology - Journal de Neuroradiologie
0151-0479 Cahiers C E R T-C I R C E†
0151-0509 Academie des Sciences. Comptes Rendus Hebdomadaires des Seances. Series A-B: Sciences Mathematiques *see* 0764-4442
0151-0517 Societe Entomologique de France. Bulletin
0151-0592 B.O.P.I. Abreges *see* 0750-7674
0151-0827 Documents
0151-1335 Academie d'Agriculture de France. Comptes Rendus des Seances *see* 0989-6988
0151-1408 Demographie Africaine: Bulletin de Liaison
0151-1475 France. Institut National de la Statistique et des Etudes Economiques. Informations Rapides
0151-1793 Economie Champenoise
0151-1998 Sante de l'Homme
0151-2137 Psychologie et Education
0151-2943 Indicateur Bertrand *changed to* Indicateur Bertrand Paris - Banlieu.
0151-3605 Visages du Vingtieme Siecle
0151-3648 Special Bricolage
0151-4016 Renaitre 2000
0151-4695 Jardineries *changed to* Jardineries Vegetal.
0151-5055 Economia†
0151-5772 Royaliste
0151-5845 Psychomotricite†
0151-605X Sciences et Techniques Biomedicales
0151-6973 Techniques et Sciences Municipales Eau *see* 0299-7258
0151-6981 Aquarama
0151-7163 Al Islam
0151-7341 Alsace Historique
0151-7791 Fou Parle
0151-783X Phot 'argus (Edition Professionnelle)
0151-8720 Societe Generale pour Favoriser de Developpement du Commerce et de l'Industrie en France. Bulletin†
0151-9093 Actualite Chimique
0151-9107 Annales de Chimie: Science des Materiaux
0151-9514 France. Institut National de la Statistique et des Etudes Economiques. Courrier des Statistiques
0151-9638 Annales de Dermatologie et de Venereologie
0151-9808 Ethnopsychiatrica *see* 0762-6819
0152-0032 Po & Sie
0152-0768 Pouvoirs
0152-3058 Cuniculture
0152-3791 Cote des Arts
0152-5425 Petrole et Techniques
0152-7401 Revue Francaise d'Administration Publique
0152-7886 Phreatique
0152-9668 Annales des Ponts et Chaussees
0153-0208 Foret Privee Francaise et Revues Forestiere Europeenne *see* 0153-0216
0153-0216 La Foret Privee
0153-0313 Lengas
0153-1999 France. Ministere de l'Agriculture. Informations Rapides Commerce Exterieur Agro-Alimentaire *changed to* France. Ministere de l'Agriculture et de la Foret. Conjoncture Exterieur Agro-Alimentaire.
0153-226X Energie Solaire Actualites†
0153-3320 Cahiers de Linguistique Asie Orientale
0153-3401 Al Mostakbal
0153-3428 Watan al-Arabi

ISSN

5614 ISSN INDEX

0153-3614 L'Argus International†
0153-3657 Association pour l'Etude des Problemes d'Outre Mer. Documentation-Developpement
0153-3673 Monuments Historiques
0153-4092 Pour la Science
0153-4157 Maghreb Selection
0153-4270 Mediatheques Publiques
0153-4351 Histoire pour Tous
0153-4459 Institut d'Economie Regionale Bourgogne-Franche-Comte. Cahiers
0153-4602 Escargot Folk?†
0153-4742 Lettre Medicale
0153-5021 Etudes sur l'Egypte et le Soudan Anciens *changed to* Habitats et Societes Urbaines en Egypte et au Soudan.
0153-5048 Cahiers de Philologie
0153-5196 C.T.N.E.R.H.I. Recherchest
0153-6133 Association Francaise des Amis d'Albert Schweitzer. Cahiers
0153-6184 Institut d'Amenagement et d'Urbanisme de la Region d'Ile de France. Cahiers
0153-6540 France. Bureau de Recherches Geologiques et Minieres. Bulletin. Section 2: Geologie des Cite Mineraux *see* 0755-6365
0153-8446 Geochronique
0153-9019 Marche de l'Innovation†
0153-906X Etudes et Documentation de la R T A
0153-9396 Electro-Negoce
0153-9442 Enerpresse
0153-9604 Moules et Modeles *see* 0297-8717
0153-9620 Vagabondages
0153-985X Courrier du C N R S†
0153-9884 Interets Prives
0153-9930 Institut Europeen de Formation des Techniciens des Circuits Imprimes. Informations
0153-999X Catalogue National du Genie Climatique-Chauffage et Conditionnement d'Air
0154-0009 Tequi Electricite Electronique†
0154-0033 Bulletin Officiel du Ministere de l'Environnement et du Cadre de Vie et du Ministere des Transports
0154-0157 Institut d'Etudes Slaves, Paris. Lexiques
0154-0238 Groupe d'Etude des Rythmes Biologiques. Bulletin
0154-1757 Alpinisme et Randonnee *changed to* Alpirando.
0154-1854 Archaeonautica
0154-4101 Pulsar
0154-5604 Interference
0154-6902 Semiotique et Bible
0154-7283 Amis de l'Oeuvre et la Pensee de Georges Migot. Bulletin d'Information
0154-7313 P G - C A T M
0154-7550 France Climat†
0154-7763 Cahiers de Feminisme
0154-8530 Objectif et Action Mutualistes
0154-8840 Juri-Social†
0154-8867 Industrie Sante
0155-0144 C I S Newsletter *see* 1032-6634
0155-0179 University of Western Australia. Centre for South and Southeast Asian Studies. Research Papers†
0155-0195 University of New South Wales. Library. Information Bulletin†
0155-0306 Social Alternatives
0155-0357 Aboriginal Health Worker *see* 1037-3403
0155-0438 Corella
0155-0489 Development News Digest *see* 0815-9424
0155-0543 Musicological Society of Australia. Newsletter
0155-0659 Classicum
0155-0837 Dairy Topics†
0155-1027 Directory of Australian Academic Libraries *changed to* Directory of Australian Academic and Research Libraries.
0155-1108 School Magazine
0155-1221 A F M Exploratory Series
0155-123X New England Accounting Research Studies (No.)
0155-1264 Trolley Wire
0155-2090 C A I News *changed to* C A I News Briefs.
0155-218X Reading Time
0155-2260 Light Railway News
0155-252X Communique†
0155-2589 Industrial Arbitration Reports, New South Wales
0155-2821 Perspectives *see* 1034-4284
0155-2856 Labyrinth†
0155-2880 Quaver *see* 1035-4697
0155-2899 Clean Air Clarion
0155-2902 Mission Review†
0155-297X Australian Legal Directory
0155-3070 A.A.P.A. Newsletter
0155-3089 A.A.P.A. Technitopics *see* 0727-0003
0155-3372 New South Wales. Geological Survey. Records
0155-3380 Australian Gourmet Traveller
0155-3410 New South Wales. Geological Survey. Quarterly Notes
0155-3631 Australia. Bureau of Statistics. Queensland Office. Law and Order, Queensland
0155-3801 Australian Nurseryman *changed to* Australian Nursery.
0155-4360 Ozbike
0155-4425 Labor Forum
0155-476X F A W N S
0155-4786 Fisherman's Journal†
0155-4840 Leichhardt Historical Journal
0155-4980 Opera Australia
0155-5561 New South Wales. Geological Survey. Bulletin
0155-5588 Australian Scientific and Technological Reports†
0155-560X Library Association of Australia. Handbook
0155-5731 Australia. Bureau of Statistics. Queensland Office. Building Operations: Small Area Statistics *see* 0728-6546
0155-5936 Sydney Gay Guide
0155-6002 Australasian Corrosion Association. Annual Conference Proceedings
0155-6134 Australian Jockey Club Thoroughbred Stallion Register†
0155-6215 Pocket Australian Stamp Catalogue
0155-6223 Research Development in Higher Education. Publications
0155-624X Australian National University. Research School of Physical Sciences. Annual Report *changed to* Australian National University. Research School of Physical Sciences and Engineering. Annual Report.
0155-6282 Monash University. Department of Civil Engineering. Civil Engineering Research Report
0155-6320 New South Wales, Australia, Government Gazette
0155-6894 Word in Life
0155-7157 Cane Toad Times
0155-7742 Commonwealth Scientific and Industrial Research Organization. Division of Animal Production. Report
0155-7785 Speculations in Science and Technology
0155-7831 Australian Women's Chess Bulletin
0155-8234 Action for Public Transport Newsletter
0155-8498 Australasian Stamp Catalogue
0155-8560 Galleries and Craft Shops in Australia
0155-8633 Push from the Bush *changed to* The Push: A Journal of Early Australian Social History.
0155-8862 A.C.P.C. Forum†
0155-8870 Australian S F News
0155-9044 Helix
0155-9060 Pacific Research Monograph
0155-9222 Primary Industry Newsletter
0155-9397 S W A N S†
0155-9419 Australian Mineral Industry. Quarterly†
0155-9435 Western Australia. Department of Fisheries and Wildlife. Fisheries Research Bulletin *changed to* Western Australia. Fisheries Department. Fisheries Research Bulletin.
0155-9508 Annual Review of the Residential Property Market *changed to* Annual Review of Major Residential Property Markets in Australia.
0155-9567 National Directory of Internships, Residencies & Registrarships
0155-9648 Truckin' Life
0155-9664 Queensland. Department of Forestry. Technical Paper *see* 1035-9826
0155-977X Social Analysis
0155-9982 Accounting Forum
0156-0107 Australian Youth Hostels Handbook *changed to* Y H A Hostels in Australia.
0156-0115 Hostel Yarn *changed to* Hostel Travel.
0156-0166 Convention Rostrum
0156-0182 Asian Studies Association of Australia. Conference Papers
0156-0301 Australian Journal of Reading
0156-0352 Food and Liquor Retailer
0156-0417 Australian Journal of Clinical and Experimental Hypnosis
0156-0433 P S
0156-0905 New Education
0156-0913 University of New England. Department of Agricultural Economics and Business Management. Farm Management Report
0156-0972 Australian Plant Pathology Society. Newsletter *see* 0815-3191
0156-0999 Australian Early Childhood Research Booklets *changed to* Australian Early Childhood Resource Booklets.
0156-1006 U N E Convocation Bulletin & Alumni News
0156-1103 Links
0156-1383 Bird Behaviour
0156-1596 Inside Asean†
0156-160X A N S O L Bibliography Series *see* 0725-2803
0156-1650 Religious Traditions
0156-174X Metals Australasia *see* 0818-3597
0156-1766 A P M A A Report (No.)†
0156-191X Bulletin of Christian Affairs†
0156-1987 V I S E Handbook *changed to* V C A B Handbook.
0156-2126 Civil Engineering Working Papers
0156-2444 Commonwealth Scientific and Industrial Research Organization. Division of Tropical Crops and Pastures. Research Report
0156-255X New South Wales. Department of Agriculture. Annual Report
0156-2681 Australian Meat Industry Bulletin
0156-2703 Inpharma
0156-2878 Community Education Newsletter†
0156-3394 Australia. Bureau of Industry Economics. Research Report
0156-3491 Forceps *changed to* A C O R N Journal.
0156-3548 Fintas†
0156-3661 Australian Exports *see* 1032-2116
0156-3688 Hospitality Buyers Guide *see* 0817-0398
0156-3696 Travelweek Hotel, Motel and Travel Directory *see* 0813-4790
0156-370X Metal and Engineering Industry Handbook *see* 0314-1586
0156-3726 Pacific Aviation Yearbook†
0156-403X Professional Fisherman
0156-4374 Public Libraries of Victoria. Annual Statistical Bulletin *see* 1035-4832
0156-4420 Studies in Society
0156-4579 Freewheeling *changed to* Cycling World.
0156-4714 Health Education News and Views†
0156-4722 Australia. Bureau of Statistics. Publications Advice
0156-4919 Pursuit
0156-4943 Sociology Occasional Publications
0156-5788 Australian Health Review
0156-5826 Journal of Australian Political Economy
0156-5842 Great Barrier Reef Marine Park Authority Workshop Series
0156-5907 Australian Pork Journal *see* 1032-3759
0156-594X Australian Marc Record Service†
0156-6148 Western Intelligence Report†
0156-6296 On Being
0156-6342 Science Fiction News†
0156-6555 Exceptional Child *changed to* International Journal of Disability, Development and Education.
0156-6717 Guidelines
0156-6962 Recreation and Tourism Research Unit. Occasional Paper†
0156-7365 Australian Journal of Chinese Affairs
0156-7373 Australia. Sea Transport Statistics. Trade and Cargo Review†
0156-7381 Australia. Sea Transport Statistics. Stevedoring Labour Review *changed to* Australia. Stevedoring Statistics. Stevedoring Labour Review.
0156-742X Australian International U F O Flying Saucer Research
0156-7446 Australia. Bureau of Agricultural Economics. Quarterly Review of the Rural Economy *see* 1032-9722
0156-7470 Zadok Centre. Series No.1
0156-7489 Zadok Centre. Series No.2
0156-7500 Zadok Centre Reading Guides
0156-7594 The Rationalist News
0156-7799 Reflections
0156-7918 Australia. Bureau of Statistics. Tasmanian Office. Motor Vehicle Census†
0156-806X Notes & Furphies
0156-8124 Island Magazine
0156-8221 Nation Review
0156-8698 The Great Circle
0156-8760 New South Wales. Department of Technical and Further Education. T A F E Quarterly†
0156-904X Human Resource Management Australia *see* 1032-3627
0156-9236 Geography Teachers Association of New South Wales. Geography Bulletin
0156-9643 Australia. Library Information Service. Catalogue of Serials†
0156-9732 The Labour Force, Victorian Region *see* 1030-536X
0156-9945 Commonwealth Scientific and Industrial Research Organization. Institute of Earth Resources. Technical Communication *see* 0726-1772
0156-9953 Commonwealth Scientific and Industrial Research Organization. Institute of Earth Resources. Investigation Report. *see* 0726-1780
0157-0188 University of New England. Department of Econometrics. Working Papers in Econometrics and Applied Statistics
0157-0919 V I S E Circular†
0157-0994 Push On *see* 1034-3016
0157-1079 University of Queensland. Undergraduate Degree Handbook *changed to* University of Queensland. Calendar. Volume 2. Student Handbook: Metropolitan Campuses.
0157-1133 University of Queensland. Higher Degree Handbook *changed to* University of Queensland. Calendar. Volume 2. Student Handbook: Metropolitan Campuses.
0157-1338 Geo (Australia)
0157-1532 Australian Journal of Audiology
0157-1672 Surveying Australia
0157-1729 Guns Australia
0157-177X A.C.T. - S.T.A. Journal *see* 0818-2019
0157-1826 H E R D S A News
0157-1923 New South Wales. Department of Decentralisation. Regional Developer†
0157-2024 Register of Australian Drug and Alcohol Research†
0157-2083 Australian Mining and Petroleum Law Journal *see* 0812-857X
0157-2229 N T Newsletter *changed to* Paraphernalia.

ISSN

ISSN INDEX 5615

0157-2431 Railway Digest
0157-244X Australian Science Education Research Association. Research in Science Education
0157-258X South Australia. State Library. Monthly List of Publications†
0157-2601 Organic Grower
0157-2784 Directory of Internships, Residencies and Registrarships Available in Victorian Hospitals
0157-2849 University of Queensland. Calendar *changed to* University of Queensland. Calendar. Volume 2. Student Handbook: Metropolitan Campuses.
0157-2849 University of Queensland. Calendar *changed to* University of Queensland. Calendar. Volume 1. The University.
0157-2849 University of Queensland. Calendar *changed to* University of Queensland. Calendar. Volume 3. Gatton College Handbook.
0157-2938 Tasmanian Tramp
0157-3039 Australian Canegrower
0157-308X Australian Littoral Society. Bulletin
0157-3136 Veterinary Prescribers Index
0157-3276 Biblionews and Australian Notes and Queries
0157-3357 Practising Administrator
0157-3381 Mulga Wire
0157-3470 Release
0157-3608 Directory of Research and Developmental Projects
0157-3705 C R N L E Reviews Journal
0157-3713 Queensland at a Glance
0157-3845 Free Palestine
0157-3942 Infocus Newsletter
0157-3977 Hosteller
0157-4159 Melbourne Papers on Australian Defence†
0157-4310 A.D.A. Journal *see* 0811-6407
0157-4566 Australian Coal Report
0157-5295 Fun Runner
0157-5317 Justinian
0157-5619 Brandywine Keepsake
0157-5740 R.H.S.V. History News
0157-5767 Australian National University. Development Studies Centre. Monograph†
0157-5783 Community and Real Estate News
0157-6011 Justice Trends
0157-6054 Australia. Sea Transport Statistics. Report of Manhours Lost by Operational Employees of Stevedoring Companies Due to Industrial Disputes†
0157-6127 Local Museum *changed to* Community History.
0157-6178 Australia. Public Service Board. Bulletin
0157-6224 A A E C Nuclear News (Australian Atomic Energy Commission) *changed to* A N S T O Technology.
0157-6232 Australian National University. Development Studies Centre. Demography Teaching Notes *changed to* Australian National University. National Centre for Development Studies. Demography Teaching Notes.
0157-6321 Australian Social Welfare: Impact *changed to* Impact (Sydney).
0157-6402 Directory of Australian Music Organisations
0157-6429 Australian Marine Sciences Association. Bulletin *changed to* Australian Marine Science Bulletin.
0157-6461 Non-Destructive Testing - Australia
0157-650X Riv Lib File *see* 1034-8042
0157-7204 C S I R O Directory
0157-7271 Reactions
0157-731X Gas Industry Statistics (Year)
0157-759X Vinculum
0157-7662 New Zealand Books in Print
0157-7786 Queensland Agricultural Journal†
0157-7794 Queensland Journal of Agricultural and Animal Sciences†
0157-8081 Commonwealth Scientific and Industrial Research Organization. Marine Laboratories. Fishery Situation Report†
0157-809X Queensland. Department of Forestry. Research Paper *see* 1035-9796
0157-8103 Western Australia (Perth, 1979)†
0157-8200 Australia. National Information Service on Drug Abuse. Technical Information Bulletin
0157-8243 Northern Territory. Department of Primary Production. Agnotes *changed to* Northern Territory. Department of Primary Industry and Fisheries. Agnotes.
0157-8464 Southern Caver
0157-8804 FitzHardinge's Nobiliary
0157-9169 Ozarts
0157-9509 E T C H
0157-9630 Australian Fishing Industry Directory (Year)
0157-9711 Commonwealth Scientific and Industrial Research Organization. Division of Tropical Crops and Pastures. Tropical Agronomy Technical Memorandum
0157-9762 Chemical Engineering in Australia
0157-9789 Australian Association for Adolescent Health. Newsletter
0158-0140 Interdom Christian Referdex *changed to* Christian Referdex.
0158-0531 Mission Probe
0158-0604 University of New England. Information Office Specialists List
0158-0655 Australian Penthouse
0158-0760 General and Applied Entomology
0158-0779 Margaret Gee's Media Guide
0158-0876 InCite
0158-099X Lowdown
0158-1090 Sower
0158-1309 Australia. Department of Primary Industry. Annual Report *see* 1032-4054
0158-1570 Royal Australasian College of Dental Surgeons. Annals
0158-1589 Victorian Government Directory
0158-1597 Clinical and Experimental Neurology
0158-1953 S E A R M G Newsletter†
0158-1996 State Reports W.A.
0158-202X Australia. Bureau of Statistics. Victorian Office. Monthly Summary of Statistics, Victoria
0158-2496 Australia. Bureau of Statistics. Apparent Consumption of Selected Foodstuffs, Australia, Preliminary
0158-2658 Australian Camera Craft
0158-2720 Petty Sessions Review
0158-3026 Literacy Link
0158-3158 P E News *changed to* Professional Engineer.
0158-3301 Western Australian Institute of Technology. Department of Biology. Bulletin *changed to* Curtin University. School of Biology. Bulletin.
0158-3778 Filmviews†
0158-3921 Victorian Fiction Research Guides
0158-3999 Australian Standard
0158-4138 Australian Motor Racing Year
0158-4154 Cantrills Filmnotes
0158-4197 Emu
0158-4243 Comet
0158-4960 Australian Journal of Medical Science
0158-5126 Words and Visions†
0158-5231 Biochemistry International
0158-538X C S I R O Tropical Crops and Pastures. Divisional Report *see* 0816-8474
0158-5460 Link-Up
0158-5711 Federation News (Sydney)
0158-572X The Australian Angler's Fishing World
0158-5789 Pacific Affairs Current Awareness Bulletin
0158-6041 South East Asian Monograph Series
0158-6262 World Missions Update
0158-6289 School Mathematics Journal†
0158-6319 P A T E F A News Bulletin
0158-6602 A I M M Bulletin *see* 1034-6775
0158-6610 Auchmuty Library Publication
0158-6912 Home Economics Association of Australia. Journal
0158-698X Cinema Papers Yearbook†
0158-7048 Craft Victoria
0158-7102 Regional Journal of Social Issues
0158-7110 L R C Employment Bulletin *see* 0725-0290
0158-7285 Australia. Bureau of Mineral Resources, Geology and Geophysics. Yearbook
0158-7366 Oral History Association of Australia. Journal
0158-7374 Period Building Restoration Trades & Suppliers Directory
0158-7382 Commonwealth Scientific and Industrial Research Organization. Bureau of Scientific Services. Annual Report†
0158-7390 Commonwealth Scientific and Industrial Research Organization. Institute of Animal and Food Sciences. Annual Report *changed to* C S I R O Rural Sector Report.
0158-7412 Commonwealth Scientific and Industrial Research Organization. Institute of Earth Resources. Annual Report. *see* 0729-056X
0158-7447 Australian Administrator
0158-7765 Zinc Today
0158-779X Unesco Review *changed to* Unesco Australia.
0158-7919 Distance Education
0158-9172 School Libraries in Australia†
0158-9539 Network News
0158-9830 Research Discussion Papers†
0158-9857 Pulse Survey of Victorian Manufacturing *see* 1033-9094
0158-9911 Nature and Health
0158-9938 Australasian Physical & Engineering Sciences in Medicine
0159-0030 Australian Hi-Fi *changed to* Australian Hi-Fi and Music Review.
0159-0073 Butterworths Trade Practices†
0159-0219 Commonwealth Scientific and Industrial Research Organization. Division of Atmospheric Research. Research Report
0159-0340 Guiding in Australia
0159-060X National Union Catalogue of Library Materials for the Handicapped *see* 1032-8149
0159-0677 Tasmanian Ancestry
0159-1088 Instep†
0159-1096 Contact (Sydney, 1976)†
0159-110X Now†
0159-1193 Practicing Manager
0159-1428 South Australia. Department of Agriculture. Rural Marketing and Policy†
0159-1487 Australian Journal of Sex, Marriage and Family *see* 1034-652X
0159-1878 Who's Drilling
0159-1991 Everyone's Songs. Series
0159-2033 Lab Talk
0159-2068 Institution of Engineers, Australia. Transactions. Civil Engineering
0159-2319 Australian Lithographer, Printer, and Packager
0159-2483 Legal Reporter
0159-2947 Australian Electronics Directory
0159-2955 Australian Engineering Directory
0159-3285 Victorian Bar News
0159-3641 South Australia. Department of Environment and Planning. Directory of Non-Government Environmental Groups in South Australia†
0159-3803 Quest†
0159-3935 Process Engineering News *changed to* Process Engineering.
0159-3951 Australia. Bureau of Statistics. Government Financial Estimates, Australia
0159-396X Australia. Air Transport Statistics. Domestic Air Transport *see* 1037-1273
0159-4672 Professional Administrator *see* 1034-0408
0159-6012 Crane Australasia†
0159-6071 Commonwealth Scientific and Industrial Research Organization. Division of Tropical Crops and Pastures. Genetic Resources Communication
0159-6306 Discourse
0159-6330 Dance Australia
0159-6861 Bargain Shopper's Guide to Melbourne
0159-7027 Coiffuret
0159-7043 South Australia. Department of Mines and Energy. Annual Report
0159-7191 Morocco Bound
0159-7302 Network (Melbourne)
0159-7345 News Digest - International
0159-7477 Library Service of Western Australia. Newsletter *changed to* Library and Information Service of Western Australia. Newsletter.
0159-7485 Regional Information Series *changed to* See Australia Regional Information Series.
0159-7531 Australian Law News
0159-7841 Matilda Literary Magazine *changed to* Matilda Magazine: Literary and Art Magazine.
0159-8090 Clinical Biochemist Reviews
0159-818X Nomen Nudum
0159-8821 Northern Territory. Conservation Commission. Annual Report
0159-8872 Challenge (Petersham North)
0159-8880 Professional Photography in Australia
0159-8910 Australian Journal of Geodesy, Photogrammetry & Surveying
0159-897X Victorian Scout *see* 0815-4627
0159-9011 Australian Journal of Developmental Disabilities *see* 0726-3864
0159-9062 Science Magazine *changed to* Australasian Science Magazine.
0159-9100 Hospital Equipment and Supplies Directory (Year)
0159-9143 Institute of Family Studies *see* 1030-2646
0159-9178 Commonwealth Scientific and Industrial Research Organization. Institute of Energy and Earth Resources. Minerals & Energy Bulletin
0159-9321 Pocket Yearbook of New South Wales
0159-9399 Hume News *see* 1034-9596
0159-950X Monash Review†
0159-9585 Photoworld Buyer's Guide. Index†
0159-9593 Photoworld Buyer's Guide. Darkroom†
0159-9607 S W R C Reports and Proceedings *changed to* S P R C Reports and Proceedings.
0159-9615 S W R C Newsletter *changed to* S P R C Newsletter.
0159-9976 It's a Math Math World *changed to* Math Math World.
0160-001X Washington Report (Washington, 1966)†
0160-0028 Drug Abuse and Alcoholism Newsletter
0160-0036 U.S. Health Care Financing Administration Record *changed to* U.S. Health Care Financing Administration Forum.
0160-0044 American Society for Information Science. Annual Meeting. Proceedings
0160-0168 Bulletin of Research in the Humanities†
0160-0176 International Regional Science Review
0160-0184 Pediatric Alert
0160-0281 American Journal of Trial Advocacy
0160-0303 Graphic Communications Marketplace
0160-0311 Military Journal†
0160-0338 Texas Woman†
0160-0346 Logging Management†
0160-0354 Spiritual Community Guide†
0160-0362 Professional Marketing Report†
0160-0419 French-American Review†
0160-0583 New York Times Theatre Reviews
0160-063X Face the Nation (Annual)†
0160-0664 Collections (Buffalo)
0160-0680 Sulphur in Agriculture
0160-0699 Umbrella
0160-0850 Fiddle and a Bow†
0160-0885 United Methodist Church. Curriculum Plans†
0160-0893 Cornell Review†
0160-0923 Helios (Lubbock)

ISSN

0160-0974 Colorado. Water Conservation Board. Ground Water Series. Circular *see* 0092-2684
0160-1040 I A
0160-1059 Electric Vehicle - Battery Technology *see* 0271-7093
0160-1067 Society for Industrial Archeology Newsletter
0160-1075 New Directions for Women
0160-1083 Growth Industry News *see* 0885-0003
0160-1148 Electronotes
0160-127X Interface (Carmel)†
0160-1296 Educators Guide to Free Audio and Video Materials
0160-130X Bank Expansion Quarterly
0160-1342 Safety Science Abstracts Journal *see* 0892-9351
0160-1504 D I S C U S Facts Book†
0160-1512 International Energy Biweekly Statistical Review *see* 0163-3724
0160-1571 Schwann-1 Record and Tape Guide *see* 1047-2355
0160-1644 Motor Early Model Crash Estimating Guide
0160-1725 Historical Geography Newsletter
0160-1741 U.S. National Bureau of Standards. Journal of Research *see* 1044-677X
0160-1792 Ariset
0160-1830 Sports Afield Deer†
0160-1857 Left Curve
0160-1997 Health and Society *see* 0887-378X
0160-2004 Resources in Vocational Education†
0160-2047 Log *changed to* Seafarers Log.
0160-2071 Micropaleontology Special Papers
0160-2098 Journal of Juvenile Law
0160-2144 Great River Review
0160-2179 Advances in Polyamine Research†
0160-2195 Forum (New York, 1976)
0160-2217 New Brooklyn
0160-225X American Shipper
0160-2365 American Musical Instrument Society. Newsletter
0160-2373 Gleanings (Cambridge)†
0160-239X Great Basin Naturalist Memoirs
0160-242X Comprehensive Endocrinology
0160-2438 E E G Interpretation†
0160-2446 Journal of Cardiovascular Pharmacology
0160-2454 M.D. Anderson Clinical Conferences on Cancer
0160-2462 Membrane Transport Processes†
0160-2470 Nutrition in Health and Disease†
0160-2489 Seminars in Neurological Surgery
0160-2497 S I G C P R Newsletter
0160-2500 Case Western Reserve University. Warner Swasey Observatory. Publications
0160-2527 International Journal of Law and Psychiatry
0160-2543 Cynegeticus†
0160-2551 Critical Care Quarterly *changed to* Critical Care Nursing Quarterly.
0160-256X Association for Women in Science. Newsletter *changed to* A W I S Magazine.
0160-2578 American Bench-Judges of the Nation
0160-2624 Coaching: Women's Athletics†
0160-2659 Kansas Water Resources Research Institute. Annual Report
0160-2667 Verdi Newsletter
0160-2675 Policy Grants Directory
0160-2713 Journal of African-Afro-American Affairs†
0160-2748 Neurotoxicology†
0160-2780 Urbanism Past and Present *see* 0703-0428
0160-2853 Georgetown University Papers on Languages and Linguistics†
0160-287X Wassaja *see* 0199-9052
0160-2896 Intelligence (Norwood)
0160-3000 Woodall's Trailer & R V Travel†
0160-3027 University of Illinois at Urbana-Champaign. Department of Agricultural Economics. Landlord and Tenant Shares *changed to* University of Illinois at Urbana-Champaign. Department of Agricultural Economics. Lease Shares and Farm Returns.
0160-3078 University of Oklahoma. Archaeological Research and Management Center. Project Report Series
0160-3086 University of Oklahoma. Archaeological Research and Management Center. Research Series
0160-3094 Public Accounting Report
0160-323X State and Local Government Review
0160-3248 Special Children *see* 0741-9325
0160-3280 Boys Gymnastics Rulebook
0160-3302 Illinois Manufacturers Directory
0160-3329 Backpacker (1973) *see* 0277-867X
0160-3345 Alaska Economic Trends
0160-3361 Rockefeller University. Institute for Comparative Human Development. Quarterly Newsletter†
0160-337X Enhanced Oil-Recovery Field Reports
0160-3450 American Pharmacy
0160-3469 Sociological Forum *see* 0273-2173
0160-3477 Journal of Post Keynesian Economics
0160-3493 Hispano-Italic Studies†
0160-3515 Pulpit Preaching *see* 0160-838X
0160-3566 Black Sociologist†
0160-3574 S P E C Flyer *see* 0160-3582
0160-3582 S P E C Kit
0160-3604 Energy Research Abstracts
0160-3671 Solar Thermal Power Generation *changed to* Solar Energy Utilization: a Bibliography. Vol. 1. Solar Power Generation.
0160-368X Solar Energy Utilization: a Bibliography. Vol. 3. Solar Thermal Heating and Cooling†
0160-371X Tabs†
0160-3728 Who's Who in Religion
0160-3779 Mineral Economics Abstracts†
0160-3787 Isozymes: Current Topics in Biological and Medical Research
0160-3817 Weaver's Journal†
0160-3825 Student Press Law Center Report
0160-3876 Musical Heritage Review Magazine
0160-3906 Fodor's Canada
0160-3914 Fodor's Cruises Everywhere†
0160-3930 N I T A *see* 0896-5846
0160-4074 Industrial Research and Development *see* 0746-9179
0160-4074 Research and Development Telephone Directory *changed to* Research & Development Product Source Telephone Directory.
0160-4090 Zip *see* 0889-5333
0160-4112 Fatigue of Engineering Materials and Structures *see* 8756-758X
0160-4120 Environment International
0160-4139 Progress in Analytical Atomic Spectroscopy *see* 0958-319X
0160-4147 Downtown Implementation Guide†
0160-4163 Conference of Insurance Legislators†
0160-4198 Journal of Health and Human Resources Administration
0160-4201 Voice of Youth Advocates
0160-4309 Exceptional Child Education Resources
0160-4317 Freshwater and Marine Aquarium
0160-4341 Humboldt Journal of Social Relations
0160-449X Labor Studies Journal
0160-4570 F & O S Motor Carrier Annual Report
0160-4635 Handbook of International Sociometry *see* 0731-1273
0160-4651 Travel Outlook Forum Proceedings *changed to* Outlook for Travel and Tourism.
0160-4724 Chief Executive Magazine
0160-4767 Pizzazz†
0160-4848 Arnoldian *changed to* Nineteenth-Century Prose.
0160-4872 Weekly Insiders Poultry Report
0160-4880 Fiction Catalog
0160-4910 Weekly Insiders Turkey Letter
0160-4929 Politics Today (Santa Barbara)
0160-4953 Collection Building
0160-4961 Health Services Administration Education
0160-5119 Florida Friends of Bluegrass Society. Newsletter
0160-5151 U.S. Bureau of Mines. Mineral Commodity Summaries
0160-5178 Commercial Finance Journal *see* 0888-255X
0160-5216 Power Engineering (U S S R Academy of Sciences)
0160-5305 Idaho: The University Magazine
0160-5402 Journal of Pharmacological Methods *see* 1056-8719
0160-5429 International Education
0160-5534 Perekrestki *see* 0888-5257
0160-5569 School Psychology Digest *see* 0279-6015
0160-5607 Construction News
0160-564X Artificial Organs
0160-5682 Operational Research Society. Journal
0160-5704 Horse, of Course!†
0160-5720 M L A Newsletter (New York)
0160-5739 Florida Retirement Living
0160-5836 Defense Foreign Affairs Handbook
0160-5852 Organizational Communications Abstracts *see* 0149-1644
0160-5895 House & Garden Decorating Guide†
0160-5976 Humanity & Society
0160-5992 In These Times
0160-6042 Lawn Care Industry
0160-6077 Directory of Library Reprographic Services†
0160-6107 Van Life and Family Trucking *see* 0744-074X
0160-6123 Information Manager†
0160-6131 McCall's Working Mother *see* 0278-193X
0160-614X Made in U S A
0160-6158 Standard (New York)
0160-6166 Club Living
0160-6174 Diamond Report†
0160-6271 School Food Service Journal
0160-628X Blake: An Illustrated Quarterly
0160-6352 P T J. Passenger Train Journal *see* 0160-6913
0160-6360 Chemical New Product Directory†
0160-6379 Family and Community Health
0160-6395 N A E A News
0160-6425 Dimensions (Little Rock)
0160-6433 Timber Harvesting
0160-6476 National Zip Code Directory *see* 0731-9185
0160-6506 Atlantic *see* 0276-9077
0160-6514 Atlantic Monthly *see* 0276-9077
0160-6557 N J E B: Nebraska Journal of Economics and Business *see* 0747-5535
0160-6565 Guest Author
0160-659X Common Law Lawyer
0160-6662 National Conference on Individual Onsite Wastewater Systems. Proceedings†
0160-6689 Journal of Clinical Psychiatry
0160-6719 American Peanut Research and Education Association. Proceedings *see* 0197-8748
0160-6824 Golf Industry
0160-6840 Wide Angle
0160-6891 Research in Nursing & Health
0160-6913 Passenger Train Journal
0160-6972 Journal of Oral Implantology
0160-6980 Continuing Education for Health Care Providers†
0160-7006 Health Care Education†
0160-7014 Year in Hematology *see* 0197-3649
0160-7049 Conference of Presidents of Major American Jewish Organizations. Annual Report *see* 0160-7057
0160-7057 Conference of Presidents of Major American Jewish Organizations. Annual Report
0160-7065 Diesel Car Digest
0160-7081 Foundation of Thanatology. Archives
0160-7146 Jacob Marschak Interdisciplinary Colloquium on Mathematics in the Behavioral Sciences
0160-7219 Perinatal Press
0160-7227 Health Law Newsletter *see* 0272-7102
0160-7243 Stone in America
0160-7278 Army - Navy Store & Outdoor Merchandiser
0160-7308 Trial Diplomacy Journal
0160-7332 Amateur Boxer†
0160-7340 Guide to Manufactured Homes†
0160-7375 Frank Lloyd Wright Newsletter
0160-7383 Annals of Tourism Research
0160-7391 West Virginia State Industrial Directory *see* 0740-4328
0160-7413 Compost Science - Land Utilization *see* 0276-5055
0160-7472 International Telephone Directory of the Deaf *changed to* International Telephone Directory of T D D Users (Year).
0160-7480 Modern Healthcare (Year)
0160-7499 Irrigation Association. Technical Conference Proceedings
0160-7545 Ellen Glasgow Newsletter
0160-7553 I D O C/International Documentation†
0160-7561 Philosophical Studies in Education
0160-757X Infusion
0160-7596 S I O Scripps Institution of Oceanography *see* 1046-9443
0160-7618 Health and Medical Care Services Review *see* 0735-9683
0160-7626 Infertility
0160-7634 American Mathematical Society. Symposia in Applied Mathematics. Proceedings
0160-7642 American Mathematical Society. C B M S Regional Conference Series in Mathematics
0160-7650 Crafts Report *changed to* Crafts Report.
0160-7677 Slackwater Review†
0160-7685 Journal of Continuing Education in Dermatology *see* 0198-6643
0160-7693 Journal of Continuing Education in Pharmacy *changed to* Journal of Continuing Education in Hospital and Clinical Pharmacy.
0160-7707 Journal of Continuing Education in Orthopedics *see* 0198-6376
0160-7715 Journal of Behavioral Medicine
0160-7731 Bill of Rights in Action
0160-7766 Journal of Continuing Education in Pediatrics *see* 0198-6341
0160-7774 Journal of Supervision and Training in Ministry
0160-7782 Geothermal Resources Council. Bulletin
0160-7790 Billboard's International Recording Equipment & Studio Directory
0160-7847 Fundamenta Scientiae
0160-788X Reclamation Review†
0160-791X Technology in Society
0160-7952 Metals Forum *changed to* Materials Forum.
0160-7960 Counseling and Values
0160-7987 Medical Anthropology *see* 0277-9536
0160-7995 Medical Economics *see* 0277-9536
0160-8002 Medical Geography *see* 0277-9536
0160-8010 Toys, Hobbies & Crafts†
0160-8029 U.S. Library of Congress. Cataloging Service Bulletin
0160-8037 Developing Country Courier†
0160-8045 Latin American Indian Literatures *see* 0888-5613
0160-8053 Food, Nutrition & Health Newsletter
0160-8061 Journal of Organizational Behavior Management
0160-807X Research Resources Reporter
0160-8126 Public Education Directory
0160-8134 Executive Female Digest *see* 0199-2880
0160-8177 Practical Law Books Review†
0160-8266 A P A Planning Advisory Service Reports
0160-8320 Athletic Training *changed to* Journal of Athletic Training.
0160-8347 Estuaries

0160-8371 I E E E Photovoltaic Specialists Conference. Conference Record
0160-838X Pulpit Digest (1978)
0160-8398 Viewpoints in Teaching and Learning†
0160-8401 Solar Age *see* 0895-2493
0160-8428 National Conference on Fluid Power. Proceedings
0160-8460 Annotation
0160-8495 Pennsylvania Law Journal *changed to* Pennsylvania Law Journal Reporter.
0160-8533 Cleveland Magazine
0160-8584 Laboratory and Research Methods in Biology and Medicine†
0160-8592 I A S Annual Meeting. Conference Record *see* 0197-2618
0160-8665 Mime, Mask & Marionette†
0160-8673 World of Opera†
0160-8703 Literary Onomastics Studies
0160-8746 Oklahoma Geological Survey. Educational Publication
0160-8754 Remote Sensing of Natural Resources: A Quarterly Literature Review *see* 1055-9922
0160-8770 Lexington Theological Quarterly
0160-8797 Master's Theses in the Arts and Social Sciences
0160-8819 Bibliography of Corporate Social Responsibility†
0160-8843 American Association of Stratigraphic Palynologists. Contributions Series
0160-8894 Grocers Report
0160-8908 Claude Hall's International Radio Report
0160-8916 Computer Dealer *changed to* Reseller Management.
0160-8959 C A Selects. Analytical Electrochemistry
0160-8967 C A Selects. Colloids (Applied Aspects)
0160-8975 C A Selects. Colloids (Physicochemical Aspects)
0160-8991 Fodor's Southeast Asia
0160-9009 Frontiers: a Journal of Women Studies
0160-9025 C A Selects. Computers in Chemistry
0160-9041 C A Selects. Environmental Pollution
0160-905X C A Selects. Organofluorine Chemistry
0160-9068 C A Selects. Fungicides
0160-9076 C A Selects. Gaseous Waste Treatment
0160-9084 C A Selects. Herbicides
0160-9092 C A Selects. Insecticides
0160-9106 C A Selects. Liquid Waste Treatment
0160-9114 C A Selects. Metallo Enzymes & Metallo Coenzymes
0160-9130 C A Selects. Organo-Transition Metal Complexes
0160-9149 C A Selects. Pollution Monitoring
0160-9157 C A Selects. Recovery & Recycling of Wastes
0160-9165 C A Selects. Solid & Radioactive Waste Treatment
0160-9173 C A Selects. Steroids (Biochemical Aspects)
0160-9181 C A Selects. Steroids (Chemical Aspects)
0160-919X C A Selects. Trace Element Analysis
0160-9203 Update (Washington)
0160-9211 U.S. Library of Congress. National Library for the Blind and Physically Handicapped. News *changed to* U.S. Library of Congress. National Library Service for the Blind and Physically Handicapped. News.
0160-922X Library Company of Philadelphia. Annual Report
0160-9289 Clinical Cardiology
0160-9300 Chronicle College Counseling for Transfers *see* 0276-0363
0160-9327 Endeavour (Tarrytown)
0160-9394 Folia Slavica†
0160-9416 Newsfront International†
0160-9459 Hospital Therapy *see* 1052-1372
0160-9475 Spina Bifida Therapy
0160-9513 Social Work with Groups
0160-9572 Seybold Report on Office Systems *see* 1057-8889
0160-9580 National Beverage Marketing Directory (Year) *changed to* Beverage Marketing Directory (Year).
0160-9602 Northeastern Nevada Historical Society Quarterly
0160-9629 E-R-C Directory
0160-9645 Ancient World
0160-967X Addiction and Substance Abuse Report *see* 1040-4163
0160-9688 Criminal Justice and the Public†
0160-9696 Success with Youth Report†
0160-970X Book Industry Trends
0160-9734 Grants Magazine†
0160-9742 Network Planning Paper
0160-9769 High Performance
0160-9807 Unexplored Deviance†
0160-9815 Annual Editions: Urban Society
0160-984X Palestine-Israel Bulletin
0160-9939 Marathoner†
0160-9947 Future Life†
0160-9963 Applied Radiology
0160-9963 Applied Radiology Directory†
0160-998X Index to Audio Visual Serials in the Health Sciences†
0161-0007 O H Osteopathic Hospitals *changed to* A O H A Today.
0161-0155 Broward Life
0161-0287 Practice Digest†
0161-0295 T I M S - O R S A Meeting Bulletin
0161-0325 Highway & Vehicle - Safety Report
0161-0333 Together (Washington, 1975) *see* 0193-3922
0161-035X Solid Wastes Management - Refuse Removal Journal and Liquid Wastes Management *see* 0745-6921
0161-0376 Analytical & Enumerative Bibliography
0161-0384 Business International Money Report
0161-0457 Scanning
0161-0511 Sons of the American Revolution Magazine
0161-052X River World†
0161-0546 Artist's Market
0161-0554 Craftworker's Market†
0161-0562 Current Career and Occupational Literature (Year)
0161-0619 Housing†
0161-0627 Iran Economic News
0161-0694 O T C Review *changed to* Equities.
0161-0708 University of Puget Sound Law Review
0161-0724 American Universities Field Staff Reports *see* 0743-9644
0161-0775 Theater (New Haven)
0161-0902 Population and Family Planning Programs†
0161-0945 American Congress on Surveying and Mapping. Proceedings of Annual Meeting *see* 0277-2876
0161-0996 Eighteenth Century: A Current Bibliography
0161-1054 Ski X - C
0161-1089 State and Mind *changed to* New Studies on the Left.
0161-1119 Adventist Review
0161-1127 Government R and D Report†
0161-1135 A M R Reporter: Managing Without Interference†
0161-1178 American Family (Washington)
0161-1186 Cum Notis Variorum†
0161-1194 Cryptologia
0161-1232 Art - Antiques Investment Report
0161-1259 P G A Magazine
0161-1267 Bottom Line (Lansing)
0161-1364 P I M A *see* 1046-4352
0161-1372 Surgical Rounds
0161-1380 Integral Yoga
0161-1402 A S I L S International Law Journal *changed to* I L S A Journal of International Law.
0161-1461 Language, Speech and Hearing Services in Schools
0161-1496 Modern Recording's Buyer's Guide *see* 0276-9239
0161-1577 Brilliant Corners†
0161-1593 C R C Critical Reviews in Solid State and Materials Sciences *see* 1040-8436
0161-164X New Women's Times†
0161-1674 U.S. Department of Energy. Office of State and Local Assistance Programs. Annual Report to the President and the Congress on the State Energy Conservation Program
0161-1704 Music O C L C Users Group. Newsletter
0161-1712 International Journal of Mathematics and Mathematical Sciences
0161-1747 Music Country
0161-1755 Airline and Travel Food *see* 0892-4236
0161-178X Taxation for Lawyers
0161-1798 VeloNews
0161-1801 Socialist Review (San Francisco)
0161-181X Asante Seminar *see* 0272-8419
0161-1828 Overseas Outlook (Large Print Edition)
0161-1836 Birding
0161-1895 I.D.E.A.S.
0161-1933 Parenteral Drug Association. Journal *see* 0279-7976
0161-1941 Petroleum Market Shares: Report on Sales of Refined Petroleum Products†
0161-1976 Agenda *see* 0735-1755
0161-1992 Bride's *changed to* Bride's & Your New Home.
0161-2018 Street & Smith's Baseball
0161-2042 Successful Business†
0161-2085 Whole Earth Papers†
0161-2107 Maine EnvironNews
0161-2115 N C J W Journal
0161-2131 Outlook (Alexandria, 1974)†
0161-2158 International Association of Fire Chiefs. Official Publication *changed to* I A F C On Scene.
0161-2190 Vogue Beauty & Health Guide†
0161-2328 Analog Science Fiction & Fact
0161-2336 House & Garden Plans Guide†
0161-2387 Federal Reserve Bank of Kansas City. Economic Review
0161-2395 Delta Nu Alphian *changed to* Transportation Worldwide.
0161-2425 Personnel Consultant
0161-245X Equal Employment Opportunity Statistics *changed to* Affirmative Employment Statistics.
0161-2492 Callaloo
0161-2506 Bloodroot (Grand Forks)†
0161-2514 Aging and Work†
0161-2549 Gallimaufry
0161-259X Chemical Industry Products News *see* 0009-2630
0161-2638 Directory of Jewish Federations, Welfare Funds and Community Councils
0161-2654 Music Clubs Magazine
0161-2689 Magazines (Washington) *see* 0889-6518
0161-2719 Tull Tracing†
0161-2778 Journal of Personality and Social Systems†
0161-2786 Earnshaw's Infants, Girls and Boys Wear Review
0161-2832 Boston College International and Comparative Law Journal *see* 0277-5778
0161-2840 Issues in Mental Health Nursing
0161-2875 World Meetings: Medicine
0161-2905 Literary Market Place
0161-2972 Weekly Regulatory Monitor†
0161-3065 American Journal of Intravenous Therapy *changed to* Intravenous Therapy News.
0161-3081 Tune Up *changed to* Philadelphia Folksong Society Newsletter.
0161-3162 Social Sciences Citation Index Journal Citation Reports
0161-3170 Science Citation Index Journal Citation Report
0161-3189 Mississippi Pharmacist
0161-3243 University of Alaska. Biological Papers. Special Reports *see* 0568-8604
0161-326X A J O T: The American Journal of Occupational Therapy *see* 0272-9490
0161-3332 International Association of Fish and Wildlife Agencies. Proceedings of the Convention
0161-3340 General Social Surveys
0161-3448 Satellite News
0161-3464 Dax Dynamic Showcase
0161-3499 Veterinary Surgery
0161-3561 Water, Woods & Wildlife
0161-357X McGraw-Hill's Construction Contracting *see* 0270-1588
0161-3626 Analog Dialogue
0161-3650 N A G W S Guide. Basketball, Volleyball†
0161-3871 Tennessee Sportsman
0161-4002 Annual Institute on Securities Law and Regulations. Proceedings†
0161-4010 Copyright Management†
0161-4029 Index to Reviews of Bibliographical Publications
0161-4126 Communication Outlook
0161-4169 National Science Foundation. Summaries of Projects Completed†
0161-4193 Parents' Magazine *see* 0195-0967
0161-4223 Lightworks
0161-4274 National Food Review
0161-4282 Seminars
0161-4312 Racquetball Illustrated *see* 0161-7966
0161-4339 Farm Industry News - West *see* 0199-6924
0161-4347 Farm Industry News - South *see* 0199-6924
0161-4355 Asia†
0161-4363 Bacon's International Publicity Checker
0161-4371 High Fidelity's Buying Guide to Tape Systems†
0161-4428 Focus on Alcohol and Drug Issues *changed to* Focus - Education Professionals in Family Recovery.
0161-4452 Science Museum of Minnesota. Scientific Publications, New Series
0161-4479 Treteaux
0161-4576 Journal of Sex Education and Therapy
0161-4622 Italian Culture†
0161-4630 Prostaglandins and Medicine *see* 0952-3278
0161-4681 Teachers College Record
0161-4703 Horn of Africa
0161-472X Report on Survival Studies of Patients With Cystic Fibrosis *see* 0197-7423
0161-4738 North Carolina State Industrial Directory *changed to* MacRae's State Industrial Directory: North Carolina - South Carolina - Virginia.
0161-4754 Journal of Manipulative and Physiological Therapeutics *changed to* J M P T: Journal of Manipulative and Physiological Therapeutics.
0161-4835 Death
0161-4843 Casino-East
0161-4851 Gas Digest
0161-486X Columbia: A Magazine of Poetry and Prose
0161-4878 Ohio Industrial Directory *see* 0888-8140
0161-4886 Denver Magazine
0161-4908 Asian Theatre Reports *see* 0742-5457
0161-4924 Annual New Mexico Water Conference. Proceedings
0161-4932 Florida Genealogist
0161-4940 Catalysis Reviews: Science and Engineering
0161-5092 Impact (Sunnyvale)
0161-5114 Re-View†
0161-522X Marine Recreational Fisheries
0161-5238 Brethren Missionary Herald
0161-5246 Issues in Health Care of Women *see* 0739-9332
0161-5262 Income - Expense Analysis: Apartments, Condominiums and Cooperatives *see* 0194-1941
0161-5262 Income-Expense Analysis. Apartments, Condominiums and Cooperatives *see* 0191-2208

0161-5319 Frontiers of Power Technology Conference. Proceedings *changed to* Frontiers of Power Conference. Proceedings.
0161-5378 Highlander (Barrington)
0161-5386 Taxation with Representation Newsletter†
0161-5394 A M A Management Digest†
0161-5408 Ag Alert
0161-5440 Historical Methods
0161-5475 Country Profiles
0161-5491 Journal of Holistic Health†
0161-5505 Journal of Nuclear Medicine
0161-5556 Book-Mart†
0161-5653 School Social Work Journal
0161-5661 Graduate Woman *changed to* A A U W Outlook.
0161-570X Alternative Lifestyles *changed to* Journal of Family and Economic Issues.
0161-5785 Printing Paper†
0161-5807 U.S. Energy Information Administration. Annual Report to Congress
0161-5815 Prorodeo Sports News
0161-5823 Broadcasting and the Law
0161-5866 Money Business: Grants and Awards for Creative Artists†
0161-5874 Health Science *see* 0883-8216
0161-5882 National Association of Realtors. Home Sales
0161-5890 Molecular Immunology
0161-5947 Chorister *changed to* Young Chorister.
0161-5971 Songwriter's Market
0161-5998 Academy of Management Newsletter
0161-6005 A P I C Journal *see* 0196-6553
0161-603X U.S. National Institute on Drug Abuse. Statistical Series D. Data from the Client Oriented Data Acquisition Process. Quarterly Report. Provisional Data
0161-6048 Energy Technology Conference. Proceedings
0161-6072 I C U I S Justice Ministries†
0161-6080 Successful Dealer
0161-6129 Police Magazine†
0161-6234 Linn's Stamp News
0161-6242 Scholia Satyrica†
0161-6277 U.S. Environmental Protection Agency. Grants Administration Division. Awards Register, Grants Assistance Programs†
0161-6293 B P C (Building Products Catalog) *changed to* Hutton's Building Products Catalog.
0161-6315 Cost Engineering (1978) *see* 0274-9696
0161-6323 American Seaport *changed to* W W S - World Wide Shipping.
0161-6331 Wings†
0161-6412 Neurological Research
0161-6420 Ophthalmology
0161-6439 Journal of Otolaryngology and Head and Neck Surgery *see* 0194-5998
0161-6447 Michigan Restaurateur
0161-6463 American Indian Culture and Research Journal
0161-651X Mine Safety & Health†
0161-6528 Atlas World Press Review *see* 0195-8895
0161-6536 Encore American & Worldwide News
0161-6544 Friends of George Sand Newsletter *changed to* George Sand Studies.
0161-6587 Boston College Law Review
0161-6595 Energy Conservation News
0161-6641 Current Issues (Alexandria)
0161-6668 Connoisseurs Guide to California Wine
0161-6684 Human Rights and the U.S. Foreign Assistance Program†
0161-6706 Sports 'n Spokes
0161-6730 Virginia Road Builder†
0161-6749 Interaction (Washington, 1977)†
0161-6765 Health, Safety & Education†
0161-6773 Long Term Care and Health Services Administration Quarterly†
0161-6781 Health Manpower Report *see* 0888-9465
0161-682X The Romantist
0161-6838 Teacher Information Exchange†
0161-6846 Public Library Quarterly
0161-6854 American Photographer *see* 1046-8986
0161-6862 Computer Products†
0161-7001 Best Buys in Print†
0161-7036 F T C Freedom of Information Log
0161-7095 University of Detroit Journal of Urban Law *changed to* University of Detroit Law Review.
0161-7109 Juvenile and Family Court Journal
0161-7133 Missionary Monthly
0161-715X Sibyl-Child
0161-7184 Travel *changed to* Travel - Holiday.
0161-7222 Studia Mystica
0161-7230 Research in Political Economy
0161-7249 Research in Philosophy and Technology
0161-7257 Current Construction Costs
0161-7303 Literature of Liberty†
0161-7311 Producer Prices and Price Indexes *changed to* Producer Price Indexes.
0161-7338 New York Running News
0161-7346 Ultrasonic Imaging
0161-7354 Journal of Applied Biochemistry *see* 0885-4513
0161-7362 Sierra
0161-7370 Popular Science
0161-7389 U S A Today
0161-7397 International Association of Orientalist Librarians. Bulletin†
0161-7400 School Social Work Quarterly†
0161-7419 Fairfield County Executive
0161-7427 Microelectronic Manufacturing and Testing *changed to* Microelectronics Manufacturing Technology.
0161-7435 George Herbert Journal
0161-7443 National Passive Solar Conference. Proceedings. *changed to* American Solar Energy Society. Passive Conference. Annual Meeting.
0161-7451 Ex - P O W Bulletin
0161-746X Florida Pharmacy Journal *changed to* Florida Pharmacy Today.
0161-7478 Forum on Medicine†
0161-7486 Harvard Medical School Health Letter *see* 1052-1577
0161-7494 Public Employee (Washington)
0161-7508 Distributed Processing Report *changed to* Distributed Processing Product Reports.
0161-7516 Radiology - Nuclear Medicine International†
0161-7567 Journal of Applied Physiology: Respiratory, Environmental and Exercise Physiology *see* 8750-7587
0161-7605 CableLibraries†
0161-7648 Towson State University Journal of Psychology†
0161-7656 Benchmark Papers in Genetics†
0161-7672 World Smoking & Health
0161-7710 Bflo†
0161-7729 Scholars' Facsimiles & Reprints
0161-7745 Best's Review. Property - Casualty Insurance Edition
0161-7753 Arkansas Educator
0161-7761 Anthropology & Education Quarterly
0161-777X Sludge Magazine†
0161-7796 U.S. Environmental Protection Agency. Radiation Protection Activities†
0161-780X Current Neurology
0161-7826 D Magazine
0161-7885 Illinois Horizons†
0161-7915 Pacific Search *see* 0199-6363
0161-7966 National Racquetball
0161-7982 N Y E A Advocate *changed to* N E A New York.
0161-8032 Predicasts Overview of Markets and Technology
0161-8040 I F I Fabricare News
0161-8059 Practical Sailor
0161-8091 Energy Developments in Japan†
0161-8105 Sleep
0161-8113 Zoning and Planning Law Report
0161-813X Neurotoxicology (Park Forest South)
0161-8202 Journal of Arachnology
0161-8229 Sales Training *see* 0193-2136
0161-8237 American Agriculturist
0161-8245 Index to Periodical Articles By and About Negroes *changed to* Index to Black Periodicals.
0161-8318 Assembling *changed to* Assembling Annual.
0161-8342 Antique Trader Weekly
0161-8369 University of North Carolina. Sea Grant College Newsletter *changed to* Coastwatch.
0161-8415 Pharmaceutical Representative
0161-8423 Theodore Roosevelt Association Journal
0161-8458 Journal of Mechanical Design *see* 1048-9002
0161-8458 Journal of Mechanical Design *see* 1050-0472
0161-8490 E P A Activities Under the Resource Conservation and Recovery Act of 1976†
0161-8555 Cosmic Search†
0161-8571 Georgia State Industrial Directory *see* 0740-2910
0161-8644 Bilalian News *changed to* A M Journal.
0161-8660 New Roots *changed to* Renewable Energy News: Northeast.
0161-8695 Vital Statistics of Iowa
0161-8741 Dallas-Fort Worth Home & Garden†
0161-8768 Officemation Product Reports
0161-8784 Realites (Horsham)
0161-8792 Perspectives in Ophthalmology†
0161-8938 Journal of Policy Modeling
0161-8954 Advances in Aquatic Microbiology†
0161-9004 Statistics of Privately Owned Electric Utilities in the United States *changed to* Financial Statistics of Selected Electric Utilities.
0161-9055 Home Video Report *see* 0748-0792
0161-9152 Age
0161-9225 I & L
0161-9241 California State Bar Journal *see* 0279-4063
0161-9268 Advances in Nursing Science
0161-9276 Clergy Tax Tips *see* 0045-6861
0161-9284 The Magazine Antiques
0161-9292 Union Leader *see* 0019-3291
0161-9314 International President's Bulletin
0161-9330 In Public Service *changed to* P E D Forum.
0161-9373 Maritime Newsletter
0161-9500 Executive Educator
0161-9543 Musician, Player and Listener *see* 0733-5253
0161-9640 Clinical Chemistry News
0161-9705 Chinese Literature: Essays, Articles, Reviews
0161-9721 Journal of Surgical Practice
0161-973X RetailWeek†
0161-987X Notre Dame Magazine
0161-9896 Highlands Voice
0161-990X Construction Labor News
0162-0029 Garcia Lorca Review†
0162-0045 Food Monitor *changed to* Why.
0162-0061 Pawn Review†
0162-007X Physical Education - Sports Index
0162-0088 World Wide Shipping Guide
0162-0126 Cinemonkey
0162-0134 Journal of Inorganic Biochemistry
0162-0169 Red M(irage)
0162-0177 C R: Centennial Review
0162-0223 Media Index *see* 0199-9273
0162-0266 Hit Parader
0162-0274 Bowling Magazine
0162-0290 Directory and Statistics of Oregon Libraries
0162-0363 Catholic Sentinel (Diocese of Baker)
0162-0401 Frets Magazine†
0162-0436 Qualitative Sociology
0162-0444 Significant Decisions of the Supreme Court†
0162-0517 Swift River†
0162-0525 Journal of Juvenile and Family Courts *see* 0161-7109
0162-0533 Builder (Washington) *see* 0744-1193
0162-0606 E E Report *see* 0840-5662
0162-069X X, a Journal of the Arts *see* 0195-7848
0162-0789 China Geographer†
0162-0800 Olmstead's Genealogy Recorded†
0162-0843 Health Sciences Serials
0162-0878 South Carolina State Industrial Directory *see* 0733-4931
0162-0886 Reviews of Infectious Diseases *changed to* Clinical Infectious Diseases.
0162-0894 Tamarack
0162-0908 Year Book of Sports Medicine
0162-0916 Where to Write for Marriage Records: United States and Outlying Areas†
0162-0932 Verbatim
0162-1017 Tamarisk
0162-1025 Fleet Owner: Small Fleet Edition†
0162-1033 Collectors News & the Antique Reporter
0162-1041 El Paso Business Review *see* 8750-6033
0162-105X Personnel Alert†
0162-1068 Spotlight (Bethlehem)
0162-1149 Gargoyle
0162-1211 Bar Journal (Trenton) *see* 0195-0983
0162-122X Products Liability Reporter
0162-1238 Pollution Control Guide†
0162-1262 Texas Business and Texas Parade *see* 0164-7628
0162-1289 Seven Days†
0162-1297 Rugby
0162-1300 Impact Journal
0162-1327 Peninsula Magazine
0162-1343 Play Meter
0162-1378 Mode
0162-1386 Traditional Home Ideas *changed to* Traditional Home.
0162-1394 Once *changed to* Young Once.
0162-1408 Residential and Community Child Care Administration *see* 0886-571X
0162-1416 Child Behavior Therapy *see* 0731-7107
0162-1424 Home Health Care Services Quarterly
0162-1432 A S A I O Journal†
0162-1440 Tree Tracers
0162-1459 J A S A. Journal of the American Statistical Association
0162-1467 N C A A Directory
0162-153X American Shotgunner
0162-1564 Tennessee Librarian
0162-1599 New England States Limited†
0162-1602 N A R D Newsletter
0162-1718 Utilities Law Reports
0162-1726 Boycott Law Bulletin
0162-1815 Tax Court Reports
0162-1831 National Forum (Auburn)
0162-184X Center for Southern Folklore Newsletter *see* 0195-4903
0162-1858 Exchange - The Organizational Behavior Teaching Journal *see* 1052-5629
0162-1866 S T T H
0162-1890 Evangel
0162-1904 Zone
0162-1912 Western Journal of Agricultural Economics
0162-1939 Illinois. State Museum. Guidebooklet Series†
0162-1955 Accent (Birmingham)
0162-1963 General Science Index
0162-1971 Contempo
0162-198X Discovery (Birmingham)
0162-2021 Political Methodology†
0162-2048 Serial Sources for the BIOSIS Previews Database
0162-2102 Catholic Sentinel (Archdiocese of Portland, Oregon)
0162-2110 World of Rodeo and Western Heritage
0162-217X Charles Redd Monographs in Western History
0162-2188 Isaac Asimov's Science Fiction Magazine

ISSN INDEX 5619

0162-220X Cancer Nursing
0162-2226 Professional Remodeling†
0162-2234 Assemblies of God Home Missions†
0162-2242 SportStyle
0162-2250 Journal of Commerce & Industry
0162-2269 Clinical Behavior Therapy Review†
0162-2285 Medical Selfcare†
0162-234X Philosopher's Annual†
0162-2404 Soviet World Outlook†
0162-2412 Iowa R E C News
0162-2439 Science, Technology & Human Values
0162-2471 News and Views from Federally Employed Women *see* 0895-3619
0162-2498 Book Collector's Market *see* 0196-5654
0162-2617 Tennessee Farm Bureau News
0162-2641 Journal of Instructional Development *see* 1042-1629
0162-2692 Young Spartacus†
0162-2706 Society of Chartered Property and Casualty Underwriters. Journal
0162-2714 Coal Outlook
0162-2730 Fuel Oil Week†
0162-2749 International Family Planning Perspectives and Digest *see* 0190-3187
0162-2757 Detroit in Perspective†
0162-2765 Goodfellow Review of Crafts†
0162-2773 L A E Journal†
0162-2811 Communication Abstracts
0162-282X Memphis
0162-2846 P E R Report†
0162-2870 October
0162-2889 International Security
0162-2897 California History (San Francisco)
0162-2900 Los Angeles Lawyer
0162-296X Orpheus
0162-2978 Adobe Today *changed to* Solar Earthbuilder International.
0162-2994 Washington Drug and Device Letter *see* 0194-1291
0162-3036 Engineering Index Monthly and Author Index *see* 0742-1974
0162-3052 L A E News
0162-3095 Ethology and Sociobiology
0162-3109 Immunopharmacology
0162-3125 Bacon's Publicity Checker
0162-3133 Washington Spectator *see* 0887-428X
0162-3141 U.S. Army Recruiting and Re-Enlisting Journal *changed to* Recruiter Journal.
0162-315X Weimaraner Magazine
0162-3168 Construction Contractor
0162-3176 Construction Briefings
0162-3192 Journal of Guidance and Control *see* 0731-5090
0162-3206 National Security Record†
0162-3214 Petersen's 4 Wheel & Off-Road
0162-3230 Flower and Garden. Southern Edition *see* 0162-3249
0162-3249 Flower and Garden
0162-3257 Journal of Autism and Developmental Disorders
0162-3273 Computer Graphics (Eugene) *see* 0271-4159
0162-3281 Related Patent Index†
0162-329X Dual Dictionary to Petroleum Abstracts†
0162-3338 Professional Woman
0162-3346 Perspectives (Pittsburgh) *changed to* Managing (Pittsburgh).
0162-3354 Periodical Update†
0162-3362 Prep
0162-3370 Better Living
0162-3389 Actuator Systems†
0162-3397 American Lawyer
0162-3400 Savor†
0162-3451 Moneytree
0162-3486 Taxes on Parade
0162-3494 Standard Federal Tax Reports
0162-3532 Journal for the Education of the Gifted
0162-3559 P S B A Bulletin
0162-3567 Unity (Unity Village)
0162-3583 Rifle
0162-3591 A A A Traveler (Madison) *see* 0277-1004
0162-3605 Health Policy & Biomedical Research: The Blue Sheet
0162-3613 B S C S Journal *changed to* B S C S: The Natural Selection.
0162-3621 Annual Editions. Focus: Aging *see* 0272-3808
0162-3656 Agency Sales Magazine *see* 0749-2332
0162-3664 Young World *see* 0009-3971
0162-3737 Educational Evaluation & Policy Analysis
0162-3745 Communique (Washington)†
0162-3753 Crystal Structure†
0162-3761 Contemporary Pharmacy Practice†
0162-3788 Charge, Spin and Momentum Density†
0162-3796 Campground Management
0162-380X Southwestern Musician Combined with The Texas Music Educator
0162-3818 Nebula Winners
0162-3869 United Rubber Worker
0162-3885 Business Communications Review
0162-3893 Columbia (New York)
0162-3907 American Physical Therapy Association. Progress Report
0162-3923 Supercycle
0162-3958 Energy Resources and Technology *see* 0278-5099
0162-3974 Neighbors
0162-4024 Continuum (Washington) *changed to* Continuing Higher Education Review.
0162-4040 Financial Review (New York)†
0162-4067 World Naturopathic Journal†
0162-4075 Concrete International: Design & Construction
0162-4083 E P O†
0162-4105 Database (Weston)
0162-4148 Advanced Bible Study
0162-4156 Adult Bible Study
0162-4164 Adult Bible Teacher
0162-4164 Adult Bible Teacher. Large Print Edition†
0162-4172 Adult Leadership
0162-4180 Baptist Adults
0162-4199 Baptist Youth
0162-4202 Bible Book Study for Adult Teachers
0162-4237 Cemetery Business & Legal Guide†
0162-4245 Family Heritage
0162-4253 Living (Nashville)
0162-4261 Living with Teenagers
0162-427X Mature Living
0162-4288 More
0162-4296 Open Windows
0162-430X Opus One
0162-4318 Outreach (Nashville) *see* 0274-8568
0162-4326 Proclaim (Nashville)
0162-4334 Southern Baptist Convention. Sunday School Board. Quarterly Review
0162-4342 El Interprete
0162-4350 Living with Preschoolers
0162-4369 Look and Listen
0162-4377 Music Makers (Nashville)
0162-4385 On the Wing
0162-4393 Preschool Leadership
0162-4407 Sunday School Lesson Illustrator *see* 0195-1351
0162-4415 Exploring A *see* 0745-032X
0162-4423 Exploring A for Leaders *see* 0745-0346
0162-4458 Exploring C *changed to* Exploring 2.
0162-4466 Exploring C for Leaders *see* 0745-0354
0162-4474 Guide A for Preschool Teachers *changed to* Preschool Bible Teacher A.
0162-4482 Guide B for Preschool Teachers *see* 0732-944X
0162-4490 Guide C for Preschool Teachers *see* 0732-9458
0162-4504 La Fe Bautista
0162-4512 Growing (Nashville)
0162-4539 Care for Leaders†
0162-4547 Encounter!
0162-4571 Collegiate Bible Study†
0162-458X Come Alive†
0162-4598 Come Alive for Leaders†
0162-461X Children's Leadership
0162-4644 Simplified Bible Study *see* 0748-5409
0162-4652 Church Recreation Magazine
0162-4660 Bible Learners. Teacher
0162-4679 Bible Learners
0162-4687 Bible Discoverers Teacher
0162-4695 Bible Discoverers
0162-4709 Youth Leadership
0162-4733 Senior Adult Bible Study
0162-4741 Bible Study Pocket Commentary
0162-475X Bible Study Leaflet
0162-4768 Youth in Discovery Teacher
0162-4776 Youth in Discovery
0162-4784 Youth in Action
0162-4792 Youth in Action Teacher
0162-4806 Young Adults in Training *see* 0195-136X
0162-4814 Young Adult Bible Study
0162-4822 Bible Book Study for Youth
0162-4830 Bible Book Study for Youth Teachers
0162-4849 Bible Book Study for Adults
0162-4849 Bible Book Study for Adults. Large Print Edition
0162-4857 Bible Lesson Digest
0162-4865 Youth Teacher *changed to* Sunday School Youth Teacher.
0162-4873 Sunday School Lessons Simplified *see* 0748-5360
0162-4881 Sunday School Youth A *changed to* Sunday School Youth.
0162-489X Sunday School Youth B†
0162-4903 Sunday School Young Adults
0162-4911 Sunday School Adults
0162-492X C L A S S Forum†
0162-4962 Biography (Honolulu)
0162-4989 Impact (Washington)
0162-5047 Livestock Weekly
0162-5055 Juvenile Law Digest *see* 0279-2257
0162-5098 Crops and Soils Magazine†
0162-5101 Michigan State Bar Journal *see* 0164-3576
0162-5136 Candy Wholesaler
0162-5144 Eagle (Champaign)†
0162-5152 Insiders' Chronicle
0162-5160 Pennsylvania Township News
0162-5179 Oregon Farm Bureau News
0162-5217 R-A-D-A-R
0162-5233 Washington Food Report *see* 0745-4503
0162-5241 Profile (Omaha)
0162-5276 Kiwanis Magazine
0162-5284 New Hampshire Audubon
0162-5306 Action Line (Memphis)†
0162-5314 Bibliographic Guide to Latin American Studies
0162-5322 Bibliographic Guide to Soviet and European Studies
0162-5330 Ceramic Mold Mart†
0162-5381 Planbook for Leaders of Children *changed to* Curriculum Plans.
0162-5403 Alaska Review of Social and Economic Conditions
0162-5411 Official Baseball Dope Book†
0162-542X Official Baseball Register
0162-5446 Dermatology *see* 0273-2254
0162-5454 Seminars in Infectious Disease†
0162-5586 World Agricultural Supply and Demand Estimates
0162-5594 Intercontinental Press Combined with Imprecor *changed to* Intercontinental Press.
0162-5616 Florida Folk Arts Directory *changed to* Florida Folklife Resource Directory.
0162-5632 Miniature Magazine *see* 0146-6607
0162-5667 Hearing & Speech Action†
0162-5683 B N A's Washington Memorandum *see* 0886-0475
0162-5691 Corporate Practice Series
0162-5721 Atlanta Historical Journal *see* 0896-3975
0162-573X Daisy†
0162-5748 Review of Higher Education
0162-5764 Licensing Law and Business Report
0162-5810 Alembic†
0162-5837 Who
0162-5853 Computer Business News *see* 0746-6765
0162-5861 Dining In & Out†
0162-5896 Chilton's Hardware Age *see* 8755-254X
0162-5918 Alpha
0162-5934 S W L
0162-5942 Emergency
0162-5950 On-Your-Own Guide to Asia†
0162-5977 C S P Directory of Suppliers of Educational Foreign Language Materials†
0162-5993 D I S C U S Newsletter†
0162-6019 Message Magazine *see* 0026-0231
0162-6108 Frozen Fishery Products. Annual Summary
0162-6175 Monthly Coke Report *changed to* U.S. Energy Information Administration. Quarterly Coal Report.
0162-6191 Constructor
0162-6205 Highway Safety Highlights *changed to* Highway Safety Directions.
0162-6221 Metro (Redondo Beach)
0162-6272 Opiniones Latinoamericanas *changed to* Opiniones.
0162-6280 Folklore and Mythology Studies
0162-6302 New York (State) Department of Social Services. Bureau of Data Management and Analysis. Program Brief
0162-6329 Defenders of Wildlife Magazine *see* 0162-6337
0162-6337 Defenders
0162-6345 Footwear Focus†
0162-6353 Carolinas Companies†
0162-637X Chemical Worker
0162-6396 Sexology (1978) *see* 0199-7149
0162-6418 20th Century Christian
0162-6426 Library of Congress†
0162-6434 Journal of Special Education Technology
0162-6477 Correspondence Society of Surgeons. Collected Letters
0162-6493 Infectious Disease Practice
0162-654X United States Hockey and Arena Biz *see* 8756-3789
0162-6566 American Journal of Proctology, Gastroenterology & Colon & Rectal Surgery
0162-6574 Journal of Experiential Learning and Simulation†
0162-6604 Aftermarket Executive†
0162-6612 A L S C Newsletter
0162-6620 Action in Teacher Education
0162-6639 Index of N L M Serial Titles†
0162-6663 Handy Andy Magazine *see* 0195-0967
0162-6671 Primroses
0162-6728 American Fisheries Directory and Reference Book†
0162-6760 Spirituality Today†
0162-6795 Journal of Asian Culture
0162-6809 Official Guide: Tractors and Farm Equipment
0162-6817 Market Logic
0162-6825 Dimension (Birmingham)
0162-6833 Aware
0162-6841 Start (Birmingham)
0162-6876 Sharing (Rockville)
0162-6906 Monographs in Developmental Pediatrics†
0162-6957 Behavioral Medicine†
0162-6973 Cadence (Redwood)
0162-6981 Skyline†
0162-704X Conference Papers Index
0162-7082 R, D & A
0162-7090 Ceramic Teaching Projects and Trade News *changed to* Ceramics (Livonia).
0162-7104 Indiana Prairie Farmer
0162-7139 Decade
0162-7155 Journal of Nursing Care *changed to* Licensed Practical Nurse.
0162-7163 L A C M A Physician
0162-7171 Synopsis of Family Therapy Practice
0162-7295 Legal Times *changed to* Legal Times.
0162-7317 Dental Dealer International Product News

ISSN

0162-7325 National Law Journal
0162-7333 New York Theatre Annual *see* 0195-945X
0162-7341 Journal of Sport Behavior
0162-735X O A G Travel Planner and Hotel-Motel Guide. European Edition *see* 0894-1718
0162-7376 Woodall's Campground Directory. Texas Edition *changed to* Woodall's Campground Directory. Texas, Mexico Edition.
0162-7384 Woodall's Campground Directory. Arizona Edition *changed to* Woodall's Campground Directory. Arizona, New Mexico Edition.
0162-7392 Woodall's Campground Directory. California Edition *changed to* Woodall's Campground Directory. California, Nevada, Mexico Edition.
0162-7406 Woodall's Campground Directory. Eastern Edition
0162-7414 Woodall's Campground Directory. Western Edition
0162-7422 Bank Loan Officers Report†
0162-7430 Bank Marketing Report†
0162-7449 Bank Personnel Report *changed to* Bank Human Resouces Report.
0162-7457 Bank Security Report
0162-7465 Bank Tax Report
0162-7473 Bank Teller's Report
0162-7481 Branch Banker's Report†
0162-7503 Executive Compensation Report *changed to* Employee Benefits Report.
0162-7511 Kess Tax Practice Report†
0162-752X Real Estate Law Report
0162-7538 Real Estate Tax Ideas
0162-7546 Reviews of Chemical Intermediates *see* 0922-6168
0162-7570 Washington University Magazine
0162-7635 Yachtsman's Guide to the Greater Antilles *see* 0735-9020
0162-766X Middle East: Abstracts and Index†
0162-7686 C A Selects. Adhesives
0162-7694 C A Selects. Animal Longevity and Aging
0162-7708 C A Selects. Batteries & Fuel Cells
0162-7716 C A Selects. Biogenic Amines & the Nervous System
0162-7724 C A Selects. Biological Information Transfer
0162-7732 C A Selects. Blood Coagulation
0162-7740 C A Selects. Crystal Growth
0162-7767 C A Selects. Detergents, Soaps, & Surfactants
0162-7775 C A Selects. Drug & Cosmetic Toxicity
0162-7783 C A Selects. Electrodeposition
0162-7791 C A Selects. Energy Reviews & Books
0162-7805 C A Selects. Flammability
0162-7813 C A Selects. Food Toxicity
0162-7821 C A Selects. Heat-Resistant and Ablative Polymers
0162-783X C A Selects. Organophosphorous Chemistry
0162-7848 C A Selects. Organic Reaction Mechanisms
0162-7864 C A Selects. Thermochemistry
0162-7872 C A Selects. X-Ray Analysis & Spectroscopy
0162-7880 Who's Who in American Law
0162-7899 Groundswell (Washington)
0162-7902 El Quetzal
0162-7910 A A H E Bulletin
0162-7929 Concordia Commentator†
0162-7937 A L S A Forum *see* 0894-5993
0162-7961 Social Work in Education
0162-7996 Antitrust
0162-8003 Advances in Archaeological Method and Theory *see* 1043-1691
0162-8046 U F O Annual†
0162-8127 Horse Care†
0162-816X Medical Equipment Classified
0162-8178 I T E Journal
0162-8208 Altadena Review†
0162-8216 Communication Theory in the Cause of Man *changed to* Communication Theory in the Cause of Humanity.
0162-8267 Heritage Review
0162-8283 American Historical Society of Germans from Russia. Journal
0162-8291 Sea World†
0162-8305 Galileo (Boston)†
0162-8321 Monographs of Marine Mollusca
0162-833X Journal of the New Alchemists†
0162-8356 Confluencia†
0162-8372 University of Arkansas at Little Rock Law Journal
0162-8402 Hydrogen Progress†
0162-8410 Nashville! *see* 1052-4215
0162-8445 Arts & Humanities Citation Index
0162-8453 Journal of Curriculum Theorizing *changed to* J C T.
0162-8488 Pre-Raphaelite Review *see* 0835-7099
0162-8496 Mail Order Product *changed to* Key (Battleground).
0162-8534 Electrical Business†
0162-8623 Wind Energy Report
0162-8658 Small Business Tax Control
0162-8666 Pets, Supplies, Marketing
0162-8712 California Sociologist
0162-8739 A Different Drummer
0162-8763 Santa Clara County Business Magazine
0162-8771 New England Printer and Publisher
0162-8801 Home and Auto *changed to* Aftermarket Business.
0162-8801 Home and Auto Buyer's Guide *changed to* Aftermarket Business Buyer's Guide.
0162-881X Flooring
0162-8828 I E E E Transactions on Pattern Analysis and Machine Intelligence
0162-8836 Housewares†
0162-8887 Standard Rate and Data Service. Community Publication Rates and Data
0162-8895 Standard Rate and Data Service. Weekly Newspaper and Shopping Guide Rates and Data *see* 0162-8887
0162-8917 Sassy†
0162-8933 Character *see* 0883-1718
0162-8941 Equine Practice
0162-895X Political Psychology
0162-8968 Inc.
0162-8976 Prairie Sun†
0162-8984 Practical Politics
0162-9050 New Issues
0162-9069 Nursing Job Guide to Over 7000 Hospitals *changed to* Nursingworld Journal Nursing Job Guide.
0162-9077 Home Lighting & Accessories
0162-9085 Nahuatzen†
0162-9093 Communications and the Law
0162-9107 Januz Direct Marketing Letter†
0162-9123 Workbasket
0162-9131 Energy User News
0162-9158 H F D - Retailing Home Furnishings
0162-9166 Southeastern Camping *see* 0731-5112
0162-9174 University of Dayton Law Review
0162-9182 Journal of International Relations *see* 0191-8028
0162-9301 Bible and Spade *changed to* Archaeology and Biblical Research.
0162-9360 Journal of Clinical Hematology and Oncology†
0162-9379 Orthopaedic Transactions
0162-945X Update (Alexandria)†
0162-9468 Textile Products and Processes†
0162-9506 Spokane†
0162-9646 C I C's State School Directories
0162-9689 Bus World
0162-9700 Journal of Applied Metalworking *see* 0931-704X
0162-9719 Journal of Materials for Energy Systems *see* 0931-7058
0162-976X A A B S Newsletter
0162-9778 Journal of Baltic Studies
0162-9794 Forum on Taxing and Spending *see* 0272-7595
0162-9808 Young Crusader
0162-9816 TravLtips
0162-9824 Nathaniel Hawthorne Society. Newsletter *see* 0890-4197
0162-9832 World Refugee Survey Report *see* 0197-5439
0162-9859 Juvenile and Family Court Newsletter
0162-9867 International Gymnast *see* 0276-1041
0162-9875 Extension Review
0162-9883 A's and B's of Merit Scholarships *changed to* A's & B's of Academic Scholarship.
0162-9905 Restoration: Studies in English Literary Culture, 1660-1700
0162-9972 Hotel and Travel Index
0162-9999 Group for the Use of Psychology in History. Newsletter *see* 0363-891X
0163-0008 Ohio Monthly Record
0163-0016 Working Papers in Applied Linguistics *changed to* Ohio University. Working Papers in Linguistics and Language Teaching.
0163-0040 American Hungarian Educator
0163-0067 Information World†
0163-0075 Cincinnati Medicine
0163-0083 Woodall's Campground Directory. New England States Edition†
0163-0105 Woodall's Campground Directory. Wisconsin Edition *changed to* Woodall's Campground Directory. Minnesota, Wisconsin Edition.
0163-0113 Woodall's Campground Directory. New Jersey, New York Edition *changed to* Woodall's Campground Directory. New York Edition.
0163-0121 Woodall's Campground Directory. Michigan Edition†
0163-0172 Focus (Seattle)†
0163-0180 Research in Sociology of Knowledge, Science and Art *see* 0278-1557
0163-0229 Korean Review
0163-0253 Life Lines†
0163-030X Chilton's I A M I Iron Age Metalworking International†
0163-0334 Diet and Exercise *changed to* Better Homes and Gardens Low-Calorie Recipes.
0163-0350 Latin American Music Review
0163-0369 New Farm
0163-0415 Dieciocho
0163-0423 Identity†
0163-0458 Health Devices Alerts
0163-0466 Index to New England Periodicals
0163-0504 Genealogical Forum of Portland, Oregon. Bulletin *changed to* Genealogical Forum of Oregon. Bulletin.
0163-0512 Facets (Chicago)
0163-0539 Genealogical Society of Portland, Oregon. Monthly Bulletin *changed to* Genealogical Forum of Oregon. Bulletin.
0163-0547 Computers and Medicine (Glencoe)
0163-0563 Numerical Functional Analysis and Optimization
0163-0571 Journal of Immunopharmacology *see* 0892-3973
0163-0628 Fodor's Brazil
0163-0644 Sulphur Research & Development†
0163-0652 Limited Partners Letter
0163-0660 Allergy Information Exchange *see* 0192-995X
0163-0679 Chilton's Control Equipment Master†
0163-0741 Wind Technology Journal†
0163-075X Kenyon Review
0163-0768 Forum Linguisticum
0163-0784 Massachusetts Nurse
0163-0881 Philosophy of Science Association Newsletter
0163-089X Wall Street Journal (Midwest Edition)
0163-0911 Antiques World†
0163-092X Portfolio
0163-0938 Fashion Rage
0163-0946 Odyssey (Peterborough)
0163-0954 Icarus(Baltimore)†
0163-0989 Earth's Daughters
0163-1004 Fuego de Aztlan†
0163-1020 U S News Washington Letter†
0163-1047 Behavioral and Neural Biology
0163-108X Policy Studies Review Annual
0163-1101 Shepard's Military Justice Citations
0163-1128 Bookwoman
0163-1136 Connecticut
0163-1144 Flying Annual & Buyers' Guide†
0163-1152 Maine Historical Society Quarterly
0163-1187 Chronicles of Culture *see* 0887-5731
0163-1209 Cumberlands†
0163-1241 Abingdon Clergy Income Tax Guide
0163-1268 Small Business Computers†
0163-1276 New York Production Manual *see* 0732-6653
0163-1284 Platt's Oilgram News
0163-1306 Family Circle's Great Ideas
0163-1314 Acupuncture Letter
0163-1322 Hospital Purchasing Management *see* 0888-3068
0163-1365 American Jewish Congress. Congress Monthly
0163-1373 L A M P Occasional Newsletter *see* 1044-8756
0163-1411 Massachusetts Law Review
0163-1438 Abstract Newsletter: Natural Resources and Earth Sciences *changed to* N T I S Alerts: Natural Resources & Earth Sciences.
0163-1446 Abstract Newsletter: Physics *changed to* N T I S Alerts: Physics.
0163-1454 Abstract Newsletter: Civil Engineering *changed to* N T I S Alerts: Civil Engineering.
0163-1462 Abstract Newsletter: Electrotechnology *changed to* N T I S Alerts: Electrotechnology.
0163-1489 Procurement Systems Digest *changed to* Federal Computer Market Report.
0163-1497 Abstract Newsletter: Biomedical Technology and Human Factors Engineering *changed to* N T I S Alerts: Biomedical Technology & Human Factors Engineering.
0163-1500 Abstract Newsletter: Building Industry Technology *changed to* N T I S Alerts: Building Industry Technology.
0163-1519 Abstract Newsletter: Chemistry *changed to* N T I S Alerts: Chemistry.
0163-1527 Abstract Newsletter: Transportation *changed to* N T I S Alerts: Transportation.
0163-1535 Abstract Newsletter: Urban and Regional Technology and Development
0163-1543 Psychotherapy Finances
0163-1578 Advances in Asthma & Allergy†
0163-1586 N Y State Pharmacist
0163-1608 American Revenuer
0163-1640 18 Almanac†
0163-1667 Texas. Department of Health Resources. Biennial Report *changed to* Texas. Department of Health. Annual Report.
0163-1675 Cardiology Update
0163-1691 Dermatology Update†
0163-1721 Psychiatric Medicine Update†
0163-1748 Professional Salesman's Letter *see* 1043-4364
0163-1756 Children's Books International. Proceedings
0163-1780 World Traveling
0163-1799 Today's Christian Woman
0163-1810 Institute of Industrial Engineers. Fall Industrial Engineering Conference. Proceedings *changed to* Institute of Industrial Engineers. Industrial Engineering Conference. Proceedings.
0163-1829 Physical Review B (Condensed Matter)
0163-1853 Polamerica *changed to* Poland Today.
0163-1861 Kent Collector
0163-1918 International Electron Devices Meeting. I E D M Technical Digest
0163-1926 Cat World
0163-1942 American Journal of Forensic Psychiatry

0163-1950 Woodall's Campground Directory. Ohio, Pennsylvania Editions *changed to* Woodall's Campground Directory. New Jersey, Ohio, Pennsylvania Editions.
0163-1977 Mobile-Modular Housing Dealer *changed to* M H Business.
0163-2027 50 Plus *see* 1041-6277
0163-206X Data Resources Steel Industry Review *changed to* D R I - McGraw-Hill Steel Industry Review.
0163-2078 Judicial Newsletter *changed to* Tennessee Judicial Newsletter.
0163-2116 Digestive Diseases and Sciences
0163-2124 National Contract Management Quarterly Journal *changed to* National Contract Management Journal (1980).
0163-2175 Gifts & Tableware(New York)†
0163-2183 Synerjy
0163-2205 L I N K S
0163-2213 C A R C H News *changed to* C C C N.
0163-223X Nursing Job News *changed to* Nursingworld Journal.
0163-2248 New England Senior Citizen†
0163-2280 Censored *see* 0883-282X
0163-2396 Studies in Symbolic Interaction
0163-240X Woodall's Campground Directory. Ontario Edition†
0163-2418 Quality Control Reports: The Gold Sheet
0163-2426 Medical Devices, Diagnostics & Instrumentation Reports: The Gray Sheet
0163-2469 Milford Series
0163-2485 Woodall's Campground Directory. Illinois, Indiana Edition†
0163-2493 Woodall's Campground Directory. Idaho, Oregon, Washington Edition *changed to* Woodall's Campground Directory. Idaho, Oregon, Washington, British Columbia Edition.
0163-2566 E D F Letter
0163-2574 Current Contents: Physical, Chemical & Earth Sciences
0163-2582 Physical Fitness - Sports Medicine
0163-2590 Allied Medical Education Directory *see* 0194-3766
0163-2647 Universal Human Rights *see* 0275-0392
0163-2655 Psychiatric Opinion†
0163-2728 Patterson's American Educational Directory *see* 0079-0230
0163-2787 Evaluation and the Health Professions
0163-2795 Handbook for Recruiting at Minority Colleges *changed to* C C D M Minority Student Recruitment Guide.
0163-2809 Children's Language
0163-2817 Official National Collegiate Athletic Association Basketball Rules and Interpretations *changed to* N C A A Men's and Women's Basketball Rules and Interpretations.
0163-2825 Mountain State Geology
0163-2833 S A R Statistics
0163-2841 Modern Psychotherapy
0163-285X North American Yacht Register
0163-2876 Commercial and Financial Chronicle
0163-2884 Swimming and Diving Rules *changed to* Swimming and Diving and Water Polo Rulebook.
0163-2914 State Laws and Regulations†
0163-2922 State, Local, and Urban Law Newsletter *see* 0195-7686
0163-2965 Studia Africana
0163-299X Today's Professionals
0163-3007 Black Stars†
0163-3015 Boston Phoenix
0163-3023 Commonsense†
0163-3031 Corporate Finance Sourcebook
0163-3058 Magill's Literary Annual
0163-3066 New Hampshire Times
0163-3139 Sonshine Times
0163-3155 Current Contents: Arts & Humanities
0163-3171 Global Tectonics and Metallogeny
0163-3198 Large Type Books in Print *see* 0000-1120
0163-321X R F Design
0163-3228 Diagnosis†
0163-3252 Journal of Studies in Technical Careers
0163-3287 Employment Information in the Mathematical Sciences
0163-3295 Urthkin
0163-3341 Entrepreneur
0163-3422 Team Horizons
0163-3449 Organic Gardening *see* 0884-3252
0163-3457 E D A Research Review†
0163-3562 Dynamite
0163-3570 Scholastic Action
0163-3589 Scholastic Sprint
0163-3597 Scholastic Search *see* 0745-7065
0163-3651 Art Teacher *see* 0004-3125
0163-366X West Virginia University Alumni Quarterly *changed to* West Virginia University Alumni Magazine.
0163-3724 International Energy Statistical Review
0163-3767 Semiconductor International
0163-3813 Contributions in Comparative Colonial Studies
0163-3821 Contributions in Drama and Theatre Studies
0163-3848 Edward Sapir Monograph Series in Language, Culture, and Cognition
0163-3856 Fusion Energy Update†
0163-3864 Journal of Natural Products
0163-3872 Porch†
0163-3929 Historical Journal of Western Massachusetts *see* 0276-8313
0163-3937 Books of the Times†
0163-3945 National Guard
0163-3996 Health Law Project Library Bulletin†
0163-4070 Soccer America
0163-4089 American Demographics
0163-4100 Chronicle Annual Vocational School Manual *see* 0276-0371
0163-4119 Feed and Grain Times *changed to* Feed and Grain.
0163-4143 Studies in Contemporary Satire
0163-416X ZooGoer
0163-4186 Copper: Quarterly Report†
0163-4267 N A G W S Guide. Synchronized Swimming†
0163-4275 Environmental Ethics
0163-4313 Woodall's Florida and Southern States Retirement and Resort Communities Directory *see* 0731-6526
0163-4321 Woodall's Senior Exchange†
0163-433X Journal of Sport Psychology *see* 0895-2779
0163-4348 Science Fiction and Fantasy Book Review *changed to* Science Fiction and Fantasy Book Review Annual.
0163-4356 Therapeutic Drug Monitoring
0163-4372 Journal of Gerontological Social Work
0163-4399 Formed Fabrics Industry *see* 0163-4429
0163-4429 Nonwovens Industry
0163-4437 Media Culture and Society
0163-4445 Journal of Family Therapy
0163-4453 Journal of Infection
0163-4461 Humanities in Society†
0163-447X B C & T News
0163-4488 Supermarket Trends *see* 0278-6346
0163-4518 Farm Show Magazine
0163-4526 Journal of Water Borne Coatings†
0163-4534 Polyphony *see* 0884-4720
0163-4542 Powder Coatings†
0163-4585 Let's Go: The Budget Guide to Europe.
0163-4593 Next†
0163-4615 Handbook of Business Finance and Capital Sources
0163-4631 Precisely
0163-464X Pharmacy Management *see* 0730-7780
0163-4674 U.S. Federal Railroad Administration. Office of Safety. Accident - Incident Bulletin
0163-4712 Florida State Industrial Directory *see* 0740-4697
0163-4747 N A G W S Guide. Soccer†
0163-4763 National Federation of State High School Associations. Soccer Rules *see* 0731-9541
0163-4828 Weekly Reader Eye *changed to* Weekly Reader, Edition 5.
0163-4844 Know Your World Extra
0163-4852 Senior Weekly Reader *see* 0890-3239
0163-4860 Weekly Reader News Parade *changed to* Weekly Reader, Edition 4.
0163-4879 Weekly Reader News Patrol *see* 0890-3204
0163-4887 Weekly Reader Surprise *see* 0890-3166
0163-4895 Buddy's Weekly Reader *see* 0890-3220
0163-4909 Weekly Reader News Hunt *see* 0890-3212
0163-4917 Medicaid Management Reports†
0163-4941 Aeronautical Engineering: A Continuing Biography with Indexes
0163-495X American Petroleum Institute. Refining Department. Proceedings†
0163-4976 Iowa. Crop and Livestock Reporting Service. Weather and Field Crops *changed to* Iowa Agricultural Statistics.
0163-4984 Biological Trace Element Research
0163-4992 Cell Biophysics
0163-5018 C S I Newsdigest
0163-5026 Impact Two†
0163-5069 Film Criticism
0163-5077 Labor Relations and Employment *see* 0193-5739
0163-5085 World Development Report
0163-5093 Information Moscow *changed to* Information Moscow, Western Edition.
0163-5107 Health Policy Quarterly†
0163-5123 Annual Index to Motion Picture Credits
0163-514X Journal of Prevention *see* 0278-095X
0163-5158 Ageing International
0163-5182 Human Factors Society Annual Meeting. Proceedings
0163-5255 Rockford Papers†
0163-5271 Mixed Pickles
0163-528X Folk Dance Directory
0163-5298 Journal of Continuing Education in Radiology
0163-531X Business (Atlanta)†
0163-5328 Woodall's Campground Directory. Arkansas, Missouri Edition†
0163-5336 Woodall's Campground Directory. Kentucky, Tennessee Edition†
0163-5344 Woodall's Campground Directory. Colorado Edition†
0163-5352 Woodall's Campground Directory. North Carolina, South Carolina Edition†
0163-5379 Advances in Instructional Psychology
0163-5387 Persuasion at Work *see* 0892-2691
0163-5425 Focus: Teaching English Language Arts
0163-5433 Wyoming Issues†
0163-545X Environmental Law Newsletter
0163-5468 Field & Stream Bass Fishing Annual
0163-5476 Middle East Contemporary Survey
0163-5484 Northeastern Agricultural Economics Council. Journal *changed to* Northeastern Journal of Agricultural Economics and Resource Economics.
0163-5506 Public Libraries
0163-5514 Federal Controls†
0163-5530 Writing (La Mesa)†
0163-5549 Journal of Integral Equations†
0163-5573 American Institute of Industrial Engineers. Proceedings of the Spring Annual Conference *see* 0278-8012
0163-5581 Nutrition and Cancer
0163-559X International Society of Magnetic Resonance. Bulletin†
0163-5662 Energy Guidebook *changed to* Power's Energy Systems Guidebook.
0163-5689 Progress in Communication Sciences
0163-5700 S I G A C T News
0163-5719 S I G A R T Newsletter
0163-5727 S I G C A P H Newsletter
0163-5778 S I G N U M Newsletter
0163-5808 S I G M O D Record
0163-5824 S I G S A M Bulletin
0163-5840 S I G I R Forum
0163-5905 Nordic
0163-5948 Software Engineering Notes
0163-5956 Journal of Computer Documentation
0163-5964 S I G A R C H Computer Architecture News
0163-5980 Operating Systems Review
0163-5999 S I G M E T R I C S Performance Evaluation Review
0163-6006 A P L Quote Quad
0163-6065 Directory of Blood Establishments Registered Under Section 510 of the Food, Drug, and Cosmetic Act *changed to* Directory of Blood Service Establishments.
0163-6103 S I G S I M Simuletter
0163-6111 Peterson's Annual Guides to Graduate Study. Graduate Programs in the Physical Science and Mathematics. *see* 0894-9379
0163-6170 Recent Advances in Nuclear Medicine
0163-6197 Electronic Business
0163-6200 Football Case Book
0163-6251 Forgotten Fantasy Library
0163-626X Voice of Z-39 *see* 1041-0031
0163-6278 Current Chemical Reactions
0163-6359 Wildlifer
0163-6367 P G R Bulletin *changed to* P G R S A Quarterly.
0163-6383 Infant Behavior and Development
0163-6391 Canada - United States Law Journal
0163-6413 Durak†
0163-6480 Moral Education Forum†
0163-6499 Urban Innovation Abroad *see* 0887-4468
0163-6529 Urban Transit Abroad *see* 0887-4468
0163-6537 Directory of Personal Image Consultants
0163-6545 Radical History Review
0163-657X Stanford French Review
0163-660X Washington Quarterly
0163-6618 P-S-R-O Reports *see* 0277-8548
0163-6626 Interface: the Computer Education Quarterly
0163-6642 Family Practice Recertification
0163-6650 Eberly's Michigan Journal
0163-6693 F and S Index of Corporate Change *see* 0744-2785
0163-6715 Gospel Teacher†
0163-6723 Worldcasts: Product Edition
0163-6731 Worldcasts: Regional Edition
0163-6766 Biomass Digest *see* 1056-7194
0163-6774 Acronyms
0163-6782 Savings and Loan Market Study†
0163-6804 I E E E Communications Magazine
0163-6812 I E E E Circuits and Systems Magazine†
0163-6855 Eastern Finance Association. Proceedings of the Annual Meeting *see* 0732-8516
0163-6952 People and Energy†
0163-7010 Oxbridge Directory of Newsletters
0163-7029 Modern Technics in Surgery. Cardiac - Thoracic Surgery†
0163-7037 Modern Technics in Surgery. Neurosurgery
0163-7088 Notes on Teaching English
0163-710X Family Advocate
0163-7134 Sawyer's Gas Turbine International *see* 0149-4147
0163-7169 China Business Review
0163-7177 Internal Revenue Code
0163-7193 Industrial Gas and Energy Utilization *see* 0164-4262
0163-7207 Boating Registration Statistics
0163-7258 Pharmacology and Therapeutics
0163-7266 Railfan & Railroad
0163-7274 Purpose
0163-7282 Exetasis
0163-7290 U.S. Copyright Office. Catalog of Copyright Entries. Fourth Series. Part 1: Nondramatic Literary Works
0163-7304 U.S. Copyright Office. Catalog of Copyright Entries. Fourth Series. Part 2: Serials and Periodicals

5622 ISSN INDEX

0163-7312 U.S. Copyright Office. Catalog of Copyright Entries. Fourth Series. Part 3: Performing Arts
0163-7320 U.S. Copyright Office. Catalog of Copyright Entries. Fourth Series. Part 4: Motion Pictures and Filmstrips
0163-7339 U.S. Copyright Office. Catalog of Copyright Entries. Fourth Series. Part 5: Visual Arts Excluding Maps
0163-7347 U.S. Copyright Office. Catalog of Copyright Entries. Fourth Series. Part 6: Maps
0163-7355 U.S. Copyright Office. Catalog of Copyright Entries. Fourth Series. Part 7: Sound Recordings
0163-7363 U.S. Copyright Office. Catalog of Copyright Entries. Fourth Series. Part 8: Renewals
0163-7428 Women's Sports *see* 8750-653X
0163-7452 Board & Sail Magazine
0163-7460 Art Product News *see* 1055-2286
0163-7479 Texas International Law Journal
0163-7517 S and M M Sales and Marketing Management *changed to* Sales & Marketing Management.
0163-7525 Annual Review of Public Health
0163-7533 Sea, Eastern Edition *see* 0746-8601
0163-755X M E L U S
0163-7584 Medicaid Statistics *see* 0277-5611
0163-7606 Federal Communications Law Journal
0163-7622 Milwaukee History
0163-7665 Federal Personnel Guide
0163-7673 Reviews in Biochemical Toxicology
0163-769X Endocrine Reviews
0163-772X T C A Report
0163-7770 Haiti Report†
0163-7789 Bulletin Exterieur†
0163-7800 Current Pulmonology
0163-7827 Progress in Lipid Research
0163-7843 Pacific Horticulture
0163-7851 Horticultural Reviews
0163-786X Research in Social Movements, Conflicts and Change
0163-7878 Research in Population Economics
0163-7894 Primary Care Physician's Guide to Practical Gastroenterology *see* 0277-4208
0163-7908 Re: Act†
0163-7916 Untitled
0163-8130 Attenzione - U S A
0163-8211 American Rag
0163-822X Illinois School Research and Development
0163-8238 University of Puerto Rico. Agricultural Experiment Station. Bulletin
0163-8246 N M A L: Notes on Modern American Literature
0163-8262 Impact (Syracuse)†
0163-8270 Federal Civilian Workforce Statistics. Monthly Release *changed to* Federal Civilian Workforce Statistics. Employment and Trends.
0163-8289 Congressional Record Index†
0163-8297 Public Welfare Directory
0163-8300 American Public Welfare Association. W - Memo
0163-8343 General Hospital Psychiatry
0163-836X Annual Editions: Readings in Human Sexuality *changed to* Annual Editions: Human Sexuality.
0163-8386 Guide to Microforms in Print. Subject
0163-8440 Commercial Remodeling *changed to* Commercial Renovation.
0163-8475 Community Review
0163-8483 World Higher Education Communique†
0163-8491 Holistic Health Review *see* 0195-5977
0163-8505 Sociological Practice
0163-853X Discourse Processes
0163-8548 Human Studies
0163-8602 President's National Urban Policy Report
0163-8653 Convention of the International Association of Fish and Wildlife Agencies *see* 0161-3332
0163-8912 National Underwriter. Property & Casualty Insurance Edition
0163-8971 Group (Loveland)
0163-898X O C L C Newsletter
0163-8998 Annual Review of Nuclear and Particle Science
0163-903X Washington Review
0163-9048 Human Rights Internet Newsletter *see* 0275-049X
0163-9056 Criminology Review Yearbook†
0163-9153 Colorado School of Mines Quarterly
0163-9218 Massachusetts Institute of Technology. Research Laboratory of Electronics. R L E Progress Report
0163-9226 M S I - L S I Memory D.A.T.A. Book *see* 1048-2598
0163-9234 Package Printing *changed to* Package Printing & Converting.
0163-9242 Chronicle College Charts *see* 0191-3670
0163-9242 Chronicle College Charts *see* 0191-3662
0163-9250 Darkroom Photography *see* 1056-8484
0163-9269 Behavioral & Social Sciences Librarian
0163-9277 Goodstay: Your Hospital Stay Magazine
0163-9285 Southeast Optician
0163-9293 Southwest Optician
0163-9307 Far West Optician
0163-9323 Great Lakes Optician
0163-9358 Emergency Medical Services Quarterly *see* 0886-9723
0163-9366 Journal of Nutrition for the Elderly
0163-9374 Cataloging & Classification Quarterly
0163-9404 Feature†
0163-9412 Advertising World *see* 0885-3363
0163-9439 C B M S. N S F. Regional Conference Series in Applied Mathematics
0163-948X Inside F.E.R.C.
0163-9498 Open Chain†
0163-9528 Supermarket Shopper†
0163-9536 Impact American Distilled Spirits Market Review and Forecast *changed to* The U S Distilled Spirits Market: Impact Databank Review and Forecast.
0163-9544 Impact American Wine Market Review and Forecast *changed to* The U S Wine Market: Impact Databank Review and Forecast.
0163-9552 Friends of Photography. Newsletter *see* 0891-5326
0163-9587 Mossbauer Effect Reference and Data Journal
0163-9609 U.S. National Diabetes Advisory Board. Annual Report†
0163-9617 AmStat News
0163-9625 Deviant Behavior
0163-9633 Clinical Preventive Dentistry
0163-9641 Infant Mental Health Journal
0163-9684 White Book of Ski Areas. U S and Canada
0163-9706 View (Oakland)
0163-9730 Public Works Manual
0163-9803 Bioethics Quarterly *see* 1041-3545
0163-9854 Telecommunications Reports
0163-9897 Gay Insurgent
0163-9900 Herb Quarterly
0163-9927 A E I Foreign Policy and Defense Review†
0163-9943 Claymore
0163-9951 Clan MacNeil Association of America. Galley
0163-996X Federal Tax Coordinator 2d. Weekly Alert
0163-9986 Research Institute of America. Estate Planners Alert *changed to* Estate and Financial Planners Alert.
0163-9994 Research Institute Lawyers Tax Alert†
0164-002X Optoelectronics D.A.T.A. Book *see* 1040-0907
0164-0038 Power Semiconductors D.A.T.A. Book *see* 1040-0214
0164-0046 Advances in Space Exploration *see* 0273-1177
0164-0070 Carolina Planning
0164-0089 Chilton's Instruments and Control Systems *changed to* Instrumentation and Control Systems.
0164-0119 Interface I Cs D.A.T.A. Book *see* 1057-4522
0164-0135 Microwave Tubes *see* 0271-0773
0164-0143 Short Stories in Spanish†
0164-016X National Center Reporter *see* 0190-1168
0164-0178 American Jewish History
0164-0186 Better Homes and Gardens Bedroom and Bath Decorating Ideas *changed to* Better Homes and Gardens Bedroom and Bath Ideas.
0164-0259 Knowledge: Creation, Diffusion, Utilization
0164-0267 Law and Policy Quarterly *see* 0265-8240
0164-0275 Research on Aging
0164-0283 Sage Family Studies Abstracts
0164-0291 International Journal of Primatology
0164-0305 Journal of Behavioral Assessment *see* 0882-2689
0164-0313 Journal of Fusion Energy
0164-0356 50 State Legislative Review
0164-0364 American Criminal Law Review
0164-0372 Probate & Property
0164-0496 Missouri Union List of Serial Publications
0164-0534 Topics in Clinical Nursing *changed to* Holistic Nursing Practice.
0164-0542 Group Health News *see* 1050-9038
0164-0593 Associated Equipment Distributors. Rental Rates Compilation
0164-0674 Catholic Near East Magazine
0164-0682 Economic Perspectives
0164-0704 Journal of Macroeconomics
0164-0712 National Wetlands Newsletter
0164-0720 Running Times Yearbook†
0164-0739 Guide to Microforms in Print. Supplement
0164-0747 Guide to Microforms in Print. Author - Title
0164-0763 Library Research *see* 0740-8188
0164-0771 Philosophy Research Archives *see* 1053-8364
0164-078X Psychotherapy Digest
0164-0828 Bank Note Reporter
0164-0836 Car Exchange *see* 0164-5552
0164-0917 A E E Directory of Energy Professionals†
0164-0925 A C M Transactions on Programming Languages and Systems
0164-0941 Fishing in Maryland
0164-095X Forest Products Review†
0164-0968 Task Force on Environmental Cancer and Heart and Lung Disease. Annual Report to Congress
0164-1085 Silverfish Review
0164-1093 Science Fiction Voices
0164-1212 Journal of Systems and Software
0164-1220 Futurics
0164-1239 Annals of the History of Computing *see* 1058-6180
0164-1247 Comparative Studies in Sociology *see* 0195-6310
0164-1255 Fundamental Concepts of Estate Administration†
0164-1263 Pediatric Dentistry
0164-1298 Artpark†
0164-1336 Michigan Health Educator
0164-1352 Checklist of State Publications *see* 0197-5668
0164-1360 Notes on Modern American Literature *see* 0163-8246
0164-1433 South Jersey
0164-1441 Bostonia
0164-145X Higginson Journal
0164-1484 Periodically Speaking†
0164-1492 Dickinson Studies
0164-1514 Washington Health Record
0164-1522 Collaboration
0164-1530 California Work Injuries and Illnesses
0164-1662 Florida Journal of Anthropology
0164-1670 Directory of Residency Training Accredited by the Accreditation Council for Graduate Medical Education *changed to* Directory of Graduate Medical Education.
0164-1689 Transportation Law Seminar. Papers and Proceedings *changed to* Transportation Law Institute Papers and Proceedings.
0164-1697 Occupational Injuries and Illnesses in California *see* 0164-2707
0164-1700 Pain Control in Dentistry
0164-1743 Media Guide International. Business - Professional Publications Edition *changed to* International Media Guides. Business - Professional Publications Edition.
0164-176X P I P E R
0164-1867 D R C Historical and Comparative Disasters Series
0164-1875 D R C Book & Monograph Series
0164-1883 Trouser Press†
0164-1905 Artes Graficas U S A *see* 1054-2434
0164-1999 American Animal Hospital Association. Annual Meeting Scientific Proceedings
0164-2049 Geoscience Wisconsin
0164-2103 Cosecha - Harvest *see* 0145-2681
0164-2111 Fantastica *changed to* Fangoria.
0164-212X Occupational Therapy in Mental Health
0164-2340 Topics in Emergency Medicine
0164-2472 Social Text
0164-2502 Journal of Career Education *see* 0894-8453
0164-2537 Karikazo†
0164-2707 Work Injuries and Illnesses in California. Quarterly†
0164-2790 Analysis of Jewish Policy Issues
0164-2847 National Association of Schools of Music. Handbook
0164-2863 Air Gun
0164-288X Forum (College Park) *changed to* Forum International.
0164-3010 Springfield/Hartford
0164-3037 Bird Watcher's Digest
0164-3150 American Organist
0164-3169 Perspectiva Mundial
0164-3177 New England Review *see* 1053-1297
0164-3207 Democratic Left
0164-3215 Showcase U S A
0164-3223 Drum Corps World
0164-324X Fiberarts
0164-3290 Nutshell News
0164-3304 Oregon Geology
0164-3320 Security Dealer
0164-3371 M S N Microwave Systems News *changed to* Microwave Systems News.
0164-3452 Hang Glider Magazine†
0164-3495 Emmy
0164-3509 Skinned Knuckles
0164-3525 Economic World
0164-3533 New England Business†
0164-3576 Michigan Bar Journal
0164-3622 Louisiana Municipal Review
0164-3711 Game Bird Breeders, Aviculturists, Zoologists, & Conservationists Gazette
0164-3746 Gulf Coast Fisherman
0164-3754 South-West Foodservice
0164-3762 Electronic Field Engineer
0164-3835 Barclays Law Monthly
0164-3851 Schools and the Courts
0164-386X Sheet Music *see* 0197-3495
0164-3959 K E A News
0164-3967 New Age Magazine *see* 0746-3618
0164-4076 Military Electronics Countermeasures†
0164-4092 Aviation Engineering and Maintenance *changed to* Military Science and Technology.
0164-4114 Woodsmith
0164-4211 Verona Missions *see* 0279-3652
0164-4238 Surgical Technologist
0164-4262 Modern Industrial Energy†
0164-4289 Kennel Review
0164-4297 Arizona State Law Journal
0164-4335 Meat, Poultry & Seafood Digest†
0164-4343 Marketing Communications *see* 0032-5619
0164-4386 Nephrology Nurse†

ISSN

0164-4483 Siberian World†
0164-4556 Southwest Magazine
0164-4645 Glaucoma
0164-4742 Words *changed to* A I S P Dialogue.
0164-4769 Photo Lab Management
0164-4777 Jordan (Washington)†
0164-4858 Spa and Sauna *changed to* Aqua: The Business Magazine for the Spa and Pool Industry.
0164-4882 Joyful Woman
0164-4904 Automotive Design & Development††
0164-503X Motorhome Life *see* 0744-074X
0164-5048 Dromenon
0164-5056 Primal Institute Newsletter
0164-5080 American Auditory Society. Journal *see* 0196-0202
0164-5137 Chilton's Iron Age *see* 0897-4365
0164-517X Dun and Bradstreet Reports *see* 0746-6110
0164-5196 Police Product News *see* 0893-8989
0164-5218 Black Odyssey
0164-5226 Rainbow (Minneapolis)†
0164-5242 Specifying Engineer *see* 0892-5046
0164-5285 New Era (Salt Lake City)
0164-5315 Biweekly List of Papers on Radiation Chemistry and Photochemistry
0164-5323 Chosen People
0164-5331 California - Arizona Farm Press
0164-534X Cause - Effect Magazine
0164-5382 Small Business Reports (New York)
0164-5390 Law Office Information Service
0164-5412 Michigan Real Estate Magazine†
0164-5420 A P A News†
0164-5455 Compendium on Continuing Education for the Small Animal Practitioner *see* 0193-1903
0164-5463 International Motorcycle Trade Journal†
0164-5528 Christian Social Action
0164-5552 Car Collector and Car Classics
0164-5560 Classic Film - Video Images *see* 0275-8423
0164-5587 Contrast†
0164-5595 City Weekly *see* 0164-5935
0164-5609 Council of Biology Editors. Newsletter *changed to* C B E Views.
0164-5617 Motor Inn Journal *see* 0018-6082
0164-5706 Paint Horse Journal
0164-5722 American Hiker Newsletter
0164-5749 Flotation Sleep Industry *changed to* Aqua: The Business Magazine for the Spa and Pool Industry.
0164-5757 A L I Reporter
0164-5765 Laundry News
0164-5781 Real Estate Center Journal
0164-5811 Personnel Advisory Bulletin *changed to* Personnel Manager's Letter.
0164-582X Ideal Beef Memo†
0164-5846 Recreational Computing†
0164-5854 G S A News and Information *see* 1052-5173
0164-5870 Phoenix Living *see* 0741-5516
0164-5889 Subway
0164-5897 Pizza Maker
0164-5919 Tidewater Life
0164-5935 Nation's Cities Weekly
0164-5951 O W N
0164-6028 Update (Minneapolis)†
0164-6060 Co-Op News (Berkeley)
0164-6079 Human Services Reporter
0164-6109 Hexagon
0164-6117 Cuisine†
0164-6168 Texas Thoroughbred
0164-6184 Possessions
0164-6214 House Beautiful's Colonial Homes *see* 0195-1416
0164-6249 Real Estate Washington *changed to* Regardie's.
0164-6257 Federal Veterinarian
0164-6273 Arkansas Times
0164-632X Ocean World†
0164-6338 Pro Sound News
0164-6346 Motor Imported Car Crash Estimating Guide
0164-6397 Fire and Police Personnel Reporter
0164-6419 Internist's Intercom
0164-6427 Florida Bar Case Summary Service†
0164-6451 Church Teachers
0164-646X J O H: Journal of Housing *see* 0272-7374
0164-6486 Dairymen's Digest: Southern Region Edition
0164-6532 Twin Cities
0164-6540 Snowmobile West Magazine
0164-6559 Shelter
0164-6605 Stanford G S B *see* 0883-265X
0164-6613 Evener *see* 0889-2970
0164-6656 Quarter Horse Journal
0164-6699 Mississippi Magazine
0164-6753 Expo (Philadelphia) *see* 0199-7602
0164-6761 North Carolina Tarheel Coast†
0164-6796 New Mexico Business Journal
0164-6826 Pharmaceutical Technology International
0164-6834 Video Management *see* 0747-1335
0164-6850 North Carolina State Bar Quarterly
0164-694X Jogger *see* 0898-5162
0164-7016 Investigative Reporters & Editors Journal
0164-7059 Business Viewpoint††
0164-7083 Keeping Abreast Journal of Human Nurturing†
0164-7148 Squash News
0164-7164 Inform†
0164-7172 Ohio Magazine
0164-7180 Music Time
0164-7202 Nutrition Health Review
0164-7253 Mountain Movers
0164-7288 Virtue
0164-7296 Municipal Management
0164-730X Fly Tyer *changed to* American Angler.
0164-7318 Deer & Deer Hunting
0164-7415 National Right to Life News
0164-7547 National Knife Collector *changed to* National Knife Magazine.
0164-761X Billiards Digest
0164-7628 Texas Business†
0164-7695 Hardware Retailing *changed to* Do-it-Yourself Retailing.
0164-7709 Insights (Springfield) *changed to* Insights for Preachers.
0164-7725 Issues in Bank Regulation
0164-7741 Science - Ciencia
0164-775X Communique (Silver Spring)
0164-7768 Personal Finance: The Inflation Survival Letter *changed to* Personal Finance.
0164-7792 Muscle Digest†
0164-7822 Pennsylvania Naturalist†
0164-7830 Calculators - Computers Magazine†
0164-7857 Current Concepts in Hospital Pharmacy Management
0164-7881 Shooting Sportsman†
0164-7954 International Journal of Acarology
0164-7970 New Directions for Student Services
0164-7989 New Directions for Program Evaluation
0164-8047 Arena News
0164-8071 Atlanta Business Chronicle
0164-8098 New York Theatre Review†
0164-8128 Internews International Bulletin
0164-8136 American Firearms Industry
0164-8152 New Hampshire Business Review
0164-8195 Denver Monthly†
0164-8233 Specialty Salesman and Business Opportunities *see* 0738-4211
0164-8241 National Wood Stove and Fireplace Journal *see* 0279-4357
0164-825X Sierra Atlantic
0164-8276 Texas & Southern Quarter Horse Journal
0164-8314 Deke Quarterly
0164-8330 Alaska Fisherman's Journal
0164-8349 Motorcycle Product News
0164-8470 Interiors: For the Contract Design Professional
0164-8489 T V C *see* 0745-2802
0164-8497 Vegetarian Times
0164-8500 In League†
0164-8527 Child Care Information Exchange
0164-856X Solidarity (Detroit)
0164-8578 Rural Missouri
0164-8675 Irish Wolfhound Quarterly
0164-8683 Mississippi Educator
0164-8756 Computer-Law Journal
0164-8780 Ranch & Coast
0164-887X Oilpatch Magazine
0164-8942 Skateboarder *see* 0279-8689
0164-8985 Audio & Electronics Digest†
0164-9175 VocEd *see* 0884-8009
0164-9183 Bowlers Journal
0164-9191 Craft Horizons with Craft World *see* 0194-8008
0164-9221 Texas Government Newsletter
0164-923X United States Specialist
0164-9248 Circus Weekly *changed to* Circus.
0164-9256 Motorcyclist's Post
0164-9329 Everybody's
0164-9345 Kentucky Bench & Bar
0164-9353 United Caprine News
0164-9442 Oklahoma Dental Association Journal
0164-9507 Dialogues in Pediatric Urology
0164-9515 Woman Executive's Bulletin†
0164-9531 Animal Keepers' Forum
0164-9566 Library P R News
0164-9574 Product Liability Trends
0164-9612 Diving World
0164-9620 Electronics Test *see* 0744-1657
0164-9655 Millimeter
0164-9698 Financial Planning Today *changed to* Journal of Financial Planning Today.
0164-971X Gull
0164-9728 G C T (Gifted, Creative, Talented Children) *see* 0892-9580
0164-9760 C T A - N E A Action *see* 0742-2121
0164-9787 Houston Engineer
0164-985X Clinical Cancer Letter
0164-9876 Marketing Bestsellers *see* 0744-3102
0164-9914 Chain Drug Review
0164-9922 Spray *changed to* Water Ski.
0164-9930 Oregon Magazine *see* 0199-6363
0164-9957 Mix Magazine
0164-9981 Computer Systems News *changed to* Systems and Networks Integration.
0164-999X Broadcast Communications *changed to* Television Broadcast.
0165-0009 Climatic Change
0165-0025 Praktijkgids
0165-005X Culture, Medicine and Psychiatry
0165-0068 Urban Law and Policy†
0165-0076 Proces
0165-0106 Erkenntnis
0165-0114 Fuzzy Sets and Systems
0165-0122 Tijdschrift voor de Politie
0165-0157 Linguistics and Philosophy
0165-0165 Journal of Comparative Corporate Law and Securities Regulation *see* 0891-9895
0165-0173 Brain Research Reviews
0165-019X Z T (Ziekenhuistechniek) *changed to* Infomedica.
0165-0203 Natural Resources Forum
0165-0211 Zenit
0165-022X Journal of Biochemical and Biophysical Methods
0165-0254 International Journal of Behavioral Development
0165-0262 Outlook on Science Policy
0165-0270 Journal of Neuroscience Methods
0165-0300 Review of Socialist Law
0165-0327 Journal of Affective Disorders
0165-0378 Journal of Reproductive Immunology
0165-0386 Marget†
0165-0424 Aquatic Insects
0165-0432 Naamlooze Venootschap
0165-0475 Journal of Clinical Neuropsychology *see* 0168-8634
0165-0505 Bijdragen en Mededelingen Betreffende de Geschiedenis der Nederlanden
0165-0513 Recueil des Travaux Chimiques des Pays-Bas
0165-0521 Studies on Neotropical Fauna and Environment
0165-0572 Resources and Energy
0165-0610 Instituut voor Cultuurtechniek en Waterhuishouding. Jaarverslag *see* 0924-0160
0165-0629 International Review of Social History
0165-0653 International Journal for the Advancement of Counselling
0165-070X Netherlands International Law Review
0165-0750 Common Market Law Review
0165-0807 Moon and the Planets *see* 0167-9295
0165-084X Spektator
0165-0890 Tikker
0165-1005 Core Journals in Ophthalmology
0165-1048 Bibliotheek en Samenleving
0165-1056 Core Journals in Clinical Neurology
0165-1110 Mutation Research - Reviews in Genetic Toxicology
0165-1153 Itinerario
0165-1218 Mutation Research - Genetic Toxicology Testing
0165-1269 International Journal of Invertebrate Reproduction *see* 0168-8170
0165-1404 Hydrobiological Bulletin *changed to* Netherlands Journal of Aquatic Ecology.
0165-1439 Tijdschrift voor Marketing
0165-148X Overzicht-Internationale Universitaire Samenwerking *changed to* Overzicht Onderwijs, Onderzoek en Ontwikkelingssamenwerking.
0165-1587 European Review of Agricultural Economics
0165-1595 Bakker *changed to* Bakkerij.
0165-1625 Beleid en Maatschappij
0165-1633 Solar Energy Materials *see* 0927-0248
0165-1641 Foodmagazine
0165-1676 Sociodrome
0165-1684 Signal Processing
0165-1722 M & O
0165-1730 Current Bibliography of Agriculture in China†
0165-1765 Economics Letters
0165-1773 Kennis en Methode
0165-1781 Psychiatry Research
0165-182X Tijdschrift voor Criminologie
0165-1838 Journal of the Autonomic Nervous System
0165-1854 Current Topics in Materials Science
0165-1889 Journal of Economic Dynamics and Control
0165-1943 Tweewieler
0165-1951 Rijks Geologische Dienst. Mededelingen. Nieuwe Serie
0165-2079 Air Law
0165-2117 Energiespectrum
0165-2125 Wave Motion
0165-2176 Veterinary Quarterly
0165-2222 Excerpta Medica. Section 51: Leprosy and Related Subjects *see* 0168-8944
0165-2273 Geo-Processing†
0165-2281 Health Policy and Education *see* 0168-8510
0165-232X Cold Regions Science and Technology
0165-2370 Journal of Analytical and Applied Pyrolysis
0165-2427 Veterinary Immunology and Immunopathology
0165-2478 Immunology Letters
0165-2516 International Journal of the Sociology of Language
0165-2524 Esperanto-Dokumentoj. Nova Serio
0165-2575 Esperanto Documents
0165-2583 N B L C Info Bulletin
0165-2656 Siboga Expedition
0165-2672 Lingvaj Problemoj Kaj Lingvo-Planado *see* 0272-2690
0165-280X Contributions to Tertiary and Quaternary Geology†
0165-2818 Outlook on Research Libraries *see* 0961-7612
0165-2826 Intertax
0165-2966 Fiscale en Administratieve Praktijkvragen
0165-2974 Sjow *changed to* Tijdschrift voor Jeugdhulpverlening en Jeugdwerk.
0165-3687 Kunst & Antiekrevue
0165-3806 Developmental Brain Research

5624 ISSN INDEX
ISSN

0165-4004 Folia Linguistica
0165-4055 International Journal of Psycholinguistics†
0165-4101 Journal of Accounting and Economics
0165-4373 Prana
0165-4543 Meubel
0165-4608 Cancer Genetics & Cytogenetics
0165-4748 Key to Economic Science
0165-4772 De Wereld van het Jonge Kind
0165-4888 Text
0165-4896 Mathematical Social Sciences
0165-5108 Aandrijftechniek
0165-5302 Mobilia
0165-5477 Koeltechniek *changed to* Koude Magazine.
0165-5515 Journal of Information Science
0165-5523 Klimaatbeheersing
0165-5701 International Ophthalmology
0165-5728 Journal of Neuroimmunology
0165-5752 Systematic Parasitology
0165-5817 Philips Journal of Research
0165-5876 International Journal of Pediatric Otorhinolaryngology
0165-5949 H B Modelbouw en Techniek *see* 0922-2170
0165-6031 Aardappelwereld
0165-604X Trends in Pharmacological Sciences
0165-6074 Microprocessing and Microprogramming
0165-6090 Thymus
0165-6104 Radio Bulletin Elektronica Computers *changed to* R B Elektronica Magazine.
0165-6449 Kleio
0165-6473 Centraal Bureau voor Genealogie. Mededelingen
0165-6546 Moesson
0165-6643 Onderneming
0165-6759 Student
0165-7089 N V R - Informatief
0165-7119 International Sedimentary Petrographical Series†
0165-716X Amsterdam Studies in the Theory and History of Linguistic Science. Series 2: Classics in Psycholinguistics
0165-7194 Bestuurswetenschappen
0165-7208 Pharmacochemistry Library
0165-7224 Documentatiegroep 40-45. Maandorgaan *see* 0920-3958
0165-7267 Amsterdam Studies in the Theory and History of Linguistic Science. Series 5: Library and Information Sources in Linguistics
0165-7305 Amsterdamer Beitraege zur Aelteren Germanistik
0165-7380 Veterinary Research Communications
0165-7569 Lingvisticae Investigationes: Supplementa
0165-7607 Recht en Kritiek
0165-7666 Vicus Cuadernos: Linguistica†
0165-7712 Linguistic & Literary Studies in Eastern Europe
0165-7720 K.N.G.M.G. Nieuwsbrief
0165-7747 Systems, Objectives, Solutions *see* 0378-7206
0165-7763 Studies in Language Companion Series
0165-7836 Fisheries Research
0165-7992 Mutation Research Letters
0165-8042 Lover
0165-8107 Neuro-Ophthalmology
0165-8182 Zeewezen
0165-8220 Nu
0165-8379 Welzijn *changed to* C F O - Magazine.
0165-8476 W P N R
0165-8573 Zuivelzicht
0165-859X Marine Biology Letters†
0165-8603 Advent
0165-8646 Photobiochemistry and Photobiophysics†
0165-8654 Beeldenaar
0165-8719 Core Journals in Gastroenterology
0165-8743 Purdue University Monographs in Romance Language
0165-8794 Science of Religion
0165-8867 Pen en Toets
0165-9030 Van Taal Tot Taal
0165-9227 Grazer Philosophische Studien
0165-9367 Bulletin Antieke Beschaving
0165-9375 C S M Informatie
0165-9405 Core Journals in Cardiology
0165-9545 Milieudefensie
0165-9618 Costerus
0165-9677 Finish†
0165-988X Wereld en Zending
0165-9936 Trends in Analytical Chemistry
0166-0012 Journal of Italian Linguistics†
0166-0268 Netherlands. Centraal Bureau voor de Statistiek. Maandschrift
0166-0373 Amandla
0166-0462 Regional Science & Urban Economics
0166-0535 Muziek en Dans *see* 0924-560X
0166-0586 Het Nederlandse Boek
0166-0616 Studies in Mycology
0166-0667 Volkskundig Bulletin
0166-0829 Linguistik Aktuell
0166-0926 Nieuwe Geografenkrant
0166-0934 Journal of Virological Methods
0166-1280 Journal of Molecular Structure: Theochem
0166-1302 Columbia Studies in the Classical Tradition
0166-137X Betoniek
0166-1426 Boogie Woogie and Blues Collector
0166-1868 Tweede Ronde
0166-1922 R A I Actueel
0166-1973 S E K - Lesbisch en Homoblad
0166-2031 Metamedicine *see* 0167-9902
0166-218X Discrete Applied Mathematics
0166-2236 Trends in Neurosciences
0166-2287 Developments in Agricultural and Managed Forest Ecology
0166-2309 Doctor Jazz Magazine
0166-2481 Developments in Psychiatry
0166-2694 Documentatieblad: The Abstracts Journal of the African Studies Centre Leiden
0166-2767 Niet Zo Benauwd
0166-3097 Resources and Conservation *see* 0921-3449
0166-3178 Molecular Physiology†
0166-3437 Philatelie
0166-3488 Clamavi
0166-3542 Antiviral Research
0166-3615 Computers in Industry
0166-3704 Kleine Aarde
0166-3917 M.3
0166-4069 Ruimzicht
0166-4298 Raakpunt
0166-4301 Westerheem
0166-4328 Behavioral Brain Research
0166-4360 In Search
0166-445X Aquatic Toxicology
0166-4786 Aarde en Kosmos - D J O
0166-4972 Technovation
0166-5030 Philosophia Patrum
0166-5057 Economic Titles - Abstracts
0166-5162 International Journal of Coal Geology
0166-5316 Performance Evaluation
0166-5324 Journal of Pipelines†
0166-5618 Diepzee
0166-5677 Van Horen Zeggen
0166-574X Demografie *see* 0169-1473
0166-5766 Ports and Dredging
0166-5790 Glot
0166-5855 Pedagogisch Tijdschrift
0166-6002 Verbum
0166-6061 Studies in Modern Thermodynamics
0166-610X Penitentiaire Informatie *changed to* Sancties.
0166-6231 Criminology and Penology Abstracts *changed to* Criminology, Penology & Police Science Abstracts.
0166-6258 Pragmatics and Beyond *see* 0922-842X
0166-6282 Formed by the merger of Police Science Abstracts *changed to* Criminology, Penology & Police Science Abstracts.
0166-6444 Bijenteelt
0166-6584 Notulae Odonatologicae
0166-6622 Colloids and Surfaces
0166-6789 Registratie†
0166-6797 Bericht over Rassenkeuze *changed to* Rassenbericht.
0166-6851 Molecular and Biochemical Parasitology
0166-6983 Structure Reports. Section A
0166-7025 Jazz Nu
0166-7033 Structure Reports. Section B
0166-7688 Analyse
0166-7831 Contour
0166-8072 Landbouw-Economisch Instituut. Maandblad Prijsstatistiek
0166-8528 B & G
0166-8595 Photosynthesis Research
0166-8641 Topology and Its Applications
0166-9028 Overheidsdocumentatie *see* 0923-6600
0166-9087 Netherlands. Centraal Bureau voor de Statistiek. Conjunctuurtest
0166-9222 Beleidsanalyse
0166-9281 Netherlands. Centraal Bureau voor de Statistiek. Maandstatistiek van de Binnenlandse Handel en Dienstverlening
0166-932X Berichten aan Zeevarenden
0166-9680 Netherlands. Centraal Bureau voor de Statistiek. Statistisch Bulletin
0166-977X P K B - Berichten over Planologische Kernbeslissingen *see* 0923-7674
0166-9834 Applied Catalysis
0166-9966 Bibliografie van Nederlandse Proefschriften
0167-0115 Regulatory Peptides
0167-0247 Volleybal
0167-0441 Doopsgezinde Bijdragen
0167-093X Linksaf
0167-1200 Concilium
0167-1340 Databus†
0167-1359 Tijdschrift voor Arbitrage
0167-1618 Oncodevelopmental Biology and Medicine *see* 1010-4283
0167-1731 Fertilizer Research
0167-174X I F O R Report *changed to* Reconciliation International.
0167-1839 French-Language Psychology†
0167-1847 Atlantisch Perspektief
0167-188X Engineering Costs and Production Economics *see* 0925-5273
0167-1936 Material Flow *see* 0925-5273
0167-1987 Soil and Tillage Research
0167-2088 Tijdschrift voor de Geschiedenis der Geneeskunde, Natuurwetenschappen, Wiskunde en Techniek *changed to* Gewina.
0167-2185 Deutsche Buecher
0167-2231 Carnegie-Rochester Conference Series on Public Policy
0167-224X Speleo Nederland
0167-238X Kwartaalschrift voor Directieve Therapie en Hypnose
0167-2533 Human Systems Management
0167-2681 Journal of Economic Behavior & Organization
0167-2738 Solid State Ionics
0167-2746 Chemisch Magazine
0167-2789 Physica D - Nonlinear Phenomena
0167-2878 Dutch Birding
0167-3157 Pharmacy International *see* 1010-0423
0167-319X Sponsorbulletin†
0167-3572 Planning
0167-3696 Ins and Outs
0167-3831 Grotiana
0167-3882 Assurantie Magazine
0167-3890 Durability of Building Materials†
0167-3998 De Nederlandsche Bank N.V. Annual Report
0167-4048 Computers & Security
0167-4102 Studien zur Oesterreichischen Philosophie
0167-4110 Natural Resources Forum Library†
0167-420X Large Scale Systems: Theory and Applications *see* 0923-0408
0167-4366 Agroforestry Systems
0167-4412 Plant Molecular Biology
0167-4544 Journal of Business Ethics
0167-4730 Structural Safety
0167-4749 Paedo Alert News Magazine
0167-4757 Selected Annotated Bibliography of Population Studies in the Netherlands
0167-4765 Boekblad
0167-4773 T T T Interdisciplinair Tijdschrift voor Taal- en Tekstwetenschap
0167-4781 B B A - Gene Structure and Expression
0167-479X Spartacus Magazine *changed to* Spartacus Travel Magazine.
0167-482X Journal of Psychosomatic Obstetrics and Gynaecology
0167-4838 B B A - Protein Structure and Molecular Enzymology
0167-4870 Journal of Economic Psychology
0167-4889 B B A - Molecular Cell Research
0167-4919 Immunology Today
0167-4943 Archives of Gerontology and Geriatrics
0167-4994 Caert-Thresoor
0167-5036 Japan Annual Reviews in Electronics, Computers & Telecommunications. Amorphous Semiconductor Technologies & Devices
0167-5087 Nuclear Instruments and Methods in Physics Research *see* 0168-9002
0167-5087 Nuclear Instruments and Methods in Physics Research *see* 0168-583X
0167-5133 Journal of Semantics
0167-5249 Law and Philosophy
0167-5257 Naamkunde
0167-5265 Information Services & Use
0167-5273 International Journal of Cardiology
0167-5303 Butt†
0167-5311 Spanish-Language Psychology†
0167-5419 Engineering Management International *see* 0923-4748
0167-5427 Aquatic Mammals
0167-5516 Tijdschrift voor Theaterwetenschap
0167-5567 Handbook of Inflammation
0167-5583 Uranium†
0167-5710 Office - Technology and People *see* 0959-3845
0167-5729 Surface Science Reports
0167-577X Materials Letters
0167-5796 Core Journals in Dermatology
0167-580X Sociology of Leisure and Sport Abstracts *see* 0838-4061
0167-5818 Coptic Studies
0167-5826 Energy in Agriculture *see* 0960-8524
0167-5850 Justitiele Verkenningen
0167-5877 Preventive Veterinary Medicine
0167-5907 Paidika
0167-5923 Population Research and Policy Review
0167-594X Journal of Neuro-Oncology
0167-5966 Zien Magazine *see* 0923-6511
0167-6059 Behavior Research of Severe Developmental Disabilities†
0167-6105 Journal of Wind Engineering and Industrial Aerodynamics
0167-6164 Journal of African Languages and Linguistics
0167-6172 Plan and Action
0167-6245 Information Economics and Policy
0167-6296 Journal of Health Economics
0167-6318 Linguistic Review
0167-6369 Environmental Monitoring and Assessment
0167-6377 Operations Research Letters
0167-6393 Speech Communication
0167-6423 Science of Computer Programming
0167-644X Reclamation and Revegetation Research *see* 0169-2046
0167-6547 Mini - Microcomputer
0167-6563 Crustaceana. Supplements
0167-6636 Mechanics of Materials
0167-6644 Netherlands. Ministerie van Onderwijs en Wetenschappen. Onderwijsliteratuur
0167-6679 Studies in Classical Antiquity
0167-6687 Insurance: Mathematics & Economics
0167-6695 Isotope Geoscience *see* 0168-9622
0167-6784 Ophthalmic Paediatrics and Genetics
0167-6806 Breast Cancer Research and Treatment
0167-6830 Orbit
0167-6857 Plant Cell, Tissue and Organ Culture†

ISSN INDEX 5625

0167-6865 International Journal of Microcirculation: Clinical & Experimental
0167-6903 Plant Growth Regulation
0167-6911 Systems and Control Letters
0167-692X Energy Research
0167-6962 Transnational Data Report *see* 0892-399X
0167-6989 Reactive Polymers, Ion Exchangers, Sorbents *see* 0923-1137
0167-6997 Investigational New Drugs
0167-7012 Journal of Microbiological Methods
0167-7055 Computer Graphics Forum
0167-7063 Journal of Neurogenetics
0167-7136 Computer Compacts†
0167-7152 Statistics & Probability Letters
0167-7187 International Journal of Industrial Organization
0167-7314 International Journal of Crude Drug Research *see* 0925-1618
0167-7322 Journal of Molecular Liquids
0167-7349 Elex
0167-7373 Typological Studies in Language
0167-739X Future Generation Computer Systems
0167-7411 Topoi
0167-7551 Universite des Sciences Humaines de Strasbourg. Centre de Recherche sur le Proche Orient et la Grece Antiques. Travaux
0167-7659 Cancer Metastasis Reviews *changed to* Cancer and Metastasis Reviews.
0167-7764 Journal of Atmospheric Chemistry
0167-7861 Journal of Inclusion Phenomena *see* 0923-0750
0167-7888 T R W Series of Software Technology†
0167-7977 Computer Physics Reports†
0167-8000 United Nations. Economic Commission for Europe. Statistical Journal
0167-8019 Acta Applicandae Mathematicae
0167-8051 Computers and Standards *see* 0920-5489
0167-806X Natural Language and Linguistic Theory
0167-8094 Order
0167-8116 International Journal of Research in Marketing
0167-8140 Radiotherapy & Oncology
0167-8175 Utrecht Publications in Comparative Literature
0167-8191 Parallel Computing
0167-8272 Bibliografie Nederlandse Sociologie *changed to* Bibliografie Nederlandse Sociale Wetenschappen.
0167-8299 Reviews in Chemical Engineering
0167-8329 Education for Information
0167-8353 Excerpta Medica. Section 52: Toxicology
0167-8396 Computer-Aided Geometric Design
0167-8442 Theoretical and Applied Fracture Mechanics
0167-8493 Robotics *see* 0921-8890
0167-8507 Multilingua
0167-8558 Insurance Abstracts and Reviews†
0167-8590 Kema Scientific & Technical Reports†
0167-8612 Monographs in Ophthalmology
0167-8647 Tijdschrift voor Gezondheid en Politiek†
0167-8655 Pattern Recognition Letters
0167-871X Effective Health Care *see* 0168-8510
0167-8760 International Journal of Psychophysiology
0167-8809 Agriculture, Ecosystems and Environment
0167-8817 Mutation Research - D N A Repair - Reports *see* 0921-8777
0167-899X Nuclear Engineering and Design, Fusion *see* 0920-3796
0167-9031 Mining Science and Technology *see* 0013-7952
0167-9104 Perspektief
0167-9163 Comenius
0167-9236 Decision Support Systems
0167-9260 Integration
0167-9287 Education & Computing
0167-9295 Earth, Moon and Planets
0167-9317 Microelectronic Engineering
0167-9368 Space Communication and Broadcasting *see* 0924-8625
0167-9392 Faux Titre
0167-9430 Trends in Biotechnology
0167-9457 Human Movement Science
0167-9473 Computational Statistics and Data Analysis
0167-9554 Dia Regno
0167-9597 Kunststof en Rubber
0167-9643 Excerpta Medica. Section 30: Pharmacology *see* 0927-2798
0167-9708 Eindhoven University of Technology. Research Reports
0167-9732 Novum Testamentum. Supplements
0167-9767 South African Panorama (Dutch Edition)†
0167-9848 Husserl Studies
0167-9856 European Environmental Science Synopses. Part A: Water Pollution†
0167-9899 International Journal of Cardiac Imaging
0167-9902 Theoretical Medicine
0167-9945 International Journal of Clinical Monitoring and Computing
0167-9988 Tijdschrift voor Zeegeschiedenis
0168-0072 Annals of Pure and Applied Logic
0168-0102 Neuroscience Research
0168-0617 Neuroendocrine Perspectives
0168-1168 Pluimvee Documentatie
0168-1176 International Journal of Mass Spectrometry and Ion Processes
0168-1591 Applied Animal Behaviour Science
0168-1605 International Journal of Food Microbiology
0168-1656 Journal of Biotechnology
0168-1672 Armamentaria
0168-1699 Computers and Electronics in Agriculture
0168-1702 Virus Research
0168-1850 Leidraad
0168-1923 Agricultural and Forest Meteorology
0168-2555 Foundations of Semiotics
0168-2563 Biogeochemistry
0168-275X Krisis
0168-2857 Maandblad Aktiviteitensektor
0168-2997 Andon
0168-3330 Netherlands. Centraal Bureau voor de Statistiek. Statistiek van de Spaargelden
0168-3381 Netherlands. Centraal Bureau voor de Statistiek. Beleggingen van Institutionele Beleggers *changed to* Netherlands. Centraal Bureau voor de Statistiek. Institutionele Beleggers.
0168-3411 Netherlands. Centraal Bureau voor de Statistiek. Vakantieonderzoek
0168-3462 Netherlands. Centraal Bureau voor de Statistiek. Statistiek van de Openbare Bibliotheken
0168-3489 Netherlands. Centraal Bureau voor de Statistiek. Nationale Rekeningen
0168-3519 Netherlands. Centraal Bureau voor de Statistiek. Muziek en Theater
0168-3659 Journal of Controlled Release
0168-3667 Netherlands. Centraal Bureau voor de Statistiek. Statistiek Werkzame Personen
0168-3705 Netherlands. Centraal Bureau voor de Statistiek. Statistisch Zakboek
0168-373X Netherlands. Centraal Bureau voor de Statistiek. Statistiek der Rijksfinancien
0168-3748 Allicht
0168-3853 Population of the Municipalities of the Netherlands
0168-3888 Netherlands. Centraal Bureau voor de Statistiek. Vermogensverdeling. Regionale Gegevens
0168-3918 Netherlands. Centraal Bureau voor de Statistiek. Statistiek van de Land- en Tuinbouw/Statistics of Agriculture
0168-4000 Netherlands. Centraal Bureau voor de Statistiek. Jaarstatistiek van de Bevolking
0168-4019 Landbouwcijfers
0168-4035 Statistiek der Vakbeweging in Nederland
0168-4086 Netherlands. Centraal Bureau voor de Statistiek. Statistiek van de Algemene Bijstand
0168-4094 Netherlands. Centraal Bureau voor de Statistiek. Naamlijsten voor de Statistiek van de Buitenlandse Handel†
0168-4108 Netherlands. Centraal Bureau voor de Statistiek. Diagnosestatistiek Bedrijfsverenigingen (Omslagleden)
0168-4167 Netherlands. Centraal Bureau voor de Statistiek. Statistiek van de Visserij†
0168-423X Netherlands. Centraal Bureau voor de Statistiek. Statistiek van de Voorlichting Bij Scholen en Beroepskeuze†
0168-4248 Netherlands. Centraal Bureau voor de Statistiek. Statistiek van de Inkomsten en Uitgaven der Overheid voor Cultuur en Recreatie
0168-4280 Netherlands. Centraal Bureau voor de Statistiek. Criminele Statistiek *changed to* Netherlands. Centraal Bureau voor de Statistiek. Criminaliteit en Strafrechtspleging.
0168-4361 Netherlands. Centraal Bureau voor de Statistiek. Produktiestatistieken: Papier- en Kartonindustrie
0168-4590 Netherlands. Centraal Bureau voor de Statistiek. Hypotheken. Statistics of Mortgages
0168-468X Speur- en Ontwikkelingswerk in Nederland
0168-4809 Nederlandse Jeugd en Haar Onderwijs
0168-4825 Netherlands. Centraal Bureau voor de Statistiek. Statistiek van Aan-, Af- en Doorvoer. Goederenvervoer per Goederensoort van en naar de Zeehavens van Rotterdam en Amsterdam
0168-485X Netherlands. Centraal Bureau voor de Statistiek. Voortgezet Onderwijs Regionaal Bezien
0168-4876 Netherlands. Centraal Bureau voor de Statistiek. Statistiek van de Aan-, Af- en Doorvoer. Goederenvervoer van en naar Nederland
0168-4884 Netherlands. Centraal Bureau voor de Statistiek. Statistiek der Verkiezingen. Gemeenteraden
0168-4906 Netherlands. Centraal Bureau voor de Statistiek. Statistiek van het Erkende Schriftelijk Onderwijs
0168-4973 Netherlands. Centraal Bureau voor de Statistiek. Statistiek der Motorvoertuigen
0168-5023 Netherlands. Centraal Bureau voor de Statistiek. Statistiek van de Verkeersongevallen op de Openbare Weg
0168-5058 Netherlands. Centraal Bureau voor de Statistiek. Statistiek van Het Wetenschappelijk Onderwijs
0168-5074 Netherlands. Centraal Bureau voor de Statistiek. Statistiek van het Personenvervoer
0168-518X Netherlands. Centraal Bureau voor de Statistiek. Productie Statistiek van de Zuivelindustrie
0168-5236 Netherlands. Centraal Bureau voor de Statistiek. Nederlandse Energiehuishouding
0168-5244 Netherlands. Centraal Bureau voor de Statistiek. Statistiek van de Gemeentewege per Leerling Beschikbaar Gestelde Bedragen voor het Lager Onderwijs.†
0168-5287 Netherlands. Centraal Bureau voor de Statistiek. Produktiestatistieken: Suikerindustrie
0168-5325 Netherlands. Centraal Bureau voor de Statistiek van het Binnenlands Goederenvervoer. Statistics of Internal Goods Transport in the Netherlands
0168-5333 Netherlands. Centraal Bureau voor de Statistiek. Produktiestatistieken: Veevoederindustrie
0168-5376 Netherlands. Centraal Bureau voor de Statistiek. Statistiek van de Internationale Binnenvaart
0168-5406 Netherlands. Centraal Bureau voor de Statistiek. Statistiek van het Beroepsonderwijs: Huishoud- en Nijverheidsonderwijs†
0168-5422 Netherlands. Centraal Bureau voor de Statistiek. Statistiek van de Zeevaart
0168-5457 Netherlands. Centraal Bureau voor de Statistiek. Statistiek van het Beroepsonderwijs: Technisch en Nautisch Onderwijs
0168-549X Netherlands. Centraal Bureau voor de Statistiek. Sociaal-Economische Maandstatistiek
0168-5503 Netherlands. Centraal Bureau voor de Statistiek. Statistiek van het Beroepsonderwijs: Kunstonderwijs. Art Colleges
0168-552X Netherlands. Centraal Bureau voor de Statistiek. Statistiek van de Luchtvaart
0168-5538 Netherlands. Centraal Bureau voor de Statistiek. Statistiek Vreemdelingenverkeer.
0168-5597 Evoked Potentials
0168-5600 Netherlands. Centraal Bureau voor de Statistiek. Statistiek van het Beroepsonderwijs: Sociaal-Pedagogisch Onderwijs
0168-5686 Netherlands. Centraal Bureau voor de Statistiek. Statistiek der Verkiezingen. Tweede Kamer der Staten-Generaal
0168-5708 Netherlands. Centraal Bureau voor de Statistiek. Statistiek van het Beroepsonderwijs: Beroepsbegeleidend Onderwijs Leerlingwezen
0168-5732 Netherlands. Centraal Bureau voor de Statistiek. Statistiek der Verkiezingen. Provinciale Staten
0168-5767 Netherlands. Centraal Bureau voor de Statistiek. Produktiestatistieken: Alcoholfabrieken, Bierbrouwerijen en Mouterijen, Distilleerderijen en Frisdrankenindustrie
0168-583X Nuclear Instruments & Methods in Physics Research. Section B. Beam Interactions with Materials and Atoms
0168-5856 Netherlands. Centraal Bureau voor de Statistiek. Statistiek van het W V O, H A V O en M A V O: Scholen en Leerlingen
0168-5864 Netherlands. Centraal Bureau voor de Statistiek. Produktiestatistieken: Rijwiel- en Motorrijwielindustrie
0168-5988 Bibliografie van Regionale Onderzoekingen op Sociaal-wetenschappelijk Terrein
0168-6054 Annales de Readaptation et de Medecine Physique
0168-6151 Modern Quaternary Research in Southeast Asia
0168-6208 Paleoecology of Africa
0168-6259 Indo-Malayan Zoology†
0168-6291 Irrigation and Drainage Systems
0168-6445 F E M S. Microbiology Reviews
0168-6496 F E M S. Microbiology Ecology
0168-6577 European Journal of Population
0168-6674 Delft Hydroscience Abstracts†
0168-6682 Konteksten
0168-7034 Journal of Consumer Policy
0168-7166 Export Magazine
0168-7298 Bollettino di Italianistica†
0168-7336 Reactivity of Solids *see* 0167-2738
0168-7433 Journal of Automated Reasoning
0168-7484 Beschrijvende Rassenlijst voor Landbouwgewassen
0168-7565 Veeteelt
0168-7697 New in Chess Yearbook
0168-7778 Journal of Management Consulting
0168-7840 Elektronica

ISSN

0168-7905 Netherlands. Centraal Bureau voor de Statistiek. Statistiek van de Uitgaven der Overheid voor Onderwijs
0168-7956 Netherlands. Centraal Bureau voor de Statistiek. Statistiek van de Investeringen in Vaste Activa in de Nijverheid
0168-8162 Experimental & Applied Acarology
0168-8170 Invertebrate Reproduction and Development
0168-8227 Diabetes Research and Clinical Practice
0168-8278 Journal of Hepatology
0168-8308 Apple Blad 2 - Macintosh Blad *changed to* Apple Macintosh Blad.
0168-8413 Lust & Gratie
0168-8448 Alternative Medicine†
0168-8472 Nederlandse Vereniging voor Klinische Chemie. Tijdschrift
0168-8510 Health Policy
0168-8561 Biogenic Amines
0168-8626 Tijdschrift voor Agologie
0168-8634 Journal of Clinical and Experimental Neuropsychology
0168-874X Finite Elements in Analysis and Design
0168-8782 New in Chess Magazine
0168-8944 Excerpta Medica. Section 51: Mycobacterial Diseases: Leprosy, Tuberculosis and Related Subjects†
0168-9002 Nuclear Instruments & Methods in Physics Research. Section A. Accelerators, Spectrometers, Detectors, and Associated Equipment
0168-9274 Applied Numerical Mathematics
0168-9444 Harvard Holland Review
0168-9452 Plant Science
0168-9479 Trends in Genetics
0168-9533 Pigs
0168-9622 Chemical Geology. Isotope Geoscience Section
0168-9630 De Schoonheidsspecialist
0168-9673 Acta Mathematicae Applicatae Sinica
0168-9770 Forschungsberichte zur D D R-Literatur
0168-9827 Nieuwe Nederlandse Bijdragen Tot de Geschiednis der Geneeskunde en der Natuurwetenschappen
0168-9843 Instituut voor Rassenonderzoek van Landbouwgewassen. Jaarverslag *changed to* Centrum voor Rassenonderzoek en Zaadtechnologie. Jaarsverslag.
0168-9924 Verpleegkundig Historische Cahiers
0168-9959 Tijdschrift voor Theologie
0168-9975 Verpleegkundig Historische Monografieen
0169-0124 Studies in Slavic and General Linguistics
0169-0175 Studies in Slavic Literature and Poetics
0169-0221 Amsterdamer Publikationen zur Sprache und Literatur
0169-023X Data & Knowledge Engineering
0169-0272 Amsterdam Studies in Theology
0169-0337 H I V O S - Projectbericht
0169-0361 University of Pennsylvania Studies on South Asia†
0169-037X Indices Zum Altdeutschen Schrifttum†
0169-0426 Quellen und Forschungen zur Erbauungsliteratur des Spaeten Mittelalters und der Fruehen Neuzeit†
0169-0477 Beschreibende Bibliographien†
0169-0930 Kleur
0169-0965 Language and Cognitive Processes
0169-1007 Agrarisch Onderwijs *changed to* Netherlands. Centraal Bureau voor de Statistiek. Statistiek van het Hoger Beroepsonderwijs: Agrarisch Onderwijs.
0169-1015 Spatial Vision
0169-1023 Genootschap Delfia Batavorum. Serie-Uitgave
0169-1066 Japanese Anaesthesia Journals Review†
0169-1112 The Pain Clinic
0169-1163 Japanese Journal of Rheumatology
0169-1198 The Hoogsteder Mercury
0169-121X Mathematical Engineering in Industry
0169-1244 Current Titles and Abstracts in Immunology, Transplantation and Allergy†
0169-1317 Applied Clay Science
0169-1368 Ore Geology Reviews
0169-1422 Population and Family in the Low Countries
0169-1473 Demos
0169-1724 Viennese Heritage
0169-1767 Economic Forecasts
0169-1864 Advanced Robotics
0169-1872 Nederlands Tijdschrift voor Opvoeding, Vorming, en Onderwijs
0169-2046 Landscape and Urban Planning
0169-2070 International Journal of Forecasting
0169-2305 Gebouwmanagement *changed to* Facility Management Magazine.
0169-2313 Netherlands Fertilizer Technical Bulletin
0169-2577 Water Supply and Wastewater Disposal - International Almanac
0169-2607 Computer Methods & Programs in Biomedicine
0169-2763 Infomediary
0169-2801 Groniek
0169-281X Leidinggeven & Organiseren
0169-2895 Soviet Journal of Numerical Analysis and Mathematical Modelling
0169-2968 Fundamenta Informaticae
0169-3255 Landbouw-Economisch Bericht
0169-328X Molecular Brain Research
0169-3298 Surveys in Geophysics
0169-3441 Netherlands Quarterly of Human Rights. Newsletter
0169-3662 Stygologia
0169-3816 Journal of Cross-Cultural Gerontology
0169-3867 Biology and Philosophy
0169-3913 Transport in Porous Media
0169-409X Advanced Drug Delivery Reviews
0169-4146 Journal of Industrial Microbiology
0169-4197 International Journal of Pancreatology
0169-4243 Journal of Adhesion Science and Technology
0169-4286 New Forests
0169-4332 Applied Surface Science
0169-4375 Belmontia
0169-4405 Poultry *changed to* Misset World Poultry.
0169-4758 Parasitology Today
0169-4839 Nederlandse Geografische Studies
0169-4901 Agricultural Science in the Netherlands
0169-5002 Lung Cancer
0169-5126 Kerngetallen-Testbeeloen
0169-5150 Agricultural Economics
0169-5347 Trends in Ecology and Evolution
0169-5401 De Spaarbank
0169-555X Geomorphology
0169-5606 Visible Religion
0169-5614 Volkscultuur
0169-5959 The Gist
0169-5983 Fluid Dynamics Research
0169-6009 Bone and Mineral
0169-605X Abstracts on Rural Development in the Tropics
0169-6149 Origins of Life and Evolution of the Biosphere
0169-6165 Bochumer Anglistische Studien
0169-622X Techniek in de Gezondheidszorg
0169-6270 R O M *see* 0923-7674
0169-6289 C B S Newsletter
0169-6424 New Polymeric Materials
0169-6459 Molens
0169-6726 Nederlands Kunsthistorisch Jaarboek
0169-6750 Rassenlijst voor Fruitgewassen
0169-6939 Studies in Banking and Finance *see* 0378-4266
0169-7226 Oudtestamentische Studien
0169-7269 Opstap†
0169-7293 Acta Collegii Historiae Urbanae
0169-734X Arbeiten zur Geschichte des Antiken Judentums und des Urchristentums
0169-7390 Arbeiten zur Literatur und Geschichte des Hellenistischen Judentums
0169-7439 Chemometrics and Intelligent Laboratory Systems
0169-7471 Zelfbestuur†
0169-7528 Corruption and Reform
0169-7544 Behaviour. Supplements†
0169-7552 Computer Networks and I S D N Systems
0169-7692 Cincinnati Classical Studies. New Series
0169-7722 Journal of Contaminant Hydrology
0169-7749 Coptic Gnostic Library *see* 0169-9350
0169-779X Cornell Linguistic Contributions
0169-7846 Contributions to the Sociology of Jewish Languages
0169-7897 Academie Internationale d'Histoire des Sciences. Collection des Travaux
0169-7943 Documenta et Monumenta Orientis Antiqui
0169-796X Contributions to Asian Studies *changed to* Journal of Developing Societies.
0169-7994 Davis Medieval Texts and Studies
0169-801X Studia Ad Corpus Hellenisticum Novi Testamenti
0169-8028 Studien und Texte zur Geistesgeschichte des Mittelalters
0169-8036 Iconography of Religions. Section 15, Mesopotamia and the Near East
0169-8060 Dutch Archaeological and Historical Society. Studies
0169-8087 Iconography of Religions. Section 5, Australia
0169-8095 Atmospheric Research
0169-8125 Studia in Veteris Testamenti Pseudepigrapha
0169-8133 Iconography of Religions. Section 13, Indian Religions
0169-8141 International Journal of Industrial Ergonomics
0169-815X Etudes sur le Judaisme Medieval
0169-8184 Iconography of Religions. Section 10, North America
0169-8206 Griekse en Latijnse Schrijvers
0169-8230 Iconography of Religions. Section 7, Africa
0169-8257 De Goeje Stichting. Uitgaven
0169-8273 Textus Minores†
0169-8281 Iconography of Religions. Section 23, Judaism
0169-8311 Studia Gaianat†
0169-832X T'oung Pao. Monographies
0169-8338 Iconography of Religions. Section 16, Egypt
0169-8354 Jewish Law Annual
0169-8362 Studies in the History of Leiden University
0169-8370 Theokratia: Jahrbuch des Institutum Judaicum Delitzschianum
0169-8389 Iconography of Religions. Section 22, Islam
0169-8400 Jewish Law Annual Supplements
0169-8435 Iconography of Religions. Section 20, Manichaeism
0169-8451 Kerkhistorische Bijdragen
0169-8508 Leiden Botanical Series
0169-8559 Leidse Germanistische en Anglistische Reeks
0169-8575 Leidse Kunsthistorische Reeks†
0169-8605 Leidse Juridische Reeks
0169-8656 Leidse Romanistische Reeks
0169-8672 Codices Manuscripti Bibliothecae Universitatis Leidensis
0169-8702 Litterae Textuales
0169-8729 Islamic Philosophy, Theology and Science
0169-877X Iranica Antiqua Supplementa
0169-880X Delegation Archeologique Francaise en Iran. Memoires
0169-8834 Numen Supplements
0169-8850 Monumenta Graeca et Romana
0169-8885 Numen Supplements, Altera Series *see* 0169-8834
0169-8907 Kern Institute, Leiden. Memoirs
0169-8923 Netherlands Institute of Archaeology and Arabic Studies in Cairo. Publications
0169-8931 Sir Thomas Browne Institute. Publications. General Series *changed to* Sir Thomas Browne Institute. Publications. New Series.
0169-8958 Mnemosyne. Supplements
0169-8982 Sir Thomas Browne Institute. Publications. Special Series *changed to* Sir Thomas Browne Institute. Publications. New Series.
0169-9008 Peshitta Institute, Leiden. Monographs
0169-9024 Studies in the History of the Ancient Near East
0169-9032 Rechtshistorisch Instituut Leiden. Series 1
0169-9059 Medieval and Renaissance Authors
0169-9105 Medieval and Renaissance Texts
0169-9202 Monographs and Theoretical Studies in Sociology and Anthropology in Honour of Nels Anderson
0169-930X Nisaba
0169-9350 Nag Hammadi Studies
0169-9377 Handbuch der Orientalistik. 2. Abteilung. Indien
0169-9423 Handbuch der Orientalistik. 1. Abteilung. Der Nahe und der Mittlere Osten
0169-9431 N E V A C Blad
0169-9458 Orientalia Monspeliensia
0169-9474 Handbuch der Orientalistik. 7. Abteilung. Kunst und Archaeologie
0169-9504 Orientalia Rheno-Traiectina
0169-9512 Studies in Greek and Roman Religion
0169-9520 Handbuch der Orientalistik. 4. Abteilung. China
0169-9555 Oekumenische Studien
0169-9563 Sinica Leidensia
0169-9571 Handbuch der Orientalistik. 3. Abteilung. Indonesien, Malaysia und die Philippinen
0169-9601 Probleme der Aegyptologie
0169-961X Studies in Judaism in Late Antiquity
0169-9628 Iconography of Religions. Section 8, Arctic Peoples
0169-9652 Papyrologica Lugduno-Batava
0169-9660 Studies in Judaism in Modern Times
0169-9679 Iconography of Religions. Section 19, Ancient Europe
0169-9717 Studia Post-Biblica
0169-9725 Iconography of Religions. Section 12, East and Central Asia
0169-975X Roma Aeterna†
0169-9776 Iconography of Religions. Section 21, Mandaeism
0169-9806 Rechtshistorische Studies†
0169-9814 Studies on Religion in Africa
0169-9822 Iconography of Religions. Section 17, Greece and Rome
0169-9857 Studien zur Problemgeschichte der Antiken und Mittelalterlichen Philosophie
0169-9865 Studies in South Asian Culture
0169-9873 Iconography of Religions. Section 14, Iran
0169-9903 Studies in Arabic Literature
0169-9911 Semitic Study Series
0169-992X Iconography of Religions. Section 24, Christianity
0169-9954 Studia Biblica
0169-9962 Studies on the Texts of the Desert of Judah
0169-9970 Iconography of Religions. Section 11, Ancient America
0170-0006 Bochumer Jahrbuch zur Ostasienforschung
0170-0189 Bacillaria†
0170-026X Zeitschrift fuer Arabische Linguistik
0170-0413 Zeitschrift fuer Deutsches und Internationales Baurecht
0170-0456 Die Chemische Produktion
0170-0499 Fleisch-Lebensmittel-Markt
0170-0510 Welt der Modell- und Eisenbahn
0170-0537 Psychologie und Gesellschaftskritik
0170-0553 Bioscience Journal†
0170-0561 Genetik.Grundlagen und Perspektiven†
0170-057X Gestalt Theory
0170-060X Praxis der Psychomotorik
0170-0618 Columbus†
0170-0723 Erziehung und Wissenschaft Niedersachsen

0170-0839 Polymer Bulletin
0170-0847 Oesterreichisches Jahrbuch fuer Politik
0170-0863 Biologica Didactica†
0170-0944 Sachunterricht und Mathematik in der Grundschule
0170-1002 Deutsche Bibliographie. Zeitschriften-Verzeichnis†
0170-1029 Deutsche Bibliographie. Musiktontraeger-Verzeichnis *changed to* Deutsche Nationalbibliographie. Musiktontraeger-Verzeichnis.
0170-1037 Deutsche Bibliographie. Woechentliches Verzeichnis. Ausgabe 1 Amtsblatt der Deutschen Bibliothek *changed to* Deutsche Nationalbibliographie. Woechentliches Verzeichnis. Ausgabe 1 Amtsblatt der Deutschen Bibliothek.
0170-124X Deutsche Bibliographie: Musikalien-Verzeichnis *changed to* Deutsche Nationalbibliographie: Verzeichnis der Musikalien und Musikschriften.
0170-1304 Weltweit Hoeren
0170-1320 Specimina Philologiae Slavicae
0170-1452 Jura
0170-1509 Deutsche Volleyball Zeitschrift
0170-1533 Freie Universitaet Berlin. Osteuropa-Institut. Balkanologische Veroeffentlichungen
0170-1541 Mathematica Didactica
0170-155X Technica Didactica *changed to* Didaktik-Arbeit, Technik, Wirtschaft.
0170-1665 Berliner Kunstblatt *changed to* Kunstblatt.
0170-1703 E T Z Archiv *see* 0939-3072
0170-1711 Elektrotechnische Zeitschrift *changed to* E T Z.
0170-1754 Media Perspektiven
0170-1789 Zeitschrift fuer Differentielle und Diagnostische Psychologie
0170-1800 Chef International
0170-1819 ModellWerft
0170-1916 Bochumer Materialen zur Entwicklungsforschung und Entwicklungspolitik†
0170-2025 Jahrbuch fuer Westdeutsche Landesgeschichte
0170-2033 Elektrische Energie Technik
0170-2041 Liebigs Annalen der Chemie
0170-219X Semiosis
0170-236X Germany (Federal Republic, 1949-) Bundesaufsichtsamt fuer das Versicherungswesen. Veroeffentlichungen
0170-2408 Hiersemanns Bibliographische Handbuecher
0170-2416 Uebersee-Museum, Bremen. Veroeffentlichungen. Reihe E: Human-Oekologie
0170-2513 Magazin fuer Amerikanistik
0170-2653 Ahnenlisten Kartei
0170-2793 Ersatzkassen-Report
0170-284X Deutsche Branchen-Fernsprechbuch *changed to* Liefern und Leisten.
0170-2971 Spektrum der Wissenschaft
0170-3013 Modern German Studies
0170-303X Technique du Roulemont *see* 0934-926X
0170-3056 Tecnica de los Rodamientos *see* 0934-9278
0170-3080 Deutsche Handelsakten des Mittelalters und der Neuzeit
0170-3099 Universitaet Frankfurt. Seminar fuer Voelkerkunde. Arbeiten
0170-3102 Bibliotheca Islamica
0170-3137 Beitraege zur Suedasienforschung
0170-3153 Deutsche Sprache in Europa und Uebersee
0170-3188 Erdwissenschaftliche Forschung
0170-3196 Aethiopistische Forschungen
0170-3218 Beitraege zur Aegyptischen Bauforschung und Altertumskunde
0170-3226 Frankfurter Historische Abhandlungen
0170-3242 Alt- und Neu-Indische Studien
0170-3250 Geoecological Research
0170-3285 Freiburger Islamstudien
0170-3293 Frankfurter Historische Vortraege
0170-3307 Freiburger Altorientalische Studien
0170-3315 Beitraege zur Literatur des 15.-18. Jahrhunderts
0170-334X Materialfluss
0170-3447 Veroeffentlichungen zur Geschichte des Glases und der Glashuetter in Deutschland
0170-3455 Glasenapp-Stiftung
0170-3463 Industriegewerkschaft Druck und Papier. Schriftenreihe fuer Betriebsrate *changed to* Industriegewerkschaft Medien. Schriftenreihe fuer Betriebsrate.
0170-348X Uebersetzungen Auslaendischer Arbeiten zur Antiken Sklaverei
0170-3544 Studien zur Kulturkunde
0170-3560 Mainzer Studien zur Sprach- und Volksforschung
0170-3579 Wissenschaftliche Paperbacks
0170-3595 Quellen und Studien zur Geschichte des Oestlichen Europa
0170-3617 I F O Spiegel der Wirtschaft
0170-3633 Verschollene und Vergessene
0170-365X Institut fuer Europaeische Geschichte, Mainz. Veroeffentlichungen. Abteilung Universalgeschichte. Beihefte
0170-3668 Muenchener Ostasiatische Studien
0170-3676 Muenchener Ostasiatische Studien. Sonderreihe
0170-3684 Studien zur Ostasiatischen Schriftkunst
0170-3692 Universitaet zu Koeln. Kunsthistorisches Institut. Abteilung Asien. Publikationen
0170-3706 Sinologica Coloniensia
0170-3722 Praxis Grundschule
0170-3730 Hermannstrase 14†
0170-379X Die Lokrundschau
0170-3803 Lendemains
0170-3846 Lutherische Theologie und Kirche
0170-4044 Oberflaeche und J O T *see* 0940-8789
0170-4060 A V R
0170-4176 Media Daten: Zeitschriften
0170-4192 Media Daten: Fachzeitschriften
0170-4214 Mathematical Methods in the Applied Sciences
0170-4249 Esoterik und Wissenschaft
0170-4478 Betriebswirtschaftlicher Informationsdienst†
0170-4605 Lehrerzeitung Baden-Wuerttemberg
0170-4613 S P W
0170-4621 L O K Report Reisefuehrer
0170-4761 Kritik†
0170-4818 Englera
0170-5067 B P S - Report
0170-5091 Basler Afrika Bibliographien. Mitteilungen†
0170-5105 Buchhandelsgeschichte. Zweite Folge
0170-5148 Christ in der Gegenwart
0170-5253 Roll on Roll off in Europe
0170-5261 Zeitschrift fuer Vegetationstechnik†
0170-5288 Eisenbahn-Kurier
0170-5334 Anaesthesiologie und Intensivmedizin
0170-5385 Garten Organisch
0170-5458 W M Teil IIb: Sammelliste Gekuendigter und Verloster Wertpapiere
0170-5504 Fliegermagazin
0170-5598 Arbeitsgemeinschaft der Parlaments- und Behoerdenbibliotheken. Mitteilungen
0170-5652 Studien zur Verkehrswirtschaft
0170-5660 Studien zur Industriewirtschaft
0170-5679 Ciret Studien
0170-5687 Studien zur Bauwirtschaft
0170-5695 I F O Institut fuer Wirtschaftsforschung. Studien zu Handels- und Dienstleistungsfragen
0170-5725 Ur- und Fruehzeit†
0170-5768 Schrifttums fuer den Bereich Haushalt und Verbauch. Bibliographie
0170-5776 Archaeologische Mitteilungen aus Nordwestdeutschland
0170-5792 Motorik
0170-5946 Sprache und Geschichte in Afrika
0170-5989 N M R
0170-6012 Informatik-Spektrum
0170-608X Daten und Dokumente Zum Umweltschutz†
0170-6128 Schoenberger Hefte
0170-6136 Weg und Wahrheit *changed to* Evangelische Kirchenzeitung.
0170-6225 Kunst und Unterricht
0170-6233 Berichte zur Wissenschaftsgeschichte
0170-6241 Zeitschrift fuer Semiotik
0170-625X Kindheit
0170-6632 Chip
0170-6640 Internationales Energie Forum
0170-6659 Bankfachklasse
0170-6802 An Rems und Murr
0170-6845 Steuer Training
0170-6977 Wissenschaft und Umwelt†
0170-6993 Instandhaltung
0170-7140 V O P - Fachzeitschrift fuer die Oeffentliche Verwaltung
0170-7213 Who's Who at the Frankfurt Book Fair
0170-7256 Datenschutz-Berater
0170-7302 Katholisches Leben und Kirchenreform im Zeitalter der Glaubensspaltung
0170-7337 Jahrbuch zur Frage der Suchtgefahren *changed to* Jahrbuch Sucht.
0170-7353 Wer und Was in der Deutschen Fleisch- Fisch- und Feinkost-Industrie
0170-7434 Physics Briefs - Physikalische Berichte
0170-7558 Quickborn
0170-7620 Steuer Telex
0170-7663 I F O Digest
0170-7671 Agrarsoziale Gesellschaft. Kleine Reihe
0170-768X Kurier (Duesseldorf)
0170-7779 Studien zur Energiewirtschaft
0170-7787 South Asian Digest of Regional Writing
0170-7809 Z M P Bilanz Getreide-Futtermittel
0170-7922 Schulleiter Handbuch
0170-8007 Balkan-Archiv Neue Folge
0170-8058 Tribuna Alemat
0170-8090 Landschaftsverband Westfalen-Lippe *changed to* Volkskuendlichen Kommission fuer Westfalen. Schriften.
0170-821X Bonner Romanistische Arbeiten
0170-8287 E E G Labor
0170-8309 Technische Universitaet Berlin. Institut fuer Sozialoekonomie der Agrarentwicklung. Annual Report (Abridged Edition) *see* 0177-6673
0170-8376 Technische Universitaet Berlin. Institut fuer Sozialoekonomie der Agrarentwicklung. Jahresbericht *see* 0177-6673
0170-8406 Organization Studies
0170-8643 Lecture Notes in Control and Information Sciences
0170-866X W & M
0170-8791 N Z: Neue Zeitschrift fuer Musik
0170-8864 Monographien zur Indischen Archaeologie, Kunst und Philologie
0170-8929 Muenchener Zeitschrift fuer Balkankunde
0170-8988 Archiv fuer das Post - und Fernmeldewesen
0170-902X Das Band
0170-9135 Mainzer Studien zur Amerikanistik
0170-9267 Bautenschutz und Bausanierung
0170-9291 Europaisches Patentamt. Amtsblatt
0170-9348 International Books in Print
0170-9364 Die Alte Stadt
0170-9496 Siemens Energietechnik *see* 0939-205X
0170-9526 V D I Informationsdienst. Blechbearbeitung
0170-9550 V D I Informationsdienst. Kaltmassivumformung
0170-9569 V D I Informationsdienst. Elektrisch Abtragende Fertigungsverfahren
0170-9577 T Z fuer Metallbearbeitung†
0170-9615 B M F T Journal
0170-9690 V G A Nachrichten
0170-9739 Zeitschrift fuer Physik. Section C: Particles and Fields
0170-9828 Allgemeine Fleischer Zeitung
0170-9925 Archives of Gynecology *see* 0932-0067
0170-9933 Metal Statistics (Years)
0171-0079 Atalanta
0171-0087 Basler Afrika Bibliographien. Nachrichten†
0171-0125 Bibliographien zur Romanistik
0171-0796 Rheinische-Westfaelischer Jaeger
0171-0826 Lexikon des Steuer- und Wirtschaftsrechts
0171-0834 Kodikas - Code - Ars Semeiotica
0171-0958 E L C O M P Magazine
0171-1091 Urologic Radiology
0171-1342 D F V L R - Forschungsberichte und D F V L R - Mitteilungen *changed to* D L R - Forschungsberichte.
0171-1555 B B A Planen und Bauen
0171-1644 Bromberg
0171-1660 Beitraege zur Afrikakunde
0171-1687 Geomethodica
0171-1741 European Journal of Applied Microbiology and Biotechnology *see* 0175-7598
0171-1814 Anaesthesiologie und Intensivmedizin
0171-1873 Springer Series in Solid State Sciences
0171-1970 Briefmarkenwelt
0171-2004 Handbook of Experimental Pharmacology
0171-2063 Humboldtiana *changed to* Bibliographia Humboldtiana.
0171-2160 Topics in Infectious Diseases
0171-2268 Uni Hannover
0171-2802 Polizeiliche Kriminalstatistik N - W
0171-290X Portugiesische Forschungen der Goerresgesellschaft. Reihe 3: Vieira-Texte und Vieira-Studien†
0171-2985 Immunobiology
0171-3159 Spak-Forum
0171-3183 Perspektiven†
0171-3191 Kernforschungszentrum Karlsruhe. Ergebnisbericht ueber Forschung und Entwicklung
0171-3302 Berliner Wissenschaftlicher Gesellschaft. Jahrbuch
0171-3426 Pulheimer Beitraege zur Geschichte und Heimatkunde
0171-3434 Psychosozial
0171-3469 Reformationsgeschichtliche Studien und Texte
0171-3604 Prisma (Kassel)
0171-3647 V D I Informationsdienst. Schmieden und Pressen
0171-3655 Projektbereich Auslaendische Arbeiter. Materialien†
0171-3698 Marxistische Studien
0171-3736 Provinzialinstitut fuer Westfaelische Landes- und Volkforschung. Veroeffentlichungen *changed to* Provinzialinstitut fuer Westfaelische Landes- und Volksforschung des Landschaftsverbandes Westfalen-Lippe. Veroeffentlichungen.
0171-3876 Medikament & Meinung
0171-4090 Articulata
0171-4163 Test-Index
0171-4171 Lebendige Katechese
0171-4341 Wer und Was in der Deutschen Koerperpflege-, Wasch- und Reinigungsmittel-Industrie
0171-4449 Wer und Was in der Deutschen Pharmazeutischen - Industrie
0171-4457 Wer und Was in der Deutschen Getraenke - Industrie
0171-4511 M P T - Metallurgical Plant and Technology
0171-4538 Sozialpsychiatrische Informationen
0171-4937 Sekretariat
0171-4996 Italienisch
0171-5038 W E M A Bezugsquellenverzeichnis†
0171-5046 G V A Mitgliederverzeichnis
0171-5062 Fertigung und Betrieb
0171-5089 Der Weihenstephaner
0171-5178 Praxis Geographie
0171-5208 Kullerаugen
0171-5216 Journal of Cancer Research and Clinical Oncology

0171-5410 Arbeiten aus Anglistik und Amerikanistik
0171-5445 Bauphysik
0171-5658 Hoppenstedt Boersenfuehrer
0171-5747 Atomkernergie - Kerntechnik *see* 0932-3902
0171-5860 Analyse & Kritik
0171-5976 Menschenrechte
0171-6026 Homosexuelle Emanzipation†
0171-6042 Made in Europe. Furniture and Interiors†
0171-6204 Erneuerung in Kirche und Gesellschaft
0171-6298 Spiridon Laufmagazin
0171-6425 Thoracic and Cardiovascular Surgeon
0171-645X Beitraege zur Hochschulforschung
0171-6468 O R Spektrum
0171-6530 Aurora-Buchreihe
0171-6794 Studies in Descriptive Linguistics
0171-6913 Information†
0171-709X Polymers - Properties and Applications
0171-7111 Haematology and Blood Transfusion *see* 0440-0607
0171-712X Recht der Elektrizitaetswirtschaft
0171-7227 Anwaltsblatt
0171-7243 Amusement-Industrie
0171-726X Utah Studies in Literature and Linguistics
0171-7383 Angler Rinderzucht
0171-7456 I F O A M *changed to* Oekologie und Landbau.
0171-791X Praxis der Psychotherapie und Psychosomatik
0171-7936 Offenbacher Verein fuer Naturkunde. Abhandlungen
0171-7952 Bauen fuer die Landwirtschaft
0171-7995 Ballett Info *see* 0722-6268
0171-8096 Technisches Messen - T M
0171-8177 Entomologia Generalis
0171-838X B T E Marketing-Berater
0171-8495 B L L V Bayerische Schule
0171-8630 Marine Ecology-Progress Series
0171-8649 Geographie und Schule
0171-8738 Sozial Report
0171-8789 B F G: Aussenhandelsdienst
0171-8819 Arbeit und Soziales
0171-8932 Zeitschriften - Datenbank (Z D B)
0171-9262 Wirtschaftsschutz *changed to* Wirtschaftsschutz und Sicherheitstechnik.
0171-9289 Freibeuter
0171-9319 Begegnen und Helfen
0171-9327 Sozial Paediatrie
0171-9335 European Journal of Cell Biology
0171-9378 Studien zu Nichteuropaeischen Rechtstheorien
0171-9386 Junges Forum
0171-953X Journal fuer Geschichte *see* 0173-539X
0171-9599 Contactologia
0171-9629 Sonderschulmagazin *see* 0930-696X
0171-967X Calcified Tissue International
0171-9718 Behindertenhilfe Durch Erziehung, Unterricht und Therapie
0171-9750 Archives of Toxicology. Supplement
0172-0015 Photorin *changed to* Lichtenberg-Jahrbuch.
0172-0171 Bildung und Wissenschaft
0172-0457 Literarisches Arbeitsjournal†
0172-049X Wettbewerb in Recht und Praxis
0172-0570 Agrarmeteorologischer Wochenhinweis fuer das Gebiet Bundesrepublik Deutschland
0172-0589 Brauerei Journal
0172-0643 Pediatric Cardiology
0172-0686 Steuern in der Elektrizitaetswirtschaft
0172-0872 Blaetter fuer Oberdeutsche Namenforschung
0172-0899 Micro Extra
0172-0929 Priesterjahrheft
0172-1232 Current Diagnostic Pediatrics
0172-1518 Forschung
0172-1526 German Research
0172-1623 Wechselwirkung
0172-1631 Natur und Recht
0172-1658 Literaturinformationen zur Beruflichen Bildung
0172-1879 Westdeutsche Gesellschaft fuer Familienkunde. Mitteilungen
0172-1984 K I - Klima, Kaelte, Heizung
0172-200X Bau & Heimwerker Markt
0172-2115 Materialen zur Kunst des Neunzehnten Jahrhunderts†
0172-2131 Akademie fuer Oeffentliches Gesundheitswesen. Schriftenreihe
0172-2182 Made in Europe Buyers' Guide
0172-2190 World Patent Information
0172-2255 Der Chorsaenger
0172-2476 Handballtraining
0172-2514 Wuerttembergische Bau-Berufsgenossenschaft. Mitteilungen
0172-2522 Amtsblatt der Stadt Koeln
0172-2530 Vorteilhafte Geldanlagen
0172-2611 Process Automation-P A†
0172-2751 Arbeitsmarkt in Hessen
0172-2859 Exlibriskunst und Graphik. Jahrbuch
0172-2867 D L W Nachrichten
0172-2875 Zeitschrift fuer Berufs- und Wirtschaftspaedagogik
0172-3006 Institut fuer Bautechnik. Mitteilungen
0172-3146 Internationale Aufgaben der D G D†
0172-3227 Diplomatic Observer
0172-3456 Symbol
0172-3510 Bielefelder Beitraege zur Sprachlehrforschung
0172-360X Handbuch der Finanzstatistik
0172-3790 Hygiene & Medizin
0172-388X Stereoplay
0172-3960 Bibliographie Linguistischer Literatur
0172-4029 Stadion
0172-4207 Advanced Series in Agricultural Sciences
0172-4525 Guten Tag
0172-4533 Stadt Duisburg. Statistisches Jahrbuch
0172-4541 Duisburg. Amt fuer Statistik und Stadtforschung. Daten und Information *changed to* Daten und Information.
0172-4568 Applications of Mathematics
0172-4606 Aktuelle Endokrinologie und Stoffwechsel
0172-4614 Ultraschall in der Medizin
0172-4622 International Journal of Sports Medicine
0172-4665 Cell Biology Monographs
0172-4770 Beitraege Zum Auslaendischen Oeffentlichen Recht und Voelkerrecht
0172-4827 Comprehensive Manuals of Surgical Specialities
0172-4843 Comprehensive Manuals in Radiology
0172-4878 Das Neue China
0172-5076 Crystals: Growth, Properties and Applications
0172-5203 Fachberichte Messen - Steuern - Regeln
0172-5238 Fachschwester - Fachpfleger
0172-5300 Vox Latina
0172-5408 Der Schulgeograph
0172-5505 Musiktherapeutische Umschau
0172-5564 Zentralblatt fuer Bakteriologie, Mikrobiologie und Hygiene *see* 0723-2020
0172-570X Studies in the History of Mathematics and Physical Sciences
0172-5726 Springer Series in Computational Physics
0172-5734 Springer Series in Electrophysics
0172-5742 Studies of Brain Function
0172-5912 Sonnenenergie und Waermepumpe
0172-5939 Universitexts
0172-5963 Wirtschaftspolitische Studien
0172-5998 Texts and Monographs in Physics
0172-603X Texts and Monographs in Computer Science
0172-6056 Undergraduate Texts in Mathematics
0172-6099 Acta Medico Technica†
0172-6145 Geotechnik
0172-6153 Elektronik Entwicklung
0172-6161 Springer Series on Environmental Management
0172-6188 Springer Series in Experimental Entomology
0172-620X Springer Series in Language and Communication
0172-6218 Springer Series in Chemical Physics
0172-6226 Springer Advanced Texts in Life Sciences
0172-6315 Sources in the History of Mathematics and Physical Sciences
0172-6323 Springer Advanced Texts in Chemistry
0172-6331 Springer Series in Microbiology
0172-6374 Kunststoffberater
0172-6390 Hepato-Gastroenterology
0172-6404 Historical Social Research
0172-6412 Rehabilitation und Praevention
0172-6625 Proceedings in Life Sciences
0172-6641 Perspectives in Mathematical Logic
0172-665X Schriftenreihe des Bayerisches Landesamtes fuer Wasserwirtschaft
0172-7028 European Photography
0172-7117 Industriebedarf
0172-7214 Das Steuer A B C
0172-7249 Der Allgemeinarzt
0172-7265 Kunstreport
0172-7311 Arbeitsgemeinschaft fuer Klinische Nephrologie. Mitteilungen
0172-732X O L B G - Info
0172-7362 Varieties of English around the World
0172-7389 Springer Series in Synergetics
0172-7397 Springer Series in Statistics
0172-7400 Kreditpraxis
0172-7419 Anlagepraxis
0172-7478 Praxis in der Gemeinde
0172-7567 Chimica Didactica
0172-7699 Human Genetics. Supplement
0172-7788 Lecture Notes in Medical Informatics
0172-780X Neuroendocrinology Letters
0172-7966 Inorganic Chemistry Concepts
0172-8008 Ingenieurbauten
0172-8083 Current Genetics
0172-8113 Der Pathologe
0172-8172 Rheumatology International
0172-8237 Internationale Schulbuchforschung
0172-8253 Hoch- und Niedrigwasserzeiten fuer die Deutsche Bucht und deren Flussgebiete
0172-8261 Audiologisch Akustik
0172-8296 Education, Sociedad y Politica. Anuario *changed to* Anuario: Muensteraner Beitraege zur Latein Amerika Forschung.
0172-8334 Humane Produktion, Humane Arbeitsplaetze†
0172-8512 Jahrbuch Ueberblicke Mathematik†
0172-8539 Marineforum
0172-8563 Mannheimer Hefte fuer Schriftvergleichung
0172-8717 Kontakte (Darmstadt)
0172-875X Arbeitskreis fuer Mammillarienfreunde. Mitteilungsblatt
0172-8865 English World Wide
0172-8989 Musikblatt
0172-9039 Experimental Brain Research. Supplementa
0172-9047 Lohn und Gehalt
0172-908X Magnesium Bulletin
0172-9160 Medica *changed to* Medica Report.
0172-9179 Facies
0172-9209 Komparatistische Hefte†
0172-9314 Cargoworld
0172-9322 Der Akupunkturarzt - Aurikulotherapeut
0172-9357 Zeus
0172-9403 Agrarmeteorologischer Wochenbericht fuer Nordrhein - Westfalen
0172-9527 Der Standpunkt (Hamburg)
0172-9624 Kongressbericht Bundesschulmusikwoche *changed to* Bundesschulmusikwoche.
0172-9683 Gitarre & Laute
0173-007X Diskurs†
0173-0266 Vogel und Umwelt
0173-0274 Ingenieurwissenschaftliche Bibliothek
0173-0282 International Boehringer Mannheim. Symposia
0173-0290 Blickpunkt Strassenbahn
0173-0339 Religionspaedagogische Beitraege
0173-0568 Zeitschrift fuer Schadensrecht
0173-0614 Lernen in Deutschland
0173-0665 I D - Informationsdienst fuer die Personalabteilung
0173-0835 Electrophoresis
0173-0843 Dokumente zum Hochschulsport
0173-0851 A Q†
0173-0967 Beitraege zur Psychologie und Soziologie des Kranken Menschen
0173-0975 Studienreihe Paedagogische Psychologie
0173-1637 Bibliographie zur Kunstgeschichtlichen Literatur in Ost- und Suedosteuropaeischen Zeitschriften
0173-1688 Fundheft fuer Arbeits- und Sozialrecht
0173-170X Disorders of Human Communication
0173-1718 Oesterreichische Zeitschrift fuer Oeffentliches Recht und Voelkerrecht. Supplement
0173-1726 Siemens Components
0173-1831 Bibliographien zur Philosophie
0173-184X Peripherie
0173-1882 Apotheke Heute
0173-1904 Abhandlungen des Deutschen Palaestinavereins
0173-1955 Von Deutschland Nach Amerika
0173-2110 Das Schaufenster (Stuttgart) *see* 0173-1882
0173-2153 Historisch Sozialwissenschaftliche Forschungen†
0173-2307 Arbeiten und Text zur Slavistik
0173-2323 G D S - Zeitung
0173-2358 Goettinger Orientforschungen. Reihe II: Studien zur Spaetantiken und Fruehchristlichen Kunst
0173-2404 Reiterjournal
0173-2412 Feuerverzinkent
0173-2471 Institut zur Erforschung der Europaeischen Arbeiterbewegung. Mitteilungsblatt
0173-2528 Sportpraxis
0173-2595 Z P A
0173-2803 Makromolekulare Chemie. Rapid Communications
0173-2986 Abstracts in German Anthropology
0173-3028 Rheinischer Merkur
0173-329X Wirtschaft am Bayerischen Untermain
0173-3524 Werkstattschriften zur Sozialpsychiatrie
0173-363X U - das Technische Umweltmagazin *see* 0341-1206
0173-3842 Materialien aus der Bildungsforschung
0173-430X Dr. Med. Mabuse
0173-4415 W S T Knitting Technik *see* 0177-4875
0173-458X Suizidprophylaxe
0173-4784 Kirche im Sozialismus *changed to* Uebergaenge.
0173-4911 Journal of Optical Communication
0173-4970 Film und Fernsehen in Forschung und Lehre
0173-5187 Forum Musikbibliothek
0173-5322 Journal fuer Mathematik-Didaktik
0173-5365 Bauhandwerk
0173-5373 Amphibia Reptilia
0173-539X G - Geschichte mit Pfiff
0173-5403 Arbeitshefte zur Sozialistischen Theorie und Praxis
0173-5500 Seifen, Oele, Fette, Wachse
0173-5543 Fraenkischer Hauskalender und Caritaskalender
0173-5896 Statistical Software Newsletter *see* 0167-9473
0173-606X Touristik R.E.P.O.R.T.
0173-6213 Logistik Heute
0173-6264 Luft- und Raumfahrt
0173-6280 D V W Hessen Mitteilungen
0173-6310 Silhouette
0173-6388 Bayerische Staatsbibliothek. New Contents Slavistics. Inhaltsverzeichnisse Slavistischer Zeitschriften - ISZ
0173-6469 Jahrbuch der Deutschdidaktik
0173-6507 Zahlentafeln der Physikalisch-Chemischen Untersuchungen des Rheinwassers
0173-6574 Beitraege zur Arbeitsmarkt- und Berufsforschung
0173-6582 Brasilien Nachrichten
0173-6612 I K
0173-6647 Klinische Chemie

ISSN INDEX 5629

0173-6973 Annales Universitatis Saraviensis. Medicinae
0173-7007 Weilheimer Heimatblaetter
0173-7074 Berliner Naturschutzblaetter
0173-7260 Deutsches Gewaesserkundliches Jahrbuch. Rheingebiet Teil 2: Main
0173-7481 Naturwissenschaftlicher Verein in Hamburg. Verhandlungen
0173-749X Naturwissenschaftlicher Verein in Hamburg. Abhandlungen und Verhandlungen *see* 0301-2697
0173-749X Naturwissenschaftlicher Verein in Hamburg. Abhandlungen und Verhandlungen *see* 0173-7481
0173-7597 Krankenhauspharmazie
0173-7600 Jahrbuch fuer Regionalwissenschaft
0173-783X Beitraege zur Tabakforschung International
0173-7872 Z S Magazin *changed to* Bevoelkerungsschutz-Magazin.
0173-7937 Psychotherapie - Psychosomatik - Medizinische Psychologie
0173-8046 A I T
0173-8062 Zeitschrift fuer Logistik
0173-8585 Bausteine Kindergarten
0173-8593 International Journal of Biological Research in Pregnancy *changed to* Biological Research in Pregnancy and Perinatology.
0173-8607 Piano-Jahrbuch
0173-8720 Umwelt und Energie
0173-8895 Muelheimer Statistik
0173-8925 Duisburg. Amt fuer Statistik und Stadtforschung. Statistischer Monatsbericht *changed to* Statistischer Monatsbericht.
0173-9387 Fusion
0173-9522 Zielsprache Russisch
0173-9565 Marine Ecology
0173-9573 Geistige Behinderung
0173-959X Redaktions Adress
0173-9832 Bio-land
0173-9913 Ceramic Forum International
0173-9980 Bulk Solids Handling
0174-0156 Rechtspfleger - Studienhefte
0174-0164 Deutsche Drogisten Zeitung
0174-0202 Zeitschrift fuer Rechtssoziologie
0174-0288 Allgemeine Zeitschrift fuer Parapsychologie *see* 0934-4535
0174-0350 Der Sonntagsbrief
0174-0431 Dresdener Bank - Economic Quarterly *changed to* Trends.
0174-0512 Bayerns Pferde Zucht und Sport
0174-0601 Literatur aus der Bildungsforschung *changed to* Literaturinformationen aus der Bildungsforschung.
0174-0652 Ural-Altaische Jahrbuecher. Neue Folge
0174-0830 Zeitschrift fuer Berufs- und Wirtschaftspaedagogik. Beihefte
0174-1004 Charadrius
0174-1098 Zeitschrift fuer Laermbekaempfung
0174-1144 Sporthandbuch Nordrhein-Westfalen
0174-1152 Sporthandbuch Niedersachsen
0174-1187 Handbuch des Sports in Hessen
0174-1195 Handbuch des Hamburger Sports
0174-1209 Handbuch des Berliner Sports
0174-1217 Handbuch des Bremer Sports
0174-1284 Hoppenstedt Kurstabellen - Kursanalysen
0174-1446 Recycling
0174-1551 Cardiovascular and Interventional Radiology
0174-1578 Journal of Comparative Physiology. B: Biochemical, Systematic, and Environmental Physiology
0174-173X Collagen and Related Research *see* 0934-8832
0174-1764 L W B Dokumentation. Report
0174-1837 Anaesthesie - Intensivtherapie - Notfallmedizin *see* 0939-2661
0174-1985 Baubedarf Manager *changed to* Baubedarf Einkaufen, Beraten, Verkaufen.
0174-2108 Informationsbrief Auslaenderrecht
0174-2116 Kirchenmusikalische Mitteilungen
0174-2132 Schreibheft
0174-2345 Schuetz-Jahrbuch
0174-2450 Colo-Proctology
0174-2477 Berliner Islamstudien
0174-2582 Kulleraugen - Materialsammlung
0174-2655 Blitz Magazin *changed to* Blitz-Terminal.
0174-2752 Klinische und Experimentelle Urologie
0174-2795 Zentralinstitut fuer Versuchstierzucht. Jahresbericht
0174-2809 Deutscher Studienkreis
0174-2876 Rheinland - Pfalz Heute
0174-2914 Rheinland-Pfalz. Statistisches Landesamt Rheinland-Pfalz. Statistische Monatshefte
0174-3015 Zentralblatt fuer Bakteriologie, Parasitenkunde, Infektionskrankenheiten und Hygiene. Series B: Krankenhaushygiene - Praeventive Medizin - Betriebshygiene *see* 0934-8859
0174-3031 Zentralblatt fuer Bakteriologie, Parasitenkunde, Infektionskrankheiten und Hygiene. Series A: Medizinische Mikrobiologie und Parasitologie *see* 0934-8840
0174-304X Neuropediatrics
0174-3058 Bauspar-Journal
0174-3082 Zeitschrift fuer Kinderchirurgie
0174-3120 W Z B - Mitteilungen
0174-3163 F L F
0174-3279 Airport Forum News
0174-335X HarvardManager
0174-3384 Braunschweiger Naturkundliche Schriften
0174-3465 Die Eule
0174-352X Kunstpreis-Jahrbuch
0174-3538 V T F-Post
0174-3597 Helgolaender Meeresuntersuchungen
0174-3805 Catalogue: English Translations of German Standards (Year)
0174-4224 Early Man News
0174-4631 Landkreises Birkenfeld. Heimatkalender
0174-4704 Human Rights Law Journal
0174-4747 Analysis
0174-478X Gesetzblatt fuer Baden-Wuerttemberg
0174-4879 International Journal of Clinical Pharmacology, Therapy and Toxicology
0174-4895 Schmerz (Heidelberg) *see* 0939-6365
0174-5336 D S B
0174-5395 Betriebspruefung
0174-5522 E I
0174-559X Transportrecht
0174-5603 Africana Marburgensia
0174-5735 Magazin fuer Heimwerker†
0174-5832 Stafette
0174-5980 Phillip Journal
0174-6146 Industrie Service
0174-6162 Der Verwaltungswirt
0174-6170 Wirtschaft und Erziehung
0174-6200 Basistexte Personalwesen
0174-6227 Fussballtraining
0174-6324 Lateinamerika Nachrichten
0174-6367 Moderne Medizin fuer die Praxis *see* 0931-5594
0174-6545 Epigraphica Anatolica
0174-6944 Instant
0174-7207 Melos
0174-7215 Industrie-Ausruestungs-Magazin
0174-7312 K E M - European Design Engineering
0174-7371 Trace Elements in Medicine
0174-738X Verdauungskrankheiten
0174-7398 Virchows Archiv. Section A: Pathological Anatomy and Histopathology
0174-786X Deutsche Waldenser
0174-8726 Alt-Offenbach
0175-0038 Neue Kunst in Europa *changed to* N I K E.
0175-0135 Dilthey-Jahrbuch
0175-0143 Pilot und Flugzeug
0175-0488 Zeitschrift fuer Entwicklungspaedagogik
0175-0992 Forschung Frankfurt
0175-1344 Segelsport
0175-2103 G A L - Bulletin
0175-2200 Fachdienst Germanistik
0175-2723 Beispiele
0175-274X Sicherheit und Frieden
0175-3053 Medizinische Kongresse
0175-3851 Intensivmedizin und Notfallmedizin
0175-4521 G S F Mensch und Umwelt
0175-4548 F & W - Fuehren und Wirtschaften im Krankenhaus
0175-4750 Micro *see* 0724-469X
0175-4815 Deutsches Polizeiblatt
0175-5021 Fossilien
0175-5161 K A B
0175-5293 Dokumentation Deutsche Finanzrechtsprechung
0175-5811 Aerzte Zeitung
0175-5838 Oekumene am Ort†
0175-5854 Behindertenzeitschrift *see* 0939-4702
0175-5889 Theaterpaedagogik
0175-5943 Beitraege zur Psychopathologie
0175-6206 Lexicographica
0175-6273 Aluminium-Kurier
0175-6281 European Truck & Trailer†
0175-6486 Wissenschaft und Gegenwart. Geisteswissenschaftliche Reihe
0175-6508 Philosophische Abhandlungen
0175-6524 Lansky: Bibliotheksrechtliche Vorschriften
0175-6532 Max-Planck-Institute fuer Europaische Rechtsgeschichte. Veroeffentlichungen. Ius Commune. Sonderhefte
0175-6559 Sozialwissenschaftliche Literatur Rundschau
0175-6575 F T B-Handel
0175-6796 Bibliotheken der Bundesrepublik Deutschland. Datierte Handschriften
0175-6877 DX Magazine
0175-6893 D B I - Pressespiegel
0175-7016 Hebraeische Beitraege zur Wissenschaft des Judentums
0175-7024 Israel und Palaestina
0175-7571 European Biophysics Journal
0175-758X European Archives of Psychiatry and Neurological Sciences
0175-7598 Applied Microbiology and Biotechnology
0175-7601 Das Logbuch
0175-761X Siebenbuergische Familienforschung
0175-7695 E M W - Informationen
0175-7784 Zeitschrift fuer Stomatologie
0175-7881 Allgemeine Homoeopathische Zeitung
0175-8152 Laurentius
0175-825X Badminton - Report
0175-8292 Vitis - Viticulture and Enology Abstracts
0175-8314 Alles Ueber Wein
0175-8659 Journal of Applied Ichthyology
0175-9191 Allensbacher Jahrbuch der Demoskopie
0175-9302 Universitaet Kiel. Geologisch-Palaeontologisches Institut. Berichte - Reports
0175-9485 Wir Selbst
0175-9531 Das Auto-International-in Zahlen
0175-9698 Markt fuer Klassische Automobile und Motorraeder
0175-9809 Mensch Guten Willens†
0176-036X Uni Ulm Intern
0176-0599 Deutsche Tennis Zeitung
0176-0629 Carolo-Wilhelmina Mitteilungen
0176-0750 P D S
0176-0882 Tennis Aktuell
0176-0947 Sozialistische Praxis
0176-0971 Zupfmusik Magazin
0176-1110 Filmfaust
0176-1188 Die Schaubuehne
0176-1196 Volkskunde in Niedersachsen
0176-1285 Lapis
0176-148X Geologie und Palaeontologie in Westfalen
0176-1617 Journal of Plant Physiology
0176-1625 Gummi, Asbest, Kunstoffe *changed to* Gummi, Fasern, Kunststoffe.
0176-1633 Fernerkundung in Raumordung und Stadtebau
0176-1714 Social Choice and Welfare
0176-1749 Lung and Respiration
0176-1897 Arzthelferin Aktuell
0176-1900 Goldmann-Nachrichten
0176-2044 E P D Film
0176-2257 Die Schachwoche
0176-2265 Particle Characterization *see* 0934-0866
0176-232X Forum Buero Wirtschaft
0176-2397 Bibliothek fuer Alle
0176-2400 Computer-Schach und -Spiele
0176-246X Kontakt (Esslingen am Neckar)
0176-2494 Bio Garten†
0176-263X Forschung Aktuell
0176-2656 Sekundaer-Rohstoffe
0176-2680 European Journal of Political Economy
0176-2710 Ministranten Post†
0176-2753 Fundevogel
0176-2982 Paten
0176-3008 Spiegel der Forschung
0176-3148 Gypsy
0176-3156 Videofilmen
0176-3261 P K V Publik
0176-3288 Datacom
0176-3296 Mikrofauna Marina
0176-3539 Maueranker
0176-358X TransportMarkt
0176-3660 T I
0176-3679 Pharmacopsychiatry
0176-3687 Das Forum (Munich)
0176-3717 Arbeiten und Lernen *changed to* Arbeiten & Lernen: Technik und Wirtschaft.
0176-3814 Neue Zeitschrift fuer Arbeits- und Sozialrecht
0176-3849 Medien-Kritik
0176-3946 Soester Zeitschrift
0176-3997 Carolinea
0176-4225 Diachronica
0176-4241 Medienwissenschaft
0176-4268 Journal of Classification
0176-4276 Constructive Approximation
0176-4594 Spektrum Film†
0176-4624 Scouting
0176-473X Kehrwieder
0176-4853 Katzen Extra
0176-490X Pferde Heute
0176-4985 B T F - Biotech Forum *see* 0938-7501
0176-5035 Lecture Notes in Engineering
0176-5116 Mediatus
0176-5124 Milch-Marketing
0176-5183 Nierenpatient
0176-5248 Presse-Portraets
0176-5388 Abenteuer & Reisen
0176-540X Exporama
0176-5493 Katholischer Arbeitskreis fuer Zeitgeschichtliche Fragen. Informationsdienst.
0176-5833 Memo-Forum
0176-6023 Nassauer Gespraeche der Freiherr-vom-Stein-Gesellschaft
0176-604X Neue Politische Literatur. Beihefte.
0176-6058 Werkstoffe - Betriebsleitung Technik *changed to* Werkstoffe - in der Fertigung.
0176-6449 Zentralblatt fuer Jugendrecht
0176-6511 Tibia
0176-6619 Neue Medien
0176-7437 Handarbeiten und Hauswirtschaft *changed to* H T W Praxis.
0176-7615 Modern Synthetic Methods
0176-7739 D L R - Mitteilungen
0176-7771 Finanz-Rundschau Ausgabe A
0176-778X Finanz-Rundschau Ausgabe B
0176-781X Dokumentationsdienst Bibliothekswesen
0176-7836 Blind - Sehbehindert
0176-7879 Etudes de Phonologie, Phonetique et Linguistique Descriptive du Francais
0176-8018 Equine Abstracts†
0176-8123 Hydronymia Europaea
0176-8204 Menschenskinder
0176-8220 Buchreport
0176-8522 Archaeologie in Deutschland
0176-8530 Atelier
0176-8565 Image
0176-8573 Botschaft Heute

ISSN

ISSN INDEX

ISSN	Title
0176-8581	Gottesdienste mit Kindern und Jugendlichen *changed to* Familien und Jugend - Gottesdienste.
0176-859X	Ideen Archiv
0176-862X	Sonntagsdienste
0176-8654	UNIX - Mail
0176-8700	Betrifft Sport
0176-8751	Deutsch - Finnische Rundschau
0176-8816	Besseres Leben
0176-9146	Familienpolitische Informationen
0176-9243	Heim and Anstalt
0176-9251	Allensbacher Berichte
0176-9324	Beruf und Leben
0176-9340	Advances in Soil Sciences
0176-9375	Structured Language World *see* 0935-1183
0176-9391	Sauria
0176-943X	Geschichte Betrifft Uns
0176-9448	Politik Betrifft Uns
0176-9502	Fleischerei-Technik
0176-9707	Journalisten Jahrbuch
0176-9723	Wildhaltung
0176-9855	Zeitschrift fuer Transaktionsanalyse in Theorie und Praxis
0177-011X	Freundeskreis Blaetter
0177-0608	K: Plastic und Kautschuk Zeitung
0177-0667	Engineering with Computers
0177-0942	Video Gesamtkatalog B V V
0177-0950	Muenchner Geowissenschaftliche Abhandlungen. Reihe A: Geologie und Palaeontologie
0177-0969	Sahara Info
0177-1116	Schiffsbetriebstechnik Flensburg
0177-1361	Trafik
0177-1426	Materialien aus der Arbeitsmarkt- und Berufsforschung
0177-1469	C P & T
0177-1531	Du Darfst†
0177-1612	Bonsai-Magazin *changed to* Bonsai - das Spezial Magazin.
0177-1647	Middle Eastern Culture Center, Japan. Bulletin
0177-1817	Gruss aus der Weltweiten Brueder-Unitaet - Daheim und Draussen
0177-185X	Evangelischer Digest
0177-1965	Zivildienst
0177-2074	Literatur im Historischen Prozess (Neue Folge)†
0177-2309	Der Notarzt
0177-2392	Tropical Medicine and Parasitology
0177-2538	Der Heimatpfleger
0177-2872	Katholischer Digest
0177-2899	Heimatstimmen aus dem Kreis Olpe
0177-2945	High Quality
0177-2953	Reisen in Deutschland: Reisefuehrer Volume 2 *changed to* Reisen in Deutschland: Zimmerkatalog.
0177-2961	
0177-3100	Zentralblatt fuer Bakteriologie, Mikrobiologie und Hygiene. Abstracts
0177-3348	Fortschritte der Zahnaerztliche Implantologie *changed to* Zeitschrift fuer Zahnaerztliche Implantologie.
0177-350X	Musikpsychologie
0177-3518	Der Wirtschaftsredakteur
0177-3542	Alpin-Magazin
0177-3747	Deutsche Gesellschaft fuer Unfallheilkunde. Mitteilungen und Nachrichten
0177-3836	Zentraler Bewerberanzeiger Markt und Chance
0177-3941	Gourmed
0177-4042	Frauen und Schule†
0177-4050	Reisefieber
0177-4093	Jahrbuch fuer Vergleichende Sozialforschung
0177-4182	Musiktheorie
0177-4247	Jugendbuchmagazin
0177-4476	Neuland Ansaetze zur Musik der Gegenwart†
0177-4492	Schoenere Heimat
0177-4557	Eurokunst Magazin Reisen *changed to* Eurokunst: Besser Reisen & Mehr Erleben.
0177-4565	K E S
0177-4573	Polizei Info Polizeiforum
0177-4603	Computer Katalog
0177-462X	Evangelium-Gospel
0177-4743	Turcologica
0177-4832	Steel Research - Archiv fuer das Eisenhuettenwesen
0177-4840	Archaelogica Venatoria. Mitteilungsblatt
0177-4859	Baltisches Jahrbuch
0177-4875	Knitting Technique
0177-4891	Wege... *changed to* Wege Magazin.
0177-4913	Station to Station
0177-5006	T A S P O
0177-5014	T A S P O - Magazin
0177-5103	Diseases of Aquatic Organisms
0177-5251	W I K
0177-526X	Migration und Ethnizitaet *changed to* Bibliographische Informationen zu Migration und Ethnizitaet.
0177-5332	Materialy Samizdata
0177-5375	Bayerischer Waldbesitzerverband
0177-5499	Net
0177-5529	Jahrbuch Schienenverkehr†
0177-5537	Der Unfallchirurg
0177-5928	W L A Selecta
0177-6126	T A S P O Gartenkurier
0177-6185	Spektrum des Geistes
0177-6487	Wuerttembergische Blaetter fuer Kirchenmusik
0177-6657	I N P R E K O R R
0177-6673	Technische Universitaet Berlin. Institut fuer Sozialoekonomie der Agrarentwicklung. Schriftenreihe des Fachbereichs
0177-672X	Magazin 2000
0177-6738	Die Neue Gesellschaft - Frankfurter Hefte
0177-6894	D F N Mitteilungen
0177-7114	Woodworking International
0177-7173	Marktforschungsreport
0177-7238	Berufliche Eingliederung Behinderter
0177-7351	Frankfurter Statistische Berichte
0177-7459	Konstruktion & Elektronik
0177-7483	Dent - Tax
0177-7491	Maerkte im Saarland
0177-7513	V H F Communications
0177-7726	Pferdeheilkunde
0177-7955	Neuro-Orthopedics
0177-7963	Few-Body Systems. Acta Physica Austriaca. New Series
0177-7971	Meteorology and Atmospheric Physics
0177-798X	Theoretical and Applied Climatology
0177-8005	Theosophie Heute
0177-8285	Bulldok Bauschaeden
0177-8358	Arbeitsgemeinschaft Katholisch-Theologischer Bibliotheken. Mitteilungsblatt
0177-8374	Praxis der Naturwissenschaften. Physik
0177-8390	Live
0177-8617	Heilpraxis - Magazin
0177-8706	Evangelikale Missiologie
0177-8722	Intern
0177-8978	Zentralinstitut fuer Kunstgeschichte. Jahrbuch
0177-9095	Jatros Paediatrie
0177-9109	Jatros Gynaekologie
0177-9249	Kabel & Satellit
0177-9265	Agora
0177-9303	Entscheidungen zum Wirtschaftsrecht - E W I R
0177-9419	Zeitungs - Dokumentation Bildungswesen
0177-9540	Contrapunct†
0177-9591	Apotheke und Krankenhaus
0177-963X	Auszuege aus den Europaeischen Patentanmeldungen. Teil 2. Elektrotechnik, Physik, Feinmechanik und Optik, Akustik
0177-9648	Auszuege aus den Europaeischen Patentanmeldungen. Teil 3. Uebrige Verarbeitungsindustrie und Arbeitsverfahren, Maschinen- und Fahrzeugbau, Ernaehrung, Landwirtschaft
0177-9656	Steuer Seminar
0177-9664	Steuer-Lexikon Teil II
0177-9761	V K G - Nachrichten†
0177-9788	Wettbewerbe *changed to* Wettbewerbe Aktuell.
0177-9796	Guss Produkte†
0178-000X	Bateria
0178-0026	Robotersysteme
0178-0166	Kraut und Rueben
0178-0182	Sueddeutsche Eisen- und Stahl-Berufsgenossenschaft. Mitteilungen
0178-0239	Vogelkundliche Hefte Edertal
0178-0409	Fliegenfischen
0178-0417	Deutsch - Betrifft Uns
0178-0522	Myositis
0178-0727	Trend Aktuell
0178-1014	Sport Inform
0178-1073	Ariadne
0178-1421	Gruenstift (Berlin)
0178-1448	Betriebsecho†
0178-1510	Baustoff, Recycling und Deponietechnik
0178-1529	M I S - Motor Im Schnee
0178-1677	Wandermagazin
0178-1715	O P Journal
0178-1723	Beitraege zur Phonetik und Linguistik
0178-1766	Softwarefuehrer fuer Personal-Computer
0178-1928	Meerestechnik *changed to* Meerestechnik.
0178-1944	Praxis Sonderschule†
0178-2010	R F L - Rundschau Fleischhyiene und Lebensmittelueberwachung
0178-2029	Bio-Engineering
0178-2177	Schottische Terrier Gazette
0178-2312	Automatisierungstechnik
0178-2320	Automatisierungstechnische Praxis
0178-2436	Bahnengolfer
0178-2495	German Maritime Industry Journal
0178-2509	Wohnbaden
0178-2525	Rettungsdienst
0178-269X	C Q - D L
0178-2762	Biology and Fertility of Soils
0178-2770	Distributed Computing
0178-2789	Visual Computer
0178-2835	Siebdruck
0178-2983	Handball Magazin
0178-3351	Deguo Yixue
0178-3556	Manipulator
0178-3564	Informatik - Forschung und Entwicklung
0178-4099	Transfer
0178-4218	Museen der Stadt Koeln. Bulletin *see* 0933-257X
0178-4226	Niedersaechsischer Staedtetag
0178-4250	Auszuege aus den Patentschriften
0178-4536	Hoergeraete-Akustiker *see* 0933-1980
0178-4617	Algorithmica
0178-4625	Deutsche Gesellschaft fuer Urologie. Mitteilungen
0178-4757	Johannes Gutenberg-Universitaet Mainz. Forschungsmagazin
0178-4811	Auto and Service†
0178-501X	Die Fuehrungskraft
0178-5052	In Leder
0178-5109	Grauer Panther
0178-515X	Bioprocess Engineering
0178-5214	Der Feuerwehrmann
0178-5338	Ruprecht Karls Universitaet Heidelberg. Personal- und Informationsverzeichnis
0178-5516	Muenchens Feine Adressen
0178-5540	Koeln - Bonns Feine Adressen
0178-5745	Greenpeace Nachrichten *see* 0939-3234
0178-5893	Verkaufsleiter Service
0178-594X	K M I Buerowirtschaft - Lehre und Praxis
0178-6083	Wir Frauen
0178-6156	HiFi Vision
0178-6199	Allgaeuer Geschichtsfreund
0178-644X	Sprachreport
0178-6563	Forum Wissenschaft
0178-658X	Agenturen und Marken
0178-6768	Wissenschaften in der D.D.R.†
0178-6849	Sheet Metal Tubes Sections†
0178-6857	Literatur in Bayern
0178-692X	Schmerzdiagnostik und Therapie
0178-7128	Aufklaerung
0178-7241	Buchjournal
0178-7276	Deutsche Zeitschrift fuer Biologische Zahnmedizin
0178-7438	China-Handel†
0178-7470	Arterien und Venen *changed to* Cerebro.
0178-7527	Jatros Urologie
0178-7535	Jatros Neurologie - Psychiatrie
0178-7578	Kurzberichte aus der Bauforschung
0178-7608	Oeko-Test Magazin
0178-7624	Orthomolekular
0178-7659	Elemente
0178-7667	Forum der Psychoanalyse
0178-7675	Computational Mechanics
0178-7683	Zeitschrift fuer Physik. Section D: Atoms, Molecules and Clusters
0178-7691	Krisis
0178-7764	Internationales Sauna - Archiv
0178-7810	Geographie Aktuell
0178-787X	Neue Aerztliche†
0178-7888	Mycotoxin Research
0178-8051	Probability Theory and Related Fields
0178-8310	Studien zur Modernen Geschichte
0178-837X	Der Staudengarten
0178-8574	B G W Mitteilungsblatt *see* 0937-0811
0178-8728	Cogito
0178-8876	Aussenwirtschaftsbrief
0178-8884	MusikTexte
0178-8906	Kirchlicher Dienst in der Arbeitswelt
0178-8930	Recht der Datenverarbeitung
0178-8965	Deutscher Forschungsdienst Magazin
0178-9090	Infektionen und Klinikhygiene
0178-9104	Der Vegetarier
0178-9279	Basketball
0178-9287	International Listening Guide
0178-9562	Fortschritt-Berichte V D I. Reihe 13: Foerdertechnik
0178-9945	Swingtrend
0178-9953	Der Punkt†
0178-9988	Buskursbuch
0179-0102	Missionsblaetter
0179-0153	T U S Info
0179-0161	Steuer Aktuell
0179-017X	D N R - Kurier
0179-0315	Beto
0179-0358	Pediatric Surgery International
0179-0374	Applied Agricultural Research
0179-0404	Medizin Heute
0179-0463	Informatik und Recht†
0179-051X	Dysphagia
0179-0811	V D I - V D E Dokumentation Regelungstechnik *changed to* V D I. Informationsdienst Regelungstechnik.
0179-1028	Construction Machinery and Building Supplies
0179-1133	Praxis Computer
0179-1419	Berg (Year)
0179-1591	Schloss & Beschlag & Markt
0179-1613	Ethology
0179-1621	Mediterranean Language and Culture Monograph Series
0179-163X	Erinnyen
0179-1796	Fertilitaet, Sterilitaet, In-Vitro Fertilisation, Sexualitaet, Kontrazeption
0179-1826	Medical Corps International
0179-1842	Ludwigsburger Geschichtsblaetter
0179-1869	Hoeruebersicht International
0179-1958	International Journal of Colorectal Disease
0179-1990	Computer und Recht
0179-2415	Fleischwirtschaft International
0179-2466	Brauerei-Forum
0179-261X	Monumenta Serica Monograph Series
0179-2636	Przeglad Tygodnia
0179-2679	C I M Management
0179-2776	Betrifft Justiz
0179-2830	Kritische Vierteljahresschrift fuer Gesetzgebung und Rechtswissenschaft
0179-2857	Bausubstanz
0179-2938	Rechtsrheinisches Koeln
0179-3004	Wie Geht's Heute?
0179-3063	That's Yugoslavia
0179-3071	Ost-Dienst
0179-3187	Erdoel - Erdgas - Kohle
0179-3233	Deutsche Dialektgeographie

ISSN INDEX 5631

0179-342X Heart & Circulation
0179-3462 I W L - Umweltbrief
0179-3551 Glaube und Lernen
0179-356X Musica Sacra
0179-3683 Muenzen- und Medaillensammler Berichte
0179-3780 Colloquium Helveticum
0179-3799 Mindener Klinikschriften
0179-387X Die Alten Sprachen im Unterricht
0179-3896 Studia Spinozana
0179-3934 Europa-Rochade
0179-4043 N J W - Rechtsprechungs-Report Zivilrecht
0179-4051 Zeitschrift fuer Gesetzgebung
0179-4078 Auto Aktuell
0179-4639 Zeitschrift fuer Geschichte der Arabisch-Islamischen Wissenschaften
0179-4744 L U Journal
0179-4922 Ambacher Schriften
0179-499X Materialwirtschaft im Unternehmen *see* 0937-4183
0179-5295 Biologische Zeitschrift
0179-5341 Tools and Hardware†
0179-5376 Discrete and Computational Geometry
0179-5627 Raumfahrt Wirtschaft
0179-5775 I P N - Blaetter
0179-5813 Ornithologischer Verein zu Hildesheim. Mitteilungen
0179-5961 Kroatische Berichte
0179-5988 Druck
0179-6089 A D A C Campingfuehrer. Band 1: Suedeuropa
0179-6100 Westen
0179-6356 Forschungsstelle Ostmitteleuropa an der Universitaet Dortmund. Studien
0179-6429 Schreisset†
0179-647X Art Aurea
0179-6607 Fh-Bo-Journal
0179-6658 Zur Debatte
0179-6755 Universitaet Goettingen. Veroeffentlichungen des Seminars fuer Indologie
0179-6844 Textcontext
0179-714X Deutsche Zeitschrift fuer Biologische Veterinaermedizin *changed to* Zeitschrift fuer Ganzheitliche Tiermedizin.
0179-7158 Strahlentherapie und Onkologie
0179-7166 Cardiologisch-Angiologisches Bulletin†
0179-7182 Uni Report
0179-7298 Praktika
0179-7360 Prima Vita
0179-7379 C A K†
0179-7417 Listen
0179-745X Wohnungswirtschaft
0179-7514 Universitaetsfuehrer
0179-7565 Indiviualitaet†
0179-7581 Hufeland - Journal
0179-7603 Agrarsoziale Gesellschaft. Laendlicher Raum Rundbriefe
0179-7743 Binnenschiffahrts-Nachrichten
0179-7824 Amtsblatt der Deutschen Bundesbahn
0179-7883 Mobilitaet und Normenwandel
0179-7948 W I - Wohnungswirtschaftliche Informationen
0179-7999 Adventecho
0179-8170 Oboe - Klarinette - Fagott
0179-8596 Mein Erlebnis
0179-8669 Theoretical Surgery
0179-8715 K S B Technische Berichte
0179-8790 Heimatgemeinschaft Eckernfoerde. Jahrbuch
0179-8863 Informationen zum Arbeitslosenrecht und Sozialhilferecht *
0179-9088 Uni Journal
0179-9401 Paedagogik Heute *changed to* Paedagogik Heute - Paedagogische Beitraege.
0179-9541 Plant Breeding
0179-9592 Sensor Report
0179-9711 Palette
0179-9738 Informationstechnik - I T
0179-9932 Energie Spektrum
0179-9959 Oekumenischer Informationsdienst
0180-0817 Urgence
0180-2410 Federation Nationale des Foyers Ruraux de France. Bulletin d'Information *changed to* Animer.
0180-3344 Palais de la Decouverte. Revue
0180-3573 Depeche Veterinaire
0180-3905 Demeures et Chateaux en France *see* 0291-1191
0180-4103 Notes Bibliographiques Caraibes
0180-4561 Maisons & Decors Mediterranee
0180-5738 Chirurgie Pediatrique *see* 0939-7248
0180-6734 Combustibles et Carburants
0180-7307 Revue d'Economie Regionale et Urbaine
0180-7811 Liaisons Transports Equipement
0180-7897 Europ
0180-8214 Commentaire
0180-8567 Amitie Charles Peguy. Bulletin d'Informations et de Recherches
0180-9105 Bloc-Notes de l'Observatoire Economique de Paris
0180-9210 Bulletin de Mineralogie *see* 0935-1221
0180-9237 Plastiques Flash
0180-9261 Cahiers du Memontois
0180-9296 Bulletin Signaletique. Part 527: Histoire et Sciences des Religions
0180-930X Annales de la Recherche Urbaine
0180-9350 Andre Gide
0180-9385 Arthur Rimbaud
0180-9555 Documents Pedozoologiques
0180-961X Parc National de La Vanoise. Travaux Scientifiques
0180-9741 Education Menagere†
0180-9822 Voies†
0180-9849 Revue de Droit Immobilier
0180-989X Annuaire des Marees pour l'An. Tome 1. Ports de France
0180-9938 Avis aux Navigateurs
0180-9954 Cahiers de l'Indo-Pacifique†
0180-9962 Annuaire des Marees pour l'An. Tome 2. Ports d'Outre Mer
0180-9970 Recueil des Corrections de Cartes (Year)
0180-9989 Bulletin Signaletique. Part 361: Reproduction. Embryologie. Endocrinologie *see* 0761-1919
0181-0006 Bulletin Signaletique. Part 364: Protozoaires et des Invertebres. Zoologie Generale et Appliquee *see* 0761-1714
0181-0014 Bulletin Signaletique. Part 365: Zoologie des Vertebres. Ecologie Animale. Physiologie Appliquee Humaine *see* 0761-1900
0181-0014 Zoologie des Vertebres. Ecologie Animale. Physiologie Appliquee Humaine *see* 0246-1153
0181-0030 Bulletin Signaletique. Part 380: Produits Alimentaires†
0181-0146 Promethee
0181-0197 Archistra: Archives - Histoire - Traditions
0181-0626 Museum National d'Histoire Naturelle. Bulletin - Section A (Zoologie et Ecologie Animales)
0181-0642 Museum National d'Histoire Naturelle. Bulletin - Section C (Sciences de la Terre: Paleontologie, Geologie, Mineralogie)
0181-0804 France. Caisse Nationale des Allocations Familiales. Statistiques Action Sociale
0181-0839 Cahiers Geographiques de Rouen
0181-110X Informatique et Sciences Juridiques
0181-1223 Lettre d'Information Metaux
0181-1304 Universite Rene Descartes. Bulletin†
0181-1347 Alpes - Region†
0181-1525 Musee National d'Art Moderne. Cahiers
0181-1568 Cryptogamie: Algologie
0181-1576 Cryptogamie: Bryologie et Lichenologie
0181-1584 Cryptogamie: Mycologie
0181-1789 Actualites Botaniques
0181-1797 Lettres Botaniques
0181-1835 Artus
0181-1878 Le Rail et le Monde *changed to* Le Rail.
0181-1894 Bulletin Signaletique. Part 525: Prehistoire et Protohistoire
0181-1916 Reproduction, Nutrition, Development
0181-2874 Action Juridique (Paris, 1978)
0181-3048 Connaissance des Temps
0181-4087 Peuples Noirs, Peuples Africains
0181-4095 Langage et Societe
0181-4141 Filmechange
0181-513X Dossiers de l'Etudiant *see* 0766-6330
0181-5210 Paris Voices
0181-5334 Systeme d'Information sur les Transports de Marchandises: Resultats Generaux, Trafic Interieur et International
0181-5512 Journal Francais d'Ophtalmologie
0181-561X Universite de Haute Bretagne. Centre d'Etudes Irlandaises. Cahier†
0181-687X 4 Taxis
0181-7450 Elektor - Electronique
0181-7582 Revue de Cytologie et de Biologie Vegetales - Le Botaniste
0181-7671 Centre Protestant d'Etudes et de Documentation. Bulletin
0181-8120 Entretien des Textiles
0181-9224 Champion d'Afrique
0181-9445 Intellect
0181-9801 Feuillets de Radiologie
0181-995X Agriculture et Cooperation
0182-0176 Moyen-Orient Selection *changed to* Marches Arabes.
0182-0230 Argus de la Miniature
0182-0346 Grands Reportages
0182-0745 Oceanis
0182-1377 Medecine et Troisieme Age *changed to* Practiciens et 3eme Age.
0182-1598 France. Caisse Nationale des Allocations Familiales. Statistiques Prestations Familiales. Resultats Generaux: Recettes, Depenses, Beneficiaires
0182-1717 Faire Part
0182-2322 Afrique Defense†
0182-2411 Histoire
0182-2705 Cahiers de l'Avenir de la Bretagne
0182-3329 Batiment International, Building Research and Practice *see* 0961-3218
0182-4295 Fondation Louis de Broglie. Annales
0182-564X Chronique de la Recherche Miniere
0182-5887 Verbum
0182-7103 Philosophie (Toulouse) *see* 1148-9227
0182-8843 C.T.N.E.R.H.I. Etudes†
0183-0139 Van et le Camping-Car *changed to* Camping-Car.
0183-3189 Pour la Danse
0183-3634 Philatelie Francaise
0183-3898 Tout le Tricot - Le Crochet et le Tricot d'Art *changed to* Crochet d'Art.
0183-3901 Tout le Tricot
0183-391X Tout le Tricot - Ouvrages au Crochet *changed to* Ouvrages au Crochet.
0183-3928 Tout le Tricot - Tricot d'Art
0183-3944 Toute la Broderie - Point de Croix
0183-4037 Chambre de Commerce et d'Industrie d'Auxerre. Documentation Economique
0183-4150 Dossiers Histoire de la Mer
0183-455X Stores et Fermetures
0183-4568 Generaliste
0183-4738 Tous les Ouvrages - Toute la Broderie
0183-5173 Journal d'Agriculture Traditionnelle et de Botanique Appliquee†
0183-5688 Societe de Biometrie Humaine. Revue *see* 0758-2714
0183-6242 Centre Genealogique de l'Ouest. Revue Trimestrielle
0183-7516 Officiel de l'Equipement Menager *see* 0399-8290
0183-7591 Etudes sur Pezenas et l'Herault *see* 0249-1664
0183-8490 Cartes Postales et Collections
0183-8636 Revue Francaise des Telecommunications *changed to* France Telecom.
0183-9187 Revue de Nematologie *changed to* Fundamental and Applied Nematology.
0183-973X Etudes Irlandaises
0184-0584 Journal du Travail Temporaire et des Services
0184-0932 Cahiers de Combat pour la Paix
0184-3540 A S S U (Association du Sport Scolaire et Universitaire) *see* 0221-0142
0184-5055 Annee Bateaux Magazine *changed to* Mer & Bateaux.
0184-6469 France. Caisse Nationale des Allocations Familiales. Statistiques Prestations de Logement
0184-6531 C L E I R P P A Annees - Documents
0184-6892 France. Ministere de l'Urbanisme et du Logement. Statistiques et Etudes Generales
0184-6949 Annee Philologique
0184-7473 Combat Nature
0184-7589 Geographie et Recherche
0184-7678 Cahiers Elisabethains
0184-7783 Population et Societes
0184-8100 Jalons
0184-8895 Banc-Titre - Animation Stand†
0184-9662 Agri-Afrique†
0184-9670 Afrique Informations *changed to* Marches Africains.
0184-9697 Equip-Afric†
0184-9719 Banque Afrique
0185-0008 Ciencia y Desarrollo
0185-0059 Boletin I I E
0185-0067 Universidad Nacional Autonoma de Mexico. Instituto de Investigaciones Bibliografica. Instrumenta Bibliographica
0185-0083 Bibliotecas y Archivos†
0185-0113 Dialogos†
0185-0121 Nueva Revista de Filologia Hispanica
0185-013X Foro Internacional
0185-0148 Demografia y Economia†
0185-0164 Estudios de Asia y Africa
0185-0172 Historia Mexicana
0185-0261 Informacion Cientifica y Tecnologica
0185-027X Cuadernos Politicos†
0185-0288 Agrociencia
0185-0326 Biotica†
0185-0369 I N I R E B Informa *changed to* Instituto de Ecologia. Informa.
0185-0431 Palabra y el Hombre
0185-0547 Educacion
0185-058X Mexico Indigena
0185-0601 Comercio Exterior
0185-061X Cuadernos de Marcha
0185-0644 Universidad Nacional Autonoma de Mexico. Instituto de Matematicas. Anales
0185-0679 Gaceta Informativa *changed to* Gaceta Informativa I N E G I.
0185-075X Ciencia
0185-0814 Relaciones Internacionales
0185-0830 Universidad Veracruzana. Centro de Investigaciones Linguistico-Literarias. Texto-Critico
0185-0903 C L A S E. Citas Latinoamericanas en Sociologia, Economia, y Humanidades *changed to* C L A S E.
0185-0962 Universidad Nacional Autonoma de Mexico. Instituto de Geologia. Revista
0185-0970 Enfermera al Dia
0185-0997 Instituto Politecnico Nacional. Escuela Nacional de Ciencias Biologicas. Boletin Bibliografico
0185-1004 Periodica. Indice de Revistas Latinoamericanas en Ciencias
0185-1012 Revista Mexicana de Anestesiologia
0185-1101 Revista Mexicana de Astronomia y Astrofisica
0185-1136 Monetaria
0185-125X K I N A M†
0185-1268 Mercado de Valores
0185-1276 Universidad Nacional Autonoma de Mexico. Instituto de Investigaciones Esteticas. Anales
0185-1284 Revista Latinoamericana de Estudios Educativos

ISSN

5632 ISSN INDEX

0185-1322 Universidad Nacional Autonoma de Mexico. Anuario de Geografia
0185-1357 Naturaleza†
0185-156X Cuadernos Americanos
0185-1578 Bibliografia Historica Mexicana
0185-1594 Ensenanza e Investigacion en Psicologia
0185-1616 Estudios Politicos
0185-1659 Cuicuilco
0185-1691 Cuadernos de Historia del Arte
0185-1799 Universidad Nacional Autonoma de Mexico. Instituto de Investigaciones Esteticas. Monografias de Arte
0185-1896 Cuadernos de Musica
0185-1918 Revista Mexicana de Ciencias Politicas y Sociales
0185-1926 Mexico. Archivo General de la Nacion. Boletin†
0185-1934 Compendium de Investigaciones Clinicas Latinoamericanas†
0185-1977 Universidad Nacional Autonoma de Mexico. Instituto de Geografia. Boletin *changed to* Investigaciones Geograficas.
0185-1985 Decision
0185-2027 Boletin Bibliografico Mexicano
0185-2248 Nuestra America
0185-2310 Instituto Nacional de Investigaciones Forestales. Boletin Tecnico
0185-2361 Instituto Nacional de Investigaciones Forestales. Boletin Divulgativo
0185-2418 Instituto Nacional de Investigaciones Forestales. Ciencia Forestal
0185-2426 Caribe Contemporaneo
0185-2477 Cuento
0185-2493 C N I D A Informa
0185-2523 Estudios de Historia Novohispana
0185-2558 Universidad Nacional Autonoma de Mexico. Instituto de Investigaciones Filosoficas. Cuadernos
0185-2566 Instituto Nacional de Investigaciones Forestales. Publicacion Especial
0185-2604 Cuadernos de Critica (Mexico)
0185-2698 Perfiles Educativos
0185-2876 Historia Obrera†
0185-2884 Bibliografia Latinoamericana: Part I
0185-2930 Bibliografia Latinoamericana: Part II
0185-3082 Acta Poetica
0185-3198 Asociacion Latinoamericana de Psicologia Social. Revista†
0185-3295 Anuario Juridico
0185-3309 Revista Mexicana de Fitopatologia
0185-3325 Salud Mental
0185-3481 Revista de Filosofia
0185-3597 Docencia Postsecundaria
0185-3619 Sociedad Botanica de Mexico. Boletin
0185-3929 Relaciones
0185-4003 Sociedad Mexicana de Mecanica de Suelos. Boletin
0185-4011 Nabor Carrillo Lecture Series. Proceedings
0185-402X Mexican Society for Soil Mechanics Meeting. Proceedings
0185-4038 Dermatologia
0185-4143 Universitarios
0185-4186 Estudios Sociologicos
0185-4399 Informet†
0185-4445 Instituto Nacional de Investigaciones Forestales. Catalogo
0185-4534 Revista Mexicana de Analisis de la Conducta
0185-4925 Plural
0185-4968 Nacional Financiera. Annual Report
0185-5093 Quipu
0185-5107 Sociedad Latinoamericana de Historia de las Ciencias y la Tecnologia. Boletin Informativo
0185-6235 Atencion Medica
0185-6278 Indian News from the Americas
0185-6286 T R A C E
0185-6588 Perfumeria Moderna
0185-8114 Comunidad Informatica
0186-0437 Catalogo (Year) Productos del I N E G I
0186-0445 Cuaderno de Informacion Oportuna
0186-0453 Agenda Estadistica
0186-0461 Boletin de Politica Informatica
0186-047X Cuaderno de Informacion Oportuna Regional
0186-0496 Estadisticas del Comercio Exterior de Mexico. Informacion Preliminar
0186-050X Sector Electrico en Mexico
0186-1166 Muebletecnic†
0186-2243 Libros de Mexico
0186-2707 Mexico. Instituto Nacional de Estadistica, Geografia e Informatica. Revista de Estadistica
0186-2715 Revista de Geografia
0186-3266 Instituto Mexicano del Petroleo. Boletin Informativo†
0186-3401 Pemex. Boletin Bibliografico
0186-4076 Ingenieria Hidraulica en Mexico
0186-5609 Management Today
0186-5730 Tiempos de Ciencia
0186-5757 El Correo Fronterizo
0186-6486 Empresa Publica
0186-7067 Infame Turba
0186-7180 Universidad Autonoma de Yucatan. Revista
0186-7210 Estudios Demograficos y Urbanos
0186-7229 Centro de Estudios Monetarios Latinoamericanos. Boletin Bimensual
0186-9027 Boletin de Informacion Oportuna del Sector Alimentario
0187-0203 Universidad Nacional Autonoma de Mexico. Instituto de Investigaciones Juridicas. Cuadernos
0187-3180 Revista Mexicana de Micologia
0187-358X Investigacion Bibliotecologica
0187-4519 Revista Mexicana de Oftalmologia
0187-4780 Universidad Nacional Autonoma de Mexico. Instituto de Matematicas. Monografias
0187-4853 Finanzas Publicas Estatales y Municipales de Mexico
0187-487X Industria Petrolera en Mexico
0187-4888 Industria Quimica en Mexico
0187-4942 Avance de Informacion Economica. Balanza Comercial
0187-4950 Avance de Informacion Economica. Industria de la Construccion
0187-4969 Avance de Informacion Economica. Empleo
0187-4977 Avance de Informacion Economica. Indicadores del Sector Manufacturero
0187-4985 Avance de Informacion Economica. Ciudad de Mexico: Encuesta sobre Establecimientos Comerciales
0187-5000 Avance de Informacion Economica. Cuidad de Monterrey: Encuesta sobre Establecimientos Comerciales
0187-5019 Avance de Informacion Estadistica. Industria Maquiladora de Exportacion
0187-5027 Avance de Informacion Economica. Industria Minerometalurgica
0187-5841 Gaceta Informativa de Legislacion, Jurisprudencia y Bibliografia *changed to* Gaceta Informativa de Legislacion.
0187-6074 Arqueologia
0187-6708 Avance de Informacion Economica. Ciudad de Guadalajara: Encuesta sobre Establecimientos Comerciales
0187-7372 Frontera Norte
0187-7615 Money Affairs
0187-7658 Industria Alimentaria
0187-7895 Construccion y Tecnologia
0187-8492 Pan
0187-8506 Pan Directorio de Proveedores
0187-8999 Golden Penthouse
0188-0012 Perspectivas en Salud Publica
0188-0861 Universidad Nacional Autonoma de Mexico. Instituto de Investigaciones Esteticas. Monografias. Serie Mayor
0188-2503 Revista Mexicana de Sociologia
0188-3631 Revista de Arqueologia Mexicana
0188-3984 Divulgacion
0188-3992 Apoyo a la Docencia
0188-4018 Icones Orchidacearum
0188-476X Biblioteca de Mexico
0188-6673 Bibliografia sobre la Economica Mexicana. Libros
0189-0514 Nigeria. National Animal Production Research Institute. Journal
0189-0557 Today's Challenge
0189-0816 Nigeria Forum
0189-0840 Nigerian Institute of International Affairs. Dialogues
0189-0913 Nigerian Journal of Nutritional Sciences
0189-207X Nigerian Current Law Review
0189-2207 Annals of Borno
0189-255X Heritage (Lagos, 1981)
0189-2568 Nigerian Management Review
0189-2916 Nigeria Educational Forum. Journal
0189-3319 Nigerian Journal of Financial Management
0189-3963 Headlines
0189-4412 Nigerian Library and Information Science Review
0189-5036 Nigerian Business Journal
0189-5117 Tropical Journal of Obstetrics and Gynaecology
0189-6652 Journal of English Studies
0189-6709 African Journal of Academic Librarianship
0189-8892 Newswatch
0189-9228 Fun Times
0190-0005 City Hall Digest
0190-0013 Philosophy and Literature
0190-0226 Boarding Kennel Proprietor†
0190-0234 Inklings†
0190-0242 Children's Rights Report†
0190-0250 E I S Cumulative
0190-0331 Allied Health and Behavioral Sciences†
0190-0412 Gestalt Journal
0190-0447 Cross-Reference on Human Resources Management *see* 0740-9982
0190-0471 Analytical and Quantitative Cytology *changed to* Analytical and Quantitative Cytology and Histology.
0190-0528 Rangelands
0190-0536 Philosophical Investigations
0190-0684 Journal of Civil Engineering Design *see* 0730-8213
0190-0692 International Journal of Public Administration
0190-0870 St. Louis Labor Tribune *changed to* St. Louis - Southern Illinois Labor Tribune.
0190-0943 I T E M
0190-1028 Behavioral Counseling Quarterly *see* 0749-1301
0190-1052 American Society for Engineering Education. Annual Conference Proceedings
0190-1168 New Spirit†
0190-1192 Community Association Law Reporter
0190-1206 Cancer Clinical Trials *see* 0277-3732
0190-1249 Sports Afield Outdoor Almanac†
0190-1281 Research in Economic Anthropology
0190-129X Louisiana State Industrial Directory *see* 0733-3234
0190-1311 Tennessee State Industrial Directory *see* 0740-4646
0190-132X Virginia State Industrial Directory *see* 0740-2902
0190-1338 Michigan State Industrial Directory *see* 0733-4958
0190-1346 Mississippi State Industrial Directory *see* 0740-4654
0190-1354 Kentucky State Industrial Directory *see* 0740-4328
0190-1362 Indiana State Industrial Directory *see* 0740-6045
0190-1370 Electrical Apparatus
0190-1397 Forge
0190-1400 Photoletter
0190-1427 A J S Update *changed to* Update (Chicago).
0190-1435 Dr. Dobb's Journal of Computer Calisthenics and Orthodontia *see* 1044-789X
0190-1451 Laser Focus with Fiberoptic Communications *see* 1043-8092
0190-1486 Current Topics in Hematology†
0190-1494 I E E E International Symposium on Electromagnetic Compatibility.
0190-1559 Banjo Newsletter
0190-1567 Free Stock Photography Directory†
0190-1575 International Advances in Surgical Oncology†
0190-1737 Street Magazine†
0190-1761 Earthwise News *changed to* Earthwise Review.
0190-1761 Earthwise Literary Calendar
0190-1788 Poetry in Motion†
0190-1796 Professional Women and Minorities
0190-1966 Penny Power *see* 1050-8163
0190-1974 Learning Resources (Washington)†
0190-1982 C B S News Review
0190-1990 New York Times Current Events Edition
0190-2008 Journal of Caribbean Studies
0190-2024 Implantologist *changed to* International Journal of Oral Implantology.
0190-2040 Patient Counselling and Health Education *see* 0738-3991
0190-2067 History of Sociology: An International Review
0190-2075 Speech Communication Directory
0190-2148 Experimental Lung Research
0190-2172 Pulp and Paper Industry Technical Conference. Conference Record
0190-2180 Humanities Report†
0190-2199 Counselor Education Directory: Personnel and Programs *see* 0271-5368
0190-2210 State Consumer Action†
0190-2229 Pacific Coast Council on Latin American Studies. Proceedings *changed to* Review of Latin American Studies.
0190-2253 Gusto†
0190-2261 Journal Fee-Based Information Services *changed to* Information Broker.
0190-230X Family and Child Mental Health Journal *see* 0738-0151
0190-2318 Obesity and Metabolism *see* 0731-4361
0190-2334 Regional Council Directory *changed to* Directory of Regional Councils.
0190-2342 Chutzpah
0190-2350 Legal Aspects of Medical Practice†
0190-2369 Modern Chinese Literature
0190-2377 Tennessee Out-of-Doors†
0190-2407 Studies in the Age of Chaucer
0190-2423 Agri-Fieldman and Consultant *changed to* Ag Consultant.
0190-2458 In Business (Emmaus)
0190-2482 White Cloud Journal
0190-2555 Juvenile and Adult Correctional Departments, Institutions, Agencies, and Paroling Authorities of the United States and Canada
0190-2563 Corrections Today
0190-2571 On the Line (Laurel)
0190-2709 Academy of Sciences of the U S S R. Special Astrophysical Observatory-North Caucasus. Bulletin
0190-2717 Academy of Sciences of the U S S R. Crimean Astrophysical Observatory. Bulletin
0190-2725 Social Psychology Quarterly
0190-2733 Examiner (Raleigh)
0190-2741 Co-Op (Ann Arbor)†
0190-275X H U D Statistical Yearbook *see* 0147-7870
0190-2903 Plate Collector
0190-2911 MidAmerica
0190-292X Policy Studies Journal
0190-2946 Academe
0190-2954 U.S. Office of Consumer Affairs. Directory: Federal, State, County, and City Government Consumer Offices *see* 0190-2962
0190-2962 U.S. Office of Consumer Affairs. Directory: Federal, State, and Local Government Consumer Offices†
0190-2970 Current Topics in Eye Research†
0190-2989 Health Sciences Audiovisual Resource List *changed to* Nursing Audiovisual Resource List.

ISSN

ISSN INDEX 5633

0190-2997 Summary of Rate Schedules of Natural Gas Pipeline Companies as Filed with the Federal Energy Regulatory Commission and the National Energy Board of Canada *changed to* Summary of Rate Schedules of Natural Gas Pipeline Companies.
0190-3012 Northern New England Review
0190-3047 Directory of Manufacturers, State of Hawaii†
0190-3055 Rhode Island Genealogical Register
0190-3071 Encyclopedia of American Associations *see* 0071-0202
0190-3101 Truck & Van Buyer's Guide†
0190-3136 World Food Situation *see* 0084-1358
0190-3160 Community and Junior College Journal *changed to* Community, Technical, and Junior College Journal.
0190-3187 International Family Planning Perspectives
0190-3225 Management Aids for Small Business Annual†
0190-3233 Review (Charlottesville)
0190-3241 Future Survey
0190-325X Policy Report *see* 0743-605X
0190-3276 Copley Mail Order Advisor
0190-3284 Zero
0190-3292 N A S A Activities *changed to* N A S A Magazine.
0190-3306 Faceplate†
0190-3314 Green Feather
0190-3330 Thinking
0190-3349 Food Marketing Industry Speaks
0190-3357 Foundation Center. Annual Report
0190-3373 Anthropological Literature
0190-339X Chronicle Student Aid Annual *changed to* Chronicle Financial Aid Guide.
0190-3586 Bostonian Society. Proceedings.†
0190-3608 Conser Tables†
0190-3632 A R R L Repeater Directory
0190-3640 Sez
0190-3659 Boundary 2
0190-3705 Video Register and Teleconferencing Resources Directory
0190-373X U.S. Community Services Administration. Annual Report
0190-3748 Food Topics *see* 0196-5700
0190-3799 National Municipal Review *see* 0027-9013
0190-3802 High Adventure
0190-3845 Live (Springfield)
0190-3896 U.S. Administration on Aging. Elderly Population: Estimates by County†
0190-3918 International Conference on Parallel Processing. Proceedings
0190-4019 American Journal of Clinical Biofeedback *see* 0827-1038
0190-406X Museums New York
0190-4094 Chemical, Biomedical and Environmental Instrumentation *see* 0743-5797
0190-4132 International Conference on Lasers. Proceedings
0190-4167 Journal of Plant Nutrition
0190-4175 Electric Vehicle Progress
0190-4183 Practical Parenting†
0190-4205 St. Louis Home - Garden
0190-4213 Peterson's Annual Guide to Careers and Employment for Engineers, Computer Scientists, and Physical Scientists *see* 1048-342X
0190-4302 Material Handling and Industrial Engineer *changed to* American Institute of Industrial Engineers. Material Handling Institute. Proceedings.
0190-4329 National Collegiate Championships
0190-4361 Journal of Jewish Lore and Philosophy *see* 0360-9049
0190-4507 Boating Product News†
0190-4523 Duke Divinity School Bulletin *see* 0012-7078
0190-4620 Woman's Touch
0190-4639 Paraclete
0190-4655 Cooperative Education Quarterly
0190-4663 Chronicle Career Index Annual *see* 0276-0355
0190-4701 Furman Studies
0190-4752 Paragraph†
0190-4817 Advances in Cancer Chemotherapy†
0190-485X Counter Pentagon†
0190-4876 Energy Research Reports†
0190-4906 Black Review
0190-4914 Business Owner
0190-4922 Contributions to Music Education
0190-4949 C A Selects. Zeolites
0190-4981 Combined Cumulative Index to Pediatrics
0190-499X Foreign Trade Reports. U.S. Exports - Schedule E - Commodity Groupings Commodity by Country *see* 1057-9680
0190-5066 Same-Day Surgery
0190-5074 International Psoriasis Bulletin†
0190-5104 Sage Annual Reviews of Drug and Alcohol Abuse†
0190-521X Political Science Discussion Papers†
0190-5244 What's New in Collective Bargaining Negotiations & Contracts
0190-5252 United States Law Week Summary and Analysis
0190-5260 Union Labor Report Weekly Newsletter
0190-5279 American Druggist
0190-535X Oncology Nursing Forum
0190-5422 U.S. National Arthritis Advisory Board. Annual Report *changed to* Advisory Board for Arthritis and Musculoskeletal and Skin Diseases. Annual Report.
0190-5570 Telescope Making†
0190-5589 Semi-Annual Electric Power Survey *changed to* Electric Power Annual Report.
0190-5600 Annual Electric Power Survey *changed to* Electric Power Annual Report.
0190-5619 Electric Power Survey *changed to* Electric Power Annual Report.
0190-5724 Carnivore
0190-5821 I L A Newsletter
0190-5848 Frontiers in Education Conference. Proceedings
0190-5856 Baptist Review and Expositor *see* 0034-6373
0190-5872 Meeting Site Selector
0190-5961 Center for Cuban Studies. Newsletter *see* 0197-5277
0190-597X SciQuest†
0190-6003 International Directory of Research and Development Scientists *see* 0882-2360
0190-6003 International Directory of Research and Development Scientists *changed to* Current Contents Address Directory - Social Sciences, Arts & Humanities.
0190-6011 Journal of Orthopaedic and Sports Physical Therapy
0190-602X China Facts and Figures Annual
0190-6100 Wesleyan Methodist *see* 0043-289X
0190-6275 Business America
0190-647X Culture and Language Learning Newsletter *changed to* East-West Culture Learning Institute Report.
0190-6526 Flying Yearbook†
0190-6569 Light' n' Heavy†
0190-6577 Folk Music Magazine
0190-6585 DataWorld
0190-6593 Western New England Law Review
0190-6607 Administrative Directory of College and University Computer Science Departments and Computer Centers *changed to* A C M Administrative Directory of College and University Computer Science - Data Processing Programs and Computer Facilities.
0190-6623 State Government Research Checklist
0190-6631 A C H Newsletter
0190-6690 Official Intermodal Equipment Register
0190-6704 Official Railway Guide. North American Freight Service Edition
0190-6739 R V Aftermarket†
0190-6798 Speedy Bee
0190-7034 Boston College Environmental Affairs Law Review
0190-731X Scriblerian and the Kit-Cats
0190-7409 Children and Youth Services Review
0190-745X Bulletin of Bibliography
0190-7476 National Directory of Children & Youth Services†
0190-7492 Marketing California Ornamental Crops
0190-7654 Financial Education *see* 0093-3961
0190-7662 National Education Association of the United States. Proceedings of the Annual Meeting *changed to* National Education Association of the United States. Proceedings of the Representative Assembly.
0190-7808 National Waste News†
0190-7956 Yacht Racing and Cruising *see* 0889-4094
0190-8049 National Arts Guide
0190-8189 Folk and Kinfolk of Harris County†
0190-8197 New Information Systems and Services *changed to* Information Industry Directory Supplement.
0190-8227 Applewood Journal†
0190-8294 American Society of Civil Engineers. Energy Division. Journal *see* 0733-9402
0190-8340 A P I C S International Technical Conference Proceedings *changed to* American Production and Inventory Control Society. Annual International Conference Proceedings.
0190-8553 Commercial Kitchen & Institutional Dining Room†
0190-8715 Reports on Research Assisted by the Petroleum Research Fund
0190-8766 ProFile (Topeka)
0190-9177 Journal of Heat Treating
0190-9185 Monitoring the Future
0190-9215 Carnivorous Plant Newsletter
0190-9320 Political Behavior
0190-9363 N A G W S Guide. Flag Football, Speedball, Speed-a-Way†
0190-9398 C A Selects. Chemical Hazards, Health & Safety
0190-9401 C A Selects. Carbon & Heteroatom N M R
0190-941X C A Selects. Proton Magnetic Resonance
0190-9428 C A Selects. Infrared Spectroscopy (Organic Aspects)
0190-9436 C A Selects. Infrared Spectroscopy (Physicochemical Aspects)
0190-9444 C A Selects. Colloids (Macromolecular Aspects)
0190-9622 American Academy of Dermatology. Journal
0190-9649 Billboard's International Talent Directory *see* 0732-0124
0190-9789 Green Scene
0190-9797 U.S. Civil Service Commission. Annual Report†
0190-9819 National Preservation Report†
0190-9827 Audiovisual Materials *changed to* National Union Catalog. Audiovisual Materials.
0190-9835 White Walls
0190-9851 Private Label
0190-986X Lens' on Campus†
0190-9940 Archaeoastronomy
0191-0043 Search *see* 0199-6363
0191-0051 O'Dwyer's Directory of Public Relations Executives
0191-0132 Asian Wall Street Journal Weekly
0191-0167 Restoration Witness
0191-0221 Martindale-Hubbell Law Directory
0191-0310 Statistical Abstract of Oklahoma
0191-0329 Fielding's Favorites: Hotels & Inns, Europe†
0191-040X Catalyst (New York, 1978) *see* 1042-8232
0191-0574 Index to Social Sciences & Humanities Proceedings
0191-0647 Optical Industry and Systems Purchasing Directory *see* 1044-1425
0191-0760 Gravida
0191-0833 C N I Weekly Report *see* 0736-0096
0191-0914 Reading Research. Advances in Theory and Practice†
0191-0930 Texas Journal of Political Studies
0191-0965 Yoga Journal
0191-1031 Kentucky Review
0191-1058 Illinois. State Library, Springfield. Publications of the State of Illinois.
0191-118X Analysis of Workers' Compensation Laws
0191-1295 Library Computer Equipment Review *changed to* Library Computer Systems & Equipment Review.
0191-135X Sealift†
0191-1422 Congressional Yellow Book
0191-1503 A R M A Records Management Quarterly *see* 1050-2343
0191-1538 O A G North American Pocket Flight Guide *changed to* O A G Pocket Flight Guide North American Edition.
0191-1554 Performing Woman
0191-1562 Minnesota Statutes
0191-1600 Developmental Disabilities Abstracts†
0191-1619 Official Airline Guide. North American Edition
0191-1643 Fact Book on Higher Education in the South
0191-1686 Nuclear Science Applications *changed to* Nuclear Science Applications - Section A: Short Reviews, Research Papers, and Comments.
0191-1686 Nuclear Science Applications *changed to* Nuclear Science Applications - Section B: In Depth Reviews.
0191-1708 Fundamentals of Pure and Applied Economics Series
0191-1759 National Health†
0191-1767 Foundry World *see* 0887-9060
0191-1783 American Production and Inventory Control Society. Annual Conference Proceedings *changed to* American Production and Inventory Control Society. Annual International Conference Proceedings.
0191-1813 Journal of American Culture
0191-183X Florida Business Publications Index
0191-1872 Update in Clinical Dentistry†
0191-1937 Research in Corporate Social Performance and Policy
0191-1953 Full Blast†
0191-1961 Missouri Review
0191-2151 Science in Alaska *changed to* Arctic Science Conference. Proceedings.
0191-2186 Focus on Poverty Research *see* 0195-5705
0191-2208 Expense Analysis: Condominiums, Cooperatives and Planned Unit Developments
0191-2216 I E E E Conference on Decision and Control, Including the Symposium on Adaptive Processes. Proceedings *changed to* I E E E Conference on Decision and Control. Proceedings.
0191-2259 Black Box†
0191-2283 High - Low Report†
0191-2291 Nurses' Drug Alert
0191-2321 Fodor's Australia, New Zealand and the South Pacific *changed to* Fodor's Australia and New Zealand.
0191-2453 Current Topics in Nutrition and Disease
0191-2607 Transportation Research. Part A: General
0191-2615 Transportation Research. Part B: Methodological
0191-2690 Ballet News†
0191-2763 Loss Prevention and Control†
0191-2771 Metabolic and Pediatric Ophthalmology *see* 0882-889X
0191-278X Nuclear Tracks *changed to* International Journal of Radiation Applications and Instrumentation. Part D: Nuclear Tracks and Radiation Measurements.
0191-2836 Arthritis Foundation Annual Report

ISSN

5634 ISSN INDEX

0191-2917 Plant Disease
0191-2925 Stamp Show News & Philatelic Review†
0191-2933 Plants, Sites & Parks
0191-2941 Nature and System†
0191-295X Bubblegum Gazette. Summer Weekly . Reader *see* 0899-6121
0191-2968 Peppermint Press *changed to* Weekly Reader. Summer Edition B. Grades 2-6.
0191-2976 Jellybean Jamboree *changed to* Weekly Reader. Summer Edition A. Pre K - Grade 1.
0191-3026 Research in Marketing
0191-3034 Jewish Civilization: Essays and Studies
0191-3085 Research in Organizational Behavior
0191-3123 Ultrastructural Pathology
0191-328X Alaska Today†
0191-3352 Agni Review *changed to* Agni.
0191-3379 International Forum for Logotherapy
0191-3387 Pacific Basin Quarterly†
0191-3417 Audiovisual Instruction with Instructional Resources *see* 8756-3894
0191-3441 National Governors' Association. Annual Meeting. Proceedings†
0191-345X Restaurant Design *see* 0745-4929
0191-3468 Sunset Western Travel Adventures†
0191-3522 Man at Arms
0191-3530 Venture (New York)†
0191-3557 Journal of California and Great Basin Anthropology
0191-3581 Neurobehavioral Toxicology *see* 0892-0362
0191-359X National Librarian
0191-3654 Turtle
0191-3662 Chronicle Two-Year College Databook
0191-3670 Chronicle Four-Year College Databook
0191-3700 East West Journal *see* 0888-1375
0191-3727 How to Evaluate Health Programs†
0191-3794 Cancer Control Journal
0191-3867 Almanac for Computers†
0191-3875 Desert Tortoise Council. Proceedings of Symposium
0191-3883 Hammond Almanac of a Million Facts, Records, Forecasts *changed to* Hammond Almanac: One-Volume Encyclopedia of a Million Facts & Records (year).
0191-3905 Draper Fund Report†
0191-3913 Journal of Pediatric Ophthalmology and Strabismus
0191-3999 Garden (Bronx)†
0191-4006 Business Library Newsletter
0191-4022 Modulus
0191-4030 Stereo World
0191-4138 Man in the Northeast
0191-4146 University Publishing†
0191-4219 Studying Adult Life and Work Lessons
0191-426X Argosy (1979)†
0191-4294 Christian Single
0191-4421 Mineral Industry Surveys. Platinum - Group Metals
0191-4502 Oxbridge Directory of Religious Periodicals†
0191-4537 Philosophy and Social Criticism
0191-4545 Europe
0191-4588 Quick Printing
0191-4618 Florida Forum
0191-4626 Starlog
0191-4634 Web†
0191-4650 Iowa Beverage Journal *changed to* Beverage Alcohol Business Scene.
0191-4685 Missouri Beverage Journal *see* 0747-3192
0191-474X Keepin' Track of Vettes *see* 0195-1661
0191-4766 Pet Business
0191-4847 Radical Teacher
0191-4898 Broadcast Programming and Production†
0191-491X Studies in Educational Evaluation
0191-5096 Journal of Sociology and Social Welfare
0191-5142 South Bay†
0191-5207 Truth Consciousness Journal *see* 1040-7448
0191-5215 Enterprise (Washington)†
0191-524X Virginia Federation of Business and Professional Women's Clubs. Federation Notes†
0191-5258 Georgia Disabled American Veterans†
0191-5320 Alaska Beverage Analyst†
0191-5355 West Virginia State Firemen's Association Journal†
0191-5371 Ion-Selective Electrode Reviews *see* 0894-3923
0191-538X Advances in Earth-Oriented Applications of Space Technology *see* 0892-9270
0191-5398 Environmental Professional
0191-5401 Behavioral Assessment
0191-541X Lighting Dimensions
0191-5428 Communications - Engineering and Design
0191-5592 Colorado Woman†
0191-5606 MobileTimes†
0191-5614 Live and Invest
0191-5622 Solubility Data Series
0191-5657 High Country News
0191-5665 Mechanics of Composite Materials
0191-5681 Behavioral Group Therapy†
0191-5738 Lawman†
0191-5835 Racquetball Industry†
0191-5851 Tennis Industry
0191-586X Florida Grocer
0191-5886 Journal of Nonverbal Behavior
0191-5959 Grain & Feed Review (Des Moines)†
0191-5967 Magnolia L P N
0191-5975 Maryland's Highlights†
0191-5983 Palmetto Licensed Practical Nurse
0191-5991 Senior Circle
0191-6017 Spyglass†
0191-6025 Tennessee Fireman
0191-6084 T.L.P.N.A. Bulletin†
0191-6122 Palynology
0191-6181 Food Production - Management
0191-6246 U S Medicine
0191-6394 Pharmacy West
0191-6408 Rotor and Wing International
0191-6505 Maryland Magazine of Genealogy *see* 0025-4258
0191-6521 Africa News
0191-6599 History of European Ideas
0191-6734 Handicapped Rights and Regulations *see* 1043-1209
0191-6750 Mental Health Report
0191-6769 C I R A Scope (Chicago and Illinois Restaurant Association) *changed to* Illinois Food Service News.
0191-6777 Heavy-Duty Distribution *see* 0895-3856
0191-6785 Hurdy Gurdy
0191-6793 N-C Commline *see* 0744-2386
0191-6807 Northern Hardware Trade *changed to* Hardware Trade.
0191-6815 Outlook *changed to* Ingram's Magazine.
0191-6823 Professional Car Washing *changed to* Professional Car Washing & Detailing.
0191-6904 Model Retailer
0191-6912 Miniatures and Doll Dealer *changed to* Miniatures Dealer.
0191-6939 Generations (Baltimore)
0191-6963 Drawing
0191-6971 National Zip Code and Post Office Directory *see* 0731-9185
0191-717X Golf Traveler
0191-7390 Nethula Journal of Contemporary Art & Literature
0191-7579 American Logger and Lumberman†
0191-7587 Drug Store News
0191-765X Evaluation in Education - International Progress *see* 0883-0355
0191-7706 Equine Events†
0191-7714 Eastern-Western Quarter Horse Journal
0191-7730 Archaeology on Kaua'i
0191-7757 Harvard Medical Alumni Bulletin
0191-7870 Clinical Biomechanics
0191-7935 Photo Star
0191-8028 International Security Review†
0191-8036 E N. Evaluation News *see* 0886-1633
0191-8087 United Nations Documents *changed to* United Nations Documents and Publications.
0191-8095 Snow Goer *see* 0274-8363
0191-8133 National Dean's List
0191-8141 Journal of Structural Geology
0191-815X Nuclear and Chemical Waste Management *see* 0956-053X
0191-8176 Wisconsin Trillium†
0191-8206 Latitude 20†
0191-8257 Urban Health *changed to* Urban Practice.
0191-8273 Printing Journal
0191-8397 Pacific Goldsmith *see* 0274-7456
0191-8427 Archery Retailer *changed to* Archery Business.
0191-8443 Design Professional Product Bulletin Directory†
0191-8508 Fastener Technology *see* 0746-2441
0191-8575 Ocean Yearbook
0191-8591 Panorama (New York)†
0191-863X Altman Weil Pensa Report to Legal Management
0191-8699 Sojourner
0191-8745 Landscape West and Irrigation News *see* 0745-3795
0191-8753 World of Golf-Tennis & Resorts
0191-877X Defense Manual
0191-8796 Sacramento Magazine
0191-880X Stockton's Port Soundings†
0191-8818 Connecticut Beverage Journal
0191-8826 Apartment Owner
0191-8834 Pig International. Europe, Africa and Asia - Pacific *changed to* Pig International. Europe, Africa and Asia - Pacific and Latin America.
0191-8869 Personality and Individual Differences
0191-8877 Substance and Alcohol Actions - Misuse *see* 0741-8329
0191-8923 Westchester Illustrated†
0191-9016 North Central Journal of Agricultural Economics
0191-9040 Insect Science and Its Application
0191-9059 Physicochemical Hydrodynamics *see* 0301-9322
0191-9067 Space Power Review *see* 0883-6272
0191-9075 Electronic Distributing *changed to* Electronic Purchaser.
0191-9113 Alabama & Gulf Coast Retailing News
0191-9121 Georgia Retailing News
0191-913X Population Research Center Papers
0191-9199 French 17
0191-9202 Physical Education Index
0191-9210 Coffee Break†
0191-9237 Purchasor - New York State†
0191-9245 Syracuse Magazine†
0191-927X General Aviation News: The Green Sheet *see* 1052-9136
0191-9288 Hudson Valley Magazine
0191-9318 Susquehanna *see* 1047-3068
0191-9334 Feed Industry Review†
0191-9458 Administrative Officials Classified by Functions *see* 0561-8630
0191-9474 Greater Salt Lake Builder†
0191-9482 Mountainwest Magazine†
0191-9512 Ozone
0191-9539 Journal of Engineering & Applied Sciences†
0191-9601 Pediatrics in Review
0191-961X Rx Home Care†
0191-961X Rx Home Care Buyer's Guide *changed to* Rx Home Care Directory.
0191-9679 U.S. Department of Housing and Urban Development. Office of International Affairs. International Review†
0191-975X Field Artillery Journal *see* 0899-2525
0191-9768 Mobile - Manufactured Home Merchandiser *changed to* Manufactured Home Merchandiser.
0191-9776 Computer and Information Systems Abstracts Journal
0191-9792 Working Arts†
0191-9822 Willamette Law Review
0191-9873 Contemporary Administrator *changed to* Contemporary Long-Term Care.
0192-0030 Apartment Age
0192-0103 G A T N *changed to* German American Trade.
0192-0219 Motorcycle DealerNews *see* 0888-4234
0192-0227 Design Cost and Data for the Construction Industry *changed to* Design Cost & Data.
0192-0359 National Utility Contractor
0192-0561 International Journal of Immunopharmacology
0192-0596 Training and Development Alert
0192-060X Washington Representatives
0192-0618 c/o: Journal of Alternative Human Services†
0192-0790 Journal of Clinical Gastroenterology
0192-0812 Research in Community and Mental Health
0192-0839 F R E S Newsletter (Federal Regulation of Employment Service) *changed to* Employment Coordinator.
0192-0855 Business Atlanta
0192-0863 Pecan South *see* 8750-5797
0192-0871 Undercurrent
0192-091X New Consultants
0192-0944 Diplomat International Calendar
0192-0952 Fodor's Germany: West and East *changed to* Fodor's Germany.
0192-0987 Automotive Aftermarket News *see* 0193-3264
0192-0995 Automotive Body Repair News
0192-1118 Plant Energy Management *changed to* Energy Management Technology.
0192-1193 Journal of Clinical and Experimental Gerontology
0192-1207 Keltica
0192-1215 Irish Echo
0192-1223 N A P S A C News
0192-1266 Biomedical Products
0192-1274 C E E *changed to* Electrical Construction Technology.
0192-1290 Engineer's Digest (Overland Park)
0192-1304 20-20
0192-1312 Development Communication Report
0192-1347 Fastfacts European Hotel Locator†
0192-1371 College Administrator and the Courts
0192-1460 MacNeil - Lehrer Report
0192-1487 Designers West
0192-1487 Designers West Resource Directory
0192-1533 Equal Opportunity Forum†
0192-1541 Electronic Engineering Times
0192-1622 American Inventor†
0192-1630 Southeast Real Estate News
0192-1657 Installation & Cleaning Specialist
0192-1703 Sun Coast Architect - Builder
0192-1711 Plumbing Engineer†
0192-1746 Solid State Power Conversion *see* 0885-0259
0192-1878 Apparel Industry Magazine
0192-1975 Leisure Cooking
0192-2238 Petersen's Pro Basketball
0192-2262 Hospital Materiel Management Quarterly
0192-2270 Rocky Mountain Magazine
0192-2297 Directory of Architects for Health Facilities†
0192-2319 New Magazine Review†
0192-2327 Restaurant Employee
0192-236X Council on Foreign Relations. Annual Report
0192-2378 Fodor's People's Republic of China *changed to* Fodor's China.
0192-2394 Nursing (Year) Career Directory
0192-2408 New Pacific *changed to* Pacific Magazine.
0192-2467 Greater Ohio Valley Retailer†
0192-2475 Retail Reporter *changed to* Retail News Reporter.
0192-2491 M B News
0192-2505 Park Maintenance and Grounds Management *see* 1057-204X
0192-2521 Environmental Mutagenesis *see* 0893-6692
0192-253X Developmental Genetics

ISSN

ISSN INDEX 5635

0192-2718 Military Clubs & Recreation
0192-2807 Meat Plant Magazine *changed to* Meat Business Magazine.
0192-2815 Livestock†
0192-2858 Annals of Scholarship
0192-2874 Book Production Industry and Magazine Production *see* 0273-8724
0192-2882 Theatre Journal (Baltimore)
0192-2890 Dreamworks†
0192-2912 Conservation Administration News
0192-2920 Let's Go: The Budget Guide to Italy
0192-2963 Physician East
0192-298X R.N. Idaho
0192-3021 I D: International Design Magazine
0192-303X InTech
0192-3048 Golf Course Management
0192-3056 Missouri Beef Cattleman
0192-3064 Industry and Commerce
0192-3072 Simmental Shield
0192-3080 Topeka Magazine
0192-3102 Bay Views (San Rafael)
0192-3137 Direct Marketing Market Place
0192-3145 Forensic Services Directory
0192-3153 Renews†
0192-3161 Animal Hospital Product News†
0192-3196 PhotographiConservation†
0192-320X Naval Abstracts†
0192-3250 Farmerage
0192-3293 Construction Equipment Maintenance†
0192-3307 College Union *changed to* College Union & On-Campus Hospitality.
0192-3315 A A I I Journal
0192-3323 Criminal Law Review
0192-334X Discographies
0192-3404 Oil Pollution Reports *see* 0270-4315
0192-3412 Fodor's New England
0192-3420 Kite Tales *see* 0192-3439
0192-3439 KiteLines
0192-3498 Florida Hotel and Motel News *see* 8750-6807
0192-3595 Eastern Aftermarket Journal
0192-3641 Hunt Institute for Botanical Documentation. Journal *changed to* Hunt Institute for Botanical Documentation. Bulletin.
0192-3706 Decorating and Craft Ideas *changed to* Creative Ideas for Living.
0192-3730 Fodor's Far West†
0192-3749 Chinese Music
0192-3757 Black Collegian
0192-382X Port of New Orleans. Weekly Bulletin
0192-3838 Louisiana Pharmacist
0192-3846 Marina Management/Marketing
0192-3951 Rocky Mountain Construction (South Edition)
0192-396X Buddhist Research Information *see* 0888-5869
0192-3978 Construction Equipment
0192-3994 I T S Review
0192-401X O R T E S O L Journal†
0192-4036 International Journal of Comparative and Applied Criminal Justice
0192-4044 Journal of Superstition & Magical Thinking†
0192-4117 California Transportation and Public Works Conference. Selected Papers†
0192-415X American Journal of Chinese Medicine
0192-4168 Southern Tier Town and Country Living
0192-4176 Bradford-Tioga-Sullivan-Potter-Wyoming Farm and Home News
0192-4184 Seven County Farm and Home News
0192-4214 Southwest Art
0192-4230 Construccion Pan-Americana
0192-4265 Sarasota Magazine
0192-429X Journal of Electronic Defense
0192-4311 Purchasing Administration *see* 0279-4799
0192-432X Medical Products Salesman *see* 0279-4802
0192-4389 Gulf Coast Lumberman
0192-4397 Year Book of Pediatrics Newsletter†
0192-4400 Griffin Report of Food Marketing
0192-4486 Carpet & Rug Industry
0192-4575 Kilobaud Microcomputing *see* 0744-4567
0192-4583 Kilobaud *see* 0744-4567
0192-4699 American Association of Textile Chemists and Colorists. National Technical Conference. Book of Papers
0192-4729 Music-in-Print Annual Supplement†
0192-4745 Mine Safety & Health Reporter†
0192-477X Transatlantic Perspectives
0192-4788 Activities, Adaptation & Aging
0192-4893 New Homes Magazine
0192-4907 Twin Cities Woman
0192-4923 Minicomputer News *changed to* Computer Times.
0192-4974 Urban Interest Journal *see* 0735-2166
0192-5059 Plantation Society in the Americas
0192-5067 A S L A Members Handbook
0192-5083 Lincoln Review
0192-5121 International Political Science Review
0192-513X Journal of Family Issues
0192-5148 Epigraphic Society. Occasional Publications *changed to* Epigraphic Society. Occasional Papers.
0192-5164 Senior Profile
0192-5199 Truck Tracks
0192-5210 Yankee Horsetrader
0192-5237 Farm and Ranch
0192-5245 Antiques Observer
0192-527X Capital District Business Review
0192-5318 International Interdisciplinary Seminar on Piagetian Theory and Its Implications for the Helping Professions. Proceedings†
0192-5326 Fielding's Europe
0192-5482 Athletic Purchasing and Facilities *see* 0747-315X
0192-5490 Personal Computing *changed to* Personal Computing.
0192-5539 Friendscript
0192-5571 Fodor's Midwest†
0192-558X Advances in the Economics of Energy and Resources
0192-5709 American Tool, Die and Stamping News *changed to* Diemaking, Stamping & EDMing.
0192-5717 Ann Arbor Observer
0192-5725 Ann Arbor Scene Magazine
0192-5776 Amicus *see* 0276-7201
0192-5784 Official (Los Angeles)
0192-5792 Southern Pharmacy Journal
0192-5857 American Mathematical Society. Abstracts of Papers Presented.
0192-5881 Comic Art Collection
0192-592X T.H.E. Journal
0192-5938 B B W: Big Beautiful Woman Magazine
0192-6071 All Volunteer *changed to* Recruiter Journal.
0192-6152 Legal Memorandum *changed to* N A S S P Legal Memorandum.
0192-6160 N A S S P Practitioner
0192-6179 Mineral & Energy Resources†
0192-6187 American Journal of Family Therapy
0192-6225 Microwave Journal (International Edition)
0192-6233 Toxicologic Pathology
0192-6268 Minnesota. Geological Survey. Guidebook Series
0192-6314 Printers Hot Line
0192-6330 Contractors Hot Line
0192-6365 N A S S P Bulletin
0192-6411 Kentucky Sports World†
0192-642X Kentucky Business Ledger
0192-6438 Southern Advertising - Markets *see* 8756-6389
0192-6551 Progress in Biomass Conversion†
0192-6667 Daily Planet†
0192-6675 Healthways Magazine Digest *changed to* Health Perspective.
0192-6756 Texas Child Care Quarterly *see* 1049-9466
0192-6764 Brahman Journal
0192-6772 National Home Center News
0192-6802 Current World Leaders
0192-6845 W A A *changed to* Agricultural Aviation.
0192-6918 Studies in the Anthropology of Visual Communications *see* 0276-6558
0192-6942 Ohio Media Spectrum
0192-6950 Metropolitan Museum of Art. Notable Acquisitions†
0192-6985 Biological Abstracts - R R M
0192-6985 Biological Abstracts - R R M Cumulative Index
0192-7000 N O O N (National Outdoor Outfitters News) *changed to* Outside Business Magazine.
0192-7027 My Little Salesman Truck Catalog
0192-7051 Journal of Prison Health *see* 0731-8332
0192-7116 Chef Institutional
0192-7124 Logger and Lumberman
0192-7132 Processed Prepared Foods *see* 0747-2536
0192-7140 Stockman Farmer *changed to* Stockman - Grass Farmer.
0192-7159 Pacific Coast Nurseryman and Garden Supply Dealer
0192-7167 Moody's O T C Industrial Manual
0192-7175 Electronic Technician-Dealer *see* 0278-9922
0192-7256 Graphics (Kissimmee) *see* 0274-774X
0192-7272 American Association of Stratigraphic Palynologists. Abstracts of Papers Presented at the Annual Meetings.
0192-7299 American Association of Stratigraphic Palynologists. Newsletter
0192-7310 Health Practitioner, Physician Assistant *changed to* Physician Assistant.
0192-7329 National Independent Coal Leader
0192-7345 Voice (Honolulu)
0192-7361 Skydiving
0192-737X American Association of Stratigraphic Palynologists Foundation. Field Trip Guide
0192-7388 U.S. Library of Congress. Accessions List, Eastern Africa: Annual Serial Supplement
0192-7396 Small Boat Journal *see* 1059-5155
0192-740X Gerontopics†
0192-7450 In Business (Madison)
0192-7469 Exhaust News
0192-7507 Accent (New York)
0192-7558 Outdoor Power Equipment
0192-7590 Building Construction News
0192-7639 Domestic and International Commercial Loan Charge-Offs *changed to* Report on Domestic and International Commercial Loan Charge-Offs.
0192-7663 Media Management Monographs *changed to* Publishing Trends and Trendsetters.
0192-7671 Welding Distributor
0192-7922 Ad East†
0192-7973 Metropolitan Purchasor
0192-7981 Club and Food Service *see* 0886-8832
0192-799X Furniture Manufacturing Management
0192-8015 Gas Phase Molecular Structure†
0192-804X New Orleans *see* 0897-8174
0192-8058 F D M - Furniture Design & Manufacturing
0192-818X Music Retailer *changed to* Music Video Retailer.
0192-8198 Patent Law Handbook
0192-8201 Industrial Maintenance and Plant Operation *see* 8755-2523
0192-8228 National Jail and Adult Detention Directory
0192-8287 Fodor's Budget Travel in America *changed to* Fodor's Great Travel Values: American Cities.
0192-8309 Land Use & Environment Law Review
0192-8325 Industrial Safety Product News *see* 8755-2566
0192-8333 Carbide and Tool Journal†
0192-8430 Entertainment Bits
0192-8457 Insulator's Guide *see* 0273-5954
0192-8473 Accent Grand Rapids *changed to* West Michigan Magazine.
0192-8481 Porsche ueber Alles
0192-8546 Dallas - Fort Worth Living *changed to* Dallas - Fort Worth Home Buyer's Guide.
0192-8562 American Journal of Pediatric Hematology - Oncology
0192-8570 American Men and Women of Science
0192-8651 Journal of Computational Chemistry
0192-8694 Fairfield County
0192-8716 Pikestaff Forum
0192-8724 Pikestaff Review†
0192-8732 Stores of the Year
0192-8740 Air Traffic Control Association. Fall Conference Proceedings
0192-8902 Bus Ride
0192-8929 Wind Sock
0192-8953 Iowa Snowmobiler†
0192-8961 Minnesota Snowmobiler†
0192-8988 Sunflower (Bismarck)
0192-8996 Applied Geography Conferences
0192-9062 Interface. Banking Industry *see* 0892-6778
0192-9100 Denver Living *changed to* Denver Housing Guide.
0192-9143 Houston Living *changed to* Houston Living Housing Guide.
0192-9194 Southwest Real Estate News
0192-9216 Texas Contractor
0192-9240 Detroit Industrial Market News
0192-9259 Chevy 4 x 4
0192-9275 Printing History
0192-9453 Land & Water
0192-9488 Baltimore Purchaser *changed to* Maryland Purchasing & Material Management.
0192-9496 Drug Update†
0192-950X Midwest Dairyman†
0192-9526 Agri-Equipment Today *changed to* Agri-Equipment and Chemical.
0192-9550 Tile and Decorative Surfaces
0192-9569 Reynolds Review
0192-9593 Oklahoma Business
0192-9607 Purchasing Professional†
0192-9755 Seminars in Respiratory Medicine
0192-9763 American Journal of Otology
0192-9828 Chinese Studies in Archeology†
0192-9917 Journal of Magic History†
0192-9925 Fodor's California
0192-9933 American Printer and Lithographer *see* 0744-6616
0192-995X Living with Allergies†
0192-9968 American Indian Art Magazine
0193-0044 Mineral Industry Surveys. Cadmium
0193-0176 Utility Specifier Engineer†
0193-0184 Gothic Chapbook Series *changed to* Gothic.
0193-0257 Michigan Banking and Business News *changed to* Michigan Banker.
0193-0265 New England Sportsman
0193-0281 Progress (Framingham)
0193-032X Ophthalmology Times
0193-0400 Hardhat (Oklahoma City)
0193-0451 L A M A Newsletter (Library Administration and Management Association) *see* 0888-4463
0193-0516 Insurance Conference Planner
0193-0540 Law Enforcement Communications *see* 0747-3680
0193-0559 Luggage and Travelware *changed to* Travelware.
0193-0613 Southern Beverage Journal
0193-0648 What's New in Plant Physiology†
0193-0818 Research Communications in Substances of Abuse
0193-0826 Journal of Library Administration
0193-0834 Shenandoah Valley *see* 0743-4243
0193-0869 New Venturest
0193-0885 M U G Quarterly *see* 1060-7684
0193-0915 Fashion Accessories (East Norwalk) *changed to* Accessories.
0193-0982 Special Topics in Endocrinology and Metabolism†
0193-1075 Slovene Studies
0193-1091 American Journal of Dermatopathology
0193-1105 American Journal of Diagnostic Gynecology and Obstetrics *see* 0196-9617

ISSN

0193-113X Volunteers Who Produce Books
0193-1199 Chain Store Age Executive with Shopping Center Age *see* 0731-1303
0193-1202 Dance Magazine College Guide
0193-1229 F and S Europe *see* 0270-4536
0193-1350 Chain Store Age General Merchandise Group *changed to* Chain Store Age General Merchandise Trends.
0193-1369 Chain Store Age Supermarkets†
0193-1466 Sikh Religious Studies Information *see* 0888-5869
0193-1504 Whole Foods
0193-1636 Survey of Marketing Research†
0193-1709 Academic Psychology Bulletin
0193-1725 Speakers, Tours and Films
0193-175X Political Handbook of the World
0193-1814 News Circle
0193-1830 A M H C A Journal *see* 1040-2861
0193-1849 American Journal of Physiology: Endocrinology and Metabolism
0193-1857 American Journal of Physiology: Gastrointestinal and Liver Physiology
0193-1865 Registered Representative
0193-189X Mideast Business Exchange†
0193-1903 Compendium on Continuing Education for the Practicing Veterinarian
0193-1911 Kinesis Report *see* 0023-1568
0193-1954 Mechanical and Electrical Cost Data *changed to* Means Mechanical Cost Data (Year).
0193-1962 Aircraft Owners Bulletin. Kansas-Missouri-Southern Illinois Edition†
0193-1997 Heart of America Aquarium Society News
0193-2012 Horses Unlimited†
0193-2020 Kansas City Magazine
0193-2039 Mid-Continent Purchaser
0193-2047 Mid-America Commerce & Industry
0193-2055 Modern Jeweler. South-East†
0193-2063 Modern Jeweler. North Central†
0193-2071 Modern Jeweler. South-Central†
0193-208X Modern Jeweler. National Executive
0193-2098 Modern Jeweler. Western†
0193-2101 Modern Jeweler. North-East†
0193-211X Pilot News†
0193-2128 Service Reporter
0193-2136 Training World
0193-2241 Wall Street Journal (Western Edition)
0193-225X Wall Street Journal (Southwest Edition)
0193-2276 Graduating Engineer
0193-2284 Cigar Magazine†
0193-2306 Research in Experimental Economics
0193-2381 Fodor's Budget Britain *changed to* Fodor's Affordable Great Britain.
0193-239X Connecticut Honey Bee
0193-2446 Southern Changes
0193-2551 Giftware News
0193-2586 Inside Contracting *see* 0888-0387
0193-2683 Home Health Review *see* 0738-467X
0193-2691 Journal of Dispersion Science and Technology
0193-2713 Operant Subjectivity
0193-273X S O L I N E W S
0193-2748 Studies in Formative Spirituality
0193-2799 Truck Stop Management†
0193-2861 Satellite Week
0193-2993 Rancho Bernardo†
0193-3086 O D L Source
0193-3108 New Florida†
0193-3140 Aquaculture Digest *see* 1047-5672
0193-3140 Aquaculture Digest *changed to* Mollusk Farming U S A.
0193-3221 Business Opportunities Journal
0193-323X Chilton's Food Engineering
0193-3248 Chilton's Distribution Worldwide *see* 0273-6721
0193-3264 Chilton's Automotive Marketing
0193-3299 O A G Travel Planner and Hotel-Motel Guide. North American Edition *see* 1053-0002
0193-3329 World Opinion Update
0193-3396 Science and Nature†
0193-340X Contemporary Metabolism
0193-3418 Annual National Conference on Labor at New York University. Proceedings
0193-3434 Speech and Language: Advances in Basic Research and Practice†
0193-3442 Ukrainian American Index: The Ukrainian Weekly†
0193-3450 Fish Kills Report *see* 0193-3558
0193-3469 Communist†
0193-3477 Clear Track
0193-3485 Revolutionary Worker
0193-3507 Pacific Boating Almanac. Southern California, Arizona, Baja
0193-3515 Pacific Boating Almanac. Northern California & Nevada
0193-3558 U.S. Environmental Protection Agency. Fish Kills Caused by Pollution†
0193-3604 Journal of Religious Studies
0193-3612 Revolution
0193-3639 Cable and Station Coverage Atlas and 35-Mile Zone Maps *changed to* Cable and Station Coverage Atlas.
0193-3655 Early Warning Report
0193-3663 Public Broadcasting Report
0193-3736 Advances in Agricultural Technology†
0193-3760 Agricultural Reviews and Manuals†
0193-3817 Agricultural Research Results†
0193-3876 Coal Industry News†
0193-3892 Coronica
0193-3906 Military Law Reporter
0193-3914 Pulpit Helps
0193-3922 Journal for Specialists in Group Work
0193-3949 Printing Trades Blue Book. Delaware Valley-Ohio Edition *see* 1044-7970
0193-3973 Journal of Applied Developmental Psychology
0193-4015 Pretrial Reporter
0193-4066 C E P Newsletter *changed to* C E P Research Report.
0193-4120 Test Engineering & Management
0193-418X Schools & Civil Rights News†
0193-4198 Water Flying Annual
0193-4201 Significant Issues Facing Directors
0193-421X Greyledge Review†
0193-4279 Directorship
0193-4287 New Special Libraries
0193-4295 Digital I Cs D.A.T.A. Book *changed to* Digital I Cs D.A.T.A. Digest.
0193-4309 Tar Heel Libraries
0193-4406 Brimleyana
0193-4414 Business Advocate *changed to* Business Counsel.
0193-4422 R T C A Digest
0193-4457 Advertising - Communications Times
0193-4503 Navajo Education Newsletter *changed to* Navajo Area Newsletter.
0193-4511 Science (Year)†
0193-4600 Blue Chip Economic Indicators
0193-4716 Ways & Means
0193-4783 Across the Seas†
0193-4791 Hudson Forum†
0193-4864 Intellectual Property Law Review
0193-4872 Harvard Journal of Law and Public Policy
0193-4929 Reviews in Inorganic Chemistry
0193-4953 Towers Club U S A Newsletter
0193-497X Wine Spectator
0193-5011 American Chemical Society. Directory of Graduate Research
0193-502X Focus - Metropolitan Philadelphia's Business Newsmagazine
0193-5135 P R N Radio Guide†
0193-5151 American Petroleum Institute. Central Abstracting and Indexing Service. Thesaurus *changed to* American Petroleum Institute. Central Abstracting & Information Services. Thesaurus.
0193-5186 Neurochemical Transmitters and Modulators†
0193-5216 Hillside Journal of Clinical Psychiatry†
0193-5321 St. Louis Bowling Review
0193-533X Gazette (New York)
0193-5356 New Mexico Independent
0193-5364 Recent Researches in the Music of the Nineteenth and Early Twentieth Centuries
0193-5372 American Suzuki Journal
0193-5380 Eighteenth Century: Theory and Interpretation
0193-5399 Solar Energy Digest *changed to* International Solar Energy Intelligence Report.
0193-5488 Cognition and Brain Theory†
0193-550X Legislative Manual *changed to* Refusal of Treatment Legislation (Year).
0193-5615 Anthropology and Humanism Quarterly
0193-5712 Louisiana Business Survey
0193-5739 Labor & Employment Law
0193-5755 Smoloskyp†
0193-5771 Tax Angles†
0193-578X A I T Newsletter *see* 1060-5649
0193-5798 Enclitic
0193-5895 Research in Law and Economics
0193-5933 Geothermal Resources Council. Transactions
0193-5941 Journal of Social and Political Studies *see* 0278-839X
0193-5968 Living City
0193-600X International Association of Buddhist Studies. Journal
0193-6093 A C S U S Newsletter *see* 0272-2011
0193-6131 Junior Eagle†
0193-614X Chilton's E C N - Electronic Component News
0193-6174 Chilton's Instrument and Apparatus News *changed to* Instrumentation & Automation News.
0193-628X Chilton's C C J *see* 0734-1423
0193-6301 Black Warrior Review
0193-6336 By Valor & Arms†
0193-6417 U S Book Publishing Yearbook and Directory†
0193-645X Lighting Supply & Design
0193-6468 Econoscope View
0193-6484 Chemistry International
0193-6530 I E E E International Solid State Circuits Conference. Digest of Technical Papers
0193-6581 American Academy of Actuaries. Journal†
0193-6700 Western Journal of Speech Communication *see* 1057-0314
0193-6808 Managing Housing Letter
0193-6832 Buss†
0193-6840 Directory of Online Databases
0193-6859 American Popular Culture
0193-6867 Art Reference Collection
0193-6875 Contributions to the Study of Science Fiction and Fantasy
0193-6883 Denominations in America
0193-6891 Popular Culture Bio-Bibliographies
0193-6913 Robotics Today
0193-693X C L E Register *changed to* C L E Journal and Register.
0193-6956 Artspace (Albuquerque)
0193-7022 Chilton's Motor Age
0193-7103 Mary Wollstonecraft Journal *see* 0147-1759
0193-7146 American Humor *see* 0095-280X
0193-7189 Policy Analysis and Information Systems *see* 0195-9301
0193-7197 Journal of Vinyl Technology
0193-7235 Journal of Sport and Social Issues
0193-726X Brake and Front End
0193-7308 A I P R (American Industrial Properties Report) *see* 0746-0023
0193-7367 Judicial Conduct Reporter
0193-7375 Counseling and Human Development
0193-7383 Editorial Eye
0193-7391 Publishing in the Output Mode†
0193-7405 Central Serials Record†
0193-7421 Child Behavior and Development
0193-7472 Builder Architect-Contractor Engineer *changed to* Builder Architect.
0193-7480 Arizona Business - Industry
0193-757X Zoning Law Anthology†
0193-7618 California Women
0193-7626 Extracts *see* 0193-8991
0193-7642 National Farm Tractor & Implement Blue Book
0193-7677 Travel Marketing *changed to* Travel Market Yearbook (1980).
0193-7758 I R B: A Review of Human Subjects Research
0193-7774 Chinoperl Papers
0193-7782 A F T A *changed to* Crow.
0193-7812 New England Report *changed to* First National Bank of Boston. Economic Review.
0193-7871 World Eagle
0193-7901 Agrow-Marketer *see* 0886-4780
0193-791X Neighborhood Works
0193-7928 Health Funds Development Letter
0193-7944 South America (New York)
0193-8010 Gilbert Law Summaries. Criminal Procedure
0193-8029 Congressional Research Service Review
0193-8037 Growing Parent Newsletter
0193-8061 Phoebus (Tempe)
0193-8118 American Romanian Review†
0193-8207 American Indian Libraries Newsletter
0193-8274 Sharing the Practice
0193-8312 Women's Track World
0193-8320 Gospel in Context *see* 0272-6122
0193-8339 Contemporary Poetry *changed to* Poesis: A Journal of Criticism.
0193-8355 Natural Hazards Observer
0193-8371 City & Town (North Little Rock)
0193-8398 Comm-Ent: Hastings Journal of Communications and Entertainment Law *changed to* Hastings Communications and Entertainment Law Journal (Comm - Ent).
0193-8401 Sporting Goods Market
0193-841X Evaluation Review
0193-8452 Contemplative Review *see* 0890-5568
0193-8487 Farm and Garden Index†
0193-8495 Annual Hardwood Symposium. Proceedings
0193-8509 Arizona-Nevada Academy of Science. Journal
0193-855X Anthropology
0193-8568 Modern Technics in Surgery. Urologic Surgery
0193-8576 Electron Device Letters *see* 0741-3106
0193-8584 Bicycle Resource Guide†
0193-8622 Educational Resources Directory
0193-8630 Hub Rail *see* 0017-7857
0193-869X Synthesis (San Francisco) *changed to* Social Justice.
0193-8703 Contemporary Marxism *changed to* Social Justice.
0193-8738 Latin American Petroleum Directory†
0193-8770 Chicago Genealogical Society. Newsletter
0193-8991 Melville Society Extracts
0193-9009 Human Services in the Rural Environment
0193-9025 Food Research Institute Studies
0193-9033 Fodor's Budget Germany *changed to* Fodor's Affordable Germany.
0193-9041 Contributions to the Study of Music and Dance
0193-905X Index to International Public Opinion
0193-9106 Green Markets Fertilizer Price Handbook†
0193-9122 Fodor's Budget Caribbean *changed to* Fodor's Great Travel Values: Caribbean.
0193-919X Convenience Stores *see* 0274-869X
0193-9211 Word & Spirit
0193-922X Criminal Practices *see* 0193-8010
0193-9270 International Petroleum Finance
0193-936X Epidemiologic Reviews
0193-9416 New Directions for Mental Health Services
0193-9459 Western Journal of Nursing Research
0193-953X Psychiatric Clinics of North America
0193-9556 Fodor's Florida
0193-9564 Worcester Art Museum. Journal†
0193-9599 Videolog: Programs for Business and Technology *see* 0731-454X

0193-9602 Programs for General Interest and Entertainment *changed to* General Interest and Education Videolog.
0193-9629 University of Wisconsin, Madison. Engineering Experiment Station. Annual Report
0193-970X Public Administration Series: Bibliography†
0193-9777 Irish Renaissance Annual†
0193-9866 Military Images Magazine *see* 1040-4961
0193-9920 Directory of Top Computer Executives
0193-9939 Hospital Fund Raising Newsletter *changed to* Healthcare Fund Raising Newsletter.
0194-0090 Nephrology Reviews†
0194-0104 NoLoad Fund X
0194-0139 Refundle Bundle
0194-0147 Water Pollution Control
0194-0236 Focus on Learning†
0194-0252 Inside N R C
0194-0287 Environmental Science and Technology: A Wiley-Interscience Series of Texts and Monographs
0194-0406 B I N California Goldbook†
0194-0430 Journal of Contemporary Business†
0194-0449 Unite (Chicago)
0194-0465 Seminars in Family Medicine†
0194-049X Rutgers Art Review
0194-0538 Biochemistry: Series of Monographs
0194-0546 Conference Papers Annual Index
0194-0589 Colorado North Review
0194-0694 Information Intelligence Online Newsletter *changed to* Online Newsletter.
0194-0767 National Employment Listing Service for the Criminal Justice System. Bulletin *changed to* National Employment Listing Service (N E L S) Bulletin.
0194-0775 National Employment Listing Service for Human Services. Bulletin *changed to* National Employment Listing Service (N E L S) Bulletin.
0194-083X Green Book of Home Improvement Contractors†
0194-0856 C P P A X Newsletter
0194-0902 S I S T M Quarterly Incorporating Brain Theory Newsletter (Society for the Interdisciplinary Study of the Mind) *see* 0193-5488
0194-0910 National Hardwood Magazine
0194-0929 Rice Farming and Rice Industry News
0194-0937 Southeast Farm Press
0194-0953 Criminal Justice History
0194-0988 Transfer Credit Practices of Designated Educational Institutions
0194-1038 Risk Management News
0194-1062 Not Man Apart *changed to* Friends of the Earth. Magazine.
0194-1070 Art - World
0194-1089 Hudson Home Magazine *see* 0278-2839
0194-1240 Tennessee Journal
0194-1259 Tennessee Attorneys Memo *changed to* Tennessee Attorneys Memo, Permanent Edition.
0194-1291 Washington Drug Letter (Washington, 1979)
0194-1305 American Arts *see* 0748-6723
0194-1313 Mickle Street Review†
0194-1321 Home Center Magazine *see* 1045-9367
0194-1356 Architecture Series: Bibliography†
0194-1380 Pool News Directory *changed to* Pool & Spa News Source Book.
0194-1410 Chilton's Truck and Off-Highway Industries *changed to* Truck & Off-Highway Industries.
0194-1429 Specialty Food Merchandising
0194-1445 Catalyst for Environment - Energy
0194-1453 Northeastern Geology
0194-1461 Measurements & Control News
0194-150X Log Trucker
0194-1526 Film News Omnibus
0194-1607 Media Science Newsletter *changed to* The Marketing Pulse.
0194-164X Hungarian Studies Newsletter
0194-1658 Journal of Intravenous Therapy
0194-1666 Commentaries on Research in Breast Disease†
0194-1682 California Correctional News
0194-1690 Visions *changed to* Visions International.
0194-1704 National Employment Listing Service for the Criminal Justice System. Federal Employment Information Directory†
0194-1720 Seminars in Ultrasound *see* 0887-2171
0194-178X Directory of Nightclubs, Hotels, Theatres, Lounges & Discotheques
0194-1879 Houston Journal of International Law
0194-1895 Annual Microprogramming Workshop. Proceedings *changed to* Microprogramming and Microarchitecture Workshop. Proceedings.
0194-1909 Critical Issues
0194-1941 Income - Expense Analysis: Conventional Apartments
0194-195X Data Communications Buyers' Guide
0194-1968 Shelby Report of the Southeast
0194-2158 Journal of Community Communications†
0194-2174 Dispensing Optician†
0194-2190 Broadcast Equipment Exchange *see* 0274-8541
0194-2212 Student Aid News
0194-2239 Higher Education Daily *see* 0013-1261
0194-2247 Federal Grants & Contracts Weekly
0194-2255 Education of the Handicapped
0194-2263 Nation's Schools Report†
0194-2271 School Law News
0194-228X Tax-Exempt News *changed to* NonProfit Insights.
0194-231X Education and Work *changed to* Vocational Training News.
0194-2344 Equal Opportunity in Higher Education *see* 0194-2271
0194-2352 Health Grants & Contracts Weekly
0194-2360 Labor Relations in Education *changed to* Employee Relations in Education.
0194-2387 Executive Golfer
0194-2468 Gas Industries E and A News *changed to* Gas Industries Magazine.
0194-2484 Home Video†
0194-2492 Babcox's Importcar *see* 0735-7877
0194-2506 Magazine Age *changed to* Inside Media.
0194-2514 Diagnostic Imaging
0194-2557 Cardiac Alert
0194-2581 Savvy *changed to* Savvy Woman.
0194-259X Journal of Respiratory Diseases
0194-2603 Los Angeles Business Journal
0194-262X Science & Technology Libraries
0194-2638 Physical & Occupational Therapy in Pediatrics
0194-2670 University of New Mexico. Division of Government Research. Monograph Series
0194-2778 Biomedical Engineering and Computation Series
0194-2816 Scripps Institution of Oceanography (Year) *see* 1046-9443
0194-2859 Teacher Update
0194-2875 Industrial Organization Review
0194-2883 Cincinnati Historical Society Bulletin *see* 0746-3472
0194-2905 Chilton's Jewelers' Circular-Keystone
0194-2913 California Communities
0194-2948 Puppetry in Education News
0194-2972 Price Trends of Food Ingredients Newsletter
0194-2980 Food Packaging and Labeling Newsletter
0194-2999 Watermark *changed to* Letter to Libraries.
0194-3022 Catalog Showroom Merchandiser *changed to* C S M.
0194-3030 Wilderness Record
0194-3057 Research in Labor Economics
0194-3073 C P E R
0194-3081 New Directions for Community Colleges
0194-3243 Presstime
0194-3294 Vette'n U S A
0194-3340 World Record Game Fishes
0194-3359 Technology & Society†
0194-3413 Archaeological News
0194-3448 American Journal of Theology & Philosophy
0194-3502 Crossroad
0194-3510 Leaders
0194-357X Compute
0194-3588 D M News
0194-360X Furniture - Today
0194-3650 Harvard Architecture Review
0194-3766 Allied Health Education Directory
0194-3790 Handbook of the Nations
0194-3812 Dog Groomers Gazette *changed to* Groomers Gazette.
0194-3847 Nielsen's New Products Bulletin *see* 0738-0690
0194-388X Mississippi Libraries
0194-3901 Hall Radio Report *see* 0273-3056
0194-3944 Wet
0194-3960 Research in Human Capital and Development
0194-4053 Congressional Studies *see* 0734-3469
0194-407X Council for Agricultural Science and Technology. Special Publications
0194-4088 Council for Agricultural Science and Technology. Task Force Reports
0194-4096 Comments from C A S T
0194-410X Association of Collegiate Schools of Architecture. Proceedings of the Annual Meeting
0194-4118 Newscribes
0194-4134 Computer Law Monograph Series†
0194-4150 Fodor's Budget France *changed to* Fodor's Affordable France.
0194-4185 Critical Mass Energy Journal *changed to* Connections (Washington).
0194-4193 Stumpwork Society Chronicle
0194-4231 Quarterly West
0194-4282 Beefmaster Cowman
0194-4312 Lifetimes
0194-4320 North American Hunter
0194-4339 Filmmakers' Monthly
0194-4347 Dental Graduate *see* 0199-736X
0194-4363 American Planning Association. Journal
0194-4371 Mariah - Outside *see* 0278-1433
0194-438X New Wine *see* 0892-9300
0194-4444 Fluid and Lubricant Ideas *see* 0747-2722
0194-4495 Seeds
0194-4517 Earth Shelter Digest and Energy Report *changed to* Earth Shelter Living. Newsletter.
0194-4525 Midlands Business Journal
0194-4533 Modern Drummer
0194-4584 Africa Update
0194-4592 Fashions Magazine†
0194-4622 Great Lakes Sailing Scanner
0194-4665 P.R.O.'s Magazine
0194-472X Journal of Marital and Family Therapy
0194-4746 Electrical Energy Management†
0194-4800 Florida Administrative Law Reports
0194-4851 TypeWorld
0194-4908 Abstracts of Health Care Management Studies†
0194-5025 68 Micro Journal
0194-5041 Nostalgia World
0194-5068 Midwest Flyer Magazine
0194-5092 Air Progress Aviation Review†
0194-5106 Journal of Kansas Pharmacy
0194-5181 Today's O R Nurse
0194-5246 Emphasis on Faith and Living
0194-5254 Eastern Grape Grower and Winery News *see* 1047-4951
0194-5297 Saluki Quarterly
0194-5343 Health Foods Communicator
0194-5351 Pool & Spa News
0194-5386 Earthton†
0194-5408 Intermountain Golf News†
0194-5416 Washington Actions on Health *see* 0886-2095
0194-5467 Photographer's Forum
0194-5475 Writing (Northbrook)
0194-5483 Air Trails Classic Flying Models†
0194-5572 Current Energy and Ecology *changed to* Biology Bulletin Monthly.
0194-567X Kentucky Pharmacist
0194-570X Van, Pickup and Offroad World†
0194-5769 Dakota Country
0194-5785 Civitan Magazine
0194-5823 Retriever International†
0194-5874 H P M (Heating and Plumbing Merchandiser) *changed to* Heating, Air Conditioning & Plumbing Products.
0194-5912 Maintenance Supervisor's Bulletin
0194-5955 Timber Mart-South
0194-598X Missouri Police Chief
0194-5998 Otolaryngology - Head and Neck Surgery
0194-603X Handling and Shipping Management *see* 0895-8548
0194-6161 World Meetings: Social & Behavioral Sciences, Human Services and Management
0194-6196 Payroll Exchange
0194-6218 Propeller
0194-6277 Michigan Food & Beverage†
0194-634X Kansas Insurance
0194-6404 Old Cars Price Guide
0194-6420 I C C A's Newsletter *see* 0885-6788
0194-6455 Thermophysics and Electronics Newsletter
0194-648X Chic Magazine
0194-6498 A W P Newsletter *changed to* A W P Chronicle.
0194-6536 American Chiropractor
0194-6552 Inside Running
0194-6587 B I D Service Weekly
0194-6595 International Journal of the Sociology of Law
0194-6625 AgReview†
0194-6706 Dog Sports
0194-6730 Skeptical Inquirer
0194-6803 Arabian Horse Express
0194-6900 Real Estate Intelligence Report†
0194-6919 People & Taxes†
0194-7060 Southern California Contractor
0194-7079 Model Builder
0194-7176 A H E A Action
0194-7206 Newf-Tide
0194-7249 La Bobina - Notivest
0194-7257 Landscape Contractor
0194-729X A G D Impact
0194-7419 Heavy Duty Aftermarket Exchange *see* 0198-6678
0194-7435 Arizona Professional Engineer†
0194-7508 Immunology and Allergy Practice
0194-7613 Stock Service Digest
0194-763X United Fresh Fruit and Vegetable Association. Monthly Supply Letter†
0194-7648 Journal of Legal Medicine
0194-7818 Handicapped Requirements Handbook
0194-7869 Comics Journal
0194-7885 Electronic Warfare - Defense Electronics *see* 0278-3479
0194-7893 Lacrosse
0194-7958 Sophia
0194-7990 Amerikai Magyar Szo
0194-8008 American Craft
0194-8032 Heartbeat (Orlando)
0194-8075 OnComputing *see* 0279-4721
0194-8083 Knitting World
0194-8121 The Forum (New York, 1978)
0194-813X New Mexico Beverage Analyst
0194-8261 C A H P E R Journal/Times *see* 0273-6896
0194-827X Aircraft Owners Bulletin. Eastern Nebraska-Iowa-Western Illinois Edition†
0194-8326 Caribbean Business
0194-8369 Soundings Trade Only
0194-8431 Pittsburgh
0194-844X Medical Device & Diagnostic Industry
0194-8490 DollarSense

ISSN

5638 ISSN INDEX

0194-8652 A C Flyer
0194-8660 Government-Sponsored Research on Foreign Affairs
0194-8717 Supervisor's Safety Clinic†
0194-8814 Horse & Chariot†
0194-8822 Tax, Financial and Estate Planning for the Owner of a Closely-Held Corporation *changed to* Closely Held Corporation: Tax, Financial and Estate Planning.
0194-8849 A E A Advocate
0194-8857 Florida Gulf Coast Living *changed to* Florida Gulf Coast Homebuyer's Guide.
0194-8903 Construction Dimensions Magazine
0194-9039 Flight Reports
0194-9071 A I Art Insight *changed to* Art Insight Southwest.
0194-9098 Tennis Week
0194-9101 Mercer Business Magazine
0194-911X Hypertension
0194-9144 Fashionews†
0194-9225 News Front Business Trends†
0194-9268 N A H R O Monitor
0194-9314 Surfing
0194-939X National Bus Trader
0194-9535 Esquire (1979)
0194-9543 Angus Journal
0194-9756 Dog (Marshall)
0194-9772 Cotton Grower
0194-9845 Impact: Information Technology *see* 0739-8182
0194-9888 Choppers & Big Bike Magazine†
0194-9977 Space Gamer†
0195-0118 Textile Rental
0195-0207 Exeter
0195-0223 Eastern Basketball Magazine
0195-0282 American Journal of Intravenous Therapy and Clinical Nutrition *changed to* Intravenous Therapy News.
0195-0304 International Federation of Organic Agriculture Movements. Bulletin
0195-0347 Aviators Hot Line
0195-0363 U F C W Action
0195-038X Muzzleloading Artilleryman *see* 0884-4747
0195-0495 Specialty Advertising Business
0195-0509 Sport Trucking†
0195-0673 Washington Agricultural Record
0195-072X Gallery
0195-0738 Journal of Energy Resources Technology
0195-0819 Chicago Apparel News
0195-0894 Springfield! Magazine
0195-0932 Abrasive Engineering Society Magazine
0195-0967 Parents
0195-0983 New Jersey Lawyer
0195-1017 Film News (1979) *changed to* Film & Video News (1979).
0195-1157 Community Jobs (Washington)
0195-1351 Biblical Illustrator
0195-136X Baptist Young Adults
0195-1386 Garden Supply Retailer†
0195-1386 Garden Supply Retailer Green Book
0195-1416 Colonial Homes
0195-1513 N F I B
0195-153X S N E A Impact: The Student Voice of the United Teaching Profession
0195-1548 Pulpit Resource
0195-1564 Automotive Executive
0195-1599 New Gun Week
0195-1661 Corvette Fever
0195-1688 Women's Political Times
0195-1696 Obscenity Law Bulletin
0195-1718 Soundview Executive Book Summaries
0195-1777 A A R Times *see* 0893-8520
0195-1785 Solar Law Reporter†
0195-1793 Minnesota (St. Paul)†
0195-1858 Insurance Litigation Reporter
0195-1874 Home Energy Digest & Wood Burning Quarterly†
0195-1920 Phalanx
0195-198X Southwest Business and Economic Review *see* 8750-4294
0195-2013 Old Time Crochet Patterns and Designs *see* 1050-9518
0195-2056 Asian Week
0195-2064 Journal of Retail Banking
0195-2099 Illinois Pharmacist
0195-2137 Teens' and Boys' Magazine†
0195-2196 HomeOwner†
0195-2242 New Directions for Continuing Education *changed to* New Directions for Adult and Continuing Education.
0195-2250 Global Communications
0195-2269 New Directions for Child Development
0195-2358 Informer (Washington)†
0195-2366 Material Handling Product News
0195-2390 Equal Employment News
0195-2439 Women's Circle Home Cooking *changed to* Home Cooking.
0195-2552 Yankee Food Service
0195-2617 Federal Grants Management Handbook
0195-2633 British Heritage
0195-265X Billy James Hargis' Christian Crusade
0195-2692 Lost Treasure
0195-2781 P T A Today
0195-282X Carolina Lifestyle†
0195-2889 Journal Francais d'Amerique
0195-2900 Indianapolis Monthly
0195-2986 A A P G Explorer
0195-3036 Cosmetic Technology†
0195-3117 True Story
0195-315X Internal Medicine Alert
0195-3184 Home Textiles Today
0195-3192 New Jersey Reporter
0195-3346 F C X Carolina Cooperator†
0195-3354 Nursing Abstracts
0195-3370 Technology Tomorrow†
0195-3389 Education Tomorrow†
0195-3397 Business Tomorrow†
0195-3419 Friends of the Library National Notebook *changed to* Friends of Libraries U S A National Notebook.
0195-3443 Maryland Documents
0195-3478 Inside Sports
0195-3508 Channel (Los Angeles)†
0195-3516 Exit
0195-3524 Oil Spill Intelligence Report
0195-3532 San Francisco Business Journal†
0195-3567 Computer Law Bibliography†
0195-3591 C F T C Databook†
0195-3613 Journal of Labor Research
0195-363X A L L-O-Grams
0195-3729 Giustizia†
0195-3737 Justicia
0195-3761 Checklist of Congressional Hearings and Committee Prints *changed to* Congress in Print.
0195-377X L A C U S Forum
0195-3842 Current Clinical Topics in Infectious Diseases
0195-3850 Darkroom & Creative Camera Techniques
0195-3869 H R A F Newsletter†
0195-3966 M M I Press Symposium Series
0195-3974 World Trade & Business Digest†
0195-3982 Griffith Observer
0195-3990 College and University Administrators Directory
0195-4016 Finger Lakes Library System. Newsletter
0195-4024 Environmental Nutrition Newsletter *see* 0893-4452
0195-4121 County Lines
0195-4156 Careers (Saratoga)
0195-4202 Oxbridge Directory of Ethnic Periodicals†
0195-4210 Symposium on Computer Applications in Medical Care. Proceedings
0195-4296 Marketing and Media Decisions *see* 1055-176X
0195-4326 Design Directory *see* 0889-7611
0195-4342 Hellenic American Society. Journal *see* 0364-2976
0195-4350 Journal of Digital Systems *see* 0888-224X
0195-4407 Appraisal Review and Mortgage Underwriting Journal
0195-4474 Energy Conservation Digest
0195-4636 Workbook
0195-475X Journal of Mayan Linguistics
0195-4865 Association of Food and Drug Officials Quarterly Bulletin *changed to* Association of Food and Drug Officials. Journal.
0195-4903 Center for Southern Folklore Magazine†
0195-4911 C A Selects. Atomic Spectroscopy
0195-4938 C A Selects. Chemical Instrumentation
0195-4946 C A Selects. Chemical Processing Apparatus
0195-4962 C A Selects. Electrophoresis
0195-4970 C A Selects. Emulsion Polymerization
0195-4989 C A Selects. Fluidized Solids Technology
0195-4997 C A Selects. Fuel & Lubricant Additives
0195-5012 C A Selects. Inorganic & Organometallic Reaction Systems
0195-5020 C A Selects. Ion-Containing Polymers
0195-5039 C A Selects. Laser Applications
0195-5063 C A Selects. Optical and Photosensitive Materials
0195-5071 C A Selects. Optimization of Organic Reactions
0195-508X C A Selects. Organic Stereochemistry
0195-5101 C A Selects. Organotin Chemistry
0195-511X C A Selects. Plastic Films
0195-5128 C A Selects. Polymer Morphology
0195-5136 C A Selects. Porphyrins
0195-5152 C A Selects. Surface Analysis
0195-5160 C A Selects. Synfuels
0195-5179 C A Selects. Synthetic Macrocyclic Compounds
0195-5187 C A Selects. Thermal Analysis
0195-5195 C A Selects. Ultrafiltration
0195-5209 C A Selects. Ultraviolet & Visible Spectroscopy
0195-5217 C A Selects. High Performance Liquid Chromatography
0195-5241 National Center for State Courts. Report
0195-5314 Pennmarva†
0195-5365 Science Fiction Chronicle
0195-5373 Atomic Spectroscopy
0195-539X Who's Who in California Business and Finance†
0195-5616 Veterinary Clinics of North America: Small Animal Practice
0195-5624 Mid-Am Reporter
0195-5632 Army Motors
0195-5705 Focus (Madison)
0195-5764 Landscape Architecture Technical Information Series
0195-5780 Plate World
0195-5810 Massachusetts Directory of Manufacturers
0195-5853 Memory I Cs D.A.T.A. Book *see* 1048-2598
0195-590X Canadian Oil Industry Directory†
0195-5926 Pediatric Social Work
0195-5969 Stepfamily Bulletin *changed to* Stepfamilies.
0195-5977 Journal of Holistic Medicine†
0195-6000 Journal of Public and International Affairs†
0195-6051 Journal of Popular Film and Television
0195-6094 Gray Herbarium. Contributions†
0195-6108 A J N R
0195-6116 Journal of Offender Counseling, Services and Rehabilitation *see* 1050-9674
0195-6124 Outdoor Writers Association of America. Directory
0195-6140 People's Computers *see* 0164-5846
0195-6167 Music Theory Spectrum
0195-6175 California Political Week
0195-6183 Woman Poet
0195-623X International Symposium on Multiple-Valued Logic. Proceedings
0195-6310 Comparative Social Research
0195-6353 Index to the Chicago Tribune†
0195-6361 Index to Washington Post†
0195-6396 Index to the San Francisco Chronicle *see* 0893-2425
0195-640X Index to the New Orleans Times-Picayune *see* 0893-2484
0195-6418 Index to the Los Angeles Times *see* 0742-4817
0195-6426 Bell and Howell Newspaper Index to the American Banker *changed to* Index to the American Banker.
0195-6434 Index to the Denver Post *see* 0893-2441
0195-6442 Index to the Chicago Sun-Times†
0195-6450 Defense Monitor
0195-6515 Pacific Fishing
0195-654X Home Fashion Textiles *see* 0896-7962
0195-6574 Energy Journal
0195-6582 Rodale's New Shelter *see* 1042-4601
0195-6612 Communications and Information Handling Equipment & Services: Semi-Annual Directory/Index†
0195-6639 State Legislative Leadership, Committees and Staff
0195-6655 Inter-American Music Review
0195-6663 Appetite
0195-6671 Cretaceous Research
0195-668X European Heart Journal
0195-6698 European Journal of Combinatorics
0195-6701 Journal of Hospital Infection
0195-6728 Discotheque Magazine
0195-6744 American Journal of Education
0195-6752 Journal of Historical Review
0195-6760 Swim Swim
0195-6779 Media History Digest
0195-6787 International Journal of Oral History *changed to* International Annual of Oral History.
0195-6817 New Jersey Media Directory *see* 0883-9778
0195-6876 Engineering Times
0195-6884 Eton Journal of Real Estate Investment†
0195-6981 Association of Executive Recruiting Consultants. Directory†
0195-7031 C I S Highlights†
0195-7082 Arizona State Industrial Directory *see* 0739-8476
0195-7112 Minnesota State Industrial Directory *see* 0740-6061
0195-7120 Montana State Industrial Directory *see* 0740-6088
0195-7139 Nevada State Industrial Directory *see* 0740-6126
0195-7147 Oregon State Industrial Directory *see* 0740-610X
0195-7155 Wisconsin State Industrial Directory *see* 0740-6053
0195-7163 Arcadia Bibliographica Virorum Eruditorum
0195-7244 Chilton's Distribution *see* 0273-6721
0195-7260 Papers in Romance†
0195-7279 Pleasures of Cooking†
0195-7287 E F T Report
0195-7295 Videolog: Programs for the Health Sciences *see* 0731-5945
0195-7384 Je Me Souviens
0195-7430 C M J Progressive Media *changed to* C M J New Music Report.
0195-7449 Research in Race and Ethnic Relations
0195-7473 Political Communication and Persuasion
0195-749X Federal Regulatory Directory
0195-7554 International Journal for the Study of Animal Problems†
0195-7589 U S Import Weekly *see* 0748-0172
0195-7597 Journal for Vocational Special Needs Education
0195-7600 New Roots; for the Northeast *changed to* Renewable Energy News: Northeast.
0195-7619 Directory of New England Newspapers, College Publications, Periodicals, and Radio and Television Stations *see* 0883-9999
0195-7678 The Comparatist
0195-7686 Urban, State, and Local Law Newsletter
0195-7708 Sexually Transmitted Diseases. Abstracts and Bibliography *changed to* Survey of Research for Sexually Transmitted Diseases.

ISSN

ISSN INDEX 5639

ISSN	Title
0195-7716	Volumes: The Jewish Book Report†
0195-7732	Women & Politics
0195-7740	National Council on Radiation Protection and Measurements. Proceedings of the Annual Meeting
0195-7783	Illinois Government Research†
0195-7791	Social Science Monitor†
0195-7848	Cumberland Journal†
0195-7910	American Journal of Forensic Medicine and Pathology
0195-7988	Social Planning - Policy & Development Abstracts
0195-7996	United States Pharmacopeia - National Formulary
0195-8011	A M S Studies in the Renaissance
0195-802X	Hofstra University Cultural and Intercultural Studies†
0195-8054	Silver and Gold Report
0195-8062	Air California Magazine *changed to* AirCal.
0195-8100	Sports Literature Index
0195-8127	Journal of Psychiatric Treatment and Evaluation†
0195-8178	Alarm Installer and Dealer *changed to* Security Sales.
0195-8186	Interloop†
0195-8194	Mobility (Washington)
0195-8208	Art & Antiques
0195-8267	American Classic Screen
0195-8402	Health Education Quarterly
0195-8437	Farm, Ranch and Country Vacations
0195-8445	Adventure Travel (New York) *changed to* Adventure Travel North America.
0195-8453	Rocky Mountain Medieval and Renaissance Association. Journal
0195-8461	Blue Book of Major Home Builders
0195-847X	Gold Book of MultiHousing
0195-8496	Plumbers Ink†
0195-8550	Economic Forum (Salt Lake City)†
0195-8569	Electric Vehicle Council Newsletter†
0195-8631	Health Care Financing Review
0195-8682	Metas
0195-8690	National Cancer Institute. Annual Report†
0195-878X	Advances in Shock Research†
0195-8798	University of Virginia Alumni News
0195-8895	World Press Review
0195-8933	Human Sexuality Update†
0195-8941	Hudson Home Products Directory†
0195-895X	Best Newspaper Writing
0195-9085	Horizons in Biblical Theology
0195-9107	Hazardous Materials Management Journal†
0195-9131	Medicine and Science in Sports and Exercise
0195-914X	Abraham Lincoln Association. Papers *see* 0898-4212
0195-9204	Leadership (Washington)
0195-9212	Baha'i News†
0195-9255	Environmental Impact Assessment Review
0195-9263	Hyperbaric Oxygen Review *see* 0884-1225
0195-9271	International Journal of Infrared and Millimeter Waves
0195-928X	International Journal of Thermophysics
0195-9298	Journal of Nondestructive Evaluation
0195-9301	International Journal of Policy Analysis and Information Systems†
0195-931X	Western Wood Products Association. Statistical Yearbook
0195-9336	Destination of Shipments of Western Wood Species by State
0195-9344	Western Wood Products Association. Quarterly Injury & Illness Incidence Report
0195-9379	Starship *see* 0195-5365
0195-9387	Christian Anti-Communism Crusade. Newsletter
0195-9395	Lumber Price Index. Inland Index
0195-9409	Western Wood Products Association. Monthly F.O.B. Price Summary, Past Sales. Inland Mills
0195-9417	Infection Control *see* 0899-823X
0195-9425	Journal of Security Administration
0195-945X	American Theatre Annual†
0195-9468	Spenser Studies
0195-9492	Index to Government Regulation *changed to* Index to Chemical Regulations.
0195-9611	Pacific Skipper *see* 0274-905X
0195-9646	Packet
0195-9670	Political Animal *see* 0747-5659
0195-9700	Education's Federal Funding Alert†
0195-9735	Contest Hotline
0195-9743	Woman in History
0195-9751	University - Government - Industry Microelectronics Symposium. Proceedings
0195-9883	E T Journal *see* 0270-1170
0195-9948	Journal of Financial Planning *changed to* Journal of Financial Planning Today.
0196-0016	F T C: Watch
0196-0040	Facts on File. Yearbook
0196-0075	Library & Archival Security
0196-0091	E P A Publications Bibliography Quarterly Abstracts Bulletin
0196-0148	New Book of Knowledge Annual
0196-0172	Encyclopedia Year Book
0196-0180	Americana Annual
0196-0202	Ear and Hearing
0196-0229	Recombinant D N A Technical Bulletin
0196-0237	Museology
0196-0253	Coffee Market *changed to* Mercadeo de Cafe nos Estados Unidos e no Canada.
0196-0555	Directory of World Chemical Producers (Year)
0196-058X	Occupational Health & Safety Letter
0196-0598	Environmental Health Letter
0196-0644	Annals of Emergency Medicine
0196-0660	Franchise Adviser
0196-0709	American Journal of Otolaryngology
0196-0717	Southwest & Texas Water Works Journal†
0196-0768	Smithsonian Contributions to the Marine Sciences
0196-0784	Congressional Insight
0196-0806	U.S. Federal Highway Administration. Monthly Motor Gasoline Reported by States
0196-0830	Cuba Update
0196-0873	Mission (Washington)†
0196-0881	Mapline
0196-0903	Book Publishers Directory *see* 0742-0501
0196-0911	Equipping Youth
0196-0938	Youth Alive
0196-0946	The Youth Disciple
0196-1004	C P C Salary Survey
0196-1063	Northern Social Science Review†
0196-108X	Seminars in Speech, Language and Hearing *see* 0734-0478
0196-108X	Seminars in Speech, Language and Hearing *see* 0734-0451
0196-1098	Georgia. Office of Planning and Budget. State Investment Plan†
0196-1152	Research in Social Problems and Public Policy
0196-125X	Arms Control Today
0196-1276	Overseas Private Investment Corporation. Annual Report
0196-1292	Consultants and Consulting Organizations Directory
0196-1306	Columns (Madison)
0196-1365	International Journal of Therapeutic Communities
0196-1373	Revista Interamericana *see* 0360-7917
0196-1446	On the Rock
0196-1454	Platt's C H A Digest *see* 0278-226X
0196-1489	Northrop University Law Journal of Aerospace, Energy and the Environment *see* 0887-4301
0196-1683	Small Town
0196-1721	National Humanities Center Newsletter
0196-173X	Research Libraries Group News
0196-1748	Journal of Climatology *see* 0899-8418
0196-1756	Compendium of Continuing Education in Dentistry
0196-1772	Sulfur Reports
0196-1780	Current Law Index
0196-1799	L I T A Newsletter
0196-1810	Retailer Owned Cooperative Chains, Voluntary Chains and Wholesale Grocers *see* 0277-1969
0196-1829	Fodor's Budget Mexico *changed to* Fodor's Great Travel Values: Mexico.
0196-1845	Directory of Supermarket, Grocery & Convenience Store Chains (Year)
0196-1853	Sinister Wisdom
0196-1918	Modern Technics in Surgery. Abdominal Surgery†
0196-1934	Advances in Thanatology
0196-1969	Challenge (Washington)†
0196-1977	Library Insights, Promotion & Programs
0196-2000	Journal of Social Reconstruction†
0196-2035	Denver Journal of International Law and Policy
0196-2043	Oregon Law Review
0196-206X	Journal of Development and Behavioral Pediatrics *changed to* Journal of Developmental and Behavioral Pediatrics.
0196-2094	U.S. Forest Service. Pacific Southwest Forest and Range Experiment Station. General Technical Report P S W
0196-2116	Corporate Director *see* 0746-8652
0196-2183	Solomon Goldman Lectures
0196-2213	Gaming Business *changed to* Gaming & Wagering Business.
0196-2221	Anthology of Magazine Verse and Yearbook of American Poetry
0196-2256	J G R: Journal of Geophysical Research: Oceans and Atmospheres. C - D *changed to* J G R: Journal of Geophysical Research: Oceans.
0196-2280	University of Hartford Studies in Literature
0196-2337	Stanza
0196-2418	Cystic Fibrosis G A P Conference Reports†
0196-2434	Cost and Production Survey Report
0196-2604	Moody Street Irregulars
0196-2701	Dentists Medical Digest†
0196-2787	Neuroimmunology†
0196-2809	Countries of the World and Their Leaders Yearbook
0196-2884	San Fernando Poetry Journal
0196-2892	I E E E Transactions on Geoscience and Remote Sensing
0196-3031	J Q: Journalism Quarterly
0196-3171	N A R D A's Costs of Doing Business Survey
0196-3228	Northwestern Journal of International Law & Business
0196-3295	N S F R E Journal
0196-3309	C M L E A Journal
0196-3341	Organization of American Historians Newsletter
0196-335X	Government Publications Review. Part A: Research Articles *see* 0277-9390
0196-3368	Acquisitions Guide to Significant Government Publications at All Levels *see* 0277-9390
0196-3422	N A R A S Institute Journal†
0196-3538	Arab-Asian Affairs
0196-3546	Gold & Silver Survey
0196-3570	World Literature Today
0196-3597	Armed Forces Journal International
0196-3627	Veterinary Radiology *see* 1058-8183
0196-3635	Journal of Andrology
0196-3643	Information Chicago
0196-3716	Genetic Engineering
0196-3767	Hazardous Substance Advisor *changed to* Environment Advisor.
0196-3821	Research in Finance
0196-3929	New Mexico Blue Book *see* 0732-3093
0196-3988	Pacific Basin Economic Indicators†
0196-4003	National Association of Regional Councils. Washington Report *changed to* National Association of Regional Councils. Regional Reporter.
0196-4127	Personal Composition Report
0196-4151	Applied Social Psychology Annual *changed to* Social Psychological Applications to Social Issues.
0196-4186	Arts Reporting Service *see* 0270-8159
0196-4240	Native Self-Sufficiency†
0196-4283	Journal of Foodservice Systems
0196-4305	Industrial and Engineering Chemistry Process Design and Development *see* 0888-5885
0196-4313	Industrial and Engineering Chemistry Fundamentals *see* 0888-5885
0196-4321	Industrial and Engineering Chemistry Product Research and Development *see* 0888-5885
0196-433X	Ovation†
0196-4399	Clinical Microbiology Newsletter
0196-4402	Guide to Recognized Accrediting Agencies *changed to* Guide to C O P A Recognized Accrediting Bodies.
0196-4429	Video Marketing Newsletter *changed to* Video Marketing News.
0196-4445	Computer Consultant†
0196-447X	Index to Book Reviews in the Sciences†
0196-4542	Readings in Environment *see* 0272-9008
0196-4690	Marine Mammal Protection Act of 1972 Annual Report
0196-4763	Cytometry (New York)
0196-4801	Social Anarchism
0196-4984	Basic Education
0196-5034	Philatelic Foundation Quartely
0196-5042	Educational Research Quarterly
0196-5069	U S Publicity Directory. Radio & TV†
0196-5093	U S Publicity Directory. Business & Finance†
0196-5107	U S Publicity Directory. Communication Services†
0196-514X	Financial Freedom Report
0196-5204	S I A M Journal on Scientific and Statistical Computing
0196-5212	S I A M Journal on Algebraic and Discrete Methods *see* 0895-4801
0196-5212	S I A M Journal on Algebraic and Discrete Methods *see* 0895-4798
0196-5220	Seymour Britchky's Restaurant Letter
0196-5530	Quarterly Index to Current Contents - Life Sciences†
0196-5549	3 - Wheeling†
0196-5581	Biological Oceanography Journal†
0196-559X	Digital Systems for Industrial Automation†
0196-5603	Institute Scholar
0196-5654	American Book Collector
0196-5700	Supermarket Business
0196-5816	E D A M Newsletter *see* 1048-9401
0196-5875	Art Ink
0196-5905	Video Week
0196-5913	Pudding Magazine
0196-5921	Zymurgy
0196-5964	Engineering Thermophysics in China†
0196-5972	Annual Report on Medicare
0196-6006	SciTech Book News
0196-612X	Current American Government
0196-6138	Parker Directory of California Attorneys
0196-6146	S S P Proceedings *see* 0734-8509
0196-6197	Dermatology Times
0196-6219	Ceramic Engineering and Science Proceedings
0196-6227	Cashflow *see* 1040-0311
0196-6243	Senior Sports News
0196-626X	G M P Letter
0196-6286	William Carlos Williams Review
0196-6316	Awards, Honors and Prizes
0196-6324	American Journal of Mathematical and Management Sciences
0196-6332	Group Health Journal *see* 0888-4250
0196-6456	Northeastern Camping *see* 0732-7315
0196-6545	American Psychological Association. Directory
0196-6553	American Journal of Infection Control

5640 ISSN INDEX

0196-6561 A M S Studies in the Eighteenth Century
0196-657X A M S Studies in the Nineteenth Century
0196-6677 In Common *see* 0271-9592
0196-6693 Synfuels Week *see* 0883-9735
0196-6707 Pittsburgh Regional Library Center. Newsletter
0196-6715 Education Law and the Public Schools. Bulletin and Update Subscription Service†
0196-674X American Society of Photogrammetry Fall Convention. Proceedings *changed to* American Society for Photogrammetry and Remote Sensing Fall Convention. Technical Papers.
0196-6774 Journal of Algorithms
0196-6790 The Nurse, the Patient and The Law
0196-6871 New York Medical Quarterly†
0196-691X Artful Dodge
0196-6928 J G R: Journal of Geophysical Research: Space Physics
0196-6936 J G R: Journal of Geophysical Research: Solid Planets. B *changed to* J G R: Journal of Geophysical Research: Solid Earth.
0196-6936 J G R: Journal of Geophysical Research: Solid Earth and Planets *changed to* J G R: Journal of Geophysical Research: Planets.
0196-6960 Exceptional Education Quarterly *see* 0741-9325
0196-6979 Instructional Innovator *see* 8756-3894
0196-7037 Renaissance Manuscript Studies
0196-7053 Contributions to the Study of Religion
0196-707X Contributions to the Study of Education
0196-7088 Contributions in Ethnic Studies
0196-7134 Documentary Editing
0196-7150 Air Pollution Control (Washington)
0196-7185 George D. Hall's Massachusetts Service Directory
0196-7207 Georgetown University Round Table on Languages and Linguistics
0196-7223 B R S Bulletin
0196-7304 Survey of Judicial Salaries in State Court Systems *changed to* Survey of Judicial Salaries.
0196-7355 Nevada Public Affairs Review
0196-7525 Chicago M B A
0196-755X List of Serials and Monographs Indexed for Online Users *see* 0736-7139
0196-7622 Belgian - American Chamber of Commerce in the United States. Directory
0196-7703 Idaho Museum of Natural History. Occasional Papers
0196-786X Professional Educator
0196-7967 Sonneck Society Newsletter *changed to* Sonneck Society Bulletin.
0196-7975 Guidebook to Fair Employment Practices
0196-8017 Mass Communication Review Yearbook†
0196-8092 Lasers in Surgery and Medicine
0196-8203 Disclosure
0196-8211 Materials Management & Physical Distribution Abstracts
0196-822X Practices of the Wind
0196-8238 Cottonboll
0196-8262 Nationwide Directory of Premium, Incentive & Travel Buyers
0196-8270 George D. Hall's Directory of Connecticut Manufacturers
0196-8319 Archaeological Society of New Jersey Bulletin
0196-8432 Magic Changes
0196-8599 Journal of Communication Inquiry
0196-8602 Business and Trade *see* 0731-7727
0196-8602 Business and Trade *see* 0731-7700
0196-8696 Advances in Data Processing Management
0196-870X Advances in Computer Programming Management†
0196-8718 Advances in Data Base Management†
0196-8793 Video Review (New York)†
0196-8858 Advances in Applied Mathematics
0196-8882 Tax Alert for Management†
0196-8904 Energy Conversion and Management
0196-8939 U.S. Department of State. Bureau of Public Affairs. Current Policy *changed to* Dispatch (Washington).
0196-8998 Byron Society Newsletter
0196-903X Interpretations *see* 0890-4944
0196-9072 Journal of Pastoral Practice
0196-9110 Encyclia
0196-9323 Peter Dag Investment Letter
0196-9358 Official National Collegiate Athletic Association Track and Field Guide *see* 0736-7783
0196-9455 Management Update (Denver)
0196-9536 Revenue Sharing Bulletin *changed to* Thompson's Washington's Bulletin for Local Governments.
0196-9617 Diagnostic Gynecology and Obstetrics†
0196-9641 Thresholds in Education
0196-9668 Youth - Serving Organizations Directory
0196-9722 Cybernetics and Systems (Bristol)
0196-9781 Peptides
0196-979X A.L.S. Forum and Newsletter†
0196-9846 Veterinary Clinics of North America: Large Animal Practice†
0197-0062 Electric Company Magazine *changed to* Kid City.
0197-0070 Journal of Adolescent Health Care *see* 1054-139X
0197-0100 Journal of Jewish Music and Liturgy
0197-0127 Goldsmith's Journal *see* 0270-1146
0197-0178 I D P Report
0197-0186 Neurochemistry International
0197-0208 Stolen Art Alert *see* 8756-7172
0197-0216 Bulletin of Alloy Phase Diagrams *see* 1054-9714
0197-0348 Chronicle of the Catholic Church in Lithuania
0197-0364 Antiquarian Trade List Annual†
0197-0380 M L A Directory of Periodicals
0197-0542 Annual Editions: Readings in Psychology *see* 0272-3794
0197-0690 Research in Health Economics *see* 0731-2199
0197-0747 Acquisitive Librarian†
0197-0771 Campaigns and Elections
0197-0798 Christian Family Chroniclest
0197-1042 Philosophy Teacher's Handbook†
0197-1077 Marine Management Letter†
0197-1085 Portage†
0197-1093 Art & Auction
0197-1115 Inland Towboat Newsletter†
0197-1131 Guide to American Offshore Fleets, Offshore Service Vessels *see* 0887-6827
0197-1212 Universitas (Albany)†
0197-1220 Maine, Vermont and New Hampshire Directory of Manufacturers
0197-128X Guide to Leadership Development Opportunities for College and University Administrators†
0197-1360 American Institute for Conservation of Historic & Artistic Works. Journal
0197-1387 West Virginia Forestry Notes
0197-1433 Advances in Distributed Processing Management
0197-1441 Comuniunea Romaneasca
0197-1468 Genealogist (Salt Lake City)
0197-1476 Advances in Data Communications Management
0197-1484 Psycscan: Clinical Psychology
0197-1492 Psycscan: Developmental Psychology
0197-1506 Pipeline Digest
0197-1514 Advances in Computer Security Management†
0197-1522 Journal of Immunoassay
0197-1816 Manufactured Housing Newsletter
0197-1859 Clinical Immunology Newsletter
0197-1867 Chrysalis
0197-1905 Robotics Age *changed to* Robotics Engineering.
0197-2030 Solar Collector Manufacturing Activity
0197-2103 Connecticut Ancestry
0197-212X Older Boat Price Guide *changed to* Used Boat Price Guide.
0197-2138 Psi - M
0197-2146 Literary Voicest
0197-2219 Rubber & Plastics News II
0197-2227 Classical and Modern Literature: A Quarterly
0197-2243 Information Society
0197-2251 Annual Review of Rehabilitation *changed to* Advances in Clinical Rehabilitation.
0197-2340 Texas Natural Resources Reporter
0197-2367 Collector-Investor†
0197-2375 Crain's Cleveland Business
0197-2456 Controlled Clinical Trials
0197-2510 J E M S
0197-2588 Bar Bulletin *see* 0162-2900
0197-260X Chess Life
0197-2618 Industry Applications Society. I E E E - I A S Annual Meeting. Conference Record
0197-2669 National Conference of Referees in Bankruptcy. Journal *see* 0027-9048
0197-2715 Gospel Music *changed to* Gospel Music Association. Resource Guide.
0197-2839 Reviews in Pure and Applied Pharmacological Sciences *changed to* Journal of Basic and Clinical Physiology and Pharmacology.
0197-288X Fiscal Letter
0197-3045 Bride of Christ
0197-3096 Human Development (Hartford)
0197-3118 Cardiovascular Reviews & Reports
0197-3177 Hazardous Materials Transportation
0197-3355 C R C Critical Reviews in Immunology *see* 1040-8401
0197-3371 Helicon Nine†
0197-3428 Tributaries†
0197-3444 Workshop on Color Aerial Photography in the Plant Sciences. Proceedings
0197-3460 Sea Grant Today†
0197-3479 Ski Industry Letter
0197-3495 Sheet Music. Standard Organ Edition†
0197-3533 Basic and Applied Social Psychology
0197-3592 Ostaro's Market Newsletter
0197-3606 Free-Lance West
0197-3622 U M A P Journal
0197-3649 Contemporary Hematology - Oncology
0197-3657 House Ear Institute. Progress Report†
0197-3681 International Journal of Clinical Neuropsychology
0197-369X United States Imports and Exports of Natural Gas†
0197-3738 Health Care Labor Manual
0197-3746 Summer Institute of Linguistics. Museum of Anthropology Publication *see* 0895-9897
0197-3762 Visual Resources
0197-3789 American Bamboo Society. Journal
0197-3800 Arkansas State Industrial Directory *see* 0740-4670
0197-3827 North Dakota State Industrial Directory *see* 0739-8468
0197-3835 Nebraska State Industrial Directory *see* 0740-428X
0197-3851 Prenatal Diagnosis
0197-3975 Habitat International
0197-3991 Paper Industry *see* 1046-4352
0197-4009 Poetry East
0197-4025 Aging Service News *see* 0146-3640
0197-4041 Ligand Review
0197-4084 Potpourri from Herbal Acres
0197-4106 Propagation & Distribution of Fishes from National Fish Hatcheries for the Fiscal Year
0197-4254 Atlantic Economic Journal
0197-4327 Western Journal of Black Studies
0197-4556 The Arts in Psychotherapy
0197-4564 U C Davis Law Review
0197-4572 Geriatric Nursing
0197-4580 Neurobiology of Aging
0197-4610 Jersey Woman Magazine *changed to* New Jersey Woman Magazine.
0197-4637 Multinational Monitor
0197-467X Police Beat†
0197-4696 Gas Phase Ion-Molecule Reactions†
0197-4777 Waterways
0197-4874 New Wilderness Letter†
0197-4998 Fodor's Budget Europe *changed to* Fodor's Affordable Europe.
0197-5056 Horizons (Chicago)†
0197-5072 Inside Track†
0197-5080 Research in Sociology of Education and Socialization
0197-5102 American Enterprise Institute for Public Policy Research. Review, Session of the Congress†
0197-5110 Journal of Receptor Research
0197-5129 Annual Summary of Investigations Relating to Reading
0197-5153 Technical Association of the Pulp and Paper Industry. Papermakers Conference Proceedings (Year)
0197-5277 Cuba in Focus†
0197-5323 Journal for Special Educators *see* 0741-9325
0197-534X Catalysis in Organic Syntheses†
0197-5374 Education Times†
0197-5382 Managed Accounts Reports
0197-5390 Futures Industry *see* 0197-5382
0197-5439 World Refugee Survey
0197-5455 American College of Physicians. Directory†
0197-5579 C A A S Newsletter *see* 1051-4589
0197-5587 Library Imagination Paper
0197-5617 Farm Bureau News
0197-5668 State Publications Index†
0197-5676 Response (Solana Beach) *see* 1041-0651
0197-5684 Pesticide Handbook *see* 0553-8521
0197-5897 Journal of Public Health Policy
0197-5919 Annual Review of Research in Religious Education†
0197-5927 Bread & Roses
0197-596X Lymphokine Reports *see* 0277-013X
0197-5986 Modern Photography's Guide to the World's Best Cameras†
0197-6044 Highroller *changed to* High Roller.
0197-6052 Reporter's Report†
0197-6060 Ragan Report
0197-6338 Poets in the South†
0197-6524 Information Management (Sioux City)
0197-6656 Student Guide to Summer Law Study Programs
0197-6664 Family Relations
0197-6672 Missouri. Emergency Management Agency. Newsletter
0197-6729 Journal of Advanced Transportation
0197-6745 Dictionaries
0197-6753 T M R Travel Marketing Report
0197-677X International Videotex Teletext News *changed to* Information & Interactive Services Report.
0197-6788 Soviet Mathematics - Doklady
0197-6796 Contact 2
0197-680X Phantasmagoria†
0197-6818 Snippets†
0197-6826 Pastiche†
0197-6931 North American Archaeologist
0197-6966 Data Resources Review of the U.S. Economy *changed to* D R I - McGraw-Hill Review of the U.S. Economy.
0197-7016 Blue Unicorn
0197-7024 Polygraph (Severna Park)
0197-7032 National Right to Work Newsletter
0197-7040 The Anderson Report
0197-7075 Cash Manager *see* 0896-2987
0197-7083 Donoghue's Moneyletter
0197-7091 I B C - Donoghue's Money Fund Report
0197-713X Physician Assistant - Health Practitioner *changed to* Physician Assistant.
0197-7156 Soviet Mathematics - Iz. V U Z
0197-7164 Directive Teacher†
0197-7261 Lithic Technology
0197-7296 Aura
0197-7342 Keywords
0197-7385 Oceans. Conference Record
0197-7393 International Goat and Sheep Research *see* 0921-4488
0197-7423 Report of the Patient Registry†

ISSN

ISSN INDEX

ISSN	Title
0197-744X	California. Department of Education. Annual Report on Publicly Subsidized Child Care Services†
0197-7520	Society of Petroleum Engineers Journal†
0197-7547	California Weekly Explorer
0197-7636	Harvard College Economist
0197-7709	Urology Digest (1979)
0197-7717	Behavioral Medicine Abstracts see 0883-6612
0197-7792	Fortune World Business Directory changed to Global 500 Directory.
0197-7830	Africa - Middle East Petroleum Directory see 0748-4089
0197-7873	Stanford Environmental Law Annual see 0892-7138
0197-7903	Art Hazards News
0197-7997	Replacement Parts Guide†
0197-8004	New York Times Annual Review†
0197-8039	Radiation Curing Buyer's Guide†
0197-8071	Society for the Study of Southern Literature. Newsletter
0197-8098	Brown's Directory of North American and International Gas Companies
0197-8101	Human Rights Directory see 0270-2282
0197-8160	Human Genetics, Informational and Educational Materials. Supplement
0197-8322	Advances in Inflammation Research
0197-8357	Journal of Interferon Research
0197-8381	Upton Sinclair Quarterly†
0197-8454	Clinical Lab Letter
0197-8462	Bioelectromagnetics
0197-8497	Images and Issues Magazine
0197-8527	Hawaii on 25 Dollars a Day changed to Hawaii on 60 Dollars a Day.
0197-8748	A P R E S Proceedings
0197-8896	Witness (Detroit)
0197-890X	Tendril
0197-8969	Phytochemical Society of Europe. Annual Proceedings
0197-9035	Public Policy Book Forecast see 0190-3241
0197-9140	Water Pollution Research Journal of Canada
0197-9175	Migration Today changed to Migration World.
0197-9183	International Migration Review
0197-9272	Sage Annual Reviews of Studies in Deviance†
0197-9280	Industrial Robots International see 0885-5684
0197-9299	Pennsylvania Library Association. Bulletin
0197-9337	Earth Surface Processes and Landforms
0197-9353	Journal of Preventive Psychiatry see 1049-6343
0197-9361	Olsen's Agribusiness Report
0197-937X	Corporate 500: the Directory of Corporate Philanthropy
0197-9388	ScriptWriter see 0279-9596
0197-9426	Annual National Conference on Recreation Planning and Development. Proceedings†
0197-9477	Fastfacts U S A Hotel Motel Locator†
0197-9906	New York Sea Grant Law and Policy Journal†
0197-9930	Early Man†
0197-9973	Resources in Education Annual Cumulation
0197-9981	Legal Medicine
0198-0068	Banbury Reports
0198-0092	Modeling and Simulation
0198-0106	M A S C A Journal changed to M A S C A Research Papers in Science and Archaeology.
0198-0149	Deep-Sea Research. Part A: Oceanographic Research Papers
0198-0211	Foot & Ankle
0198-0238	D N A see 1044-5498
0198-0246	Food for Thought (Los Angeles)
0198-0254	Deep-Sea Research. Part B: Oceanographic Literature Review
0198-0289	Connecticut Law Tribune
0198-1021	Carta Abierta
0198-103X	Advances in the Management of Cardiovascular Disease†
0198-1056	Cinefex
0198-1064	Cinemacabre
0198-1080	Purser's Magazine†
0198-1501	Safe Boating†
0198-6171	Northwestern Farmer changed to The Farmer - The Dakota Farmer.
0198-6201	Beginning (Nashville)
0198-6228	International Marketing Report see 0885-3363
0198-6252	Ukrainian Philatelist
0198-6325	Medicinal Research Reviews
0198-6341	Pediatrics Digest (1979)†
0198-635X	Al Urdun†
0198-6376	Orthopedics Digest (1979)†
0198-6449	Halcyon
0198-6473	Cancer Biology Reviews†
0198-6503	Federal Reporter
0198-6511	Bread for the World see 1045-1005
0198-6597	Sports Collectors Directory
0198-6643	Dermatology Digest (1979)†
0198-666X	Grace Theological Journal
0198-6678	Heavyduty Marketing†
0198-6686	Thrust (Gaithersburg) changed to Quantum (Gaithersburg).
0198-6759	Foreign Trade Reports. U.S. Exports - Schedule E - Commodity by Country see 1057-9680
0198-683X	Ohio Underwriter
0198-6856	Theological Educator
0198-6880	Chemical Technology Review†
0198-6945	Just Pulp
0198-697X	Online Terminal-Microcomputer Guide and Directory see 0734-5097
0198-7038	O.R.L. & Allergy Digest†
0198-7089	Advances in Behavioral Pediatrics changed to Advances in Developmental and Behavioral Pediatrics.
0198-7097	Radiology Management
0198-7100	Simplicity Today Incorporating Home Catalog changed to Simplicity Magazine.
0198-7194	North American Society for Oceanic History. Proceedings changed to North American Society for Oceanic History. Newsletter.
0198-7208	Ohio Monitor
0198-7224	High Fidelity's Buying Guide to Stereo Components†
0198-7275	Melliand Textilberichte (English Edition)
0198-7356	Bartonia
0198-7364	Hamline Law Review
0198-7399	Socioeconomic Issues of Health†
0198-7429	Behavioral Disorders Journal
0198-7518	Annual Editions: Educating Exceptional Children
0198-7542	South Texas Journal of Research and the Humanities see 0276-9220
0198-7569	International Journal of Periodontics & Restorative Dentistry
0198-7593	Journal of Heat Recovery Systems see 0890-4332
0198-7607	Objectivist Forum†
0198-7992	Thai Philately
0198-8085	Current Gastroenterology
0198-8093	Current Hepatology
0198-8107	Writ
0198-8174	Campbell Law Review
0198-8190	Sportsguide for Team Sports†
0198-8212	Handwoven
0198-8239	Spin-Off
0198-831X	Colorado Shakespeare Festival Annual changed to On - Stage Studies.
0198-8344	R A S D Update
0198-8360	U.S. Nuclear Regulatory Commission. Occupational Radiation Exposure. Annual Report changed to U.S. Nuclear Regulatory Commission. Occupational Radiation at Commercial Nuclear Power Reactors and Other Facilities. Annual Report.
0198-8379	Scholastic Math
0198-8387	Fiberscope†
0198-8425	Fact Book for Academic Administrators changed to Fact Book for Higher Education.
0198-8433	California Academic Libraries List of Serials†
0198-8549	Northern Kentucky Law Review
0198-8557	Management (Washington)
0198-8611	N E A Advocate
0198-8700	U.S. National Science Foundation. Federal Funds for Research, Development, and other Scientific Activities changed to U.S. National Science Foundation. Federal Funds for Research Development.
0198-8719	Political Power and Social Theory
0198-8778	Specialty Law Digest: Health Care
0198-8786	Society for the Right to Die. Handbook changed to Refusal of Treatment Legislation (Year).
0198-8794	Annual Review of Gerontology & Geriatrics
0198-8816	American Chianina Journal
0198-8840	C O I N T Reports†
0198-8859	Human Immunology
0198-9006	Quarterly Strategic Bibliography see 1050-4850
0198-9014	Index to the Code of Federal Regulations
0198-9073	American Taxation Association. Journal
0198-9103	Compendium Newsletter
0198-912X	Annual Editions: Personal Growth and Behavior
0198-9197	Ob-Gyn Digest (Year)†
0198-9375	Gateway Heritage
0198-9391	Amie†
0198-9405	Medieval Prosopography
0198-9456	Videodisc - Teletext see 1054-9692
0198-9561	International Bonsai
0198-9618	Mariner's Catalog†
0198-9634	Contact Quarterly
0198-9715	Computers, Environment and Urban Systems
0198-9731	Annual Review of Family Therapy†
0198-9855	Sing Heavenly Muse!
0198-9871	Contributions to the Study of Popular Culture
0198-9901	Blueline
0198-9936	Powell Alert†
0198-9952	Impact American Beer Market Review and Forecast changed to The U S Beer Market: Impact Databank Review and Forecast.
0198-9987	Sportsguide for Individual Sports†
0198-9995	Dairy Field
0199-0012	True Experience
0199-0020	True Romance
0199-0039	Population and Environment
0199-0071	Z P G Reporter
0199-0128	Baseball Bulletin
0199-0144	Pythian International
0199-0152	Richmond LifeStyle see 0010-3365
0199-0187	Journal of Veterinary Orthopedics†
0199-0217	Christmas Trees Magazine
0199-0330	City Limits
0199-0349	Hispanic Business Magazine
0199-0357	Gourmet Retailer
0199-0462	Glos Polek
0199-0497	Shooting Commercials and Industrials see 0273-2246
0199-0586	Alaskafest changed to Alaska Airlines Magazine.
0199-0640	International Cat Fancy see 0892-6514
0199-0683	Corporate Accounting Reporter see 1044-8136
0199-0691	Information Systems News changed to Information Week.
0199-0802	Civil Litigation Reporter
0199-0837	Nautical Quarterly†
0199-0918	Ohio P T A News
0199-1035	80-U.S. changed to Basic Computing.
0199-1248	Nevada
0199-1272	Medical Liability Advisory Service
0199-1329	Office Products Dealer changed to Office Products Dealer Buying Guide and Directory.
0199-1337	Sea Power
0199-137X	University of Hawaii. Sea Grant College Program. Sea Grant Quarterly†
0199-1388	Aquaculture Magazine
0199-1531	Austin Homes & Gardens†
0199-1574	Atlanta Skier
0199-1604	Pattern World†
0199-1639	Wisconsin Master Plumber changed to Wisconsin P-H-C Contractor.
0199-1728	Greater Portland Magazine
0199-1795	Dance Teacher Now
0199-1833	Medical Liability Reporter
0199-1876	Advocate (Los Angeles, 1973)
0199-1884	Power Conversion International see 0885-0259
0199-1892	Woodworker's Journal
0199-1914	Model Railroading
0199-2066	Chicago Nurse
0199-2139	Bicycle U S A
0199-2155	Northeast Optician
0199-2333	Kind†
0199-2376	Kliatt Young Adult Paperback Book Guide
0199-2414	C A L Underwriter
0199-2422	News Photographer
0199-2511	Word Processing Systems see 0279-7992
0199-2678	Afghan Quarterly changed to Afghan World.
0199-2686	Commuter Air see 1054-7436
0199-2716	Massachusetts General Hospital Biological Therapies in Psychiatry Newsletter see 1044-422X
0199-2805	Southeast Food Service News
0199-2864	Adweek (New York)
0199-2880	Executive Female
0199-2899	Long Island Jewish World
0199-3046	Yakima Nation Review
0199-3097	Backpacker Including Wilderness Camping see 0277-867X
0199-3100	Benefits News Analysis
0199-3151	Fantasy Newsletter changed to Science Fiction and Fantasy Book Review Annual.
0199-3178	Toxic Substances Journal
0199-3186	Director
0199-3240	Mississippi Outdoors see 1041-9306
0199-3313	Keyboard World
0199-3372	Southern Outdoors
0199-3410	Oil and Gas Regulation Analyst changed to Natural Gas.
0199-350X	People (Palo Alto)
0199-3518	New Horizons (Horsham)
0199-3550	E D M Digest changed to Diemaking, Stamping & EDMing.
0199-3607	Kansas Business News
0199-3658	Utmost
0199-3704	I U D Digest
0199-378X	Music World†
0199-3933	House & Garden Building & Remodeling Guide†
0199-3941	Nit & Wit
0199-3992	Texas Homes†
0199-4050	The Short Line
0199-4220	American Cowboy†
0199-4239	Holstein World
0199-4328	American Paint and Wallcoverings Dealer see 1045-5914
0199-4336	Grain Storage and Handling†
0199-4433	Mission Journal†
0199-4441	Jewish World
0199-4468	Import Automotive Parts & Accesories
0199-4514	Tole World
0199-4557	New Jersey Interact†
0199-4581	Insurance Sales see 1053-2838
0199-4654	Sensible Sound
0199-4743	Adweek (Los Angeles)
0199-4905	Medical Sciences Bulletin
0199-4913	Petersen's Photographic
0199-4972	Action Sports Retailer
0199-5014	Indian River Life
0199-5030	Supreme Court Bulletin
0199-5103	Group Practice Journal

0199-5111 Cruise Travel
0199-5197 Cobblestone
0199-5219 F and S Index Europe *see* 0270-4536
0199-5243 M A P A Log
0199-5278 Sportswear Graphics†
0199-5405 Hustler Humor
0199-5421 Mainline Modeler
0199-5456 Bovine Practice *see* 0745-452X
0199-5510 Nutrition Action *changed to* Nutrition Action Healthletter.
0199-5529 Western Office Dealer *see* 0584-455X
0199-5553 Museum Magazine†
0199-5650 Energy Management†
0199-5707 Chevron U S A *see* 0886-5418
0199-5723 Network (Washington, 1971) *changed to* Network Connection.
0199-574X Weekly World News
0199-5820 International Fiber Optics and Communications†
0199-5839 Florida Realtor
0199-5847 Environmental Regulation Analyst *see* 0732-7927
0199-5855 Whitchappel's Herbal†
0199-5979 Bird World
0199-6096 Bus Tours Magazine
0199-6134 Municipal Finance Journal
0199-6223 Quality Control Supervisor's Bulletin *see* 1040-0664
0199-6231 Journal of Solar Energy Engineering
0199-6258 Wrestling U.S.A. Magazine
0199-6290 Back Home in Kentucky
0199-6304 Employee Health and Fitness
0199-6312 Hospital Risk Management
0199-6363 Pacific Northwest
0199-6460 Ag Consultant and Fieldman *changed to* Ag Consultant.
0199-6487 Chinmaya Mission West News
0199-6495 Terrier Type
0199-6509 Management Digest (Chicago)†
0199-6517 Georgia Sportsman
0199-6584 M D A Journal *changed to* Missouri Dental Journal.
0199-6614 Journal of Cardiovascular Medicine *see* 0363-5104
0199-6649 InfoWorld
0199-6657 Kicks
0199-669X California Business Law Reporter
0199-672X Nebraska Fertilizer and Ag-Chemical Digest
0199-6738 Setter Quarterly†
0199-6789 80 Microcomputing *see* 0744-7868
0199-6835 Alarm Signal†
0199-686X C B I A News
0199-6908 AutoInc.
0199-6916 Environmental Education Report *see* 0840-5662
0199-6924 Farm Industry News
0199-6991 A A U News *see* 0279-9863
0199-7068 Model Ship Builder
0199-7114 Program Manager
0199-7149 Sexology Today†
0199-7173 Lake Superior Port Cities *see* 0890-3050
0199-7211 Military Police Law Enforcement Journal *see* 0895-4208
0199-7238 Cape Cod Life
0199-7297 American Brittany
0199-7300 Film Journal
0199-7327 Scale R - C Modeler
0199-7335 Pet Gazette†
0199-7343 Colorado Medicine
0199-736X Dental Practice†
0199-7424 Israel Scene
0199-7580 Ohio Holstein News *see* 0899-4862
0199-7602 Inside (Philadelphia)
0199-7610 Specialist (Radnor)†
0199-7661 Leadership (Carol Stream)
0199-7696 Foodservice Product News
0199-7742 Professional Roofing
0199-7793 County (Des Moines) *see* 0892-3795
0199-7890 Vette
0199-7912 Drug Metabolism Newsletter
0199-7920 Speaker Builder
0199-7947 Senior Citizen Sentinel
0199-7955 Microsystems†
0199-8013 Plant Services
0199-8196 Current Consumer *see* 0745-0265
0199-820X Current Health 1
0199-8218 Current Lifestudies *see* 0745-0265
0199-8285 Wittenburg Door *see* 1044-7512
0199-8293 World Around You
0199-8323 Contact High *see* 0747-3818
0199-8366 Groom & Board
0199-8374 Chicago Lawyer
0199-8463 Northeast Outdoors
0199-8498 Sugar Producer
0199-8501 Inside Kung Fu
0199-8536 Powerlifting U S A
0199-8595 Energy Engineering
0199-865X V F W Auxiliary
0199-8668 Southern Struggle†
0199-8714 Unfinished Furniture Industry
0199-8730 Biz†
0199-8765 Bema
0199-8838 M I S Week†
0199-8854 Southwest Homefurnishings News *changed to* Home Furnishings Review.
0199-8951 Systems User
0199-8994 N C E E Registration Bulletin *changed to* N C E E S Registration Bulletin.
0199-901X News India
0199-9028 Communique (Chicago)
0199-9052 Wassaja/The Indian Historian†
0199-9060 Soil and Water Conservation News
0199-9184 Miniature Collector
0199-9230 Crossroads (Evanston)†
0199-9249 Internos *see* 0744-1223
0199-9257 Prevue
0199-9273 Media Review†
0199-929X Collector Editions Quarterly *see* 0733-2130
0199-9303 Los Angeles Home and Garden Magazine†
0199-9311 Credit Union News
0199-9346 Communities
0199-9370 Sunshine Artists U S A
0199-9419 Asia Record†
0199-9435 A R C
0199-946X Baseball Hobby News
0199-9664 Nebraska State Historical Society. Historical Newsletter
0199-9753 Diamond Registry. Bulletin
0199-9788 Games
0199-9796 New Books on Asia Announced for Publication in the Soviet Union
0199-9818 American Academy of Arts and Sciences. Proceedings *see* 0011-5266
0199-9869 Solutions
0199-9885 Annual Review of Nutrition
0199-9915 Retail Automation Report†
0199-994X Geographical Perspectives
0199-9974 Weekly Government Abstracts. Health Planning and Health Services Research *changed to* N T I S Alerts: Health Care.
0200-0156 Hungarica Kulfoldi Folyoiratszemle *see* 0133-7505
0200-0202 Konyvtari Tajekoztato *changed to* Konyvtari Figyelo. Uj Folyam.
0200-0679 Magyar Zenemuvek Bibliografiaja *see* 0133-5782
0200-2396 Weekly Bulletin *see* 0024-8495
0200-5344 Zalai Tukor†
0200-5352 Magyar Nepmuveszet Evszazadai†
0201-419X Kul'tura Slova
0201-5307 Signal'naya Informatsiya. Kvantovaya Radiotekhnika - Kriogennaya Radioehlekrtronika†
0201-5315 Signal'naya Informatsiya. Antenny - Volnovody - Ob'emnye Rezonatory - Rasprostranenie Radiovoln†
0201-5323 Signal'naya Informatsiya. Ehlektrosvyaz†
0201-5331 Signal'naya Informatsiya. Radiolokatsiya - Radionavigatsiya - Televidenie - Impul'snaya Tekhnika†
0201-7369 Akademiya Meditsinskikh Nauk S.S.S.R. Vsesoyuznyi Kardiologicheskii Nauchnyi Tsentr. Byulleten'
0201-7474 Khimiya Drevesiny
0201-7563 Anesteziologiya i Reanimatologiya
0201-7822 Shakhmaty *changed to* Baltiiskie Shakhmaty.
0201-8039 Latviesu Valodas Kulturas Jautajumi†
0201-8101 Sahs *changed to* Sahs Baltija.
0201-8128 Akademiya Nauk Estonskoi S.S.R. Izvestiya. Khimiya *changed to* Eesti Teaduste Akadeemia. Toimetised. Keemia.
0201-8136 Akademiya Nauk Estonskoi S.S.R. Izvestiya. Geologiya *changed to* Eesti Teaduste Akadeemia. Toimetised. Geoloogia.
0201-8446 Akademiya Nauk Ukrainskoi S.S.R. Doklady. Seriya A. Fiziko-Matematicheskie i Tekhnicheskie Nauki
0201-8454 Akademiya Nauk Ukrainskoi S.S.R. Doklady. Seriya B. Geologicheskie, Khimicheskie i Biologicheskie Nauki
0201-8462 Mikrobiologichnyi Zhurnal
0201-8470 Ukrain'skyi Biokhimichnyi Zhurnal
0201-8489 Fiziologicheskii Zhurnal (Kiev)
0202-0726 Itogi Nauki i Tekhniki: Geodeziya i Aeros'emka
0202-0734 Itogi Nauki i Tekhniki: Issledovanie Kosmicheskogo Prostranstva
0202-0742 Itogi Nauki i Tekhniki: Astronomiya
0202-0769 Itogi Nauki i Tekhniki: Radiotekhnika
0202-1870 Soviet Literature
0202-2001 Lituanistika v S.S.S.R. Filosofiya i Psikhologiya†
0202-201X Lituanistika v S.S.S.R. Yazykoznanie†
0202-2028 Lituanistika v S.S.S.R. Pravo†
0202-2036 Obshchestvennye Nauki v S.S.S.R. Seriya 1: Problemy Nauchnogo Kommunizma
0202-2044 Obshchestvennye Nauki v S.S.S.R. Ekonomika
0202-2052 Obshchestvennye Nauki v S.S.S.R. Filosofskie Nauki
0202-2060 Obshchestvennye Nauki v S.S.S.R. Gosudarstvo i Pravo
0202-2079 Obshchestvennye Nauki v S.S.S.R. Istoriya
0202-2087 Obshchestvennye Nauki v S.S.S.R. Yazykoznanie
0202-2095 Obshchestvennye Nauki v S.S.S.R. Literaturovedenie
0202-2109 Obshchestvennye Nauki za Rubezhom. Gosudarstvo i Pravo
0202-2117 Obshchestvennye Nauki za Rubezhom. Literaturovedenie
0202-2125 Obshchestvennye Nauki za Rubezhom. Problemy Nauchnogo Kommunizma
0202-2133 Obshchestvennye Nauki za Rubezhom. Yazykoznanie
0202-2141 Obshchestvennye Nauki za Rubezhom. Naukovedenie
0202-2540 Novaya Sovetsakaya i Inostrannaya Literatura po Obshchestvennym Naukam. Sotsialisticheskaya Respublika Rumyniya *changed to* Novaya Sovetskaya i Inostrannaya Literatura po Obshchestvennym Naukam. Rumyniya.
0202-3261 Istorija
0202-327X Geografija ir Geologija *changed to* Geografija ir Krastotvarka.
0202-3296 Literatura
0202-330X Kalbotyra
0202-3776 Obogashchenie Rud
0202-4098 Referativnyi Zhurnal. Avtomatika, Telemekhanika i Vychislitel'naya Tekhnika *changed to* Referativnyi Zhurnal. Avtomatika i Vychislitel'naya Tekhnika.
0202-4195 Ekologiya Ptits Litovskoi S.S.R.
0202-5132 Referativnyi Zhurnal. Farmakologiya Effektornykh Sistem. Khimioterapevticheskie Sredstva
0202-5140 Referativnyi Zhurnal. Ekologiya Cheloveka
0202-6309 Mestnyi Proizvodstvennyi Opyt v Promyshlennosti
0202-6317 Mestnyi Proizvodstvennyi Opyt v Stroitel'stve
0202-6325 Mestnyi Proizvodstvennyi Opyt v Sel'skom Khozyaistve
0202-7003 Itogi Nauki i Tekhniki: Biofizika *see* 0234-2979
0202-702X Itogi Nauki i Tekhniki: Zoologiya Pozvonochnykh
0202-7070 Itogi Nauki i Tekhniki: Molekulyarnaya Biologiya
0202-7127 Itogi Nauki i Tekhniki: Onkologiya
0202-716X Itogi Nauki i Tekhniki: Rastenievodstvo
0202-7208 Itogi Nauki i Tekhniki: Geografiya Zarubezhnykh Stran
0202-7216 Itogi Nauki i Tekhniki: Geografiya SSSR†
0202-7240 Itogi Nauki i Tekhniki: Kartografiya
0202-7275 Itogi Nauki i Tekhniki: Geomagnetizm i Vysokie Sloi Atmosfery
0202-7321 Itogi Nauki i Tekhniki: Okhrana Prirody i Vosproizvodstvo Prirodnykh Resursov
0202-7348 Itogi Nauki i Tekhniki: Geokhimiya - Mineralogiya - Petrografiya
0202-7356 Itogi Nauki i Tekhniki: Gidrogeologiya. Inzhenernaya Geologiya
0202-7372 Itogi Nauki i Tekhniki: Obshchaya Geologiya
0202-7380 Itogi Nauki i Tekhniki: Rudnye Mestorozhdeniya
0202-7410 Itogi Nauki i Tekhniki: Razrabotka Mestorozhdenii Tverdykh Poleznykh Iskopaemykh
0202-7429 Itogi Nauki i Tekhniki: Razrabotka Neftyanykh i Gazovykh Mestorozhdenii
0202-7437 Itogi Nauki i Tekhniki: Obogashchenie Poleznykh Iskopaemykh
0202-7445 Itogi Nauki i Tekhniki: Algebra - Topologiya - Geometriya
0202-7453 Itogi Nauki i Tekhniki: Matematicheskii Analiz
0202-7461 Itogi Nauki i Tekhniki: Problemy Geometrii
0202-747X Itogi Nauki i Tekhniki: Sovremennye Problemy Matematiki†
0202-7488 Itogi Nauki i Tekhniki: Teoriya Veroyatnostej - Matematicheskaya Statistika-Teoreticheskaya Kibernetika
0202-7542 Itogi Nauki i Tekhniki: Dvigateli Vnutrennego Sgoraniya
0202-7585 Itogi Nauki i Tekhniki: Metrologiya i Izmeritel'naya Tekhnika†
0202-7739 Itogi Nauki i Tekhniki: Metallovedenie i Termicheskaya Obrabotka
0202-7747 Itogi Nauki i Tekhniki: Metallurgiya Tsvetnykh Metallov
0202-7755 Itogi Nauki i Tekhniki: Metallurgicheskaya Teplotekhnika
0202-778X Itogi Nauki i Tekhniki: Svarka
0202-7798 Itogi Nauki i Tekhniki: Teoriya Metallurgicheskikh Protsessov†
0202-781X Itogi Nauki i Tekhniki: Mekhanika Zhidkosti i Gaza
0202-7836 Itogi Nauki i Tekhniki: Obshchaya Mekhanika†
0202-7844 Itogi Nauki i Tekhniki: Avtomobil'nyi i Gorodskoi Transport
0202-7879 Itogi Nauki i Tekhniki: Vodnyi Transport
0202-7887 Itogi Nauki i Tekhniki: Vozdushnyi Transport
0202-7909 Itogi Nauki i Tekhniki: Promyshlennyi Transport
0202-7917 Itogi Nauki i Tekhniki: Truboprovodnyi Transport
0202-795X Itogi Nauki i Tekhniki: Biologicheskaya Khimiya
0202-7968 Itogi Nauki i Tekhniki: Kinetika. Kataliz
0202-7976 Itogi Nauki i Tekhniki: Korroziya i Zashchita ot Korrozii
0202-7984 Itogi Nauki i Tekhniki: Kristallokhimiya
0202-8018 Itogi Nauki i Tekhniki: Protsessy i Apparaty Khimicheskoi Tekhnologii
0202-8050 Itogi Nauki i Tekhniki: Khimicheskaya Termodinamika i Ravnovesiya†

0202-8069 Itogi Nauki i Tekhniki: Khimiya i Tekhnologiya Vysokomolekulyarnykh Soedinenii
0202-8093 Itogi Nauki i Tekhniki: Elektrokhimiya
0202-8190 Itogi Nauki i Tekhniki: Kotel'nye Ustanovki i Vodopodgotovka†
0202-8247 Itogi Nauki i Tekhniki: Teplo- i Massoobmen†
0202-8301 Itogi Nauki i Tekhniki: Elektricheskie Apparaty
0202-831X Itogi Nauki i Tekhniki: Elektricheskie Mashiny i Transformatory†
0202-8328 Itogi Nauki i Tekhniki: Elektricheskie Stantsii, Seti i Sistemy *changed to* Itogi Nauki i Tekhniki: Elektricheskie Stantsii i Seti.
0202-8387 Signal'naya Informatsiya. Genetika Cheloveka†
0202-8395 Signal'naya Informatsiya. Ikhtiologiya†
0202-8425 Signal'naya Informatsiya. Obmen Veshchestv, Pitanie i Pishchevarenie†
0202-8433 Signal'naya Informatsiya. Obshchaya Genetika†
0202-8441 Signal'naya Informatsiya. Obshchaya Mikrobiologiya†
0202-845X Signal'naya Informatsiya. Obshchie Problemy Biologii†
0202-8468 Signal'naya Informatsiya. Obshchie Problemy Fiziologii Cheloveka i Zhivotnykh. Prikladnaya Fiziologiya†
0202-8476 Signal'naya Informatsiya. Onkologiya: Opukholi u Cheloveka†
0202-8484 Signal'naya Informatsiya. Onkologiya: Terapiya Opukholei†
0202-8492 Signal'naya Informatsiya. Onkologiya: Eksperimental'naya†
0202-8506 Signal'naya Informatsiya. Prikladnaya Mikrobiologiya†
0202-8514 Signal'naya Informatsiya. Toksikologiya *see* 0233-6588
0202-8522 Signal'naya Informatsiya. Farmakologiya: Khimioterapevticheskie Sredstva†
0202-8530 Signal'naya Informatsiya. Fiziologiya Krovoobrashcheniya i Dykhaniya: Pochki†
0202-8549 Signal'naya Informatsiya. Tsitologiya - Tsitogenetika†
0202-8565 Signal'naya Informatsiya. Analiticheskaya Khimiya-Oborudovanie Laboratorii *see* 0234-9744
0202-8638 Signal'naya Informatsiya. Vysokomolekulyarnye Soedineniya†
0202-8646 Signal'naya Informatsiya. Zhiry, Masla, Moyushchie Sredstva i Dushistye Veshchestva†
0202-8662 Signal'naya Informatsiya. Kinetika - Kataliz - Fotokhimiya - Radiatsionnaya Khimiya†
0202-8670 Signal'naya Informatsiya. Korroziya i Zashchita ot Korrozii
0202-8689 Signal'naya Informatsiya. Kristallokhimiya i Kristallografiya†
0202-8697 Signal'naya Informatsiya. Laki - Kraski - Organicheskie Pokrytiya
0202-8727 Signal'naya Informatsiya. Natural'nyi Kauchuk-Rezina†
0202-8735 Signal'naya Informatsiya. Neorganicheskaya Khimiya-Kompleksnye Soedineniya-Radiokhimiya†
0202-8743 Signal'naya Informatsiya. Obshchie Voprosy Khimii†
0202-8751 Signal'naya Informatsiya. Obshchie i Teoreticheskie Voprosy Organicheskoi Khimii†
0202-876X Signal'naya Informatsiya. Osnovy Khimicheskoi Tekhnologii†
0202-8778 Signal'naya Informatsiya. Pererabotka Tverdykh Goryuchikh Iskopaemykh, Nefti, Gazov, Drevesiny†
0202-8786 Signal'naya Informatsiya. Pestitsidy†
0202-8794 Signal'naya Informatsiya. Pishchevaya, Brodil'naya i Sakharnaya Promyshlennost'†
0202-8808 Signal'naya Informatsiya. Plastmassy i Ionoobmennye Materialy†
0202-8816 Signal'naya Informatsiya. Poverkhnostnye Yavleniya - Khimiya Kolloidov†
0202-8824 Signal'naya Informatsiya. Prirodnye Soedineniya i Ikh Sinteticheskie Analogi†
0202-8832 Signal'naya Informatsiya. Promyshlennyi Organicheskii Sintez i Sintez Krasitelei†
0202-8840 Signal'naya Informatsiya. Silikatnye Materialy†
0202-8859 Signal'naya Informatsiya. Sinteticheskaya Organicheskaya Khimiya†
0202-8867 Signal'naya Informatsiya. Sinteticheskie i Prirodnye Lekarstvennye Veshchestva†
0202-8875 Signal'naya Informatsiya. Stroenie Molekul i Khimicheskaya Svyaz'†
0202-8883 Signal'naya Informatsiya. Struktura i Svoistva Vysokomolekulyarnykh Soedinenii†
0202-8891 Signal'naya Informatsiya. Termodinamika - Termokhimiya - Ravnovesiya - Rastvory†
0202-8905 Signal'naya Informatsiya. Tekhnika Bezopasnosti. Sanitarnaya Tekhnika
0202-8921 Signal'naya Informatsiya. Tekhnologiya Neorganicheskikh Veshchestv†
0202-893X Signal'naya Informatsiya. Khimicheskie Volokna - Tekstil - Kozha - Mekh†
0202-8948 Signal'naya Informatsiya. Khimiya Vody
0202-8956 Signal'naya Informatsiya. Khimiya Tverdogo Tela - Gazy - Zhidkosti - Amorfnye Tela†
0202-8980 Signal'naya Informatsiya. Enzimologiya
0202-8999 Signal'naya Informatsiya. Razrabotka Neftyanykh i Gazovykh Mestorozhdenii†
0202-912X Referativnyi Zhurnal. Bionika - Biokibernetika - Bioinzheneriya
0202-9138 Referativnyi Zhurnal. Genetika i Selektsiya Vozdelyvaemykh Rastenii
0202-9146 Referativnyi Zhurnal. Genetika Cheloveka
0202-9154 Referativnyi Zhurnal. Immunologiya - Allergologiya
0202-9162 Referativnyi Zhurnal. Klinicheskaya Farmakologiya
0202-9170 Referativnyi Zhurnal. Molekulyarnaya Biologiya†
0202-9189 Referativnyi Zhurnal. Obshchie Voprosy Patologii *changed to* Referativnyi Zhurnal. Obshchie Voprosy Patologicheskoi Anatomii.
0202-9197 Referativnyi Zhurnal. Onkologiya
0202-9200 Referativnyi Zhurnal. Rastenievodstvo (Biologicheskie Osnovy)
0202-9219 Referativnyi Zhurnal. Toksikologiya
0202-9227 Referativnyi Zhurnal. Farmakologiya. Khimioterapevticheskie Sredstva. Toksikologiya†
0202-9235 Referativnyi Zhurnal. Fitopatologiya
0202-9332 Referativnyi Zhurnal. Okhrana Prirody i Vosproizvodstvo Prirodnykh Resursov
0202-9898 Referativnyi Zhurnal. Pozharnaya Okhrana
0202-9952 Referativnyi Zhurnal. Organizatsiya i Bezopasnost' Dorozhnogo Dvizheniya
0203-1272 Mekhanika Kompozitnykh Materialov
0203-3100 Geofizicheskii Zhurnal
0203-3119 Sverkhtverdye Materialy
0203-3275 Kompositsionnye Polimernye Materialy
0203-3569 Sel'skaya Molodezh
0203-3933 Soviet Shipping
0203-3941 Bibliograficheskie Posobiya Belorusskoi S.S.R.
0203-4425 Nauka v S.S.S.R.
0203-4646 Ekologiya Morya
0203-4654 Fizika i Tekhnika Vysokikh Davlenii
0203-5189 Referativnyi Zhurnal. Elektrotekhnika i Elektroenergetika *see* 0203-5316
0203-5308 Referativnyi Zhurnal. Energetika
0203-5316 Referativnyi Zhurnal. Elektrotekhnika
0203-5405 Itogi Nauki i Tekhniki: Obshchie Problemy Biologii
0203-5413 Signal'naya Informatsiya. Metallurgiya Blagorodnykh, Redkikh, Redkozemel'nykh i Radioaktivnykh Metallov i Splavov. Proizvodstvo Tsvetnykh Metallov i Splavov iz Vtorichnogo Syr'ya†
0203-5421 Signal'naya Informatsiya. Metallurgiya Legkikh i Tyazhelykh Metallov i Splavov†
0203-543X Signal'naya Informatsiya. Metallurgicheskaya Teplotekhnika†
0203-5448 Signal'naya Informatsiya. Metodika Issledovanii Metallov i Splavov i Laboratornoe Oborudovanie. Termicheskaya i Khimiko-Termicheskaya Obrabotka Metallov i Splavov†
0203-5456 Signal'naya Informatsiya. Obshchie Voprosy Metallovedenya i Termicheskoi Obrabotki. Fazovye Ravnovesiya Metallov i Splavov. Fazovye i Strukturnye Prevrashcheniya v Metallakh i Splavakh†
0203-5464 Signal'naya Informatsiya. Obshchie Voprosy Prokatnogo Proizvodstva. Teoriya Prokatki Metallov. Proizvodstvo Blyumov, Slyabov, Zagotovok i Profilei Prokata Chernykh Metallov†
0203-5472 Signal'naya Informatsiya. Obshchie Voprosy Tsvetnoi Metallurgii. Obogashchenie Rud Tsvetnykh Metallov†
0203-5480 Signal'naya Informatsiya. Obshchie Voprosy Chernoi Metallurgii. Obshchezavodskoe Khozyaistvo Chernoi Metallurgii†
0203-5499 Signal'naya Informatsiya. Podgotovka Syr'evykh Materialov Chernoi Metallurgii. Proizvodstvo Chuguna i Ferrosplavov. Pryamoe Poluchenie Zheleza i Stali†
0203-5502 Signal'naya Informatsiya. Proizvodstvo Listov Chernykh Metallov†
0203-5510 Signal'naya Informatsiya. Proizvodstvo Zagotovok, Profilei, Katanki, Listov i Fol'gi iz Tsvetnykh Metallov i Splavov. Volochil'noe i Metiznoe Proizvodstvo. Proizvodstvo Trub†
0203-5529 Signal'naya Informatsiya. Proizvodstvo Stali†
0203-5537 Signal'naya Informatsiya. Struktura i Svoistva Tsvetnykh Metallov i Splavov i Kompozitsionnykh Materialov na Ikh Osnove. Metally i Splavy v Atomnoi i Termoyadernoi Ehnergetike†
0203-5545 Signal'naya Informatsiya. Atomnoe Yadro
0203-5553 Signal'naya Informatsiya. Nelineinaya Optika i Kvantovaya Elektronika
0203-5561 Signal'naya Informatsiya. Struktura i Dinamika Reshetki Tverdykh Tel
0203-5847 Literaturnaya Ucheba
0203-6223 Referativnyi Zhurnal. Ekonomika Promyshlennosti
0203-6436 Referativnyi Zhurnal. Teplo i Massobmen
0203-6495 F I D - R I Series on Problems of Information Science†
0203-7343 Polutehniline Instituut Tallinn. Teoriya i Raschet Tonkostennykh i Prostranstvennykh Konstruktsii *see* 0868-4138
0203-7483 Protection of Atmosphere Against Pollution
0203-8889 Ekspress-Informatsiya. Informatika
0203-9494 Problemy Slov'iyanoznavstva
0203-9699 Polutehniline Instituut Tallinn. Narodonaselenie i Rabochaya Sila†
0203-9702 Polutehniline Instituut Tallinn. Neustanovivsheesya Dvizheniya Zhidkosti v Trubakh *see* 0868-4103
0203-9710 Polutehniline Instituut Tallinn. Teoriya i Tekhnologiya Polucheniya Stroitel'nykh Materialov iz Zol Tverdykh Toplivt
0203-9737 Polutehniline Instituut Tallinn. Problemy Podzemnoi Otkrytoi Razrabotki Goryuchikh Slantsev i Nerudnykh Materialov *see* 0868-4189
0203-9745 Polutehniline Instituut Tallinn. Optimal'nye Sistemy i Algoritmy†
0203-9788 Polutehniline Instituut Tallinn. Voprosy Povysheniya Kachestva Pishchevykh Produktov†
0204-2177 Olimpiiskaya Panorama
0204-3548 Mineralogicheskii Zhurnal
0204-3556 Khimiya i Tekhnologiya Vody
0204-3564 Eksperimental'naya Onkologiya
0204-3572 Elektronnoe Modelirovanie
0204-3580 Metallofizika
0204-3599 Tekhnicheskaya Elektrodinamika
0204-3602 Promyshlennaya Teplotekhnika
0204-4005 Sofiiski Universitet. Istoricheski Fakultet. Godishnik.
0204-4013 Izvestiya na Muzeite v Severozapadna Bulgariya†
0204-4021 Palaeobulgarica
0204-403X Izvestiya na Muzeite ot Iugoiztochna Bulgariya
0204-4048 Godishnik na Muzeite ot Severna Bulgariia
0204-4056 Otechestvo
0204-4072 Izvestiya na Muzeite ot Iuzhna Bulgariya
0204-4080 Voenno Istoricheski Sbornik
0204-4099 Natsionalen Muzei na Revoliutsionnogo Dvizhenie v Bulgariya. Godishnik†
0204-4110 Serdika; Bulgarsko Matematichesko Spisanie
0204-4684 Statisticeski Danni za Bibliotekite v Bulgaria
0204-5109 Neftena i Vuglistna Geologiia
0204-5311 Rudoobrazuvatelni Protsesi i Mineralni Nakhodishta
0204-577X Abstracts of Bulgarian Scientific Literature. Industry, Building and Transport
0204-5958 Fiziko-Khimicheska Mekhanika
0204-6083 Abstracts of Bulgarian Scientific Literature. Economics and Law
0204-6253 Teatur
0204-6350 Putishta
0204-6989 Iaderna Energiia
0204-7373 Bibliografia na Bulgarskata Bibliografiia
0204-7438 Bibliotekar
0204-7535 Materialoznanie i Tekhnologiia
0204-7594 Biomekhanika
0204-7667 Bulletin d'Analyses de la Litterature Scientifique Bulgare. Linguistique et Litterature *see* 0861-0843
0204-7675 Ekologiia
0204-7934 Inzenerna Geologiia i Khidrogeologiia
0204-8213 Bulgaro-Suvetska Druzhba
0204-8248 Vodni Problemi
0204-8418 Discover Bulgaria
0204-8701 S'postavitelno Ezikoznanie
0204-8728 Tantsovo Izkustvo
0204-8809 Acta Microbiologica Bulgarica
0204-8892 Bulgarian Foreign Trade
0204-8906 Bulgarian Historical Review
0204-9260 Istoriya i Obshtestvoznanie
0204-9384 Abstracts of Bulgarian Scientific Literature. Biology and Biochemistry *changed to* Abstracts of Bulgarian Scientific Literature. Biology.
0204-9406 Abstracts of Bulgarian Scientific Literature. Geosciences
0204-9449 Abstracts of Bulgarian Scientific Literature. Mathematical and Physical Sciences
0204-9619 Sofiiski Universitet. Katedra po Nauchen Komunizm. Godishnik
0204-9627 Sofiiski Universitet. Katedra po Politiceska Ikonomiya. Godisnik
0204-9848 Problemi na Tekhnicheskata Kibernetika i Robotika
0205-0617 Naselenie
0205-0625 Uspehi na Moleculiarnata Biologia
0205-1109 Narodna Kultura

ISSN	Title
0205-1281	Televiziia. Radio
0205-1656	Savremenna Zhurnalistika
0205-194X	Rodoliubie
0205-3217	Mathematica Balkanica†
0205-3772	Abstracts of Bulgarian Scientific Literature. History, Archaeology and Ethnography
0205-9606	Voprosy Istorii Estestvoznanya i Tekhniki
0206-0515	Index of Current Medical Literature in the U S S R
0206-3131	Nadezhnost' i Dolgovechnost' Mashin i Sooruzhennii
0206-3441	Khemoretseptsiya Nasekomykh
0206-3638	Fizika Mnogochastichnykh Sistem
0206-4952	Immunologiya
0206-510X	Soviet Union
0206-538X	Signal'naya Informatsiya. Radioveshchanie - Ehlektroakustika - Zapis' i Vosproizvedenie Elektricheskikh Signalov†
0206-5398	Signal'naya Informatsiya. Tekhnologiya Proizvodstva Radioapparatury†
0206-5401	Signal'naya Informatsiya. Ehlektrovakuumnye Pribory i Ustroistva†
0206-541X	Signal'naya Informatsiya. Materialy Elektronnoi Tekhniki†
0206-5428	Signal'naya Informatsiya. Optoehlektronnye Pribory†
0206-5452	Referativnyi Zhurnal. Elektronika
0206-5525	Referativnyi Zhurnal. Veterinariya†
0206-5533	Referativnyi Zhurnal. Zhivotnovodstvo changed to Referativnyi Zhurnal. Biologiya Sel'skokhozyaistvennykh Zhivotnykh.
0206-572X	Mekhanizatsiya i Elektrifikatsiya
0206-6130	Referativnyi Zhurnal. Tekhnologicheskie Aspekty Okhrany Okruzhayushchei Sredy
0206-6149	Referativnyi Zhurnal. Sіstemy, Pribory i Metody Kontrolya Kachestva Okruzhayushchei Sredy
0206-6157	Referativnyi Zhurnal. Okhrana i Uluchshenie Gorodskoi Sredy
0206-8214	Avtomatika i Vychislitel'naya Tekhnika (Minsk)
0207-0111	Gibridnye Vychislitel'nye Mashiny i Kompleksy
0207-0383	Demograficheskie Issledovaniya
0207-1266	Lituanistika v S.S.S.R. Ekonomika†
0207-1274	Lituanistika v S.S.S.R. Literaturovedenie†
0207-1371	Referativnyi Zhurnal. Raketostroenie changed to Referativnyi Zhurnal. Raketostroenie i Kosmicheskaya Tekhnika.
0207-141X	Referativnyi Zhurnal. Fiziologiya i Morfologiya Cheloveka i Zhivotnykh
0207-2165	Maslichnye Kul'tury
0207-5008	Ekspress-Informatsiya. Aviastroenie
0207-5016	Ekspress-Informatsiya. Organizatsiya Perevozok, Avtomatizirovanie, Telemekhanika i Svyaz' na Zheleznykh Dorogakh changed to Ekspress-Informatsiya. Organizatsiya Perevozok. Avtomatizirovannie Sistemy Upravleniya Transportom.
0207-5024	Ekspress-Informatsiya. Protsessy i Apparaty Khimicheskikh Proizvodstv i Khimicheskaya Kibernetika
0207-5032	Ekspress-Informatsiya. Pryamoe Preobrazovanie Teplovoi i Khimicheskoi Energii v Elektricheskuyu
0207-9003	Belorusskaya S.S.R. v Pechati S.S.S.R. i Drugikh Zarubezhnykh Stran
0208-0052	Novaya Sovetskaya Literatura po Obshchestvennym Naukam. Nauchnyi Kommunizm
0208-0613	Molekulyarnaya Genetika, Mikrobiologiya i Virusologiya
0208-0621	V Mire Nauki
0208-0656	Signal'naya Informatsiya. Poverkhnost'
0208-0710	Kiiv
0208-2438	Santechnika ir Hidraulika
0208-287X	Otkrytiya, Izobreteniya
0208-2888	Promyshlennye Obraztsy. Tovarnye Znaki
0208-404X	Studia i Materialy do Dziejow Teatru Polskiego
0208-4058	Polska Akademia Nauk. Instytut Slawistiki. Prace Slawistyczne
0208-4082	Pomorskie Monografie Toponomastyczne
0208-4090	Polska Mysl Polityczna XIX i XX Wieku
0208-4147	Probability and Mathematical Statistics
0208-4198	Archiwum Combustionis
0208-421X	Studia i Materialy Oceanologiczne
0208-4228	Linguistica Silesiana
0208-4252	Bibliografia Prac Magisterskich, Doktorskich i Habilitacyjnych Przyjetych w S G G W w Warszawie
0208-4260	Bibliografia Publikacji Pracownikow w S G G W w Warszawie
0208-4325	Gazeta Obserwatora I M G W
0208-4333	Bibliotekarz
0208-4449	Acta Universitatis Nicolai Copernici. Biologia
0208-4562	Uniwersytet Gdanski. Wydzial Humanistyczny. Zeszyty Naukowe. Psychologia
0208-4589	Uniwersytet Warszawski. Wydzial Geografii i Studiow Regionalnych. Prace i Studia Geograficzne
0208-4600	Uniwersytet Warszawski. Instytut Archeologii. Studia i Materialy Archeologiczne
0208-4678	Uniwersytet Gdanski. Wydzial Humanistyczny. Zeszyty Naukowe. Filologia Rosyjska
0208-4732	Uniwersytet Gdanski. Wydzial Humanistyczny. Zeszyty Naukowe. Nauki Polityczne
0208-4740	Uniwersytet Gdanski. Wydzial Humanistyczny. Zeszyty Naukowe. Slawistyka
0208-4775	Uniwersytet Gdanski. Wydzial Ekonomiki Produkcji. Zeszyty Naukowe. Zagadnienia Finansowe changed to Uniwersytet Gdanski. Wydzial Ekonomiki Produkcji. Zeszyty Naukowe. Finanse i Rachunek Ekonomiczny.
0208-4783	Uniwersytet Gdanski. Wydzial Ekonomiki Produkcji. Zeszyty Naukowe. Zagadnienia Ekonomiki Przemyslu
0208-4791	Uniwersytet Gdanski. Wydzial Ekonomiki Produkcji. Zeszyty Naukowe. Organizacja Pracy i Zarzadzanie
0208-4805	Uniwersytet Gdanski. Wydzial Ekonomiki Produkcji. Zeszyty Naukowe. Cybernetyka Ekonomiczna i Informatyka
0208-4813	Uniwersytet Gdanski. Wydzial Ekonomiki Transportu. Zeszyty Naukowe. Instytut Ekonomii Politycznej. Prace i Materialy
0208-4821	Uniwersytet Gdanski. Wydzial Ekonomiki Transportu. Zeszyty Naukowe. Ekonomika Transportu Ladowego
0208-483X	Uniwersytet Gdanski. Wydzial Ekonomiki Transportu. Zeszyty Naukowe. Ekonomika Transportu Morskiego
0208-4864	Uniwersytet Gdanski. Wydzial Ekonomiki Transportu. Zeszyty Naukowe. Ekonomika Handlu Zagranicznego. Prace i Materialy changed to Uniwersytet Gdanski. Wydzial Ekonomiki Transportu. Zeszyty Naukowe. Instytut Ekonomiki Handlu Zagranicznego. Prace i Materialy.
0208-4872	Uniwersytet Gdanski. Wydzial Matematyki, Fizyki i Chemii. Zeszyty Naukowe. Problemy Dydaktyki Fizyki
0208-4910	Uniwersytet Gdanski. Wydzial Prawa i Administracji. Zeszyty Naukowe. Prawo
0208-4929	Uniwersytet Gdanski. Wydzial Prawa i Administracji. Zeszyty Naukowe. Prace Instytutu Administracji i Zarzadzania changed to Uniwersytet Gdanski. Wydzial Prawa i Administracji. Zeszyty Naukowe. Prace z Zakresu Administracji i Zarzadzania.
0208-4937	Uniwersytet Gdanski. Wydzial Biologii i Nauk o Ziemi. Zeszyty Naukowe. Geografia changed to Uniwersytet Gdanski. Wydzial Biologii, Geografii i Oceanologii. Zeszyty Naukowe. Geografia.
0208-4961	Uniwersytet Gdanski. Wydzial Biologii i Nauk o Ziemi. Zeszyty Naukowe. Biologia changed to Uniwersytet Gdanski. Wydzial Biologii, Geografii i Oceanologii. Zeszyty Naukowe. Biologia.
0208-497X	Wydzial Filologiczno-Filozoficzny. Prace
0208-4996	Lubelskie Towarzystwo Naukowe. Wydzial Humanistyczny. Prace. Monografie
0208-5003	Uniwersytet Slaski w Katowicach. Prace Naukowe. Z Problematyki Prawa Pracy i Polityki Socjalnej
0208-5011	Uniwersytet Slaski w Katowicach. Prace Naukowe. Z Teorii i Praktyki Dydaktycznej Jezyka Polskiego
0208-502X	Uniwersytet Slaski w Katowicach. Prace Naukowe. Studia Iuridica Silesiana
0208-5038	Uniwersytet Slaski w Katowicach. Prace Naukowe. Rusycystyczne Studia Literaturoznawcze
0208-5046	Acta Biologica see 0860-2441
0208-5054	Uniwersytet Slaski w Katowicach. Prace Naukowe. Geographia: Studia et Dissertationes
0208-5062	Muzeum Archeologiczne i Etnograficzne, Lodz. Prace i Materialy. Seria Numizmatyczna i Konserwatorska
0208-5240	Uniwersytet Gdanski. Wydzial Humanistyczny. Zeszyty Naukowe. Filologia Angielska
0208-5259	Acta Universitatis Nicolai Copernici. Filologia Germanska
0208-5267	Acta Universitatis Nicolai Copernici. Socjologia Wychowania
0208-5283	Acta Universitatis Nicolai Copernici. Prawo
0208-5291	Acta Universitatis Nicolai Copernici. Geografia
0208-5305	Acta Universitatis Nicolai Copernici. Ekonomia
0208-5321	Acta Universitatis Nicolai Copernici. Filologia Polska
0208-533X	Acta Universitatis Nicolai Copernici. Zabytkoznawstwo i Konserwatorstwo
0208-5348	Acta Universitatis Nicolai Copernici. Prace Limnologiczne
0208-5402	Uniwersytet Slaski w Katowicach. Prace Naukowe. Prace Wydzialu Techniki
0208-5410	Uniwersytet Slaski w Katowicach. Prace Matematyczne changed to Uniwersytet Slaski w Katowicach. Prace Naukowe. Annales Mathematicae Silesianae.
0208-5429	Uniwersytet Slaski w Katowicach. Prace Naukowe. Prace Pedagogiczne
0208-5437	Uniwersytet Slaski w Katowicach. Prace Naukowe. Prace z Nauk Spolecznych. Folia Philosophica
0208-5445	Uniwersytet Slaski w Katowicach. Prace Naukowe. Prace Jezykoznawcze
0208-5453	Uniwersytet Slaski w Katowicach. Prace Naukowe. Prace Historycznoliterackie
0208-5488	Uniwersytet Slaski w Katowicach. Prace Naukowe. Problemy Prawne Gornictwa
0208-5496	Uniwersytet Slaski w Katowicach. Prace Naukowe. Problemy Prawne Handlu Zagranicznego
0208-550X	Problemy Prawa Wynalazczego i Patentowego†
0208-5518	Uniwersytet Slaski w Katowicach. Prace Naukowe. Problemy Prawa Przewozowego
0208-5526	Uniwersytet Slaski w Katowicach. Prace Naukowe. Pedagogika Pracy Kulturalno-Oswiatowej
0208-5534	Uniwersytet Slaski w Katowicach. Prace Naukowe. Geologia
0208-5550	Uniwersytet Slaski w Katowicach. Prace Naukowe. Neophilologica
0208-5569	Uniwersytet Slaski w Katowicach. Prace Naukowe. Psychologiczne Problemy Funkcjonowania Czlowieka w Sytuacji Pracy
0208-5577	Uniwersytet Slaski w Katowicach. Prace Nukowe. Problemy Prawa Karnego
0208-5615	Innowacje see 0137-8783
0208-5623	Accademia Polacca delle Scienze. Conferenze e Studi see 0239-8605
0208-564X	Acta Universitatis Nicolai Copernici. Filozofia
0208-5666	Politechnika Gdanska. Zeszyty Naukowe. Ekonomia
0208-5704	Warsaw Agricultural University. S G G W - A R. Annals. Forestry and Wood Technology changed to Warsaw Agricultural University. S G G W. Annals. Forestry and Wood Technology.
0208-5712	Warsaw Agricultural University. S G G W - A R. Annals. Agriculture changed to Warsaw Agricultural University. S G G W. Annals. Agriculture.
0208-5720	Warsaw Agricultural University. S G G W - A R. Annals. Agricultural Economics and Rural Sociology changed to Warsaw Agricultural University. S G G W. Annals. Agricultural Economics and Rural Sociology.
0208-5739	Warsaw Agricultural University. S G G W - A R. Annals. Animal Science changed to Warsaw Agricultural University. S G G W. Annals. Animal Science.
0208-5747	Warsaw Agricultural University. S G G W - A R. Annals. Horticulture changed to Warsaw Agricultural University. S G G W. Annals. Horticulture.
0208-5755	Warsaw Agricultural University. S G G W - A R. Annals. Food Technology and Nutrition changed to Warsaw Agricultural University. S G G W. Annals. Food Technology and Nutrition.
0208-5763	Warsaw Agricultural University. S G G W - A R. Annals. Veterinary Medicine changed to Warsaw Agricultural University. S G G W. Annals. Veterinary Medicine.
0208-5771	Warsaw Agricultural University. S G G W - A R. Annals. Land Reclamation changed to Warsaw Agricultural University. S G G W. Annals. Land Reclamation.
0208-578X	Uniwersytet Slaski w Katowicach. Prace Naukowe. Fizyka i Chemia Metali
0208-5925	Instytut Sadownictwa i Kwiaciarstwa w Skierniewicach. Prace. Seria B: Rosliny Ozdobne
0208-5933	Instytut Sadownictwa i Kwiaciarstwa w Skierniewicach. Seria A: Prace Doswiadczalne z Zakresu Sadownictwa
0208-5992	Rocznik Chopinowski
0208-600X	Acta Universitatis Lodziensis: Folia Sociologica
0208-6018	Acta Universitatis Lodziensis: Folia Oeconomica
0208-6034	Acta Universitatis Lodziensis: Folia Archaeologica
0208-6042	Acta Universitatis Lodziensis: Folia Ethnologica
0208-6050	Acta Universitatis Lodziensis: Folia Historica
0208-6069	Acta Universitatis Lodziensis: Folia Iuridica
0208-6077	Acta Universitatis Lodziensis: Folia Linguistica

ISSN INDEX

ISSN	Title
0208-6085	Acta Universitatis Lodziensis: Folia Litteraria
0208-6093	Acta Universitatis Lodziensis: Folia Paedagogica et Psychologica
0208-6107	Acta Universitatis Lodziensis: Folia Philosophica
0208-6123	Acta Universitatis Lodziensis: Folia Geographica
0208-6131	Acta Universitatis Lodziensis: Folia Sozologica
0208-614X	Acta Universitatis Lodziensis: Folia Biochimica et Biophysica
0208-6158	Acta Universitatis Lodziensis: Folia Limnologica
0208-6166	Acta Universitatis Lodziensis: Folia Zoologica et Anthropologica
0208-6174	Acta Universitatis Lodziensis: Folia Botanica
0208-6182	Acta Universitatis Lodziensis: Folia Chimica
0208-6190	Acta Universitatis Lodziensis: Folia Physica
0208-6204	Acta Universitatis Lodziensis: Folia Mathematica
0208-6263	Instytut Meteorologii i Gospodarki Wodnej. Wiadomosci
0208-6425	Inzynieria Chemiczna *changed to* Inzynieria Chemiczna i Procesowa.
0208-645X	Panstwowy Instytut Geologiczny. Prace
0208-6573	Functiones et Approximatio Commentarii Mathematici
0208-6808	Socjolingwistyka
0208-7286	Politechnika Slaska. Zeszyty Naukowe. Informatyka
0208-7359	Polish Historical Library. Anthologies. Monographs. Opera Minora
0208-7375	Polish Political Science
0208-7448	Mechanizacja i Automatyzacja Gornictwa
0208-7596	Archiwum Tlumaczen z Teorii Literatury i Metodologii Badan Literackich
0208-7669	Akademia Rolnicza w Szczecinie. Zeszyty Naukowe. Nauki Spoleczne i Ekonomiczne
0208-7944	Akademia Ekonomiczna, Krakow. Zeszyty Naukowe
0208-8045	Tygodnik Solidarnosc
0208-8061	Polish Academy of Sciences. Institute of Geophysics. Publications. Series G. Numerical Methods in Geophysics†
0208-8193	Muzeum Narodowe w Krakowie. Katalogi Zbiorow
0208-8363	Punkt
0208-8371	Politechnika Wroclawska. Studium Praktycznej Nauki Jezykow Obcych. Prace Naukowe. Monografie *changed to* Politechnika Wroclawska. Studium Nauki Jezykow Obcych. Prace Naukowe. Monografie.
0208-841X	Planetary Geodesy
0208-8428	Space Physics
0208-8436	Akademia Rolnicza, Poznan. Roczniki. Rozprawy Naukowe
0208-8665	Studia Jezykoznawcze
0208-8932	Akademia Rolnicza, Poznan. Roczniki. Melioracje Wodne *changed to* Akademia Rolnicza, Poznan. Roczniki. Melioracje.
0208-8940	Akademia Rolnicza, Poznan. Roczniki. Fizyka, Chemia
0208-9068	Annales Societatis Geologorum Poloniae
0208-9386	Krzepniecie Metali i Stopow
0208-9564	Wyzsza Szkola Pedagogiczna, Opole. Zeszyty Naukowe. Seria A. Psychologia
0208-9963	Biblioteka Res Facta
0209-0112	Zbiorcza Szkola Gminna *changed to* Problemy Oswiaty na Wsi.
0209-0260	Polish Engineering
0209-0724	Instytut Gornictwa Naftowego i Gazownictwa. Prace
0209-0961	Stosunki Miedzynarodowe
0209-1186	Instytut Medycyny Pracy w Przemysle Wlokienniczym i Chemicznym. Zeszyty Metodyczno-Organizacyjne *changed to* Instytut Medycyny Pracy. Zeszyty Metodyczno-Organizacyjne.
0209-1577	Polish Academy of Sciences. Institute of Geography and Spatial Organization. Geographical Studies. Special Issue
0209-1593	Instytut Maszyn Matematycznych. Prace Naukowo-Badawcze
0209-1607	Firma
0209-164X	Zywienie Czlowieka *changed to* Zywienie Czlowieka.
0209-1674	Akademia Ekonomiczna, Krakow. Zeszyty Naukowe. Seria Specjalna: Monografie
0209-1747	Wprost
0209-2077	Etnografia
0209-2573	Politechnika Wroclawska. Instytut Sterowania i Techniki Systemow. Prace Naukowe. Monografie
0209-3316	Acta Magnetica
0209-3324	Politechnika Slaska. Zeszyty Naukowe. Transport
0209-3413	Przeglad Dokumentacyjny Obrobki Plastycznej
0209-3731	Uniwersytet Slaski w Katowicach. Prace Naukowe. Jezyk Artystyczny
0209-3928	Novosti Farmatsii i Meditsiny
0209-4002	Hungary. Kozponti Statisztikai Hivatal. Iparstatisztikai Evkonyv
0209-4010	Hungary. Kozponti Statisztikai Hivatal. Beruhazasi-Epitoipari Adatok†
0209-4401	Made in Hungary Yearbook
0209-4819	Idegenforgalmi Statisztika *see* 0230-4414
0209-5033	Muszaki Lapszemle. Gepeszet-Gepgyartastechnologia *see* 0231-0694
0209-5327	Hazai es Kulfoldi Roplapok, Prospektusok, Kulonlenyomatok, Szabvanyok es Szabadamak az Agroinform Allomanyabant
0209-5386	Hungarian Digest
0209-5513	Hungary. Kozponti Statisztikai Hivatal. Lakasepites es Megszunes *changed to* Hungary. Kozponti Statisztikai Hivatal. Beruhazasi, Epitoipari, Lakasepitesi Evkonyu.
0209-6145	Pest Megyei Konyvtaros
0209-6919	Hungary. Kozponti Statisztikai Hivatal. Agazati Kapcsolatok Merleget
0209-7915	Hungary. Kozponti Statisztikai Hivatal. Vizgazdalkodasi Statisztikai Zsebkonyv
0209-8393	Konyvtari Kiadvanyok†
0209-9403	Studia Poetica
0209-9543	Acta Universitatis Szegediensis de Attila Jozsef Nominatae. Sectio Ethnographica et Linguistica
0209-9578	Textil- es Textilruhazati Ipari Szakirodalmi Tajekoztatot
0209-9683	Combinatorica
0209-9853	Gyorsindex - Epitest
0210-0002	Revistas Espanolas en Curso de Publicacion†
0210-0045	Awraq *see* 0214-834X
0210-0118	Novamaquina 2000
0210-0134	Integral
0210-0177	Actualidad Bibliografica Iberoamericana
0210-0223	Sistema
0210-024X	Petrogas
0210-0266	Consejo Superior de Investigaciones Cientificas. Cuadernos de Economia
0210-0274	Batik
0210-0320	Yate y Motonautica
0210-0347	Boletin Informativo de Medio Ambiente†
0210-0363	Estudios Trinitarios
0210-0398	Ciencia Tomista
0210-0436	Perspectiva Social
0210-0479	Cimbra
0210-0487	Ciudad y Territorio
0210-0525	Estudios
0210-0541	Selecciones Avicolas
0210-055X	Metales y Maquinas *changed to* Metales y Metalurgia.
0210-0576	Revista Espanola de Ortodoncia
0210-0592	Sumario Actual de Revistas
0210-0614	Revista Espanola de Documentacion Cientifica
0210-0630	Cuadernos de Pedagogia
0210-0657	Clinica y Analisis Grupal
0210-069X	Spain. Servicio Social de Higiene y Seguridad del Trabajo. Boletin Bibliografico *see* 0213-943X
0210-0711	Colectanea de Jurisprudencia Canonica *see* 0034-9372
0210-0738	Confederacion Espanola de Cajas de Ahorros. Fundacion Fondo para la Investigacion Economica y Social. Coyuntura Economica
0210-0746	Cuadernos de Filologia Clasica
0210-0762	Maestria Industrial
0210-0770	Embalajes *see* 0210-1084
0210-0800	Revista de la Industria Textil
0210-0819	Ciencia e Industria Farmaceutica
0210-0827	Instituto de Investigaciones Pesqueras. Datos Informativos†
0210-0835	Nueva Estafeta†
0210-0851	Moralia
0210-086X	Cuadernos de Geografia
0210-0975	Instituto de Estudios de Administracion Local. Secretariado Iberoamericano de Municipios. Boletin de Informacion *changed to* Informacion Iberoamericana.
0210-1017	Panorama Veterinario
0210-1025	Revista Espanola de Economia
0210-1084	Embalajes y Plasticos y Manufacturas
0210-1122	Boletin del Mutualismo Laboral†
0210-1130	Revista de Citologia
0210-1157	Spain. Ministerio de Justicia. Diccionarios Indice de Jurisprudencia Penal
0210-1165	Spain. Ministerio de Justicia. Diccionarios Indice de Jurisprudencia Civil
0210-1173	Hacienda Publica Espanola
0210-1203	Edicion
0210-122X	Proceso de Datost
0210-1297	Escuela Tecnica Superior de Ingenieros de Montes. Biblioteca. Boletin Bibliografico y Documental *see* 0212-226X
0210-1343	Anuario de Filologia
0210-136X	Investigacion y Ciencia
0210-1416	Estudios de Historia Social
0210-1432	Comentario Sociologico†
0210-1459	Revista de Musicologia
0210-1475	Sociedad Castellonense de Cultura. Boletin
0210-1513	Manipulacion de Materiales en la Industria
0210-1521	Investigaciones Economicas. Revista
0210-1580	Boletin de Estadistica y Coyuntura
0210-1602	Teorema
0210-1610	Estudios Eclesiasticos
0210-1688	Banca Espanola
0210-1718	Laboreo
0210-1742	Revista de Extension Agraria
0210-1777	I M H E
0210-1785	Anuario de Sociologia y Psicologia Juridicas†
0210-1793	Facultad de Medicina de Barcelona. Departamento de Psiquiatria. Revista *see* 0213-7429
0210-1815	Industria Internacional
0210-1831	Boletin Merksa de Estudios de Mercado
0210-184X	M I
0210-1874	Revista Espanola de Linguistica
0210-1912	Cunicultura
0210-1920	Confiteria Espanola
0210-1947	Boletin Economico de la Construccion
0210-1963	Arbor
0210-2056	Energia
0210-2064	Ingenieria Quimica
0210-2137	Gaceta Numismatica
0210-2153	Luz y Fuerza
0210-2196	Revista Quirurgica Espanola *see* 0214-2376
0210-220X	Jano "Medicina y Humanidades"
0210-2307	Industria Minera
0210-2315	Boletin de la Normalizacion Espanola
0210-2331	Perspectiva Escolar
0210-2463	Spain. Instituto Nacional de Investigaciones Agrarias. Anales. Serie: General†
0210-2471	Spain. Instituto Nacional de Investigaciones Agrarias. Anales. Serie: Recursos Naturales *see* 0211-9102
0210-2498	Spain. Instituto Nacional de Investigaciones Agrarias. Anales. Serie: Higiene y Sanidad Animal *see* 0213-5035
0210-2501	Proteccion Vegetal *see* 0213-5000
0210-251X	Instituto de Investigacion Textil y de Cooperacion Industrial. Boletin *see* 0212-6699
0210-2536	Ecologia
0210-2560	Spain. Instituto Nacional de Investigaciones Agrarias. Comunicaciones. Serie: Tecnologia Agraria
0210-2579	Comercio Industrial†
0210-2595	Comercio e Industria. Suplemento Quicenal *see* 0213-0637
0210-2692	Zona Abierta
0210-282X	Tecnica Topografica
0210-2854	Revista de Estudios Extremenos
0210-2870	Dialogo Ecumenico
0210-2897	Revista de Derecho Publico
0210-2919	Cronica Tributaria
0210-2943	Memorias de Historia Antigua
0210-3001	Derecho Penal y Ciencias Penales. Anuario
0210-301X	Derecho Civil. Anuario
0210-3168	Alforja
0210-3206	Informacion Economica Mundial†
0210-3214	Camp de l'Arpa
0210-329X	Spain. Instituto Nacional de Investigaciones Agrarias. Comunicaciones. Serie: Produccion Vegetal
0210-3303	Spain. Instituto Nacional de Investigaciones Agrarias. Comunicaciones. Serie: Produccion Animal
0210-3311	Spain. Instituto Nacional de Investigaciones Agrarias. Comunicaciones. Serie: General
0210-332X	Spain. Instituto Nacional de Investigaciones Agrarias. Comunicaciones. Serie: Economia y Sociologia Agrarias *see* 0214-0357
0210-3338	Spain. Instituto Nacional de Investigaciones Agrarias. Comunicaciones. Serie: Recursos Naturales
0210-3397	Avances en Terapeutica†
0210-3419	Spain. Ministerio de Justicia. Secretaria General Tecnica. Documentacion Juridica
0210-3427	Sentencias en Apelacion de las Audiencias Provinciales
0210-3516	Letras de Deusto
0210-3559	Pastoral Misionera
0210-3605	Vida Silvestre
0210-3664	Cuadernos de Investigacion: Geografia e Historia *see* 0211-6820
0210-3664	Cuadernos de Investigacion: Geografia e Historia *see* 0214-4670
0210-3680	Revista de Acustica
0210-3737	Banco de Espana. Boletin Economico
0210-3761	T G
0210-377X	Verba
0210-3869	Delta (Barcelona) *changed to* Delta (Barcelona).
0210-4083	Monsalvat
0210-4105	Astrum
0210-4113	Fomento Social *see* 0015-6043
0210-4148	Fundacion Juan March. Boletin Informativo
0210-4164	A N A B A D Boletin
0210-4245	Nueva Estetica
0210-4261	Eikonos
0210-4296	Revista Juridica de Cataluna
0210-4326	Parapsicologia†
0210-4334	Quimica Analitica
0210-4466	Asclepio

5646 ISSN INDEX

0210-4547 Anales de Literatura Hispanoamericana
0210-4563 C.A.U.
0210-461X Clinica Hematologica†
0210-4628 Clinica Gastroenterologica†
0210-4636 Clinica Endocrinologica†
0210-4644 Clinica Radiologica†
0210-4660 Clinica Anestesiologica†
0210-4792 Revista de Seguridad Social
0210-4822 Real Academia Espanola. Boletin
0210-4857 Cuadernos Salmantinos de Filosofia
0210-489X Informacion Arqueologica
0210-4903 Universidad de Murcia. Miscelanea Medieval Murciana
0210-4911 Universidad de Murcia. Estudios Romanicos
0210-492X Universidad de Murcia. Didactica Geografica†
0210-4938 Clinica Ginecologica†
0210-5004 Mediterranea
0210-508X I.Q.S.
0210-5187 Medicina Cutanea Ibero-Latino-Americana
0210-5233 Revista Espanola de Investigaciones Sociologicas
0210-5381 Spain. Ministerio de Agricultura, Pesca y Alimentacion. Boletin Mensual de Informacion de Prensa Extranjera *see* 0213-0602
0210-539X Universidad de Murcia. Anales de Derecho†
0210-5462 Cuadernos Geograficos
0210-5489 Euromueble
0210-5527 Universidad de Oviedo. Facultad de Medicina. Archivos
0210-5535 Panorama Harinero
0210-5578 Diario de Congresos Medicos
0210-5608 Ethnica†
0210-5616 Tria
0210-5632 Consulta†
0210-5659 Nuestra Cabana
0210-5705 Gastroenterologia y Hepatologia
0210-5713 American Journal of Medicine (Spanish Edition)†
0210-5721 Pediatrics (Edicion Espanola)
0210-573X Clinica e Investigacion en Ginecologia y Obstetricia
0210-5810 Anuario de Estudios Americanos
0210-5845 Federacion Espanola de Natacion. Anuario.†
0210-5888 Poesia
0210-5977 Presupuesto y Gasto Publico
0210-6000 Revista Catalana de Geografia
0210-6035 Revista de Estudios Penitenciarios
0210-6086 Estudios Filosoficos
0210-6302 Actualidad Electronica
0210-637X Anuario Hortofruticola Espanol
0210-6485 Rotacion de la Tierra
0210-6493 Instituto y Observatorio de Marina. Boletin Astronomico *changed to* Real Instituto y Observatorio de la Armada. Boletin Astronomico.
0210-6566 Cuadernos de Historia de la Farmacia
0210-6604 Revista Iberoamericana de Corrosion y Proteccion
0210-6825 Alerta Informativa. Serie B: Fisica Aplicada†
0210-6833 Diputacio Provincial. Biblioteca Catalunya Cataleg la Produccion Editorial Barcelonesa†
0210-685X Deformacion Metalica
0210-6868 Piscinas
0210-7007 Alerta Informativa. Serie D: el Mundo Rural†
0210-7023 Alerta Informativa. Serie E: Economia de la Empresa†
0210-7074 Estudios Josefinos
0210-7090 Noticiario Arqueologico Hispanico: Arqueologia *see* 0211-1748
0210-7112 Revista Espanola de Teologia
0210-7171 Avances en Obstetricia y Ginecologia†
0210-7228 Instituto Gemologico Espanol. Boletin
0210-7295 Tribuna Cooperativa
0210-7309 O.R.L. Dips
0210-735X Instituto y Observatorio de Marina. Almanaque Nautico *changed to* Real Instituto y Observatorio de la Armada. Almanaque Nautico.
0210-7465 Annals de Medicina
0210-7570 Faventia†
0210-7597 Acta Botanica Barcinonensia
0210-7651 Universidad Hispalense. Anales. Facultad de Medicina *changed to* Universidad de Sevilla. Serie: Medicina.
0210-7678 Universidad Hispalensa. Anales. Serie: Filosofia y Letras *changed to* Universidad de Sevilla. Serie: Filosofia y Letras.
0210-7686 Universidad Hispalense. Anales. Serie: Derecho *changed to* Universidad de Sevilla. Serie: Derecho.
0210-7694 Revista Habis
0210-7708 Revista Lagascalia
0210-7716 Revista Historia, Instituciones, Documentos
0210-7732 Sociedad de Eusko Folklore. Anuario
0210-7775 Medios Audiovisuales
0210-7953 Estudios de Filologia Inglesa
0210-7988 Revista de Ferreteria
0210-8038 Spain. Ministerio de Agricultura, Pesca y Alimentacion. Servicio de Defensa Contra Plagas e Inspeccion Fitopatologica. Boletin *see* 0213-6910
0210-8046 Almanaque Nautico Reducido para Uso con Maquinas de Calcular
0210-8062 Institut Botanic de Barcelona. Treballs
0210-8089 Vergel
0210-8119 Ocultaciones de Estrellas por la Luna
0210-8127 Fenomenos Astronomicos
0210-8135 M T A Pediatria
0210-8143 Museo del Prado. Boletin
0210-8291 Quaderns de Treball†
0210-8348 Psiquis
0210-8356 Revista de Minas
0210-8372 Bibliografia Espanola. Suplemento de Publicaciones Periodicas
0210-8488 Indice Espanol de Humanidades *changed to* Indice Espanol de Humanidades. Series A: Art.
0210-8488 Indice Espanol de Humanidades *see* 1130-099X
0210-8488 Indice Espanol de Humanidades *see* 1130-1163
0210-8623 Centro de Edafologia y Biologia Aplicada. Anuario†
0210-8836 Spain. Instituto de Estudios Laborales y de la Seguridad Social. Jurisprudencial Laboral y de Seguridad Social.†
0210-8852 F A C: Revista Practica de Medicina
0210-9107 Papeles de Economia Espanola
0210-9174 Revista de Filologia Espanola
0210-9220 Spain. Ministerio del Interior. Direccion General de Trafico. Boletin Informativo
0210-9409 Indice Espanol de Ciencia y Tecnologia
0210-9425 Investigaciones Historicas
0210-9492 Centro de Informacion Documental de Archivos. Boletin de Informacion
0210-9506 Acta Botanica Malacitana
0210-9522 Miscelanea Comillas
0210-9603 Anuario de Historia Moderna y Contemporanea
0210-9743 Universidad Complutense de Madrid. Centro de Calculo. Boletin†
0210-9999 Tiempos Medicos
0211-0105 Boletin Oficial de la Propiedad Industrial. 1: Marcas y Otros Signos Distintivos
0211-0113 Boletin Oficial de la Propiedad Industrial. 2: Patentes, Modelos y Dibujos *see* 0211-0121
0211-0113 Boletin Oficial de la Propiedad Industrial. 2: Patentes, Modelos y Dibujos *see* 0211-013X
0211-0121 Boletin Oficial de la Propiedad Industrial. 2: Patentes y Modelos de Utilidad
0211-013X Boletin Oficial de la Propiedad Industrial. 3: Modelos y Dibujos Industriales y Artisticos
0211-030X Agrishell
0211-0334 Boletin de Estudios y Documentacion de Servicios Sociales†
0211-0547 Cuadernos de Investigacion Filologica
0211-0768 D'Art
0211-1136 Fluidos
0211-1268 Boletin de Coyuntura y Estadistica del Pais Vasco
0211-1284 Coyuntura Industrial y Utilizacion de la Capacidad Productiva de Alava†
0211-1314 Spain. Instituto Nacional de Investigaciones Agrarias. Comunicaciones. Serie: Higiene y Sanidad
0211-1322 Jardin Botanico de Madrid. Anales
0211-1373 Indice Espanol de Ciencias Sociales *see* 0213-019X
0211-139X Revista Espanola de Geriatria y Gerontologia
0211-142X Quaderns d'Historia Tarraconense
0211-1578 Comercio Industria y Navegacion *changed to* La Camara.
0211-1748 Noticiario Arqueologico Hispanico
0211-187X Boletin Oficial de la Propiedad Industrial. Informacion Tecnologica de Patentes *changed to* Boletin Oficial de la Propiedad Industrial. 4: Resumenes de Patentes.
0211-1993 Revistas Espanolas con I S S N
0211-2299 Endocrinologia
0211-2329 Instituto de Estudios Gerundenses. Anales
0211-2477 Instituto de Estudios Gerundenses. Serie Monografica
0211-2728 Agricola Vergel
0211-2892 Rotacion
0211-2930 Cambus
0211-304X Sernaval
0211-3325 Quimera
0211-3333 Revista Internacional de Comunicacion y Relaciones Publicas
0211-3465 Ciencia Pediatrika
0211-3538 Anuario Musical
0211-3589 Al Qantara
0211-3732 Defensa
0211-3767 Frisona Espanola
0211-3945 Revista de Libreria Antiquaria
0211-4046 Boletin de Traducciones
0211-4143 Actualidad Bibliografica de Filosofia y Teologia
0211-4364 Revista de Estudios de Juventud
0211-4410 Guia de Centros Educativos Catolicos
0211-450X Museo Canario
0211-4526 Persona y Derecho
0211-4569 Sal Terrae
0211-4674 Spain. Instituto Nacional de Investigaciones Agrarias. Anales. Series: Ganaderia *see* 0213-5035
0211-4682 Spain. Instituto Nacional de Investigaciones Agrarias. Anales. Serie: Agricola *see* 0213-5000
0211-4704 Campo y Mecanica
0211-5174 Trabajos de Arqueologia Navarra
0211-5379 Coyuntura Comercial. Alava†
0211-5468 Informe Economico de Aragon
0211-5549 Psicopatologia
0211-5581 Revista Politica Comparada
0211-5611 Anthropos
0211-5638 Fisioterapia
0211-5913 Revista Canaria de Estudios Ingleses
0211-6057 Nutricion Clinica
0211-6243 Real Sociedad Espanola de Fisica y Quimica. Anales de Fisica *changed to* Real Sociedad Espanola de Fisica. Anales de Fisica.
0211-6529 Miscel.lania Zoologica
0211-6561 Mensajero
0211-6820 Cuadernos de Investigacion Geografica
0211-6839 Cuadernos de Investigacion Historia *see* 0214-4670
0211-6901 Gine Dips
0211-7142 Banco Central. Boletin Informativo
0211-7290 Tecnica Ceramica
0211-7959 Arte Regalo
0211-7967 Azulejo
0211-7975 Textiles para el Hogar
0211-8173 Tecnologia del Agua
0211-8181 Equivalencias
0211-8335 B I B E Quarterly Bulletin
0211-8335 B I B E Annual Summary
0211-836X Resultados Expediciones Cientificas†
0211-8394 Agricultura y Sociedad
0211-8734 Informe Economico Regional
0211-8866 Region Exporta *changed to* Comercio Exterior de la Comunidad Valenciana.
0211-8998 Institucion Fernan-Gonzalez. Boletin
0211-9102 Spain. Instituto Nacional de Investigaciones Agrarias. Anales. Serie: Forestal†
0211-9323 Coyuntura Industrial de la Region Valenciana†
0211-9536 Dynamis
0211-9714 Studia Botanica
0211-9749 Vida Religiosa
0211-9897 Spain. Ministerio de Agricultura, Pesca y Alimentacion. Boletin Mensual de Estadistica Agraria
0212-0151 Lancet (Edicion Espanola)
0212-0208 Pensamiento Iberoamericano
0212-033X Spain. Ministerio de Relaciones con las Cortes y de la Secretaria del Gobierno. Boletin Official del Estado *changed to* Spain. Boletin Oficial del Estado.
0212-0542 Gaseta Sanitaria de Barcelona *see* 0213-9111
0212-0550 Cuadernos de Traduccion e Interpretacion
0212-0607 Horizonte Empresarial
0212-0771 Sociedad Andaluza de Ortopedia y Traumatologia. Revista
0212-1514 M T A Medicina Interna
0212-1565 Spain. Instituto Espanol de Oceanografia. Informes Tecnicos
0212-159X Andalucia Islamica. Textos y Estudios
0212-1689 Alimentacion
0212-1808 Clinica Cardiovascular
0212-1964 Teologia y Catequesis
0212-2138 Revista del Caucho
0212-2146 Campo
0212-226X Escuela Tecnica Superior de Ingenieros de Montes. Biblioteca. Boletin Bibliografico y Documental. Informacion Forestal. Serie A: Monografias
0212-2278 Escuela Tecnica Superior de Ingenieros de Montes. Biblioteca. Boletin Bibliografico y Documental. Informacion Forestal. Serie B: Publicaciones Periodicas
0212-2359 Instituto Nacional de Seguridad e Higiene en el Trabajo. Boletin Bibliografico *see* 0213-943X
0212-3215 Sociedad de Estudios Vascos. Cuadernos de Seccion. Artes Plasticas y Monumentales
0212-3223 Sociedad de Estudios Vascos. Cuadernos de Seccion. Lengua y Literatura
0212-3231 Poder y Libetad
0212-324X Vindicacion Feminista *changed to* Poder y Libertad.
0212-3754 Revista de Robotica *changed to* Automatizacion Integrada y Revista de Robotica.
0212-3800 Infectologika†
0212-4009 Apunts
0212-4130 Revista de Filologia
0212-4173 Sociedad de Estudios Vascos. Cuadernos de Seccion. Ciencias Naturales
0212-4416 Revista de Historia Contemporanea
0212-4572 Analisis Clinicos
0212-4688 Revista Espanola de Endodoncia
0212-4696 C Q Radio Amateur
0212-4939 Estomodeo
0212-5218 Enfermedades Infecciosas *see* 0213-005X
0212-5226 Equipack
0212-5382 Nursing (Year) (Edicion Espanola)
0212-5625 Caza y Pesca
0212-5633 El Croquis de Arquitectura y de Diseno
0212-5765 Inmunologia *see* 0213-9626

ISSN

ISSN INDEX 5647

0212-5773 Spain. Ministerio de Transportes, Turismo y Comunicaciones. Secretaria General de Turismo. Anuario de Estadisticas de Turismo
0212-5919 Thalassas
0212-5978 Razon Espanola†
0212-5994 Suplementos sobre el Sistema Financiero de Papeles de Economia Espanola
0212-6052 Ciencia Medica
0212-6109 Historia Economica
0212-6397 Sociedad de Estudios Vascos. Cuadernos de Seccion. Historia y Geografia
0212-6400 Alimentec
0212-6532 Spain. Instituto Nacional de Estadistica. Encuesta de Poblacion Activa. Principales Resultados
0212-6559 Universidad de Murcia. Anales de Historia Contemporanea
0212-6699 Instituto de Investigacion Textil y de Cooperacion Industrial. Boletin INTEXTER
0212-6818 Electro-Ocio
0212-6982 Revista Espanola de Medicina Nuclear
0212-6990 Spain. Instituto Nacional de Estadistica. Encuesta de Poblacion Activa. Resultados Detallados
0212-7016 Revista Internacional de los Estudios Vascos
0212-7202 Industrias Pesqueras
0212-7512 Tribuna Medica
0212-7547 Sociedad de Estudios Vascos. Cuadernos de Seccion. Folklore
0212-8047 Universidad de La Laguna. Anuarios
0212-8322 Universidad de Murcia. Anales de Pedagogia
0212-8519 Instalaciones Deportivas
0212-8594 Revista de Estudios Andaluces
0212-8780 Revista Canaria de Filosofia y Ciencia Social
0212-8799 Archivos de Medicina del Deporte
0212-8977 Universidad de Oviedo. Revista de Biologia
0212-9108 Ruizia
0212-9248 Museu Arxiu de Santa Maria. Fulls
0212-9280 Topografia y Cartografia
0212-9442 Hora de Poesia
0212-9698 Universidad de Murcia. Anales de Filosofia
0212-9701 Revista de Actualidades de Estomatologica Espanola *see* 1130-0094
0212-9728 Universidad de Murcia. Anales de Psicologia
0212-9744 Geriatrika
0213-005X Enfermedades Infecciosas y Microbiologia Clinica
0213-0157 Revista de Farmacologia Clinica y Experimental
0213-019X Indice Espanol de Ciencias Sociales. Series A: Psychology and Educational Sciences
0213-019X Indice Espanol de Ciencias Sociales *see* 0213-0521
0213-019X Indice Espanol de Ciencias Sociales *see* 0213-4683
0213-019X Indice Espanol de Ciencias Sociales *see* 1130-3700
0213-019X Indice Espanol de Ciencias Sociales *see* 0214-1086
0213-019X Indice Espanol de Ciencias Sociales *see* 1130-9105
0213-0289 Sociedad de Estudios Vascos. Cuadernos de Seccion. Medios de Comunicacion
0213-0297 Sociedad de Estudios Vascos. Cuadernos de Seccion. Antropologia y Etnografia
0213-0467 Canelobre
0213-0483 Sociedad de Estudios Vascos. Cuadernos de Seccion. Derecho
0213-0521 Indice Espanol de Ciencias Sociales. Series B: Economics, Sociology and Political Science
0213-053X Anuario de Linguistica Hispanica
0213-0602 Spain. Instituto de Relaciones Agrarias. Boletin de Informacion Extranjera
0213-0610 Guiniguada
0213-0637 Comercio Industria
0213-0750 Temas Laborales
0213-0815 Sociedad de Estudios Vascos. Cuadernos de Seccion. Musica
0213-0823 Nueva Ferreteria
0213-1005 Vida Apicola
0213-1021 Heladeria Internacional
0213-120X Joyas & Joyeros
0213-1269 Cuestiones Pedagogicas
0213-1773 Cinematograf
0213-1781 Universidad de Murcia. Papeles de Geografia
0213-196X Agricultor Practico y Ganadero
0213-2230 Revista Matematica Iberoamericana
0213-2257 Miscelanea de Textos Medievales *changed to* Miscel.lania de Textos Medievals.
0213-2273 Situacion. Suplemento de Coyuntura
0213-2648 Banco de Bilbao. Informacion Semanal de Valores
0213-2699 Banco de Espana. Estudios Economicos
0213-2818 Tabona
0213-2958 Universidad de Murcia. Anales de Filologia Francesa
0213-3024 Sociedad de Estudios Vascos. Cuadernos de Seccion. Prehistoria y Arqueologia
0213-3091 Inter-Transport
0213-3113 Automatica e Instrumentacion
0213-3601 Sociedad de Estudios Vascos. Cuadernos de Seccion. Ciencias Medicas
0213-3636 Sociedad de Estudios Vascos. Cuadernos de Seccion. Educacion
0213-3792 Espana Agricola y Ganadera
0213-392X Universidad de Murcia. Imafronte. Departamento de Historia del Arte
0213-3938 Universidad de Murcia. Anales de Biologia. Seccion Especial†
0213-3954 British Medical Journal. Edicion Espanola
0213-3997 Universidad de Murcia. Anales de Biologia. Seccion Biologia Animal
0213-4004 Universidad de Murcia. Anales de Biologia. Seccion Biologia Ambiental
0213-4012 Policia
0213-4020 Monografias de Zoologia Marina
0213-4098 Societat d'Onomastica. Butlleti Interior
0213-4101 Microbiologia
0213-4128 Cuadernos de Fitopatologia
0213-4144 Archivos de Odontoestomatologia
0213-4365 Universidad de Murcia. Anales de Filologia Hispanica
0213-4403 Gavagai
0213-4675 Revista de Estudios de Administracion Local y Autonomica
0213-4683 Indice Espanol de Ciencias Sociales. Series C: Law
0213-4845 Hospital Practice (Edicion Espanola)
0213-4853 Neurologia
0213-5000 Investigacion Agraria. Produccion y Proteccion Vegetales
0213-5035 Investigacion Agraria. Produccion y Sanidad Animales
0213-540X Revista Doyma de Inmunologia *see* 0213-9626
0213-5434 Anales de Veterinaria de Murcia
0213-5442 Universidad de Murcia. Anales de Biologia. Seccion Biologia General *changed to* Universidad de Murcia. Anales de Biologia. Seccion Biologia Molecular y Microbiana.
0213-5450 Universidad de Murcia. Anales de Biologia. Seccion Biologia Vegetal
0213-5469 Universidad de Murcia. Anales de Ciencias
0213-5477 Contrastes: Revista de Historia Moderna
0213-5485 Universidad de Murcia. Cuadernos de Filologia Inglesa
0213-5574 Industria Farmaceutica
0213-571X Productronica
0213-6171 Proyecto 2000
0213-635X Investigacion Agraria. Economia
0213-6449 Saber Leer
0213-6635 Awraq Yadida *see* 0214-834X
0213-683X Geogaceta
0213-6856 Politica Exterior
0213-6910 Spain. Ministerio de Agricultura, Pesca y Alimentacion. Boletin de Sanidad Vegetal: Plagas
0213-7410 Spain. Instituto Nacional de Estadistica. Indices de Precios de Consumo. Boletin Informativo
0213-7429 Facultad de Medicina de Barcelona. Revista de Psiquiatria
0213-7488 Tecno 2000
0213-7534 Catalonia Culture
0213-7569 Anales de Estudios Economicos y Empresariales
0213-7585 Asimetria†
0213-7674 Myrtia: Revista de Filologia Clasica
0213-8239 Noray
0213-831X SoProDen
0213-8328 Control de Calidad Asistencial
0213-8360 Petroleo
0213-8409 Limnetica
0213-8514 Sociedad Espanola de Quimica Clinica. Revista
0213-8948 Revista de Edificacion
0213-8980 Verde. Boletin
0213-9014 Audioptica
0213-9111 Gaseta Sanitaria
0213-9251 Piel
0213-943X E R G A. Bibliografico
0213-9472 Revista de Historia de Canarias
0213-9480 Revista de Geografia Canaria
0213-9529 Campo Abierto
0213-9626 Inmunologia
0213-9634 Minerva: Revista de Filologia Clasica
0214-0357 Spain. Instituto Nacional de Investigaciones Agrarias. Comunicaciones. Serie: Economia
0214-0381 Algo 2000
0214-0446 C I M†
0214-0578 Frut
0214-0934 Drug News & Perspectives
0214-0985 Quintessence (Edicion Espanola)
0214-1086 Indice Espanol de Ciencias Sociales. Series D: Science and Scientific Information
0214-1221 Cirugia Pediatrica
0214-1582 Revista de Senologia y Patologia Mamaria
0214-1949 Instituto Espanol de Oceanografia. Monografias
0214-2376 British Journal of Surgery (Edicion Espanola)
0214-2694 Delibros
0214-3089 Catalan Writing
0214-3127 Renovatec
0214-3135 Promecanica†
0214-3143 Maquinaria Agricola *changed to* Agricola XXI.
0214-3151 Animalia
0214-3429 Revista Espanola de Quimioterapia
0214-3941 Revista Iberoamericana de Trombosis y Hemostasia
0214-3984 Panaderia Noticias
0214-4131 Disposiciones Generales
0214-4441 Bibliografia Espanola. Suplemento de Cartografia
0214-4565 Botanica Complutensis
0214-462X Cuadernos Cinematograficos
0214-4670 Cuadernos de Investigacion Historica. Brocar
0214-4689 Guia de Congresos Medicos Jano
0214-4727 Anales de Arquitectura
0214-4832 Composicion Arquitectonica
0214-5979 Manos Unidas
0214-6215 Barcelona. Metropolis Mediterrania
0214-6541 Universitat de Barcelona. Biblioteca
0214-6967 Kobie Revista de Bellas Artes y Ciencias: Serie Ciencias Naturales
0214-7122 Juguetecnica
0214-7378 Instituto Espanol de Oceanografia. Publicaciones Especiales
0214-7939 Kobie Revista de Bellas Artes y Ciencias: Serie Antropologia Cultural
0214-7955 Kobie Revista de Bellas Artes y Ciencias: Serie Bellas Artes
0214-7971 Kobie Revista de Bellas Artes y Ciencias: Serie Paleoanthropologia
0214-834X Revista Awraq
0214-8900 Revista Internacional de Ajedrez
0214-8919 Gestion Hospitalaria
0214-8935 Farmacoterapia
0214-9028 Catering
0214-9117 Boletin Galego de Literatura
0214-9168 Clinica e Investigacion en Arteriosclerosis
0214-9958 Spain. Registro Mercantil. Boletin Oficial
0214-9982 Balsa de la Medusa
0215-028X Forest Research Bulletin
0215-1510 Cocommunity
0215-840X Yuridika
0216-0021 Pusat Penelitian Perkebunan Gula Indonesia. Prosiding
0216-0269 Kabar
0216-0412 Bulletin Ekonomi Indonesia
0216-0803 Index of Biology, Agriculture and Agro Economy *changed to* Indonesian Biological and Agricultural Index.
0216-1052 Indonesian Importers Directory
0216-1265 University of Indonesia. Institute of Management. Newsletter†
0216-1273 Berita Bibliografi
0216-3217 Indonesia. Lembaga Pertahanan Nasional. National Resilience
0216-3527 Indonesian Journal of Public Health
0216-4000 Jepara. Shrimp Culture Research Centre. Bulletin *see* 0126-1924
0216-4027 Mantap: Majalah Ilmaih P K M I
0216-4167 Sari Karangan Indonesia
0216-4760 Buletin Penelitian Hutan *see* 0215-028X
0216-6216 Index of Indonesian Learned Periodicals
0216-7204 Indonesian Journal of Bioanthropology
0216-9967 Pusat Penelitian Perkebunan Gula Indonesia. Annual Report
0217-0590 Social Dimension
0217-0914 Institute of Southeast Asian Studies. Library Bulletin
0217-104X Management Abstracts of Singapore *changed to* A S E A N Management Abstracts.
0217-1058 Her World Annual
0217-1546 Singapore. National Library. Annual Report
0217-247X Technonet Asia Newsletter and Digest
0217-2992 Contributions to Southeast Asian Ethnography
0217-3077 R E L C Newsletter
0217-3476 Singapore Stock Exchange Journal
0217-3891 Telecommunication Authority of Singapore. Telecoms Annual Report *changed to* Telecommunication Authority of Singapore. Singapore Telecom Annual Report.
0217-4456 Singapore Accountant
0217-4472 A S E A N Economic Bulletin
0217-4561 Asia Pacific Journal of Management
0217-4936 Singapore Computer Society. Bulletin
0217-5487 Singapore. Ministry of the Environment. Annual Report
0217-5541 Building & Construction News
0217-5851 Accent
0217-5908 Singapore Economic Review
0217-6009 Times Business Directory of Singapore
0217-6440 R & D Survey
0217-6602 Oil and Gas News
0217-6998 Mabuhay
0217-7099 Institute of Southeast Asian Studies. Field Reports Series
0217-717X Malaysian Accountant†
0217-7323 Modern Physics Letter A
0217-7447 Tradelink - S M A Annual Directory (Year)
0217-751X International Journal of Modern Physics A
0217-7528 Singapore Trade News

ISSN

0217-7587 Politeia
0217-765X Go
0217-7668 S I A Yearbook
0217-7757 Singapore This Week†
0217-7773 Singapore Facts and Pictures
0217-8311 Directory of Certified Products in Singapore *changed to* Directory of Certified Products & Companies & Accredited Laboratories in Singapore.
0217-913X University of Singapore. History Society. Journal
0217-9520 Sojourn
0217-9563 Singapore. Department of Statistics. Report on the Household Expenditure Survey
0217-9687 Asia Pacific Journal of Pharmacology
0217-9725 Zhongguo Kexueyuan Daqi Wulisuo Nianbao†
0217-9776 Chinese Journal of Acoustics
0217-9792 International Journal of Modern Physics B
0217-9822 Journal of Electronics
0217-9849 Modern Physics Letter B
0218-0006 Southeast Asian Bulletin of Mathematics
0218-0014 International Journal of Pattern Recognition and Artificial Intelligence
0218-0367 Implants in Ophthalmology
0218-0553 South East Asia Traveller
0218-1029 Reviews of Solid State Science
0218-1266 Journal of Circuits, Systems and Computers
0218-1274 International Journal of Bifurcations and Chaos in Applied Sciences and Engineering
0218-1924 Pacific Strategic Papers
0218-1932 International Journal of Genome Research
0218-1940 International Journal of Software Engineering and Knowledge Engineering
0218-1959 International Journal of Computational Geometry and Applications
0218-1967 International Journal of Algebra and Computation
0218-1991 International Journal of Nonlinear Optical Physics
0218-2025 Mathematical Models and Methods in Applied Sciences
0218-2114 I S E A S Current Economic Affairs Series
0218-2130 International Journal of Artificial Intelligence Tools
0218-2157 International Journal of Intelligent and Cooperative Information Systems
0218-2165 Journal of Knot Theory and Its Ramifications
0218-2173 Singapore Journal of Legal Studies
0218-236X Travel Directory (Year)
0218-253X What's New in Computing
0218-2610 Die & Mould Technology International
0218-2734 Asia Pacific Food Industry
0218-2831 Singapore Contractors' Equipment Catalogue
0218-3153 Singapore Source Book Architects & Designers
0218-3161 Singapore Law Reports
0218-3188 Synergy
0219-5550 Commodities *see* 0746-2468
0220-0546 Lettre d'Intergeo
0220-0562 France. Office National d'Information sur les Enseignements et les Professions. Bulletin d'Information.
0220-2352 Bulletin Comptable & Financier
0220-2425 Campost†
0220-2476 Information Cardiologique
0220-276X Gwechall
0220-3294 Industrie du Petrole - Gaz - Chimie
0220-5157 Plume Limousine
0220-5270 Revue de l'Offshore†
0220-5424 Bulletin des Consommateurs
0220-5610 Cahiers Victoriens et Edouardiens
0220-6102 Tiers-Monde Engineering *changed to* Tiers Monde Ingenierie.
0220-6137 Carrousel†
0220-6617 Revue Archeologique du Centre de la France
0220-6668 Ecole Buissonniere
0220-6862 International Executive Search Newsletter *see* 0752-4676
0220-746X Collection Oralites-Documents
0220-8156 Ville de Paris *see* 1153-026X
0220-8245 Geo (France)
0220-8482 Nouvel Automatisme *see* 1148-7305
0220-9241 Chambre de Commerce et d'Industrie de la Provence - Cote d'Azur - Corse. Conjoncture
0220-9535 L C I E Informations
0220-9896 Revue de la Concurrence et de la Consommation
0220-9926 Realites Familiales
0221-0142 Sport Scolaire
0221-0436 Mondes et Cultures
0221-0665 Annales Francaises de Chronometrie et de Microtechniques *see* 0294-1228
0221-2536 France. Bureau de Recherches Geologiques et Minieres. Documents
0221-2781 Politique Internationale
0221-301X Presse du Vin-Vinetec
0221-5225 Bigre
0221-5780 Cote-d'Ivoire Selection
0221-5896 Ktema
0221-5918 Centre National de la Recherche Scientifique. Annuaire Europeen d'Administration Publique
0221-7945 Societe Theophile Gautier. Bulletin
0221-8747 Metabolic Bone Disease and Related Research *see* 8756-3282
0222-0377 Charcuterie et Gastronomie
0222-1543 Russkoe Vozrozhdenie
0222-3074 Tutti
0222-3856 Audition et Parole†
0222-3996 Auto Verte
0222-4275 N R S
0222-447X Minis Autos
0222-4828 Jeux d'Afrique
0222-4844 Connaissance du Rail
0222-5069 International Journal of Microsurgery
0222-5220 France. Ministere de l'Agriculture. Situation Agricole en France. Conjoncture Generale *changed to* France. Ministere de l'Agriculture et de la Foret. Conjoncture Generale.
0222-559X Securite Civile et Industrielle
0222-593X Bamerkhav†
0222-5956 Cahiers Confrontation
0222-6618 Commerce et Cooperation
0222-6766 Cercle Genealogique et Heraldique de Normandie *see* 0294-7382
0222-6782 Revue Francaise de Genealogie
0222-7762 Institut de Recherches Marxistes. Issues *changed to* Institut des Recherches Marxistes. Issues.
0222-8394 France. Laboratoire Central des Ponts et Chausees. Rapport de Recherche
0222-9617 Neuropsychiatrie de l'Enfance et de l'Adolescence
0222-9714 Cahiers Evangile
0223-0038 Air Fan
0223-0100 Sigma (Aix-en-Provence)
0223-0127 Videoglyphes
0223-0135 Revue Technique Machinisme Agricole
0223-0232 Pour l'Enfant Vers l'Homme
0223-0844 P L G P P U R
0223-0976 Ovni-Presence
0223-1077 A B C D
0223-1603 Galerie des Arts
0223-3290 Hommes et Migrations
0223-3398 B.O.P.I. Dessins & Modeles
0223-3401 B.O.P.I. Marques
0223-341X Bulletin Signaletique. Part 520: Sciences de l'Education
0223-3533 Nouveau Commerce de la Lecture
0223-3843 Medieviste et l'Ordinateur
0223-4092 B.O.P.I. Listes†
0223-4238 Bulletin Signaletique. Part 381: Sciences Agronomiques. Productions Vegetales†
0223-4246 Bulletin Signaletique. Part 891: Industries Mecaniques *changed to* P A S C A L Folio. F 10: Mecanique et Acoustique et Transfert de Chaleur.
0223-4254 Bulletin Signaletique. Part 892: Batiment. Travaux Publics. Transports *see* 1146-5093
0223-4254 Bulletin Signaletique. Part 892: Batiment. Travaux Publics. Transports *see* 0761-1803
0223-4270 Connaissance de la Region
0223-4335 Societe Francaise du Vide. Comptes Rendus des Travaux des Congres et Colloques
0223-4580 Situation du Marche Vinicole
0223-4637 Semaine Sociale Lamy
0223-4696 Flash-Informations
0223-4718 Revue Fiduciaire
0223-4726 Legi-Social
0223-4734 Croire Aujourd'hui†
0223-4866 Enjeux
0223-4912 France. Ministere de l'Agriculture. Informations Rapides. Production Animale *changed to* France. Ministere de l'Agriculture et de la Foret. Conjoncture Productions Animales.
0223-4920 France. Ministere de l'Agriculture. Informations Rapides. Secteur Avicole *changed to* France. Ministere de l'Agriculture et de la Foret. Series Avicuture.
0223-4939 France. Ministere de l'Agriculture. Informations Rapides. Statistique Laitiere *changed to* France. Ministere de l'Agriculture et de la Foret. Conjoncture Lait et Produits Laitiers.
0223-5137 Neuroptera International
0223-5145 Entreprise et Formation Permanente†
0223-534X Instructions Nautiques
0223-5358 Feux et Signaux de Brume
0223-5420 Accueillir
0223-5714 Proletariat†
0223-5730 Realities Franc-Comtoises
0223-5749 Reforme
0223-5765 Parlements et Francophonie
0223-5773 Cahiers D'Action Francaise *changed to* Aspects de la France.
0223-5846 Hommes et Commerce
0223-5854 Eglise Aujourd'hui *see* 0985-5734
0223-5951 Territoires - Correspondance Municipale
0223-5986 Enseignement Public
0223-7237 Genealogies Bourbonnaises et du Centre
0223-9159 C D I U P A. Bulletin Bibliographique *see* 0245-985X
0223-9353 Masques
0223-9434 Lettre du Psychiatre
0223-9469 Universite de Saint Etienne. Centre Jean Palerne. Memoires
0224-0424 Strategique
0224-098X Stateco
0224-1196 Special Motoculteurs et Tondeuses a Gazon *see* 0752-4250
0224-2265 Semaine de l'Energie
0224-2435 Syndicat General des Commerces et Industries du Caoutchouc et des Plastiques. Guide *changed to* Union des Industries et de la Distribution des Plastiques et du Caoutchouc. Guide.
0224-2680 Asie du Sud-Est et Monde Insulindien
0224-2702 Memoires et Documents Geographie
0224-4365 Travail et Emploi
0224-4772 Geopolitique du Petrole†
0224-5027 Boulanger-Patissier, Confiseur, Glacier
0224-7232 Casse-Tete Magazine
0224-8042 C.T.N.E.R.H.I. Documents†
0225-0233 Bonne Nouvelle
0225-0462 Journal des Voyages *see* 0836-205X
0225-0500 Canadian Journal of Netherlandic Studies
0225-0608 Canadian Taxpayer
0225-1205 Minjoong Shinmoon
0225-1485 Canadian Heritage†
0225-1507 Canada. Statistics Canada. Coastwise Shipping Statistics†
0225-1574 Canadiana Authorities
0225-1582 Moebius
0225-168X Insurance Institute of Canada. Newsletter *changed to* Insurance Institute of Canada. Perspectives.
0225-1701 In Ontario
0225-1760 U T L A S Newsletter†
0225-2112 Feuillet Biblique
0225-2279 Canadian Native Law Reporter
0225-2287 Legal Information Service Reports†
0225-2910 Banque Nationale du Canada. Revue Economique†
0225-3194 Terminogramme
0225-3216 Canadiana on Microfiche
0225-3488 Western Hog Journal
0225-3550 S P E A Q Journal
0225-3895 Medicine North America
0225-4115 Justice - Directory of Services
0225-4190 Handbook of Canadian Consumer Markets
0225-4212 Plasmapheresis and Plasma Exchange†
0225-4484 Boreal Institute for Northern Studies. Library Bulletin *changed to* Canadian Circumpolar Library. Bulletin.
0225-4530 Quebec (Province) Pension Board. Supplemental Pension Plans-Characteristics and Membership Statistics†
0225-4565 Agent West Weekly *see* 0834-0471
0225-4700 Ma Caisse
0225-4913 Horses All
0225-509X British Columbia. Housing Management Commission. Annual Report
0225-5170 A S T I S Occasional Publications
0225-5189 Canadian Journal of Development Studies
0225-5316 Ontario Geological Survey. Geoscience Research Grant Program. Summary of Research
0225-5383 Moving to Saskatchewan *changed to* Moving to & Around Saskatchewan.
0225-5642 Canada. Statistics Canada. List of Canadian Hospitals and Special Care Facilities *see* 0831-7313
0225-5804 Resilog
0225-5847 Canadian Legislative Report†
0225-6002 Canadian Earthquakes - Tremblements de Terre Canadiens *see* 0068-7650
0225-6320 C T M: the Human Element
0225-6363 Coatings
0225-6398 Landscape Trades
0225-6533 Adventuring in Conservation
0225-6843 Broadside
0225-686X Musicworks
0225-6932 Canadian Federation for the Humanities. Annual Report†
0225-7068 Mandate
0225-7068 Mandate "Special"
0225-7165 Atlantic Salmon Newsletter *changed to* Salar.
0225-7270 Theodolite *see* 0849-0899
0225-7351 Chess Canada Echecs *see* 0822-5672
0225-7459 Canadian News Index
0225-7572 Logging & Sawmilling Journal
0225-8013 Economic Council of Canada. Discussion Papers†
0225-851X Professional Engineer *changed to* Engineer.
0225-9036 Index to Commonwealth Legal Periodicals†
0225-9044 Spirale
0225-9435 Canadian Music Trade
0225-9591 Medecin Veterinaire du Quebec
0225-9958 Canadian Review of Physical Anthropology†
0226-0336 Canada Mortgage and Housing Corporation. Annual Report
0226-0344 Cottager Magazine†
0226-0786 Forintek Canada Corp., Western Laboratory. Review Reports†
0226-0840 The Pottersfield Portfolio
0226-093X Canadian Homeowner
0226-1472 International Journal of Energy Systems

ISSN	Title
0226-1480	M I M I
0226-1510	Healthsharing
0226-1537	Index of Industrial Relations Literature†
0226-157X	Canadian Railway Club. Newsletter
0226-1685	A S T I S Bibliography
0226-1804	Repertoire Theatral du Quebec (Year)†
0226-1928	Ethnocultural Directory of Ontario†
0226-210X	Quebecensia
0226-2169	Le Sagamien
0226-224X	Economic Council of Canada. Au Courant
0226-2320	Canada. Statistics Canada. Restaurant, Caterer and Tavern Statistics
0226-2576	Marche du Travail
0226-2630	Track & Field Journal
0226-3068	Zapad
0226-3300	University of Guelph Library. Collection Update
0226-3440	U.C. Review
0226-3491	Studies in Aboriginal Rights†
0226-3882	Negotiated Working Conditions from Collective Agreements in Nova Scotia
0226-3890	Nova Scotia. Department of Labour and Manpower. Compendium of Grievance Arbitration Decisions *changed to* Nova Scotia. Department of Labour. Compendium of Grievance Arbitration Decisions.
0226-4781	Ici Radio Canada Television†
0226-5036	Manitoba History
0226-5125	Canadian Theatre Checklist†
0226-5346	Quebec (Province) Regie de l'Assurance-Maladie. Statistiques Annuelles
0226-5419	Directory of Long-Term Care Centres in Canada
0226-5478	C A H P E R Journal *see* 0834-1915
0226-5664	Canadian Collector
0226-5702	Ontario Water Skier
0226-5761	Theatre History in Canada
0226-577X	Canadian Amateur Softball Association. Facts & Figures†
0226-5788	Health Care (Don Mills)†
0226-5893	Policy Options
0226-5923	C H A C Review
0226-6105	Generations (Winnipeg)
0226-6121	Age d'Or - Vie Nouvelle
0226-6156	Brayon *changed to* Societe Historique du Madawaska. Revue.
0226-6245	Entraide Genealogique
0226-6326	Guelph This Week
0226-6342	Canada. Environment Canada. Information Reports Digest - Digest des Rapports d'Information *see* 1183-7918
0226-6601	Tourisme Plus *see* 0836-205X
0226-661X	Inter-Church Committee on Human Rights in Latin America. Newsletter
0226-6628	Thyroid Disorders†
0226-6776	Moving to Houston†
0226-6822	Financial Accounting Problems with Detailed Solutions
0226-6881	Dialogues et Cultures
0226-7004	Summer Breezes†
0226-7063	Cahiers d'Histoire de Deux-Montagnes
0226-7101	Kingston Business Review†
0226-7209	Toronto Historical Board. Year Book
0226-7365	Quality of Working Life†
0226-7446	Canadian Gemmologist
0226-7454	Universites
0226-7462	Whiskey Jack†
0226-7470	Canadian Nuclear Society. Transactions *see* 0227-0129
0226-7527	Carleton University. Library. Serials List†
0226-7551	Shopping Centre Canada†
0226-7586	McGill University. Register
0226-7616	Centre for Resources Studies. Working Papers
0226-7705	Quebec Farmers Association. Newsletter *see* 0714-9158
0226-773X	Federation of Canadian Archers. Rules Book
0226-7829	Moving to Toronto and Area *see* 0713-8377
0226-7837	Moving to Ottawa - Hull
0226-7934	Laurentian University. Gazette
0226-8043	Quaderni d'Italianistica
0226-8086	Fuse *see* 0838-603X
0226-8264	Canadian Real Estate Journal†
0226-8361	Marine Affairs Bibliography
0226-840X	Samisdat†
0226-854X	I P Sharp Newsletter†
0226-8841	Health Law in Canada
0226-8922	Conventions & Meetings Canada
0226-8965	Coaching Science Update†
0226-9031	Freelance Editors' Association of Canada. Directory of Members
0226-9317	Indian Life
0226-9325	O S C Bulletin
0226-9368	British Columbia. Ministry of Forests. Research Notes
0226-9422	At the Centre
0226-9430	British Columbia. Ministry of Energy, Mines and Petroleum Resources. Paper Series
0226-9597	Practical Homes
0226-9686	Suburban
0226-9708	Photo Selection
0226-9759	Canada. Environment Canada. Insect and Disease Conditions in Canada *changed to* Canada. Forestry Canada. Insect and Disease Conditions in Canada.
0226-9902	Femmes d'Action
0227-0072	University of Manitoba Anthropology Papers
0227-0129	Canadian Nuclear Society. Annual Conference Summaries
0227-017X	Canada. Statistics Canada. Retail Chain and Department Stores
0227-0315	Filles d'Aujourd'hui
0227-034X	Service
0227-0382	Communications Week *see* 0825-3021
0227-0390	Federal Court of Appeal Decisions
0227-0579	Alberta Wild Rose Quarter Horse Journal
0227-0595	Buildcore Index
0227-0668	Quebec (Province) Bureau of Statistics. Statistiques
0227-0773	Island (Lantzville)
0227-0994	Family Genealogies
0227-1001	Wood Technology Notes *see* 0821-1841
0227-1192	Chronicle
0227-1230	Juice & Cookie
0227-1265	Tax Principles to Remember
0227-1311	Conflict Quarterly
0227-1338	Indexing and Abstracting Society of Canada. Bulletin
0227-1362	Trends in Collective Agreement Settlement Wage Rate Changes in Nova Scotia†
0227-1370	Gaspesie
0227-1397	Ontario Business†
0227-1400	Annual Bibliography of Victorian Studies
0227-1427	Coordinating Council on Deafness of Nova Scotia. Newsletter *changed to* Atlantic Silent News.
0227-1435	Access (Halifax) *changed to* Atlantic Silent News.
0227-1524	North American Anarchist *see* 0712-1539
0227-1559	U F O Update
0227-1656	Financial Post Survey of Mines and Energy Resources
0227-1699	Lyman's Standard Catalogue of Canada-B N A Postage Stamps
0227-1796	Canada. Statistics Canada. Estimation of Population by Marital Status, Age and Sex, Canada and Provinces/ Estimations de la Population Suivant l'Etat Matrimonial, l'Age et le Sexe, Canada et Provinces†
0227-1834	Soccer Canada†
0227-1907	Canadian Nuclear Society. Annual Conference Proceedings
0227-2083	Professional Circle *see* 0227-2091
0227-2091	Circle
0227-2199	University of Waterloo Courier
0227-227X	Liaison
0227-2393	F A M L I
0227-2636	L M G Report on Data and Word Processing
0227-2652	Cross-Canada Writers' Quarterly *changed to* Paragraph.
0227-2406	Graphic Monthly
0227-2865	National Bank of Canada. Economic Review
0227-289X	Quebec (Province) Centrale des Bibliotheques. Services et Publications *changed to* Quebec (Province) Centrale des Bibliotheques. Produits et Services Documentaires.
0227-3020	Transport - Action
0227-3160	Helicopters in Canada *changed to* Helicopters Magazine Canada.
0227-3268	Ontario. Federal Cabinet. Orders-in-Council
0227-3330	Canadian Pool & Spa Marketing
0227-3357	Alberta Drilling Progress and Pipeline Receipts. Weekly Report *changed to* Alberta Drilling Progress Weekly Report.
0227-3748	Canadian Health Record Association. Bulletin *changed to* C H R A Progress Notes.
0227-3780	School Libraries in Canada
0227-3802	British Columbia. Ministry of Agriculture and Food. Agricultural Aid to Developing Countries†
0227-4272	Style
0227-437X	Brown Chart for All Lines of General Insurance. Provincial Results. Reports *see* 0585-3680
0227-4752	Nova Scotia Historical Review
0227-5023	Chansons d'Aujourd'hui
0227-5090	Scrivener
0227-5147	Engineering Dimensions
0227-5317	Family Newsletter Directory *see* 0828-4466
0227-5910	Crisis
0227-6038	Financial Post Canadian Markets
0227-6178	Court Cases of Interest to the Ombudsman Institution†
0227-6755	Vibrations
0227-7506	British Columbia. Ministry of Environment. Annual Report *see* 1181-8336
0227-7514	Saskatchewan Archaeological Society Newsletter
0227-7980	Canadian Pest Management Society Proceedings
0227-8243	Canadian Ecumenical News
0227-8332	Informatique & Bureautique
0227-8669	Canadian Business Index
0227-8731	Micro-Scope†
0227-9363	Journal de Radiologie
0227-9916	Ontario Hydro Research Review
0228-0078	British Columbia. Ministry of Energy, Mines and Petroleum Resources. Annual Report *see* 0825-6896
0228-0108	Supreme Court Law Review
0228-0620	J A M
0228-0736	Canada. Petawawa National Forestry Institute. Information Reports
0228-0760	Wild Rose Quarter Horse Country *see* 0227-0579
0228-0906	Victorian Order of Nurses for Canada. National Office. Newsletter†
0228-0914	Canadian School Executive
0228-1082	Alberta Motorist *changed to* Westworld Alberta Magazine.
0228-1244	Ennui
0228-1635	Journal of Ukrainian Studies
0228-1686	Producteur de Lait Quebecois
0228-1821	C R S Perspectives
0228-1961	Canadian Competition Policy Record
0228-2194	Nicola Indian†
0228-2356	Aspent
0228-250X	Tricolorul
0228-2518	In Summary
0228-2828	Messenger
0228-2984	Westminster Institute Review†
0228-3344	Potboiler Magazine
0228-3409	Canadian Customs and Excise Reports *changed to* National Trade and Tariff Service.
0228-3530	La Plongee
0228-359X	GATT-Fly Report *changed to* Economic Justice Report.
0228-4642	Ontario Science Centre. Newscience
0228-491X	Canadian Philosophical Reviews
0228-5134	Canada. Statistics Canada. Listing of Supplementary Documents
0228-5215	Media Editorial Profile Edition *changed to* Publication Profiles.
0228-5452	La Barrique
0228-5479	La Vie en Rose
0228-5584	Agriweek
0228-5630	Drilling Activity Report
0228-5843	Noticias do Canada†
0228-5851	Regina Geographical Studies
0228-586X	Alive
0228-6033	Baseball America
0228-6157	Wine Tidings
0228-6203	International Journal of Modelling & Simulation
0228-6211	B.C. Business Bulletin *see* 0821-0020
0228-6246	Science Council of Canada. Annual Review†
0228-653X	Corpus Chemical Report *changed to* Camford Chemical Report.
0228-6637	Arpenteur-Geometre
0228-6726	Video Guide
0228-6939	Studies in History and Politics
0228-6963	Landscape Architectural Review
0228-7153	Moving to & Around Maritimes & Newfoundland
0228-7404	Moosehead Review
0228-7587	Drillsite†
0228-7730	Association des Colleges du Quebec Annuaire
0228-7781	Sound Heritage Series†
0228-7951	Ecriture Francaise dans le Monde†
0228-8117	British Columbia. Ministry of Agriculture. Field Crop Production Guide *changed to* British Columbia. Ministry of Agriculture Fisheries and Food. Field Crop Production Guide.
0228-8397	Canadian Association of African Studies. Newsletter
0228-8605	Papers in Mediaeval Studies
0228-863X	Directory of Alcohol and Drug Treatment Resources in Ontario
0228-8648	Substance Abuse Book Review Index†
0228-877X	Ontario Medical Technologist†
0228-8788	Construction Canada
0228-8877	Memorial University of Newfoundland. Gazette
0228-9636	Les Diplomes
0228-9806	Science Express
0228-9989	Canada. Environment Canada. Forestry Service Research Notes†
0229-0243	Royal Bank Letter
0229-1134	Coptologia
0229-1320	Ontario Craft
0229-1622	British Columbia. Ministry of Forests. Land Management Handbooks
0229-1665	Economic Accounts
0229-1916	Quaker Concern
0229-1932	New Canadian Fandom
0229-2181	International Ombudsman Institute. Newsletter
0229-2548	Canadian Parliamentary Review
0229-2947	Projection (Toronto)
0229-3196	Toronto Clarion
0229-3404	Les Affaires
0229-3455	Champion†
0229-3803	Vie Ouvriere *see* 0849-035X
0229-3811	Quebec (Province) Department of Recreation, Fish and Game. Annual Report
0229-4362	Transporteur

5650 ISSN INDEX

0229-4435 Artisan†
0229-480X Women and Environments
0229-4931 Source *see* 0832-9354
0229-4958 Collective Agreement Expiration in Nova Scotia†
0229-4966 Athletics
0229-5024 Birdfinding in Canada†
0229-5032 Moving to Washington, D.C.†
0229-5113 Refuge
0229-527X British Columbia Genealogical Society. Newsletter
0229-5415 Spartacist Canada
0229-5679 R I A Digest†
0229-6098 Canada. Statistics Canada. Mineral Wool Including Fibrous Glass Insulation
0229-6373 Clan Suibhne Association. Newsletter†
0229-7094 Fifth Column
0229-7108 Alberta Insurance Report *changed to* Superintendent of Insurance Annual Report.
0229-7175 His Dominion†
0229-7256 Canadian Research Institute for the Advancement of Women. Newsletter
0229-7345 Canadian Nurses Association. Nursing Programs and Entrance Requirements at Canadian Universities *see* 1180-4920
0229-737X Sugar World
0229-7558 Federation des Enseignants du Nouveau-Brunswick. Nouvelles *changed to* Association des Enseignantes et des Enseignants Francophones du Nouveau-Brunswick. Nouvelles.
0229-7876 Producteur de Porc Quebecois
0229-8090 Grainews
0229-8325 Canada. Mineral Policy Sector. Mineral Survey†
0229-8546 Alberta's Reserve of Gas: Complete Listing
0229-8651 R S S I
0229-8910 Bedford Institute of Oceanography. Review *changed to* Bedford Institute of Oceanography. Science Review.
0229-8961 Canadian Art Sales Index
0229-9119 Varsity Student Handbook
0229-9992 Magazine Affaires *see* 0836-6942
0230-1202 Ez a Divat
0230-1806 Egyutt
0230-1814 Allattenyeztes es Takarmanyozas
0230-1911 Adam
0230-2241 Szolotermesztes es Boraszat
0230-2780 Acta Universitatis de Attila Jozsef Nominatae. Papers in English and American Studies
0230-3337 A Testnevelesi Foiskola Kozlemenyei
0230-4066 Hungary. Kozponti Statisztikai Hivatal. Mezogazdasagi Statisztikai Evkonyv *changed to* Hungary. Kozponti Statisztikai Hivatal. Mezogazdasagi Elelmiszeripari Statisztikai Evkonyv.
0230-4414 Hungary. Kozponti Statisztikai Hivatal. Idegenforgalmi Evkonyv
0230-4430 Rovid Uton
0230-4619 Informatika es Tudomanyelemzes
0230-5151 Levelezesi Sakkhirado
0230-5348 Anyagmozgatasi es Csomagolasi Szakirodalmi Tajekoztato
0230-581X Magyar Korhazak es Klinikak Evkonyve
0230-5828 Magyarorszag
0230-7065 Geologiai es Geofizikai Szakirodalmi Tajekoztato
0230-8452 Monumenta Linguae Mongolicae Collecta
0230-9718 Public Finance in Hungary
0231-0643 Automatizalasi, Szamitastechnikai es Merestechnikai Szakirodalmi Tajekoztato
0231-0651 Banyaszati Szakirodalmi Tajekoztato
0231-066X Elektronikai es Hiradastechnikai Szakirodalmi
0231-0678 Energiaipari es Energiagazdalkodasi Tajekoztato
0231-0686 Gepeszeti Szakirodalmi Tajekoztato
0231-0694 Gepgyartastechnologiai es Szerszamgepipari Szakirodalmi Tajekoztato
0231-0708 Kohaszati es Onteszeti Szakirodalmi Tajekoztato
0231-0716 Kornyezetvedelmi Szakirodalmi Tajekoztato
0231-0724 Kozuti Kozlekedesi Szakirodalmi Tajekoztato
0231-0732 Melyepitesi es Vizepitesi Szakirodalmi Tajekoztato
0231-0740 Papiripari es Nyomdaipari Szakirodalmi Tajekoztato
0231-0759 Vallalatszervezesi es Ipargazdasagi Szakirodalmi Tajekoztato
0231-0767 Vasuti Kozlekedesi Szakirodalmi Tajekoztato
0231-0775 Vegyipari Szakirodalmi Tajekoztato
0231-0783 Elektrotechnikai Szakirodalmi Tajekoztato
0231-1941 Hajozasi Szakirodalmi Tajekoztato
0231-195X Ipari Formatervezesi Szakirodalmi Tajekoztato
0231-2255 Studia Latino-Americana *see* 0324-6965
0231-2379 Audio-Vizualis Kozlemenyek - Audio-Visual Review *changed to* A -V Kommunikacio.
0231-2522 Tarsadalomkutatas
0231-2662 Finommechanika, Mikrotechnika
0231-2670 Acta Universitatis Szegediensis de Attila Jozsef Nominatae. Sectio Philosophica
0231-3146 Acta Chimica Hungarica
0231-3316 Szamitogepes Muszaki Tervezes
0231-3928 Repulesi Szakirodalmi Tajekoztato
0231-4231 Kutatas - Fejlesztes *see* 0866-5192
0231-424X Acta Physiologica Hungarica
0231-441X Acta Paediatrica Hungarica
0231-4428 Acta Physica Hungarica
0231-4592 Magyar Nemzeti Bibliografia. Idoszaki Kiadvanyok Bibliografiaja
0231-4614 Acta Chirurgica Hungarica
0231-4622 Acta Microbiologica Hungarica
0231-4932 Technical and Scientific Films *see* 0236-9702
0231-5025 Univerzita J.E. Purkyne. Filozoficka Fakulta. Sbornik Praci. F: Rada Umenovedna *changed to* Masarykova Univerzita. Filozoficka Fakulta. Sbornik Praci. F: Rada Umenovedna.
0231-5122 Univerzita J.E. Purkyne. Filozoficka Fakulta. Sbornik Praci. G: Rada Socialnevedna *changed to* Masarykova Univerzita. Filozoficka Fakulta. Sbornik Praci. G: Rada Socialnevedna.
0231-522X Univerzita J.E. Purkyne. Filozoficka Fakulta. Sbornik Praci. H: Rada Hudebnevedna *changed to* Masarykova Univerzita. Filozoficka Fakulta. Sbornik Praci. H: Rada Hudebnevedna.
0231-5300 Ceskoslovenske Geograficke Spolecnosti. Sbornik
0231-5335 Acta Dendrobiologica
0231-5351 Univerzita J.E. Purkyne. Filozoficka Fakulta. Sbornik Praci. K: Rada Germanisticko - Anglisticka *changed to* Masarykova Univerzita. Filozoficka Fakulta. Sbornik Praci. K: Rada Germanisticko - Anglisticka.
0231-567X Sbornik U V T I Z - Zahradnictvi *changed to* Zahradnictvi.
0231-5688 Sbornik U V T I Z - Sociologie Zemedelstvi *changed to* Sociologie Venkova a Zemedelstvi.
0231-5823 Archaeologia Historica
0231-5882 General Physiology and Biophysics
0231-5955 Acta Comeniana. Archiv pro Badani o Zivote a Dile Jana Amose Komenskeho
0231-6005 Acta Historiae Rerum Naturalium nec non Technicarum
0231-6153 Sbornik k Dejinam 19 a 20 Stoleti
0231-620X Sbornik k Problematice Dejin Imperialismu
0231-6358 Zpravodaj Mistopisne Komise C S A V *see* 0232-0266
0231-6471 Prakticka Zena
0231-6811 Rozhlas *changed to* Tydenik Rozhlas.
0231-7494 Folia Historica Bohemica
0231-7532 Univerzita J.E. Purkyne. Filozoficka Fakulta. Sbornik Praci. L: Rada Romanisticka *changed to* Masarykova Univerzita. Filozoficka Fakulta. Sbornik Praci. L: Rada Romanisticka.
0231-7540 Hospodarske Dejiny
0231-7567 Univerzita J.E. Purkyne. Filozoficka Fakulta. Sbornik Praci. A: Rada Jazykovedna *changed to* Masarykova Univerzita. Filozoficka Fakulta. Sbornik Praci. A: Rada Jazykovedna.
0231-7648 Krajske Muzeum v Teplicich. Zpravy a Studie *changed to* Regionalni Muzeum v Teplicich. Zpravy a Studie.
0231-7664 Univerzita J.E. Purkyne. Filozoficka Fakulta. Sbornik Praci. B: Rada Filozoficka *changed to* Masarykova Univerzita. Filozoficka Fakulta. Sbornik Praci. B: Rada Filozoficka.
0231-7710 Univerzita J.E. Purkyne. Filozoficka Fakulta. Sbornik Praci. C: Rada Historicka *changed to* Masarykova Univerzita. Filozoficka Fakulta. Sbornik Praci. C: Rada Historicka.
0231-7737 Results of Geomagnetic Observations at the Hurbanovo Geomagnetic Observatory
0231-7818 Univerzita J.E. Purkyne. Filozoficka Fakulta. Sbornik Praci. D: Rada Literarnevedna *changed to* Masarykova Univerzita. Filozoficka Fakulta. Sbornik Praci. D: Rada Literarnevedna.
0231-7915 Univerzita J.E. Purkyne. Filozoficka Fakulta. Sbornik Praci. E: Rada Archeologicko-Klasicka *changed to* Masarykova Univerzita. Filozoficka Fakulta. Sbornik Praci. E: Rada Archeologicko-Klasicka.
0231-9004 Slovak Academy of Sciences. Geophysical Institute. Contributions. Series of Meteorology
0231-9128 Vysoka Skola Zemedelska. Information Bulletin
0231-9136 Monographia Historica Bohemica
0232-0150 Dejiny Socialistickeho Ceskoslovenska
0232-0266 Ceskoslovenska Akademie Ved. Ustav pro Jazyk Cesky. Onomasticky Zpravodaj
0232-041X Bibliograficky Katalog C S S R: Ceske Knihy. Ceske Disertace *see* 0862-8599
0232-0533 Czechoslovak Academy of Sciences. Hydrobiological Institute. Annual Report
0232-0568 Sbornik U V T I Z - Potravinarske Vedy *changed to* Potravinarske Vedy.
0232-0576 Revue Fotografie†
0232-0851 Ceskoslovenska Zemedelska Bilbiografie
0232-1300 Crystal Research and Technology
0232-1351 Informatik - Kybernetic - Rechentechnik. Schriftenreihe *changed to* Informatik - Kybernetik - Rechentechnik.
0232-1459 Corpus Vitrearum Medii Aevi
0232-1513 Experimental Pathology *see* 0940-2993
0232-1556 Beitraege zur Alexander-von Humboldt-Forschung
0232-2064 Zeitschrift fuer Analysis und Ihre Anwendungen
0232-2609 Restaurierung und Museumstechnik
0232-265X Weimarer Monographien zur Ur- und Fruehgeschichte
0232-2714 Beitraege zur Erforschung der Deutschen Sprache *see* 0005-8076
0232-2765 Baustoffindustrie
0232-2803 Beitraege zur Kritik der Buergerlichen Ideologie und des Revisionismus†
0232-2900 Griechischen Christlichen Schriftsteller der ersten Jahrhunderte
0232-3001 Hilprecht: Sammlung
0232-315X Literatur und Gesellschaft
0232-3257 Papyri aus den Staatlichen Museen zu Berlin
0232-346X Kleine Naturwissenschaftliche Bibliothek
0232-3516 Biographien Hervorragender Naturwissenschaftler, Techniker und Mediziner†
0232-3702 Volksmaerchen
0232-3869 Technische Mechanik
0232-3907 Thuringen-Bibliographie
0232-4393 Zentralblatt fuer Mikrobiologie
0232-4768 Die Wirtschaft
0232-4814 Deutsches Sportecho: Reihe B†
0232-4865 Bibliographie zur Archaeo-Zoologie und Geschichte der Haustiere†
0232-489X Gnadauer Mitteilungen†
0232-5020 Potsdamer Kirche *changed to* Berlin - Brandenburgisches Sonntagsblatt.
0232-5160 Arbeitsmedizininformation†
0232-5381 Altenburger Naturwissenschaftliche Forschungen
0232-5446 Landesmuseum fuer Vorgeschichte, Dresden. Kleine Schriften
0232-5519 Annalen fuer Ornithologie
0232-5616 Saechsische Landesbibliothek. Bibliographie Illustrierte Buecher der Deutschen Demokratischen Republik
0232-5780 Trade and Technical Review
0232-5810 Bibliographie Bildende Kunst
0232-6086 Adventgemeinde†
0232-6310 Evangelische Kirche der Kirchenprovinz Sachsen. Amtsblatt
0232-6833 E D V - Aspekte
0232-704X Annals of Global Analysis and Geometry
0232-7090 Charite Annalen. Neue Folge
0232-7287 Arbeitshygienische Information Bauwesen†
0232-7295 Zeitschrift fuer Experimentelle Chirurgie†
0232-7384 Experimental and Clinical Endocrinology
0232-7503 Referatedienst Rehabilitationspaedagogik†
0232-7546 Dienstleistungen. Ausgabe A: Fachzeitschrift fuer Theorie und Praxis der Haus- und Stadtwirtschaftlichen Dienstleistungen
0232-7643 Deutsches Patentamt. Bekanntmachungen 1. Grund- und Rohstoffindustrie, Chemie und Huettenwesen, Bauwesen und Bergbau
0232-766X Biomedica Biochimica Acta
0232-7678 Bibliographie Musik
0232-7694 Deutsches Patentamt. Bekanntmachungen 2. Elektrotechnik, Physik, Feinmechanik und Optik, Akustik
0232-7740 Deutsches Patentamt. Bekanntmachungen 3. Uebrige Verarbeitungsindustrie und Arbeitsverfahren, Maschinen- und Fahrzeugbau, Ernaehrung, Landwirtschaft
0232-8399 Dienstleistungen. Ausgabe B: Fuer Testilreinigung und Hauswirtschaftliche Dienstleistungen
0232-8410 Asien - Afrika - Lateinamerika. Jahrbuch†
0232-8461 Altorientalische Forschungen
0232-8798 Referateblatt Philosophie
0232-9042 Verkehrsgeschichtliche Blaetter
0232-9298 Systems Analysis Modelling Simulation
0232-9387 Zeitgenoessisches Musikschaffen in der Deutschen Demokratischen Republik. Urauffuehrungen
0232-9476 Gesellschaft Krankenwesen der D.D.R. Mitteilungen
0233-0016 Hochschule fuer Verkehrswesen "Friedrich List". Bibliographie Verkerswesen†
0233-0105 Beitraege zur Bach-Forschung
0233-030X Fernsehdienst

ISSN

ISSN INDEX

ISSN	Title
0233-0741	Korrosiont
0233-089X	Philosophiehistorische Texte
0233-0911	Teubner-Texte zur Physik
0233-0946	Oekonomiehistorische Texte
0233-0962	Teubner-Archiv zur Mathematik
0233-1063	Mathematik und ihre Anwendungen in Physik und Technik
0233-1098	Saechsische Landesbibliothek. Neuewerbungen und Nachrichten *changed to* Saechsische Landesbibliothek. Neuerwerbungen.
0233-111X	Journal of Basic Microbiology
0233-173X	Mauritiana (Altenburg)
0233-1934	Series Optimization *changed to* Optimization.
0233-2213	Congress Calendar G D R†
0233-2264	Kongresstermindienst: Naturwissenschaftlich-technische Veranstaltungen im Sozialistischen Auslandt
0233-2655	Agroselekt. Reihe 1: Landtechnik
0233-2701	Agroselekt. Reihe 2: Pflanzenproduktion
0233-2752	Agroselekt. Reihe 3: Tierproduktion
0233-2809	Agroselekt. Reihe 4: Veterinaermedizin
0233-2930	Beitraege zur Hochschul- und Wissenschaftsgeschichte Erfurts
0233-5816	Problemy Bol'shikh Gorodov
0233-6588	Signal'naya Informatsiya. Toksikologiya Lekarstvennaya
0233-6618	Signal'naya Informatsiya. Fiziologiya i Morfologiya Cheloveka i Zhivotnykh: Krov' i Limfa
0233-7029	Revmatologiya
0233-7525	Antibiotiki i Meditsinskaya Biotekhnologiya *see* 0235-2990
0233-7568	Matematicheskaya Fizika i Nelineinaya Mekhanika
0233-9897	Tekhnicheskii Progress i Effektivnost' Proizvodstva
0234-0852	Algebra i Analiz
0234-0860	Diskretnaya Matematika
0234-2979	Itogi Nauki i Tekhniki: Biofizika Membran
0234-4483	Ionnye Rasplavy i Tverdye Elektrolity
0234-4742	Itogi Nauki i Tekhniki. Organizatsiya i Bezopasnost' Dorozhnogo Dvizheniya
0234-5730	Gematologiya i Transfusiologiya
0234-7059	Referativnyi Zhurnal. Environment Management Abstracts
0234-9647	Referativnyi Zhurnal. Volokonno-opticheskie Systemy
0234-968X	Signal'naya Informatsiya. Khimiya Vysokikh Energii
0234-9698	Signal'naya Informatsiya. Sorbenty. Poverkhnostno-Aktivnye Veshchestva
0234-9701	Signal'naya Informatsiya. Ochistka i Utilizatsiya Otkhodov Khimicheskikh Proizvodstv
0234-971X	Signal'naya Informatsiya. Napolnennye i Armirovannye Plastiki
0234-9736	Signal'naya Informatsiya. Kataliz i Katalizatory
0234-9744	Signal'naya Informatsiya. Analiticheskaya Khimiya
0234-9752	Signal'naya Informatsiya. Neiropeptidy
0234-9760	Signal'naya Informatsiya. Ishemicheskaya Boleznʹ Serdtsa
0235-0904	Introduktsiva i Akklimatyzatsiva Rastenii
0235-2222	Referativnyi Zhurnal. Izdatel'skoe Delo i Poligrafiya
0235-2427	Ekonomika i Organizatsiya Promyshlennogo Proizvodstva
0235-2508	Khleboprodukty
0235-2613	Khozyain (Moscow)
0235-277X	Atmospheric Optics
0235-2990	Antibiotiki i Khimioterapiya
0235-3393	Knigi Belorusskoi S.S.R.
0235-4241	Rasskaz
0235-4519	Solnechnaya Radiatsiya i Radiatsionnyi Balans. Mirovaya Set'
0235-5116	Pod'emno-Transportnaya Tekhnika i Sklady
0235-6821	Obshchestvennye Nauki za Rubezhom. Kitavedenie
0235-7488	Eesti Naine
0235-8611	Akademiya Nauk S.S.S.R. Dal'nevostochnoe Otdelenie. Vestnik
0235-8964	Superconductivity: Physics, Chemistry, Technology
0236-2007	Chelovek
0236-3062	Academie de Stiinte a R.S.S. Moldova. Filosofie si Drept
0236-3070	Academie de Stiinte a R.S.S. Moldova. Buletinul. Economie se Sociologie
0236-3100	Revista de Istorie a Moldovei
0236-3933	Moskovskii Gosudarstvennyi Tekhnicheskii Universitet. Vestnik. Priborostroenie
0236-4964	Radiolyubitel'
0236-5200	Konyvtari es Informatikai Kozponti Gyarapodasi Jegyzekt
0236-5278	Acta Geologica Hungarica
0236-5286	Acta Medica Hungarica
0236-5294	Acta Mathematica Hungarica
0236-5391	Acta Morphologica Hungarica
0236-5731	Journal of Radioanalytical and Nuclear Chemistry *changed to* Journal of Radioanalytical and Nuclear Chemistry. Articles.
0236-5731	Journal of Radioanalytical and Nuclear Chemistry *changed to* Journal of Radioanalytical and Nuclear Chemistry. Letters.
0236-6290	Acta Veterinaria Hungarica
0236-6495	Acta Botanica Hungarica
0236-6568	Hungarian Studies
0236-705X	Elelmiszertudomanyi es Elelmiszeripari Szakirodalmi Tajekoztato
0236-7130	Acta Zoologica Hungarica
0236-7408	Muszaki Konyv-Magazin
0236-8722	International Agrophysics
0236-9524	Hungary. Kozponti Statisztikai Hivatal. Lakasstatisztikai Evkonyu *changed to* Hungary. Kozponti Statisztikai Hivatal. Beruhazasi, Epitoipari, Lakasepitesi Evkonyu.
0236-9702	Scientific Films and Videocassettes†
0237-0115	Biotechnology Information
0237-028X	Acta I M E K O
0237-0298	Hungary. Kozponti Statisztikai Hivatal. Epitoipari Arak Alakulasat
0237-0719	Baranyai Konyvtarost
0237-0808	Hungarian R and D Abstracts. Science and Technology
0237-0840	Kulfoldi Kozgazdasagi Irodalmi Szemle. Series A†
0237-0859	Kulfoldi Kozgazdasagi Irodalmi Szemle. Series B†
0237-322X	Tudomany
0237-384X	Vasarnapi Hirek
0237-6261	Acta Biochimica et Biophysica Hungarica
0237-8280	Hungary. Kozponti Statisztikai Hivatal. Kozlekedesi Evkonyv
0238-0161	Acta Agronomica Hungarica
0238-0196	Hungaria Informacio
0238-0218	Antaeus
0238-079X	Acta Universitatis Szegediensis de Attila Jozsef Nominatae. Acta Germanistica
0238-1249	Academia Scientiarum Hungarica. Acta Phytopathologica et Entomologica
0238-132X	Danubian Historical Studies
0238-1486	European Review of Native American Studies
0238-4000	Focit
0238-4043	Notarius
0238-4086	Feherje *changed to* Feherje es Biotermek.
0238-602X	Hungarian Trade Journal†
0238-7891	Hungary. Kozponti Statisztikai Hivatal. Mezogazdasagi Elelmiszeripari Statisztikai Zsebkonyv
0238-8197	Agrarvilagt
0238-9401	Hungarian Music Quarterly
0238-969X	Polish Export-Import *see* 0032-2881
0238-9916	Hungary. Kozponti Statisztikai Hivatal. Belkereskedelmi Statisztikai Evkonyv *see* 0866-1146
0238-9932	Hungarian Observer
0239-0094	Politechnika Poznanska. Instytut Nauk Ekonomicznych i Spolecznych. Prace Naukowe *see* 0239-9423
0239-0345	Soon to Appear...
0239-1333	Konyvtari Expressz *see* 0865-1329
0239-1589	Hungary. Kozponti Statisztikai Hivatal. Gazdasag es Statisztika
0239-2356	Wyzsza Szkola Pedagogiczna im. Komisji Edukacji Narodowej w Krakowie. Rocznik Naukowo-Dydaktyczny. Prace Pedagogiczne
0239-3174	Projektowanie i Systemy
0239-3182	Politechnika Wroclawska. Instytut Konstrukcji i Eksploatacji Maszyn. Prace Naukowe. Wspolpraca
0239-3204	Politechnika Wroclawska. Instytut Nauk Ekonomiczno-Spolecznych. Prace Naukowe. Monografie
0239-3212	Politechnika Wroclawska. Instytut Nauk Ekonomiczno-Spolecznych. Prace Naukowe. Studia i Materialy
0239-3271	Czlowiek i Spoleczenstwo
0239-3433	Politechnika Wroclawska. Instytut Sterowania i Techniki Systemow. Prace Naukowe. Konferencja
0239-4243	Annales Universitatis Mariae Curie-Sklodowska. Sectio EE. Zootechnika
0239-4251	Annales Universitatis Mariae Curie-Sklodowska. Sectio F. Historia
0239-426X	Annales Universitatis Mariae Curie-Sklodowska. Sectio FF. Philologiae
0239-4421	Bibliografia Wydawnictw Ciaglych
0239-488X	Politechnika Poznanska. Zeszyty Naukowe. Geometria
0239-5274	Akademia Gorniczo-Hutnicza im. Stanislawa Staszica. Zeszyty Naukowe. Elektrotechnika. Kwartalnik
0239-5282	Akademia Gorniczo-Hutnicza im. Stanislawa Staszica. Zeszyty Naukowe. Mechanika. Kwartalnik
0239-5312	Akademia Gorniczo-Hutnicza im. Stanislawa Staszica. Zeszyty Naukowe. Elektrotechnika
0239-5320	Akademia Gorniczo-Hutnicza im. Stanislawa Staszica. Zeszyty Naukowe. Mechanika
0239-541X	Przeglad Dokumentacyjny z Zakresu Handlu Wewnetrznego i Uslug
0239-5495	Politechnika Wroclawska. Instytut Technologii Organicznej i Tworzyw Sztucznych. Prace Naukowe. Monografie
0239-5568	Roczniki Socjologii Morskiej
0239-5622	Akademia Gorniczo-Hutnicza im. Stanislawa Staszica. Zeszyty Naukowe. Zagadnienia Spoleczno-Filozoficzne
0239-6025	Wyzsza Szkola Pedagogiczna im. Komisji Edukacji Narodowej w Krakowie. Prace Monograficzne
0239-622X	Bibliografia Gospodarki i Inzynierii Wodnej
0239-6238	Instytut Meteorologii i Gospodarki Wodnej. Materialy Badawcze. Seria: Gospodarka Wodna i Ochrona Wod
0239-6246	Bibliografia Hydrologii i Oceanologii
0239-6254	Instytut Meteorologii i Gospodarki Wodnej. Materialy Badawcze. Seria: Inzynieria Wodna
0239-6262	Instytut Meteorologii i Gospodarki Wodnej. Materialy Badawcze. Seria: Meteorologia
0239-6270	Bibliografia Meteorologii
0239-6297	Instytut Meteorologii i Gospodarki Wodnej. Materialy Badawcze. Seria: Hydrologia i Oceanologia
0239-6556	Wyzsza Szkola Pedagogiczna im. Komisji Edukacji Narodowej w Krakowie. Rocznik Naukowo-Dydaktyczny. Prace Romanistyczne
0239-670X	Wyzsza Szkola Pedagogiczna, Opole. Zeszyty Naukowe. Seria A. Nauki Spoleczno-Polityczne
0239-6769	Wyzsza Szkola Pedagogiczna im. Komisji Edukacji Narodowej w Krakowie. Problemy Studiow Nauczycielskich
0239-7269	Polish Academy of Sciences. Bulletin. Mathematical Sciences
0239-7277	Polish Academy of Sciences. Bulletin. Earth Sciences
0239-7285	Polish Academy of Sciences. Bulletin. Chemical Sciences
0239-7404	Problemy Projektowe *changed to* Problemy Projektowe Przemyslu i Budownictwa.
0239-751X	Polish Academy of Sciences. Bulletin. Biological Sciences
0239-7528	Polish Academy of Sciences. Bulletin. Technical Sciences
0239-7846	Instytut Zachodni. Studium Niemcoznawcze
0239-7951	Wyzsza Szkola Pedagogiczna im. Komisji Edukacji Narodowej w Krakowie. Roczni Naukowo-Dydaktyczny. Prace Ekonomiczno-Spoleczne
0239-796X	Wyzsza Szkola Pedagogiczna im. Komisji Edukacji Narodowej w Krakowie. Rocznik Nukowo-Dydaktyczny. Prace Geograficzne
0239-7978	Wyzsza Szkola Pedagogiczna im. Komisji Edukacji Narodowej w Krakowie. Rocznik Naukowo-Dydaktyczny. Prace Matematyczne
0239-7986	Wyzsza Szkola Pedagogiczna im. Komisji Edukacji Narodowej w Krakowie. Rocznik Naukowo-Dydaktyczny. Prace Rusycystyczne
0239-7994	Wyzsza Szkola Pedagogiczna im. Komisji Edukacji Narodowej w Krakowie. Rocznik Naukowo-Dydaktyczny. Prace Zoologiczne
0239-8524	Folia Praehistorica Posnaniensia
0239-8605	Accademia Polacca delle Scienze. Conferenze
0239-8613	Szkola Glowna Gospodarstwa Wiejskiego. Rozprawy Naukowe i Monografie
0239-8818	Hemispheres
0239-8931	Centralny Katalog Zagranicznych Wydawnictw Ciaglych w Bibliotekach Polskich
0239-9148	Szkice o Kulturze Muzycznej XIX Wieku. Studia i Materialy
0239-9180	Akademia Rolnicza w Szczecinie. Zeszyty Naukowe. Rybactwo Morskie i Technologia Zywnosci
0239-9415	Politechnika Poznanska. Zeszyty Naukowe. Organizacja i Zarzadzanie
0239-9423	Politechnika Poznanska. Instytut Nauk Ekonomicznych i Spolecznych. Zeszyty Naukowe
0239-958X	Bibliografia Agrometeorologii
0239-9679	Budownictwo Weglowe. Projekty - Problemyt
0239-989X	Polish Trade Magazine
0239-9997	Studies in the Theory and Philosophy of Law
0240-0154	Francaise Frisonne *changed to* La Prim Holstein.
0240-1568	Alternative
0240-2041	Langues et Civilisations a Tradition Orale
0240-2955	Universite de Toulouse. Faculte des Sciences. Annales *changed to* Universite Paul Sabatier. Faculte des Sciences. Annales.
0240-3803	Special Scies a Moteur et Accessoires *see* 0998-495X
0240-396X	Echange - Travail
0240-4656	Celebrer

5652 ISSN INDEX

0240-5024 Jardin Familial de France
0240-5407 Tour de l'Orle d'Or *see* 0989-9200
0240-6411 Avenir et Sante
0240-642X Acta Endoscopica
0240-7418 Chroniques d'Histoire Maconnique
0240-7426 Commerce et Industrie†
0240-7914 Journal Francais d'Orthoptique
0240-8368 Epimenides
0240-8376 Epidecides Lunaires
0240-8430 Perspectives Mediterraneennes
0240-8473 Bulletin Signaletique. Part 172: Chimie Analytique *see* 0761-1749
0240-8481 Bulletin Signaletique. Part 173: Chimie Minerale et Organique *see* 0761-1757
0240-849X Astronomie - Physique Spatiale - Geophysique *see* 0761-2109
0240-849X Bulletin Signaletique. Part 120: Astronomie - Physique Spatiale - Geophysique *see* 0761-2117
0240-8503 Bulletin Signaletique: Bibliographie des Sciences de la Terre. Section 225: Tectonique Geophysique Interne *see* 0761-1862
0240-8546 Bulletin Signaletique. Part 370: Biologie et Physiologie Vegetales. Sylviculture *see* 0761-1927
0240-8554 Eldoc-Electronique *see* 0246-1161
0240-8562 Eldoc-Electrotechnique. *see* 0761-1773
0240-8740 Bulletin Signaletique. Part 401: Congres. Rapports. Theses *changed to* P A S C A L Explore. Part 99: Congres. Rapports. Theses.
0240-8759 Vie et Milieu
0240-8783 Revue d'Hydrobiologie Tropicale
0240-8813 Sciences des Aliments
0240-8864 Centre Aixois de Recherches Anglaises. Actes du Colloque
0240-8910 Abstracta Iranica
0240-8937 Museum National d'Histoire Naturelle. Bulletin - Section B - Adansonia (Botanique, Phytochimie)
0240-902X Alta Nizza
0240-9542 Industrie Minerale. Techniques *see* 0766-1207
0240-9925 Inter Regions
0241-0389 Viandes et Produits Carnes
0241-0702 Tricot Prestige
0241-2640 Infotecture
0241-2799 Cahiers Philosophiques
0241-5453 Cahiers Critiques de Therapie Familiale et de Pratiques de Reseaux
0241-6794 Cahiers Techniques du Batiment
0241-7375 Info Dechets. Environment et Technique
0241-8185 A - Ya
0241-8622 Moteurs Loisirs
0242-035X International Association of Literary Critics. Revue
0242-1283 Commutation et Transmission
0242-2085 Series: Graph-Agri
0242-3502 Hudson Letter
0242-3782 Agence Telegraphique Juive. Bulletin
0242-3960 Interbloc
0242-4002 Association Nationale d'Etude et de Lutte Contre les Fleaux Atmospheriques. Rapport de Campagne
0242-5017 Annales de Virologie *see* 0923-2516
0242-5149 Revue Imprevue
0242-5769 Monde Informatique
0242-5815 Banque de France. Enquete Mensuelle de Conjoncture
0242-5823 Argus du Livre Ancien et Moderne *changed to* Argus du Livre de Collection.
0242-5874 Bulletin Social
0242-5912 Bulletin Fiscal
0242-6277 R G S
0242-648X Journal de Readaptation Medicale
0242-6498 Annales de Pathologie
0242-6536 Observatoire de Strasbourg. Centre de Donnees Stellaires. Information Bulletin
0242-6862 Tonus Dentaire
0242-7540 Annuaire de l'Afrique du Nord
0242-7818 Economie Prospective Internationale
0242-8903 Revue de l'Ameublement
0242-9284 Auto-Loisirs
0242-9616 Psychoanalistes
0242-9780 Revue Francaise de Gestion Industrielle
0243-0738 Echo de l'Union
0243-1181 Revue de l'Artisan Electricien *see* 0761-0076
0243-1203 Journal Europeen de Radiotherapie†
0243-1327 Casus Belli
0243-1335 Ca m'Interesse
0243-1947 C.E.P.I.I. Lettre
0243-5314 Institut Appert. Bulletin Analytique Cie
0243-6108 France. Ministere de l'Agriculture. Informations Rapides. Fruits *changed to* France. Ministere de l'Agriculture et de la Foret. Conjoncture Fruits.
0243-6140 France. Ministere de l'Agriculture. Informations Rapides. Legumes *changed to* France. Ministere de l'Agriculture et de la Foret. Conjoncture Legumes.
0243-6167 France. Ministere de l'Agriculture. Informations Rapides. Statistiques des Entreprises *changed to* France. Ministere de l'Agriculture et de la Foret. Donnees Chiffrees. I A A.
0243-6175 France. Ministere de l'Agriculture. Situation Agricole en France. Note de Conjoncture Production Porcine *changed to* Animaux Hebdo.
0243-6183 France. Ministere de l'Agriculture. Situation Agricole en France. Note de Conjoncture Production Avicole
0243-6248 France. Ministere de l'Agriculture. Situation Agricole en France. Note de Conjoncture Production Vegetale *changed to* France. Ministere de l'Agriculture et de la Foret. Conjoncture Legumes.
0243-6248 France. Ministere de l'Agriculture. Situation Agricole en France. Note de Conjoncture Production Vegetale *changed to* France. Ministere de l'Agriculture et de la Foret. Conjoncture Fruits.
0243-6248 France. Ministere de l'Agriculture. Situation Agricole en France. Note de Conjoncture Productions Vegetale *changed to* France. Ministere de l'Agriculture et de la Foret. Conjoncture Grandes Cultures.
0243-6248 France. Ministere de l'Agriculture. Note de Conjoncture Production Vegetale *changed to* France. Ministere de l'Agriculture et de la Foret. Donnees.
0243-6280 France. Ministere de l'Agriculture. Situation Agricole en France. Note de Conjoncture Production Bovine *changed to* Animaux Hebdo.
0243-6345 France. Ministere de l'Agriculture. Situation Agricole en France. Note de Conjoncture Production Animale†
0243-6450 M O T S: Mots, Ordinateurs, Textes, Societes
0243-6566 France. Ministere de l'Agriculture. Series "S". Production Animales *changed to* France. Ministere de l'Agriculture et de la Foret. Donnees Chiffres Agriculture.
0243-6574 France. Ministere de l'Agriculture. Series "S". Departements d'Outre-Mer *changed to* France. Ministere de l'Agriculture et de la Foret. Donnees Chiffres Agriculture.
0243-6639 France. Mininstere de l'Agriculture. Series "S". Structure et Environnement des Exploitations *see* 0998-4186
0243-6647 France. Ministere de l'Agriculture. Series "S". Industries Agricoles et Alimentaires *changed to* France. Ministere de l'Agriculture et de la Foret. Donnees Chiffrees. I A A.
0243-6647 France. Ministere de l'Agriculture. Series "S". Industries Agricoles et Alimentaires *changed to* France. Ministere de l'Agriculture et de la Foret. Donnees.
0243-6825 Annuaire de Statistique Agricole†
0243-7090 Afram Newsletter
0243-7651 Oecologica Plantarum *see* 1146-609X
0243-766X Oecologia Generalis *see* 1146-609X
0243-7678 Oecologia Applicata *see* 1146-609X
0243-8283 France. Ministere de l'Agriculture. Situation Agricole en France. Commerce Exterieur Bois et Derives *changed to* France. Ministere de l'Agriculture et de la Foret. Serie Commerce Exterieur Bois et Derives.
0243-8828 France. Direction des Affaires Economiques et Internationales. Tableau de Bord Conjoncture
0244-0008 Amina
0244-0342 African Defence Journal†
0244-1179 France. Ministere de l'Economie, des Finances et du Budget. Notes Bleues
0244-1462 Temoignage Chretien
0244-2019 Isolation
0244-4046 Animer mon Pays, mon Village *changed to* Animer.
0244-5271 France. Ministere de l'Agriculture. Series "S". Synthese Statistique Comptes et Revenus *see* 0998-4186
0244-6014 Societe Francaise de Photogrammetrie et de Teledetection. Bulletin
0244-710X Francexport
0244-7118 France. Service d'Etude des Strategies et des Statistiques Industrielles. Collections: Traits Fondamentaux du Systeme Industriel Francais
0244-7819 France. Observatoire Economique et Statistique des Transports. Note de Conjoncture
0244-7827 Politique Africaine
0244-7878 Le Nouvel Humanisme
0244-9358 Revue Trimestrielle de Droit Commercial et du Droit Economique
0244-9404 Centre d'Histoire Contemporaine du Languedoc-Roussillon. Bulletin
0244-9870 Traitement de Texte
0245-0283 French Engineering Catalog
0245-1301 Annuaire National de la Conserve *changed to* Annuaire des Industries de la Conserve.
0245-2030 Communautes Educatives
0245-3614 Cheval Magazine
0245-5552 Journal d'Echographie et de Medecine par Ultrasons
0245-5919 Motricite Cerebrale: Readaptation Neurologie du Developpement.
0245-6001 Messages des P T T
0245-7318 Cheminot de France
0245-761X Banque de l'Union Europeenne. Chiffres et Commentaires
0245-8292 Revue de Metallurgie. Memoires et Etudes Scientifiques
0245-8756 Aeroports de Paris. Bulletin Mensuel de Statistiques
0245-8969 Education Physique et Sport
0245-8977 Education Physique et Sportive au 1er Degre
0245-9132 Economie et Humanisme
0245-9310 Guide Offshore
0245-9337 International Pediatric Association. Bulletin†
0245-9345 France. Bureau de Recherches Geologiques et Minieres. Manuels et Methodes
0245-940X Chimie Magazine
0245-9418 Oceanographie Tropicale†
0245-954X Bulletin Signaletique. Part 215: Biotechnologies (French Edition) *see* 0761-165X
0245-9558 Bulletin Signaletique. Part 233: Medecine Tropicale *see* 0761-1676
0245-985X Bibliographie Internationale des Industries Agro-Alimentaires
0245-9868 Bulletin Signaletique. Part 215: Biotechnology (English Edition) *changed to* P A S C A L Thema. Part 216: Biotechnology (English Edition).
0245-9884 Bulletin Signaletique. Part 361: Reproduction. Gynecologie. Obstetrique. Embryologie. Endocrinologie *see* 0761-1919
0245-9884 Bulletin Signaletique. Part 361: Reproduction. Gynecologie. Obstetrique. Embryologie. Endocrinologie *see* 0761-2168
0245-9884 Bulletin Signaletique. Part 361: Reproduction. Gynecologie. Obstetrique. Embryologie. Endocrinologie *see* 0761-229X
0245-9981 Bureaux d'Etudes *see* 1148-7305
0246-0203 Institut Henri Poincare. Annales. Probabilites et Statistiques
0246-1153 P A S C A L Folio. F 56: Ecologie Animale et Vegetale
0246-1161 P A S C A L Explore. E 20: Electronique et Telecommunications
0246-117X P A S C A L Explore. E 36: Pollution de l'Eau, de l'Air et du Sol, Dechets, Bruit
0246-1196 Musee National d'Histoire Naturelle, Paris. Memoires. Nouvelle Serie. Serie C. Sciences de la Terre
0246-1234 Reanimation et Medecine d'Urgence *see* 0765-5290
0246-1447 P A S C A L Explore. E 58: Genetique
0246-1528 Hydrologie Continentale
0246-1579 Parc Naturel Regional et des Reserves Naturelles de Corse. Travaux Scientifiques
0246-1641 France. Bureau de Recherches Geologiques et Minieres. Hydrogeologie
0246-2303 Institut d'Elevage et de Medecine Veterinaire des Pays Tropicaux. Rapport d'Activite
0246-2346 Debat
0246-2958 Audio Video Magazine
0246-4438 Education par le Jeu et l'Environnement
0246-5957 Magic Crochet
0246-9367 Recherches en Didactique des Mathematiques
0246-9405 Revolution
0246-9715 Innovation et Produits Nouveaux *changed to* Telecommunications.
0246-9731 Institut de Recherches Marxistes. Cahiers d'Histoire *changed to* Cahiers d'Histoire (Paris).
0247-0357 Paroles et Musique
0247-1086 Centre d'Entraide Genealogique de Franche-Comte. Bulletin *changed to* Genealogie Franc - Comtoise.
0247-1906 Neige Magazine†
0247-3518 Informations du Caoutchouc et des Plastiques
0247-381X Criticon
0247-400X Annuaire des Pays de l'Ocean Indien
0247-4352 Videotex
0247-4468 France. Ministere de la Cooperation. Services des Etudes et Questions Internationales. Etudes et Documents *changed to* France. Ministere des Relations Exterieures. Sous-Directions des Etudes et Developpement. Etudes et Documents.
0247-4808 Opto Electronique
0247-5421 Profils Economiques
0247-6355 Mutu
0247-7181 Chausser
0247-8277 Eco 3
0247-8315 Gabon Selection
0247-8390 Cartonnages & Emballages Modernes
0247-8633 D'onte Ses
0247-9095 Differences
0247-915X Contrastes
0248-0018 Journal d'Urologie
0248-1294 Fruits
0248-1308 Fruits A *see* 0248-1294
0248-1316 Fruits B *see* 0248-1294

ISSN

0248-1758 Psychiatrie du Praticien *changed to* Pratique Medicale.

0248-3165 Feuille de Route

0248-3807 Institut d'Ethnologie. Archives et Documents, Micro Edition. Sciences Naturelles

0248-3912 Institut d'Ethnologie. Archives et Documents, Micro Edition. Sciences Humaines

0248-4684 Cahiers d'Information Therapeutique†

0248-4900 Biology of the Cell

0248-5516 Sources et Travaux d'Histoire Haut-Pyreneenne

0248-8663 Revue de Medecine Interne

0248-9708 Banque et Informatique

0249-1605 Rayons Jardin

0249-1664 Etudes sur l'Herault

0249-1729 E L F - Aquitaine News

0249-2644 Scout - Avenir

0249-3136 Fonderie, Fondeur d'Aujourd'hui

0249-3446 Alea *changed to* L'Ennemi.

0249-4744 Economie et Prevision

0249-5163 Opportunites Industrielles Bulletin

0249-5430 Marche des Dechets Industriels

0249-5570 Cahiers de Recherche en Gestion des Entreprises

0249-5619 Recherches d'Histoire et de Sciences Sociales

0249-5627 Agronomie

0249-5635 Universite de Bordeaux II. Cahiers Ethnologiques

0249-5686 C E M A G R E F Nouvelles†

0249-5740 France. Centre de Recherche Zootechnique. Departement de Genetique Animale. Bulletin Technique†

0249-5805 Societe Sciences Nat. Bulletin

0249-5872 Electricite de France. Bulletin de Documentation *see* 1142-3153

0249-5902 Centre d'Histoire Economique et Sociale de la Region Lyonnaise. Bulletin

0249-6208 Journal de Medecine Legale Droit Medical

0249-6216 Journal de Toxicologie Medicale *see* 0753-2830

0249-6267 Modeles Linguistiques

0249-6356 Revue Co-Textes

0249-6399 Institut National de Recherche en Informatique et en Automatique. Rapports de Recherche

0249-6402 Toxicological European Research†

0249-6550 Journal d'Ergotherapie

0249-6704 Fils, Tubes, Bandes et Profiles

0249-6739 Orientation Scolaire et Professionnelle

0249-7069 Societe d'Etudes Linguistiques et Anthropologiques de France. Numeros Speciaux

0249-7271 Recueil des Decisions du Conseil d'Etat

0249-7344 Bibliotheque Nationale. Revue

0249-7395 Revue d'Ecologie: La Terre et la Vie

0249-7522 Association pour le Developpement International de l'Observatoire de Nice. Bulletin

0249-7549 Societe Geologique de France. Memoires

0249-7557 Reunion Annuelle des Sciences de la Terre *changed to* Reunion des Sciences de la Terre.

0249-9185 Cahiers de Psychologie Cognitive

0250-0019 Dyers Dyegest *see* 0254-0533

0250-0027 Dynamica

0250-0116 Africa Seminar: Collected Papers†

0250-0167 Communicatio

0250-0213 Cormorant *see* 1018-3337

0250-0329 De Rebus

0250-0418 Electron Microscopy Society of Southern Africa. Proceedings

0250-054X Architecture S.A. (Cape Town)

0250-0817 Black Who's Who of Southern Africa†

0250-0868 Tissue Reactions

0250-104X Cripple Care News *changed to* Towards Independence.

0250-1163 Johannesburg Historical Foundation. Journal *changed to* Between the Chains.

0250-1236 N T K - Nuus *changed to* S A Co-op.

0250-1325 South African Laundry and Cleaning Review *changed to* S A Cleaning Review.

0250-1333 South African Shoemaker and Leather Review

0250-152X Educamus

0250-1619 Centre d'Etudes et de Documentation Africaines. Cahiers

0250-1651 Republic of China. National Science Council Monthly

0250-1910 Informa†

0250-1961 I S S U P Strategic Review *see* 1013-1108

0250-2003 Contacts

0250-216X University of Cape Town. Department of Geology. Precambrian Research Unit. Annual Report

0250-2399 Bibliography of Foreign Publications About South Africa†

0250-2402 Barclays Business Brief *changed to* Business Brief.

0250-2410 Small Business News

0250-2887 Sugar Industry Abstracts *see* 0957-5022

0250-2992 Cookeia

0250-300X Smithersia *see* 1011-7881

0250-3018 Zimbabwea

0250-3190 Revista A I B D A

0250-3212 Beitraege zur Urologie

0250-3220 Contributions to Oncology

0250-3255 Soochow Journal of Mathematics

0250-3263 Dongwuxue Zazhi

0250-3301 Huanjing Kexue

0250-3328 Asian Medical News

0250-3360 Korean Journal of Breeding

0250-362X Kuwait Bulletin of Marine Science

0250-3654 Pakistan Hotel Guide

0250-3662 Pakistan Hotel and Travel Review

0250-3670 Revista Universitaria

0250-3689 Gesundheit

0250-3697 Societe pour le Developpement Minier de la Cote d'Ivoire. Rapport Annuel

0250-3751 Developments in Ophthalmology

0250-3778 Khanya Theological Education by Extension Newsletter†

0250-3786 Aeronautical Society of South Africa. Journal *see* 0257-8573

0250-3794 World Health Statistics Annual

0250-3891 E I B - Information

0250-4057 Social Security Documentation: Asian Series

0250-4065 Kuwait Institute for Scientific Research. Annual Research Report

0250-4162 Scopus

0250-4197 Advances in Clinical Enzymology

0250-4235 Bulletin C I S *see* 1010-7061

0250-4278 O E C D. Indicators of Industrial Activity

0250-4324 Estadistica Panamena. Situacion Economica. Seccion 312. Siembra y Cosecha de Hortilizas†

0250-4340 Pakistan Hotel and Restaurant Guide

0250-4367 Medicinal and Aromatic Plants Abstracts

0250-4375 Nuclear Science Research Conference Series

0250-4421 Blues Life

0250-443X Wiener - Goethe - Verein. Jahrbuch

0250-4731 Hjukrun

0250-474X Indian Journal of Pharmaceutical Sciences

0250-4782 Fact Technical Society. Journal

0250-4928 Transnational Associations

0250-4952 Therapie Familiale

0250-4960 Nephrologie

0250-4987 Revue Celinienne

0250-5045 Aviation Medicine

0250-5053 Bibliografia Kombetare e Republikos Popullore Socialiste te Shquperise. Librit Shqip *changed to* Bibliografia Kombetare e Librit Shqip.

0250-5061 Bibliografia Kombetare e Republikes Popullore Socialiste te Shqiperise. Artikujt e Periodikut Shqip. *changed to* Bibliografia Kombetare e Periodikeve Shqip.

0250-5118 International Dairy Federation. Annual Bulletin

0250-5193 Gujarat Agricultural University Research Journal

0250-524X Indian Journal of Forestry

0250-5266 Indian Veterinary Medical Journal

0250-5363 Karachi Journal of Science

0250-5371 Legume Research

0250-538X Maadini

0250-541X National Academy of Sciences, India. Science Letters

0250-5584 U N D O C: Current Index

0250-5592 University of Dar es Salaam. University Science Journal *see* 0856-1761

0250-5657 Zambian Geographical Journal

0250-5673 Bibliographie der Berner Geschichte

0250-5754 E P News

0250-5789 Euronet Diane News *see* 1017-6950

0250-5886 Green Europe

0250-5940 Rechtsbibliographie

0250-5959 I I C A in the Americas

0250-5967 E C Agricultural Price Indices *changed to* Agricultural Statistics Series No.3: European Communities Index of Agricultural Prices.

0250-5991 Journal of Biosciences

0250-6009 Indian Institute of Tropical Meteorology. Research Report *see* 0252-1075

0250-6017 Indian Institute of Tropical Meteorology. Annual Report

0250-6041 Documentacion de la Seguridad Social Americana

0250-6068 Pharmanual†

0250-6114 Chiefs of State and Cabinet Ministers of the American Republics

0250-6130 Educacion

0250-6173 Juventud†

0250-6211 Organization of American States. Directory

0250-6262 Revista Interamericana de Bibliografia

0250-6270 Inter-American Review of Bibliography

0250-6289 Organization of American States. Statistical Bulletin

0250-6327 Bulletin of Materials Science

0250-6335 Journal of Astrophysics and Astronomy

0250-6386 Arnoldia Zimbabwe

0250-6394 N A F O Statistical Bulletin

0250-6408 Journal of Northwest Atlantic Fishery Science

0250-6416 N A F O Scientific Council Reports

0250-6432 N A F O Scientific Council Studies

0250-6440 Der Gesellschafter

0250-6459 Zeitschrift fuer Neuere Rechtsgeschichte

0250-6505 Regional Development Dialogue

0250-6521 Universidad de la Republica. Facultad de Humanidades y Ciencias. Revista. Serie Ciencias de la Tierra

0250-653X Universidad de la Republica. Facultad de Humanidades y Ciencias. Revista. Serie Ciencias Biologicas

0250-6548 Universidad de la Republica. Facultad de Humanidades y Ciencias. Revista. Serie Linguistica

0250-6556 Universidad de la Republica. Facultad de Humanidades y Ciencias. Revista. Serie Letras

0250-6564 Universidad de la Republica. Facultad de Humanidades y Ciencias. Revista. Serie Ciencias Antropologicas

0250-6580 Statistical Office of the European Communities. Animal Production *changed to* Agricultural Statistics Series No.2: Animal Production.

0250-6793 Stem Cells *see* 0254-7600

0250-6807 Annals of Nutrition and Metabolism

0250-6831 Belizean Studies

0250-6874 Sensors and Actuators *see* 0924-4247

0250-6874 Sensors and Actuators *see* 0925-4005

0250-6971 Revue de Theologie et de Philosophie. Cahiers

0250-7005 Anticancer Research

0250-7013 Fauna & Flora (English Edition) *see* 0046-3388

0250-7102 Naturopa

0250-7161 Revista Latinoamericana de Estudios Urbano Regionales

0250-7188 Hamdard Medicus

0250-7196 Hamdard Islamicus

0250-720X Fiji. Geological Survey. Long Report *changed to* Fiji. Mineral Resources Department. Report.

0250-7234 Fiji. Mineral Resources Division. Report *changed to* Fiji. Mineral Resources Department. Report.

0250-7242 Fiji. Geological Survey. Bulletin *changed to* Fiji. Mineral Resources Department. Bulletin.

0250-7269 Fiji. Geological Survey. Memoir *changed to* Fiji. Mineral Resources Department. Memoir.

0250-7277 Fiji. Mineral Resources Department. Geothermal Report

0250-7366 International Monetary Fund. Annual Report on Exchange Arrangements and Exchange Restrictions

0250-7374 International Monetary Fund. Government Finance Statistics Yearbook

0250-7463 International Financial Statistics Yearbook

0250-7498 International Monetary Fund. Annual Report of the Executive Board

0250-7544 Organization of American States. Department of Scientific Affairs. Newsletter.†

0250-7595 Index Indiana

0250-7609 Geosur

0250-7617 Carindex: Social Sciences and Humanities

0250-7633 I D O C Monthly Bulletin†

0250-7730 International Designs Bulletin

0250-7757 P C T Gazette

0250-7765 Petroleum News

0250-7781 European Parliament's Official Handbook†

0250-779X Unesco Yearbook on Peace and Conflict Studies

0250-7811 N A F O List of Fishing Vessels

0250-782X Modell-Eisenbahn

0250-7862 Kexue Tongbao (Foreign Language Edition) *see* 1001-6538

0250-7935 Industry and Development

0250-801X United Nations Industrial Development Organization. Development and Transfer of Technology Series†

0250-8052 E P P O Bulletin

0250-8060 Water International

0250-8079 Polymer Engineering. Journal *see* 0334-6447

0250-8087 Pseudo-Allergic Reactions†

0250-8095 American Journal of Nephrology

0250-8109 Z G A Occasional Studies

0250-8117 Z G A School Supplement

0250-8125 Z G A Bibliographic Series

0250-8133 Zambia Geographical Association. Regional Handbook

0250-8257 Kenya Journal of Science and Technology. Series A: Physical and Chemical Sciences *changed to* Kenya Journal of Sciences. Series A: Physical and Chemical Sciences.

0250-8281 Tourism Recreation Research

0250-829X Indian Journal of Botany

0250-832X Dento Maxillo Facial Radiology

0250-8346 Journal of Himalayan Studies and Regional Development

0250-8443 A F R O Technical Report Series

0250-8613 I A R C Biennial Report

0250-8621 A F R O Technical Papers

0250-863X Environmental Health Criteria

0250-8710 Euro Reports and Studies†

0250-9040 World Meteorological Organization. Regional Association V (South West Pacific). Abridged Final Report of the (No.) Session

0250-9121 World Meteorological Organization. Regional Association IV (North America and Central America). Abridged Final Report of the (No.) Session

5654 ISSN INDEX

0250-9172 World Meteorological Organization. Commission for Atmospheric Sciences. Abridged Final Report of the (No.) Session
0250-9393 World Meteorological Organization. Weather Reporting. Volume A: Observing Stations
0250-9407 World Meteorological Organization. Weather Reporting. Volume B: Data Processing
0250-9415 World Meteorological Organization. Weather Reporting. Volume C: Transmissions
0250-9423 World Meteorological Organization. Weather Reporting. Volume D: Information for Shipping
0250-944X International Fruit World
0250-9555 I A R C Monographs on the Evaluation of Carcinogenic Risk of Chemicals to Man *changed to* I A R C Monographs on the Evaluation of Carcinogenic Risks to Humans.
0250-9601 Agricultural Markets: Places
0250-961X Inside China Mainland
0250-9628 Journal of Combinatorics, Information & System Sciences
0250-9636 Indian Society of Statistics and Operations Research. Journal
0250-9660 I C S S R Journal of Abstracts and Reviews: Political Science
0250-9679 Indian Psychological Abstracts
0250-9687 I C S S R Journal of Abstracts and Reviews: Geography
0250-9695 I C S S R Journal of Abstracts and Reviews: Economics
0250-9709 Indian Dissertation Abstracts
0250-9717 Asian Banking and Corporate Finance *changed to* AsiaBanking.
0250-9725 Biblioteek voor Hedendaagse Dokumentatie. Bulletin
0250-975X Bhashavimarsa†
0250-9784 Mechanical and Corrosion Properties *changed to* Key Engineering Materials.
0250-9784 Mechanical and Corrosion Properties *changed to* Crystal Properties and Preparation.
0250-9792 Resumen Semanal
0250-9806 QueHacer
0250-9814 Serie Praxis
0250-9873 Yearbook of Industrial Statistics *see* 0257-7208
0250-9881 Arab Mining Journal
0250-9903 Annual Bulletin of Steel Statistics for Europe
0250-9989 Ecoforum
0251-0006 M & K Computer
0251-0073 Statistical Indicators of Short Term Economic Changes in E.C.E. Countries
0251-0081 Annual Bulletin of Trade in Chemical Products
0251-012X Indian Musicological Society. Journal
0251-0146 I S P T Journal of Research in Educational & Psychological Measurement
0251-0154 Luso
0251-0170 Experimental Hematology Today†
0251-0332 Executive
0251-0480 Pakistan Journal of Agricultural Research
0251-091X Notas e Estudos, Serie Recursos e Ambiente Aquaticos *see* 0870-1245
0251-0936 E B U Technical Review
0251-0944 Revue de l'Ingenieur Industriel *see* 0775-2962
0251-0952 Seed Science and Technology
0251-0979 Ingenieurs et Architectes Suisses
0251-1088 Environmentalist
0251-110X Institution of Engineers (India). Environmental Engineering Division. Journal
0251-1118 Institution of Engineers (India). Interdisciplinary and General Engineering Journal *see* 0970-9843
0251-1223 Geobios
0251-1339 International Social Security Association. Reports of the General Assemblies of the ISSA
0251-1495 Training for Agriculture and Rural Development
0251-1525 F A O Fertilizer Yearbook
0251-1630 Indian Institute of World Culture. Bulletin
0251-1649 International Journal of Clinical Pharmacology Research
0251-1711 Biblioteca Nacional de Portugal. Revista
0251-172X Odonto-Stomatologie Tropicale
0251-1746 Shree Hari Katha
0251-1762 Schweizerischer Medizinalkalender *changed to* Schweizerischer Medizinalkalender und Arzneimitteluebersicht.
0251-1770 Journal of Engineering Production†
0251-1789 Invasion and Metastasis
0251-1800 Statistical Office of the European Communities. Balance of Payments *changed to* Balance of Payments Statistical Yearbook.
0251-1924 Nyala
0251-1940 Handbok Baenda
0251-2068 Concepts in Pediatric Neurosurgery
0251-2408 De Franse Nederlanden
0251-2432 World Health Forum
0251-2440 Agricultural Abstracts for Tanzania
0251-2459 Industrial Abstracts for Tanzania
0251-2467 Child Health and Development†
0251-2483 Estudios Paraguayos
0251-2491 Andean Report
0251-2513 Bulletin A I O S P-I A E V G-I V S B B *changed to* Educational and Vocational Guidance - Bulletin A I O S P, I A E V G, I V S B B.
0251-2645 D S T C Newsletter *see* 0255-0806
0251-2661 Bunadarrit
0251-2920 C E P A L Review
0251-3056 Journal of Government and Political Studies
0251-3099 Revista de Istorie *see* 0567-6304
0251-317X Development Policy and Administrative Review
0251-348X Social Sciences Research Journal
0251-3552 Nueva Sociedad
0251-3609 Franciat†
0251-3625 D I S P
0251-401X Commodity Trade and Price Trends
0251-4133 Switzerland. Eidgenoessische Anstalt fuer das Forstliche Versuchswesen. Mitteilungen
0251-4141 Associacao Portuguesa de Bibliotecarios Arquivistas e Documentalistas. Noticia
0251-4184 Acta Mathematica Vietnamica
0251-4265 United Nations Commission on International Trade Law. Yearbook
0251-4796 National Central Library News Bulletin *changed to* National Central Library Bulletin.
0251-5342 Frontiers in Diabetes
0251-5350 Neuroepidemiology
0251-6365 International Monetary Fund. Occasional Papers
0251-6616 United Nations Library. Monthly Bibliography. Part 1: Books, Official Documents, Serials
0251-6624 United Nations Library. Monthly Bibliography. Part 2: Selected Articles
0251-6632 Development Forum
0251-6802 Bulletin on Ageing
0251-6810 International Colloquium on Prospective Biology (Proceedings)†
0251-6861 Populi
0251-690X Everyone's United Nations
0251-7019 Human Rights Bulletin
0251-7256 Bulletin C I L A
0251-7329 U N Chronicle
0251-737X Psychotherapies
0251-7396 Hey *changed to* S O H-Info.
0251-7469 International Conference on Data Processing in the Field of Social Security. Reports
0251-7493 Oesterreichische Geologische Gesellschaft. Mitteilungen
0251-7604 Population Bulletin of the United Nations
0251-8775 World Meteorological Organization. Commission for Hydrology. Abridged Final Report of the (No.) Session
0251-8783 World Meteorlogical Organization. Commission for Instruments and Methods of Observation. Abridged Final Report of the (No.) Session
0251-8945 World Meteorological Organization. Commission for Special Applications of Meteorology and Climatology. Abridged Final Report of the (No.) Session†
0251-8953 World Meteorological Organization. Commission for Basic Systems. Abridged Final Report of the (No.) Session
0251-9089 Caribbean Documentation Centre. Current Awareness Bulletin
0251-9410 United Nations Economic and Social Council. Resolutions and Decisions
0251-9445 Boletin Estadistico de America Latina *see* 1014-0697
0251-9453 Notas Sobre la Economia y el Desarrollo de America Latina *see* 0257-2168
0251-9461 International Trade and Development Statistics. Handbook
0251-9518 Disarmament
0252-0397 Journal of Higher Education
0252-0508 European Information Centre for Nature Conservation. Newslettter *changed to* Council of Europe. Centre Naturopa. Newsletter.
0252-0591 Council of Europe. Documentation Centre for Education in Europe. Newsletter
0252-063X International Exchange of Information on Current Criminological Research Projects in Member States†
0252-0648 Exchange of Information on Research in European Law
0252-0656 Council of Europe. Parliamentary Assembly. Documents: Working Papers
0252-0664 Council of Europe. Parliamentary Assembly. Official Report of Debates.
0252-0753 Council of Europe. Information Bulletin - Municipal and Regional Matters *see* 0253-1968
0252-0869 Cultural Policy
0252-0877 Council of Europe. Directorate of Legal Affairs. Information Bulletin on Legislative Activities
0252-0958 Council of Europe Forum
0252-1024 Asian Banking Directory *changed to* Triple A.
0252-1032 Acta de Odontologia Pediatrica
0252-1059 Mechanical and Corrosion Properties. Series A. Key Engineering Materials *changed to* Key Engineering Materials.
0252-1067 Mechanical and Corrosion Properties. Series B. Single Crystal Properties *changed to* Crystal Properties and Preparation.
0252-1075 Indian Institute of Tropical Meteorology. Contributions
0252-1105 Information Resources Annual†
0252-1121 Bulletin Celinien
0252-1148 Geneva Papers on Risk and Insurance *see* 0926-4957
0252-1156 Magnesium *see* 1015-3845
0252-1164 Clinical Physiology and Biochemistry†
0252-1172 Applied Pathology†
0252-1865 Apuntes
0252-1881 Schweizerische Gesellschaft fuer Ur- und Fruehgeschichte. Jahrbuch
0252-1903 Revista Cubana de Administracion de Salud *see* 0864-3466
0252-1962 Revista de Investigaciones Marinas
0252-2195 Cuadernos de la C E P A L
0252-2462 Fiji. Mineral Resources Department. Annual Report
0252-2470 Fiji. Department of Lands and Mineral Resources. Annual Report *see* 0252-2462
0252-2489 Fiji. Geological Survey. Annual Report *see* 0252-2462
0252-2497 Fiji Mineral Resources Division. Memoir *changed to* Fiji. Mineral Resources Department. Memoir.
0252-2527 Echo der Liebe
0252-2535 Mirror
0252-2659 Weekly Analysis of Ecuadorian Issues
0252-2667 Journal of Information & Optimization Sciences
0252-2683 Informations Recentes sur les Comptes Nationaux des Pays en Developpement
0252-2942 World Bank. Annual Report
0252-2969 Schweizerischen Naturforschenden Gesellschaft. Jahrbuch†
0252-3051 International Monetary Fund. Balance of Payments Statistics
0252-306X Direction of Trade Statistics
0252-3116 Tushu Qingbao Gongzuo
0252-3213 Infoterra
0252-3353 Date Palm Journal
0252-337X Academia de Geografia e Historia de Guatemala. Anales
0252-3426 Small Industry Bulletin for Asia and the Pacific
0252-354X R I S S: Regional Information Support Service
0252-3639 Population Headliners
0252-3647 United Nations Economic and Social Commission for Asia and the Pacific. Statistical Newsletter
0252-3655 Statistical Yearbook for Asia and the Pacific
0252-4392 Transport & Communications Bulletin for Asia & the Pacific
0252-4406 Electric Power in Asia and the Pacific
0252-4422 A D O P T†
0252-4457 Statistical Indicators for Asia and the Pacific
0252-4481 Industry and Technology Development News - Asia and the Pacific
0252-452X United Nations Economic and Social Commission for Asia and the Pacific. Social Development Division. Social Work Education and Development
0252-4538 Foreign Trade Statistics of Asia and the Pacific. Series A *see* 1011-4858
0252-4546 Foreign Trade Statistics of Asia and the Pacific. Series B *see* 1011-4858
0252-5216 Trade and Development: An U N C T A Review *changed to* U N C T A D Review.
0252-5232 U N C T A D Monthly Bulletin *see* 0259-3181
0252-5321 United Nations. Treaty Series. Cumulative Index
0252-5348 Mekong Bulletin†
0252-5607 United Nations Disarmament Yearbook
0252-5704 Economic and Social Survey of Asia and the Pacific
0252-7308 Interfaces in Computing *see* 0920-5489
0252-791X Refugees
0252-7979 Guide to Current Literature in Environmental Health Engineering and Science
0252-8088 Conditions of Work: A Cumulative Digest *see* 0257-3512
0252-8150 Zygos (1982)†
0252-8169 Journal of Comparative Literature and Aesthetics
0252-8177 N S C Symposium Series
0252-8274 Ernstia
0252-8290 Revue d'Etudes Palestiniennes
0252-8347 Papua New Guinea National Bibliography
0252-8398 Bibliography of the Geology of Fiji
0252-841X Boletin de Antropologia Americana
0252-8479 Repertorio Americano
0252-855X C E D E F O P News†
0252-8576 International Journal of Educational Sciences
0252-8584 Economia y Desarrollo
0252-8754 Inforpress Centroamericana

ISSN

ISSN INDEX 5655

0252-8843 Revista de Critica Literaria Latinoamericana
0252-886X Amazonia Peruana
0252-9114 European Commission of Human Rights. Annual Review/Compte Rendu Annual†
0252-9203 Social Sciences in China
0252-9246 C I E - Journal†
0252-9416 Mausam
0252-9505 Transnational Perspectives
0252-9521 Ciencias Economicas
0252-9564 Survey of Immunologic Research *see* 0257-277X
0252-9599 Chinese Annals of Mathematics. Series B
0252-9610 Cargonews Asia
0252-9629 Travel News Asia
0252-967X Saudi Economic Survey
0252-9769 Revista Geofisica
0252-9793 Armada International
0252-9920 Unemployment Monthly Bulletin
0252-9939 Caribbean Geography
0252-9963 Mesoamerica
0252-9971 Centro de Investigaciones Regionales de Mesoamerica. Serie Monografica
0252-998X Educacion Especial
0253-0015 Boletin de Lima
0253-004X Phonographic Bulletin
0253-0090 United Nations. Economic Commission for Europe. Information
0253-035X Schweizerische Gesellschaft fuer Klinische Chemie. Bulletin
0253-0538 Carib-Latin Energy Consultant
0253-066X Caribbean Journal of Religious Studies
0253-0716 Iranian Journal of Medical Sciences
0253-0910 Oikogeneia kai Scholeio
0253-1062 Geotermia
0253-1119 Institutul Politehnic "Gheorghe Asachi" din Iasi. Buletinul. Sectia VII: Textile, Pielarie
0253-1216 Universite d'Ankara. Faculte des Sciences. Communications. Serie C1. Geologie
0253-1321 F I O D S Revue
0253-1445 Refugee Abstracts
0253-1453 Botanica Helvetica
0253-1496 Agricultural Reviews
0253-150X Agricultural Science Digest
0253-1607 Monumentet
0253-1674 Didaskalia
0253-1801 Revue Roumaine de Medecine. Serie Endocrinologie *changed to* Revue Roumaine d'Endocrinologie.
0253-1933 O.I.E. Revue Scientifique et Technique
0253-1941 Pakistan and Gulf Economist
0253-195X Unir Cinema
0253-1968 Regional and Local Affairs News†
0253-200X Synthetic Methods of Organic Chemistry
0253-2069 Biology International: I U B S Newsmagazine
0253-2093 Advances in Pharmacotherapy†
0253-2158 Russischer Samisdat *see* 0254-1521
0253-2182 Comite International des Poids et Mesures. Comite Consultatif pour la Definition du Metre (Rapport et Annexes)
0253-2239 Guangxue Xuebao
0253-2263 Chengdu Keji Daxue Xuebao
0253-228X Dongbei Nongxueyuan Xuebao
0253-2301 Fujian Nongye Keji
0253-231X Gongcheng Re-Wuli Xuebao
0253-2344 Shanghai Jinshu
0253-2379 Tianti Wuli Xuebao
0253-2409 Ranliao Huaxue Xuebao
0253-2468 Huanjing Kexue Xuebao
0253-2492 Consejo Nacional para Investigaciones Cientificas y Tecnologicas, Costa Rica. Informe Anual
0253-2654 Weishengwuxue Tongbao
0253-2700 Yunnan Zhiwu Yanjiu
0253-2727 Zhonghua Xueyexue Zazhi
0253-2743 Shuli Kexue yu Huaxue
0253-2778 Zhongguo Kexue Jishu Daxue Xuebao
0253-2786 Youji Huaxue
0253-2859 World Debt Tables
0253-2875 Newsletter for Research in Chinese Studies
0253-2913 Point Series
0253-293X New Muses
0253-2948 Revista Costarricense de Ciencias Medicas
0253-3014 Daihan Mingug Tongyei Nyengam *see* 0075-6873
0253-3073 Korean Journal of Pharmacognosy
0253-3162 Taehan Misaengmul Hakhoe Chi
0253-3219 He Jishu
0253-3316 Acta Academiae Medicinae Wuhan *see* 0257-716X
0253-3340 Geobios New Reports
0253-3367 Electricidade, Energia, Electronica *see* 0870-5364
0253-3413 Boletim de Bibliografia Portuguesa. Monografias
0253-3421 Boletim de Bibliografia Portuguesa. Publicacoes em Serie
0253-343X Boletim de Bibliografia Portuguesa. Documentos nao Textuais
0253-3596 Yuanzineng Nongye Yingyong
0253-360X Hanjie Xuebao
0253-3618 Hangzhou Daxue Xuebao (Ziran Kexue Ban)
0253-3634 Acta Physica Temperaturae Humilis Sinica: Cryophysics *see* 1000-3258
0253-3707 Baiqiu'en Yike Daxue Xuebao
0253-3715 Internationale Berg- und Seilbahn-Rundschau *changed to* Internationale Seilbahn-Rundschau.
0253-3782 Dizhen Xuebao
0253-3790 Yuanzihe Wuli
0253-3804 Journal of Civil and Hydraulic Engineering
0253-3839 Chinese Institute of Engineers. Journal
0253-3952 Social Dynamics
0253-4088 Zhongshan Daxue Xuebao (Ziran Kexue Ban)
0253-4096 Indian Academy of Sciences. Proceedings. Engineering Sciences *see* 0256-2499
0253-410X Indian Academy of Sciences. Proceedings. Plant Sciences *see* 0250-5991
0253-4118 Indian Academy of Sciences. Proceedings. Animal Sciences *see* 0250-5991
0253-4126 Indian Academy of Sciences. Proceedings. Earth and Planetary Sciences
0253-4134 Indian Academy of Sciences. Proceedings. Chemical Sciences
0253-4142 Indian Academy of Sciences. Proceedings. Mathematical Sciences
0253-4177 Bandaoti Xuebao
0253-4193 Haiyang Xuebao
0253-424X Dirasat. Series B: Pure and Applied Sciences
0253-4258 Dongbei Gongxueyuan Xuebao
0253-4290 Sichuan Yixueyuan Xuebao - Acta Academiae Medicinae Sichuan *see* 0257-7712
0253-4320 Modern Chemical Industry
0253-4347 Zhongnan Kuangye Xueyuan Xuebao
0253-4398 Survey of Digestive Diseases *see* 0257-2753
0253-4401 Naturhistorisches Museum Bern. Jahrbuch
0253-4533 Sprache & Kognition
0253-4754 International Journal of Structures
0253-4770 King Faisal Specialist Hospital Medical Journal *see* 0256-4947
0253-4827 Applied Mathematics and Mechanics
0253-4851 Tropical Veterinarian†
0253-486X Geochemistry *see* 1000-9426
0253-4878 Schweizer Waffen-Magazin *changed to* Internationales Waffen-Magazin.
0253-4886 Digestive Surgery
0253-4894 I C M E News†
0253-4959 Dicengxue Zazhi
0253-4967 Dizhen Dizhi
0253-4975 Guoji Dizhen Dongtai
0253-5033 Boletin S I N I C Y T
0253-505X Acta Oceanologica Sinica
0253-5068 Blood Purification
0253-5076 Complement *see* 1012-8204
0253-5092 Anthropologika
0253-5106 Chemical Society of Pakistan. Journal
0253-5114 Current Practices in Environmental Engineering *changed to* Progress in Environmental Science & Technology.
0253-5122 Current Practices in Geotechnical Engineering *changed to* Progress in Geotechnical Engineering.
0253-519X Discourse
0253-5416 Bangladesh Journal of Botany
0253-5467 Dacca University Studies. Part B: Science *changed to* Dhaka University Studies. Part B: Science.
0253-5572 I C S U AB News *changed to* I C S U Newsletter.
0253-5696 Jardin Botanico Nacional. Revista
0253-5823 Scientia Sinica. Series B: Chemistry, Life Sciences and Earth Sciences *see* 1001-652X
0253-5831 Scientia Sinica. Series A: Mathematics, Physics, Astronomy and Technological Sciences *see* 1001-6511
0253-584X Unir: Echo de Saint Louis
0253-5858 Unir Cine Media
0253-5890 Egyptian Society of Parasitology. Journal
0253-5904 Die Makromolekulare Chemie. Supplement
0253-6005 A R P E L Boletin Tecnico
0253-6102 Communications in Theoretical Physics
0253-6137 Shuxue Niankan *see* 0252-9599
0253-6137 Shuxue Niankan *changed to* Chinese Annals of Mathematics. Series A.
0253-6269 Archives of Pharmacal Research
0253-6455 A B C Human Rights Teaching
0253-651X Korean Journal of Mycology
0253-6544 Supreme Court Cases (Criminal)
0253-6552 Supreme Court Cases (Labour and Services)
0253-6560 Supreme Court Cases (Taxation)†
0253-6579 Current Central Legislation
0253-6587 Uttar Pradesh Services Cases†
0253-6595 Asian Journal of Dairy Research
0253-665X Progress in Ecology *see* 0971-1708
0253-6730 Revue de Paleobiologie
0253-6749 Cyprus. Agricultural Research Institute. Miscellaneous Reports
0253-6757 N I H F W Technical Reports
0253-682X Arogya
0253-7141 Indian Journal of Environmental Protection
0253-7176 Indian Journal of Psychological Medicine
0253-7206 International Bio-Sciences Monographs
0253-7222 Journal of Dharma
0253-7230 Journal of Scientific Research
0253-7249 Journal of Scientific Research in Plants & Medicines
0253-7257 Acoustical Society of India. Journal
0253-7273 Journal of Zoological Research
0253-7303 Popular Plastics
0253-7370 West Indian Law Journal
0253-7397 Ciencias Tecnicas Fisicas y Matematicas
0253-7400 Archiv der Geschichte der Naturwissenschaften
0253-7419 Medequip
0253-7427 Eurosocial Newsletter
0253-7435 Oberoesterreich
0253-7583 Physics News
0253-7605 Journal of Cytology and Genetics
0253-7613 Indian Journal of Pharmacology
0253-8083 News from Iceland
0253-8296 Speleological Abstracts
0253-8318 Pakistan Veterinary Journal
0253-8482 Sierra Leone Medical and Dental Association. Journal
0253-8539 Industriearchaeologie
0253-8555 Cyprus. Department of Statistics and Research. Economic Indicators
0253-8563 Tourism, Migration and Travel Statistics†
0253-858X Cyprus. Department of Statistics and Research. Imports and Exports Statistics
0253-8598 Cyprus. Department of Statistics and Research. Services Survey†
0253-8601 Health Statistics†
0253-8628 Hospital Statistics†
0253-8636 Sales of Vine Products Manufactured in Cyprus†
0253-8660 Cyprus. Department of Statistics and Research. Wages, Salaries and Hours of Work†
0253-8687 Cyprus. Department of Statistics and Research. Analysis of Wholesale and Retail Trade†
0253-8695 Cyprus. Department of Statistics and Research. Criminal Statistics
0253-8709 Cyprus. Department of Statistics and Research. Tourism, Migration and Travel Statistics
0253-8725 Cyprus. Department of Statistics and Research. Construction and Housing Report *changed to* Cyprus. Department of Statistics and Research. Construction and Housing Statistics.
0253-8733 Statistics of Education in Cyprus *changed to* Cyprus. Department of Statistics and Research. Education Statistics.
0253-8741 Cypriot Students Abroad†
0253-875X Cyprus. Department of Statistics and Research. Statistical Abstract
0253-8776 J I S T A
0253-8830 Taiwan Fisheries Research Institute, Keelung. Bulletin. *see* 1018-7324
0253-9071 Language Forum
0253-9268 Revista Cubana de Fisica
0253-9276 Tecnologia Quimica
0253-9306 Research Journal: Science
0253-9365 Bangalore Theological Forum
0253-9403 United Nations. International Narcotics Control Board. Statistics on Psychotropic Substances Furnished by Governments in Accordance with the Convention of 1971 on Psychotropic Substances *changed to* International Narcotics Control Board. Statistics on Psychotropic Substances for (Year).
0253-9454 Greece. National Statistical Service. Social Welfare and Health Statistics
0253-9527 Third World International *changed to* Thirdworld.
0253-9535 World Bank. Abstracts of Current Studies
0253-9608 Ziran Zazhi
0253-9683 Shanghai Huagong Xueyuan Xuebao
0253-9713 Beijing Yixue
0253-9756 Zhongguo Yaoli Xuebao
0253-9772 Yichuan
0253-9810 Recht
0253-9837 Cuihua Xuebao
0253-9888 Wuhan Daxue Xuebao (Ziran Kexue Ban)
0253-9896 Tianjin Yiyao
0253-9926 Shanxi Yiyao Zazhi
0253-9934 Shanghai Yixue
0253-9942 Shanghai Jiaotong Daxue Xuebao
0253-9950 He-Huaxue yu Fangshe Huaxue
0253-9977 Xibao Shengwuxue Zazhi
0253-9993 Meitan Xuebao
0254-0002 Daqi Kexue
0254-0053 Shanghai Lixue
0254-0096 Taiyang Neng Xuebao
0254-010X Turang Xue Jinzhan
0254-0126 International Journal of Tropical Plant Diseases
0254-0185 Studies in Education and Teaching Techniques
0254-0193 Series in English Language and Literature
0254-0207 Language Forum Monograph Series
0254-0215 Series in Sikh History and Culture
0254-0525 Revista de Ciencias Quimicas

ISSN

0254-0533 Textile Industries Dyegest Southern Africa
0254-0576 I S S A. Social Security Documentation. Caribbean Series
0254-0584 Materials Chemistry and Physics
0254-0649 Statistical Office of the European Communities. Industrial Production
0254-0657 Melanesian Law Journal
0254-0665 Research in Melanesia
0254-0770 Universidad de Zulia. Facultadad de Ingenieria. Revista Tecnica
0254-0819 Acute Care†
0254-0886 N I M H A N S Journal
0254-105X Progress in Reproductive Biology and Medicine
0254-1106 Revista Critica de Ciencias Sociais
0254-1114 Asian Sources Electronics
0254-1122 Asian Sources Electronics Components
0254-1130 Asian Sources Fashion Accessories
0254-1149 Asian Sources Hardwares
0254-1157 Asian Sources Gifts & Home Products
0254-1173 Asian Sources Timepieces
0254-1270 Karger Continuing Education Series†
0254-1300 Review of Tropical Plant Pathology
0254-1378 Islensk Bokaskra
0254-1408 Zhonghua Liliao Zazhi
0254-1424 Zhonghua Wuli Yixue Zazhi
0254-1432 Zhonghua Xiaohua Zazhi
0254-1521 Samisdat
0254-1572 Artesania y Folklore de Venezuela
0254-1793 Yaowu Fenxi Zazhi
0254-1807 Scriptura
0254-1858 South African Journal of Zoology
0254-217X Asian Computer Monthly†
0254-2307 Romanian Journal of Gerontology and Geriatrics
0254-2412 Development Information Abstracts
0254-2471 Central America Report
0254-2528 Interamerican Society for Tropical Horticulture. Proceedings
0254-2536 International Institute on the Prevention and Treatment of Addictions. Selected Papers
0254-2757 Questiones Informaticae *see* 1015-7999
0254-2935 Cell and Chromosome Research Journal
0254-296X Vaccination Certificate Requirements for International Travel and Health Advice to Travellers *changed to* International Travel and Health: Vaccination Requirements and Health Advice.
0254-3028 Ariel
0254-3036 I F D A Dossier
0254-3052 Gaoneng Wuli yu He Wuli
0254-3079 Yingyong Shuxue Xuebao
0254-3486 Suid Afrikaanse Tydskrif vir Natuurwetenskap en Tegnologie
0254-3494 Paper Southern Africa
0254-3729 Asian Business
0254-3915 I A W A Bulletin
0254-3923 Animals International
0254-4059 Chinese Journal of Oceanology and Limnology
0254-4067 Islensk Hljodritaskra
0254-4091 Indian Botanical Reporter
0254-4105 Indian Journal of Veterinary Surgery
0254-4156 Zidonghua Xuebao
0254-4164 Jisuanji Xuebao
0254-4296 Annales Aequatoria
0254-4318 Elektronikschau
0254-4326 O E G A I Journal
0254-4334 Christliche Demokratie
0254-4377 Glaube in der 2. Welt
0254-4474 Language Research
0254-4539 Bano Biggyan Patrika *changed to* Bangladesh Journal of Forest Science.
0254-4733 Hagskyrslur Islands
0254-4784 Library Association of China. Newsletter
0254-4903 Chinese Science Abstracts. Part B
0254-4962 Psychopathology
0254-5012 Computermarkt
0254-5020 Medicine and Sport Science
0254-5047 P R O S I
0254-508X Zhongguo Zaozhi
0254-5179 Chinese Science Abstracts. Part A
0254-5195 Progress in Applied Microcirculation
0254-5233 Prison Information Bulletin
0254-5241 J B I Journal
0254-5268 Business India
0254-5276 Buletini i Shkencave Gjeologjike
0254-5284 F A O Irrigation and Drainage Papers
0254-5292 Reiseland Oesterreich *changed to* Euro-City.
0254-5306 Output Oesterreich
0254-5330 Annals of Operations Research
0254-5357 Yankuang Ceshi
0254-5373 Karger Biobehavioral Medicine Series†
0254-5586 Asian Sources Computer Products
0254-5861 Jiegou Huaxue
0254-6051 Jinshu Rechuli
0254-6094 Huagong Jixie
0254-6108 Huanjing Huaxue
0254-6124 Kongjian Kexue Xuebao
0254-6183 Asian Literary Market Review
0254-6205 Knanayamithram
0254-6221 Daseinsanalyse
0254-623X Progress in Critical Care Medicine†
0254-6299 South African Journal of Botany
0254-6426 Evergreen
0254-6493 Aquaculture
0254-7104 Institutului Politehnic Din Iasi. Buletinul. Sectia II: Chimie. Si Inginerie Chimica
0254-7147 Consulting Medical Laboratories. Bulletin
0254-7600 Natural Immunity and Cell Growth Regulation
0254-7694 Short Book Reviews
0254-7791 Jisuan Shuxue
0254-7805 Guti Lixue Xuebao
0254-7848 V A C News *see* 0970-2334
0254-7856 Al-Mushir
0254-797X Garabato
0254-802X Barricada Internacional
0254-8178 Nemity
0254-8186 Revue Internationale d'Histoire Militaire
0254-8275 Beitraege zur Intensiv- und Notfallmedizin
0254-8305 Dryland Resources and Technology *changed to* Dryland Resources and Technology Annual (Year).
0254-8356 Neotestamentica
0254-8704 Journal of Environmental Biology
0254-8739 Concepts in Toxicology†
0254-8747 Advances in Audiology
0254-8755 International Journal of Tropical Agriculture
0254-8763 Kexue Dui Shehui de Yingxiang
0254-8798 Environmental Awareness
0254-8801 Agrindex
0254-881X Diagnostic Imaging in Clinical Medicine†
0254-8844 International Organization of Plant Biosystematists. Newsletter
0254-8852 Discussions in Neuroscience
0254-8860 Indian Journal of Gastroenterology
0254-8992 Steuerentscheid
0254-9026 Zhonghua Laonian Yixue Zazhi
0254-9034 Zhong-Xiyi Jiehe Zazhi
0254-9166 Touche Ross European Commentary *changed to* European Update.
0254-9204 Pakistan Journal of Applied Economics
0254-9212 Anthropologica (Lima)
0254-9239 Lexis
0254-9247 Revista de Psicologia
0254-9298 Lebensmittel- und Biotechnologie
0254-9379 Proche-Orient Etudes Economiques†
0254-9395 Indian Journal of Leprosy
0254-9409 Journal of Computational Mathematics
0254-9433 Geobotanisches Institut E T H, Stiftung Ruebel, Zurich. Veroeffentlichungen
0254-9441 Praxis des Bundesgerichts
0254-945X Zeitschrift fuer Schweizerisches Recht
0254-9492 Arab Medical Bulletin
0254-9522 Manual Medicine *see* 0935-6339
0254-9549 The New Voices
0254-9565 Nova Giulianiad
0254-9611 Majallah-i Fizik
0254-962X Caricom Perspective
0254-9662 Youth of the 21†
0254-9670 Experimental and Clinical Immunogenetics
0254-9727 F A O Plant Protection Bulletin (Miltilingual Edition)
0254-9743 Earthscan Bulletin†
0254-9794 Calcutta Historical Journal
0254-9808 Tibetan Bulletin
0254-9948 Monumenta Serica
0255-0008 I L C A Bulletin
0255-0024 I L C A Newsletter
0255-0040 I L C A Annual Report
0255-0067 Bermuda National Bibliography
0255-0172 Transvaal Museum. Monographs
0255-0326 I F H O H Journal
0255-0695 Zambia Educational Review
0255-0717 European Communities. Economic and Social Committee. Opinions and Reports *changed to* European Communities. Economic and Social Committee. Commission Documents.
0255-0776 Social Europe
0255-0806 Innovation and Technology Transfer
0255-0822 O E C D Economic Studies
0255-0849 International Bibliography of Historical Demography
0255-0903 Groupe International d'Etude de la Ceramique Egyptienne. Bulletin de Liaison
0255-0962 Institut Francais d'Archeologie Orientale du Caire. Bulletin
0255-2701 Chemical Engineering and Processing
0255-271X U N C H S Habitat News
0255-2760 International Whaling Commission. Special Issues
0255-2779 Literary Endeavour
0255-2809 Litterae Numismaticae Vindobonenses
0255-2914 Yunnan Zhongyi Zazhi
0255-3139 International Council on Archives. Committee on Conservation and Restoration. Committee on Archival Reprography (Bulletin)
0255-3147 Comite International des Poids et Mesures. Comite Consultatif pour les Etalons des Mesure des Rayonnements Ionisants (Rapport et Annexes)
0255-3627 O E C D. Quarterly Labour Force Statistics
0255-3678 Kriminalsoziologische Bibliographie†
0255-3686 Progress in Veterinary Microbiology and Immunology†
0255-3813 N A T O Review
0255-3910 Pain and Headache
0255-4062 Eye Care
0255-4070 Ahfad Journal
0255-4100 Cocos
0255-4119 Coconut Bulletin
0255-4216 C T C Reporter *changed to* Transnational Corporations.
0255-4291 Annual Review of the Chemical Industry
0255-4399 N S C Review
0255-4429 World Badminton
0255-4437 International Badminton Federation. Annual Statute Book
0255-4607 Trade and Development Report
0255-5018 Disaster Management
0255-5085 Yearbook of World Energy Statistics *see* 0256-6400
0255-5352 O C E A C Bulletin de Liaison et de Documentation
0255-5476 Materials Science Forum
0255-5484 Documentation Indian National Affairs†
0255-5514 World Labour Report
0255-5581 Taiwan Sugar Research Institute. Annual Report
0255-5697 Taiwan Economy
0255-6472 Lesotho Law Journal
0255-6510 Statistical Office of the European Communities. Eurostat. Money and Finance.
0255-6588 Republic of China. National Science Council. Proceedings. Part A: Physical Science and Engineering
0255-6596 Republic of China. National Science Council. Proceedings. Part B: Life Sciences
0255-6715 Studien zur Kinderpsychoanalyse. Jahrbuch
0255-6766 Statistical Yearbook of China *see* 1052-9225
0255-6790 Revista Mjekesore
0255-6863 Tamkang Journal of Management Sciences *see* 1017-1819
0255-6871 Transport Rundschau
0255-6898 Schweizer Baumarkt
0255-6944 Precision
0255-6979 O E C D Financial Statistics. Part 2: Financial Accounts
0255-7010 Seoul National University. Agricultural Research *changed to* Seoul National University Journal of Agricultural Sciences.
0255-7134 N A T O Scientific Publications. Newsletter
0255-7193 Clay Research
0255-7223 Yiyao Gongye *see* 1001-8255
0255-724X United Nations. Multilateral Treaties Deposited with the Secretary-General
0255-7312 Business Traveller Asia-Pacific
0255-7320 Asia Travel Trade
0255-7460 Central Bank of Barbados. Economic Review
0255-755X C E D E J Departement des Sciences Sociales. Bulletin *see* 0752-4412
0255-7592 I S S A. Committee on Provident Funds. Reports
0255-7614 International Journal of Music Education
0255-769X Managment Forum†
0255-7800 Daziran
0255-7924 Boletin de Biotecnologia
0255-7975 Pediatric Neuroscience *see* 1016-2291
0255-7983 Concepts in Immunopathology
0255-8033 Dirasat. Series A: Humanities
0255-8106 Journal of International Arbitration
0255-8165 National Buildings Construction Corporation. Bulletin
0255-8173 I C R A F Newsletter *see* 1013-9591
0255-8203 Nyam News
0255-8246 Swiss Review of International Competition Law *see* 1011-4548
0255-8254 Stamps World
0255-8297 Yingyong Kexue Xuebao
0255-8319 Cagrindex: Abstracts of the Agricultural Literature of the Caribbean
0255-8386 Labour Statistics Report *changed to* Labour Statistics.
0255-8432 Central Bank of Barbados. Balance of Payments
0255-8440 Central Bank of Barbados. Annual Statistical Digest
0255-8572 Arab Construction World
0255-8580 Arab Water World
0255-8831 Imago Musicae
0255-8858 Theologia Evangelica
0255-9005 Archaeologie der Schweiz
0255-9293 Annual Review of Engineering Industries and Automation
0255-9358 Guide to U N C T A D Publications
0255-9587 Zoological Survey of India. Bulletin
0255-9625 International Journal of Immunotherapy
0255-9870 Free China Journal
0255-996X Olivae
0256-002X Scenaria
0256-0038 Chromium Review
0256-0054 Ecquid Novi
0256-0070 Jagger Journal†
0256-0100 South African Journal of Education
0256-0119 G A T T Focus
0256-0240 Frontline
0256-0356 Odyssey
0256-0437 Toktokkie (English Edition)
0256-0550 S A Motorscene *changed to* Chequered Flag.
0256-0569 South African Runner
0256-064X Weekend Workshop†
0256-0666 Hit

0256-0771 Amnesty International Australian Newsletter
0256-0909 Vikalpa
0256-0917 Parkett
0256-0925 Community Education International
0256-1042 International Bibliography: Publications of Intergovernmental Organizations
0256-1069 Cyprus Time Out
0256-1425 Fiziologiya i Biokhimiya Kul'turnykh Rastenii
0256-1514 Endocytobiosis and Cell Research
0256-1530 Advances in Atmospheric Sciences
0256-1565 University of Lausanne. Departement des Langues et des Sciences du Langage. Cahiers
0256-159X Book People
0256-1603 Economic Review
0256-1654 Bulletin of Electrochemistry
0256-1697 Geological Survey of South West Africa - Namibia. Communications *changed to* Geological Survey of Namibia. Communications.
0256-1824 Falkland Islands Journal
0256-1883 Zhenjun Xuebao
0256-1891 Minzu Yanjiu
0256-193X Central Bank of Iceland. Economic Statistics
0256-2308 Year in Immunology
0256-2332 O E C D. International Energy Agency. Energy Prices and Taxes
0256-2456 U N E P News *see* 1013-7394
0256-2480 Hamlet Studies
0256-2499 Sadhana
0256-257X Journal of Taiwan Museum
0256-2804 Africa Insight
0256-2901 Papua New Guinea Institute of Medical Research. Monograph Series
0256-2928 European Journal of Psychology of Education
0256-3061 Estudios de Ciencias y Letras
0256-307X Chinese Physics Letters
0256-3096 S C A D Bulletin
0256-310X Mycologia Helvetica
0256-3525 Economic and Financial Prospects
0256-3533 Monat
0256-355X Haiti. Bureau National d'Ethnologie. Bulletin
0256-3568 Greece. National Statistical Service. Public Finance Statistics
0256-3576 Greece. National Statistical Service. Labour Force Survey
0256-3584 Greece. National Statistical Service. Results of Sea Fishery Survey by Motor Vessels
0256-3592 Greece. National Statistical Service. Statistical Bulletin of Public Finance
0256-3606 Greece. National Statistical Service. Cultural Statistics
0256-3614 Greece. National Statistical Service. Bulletin de Statistique du Commerce Exterieur†
0256-3630 Enquete Annuelle sur l'Activite des Organismes de Securite Sociale
0256-3657 Greece. National Statistical Service. Transport and Communication Statistics
0256-3665 Greece. National Statistical Service. Statistics on Civil, Criminal and Reformatory Justice
0256-4017 Indian Architects Directory
0256-4025 Directory of Interior Designers
0256-4033 Werbeforschung und Praxis
0256-4106 Informat
0256-4203 Travel Directory
0256-4246 Universitaet fuer Bodenkultur in Wien. Dissertationen
0256-4319 Protector
0256-436X Journal of Plant Anatomy and Morphology
0256-4491 Indian Council of Social Research. Annual Report
0256-4513 I A W P R C Newsletter *see* 0892-211X
0256-4548 Arab Gulf Journal of Scientific Research *see* 1015-4442
0256-4602 I E T E Technical Review
0256-4637 Journal of Pure and Applied Ultrasonics
0256-4653 Walter Roth Museum of Anthropology. Journal
0256-4718 Journal of Literary Studies
0256-4726 Go
0256-4912 I P D Cahier
0256-4947 Annals of Saudi Medicine
0256-4971 Maktabat al-Idarah†
0256-5056 Information Market *see* 1017-6950
0256-520X Pedagogiekjoernaal
0256-5374 Revista Cubana de Ciencias Matematicas
0256-5935 H C J Communications Report
0256-5994 Fasette
0256-6044 Semitics†
0256-6141 Energy in Europe
0256-6400 Energy Statistics Yearbook
0256-6524 Journal of Agricultural Engineering
0256-6575 Lebensmittel-Technologie
0256-663X Cognitive Systems
0256-6672 International Quarterly of Entomology
0256-6702 Grassland Society of Southern Africa. Journal
0256-6710 S A I L I S Newsletter
0256-6877 World Economic Outlook
0256-6966 Economic Outlook *see* 1017-141X
0256-6974 Lighting Review†
0256-6982 Publico
0256-6990 Studies in Marxism†
0256-7008 Vector
0256-7032 Middle East Food
0256-7040 Child's Nervous System
0256-7121 Commission of the European Communities. Monthly Catalogue. Part A: Publications†
0256-7172 Wood Southern Africa
0256-730X Safety Evaluation and Regulation of Chemicals†
0256-7415 Xinzhongyi
0256-7423 University of Durban-Westville. Bulletin for Academic Staff
0256-7431 South African Yachting, Sail, Power and Waterski *changed to* South African Yachting.
0256-7512 Bulletin of Agricultural Research in Botswana
0256-7660 Acta Chimica Sinica (English Edition) *see* 1001-604X
0256-7679 Chinese Journal of Polymer Science
0256-7709 National Bibliography of Barbados
0256-7822 International Defense Directory
0256-7865 Universite d'Ankara. Faculte des Sciences. Communications. Serie C. Biologie
0256-7873 Commission of the European Communities. Terminology and Computer Applications. Translation and Terminology Bulletin *changed to* Terminologie et Traduction.
0256-7911 Journal of Solar Energy Research
0256-7970 Greece. National Statistical Service. Building Activity Statistics
0256-8004 Greece. National Statistical Service. Employment Survey Conducted in Urban and Semi-Urban Areas *see* 0256-3576
0256-8314 Cyprus. Ministry of Labour and Social Insurance. Labour Review†
0256-8446 Skirnir
0256-8462 Hid Islenzka Fornleifafelag. Arbok
0256-8543 Journal of Research in Childhood Education
0256-8551 Journal of Microbial Biotechnology
0256-856X Melanesian Journal of Theology
0256-8837 Musicus
0256-8853 Progressio
0256-8861 South African Journal of Library and Information Science
0256-8888 I S D S Register (Tape Edition)
0256-8896 U N I S A Psychologia
0256-9043 Sinorama
0256-9159 Morocco. Direction de la Statistique. Bulletin Mensuel des Statistiques
0256-9701 Soilless Culture
0256-971X Uttar Pradesh Journal of Zoology
0256-9728 Insight *changed to* Zimbabwe Insight.
0256-9795 Estudios e Informes de la C E P A L
0257-0017 Dialogue
0257-0114 Paginas de Contenido: Ciencias de la Informacion
0257-0130 Queueing Systems
0257-0149 Baogao Wenxue
0257-0165 Dangdai
0257-0173 Dianying Chuangzuo
0257-0181 Dianying Yishu
0257-019X Dili Zhishi
0257-0203 Fangyan
0257-0211 Fujian Xiju
0257-022X Guangzhou Wenyi
0257-0238 Gushihui
0257-0246 Shehui Kexue Zhanxian
0257-0254 Wenyi Lilun Yanjiu
0257-0262 Beijing Wenxue
0257-0270 Du Shu
0257-0289 Fudan Xuebao (Shehui Kexue Ban)
0257-0297 Fujian Wenxue
0257-0521 E A R S L Newsletter
0257-053X E A R S L Directory
0257-067X United Nations. Security Council. Official Records. Supplement
0257-1420 International Angler
0257-1625 Artesanias de America
0257-1749 Tecnologica
0257-1862 South African Journal of Plant and Soil
0257-1870 Yearbook of International Commodity Statistics *see* 1012-0793
0257-1897 Disarmament Newsletter
0257-1978 Institution of Municipal Engineers of Southern Africa. Journal
0257-1994 Meson†
0257-2001 Rossing Magazine
0257-201X South African Poultry Bulletin
0257-2028 Pharmaceutical & Cosmetic Review
0257-2036 Ensovoort
0257-2044 Golden Fleece
0257-2095 South African Citrus and Sub-Tropical Fruit Journal
0257-2109 N A C News
0257-2117 South African Journal of African Languages
0257-2141 Defence Journal
0257-2168 Notas Sobre la Economia y el Desarrollo
0257-2184 Economic Survey of Latin America and the Caribbean
0257-2222 I S D S Register (Microfiche Edition)
0257-2354 Hellenic Veterinary Medical Society. Bulletin
0257-2605 Ethiopian Journal of Agricultural Sciences
0257-2753 Digestive Diseases
0257-2761 Pathology and Immunopathology Research *see* 1015-2008
0257-277X Immunologic Research
0257-2788 Fetal Therapy *see* 1015-3837
0257-2826 Jiaoxue yu Yanjiu
0257-2850 Minzu Wenxue
0257-2885 Nanfeng
0257-2915 Jinyang Wenyi
0257-3032 World Bank Research Observer
0257-3199 Allgemeinmedizin
0257-3202 Arab Health
0257-3229 I A S L Conference Proceedings
0257-3245 Research and Development Reporter
0257-3423 Institution of Engineers (India). Aerospace Engineering Division. Journal
0257-3431 Institution of Engineers (India). Agricultural Engineering Division. Journal
0257-344X Institution of Engineers (India). Architectural Engineering
0257-3512 Conditions of Work Digest
0257-3555 Libros Paraguayos
0257-3563 Island Sun
0257-3636 Hong Kong Countdown: Perspectives on Change
0257-3717 International Narcotics Control Board. Report for (Year)
0257-3822 Medien und Recht International
0257-3830 Neue Helvetische Gesellschaft. Mitteilungen
0257-3849 Interface
0257-3881 Nauchnaya Apparatura
0257-4284 Tidal Gravity Corrections
0257-4292 Tipografia
0257-4306 Universidad de la Habana. Direccion de Informacion Cientifica y Tecnica. Investigacion Operacional
0257-4322 Revista Cubana de Psicologia
0257-4411 Institution of Engineers (India). Metallurgy & Material Science Division. Journal
0257-442X Institution of Engineers (India). Mining Engineering Division. Journal
0257-4438 Institution of Engineers (India). Textile Engineering Division. Journal
0257-4829 Zhiwu Shengli Xuebao
0257-4985 Pakistan Journal of Otolaryngology
0257-4993 Journal of Potassium Research
0257-5035 Agro-Chemicals News in Brief
0257-540X Transkei Official Gazette *see* 0257-5418
0257-5418 Transkei Government Gazette Index
0257-5426 Wiel
0257-5604 Xiaoshuo Xuankan
0257-5647 Xin Wenxue Shiliao
0257-5655 Kaohsiung Journal of Medical Sciences
0257-5663 China, Republic. Executive Yuan. Directorate-General of Budget, Accounting & Statistics. Quarterly National Economic Trends, Taiwan Area
0257-5671 China, Republic. Executive Yuan. Directorate-General of Budget, Accounting & Statistics. National Income in Taiwan Area, R.O.C.
0257-5698 Commodity Price Monthly
0257-5728 Commodity Price Statistics Monthly
0257-5736 China, Republic. Executive Yuan. Directorate-General of Budget, Accounting & Statistics. Social Indicators (Year)
0257-5752 China, Republic. Executive Yuan. Directorate-General of Budget, Accounting & Statistics. Report on the Survey of Personal Income Distribution in Taiwan Area
0257-5779 Minzu Yuwen
0257-5795 Qinghai Hu
0257-5809 Sanwen
0257-5817 Shandong Wenxue
0257-5833 Shehui Kexue (Shanghai)
0257-5841 Shi Yue
0257-585X Shuofang
0257-5876 Wenyi Yanjiu
0257-5892 Nanjing Daxue Xuebao (Zhexue Shehui Kexue Ban)
0257-5906 Shanxi Wenxue
0257-5914 Wenxue Yichan
0257-5930 Xinwen Zhanxian
0257-6074 Culture Populaire Albanaise
0257-6082 Kultura Popullore
0257-6406 I J A. Research Reports
0257-6430 Studies in History (Newbury Park)
0257-6457 Cuadernos de Poetica
0257-6562 Ertong Wenxue
0257-6708 Institution of Engineers (India). Production Engineering Division. Journal
0257-7046 Paiperlekt†
0257-7070 Paraguay
0257-716X Tongji Medical University. Journal
0257-7208 Industrial Statistics Yearbook
0257-7240 Greek Economy in Figures (Year)
0257-7305 Manushi
0257-7348 South Asian Anthropologist
0257-7364 South East Asian Review
0257-7402 16 de Abril
0257-7712 Huaxi Yike Daxue Xuebao
0257-7739 Message of the Library
0257-7747 Tydskrif vir die Suid-Afrikaanse Reg
0257-7860 Special United Nations Services†
0257-7941 Ancient Science of Life
0257-8034 Fertiliser Marketing News
0257-8069 A S C I Journal of Management
0257-8131 Shanghai Yike Daxue Xuebao

ISSN

0257-8166	Target Electronics Industry *changed to* Taiwan Electronics Industry.
0257-8174	Target Electronics Industry Components†
0257-8573	Aeronautica Meridiana
0257-859X	Rubber Reporter
0257-8611	Boletin de Geociencias
0257-8646	Engineering News
0257-8697	Upbeat
0257-8700	Water Sewage and Effluent
0257-8867	South African Food Review
0257-8891	Skrif en Kerk
0257-893X	Asian Advertising and Marketing
0257-8972	Surface and Coatings Technology
0257-9073	United Nations. Department of International Economic and Social Affairs. Statistical Office. Construction Statistic Yearbook
0257-912X	Vaccination Certificate Requirements and Health Advice for International Travel *changed to* International Travel and Health: Vaccination Requirements and Health Advice.
0257-9146	South Pacific Bibliography
0257-9413	Xiaoshuo Yuebao
0257-943X	Xiju Yishu
0257-9448	Yuyan Jiaoxue yu Yanjiu
0257-9456	Mainland China Monthly
0257-9472	Dachauer Hefte
0257-9774	Anthropos
0258-0004	Xiandai Zuojia *changed to* Sichuan Wenxue.
0258-0136	South African Journal of Philosophy
0258-0144	South African Journal of Sociology
0258-0276	Words of Wisdom
0258-0284	Telecoms Technical Quarterly
0258-0322	Makromolekulare Chemie. Macromolecular Symposia
0258-0330	Current Studies in Hematology and Blood Transfusion
0258-0357	Acta Anthropogenetica
0258-0365	Aligarh Journal of English Studies
0258-0381	New Quest
0258-042X	Management and Labour Studies
0258-0446	Man & Environment
0258-0500	Indian Roads Congress. Journal
0258-0764	Arbido-B
0258-0772	Arbido-R
0258-0861	Consumer Price Indices *changed to* Consumer Price Index.
0258-0918	He Kexue yu Gongcheng
0258-1469	Neng Yuan
0258-1647	Nursing R S A Verpleging
0258-1698	Studies in History (Sahibabad)
0258-1701	Review Journal of Philosophy and Social Science
0258-1825	Kongqi Donglixue Xuebao
0258-1914	E S C W A Population Bulletin
0258-1922	Industrial Trends
0258-2015	Die Funktionskrankheiten des Bewegungsapparates
0258-2171	Turk Mikrobiyologi Cemiyeti Dergisi
0258-218X	Asian Printing Directory
0258-2228	Building
0258-2279	Literator
0258-2422	Journal for Contemporary History
0258-2473	South African Historical Journal
0258-249X	Industrial Law Journal
0258-252X	Journal for Juridical Science
0258-3038	Mechanical & Electronic Industries Yearbook of China†
0258-3046	China's Customs Statistics
0258-3054	China Market
0258-3062	China Coal Industry Yearbook
0258-3135	Historia de las Geociencias en Venezuela. Boletin
0258-3240	Zhongguo Haiyun
0258-3259	China Transport
0258-3267	Medical China†
0258-3313	Conserva
0258-3321	South African Journal of Dairy Science
0258-3569	Statistical Office of the European Communities. Energy *changed to* Statistical Office of the European Communities. Energy Statistics Monthly Bulletin.
0258-3690	I C S I D Review: Foreign Investment Law Journal
0258-4069	Cansang Tongbao
0258-4212	Space Markets†
0258-4425	American Journal of Noninvasive Cardiology
0258-4476	Tea Research Foundation of Central Africa. Annual Report *changed to* Tea Research Foundation. Annual Report.
0258-4913	Africa Media Review
0258-5081	S A Irrigation
0258-509X	South African Journal of Musicology
0258-5812	Pesca y Marina
0258-5936	Cultivos Tropicales
0258-6002	Revista de Ciencias Biologicas
0258-6096	Food and Agriculture Organization of the United Nations. European Inland Fisheries Advisory Commission. Occasional Papers
0258-6169	Women of Europe *see* 1012-1935
0258-6428	Chinese Journal of Physiological Sciences
0258-6436	Bibliotecologia y Documentacion Paraguaya
0258-655X	Ploutarkhos
0258-6568	S A Publiekreg
0258-6746	Abstracts of Chinese Geological Literature
0258-6754	Nedcor Group. Guide to the Economy *changed to* Nedbank. Guide to the Economy.
0258-6770	World Bank Economic Review
0258-6819	Wiener Slawistischer Almanach
0258-7025	Zhongguo Jiguang
0258-7033	Zhongguo Xumu Zazhi
0258-7130	Bangladesh Journal of Nuclear Agriculture
0258-7149	Book Parade
0258-7173	Growth
0258-7181	Industrial Relations Journal of South Africa
0258-719X	Momentum
0258-7203	South African Journal on Human Rights
0258-7211	Staffrider
0258-7246	Race Relations Survey
0258-7254	Accountancy S A
0258-7262	Gold Patent Digest *see* 0017-1557
0258-7270	International Affairs Bulletin
0258-7416	Upstream *changed to* New Contrast.
0258-7440	International Monetary Fund. World Economic and Financial Surveys
0258-798X	Dianzi Kexue Xuekan
0258-8218	Renmin Wenxue
0258-8226	Wenyi Bao
0258-8412	Ssu yu Yen
0258-8498	Dudu
0258-8501	Journal of West Indian Literature
0258-851X	In Vivo
0258-8536	Instituto de Estudios Aymaras. Boletin
0258-8757	Chinese Academy of Medical Sciences and Peking Union Medical College. Proceedings - Zhongguo Yixue Kexueyuan, Zhongguo Xiehe Yike Daxue Xuebao *see* 1001-9294
0258-8811	Beijing Zhongyi Xueyuan Xuebao
0258-8900	Bulletin of Volcanology
0258-8951	Skipper
0258-9001	Journal of Contemporary African Studies†
0258-9052	Tshiingamo
0258-9079	Xihondzo Xo Rindza
0258-9109	Institutului Politehnic Din Iasi. Buletinul. Sectia III: Electrotehnica, Energetica, Electronica, Automatizari
0258-9281	Truck & Bus, South Africa
0258-929X	Update
0258-9311	University of Stellenbosch. Bureau for Economic Research. Trade and Commerce
0258-9338	University of Stellenbosch. Bureau for Economic Research. Manufacturing Survey
0258-9346	Politikon
0258-9680	Journal of European Studies
0258-9737	Rubber Southern Africa
0258-977X	China Sources†
0258-9834	United Nations Research Institute for Social Development. Research Notes *see* 1014-8361
0259-000X	List of Serial Title Word Abbreviations
0259-0026	Vitae
0259-0034	Vitae Yearbook *changed to* Vitae Guide to S A Assurers.
0259-0069	Communicare
0259-0115	Brucka
0259-0182	Wolnuus
0259-0190	Kronos
0259-0336	Gleaner Index
0259-0360	Conscience et Liberte
0259-0492	Earnings - Industry and Services
0259-059X	Asian Security & Safety Journal
0259-0654	Beihefte zur Wiener Zeitschrift fuer die Kunde des Morgenlandes
0259-0662	Beitraege zur Sprachinselforschung
0259-0670	Conceptus-Studien
0259-0689	Johannes-Kepler-Universitaet Linz. Dissertationen
0259-0697	Technische Universitaet Wien. Dissertationen
0259-0700	Universitaet Salzburg. Dissertationen
0259-0719	Wirtschaftsuniversitaet Wien. Dissertationen†
0259-0727	Kanon
0259-0735	Kirche und Recht
0259-0743	Klagenfurter Beitraege zur Philosophie
0259-0751	Leobener Gruene Hefte. Neue Folge
0259-076X	Musik und Gesellschaft
0259-0778	Oesterreichische Volkskundliche Bibliographie
0259-0786	Quellen zur Theatergeschichte
0259-0794	Salzburger Beitraege zur Paracelsusforschung
0259-0816	Law & Anthropology
0259-0824	Polyaisthesis
0259-0972	Institute of Medicine. Journal
0259-1146	Directory of Chinese External Economic Organizations & Industrial/Commercial Enterprises
0259-1162	Anaesthesia Essays and Researches
0259-1235	Electronic News for China
0259-1278	Brain Dysfunction
0259-1340	Models in Dermatology
0259-1855	South African Exporters
0259-1871	University of Pretoria. Annual Report
0259-188X	Indicator South Africa
0259-191X	Orion
0259-1944	Studies in the History of Cape Town
0259-2010	Namibiana
0259-2029	Education & Culture
0259-207X	Education Journal
0259-2290	European Political Cooperation Documentation Bulletin
0259-238X	Asia - Pacific Population Journal
0259-2460	F A O Economic and Social Development Paper
0259-2495	F A O Fertilizer and Plant Nutrition Bulletin
0259-2509	F A O Fisheries Series
0259-3009	United Nations. National Accounts Statistics. Government Accounts and Tables
0259-3017	United Nations. National Accounts Statistics. Analysis of Main Aggregates
0259-3025	United Nations. National Accounts Statistics. Main Aggregates and Detailed Tables
0259-3092	Eidgenoessische Anstalt fuer das Forstliche Versuchswesen. Berichte
0259-3181	U N C T A D Bulletin
0259-3238	Commercial Agriculture in Zimbabwe
0259-3602	S A B S Catalogue (English Edition) *see* 1018-4295
0259-3610	S A B S Katalogus (Afrikaans Edition) *see* 1018-4295
0259-3629	Disarmament Times
0259-3637	Tsunami Newsletter
0259-3696	International Children's Rights Monitor
0259-3742	Soochow University Journal of Chinese Art History†
0259-3750	Soochow Law Review
0259-3769	Soochow Journal of Economics and Business
0259-3777	Soochow Journal of Foreign Languages and Literatures
0259-3785	Soochow Journal of Political Science & Sociology
0259-3793	Index to Chinese Legal Periodicals
0259-4285	United Nations University. Work in Progress
0259-4374	Envio
0259-4382	Central American Historical Institute. Update *see* 0259-4374
0259-4862	University of Stellenbosch. Bureau for Economic Research. Economic Prospects
0259-5419	Anderschume - Kontiki
0259-5591	Die Unie
0259-563X	Denteksa
0259-5796	Africa Press Clips
0259-5818	Vierte Internationale
0259-6415	Simpliciana
0259-6512	V W A
0259-7349	Photographia
0259-7373	Bulletin Critique des Annales Islamologiques
0259-7381	Cahiers de la Ceramique Egyptienne
0259-7454	Papier und Druck
0259-8213	World Market for Dairy Products
0259-8264	World Translation Index
0259-8272	Asian Journal of Public Administration
0259-8280	Camera International†
0259-8388	International Quarterly of Analytical Chemistry†
0259-8396	International Quarterly of Antibiotic Research
0259-840X	International Quarterly of Cancer Research
0259-8418	International Quarterly of Materials Science
0259-8426	International Quarterly of Virology
0259-8930	Arab Gulf Journal of Scientific Research. Section A: Mathematical and Physical Sciences *see* 1015-4442
0259-8949	Agricultural and Biological Sciences *see* 1015-4442
0259-9082	Majallah-i Zabanshinasi
0259-9147	International Disability Studies *see* 0963-8288
0259-9171	Economic Review (Year)
0259-9198	South African Panorama (French Edition)†
0259-9201	South African Panorama (Italian Edition)†
0259-921X	South African Panorama (Spanish Edition)†
0259-9228	South African Panorama (Portuguese Edition)†
0259-9236	South African Panorama (German Edition)†
0259-9422	Hervormde Teologiese Studies
0259-949X	Die Hervormer
0259-9570	Tydskrif vir Taalonderrig
0259-9791	Journal of Mathematical Chemistry
0259-9805	Muon Catalyzed Fusion
0259-9864	Proceso
0259-9880	Trade Winds Monthly
0259-9880	Trade Winds Monthly
0260-0005	Serials in the British Library
0260-0072	Butterworths International Medical Reviews: Clinical Endocrinology†
0260-0099	Butterworths International Medical Reviews: Clinical Pharmacology and Therapeutics†
0260-0102	Butterworths International Medical Reviews: Otolaryngology
0260-0110	Butterworths International Medical Reviews: Gastroenterology†
0260-0137	Butterworths International Medical Reviews: Neurology†
0260-0145	Butterworths International Medical Reviews: Ophthalmology
0260-0153	Butterworths International Medical Reviews: Orthopaedics†

0260-0161 Butterworths International Medical Reviews: Pediatrics†
0260-0218 Scottish Council of Social Service. News Bulletin†
0260-0226 Multiracial Education†
0260-0234 Printers Pie†
0260-0250 Clwyd Historian
0260-0293 Cityscope *changed to* Godwins Cityscope.
0260-0315 Bookmark
0260-0366 Museum Ethnographers Group. Newsletter
0260-0374 Lincolnshire Dragon
0260-0382 The Shepherd
0260-0439 English Horizon†
0260-0447 Current Transnational Corporations Bibliography†
0260-0463 Geologist's Directory
0260-0471 Great Britain. Department of Education and Science. Architects and Building Branch. Broadsheets
0260-0498 Eurovet Bulletin†
0260-0544 Castle Lodge News and Views†
0260-0552 Alternative Alternative
0260-0587 North West England Industrial Classified Directory *changed to* North West England Directory of Industry and Commerce.
0260-0595 Paperback Inferno
0260-0617 Scottish Episcopal Church Yearbook
0260-0625 I S T C Banner *changed to* I S T C Phoenix.
0260-0684 University of Liverpool. Research Report†
0260-0706 Graduate Careers in Sales and Marketing for Graduates and Postgraduates *changed to* Directory of Opportunities for Graduates. Vol.6: Buying, Marketing, Selling.
0260-0749 Financial Aid for First Degree Study at Commonwealth Universities
0260-0765 I B I D†
0260-0781 Qarch
0260-079X County Trades Finder. Section 2: Central
0260-0803 B A A F Practice Series
0260-0811 B A A F Research Series
0260-082X B A A F Discussion Series
0260-0854 Oxford Reviews of Reproductive Biology
0260-0935 Technical Papers for the Bible Translator
0260-0943 Practical Papers for the Bible Translator
0260-0951 British Shipper *changed to* British Shipper and Forwarder.
0260-096X Business Review of Burton upon Trent and District *changed to* Business Review for the Burton-on-Trent and Surrounding Areas.
0260-0986 Popular D I Y†
0260-0994 Educational Analysis *changed to* Contemporary Analyses in Education.
0260-1001 Estate Agent
0260-101X Retail Security & Fire Prevention†
0260-1036 Leeds Naturalists' Club and Scientific Association. Newsletter
0260-1044 Herefordshire Family History Society. Journal
0260-1060 Nutrition and Health
0260-1079 Journal of Interdisciplinary Economics
0260-1087 International Bulk Journal
0260-1117 A C T H and Related Peptides†
0260-1141 Purines†
0260-115X Energy Review†
0260-1176 Finance Director's Review†
0260-1222 Mental Handicap Bulletin
0260-1230 Journal of Molluscan Studies
0260-1249 Environmental Data Services. Report
0260-1265 Yearbook and Philatelic Societies' Directory
0260-1362 School Organisation
0260-1370 International Journal of Lifelong Education
0260-146X Barclays U.K. Financial Survey†
0260-1508 Exhibitor's Handbook†
0260-1532 British Telecom Journal *see* 0953-8429
0260-1559 Focus on Tourism†
0260-1656 Electrical Products
0260-1729 Trent Papers in Education
0260-1745 Kitchens
0260-1753 Hel Achau
0260-180X Bus News†
0260-1818 Royal Society of Chemistry. Annual Reports on the Progress of Chemistry. Section A: Inorganic Chemistry
0260-1826 Royal Society of Chemistry. Annual Reports on the Progress of Chemistry. Section C: Physical Chemistry
0260-1842 Phototrain Express
0260-1869 Manpower: Glass Industry
0260-194X Business News Index *changed to* M I R A Automotive Business Index.
0260-1974 Food World News
0260-2040 Agricultural Manpower
0260-2067 Irish Slavonic Studies
0260-2105 Review of International Studies
0260-2113 Ecuatorial
0260-2199 The Conference Green Book
0260-2202 Cubit†
0260-2245 Sorby Record
0260-2288 Sensor Review
0260-2334 Medicine International. Southern African Edition
0260-2342 Medicine in Practice†
0260-2350 Palestine Report†
0260-2377 Brazilian Agriculture & Commodities
0260-2385 Brokers' Monthly & Insurance Adviser
0260-2393 Fur Review†
0260-2407 Nationalism Today *see* 0959-5031
0260-2415 North of Scotland Visitor†
0260-2423 Radio Advertisers' Guide
0260-2431 The Conference Blue Book
0260-2474 Aspis
0260-2504 Grampian English Views†
0260-2547 Poole - Commercial Users Handbook *changed to* Poole Handbook.
0260-2563 Student Nationalist
0260-261X Barclays Commodities Survey†
0260-2695 N B A Technical Note†
0260-2725 Royal Society News
0260-2733 Leeds and Harrogate Graphic
0260-2776 Writer (Penzance)
0260-2784 Marine Biological Association of the United Kingdom. Occasional Papers *changed to* Marine Biological Association of the United Kingdom. Occasional Publications.
0260-2806 S.I.S. Workshop *see* 0951-5984
0260-2814 Society for Radiological Protection. Journal *see* 0952-4746
0260-2911 Practical Classics
0260-2938 Assessment and Evaluation in Higher Education
0260-2954 Avon Past
0260-2970 Locomotives Large & Small
0260-3004 Smash Hits
0260-3020 Atomic Energy News†
0260-3055 Annals of Glaciology
0260-3063 Muslim World Book Review
0260-3098 Fire Statistics United Kingdom
0260-311X Educational Drama Association. Newsletter
0260-3233 Vegetarian *changed to* Vegetarian Living.
0260-3268 New Tolkien Newsletter
0260-3322 Rutland Record
0260-3330 New Gandy Dancer
0260-3403 World Copper Survey *see* 0950-2262
0260-3438 International Directory of Software
0260-3594 Comments on Inorganic Chemistry
0260-3667 American Trust for the British Library. Newsletter
0260-3675 Transit Packaging†
0260-3683 Fuel Poverty News
0260-3691 W E F Communications Report†
0260-3705 Theological News
0260-373X Institute of Management Consultants. Yearbook
0260-3756 Local Authority Specifiers' Reference Book and Buyers Guide
0260-3810 Labour Party. Campaign Briefing
0260-3837 Cats
0260-3853 Conspectus For...Of Further Education in the Inner and Outer London Region†
0260-387X World Poultry Industry†
0260-3888 B A A F News
0260-390X Clarinet and Saxophone
0260-3926 Whillans's Tax Tables
0260-3934 Edinburgh Medicine
0260-3985 British-Israel Trade
0260-3993 Vive la Difference
0260-4000 Arclight *see* 0144-9745
0260-4019 Intercede (Manchester)
0260-4027 World Futures
0260-4043 Ultrasound Patents & Papers
0260-406X Chartered Institute of Public Finance and Accountancy. Housing Rents Statistics. Actuals
0260-4078 Chartered Institute of Public Finance and Accountancy. Housing Revenue Accounts Statistics. Actuals†
0260-4086 Chartered Institute of Public Finance and Accountancy. Housing Statistics. Estimates *changed to* Chartered Institute of Public Finance and Accountancy. Housing Revenue Account Statistics. Estimates.
0260-4094 Housing Corporation. Quarterly Review
0260-4116 Traditional Kent Buildings
0260-4140 Royal Society of Chemistry. Information Services. Newsletter *changed to* Royal Society of Chemistry. Database Newsletter.
0260-4256 Textile Digest†
0260-4272 Arabia: The Islamic World Review
0260-4280 Perspective of Physics (New York)
0260-4299 International Coal Report
0260-4353 Fluid Mechanics of Astrophysics and Geophysics
0260-437X Journal of Applied Toxicology
0260-4388 Manchester Training Handbooks
0260-440X Carnivorous Plant Society Journal
0260-4426 West of Scotland Visitor†
0260-4450 Adhesion
0260-4523 Architectural Psychology Newsletter
0260-4531 Spindrift†
0260-454X Afrosport
0260-4604 International Who's Who in Water Supply *changed to* I W S A Year Book.
0260-4620 Company Law Digest
0260-4639 Clinics in Immunology and Allergy *see* 0889-8561
0260-4698 Expired British Patents & Licences of Right
0260-471X Short Stories Magazine
0260-4736 Sandgrouse
0260-4752 Practical English Teaching
0260-4760 Toys International and Toy Buyer
0260-4779 International Journal of Museum Management and Curatorship *changed to* Museum Management and Curatorship.
0260-4817 N M I News *changed to* British Maritime Technology News.
0260-4833 I E S Proceedings
0260-4868 European Human Rights Reports
0260-4876 I. P. Reports from Socialist Countries†
0260-4884 Dozenal Journal
0260-4892 Threshing Floor
0260-4906 Top Fruit Times†
0260-4914 London and Middlesex Genealogical Directory†
0260-4922 Engineering Distributor
0260-4930 Graphics World. Services and Supplies Directory†
0260-4957 Heritage
0260-4965 Fighters Monthly *changed to* Fighters.
0260-5007 Directory of Land and Hydrographic Survey Services in the United Kingdom†
0260-504X Wind and Water Mills
0260-5058 F E R N Journal
0260-5090 Movie News†
0260-5112 Free Life
0260-5120 B J - Builder's Journal *changed to* Professional Builder.
0260-5139 Gloucestershire Local History Newsletter
0260-5163 Student Update *changed to* Trainee.
0260-5171 Business History Newsletter
0260-518X O T C Medication *changed to* Community Pharmacy.
0260-5236 Finders Keepers (Wellingborough) *changed to* Collectors Mart.
0260-5244 Community View†
0260-5252 Mental Health Statistics for Wales
0260-5295 Home Care Services, Day Care Establishments, Day Services - Scotland
0260-5317 European Rubber Journal
0260-5333 Period Piece and Paperback *see* 0954-0881
0260-535X British National Formulary
0260-5414 Extro
0260-5503 The Manchester Geographer
0260-5511 Abstracts on Hygiene and Communicable Diseases
0260-5546 Chartered Institute of Public Finance and Accountancy. Revenue Collection Statistics. Actuals
0260-5554 Problem-Solving News
0260-5562 Phase Two *changed to* Micros in Scottish Education.
0260-5570 Handbooks in Maritime Archaeology†
0260-5597 Scottish Society for the Conservation and Restoration of Historic and Artistic Works. Newsletter *see* 0264-9039
0260-5600 Cambridge Medieval Celtic Studies
0260-5619 Catalogue of British Official Publications Not Published by H.M.S.O.
0260-5627 Labrador Retriever Club of Wales. Yearbook
0260-5716 Light and Design International
0260-5724 Business Computing
0260-5732 Shetland Life
0260-5805 British Herpetological Society. Bulletin
0260-5813 Clapham Omnibus *changed to* Consumer Voice.
0260-5821 C T O
0260-583X Kington History Society. Papers
0260-5848 Royal College of Midwives. Current Awareness Service
0260-5864 Holdsworth Law Review
0260-5872 Clinical Cytogenetics
0260-5880 Haemic and Lymphatic Cell Culture†
0260-5902 Plant Biotechnology
0260-5910 Development of Social Skills†
0260-5929 University of London. Institute of Germanic Studies. Research in Germanic Studies
0260-597X Turner Studies
0260-5988 Timecraft†
0260-6003 Bicycle Trade Times
0260-6054 Kelly's Directory of British Industry & Services in Eastern England†
0260-6097 Bicycle Times
0260-6127 Workers Education Association. Women's Studies Newsletter
0260-6151 Kelly's Directory of British Industry & Services in Northern England†
0260-6186 Guide to Banks & Other Financial Institutions in Asia (Including Iran & the Arab Region)
0260-6194 Kelly's Directory of British Industry & Services in The Midlands†
0260-6208 Bulletin of Scottish Politics
0260-6216 B C I S Quarterly Review of Building Prices
0260-6267 International Journal of Pharmaceutical Technology & Product Manufacture
0260-6275 Journal of Separation Process Technology
0260-6313 Crosscurrent
0260-6321 Glass and Glazing News

0260-633X Kelly's Directory of British Industry & Services in Scotland and Northern Ireland†
0260-6348 Lyle Official Books Review†
0260-6356 Homeopathic Alternative†
0260-6364 L S A Quarterly *changed to* L S A Newsletter.
0260-6372 Chartered Institute of Public Finance and Accountancy. Trading Standards Statistics. Actuals
0260-6399 Steel Industry Monitor†
0260-6402 Outsider
0260-6429 C O A D Words†
0260-6445 P.S. (London)
0260-647X Adverse Drug Reactions and Acute Poisoning Reviews *changed to* Adverse Drug Reactions and Toxicological Reviews.
0260-6488 A - Z of U.K. Marketing Data
0260-6496 Institute of Chartered Accountants in England and Wales. Tax Digest
0260-650X Irish in Britain Directory
0260-6518 Textile Horizons
0260-6526 Large Stores Directory
0260-6534 Home Entertainment *changed to* Television: the New Era.
0260-6542 Euromonitor Reports on D I Y and Home Improvement Markets *see* 0263-5437
0260-6550 Bulletin of Northern Ireland Law
0260-6593 Current Technology Index
0260-6615 Labour & Ireland
0260-664X Austin Healey Year Book
0260-6666 Monitor (Abingdon)
0260-6674 Sheffield Studies in Japanese†
0260-6704 People's Power†
0260-6739 Philatelist and Philatelic Journal of Great Britain
0260-6747 Euromoney Syndication Guide *changed to* Euromoney Capital Markets Guide.
0260-6755 Parliaments, Estates & Representation
0260-6771 Rabbits *changed to* Fur & Feather.
0260-6801 Arts London Review
0260-681X Cephalopod Newsletter
0260-6844 Terminus
0260-6879 Information and Library Manager *see* 0957-6053
0260-6887 Workshop Equipment News *see* 0267-307X
0260-6917 Nurse Education Today
0260-6941 Scientific & Technical Books†
0260-695X Newth-Nuth Family History Society. Newsletter
0260-6976 South
0260-7050 Computer Price Guide for Large Computers†
0260-7069 Micrographics Year Book *changed to* Micrographics and Optical Storage Buyer's Guide.
0260-7123 Combat (Cleckheaton)
0260-714X Black Country Geologist
0260-7174 Wiltshire Family History Society. Journal
0260-7212 Marxist Humanism
0260-7247 Infomatics
0260-728X Sea Angling Monthly†
0260-7336 Socialist Youth *changed to* Labour Student.
0260-7387 List of Shipowners
0260-7409 International Packaging Abstracts
0260-7417 Journal of Educational Television
0260-7425 Tonic
0260-745X Cranes Today Handbook
0260-7468 European Racehorse
0260-7476 Journal of Education for Teaching
0260-7492 Wild Cat
0260-7522 I C S A Bulletin
0260-7530 What Video?
0260-7549 Twirling Times
0260-7557 Liverpool Family History Society *see* 0260-759X
0260-7565 Oxfordshire Local History
0260-759X Liverpool Family Historian
0260-7603 Chartered Institute of Public Finance and Accountancy. Waste Collection Statistics. Actuals
0260-762X Model Cars
0260-7638 Liverpool Software Gazette
0260-7654 Zip
0260-7727 Chartered Institute of Building. Year Book *changed to* Chartered Institute of Building. Handbook.
0260-7735 National Council on Inland Transportation. Newsletter
0260-7743 London Federation of Museum and Art Galleries. Newsletter
0260-7751 P.P.A. North West Region Newsletter†
0260-776X Conferences Meetings & Exhibitions Welcome†
0260-7786 Hong Kong Handbook
0260-7794 Darlington Astronomical Society. Newsletter
0260-7808 Early Childhood†
0260-7816 Past and Present *changed to* Irish Heritage Links.
0260-7840 Modern Power Systems
0260-7883 Agricultural Administration Network. Newsletter *see* 0951-1865
0260-7921 Fellowship in Prayer†
0260-7948 New Hope International *changed to* New Hope International Writing.
0260-7964 Irish Drama Selections
0260-7972 Scottish Pottery Studies
0260-8049 Shearsman *see* 0264-6773
0260-8065 Strathclyde's Budget *changed to* Strathclyde Regional Council. Annual Report & Financial Statement.
0260-8081 Fairfield Experimental Horticulture Station. Summary Annual Review
0260-809X Energy Matters†
0260-8103 Equit
0260-8111 Equestrian Year†
0260-8154 Irish Studies in Britain
0260-8189 Probe Report
0260-8235 Manchester Papers on Development *see* 0954-1748
0260-8251 Fantasy Macabre
0260-8278 Creative Mind
0260-8294 Nottingham Licensed Taxi Owners & Drivers Association. Newsletter
0260-8308 Everything Has a Value†
0260-8316 Conferences and Exhibitions International†
0260-8324 Illustrators Despatch†
0260-8359 Journal of Economic Affairs *see* 0265-0665
0260-8367 Clinical Research Reviews†
0260-8391 Caraher Family History Society. Journal
0260-8405 Lincolnshire Population†
0260-8448 Praxis International
0260-8456 Faba Bean Abstracts
0260-8464 Lentil Abstracts *see* 0961-3501
0260-8472 Microcomputer News International *see* 0263-6522
0260-8480 Irish Studies†
0260-8499 Reflections
0260-8502 Manchester Polytechnic. Department of Library and Information Studies. Occasional Papers
0260-8537 Studio Sound's Pro-Audio Yearbook *changed to* Studio Sound's Pro-Audio Directory.
0260-8553 Knitting Industry Technical Review†
0260-8634 Business News†
0260-8677 Epoxy Resins & Plastics†
0260-8685 Head and Hand
0260-8693 Handgunner: Britain's Foremost Firearms Journal
0260-8707 Historic House
0260-8723 Arts Report†
0260-8774 Journal of Food Engineering
0260-8790 Correlation
0260-8804 Clydesdale Bank Scottish Football League Review *changed to* B & Q Scottish Football League Review.
0260-8812 Forecast of Shop Rents†
0260-8820 Directory of Private Hospitals and Health Services *changed to* Directory of Independent Hospitals and Health Services.
0260-8839 London Port Handbook 1984
0260-8855 Knitstats
0260-8944 ComLon†
0260-8952 Bradford Center Occasional Papers
0260-8979 Euroednews
0260-9061 Weekender
0260-907X Rent Review *see* 0263-7499
0260-9088 Soil Survey and Land Evaluation†
0260-9096 British Journal of Administrative Management *see* 0951-5062
0260-910X Visit California with Fyfe Robertson†
0260-9126 Journal of Education in Museums
0260-9150 New Computer Careers
0260-9169 Barbour Compendium Building Products
0260-9177 Pelham Golf Year†
0260-9215 British Pirandello Society. Yearbook *changed to* Society for Pirandello Studies. Yearbook.
0260-924X Ireland Ports & Shipping Handbook
0260-9282 Falmouth Port and Industry Handbook 1984
0260-9290 City Handbook†
0260-9339 Poetry and Little Press Information
0260-9355 Edmonton Hundred Historical Society. Chronicle
0260-9363 Instant Record
0260-938X F O L K Magazine *changed to* Nama Hatta Newsletter.
0260-9398 Stereotype
0260-9428 A L P S P Bulletin *changed to* Learned Publishing: A L P S P Bulletin.
0260-9436 Polymicros†
0260-9452 Boating Business and Marine Trade News
0260-9460 Biblical Creation
0260-9517 Great Yarmouth Port and Industry Handbook
0260-9541 Archives of Natural History
0260-955X Annual Register of Pharmaceutical Chemists
0260-9584 Quaker Peace & Service. Annual Report
0260-9592 London Review of Books
0260-9762 Chartered Institute of Public Finance and Accountancy. Local Government Comparative Statistics. Estimates
0260-9770 Multicultural Education Abstracts
0260-9819 Communist Affairs†
0260-9827 Political Geography Quarterly
0260-9835 T.E. Lawrence Studies Newsletter
0260-986X Irish Hare
0260-9886 Chartered Institute of Public Finance and Accountancy. Highways and Transportation. Actuals†
0260-9894 Chartered Institute of Public Finance and Accountancy. Highways and Transportation Statistics. Estimates
0260-9924 Canterbury Diocesan News Service
0260-9959 Chartered Institute of Public Finance and Accountancy. Cemeteries Statistics. Actuals *see* 0263-2969
0260-9967 Chartered Institute of Public Finance and Accountancy. Local Authority Airports. Accounts and Statistics *changed to* Chartered Institute of Public Finance and Accountancy. Local Authority Airports. Accounts and Statistics. Actuals.
0260-9975 Chartered Institute of Public Finance and Accountancy. Airport Financial Statistics. Estimates†
0260-9983 U K I R T Report
0260-9991 Journal of Art and Design Education
0261-0094 Anbar Management Publications Joint Index†
0261-0108 Anbar Management Publications Bibliography *changed to* Management Bibliographies & Reviews.
0261-0124 Aireings
0261-0140 Progress in Obstetrics and Gynaecology†
0261-0159 Equal Opportunities International
0261-0183 C S P: Critical Social Policy
0261-0191 Catchword and Trade Name Index
0261-023X Bulletin of Inventions and Summary of Patent Specifications
0261-0272 Reviewing Sociology
0261-0302 Average Prices of British Academic Books
0261-0310 International Who's Who in the Arab World
0261-0329 Glazed Expressions
0261-0337 Training Action†
0261-0345 Diesel Engineers and Users Association. Transactions *changed to* Institution of Diesel and Gas Turbine Engineers. Transactions.
0261-0353 Bradford Occasional Papers
0261-0361 Citizens' Band
0261-0388 Afghan Voice
0261-0477 New Growth *see* 0264-4614
0261-0558 Curious Woman
0261-0604 Nucleus (Cambridge)†
0261-0655 Property Guide: Homes in Beds/Bucks/Berks & Oxon†
0261-0663 Estuaries and Coastal Waters of the British Isles
0261-068X I A M S Newsletter
0261-0752 Lincolnshire, Housing†
0261-0760 Resources†
0261-0795 Poetry into Print†
0261-0833 Independent Retailer and Caterer *see* 0267-9361
0261-0868 Magpie
0261-0876 Al-Majalla
0261-0892 Popular Astronomy
0261-099X Strathclyde Modern Language Studies
0261-1023 Okikiolu Scientific and Industrial Organization. Bulletin of Mathematics
0261-1066 Literary Drivel Society. Transactions
0261-1104 Cronicl Powys
0261-1139 Greentrees
0261-1171 Crimp Journal
0261-1252 Chartered Institute of Public Finance and Accountancy. Public Money *see* 0954-0962
0261-1260 Telegram (London) *see* 0264-6773
0261-1279 Early Music History
0261-1309 Screenprinting *changed to* Screen Process.
0261-1325 I S Annual†
0261-1341 Moz-Art†
0261-135X Shropshire Family History Journal
0261-1376 Explorations in Knowledge
0261-1392 Leisure, Recreation and Tourism Abstracts
0261-1430 Popular Music
0261-1465 Benn's Hardware Directory and D-I-Y Buyers Guide *see* 0954-8548
0261-1473 Middle East Industry and Transport *changed to* Middle East Transport.
0261-152X International Federation of Library Associations and Institutions. Section of Art Libraries. Newsletter
0261-1538 Liverpool Monographs in Hispanic Studies
0261-1589 Fire Research News
0261-1600 Beatles Book
0261-1635 Westgate Tax Planner's Letter
0261-1678 School Libraries Group News
0261-1686 Zerb
0261-1708 Network (London, 1965)†
0261-1724 R L C: Roskill's Letter from China†
0261-1732 Information Technology and People†
0261-1740 Retail Banker International
0261-1783 Great Britain. Central Statistical Office. Regional Trends
0261-1791 Great Britain. Central Statistical Office. Guide to Official Statistics
0261-1821 Appendix *see* 0264-6420
0261-1848 Merchant Shipbuilding Return
0261-1899 Stamp and Postal History News *see* 0953-5241
0261-1902 Pop Puzzles
0261-1910 International Video Yearbook *see* 0266-2256
0261-1929 Alternatives to Laboratory Animals: A T L A

0261-1953 S O A P
0261-1961 Unexplained
0261-197X T P A S Notes
0261-1988 Heritage Outlook
0261-2038 Fried Fish Caterer *changed to* Friers Catering Advertiser.
0261-2089 Scottish Anti-Vivisection Society. Newsletter *changed to* Animal Concern.
0261-2127 Electricity Consumers Council. Annual Report
0261-2135 Craftsman's Directory (Year) Part 1
0261-2143 Somerset Mines Research Group. Newsletter *changed to* Somerset Mines Research Group. Journal.
0261-216X Essays by Divers Hands
0261-2178 British Library Research Reviews
0261-2194 Crop Protection
0261-2208 Countryside Monthly *see* 0268-9502
0261-2267 International Automotive Review
0261-2275 Mid Glamorgan Industrial Directory (Year) *changed to* Mid Glamorgan Business Directory (Year).
0261-2305 Barclays U.K. Economic Survey†
0261-2313 African Air Transport
0261-2356 Fairplay World Ports Directory
0261-2364 T E S T Bureau. Technical Reports
0261-2399 World Airnews
0261-2429 Cancer Surveys
0261-2437 Current Fluid Engineering Titles†
0261-2445 Devon County Planning Department. Tourism and Recreation. Topic Report *see* 0269-0551
0261-2453 Devon County Planning Department. Conservation and Primary Industries. Annual Report *changed to* Devon. Property Department. Conservation and Primary Industries. Annual Report.
0261-250X Record Collector
0261-2534 Good 6500 *changed to* Good Food.
0261-2550 Collectors Items
0261-2593 Library Science Book Distribution Service. Quality Monitor *changed to* Library Science Book Distribution Service. Library and Information Science Update.
0261-2607 Protect and Survive Monthly and British Civil Defence News *see* 0264-4525
0261-2631 Northern Ireland Council for Educational Research. Research Unit. Staffing Needs of Post-Primary Schools†
0261-2666 Electrosonic World
0261-2674 English Hops†
0261-2712 Casualty Return Statistical Summary of Merchant Ships Totally Lost, Broken Up, Etc *see* 0268-0815
0261-2720 Annual Summary of Merchant Ships Completed in the World
0261-2747 European Information Service
0261-2755 School Organisation & Management Abstracts
0261-281X Medway Ports Shipping Handbook
0261-2828 Homoeopathy Today *changed to* Health and Homoeopathy.
0261-2836 Pennine Magazine
0261-2909 Nueva Historia
0261-2917 Laboratory Hazards Bulletin
0261-2925 Arab Banker
0261-2933 B M C I S Building Maintenance Price Book *changed to* B M I Building Maintenance Price Book.
0261-2992 Current Awareness Bulletin for Librarians and Information Scientists *see* 0954-9196
0261-300X Pelham Horse Year†
0261-3018 Scottish Society of Composers. Newsletter *changed to* Stretto.
0261-3042 Riverside Interviews
0261-3050 Bulletin of Latin American Research
0261-3069 Materials in Engineering *see* 0264-1275
0261-3107 Philatelic Magazine *see* 0953-5241
0261-3115 Investors Chronicle (London, 1860)
0261-3131 Ecologist (1979)
0261-314X C E C T A L Conference Papers Series
0261-3158 Milnholm Cross Newsletter
0261-3182 Software and Microsystems *see* 0268-6961
0261-3220 National Galleries of Scotland. News *see* 0953-024X
0261-3247 Oil Spot
0261-3263 Video Review†
0261-331X Computer Applications (Bradford)†
0261-3344 Risk Measurement Service
0261-3379 Scottish Democrat
0261-3409 Archaeologia
0261-3417 Archaeologia Aeliana
0261-3425 A N: Artists Newsletter
0261-3468 Wagner News
0261-3506 Japan Electronics Today News *changed to* Nikkei High Tech Report.
0261-3530 Journal of Area Studies†
0261-3646 Medical Forum†
0261-3654 I B M User
0261-3697 Computer & Video Games
0261-3735 America Latina Informe Economico *see* 0263-5372
0261-3743 America Latina Informe Politico *see* 0263-5372
0261-3751 America Latina Informe de Mercados *see* 0263-5372
0261-3786 Barclay's Industrial Survey†
0261-3794 Electoral Studies
0261-3808 Edinburgh Rape Crisis Centre. Report
0261-3816 Garden Trade News
0261-3824 Council of Civil Service Unions. Bulletin
0261-3867 Problem Solver†
0261-3875 Legal Studies
0261-3883 Petroleum Times Price Report
0261-3891 Investment Trust Year Book *see* 0953-8453
0261-3921 Scottish Medicine
0261-3948 International Dollmaking & Collecting
0261-3956 Wining & Dining
0261-3964 City News (Newcastle upon Tyne)
0261-4014 Links (Oxford)
0261-4022 Kampuchea Bulletin†
0261-4049 Welfare and Social Services Journal *changed to* Welfare Journal.
0261-4057 Scottish Theatre News
0261-4065 Trailer World†
0261-4073 Product Finder: Swift-Sasco Buyers Guide
0261-409X S T O R M
0261-4103 Information Age *see* 0960-3395
0261-4146 Beauty Salon *changed to* Health & Beauty Salon.
0261-4170 Lloyd's European Loading List†
0261-4189 E M B O Journal
0261-4200 Popular Video
0261-4227 Book Choice *changed to* Books.
0261-4251 Super Marketing
0261-426X European and North American Scrap Directory *changed to* International Scrap Directory.
0261-4286 Journal of World Forest Resource Management
0261-4294 Gifted Education International
0261-4316 Catholic Archives
0261-4324 Medical News Weekly†
0261-4332 Archaeological Review from Cambridge
0261-4340 Italianist
0261-4359 I Guide *changed to* Golden Keys Magazine.
0261-4367 Leisure Studies
0261-4375 Family Law Reports
0261-4391 World Book News†
0261-4413 International Agricultural Development
0261-4421 Laundry & Cleaning News International
0261-4448 Language Teaching
0261-4499 Microcomputer Printout
0261-4510 Anaesthesia (Sheffield)†
0261-4553 ATPases
0261-4561 Biliary Tract†
0261-4596 Blood Transfusion
0261-4626 Enzyme Isolation and Purification†
0261-4634 Epilepsy†
0261-4650 Fetal Physiology†
0261-4669 Gastric and Duodenal Ulcer†
0261-4707 High Performance Liquid Chromatography
0261-4723 Intestinal Malfunction†
0261-4731 Killer Cells and Cytotoxicity†
0261-474X Leukemia Research†
0261-4758 Liver Function†
0261-4766 Muscle Biochemistry†
0261-4774 Muscle Physiology†
0261-4790 Myocardium†
0261-4804 Neural Tube Defects†
0261-4820 Oral Biology†
0261-4847 Parathyroid Hormones†
0261-4898 Pregnancy†
0261-4901 Protein Separation†
0261-4928 Smooth Muscle
0261-4952 Invertebrate Neurobiology
0261-4960 Monoclonal Antibodies
0261-4979 Recombinant D N A
0261-4987 Catecholamines and Adrenergic Receptors *see* 0950-0502
0261-4995 Intestinal Function
0261-5002 Micronutrient News *see* 0957-4360
0261-5061 Retrospect
0261-507X Omnibus (London)
0261-5096 Northumbrian Pipers' Society Magazine
0261-510X British Journal of Developmental Psychology
0261-5118 Municipal Review and A M A News
0261-5142 Microdecision
0261-5150 Arab Gulf Journal†
0261-5169 Pims Media Directory *changed to* Pims U K Media Directory.
0261-5177 Tourism Management
0261-5207 Guide to In-Career Training Courses for Civil Engineers
0261-5223 Trackwise†
0261-524X Independent Grocer
0261-5282 London Theatre Record *see* 0962-1792
0261-5304 Building Society News *changed to* Mortgage Finance Monthly.
0261-5312 Coarse Fishing Monthly†
0261-5339 Fraud Report
0261-5355 Aquatechnic International
0261-5363 New Bookbinder
0261-5479 Social Work Education
0261-5487 I R P I: International Reinforced Plastics Industry
0261-5495 Scandinavian Contact
0261-5525 Lincolnshire Bird Report
0261-5584 Sell's Directory
0261-5606 Journal of International Money and Finance
0261-5614 Clinical Nutrition
0261-5622 European Journal of Sexually Transmitted Diseases†
0261-5630 Agape†
0261-5649 Ruskin College, Oxford. Library. Occasional Publication
0261-5657 Electro Optics Newsletter
0261-5665 Sports Industry
0261-5703 Schools of Prayer
0261-5711 Welsh Books & Writers†
0261-5746 Paint and Resin
0261-5754 W.E.A. Arts Newsletter†
0261-5770 World Hi-Fi Guide†
0261-5789 World Fertilizer News Summary†
0261-586X Fort
0261-5878 Fluids Handling *changed to* Fluids Handling Technology.
0261-5886 International Freighting Management†
0261-5894 Copperplate
0261-5924 Activity Holidays in Britain†
0261-5932 Angus District Council. Housing Plans and Programmes
0261-6025 Childrens Clothing International
0261-6033 Alternative Times
0261-6386 B S A European Bulletin†
0261-6394 B S A Bulletin *see* 0955-3800
0261-6416 Building Societies Association. Monthly Figures Press Release
0261-6505 Richmond Collage†
0261-6513 Airports International Directory *changed to* Airports International Magazine.
0261-653X Society (London)
0261-6548 Stand To!
0261-6688 Lloyd's Register of Classed Yachts
0261-6777 Ocean Voice
0261-6793 Arabian Government and Public Services
0261-6823 A A Files
0261-6866 Coin Slot Location†
0261-6912 New Socialist
0261-6920 C A D - C A M International
0261-6939 2D: Drama, Dance
0261-7005 Science and Engineering Research Council. Report
0261-7048 Artefact/Pin Up†
0261-7099 Mediscope
0261-7102 Small Computer Program Index†
0261-7129 Consumer Education Newsletter - Cylchlythyr Addysg Defnyddwyr *see* 0953-1475
0261-7188 Mechanical Engineering Technology *see* 0954-6529
0261-7226 Sarawak Journal
0261-7277 Soil Dynamics and Earthquake Engineering
0261-7358 Natural World
0261-7374 European Energy Profile†
0261-7404 Message to the Anglo-Saxon and Celtic Peoples *changed to* Wake-up! (Ayrshire).
0261-7412 Process Equipment News
0261-7420 Quilters Guild. Newsletter *changed to* The Quilter.
0261-7633 World Energy Business Centre Reference Book and Buyers' Guide†
0261-7641 Institution of Engineering Designers Official Reference Book and Buyers Guide
0261-7943 Fishing Handbook†
0261-7951 Gardening Handbook†
0261-796X Business Location Handbook
0261-8028 Journal of Materials Science Letters
0261-8044 Flesh and Blood
0261-8222 Fender Musician†
0261-8230 Executive Health Club
0261-8249 European Review†
0261-8273 B E C A N Instrumentation and Techniques in Cardiology†
0261-8281 B E C A N Electrodes for Medicine and Biology†
0261-8451 Office Automation Report†
0261-8567 Wholistic Health†
0261-863X European Policies and Legislative Proposals†
0261-8648 Institute of Grocery Distribution. Economic Bulletin *see* 0954-1683
0261-8664 Touche Ross & Company. Tax Newsletter
0261-8761 Building Products
0261-8818 Poynton Local History Society Newsletter
0261-8834 Rajneesh Buddafield European Newsletter†
0261-8850 Aspects of Edenbridge
0261-8877 Falkirk Central Community Council. News Letter
0261-8966 Education in the Royal County of Berkshire
0261-8982 D & B Creditnews
0261-9180 High Temperature Technology *see* 0960-3409
0261-9253 Industrial Chemistry Bulletin†
0261-927X Journal of Language and Social Psychology
0261-9288 Immigrants & Minorities
0261-9296 Orchard Lodge Studies of Deviancy†
0261-9768 European Journal of Teacher Education
0261-9776 Personnel Executive†
0261-9784 Quaternary Studies
0261-9857 Anglo-Norman Studies
0261-9873 Clinics in Oncology *see* 0889-8588
0261-9881 Clinics in Anaesthesiology *see* 0950-3501
0261-989X Life Support Systems *see* 0391-3988
0261-9903 Journal of Advertising *see* 0265-0487

5662 ISSN INDEX

0261-9911 Facts about Lewisham†
0261-9962 Brazil, Land of the Present†
0261-9970 Library Association. Local Studies Group. Newsletter *see* 0263-0273
0261-9997 Mental Handicap
0262-0022 Microfilm & Video Systems†
0262-0030 Food Law Monthly
0262-0057 N E I News†
0262-0073 Middle East Hospital†
0262-0200 Maternal & Child Health
0262-0219 Top 2,000 Directories and Annuals: A Guide to the Major Titles Used in British Libraries *see* 0268-9928
0262-0227 Plant & Works Engineering
0262-0251 Media in Education & Development
0262-0308 British Tourism Yearbook†
0262-0383 Northern Economic Review
0262-0413 Theatre International†
0262-0448 Helicopter World
0262-0456 East European Markets
0262-0669 Turf Management
0262-0782 T H S: Times Health Supplement†
0262-0812 Gramophone Spoken Word and Miscellaneous Catalogue *changed to* Gramophone Spoken Word Catalogue.
0262-0820 Fish Farming International
0262-0839 Resources Supplement†
0262-0855 International Development Abstracts
0262-0898 Clinical and Experimental Metastasis
0262-0995 International Directory of Laboratory Accreditation Systems and other Schemes of Testing Laboratories *changed to* International Directory of Testing Arrangements and Testing Laboratory Accreditation Systems.
0262-1010 G P Guide to Emergency & Medical Services
0262-1037 Creative Review
0262-1045 Schooling & Culture†
0262-1053 Scottish Tynedale Bulletin *see* 0265-4547
0262-1061 White Fathers - White Sisters
0262-107X Contact (Sutton Coldfields)
0262-1126 19
0262-1150 Solvent News *changed to* Cleaning Technology News.
0262-1169 Southern Arts Bulletin *changed to* The Arts Business.
0262-1193 Themes in Family Planning†
0262-1215 Rothamsted Experimental Station Report *see* 0955-9051
0262-1452 Lincolnshire Information. Employment
0262-1533 Metamorphic Association Newsletter *changed to* Metamorphosis.
0262-1533 Metamorphic Association Newsletter *changed to* Metamorphic Association Programme.
0262-1584 Developments in Rubber Technology
0262-1622 Goole Port Handbook
0262-1630 Associated British Ports Handbook
0262-1657 Airline Fleets *changed to* Air-Britain Airline Fleets.
0262-1703 Journal of International Marketing†
0262-1711 Journal of Management Development
0262-172X H V A Current Awareness Bulletin
0262-1762 World Pumps
0262-1789 G D R - Monitor Special Series
0262-1819 Footloose
0262-1940 Badminton Association of England. Annual Handbook
0262-2203 Conservation Education
0262-2238 Animal Pharm
0262-2270 Choice
0262-236X Behavioural Abstracts†
0262-2394 Agricultural Statistics, England
0262-2513 Better Business†
0262-2548 Topics (Cambridge)
0262-2556 R E News *see* 0955-5188
0262-2564 Chemical Engineering Bulletin†
0262-2572 Radio & Electronics World†
0262-2726 Traveller
0262-2734 What's New in Computing
0262-2742 What's New in Interiors
0262-2750 French Studies Bulletin
0262-2793 C O S P E N News
0262-2874 Good News (Birmingham)
0262-2955 Laboratory Microcomputer
0262-2963 Biotech Quarterly†
0262-298X Book World Advertiser *changed to* Book World.
0262-3080 London Housing†
0262-3099 A A E News
0262-3102 Small Business
0262-3110 British Association for Behavioural Psychotherapy. Newsletter *changed to* Behavioural Psychotherapist.
0262-3145 Hospital Doctor
0262-3153 Directory of Social Action Programmes *changed to* Action Stations: The Directory of Social Action Programmes.
0262-3161 Industrial Planning and Development *changed to* Regional Development International.
0262-3196 E C I: Electronic Components and Instruments†
0262-3226 Industrial Safety Data File
0262-3234 Anthony and Berryman's Magistrates' Court Guide
0262-3242 Fire World
0262-3269 Great Britain. Sea Fish Industry Authority. Household Fish Consumption in Great Britain
0262-3315 Flat Glass International *see* 0964-6779
0262-3358 Hospital Acquired Infection†
0262-3439 Travel and Leisure (Belfast)
0262-3447 L R D Book of Wage Rates, Hours and Holidays *see* 0143-2680
0262-3579 I - D
0262-3617 Everyday Electronics
0262-3765 Commercial Grower Weekly†
0262-3781 Briefing Paper on Southern Africa
0262-3803 Oxfam News
0262-3943 Guide to Steam Trains in the British Isles *changed to* British Coal Guide to Steam Trains in the British Isles.
0262-4001 Popular Caravan†
0262-401X British Telecommunications Engineering
0262-4087 British Psychological Society. Education Section. Review
0262-4109 Behavioural Approaches with Children†
0262-4206 Scoop Sport Annual
0262-4230 Manufacturing Chemist
0262-4249 Air Travel and Interline News *changed to* Air & Business Travel.
0262-4257 Investment Opportunities
0262-4303 Local Government Review
0262-4338 Squash Player International
0262-4354 Logistics Today
0262-4389 Scottish Archaeological Review
0262-4427 Peterborough & District Family History Society Journal
0262-4435 Leithead Family Newsletter
0262-4451 Fire News (London)
0262-4478 Keyways
0262-4508 International Road Haulage by British Registered Vehicles *see* 0262-6195
0262-4540 Practical Alternatives
0262-4583 Tolley's Tax Data (Year)
0262-4591 Searchlight
0262-4605 Scoop (London)†
0262-4648 Cash & Carry Wholesaler
0262-4672 Gwent Family History Society. Journal
0262-4710 Pace Motor Racing Directory†
0262-4737 Nigerian Criminal Reports†
0262-4745 Rothmans Rugby League Yearbook
0262-4753 Grass-Roots (Poole)†
0262-4842 Journal of One-Name Studies
0262-4850 Rothmans F.A. Non-League Football Yearbook†
0262-4885 S N H A T News Bulletin *see* 0950-5458
0262-4893 Cellular Polymers
0262-4923 Archive (Air-Britain)
0262-4966 Churchscape
0262-5008 Camera Counter
0262-5016 Best of London Eating†
0262-5024 British Journal of Geriatric Nursing *changed to* Nursing the Elderly.
0262-5032 British Journal of Psychiatric Nursing†
0262-5075 International Journal of Cement Composites and Lightweight Concrete *changed to* Cement and Concrete Composites.
0262-5091 Nuclear Engineer
0262-5113 Atholl & Breadalbane Community Comment
0262-5156 E C J R: European Court of Justice Reporter†
0262-5229 Great Britain. Department of Education and Science. Safety in Education
0262-5245 Music Analysis
0262-5253 Oxford Journal of Archaeology
0262-5288 Technology Week
0262-5296 Energy Action Bulletin *changed to* Energy Action.
0262-5326 Buttons
0262-5334 Commercial and Industrial Floorspace Statistics†
0262-5342 Bygone Kent
0262-5377 Psychiatry in Practice
0262-5407 Asia and Pacific *changed to* Asia & Pacific Review.
0262-5415 Latin America and Caribbean *changed to* Americas Review.
0262-5458 Sinclair User
0262-5474 Epilepsy Now! *changed to* Epilepsy Today.
0262-5504 Dermatology in Practice†
0262-5512 Rheumatology in Practice *changed to* Gastroenterology in Practice.
0262-5547 Cardiology in Practice
0262-558X New Arcadian Journal
0262-5636 Cognitive Development Abstracts†
0262-5644 Studies on Women Abstracts
0262-5695 Finance Confidential
0262-5717 Primary and Middle School Equipment *changed to* Primary & Middle School Equipment.
0262-575X L T P†
0262-5768 Adventure Sports & Travel†
0262-5849 Pet Product Marketing
0262-5873 Civil Engineering and Public Works Review *see* 0956-9189
0262-5881 Chemist & Druggist Directory
0262-5938 Coffee & Cocoa International
0262-5946 Gifts International
0262-5954 O S E A P Journal
0262-5997 Lifeskills Teaching Magazine†
0262-6004 Suffolk Institute of Archaeology and History. Proceedings
0262-6063 Builders and Timber Merchant *changed to* Builders Merchants Journal.
0262-6071 Timber Trades Journal and Wood Processing
0262-6101 Print Buyer *changed to* Print Buying.
0262-6195 International Road Haulage by United Kingdom Registered Vehicles
0262-6373 Newstime (London) *see* 0954-9021
0262-6381 Black Insight
0262-642X Welding Review *changed to* Welding Review International.
0262-6438 Chemical Engineering Abstracts
0262-6454 Metal Bulletin Handbook *see* 0269-1698
0262-6470 Television & Radio†
0262-6489 Fur and Feather *changed to* Fur & Feather.
0262-6497 Insuror
0262-6616 Impulse Foods *see* 0015-6671
0262-6624 Kerrang!
0262-6659 Highland Family History Society Journal
0262-6667 Hydrological Sciences Journal
0262-6756 IMS Monitor Report *changed to* Marketletter.
0262-6845 Monitor Weekly
0262-6853 I A P A Bulletin
0262-6896 C A S Newsletter
0262-6942 Bowls International
0262-6950 Flypast
0262-6969 International Financial Law Review
0262-6993 Radical Scotland†
0262-7035 Art & Craft
0262-7043 Respiratory Disease in Practice
0262-7051 A X 5
0262-706X Community Education Network
0262-7078 Collusion
0262-7108 Energy Economist
0262-7116 Hazards, Pollution and Legislation in the Coatings Field†
0262-7140 Crested Circle
0262-7159 C B S Newsletter (Glasgow) *changed to* Community Business News.
0262-7183 Biotech Business Bulletin†
0262-7221 N A T T A Newsletter *changed to* Renew Newsletter.
0262-723X Calder Voice
0262-7280 South Asia Research
0262-7299 Abortion Review
0262-7310 International Tax and Duty Free Buyers' Index
0262-7507 Child Education Special *see* 0269-9524
0262-7515 Junior Education Special *see* 0269-9532
0262-754X Schools Council Project, Art and the Built Environment. Working Parties Project. Bulletin†
0262-7574 Leicestershire Family History Society. Newsletter
0262-7612 Enlightenment and Dissent
0262-7620 Industry, Commerce, Development†
0262-7639 Tax Case Analysis
0262-7647 Law & Tax Review
0262-7655 Cheshire Ornithological Association. Bird Report
0262-7663 Exchange Rate Movements Year Book†
0262-7671 S E R C Bulletin
0262-7701 Captive Insurance Company Review
0262-7760 B E C A N Equipment for the Disabled Population†
0262-7779 B E C A N Biomechanics & Orthopaedics†
0262-7795 O S E A P Centre Update
0262-7841 Library Micromation News *see* 0964-7627
0262-785X S C A D Newsheet†
0262-7884 Practical Biotechnology
0262-7922 End Papers
0262-7965 Mines and Mining Equipment Companies Worldwide *changed to* Mines & Mining Equipment and Service Companies Worldwide (Year).
0262-7981 Fire Surveyor
0262-8015 Ditchley Newsletter
0262-804X Gamer†
0262-8074 Computer Business Europe†
0262-8090 Tractor & Farm Machinery Trader
0262-8104 Waterlines
0262-8120 Foster Care
0262-8155 Building Societies Association. Report of the Council *changed to* B S A Annual Report.
0262-8163 N I C E R Bulletin
0262-818X Mideast File†
0262-8201 Flying M
0262-8228 Francis Bacon Research Trust Journal
0262-8236 G E C Journal for Industry *see* 0267-9337
0262-8260 Music & Automata
0262-8279 Electric Living Journal
0262-8295 Digest of Welsh Statistics
0262-8309 Welsh Economic Trends
0262-8317 Statistics of Education in Wales *see* 0951-1237
0262-8317 Statistics of Education in Wales *see* 0951-1245
0262-8376 Futures World *changed to* Futures & Options World.
0262-8406 Scale Trains *changed to* Scale Model Trains.
0262-8457 Superbike
0262-8481 What C B†
0262-852X Smoke
0262-8597 Business South East
0262-8600 P I R A Annual Review of Research & Services
0262-8643 Northern Ireland Local Studies *see* 0959-8812
0262-8759 Community Outlook

ISSN

ISSN INDEX 5663

0262-8805 Railpower
0262-8856 Image and Vision Computing
0262-8864 Greek Review International
0262-8880 Forth Ports Handbook 1984
0262-8937 Dowry†
0262-9003 Uren There†
0262-9070 Body Shop News†
0262-9208 Girl Annual†
0262-9216 E D C Newsletter
0262-9224 Tennis Magazine
0262-9232 Your Health
0262-9240 Trading Law
0262-9267 Stride†
0262-9275 Royal College of General Practitioners. Official Reference Book
0262-9283 Psychiatric Developments†
0262-9356 Share It
0262-9380 E E C Information Services†
0262-9488 Foreign Exchange Outlook†
0262-9577 Chart Watch
0262-9615 Fish Farmer
0262-9763 British Paperbacks in Print†
0262-9798 Youth and Policy
0262-9828 B A A R G Bulletin *changed to* B A A S Bulletin.
0262-9860 Shakti
0262-9909 Water Bulletin
0262-9925 Race and Immigration: Runnymede Trust Bulletin *changed to* Runnymede Bulletin.
0262-9941 Welcome to London†
0263-0001 Initiatives *see* 0952-0430
0263-0052 Bedford Operator†
0263-0060 Brazing and Soldering *changed to* Soldering & Surface Mount Technology.
0263-0079 Bulletin of Archaeology for Schools *see* 0952-9748
0263-0095 Green Drum
0263-0125 Blastpipe
0263-015X County Border Times
0263-0249 Liszt Saeculum
0263-0257 Civil Engineering Systems†
0263-0273 Local Studies Librarian†
0263-0338 African Archaeological Review
0263-0346 Laser and Particle Beams
0263-0354 Association of Football Statisticians. Annual
0263-0362 Cardiff Working Papers in Welsh Linguistics
0263-0664 Education Social Worker
0263-080X Structural Survey
0263-0869 Multicultural Teaching
0263-0885 Your Computer
0263-0915 Wind Engineering Abstracts
0263-0923 Journal of Low Frequency Noise & Vibration
0263-0982 Computers in Schools *changed to* Information Technology & Learning.
0263-1008 Apparel International
0263-1040 B R A D Directories and Annuals *see* 0263-3515
0263-1067 Business in Yorkshire
0263-1083 V B R A Directory of Members *changed to* V B R A Industry Yearbook.
0263-1091 Bristol and Avon Archaeology
0263-1210 The Face
0263-1385 Civil Aircraft Registrations†
0263-1407 C J A and H S A Newsletter
0263-1474 Electronic Product Design
0263-1644 Gadfly (Retford)†
0263-175X Business Information Technology†
0263-1768 Approved Courses for Accountancy Education
0263-1776 Wellsian
0263-1911 Media Project News *see* 0953-9492
0263-1989 African National Congress of South Africa. Newsbriefings†
0263-2012 Aerospace Dynamics
0263-2039 I C R News†
0263-2047 British Institute of Interior Design Members' Reference Book
0263-2098 Welfare Rights Bulletin
0263-211X Educational Management & Administration
0263-2128 Pi
0263-2136 Family Practice
0263-2160 Litigation
0263-2187 On Line (Sunbury-on-Thames)
0263-2217 Meat and Livestock Commission, Bucks, England. International Meat Market Review
0263-2241 Measurement
0263-2268 Journal of African Marxists
0263-2276 Chartered Institute of Public Finance and Accountancy. Return of Rates *changed to* Chartered Institute of Public Finance and Accountancy. Finance and General Statistics. Estimates.
0263-2306 News of Hymnody
0263-2322 London Theatre Index (Year)
0263-2373 European Management Journal
0263-2381 Scottish Criminal Case Reports
0263-242X Britain's Top 1000 Foreign-Owned Companies *changed to* Britain's Top 2500 Foreign-Owned Companies.
0263-2446 Britain's Top 500 Electrical & Electronic Companies
0263-2462 British Newspaper Industry *changed to* British Newspaper and Magazines Industry.
0263-2500 North West European Continental Shelf Oil & Gas Field Development Survey *changed to* North West Europe Offshore Development.
0263-2543 Blitz Magazine
0263-2632 Chorleywood Digest
0263-2659 A S M Translations Index *see* 0278-4238
0263-2721 Henley Centre for Forecasting. Director's Guide to the U.K. Economy *see* 0952-5467
0263-2764 Theory Culture & Society
0263-2772 Facilities
0263-2926 Creativity and Innovation Network *see* 0953-4199
0263-2942 Parnasse
0263-2969 Chartered Institute of Public Finance and Accountancy. Cemeteries & Crematoria Statistics. Actuals
0263-2977 Chartered Institute of Public Finance and Accountancy. Direct Labour Statistics. Actuals *changed to* Chartered Institute of Public Finance and Accountancy. Direct Labour Organisation Statistics. Actuals.
0263-2985 Chartered Institute of Public Finance and Accountancy. Capital Expenditure and Debt Financing Statistics. Actuals
0263-3019 Thoroughbred†
0263-3094 Health and Safety: Quarries
0263-3183 Classic & Sportscar
0263-3191 Society of Antiquaries of Scotland. Monograph Series
0263-3205 East Europe Agriculture *changed to* East Europe & USSR Agriculture & Food.
0263-3213 Black Beauty & Hair
0263-3221 Ditchley Conference Reports
0263-323X Journal of Law and Society
0263-3248 Computers in Genealogy
0263-3272 Airline Data News *see* 0951-8673
0263-3396 Table Tennis
0263-3515 British Rate and Data
0263-3523 British Economy Survey
0263-3604 C L W Contents†
0263-3612 Library Link†
0263-3620 Reed's Mediterranean Navigator
0263-3639 Nationwide Anglia Building Society. House Prices
0263-3655 British Security Companies *changed to* Britain's Security Industry.
0263-368X British Hotel Industry
0263-3698 British Distilling Industry†
0263-3701 C O M E C O N Data
0263-3809 Sponsorship News
0263-3817 S B B Tax News *see* 0262-3102
0263-3868 Administrator
0263-3957 Politics
0263-404X East Midlands Chamber of Commerce Regional Directory *changed to* East Midlands Business Directory.
0263-4066 Golf Guide - Where to Play and Where to Stay
0263-4228 Large Mixed Retailing†
0263-4236 Carpet & Floorcoverings Review
0263-4260 Panama Handbook 1983
0263-4368 International Journal of Refractory and Hard Metals *see* 0958-0611
0263-4384 Offset Printing & Reproduction
0263-4430 Busy Solicitors' Digest
0263-4457 Journal of Applied Language Study†
0263-4465 Journal of District Nursing
0263-4503 Marketing Intelligence & Planning
0263-4538 Current Research in French Studies at Universities and University Colleges in the United Kingdom *changed to* Current Research in French Studies at Universities and Polytechnics in the United Kingdom and Ireland.
0263-4600 U F A W Annual Report and Accounts
0263-4635 Litmus
0263-466X Christian Brethren Review *changed to* Partnership Christian Brethren Review.
0263-4759 Engineering Computers
0263-4929 Journal of Metamorphic Geology
0263-4937 Central Asian Survey
0263-497X Ink and Print *changed to* Ink & Print International.
0263-502X B I S F A Magazine *see* 0952-7419
0263-5038 Spon's Plant and Equipment Price Guide
0263-5046 First Break
0263-5054 Aberdeen Petroleum Report
0263-5062 Defence Helicopter World *see* 0963-116X
0263-5070 Oil & Gas: Law and Taxation Review
0263-5100 Human Potential Resources *see* 0955-4815
0263-5143 Research in Science & Technological Education
0263-5372 Informe Latinoamericano
0263-5402 Institute of Development Studies. Commissioned Studies
0263-5437 Do-It-Yourself Report
0263-547X Recent Polar and Glaciological Literature *see* 0957-5073
0263-5488 International Tax-Free Trade Buyers Guide & Directory
0263-5569 F T London Policy Guide *changed to* World Policy Guide.
0263-5720 P C User
0263-5739 Refrigeration and Air Conditioning
0263-5747 Robotica
0263-5798 Papers in Slavonic Linguistics†
0263-5909 Journal of Community Education
0263-5917 Critical Reports on Applied Chemistry
0263-5933 Royal Society of Edinburgh. Transactions. (Earth Sciences)
0263-5976 Warwick Papers in Industry, Business and Administration *changed to* Warwick Business School Research Papers.
0263-6050 World Cement
0263-6085 Beauty Counter and Perfumery and Toiletries Buyer *changed to* Beauty Counter.
0263-6107 Teaching Science
0263-6115 Australian Mathematical Society. Journal. Series A. Pure Mathematics and Statistics
0263-614X P I T C O M *see* 0266-8513
0263-6166 Public Relations†
0263-6182 Postgraduate Courses in United Kingdom Universities *changed to* British Universities' Guide to Graduate Study.
0263-6190 C A D - C A M Digest
0263-6212 Keyboards and Music Player
0263-6263 Truck and Bus Builder
0263-6336 Robotics in Japan†
0263-6344 Theatre Ireland
0263-6352 Journal of Hypertension
0263-6395 International Media Law
0263-6484 Cell Biochemistry and Function
0263-6506 North West Kent Family History
0263-6522 Integrated Circuits International
0263-6530 D E C User
0263-6565 Fiction Magazine
0263-6697 Compass Sport - Orienteer
0263-6700 Policy Market
0263-6727 Atlantic Quarterly†
0263-6735 Information Technology Training†
0263-6743 Clarity
0263-6751 Anglo-Saxon England
0263-676X Themes in Drama
0263-6778 Abstracts in BioCommerce
0263-6786 Vox Evangelica
0263-6794 Tube International
0263-6832 A C O L A M Newsletter
0263-6921 Young Farmer†
0263-7022 James Hogg Society. Newsletter *see* 0960-6025
0263-7057 Golfing Handbook†
0263-7073 Canary Islands Shipping Handbook 1983
0263-7081 Wheels & Tracks
0263-709X Art Book Review
0263-7103 British Journal of Rheumatology
0263-7138 Power and Process Engineering *changed to* Institution of Mechanical Engineers. Proceedings. Part A: Journal of Power and Energy.
0263-7146 Institution of Mechanical Engineers. Proceedings. Part B: Management and Engineering Manufacture *see* 0954-4054
0263-7154 Institution of Mechanical Engineers. Proceedings. Part C: Mechanical Engineering Science *changed to* Institution of Mechanical Engineers. Proceedings. Part C: Journal of Mechanical Engineering Science.
0263-7227 Bacterial Cell Surface†
0263-7235 Beta Lactams†
0263-7243 Cardiovascular Pharmacology
0263-7251 Cell Cycle
0263-726X Cell Differentiation
0263-7286 Complement (Sheffield)†
0263-7294 Diabetes Mellitus
0263-7324 Hearing†
0263-7340 Motor Activity†
0263-7359 Neonatal Physiology†
0263-7367 Polyamines†
0263-7383 Annales Benjamin Constant
0263-7472 Property Management
0263-7480 Journal of Valuation *changed to* Journal of Property Valuation and Investment.
0263-7499 Rent Review and Lease Renewal
0263-7553 Picture House
0263-7561 Beebug
0263-760X Cave Science: Transactions of the British Cave Research Association
0263-7685 Executive Travel
0263-7693 Floors
0263-7707 The Medal
0263-774X Environment and Planning C: Government & Policy
0263-7758 Environment and Planning D: Society & Space
0263-7774 Leisure Futures
0263-7855 Journal of Molecular Graphics
0263-7863 International Journal of Project Management
0263-788X Municipal Engineer
0263-7898 Which World Processor and Office System? *see* 0265-6965
0263-7928 Partnership Management
0263-7936 Professional Builder and House Remodeller *changed to* Professional Builder.
0263-7952 Industrial Research in United Kingdom
0263-7960 Built Environment†
0263-7987 World Calendar
0263-8029 Biotech News
0263-8134 Harpers Sports & Leisure
0263-8223 Composite Structures
0263-8231 Thin-Walled Structures

ISSN

5664 ISSN INDEX

0263-8371 Changes
0263-841X In Practice
0263-8495 Human Nutrition. Applied Nutrition *see* 0952-3871
0263-8665 Petcare†
0263-8746 Sports Teacher
0263-8762 Chemical Engineering Research & Design
0263-8894 Orbit†
0263-8908 Microcomputer Newsletter *changed to* Computer Newsletter (Bracknell).
0263-9041 Wisden Cricket Monthly
0263-9106 Which Camera?
0263-9114 European Journal of Chiropractic
0263-9203 Middle East Computing†
0263-9254 Current Research in Library & Information Science
0263-9327 Computer-Aided Engineering Journal
0263-936X Pickup in Progress
0263-9378 Community Transport Magazine
0263-9432 Whitaker's Classified Monthly Book List†
0263-9459 Cruciferae Newsletter
0263-9475 C I R C A Art Magazine
0263-953X What Investment
0263-9661 World Precious Metals Survey *changed to* World Precious Metals Databook.
0263-9688 Hampstead Clinic. Bulletin *see* 0267-3061
0263-9696 National Association of Inspectors and Educational Advisors. Journal
0263-9777 F M S Magazine *see* 0957-6061
0263-9874 Information on TV Directory *changed to* Professional T V & Radio Media Directory.
0263-9904 Romance Studies
0263-9947 V A T Intelligence
0263-9963 Bethlem and Maudsley Gazette
0264-0155 Euro-Asia Business Review†
0264-0163 Garage and Automotive Retailer
0264-0201 International Council for Distance Education. Bulletin
0264-0236 Concrete Plant and Production
0264-0295 G E C Engineering *see* 0267-9337
0264-0325 Royal Society of Health Journal
0264-0406 British Naturism
0264-0414 Journal of Sports Sciences
0264-0422 Glasgow Magazine†
0264-0449 Sinclair Projects†
0264-0473 Electronic Library
0264-0643 A D I U Report†
0264-0724 Mackintosh Yearbook of International Electronics Data *see* 0954-0172
0264-0732 World Leasing Yearbook
0264-0775 World Ports and Harbours Abstracts
0264-0783 World Ports and Harbours News†
0264-0821 Land Development Studies *see* 0959-9916
0264-083X The World of Interiors
0264-0856 Cencrastus
0264-0961 Intercon
0264-1011 Templar†
0264-1062 Model Flyer†
0264-1127 Law Reports: Queen's Bench Division
0264-1240 Fish Stock Record *see* 0955-2855
0264-1259 Antwerp Handbook 1984†
0264-1275 Materials & Design
0264-1283 British Micro Software News
0264-1291 Horticultural Trades Association Members' Reference Book†
0264-1372 Missionary Herald
0264-1453 Amar Deep
0264-1615 Interlending and Document Supply
0264-1674 Current Military Literature *see* 0954-3589
0264-1755 Advertising Age's Focus *see* 0001-8899
0264-1828 Arts & the Islamic World
0264-1887 Technology
0264-2069 Service Industries Journal
0264-2212 Signal Review *changed to* Signal Selection of Children's Books.
0264-2220 Model Shipwright
0264-2247 International Pharmaceutical Technology & Product Manufacture Abstracts†
0264-2425 Reading in a Foreign Language
0264-2441 U A P Newsletter
0264-2506 Finishing
0264-2549 Health and Fitness (Bicester)
0264-2557 Amateur Radio
0264-2751 Cities
0264-2824 Parliamentary History
0264-2867 Latin American Special Reports
0264-2875 Dance Research
0264-312X Shaw's Directory of Courts in the United Kingdom
0264-3200 Sales and Marketing Management
0264-3219 Book Marketing News
0264-3227 What's on & Where to go *changed to* What's on in London (London, 1966).
0264-3294 Cognitive Neuropsychology
0264-3340 Asian Electricity
0264-3375 Journal of Semi-Custom I Cs *see* 0026-2692
0264-3383 Music and Video Week Directory *changed to* Music Week Directory.
0264-3391 Current Biotechnology Abstracts
0264-3405 British Cactus & Succulent Journal
0264-3413 Journal of Chemical Technology and Biotechnology. Part A: Chemical Technology *see* 0268-2575
0264-3421 Biotechnology *see* 0268-2575
0264-357X Fashion Buyers Diary *see* 0014-8679
0264-3596 Interzone
0264-3642 Modern Railways Pictorial Profile†
0264-3693 Bookplate Journal
0264-3707 Journal of Geodynamics
0264-3723 Weekly Law Digest
0264-3731 Justice of the Peace Reports
0264-3758 Journal of Applied Philosophy
0264-3898 Society for Italic Handwriting. Bulletin *changed to* Society for Italic Handwriting. Newsletter.
0264-3944 Pastoral Care in Education
0264-4002 Rural Viewpoint
0264-4037 Food Industry Directory *changed to* European Food Trades Directory.
0264-4088 Community Currents
0264-410X Vaccine
0264-4134 Asian Timber Trades Journal *changed to* Asian Timber.
0264-4169 Electrical and Mechanical Executive Engineer (EMEE) *see* 0266-2450
0264-441X What Micro?
0264-4479 Computer Answers†
0264-4495 Country Profile. Germany
0264-4509 Video Retailer†
0264-4525 Journal of Practical Civil Defence
0264-4584 A & B Computing
0264-4606 B O C A A D†
0264-4614 Maladjustment and Therapeutic Education
0264-4649 Combat Craft *see* 0144-3194
0264-4703 Precision Toolmaker
0264-4754 Animal Technology
0264-4770 Texas Personal Injury Law Reporter
0264-4886 Country Profile. Netherlands
0264-4924 Archives of Emergency Medicine
0264-4932 Industry Northwest
0264-4940 Ideas and Productions
0264-5130 Fisheries Research Data Report
0264-5181 Housing Year Book
0264-519X Research, Policy and Planning
0264-522X The Regionalist Seminar
0264-5378 Coffee International Directory
0264-5394 Tobacco Directory and Diary *changed to* Tobacco Trade Directory and Diary.
0264-5467 Research and Development in Agriculture†
0264-5483 C P N A Journal *see* 0265-7007
0264-5491 Oxford Agrarian Studies
0264-5505 Probation Journal
0264-553X Microprocessor Software Quarterly†
0264-5564 Vinaver Studies in French
0264-5572 Scottish Church History Society. Records
0264-5629 Microprofile *see* 0958-4668
0264-5637 British Book News Children's Books *see* 0143-909X
0264-5661 Vancouver Port Handbook
0264-567X Sydney Ports Handbook (Year)†
0264-5688 Scottish Health Education Group Bulletin†
0264-5807 Society for Environmental Therapy. Newsletter
0264-5890 Formaos
0264-598X Christian Arena
0264-6021 Biochemical Journal
0264-6137 Bare Nibs
0264-6196 British Journal of Visual Impairment
0264-6307 Texas Insurance Law Reporter *changed to* Texas Insurance Law Journal.
0264-6358 Videodisc Newsletter†
0264-6412 Rad for Radiographers, Radiologists and Radiotherapists
0264-6420 Maritime Guide
0264-6501 Uncensored Poland News Bulletin†
0264-6544 Chartered Institute of Public Finance and Accountancy. Probation. Estimates
0264-6552 Chartered Institute of Public Finance and Accountancy. Administration of Justice. Estimates
0264-6579 Irish Christian Study Centre. Journal
0264-6706 Euromoney Trade Finance Report *changed to* Trade Finance & Banker International.
0264-6714 Key Statistical Indicators for National Health Service Management in Wales
0264-6773 Ninth Decade†
0264-6781 Imprint (York)
0264-6811 Journal of Energy and Natural Resources Law
0264-682X Engineering Analysis *see* 0955-7997
0264-6854 Construction Computing
0264-6900 Cerebral Circulation and Metabolism
0264-6943 Graduate Management Research
0264-7028 Main Line
0264-7125 Chartered Institute of Public Finance and Accountancy. Education Statistics. Unit Costs†
0264-715X Converting Today
0264-7230 Craftwork†
0264-7249 Fibre Optics Newsletter
0264-729X Physics and Chemistry of Materials Treatment
0264-7303 Metallic Materials
0264-732X Litho Week
0264-7362 European Access
0264-7419 Technology and Science of Informatics
0264-7478 Gastroenterology in Practice *changed to* Gastroenterology in Practice.
0264-7494 Intensive Therapy & Clinical Monitoring†
0264-7540 Devon Archaeology
0264-7664 Travel Managers Reference Book *see* 0952-0899
0264-7699 Arts Yorkshire *see* 0951-9084
0264-7753 High Performance Plastics
0264-7761 Temporary Occupations and Employment *changed to* Jobs in the 'Gap' Year.
0264-7834 Capital Taxes News & Reports
0264-7877 Conference Papers in Applied Physical Sciences†
0264-8059 Marine Pollution Research Titles
0264-8121 New Law for General Practice Surveyors *changed to* New Law for Surveyors.
0264-8148 Designers' Journal
0264-8156 Designing and Making *see* 0943-612X
0264-8164 Asian Building & Construction
0264-8172 Marine and Petroleum Geology
0264-827X Pubcaterer
0264-8296 Media Information - UK†
0264-8334 Paragraph
0264-8342 Pater Newsletter
0264-8377 Land Use Policy
0264-8466 Training and Education *changed to* Personnel, Training and Education.
0264-8474 Focus on Nature Conservation
0264-8555 Fashion Extras
0264-8563 Housewares
0264-8571 Society for Renaissance Studies. Bulletin
0264-858X Comeback
0264-861X Oxford Surveys of Plant Molecular and Cell Biology
0264-8644 Industrial Jetting Report
0264-8717 S C O L A G
0264-8725 Biotechnology and Genetic Engineering Reviews
0264-8741 C J A and H S A Annual Report and Accounts
0264-8768 Primary Teaching and Micros†
0264-8822 Countryside Commission News
0264-8873 Home Farm
0264-8970 Benn's Direct Marketing Service
0264-9039 Scottish Society for Conservation and Restoration. Bulletin
0264-908X Semi-Custom I C Yearbook *see* 0026-2692
0264-9152 I T Focus *changed to* Key Abstracts - Business Automation.
0264-9187 G E C Journal of Research
0264-9314 Trade U S A†
0264-9373 British Journal of Sports History *see* 0952-3367
0264-9381 Classical and Quantum Gravity
0264-9403 Neural Circulation and C S F†
0264-9411 Neural Organisation†
0264-9438 International Zinc & Galvanising Survey†
0264-9551 Immunoparasitology†
0264-956X Immunosuppression†
0264-9586 Lymphokines *see* 0964-7554
0264-9594 Microsomes†
0264-9624 Phospholipids
0264-9640 Chloroplasts
0264-9659 Liposomes
0264-9675 Quarterly Economic Review of Venezuela, Suriname, Netherland Antilles *see* 0269-6754
0264-9683 Modus
0264-9780 Fireworks
0264-9829 National Housing and Town Planning Council. Conference and Exhibition Guide
0264-9993 Economic Modelling
0265-0096 Electronic Systems News *changed to* Electronics Education.
0265-0193 British Telecom Technology Journal
0265-0215 European Journal of Anaesthesiology
0265-0231 Railways Today
0265-024X Sea Fishing Today
0265-0266 Great Britain. Civil Aviation Authority. C A A Monthly Operating and Traffic Statistics *changed to* Great Britain. Civil Aviation Authority. U.K. Airlines Monthly Operating & Traffic Statistics.
0265-0266 Great Britain. Civil Aviation Authority. C A A Monthly Operating and Traffic Statistics *changed to* Great Britain. Civil Aviation Authority. U.K. Airports Monthly Statements of Movements, Passengers and Cargo.
0265-0290 Economic Review
0265-041X Library Conservation News
0265-0487 International Journal of Advertising
0265-0495 Woodworking Crafts *changed to* Woodworking.
0265-0517 British Journal of Music Education
0265-0525 Social Philosophy and Policy
0265-0533 Journal of Social Work Practice
0265-0568 Natural Product Reports
0265-0584 Industrial Corrosion
0265-0665 Economic Affairs
0265-0673 Pharmaceutical Medicine (Houndmills)
0265-0681 Good Beer Guide
0265-069X Benn's Hardware Price List†
0265-0711 Oxford Survey in Information Technology
0265-072X Oxford Surveys in Evolutionary Biology
0265-0738 Oxford Surveys on Eukaryotic Genes
0265-0746 I M A Journal of Mathematics Applied in Medicine & Biology
0265-0754 I M A Journal of Mathematical Control & Information

ISSN

0265-0762 Mircen - Journal of Applied Microbiology & Biotechnology *see* 0959-3993
0265-086X Bradleya
0265-0916 International Journal of Rapid Solidification
0265-0940 Abstracts on Productivity, Technology and Training *changed to* Productivity Insights.
0265-0959 Benn Electronics Executive†
0265-0975 I P C S Bulletin *see* 0958-5222
0265-0983 Metals International *see* 0959-6127
0265-1025 Spon's Civil Engineering Price Book *see* 0957-171X
0265-1033 British Journal of Experimental and Clinical Hypnosis *see* 0960-5290
0265-1068 Seventeenth Century French Studies
0265-1076 Historian
0265-1084 Fashion Update
0265-1092 Design International†
0265-1165 Dover Port Handbook
0265-1173 Mersey Ports Handbook (Year)
0265-1181 Tees and Hartlepool Ports
0265-1211 Law Reports: Chancery and Family Division
0265-122X Law Reports: Appeal Cases
0265-1270 Fiesta
0265-1289 Knave
0265-1300 Advance
0265-1327 Survival International News *changed to* Survival (London, 1983).
0265-1335 International Marketing Review
0265-1351 Microbiological Sciences *see* 0950-382X
0265-1386 India Office Library and Records Oriental Collections Newsletter *see* 0960-7935
0265-1416 International Construction Law Review
0265-1432 Third World Book Review
0265-1459 Childright
0265-1513 Stock Exchange Fact Sheet Monthly *changed to* International Stock Exchange Fact Sheet Monthly.
0265-1521 London. Stock Exchange. Stock Exchange Companies *changed to* International Stock Exchange. Quality of Market Companies Book.
0265-1548 Music Week
0265-1580 Anglo Orthodoxy
0265-1602 Education and Health
0265-1610 Guidance and Assessment Review *see* 0963-2638
0265-1653 Property Business†
0265-1661 Financial Technology Bulletin
0265-167X Automated Office Profiles *see* 0957-3224
0265-1688 Computer Security and Privacy Profiles *see* 0958-1413
0265-1696 Software Systems and Techniques *see* 0958-465X
0265-170X Telecomms Profile *see* 0957-4611
0265-1718 C A D - C A M Profiles *see* 0958-1499
0265-1726 Yearbook of Adult Continuing Education
0265-1734 Energy Focus†
0265-1785 Society of Antiquaries of Newcastle Upon Tyne. Monograph Series
0265-1831 Theory, Computational Science & Computing
0265-184X Lisbon Letter†
0265-1858 W F S A Lectures *see* 0267-0003
0265-1874 International Hospital Federation. Official Handbook *see* 0953-9743
0265-1904 Institution of Mechanical Engineers. Proceedings. Part D: Transport Engineering *see* 0954-4070
0265-1920 Chemical Engineer Diary and Institution News *see* 0302-0797
0265-1947 B U F O R A Bulletin†
0265-203X Food Additives and Contaminants
0265-2048 Journal of Microencapsulation
0265-2072 Purchasing and Supply Management
0265-2099 Credit Management
0265-2196 Medical Association for Prevention of War. Journal *see* 0748-8009
0265-2269 Armstrong News
0265-2285 Giant Steps†
0265-2323 International Journal of Bank Marketing
0265-2455 Lloyd's Ship Manager
0265-2501 Independent Solicitor
0265-2587 Assignation
0265-2609 Theatrephile
0265-2641 Philatelic Quill
0265-2706 Guiding
0265-2722 Metals Society World *see* 0266-7185
0265-2730 Guide to Postgraduate Degrees, Diplomas and Courses in Medicine
0265-2897 Buddhist Studies Review
0265-2900 Buddhist Forum†
0265-2927 Satellite and Cable Television News†
0265-301X Electronics Manufacture and Test
0265-3028 Hybrid Circuits
0265-3036 International Biodeterioration
0265-3273 Scottish Slavonic Review
0265-3389 American Studies Library Newsletter
0265-3400 P H L S Microbiology Digest
0265-3435 Analytical Instrument Industry Report
0265-3443 New Materials - Japan
0265-3656 B B C Wildlife
0265-3664 Heritage Interpretation *changed to* Interpretation Journal.
0265-377X Cubism
0265-3788 Transformation
0265-3818 Jane's Defence Weekly
0265-3834 History of Nursing Bulletin *see* 0960-2348
0265-3842 Kew Magazine
0265-3877 International Biotechnology Directory *changed to* Biotechnology Directory (Year).
0265-3990 Pipelines Abstracts
0265-4024 A B C Air Asia *changed to* A B C Executive Flight Planner: Asia Planner.
0265-4040 Micro User
0265-4075 Journal of Social and Personal Relationships
0265-4210 Land and Minerals Surveying
0265-4245 Methods in Organic Synthesis
0265-4385 University Computing
0265-4415 Thomas Cook Airport Links *see* 0266-9404
0265-444X Mauritian International
0265-4458 Conference & Common Room
0265-4490 Database and Network Journal
0265-4504 Commuter World
0265-4512 University (Bristol)†
0265-4547 Scottish Bulletin of Evangelical Theology
0265-4571 Heating, Ventilating & Plumbing
0265-4601 Thomas Callander Memorial Lectures
0265-4792 The Safety & Health Practitioner
0265-4822 Afghan Studies *see* 0266-6030
0265-4881 Salisbury Review
0265-5012 I D S Bulletin
0265-5039 North Sea Oil & Gas Directory
0265-5071 Industrial Heritage Magazine
0265-511X Open Mind
0265-5136 Irrigation News
0265-5209 Charity
0265-5217 British Journal of Healthcare Computing
0265-5241 Intensive & Critical Care Digest
0265-5292 Middle East Education & Training†
0265-5322 Language Testing
0265-5373 Farm Buildings and Engineering
0265-539X Community Dental Health
0265-5497 Self Health *see* 0957-1728
0265-5500 Rock Garden
0265-5527 Howard Journal of Criminal Justice
0265-5543 Scorpion
0265-5683 O'Neill Clan News
0265-5691 Maguire Bulletin
0265-5705 Crawford Chronicle
0265-5721 Chemical Hazards in Industry
0265-573X Great Britain. Home Office. Probation Statistics England & Wales (Year)
0265-5802 Adventure Education *changed to* Adventure Education and Outdoor Leadership.
0265-5810 Little Red Book *changed to* Guide to International Journals & Periodicals.
0265-5837 Quarterly Serial Bulletin†
0265-5896 Subject Guide: Recent and Forthcoming British Books
0265-5918 International Journal of Bulk Solids Storage in Silos
0265-5942 Journal of Newspaper and Periodical History
0265-5985 Diabetes Research
0265-6000 I L A M Journal *see* 0267-3754
0265-6027 European Semiconductor Design and Production *changed to* European Semiconductor.
0265-6159 Scottish Current Law Year Book
0265-6183 Performance Car
0265-6248 Venture Capital Report
0265-6272 World: Quarterly Energy Review†
0265-637X Urethanes Technology
0265-640X Oil and Gas Industry *changed to* Oil and Oil Field Equipment & Service Companies Worldwide.
0265-6469 Middle East Food Trade and Catering Equipment *changed to* Asia and Middle East Food Trade.
0265-6582 Journal of Synthetic Lubrication
0265-6590 Child Language Teaching and Therapy
0265-6647 Health Libraries Review
0265-671X International Journal of Quality & Reliability Management
0265-6736 International Journal of Hyperthermia
0265-6760 Mini Micro Software *see* 0954-2833
0265-6817 B U F V C Newsletter *see* 0952-4444
0265-6868 Highways and Transportation
0265-6906 Quarterly Economic Review of Hong Kong, Macau *see* 0269-6762
0265-6914 European History Quarterly
0265-6922 Greek Orthodox Calendar
0265-6930 New Home Economics
0265-6957 Social Services Research
0265-6965 Which Office System?†
0265-6981 Malpas History†
0265-7007 Community Psychiatric Nursing Journal
0265-7015 Potato World†
0265-7066 16 Bit Computing
0265-7074 Deaf Newsletter
0265-7155 Directory of Agricultural, Horticultural and Fishery Co-Operatives in the United Kingdom *changed to* Directory of Agricultural Co-Operatives in the United Kingdom.
0265-7198 Photography
0265-7260 B A I E Magazine†
0265-7295 North Wind
0265-7406 Sugar Cane
0265-7465 Financial Marketing News *changed to* Financial Marketing Update.
0265-7473 Smallholder
0265-766X All England Law Reports. Annual Review
0265-7759 Motorcycle Enthusiast
0265-7848 Q P S Reporter†
0265-7880 Wheat, Barley and Triticale Abstracts
0265-7899 Heating & Plumbing Monthly Inc. Ventilation
0265-7937 Wilkinson's Road Traffic Law Bulletin
0265-7988 Banking & Financial Training
0265-8038 Durham Archaeological Record *changed to* Durham Archaeological Journal.
0265-8062 Phonology Yearbook *see* 0952-6757
0265-8119 Swedish Book Review
0265-8135 Environment and Planning B: Planning & Design
0265-8143 Glad Rag
0265-8178 British Columbia Ports Handbook 1984
0265-8186 Montreal Port and Shipping Handbook (Year)
0265-8194 Turkey Port and Shipping Handbook (Year)
0265-8216 Stamp News *see* 0953-5241
0265-8240 Law & Policy
0265-8275 Directory of British Biotechnology
0265-8291 Shipyard Orders. Weekly Report
0265-8305 Print Quarterly
0265-833X Asian Agriculture Buyers Guide *changed to* Agri-Technology Buyers Guide.
0265-8399 Small Business Confidential
0265-8410 Marine and Aviation Insurance Report
0265-8429 Outwrite Women's Newspaper
0265-8445 Commons, Open Spaces and Footpaths Preservation Society. Annual Report *changed to* Open Spaces.
0265-8569 Aerogram
0265-8739 R I B A Product Selector
0265-9190 Hampshire Field Club and Archaeological Society. Section Newsletters
0265-9220 Contents Pages in Education
0265-9239 Electronic Banking and Finance *see* 0961-5342
0265-9247 BioEssays
0265-9271 Current Awareness Bulletin *changed to* Current Awareness Abstracts.
0265-928X Biosensors *see* 0956-5663
0265-931X Journal of Environmental Radioactivity
0265-9344 Action Resources *changed to* Action & Resources for Quaker Peace and Service.
0265-9387 Review of the Economy and Employment
0265-9484 World Banking Abstracts
0265-9646 Space Policy
0265-9786 Landscape Issues
0265-9808 Sightline
0265-9883 British Journal of Psychotherapy
0265-9999 Senior Nurse (W. Sussex)
0266-0016 Folio Poetry Magazine
0266-0032 Soil Use and Management
0266-0180 Index to Business Reports
0266-0210 Publishing and Bookselling Directory *changed to* Professional Publishing Media Directory.
0266-0504 Flightline
0266-0539 Hardware and Garden Review
0266-0598 Leibniz Newsletter
0266-0644 Los Angeles Port and Shipping Handbook
0266-0652 New South Wales Ports Handbook
0266-0776 Welsh Hospital Waiting List Bulletin
0266-0784 English Today
0266-0806 Texas Health Law Reporter
0266-0814 Texas Evidence Reporter
0266-0822 Serica
0266-0830 Studies in the Education of Adults
0266-0865 Banking Technology
0266-0962 British Isles Airlines Schedule†
0266-1063 Opus Building Services Design File
0266-111X Issue One
0266-1144 Geotextiles and Geomembranes
0266-1322 Perspectives in American History New Series†
0266-139X Civil Engineering Surveyor
0266-1411 Geology of Nonmetallics *changed to* Geology and World Deposits.
0266-1500 Linen Hall Review
0266-1616 INSPEC Matters
0266-1640 Pteridologist
0266-1667 Escape
0266-1713 B P I C S Control *changed to* Control.
0266-1772 Warburg Institute. Surveys and Texts
0266-1802 Distributive Trades Survey *changed to* C B I Financial Times Distributive Trades Survey.
0266-2043 Great Britain. Economic and Social Research Council. Annual Report
0266-206X Scandinavian Institute of Asian Studies. Occasional Papers
0266-2078 Medical Textiles
0266-2094 Middle East Financial Directory†
0266-2108 Laser and Optics International†
0266-2132 Airfinance Annual
0266-2140 International Labour Reports†
0266-2175 Shuttle Story *see* 0268-4713
0266-2183 Muhyiddin Ibn Arabi Society. Journal
0266-2205 Subsea Engineering News

0266-2256 Professional Video International Yearbook†
0266-2329 British Music Education Yearbook
0266-2426 International Small Business Journal
0266-2450 Electrotechnical News
0266-2450 I I E X E Newsletter
0266-2493 Control Systems
0266-2671 Economics and Philosophy
0266-268X Computing Decisions *changed to* Computing and Communications Decisions.
0266-2698 Local History *changed to* Local History Magazine.
0266-2701 Afkar Inquiry†
0266-2914 Informes Especiales
0266-2922 International Powder & Bulk Solids Abstracts
0266-2930 International Process Technology Abstracts
0266-2949 Chartered Institute of Public Finance and Accountancy. School Meals Statistics†
0266-2957 Ghana Studies Bulletin
0266-299X What Telephone and Communication News *changed to* Communications Now.
0266-304X Binary: Computing in Microbiology
0266-3082 Bioengineering and the Skin *see* 1011-0283
0266-3112 Offshore Fleet Economics
0266-3120 Destiny†
0266-3147 International Banking & Financial Law Bulletin†
0266-3198 Ferro Alloy Directory *see* 0953-721X
0266-321X P C Review†
0266-3228 Miniature Wargames
0266-3244 Electronics World & Wireless World
0266-3368 Educational Technology Abstracts
0266-3392 Selly Oak Journal†
0266-3414 Dentist
0266-3481 Atomisation and Spray Technology *see* 0278-6826
0266-349X Journal of Micronutrient Analysis *see* 0308-8146
0266-3511 Space Structures†
0266-352X Computers and Geotechnics
0266-3538 Composites Science and Technology
0266-3554 German History
0266-3597 Hazell's Guide to the Judiciary and the Courts with the Holborn Law Society's List of Barristers by Chambers *changed to* Hazell's Guide to the Judiciary & the Courts with the Holborn Law Society's Bar List.
0266-366X Peter Warlock Society Newsletter
0266-3791 Kelly's Post Office London Business Directory
0266-3821 Business Information Review
0266-3848 Port Rashid: Dubai Shipping Handbook
0266-3856 Port Kelang Shipping Handbook
0266-3880 Biology and Society†
0266-3988 International Cargo Crime Prevention *see* 1012-2710
0266-4070 International Industry†
0266-4194 Economic Development Digest
0266-4208 Booknews
0266-4216 C.B.F. News
0266-4232 Children's Books of the Year
0266-4283 Computing Equipment
0266-4348 Genitourinary Medicine *changed to* Genitourinary Medicine: The Journal of Sexual Health, STDs and HIV.
0266-4356 British Journal of Oral and Maxillofacial Surgery
0266-4372 Quarterly Economic Review of Zimbabwe, Malawi *see* 0269-4255
0266-4380 Architectural Periodicals Index
0266-4429 Holiday Parks†
0266-4437 Camping and Caravan Site Selector
0266-447X Practical Diabetes
0266-4623 International Journal of Technology Assessment in Health Care
0266-4631 Computer Newsletter (Cambridge) *see* 0010-4531
0266-464X New Theatre Quarterly
0266-4658 Economic Policy
0266-4666 Econometric Theory
0266-4674 Journal of Tropical Ecology
0266-4720 Expert Systems
0266-4755 Report on British Palaeobotany & Palynology
0266-4763 Journal of Applied Statistics
0266-4771 Harvest
0266-4801 Computer Law & Practice
0266-4828 Building Societies in (Year) *changed to* Housing Finance Fact Book (Year).
0266-4879 MicroIndexer
0266-4909 Journal of Computer Assisted Learning
0266-5174 Crops
0266-5182 Fast Lane
0266-5433 Planning Perspectives
0266-5441 Scotlink
0266-5611 Inverse Problems
0266-5883 Frontier
0266-5905 Middle East Agribusiness†
0266-6014 P A X
0266-6030 South Asian Studies
0266-6073 Dental Annual
0266-6081 S R H E Bulletin *changed to* S R H E News.
0266-612X Intensive Care Nursing
0266-6138 Midwifery
0266-6154 Physiotherapy Practice†
0266-6189 Lloyd's Monthly List of Laid up Vessels
0266-6197 Lloyd's Ports of the World (Year)
0266-6200 Across Architecture
0266-6278 A C E Bulletin
0266-6286 Word & Image
0266-6294 Blood Coagulation Factors
0266-6308 D N A Probes
0266-6316 Biocompatible Materials†
0266-6340 Immunodeficiency†
0266-6375 Mammary Gland†
0266-6421 Issues in the Islamic Movement
0266-660X Reproductive Immunology†
0266-6618 Thymus†
0266-6669 Information Development
0266-6677 African Technical Review *see* 0954-6782
0266-6731 Africa Bibliography†
0266-6898 Scottish Museum News
0266-6952 Institute of Muslim Minority Affairs. Journal
0266-6960 Information Media & Technology
0266-6979 Geology Today
0266-7002 Euromoney Corporate Finance *changed to* Corporate Finance.
0266-7037 Intensive Care World
0266-7061 Computer Applications in the Biosciences
0266-707X Who's Who in Arts Management†
0266-7088 Congregational Year Book
0266-7142 Optical & Electron Microscopy†
0266-7169 Laboratory News
0266-7177 Modern Theology
0266-7185 Metals and Materials
0266-7207 Future Computing Systems†
0266-7215 European Sociological Review
0266-7223 Yearbook of European Law
0266-7274 Virginia Ports and Shipping Handbook
0266-7320 Progress in Rubber and Plastics Technology
0266-7339 City University Business School. Economic Review†
0266-7347 World Wrought Copper Statistics
0266-7363 Educational Psychology in Practice
0266-7398 Cricketer International
0266-7401 Cricketer Quarterly Facts and Figures
0266-7428 Scottish Industrial History
0266-7452 Trolleybus Magazine
0266-7460 Television and Video Production *changed to* Television Producer.
0266-7525 Third World Women's News
0266-7606 British Ceramic Society. Journal *see* 0307-7357
0266-7681 Journal of Hand Surgery: British Volume
0266-7703 Profitable Greetings
0266-7800 European Paint and Resin News
0266-7835 New Ground
0266-7878 Camping and Trailer *see* 0952-5106
0266-7908 International Management Development Review
0266-7924 Royal Agricultural Society of England Reference Book and Buyers' Guide
0266-7932 University of London. Institute of Germanic Studies. Bithell Series of Dissertations
0266-8009 Communications
0266-8017 African Farming and Food Processing
0266-8025 Far Eastern Agriculture
0266-8033 Memory Lane
0266-8068 National Trust
0266-8130 Professional Nursing *changed to* Professional Nurse.
0266-836X Amateur Entomologists Society. Bulletin
0266-8394 Knitting International
0266-8459 Directory of Post-Graduate and Post-Experience Courses
0266-8467 Directory of First Degree and Diploma of Higher Education Courses *changed to* Directory of First Degree and Undergraduate Courses.
0266-8505 Machine Knitting News
0266-8513 Information Technology and Public Policy
0266-8521 Altrive Chapbooks†
0266-8548 Quarterly Journal of Social Affairs†
0266-8599 Shadow
0266-8653 Reinsurance Market Report
0266-867X World Marxist Review
0266-8688 Media International
0266-8750 Liverpool Link
0266-8769 Lampada *see* 0029-6570
0266-8831 Label
0266-8920 Probabilistic Engineering Mechanics
0266-8963 Sport & Fitness
0266-8971 100A1
0266-898X Japanese Motor Business
0266-9013 Chartered Institute of Public Finance and Accountancy. Block Grant Statistics†
0266-903X Oxford Review of Economic Policy
0266-9064 City of Birmingham Directory of Industry & Commerce
0266-9080 Irish Philosophical Journal
0266-9102 Leisure Management
0266-9129 Network (London, 1984) *changed to* Community Network.
0266-9145 Education for Tomorrow
0266-9153 Sikh Messenger
0266-9390 Optical Receptionist
0266-9404 Thomas Cook Airports Guide Europe
0266-9412 U S Business Briefing†
0266-9455 Landscape Industry International
0266-9463 Microsoftware for Engineers *see* 0965-9978
0266-9536 Anti-Cancer Drug Design
0266-9544 E.I.D.C.T. - C.D.T. Year Book†
0266-9552 Chartered Institute of Public Finance and Accountancy. Environmental Health Statistics. Actuals
0266-9560 Chartered Institute of Public Finance and Accountancy. Leisure Usage. Actuals
0266-9587 Quarterly Economic Review of Australia *see* 0269-7106
0266-9595 Quarterly Economic Review of New Zealand *see* 0269-7114
0266-9609 Quarterly Economic Review of Pacific Islands - Papua New Guinea, Fiji, Solomon Islands, Western Samoa, Vanuatu, Tonga *see* 0269-7122
0266-9617 Quarterly Economic Review of Jamaica, Belize, Bahamas, Bermuda *see* 0269-7130
0266-9625 Quarterly Economic Review of Trinidad and Tobago, Guyana, Barbados, Windward and Leeward Islands *see* 0269-7149
0266-9633 Quarterly Economic Review of Colombia *see* 0269-7157
0266-9641 Quarterly Economic Review of Ecuador *see* 0269-7165
0266-965X Quarterly Economic Review of Pakistan, Afghanistan *see* 0269-7173
0266-9668 Quarterly Economic Review of Bangladesh *see* 0269-431X
0266-9676 Quarterly Economic Review of Ghana, Sierra Leone, Liberia *see* 0269-7181
0266-9684 Quarterly Economic Review of Senegal, The Gambia, Guinea-Bassau, Cape Verde *see* 0269-719X
0266-9692 Quarterly Economic Review of Guinea, Mali, Mauritania *see* 0269-7203
0266-9706 Quarterly Economic Review of Syria *see* 0269-7211
0266-9714 Quarterly Economic Review of Jordan *see* 0269-722X
0266-9722 Quarterly Economic Review of Libya *see* 0269-4328
0266-9730 Quarterly Economic Review of Tunisia, Malta *see* 0269-7238
0266-9749 Quarterly Economic Review of Congo, Gabon, Equatorial Guinea *see* 0269-7246
0266-9757 Quarterly Economic Review of Cameroon, Central African Republic, Chad *see* 0269-4336
0266-9765 Quarterly Economic Review of Cote d'Ivoire *see* 0269-7254
0266-9773 Quarterly Economic Review of Togo, Niger, Benin, Burkina Faso *see* 0269-7262
0266-9781 Quarterly Economic Review of Angola, Sao Tome & Principe *changed to* Country Report. Angola, Sao Tome & Principe.
0266-9838 Environmental Software
0266-9870 River and Flood Control Abstracts†
0266-996X Aquaculture and Fisheries Management
0267-0003 Lectures in Anaesthesiology†
0267-0054 Housing Information Digest
0267-0224 End Journal†
0267-0267 Athletics Coach
0267-0275 Postgraduate Doctor: Caribbean
0267-033X Sesame
0267-0348 Selected Bibliographies on Ageing
0267-0372 C E G B Abstracts†
0267-050X Road Engineering Intelligence and Research
0267-064X British Library. Lending Division Newsletter *see* 0952-892X
0267-0712 Social Studies Review
0267-0763 Advertising Law and Practice *see* 0144-0373
0267-0771 Insolvency Law & Practice
0267-078X Professional Negligence
0267-0801 R I B A Interior Design Product Selector *changed to* R I B A Interior Design Selector.
0267-0836 Materials Science and Technology
0267-0844 Surface Engineering
0267-0879 Fairplay Marine Computing Guide
0267-0887 Free Associations
0267-1085 International Underwater System Design
0267-1131 Family Tree Magazine
0267-1166 Golf Club Management & Equipment News
0267-1174 Chartered Institute of Public Finance and Accountancy. Teaching Hospital Statistics. Actuals†
0267-1182 Chartered Institute of Public Finance and Accountancy. Non-Teaching Hospital Costs. Statistics†
0267-1190 Royal Bank of Scotland Review
0267-1212 Scottish Business Survey *changed to* Scottish Chambers Business Survey.
0267-1247 Protostar *see* 0963-2700
0267-1263 London Energy News
0267-131X Mini Micro News
0267-1344 Delawarr Laboratories Information Service Newsletter†
0267-1360 Writers' Own Magazine
0267-1379 Current Opinion in Gastroenterology
0267-1395 Communications Systems Worldwide†
0267-1425 Scottish Library and Information Resources

ISSN	Title
0267-1441	Directory of Electronics, Instruments and Computers *changed to* Electronics & Instruments Directory.
0267-145X	Butterworths Company Law Cases
0267-1468	Britain's Best Holidays - A Quick Reference Guide
0267-1484	Telecom Markets
0267-1506	Food Manufacture International
0267-1522	Research Papers in Education
0267-1530	London. Stock Exchange. Stock Exchange Quarterly *changed to* International Stock Exchange. Quality of Markets Quarterly.
0267-1557	Codex: Journal of the Centre for the Study of Christianity in Islamic Lands
0267-1611	British Psychology Society. Division of Educational and Child Psychology. Papers *changed to* Educational & Child Psychology.
0267-1689	Institution of Electronic and Radio Engineers. Journal *see* 0954-0695
0267-1700	Religion Today
0267-1719	Management Digest†
0267-1832	Institute of Grocery Distribution. Economics and Finance. Bulletin *see* 0954-1683
0267-1891	Pelargonium News
0267-1905	Annual Review of Applied Linguistics
0267-1913	Worldwide Tanker Nominal Freight Scale *see* 0953-9336
0267-1948	Current Research in Britain. Physical Sciences
0267-1956	Current Research in Britain. Biological Sciences
0267-1964	Current Research in Britain. Social Sciences
0267-1972	Current Research in Britain. Humanities
0267-1980	Computer Applications in Social Work and Allied Professions *see* 0959-0684
0267-2006	Institute of Chartered Shipbrokers. Reference Book and List of Members (Year)
0267-2022	Local Government Administrators' Official Source Book
0267-2049	Plant Manager's Directory
0267-2073	Journal of Paediatric Dentistry *see* 0960-7439
0267-2103	Recreation Managers' Association of Great Britain Year Book *changed to* Leisure and Fitness.
0267-2243	Boston Sea and Air Port Handbook
0267-2251	Major Companies of the Far East
0267-2286	Darts Player
0267-2294	Everywoman
0267-2316	Sharjah Ports Handbook
0267-2499	Third World Affairs†
0267-2502	Start *changed to* Start Magazine of Literature and the Arts.
0267-2537	S I P R I Chemical & Biological Warfare Studies
0267-2561	Building Market Report
0267-257X	Journal of Marketing Management
0267-2618	N E M S News
0267-2669	Bulletin of Islamic Studies†
0267-2871	Farm Holiday Guide (England Edition) *changed to* Farm Holiday Guide (England, Wales & Ireland).
0267-288X	Farm Holiday Guide (Scotland Edition)
0267-2898	Farm Holiday Guide (Wales Edition) *changed to* Farm Holiday Guide (England, Wales & Ireland).
0267-2928	I M L S Gazette
0267-2952	Your Car Magazine *changed to* Top Car Magazine.
0267-2987	Maize Abstracts
0267-3037	Housing Studies
0267-3053	Third Sector *changed to* Third Sector Fortnight and Inform.
0267-3061	Anna Freud Centre. Bulletin
0267-307X	O E M Newsletter
0267-3231	European Journal of Communication
0267-3258	British Association for Immediate Care. Journal
0267-3304	Sport and Recreation Information Group Bulletin
0267-3355	Guide to Caravan and Camping Holidays
0267-3363	Bed & Breakfast Stops
0267-3371	Heritage Britain. Where to Visit: Where to Stay†
0267-338X	Scotland's Best Holidays†
0267-3398	England's Best Holidays†
0267-3401	Holidays in Wales *changed to* Wales Best Holidays.
0267-341X	Mini-Break Holidays in Britain *changed to* Recommended Short Break Holidays.
0267-3428	Recommended Country Hotels of Britain
0267-3436	Bed and Breakfast in Britain
0267-3460	Root
0267-3517	Bulletin of Forthcoming Anglo-Hellenic Events
0267-3584	Videotex Viewpoint
0267-3622	Clothing World
0267-3649	Computer Law and Security Report
0267-3754	Leisure Manager
0267-3762	International Journal of High Technology Ceramics *see* 0955-2219
0267-3843	International Journal of Adolescence and Youth
0267-3851	Catering and Health
0267-3932	I E E Proceedings Part J: Optoelectronics
0267-3991	Art and Design
0267-4009	Advances in Special Electrometallurgy
0267-4041	Optical Management†
0267-4173	Property Monthly Review†
0267-4181	Spon's Landscape & External Works Pricebook
0267-4319	Canada - U.K. Link *changed to* Can - U.K. Link.
0267-4343	Preservation in Action
0267-4394	Food Marketing *see* 0007-070X
0267-4424	Financial Accountability & Management
0267-4599	Self-Catering and Furnished Holidays
0267-4602	Women in Management Review
0267-4610	Your Stars†
0267-4629	4x4
0267-4637	Modern Farming
0267-4645	Disability, Handicap & Society
0267-4653	Sexual and Marital Therapy
0267-4823	Port Development International
0267-484X	Atlas
0267-4874	Advances in Contraception
0267-4920	Journal of Oil and Gas Accountancy *see* 0962-3752
0267-5080	Women's Review
0267-5145	Engineering News
0267-5153	Civil Liberty *changed to* Civil Liberty Agenda.
0267-5307	Technical Review. Middle East
0267-5315	Portuguese Studies
0267-5374	Employment Affairs Report
0267-5382	Media Bulletin
0267-5439	Biomedical Polymers *see* 0955-7717
0267-5447	Data Storage Report†
0267-5498	Linguistics Abstracts
0267-5501	Micromath
0267-5528	Professional Promotion Media Directory†
0267-565X	Broadcast Systems Engineering *changed to* Broadcast Systems International.
0267-5730	International Journal of Technology Management
0267-5900	Chemtronics *see* 1057-9257
0267-5943	Railwatch
0267-6133	Remote Sensing Yearbook†
0267-615X	Muslim Educational Quarterly
0267-6192	Computer Systems Science and Engineering
0267-6222	Acid Rain Update†
0267-6230	Social and Economic Impact of New Technology†
0267-6281	Royal Observatory. Research and Facilities
0267-629X	Energy Shipping
0267-6303	E I U Business Update *changed to* E I U Europe - Pacific Update.
0267-6362	Africa Events
0267-6583	Second Language Research
0267-6591	Perfusion
0267-6605	Clinical Materials
0267-6621	Applied Computer and Communications Law
0267-6648	Universalist
0267-6664	Field Service and Repair
0267-6672	Edinburgh Review
0267-6761	Libertarian Alliance. Foreign Policy Perspectives
0267-677X	Libertarian Alliance. Cultural Notes
0267-6788	Libertarian News
0267-6796	Libertarian Reprints
0267-6850	P H L S Library Bulletin
0267-7059	Libertarian Alliance. Political Notes
0267-7067	Libertarian Alliance. Scientific Notes
0267-7083	Libertarian Alliance. Legal Notes
0267-7091	Libertarian Alliance. Philosophical Notes
0267-7105	Libertarian Alliance. Historical Notes
0267-7113	Libertarian Alliance. Sociological Notes
0267-7121	Libertarian Alliance. Background Briefings
0267-7156	Libertarian Alliance. Personal Perspectives
0267-7164	Libertarian Alliance. Economic Notes
0267-7172	Libertarian Alliance. Psychological Notes
0267-7180	Libertarian Alliance. Study Guides
0267-7199	Libertarian Student
0267-7253	Piano Journal
0267-7296	Hazards
0267-7350	Melbourne Port and Shipping Handbook
0267-7369	Penang Port Handbook
0267-7377	Aberdeen Port Handbook
0267-7385	Planning Information Digest *changed to* Planning and Development Digest.
0267-744X	International Property Review†
0267-7563	Geofile
0267-7571	Service Compris†
0267-761X	Modern and Contemporary France
0267-7717	International Executive Transfers†
0267-7768	Construction Science *changed to* Construction History.
0267-7806	Journal for Weavers, Spinners & Dyers
0267-7814	Exploring Local History
0267-8071	O P A L Journal
0267-8101	Radio Control Scale Aircraft Quarterly
0267-8128	England. Economic and Social Research Council. Research Programme Bulletin
0267-8136	Manpower Policy & Practice†
0267-8179	Journal of Quaternary Science
0267-8225	International Motor Business
0267-8233	European Motor Business
0267-8292	Liquid Crystals
0267-8306	Texas Lawyer
0267-8349	Joint Association of Classical Teachers. Bulletin
0267-8357	Mutagenesis
0267-8373	Work and Stress
0267-8411	Transport Operator
0267-8470	Orthodox News
0267-8497	Undercut
0267-8500	Lib Ed
0267-8519	Company Car (Redhill)
0267-8594	Museum Abstracts
0267-8829	Moores & Rowland's Tax Guide
0267-8837	Science and Business Link-Up *changed to* Science & Business.
0267-8853	Oils & Fats International
0267-8896	Texas Real Estate Law Reporter
0267-8926	Pumps and Turbines†
0267-9035	Pensions Intelligence
0267-9264	International Journal for Artificial Intelligence in Engineering *see* 0954-1810
0267-9299	International Electronics for China†
0267-9310	Seabird
0267-9337	G E C Review
0267-9353	Hostelling News *changed to* Triangle.
0267-9361	Convenience Store
0267-937X	Journal of International Banking Law
0267-9442	Jumbo Cross
0267-9469	Comments & Criticisms
0267-9477	Journal of Analytical Atomic Spectrometry
0267-9515	Online Business Information
0267-954X	Space (Burnham)
0267-9612	Finnegans Wake Circular
0267-9698	Directory of Museums & Living Displays†
0267-9841	Back Street Heroes
0267-9981	I S C O Careers Bulletin *changed to* Careers Cop: I S C O Careers Bulletin.
0268-0033	Clinical Biomechanics
0268-005X	Food Hydrocolloids
0268-0106	International Journal of Estuarine and Coastal Law
0268-0130	Herpetological Journal
0268-0149	Public Eye
0268-0165	Geodrilling
0268-0181	J A C T Review
0268-0408	Food Market Abstracts
0268-0432	African Concord
0268-0440	Caravan Magazine
0268-0491	Carbon & High Performance Fibres Directory
0268-053X	Scottish Ambassador†
0268-0556	Arab Law Quarterly
0268-0572	British Health and Safety Society. Reviews Bulletin *see* 0954-576X
0268-0580	British Health and Safety Society. Newsletter *see* 0954-576X
0268-0599	Personal Investor
0268-0645	Postgraduate Study at the University of Liverpool *changed to* University of Liverpool Post Graduate Prospectus.
0268-0661	South America, Central America and the Caribbean (Year)
0268-067X	Sinclair Q L World
0268-0696	Lloyd's Maritime Law Newsletter
0268-0750	Making Better Movies *changed to* Video Maker.
0268-0815	Casualty Return
0268-0831	Motor Racing†
0268-0858	Articles in Hospitality and Tourism
0268-0882	Journal of Interventional Radiology
0268-0890	Current Orthopaedics
0268-0939	Journal of Education Policy
0268-1056	Polin
0268-1064	Mind & Language
0268-1072	New Technology, Work & Employment
0268-1080	Health Policy and Planning
0268-1099	Health Promotion *changed to* Health Promotion International.
0268-1102	Information Technology for Development†
0268-1110	Dynamics and Stability of Systems
0268-1129	I M A Journal of Mathematics in Management *see* 0953-0061
0268-1137	Oxford Magazine
0268-1153	Health Education Research
0268-1161	Human Reproduction
0268-117X	The Seventeenth Century
0268-1188	Automated Manufacturing Directory†
0268-1218	Journal of Medical & Veterinary Mycology
0268-1242	Semiconductor Science and Technology
0268-1331	Contemporary German Studies: Occasional Papers
0268-1358	Laboratory Science and Technology†
0268-1374	Offshore Engineering Abstracts
0268-1390	Poetry World†
0268-1455	Uterus†
0268-1463	Trace Elements†
0268-148X	Speech†
0268-1498	Sleep (Substances)†
0268-1501	Pineal Gland†
0268-151X	Microscopy and 3D Imaging†
0268-1528	Energy Balance†
0268-1536	Blood Vessel Walls†
0268-1544	Aging
0268-1552	Peptide Hormone Receptors
0268-1587	Immunologic Receptors†
0268-1595	Growth Factors *see* 0964-7554

0268-1609 Fertilisation†
0268-1617 Extracellular Matrix
0268-1625 Cytoskeleton
0268-1633 Bioelectronics *see* 0952-0384
0268-1641 Atrial Natriuretic Factors
0268-1781 Butcher and Processor
0268-1900 International Journal of Materials & Product Technology
0268-1935 Insurance Systems Bulletin
0268-2117 Pims Financial Directory *changed to* Pims Business, Investor and Government Relations Directory.
0268-2125 Learning Resources Journal
0268-2141 Support for Learning
0268-2184 Economic Development Briefing
0268-2222 Arab Commercial Law Review†
0268-2230 Business Finance Review†
0268-2249 Sunday Telegraph Business Finance Directory *changed to* U K Business Finance Directory (Year).
0268-2257 Asian Living Costs†
0268-2265 Budget Representations to the Chancellor
0268-2273 C B I Annual Report
0268-2281 North American Living Costs†
0268-2311 Major Energy Companies of Europe *changed to* Major Energy Companies of Europe.
0268-232X Major Banks, Finance and Investment Companies of Continental Europe *changed to* Major Financial Institutions of Continental Europe (Year).
0268-2338 Major Companies of the United States of America (Year)†
0268-2362 University of Liverpool Prospectus
0268-2400 British Bulletin of Publications on Latin America, the Caribbean, Portugal and Spain
0268-2419 Pep Talk
0268-246X Bookselling News
0268-2478 Construction Management: Register of Members
0268-2494 Topical Issues†
0268-2575 Journal of Chemical Technology and Biotechnology
0268-2605 Applied Organometallic Chemistry
0268-2656 R U S I Newsbrief
0268-2664 Urban Wildlife News
0268-2877 V.C.F. Newsletter
0268-2885 Science and Faith *see* 0954-4194
0268-294X Spokes *changed to* New Spokes.
0268-2966 International Carpet Bulletin
0268-3091 Royal Society of Medicine. Round Table Series
0268-3105 Kelly's United Kingdom Exports Directory
0268-313X Agrow
0268-3253 Lloyd's Marine Equipment Guide *changed to* Lloyd's International Marine Equipment Guide (Year).
0268-327X Lloyd's Maritime Directory (Year)
0268-3296 British Gas Corporation. Monitor *changed to* British Gas. Monitor.
0268-330X R & D Digest
0268-3369 Bone Marrow Transplantation
0268-3393 B C I R A Abstracts of International Literature on Metal Castings Production
0268-3539 University Library Expenditure Statistics
0268-3555 Phlebology
0268-3768 International Journal of Advanced Manufacturing Technology
0268-3830 Verse
0268-3903 International Journal of Retailing *see* 0959-0552
0268-3911 Industrial Marketing and Purchasing *see* 0265-1335
0268-392X International Review of Economics and Ethics *see* 0306-8293
0268-3946 Journal of Managerial Psychology
0268-3954 I T Intelligence†
0268-3962 Journal of Information Technology
0268-4012 International Journal of Information Management
0268-4020 Papers in the Administration of Development
0268-4047 This Caring Business
0268-4055 Complementary Medical Research
0268-4160 Continuity and Change
0268-4268 Henston Veterinary Vade Mecum (Small Animals)
0268-4276 Henston Veterinary Vade Mecum (Large Animals)
0268-4306 F R A M E News
0268-4527 Intelligence and National Security
0268-4535 Journal of Communist Studies
0268-4594 Mobile & Holiday Homes
0268-4705 Current Opinion in Cardiology
0268-4713 Spaceflight News†
0268-4764 Textile Outlook International
0268-490X Science and Public Affairs
0268-4993 Abstracts: Cellular Pathology
0268-5000 Jennings Magazine†
0268-5175 Audrey Babington's Workbox
0268-523X What's New in Processing
0268-5248 Radio Control Boat Modeller
0268-5280 Aluminium Industry
0268-537X Journal of Irish Archaeology
0268-5418 Thomas Hardy Journal
0268-5485 Optometry Today
0268-5558 Caravan Business Plus Caravan Industry
0268-5655 Simplified Spelling Society Newsletter *see* 0950-9585
0268-5663 Catering Manager's Buyer's Guide (Year) *see* 0956-9146
0268-5671 International Meeting Place
0268-568X British Security Industry Buyer's Guide (Year) *see* 0956-9170
0268-5795 Countryside Campaigner
0268-5809 International Sociology
0268-5949 Electricity for China†
0268-5957 I C L Today
0268-5965 Linguist
0268-5973 Health Information Service
0268-5981 Rialto
0268-6112 Irish Biblical Studies
0268-6287 Chromatography Abstracts
0268-6309 Marine Money†
0268-6376 Radical Statistics
0268-6384 Business
0268-6481 Oakland Port and Shipping Handbook
0268-649X Cherbourg Port Handbook
0268-6503 Darwin Port Handbook†
0268-6511 Southampton Port Handbook
0268-652X Ada User
0268-6538 Books at Boston Spa
0268-6635 Cash Management News
0268-6643 British Association of Psychotherapists. Bulletin *see* 0954-0350
0268-6716 Historical Research for Higher Degrees in the United Kingdom. Part 1: Theses Completed
0268-6724 Historical Research for Higher Degrees in the United Kingdom. Part 2: Theses in Progress
0268-6732 Teachers of History in the Universities and Polytechnics of the United Kingdom
0268-6856 Hydrosoft *see* 0309-1708
0268-6902 Managerial Auditing Journal
0268-6910 Expatriate
0268-6961 Software Engineering Journal
0268-702X Rouen Port and Shipping Handbook
0268-7038 Aphasiology
0268-7143 Equal Opportunities Review
0268-7232 Fund Management International†
0268-7291 Biotechnology Insight
0268-7305 Platinum (Year)
0268-7402 U K Centre for Economic and Environmental Development Bulletin
0268-750X Church Monuments Society Newsletter *see* 0268-7518
0268-7518 Church Monuments
0268-7615 Airline Business
0268-764X Benefits & Compensation International
0268-7844 Weekly Petroleum Argus
0268-7860 Industrial Computing
0268-7941 Geological Abstracts: Geophysics and Tectonics *see* 0954-0512
0268-800X Economic Geology *see* 0954-0512
0268-8018 Palaentology and Stratigraphy *see* 0954-0512
0268-8050 Condition Monitor
0268-8115 Dealerama *changed to* Photo and Electronics Marketing.
0268-8123 Technical Ceramics Bulletin *changed to* Technical Ceramics International.
0268-8212 Impact International
0268-8336 Law Library Information Reports
0268-8352 Link International: Educational Newsletter
0268-8360 A I D S Newsletter
0268-8387 Institute of Qualified Private Secretaries. Career Secretary
0268-8395 Franchise Magazine
0268-8654 Proprietary Articles Trade Association. Publication
0268-8697 British Journal of Neurosurgery
0268-8786 One to One
0268-8867 Project Appraisal
0268-8921 Lasers in Medical Science
0268-893X Public Library Journal
0268-8948 Government Contracting Review
0268-9146 Animal Genetics
0268-9219 Liquids Handling
0268-9499 Fibrinolysis
0268-9502 Dog & Country†
0268-9510 Trading Law Reports
0268-960X Blood Reviews
0268-9650 B M T Abstracts
0268-9669 Professional Liability Today
0268-9707 British Library. Bibliographic Services. Newsletter *changed to* Select: National Bibliographic Service Newsletter.
0268-9766 Surface Coating & Raw Material Directory
0268-9812 Polymers and Rubber Asia
0268-9847 Advanced Ceramics Report
0268-9928 Top 3,000 Directories and Annuals: A Guide to the Major Titles Used in British Libraries
0268-9944 ManTech Analyst†
0269-0004 British Journal of Education and Work
0269-0012 Current British Journals
0269-0136 International Journal of Mining and Gelogical Engineering *see* 0960-3182
0269-0144 Clinical Psychology Forum
0269-0225 Diagnostic Engineering
0269-0292 Music Business
0269-0357 International Public Relations Review
0269-0365 M O D Contracts Bulletin
0269-0403 Royal Musical Association. Journal
0269-0411 Professional Teacher
0269-0489 D E C Today
0269-0497 British Journal of Academic Librarianship
0269-0500 International Review of Children's Literature and Librarianship
0269-0543 Agricultural Zoology Reviews
0269-0551 Devon Tourism Review
0269-056X C L W Contents Monthly†
0269-0616 Christian Woman *see* 0962-2152
0269-0640 P.C. Management
0269-0675 Gridiron
0269-0756 Snooker Scene
0269-0780 N A G Newsletter
0269-0802 European Patent Office Reports
0269-0810 R I B A Directory of Practices
0269-0934 Guide to Over 100 Properties
0269-0942 Local Economy
0269-0977 Tradimus *see* 0029-6570
0269-1175 British Library. Document Supply Centre. Newsletter *see* 0952-892X
0269-1191 French History
0269-1205 Literature and Theology
0269-1213 Renaissance Studies
0269-1396 Pratique
0269-1469 Sheppard's Bookdealers in North America
0269-1477 Microsystem Design
0269-1698 Metal Bulletin Prices & Data Book
0269-1701 Industrial Minerals Directory - World Guide to Producers and Processors
0269-1728 Social Epistemology
0269-1736 Journalist's Handbook
0269-1752 Press Briefing†
0269-1760 Centre for South-East Asian Studies. Bibliography and Literature Series
0269-1779 Centre for South-East Asian Studies. Occasional Papers
0269-1787 Scottish Photography Bulletin
0269-1906 British Archaeological News
0269-1922 Denning Law Journal
0269-2104 Health Care Management *see* 0952-6862
0269-2139 Protein Engineering
0269-2155 Clinical Rehabilitation
0269-2163 Palliative Medicine
0269-2171 International Review of Applied Economics
0269-2309 Electronics Showcase
0269-2317 Local Studies Index
0269-2333 Post Marketing Surveillance
0269-2457 Agriculture International
0269-2511 Constitutional Reform
0269-2554 E S R C Studentship Handbook
0269-2600 World Cinema
0269-2619 Princess Grace Irish Library
0269-2694 Butterworths Journal of International Banking and Financial Law
0269-2716 Suffolk Business Directory
0269-2805 Butterworths Trading Law Cases†
0269-2813 Alimentary Pharmacology and Therapeutics
0269-2821 Artificial Intelligence Review
0269-283X Medical & Veterinary Entomology
0269-2848 Surfacing Journal International *see* 0267-0844
0269-3046 Office Magazine
0269-3208 On the Move†
0269-3259 Anthroposophy Today
0269-3291 County Court Practice
0269-3658 Paterson's Licensing Acts
0269-3682 Stone's Justices' Manual
0269-3712 Yearbook of Law Computers and Technology
0269-3720 Tax Practitioner's Diary
0269-3747 International Tourism Reports
0269-3755 Travel & Tourism Analyst
0269-3798 International Journal of Geographical Information Systems
0269-381X CoalTrans
0269-3836 Keyboard Player
0269-3879 Biomedical Chromatography
0269-4158 Country Report. Belgium, Luxembourg
0269-4166 Country Report. Canada
0269-4174 Country Report. Sri Lanka
0269-4182 Country Report. Norway
0269-4190 Country Report. Yugoslavia
0269-4204 Country Report. Nigeria
0269-4220 Country Report. Guatemala, El Salvador, Honduras
0269-4239 Country Report. Kenya
0269-4247 Country Report. Nicaragua, Costa Rica, Panama
0269-4255 Country Report. Zimbabwe, Malawi
0269-4263 Country Report. Spain
0269-4271 Country Report. Zambia
0269-428X Country Report. Philippines
0269-4298 Country Report. Czechoslovakia
0269-4301 Country Report. Hungary
0269-431X Country Report. Bangladesh
0269-4328 Country Report. Libya
0269-4336 Country Report. Cameroon, Central African Republic, Chad
0269-4352 Country Profile. Belgium, Luxembourg
0269-4360 Country Profile. Zimbabwe
0269-4379 Country Profile. Canada
0269-4387 Country Profile. Guatemala, El Salvador, Honduras
0269-5502 Country Report. Iraq
0269-4395 Country Profile. Iraq
0269-4409 Country Profile. Nicaragua, Costa Rica, Panama
0269-4417 Country Profile. Guinea, Mali, Mauritania
0269-4212 Country Report. Argentina
0269-4468 Country Profile. Argentina

0269-4476 Country Profile. Australia
0269-4484 Country Profile. Austria
0269-4492 Country Profile. Brazil
0269-4506 Country Profile. Jamaica
0269-4514 Country Profile. Belize, Bahamas, Bermuda
0269-4522 Country Profile. Malawi
0269-4530 Country Profile. Kenya
0269-4549 Country Profile. Ghana
0269-4565 Epitheliat†
0269-4670 Underground
0269-4689 Christian Family
0269-4727 Journal of Clinical Pharmacy and Therapeutics
0269-4735 Pro Sound News (Europe)
0269-4824 Tuba
0269-4921 Expatriates Tax & Investment Intelligence†
0269-4999 London Energy Group Data Book and Diary *changed to* Energy Data Book and Diary.
0269-5006 France & Colonies Philatelic Society of Great Britain. Journal
0269-5022 Paediatric & Perinatal Epidemiology
0269-5030 Scottish Economic and Social History
0269-5057 Country Profile. Sierra Leone, Liberia
0269-5065 Country Profile. Thailand, Burma
0269-5073 Country Profile. Sri Lanka
0269-5081 Country Profile. Chile
0269-509X Country Profile. China, North Korea
0269-5103 Country Profile. Colombia
0269-5111 Country Profile. Cuba
0269-512X Country Profile. Dominican Republic, Haiti, Puerto Rico
0269-5138 Country Profile. Denmark, Iceland
0269-5154 Country Report. Madagascar, Mauritius, Seychelles, Comoros
0269-5162 Country Report. United Arab Emirates
0269-5170 Country Report. Austria
0269-5189 Country Report. Thailand, Burma
0269-5197 Country Report. Chile
0269-5219 Country Profile. Poland
0269-5227 Country Profile. Egypt
0269-5251 Country Report. Cuba, Dominican Republic, Haiti, Puerto Rico
0269-526X Country Report. Egypt
0269-5278 Country Report. Ireland
0269-5286 Country Report. France
0269-5294 Country Report. India, Nepal
0269-5324 Country Profile. Ireland
0269-5332 Country Profile. Finland
0269-5340 Country Profile. France
0269-5359 Country Profile. India, Nepal
0269-5367 Country Profile. Greece
0269-5375 Country Profile. Indonesia
0269-5383 Country Profile. Israel
0269-5391 Country Profile. Italy
0269-5405 Country Report. Japan
0269-5405 Country Profile. Japan
0269-5413 Country Report. Indonesia
0269-5421 Country Report. Italy
0269-543X Country Report. Peru, Bolivia
0269-5448 Country Report. Iran
0269-5456 Country Report. Portugal
0269-5464 Country Report. Turkey
0269-5472 Country Report. United Kingdom
0269-5480 Country Report. U S S R *changed to* Country Report. Commonwealth of Independent States.
0269-5499 Country Report. West Germany *changed to* Country Report. Germany.
0269-5510 Country Report. Zaire, Rwanda, Burundi
0269-5588 Country Profile. Malaysia, Brunei
0269-5596 Country Report. Mexico
0269-5596 Country Profile. Mexico
0269-5618 Country Profile. New Zealand
0269-5626 Country Profile. Norway
0269-5634 Country Profile. Pakistan, Afghanistan
0269-5669 Country Report. Romania, Bulgaria, Albania
0269-5677 Country Report. Indochina: Vietnam, Laos, Cambodia
0269-5685 Country Report. Uganda, Ethiopia, Somalia, Djibouti
0269-5693 Country Report. Lebanon, Cyprus
0269-5715 Country Report. Kuwait
0269-5723 Country Report. Algeria
0269-5731 Country Report. Brazil
0269-574X Country Report. Denmark, Iceland
0269-5782 Trust Law and Practice *changed to* Trust Law International.
0269-5790 O F I Occasional Papers
0269-5839 International Review of Ergonomics: Current Trends in Human Factors Research and Practice†
0269-588X Gabbitas, Truman & Thring Education after 16
0269-5901 Country Report. Finland
0269-591X Country Report. Greece
0269-5928 Country Report. Israel
0269-5944 Country Profile. Peru
0269-5952 Country Profile. Bolivia
0269-5960 Country Profile. Iran
0269-5979 Country Profile. Philippines
0269-5987 Country Profile. Portugal
0269-5995 Country Profile. Spain
0269-6002 Country Profile. Sweden
0269-6010 Country Profile. Switzerland
0269-6037 Country Profile. Senegal
0269-6045 Country Profile. Syria
0269-6053 Country Profile. Algeria
0269-607X Country Profile. Venezuela, Suriname, Netherlands Antilles
0269-6126 Country Report. Morocco
0269-6134 Country Report. Netherlands
0269-6142 Country Report. Sweden
0269-6150 Country Report. Sudan
0269-6169 Country Report. Switzerland
0269-6177 Country Report. Uruguay, Paraguay
0269-6185 Country Report. U S A
0269-6193 Country Report. Poland
0269-6207 Country Report. East Germany *changed to* Country Report. Germany.
0269-6215 Country Report. Saudi Arabia
0269-6223 Country Report. Tanzania, Mozambique
0269-6231 Country Report. China, North Korea
0269-6320 Country Profile. Zaire, Rwanda, Burundi
0269-6339 Country Profile. Nigeria
0269-6347 Country Profile. Libya
0269-6355 Country Profile. Saudi Arabia
0269-6363 Country Profile. Congo
0269-6371 Country Profile. Gabon, Equatorial Guinea
0269-638X Country Profile. Romania
0269-6398 Country Profile. Bulgaria, Albania
0269-6606 Country Profile. United Arab Emirates
0269-6614 Country Profile. Morocco
0269-6622 Country Profile. Indochina: Vietnam, Laos, Cambodia
0269-6630 Country Profile. Tanzania
0269-669X Country Report. South Korea
0269-6703 Country Report. Malaysia, Brunei
0269-6711 Country Report. Singapore
0269-672X Country Report. Taiwan
0269-6738 Country Report. South Africa
0269-6746 Country Report. Namibia, Botswana, Lesotho, Swaziland
0269-6754 Country Report. Venezuela, Suriname, Netherlands Antilles
0269-6762 Country Report. Hong Kong, Macau
0269-6924 Institute of Refractories Engineers. Journal
0269-7017 Country Profile. Mozambique
0269-7025 Country Profile. Taiwan
0269-7041 Country Profile. Singapore
0269-705X Country Profile. Sudan
0269-7068 Country Profile. Cote d'Ivoire
0269-7076 Country Profile. Uganda
0269-7084 Country Profile. Ethiopia, Somalia, Djibouti
0269-7092 Country Profile. Angola, Sao Tome & Principe
0269-7106 Country Report. Australia
0269-7114 Country Report. New Zealand
0269-7122 Country Report. Pacific Islands: Papua New Guinea, Fiji, Solomon Islands, Western Samoa, Vanuatu, Tonga
0269-7130 Country Report. Jamaica, Belize, Bahamas, Bermuda
0269-7149 Country Report. Trinidad & Tobago, Guyana, Barbados, Windward & Leeward Islands
0269-7157 Country Report. Colombia
0269-7165 Country Report. Ecuador
0269-7173 Country Report. Pakistan, Afghanistan
0269-7181 Country Report. Ghana, Sierra Leone, Liberia
0269-719X Country Report. Senegal, The Gambia, Guinea-Bassau, Cape Verde
0269-7203 Country Report. Guinea, Mali, Mauritania
0269-7211 Country Report. Syria
0269-722X Country Report. Jordan
0269-7238 Country Report. Tunisia, Malta
0269-7246 Country Report. Congo, Gabon, Equatorial Guinea
0269-7254 Country Report. Cote d'Ivoire
0269-7262 Country Report. Togo, Niger, Benin, Burkina Faso
0269-7300 Country Profile. Zambia
0269-7319 Country Profile. Hong Kong, Macau
0269-7327 Country Profile. Kuwait
0269-5707 Country Report. Bahrain, Qatar
0269-7335 Country Profile. Bahrain, Qatar
0269-7343 Country Profile. Oman, Yemen
0269-7351 Country Profile. Lebanon, Cyprus
0269-736X Country Profile. Madagascar, Comoros
0269-7378 Country Profile. Mauritius, Seychelles
0269-7386 Country Profile. Namibia
0269-7394 Country Profile. Botswana, Lesotho, Swaziland
0269-7459 Planning Practice and Research
0269-7483 Biological Wastes *see* 0960-8524
0269-7491 Environmental Pollution
0269-7513 Electricity Council Abstracts Bulletin†
0269-7572 Biorecovery
0269-7580 International Review of Victimology
0269-7653 Evolutionary Ecology
0269-7696 Catering Update
0269-770X Glass (Leicester)
0269-7726 Container Management
0269-7769 Premiere
0269-7815 International Industrial Biotechnology *see* 0959-020X
0269-7890 Foundry Focus†
0269-7955 Country Profile. South Korea
0269-7963 Country Profile. Cameroon, Central African Republic, Chad
0269-7971 Country Profile. Ecuador
0269-798X Country Profile. United Kingdom
0269-7998 Country Profile. Uruguay, Paraguay
0269-8005 Country Profile. United States of America
0269-803X Country Profile. Yugoslavia
0269-8048 Country Profile. Czechoslovakia
0269-8056 Country Profile. Togo, Benin
0269-8064 Country Profile. Niger, Burkina Faso
0269-8072 Country Profile. Jordan
0269-8080 Country Profile. Pacific Islands: Fiji, Solomon Islands, Western Samoa, Vanuatu, Tonga
0269-8099 Country Profile. Papua New Guinea
0269-8102 Country Profile. Trinidad & Tobago
0269-8110 Country Profile. Guyana, Barbados, Windward & Leeward Islands
0269-8129 Country Profile. Tunisia
0269-8137 Country Profile. Malta
0269-8145 Country Profile. Bangladesh
0269-8153 Country Profile. South Africa
0269-8269 Ham Radio Today
0269-8277 Your Commodore†
0269-8293 Photoplay†
0269-8315 Radio Control Model Cars
0269-834X Scale Models International
0269-8358 Benn's Media Directory. U.K. Media *changed to* Benn's Media Directory. U.K. Edition.
0269-8366 Benn's Media Directory. Overseas Press *changed to* Benn's Media Directory. International Edition.
0269-8390 South Western Catholic History
0269-8463 Functional Ecology
0269-8579 Oil and Chemical Pollution *see* 0141-1136
0269-8595 International Studies in the Philosophy of Science - the Dubrovnik Papers *changed to* International Studies in the Philosophy of Science.
0269-8730 Caravan & Chalet Parks Guide
0269-8803 Journal of Psychophysiology
0269-8811 British Association for Psychopharmacology. Journal *changed to* Journal of Psychopharmacology.
0269-8862 Turing Institute Abstracts in Artificial Intelligence
0269-8889 Knowledge Engineering Review
0269-8897 Science in Context
0269-8951 Medical Science Research
0269-8986 I O P Short Meetings Series
0269-9052 Brain Injury
0269-9079 Paediatric Nursing
0269-9141 A World to Win
0269-915X Mycologist
0269-9184 Electrosoft
0269-9206 Clinical Linguistics & Phonetics
0269-9214 Westwords
0269-9222 British Journal of Canadian Studies
0269-9265 Kelly's Business Directory
0269-9281 Kelly's Business Link
0269-9354 Which Video?†
0269-9370 A I D S
0269-9451 Hi-Fi Answers *see* 0959-7697
0269-9524 Infant Projects
0269-9532 Junior Projects
0269-9567 Middle East Communications
0269-9575 On Board International
0269-9591 History and Archaeology Review†
0269-963X Library Equipment Report
0269-9648 Probability in the Engineering and Informational Sciences
0269-9702 Bioethics
0269-9710 L.S.E. Quarterly†
0269-9761 Machine Knitting Monthly
0269-9834 Packaging Industry Directory
0269-9915 Nnidnid: Surreality
0269-9931 Cognition and Emotion
0269-994X Applied Psychology
0269-9982 Canoeist
0269-9990 Back Brain Recluse
0270-0069 Deer Hunting (Los Angeles) *changed to* Big Game Hunting.
0270-0255 Mathematical Modelling *see* 0895-7177
0270-031X Annual Directory of Vegetarian Restaurants†
0270-0352 F M I Monthly Index Service *changed to* Reference Point: Food Industry Abstracts.
0270-0360 Wildlife News
0270-045X International Economic Scoreboard
0270-0476 Frontiers in Immunoassay *changed to* Frontiers in Immunoassay and Biotech Update.
0270-0484 American Real Estate and Urban Economics Association. Journal
0270-0662 News from the Hill (Washington)
0270-0794 Advances in Cellular Neurobiology *changed to* Cellular Neurobiology.
0270-0808 Current Governments Reports: State Government Tax Collections *changed to* Current Governments Reports: State Government Tax Collections.
0270-0999 Consumer Affairs Letter
0270-1111 Directory of Environmental Organizations
0270-1146 Metalsmith
0270-1170 Journal of Enterostomal Therapy
0270-1197 Building Standards
0270-1200 Policy Research Centers Directory
0270-1235 Asia - Pacific Petroleum Directory *see* 0748-4089
0270-1308 Publications in Archaeology
0270-1316 American Association of Stratigraphic Palynologists. Proceedings of the Annual Meeting *see* 0191-6122
0270-1367 Research Quarterly for Exercise and Sport

ISSN

0270-1421 Kentucky Economy: Review and Perspective *changed to* University of Kentucky. Center for Business and Economic Research. Review & Perspective.
0270-1448 Readings on Equal Education
0270-1456 Harvard Women's Law Journal
0270-1480 Annual Student Symposium on Marine Affairs. Proceedings
0270-157X How to Evaluate Education Programs *see* 0034-4699
0270-1588 Construction Contracting†
0270-160X Who's Who in the Fish Industry
0270-1618 Korean Culture
0270-1626 Engelsman's General Construction Cost Guide†
0270-1642 University of Michigan. Museums of Art and Archaeology. Bulletin
0270-1707 Philatelic Literature Review
0270-1715 Accredited Institutions of Postsecondary Education
0270-174X Nouvelles *see* 0047-4576
0270-1812 Sport Scene
0270-1847 Cold Spring Harbor Monograph Series
0270-1960 Gerontology & Geriatrics Education
0270-1987 Review of Personality and Social Psychology
0270-2010 Journal of Soviet Laser Research
0270-2029 Girls Gymnastics Rules *changed to* Girls Gymnastics Rules and Manual.
0270-207X Outreach (Chicago)
0270-2088 Controversies in Nephrology†
0270-2150 Western Reserve Law Review *see* 0008-7262
0270-2282 North American Human Rights Directory†
0270-2304 Family Practice Research Journal
0270-2347 Current Christian Books
0270-238X Kentucky. Council of Economic Advisors. Annual Report *changed to* Commonwealth of Kentucky. Annual Economic Report (Year).
0270-2398 Travelore Report
0270-2460 Commercial News U S A. New Products Annual Directory†
0270-2487 Government Union Review
0270-2495 Journal of African Civilizations
0270-2525 Andy Awards Souvenir Journal
0270-2592 Journal of Financial Research
0270-2614 Skenectada
0270-2673 American Association of Tissue Banks Newsletter
0270-2703 Prison Decisions
0270-2711 Reading Psychology
0270-272X William Mitchell Law Review
0270-2738 International Data Networks News *see* 0735-1844
0270-2746 Cycle World Test Annual and Buyers Guide
0270-2762 Retail Deposit Services Report
0270-2894 Continental Birdlife†
0270-2959 Flying Needle
0270-2975 House and Garden Building Guide *see* 0199-3933
0270-2983 A M S Studies in Modern Literature
0270-2991 A M S Studies in Criminal Justice
0270-3041 Gardening
0270-305X House & Garden Kitchen & Bath Guide†
0270-3092 Applied Research in Mental Retardation *see* 0891-4222
0270-3106 Advances in Alcohol and Substance Abuse *see* 1055-0887
0270-3114 Prevention in Human Services
0270-3122 Journal of Aged Care *see* 0731-7115
0270-3149 Women & Therapy
0270-3157 Special Collections *see* 1042-8216
0270-3173 Resource Sharing and Library Networks *see* 0737-7797
0270-3181 Physical & Occupational Therapy in Geriatrics
0270-319X Legal Reference Services Quarterly
0270-3211 Teratogenesis, Carcinogenesis, and Mutagenesis
0270-322X Pediatric Pharmacology†
0270-3416 Behind the Scenes *see* 0278-467X
0270-3424 Legal Connection: Corporations and Law Firms
0270-3513 Sportsmans Book of U.S. Records†
0270-3521 Mississippi Valley Review
0270-353X Political Finance - Lobby Reporter *changed to* P A Cs & Lobbies.
0270-3572 Business and the Media†
0270-3580 Gizeh
0270-3602 Hoyan
0270-3637 Network (Durham)
0270-3653 Borgo Reference Library *see* 0891-9607
0270-370X United States Foreign Policy
0270-3718 Foster Oil Pipeline Report from Washington†
0270-3750 Dictionary, Encyclopedia, Handbook Review†
0270-3777 Dangerous Properties of Industrial Materials Report
0270-3793 Laurels *see* 1052-3952
0270-3807 I E E E Power Engineering Society. Discussions and Closures of Abstracted Papers from the Winter Meeting†
0270-3831 Entertainment Law Reporter
0270-384X California Fresh Fruit and Vegetable Shipments by Rail, Truck, and Air
0270-3866 Year Book of General Therapeutics *see* 0084-3733
0270-3904 Anthology of Magazine Verse *see* 0196-2221
0270-3920 Advances in School Psychology
0270-3963 Insulation Outlook *changed to* Outlook (Alexandria, 1953).
0270-4013 Advances in Special Education
0270-4021 Advances in Early Education and Day Care
0270-403X Air Force Journal of Logistics
0270-4048 Jazz Rag
0270-4056 Advances in Myocardiology†
0270-4110 Artists - Prints†
0270-4137 The Prostate
0270-4145 Journal of Craniofacial Genetics and Developmental Biology
0270-4153 Weekly Insiders Dairy & Egg Letter
0270-4161 Restaurant Buyers Guide *changed to* H R I - Buyers Guide.
0270-417X Seafood Price-Current
0270-4218 Baseball Case Book
0270-4226 Basketball Officials Manual
0270-4234 National Society to Prevent Blindness. Report
0270-4315 Oil Pollution Abstracts†
0270-4331 Kansas. Legislative Research Department. Report on Kansas Legislative Interim Studies
0270-434X Federal Government and Cooperative Education *see* 0277-7002
0270-4374 M I B Mineral Industries Bulletin *see* 0192-6179
0270-4390 Reverse Acronyms, Initialisms and Abbreviations Dictionary
0270-4404 Acronyms, Initialisms and Abbreviations Dictionary
0270-4447 Safety News (Denver)
0270-448X Commuter Air Carrier Traffic Statistics *changed to* Air Carrier Industry Schedule Service Traffic Statistics. Medium Regional Carriers.
0270-451X Light (Brooklyn)
0270-4528 Predicasts F & S Index International
0270-4536 Predicasts F & S Index Europe
0270-4544 Predicasts F & S Index United States
0270-4676 Bulletin of Science Technology and Society
0270-4684 Analysis and Intervention in Developmental Disabilities *see* 0891-4222
0270-4730 Studies in High Energy Physics Series
0270-4757 Signcraft
0270-4811 Government Research Centers Directory *see* 0882-3766
0270-4846 Computer Literature Index
0270-4862 California International Trade Register
0270-4870 Directory of Communications Management†
0270-4889 American Bar Association. Section of Labor and Employment Law. Committee Reports.†
0270-4919 Historical Intelligencer†
0270-4935 Electromagnetic News Report
0270-4986 Kodak Laboratory Chemicals Bulletin *changed to* Eastman Fine Chemicals News.
0270-5036 One Hundred and One Electronics Projects†
0270-5052 C B Yearbook†
0270-5060 Journal of Freshwater Ecology
0270-5087 Export-Import Bank of the United States. Statement of Condition *see* 0270-5109
0270-5109 Export-Import Bank of the United States. Annual Report
0270-5117 Acoustical Imaging: Recent Advances in Visualization and Characterization *changed to* Acoustical Imaging.
0270-5133 International Symposium on Cartography and Computing. Proceedings *changed to* International Symposium on Automated Cartography. Proceedings.
0270-515X Kentucky. Council of Economic Advisors. Policy Papers Series†
0270-5168 Kentucky. Council of Economic Advisors. Studies in Applied Economics†
0270-5176 International Air Safety Seminar Proceedings
0270-5184 Export-Import Markets
0270-5206 Bender's Dictionary of 1040 Deductions
0270-5214 Johns Hopkins A P L Technical Digest
0270-5222 Southern Pulp & Paper
0270-5230 Topics in Health Record Management
0270-5257 International Conference on Software Engineering. Proceedings
0270-5281 Cemetery Management
0270-529X Shepard's Texas Briefcase
0270-5311 Research Libraries Group. Annual Report *see* 0196-173X
0270-532X Constantian
0270-5338 Stokvis Studies in Historical Chronology & Thought
0270-5346 Camera Obscura
0270-5354 Edmund's Auto-Pedia *changed to* Edmund's Car Savvy.
0270-5370 Alaska Almanac - Facts About Alaska *see* 1051-5623
0270-5443 Ohio Biological Survey. Informative Circular
0270-5451 Geological Society of the Oregon Country. Geological Newsletter
0270-5494 Tax Notes
0270-5508 Szivarvany
0270-5524 Sea Heritage News
0270-5540 Energy News Digest
0270-563X Federal Executive Directory
0270-5664 International Studies in Philosophy
0270-5672 Farmline Magazine
0270-5699 Cornerstone (Lincoln)
0270-6091 C A E D Report *see* 0271-7190
0270-6229 A I Ch E M I Modular Instruction. Series A: Process Control
0270-6253 A M S Studies in Social History
0270-6261 A M S Studies in the Middle Ages
0270-6296 Journal of Soviet Oncology†
0270-630X Journal of Soviet Cardiovascular Research†
0270-6334 Anales de la Narrativa Espanola Contemporanea *see* 0272-1635
0270-6377 Genetic Engineering News
0270-6474 Journal of Neuroscience
0270-6636 Nursing Law and Ethics *see* 0277-8459
0270-6644 Clinical Psychiatry News
0270-6679 Feminist Issues
0270-6687 Corona
0270-6717 Interface (Chicago)
0270-675X Toxic Substances Reporter†
0270-6776 P C A S Newsletter
0270-6822 M U F O N - U F O Journal
0270-6881 N A E N Bulletin
0270-7012 New Directions in Middle East Studies Newsletter†
0270-7284 S N A Perspective
0270-7306 Molecular and Cellular Biology
0270-7314 The Journal of Futures Markets
0270-7446 China International Business†
0270-7454 Pat-Ab: U S Patent Abstracts & Background, Solar Thermal Energy†
0270-7497 Great Issues of the Day
0270-7500 Pennsylvania Heritage
0270-7527 Resume
0270-7543 Directors Encyclopedia of Newspapers
0270-756X U.S. Department of Energy. Annual Report to Congress on the Automotive Technology Development Program
0270-7624 A I Ch E M I Modular Instruction. Series B: Stagewise and Mass Transfer Operations
0270-7632 A I Ch E M I Modular Instruction. Series C: Transport
0270-7640 A I Ch E M I Modular Instruction. Series D: Thermodynamics
0270-7659 A I Ch E M I Modular Instruction. Series E: Kinetics
0270-7667 A I Ch E M I Modular Instruction. Series F: Material and Energy Balances
0270-7780 Virginia Nurse
0270-787X Fodor's Budget Italy *changed to* Fodor's Affordable Italy.
0270-7888 Fodor's Budget Spain *changed to* Fodor's Great Travel Values: Spain.
0270-7950 N C I Fact Book
0270-7969 Business Traveler's Report†
0270-7993 Woman's Art Journal
0270-8027 Small-Scale Master Builder†
0270-8159 Charles Christopher Mark's Arts Reporting Service
0270-8183 Fodor's Central America
0270-8191 National Directory of Health/Medicine Organizations
0270-823X Energy Research Digest *see* 0883-9735
0270-8248 Improving Urban Mobility *see* 0270-8264
0270-8264 Directory of Research, Development and Demonstration Projects†
0270-8302 Adweek: Southeast Advertising News *see* 8756-6389
0270-8337 E E R I Newsletter
0270-8388 Art of Negotiating Newsletter
0270-8523 Microforms Annual
0270-8531 H P L C: Advances and Perspectives
0270-854X John Marshall Law Review
0270-8663 Audio-Cassette Newsletter†
0270-868X Phoebe
0270-8841 Cable T V Security†
0270-885X Cable T V Advertising
0270-8973 Public Sector - Health Care Risk Management *see* 0883-6671
0270-8981 Dance Films Association. Bulletin *changed to* Dance on Camera News.
0270-899X 16 Magazine
0270-9015 Command Policy†
0270-9031 Weather Guide Calendar *changed to* Minnesota Weather Guide Calendar.
0270-904X Review of Afro-American Issues and Culture†
0270-9074 Archives of Family Practice†
0270-9139 Hepatology (St. Louis)
0270-9155 Energy Technology Review†
0270-9163 Energy Law Journal
0270-9171 Dancer's Digest *changed to* Dancer's Digest & Off Broadway.
0270-9228 Advances in Family Intervention, Assessment and Theory
0270-9287 United Methodist Board of Higher Education and Ministry. Quarterly Review
0270-9295 Seminars in Nephrology
0270-9325 Guitar and Mandolin
0270-9341 Phoenix Home & Garden

0270-935X National Center for a Barrier Free Environment. Report†
0270-9368 Shaker Messenger
0270-9384 U.S. Foreign Broadcast Information Service. Daily Reports: Middle East and North Africa *changed to* U.S. Foreign Broadcast Information Service. Daily Reports: Near East & South Asia.
0270-9392 Conference on Modern Jewish Studies Annual *see* 0270-9406
0270-9406 Modern Jewish Studies Annual
0270-9465 Discontinued Diodes D.A.T.A. Book *changed to* Diode Discontinued Devices D.A.T.A. Book.
0270-9635 Telephone Marketing Report†
0270-9872 Dataguide†
0270-9899 House and Garden Gardening Guide *see* 0270-3041
0270-9988 Linear I Cs D.A.T.A. Book *changed to* Linear I Cs D.A.T.A. Digest.
0271-0129 Discontinued Integrated Circuit D.A.T.A. Book *changed to* Digital & Audio-Video Discontinued Devices D.A.T.A. Book.
0271-0137 Journal of Mind and Behavior
0271-0145 Las Vegas Insider
0271-0269 U.S. Foreign Broadcast Information Service. Daily Reports: Western Europe
0271-0315 Oil Shale Symposium Proceedings
0271-0323 E E R C Reports
0271-0498 Middle East Executive Reports
0271-0552 New Directions for Methodology of Behavioral Science *see* 0271-1249
0271-0560 New Directions for Higher Education
0271-0579 New Directions for Institutional Research
0271-0587 New Directions for Institutional Advancement†
0271-0595 New Directions for Experiential Learning†
0271-0609 New Directions for Testing and Measurement†
0271-0617 New Directions for College Learning Assistance†
0271-0625 New Directions for Exceptional Children†
0271-0633 New Directions for Teaching and Learning
0271-0641 Arizona State University Anthropological Research Papers
0271-065X A O P A's Airport U S A *see* 1056-7704
0271-0668 American Land†
0271-0706 Nuclear Index
0271-0722 Discontinued Transistors D.A.T.A. Book *see* 0730-4846
0271-0730 Arba Sicula
0271-0749 Journal of Clinical Psychopharmacology
0271-0773 Microwave D.A.T.A. Book†
0271-079X D.A.T.A. Books Master Type Locator *see* 1048-6607
0271-0811 Response: The New Sexuality
0271-0838 Photograph Collector
0271-0927 Best's Directory of Recommended Independent Insurance Adjusters *changed to* Best's Directory of Recommended Insurance Adjusters.
0271-0951 VideoPrint†
0271-0986 Hispanic Journal
0271-0994 New Publications for Architecture Librariest
0271-1001 Desert Research Institute Publications in the Social Sciences
0271-1044 National Weather Association Newsletter
0271-1052 National Weather Digest
0271-1079 N C ShopOwner†
0271-1206 Topics in Hospital Pharmacy Management
0271-1214 Topics in Early Childhood Special Education
0271-1222 Topics in Health Care Planning and Marketing Quarterly *changed to* H C P and M: Health Care Planning and Marketing.
0271-1249 New Directions for Methodology of Social & Behavioral Science†
0271-1265 Audio-Digest Anesthesiology
0271-1273 Audio-Digest Surgery *changed to* Audio-Digest General Surgery.
0271-1281 Audio-Digest Ophthalmology
0271-129X Audio-Digest Obstetrics - Gynecology
0271-1303 Audio-Digest Internal Medicine
0271-1311 Audio-Digest Psychiatry
0271-132X Audio-Digest Orthopaedics
0271-1338 Audio-Digest Urology
0271-1346 Audio-Digest Pediatrics
0271-1354 Audio-Digest Otolaryngology - Head and Neck Surgery
0271-1362 Audio-Digest Family Practice
0271-1400 Advertising Research Foundation. Yearbook *changed to* Advertising Research Foundation. Annual Report and Yearbook.
0271-1427 Southwest Folklore†
0271-1435 Journal of Pre-Raphaelite Studies *see* 0835-7099
0271-1443 Weekly Reader Funday *see* 0890-3174
0271-1478 Chemical Substances Control
0271-1494 Topics in Learning and Learning Disabilities *see* 0741-9325
0271-1567 U.S. Department of Labor. Employee Retirement Income Security Act. Report to Congress
0271-1575 Journal of Neurological and Orthopaedic Surgery *see* 0890-6599
0271-1591 Vegetarian Voice
0271-1672 N A S P A Forum
0271-1699 Gravure Environmental Newsletter
0271-1702 Learning Traveler. Vacation Study Abroad *changed to* Vacation Study Abroad.
0271-1761 Index: Foreign Broadcast Information Service Daily Reports: China
0271-1966 Classical Calliope *see* 1050-7086
0271-1990 The Korbin Letter
0271-2040 Johnson Outboards Boating†
0271-2067 Cost Data for Landscape Construction
0271-2075 Public Administration and Development
0271-2083 Atlanta Art Papers *see* 0278-1441
0271-2091 International Journal for Numerical Methods in Fluids
0271-2172 R D P
0271-2199 N A G W S Guide. Competitive Swimming and Diving†
0271-2202 Transnational Immigration Law Reporter
0271-2229 A A A S Publications Catalog
0271-2334 Advances in Transport Processes†
0271-2482 T A T Journal
0271-2512 Space and Time
0271-2555 U S M A Newsletter *see* 1050-5628
0271-258X Real Estate Appraiser and Analyst *changed to* Real Estate Appraiser.
0271-2601 Hazardous Waste Report
0271-2636 Petersen's Pro Hockey†
0271-2687 Symphony Magazine
0271-2709 Dispute Resolution
0271-2776 Fodor's Alaska
0271-2792 Survey of Law†
0271-2849 St. Louis Law Review *see* 0043-0862
0271-2938 Glass Science and Technology
0271-2946 Ocean Thermal Energy Conversion Workshop. Workshop Proceedings
0271-3012 Seven (Lakewood)†
0271-3020 Design & Management for Resource Recovery†
0271-3136 Theatre Directory
0271-3179 Key Issues†
0271-3225 Stepparent News *changed to* Stepfamilies & Beyond.
0271-3241 Key, Lock and Lantern
0271-3276 Alaska Journal of Commerce & Pacific Rim Reporter
0271-3284 Immunology Tribune†
0271-3306 Library Management Quarterly
0271-3462 Discipline and Grievances: White Collar Edition†
0271-3519 Arab Studies Quarterly
0271-3586 American Journal of Industrial Medicine
0271-3659 Executive Speaker
0271-3667 School Librarian's Workshop
0271-3683 Current Eye Research
0271-3829 Photograph†
0271-3977 England and Scotland on Twenty Dollars a Day *see* 1042-8399
0271-3993 Sylloge Nummorum Graecorum
0271-4019 Ancient Coins in North American Collections
0271-4043 American Society of Photogrammetry Fall Convention. Technical Papers *changed to* American Society for Photogrammetry and Remote Sensing Fall Convention. Technical Papers.
0271-4132 Contemporary Mathematics
0271-4159 Computer Graphics World
0271-4299 Columbia Road Review†
0271-437X Eastern Transportation Law Seminar Papers and Proceedings *changed to* Transportation Law Institute Papers and Proceedings.
0271-4396 Western Transportation Law Seminar Papers and Proceedings *changed to* Transportation Law Institute Papers and Proceedings.
0271-4450 American Railway Engineering Association. Proceedings, Technical Conference *changed to* American Railway Engineering Association. Proceedings.
0271-4477 Computer - Readable Databases
0271-4655 I E E E International Symposium on Information Theory. Abstracts of Papers
0271-4760 Fodor's Caribbean and Bahamas *changed to* Fodor's Caribbean.
0271-4760 Fodor's Caribbean and Bahamas *changed to* Fodor's Bahamas.
0271-4787 Employment and Earnings: United States
0271-4795 C R I Communications Update Service
0271-5023 En Passant Poetry
0271-5031 Scottish-American Genealogist†
0271-5090 Woodstove, Coalstove, Fireplace and Equipment Directory *see* 1045-8069
0271-5147 Northern Ohio Live
0271-5198 Clinical Hemorheology
0271-5287 Federal Reserve Bank of Minneapolis. Quarterly Review
0271-5309 Language & Communication
0271-5317 Nutrition Research
0271-5333 Radiographics
0271-535X Insider's Guide to Prep Schools†
0271-5368 Counselor Preparation (Year)
0271-5376 Coastal Research
0271-5384 Medical Psychology *see* 0277-9536
0271-5430 Telephone News
0271-5481 Liability Reporter
0271-5783 Schwann-2 Record and Tape Guide *see* 1047-2371
0271-5848 Labor Unity
0271-5880 Co-Op Directory
0271-5902 A S E E Computers in Education Division. CoED Transactions *changed to* Computers in Education Journal.
0271-5945 Repair and Remodeling Cost Data *changed to* Means Repair and Remodeling Cost Data (Year).
0271-5988 Children in Crisis *see* 0732-7420
0271-6062 Principal (Alexandria)
0271-6100 Florida Keys Magazine†
0271-6283 New York State Criminal Law Review
0271-6437 Brooklyn Engineer
0271-6445 U.S. Library of Congress. Accessions List: South Asia
0271-6518 Admission Requirements of American Medical Colleges, Including Canada *see* 0066-9423
0271-6577 Caribbean Studies Newsletter
0271-6585 Cell Motility *see* 0886-1544
0271-6607 French Literature Series
0271-6615 California Services Register
0271-6623 Micropolitics†
0271-6712 Importcar (Akron) *see* 0735-7877
0271-6771 A V S Biomedical Bulletin *changed to* Biomedical Bulletin.
0271-678X Journal of Cerebral Blood Flow and Metabolism
0271-6798 Journal of Pediatric Orthopedics
0271-6801 Journal of Molecular and Applied Genetics†
0271-6925 Ripley P. Bullen Monographs in Anthropology and History
0271-7085 Enhanced Energy Recovery News
0271-7093 Battery & E V Technology News
0271-7107 Applied Genetics News
0271-7123 Social Science and Medicine. Part A: Medical Sociology *see* 0277-9536
0271-7190 C A R D Report (Ames, 1971)†
0271-7204 Field Afar *changed to* Maryknoll Fathers and Brothers.
0271-7220 Old-House Journal Catalog
0271-7352 American Journal of Reproductive Immunology *see* 8755-8920
0271-7506 Psycscan: Applied Psychology
0271-7514 N A G W S Guide. Bowling-Fencing *changed to* N A G W S Guide. Archery-Fencing.
0271-7557 Naropa Institute Journal of Psychology *see* 0894-8577
0271-7565 Police and Security Bulletin†
0271-759X Country Magazine *see* 0888-1022
0271-7662 Directory of Food Service Distributors (Year)
0271-7735 Little Balkans Review
0271-7751 Money Market Fund Survey
0271-7794 Masters of Science Fiction†
0271-7808 Fantasy Voices†
0271-7956 Year Book of Clinical Pharmacy†
0271-7964 Year Book of Emergency Medicine
0271-8006 Directory of Retailer Owned Cooperative Chains, Wholesaler Sponsored Voluntary Chains, Wholesale Grocers *see* 0277-1969
0271-8014 Entertainment Industry Directory
0271-8022 Indiana Theory Review
0271-8057 Journal of Tissue Culture Methods
0271-8170 Sporting News National Basketball Association Register *see* 0739-3067
0271-8189 Best of Micro†
0271-8197 New Pages
0271-8200 Journal of Precision Teaching
0271-8219 Modern Technics in Surgery. Head and Neck Surgery
0271-8227 Iowa Woman
0271-8235 Seminars in Neurology
0271-8294 Topics in Language Disorders
0271-8472 News on Tests
0271-8510 A A P G Studies in Geology Series
0271-860X N C A A Water Polo Rules *see* 0734-0508
0271-8677 Directory of Dental and Allied Dental Educators *changed to* Directory of Dental Educators.
0271-8685 Midwest Historical and Genealogical Register. Quarterly
0271-8707 Drug Interactions Newsletter *changed to* Drug Interactions and Updates.
0271-8774 Paleo Data Banks†
0271-8987 Alaska Shippers Guide†
0271-9002 Micro†
0271-9029 Alternate Energy Transportation Newsletter†
0271-9045 Business Law Memo *see* 0884-1977
0271-9061 I.O. Evans Studies in the Philosophy & Criticism of Literature
0271-9126 Landscaping, Lawns and Gardens
0271-9142 Journal of Clinical Immunology
0271-9150 National Consultor
0271-9274 Studies in American Jewish Literature
0271-9347 Wistar Symposium Series†
0271-9355 Biological Regulation & Development
0271-9479 Graphic Arts Research Center. G A R C Newsletter *see* 0895-6529
0271-9487 American Man†
0271-9509 Greenwood Encyclopedia of American Institutions
0271-9517 N A C A D A Journal

5672 ISSN INDEX

0271-955X Frontiers in Aging Series
0271-9592 Common Cause Magazine
0271-9746 Trustee Quarterly
0271-9800 Annual of Armenian Linguistics
0271-9894 B I N Merchandiser
0271-9940 Dance Book Forum
0271-9959 Technical Association of the Pulp and Paper Industry. Engineering Conference Proceedings (Year)
0271-9983 Clinical Respiratory Physiology *see* 0903-1936
0272-0035 Arthur Frommer's Dollarwise Guide to Germany *see* 1044-2405
0272-0051 Appraisal Manual *see* 0732-815X
0272-0086 China Exchange News
0272-0108 Nuclear Medicine Annual
0272-0116 Construction Lawyer
0272-0167 Directory of Home Center Operators & Hardware Chains (Year)
0272-0264 Greenwood Encyclopedia of Black Music
0272-0280 Niepodleglosc
0272-0299 Corporate E F T Report
0272-0310 International Micrographics Source Book *changed to* International Imaging Source Book.
0272-037X D L A Bulletin
0272-0396 Entrepreneurial Manager's Newsletter
0272-0426 Ancestoring
0272-0434 Advances in the Mechanics and Physics of Surfaces Series
0272-0485 Metals Daily†
0272-0493 Wise Giving Bulletin†
0272-0515 Women & Health Roundtable Reports
0272-0558 Enterprise (Cincinnati)†
0272-0582 Psychological Cinema Register
0272-0590 Fundamental and Applied Toxicology
0272-0671 Policy Publishers and Associations Directory
0272-068X Advances in Human Psychopharmacology
0272-0701 Free Inquiry
0272-0809 Evolutionary Monographs
0272-0817 Rental House & Condo Investor†
0272-0825 National Fund Raiser
0272-0868 Forecasts & Strategies
0272-0884 Technicalities
0272-0906 American Institute of Architects. International Directory†
0272-0965 Pneuma
0272-1015 Irish-American Genealogist†
0272-1074 George D. Hall's New York Manufacturers Directory
0272-1082 Century
0272-1104 Directory of Apparel Specialty Stores. Women's and Children's *see* 0277-9617
0272-1112 Directory of Men's and Boy's Specialty Stores *see* 0277-9625
0272-1155 Heritage Lectures
0272-1163 American Export Register
0272-1171 I C P Directory†
0272-1236 Video Programs Index†
0272-1279 St. Louis
0272-1406 Tampa Bay History
0272-1570 Northwest Discovery
0272-1635 Anales de la Literatura Espanola Contemporanea
0272-1708 Control Systems Magazine *see* 0888-0611
0272-1716 I E E E Computer Graphics and Applications
0272-1724 I E E E Power Engineering Review
0272-1732 I E E E Micro
0272-1740 Advances in Substance Abuse: Behavioral and Biological Research
0272-1775 International Golf Directory *changed to* Golf Index.
0272-1902 New Hearer
0272-1953 American Subsidiaries of German Firms
0272-1961 Legal Assistants Update
0272-197X Falconer's Current Drug Handbook†
0272-1988 Reference Book Review
0272-1996 W L W Journal
0272-2011 American Review of Canadian Studies
0272-2046 Marijuana and Health: Annual Report to the U.S. Congress from the Secretary of Health, Education and Welfare†
0272-2062 International Banjo
0272-2089 Family Journal
0272-2135 Directory of College Recruiting Personnel†
0272-2275 Moped and Economy Motorcycle Buyer's Guide†
0272-2348 Journal of Refugee Resettlement†
0272-2380 E S P Journal *see* 0889-4906
0272-2410 Pace Law Review
0272-2461 Accent on Living Buyer's Guide
0272-247X National Directory of Landscape Architecture Firms†
0272-2488 Contemporary Concepts in Physics
0272-2631 Studies in Second Language Acquisition
0272-2666 Perfumer & Flavorist
0272-2690 Language Problems and Language Planning
0272-2712 Clinics in Laboratory Medicine
0272-2720 Hollywood Drama-Logue *changed to* Drama-Logue.
0272-2747 Ram's Horn
0272-2801 Research in the Interweave of Social Roles
0272-2836 U.S. National Toxicology Program. Annual Report on Carcinogens
0272-3271 Bank Personnel News
0272-3328 N R D C Newsletter†
0272-3336 Datapro Reports on Word Processing†
0272-3387 Directory of Professional Genealogists and Related Services *changed to* Directory of Professional Genealogists.
0272-3417 Farming Uncle
0272-3425 Moebius *see* 0894-1912
0272-3433 The Public Historian
0272-345X Executive Bio-Pictorial Directory (Year) *changed to* The President's Team.
0272-3530 Drug-Nutrient Interactions†
0272-3565 Benzene Magazine†
0272-3573 Today's Education (General Edition) *see* 0734-7219
0272-3581 Today's Education: Social Studies Edition†
0272-359X Today's Education: Elementary Edition†
0272-3638 Urban Geography
0272-3646 Physical Geography
0272-3727 American Institute for Conservation of Historic and Artistic Works. Preprints of Papers Presented at the Annual Meeting *changed to* American Institute for Conservation of Historic and Artistic Works. Abstracts of Papers Presented at the Annual Meeting.
0272-3751 Pets and People of the World
0272-3794 Annual Editions: Psychology
0272-3808 Annual Editions: Aging
0272-3816 Annual Editions: Criminal Justice
0272-3875 Index: Foreign Broadcast Information Service Daily Reports: Asia and Pacific *changed to* Index: Foreign Broadcast Information Service Daily Reports: East Asia.
0272-3913 T S F Bulletin†
0272-3921 Nuclear Technology - Fusion *see* 0748-1896
0272-4030 Houston Review: History and Culture of the Gulf Coast
0272-4057 Chemical Engineering Equipment Buyer's Guide
0272-4065 Directory of Corporate Counsel†
0272-4103 Today's Education: Vocational-Career Education Edition†
0272-4111 Today's Education: Mathematics-Science Edition†
0272-4154 Better Homes and Gardens Brides Book†
0272-4294 Seafood America
0272-4308 International Journal of Partial Hospitalization
0272-4316 Journal of Early Adolescence
0272-4324 Plasma Chemistry & Plasma Processing
0272-4332 Risk Analysis
0272-4340 Cellular & Molecular Neurobiology
0272-4359 Another Chicago Magazine
0272-4367 Freedom Socialist
0272-4383 American Kennel Club. Show, Obedience and Field Trial Awards *see* 0888-627X
0272-4391 Drug Development Research
0272-4464 Annual Editions: Social Problems
0272-4499 McCall's Country Decorating†
0272-4537 Faxon Librarians' Guide to Continuations†
0272-4553 Computer and Communications Buyer
0272-4561 Construction Claims Monthly
0272-457X Hybridoma
0272-4588 Monoclonal Antibody News *see* 1047-871X
0272-4626 European Applied Research Reports: Environmental and Natural Resources Section†
0272-4634 Journal of Vertebrate Paleontology
0272-4685 Conference of Electrical Engineering Problems in the Rubber and Plastics Industries. I E E E Conference Record
0272-4715 Simulation Symposium. Record of Proceedings
0272-4782 British Defence Directory
0272-4790 Advances in Drying
0272-4847 Annual Symposium on Switching and Automata Theory. Proceedings *see* 0272-5428
0272-4855 Office Automation Conference Digest†
0272-4936 Annals of Tropical Paediatrics
0272-4944 Journal of Environmental Psychology
0272-4952 Power Industry Research†
0272-4960 I M A Journal of Applied Mathematics
0272-4979 I M A Journal of Numerical Analysis
0272-4987 Quarterly Journal of Experimental Psychology. Section A: Human Experimental Psychology
0272-4995 Quarterly Journal of Experimental Psychology. Section B: Comparative and Physiological Psychology
0272-5045 American Society of International Law. Proceedings of the Annual Meeting
0272-5088 Accelerators and Storage Rings Series
0272-5231 Clinics in Chest Medicine
0272-5371 Western Bank Directory
0272-5428 Symposium on Foundations of Computer Science. Proceedings
0272-5436 Archaeoastronomy Bulletin *see* 0190-9940
0272-5444 Small Systems World *see* 1055-7768
0272-5460 Internships
0272-5495 OncoLogic†
0272-5509 Current Industrial Reports: Finished Fabrics. Production, Inventories, and Unfilled Orders *changed to* Current Industrial Reports: Broadwoven Fabrics (Gray).
0272-5541 Masson Today†
0272-5657 Me
0272-5665 Journal of Therapeutic Humor†
0272-569X Travel Expense Management
0272-572X JazzTimes
0272-5754 N C A A Illustrated Basketball Rules *changed to* N C A A Men's and Women's Illustrated Basketball Rules.
0272-5827 Search (Brattleboro)
0272-5959 Libertarian Digest
0272-5967 Maize†
0272-6017 Changing Public Attitudes on Governments and Taxes
0272-6122 International Bulletin of Missionary Research
0272-6300 C B O Management Report *see* 0747-6086
0272-6319 Childbirth Alternatives Quarterly†
0272-6327 Perspectives in Biomechanics
0272-6343 Electromagnetics
0272-6351 Particulate Science and Technology
0272-636X Director of Nursing Labor Alert *changed to* Health Labor Relations Alert.
0272-6378 Mark Twain Society Bulletin
0272-6386 American Journal of Kidney Diseases
0272-6440 Journal of Research in Singing *changed to* Journal of Research in Singing and Applied Vocal Pedagogy.
0272-6513 Connections (New York)†
0272-6521 Pyrotechnica
0272-6742 Woodrose†
0272-6750 Democracy†
0272-6807 Sculpture *see* 0747-5284
0272-684X International Quarterly of Community Health Education
0272-6904 Colorado Homes & Lifestyles
0272-6939 Tentmaker's Journal
0272-6955 Your Patient and Cancer *see* 0743-8176
0272-6963 Journal of Operations Management
0272-7064 Osteopathic Physician's Compendium of Drug Therapy *see* 0276-4318
0272-7102 N H E L P Health Advocate
0272-7145 Children's Digest (1980)
0272-717X Mid-Hudson Language Studies†
0272-720X S I G Small Newsletter
0272-7250 Albanian Catholic Bulletin
0272-7269 Technical Association of the Pulp and Paper Industry. Annual Meeting Proceedings *see* 1046-4166
0272-7323 Rep Talk
0272-7331 F T Fastener Technology *see* 0746-2441
0272-7358 Clinical Psychology Review *issued with* 0009-9244
0272-7358 Clinical Psychology Review
0272-7374 Journal of Housing
0272-7404 Comedy
0272-7595 Journal of Contemporary Studies†
0272-7617 Death Penalty Reporter†
0272-7625 Nedrud: the Criminal Law *see* 0278-1816
0272-765X Social Action and the Law
0272-7714 Estuarine, Coastal and Shelf Science
0272-7730 Starmont Reader's Guides
0272-7749 Diagnostic Histopathology *see* 0022-3417
0272-7757 Economics of Education Review
0272-7838 U S Woman Engineer
0272-7846 S E C Monthly Statistical Review†
0272-7897 Annual Editions: Marriage and Family
0272-7900 Pulmonary Disease Reviews†
0272-7919 International Journal of Turkish Studies
0272-7951 Accent on Liturgy *see* 0276-2358
0272-8060 Houston Monthly Magazine
0272-8079 Speechwriter's Newsletter
0272-8087 Seminars in Liver Diseases
0272-8095 N C A A Swimming *see* 0736-5128
0272-8117 Delaware Directory of Commerce and Industry
0272-8141 I S A Directory of Instrumentation
0272-8362 Setting Municipal Priorities
0272-8397 Polymer Composites
0272-8419 Asantesem†
0272-8443 Health Facilities Energy Report
0272-846X Journal of Clinical Neuro-Ophthalmology
0272-8486 Bulletin on Training
0272-8494 Folklore Bibliography for (Year)†
0272-8532 Base Line
0272-8540 Chicago History
0272-8559 Professional Consultant and Seminar Business Report *changed to* Professional Consultant.
0272-8583 Minnesota Industrial Minerals Directory
0272-863X N A G W S Guide. Tennis†
0272-8745 National Service Data: Domestic *changed to* Domestic Cars Service & Repair.
0272-8761 Life Insurance Index†
0272-8818 Trade Names Dictionary *changed to* Brands and Their Companies.
0272-8826 New Trade Names *changed to* Brands and Their Companies Supplement.
0272-8842 Ceramics International
0272-8850 Periodicals Digest in Dentistry
0272-8869 Bibliography of Fossil Vertebrates

ISSN

ISSN INDEX 5673

0272-8893 Focus on Learning Problems in Mathematics
0272-8907 Colorado Heritage News *see* 0895-0083
0272-8923 Cycle Street and Touring Guide
0272-8931 Capstone Journal of Education†
0272-8958 Consultation on Church Union. Official Record *changed to* Consultation on Church Union. Digest.
0272-8966 Sanctuary
0272-8974 U.S. Urban Initiatives Anti-Crime Program. Annual Report to Congress
0272-9008 Annual Editions: Environment
0272-9016 University of Southern California. School of Social Work. Social Work Papers†
0272-9032 Genetic Technology News
0272-9075 University of California. Lawrence Berkeley Laboratory. Biology and Medicine Division. Annual Report
0272-9172 Materials Research Society Symposium Proceedings
0272-9199 Pedalpoint
0272-9296 Legal Resource Index
0272-9377 Colorado Heritage
0272-9490 American Journal of Occupational Therapy
0272-9504 Advances in Plastics Technology *see* 0730-6679
0272-9520 Tarakan Music Letter†
0272-9598 RiverSedge
0272-9601 Prooftexts
0272-9660 Telematics†
0272-9709 Promoting Health†
0272-9741 American Board of Medical Specialties. Annual Report & Reference Handbook
0272-9784 Evaluation Notes†
0272-9873 South Carolina Geology
0272-9881 Clinical Biochemistry Reviews (Tarrytown)†
0272-989X Medical Decision Making
0272-9903 Selecta Mathematica Sovietica
0273-0197 Needle and Bobbin Club Bulletin
0273-0200 Harris Postage Stamp Price Index†
0273-0227 Linda Hall Library. Miscellany†
0273-0278 Postgraduate Radiology
0273-0324 Source (Jamaica)†
0273-0340 Henry James Review
0273-043X Holly Society of America. Proceedings *see* 0738-2421
0273-0685 Securities and Federal Corporate Law Report
0273-0693 Scotia
0273-0839 Alternatives *see* 0361-6908
0273-0979 American Mathematical Society. Bulletin. New Series
0273-0995 Brief (Chicago)
0273-1037 Harris Poll
0273-1061 Federal Librarian
0273-1134 National Academy of Sciences of the United States of America. Proceedings. Biological Sciences *changed to* National Academy of Sciences of the United States of America. Proceedings.
0273-1177 Advances in Space Research
0273-1223 Water Science and Technology
0273-1231 Studies in Freedom
0273-124X Contributions to the Study of Childhood and Youth
0273-1266 World Faiths Insight *changed to* World Faiths Encounter.
0273-1347 Comparative State Politics Newsletter *see* 1047-1006
0273-1398 Fine Homebuilding
0273-141X G T E Automatic Electric World-Wide Communications Journal†
0273-1428 Country Music Sourcebook
0273-1576 Sesame Street Parents' Newsletter†
0273-1606 Metamorfosis†
0273-1665 Plum Magazine
0273-1673 E E R Energy Price Forecast†
0273-1800 Gulf Solidarity
0273-1916 Alaska. Oil and Gas Conservation Commission. Statistical Report†
0273-2017 Survival Tomorrow
0273-2033 One Show
0273-2041 B H M Support†
0273-2068 Association of Graduate Dance Ethnologists U C L A Journal *see* 0884-3198
0273-2076 California Alcohol Program Plan *changed to* California Alcohol Program: Report to the Legislature (Year).
0273-2122 National Center for Professional Responsibility Advance Sheets†
0273-2157 Directory of Special Opportunities for Women†
0273-2173 Sociological Spectrum
0273-2238 Water - Engineering and Management
0273-2246 Shooting Commercials (Melville)
0273-2254 Dermatology & Allergy†
0273-2289 Applied Biochemistry and Biotechnology
0273-2297 Developmental Review
0273-2300 Regulatory Toxicology and Pharmacology
0273-2335 Los Chihuahuas
0273-2343 S H A R E†
0273-2351 Research Libraries in O C L C: A Quarterly
0273-236X Employee Benefit Cases
0273-2378 Energy Purchasing Report†
0273-2696 Syntax†
0273-270X New Jersey Monthly
0273-2726 Kerr Report *changed to* Mobilehome Parks Report.
0273-2742 Arkansas Report
0273-2858 Metropolitan Home
0273-2866 Dairy and Food Sanitation *see* 1043-3546
0273-2904 Biofuels Report *see* 1050-2483
0273-2920 Song of Zion
0273-298X Current Energy Patents†
0273-2998 European Applied Research Reports Special Topics Series
0273-3013 Benchmark Soils News†
0273-3048 Asbestos Litigation Reporter
0273-3056 RadioNews†
0273-3072 Cato Journal
0273-3080 S C A N Newsletter
0273-3102 Energy Clearinghouse†
0273-3145 Action (Winona Lake)†
0273-3153 Children's Bible Study Teacher
0273-3161 Children's Bible Study Older Pupil
0273-317X Children's Bible Study Younger Pupil
0273-3188 Defense Week
0273-3196 Initiative News Report†
0273-320X Nursing (Year) Drug Handbook
0273-3218 A W W A Mainstream
0273-3226 Biotechnology News
0273-3234 Work Related Abstracts
0273-3242 Resophonic Echoes *see* 0733-8759
0273-3250 C T I Journal
0273-3315 C C L M News *changed to* C L M P Newsletter.
0273-3323 Central Park
0273-3382 Journal of International Student Personnel
0273-3463 Missouri Dental Association Journal *changed to* Missouri Dental Journal.
0273-3560 Fairshare
0273-3579 Psychology Information Guide Series†
0273-3617 Risk Management Report - Medical Records *see* 0883-6671
0273-3706 Extractive and Process Metallurgy *see* 0882-7508
0273-3722 Yearbook of Substance Use and Abuse
0273-3951 Virginia Librarian Newsletter *changed to* Virginia Librarian.
0273-3994 Predicasts Index of Corporate Change *see* 0744-2785
0273-4079 Dial†
0273-4125 Findex
0273-4257 Professional Practice Management†
0273-429X Chinese Physics
0273-4346 Education Directory. Local Education Agencies *changed to* Directory of Public Elementary and Secondary Education Agencies.
0273-4419 Whalewatcher
0273-4435 Federal Funding Guide
0273-4443 Education Funding News
0273-4451 Local Government Funding Report *see* 0741-3173
0273-446X Rural Educator
0273-4605 A L A Handbook of Organization and Membership Directory *see* 0084-6406
0273-4613 Consulting Opportunities Journal
0273-4621 Perspectives in Computing (Armonk)†
0273-4699 West Coast Sailors
0273-4753 Journal of Marketing Education
0273-480X World's Fair
0273-4931 Armstrong Oil Directories: Louisiana, Mississippi, Arkansas, Texas Gulf Coast and East Texas Edition
0273-4958 Radiology Letter *see* 0741-160X
0273-4974 National Report on Computers and Health
0273-5016 Producer's Price Current (West Coast Edition) *changed to* Urner Barry's Price Current (West Coast Edition).
0273-5024 Journal of Teaching in Physical Education
0273-5032 U.S. Bureau of Alcohol, Tobacco and Firearms. Explosives Incidents
0273-5229 Armstrong Oil Directories: Rocky Mountain - Central United States Edition
0273-5326 Performance and Instruction *see* 0884-1985
0273-5415 Precancel Forum
0273-5466 Pensions and Investment Age *see* 1050-4974
0273-5520 Restaurants and Institutions
0273-5598 Philatelic Observer
0273-5636 On Cable†
0273-5652 Art Business News
0273-5695 Wood 'n Energy *changed to* Hearth & Home.
0273-5822 Mini-Storage Messenger
0273-5830 Tampa Bay Business Journal
0273-5865 Discipleship Journal
0273-5954 Contractor's Guide
0273-5970 National Comment†
0273-6160 Better Living
0273-6187 Intermountain Catholic
0273-6225 Builder Developer West
0273-6241 S Gaugian
0273-625X Locksmith Ledger - Security Guide and Directory *changed to* Locksmith Ledger - International Directory.
0273-6314 Executive Intelligence Review
0273-6357 Mergers and Corporate Policy
0273-642X Skier's World†
0273-6462 Sheet Music Magazine. Standard Piano-Guitar Edition
0273-6497 Adoptalk
0273-6519 Appaloosa World
0273-6527 This People
0273-6535 Contemporary Dialysis *see* 0899-837X
0273-6551 Broker World
0273-656X Chilton's Automotive Industries *changed to* Automotive Industries.
0273-6608 I M - Internal Medicine for the Specialist
0273-6624 Nelson Survey of Industry Research *see* 0740-5103
0273-6691 Gray's Sporting Journal
0273-6705 Quote
0273-6721 Chilton's Distribution Magazine
0273-6748 V W and Porsche Etc *changed to* European Car.
0273-6837 The Wall Paper
0273-6896 C A H P E R D Journal/Times
0273-6950 Arizona Business Gazette
0273-6969 Epiphany Journal
0273-6977 M S U Alumni Magazine
0273-7027 Estate Planning and California Probate Reporter
0273-7086 Housewares Retailing†
0273-7175 Brandeis Quarterly *changed to* Brandeis Review.
0273-7183 Global Church Growth Bulletin *see* 0731-1125
0273-7353 E S A Newsletter
0273-7434 Bowhunter
0273-7469 Bedroom
0273-7485 I S
0273-7574 Kick Illustrated *changed to* Inside Karate.
0273-7582 Children's Digest and Children's Playcraft *see* 0272-7145
0273-7590 Humpty Dumpty's Magazine
0273-7612 Executive Compensation & Taxation Coordinator
0273-7620 Common Faith†
0273-7639 Avionics
0273-7655 Surgical Practice News
0273-768X Employee Benefits Compliance Coordinator
0273-7752 Low Priced Stock Survey
0273-7884 B G R Newsletter†
0273-7892 Spray's Water Ski Magazine *changed to* Water Ski.
0273-7930 Indiana Business
0273-7957 Crafts Fair Guide
0273-7973 Winning Negotiator†
0273-8023 Alliance Update
0273-804X California Optometry
0273-8139 Pharmaceutical Engineering
0273-8163 Alternative Energy Retailer
0273-8236 S R E A Briefs *see* 0899-8779
0273-8333 Lhasa Apso Reporter
0273-835X Outlook (Palo Alto)
0273-8392 View (New York)
0273-8414 Lambda *changed to* High Performance Systems.
0273-8457 Polar Geography and Geology
0273-8481 Journal of Burn Care and Rehabilitation
0273-8546 Brain - Mind Bulletin *changed to* New Sense Bulletin.
0273-8562 Taegliche Andachten
0273-8570 Journal of Field Ornithology
0273-8589 Diver
0273-8708 A M U S. Log
0273-8724 Book and Magazine Production†
0273-8902 Music & Sound Output†
0273-8910 E A P Digest
0273-9046 Executive Compensation and Employee Benefits Report *changed to* Employee Benefits Report.
0273-9097 R U R: Rural and Urban Roads *see* 8750-9229
0273-9178 N A M R P Quarterly
0273-9194 Racquet (New York)
0273-9240 Creative Products News
0273-9267 Credit Union Management
0273-9313 Industrial Chemical News†
0273-9348 Ukrainian Weekly
0273-9380 Leading Edge†
0273-9399 SpeciaList
0273-9402 Truck Blue Book
0273-9526 Keyboard Classics
0273-9550 Print & Graphics
0273-9569 Compliance Management Report†
0273-9607 Casting Engineering and Foundry World *see* 0887-9060
0273-9615 Children's Health Care Journal
0273-9623 Credit and Collection Management Bulletin *changed to* Credit & Collection Manager's Letter.
0273-964X Office Guide
0273-9658 Official Railway Guide. North American Travel Edition
0273-9682 P.S. for Professional Secretaries *changed to* Professional Secretary - Administrative Support Letter.
0273-9712 West Plains Gazette†
0273-9747 Florida Funeral Director
0273-978X Stamp Dealer†
0273-9836 New Times Weekly
0273-9917 Education in Photojournalism. Journal†
0273-9933 Indiana Musicator
0273-9968 Corporate Report-Kansas City *changed to* Ingram's Magazine.

ISSN

5674 **ISSN INDEX**

0273-9976 American Medical Record Association. Journal *changed to* American Health Information Management Association. Journal.
0273-9992 Producers' Price-Current *changed to* Urner Barry's Price-Current.
0274-4791 Good Housekeeping's Country Living *see* 0732-2569
0274-4805 Bottom Line - Personal
0274-4856 Folio - K P F K *changed to* Folio (North Hollywood).
0274-4929 Indianapolis Business Journal
0274-497X Journal of Biological Photography
0274-4996 Packaging Technology†
0274-5046 Goucher Quarterly *changed to* Goucher Quarterly.
0274-5097 Prints (Alton)
0274-5178 Fighting Stars *see* 0898-4786
0274-5186 Foundation Drilling
0274-5437 Motorcycle Industry Shopper *see* 0884-626X
0274-5453 Seattle Business Journal *changed to* Puget Sound Business Journal.
0274-547X Indiana Beverage Journal
0274-5496 Greater Washington Board of Trade News
0274-5526 Plexus
0274-5542 Internal Medicine News & Cardiology News
0274-5569 Increase
0274-564X Ornithological Newsletter
0274-5720 Muzzleloader
0274-5852 William Winter Comments
0274-5887 This Is Arkansas *changed to* Arkansas Journal.
0274-5925 New England Fashion Retailer *changed to* Fashion Retailer.
0274-5933 San Francisco Focus
0274-5941 Landscape and Turf Industry *changed to* Southern Golf - Landscape & Resort Management.
0274-5968 Resource Management Journal
0274-5976 Graphic Arts Product News (Chicago)
0274-600X Prayers for Worship
0274-6050 Big Farmer Entrepreneur†
0274-6107 Corporate Controllers Report†
0274-6263 Gourmet Today (1979) *see* 1052-4630
0274-631X Computers in Hospitals *see* 0745-1075
0274-6328 Ad Forum *see* 0892-8274
0274-6441 Second Boat
0274-645X Supervisory Sense
0274-6506 Personnel Manager's Legal Reporter *changed to* Human Resource Manager's Legal Reporter.
0274-6530 I R T Communication Quarterly
0274-6549 Oregon Optometry
0274-6565 American Farriers Journal
0274-6816 Living Alternatives Magazine
0274-6905 Beatlefan
0274-7014 Arizona Farm Bureau News
0274-7057 Franchising Today
0274-7073 Art New England
0274-7111 Bank Advertising News
0274-712X Quilter's Newsletter Magazine
0274-7138 Grain Journal
0274-7154 Hawaiian Church Chronicle
0274-7170 Skateboarder's Action Now *see* 0279-8689
0274-726X Contraceptive Technology Update
0274-7286 Siberian Quarterly
0274-7294 Ohio District Court Review
0274-7405 Wings of Gold
0274-7456 Goldsmith†
0274-7472 Wisconsin Restaurateur
0274-7499 Graphic Design: U S A
0274-7529 Discover (Burbank)
0274-774X Southern Graphics
0274-7766 Premiere *see* 0279-0041
0274-7774 The A V Magazine
0274-8096 Printed Circuit Fabrication
0274-8193 Jewelry Making, Gems and Minerals
0274-8282 Alaska Outdoors
0274-8304 Compliance Guide for Plan Administrators
0274-8363 Snowmobile
0274-8525 Mid-South Business *see* 0747-167X
0274-8533 Florida Law Weekly
0274-8541 Radio World
0274-855X Perspectives: A Civil Rights Quarterly *changed to* New Perspectives.
0274-8568 Sunday School Leadership
0274-8606 West Virginia School Journal
0274-8622 Minnesota Sportsman
0274-8630 Softside
0274-869X C-Store Business†
0274-8762 Acorn *changed to* Acorn Storyteller.
0274-8800 Southwest Purchasing†
0274-8843 Metal Construction News
0274-8916 Association for the Care of Children's Health. Journal *see* 0273-9615
0274-8983 Florida Homefurnishings†
0274-9041 B I N - Beverage Industry News
0274-905X Sea and Pacific Skipper *see* 0746-8601
0274-905X Sea & Pacific Skipper
0274-9068 Rudder *see* 0746-8601
0274-9076 Lakeland Boating Incorporating Sea *see* 0744-9194
0274-9149 Northwest Skier and Northwest Sports *changed to* Northwest Skier.
0274-9394 New England Offshore *changed to* Offshore (Needham).
0274-9459 O M S Outreach
0274-9483 Association for the Severely Handicapped. Journal (JASH) *changed to* Association for Persons with Severe Handicaps. Journal.
0274-9491 Tennessee Realtor
0274-9513 Soldier Support Journal†
0274-9629 Softalk for Apple Computers†
0274-9696 Cost Engineering (Morgantown, 1980)
0274-9777 Student Press Service†
0274-984X Regardie's Business and Real Estate Washington *changed to* Regardie's.
0274-9874 A P I C S News *see* 1057-2341
0274-9882 F M O News
0274-9912 Kansas Citian
0275-0031 Wise Giving Guide
0275-004X Retina
0275-0066 Cardiology (Year)
0275-0147 Radix
0275-0155 University of Chicago. Division of Biological Sciences and Pritzker School of Medicine. Report
0275-0198 Chopper Noise *see* 0271-9029
0275-0201 Moody's Commercial Paper Record†
0275-0236 Infection Control Digest†
0275-0244 Hazardous Waste Litigation Reporter
0275-0252 National Bankruptcy Reporter
0275-0260 Successful Woman *changed to* Successful Woman in Business.
0275-0392 Human Rights Quarterly
0275-0430 Inteltrade†
0275-0457 Fiber Optics and Communications
0275-0473 International Telecommunications Energy Conference. Proceedings
0275-049X Human Rights Internet Reporter
0275-0503 Professional Liability†
0275-0589 Gamut
0275-0686 ViewText (Potomac)†
0275-0732 Sporting News Baseball Yearbook
0275-0740 American Review of Public Administration
0275-0759 Chapter I Handbook: Understanding and Implementing the New Regulations *see* 0737-2094
0275-0813 Datapro Reports on Minicomputers†
0275-0899 Technical Association of the Pulp and Paper Industry. Pulping Conference Proceedings (Year)
0275-0902 Regulatory Watchdog Service
0275-0929 Oklahoma Geological Survey. Special Publication Series
0275-0945 Best Sellers and Best Choices (Year) *see* 8755-9633
0275-1062 Chinese Astronomy and Astrophysics
0275-1089 Directory of Louisiana Manufacturers
0275-1100 Public Budgeting and Finance
0275-1178 Mennonite Yearbook and Directory
0275-1275 Journal of the Early Republic
0275-1356 American Council on Consumer Interests. Proceedings of the Annual Conference
0275-1364 Joyful Noise†
0275-1380 Neurobehavioral Toxicology and Teratology *see* 0892-0362
0275-1399 Laser Focus with Fiberoptic Technology *see* 1043-8092
0275-1410 Threepenny Review
0275-1429 Journal of Cardiac Rehabilitation *see* 0883-9212
0275-1569 American Society of Bookplate Collectors and Designers. Year Book
0275-1607 Raritan
0275-1739 Poetry - L A
0275-1836 MacRae's New Mexico State Industrial Directory *see* 0739-8476
0275-1852 MacRae's Wyoming State Industrial Directory *see* 0740-6088
0275-1879 Special Care in Dentistry
0275-1909 Rhode Island Media Directory†
0275-2069 Communication and the Human Condition
0275-2107 Specialty Law Digest: Education†
0275-2123 Fiction Writer's Market *see* 0897-9812
0275-2220 Ocean Science and Engineering *see* 0890-5460
0275-2271 State - E P A Agreements. Annual Report
0275-2484 Centaur (Gaithersburg)†
0275-2565 American Journal of Primatology
0275-2581 Current Topics in Environmental and Toxicological Chemistry
0275-2743 Cornerstone (Chicago)
0275-276X Year-End Regulatory Review
0275-2786 American Land Forum *changed to* New American Card.
0275-2832 Employers Guide to A B A Approved N A L P Member Law Schools *changed to* Employers Guide to Law Schools.
0275-2883 Caribbean - American Directory
0275-2905 Energy Executive Directory†
0275-3030 Volunteering
0275-3049 Advances in Developmental Psychology
0275-3065 Hoosharar - Mioutune
0275-3073 Day Tonight - Night Today†
0275-3081 Industrial Relations Research Association. Proceedings of Annual Winter Meeting *changed to* Industrial Relations Research Association. Proceedings of the Annual Meeting.
0275-309X Covert Action Information Bulletin
0275-3502 Source (Boca Raton)†
0275-3510 Series in Death Education, Aging, and Health Care
0275-3529 Religious Freedom Reporter
0275-3545 Travel Marketing and Agency Management Guidelines
0275-357X Piedmont Literary Review
0275-3588 Journal of Arab Affairs
0275-3596 Pacific Studies
0275-360X Modern Aging Research
0275-3618 Prostaglandin and Related Lipids†
0275-3650 Journal of Library History, Philosophy and Comparative Librarianship *see* 0894-8631
0275-3685 McGraw-Hill's Biotechnology Newswatch
0275-3707 Radioactive Waste Management (Oak Ridge)
0275-3715 Aurora (Madison)
0275-3723 Journal of Supramolecular Structure and Cellular Biochemistry *see* 0730-2312
0275-374X Hazardous Waste News
0275-3758 U S Rail News
0275-3766 Toxic Materials Transport *changed to* HazMat Transport.
0275-3774 Minerals Report *see* 0278-5099
0275-3782 Emergency Preparedness News
0275-3812 Art Express
0275-3820 Directory of Publishing Opportunities in Journals and Periodicals†
0275-3871 European Petroleum Directory
0275-3901 U V/E B News†
0275-391X Car Care
0275-3987 Psychomusicology
0275-3995 A A G Newsletter
0275-4002 Policy Studies Personnel Directory
0275-4088 Legal Looseleafs in Print
0275-410X Lamar Journal of the Humanities
0275-4177 Microcirculation†
0275-4207 BioEngineering News
0275-4347 Journal of Educational Equity and Leadership†
0275-4371 Value Engineering and Management Digest - Defense Contract Guide
0275-4401 Plain Speaking†
0275-4452 Labor Notes
0275-4479 New York Stock Exchange. Statistical Highlights†
0275-4487 Sporting News Super Bowl Book
0275-4509 Soya Bluebook
0275-4592 Interstate Compact for Education *see* 0736-7511
0275-4681 Cosmetic Insider's Report
0275-469X New Glass Review
0275-4770 Real Times
0275-4797 Medical Detective†
0275-4819 How to Get Help for Kids†
0275-4924 Focus: on the Center for Research Libraries
0275-4959 Research in the Sociology of Health Care
0275-5122 Planned Parenthood Review†
0275-519X Pandora
0275-5203 Sonora Review
0275-522X Inform Reports
0275-5270 Word & World
0275-5289 Energy and the Environment†
0275-5319 Research in International Business and Finance
0275-5327 Journal of Southern African Affairs
0275-5351 Trialogue
0275-5408 Ophthalmic and Physiological Optics
0275-5416 Advances in Tunnelling Technology and Subsurface Use *see* 0886-7798
0275-5580 Directories in Print
0275-5599 Washington Report on the Hemisphere
0275-5629 Maenad
0275-5637 Inspirational Review†
0275-5696 A A P T Announcer
0275-5742 Advances in Medical Social Science
0275-5769 Food and Nutrition in History and Anthropology
0275-5777 Polymer Monographs
0275-5785 Stochastics Monographs
0275-5793 Caribbean Studies (New York)
0275-5807 Studies in Cybernetics
0275-5815 Topics in Computer Mathematics
0275-5823 Military Operations Research
0275-584X Perspectives on the American South
0275-5866 Monographs on Musicology
0275-5874 Economic Handbook of the World†
0275-5947 North American Journal of Fisheries Management
0275-5971 Theatre Communications†
0275-598X Soviet Sports Review
0275-6013 Mid-America Folklore
0275-6048 Turkish Studies Association Bulletin
0275-6064 Guide to Federal Energy Development and Assistance Programs†
0275-6072 Journal of Law and Education
0275-6080 Bravo
0275-6099 Fiber - Laser News *see* 8756-2049
0275-6145 First Catholic Slovak Union of America. Minutes of Annual Meeting
0275-634X In Defense of the Alien
0275-6358 Advances in Cell Culture
0275-6587 Bear & Company†
0275-6595 Microwave News
0275-6617 System Development
0275-6625 Alabama Forests
0275-6633 Mono Lake Committee Newsletter
0275-665X Obstetric Anesthesia Digest
0275-6668 Journal of Business Strategy
0275-6692 A I D Bulletin
0275-6706 We Proceeded On

ISSN

ISSN INDEX 5675

0275-6722 Small Computers in Libraries *see* 1041-7915
0275-6757 Sapphic Touch
0275-6765 Christian Legal Society Quarterly *see* 0736-0142
0275-682X Reprint Bulletin Book Reviews
0275-6870 Typography
0275-6889 Manhattan Review
0275-6919 Saguaroland Bulletin *changed to* Sonoran Quarterly.
0275-6935 Revision
0275-6951 Tax Regulation Series *changed to* Law Reprints: Tax Law Series.
0275-696X B N A's Law Reprints: Securities Regulation Series *changed to* Law Reprints: Securities Regulation Series.
0275-6978 B N A's Law Reprints: Trade Regulation Series *changed to* Law Reprints: Trade Regulation Series.
0275-6986 B N A's Law Reprints: Criminal Law Series *changed to* Law Reprints: Criminal Law Series.
0275-6994 B N A's Law Reprints: Labor Law Series *changed to* Law Reprints: Labor Law Series.
0275-7001 B N A's Law Reprints: Patent, Trademark and Copyright Series *changed to* Law Reprints: Patent, Trademark & Copyright Series.
0275-701X C A Selects. Amino Acids, Peptides and Proteins
0275-7028 C A Selects. Antioxidants
0275-7036 C A Selects. Coatings, Inks, & Related Products
0275-7044 C A Selects. Cosmetic Chemicals
0275-7052 C A Selects. Distillation Technology
0275-7060 C A Selects. Epoxy Resins
0275-7079 C A Selects. Fats & Oils
0275-7087 C A Selects. Inorganic Analytical Chemistry
0275-7095 C A Selects. Inorganic Chemicals & Reactions
0275-7117 C A Selects. Organic Analytical Chemistry
0275-7125 C A Selects. Plastics Fabrication & Uses
0275-7133 C A Selects. Plastics Manufacture & Processing
0275-7168 C A Selects. Synthetic High Polymers
0275-7184 Commercial Food Patents†
0275-7206 History and Anthropology
0275-7214 Mathematical Reports
0275-7222 Comprehensive Psychotherapy
0275-7230 Electrocomponent Science Monographs
0275-7257 Remote Sensing Reviews
0275-7265 M M I Press Polymer Monograph Series
0275-7273 Radioactive Waste Management Series
0275-7427 Top 1,500 Private Companies *changed to* Trinet Directory of Leading U S Companies: Top 1,500 Private.
0275-7435 Top 1,500 Companies *changed to* Trinet Directory of Leading U S Companies: Top 1,500.
0275-7443 Second 1,500 Companies *changed to* Trinet Directory of Leading U S Companies: Second 1,500.
0275-746X Congressional District Business Patterns†
0275-7478 Northern Great Plains Research Center. Annual Research Report†
0275-7524 Social Orders Series
0275-7540 Chemistry and Ecology
0275-7567 C1 Molecule Chemistry
0275-7575 I S P R A Courses on Nuclear Engineering and Technology Series
0275-7613 The Relocation Report
0275-7656 Tanner Lectures on Human Values
0275-7664 Great Plains Quarterly
0275-7672 Vanderbilt Review†
0275-777X Indiana Libraries
0275-7796 Soviet Scientific Reviews Supplement Series. Section A: Physics
0275-780X Soviet Scientific Reviews Supplement Series. Section B: Chemistry
0275-7893 Soviet Technology Reviews. Section A: Energy Reviews
0275-7915 Advances in Irrigation†
0275-7966 Energy Economics, Policy and Management *see* 1048-5236
0275-7982 Studies in Communications
0275-8032 New Poetic Drama†
0275-8059 F M I Issues Bulletin
0275-8113 Milkweed Chronicle†
0275-8148 Pioneer *see* 1042-7732
0275-8210 U.S. Department of Health, Education and Welfare. Catalog of Publications *see* 0278-0143
0275-8393 Guide to Federal Funding for Education
0275-8407 A M S Studies in Modern Society
0275-8423 Classic Images
0275-844X Trace Analysis
0275-8466 Faxon Librarians' Guide to Serials *changed to* Faxon Guide to Serials.
0275-8539 J P S Bookmark *see* 0006-7407
0275-8555 Mississippi Geology
0275-858X Bell & Howell Newspaper Index to the St. Louis Post-Dispatch *see* 0893-2417
0275-8598 Journal of Offender Counseling *see* 1055-3835
0275-8709 Science, Technology and American Diplomacy (Washington)†
0275-8717 Progress in Cybernetics and Systems Research†
0275-8873 Apparel Plant Wages Survey
0275-889X Annual of American Architecture†
0275-8911 Georgia Journal of Accounting†
0275-9098 Current Topics of Contemporary Thought
0275-911X Soviet Journal of Remote Sensing
0275-9128 Geophysical Journal
0275-9136 Electronic Modeling
0275-9144 Physics of Metals
0275-9187 Rock Yearbook
0275-9306 I E E E Power Electronics Specialists Conference. Record
0275-9314 Swedish American Genealogist
0275-9322 Public Eye (Boston)
0275-9381 Symphony Gold Book
0275-9470 A I G A Graphic Design U S A
0275-9489 Commodities Magazine Reference Guide to Futures Markets *changed to* Futures Magazine Reference Guide to Futures Markets.
0275-9527 South Asian Review
0275-9586 Methods in Microanalysis
0275-9594 Demographic Monographs
0275-9608 Ferroelectricity and Related Phenomena
0275-9616 U.S. Library of Congress. Manuscript Division. Acquisitions
0275-9624 Journal of Somatic Experience†
0275-9632 Profiles in Healthcare Marketing
0275-9667 Ages 3-4 Church and Home Leaflets†
0275-973X World Jazz Calendar of Festivals & Events *changed to* Jazz Festivals International Directory.
0275-9802 Himalayan *see* 0891-6144
0275-9926 Journal of Energy Law and Policy *see* 1053-377X
0275-9942 Journal of Linguistic Research†
0275-9993 Hebrew Union College Annual Supplements
0276-0037 Journal of Telecommunication Networks *see* 0888-2223
0276-0045 Review of Contemporary Fiction
0276-0142 Journal of Freshwater†
0276-0231 Colorado. Division of Wildlife. Division Report
0276-0290 Nous Letter *see* 0090-2586
0276-0347 Cosmetic Surgery†
0276-0355 Chronicle Career Index
0276-0363 Chronicle Guide for Transfers†
0276-0371 Chronicle Vocational School Manual
0276-0401 Research and Invention†
0276-0428 C A I News†
0276-0436 Pulpsmith (Year)†
0276-0444 Mananam Publication Series
0276-0460 Geo-marine Letters
0276-0606 Kastlemusick Monthly Bulletin†
0276-072X Rural - Regional Education News *see* 0036-0023
0276-0738 Fodor's Europe on a Budget *changed to* Fodor's Affordable Europe.
0276-0770 Journal of Religious Education of the African Methodist Episcopal Church *changed to* Journal of Christian Education of the African Methodist Episcopal Church.
0276-0843 Public Affairs Review†
0276-086X Psi News†
0276-0908 The Community Bank President
0276-0916 Leisure Industry Digest *changed to* Leisure Industry Report.
0276-0959 Modern's Market Guide†
0276-1017 N C A A Basketball
0276-1041 International Gymnast Magazine
0276-1076 Interferon
0276-1092 Year Book of Orthopedics
0276-1106 University of Texas Publications in Astronomy†
0276-1114 Modern Judaism
0276-1416 Byelorussian Times
0276-1432 Jewish Jurisprudence Series
0276-1440 Computer Graphics News†
0276-1459 Multiphase Science and Technology
0276-1467 Journal of Macromarketing
0276-1491 Federation Reports *see* 0882-5793
0276-1505 Bench & Bar of Minnesota
0276-153X Screen
0276-1564 Bloomsbury Review
0276-1572 Channels of Communications *changed to* Channels: the Business of Communications.
0276-1599 Occupational Therapy Journal of Research
0276-1610 Psychic Studies
0276-1653 Research in Domestic and International Agribusiness Management
0276-1661 Court Management Journal†
0276-1696 Drivers License Guide *see* 1041-5793
0276-170X Farm & Ranch Living
0276-1769 University of Illinois at Urbana-Champaign. Graduate School of Library and Information Science. Occasional Papers
0276-1858 Energy Newsletter Index
0276-1866 Datapro Directory of Small Computers *changed to* Datapro Directory of Microcomputer Hardware.
0276-1882 Genetic Engineering Letter
0276-2021 New York University Institute of Finance. Bulletin *changed to* New York University. Salomon Center. Monograph Series.
0276-203X Center for Law and Education. Newsnotes
0276-2056 I S T F News
0276-2072 Fat Tuesday
0276-2080 Philosophical Topics
0276-2110 New Hampshire Marketing Directory *changed to* New Hampshire Manufacturing Directory.
0276-2129 Petersen's College Football
0276-2226 A R C Bulletin†
0276-2234 Oncology Times
0276-2277 World Pharmaceutical Directory
0276-2285 Journal of Rural Community Psychology
0276-2293 National Reye's Syndrome Foundation†
0276-2307 Sporting News Pro Football Yearbook
0276-2323 Hospital Safety Information Service
0276-2358 Accent on Worship
0276-2366 Imagination, Cognition and Personality
0276-2374 Empirical Study of the Arts
0276-2552 Fodor's Budget Japan *changed to* Fodor's Great Travel Values: Japan.
0276-2560 Fodor's Rome
0276-2854 Erasmus of Rotterdam Society Yearbook
0276-2870 State Regulation Report
0276-2889 Handicapped Americans Report *see* 1043-1209
0276-2897 Nuclear Waste News
0276-2900 U S Census Report *changed to* American Marketplace.
0276-2919 Fusion Power Report
0276-2935 Yacht Racing *see* 0889-4094
0276-3052 Interval
0276-3095 BIOSIS CAS Selects: Allergy and Antiallergy *see* 1047-8191
0276-3109 BIOSIS CAS Selects: Biochemistry of Fermented Foods†
0276-3117 BIOSIS CAS Selects: Biological Clocks†
0276-3125 BIOSIS CAS Selects: Cancer Immunology†
0276-3133 BIOSIS CAS Selects: Endorphins†
0276-3141 BIOSIS CAS Selects: Geriatric Pharmacology†
0276-315X BIOSIS CAS Selects: Histochemistry and Cytochemistry†
0276-3168 BIOSIS CAS Selects: Immunochemical Methods *see* 1048-874X
0276-3176 BIOSIS CAS Selects: Interferon†
0276-3184 BIOSIS CAS Selects: Mammalian Birth Defects†
0276-3192 BIOSIS CAS Selects: Pediatric Pharmacology†
0276-3206 BIOSIS CAS Selects: Plant Genetics†
0276-3214 BIOSIS CAS Selects: Schizophrenia†
0276-3222 BIOSIS CAS Selects: Transplantation†
0276-3338 Old Mill News
0276-3362 Hemingway Review
0276-3397 The Tamarind Papers
0276-3427 Children's Leader *changed to* Leader in the Church School Today.
0276-3435 Ages 4-6 Church and Home Leaflets *changed to* Ages 5-6 Church and Home Leaflets.
0276-3478 International Journal of Eating Disorders
0276-3494 Moving Image†
0276-3508 Advances in Ophthalmic Plastic & Reconstructive Surgery
0276-3516 Moody's Handbook of O T C Stocks
0276-3583 Boston Third World Law Journal
0276-3605 Black Music Research Journal
0276-3621 Proletarian Internationalism†
0276-363X Workers' Advocate
0276-3656 Insecticide and Acaricide Tests
0276-3680 Ocean Construction Locator *see* 1058-5869
0276-3737 The Poe Messenger
0276-3826 U.S. Environmental Protection Agency. Monthly Listing of Awards for Construction Grants for Waste Water Treatment Works†
0276-3850 Journal of Social Work and Human Sexuality
0276-3869 Medical Reference Services Quarterly
0276-3877 Reference Librarian
0276-3885 Women & History†
0276-3893 Journal of Housing for the Elderly
0276-3915 Community & Junior College Libraries
0276-3923 Business Management *see* 0090-4309
0276-4040 International Gas Technology Highlights
0276-4148 Himalayan International Institute. Eleanor N. Dana Laboratory. Research Bulletin†
0276-4156 Wisconsin Preservation: National Register of Historic Places. Newsletter
0276-4164 Palmetto
0276-4245 Broadcast Databook†
0276-4253 Bank Compliance *see* 0887-0187
0276-4318 Family Physician's Compendium of Drug Therapy
0276-4342 Internist's Compendium of Drug Therapy
0276-4415 Housing Finance Review†
0276-4482 Schools in the Middle
0276-4512 Marriage & Family†
0276-461X N A P E H E Proceedings†
0276-4644 Costa Rica Report
0276-4652 Discharge Planning Update
0276-4679 Fulness†
0276-4695 Cold Spring Harbor Reports in the Neurosciences†
0276-4717 Transitions Abroad

ISSN

0276-4741 Mountain Research and Development
0276-4768 Saxophone Journal
0276-4792 Real Estate Investment Digest†
0276-4806 B I S G Bulletin†
0276-4830 Pro Rege
0276-4849 U.S. Hydrographic Conference. Biennial Meeting. Proceedings
0276-4857 Knox County, Kentucky Kinfolk
0276-4865 Worldwide Hunting Annual†
0276-4881 Firehouse Magazine Buyers Guide
0276-489X Municipal Year Book Directories†
0276-4954 Estandarte Obrero
0276-5047 Arteriosclerosis *see* 1049-8834
0276-5055 BioCycle
0276-5098 Microcomputer Systems D.A.T.A. Book†
0276-5101 Consumer I C's D.A.T.A. Book *changed to* Audio-Video I C's D.A.T.A. Book.
0276-511X Microprocessor I C's D.A.T.A. Book *see* 1049-2445
0276-5241 Newport Review
0276-5276 National Recreational, Sporting and Hobby Organizations of the United States *changed to* National Avocational Organizations.
0276-5284 Nursing and Health Care
0276-5322 Small Business Tax Review
0276-5330 Critical Perspectives on Contemporary Psychology†
0276-5349 Association of American Publishers. Annual Report
0276-5365 Directory of Legal Aid and Defender Offices in the United States *changed to* Directory of Legal Aid and Defender Offices in the United States and Territories.
0276-539X O P D Chemical Buyers Directory
0276-5497 Clinical and Experimental Dialysis and Apheresis *see* 0886-022X
0276-5500 Fodor's India and Nepal *changed to* Fodor's India.
0276-5519 American Register of Printing and Graphic Arts Services
0276-556X Export Documentation Handbook†
0276-5594 Group and Family Therapy†
0276-5608 Chemical Dependencies: Behavioral & Biomedical Issues†
0276-5624 Research in Social Stratification and Mobility
0276-5675 D E S Litigation Reporter
0276-5683 Thomas Wolfe Review
0276-5713 Cable T V Technology
0276-5721 Data Base Monthly *changed to* D G Review.
0276-5756 Computing Resources for the Professional†
0276-5853 E E O Report†
0276-606X Health of Kansas Chart Book†
0276-6256 Journal of Children in Contemporary Society†
0276-6264 Children in Contemporary Society *see* 0276-6256
0276-6345 Syracuse Scholar†
0276-6353 Operating Room Research Institute. Journal†
0276-6469 U.S. International Development Cooperation Agency. Congressional Presentation, Fiscal Year
0276-6493 Georgia Genealogical Survey†
0276-6515 Richmond Quarterly
0276-6531 C D F Reports
0276-6558 Studies in Visual Communication†
0276-6566 U.S. Bureau of the Census. State and Metropolitan Area Data Book
0276-6574 Computers in Cardiology
0276-6582 Surfboard
0276-6701 S.O.S. Directory†
0276-6744 Yearbook of Podiatric Medicine and Surgery†
0276-6779 Let's Go: The Budget Guide to Greece, Israel and Egypt *changed to* Let's Go: The Budget Guide to Greece, Israel and Egypt - Including Cyprus & Turkish Coast.
0276-6795 Ex Tempore
0276-6949 Bibliography of the English-Speaking Caribbean†
0276-6965 Probation and Parole Law Reports
0276-7031 New on the Charts
0276-7066 Network (Washington, 1981)
0276-7074 Driving Digest Magazine
0276-7090 Tournament Chess
0276-7120 Q C: The Magazine of Queens County
0276-7155 Southwestern Review
0276-7163 State Executive Directory
0276-718X Education Law Bulletin†
0276-7201 Amicus Journal
0276-721X Cost Engineering Magazine *see* 0274-9696
0276-7244 United States Postal Card Catalog
0276-7309 Television and Children *changed to* Television & Families.
0276-7333 Organometallics
0276-7430 European Review *changed to* D R I - McGraw-Hill European Review.
0276-7449 Journal of the Alleghenies
0276-7473 Recycling News†
0276-749X Computer Aided Design Report
0276-7511 New England Society of Allergy. Proceedings *see* 1046-9354
0276-752X Client Counseling Update *changed to* Competitions (Chicago).
0276-7546 National Law Review Reporter
0276-7554 Motions in Proteins, Peptides & Amino Acids†
0276-7562 Phase-Transfer Reactions†
0276-7570 U C M P Quarterly
0276-7589 Effective Speech Writer's Newsletter†
0276-7597 Airbrush Digest
0276-7651 State Laws and Published Ordinances, Firearms
0276-7783 M I S Quarterly
0276-7805 Directory of Faculty Contracts and Bargaining Agents in Institutions of Higher Education
0276-783X Directory of Consumer Finance Companies†
0276-7856 Chimeres: A Journal of French and Italian Literature†
0276-7872 Burrelle's Pennsylvania Media Directory (Year)
0276-7899 Second Century
0276-7910 Ga'vea - Brown
0276-7945 Baptist Reformation Review *see* 0739-2281
0276-7953 Journal of Industrial Fabrics†
0276-7961 Microwave World
0276-7988 Women's Annual†
0276-8038 Clinical Management in Physical Therapy *changed to* Clinical Management.
0276-8135 Short-Timer's Journal
0276-8151 Peter W. Rodino Institute of Criminal Justice. Annual Journal†
0276-816X Something about the Author
0276-8178 Twentieth - Century Literary Criticism
0276-8186 National Parks
0276-8208 Florida Builders and Contractors Directory
0276-8259 Technology (Boulder)†
0276-8267 Computer State of the Art Reports†
0276-8275 Washington Tariff & Trade Letter
0276-8283 C P T
0276-8291 Abbey Newsletter
0276-8313 Historical Journal of Massachusetts
0276-8429 C E C - Chemical Engineering Catalog
0276-8542 Analog-Hybrid Computer Educational Society. A C E S Transactions *changed to* Computers in Education Journal.
0276-8577 Comments on Geochemistry and Cosmochemistry†
0276-8585 Journal of Ecological and Life Chemistry†
0276-8593 Multichannel News
0276-8607 Occasional Publications in Northeastern Anthropology
0276-8631 Specialized Transportation Planning and Practice†
0276-864X U C L A Historical Journal
0276-8704 Protein Semisynthesis†
0276-8712 Current Awareness Profile on Chemical Information†
0276-8739 Journal of Policy Analysis and Management
0276-8747 Op
0276-8771 Pacific Boating Almanac. Oregon, Washington, British Columbia & Southeastern Alaska
0276-8798 New York Agricultural Statistics
0276-8836 Institutions, Etc. *changed to* Augustus.
0276-8860 Journal of Clinical Laboratory Automation†
0276-8895 Sports Afield Hunting†
0276-8968 Travel and Tourism Research Association. Proceedings of the Annual Conference
0276-8976 Applications of Management Science
0276-900X Lambert's Worldwide Government Directory *see* 0894-1521
0276-9018 Fodor's Colorado†
0276-9077 The Atlantic
0276-9220 Borderlands Journal
0276-9239 Modern Recording & Music's Buyer's Guide†
0276-928X Journal of Staff Development
0276-9298 Urban Academic Librarian
0276-9387 Modern Technics in Surgery. Plastic Surgery†
0276-9433 Grower Talks Magazine
0276-959X Directory of Government Document Collections and Librarians
0276-9603 Juvenile Law Reports
0276-9611 T and E Center Newsletter *see* 0895-6529
0276-9751 Advertising Age Yearbook†
0276-9883 Crime Digest†
0276-9891 Guide to Federal Procurement *changed to* Doing Business with the Federal Government: A Procurement Guide.
0276-9905 In-Fisherman
0276-9913 Advances in Descriptive Psychology
0276-993X Tennessee Williams Review†
0276-9948 University of Illinois Law Review
0276-9956 Enfo
0276-9964 Sunspeak†
0276-9972 Computer Publicity News
0277-0008 Pharmacotherapy
0277-0059 Micro Moonlighter†
0277-0113 Dallas Civic Opera Magazine *see* 0731-8529
0277-013X Lymphokines†
0277-0156 Pulp & Paper Week Price - Export-Import Databook†
0277-0180 O P E C Review
0277-0288 Library Systems Newsletter
0277-0296 Sportsguide *changed to* Sports Market Place.
0277-0326 Seminars in Anesthesia
0277-0334 How to Double Your Income
0277-0342 Cityguide - The San Francisco Bay Area and Northern California
0277-0369 Trade Names Dictionary: Company Index *see* 1047-6393
0277-0385 National Women's Health Network Newsletter *see* 8755-867X
0277-0393 Clinical Engineering Information Service
0277-0415 Platt's Oil Marketing Bulletin
0277-0474 Biblical Scholarship in North America
0277-0490 Visual Arts *changed to* N E A Grantmaking Programs: Visual Arts.
0277-0598 Selecta (Corvallis)
0277-0628 Uncoverings
0277-0679 Communications Daily
0277-0687 Advances in Disease Prevention†
0277-0709 Window Energy Systems *see* 0886-9669
0277-0717 Fantasy Book
0277-0725 Knives (Year)
0277-0768 Science Fiction Digest†
0277-0784 Access: Microcomputers in Libraries
0277-0792 Keynotes (New Orleans)
0277-0814 U.S. Department of Agriculture. Poultry and Egg Outlook and Situation *changed to* U.S. Department of Agriculture. Livestock and Poultry Situation and Outlook.
0277-0865 Computer Security Journal
0277-0903 Journal of Asthma (New York)
0277-092X International Yoga Guide
0277-0938 Pediatric Pathology
0277-0946 Mexico Report
0277-0954 Land Drilling and Oilwell Servicing Contractors Directory†
0277-0962 Worldwide Refining and Gas Processing Directory
0277-0970 National Parking Association Newsletter *see* 0031-2193
0277-0997 Northern Raven†
0277-1004 A A A World: Wisconsin Edition
0277-1071 A A R Academy Series
0277-108X Group Headquarters Directory†
0277-1098 Play the Red
0277-1152 Mississippi College Law Review
0277-1233 Engineer of California
0277-1292 Country Song Roundup. Yearbook *see* 0011-0248
0277-1314 Massachusetts Political Almanac
0277-1322 Res
0277-1330 I C B P Parrot Working Group Meeting. Proceedings *changed to* I C B P Technical Publications.
0277-1349 Hindu Text Information *see* 0888-5869
0277-1365 N C T M News Bulletin
0277-1403 A A A World (Heathrow)
0277-1446 Continuity
0277-1470 A's and B's of Academic Scholarships *changed to* A's & B's of Academic Scholarship.
0277-1497 Loans Closed and Servicing Volume for the Mortgage Banking Industry†
0277-1527 World Factbook
0277-1535 La Palabra
0277-1551 Best's Directory of Recommended Insurance Attorneys
0277-1659 A - E - C Automation Newsletter
0277-1667 Executive's Personal Health Advisor *changed to* Executive Productivity.
0277-1675 Challenge (Convent Station)
0277-1683 Personal Tax Strategist†
0277-1705 Journal of Community Action†
0277-1764 Aviation Safety
0277-1926 Ground Water Monitoring Review
0277-1942 Water and Power Era *see* 0733-6446
0277-1950 Apple Orchard†
0277-1969 Directory of Cooperatives, Voluntaries & Wholesale Grocers (Year)
0277-1985 Directory of General Merchandise, Mail Order Firms and Family Centers *changed to* Directory of General Merchandise, Variety & Specialty Stores (Year).
0277-2027 Business & Professional Ethics Journal
0277-2086 Champaign County Genealogical Society Quarterly
0277-2094 American Society of Photogrammetry. Technical Papers from the Annual Meeting *changed to* American Society for Photogrammetry and Remote Sensing. Technical Papers from the Annual Meeting.
0277-2108 O A G Frequent Flyer
0277-2116 Journal of Pediatric Gastroenterology and Nutrition
0277-2132 Washington Book Review
0277-2140 Wind Energy Abstracts
0277-2159 Pipes & Filters *see* 0742-1206
0277-2248 Toxicological and Environmental Chemistry
0277-2272 Voice (Newark)
0277-2280 Armstrong Oil Directories: Texas Including Southeast New Mexico Edition
0277-2302 Instauration
0277-2310 U.S. Department of Transportation. Highway Safety Stewardship Report
0277-2361 American Bar Association. Section of Taxation. Newsletter
0277-2418 Alternative Source†
0277-2426 Landscape Journal

0277-2434 Philosophy in Science
0277-2442 International Living
0277-2469 Psychology and Social Theory
0277-2736 Discussions on Teaching
0277-2833 Research in the Sociology of Work
0277-2876 American Congress on Surveying and Mapping. Technical Papers
0277-2922 Iranian Assets Litigation Reporter
0277-2930 Commodities Law Letter
0277-2981 High Technology *see* 0895-8432
0277-299X Technology Illustrated†
0277-3015 New Methods
0277-3074 U.S. Department of Energy. Patents Available for Leasing *changed to* U.S. Department of Energy. D.O.E. Patents Available for Licensing.
0277-3082 New E R A Newsletter *see* 0887-1043
0277-3171 Rabbits *changed to* Rabbit Gazette.
0277-318X Rutgers Law Journal
0277-3236 G A L A Review *changed to* G A L A Realist.
0277-3317 Video Source Book
0277-3325 Federal Civilian Work Force Statistics. Work Years and Personnel Costs. Executive Branch, United States Government
0277-335X South Atlantic Review
0277-3368 Stamp World†
0277-3376 National Health Practitioner Program Profile *see* 1051-600X
0277-3538 Design Solutions
0277-3619 A S D A Handbook
0277-3627 A S D A News (Year)
0277-3635 Dentistry (Year)
0277-3678 Broadcasting - Cablecasting Yearbook *changed to* Broadcasting & Cable Market Place (Year).
0277-3708 Colorado Legislative Almanac
0277-3716 Drug Store Market Guide
0277-3732 American Journal of Clinical Oncology
0277-3740 Cornea
0277-3775 Civil Engineering for Practicing & Design Engineers†
0277-3791 Quaternary Science Reviews
0277-3813 Journal of Wood Chemistry and Technology
0277-3899 Stamp Collector
0277-3945 Rhetoric Society Quarterly
0277-3988 Standard & Poor's Bond Guide
0277-4178 Problems of Industrial Psychiatric Medicine Series
0277-4208 Practical Gastroenterology
0277-4232 Education Week
0277-4275 Wire Journal International
0277-4275 Wire Journal International Reference Guide
0277-433X Plymouth Colony Genealogist†
0277-4356 Letras Femeninas
0277-4461 Dawn (Honesdale) *see* 1055-7911
0277-447X Swift Kick
0277-4488 Earth-Oriented Applications of Space Technology *see* 0892-9270
0277-450X University of Texas at Austin. General Libraries. Library Bulletin
0277-4720 St. John's Review
0277-4933 Defense & Foreign Affairs
0277-5166 Negative Capability
0277-5212 Wetlands
0277-5247 Braille Books (Large Print Edition)
0277-5263 COMEXAZ: News Monitoring Service
0277-5271 Survive *changed to* Guns & Action.
0277-5379 European Journal of Cancer and Clinical Oncology *see* 0964-1947
0277-5387 Polyhedron
0277-5395 Women's Studies International Forum
0277-5417 Loyola of Los Angeles International and Comparative Law Journal
0277-5565 Lottery Player's Magazine
0277-559X Official Read-Easy Basketball Rules *see* 0736-5195
0277-5611 National Monthly Medicaid Statistics†
0277-5727 Search (Niles)
0277-576X Popular Woodworker *see* 0884-8823
0277-5778 Boston College International and Comparative Law Review
0277-5883 Topics in Chemical Engineering
0277-5891 CineFan†
0277-5913 Genealogical Computing
0277-5921 Contributions to Political Economy
0277-593X Ismael Reed and Al Young's Quilt†
0277-5948 Recommended Reference Books for Small & Medium-Sized Libraries and Media Centers
0277-5956 Connecticut News Handbook
0277-5980 Jazz Echo *changed to* Jazz World.
0277-6030 Space News†
0277-609X Naturalists' Directory International *changed to* Naturalists' Directory and Almanac International.
0277-612X For Parents
0277-6146 Telescope (Baltimore)†
0277-6189 Community Service Newsletter
0277-6197 U.S. National Weather Service. Oceanographic Monthly Summary *changed to* U.S. Department of Commerce. National Oceanic and Atmospheric Administration. Oceanographic Monthly Summary.
0277-6308 Arkansas Archeological Survey. Publications on Archeology. Research Reports
0277-6448 Family Festivals *changed to* Festivals.
0277-6456 Passive Solar Journal: Heating, Cooling, Hybrid Technologies and Strategies for Sustainable Design†
0277-6464 Family Therapy News
0277-6626 Annual American Music Export Buyers Guide†
0277-6693 Journal of Forecasting
0277-6707 Human Learning *see* 0888-4080
0277-6715 Statistics in Medicine
0277-6723 Cover
0277-674X I E E E International Symposium on Circuits and Systems. Proceedings
0277-6766 Lymphokine Research *changed to* Lymphokine and Cytokine Research.
0277-6774 Community Junior College: Quarterly of Research and Practice
0277-6782 Coleccion Vortex *changed to* Asociacion de Hispanistas de las Americas. Coleccion Monografias.
0277-6812 International Oil Scouts Association. Official Publication
0277-6820 Mind Your Own Business at Home
0277-6863 Crit
0277-6944 Energy Stocks Handbook *changed to* Oil & Gas Stocks Handbook.
0277-6987 Don't Miss Out: The Ambitious Student's Guide to Financial Aid
0277-6995 Cervantes
0277-7002 Earn & Learn: Cooperative Education Opportunities Offered by the Federal Government
0277-7010 Individual Psychology
0277-7037 Mass Spectrometry Reviews
0277-7053 Art on the Line Series†
0277-7061 Imprint (Brooklyn Heights)
0277-707X Recreation, Sports and Leisure *changed to* Recreation Resources.
0277-710X Kairos
0277-7126 American Journal of Semiotics
0277-7207 U.S. Department of Commerce. Publications Catalog†
0277-7223 Chiricu
0277-724X Directory of Nonprofit Immigration Counseling Agencies
0277-7312 Bricker's International Directory *see* 1054-7835
0277-7312 Bricker's International Directory *see* 1054-7843
0277-7347 Industrial Relations Research Association. Proceedings of the Annual Winter Meeting *changed to* Industrial Relations Research Association. Proceedings of the Annual Meeting.
0277-7398 Managing the Human Climate
0277-7436 Fisheries Research Review *see* 0588-4462
0277-7460 National Senior Citizens Law Center Weekly
0277-7533 Big Mama Rag†
0277-7576 International Instrumentation Symposium
0277-7738 Joy of Travel *see* 0741-5826
0277-7746 Infections in Surgery *see* 1053-749X
0277-7770 Connecticut Poetry Review
0277-7789 Writing Instructor
0277-7800 Threshold of Fantasy†
0277-7835 Puns Upon a Time†
0277-7843 Reborn *changed to* Churchyard.
0277-7983 Solid-State Circuits Conference. Digest of Technical Papers *see* 0193-6530
0277-7991 World Food Problems and United States Food Politics and Policies†
0277-8033 Journal of Protein Chemistry
0277-8041 Contemporary Psychiatry†
0277-805X Medical Grand Rounds†
0277-8068 Journal of Crystallographic and Spectroscopic Research
0277-8114 Soul Teen
0277-8173 American Journal of Social Psychiatry†
0277-8181 Blatant Image†
0277-8254 Federal Grants Handbook Annual†
0277-8270 International Journal for Hybrid Microelectronics
0277-8289 Oklahoma. Department of Human Services. Annual Report
0277-8300 Transmission Digest
0277-8327 Joint Commission Perspectives†
0277-836X Better Homes and Gardens Window & Wall Ideas
0277-8416 Discovercard Directory of Cities and Hotels†
0277-8432 Imprimis
0277-8459 Law, Medicine & Health Care
0277-8491 Housing Law Bulletin
0277-8548 Washington Health Costs Letter†
0277-8556 National Productivity Review
0277-8610 Means Historical Cost Indexes (Year)†
0277-867X Backpacker
0277-8688 American Mining Congress Journal *see* 0891-6209
0277-8696 Mine Regulation and Productivity Report *see* 0149-578X
0277-870X International Solid Fuel Buyer's Guide Directory
0277-8726 Markers
0277-8750 N A P C A E Exchange†
0277-8920 E D P Performance Management Handbook *changed to* I S Capacity Management Handbook Series.
0277-8939 Library School Review Newsletter *changed to* Infocus (Emporia).
0277-8947 National Medico-Legal Symposium. Medicolegal Proceedings†
0277-8955 Communicator (Chicago)†
0277-9048 Airpower Historian *see* 1044-016X
0277-9110 Astro Annual *changed to* New Age Astrology Guide (Year).
0277-9137 Petro Engineering News *see* 1050-2483
0277-9196 Lauriston S. Taylor Lecture Series
0277-9250 Information Intelligence Online Hotline *see* 1040-6646
0277-9269 Journal of Musicology
0277-9277 Market Watch
0277-9315 Annual Editions: Sociology
0277-9366 Clinical Immunology Reviews *see* 0882-0139
0277-9374 Applied Physics Communications
0277-9382 Metabolic, Pediatric, and Systemic Ophthalmology *see* 0882-889X
0277-9390 Government Publications Review
0277-9536 Social Science & Medicine
0277-9609 Apparel World *see* 0023-2300
0277-9617 Directory of Women's & Children's Wear Specialty Stores (Year)
0277-9625 Directory of Men's and Boys' Wear Specialty Stores (Year)
0277-9668 Yellowjacket
0277-9714 Drug Facts and Comparisons
0277-9722 Packaging Letter *see* 0892-7146
0277-9781 Wind Industry News Digest†
0277-979X FineScale Modeler
0277-9803 CinemaScore *see* 0771-6303
0277-9846 Electronic Publisher†
0277-9870 International Guide to Psi-Periodicals *see* 0734-9033
0277-9897 Post Script (Commerce)
0277-9900 U.S. Department of Agriculture. Vegetable Outlook and Situation *changed to* U.S. Department of Agriculture. Vegetable and Specialty Crop Situation and Outlook.
0277-9935 Journal of Christian Education *changed to* Christian Education Journal.
0277-9943 Advertising Compliance Service Newsletter
0277-9951 Modern Applications News
0277-996X New England Journal of Human Services
0277-9986 Directory of Real Estate Investors *changed to* Real Estate Sourcebook.
0278-002X P S F Q†
0278-0038 Going Public - The I P O Reporter
0278-0046 I E E E Transactions on Industrial Electronics
0278-0062 I E E E Transactions on Medical Imaging
0278-0070 I E E E Transactions on Computer-Aided Design of Integrated Circuits and Systems
0278-0097 I E E E Technology and Society Magazine
0278-0119 Directory of Industry Data Sources, U.S. and Canada†
0278-0127 U.S. Department of Agriculture. Feed Outlook and Situation *changed to* U.S. Department of Agriculture. Feed Situation and Outlook.
0278-0135 Predicasts Forecasts
0278-0143 U.S. Department of Health and Human Services. Publication Catalog†
0278-016X Social Cognition
0278-0178 J L A G Review†
0278-0208 Goldfinch
0278-0224 Parity
0278-0232 Hematological Oncology
0278-0240 Disease Markers
0278-0372 Journal of Crustacean Biology
0278-0410 S A C Movie News†
0278-047X Wine Country
0278-0569 N A S S P Newsleader
0278-0585 American Sentinel
0278-0763 Moravian Music Journal
0278-0771 Journal of Ethnobiology
0278-0801 Cargo Facts
0278-081X Circuits, Systems, and Signal Processing
0278-0828 Passages North
0278-0844 1001 Home Ideas†
0278-0879 Attorney's Directory of Forensic Psychiatrists in the United States and Canada†
0278-0895 Nondestructive Testing Communications *changed to* Nondestructive Testing and Evaluation.
0278-0933 Lips (Montclair)
0278-095X Journal of Primary Prevention
0278-0984 Advances in Applied Microeconomics
0278-0992 Compensation in Manufacturing - Engineers and Managers
0278-1018 Soviet Christian Prisoner List *changed to* Christian Prisoners in the U.S.S.R.
0278-1042 Journal of Probation and Parole
0278-1077 Complex Variables: Theory and Application
0278-1093 Congress Watcher *see* 0738-5927
0278-1174 Catholic New York
0278-1190 Mendocino Review†
0278-1204 Current Perspectives in Social Theory
0278-1263 Trump's†
0278-1301 Municipal Litigation Reporter
0278-1336 Home Video Yearbook *see* 0735-469X
0278-1360 Index: Foreign Broadcast Information Service Daily Reports: Latin America
0278-1387 Speakers†
0278-1409 Parents Home *see* 0195-0967

ISSN

5678 ISSN INDEX

0278-1425 Professional Surveyor
0278-1433 Outside (Chicago, 1980)
0278-1441 Art Papers
0278-145X Seminars in Dermatology
0278-1506 A M S Guide to Management Compensation *changed to* A M S Management Salaries Report.
0278-1530 Product Marketing and Cosmetic and Fragrance Retailing
0278-1557 Knowledge and Society
0278-1565 American Bus Association. Report†
0278-159X Robotics Industry Directory *changed to* International Robotics Product Database.
0278-1603 Wildrows†
0278-1743 Research Services Directory
0278-1808 Focal Points†
0278-1816 Criminal Law Monthly†
0278-1832 Chemical Abstracts - Physical, Inorganic and Analytical Chemistry Sections
0278-1859 State (Washington)
0278-1891 Pynchon Notes
0278-193X Working Mother (New York)
0278-2219 A S A News
0278-2227 Inside Energy With Federal Lands
0278-226X Platt's Energy Litigation Report†
0278-2308 International Social Science Review
0278-2316 I D N - Infectious Diseases Newsletter
0278-2324 Conjunctions
0278-2340 B I H E P†
0278-2359 Advances in the Psychology of Human Intelligence
0278-2367 Advances in Personality Assessment
0278-2383 Information and Referral
0278-2391 Journal of Oral and Maxillofacial Surgery
0278-2448 International Construction Week: Asia Construction Business Report†
0278-2456 International Construction Week: Latin America Construction Business Report†
0278-2464 International Construction Week: Mideast Construction Business Report†
0278-257X Directory of Computer Software and Related Technical Reports *see* 0748-1543
0278-260X Computer Equipment Review *changed to* Library Computer Systems & Equipment Review.
0278-2618 Washington Letter on Latin America†
0278-2626 Brain and Cognition
0278-2634 Software Review (Westport) *see* 0742-5759
0278-2642 Quality Circle Digest *changed to* Quality Digest.
0278-2677 Clinical Pharmacy
0278-2693 Sports Collectors Digest
0278-2715 Health Affairs
0278-2731 International Research Centers Directory
0278-2774 Computer Graphics Marketplace†
0278-2790 Photographer's Market Newsletter†
0278-2820 Abstracts Strengthening Research Library Resources Program
0278-2839 Home
0278-2863 Community Animal Control
0278-2871 Rock Art
0278-2898 I S I Atlas of Science *changed to* I S I Atlas of Science: Vol. 1: Biochemistry and Molecular Biology.
0278-2901 Journal of Photoacoustics†
0278-291X Rocky Mountain Symposium on Microcomputers: Systems, Software, Architecture. Proceedings†
0278-2936 Roanoke Valley Historical Society Journal
0278-2944 Journal of Psychoanalytic Anthropology *see* 0145-3378
0278-310X University of Mississippi Studies in English
0278-3118 Nautilus Magazine *changed to* Nautilus (Independence).
0278-3126 School Age Notes
0278-3134 Smith Papers
0278-3177 New Hampshire Media Directory†
0278-3258 Electronic Learning
0278-3274 Novitates Arthropodae†
0278-3282 Spring (Emmaus)†
0278-3428 Los Angeles Business and Economics *see* 0733-2408
0278-3452 Health Devices Sourcebook
0278-3479 Defense Electronics
0278-3479 Defense Electronics. Marketing Directory and Buyers Guide†
0278-355X Property & Liability Insurance Index†
0278-3649 International Journal of Robotics Research
0278-372X How to Find Information About Companies
0278-3738 Neuroscience Newsletter
0278-3770 Utah Statistical Abstract
0278-3819 Transportation Studies
0278-3916 Law - Technology
0278-4017 Science and Technology Series
0278-4033 Association for Jewish Studies Newsletter†
0278-405X Directory of Statisticians
0278-4092 Connecticut Nursing News
0278-4114 Loose Change
0278-4149 Legal Systems Letter†
0278-4165 Journal of Anthropological Archaeology
0278-4173 Hot Water Review
0278-419X Hollywood Reporter Studio Blu-Book Directory
0278-4238 Translations Index
0278-4246 Ruralamerica†
0278-4254 Journal of Accounting and Public Policy
0278-4262 Astrology for the 80's†
0278-4270 E M C Technology & Interference Control News
0278-4289 Annals of Public Administration
0278-4297 Journal of Ultrasound in Medicine
0278-4300 Ecology of Disease†
0278-4319 International Journal of Hospitality Management
0278-4327 Progress in Retinal Research
0278-4335 World Language English *see* 0883-2919
0278-4343 Continental Shelf Research
0278-436X J A P O S Bulletin†
0278-4378 Source I
0278-4386 Source II
0278-4408 Northern Sun News
0278-4416 Policy Studies Review
0278-4424 Manufacturing Technology Horizons†
0278-4440 Organizing Notes†
0278-4491 Environmental Progress (New York)
0278-4513 Plant - Operations Progress
0278-4521 Energy Progress†
0278-4602 Psychiatry Digest (1979)†
0278-4653 Annual Editions: Health
0278-467X Tours and Visits Directory
0278-4726 Construction Industry Litigation Reporter†
0278-4750 Problems of Desert Development
0278-4807 Rehabilitation Nursing
0278-4823 School Library Media Quarterly
0278-4858 Washington State Library News
0278-4882 Occasional Papers in Middle Eastern Librarianship
0278-4912 U.S. National Center for Health Statistics. Catalog of Publications
0278-4920 Trade and Technical Careers and Training *changed to* Career Education That Works for America.
0278-4947 What's Cooking in Congress?
0278-4955 Hockey Guide
0278-4998 Pediatric Mental Health
0278-5013 Movie - Video Age International
0278-503X Cable T V Programming
0278-5048 Sales Rep's Advisor
0278-5099 Energy & Minerals Resources†
0278-5161 Lab Report for Physicians Newsletter *see* 1045-7313
0278-520X I E E E Technical Activities Guide
0278-5226 Journal of Arboriculture
0278-5277 Criminal Justice Career Digest†
0278-5293 Electronic Education
0278-5307 Libertas Mathematica
0278-5374 U.S. National Institutes of Health. Division of Research Resources. Program Highlights *changed to* U.S. National Institutes of Health. National Center for Research Resources. Program Highlights.
0278-551X Axios
0278-5595 Poultryman *see* 0885-3371
0278-5633 Rutgers Journal of Computers, Technology, and the Law *see* 0735-8938
0278-5641 O'Casey Annual†
0278-565X Pockets
0278-5676 Microwave Discontinued Devices
D.A.T.A. Book†
0278-5692 U.S. Federal Deposit Insurance Corporation. Trust Assets of Banks and Trust Companies
0278-5706 Job Catalog
0278-5846 Progress in Neuro-Psychopharmacology and Biological Psychiatry
0278-5854 U S Law Library Alert *see* 0883-1297
0278-5919 Clinics in Sports Medicine
0278-5927 Journal of American Ethnic History
0278-5943 American Classical Studies
0278-5994 Diesel & Gas Turbine Worldwide
0278-6052 California Journal of Teacher Education *see* 0737-5328
0278-6060 Psychoenergetics *see* 0894-2528
0278-6079 Nightsun
0278-6087 Journal of Business Forecasting Methods and Systems
0278-6117 Sulfur Letters
0278-6125 Journal of Manufacturing Systems
0278-6133 Health Psychology
0278-6273 Laser Chemistry
0278-6281 Life Chemistry Reports
0278-632X Kidstuff
0278-6346 Trends: Consumer Attitudes and the Supermarket Update
0278-6397 Reruns
0278-6419 Moscow University Computational Mathematics and Cybernetics
0278-6508 Dr. Dobb's Journal for the Experienced in Microcomputing *see* 1044-789X
0278-6524 Market Guide Continental Europe
0278-6532 Babcox's ImportCar *see* 0735-7877
0278-6567 Financial Statements and Operating Ratios for the Mortgage Banking Industry
0278-663X Terrorism (Minneapolis)
0278-6648 I E E E Potentials
0278-6656 Classical Antiquity
0278-6664 W W S - World Ports *changed to* W W S - World Wide Shipping.
0278-6680 International Country Risk Guide
0278-6702 Airline Executive *see* 1051-631X
0278-6745 Legal Notes and Viewpoints Quarterly†
0278-6826 Aerosol Science and Technology
0278-6850 PharmAlert
0278-6915 Food and Chemical Toxicology
0278-694X Statistical Reference Index
0278-7016 Raise the Stakes
0278-7032 I E E E Symposium on Research in Security and Privacy. Proceedings
0278-7067 Welding and Fabricating Data Book
0278-7121 Publishing Abstracts†
0278-7210 Children's Legal Rights Journal
0278-7261 Critica Hispanica
0278-7288 Literatura Chilena en el Exilio *see* 0730-0220
0278-7334 Parks & Recreation Resources†
0278-7393 Journal of Experimental Psychology: Learning, Memory, and Cognition
0278-7407 Tectonics
0278-7431 Western Pennsylvania Genealogical Society Quarterly
0278-7490 Better Homes and Gardens Holiday Crafts
0278-7504 Better Homes and Gardens 100's of Needlework and Craft Ideas *changed to* Better Homes and Gardens Needlework & Craft Ideas.
0278-7857 Directory of Library Resources for the Blind and Physically Handicapped *see* 0364-1236
0278-7946 O M S Annual Report†
0278-8012 Institute of Industrial Engineers. Proceedings of the Spring Annual Conference†
0278-8020 Batteries Today *changed to* I B D B Bulletin.
0278-8063 World Agricultural Regional Supplement: Africa and the Middle East *changed to* World Agriculture Regional Supplement: Middle East and North Africa.
0278-8217 Safety Products News *see* 8755-2566
0278-8225 Mainstream (San Diego)
0278-8322 Phenomenology Information Bulletin *see* 0885-3886
0278-8381 Economic Indicators (Charleston)
0278-839X Journal of Social, Political and Economic Studies
0278-842X Who's Who in Special Libraries
0278-8799 Dun's Industrial Guide - The Metalworking Directory
0278-8888 Annual Insider Index to Public Policy Studies†
0278-8896 Bondweek (1972)†
0278-8950 Light Plane Maintenance
0278-8969 Afro-Hispanic Review
0278-906X Handbook of Food Preparation†
0278-9078 Ethnic Forum
0278-9175 Computing Teacher
0278-9183 Videodisc - Videotex *see* 1054-9692
0278-9213 Cross Country Skier
0278-923X U.S. Department of Agriculture. Livestock and Meat Outlook and Situation *changed to* U.S. Department of Agriculture. Livestock and Poultry Situation and Outlook.
0278-9353 Journal: Asset-Based Financial Services Industry *see* 0888-255X
0278-937X Washington Papers
0278-9396 International Omega Association. Proceedings of Annual Meeting
0278-940X C R C Critical Reviews in Biomedical Engineering *changed to* Critical Reviews in Biomedical Engineering.
0278-9426 Glass Art Society Journal
0278-9434 Transportation Quarterly
0278-9442 Yet Another Small Magazine
0278-9469 PaLiNet News
0278-9485 Livability Digest
0278-9493 Psychiatric Aspects of Mental Retardation Newsletter *see* 1057-3291
0278-9507 American Ceramics
0278-9523 Journal of Bioethics *see* 1041-3545
0278-954X Siddha Path *see* 0892-130X
0278-9566 Bi-Annual Review of Allergy†
0278-9612 Wrestling's Main Event
0278-9647 Computer Technology Review
0278-9671 Literature & Medicine
0278-9698 Directory of Convenience Store Companies *changed to* Progressive Grocer's Directory of Convenience Stores.
0278-9728 Biotechnology Law Report
0278-9736 Agricultural Genetics Report†
0278-9744 University of Kansas. Paleontological Contributions. Monographs *see* 1046-8390
0278-9752 Borgo Political Scenarios
0278-9760 Fit *changed to* Ujena Girl.
0278-9779 Medico Interamericano
0278-9817 Lawyers Alert
0278-9841 Informs
0278-9892 Washington Blade
0278-9922 Electronic Servicing & Technology
0278-999X Management (Los Angeles)†
0279-0041 American Premiere Magazine
0279-0106 Arbor Age
0279-0327 Typographer
0279-0424 Charisma
0279-0432 Picture Magazine *see* 0732-1511
0279-0491 Illinois Vocational Education Journal
0279-0548 Services

ISSN

ISSN INDEX 5679

ISSN	Title
0279-067X	Essex Genealogist
0279-0688	Education and Psychological Research
0279-070X	Computers and Programming†
0279-0718	Black Family
0279-0726	Food Development see 0747-2536
0279-0734	Media General Financial Weekly†
0279-0742	M D A News see 8750-2321
0279-0750	Pacific Philosophical Quarterly
0279-0785	The Chamber Today
0279-0815	Uncle Sam
0279-0858	Clavier's Piano Explorer
0279-0882	Rhode Island Lawyers Weekly
0279-0998	Sporting Classics
0279-1021	C P A Marketing Report
0279-103X	Objector
0279-1072	Journal of Psychoactive Drugs
0279-1102	Construction Litigation Reporter
0279-1110	Toiletries, Fragrances and Skin Care: The Rose Sheet
0279-1153	College and Junior Tennis
0279-1196	Communicare†
0279-120X	N A T O News & Views
0279-1250	Letters Magazine (Teaneck)
0279-1293	Serbian Struggle
0279-1323	Orlando Magazine
0279-134X	Swimming Pool Age and Spa Merchandiser see 0899-1022
0279-134X	Swimming Pool Age Data and Reference Annual see 0899-1022
0279-1420	Buying for the Farm†
0279-1447	Robb Report
0279-151X	Radio World International
0279-1536	Survey of Wall St. Research see 0740-5103
0279-1552	Buildings Journal†
0279-1579	Unisphere
0279-165X	Texas Farmer-Stockman
0279-1706	Amazing Science Fiction Stories see 1058-0751
0279-1749	Sportsman Pilot
0279-1889	Bottomline (Austin)
0279-1935	N B A Today see 0749-5285
0279-1978	Women's Circle Crochet
0279-2125	New Health
0279-2176	Truck & Equipment Salesman†
0279-2230	Federal Career Opportunities
0279-2257	Juvenile and Family Law Digest
0279-2338	Saving Energy
0279-2435	G W Times changed to G W Magazine.
0279-246X	Epic Illustrated†
0279-2508	National Dairy News changed to Cheese Market News.
0279-2664	Interact
0279-2680	Your Life and Health see 0749-3509
0279-2737	On Track
0279-2834	V L S I Design changed to High Performance Systems.
0279-2893	Non-Store Marketing Report
0279-3016	Founders Hall
0279-3040	Dun's Business Month see 0892-4090
0279-3083	National Motorist
0279-3091	Nursing Life†
0279-3156	Oregon Outdoors
0279-3229	Zontian
0279-3369	Instructor and Teacher see 1049-5851
0279-3415	B'nai B'rith International Jewish Monthly
0279-3547	Health
0279-358X	American Cocker Magazine
0279-361X	Wombat†
0279-3652	Comboni Missions
0279-3695	Journal of Psychosocial Nursing and Mental Health Services
0279-3709	The Petro-Philatelist
0279-375X	State Bar of New Mexico. News and Views changed to State Bar of New Mexico. Bar Bulletin.
0279-3768	California (Los Angeles)†
0279-3857	Georgia Business and Economic Conditions
0279-3911	The Messenger (Belleville)
0279-4004	Cable Age
0279-4039	Dynamic Business
0279-4063	California Lawyer
0279-4071	Contracting Business
0279-408X	Directions (Lawrenceville) changed to Rider College Magazine.
0279-4160	Acquisition - Divestiture Weekly Report
0279-4187	Converting Product News see 0746-7141
0279-4195	Daily Commerce
0279-4268	Gung-Ho†
0279-4357	National Energy Journal
0279-4438	Facilities Design and Management
0279-4462	Lutheran Perspective†
0279-4470	American Import-Export Management changed to Global Trade.
0279-4519	Revista Aerea
0279-4527	New Orleans CityBusiness
0279-4616	Roofer Magazine
0279-4659	Windrider changed to Windsurfing.
0279-4691	Federal Bar News & Journal
0279-4705	Concrete see 0899-8671
0279-4721	Popular Computing (Peterborough)†
0279-473X	New Dimensions (Reston) changed to D E C A Dimensions.
0279-4756	Gifted Children Newsletter changed to Gifted Children Monthly.
0279-4799	Hospital Purchasing News
0279-4802	Medical Products Sales
0279-4853	Endless Vacation
0279-4888	Dallas Apparel News
0279-4896	New York's Inside Design†
0279-490X	Childbirth Educator†
0279-4918	Draperies & Window Coverings
0279-4942	Group Practice News changed to Group Practice Managed Healthcare News.
0279-4969	Coltsfoot
0279-4977	Metropolis
0279-5027	Modern Textile Business†
0279-5051	S E M A News
0279-5086	Gun Dog
0279-5272	Pharmacy Student
0279-5337	Western City
0279-5345	Missions U S A
0279-5353	Consumers Union News Digest changed to Consumer Reports News Digest.
0279-540X	N T E U Bulletin
0279-5418	B N A Policy and Practice Series. Compensation
0279-5442	Critical Care Nurse
0279-5523	Will Eisner's Spirit see 0886-7267
0279-5590	Whole Life Times
0279-5647	Orthopedics Today
0279-568X	Dialogue (Columbus)
0279-5701	Sync†
0279-571X	Video Business
0279-5787	Legal Contents†
0279-585X	Science and Electronics see 0279-070X
0279-5957	Rural Sociologist
0279-6015	School Psychology Review
0279-6090	Rod Serling's the Twilight Zone Magazine†
0279-6139	U S C S Log
0279-6163	Coordinator (Memphis)
0279-6198	Watch and Clock Review
0279-6309	Realtor News
0279-6368	Builder-Dealer
0279-6406	Weekly: Seattle's Newsmagazine changed to Seattle Weekly.
0279-6430	A E D C Journal†
0279-6481	New Jersey Tax Court. Reports
0279-6503	Land Line Magazine
0279-6570	Pharmaceutical Executive
0279-6678	Sports Retailer see 1045-2087
0279-6694	GyroScope
0279-6716	S O W
0279-6740	Food & Wine
0279-6791	Lousiana Life
0279-6848	Dragon Magazine
0279-6910	Clinical Prosthetics and Orthotics see 1040-8800
0279-7739	National Drillers Buyers Guide
0279-7798	Northeast Oil Reporter see 0884-4771
0279-7801	Oil Price Information Service
0279-781X	Synthesis (Bolton)†
0279-7828	Parish Communication
0279-7844	New York Apparel News
0279-7976	Journal of Parenteral Science and Technology
0279-7984	Jax Fax Travel Marketing Magazine
0279-7992	Word Processing and Information Services†
0279-8085	Empire for the S F Writer changed to Waystation for the S F Writer.
0279-8123	Hardcopy
0279-8174	Mid-South Business Journal
0279-8182	Biblical Recorder
0279-8204	Cow Country
0279-8301	Napa Valley Magazine's Wine Country see 0278-047X
0279-8344	MassBay Antiques
0279-8468	Destinations (Washington)
0279-8484	Kiplinger Texas Letter
0279-8557	New Jersey Education Law Report
0279-8611	New York Holstein News
0279-8689	Action Now†
0279-8743	Legislative Monitor changed to Professional Monitor.
0279-8824	Louisiana Market Bulletin
0279-8891	Cable Marketing†
0279-8905	Vital†
0279-9030	Kansas Wildlife changed to Kansas Wildlife & Parks.
0279-9065	Outdoor News
0279-9111	Bond
0279-9162	New England Farm Bulletin changed to New England Farm Bulletin and Garden Gazette.
0279-9200	Sheep! Magazine
0279-9308	Flying Safety
0279-9316	A S M E News
0279-9340	Medical Tribune (1980)
0279-9359	Wind Surf
0279-9456	Groundwater Digest
0279-9472	American Hiker
0279-9529	American College of Physicians Observer
0279-9553	American Sailor
0279-9588	Religious Book Review†
0279-9596	ScriptWriter News†
0279-960X	Marple's Business Newsletter
0279-9626	County Bar Update
0279-9634	Ohio Runner
0279-9693	Retriever Field Trial News
0279-9766	Staten Island
0279-9782	Software News (Hudson) see 0897-8085
0279-9812	Woodland Report
0279-9855	Susquehanna Monthly Magazine see 1047-3068
0279-9863	Info A A U
0280-1078	Kungliga Tekniska Hoegskolan. Flygteknisk Institutionen. K T H Aero Memo F It
0280-1183	Transportraadet Rapport†
0280-185X	Ekonomisk Dokumentation
0280-2171	Current African Issues
0280-2783	Stressforskningsrapporter
0280-2791	Scandinavian Journal of Development Alternatives
0280-3038	Cykling
0280-3046	Riksarkivets Rapporter
0280-378X	New Swedish Technology see 1100-956X
0280-3887	Goeteborgs Etnografiska Museum. Aarstryck - Annals
0280-3984	Slaekthistoriskt Forum
0280-4026	Chalmers University of Technology. Department of Sanitary Engineering. Publications
0280-4131	Sweden. Statens Planverk. Plan o Bygg Aktuellt
0280-4182	Riksgaeldkontoret. Statistisk Aarsbok
0280-4239	Bergsmannen med Jernkontorets Annaler see 0284-0448
0280-4557	L K B News with Science Tools changed to L K B News.
0280-4603	Kyrkans Tidning
0280-4638	Hjaerta Kaerl Lungor changed to Hjaert-Lungfonden.
0280-4743	Wages and Total Labour Costs for Workers: International Survey
0280-6347	Din Fastighet
0280-6495	Tellus. Series A: Dynamic Meteorology and Oceanography
0280-6509	Tellus. Series B: Chemical and Physical Meteorology
0280-6983	Socialt Arbete
0280-7610	Sweden. Statistiska Centralbyraans Bibliotek. Statistik Fraan Enskilda Laender
0280-7629	Sweden. Statistiska Centralbyraan Bibliotek. Internationella Organ. Statistik changed to Sweden. Statistiska Centralbyraan Bibliotek.
0280-7637	Sweden. Statistiska Centralbyraans Bibliotek. Nyfoervaerv
0280-7815	Nya Byggnormer see 0281-7276
0280-8234	Loggen changed to Loggen Magazine.
0280-8331	Systema Ascomycetum
0280-8463	Kattegat-Skagerrak-Projectet. Meddelelser†
0280-8633	Studia Anthroponymica Scandinavica
0280-8773	Invandrarfraagor. Aarsbok†
0280-896X	V T I Topics†
0280-9060	Sindikalne Novosti
0280-9311	Montage
0281-0018	Scandinavian Institute of African Studies. Seminar Proceedings
0281-0557	Sindikalistika Nea changed to Trade Union News.
0281-0662	Journal of Social Administrative Pharmacy
0281-0891	Skola och Vuxenutbilning see 1100-5491
0281-1189	Elektronikvarlden
0281-1278	Kloeverbladet
0281-1847	Physica Scripta Topical Issues
0281-2584	Tidskrift foer Raettssociologi
0281-2851	Stockholm Studies in Social Work
0281-286X	Kyrkomusikernas Tidning
0281-2932	Ute-Magasinet
0281-3408	Swedish Research on Higher Education see 0283-7692
0281-3505	Advokaten
0281-4447	Swedish Road Safety Office. Analysis Section Report
0281-4528	Studia Orientalia Lundensia
0281-5087	Acid News
0281-5443	Svensk Gymnastik
0281-5737	Scandinavian Housing and Planning Research
0281-627X	I L G A Bulletin
0281-658X	Building and Technic
0281-6776	Pedagogiska Rapporter
0281-6881	Sweden Sjukvaardens och Socialvaardens Planerings och Rationaliseringsins
0281-7276	Nya Byggregler
0281-7446	Arbetarhistoria
0281-7527	Scandinavian Journal of Management
0281-8205	Noetkoett
0281-8515	Energy, Environment and Development in Africa†
0282-0080	Glycoconjugate Journal
0282-0145	Goeteborg. Stadskansli. Boersmeddelandent
0282-0196	Acid Magazine see 1101-7341
0282-0390	Restauranger & Storkoek
0282-0595	Kyrkogarden
0282-1001	S S R - Tidningen Socionomen see 0283-1910
0282-1540	Acidification Research in Sweden†
0282-2024	Sweden. Statens Jaernvaegars Huvudkontor. Geoteknik och Ingenjoergeologi. Meddelandent
0282-3497	Sweden. Statistiska Centralbyraan. Statistiska Meddelanden. Subgroup O (Offtentliga Finanser-Public Finances)
0282-3500	Sweden. Statistiska Centralbyraan. Statistiska Meddelanden. Subgroup Na (Natural Resources and the Environment)

ISSN	Title
0282-3519	Sweden. Statistiska Centralbyraan. Statistiska Meddelanden. Subgroup Ku
0282-4175	Guldsmedstidningen
0282-423X	Journal of Official Statistics
0282-4485	Landstingsvaerlden
0282-4655	Initiativ
0282-4736	Skolvux-soe see 1100-5491
0282-5902	Kulturens Vaerld
0282-5996	Sweden. Statens Vaeg- och Trafikinstitut. Verksamhetsberaettelse
0282-6283	C B I Informerar
0282-7298	Sweden. Swedish Environmental Protection Agency. Report
0282-7581	Scandinavian Journal of Forest Research
0282-7654	Buss - Svensk Omnibustidning
0282-8006	Strindbergiana
0282-860X	Aarets Ishockey
0282-8618	Teknik i Jordskog see 0023-8449
0282-8677	Studies in Plant Ecology
0282-8928	Acta Universitatis Upsaliensis
0282-8952	Musikmuseets Skrifter
0283-071X	Svensk Numismatisk Tidskrift
0283-1155	Brand & Raeddning
0283-1511	I V L - Referat
0283-1686	Kiruna Geophysical Institute. Annual Report see 0284-169X
0283-1694	Kiruna Geophysical Institute. Scientific Report see 0284-1703
0283-1910	S S R - Tidningen
0283-2380	Acta Philosophica Gothoburgensia
0283-2399	Goeteborg Women's Studies
0283-2631	Nordic Pulp & Paper Research Journal
0283-2852	Faaglar i Kvismaren
0283-2925	Communidad
0283-3190	Stim Nytt
0283-4669	Verko
0283-5452	Skydd & Saekerhet
0283-6831	Svensk Papperstidning - Nordisk Cellulosa
0283-7021	V T I Annual Report
0283-7692	Studies of Higher Education and Research
0283-8400	Militaerhistorisk Tidskrift
0283-8486	Journal of Prehistoric Religion
0283-8974	Industrial Institute for Economic and Social Research. Yearbook
0283-9652	Smaafoeretagartidningen changed to Tidningen Foeretagarna.
0284-0448	Bergsmannen
0284-074X	Transport Teknik Scandinavia changed to Transport i Dag.
0284-0758	Scan Ref
0284-169X	Swedish Institute of Space Physics. Annual Report
0284-1703	Swedish Institute of Space Physics. Scientific Report
0284-1711	Swedish Institute of Space Physics. Preprint†
0284-172X	Swedish Institute of Space Physics. Software Report
0284-1738	Swedish Institute of Space Physics. Technical Report
0284-4524	Oern Bladet
0284-5075	Lund Studies in Economics and Management
0284-5342	Svensk Medicin
0284-6152	Textil Magazine
0284-6578	Goeteborg Studies in Conservation
0284-7035	Fotografisk Tidskrift
0284-9321	Bio Science Abstracts
0284-9941	Kristdemokraten
0285-0028	Taikabutsu Overseas
0285-0257	Akita Shizenshi Kenkyu
0285-0303	Nippondenso Technical Disclosure. Journal
0285-0354	Musashi Kogyo Daigaku. Genshiryoku Kenkyujo. Kenkyujoho
0285-0370	Oyo Tokeigaku
0285-0435	Shizuoka Daigaku Kyoyobu Kenkyu Hokoku. Shizen Kagaku Hen
0285-0494	Enerugi Shigen
0285-0508	Journal of Dental Hygiene
0285-0516	Journal of Dental Office†
0285-0796	Immuno-Advance†
0285-0850	Raiken
0285-0877	Yobo Igaku
0285-1008	Bessatsu Saiensu
0285-1350	National Rehabilitation Center for the Disabled. Research Bulletin
0285-1601	African Study Monographs
0285-1806	Hokkaido Eiyo Syokuryo Gakkaishi
0285-211X	Minami-Kyushu Daigaku Engeigakubu Kenkyu Hokoku. Shizen Kagaku, Jinbun Shakai Kagaku
0285-2608	I H J Bulletin
0285-2861	I S A S Nyusu
0285-2926	Jisuberi
0285-2969	Kyowa Engineering News
0285-3167	Denki Tetsudo
0285-3205	Kansai Shizen Kagaku
0285-3760	Hokuriku Journal of Zootechnical Science
0285-3809	Tradescope
0285-3817	Tohoku Kogyo Daigaku Kiyo, 1. Rikogaku Hen
0285-3825	Tohoku Institute of Technology. Memoirs. Series 2: Humanities and Social Science
0285-3833	Japan Electronic Materials Society. Bulletin
0285-3922	Nichi-Futsu Rikoka Kaishi
0285-4333	Waseda University. Science and Engineering Research Laboratory. Report
0285-4538	Nagoya Keizai Daigaku, Ichimura Gakuen Tanki Daigaku Shizen Kagaku Kenkyukai Kaishi
0285-4600	Nikkei Biotechnology
0285-4619	Nikkei Computer
0285-4821	Historia Scientiarum
0285-4937	Pharma Japan
0285-5100	Current Bibliography on Science and Technology: Life Sciences
0285-5518	Isotope News
0285-5615	Hiwa Kagaku Hakubutsukan Kenkyu Hokoku
0285-5844	Shashin Sokuryo to Rimoto Senshingu
0285-5887	Nihon Kaihatsu Ginko. Chosabu. Chosa
0285-6018	Doro to Konkurito
0285-6085	Nagaoka-shiritsu Kagaku Hakubutsukan Kenkyu Hokoku
0285-6425	Micomlife
0285-6808	Institute of Space and Astronautical Science. Report
0285-6905	Kiso, Kankyo Kagaku Kenkyu
0285-7006	Bifidos-Flores et Frictus†
0285-7529	China Newsletter
0285-7677	Tokei
0285-7685	Okayama Rika Daigaku Kiyo A. Shizen Kagaku
0285-7790	Sokuryo
0285-7928	Kokusai Kyoryoku
0285-7960	Kagaku Keisatsu Kenkyujo Hokoku Hokagaku Hen
0285-8150	Shizen Kagaku Ronso
0285-8258	Meiji Daigaku Kagaku Gijutsu Kenkyujo Hokoku. Sogo Kenkyu
0285-8576	Miyazaki Daigaku Kyoikugakubu Kiyo. Shizen Kagaku
0285-9033	Toyota Foundation Occasional Report
0285-9394	Data Communications and Processing
0285-9521	Fire Science and Technology
0285-9556	Journal of Japanese Trade and Industry
0285-9610	Toyama Daigaku Kyoikugakubu Kiyo, B. Rikakei
0285-9947	Japan Society for Simulation Technology. Journal
0286-0376	Go World
0286-0406	Science and Technology in Japan
0286-0619	Earthquake Prediction Research
0286-0627	Hokkaido no Shizen
0286-0635	Japan Aviation Directory
0286-0651	Newton
0286-1208	Kagoshima-kenritsu Tanki Daigaku Kiyo. Shizen Kagaku Hen
0286-1410	Japan Statistical Association. Annual Report on the Migration in Japan Derived from the Basic Resident Registers
0286-2743	Niihama Kogyo Koto Senmon Gakko Kiyo. Rikogaku Hen
0286-2832	Doshisha Studies in Foreign Literature
0286-3189	Hokkaido Daigaku Oyo Denki Kenkyujo Gijutsu Hokoku
0286-4010	Japanese Society for Strength and Fracture of Materials. Journal
0286-4215	Keio Science and Technology Reports
0286-4312	Kuruma no Techo
0286-4339	Iwate University Forests. Bulletin
0286-4487	Rigaku Senkoka Zasshi†
0286-4568	Kyoto Daigaku. Reichorui Kenkyujo Nenpo
0286-4932	Sei Marianna Ika Daigaku Kiyo. Ippan Kyoiku.
0286-5092	Tezukayama Tanki Daigaku Kiyo. Shizen Kagaku Hen
0286-522X	Bulletin of Informatics and Cybernetics
0286-5300	Omni Japan†
0286-5769	Kumamoto Daigaku Kyoyobu Kiyo. Shizen Kagaku Hen
0286-6102	Shokuchu Shokubutsu Kenkyukai Kaishi
0286-6293	Utsunomiya Daigaku Kyoyobu Kenkyu Hokoku. Dai-2-bu
0286-6722	Radiation Chemistry
0286-7125	Niigata Rikagaku
0286-715X	Recent Progress of Natural Sciences in Japan†
0286-7311	Shizuoka Daigaku Kyoikugakubu Kenkyu Hokoku. Shizen Kagaku Hen
0286-7427	Marine Technology Research Abstracts & Index (MATRAX)
0286-7583	Hokkaido Chika Shigen Chosa Hokoku see 0441-0785
0286-8210	Japan Semiconductor Technology News†
0286-8660	Ishikawa-ken Hakusan Shizen Hogo Senta Kenkyu Hokoku
0286-8768	Tokyo-to Takao Shizen Kagaku Hakubutsukan Kenkyu Hokoku
0286-9152	Kaiji Sangyo Kenkyujoho
0286-9241	Shin Boei Ronshu
0286-9306	Bifidobacteria and Microflora
0286-9500	Kuoku
0286-9640	University of the Ryukyus. College of Science. Bulletin
0286-9667	African Study Monographs. Supplementary Issue
0286-9810	Entomological Review of Japan
0287-0002	Fukuoka Daigaku Sogo Kenkyujo. Shizen Kagaku Hen
0287-0029	Japan. Ministry of Agriculture, Forestry and Fisheries. National Research Institute of Agricultural Engineering. Technical Report
0287-0185	Arerugia
0287-0517	Environmental Medicine
0287-0606	Hozon Kagaku
0287-0916	Oita Daigaku Keizai Kenkyujo Kenkyujoho
0287-1238	Japanese Cosmetic Science Society. Journal
0287-1254	Fukuoka-Ken Eisei Kogai Senta Nenpo
0287-1319	Nagasaki Daigaku Kyoyobu Kiyo. Shizen Kagaku Hen
0287-1394	Osaka Sangyo Daigaku Ronshu. Shizen Kagaku Hen
0287-1688	Tottori-kenritsu Hakubutsukan Kenkyu Hokoku
0287-1785	I C M R Annals
0287-2404	L T C B Research
0287-2633	Kaijo Hoan-cho. Suiro-bu Kansoku Hokoku. Tenmon Sokuchi Hen
0287-2900	Utan
0287-3052	Needs
0287-3516	Japanese Society of Nutrition and Food Science. Journal
0287-3532	Iwatani Naoji Kinen Zaidan Kenkyu Hokokusho
0287-4466	Setsunan University. Scientific Review. Series A, Natural Sciences
0287-5012	Renewable Energy see 0912-2311
0287-5128	Japan Shipbuilding Information Notes†
0287-5306	Monetary and Economic Studies
0287-5594	Mediya Sakuru
0287-6051	Asiatic Society of Japan. Transactions
0287-6507	Kobe University. Graduate School of Science and Technology. Memoirs. Series A
0287-6515	Kobe Daigaku Daigakuin Shizen Kagaku Kenkyuka Kiyo B
0287-7007	Waseda Seiji Keizaigaku Zasshi
0287-7082	Kanagawa University. Institute for Humanities Research. Bulletin
0287-7112	Japan Press Weekly: News & Comments
0287-718X	Rikagakkaishi
0287-7775	Seicho
0287-7791	Kagoshima Daigaku. Nankanen Shiryo Senta. Hokoku
0287-7902	Kyoto Sangyo Daigaku Ronshu. Shizen Kagaku Keiretsu
0287-802X	Chosen Shogakkai Gakujutsu Ronbunshu
0287-8321	Jidosha Gijutsukai Ronbunshu
0287-864X	Nihon Rikagaku Kyokai. Kenkyu Kiyo
0287-9433	Hokkaido Kaitaku Kinenkan Kenkyu Nenpo
0287-9506	Nikkei Personal Computing
0287-9530	Japan Directory of Professional Associations
0287-9549	Nara Joshi Daigaku Hoken Kanri Senta Nenpo
0287-9980	Kyushu Daigaku Kyoyobu Sugaku Zasshi
0288-0490	Netsu Shori
0288-089X	Kaihatsu Ronshu
0288-1012	Shika Yakubutsu Ryoho
0288-1829	Donan Igakukai
0288-1977	Tenmon Gaido
0288-2043	Radiation Medicine
0288-2329	Tokyo-to no Shizen
0288-2930	S G I
0288-3139	Mogura
0288-3422	Niigata Daigaku Kyoikugakubu Kiyo. Shizen Kagaku Hen
0288-349X	Gakujutsu Zasshi
0288-3635	New Generation Computing
0288-3864	Packaging Japan
0288-4046	Sushiki Shori Tsushin
0288-4216	Gekkan Tenmon
0288-4232	Yamaguchi-kenritsu Yamaguchi Hakubutsukan Kenkyu Hokoku
0288-4240	Yamaguchi-ken no Shizen
0288-433X	Institute of Space and Astronautical Science. Report. Special Publication
0288-500X	Nanzan University. Nanzan Academic Society. Bulletin
0288-5026	Nikkei New Media
0288-5530	Tokyo Denki University. Faculty of Engineering. General Education. Research Reports
0288-5611	Saitama-kenritsu Shizenshi Hakubutsukan Kenkyu Hokoku
0288-6022	Current Science and Technology Research in Japan
0288-6030	Musashino Art University. Bulletin
0288-6103	Dempa Digest
0288-6340	Kokugakuin University Economic Review
0288-738X	Kinki Daigaku Kyushu Kogakubu Kenkyu Hokoku. Rikogaku Hen
0288-7436	Yamaguchi-ken Eisei Kenkyujo Nenpo see 0915-048X
0288-7622	Local Government Review in Japan
0288-7975	Komatsu-shiritsu Hakubutsukan Kenkyu Kiyo
0288-8491	Fukui Prefectural General Green Center. Forest Research Division. Annual Report
0288-8726	Ochanomizu Chiri
0288-8750	Daigakuin Kenkyu Nenpo. 3: Rikogaku Kenkyuka Hen
0288-9102	Kyodo to Hakubutsukan
0288-920X	Japan. Statistics Bureau. Monthly Report on the Consumer Price Index
0288-9307	Japan Company Handbook. First Section

0288-9315 Second Section Firms *changed to* Japan Company Handbook. Second Section.
0288-9617 Kanagawa-ken Seishin Igakkaishi
0289-0003 Zoological Science
0289-0011 Biotronics
0289-0542 Meat Science
0289-0739 Saitama Mathematical Journal
0289-0755 Hoigaku no Jissai to Kenkyu
0289-0968 Japanese Journal of Child & Adolescent Psychiatry
0289-1239 Cross Currents
0289-1301 Japan Statistical Association. Annual Report on the Labour Force Survey
0289-1522 Financial Statistics of Japan
0289-1956 Japan Times
0289-2057 I-bunpi Kenkyukaishi
0289-2316 Japanese Journal of Mathematics
0289-3096 Tochigi Prefectural Dairy Experimental Institute. Bulletin
0289-3363 Lake Biwa Study Monographs
0289-3428 Kagaku Tetsugaku
0289-3606 Ongaku no Tomo
0289-3614 Record Geijutsu
0289-3622 Stereo
0289-3630 Musica Nova
0289-3657 Ongaku Kyoiku Kenkyu
0289-3673 M A Journal
0289-405X Japan Comparative Education Society. Bulletin
0289-4092 Hakubutsukan Dayori
0289-4238 Japan. Ibaraki National Institute of Animal Industry. Annual Report
0289-4947 Journal of Practical Diabetes
0289-5242 Ariake Fisheries Experiment Station. Annual Report
0289-5447 Tumour Biology *see* 1010-4283
0289-551X The Yoke
0289-5560 Sogo Kenkyujo Hokoku
0289-5773 Plant Tissue Culture Letters
0289-6214 Mining and Materials Processing Institute of Japan. Metallurgical Review
0289-6389 Sado Marine Biological Station. Report
0289-6508 Nikkei Byte
0289-6516 Nikkei Venture
0289-6540 Computer Software
0289-7016 S U T Bulletin
0289-730X Medical and Pharmaceutical Society for Wakan-Yaku. Journal
0289-7520 University of Tokyo. College of Arts and Sciences. Scientific Papers
0289-7806 Doboku Gakkai Ronbunshu
0289-7911 Nihon Rimoto Senshingu Gakkaishi
0289-8322 Container Age
0289-842X Riken. Accelerator Progress Report
0289-8888 Osaka Joshi Daigaku Kiyo. Kiso Rigaku Hen, Taiikugaku Hen
0289-890X K K C Brief†
0289-9051 Kobe Journal of Mathematics
0289-9841 Nikkei Aerospace
0289-9922 Drug Approval and Licensing Procedures in Japan
0289-9957 Tokyo Daigaku Kogakubu. Denki Kogaku Iho *see* 0563-7929
0290-7747 Tchad Nouvelles
0290-8271 International Silk Association. Monthly Newsletter
0291-1191 Demeures et Chateaux
0291-1981 Journal de Pharmacie Clinique
0291-2066 Iris
0291-2430 Bio
0291-5871 France. Ministere de l'Education Nationale. Bulletin Officiel
0291-6207 France. Ministere de l'Education Nationale. Bulletin Officiel Complementaire†
0291-8099 Neo Restauration Hotellerie Collectives *see* 1145-377X
0291-8102 France. Ministere de l'Agriculture. Series "S". Reseau d'Information Comptable Agricole *see* 0998-4186
0291-8234 Electricite Automobile
0291-8404 Cahiers de l'Animation†
0291-8692 Tableaux Economiques de Midi-Pyrenees
0291-8706 Dossiers Antilles Guyane. Etudes Diverses
0291-8897 France. Direction des Affaires Economiques et Internationales. Informations Rapides
0292-1782 E C O D O C
0292-3238 Mot Pour Mot†
0292-384X Nouveau Centre de Sante
0292-627X Annales des Composites
0292-6792 Dossiers de l'Economie Reunionnaise
0292-7292 Cinema Francais Production
0292-7616 Groupe de Demographie Africaine. Etudes et Documents†
0292-7934 Magyar Fuzetek
0292-7993 Habone
0292-8418 Bio-Sciences
0292-935X Digest Documentation Organique
0292-9406 Phytotherapy *changed to* Revue de Phytotherapy Pratique.
0293-0773 Amis de Ramuz. Bulletin
0293-0781 Paris Passion
0293-1176 Cahiers de Paleoanthropologie
0293-2407 Prima
0293-3055 Lettre de Solagral *see* 1161-8043
0293-311X Recherches Pyreneennes
0293-5090 Arteres et Veines
0293-6852 Lien Horticole
0293-7107 Materiaux pour l'Etude de l'Asie Orientale Moderne et Contemporaine
0293-8286 Voix de l'Ecole
0293-9274 Connaissance des Arts
0293-9320 Ecrit du Temps†
0293-9339 Archipelago†
0293-9436 Michelin Green Guide Series: Jura
0293-9614 Bulletin Signaletique d'Information Administrative
0293-9908 Comptes Rendus de Therapeutique et de Pharmacologie Clinique
0293-9932 Voix d'Afrique
0293-9967 Annuaire Officiel de la Charcuterie *changed to* Annuaire des Industries Charcuteries.
0294-0000 Livres Hebdo
0294-0051 Perspectives (Paris)†
0294-0337 Sciences Sociales et Sante
0294-0442 Journal of the Short Story in English
0294-0701 Guide Europeen des Progiciels *see* 0985-0791
0294-0736 Journal d'Economie Medicale
0294-0809 Dossiers de l'Education
0294-0817 Medecine Aeronautique et Spatiale
0294-0957 Filmo†
0294-1228 Annales Francaises de Microtechniques et de Chronometrie
0294-1260 Annales de Chirurgie Plastique et Esthetique
0294-1449 Institut Henri Poincare. Annales: Analyse Non Lineaire
0294-1759 Vingtieme Siecle: Revue d'Histoire
0294-1805 Philosophie (Paris)
0294-2623 Revue de Parapsychologie
0294-2925 International Viewpoint
0294-3069 Institut des Recherches Marxistes. Recherches Internationales
0294-3506 Biofutur
0294-4030 Nouvelle Tour de Feu
0294-4081 Cahiers de la Photographie
0294-4480 O R A C L
0294-5495 Societe Speleologique et Prehistorique de Bordeaux. Memoire
0294-6475 Indian Ocean Newsletter
0294-6831 Cahiers du Tourisme. Serie D: Statistiques
0294-6939 Cahiers de la Guitare
0294-7382 Revue Genealogique Normande
0294-7544 Infotecture
0294-7579 Youthlink
0294-8141 Intersocial†
0294-8281 Dirigeant
0294-8303 Cooperation-Distribution-Consommation
0294-8397 C F D T Aujourd'hui
0294-8400 France. Centre d'Etudes de l'Emploi. Lettre d'Information
0294-8508 Marine Marchande *see* 0983-0537
0294-8567 Archi-Cree
0295-0448 Aqua Review
0295-060X Centre International de Documentation Arachnologique. Liste des Travaux Arachnologiques
0295-1630 Pleine Marge
0295-2319 Politix
0295-3722 Analyse Musicale
0295-4192 Logistiques Magazine
0295-5652 Pardes
0295-5717 Centre Technique du Bois et de l'Ameublement. Revue Documentaire *changed to* Centre Technique du Bois et de l'Ameublement. Profils.
0295-5725 Piscines - Spas Magazine
0295-6322 Genie Logiciel et Systemes Experts
0295-9151 Ethnies
0295-9909 Cahiers du G I T A
0296-1598 R A I R O APII Automatique - Productique Informatique Industrielle
0296-3353 France Peche International
0296-4333 Solidarite Atlantique
0296-4449 Ecoflash
0296-5569 N C G R Journal
0296-6867 Societe des Poetes Francais. Bulletin Trimestriel
0296-8517 Bureaux d'Etudes Automatise *see* 1148-7305
0296-8541 C T B Info
0296-8746 Ami du Professionnel en Alimentation
0296-8770 Psychologie et Psychometrie
0297-8148 Marine Microbial Food Webs
0297-8717 Moules, Modeles et Maquettes
0298-248X Cahiers de Paleontologie Est-Africaine
0298-2900 Association des Medecins Israelites de France. Revue Medicale *see* 0299-3953
0298-6663 Sciences de l'Eau
0298-7139 Filigrane†
0298-7783 Revue Generale Nucleaire: International Edition
0298-7899 Cahiers d'Etude et de Recherche
0298-7902 Notebooks for Study and Research
0298-7996 Cahiers de Montpellier *see* 0765-0531
0298-9239 Lettre du Sponsoring et du Mecenat
0299-061X Cahiers de l'Economie Meridionale
0299-3007 Afrique Medecine et Sante
0299-3678 Profession Textile
0299-3953 J A M I F
0299-6898 Panorama
0299-7258 Techniques - Sciences - Methodes. Genie Urbain Rural
0299-8572 Afrique Elite
0299-8661 Bulletin Technique du Machinisme et de l'Equipement Agricoles
0300-0087 Annali di Ostetricia Ginecologia Medicina Perinatale
0300-0109 Archivio e Rassegna Italiana di Ottalmologia†
0300-0214 Canada. Statistics Canada. Rubber Products Industries *see* 0835-0027
0300-0249 Canada. Statistics Canada. Tobacco Products Industries *see* 0835-0019
0300-0265 Canada. Statistics Canada. Wool Production and Supply†
0300-0273 Canadian Statistical Review. Weekly Supplement/Supplement Hebdomadaire de la Revue Statistique du Canada†
0300-0443 Psychological Reader's Guide†
0300-0486 Society of Biological Chemists. Proceedings
0300-0508 Physiotherapy Canada
0300-0524 Rendiconti Romani di Gastro-Enterologia *see* 0392-0623
0300-0559 Revue de Medecine du Travail
0300-0583 Caraibe Medical
0300-0605 Journal of International Medical Research
0300-0621 Steroids and Lipids Research *see* 0301-0163
0300-0664 Clinical Endocrinology
0300-0672 Rassegna Italiana d'Ottalmologia *see* 0300-0109
0300-0729 Rhinology
0300-0753 Dairy Review
0300-0877 Rendiconti di Gastroenterologia *see* 0392-0623
0300-0893 Biomedicine *see* 0753-3322
0300-0923 W H O Food Additives Series†
0300-0958 Flora of New South Wales.†
0300-0990 Arbeitsgemeinschaft fuer Juristisches Bibliotheks- und Dokumentationswesen. Mitteilungen
0300-1016 Versuchstierkunde
0300-1067 Studia Phonologica
0300-1156 Norwegian Journal of Botany *see* 0107-055X
0300-1164 Bulletin Mensuel de la Normalisation Francaise *see* 0223-4866
0300-1172 Banque du Zaire. Rapport Annuel
0300-1199 Canada. Statistics Canada. Household Furniture Manufacturers/Industrie des Meubles de Maison†
0300-1202 Canada. Statistics Canada. Wool Yarn and Cloth Mills/Filature et Tissage de la Laine†
0300-1237 European Journal of Forest Pathology
0300-1245 Pediatrician†
0300-1261 Chemoreception Abstracts
0300-1342 New Zealand Journal of Dairy Science and Technology†
0300-1385 Cocoa Research Institute. Annual Report
0300-1407 Carbohydrate Chemistry and Metabolism Abstracts†
0300-1547 Annual Reports on Competition in O E C D Member Countries *changed to* Competition Policy in O E C D Countries.
0300-1555 South Africa. Prisons Department. Report of the Commissioner of Prisons†
0300-1628 International Tax Report
0300-1652 Nigerian Medical Journal
0300-1679 Guinness Book of World Records *see* 1057-4557
0300-1695 Pilot (Clapham)
0300-1725 Current Problems in Clinical Biochemistry†
0300-1881 Nigeria. Federal Ministry of Trade. Quarterly Information Bulletin†
0300-1989 Karl-May-Gesellschaft. Jahrbuch
0300-2012 Wolfenbuettler Beitraege
0300-208X Who's Notable in Mexico
0300-211X Radical Philosophy
0300-2144 Management Journal
0300-2233 European Law Newsletter *changed to* Business Law Brief.
0300-2241 Liberia. Department of State. Newsletter
0300-225X World Peace
0300-2373 Kenya. Central Bureau of Statistics. Agricultural Census (Large Farm Areas)
0300-2403 Nigeria. Federal Department of Forest Research. Research Paper
0300-2446 Literarni Mesicnik
0300-2497 Neki Pokazatelji Tehnickog Razvoja Privrede Jugoslavije
0300-2519 U N I S I S T Newsletter
0300-2527 Drustveni Proizvod i Narodni Dohodak
0300-2535 Licni Dohoci
0300-2594 Institut d'Etudes Slaves, Paris. Documents Pedagogiques
0300-2608 Enseignement du Russe
0300-2659 Prevent
0300-2667 Management Information Service
0300-2713 Oriental Insects Supplements Series†
0300-2721 Insaat Muhendisleri Odasi. Teknik Bulten†
0300-2772 Austria. Bundesministerium fuer Wissenschaft und Forschung. Bericht der Bundesregierung an den Nationalrat
0300-2829 Arable Farming
0300-287X Bibliothekspraxis
0300-2896 Archivos de Bronconeumologia
0300-2977 Netherlands Journal of Medicine
0300-3000 I S D S Bulletin *see* 0257-2222
0300-306X Nippon Steel Technical Report
0300-3094 Nordisk Statutsamling

ISSN INDEX

0300-3108 Travelgram see 0041-204X
0300-3124 Teollisuusanomat see 0358-7673
0300-3132 Tavola Rotonda†
0300-3159 Tekawennake
0300-3167 Umformtechnik
0300-3175 Valori Umani
0300-3183 Vida Hospitalar†
0300-3205 Voice of Malta
0300-3213 Voxair
0300-3221 Work - Environment - Health see 0355-3140
0300-3256 Zoologica Scripta
0300-3264 Young Soldier
0300-3272 Talyllyn News
0300-3280 Swing changed to On the Agenda.
0300-3299 Nepal Science Magazine changed to Nepalese Journal of Science.
0300-3302 Sun Yat-sen Cultural Foundation Bulletin
0300-3310 Skip
0300-3329 Sicherheitsingenieur
0300-3337 Sicherheitsbeauftragter
0300-3361 Science Chelsea
0300-337X Scottish Genealogist
0300-3388 Salamandra
0300-3396 Rheumatology and Rehabilitation see 0263-7103
0300-340X Rivista Storica dell'Antichita
0300-3434 Renal Physiology
0300-3442 Hospital Career†
0300-3450 Rechentechnik - Datenverarbeitung
0300-3469 Reader
0300-3477 Razza Bovina Piemontese
0300-3485 Rassegna di Diritto, Legislazione e Medicina Legale Veterinaria
0300-3493 Foreign Compound Metabolism in Mammals†
0300-3507 Rank & File see 0141-8688
0300-3515 Rally†
0300-3523 Protee
0300-3531 Processeans changed to Founders.
0300-3558 Prison Service Journal
0300-3574 Pollustop
0300-3582 Plastics and Polymers see 0309-4561
0300-3604 Photosynthetica
0300-3612 University of the Philippines. Institute of Library Science. Newsletter
0300-3620 Civil Service Reporter
0300-3639 Phenix
0300-3655 Personalhistorisk Tidsskrift
0300-3663 Periodex changed to Point de Repere.
0300-368X Nigerian Agricultural Journal
0300-3701 Orquidea (Mex)
0300-371X Notes on the Science of Building
0300-3728 Nova Scotia Historical Quarterly see 0227-4752
0300-3736 New Spectator see 0314-6200
0300-3752 New Linguist†
0300-3779 Muchachas†
0300-3787 Mundo Electronico
0300-3809 Natun Thikana
0300-3817 Magyar Tortenelmi Szemle
0300-3825 Medicot
0300-3868 Medical Technician see 0309-2666
0300-3884 Mundo Financiero
0300-3906 Mindanao Mail
0300-3922 Multinational Business
0300-3930 Local Government Studies
0300-3957 Kerala Homoeo Journal
0300-3965 Interdit see 0228-9636
0300-3973 Informazione Radio TV
0300-3981 Informationen zur Orts-, Regional- und Landesplanung see 0251-3625
0300-4007 Indranil
0300-4015 Korean Journal of Physiology
0300-4023 Indochina
0300-4031 In Terris
0300-4058 International Law Reporter
0300-4074 Kanara Chamber of Commerce & Industry Journal
0300-4112 Forstarchiv
0300-4139 Germinal
0300-4155 Impact
0300-4163 I P P F - S E A O R News see 0126-8031
0300-4171 I D E
0300-418X Hong Kong Monthly Digest of Statistics
0300-421X British Baking Industries Research Association. Abstracts see 0430-7941
0300-4228 Fleet Street Letter
0300-4236 Evangelische Kommentare
0300-4252 European Federation of Finance House Associations. Newsletter
0300-4260 English Golf Union. News and Fixtures changed to English Amateur Golf.
0300-4279 Education Three-Thirteen
0300-4287 Economics
0300-4309 Dhandha
0300-4317 Desarrollo del Tropico Americano†
0300-4325 British Clayworker changed to Ceramic Industries International.
0300-4333 University of Calgary Gazette
0300-4341 Business Japan changed to Japan 21st.
0300-435X Canadian Guider
0300-4368 Charadista
0300-4384 Concord
0300-4406 Common Market News
0300-4414 Dejiny Ved a Techniky
0300-4422 Deputazione di Storia Patria per l'Umbria. Bollettino
0300-4430 Early Child Development and Care
0300-4465 Cooperator†
0300-4473 Cidade†
0300-4481 Cerveza y Malta
0300-449X Transport and Tourism Journal
0300-4503 Case Studies in Atomic Physics see 0370-1573
0300-4511 Canada Rides
0300-452X Camouflage Air Journal
0300-4538 Cahiers de la Presse Francaise†
0300-4546 Society and Commerce
0300-4554 B I P
0300-4562 British Lichen Society Bulletin
0300-4570 British Ceramic Abstracts see 0957-8897
0300-4589 Bollettino di Collegamento
0300-4600 Athletic Echo
0300-4619 Brewing Industry Research Foundation. Bulletin of Current Literature changed to Brewing Research Convention. Current Awareness Monthly.
0300-4627 Blatt fuer Sortenwesen
0300-4651 Odini
0300-466X Artbibliographies Modern
0300-4678 Action (Fitzroy)
0300-4686 Acrida
0300-4708 A M A Gazette see 0729-9745
0300-4716 Canada Manpower Review see 0318-4099
0300-4732 Dansk Forsikrings Tidende - Assurandoeren see 0105-4260
0300-4740 Cayman Islands. Legislative Assembly. Minutes
0300-483X Toxicology
0300-4864 Journal of Neurocytology
0300-4880 Public Health in Europe†
0300-4910 Annales d'Immunologie see 0923-2494
0300-4937 Medecine et Armees
0300-4953 Artes de Mexico
0300-4961 Rocky Mountain Social Science Association. Newsletter changed to Western Social Science Association Newsletter.
0300-4988 Chez Nous changed to Chester Zoo News.
0300-5038 I A R C Scientific Publications
0300-5054 Actas Espanolas de Neurologia y Psiquiatria see 0300-5062
0300-5062 Actas Luso Espanolas de Neurologia Psiquiatria y Ciencias Afines
0300-5089 Clinics in Gastroenterology see 0889-8553
0300-5127 Biochemical Society, London. Transactions changed to Biochemical Society. Transactions.
0300-5143 Clean Air
0300-5186 Monographs in Neural Sciences
0300-5194 Excerpta Medica. Section 46: Environmental Health and Pollution Control
0300-5224 Nieren- und Hochdruckkrankheiten
0300-5232 Society of Chemical Industry. Bulletin
0300-5275 Ontario Dentist
0300-5283 Medical Journal of Malaysia
0300-5305 Architektura C S R changed to Architektura.
0300-5321 Excerpta Medica. Section 36: Health Economics and Hospital Management see 0921-8068
0300-533X Institute of Child Health, Calcutta, Annals†
0300-5356 Arhitectura
0300-5364 British Journal of Audiology
0300-5372 Excerpta Medica. Section 29: Clinical Biochemistry see 0927-278X
0300-5402 Acta Universitatis Carolinae: Geographica
0300-5410 Annales de Microbiologie see 0923-2508
0300-5429 Environmental Physiology & Biochemistry†
0300-5453 New Al-Hoda
0300-5461 Hospital and Health Service Purchasing†
0300-5488 Studies on the Fauna of Suriname and Other Guyanas
0300-550X Agricultural Association of China. Journal
0300-5526 Intervirology
0300-5534 Natuurwetenschappelijke Studiekring voor Suriname en de Nederlandse Antillen. Uitgaven
0300-5550 Revista Espanola de Lecheria
0300-5577 Journal of Perinatal Medicine
0300-5607 Courses et Elevage
0300-5623 Urological Research
0300-5658 Eperont
0300-5704 Aktuelle Gerontologie see 0044-281X
0300-5712 Journal of Dentistry
0300-5720 Hospital Development
0300-5747 South Africa. Maize Board. Report on Grain Sorghum and Buckwheat for the Financial Year†
0300-5755 Alimentaria
0300-5763 Biological Membrane Abstracts see 8756-7504
0300-5771 International Journal of Epidemiology
0300-581X Arbeitsmedizin, Sozialmedizin, Praeventivmedizin
0300-5852 Behavioural Biology Abstracts, Section A: Animal Behaviour see 0301-8695
0300-5860 Zeitschrift fuer Kardiologie
0300-5879 Medical Technologist see 0309-2666
0300-5925 Public Health Engineer†
0300-595X Clinics in Endocrinology and Metabolism see 0889-8529
0300-5992 Terpenoids and Steroids†
0300-600X Venture Management†
0300-6018 New Dimensions in Legislation see 0146-9584
0300-6026 Trends in Housing
0300-6034 Consumer Credit and Truth-In-Lending Compliance Report
0300-6050 Texas State and Region Newsletter†
0300-6069 New Jersey Register
0300-6077 Under Twenty-Five Newsletter
0300-6107 California Teachers Association. Chapter News Service†
0300-6115 New Jersey Savings League Guide changed to New Jersey Savings League News.
0300-6123 Rubber & Plastics News
0300-6131 San Diego County. Planning Department. Population and Housing changed to Info Bulletin-Population and Housing Estimates.
0300-6158 Miesiecznik Franciszkanski
0300-6166 T A A Newsletter changed to Sister City News.
0300-6182 South Dakota Municipalities
0300-6190 Tube Topics
0300-6204 Business & Government Insider Newsletter†
0300-6212 Svithiod Journal
0300-6239 Southern Tobacco Journal†
0300-6247 Talking Leaf
0300-6298 Teacher Advocate changed to I S T A Advocate.
0300-6301 Motor North
0300-6328 Rawhide Press
0300-6336 Union W.A.G.E.†
0300-6379 Rainbow (Jersey City)
0300-6387 Sports Cart
0300-6409 N A H R O Letter see 0194-9268
0300-6425 Recovering Literature
0300-6433 T E P S A Journal
0300-6441 Regional Plan Association Library Acquisitions changed to Regional Plan Association Selected Library Acquisitions.
0300-645X Virginia Genealogist
0300-6468 Rhode Island Statewide Planning Program Monthly Progress Report changed to Rhode Island Division of Planning Monthly Progress Report.
0300-6484 Palestine Digest†
0300-6506 Transportation Business Report††
0300-6514 Pan-American Trader†
0300-6530 West Virginia Record and West Virginia Merchant
0300-6557 Trailer Boats
0300-6565 Whispering Wind
0300-6573 Whitmore Investment Letter†
0300-659X Womanpower see 0195-2390
0300-6603 Twin Cities Courier
0300-6611 Women's Advocate†
0300-662X Western Mining News
0300-6638 Voluntary Action News see 0149-6492
0300-6646 National On-Campus Report
0300-6654 R H G H Vital Signs
0300-6662 N Y D H I C Improver see 0145-9112
0300-6670 N S A A Newsletter changed to N S A A News.
0300-6689 N A T E News
0300-6700 Technology and Human Affairs changed to I I T Technology and Human Affairs.
0300-6727 North Carolina Agribusiness†
0300-6743 Noticiero Obrero Norteamericano†
0300-676X Oshkosh Advance-Titan
0300-6778 Nichols Alumnus changed to Nichols News.
0300-6786 Post Eagle
0300-6794 Nostalgia Newsletter†
0300-6816 P A A Affairs
0300-6824 Northwest Investment Review see 0886-3768
0300-6832 North Dakota Publisher†
0300-6840 Northwest Investment Tablistics see 0147-2410
0300-6859 Urban Affairs Abstracts
0300-6867 W E A L Washington Report
0300-6883 I A L News
0300-6891 A.D. Presbyterian Life Edition changed to United Presbyterian A.D.
0300-6905 Highway Safety Literature†
0300-6921 Chicago Reporter
0300-693X Daphnis
0300-6948 Arts in Common see 0748-6723
0300-6956 Current Programs see 0162-704X
0300-6964 Augsburg College Now
0300-6972 Abortion Surveillance changed to U.S. Centers for Disease Control. Abortion Surveillance. Annual Summary.
0300-6999 Federation Forum changed to Planning and Action Newsletter.
0300-7006 World Education Reports†
0300-7014 Feminist Art Journal†
0300-7022 A D R I S Newsletter
0300-7030 Concerned Business Students' Report††
0300-7057 Video Publisher see 0748-0792
0300-7065 A C A Word from Washington see 1054-3570
0300-7073 Family Practice News

ISSN	Title
0300-7081	Chicago. Municipal Reference Library. Recent Additions
0300-7103	Essecondsext
0300-7111	Fashion Newsletter
0300-712X	Chicago. Municipal Reference Library. Checklist of Publications Issued by the City of Chicago
0300-7138	Du Pont Context†
0300-7154	Michael Reese Hospital & Medical Center. Medical Staff Newsletter changed to Rounds.
0300-7162	Diacritics
0300-7170	Environmental Pollution Control Journal†
0300-7197	Drywall Newsmagazine see 0194-8903
0300-7200	Medic Alert Newsletter†
0300-7219	American Challenge
0300-7227	Bibliography and Index of Micropaleontology
0300-7235	Bay View†
0300-7243	Clyde LaMotte's Washington Energy Memo
0300-7251	Metro New Orleans see 0897-8174
0300-7278	American Indian News†
0300-7308	Metric Association Newsletter see 1050-5628
0300-7316	Discovery (Richmond)
0300-7324	Dow Theory Forecasts
0300-7340	D C A T Bulletin changed to D C A T Digest.
0300-7359	Media Ecology Review†
0300-7367	Commodity Exchange Bulletin
0300-7375	Consumer Newsweek changed to Consumer Newsweekly.
0300-7391	Contents of Current Legal Periodicals see 0279-5787
0300-7405	Intermountain Logging News†
0300-7421	American University Report changed to American.
0300-743X	C O R E Magazine
0300-7448	American Dance Guild Newsletter
0300-7472	Afterimage
0300-7480	Beer Marketer's Insights
0300-7499	Buffalo Spree
0300-7502	Maryland Travel Scene changed to Maryland Travelgram.
0300-7510	Bnai Yiddish†
0300-7529	Connecticut Business Journal see 0887-2252
0300-7553	Margins†
0300-7561	Crab
0300-757X	Inside R & D
0300-7588	Inter-Society Color Council Newsletter see 0731-2911
0300-7618	Poblacion†
0300-7626	American White Water
0300-7634	Correio Operario Norteamericano†
0300-7669	Your Clipping Analyst changed to Burrelle's Clipping Analyst.
0300-7677	Indian Legal Information Development Service Legislative Review see 0145-7993
0300-7685	Industrial Television News changed to International Television News.
0300-7693	Performance Guide Publications. Mutual Funds and Timing†
0300-7707	M A S C D Newsletter changed to Focus Magazine (Detroit).
0300-7715	Payment Systems Newsletter†
0300-7723	Photo Industry Newsletter
0300-7766	Popular Music & Society
0300-7782	Headlines changed to Profile (Los Angeles).
0300-7804	Live Steam Magazine see 0364-5177
0300-7812	Goddard Journal†
0300-7820	Suomi-Opiston Viesti†
0300-7839	Human Ecology (New York)
0300-7898	New York (State) University. Division of Continuing Education. Newsletter†
0300-7901	Know News Service†
0300-7928	Ripon College Magazine
0300-7936	Robinson Jeffers Newsletter
0300-7952	Kitchen Planning see 0744-1916
0300-7960	Shmuessen mit Kinder Un Yugent
0300-7995	Current Medical Research and Opinion
0300-8002	Junior High-Middle School Bulletin†
0300-8029	Inforasia†
0300-8037	Scandinavian Journal of Social Medicine
0300-8053	International Jugglers Association Newsletter changed to Juggler's World Magazine.
0300-807X	Geographia Medica
0300-8096	D T. It
0300-810X	Italian Heritage Newsletter†
0300-8126	Infection
0300-8134	Journal of Human Ergology
0300-8169	Medicina e Historia†
0300-8177	Molecular and Cellular Biochemistry
0300-8185	Pakistan Journal of Biochemistry†
0300-8207	Connective Tissue Research
0300-8258	Connecticut Fireside
0300-8274	Actualites Psychiatriques
0300-8282	E D V in Medizin und Biologie - E D V in Medicine and Biology see 0934-9235
0300-8320	Helminthological Abstracts. Series B: Plant Nematology see 0957-6797
0300-8339	Helminthological Abstracts. Series A: Animal and Human Helminthology see 0957-6789
0300-8347	Health & Social Service Journal
0300-8355	Gem City News changed to Idaho Cities.
0300-8371	Neue Muenchner Beitraege zur Geschichte der Medizin und Naturwissenschaften. Medizinhistorische Serie
0300-838X	Microbiology Abstracts: Section A. Industrial & Applied Microbiology
0300-8398	Microbiology Abstracts: Section B. Bacteriology
0300-8428	Basic Research in Cardiology
0300-8436	Jahresverzeichnis der Verlagsschriften und Einer Auswahl der Ausserhalb des Buchhandels Erschienenen Veroeffentlichungen der D.D.R., der B.R.D. und Westberlins Sowie der Deutschsprachigen Werke Anderer Laender†
0300-8452	Forecast FM changed to Forecast (Silver Spring).
0300-8495	Australian Family Physician
0300-8509	Fore
0300-8533	Oyo Yakuri
0300-8584	Medical Microbiology and Immunology
0300-8592	Roentgen Blaetter see 0939-267X
0300-8622	Leber Magen Darm
0300-8630	Klinische Paediatrie
0300-8665	Verein fuer Wasser-, Boden- und Lufthygiene. Schriftenreihe
0300-869X	Zeitschrift fuer Klinische Psychologie und Psychotherapie
0300-8703	Studebaker Story
0300-8711	Zentralblatt fuer Veterinaermedizin. Series A see 0931-184X
0300-872X	Zeitschrift fuer Immunitaetsforschung, Experimentelle und Klinische Immunologie see 0171-2985
0300-8754	Housing and Community Development News see 0194-2913
0300-8819	Neurobiology†
0300-8827	Acta Orthopaedica Scandinavica. Supplementum
0300-8835	Acta Obstetrica et Gynecologica Scandinavica. Supplement
0300-8843	Acta Paediatrica Scandinavica, Supplement see 0803-5326
0300-8851	Herold der Wahrheit
0300-8908	Nevada Planner†
0300-8924	Acta Vitaminologica et Enzymologica†
0300-8932	Revista Espanola de Cardiologia
0300-8959	New Alaskan
0300-8967	Acta Psychiatrica Belgica
0300-9009	Acta Neurologica Belgica
0300-9033	Acta Gastroenterologica Latinoamericana
0300-9084	Biochimie
0300-9092	Akusherstvo i Ginekologiya
0300-9130	Research in Experimental Medicine
0300-922X	Royal Society of Chemistry. Journal: Perkin Transactions 1
0300-9238	Faraday Transactions 2 see 0956-5000
0300-9246	Royal Society of Chemistry. Journal: Dalton Transactions
0300-9254	National Science Council of Sri Lanka. Journal
0300-9262	Bulletin Signaletique: Bibliographie des Sciences de la Terre. Section 220. Mineralogie. Geochimie. Geologie Extraterrestre see 0761-1811
0300-9270	Bulletin Signaletique: Bibliographie des Sciences de la Terre. Section 221. Cahier B. Gitologie, Economie Miniere see 0761-182X
0300-9289	Bulletin Signaletique: Bibliographie des Sciences de la Terre. Section 222: Roches Cristallines see 0761-1838
0300-9297	Bulletin Signaletique: Bibliographie des Sciences de la Terre. Section 223. Roches Sedimentaires. Geologie Marine see 0761-1846
0300-9300	Bulletin Signaletique: Bibliographie des Sciences de la Terre. Section 224. Stratigraphie, Geologie, Regionale et Geologie Generale. see 0761-1854
0300-9319	Bulletin Signaletique-Bibliographie des Sciences de la Terre. Section 225. Tectonique see 0761-1862
0300-9327	Bulletin Signaletique: Bibliographie des Sciences de la Terre. Section 226: Hydrologie. Geologie de l'Ingenieur. Formations Superficielles see 0761-1870
0300-9335	Bulletin Signaletique: Bibliographie des Sciences de la Terre. Section 227: Paleontologie see 0761-1889
0300-9351	France. Bureau de Recherches Geologiques et Minieres. Bulletin. Section 2. Geologie Appliquee- Chronique des Mines see 0755-6365
0300-936X	France. Bureau de Recherches Geologiques et Minieres. Bulletin. Section 3: Hydrologie-Geologie de l'Ingenieur see 0246-1641
0300-9432	Forensic Science see 0379-0738
0300-9467	Chemical Engineering Journal changed to Chemical Engineering Journal and Biochemical Engineering Journal.
0300-9475	Scandinavian Journal of Immunology
0300-9483	Boreas
0300-9505	Revue d'Histoire de l'Eglise de France
0300-9513	Revue Francaise d'Histoire d'Outre-Mer changed to Revue Francaise d'Histoire d'Outre-Mer, Explorations, Colonisations, Independences.
0300-953X	Societe des Oceanistes. Journal
0300-9556	Paediatrie und Paedologie. Supplement
0300-9564	Journal of Neural Transmission
0300-9572	Resuscitation
0300-9580	Royal Society of Chemistry. Journal: Perkin Transactions 2
0300-9599	Royal Society of Chemistry. Journal: Faraday Transactions 1 see 0956-5000
0300-9629	Comparative Biochemistry and Physiology. Part A: Comparative Physiology
0300-9637	Biochemistry, General and Molecular see 0024-3205
0300-9653	Life Sciences. Part 1: Physiology and Pharmacology see 0024-3205
0300-967X	Zeitschrift fuer Geburtshilfe und Perinatologie
0300-970X	Acta Hepato-Gastroenterologica see 0172-6390
0300-9718	Revista de Quimica Textil
0300-9734	Uppsala Journal of Medical Sciences
0300-9742	Scandinavian Journal of Rheumatology
0300-9750	Acta Endocrinologica Congress. Advance Abstracts†
0300-9777	Journal of Oral Pathology see 0904-2512
0300-9785	International Journal of Oral Surgery see 0901-5027
0300-9815	Revue d'Odonto-Stomatologie
0300-9823	O.I.E. Bulletin
0300-9831	International Journal for Vitamin and Nutrition Research
0300-984X	Archiv fuer Genetik†
0300-9858	Veterinary Pathology
0300-9920	Journal of Tropical Pediatrics and Environmental Child Health see 0142-6338
0300-9947	Nursing Bibliography
0300-9963	Selected Annual Reviews of the Analytical Sciences†
0300-9998	International Journal of Chronobiology†
0301-0015	Journal of Physics A: Mathematical, Nuclear and General see 0305-4470
0301-0023	Society of Occupational Medicine. Journal changed to Occupational Medicine.
0301-0066	Perception
0301-0074	Organometallic Chemistry
0301-0082	Progress in Neurobiology
0301-0104	Chemical Physics
0301-0112	Abstracts on Police Science changed to Criminology, Penology & Police Science Abstracts.
0301-0139	Pigment Cell
0301-0147	Haemostasis
0301-0155	Frontiers of Matrix Biology†
0301-0163	Hormone Research
0301-0171	Cytogenetics and Cell Genetics
0301-018X	Australasian Nurses Journal†
0301-0244	Polish Journal of Pharmacology and Pharmacy
0301-0260	Presence Croix-Rouge
0301-0279	Revue Francaise des Maladies Respiratoires see 0761-8425
0301-0287	Psychiatries
0301-0295	Biochimie, Biophysique Moleculaire see 0761-1897
0301-0333	Kenya Nursing Journal
0301-035X	Bangladesh Medical Journal
0301-0368	Asian Archives of Anaesthesiology and Resuscitation
0301-0376	Modern Medicine of Asia†
0301-0384	Health of the People
0301-0422	Public Health Reviews
0301-0430	Clinical Nephrology
0301-0449	Pediatric Radiology
0301-0457	Behring Institute Mitteilungen
0301-0481	Zeitschrift fuer Hautkrankheiten H und G
0301-049X	Food Irradiation Information†
0301-0503	Journal of Maxillofacial Surgery see 1010-5182
0301-0511	Biological Psychology
0301-0546	Allergologia et Inmunopathologia
0301-0554	Malaysian Journal of Science
0301-0597	Ceskoslovenska Neurologie a Neurochirurgie
0301-0635	Sciences Pharmaceutiques et Biologique de Lorraine†
0301-0643	Epoch (Croydon)
0301-0708	Biosynthesist
0301-0716	Radiochemistry†
0301-0724	Folia Veterinaria Latina†
0301-0732	South African Veterinary Association. Journal changed to South African Veterinary Association. Scientific Journal.
0301-0740	World Health Organization. World Health Assembly and the Executive Board. Handbook of Resolutions and Decisions. changed to World Health Organization. Handbook of Resolutions and Decisions of the World Health Assembly and the Executive Board.
0301-0791	Cahiers de Chirurgie†
0301-0813	F.N.I.B. - Info
0301-0821	Queen's Nursing Journal†
0301-0864	Anaesthesia, Resuscitation and Intensive Therapy†

5684 ISSN INDEX

0301-0902 Aichi Medical University Association. Journal
0301-0996 Goeteborg Psychological Reports
0301-102X John Rylands University Library of Manchester. Bulletin
0301-1208 Indian Journal of Biochemistry and Biophysics
0301-133X Bulletin Signaletique. Part 349: Anesthesie. Reanimation *see* 0761-2303
0301-1402 Klassische Homeopathie *see* 0935-0853
0301-1445 Giornale di Batteriologia, Virologia ed Immunologia ed Annali dell'Ospedale Maria Vittoria di Torino. Parte 2. Sezione Clinica *see* 0390-5454
0301-1453 Giornale di Batteriologia, Virologia ed Immunologia ed Annali dell'Ospedale Maria Vittoria di Torino. Parte 1. Microbiologia *see* 0390-5462
0301-150X Electromyography and Clinical Neurophysiology
0301-1518 Nouvelle Presse Medicale *see* 0755-4982
0301-1526 Vasa
0301-1569 O R L
0301-1607 Z W R - Zahnaerztliche Welt, Zahnaerztliche Rundschau *see* 0044-166X
0301-1623 International Urology and Nephrology
0301-2115 European Journal of Obstetrics, Gynecology and Reproductive Biology
0301-2123 Acta Biologica Paranaense
0301-2190 Hospital and Health Administration *changed to* Australian Hospital.
0301-2204 Gynecologie
0301-2212 Social Behavior and Personality
0301-2255 Anali Klinicke Bolnice "Dr. M. Stojanovic"
0301-228X British Journal of Orthodontics
0301-2328 Microbiology Abstracts: Section C. Algology, Mycology and Protozoology
0301-2425 Biofizika Zhivoi Kletki
0301-2514 Acta Universitatis Palackianae Olomucensis. Facultatis Medicae
0301-2603 Neurological Surgery
0301-2611 Kensa to Gijutsu
0301-2662 Josai Shika Daigaku Kiyo *see* 0916-0701
0301-2689 Berichte ueber Landwirtschaft. Sonderhefte
0301-2697 Naturwissenschaftlicher Verein in Hamburg. Abhandlungen
0301-2719 Gaertnerische Berufspraxis
0301-2727 Advances in Plant Breeding
0301-2735 Advances in Agronomy and Crop Science
0301-2743 Advances in Animal Physiology and Animal Nutrition
0301-276X Monumenta Venatoria†
0301-2778 Mammalia Depicta
0301-2794 Advances in Veterinary Medicine
0301-2808 Advances in Ethology
0301-2891 Calendar of Congresses of Medical Sciences
0301-2980 Datenverarbeitung im Recht†
0301-2999 Vierteljahresschrift fuer Sozialrecht
0301-3006 Analytische Psychologie
0301-3057 Monographs on Drugs†
0301-3073 Frontiers of Hormone Research
0301-3081 Contributions to Microbiology and Immunology
0301-3243 Infusionstherapie und Klinische Ernaehrung *see* 1011-6966
0301-326X European Ophthalmological Society. Congress Acta
0301-3294 Zeitschrift fuer Germanistische Linguistik
0301-3308 Electrotechnique *see* 0761-1773
0301-3316 Electronique *see* 0246-1161
0301-3324 Bulletin Signaletique. Part 346: Ophtalmologie *see* 0761-2184
0301-3332 Bulletin Signaletique. Part 160: Physique de l'Etat Condense *see* 0761-196X
0301-3340 Bulletin Signaletique. Part 161. Cristallographie *see* 0761-1978
0301-3359 Atomes et Molecules. Physiques des Fluides et Plasmas *see* 0761-1951
0301-3375 Bulletin Signaletique. Part 347: Oto-Rhino-Laryngologie, Stomatologie, Pathologie Cervicofaciale *see* 0761-2192
0301-3383 Bulletin Signaletique. Part 348: Dermatologie - Venerologie *see* 0761-2206
0301-3391 Bulletin Signaletique. Part 362: Maladies de l'Appareil Respiratoire du Coeur et des Vaisseaux. Chirurgie Thoracique et Vasculaire *see* 0761-2214
0301-3405 Bulletin Signaletique. Part 354: Maladies de l'Appareil Digestif. Chirurgie Abdominale *see* 0761-2230
0301-3413 Bulletin Signaletique. Part 355: Maladies des Reins et des Voies Urinaires. Chirurgie *see* 0761-2249
0301-3421 Bulletin Signaletique. Part 356: Maladies du Systeme Nerveux Myopathies-Neurochirurgie *see* 0761-2257
0301-343X Bulletin Signaletique. Part 357: Maladies des Os et des Articulations. Chirurgie Orthopedique. Traumatologie *see* 0761-2265
0301-3448 Bulletin Signaletique. Part 359: Maladies du Sang *see* 0761-2273
0301-3456 Bulletin Signaletique. Part 360. Biologie Animale. Physiologie-Pathologie des Invertebres. Ecologie *see* 0761-1714
0301-3464 Bulletin Signaletique. Part 363: Genetique *see* 0246-1447
0301-3472 Bulletin Signaletique. Part 365. Physiologie des Vertebres *see* 0761-1900
0301-3480 Bulletin Signaletique. Part 745: Soudage, Brasage et Techniques Connexes *see* 0761-1692
0301-3499 Bulletin Signaletique. Part 885: Nuisances *see* 0246-117X
0301-3537 Bulletin Signaletique. Part 110: Informatique-Automatique-Recherche Operationnelle-Gestion-Economie *see* 0761-2060
0301-3693 Nuovo Archivio Italiano di Otologia, Rinologia e Laringologia *changed to* Otorinolaringologica.
0301-374X New Techniques in Biophysics and Cell Biology†
0301-3782 Basel Institute for Immunology. Annual Report
0301-3901 Institut d'Hygiene des Mines. Revue†
0301-391X Itogi Nauki i Tekhniki: Genetika Cheloveka
0301-3952 Journal de Biologie Buccale
0301-4150 A G E Current Awareness Service
0301-4169 Asian Geotechnical Engineering Abstracts *changed to* A G E Refdex.
0301-4185 Digital Processes†
0301-4193 Contributions to Human Development
0301-4207 Resources Policy
0301-4215 Energy Policy
0301-4223 New Zealand Journal of Zoology
0301-4231 Contributions to Primatology
0301-4347 Zimbabwe. National Archives. Annual Report
0301-4355 Instituto Interamericano de Ciencias Agricolas de la O E A. Documentos Oficiales *changed to* Instituto Interamericano de Cooperacion para la Agricultura - O E A. Documentos Oficiales.
0301-438X Inter-American Centre for Agricultural Documentation and Information. Documentacion e Informacion Agricola†
0301-441X Excelsa
0301-4428 Theoretical Linguistics
0301-4436 R & D Projects in Documentation and Librarianship†
0301-4444 Annales de Medecine de Reims Champagne- Ardennes†
0301-4460 Annals of Human Biology
0301-4495 Annee Therapeutique et Clinique en Ophtalmologie
0301-4606 Bangladesh Pharmaceutical Journal
0301-4614 Bibliographie der Bibliographien
0301-4622 Biophysical Chemistry
0301-4657 Current Research and Development Projects in Israel: Natural Sciences and Technology†
0301-4665 Deutsche Bibliographie. Hochschulschriften-Verzeichnis *changed to* Deutsche Nationalbibliographie. Hochschulschriften-Verzeichnis.
0301-4681 Differentiation
0301-469X Eastern Archives of Ophthalmology†
0301-4703 Essays in Fundamental Immunology†
0301-4711 European Journal of Cardiology *see* 0167-5273
0301-472X Experimental Hematology
0301-4738 Indian Journal of Ophthalmology
0301-4746 Industrial Safety Chronicle
0301-4797 Journal of Environmental Management
0301-4800 Journal of Nutritional Science and Vitaminology
0301-4827 Kerala Medical Journal
0301-4835 Die Krankenversicherung
0301-4843 Kupat-Holim Yearbook
0301-4851 Molecular Biology Reports
0301-486X Mycopathologia
0301-5017 Revue Internationale du Trachome et de Pathologie Tropicale et Subtropicale
0301-5068 Egyptian Journal of Pharmaceutical Sciences
0301-5076 United Arab Republic Journal of Pharmaceutical Sciences *see* 0301-5068
0301-5092 Veterinaria Mexico
0301-5106 Who's Who in India (Calcutta)
0301-5149 Developments in Biological Standardization
0301-5165 Chinese National Bibliography
0301-536X Frontiers of Oral Physiology
0301-5521 New Zealand Journal of Experimental Agriculture *see* 0114-0671
0301-5548 European Journal of Applied Physiology and Occupational Physiology
0301-5556 Advances in Anatomy, Embryology and Cell Biology
0301-5564 Histochemistry
0301-5572 British Journal of Sexual Medicine
0301-5629 Ultrasound in Medicine & Biology
0301-5645 People
0301-5661 Community Dentistry and Oral Epidemiology
0301-567X Beitraege zur Tropischen Landwirtschaft und Veterinaermedizin
0301-5718 Update
0301-5769 Schmuck†
0301-5785 Australian Outlook
0301-584X Kongresszentralblatt fuer die Gesamte Innere Medizin. Sektion A: Zentralblatt Praktische Innere Medizin und Grenzgebiete - Internal Medicine *see* 0931-4695
0301-5912 Biotelemetry *see* 0254-0819
0301-603X South African Society for Agricultural Extension. Journal *changed to* South African Journal of Agricultural Extension.
0301-6129 Acta Diurna Historica†
0301-6145 C S I R Publications†
0301-620X Journal of Bone and Joint Surgery: British Volume
0301-6226 Livestock Production Science
0301-6242 Petroleum International
0301-6269 Indonesian Indicator *see* 0126-270X
0301-6307 Quaderni Storici
0301-634X Radiation and Environmental Biophysics
0301-6366 Mensuel du Medecin Acupuncteur
0301-6374 N G M
0301-6404 North-Eastern Affairs
0301-6412 Neurolinguistics†
0301-6420 Studia Historica Slavo-Germanica
0301-6528 Rockville International
0301-6536 Building Services Engineer *changed to* Building Services.
0301-6587 Anthropologica
0301-6625 Central Bank of Yemen. Annual Report
0301-6722 Universidade Federal do Para. Revista†
0301-679X Tribology International
0301-6811 Zeitschrift fuer Kinder- und Jugendpsychiatrie
0301-6897 Matematicheskie Problemy Geofiziki
0301-6900 Lingvisticheskie Issledovaniya
0301-6919 Voprosy Fiziki Tverdogo Tela
0301-6943 Veterinary History
0301-7028 Water Services
0301-7036 Problemas del Desarrollo
0301-7095 Malaysia in Brief
0301-7214 Guitar *see* 0958-6342
0301-7230 Financas Publicas
0301-7249 Faraday Discussions
0301-7257 Byron Journal
0301-7265 Community Medicine†
0301-7303 Revue Roumaine de Medecine. Serie Neurologie et Psychiatrie *changed to* Revue Roumaine de Neurologie et Psychiatrie.
0301-7338 Revista de Igiena, Bacteriologie, Virusologie, Parazitologie, Pneumoftiziologie. Bacteriologie, Virusologie, Parazitologie, Epidemiologie
0301-7443 Anuario Financiero y de Sociedades Anonimas de Espana
0301-7478 Survey of Construction Activities of the Private Sector in Urban Areas of Iran
0301-7516 International Journal of Mineral Processing
0301-7524 Greater London Council. Housing Facts and Figures†
0301-7559 Financial Statistics of Education in Cyprus†
0301-7567 Guia de Reuniones Cientificas y Tecnicas en la Argentina
0301-7575 Electron Spin Resonance Spectroscopy Abstracts
0301-7605 Critique
0301-7621 Almanak Jakarta
0301-7729 Universidade Federal de Minas Gerais. Faculdade de Medicina. Anais†
0301-7737 Annales Universitatis Mariae Curie-Sklodowska. Sectio DD. Medicina Veterinaria
0301-7753 Cameroon Year Book
0301-7788 Iter†
0301-7796 Facts and Figures
0301-7818 Argentina. Congreso de la Nacion. Biblioteca. Boletin Legislativo
0301-7850 Magyar Belorovosi Archivum es Ideggyogyaszati Szemle *see* 0133-5464
0301-7877 Finish Digest†
0301-8059 Sociedade Entomologica do Brasil. Anais
0301-8105 South Africa. Department of Statistics. Census of Electricity, Gas and Steam *changed to* South Africa. Central Statistical Service. Census of Electricity, Gas and Steam.
0301-8156 Rio Grande do Sul, Brazil. Fundacao de Economia e Estatistica. Indicadores Sociais†
0301-8172 Egyptian Journal of Microbiology
0301-8407 National Dairy Research Institute. Annual Report
0301-8423 Gambia. Produce Marketing Board. Annual Report
0301-861X Contraception - Fertilite - Sexualite
0301-8636 Archives Belges de Dermatologie†
0301-8660 Egyptian Journal of Physiological Science
0301-8695 Animal Behavior Abstracts
0301-8768 Intergeo *see* 0396-5880
0301-8849 Egyptian Journal of Bilharziasis

ISSN

ISSN INDEX 5685

0301-8881 Let's Square Dance
0301-8938 Fluorocarbon and Related Chemistry†
0301-9020 Botswana Handbook
0301-9039 Clean Air Conference (Gt. Brit.)
0301-9047 Democratic World
0301-9055 Democratic Forum
0301-9063 Derecho
0301-908X Finnish Fisheries Research
0301-9101 Ideas
0301-9195 British Pteridological Society. Bulletin
0301-9217 Exports of the Republic of China
0301-9225 Handbuch der Oeffentlichen Bibliotheken
0301-9233 Ironmaking and Steelmaking
0301-9268 Precambrian Research
0301-9322 International Journal of Multiphase Flow
0301-9349 Confederacion General de la Industria. Memoria y Balance General
0301-9780 Japan. Ministry of Agriculture, Forestry and Fisheries. National Food Research Institute. Report
0302-0029 Acta Criminologiae et Medicae Legalis Japonica
0302-0231 Japan Map Center News
0302-0282 Nihon no Minken Kyoiku
0302-0479 Kanazawa Daigaku Kyoyobu Ronshu. Shizen Kagaku Hen
0302-0622 Euro Cooperation; Economic Studies on Europe
0302-0657 Gesamtverzeichnis der Zeitschriften und Serien in Bibliotheken der Bundesrepublik Deutschland Einschliesslich Berlin (West) *see* 0171-8932
0302-0665 Bibliotheca Gastroenterologica *changed to* Frontiers of Gastrointestinal Research.
0302-0681 South Africa. Official Yearbook of the Republic of South Africa
0302-069X Geological Correlation
0302-072X Journal de Physique - Lettres†
0302-0738 Journal de Physique *changed to* Journal de Physique I.
0302-0762 Hot Buttered Soul†
0302-0797 Chemical Engineer
0302-0800 Medecine - Biologie - Environnement
0302-0851 National Institute for Research in Dairying. Report†
0302-086X Mauri Ora *see* 0113-7492
0302-1033 Annales Musei Goulandris
0302-1114 Greece. National Statistical Service. Statistics on the Declared Income of Physical Persons and Its Taxation
0302-1122 Anthropines Scheseis
0302-1173 Koinonike Epitheoresis†
0302-1254 Big Beat†
0302-1289 Netsu Kanri to Kogai - Heat Management and Pollution Control *see* 0387-1819
0302-1319 Journal of Indian Writing in English
0302-1416 Greece. National Statistical Service. Statistics of the Declared Income of Legal Entities and Its Taxation
0302-1440 Study of Nursing Care: Research Project Series
0302-1475 Sign Language Studies
0302-1599 Himalangue
0302-1610 Indian Journal of Psychiatric Social Work
0302-167X P T A Heute
0302-1688 Origins of Life *see* 0169-6149
0302-1742 Crystal Structure Communications *see* 0108-2701
0302-1750 Rivista di Farmacologia e Terapia†
0302-184X Ocean Management *changed to* Ocean and Coastal Management.
0302-1998 National Children's Bureau. Annual Review
0302-2013 Bank Indonesia. Data Kredit Perbankan†
0302-203X Forest Products Trade Statistics of Indonesia *changed to* Indonesian Statistics on Trade of Forest Products.
0302-2048 Schweizerische Gesellschaft fuer Marktforschung. Geschaeftsbericht
0302-2056 National Accounts of Botswana
0302-2129 Industrie Minerale *changed to* Industrie Minerale Mines et Carrieres.
0302-2137 Medical Biology†
0302-217X Universidade Federal do Rio Grande do Sul. Instituto de Filosofia e Ciencias Humanas. Revista†
0302-2196 Internationales Verzeichnis der Wirtschaftsverbaende
0302-2277 Observatorio Astronomico Municipal de Rosario. Boletin
0302-2293 Monographs on Standardization of Cardioangiological Methods†
0302-2315 Uniwersytet Gdanski. Wydzial Humanistyczny. Zeszyty Naukowe. Filologia Polska. Prace Jezykoznawcze
0302-2358 Archives Internationales Claude Bernard
0302-2366 Advances in Neurosurgery
0302-2374 Statistical Yearbook of Bangladesh
0302-2404 Postgraduate Institute of Medical Education and Research, Chandigarh. Bulletin
0302-2420 Estudios Interdisciplinarios
0302-2439 Universidade de Sao Paulo. Departamento de Botanica. Boletim de Botanica
0302-2447 Budkavlen
0302-2471 Chemical Senses and Flavour *see* 0379-864X
0302-248X Archiv for Pharmaci og Chemi. Scientific Edition *see* 1100-1801
0302-2528 Siemens Zeitschrift
0302-2536 Revue Siemens†
0302-2587 G E C Journal of Science and Technology *see* 0264-9187
0302-2684 Sciences Geologiques - Memoires
0302-2692 Sciences Geologiques. Bulletin
0302-2706 R A D I A L S Bulletin *see* 0263-9254
0302-2773 Applied Neurophysiology *see* 1011-6125
0302-2781 Biosciences Communications *see* 0378-9845
0302-2803 Child's Brain *see* 0256-7040
0302-2803 Child's Brain *see* 1016-2291
0302-2811 Mental Health and Society†
0302-282X Neuropsychobiology
0302-2838 European Urology
0302-2870 Pumps and Other Fluids Machinery Abstracts
0302-2927 Annals of Nuclear Science and Engineering *see* 0306-4549
0302-2935 Malaysian Forester
0302-2951 Goeteborg. Stadskontor. Statistiska Meddelanden *see* 0282-0145
0302-3052 Mondes en Developpment
0302-3060 Chancellor College. Journal of Social Science *changed to* Malawi Journal of Social Science.
0302-3125 Uniwersytet Gdanski. Wydzial Biologii i Nauk o Ziemi. Zeszyty Naukowe. Oceanografia *changed to* Uniwersytet Gdanski. Wydzial Biologii, Geografii i Oceanologii. Zeszyty Naukowe. Oceanografia.
0302-3176 Ayrshire Collections *changed to* Ayrshire Monographs.
0302-3184 Baptist Union Directory
0302-3249 Institute of Trading Standards Administration Monthly Review *see* 0953-8704
0302-329X Civil Service Year Book
0302-3338 Human Experimentation & Toxicology Abstracts†
0302-3354 Liquid Scintillation Counting.†
0302-3427 Science and Public Policy
0302-3451 Audiovisual Librarian
0302-3478 Underwater Information Bulletin†
0302-3494 Summary of Postgraduate Diplomas and Courses in Medicine *see* 0265-2730
0302-3524 Estuarine and Coastal Marine Science *see* 0272-7714
0302-4091 Who Owns Whom. Australasia and Far East
0302-4148 Merseyside Chamber of Commerce and Industry. Directory
0302-4172 M I M S Middle East
0302-4180 Paper Review of the Year
0302-4261 East African Journal of Medical Research†
0302-427X Annales de Kinesitherapie
0302-4326 Maternidade Dr. Alfredo da Costa, Lisbon. Arquivo Clinico†
0302-4342 Anales Espanoles de Pediatria
0302-4350 Aktuelle Neurologie
0302-4369 Organic Chemistry and Biochemistry *see* 0904-213X
0302-4377 Acta Chemica Scandinavica. Series A: Physical and Inorganic Chemistry *see* 0904-213X
0302-4466 Acta Dermatovenerologica Iugoslavica
0302-4520 Egyptian Journal of Animal Production
0302-4555 Sugar Technologists' Association of Trinidad and Tobago. Proceedings
0302-4598 Bioelectrochemistry and Bioenergetics
0302-4601 Aktuelle Literaturinformationen aus dem Obstbau
0302-4717 Rivista di Patologia e Clinica della Tubercolosi e di Pneumologia
0302-4814 Universite de Brazzaville. Annales *changed to* Universite Marien Ngouabi. Annales.
0302-4822 Mexico. Comision Nacional de los Salarios Minimos. Informe de Labores
0302-4881 Rajasthan State Tanneries Limited. Annual Report
0302-4946 Landbrugsaarbog
0302-5004 Mexico. Secretaria del Trabajo y Prevision Social. Subdireccion de Documentacion. Resena Laboral
0302-5047 Zambia. Meteorological Department. Totals of Monthly and Annual Rainfall
0302-5063 Quarto Potere
0302-508X N C E R T Newsletter
0302-5128 Sleep†
0302-5144 Contributions to Nephrology
0302-5160 Historiographia Linguistica
0302-5195 Precos Pagos Pelos Agricultores
0302-5233 Ecuador. Instituto Nacional de Estadistica y Censos. Encuesta Anual de Manufactura y Mineria†
0302-5268 Investigacion e Informacion Textil y de Tensioactivos
0302-5349 Dansk Maskinhandlerforening. Handbog
0302-5403 Kongeriget Danmarks Handels-Kalender
0302-542X Itogi Nauki i Tekhniki: Mestorozhdeniya Goryuchikh Poleznykh Iskopaemykh
0302-5489 We Represent in Israel and Abroad
0302-5608 Germany (Federal Republic, 1949-). Bundesaufsichtsamt fuer das Versicherungswesen. Geschaeftsbericht
0302-5640 Cultures au Zaire et en Afrique
0302-5691 Antartida
0302-5705 Argentina. Servicio Nacional de Parques Nacional. Anales
0302-5756 L E M I T. Anales†
0302-5802 Timber Trade Review†
0302-5926 Johann Wolfgang Goethe Universitaet. Studienfuehrer
0302-6248 Karka
0302-6256 Vedere-International
0302-6329 Arbeitskreis Zweiter Weltkrieg. Bulletin *changed to* Bulletin Faschismus - Zweite Weltkrieg.
0302-6574 Review of Economics and Business
0302-6620 States of Malaya Chamber of Mines. Council Report *changed to* Malaysian Chamber of Mines. Council Report.
0302-6655 Revista Juridica Panamena†
0302-6671 Management Heute und Marktwirtschaft
0302-668X Management Heute *see* 0302-6671
0302-6701 Egyptian Journal of Soil Science
0302-671X Bonner Zoologische Monographien
0302-6736 Makerere Institute of Social Research. Research Abstracts and Newsletter†
0302-6744 Indian Records
0302-6795 Bank Eksport Import Indonesia. Annual Report
0302-6809 Barclays National Review *changed to* Business Brief.
0302-6957 Anales de Ciencias Humanas†
0302-6965 Anuario del Arte Espanol
0302-6973 National Debate
0302-6981 Yuva Bharati
0302-7104 Agroanimalia†
0302-7112 Agrochemophysica†
0302-7120 Phytophylactica
0302-7139 Agroplantae†
0302-7368 Magyar Tudomanyos Akademia. Acta Alimentaria *see* 0139-3006
0302-7384 Symbolae Philologorum Posnaniensium
0302-7406 Instituto Antituberculoso Francisco Moragas. Publicaciones
0302-7481 University of the North. Department of Bantu Languages. Communications
0302-7503 Deutsche Wochen-Zeitung
0302-752X Folclorica
0302-7546 I C S S R Journal of Abstracts and Reviews *changed to* I C S S R Journal of Abstracts and Reviews: Sociology & Social Anthropology.
0302-7554 Indian Biologist
0302-7562 Indian Journal of Zoology
0302-7600 Praktische Anaesthesie *see* 0939-2661
0302-7651 C I S Abstracts *see* 1010-7053
0302-766X Cell and Tissue Research
0302-7678 Chemical Industry Developments *changed to* Chemical Business.
0302-7724 Cuadernos de Realidades Sociales
0302-7775 Ingegneria Ambientale Inquinamento e Depurazione *see* 0394-5871
0302-7902 World Transport Data
0302-8003 Revista E A C†
0302-8070 Balneologia Bohemica
0302-8127 Immanuel
0302-8143 Adrikhalut *changed to* A-A.
0302-816X Israel. Central Bureau of Statistics. Immigration to Israel
0302-8178 Bay Zikh
0302-8186 Folk, Velt un Medine
0302-8194 Biaf - Israel Aviation and Space Magazine
0302-8267 Israel. Ministry of the Interior. City and Region - Ir ve Ezor
0302-833X Mejeribrugets Uge-Nyt
0302-8348 Sydsvenska Ortnamnssaellskapet. Aarsskrift
0302-8429 Academie des Sciences. Comptes Rendus Hebdomadaires des Seances. Serie A. Sciences Mathematiques *see* 0764-4442
0302-8437 Academie des Sciences. Comptes Rendus Hebdomadaires des Seances. Serie B. Sciences Physiques *see* 0764-4442
0302-8585 Uniwersytet Jagiellonski. Zeszyty Naukowe. Prace Botaniczne
0302-8755 Spain. Instituto Nacional de Investigaciones Agrarias. Serie: Produccion y Proteccion Vegetales
0302-8844 Addab Journal
0302-8852 Revisor
0302-8933 Archives of Microbiology
0302-8984 Psychotherapie und Medizinische Psychologie *see* 0173-7937
0302-9069 Liteinoe Proizvodstvo, Metallovedenie i Obrabotka Metallov Davleniem
0302-9085 Issledovania po Teorii Algorifmov i Matematicheskoi Logike
0302-9263 Mediterranee Medicale
0302-9336 Jamaica. Department of Statistics. Consumer Price Indices *changed to* Statistical Institute of Jamaica. Consumer Price Indices Bulletin.
0302-9379 Laryngologie, Rhinologie, Otologie und ihre Grenzgebiete *see* 0935-8943
0302-9417 Tropische und Subtropische Pflanzenwelt
0302-9468 B G S
0302-9530 Archives of Oto-Rhino-Laryngology

ISSN

0302-9611 Banco de la Republica. Registros de Exportacion e Importacion†
0302-9697 Etesia Statistike. Erevna tou Karkinou
0302-9743 Lecture Notes in Computer Science
0302-9794 Novum Gebrauchsgraphik
0302-9840 Vincent†
0303-0849 Chung-Wai Literary Monthly
0303-111X Sovetskie Ljudi Segodnja
0303-1179 Asterisque
0303-1187 Institut Henri Poincare and Societe Mathematique de France. Circulaire d'Informations†
0303-1241 Betriebs- und Marktwirtschaft im Gartenbau
0303-125X One World
0303-1268 Euromicro Journal *see* 0165-6074
0303-1276 Bulletin de Liaison de la Recherche en Informatique et en Automatique
0303-1705 Portugal. Instituto Nacional de Estatistica. Delegacao do Funchal. Boletim Trimestral de Estatistica - Arquipelago de Madeira *changed to* Madeira. Servico Regional de Estatistica. Boletim Trimestral de Estatistica.
0303-1829 Centro Latinoamericano de Demografia. Notas de Poblacion
0303-1896 Akroterion
0303-190X Philippine National Bibliography
0303-1969 Data-Data Iklim di Indonesia
0303-2019 Muszaki Lapszemle. Hiradastechnika - Technical Abstracts. Telecommunication *see* 0231-066X
0303-2221 C S S R. Kronika Vnitropolitickych Udalosti†
0303-223X Bilten Dokumentacije. Savremena Organizacaija i Ekonomija Radnih Organizacija *see* 0351-4048
0303-2361 Itogi Nauki i Tekhniki: Tekhnologiya Organicheskikh Veshchestv†
0303-240X Revue de l'Energie
0303-2434 I T C Journal
0303-2485 Kuukausikatsaus Suomen Ilmastoon
0303-2493 Informationen zur Raumentwicklung
0303-2515 South African Museum. Annals
0303-254X Monographs in Anaesthesiology
0303-2582 Indian Journal of Clinical Psychology
0303-2590 Roentgen Technology
0303-2647 Biosystems
0303-2728 Ahram Index
0303-2876 Majalah B A T A N
0303-2884 Berita Hasil Hutan *changed to* Statistik Kehutanan Indonesia.
0303-2906 Prayaasa
0303-2949 Gunakesari†
0303-3007 International Journal of Korean Studies
0303-3074 Sarvotkrushta Marathi Katha
0303-3171 Manusia dan Masyarakat
0303-321X Sangkakala Peradilan
0303-3309 I S O Catalogue
0303-3317 I S O Annual Review†
0303-3821 Bhartiya Krishi Anusandhan Patrika
0303-3848 Brass Bulletin
0303-3856 Revolutionary World†
0303-3880 Universite Catholique de Louvain. Institut de Linguistique. Cahiers *see* 0771-6524
0303-3899 Educational Documentation and Information - Documentation et Information Pedagogiques *changed to* International Bureau of Education. Bulletin.
0303-3902 Interface
0303-3910 Irish Journal of Psychology
0303-3929 Mathematical Programming Studies†
0303-3937 Orbis Musicae
0303-4011 Plasticos Universales
0303-402X Colloid and Polymer Science
0303-4070 Kumamoto University. Department of Physics. Physics Reports
0303-4097 Indian Journal of Mycology and Plant Pathology
0303-4100 Finnish Chemical Letters†
0303-4135 Academiae Medicae Gedanensis. Annales
0303-4151 International Commission for the Northwest Atlantic Fisheries. Annual Report *see* 0704-4798
0303-416X Toshiba Review†
0303-4178 Poetica
0303-4208 Tropenmedizin und Parasitologie *see* 0177-2392
0303-4216 Topics in Applied Physics
0303-4224 Studien und Mitteilungen zur Geschichte des Benediktiner. Ordens und Seiner Zweige
0303-4240 Reviews of Physiology, Biochemistry and Experimental Pharmacology
0303-4259 Psychiatrische Praxis
0303-4283 Leben und Umwelt
0303-4305 Innere Medizin
0303-4461 Oesterreichische Krankenpflegezeitschrift
0303-4534 Zeitschrift fuer Geologische Wissenschaften
0303-4550 Bulletin of Reprints†
0303-4569 Andrologia
0303-4992 Indonesia. Lembaga Pertahanan Nasional. Ketahanan Nasional
0303-5220 Reproduccion†
0303-5344 Hungary. Kozponti Statisztikai Hivatal. Teruleti Statisztikai Evkonyv
0303-5395 Uttar Pradesh
0303-5476 Chiba Igaku Zasshi
0303-5980 Studia Leibnitiana. Supplementa
0303-5999 Bibliographie der Deutschsprachigen Psychologischen Literatur
0303-6200 Intensivmedizinische Praxis†
0303-6251 Intensivmedizin *see* 0175-3851
0303-6286 Tieraerztliche Praxis
0303-6294 Tips fuer die Gastroenterologische Praxis
0303-6448 Statistical Yearbook of the Netherlands
0303-6464 Zahn- Mund- und Kieferheilkunde
0303-6537 Sweden. Sjukvaardens och Socialvaardens Planerings- och Rationaliseringsinstitut. S P R I Raad 7†
0303-6634 Geography of World Agriculture
0303-6758 Royal Society of New Zealand. Journal
0303-6812 Journal of Mathematical Biology
0303-6847 Blood Vessels *see* 1018-1172
0303-6898 Scandinavian Journal of Statistics
0303-691X West African Journal of Pharmacology and Drug Research
0303-6936 Hydrological Sciences Bulletin *see* 0262-6667
0303-6960 Indian Journal of Nematology
0303-6979 Journal of Clinical Periodontology
0303-6987 Journal of Cutaneous Pathology
0303-6995 Journal of Neural Transmission. Supplement
0303-7002 Kerrygold International†
0303-7169 Singapore Bulletin
0303-7193 New Zealand Journal of Physiotherapy
0303-7207 Molecular and Cellular Endocrinology
0303-7339 Tijdschrift voor Psychiatrie
0303-7479 Groupement International pour la Recherche en Stomatologie et Odontologie. Bulletin
0303-7495 Institut Francais d'Etudes Andines. Bulletin
0303-7584 Instituto de Tonantzintla. Boletin *changed to* Instituto Nacional de Astrofisica, Optica y Electronica. Boletin.
0303-7657 Revista Brasileira de Saude Ocupacional
0303-7762 Instituto de Higiene e Medicina Tropical. Anais
0303-7819 Encyclopaedia Judaica Year Book
0303-7932 Majalah Kedokteran Surabaya
0303-7940 Archifacts†
0303-7967 Prakriti Vani
0303-805X I S O Bulletin (English Edition)
0303-8106 Audiology Japan
0303-8122 Science Society of Thailand. Journal
0303-8157 Poznan Studies in the Philosophy of the Sciences and the Humanities
0303-8173 Acta Medica Austriaca
0303-8246 Southeast Asian Journal of Social Sciences
0303-8300 Social Indicators Research
0303-8432 Folia Allergologica et Immunologica Clinica†
0303-8459 Excerpta Medica. Section 49: Forensic Science Abstracts
0303-8467 Clinical Neurology and Neurosurgery
0303-853X Economic Survey of Liberia
0303-8688 Belize Institute of Social Research and Action. National Studies *see* 0250-6831
0303-8874 Anales Otorrinolaringologicos Ibero-Americanos
0303-8971 Institut Economique Agricole. Cahiers†
0303-9021 Vlaams Diergeneeskundig Tijdschrift
0303-903X Belgium. Rijksstation voor Sierplantenteelt. Mededelingen†
0303-9056 Belgium. Rijksstation voor Landbouwtechniek. Mededelingen
0303-9072 Belgium. Rijksstation voor Zeevisserij. Mededelingen
0303-9099 Annales de Gembloux
0303-9102 Rijksuniversiteit te Gent. Mededelingen van de Fakulteit Diergeneeskunde†
0303-9145 Institut Royal Belge pour l'Amelioration de la Betterave. Publication Trimestrielle†
0303-9153 Jardin Botanique National de Belgique. Bulletin
0303-9382 M E R A D O News†
0303-9676 Estudios Sociales Centroamericanos
0303-9692 Schweizerische Zeitschrift fuer Volkswirtschaft und Statistik
0303-9714 Studi Parlamentari e di Politica
0303-9722 Amministrazione Italiana
0303-9862 Revista de Ciencias Sociais
0303-9889 Revista de Estudios Sociales
0303-9919 Anales de Economia
0303-9927 Spain. Ministerio de Justicia. Secretaria General Tecnica. Informacion Juridica *see* 0210-3419
0303-9951 Indian Journal of Politics
0303-9986 Revista de Derecho (Concepcion)
0304-0003 L I A S: Sources and Documents Relating to the Early Modern History of Ideas.
0304-0062 U N I S I S T Boletin de Informacion
0304-0089 Yearbook of World Problems and Human Potential *changed to* Encyclopedia of World Problems and Human Potential.
0304-0100 I I C A en America†
0304-0119 Indice Agricola de America Latina y el Caribe†
0304-0224 L I B E R Bulletin *changed to* European Research Library Cooperation.
0304-0313 Patologia e Clinica Ostetrica e Ginecologica
0304-0550 Istituto Sperimentale per la Floricoltura. Annali
0304-0593 Rivista di Ingegneria Agraria
0304-0615 Annali dell'Istituto Sperimentale Agronomico
0304-0666 Annuario dell'Agricoltura Italiana
0304-0704 Planeur *changed to* Aeronovum.
0304-0720 Amsterdam Studies in the Theory and History of Linguistic Science. Series 3: Studies in the History of the Language Sciences
0304-0763 Amsterdam Studies in the Theory and History of Linguistic Science. Series 4: Current Issues in Linguistic Theory
0304-078X Cultures†
0304-0798 Natal Museum. Annals
0304-0941 Decision
0304-095X Bangladesh Development Studies
0304-100X Services Law Cases
0304-1042 Japanese Journal of Religious Studies
0304-1131 Agriculture and Environment *see* 0167-8809
0304-1158 Indian School of Mines. Annual Report
0304-1166 Chemical India Annual
0304-1190 Ghana
0304-1204 Free China Today†
0304-1298 Bulletin Signaletique. Part 161: Structure de l'Etat Condense. Cristallographie *see* 0761-1978
0304-1301 Bibliographie des Sciences de la Terre. Section 221. Gisements Metalliques et Non Metalliques *see* 0761-182X
0304-1409 Atheist
0304-1425 Societe Royale Belge d'Anthropologie et de Prehistoire. Bulletin
0304-1646 Industry and Society *see* 0007-5116
0304-1735 New Zealand. Soil Bureau. Scientific Report†
0304-1743 Norwegian Maritime Research†
0304-1786 Prospect†
0304-2138 Fundacao Servicos de Saude Publica. Revista
0304-2146 Japanese Journal of Tropical Medicine and Hygiene
0304-2154 Akademie der Wissenschaften der D.D.R. Jahrbuch
0304-2162 Le Mois
0304-2170 Indonesian Quarterly
0304-2189 Irian: Bulletin of Irian Jaya
0304-2197 Jahrbuch Internationale Politik und Wirtschaft†
0304-2251 Royal Asiatic Society. Malaysian Branch. Journal
0304-226X Siam Society. Journal
0304-2286 University of Bombay. Journal
0304-2308 Pesquisa e Planejamento *see* 0100-0551
0304-2421 Theory and Society
0304-243X Trabalhos de Antropologia e Etnologia
0304-2448 Toho Gakuho
0304-2499 Tecnica Pesquera†
0304-2502 Pastizales
0304-2529 Actividades en Turrialba†
0304-2553 Bangladesh Economic Review *see* 0304-095X
0304-2634 Boletin de Estudios Latinoamericanos y del Caribe *see* 0924-0608
0304-2669 Cadernos de Estudos Rurais e Urbanos†
0304-2685 Ciencia & Tropico
0304-2731 Drejtesia Popullore
0304-274X National Bank of Egypt. Economic Bulletin
0304-2758 Estudios de Economia
0304-2839 Documentacion e Informacion para el Desarrollo Agricola†
0304-2847 Facultad Nacional de Agronomia Medellin. Revista
0304-2863 Colloquium Internationale†
0304-2871 European Organization for Nuclear Research. Liste des Publications Scientifiques/List of Scientific Publications
0304-288X C E R N Courier
0304-2898 C E R N School of Computing. Proceedings
0304-324X Gerontology
0304-3274 Perspectives Economiques de l'O E C D
0304-3282 O E C D. Guide to Legislation on Restrictive Business Practices Supplements†
0304-3312 Organization for Economic Cooperation and Development. Labour Statistics *see* 0255-3627
0304-3320 Recherche en Matiere d'Economie des Transports
0304-3371 O E C D Financial Statistics
0304-341X Nuclear Law Bulletin
0304-3428 Bulletin de Droit Nucleaire *see* 1016-4995
0304-3460 Goodwin Series. Occasional Papers
0304-3479 Russian Literature
0304-3487 Russian Linguistics
0304-3495 Rumanian Studies
0304-3509 Revista Pedagogjike
0304-3568 Experimental Cell Biology *see* 1015-2008
0304-3584 Actualidades Biologicas
0304-3606 Irrinews†
0304-3622 International Association for Shell and Spatial Structures. Bulletin
0304-3681 Extern†

ISSN INDEX 5687

0304-3703 Vinculos
0304-3711 Brenesia
0304-3738 O E C D. Quarterly National Accounts
0304-3746 Agro-Ecosystems†
0304-3754 Alternatives
0304-3762 Applied Animal Ethology *see* 0168-1591
0304-3770 Aquatic Botany
0304-3797 European Journal of Engineering Education
0304-3800 Ecological Modelling
0304-3835 Cancer Letters
0304-3843 Hyperfine Interactions
0304-3851 Journal of Applied Science and Engineering Section A. Electrical Power and Information Systems†
0304-386X Hydrometallurgy
0304-3878 Journal of Development Economics
0304-3886 Journal of Electrostatics
0304-3894 Journal of Hazardous Materials
0304-3908 Journal of Industrial Aerodynamics *see* 0167-6105
0304-3924 Landscape and Planning *see* 0169-2046
0304-3932 Journal of Monetary Economics
0304-3940 Neuroscience Letters
0304-3959 Pain
0304-3967 Resource Recovery and Conservation *see* 0921-3449
0304-3975 Theoretical Computer Science
0304-3991 Ultramicroscopy
0304-4009 Urban Ecology *see* 0169-2046
0304-4017 Veterinary Parasitology
0304-4025 Wave Electronics†
0304-4033 Revista Centroamericana de Nutricion y Ciencias de Alimentos†
0304-4041 Excerpta Medica. Section 40: Drug Dependence *see* 0925-5958
0304-405X Journal of Financial Economics
0304-4068 Journal of Mathematical Economics
0304-4076 Journal of Econometrics
0304-4084 Excerpta Medica. Section 47: Virology *see* 0927-2771
0304-4092 Dialectical Anthropology
0304-4114 Mass Emergencies†
0304-4130 European Journal of Political Research
0304-4149 Stochastic Processes and Their Applications
0304-4157 B B A - Reviews on Biomembranes
0304-4165 B B A - General Subjects
0304-4173 B B A Reviews on Bioenergetics†
0304-4181 Journal of Medieval History
0304-419X B B A - Reviews on Cancer
0304-4203 Marine Chemistry
0304-4211 Plant Science Letters *see* 0168-9452
0304-422X Poetics
0304-4238 Scientia Horticulturae
0304-4246 Contributions to Gynecology and Obstetrics
0304-4254 Pediatric and Adolescent Endocrinology
0304-4262 Progress in Reproductive Biology *see* 0254-105X
0304-4270 INSEAD Address Book
0304-4289 Pramana
0304-4297 European Research *see* 0923-5957
0304-4319 Historia del Derecho Espanol. Anuario
0304-4556 Iranian Journal of Public Health
0304-4602 Academy of Medicine, Singapore. Annals
0304-4815 Revista Espanola de Reumatologia
0304-4858 Gaceta Medica de Bilbao
0304-4920 Chinese Journal of Physiology
0304-5013 Progresos de Obstetricia y Ginecologia
0304-5056 Revista Espanola de Cirugia Osteoarticular
0304-5102 Journal of Molecular Catalysis
0304-5188 Institutul Politehnic Iasi. Buletinul. Sectia I: Matematica, Mecanica Teoretica, Fizica *changed to* Institutul Politehnic "Gheorghe Asachi" din Iasi. Buletinul. Sectia I: Mecanica Matematica, Fizica.
0304-520X Technika Poszukiwan Geologicznych *changed to* Technika Poszukiwan Geologicznych, Geosynoptyka i Goetermia.
0304-5218 Islamabad Journal of Sciences
0304-5242 Journal of Plantation Crops
0304-5250 Indian Journal of Ecology
0304-5293 Academia Sinica. Institute of Physics. Annual Report
0304-5307 National Museums and Monuments of Rhodesia. Occasional Papers. Series A: Human Sciences. *changed to* National Museums and Monuments Administration. Occasional Papers. Series A: Human Sciences.
0304-5315 Natural Sciences *see* 1011-7881
0304-5323 Museum Memoir†
0304-534X I N S D O C. Russian Scientific and Technical Publications. Accessions List
0304-5358 Contents List of Soviet Scientific Periodicals
0304-5374 Comparative Animal Nutrition
0304-5439 C I M M Y T Report on Wheat Improvement†
0304-5447 C I M M Y T Today†
0304-5463 C I M M Y T Review†
0304-548X C I M M Y T Report on Maize Improvement†
0304-551X C I M M Y T Information Bulletin†
0304-5579 Investigacion y Progreso Agricola *see* 0716-5331
0304-5609 Ciencia e Investigacion Agraria
0304-5617 Investigacion Agricola†
0304-5692 Zaire. Institut National de la Statistique. Annuaire des Statistiques du Commerce Exterieur†
0304-5714 Institut Oceanographique. Memoires
0304-5722 Institut Oceanographique. Bulletin
0304-5757 Conjonction
0304-5765 Tropical Grain Legume Bulletin†
0304-582X F A O Documentation - Current Bibliography
0304-5935 Abstracts of Geochronology and Isotope Geology†
0304-5951 Abstracts on Tropical Agriculture
0304-5978 G E R V Activiteitsverslag†
0304-6125 Afghanistan Journal†
0304-6133 Afghanistan Republic Annual
0304-615X Africanus
0304-6184 Madhya Pradesh. Directorate of Agriculture. Agricultural Statistics
0304-6214 A I I S Quarterly Newsletter
0304-6257 Amsterdamer Beitraege zur Neueren Germanistik
0304-6451 Association of Urban Authorities. Annual Bulletin
0304-6478 Pakistan. Finance Division. Annual Budget Statement (Final)
0304-6729 Arab Fund for Economic and Social Development. Annual Report
0304-6796 Central Bank of Barbados. Annual Report
0304-6818 Central Sericultural Research and Training Institute. Annual Report
0304-6907 Cotton Corporation of India. Annual Report
0304-6966 Deposit Insurance Corporation. Annual Report: Directors' Report, Balance Sheet and Accounts
0304-7032 Indian Council of Historical Research. Annual Report
0304-7067 Indian Veterinary Research Institute. Annual Report
0304-7083 Institute of Secretariat Training and Management. Annual Report
0304-7091 International Centre for Theoretical Physics. Annual Report
0304-7164 Jammu & Kashmir Minerals Limited. Annual Report
0304-7245 Madhya Pradesh State Agro-Industries Development Corporation Ltd. Annual Report
0304-727X Liberia. Ministry of Finance. Annual Report
0304-7296 Liberia. Ministry of Lands and Mines. Annual Report *changed to* Liberia. Ministry of Lands, Mines and Energy. Annual Report.
0304-730X Liberia. Ministry of Local Government, Rural Development & Urban Reconstruction. Annual Report
0304-7326 Liberia. Ministry of Public Works. Annual Report
0304-7350 Singapore. National Statistical Commission. Annual Report†
0304-7423 Israel Oceanographic and Limnological Research. Biennial Report
0304-7628 Focus on Rhodesia *changed to* Spotlight on Zimbabwe.
0304-8101 Punjab National Bank. Annual Report
0304-8152 Salar Jung Museum. Annual Report
0304-8179 Shellac Export Promotion Council. Annual Report
0304-8349 United Planting Association of Malaysia. Annual Report
0304-8551 Arab Oil & Gas Directory
0304-8594 Architects Trade Journal *see* 0970-6852
0304-8608 Archives of Virology
0304-8616 Archivos de Farmacologia y Toxicologia
0304-8624 Armenian Studies
0304-8632 Art Spectrum *see* 0004-3230
0304-8675 Asian Profile
0304-8683 Asiryada
0304-8705 Astronautical Research†
0304-8713 Austria Today
0304-8721 Automobil
0304-8764 Medio Ambiente
0304-8802 Agro Sur
0304-8845 P T L†
0304-8853 Journal of Magnetism and Magnetic Materials
0304-8861 Anuario Bibliografico Uruguayo
0304-8942 Food and Nutrition†
0304-9027 Bangladesh Journal of Zoology
0304-9191 Spain. Ministerio del Interior. Direccion General de Trafico. Boletin Informativo: Anuario Estadistico General
0304-9272 Brahmana-Gaurava
0304-9523 Astronomical Society of India. Bulletin
0304-9558 Indian Institute of History of Medicine. Bulletin (New Delhi)
0304-9566 Osmania Medical College. Institute of History of Medicine. Bulletin *see* 0304-9558
0304-9620 Societe des Naturalistes Luxembourgeois. Bulletin
0304-968X Buy from India
0304-9701 International Forum on Information and Documentation
0304-971X Revista de Biologia del Uruguay
0304-9841 C S I O Communications
0304-985X Delft Progress Report
0304-9884 Indian Journal of Engineering Mathematics
0305-0009 Journal of Child Language
0305-0017 Geocom Programs *see* 0098-3004
0305-0033 Aslib Information
0305-0041 Cambridge Philosophical Society. Mathematical Proceedings
0305-005X Emergency Post *see* 0954-562X
0305-0068 Comparative Education
0305-0076 Review of Applied Entomology. Series A: Agricultural *see* 0957-6762
0305-0084 Review of Applied Entomology. Series B: Medical and Veterinary *see* 0957-6770
0305-0122 Bulk Carrier Register
0305-0130 Local Government Companion
0305-0165 Current Clinical Chemistry *see* 0885-1980
0305-0262 Waste Materials Biodegradation Research Titles *see* 0265-3036
0305-0270 Journal of Biogeography
0305-0297 Labour Leader *see* 0951-2187
0305-0319 Cosmetic World News
0305-0351 C I P Descriptions of Plant-Parasitic Nematodes
0305-036X Arabian Studies
0305-0424 News from Victoria (Australia) *changed to* Economic Review.
0305-0440 Historical Breechloading Smallarms Association. Journal
0305-0467 Freezer Foods†
0305-0483 Omega (Tarrytown)
0305-0491 Comparative Biochemistry and Physiology. Part B: Comparative Biochemistry
0305-0548 Computers & Operations Research
0305-0629 International Interactions
0305-0637 Classified World
0305-0653 Work Study and O and M Abstracts *see* 0952-4614
0305-0661 Marketing & Distribution Abstracts
0305-067X Personnel & Training Abstracts
0305-0718 Commonwealth Law Bulletin
0305-0734 The Middle East
0305-0777 Refrigeration and Air Conditioning Year Book
0305-0785 Scottish Literary Journal
0305-0831 Aerospace
0305-0904 Thomas Cook News *changed to* Internationally Speaking.
0305-0920 Appropriate Technology
0305-0963 Radical Science Journal *see* 0950-5431
0305-0998 Norwegian Chamber of Commerce. Year Book and Directory of Members
0305-103X Urban Abstracts *changed to* Urban Abstracts.
0305-1048 Nucleic Acids Research
0305-1129 Stock Exchange, London. Members and Firms of the Stock Exchange *changed to* I S E Firms and Members.
0305-1277 National Institute of Agricultural Botany, Cambridge, England. Farmers Leaflets
0305-1420 British Railways Board. Annual Report and Accounts
0305-1471 N M M News†
0305-1498 Oxford Literary Review *changed to* Oxford Literary Review.
0305-1536 Home and School
0305-165X Librarians for Social Change *changed to* Social Change and Information Systems.
0305-1668 Systems International
0305-1706 Film Dope
0305-1781 C I R I A Technical Note
0305-179X Tanker Register
0305-1803 Liquid Gas Carrier Register
0305-1811 Journal of Immunogenetics *see* 0960-7420
0305-182X Journal of Oral Rehabilitation
0305-1838 Mammal Review
0305-1846 Neuropathology and Applied Neurobiology
0305-1862 Child: Care, Health and Development
0305-1870 Clinical and Experimental Pharmacology and Physiology
0305-196X Ecological Abstracts
0305-1978 Biochemical Systematics and Ecology
0305-2001 Royal Observatory, Edinburgh. Publications†
0305-2044 Association of County Councils. Yearbook
0305-2109 Communications International
0305-215X Engineering Optimization
0305-2176 I C E Abstracts *see* 0332-4095
0305-2249 Audio Visual
0305-2257 National Electronics Review†
0305-2303 South East Hampshire Genealogical Society. Journal *see* 0306-6843
0305-2346 Institute of Physics, London. Conference Series. Proceedings
0305-2524 Commonwealth Bureau of Soils. Annotated Bibliographies *changed to* C.A.B. International. Bureau of Soils. Annotated Bibliographies.
0305-2680 Descriptions of Plant Viruses†
0305-2729 C I P Keys to the Nematode Parasites of Vertebrates†
0305-3040 Applied Ecology Abstracts *see* 0143-3296
0305-3091 Electrocomponent Science & Technology†
0305-3105 Water *see* 0262-9909
0305-3121 Machinery Buyers' Guide
0305-3199 Adhesives Directory

ISSN

0305-3210 Middle East Review
0305-3253 Higher Education Exchange *changed to* Educational International.
0305-3342 Medical Directory
0305-3504 Mintel *changed to* Market Intelligence.
0305-3601 Communication & Broadcasting†
0305-3679 Essex Union List of Serials
0305-3695 Corporate Planning Journal *changed to* Local Government Policy Making.
0305-3709 Bulk: Storage, Movement, Control *changed to* Bulk Handling: Storage, Movement, Control.
0305-3717 Zambezi Press International
0305-3849 Par Golf
0305-3873 Surface and Defect Properties of Solids *see* 0142-3401
0305-4012 Stores, Shops, Hypermarkets Retail Directory *changed to* Retail Directory.
0305-4039 Bale Catalogue of Palestine and Israel Stamps *changed to* Bale Catalogue of Israel Postage Stamps.
0305-4047 C I R I A Annual Report
0305-408X C I R I A Report
0305-4136 Hospital Update
0305-4179 Burns
0305-4233 Communication (London, 1975)
0305-4284 Offshore Drilling Register†
0305-4322 Ditchley Journal *see* 0262-8015
0305-4349 Druglink
0305-439X Processing
0305-4403 Journal of Archaeological Science
0305-4438 Music and Liturgy
0305-4470 Journal of Physics A: Mathematical and General
0305-4543 Spon's Mechanical & Electrical Services Price Book
0305-4608 Journal of Physics F: Metal Physics *see* 0953-8984
0305-4616 Journal of Physics G: Nuclear Physics *see* 0954-3899
0305-4624 Physics in Technology *see* 0953-8585
0305-4659 Northamptonshire Archaeology
0305-4756 Camden History Review
0305-4829 Heat Treatment of Metals
0305-4934 Ornamental Horticulture
0305-4985 Oxford Review of Education
0305-5000 Dental Update
0305-5167 British Library Journal
0305-5183 British Library. Lending Division. Index of Conference Proceedings Received *see* 0959-4906
0305-5280 Current Archaeological Offprints and Reports *see* 0269-1906
0305-5426 Programming Index†
0305-5620 Framework Forecasts for the United Kingdom
0305-5698 Educational Studies
0305-5728 Vine
0305-5736 Policy and Politics
0305-5752 Property Studies in the U.K. and Overseas
0305-5795 Devon Archaeological Society. Proceedings
0305-5892 Register of Thoroughbred Stallions†
0305-5906 Municipal Year Book
0305-5914 Geographical Papers
0305-5973 B S R I A Application Guides
0305-5981 Omnibus (Bracknell)†
0305-6104 Independent Broadcasting†
0305-6139 British Society for Middle Eastern Studies. Bulletin *changed to* British Journal of Middle East Studies.
0305-6147 Radical Education
0305-6155 R U S I and Brassey's Defence Yearbook
0305-6198 Saturated Heterocyclic Chemistry†
0305-6244 Review of African Political Economy
0305-6252 Minority Rights Group. Reports
0305-6473 Civil Engineering *see* 0956-9189
0305-6481 I R C S Journal of Medical Science†
0305-649X I R C S Medical Science: Classified List†
0305-6503 B L L Review *see* 0264-1615
0305-652X Pick
0305-6562 Scotland's Regions
0305-6589 Laxton's Building Price Book *changed to* Laxton's Building Price Book.
0305-6686 I R C S Medical Science: Anatomy and Human Biology *see* 0269-8951
0305-6694 I R C S Medical Science: Anesthetics†
0305-6708 Biochemistry *see* 0269-8951
0305-6716 Biomedical Technology *see* 0269-8951
0305-6724 Cancer *see* 0269-8951
0305-6732 Cardiovascular System *see* 0269-8951
0305-6848 I R C S Medical Science: Neurobiology and Neurophysiology†
0305-6856 I R C S Medical Science: Neurology and Neurosurgery†
0305-6864 I R C S Medical Science: Pediatrics†
0305-6899 I R C S Medical Science: Psychiatry and Clinical Psychology†
0305-6902 I R C S Medical Science: Psychology†
0305-6910 I R C S Medical Science: Radiology and Nuclear Medicine†
0305-6961 I R C S Medical Science: Veterinary Science†
0305-697X Inorganic Chemistry of the Main Group Elements†
0305-6996 B K S T S Journal *see* 0950-2114
0305-7046 Clothing Machinery Times
0305-7054 Consumer Bulletin *see* 0265-6930
0305-7070 Journal of Southern African Studies
0305-7100 Kemps Music and Record Industry Year Book International *changed to* Kemps International Music Book.
0305-716X Journal of Flour and Animal Feed Milling *changed to* Milling Feed and Farm Supplies.
0305-7194 C E G B Research†
0305-7224 Psychoenergetic Systems *see* 0894-2528
0305-7232 Cancer Biochemistry Biophysics
0305-7240 Journal of Moral Education
0305-7259 Mathematics in School
0305-7291 Education for Development *changed to* Welsh Journal of Education.
0305-7321 Brushes International *changed to* Brushes International.
0305-733X Blinds and Shutters
0305-7348 Ideas†
0305-7356 Psychology of Music
0305-7364 Annals of Botany
0305-7372 Cancer Treatment Reviews
0305-7399 Clinical Oncology *see* 0748-7983
0305-7402 Containerisation International Yearbook
0305-7429 Modern China Studies. International Bulletin†
0305-7445 International Journal of Nautical Archeology and Underwater Exploration *see* 1057-2414
0305-7453 Journal of Antimicrobial Chemotherapy
0305-7488 Journal of Historical Geography
0305-7496 Educational Administration *see* 0263-211X
0305-750X World Development
0305-7518 Leprosy Review
0305-7593 Modern Languages in Scotland†
0305-7615 Applied Health Physics Abstracts and Notes
0305-7623 Ceramics Industries Journal *changed to* Ceramic Industries International.
0305-7631 British Journal of In-Service Education
0305-764X Cambridge Journal of Education
0305-7658 Conference *see* 0265-4458
0305-7682 British Exports. Export Services. *changed to* British Exports.
0305-7704 Reaction Kinetics *see* 0309-6890
0305-7712 Environmental Chemistry†
0305-7755 Teaching English
0305-7798 Sheet Metal Industries Year Book
0305-781X Association of British Theological and Philosophical Libraries. Bulletin
0305-7828 Aether
0305-7860 Therapeutic Education *see* 0264-4614
0305-7879 Vocational Aspects of Education
0305-7887 British Library. Annual Report
0305-7917 Spectrum
0305-7925 Compare
0305-795X Scottish Journal of Adult Education
0305-7984 University of Manchester. School of Education. Gazette†
0305-7992 Proof†
0305-8018 Teaching Geography
0305-8034 London Journal
0305-8077 A B C Air - Rail Europe *changed to* A B C Executive Flight Planner: Europe, Middle East & Africa.
0305-8107 Journal of Occupational Psychology *see* 0963-1798
0305-8123 Brewery Manual and Who's Who in British Brewing†
0305-8131 B C R A Review†
0305-814X Reading in Political Economy
0305-8174 Offshore Fishing†
0305-8182 Jabberwocky
0305-8190 University of Oxford. School of Geography. Research Papers
0305-8204 Current Topics in Immunology
0305-8220 Regular Savings Plans *changed to* Unit-Linked Regular Savings Plans.
0305-8255 Inorganic Reaction Mechanisms†
0305-8298 Millennium
0305-8336 N E R C News Journal *see* 0951-5305
0305-8344 New Review†
0305-8441 Coombe Lodge Report
0305-8468 Focus on International and Comparative Librarianship
0305-8476 European Law Digest†
0305-8549 Devon Historian
0305-859X British Cave Research Association. Transactions *see* 0263-760X
0305-862X African Research and Documentation
0305-8646 University of Glasgow. Institute of Latin American Studies. Occasional Papers
0305-8654 Vice-Chancellor's Annual Report
0305-8689 Background Data on the Common Market†
0305-8697 Award for Commonwealth University Staff *see* 0964-2706
0305-8751 Home and Freezer Digest
0305-876X Offshore Engineer
0305-8913 British Journal of Teacher Education *see* 0260-7476
0305-8921 Tolley's Income Tax (Year)
0305-8964 Tropical Storage Abstracts *see* 0041-3291
0305-8972 M I R A Abstracts *see* 0309-0817
0305-8980 Glasgow Archaeological Journal
0305-9006 Progress in Planning
0305-9014 Public Finance and Accountancy
0305-9049 Oxford Bulletin of Economics and Statistics
0305-9154 Plant Growth Regulator Abstracts
0305-9162 Maize Quality Protein Abstracts *see* 0267-2987
0305-9189 State Librarian
0305-9219 Viking Society for Northern Research. Saga Book
0305-9227 University of Liverpool Calendar
0305-9235 Fluid Flow Measurement Abstracts
0305-9243 Omnibus Magazine
0305-9251 Theatrefacts *changed to* Theatrefacts - Theatrelogs.
0305-926X Housman Society Journal
0305-9308 Writer (Zennor)†
0305-9324 Fellowship for Freedom in Medicine. Newsletter
0305-9332 Industrial Law Journal
0305-9340 Health and Welfare Libraries Quarterly
0305-9367 Insurance†
0305-9421 Quarry Management and Products *changed to* Quarry Management.
0305-9456 Civil Engineering Hydraulics Abstracts
0305-9499 Applecon†
0305-9529 New Internationalist
0305-9537 Handbook and Directory of Crematoria *see* 0143-3164
0305-9545 Carbonization Research Report†
0305-9553 Standard Chartered Review†
0305-9561 Eurolaw Commercial Intelligence†
0305-960X Religious Books in Print
0305-9669 Family Practitioner Services†
0305-9707 Alkaloids†
0305-9715 Aromatic and Heteroaromatic Chemistry†
0305-9723 Colloid Science†
0305-9731 Chemical Thermodynamics†
0305-974X Dielectric and Related Molecular Processes†
0305-9758 Electron Spin Resonance *changed to* Electron Spin Resonance. Part A.
0305-9758 Electron Spin Resonance *changed to* Electron Spin Resonance. Part B.
0305-9766 Electronic Structure & Magnetism of Inorganic Compounds†
0305-9774 Inorganic Chemistry of the Transition Elements†
0305-9782 Molecular Spectroscopy†
0305-9790 Molecular Structure by Diffraction Methods†
0305-9804 Nuclear Magnetic Resonance
0305-9812 Organic Compounds of Sulphur, Selenium and Tellurium†
0305-9839 Hard Cheese
0305-9855 A L L C Bulletin *see* 0951-1474
0305-9863 Buying Antiques
0305-988X Modern Purchasing†
0305-9898 Borthwick Institute Bulletin†
0305-9928 Henley Centre for Forecasting. Costs & Prices
0305-9936 Framework Forecast for the E E C Economies
0305-9944 Forecasts of Exchange Rate Movements *see* 0143-0769
0305-9960 Statistical Mechanics†
0305-9979 Electrochemistry†
0305-9987 Mass Spectrometry
0305-9995 Theoretical Chemistry†
0306-0004 Amino Acids, Peptides and Proteins *changed to* Amino Acids and Peptides.
0306-0012 Royal Society of Chemistry. Reviews
0306-0020 Mantatoforost
0306-0039 I S M E C Bulletin *see* 0896-7113
0306-0128 Dance Gazette
0306-0152 Great Britain. Property Services Agency. Construction References†
0306-0160 Leicestershire, Northamptonshire & Rutland Farmer
0306-0179 Engineering Capacity
0306-0195 Poetry Post
0306-0209 Naval Architect
0306-0225 Sub-Cellular Biochemistry
0306-0233 Health Services Manpower Review *see* 0955-2065
0306-0241 Dundee Tayside
0306-0284 Bibliography of Insecticide Materials of Vegetable Origin†
0306-0314 C I P A
0306-0322 African Book Publishing Record
0306-0349 Airtrade
0306-0357 Organ Club Journal
0306-0373 Delius
0306-0381 O E M Design
0306-039X Pharmacology and Therapeutics. Part B. General and Systematic Pharmacology *see* 0163-7258
0306-0403 Swimming Teacher
0306-042X B M S - Biomedical Mass Spectrometry *see* 1052-9306
0306-0438 Thermal Analysis Abstracts *see* 0956-2265
0306-0462 Craft Teacher News *changed to* Craft, Design & Technology News.
0306-0497 Self & Society
0306-0519 Furniture Manufacturer
0306-056X Street Research Bulletin
0306-0586 High-Speed Ground Transportation and Urban Rapid Transit Systems Bibliography Service†
0306-0594 Air-Cushion and Hydrofoil Systems Bibliography Service†
0306-0624 University of York. Institute of Advanced Architectural Studies. Research Papers
0306-0632 Progress in Food & Nutrition Science
0306-0659 Stable Management
0306-0691 Screen Education†

ISSN

0306-0713 Organophosphorus Chemistry
0306-0772 Facts
0306-0837 Llafur
0306-0845 Urban History Yearbook
0306-087X Theological and Religious Index *changed to* Theological and Religious Bibliographies.
0306-0896 Pacifica
0306-090X Civic Trust News *see* 0261-1988
0306-0942 Service Point
0306-0985 Cargo Systems International
0306-1000 B A I E News
0306-1043 Great Britain. Departments of the Environment and Transport. Library. Library Bulletin *see* 0140-170X
0306-1051 Antiques Trade Gazette
0306-1078 Early Music
0306-1108 University of Sussex. Centre for Continuing Education. Occasional Paper
0306-1124 Commonwealth Bibliographies
0306-1132 Football News
0306-1140 Romford Record
0306-1159 Audio Arts
0306-1256 Gallery
0306-1264 A B L C News *changed to* Textile Services.
0306-1353 Annual Reports on Analytical Atomic Spectroscopy *see* 0267-9477
0306-1396 Chemical Society. Analytical Division. Proceedings *see* 0144-557X
0306-140X Pennine Platform
0306-1426 Women's Report†
0306-1450 B I A S Journal
0306-1477 Voices of North Devon†
0306-1485 Hoversport†
0306-1493 Hovercraft Contact Book and International ACV Directory†
0306-1531 Public Health Laboratory Service Board. Year Book *see* 0142-3517
0306-154X After the Battle
0306-1582 Poultry Abstracts
0306-1604 Clockwork
0306-1639 Digest of English - Language Textile Literature *see* 0260-4256
0306-1647 Motorcycle Rider
0306-1655 Verifact†
0306-1701 Emigrante†
0306-1728 Schedule of Postgraduate Courses in United Kingdom Universities *changed to* British Universities' Guide to Graduate Study.
0306-1736 Scholarships Guide for Commonwealth Postgraduate Students *see* 0960-7986
0306-1744 Higher Education in the United Kingdom
0306-1841 Euroclay *see* 0959-6127
0306-1884 New Towns Bulletin†
0306-1892 Workers' Control Bulletin†
0306-1914 Current Information in the Construction Industry
0306-1922 Procurement Weekly
0306-1973 Literature & History
0306-1981 I L E A Contact†
0306-2015 Children's Literature Abstracts
0306-204X European Glass Directory and Buyer's Guide
0306-2074 Spore Research†
0306-2082 Music and Man *see* 0141-1896
0306-2090 Experimental Embryology and Teratology†
0306-2104 Liquid Chromatography Abstracts
0306-2163 Industrial Cases Reports
0306-2201 Sussex Business Times
0306-2252 Transport News Digest
0306-2279 European Industrial & Commercial Review†
0306-2295 Outlook *changed to* Newscan.
0306-2309 Offshore Services *changed to* Offshore Services & Technology.
0306-2392 Undercurrents *see* 0034-5970
0306-2406 Certified Accountant
0306-2414 Natural Gas for Commerce†
0306-2465 A T L A Abstracts *see* 0261-1929
0306-2473 Yearbook of English Studies
0306-2481 Sociological Analysis & Theory
0306-252X Paper Technology and Industry *changed to* Paper Technology.
0306-2538 Staff and Welfare Caterer†
0306-2597 Liquid Crystals Abstracts†
0306-2619 Applied Energy
0306-2643 International Review of Psycho-Analysis
0306-2686 Plant Foods for Man *changed to* Food Science.
0306-2708 Society for General Microbiology Proceedings *see* 0142-7547
0306-2732 International Symposium on Jet Cutting Technology. Proceedings
0306-2740 Queen Mary College. Department of Geography. Occasional Papers *changed to* Queen Mary and Westfield College. Department of Geography. Research Papers in Geography.
0306-283X Quaker Service *see* 0265-7848
0306-2856 Quality Assurance *see* 0959-3268
0306-2864 Diagnostics Index†
0306-2880 Reprographics Quarterly *see* 0266-6960
0306-2910 I B C A M Journal *changed to* I B C A M Journal.
0306-2945 Lloyd's Maritime & Commercial Law Quarterly
0306-2988 Stainless Steel Industry
0306-3003 Intestinal Absorption *see* 0261-4995
0306-3046 Spon's Architects' & Builders' Price Book
0306-3054 Spon's Landscape Handbook *see* 0267-4181
0306-3062 Recreation Management Yearbook *see* 0144-624X
0306-3070 Journal of General Management
0306-3089 Financial Times Tax Newsletter *see* 0141-0741
0306-3127 Social Studies of Science
0306-3151 Gwynedd Archives Service. Bulletin†
0306-316X Scotia Review
0306-3208 International Journal of Criminology and Penology *see* 0194-6595
0306-3216 Building Trades Journal *see* 0954-0652
0306-3224 Contents Pages in Management
0306-3275 Molecular Aspects *see* 0264-6021
0306-3283 Biochemical Journal. Part 1: Cellular Aspects *see* 0264-6021
0306-3291 Current Advances in Ecological Sciences *see* 0955-6648
0306-3313 N A P V Newsletter
0306-3321 Guerrilheiro†
0306-333X Electronic Production
0306-3348 Guardian Gazette *changed to* Law Society's Guardian Gazette.
0306-3356 Clinics in Obstetrics and Gynaecology *see* 0889-8545
0306-3380 British Geomorphological Research Group. Technical Bulletin†
0306-3410 Jane's Infantry Weapons
0306-3437 Footwear World†
0306-3461 Meridian†
0306-347X Marine Week†
0306-3534 European Plastics News
0306-3542 Progress of Rubber Technology *see* 0266-7320
0306-3550 Accidents to Aircraft on the British Register
0306-3569 Great Britain. Civil Aviation Authority. Annual Report and Accounts
0306-3577 Great Britain. Civil Aviation Board. C A A Monthly Statistics *changed to* Great Britain. Civil Aviation Authority. U.K. Airlines Monthly Operating & Traffic Statistics.
0306-3585 Heating, Ventilating and Air Conditioning Year Book *changed to* The Specifier's Guide to Heating, Ventilating, Air Conditioning, and Refrigeration.
0306-3593 Boatbuilders' and Chandlers' Directory of Suppliers *changed to* Boat Equipment Buyers' Guide.
0306-3607 Reinforced Plastics Congress *changed to* Reinforced Plastics. Composite Papers.
0306-3623 General Pharmacology
0306-3631 Journal of Commonwealth & Comparative Politics
0306-364X Renewable Energy Bulletin
0306-3666 Men of Achievement
0306-3674 British Journal of Sports Medicine
0306-3704 British Journal of Law and Society *see* 0263-323X
0306-3712 Brass Band Review†
0306-3747 Additives for Polymers
0306-3763 N C A V A E. E D U. Technical Reports *see* 0261-2364
0306-3860 St. Thomas's Gazette *changed to* St. Thomas's Hospital Gazette.
0306-3879 Double Glazing - Domestic, Industrial and Commercial *changed to* Window Industries.
0306-3895 Business Graduate†
0306-3909 Creative Camera International Year Book *changed to* Creative Camera Collection.
0306-3933 Merrill Lynch - Euromoney Directory
0306-395X Petroleum Economist
0306-3968 Race and Class
0306-3992 Equals *see* 0140-9506
0306-400X International Water Power and Dam Construction
0306-4034 University of Birmingham. Centre for Urban and Regional Studies. Research Memorandum
0306-4069 Hydraulic Pneumatic Mechanical Power *see* 0950-1487
0306-4077 Bindery Data Index†
0306-4123 Board Manufacture & Processing
0306-4190 International Journal of Mechanical Engineering Education
0306-4212 Foundry Yearbook
0306-4220 Index on Censorship
0306-428X S R L News *see* 0951-4635
0306-4336 International Tourism Quarterly *see* 0269-3747
0306-4379 Information Systems (Tarrytown)
0306-4395 Harpsicord Magazine *changed to* Harpsichord and Fortepiano.
0306-4409 Recorder and Music Magazine *see* 0961-3544
0306-4484 Current Advances in Plant Science
0306-4492 Comparative Biochemistry and Physiology. Part C: Comparative Pharmacology *see* 0742-8413
0306-4522 Neuroscience
0306-4530 Psychoneuroendocrinology
0306-4549 Annals of Nuclear Energy
0306-4565 Journal of Thermal Biology
0306-4573 Information Processing & Management
0306-4603 Addictive Behaviors
0306-462X Life and Health†
0306-4824 World Trade Union Movement†
0306-4859 Society for Lincolnshire History and Archaeology. Annual Report and Statement of Accounts
0306-4905 Imperial Cancer Research Fund. Scientific Report
0306-4964 Foundation
0306-4980 I D F Bulletin
0306-5030 Manchester Free Press
0306-5049 Business Economist
0306-5065 British Mensa Newsletter *changed to* Mensa Magazine.
0306-5103 Collect Channel Islands Stamps *changed to* Collect Channel Islands and Isle of Man Stamps.
0306-512X New Humanist
0306-5154 Shirley Institute Publications. S: Series *changed to* Shirley Publications. S: Series.
0306-5162 European Market Report†
0306-5197 Chigwell Local History Society. Transactions
0306-5251 British Journal of Clinical Pharmacology
0306-526X Metallurgist and Materials Technologist *see* 0266-7185
0306-5278 Northern Scotland
0306-5286 Road Traffic Reports
0306-5332 Museums Association Information Sheets†
0306-5367 Spur
0306-543X Who's Who in Football
0306-5456 British Journal of Obstetrics & Gynaecology
0306-5472 B M A News Review
0306-5480 H.G. Wells Society Newsletter
0306-5499 Institute of United States Studies Monographs†
0306-5502 European Plastics Buyers Guide†
0306-5529 Prospect *changed to* Swansea Review.
0306-5537 Key Abstracts - Solid State Devices *see* 0950-4850
0306-5553 Key Abstracts - Systems Theory *see* 0950-477X
0306-5561 Key Abstracts - Power Transmission and Distribution *see* 0950-4834
0306-557X Key Abstracts - Electronic Circuits
0306-5588 Key Abstracts - Communications Technology *see* 0950-4877
0306-5596 Key Abstracts - Industrial Power and Control Systems *see* 0950-4842
0306-5618 Sales Engineering *see* 0264-3200
0306-5634 Air International
0306-5650 North West Business
0306-5677 Catholic Directory for Scotland
0306-5693 Esperanto News *see* 0007-067X
0306-5707 Challenge†
0306-5723 Outdoors *see* 0954-6693
0306-5758 Manchester Chamber of Commerce and Industry. Yearbook *changed to* Manchester Regional Business Directory.
0306-5766 References to Scientific Literature on Fire *changed to* Fire Science Abstracts.
0306-5774 Mackintosh Yearbook of West European Electronics Data *changed to* Yearbook of World Electronics Data Vol. 1: West Europe.
0306-5790 Anglesey Antiquarian Society Transactions
0306-5839 Mobile Home and Holiday Caravan *see* 0268-4594
0306-5928 British Music Yearbook
0306-6045 International Tax-Free Trader & Duty-Free World
0306-6061 Political Social Economic Review
0306-610X Crafts
0306-6118 Security Surveyor
0306-6142 C A T M O G
0306-6150 Journal of Peasant Studies
0306-6185 D I A Yearbook - Design Action *changed to* D I A Yearbook.
0306-6193 Educational Yearbook†
0306-624X International Journal of Offender Therapy and Comparative Criminology
0306-6266 Natural Food Trade Journal *changed to* Natural Food Retailer.
0306-6274 Motor Report International
0306-6304 Language Teaching and Linguistics Abstracts *see* 0261-4448
0306-6312 750 Bulletin
0306-6398 East Malling Research Station. Annual Report *see* 0963-3235
0306-6444 Gas Engineering & Management
0306-6479 New Law Journal
0306-6495 Practical Hi-Fi & Audio *changed to* Hi-Fi Today.
0306-6509 Solid Wastes *changed to* Wastes Management.
0306-6517 International Flavours and Food Additives *changed to* Food Ingredients & Processing International.
0306-6541 Pram and Nursery Trader Year Book *changed to* Toy Directory.
0306-6568 Sea Angler
0306-6649 W R C Information *see* 0748-2531
0306-6673 Personnel and Training Management Yearbook *changed to* Human Resource Management Yearbook.
0306-672X Hertfordshire Countryside

0306-6746 Progress in Water Technology *see* 0273-1223
0306-6800 Journal of Medical Ethics
0306-6843 Hampshire Family Historian
0306-686X Journal of Business Finance & Accounting
0306-6886 Computer Report
0306-6908 Middle East Week†
0306-6916 British Hydromechanics Research Association. Proceedings of Hydrotransport
0306-7041 British Airways Executive
0306-7068 Monotype Pictorial†
0306-7076 British Ceramic Review
0306-719X Farm Business Review†
0306-7262 Reform
0306-7297 Journal of Human Movement Studies
0306-7319 International Journal of Environmental and Analytical Chemistry
0306-7327 Irrigation and Drainage Abstracts
0306-7335 Challenger Society. Newsletter *changed to* Ocean Challenge.
0306-7351 Ocean Energy†
0306-7408 University of Strathclyde, Fraser of Allander Institute for Research on the Scottish Economy. Research Monograph
0306-7432 Association of Teachers of Russian. Newsletter
0306-7440 Traditional Music
0306-7475 Antiquarian Book Monthly Review
0306-7548 Recent Advances in Obesity Research
0306-7556 Crop Physiology Abstracts
0306-7564 Dynamica *see* 0883-7066
0306-7580 Small Animal Abstracts *see* 0961-3501
0306-7645 JustPeace
0306-7661 Framework
0306-7696 International Newsletter on Chemical Education
0306-770X Oil World Statistics *see* 0141-4305
0306-7734 International Statistical Review
0306-7858 Tape Teacher†
0306-7866 University of Strathclyde. Fraser of Allander Institute for Research on the Scottish Economy. Quarterly Economic Commentary
0306-7912 Beermat Magazine
0306-7920 Lawn Tennis *changed to* Tennis.
0306-7947 British Model Soldier Society. Bulletin
0306-7963 L A G Bulletin *changed to* Legal Action.
0306-7971 Spare Rib
0306-798X B U F O R A Journal *see* 0265-1947
0306-7998 Jewish Historical Society of England. Annual Report and Accounts for the Session
0306-8099 Opera North†
0306-8129 Forestry and Home Grown Timber *see* 0308-7638
0306-8145 Canada Today
0306-817X Art Design Photo†
0306-8234 Paper
0306-8285 Industrial Pollution Control Yearbook†
0306-8293 International Journal of Social Economics
0306-8374 Asian Affairs
0306-8404 Bandersnatch
0306-8412 Africa Currents†
0306-8463 Postal History International†
0306-8471 Eugenics Society Bulletin *see* 0266-3880
0306-848X Radnorshire Society. Transactions
0306-8536 Manxman†
0306-8552 Electrotechnology
0306-8560 Livestock International *see* 0269-2457
0306-8765 Intermusik
0306-8781 Amon Hen
0306-879X Italiano†
0306-882X Flora *changed to* Flora International.
0306-8838 Bradwell Abbey Field Centre for the Study of Archaeology, Natural History & Environmental Studies. Occasional Papers†
0306-8919 Optical and Quantum Electronics
0306-8927 Hostelling News *changed to* Triangle.
0306-8943 Stainless
0306-9001 Northamptonshire and Bedfordshire Life *changed to* Northamptonshire Life.
0306-9001 Northamptonshire and Bedfordshire Life *changed to* Bedfordshire Life.
0306-9028 Window *changed to* Junkanoo.
0306-9079 Cornish Banner
0306-9192 Food Policy
0306-9206 North Cheshire Family Historian
0306-9338 Bangor Occasional Papers in Economics†
0306-9346 B B C Modern English†
0306-9389 Tabs *see* 0950-0634
0306-9397 Conferences and Exhibitions *see* 0260-8316
0306-9400 Law Teacher
0306-9419 International Journal of Forensic Dentistry
0306-9427 Welding Research International†
0306-9435 Transport Manager's Handbook *changed to* Transport Manager's and Operator's Handbook.
0306-9516 African Books in Print
0306-9524 Index Islamicus
0306-9532 Chartered Mechanical Engineer *see* 0953-6639
0306-9540 M E N (Mechanical Engineering News) *see* 0267-5145
0306-9559 Chartered Institute of Transport. Handbook†
0306-9575 Contact Lens Journal
0306-9699 Midwife, Health Visitor and Community Nurse
0306-977X Ilkeston and District Local History Society. Occasional Paper†
0306-9788 City of London Law Review *changed to* City of London. Law Faculty. Journal.
0306-9796 Cambria: A Welsh Geographical Review
0306-9869 Electron Microscopy Abstracts
0306-9877 Medical Hypotheses
0306-9885 British Journal of Guidance and Counselling
0306-9915 U F O Research Review *changed to* Hidden History.
0306-9931 Building Research and Practice *see* 0961-3218
0307-0018 Cranes Today
0307-0042 Social Science Monographs
0307-0131 Byzantine and Modern Greek Studies
0307-0158 Birmingham & West Midlands Chambers of Commerce Directory
0307-0220 Fairplay International Shipping Weekly
0307-0255 F A S Journal†
0307-0298 Harrington Family Miscellany
0307-0360 London Currency Report
0307-0387 Middle East Currency Reports
0307-0395 Young Drama†
0307-0409 Anbar Yearbook *changed to* Compleat Anbar.
0307-0417 Greater London Arts Association. Annual Report and Yearbook *see* 0309-1945
0307-0441 Local Government Trends†
0307-0468 Chartered Institute of Public Finance and Accountancy. Housing Maintenance & Management. Actuals Statistics†
0307-0484 Azania Combat
0307-0506 Chartered Institute of Public Finance and Accountancy. Local Health and Social Services Statistics *see* 0309-653X
0307-0514 Chartered Institute of Public Finance and Accountancy. Education Statistics. Estimates
0307-0522 Chartered Institute of Public Finance and Accountancy. Public Library Statistics. Estimates
0307-0565 International Journal of Obesity
0307-0573 Chartered Institute of Public Finance and Accountancy. Fire Service Statistics. Estimates
0307-0603 Digest of United Kingdom Energy Statistics
0307-062X Official Guide to Hotels and Restaurants in Great Britain, Ireland and Overseas *changed to* Hotels and Restaurants of Britain.
0307-0654 University of Durham. Centre for Middle Eastern and Islamic Studies. Occasional Papers Series.
0307-0697 Power and Works Engineering†
0307-0719 University College London. Institute of Jewish Studies. Bulletin†
0307-076X National Institute for Medical Research. Scientific Report *see* 0141-2116
0307-0778 Paper and Board Abstracts
0307-0786 Ostrich
0307-0794 Marketing Abstracts *see* 0308-2172
0307-0808 Studies in Library Management
0307-0832 Navin Weekly
0307-093X Social Services Yearbook
0307-0980 New Humanity Journal
0307-1006 Discourse Analysis Monographs
0307-1022 Social History
0307-112X Immunology Abstracts
0307-1146 Great Britain. Electricity Council. Annual Report and Accounts†
0307-1154 Garage and Transport *see* 0264-0163
0307-1170 Shaw's Wine Guide†
0307-1189 About Wine Newsletter
0307-1243 Garden History
0307-1308 Chartered Institute of Public Finance and Accountancy. Housing Part 1: Rents. Actuals Statistics *see* 0260-406X
0307-1316 Chartered Institute of Public Finance and Accountancy. Housing Part 2: Revenue Accounts. Actuals Statistics *see* 0260-4078
0307-1375 Arboricultural Journal
0307-1391 S S R C Survey Archive Bulletin *changed to* E S R C Data Archive Bulletin.
0307-1448 Donizetti Society. Journal
0307-1456 S A L G Newsletter
0307-1596 Food Machinery and Ingredients Export News†
0307-1634 E A A Review
0307-1642 Thomas Hardy Society. Review *see* 0268-5418
0307-1677 Industrial Past *see* 0265-5071
0307-174X International Polymer Science and Technology
0307-1782 Water Services Handbook *changed to* Water Services Year Book.
0307-1790 Youth in Society *see* 0956-2842
0307-1804 Locomotives Illustrated
0307-1847 R U S I Journal
0307-1901 E S S R A Magazine†
0307-191X Pensions World
0307-1936 Contact (London, 1973)†
0307-2029 Calgacus†
0307-2053 Home Economics *see* 0265-6930
0307-2061 British National Association for Soviet and East European Studies. Information Bulletin†
0307-2118 Fitech International
0307-2169 Black Music and Jazz Review *see* 0045-2297
0307-2274 Association of Commonwealth Universities. Annual Report of the Council Together with the Accounts of the Association
0307-2312 Teaching over 13s†
0307-2401 Electronics Industry†
0307-2444 Studies for Trade Unionists
0307-2460 East Anglian Archaeology. Report
0307-2509 Yorkshire Library News
0307-2517 Knitting World & Textile Manufacturer†
0307-2576 Soil Association. Quarterly Review *see* 0954-1098
0307-2606 Locke Newsletter
0307-2614 S E E Journal
0307-2630 U K Plant Hire Guide *changed to* Contract Journal (1979).
0307-2649 Journal of A T E *changed to* Test.
0307-2657 B S B I Abstracts
0307-2770 New German Studies
0307-2827 C H E C News *changed to* C H E C Journal.
0307-2851 Midland Ancestor
0307-2894 International Who's Who in Music and Musicians' Directory
0307-2916 Fireweed†
0307-2991 What Car?
0307-3033 Japan News
0307-3084 Gas Directory and Who's Who *see* 0954-853X
0307-3149 Jane's Ocean Technology†
0307-319X Illustrators†
0307-3262 Iberian Studies
0307-3289 Institute of Health Education. Journal
0307-3319 Great North Review
0307-3335 Matrix
0307-3378 Bulletin of Economic Research
0307-3408 Bard
0307-3424 Tass Journal *changed to* M S F Journal.
0307-3513 Youth Social Work Bulletin *see* 0956-2842
0307-353X Insight: Soviet Jews†
0307-3572 Tennyson Society, Lincoln, England. Occasional Papers
0307-3580 Management Review and Digest *changed to* Management News.
0307-4293 New Fiction†
0307-4331 Austria
0307-434X British Directory of Little Magazines and Small Presses†
0307-4358 Managerial Finance
0307-4412 Biochemical Education
0307-4463 Population Trends
0307-4536 Greek Review *changed to* Greek Institute Review.
0307-4552 Barclays Country Reports
0307-4617 Screen International
0307-4625 Centerpiece†
0307-4722 Art Libraries Journal
0307-4730 British Journal of Clinical Equipment†
0307-4757 Policy Publications Review *changed to* Publications Review-Innovation & Management.
0307-4803 New Library World
0307-4811 Vegan
0307-4870 Journal of Planning and Environment Law
0307-5036 Royal Scottish Museum Information Series: Natural History†
0307-5044 Royal Scottish Museum Information Series: Technology†
0307-5052 Royal Scottish Museum Information Series: Geology†
0307-5079 Studies in Higher Education
0307-5087 Contrebis
0307-5095 Journal of Electrophysiological Technology
0307-5133 Journal of Egyptian Archaeology
0307-5281 Watford and District Industrial History Society. Journal
0307-5354 S P E L†
0307-5400 European Law Review
0307-5451 History of Technology
0307-546X Tangent
0307-5494 Microbios Letters *see* 0961-088X
0307-5508 Community Care
0307-5540 Industrial Relations Legal Information Bulletin
0307-5583 Cromwelliana
0307-5591 Industrial Relations Law Reports
0307-5656 Institute of Medical Laboratory Sciences. Gazette *see* 0267-2928
0307-580X Jeweller†
0307-5826 Library Association. Rare Books Group. Newsletter *see* 0959-1656
0307-5966 Journal of Meteorology
0307-5974 Religion in Communist Lands *see* 0963-7494
0307-5982 Together (London, 1956)
0307-6008 India Office Library and Records Newsletter *see* 0960-7935
0307-6032 Who's Who in Finance†

ISSN INDEX 5691

0307-6067 Community Work†
0307-6075 Dissertation Abstracts International. Section C: European Abstracts *see* 1042-7279
0307-6091 Federation for Children's Book Groups. Yearbook *changed to* Pick of the Year.
0307-6113 International Directory of Current Research in the History of Cartography and in Carto-Bibliography†
0307-6164 British Plastics and Rubber Magazine
0307-6202 Sheffield University Calendar
0307-6334 Church Music Quarterly
0307-6474 Wedding and Home
0307-6490 Automotive Engineer
0307-6539 Commonwealth Magistrates' Conference. Report
0307-6547 Great Britain. Department of Energy. Report on Research and Development†
0307-6571 Coin Yearbook
0307-6601 Exhibitions & Conferences
0307-6628 Cheshire Archaeological Bulletin
0307-6652 Notes on Water Research†
0307-6679 Stamp Magazine
0307-6687 Tolley's Tax Tables (Year)
0307-6695 New Aspects of Breast Cancer†
0307-6717 Criminal Statistics, Scotland.
0307-6741 Toy Retailing News†
0307-6768 Management Services
0307-6776 R A I N: Royal Anthropological Institute News *changed to* Anthropology Today.
0307-6784 Lewisletter
0307-6792 Society for the Social History of Medicine. Bulletin *see* 0951-631X
0307-6822 Road Accidents in Great Britain
0307-6857 International Planned Parenthood Federation. Annual Report *changed to* I P P F Annual Report.
0307-689X Directory of Agricultural Co-Operatives in the United Kingdom *changed to* Directory of Agricultural Co-Operatives in the United Kingdom.
0307-6903 S C O C L I S News†
0307-6911 Roof
0307-692X Australian Journal of Ecology
0307-6938 Clinical and Experimental Dermatology
0307-6946 Ecological Entomology
0307-6962 Physiological Entomology
0307-6970 Systematic Entomology
0307-7004 Triticale Abstracts *see* 0265-7880
0307-7039 Politics Today
0307-7098 Collect Isle of Man Stamps†
0307-7144 Lore and Language
0307-7195 Printing Industries
0307-7225 Church of England. General Synod. Report of Proceedings
0307-7233 German Political Studies†
0307-7276 Weyfarers
0307-7349 Soviet Non-Ferrous Metals Research†
0307-7357 British Ceramic Society. Transactions and Journal
0307-7365 Surfacing Journal *see* 0267-0844
0307-7411 Air Extra†
0307-742X Clinics in Rheumatic Diseases *see* 0950-3579
0307-7497 Occasional Papers in German Studies
0307-7535 Fabian Tract *changed to* Fabian Pamphlet.
0307-7543 Trade Union Register†
0307-7608 International Steel Statistics - United Kingdom
0307-7640 Medical Informatics
0307-7667 Quarterly Review of Marketing†
0307-7675 Museums Yearbook
0307-7683 New Civil Engineer
0307-7691 National Coal Board Statistical Tables†
0307-7713 Civil Engineering Technician *changed to* Civil Engineering Technology.
0307-7772 Clinical Otolaryngology and Allied Sciences
0307-7780 Securitech *changed to* Securitech Europe.
0307-7861 Accountants Weekly†
0307-7896 Metal Construction *changed to* Joining and Materials.
0307-7942 Energy World
0307-7950 Heating and Air Conditioning Journal
0307-7969 Key Abstracts - Physical Measurements and Instrumentation *see* 0950-4818
0307-7977 Key Abstracts - Electrical Measurements and Instrumentation *see* 0950-480X
0307-8000 Comparison *see* 0950-5814
0307-8051 Courtauld Institute Illustration Archives. Archive 1
0307-806X Courtauld Institute Illustration Archives. Archive 2
0307-8078 Courtauld Institute Illustration Archives. Archive 3
0307-8086 Courtauld Institute Illustration Archives. Archive 4
0307-8108 Football *changed to* Football Monthly.
0307-8140 Northumberland & Durham Family History Society. Journal
0307-823X Sussex Anthropology†
0307-8329 Chartered Institute of Public Finance and Accountancy. Planning Estimates Statistics. Actuals *see* 0144-901X
0307-8337 English Language Teaching Journal
0307-8353 Institution of Civil Engineers. Proceedings. Part 1: Design and Construction†
0307-8361 Institution of Civil Engineers. Proceedings. Part 2: Research and Theory†
0307-8388 Themelios
0307-8477 Newscheck
0307-8515 Clothing Institute Year Book and Membership Register *changed to* Clothing and Footwear Institute Year Book and Membership Register.
0307-8531 Rare Earth Bulletin
0307-8558 Management Services in Government *changed to* Management in Government.
0307-8590 Maritime Monographs and Reports†
0307-8604 Coop Marketing & Management *changed to* Retail Marketing & Management.
0307-8612 New Universities Quarterly *see* 0951-5224
0307-8647 Bar Quarterly†
0307-8698 Ringing and Migration
0307-8833 Theatre Research International
0307-8884 Seed
0307-8957 Robert Burns Chronicle
0307-8965 Computing Europe *changed to* Computing.
0307-9007 N R Technology *changed to* Rubber Developments.
0307-9023 Research Intelligence *see* 0141-1926
0307-904X Applied Mathematical Modelling
0307-9058 Great Britain. Centre for Overseas Pest Research. Miscellaneous Report†
0307-9066 Mining Department Magazine
0307-9074 Stream
0307-9082 Great Britain. Centre for Overseas Pest Research. Report†
0307-9112 London Mystery Selection†
0307-9163 Association of Art Historians. Bulletin
0307-9201 Sage Race Relations Abstracts
0307-9244 Le Nurb
0307-9252 Communicator†
0307-9341 Lakeland Dialect Society. Journal *changed to* Lakeland Dialect.
0307-9457 Avian Pathology
0307-9481 British Library News
0307-9562 Thames Poetry†
0307-9570 Moonshine†
0307-9589 Great Britain. Civil Service Department. Report†
0307-9597 Scottish Social Work Statistics *see* 0260-5295
0307-9708 School and Community†
0307-9732 International Yearbook of Educational and International Technology *changed to* International Yearbook of Educational & Training Technology.
0307-9767 New Library Buildings†
0307-9813 Gay Left
0307-9821 Halsbury's Laws of England Monthly Review
0307-9864 Annual Bibliography of Scottish Literature
0307-9929 Under 5
0308-003X Tape and Hi-Fi Test†
0308-0110 Medical Education
0308-0129 English Philological Studies†
0308-0137 Rural Recreation and Tourism Abstracts *see* 0261-1392
0308-0161 Pressure Vessels and Piping *changed to* International Journal of Pressure Vessels and Piping.
0308-017X Thomas Hardy Society. Newsletter†
0308-0188 I S R - Interdisciplinary Science Reviews
0308-0226 British Journal of Occupational Therapy
0308-0234 Hospital and Health Services Review *see* 0953-8534
0308-0404 Enthusiasm†
0308-0455 Business Graduates Association Address Book *changed to* Association of M B A Address Book.
0308-0501 F A M - Fire and Materials
0308-051X Pharmatherapeutica
0308-0528 Middle East Construction†
0308-0587 Modern English Teacher
0308-0617 Catholic Life†
0308-0633 Contact (London, 1961)
0308-0676 Warfare
0308-0765 Human Rights Review†
0308-082X Town and Country Planning Association. Annual Report
0308-0838 Fern Gazette
0308-0854 Fine Art Trade Guild Journal
0308-0862 British Plumbing and Heating *changed to* Plumb and Heat.
0308-0889 Four Decades†
0308-0935 Great Britain. Ministry of Agriculture, Fisheries and Food. Directorate of Fisheries Research. Fishing Prospects *see* 0955-2855
0308-0943 Skinner's British Textile Register†
0308-0951 Charles Lamb Bulletin
0308-1060 Transportation Planning and Technology
0308-1079 International Journal of General Systems
0308-1087 Linear and Multilinear Algebra
0308-1125 Great Britain. Natural Environment Research Council. Report
0308-1206 Comments on Solid State Physics *see* 0885-4483
0308-1222 Energy Trends
0308-1230 On Target
0308-1273 Netherlands-British Trade Directory
0308-129X Royal Society of Edinburgh. Communications, Physical Sciences†
0308-1400 International Dredging Abstracts *see* 0264-0775
0308-1419 Great Britain. Department of Employment. New Earnings Survey
0308-1443 Printing Industries Annual *changed to* Printers Yearbook.
0308-1451 Royal Institution of Chartered Surveyors Year Book†
0308-146X Great Britain. Central Statistical Office. Regional Statistics *see* 0261-1783
0308-1656 Akhbar-e-Watan Urdu Newsweekly *changed to* Watan Weekend.
0308-1729 Savings Market
0308-1745 Great Britain. Department of the Environment. Local Government Financial Statistics: England and Wales
0308-1796 National Review
0308-180X Natural History Book Reviews
0308-1907 N A T F H E Journal
0308-1958 Impact of Tax Changes on Income Distribution†
0308-1990 Footnote†
0308-2024 Writing Magazine *see* 0957-3577
0308-2075 Occasional Papers in Linguistics and Language Learning
0308-2091 Artefact *see* 0261-7048
0308-2105 Royal Society of Edinburgh. Proceedings. Section A (Mathematics)
0308-2113 Royal Society of Edinburgh. Proceedings. (Natural Environment) *changed to* Royal Society of Edinburgh. Proceedings. Section B (Biological Sciences).
0308-2172 Management and Marketing Abstracts
0308-2199 British Mining
0308-2261 Clinics in Haematology *see* 0889-8588
0308-230X British Library. Bibliographic Services Division. Newsletter *changed to* Select: National Bibliographic Service Newsletter.
0308-2342 Journal of Chemical Research
0308-244X British Journal of Music Therapy *see* 0951-5038
0308-2636 Poetry Nation *see* 0144-7076
0308-2695 Chapman
0308-2741 Society for Lincolnshire History and Archaeology. Newsletter *see* 0960-9555
0308-275X Critique of Anthropology
0308-2776 Prospice†
0308-2792 New Age Concern Today *see* 0144-6630
0308-2857 Survival International Review†
0308-2881 Christian Educator†
0308-2938 International Marketing Data and Statistics
0308-2962 Tropical Oil Seeds Abstracts *see* 0961-351X
0308-2970 Sorghum and Millets Abstracts
0308-2997 Feeding-Weight and Obesity Abstracts†
0308-3047 Market Research Great Britain
0308-308X Elektor *see* 0013-5895
0308-3098 Pipeline Industries Guild Journal *see* 0032-020X
0308-3217 International†
0308-3233 Issues in Race and Education
0308-3268 Horticulture Industry *see* 0262-3765
0308-3276 S I S Review *changed to* Chronology & Catastrophism Review.
0308-3306 Farming Industry†
0308-3322 Great Britain. Royal Greenwich Observatory. Annual Report†
0308-3381 Bananas
0308-342X Surrey Archaeological Society. Research Volumes
0308-3446 Market Research Europe
0308-3535 Royal College of Art, Journal *changed to* Ark (1978).
0308-356X Learning Together with 11-14's
0308-3586 Focus on Political Repression in Southern Africa
0308-3594 Local Council Review
0308-3616 Medical Laboratory Sciences
0308-3675 Great Britain. Institute of Terrestrial Ecology. Merlewood Research and Development Paper
0308-3705 Consuming Interest†
0308-373X Plumbing and Heating Equipment News *changed to* Plumbing and Heating News.
0308-3756 Pali Buddhist Review *see* 0265-2897
0308-3764 Court†
0308-4035 South East Asia Library Group Newsletter
0308-4086 Journal of Crystal and Molecular Structure *see* 0277-8068
0308-4094 B L L D Announcement Bulletin *see* 0959-4922
0308-4159 I C E Yearbook *changed to* I C E List of Members.
0308-4183 Bristol and Avon Family History Society. Journal
0308-4205 Professional Printer
0308-4213 Cable Television Engineering *changed to* International Cable.
0308-4221 Computer Applications†
0308-423X I B A Technical Review†
0308-4272 Radiological Protection Bulletin
0308-4353 Consumer Europe (Year)

ISSN

5692 ISSN INDEX

0308-437X Acoustics Bulletin
0308-4388 Halsbury's Laws of England Annual Abridgment
0308-4426 Journal of Maternal and Child Health *see* 0262-0200
0308-4450 West African Journal of Sociology and Political Science
0308-4469 International Cocoa Organization. Quarterly Bulletin of Cocoa Statistics
0308-4485 Offset Data Index†
0308-4507 Carpet Review Weekly *see* 0263-4236
0308-4531 Stella Polaris
0308-454X Television (London, 1927)
0308-4558 Royal Historical Society. Annual Bibliography of British and Irish History
0308-4574 Bracton Law Journal
0308-4590 International Metals Review *see* 0950-6608
0308-4698 British Country Music Association. Yearbook
0308-4752 Omens
0308-4787 Limestone Literary Magazine *see* 0263-4635
0308-4795 Diesel Engineering†
0308-4809 Northumbriana
0308-4892 Committee on Invisible Exports. Annual Report *changed to* British Invisible Exports Council. Annual Report.
0308-4922 British Paedodontic Society. Proceedings *see* 0960-7439
0308-4930 A and S *changed to* Architect & Surveyor.
0308-4949 Royal British Legion. Journal.†
0308-4957 Vida Hispanica
0308-499X Great Britain. Department of Trade. Insurance Business: Annual Report
0308-5074 Great Britain. Royal Greeenwich Observatory. Bulletin†
0308-5082 Great Britain. Institute of Geological Sciences. Seismological Bulletins *changed to* Great Britain. British Geological Survey. Seismological Bulletins.
0308-5090 United Kingdom Mineral Statistics *see* 0957-4697
0308-5147 Economy and Society
0308-518X Environment and Planning A
0308-5198 Defence Materiel†
0308-5201 Maritime Defence International *changed to* Maritime Defence.
0308-521X Agricultural Systems
0308-5252 C W I Herald
0308-5279 Bank of England. Report and Accounts
0308-5325 Great Britain. Institute of Geological Sciences. Overseas Memoirs *see* 0951-6646
0308-5333 Great Britain. Institute of Geological Sciences. Mineral Assessment Report *changed to* Great Britain. British Geological Survey. Mineral Assessment Report.
0308-5376 B U F C Newsletter *see* 0952-4444
0308-5384 Biological Structure and Function
0308-5457 Royal Horticultural Society. Garden Journal *changed to* The Garden.
0308-5473 Librarians' Christian Fellowship Newsletter
0308-5538 Documents on International Affairs†
0308-5554 Sounding Brass *changed to* Brass International.
0308-5562 Oxoniensia
0308-5570 Great Britain. Ministry of Agriculture, Fisheries and Food. Directorate of Fisheries Research. Report of the Director of Fisheries Research. *changed to* Great Britain. Ministry of Agriculture, Fisheries and Food. Research into Fisheries and the Marine Environment. Report of the Director of Fisheries Research.
0308-5589 Great Britain. Ministry of Agriculture, Fisheries and Food. Directorate of Fisheries Research. Fisheries Research Technical Report
0308-5597 A A R P Journal *see* 0393-5183
0308-5651 Buildings Maintenance and Services *changed to* Cleaning Maintenance.
0308-5694 Imago Mvndi
0308-5732 Agricultural Engineer
0308-5759 Adoption and Fostering
0308-5791 British Flower
0308-5864 I D S Discussion Paper
0308-5899 Fortean Times
0308-5910 Oil Paintings, Drawings and Watercolours *changed to* Art Sales Index: Oil Paintings, Drawings, Water Colours and Sculpture.
0308-5953 Microprocessors *see* 0141-9331
0308-5961 Telecommunications Policy
0308-597X Marine Policy
0308-6003 Chemical Society. Annual Reports on the Progress of Chemistry. Section A: Physical and Inorganic Chemistry *see* 0260-1818
0308-602X Chest, Heart and Stroke Journal†
0308-6100 Craft & Hobby Dealer
0308-6119 University of London. Contemporary China Institute. Research Notes and Studies
0308-6135 Portsmouth Magazine
0308-616X Housing Outlook†
0308-6194 Christian Parapsychologist
0308-6224 B S R I A Statistics Bulletin
0308-6259 Commercial Food Information
0308-6283 New Poetry†
0308-6305 Ushaw Magazine
0308-6348 Nottinghamshire Historian
0308-6380 Marfleet Society Newsletter
0308-650X General Engineer *see* 0954-6529
0308-6534 Journal of Imperial and Commonwealth History
0308-6569 Anglo-American Law Review
0308-6577 Cotton and Tropical Fibres Abstracts *see* 0961-3528
0308-6593 Journal of Clinical Pharmacy *see* 0269-4727
0308-6631 Mining Magazine
0308-664X Phosphorous and Sulfur and the Related Elements *see* 1042-6507
0308-6666 Great Britain. Central Statistical Office. Monthly Digest of Statistics
0308-6674 Mallorn
0308-6712 British Toys and Hobbies *changed to* British Toys & Hobbies Briefing.
0308-6739 Freshwater Biological Association. Occasional Publications
0308-6747 Architecture West Midlands†
0308-678X Africa Guide *changed to* Africa Review.
0308-6801 J C A T S *changed to* C.A.T.S. Reports.
0308-6852 Red Letters
0308-6860 Ethnic Groups
0308-6887 Amnesty International Newsletter
0308-6895 A T P A S Printing Education & Training Journal
0308-6909 C O R E
0308-6925 Communicator of Scientific and Technical Information *see* 0953-3699
0308-6925 Communicator News Supplement†
0308-6992 Geographers
0308-7018 Cassell's Directory of Publishing in Great Britain, the Commonwealth, Ireland, South Africa and Pakistan *changed to* Cassell and Publishers Association Directory of Publishing in the United Kingdom, Commonwealth and Overseas.
0308-7026 Gas Marketing
0308-7107 Sell's Health Service Buyers Guide *see* 0140-5748
0308-7123 Directory of Summer Jobs Abroad
0308-7174 Electrical Contractor (London)
0308-7212 In Touch (London)
0308-7298 History of Photography
0308-731X Cherwell
0308-7344 Potato Abstracts
0308-7379 Scottish Diver
0308-7387 Extel Book of Prospectuses and New Issues *changed to* Extel Prospectuses and New Issues Fiche Service.
0308-7395 Quarterly Index Islamicus
0308-7417 Historical Research for University Degrees in the United Kingdom. Part 1: Theses Completed *see* 0268-6716
0308-7425 Historical Research for University Degrees in the United Kingdom. Part 2: Theses in Progress *see* 0268-6724
0308-745X Partners
0308-7484 Registered Accountant†
0308-7506 Tertiary Research Group. Special Papers *changed to* Tertiary Research Special Papers.
0308-7565 Canoeing†
0308-762X International Newsletter†
0308-7638 Forestry & British Timber
0308-7646 Gifts *see* 0262-5946
0308-7654 Gas World *changed to* Gas World International.
0308-7670 Scottish Ophthalmic Practitioner *changed to* Scottish Optometrist.
0308-7751 Planning Consumer Markets
0308-7786 European Scrap Directory *changed to* International Scrap Directory.
0308-7794 Metallurgical Plantmakers of the World
0308-7808 Therapy Weekly
0308-7816 Residential Social Work†
0308-7840 Community Home Schools Gazette *changed to* Community Homes Gazette.
0308-7883 Income Tax Digest and Accountants' Review *see* 0143-294X
0308-7948 Whillan's Tax Tables and Tax Reckoner *see* 0260-3926
0308-7999 Gazelle Review of Literature on the Middle East†
0308-8006 Steel Traders of the World
0308-8022 Scottish Fisheries Research Reports
0308-8030 Simon's Tax Cases
0308-8049 Simon's Tax Intelligence
0308-809X Arlis News-Sheet
0308-812X Ley Hunter
0308-8146 Food Chemistry
0308-8197 Dairy Industries International
0308-8219 Bar List of the United Kingdom†
0308-8227 Rights *changed to* Civil Liberty Agenda.
0308-8359 Materials Handling Index *changed to* Manufacturing and Materials Handling Index.
0308-8367 Laboratory Equipment Index†
0308-8375 Electronic Engineering Index
0308-8383 Engineering Components and Materials Index *changed to* Engineering Design and Manufacturing Index.
0308-8391 Chemical Engineering Index *changed to* Process Engineering Index.
0308-8405 Manchester United Football Book†
0308-8456 Archaeology in Britain (Year)
0308-8464 Financial Times International Year Books: World Hotel Directory
0308-8480 C A B News†
0308-8499 Extel Issuing House Year Book *changed to* Professional Advisers to New Issues.
0308-8537 Bectis Bulletin
0308-8561 Domestic Heating Plus Plumbing: Bathrooms-Kitchens *changed to* Domestic Heating Plus Plumbing: Bathrooms.
0308-8669 Labour Weekly†
0308-8677 L A N S A
0308-8766 Society of Osteopaths. Journal†
0308-8774 Latest Literature in Family Planning†
0308-8839 Maritime Policy and Management
0308-8855 World Cement Technology *see* 0263-6050
0308-8863 Agricultural Engineering Abstracts
0308-888X Essays in Poetics
0308-8987 Kitchin's Road Transport Law
0308-9002 Interest Rate Service
0308-9037 Kent Family History Society. Record Publication
0308-9053 C A S S News *see* 0260-390X
0308-9088 City Directory (Year)
0308-9126 N D T International
0308-9134 Security and Protection *changed to* Security and Protection Equipment.
0308-9142 Iron and Steel International *see* 0143-7798
0308-9274 A G M Service
0308-9290 Research Fields in Physics at United Kingdom Universities and Polytechnics
0308-9304 A B C Freight Guide
0308-9347 Music Master *changed to* Music Master Catalogue.
0308-9398 Footwear Industry Statistical Review
0308-9533 Highways and Road Construction International *changed to* Highways.
0308-9541 Journal of Applied Systems Analysis *see* 0960-085X
0308-9568 L A C News†
0308-9584 Agent's Hotel Gazetteer: Tourist Cities *changed to* Agent's Hotel Gazetteer: Cities of Europe.
0308-9614 Domestic Heating and Air Conditioning
0308-9649 Tertiary Research†
0308-9673 Extel Handbook of Market Leaders
0308-9703 Epilepsy News *changed to* Epilepsy Today.
0308-9762 Classical Music Weekly *see* 0961-2696
0308-9770 Iron and Steel Industry: Monthly Statistics†
0308-9789 I M M Bulletin *see* 0955-2847
0308-9819 Great Britain. Department of the Environment. Housing and Construction Statistics
0308-9886 Body Lines
0309-0019 Performing Right News *changed to* P R S News.
0309-0078 National Association of Pension Funds. Annual Survey
0309-0108 Royal Observatory, Edinburgh. Annual Report†
0309-0132 Great Britain. Medical Research Council. Handbook (Year)
0309-0167 Histopathology
0309-0175 Independent Broadcasting Authority. Annual Report and Accounts†
0309-0191 University of Sheffield. Newsletter Diary *changed to* University of Sheffield. Diary of Events.
0309-0191 University of Sheffield. Newsletter Diary *changed to* University of Sheffield. Newsletter.
0309-023X Soil and Water *see* 0308-5732
0309-0248 B S R I A Technical Notes
0309-0256 Media Reporter
0309-0264 Food Trades Directory and Food Buyer's Yearbook *changed to* European Food Trades Directory.
0309-0329 Canada - U.K. Year Book
0309-0388 Commonwealth Diary of Coming Events *see* 0141-8513
0309-0396 Shaw Newsletter *changed to* Shaw Society Newsletter.
0309-040X Offshore Service Vessel Register
0309-0531 Nutrition Information Centre. Bulletin†
0309-0558 Managerial Law
0309-0566 European Journal of Marketing
0309-0574 Recommended Recordings
0309-0582 Management Bibliographies and Reviews
0309-0590 Journal of European Industrial Training
0309-0655 British Library. Lending Division. Current Serials Received *see* 0959-4914
0309-0698 Monographs on Physical Biochemistry
0309-0728 Industrial Archaeology Review†
0309-0736 Planned Parenthood in Europe
0309-0787 Journal for the Study of the Old Testament. Supplement Series
0309-0809 Milk Bulletin
0309-0817 M I R A Automobile Abstracts
0309-0884 Performing Right Year Book

ISSN

0309-0892 Journal for the Study of the Old Testament
0309-099X Royal Observatory. Occasional Reports
0309-1031 Dog News and Family Pets
0309-1082 Great Britain. Land Resources Development Centre. Progress Report *changed to* Great Britain. Natural Resources Institute. Annual Report.
0309-1112 Family Planning Today
0309-1139 Cadmium Abstracts *changed to* Cadscan.
0309-118X InterMedia
0309-1252 Bristow's Book of Yachts
0309-1287 Protozoological Abstracts
0309-1295 Nutrition Abstracts and Reviews. Series A: Human and Experimental
0309-1309 Mervyn Peake Review
0309-1317 International Journal of Urban and Regional Research
0309-1325 Progress in Human Geography
0309-1333 Progress in Physical Geography
0309-135X Nutrition Abstracts and Reviews. Series B: Livestock Feeds and Feeding
0309-1376 Meccano Magazine
0309-1384 Planner
0309-1384 Planner *issued with* 0078-2114
0309-1422 Waterways World
0309-1449 British Quarrying & Slag Federation. Technical Review *see* 0141-6936
0309-1465 Developing Railways
0309-1600 Institution of Water Engineers and Scientists. Journal†
0309-1619 Powys Review
0309-1627 Faith & Worship
0309-1635 British Journal of Alcohol and Alcoholism *see* 0735-0414
0309-1643 Land Resource Bibliography†
0309-1651 Cell Biology International Reports
0309-166X Cambridge Journal of Economics
0309-1708 Advances in Water Resources
0309-1740 Meat Science
0309-1783 Hobart Paperbacks
0309-1821 Guinea-Pig News Letter†
0309-1848 Rat News Letter†
0309-1902 Journal of Medical Engineering & Technology
0309-1929 Geophysical and Astrophysical Fluid Dynamics
0309-1945 Greater London Arts Association. Annual Report†
0309-1953 Heat Transfer and Fluid Flow Digest *changed to* H T F S Digest.
0309-1961 Lectures in Commercial Diplomacy *see* 0378-5920
0309-2003 Middle East Health
0309-2097 O E Report
0309-2143 Converter Directory
0309-2151 Artscribe
0309-2178 University of London King's College. Department of Geography. Occasional Paper†
0309-2216 International Copper Information Bulletin
0309-2224 Conservation News
0309-2232 Library Research Occasional Paper *see* 0143-5124
0309-2275 Oxfordshire Family Historian
0309-233X Vision†
0309-2356 U K Chemical Industry Statistics Handbook†
0309-2402 Journal of Advanced Nursing
0309-2445 Publishing History
0309-2534 Advances in Raman Spectroscopy†
0309-2658 Action (Horsham) *changed to* Action Research.
0309-2666 Medical Technologist and Scientist
0309-2968 Sutton Bridge Annual Review
0309-2984 History Workshop
0309-300X Latin America Commodities Report *see* 0960-8702
0309-3018 Finishing Industries *see* 0264-2506
0309-3077 L P Gas Review
0309-3093 Berkshire Archaeological Journal
0309-3115 United Kingdom Temperance Alliance. Alliance News *changed to* U K Alcohol Alert.
0309-314X Online Review
0309-3204 Council for British Archaeology. Newsletter and Calendar of Excavations *see* 0269-1906
0309-3247 Journal of Strain Analysis for Engineering Design
0309-3263 Reading Geographer†
0309-3298 In the Making
0309-331X Coffee International *see* 0262-5938
0309-3328 Counterpoint†
0309-3336 What Hi-Fi?
0309-345X African Environment Special Reports†
0309-3468 Wiltshire Natural History Magazine *changed to* Wiltshire Archaeological and Natural History Magazine (1982).
0309-3476 Wiltshire Archaeological Magazine *changed to* Wiltshire Archaeological and Natural History Magazine (1982).
0309-3484 Junior Education
0309-3492 Third Way (London, 1977)
0309-3557 Recycling and Waste Disposal†
0309-3573 A E P Journal *see* 0266-7363
0309-3646 Prosthetics and Orthotics International
0309-3654 Messenger (Grantham)
0309-3700 Liverpool Classical Monthly
0309-3786 G L A D Journal†
0309-3891 Journal of Consumer Studies & Home Economics
0309-3913 African Journal of Medicine & Medical Sciences
0309-393X Royal Scottish Museum Information Series: Art & Archaeology†
0309-3948 Institute of Marine Engineers. Technical Reports *changed to* Marine Management Holdings. Transactions.
0309-3980 Free Nation *changed to* Freedom Today.
0309-4073 Leveller†
0309-409X Chelsea Spelaeological Society. Records
0309-4170 Christian Librarian
0309-426X Advances in Infrared and Raman Spectroscopy†
0309-4294 Great Britain. Sea Fish Industry Authority. Fisheries Economics Newsletter
0309-4308 Liturgy
0309-4359 Gramophone Popular Catalogue†
0309-4367 Gramophone Classical Catalogue *changed to* The Classical Catalogue.
0309-4405 Elgar Society. Newsletter *see* 0143-1269
0309-4413 Directory for Disabled People
0309-4472 Institute of Oceanographic Sciences. Annual Report *changed to* Institute of Oceanographic Sciences. Deacon Laboratory. Annual Report.
0309-4545 Fertility and Contraception†
0309-4561 Plastics and Rubber International
0309-457X Maghreb Review
0309-4693 Social Service Abstracts
0309-4707 Middle East Electricity
0309-474X European Bulletin and Press
0309-4898 Style Pattern Book *changed to* Style Magazine.
0309-4928 Chartered Insurance Institute, London. Journal *see* 0957-4883
0309-4944 International Petroleum Abstracts
0309-4960 Worldwide Marketing Opportunities Digest
0309-4979 Coal Abstracts
0309-4995 Employment Digest
0309-510X Practical Self-Sufficiency *see* 0264-8873
0309-5118 Hatcher Review
0309-5134 Daily Mail Skier's Holiday Guide *changed to* Audi - Daily Mail Skier's Holiday Guide.
0309-5150 Optics Abstracts†
0309-5207 Journal of Beckett Studies
0309-524X Wind Engineering
0309-5258 Leasing Digest *changed to* Asset Finance and Leasing Digest.
0309-5290 Directory of Technical and Further Education
0309-5304 L G O R U Transportation News†
0309-5312 X-Ray Diffraction Abstracts
0309-5320 Laser Raman & Infrared Spectroscopy Abstracts
0309-5339 Directory of European Associations. Part 2: National Learned, Scientific and Technical Societies *changed to* Directory of Professional & Learned Societies.
0309-5355 Popular Hi-Fi and Sound *changed to* High Fidelity.
0309-5371 Statistics - Asia & Australasia: Sources for Market Research†
0309-5398 Waste Management Information Bulletin *see* 0954-495X
0309-5444 Microcomputer Analysis *see* 0263-6522
0309-5541 Arca
0309-5614 Chartered Institute of Public Finance and Accountancy. Education Statistics. Actuals
0309-5630 Chambers Trades Register of Scotland and North East England†
0309-5649 Chambers Trades Register of the Wirral to the Wash†
0309-5703 Tenders and Contracts Journal
0309-5770 Catalysts in Chemistry
0309-5789 T S B Gazette
0309-5991 Semiconductors and Insulators
0309-6149 Croydon Natural History & Scientific Society. Bulletin
0309-6157 A B C World Airways Guide
0309-622X Chartered Institute of Public Finance and Accountancy. Fire Service Statistics. Actuals
0309-6254 Nautical Review *see* 0265-2455
0309-6270 Logophile
0309-653X Chartered Institute of Public Finance and Accountancy. Personal Social Services Statistics. Actuals
0309-6629 Chartered Institute of Public Finance and Accountancy. Public Library Statistics. Actuals
0309-6653 M D A Information†
0309-667X Great Britain. Civil Aviation Authority. General Aviation Safety Information Leaflets
0309-6688 Finite Element News
0309-6858 International Association of Dentistry for Children. Journal *see* 0960-7439
0309-6866 Fire Prevention
0309-6890 Gas Kinetics and Energy Transfer†
0309-6904 I P P F Co-operative Information Service†
0309-7013 Aristotelian Society. Proceedings. Supplementary Volume
0309-703X Company Secretary's Review
0309-7234 European Industrial Relations Review
0309-7242 Purchasing and Supply *see* 0265-2072
0309-7285 Cienfuegos Press Anarchist Review
0309-7323 Scottish Opera News†
0309-7374 North West Industrial Development Association. Newsletter†
0309-7463 Institute of Oceanographic Sciences. Collected Reprints†
0309-7471 Material Matters
0309-7498 Hospital Engineering *see* 0957-7742
0309-751X Financial Times International Year Books: World Insurance
0309-7552 Science Bulletin†
0309-7560 Forth Naturalist and Historian
0309-7676 International Business Lawyer
0309-7684 International Legal Practitioner
0309-7714 Journal of Environmental Planning and Pollution Control†
0309-7757 British Journal of Projective Psychology
0309-7765 Bronte Society Transactions
0309-7773 British Psychological Society. Annual Report
0309-7803 Surrey Archaeological Collections
0309-7846 Hydrographic Journal
0309-7854 Economic Bulletin (London)
0309-7900 Tax Planning International Review
0309-7935 Bookplate Society Newsletter
0309-7951 Texture of Crystalline Solids *see* 0730-3300
0309-7978 Breaking Chains
0309-7986 Cumberland and Westmorland Antiquarian and Archaeological Society. Transactions
0309-7994 Devonshire Association for the Advancement of Science, Literature and Art. Report and Transactions
0309-8036 Theatre Papers†
0309-8044 British Federation of Music Festivals. Yearbook *changed to* British Federation of Festivals. Yearbook.
0309-8079 Handicapped Children
0309-8168 Capital and Class
0309-8230 Noise Control, Vibration and Insulation *see* 0957-4565
0309-8249 Journal of Philosophy of Education
0309-8265 Journal of Geography in Higher Education
0309-8273 East Coast Digest *changed to* Coast and Country.
0309-8338 Cumbria Guide Industry and Commerce
0309-8346 Huguenot Society of London. Proceedings *changed to* Huguenot Society of Great Britain and Ireland. Proceedings.
0309-8354 Huguenot Society of London. Quarto Series *changed to* Huguenot Society of Great Britain and Ireland. Quarto Series.
0309-8389 Kirklees Chamber of Commerce. Member's Directory
0309-8397 Bradford and Halifax Chambers of Commerce Members Directory
0309-8486 Northamptoniana
0309-8524 Tourism International Research - Caribbean†
0309-8559 Family History News and Digest
0309-8567 Tourism International Policy†
0309-8575 Tourism International History†
0309-8591 Croydon Bibliographies for Regional Survey
0309-8613 Tourism International Research - Pacific†
0309-8621 Tourism International Airletter†
0309-8648 Dozenal Review *see* 0260-4884
0309-8656 Croydon Natural History & Scientific Society. Proceedings and Transactions
0309-8710 Israel Physical Society. Annals
0309-8729 Infuset
0309-877X Journal of Further and Higher Education
0309-8885 Computing Journal Abstracts
0309-8907 University of Leeds English Society Paper *see* 0144-3399
0309-8990 Trent Law Journal *see* 0965-0660
0309-9105 Scottish Fisheries Information Pamphlets
0309-9113 Higher Education Current Awareness Bulletin†
0309-913X Hertfordshire People
0309-9156 Ideology and Consciousness *changed to* I & C.
0309-9210 Thoroton Society of Nottinghamshire. Transactions
0309-9253 New Vegetarian *changed to* Vegetarian Living.
0309-9334 Business Traveller
0310-0014 Australian Law Reports
0310-0049 Australian Mammalogy
0310-0081 Droughtmaster Digest
0310-0103 New South Wales. Higher Education Board. Higher Education Handbook†
0310-0111 Hunter's Hill Trust Journal
0310-0138 Massada Quarterly *changed to* Emet.
0310-0189 Space
0310-0294 Eco Info *changed to* Queensland Conservation Council Newsletter.
0310-0308 F.A.A. Journal
0310-0316 Impact (Dundas)
0310-0367 Water
0310-0391 Bookmark
0310-0405 Australian Weed Control Handbook
0310-0537 Agriscene Australia

0310-057X Anaesthesia and Intensive Care Journal *changed to* Anaesthesia and Intensive Care.
0310-0634 Audio Visual Australia†
0310-0677 Australia†
0310-0685 Australia. Bureau of Agricultural Economics. Meat Situation *see* 0311-0885
0310-0871 Australia. Bureau of Statistics. South Australian Office. Manufacturing Establishments *changed to* Australia. Bureau of Statistics. South Australian Office. Manufacturing Establishments: Details of Operations by Industry.
0310-1010 Autosafe†
0310-1029 Australian Acoustical Society. Bulletin *see* 0814-6039
0310-1045 Australian Association of Permanent Building Societies. National Newsletter†
0310-1053 Australian Business Law Review
0310-1118 Australian Family Circle
0310-1258 Australian Pipeliner
0310-1304 Australian Shell News
0310-1347 Australian Superannuation and Employment Benefits Planning in Action *changed to* Australian Superannuation Law and Practice.
0310-138X Australian Veterinary Practitioner
0310-1398 Australian Wool Corporation. Bi-Monthly Market Report *changed to* Australian Wool Corporation. Wool Market News: Monthly Perspective.
0310-1444 Bell Bryant News
0310-1452 Belle
0310-1584 Cabbages and Kings
0310-1649 Canberra Papers in Continuing Education
0310-1797 Cleo
0310-186X New South Wales. Department of Agriculture. Commodity Bulletin
0310-1878 C C E A Newsletter
0310-1886 Commonwealth Police Officers' Association Journal
0310-1894 Commonwealth Scientific and Industrial Research Organization. Division of Geomechanics. Abstracts of Published Papers
0310-1908 Commonwealth Scientific and Industrial Research Organization. Division of Atmospheric Physics. Annual Report *see* 0159-0219
0310-2076 Cosmopolitan (Australia)
0310-2084 Australia. Department of Agriculture. Marketing Division. Cotton Market News *changed to* Australia. Department of Primary Industries and Energy. Cotton Market News.
0310-2157 Deed†
0310-2165 Digger
0310-222X Earth Garden
0310-2246 Economic Newsletter†
0310-2467 Bronze Swagman Book of Bush Verse
0310-270X Environmental Control†
0310-2890 Grass Roots
0310-2920 Guide to Book Outlets in Australia†
0310-2939 Habitat Australia
0310-2971 Herd Book for Angora Goats in Australia
0310-3064 Australian Council of Employers Federation. Economic Newsletter *changed to* C A I News Briefs.
0310-3137 Jaguar Journal of Australia†
0310-3145 Keep Australia Beautiful News†
0310-320X Landline in Australia
0310-3242 Learning Exchange†
0310-334X Manifest
0310-3439 Metropolitan Speleological Society. Newsletter
0310-3471 Minie News
0310-3625 National Water Well Association. Journal *see* 1037-3535
0310-3684 New South Wales. Attorney-General. Bureau of Crime Statistics and Research. Statistical Report†
0310-3706 New South Wales Clayworker†
0310-3714 New South Wales Dairyman *see* 0810-4115
0310-3722 New South Wales Dairymen's Digest
0310-3773 Niugini Caver
0310-3781 N. A. G. Newsletter†
0310-3811 Australia. Chamber of Industries, Northern Territory. Northern Territory Business Journal *changed to* Australia. Chamber of Industries, Northern Territory. N.T. Business Journal.
0310-4036 Priorities†
0310-4044 Probe†
0310-4079 Queensland. Department of Education. Research and Curriculum Branch. Curriculum Paper *changed to* Queensland. Department of Education. Curriculum Development Services. Curriculum Paper.
0310-4087 Queensland. Department of Education. Research and Curriculum Branch. Document *changed to* Queensland. Department of Education. Information and Publications Branch. Document.
0310-4095 Queensland. Department of Education. Research and Curriculum Branch. Reporting Research *changed to* Queensland. Department of Education. Research Branch. Reporting Research.
0310-4141 R. M. C. Historical Journal†
0310-4168 Refractory Girl
0310-4184 P E X: Australia's Petroleum Exploration Newsletter
0310-4257 Rydge's C C E M Industry Report and Buyers Guide†
0310-4273 Saturday Club Book of Poetry *see* 0313-685X
0310-4303 Science in New Guinea
0310-4389 Something on Paper
0310-4540 Syntec
0310-4575 Tasmanian Chamber of Industries. Service Bulletin *changed to* Enterprise (Hobart).
0310-4591 Tasmanian Official Publications†
0310-4605 Teaching Religion Today†
0310-463X Tok Tok Bilong Haus Buk
0310-4664 Training and Development in Australia
0310-4729 University of Sydney. Archives Record
0310-4923 Rural Reconstruction Authority of Western Australia. Annual Report *changed to* Rural Adjustment and Finance Corporation of Western Australia. Annual Report.
0310-5083 Ploughman's Lunch *see* 0310-6837
0310-5121 Queensland. Department of Education. Research and Curriculum Branch. Information Statement *changed to* Queensland. Department of Education. Information and Publications Branch. Information Statement.
0310-5202 South Australia. Department of Education. School Libraries Branch. Review†
0310-5296 Australian Labor Party (NSW Branch). Labor Year Book†
0310-5377 Papua New Guinea. National Statistical Office. Abstract of Statistics
0310-5415 Current Australian and New Zealand Legal Literature Index
0310-544X Australian Department of Social Security. Social Security Quarterly *changed to* Australian Department of Social Security. Social Security Journal.
0310-5466 Sydney Town Express
0310-5504 A. C. A. P. Newsletter
0310-5571 International Association for the Evaluation of Educational Achievement (Australia). Newsletter†
0310-558X I. E. A. (Australia) Report†
0310-5601 Urbanology†
0310-5652 Feedback†
0310-5695 Monash University. Higher Education Advisory and Research Unit. Notes on Higher Education†
0310-5709 Developing Education†
0310-5725 Environment Control News†
0310-5814 Ancient Society; Resources for Teachers *changed to* Ancient History; Resources for Teachers.
0310-5822 Aboriginal Child at School
0310-5857 Ekstasis†
0310-5865 Australian Computer Weekly *changed to* Pacific Computer Weekly.
0310-589X National Greyhound News
0310-5903 Australian Weight Lifting Journal†
0310-5938 Gredzens
0310-5946 New South Wales Horizons†
0310-5989 Australian Disc and Tape Review
0310-6012 Australia. National Drug Information Service. Technical Information Bulletin *see* 0157-8200
0310-6020 Filter: a Paper for Secondary Science Teachers
0310-608X Association of Teachers of English as a Foreign Language. Bulletin
0310-6152 Australia's External Aid *changed to* Australia's Overseas Development Assistance. Budget Paper.
0310-6217 Tube
0310-6276 Australia. Environment Housing and Community Development. Farm Holidays†
0310-6330 Western Australia. Main Roads Department. Technical Report†
0310-6357 Mathnews *changed to* P R I M E.
0310-6381 Australian Theatre Review†
0310-6403 Australasian Stud and Stable *see* 0311-8215
0310-6462 M.C.B. Newsletter *changed to* M.C.B. News.
0310-6500 Australian Comparative Education Society. Newsletter
0310-6578 Cities Commission Bulletin†
0310-6632 Newsletter on Soviet and East European Studies in Australia and New Zealand†
0310-6659 Indonesian Acquisitions List
0310-6721 Meatworker
0310-6748 Ball Bearing Journal
0310-6756 Parks and Wildlife†
0310-6802 Continuo
0310-6810 Australian Journal of Hospital Pharmacy
0310-6837 Ploughman†
0310-6861 St. Thomas More Society. Journal
0310-687X Queensland Architect
0310-6969 Welcare
0310-7078 South Australian Canine Journal
0310-7108 Travel News from Victoria, Australia
0310-7175 Independent Education
0310-7213 Wedgwood News
0310-723X Aboriginal News†
0310-7299 Albury/Wodonga†
0310-7345 Official Publications of Western Australia†
0310-740X Serbian Bulletin†
0310-7442 Spectrum†
0310-7531 Tasmanian Transport Bulletin *changed to* Tasmanian Transport Statistics.
0310-7582 Steel Spiel
0310-7787 W A P E T Journal†
0310-7809 W E L Spoken†
0310-7817 Australian Federal Tax Reporter
0310-7833 Australian Wildlife Research *see* 1035-3712
0310-7841 Australian Journal of Plant Physiology
0310-8031 International Telex Directory. International Service
0310-8147 Papua New Guinea. Department of Social Development and Home Affairs. Social Science Research†
0310-8163 C. S. I. R. O. Sheep and Wool Research†
0310-818X Scout Association of Australia. Review of Progress *changed to* Scout Association of Australia. Annual Report.
0310-8198 News Exchange†
0310-8228 Consequences†
0310-8252 Australian Marxist Review
0310-8279 Cattle *changed to* Australian Cattle Magazine.
0310-8341 Aboriginal Medical Service. Newsletter
0310-8368 Australian Speedway Yearbook *changed to* Peter Webster's International Speedway Review.
0310-8465 Interprobe *changed to* Business Week.
0310-8546 Victoria, Australia. Directory of Government Departments and Authorities *see* 0158-1589
0310-8554 Graduate Careers Council of Australia. Digest of Research†
0310-8562 Australian Estate and Gift Duty Reporter†
0310-8651 Executive Briefing†
0310-8740 J E T R O Information Bulletin *changed to* J E T R O News Digest.
0310-8813 Australian Corporate Affairs Reporter *see* 0726-6065
0310-8856 Australian Advisory Council on Bibliographical Services. Library Services for Australia *see* 0812-6267
0310-8880 Irrigation Farmer†
0310-8902 Australian Hi-Fi Annual
0310-8937 Informed Opinion†
0310-897X Western Australia. Department of Agriculture. Rangeland Management Section. Rangeland Bulletin†
0310-9011 Landscape Australia
0310-9054 A. P. E. A. News†
0310-9062 Women's Electoral Lobby (South Australian) Newsletter
0310-9070 C S I R O Food Research Quarterly
0310-9089 Australian Journal of Zoology, Supplementary Series *see* 0818-0164
0310-9100 Science and Technology†
0310-9143 Retrieval
0310-916X Institute of Economic Democracy. Information Bulletin
0310-9178 Artificial Breeding News *changed to* T H I O News!
0310-9186 Iris and Res Novissimae *changed to* Iris.
0310-9267 Art Dialogue
0310-933X Australian Process Engineering *changed to* Process Engineering.
0310-9348 On the Move (Melbourne, 1973)†
0310-9356 Cricket Quadrant
0310-9399 Soaring in the A.C.T.†
0310-9534 B.N.I.A. *changed to* Build.
0310-9593 Tariff Insight *see* 1035-4107
0310-964X Liberation
0310-9658 Ecology Action Newsletter
0310-9666 Murray Grey World
0310-9674 M L T A News
0310-9704 Marine Board of Hobart. Newsletter†
0310-9879 Australian and Pacific Book Prices Current†
0310-9917 Australia. Bureau of Agricultural Economics. Wheat: Situation and Outlook†
0310-9968 Gegenschein
0311-0001 Caspa *changed to* Pool & Spa Review.
0311-0079 National Bottle Review
0311-0095 Artviews
0311-015X Steel Fabrication Journal *see* 1030-2581
0311-0184 Pharmaceutical Society of Victoria. Bulletin *changed to* Pharmaceutical Society of Australia (Victorian Branch). Bulletin.
0311-0192 Insurance and Banking Record *see* 0725-4644
0311-0222 Pivot†
0311-0230 Electronics News
0311-0265 Australian Securities Law Reporter
0311-0273 Mitsui News†
0311-029X Credit Scene *changed to* Credo.
0311-0311 I F A P News *changed to* Safety W A.
0311-032X Moonbi
0311-0346 Australian Racing Drivers Club Journal *changed to* Australian Racing Drivers Club Newsletter.
0311-0362 Garamut *see* 0158-6262

ISSN INDEX 5695

0311-0370 Agribusiness Decision
0311-0389 Director's Law Reporter *changed to* Company Director.
0311-0400 Australian Golf Instructional *changed to* Australian Golf Digest.
0311-0419 Kabar
0311-046X Craft Australia†
0311-0478 Society for Mass Media and Resource Technology. Journal†
0311-0486 Challenge
0311-0559 Flautist
0311-0567 Impact†
0311-0621 I M U Canberra Circular
0311-0699 Dental Anaesthesia and Sedation†
0311-0710 University of Sydney. Department of Architectural Science. General Reports†
0311-0729 Australian Mathematical Society Gazette
0311-0737 Checkpoint
0311-0745 Nature Conservation Council of N.S.W. Bulletin *changed to* Nature Conservation News.
0311-0753 Plain Turkey
0311-0761 Dane Digest
0311-0788 Australia. Bureau of Agricultural Economics. Coarse Grains: Situation and Outlook†
0311-0826 Pacific Travel Directory
0311-0842 A.M.R.C. Review†
0311-0850 Canberra Bulletin†
0311-0885 Australia. Bureau of Agricultural Economics. Meat: Situation and Outlook†
0311-0893 Queensland. Department of Forestry. Division of Technical Services. Report of Research Activities *changed to* Queensland Forest Service. Research Report.
0311-0931 Australian and New Zealand Environmental Report†
0311-094X Australian Tax Review
0311-0982 C A T Newsletter†
0311-1008 Engineering Associate *changed to* Engineers Australia.
0311-1016 Nurungi
0311-1032 A.B.O.A. Newsletter (Australian Bank Officials Association) *changed to* A.B.E.U. Newsletter.
0311-1172 Your Chamber Reporting†
0311-1180 Concrete Masonry Association of Australia. Project Review†
0311-1199 Australian Speedway†
0311-1229 Caesarian *changed to* Curio.
0311-1237 Australia. Department of Manufacturing Industry. Technical Newsletter†
0311-1245 Cor Serpentis
0311-1253 A I M T Newsletter *changed to* A I M S Newsletter.
0311-127X V.C.M. File *see* 1035-395X
0311-1334 Australian Overseas Information Service. Science Newsletter *see* 0815-4171
0311-1342 Primary Journal *changed to* Primary Journal K-7.
0311-1385 Baker and Miller's Journal *changed to* Pastrycooks & Bakers News Monthly.
0311-1431 Farming Forum *see* 1035-1914
0311-175X Big League
0311-1784 Words and Windmills
0311-1822 Prod†
0311-1873 Nexust
0311-1881 Australian Entomological Magazine
0311-1903 Chartered Builder†
0311-1911 Power Farming
0311-1938 South Australia. Department of Agriculture. Agricultural Record†
0311-1954 Australian Journal of Remedial Education
0311-1962 Polycom†
0311-2136 South Pacific Journal of Teacher Education
0311-2144 Hereford Quarterly *see* 0814-7663
0311-2152 Australia. Patent Office. Annual Report of Activities *changed to* Australia. Patent, Trade Marks and Designs Offices. Activities Report.
0311-2160 Manufacturing News in Australia *changed to* Factory Management.
0311-2179 Travel Consultant†
0311-2195 Tourism Australia†
0311-2209 Australia. Department of Manufacturing Industry. Bulletin *changed to* Australia. Department of Industry and Commerce. Bulletin.
0311-2217 Sound News
0311-2225 Adbrief
0311-2233 Studium†
0311-2349 Q I E R Journal *see* 0818-545X
0311-2373 Serials in Education in Australian Libraries: a Union List†
0311-2381 New Products Bulletin†
0311-2497 Cordell's Building Cost Book and Estimating Guide. New South Wales *changed to* Cordell's Building Cost Guide. Commercial and Industrial.
0311-2519 Business Outlook†
0311-2543 Education Research and Perspectives
0311-2659 Gay Liberation Press *see* 0312-7915
0311-2667 Australian Key Business Directory
0311-2756 South Australian Genealogist
0311-2764 Australian Composer†
0311-2772 Teacher Feedback *see* 0013-1156
0311-2780 Mitchell Business Review†
0311-2810 Poets of Australia
0311-290X Southeast Asian Research Materials Group. Newsletter *see* 0158-1953
0311-2926 Ark
0311-2934 Australian Copyright Council. Bulletin
0311-2950 Australia. Bureau of Agricultural Economics. Fibre Review†
0311-2969 Hospitality Yearbook *see* 0817-0398
0311-3000 Australian Council on Awards in Advanced Education. Bulletin†
0311-306X Cancer Forum
0311-3078 South Australia. State Library. Reference Services Branch. Reference Services Bibliographies†
0311-3140 Monash University Law Review
0311-323X Australian Audio-Visual Reference Book†
0311-3248 A N Z H E S Journal *changed to* History of Education Review.
0311-3531 Earth Science and Related Information
0311-354X Municipal Engineering in Australia
0311-3558 Waste Disposal and Water Management in Australia
0311-3612 Australian Podiatrist
0311-3655 Chart Book of the Melbourne Share Price Index†
0311-368X Community†
0311-3760 Migration Action
0311-3930 Globe
0311-4015 Goodwill†
0311-4023 Impact†
0311-4031 Play
0311-404X Splashdown†
0311-4074 Australia. Department of Aboriginal Affairs. Western Australian Office. Newsletter†
0311-4163 Restored Cars
0311-4198 Hecate
0311-4201 Graduate Careers†
0311-4511 Administration for Development†
0311-4546 Ecos
0311-4627 Canberra Linguist
0311-4775 Unicorn
0311-4805 South Australia. Department of Environment and Planning. Coastline†
0311-5070 Business Who's Who Australian Buying Reference *changed to* The Business Who's Who Australian Products and Trade Names Guide.
0311-5518 Alcheringa
0311-5836 C S I R O Index
0311-5984 Australian Law Librarians' Group. Newsletter
0311-628X Australian Transport†
0311-6336 Australian Bulletin of Labour
0311-6603 Australian Institute of Criminology. Information Bulletin *changed to* Cinch. Australian Criminology Database.
0311-662X N A T A News
0311-6875 Australian Education Review
0311-6999 Australian Educational Researcher
0311-7057 Scarlet Letter
0311-7189 Australia. Environment Housing and Community Development. Annual Report†
0311-7472 Cordell's Price Index of Building Materials
0311-7731 Modern Office and Data Management *see* 0810-9451
0311-7839 Australian Sea Spray
0311-7979 A W R C Activities†
0311-7987 Australian Water Resources Council. Water Resources Newsletter *changed to* Australian Water Resources Council. Water News.
0311-7995 Australian Foreign Affairs Record *changed to* Australian Foreign Affairs and Trade: The Monthly Record.
0311-8150 Australian Birds
0311-8215 Stud and Stable
0311-8223 Australian Parks & Recreation
0311-8347 Thoroughbred Breeders' Handbook
0311-8576 New South Wales. Department of Agriculture. Technical Bulletin
0311-8665 Australian Farm Management Society Newsletter *see* 1035-1914
0311-8754 Right to Choose
0311-8789 Australia. Bureau of Agricultural Economics. Oilseeds: Situation and Outlook†
0311-8835 Australia. Bureau of Agricultural Economics. Situation and Outlook (Year). Cotton†
0311-8843 Australia. Bureau of Agricultural Economics. Dairy Products: Situation and Outlook†
0311-8924 Historical Journal†
0311-8959 Australia. Fishing Industry Research Committee. Annual Report *changed to* Australia. Fishing Industry Research and Development Council. Annual Report.
0311-8975 Australia. Bureau of Statistics. Mineral Production, Australia
0311-8983 National Acoustic Laboratories, Sydney. Annual Report†
0311-905X Current Therapeutics
0311-9300 University of New England. Management Forum
0311-9319 Overseas Map Acquisitions†
0311-9491 Queensland. Department of Local Government. Conference of Local Authority Engineers. Proceedings†
0311-9629 Australian Directory of Services for Alcoholism and Drug Dependence†
0311-9882 Australian Wool Sale Statistics. Statistical Analysis. Part A & B & C
0312-0007 University of Wollongong. Calendar *see* 0726-4844
0312-0007 University of Wollongong. Calendar *changed to* University of Wollongong. Undergraduate Calendar.
0312-0007 University of Wollongong. Calendar *changed to* University of Wollongong. Postgraduate Calendar.
0312-004X Stereo Buyer's Guide. Directory†
0312-0058 Stereo Buyer's Guide. Manual *see* 0819-0216
0312-0066 Stereo Buyer's Guide. Turntables *see* 0819-0208
0312-0074 Stereo Buyer's Guide. Speakers†
0312-0104 Stereo Buyer's Guide. Cassettes†
0312-0112 Australasian Small Press Review†
0312-0325 Australian Women's Wear†
0312-0627 International Research and Information Association. Survey
0312-1356 Australia. Bureau of Statistics. Tasmanian Office. Public Justice†
0312-1372 Chain Reaction
0312-1437 Australia. Bureau of Statistics. Trade Union Statistics, Australia
0312-1658 Queensland Lawyer
0312-1674 New South Wales Law Reports
0312-200X C H O M I - Das†
0312-2115 Australian Road Index†
0312-2417 Australian Archaeology
0312-259X Australia. National Library. Acquisitions Newsletter†
0312-2654 Metro
0312-3162 Western Australian Museum. Records
0312-3480 Working Kelpie Council. National Stud Book
0312-3685 Mathematical Scientist
0312-3898 Playgroup *changed to* Playtimes.
0312-4029 Industrial Arbitration Service *see* 0728-8417
0312-407X Australian Social Work
0312-4134 A F C O Quarterly†
0312-4371 Cataloguing Australia
0312-4428 Australia. Bureau of Statistics. Perinatal Deaths (Canberra) *see* 1031-0053
0312-4460 Earnings and Hours of Employees, Distribution and Composition, Preliminary (Canberra) *see* 1031-0231
0312-4479 Australia. Bureau of Statistics. Public Authority Finance. Public Authority Estimates *see* 0159-3951
0312-455X Work and People
0312-4681 Fleetline
0312-4738 Endocrine Society of Australia. Proceedings
0312-4746 Australia. Bureau of Statistics. Official Year Book of Australia *see* 0810-8633
0312-5033 Australian Journal of Early Childhood
0312-5041 Humanities Research Centre Bulletin
0312-5211 C S I R O Wool Textile News
0312-5327 Australian Giftguide Magazine
0312-5378 University of Technology, Sydney. Research Report *changed to* University of Technology, Sydney. Research and Consultancy Report.
0312-5467 Australia. Working Papers in Language and Linguistics
0312-5599 Australian Hospitals and Health Services Yearbook
0312-5807 Australian Naval Institute. Journal
0312-5963 Clinical Pharmacokinetics
0312-6072 Australia. Bureau of Statistics. Western Australian Office. Local Government, Western Australia
0312-6137 University of New South Wales. Faculty Handbooks: Medicine
0312-620X Rebuild *see* 1032-9315
0312-6242 Australia. Bureau of Statistics. Value of Primary Production, Excluding Mining, and Indexes of Quantum and Unit Gross Value of Agricultural Production *see* 1031-0789
0312-6447 Australia. Bureau of Statistics. Dairying Industry *changed to* Australia. Bureau of Statistics. Dairying and Dairy Products, Australia.
0312-6986 Australian Historical Association. Bulletin
0312-6994 Australia. Law Reform Commission. Annual Report
0312-7397 Australia. Bureau of Statistics. Queensland Office. List of Publications†
0312-7559 Nepean Review†
0312-7567 Natural Family Planning Council of Victoria. Bulletin
0312-7850 Australia. Bureau of Statistics. Tasmanian Office. Local Government Finance *changed to* Australia. Bureau of Statistics. Tasmanian Office. Government Finance Statistics.
0312-7915 Working Papers in Sex, Science and Culture†
0312-7923 Royal Australian College of Dental Surgeons. Annals *see* 0158-1570
0312-8008 Australian Prescriber
0312-8059 A N Z A A S Congress Papers
0312-827X Australian Journal for Health, Physical Education and Recreation *see* 0813-2283

ISSN

0312-8318 Aus Education Information *see* 0726-2639
0312-8741 University of New England. Department of Geography and Planning. Monograph Series (No.)
0312-875X Modern Medicine *see* 1030-3782
0312-889X Professional Farm Management Guidebook
0312-8962 Australian Journal of Management
0312-8989 Quandong
0312-8997 West Australian Nutgrowing Society Yearbook *see* 0810-6681
0312-9152 Industrial Arts Education *see* 1034-6902
0312-9217 Australia's Overseas Development Assistance *changed to* Australia's Overseas Development Assistance. Budget Paper.
0312-9225 Commonwealth Scientific and Industrial Research Organization. Division of Chemical Technology. Research Review *changed to* Commonwealth Scientific and Industrial Research Organization. Division of Chemical & Wood Technology. Research Review.
0312-9608 B M R Journal of Australian Geology and Geophysics
0312-9616 Media Information Australia
0312-9640 Historical Society of South Australia. Journal
0312-9764 Telopea
0312-9837 Petroleum Newsletter
0312-9888 Luna
0313-0096 University of New South Wales Law Journal
0313-0568 Thomson's Liquor Guide
0313-0797 2 M B S - F M Stereo F M Radio Program Guide
0313-0835 Management Review
0313-122X Western Australian Museum. Records. Supplement
0313-1459 Span
0313-153X Reform
0313-1912 Australia. Bureau of Statistics. Queensland Office. Labour Force, Queensland
0313-1971 National Library of Australia. Annual Report
0313-2080 Theatre Australia
0313-2153 New Doctor
0313-220X Art Almanac
0313-2463 Victorian Government Publications
0313-251X Ancestral Searcher
0313-2773 Australia. Bureau of Statistics. Balance of Payments (Canberra, 1976)
0313-2781 Australia. Department of Primary Industry. Australian Plague and Locust Commission. Annual Report
0313-2919 Health Action†
0313-3133 Australia. Bureau of Statistics. Queensland Office. Pre-schools Training and Child Minding, Queensland *see* 0818-1993
0313-3192 Australian Plant Introduction Review
0313-3249 Instead
0313-3311 Australian Computer Society. Conference Proceedings†
0313-363X Skysailor
0313-377X Agricultural Economics Bulletin (No.)
0313-3788 University of New England. Department of Agricultural Economics and Business Management. Agricultural Economics Miscellaneous Publication (No.)
0313-4075 Ports of New South Wales Journal†
0313-4083 Adelaide Botanic Gardens. Journal
0313-4245 Brunonia *see* 1030-1887
0313-4253 Queensland Law Society Journal
0313-427X University of New South Wales. Library. Annual Report
0313-4288 L I P
0313-4334 Pedal Power *changed to* Canberra Cyclist.
0313-4393 Industrial and Commercial Photography *changed to* Commercial Photography.
0313-4423 Scarlet Woman
0313-4504 Rhombus *changed to* Cross Section.
0313-4954 Skindiving in Australia and the South Pacific *changed to* Sportdiving in Australia and the South Pacific.
0313-5047 Tomorrow's Business Decisions *see* 0313-5055
0313-5055 McCabe-McMiles Letter
0313-5136 Commonwealth Record
0313-5276 Custom Vans & Trucks†
0313-5381 A I C C M Bulletin
0313-5519 Institutions of Engineers, Australia. Mechanical Engineering Transactions *see* 0727-7369
0313-5780 University of Tasmania. Centre for Environmental Studies. Working Papers
0313-5861 Southern Cross
0313-5934 J A S S A
0313-5977 Canberra Historical Journal
0313-6086 Mineral Industry Quarterly
0313-6221 Parergon
0313-6620 Australian Citizen Limited *see* 0818-6286
0313-6647 Australian Journal of Public Administration
0313-6701 Heritage News
0313-6728 Queensland. Department of Education. Division of Special Education. Special Education Bulletin
0313-6744 Tableaus
0313-6825 Function
0313-685X S C O P P
0313-6906 University of Wollongong. Annual Report
0313-7031 Australian Film Institute Newsletter
0313-704X A E S I S Quarterly
0313-7112 Australian Graduate School of Management. Handbook
0313-7384 Australian Society of Endodontology. Newsletter
0313-7414 Australian National University. Centre for Resource and Environmental Studies. Working Papers
0313-7465 Australia. Bureau of Statistics. Queensland Office. Public Finance: Government Authorities *see* 1031-2269
0313-766X Australian Powerboat
0313-7813 Queensland Government Publications
0313-7864 Enterprise: Western Australia†
0313-7872 Beach Conservation
0313-8143 Queensland Education Digest†
0313-8410 Monash Publications in Geography
0313-8445 Australian Company Law Reports *see* 1033-7466
0313-8461 Australian Film, Television and Radio School Handbook
0313-8518 Australia. Bureau of Statistics. Queenslnad Office. Primary and Secondary Education, Queensland *see* 0818-2582
0313-8704 University of Sydney. Department of Agricultural Economics. Agricultural Extension Bulletin†
0313-8747 Explore
0313-8860 Western Geographer
0313-895X Australian Road Research Board. Technical Manuals
0313-9050 Australian Computer Bulletin†
0313-9549 Environment W.A. *changed to* Environment.
0313-9581 University of Western Australia. Centre for East Asian Studies. Occasional Papers†
0313-9603 Australian Commonwealth Specialists' Catalogue†
0313-9611 Australian Banknote Catalogue†
0313-9727 Australia - Israel Review
0313-9921 University of Wollongong. Research Bulletin†
0313-9948 Australia. National Capital Development Commission. Technical Papers†
0313-9980 Australian National University. National Centre for Development Studies. Newsletter *see* 1035-1132
0314-0164 Complan Handbook
0314-0377 Australasian Shipping Record
0314-0679 Graduate Outlook
0314-1004 Nutrition Society of Australia. Proceedings
0314-1039 Defence Force Journal *changed to* Australian Defence Force Journal.
0314-111X National Rehabilitation Digest *see* 0728-490X
0314-1160 Criminal Law Journal
0314-1306 Wool Outlook†
0314-1357 Research Laboratories Review of Activities
0314-1438 Australian Forest Resources
0314-1551 Hospitality Buyers Guide and Diary *see* 0817-0398
0314-1578 D P Index *see* 1036-0352
0314-1586 M T I A Metal & Engineering Industry Yearbook
0314-1608 Salssah on Com†
0314-1640 Tasmanian Pocket Yearbook
0314-1659 Australia. Bureau of Statistics. Tasmanian Office. Agricultural Industry *changed to* Australia. Bureau of Statistics. Tasmanian Office. Agriculture, Tasmania.
0314-1667 Australia. Bureau of Statistics. Tasmanian Office. Fruit Production *changed to* Australia. Bureau of Statistics. Tasmanian Office. Agricultural Statistics, Tasmania.
0314-1705 Australia. Bureau of Statistics. Tasmanian Office. Education†
0314-1888 Australia. Bureau of Statistics. Tasmanian Office. Mining Tasmania
0314-2094 Australia. Bureau of Statistics. Tasmanian Office. Monthly Summary of Statistics Tasmania *changed to* Australia. Bureau of Statistics. Tasmanian Office. Tasmanian Statistical Indicators.
0314-2205 A R R B Regional Symposium
0314-2531 Panorama (Hobart)†
0314-254X Commonwealth Scientific and Industrial Research Organization. Division of Protein Chemistry. Annual Report *changed to* Commonwealth Scientific and Industrial Research Organization. Division of Biomolecular Engineering. Annual Report.
0314-2779 Australia. Bureau of Statistics. Labour Statistics, Australia
0314-285X Inprint†
0314-2868 A C T U Bulletin†
0314-2876 Australian Society of Exploration Geophysicists. Bulletin *see* 0812-3985
0314-2981 Helen Vale Foundation. Journal†
0314-3155 Simply Living
0314-3171 Australian Institute of Petroleum. Annual Report
0314-3287 Australia. Bureau of Statistics. Queensland Office. Sawmill Statistics, Queensland†
0314-3457 Queensland Geographer
0314-3767 Australian Society of Indexers Newsletter
0314-4224 Earthmover and Civil Contractor
0314-4240 Chemistry in Australia†
0314-4321 Monitor *see* 0725-2986
0314-4607 Mining Review
0314-464X Australian Musician
0314-5204 Victorian Statutes Cumulative Supplement
0314-5468 Sports Coach
0314-5514 Life: Be in It /Y S R News†
0314-6057 New South Wales Institute of Technology Calendar *see* 1030-5947
0314-6162 Howard Florey Institute of Experimental Physiology & Medicine. Annual Report and Notice of Meeting
0314-6200 Church & Nation
0314-6235 Journey (Brisbane)
0314-6316 Pharmacy Review
0314-6464 Australian Journal of Art
0314-6510 Reeflections (Townsville)
0314-660X Patient Management (Australia)
0314-6677 Science Fiction
0314-6820 Statistical Society of Australia. Newsletter
0314-7134 Victoria, Australia. Women's Bureau. Women and Work Newslettter *changed to* Women & Work.
0314-724X V I S E News†
0314-7312 Fleece and Flock
0314-7320 Currency†
0314-7487 Energy†
0314-7495 New Literatures Review
0314-7533 Asian Studies Association of Australia. Review *see* 1035-7823
0314-755X Monthly Summary of Australian Conditions *changed to* National Quarterly Summary.
0314-7592 Journal of Industry and Commerce
0314-7606 Sigma *changed to* Cross Section.
0314-769X Journal of Australian Studies
0314-7762 Australian Mining Year Book *changed to* Australian Mining Product Register.
0314-7894 Candy Family History Newsletter†
0314-8009 Compass†
0314-853X University of New South Wales. Centre for Applied Economic Research. Paper
0314-8580 A I I Journal
0314-8769 Aboriginal History
0314-9099 Canberra Anthropology
0315-0003 Accessible *see* 0027-9633
0315-0054 Dalhousie University. School of Library Service. Newsletter *changed to* Dalhousie University. School of Library and Information Studies. Newsletter.
0315-0062 Canadian Frontier†
0315-0097 Encounter *changed to* Liberation.
0315-0143 Urban Focus†
0315-0208 Spear
0315-0380 Eco-Log Week
0315-047X Decormag
0315-0496 Stuffed Crocodile†
0315-0518 Recreation Property *changed to* Ontario Cottager.
0315-0542 Outdoor Canada
0315-0550 Cuttings and Comments†
0315-0607 Articles et Commentaires†
0315-0623 Lodgistiks†
0315-0631 Directory of Community Services in Metropolitan Toronto
0315-0720 Titmouse Review *changed to* Titmouse Annual.
0315-0771 Ottawa Ethnic Groups Directory
0315-0836 Canadian Theatre Review
0315-0860 Historia Mathematica
0315-0879 Canadian Key Business Directory
0315-0887 Volleyball Technical Journal†
0315-0895 Guide to Departments of Sociology and Anthropology in Canadian Universities *see* 0316-1854
0315-0909 Canadian Amateur Boxing News†
0315-0917 Beale's Letter
0315-0941 Geoscience Canada
0315-095X Y Canada *see* 0838-6536
0315-1042 On Continuing Practice
0315-1131 M S Canada
0315-1174 T.S. Eliot Newsletter *see* 0704-5700
0315-1182 AudioScene Canada *changed to* Sound & Vision.
0315-1204 Cooperateur Agricole
0315-1298 Heritage Canada *see* 0225-1485
0315-1301 Cosmetics
0315-1409 Canadian and International Education
0315-1433 Canadian Annual Review of Politics and Public Affairs
0315-1468 Canadian Journal of Civil Engineering
0315-162X Journal of Rheumatology
0315-1654 Energy Analects
0315-1840 L S M News†
0315-1859 The Charlatan
0315-1867 Le Consommateur Canadien
0315-2022 Western Geographical Series
0315-2081 Eau du Quebec *see* 0823-0269
0315-2138 Bivoie
0315-2146 Entomological Society of Manitoba. Proceedings
0315-2235 Venture Forth

0315-226X Corporation Professionnelle des Medecins du Quebec. Annuaire Medical
0315-2286 Canadian Bar National
0315-2316 R A D A R *changed to* Point de Repere.
0315-2340 Documentation et Bibliotheques
0315-2359 Beaux-Arts
0315-2456 Filet†
0315-2464 Canadian Police Chief *see* 0713-4517
0315-2561 Information North
0315-257X C P I Management Service *changed to* Camford Chemical Report.
0315-2588 Polyfacts *changed to* Camford Chemical Report.
0315-260X Quebec Chasse et Peche *see* 0711-7957
0315-2685 Jewish Dialogue
0315-2804 Raincoast Chronicles†
0315-2979 Corporation Professionnelle des Medecins du Quebec. Bulletin
0315-3002 U R A M Newsletter
0315-3010 Westwater†
0315-3037 Ego
0315-3088 Where to Eat in Canada
0315-310X Hellenic View
0315-3118 Skimania†
0315-3223 Biomass Energy Institute. Newsletter *changed to* Bio-Joule.
0315-3339 Accelerator (Ottawa)†
0315-3371 History Collection: Canadian Catholic Church†
0315-3452 Canadian Layman
0315-3495 Canadian Defence Quarterly
0315-3525 Canadian Rehabilitation Council for the Disabled. Employment Bulletin†
0315-3541 Canadian Association of University Schools of Music. Journal. *see* 0710-0353
0315-355X Alberta-Westmorland-Kent Regional Library. Extension Department. News†
0315-3584 Pathfinder Travel Parks Directory
0315-3606 Body Politic†
0315-3630 Northern Journey†
0315-369X Reporting Classroom Research
0315-3754 Capilano Review
0315-3770 Event
0315-3800 Alberta Hog Journal *see* 0225-3488
0315-3819 E D P In-Depth Reports
0315-3835 British Columbia Genealogist
0315-3843 C R E A Reporter *changed to* Canadian Real Estate.
0315-3932 Waves†
0315-3959 Canadian Dancers News
0315-3967 Cahiers Linguistiques d'Ottawa
0315-3975 Video-Presse
0315-4025 Cahier de Linguistique *see* 0710-0167
0315-4114 Concern International
0315-4149 International Fiction Review
0315-4254 C B Newsletter†
0315-4297 Journal of Canadian Art History
0315-4351 Comment on Education†
0315-4459 Forgotten People
0315-4661 Computernews
0315-467X Chien d'Or
0315-4785 Arctic and Northern Development Digest *see* 0824-4952
0315-4793 Better Vending & Catering†
0315-484X Actrascope News†
0315-4874 Landscape/Paysage Canada†
0315-4998 Ligne Directe *see* 0710-5568
0315-5064 Manitoba Nature†
0315-5153 Vie Medicale au Canada Francais†
0315-5226 Vanguard (Vancouver)†
0315-5463 Canadian Institute of Food Science and Technology. Journal - Institut Canadien de Science et Technologie Alimentaires. Journal *see* 0963-9969
0315-5943 Repertoire de l'Edition au Quebec†
0315-5986 I N F O R Journal
0315-6168 Canadian Parliamentary Guide (Year)
0315-6230 Canadian Banker and I C B Review *see* 0822-6830
0315-6621 C M P A Newsletter
0315-6877 Canadian Society for Horticultural Science. Journal *changed to* Canadian Society for Horticultural Science. Newsletter.
0315-6915 Shaver Focus
0315-6923 Newsletter Called Fred *see* 0840-4313
0315-694X Mark II *changed to* Sales & Marketing Manager Canada.
0315-6966 Motion
0315-7083 Corpus Almanac *see* 0823-1133
0315-727X C S S E Yearbook†
0315-7288 Guide to Periodicals and Newspapers in the Public Libraries of Metropolitan Toronto
0315-7326 Sixteen Mm Films Available in the Public Libraries of Metropolitan Toronto
0315-7423 Grain
0315-7466 Atlantic Sport News†
0315-7555 Short Guide to Canadian Universities and Colleges†
0315-7601 Canada: an Historical Magazine†
0315-761X Canadian Archaeological Association. Bulletin *see* 0705-2006
0315-7725 Pakistan Forum *see* 0899-2851
0315-7784 Black Images†
0315-7911 City Magazine
0315-7970 Le Sauveur
0315-7997 Historical Reflections
0315-8020 Kateri
0315-8098 Corporate Insurance in Canada *see* 0008-3879
0315-8101 Mennonite Mirror
0315-811X Digest, Business & Law Journal
0315-8179 Ascent (Kootenay Bay)
0315-8233 Canadian Gas Association. Membership Directory†
0315-8349 Directory of Gas Utilities *changed to* Directory of Natural Gas Company Operations.
0315-8527 Horizon (Vancouver)
0315-8691 Foreign Focus†
0315-8705 Canadian Ethnic Studies Association. Bulletin
0315-8748 A I M E†
0315-8756 Log House†
0315-8888 Emergency Librarian
0315-8934 Automatic Control: Theory and Applications *see* 0730-9538
0315-8977 Canadian Society for Mechanical Engineering. Transactions
0315-9000 Council of Ontario Universities. Annual Review *changed to* Council of Ontario Universities Quadrennial Review.
0315-9027 Discovery Through Art *see* 0708-5354
0315-906X Classmate
0315-9116 Manitoba Social Science Teacher
0315-9124 M S L A V A Journal
0315-9140 Canadian Mining Journal's Reference Manual & Buyers' Guide
0315-9159 Manitoba Science Teacher
0315-9183 Plant Management and Engineering *see* 0845-4213
0315-9337 Canadian Micrographic Society. Micro Notes *changed to* Canadian Information & Image Management Society. Newsletters.
0315-9388 Educational Planning
0315-9396 Digger's Digest
0315-940X Universities Art Association of Canada. Journal
0315-9566 Humanities Research Council of Canada. Bulletin *see* 0707-8048
0315-9590 Council of Ontario Universities Triennial Review *changed to* Council of Ontario Universities Quadrennial Review.
0315-985X Canadian Chemical Register†
0315-9884 Cancer in Ontario
0315-9892 Intercom
0315-9906 R A C A R
0315-9922 About Unions
0315-9930 Argus (Montreal)
0315-9981 I D R C Reports
0316-0033 Probe *changed to* S E S Newsletter.
0316-0041 Criminologie
0316-0068 Centre for Urban and Community Studies. Research Papers
0316-0114 National Research Council, Canada. Associate Committee on Scientific Criteria for Environmental Quality. Status Report†
0316-0173 British Columbia English Teachers' Association. Journal
0316-0297 Directory of Federally Supported Research in Universities†
0316-0300 Essays on Canadian Writing
0316-0343 Canadian Plains Bulletin
0316-0386 Notes on Unions†
0316-0513 L'Ancetre
0316-0602 Lifeline (Cornwall) *changed to* Writer's Lifeline.
0316-0661 Environmental Management for the Public Health Inspector†
0316-0688 Dalhousie Labour Institute for the Atlantic Provinces. Proceedings†
0316-0696 Canadian Essay and Literature Index†
0316-0734 Directory of Associations in Canada
0316-0769 Subsidia Mediaevalia
0316-0874 Mediaeval Sources in Translation
0316-0955 Association pour l'Avancement des Sciences et des Techniques de la Documentation. Rapport Annuel
0316-0963 Association pour l'Avancement des Sciences et des Techniques de la Documentation. Nouvelles de l'ASTED
0316-1218 Canadian Journal of Higher Education
0316-1226 Directory of Accredited Camps
0316-1234 Cours de Perfectionnement du Notariat
0316-1269 Royal Ontario Museum. History, Technology and Art Monographs
0316-1277 Royal Ontario Museum. Ethnography Monograph†
0316-1285 Royal Ontario Museum. Archaeology Monographs
0316-1323 Canadian Theatre Review Yearbook *changed to* Canadian Theatre Review (Annual).
0316-1544 British Columbia Art Teachers' Association. Journal
0316-1552 Alberta History
0316-1609 Room of One's Own
0316-1617 Ontario Government Publications, Monthly Checklist
0316-1854 Guide to Departments of Sociology, Anthropology and Archaeology in Universities and Museums in Canada
0316-1862 National Museum of Man. Mercury Series. Canadian Ethnology Service. Papers
0316-1897 National Museum of Man. Mercury Series. Canadian Centre for Folk Culture Studies. Papers
0316-1900 National Museum of Man. Mercury Series. History Division. Papers
0316-1919 National Museum of Man. Mercury Series. Canadian War Museum. Papers
0316-2281 Mining in Canada - Facts & Figures
0316-2397 T V Magazine
0316-2494 Tailspinner
0316-2508 Vexillum
0316-2516 Sound Heritage *see* 0228-7781
0316-2540 Talespinner *see* 0316-2494
0316-2672 Etudes Francaises dans le Monde *see* 0226-7454
0316-2702 Grand Manan Historian
0316-280X Canadian Camper
0316-2893 Accelerator Newsletter
0316-2907 Canadian Gideon
0316-2915 Torch and Trumpet *see* 0316-2907
0316-2923 Philosophiques
0316-2931 Torch Runner
0316-3040 Come and See
0316-3083 Canadian Communications Reports *see* 0825-3021
0316-313X Social Development *changed to* Social Development Overview.
0316-327X PSST†
0316-3334 Perspectives (Saskatoon)
0316-3350 Wildland News
0316-3393 L A W G Letter
0316-3423 Profitable Outdoor Occupations *see* 0316-3431
0316-3431 Outdoor Careers†
0316-3458 Winnipeg Industrial Topics†
0316-3547 Canadian Gas Facts
0316-3571 Canadian Tax Foundation. Tax Conference. Report of Proceedings
0316-3768 Writ
0316-3903 O T F - F E O Interaction
0316-3938 Canadian Locations of Journals Indexed in Index Medicus *see* 0707-7629
0316-4004 Pulp & Paper Canada
0316-4047 National Research Council of Canada. Annual Report on Scholarships and Grants in Aid of Research *changed to* Natural Sciences and Engineering Research Council of Canada. List of Scholarships and Grants in Aid of Research.
0316-4055 Ontario Review
0316-4241 Canadian Pulp and Paper Association. Annual Newsprint Supplement
0316-4357 Genetics Society of Canada Bulletin
0316-4454 Rehabilitation Institute of Montreal. Bulletin *changed to* Institut de Readaptation de Montreal. Bulletin.
0316-4543 Canadian Association of University Business Officers. Bulletin
0316-4608 Profile Index to Canadian and Municipal Government Publications *see* 0839-1289
0316-4616 Royal Society of Canada. Proceedings and Transactions *see* 0035-9122
0316-4616 Royal Society of Canada. Proceedings and Transactions *see* 0080-4517
0316-4675 University of Western Ontario. Department of Psychology. Research Bulletin†
0316-4683 University of Alberta. Department of Computing Science. Technical Reports
0316-4691 Centre for Urban and Community Studies. Bibliographic Series
0316-473X Alberta Catholic Directory
0316-4853 Pulp and Paper Research Institute of Canada. Logging Research Reports†
0316-4969 History and Social Science Teacher *changed to* Canadian Social Studies: History and Social Science Teacher.
0316-5000 Index of Feature Length Films *see* 0316-5019
0316-5019 Index of 16 mm & 35 mm Feature Length Films Available in Canada†
0316-5078 Queen's University. Institute for Economic Research. Discussion Paper
0316-5183 Ontario Genealogical Society. Kingston Branch. Newsletter *see* 1188-1089
0316-5310 Law Society of Upper Canada. Special Lectures
0316-5329 Nineteenth Century Theatre Research *see* 0893-3766
0316-5345 Science et Esprit
0316-5515 Canadian Film Digest Yearbook†
0316-5779 S M T S Journal - Newsletter
0316-5973 Modernist Studies: Literature and Culture, 1920-1940†
0316-5981 Atlantic Provinces Book Review
0316-618X Gnosis
0316-6198 Motor Vehicle Data Book
0316-6260 International Corner *see* 0829-4976
0316-6325 Nova Scotia Law News
0316-6368 Universite de Moncton. Revue
0316-6414 Madison's Canadian Lumber Directory
0316-6546 Institute of Chartered Accountants of Alberta. Monthly Statement *changed to* Institute of Chartered Accountants of Alberta. C A Monthly Statement.
0316-6570 McGill University, Montreal. Centre for Developing-Area Studies. Bibliography Series†

0316-6597 Serials Holdings in the Libraries of Memorial University of Newfoundland, St. John's Public Library and College of Trades and Technology *see* 0709-0536
0316-6600 Memorial University of Newfoundland. Library. Serials Holdings in the Libraries of Memorial University of Newfoundland and St. John's Public Library *see* 0709-0536
0316-6724 Charlottes
0316-7437 Books in Bengali†
0316-7518 New Canadian Stories *see* 0703-9476
0316-7631 Export News Bulletin *see* 0713-0341
0316-7739 Grand News
0316-7771 Canadian Sporting Goods & Playthings. Directory
0316-778X Queen's Law Journal
0316-7828 Boreal Institute, Edmonton. Report of Activities *changed to* Canadian Circumpolar Library. Report of Activities.
0316-7852 Point *see* 0380-9811
0316-7917 Canadian Journal of Research in Semiotics *see* 0229-8651
0316-7933 Canadian Urban Transit Association. Proceedings†
0316-7941 Canadian Transit Association. Proceedings *see* 0316-7933
0316-7984 University of Manitoba. Center for Transportation Studies. Research Report†
0316-800X Lutheran Churches in Canada. Directory
0316-8131 Canadian and Provincial Golf Records
0316-8212 Royal Canadian Golf Association. National Tournament Records *see* 0316-8131
0316-8433 News News News†
0316-8484 Canadian Children's Annual
0316-8549 Ontario Directory of Education
0316-8565 Canadian Journal of Social Work Education *see* 0820-909X
0316-859X Canadian Logger & Pulpwood Contractor†
0316-8603 German-Canadian Yearbook
0316-8670 Words from Inside†
0316-8743 Canadian Religious Conference. Bulletin
0316-8840 Revolting Librarian†
0316-8891 Index to Canadian Legal Periodical Literature
0316-8913 My Brother and I
0316-8956 Canadian Information Processing Society. Computer Census
0316-9014 Humane Viewpoint *changed to* Animal Talk.
0316-9200 Ordre des Architectes du Quebec. Bulletin
0316-9235 Art & Literary Review *see* 0316-9243
0316-9243 Muskeg Review†
0316-9375 Canadian Construction Association. Documentation de Reference†
0316-9448 Current Canadian Books
0316-9537 Blue Book of Food Store Operators & Wholesalers
0317-0209 Journal of Orthomolecular Psychiatry *changed to* Journal of Orthomolecular Medicine.
0317-0349 Ontario Education Dimensions†
0317-0403 All About Boating†
0317-0500 Chesterton Review
0317-0535 Canadian Labour Relations Board Reports
0317-056X From the Ground Up
0317-0659 Third World Forum
0317-0691 Okangan Historical Society. Report *see* 0830-0739
0317-0713 Cahiers de Psychologie et de Reeducation†
0317-0756 Canadian Trapper
0317-0802 English Studies in Canada
0317-0845 Repository†
0317-0861 Canadian Public Policy
0317-0926 C I M Bulletin
0317-1272 Insurance Marketer†
0317-1280 R T A C News *changed to* T A C News.
0317-1485 Dogs in Canada
0317-1493 Consensus (Winnipeg)†
0317-1655 Jewish Historical Society of Western Canada. Annual Publication *changed to* Jewish Life and Times.
0317-1663 Dalhousie Law Journal
0317-1671 Canadian Journal of Neurological Sciences
0317-1817 Fisheries Fact Sheet.†
0317-1892 Canadian Grain Commission Grain Research Laboratory. Annual Report
0317-2023 Canadian Fisherman *changed to* Canadian Fisherman.
0317-2031 Arts Victoria†
0317-2147 Chelsea Journal†
0317-2244 National Museum of Man. Mercury Series. Archaeological Survey of Canada. Papers
0317-2333 Cinema Quebec
0317-2473 Population Research Laboratory. Discussion Paper Series *changed to* Population Research Laboratory. Research Discussion Paper Series.
0317-2481 Flypaper
0317-2546 Queen's University. Industrial Relations Centre. Research and Current Issues Series†
0317-2635 Chatelaine (French edition)
0317-266X Evangelical Baptist Churches in Canada. Fellowship Yearbook
0317-2716 Canada. National Museum of Man. Mercury Series. Communications Division. Papers†
0317-2775 Canadian Urban Sources *see* 0839-1289
0317-2791 Canadian Pool and Patio†
0317-2937 Voix de l'Ancai
0317-2961 Vernon's City of Guelph (Ontario) Directory
0317-297X British Columbia Provincial Judges' Association. Annual Conference†
0317-3100 Population Research Laboratory. Population Reprint Series
0317-3119 University of Alberta. Department of Sociology. Population Research Laboratory. Alberta Series Report†
0317-3348 University of Waterloo Biology Series
0317-3445 Canada. Statistics Canada. Railway Freight Traffic/Trafic Marchandises Ferroviaire†
0317-3518 Emergency Planning Digest *see* 0837-5771
0317-3526 Nova Scotia. Environmental Control Council. Annual Report
0317-3550 Pulp and Paper Canada Business Directory *see* 0708-501X
0317-3720 Canada. Statistics Canada. Surgical Procedures and Treatments†
0317-3739 Administration Hospitaliere et Sociale
0317-3798 Autosport Canada
0317-3925 Alberta Statistical Review
0317-3992 Ontario School Counsellors' Association. Newsletter *see* 0383-9931
0317-4018 Svetovy Kongres Slovakov. Bulletin.
0317-4026 Canadian Business Review
0317-4085 Canada. Energy, Mines and Resources Canada. Indian and Northern Affairs. Canada Oil and Gas Lands Administration Released Geophysical-Geological Data *changed to* Canada. Energy, Mines and Resources Canada. Indian and Northern Affairs. Canada Oil and Gas Lands Administration Frontier Lands Released Information.
0317-4336 Social Services in Nova Scotia *changed to* Nova Scotia Department of Community Services (Year).
0317-4344 Saskatchewan. Department of Culture and Youth. Annual Report *changed to* Saskatchewan. Department of Culture and Recreation. Annual Report.
0317-4514 In Search†
0317-4522 Living†
0317-4530 Prince Edward Island. Department of Health. Annual Report *changed to* Prince Edward Island. Department of Health and Social Services. Annual Report.
0317-4611 Saskatchewan. Department of the Environment. Annual Report *changed to* Saskatchewan. Department of the Environment and Public Safety. Annual Report.
0317-4654 Canadian Materials *changed to* C M: A Reviewing Journal of Canadian Materials for Young People.
0317-4670 British Columbia. Ministry of Human Resources. Services for People *changed to* British Columbia. Ministry of Social Services and Housing. Services for People. Annual Report (Year).
0317-4697 Canada. Department of Manpower and Immigration. Strategic Planning and Research. Supply, Demand and Salaries: New Graduates of Universities and Community Colleges. Offre, Demande et Salaires.: Nouveaux Diplomes d'Universites et de Colleges.†
0317-4808 Incite Magazine
0317-4859 Reports of Family Law (3rd Series)
0317-4921 Public Libraries in Canada†
0317-4956 Germano-Slavica
0317-4980 Canada. Grain Commission. Economics and Statistics Division. Canadian Grain Exports
0317-5065 Cahiers des Etudes Anciennes
0317-5073 S M E A. Journal *see* 0703-8380
0317-5375 Canada. Statistics Canada. Exports - Merchandise Trade *see* 0844-8361
0317-543X Canadian Society for Legal History. Newsletter†
0317-5545 Krzyk
0317-5642 National Museum of Natural Sciences. Natural History Series†
0317-5685 Canadian Communications Research Information Centre. Newsletter†
0317-5693 Canadian Commission for Unesco. Annual Report
0317-5766 National Science Library. Health Sciences Resources Centre. Conference Proceedings in the Health Sciences Held by the National Science Library/ Comptes Rendus des Conferences sur les Sciences de la Sante Qui Se Trouvent a la Bibliotheque Scientifique Nationale†
0317-5839 Conservation News *see* 0383-6479
0317-5979 Tournee de Spectacles *changed to* Tourarts.
0317-6045 C M A Gazette - A M C Gazette *see* 0820-0165
0317-607X Bond Record
0317-6126 Ahoy
0317-6193 Captain George's Penny Dreadful
0317-6207 Dairy Facts and Figures at a Glance
0317-6282 Prairie Forum
0317-6436 Ontario. Ministry of Education. Report
0317-6495 Canadian Current Tax
0317-6525 Consulting Engineers - Canada - Ingenieurs Conseils *changed to* Association of Consulting Engineers of Canada. Directory of Member Firms and Their Services.
0317-6649 Canada Business Corporations Act with Regulations
0317-6673 Conservation Canada†
0317-6738 Canada. Statistics Canada. Travel Between Canada and Other Countries *see* 0838-3952
0317-6789 Economic Council of Canada. Economic and Social Indicators†
0317-6878 C A Magazine
0317-6908 Canada. Forestry Service. Bi-Monthly Research Notes *see* 0228-9989
0317-6983 Maltese Directory: Canada, United States *changed to* Maltese Directory: Canada.
0317-7025 Perspectives and Plans for Graduate Studies
0317-7076 Decks Awash
0317-7114 University of Waterloo. Solid Mechanics Division. Reports
0317-7130 University of Waterloo. Solid Mechanics Division. Papers
0317-7173 Cartographica
0317-7254 Carleton Germanic Papers
0317-7262 Manitoba. Horse Racing Commission. Annual Report
0317-7335 Saskatchewan Labour Report
0317-7483 Canada's Trade in Agricultural Products
0317-7645 Dimensions in Health Service *changed to* Leadership in Health Services.
0317-7785 Canadian Rodeo News
0317-7831 Model Aviation Canada
0317-7882 Canada. Statistics Canada. Aggregate Productivity Measures
0317-7904 Canadian Review of Studies in Nationalism
0317-7920 Canadian Art Auction Record†
0317-8064 Chess Federation of Canada. Bulletin *see* 0822-5672
0317-8161 Ontario. Ministry of Consumer and Commercial Relations. Statistical Review†
0317-8196 Canada. Road and Motor Vehicle Traffic Safety Branch. Road Safety Annual Report. Rapport Annuel, Securite Routiere
0317-8382 Papers on European and Mediterranean Societies†
0317-851X En Eglise
0317-8536 Directory of Libraries in Manitoba
0317-8552 Free Press Report on Farming†
0317-8625 Contact (Waterloo) *see* 0711-6780
0317-8633 University of Waterloo. Division of Environmental Studies. Occasional Paper *changed to* University of Waterloo. Faculty of Environmental Studies. Occasional Paper.
0317-8668 Lawyer's Phone Book (Year)
0317-8722 Youth Science News†
0317-8765 Anglican Year Book
0317-8781 Scott's Industrial Directory. Western Provinces *see* 0317-879X
0317-879X Scott's Directories - Western Manufacturers
0317-882X Canadian Pulp and Paper Association. Technical Section. Transactions *see* 0826-6220
0317-9044 Canadian Drama†
0317-9095 Kinesis
0317-9311 U F O - Quebec†
0317-9443 Toy and Decoration Fair Directory
0317-946X Canadian Tax Foundation. Provincial and Municipal Finances
0317-9508 Mining - What Mining Means to Canada
0317-9575 Long Point Bird Observatory Newsletter
0317-9656 Universite de Sherbrooke. Revue de Droit
0317-9672 Canada. Statistics Canada. Production and Value of Maple Products†
0317-9893 University of Toronto. Department of Geography. Discussion Paper Series
0318-000X Indian Education Newsletter†
0318-0069 Cable Communications Magazine
0318-0077 Learning Resources
0318-0107 Gargoyle
0318-0123 Donum Dei
0318-0247 O L A Focus *changed to* Focus (Toronto).
0318-0344 Fraser's Construction & Building Directory†
0318-0468 Water and Pollution Control. Directory and Handbook *changed to* Water & Pollution Control. Directory and Buyers' Guide.
0318-0492 Quebec Astronomique *see* 1183-5362
0318-0522 Canadian Structural Engineering Conference. Proceedings†

ISSN INDEX 5699

0318-0646 Professional Institute of the Public Service of Canada. Communications
0318-0743 Ontario. Provincial-Municipal Affairs Secretariat. Municipal Directory
0318-0794 Canadian Environmental Control Newsletter
0318-0859 Canadian Process Equipment & Control News
0318-0867 The Canadian Amateur
0318-0913 Simmental Scene *changed to* Simmental Country.
0318-0948 Reviewing Librarian *changed to* Teaching Librarian.
0318-1006 Nursing Papers - Perspectives en Nursing *changed to* Canadian Journal of Nursing Research.
0318-1049 Meetings & Incentive Travel
0318-1235 University of Toronto-York University Joint Program in Transportation. Newsletter†
0318-1251 University of Toronto - York University. Joint Program in Transportation. Annual Report
0318-1340 Liaison†
0318-1723 N A P E News *changed to* Communicator (St. John's).
0318-1766 Mining Exploration and Development Review *see* 0711-3277
0318-1944 Canadian Information Processing Society. Canadian Salary Survey†
0318-1960 C A H P E R News *see* 0848-1733
0318-2037 Current Soviet Leaders†
0318-2096 Canadian Psychological Review *see* 0708-5591
0318-2118 Manitoba Spectra
0318-2126 Association of New Brunswick Land Surveyors. Annual Report
0318-2274 Canada. Statistics Canada. Private and Public Investment in Canada. Outlook *see* 0823-065X
0318-2460 Windsor This Month
0318-2592 Stereo Guide *see* 0833-9570
0318-2789 Canadian Conservation Directory†
0318-2851 Association of Canadian Map Libraries. Bulletin *see* 0840-9331
0318-2967 Dairy Policy
0318-3122 University of Waterloo. Solid Mechanics Division. Studies Series
0318-3270 Introductions from an Island *see* 0826-5909
0318-3319 Erasmus Studies
0318-3610 Matrix
0318-3661 British Colombia. Ministry of Agriculture. Vegetable Production Guide *changed to* British Columbia. Ministry of Agriculture Fisheries and Food. Vegetable Production Guide.
0318-3742 Captain Lillie's Coast Guide and Radiotelephone Directory
0318-3874 Canada. Statistics Canada. Salaries and Qualifications of Teachers in Public, Elementary and Secondary Schools†
0318-3912 Manitoba. Water Services Board. Annual Report
0318-3971 Alberta Opportunity Company. Annual Report
0318-4099 Canada Manpower and Immigration Review
0318-4137 Recherches Amerindiennes au Quebec
0318-4277 Canadian Forest Industries
0318-434X Annals of Good St. Anne
0318-4390 Touring & Travel
0318-4552 Housing Ontario *changed to* Community Ontario.
0318-4560 Commerce Montreal
0318-4684 Saskatchewan. Tourism and Renewable Resources Annual Report *changed to* Saskatchewan. Parks, Recreation and Culture. Annual Report.
0318-4935 Canadian Bar Association. Annual Report of Proceedings
0318-4943 Alberta Fishing Guide
0318-5036 Canadian Association of Administrative Sciences. Proceedings, Annual Conference *changed to* Administrative Sciences Association of Canada. Proceedings, Annual Conference.
0318-5133 Canadian Society of Environmental Biologists Newsletter
0318-5184 Canada. Statistics Canada. Survey of Canadian Nursery Trades Industry
0318-5273 Canada. Statistics Canada. Household Facilities and Equipment
0318-5303 Quebec (Province). Commission des Transports. Rapports des Activites de la Commission des Transports du Quebec *see* 0702-0996
0318-5311 Issues in Canadian Science Policy†
0318-5540 Alberta Naturalist
0318-5729 Amigo
0318-5737 Amisol
0318-5753 Amber
0318-6075 Cross Country
0318-6210 Training Aids Action Service†
0318-6229 Careers for Graduates†
0318-6237 Short Courses and Seminars
0318-6288 Carleton Lecture Note Series *changed to* Lecture Notes in Mathematics.
0318-6342 T.S. Eliot Review *see* 0704-5700
0318-6385 Metric Message†
0318-6415 Manitoba Community Reports *changed to* Manitoba. Economic Development Network. Community Profile Information System.
0318-6431 Canadian Journal of Sociology
0318-658X Agronews *see* 0840-8289
0318-6644 Artmagazine
0318-6717 Canadian Business Periodicals Index *see* 0227-8669
0318-675X Canadian Government Publications: Catalogue†
0318-6954 Archivaria
0318-7020 Parachute (Montreal)
0318-708X Canada. Statistics Canada. National Income and Expenditure Accounts - Comptes Nationaux des Revenus et des Depenses *changed to* Canada. Statistics Canada. National Income and Expenditure Accounts.
0318-7128 Canada. Statistics Canada. Sawmills and Planing Mills and Shingle Mills *see* 0835-0078
0318-7160 Canada. Statistics Canada. Statistical Information on Schools of Social Work in Canada/Information Statistique sur les Ecoles de Service Social au Canada†
0318-7179 University and College Libraries in Canada†
0318-7306 Action Canada France
0318-7403 Dalhousie University. School of Library Service. Occasional Papers *changed to* Dalhousie University. School of Library and Information Studies. Occasional Papers.
0318-742X C G A Magazine
0318-7446 Land *see* 0700-1770
0318-7454 Forestalk *see* 0700-1770
0318-7500 Fotoflash
0318-7527 Ontario Municipal Board Reports
0318-7551 Eskimo
0318-7632 Hiballer Magazine *see* 0708-2169
0318-7888 Canada. Statistics Canada. Report on Fur Farms
0318-7985 Italian Chamber of Commerce Bulletin *changed to* Italcommerce.
0318-8116 L U A C Monitor†
0318-8140 Urban Forum†
0318-8272 Huxley Institute - C S F Newsletter *see* 0831-8530
0318-8329 Inventory of Research into Higher Education in Canada†
0318-8442 Canadian Issues
0318-8515 Quincaillier *see* 0318-8531
0318-8531 Quincaillerie Materiaux
0318-8647 Indian-Ed *see* 0710-1481
0318-8701 Fashion Textiles Mode
0318-871X Fem Ego
0318-8752 Franchise Annual
0318-8779 Quebec (Province) Direction Generale des Peches Maritimes. Direction de la Recherche. Rapport Annuel *changed to* Quebec (Province) Direction de la Recherche Scientifique et Technique. Activites (Year).
0318-8787 Canada. Statistics Canada. Selected Financial Statistics of Charitable Organizations/Certaines Statistiques Financieres des Oeuvres de Charite†
0318-8809 Canada. Statistics Canada. Building Permits
0318-8841 Canada. Statistics Canada. Contract Drilling for Petroleum and Other Contract Drilling/Forage de Puits de Petrole a Forfait et Autre Forage a Forfait†
0318-8868 Canada's International Investment Position *changed to* Canada. Statistics Canada. System of National Accounts, Canada's International Investment Position.
0318-8876 Canada. Statistics Canada. Provincial Government Finance: Assets, Liabilities, Sources and Uses of Funds *see* 0710-1023
0318-8914 Canada. Statistics Canada. Shipping Report. Part 1: International Seaborne Shipping (by Country) /Transport Maritime. Partie 1: Transport Maritime International (Par Pays)†
0318-8930 Canada. Statistics Canada. Shipping Report. Part 3: Coastwise Shipping/ Transport Maritime. Partie 3: Navigation Nationale†
0318-8949 Canada. Statistics Canada. Shipping Report. Part 5: Origin and Destination for Selected Commodities/Transport Maritime. Partie 5: Origine et Destination de Certaines Marchandises†
0318-9007 Canada. Statistics Canada. Estimates of Labour Income
0318-9090 Canadian Journal of University Continuing Education
0318-9171 University of British Columbia. Faculty of Forestry. Bulletin†
0318-9201 Voix et Images
0318-9236 Poumons†
0318-9244 Metropolitan Toronto Library Board. News *see* 0842-9707
0318-9392 Vie Oblate
0318-9422 Sanford Evans Gold Book of Snowmobile Data and Used Prices
0318-952X Current Industrial Relations Scene in Canada†
0318-9600 Canadian Aural/Oral History Association. Bulletin *see* 0383-6576
0318-9651 Apartment & Building
0318-9872 Echo Missionaire
0318-9937 American Society for Information Science. Western Canada Chapter. Annual Meeting Proceedings
0319-003X Atlantic Canada Economics Association. Annual Conference: A C E A Papers
0319-0080 C C L
0319-0161 Computing Canada
0319-0188 Sphinx
0319-0358 North Shore Numismatic Society. Bulletin *see* 0380-8866
0319-0382 Canada. Epidemiology Division. Venereal Disease in Canada *changed to* Sexually Transmitted Diseases in Canada.
0319-0404 British Columbia. Labour Relations Board. Annual Report *changed to* British Columbia. Industrial Relations Council. Annual Report.
0319-0412 British Columbia Economic Outlook Survey *changed to* Economic Review and Outlook.
0319-051X Canadian Review of Comparative Literature
0319-0552 York Dance Review†
0319-0560 Swim Canada
0319-0595 Harlequin†
0319-0684 B C S T A Convention Reporter *see* 0703-766X
0319-0994 Women Can *see* 0319-1001
0319-1001 Pedestal
0319-1095 Interuniversity Centre for European Studies. Bulletin
0319-1249 Chateauguay Valley Historical Society Annual Journal
0319-1362 Bull & Bear Financial Newspaper
0319-1443 Family Involvement
0319-1648 Kabalarian Courier†
0319-1729 Canadian Society for Cell and Molecular Biology Bulletin
0319-1915 Canadian Gladiolus Society. Annual
0319-1974 Canadian Research†
0319-2008 Uncertified Human *see* 0711-7388
0319-2121 Forum (Toronto) *see* 0840-9269
0319-2148 Canadian Office†
0319-2156 Connection†
0319-2431 Canadian Tax News
0319-2547 Canadian Appaloosa Journal†
0319-2563 Directory of Special Libraries in the Montreal Area
0319-2571 Canadian Archer *changed to* Canadian Archer.
0319-258X Directory of Community Services of Greater Montreal
0319-2636 Order of Nurses of Quebec. News and Notes *see* 0381-6419
0319-2644 Canadian Public Health Association. Proceedings of the Annual Meeting†
0319-2709 Mart *see* 0035-3728
0319-2776 Gulf Wings†
0319-2822 Cycle Canada
0319-2865 Moto Journal
0319-2962 Canada News *changed to* Korea Times Toronto.
0319-3098 Jardin Botanique de Montreal. Annuelles et Legumes: Resultats des Cultures d'Essai *changed to* Jardin Botanique de Montreal. Legumes: Resultats des Cultures d'Essai.
0319-3101 Jardin Botanique de Montreal. Annuelle *changed to* Jardin Botanique de Montreal. Legumes: Resultats des Cultures d'Essai.
0319-3225 Canadian Funeral Director
0319-3322 Canadian Business Law Journal
0319-3403 Canadian Energy News
0319-3535 Alberta Hail and Crop Insurance Corporation. Annual Report
0319-3578 Saskatchewan. Department of Agriculture. Annual Report *see* 0713-1844
0319-3608 Environment News *see* 0701-9637
0319-3780 Routes et Transports
0319-3799 Canada. Statistics Canada. Honey Production - Production de Miel *see* 0829-3163
0319-3896 CanPara
0319-3934 Canadian Quaker Historic Newsletter *see* 1180-968X
0319-4019 Monarchy Canada
0319-4027 Industrial Manager *see* 0045-5156
0319-423X Alberta. Alcoholism and Drug Abuse Commission. Annual Report *changed to* Alberta. Alcohol and Drug Abuse Commission. Annual Report.
0319-4264 Alberta Economic Accounts
0319-4434 Canadian Journal of Radiography, Radiotherapy, Nuclear Medicine *see* 0820-5930
0319-4477 Canadian Newsletter of Research on Women *see* 0707-8412
0319-4558 A P T Communique
0319-4604 R N A N S Bulletin *see* 0849-3383
0319-4620 Centre for Urban and Community Studies. Major Report Series
0319-4639 Cape Breton's Magazine
0319-4728 Centre Stage†
0319-4787 Canadian Nurses Association. Entrance Requirements for Diploma Schools of Nursing and Schools of Practical Nursing *see* 1180-4920
0319-485X Religious Studies Review

ISSN

5700 ISSN INDEX

0319-4930 Canada. Statistics Canada. Labour Costs in Canada: Finance, Insurance and Real Estate/Couts de la Main-d'Oeuvre au Canada: Finances, Assurances, et Immeublet†
0319-4957 Canada. Statistics Canada. Feldspar and Quartz Mines/Mines de Feldspath et de Quartz†
0319-5023 Action *changed to* P M A C News.
0319-5082 Summer in Canada†
0319-5147 Polish Canadian Courier
0319-5228 Canoma
0319-5376 Canadian Association of Law Libraries. Newsletter *see* 1180-176X
0319-5724 Canadian Journal of Statistics
0319-5759 Energy Processing - Canada
0319-583X Canada North Almanac
0319-5864 Canada. National Museums of Canada. Journal†
0319-616X Floor Covering News
0319-6348 Canadian Quarter Horse Journal *see* 0702-9071
0319-6356 Canadian Music Teacher
0319-6658 League of Canadian Poets. Newsletter *changed to* Museletter.
0319-6771 Environmental Health Review
0319-681X Cegepropos
0319-6879 C V 2 *see* 0831-9502
0319-6887 Bharati
0319-6984 Alerte au Quebec
0319-7018 Building Management Maintenance News *changed to* Building Operating Manager.
0319-7093 Canadian Travel News Weekly†
0319-7107 Canadian Travel News
0319-7336 Hume Studies
0319-7468 Communique (Ottawa)
0319-7549 Common Sense Economics†
0319-7581 Corinthian *see* 0829-2930
0319-7697 Manitoba Moods†
0319-7751 Ontario Statistics†
0319-7778 Communications *see* 0827-0678
0319-7832 CraftNews
0319-7840 Craftsman *see* 0229-1320
0319-7980 Alberta Decisions, Civil and Criminal Cases
0319-7999 Saskatchewan Decisions, Civil and Criminal Cases
0319-8014 Canada. Statistics Canada. Hospitals Section. List of Canadian Hospitals and Related Institutions and Facilities *see* 0831-7313
0319-8030 Canada. Statistics Canada. Federal Government Expenditures on the Human Sciences *see* 0319-8049
0319-8049 Canada. Statistics Canada. Federal Government Activities in the Human Sciences/Activites de l'Administration Federale en Sciences Humaines†
0319-8227 Canada. Statistics Canada. Statistics of Criminal and Other Offences/Statistique de la Criminalite†
0319-8251 Canada. Statistics Canada. Construction Price Statistics. Quarterly Report/Statistiques des Prix de la Construction Rapport Trimestriel†
0319-8278 Canada. Statistics Canada. Housing Starts and Completions†
0319-8294 Industrial Business Management *see* 0833-1146
0319-8316 Library Selections *see* 0836-1525
0319-8413 Design Product News
0319-8480 Discovery
0319-8499 Saskatchewan Registered Nurses' Association. Bulletin *changed to* Saskatchewan Conce R N.
0319-8561 Cross Trail News
0319-8588 Dome *changed to* Union Matters.
0319-8650 Envers du Decor
0319-8693 Asia Times
0319-8715 Canadian India Star
0319-8774 Quebec (Province). Conseil de la Protection du Consommateur. Rapport Annuel *changed to* Quebec (Province). Office de la Protection du Consommateur. Rapport Annuel.
0319-891X Canada. Statistics Canada. Textile Products Industries
0320-0108 Pis'ma v Astronomicheskii Zhurnal
0320-0647 Naryzy z Istoriyi Pryrodoznavstva i Tekhniky *changed to* Ocherki po Istorii Estestvoznaniya i Tekhniki.
0320-1031 Druzhba
0320-1058 Ekspress-Informatsiya. Peredacha Informatsii
0320-2259 Sovetskaya Militsiya
0320-2372 Inozemna Filolohija
0320-3123 Signal'naya Informatsiya. Akustika
0320-314X Signal'naya Informatsiya. Fizika Yadernykh Reaktorov
0320-3166 Signal'naya Informatsiya. Elektricheskie Svoistva Tverdykh Tel
0320-3182 Signal'naya Informatsiya. Chastitsy i Polya
0320-3336 Polutehniline Instituut Tallinn. Issledovanie Elektromagnitnykh i Elektromashinnykh Ustroistv Upravleniya i Kontrolya Spetsial'nogo Naznacheniya *see* 0868-4278
0320-3344 Polutehniline Instituut Tallinn. Trenie i Iznos v Mashinakh *see* 0868-4162
0320-3352 Polutehniline Instituut Tallinn. Issledovanie Dvumernogo Vozmushchennogo Polya Napryazheniya†
0320-3379 Polutehniline Instituut Tallinn. Neorganicheskaya Khimiya i Tekhnologiya†
0320-3409 Polutehniline Instituut Tallinn. Postroenie Translyatorov, Obrabotka Dannykh, Voprosy Programmirovaniya *changed to* Tallinna Tehnikaulikool. Data Processing, Compiler Writing, Programming.
0320-3433 Polutehniline Instituut Tallinn. Teoretichekoe i Eksperimental'noe Issledovanie Avtomobil'nykh Dorog i Avtomobil'nogo Transporta Estonskoi S.S.R. v Usloviyakh Intensivnoi Avtomobilizatsii *changed to* Tallinna Tehnikaulikool. Povyshenie Kachestva Proektirovaniya, Stroitel'stva i Ekspluatatsii Avtodorog i Gorodskikh Ulits.
0320-3468 Polutehniline Insituut Tallinn. Sintez i Primenenie Polikondensatsionnykh Kleev *see* 0868-4197
0320-4421 Istoriya Narodnogo Gospodarstva ta Ekonomichnoi Dumki Ukrainskoi R.S.R.
0320-4650 Mody Stran Socializma
0320-5223 Referativnyi Zhurnal. Ekonimika, Organizatsiya, Tekhnologiya i Oborudovanie Poligraficheskogo Proizvodstva *see* 0235-2222
0320-7218 Absorbtsiya i Absorbenty†
0320-734X Aktual'nye Problemy Leksikologii i Slovoobrazovaniya†
0320-7544 Belarus'
0320-7552 Belarusskaya Linhvistika
0320-7986 Twentieth Century and Peace
0320-8044 Veselye Kartinki
0320-8370 Vsesvit
0320-8907 Voprosy Istorii K.P.S.S.
0320-930X Astronomicheskii Vestnik
0320-9407 Arkheologiya
0320-9512 Tbilisskii Universitet. Institut Prikladnoi Matematiki. Seminar. Dokladi
0320-9695 Biologiya Morya *see* 0203-4646
0321-0359 Belaruski Dziarzhauny Universitet. Vesnik. Seryia 3; Historiya, Filosofiya, Navukovy Kamunism, Ekanomika, Prava
0321-0596 Vodnye Resursy
0321-0642 Stupeni
0321-0669 Vokrug Sveta
0321-1576 Zhurnal Mod
0321-1649 Akademiya Navuk Belarusskai S.S.R. Vestsi. Seriya Gramadskikh Navuk
0321-1657 Akademiya Navuk Belarusskai S.S.R. Vestsi. Seriya Sel'skogaspadarchykh Navuk
0321-1673 Akademiya Nauk Latviiskoi S.S.R. Izvestiya. Seriya Fizicheskikh i Tekhnicheskikh Nauk
0321-1738 Akademiyai Fanhoi R.S.S. Tojikiston. Shu'Bai Fanhoi Jam'iiati. Akhboroti
0321-186X Leningradskii Universitet. Vestnik. Seriya Biologiya
0321-1975 Mekhanika Tverdogo Tela
0321-2068 S.Sh.A.
0321-2653 Severo-Kavkazskii Nauchnyi Tsentr Vysshei Shkoly. Tekhnicheskie Nauki. Izviestiya
0321-3005 Severo-Kavkazskii Nauchnyi Tsentr Vysshei Shkoly. Estestvennye Nauki. Izvestiya
0321-3056 Severo-Kavkazskii Nauchnyi Tsentr Vysshei Shkoly. Obshchestvennye Nauki. Izvestiya
0321-3668 Ekspress-Informatsiya. Promyshlennyi Organicheskii Sintez
0321-3803 Studencheskii Meridian
0321-3900 Teoriya Sluchainykh Protsessov
0321-4095 Voprosy Khimii i Khimicheskoi Tekhnologii
0321-4419 Teoriya Mekhanizmov i Mashin
0321-4427 Teoriya Funktsii, Funktsional'nyi Analiz i ikh Prilozheniya
0321-4508 Kosmicheskie Issledovaniya na Ukraine *changed to* Kosmicheskaya Nauka i Tekhnika.
0321-5040 Kosmicheskaya Biologiya i Aviakosmicheskaya Meditsina
0322-7154 Silnicni Obzor
0322-7189 Nezelezne Kovy
0322-7243 Metodicky Zpravodaj Cs. Soustavy Vedeckych, Technickych a Ekonomickych Informaci†
0322-7340 Plasty a Kaucuk
0322-807X Kniznice a Vedecke Informacie†
0322-8509 Ceskoslovenska Informatika *see* 0862-9382
0322-8959 Novinky Literatury: Geologie-Geografie†
0322-9378 Novinky Literatury: Jazykoveda. Literarni Veda†
0322-9564 Prumyslove Informace†
0322-9572 Amaterske Radio A
0322-9653 Financni Zpravodaj
0323-0287 Folia Facultatis Scientiarum Naturalium Universitatis Purkynianae Brunensis: Physica *changed to* Folia Facultatis Scientiarum Naturalium Universitatis Masarykianae Brunensis: Physica.
0323-0465 Acta Physica Slovaca
0323-052X Casopis Matice Moravske
0323-0562 Acta Universitatis Carolinae. Historia Universitatis Carolinas Pragensis
0323-0570 Moravske Zemske Museum. Casopis. Vedy Spolecenske *changed to* Acta Musei Moraviae - Scientiae Sociales.
0323-0678 Slezske Muzeum. Casopis. Serie B. Vedy Historicke
0323-0937 Historicka Demografie
0323-0988 Historicka Geografie
0323-1119 Anthropologie
0323-1267 Archeologicke Rozhledy
0323-1283 Hudebni Nastroje
0323-1313 Ceskoslovenska Akademie Ved. Archivni Zpravy
0323-1364 Atletika†
0323-1445 Lyzarstvi†
0323-1569 Bibliograficky Katalog C S S R: Ceske Hudebniny a Gramofonove Desky *see* 0862-8580
0323-1615 Bibliograficky Katalog C S S R: Ceske Knihy *see* 0862-9218
0323-164X Marxismus a Soucasnost†
0323-1666 Bibliograficky Katalog C S S R. Ceske Knihy. Zvlastni Sesit. Bibliografie A V T I *see* 0139-8539
0323-1712 Bibliograficky Katalog C S S R. Ceske Knihy. Ceska Grafika a Mapy za Rok (Year) *see* 0862-9226
0323-1763 Bibliograficky Katalog C S S R: Ceske Knihy. Ceskoslovenske Disertace *see* 0862-8599
0323-1860 Bibliograficky Katalog C S S R. Ceske Knihy. Soupis Ceskych Bibliografii *see* 0862-9234
0323-214X Myslivost
0323-2220 Studia Comeniana et Historica
0323-2581 Vlastivedny Vestnik Moravsky
0323-2719 Bulletin of Czechoslovak Law
0323-3022 Neue Erziehung im Kindergarten
0323-3049 Organisation
0323-312X Modellbau Heute
0323-3154 Bibliographie Fremdsprachiger Germanica
0323-3162 Landschaftsarchitektur
0323-3189 Federball
0323-3227 Film und Fernsehen
0323-326X Forschung, Lehre, Praxis†
0323-3308 Agrartechnik (Berlin)†
0323-3413 Architektur
0323-3472 Deutscher Angelsport *changed to* Rute und Rolle.
0323-3499 Wissenschaftliche Mitteilungen†
0323-3545 Handelshochschule Leipzig. Wissenschaftliche Zeitschrift
0323-3553 D E T†
0323-357X Der Falke
0323-3596 Deutsche Nationalbibliographie. Reihe A: Neuerscheinungen des Buchhandels
0323-3642 Deutsche Nationalbibliographie. Reihe B: Neuerscheinungen Ausserhalb des Buchhandels
0323-3677 Ganztaegige Bildung und Erziehung
0323-3715 Sprachpraxis
0323-374X Deutsches Buecherverzeichnis
0323-3766 Literarisches Sonderheft†
0323-3790 Asien, Afrika, Lateinamerika
0323-3804 Textiltechnik
0323-3847 Biometrical Journal
0323-3901 I P W Forschungshefte†
0323-3944 Series Statistics *changed to* Statistics.
0323-4045 Savigny-Stiftung fuer Rechtsgeschichte. Zeitschrift. Germantische Abteilung
0323-4096 Savigny-Stiftung fuer Rechtsgeschichte. Zeitschrift. Romanistische Abteilung
0323-410X Frisur und Kosmetik
0323-4134 Leichtathlet
0323-4142 Savigny-Stiftung fuer Rechtsgeschichte. Zeitschrift. Kanonistische Abteilung
0323-4207 Goethe-Jahrbuch
0323-4290 Zidis-Information *changed to* Zidis.
0323-4304 Standpunkt (Berlin)
0323-4320 Acta Hydrochimica et Hydrobiologica
0323-4339 Neue Deutsche Presse
0323-4347 Folia Haematologica†
0323-4355 Bibliographie Geschichte der Technik
0323-438X Musik - Information†
0323-4398 Allergie und Immunologie
0323-4436 Saat- und Pflanzgut†
0323-4444 Leopoldina
0323-455X Jahresverzeichnis der Hochschulschriften der D D R, der B R D und Westberlins
0323-4568 Arbeit und Arbeitsrecht
0323-4614 D D R - Medizin-Report†
0323-4630 Rostock Universitaet. Wissenschaftliche Zeitschrift. Gesellschafts-Wissenschaftliche Reihe
0323-4657 Nachrichtentechnik - Elektronik
0323-4673 Beitraege fuer die Forstwirtschaft
0323-4681 Rostock Universitaet. Wissenschaftliche Zeitschrift. Naturwissenschaftliche Reihe
0323-4711 Forschung der Sozialistischen Berufsbildung†
0323-4762 Gastronomie
0323-4835 Gartenbau
0323-4886 Baustoffindustrie. Ausgabe A. Primaerbaustoffe *see* 0232-2765
0323-4916 Koerpererziehung
0323-4932 Folia Ophthalmologica
0323-4967 Kultur im Heim *see* 0863-4076
0323-5017 Kultur und Freizeit
0323-5033 H N O - Praxis
0323-5084 Fortschritte der Onkologie

ISSN

ISSN INDEX 5701

ISSN	Title
0323-5106	Musikforum†
0323-5130	Beitraege zur Forschungstechnologie
0323-5254	Militaergeschichte
0323-5270	Technische Hochschule Carl Schorlemmer Leuna-Merseburg. Wissenschaftliche Zeitschrift.†
0323-5297	Theorie und Praxis
0323-5386	Medizin Aktuell
0323-5394	Warenzeichen- und Musterblatt
0323-5408	Archiv fuer Phytopathologie und Pflanzenschutz
0323-5424	Milchforschung - Milchpraxis†
0323-5610	Aquarien Terrarien see 0723-4066
0323-5637	Zeitschrift fuer Medizinische Laboratoriumsdiagnostik†
0323-5750	F D G B. Rundschau†
0323-5815	Neues Leben see 0863-3045
0323-5947	Fuer Dicht
0323-598X	Journal fuer Signalaufzeichnungsmaterialien see 0863-0453
0323-5998	Rundfunk- und Fernsehprogramm
0323-6021	Kontakt†
0323-6315	Mitteilungen P T†
0323-6471	Bauern-Echo
0323-6862	Gelditschia
0323-6927	Technischen Hochschule Zwickau. Wissenschaftliche Zeitschrift
0323-7117	C L G - Information
0323-7168	Handelswoche - Konsum-Genossenschafter see 0863-4084
0323-7532	Ordinariate und Bischoefliche Aemter in der D D R. Kirchliche Amtsblatt. Ausgabe der Apostlichen Administratur Goerlitz†
0323-7583	Ordinariate und Bischoeflichen Aemter in der D D R. Kirchliche Amtsblatt. Ausgabe des Bischoeflichen Amtes Magdeburg†
0323-763X	Ordinariate und Bischoefliche Aemter in der D D R. Kirchliche Amtsblatt. Ausgabe des Bischoeflichen Amtes Erfurt-Meiningen†
0323-7648	Acta Polymerica
0323-7680	Ordinariate und Bischoefliche Aemter in der D D R. Kirchliche Amtsblatt. Ausgabe des Bistums Dresden-Meissen†
0323-7737	Ordinariate und Bischoefliche Aemter in der D D R. Kirchliche Amtsblatt. Ausgabe des Bischoefliche Amtes Schwerin†
0323-7982	Zeitschrift fuer Germanistik
0323-8105	Jahrbuch Peters
0323-8202	Glaube und Heimat
0323-8253	Landschaftspflege und Naturschutz in Thueringen
0323-830X	Around the World - A Travers le Monde - Po Svetu changed to Po Svetu.
0323-8407	Fuwo
0323-8474	Journal of Information Processing†
0323-8490	Bauinformation Wissenschaft und Technik†
0323-8628	Deutsches Sportecho: Reihe A†
0323-8709	Trommel†
0323-8725	Hochschule fuer Seefahrt Warnemuende-Wustrow. Wissenschaftliche Zeitschrift
0323-8776	Z F I - Mitteilungen†
0323-8806	Froesi†
0323-8865	Galerie - Informationen†
0323-8903	Atze†
0323-8946	Schriftenreihe fuer Geologische Wissenschaften
0323-8954	Bummi
0323-8962	Numismatische Beitraege
0323-9004	Narodnostopanski Arkhiv
0323-9217	Bulgarian Journal of Physics
0323-9268	Bulgarska Etnografiia
0323-9365	Bulgarski Gramofonni Plochi
0323-9411	Bulgarski Disertacii
0323-956X	Bulgarski Zhurnalist
0323-9578	Dukhovna Akademiya SV. Kliment Okhridski. Godishnik
0323-9667	Bulgarski Knigopis. Seriia 2: Sluzhebni Izdaniia i Disertatsii
0323-9748	Istoricheski Pregled
0323-9764	Bulgarski Periodichen Pechat
0323-9780	Izvestiia na Darzhavnite Arkhivi
0323-9799	Istoriya i Osnovi na Komunizma see 0204-9260
0323-9861	Bulgarski Folklor
0323-9950	Acta Physiologica et Pharmacologica Bulgarica
0323-9969	Bulgaria v Chuzhdata Literatura
0323-9985	Bulgarska Akademiia na Naukite. Institut za Istoriia. Izvestiia
0323-9993	Kinoizkustvo
0324-0037	Sofiya
0324-024X	Filosofska Misul
0324-0282	Institut po Istoriia na B K P. Izvestiia
0324-0290	Fiziologiia na Rasteniiata
0324-0347	Letopis na Statiite ot Bulgarskite Vestnitsi
0324-0398	Letopis na Statiite ot Bulgarskite Spisaniia i Sbornitsi
0324-0495	Literaturna Misal
0324-0525	Sofiiski Universitet. Geologo-Geografski Fakultet. Geografiia. Godisnik
0324-0770	Acta Zoologica Bulgarica
0324-0835	Natsionalen Voennoistoricheski Muzei, Sofia. Izvestiia
0324-0878	Okeanologiia
0324-0894	Geologica Balcanica
0324-0924	Hydrobiology
0324-0959	Akuserstvo i Ginekologija
0324-0967	Vekove
0324-0975	Fitologija
0324-1092	Mezhdunarodni Otnosheniya
0324-1114	Vissha Geodeziia
0324-1130	Izvestiia po Khimiia
0324-119X	M B I
0324-1203	Arkheologiia
0324-1459	Astrofizicheskie Issledovaniia
0324-1491	Pneumologia i Ftiziatria
0324-1572	Sociologiceski Problemi
0324-1653	Linguistique Balkanique
0324-1661	Geotektonika, Tektonofizika i Geodinamika
0324-1718	Geokhimiia, Mineralogiia i Petrologiia
0324-1793	Muzei i Pametnitsi na Kulturata†
0324-1858	Bibliotekoznanie, Bibliografiia, Knigoznanie, Nauchna Informatsiia
0324-1998	Obsta i Sravnitelna Patologiia
0324-2048	Computational Linguistics and Computer Languages†
0324-3044	Fortnightly Bulletin see 0024-8495
0324-3451	Hungarian Book Review†
0324-4202	Kulgazdasag
0324-4628	Publications of the Technical University for Heavy Industry. Series A, Mining
0324-4652	Neohelicon
0324-4679	Publications of the Technical University for Heavy Industry. Series B, Metallurgy
0324-5268	Attila Jozsef University. Acta Geographica
0324-542X	Alba Regia
0324-5934	Studia Iuridica Auctoritate Universitatis Pecs Publicata
0324-6051	Periodica Polytechnica. Mechanical Engineering
0324-6817	Severni Morava
0324-6965	Acta Universitatis Szegediensis de Attila Jozsef Nominatae. Acta Historica
0324-7007	Pravnik
0324-7171	Allam es Igazgatas
0324-721X	Attila Jozsef University. Acta Cybernetica
0324-7228	Valosag
0324-7260	Acta Universitatis Szegediensis de Attila Jozsef Nominatae. Sectio Paedagogica et Psychologica
0324-7341	Modszertani Kiadvanyok†
0324-7473	New Hungarian Exporter see 0238-602X
0324-7627	Honismeret
0324-7880	Studias Humanitas
0324-7961	Spolecenske Vedy ve Skole
0324-8003	Kartkowy Katalog Nowosci
0324-802X	Politechnika Slaska. Zeszyty Naukowe. Hutnictwo
0324-8038	Politechnika Slaska. Zeszyty Naukowe. Jezyki Obce†
0324-8194	Zagadnienia Informacji Naukowej
0324-8208	Teksty see 0867-0633
0324-8232	Sztuka
0324-8240	Szpitalnictwo Polskie†
0324-8283	Studies on International Relations†
0324-8291	Studies in Physical Anthropology
0324-833X	Postepy Biologii Komorki
0324-8429	Annales Societatis Mathematicae Polonae. Seria 4: Fundamenta Informaticae†
0324-8453	Magazyn Fotograficzny FOTO
0324-8461	Archiwum Ochrony Srodowiska
0324-850X	Fotografia
0324-8534	Immunologia Polska
0324-8569	Control and Cybernetics
0324-8739	Przemyslowy Instytut Maszyn Rolniczych. Prace†
0324-8747	Foundations of Control Engineering changed to Foundation of Computing and Decision Sciences.
0324-8763	Polish Ecological Studies
0324-8828	Environment Protection Engineering
0324-8844	Plastyka w Szkole changed to Plastyka i Wychowanie w Szkole.
0324-8895	Uniwersytet Gdanski. Wydzial Humanystyczny. Zeszyty Naukowe. Studium Praktycznej Nauki Jezykow Obcych
0324-8925	Muzeum Literatury im. Adama Mickiewicza. Blok-Notes
0324-8968	Wyzsza Szkola Pedagogiczna, Opole. Zeszyty Naukowe. Seria A. Dydaktyka
0324-8976	Uniwersytet Slaski w Katowicach. Prace Fizyczne†
0324-8992	Wyzsza Szkola Pedagogiczna, Opole. Zeszyty Naukowe. Seria A. Nauki Techniczne
0324-9034	Wyzsza Szkola Pedagogiczna, Opole. Zeszyty Naukowe. Seria A. Chemia
0324-9050	Wyzsza Szkola Pedagogiczna, Opole. Zeszyty Naukowe. Seria A. Filologia Polska
0324-9085	Akademia Rolnicza, Warsaw. Zeszyty Naukowe. Weterynaria changed to Warsaw Agricultural University. S G G W. Annals. Veterinary Medicine.
0324-9166	Akademia Rolniczo-Techniczna. Zeszyty Naukowe. Ekonomika see 0860-2948
0324-9174	Akademia Rolniczo-Techniczna. Zeszyty Naukowe. Geodezja i Urzadzenia Rolne see 0860-262X
0324-9182	Akademia Rolniczo-Techniczna w Olsztynie. Zeszyty Naukowe. Mechanika i Budownictwo Ladowe see 0860-2956
0324-9190	Akademia Rolniczo-Techniczna. Zeszyty Naukowe. Ochrona Wod i Rybactwo Srodladowe see 0860-2611
0324-9204	Akademia Rolniczo-Techniczna. Zeszyty Naukowe. Rolnictwo see 0860-2832
0324-9212	Akademia Rolniczo-Techniczna. Zeszyty Naukowe. Technologia Zywnosci see 0860-2859
0324-9220	Akademia Rolniczo-Techniczna. Zeszyty Naukowe. Weterynaria see 0860-2840
0324-9239	Akademia Rolniczo-Techniczna. Zeszyty Naukowe. Zootechnika see 0860-2603
0324-931X	Politechnika Wroclawska. Instytut Ukladow Elektromaszynowych. Prace Naukowe. Konferencje
0324-9328	Politechnika Wroclawska. Instytut Telekomunikacji i Akustyki. Prace Naukowe. Monografie
0324-9336	Politechnika Wroclawska. Instytut Telekomunikacji i Akustyki. Prace Naukowe. Studia i Materialy
0324-9344	Politechnika Wroclawska. Instytut Telekomunikacji i Akustyki. Prace Naukowe. Konferencje
0324-9352	Politechnika Wroclawska. Instytut Technologii Budowy Maszyn. Prace Naukowe. Monografie changed to Politechnika Wroclawska. Instytut Technologii Maszyn i Automatyzacji. Prace Naukowe. Monografie.
0324-9360	Politechnika Wroclawska. Instytut Technologii Budowy Maszyn. Prace Naukowe. Studia i Materialy changed to Politechnika Wroclawska. Instytut Technologii Maszyn i Automatyzacji. Prace Naukowe. Studia i Materialy.
0324-9379	Politechnika Wroclawska. Instytut Technologii Budowy Maszyn. Prace Naukowe. Konferencje changed to Politechnika Wroclawska. Instytut Technologii Maszyn i Automatyzacji. Prace Naukowe. Konferencje
0324-9387	Politechnika Wroclawska. Instytut Techniki Cieplnej i Mechaniki Plynow. Prace Naukowe. Monografie
0324-9395	Politechnika Wroclawska. Instytut Techniki Cieplnej i Mechaniki Plynow. Prace Naukowe. Konferencje
0324-9409	Politechnika Wroclawska. Instytut Techniki Cieplnej i Mechaniki Plynow. Prace Naukowe. Studia i Materialy
0324-9441	Politechnika Wroclawska. Instytut Podstaw Elektrotechniki i Elektrotechnologii. Prace Naukowe. Konferencje
0324-945X	Politechnika Wroclawska. Instytut Podstaw Elektrotechniki i Elektrotechnologii. Prace Naukowe. Monografie
0324-9468	Politechnika Wroclawska. Instytut Organizacji i Zarzadzania. Prace Naukowe. Studia i Materialy
0324-9484	Politechnika Wroclawska. Instytut Organizacji i Zarzadzania. Prace Naukowe. Konferencje
0324-9492	Politechnika Wroclawska. Instytut Organizacji i Zarzadzania. Prace Naukowe. Monografie.
0324-9506	Politechnika Wroclawska. Instytut Nauk Spolecznych. Prace Naukowe. Monografie see 0239-3204
0324-9514	Politechnika Wroclawska. Instytut Nauk Spolecznych. Prace Naukowe. Studia i Materialy see 0239-3212
0324-9530	Politechnika Wroclawska. Instytut Metrologii Elektrycznej. Prace Naukowe. Przemysl†
0324-9549	Politechnika Wroclawska. Instytut Metrologii Elektrycznej. Prace Naukowe. Monografie
0324-9557	Politechnika Wroclawska. Instytut Metrologii Elektrycznej. Prace Naukowe. Konferencje
0324-9565	Politechnika Wroclawska. Instytut Materialoznawstwa i Mechaniki Technicznej. Prace Naukowe. Monografie
0324-9573	Politechnika Wroclawska. Instytut Materialoznawstwa i Mechaniki Technicznej. Prace Naukowe. Konferencje
0324-9603	Politechnika Wroclawska. Instytut Matematyki. Prace Naukowe. Monografie
0324-9611	Politechnika Wroclawska. Instytut Matematyki. Prace Naukowe. Studia i Materialy
0324-962X	Politechnika Wroclawska. Instytut Konstrukcji i Eksploatacji Maszyn. Prace Naukowe. Monografie
0324-9638	Politechnika Wroclawska. Instytut Konstrukcji i Eksploatacji Maszyn. Prace Naukowe. Studia i Materialy
0324-9646	Politechnika Wroclawska. Instytut Konstrukcji i Eksploatacji Maszyn. Prace Naukowe. Konferencje

5702 ISSN INDEX

0324-9654 Politechnika Wroclawska. Instytut Historii Architektury, Sztuki i Techniki. Prace Naukowe. Studia i Materialy
0324-9662 Politechnika Wroclawska. Instytut Historii Architektury, Sztuki i Techniki. Prace Naukowe. Monografie
0324-9670 Politechnika Wroclawska. Instytut Gornictwa. Prace Naukowe. Konferencje
0324-9689 Politechnika Wroclawska. Instytut Gornictwa. Prace Naukowe. Monografie
0324-9697 Politechnika Wroclawska. Instytut Fizyki. Prace Naukowe. Studia i Materialy
0324-9719 Politechnika Wroclawska. Instytut Inzynierii Ochrony Srodowiska. Prace Naukowe. Konferencje
0324-9727 Politechnika Wroclawska. Instytut Inzynierii Ladowej. Prace Naukowe. Monografie
0324-9735 Politechnika Wroclawska. Instytut Inzynierii Ladowej. Prace Naukowe. Konferencje
0324-9743 Politechnika Wroclawska. Instytut Inzynierii Chemicznej i Urzadzen Cieplnych. Prace Naukowe. Konferencje
0324-9751 Politechnika Wroclawska. Instytut Inzynierii Chemicznej i Urzadzen Cieplnych. Prace Naukowe. Studia i Materialy
0324-976X Politechnika Wroclawska. Instytut Energoelektryki. Prace Naukowe. Monografie
0324-9778 Politechnika Wroclawska. Instytut Energoelektryki. Prace Naukowe. Konferencje
0324-9786 Politechnika Wroclawska. Instytut Cybernetyki Technicznej. Prace Naukowe. Monografie
0324-9794 Politechnika Wroclawska. Instytut Cybernetyki Technicznej. Prace Naukowe. Konferencje
0324-9808 Politechnika Wroclawska. Instytut Cybernetyki Technicznej. Prace Naukowe. Studia i Materialy
0324-9816 Politechnika Wroclawska. Instytut Chemii Organicznej i Fizycznej. Prace Naukowe. Monografie
0324-9824 Politechnika Wroclawska. Instytut Chemii Organicznej i Fizycznej. Prace Naukowe. Konferencje
0324-9832 Politechnika Wroclawska. Instytut Chemii Nieorganicznej i Metalurgii Pierwiastkow Rzadkich. Prace Naukowe. Konferencje
0324-9840 Politechnika Wroclawska. Instytut Chemii Nieorganicznej i Metalurgii Pierwiastkow Rzadkich. Prace Naukowe. Monografie
0324-9859 Politechnika Wroclawska. Instytut Chemii i Technologii Nafty i Wegla. Prace Naukowe. Monografie
0324-9867 Politechnika Wroclawska. Instytut Chemii i Technologii Nafty i Wegla. Prace Naukowe. Konferencje
0324-9875 Politechnika Wroclawska. Instytut Budownictwa. Prace Naukowe. Monografie
0324-9883 Politechnika Wroclawska. Instytut Budownictwa. Prace Naukowe. Konferencje
0324-9891 Politechnika Wroclawska. Instytut Architektury i Urbanistyki. Prace Naukowe. Studia i Materialy
0324-9905 Politechnika Wroclawska. Instytut Architektury i Urbanistyki. Prace Naukowe. Monografie
0325-0075 Archivos Argentinos de Pediatria *see* 0325-3767
0325-0202 Metalurgia Moderna
0325-0210 Ceramica y Cristal *see* 0325-0229
0325-0229 Ceramica y Cristal
0325-0245 Tesis Presentadas a la Universidad de Buenos Aires†
0325-0253 Asociacion Argentina de Mineralogia, Petrologia y Sedimentologia. Revista
0325-0288 Anales de Arqueologia y Etnologia
0325-0326 Industria Azucarera
0325-0342 Physis
0325-0407 Noticiero del Plastico - Elastomeros
0325-0415 Envasamiento
0325-0431 C L A C S O Boletin *changed to* David y Goliath.
0325-0474 Revista Latinoamericana de Ingenieria Quimica y Quimica Aplicada†
0325-058X Revista de la Union Industrial†
0325-0598 Liberacion y Derecho†
0325-0601 Revista de Ciencias Juridicas Sociales
0325-0679 Indice de la Literatura Dental en Castellano
0325-0695 Psicologia Medica
0325-0725 Revista Latinoamericana de Filosofia
0325-0792 Argentina. Escuela de Defensa Nacional. Revista
0325-0806 Revista de Ciencias Economicas. Temas de Administracion *changed to* Administracion.
0325-0822 Revista de Ciencias Economicas. Temas de Economia *see* 0325-0830
0325-0830 Economia
0325-1071 Universidad Nacional de Cordoba. Facultad de Odontologia. Revista
0325-1209 Universidad de Buenos Aires. Instituto de Historia Antigua Oriental. Revista
0325-1276 Bolsa de Cereales. Revista *see* 0045-2467
0325-1306 Centro de Investigacion y Accion Social. Revista
0325-1675 Integracion Latinoamericana
0325-1772 Instituto Nacional de Tecnologia Agropecuaria. Estacion Experimental Regional Agropecuaria. Boletin de Divulgacion Tecnica
0325-1799 Estacion Experimental Region Agropecuaria Pergamino. Informe Tecnico
0325-1888 Revista Argentina de Relaciones Internacionales *changed to* Ceinar.
0325-1950 Argentina. Instituto Nacional de Estadistica y Censos. Boletin de Estadistica y Censos *see* 0326-6214
0325-1969 Argentina. Instituto Nacional de Estadistica y Censos. Boletin Estadistico Trimestral
0325-223X Mendeliana
0325-2280 Patristica et Mediaevalia
0325-2345 Quiron
0325-2388 Economic Information on Argentina
0325-2698 Sociedad Argentina de Estudios Geograficos Boletin
0325-2787 Revista Argentina de Dermatologia
0325-2809 Asociacion de Ciencias Naturales del Litoral. Revista
0325-2868 Archivo General de la Nacion. Revista
0325-3082 Revista Nacional de Aeronautica y Espacial *see* 0001-9127
0325-3147 Argentina. Congreso de la Nacion. Biblioteca. Serie Bibliografica
0325-3228 Rassegna. Revista de Informacion Medica y Cultural
0325-3732 Hickenia†
0325-3767 Pediatria†
0325-383X Argentina. Ministerio de Economia, Hacienda y Finanzas. Boletin Semanal de Economia
0325-3856 Argentina. Museo Provincial de Ciencias Naturales. Comunicaciones. Nueva Serie
0325-3899 Anuario Interamericano de Archivos
0325-4194 Argos
0325-4216 F A C E N A
0325-4453 Nudos en la Cultura Argentina
0325-4615 Summa
0325-5182 Acta Oceanographica Argentina†
0325-5387 Ethos
0325-6146 S C A R Boletin
0325-6251 Bibliotecologia y Documentacion Argentina
0325-6278 Argentina. Instituto Nacional de Tecnologia Industria. Boletin Tecnico†
0325-6375 Instituto Nacional de Investigacion y Desarrollo Pesquero. Revista
0325-6448 Summarios
0325-6502 Psychologica†
0325-6790 Instituto Nacional de Investigacion y Desarrollo Pesquero. Serie Contribuciones
0325-6987 Instituto Nacional de Investigacion y Desarrollo Pesquero. Memoria
0325-7150 Fotomundo
0325-7479 Circulo Argentino de Odontologia. Revista
0325-7541 Revista Argentina de Microbiologia
0325-7592 Limnobios†
0325-7622 Instituto de Numismatica e Historia de San Nicolas de los Arroyos. Boletin
0325-7657 Cuadernos de Numismatica y Ciencias Historicas
0325-8203 Interdisciplinaria
0325-8238 Folia Historica del Nordeste
0325-8637 Lectura y Vida
0325-8815 Boletin de Educacion y Cultura†
0325-8955 Colegio de Abogados de Buenos Aires. Revista
0325-8963 Notas de Geometria y Topologia
0325-9064 Instituto para el Desarrollo de Ejecutivos en la Argentina. Revista
0325-9153 Encuesta de Expectativas Agropecurias†
0325-9161 Situacion Coyuntural del Sector Agropecuario†
0325-9293 Aeronavegacion Comercial Argentina
0325-934X I N T I†
0325-9404 Documentos de Geohistoria Regional
0325-9676 Critica y Utopia
0325-9781 Argentina. Direccion de Investigaciones Forestales. Folleto Tecnico Forestal†
0326-0011 El Rey
0326-0658 Revista Patagonica
0326-0666 Mutantia
0326-0690 Instituto de Matematica Beppo Levi. Cuadernos
0326-0992 Gaceta Agronomica
0326-1190 Jurisprudencia Argentina
0326-1336 Notas de Matematica Discreta
0326-1352 Historia
0326-1417 Centro de Estudios Urbanos y Regionales. Cuadernos
0326-1913 Interdisciplinaria Monographs
0326-1956 Comunicaciones Biologicas
0326-1980 Bimestre
0326-226X L E A
0326-2928 Letras de Buenos Aires
0326-2944 Argentina. Centro Nacional de Documentacion e Informacion Educativa. Boletin Bibliografico
0326-3142 Microscopia Electronica y Biologia Celular
0326-3169 Ciencia del Suelo
0326-3193 Slovensky Zivot
0326-386X Ideas en Ciencias Sociales
0326-3878 Ideas en Arte y Tecnologia
0326-4068 Contribuciones
0326-4629 Veterinaria Argentina
0326-4807 Arte al Dia
0326-5730 Nueva Economia
0326-6214 Argentina. Instituto Nacional de Estadistica y Censos. Estadistica Mensual
0326-6400 Revista Argentina de Linguistica
0326-6427 Revista Argentina de Estudios Estrategicos
0326-6672 Actividad Minera
0326-6680 Bibliografia Teologica Comentada del Area Iberoamericana
0326-677X Plural
0326-6982 Hueso Perdido
0326-7296 Revista Agronomica de Manfredi *see* 0327-151X
0326-7458 Estudios Migratorios Latinoamericanos
0326-7512 Fisica
0326-7857 Boletin de Medio Ambiente y Urbanizacion
0326-7997 Studia Croatica
0326-8071 Lucanor
0326-8101 Argentina Tecnologica
0326-8470 Centro de Estudios Urbanos y Regionales. Boletin
0326-9000 Industria Alimentaria
0326-9442 Etica & Ciencia
0326-9779 Ultimo Reino
0327-022X Revista de Investigacion Contable (Teuken)
0327-0793 Latin American Applied Research
0327-151X Revista Agropecuario de Manfredi y Marcos Juarez
0327-2214 Discurso y Realidad
0327-2915 Indice de Contenidos - Serie 1: Ciencias de la Informacion
0327-330X Revista de Arquitectura
0327-5930 Mundo Israelita
0330-8081 Arab Historical Review for Ottoman Studies
0330-8480 Revue Tunisienne de Communication
0330-8553 Tunisia. Ministere des Travaux Publics et de l'Habitat. Travaux Publics et Habitat *changed to* Revue Tunisienne de l'Equipement.
0330-8987 Revue d'Histoire Maghrebine
0330-9290 Guide Economique de la Tunisie
0331-0019 National Bibliography of Nigeria
0331-0086 Barrister
0331-0094 Nigerian Journal of Entomology
0331-0124 Journal of Medical and Pharmaceutical Marketing
0331-0361 Nigerian Economic Society. Proceedings of the Annual Conference
0331-0388 Association for Teacher Education in Africa. Western Council. Report of the Annual Conference
0331-0515 West African Journal of Educational and Vocational Measurement
0331-0523 Savanna
0331-0531 West African Journal of Modern Languages
0331-0566 Okike
0331-0604 Journal of Pharmaceutical and Medical Sciences
0331-0973 Nigerian Yellow Pages
0331-1481 Nsukka Library Notes
0331-1686 University of Nigeria. Annual Report
0331-2151 Nigeria Bulletin on Foreign Affairs
0331-2585 Business Times
0331-3468 Muse
0331-3646 Nigerian Journal of International Affairs
0331-3735 Nigerian Society of Physiotherapy. Journal
0331-4162 Woman's World
0331-4340 International Institute of Tropical Agriculture. Research Highlights *changed to* International Institute of Tropical Agriculture. Annual Report and Research Highlights.
0331-4448 Nigerian Nurse
0331-4782 Medipharm
0331-5967 Nigerian Engineer
0331-5975 The Truth
0331-6254 Nigerian Institute of International Affairs. Monograph Series
0331-6262 Nigerian Institute of International Affairs. Lecture Series
0331-6742 Noma
0331-7285 Samaru Journal of Agricultural Research
0331-8109 School Libraries Bulletin
0331-8400 Marketing in Nigeria
0331-8494 Healthy Living†
0331-8508 Third World First *see* 0794-3415
0331-8508 Third World First *see* 0189-255X
0331-8524 Nigerian Journal of Political Science
0331-8583 Journal of Business & Social Studies
0331-9237 Lagos Education Review
0331-9911 Positive Review
0332-0006 Dublin. National Library of Ireland. Council of Trustees Report
0332-0111 Irish Birds
0332-0189 Progressive Farmer†
0332-0197 Irish Computer
0332-0197 Telecom Report
0332-0235 Glasra
0332-0375 Irish Journal of Food Science and Technology

ISSN

ISSN INDEX

ISSN	Title
0332-0510	Irish Journal of Psychiatric Nursing†
0332-0561	Irish Rod & Gun
0332-0618	Search
0332-1150	Scripture in Church
0332-1274	Gaelic World
0332-1312	In Touch (Dublin) see 0332-4036
0332-1428	Milltown Studies
0332-1460	Irish Studies in International Affairs
0332-1541	Soundpost†
0332-1568	Aontas Review†
0332-1584	Irish Council for Civil Liberties. Bulletin see 0790-2743
0332-1592	Peritia
0332-1649	Compel
0332-1665	Irish Journal of Environmental Science†
0332-1673	Gaelic Games Monthly
0332-1711	Engineers Journal
0332-1800	Royal Dublin Society. Journal of Life Sciences†
0332-1851	Journal of Earth Sciences see 0790-1763
0332-2262	Farm Machinery†
0332-236X	Irish Veterinary News
0332-2408	Irish Farmers Monthly
0332-2491	Contact
0332-253X	Blazes
0332-2599	Central Bank of Ireland. Quarterly Statistical Bulletin see 0069-1542
0332-2629	Sherkin Island. Journal†
0332-2696	Central Bank of Ireland. Irish Economic Statistics
0332-2742	Central Bank of Ireland. Statistical Supplement to the Quarterly Bulletin see 0791-1785
0332-2793	Central Bank of Ireland. Statistical Tables of the Quarterly Bulletin see 0791-1785
0332-3102	Irish Medical Journal
0332-317X	Irish Stamp News
0332-3293	Irish Law Reports Monthly
0332-3358	Economic Research Institute. Paper changed to Economic and Social Research Institute. General Research Series.
0332-3633	Irish History Workshop
0332-3641	Institute of Guidance Counsellors. Journal
0332-4036	Identity (Dublin)†
0332-4095	International Civil Engineering Abstracts
0332-4117	Cathair na Mart
0332-4214	Scriptores Latini Hiberniae
0332-4230	Mediaeval and Modern Welsh Series
0332-4249	Scribhinni Gaeilgena na Brathar Mionur
0332-4265	Mediaeval and Modern Irish Series
0332-4273	Moorea
0332-4281	Dawn Train
0332-4338	Fisheries Bulletin
0332-4427	Irish Biblical Association. Proceedings
0332-4869	Maynooth Review
0332-4893	Irish Economic and Social History
0332-5024	Studia Musicologica Norvegica
0332-5040	Vaeret changed to Vaer og Klima.
0332-5083	Norway. Fiskeridirektoratet. Skrifter. Serie Ernaering
0332-5121	Gyldendals Aktuelle Magasin†
0332-5210	European Offshore Petroleum Newsletter
0332-5229	Jord og Myr
0332-5237	Northern Offshore see 0305-876X
0332-5326	Norges Roede Kors see 0333-2985
0332-5334	Scandinavian Oil - Gas Magazine
0332-5415	Fokus paa Familien
0332-5423	Kapital
0332-544X	Noroil see 0802-9474
0332-5466	Norsk Advokatblad changed to Advokatbladet.
0332-5474	Norsk Landbruk
0332-5482	Norsk Musikktidsskrift
0332-5512	Tidsskrift om Edruskapsspoersmaal†
0332-5520	Tekstilforum changed to Tekstilforum.
0332-558X	Skipsnytt changed to Skipsrevyen.
0332-5598	Penger og Kreditt
0332-5652	N I P H Annals
0332-5709	Norsk Institutt for Skogforskning. Meddelelser see 0803-2866
0332-5733	Mur
0332-5768	N G U Bulletin
0332-5814	Videregaaende Opplaering
0332-5865	Nordic Journal of Linguistics
0332-5938	Teknikk og Miljoe†
0332-5997	Tradisjon
0332-611X	Ingeniør - Nytt
0332-6128	Moderne Transport see 0802-5193
0332-6136	Norsk Plast
0332-6144	North Sea Observer†
0332-6152	Byggherren
0332-6179	Miljoemagasinet changed to Natur og Miljoe.
0332-6306	A M S - Varia
0332-6411	A M S - Smaatrykk
0332-6470	Norsk Psykologforening. Tidsskrift
0332-6497	Propaganda see 0025-3502
0332-656X	Synopsis
0332-6578	Norske Arkitektkonkurranser
0332-6756	Bergen Banks Kvartalsskrift†
0332-6802	Personal-Opplaering†
0332-6934	Fly-Nytt
0332-6942	Doeves Tidsskrift
0332-7078	Kjoettbransjen
0332-7094	Mot Brann see 0801-6763
0332-7124	Arbeidervern
0332-7167	Skoleforum
0332-7205	Fortidsvern
0332-7299	Norsk Utenrikspolitisk Aarbok
0332-7434	Sunnhetsbladet
0332-7566	Svineavlsnytt
0332-7590	Juristkontakt
0332-768X	Fauna Norvegica Series A. Norwegian Fauna Except Entomology and Ornithology
0332-7698	Fauna Norvegica Series B. Norwegian Journal of Entomology
0332-7701	Fauna Norvegica Series C. Norwegian Journal of Ornithology
0332-7795	Revisjon og Regnskap
0332-7841	Hjelpepleieren
0332-7906	Norway. Statistisk Sentralbyraa. Helsestatistikk
0332-7957	Norway. Statistisk Sentralbyraa. Familie Statistikk†
0332-7965	Norway. Statistisk Sentralbyraa. Alkohol og Andre Rusmidler†
0332-8015	Norway. Statistisk Sentralbyraa. Framskriving Av Folkemengden: Regionale Tall†
0332-8023	Norway. Statistisk Sentralbyraa. Kommune og Fylkestings Valget
0332-8066	Handelsbestyreren
0332-8090	Kongelige Norske Videnskabers Selskab Museet. Rapport. Botanisk Serie see 0802-2992
0332-8171	Datatid
0332-8201	Kontor og Datateknikk
0332-8244	Forum for Utviklingsstudier changed to Forum for Development Studies.
0332-8414	Bondebladet
0332-8554	Gunneria
0332-8678	NAT. Norges Apotekerforenings Tidsskrift see 0802-8400
0332-8821	El Installasjon og Handel see 0802-3212
0332-883X	Politiembetsmennenes Blad
0332-8988	Samferdsel
0332-9038	Sivilforsvarsbladet
0332-9062	Forsvarets Forum
0332-9127	Arbeidsmiljoe
0332-9410	Hold Pusten
0332-9666	Friidrett
0332-9798	Cockpit Forum
0333-001X	Norsk Institutt for Skogforskning. Rapport see 0803-2858
0333-0141	Kroppsoeving
0333-0192	Norsk Maskin-Tidende
0333-0249	Norsk Bedriftshelsetjeneste see 0803-2394
0333-0451	Avis- og Bladlista†
0333-0656	Stavanger Museum. Aarbok
0333-0664	Stavanger Museum. Skrifter
0333-0796	Fysiokjemikeren see 0801-6828
0333-0974	Maihaugen
0333-1024	Cephalagia
0333-130X	Universitets Oldsaksamling. Aarbok
0333-1342	Nordisk Sosialt Arbeid
0333-1423	Norsk Skattelovsamling
0333-144X	Stoffmisbruk
0333-1512	Acta Ad Archaeologiam et Artium Historiam Pertinentia (Miscellaneous)
0333-1555	Utemiljoe
0333-208X	Norway. Statistisk Sentralbyraa. Reiselivstatiskk
0333-2217	Forming i Skolen
0333-2241	I C L A S Bulletin†
0333-2314	Universitetet i Trondheim. Norges Tekniske Hoegskole. Biblioteket. Meldinger og Boklister†
0333-2500	Norsk Institutt for Landbruksoekonomisk Forskning. Driftsgranskinger i Jord- og Skogbruk
0333-273X	European Political Data Newsletter†
0333-2810	Skatterett
0333-2985	Roede Kors
0333-3124	Kristiansand Museum. Aarbok
0333-3302	Automatisering
0333-3329	Huseierens Magasin†
0333-354X	Moebelhandleren
0333-3620	I A S P Newsletter
0333-3728	Norway. Statistisk Sentralbyraa. Fiskeristatistikk
0333-3825	Spraaknytt
0333-3868	Skattebetaleren
0333-3914	Norway. Statistisk Sentralbyraa. Kriminalstatistikk
0333-4112	Norges Geologiske Undersoekelse. Aarsmelding
0333-4325	University of Bergen. Institute of Psychology. Psychological Report Series†
0333-5100	Baavoda Kahelatit
0333-5151	Dapim Licheker Tikufat Hashoah
0333-5194	I O L R Collected Reports
0333-5259	Physical Education and Sport
0333-5275	Geographical Research Forum changed to Geography Research Forum.
0333-533X	English Teachers' Journal (Israel)
0333-5372	Poetics Today
0333-5380	Diamond World Review
0333-5526	United States-Israel Binational Science Foundation. Project-Report Abstracts†
0333-5666	Yeda Lemeida
0333-5690	H S L changed to H S L A.
0333-5771	Israel. Atomic Energy Commission. Annual Report
0333-5844	Qedem
0333-5879	Technion - Israel Institute of Technology. Faculty of Agricultural Engineering. Publications
0333-5895	Isra - Counter-Source†
0333-5925	Israel Yearbook on Human Rights
0333-600X	Israel. Central Bureau of Statistics. Staff in Universities
0333-6018	Israel Book Trade Directory
0333-6131	Calendar of Scientific and Technological Meetings in Israel
0333-6166	Books from Israel†
0333-6190	Israel Academy of Sciences and Humanities. Section of Sciences. Proceedings
0333-6271	Out of Jerusalem
0333-6298	B'Or Ha'Torah
0333-6379	Kibbutz Studies
0333-6387	Noga
0333-6425	Israel. Geological Survey. Current Research
0333-6514	Israel Public Council for Soviet Jewry. Scientists' Committee. News Bulletin†
0333-6697	Svivot
0333-676X	Voices - Israel
0333-6867	Israel - Land and Nature see 0334-9578
0333-6875	Holy Land Postal History
0333-6883	Techumim
0333-6948	P-H'atom
0333-6964	Hebrew University of Jerusalem. Authority for Research and Development. Current Research
0333-7286	A.B. - The Samaritan News
0333-7308	Israel Journal of Psychiatry and Related Sciences
0333-7383	Torgos
0333-7413	Computers
0333-7499	Israel Museum Journal
0333-7502	Mivim
0333-7588	Hadarim
0333-7596	Yad l'Achim Wall Calendar
0333-7618	Jerusalem Cathedra see 0334-4657
0333-7685	Maydaon
0333-7715	Israel. Central Bureau of Statistics. Tourist Hotels
0333-7839	Maurice Falk Institute for Economic Research in Israel. Report and Discussion Paper Series
0333-7936	Israel. Meteorological Service. Monthly Agroclimatological Report
0333-8347	Jewish Language Review
0333-838X	Identity
0333-8428	I D F Journal†
0333-8487	Herodote
0333-8584	Kolot
0333-886X	Local Authorities in Israel: Financial Data
0333-8886	Alon Hanotea
0333-9041	Families in Israel
0333-9068	World Union of Jewish Studies
0333-9270	Oraita
0333-9319	Demama Shelanv see 0792-0814
0333-9521	Technologies
0333-953X	Israel Book News
0333-9661	Studies in Jewish Education
0333-9688	Lamed Leshonkha
0333-9793	Israel. Central Bureau of Statistics. Survey on Research and Development in Industry
0333-9815	Pamphlet for Biology Teachers
0333-9831	Jerusalem Institute for Israel Studies. Discussion Papers - Research Series changed to Israel Studies.
0333-9858	Current Contents of Periodicals on the Middle East
0333-9874	Integrated Rural Development. Publications
0333-9904	Rotem
0333-9971	Tnuah Vetachborat
0334-0082	International Journal of Turbo and Jet Engines
0334-0104	Ottot
0334-0139	International Journal of Adolescent Medicine and Health
0334-018X	Journal of Pediatric Endocrinology
0334-0236	Journal of Orthopedic Surgical Techniques
0334-0430	B'sdeh Habniya
0334-0554	Yidion
0334-0570	Hardun†
0334-0686	Dappim - Research in Literature
0334-0716	Bar-Ilan Law Studies
0334-0740	Metov Tiberia
0334-0899	Apereyon
0334-0953	Jews of the Soviet Union
0334-1003	Yalkut Lemachshava Sotzialistit
0334-1100	Interface
0334-1151	Weizmann Institute of Science. Research
0334-1208	Shappiritt
0334-1240	Tzufit see 0333-7383
0334-133X	Israel Social Science Research
0334-1380	Barkai
0334-1461	Re'em
0334-1488	Mazone Umitbach
0334-1534	Reviews in Clinical and Basic Pharmacology changed to Journal of Basic and Clinical Physiology and Pharmacology.
0334-1607	Excavations and Surveys in Israel
0334-1704	High Temperature Materials and Processes
0334-1763	Reviews in the Neurosciences
0334-1771	Studies in Zionism

5704 ISSN INDEX

0334-1798 Yisrael-Am ve-Eretz†
0334-181X Composite Materials Science *changed to* Science and Engineering of Composite Materials.
0334-1860 Journal of Intelligent Systems
0334-200X Yad Lakore
0334-2026 Israel Studies in Musicology
0334-2050 Environment in Israel. Selected Papers†
0334-2093 Israel's Banking System
0334-2123 Phytoparasitica: Israel Journal of Plant Protection Sciences
0334-2166 Dor le-Dor *see* 0792-3910
0334-2182 Kibbutz (Tel Aviv)
0334-2190 Reviews on Drug Metabolism and Drug Interactions *changed to* Drug Metabolism and Drug Interactions.
0334-2212 Kidma†
0334-2255 Beer-Sheva
0334-2263 Hed Hagan
0334-2301 Israel Dance *changed to* Israel Dance Quarterly.
0334-2336 Da'at
0334-2344 Reviews on Powder Metallurgy *see* 0379-0002
0334-2360 Gerontology
0334-2425 Trade Marks Journal
0334-2468 Current Research in Behavioral Sciences in Israel *see* 0334-7303
0334-2476 Statistics of Travel and Tourism
0334-2484 Agricultural Research Organization. Special Publications
0334-2506 Forum†
0334-2514 State, Government and International Relations
0334-2565 Eiunim Bicheinuch
0334-2573 Israel. Central Bureau of Statistics. Agricultural Statistics Quarterly
0334-2581 Hebrew University of Jerusalem. News *changed to* Hebrew University. News.
0334-2700 Australian Mathematical Society. Journal. Series B. Applied Mathematics
0334-2751 Sapanut
0334-276X Sifrut Yeladim Vanoar
0334-2786 Jerusalem Papers on Peace Problems†
0334-2808 Mid-East and World Shipping News(Information Paper) *changed to* Mediterranean and World Shipping News (Information Paper).
0334-2816 Divrei ha-Akademia ha-Leumit ha-Yisraelit Lemadaim
0334-2824 Directory of Scientific and Technical Associations in Israel
0334-2867 Ma'agalai Keri'a
0334-2875 Directory of Research Institutes and Industrial Research Units in Israel *see* 0334-3197
0334-2921 Index to Hebrew Periodicals
0334-2948 Journalism Yearbook
0334-3022 Pashosh
0334-3057 Israel Electronics
0334-3065 Rivaon ha-Yisraeli l'Misim
0334-309X Bibliography of Modern Hebrew Literature in Translation
0334-3162 Israel. Environmental Protection Service. Ekhut ha-Svivah be-Yisrael. Luakh Shnati *changed to* Israel. Ministry of the Environment. Misrad Le-Ichut ha-Svivah. Doch Shnati.
0334-3170 Baeretz Yisrael
0334-3197 Directory of Research Institutes and Industrial Laboratories in Israel†
0334-3251 Siach†
0334-326X Argamon
0334-3278 Israel. Central Bureau of Statistics. New Statistical Projects and Publications in Israel
0334-3316 Australian Mathematical Society. Journal. Series A. Pure Mathematics *see* 0263-6115
0334-3405 Slavica Hierosolymitana
0334-3510 Israel. Geological Survey. Current Bibliography of Middle East Geology
0334-357X Halochame
0334-3626 Leshonenu
0334-3650 Tarbiz
0334-3715 Levantina
0334-3774 Horizons
0334-3804 Israel Environment Bulletin
0334-3847 Innovation
0334-3863 Babniyah Building Centre of Israel Quarterly *changed to* Building Centre of Israel Bulletin.
0334-3871 Assia
0334-3898 Israel Business†
0334-3928 Eitanim
0334-3952 Ma'asef *see* 0792-2337
0334-4029 Society and Welfare
0334-4088 Pe'amim
0334-4096 Jerusalem Letter - Viewpoints
0334-4118 Jerusalem Studies in Arabic and Islam
0334-4142 Soviet Union and the Middle East
0334-4150 Michael
0334-4169 Maeda Lerofei
0334-4258 Gal-ed
0334-4266 Modern Hebrew Literature
0334-4355 Tel Aviv Journal of Archaeology
0334-438X Jews and the Jewish People - Jewish Samizdat
0334-4401 Israel Oriental Studies
0334-4479 Salit
0334-4525 Avareyanut Vestiya Cheurati
0334-4541 Bank of Israel. Annual Statistics of Israel's Banking System
0334-4568 Ha-Hinukh ha-Meshutaf
0334-4649 Crossroads
0334-4657 Cathedra
0334-4754 Alei Sefer
0334-4762 Social Research Review
0334-4770 Studies in Educational Administration and Organization
0334-4827 Alei Siach
0334-4975 Proza
0334-5076 Alon Lamorah Lesifrut
0334-5084 Alim
0334-5114 Symbiosis
0334-5262 New Reference Books
0334-5807 Water and Irrigation Review
0334-5831 Adam Chofshe
0334-5904 Yearbook for Jewish Communities and Organizations *changed to* Jewish World.
0334-5963 Assaph. Section C. Studies in the Theatre
0334-5971 Yedion *changed to* S S D A Newsletter.
0334-6080 Israel Quarterly of Psychology
0334-6447 Journal of Polymer Engineering
0334-648X Kulanu
0334-6641 Jews and Jewish Topics in Soviet and East European Publications *changed to* Jews and Jewish Topics in the Soviet Union and Eastern Europe.
0334-6943 Siratim
0334-6986 Sidra
0334-6994 Kabbalah
0334-701X Jewish History
0334-7303 Current Research in the Social Sciences in Israel
0334-7311 Michmanim
0334-7397 Inyan-Chaddash
0334-7524 Preventive Pediatrics
0334-7532 Michkar Chaklaei Beyisrael
0334-7559 Siah Mesharim
0334-7575 Main Group Metal Chemistry
0334-7613 Special Education and Rehabilitation
0334-7621 Smol
0334-7680 Elektronika Umachshavim
0334-794X Adrichalut
0334-8466 Romach
0334-8814 Megadim
0334-889X Semana
0334-8903 Dispersion y Unidad†
0334-8938 Journal of the Mechanical Behavior of Materials
0334-8954 Aurora
0334-9012 J D C - Brookdale Institute of Gerontology and Human Development in Israel. Discussion Papers
0334-908X J D C - Brookdale Institute of Gerontology and Human Development in Israel. Special Series
0334-9101 J D C - Brookdale Institute of Gerontology and Human Development in Israel. International Forum
0334-9144 Aging in the Jewish World
0334-9152 Israel Journal of Veterinary Medicine
0334-9160 Leumi Review
0334-9195 Main Group Metal Chemistry
0334-9330 Sihot
0334-9470 Lo Nishkach
0334-9527 Taglit
0334-9578 Eretz
0334-9594 Yerusholaimer Almanakh
0334-9721 Israel. Central Bureau of Statistics. Projections of Population in Judea, Samaria and Gaza Area up to 2002
0334-973X Be'emmet
0334-9748 Moreshet Derech
0334-9810 Mishkafayim
0334-9977 Journal of Social Work and Policy in Israel
0334-9985 Biton Lemorim Le'Aravit
0335-0274 I N R S Bulletin de Documentation
0335-0290 Association Francaise d'Amitie et de Solidarite avec les Peuples d'Afrique. Bulletin d'Information *see* 0339-9958
0335-0894 Migrants Formation
0335-1653 Association Francaise pour l'Etude du Sol. Science du Sol. Bulletin
0335-1971 Numismatique & Change
0335-2013 Relations Internationales
0335-2021 Construction Neuve et Ancienne
0335-2927 Theatre Public
0335-2986 Gymnastique Volontaire
0335-3559 Repertoire de Materiaux et Elements Controles du Batiment†
0335-3710 Bulletin Technique Apicole
0335-377X Pulp and Paper/Pates et Papiers†
0335-394X Guide de l'Acheteur NF†
0335-3958 Quercy Recherche
0335-4024 Reunion. Service de Statistique Agricole. Notes de Conjoncture *see* 1150-1448
0335-4105 Council of Europe. Information Bulletin on Social Policy/Bulletin d'Information sur la Politique Sociale†
0335-5012 Assemblee Nouvelle
0335-5047 Droit et Pratique du Commerce International
0335-508X Bulletin des Etudes Valeryennes
0335-5233 Archeologie en Bretagne
0335-5276 Courrier de l'Industriel du Bois et de l'Ameublement *see* 0296-8541
0335-5322 Actes de la Recherche en Sciences Sociales
0335-5330 Documents de Cartographie Ecologique *changed to* Revue d'Ecologie Alpine.
0335-5985 Archives de Sciences Sociales des Religions
0335-6280 Cinema Politique
0335-6469 Calao
0335-6566 Mineraux et Fossiles
0335-704X Escargot *see* 0153-4602
0335-7163 Centre de Promotion de la Presse Industrielle et Scientifique Francaise. Revue des Sommaires†
0335-7368 Nouvelle Revue d'Optique *see* 0150-536X
0335-7457 Revue Francaise d'Allergologie et Immunologie Clinique
0335-752X Nouvelles du Livre Ancien
0335-7619 Tribune Medicale
0335-8259 France. Centre National pour l'Exploitation des Oceans. Colloques. Actes *see* 0761-3962
0335-9190 L.S.I.
0335-9255 Sciences de la Terre: Serie Informatique Geologique
0335-9395 Combat pour la Paix *see* 0184-0932
0335-9956 Officiel
0336-030X Heimdal
0336-1357 Universite de Lyon III. Faculte de Droit. Annales *changed to* Universite Jean Moulin. Annales.
0336-1438 L'Ethnographie
0336-1454 France. Institut National de la Statistique et des Etudes Economiques. Economie et Statistique
0336-1454 France. Institut National de la Statistique et des Etudes Economiques. Economie et Statistique (Microfiche Edition)
0336-1470 Centre d'Etude des Revenus et des Couts. Documents
0336-1489 Defense Nationale
0336-1519 Ecole Francaise d'Extreme-Orient. Bulletin
0336-156X Revue des Etudes Islamiques
0336-1578 Revue des Sciences Sociales de la France de l'Est
0336-1667 Architecture Mouvement Continuite *see* 0998-4194
0336-1675 A M C *see* 0998-4194
0336-1721 Pluriel
0336-2086 A G E C O P Liaison
0336-2698 Archontes†
0336-3112 France. Centre National pour l'Exploitation des Oceans. Centre Oceanologique de Bretagne. Recueil des Travaux *changed to* France. I.F.Re.Mer. Centre de Brest. Recueil des Travaux.
0336-321X Presence des Lettres et des Arts
0336-335X Solidaires *changed to* Solidaires - Lumiere du Monde.
0336-3686 International Copyright Information Centre. Information Bulletin†
0336-3945 New Caledonia. Institut Territorial de la Statistique et des Etudes Economiques. Informations Statistiques Rapides
0336-4437 A.F.C. *see* 0395-2096
0336-4895 Recherche, Pedagogie et Culture†
0336-5522 Travaux et Documents de Geographie Tropicale *changed to* Espaces Tropicaux.
0336-5638 France. Ministere de l'Agriculture. Collections de Statistique Agricole *see* 0998-4186
0336-5697 Annuaire de Statistique Agricole du Departement de la Reunion *see* 1150-1456
0336-626X Aeroports Magazine
0336-6324 Maghreb, Machrek, Monde Arabe
0336-6979 France. Institut National de la Statistique et des Etudes Economiques. Documents Divers *changed to* Reunion. Institut National de la Statistique et des Etudes Economiques. Collection: Documents.
0336-8300 Societe Versaillaise des Sciences Naturelles. Bulletin
0336-9331 Fiches du Cinema
0336-9420 Combat Socialiste†
0336-9455 Connaissance du Pays d'Oc
0336-9609 Revue Sexpol
0336-9730 Traverses†
0336-9749 Babillard *see* 0338-5922
0336-9919 France. Ministere de l'Agriculture. Service Central des Enquetes et Etudes Statistiques. Bulletin de Statistique Agricole *changed to* France. Ministere de l'Agriculture et de la Foret. Series: Le Bulletin.
0336-9943 France. Ministere de l'Agriculture. Cahiers de Statistiques Agricoles *see* 0998-4178
0336-9994 Societe Geologique de Normandie et des Amis du Museum du Havre. Bulletin Trimestriel
0337-1573 France. Laboratoire Central des Ponts et Chaussees. Rapport General d'Activite
0337-1883 Haut-Parleur
0337-1891 Hifi Stereo
0337-2014 Paradoxes†
0337-2219 Industrie du Petrole dans le Monde - Gaz - Petrochimie *see* 0220-3294
0337-2731 Ingenierie-Information
0337-274X Ingeniere-Edition Regionale, Sud-Ouest de la France
0337-307X Futuribles

ISSN

0337-4084 C E N A D D O M Bulletin d'Information *see* 0769-3478
0337-4092 Actualite, Combustibles, Energie†
0337-5714 Repertoire General de la Production Francaise *changed to* La France de l'Industrie et ses Services.
0337-5781 Guide du Feu
0337-5927 Annuaire National M.K.D.E. France *see* 0337-5935
0337-5935 Annuaire National des Masseurs Kinesitherapeutes
0337-5978 Mots en Liberte, Bulletin d'Etudes Lexicales†
0337-5986 Lexique Dernier†
0337-6176 Universite de la Reunion. Cahier†
0337-6680 Union Genealogique du Centre. Informations Genealogiques *changed to* Union Genealogique du Centre. Informations Genealogiques du Centre.
0337-7091 Regards sur l'Actualite
0337-7393 Revue de Jurisprudence Fiscale
0337-8500 Journal des Electriciens
0337-8659 Eclats de Rire
0337-8888 Nostra
0337-9353 Loisirs Service-Sports Europe
0337-9736 Revue d'Orthopedie Dento-Faciale
0337-9965 Technicien Biologiste *see* 0766-5725
0338-0181 Khamsin
0338-0548 Bulletin d'Informations Proustiennes
0338-0610 Diagonal
0338-1439 Cahiers Medicaux†
0338-1552 Nouveau Pouvoir Judiciaire
0338-1684 Diabete & Metabolisme
0338-1757 Solidaires (Paris)
0338-1900 Oeuvres et Critiques
0338-2060 Revue Francaise d'Etudes Politiques Mediterraneennes
0338-2079 Revue du Magnetisme-Etude du Psychisme Experimental
0338-2397 Psychanalyse a l'Universite
0338-2842 H *changed to* H L M Aujourd'hui.
0338-3423 France. Ministere de la Sante et de la Securite Sociale. Sante, Securite Sociale. Statistiques et Commentaires *changed to* Solidarite - Sante.
0338-4187 D F Actualites *changed to* A Propos (Paris).
0338-4241 France. Direction de la Prevision. Rationalisation des Choix Budgetaires†
0338-4284 France. Ministere des Affaires Sociales et de la Solidarite Nationale. Bulletin Mensuel des Statistiques du Travail.
0338-4284 Participation
0338-4446 Bibliotheque Nationale Bulletin *see* 0249-7344
0338-4535 Revue Francaise de Transfusion et Immuno-Hematologie
0338-5922 France. Secretariat d'Etat aux Universities. Service des Bibliotheques. Division de la Cooperation et de l'Automatisation. Bulletin de la DICA†
0338-6473 Propriete Industrielle Bulletin Documentaire
0338-7070 Centre Lyonnais d'Acupuncture de Saint-Luc. Bulletin de Liaison
0338-7208 Cahiers Bleus
0338-8190 Inconnu
0338-9529 Handicapes Mechants
0338-9898 Revue Francaise des Laboratoires
0339-0047 Secrets de l'Histoire†
0339-0055 Presence de l'Enseignement Agricole Prive
0339-0462 Foi et Developpement
0339-0608 Collections et Monnaies *see* 0183-8490
0339-0713 Sapho
0339-0934 Citoyen
0339-1116 Centre Auvergne Gadz'arts. Bulletin Trimestriel des Ingenieurs Arts et Metiers de la Region Auvergne
0339-1493 Photoroman d'Amour
0339-1507 Sol et Murs Magazine
0339-1531 50 Millions de Consommateurs
0339-154X Consommateurs Actualites *changed to* I N C Hebdo Consommateurs Actualites.
0339-1558 Composants Mecaniques, Electriques et Electroniques *see* 1148-7305
0339-1744 Purushartha
0339-2171 Cahiers d'Etudes et de Recherche Victoriennes *see* 0220-5610
0339-2899 France. Centre National pour l'Exploitation des Oceans. Publications. Serie: Rapports Scientifiques et Techniques *see* 0761-3970
0339-2902 Resultats des Campagnes a la Mer *changed to* Campagnes Oceanographiques Francaises.
0339-2910 France. Centre National pour l'Exploitation des Oceans. Publications. Serie: Rapports Economiques et Juridiques *see* 0761-3938
0339-2945 France. Departement d'Economie et de Sociologie Rurales. Bulletin d'Information†
0339-3070 Faire
0339-3097 Cahiers de l'Analyse des Donnees
0339-3275 Interfolk
0339-3666 Profils Medico-Sociaux
0339-4212 I N E S Informations *see* 0980-3637
0339-5081 Unites Petrochimiques en Europe de l'Ouest†
0339-6460 Notes d'Informations Communautaires *changed to* Actualites Communautaires.
0339-6517 Documents Pour le Medecin du Travail
0339-6851 Actes "Cahiers d'Action Juridique"
0339-686X Champ Social
0339-6886 Revoltes Logiques
0339-722X S T A L
0339-7238 Association des Techniciens d'Animaux de Laboratoire. Bulletin Trimestriel *see* 0339-722X
0339-7513 Education Permanente
0339-7963 Cuisine Chez Sol
0339-8390 Fleurs de France
0339-8498 Belisane
0339-8617 Dossiers de Puericulture Information
0339-8811 Universite de Paris VII. Groupe de Linguistique Japonaise. Travaux *changed to* Travaux de Linguistique Japonaise.
0339-8943 Cinema Different
0339-8978 Changer le Cinema
0339-9052 Cheval Hebdo
0339-9702 Mecanisation Forestiere
0339-9958 Aujourd'hui l'Afrique
0340-000X Bibliotheksforum Bayern
0340-0026 International Journal of Clinical Pharmacology and Biopharmacy *see* 0174-4879
0340-0034 Communication and Cybernetics
0340-0050 International Classification
0340-0077 Technische Universitaet Hannover. Franzius - Institut fuer Wasserbau und Kuesteningenieurwesen. Mitteilungen *changed to* Franzius - Institut fuer Wasserbau und Kuesteningenierurwesen. Mitteilungen.
0340-0093 Medizinische Psychologie†
0340-0107 Zeitungs - Index
0340-0123 Beitraege zur Psychodiagnostik des Kindes
0340-0131 International Archives of Occupational and Environmental Health
0340-0158 Communications†
0340-0174 Zeitschrift fuer Historische Forschung
0340-0204 Journal of Non-Equilibrium Thermodynamics
0340-0220 Exakt†
0340-0255 Die Friedens - Warte
0340-031X Wissenschaftliche Forschungsberichte. Reihe 1. Grundlagenforschung und Grundlegende Methodik. Abt. C. Psychologie†
0340-0352 I F L A Journal
0340-0409 Bibliographia Cartographica
0340-0425 Leviathan
0340-0441 Scala
0340-045X International Journal of Law Libraries *see* 0731-1265
0340-0476 Materialien zur Politischen Bildung†
0340-0522 International Bulletin for Research on Law in Eastern Europe.†
0340-0603 Epitaph
0340-062X Journal of Geophysics†
0340-0700 Staatsbibliothek Preussischer Kulturbesitz. Ausstellungskataloge
0340-0727 Psychological Research
0340-0751 Deutsche Forschungsberichte *see* 0343-5520
0340-076X Zeitschrift fuer Klinische Chemie und Klinische Biochemie *see* 0939-4974
0340-0778 Stereo
0340-0794 Wilhelm Roux's Archives of Developmental Biology *see* 0930-035X
0340-0816 Auszuege aus den Offenlegungsschriften. Teil 1. Grund- und Rohstoffindustrie, Chemie und Huetten-wesen, Bauwesen und Bergbau
0340-0824 Zeitschrift fuer Archaeologie des Mittelalters
0340-0840 Funktionsanalyse Biologischer Systeme
0340-0867 Auszuege aus den Offenlegungsschriften. Teil 2. Elektrotechnik, Physik, Feinmechanik und Optik, Akustik
0340-0905 Waking and Sleeping†
0340-0913 Auszuege aus den Offenlegungsschriften. Teil 3. Uebrige Verarbeitungsindustrie und Arbeitsverfahren, Maschinen- und Fahrzeugbau, Ernaehrung, Landwirtschaft
0340-0956 Sportwissenschaftliche Dissertationen†
0340-1022 Topics in Current Chemistry
0340-1057 Biophysics of Structure and Mechanism *see* 0175-7571
0340-112X Graue Literatur zur Orts Regional- und Landesplanung
0340-1162 Immunitaet und Infektion
0340-1170 Kommunalwissenschaftliche Dissertationen
0340-1200 Biological Cybernetics
0340-1227 Virchows Archiv. Section A: Pathological Anatomy and Histology. *see* 0174-7398
0340-1294 Bergwelt *changed to* Alpin.
0340-1324 Cleveland *see* 0160-8533
0340-1332 Handbuch der Internationalen Dokumentation und Information
0340-1502 Rassegna Tecnica A E G-Telefunken†
0340-1545 Online
0340-1588 Laryngologie, Rhinologie, Otologie und ihre Grenzgebiete Vereinigt mit Monatsschrift fuer Ohrenheilkunde *see* 0935-8943
0340-160X Die Dritte Welt†
0340-1618 RoeFo. Fortschritte auf dem Gebiete der Roentgenstrahlen und der Nuklearmedizin *see* 0936-6652
0340-1626 Kunst Magazin
0340-1650 Wirtschaftwissenschaftliches Studium (WIST)
0340-1669 Monatsschrift fuer Unfallheilkunde *see* 0177-5537
0340-1677 Psychologie Heute
0340-1707 Deutsches Institut fuer Wirtschaftsforschung. Vierteljahrshefte zur Wirtschaftsforschung
0340-1723 Pflanzenschutz-Nachrichten Bayer
0340-174X Suedosteuropa - Mitteilungen
0340-1758 Zeitschrift fuer Parlamentsfragen
0340-1766 Der Freie Zahnarzt
0340-1774 Informationen zur Modernen Stadtgeschichte (I M S)
0340-1790 Bayerisches Staatsministerium fuer Arbeit und Sozialordnung. Amtsblatt.†
0340-1804 Zeitschrift fuer Soziologie
0340-1812 Monatsschrift fuer Deutsches Recht
0340-1855 Zeitschrift fuer Rheumatologie
0340-1863 Applied Sciences and Development *changed to* Applied Geography and Development.
0340-188X Mindener Geschichtsverein. Mitteilungen
0340-1898 Deutsches Tieraerzteblatt
0340-1901 Aktuelle Probleme der Intensivmedizin†
0340-1952 F und M, Feinwerktechnik und Messtechnik
0340-1960 Current Topics in Nutritional Sciences†
0340-2002 C.I.I.A. Symposia†
0340-2037 Divice†
0340-2061 Anatomy and Embryology
0340-2096 Anatomia, Histologia, Embryologia. Series C
0340-210X Aktuelle Probleme der Polymer-Physik†
0340-2118 European Journal of Applied Microbiology *see* 0175-7598
0340-2134 Physica Didactica
0340-2150 Praxis der Sozialpsychologie†
0340-2185 B T†
0340-2193 Zeitschrift fuer Physik. Section A: Atomic and Nuclei *see* 0930-1151
0340-2207 Der Fremdsprachliche Unterricht
0340-2215 Studien zur Altaegyptischen Kultur
0340-224X Zeitschrift fuer Physik. Section B. Quanta and Matter *see* 0722-3277
0340-2258 Der Deutschunterricht
0340-2266 Entomologica Germanica *see* 0171-8177
0340-2274 Staatsbibliothek Preussischer Kulturbesitz. Jahresbericht
0340-2304 Sozialwissenschaftliche Informationen fuer Unterricht und Studium
0340-2355 Suedwestdeutsche Schulblaetter†
0340-2371 Ernaehrungs Umschau
0340-2398 Zeitschrift fuer Bevoelkerungswissenschaft: Demographie
0340-241X Veroeffentlichungen aus der Pathologie
0340-2444 Zeitschrift fuer Arbeitswissenschaft
0340-2452 Fortschritte im Integrierten Pflanzenschutz†
0340-2479 Zeitschrift fuer Unternehmens- und Gesellschaftsrecht
0340-2495 Denkmalpflege in Baden-Wuerttemberg
0340-2509 Spezielle Anorganische Chemie†
0340-2541 Aktuelle Dermatologie
0340-255X Progress in Colloid and Polymer Science
0340-2592 Der Urologe. Section A
0340-2649 Unfallchirurgie
0340-2657 Der Chemieunterricht†
0340-269X Phytocoenologia
0340-2703 Wissenschaftliche Forschungsberichte. Reihe 2. Anwendungstechnik und Angewandte Wissenschaft†
0340-2827 Amerikastudien
0340-2924 Surface and Vacuum Physics Index†
0340-2940 Technik in der Medizin†
0340-2967 F und I-Bau
0340-2991 Condition
0340-3009 Buero-Wirtschaft *see* 0007-3148
0340-3017 Zahnaerzteblatt Baden-Wuerttemberg
0340-305X Phlebologie und Proktologie *see* 0939-978X
0340-3068 Ibero-Amerikanisches Archiv
0340-3130 Akupunktur: Theorie und Praxis
0340-3157 Acta Pharmaceutica Technologica *see* 0939-6411
0340-3238 Dokumentation Arbeitsmedizin - Documentation Occupational Health *see* 0932-2876
0340-3254 Mitteilungen aus der Arbeitsmarkt- und Berufsforschung
0340-3270 Landesversicherungsanstalt Wuerttemberg. Mitteilungen
0340-3289 Versorgungsbeamte *changed to* Die Versorgungsverwaltung.
0340-3297 Dokumentation Ostmitteleuropa
0340-3343 Chemiefasern - Textil-Industrie

5706 ISSN INDEX

0340-3416 Deutsche Bibliographie: Neuerscheinungen-Sofortdienst *changed to* Deutsche Nationalbibliographie: Vorankuendigungen, Monographien und Periodika.
0340-3440 A B T Informationen†
0340-3475 Dokumentation Tribologie†
0340-3491 Rationelle Buero *see* 0341-1370
0340-3505 Baden - Wuerttembergische Verwaltungspraxis
0340-3513 Elektrowaerme International. Part A: Elektrowaerme im Technischen Ausbau
0340-3521 Elektrowaerme International. Part B: Industrielle Elektrowaerme
0340-3564 Archiv fuer Wissenschaft und Praxis der Sozialen Arbeit
0340-3602 Das Krankenhaus
0340-3637 Der Gemeindetag†
0340-3645 Der Gemeindehaushalt
0340-3653 Gemeinde
0340-367X Sozialversicherungs-Beamte und -Angestellte BSBA *see* 0173-2323
0340-3696 Archives of Dermatological Research
0340-3718 Bonner Energie-Report *changed to* Bonner Umwelt und Energie Report.
0340-3734 Naturhistorischer Verein Augsburg. Bericht *see* 0720-3705
0340-3793 Applied Physics *see* 0721-7250
0340-3793 Applied Physics *see* 0721-7269
0340-3858 D G S
0340-3874 Brunnenbau, Bau von Wasserwerk, Rohrleitungsbau *see* 0937-3756
0340-3912 Architektur und Wohnwelt *see* 0173-8046
0340-3955 Dokumentation Regelungstechnik *changed to* V D I. Informationsdienst Regelungstechnik.
0340-398X K I *see* 0172-1984
0340-3998 Forschung im Strassenwesen
0340-403X Vogelkundliche Berichte aus Niedersachsen
0340-4056 Geschiebe-Sammler
0340-4099 Unterrichtswissenschaft
0340-4137 Management Wissen†
0340-4145 Goettinger Floristische Rundbriefe *changed to* Floristische Rundbriefe.
0340-4196 Hoppea
0340-4242 Germany(Federal Republic, 1949-). Bundesanstalt fuer Gewaesserkunde. Hydrologische Bibliographie†
0340-4277 Beitraege zur Naturkunde Niedersachsens
0340-4285 Transition Metal Chemistry
0340-434X Regelungstechnik *see* 0178-2312
0340-4358 Mathematischen Gesellschaft in Hamburg. Mitteilungen
0340-4366 Physikalisch-Technischen Bundesanstalt Braunschweig und Berlin. Jahresbericht
0340-4404 Mainzer Geowissenschaftliche Mitteilungen
0340-4439 Sanitaer-Installateur und Heizungsbauer *see* 0931-7775
0340-448X Die Neue Hochschule
0340-4528 Internationales Archiv fuer Sozialgeschichte der Deutschen Literatur
0340-4536 Verkehr und Technik
0340-4544 W T - Werkstattstechnik
0340-4552 Promet
0340-4560 Zeitschrift fuer Vermessungswesen
0340-4684 Blood Cells
0340-4730 Regelungstechnik Praxis *see* 0178-2320
0340-4749 Referate: Schweissen und Verwandte Verfahren
0340-4773 Progress in Botany
0340-4781 Osnabruecker Naturwissenschaftliche Mitteilungen
0340-4803 Stahl und Eisen
0340-4811 Zeitschrift fuer Naturforschung. Section A: Physics, Physical Chemistry, Cosmic Physics *see* 0932-0784
0340-4838 Hafenbautechnische Gesellschaft. Jahrbuch
0340-4897 Mathematisch-Physikalische Semesterberichte *see* 0720-728X
0340-4900 Literaturberichte ueber Wasser, Abwasser, Luft und Feste Abfallstoffe
0340-4927 Telma
0340-4951 Zeitschriften- und Buecherschau "Stahl und Eisen" *see* 0933-8934
0340-5044 Die Bautechnik. Ausgabe B
0340-5060 Thyssen Technische Berichte
0340-5079 Tiefbau, Ingenieurbau, Strassenbau
0340-5087 Zeitschrift fuer Naturforschung. Section B: Inorganic and Organic Chemistry *see* 0932-0776
0340-5109 Zentralblatt fuer Geologie und Palaeontologie. Teil I: Allgemeine, Angewandte, Regionale und Historische Geologie
0340-5133 Sprechsaal fuer Keramik, Glas, Baustoffe *see* 0341-0676
0340-5141 Vermessungswesen und Raumordnung (VR)
0340-5176 Deutsches Gewaesserkundliches Jahrbuch. Donaugebiet
0340-5184 Deutsches Gewaesserkundliches Jahrbuch. Kuestengebiet der Nord- und Ostsee
0340-5214 Zentralblatt Hals-, Nasen- und Ohrenheilkunde, Plastische Chirurgie an Kopf und Hals
0340-5303 Die Schwester - Der Pfleger
0340-5354 Journal of Neurology
0340-5362 Bremer Aerzteblatt
0340-5370 Betriebswirtschaftliche Forschung und Praxis
0340-5389 Electromedica
0340-5400 Research in Molecular Biology
0340-5419 Karl August Forster Lectures
0340-5443 Behavioral Ecology and Sociobiology
0340-5508 Medizinisch-Orthopaedische Technik
0340-5559 Dokumentation Impfschaeden-Impferfolge†
0340-5613 Zeitschrift fuer Psychosomatische Medizin und Psychoanalyse
0340-5664 Chirurgia Plastica *see* 0930-343X
0340-5702 Aerztliche Kosmetologie *changed to* T W Dermatologie.
0340-5710 Deutschland in Geschichte und Gegenwart
0340-5737 Die Maschine
0340-5745 A.G.T. Dokumentation
0340-5753 Die Rentenversicherung
0340-5761 Archives of Toxicology
0340-577X Modernes Leben-Natuerliches Heilen
0340-5796 Afrika
0340-580X Hauptschulmagazin *changed to* Lehrerjournal Hauptschulmagazin.
0340-5818 Welt der Schule†
0340-5869 Politik und Kultur†
0340-5877 Der Kinderarzt
0340-5923 Bouvier Disputanda†
0340-594X Studien zur Germanistik, Anglistik und Komparatistik
0340-5958 Studien zur Franzoesischen Philosophie des Zwanzigsten Jahrhunderts
0340-5982 Kybernetik - Datenverarbeitung - Recht†
0340-5990 Studien zur Literatur- und Sozialgeschichte Spaniens und Lateinamerikas
0340-6008 Studien zur Englischen Literatur†
0340-6040 Stahl-Report Lernen und Leisten
0340-6067 Gas Aktuell
0340-6075 Virchows Archiv. Section B: Cell Pathology
0340-6083 Goettinger Predigtmeditationen
0340-6091 Frohe Botschaft
0340-6121 Bibliographie der Wirtschaftswissenschaften
0340-613X Geschichte und Gesellschaft
0340-6199 European Journal of Pediatrics
0340-6210 Luther
0340-6229 Die Welt des Orients
0340-6245 Thrombosis and Haemostasis
0340-6253 Match
0340-6261 Freiburger Beitraege zur Indologie
0340-627X Enchoria
0340-6296 Darmstaedter Blaetter fuer Kulturelle Evolution
0340-6318 Wolfenbuetteler Barock - Nachrichten
0340-6326 Goettinger Orientforschungen. Reihe I: Syriaca
0340-6342 Goettinger Orientforschungen. Reihe IV: Aegypten
0340-6369 Giorgio Levi della Vida Conferences. Reports of the Conference.
0340-6377 Bonner Orientalistische Studien†
0340-6385 Neuindische Studien
0340-6393 Codices Arabici Antiqui
0340-6407 Oriens Christianus
0340-6423 Societas Uralo-Altaica. Veroeffentlichungen
0340-644X Saarlaendisches Aerzteblatt
0340-6490 Schriften zur Geistesgeschichte des Oestlichen Europa
0340-6628 Materialien zur Psychoanalyse und Analytisch Orientierten Psychotherapie†
0340-6652 Universitaet Frankfurt am Main. Ostasiatischen Seminars. Veroeffentlichungen *changed to* Johann-Wolfgang-Goethe-Universitaet, Frankfurt. Ostasiatische Seminar. Veroeffentlichungen. Reihe B: Ostasienkunde.
0340-6679 Submarin†
0340-6687 Ruhr-Universitaet Bochum. Ostasien Institut. Veroeffentlichungen
0340-6695 European Journal of Behavioural Analysis and Modification *changed to* Behavioural Analysis and Modification.
0340-6717 Human Genetics
0340-6725 Zoomorphologie *see* 0720-213X
0340-6792 Studies in Oriental Religions
0340-6989 Kieler Studien
0340-6997 European Journal of Nuclear Medicine
0340-7004 Cancer Immunology, Immunotherapy
0340-7047 Zentralblatt fuer Arbeitsmedizin, Arbeitsschutz und Prophylaxe
0340-7063 Die Schaltung†
0340-7071 Strassenbahn Magazin
0340-7217 Soziale Forschung und Praxis†
0340-7322 Anzeiger fuer Schaedlingskunde, Pflanzen- und Umweltschutz *see* 0340-7330
0340-7330 Anzeiger fuer Schaedlingskunde, Pflanzenschutz, Umweltschutz
0340-7349 Public International Law
0340-7373 Boersenblatt fuer den Deutschen Buchhandel. Frankfurter Ausgabe
0340-739X Eurosport und Freizeitmode *see* 0931-5381
0340-7403 Kritische Berichte
0340-7462 Propellants and Explosives *see* 0721-3115
0340-7489 Baurecht
0340-7497 Zeitschrift fuer Miet- und Raumrecht
0340-7519 Strompraxis
0340-7551 Bundesanstalt fuer Materialpruefung. Amts- und Mitteilungsblatt *changed to* Bundesanstalt fuer Materialforschung und -pruefung. Amts- und Mitteilungsblatt.
0340-7586 Bayerische Akademie der Wissenschaften. Mathematisch-Naturwissenschaftliche Klasse. Sitzungberichte
0340-7594 Journal of Comparative Physiology. A: Sensory, Neural, and Behavioral Physiology
0340-7616 Journal of Comparative Physiology. B. Systematic and Environmental Physiology *see* 0174-1578
0340-7632 Current Contents Africa
0340-7691 Bayerische Kommission fuer die Internationale Erdmessung. Veroeffentlichungen
0340-7705 Forum Ware
0340-7810 V D L - Nachrichten *changed to* V D L - Journal.
0340-7829 Die Pirsch
0340-7837 Land Aktuell
0340-7845 Psycho
0340-7853 Bibliothek der Griechischen Literatur
0340-7888 Literarischer Verein in Stuttgart. Bibliothek
0340-7896 Glueckauf
0340-7918 Betriebs-Berater
0340-7926 Recht der Internationalen Wirtschaft
0340-7969 Allgemeine Zeitschrift fuer Philosophie
0340-7993 Paepste und Papsttum
0340-8035 Monumenta Germaniae Historica. Staatsschriften des Spaeteren Mittelalters
0340-8043 Fachberichte Huettenpraxis Metallweiterverarbeitung *see* 0934-5965
0340-8051 Bibliothek des Buchwesens (B B)
0340-8094 Indices Naturwissenschaftlich-Medizinischer Periodica bis 1850†
0340-8140 Mendelssohn Studien
0340-8167 Taschenbuch fuer Lackierbetriebe (Year)
0340-8175 Giesserei-Kalender
0340-8183 M M G
0340-823X Kriminalitaet und ihre Verwalter
0340-8280 Renovatio
0340-8329 Zeitschrift fuer Luft- und Weltraumrecht
0340-8361 Zeitschrifteninhaltsdienst Theologie
0340-837X Technisches Messen - A T M *see* 0171-8096
0340-8388 Dokumentation Rheologie†
0340-8396 Deutsches Mittelalter, Kritische Studientexte der Monumenta Germaniae Historica†
0340-840X Agrarrecht
0340-8434 Arbeit und Sozialpolitik
0340-8442 Kunststoffberater, -Rundschau, -Technik *see* 0172-6374
0340-8450 Records of the Ancient Near East
0340-8469 Sozialmagazin
0340-8485 Zeitschrift fuer das Gesamte Kreditwesen
0340-8515 Physik und Didaktik
0340-8590 Demokratie und Recht
0340-8604 Deutsche Notar-Zeitschrift
0340-8612 Deutsche Richterzeitung
0340-8671 Biologische Medizin
0340-8728 Vierteljahrschrift fuer Sozial- und Wirtschaftsgeschichte
0340-8744 Empirica
0340-8825 Manuscripta Geodaetica
0340-8833 Ernst-Mach-Institut, Freiburg. Bericht
0340-8906 Grundrechte; die Rechtsprechung in Europa *see* 0341-9800
0340-8973 Forschungsdokumentation zur Arbeitsmarkt- und Berufsforschung
0340-9023 Studien zur Literatur der Moderne
0340-9031 Die Wirtschaftspruefung
0340-9058 Zeitschrift fuer Sportpaedagogik *changed to* Sportpaedagogik.
0340-9066 Fisch und Umwelt†
0340-9090 N A B D - Mitteilungen
0340-9120 Sel'skoe Khozyaistvo za Rubezhom
0340-918X Soziologie
0340-9201 Sozialisation und Kommunikation†
0340-9244 Politikwissenschaftliche Forschung†
0340-9260 Neues Steuerrecht von A bis Z
0340-9279 Betriebliches Vorschlagswesen
0340-9341 Deutsche Sprache
0340-9422 Z O R - Zeitschrift fuer Operations Research *changed to* Z O R - Methods and Models of Operations Research.
0340-9503 Die Steuerliche Betriebspruefung
0340-9511 Medizin in Recht und Ethik
0340-952X Die Tiefbauberufsgenossenschaft
0340-9716 Beitraege zur Umweltgestaltung. Reihe A
0340-9767 Kritikon Litterarum
0340-9783 Hohenheimer Arbeiten
0340-9821 Veroeffentlichungen der Astronomischen Institut der Universitaet Bonn
0340-983X Materialiensammlung Staedtebau
0340-9929 Suedkurs†

ISSN

0340-9937 Herz
0340-9961 Chemie-Technik
0340-997X Hospital-Hygiene†
0341-0013 Katechetische Blaetter
0341-0056 Historia. Einzelschriften
0341-0064 Hermes - Einzelschriften
0341-0099 Beitraege zur Geschichte der Pharmazie *see* 0939-334X
0341-0102 Universitas (Spanish Edition)
0341-0129 Universitas (English Edition)
0341-0137 Deutsche Morgenlaendische Gesellschaft. Zeitschrift
0341-017X Angestellten Magazin
0341-0218 Max-Planck-Gesellschaft. Jahrbuch
0341-0323 Neue D E L I W A - Zeitschrift
0341-0331 Holz-Kunststoff-Moebelfertigung *see* 0933-4580
0341-0382 Zeitschrift fuer Naturforschung. Section C: Biosciences
0341-0390 N V
0341-0412 D L G - Mitteilungen
0341-0455 Altenpflege
0341-0463 Archiv fuer Eisenbahntechnik
0341-0498 Grundlagen und Fortschritte der Lebensmitteluntersuchung und Lebensmitteltechnologie
0341-0501 Aktuelle Ernaehrungsmedizin
0341-051X Aktuelle Rheumatologie
0341-0528 Bundesanstalt fuer Materialpruefung. Jahresbericht *see* 0934-9456
0341-0544 Referateorgan: Zerstoerungsfreie Pruefung
0341-0552 Z I International
0341-0595 Informationsdienst Krankenhauswesen
0341-0609 Kopfklinik†
0341-0668 Rundschau fuer Fleischuntersuchung und Lebensmittelueberwachung *see* 0178-2010
0341-0676 Sprechsaal
0341-0730 Medizin in Unserer Zeit†
0341-0749 Gedenktage des Mitteldeutschen Raumes
0341-0765 Studia Leibnitiana. Sonderhefte
0341-0773 Sudhoffs Archiv. Beihefte
0341-0781 Melliand Textilberichte
0341-079X Archiv fuer Rechts- und Sozialphilosophie. Beihefte
0341-0803 Deutsche Morgenlaendische Gesellschaft. Zeitschrift. Supplementa
0341-0811 Zeitschrift fuer Franzoesische Sprache und Literatur. Beihefte. Neue Folge
0341-082X Wort in der Welt *see* 0723-6204
0341-0838 Zeitschrift fuer Dialektologie und Linguistik. Beihefte
0341-0846 Vierteljahrschrift fuer Sozial- und Wirtschaftsgeschichte. Beihefte
0341-0854 Acta Pharmaceutica Technologica. Supplementa†
0341-0862 Hamburger Hafen - Nachrichten
0341-0900 Angewandte Arbeitswissenschaft
0341-0935 Betriebsverpflegung†
0341-0943 Kritische Medizin im Argument
0341-0951 Forschung Stadtverkehr†
0341-096X Bau
0341-0978 Die Konjunktur im Handwerk†
0341-0986 Internationales Jahrbuch fuer Kartographie
0341-101X Haerterei-Technische Mitteilungen
0341-1052 Die Bautechnik. Ausgabe A
0341-1060 Braunkohle
0341-1117 Sozialpolitische Informationen
0341-1184 Acta Praehistorica et Archaeologica
0341-1206 Umweltmagazin
0341-1222 Archaeologische Ausgrabungen
0341-1230 Aurora
0341-1281 Aerokurier
0341-1362 Electrotechnische Zeitschrift E T Z *changed to* E T Z.
0341-1370 B T S
0341-1478 Korrespondenz Abwasser
0341-1486 Augenaerztliche Fortbildung
0341-1869 I K O - Innere Kolonisation - Land und Gemeinde†
0341-1893 Mineroeltechnik
0341-1915 Neue Juristische Wochenschrift
0341-1966 Kriminologisches Journal
0341-1982 Niedersaechsische Wirtschaft
0341-2016 Der Oeffentlich Bestellte und Vereidigte Sachverstaendige
0341-2032 T A B
0341-2040 Lung
0341-2067 Kleinbrennerei
0341-2075 Blumen Einzelhandel
0341-2091 Deutscher Gartenbau
0341-2105 Gartenpraxis
0341-2172 Wuppertaler Schriftenreihe Literatur
0341-2210 Verkehrsunfall *changed to* Verkehrsunfall und Fahrzeugtechnik.
0341-2253 Wolfenbuetteler Notizen zur Buchgeschichte
0341-2261 Eildienst: Bundesgerichtliche Entscheidungen
0341-2334 Zeitschrift fuer Verkehrserziehung
0341-2350 Klinikarzt
0341-2377 Reactivity and Structure: Concepts of Organic Chemistry
0341-2431 Dokumentation zur Raumentwicklung†
0341-244X Forschungen zur Raumentwicklung
0341-2458 Aerztin
0341-2474 Denkmaeler der Buchkunst
0341-2512 Referateblatt zur Raumentwicklung
0341-2520 Agraringenieur und Agrarmanager
0341-2601 C C B†
0341-261X Lohnunternehmen in Land- und Forstwirtschaft
0341-2679 Wasser, Luft und Betrieb *see* 0938-8303
0341-2695 International Orthopaedics
0341-2709 Aquarium
0341-2717 Baumarkt
0341-275X Vereinigung von Afrikanisten in Deutschland. Schriften
0341-2784 Architektur und Wettbewerbe *changed to* Architecture & Competitions.
0341-2792 Personal-Buero in Recht und Praxis
0341-2903 Notfallmedizin
0341-2911 Medizin *see* 0931-5594
0341-2954 Steuer und Wirtschaft
0341-2970 Europaeischer Wetterbericht
0341-3055 Atemwegs- und Lungenkrankheiten
0341-3063 Intensivbehandlung *changed to* Intensiv- und Notfallbehandlung.
0341-3071 Jugendscala *see* 0940-4961
0341-3098 Muenchener Medizinische Wochenschrift
0341-311X Fenno-Ugrica
0341-3136 Universitaet Bonn. Institut fuer Kommunikationsforschung und Phonetik. Forschungsberichte
0341-3144 Forum Phoneticum
0341-3152 Hamburger Beitraege zur Archaeologie
0341-3187 Hamburger Phonetische Beitraege *see* 0178-1723
0341-3195 Papiere zur Textlinguistik
0341-3209 Romanistik in Geschichte und Gegenwart
0341-3217 Bibliotheca Russica
0341-3225 Linguarum Minorum Documenta Historiographica
0341-3233 Universitaet Hamburg. Institut fuer Internationale Angelegenheiten. Veroeffentlichungen
0341-3241 Universitaet Hamburg. Institut fuer Internationale Angelegenheiten. Werkhefte
0341-3276 Dokumente zur Deutschlandpolitik. Beihefte
0341-3322 Regnum
0341-339X Wirtschaft und Berufs - Erziehung
0341-3403 Atem und Mensch
0341-3489 Industrie der Steine und Erden
0341-3624 Baum-Zeitung
0341-3659 Bau- und Moebelschreiner
0341-3667 Bank und Markt *changed to* Bank und Markt und Technik.
0341-3675 Deutsch Lernen
0341-3683 Diebold Management Report
0341-3756 Die Industriefeuerung
0341-3772 Scripta Geobotanica
0341-3780 Goettinger Geographische Abhandlungen
0341-3810 Bauwirtschaft. Ausgabe A
0341-3896 B I
0341-3918 Bayerische Vorgeschichtsblaetter
0341-4000 Bau-Zentralblatt *see* 0723-6131
0341-4027 Geologisches Jahrbuch Hessen
0341-4035 Nachrichten-Elektronik *changed to* Nachrichten - Elektronik und Telematik.
0341-4043 Geologische Abhandlungen Hessen
0341-406X Drosera
0341-4159 Kunst & Antiquitaeten
0341-4175 E L O†
0341-4183 Bibliothek Forschung und Praxis
0341-4191 Studien zur Indologie und Iranistik
0341-4213 A T W News
0341-440X R A K - Riechstoffe, Aromen, Kosmetica
0341-4434 Arzt und Auto
0341-4477 Betrieb und Meister
0341-4507 Beschaffung Aktuell
0341-4558 Fleisch und Lebensmittelkontrolle *changed to* Fleisch- und Lebensmittelhygiene.
0341-468X Kraftfahrt-Bundesamt. Statistische Mitteilungen
0341-4698 Personalwirtschaft
0341-471X Schulbibliothek Aktuell
0341-4728 Schnellstatistik Allgemeiner Oeffentlicher Bibliotheken†
0341-4817 Haustechnik†
0341-5104 Modell Fan
0341-5112 Mobil†
0341-5163 Nachrichten aus Chemie, Technik und Laboratorium
0341-5198 Archiv fuer Presserecht
0341-5244 Bus-Fahrt
0341-5279 Geographie Heute
0341-5295 Rationelle Hauswirtschaft
0341-5309 Lebensmittel und Gerichtliche Chemie *changed to* Lebensmittelchemie.
0341-5376 Monographs on Theoretical and Applied Genetics
0341-5406 Die Computer-Zeitung
0341-5449 D S W R
0341-5457 D D R Report†
0341-549X D F Z Wirtschaftsmagazin
0341-5570 Techno-Tip†
0341-5589 Elektronikpraxis
0341-5600 Werbeartikel - Berater
0341-5694 Unfallheilkunde *see* 0177-5537
0341-5759 Du und das Tier
0341-5775 Maschinenmarkt
0341-5783 Europa Industrie Revue†
0341-5805 Institut fuer Stadtbauwesen. Veroeffentlichungen
0341-5864 Zielsprache Deutsch
0341-5872 Forschungsarbeiten aus dem Strassenwesen. Schriftenreihe
0341-5910 Publikationen zu Wissenschaftlichen Filmen. Sektion Ethnologie
0341-5929 Publikationen zu Wissenschaftlichen Filmen. Sektion Medizin
0341-5937 Publikationen zu Wissenschaftlichen Filmen. Sektion Geschichte, Publizistik
0341-6151 Law and State
0341-616X Institute for Scientific Co-operation with Developing Countries. Economics
0341-6208 Bankhistorisches Archiv
0341-633X Lecture Notes in Biomathematics
0341-6399 Geologisches Jahrbuch. Reihe A: Allgemeine und Regionale Geologie B.R. Deutschland und Nachbargebiete, Tektonik, Stratigraphie, Palaeontologie
0341-6402 Geologisches Jahrbuch. Reihe B: Regionale Geologie Ausland
0341-6410 Geologisches Jahrbuch. Reihe C: Hydrogeologie. Ingenieurgeologie
0341-6429 Geologisches Jahrbuch. Reihe D: Mineralogie. Petrographie, Geochemie, Lagerstaettenkunde
0341-6437 Geologisches Jahrbuch. Reihe E: Geophysik
0341-6445 Geologisches Jahrbuch. Reihe F: Bodenkunde
0341-6569 Components Report *see* 0173-1726
0341-6593 D T W - Deutsche Tieraerztliche Wochenschrift
0341-6631 China Aktuell
0341-6771 Deike Gedenktage
0341-6836 Meeresforschung
0341-6860 Medien & Erziehung
0341-6879 Gruppe und Spiel
0341-695X Agrartechnik International *changed to* Agrartechnik (Wuerzburg).
0341-6992 Verein fuer Heimatkunde im Landkreis Birkenfeld und der Heimatfreunde Oberstein. Mitteilungen
0341-7115 Brauindustrie
0341-7158 Was und Wie?
0341-7182 Freizeit Pferde†
0341-7190 Kindergottesdienst/Lass mich Hoeren
0341-7212 Aesthetik und Kommunikation
0341-7239 Deutsch-Brasilianische Hefte
0341-7301 Behindertenpaedagogik
0341-7387 Leistungssport
0341-7492 Beiheft zu Leistlingssport†
0341-7522 Geowissen Kompakt
0341-7581 Euro-Revue *see* 0724-4509
0341-759X Meister - Zeitung *changed to* Industrie Meister.
0341-7603 Schule und Museum†
0341-7638 Journal of Literary Semantics
0341-7727 M P G Spiegel
0341-7743 Musikbibliothek Aktuell†
0341-7778 Max-Planck-Gesellschaft zur Foerderung der Wissenschaften Berichte und Mitteilungen
0341-7816 Finnisch-Ugrische Mitteilungen
0341-7840 Germany (Federal Republic, 1949-). Bundesministerium fuer Arbeit und Sozialordnung. Hauptergebnisse der Arbeits- und Sozialstatistik
0341-7948 Praxis des Rechnungswesens
0341-8022 Dokumentation Gefaehrdung durch Alkohol, Rauchen, Drogen, Arzneimittel†
0341-8057 Geographie im Unterricht
0341-8073 Presse Report
0341-8162 Catena
0341-8235 Schul-Management
0341-8243 Lehrmittel Aktuell *changed to* Lehrmittel Aktuell - Lehrmittel Computer.
0341-826X Diakonie
0341-8324 Archiv fuer Frankfurts Geschichte und Kunst
0341-8332 Archiv fuer Angewandte Sozialpaedagogik
0341-8340 Arbeitsinformationen ueber Studienprojekte auf dem Gebiet der Geschichte des Deutschen Judentums und des Antisemitismus
0341-8383 Anzeiger des Germanischen Nationalmuseums *see* 0934-5191
0341-8391 Spixiana
0341-8448 Iconographia Ecclesiae Orientalis†
0341-8510 Praxis der Naturwissenschaften. Biologie
0341-8588 Ost-West Commerz
0341-8634 Museum
0341-8642 Indiana
0341-8669 Umsatzsteuer-Rundschau
0341-8677 Gynaekologische Praxis
0341-8685 International Journal of Physical Education
0341-8693 Internationale Katholische Zeitschrift
0341-8707 Schleswig-Holsteinisches Aerzteblatt
0341-8723 Wissenschaftlicher Literaturanzeiger
0341-8766 Deutsche Verkehrsteuer-Rundschau *changed to* Umsatzsteuer- und Verkehrsteuer-Recht.
0341-8812 Diabetes-Journal
0341-8839 D D S - Der Deutscher Schreiner und Tischler
0341-8960 Religionsunterricht an hoeheren Schulen
0341-8995 Zahnaerztliche Mitteilungen
0341-9002 Schmuck und Uhren
0341-907X Mineralien Magazin†

ISSN INDEX

ISSN	Title
0341-910X	Beitraege Archaeologie des Romischen Rheinlands
0341-9142	Istanbuler Mitteilungen
0341-9150	Bayerische Denkmalpflege. Jahrbuch
0341-9177	Jahrbuch der Historischen Forschung in der Bundesrepublik Deutschland†
0341-9185	Beitraege zur Archaeologie des Mittelalters
0341-9193	Beitraege zur Urgeschichte des Rheinlandes
0341-9258	Geographie *changed to* Uebersee-Museum, Bremen. Veroeffentlichungen. Reihe C: Geographie.
0341-9274	Uebersee-Museum, Bremen. Veroeffentlichungen. Reihe D: Voelkerkundliche Monographien
0341-9312	Romisch-Germanischen Kommission. Berichte
0341-9363	Bibliographie der Deutschen Sprach- und Literaturwissenschaft
0341-938X	Psychologie und Gesellschaft†
0341-9452	Blaetter fuer Pfaelzische Kirchengeschichte und Religioese Volkskunde
0341-9479	Blaetter fuer Wuerttembergische Kirchengeschichte
0341-9495	Quaterner
0341-9622	Bremisches Jahrbuch
0341-9665	Pollichia. Mitteilungen
0341-9681	K F Z Anzeiger
0341-9738	Spektrum der Psychiatrie und Nervenheilkunde
0341-9746	H N O (Cologne)
0341-9754	Arzt und Krankenhaus†
0341-9762	Libertas
0341-9770	Bunte Tierwelt
0341-9789	Rasen - Turf - Gazon
0341-9797	Garten als Jungborn *see* 0930-6749
0341-9800	Europaeische Grundrechte Zeitschrift
0341-9835	Z F A mit Kartei der Praktischen Medizin
0342-0019	Duesseldorfer Jahrbuch
0342-0078	Frankfurter Judaistische Beitraege
0342-0124	Stiftung Preussische Kulturbesitz. Jahrbuch
0342-0175	Jugend Beruf Gesellschaft
0342-0221	Bayerische Staatsbibliothek. Jahresbericht
0342-0329	Aktueller Informationsdienst Moderner Orient
0342-037X	Dokumentationsdienst Lateinamerika
0342-0388	Spiegel der Lateinamerikanischen Presse
0342-0396	Aktueller Informationsdienst Afrika
0342-040X	Dokumentationsdienst Afrika. Ausgewaehlte Neuere Literatur
0342-0442	Dokumentationsdienst Afrika. Reihe A
0342-0477	Sprache - Stimme - Gehoer
0342-0493	S B Warenhaus†
0342-0523	Orgadata
0342-0531	B I B - Report
0342-0671	Erziehung und Wissenschaft
0342-068X	Zeitschrift fuer Flugwissenschaften und Weltraumforschung
0342-0736	Die Kunde
0342-0752	Verein fuer Niederdeutsche Sprachforschung. Korrespondenzblatt.
0342-0787	Kieler Arbeitspapiere
0342-0795	Dokumentation Medizin im Umweltschutz
0342-0809	Kompass
0342-0817	Die Betriebskrankenkasse
0342-0876	Lippische Mitteilungen aus Geschichte und Landeskunde
0342-0884	Linguistica Biblica
0342-0930	Der Langfristige Kred1t
0342-0957	D M I - Die Medizinische Information†
0342-0965	Geschichtsblaetter fuer Waldeck
0342-1058	Spanische Forschungen der Goerresgesellschaft. Reihe 1: Gesammelte Aufsaetze zur Kulturgeschichte Spaniens
0342-1104	Hannoversche Geschichtsblaetter
0342-1120	Algological Studies
0342-1171	Mennonitische Geschichtsblaetter
0342-118X	Deutsche Orient-Gesellschaft. Mitteilungen
0342-1295	Deutsches Archaeologisches Institut. Athenische Abteilung. Mitteilungen - Athenische Mitteilungen
0342-1341	Beitraege zur Geschichte des Alten Moenchtums und des Benediktinerordens
0342-1406	Nachrichten aus Niedersachsens Urgeschichte
0342-1422	Nietzsche-Studien
0342-1430	Theologische Quartalschrift
0342-1457	Theologie der Gegenwart
0342-1465	Una Sancta
0342-1503	Ortenau
0342-1589	Diskussion Deutsch
0342-1643	Diakonie Report
0342-1694	Archiv fuer Arzneitherapie†
0342-1716	Kultur Vorschau Europa
0342-1724	Sport-Vorschau
0342-1732	Deike-Press
0342-1783	Zeitschrift fuer Wirtschafts- und Sozialwissenschaften
0342-1791	Physics and Chemistry of Minerals
0342-1805	Rheinische Heimatpflege
0342-1821	Rechtsprechung zum Wiedergutmachungsrecht†
0342-183X	Psychologie in Erziehung und Unterricht
0342-1864	Iberoamericana
0342-1902	Eisenbahn Modellbahn Magazin
0342-1945	Recht der Arbeit
0342-1953	Fraunhofer-Gesellschaft. Berichtet
0342-197X	Sammlung der Entscheidungen des Bundesfinanzhofs
0342-202X	Forum Staedte-Hygiene
0342-2046	Roemisches Jahrbuch fuer Kunstgeschichte *changed to* Bibliotheca Hertziana. Roemisches Jahrbuch.
0342-2062	Karst und Mozlen Neue Forschungen und Berichte†
0342-2070	Verein fuer Geschichte des Bodensees und seiner Umgebung. Schriften
0342-2119	Z P F - Zeitschrift fuer das Post- und Fernmeldewesen *changed to* Z P T.
0342-2186	Selbstverwaltung und Selbstverantwortung
0342-2216	Textil Report *changed to* Fashion.
0342-2224	Textil Mitteilungen
0342-2259	Der Landkreis
0342-2364	Ulm und Oberschwaben
0342-2372	Theologische Beitraege
0342-2380	Sportwissenschaft
0342-2399	Top Agrar: Ausgabe S - R
0342-2402	Sportunterricht
0342-2410	Verkuendigung und Forschung
0342-2461	Lehrhilfen fuer den Sportunterricht
0342-2534	Verwaltungsprechsprechung in Deutschland *see* 0721-880X
0342-2747	Familiendynamik
0342-2852	Zeitschrift fuer Unternehmensgeschichte
0342-2860	Rad und Sparren
0342-2895	Franzoesisch Heute
0342-2968	Kosmetik Journal
0342-2976	Kosmetik International
0342-300X	W S I Mitteilungen
0342-3018	Tierfreund
0342-3026	Laboratoriums Medizin
0342-3042	Fracht Management
0342-3158	Graphische Kunst
0342-3247	Mikrofauna des Meeresbodens *see* 0176-3296
0342-328X	Z F A
0342-3344	Zeitschrift fuer die Geschichte und Altertumskunde Ermlands
0342-3468	Zeitschrift fuer Zivilprozess
0342-3476	Z L R - Zeitschrift fuer das Gesamte Lebensmittelrecht
0342-3484	Zeitschrift fuer Zoelle und Verbrauchsteuern
0342-3514	Zeitschrift fuer Strafvollzug und Straffaelligenhilfe
0342-3557	Gesetz und Verordnungsblatt fuer das Land Hessen
0342-3573	Bindereport
0342-3689	Mode im Verkauf
0342-376X	G V - Praxis mit Tiefkuehlpraxis *changed to* G V - Praxis.
0342-3816	Die Neueren Sprachen
0342-3867	Heer
0342-3875	Beihefte zur Internationalen Wissenschaftlichen Korrespondenz zur Geschichte der Deutschen Arbeiterbewegung
0342-393X	Zeitschrift fuer Individualpsychologie
0342-3956	Zeitschrift fuer Unternehmensgeschichte. Beihefte
0342-3964	Bibliographie Sozialisation und Sozialpaedagogik†
0342-4022	Abwassertechnik mit Abfalltechnik *see* 0932-3708
0342-4030	Universitaetssternwarte zu Wien. Annalen
0342-4103	Medizinische Informatik und Statistik
0342-4111	Springer Series in Optical Sciences
0342-4316	Zeitschrift fuer Bayerische Kirchengeschichte
0342-4340	Wolfenbuetteler Renaissance Mitteilungen
0342-4553	Schauspielfuehrer
0342-457X	Sportwissenschaft und Sportpraxis
0342-4626	Kraus-Hefte
0342-4634	I S B N Review
0342-4642	Intensive Care Medicine
0342-4650	Garten- und Freizeitmarkt
0342-4758	Freizeit Im Sattel
0342-4774	Fremdenverkehr und das Reisebuero *changed to* European Tourism & Congress - Der Fremdenverkehr.
0342-4839	Schriften des Oesterreichischen Kulturinstituts Kairo. Archaeologisch-Historische Abteilung
0342-4871	Bibliotheca Nostratica
0342-4898	Hoergeschaedigten-Paedagogik
0342-4901	Lecture Notes in Chemistry
0342-491X	Schiffahrt International
0342-4960	Informationsdienst fuer den K F Z-Zubehoer und Ersatzteile-Fachhandel†
0342-507X	Halbjaehrliches Verzeichniss Taschenbuecher
0342-5088	Hauswirtschaftliche Bildung
0342-5142	Glas und Rahmen
0342-5169	Hoch- und Tiefbau
0342-5258	Unsere Jugend
0342-5282	International Journal of Rehabilitation Research
0342-5487	Naturwissenschaften im Unterricht. Biologie
0342-5592	Verwaltungsrundschau
0342-5622	Oil Gas European Magazine
0342-5665	Energy Developments *changed to* Energie Spektrum International.
0342-5681	Bergbau
0342-5746	Politik - Aktuell fuer den Unterricht
0342-5789	Antimilitarismus Information
0342-5800	Confructa
0342-5835	Jahrbuch des Kreises Dueren
0342-5843	Zeitschrift fur Verbraucherpolitik *see* 0168-7034
0342-5851	Zeitlupe
0342-5916	Waegen und Dosieren
0342-5967	Wohnmedizin
0342-5991	Bayerische Akademie der Wissenschaften. Philosophisch-Historische Klasse. Sitzungsberichte
0342-6017	Wirtschaft und Gesellschaft im Unterricht *changed to* Wirtschaft und Gesellschaft im Beruf.
0342-6173	Zielsprache Englisch
0363-619X	Zielsprache Spanisch†
0342-6203	Zielsprache Franzoesisch
0342-6270	Archiv und Wirtschaft
0342-6300	Jahrbuch Deutsch Als Fremdsprache
0342-6319	I W - Report
0342-6335	Weltkonjunkturdienst
0342-6378	Wort und Antwort
0342-6386	Jetzt
0342-6505	Ja
0342-6513	Ja, Das Wort Fuer Alle
0342-6521	Der Zimmermann
0342-6580	Brennstoffspiegel
0342-6610	Uebersee-Museum, Bremen. Veroeffentlichungen. Reihe G: Bremer Suedpazifik-Archiv
0342-6777	Politische Didaktik†
0342-6785	Alexander von Humboldt Foundation. Annual Report
0342-6793	Topics in Current Physics
0342-6831	Integrative Therapie
0342-684X	Veroeffentlichungen fuer Naturschutz und Landschatspflege in Baden-Wuerttemberg
0342-6866	Metamed *see* 0167-9902
0342-6874	W M Allgemeine Verlosungstabelle
0342-6882	W M: Wertpapierberatung
0342-6904	Zur Zeit
0342-6939	W M Teil II: Nachrichten Ueber Deutsche Festverzinsliche Werte
0342-6947	European Petroleum Yearbook
0342-6955	W M Teil III: Nachrichten Ueber Deutsche Aktien, Anteile, Genussscheine, Kuxe
0342-6998	W M Teil Va: Nachrichten Ueber Auslaendische Aktien und Aktienaehnliche Werte
0342-7064	Die Betriebswirtschaft
0342-7102	Konstruktion Elemente Maschinenbau
0342-7145	Theorie und Praxis der Sozialpaedagogik
0342-7161	Teddy
0342-7188	Irrigation Science
0342-7196	Cardiovascular Radiology *see* 0174-1551
0342-7269	Fussboden Forum
0342-734X	Archaeologisches Korrespondenzblatt
0342-7358	Textilarbeit und Unterricht
0342-7439	Arnes Journal fuer Guten Geschmack
0342-7471	Schiedsmanns Zeitung
0342-7498	Praxis und Klinik der Pneumologie *see* 0934-8387
0342-7609	Koelner Aerztliche Nachrichten†
0342-7641	Leder- und Haeutemarkt
0342-765X	Landwirtschaftliches Wochenblatt Westfalen-Lippe: Ausgabe A
0342-7684	Sammler Journal
0342-7706	Staedte- und Gemeindebund *changed to* Stadt und Gemeinde.
0342-7722	Schwartzsche Vakanzen-Zeitung
0342-7749	Der Spediteur
0342-7757	Unsere Katze†
0342-7951	T W
0342-7978	Zeitschrift fuer Plastische Chirurgie *see* 0722-1819
0342-801X	D I N - Taschenbuecher
0342-8036	Bargfelder Bote
0342-8095	Bimbo
0342-815X	Sozialpaedagogische Blaetter
0342-8184	S B Z - Sanitaer, Heizungs- und Klimatechnik
0342-8206	S B Z-monteur
0342-8257	Paedagogische Welt
0342-8281	Rudersport
0342-829X	Die Realschule
0342-8419	Der Uebungsleiter
0342-8613	Photoblaetter
0342-8699	Altfraenkische Bilder und Wappenkalender†
0342-8745	Praxis der Naturwissenschaften. Chemie
0342-8834	Und-oder-Nor und Steuerungstechnik *changed to* Und-oder-nor.
0342-8893	Cancer Campaign†
0342-8915	Bayern Tennis
0342-8974	Wochenschau fuer Politische Erziehung, Sozial- und Gemeinschaftskunde. Ausgabe fuer Sekundarstufe II
0342-8982	Studium Linguistik†
0342-8990	Wochenschau fuer Politische Erziehung, Sozial- und Gemeinschaftskunde. Ausgabe fuer Sekundarstufe I
0342-9148	Nachrichtentechnik
0342-9423	Zeitschrift fuer Mission

ISSN INDEX 5709

0342-9512 Lebensmittel Zeitung
0342-9547 Neue Beitraege zur George-Forschung
0342-9601 Medizinische Monatsschrift fuer Pharmazeuten
0342-9857 Neue Praxis
0343-0103 Loyal
0343-0170 Lernzielorientierter Unterricht†
0343-0200 Die Milchpraxis und Rindermast
0343-0235 Olympische Jugend
0343-0405 Echo aus Deutschland
0343-043X Maschinen Anlagen Verfahren
0343-0510 Bergbau-Berufsgenossenschaft. Geschaeftsbericht *see* 0933-0127
0343-0545 M und A Tagungsplaner Europa *changed to* T W Veranstaltungsplaner.
0343-0553 Ueberblick
0343-0642 M D
0343-0987 Beitraege zur Hydrologie
0343-1002 Medizin Bibliothek Dokumentation†
0343-1088 Kleine Aegyptische Texte
0343-1258 Gratia
0343-1401 Publik-Forum
0343-1657 Literatur fuer Leser
0343-1711 Bergische Handwerk
0343-1762 Althaus Modernisierung *changed to* Modernisieren.
0343-186X Aus dem Antiquariat
0343-1975 Business Report (Abridged Version)
0343-2009 Saecula Spiritalia
0343-2092 Gas
0343-2181 Minerals and Rocks
0343-2246 K K - die Kaelte und Klimatechnik
0343-2319 Office Management
0343-2432 Dermatosen in Beruf und Umwelt
0343-2521 GeoJournal
0343-267X Controller Magazin
0343-2734 Suesswaren-Markt *changed to* Suesswaren-Wirtschaft.
0343-2793 Offenbacher Verein fuer Naturkunde. Bericht
0343-2963 Yorkshire Terrier Journal
0343-3005 Informatik-Fachberichte
0343-3048 Zentralblatt Haut- und Geschlechtskrankheiten
0343-3129 Kunststoffe im Bau†
0343-3137 Deutsche Zeitschrift fuer Mund, Kiefer- und Gesichtschirurgie
0343-3218 Diaconia XP *see* 0933-0771
0343-3226 Selbstbedienung-Dynamik im Handel *see* 0722-6950
0343-3277 Duisburger Journal
0343-334X I P E - Industrial and Production Engineering *changed to* E P E.
0343-3366 Lady International
0343-3420 Dokumentation Neusprachlicher Unterricht†
0343-3463 Elektro Boerse
0343-3528 Primate Report
0343-3560 Schadenprisma
0343-3587 Progress in Orthopaedic Surgery†
0343-3668 Deutsches Schiffahrtsarchiv
0343-382X Der Dachdeckermeister
0343-3838 Der Deutsche Badebetrieb
0343-3846 Deutsche Bauern-Korrespondenz
0343-3919 Getraenke Revue *changed to* Getraenke Handel.
0343-3935 Contrapunkt
0343-4052 Handwerk Aktuell†
0343-4060 Accessories
0343-4079 Das Maler- und Lackiererhandwerk
0343-4109 Soziologische Revue
0343-4117 Bibliographie zur Geschichte der Deutschen Arbeiterbewegung
0343-4125 Contributions to Sedimentology
0343-4133 P z L - Papiere zur Linguistik
0343-4184 Paderborner Almanach
0343-4192 Links und Rechts der Autobahn
0343-4206 HiFi und TV
0343-4346 Deutsche Handwerks Zeitung
0343-4494 Schrifttum Bauwesen: Gesamtausgabe *see* 0722-060X
0343-4648 Geschichte, Politik und ihre Didaktik
0343-4842 Drug Development and Evolution
0343-5121 Express
0343-5156 Winzer Kurier *changed to* Weinwirtschaft Anbau.
0343-5199 Polygraph International
0343-5202 Sprache und Datenverarbeitung
0343-5318 Deutsches Turnen
0343-5334 Didaktik der Mathematik
0343-5377 Zeitschrift fuer Energiewirtschaft
0343-5520 Forschungsberichte aus Technik und Naturwissenschaften
0343-5539 German Chemical Engineering *see* 0930-7516
0343-5555 Husumer Monatshefte
0343-5563 Deutsche Universitaetszeitung *changed to* Deutsche Universitaets-Zeitung.
0343-5571 Film und TV Kameramann
0343-5598 D N V
0343-5733 Arztrecht
0343-5881 Einkaufs 1x1 der Deutschen Industrie
0343-589X Deutsches Bundes-Adressbuch: Industrie, Gross- und Aussenhandel, Dienstleistungen, Organisationen
0343-6047 Das Farbenfachgeschaeft *see* 0175-6575
0343-6098 Anatomica Clinica *see* 0930-312X
0343-639X Fachbuchverzeichnis Mathematik - Physik (Year)
0343-6403 Fachbuchverzeichnis Bauwesen - Architecktur (Year)
0343-6411 Fachbuchverzeichnis Maschinenbau (Year)
0343-642X Fachbuchverzeichnis Elektrotechnik - Elektronik (Year)
0343-6438 Fachbuchverzeichnis Chemie (Year)
0343-6462 Entwicklung und Laendlicher Raum
0343-6519 Entwurf
0343-656X Entscheidungen der Spruchstellen fuer Fuersorgestreitigkeiten
0343-6586 Germany, Federal Republic (1949-). Bundesinstitut fuer Sportwissenschaft. Sportwissenschaftliche Forschungsprojekte Erhebung (Year)
0343-6594 Monatsbericht der Angezeiten Flugunfalluntersuchungsstelle
0343-6667 E G Magazin†
0343-6675 Elektronik Informationen
0343-6691 Erfolg
0343-6705 Erdoel-Informationsdienst
0343-6993 Mathematical Intelligencer
0343-7051 Abhandlungen aus dem Gebiet der Auslandskunde. Series B & C
0343-7108 Der Deutsch Eisenbahner
0343-7140 Alte Uhren *see* 0932-2655
0343-7167 Zeitschrift fuer Umweltpolitik
0343-7183 Packung und Transport
0343-7256 Geographie und ihre Didaktik
0343-7477 Germany (Federal Republic, 1949-). Bundesministerium Fuer Ernaehrung, Landwirtschaft und Forsten. Jahresbericht. Forschung im Geschaeftsbereich des Bundesministers fuer Ernaerung, Land, Wirtschaft und Forsten
0343-7493 Universitaet Muenchen. Geophysikalisches Observatorium, Fuerstenfeldbruck. Veroeffentlichungen. Serie A
0343-7507 P V - Report
0343-754X Economic Bulletin (Aldershot)
0343-7620 Philippia
0343-7647 A Z - Nachrichten
0343-7744 Forum Religion
0343-7868 Informationen - Bildung, Wissenschaft
0343-7892 Deutsche Gemmologische Gesellschaft. Zeitschrift
0343-7906 Stuttgarter Geographische Studien
0343-8090 Institut fuer Wasserwirtschaft, Hydrologie und Landwirtschaftlichen Wasserbau. Mitteilungen
0343-8198 Unser Betrieb
0343-835X Freie Universitaet Berlin. Osteuropa-Institut. Rechtswissenschaftliche Veroeffentlichungen
0343-8449 Fakten
0343-8554 Zeitschrift fuer Lymphologie
0343-8651 Current Microbiology
0343-8732 Gottesdienst
0343-8740 Geldinstitute
0343-8759 Handling
0343-9003 Junge Radio-, Fernseh- und Industrie-Elektroniker
0343-9011 K F Z Zeitschrift fuer den Nachwuchs des Kraftfahrzeuhandwerks
0343-9062 Federal Republic of Germany - Partner of the World
0343-9321 P K V Informationdienst
0343-9429 Klinische Psychologie und Psychopathologie
0343-9445 Schott Intern
0343-9196 Deutsche Verwaltungspraxis
0343-9704 Die Ernaehrungsindustrie
0343-9771 Recht und Schaden
0344-0079 Fruchthandel Adressbuch
0344-015X Liste Pharmindex *changed to* Gelbe Liste Pharmindex.
0344-0249 Wirtschafts-Nachrichten fuer den Linken Niederrhein *changed to* Wirtschafts - Nachrichten.
0344-0338 Pathology, Research and Practice
0344-0354 Alexander von Humboldt-Stiftung. Mitteilungen
0344-0397 Agrarmeteorologischer Wochenbericht fuer Norddeutschland
0344-0591 Sammlung Groos
0344-0915 Universitaet Hohenheim Forschungsbericht
0344-1296 Forst, Holz und Jagd Taschenbuch
0344-1369 Marketing
0344-1407 Taschenbuch fuer Liturgie Kirchenmusik und Musikerziehung†
0344-1415 Die Frauenfrage in Deutschland. Bibliographie
0344-1466 Evangelische Fachhochschulen Darmstadt, Freiburg, Ludwigshafen, Reutlingen. Hochschulbrief
0344-1733 LaborPraxis
0344-1741 Aerztekammer Nordrhein. Bezirksstelle Duesseldorf. Mitteilungsblatt†
0344-1857 Bonner Akademische Reden
0344-208X Advances in Animal Breeding and Genetics
0344-2101 Ganztagsschule
0344-2292 Geschaeftsidee
0344-2330 Haustechnische Rundschau
0344-239X Arbeit und Sicherheit
0344-242X Gulliver
0344-2667 Anschlaeget†
0344-2934 Deutscher Hugenotten-Verein E.V. Geschichtsblaetter
0344-3094 German Yearbook of International Law
0344-3418 Zeitschrift fuer Siebenbuergische Landeskunde
0344-3531 Politik und Unterricht
0344-385X Goettinger Miszellen
0344-4023 T U S - Turnen und Sport
0344-4201 Die Internistische Welt
0344-4317 Uebersee-Museum, Bremen. Veroeffentlichungen. Reihe F: Bremer Afrika-Archiv
0344-4325 Springer Seminars in Immunopathology
0344-4376 Kueche
0344-4422 Restaurant and Hotel Management
0344-4430 Informationsaufnahme und Informationsverarbeitung im Lebenden Organismus†
0344-449X Materialia Turcica
0344-4570 Der Konstrukteur
0344-4686 Backtechnik *changed to* Brot- und Backwaren.
0344-4724 Telecom Report
0344-4880 Telcom Report International
0344-5062 Allergologie
0344-5089 Berliner Beitraege zur Archaeometrie
0344-5208 Labo
0344-5259 Internationales Hydrologisches Programm: Operationelles Hydrologisches Programm: Jahrbuch Bundesrepublik Deutschland und Berlin (West)
0344-5372 D G D Schriftenreihe
0344-5399 Jazz Index†
0344-5542 Tungusica
0344-5550 Staat und Wirtschaft in Hessen
0344-5607 Neurosurgical Review
0344-5615 Institut fuer Allgemeine Botanik und Botanischer Garten. Mitteilungen
0344-5631 Der Mann Magazin†
0344-5690 Kultur und Technik
0344-5704 Cancer Chemotherapy and Pharmacology
0344-5712 Agrarsoziale Gesellschaft. Materialsammlung
0344-5836 Moderne Medizin *see* 0931-5594
0344-5909 Germanistische Mitteilungen
0344-5925 Deutsche Zeitschrift fuer Sportmedizin
0344-5933 Klinikarzt mit Medizinstudent. Ausgabe B†
0344-5941 Der Betriebsleiter
0344-5984 Kontraste Impuls
0344-6026 Orthopaedie-schuhtechnik
0344-6034 Konstruktion und Design *see* 0177-7459
0344-6190 International Book Trade Directory
0344-6379 Versicherungsbetriebe
0344-6492 Sport- Baeder- Freizeitbauten
0344-6581 Jahrbuch fuer das Elektrohandwerk (Year)
0344-6727 Linguistische Arbeiten
0344-676X Romanistische Arbeitshefte
0344-6816 Der Doemensianer
0344-6891 I F L A Publications
0344-7006 Prager Nachrichten
0344-7022 Neue Stadt
0344-7030 Ost-Wirtschaftsreport
0344-7065 Profil
0344-7103 Deutsche Optikerzeitung
0344-7138 H R C and C C *changed to* H R C.
0344-7146 L O K Report
0344-7154 Pharmakotherapie†
0344-726X P B S Report
0344-7596 Moderne Fertigung *changed to* Fertigung.
0344-7758 Informationsdienst Laerm
0344-7071 Recht und Politik
0344-8029 Computing Supplementa
0344-824X Studien ueber Wirtschaft- und Systemvergleiche
0344-8266 Anglistik und Englischunterricht
0344-8274 Wunderblock
0344-8444 Archives of Orthopaedic and Traumatic Surgery
0344-8614 Sielmanns Tierwelt†
0344-8622 Curare
0344-8657 Zuckerindustrie
0344-8711 Stuckgewerbe *changed to* Das Stukkateur.
0344-8738 Der Wohnungseigentuemer
0344-8746 Sicherheits-Berater
0344-8789 S I Informationen
0344-8843 Markt & Technik
0344-9033 Tribuna Tedesca†
0344-9041 Tribune D'Allemagne
0344-9068 Technische Kulturdenkmale
0344-9084 Deutsche Gesellschaft fuer Allgemeine und Angewandte Entomologie. Mitteilungen
0344-9092 Liturgie Konkret
0344-9106 E Z W - Texte
0344-9122 Sanitaer und Heizungs Report
0344-9130 Germany (Federal Republic, 1949-). Deutscher Bundestag. Wissenschaftliche Dienste. Materialien
0344-9270 Die Voliere
0344-9300 Publikationen zu Wissenschaftlichen Filmen. Sektion Psychologie, Paedagogik
0344-9416 Medizintechnik
0344-9602 Report Psychologie
0344-9696 Technologie-Nachrichten - Management-Informationen
0344-9750 Technologie-Nachrichten - Programm-Informationen
0344-9777 Zeitschrift fuer Oeffentliche und Gemeinwirtschaftliche Unternehmen
0344-9823 Transnational
0344-984X Schiefertafel†
0345-0074 Striae

ISSN

5710 ISSN INDEX

0345-0112 Text
0345-0139 Stockholms Universitet. Psykologiska Institutionen. Report Series
0345-0155 Umeaa Studies in the Humanities
0345-0171 Sweden. Socialstyrelsen. Legitimerade Laekare
0345-021X Stockholms Universitet. Psykologiska Institutionen. Reports. Supplement Series†
0345-0295 Aneks†
0345-0406 Accent
0345-049X Aktiespararen
0345-0635 Aktuellt i Politiken
0345-0732 Alkohol och Narkotika
0345-0759 Allas Veckotidning
0345-0813 Allt om M C
0345-1097 Bibliotekariesamfundet Meddelar
0345-1135 B i S
0345-1402 Scandinavian Journal of Behaviour Therapy
0345-1453 Biblicum
0345-1593 Blaaklint - Livlinant†
0345-178X Bryggan
0345-1798 Bridge
0345-181X Broed-Konditorn *changed to* Broed.
0345-1941 Byggreferat
0345-200X Clinical Chemistry Lookout
0345-2131 Dans†
0345-2212 Daa och Nu
0345-2328 Development Dialogue
0345-2409 Djurens Raett
0345-2417 Djurfront *see* 0345-2409
0345-2581 Entre
0345-2719 Svenska Bankfoereningen. Ekonomiska Meddelanden
0345-2980 Evangelii Haerold
0345-3251 Fasaden
0345-3286 F B R Aktuellt†
0345-3685 Frihetlig Socialistisk Tidskrift
0345-3766 Affaersvaerlden
0345-3901 Foersaekrings Vaerlden
0345-3979 Golv till Tak
0345-4347 Hockey
0345-4495 Handelskammartidningen
0345-4630 Hemmets Veckotidning
0345-469X Historisk Tidskrift
0345-4789 Haeften foer Kritiska Studier
0345-4797 Haelsa
0345-4843 Haent i Veckan
0345-486X Haesten
0345-4983 Invandrartidningen Information *see* 0349-554X
0345-4991 Invandrartidningen (Weekly)
0345-5068 I C A - Kuriren
0345-5300 Information-Ekonomi och Miljoe, Vetenskap och Humanism
0345-5440 International Union of Tenants. International Information
0345-5505 Invandrarrapport
0345-5564 Journal of Traffic Medicine
0345-5653 Jefferson
0345-6005 Kvaekartidskrift
0345-6471 Kontakten
0345-6706 Kustbon
0345-696X Tidskriften Laboratoriet
0345-7001 Lantbruksnytt†
0345-7044 Ledarbladet Samspel†
0345-7133 Leveranstidningen Entreprenad
0345-7389 Lutersk Barntidning
0345-7605 Arkivet foer Folkets Historia. Meddelanden *see* 0349-6279
0345-7656 Modern Elektronik
0345-7699 Musiktidningen
0345-7737 Moebler och Miljoe
0345-7788 MaskinKontakt
0345-780X Mat foer Millioner†
0345-7842 Laerarnas Missionsfoerening. Meddelande till L M F.
0345-7850 Forbundet foer Art, Bild, Copy och Design. Meddelandet
0345-7982 Bygd och Natur
0345-8199 M S-Brevet *see* 0348-8071
0345-8202 Munskaenken
0345-830X Nordisk Mejeriindustri - Scandinavian Dairy Industry *see* 1101-8399
0345-8326 Nord Refo
0345-8539 Nordisk Posttidsskrift
0345-8660 Ny i Sverige
0345-8768 Nysvenska Studier
0345-9225 Pro - Pensionaeren
0345-9616 P S O Aktuellt
0346-0479 Skandanavisk Numismatik *see* 0029-134X
0346-0479 Skandinavisk Numismatik *changed to* Nordisk Filateli med Mynt - Magazinet.
0346-0576 Hifi & Musik
0346-0762 S C C News†
0346-0770 Schacknytt
0346-0827 Scout
0346-1025 Ship Abstracts
0346-1033 Skogsindustriarbetaren
0346-1238 Scandinavian Actuarial Journal
0346-1300 Skohandlaren
0346-1351 Skorstensfejarmaestaren
0346-1386 Skraedderi
0346-1602 Sparbankerna†
0346-2099 Svensk Froetidning
0346-2250 Svensk Veterinaertidning
0346-2471 Svinskoetsel
0346-251X System
0346-2765 Tobakshandlaren
0346-2773 Transport och Hantering
0346-2846 Traeindustrin
0346-3001 Teratology Lookout†
0346-329X Tonfallet
0346-3605 Undervisningsteknologi†
0346-363X Ung Vaerld†
0346-3788 Utsikt
0346-4644 V V S - Forum
0346-4687 Vaar Ponny
0346-4997 Vaextskydds - Kuriren
0346-5004 Pedagogisk-Psykologiska Problem
0346-5020 Didakometry and Sociometry
0346-5039 Pedagogisk Dokumentation
0346-5047 Pedagogiska Hjaelpmedel
0346-5365 Sveriges Socialfoerbunds Tidskrift
0346-5438 Bibliotheca Historico-Ecclesiastica Lundensis
0346-5764 Sweden. Statens Lantmaeteriverk. L M V Information†
0346-5799 Sweden. Socialstyrelsen. Redovisar *see* 1100-2808
0346-5837 Sweden. Medicinalvaesendet. Foerfattningssamling *see* 0346-6000
0346-5837 Sweden. Medicinalvaesendet. Foerfattningssamling *see* 0346-6019
0346-6000 Sweden. Socialstyrelsen. Foerfattningssamling: Medical
0346-6019 Sweden. Socialstyrelsen. Foerfattningssamling: Social
0346-606X Sweden. Statistiska Centralbyraan. Statistiska Meddelanden. Subgroup F (Entreprises)
0346-6078 Sweden. Statistiska Centralbyraan. Statistiska Meddelanden. Subgroup K (Kreditmarknad-Credit Market, Banking and Insurance)
0346-6159 Paa Fritid *see* 0347-5484
0346-6175 Educational Development *see* 0283-7692
0346-6310 Elteknik Aktuell Elektronik
0346-640X Dagens Industri
0346-6493 Uppsala Studies in Economic History
0346-6620 Stockholm Studies in Politics
0346-6728 Norna - Rapporter
0346-6868 Swedish Natural Science Research Council. Ecological Bulletins *changed to* Ecological Research Committee. Ecological Bulletins.
0346-6906 C B I Forskning - Research
0346-7090 Svenska Traeskyddsinstitutet. Meddelanden
0346-7104 Naeringsforskning
0346-7236 Lantbrukshoegskolan Institutionen foer Vaextodling. Rapporter och Arhandlingar *changed to* Sveriges Lantbruksuniversitet. Institutionen foer Vaextodling. Rapporter och Avhandlingar.
0346-7341 Vaar Foeda. Supplement
0346-735X Vaextekologiska Studier *see* 0282-8677
0346-8186 Eastern Business Magazine
0346-8240 C B I Rapporter - Reports
0346-8445 Sweden. Sjukvaardens och Socialvaardens Planerings- och Rationaliseringsinstitut. S P R I Informerar
0346-8488 Skrifter Utgivna av Svenska Riksarkivet
0346-8666 Sweden. Fishery Board. Institute of Marine Research. Report†
0346-8712 Slavica Lundensia
0346-8755 Scandinavian Journal of History
0346-895X L O Tidningen
0346-8992 Sweden. Statistiska Centralbyraan. Statistiska Meddelanden. Subgroup HS (Public Health and Medical Care)
0346-9018 Hembygden
0346-9158 Afrikabulletinen
0346-9190 Allt om Husvagn och Camping
0346-9212 Antik & Auktion
0346-9468 Current Business in Sweden
0346-9670 Foereningsbankerna†
0346-9735 Historiska Institutionens Tidskrift†
0347-030X Railway Scene†
0347-0342 S A C O - S R-Tidningen
0347-0520 Scandinavian Journal of Economics
0347-0547 Saagrevyn *changed to* Skog & Saag.
0347-0822 Etudes Romanes de Lund
0347-0989 Motpol
0347-1314 Uppsala Studies in Education
0347-1748 Kullagertidningen
0347-2205 World Armaments and Disarmament: S I P R I Yearbook *changed to* S I P R I Yearbook: World Armaments and Disarmament.
0347-2558 Travaux de l'Institute de Linguistique de Lund
0347-2787 Bible Researcher
0347-2965 Arbetarroerelsens Aarsbok
0347-3139 Skandinaviska Enskilda Banken Quarterly Review
0347-3198 Sveriges Riksbank. Foervaltningsberaettelse
0347-3236 Vaextskyddsrapporter
0347-3449 Registreringstidning foer Varumaerken. Part A (Publications for Opposition) *see* 0348-324X
0347-3457 Registreringstidning foer Varumaerken. Part C (Renewals, Changes of Ownership) *see* 0348-3266
0347-3465 Registreringstidning foer Varumaerken. Part B (Publications of Registrations) *see* 0348-3258
0347-3899 Praktiskt Butiksarbete
0347-4135 Tidningsteknik
0347-416X Kyrkosaangsfoerbundet *see* 0281-286X
0347-4178 Svensk Kyrkomusik (Edition B for Choir Members)†
0347-4240 A I C A R C Bulletin
0347-4585 R A - Nytt
0347-4917 Acta Regiae Societatis Scientiarum et Litterarum Gothoburgensis. Botanica
0347-4925 Acta Regiae Societatis Scientiarum et Litterarum Gothoburgensis. Interdisciplinaria
0347-4976 R & D for Higher Education *see* 0283-7692
0347-5301 Naturvaardsverkets Foerfattningssamling
0347-5387 Svenska Barnboksinstitutet. Skrifter
0347-5484 Kommun-Aktuelt
0347-5719 Documenta
0347-5867 Sskk Bulletinen
0347-6030 V T I Rapport
0347-6049 V T I Meddelande
0347-6154 Konsumentraett och Ekonomi
0347-6405 Kiruna Geophysical Institute. Report *see* 0284-1703
0347-6820 Utlaendska Nyfoervaerv till Stoerre Svenska Folkbibliotek
0347-7169 Sweden. Finansdepartmentet. Regeringens Budgetfoerslag
0347-7193 Sweden. Statistiska Centralbyraan. Levnadsfoerhaallanden. Rapport
0347-772X Barnboken
0347-8173 Sweden. Statens Naturvaardsverk. Naturvaardsverkets Aarsbok†
0347-8262 Plastforum Scandinavia
0347-8785 Svenskt Raattsforum
0347-884X Goeteborgs Universitet. Universitetsbibliotek. Aarsberaettelse†
0347-9331 Lill-Allers†
0347-9706 Department of Animal Breeding and Genetics. Report
0347-9994 Swedish Dental Journal
0348-0356 Aakeri & Transport
0348-0593 Swedish University of Agricultural Sciences. Department of Farm Buildings. Special Reports
0348-0755 Statens Geotekniska Institut. Rapport
0348-1093 Scripta Academica
0348-1964 Studies of Law in Social Change and Development†
0348-2219 Goeteborgs Universitet. Institutionen foer Praktisk Pedagogik. Rapport
0348-2251 Sweden. Luftfartsverket. Aarsbok
0348-243X S K R-Meddelanden†
0348-2456 Lund Universitet. Vaextekologiska Institutionen. Meddelanden†
0348-2480 Accessionskatalog over Utlaendsk Litteratur i Svenska Forskningsbibliotek
0348-2626 S A R E C Report
0348-2650 S T F I Meddelande. Series A
0348-2790 C B I Rekommendationer-Recommendations *see* 0282-6283
0348-3118 Transport-Journalen
0348-324X Svensk Varumaerkestidning - Swedish Trademark Journal. Part A (Publications for Opposition)
0348-3258 Svensk Varumaerkestidning - Swedish Trademark Journal. Part B (Publications of Registrations)
0348-3266 Svensk Varumaerkestidning - Swedish Trademark Journal. Part C (Renewals, Changes of Ownership)
0348-3304 Svenska Motor-Magasinet
0348-4009 Svenska P C World
0348-4076 Gothenburg Studies in Social Anthropology
0348-4114 Gothenburg Studies in Art and Architecture
0348-4386 Striolae
0348-4599 Sveriges Lantbruksuniversitet. Institutionen foer Virkeslaera. Rapporter
0348-4769 Folkhoegskolan
0348-4998 Datornytt, med Maskin- och Programvara
0348-5099 Uppsala Studies in Cultural Anthropology
0348-5153 Sveriges Riksbank. Kredit- och Valutaoeversikt *see* 1100-5815
0348-5242 Personal
0348-5552 Fastighetstidningen
0348-5676 Centre for Development Research. Publications
0348-6087 Civilingenjoeren
0348-6133 Samlaren
0348-6397 Sweden. Statistiska Centralbyraan. Utbildningsstatistisk Aarsbok
0348-6508 Sweden Business Report
0348-6516 Nordisk Foersaekringstidskrift
0348-6613 Foeredrag vid Pyroteknikdagen
0348-6788 Gothenburg Studies in the History of Science and Ideas
0348-7032 Tidskrift foer Frukt- och Baerodling
0348-7148 Byggnadsstyrelsens Tidskrift†
0348-7342 Sveriges Riksbank. Statistisk Aarsbok
0348-7369 Energy Technology†
0348-7377 Qufo
0348-7741 Meijerbergs Arkiv for Svensk Ordforskning
0348-7962 Ny Litteratur om Kvinnor: En Bibliografi
0348-7997 Tvaersnitt
0348-8071 Handikapp - Reflex
0348-811X Sweden. Statistiska Centralbyraan. Statsanstaelldat
0348-8691 Africana in the Library of the Scandinavian Institute of African Studies

ISSN

ISSN INDEX 5711

0348-8799 Annual Report on the Results of Treatment in Gynecological Cancer
0348-9078 Revisionist History
0348-9221 Byggnormindex *changed to* Byggregler (Year).
0348-9388 Pedagogiska Rapporter Umeaa *see* 0281-6776
0348-9698 Ethnologia Scandinavica
0348-971X Fataburen
0349-0068 International Meteorological Institute in Stockholm. Annual Report
0349-0297 Soermlandsbygden
0349-0505 Arkiv, Samhaelle och Forskning
0349-0564 Acta Wexionensia. Serie 1: History & Geography
0349-0823 Fauna Norrlandica†
0349-0874 S A R E C Annual Report
0349-1048 Foereningen Armemusei Vaenner. Meddelande: Kungliga Armemuseum *changed to* Meddelande Armemuseum. Yearbook.
0349-1714 Svenska Antavlor
0349-2559 Till Tjaenst
0349-2656 Kiruna Geophysical Institute. Preprint *see* 0284-1711
0349-2664 Kiruna Gephysical Institute. Software Report *see* 0284-172X
0349-2672 Kiruna Geophysical Institute. Technical Report *see* 0284-1738
0349-2680 Uppsala Ionospheric Observatory. Technical Reports *changed to* Swedish Center of Space Physics. Uppsala Division. Technical Reports.
0349-2699 Uppsala Ionospheric Observatory. Scientific Reports *changed to* Swedish Institute of Space Physics. Uppsala Division. Scientific Reports.
0349-2702 Uppsala Ionospheric Observatory. Administrative Reports†
0349-2737 Duty and Tax-Free Shop World Guide Series *see* 1100-3006
0349-3210 Nytt fraan D F I†
0349-3733 Byggindustrin
0349-5264 Sveriges Natur
0349-5299 Sweden. Statistiska Centralbyraan. Statistiska Meddelanden. Subgroup E (Energy)
0349-5426 Kommunal Litteratur
0349-554X Invandrartidningen (Monthly)†
0349-5612 Educational Reports Umeaa†
0349-5949 Nordicom - Information om Masskommunikationsforskning i Norden
0349-6244 Nordicom Review of Nordic Mass Communication Research
0349-6279 Folkets Historia
0349-6287 Raw Materials Report
0349-652X Acta Radiologica. Series 2: Oncology, Radiation Therapy, Physics and Biology
0349-6740 S A F - Tidningen
0349-7038 Nordiskt Lantbruk
0349-7143 Lag och Avtal
0349-764X Tjustbygden
0349-8476 Industriell Datateknik
0349-9375 Social Debatt
0349-9464 Svensk Handel *see* 0346-640X
0349-988X Musical Interpretation Research
0350-0012 Wissenschaftliche Mitteilungen des Bosnisch-Herzegowinischen Landesmuseums. Naturwissenschaft
0350-0020 Akademija Nauka i Umjetnosti Bosne i Hercegovine. Centar za Balkanoloska Ispitivanja. Godisnjak
0350-0039 Akademija Nauka i Umjetnosti Bosne i Hercegovine. Odjeljenje Drustvenih Nauka. Radovi
0350-0055 Bilten Dokumentacije. Zavarivanje†
0350-0063 Zdravstveni Vestnik
0350-0071 Akademija Nauka i Umjetnosti Bosne i Hercegovine. Odeljenje Medicinskih Nauka. Radovi†
0350-0101 Bilten Dokumentacje. Serija D6. Analiticka Hemija *see* 0352-633X
0350-011X Naucni i Strucni Skupovi u Jugoslavii i u Inostranstvu
0350-0144 Survey Sarajevo
0350-0152 Bilten Dokumentacije. Otpadne Vode i Zagadjenje Vazduha†
0350-0179 Balcanoslavica
0350-0209 Bilten Dokumentacije. Iskoriscenje Otpadaka *see* 0352-1036
0350-0241 Starinar
0350-025X Bilten Tehnickih Informacija Iz Oblasti Industrije Gume†
0350-0306 Bilten Dokumentacije. Zastita na Radu
0350-0322 Etnografski Muzej u Beogradu. Glasnik
0350-0330 Slovenski Etnograf
0350-0349 Bibliografija Jugoslavije. Serijske Publikacije
0350-0357 Bilten Dokumentacije. Serija I1. Informatika *see* 0352-6437
0350-0365 Institut za Javno Upravo. Vestnik
0350-0403 O A P Automatika Obrada Podataka. Bibliografija *see* 0351-3548
0350-0411 Katalog Tekucih Stranih Publikacija u Bibliotekama Jugoslavije *see* 0352-132X
0350-0454 Bilten Dokumentacije. Drzavni Organi. Drustvene Politicke Zajednice. Privreda. Drustvene Sluzbe. Pravo†
0350-0470 Zbornik za Slavistiku
0350-0578 Vojnoekonomski Pregled *see* 0351-3912
0350-0594 Tehnicka Fizika
0350-0667 Naucno-tehnicki Pregled
0350-1019 Komercijalist
0350-106X Filozofske Studije
0350-1094 Vaspitanje i Obrazovanje
0350-1159 Prilozi
0350-1256 Pregled (Sarajevo, 1964)
0350-1272 Dijalektika
0350-1299 Centar Jugoslavenske Akademije Znanosti i Umjetnosti u Zadru. Radovi *see* 0351-6709
0350-1302 Publications de l'Institut Mathematique
0350-1388 Nauka u Praksi
0350-1418 Gazi Husrevbegova Biblioteka. Anali
0350-1442 Zavod za Mentalno Zdravlje. Anali *see* 0350-2538
0350-1450 Bibliografija Domacih i Stranih Knjiga
0350-1531 Organizacija in Kadri
0350-154X Revija za Sociologiju
0350-1558 Bulletin Scientifique. Section A: Sciences Naturelles, Techniques et Medicales
0350-1604 Bulletin Scientifique. Section B: Sciences Humaines
0350-1655 Sodobno Kmetijstvo
0350-1698 Makedonski Akademija na Naukite i Umetnostite. Oddelenie za Opstestveni Nauki. Prilozi
0350-1701 Gradjevinski Fakultet. Institut za Materijale i Konstrukcije. Zbornik Istrazivackih Radova *see* 0353-4146
0350-1728 Makedonski Arhivist
0350-185X Juznoslovenski Filolog
0350-1892 Diabetologia Croatica
0350-1906 Srpski Dijalektoloski Zbornik
0350-1914 Makedonska Akademija na Naukite i Umetnostite. Oddelenie za Lingvistika i Literaturna Nauka. Prilozi
0350-2058 Univerzitet u Zagrebu. Pravni Fakultet. Zbornik
0350-2104 Medjunarodni Radnicki Pokret†
0350-2155 Jugoslovensko Vocarstvo
0350-218X Termotehnika
0350-2252 Yugoslav Law
0350-2325 Informatica Museologica
0350-2457 Veterinarski Glasnik
0350-2538 Psihijatrija Danas
0350-2562 Licki Vjesnik
0350-2570 Sahovki Glasnik
0350-2597 Tehnika
0350-2619 Nase Gradevinarstvo
0350-2627 Rudarstvo - Geologija - Metalurgija
0350-2643 Acta Biologica Iugoslavica. Serija G: Biosistematika
0350-2651 Kinematografija u Srbiji *changed to* Kinematografija u Srbiji - Uporedo S F R J.
0350-2694 Institut za Kriminoloska i Socioloska Istrazivanja. Zbornik
0350-2791 Prilozi za Istrazivanje Hrvatske Filozofske Bastine
0350-2856 Arhivist
0350-2929 Goriski Letnik
0350-2953 Savremena Poljoprivredna Tehnika
0350-3089 Macedonian Review
0350-3097 Sveuciliste u Zagrebu. Fakultet Strojarstva i Brodogradnje. Zbornik Radova
0350-3283 University of Belgrade. Faculty of Sciences. Department of Astronomy. Publications
0350-350X Goriva i Maziva
0350-3569 Narodna in Univerzitetna Knjiznica. Zbornik
0350-3577 Obvesila Republiske Maticne Sluzbe *see* 0353-9237
0350-3585 Slovenska Bibliografija *see* 0353-1716
0350-3615 Fragmenta Herbologica Jugoslavica
0350-3623 Filozofski Fakultet - Zadar. Razdio Filoloskih Znanosti. Radovi
0350-3631 Acta Historico-Oeconomica Iugoslaviae
0350-3658 Acta Parasitologica Iugoslavica†
0350-3666 Arhitektura
0350-3771 Energeticar
0350-4034 I T D *see* 0350-7564
0350-4115 Knjizevna Rec
0350-414X Latina et Graeca
0350-4158 Letunk
0350-4247 Mesecni Statisticki Pregled
0350-4603 Ruske Slovo
0350-4697 Slovenski Cebelar
0350-4778 Spone
0350-5421 Izgradnja
0350-5510 Acta Entomologica Jugoslavica
0350-5537 Koncar Strucne Informacije
0350-5596 Informatica
0350-5669 Financijska Praksa
0350-5723 Primorska Srecanja
0350-5774 Zgodovinski Casopis
0350-5928 Agroekonomika
0350-6134 Collegium Antropologicum
0350-6398 Jukic
0350-6525 Mostovi
0350-6541 Nastava Povijesti
0350-6584 Odzivi
0350-6673 Prilozi za Knjizevnost, Jezik, Istoriju i Folklor
0350-6746 Centro di Ricerche Storiche, Rovigno. Quaderni
0350-6789 Ribolov
0350-6886 Sigurnost
0350-6894 Slavisticna Revija
0350-7130 Vestnik Koroskih Partizanov
0350-7165 Arheoloski Muzej u Zagrebu. Vjesnik
0350-7335 Zivot i Zdravije
0350-7483 Sam
0350-7564 Teleks†
0350-7696 Komisija za Ispitivanje S-Uredjaja. Bilten
0350-8080 M A K
0350-820X Science of Sintering
0350-8498 Zbornik Obcine Grosuplje
0350-8765 Covjek i Promet
0350-9370 Muzejski Vjesnik
0350-9400 Obelezja
0350-9419 Povijest Sporta
0350-9427 Privreda (Osijek)
0350-9494 Varstvo Spomenikov
0350-9508 Yugoslav Information Bulletin
0350-9516 Zdravstveni Obzornik
0350-9559 Neurologija *see* 0353-8842
0350-9974 Bibliografija Prevoda U S F R J
0351-0085 Yugoslav Chemical Papers†
0351-0123 I R C I H E Bulletin
0351-0174 Informativni Bilten Urbanisticnega Instituta SR Slovenije. Sporocila†
0351-0557 Kulturna Bastina
0351-0603 Yugoslavia. Savezni Zavod za Statistiku. Metodoloske Studije, Rasprave i Dokumentacija
0351-0697 Revija Obrazovanja
0351-0891 Historijski Arhiv u Rijeci i Pazinu. Vjesnik *see* 0353-9520
0351-0999 Zito Hleb
0351-1030 Naucni Podmladak: Tehnicke Nauke
0351-1189 Primerjalna Knjizevnost
0351-1375 Sahovski Informator
0351-1537 Bibliografija Roto Stampe i Stripova
0351-1677 Endocrinologia Iugoslavica
0351-1685 Marksisticke Teme *changed to* Teme.
0351-1871 Polimeri
0351-1898 Suvremeni Promet
0351-2045 Annales Forestales
0351-2142 Zavod za Hrvatsku Povijest. Radovi
0351-2177 Beogradski Univerzitet. Elektrotehnicki Fakultet. Publikacije. Serija: Elektronika, Telekomunikacije, Automatika
0351-2274 Teorja
0351-2312 Bilten Dokumentacije. Poljoprivreda. Biljna Proizvodnja
0351-2320 Bilten Dokumentacije. Poljoprivreda-Stocna Proizvodnja
0351-238X Bilten Dokumentacije. Elektroprivreda
0351-2398 Bilten Dokumentacije. Elektrotehnika i Elektronika *changed to* Bilten Dokumentacije. Elektrotehnika i Elektronika. Proizvodnja Elektricnih Masina i Aparata. Ptt Usluge.
0351-2479 Bilten Dokumentacije. Proizvodnja Prehrambenih Proizvoda. Proizvodnja Pica
0351-2509 Bilten Dokumentacije. Prerada Nemetalnih Minerala-Proizvodnja Gradjevinskog Materijala
0351-2576 Bilten Dokumentacije. Gradjevinarstvo - Niskogradnja i Hidrogradnja
0351-2592 Bilten Dokumentacije. Urbanizam i Arhitektura
0351-2657 Hvar Observatory Bulletin
0351-2665 Engrami
0351-2797 Sunceva Energija
0351-2800 Institute of International Law and International Relations. Contributions to the Study of Comparative and International Law
0351-2819 Arheografski Prilozi
0351-2843 Bibliografija Zvanicnih Publikacija S F R J
0351-286X Economic Analysis and Workers Management
0351-2886 Gerontolosko Drustvo S R Srbije
0351-2908 Slovensko Etnolosko Drustvo. Glasnik
0351-3211 Narodna Banka Jugoslavije. Bilten
0351-3238 Geographica Iugoslavica
0351-3246 Makedonska Akademija na Naukite i Umetnostite. Oddelenie za Matematicki i Tehnicki Nauki. Prilozi
0351-3254 Makedonska Akademija na Naukite i Umetnostite. Oddelenie za Bioloski i Medicinski Nauki. Prilozi
0351-3297 Jugoslavenska Akademija Znanosti i Umjetnosti. Razred za Prirodne Znanosti. Rad
0351-3386 Tekstilec
0351-3548 A O P Bibliografija
0351-3769 Razvitok
0351-3912 Pozadina
0351-3947 Obnovljeni Zivot
0351-4048 Bilten Dokumentacije. Savremena Organizacija i Ekonomija Organizacija Udruzenog Rada
0351-4056 Bilten Dokumentacije. Serija I1, 1. Informatika *see* 0352-6437
0351-434X Zavod za Jezik. Rasprave *changed to* Zavod za Hrvatski Jezik. Rasprave.
0351-4471 Naucna Sveska
0351-4501 Mediterranean Journal of Social Psychiatry
0351-4595 Zbornik Objavljenih Radova Saradnika Instituta
0351-4706 Filozofska Istrazivanja†
0351-4714 Pozar Eksplozija Preventiva
0351-4889 Odgoj i Samoupravljanje
0351-496X Cerkveni Glasbenik
0351-5494 Dokumenti - Informacije
0351-5699 Naucni Podmladak: Drustvene Nauke i Filozofija

ISSN

5712 ISSN INDEX

0351-5796 International Review of the Aesthetics and Sociology of Music
0351-580X Acta Stereologica
0351-5915 Bilten Dokumentacje. Serija D6, 1. Analiticka Hemija *see* 0352-633X
0351-6245 Vesnik
0351-627X Strucni Casopis Duro Dakovic
0351-6652 Presek
0351-6687 Vjesnik Drustava Medicinskih Sestara i Medicinskih Tehnicara SR Hrvatske *see* 0352-3721
0351-6709 Jugoslavenska Akademija Znanosti i Umjetnosti. Zavod za Provijesne Znanosti. Radovi
0351-6768 Mikrografija u Informacionim Sistemima
0351-6881 Institut za Marksisticne Studije. Vestnik *see* 0353-4510
0351-689X Nuklearna Tehnologija
0351-6962 Univerzitet Svetozar Markovic u Kragujevcu. Prirodno-Matematicki Fakultet. Zbornik Radova
0351-7160 Zbornik Radova Muzeja Rudarstva i Metalurgije Bor
0351-7543 Bilten Dokumentacije. Rudarstvo i Geologija
0351-756X Bilten Dokumentacije. Serija D1. Hemija i Hemijska Industrija
0351-7586 Bilten Dokumentacije. Serija E2. Saobracaj *see* 0352-6402
0351-8892 Prevodilac
0351-8906 Bilten Dokumentacije. Metalopreradjivacka Delatnost. Proizvodnja Raznovrsnih Proizvoda
0351-8949 Nasa Knjiga
0351-9120 Godisnjak Jugoslovenskih Pozorista
0351-9430 Bilten za Hmelj, Sirak i Lekovito Bilje
0351-9716 Vakuumist
0351-9783 Zastita od Pozara
0352-0447 Traditiones
0352-0781 DrustvO Ekologa Bosne i Hercegovine. Bilten. Serija A - Ekoloske Monografije
0352-0811 Bilten Drustva Ekologa Bosne i Hercegovine. Serija B - Naucni Skupovi i Savjetovanja
0352-082X Gastroenterohepatoloski Arhiv
0352-0870 D I T
0352-0900 Univerzitet u Novom Sadu. Prirodno-Matematicki Fakultet. Zbornik Radova. Serija za Matematiku
0352-1028 Bilten Dokumentacije. Gradjevinarstvo - Visokogradnja i Zavrsni Radovi u Gradjevinarstvu
0352-1036 Bilten Dokumentacije. Zastita Covekove Okoline i Iskoriscenje Otpadaka
0352-115X Sahovska Kompozicija
0352-1168 Centar za Drustvena Istrazivanja Slavonije i Baranje. Zbornik *see* 0352-8650
0352-1311 Jugoslavenska Medicinska Biokemija
0352-132X Katalog Stranih Serijskih Publikacija u Bibliotekama Jugoslavije
0352-1362 Osogovski Glas
0352-1427 Centro di Ricerche Storiche, Rovigno. Atti
0352-1443 Muzej Brodskog Posavlja. Vijesti
0352-1605 Revija za Psihologiju
0352-1753 Podravka
0352-1818 Agrometeorolosko Porocilo
0352-2253 Ucitelj
0352-2393 Bibliografija Jugoslavije. Naucni i Strucni Radovi u Serijskim Publikacijama. Serija B: Prirodne, Primenjene, Medicinske i Tehnicke Nauke *see* 0352-5945
0352-2873 Start
0352-3055 Filoloski Fakultet. Katedra za Istocnoslovenski i Zapadnoslovenski Jazici i Knizeunosti. Slavisticki Studii
0352-3306 Godisnjak za Povijest Filozofije
0352-3314 Narodna Banka Jugoslavije. Godisnji Izvestaj
0352-3349 Statisticki Kalendar Jugoslavije
0352-3659 Geofizika
0352-3721 Vjesnik Medicinskih Sestara i Medicinskih Tehnicara Hrvatske
0352-4000 Crkva u Svijetu
0352-4728 Razvoj
0352-4973 Luca
0352-5139 Serbian Chemical Society. Journal
0352-5562 Yugoslav Gynecology and Perinatology
0352-5600 Migracijske Teme
0352-5708 Veritas
0352-5740 Academie Serbe des Sciences et des Arts. Classe des Sciences Mathematiques et Naturelles. Bulletin. Sciences Naturelles
0352-5856 Naucni Podmladak: Medicinske Nauke
0352-5899 Bibliografija Jugoslavije. Clanci i Prilozi u Serijskim Publikacijama. Serija A: Drustvene Nauke
0352-5945 Bibliografija Jugoslavije. Clanci i Prilozi u Serijskim Publikacijama. Serija B: Prirodne, Primenjene, Medicinske i Tehnicke Nauke
0352-5996 Bibliografija Jugoslavije. Clanci i Prilozi u Serijskim Publikacijama. Serija C: Umetnost, Sport, Filologija, Knjizevnost
0352-633X Bilten Dokumentacije. Serija D6. Analiticka Hemija
0352-6402 Bilten Dokumentacije. Serija S1. Saobracaj
0352-6437 Bilten Dokumentacije. Serija I1. Informatika
0352-6712 Filozofski Fakultet - Zadar. Razdio Povijesnih Znanosti. Radovi
0352-6798 Filozofski Fakultet - Zadar. Razdio Filozofije, Psihologije, Sociologije i Pedagogije. Radovi
0352-7417 Novogradiski Zbornik
0352-7654 Quorum
0352-7670 Development and South-South Cooperation *changed to* Development and International Cooperation.
0352-7921 Univerza Edvarda Kardelja v Ljubljani. Filozofska Fakulteta. Oddelek za Geografijo. Dela *changed to* Univerza v Ljubljani. Filozofska Fakulteta. Oddelek za Geografijo. Dela.
0352-8456 Lola Saopstenja
0352-8553 Razvoj: Development - International
0352-8650 Slavonski Povijesni Zbornik†
0352-8685 Biomedicina Iugoslavica
0352-8936 Livarstvo
0352-9029 Pesticidi
0352-9193 Prehrambeno-Tehnoloska i Biotehnoloska Revija
0352-9568 Chemical and Biochemical Engineering Quarterly
0352-9657 Folia Anatomica Iugoslavica
0353-0329 Prispevki za Novejso Zgodovino
0353-0353 C S S Papers
0353-0434 Znaci Vremena
0353-0477 Salezijanski Vestnik
0353-0973 Indos†
0353-1007 Slovenijales
0353-1074 M I
0353-118X Slovenija
0353-1716 Slovenska Bibliografija. Knjige
0353-1783 Vinograd Gospodnji
0353-1805 Slatki Grozdovi Vinograda Gospodnjeg
0353-2976 Evropa Danas†
0353-3271 Centro di Ricerche Storiche, Rovigno. Etnia
0353-328X Centro di Ricerche Storiche, Rovigno. Monografie
0353-3301 Centro di Ricerche Storiche, Rovigno. Collana degli Atti
0353-3832 Pogledi (Kragujevac)
0353-4146 Zbornik Istrazivackih Radova iz Oblasti Materijala i Konstrukcija u Gradjevinarstvu
0353-4510 Slovenska Akademija Znanosti in Umetnosti. Filozofski Vestnik
0353-474X Centro di Ricerche Storiche, Rovigno. Ricerche Sociali
0353-4855 Etnolog *see* 0350-0330
0353-4960 Arhiv Hrvatske. Bilten
0353-5746 Glasilo M S
0353-8052 Nova Matica
0353-8842 Neurologia Croatica
0353-9237 Knjiznicarske Novice
0353-9245 Experimental and Clinical Gastroenterology
0353-9520 Historijski Arhiv Rijeka. Vjesnik
0354-0243 Yugoslav Journal of Operations Research
0354-0650 Hrvatski Planinar
0355-001X Suomen Kirjallisuus
0355-0036 Signum
0355-0044 Kansallis-Osake-Pankki. Taloudellinen Katsaus
0355-0079 Yearbook of Finnish Foreign Policy
0355-0087 Annales Academiae Scientiarum Fennicae. Series A, I: Mathematica Dissertationes
0355-0133 Union Bank of Finland. Annual Report
0355-0192 Societe Neophilologique de Helsinki. Memoires
0355-0206 N I F Newsletter
0355-0214 Suomalais-Ugrilaisen Seuran. Aikakauskirja
0355-0303 Kanava
0355-0311 Kalevalaseuran Vuosikirja
0355-0346 Business Contacts in Finland
0355-0451 Maamies†
0355-0532 Mejeritidskrift foer Finlands Svenskbygd
0355-0567 Teho A
0355-0648 Riista- ja Kalatalouden Tutkimuslaitos. Kalantutkimusosasto. Tiedonantoja†
0355-0680 Lantman och Andelsfolk
0355-0729 Koneviesti
0355-0982 Finland. Vestientutkimuslaitos. Julkaisuja
0355-1008 International Peat Society. Bulletin
0355-1059 Musiikki
0355-113X Annales Academiae Scientiarum Fennicae. Dissertationes Humanarum Litterarum
0355-1253 Finnisch-Ugrische Forschungen
0355-1350 Helsingin Yliopiston Kirjaston. Julkaisuja
0355-1393 Keski-Suomi
0355-1407 SETA
0355-1466 Valokuva
0355-1555 Koti
0355-1628 Kemia - Kemi
0355-1644 Aarni
0355-1717 Finland. Ilmatieteen Laitos. Tutkimusselostet†
0355-1733 Finnish Meterological Institute. Technical Report†
0355-1784 Ylioppilasaineita
0355-1792 Acta Philosophica Fennica†
0355-1806 Suomen Museo
0355-1814 Finskt Museum
0355-1822 Suomen Muinaismuistoyhdistyksen Aikakauskirja
0355-1830 Kansatieteellinen Arkisto
0355-1849 Paasikivi - Society. Mimeograph Series
0355-1865 Pientalo-Omakoti†
0355-1873 Tee Itse†
0355-189X Suur-Seura *changed to* Seura (1979)
0355-1903 T H Kotilaakari
0355-1911 Non Stop†
0355-192X Muoti & Kauneus
0355-1962 Suomen Geodeettisen Laitoksen. Tiedonantoja
0355-2004 Finnish Meteorological Institute. Observations of Satellites. Visual Observations of Artificial Earth Satellites in Finland†
0355-2063 Finland. Tilastokeskus. Kaesikirjoja
0355-2071 Finland. Tilastokeskus. Tutkimuksia
0355-208X Finland. Tilastokeskus. Tilastollisia Tiedonantoja *changed to* Finland. Tilastokeskus. Tilastollisia Tiedonantoja. Kotitaloustiedustelu.
0355-2098 Suuri Kasityokerho
0355-2101 Aku Ankka
0355-211X Finland. Tilastokeskus. Tulo- ja Omaisuustilasto *see* 0780-9352
0355-2128 Finland. Tilastokeskus. Kuolleisuus- Ja Eloonjaamistauluja *changed to* Finland. Tilastokeskus. Kuolleisuus. Kuolleisuus- Ja Eloonjaamistauluja.
0355-2136 Finland. Tilastokeskus. Vaestolaskenta *changed to* Finland. Tilastokeskus. Vaestoe- ja Asuntolaskenta.
0355-2144 Finland. Tilastokeskus. Kuolemansyyt
0355-2152 Finland. Tilastokeskus. Asuntotuotanto†
0355-2160 Finland. Tilastokeskus. Rikollisuus. Poliisin Tietoon Tullut Rikollisuus
0355-2179 Finland. Tilastokeskus. Rikollisuus. Tuomioistuinten Tutkimat Rikokset
0355-2187 Finland. Tilastokeskus. Tuomioistuinten Toiminta
0355-2195 Finland. Tilastokeskus. Valtiolliset Vaalit. Tasavallan Presidentin Vaalit Valisijamiesten
0355-2209 Finland. Tilastokeskus. Kansanedustajain Vaalit *changed to* Finland. Tilastokeskus. Valtiolliset Vaalit. Kansanedustajain Vaalit.
0355-2217 Finland. Tilastokeskus. Kunnallisvaalit
0355-2225 Finland. Tilastokeskus. Korkeakoulut†
0355-2233 Finland. Tilastokeskus. Tutkimustoiminta†
0355-2276 Finland. Tilastokeskus. Tilastotiedotus KT. Kansantalouden Tilinpito/National Raekenskaper/National Accounts
0355-2284 Finland. Tilastokeskus. Tieliikenneonnettomuudet
0355-2306 Tilastotiedotus P A *see* 0784-8374
0355-2373 Tilastotiedotus YR *see* 0784-8463
0355-2381 Finland. Tilastokeskus. Indeksitiedotus KH. Kuluttajahintaindeksi
0355-239X Finland. Tilastokeskus. Indeksitiedotus RK. Rakennuskustannusindeksi
0355-2403 Finland. Tilastokeskus. Indeksitiedotus TH. Tuottajahintaiset Indeksit
0355-2411 Finland. Tilastokeskus. Indeksitiedotus TR. Tienrakennuskustannusindeksi
0355-2446 Finland. Tilastokeskus. Yleissivistaevaet Oppilaitokset†
0355-2454 Tilastokeskus. Pankit *see* 0784-8382
0355-2527 Teho B
0355-256X Commentationes Scientiarum Socialium
0355-2624 Vaasan Kauppakorkeakoulu. Julkaisuja. Opetusmonisteita *see* 0788-6659
0355-2632 Vaasan Kauppakorkeakoulu. Julkaisuja. Tutkimuksia *see* 0788-6667
0355-2667 Acta Wasaensia
0355-2691 Suomen Autolehti
0355-2705 Acta Polytechnica Scandinavica. Civil Engineering and Building Construction Series
0355-2713 Acta Polytechnica Scandinavica. Mathematics and Computer Science Series
0355-2721 Acta Polytechnica Scandinavica. Applied Physics Series
0355-2764 Jermu
0355-2772 Seksi
0355-2896 Autolla Ulkomaille
0355-2950 Avotakka
0355-2969 Katso
0355-2977 Elamani Tarinat†
0355-2985 Eeva
0355-3000 Ravi ja Ratsastus†
0355-3035 Anna
0355-3043 U M: Uusi Maailma†
0355-3051 Apu
0355-3078 Kauppias *see* 0783-5167
0355-3086 Rautaviesti *see* 0786-1443
0355-3108 Iskos
0355-3140 Scandinavian Journal of Work, Environment & Health
0355-3221 Acta Universitatis Ouluensis. Series D. Medica
0355-3256 Myyntineuvoja
0355-337X Technical Research Centre of Finland. Publication. Building Technology and Community Development†
0355-3388 Technical Research Centre of Finland. Publication. Materials and Processing Technology†

ISSN

ISSN INDEX 5713

ISSN	Title
0355-3396	Technical Research Centre of Finland. Publication. Electrical and Nuclear Technology†
0355-3434	Valtion Teknillinen Tutkimuskeskus. Kojetekniikan Laboratorio. Tiedonantot
0355-3450	Valtion Teknillinen Tutkimuskeskus. Geotekniikan Laboratorio. Tiedonantot
0355-3477	Valtion Teknillinen Tutkimuskeskus. Maankayton Laboratorio. Tiedonantot
0355-3485	Valtion Teknillinen Tutkimuskeskus. Palotekniikan Labboratorio. Tiedonantot
0355-354X	Valtion Teknillinen Tutkimuskeskus. Biotekniikan Labboratorio. Tiedonantot
0355-3558	Valtion Teknillinen Tutkimuskeskus. Elintarvikelabboratorio. Tiedonantot
0355-3566	Valtion Teknillinen Tutkimuskeskus. Graafinen Labboratorio. Tiedonantot
0355-3574	Valtion Teknillinen Tutkimuskeskus. Kemian Laboratorio. Tiedonantot
0355-3590	Valtion Teknillinen Tutkimuskeskus. Poltti- ja Voiteluaineelaboratorio. Tiedonantot
0355-3639	Valtion Teknillinen Tutkimuskeskus. Tekstiililaboratorio. Tiedonantot
0355-3663	Valtion Teknillinen Tutkimuskeskus. Reaktorilaboratorio. Tiedonantot
0355-3671	Valtion Teknillinen Tutkimuskeskus. Sahkotekniikan Laboratorio. Tiedonantot
0355-368X	Valtion Teknillinen Tutkimuskeskus. Teletekniikan Laboratorio. Tiedonantot
0355-3698	Valtion Teknillinen Tutkimuskeskus. Ydinvoimatekniikan Laboratorio. Tiedonantot
0355-3701	Valtion Teknillinen Tutkimuskeskus. Teknillinen Informaatiopalvelulaitos. Tiedonantot
0355-3736	Lapset Ja Yhteiskunta see 0786-0188
0355-3752	Tuottavuus
0355-3779	Siirtolaisuus
0355-3817	E - Lehti changed to Meidan Liike.
0355-3930	Suomen Antropologi
0355-3949	Help†
0355-3957	Joensuun Korkeakoulu. Julkaisuja. Sarja B see 0355-6832
0355-3965	Opettaja
0355-4031	Aabo Akademi. Statsvetenskapliga Fakulteten. Meddelanden. Serie A see 0358-5654
0355-4074	Suomen Sanomalehtien Mikrofilmit
0355-4201	J P Joka Poika see 0781-7177
0355-4236	Jaanat
0355-4252	Kaks Plus
0355-4260	Suosikki
0355-4287	Tekniikan Maailma
0355-4295	Vauhdin Maailma
0355-4317	Hymy
0355-4465	Aabo Akademi. Statsvetenskapliga Fakulteten. Meddelanden. Serie B see 0358-5654
0355-4481	Finland. Patentti- ja Rekisterihallitus. Mallioikeuslehti
0355-4503	Elecktroniikka changed to Elektroniikka & Automaatio.
0355-4651	Finnish Dental Society. Proceedings. Supplement
0355-4759	Finland. Sosiaalihallitus. Huoltoapu
0355-4767	Finland. Sosiaalihallitus. Kodinhoitoapu.
0355-4813	Finland. Kansanelakelaitos. Julkaisuja. Sarja AL
0355-4821	Finland. Kansanelakelaitos. Julkaisuja. Sarja M
0355-483X	Finland. Kansanelakelaitos. Julkaisuja. Sarja ML
0355-4848	Finland. Kansanelakelaitos. Julkaisuja. Sarja E
0355-4856	Finland. Kansanelakelaitos. Julkaisuja. Sarja EL
0355-5003	Finland Kansanelakelaitos. Toimintakertomus
0355-502X	Philatelia Fennica changed to Filatelisti.
0355-5054	Rondo
0355-5089	Lastenhoitajalehti see 0358-4038
0355-550X	Rakentajain Kalenteri
0355-5526	Rakennustuotanto see 0033-9121
0355-5534	Rakennusalan Suomalaisen Kirjallisuuden Kuukausikatsaus see 0781-8904
0355-5615	Numismaatikko
0355-578X	Acta Academiae Aboensis. Series A: Humaniorat
0355-5798	Aabo Akademi. Aarsskriftt
0355-6034	Suomen Pankki. Julkaisuja. Sarja A
0355-6042	Suomen Pankki. Julkaisuja. Sarja D
0355-6050	Suomen Pankki. Julkaisuja. Kasvututkimuksia
0355-6093	Finlands Kommunaltidskrift
0355-6395	Valtion Teknillinen Tutkimuskeskus. Metallilaboratorio. Tiedonantot
0355-6654	Liikenneturva. Reports
0355-6735	Radiokauppias see 0783-4632
0355-6832	Joensuun Korkeakoulu. Julkaisuja. Sarja B2†
0355-6980	Purjehtija
0355-6999	Kenkaalusikka
0355-7073	Liikuntakasvatus
0355-7227	Et-Lehti
0355-7235	Koiramme - Vaara Hundar
0355-726X	Toimiupseeri
0355-7286	Ammattiautoilija
0355-7294	Vakuutussanomat
0355-7308	Foersaekringstidning
0355-7421	Kotiteollisuus - Vaar Hoemsleojd changed to Taito.
0355-7596	Metsanhoitaja
0355-7693	Psychiatria Fennica. Julkaisusarja changed to Psychiatria Fennica. Reports.
0355-7707	Psychiatria Fennica. Monografiasarja
0355-7839	Muoviuutiset†
0355-7855	Tie ja Liikenne
0355-7871	Navigator
0355-7898	Teksi
0355-8096	Suomen Shakki
0355-841X	Regina
0355-8614	Rakentaja
0355-8878	Finland. Valtioneuvoston Kanslian. Julkaisuja
0355-8991	Tekstiiliopettaja
0355-9076	Valtion Teknillinen Tutkimuskeskus. Sairaalatekniikan Laboratorio. Tiedonantot
0355-9106	Narinkka
0355-9378	Y V†
0355-9483	Turun Yliopisto. Julkaisuja. Sarja D. Medica - Odontologica
0355-9521	Annales Chirurgiae et Gynaecologiae
0355-953X	Puumies
0355-9610	Aja
0355-9637	Nykyposti
0355-9912	Uudistuva Konttori
0356-0023	Meri
0356-004X	Valtion Teknillinen Tutkimuskeskus. A T K-Palvelutoimisto. Tiedonantot
0356-0732	Veckan med Radio och T V see 0788-6632
0356-0805	Leirinta ja Retkeily changed to Matkailu.
0356-0910	Nordenskiold-Samfundets Tidskrift
0356-1062	Biological Research Reports from the University of Jyvaskyla
0356-1364	University of Helsinki. Department of Co-operative Studies. Publications
0356-1496	Historiska Samfundet i Abo. Skrifter Utgivna
0356-1704	Vapaa-Aika-Eurosport†
0356-178X	Fink-S changed to Finuc-S.
0356-276X	Savon Luonto
0356-2913	Finland. Tilastokeskus. Maatilatalous
0356-3014	Mallas ja Olut
0356-3081	Syopa
0356-3189	Savonia
0356-3316	Finland. Tilastokeskus. Tyovoimatiedustelu see 0781-5611
0356-3464	Era
0356-3472	P.S.†
0356-4096	Projektio
0356-4827	Auto ja Liikenne see 0359-7636
0356-5092	Hinnat ja Kilpailu†
0356-5106	Talouselama
0356-5327	Tehokas Yritys see 0358-4208
0356-5629	Faravid
0356-6110	Rakennusviesti changed to Meidan Talo.
0356-6927	Academia Scientiarum Fennica. Yearbook
0356-7133	Aqua Fennica
0356-7249	I T - Invalidityoe
0356-7753	Finnish Boatbuilding Industry
0356-780X	Institute for Migration, Turku. Migration Studies changed to Migration Institute. Migration Studies.
0356-7818	Kemistin Kalenteri
0356-7826	Suomen Vakuutusvuosikirja
0356-7842	Laeraren
0356-7850	Liikearkisto
0356-7869	Maankaytto
0356-7893	Current Research on Peace and Violence†
0356-7915	Markkinointi changed to Mark Markkinoinnin Ammattilehti.
0356-7923	Muusikko
0356-7931	Osto†
0356-794X	Pistis†
0356-8067	Tahti
0356-8075	Valokuvauksen Vuosikirja
0356-8083	Vaatturi
0356-8091	Valtionyhtiot
0356-8105	U I T B B Information changed to U I T B B Bulletin.
0356-8156	A Fin L A Yearbook
0356-8164	Helsingin Kauppakorkeakoulu. Julkaisusarja D. Laitosjulkaisuja
0356-8199	Studia Historica Septentrionalia
0356-8202	Makasiinit
0356-827X	Finland
0356-8741	Turun Yliopisto. Psykologian Tutkimuksia
0356-9489	Helsingin Kaupunki Tilastolunen Vuosikirja see 0785-8736
0356-9624	Nordinfo-Nytt
0356-9993	Insurance in Finland
0357-0614	Finland. Tilastokeskus. Valtion Tilastojulkaisut
0357-0738	Hifi
0357-1076	Finnish Marine Research
0357-1831	Valtion Teknillinen Tutkimuskeskus. Metallurgian ja Mineraalitekniikan Laboratorio. Tiedonantot
0357-1955	N O S P - Mikro
0357-2498	Bibliografia Eritysiryhmien Liikunnan Tutkimuksesta
0357-2625	Finland. Tilastokeskus. Ammatilliset Oppilaitokset†
0357-2714	Koululainen
0357-2862	Mark Uusi Markkinointilehti changed to Mark Markkinoinnin Ammattilehti.
0357-2943	Kuva ja Aani see 0780-4199
0357-3362	Helsingin Kaupungin Tilastokeskuksen Neljannesvuosikatsaus
0357-3486	Vaasa School of Economics. Proceedings. Discussion Papers see 0358-870X
0357-3737	Valtion Teknillinen Tutkimuskeskus. Betoni- ja Silikaattitekniikan Laboratorio. Tiedonantot
0357-3796	R T - Uutiset see 0781-8904
0357-4121	Prosessori
0357-4776	Suomen Pankki. Julkaisuja. Sarja B
0357-542X	Alibi
0357-5632	Scandinavian Journal of Sports Sciences see 0905-7188
0357-7031	Valtion Teknillinen Tutkimuskeskus. Rakennetekniikan Laboratorio. Tiedonantot
0357-7201	Finland. Tilastokeskus. Indeksitiedotus AT. Palkansaajien Ansiotasoindeksi
0357-749X	Vitriini
0357-816X	Sotahistoriallinen Aikakauskirja
0357-8682	Kalastaja
0357-8747	Elainmaailma
0357-8755	Roope-Seta
0357-9387	V T T Symposium
0357-9492	Sukuviesti
0357-9921	Jyvaskyla Studies in Computer Science, Economics and Statistics
0358-0520	Scanp
0358-0628	Kehittyva Yritys
0358-1039	Tiede 2000
0358-1071	Kirjeshakki
0358-2019	Finland. Tilastokeskus. Energiatilastot see 0785-3165
0358-2671	Finland. Ilmatieteen Laitos. Ilmasahkohavaintojat
0358-2825	Tilastokeskus. Tulonjakotilasto see 0784-8420
0358-2973	Helsingin Kauppakorkeakoulu. Julkaisusarja F. Tyopapereita
0358-3414	Arx Tavastica
0358-3511	Muoto changed to Finnish Design Magazine Muoto.
0358-4038	Tehy
0358-4208	Yritystalous
0358-495X	Finland. Kehittaemistiedote changed to Finland. Rakennushallitus. Tutkimus-ja Kehitystoiminnan. Tiedote.
0358-5069	Technical Research Centre of Finland. Publications see 1235-0621
0358-5077	Valtion Teknillinen Tutkimuskeskus. Tutkimuksia see 1235-0613
0358-5085	Valtion Teknillinen Tutkimuskeskus. Tiedotteita see 1235-0605
0358-5581	Opusculum
0358-5654	Aabo Akademi. Ekonomisk-statsvetenskapliga Fakulteten. Meddelanden
0358-626X	Fakta
0358-6758	Walter and Andree de Nottbeck Foundation Scientific Reports
0358-7045	N O R D I N F O Publikation
0358-7088	S S I D Liaison Bulletin
0358-710X	Scripta Historica
0358-7673	Teollisuusviikko
0358-7703	Blue Wings
0358-7711	V R - Express
0358-8424	Helsingfors Slaktforskare. Skrifter Utgivna
0358-870X	University of Vaasa. Proceedings. Discussion Papers
0358-8882	Tiede ja Ase
0358-8904	Form Function Finland
0358-9080	Vaasan Korkeakoulu. Julkaisuja. Tutkimuksia see 0788-6667
0358-9110	Vaasan Korkeakoulu. Julkaisuja. Opetusmonisteita see 0788-6659
0358-9609	Communicationes Instituti Forestalis Fenniae†
0359-0216	University of Turku. Psychological Research Reports
0359-0267	Sinamina
0359-0607	Suomen Matkailu - Tourism of Finland changed to Matkailu.
0359-081X	Finland. Tilastokeskus. Kuntien Talous
0359-3223	Historiallinen Kirjasto
0359-4947	Tietokone
0359-6079	Primat
0359-7008	Technik aus Finnland
0359-7016	Finlande Industrielle
0359-7601	Nordisk Komite for Transport Forskning. Publikation
0359-7636	Moottori (Year)
0359-8543	Tietoviikko
0359-9108	Tulosuunta
0359-9329	Kuluttajatietoa†
0359-968X	Metsatilastollinen Vuosikirja
0360-0017	Multiple Sclerosis Indicative Abstracts†
0360-0025	Sex Roles
0360-005X	Maine Fish and Wildlife
0360-0114	Florida Bar News
0360-0157	Young Socialist
0360-0181	New Conversations
0360-0270	Illinois. State Museum. Reports of Investigations
0360-0289	Illinois. State Museum. Story of Illinois Series
0360-0297	Illinois. State Museum. Popular Science Series
0360-0300	A C M Computing Surveys

0360-0319 Street Drug Survival *changed to* Preview (Tempe).
0360-0327 Soviet Astronomy Letters
0360-0335 Soviet Journal of Low Temperature Physics
0360-0343 Soviet Journal of Plasma Physics
0360-0467 Areito†
0360-0521 U.S. Department of Agriculture. Economic Research Service. Sugar and Sweetener Situation *changed to* U.S. Department of Agriculture. Sugar and Sweetener Situation and Outlook.
0360-0556 Civil Engineering A S C E
0360-0564 Advances in Catalysis
0360-0572 Annual Review of Sociology
0360-0637 Ebsco Bulletin of Serials Changes
0360-0661 Index to Scientific Reviews
0360-0696 Behavior Change†
0360-0726 Rehabilitation - World†
0360-0815 National Panorama of American Youth
0360-0939 A C A Bulletin
0360-0971 Information Reports and Bibliographies
0360-1005 Mandate
0360-1013 Ohio Review
0360-1021 Archaeology of Eastern North America
0360-1048 New Mexico Almanac *changed to* New Mexico Digest.
0360-1056 North Carolina Genealogical Society Journal
0360-1102 Needlework Guild of America. Annual Report†
0360-120X Soviet Technical Physics Letters
0360-1218 Journal of Structural Mechanics *see* 0890-5452
0360-1226 Journal of Environmental Science and Health. Part A: Environmental Science and Engineering
0360-1234 Journal of Environmental Science and Health. Part B: Pesticides, Food Contaminants, and Agricultural Wastes
0360-1250 Current Book Review Citations†
0360-1269 Earth Surface Processes *see* 0197-9337
0360-1277 Educational Gerontology
0360-1285 Progress in Energy and Combustion Science
0360-1293 Acupuncture and Electro-Therapeutics Research
0360-1307 Iranian Journal of Science and Technology†
0360-1315 Computers & Education
0360-1323 Building and Environment
0360-1358 Contact and Intraocular Lens Medical Journal *see* 0733-8902
0360-1390 Suicide *see* 0363-0234
0360-1420 Journal of Christian Reconstruction
0360-1439 Legal Economics *see* 1045-9081
0360-1455 New River Review†
0360-151X Brigham Young University Law Review
0360-1560 Lumberman and Wood Industries *see* 0015-7430
0360-165X A E I Review, Session of the Congress and Index of A E I Publications *see* 0197-5102
0360-1676 Florida Dental Journal *see* 1048-5317
0360-1684 National Association of Chiropodists. Journal *see* 8750-7315
0360-1722 Ongoing Current Bibliography of Plastic and Reconstructive Surgery *see* 0149-5348
0360-1757 E I A Electronics Multimedia Handbook†
0360-1773 Market Chronicle†
0360-179X Papers in Slovene Studies *see* 0193-1075
0360-1846 Great Lakes Review *see* 0439-237X
0360-1862 TeleSystems Journal†
0360-1889 Astrologia†
0360-1897 Pacific Theological Review
0360-1927 Journal of Latin American Lore
0360-1935 Main Title†
0360-1943 Music Book Guide *see* 0360-2753
0360-1978 Richmond Historian†
0360-1986 Women's Work (Washington)
0360-2044 Forum Law Journal *changed to* The Law Forum.
0360-2087 Houston Home and Garden *changed to* Houston Metropolitan.
0360-2109 Paul's Record Magazine
0360-2133 Metallurgical Transactions A - Physical Metallurgy and Materials Science
0360-2141 Metallurgical Transactions B - Process Metallurgy
0360-215X Dictionary of Contemporary Quotations
0360-2184 U.S. Department of Agriculture. Economics Management Staff. Cotton and Wool Situation *changed to* U.S. Department of Agriculture. Cotton and Wool Situation and Outlook.
0360-2192 Masks†
0360-2206 Balkanistica†
0360-2230 Plymouth Colony Genealogical Helper *see* 0277-433X
0360-2265 E P A Reports Bibliography Quarterly *see* 0196-0091
0360-2273 Popular Mechanics Do-It-Yourself Yearbook
0360-2397 Harper's Weekly†
0360-2400 Management Contents
0360-2508 Current Governments Reports: Chart Book on Government Data. Organization, Finances and Employment†
0360-2516 Billboard Index†
0360-2532 Drug Metabolism Reviews
0360-2540 Separation and Purification Methods
0360-2559 Polymer-Plastics Technology and Engineering
0360-2672 Scree
0360-2699 Bibliographic Guide to Art and Architecture
0360-2702 Bibliographic Guide to Business and Economics
0360-2710 Bibliographic Guide to Black Studies
0360-2729 Bibliographic Guide to Conference Publications
0360-2737 Bibliographic Guide to Dance
0360-2745 Bibliographic Guide to Law
0360-2753 Bibliographic Guide to Music
0360-2761 Bibliographic Guide to Technology
0360-277X Bibliographic Guide to Psychology
0360-2788 Bibliographic Guide to Theatre Arts
0360-2796 Bibliographic Guide to Government Publications - U S
0360-280X Bibliographic Guide to Government Publications - Foreign
0360-2834 Maryland Register
0360-2834 Maryland Register. State Contract Supplement
0360-2877 Concrete Pipe Industry Statistics
0360-2915 Trinity Studies *see* 0360-3032
0360-3016 International Journal of Radiation: Oncology - Biology - Physics
0360-3024 Family Motor Coaching
0360-3032 Trinity Journal
0360-3059 Vermont. Agency of Environmental Conservation. Biennial Report†
0360-3083 Wood Industry Abstracts†
0360-3091 Portland Review *changed to* Portland Review Magazine.
0360-3164 Plating and Surface Finishing
0360-3180 Yale Art Gallery Bulletin *see* 0084-3539
0360-3199 International Journal of Hydrogen Energy
0360-3245 U.S. Federal Bureau of Investigation. Bomb Summary
0360-3326 New York State Sea Grant Program. Annual Report *changed to* New York Sea Grant Institute. Annual Report.
0360-3334 Calendar of Folk Festivals and Related Events†
0360-3342 Liberty, Then and Now†
0360-3350 L A D O C
0360-3385 Tristania
0360-3431 Sourcebook of Criminal Justice Statistics
0360-3482 Microorganisms and Infectious Diseases†
0360-3520 Body Fashions - Intimate Apparel
0360-3571 E R D A Energy Research Abstracts *see* 0160-3604
0360-3598 Family in Historical Perspective *see* 0363-1990
0360-3601 Genesis III†
0360-361X A.D. United Church of Christ Edition *changed to* United Church of Christ A.D.
0360-3628 A.D. United Presbyterian Edition *changed to* United Presbyterian A.D.
0360-3636 Arithmoi†
0360-3679 Institutes of Religion and Health. Institutes Reporter†
0360-3687 A I I S Annual Report *changed to* American Institute of Indian Studies. Biennial Report.
0360-3695 Film & History
0360-3709 American Poetry Review (Philadelphia)
0360-3725 A.M.E. Church Review
0360-3733 Theological Currents†
0360-3741 Black Church†
0360-375X Decision Sciences Institute. Annual Meeting Proceedings
0360-3768 Candler Review†
0360-3814 Performing Arts Resources
0360-3857 The Virginia Bar Association Journal
0360-3881 Alaska. Division of Geological and Geophysical Surveys. Special Report
0360-389X Adventist Heritage
0360-392X U.S. National Transportation Safety Board. Briefs of Accidents Involving Midair Collisions, U.S. General Aviation†
0360-3938 Business Outlook†
0360-3954 U.S. National Transportation Safety Board. Listing of Aircraft Accidents-Incidents by Make and Model, U.S. Civil Aviation†
0360-3989 Human Communication Research
0360-3997 Inflammation
0360-4012 Journal of Neuroscience Research
0360-4020 Association of Military Dermatologists. Journal
0360-4039 Nursing (Year) (Springhouse)
0360-4055 C S Journal
0360-4071 Quality Rock Reader
0360-4098 Agricultural Situation in the Soviet Union *changed to* World Agriculture Regional Supplement: U S S R.
0360-4152 B O C A Basic Mechanical Code *changed to* B O C A National Mechanical Code.
0360-4209 Notre Dame Journal of Legislation *see* 0146-9584
0360-4217 National Journal
0360-4225 Visual Dialog†
0360-4233 A S P A News and Views *see* 0149-8797
0360-4357 D P I Yellow Pages *changed to* Directory of Nebraska Services.
0360-4365 In Theory Only
0360-4381 River City
0360-439X Tobacco Stocks
0360-4411 Who's Where in Music
0360-4438 Appalachian Notes†
0360-4497 Soviet Journal of Bioorganic Chemistry
0360-4500 Scottish Genealogical Helper *see* 0271-5031
0360-4519 Irish Genealogical Helper *see* 0272-1015
0360-4527 Fleet Specialist *see* 0199-7610
0360-4543 U.S. Department of the Interior. Oil Shale Environmental Advisory Panel. Annual Report†
0360-4594 U.S. Food and Nutrition Service. Food and Nutrition Programs
0360-4608 Record (Nashville)
0360-473X Directions (Bridgewater)
0360-487X U.S. Social and Rehabilitation Service. Annual Report of Welfare Programs†
0360-4918 Presidential Studies Quarterly
0360-4969 American Health Care Association. Journal *changed to* American Health Care Association. Provider.
0360-4985 Environmental Report Data System *changed to* Electric Power Industry Abstracts.
0360-4993 Budget Decorating & Remodeling†
0360-5027 Journal of Teaching and Learning *see* 0887-9486
0360-5043 Soviet Journal of Glass Physics and Chemistry
0360-506X Retailing Today
0360-5094 Midwestern Advocate *see* 0198-7364
0360-5108 Looking Back to Those Wonderful Days Gone by†
0360-5132 Official Gazette of the United States Patent and Trademark Office. Trademarks Supplements
0360-5159 Metal Industry (New York) *see* 0026-0576
0360-5167 American Hospital Association. House of Delegates. Proceedings†
0360-523X Conference Board. Utility Investment Statistics. Utility Appropriations *see* 0896-2510
0360-5248 Who's Who Among Students in American Vocational and Technical Schools *see* 0148-6381
0360-5272 Rail Transit Directory†
0360-5280 Byte
0360-5302 Communications in Partial Differential Equations
0360-5310 Journal of Medicine and Philosophy
0360-5361 N A D L Journal *changed to* Trends & Techniques in the Contemporary Dental Laboratory.
0360-5388 Ais-Eiri *changed to* An Gael.
0360-5434 Occupational Education
0360-5442 Energy
0360-5450 Vertica†
0360-5477 Tennessee Manufacturers Directory
0360-5485 Affiliate (Chicago)
0360-5531 Old Northwest
0360-554X Uniformed Services Almanac. Special Reserve Forces Edition *see* 0363-860X
0360-5558 Alaska. Department of Natural Resources. Division of Oil and Gas. Statistical Report *see* 0273-1916
0360-5590 Texas Tech Journal of Education†
0360-5612 Loon†
0360-5639 Home Horticulture†
0360-5701 Freeing the Spirit†
0360-5779 Chronicle (Greensburg) *changed to* American Baptist Quarterly.
0360-5809 Information News and Sources *see* 0360-5817
0360-5817 Information Hotline
0360-5825 Financial Corporate Bond Transfer Service *changed to* Financial Corporate - Municipal Bond Transfer Service.
0360-5892 American Machinist (1877) *see* 1041-7958
0360-5906 R T S D Newsletter (Resources and Technical Services Division) *see* 1047-949X
0360-5949 American Philological Association. Transactions
0360-5973 Journal of Psychiatric Nursing and Mental Health Services *see* 0279-3695
0360-6031 Yearbook of Cardiovascular Medicine *see* 0145-4145
0360-6058 Bricklayers', Masons' and Plasterers' International Union of America. Journal *see* 0362-3696
0360-6112 Buddhist Text Information
0360-6171 Monday Morning
0360-618X Center for Process Studies. Newsletter
0360-6244 Living Worship *see* 0276-2358
0360-6325 L D & A
0360-6333 African Economic History Review *see* 0145-2258
0360-6376 Journal of Polymer Science. Polymer Chemistry Edition *see* 0887-624X
0360-649X Copts
0360-6503 Process Studies

ISSN

0360-652X Patristics
0360-6538 Annotated Bibliography of New Publications in the Performing Arts†
0360-6724 Obsidian: Black Literature in Review *see* 0888-4412
0360-683X Nebraska. Indian Commission. Report
0360-6848 U.S. Social Security Administration. Applications and Case Dispositions for Public Assistance *changed to* Quarterly Public Assistance Statistics.
0360-6864 Columbia River Water Management Report
0360-6899 American Public Works Association. Directory
0360-6929 American Society for Quality Control. Annual Technical Conference Transactions
0360-6945 Lutheran Journal
0360-697X A A C S B Newsline
0360-6996 A R T B A Officials and Engineers Directory, Transportation Agency Personnel
0360-7011 Ammonia Plant Safety and Related Facilities
0360-7046 M S U U Newsletter *changed to* M S U U Newsletter: Gleanings.
0360-7100 American Institute for Decision Sciences. Southeast Section. Proceedings
0360-7119 Reporter (St. Louis)
0360-7135 Creative World†
0360-7151 Legal Bibliographic Data Service: Weekly Listing†
0360-716X Navy Supply Corps Newsletter
0360-7178 A A M O A Reports
0360-7216 Functional Photography (Woodbury)
0360-7275 Chemical Engineering Progress
0360-7283 Health and Social Work
0360-7348 Replay
0360-7372 Survey of Law Reviews *see* 0279-5787
0360-7410 Renaissance Two
0360-7437 A A M C Directory of American Medical Education
0360-7453 Violations of Human Rights in Soviet Occupied Lithuania†
0360-7461 Arizona. Water Commission. Bulletin *changed to* Arizona. Department of Water Resources. Report.
0360-7496 Canoe
0360-750X U. S. Urban Mass Transportation Administration Report to Congress Concerning the Demonstration of Fare-Free Mass Transportation†
0360-7550 Florida. Department of Agriculture and Consumer Services. Nematology Circular
0360-7569 Current Concepts in Psychiatry
0360-7607 Hemostasis and Thrombosis; a Bibliography†
0360-7690 Nuclear Regulation Reports
0360-7739 Amicus Curiae *changed to* Friends of the Court.
0360-7860 Revista Chicano - Riquena *see* 1042-6213
0360-7887 Rackham Literary Studies *see* 0731-4817
0360-7917 Revista - Review Interamericana
0360-7941 National Development
0360-795X Journal of Corporation Law
0360-800X Utah. Division of Wildlife Resources. Biennial Report†
0360-8085 Best in Posters *changed to* Best in Covers and Posters.
0360-814X American Water Works Association. Proceedings, A W W A Annual Conference
0360-8166 U.S. National Advisory Council on Extension and Continuing Education. Annual Report *see* 0739-1382
0360-8174 I S I's Who Is Publishing in Science *see* 0882-2360
0360-8174 I S I's Who Is Publishing in Science *changed to* Current Contents Address Directory - Social Sciences, Arts & Humanities.
0360-8182 Uniquest *see* 0191-3379
0360-8212 Radical Religion†
0360-8247 People Soup *changed to* Synapse (Boston).
0360-8263 Best in Advertising Campaigns *changed to* Best in Advertising.
0360-8271 Best in Environmental Graphics
0360-8298 Cumberland Law Review
0360-8301 Massachusetts. Division of Employment Security. Employment and Wages in the Establishments Subject to the Massachusetts Employment Security Law. *changed to* Massachusetts. Department of Employment and Training. Employment and Wages State Summary.
0360-8352 Computers & Industrial Engineering
0360-8360 Current Advances in Genetics†
0360-8409 ICarbS
0360-8417 International Defense Business *changed to* Defense & Economy World Report.
0360-8425 American Foreign Service Journal *see* 0015-7279
0360-845X S P: Sociological Practice *see* 0163-8505
0360-8476 Search at the State University of New York†
0360-8484 The Matthay News
0360-8557 Engineering Index Annual
0360-8581 I E E E Engineering Management Review
0360-859X Transportation Research Board Special Report
0360-862X C A S E Currents *see* 0748-478X
0360-8654 Guide to Micrographic Equipment†
0360-8662 United Business and Investment Report *changed to* United & Babson Investment Report.
0360-8670 Aviation Quarterly
0360-8689 Best in Packaging
0360-8727 R I D I M - R C M I Newsletter
0360-8743 Best in Annual Reports
0360-8751 Stream Improvement Technical Bulletin *changed to* National Council of the Paper Industry for Air and Stream Improvement. Technical Bulletin.
0360-8778 Atmospheric Quality Improvement Technical Bulletin *changed to* National Council of the Paper Industry for Air and Stream Improvement. Technical Bulletin.
0360-8786 Current Register of American Leaders†
0360-8808 Evangelical Theological Society. Journal
0360-8816 Northeast Rising Sun†
0360-8832 International Symposium on Atomic, Molecular and Solid-State Theory and Quantum Statistics. Proceedings *changed to* International Symposium on Atomic, Molecular and Solid-State Theory, Collision Phenomena and Computational Methods. Proceedings.
0360-8840 American Accounting Association. Southeast Regional Group. Collected Papers of the Annual Meeting
0360-8859 Pennsylvania Exporters Directory†
0360-8867 Marine Geotechnology
0360-8905 Journal of Polymer Science. Polymer Symposia Edition
0360-8913 International Conference on Cybernetics and Society. Proceedings *changed to* I E E E International Conference on Systems, Man, and Cybernetics. Proceedings.
0360-8921 Argus F C and S Chart *changed to* National Underwriter Profiles.
0360-8980 U.S. Department of Transportation. Summary of National Transportation Statistics *changed to* U.S. Department of Transportation. National Transportation Statistics. Annual.
0360-8999 Foundry Management & Technology
0360-9006 Hastings Center. Recent Activities†
0360-9030 Historical Footnotes (St. Louis)
0360-9049 Hebrew Union College Annual
0360-9073 Ecumenical Trends
0360-9081 American Archivist
0360-912X Shocks†
0360-9146 Uniform Crime Report for the State of Michigan
0360-9154 Alaska Accident Statistics†
0360-9162 Illinois Air Quality Report *changed to* Illinois. Division of Air Pollution Control. Annual Air Quality Report.
0360-9170 Language Arts
0360-9197 American Association of Blood Banks. Bulletin *see* 0041-1132
0360-9235 Lodging
0360-9278 Hearing Rehabilitation Quarterly
0360-9286 Highlights *see* 0360-9278
0360-9294 American Audiology Society. Journal *see* 0196-0202
0360-9316 Survey of Hospital Charges *changed to* A H A Hospital Statistics (Year).
0360-9421 Pope Family Register†
0360-9510 Daily Reporter
0360-9553 Non-Ferrous Metal Data
0360-9588 Adherent†
0360-9642 N I D A Supported Drug Treatment Programs†
0360-9669 Horizons (Villanova)
0360-9693 Military Chaplains' Review
0360-9731 Nevada Government Today†
0360-9766 Readings in Health *see* 0278-4653
0360-9774 Short Story Index
0360-9782 United Church of Christ. Pension Boards (Annual Report)
0360-9790 Lektos†
0360-991X Z.C.L.A. Journal *changed to* Zen Writings.
0360-9928 Marathon Handbook†
0360-9936 Quality
0360-9960 Advances in Bioengineering
0360-9987 Directory of Diesel Fuel Stations Coast to Coast *changed to* Diesel Fuel Guide.
0361-0004 Modern Recording *changed to* Modern Recording & Music.
0361-0020 Retailing in Tennessee†
0361-0047 Foreign Trade Reports. Summary of U.S. Export and Import Merchandise Trade *changed to* Foreign Trade Reports. U.S. Export and Import Merchandise Trade and Supplement.
0361-0128 Economic Geology and the Bulletin of the Society of Economic Geologists
0361-0136 Applied Hydraulics and Pneumatics *see* 0018-814X
0361-0144 American Humanities Index
0361-0152 Newspaper and Gazette Report *see* 0190-9819
0361-0160 Sixteenth Century Journal
0361-0179 Aging (New York)
0361-0195 Health Systems Management
0361-0209 Journal of Electrophysiological Techniques *see* 0361-9230
0361-0233 Progress in Chemical Fibrinolysis and Thrombolysis†
0361-025X Tests in Print
0361-0268 T C A Manual *see* 0271-8057
0361-0365 Research in Higher Education
0361-0438 Commerce America *see* 0190-6275
0361-0462 International Brain Research Organization Monograph Series
0361-0470 American Society of Brewing Chemists. Journal
0361-0489 Kroc Foundation Series†
0361-0519 Ohio. Division of Geological Survey. Miscellaneous Report
0361-0527 Perspectives in Cardiovascular Research
0361-0551 Theoretical Chemistry: Advances and Perspectives†
0361-056X Campaign Practices Reports†
0361-0640 Elastomerics Rubber Red Book
0361-073X Experimental Aging Research
0361-0772 American Nurses' Association. House of Delegates. Summary Proceedings†
0361-0802 Pilgrimage: The Journal of Pastoral Psychotherapy *changed to* Pilgrimage: The Journal of Psychotherapy and Personal Exploration.
0361-0810 F G C Quarterly†
0361-0845 Coin World Almanac
0361-0853 Manufacturing Engineering
0361-0861 Southern School Law Digest
0361-0888 American Frozen Food Institute. Membership Directory and Buyer's Guide
0361-0896 Celebrate; The Annual for Cake Decorators *changed to* Wilton Yearbook of Baking and Cake Decorating.
0361-090X Cancer Detection and Prevention†
0361-0918 Communications in Statistics. Part B: Simulation and Computation
0361-0926 Communications in Statistics. Part A: Theory and Methods
0361-0942 Video Systems
0361-0977 Formal Linguistics†
0361-1043 Motorhome Life and Camper Coachman *see* 0744-074X
0361-1116 Abortion Research Notes
0361-1124 J A C E P *see* 0196-0644
0361-1175 Western Society of Malacologists. Annual Report
0361-1205 Labor-Management Alcoholism Journal†
0361-1213 Microstructural Science†
0361-1299 Rocky Mountain Review of Language and Literature
0361-1302 Samizdat Bulletin†
0361-1353 Alaska Geographic
0361-1361 Milepost
0361-137X Selected Alaska Hunting & Fishing Tales†
0361-140X Maryland. Council for Higher Education. Annual Report and Recommendations†
0361-1434 I E E E Transactions on Professional Communication
0361-1442 Computers and People
0361-1493 Directory of Drug Information and Treatment Organizations†
0361-1507 National Institute of Education. Career Education Program: Program Plan
0361-1515 Grassroots (Madison)†
0361-1531 Review of Existential Psychology and Psychiatry
0361-1582 Federal Grant-in-Aid Activity in Florida: a Summary Report†
0361-1612 Council for Tobacco Research, U.S.A. Report
0361-1647 School Media Quarterly *see* 0278-4823
0361-1663 Abraxas
0361-1671 Milwaukee County Historical Society. Historical Messenger *see* 0163-7622
0361-168X New Boston Review *see* 0734-2306
0361-1817 The Nurse Practitioner: The American Journal of Primary Health Care
0361-1833 American Association for the Advancement of Science. Meeting Program
0361-185X Selbyana
0361-1906 Journal of Theology
0361-1981 Transportation Research Record
0361-204X New York Folklore
0361-2066 Best in Covers *changed to* Best in Covers and Posters.
0361-2090 Massachusetts Municipal Association Directory
0361-2112 Dress
0361-2120 Wisconsin. Educational Communications Board. Biennial Report
0361-2147 Antique Phonograph Monthly
0361-2163 Micro Proceedings *changed to* Microprogramming and Microarchitecture Workshop. Proceedings.
0361-218X Worldwide Lodging Industry *changed to* Worldwide Hotel Industry.
0361-2198 U S Lodging Industry†

0361-221X Baton Twirling Rules and Regulations *changed to* Baton Twirling Handbook.
0361-2228 Directory of Physics & Astronomy Staff (Year)
0361-2295 North Carolina Governor's Highway Safety Program. Summary of Activities *changed to* North Carolina. Department of Transportation. Office of Highway Safety. Summary of Activities.
0361-2309 Corporate Examiner
0361-2317 Color Research and Application
0361-2325 Political Intelligence†
0361-2333 Prospects
0361-2376 Congregational Journal
0361-2422 Post American *see* 0364-2097
0361-2449 U.S. Forest Service. Research Note N C
0361-2473 Ocean Law Memo *see* 1052-6730
0361-2481 Wind
0361-249X Ophthalmic Seminars†
0361-2546 Registry of Toxic Effects of Chemical Substances
0361-2562 Resources Recovery/Energy Review†
0361-2570 Sales and Marketing Management *changed to* Sales & Marketing Management.
0361-2597 Texas. Industrial Commission. Annual Report†
0361-2635 Micropublishers' Trade List Annual
0361-2643 U.S. Social and Rehabilitation Service. Office of Management. Quality Control, States' Corrective Action Activities†
0361-2651 U.S. Department of the Army. Projects Recommended for Deauthorization, Annual Report†
0361-2678 Viewpoint (Columbus) *changed to* Artspace (Columbus).
0361-2759 History: Reviews of New Books
0361-2767 Empirical Research in Theatre *changed to* Empirical Research in Theatre Annual.
0361-2783 Auerbach Guide to Computing Equipment Specifications†
0361-2791 C T A Quarterly†
0361-2805 U.S. National Ocean Survey. Collected Reprints *changed to* U.S. National Ocean Service. Collected Reprints.
0361-2813 Home Improvement and Repair *see* 0278-2839
0361-2821 Mechanical Properties *changed to* Key Engineering Materials.
0361-2848 Wisconsin Library Service Record
0361-2929 Health Facilities Directory (Sacramento)
0361-2961 Advances in Holography†
0361-297X Alabama. Department of Industrial Relations. Annual Manpower Planning Report *changed to* Alabama. Department of Industrial Relations. Annual Planning Information.
0361-2996 Directory of Manufacturers in Arkansas *changed to* Arkansas Directory of Manufacturers.
0361-3011 Field & Stream Hunting Annual
0361-3038 N.E.S.F.A. Index: Science Fiction Magazines and Anthologies *changed to* N E S F A Index to Short Science Fiction.
0361-3046 Selected Studies in Medical Care and Medical Economics†
0361-3054 Scripps Clinic and Research Foundation. Scientific Report *changed to* Scripps Research Institute. Scientific Report.
0361-3070 Instrumentation in the Mining and Metallurgy Industries
0361-3232 Showcase (New York)
0361-3313 Electronics and Communications Abstracts Journal
0361-333X Western Reserve Magazine
0361-3372 Practical Cardiology
0361-3399 I J A L Native American Texts Series†
0361-3410 Toxicology Annual†
0361-3445 Directory of State Government Energy-Related Agencies†
0361-3453 Fine Woodworking
0361-347X A A U Official Track and Field Handbook, Rules and Records
0361-3488 International Journal of Powder Metallurgy and Powder Technology *see* 0888-7462
0361-3496 Environmental Psychology and Nonverbal Behavior *see* 0191-5886
0361-3550 Maine. Bureau of Property Taxation. Biennial Report *changed to* Maine. Bureau of Property Taxation. Annual Report.
0361-3577 Loblolly
0361-3593 Southwest Directory of Advertising and Public Relations Agencies
0361-3615 Stanford Business School Alumni Bulletin *see* 0883-265X
0361-3658 Conservation and Recycling *see* 0921-3449
0361-3666 Disasters
0361-3674 Metabolic Ophthalmology *see* 0882-889X
0361-3682 Accounting, Organizations and Society
0361-3690 Habitat (Oxford) *see* 0197-3975
0361-3712 Arlington Catholic Herald
0361-3747 Welding and Joining Digest *changed to* Welding - Brazing - Soldering Digest.
0361-3763 Lawyers' Title Guaranty Funds Newsletter
0361-3771 Directory of Psychosocial Investigators†
0361-3798 Mental Retardation and Developmental Disabilities Abstracts *see* 0191-1600
0361-3801 Fine Print
0361-381X Bicycle Dealer Showcase
0361-381X Bicycle Dealer Showcase Buyers Guide
0361-3828 Breast: Diseases of the Breast†
0361-3836 Annual Editions: Readings in Personality and Adjustment *see* 0198-912X
0361-3844 Attorneys and Agents Registered to Practice Before the U.S. Patent and Trademark Office
0361-3895 National Income and Product Accounts of the United States, 1929-1982: Statistical Tables
0361-3968 Asian Thought and Society: an International Review
0361-3976 Women's International Bowling Congress. Playing Rules†
0361-3984 Alaska Fishing Guide†
0361-4018 New York (State). Medical Care Facilities Finance Agency. Annual Report
0361-4034 Grocery Distribution
0361-4050 Employee Benefits Journal
0361-4069 Benchmark Papers in Microbiology†
0361-4166 Rehabilitation Gazette
0361-4190 Xerox Disclosure Journal
0361-4204 U.S. Federal Highway Administration. Federally Coordinated Program of Highway Research and Development
0361-4220 International Guild Guide
0361-4247 Buyer's Directory of Suppliers for General Merchandise Buyers†
0361-4255 Directory of North American Fairs, Festivals and Expositions
0361-4336 Children Today
0361-4344 F D A Drug Bulletin *changed to* F D A Medical Bulletin.
0361-4387 Cosmetics and Toiletries
0361-4425 Yale University. School of Forestry. Bulletin *changed to* Yale University. School of Forestry and Environmental Studies. Bulletin.
0361-4433 Geodesy, Mapping and Photogrammetry *see* 0749-3878
0361-4441 Cuban Studies
0361-4468 Health, United States
0361-4476 Journal of Energy and Development
0361-4506 California. State Water Resources Control Board. Annual State Strategy *changed to* California. State Water Resources Control Board. Program Guide.
0361-4514 U.S. Office of Education. Determination of Basic Grant Eligibility Index†
0361-4522 U.S. Food and Drug Administration. Pesticide-P C B in Foods Program. Evaluation Report
0361-4530 U.S. Solicitor for the Department of the Interior. Solicitor's Review†
0361-4565 Wire Technology *changed to* Wire Tech.
0361-4646 Behavioral Sciences Newsletter
0361-4654 A A U Junior Olympic Handbook†
0361-4662 Bottomline†
0361-4670 European Skinny†
0361-4689 R & D Review (Schenectady)†
0361-4719 Instrumentation in the Pulp and Paper Industry
0361-4735 Current Biographies of Leading Archaeologists
0361-4751 American Film Magazine (Washington) *changed to* American Film.
0361-476X Contemporary Educational Psychology
0361-4794 Current Mathematical Publications
0361-4948 Tourbook: Alabama, Louisiana, Mississippi
0361-4956 Tourbook: Georgia, North Carolina, South Carolina
0361-4964 Tourbook: Kentucky, Tennessee
0361-4972 Electrical Consultant *changed to* Electrical Systems Design.
0361-4999 Ithacagun Hunting & Shooting Annual†
0361-5006 Annual Symposium on Pulmonary Diseases†
0361-5030 Flight Operations
0361-5049 Educational Catalyst†
0361-5057 College Recruiting Report
0361-5065 Buoyant Flight
0361-5162 Trace Substances in Environmental Health
0361-5170 Victimology
0361-5219 Solid Fuel Chemistry
0361-5227 Modern Psychoanalysis
0361-5235 Journal of Electronic Materials
0361-526X Serials Librarian
0361-5294 Doors and Hardware
0361-5316 Professional Builder and Apartment Business *changed to* Professional Builder & Remodeler.
0361-5359 Drug Survival News *changed to* Preview (Tempe).
0361-5367 New York's Food and Life Sciences Quarterly *changed to* Cornell Focus.
0361-5383 Billboard's on Tour *see* 0732-0124
0361-5391 Wisconsin Secondary School Administrators Association. Bulletin *changed to* Association of Wisconsin School Administrators. Bulletin.
0361-5405 Helicopter Safety Bulletin *see* 0898-8145
0361-5413 History in Africa
0361-5421 M P, the Microprocessor†
0361-5499 National Geographic World
0361-5502 Hispanic American Periodicals Index
0361-5545 C B S News Almanac *changed to* Hammond Almanac: One-Volume Encyclopedia of a Million Facts & Records (year).
0361-5553 Clarinet
0361-5561 Journal of Commerce and Commercial
0361-5634 Essays in Arts and Sciences
0361-5650 Air Quality in Minnesota†
0361-5669 A R L Annual Salary Survey
0361-5685 Dance Life in New York *changed to* Dance Life.
0361-5693 Western Tobacco Journal *changed to* Tobacco Reporter.
0361-574X Historic Madison. Journal
0361-5782 Journal of Management (Tucson) *see* 0149-7901
0361-5820 Contemporary Keyboard *see* 0730-0158
0361-5855 Recorder Review†
0361-5871 Tax Guide
0361-588X Big Eight
0361-5898 A I A W Handbook - Directory†
0361-591X Kentucky Deskbook of Economic Statistics *changed to* Kentucky Economic Statistics.
0361-5952 Advances in Prostaglandin and Thromboxane Research *changed to* Advances in Prostaglandin, Thromboxane, and Leukotriene Research.
0361-5960 Cancer Treatment Reports†
0361-5995 Soil Science Society of America. Journal
0361-6029 American Schools of Oriental Research. Newsletter
0361-6061 Face-to-Face (New York)†
0361-607X Artist's Market *see* 0161-0546
0361-6118 Reading Abstracts *see* 0888-8027
0361-6193 East Tennessee Historical Society's Publications
0361-6207 South Carolina Historical Association. Proceedings
0361-6215 West Tennessee Historical Society. Papers
0361-6266 Abstracts in Human Evolution†
0361-6274 Health Care Management Review
0361-6290 W W II Journal†
0361-6347 New Titles in Bioethics
0361-638X Woman's Day Home Decorating Ideas
0361-6428 Journal of Radiation Curing *see* 1057-5715
0361-6436 New York (State) Department of Social Services. Bureau of Research. Program Brief. *see* 0162-6302
0361-6479 South Carolina State Library. Annual Report
0361-6525 Sociobiology
0361-6576 Journal of Economics (Vermillion)
0361-6584 Kronos
0361-6606 O O B A Guidebook to Theatres *see* 0732-300X
0361-6622 Selected Reports in Ethnomusicology
0361-6657 Comprehensive Dissertation Index. Supplement†
0361-6665 Wage-Price Law & Economics Review
0361-6673 U.S. Environmental Protection Agency. Office of General Counsel. a Collection of Legal Opinions†
0361-6681 Product Productivity Review *see* 1044-8039
0361-6797 U.S. Civil Service Commission. Bureau of Personnel Management Evaluation. Evaluation Methods Series†
0361-6843 Psychology of Women Quarterly
0361-6851 Alternative Higher Education *see* 0742-5627
0361-686X Abba†
0361-6878 Journal of Health Politics, Policy and Law
0361-6908 Continuation Education
0361-6916 Bibliography, Corporate Responsibility for Social Problems *see* 0160-8819
0361-6959 World of Work Report *see* 0892-5488
0361-6967 Electric Machines and Electromechanics *see* 0731-356X
0361-6975 Community Junior College Research Quarterly *see* 0277-6774
0361-6983 Detroit News. Newspaper Index *see* 0893-2433
0361-7025 California Optometrist *see* 0273-804X
0361-7092 Notes on Urban-Industrial Mission, Literature and Training†
0361-7122 South Central Research Library Council. Reports
0361-7149 Soviet Geology and Geophysics
0361-7165 Family Heritage Series†
0361-7173 Jewish Arts Quarterly†
0361-7181 Journal of California Anthropology *see* 0191-3557
0361-719X N A G W S Guide. Aquatics *see* 0271-2199
0361-7203 Computer Law & Tax Report
0361-722X Film Reader
0361-7238 Modern Plywood Techniques†
0361-7246 Journal of Historical Studies (Washington)†
0361-7300 Army Administrator *see* 0274-9513

ISSN

0361-7440 U.S. National Commission for Manpower Policy. Annual Report to the President and the Congress *changed to* U.S. National Commission for Employment Policy. Annual Report.
0361-7467 P P F Survey
0361-7483 World Coal *see* 0746-729X
0361-7491 State University of New York at Binghamton. Center for Medieval and Early Renaissance Studies. Acta
0361-753X R & D Management Digest†
0361-7629 Iowa. Geological Survey. Annual Report of the State Geologist to the Geological Board *changed to* Iowa. Geological Survey. Annual Report of the State Geologist to the Governor.
0361-7653 B & P A
0361-7688 Programming and Computer Software
0361-7734 Operative Dentistry
0361-7742 Progress in Clinical and Biological Research
0361-7823 Facts About Alaska *see* 1051-5623
0361-7858 Population Council Annual Report
0361-7874 American Association for the Advancement of Science. Handbook; Officers, Organization, Activities
0361-7882 International Journal of African Historical Studies
0361-7947 Theatre Profiles
0361-8013 Federal Reserve Bank of Minneapolis. Annual Report
0361-8021 Harvard Teachers Record *see* 0017-8055
0361-803X A J R
0361-8242 Sky *see* 0037-6604
0361-8269 Southern Speech Communication Journal *changed to* Southern Communication Journal.
0361-8374 CableVision
0361-8382 Fire Protection Reference Directory *changed to* N F P A Buyer's Guide.
0361-8412 Malpractice Lifeline *see* 0732-9636
0361-8528 Schoharie County Historical Review
0361-8552 Yellow Brick Road†
0361-8560 South Dakota State Library Newsletter†
0361-8587 Perfumer and Flavorist International *see* 0272-2666
0361-8609 American Journal of Hematology
0361-865X Mass Media Bi-Weekly Newsletter *changed to* Mass Media Newsletter.
0361-8668 Keeping You Posted
0361-8676 South Dakota History
0361-8714 Federal Reserve Bank of Boston. Conference Series
0361-8773 J C T: Journal of Coatings Technology
0361-8854 Context
0361-8862 Congregation†
0361-8927 Guide to Four-Year College Databook *see* 0191-3670
0361-8935 Loyola Lawyer†
0361-8994 Career World
0361-9001 Chinese Science
0361-9095 California. Agricultural Statistics Service. Livestock Statistics
0361-9117 Women Artist Newsletter *see* 0149-7081
0361-915X Bell Journal of Economics *see* 0741-6261
0361-9168 American Society of Magazine Photographers. Bulletin
0361-9230 Brain Research Bulletin
0361-9249 Current Practice in Obstetric and Gynecological Nursing†
0361-9257 Current Practice in Pediatric Nursing†
0361-9273 Guidebook of U.S. & Canadian Postdoctoral Dental Programs†
0361-929X M C N: American Journal of Maternal Child Nursing
0361-9362 Accredited Institutions of Postsecondary Education and Programs *see* 0270-1715
0361-9397 Chilton's Motor-Age Professional Labor Guide and Parts Manual *see* 0749-5579
0361-9451 Wisconsin Sportsman
0361-946X Mediaevalia
0361-9478 W I L C O Newsletter†
0361-9486 American Bar Foundation Journal *see* 0897-6546
0361-9591 Means Construction Cost Indexes
0361-9613 Society for the Study of Pre-Han China. Newsletter *see* 0362-5028
0361-9621 Explicacion de Textos Literarios
0361-9737 U.S. National Park Service. Public Use of the National Park System: Calendar Year Report
0361-9885 Health and Education *see* 0161-6765
0361-9966 Seminar on the Acquisition of Latin American Library Materials. Resolutions and Lists of Committees†
0362-0034 Nuclear Materials Management *see* 0893-6188
0362-0050 Notebook of Empirical Petrology†
0362-0069 New York's Food and Life Sciences Bulletin†
0362-0085 Theologia 21
0362-0131 Buyer's Guide to Micrographic Equipment, Products, and Services†
0362-0204 Fodor's Europe
0362-0212 Fodor's India *changed to* Fodor's India.
0362-0247 Four Zoast
0362-028X Journal of Food Protection
0362-0298 Behavioral Engineering†
0362-0344 Trail Breakers
0362-0395 Automation in Housing-Systems Building News *see* 0899-5540
0362-0409 Choral Praise
0362-0417 Gospel Choir
0362-0425 Ironcaster *changed to* Metalcaster.
0362-0492 Unitarian Universalist Christian
0362-0506 Highway and Heavy Construction *changed to* Highway & Heavy Construction Products.
0362-0522 Spring (Dallas)
0362-0557 Pilgrim State Newsletter *changed to* Pilgrim State News.
0362-0565 Underground Space *see* 0886-7798
0362-0581 Gettysburg Seminary Bulletin *changed to* Lutheran Theological Seminary Bulletin.
0362-0603 Theological Markings†
0362-062X Journal of Reprints of Documents Affecting Women
0362-0662 Georgia Vital and Health Statistics *changed to* Georgia Vital Statistics Report.
0362-0689 Dow Jones Commodities Handbook†
0362-0697 Economic Crime Digest†
0362-0700 Sport Fishery and Wildlife Research *changed to* Fisheries and Wildlife Research.
0362-0719 Index of Patents Issued from the United States Patent and Trademark Office
0362-0794 N I C M Journal for Jews and Christians in Higher Education *changed to* Cross Currents: Religion and Intellectual Life.
0362-0808 M S S
0362-0816 Associate Reformed Presbyterian
0362-0824 Bioethics Northwest *see* 1041-3545
0362-0832 Christian Index (Atlanta)
0362-0867 Explor†
0362-0875 Film & Broadcasting Review†
0362-0905 Focus Chicago *see* 0736-3745
0362-0913 Quintessence of Dental Technology *see* 1060-1341
0362-0964 Theatre Studies
0362-0999 Microform Market Place
0362-1006 Micrographics Equipment Review *changed to* Micrographics and Optical Storage Equipment Review.
0362-1014 Microlist *see* 0164-0739
0362-1057 A J S Joint Enterprise *changed to* Update (Chicago).
0362-1065 Abstracts of Book Reviews in Current Legal Periodicals†
0362-1073 New Hampshire Law Weekly *see* 1051-4023
0362-1138 Nebraska. Department of Economic Development. Annual Economic Report†
0362-1146 New West *see* 0279-3768
0362-1162 Audiovideo International
0362-1170 Foundation Center Source Book *changed to* Foundation Center Source Book Profiles.
0362-1197 Human Physiology
0362-1219 Gone Soft *changed to* Soundings East.
0362-1235 University of Missouri, Columbia. Museum of Anthropology. Museum Briefs
0362-1243 California. Division of Oil and Gas. Annual Report of the State Oil and Gas Supervisor
0362-1251 Compact New York Times Magazine†
0362-1278 Financial Industry†
0362-1294 Literary Research Newsletter *see* 0891-6365
0362-1324 Electric Comfort Conditioning News†
0362-1332 F D A Consumer
0362-1340 S I G P L A N Notices *changed to* A C M S I G P L A N Notices.
0362-1383 Massachusetts Advocacy Center. Annual Report†
0362-1391 Georgia Genealogist†
0362-1405 Financial Industry Number Standard Directory
0362-1421 Arizona. Department of Health Services. Annual Report
0362-1472 Association of Theological Schools in the United States and Canada. Bulletin
0362-1510 News from the Congregational Christian Historical Society
0362-1529 Traditio
0362-1537 Transactional Analysis Journal
0362-1561 Michigan Foundation Directory
0362-1588 Houston Journal of Mathematics
0362-1596 Parabola
0362-1618 N E L B Link†
0362-1626 Annual Review of Energy *see* 1056-3466
0362-1642 Annual Review of Pharmacology and Toxicology
0362-1650 Atherosclerosis Reviews
0362-1669 Journal of Combustion Toxicology†
0362-1677 Journal of Consumer Product Flammability†
0362-1693 Journal of Fire Retardant Chemistry†
0362-1715 American Fisheries Society Monograph
0362-188X Air Force Engineering & Services Quarterly
0362-191X Commodity Drain Report of Florida's Primary Forest Industries *changed to* Florida Wood-Using Industry Directory.
0362-1952 Deer Sportsman
0362-1979 J. Paul Getty Museum Journal
0362-2428 Research Communications in Psychology, Psychiatry and Behavior
0362-2436 Spine (Philadelphia, 1976)
0362-2452 Body Fashions - Intimate Apparel Directory
0362-2487 Enjine!-Enjine!
0362-2525 Journal of Morphology
0362-2606 Merchandising 2 - Way Radio *changed to* Personal Communications.
0362-2622 Occasional Papers in Entomology
0362-2711 B & M Bulletin
0362-2746 Teaching Language through Literature†
0362-2770 Options (Wayne)
0362-2800 San Francisco Bay Area Rapid Transit District. Annual Report
0362-2827 Tab†
0362-2843 Southern California Rapid Transit District. Annual Report
0362-2908 Association of Feminist Consultants. Directory of Members†
0362-2916 Carrier Case Reports†
0362-2959 Musician's Guide
0362-2967 New Jersey Area Library Directory†
0362-2983 Study of Federal Tax Law. Income Tax Volume: Business Enterprises
0362-3025 Pathobiology Annual†
0362-3122 Transportation Terminal Techniques†
0362-3165 Health Planning and Manpower Report *see* 0888-9465
0362-3173 Lactation Review†
0362-3211 Toxicology Research Projects Directory†
0362-3238 C B S News Index†
0362-3246 Survey of Sources Newsletter†
0362-3254 N A G W S Guide. Basketball†
0362-3270 Official Field Hockey Rules for School Girls *changed to* Rules of the Game of Field Hockey.
0362-3289 Idaho. Department of Water Resources. Annual Report†
0362-3300 American Musical Instrument Society. Journal
0362-3459 Guide to Minority Business Directories *changed to* Guide to Obtaining Minority Business Directories.
0362-3475 Southeast Michigan Council of Governments. Annual Report
0362-3513 Indiana. Geological Survey. Annual Report of the State Geologist
0362-3548 N F I B Quarterly Economic Report for Small Business
0362-3572 Recent Researches in the Music of the Middle Ages and Early Renaissance
0362-3599 Tourbook: Arizona, New Mexico
0362-3602 Tourbook: Western Canada and Alaska
0362-3610 Understanding Financial Support of Public Schools†
0362-3637 Afroasiatic Linguistics
0362-3653 American Foreign Relations-a Documentary Record†
0362-3688 New York Times Film Reviews
0362-3696 International Union of Bricklayers and Allied Craftsmen. Journal
0362-370X M E S A†
0362-3718 Massachusetts. Bureau of Regional Planning. Regional Profiles†
0362-3750 Who's Who Among Music Students in American High Schools†
0362-3769 Bulletin of Law, Science & Technology
0362-3777 Corvette, the Sensuous American *changed to* Corvette, Sportscar of America.
0362-3793 Labor Force Status of Indiana Residents *changed to* Indiana Labor Market Letter.
0362-3815 Transport 2000 *changed to* Transport 2000 and Intermodal World.
0362-3823 Woodall's Campground Directory *changed to* Woodall's Campground Directory. North American Edition.
0362-3823 Woodall's Campground Directory *see* 0162-7414
0362-3823 Woodall's Campground Directory *see* 0162-7406
0362-3890 Facts and Figures on Footwear *see* 0095-1048
0362-3904 Georgia. State Data Center. City Population Estimates *changed to* Georgia Descriptions in Data.
0362-3912 Idaho. Department of Labor and Industrial Services. Annual Report†
0362-3920 Merchandising *see* 0888-4501
0362-3955 Sound Image
0362-4021 Group (New York)
0362-403X Issues in Child Mental Health *see* 0738-0151
0362-4048 American Rehabilitation
0362-4064 Occupational Health & Safety
0362-4102 Photo-Image†
0362-4110 California. Department of the Youth Authority. Affirmative Action Statistics
0362-4129 California. Department of Industrial Relations. Annual Report *changed to* California. Department of Industrial Relations. Biennial Report.
0362-4145 Children's Literature Review
0362-4196 Alaska. Employment Security Division. Labor Force Estimates by Industry and Area.†
0362-420X Guide to Two-Year College Majors and Careers *see* 0191-3662

0362-4250 Bestways Magazine *changed to* Bestways to Health.
0362-4285 Federal Funding Guide for Local Governments *see* 0273-4435
0362-4293 Lost in Canada?
0362-4366 Directory: Community Development Education and Training Programs Throughout the World†
0362-4439 P N I
0362-4447 Bonsai
0362-4455 Code & Symbol
0362-4463 Southern Weed Science Society. Proceedings
0362-448X L J Special Reports†
0362-4498 International Microfilm Source Book *changed to* International Imaging Source Book.
0362-451X D, the Magazine of Dallas *see* 0161-7826
0362-4528 Discothekin'
0362-4536 I E E E Student Papers
0362-4544 Journal Holdings in the Washington-Baltimore Area *see* 0893-5386
0362-4552 M I M C Microforms Annual *see* 0270-8523
0362-4595 Chicago
0362-4641 Moslem World *see* 0027-4909
0362-4668 Interdependence *changed to* Terra Una.
0362-4706 University of Chicago Record
0362-4722 Consumer Electronics†
0362-4730 D R I European Review *changed to* D R I - McGraw-Hill European Review.
0362-4749 Gun World Hunting Guide *changed to* Gun World Annual.
0362-4765 Political Science Utilization Directory
0362-4781 Texas Register
0362-4803 Journal of Labelled Compounds and Radiopharmaceuticals
0362-4846 Three Rivers Poetry Journal
0362-4889 Low Vision Abstracts
0362-4994 American Gas Association. Operating Section. Proceedings
0362-5001 A M J†
0362-501X Corporate Systems†
0362-5028 Early China
0362-5036 U.S. Department of Education. National Center for Education Statistics. Fall Enrollment in Higher Education
0362-5044 French Periodical Index
0362-5079 Population and Occupied Dwelling Units in Southeast Michigan†
0362-5214 Pig Iron
0362-5230 Study of Federal Tax Law. Income Tax Volume *changed to* Study of Federal Tax Law. Income Tax Volume: Individuals.
0362-5249 Supreme Court Historical Society. Yearbook
0362-5354 Wisconsin. Department of Natural Resources. Annual Water Quality Report to Congress
0362-5419 Gloria Vanderbilt Designs for Your Home
0362-5435 Conference Board. Quarterly Business Review†
0362-5451 Rx: R I A for Physicians†
0362-546X Nonlinear Analysis
0362-5478 Pharmacology and Therapeutics. Part A. Chemotherapy, Toxicology and Metabolic Inhibitors *see* 0163-7258
0362-5486 Pharmacology and Therapeutics. Part C. Clinical Pharmacology and Therapeutics *see* 0163-7258
0362-5524 Illinois. Board of Higher Education. Statewide Space Survey†
0362-5567 Fishing Guide†
0362-5575 Los Angeles Daily Journal
0362-5664 Clinical Neuropharmacology
0362-5699 Reviews in Perinatal Medicine
0362-5737 Truck Broker Directory†
0362-5745 Army Communicator
0362-5753 Who's Who Among Black Americans
0362-580X Journal of Social and Political Affairs *see* 0278-839X
0362-5818 E E O Today *see* 0745-7790
0362-5834 Youth Magazine†
0362-5850 Plants & Gardens: Brooklyn Botanic Garden Record
0362-5907 A G O Times *see* 0164-3150
0362-5915 A C M Transactions on Database Systems
0362-5923 Activity Programmers Sourcebook†
0362-5931 Georgia Legislative Review
0362-594X Geographic Origin and Distribution of Students, Missouri Institutions of Higher Education†
0362-5982 South
0362-6016 Policy Studies Directory
0362-6059 Accent†
0362-6075 Andover Review†
0362-613X American Journal of Computational Linguistics *see* 0891-2017
0362-6148 Chicago Daily Law Bulletin
0362-6180 Buyers' Guide for the Mass Entertainment Industry *changed to* Entertainment Facilities Buyers Guide.
0362-6199 Data Resources U S Long-Term Bulletin *changed to* D R I - McGraw-Hill Review of the U S Economy: Long Range Focus.
0362-6245 U & I c
0362-6288 Utah. Geological and Mineral Survey. Survey Notes *changed to* Utah Geological Survey. Survey Notes.
0362-6296 Hawaii. Department of Health. Mental Health Services for Children and Youth
0362-6369 Washington (State). Department of Ecology. Water Quality Assessment Report†
0362-6385 Field & Stream Fishing Annual
0362-6415 Red River Valley Historical Review†
0362-6466 Food and Drug Letter
0362-6474 Threads in Action Monograph
0362-6490 Virginia. Agricultural Opportunities Development Program. Annual Report†
0362-6520 Hudson Home Guides *see* 0278-2839
0362-6547 Red River Valley Historical Journal of World History†
0362-6563 California Department of Parks and Recreation. a Stewardship Report†
0362-6644 Your Good Health Review & Digest†
0362-6660 Kids Fashions Magazine
0362-6679 Summary of Kentucky Education Statistics *changed to* Information on Education.
0362-6741 United States Investor - Eastern Banker *see* 0148-8848
0362-6784 Curriculum Inquiry
0362-6830 Monthly Catalog of United States Government Publications
0362-6881 Bentley Historical Library Annual Report
0362-6911 Frontiers of Economics†
0362-6962 Alaska. Division of Wildlife Conservation. Annual Report of Survey - Inventory Activities
0362-7012 U S 1 Worksheets
0362-7047 Latvju Maksla
0362-7055 French Colonial Historical Society. Proceedings of the Meeting
0362-708X Academy†
0362-7152 Country Scene†
0362-7179 Directory of Services for Migrant Families†
0362-7284 Alaska. Criminal Investigation Bureau. Annual Report
0362-7373 Songwriter Magazine
0362-742X Public Welfare in California†
0362-7462 Washington (State). Department of Revenue. Forest Tax Report *changed to* Washington (State). Department of Revenue. Forest Tax Division. Forest Tax Annual Report.
0362-7470 Wisconsin. Division of Corrections. Bureau of Planning, Development and Research. Releases from Juvenile Institutions *changed to* Wisconsin. Division of Corrections. Office of Information Management. Releases from Juvenile Institutions.
0362-7705 Schoolhouse *changed to* E F L Reports.
0362-7721 Thomas Register of American Manufacturers and Thomas Register Catalog File
0362-7772 Demolition Age
0362-7799 Petroleum Marketer
0362-7888 Harvest *changed to* Connecticut Writer.
0362-7926 Texas Pharmacy
0362-7942 F A A General Aviation News *changed to* F A A Aviation News.
0362-7969 Painted Bride Quarterly
0362-7985 Review of Business and Economics Research *see* 1058-3300
0362-8078 Harvard Ukrainian Research Institute. Minutes of the Seminar in Ukrainian Studies†
0362-8140 Modern Veterinary Practice
0362-8205 S A E Handbook
0362-823X Business Research Bulletin†
0362-8302 Jam to-Day†
0362-8337 Health Careers†
0362-8353 Criminal Justice Plan (Richmond)†
0362-837X Los Angeles Bar Journal *see* 0162-2900
0362-8396 Provincetown Poets *changed to* Provincetown Magazine.
0362-8493 Across the Table
0362-8507 Intergovernmental Perspective
0362-8523 Poor Joe's Pennsylvania Almanac†
0362-854X University of Texas at Austin. General Libraries. Newsletter
0362-8558 Journal of Dialysis *see* 0886-022X
0362-8566 Self Reliance†
0362-8671 Index to Book Reviews in Historical Periodicals†
0362-868X Massachusetts Tax Primer *changed to* Massachusetts Primer.
0362-8701 Best's Insurance Securities Research Service†
0362-8736 Inter-University Consortium for Political and Social Research. Guide to Resources and Services.
0362-8744 New York Metropolitan Reference and Research Agency. Directory of Members *see* 0887-1973
0362-8787 Delaware. State Board of Education. Report of Educational Statistics
0362-8809 Journal on Political Repression†
0362-8817 Insurance Industry *see* 1054-0733
0362-8833 N R E C A - A P P A Legal Reporting Service
0362-8841 Mother Jones
0362-885X Manufacturing and Engineering *see* 0744-7698
0362-8914 American Journal of Ancient History
0362-8922 Gnostica News *see* 0145-885X
0362-8930 School Library Journal
0362-8973 Information Processing Journal *see* 0191-9776
0362-9066 F P S: a Magazine of Young People's Liberation
0362-9074 History of Anthropology Newsletter
0362-9090 Human Factor†
0362-9163 U.S. Office of Management and Budget. Special Analysis: Budget of the United States Government
0362-9198 Maryland. Division of Correction. Report
0362-9279 Idaho. Department of Health and Welfare. Annual Summary of Vital Statistics
0362-9287 Directory - Juvenile and Adult Correctional Departments, Institutions, Agencies, and Paroling Authorities of the United States and Canada *see* 0190-2555
0362-9368 Packard Cormorant
0362-9376 Plastics Design Forum
0362-9406 School Security†
0362-9473 Iowa Detailed Report of Vital Statistics *see* 0161-8695
0362-9481 N A G W S Guide. Track and Field†
0362-9511 U.S. Department of Agriculture. Sugar and Sweetener Outlook and Situation *changed to* U.S. Department of Agriculture. Sugar and Sweetener Situation and Outlook.
0362-9554 Aspen Anthology *changed to* Aspen Journal of the Arts.
0362-9651 Brand Guide and Directory
0362-9716 Ohio Inventory of Business and Industrial Change†
0362-9783 Humanistic Educator *see* 0735-6846
0362-9791 Journal of Educational Statistics
0362-9805 Legislative Studies Quarterly
0362-9821 Tourbook: Colorado, Utah
0362-9848 C A Selects. Psychobiochemistry
0362-9856 C A Selects. Photochemistry
0362-9872 C A Selects. Mass Spectrometry
0362-9880 C A Selects. Forensic Chemistry
0362-9899 C A Selects. Organosilicon Chemistry
0362-9902 C F O Journal
0362-9910 Fortitudine
0362-9945 American Philological Association. Proceedings†
0363-0021 Federal Reserve Bank of San Francisco. Economic Review
0363-0048 Preview of United States Supreme Court Cases
0363-0129 S I A M Journal on Control and Optimization
0363-0153 Archives of Pathology & Laboratory Medicine
0363-0161 Bibliography of Bioethics
0363-0188 Current Problems in Diagnostic Radiology
0363-020X Health Services Manager†
0363-0234 Suicide and Life-Threatening Behavior
0363-0242 Women & Health
0363-0250 Action for Libraries
0363-0269 Hemoglobin
0363-0277 Library Journal
0363-0307 Golden Gate University Law Review
0363-0358 National Association of Insurance Commissioners. Proceedings
0363-0366 Medical and Health Annual
0363-0404 Journal of Products Liability
0363-0447 First Principles
0363-0471 Hispamerica
0363-0617 Parks
0363-065X Access: the Index to Little Magazines†
0363-0781 Health Sciences Video Directory *see* 0731-5945
0363-079X Shout in the Street†
0363-0889 C P P R
0363-0927 Guide to External and Continuing Education†
0363-0978 Shepard's Criminal Justice Citations
0363-0994 Unified World
0363-1001 Videography
0363-101X Tennessee Valley Authority. Annual Report
0363-1028 Whistle Stop
0363-1079 Indochina Chronicle *see* 0738-050X
0363-1095 Washington Academy of Sciences. Proceedings *see* 0043-0439
0363-1133 Women's Studies Newsletter *see* 0732-1562
0363-1168 Virgin Islands Archaeological Society. Journal
0363-1192 Utah Geology†
0363-1230 Webster Review
0363-1249 History and Life. Part C: American History Bibliography *changed to* America: History and Life. Articles Abstract and Citations of Reviews and Dissertations Covering the United States and Canada.
0363-1257 METRO C A P Catalog†
0363-129X California Workers' Compensation Reporter
0363-1354 National Boat Book
0363-1370 Sunstone
0363-1540 Tourbook: New York
0363-1605 Community Mental Health Review *see* 0270-3114

ISSN INDEX 5719

0363-1621 Contact Lens Forum *changed to* Contact Lens Spectrum.
0363-1664 Laughing Man†
0363-1672 Lithuanian Mathematical Journal
0363-1699 Matchbox†
0363-1710 Mortgage Banking: Loans Closed and Servicing Volume *see* 0277-1497
0363-1788 Tourbook: Atlantic Provinces and Quebec
0363-1818 Consumer Life†
0363-1850 Eureka Review
0363-1869 Harris Michigan Manufacturers Industrial Directory *see* 0888-8167
0363-1877 Headmaster U.S.A. *changed to* Private School Quarterly.
0363-1907 Journal of Psychiatric Education *see* 1042-9670
0363-1915 CableFile†
0363-1923 Illinois Classical Studies
0363-194X Pennsylvania Illustrated†
0363-1990 Journal of Family History
0363-2024 Urban Anthropology†
0363-2067 Vermont Industrial Development Authority. Annual Report
0363-2083 E M Complaint Directory for Consumers *see* 0732-0485
0363-2091 Eastern Canada Campbook
0363-2148 University of Dayton Intramural Law Review *see* 0162-9174
0363-2164 Laughing Bear†
0363-2237 Sea Grant Publications Index†
0363-2245 Sean O'Casey Review†
0363-2318 Appalachian Heritage
0363-2369 Kidney Disease and Nephrology Index†
0363-2393 Chilton's Motor-Age Professional Automotive Service Manual
0363-2407 Executive's Tax Review†
0363-2415 Fisheries
0363-2423 Glendale Law Review
0363-2431 T F News *see* 1047-7667
0363-2504 N A G W S Guide. Softball
0363-2512 North Dakota. Geological Survey. Oil and Gas Production Statistics†
0363-2539 American Bankers Association. Operations and Automation Division. Results of the National Operations & Automation Survey
0363-2547 Audiotapes Reprints Publications†
0363-258X Electronic Warfare *see* 0278-3479
0363-2598 Improving College and University Teaching Yearbook†
0363-2601 Innovative Graduate Programs Directory
0363-2636 Lens Magazine†
0363-2644 Metric Bulletin†
0363-2679 Oklahoma Journal of Forensic Medicine *changed to* Medicolegal-Gram.
0363-2695 Tourbook: Idaho, Montana, Wyoming
0363-2717 Historical Abstracts. Part A: Modern History Abstracts, 1450-1914
0363-2725 Historical Abstracts. Part B: Twentieth Century Abstracts, 1914 to the Present
0363-2792 Image *see* 0743-5150
0363-2822 Access: the Index to Little Magazines. microform edition of 0363-065X
0363-2830 Downtown Promotion Reporter
0363-2849 International Trumpet Guild. Journal *changed to* I T G Journal.
0363-2857 International Trumpet Guild. Newsletter *changed to* I T G Journal.
0363-2865 Jerusalem Journal of International Relations
0363-2873 Journal of Libertarian Studies
0363-2903 Arete
0363-2911 Art and Cinema *changed to* Art & Cinema.
0363-2970 Algae, Bacteria, Bacteriophages, Fungi and Protozoa *changed to* American Type Culture Collection. Catalogue of Recombinant D N A Materials.
0363-2989 American Type Culture Collection. Catalogue of Viruses, Rickettsiae, Chlamydiae *changed to* American Type Culture Collection. Catalogue of Cell Lines and Hybridomas.
0363-308X Technos†
0363-311X Tibet Society Newsletter *see* 0883-7732
0363-3195 Social Indicators Newsletter *see* 0885-6729
0363-3268 Research in Economic History
0363-3276 Wilson Quarterly
0363-3519 Virginia Museum of Fine Arts Bulletin
0363-3551 Virginia Business Report
0363-3586 Biofeedback & Self Regulation
0363-3624 Nurse Educator
0363-3640 Journal of Library & Information Science
0363-3659 Maledicta
0363-3705 Tequesta
0363-373X Better Schools (Chicago) *changed to* Gas Industries Magazine.
0363-3764 Bus Ride: Bus Industry Directory
0363-3780 En Passant Poetry Quarterly *see* 0271-5023
0363-3799 Sensory Processes†
0363-3810 Union of American Hebrew Congregations. State of Our Union
0363-3918 International Review of Physiology†
0363-4132 University of Texas at Austin. Bureau of Economic Geology. Guidebook
0363-4140 Astrology Annual Reference Book *changed to* Astrology Reference Book.
0363-4183 California. Department of Housing and Community Development. Annual Report†
0363-4205 Journal of New Jersey Poets
0363-4396 C C H Tax Planning Review
0363-440X Carolinas Genealogical Society. Bulletin
0363-4426 Multinational Marketing & Employment Directory†
0363-4493 Chestnut Tree
0363-4507 Iowa Comprehensive State Plan for Drug Abuse Prevention: Annual Performance Report *changed to* Iowa Comprehensive State Plan for Substance Abuse (Year).
0363-4523 Communication Education
0363-454X Brass Research Series
0363-4558 Edward H. Tarr Series
0363-4566 Texas School Directory
0363-4574 Cornfield Review
0363-4590 Seeker (Pittsburg)
0363-4639 Hemming's Vintage Auto Almanac
0363-4655 Pharmacopeial Forum
0363-468X Journal of Studies on Alcohol. Supplement
0363-471X A S A Refresher Courses in Anesthesiology
0363-4744 Housing Market Report
0363-4779 T.U.B.A. Newsletter *see* 0363-4787
0363-4787 T.U.B.A. Journal
0363-4795 World Military and Social Expenditures
0363-4817 Pacific Area Destination Handbook *changed to* Pacific Destinations Handbook.
0363-4833 Western School Law Digest†
0363-4841 Encomia
0363-4922 Security Letter
0363-4965 N A S B O Newsletter†
0363-5023 Journal of Hand Surgery: American Volume
0363-504X Modern Liturgy
0363-5058 In Common
0363-5104 Primary Cardiology
0363-5120 Fast Service *see* 0744-0405
0363-5155 Inventory of Population Projects in Developing Countries Around the World
0363-5171 Great Lakes Fisherman
0363-5198 Kentucky Directory of Selected Industrial Services†
0363-5236 Bye Cadmos†
0363-5244 Pro Musica Magazine†
0363-5252 Davison's Salesman's Book
0363-5260 American National Metric Council. Annual Report†
0363-5341 Minnesota. Division of Fish and Wildlife. Environment Section. Special Publication†
0363-535X American Executive Travel Companion†
0363-5376 Alaska. Office of Ombudsman. Report of the Ombudsman *changed to* Alaska Ombudsman Report.
0363-5406 Window and Wall Decorating Ideas *see* 0277-836X
0363-5414 Dikta
0363-5422 Federal Budget: Focus and Perspective *changed to* Federal Budget (Year).
0363-5430 Foreign Exchange Rates and Restrictions†
0363-5465 American Journal of Sports Medicine
0363-552X Fishing in the Mid-Atlantic *changed to* Fishing in New Jersey.
0363-5538 Bob Zwirz' Fishing Annual *changed to* Fishing and Boating Illustrated.
0363-5570 Harvard Ukrainian Studies
0363-566X American Business
0363-5694 American Society for Church Architecture. Journal†
0363-5708 International Trombone Association Series
0363-5732 Abstract Journal in Earthquake Engineering
0363-5767 Casting & Jewelry Craft†
0363-5775 Los Angeles County Department of Regional Planning. Quarterly Bulletin†
0363-5783 The Gavel
0363-5872 Recent Advances in Studies on Cardiac Structure and Metabolism *see* 0270-4056
0363-5880 House & Garden Guide to American Tradition†
0363-5910 Gay Nineties *see* 0147-6165
0363-5937 International Sculpture Conference. Proceedings
0363-6100 American Journal of Physiology: Endocrinology, Metabolism and Gastrointestinal Physiology *see* 0193-1849
0363-6100 American Journal of Physiology: Endocrinology, Metabolism and Gastrointestinal Physiology *see* 0193-1857
0363-6119 American Journal of Physiology: Regulatory, Integrative and Comparative Physiology
0363-6127 American Journal of Physiology: Renal, Fluid and Electrolyte Physiology
0363-6135 American Journal of Physiology: Heart and Circulatory Physiology
0363-6143 American Journal of Physiology: Cell Physiology
0363-6291 Change in Higher Education *see* 0009-1383
0363-6380 Invention Management *changed to* Technology Management News.
0363-6399 Data Communications
0363-6437 Paperworker
0363-6445 Systematic Botany
0363-647X Annals of Phenomenological Sociology *changed to* Phenomenology and the Human Sciences.
0363-6488 Philadelphia Photo Review *changed to* Photo Review.
0363-650X Connecticut. Advisory Council on Vocational and Career Education. Vocational Education Evaluation Report *changed to* Connecticut. State Council on Vocational-Technical Education. Vocational Education Evaluation Report.
0363-6526 Current Concepts in Gastroenterology
0363-6542 1869 Times
0363-6550 Midwest Studies in Philosophy
0363-6569 Pastoral Music
0363-6690 Western Wildlands
0363-6712 Sea Boating Almanac. Southern California, Arizona, Baja *see* 0193-3507
0363-6720 Fact Book on Higher Education *changed to* Fact Book for Higher Education.
0363-6771 General Dentistry
0363-678X Commercial News for the Foreign Service *changed to* Commercial News U S A.
0363-6798 Foreign Trade Reports. Bunker Fuels†
0363-6828 U.S. Geological Survey. Board on Geographic Names. Decisions of Geographic Names in the United States
0363-6836 Current Population Reports: Population Characteristics
0363-6895 Catholic Periodical Index *see* 0008-8285
0363-6941 J E G P: Journal of English and Germanic Philology
0363-6968 New Life
0363-700X Manufacturing Engineering. Engineering Transactions *changed to* Transactions of the North American Manufacturing Research Conference. Proceedings.
0363-7107 Harvard Library Notes *see* 0017-8136
0363-7123 International Organisations in World Politics Yearbook†
0363-7158 Tennessee Public Library Statistics
0363-7166 Federal Programs, State of Arizona†
0363-7190 Empire State Report *see* 0747-0711
0363-7204 World Military Expenditures *see* 0897-4667
0363-7220 Geophysics, Astronomy, and Space *changed to* U S S R Report: Space.
0363-7239 U.S. Congress. Congressional Record
0363-7360 Osteopathic Medicine†
0363-7417 Weekly Government Abstracts. Urban Technology *see* 0163-1535
0363-7425 Academy of Management Review
0363-745X C U Directory
0363-7476 C C H Compliance Guide for Plan Administrators *see* 0274-8304
0363-7492 History News (Nashville)
0363-7530 Texas State Directory
0363-7565 Monumenta Archaeologica
0363-7700 Sea Boating Almanac. Northern California and Nevada *see* 0193-3515
0363-7719 American Journal of Health Planning
0363-7751 Communication Monographs
0363-7778 Media Review Digest
0363-7816 San Francisco Chronicle. Newspaper Index *see* 0893-2425
0363-7824 Houston Post. Newspaper Index *see* 0893-2476
0363-7832 National Observer Newspaper Index *changed to* Index to the National Observer.
0363-7867 Colorado Lawyer
0363-7891 Soviet Physics - Collection *see* 1047-4064
0363-7913 Rhode Island Medical Journal
0363-7972 Doll Castle News
0363-7980 Central School Law Digest†
0363-7999 Sea Boating Almanac. Pacific Northwest and Alaska *see* 0276-8771
0363-8006 Recent Developments in Maryland Law†
0363-8057 Gradiva
0363-8065 Abrasive Engineering Society. Conference Proceedings
0363-8111 Public Relations Review
0363-8138 Custom Bike *changed to* Custom Bike-Choppers.
0363-8197 Texas Business *see* 0164-7628
0363-8200 Diplomatic World Bulletin and Delegates World Bulletin
0363-8219 Aerospace Propulsion
0363-8227 Helicopter News
0363-8235 Computerized Tomography *see* 0895-6111
0363-826X Gayellow Pages
0363-8286 Current Housing Reports: Market Absorption of Apartments
0363-8294 Current Construction Reports: Value of New Construction Put in Place
0363-8332 Current Topics in Early Childhood Education
0363-8340 National Property Law Digests

ISSN

5720 ISSN INDEX

0363-8391 Pacific Northwest Council on Foreign Languages. Proceedings *see* 0277-0598
0363-8448 Monthly Retail Trade, Sales and Accounts Receivable *changed to* Current Business Reports: Monthly Retail Trade, Sales and Inventories.
0363-8464 U.S. Department of Defense. Index of Specifications and Standards
0363-8472 Music and Musicians: Large Print Scores and Books Catalog for the Blind and Physically Handicapped *changed to* Music & Musicians: Large-Print Scores and Books Catalog (Large Print Edition).
0363-8480 Recent Advances in Tobacco Science
0363-8529 Soviet Microelectronics
0363-8537 Current Construction Reports: New One Family Homes Sold and for Sale *changed to* Current Construction Reports: New One-Family Houses Sold and for Sale.
0363-8553 Current Business Reports: Monthly Wholesale Trade: Sales and Inventories
0363-8561 U.S. Crop Reporting Board. Crop Production
0363-8588 Uniformed Services Almanac. National Guard Edition *see* 0363-8618
0363-860X Reserve Forces Almanac
0363-8618 National Guard Almanac
0363-8642 Cements Research Progress
0363-8715 Journal of Computer Assisted Tomography
0363-874X Educational Directory of Mississippi Schools *see* 0092-7899
0363-8774 Rhode Island State Council on the Arts. Newsnotes *changed to* Arts & Cultural Times.
0363-8782 Texas Speech Communication Journal
0363-8790 Current Construction Reports: Housing Units Authorized by Building Permits and Public Contracts *changed to* Current Construction Reports: Housing Units Authorized by Building Permits.
0363-8812 Federal Design Matters†
0363-8820 Energy Reporter
0363-8855 Journal of Clinical Engineering
0363-8898 Fishing in Maryland and Virginia *see* 0164-0941
0363-891X Psychohistory Review
0363-8928 International Symposium on Fault-Tolerant Computing. Proceedings *see* 0731-3071
0363-8960 Old Time Songs and Poems (Seabrook) †
0363-8987 Financial Studies of the Small Business
0363-9029 Cassette Books
0363-9037 Maledicta Press Publications
0363-9045 Drug Development and Industrial Pharmacy
0363-9061 International Journal for Numerical and Analytical Methods in Geomechanics
0363-907X International Journal of Energy Research
0363-910X B A I Index of Bank Performance†
0363-9185 Help (Washington)
0363-9207 Ohio. Commission on Aging. Annual Report *changed to* Ohio Department of Aging. Annual Report.
0363-9282 N A G W S Guide. Gymnastics†
0363-9290 Republican Almanac
0363-9347 International League for Human Rights. Annual Report
0363-9401 S.C.A., State & County Administrator†
0363-9428 American Journal of Small Business *see* 1042-2587
0363-9444 Impact: Wine and Spirits Newsletter *changed to* Impact (New York).
0363-9452 Grand Jury Report†
0363-9460 Confrontation - Change Review
0363-9479 C L S I Newsletter *changed to* C L S I Newsletter of Library Automation.
0363-9487 T V Season†
0363-9509 Community College Frontiers†
0363-9525 37 Design & Environment Projects†
0363-9568 Nursing Administration Quarterly
0363-972X Directory of Dance Companies
0363-9762 Clinical Nuclear Medicine
0363-9797 Human Factors Society. Proceedings of the Annual Meeting *see* 0163-5182
0363-9819 U.S. Environmental Protection Agency. Radiological Quality of the Environment in the United States†
0363-9835 New York (State). Department of Social Services. Annual Report
0363-9843 New York (State). Board of Social Welfare. Annual Report *see* 0363-9835
0363-9991 Interstate
0364-0000 Cutting Edge†
0364-0078 Country Style
0364-0086 Tourbook: Mid-Atlantic
0364-0094 A J S Review
0364-0116 E D I S†
0364-0175 Smithsonian Institution Research Reports
0364-0205 Monthly Petroleum Statistics Report†
0364-0213 Cognitive Science
0364-023X Flea Market Trader
0364-0302 Libertarian Review†
0364-0337 Missouri. Disaster Operations Office. Newsletter *see* 0197-6672
0364-0396 U.S. National Center for Health Statistics. Monthly Vital Statistics Report
0364-040X U.S. Social Security Administration. Monthly Benefit Statistics *changed to* U.S. Department of Health and Human Services. Monthly Benefit Statistics.
0364-0426 Advisor, Navy Civilian Manpower Management†
0364-0531 N I A A A Information and Feature Service†
0364-071X Colt American Handgunning Annual†
0364-0728 Arkansas Vital Statistics
0364-0736 Farmer Cooperatives
0364-0752 Financial Stock Guide Service. Directory of Active Stocks
0364-0760 Charities U S A
0364-0779 Institute for Socioeconomic Studies. Journal
0364-0868 Biweekly Cryogenics Current Awareness Service†
0364-0930 U.S. Department of Housing and Urban Development. Office of International Affairs. Foreign Publications Accessions List†
0364-0981 U.S. Coast Guard Marine Safety Council. Proceedings
0364-099X Grain Market News *changed to* Grain and Feed Market News.
0364-1066 Correspondent (Appleton)
0364-1074 E I S: Key to Environmental Impact Statements *changed to* E I S: Digests of Environmental Impact Statements.
0364-1082 Group and Organization Studies *see* 1059-6011
0364-1112 Stress and Anxiety *see* 1053-2161
0364-118X E L C†
0364-1198 Female Patient
0364-1228 Current Index to Statistics
0364-1236 Library Resources for the Blind and Physically Handicapped (Large Print Edition)
0364-1287 Army Lawyer
0364-1414 Index of Federal Specifications, Standards, and Handbooks *changed to* Index of Federal Specifications, Standards and Commercial Item Descriptions.
0364-1449 Handbook on International Study for U.S. Nationals. Vol. 1: Study in Europe†
0364-152X Environmental Management (New York)
0364-1538 Stereopus
0364-1546 Dirt Bike
0364-1554 New Baby Talk *changed to* Baby Talk Magazine.
0364-1597 A L A Yearbook†
0364-1678 Federal Government†
0364-1708 Glyph
0364-1724 Law Enforcement News
0364-1732 Simplicity Home Catalog *changed to* Simplicity Magazine.
0364-1988 Journal of Marine Science *see* 0148-9836
0364-2003 Fusion Energy Foundation Newsletter *see* 0148-0537
0364-2011 E T A Interchange†
0364-202X U.S. Crop Reporting Board. Cattle on Feed
0364-2097 Sojourners
0364-2151 Environment Midwest†
0364-216X Aesthetic Plastic Surgery
0364-2178 Occasional Bulletin of Missionary Research *see* 0272-6122
0364-2194 Barbeque Planet†
0364-2216 Journal of the Graduate Music Students at the Ohio State University
0364-2232 Voice for the Defense
0364-2267 U.S. Securities and Exchange Commission. Official Summary of Security Transactions and Holdings
0364-2313 World Journal of Surgery
0364-2321 Soviet Physics - Lebedev Institute Reports
0364-2348 Skeletal Radiology
0364-2356 Gastrointestinal Radiology
0364-2410 M E L A Notes
0364-2429 Money Digest†
0364-2437 Afro-Americans in New York Life and History
0364-2569 Monographs in Pharmacology and Physiology†
0364-2577 Guidelines to Metabolic Therapy†
0364-2615 Tennessee Valley Perspective†
0364-264X Children's Book International. Proceedings and Book Catalog *see* 0163-1756
0364-2801 P A A B S Symposium Series *changed to* Pan American Association of Biochemical Societies Symposium.
0364-2968 Journal of Germanic Philology *see* 0363-6941
0364-2976 Journal of the Hellenic Diaspora
0364-3093 Offender Rehabilitation *see* 1050-9674
0364-3107 Administration in Social Work
0364-3115 Grantsmanship Center News†
0364-3190 Neurochemical Research
0364-3263 Combat Fleets of the World *changed to* Naval Institute Guide to Combat Fleets of the World.
0364-3301 Corrosion Prevention - Inhibition Digest
0364-3344 Box 749
0364-3352 Current Bibliographic Survey of National Defense *see* 1050-4850
0364-3379 Artist of the Rockies and the Golden West *see* 0192-4214
0364-3409 T P G A Journal
0364-345X Passenger Transport
0364-3476 H S R I Research *see* 0739-7100
0364-3484 Mass Transit
0364-3549 English Literature in Transition (1880-1920)
0364-359X Dragonfly
0364-3670 International CODEN Directory
0364-3735 Private Higher Education *see* 0734-6735
0364-3824 Taste
0364-3875 Official Airline Guide. WorldWide Edition
0364-3921 Nevada Public Affairs Report *see* 0196-7355
0364-3999 Micropublishing of Current Periodicals *see* 0958-9961
0364-4006 A L A Bulletin *see* 0002-9769
0364-4014 The Spirit That Moves Us
0364-4022 Poesie - U.S.A.
0364-4103 J S A C Grapevine†
0364-4529 Ninth District Quarterly *see* 0271-5287
0364-4626 Soviet Journal of Coordination Chemistry
0364-474X Electric Perspectives
0364-4782 Journal of Human Services Abstracts†
0364-491X U.S. Bureau of Labor Statistics. Employment Situation
0364-4928 Weekly Government Abstracts. Materials Sciences *changed to* N T I S Alerts: Materials Sciences.
0364-4936 Weekly Government Abstracts. Environmental Pollution and Control *changed to* N T I S Alerts: Environmental Pollution & Control.
0364-4944 Weekly Government Abstracts. Communication *changed to* N T I S Alerts: Communication.
0364-4952 Weekly Government Abstracts. Biomedical Technology and Engineering *changed to* N T I S Alerts: Biomedical Technology & Human Factors Engineering.
0364-4979 Weekly Government Abstracts. Natural Resources *changed to* N T I S Alerts: Natural Resources & Earth Sciences.
0364-507X Wisconsin Public Documents
0364-5134 Annals of Neurology
0364-5177 Live Steam
0364-5193 Bioethics Digest
0364-5215 U S B E News
0364-5274 Energy Daily
0364-5479 Informer (Los Angeles)
0364-5487 Peters Notes†
0364-5517 Seybold Report *see* 0736-7260
0364-5533 Infosystems *changed to* Information Systems (Carol Stream).
0364-5541 Journal of Mental Imagery
0364-555X Russian-English Translators Exchange†
0364-5568 Professional Translator†
0364-5711 Standard & Poor's International Stock Report†
0364-586X Downtown Mall Annual & Urban Design Report†
0364-5916 CALPHAD
0364-5924 Hayes Historical Journal
0364-6408 Library Acquisitions: Practice and Theory
0364-6424 Weekly Government Abstracts. Ocean Technology and Engineering *changed to* N T I S Alerts: Ocean Technology & Engineering.
0364-6432 Weekly Government Abstracts. Medicine and Biology *changed to* N T I S Alerts: Medicine & Biology.
0364-6440 Weekly Government Abstracts. N A S A Earth Resources Survey Program *changed to* Abstract Newsletter: N A S A Earth Resources Survey Program.
0364-6459 Weekly Government Abstracts. Problem-Solving Information for State and Local Governments *changed to* Abstract Newsletter: Problem-Solving Information for State and Local Governments.
0364-6467 Weekly Government Abstracts. Library and Information Sciences *changed to* N T I S Alerts: Library & Information Sciences.
0364-6475 N E I S S News *changed to* N E I S S Data Highlights.
0364-6483 Weekly Government Abstracts. Industrial and Mechanical Engineering *changed to* Abstract Newsletter: Industrial & Mechanical Engineering.
0364-6491 Weekly Government Abstracts. Government Inventions for Licensing *changed to* N T I S Alerts: Government Inventions for Licensing.
0364-6505 Edebiyat
0364-6521 Telesis (Washington) *see* 0277-6863
0364-6610 Physician Distribution and Medical Licensure in the U S *see* 0731-0315
0364-6645 Harvard Business School. Baker Library. Working Papers in Baker Library
0364-6653 Transportation Topics for Consumers *changed to* Transportation Consumer.
0364-6696 U.S. Office of the Secretary of the Treasury. Treasury Papers†

ISSN

ISSN INDEX 5721

0364-6718 S E C News Digest
0364-6742 International Notices to Airmen
0364-6807 U.S. Navy Medicine *changed to* Navy Medicine.
0364-6866 Nuclear Reactors Built, Being Built, or Planned in the United States
0364-698X American Wine Society Journal
0364-6998 Solar Energy Update†
0364-7064 U.S. National Cartographic Information Center. Newsletter *changed to* U.S. Earth Science Information Center. Newsletter.
0364-7072 U.S. National Earthquake Information Service. Preliminary Determination of Epicenters, Monthly Listing
0364-7129 U.S. Railroad Retirement Board. Monthly Benefit Statistics
0364-7145 Maintenance†
0364-7161 South Central Camping *changed to* South Central Campbook.
0364-717X Minnesota. Department of Employment Services. Annual Report *changed to* Minnesota. Department of Jobs and Training. Annual Report.
0364-720X Lake Superior Review†
0364-7234 World Economic Conditions in Relation to Agricultural Trade†
0364-7358 Manpower Planning *see* 0733-0332
0364-7374 American Merchant Marine Conference. Proceedings
0364-7390 Evaluation Studies Review Annual†
0364-7471 American Druggist Blue Book
0364-7501 Musical Mainstream (Large Print Edition)
0364-7609 Primavera (Chicago)
0364-7625 Access Reports *changed to* Access Reports/Freedom of Information.
0364-765X Mathematics of Operations Research
0364-7668 Rising Tide
0364-7692 Harvard University Gazette
0364-7714 Water Supply and Management†
0364-7722 Progress in Neuro-Psychopharmacology *see* 0278-5846
0364-7811 Directory of Geoscience Departments, United States and Canada *changed to* Directory of Geoscience Departments, North America.
0364-796X Weekly Government Abstracts. Computers, Control and Information Theory *changed to* N T I S Alerts: Computers, Control & Information Theory.
0364-7978 Weekly Government Abstracts. Business and Economics *changed to* N T I S Alerts: Business & Economics.
0364-7986 Weekly Government Abstracts. Administration *changed to* N T I S Alerts: Administration and Management.
0364-7994 Abstract Newsletter: Agriculture and Food *changed to* N T I S Alerts: Agriculture & Food.
0364-8117 Soviet Aeronautics - Iz. V U Z
0364-8125 A T L A Law Reporter
0364-815X Marquee (Norwalk)
0364-8184 New Horizon - Polish American Review
0364-8265 U.S. General Accounting Office. Monthly List of G A O Reports
0364-8273 Football Forecast (Year)
0364 8303 International and Comparative Public Policy†
0364-8389 R I F Newsletter
0364-8591 Old Testament Abstracts
0364-863X Postal Bulletin
0364-8664 Kentucky Romance Quarterly *see* 0883-1157
0364-8893 Associated Equipment Distributors. Rental Compilation *see* 0164-0593
0364-8958 International Fire Chief *changed to* I A F C On Scene.
0364-8966 Directory of U.S. and Canadian Marketing Surveys and Services†
0364-9008 Defense Business *changed to* Defense & Economy World Report.
0364-9024 Journal of Graph Theory
0364-9059 I E E E Journal of Oceanic Engineering
0364-9156 Directors & Boards
0364-9210 Ethnodisc Journal of Recorded Sound†
0364-9229 Astronomy Quarterly *see* 0083-6656
0364-9237 Speedhorse *changed to* Speedhorse - Racing Report.
0364-9253 Estates, Gifts and Trusts Journal *see* 0886-3547
0364-930X Alfa Owner
0364-9342 Mini-Micro Systems *changed to* Systems Integration Business.
0364-9369 E E-Electrical Equipment *changed to* E E Product News.
0364-9407 Th-Bao Ga *changed to* Vietnam Quarterly.
0364-9474 Friends of Wine
0364-9490 Delaware Journal of Corporate Law
0364-9539 National Distribution Directory of Local Cartage-Short Haul Carriers Warehousing *changed to* M C D's Warehousing Distribution Directory.
0364-9733 Saturday Evening Post. microform edition of 0048-9239
0364-9857 Research Quarterly for Exercise and Sport. microform edition of 0270-1367
0364-9865 American Artist. microform edition of 0002-7375
0364-9873 American Anthropologist. microform edition of 0002-7294
0364-989X America. microform edition of 0002-7049
0364-9911 Adult Education Quarterly. microform edition of 0741-7136
0364-9962 A S H R A E Journal. microform edition of 0001-2491
0365-0138 Astronomy and Astrophysics Supplement Series
0365-0340 Archiv fuer Acker- und Pflanzenbau und Bodenkunde
0365-0375 Asociacion Quimica Argentina. Anales
0365-0502 Universita degli Studi di Bari. Facolta di Agraria. Annali
0365-0588 Acta Botanica Croatica
0365-0596 Anais Brasileiros de Dermatologia
0365-0723 Arquivos Brasileiros de Medicina
0365-0979 Arquivos de Biologia e Tecnologia
0365-1029 Annales Universitatis Mariae Curie-Sklodowska. Sectio A. Mathematica
0365-1118 Annales Universitatis Mariae Curie-Sklodowska. Sectio E. Agricultura
0365-1576 Museo Civico di Storia Naturale di Trieste. Atti
0365-1649 Akita University. Faculty of Education. Memoirs *changed to* Akita Daigaku Kyoikugakubu Kenkyu Kiyo.
0365-1789 Advanced Energy Conversion *see* 0196-8904
0365-1800 Estacion Experimental de Aula Dei. Anales
0365-1932 Instituto Politecnico Nacional. Escuela Nacional de Ciencias Biologicas. Anales
0365-2017 Annales de l'Est
0365-2181 Universidade de Sao Paulo. Faculdade de Farmacia. Anais *changed to* Universidade de Sao Paulo. Revista de Odontologia.
0365-2181 Universidade de Sao Paulo. Faculdade de Farmacia. Anais *see* 0370-4726
0365-2459 Arkiv for det Fysiske Seminar i Trondheim *changed to* Theoretical Physics Seminar in Trondheim.
0365-2726 Agronomico
0365-2807 Chile. Instituto de Investigaciones Agropecuarias. Agricultura Tecnica
0365-2971 Instituto Superior de Agronomia. Anais
0365-3722 Aichi Kyoiku Daigaku Kenkyu Hokoku. Shizen Kagaku
0365-3927 Alluminio
0365-4052 Allattenyeztes - Animal Breeding *see* 0230-1814
0365-4184 Acta Pathologica et Microbiologica Scandinavica. Section A: Pathology *see* 0903-4641
0365-4389 Museo Civico di Storia Naturale "Giacomo Doria", Genoa. Annali
0365-4478 Acta Medica Medianae
0365-4761 Institut National de la Recherche Agronomique de Tunisie. Annales
0365-4850 Acta Naturalia Islandica
0365-4877 Analusis
0365-5237 Acta Oto-Laryngologica. Supplement
0365-5377 Ateneo Parmense. Collana di Monografie†
0365-5814 Institut Phytopathologique Benaki. Annales
0365-5946 Reale Accademia d'Italia. Classe di Scienze Fisiche, Matematiche e Naturali *see* 0392-7881
0365-5997 Studii si Cercetari de Biologie. Seria Biologie Animala
0365-5997 Studii si Cercetari de Biologie. Seria Biologie Vegetala
0365-6233 Archiv der Pharmazie
0365-6470 Saechsische Akademie der Wissenschaften, Leipzig. Mathematisch-Naturwissenschaftliche Klasse. Abhandlungen
0365-6527 Societe Belge de Medecine Tropicale. Annales
0365-6594 Universitatea "Al. I. Cuza" din Iasi. Analele Stiintifice. Sectiunea 2b: Geologie *see* 0379-7902
0365-6691 Sociedad Espanola de Oftalmologia. Archivos
0365-7086 Annaes de Sociedade de Pharmacia e Chimica de Sao Paulo *see* 0003-2441
0365-723X Commonwealth Scientific and Industrial Research Organization. Division of Soils. Technical Papers†
0365-7256 Geografie *see* 0379-7902
0365-7973 Universidad de Murcia. Anales *see* 0213-5469
0365-799X Universita degli Studi di Napoli. Facolta di Scienze Agrarie. Annali
0365-8066 Acta Universitatis de Attila Jozsef Nominatae. Acta Mineralogica - Petrographica
0365-8104 Ankara Universitesi. Tip Fakultesi. Mecmuasi
0365-8252 Aarsberetning Vedkommende Norges Fiskerier
0365-8406 Archiv fuer Zuechtungsforschung
0365-8414 Atomwirtschaft - Atomtechnik
0365-9356 British Columbia. Ministry of Energy, Mines and Petroleum Resources. Annual Report
0365-9429 Biochemical Reviews
0365-9445 Bromatologia i Chemia Toksykologiczna
0365-9542 Deutsche Keramische Gesellschaft. Berichte *see* 0173-9913
0365-9615 Byulleten' Eksperimental'noi Biologii i Meditsiny
0365-9623 Cancer Research Campaign. Annual Report
0365-9631 Deutsche Botanische Gesellschaft. Berichte *see* 0932-8629
0365-9844 Naturhistorische Gesellschaft Hannover. Berichte
0365-9860 Okayama University. Berichte des Ohara Instituts fuer Landwirtschaftliche Biologie
0366-0109 Universidad de la Republica. Facultad de Ingenieria. Boletin
0366-0168 Instituto Geologico y Minero de Espana. Boletin *see* 0366-0176
0366-0176 Boletin Geologico y Minero
0366-0281 Instituto de Tecnologia de Alimentos. Boletin†
0366-0486 Biologicke Listy
0366-077X British Journal of Dermatology. Supplement
0366-1318 Moskovskii Gosudarstviennyi Universitet. Moskovskoe Obshchestvo Ispytatelei Prirody. Otdel Geologicheskii. Byulleten
0366-1326 Societe Linneenne de Lyon. Bulletin Mensuel
0366-144X Belgisch-Nederlands Tijdschrift voor Oppervlaktetechnieken van Metalen *see* 0923-1722
0366-1644 Sociedad Chilena de Quimica. Boletin
0366-2047 Societa dei Naturalisti in Napoli. Bulletin
0366-2284 Bios
0366-2330 Bouw
0366-2403 Bollettino di Zoologia Agraria e di Bachicoltura
0366-3221 Denmark. Statens Mejeriforsoeg. Beretning†
0366-3345 Institut Textile de France. Bulletin Scientifique†
0366-3612 Kongelige Danske Videnskabernes Selskab. Biologiske Skrifter
0366-4198 Great Britain. Institute of Geological Sciences. Bulletin of the Geological Survey of Great Britain†
0366-5232 Caldasia
0366-5526 Chimika Chronika. General Edition
0366-5690 C E R N - H E R A Reports
0366-5887 Colloquium Mosbach
0366-600X Cuadernos de Geologia
0366-6123 Chagyo Gijutsu Kenkyu†
0366-6778 La Clinica†
0366-6824 Collective Phenomena†
0366-6913 Ceramica
0366-693X Chimika Chronika. New Series
0366-6964 Xumu Shouyi Xuebao
0366-6999 Chinese Medical Journal
0366-7022 Chemistry Letters
0366-757X C O D A T A Bulletin
0366-7588 Coelum†
0366-8258 Academie Internationale d'Histoire des Sciences. Collection des Travaux
0366-8681 Academie Bulgare des Sciences. Comptes Rendus
0366-8819 Electronic Engineering
0366-9092 Electrotechnical Laboratory. Bulletin
0366-9297 Electrochemistry and Industrial Physical Chemistry
0366-9424 Deutsche Molkerei-Zeitung *changed to* D M Z Lebensmittelindustrie und Milchwirtschaft.
0367-0244 Ecology of Food and Nutrition
0367-0449 Estudios Geologicos
0367-0643 Eksperimentalna Medicina i Morfologija
0367-0708 Elektrotechnika
0367-1119 Energy Digest
0367-1429 Akademiya Nauk Estonskoi S.S.R. Izvestiya. Fizika. Matematika *changed to* Eest Teaduste Akadeemia. Toimetised. Fuusika. Matemaatika.
0367-150X Environmental Pollution Management†
0367-1631 Fizika Aerodispersnykh Sistem
0367-1887 Freshwater Biological Association. Scientific Publications
0367-2174 Forstlige Forsoegsvaesen i Danmark *changed to* Danish Forest and Landscape Research.
0367-2387 Finnish Journal of Dairy Science
0367-2409 Fiziko-Khimicheskaya Mekhanika i Liofilnost' Dispersnykh Sistem
0367-2530 Flora
0367-2921 Fizika Plazmy
0367-3014 Farmatsiya
0367-326X Fitoterapia
0367-3812 Gaceta Veterinaria *see* 0326-4629
0367-3928 British Regional Geology
0367-4061 Gunma Journal of Liberal Arts and Sciences
0367-4088 Gidromekhanika
0367-4177 Getreide, Mehl und Brot
0367-4223 Gesunde Pflanzen
0367-4290 Geologicheskii Zhurnal
0367-4444 Glasnik Hemicara i Tehnologa Bosne i Hercegovine
0367-4916 Gospodarka Miesna
0367-4983 Prirodnjacki Muzej u Beogradu. Glasnik. Serija A: Minerologija, Geologija, Paleontologija
0367-5807 Korean Journal of Animal Sciences
0367-5939 Hokkaido Kyoiku Daigaku Kiyo. Dai-2-Bu, A. Sugaku, Butsuri, Kagaku, Kogaku- Hen
0367-598X Hemijska Industrija

ISSN

ISSN INDEX

ISSN	Title
0367-6234	Harbin Gongye Daxue Xuebao
0367-6439	Hirosaki University. Faculty of Science. Science Reports
0367-6447	Houtim†
0367-6722	Indian Journal of Animal Research
0367-6838	Industries Atomiques et Spatiales†
0367-7257	Indian Chemical Manufacturer
0367-7370	Iwate University. Faculty of Education. Annual Report
0367-777X	Informacion de Quimica Analitica Pura y Aplicada a la Industria see 0210-4334
0367-7850	Institution of Gas Engineers. Proceedings
0367-8113	Instituto Forestal de Investigaciones y Experiencias. Comunicacion see 0210-3338
0367-8229	Indian Journal of Agricultural Chemistry
0367-8245	Indian Journal of Agricultural Research
0367-8326	Indian Journal of Malariology
0367-8377	International Journal of Peptide & Protein Research
0367-8393	Indian Journal of Radio & Space Physics
0367-892X	Industria Mineraria d'Italia e d'Oltremare see 0391-1586
0367-9012	Indian Journal of Medical Research. Supplement
0367-939X	Industrielle Obst- und Gemueseverwertung
0367-973X	Indian Phytopathology
0368-0762	Irish Veterinary Journal
0368-0770	International Association of Theoretical and Applied Limnology. Proceedings
0368-0827	Inzynieria i Aparatura Chemiczna
0368-1327	Agricultural Society of Trinidad & Tobago. Journal†
0368-1416	Jornal Brasileiro de Ginecologia
0368-1653	Chinese Institute of Chemical Engineers. Journal
0368-1874	Journal of Electroanalytical Chemistry see 0022-0728
0368-2048	Journal of Electron Spectroscopy and Related Phenomena
0368-2145	Hokkaido University. Faculty of Science. Journal. Series 5: Botany
0368-2188	Hokkaido University. Faculty of Science. Journal. Series 6: Zoology
0368-2196	University of Tokyo. Faculty of Science. Journal. Section 3: Botany
0368-220X	University of Tokyo. Faculty of Science. Journal. Section 4: Zoology†
0368-2250	University of Tokyo. Faculty of Science. Journal. Section 2: Geology, Mineralogy, Geography, Geophysics changed to University of Tokyo. Faculty of Science. Journal. Section 2: Geology, Mineralogy, Geography, Earth and Planetary Physics.
0368-2307	Gesellschaft fuer Naturkunde in Wuerttemberg. Jahreshefte
0368-2315	Journal de Gynecologie Obstetrique et Biologie de la Reproduction
0368-2323	Geochemical Society of India. Journal
0368-2331	Geological Society of the Philippines. Journal
0368-2358	Jitsuyo Hyomen Gijutsu see 0915-1869
0368-2595	Institution of Nuclear Engineers. Journal see 0262-5091
0368-265X	Japan Pesticide Information
0368-2781	Japanese Journal of Antibiotics
0368-2803	Joken Hansha see 0388-7448
0368-2811	Japanese Journal of Clinical Oncology
0368-3141	Japan Congress on Materials Research. Proceedings
0368-4113	Hiroshima University. Journal of Science. Series B. Division 1: Zoology
0368-4253	Journal of Scientific Instruments see 0957-0233
0368-4466	Journal of Thermal Analysis
0368-4571	Shinshu University. Faculty of Textile Science and Technology. Journal. Series F: Physics and Mathematics
0368-4636	Textile Association (India). Journal
0368-4741	Kagaku Asahi
0368-492X	Kybernetes
0368-5039	Kyoto Daigaku Genshi Enerugi Kenkyujo Iho
0368-5063	Kagoshima Daigaku Igaku Zasshi
0368-5187	Koshu Eisei
0368-5209	Kokuritsu Kenko Eiyo Kenkyujo Hokoku
0368-5365	Kogyo Gijutsuin. Biseibutsu Kogyo Gijutsu Kenkyu. Kenkyu Hokoku
0368-556X	Khimicheskaya Tekhnologiya
0368-5829	Kyorin Igakkai Zasshi
0368-5918	Kagaku to Kogyo (Osaka)
0368-5942	Japan Meteorological Agency. Agricultural Meteorology. Annual Report
0368-5969	Kobe Kaiyo Kishodai Iho
0368-623X	Kita Nihon Byogaichu Kenkyu Kaiho
0368-6272	Kobunkazai no Kagaku
0368-6302	Kongelige Norske Videnskabers Selskab. Forhandlinger
0368-6310	Kongelige Norske Videnskabers Selskab. Skrifter
0368-6396	Kexue
0368-7066	Kurortologija i Fizioterapija
0368-7155	Kvantovaya Elektronika
0368-7171	Kongelige Veterinaer- og Landbohoejskole. Aarskrift†
0368-7201	Kongelige Danske Videnskabernes Selskab. Oversigt over Selskabets Virksomhed. Annual Report
0368-7368	Lab Instrumenten
0368-7481	Libyan Journal of Sciences
0368-7708	Long Ashton Research Station Annual Report see 0955-9051
0368-8720	Universidad Nacional Autonoma de Mexico. Instituto de Biologia. Anales: Serie Zoologia
0368-9379	Hokkaido University. Faculty of Engineering. Memoirs
0368-9395	Japanese Journal of Health and Human Ecology
0368-945X	Metallurgia and Metal Forming see 0141-8602
0368-9689	Kyoto University. Faculty of Science. Memoirs. Series of Physics, Astrophysics, Geophysics and Chemistry
0368-9697	International Symposium on Crop Protection. Proceedings
0369-0369	Osaka University. Institute of Scientific and Industrial Research. Memoirs
0369-0512	Kyushu Institute of Technology. Memoirs: Engineering
0369-061X	Metallurgical Engineer†
0369-1152	Molecular Crystals see 1058-725X
0369-1152	Molecular Crystals see 1058-7268
0369-1233	Monatsschrift fuer Brauerei see 0179-2466
0369-1527	Medicinski Podmladak
0369-1632	Mine and Quarry
0369-1829	Royal Astronomical Society, England. Memoirs†
0369-1950	Waseda University. School of Science and Engineering. Memoirs
0369-2043	Mauritius Sugar Industry Research Institute. Annual Report
0369-2086	Mineralia Slovaca
0369-2345	Metallgesellschaft Aktiengesellschaft. Review of the Activities
0369-3228	Nagasaki Igakkai Zasshi
0369-3546	Societa Italiana di Fisica. Nuovo Cimento A
0369-3554	Societa Italiana di Fisica. Nuovo Cimento B
0369-3562	Nihon Daigaku Bunrigakubu Shizen Kagaku Kenkyujo Kenkyu Kiyo
0369-3627	Niigata University. Faculty of Science. Science Reports. Series E: Geology and Mineralogy
0369-4194	Nihon Kogyokaishi - Mining and Metallurgical Institute of Japan. Journal see 0916-1740
0369-4313	Nihon Daigaku Rikogaku Kenkyujo Shoho
0369-4550	Japan. Society of Sea Water Science. Bulletin
0369-4577	Nippon Kagaku Kaishi
0369-5034	Nova Acta Leopoldina
0369-5050	Instituto Geologico y Minero de Espana. Notas y Comunicaciones see 0366-0176
0369-5255	Norsk Pelsdyrblad
0369-5387	Nippon Kagaku Zasshi see 0369-4577
0369-5417	Norsk Polarinstitutt. Skrifter
0369-5611	Nagoya-shiritsu Daigaku Yakugakubu Kenkyu Nenpo
0369-576X	Niigata University. Faculty of Science. Science Reports. Series A: Mathematics
0369-5816	Nuclear Structural Engineering see 0029-5493
0369-5867	New South Wales. Department of Agriculture. Science Bulletin
0369-6243	Natura
0369-6367	Ultragarsas
0369-6464	Nutrition News (Rosemont)
0369-7649	Onkologija
0369-7827	Osiris (Chicago)
0369-8203	National Academy of Sciences, India. Proceedings. Section A. Physical Sciences
0369-8211	National Academy of Sciences, India. Proceedings. Section B. Biological Sciences
0369-8599	Institution of Chemists (India). Proceedings
0369-8629	Pchelovodstvo
0369-9420	Pigment and Resin Technology
0369-9463	Physiologia Bohemoslovaca changed to Physiological Research.
0369-9560	Photographe
0369-979X	Pharmazie Heute
0370-0291	Poljoprivredna Znanstvena Smotra
0370-0755	Politechnika Wroclawska. Instytut Chemii Nieorganicznej i Metalurgii Pierwiastkow Rzadkich. Prace Naukowe. Studia i Materialy
0370-0798	Politechnika Wroclawska. Instytut Gornictwa. Prace Naukowe. Studia i Materialy
0370-081X	Politechnika Wroclawska. Instytut Chemii Organicznej i Fizycznej. Prace Naukowe. Studia i Materialy
0370-0828	Politechnika Wroclawska. Instytut Fizyki. Prace Naukowe. Monografie
0370-0836	Politechnika Wroclawska. Instytut Geotechniki. Prace Naukowe. Konferencje changed to Politechnika Wroclawska. Instytut Geotechniki i Hydrotechniki. Prace Naukowe. Konferencje.
0370-0844	Politechnika Wroclawska. Instytut Inzynierii Ladowej. Prace Naukowe. Studia i Materialy
0370-0852	Politechnika Wroclawska. Instytut Podstaw Elektrotechniki i Elektrotechnologii. Prace Naukowe. Studia i Materialy
0370-0879	Politechnika Wroclawska. Instytut Technologii Organicznej i Tworzyw Sztucznych. Prace Naukowe. Studia i Materialy
0370-0887	Politechnika Wroclawska. Instytut Technologii Elektronowej. Prace Naukowe. Konferencje
0370-0917	Politechnika Wroclawska. Instytut Materialoznawstwa i Mechaniki Technicznej. Prace Naukowe. Studia i Materialy
0370-1093	Oregon Academy of Science. Proceedings
0370-1158	Polymers Paint and Colour Journal
0370-1239	Physico-Mathematical Society of Japan. Proceedings see 0031-9015
0370-1514	Il Progresso Medico
0370-1573	Physics Reports
0370-1638	Instituti i Studimeve dhe Kerkimeve Industriale e Minerale. Permbledhje Studimesh see 0254-5276
0370-1670	Koninklijk Instituut voor de Tropen. Afdeling Agrarisch Onderzoek. Communication see 0922-7911
0370-1743	Przeglad Skorzany
0370-1859	Process Engineering
0370-1972	Physica Status Solidi (B). Basic Research
0370-2030	Agricultural Society of Trinidad & Tobago. Proceedings see 0368-1327
0370-226X	Petroleum and Petrochemical International see 0301-6242
0370-2529	Problems of Control and Information Theory
0370-2596	Comite International des Poids et Mesures. Proces-Verbaux des Seances
0370-2693	Physics Letters. Section B: Nuclear, Elementary Particle and High-Energy Physics
0370-2731	New Zealand Society of Animal Production. Proceedings
0370-372X	Revista Brasileira de Farmacia
0370-4246	University of the Ryukyus. College of Agriculture. Science Bulletin
0370-4254	Ritsumeikan Daigaku Rikogaku Kenkyujo Kiyo
0370-4343	Revista Espanola de las Enfermedades del Aparato Digestivo y de la Nutricion see 1130-4588
0370-4475	Revue d'Electroencephalographie et de Neurophysiologie Clinique see 0987-7053
0370-4726	Universidade de Sao Paulo. Revista de Farmacia e Bioquimica
0370-5048	Revue Generale des Colloides see 0021-7689
0370-5579	Japanese Journal of Clinical Ophthalmology
0370-5943	Revista Latinoamericana de Quimica
0370-6141	Revista Medica da Aeronautica do Brasil
0370-6559	Royal Society of New Zealand. Bulletin Series
0370-6583	Rodriguesia
0370-663X	Rostlinna Vyroba
0370-6648	Reports on the Progress of Applied Chemistry see 0263-5917
0370-7288	Sociedad Geologica Argentina. Revista see 0004-4822
0370-7857	Revista Electrotecnica
0370-7962	Revista Theobroma
0370-8047	Sulphuric Acid and Industry
0370-8063	Referativnyi Zhurnal. Fotokinotekhnika
0370-808X	Rezanie i Instrument
0370-8098	Referativnyi Zhurnal. Khimicheskoe, Neftepererabatyvayuschchee i Polimernoe Mashinostroenie
0370-8179	Serbian Archives of General Medicine
0370-8314	Southern African Museums Association. Bulletin
0370-8454	C S I R Annual Report changed to C S I R Annual Report - Technology Impact.
0370-9531	Seitai no Kagaku
0370-9612	Physiology and Ecology Japan
0370-9736	Siemens Forschungs- und Entwicklungsberichte†
0371-0025	Acta Acustica changed to Shengxue Xuebao.
0371-0165	Heidelberger Akademie der Wissenschaften. Mathematisch-Naturwissenschaftliche Klasse. Sitzungsberichte
0371-0459	Scandinavian Journal of Metallurgy
0371-0580	Sen'i Kikai Gakkaishi
0371-0874	Shengli Xuebao
0371-2222	Studia Pneumologica et Phtiseologica Cechoslovaca
0371-232X	Space Research see 0273-1177

ISSN INDEX 5723

0371-2672 Niigata University. Faculty of Science. Science Reports. Series D: Biology
0371-2761 Tohoku University. Science Reports of the Research Institutes. Series C: Medicine
0371-2885 Societas Scientiarum Fennica. Arsbok Vuosikirja *see* 0783-5876
0371-2885 Societas Scientiarum Fennica. Arsbok Vuosikirja *see* 0783-5892
0371-2907 Sveriges Skogsvaardsfoerbunds Tidskrift
0371-3172 Studi Sassaresi
0371-327X Saechsische Akademie der Wissenschaften, Leipzig. Mathematisch-Naturwissenschaftliche Klasse. Sitzungsberichte
0371-3385 Shiga-kenritsu Tanki Daigaku Gakujutsu Zasshi
0371-375X Towarzystwo Naukowe w Toruniu. Sprawozdania
0371-4098 Suomen Kemistilehti A *see* 0355-1628
0371-4101 Suomen Kemistilehti B *see* 0303-4100
0371-4217 Suisanzoshoku
0371-4756 Wroclawskie Towarzystwo Naukowe. Sprawozdania. Seria A
0371-5167 Takeda Research Laboratories. Journal
0371-5728 Tecnicas de Laboratorio
0371-5965 Tottori Daigaku Kyoikugakubu Kenkyu Hokoku. Shizen Kagaku
0371-6813 Tokyo Gakugei Daigaku Kiyo
0371-7208 South African Journal of Geology
0371-7453 Institution of Mining and Metallurgy. Transactions. Section B: Applied Earth Sciences
0371-750X Indian Ceramic Society. Transactions
0371-7682 Formosan Medical Association. Journal
0371-7844 Institution of Mining and Metallurgy. Transactions. Section A: Mining Industry
0371-9553 Institution of Mining and Metallurgy. Transactions. Section C: Mineral Processing & Extractive Metallurgy
0371-9588 Mining, Geological and Metallurgical Institute of India. Transactions
0372-0187 Newcomen Society for the Study of the History of Engineering and Technology. Transactions
0372-0330 Toyo Daigaku Kiyo. Kyoyo Katei Hen. Shizen Kagaku
0372-039X Toyoda Kenkyu Hokoku
0372-1418 University of Tokyo. Institute of Space and Aeronautical Science. Report
0372-2112 Dianzi Xuebao
0372-333X Taiwania
0372-4123 Ukrains'kyi Botanichnyi Zhurnal
0372-5480 Veterinarski Arhiv
0372-5715 V G B Kraftwerkstechnik,
0372-6053 Politekhnichnyi Instytut Kiev. Vestnik. Seriya Mashinostroeniya
0372-6436 Akademiya Nauk Ukrainskoi S.S.R. Visnyk
0372-6827 Veterinaria
0372-7025 Vojenske Zdravotnicke Listy
0372-7181 Waseda Daigaku Rikogaku Kenkyujo Hokoku
0372-7610 Technische Hochschule Karl-Marx-Stadt. Wissenschaftliche Zeitschrift
0372-7629 Journal of Pharmaceutical Science and Technology
0372-7726 Yokohama Medical Journal
0372-798X Weed Research
0372-8854 Zeitschrift fuer Geomorphologie
0372-9311 Zhurnal Mikrobiologii, Epidemiologii i Immunobiologii
0372-9400 Akademia Gorniczo-Hutnicza im. Stanislawa Staszica. Zeszyty Naukowe. Gornictwo
0372-9427 Akademia Gorniczo-Hutnicza im. Stanislawa Staszica. Zeszyty Naukowe. Geologia
0372-9443 Akademia Gorniczo-Hutnicza im. Stanislawa Staszica. Zeszyty Naukowe. Metalurgia i Odlewnictwo
0372-9486 Politechnika Krakowska. Zeszyty Naukowe. Mechanika
0372-9494 Politechnika Slaska. Zeszyty Naukowe. Chemia
0372-9508 Politechnika Slaska. Zeszyty Naukowe. Gornictwo
0372-9699 Politechnika Czestochowska. Zeszyty Naukowe. Nauki Techniczne. Hutnictwo
0372-9796 Politechnika Slaska. Zeszyty Naukowe. Energetyka
0372-9893 Zernovoe Khozyaistvo
0373-0034 Akademia Rolnicza, Warsaw. Zeszyty Naukowe. Melioracje Rolne *changed to* Warsaw Agricultural University. S G G W. Annals. Land Reclamation.
0373-0204 Zucker- und Suesswaren Wirtschaft
0373-0468 Bonner Geographische Abhandlungen
0373-0514 Bulletin Francais de Pisciculture *changed to* Bulletin Francais de la Peche et de la Pisciculture.
0373-0875 Societe Linneenne de Provence. Bulletin
0373-0956 Universite Scientifique et Medicale de Grenoble. Institut Fourier. Annales
0373-0999 Revista Matematica Hispano-Americana *see* 0213-2230
0373-1006 Seppyo
0373-1243 Universita e Politecnico di Torino. Seminario Matematico. Rendiconti
0373-1537 Bedi Kartlisa *see* 0991-8086
0373-1677 Tierzucht *changed to* Neue Landwirtschaft.
0373-1766 Magyar Nemzeti Bibliografia *see* 0133-6894
0373-1766 Magyar Nemzeti Bibliografia *see* 0133-5782
0373-1766 Magyar Nemzeti Bibliografia *see* 0133-6843
0373-1766 Magyar Nemzeti Bibliografia *see* 0231-4592
0373-1928 Etudes Celtiques
0373-1944 Travail et Securite
0373-1987 Bibliografia Geologiczna Polski
0373-1995 Institution of Engineers (India). Civil Engineering Division. Journal
0373-2029 Archives of Mechanics
0373-2045 International Council for the Exploration of the Sea. Bulletin Statistique *see* 1018-1571
0373-2061 Bulletin Scientifique de Bourgogne
0373-2134 Prirodnjacki Muzej u Beogradu. Glasnik. Serija B: Bioloske Nauke
0373-2266 Ardea
0373-241X Glasgow Naturalist
0373-2525 Saussurea
0373-2568 Pirineos
0373-2630 Revue d'Economie Politique
0373-2746 Tidsskrift for Praktisk Laegegering
0373-2916 Le Strade
0373-3033 Accademia delle Scienze di Torino. Memorie. Part 1. Classe di Scienze Fisiche, Matematiche e Naturali
0373-3165 Buecherei des Paediaters
0373-3181 Comite International des Poids et Mesures. Comite Consultatif des Unites (Rapport et Annexes)
0373-3297 Societe Languedocienne de Geographie. Bulletin
0373-3491 Societa Entomologica Italiana. Bollettino
0373-353X Vsesoyuznoe Geograficheskoe Obshchestvo. Izvestiya
0373-3602 Japan. Maritime Safety Agency. Hydrographic Department. Report of Hydrographic Research
0373-3629 Annales Hydrographiques
0373-3874 Dansk Naturhistorisk Forening. Videnskabelige Meddelelser†
0373-403X Chmelarstvi
0373-4064 Metal Bulletin Monthly
0373-4137 Bollettino di Zoologia
0373-4242 Entomological Society of Southern Africa. Memoirs
0373-4250 Associated Scientific and Technical Societies of South Africa. Annual Proceedings
0373-4277 Batiment International *see* 0961-3218
0373-4285 Recherche et Architecture†
0373-4331 Betonwerk und Fertigteil-Technik
0373-4447 Library and Information Science
0373-4544 Societe Entomologique de Mulhouse. Bulletin
0373-4625 Abeille de France et l'Apiculteur
0373-4633 Journal of Navigation
0373-4641 Sociedade Broteriana. Anuario
0373-4722 University of Tokyo. Faculty of Science. Journal. Section 5: Anthropology
0373-4854 Auroral Observatory. Magnetic Observations
0373-5125 Observatorio Astronomico de Madrid. Anuario
0373-529X Royal Institution of Naval Architects. Supplementary Papers *changed to* Royal Institution of Naval Architects. Soft Back Transactions. Parts A & B.
0373-5346 Railway Gazette International
0373-5354 Tudomanyos Tajekoztatas Elmelete es Gyakorlata†
0373-5478 Archives d'Histoire Doctrinale et Litteraire du Moyen Age
0373-5524 Universidade de Sao Paulo. Instituto Oceanografico. Boletim
0373-5605 Norsk Polarinstitutt. Meddelelser
0373-5796 Spain. Instituto Nacional de Investigaciones Agrarias. Anales. Serie: Economia y Sociologia Agrarias *see* 0213-635X
0373-580X Sociedad Argentina de Botanica. Boletin
0373-5893 Zoological Society, Calcutta. Proceedings
0373-5982 Postepy Astronautyki
0373-6067 Universite de Grenoble. Laboratoire d'Hydrologie et de Pisciculture. Travaux†
0373-6091 Institute of Electronics and Communication Engineering of Japan. Transactions *see* 0913-5707
0373-6121 Institute of Electronics and Communication Engineers of Japan. Journal - Denshi Tsushin Gakkaishi *see* 0913-5693
0373-6245 South African Geographical Journal
0373-6369 Bibliografija Jugoslavije. Serija A: Drustvene Nauke. Clanci i Prilozi u Casopisima, Listovima i Zbornicima *see* 0352-5899
0373-6377 Bibliografija Jugoslavije. Serija C: Umetnost, Sport, Filologija, Knjizevnost i Muzikalije *see* 0352-5996
0373-6385 Kyushu University. Faculty of Science. Memoirs. Series A: Mathematics
0373-6407 Referativnyi Zhurnal. Aviatsionnye i Raketnye Dvigateli
0373-6415 Referativnyi Zhurnal. Gornoe i Neftepromyslovoe Mashinostroenie
0373-6431 Akademiya Nauk Estonskoi S.S.R. Izvestiya. Obshchestvennye Nauki *changed to* Eesti Teaduste Akadeemia. Toimetised. Uhiskonnateadused.
0373-6512 Excerpta Medica. Section 7: Pediatrics and Pediatric Surgery
0373-6547 Polska Akademia Nauk. Instytut Geografii i Przestrzennego Zagospodarowania. Prace Geograficzne
0373-6687 Journal of Bryology
0373-6725 Aplikace Matematiky - Applied Mathematics *see* 0862-7940
0373-6873 Societas pro Fauna et Flora Fennica. Memoranda
0373-689X Zeitschrift fuer die Binnenfischerei der DDR†
0373-7101 Spain. Observatorio Astronomico Nacional. Boletin Astronomico
0373-7179 Ceskoslovensky Kras
0373-7187 Arbeiten zur Rheinischen Landeskunde
0373-7284 C.I.R.P. *see* 0007-8506
0373-7349 Association Nationale de Lutte Contre les Fleaux Atmospheriques. Rapport de Campagne *see* 0242-4002
0373-7411 Osaka Kyoiku Daigaku Kiyo. Dai-3-Bumon. Shizen Kagaku
0373-7632 Floristisch - Soziologische Arbeitsgemeinschaft. Mitteilungen *see* 0722-494X
0373-7640 Bayerische Botanische Gesellschaft. Berichte
0373-7772 Condizionamento dell'Aria *changed to* Condizionamento dell'Aria, Riscaldamento, Refrigerazione.
0373-7837 Instytut Hodowli i Aklimatyzacji Roslin. Biuletyn
0373-7896 Geobotanisches Institut E T H, Stiftung Ruebel, Zurich. Berichte
0373-8221 Mathematischen Seminar Giessen. Mitteilungen
0373-8299 Polskie Towarzystwo Matematyczne. Roczniki. Seria 1: Commentationes Mathematicae. Prace Matematyczne
0373-8361 Nippon Jui Chikusan Daigaku Kenkyu Hokoku
0373-8493 Mitteilungen aus dem Zoologischen Museum in Berlin
0373-8647 Politechnika Gdanska. Zeszyty Naukowe. Elektryka
0373-8663 Politechnika Gdanska. Zeszyty Naukowe. Budownictwo Wodne
0373-8671 Politechnika Gdanska. Zeszyty Naukowe. Budownictwo Ladowe
0373-868X Politechnika Gdanska. Zeszyty Naukowe. Budownictwo Okretowe
0373-8698 Politechnika Gdanska. Zeszyty Naukowe. Elektronika
0373-8809 Revue Pratique de Controle Industriel *see* 0766-5210
0373-8981 Staatliches Museum fuer Tierkunde Dresden. Entomologische Abhandlungen
0373-9066 Museo Argentino de Ciencias Naturales "Bernardino Rivadavia." Instituto Nacional de Investigacion de las Ciencias Naturales. Revista. Zoologia
0373-9090 A I S M. Bulletin
0373-9139 Ciel et Espace
0373-9465 Folia Entomologica Hungarica
0373-9627 Zitteliana
0373-9864 Poligrafika
0374-0412 Universidade Federal de Pernambuco. Departamento de Oceanografia. Centro de Tecnologia. Trabalhos Oceanograficos
0374-0447 International Society of Soil Science. Bulletin
0374-0463 Acta Linguistica Hafniensia
0374-0676 Information Bulletin on Variable Stars
0374-1036 Acta Entomologica
0374-1222 Schiffbautechnischen Gesellschaft. Jahrbuch
0374-1257 Mitteilungen aus dem Max-Planck-Institut fuer Stroemungsforschung
0374-1338 Reumatizam
0374-1656 Istanbul Medical Faculty. Medical Bulletin
0374-1842 Acta Geodaetica, Geophysica et Montanistica Hungarica
0374-2105 Ophthalmologia
0374-2261 Le Trefile
0374-2385 Rechentechnik-Datenverarbeitung. Beiheft *see* 0232-6833
0374-2466 Tenmon Geppo
0374-2490 Aviation Review *changed to* Aerospace & Defence Review.
0374-2636 Bauelemente der Elektrotechnik *see* 0172-6153
0374-2806 Comments on Plasma Physics and Controlled Fusion
0374-289X Data Report *changed to* Siemens-Magazin COM.
0374-3098 Elektron-International
0374-3101 Electro-Revue
0374-3225 Fluid: Apparecchiature Idrauliche e Pneumatiche
0374-3268 Geos
0374-3527 Journal of Smooth Muscle Research
0374-3535 Journal of Elasticity
0374-356X Society of Environmental Engineers. Journal *see* 0954-5824
0374-3659 Kent Technical Review†

ISSN

5724 ISSN INDEX

0374-387X Universita degli Studi di Roma. Istituto di Automatica. Notiziario†
0374-3896 Naukovedenie i Informatika
0374-4094 Podstawy Sterowania *see* 0867-2121
0374-4256 Revue Polytechnique
0374-4329 Nagoya University. Faculty of Engineering. Automatic Control Laboratory. Research Reports
0374-4345 Niigata Daigaku Kogakubu Kenkyu Hokoku
0374-4353 Research Disclosure
0374-4361 Radio & Electronics Constructor†
0374-4493 Systemes Logiques†
0374-4639 Tokyo Astronomical Observatory. Report *see* 0915-6321
0374-4663 Takenaka Gijutsu Kenkyu Hokoku
0374-4760 Akademiya Navuk Belarusskai S.S.R. Vestsi. Seriya Fizika-Energetychnykh Navuk
0374-4779 Vrashchenie i Prilivnye Deformatsii Zemli†
0374-4795 Works Management
0374-4809 X-Ray Focus†
0374-4922 Revista Brasileira de Fisica
0374-4965 Acta Anaesthesiologica Italica
0374-5031 Arquivos de Botanica do Estado de Sao Paulo *see* 0073-2877
0374-5066 Acta Botanica Islandica
0374-5295 Aichi Cancer Center Research Institute. Annual Report *changed to* Aichi Cancer Center Research Institute. Scientific Report.
0374-535X Istituto Sperimentale per la Cerealicoltura. Annali
0374-5511 Universidad Nacional Autonoma de Mexico. Instituto de Biologia. Anales: Serie Botanica
0374-5686 Arquivos de Ciencias do Mar
0374-5791 Istituto Sperimentale per l'Enologia Asti. Annali
0374-5880 Universidad Hispalense. Anales. Serie: Ciencias *changed to* Universidad de Sevilla. Serie: Ciencias.
0374-6003 Ecole Nationale Superieure d'Agronomie et des Industries Alimentaires. Bulletin†
0374-6038 Societe Royale Belge d'Entomologie. Bulletin et Annales
0374-6054 Naturhistorische Gesellschaft Hannover. Beihefte zu den Berichten
0374-6224 Instituto Bacteriologico de Chile. Boletin *see* 0716-1387
0374-6232 Institut Royal de Sciences Naturelles de Belgique. Bulletin. Serie Entomologie
0374-6240 Florida Genealogical Society Journal
0374-6291 Institut Royal des Sciences Naturelles de Belgique. Bulletin. Serie Sciences de la Terre
0374-633X British Journal of Mental Subnormality
0374-6429 Institut Royal des Sciences Naturelles de Belgique. Bulletin. Serie Biologie
0374-6569 Bionika
0374-6607 Botanical Society of Edinburgh Transactions
0374-6658 Brazil. Departamento Nacional de Obras Contra as Secas. Boletim Tecnico
0374-6852 Ceskoslovenska Gynekologie
0374-7115 Central Plantation Crops Research Institute. Annual Report
0374-7344 Danish Review of Game Biology
0374-7530 Etnologiska Studier
0374-7611 Fisheries Biology Technical Paper *see* 0429-9345
0374-7646 Freshwater Biological Association. Annual Report†
0374-776X Rofei ha-Mishpacha
0374-7999 Gayana: Miscelanea
0374-8014 Health Bulletin
0374-8030 Havsfiskelaboratoriet. Meddelande
0374-8049 Oceanological Society of Korea. Journal
0374-8189 Instituto de Economia y Producciones Ganaderas del Ebro. Comunicaciones
0374-826X Indian Journal of Heredity
0374-8278 Inmersion y Ciencia†
0374-8405 Irish Colleges of Physicians and Surgeons. Journal
0374-8731 Kanagawa Horticultural Experiment Station. Bulletin
0374-8774 Kerala Journal of Veterinary Science *see* 0971-0701
0374-8804 Kagawa Prefecture Agricultural Experiment Station. Bulletin
0374-9061 Geographische Gesellschaft in Hamburg. Mitteilungen
0374-9096 Mikrobiyologi Bulteni Supplement
0374-9118 Istituto Italiano di Idrobiologia. Memorie
0374-9444 Monitore Zoologico Italiano. Supplemento *see* 0394-6975
0374-955X Natuurhistorisch Genootschap in Limburg. Publicaties
0374-9665 National Museum, Bloemfontein. Memoirs
0374-9800 National Centre for Occupational Health. Annual Report
0374-9851 Nihon Contact Lens Gakkaishi
0374-9894 Nature Canada
0375-0183 Odonatologica
0375-0191 Osaka Kogyo Daigaku Kiyo. Riko Hen
0375-0280 Portugaliae Acta Biologica. Serie B. Sistematica, Ecologia, Biogeografia e Paleontologia
0375-0299 Palaeontographica. Abt. B: Palaeophytologie
0375-0442 Palaeontographica. Abt. A: Palaeozoologie - Stratigraphie
0375-0736 Ricerche di Biologia della Selvaggina
0375-1155 Museo Municipal de Historia Natural de San Rafael. Revista
0375-1589 South African Journal of Animal Science
0375-1651 Sellowia
0375-1821 Saito Ho-on Kai Museum of Natural History. Research Bulletin
0375-1880 South African Medical Research Council. Annual Report
0375-2038 Svenska Linne-Sallskapet Aarsskrift
0375-2062 Scottish Marine Biological Association. Annual Report *changed to* Dunstaffnage Marine Laboratory and Scottish Marine Biological Association. Annual Reports.
0375-2135 Staatliches Museum fuer Tierkunde Dresden. Faunistische Abhandlungen
0375-2682 South African Sugar Association Experiment Station. Annual Report
0375-2909 Steentrupia
0375-3220 College of Medicine of South Africa. Transactions
0375-3417 Instituto de Economia y Producciones Ganaderas del Ebro. Trabajos
0375-4588 University of New England. Annual Report
0375-4855 Zemedelske Muzeum. Vedecke Prace
0375-5223 Arbeitsgemeinschaft Oesterreichischer Entomologen. Zeitschrift
0375-5231 Staatliches Museum fuer Tierkunde Dresden. Zoologische Abhandlungen
0375-5363 Victoria University of Wellington Zoology Publications
0375-5444 Dili Xuebao
0375-5452 Acta Humboldtiana. Series Geologica, Palaeontologica et Biologica
0375-605X Canadian Rock Mechanics Symposium. Proceedings†
0375-6122 Ceskoslovenska Akademie Ved. Geograficky Ustav, Brno. Zpravy
0375-6505 Geothermics
0375-6742 Journal of Geochemical Exploration
0375-7471 Quartaer
0375-7587 Scripta Geologica
0375-7633 Societa Paleontologica Italiana. Bollettino
0375-7773 Tektonika i Stratigrafiya
0375-8338 Acta Medica Yugoslavica *changed to* Acta Medica Croatica.
0375-8427 Veterinarni Medicina
0375-8745 Chinese Chemical Society. Journal (Peiping) *see* 0009-4536
0375-8745 Chinese Chemical Society. Journal (Peiping) *see* 0567-7351
0375-8818 Die Weinwissenschaft
0375-8869 Europa Medica *see* 0014-2565
0375-8990 Gidrobiologicheskii Zhurnal
0375-9210 Journal of Applied Chemistry and Biotechnology *see* 0268-2575
0375-9229 Journal of Bone and Joint Surgery *see* 0021-9355
0375-930X Lettere al Nuovo Cimento†
0375-9350 Melliand Textilberichte International *see* 0341-0781
0375-9415 Molekulyarnaya Biologiya (Kiev)†
0375-9474 Nuclear Physics, Section A
0375-9504 Banyaszati es Kohaszati Lapok - Ontode
0375-9601 Physics Letters. Section A: General, Atomic and Solid State Physics
0375-9660 Problemy Endokrinologii
0375-9717 Referativnyi Zhurnal. Geodeziya i Aeros'emka
0376-0073 Vestnik Sel'skokhozyaistvennoi Nauki
0376-0421 Progress in Aerospace Sciences
0376-0456 Universidad Nacional del Litoral. Facultad de Ingenieria Quimica. Revista
0376-0898 Chemia Stosowana *changed to* Polish Journal of Applied Chemistry.
0376-1185 T U Sicherheit und Zuverlaessigkeit in Betrieb und Verkehr *changed to* T U - Technische Ueberwachung. Sicherheit Zuverlaessigheit und Umweltschutz in Wirtschaft und Verkehr.
0376-1568 Acta Agraria et Silvestria. Seria Zootechniczna *see* 0065-0935
0376-1843 Produccion Animal *see* 0213-5035
0376-1851 Spain. Instituto Nacional de Investigaciones Agrarias. Anales. Serie: Produccion Vegetal *see* 0213-5000
0376-2599 Visindafelag Islendinga. Rit
0376-2726 Societa Italiana di Scienze Naturali e del Museo Civico di Storia Naturale. Memorie
0376-2793 Museo Argentino de Ciencias Naturales "Bernardino Rivadavia." Instituto Nacional de Investigacion de las Ciencias Naturales. Revista. Botanica.
0376-4001 Utrechtse Geografische Studies†
0376-4052 Historica
0376-4087 S C I M A
0376-4109 Indian Philosophical Annual
0376-415X Indian Philosophical Quarterly
0376-4206 I C S S R Research Abstracts Quarterly
0376-4230 Contributions to Vertebrate Evolution†
0376-4249 Current Topics in Critical Care Medicine†
0376-4265 E S A Bulletin
0376-4699 Indian Journal of Chemistry. Section B: Organic and Medicinal Chemistry
0376-4710 Indian Journal of Chemistry. Section A: Inorganic, Physical, Theoretical and Analytical Chemistry
0376-4753 E S A R B I C A Journal
0376-4761 Pneumonologia Polska *changed to* Pneumonologia i Alergologia Polska.
0376-477X Journal of Agricultural Research of China
0376-4788 Indian Roads Congress. Highway Research Board Bulletin
0376-4796 Indian Journal of Meteorology, Hydrology and Geophysics *see* 0252-9416
0376-480X Advances in Pollen Spore Research
0376-4818 University of Kuwait. Journal (Science)
0376-4826 Steirische Beitraege zur Hydrogeologie
0376-4842 Current Awareness in Particle Technology
0376-5016 O P T I M A Newsletter
0376-5024 Asociacion de Escribanos del Uruguay. Revista
0376-5032 Print Letter
0376-5040 Core Journals in Pediatrics
0376-5059 Core Journals in Obstetrics - Gynecology
0376-5067 Trends in Biochemical Sciences
0376-5075 Computer Networks *see* 0169-7552
0376-5083 I R R I C A B: Current Annotated Bibliography of Irrigation†
0376-5091 Excerpta Medica. Section 37: Drug Literature Index†
0376-5156 Geophytology
0376-5423 Meghalaya Industrial Development Corporation. Annual Report
0376-5466 India. Department of Space. Annual Report
0376-5490 Bahamas. Ministry of Works. Annual Report *changed to* Bahamas. Ministry of Works and Utilities. Annual Report.
0376-5512 Andhra Pradesh State Trading Corporation Limited. Annual Report
0376-5725 Reserve Bank of Malawi. Financial and Economic Review
0376-5776 Congress Marches Ahead
0376-6039 Books Ireland
0376-6128 France. Ministere de la Sante et de la Famille. Bulletin de Statistiques et Sante *changed to* Solidarite - Sante.
0376-6349 Journal of Occupational Accidents *see* 0925-7535
0376-6357 Behavioural Processes
0376-6381 World Index of Scientific Translations and List of Translations Notified to the International Translation Centre *see* 0259-8264
0376-6411 Terra et Aqua
0376-642X I A T A Review
0376-6438 O E C D. Economic Surveys
0376-6608 Masihi Avaza
0376-6772 Personenvervoer
0376-7213 Construction and Property News
0376-7221 Irish Motor Industry
0376-7256 Indian Highways
0376-7272 Vaare Veger
0376-7329 Advances in Research and Technology of Seeds†
0376-7388 Journal of Membrane Science
0376-7426 S M Archives *see* 0952-4762
0376-7604 Current Management Literature
0376-7655 Cajanus
0376-7701 Caribbean Journal of Education
0376-7787 C C A I Monthly News Letter
0376-7809 C E N C U S: Central Excise and Customs Journal
0376-7833 Cerrahpasa Medical Faculty. Journal
0376-7868 Chartered Secretary
0376-7965 Conservation of Cultural Property in India
0376-8546 Directory of Public Enterprises in India
0376-8554 Directory of Scientific Research in Indian Universities
0376-8600 Directory of Special Libraries in Indonesia *changed to* Directory of Special Libraries and Information Sources (Year).
0376-8716 Drug and Alcohol Dependence
0376-8791 Economic Survey of Singapore
0376-8902 English in Africa
0376-8929 Environmental Conservation
0376-9429 International Journal of Fracture
0376-9569 Highlander
0376-9682 I C H R Newsletter
0376-9771 India International Centre Quarterly
0376-9836 Indian Historical Review
0376-9844 Indian Journal of Criminology
0376-9852 Indian Journal of Engineers
0376-9879 Indian Journal of Social Sciences
0376-9887 Indian Miller
0376-9909 Indian Railways Yearbook
0376-9976 Indonesian Shipping Directory
0376-9984 Indonesia Statistics
0377-0001 Indonesian Commercial Newsletter
0377-0036 Industrial Herald
0377-0044 Industrial Property, Statistics B *see* 1013-8374
0377-0044 Industrial Property, Statistics B *see* 1013-8382
0377-0087 Inkworld
0377-0141 International Journal of Critical Sociology
0377-015X International Journal of Ecology and Environmental Sciences

ISSN

ISSN INDEX 5725

0377-0168 International Journal of Zoonoses†
0377-0257 Journal of Non-Newtonian Fluid Mechanics
0377-0265 Dynamics of Atmospheres and Oceans
0377-0273 Journal of Volcanology and Geothermal Research
0377-0400 Journal of Applied Medicine
0377-0427 Journal of Computational and Applied Mathematics
0377-0443 Journal of Kerala Studies
0377-0451 Korean Journal of International Studies
0377-046X Journal of Molecular Medicine†
0377-0486 Journal of Raman Spectroscopy
0377-0494 Journal of Shipping, Customs, and Transport Law
0377-0648 Jawaharal Nehru University. School of Languages. Journal
0377-0737 Labor in Perspective *changed to* Labor and Development.
0377-0745 Wiener Gesellschaft fuer Theaterforschung. Jahrbuch
0377-077X Labour in the Public Sector Undertakings: Basic Information
0377-0796 Suid-Afrikaanse Unie-Lantern *changed to* Maranatha.
0377-0850 Law and Progress
0377-0907 Legal History
0377-0974 Libros Espanoles en Venta
0377-1083 Lore
0377-1121 Majalah Kedokteran Indonesia
0377-1261 Meghalaya Chronicle
0377-144X Barbados. Legislature. House of Assembly. Minutes of Proceedings
0377-1458 Barbados. Legislature. Senate. Minutes of Proceedings
0377-1482 M M T C News
0377-1490 Modern Fibres
0377-1555 Monthly Statistical Bulletin of Bangladesh
0377-1741 New Botanist
0377-1792 Norsk Sykehustidende *changed to* Helsetjenesten. Fagtidsskriftet.
0377-1806 Norwegian Offshore Index
0377-1830 Prehistoria *see* 0211-1748
0377-1962 Council of Europe. Parliamentary Assembly. Orders of the Day, Minutes of Proceedings
0377-2012 Molecular Structures and Dimensions
0377-2039 South Pacific Commission. Statistical Bulletin
0377-2063 Institution of Electronics and Telecommunication Engineers. Journal
0377-211X Portugal. Instituto Nacional de Estatistica. Estatisticas des Associqcoes Sindicais Patronais e Previdencia *see* 0870-4406
0377-2152 Portugal. Instituto Nacional de Estatistica. Boletim Mensal das Estatisticas da Agricultura e da Pesca. Continente, Acores e Madeira†
0377-2160 Boletim Mensal das Estatisticas do Comercio Externo
0377-2179 Portugal. Instituto Nacional de Estatistica. Boletim Mensal das Estatisticas Industrias. Continente, Acores e Madeira†
0377-2187 Portugal. Instituto Nacional de Estatistica. Boletim Trimestral das Estatisticas Monetarias e Financeiras. Continente, Acores e Madeira†
0377-2217 European Journal of Operational Research
0377-2233 Portugal. Estatisticas da Energia: Continente, Acores e Madeira†
0377-225X Portugal. Instituto Nacional de Estatistica. Estatisticas Agricolas *see* 0079-4139
0377-225X Portugal. Instituto Nacional de Estatistica. Estatisticas da Pesca - Statistiques de la Peche *changed to* Portugal. Instituto Nacional de Estatistica. Estatisticas da Pesca - Statistiques de la Peche. Continente, Acores e Madeira.
0377-2276 Portugal. Instituto Nacional de Estatistica. Estatisticas das Financas Publicas *changed to* Portugal. Instituto Nacional de Estatistica. Estatisticas das Financas Publicas. Continente, Acores e Madeira.
0377-2284 Portugal. Instituto Nacional de Estatistica. Estatisticas Demograficas Continente e Ilhas Adjacentes *changed to* Portugal. Instituto Nacional de Estatistica. Estatisticas Demograficas. Continente, Acores e Madeira.
0377-2292 Portugal. Instituto Nacional de Estatistica. Estatisticas dos Transportes e Communicacoes: Continente, Acores e Madeira
0377-2306 Portugal. Instituto Nacional de Estatistica. Estatisticas do Turismo. Continente, Acores e Madeira
0377-2314 Portugal. Estatisticas Industriais: Continente, Acores e Madeira. Volume 1: Industrias Extractivas, Electricidade, Gas, Agua
0377-2470 Portugal (Year) *see* 0871-8725
0377-2586 Pakistan Pictorial
0377-2713 People's Power
0377-2772 Philosophy & Social Action
0377-2780 Planning
0377-2969 Pakistan Academy of Sciences. Proceedings.
0377-3132 Psycho-Lingua
0377-3205 Qualitas Plantarum *see* 0921-9668
0377-3302 Rajasthan Forest Statistics
0377-3310 Rajasthan Journal of English Studies†
0377-3426 Reading Journal
0377-3450 R E C S A M Annual Report
0377-3515 Renditions
0377-3574 Contributions to Epidemiology and Biostatistics
0377-368X International Commission for the Conservation of Atlantic Tunas. Report
0377-3744 National Institute of Nutrition. Annual Report
0377-449X Singapore International Chamber of Commerce. Report
0377-452X South Pacific Commission. Report of Meetings
0377-4902 Homeopathic Herald
0377-4910 I C M R Bulletin
0377-5054 School
0377-5135 Sciences, Techniques, Informations C R I A C
0377-5380 Social and Labour Bulletin
0377-5437 Southeast Asian Affairs
0377-5445 Southern Africa Record
0377-547X Spices Newsletter†
0377-6093 Council of Europe. Parliamentary Assembly. Texts Adopted by the Assembly
0377-628X Revista de Filologia y Linguistica
0377-6352 Uplift
0377-6360 Vedic Light
0377-6549 Warta Kesehatan *changed to* Warta Dinas Kesehatan.
0377-6611 Working Class
0377-6719 Yearly All India Criminal Digest
0377-6832 Data India
0377-6883 Diffusion and Defect Data
0377-7154 Egyptian Computer Journal
0377-7243 Structural Engineering International
0377-7251 I A B S E Periodica - Surveys *see* 0377-7243
0377-726X I A B S E Periodica - Journal *see* 0377-7243
0377-7278 I A B S E Periodica - Proceedings *see* 0377-7243
0377-7286 I A B S E Periodica - Structures *see* 0377-7243
0377-7294 I A B S E Periodica - Bulletin *see* 0377-7243
0377-7308 Gedrag *changed to* Gedrag & Gezondheid.
0377-7316 Anuario de Estudios Centroamericanos
0377-7332 Empirical Economics
0377-7340 Indian Electronics Directory
0377-7359 Indian Films
0377-7367 Indian Library Movement
0377-7391 Industrial Welder
0377-743X Jijnasa
0377-7480 Journal of Rural Cooperation
0377-7537 Man-Made Textiles in India
0377-7553 Bank of Jamaica. Monthly Review
0377-757X Municipalities and Corporation Cases
0377-7669 North Atlantic Treaty Organization. Expert Panel on Air Pollution Modeling. Proceedings
0377-7774 Family Planning Association of India. Report
0377-7928 Singapore Periodicals Index
0377-7936 Space Science Instrumentation *see* 0004-640X
0377-8002 Tamil Nadu Journal of Co-operation
0377-8053 Water Resources Journal
0377-8231 Academie Royale de Medecine de Belgique. Bulletin et Memoires
0377-8282 Drugs of the Future
0377-8312 Von Karman Institute for Fluid Dynamics. Lecture Series
0377-8320 Psicodeia
0377-8347 Schweizerische Zeitschrift fuer Militaer- und Katastrophenmedizin
0377-8398 Marine Micropaleontology
0377-8401 Animal Feed Science and Technology
0377-841X Engineering and Process Economics *see* 0925-5273
0377-8436 Indian Journal of Textile Research *changed to* Indian Journal of Fibre & Textile Research.
0377-8487 Vignana Bharathi
0377-8533 University of Durban-Westville. Institute for Social and Economic Research. Annual Report
0377-8592 Safety Management
0377-8657 Purchasing South Africa†
0377-8711 Corrosion and Coatings
0377-8886 Norway. Statistisk Sentralbyraa. Legestatistikk *see* 0800-403X
0377-8894 N G U Skrifter
0377-8908 Norway. Statistisk Sentralbyraa. Statistisk Aarbok
0377-8967 Review of Population Reviews
0377-9017 Letters in Mathematical Physics
0377-9165 Annual Bulletin of General Energy Statistics for Europe
0377-919X Journal of Palestine Studies
0377-9211 Arabian Journal for Science and Engineering
0377-9238 Bangladesh Medical Research Council Bulletin
0377-9254 Journal of Engineering Sciences *see* 1018-3639
0377-9335 Entomon
0377-9343 Indian Journal of Chest Diseases and Allied Sciences
0377-9378 Karnataka Medical Journal
0377-9408 Tool and Alloy Steels
0377-9424 Agronomia Costarricense
0377-9459 Korean Journal of Pharmacology
0377-9688 Limnological Society of Southern Africa. Journal *changed to* Southern Africa Journal of Aquatic Sciences.
0377-9696 The Leech
0377-9890 Journal of Educational Media Sciences *see* 1013-090X
0378-0112 Index to Chinese Periodicals
0378-0392 Mineral and Electrolyte Metabolism
0378-0473 Kanina
0378-052X Ciencia y Tecnologia
0378-0600 Hong Kong Law Journal
0378-0643 Poesie
0378-0651 Muziek en Onderwijs
0378-066X Entretiens d'Actualite†
0378-0716 Academie Royale des Sciences, des Lettres et des Beaux-Arts de Belgique. Classe des Beaux-Arts. Bulletin
0378-0759 Indian Linguistics
0378-0791 Infusionstherapie und Klinische Ernaehrung - Forschung und Praxis *see* 1011-6966
0378-0856 Indo-Iranica
0378-0864 Geologische Bundesanstalt, Vienna. Abhandlungen
0378-0880 Communication and Cognition
0378-1070 C O M L A Newsletter
0378-1097 F E M S. Microbiology Letters
0378-1100 Contemporary Crises *changed to* Crime, Law and Social Policy.
0378-1119 Gene
0378-1127 Forest Ecology and Management
0378-1135 Veterinary Microbiology
0378-1186 Gerontologie *changed to* Tijdschrift voor Gerontologie en Geriatrie.
0378-1240 Garcia de Orta: Serie de Geologia
0378-1291 Arbeitsgemeinschaft fuer Elektrische Nachrichtentechnik. Mitteilungen
0378-1593 Central Bank of Swaziland. Quarterly Review
0378-178X Central Bank of Barbados. Economic and Financial Statistics
0378-181X Pedofauna
0378-1844 Interciencia
0378-1909 Environmental Biology of Fishes
0378-1917 Physics and Chemistry of Materials with Layered Structures *changed to* Physics and Chemistry of Materials with Low-Dimensional Structures.
0378-195X Metro: A Bibliography†
0378-1968 International Statistical Handbook of Urban Public Transport
0378-200X Revista Castilla
0378-2158 Kenya Uhuru Yearbook *changed to* Kenya Uhuru Factbook.
0378-2166 Journal of Pragmatics
0378-2182 Agricultural Services Bulletin *see* 1010-1365
0378-2395 Journal of Maharashtra Agricultural Universities
0378-2409 Journal of Root Crops
0378-2484 I J D L
0378-2522 Estadistica Panamena. Situacion Economica. Seccion 351. Indice de Precios al por Mayor y al Consumidor
0378-2530 Estadistica Panamena. Situacion Economica. Seccion 351. Precios Pagados por el Productor Agropecuario
0378-2557 Estadistica Panamena. Situacion Economica. Seccion 314, 321, 323, 324, 325. Industria
0378-2565 Estadistica Panamena. Situacion Economica. Seccion 312. Superficie Sembrada y Cosecha de Arroz, Maiz y Frijol de Bejuco
0378-2573 Estadistica Panamena. Situacion Economica. Seccion 312. Superficie Sembrada y Cosecha de Cafe, Tabaco y Cana de Azucar
0378-2581 Estadistica Panamena. Situacion Economica. Seccion 312. Produccion Pecuaria
0378-259X Estadistica Panamena. Situacion Politica, Administrativa y Justicia. Seccion 631. Justicia
0378-2603 Estadistica Panamena. Situacion Economica. Seccion 342. Cuentas Nacionales
0378-2611 Estadistica Panamena. Situacion Economica. Seccion 351. Precios Recibidos por el Productor Agropecuario
0378-262X Estadistica Panamena. Situacion Social. Seccion 431. Asistencia Social *changed to* Estadistica Panamena. Situacion Social. Seccion 431. Servicios de Salud.
0378-2654 Industrial Development Abstracts
0378-2662 Balance of Payments Yearbook *see* 0252-3051
0378-2689 University of Hong Kong. Centre of Asian Studies. Occasional Papers and Monographs
0378-2697 Plant Systematics and Evolution
0378-2700 Egyptian Journal of Dairy Science
0378-2778 Journal of Alcohol, Drugs and other Psychotropic Substances
0378-2808 Archivum Ottomanicum
0378-2883 Armaghan

ISSN

5726 ISSN INDEX

0378-3073 Oesterreichische Zeitschrift fuer Oeffentliches Recht und Voelkerrecht
0378-309X Biotelemetry and Patient Monitoring *see* 0254-0819
0378-3227 Portugal. Instituto Nacional de Estatistica. Serie Estatisticas Regionais
0378-3316 Rocas y Minerales
0378-3340 Revista del Pensamiento Centroamericano
0378-3472 Euro Abstracts Section II. Coal and Steel
0378-3588 Statistical Office of the European Communities. Crop Production *changed to* Agricultural Statistics Series No.1: Crop Production.
0378-3723 Statistical Office of the European Communities. External Trade - Monthly Statistics *changed to* Statistical Office of the European Communities. Monthly External Trade Bulletin.
0378-3758 Journal of Statistical Planning and Inference
0378-3766 T I M S Studies in the Management Sciences
0378-3774 Agricultural Water Management
0378-3782 Early Human Development
0378-3790 Inorganic Perspectives in Biology and Medicine†
0378-3804 Journal of Mechanical Working Technology *see* 0924-0136
0378-3812 Fluid Phase Equilibria
0378-3820 Fuel Processing Technology
0378-3839 Coastal Engineering
0378-3928 Hindustani Zaban
0378-4010 Al-Hilal
0378-4029 Geological Survey of India. News
0378-4037 International Bulletin of Sports Information
0378-4045 Progress in Clinical Neurophysiology†
0378-4053 Calendar of Scientific and Technical Meetings in South Africa *changed to* Calendar of Conferences, Meetings and Exhibitions to be Held in South Africa.
0378-407X Gereformeerde Vroueblad
0378-4088 Imbongi Yenkosi
0378-410X Molaetsa-Molaetsa
0378-4126 Murumiwa
0378-4134 Umthombo Wamandla
0378-4150 German Language and Literature Monographs†
0378-4169 Lingvisticae Investigationes
0378-4177 Studies in Language
0378-4207 Eurostat News†
0378-4215 Acta Iranica
0378-4266 Journal of Banking and Finance
0378-4274 Toxicology Letters
0378-4282 Animal Regulation Studies†
0378-4290 Field Crops Research
0378-4304 Analytica Chimica Acta - Computer Technique and Optimization *see* 0003-2670
0378-4312 Veterinary Science Communications *see* 0165-7380
0378-4320 Animal Reproduction Science
0378-4339 Protection Ecology *see* 0167-8809
0378-4347 Journal of Chromatography - Biomedical Applications
0378-4363 Physica B en C *see* 0921-4534
0378-4363 Physica B en C *see* 0921-4526
0378-4371 Physica A - Statistical and Theoretical Physics
0378-4487 Advances in Molecular Relaxation and Interaction Processes *see* 0167-7322
0378-4509 Avances en Produccion Animal
0378-4525 Zambian Ornithological Society. Bulletin†
0378-4533 Zambian Ornithological Society. Newsletter
0378-455X Economic Bulletin for Asia and the Pacific
0378-4568 Anvesak
0378-4592 Linguistic Bibliography
0378-469X Balafon
0378-4738 Water S.A.
0378-4754 Mathematics and Computers in Simulation
0378-4770 Women at Work†
0378-4789 Independent Journal of Philosophy
0378-4797 Africa Index *changed to* Africa Index to Continental Periodical Literature.
0378-4835 Oncologia
0378-4843 F C T L
0378-4916 Collectanea Cisterciensia
0378-4940 Estadistica Panamena. Indicadores Economicos y Sociales. Seccion 011. Indicadores Economicos y Sociales
0378-4967 Estadistica Panamena. Situacion Cultural. Seccion 511. Educacion
0378-4975 Estadistica Panamena. Situacion Demografica. Seccion 231. Migracion Internacional
0378-4983 Estadistica Panamena. Situacion Economica. Seccion 331. Comercio Exterior (Preliminary Report)
0378-4991 Estadistica Panamena. Situacion Economica. Seccion 352. Hoja de Balance de Alimentos
0378-5068 Vocational Training *see* 0252-855X
0378-5122 Maturitas
0378-5165 International Journal of Political Education†
0378-5173 International Journal of Pharmaceutics
0378-5254 Dietetics & Home Economics
0378-5327 South African Geographer
0378-5335 University of the North. Communique
0378-5378 D O C P A L Resumenes Sobre Poblacion en America Latina
0378-5386 Centro Latinoamericano de Demografia. Boletin Demografico
0378-5408 Labour and Society†
0378-5467 Labour Education
0378-5548 Revista Internacional del Trabajo
0378-5599 Revue Internationale du Travail
0378-5726 Etudes Mesoamericaines
0378-584X Onkologie
0378-5858 Renal Physiology *see* 1011-6524
0378-5866 Developmental Neuroscience
0378-5882 International Labour Office. Official Bulletin. Series A
0378-5890 International Labour Office. Official Bulletin. Series B
0378-5904 I L O Publications
0378-5920 The World Economy
0378-5939 Journal of Research Communication Studies *see* 0138-9130
0378-5947 Terotechnica *see* 0925-5273
0378-5955 Hearing Research
0378-5963 Applications of Surface Science *see* 0169-4332
0378-6196 N I H A E Bulletin *changed to* Health and Population: Perspectives and Issues.
0378-620X Integral Equations and Operator Theory
0378-6218 Results in Mathematics
0378-6242 Indian National Science Academy. Bulletin
0378-6307 Geophysical Research Bulletin†
0378-6323 Indian Journal of Dermatology, Venereology and Leprology
0378-6501 Drugs Under Experimental and Clinical Research
0378-651X Financial Market Trends
0378-6536 Organization for Economic Cooperation and Development. Quarterly Oil Statistics *see* 1013-9362
0378-6714 Statistical Office of the European Communities. Selling Prices of Vegetables Products *changed to* Statistical Office of the European Communities. Agricultural Prices.
0378-6722 Statistical Office of the European Communities. Selling Prices of Animal Products *changed to* Statistical Office of the European Communities. Agricultural Prices.
0378-6730 Estadistica Panamena. Situacion Economica. Seccion 343-344. Hacienda Publica y Finanzas *changed to* Estadistica Panamena. Situacion Economica. Seccion 343. Hacienda Publica.
0378-6730 Estadistica Panamena. Situacion Economica. Seccion 343-344. Hacienda Publica y Finanzas *changed to* Estadistica Panamena. Situacion Economica. Seccion 344. Finanzas.
0378-6749 Estadistica Panamena. Situacion Demografica. Seccion 221. Estadisticas Vitales - Cifras Preliminares†
0378-6757 Estadistica Panamena. Situacion Fisica. Seccion 121-Clima. Meteorologia *changed to* Estadistica Panamena. Situacion Fisica. Seccion 121. Meteorologia.
0378-6765 Estadistica Panamena. Situacion Social. Seccion 451. Accidentes de Transito
0378-6803 World Transindex *see* 0259-8264
0378-6900 Advances in Cardiovascular Physics
0378-6919 Schweizer Foerster
0378-6927 Plusminus 20†
0378-6935 Theaterzytig
0378-7192 E U D I S E D - R & D Bulletin
0378-7206 Information and Management
0378-7346 Gynecologic and Obstetric Investigation
0378-7354 Advances in Biological Psychiatry
0378-7362 I L O Judgements of the Administrative Tribunal
0378-7389 Estadistica Panamena. Situacion Economica. Seccion 333-334. Transporte y Comunicaciones *see* 1012-3555
0378-7389 Estadistica Panamena. Situacion Economica. Seccion 333-334. Transporte y Comunicaciones *see* 1012-3547
0378-7397 Estadistica Panamena. Situacion Economica. Seccion 341. Balanza de Pagos
0378-7443 Directory of Iranian Periodicals
0378-746X I R E B I†
0378-7478 Research in Tourism
0378-7494 Creative Book Selection Index
0378-7508 Library History Review
0378-7516 Asian Journal of European Studies
0378-7524 History of Agriculture
0378-7532 Management Development
0378-7540 Current Trends in Life Sciences
0378-7559 Statistical Office of the European Communities. Monthly Statistics Iron and Steel
0378-7591 Reports of Cases Before the Court of Justice of the European Communities
0378-7656 International Federation for Documentation. P-Notes
0378-7664 Schweizerischer Verband fuer Beruflichen Unterricht. Blaetter *changed to* Schweizerische Blaetter fuer Beruflichen Unterricht Blaetter.
0378-7680 Ciencia y Sociedad
0378-7699 Instituto del Mar del Peru. Boletin
0378-7702 Instituto del Mar del Peru. Informe
0378-7710 Swaziland National Bibliography
0378-7753 Journal of Power Sources
0378-7761 Fire Research *see* 0379-7112
0378-777X Environmental Policy and Law
0378-7788 Energy and Buildings
0378-7796 Electric Power Systems Research
0378-7818 Luz†
0378-7931 Deviance et Societe
0378-7958 Pharma-Flash
0378-7966 European Journal of Drug Metabolism and Pharmacokinetics
0378-7974 Revista de Estudios Hispanicos
0378-8032 Garcia de Orta: Serie de Estudos Agronomicos
0378-8059 Sudanow
0378-8121 Bangladesh Academy of Sciences. Journal
0378-8148 A T I R A Technical Digest *changed to* A C T.
0378-8156 Indian Journal of Physical Anthropology and Human Genetics
0378-8180 Journal of Oman Studies
0378-8350 Langues et Terminologies†
0378-8407 Tempo Medical
0378-8490 Karger Highlights: Nephrology†
0378-8512 Korean Journal of Biochemistry
0378-8644 Oesterreichische Akademie der Wissenschaften. Almanach
0378-8652 Oesterreichische Akademie der Wissenschaften. Philosophisch-Historische Klasse. Anzeiger
0378-8660 Oesterreichische Byzantinistik. Jahrbuch
0378-8679 Beitraege zu Infusionstherapie und Klin. Ernaehrung *see* 1011-6974
0378-8717 Science Teacher
0378-8733 Social Networks
0378-8741 Journal of Ethnopharmacology
0378-875X Ciencia Biologica: Biologia Molecular e Celular
0378-8857 Zambia Journal of Science and Technology
0378-8873 Barbados. Statistical Service. Monthly Digest of Statistics
0378-8911 Asian Culture Quarterly *changed to* Asian Pacific Culture Quarterly.
0378-892X Instituut voor Hygiene en Epidemiologie. Zwavel-Rook Meetnet *changed to* Studie van de Luchtkwaliteit in Belgie. Zwavel-Rook Meetnet.
0378-8970 Arabian Year Book
0378-9020 Building Industries Federation. Annual Report
0378-9098 South African Journal of Business Management
0378-9144 Boardroom
0378-9179 Braby's Cape Province Directory
0378-9195 Durban Corporation Directory
0378-9217 Braby's East London Directory
0378-9268 Ladysmith Directory
0378-9292 Braby's Orange Free State Directory *changed to* Braby's Orange Free State - Northern Cape Directory.
0378-9454 Vistas in Plant Sciences
0378-9519 Journal of Entomological Research
0378-9535 Urja
0378-956X Instituto Tecnologico de Santo Domingo. Documentos
0378-9608 Universidade de Coimbra. Faculdade de Farmacia. Boletim
0378-9721 Bulletin of Animal Health and Production in Africa
0378-9748 W H O Pesticide Residue Series†
0378-9837 Diagnostic Imaging *see* 0254-881X
0378-9845 Health Communications and Informatics†
0378-9853 Karger Highlights: Cardiology†
0378-9861 Human Gene Mapping
0378-9896 Universidad Catolica Nuestra Senora de la Asuncion. Centro de Estudios Antropologicos. Suplemento Antropologico
0378-9942 Bibliographie du Senegal
0378-9977 International Background†
0378-9993 Industry and Environment
0379-0002 Reviews on Powder Metallurgy & Physical Ceramics
0379-0010 F A O Monthly Bulletin of Statistics *see* 1011-8780
0379-0037 Indian Journal of Applied Linguistics
0379-0207 Oesterreichische Akademie der Wissenschaften, Vienna. Mathematisch-Naturwissenschaftliche Klasse. Denkschriften
0379-0231 Tiroler Landesmuseum Ferdinandeum, Innsbruck. Veroeffentlichungen
0379-0258 Automatic Data Processing Information Bulletin†
0379-0266 Estudios de la Seguridad Social
0379-0290 Current Research in Social Security
0379-0347 U N C R D Newsletter
0379-0355 Methods and Findings in Experimental and Clinical Pharmacology
0379-038X National Academy of Medical Sciences. Annals
0379-0401 Bismuth Institute. Bulletin

ISSN

0379-0436 Comparative Physiology and Ecology
0379-0479 Indian Journal of Cryogenics
0379-055X Tobacco Research
0379-0568 Indian Society of Desert Technology and University Centre of Desert Studies. Transactions *see* 0970-3918
0379-0584 Index to South African Periodicals
0379-0592 S A Joint Catalogue of Monographs on Microfiche, Series 1, Title Index *see* 1018-9602
0379-0606 S A Joint Catalogue of Monographs of Microfiche, Series 2, Author Index *see* 1018-9599
0379-0622 Zambezia: The Journal of the University of Zimbabwe
0379-0649 Penpals
0379-0703 Journal of Oman Studies Special Report
0379-072X Estadistica Panamena. Situacion Social. Seccion 441. Estadisticas del Trabajo
0379-0738 Forensic Science International
0379-0754 Estadistica Panamena. Situacion Economica. Seccion 323. Produccion Manufacturera *changed to* Estadistica Panamena. Situacion Economica. Seccion 323. Indice de Produccion Fisica de la Industria Manufacturera.
0379-0762 Revista Internacional de Ciencias Sociales
0379-0797 International Rehabilitation Medicine *see* 0963-8288
0379-0827 Cyprus. Agricultural Research Institute. Agricultural Economics Report
0379-0851 Cyprus. Tmimatos Georgias. Etisia Ekthesi (Year)
0379-086X Cyprus. Department of Fisheries. Annual Report on the Department of Fisheries and the Cyprus Fisheries
0379-0916 Cyprus. Meteorological Service. Summary of the Weather in Cyprus†
0379-0924 Cyprus. Department of Statistics and Research. Agricultural Statistics
0379-0932 Cyprus. Agricultural Research Institute. Technical Paper†
0379-0940 Americas
0379-1041 E U L A R Bulletin
0379-1068 Karger Highlights: Gerontology†
0379-1084 South Africa. Sea Fisheries Branch. Investigational Report *changed to* South Africa. Sea Fisheries Research Institute. Investigational Report.
0379-1130 Rubber Research Institute of Sri Lanka. Journal
0379-122X Unesco Journal of Information Science, Librarianship and Archives Administration†
0379-1424 Universitaet Wien. Dissertationen
0379-1564 Bibliographical Series on Coconut†
0379-1580 Fiji. Mineral Resources Division. Bulletin *changed to* Fiji. Mineral Resources Department. Bulletin.
0379-1653 Jaslok Hospital & Research Centre. Bulletin
0379-1726 Diqiu Huaxue
0379-1734 I L O Information
0379-1815 Belgian Environmental Research Index
0379-1998 Karger Highlights: Oncology†
0379-2005 Karger Highlights: Oral Science†
0379-217X European Economy
0379-2218 U N I S I S T Newsletter - General Information Programme
0379-2269 Children in the Tropics
0379-2285 E S A Journal
0379-2439 International Test Commission. Bulletin
0379-2463 Siren
0379-248X Information
0379-2501 Output
0379-2528 Unterhaltungs-Elektronik *changed to* Hi-Fi Vision.
0379-2862 China Letter
0379-2870 Philippine Letter
0379-2889 Japan Letter
0379-2897 Sinet
0379-2927 Journal for the History of Arabic Science
0379-296X Fiji. Mineral Resources Division. Economic Investigation *changed to* Fiji. Mineral Resources Department. Economic Investigation.
0379-3133 European File
0379-3168 Pure and Applied Mathematika Sciences
0379-3192 Uniterra *see* 1013-7394
0379-3338 World Union for the Safeguard of Youth. Bulletin
0379-3400 Teacher Education
0379-3486 European Communities Trade with ACP States and the South Mediterranean States†
0379-3532 Q R Journal
0379-3540 Zoological Survey of India. Memoirs
0379-3575 Egyptian Journal of Agronomy
0379-3621 Codices Manuscripti
0379-363X Paracelsust
0379-3664 Schweizerische Zeitschrift fuer Soziologie
0379-3680 F I D Directory
0379-3699 Annales de l'Economie Publique, Sociale et Cooperative
0379-3753 Wallonie
0379-3885 Journal of Indian Psychology
0379-3915 Studies in History of Medicine *see* 0970-5562
0379-3982 Tecnologia en Marcha
0379-3990 Thesis Abstracts
0379-4008 Haryana Agricultural University. Journal of Research
0379-4016 Trinidad Naturalist *changed to* Naturalist.
0379-4032 Islam and the Modern World
0379-4040 Nongye Zhoukan - Agri-Week *see* 1015-8367
0379-4121 Annual Drug Data Report *changed to* Drug Data Report.
0379-4148 Wuli
0379-4172 Yichuan Xuebao
0379-4229 European Applied Research Reports: Nuclear Science and Technology Section
0379-4237 Estadistica Panamena. Situacion Demografica. Seccion 221. Estadisticas Vitales
0379-4245 Estadistica Panamena. Situacion Economica. Seccion 321 y 325. Industria Encuesta
0379-4261 Estadistica Panamena. Situacion Economica. Seccion 331-Comercio. Comercio Exterior (Annual) *changed to* Estadistica Panamena. Situacion Economica. Seccion 331-Comercio. Anuario de Comercio Exterior.
0379-4288 Bangladesh Horticulture
0379-4296 Bangladesh Journal of Agricultural Sciences
0379-4318 Institution of Engineers, Bangladesh. Journal
0379-4350 South African Journal of Chemistry
0379-4369 South African Journal of Wildlife Research
0379-4377 South African Journal of Physics
0379-4407 Oesterreichische Zeitschrift fuer Wirtschaftsrecht
0379-4415 Recht der Schule†
0379-4423 Rundfunkrecht
0379-4474 Karger Highlights: Medical Imaging†
0379-4482 Periodicals in Southern African Libraries
0379-4490 Hong Kong Psychological Society. Bulletin
0379-4504 Current Literature on Science of Science
0379-458X Call of St. John
0379-4636 Caravan and Outdoor Life
0379-4695 Christiaan de Wet Annale
0379-4709 Tydskrif vir Skoonlug
0379-4792 Transport and Road Digest
0379-4857 Acta Medica Dominicana
0379-508X Acta Botanica Indica
0379-5101 Himalayan Geology
0379-511X Indian Geological Index†
0379-5128 Indian Journal of Earth Sciences
0379-5136 Indian Journal of Marine Sciences
0379-5179 Kavaka
0379-5187 Mineral Research
0379-525X Pacific Perspective†
0379-5268 Mana
0379-5284 Saudi Medical Journal
0379-5411 Acta Ciencia Indica
0379-542X Cheiron
0379-5446 Indian Foundry Journal
0379-5489 Journal of Nuclear Agriculture and Biology
0379-5527 Mechanical Engineering Bulletin
0379-556X Pharmstudent
0379-5578 Plant Biochemical Journal
0379-5594 Seed Research
0379-5608 Soaps, Detergents & Toiletries Review
0379-5721 Food and Nutrition Bulletin
0379-573X Asset
0379-5845 Chile Agricola
0379-5853 HongKongiana†
0379-6027 South African Journal of Dairy Technology *see* 0258-3321
0379-606X Revue A T E E Journal *see* 0261-9768
0379-6078 South Africa. Government Gazette Index *changed to* Juta - State Library Index to the Government Gazette.
0379-6086 University of Stellenbosch. Bureau for Economic Research. Consumer Survey *see* 0258-9311
0379-6124 National Institute for Transport and Road Research. Annual Report *changed to* South Africa. Division of Roads and Transport Technology. Annual Report.
0379-6175 South African Journal of Physiotherapy
0379-6191 University of Stellenbosch. Bureau for Economic Research. Trends
0379-6205 Journal for Studies in Economics and Econometrics
0379-637X A M P S Broadcast Media *changed to* A M P S White - Coloured - Asian Radio Diary.
0379-637X A M P S Broadcast Media *changed to* A M P S Black Radio and Television Diary.
0379-6477 Armed Forces
0379-6485 Ars Nova
0379-6531 Adler Museum Bulletin
0379-654X Animal Anti-Cruelty League. Chairman's Report
0379-6574 Africana Society of Pretoria. Journal
0379-6736 South Africa. Weather Bureau. Technical Paper
0379-6779 Synthetic Metals
0379-6787 Solar Cells *see* 0927-0248
0379-6906 Chinese Journal of Materials Science
0379-6922 Mundo Nuevo
0379-6930 African Journal of Plant Protection
0379-7007 Portugal. Instituto Nacional de Estatistica. Centro de Estudos Demograficos. Caderno
0379-704X Social Security Documentation: African Series
0379-7074 African News Sheet
0379-7082 Revista de Educacion
0379-7104 Universiteit van Pretoria. Biblioteekdiens. Verslagreeks†
0379-7112 Fire Safety Journal
0379-7368 Chinese Biochemical Society. Journal
0379-7481 Acta Oceanographica Taiwanica
0379-7651 Chemie Magazine
0379-7724 Higher Education in Europe
0379-7783 Brief *changed to* Design Brief.
0379-7856 Universitatea "Al. I. Cuza" din Iasi. Analele Stiintifice. Sectiunea 3b: Filozofie
0379-7864 Universitatea "Al. I. Cuza" din Iasi. Analele Stiintifice. Sectiunea 3c: Stiinte Economice
0379-7872 Universitatea "Al. I. Cuza" din Iasi. Analele Stiintifice. Sectiunea 3d: Stiinte Juridice
0379-7880 Universitatea "Al. I. Cuza" din Iasi. Analele Stiintifice. Sectiunea 3e: Lingvistica
0379-7899 Universitatea "Al. I. Cuza" din Iasi. Analele Stiintifice. Sectiunea 3f: Literatura
0379-7902 Universitatea "Al. I. Cuza" din Iasi. Analele Stiintifice. Geologie - Geografie
0379-7910 Taiwan Yellow Pages
0379-797X Behavioural Sciences and Rural Development *see* 0970-3357
0379-8070 World Health Statistics Quarterly
0379-8097 International Society of Applied Biology. Biological Memoirs
0379-8151 Hahnemannian Homoeopathic Sandesh
0379-8194 Journal of Sikh Studies
0379-8267 United Nations. Treaty Series
0379-8291 Cistercienser Chronik
0379-8305 Developmental Pharmacology and Therapeutics
0379-8321 Iraqi Chemical Society. Journal
0379-8364 Institutul Agronomic Ion Ionescu de la Brad. Lucrari Stiintifice. Seria Agronomie
0379-8372 Institutul Agronomic Ion Ionescu de la Brad. Lucrari Stiintifice. Seria Horticultura
0379-8402 Philosophica
0379-8410 South African Journal of Labour Relations
0379-8461 European Commission of Human Rights. Decisions and Reports
0379-8577 Curationis *see* 0258-1647
0379-8585 Architecture & Behaviour
0379-8607 Schweizerische Akademie der Medizinischen Wissenschaften. Bulletin†
0379-864X Chemical Senses
0379-8658 Greenhill Journal of Administration
0379-8674 World Bank. Monthly Operational Summary
0379-8836 Stats - Monthly Statistical and Marketing Digest
0379-8860 South African Journal of Ethnology
0379-8895 South African Yearbook of International Law
0379-9069 Suid Afrikaanse Tydskrif vir Navorsing in Sport - South African Journal for Research in Sport *changed to* Suid-Afrikaanse Tydskrif vir Navorsing in Sport, Liggaamlike Opvoedkunde en Ontspanning.
0379-9506 Garcia de Orta: Serie de Botanica
0379-9514 Garcia de Orta: Serie de Geografia
0379-9549 Asia Monitor†
0379-9786 Christian Education Advance†
0379-9867 Contree
0379-9921 Custos
0380-0008 Manitoba Decisions - Civil and Criminal Cases
0380-0067 Eastern Ontario Farmer *changed to* Ontario Farmer (Eastern Edition).
0380-0121 Mennonite Reporter
0380-013X Canadian Mennonite Reporter *see* 0380-0121
0380-0180 Marketing Social†
0380-0199 Media Message *see* 0710-4340
0380-0326 L B M A O Reporter
0380-0334 Canada. Statistics Canada. Communications Service Bulletin
0380-0342 Canada. Statistics Canada. Water Transportation *see* 0835-5533
0380-0482 Expression†
0380-0547 Canada. Statistics Canada. Infomat
0380-0555 Statistics Canada Weekly *see* 0380-0547
0380-0741 Canada. Statistics Canada. Consumer Credit†
0380-075X Financial Institutions, Financial Statistics
0380-1020 Canada. Department of Insurance. List of Securities *changed to* Canada. Office of the Superintendent of Financial Institutions. List of Securities.
0380-1039 Vintage Canada†
0380-1098 Education Today†

ISSN INDEX

ISSN	Title
0380-1314	Consensus (Ottawa)
0380-1330	Journal of Great Lakes Research
0380-1349	Canada. Statistics Canada. Imports - Merchandise Trade *see* 0844-8353
0380-1446	Critical List
0380-1462	Teaching Positions Available†
0380-1470	Trellis
0380-1489	Canadian Studies in Population
0380-1616	Ontario Genealogy Society. Newsleaf
0380-1691	Vancouver Island Regional Library Newsletter
0380-1721	Cahiers Quebecois de Demographie
0380-1799	Orchestra Canada
0380-1861	Registered Nursing Orderly
0380-1888	Ontario Society of Medical Technologists. Newsletter *see* 0228-877X
0380-1969	Ontario Technologist
0380-2019	C T M Weekly Bulletin *changed to* Travelweek Bulletin.
0380-2051	Journal du Nord-Ouest
0380-2108	Canada. Statistics Canada. Labour Costs in Canadian: Education, Libraries and Museums/Couts de la Main d'Oeuvre au Canada. Enseignement, Bibliotheques et Musees†
0380-2140	Promin
0380-2221	Canadian Financial E-Z Directory
0380-223X	Stone and Cox General Insurance Register
0380-2264	Canadian Association Executive
0380-2361	Canadian Journal of Education
0380-240X	Query
0380-2469	Anglican Church of Canada. General Synod. Journal of Proceedings *changed to* Anglican Church of Canada. General Synod. Journal.
0380-2531	Mayday
0380-2604	Tab International
0380-2639	F M Compilation of the Statutes of Canada *changed to* F M Compilation of the Statutes of Canada. Revised Statutes.
0380-2760	Milieu
0380-2795	Ontario Campus Culture Association. Newsletter†
0380-2817	NeWest Review
0380-2841	N.E.R.L.S. Newsletter *see* 0708-9066
0380-285X	Onion†
0380-2892	In a Nutshell†
0380-2906	M P A News *see* 0380-2892
0380-2914	Adagio
0380-2973	Talking Books in the Public Library Systems of Metropolitan Toronto
0380-3147	L U A C Forum
0380-321X	Foret Conservation
0380-3333	Greenmaster
0380-352X	Feather Fancier
0380-3554	Jr. Rider
0380-3651	Hog Marketplace Quarterly
0380-3945	I.F.†
0380-3988	Public Sector Management
0380-4011	Institute of Chartered Accountants of Guyana. Newsletter
0380-4100	Link & Visitor
0380-4194	Adaptation
0380-4208	Land Compensation Reports
0380-4275	Reserves of Coal, Province of Alberta
0380-4305	Schedule of Wells Drilled for Oil and Gas in Alberta†
0380-4321	Alberta Coal Industry, Annual Statistics
0380-4496	Conservation in Alberta†
0380-450X	Alberta. Environment Conservation Authority. Annual Report†
0380-4615	Canada. Statistics Canada. Oil Pipe Line Transport
0380-4623	Museogramme
0380-4674	Mini-Pegg *see* 0823-1745
0380-4852	Manitoba Highway News
0380-4933	International Commission for the Northwest Atlantic Fisheries. Selected Papers *see* 0250-6432
0380-4968	Canada. Statistics Canada. Gold Quartz and Copper-Gold-Silver Mines/Mines de Quartz Aurifere et Mines de Cuivre-Or-Argent†
0380-5107	Manpower and Immigration Review: Quebec Region
0380-5131	Music Scene†
0380-531X	Canada. Department of Employment and Immigration. Strategic Policy and Planning Division. Forward Occupational Imbalance Listing - Liste Anticipative des Desequilibres Par Profession†
0380-5476	Voice of Tourism†
0380-5522	Northern Perspectives
0380-562X	Alberta Wilderness Association. Newsletter *see* 0830-8284
0380-5689	Nova Scotia. Department of Labour. Annual Report
0380-5735	Notes on Agriculture†
0380-5921	Canadian Mathematical Congress. Research Committee. Report
0380-5948	Canada. Statistics Canada. Urban Transport *see* 0829-1756
0380-5964	Canada. Statistics Canada. Railway Operating Statistics
0380-6146	Canada. Statistics Canada. Retail Trade
0380-6197	Thunder Bay Camping Guide†
0380-6251	Ottawa R & D Report
0380-6294	Canada. Statistics Canada. Motion Picture Theatres and Film Distributors
0380-6308	Canada. Statistics Canada. Railway Carloadings
0380-6367	P T I C Bulletin†
0380-6375	P T I C Newsletter *see* 0849-3154
0380-6642	Peterborough Historical Society Bulletin
0380-6693	Sift†
0380-6804	Canada. Statistics Canada. The Labour Force
0380-6847	Canada. Statistics Canada. Coal and Coke Statistics
0380-691X	Canada. Statistics Canada. Consumer Prices and Price Indexes
0380-6928	Canada. Statistics Canada. Commercial Failures/Faillites Commerciales†
0380-6936	Canada. Statistics Canada. Employment, Earnings and Hours
0380-6952	Canada. Statistics Canada. Miscellaneous Non-Metal Mines/Mines Non Metalliques Diverses†
0380-6979	Makara†
0380-6987	Canadian Automobile Association. Communique†
0380-6995	Studies in Canadian Literature
0380-7045	Department Store Sales & Stocks
0380-7053	Canada. Statistics Canada. Investment Statistics Service Bulletin/Bulletin de Service sur la Statistique des Investissements†
0380-7150	Q L A Bulletin
0380-7177	Canada. Statistics Canada. Merchandising Inventories
0380-7223	Canada. Statistics Canada. Gypsum Products
0380-7525	Canada. Statistics Canada. Industrial Corporations, Financial Statistics
0380-7533	Canada. Statistics Canada. Causes of Death, Provinces by Sex and Canada by Sex and Age†
0380-7541	Canada. Statistics Canada. Index Numbers of Farm Prices of Agricultural Products *see* 0835-0906
0380-7797	Canada. Statistics Canada. Canada's Mineral Production: Preliminary Estimates
0380-7835	Canada. Statistics Canada. Telephone Statistics: Preliminary Report on Large Telephone Systems†
0380-7851	Canada. Statistics Canada. Primary Iron and Steel
0380-7878	Canada. Statistics Canada. Retail Chain Stores *see* 0227-017X
0380-7894	Canada. Statistics Canada. Wholesale Trade
0380-7967	Post *see* 0709-1370
0380-7975	Perceptual Post *see* 0709-1370
0380-8025	Publisher
0380-8041	S L I S Newsletter†
0380-8068	Georgian Bay Regional Library System. Directory-Member Libraries
0380-8114	Random Thoughts
0380-8238	Canada. Statistics Canada. Scrap Iron and Steel/Dechets de Fer et d'Acier†
0380-8297	Saskatchewan. Advisory Council on the Status of Women. Publication
0380-8343	Scope - Wheelers Canadian Campground†
0380-8416	Rincontro
0380-8475	Catholic Hospital Association of Canada. Directory *see* 0828-5748
0380-8688	Canadian Scout Executive *changed to* Scout Executive.
0380-8718	Canada. Grain Commission. Economics and Statistics Division. Visible Grain Supplies and Disposition
0380-8815	Prisma
0380-8823	Repertoire des Theses de Doctorat Soutenues Devant les Universites de Langue Francaise†
0380-8858	Toronto News†
0380-8866	Shore Line
0380-8890	Ecornifleux†
0380-8920	A T A News Bulletin *changed to* Truxpress.
0380-903X	Imperial Oil Limited. Review *see* 0700-5156
0380-9056	Direction (Downsview)
0380-9099	Business Life
0380-9218	Canadian Journal of Information Science
0380-9242	Nova Scotian Surveyor
0380-9366	Neologie en Marche. Serie A. Langue Generale†
0380-9420	Canadian Journal of Political & Social Theory
0380-9455	Canada on Stage: Canadian Theatre Review Yearbook *changed to* Canada on Stage: The National Theatre Yearbook.
0380-951X	Canada. Statistics Canada. Electric Power Statistics Volume 1: Annual Electric Power Survey of Capability and Load
0380-9544	Vancouver's Leisure Magazine *see* 0380-9552
0380-9552	Vancouver Magazine
0380-9633	Megadrilogica
0380-9668	B.C. Hotelman *changed to* B.C. Hoteliex.
0380-9676	University of Saskatchewan. Library. Notable Works and Collections†
0380-9773	Orienteering *see* 0382-8255
0380-979X	Manitoba. Environmental Council. Studies
0380-9803	Manitoba. Environmental Council. Annual Report
0380-9811	Revue Commerce
0380-9811	Commerce. Le Point
0380-982X	Arms Collecting
0380-9854	C C I Journal†
0381-0100	Conference Board of Canada. Quarterly Provincial Forecast *see* 0827-5785
0381-0380	Eglise de Montreal
0381-0569	Interlude†
0381-0925	Continuum
0381-095X	Communicator (Springhill)†
0381-0976	Canada. Information Canada. Municipal Report†
0381-0984	Journal of Natural Resource Management and Interdisciplinary Studies†
0381-0992	Renovation Bricolage
0381-1352	F C M Forum
0381-1387	Learning
0381-1603	Political Economy Series†
0381-1638	University of Toronto. Faculty of Law. Review
0381-1794	Society
0381-1905	Circuit†
0381-2022	Newfoundland and Labrador Provincial Libraries. Newsletter *see* 0838-360X
0381-2049	Legal Aid New Brunswick Annual Report
0381-209X	Newfoundland and Labrador Regional Libraries. Newsletter *see* 0838-360X
0381-2146	Canada. Environmental Protection Service. Canada-Ontario Agreement Research Report†
0381-2278	Saskatchewan. Alcoholism Commission. Annual Report *changed to* Saskatchewan. Alcohol and Drug Abuse Commission. Annual Report.
0381-2421	Farmers' Market
0381-243X	Geological Fieldwork
0381-2472	Grain Facts
0381-2510	British Columbia. Law Reform Commission. Annual Report
0381-2561	Canada Health Manpower Inventory *changed to* Health Personnel in Canada.
0381-260X	British Columbia Institute of Technology. Annual Report *changed to* B C I T Annual Report.
0381-2650	Ontario. Ministry of Natural Resources. Tree Improvement and Forest Biomass Institute. Forest Research Note *changed to* Ontario. Ministry of Natural Resources. Ontario Forest Research Institute. Forest Research Note.
0381-2669	Chalk River Nuclear Laboratories. Chemistry and Materials Division. Progress Report†
0381-2677	Chalk River Nuclear Laboratories. Biology and Health Physics Division. Progress Report *changed to* Chalk River Nuclear Laboratories. Health Sciences Division. Progress Report.
0381-2898	British Columbia. Department of Labour. Annual Report *changed to* British Columbia. Ministry of Labour and Consumer Services. Annual Report.
0381-2995	Canada. Environment Canada. Environment Protection Service. Annual Summary: National Air Pollution Surveillance *changed to* Canada. Environment Canada. Conservation and Protection Service. Annual Summary: National Air Pollution Surveillance. New Brunswick†
0381-3134	Nouveau-Brunswick Aujourd'hui *see* 0381-3134
0381-3142	
0381-3215	Manitoba. Pension Commission. Annual Report *changed to* Manitoba. Pension Commission. Update Study.
0381-3223	Saskatchewan Farmers' Markets Annual Report†
0381-3258	Trends in Collective Bargaining Settlements in Nova Scotia†
0381-3711	Employers of New Community College Graduates: Directory
0381-372X	Employers of New University Graduates: Directory
0381-3738	Directory of Employers Offering Employment to New University Graduates *see* 0381-372X
0381-3746	This Magazine
0381-3886	Heartline†
0381-3924	Ontario. Ministry of Natural Resources. Forest Research Report
0381-3932	Clover Leaflet
0381-4130	Calendar of Expiring Collective Agreements (Year)
0381-4319	National Research Council, Canada. Division of Building Research. D B R Paper *changed to* National Research Council, Canada. Institute for Research in Construction. Paper.
0381-4327	Alberta. Department of Social Services and Community Health. Annual Report *changed to* Alberta. Department of Family and Social Services. Annual Report.
0381-4432	Canada. Statistics Canada. New Surveys/Nouvelles Enquetes†
0381-4459	Spill Technology Newsletter

ISSN INDEX 5729

0381-4556 Telephone Echo *changed to* M T S Echo.
0381-4831 Bedford Institute of Oceanography. Computer Note†
0381-4874 International Perspectives
0381-5013 Canadian Oldtimers' Hockey News *changed to* Oldtimers' Hockey News.
0381-5250 H R I Observations *see* 0826-9947
0381-5528 Outdoor Power Products†
0381-565X Computing Services Bulletin *see* 0840-6235
0381-5730 Canadian Music Directory
0381-5765 Canadian Hotel, Restaurant, Institution & Store Equipment Directory
0381-5781 Association des Traducteurs et Interpretes de l'Ontario. InformATIO
0381-579X Yes, There Is Canadian Music†
0381-5838 Canadian Society of Laboratory Technologists. Bulletin
0381-5900 Maritime Psychological Association. Bulletin *see* 0004-6833
0381-5919 Information *see* 0707-7793
0381-5927 Agricultural Science *see* 0707-7793
0381-596X Brasier†
0381-5978 British Columbia School Trustees Association. Newsletter *changed to* Education Leader.
0381-6028 Bookmark
0381-6036 B.C. Science Teacher *see* 0834-2466
0381-6060 Anglican Church of Canada. Division of National and World Program. Bulletin *see* 0381-6079
0381-6079 Anglican Church of Canada. Bulletin†
0381-6109 Them Days
0381-6133 Canadian Association of Slavists Newsletter
0381-6206 Brome County Historical Society. Publication
0381-6419 Nursing Quebec
0381-646X Environment Probe *changed to* S E S Newsletter.
0381-6486 C - C O R E News
0381-6524 Journal of Our Time†
0381-6591 Poetry Toronto Newsletter *changed to* Poetry Toronto.
0381-6605 Journal of Otolaryngology
0381-6745 Beverage Canada
0381-6826 N A P E Journal *changed to* Communicator (St. John's).
0381-6834 Beef Today *changed to* Canadian Livestock Journal.
0381-6885 Harrowsmith
0381-6907 Quebec (Province) Centrale des Bibliotheques. Bulletin de Bibliographie†
0381-7024 Dalhousie University. Institute of Public Affairs. Occasional Papers†
0381-7032 Ars Combinatoria
0381-7059 Canadian Amateur Photographer†
0381-7245 Blue Book of Canadian Business
0381-730X Tidings *see* 0228-6157
0381-7369 Canada Quilts *changed to* Canada Quilts Magazine.
0381-7377 Conference Board of Canada. Survey of Consumer Buying Intentions *changed to* Conference Board of Canada. Index of Consumer Attitudes.
0381-7466 Celebrate
0381-7547 Philatelie au Quebec *changed to* Philatelie Quebec.
0381-7717 Native Perspective†
0381-7946 Maria†
0381-7970 New Brunswick Public Employees Association. News Letter *changed to* New Brunswick Public Employees Association. Newsline - Bulletin.
0381-8004 Ontario Industrial Arts Association. Bulletin
0381-8012 O I A A Bulletin *see* 0381-8004
0381-8047 Crucible
0381-8160 Farm Equipment Quarterly *see* 0705-3878
0381-8160 Farm Equipment Quarterly *see* 0705-3878
0381-8179 Sanford Evans Gold Book of Used Car Prices
0381-8187 Scope†
0381-8225 Revue des Fermieres *changed to* Revue Fermieres Aujourd'hui.
0381-8284 Transportation R and D in Canada *changed to* Surface Transportation R & D in Canada.
0381-8357 Archaic Notes *changed to* Ottawa Archaeologist.
0381-8454 Revue d'Histoire du Bas-Saint-Laurent
0381-8535 Fur Trade Journal of Canada
0381-856X Caledonian
0381-8632 O C S Nouvelles
0381-873X S I E C C A N Newsletter
0381-8802 Canada. Statistics Canada. Hospital Statistics: Preliminary Annual Report/ Statistique Hospitaliere: Rapport Annuel Preliminaire†
0381-8845 Canada. Statistics Canada. Tuberculosis Statistics. Volume 2: Institutional Facilities, Services and Finances/La Statistique de la Tuberculose, Volume 2: Installations, Services et Finance des Etablissements†
0381-8888 Estates and Trusts Quarterly *changed to* Estates and Trusts Journal.
0381-8950 Deutsche Katholik in Kanada
0381-8977 Sporting Goods Canada†
0381-9000 S T O P Newsletter *see* 0705-1212
0381-9027 Silahis
0381-9035 Speaking of Mime
0381-9043 International Yoga Life and Yoga Vacations *changed to* Yoga Life.
0381-9051 S M E A. Newsletter *see* 0703-8380
0381-9116 Special Education *see* 0826-4716
0381-9124 Special Education in Canada *see* 0826-4716
0381-9132 Olifant
0381-9159 Canadian Band Directors Association. Newsletter *changed to* Canadian Band Association (Ontario). Newsletter.
0381-9175 C B C: Coiffure-Beaute-Charme *see* 8750-0477
0381-9191 Herstory†
0381-9256 Canada. Statistics Canada. Miscellaneous Non-Metallic Mineral Products Industries/Industries des Produits Mineraux Non-Metalliques Divers†
0381-9280 Sporting Goods Trade *see* 0829-3716
0381-9345 Atlantic Provinces Transportation Commission. Tips & Topics
0381-9361 Teiresias
0381-9388 Societe Historique Nicolas Denys. Revue d'Histoire
0381-9418 Status of Women News†
0381-9507 Canadian L P & Tape Catalogue
0381-9515 Artviews†
0381-9582 Tema
0381-9612 Trust
0381-9663 Alberta Construction and Resource Industries Directory. Purchasing Guide†
0381-9825 Montreal Special Libraries Association. Bulletin *see* 0824-7749
0381-9833 Special Libraries Association. Montreal Chapter. Bulletin *see* 0824-7749
0381-9868 Motive Power International†
0381-9884 Jewish Public Library Bulletin†
0381-9930 Toys & Games
0381-9957 Association des Traducteurs et Interpretes de l'Ontario. Bulletin de l'A T I O *see* 0381-9965
0381-9965 Association des Traducteurs et Interpretes de l'Ontario. Translatio†
0382-0068 Voice of United Senior Citizens of Ontario
0382-0130 Ishtar Newsletter *see* 0382-0149
0382-0149 Ishtar News
0382-0157 Western Ontario Historical Notes†
0382-0203 Village Squire
0382-0262 Vie Francaise†
0382-0289 Vista
0382-0327 Voice of Radom
0382-0335 Jeu
0382-036X View *see* 0700-4400
0382-0424 Vision
0382-0467 Arctic in Colour†
0382-0610 Undzer Veg
0382-0661 U B C Library News
0382-0718 Vector
0382-0726 British Columbia Association of Mathematics Teachers. Newsletter *see* 0382-0718
0382-0734 Hollinger Mines Limited. Annual Report
0382-0750 Transition†
0382-0769 I D E E S†
0382-0831 Westmorland Historical Society. Newsletter
0382-084X Lettres Quebecoises
0382-0912 Town and Country Librarian†
0382-0920 Canada. Statistics Canada. Enrolment in Community Colleges *see* 0832-6657
0382-0939 Canada. Statistics Canada. For-Hire Trucking Survey†
0382-0971 Canada. Statistics Canada. Concrete Products Manufacturers/Fabricants de Produits en Beton†
0382-098X Canada. Statistics Canada. Principal Taxes and Rates: Federal, Provincial and Local Governments *see* 0382-0998
0382-0998 Canada. Statistics Canada. Principal Taxes in Canada†
0382-1005 Computers†
0382-1048 Novia Scotia. Department of Labour and Manpower. Monthly Summary of Activities-Industrial Relations Division†
0382-1102 Current Labour Force Statistics for Nova Scotia†
0382-1161 Canada. Commissioner of Official Languages. Annual Report
0382-1242 Wage Rates, Salaries and Hours of Labour in Nova Scotia†
0382-1315 Education Nova Scotia†
0382-1463 Canada. Law Reform Commission. Annual Report
0382-1587 Canada. Pension Review Board. Reports†
0382-1773 Trends in Collective Agreement Base Rate Changes in Nova Scotia *see* 0227-1362
0382-1838 Saskatchewan Universities Commission. Annual Report
0382-1889 Labour Research Bulletin†
0382-2028 Manitoba Grassland Projects†
0382-2273 C F D C Annual Report *changed to* Telefilm Canada Annual Report.
0382-232X Canada Diseases Weekly Report
0382-2788 Environment Ontario Legacy†
0382-3814 Education Quebec†
0382-4012 Canada. Statistics Canada. Manufacturing Industries of Canada: Sub-Provincial Areas
0382-4020 Canada. Statistics Canada. Manufacturing Industries Division. Potash Mines†
0382-4039 Young Communist *changed to* Rebel Youth.
0382-4047 Young Worker *changed to* Rebel Youth.
0382-408X Teacher (Armdale)
0382-411X Canada. Statistics Canada. Educational Staff in Community Colleges†
0382-4128 Canada. Statistics Canada. Statistical Profiles of Educational Staff in Community Colleges *see* 0382-411X
0382-4306 Anglican Crusader *see* 0382-4314
0382-4314 Crusader (Toronto)
0382-4365 Avec "Lui"
0382-4373 Aim
0382-4438 Athletica†
0382-4500 Arrow†
0382-4527 Action *see* 0847-3390
0382-4535 Swim Signals *see* 0847-3390
0382-4543 Red Cross Youth *see* 0847-3390
0382-4551 Volunteer *see* 0847-3390
0382-456X Advocate (Toronto)
0382-4624 Canadian Living
0382-4756 Banque de Commerce Canadienne Imperiale. Lettre Commerciale†
0382-4764 Canadian Historical Association. Newsletter
0382-4926 Vie Montante. Edition Canadienne
0382-5027 Current Index to Commonwealth Legal Periodicals *see* 0225-9036
0382-5078 Criteria†
0382-5124 Ateliers†
0382-5175 Alberta English Notes†
0382-5205 Urban Reader†
0382-5264 Branching out
0382-5272 British Columbia Monthly
0382-5302 Bulletin - S V P *changed to* Environnement.
0382-5310 Societe pour Vaincre la Pollution. Bulletin de Liaison *changed to* Environnement.
0382-5493 Teaching Mathematics†
0382-5507 B.C.A.M.T. Journal *see* 0382-5493
0382-5566 N B A R N News *changed to* Nursing Info (Fredericton).
0382-5574 Info *changed to* Nursing Info (Fredericton).
0382-5604 Bouscueil†
0382-5655 Blue Bill
0382-5728 Miners' Voice†
0382-5795 Canadian Hackney Stud Book
0382-5868 Long Time Coming†
0382-5876 Canadian Funeral News
0382-5906 Ontario Real Estate Law Guide
0382-5914 Repertoire des Cours d'Ete†
0382-5949 Contact *see* 0410-3882
0382-6031 Canadian Manhood†
0382-6295 Amnesty International (Toronto Group) Newsletter
0382-6333 Canadian Journal of Radiography, Radiation Therapy, Nuclear Medicine *see* 0820-5930
0382-6384 Beacon
0382-6406 Canadian Jersey Herd Record
0382-6414 Jersey Cattle Association of Canada. Record *see* 0382-6406
0382-6627 Owl
0382-6996 Heating, Plumbing, Air Conditioning Buyers' Guide
0382-7038 C L U Comment (English Edition)
0382-7046 Commentaire (Don Mills)
0382-7054 United Cooperatives of Ontario. News *changed to* Co-Op Cornerstone.
0382-7062 United Co-operatives of Ontario. Directors' Newsletter *changed to* Co-Op Communicator.
0382-7070 U C O Leader *changed to* Co-Op Communicator.
0382-7305 Dan Sha News *see* 0833-3831
0382-7437 Canadian Practitioner *see* 0382-7453
0382-7453 Canadian Practitioner and Review
0382-7518 Powell River Progress
0382-7577 Big Country Voice
0382-7658 Canadian Friend
0382-7712 Canadian Mining and Financial News
0382-7798 Communication Information *changed to* Communication.
0382-7879 School Calendar
0382-7887 Calgary Chamber of Commerce. Business News *see* 0707-8064
0382-7976 A C E H I Journal
0382-8115 Canada Crafts†
0382-8255 C O F Newsletter
0382-8352 Backgrounder
0382-8409 Challenge (Winnipeg)
0382-8476 Nurscene
0382-8522 South of Tuk *changed to* Sequel.
0382-8557 Ciao
0382-8565 Brick
0382-8662 Canadian World Federalist
0382-8727 Christian Bus Driver
0382-876X Iconomatrix†
0382-8824 Laomedon Review
0382-8832 Cultural Horizons of the Deaf in Canada†
0382-8980 Deaf Herald†
0382-909X Descant

ISSN

0382-912X Council of Ontario Universities. Research Division. Application Statistics
0382-9251 Abaka
0382-9391 Diocesan Times
0382-9812 Historical Society of Alberta Newsletter *see* 0838-7249
0383-0047 Au Fil du Bois†
0383-008X Canada. Statistics Canada. Fruit and Vegetable Production
0383-0101 Canadian Nurses Association. Library. Periodical Holdings†
0383-0152 Rythme de Notre Eglise *changed to* Actualite Diocesaine.
0383-0187 Guide to Film and Television Courses in Canada *changed to* Guide to Film, Television and Communication Studies in Canada.
0383-0470 Cite Libre *see* 0009-7489
0383-056X Revue de Modification du Comportement *changed to* Science et Comportement.
0383-0640 Stationery & Office Products†
0383-090X Metalworking Production & Purchasing
0383-1280 Canadian Music Library Association. Newsletter *see* 0383-1299
0383-1299 C A M L Newsletter
0383-1310 Catholic Dutch Canadian Association. C D C A Nieuws *see* 0383-1329
0383-1329 Nieuwe Weg (Montreal)
0383-1418 Eastern Light
0383-1620 Catholic Register
0383-1825 Microscopical Society of Canada. Bulletin
0383-2031 Waters
0383-2058 Western Livestock & Agricultural News *changed to* Western Beef Producers News.
0383-2244 Farm Trends†
0383-2368 Guide Camping *see* 0705-8314
0383-2406 Canadian Campus Career Directory†
0383-2430 Building Supply Dealers Association. Survey *see* 0829-559X
0383-2538 Ievanhel's'kyi Holos
0383-2554 Aujourd'hui Credo
0383-2759 International Migration Newsletter *see* 0383-2767
0383-2767 International Newsletter on Migration
0383-283X Squatchberry Journal†
0383-2848 Carleton University, Ottawa. Norman Paterson School of International Affairs. Bibliography Series
0383-2945 Industrials *see* 0830-1972
0383-2953 Canadian Weekly Stock Charts: Mines and Oils *see* 0829-3139
0383-2961 Nouvelle Revue Canadienne *see* 0547-0749
0383-3003 Living Places†
0383-3372 Labour Legislation in Nova Scotia
0383-3402 Electricity Today†
0383-3437 Labour Organizations in Nova Scotia
0383-3585 Rural Real Estate Values in Alberta *see* 0701-7502
0383-3712 Alberta. Legislature Library. Annual Report†
0383-3739 Alberta. Department of the Environment. Annual Report
0383-3925 Manitoba. Health Services Commission. Annual Report†
0383-3933 Manitoba. Health Services Commission. Statistical Supplement to the Annual Report *changed to* Manitoba. Health Services Commission. Annual Statistics.
0383-414X Canada. National Farm Products Marketing Council. Annual Report
0383-4301 Ecumenism
0383-4352 Saskatchewan Trading Corporation. Annual Report
0383-4379 Canada. Correctional Investigator. Annual Report
0383-4417 Grain Matters
0383-4514 Documents in the History of Canadian Art†
0383-4638 Canada. Department of National Defence. Defence (Year)
0383-4654 Cooperation Canada†
0383-4778 Ontario. Labour Relations Board. Reports. A Monthly Series of Decisions
0383-5154 Canada. Department of Industry, Trade and Commerce. Annual Report.†
0383-5391 Masterpieces in the National Gallery of Canada
0383-5405 Canadian Artists Series
0383-5472 Water Quality Data for Ontario Streams & Lakes
0383-5588 Manitoba. Human Rights Commission. Annual Report
0383-5766 Canada. Statistics Canada. Passenger Bus and Urban Transit Statistics
0383-6061 Intercom
0383-6096 Manitoba Educational Research Council. Newsletter *changed to* Manitoba Educational Research Council. Research Bulletin.
0383-6207 Dairy Contact
0383-6266 Artswest
0383-6304 Importfile
0383-6312 Smallholder
0383-6320 Sante Mentale au Quebec
0383-6347 S O S Press *see* 0705-1212
0383-6355 A D A News Information *changed to* A D A Newsletter.
0383-641X Comeback†
0383-6436 Countdown
0383-6479 Ontario Conservation News
0383-6509 Caledonia Diocesan Times
0383-6576 Canadian Oral History Association. Bulletin†
0383-6649 Canadian Appraiser
0383-669X Revue du Barreau
0383-6894 Canadian Oral History Association. Journal
0383-6908 Sound Canada *changed to* Sound & Vision.
0383-7114 Country Guide
0383-7300 Gift Magazine†
0383-7521 Derives†
0383-7645 Presbyterian Comment *changed to* Channels.
0383-7653 Prairie Harvester
0383-770X Canadian Book Review Annual
0383-7920 Canadian Rental Service
0383-7939 Bluenose Magazine *changed to* Earth & Tide.
0383-8277 Prions en Eglise - Edition Dominicale
0383-8358 Directory of Law Teachers
0383-8447 Ecole de Medecine Veterinaire, Saint-Hyacinthe, Quebec. Annuaire *see* 0383-8455
0383-8455 Universite de Montreal. Faculte de Medecine Veterinaire. Annuaire
0383-8528 Dialect
0383-8536 Nuclear Canada. Yearbook
0383-8544 Shepherd†
0383-8714 L'Actualite
0383-9133 Lillooet District Historical Society. Bulletin†
0383-9168 Pitch-In News
0383-9184 Metric Fact Sheets
0383-9230 Ontario Credit Union News†
0383-9249 Bruce Trail News
0383-9257 Landscape Ontario†
0383-9338 Broadcast Equipment Today *see* 0709-9797
0383-9494 Criminal Reports (4th Series)
0383-9567 Nova Scotia Bird Society. Newsletter *changed to* Nova Scotia Birds.
0383-9737 Commerce Journal†
0383-9745 Southam Business†
0383-9931 O S C A Reports
0384-0158 S H S B. Bulletin
0384-0174 Critere†
0384-0298 Le Colombien
0384-0417 Parapet
0384-0425 Simgames†
0384-0433 Contemporary Poetry of British Columbia†
0384-0581 B C Business
0384-059X McGill University, Montreal. Centre for Developing-Area Studies. Working Papers *see* 0821-6452
0384-0697 Reflections (North Battleford)
0384-0816 Mon Bebe
0384-093X Marsh and Maple
0384-0999 Canadian Yachting
0384-1014 Norman Mackenzie Art Gallery. Newsletter *see* 0712-9238
0384-1022 N M A G Review *see* 0712-9238
0384-1103 Annual Canadian-American Seminar. Proceedings†
0384-1367 North-South Canadian Journal of Latin American Studies *see* 0826-3663
0384-1405 Todays Generation *see* 0843-4557
0384-1642 Newspacket
0384-1677 Canadian Power Engineer†
0384-1820 Canadian Medical and Biological Engineering Society. Newsletter
0384-1839 Canadian Review of Art Education Research *changed to* Canadian Review of Art Education Research and Issues.
0384-1898 Newfoundland and Labrador Engineer†
0384-191X Calgary Archaeologist†
0384-2126 Discussion†
0384-2282 Noticiario de Canada†
0384-2304 Hebdo Canada *changed to* Reportage Canada.
0384-2312 Canada Weekly *changed to* Canada Reports.
0384-2355 Who's Who: A Guide to Federal and Provincial Departments and Agencies, Their Funding Programs and the People Who Head Them *see* 0832-865X
0384-2843 Canada. Statistics Canada. Cane and Beet Sugar Processors *see* 0835-0000
0384-2967 Canada. Statistics Canada. Foundation Garment Industry†
0384-3300 Canada. Statistics Canada. Leather Glove Factories†
0384-3343 Canada. Statistics Canada. Knitting Mills - Bonneterie†
0384-3912 Canada. Statistics Canada. Manufacturers of Soap and Cleaning Compounds†
0384-4080 Canada. Statistics Canada. Office Furniture Manufacturers†
0384-4161 Canada. Statistics Canada. Electric Lamp and Shade Manufacturers†
0384-4242 Scientific and Professional Equipment Industries *see* 0835-0191
0384-4498 Women's and Children's Clothing Industries *see* 0835-006X
0384-4633 Paper and Allied Products Industries *see* 0835-0094
0384-465X Canada. Statistics Canada. Corrugated Box Manufacturers/Fabricants de Boites en Carton Ondule†
0384-4811 Canada. Statistics Canada. Miscellaneous Leather Products Manufacturers†
0384-4935 Canada. Statistics Canada. Smelting and Refining *see* 0835-0116
0384-4951 Canada. Statistics Canada. Slaughtering and Meat Processors†
0384-5060 Computers and Medieval Data Processing†
0384-5087 Conference Catholique Canadienne. Bulletin National de Liturgie *changed to* Liturgie, Foi et Culture.
0384-5133 Musique Liturgique†
0384-5184 Canadian Children's Magazine†
0384-532X Prairie Overcomer†
0384-5753 Canadian Bar Association. British Columbia Branch. Program Report
0384-5958 Foresight
0384-661X Communicate (Beaverlodge)†
0384-6628 Focus on Winnipeg Schools *see* 0384-6636
0384-6636 Our Schools
0384-6903 Canadian Directory of Railway Museums and Displays†
0384-6970 Rapports de Pratique de Quebec *changed to* Revue de Droit Judiciaire.
0384-7322 Fraser's Potato Newsletter
0384-7411 University of Ottawa. Vanier Library. List of Serials†
0384-7446 Livre Canadien *changed to* Nos Livres.
0384-756X O V C Bulletin *see* 0384-7578
0384-7578 Ontario Veterinary College. Alumni Association. Alumni Bulletin†
0384-7802 Blue Book of C B S Stock Reports *changed to* Blue Book of Stock Reports.
0384-7810 Plein Soleil
0384-8116 Dalhousie University. Computer Centre. Newsletter *see* 0829-5425
0384-8159 Royal Ontario Museum. Life Sciences. Contributions
0384-8167 Revista Canadiense de Estudios Hispanicos
0384-8175 Island Magazine
0384-8523 Alchemist
0384-868X Versus
0384-8701 Contact C I L *changed to* I C I Spectrum.
0384-8744 Canadian Journal of Public and Cooperative Economy
0384-8833 Essence†
0384-9120 Regards sur Israel
0384-9147 New Directions
0384-9252 Canada Report†
0384-9627 Ontario Museum News *changed to* Currently: Ontario Museum News.
0384-9694 Journal of Religious Ethics
0384-9813 Publicat Index to Canadian Federal Publications *see* 0839-1289
0384-9821 Urban Canada *see* 0839-1289
0384-983X Canadian Newspaper Index *see* 0225-7459
0384-9856 Camping Canada
0384-9864 Congressus Numerantium
0385-0005 Tokai Journal of Experimental and Clinical Medicine
0385-0145 Nihon University. Journal of Oral Science
0385-0188 Senmon Toshokan
0385-0234 Kawasaki Medical Journal
0385-0285 Okinawa-kenritsu Hakubutsukan Kiyo
0385-0307 Shinshin-Igaku
0385-0447 Journal of Asia Electronics Union
0385-0749 Jeiwa Kenkyu
0385-0994 Ryuseijin Kaiho
0385-1036 Maku
0385-1109 Shima Marineland. Science Report
0385-1176 J A F S A Library News *see* 0286-7427
0385-1311 Iwate Medical University. Dental Journal
0385-1354 Akita-kenritsu Hakubutsukan Kenkyu Hokoku
0385-1362 Hokkaido Wakkanai Fisheries Experimental Station. Collected Reprints†
0385-1443 Kanagawa Dental College. Bulletin
0385-1478 Joho Kodo Kagaku Kenkyu
0385-1516 Dojin Nyusu
0385-1559 Journal of Pesticide Science
0385-1613 Matsumoto Shigaku
0385-1621 Japanese Society of Soil Mechanics and Foundation Engineering. Journal
0385-1699 Nikkei Medical
0385-1982 Shinshu University. School of Allied Medical Sciences. Treatises and Studies
0385-1990 Japan. National Institute for Educational Research. Newsletter
0385-2156 Jin to Toseki
0385-230X Kokusai Koryu
0385-2318 Japan Foundation Newsletter
0385-2342 Asian Folklore Studies
0385-2350 D K B Economic Report
0385-2377 Byoin
0385-2393 Rinsho Hinyokika
0385-2415 Utsunomiya Daigaku Kyoikugakubu Kiyo. Dai-2-bu
0385-2423 National Science Museum. Bulletin. Series A: Zoology
0385-2431 National Science Museum. Bulletin. Series B: Botany
0385-244X National Science Museum. Bulletin. Series C: Geology & Paleontology

ISSN

0385-2520 Rock Magnetism and Paleogeophysics
0385-2571 Japan Society for Composite Materials. Transactions
0385-2687 Kaiyo Jiho
0385-2776 Okayama Rika Daigaku. Hiruzen Kenkyujo Kenkyu Hokoku
0385-2792 Shoni no Hoken
0385-2946 Yamaguchi Joshi Daigaku Kenkyu Hokoku. Dai-2-bu. Shizen Kagaku
0385-3039 National Science Museum. Bulletin. Series D: Anthropology
0385-325X Kokuritsu Kokkai Toshokan Nenpo
0385-3284 Japanese National Bibliography†
0385-3292 Japanese National Bibliography Weekly List
0385-3306 Kokutritsu Kokkai Toshokan. Sanko Shosi Kenkyu
0385-3330 Monthly List of Selected Atomic Energy Publications *see* 0454-1944
0385-3780 Hydraulics and Pneumatics
0385-3985 Sennke
0385-4000 Library Journal
0385-4019 Kagoshima Daigaku Rigakubu Kiyo. Chigaku, Seibutsugaku
0385-4027 Kagoshima Daigaku Rigakubu Kiyo. Sugaku, Butsurigaku, Kagaku
0385-4035 Hokkaido Mathematical Journal
0385-406X Tohoku Gakuin University Review
0385-4132 Iwate Medical University School of Liberal Arts & Sciences. Annual Report
0385-4418 J E O L News: Analytical Instrumentation
0385-4426 J E O L News: Electron Optics Instrumentation
0385-4507 Journal of Electronic Engineering
0385-4515 Journal of the Electronics Industry
0385-5023 Dokkyo Journal of Medical Sciences
0385-5082 Hogaku
0385-5236 Japan Journal of Educational Technology
0385-5414 Heterocycles
0385-5481 Kodo Keiryogaku
0385-549X Kango Tenbo
0385-5600 Microbiology and Immunology
0385-5694 Geijutsu Shunju
0385-5988 Kango Gakusei
0385-6003 Current Bibliography on Science and Technology: Chemistry and Chemical Engineering (Japanese)
0385-6011 Current Bibliography on Science and Technology: Environmental Pollution
0385-6151 Hakkokogaku
0385-6186 Saga Daigaku Rikogakubu Shuho
0385-6305 Shoni Naika
0385-6321 Soka Gakkai News
0385-6380 Journal of Fermentation Technology *see* 0922-338X
0385-6402 Asian Culture *changed to* Asian Pacific Culture.
0385-6437 J A E R I Reports Abstracts
0385-6542 New Technology Japan
0385-6658 Computer Report
0385-6747 Contents
0385-6763 Kumamoto Journal of Science. Mathematics *see* 0914-675X
0385-6984 Bit
0385-7042 Chosa Shiryo
0385-7298 Jidosha Gijutsu
0385-7301 Boei Daigakko Rikogaku Kenkyu Hokoku
0385-7360 Diamond Industria
0385-7417 Behaviormetrika
0385-7433 Gocho
0385-7530 Japan Indexers Association. Journal
0385-759X Shizen Kyoikuen Hokoku
0385-7638 Hyogo Ika Daigaku Igakkai Zasshi
0385-7832 Research Laboratory of Precision Machinery and Electronics. Bulletin *changed to* Precision and Intelligence.
0385-812X Toyama Daigaku Kyoyobu Kiyo. Shizen Kagaku Hen
0385-8278 Kyushu University. Department of Earth and Planetary Sciences. Science Reports
0385-8472 Yokosuka-shi Hakubutsukanpo
0385-8545 Chishitsugaku Ronshu
0385-8634 Niigata Daigaku Nogakubu Kenkyu Hokoku
0385-8766 Yamanashi Daigaku Kyoikugakubu Kenkyu Hokoku. Dai-2-bunsatsu, Shizen Kagakukei
0385-8863 A.I.P.P.I. Japanese Group. Journal (International Edition)
0385-8960 Summer Institute in Linguistics. Studies in Descriptive and Applied Linguistics *changed to* International Christian University. Language Research Bulletin.
0385-9215 Japan Medical Journal
0385-9282 Japan Welding Society. Transactions
0385-9681 Jinko Dotai Tokei Maigetsu Gaisu *see* 0385-969X
0385-969X Japan. Ministry of Health and Welfare. Statistics and Information Department. Monthly Report on Vital Statistics
0385-9746 Research Journal of Educational Methods
0385-9932 Japanese Journal of Animal Reproduction *changed to* Journal of Reproduction and Development.
0386-037X Process: Architecture
0386-0655 Kitakami-shiritsu Hakubutsukan Kenkyu
0386-0744 National Institute of Polar Research. Memoirs. Special Issue.
0386-0752 Kyoto University. Institute of Atomic Energy. Research Activities
0386-0760 Gunma Reports on Medical Sciences
0386-0779 International Latitude Observatory of Mizusawa. Publications†
0386-1058 Shinrigaku Hyoron
0386-1104 I A T S S Research
0386-1163 Ikutoku Kogyo Daigaku Kenkyu Hokoku. B Rikogaku Hen
0386-118X Fukuoka Daigaku Rigaku Shuho
0386-1198 Institute for Sea Training. Journal
0386-1430 Atomu Fukushima
0386-1465 Furusato Tenbo†
0386-183X Kagaku Saron
0386-2062 Pharmaceutical Library Bulletin
0386-2143 Kagaku Shoho
0386-2186 Kobunshi Ronbunshu
0386-2194 Japan Academy. Proceedings. Series A: Mathematical Sciences
0386-2208 Japan Academy. Proceedings. Series B: Physical and Biological Sciences
0386-2240 Suri Kagaku
0386-2321 Gendai Ringyo
0386-233X Speleological Society of Japan. Journal
0386-2372 Japan Meat Processing Journal
0386-250X Vegetable and Ornamental Crops Research Station. Bulletin. Series B
0386-2755 Shiso
0386-2828 Purometeusu
0386-300X Acta Medica Okayama
0386-3042 J C A Journal
0386-3425 Snake
0386-3980 Japanese Journal of Leprosy
0386-4006 Tokyo Joshi Daigaku Kiyo. Ronshu. Kagaku Bumon Hokoku
0386-4103 Osaka City Medical Journal
0386-4138 Shizen Hogo
0386-4251 Young East
0386-426X Tohokai
0386-4286 Yokosuka-shi Hakubutsukan Shiryoshu
0386-4294 Gunma University. Faculty of Education. Annual Report: Cultural Science Series
0386-4324 Saiensu *issued with* 0285-1008
0386-4324 Saiensu
0386-443X Nagasaki Daigaku Kyoikugakubu Shizen Kagaku Kenkyu Hokoku
0386-4464 Hokkaido Kyoiku Daigaku Taisetsuzan Shizen Kyoiku Kenkyu Shisetsu Kenkyu Hokoku
0386-4472 Hokkaido Kyoiku Daigaku Kiyo. Dai-1-Bu, A. Jinbun Hen
0386-4480 Hokkaido Kyoiku Daigaku Kiyo. Dai-1-Bu, B. Shakai Kagaku Hen
0386-4499 Hokkaido Kyoiku Daigaku Kiyo. Dai-1-Bu, C. Kyoikugaku Hen
0386-4553 Kagaku Kyoiku Kenkyu
0386-4901 Hokkaido Kyoiku Daigaku Kiyo. Dai-2-Bu, C. Katei, Taiiku- Hen
0386-4928 Kinki Daigaku Rikogakubu Kenkyu Hokoku
0386-4944 Meiji Daigaku Kagaku Gijutsu Kenkyujo Kiyo
0386-4952 Meijo Daigaku Rikogakubu Kenkyu Hokoku
0386-4960 Sugaku Semina
0386-4987 Osaka Denki Tsushin Daigaku Kenkyu Ronshu. Shizen Kagaku Hen
0386-5037 Enshu no Shizen
0386-5096 Mitsubishi Electric Advance
0386-5126 Japan. Ministry of Agriculture, Forestry and Fisheries. National Research Institute of Agricultural Engineering. Abstracts from Research Reports
0386-5444 Solar Terrestrial Environmental Research in Japan
0386-5452 Japanese Antarctic Research Expedition, 1956-1962. Scientific Reports. Special Issue *see* 0386-0744
0386-5517 National Institute of Polar Research. Memoirs. Series A: Aeronomy.
0386-5525 National Institute of Polar Research. Memoirs. Series B: Meteorology.
0386-5533 National Institute of Polar Research. Memoirs. Series C: Earth Sciences.
0386-5541 National Institute of Polar Research. Memoirs. Series E: Biology and Medical Science
0386-555X National Institute of Polar Research. Memoirs. Series F: Logistics.
0386-5827 Senshu Shizen Kagaku Kiyo
0386-5924 Kawasaki Igakkai Shi
0386-5959 Shimane Journal of Medical Science
0386-5991 Kodai Mathematical Journal
0386-6076 Dentsu Japan Marketing - Advertising Yearbook
0386-6092 Acta Medica Kinki University
0386-6157 Society of Powder Technology, Japan. Journal.
0386-6165 Japan Petroleum Weekly *see* 0916-2623
0386-6262 Fukui-kenritsu Tanki Daigaku Kenkyu Kiyo
0386-6297 Price Indexes Monthly
0386-6319 Basic Sugaku
0386-6688 Pollen Science
0386-6890 Takayama Tanki Daigaku Kenkyu Kiyo
0386-7196 Cell Structure and Function
0386-720X Nanzan Institute for Religion and Culture. Bulletin
0386-7285 Far Seas Fisheries Research Laboratory. Bulletin *changed to* National Research Institute of Far Seas Fisheries. Bulletin.
0386-7293 Current Contents of Academic Journals in Japan
0386-7587 Toyo's Technical Bulletin
0386-7668 Ibaraki Daigaku Kyoikugakubu Kiyo. Shizen Kagaku
0386-8044 Infrared Society of Japan. Proceeding
0386-8141 Seitai Kagaku†
0386-8176 Ogasawara Kenkyu
0386-832X Toyama University. Mathematics Reports *see* 0916-6009
0386-8362 Sekai no Chikusan
0386-8419 Bulletin of Beef Cattle Science
0386-8435 Research and Clinical Center for Child Development. Annual Report
0386-846X Journal of Pharmacobio-Dynamics
0386-8710 Tokyo Metropolitan University. Department of Geography. Geographical Reports
0386-8761 Institute of Noise Control Engineering. Journal
0386-9555 Sugakushi Kenkyu
0386-9571 Byoin Kanri
0386-9733 Recent Advances in Reticulo Endothelial System Research†
0386-9822 Sogo Rehabilitation
0386-9849 Rigaku Ryoho to Sagyo Ryoho - Japanese Journal of Physical Therapy and Occupational Therapy *changed to* Rigaku Ryoho Janaru.
0386-9865 Rinsho Fujinka Sanka
0386-9903 Nihon Bungaku
0386-9962 Administrative Management
0387-0154 Atsuryoku Gijutsu
0387-0642 Short-Term Economic Survey of Enterprises in Japan
0387-0766 Micro Computer & Electronics†
0387-0855 Fukushima Daigaku Kyoikugakubu Ronshu. Rika Hokoku
0387-0995 Kanazawa Daigaku Kyoikugakubu Kiyo. Shizen Kagaku Hen
0387-1045 Machine Design
0387-1061 Konkuriito Kogaku
0387-1207 Gastroenterological Endoscopy
0387-172X Tohoku Nogyo Shikenjo Kenkyu Shiryo
0387-1819 Sho Enerugi
0387-2432 Mitsubishi Juko Giho
0387-2440 Gakujutsu Geppo
0387-2572 Neurologia Medico-Chirurgica
0387-2645 Gastroenterological Surgery
0387-2785 Asahi Ajia Rebyu†
0387-2793 Jinko Mondai Kenkyu
0387-2815 American Review
0387-2831 Doitsu Bungaku
0387-2882 Journal of Law and Politics
0387-3005 Katorikku Kenkyu
0387-3021 Doshisha University Economic Review
0387-3234 Nogyo Keizai Kenkyu
0387-3242 Nogyo Sogo Kenkyu
0387-3404 Waseda Shogaku
0387-3447 National Institute of Japanese Literature. Bulletin
0387-3501 Japanese Journal of Primary Care *see* 0914-8426
0387-351X Kangogaku Zasshi
0387-3528 National Institute of Special Education. Bulletin
0387-3544 Press Working
0387-382X Japan Marine Science and Technology Center. Technical Reports
0387-3870 Tokyo Journal of Mathematics
0387-3927 J P G Letter
0387-3935 Japan English Magazine Directory *see* 0910-7908
0387-4001 Current Bibliography on Science and Technology: Energy
0387-4087 Yamaguchi Daigaku Kyoyobu Kiyo. Shizen Kagaku Hen
0387-4095 Orthopaedic and Traumatic Surgery
0387-4141 Research Committee of Essential Amino Acids. Reports
0387-446X Osaka Daigaku Iryo Gijutsu Tanki Daigakubu Kenkyu Kiyo. Shizen Kagaku Iryo Kagaku Hen
0387-4532 Nagoya Daigaku Kyoyobu Kiyo B. Shizen Kagaku, Shinrigaku
0387-4745 Pacific Society. Journal
0387-4753 Seijo University Economic Papers
0387-480X Osaka University. Faculty of Pharmaceutical Sciences. Memoirs
0387-4982 Tsukuba Journal of Mathematics
0387-5040 Foreign Press Center Japan. Press Guide
0387-5245 Office Equipment and Products
0387-5512 Zugaku Kenkyu
0387-5806 Information Processing Society of Japan. Transactions
0387-5857 Standard Frequency and Time Service Bulletin
0387-5970 Dharma World
0387-6101 Journal of Information Processing
0387-6837 Rikkyo Daigaku Kenkyu Hokoku. Shizen Kagaku
0387-7000 Zasshi Shinbun Sokatarogu
0387-7019 Gekkan Media Data
0387-7434 Educational Technology Research
0387-7604 Brain and Development
0387-7647 Hiroshima Daigaku Seibutsu Seisan Gakubu Kiyo
0387-821X University of Occupational and Environmental Health. Journal

5732 ISSN INDEX

0387-8503 Japanese Periodicals Index. Medical Sciences and Pharmacology†
0387-8511 National Science Museum. Bulletin. Series E: Physical Sciences and Engineering
0387-8716 Shiretoko Hakubutsukan Kenkyu Hokoku
0387-8805 Journal of Light & Visual Environment
0387-8961 Plankton Society of Japan. Bulletin
0387-9089 Toyama-shi Kagaku Bunka Senta Kenkyu Hokoku
0387-9097 Shimane Ika Daigaku Kiyo
0387-9119 Rinboku no Ikushu
0387-9313 Saitama Daigaku Kiyo. Kyoikugakubu. Sugaku, Shizen Kagaku
0387-9348 Heron
0387-9569 Interface
0387-964X Kitakyushu-shiritsu Shizenshi Hakubutsukan Kenkyu Hokoku
0387-9844 Ogasawara Kenkyu Nenpo
0387-9925 Shimane Daigaku Rigakubu Kiyo
0388-0001 Language Sciences
0388-001X Rakuno Gakuen Daigaku Kiyo. Shizen Kagaku Hen
0388-0028 Rakuno Gakuen Daigaku Kiyo. Jinbun Shakai Kagaku Hen
0388-0117 Sado Marine Biological Station. Annual Report *see* 0289-6389
0388-0230 Kyoto University. Department of Astronomy. Contributions
0388-0311 Focus Japan
0388-0494 Japan Computer Quarterly
0388-0508 Journal of Intercultural Studies
0388-0532 Kyoto Review†
0388-0605 Monthly Finance Review
0388-0648 National Theatre of Japan
0388-0664 Nippon Tungsten Review
0388-080X Japan. Electro Technical Laboratory. Summaries of Reports
0388-0966 Tokyo University of Fisheries. Transactions
0388-1032 Wing Newsletter
0388-130X Meisei Daigaku Kenkyu Kiyo. Rikogakubu
0388-1423 A M J Newsletter†
0388-1717 Kyushu Daigaku Daigakuin Sogo Rikogaku Kenkyuka Hokoku
0388-1865 World Traders
0388-1989 Tokyo Denki University. Faculty of Science and Engineering. Research Activities
0388-2306 Ham Journal
0388-2349 Kyoto University. Kwasan and Hida Observatories. Contributions
0388-2403 Japan. National Institute of Animal Health. Bulletin
0388-3213 Japan. National Chemical Laboratory for Industry. Journal
0388-3515 Seikei Kisho Kansokujo Hokoku
0388-4112 National Defense Academy. Memoirs. Mathematics, Physics, Chemistry, and Engineering
0388-4201 Japan English Books in Print *see* 0910-7908
0388-4449 Iwate Horticulture Experiment Station. Bulletin
0388-4732 Hakusan
0388-4953 Sprout
0388-5259 Denryoku Shinpo *see* 0388-5267
0388-5267 Energy Forum
0388-550X Gifu-ken Hakubutsukan Chosa Kenkyu Hokoku
0388-5585 Kurinikaru Sutadi
0388-5593 Asian Book Development *changed to* Asian - Pacific Book Development.
0388-5607 Tohoku University. Science Reports. Series 8: Physics and Astronomy
0388-600X N K K News
0388-631X Okayama Prefectural Dairy Experiment Station. Bulletin
0388-7081 Patents and Licensing
0388-7367 Aichi Kyoiku Daigaku Kenkyu Hokoku. Geijutsu, Hoken Taiiku, Kasei, Gijutsu Kagaku
0388-7405 Japan Institute of Navigation. Journal
0388-7421 Japan. Ministry of Agriculture, Forestry and Fisheries. National Veterinary Assay Laboratory. Annual Report
0388-7448 Neurosciences
0388-7480 Kyoiku Ongaku, Shogaku-ban
0388-7502 Kyoiku Ongaku, Chugaku Koko-ban
0388-788X Gyobyo Kenkyu
0388-8738 Yoshida Kagaku Gijutsu Zaidan Nyusu
0388-886X Kansai University Review of Law and Politics
0388-9009 Kanagawa Shizenshi Shiryo
0388-9386 Tropical Agriculture Research Series
0388-9459 Kankyo Gijutsu
0388-9475 Kawasaki Steel Technical Report
0389-0244 Kochi Daigaku Gakujutsu Kenkyu Hokoku. Shizen Kagaku
0389-0252 Kochi University. Faculty of Science. Memoirs. Series A, Mathematics
0389-0341 Hoshi no Tomo
0389-0449 Kochi Daigaku Kyoikugakubu Kenkyu Hokoku. Dai-3-Bu
0389-0473 Kochi University. Agricultural Science. Research Reports
0389-0503 Economic Eye
0389-0988 Gurin Pawa
0389-1186 Japanese Slavic & East European Studies
0389-1313 Nihon Seikisho Gakkai Zasshi
0389-1836 Azabu Daigaku Juigakubu Kenkyu Hokoku†
0389-1887 Rinsho Kensagaku Zasshi
0389-1895 Shika Giko
0389-2131 Hoshi no Techo
0389-2166 Shinrin Bunka Kenkyu
0389-3057 Kagawa Daigaku Kyoikugakubu Kenkyu Hokoku. Dai-2-Bu
0389-3081 Tokai Daigaku Kiyo. Gaikokugo Kyoiku Senta
0389-3502 Japan: An International Comparison
0389-3510 Speaking of Japan†
0389-3944 Sapporo Ika Daigaku Jinbun Shizen Kagaku Kiyo
0389-4029 Bungaku
0389-4088 Kochi Gakuen College. Bulletin
0389-4304 J S A E Review
0389-5025 Suzugamine Joshi Tandai Kenkyu Shuho. Shizen Kagaku
0389-5483 Japanese Society of Lubrication Engineers. Journal. International Edition *changed to* Tribologist. International Edition.
0389-5491 Hiba Kagaku
0389-5602 Nihon Tokei Gakkaishi
0389-5610 Shinkei Gaisho
0389-5696 Medical Apparatus *see* 0289-3673
0389-584X Kobe Women's University. Faculty of Home Economics. Bulletin
0389-5858 National Research Institute of Aquaculture. Bulletin
0389-617X Tokyo Denki University. Faculty of Engineering. Research Reports
0389-6609 Seto Marine Biological Laboratory. Special Publication Series
0389-6692 Kagoshima Daigaku Kyoikugakubu Kenkyu Kiyo. Shizen Kagaku Hen
0389-6927 Gifu Prefectural Fisheries Experimental Station. Report
0389-6951 Watashitachi no Shizenshi
0389-729X Bunkazai no Chu-kin-gai
0389-7389 Abstracts of the Current Literature on Respiratory Diseases and T B†
0389-7605 Hokkyokusei Hoikakuhyo
0389-8105 Osaka-shiritsu Shizenshi Hakubutsukan Kanpo
0389-8237 Ionospheric Data at Showa Station (Antarctica)
0389-8326 Japanese Journal of Nursing
0389-9004 Japan Statistical Yearbook
0389-9047 Osaka-shiritsu Shizenshi Hakubutsukan Shuzo Shiryo Mokuroku
0389-9128 Shiga Shizen Kyoiku Kenkyu Shisetsu Kenkyu Gyoseki
0389-9136 Research Institute of Brewing. Report
0389-9225 Mie Daigaku Kyoikugakubu Kenkyu Kiyo. Shizen Kagaku
0389-9403 Shokaki Naishikyo no Shinpo
0389-9578 Kobe Tokiwa Tanki Daigaku Kiyo
0390-0010 Istituto Sperimentale per la Selvicoltura. Annali
0390-0037 Chronobiologia
0390-0134 Giornale Italiano di Ortopedia e Traumatologia
0390-0355 Terzo Occhio
0390-0444 Colture Protette
0390-0460 Micologia Italiana
0390-0479 VigneVini
0390-0487 Zootecnica e Nutrizione Animale
0390-0517 Oncologia Clinica†
0390-0541 Industrie delle Bevande
0390-0614 Universita degli Studi di Lecce. Bollettino di Storia della Filosofia
0390-0711 Medioevo Romanzo
0390-0916 Archivio Trimestrale
0390-0991 Lavoro e Sindacato
0390-1009 Archivio Storico Civico e Biblioteca Trivulziana. Libri & Documenti
0390-1068 Quaderni di Storia
0390-1106 Giornale di Astronomia
0390-1246 Ambiente Naturale e Urbano *changed to* Pro Natura Genova.
0390-1807 Cronorama
0390-1815 C S E L T Rapporti Tecnici *see* 0393-2648
0390-2153 Forme del Significato†
0390-217X Il Futuro dell'Uomo
0390-2358 I C P
0390-2420 Infanzia
0390-2439 Informatica & Documentazione
0390-346X Psicologia Contemporanea
0390-4555 Tuscia
0390-492X Memorie di Biologia Marina e di Oceanografia
0390-5179 Saggi
0390-5195 Problemi dell'Informazione
0390-5349 Giornale Italiano di Psicologia
0390-5381 Rivista degli Ospedali†
0390-5403 Cardiostimolazione
0390-5454 Annali dell'Ospedale Maria Vittoria di Torino
0390-5462 Giornale di Batteriologia, Virologia ed Immunologia
0390-5489 Italian Journal of Orthopaedics and Traumatology
0390-5527 Attualita in Chirurgia
0390-5551 Societa Italiana di Fisica. Nuovo Cimento C
0390-5748 Ricerca in Clinica e in Laboratorio *changed to* Research in Clinic and Laboratory.
0390-6035 Materials Chemistry *see* 0254-0584
0390-6078 Haematologica
0390-640X Compendio Statistico *see* 0069-7958
0390-6426 Italy. Istituto Centrale di Statistica. Annuario Statistico della Zootecnia, della Pesca e della Caccia *changed to* Italy. Istituto Centrale di Statistica. Statistiche della Zootecnia, della Pesca e della Caccia.
0390-6450 Italy. Istituto Centrale di Statistica. Annuario di Statistiche del Lavoro *changed to* Italy. Istituto Centrale di Statistica. Statistiche del Lavoro.
0390-6531 Annuario di Contabilita Nazionale Tomo 2
0390-654X Annuario di Contabilita Nazionale Tomo 1
0390-6558 Italy. Istituto Centrale di Statistica. Statistica Annuale del Commercio con l'Estero. Tomo 1
0390-6566 Italy. Istituto Centrale di Statistica. Statistica Annuale del Commercio con l'Estero. Parte 1-6 Tomo 2
0390-6574 Conti degli Italiani
0390-6582 Annuario Statistico dell'Istruzione - Tomo 1
0390-6590 Annuario Statistico dell'Istruzione - Tomo 2
0390-6620 Italy. Istituto Centrale di Statistica. Indicatori Mensili
0390-6663 Clinical and Experimental Obstetrics and Gynecology
0390-668X Rivista di Informatica
0390-6698 Tecnologie Elettriche
0390-6736 Montanaro d'Italia - Monti e Boschi *changed to* Monti e Boschi.
0390-6779 Cooperation in Education†
0390-6809 Studi Italiani di Linguistica Teorica ed Applicata
0390-6841 Quintessenza
0390-7139 Quaderni di Anatomia Pratica
0390-7368 Archivio di Ortopedia e Reumatologia
0390-7740 Rays
0390-7783 Accademia delle Scienze di Siena Detta de Fisiocritici. Atti
0390-8240 Archivio per la Storia del Movimento Sociale Cattolico in Italia. Bollettino
0390-8283 Societa Medico Chirurgica de Pavia. Bollettino
0390-8542 Diritto e Societa (Naples)
0391-108X Rocca
0391-1470 Vita Ospedaliera
0391-1527 Cronache Pompeiane
0391-1535 Cronache Ercolanesi
0391-1551 Rivista di Biologia Normale e Patologica
0391-1586 Industria Mineraria
0391-1632 Monitore Zoologico Italiano. Monografie†
0391-1683 Tecnologie Meccaniche
0391-1918 Guida di Veterinaria e Zootecnia
0391-1926 Contributi di Sociologia†
0391-1934 Capitalismo e Socialismo†
0391-1942 Strumenti Linguistici
0391-1950 Romanica Neapolitana
0391-1977 Minerva Endocrinologica
0391-1993 Minerva Dietologica e Gastroenterologica
0391-2000 Mondo Ortodontico
0391-2019 H P Trasporti
0391-2035 Clinica e Laboratorio
0391-2043 Medicina Illustrata†
0391-2221 Rivista Italiana di Chirurgia Plastica
0391-2515 Giornale Storico di Psicologia Dinamica
0391-2639 Otto-Novecento
0391-2655 Problemi di Amministrazione Pubblica
0391-2825 Rivista di Medicina del Lavoro ed Igiene Industriale
0391-3104 Quaderni del Vittoriale
0391-3163 Anthropos
0391-3171 Contributi di Sociologia. Readings†
0391-3198 Inconscio e Cultura
0391-321X Istituzioni Culturali†
0391-3228 Le Lingue e le Civilta Straniere Moderne
0391-3236 Quaderni di Analisi Matematica†
0391-3244 Scienze della Materia†
0391-3252 Serie di Matematica e Fisica *changed to* Serie di Matematica e Fisica. Testi.
0391-3260 Societa e Diritto di Roma†
0391-3279 Collana di Storia Moderna e Contemporanea
0391-3295 Teorie Economiche†
0391-3457 Dossier Europa - Emigrazione
0391-3627 Minerva Angiologica
0391-3716 Notiziario Vinciano
0391-3783 Odontostomatologia e Implantoprotesi
0391-383X Radio Kit Elettronica
0391-3848 Refrattari e Laterizi *changed to* L'Industria dei Laterizi.
0391-3953 T I M *see* 0393-599X
0391-3988 International Journal of Artificial Organs
0391-4089 Italian Journal of Sports Traumatology *see* 1120-3137
0391-4097 Journal of Endocrinological Investigation
0391-4186 Verifiche
0391-4259 Stazione Sperimentale del Vetro. Rivista
0391-4380 Musica Domani
0391-4631 Rivista di Meccanica International Edition
0391-464X Carte d'Acquisto†

ISSN

ISSN INDEX 5733

0391-4720	Banca d'Italia. Bollettino del Servizio Studi Economici *changed to* Banca d'Italia. Bollettino Statistico. Nuova Serie.
0391-4844	Medicina Geriatrica
0391-4887	Societa Italiana di Scienza dell'Alimentazione. Rivista
0391-500X	Universita degli Studi di Firenze. Facolta di Architettura. Biblioteca. Bollettino di Segnalazioni e Notizie Bibliografiche†
0391-5018	Doc; Documentazione *changed to* Doc Italia.
0391-5026	Economic Notes
0391-5115	Journal of European Economic History
0391-5352	Microbiologica
0391-5360	Energie Alternative: Habitat, Territorio, Energia
0391-5379	C S E L T Infotel
0391-5425	Armonia di Voci
0391-5433	Catechesi
0391-5468	Dimensioni Nuove
0391-5476	Espressione Giovani†
0391-5484	Mondo Erre
0391-5492	Migranti-Press
0391-5506	Presenza Nuova degli Anziani†
0391-5514	Progetto (Turin)
0391-5522	Apitalia
0391-5557	Acqua Aria
0391-5603	Urology
0391-5646	Archivio Giuridico
0391-5670	Giornale di Anestesia Stomatologica
0391-5859	Gortania
0391-5891	Lamiera
0391-5905	Giornale di Fisica. Quaderni†
0391-5972	Istituto Centrale per la Patologia del Libro. Bollettino
0391-6030	Forme Materiali ed Ideologie del Mondo Antico
0391-6049	Nuovo Medioevo
0391-6065	Dossier di le Monde Diplomatique†
0391-609X	Societa e la Scienza
0391-6103	Studi d'Economia†
0391-6138	Gazzetta della Piccola Industria
0391-6146	Quale Impresa
0391-6162	Rivista Aeronautica
0391-6200	Educazione Sanitaria e Medicina Preventiva *changed to* Educazione Sanitaria e Promozione della Salute.
0391-6367	E D P Telematica Notizie *changed to* Information e Technology.
0391-6391	Elettronica Oggi
0391-6448	Nuova Selezione Tessile
0391-6510	International Journal of Pediatric Nephrology *see* 1012-6694
0391-6723	Bozze
0391-674X	Cooperazione
0391-6812	Consorzio Provinciale per la Pubblica Lettura. Informazione Bibliografica
0391-7029	Archivio di Chirurgia Toracica e Cardiovascolare
0391-7045	Sviluppo e Organizzazione
0391-7096	Castelli Romani
0391-7231	Medicina Ospedaliera Romana
0391-7258	Basic and Applied Histochemistry
0391-7290	V G Vendogiocattoli
0391-7312	Quaderni Terzo Mondo
0391-7339	A E S
0391-7347	E D I†
0391-7363	I M U *see* 0393-599X
0391-7398	Market-Espresso
0391-7401	Plast
0391-741X	Progetto (Milan)
0391-7452	Isto Cito Patologia†
0391-7487	Ottagono
0391-7525	Giornale Italiano di Diabetologia
0391-7576	Regioni
0391-769X	Fiuggi
0391-7754	Giornale del Maiscoltore
0391-7770	Archivio Storico Italiano
0391-7789	Studi Musicali
0391-7797	Prospettiva Sindacale
0391-7819	Santo
0391-7983	Spezia Oggi
0391-8181	Accademia Nazionale dei Lincei. Classe di Scienze Morali, Storiche e Filologique. Rendiconti.
0391-8211	Istituto Storico Artistico Orvietano. Bollettino
0391-822X	Bollettino del Lavoro *see* 0394-6592
0391-8270	Bollettino dei Classici
0391-8289	Note Economiche
0391-836X	Prospettive Settanta
0391-8394	Quaderni Sardi di Economia
0391-8440	International Journal of Transport Economics
0391-8505	Cultura (Rome)
0391-8521	Qualita della Vita
0391-853X	Religione e Societa
0391-8548	Nuova Universale Studium
0391-8564	Verba Seniorum
0391-8580	I C U Papers†
0391-8599	S I P E
0391-8645	Oleodinamica - Pneumatica - Lubrificazione
0391-8718	Samnium
0391-8904	Cuore e Vasi
0391-8912	Dermatologo Ospedaliero *changed to* Il Dermatologo.
0391-8920	Ginecorama
0391-8939	Il Gastroenterologo
0391-8963	Reumatologo
0391-898X	Pediatria Oggi Medica e Chirurgica
0391-8998	Clinica Oculistica e Patologia Oculare
0391-9013	Giornale Italiano di Ostetricia e Ginecologia
0391-9048	Giornale di Neuropsicofarmacologia
0391-9056	Giornale Italiano di Senologia
0391-9064	Artibus et Historiae
0391-9293	Museo Archeologico di Tarquinia. Materiali
0391-9706	Acta Embryologiae et Morphologiae Experimentalis *changed to* Animal Biology.
0391-9714	History and Philosophy of the Life Sciences
0391-9730	Facolta di Magistero di Firenze. Istituto di Storia. Annali
0391-9749	Nematologia Mediterranea
0391-9757	Fisica e Tecnologia *see* 0393-4578
0391-9854	Bollettino d'Arte
0391-9889	Giornale Italiano di Medicina del Lavoro
0391-996X	Ricerche di Psicologia
0391-9994	Actum Luce
0392-0003	Fondazione Basso. Annali
0392-0011	Istituto Storico Italo-Germanico in Trento. Annali
0392-0038	Archeografo Triestino
0392-0062	Museo Civico di Storia Naturale, Verona. Bollettino
0392-0100	Nuova Polizia e Riforma dello Stato
0392-0143	Centro di Riferimento Italiano Diane. Notiziario
0392-0208	Journal of Nuclear Medicine and Allied Sciences *changed to* Journal of Nuclear Biology and Medicine.
0392-033X	Societa Savonese di Storia Patria. Atti e Memorie
0392-0453	Vedere Contact International
0392-047X	Folia Oncologica
0392-0550	Biblioteca Statale e Libreria Civica di Cremona. Annali
0392-0623	Italian Journal of Gastroenterology
0392-0658	Eta Evolutiva
0392-0879	Collezioni e Musei Archeologici del Veneto
0392-0887	Kokalos
0392-0895	Rivista di Archeologia
0392-0909	Sikelika. Serie Archeologica
0392-0917	Sikelika. Serie Storica
0392-0925	Novita Bibliografiche: Antichita Greca e Romana
0392-100X	Acta Otorhinolaryngologica Italica
0392-1212	Economia del Lavoro (Rome)†
0392-128X	Giornale Italiano di Oncologia
0392-131X	Largo Consumo
0392-1344	Clinica & Terapia Cardiovascolare
0392-1352	Campania Sacra
0392-1360	Rivista Italiana di Otorinolaringologia, Audiologia e Foniatria
0392-1387	Giornale Italiano di Angiologia
0392-1395	Dermatologia Clinica
0392-1417	Ortopedia e Traumatologia Oggi
0392-162X	Ricerche Storiche (Naples)
0392-1719	Studia Picena
0392-1875	Quaderni Medievali
0392-1913	Obiettivi e Documenti Veterinari
0392-1921	Diogenes (English Edition)
0392-1948	Studi di Storia dell'Educazione
0392-209X	Psichiatria e Cultura†
0392-2111	Cultura e Mass Media†
0392-2146	Studi sull'Educazione
0392-2154	Teorie e Oggetti
0392-2219	Accademia Ligure di Scienze e Lettere. Atti
0392-2227	Giornale Italiano di Chimica Clinica
0392-2278	Autonomie Locali e Servizi Sociali
0392-2294	Automazione Navale
0392-2308	Astronomia (Naples)
0392-2332	Nouvelles de la Republique des Lettres
0392-2510	Biologi Italiani
0392-2707	Bar Giornale
0392-2715	Il Bagno Oggi e Domani
0392-2723	Bagno e Accessori
0392-2790	Professionalita
0392-2804	Animazione ed Espressione - Tempo Sereno
0392-2812	Dirigenti Scuola
0392-2847	Am Albergo Moderno *changed to* In Design.
0392-2855	Analecta Augustiniana
0392-2936	European Journal of Gynecological Oncology
0392-2944	Ginecologia Clinica
0392-2960	C I News (Ceramics International) *changed to* Industrial Ceramics.
0392-3002	Aggiornamento del Medico
0392-3088	Acta Phoniatrica Latina
0392-3134	Bollettino Informativo Fiscale†
0392-3398	Centro Ricerche Biopsichiche
0392-3452	Technologie Chimiche
0392-3460	Tecnologie Elettriche International
0392-3479	Commercio Elettrico
0392-3487	Tecnologie Meccaniche International
0392-3525	Italian Journal of Surgical Sciences†
0392-3568	Italia Contemporanea
0392-3614	Giornale degli Apparecchi Domestici
0392-3622	Il Giornale della Subfornitura
0392-3630	Giornale dell'Installatore Elettrico
0392-3673	Monthly Review†
0392-3711	Notizario Bibliografico di Audiologia
0392-3800	Interplastics
0392-3886	Il Bolscevico
0392-3983	Meccanizzazione Agricola
0392-4173	Naturismo
0392-419X	Ateneo Parmense. Acta Naturalia
0392-4270	Cooperativa Centro di Documentazione. Notiziario
0392-4416	Rivista di Pediatria Preventiva e Sociale-Nipiologia
0392-4424	Societa Italiana di Fotogrammetria e Topografia. Bollettino
0392-4432	Bollettino di Storia delle Scienze Matematiche
0392-4440	Castoro Cinema
0392-4483	Giornale di Neuropsichiatria dell'Eta Evolutiva
0392-4505	Salute e Territorio
0392-4548	Medicina Oggi
0392-4556	Teresianum
0392-4564	Memoria
0392-4599	Rucuperare: Edilizia, Design, Impianti *changed to* Recuperare: Progetti Cantieri Tecnologie Prodotti.
0392-4602	Treni Oggi
0392-4629	N U A International Journal of Nephrology, Urology, Andrology
0392-4653	Bank of Italy. Economic Papers†
0392-4661	Banca d'Italia. Contributi alla Ricerca Economica *changed to* Banca d'Italia. Contributi alla Analisi Economica.
0392-467X	Banca d'Italia. Bollettino *changed to* Banca d'Italia. Bollettino Statistico. Nuova Serie.
0392-4718	Pasticceria Internazionale
0392-4815	Meccanica Pratica *see* 0393-5558
0392-4823	Progettista Industriale
0392-4831	Tecnica Ospedaliera
0392-4858	Rivista del Medico Pratico
0392-4866	Rivista degli Studi Orientali
0392-4874	Gruppo Micologico "G. Bresadola". Bollettino *see* 0394-9486
0392-4890	Ceramica per l'Edilizia Internationale
0392-5013	Volonta
0392-5021	Studi Marittimi
0392-517X	Radiotenica TV - Elettronik' Consumo *see* 0003-6668
0392-5404	Schede Medievali
0392-5439	Medaglia
0392-5544	Musica
0392-5730	L'Ambiente Cucina
0392-5773	Amici della Pipa
0392-5803	Cronache Castellane
0392-5870	Animazione Sociale
0392-5978	Annuario dei Fornitori *changed to* Glass Book.
0392-6036	Controlli Numerici Macchine a C N Robot Industriali *see* 0393-3911
0392-6044	Energia Solare e Fonti Alternative†
0392-6052	Export†
0392-6060	Latte
0392-6079	Mondo dei Gioielli
0392-6087	R C I
0392-6095	Inventario
0392-629X	Instituta et Monumenta. Serie II: Instituta
0392-6346	Messaggero Avventista
0392-6397	Misure Critiche
0392-6567	Utensil
0392-6648	Notiziario Informativo *changed to* Smalto.
0392-6664	Quaderni Costituzionali
0392-6699	Eos
0392-6702	Immunologia Clinica e Sperimentale *changed to* Immunologia Clinica.
0392-6710	Societa Sarda di Scienze Naturali. Bollettino
0392-6737	Societa Italiana di Fisica. Nuovo Cimento D
0392-6788	Studi per l'Ecologia del Quaternario
0392-6796	Le Grandi Automobili
0392-6834	CERannuario
0392-6850	CERfornitori
0392-7199	Medical Tribune
0392-7229	Rivista Giuridica del Lavoro e della Previdenza Sociale. Dottrina
0392-7296	Giornale Italiano di Entomologia
0392-7326	Studi Settecenteschi
0392-7334	Centro di Studi Vichiani. Bollettino
0392-7342	Elenchos
0392-7423	Elenchus Bibliographicus Biblicus *changed to* Elenchus of Biblica.
0392-7512	Alimentazione Nutrizione Metabolismo
0392-7571	Istituto per la Documentazione Giuridica. Bibliografia. Diritto Civile
0392-758X	Museo Regionale di Scienze Naturali, Torino. Bollettino
0392-7660	Balcanica
0392-7733	Fisiopatologia della Riproduzione
0392-7881	Accademia Nazionale dei Lincei. Classe di Scienze Fisiche Matematiche e Naturali. Rendiconti
0392-7903	Conservazione degli Alimenti†
0392-7911	Energia
0392-792X	Imbottigliamento
0392-7938	Panis†
0392-7954	Tecnologie del Filo
0392-8225	La Ceramica Moderna
0392-8241	Vetro Informazione
0392-8268	Rivista Telettra Review (English Edition)
0392-8276	Rivista Telettra Review (Italian Edition)
0392-8306	Agora (Rome)†
0392-8411	Universita degli Studi in Italia. Annuario
0392-8535	Dialoghi di Archeologia
0392-8543	Journal of Applied Cosmetology
0392-8586	Biblioteche Oggi
0392-8667	Comunicazioni Sociali
0392-8748	Rivista di Diritto Valutario e di Economia Internazionale
0392-8764	Heat and Technology†
0392-8829	Automazione Oggi

ISSN

5734 ISSN INDEX

0392-8837	Bit
0392-8888	Informatica Oggi *changed to* Informatica Oggi e UNIX.
0392-890X	Strumenti Musicali
0392-8926	Storia della Storiografia
0392-9035	Antropologia Contemporanea
0392-9043	Il Solidale
0392-9094	Seminario di Scienze Antropologiche
0392-9108	Indicatore Cartario *see* 0008-8765
0392-9116	Algologia
0392-9353	Chip†
0392-9485	Archeologia Viva
0392-9507	Journal of Foetal Medicine
0392-9515	Acta Mediterranea di Patologia Infettiva e Tropicale
0392-9590	International Angiology
0392-9639	Scienza Veterinaria e Biologia Animale
0392-9647	Sport & Medicina
0392-9663	Geriatrics
0392-9698	Acta Cardiologica Mediteranea
0392-9701	Stato e Mercato
0392-9809	Selezione Tessile *see* 0391-6448
0392-9884	Circolo Culturale B.G. Duns Scoto di Roccarainola. Atti
0393-0203	Rassegna
0393-022X	Rivista Storica Calabrese
0393-0440	Journal of Geometry and Physics
0393-0483	A M U
0393-0505	Junior Dental e Bocca Nuda†
0393-0521	Ambiente Risorse Salute
0393-0637	Lancet (Edizione Italiana)
0393-0645	Quaderni Italiani di Psichiatria
0393-0653	La Presse Medicale: Edizione Italiana
0393-0726	Antologia Medica Italiana *see* 0393-9715
0393-0882	Alta Fedelta
0393-0890	Tennis Italiano
0393-098X	E D A V
0393-1218	Uccelli d'Italia
0393-1226	Quaderni di Semantica
0393-1358	Federalist
0393-1412	Universita Cattolica. Istituto di Storia Antica. Ricerche
0393-1471	Chirurgia Epatobiliare
0393-196X	Bollettino di Oceanologia
0393-2095	Kos
0393-2214	Firenze Chirurgica†
0393-2451	Intersezioni
0393-2494	Rivista Italiana di Diritto del Lavoro
0393-2532	Studi Verdiani
0393-2648	C S E L T Technical Reports
0393-2664	Anteprima Libri
0393-2702	Universitas
0393-2729	International Spectator
0393-2842	Match-Ball†
0393-2850	Super Football†
0393-2915	Informazioni e Studi Vivaldiani
0393-330X	Datalignum
0393-3318	Ferrarissima
0393-3385	Storia Nordamericana
0393-3393	Audiologia Italiana
0393-3415	Rivista di Storia Economica
0393-3571	Istituto Ricerche Pesca Marittima. Quaderni
0393-3598	Cristianesimo nella Storia
0393-361X	Psichiatria dell'Infanzia e dell'Adolescenza
0393-3687	Studi Ecumenici
0393-3849	Ricerche Storiche Salesiane
0393-3865	SegnoCinema
0393-3903	L'Indice
0393-3911	Automazione Integrata
0393-4195	La Favilla
0393-4209	Bambini
0393-4217	Rivista della Montagna
0393-4322	Impianti Attrezzature Sportive e Ricreative *changed to* Sport e Citta.
0393-4330	Zoom (Italian Edition)
0393-439X	Arte & Cornice
0393-4403	Informobili *changed to* Macchine Accessori Componenti.
0393-4411	Riabita
0393-4454	Arredo Biancheria Casa *changed to* Arredo Tessili Complementi - Biancheria Casa.
0393-4462	Arredo Tessili Complementi *changed to* Arredo Tessili Complementi - Biancheria Casa.
0393-4470	Interfaccia†
0393-4489	Casa Classica†
0393-4500	Giornale dell'Arredamento
0393-4551	Savings and Development
0393-4578	Il Nuovo Saggiatore
0393-4586	Rassegna Amministrativa della Scuola
0393-4624	Rivista Dalmatica
0393-4853	Bollettino di Psichiatria Biologica
0393-487X	Clot and Hematologic Malignancies
0393-4977	Cittanova
0393-5132	Arredostile Middle East†
0393-5140	Casarredo Middle East†
0393-5167	Forwood International†
0393-5183	A A R P Environment Design
0393-5221	Rivista Italiana di Ortopedia e Traumatologia Pediatrica
0393-5337	Ginecologia dell'Infanzia e dell'Adolescenza
0393-5418	Fogli di Informazione
0393-5442	Centauro†
0393-5469	Itinerario
0393-5493	Sistemi Urbani
0393-554X	J A M A: The Journal of the American Medical Association (Italian Edition)
0393-5558	Meccanica Moderna
0393-5582	Rivista Italiana di Nutrizione Parenterale ed Enterale
0393-5590	Giornale Italiano di Nefrologia
0393-5744	Political Economy
0393-5949	I Tatti Studies
0393-5957	Giornale Italiano di Ricerche Cliniche e Terapeutiche
0393-5981	Brevetti & Invenzioni
0393-599X	Industria Mercato
0393-604X	Banca d'Italia. Bollettino Statistico - Servizio Studi *changed to* Banca d'Italia. Bollettino Statistico. Nuova Serie.
0393-6066	International Journal of Sports Cardiology
0393-6090	Banca d'Italia. Bollettino - Servizio Studi *changed to* Banca d'Italia. Bollettino Statistico. Nuova Serie.
0393-6147	Il Vesuvio
0393-6155	International Journal of Biological Markers
0393-6163	Studi di Psicologia dell'Educazione
0393-635X	Acta Toxicologica et Therapeutica
0393-6368	Universita e Istituti di Studio e Ricerca in Italia. Annuario D E A
0393-6376	Acta Chirurgica Mediterranea
0393-6384	Acta Medica Mediterranea
0393-6392	Acta Pediatrica Mediterranea
0393-6414	San Martino
0393-6457	Lettera dall'Italia
0393-6503	Institut International J. Maritain. Notes et Documents
0393-652X	Selezione Chimica Tintoria
0393-6740	Comunismo
0393-6775	Donne e Politica - Women and Politics *changed to* Reti - Pratiche e Saperi di Donne.
0393-697X	Societa Italiana di Fisica. Rivista del Nuovo Cimento
0393-716X	E N E A Notiziario-Energia e Innovazione
0393-7445	Lanternino
0393-7496	Quaderni di Retorica e Poetica†
0393-7526	Ruotaspring
0393-7534	Tribuna del Collezionista
0393-7542	Acta Oncologica
0393-7550	Assistenza Infermieristica del Nord America
0393-7569	Basi Razionali della Terapia *changed to* G and B.
0393-7577	Clinica Chirurgica del Nord America
0393-7585	Clinica Medica del Nord America
0393-7593	Clinica Odontoiatrica del Nord America
0393-7607	Clinica Ostetrica e Ginecologica
0393-7623	La Medicina di Laboratorio
0393-7631	Odontoiatria Oggi
0393-764X	Progressi Clinici: Chirurgia
0393-7658	Progressi Clinici: Medicina
0393-7666	Motori
0393-7801	Ultrasonica
0393-7844	Politica Meridionalista
0393-7984	Comunita Sportiva
0393-800X	J D
0393-8034	Reggio Storia
0393-8050	Fiere
0393-8069	Italian Building and Construction
0393-8077	Vie e Trasporti
0393-8131	Phytophaga
0393-8190	M C M : La Storia delle Cose
0393-8204	Tecno Show†
0393-8212	Nuovo Governo Locale
0393-8239	Autocarri e Autobus *changed to* Autobus.
0393-8263	Arsenale
0393-8379	Quaderni di Cinema
0393-8387	Auto e Design
0393-876X	Marmor
0393-8875	Natura e Societa
0393-9243	Economia e Banca
0393-9367	Hyria
0393-9375	Human Evolution
0393-9383	International Journal of Anthropology
0393-9413	Pubblico Esercizio
0393-9480	Steve
0393-9715	Rivista Internazionale di Chirurgia Vertebrale e dei Nervi Periferici
0393-9723	T I S: Il Corriere TermoldroSanitario
0393-974X	Journal of Biological Regulators and Homeostatic Agents
0393-9774	Psichiatria e Psicoterapia Analitica
0393-9898	Rivista di Psicologia dell'Arte
0393-9901	Venite Adoremus
0393-9944	Studi Sciacchiani
0394-0152	La Conchiglia
0394-0179	Art e Dossier
0394-0284	Il Cristiano
0394-0314	L'Oroptero
0394-0438	Agricoltura Mediterranea
0394-0543	Il Giornale dell'Arte
0394-0616	Studi e Ricerche sull'Oriente Cristiano
0394-0713	Societa di Ortopedia e Traumatologia dell' Italia Meridionale ed Insulare. Atti e Memorie
0394-073X	Cardiomyology†
0394-0756	Orizzonti di Chirurgia
0394-0772	Rivista di Patologia dell'Apparato Locomotore
0394-0802	Prospettiva
0394-0896	Monitor - Radio T V
0394-1434	C I R V I Bollettino
0394-1493	Flash Art Italia
0394-1531	Medicina e Psyche
0394-1582	Impiantistica Italiana
0394-1590	Costruire in Laterizio
0394-1612	Obiettivo Marca
0394-168X	Minerva Ortognatodontica
0394-2473	Diorama Letterario
0394-2503	Dermatologia Oggi
0394-2627	Medicina Moderna Oggi
0394-2694	Quaderni Veneti
0394-3402	Diabetes, Nutrition & Metabolism, Clinical and Experimental
0394-3429	Panorama Difesa
0394-3437	J P 4 Mensile di Aeronautica
0394-3453	Macplas
0394-3518	Taverna di Auerbach
0394-364X	Segni dei Tempi
0394-3682	Sposabella
0394-3704	Linea Verde
0394-3933	Journal of Regional Policy
0394-395X	Il Golfo
0394-4247	Popoli
0394-4271	Mostre e Musei
0394-4549	Rivista di Patologia e Sperimentazione Clinica
0394-5057	Speleo
0394-5073	Universita di Firenze. Dipartimento di Filosofia. Annali
0394-5103	European Earthquake Engineering
0394-5359	Padania
0394-5391	R S Rifiuti Solidi
0394-5413	Tecnologie Tessili
0394-5596	Annales Tectonicae
0394-5618	Erba d'Arno
0394-5634	L'Impianto Elettrico
0394-5871	Ingegneria Ambientale
0394-5901	Serigrafia
0394-6169	Advances in Horticultural Science
0394-6282	Rivista Internazionale di Musica Sacra
0394-6444	European Journal of International Affairs
0394-6479	A S P E
0394-6495	Rivista Internazionale dei Diritti dell' Uomo
0394-6592	Bollettino del Lavoro e dei Tributi
0394-6975	Tropical Zoology
0394-7149	Bollettino Malacologico
0394-7297	Filosofia Politica
0394-7394	Nuncius
0394-7726	Analecta Ordinis Carmelitarum
0394-7734	Archivium Historicum Carmelitanum
0394-7742	Carmel in the World
0394-7750	Carmel in the World Paperbacks
0394-7769	Collationes Mariales Instituti Carmelitani
0394-7777	Collectanea Bibliographica Carmelitana
0394-7785	Presenza del Carmelo†
0394-7793	Textus et Studia Historica Carmelitana
0394-7807	Vacare Deo
0394-8048	Linea Intima
0394-8064	Maglieria in Italia *changed to* R M 1 Maglieria in Italia.
0394-8137	Danzare
0394-8153	Voce dell'Emigrante
0394-8285	Vigile Urbano
0394-8374	Rivista Trimestrale degli Appalti
0394-8501	Achademia Leonardi Vince: Journal of Leonardo Studies and Bibliography of Vinciana
0394-8536	Tourispress Italia
0394-8625	Essecome
0394-8706	C I B Edifici Intelligenti
0394-9001	Medicina nei Secoli: Arte e Scienza
0394-901X	Diabete
0394-9028	Rivista delle Cancellerie
0394-9036	La Difesa Penale
0394-9079	Chirurgia della Testa e del Collo
0394-9109	Rivista Italiana di Colon-Proctologia
0394-9249	Zodiac (English Edition)
0394-9257	Journal of Genetics & Breeding
0394-9362	Giornale di Techniche Nefrologiche e Dialitiche
0394-9370	Ethnology, Ecology & Evolution
0394-9397	Religioni e Societa
0394-9427	Alba Pompeia
0394-9486	Rivista di Micologia
0394-9532	Aging - Clinical and Experimental Research
0394-9540	Neuropsicofarmacologia del Comportamento
0394-9575	Media Forum
0394-9583	Nuovo†
0394-9591	Target
0394-9605	Unificazione e Certificazione
0394-9850	Euntes Docete
0394-9869	Bibliografia Missionaria
0394-9877	Bollettino di Microbiologia ed Indagini di Laboratorio
0395-000X	Ordinaire du Psychanalyste
0395-0026	Cle des Mots†
0395-0530	Afro Music
0395-0840	Animation et Education
0395-1081	Kyrn
0395-1200	Cahiers Debussy
0395-1294	France Transports†
0395-160X	Maisons et Decors de l'Est *changed to* Maisons & Decors. Alsace, Lorraine, Champagne.
0395-1618	Maisons de l'Est *changed to* Maisons & Decors. Alsace, Lorraine, Champagne.
0395-1766	En Equipe au Service de l'Evangile *changed to* En Equipe A C G F au Service de l'Evangile.
0395-2061	Guide Europeen des Produits Logiciels *see* 0985-0791

ISSN

0395-2096 Forum Chirurgical
0395-2126 Hetero
0395-2673 Conseils Sols et Murs
0395-2681 Asie du Sud-Est et Monde Insulindien†
0395-269X Ex Libris Francais
0395-2894 Specialement Votre
0395-3203 Universite de Nantes. Centre de Recherches sur l'Histoire de la France Atlantique. Enquetes et Documents *see* 0983-2424
0395-3491 Sports Equestres†
0395-3599 Courses Hippiques
0395-367X Technic Hebdo
0395-3890 Bulletin Europeen de Physiopathologie Respiratoire *see* 0903-1936
0395-403X Societe Francaise de Cardiologie. Bulletin d'Informations
0395-4366 Autohebdo
0395-4374 Bulletin de Medecine Legale, Urgence Medicale, Centre Anti-Poisons *see* 0249-6208
0395-4382 Karate Cinema
0395-451X Bulletin Rapide de Droit des Affaires
0395-501X Archives d'Anatomie et de Cytologie Pathologiques
0395-5494 Marches Europeens des Fruits et Legumes *see* 0758-8526
0395-5621 C F D T Magazine
0395-6601 France. Centre National de Documentation Pedagogique. Textes et Documents pour la Classe.
0395-6989 Commonwealth
0395-7276 France. Ministere de l'Economie et des Finances. Bulletin de Liaison et d'Information *changed to* France. Ministere de l'Economie. Bulletin de Liaison et d'Information.
0395-7349 Medecine, Sciences et Documents
0395-7519 Centre de Recherches Zootechniques et Veterinaires de Theix. Bulletin Technique†
0395-7594 Federation Francaise de Sports pour Handicaps Physiques. Informations *changed to* Handisport Magazine.
0395-7691 Education Rurale
0395-773X Traduire
0395-7837 Chantiers de Pedagogie Mathematique
0395-7845 Chants des Peuples
0395-8086 Universite d'Aix-Marseille 3. Centre des Hautes Etudes Touristiques. Collection "Essais"
0395-8175 Cahiers du Credit Mutuel
0395-8183 Charolais
0395-8507 Foret - Loisirs et Equipements de Plein Air†
0395-8531 Horticulture Francaise
0395-8876 Journal de l'Ile de la Reunion
0395-9066 Sport de l'Esprit *changed to* Bouquet.
0395-9090 P E V H *see* 0223-0232
0395-9279 Journal de Microscopie et de Spectroscopie Electroniques *changed to* Microscopy Microanalysis Microstrucures.
0395-9295 A.D.M.A.: la Vie Musicale en Aquitaine†
0395-9317 Cahiers de la Mediterranee
0395-9406 Tribune de L'Assurance
0395-9481 Actuel Developpement
0396-0382 Syndicat General des Industries Medico-Chirurgicales et Dentaires. Annuaire†
0396-0595 Courrier de l'Exploitant et du Scieur *see* 0296-8541
0396-0625 Annuaire des Fournisseurs de Laboratoires Pharmaceutiques et Cosmetiques
0396-1214 Catalogue National du Traitement des Surfaces de l'Anticorrosion et des Traitements Thermiques
0396-2024 Connaissance de l'Ouest
0396-2318 Annuaire des Avocats
0396-2393 Union des Superieures Majeurs de France. Annuaire
0396-2458 Promotion†
0396-2644 Unites Petrochimiques dans les Pays de l'O P E C et de l'O P A E P†
0396-2679 Caribbean Archives
0396-2687 Centres de Recherches Exploration - Production ELF Aquitaine. Bulletin
0396-3128 Relais - Statistiques de l'Economie Picarde
0396-3640 Revue Fiduciaire Comptable
0396-4299 Guide du Cadeau et des Arts de la Table
0396-437X Chroniques d'Actualite de la S.E.D.E.I.S
0396-4388 Port Autonome du Havre. Bulletin Analytique de Documentation Generale
0396-4396 Port Autonome du Havre. Bulletin Analytique de Documentation Technique
0396-4914 Mes Premieres Grilles
0396-4957 Encyclopedie d'Utovie
0396-5015 Semaine Veterinaire
0396-5791 Courrier de la Microcopie
0396-5880 Intergeo-Bulletin
0396-6666 Achats et Entretien - Equipement Industriel
0396-7107 Therapeutiques Naturelles
0396-7115 Groupement National pour l'Organisation de la Medecine Auxiliaire. Bulletin de Liaison *see* 0396-7107
0396-714X Commerce Moderne†
0396-7360 Jeunesse du Quart Monde
0396-7549 Delta†
0396-8235 Chasseur d'Images
0396-8863 Association des Services Geologiques Africains. Bulletin d'Information et de Liaison. Information and Liaison Bulletin *changed to* Geologie Africaine.
0396-8898 Documents pour l'Enseignement Economique et Social
0396-8936 Federation Nationale des Agriculteurs Multiplicateurs de SEMENCES. Bulletin
0396-9657 Recherches Geographiques a Strasbourg
0396-969X Esprit Saint
0396-9975 Informations d'Ile de France†
0397-0051 Elan Poetique Litteraire et Pacifiste
0397-006X Ciments, Betons, Platres, Chaux
0397-0167 Lettre aux Educateurs†
0397-0280 Unions Sexuelles
0397-0736 Echanges
0397-1511 Journal du Mineur
0397-2836 Biologie et Ecologie Mediterraneene
0397-2844 Geologie Mediterraneenne
0397-3301 I N F F O - Flash
0397-331X Actualite de la Formation Permanente
0397-3816 Manutention *see* 0295-4192
0397-3999 Techniques Orthopediques
0397-4650 Chantiers de France
0397-4715 Expomat Actualites†
0397-474X Transport Public
0397-5754 Marches Agricoles-l'Echo des Halles *changed to* Marches.
0397-6424 Hi Fi Magazine†
0397-6467 Journal de la Marine Marchande et de la Navigation Aerienne *see* 0983-0537
0397-6491 Science Film†
0397-6505 Secretaires d'Aujourd'hui†
0397-6513 T E C
0397-6521 Transports Urbains
0397-7153 Biologie du Comportement†
0397-7757 Bulletin Signaletique. Part 130: Physique Mathematique, Optique, Acoustique, Mecanique, Chaleur *changed to* P A S C A L Folio. F 10: Mecanique et Acoustique et Transfert de Chaleur.
0397-7757 Bulletin Signaletique. Part 130: Physique Mathematique, Optique, Acoustique, Mecanique, Chaleur *see* 1146-5360
0397-7757 Bulletin Signaletique. Part 130: Physique Mathematique, Optique, Acoustique, Mecanique, Chaleur *see* 0761-2044
0397-7870 Revue Francaise d'Etudes Americaines
0397-7900 Revue de l'Infirmiere
0397-8060 Progres Technique
0397-8079 Revue de l'Embouteillage et des Industries du Conditionnement, Traitement, Distribution Transport *changed to* Conditionnement des Liquides-Embouteillage.
0397-8249 Annuaire de l'U R S S et des Pays Socialistes Europeens†
0397-8389 Economie Familiale
0397-8435 Centre National de la Cinematographie. Bulletin d'Information
0397-8702 Film Francais
0397-9180 Pediatre (Paris)
0397-944X Migrants Nouvelles
0397-9873 Revue Trimestrielle de Droit Civil
0398-0006 Paris Madame
0398-0022 Revue Dromoise
0398-0049 Theatre et Animation
0398-0499 Journal des Maladies Vasculaires
0398-074X Astrolab
0398-1169 Zero - Un References
0398-1851 Electronique et Applications Industrielles
0398-3145 Cadres C F D T
0398-3218 Geophysique *see* 0766-5105
0398-3765 Centre International de Documentation Occitane. Serie Etudes
0398-4346 Revue Arachnologique
0398-7515 Argus du Petrole†
0398-7620 Revue d'Epidemiologie et de Sante Publique
0398-8287 Institut Technique de l'Aviculture. Tendances des Marches
0398-8341 Sport Bowling
0398-8384 Revue des Livres pour Enfants
0398-8716 Service 2000
0398-9089 Soul Bag
0398-9372 Nouveau Photocinema *changed to* Photomagazine.
0398-9453 Biza Neira (Bise Noire)
0398-9682 Nouvelles de France
0398-9771 Journal Francais d'Oto-Rhino-Laryngologie *changed to* Journal Francais d'Oto-Rhino-Laryngologie - Audiophonologie - Chirurgie Maxillo-Faciale.
0398-9836 New Journal of Chemistry
0398-9941 Bulletin Signaletique. Part 310: Genie Biomedical. Informatique Biomedicale. Physique Biomedicale *see* 0761-2311
0398-995X Bulletin Signaletique. Part 890: Industries Mecaniques-Batiment-Travaux Public-Transports *changed to* P A S C A L Folio. F 10: Mecanique et Acoustique et Transfert de Chaleur.
0398-9968 Bulletin Signaletique. Part 165: Atomes et Molecules. Plasmas *see* 0761-1951
0399-0087 Septentrion
0399-0206 Annales du Tabac Section 1
0399-0265 Services d'Aide Medicale Urgente. Revue
0399-0281 France. Ministere de l'Amenagement du Territoire, de l'Equipement, du Logement et des Transports. Bulletin Officiel
0399-029X Journees Parisiennes de Pediatrie
0399-032X Lyon Mediterranee Medical *see* 0766-5466
0399-0346 Journal des Africanistes
0399-0354 Annales du Tabac Section 2
0399-0370 Afrique et l'Asie Modernes
0399-0435 Journal Francais de Biophysique et Medecine Nucleaire *see* 0992-3039
0399-0443 Universite de Bordeaux III. Centre de Recherches sur l'Amerique Anglophone. Annales
0399-0516 R A I R O Analyse Numerique - Numerical Analysis *see* 0764-583X
0399-0524 R A I R O Automatique - Systems Analysis and Control *see* 0296-1598
0399-0532 R A I R O Informatique - Computer Science *see* 0752-4072
0399-0540 R A I R O Informatique Theorique - Theoretical Informatics *see* 0988-3754
0399-0559 R A I R O Recherche Operationnelle
0399-0575 Revue Bryologique et Lichenologique *see* 0181-1576
0399-0648 Thesindex Medical†
0399-0656 Thesindex Dentaire†
0399-0842 Journal de Mecanique Appliquee *see* 0997-7538
0399-0842 Journal de Mecanique Appliquee *see* 0997-7546
0399-0966 Planification, Habitat, Information
0399-0974 Cybium
0399-1121 Amitie Henri Bosco. Cahiers *see* 0753-4590
0399-1148 Revue Pratique de Droit Social
0399-1156 Vie des Collectivites Ouvrieres *changed to* Revue des Comites d'Entreprise.
0399-1164 Vie Ouvriere
0399-1172 Spectra 2000
0399-1245 Analyses de la S.E.D.E.I.S.
0399-1253 Peuples Mediterraneens - Mediterranean Peoples
0399-127X Universite Scientifique et Medical de Grenoble. Institut des Sciences Nucleaires. Rapport Annuel *changed to* Institut des Sciences Nucleaires Grenoble. Rapport d'Activite.
0399-1415 Cahiers Leopold Delisle
0399-1539 Agritrop
0399-1563 Bulletin Signaletique. Part 110: Informatique-Automatique-Recherche Operationnelle-Gestion-Economie *see* 0761-2060
0399-1563 Bulletin Signaletique. Part 110: Informatique-Automatique-Recherche Operationnelle-Gestion Economie *see* 0761-2052
0399-1571 G A P H Y O R. Atomes, Molecules, Gaz Neutres Et Ionises. *see* 0761-3369
0399-1784 Oceanologica Acta
0399-1989 Recherches Germaniques
0399-2322 Bella (Milan, 1975)
0399-3558 Vititechnique *changed to* Cultivar.
0399-3752 Revue Culturelle Reunionnaise†
0399-5070 Actuels
0399-5461 Hebdocuir
0399-5747 Pelerin *see* 0399-5755
0399-5755 Pelerin
0399-6417 Medecine Aeronautique et Spatiale - Medecine Subaquatiqe et Hyperbare *see* 0294-0817
0399-6662 France. Centre Regional Archeologique d'Alet. Dossiers
0399-7014 Brud Nevez
0399-7081 Dico - Plus
0399-7189 Dependable's List Marketing Newsletter *changed to* SpeciaLists' MarketPlus Newsletter.
0399-7715 Caravanier
0399-8223 Nouveau Guide Gault-Millau *changed to* Gault - Millau Magazine.
0399-8290 Officiel des Cuisinistes, des Bainistes et des Electromenagistes
0399-8320 Gastro-Enterologie Clinique et Biologique
0399-855X Techniques de l'Energie *see* 0755-5202
0399-8975 C N P R Revue des Entreprises
0399-9505 France U.R.S.S. Magazine
0399-9726 France. Comite des Travaux Historiques et Scientifiques. Section d'Histoire Moderne et Contemporaine (Depuis 1610). Bulletin *see* 0071-8459
0399-9734 Bulletin du Bibliophile et du Bibliothecaire *see* 0399-9742
0399-9742 Bulletin du Bibliophile†
0400-132X A M I F *see* 0299-3953
0400-1559 A P R O Bulletin†
0400-163X A R E O Quarterly *see* 0003-0791
0400-1915 Air Traffic Control Association. Bulletin
0400-227X Aarbok for den Norske Kirke
0400-4043 Acta Humboldtiana. Series Geographica et Ethnographica *changed to* Acta Humboldtiana.

ISSN

5736 ISSN INDEX

0400-4620 Actualite Religieuse dans le Monde *see* 0757-3529
0400-471X Actualites Sociales Hebdomadaires
0400-5104 Adesso†
0400-5880 Adult Teacher
0400-7719 Agricoltore di Terra di Lavoro
0400-8111 Agronomia Sulriograndense
0400-8510 Air Currents
0401-3174 Alfold
0401-331X Algemeen Werkloosheidsfonds. Jaarverslag
0401-345X Algeria. Service Geologique. Bulletin *changed to* Algeria. Office Nationale de la Geologie. Bulletin.
0401-3689 Alhambra
0401-3956 Printing Times
0401-5576 Aluminum Light *changed to* Glass Workers News.
0401-6351 American Association for Automotive Medicine. Proceedings *see* 0892-6484
0402-4249 Angolite
0402-4621 Annales de Medecine Physique *see* 0168-6054
0402-5563 Anregung
0402-6233 Antoinette†
0402-6802 Anwaltsverzeichnist†
0402-7493 Arab Horse Society News
0402-7787 Der Arbeitgeber
0402-7817 Arbeits und Forschungsberichte zur Saechsischen Bodendenkmalpflege
0402-852X Archaeologia Japonica
0402-9054 Archivos de Pediatria
0402-9283 Arena
0403-0133 Argentina. Ministerio de Trabajo y Seguridad Social. Boletin de Biblioteca†
0403-0699 Arizona. State. State Land Department. Water Resources Report *changed to* Arizona. Department of Water Resources. Report.
0403-1792 Arkansas Highways
0403-3884 Arzt und Christ
0403-4457 Asiatic Society. Annual Report
0403-5542 Aspas de la Patata
0403-8894 Atomic Energy Guideletter *changed to* Washington Atomic Energy Report.
0403-9114 Chalk River Nuclear Laboratories. Physics Division. Progress Report†
0403-9319 Atoms in Japan
0404-181X Australia. Department of Primary Industry. Tobacco Industry Trust. Account Annual Report†
0404-3529 Automobil
0404-6307 Baden - Wuerttemberg
0404-6919 Ballroom Dancing Year Book *changed to* Dancing Year Book.
0404-8997 Bar North *changed to* North Dakota Stockman.
0404-9462 Bollettino di S. Nicola
0405-0738 Pflanzenschutz Kurier
0405-1033 Der Beamten-Bund *changed to* D B B Magazin.
0405-1157 Beauty & Barber Dealers World†
0405-119X Beauty School World†
0405-2161 Beitraege zur Schleswiger Stadtgeschichte
0405-5756 Die Berliner Wirtschaft
0405-6485 Betriebs- und Arbeitswirtschaft in der Praxis†
0405-6590 Better Homes and Gardens Christmas Ideas
0405-668X Better Nutrition *changed to* Better Nutrition for Today's Living.
0405-6701 Betteravier Francais
0405-6779 Bewaehrungs: Fachzeitschrift fuer Bewaehrungs, Gerichts, und Straffaelligheit
0405-721X Bibliografia Brasileira de Quimica Tecnologia *see* 0100-0756
0405-9212 Biblioteca Promocion del Pueblo
0406-1578 Bibliotekarz Zachodniopomorski
0406-3317 Biologie in der Schule
0406-3597 Plant Protection Bulletin
0406-3678 Bitumes Actualites
0406-5948 Boletin de Londres†
0406-6987 Tata Institute of Fundamental Research. Lectures on Mathematics and Physics. Mathematics *changed to* Tata Institute Lectures on Mathematics.
0406-9765 Brazil. Fundacao Instituto Brasileiro de Geografia e Estatistica. Boletim Bibliografico
0407-2294 University of British Columbia. Forest Club. Research Note†
0407-5439 Buchwissenschaftliche Beitraege *see* 0724-7001
0407-5501 Bucks County Law Reporter
0407-7202 Building and Allied Trades Official Handbook *changed to* Building and Allied Industries Official Handbook.
0407-8985 B D I-Mitteilungen†
0407-923X Bunte Illustrierte *changed to* Bunte.
0408-0904 Byoin Yoran
0408-1552 Geologisches Landesamt Baden-Wuettemberg. Abhandlungen
0408-1560 Geologisches Landesamt Baden-Wuerttemberg. Jahreshefte
0408-1714 Baden - Wuerttemberg. Statistisches Landesamt. Statistisch-Prognostischer Bericht
0408-2133 Bahrain News - Akhbar al-Bahrain *changed to* Al-Bahrain.
0408-215X Bahrain Trade Directory
0408-3075 Banca y Seguros
0408-3164 Banco Central de Costa Rica. Informacion de Estadistica Mensual *changed to* Banco Central de Costa Rica. Boletin Estadistico.
0408-3172 Banco Central de Costa Rica. Informacion Economica Semanal
0408-4284 Bank for International Settlements. Monetary and Economic Department. International Commodity Position. General Survey†
0408-4632 Bank Pembangunan Indonesia. Annual Report
0408-5655 Bardsey Observatory Report
0408-568X Bargain Paradises of the World *changed to* Retirement Paradises of the World.
0408-6104 Baseball Guidebook
0408-6392 Bastions de Geneve
0408-8107 Beitraege zum Buch- und Bibliothekswesen
0408-8344 Beitraege zur Geschichte der Reichskirche in der Neuzeit
0408-8379 Beitraege zur Geschichte der Universitaet Mainz
0408-8492 Beitraege zur Landeskunde
0408-8514 Beitraege zur Mittelamerikanischen Voelkerkunde
0408-9006 Commission Belge de Bibliographie. Bulletin *changed to* Commission Belge de Bibliographie et de Bibliologie. Bulletin.
0408-9235 Belgium. Ministere des Affaires Economiques. Direction Generale des Etudes et de la Documentation. Apercu de l'Evolution Economique *see* 0772-0831
0408-9936 Saopstenja
0409-0179 Belgrade. Univerzitet. Elektrotehnicki Fakultet. Publikacije. Serija: Telekomunikacije i Elektronika *see* 0351-2177
0409-0314 Zavod za Zdravstvenu Zastitu S R Srbije. Glasnik
0409-1132 La Berio
0409-1477 Freie Universitaet Berlin. Osteuropa-Institut. Berichte
0409-2163 Bermuda Historical Society. Occasional Publications†
0409-2570 Best Jewish Sermons†
0409-2694 Beton-Litteratur Referater†
0409-2740 Betontechnische Berichte
0409-2791 Betriebstechnik
0409-3453 Bibliografia Pomorza Zachodniego. Pismiennictwo Polskie
0409-3739 Bibliografski Vjesnik
0409-3747 Bibliographia Belgica
0409-6568 C A F Bulletin Mensuel *changed to* C A F Revue.
0409-7734 Cactus
0409-8757 Cahiers Medico-Sociaux
0409-9192 Caja de Ahorros y Monte de Piedad de las Baleares. Memoria
0410-2894 California F P
0410-3556 California Teacher
0410-3882 Calvinist Contact
0410-5389 Canada. Statistics Canada. Grain Milling Statistics/Statistiques de Mouture des Grains†
0410-5869 Canada. Statistics Canada. Road and Street Mileage and Expenditure - Voies Publiques: Longueur et Depenses *see* 0706-3105
0410-5877 Canada. Statistics Canada. Sales Financing/Financement des Ventes†
0410-904X Canadian Jewish Congress. Information and Comment, Social and Economic Studies: Fundamental Rights and Freedoms in Canada. Progress Reports†
0411-129X Carnuntum Jahrbuch†
0411-275X Catholic Truth *changed to* The Catholic.
0411-5023 Centro de Historia del Tachira. Boletin
0411-5562 Cercle Ernest Renan. Cahiers
0411-6380 Ceste i Mostovi
0411-7085 Directory of Chain Restaurant Operators (Year)
0411-8421 Zhejiang Zhongyi Zazhi
0411-8634 Chemia w Szkole
0411-8871 Chemical Spotlight
0411-8987 Chemische Gesellschaft der DDR. Mitteilungsblatt†
0412-0787 Jianzhu Gongren
0412-0914 Zhiwu Bingli Xuebao
0412-0922 Zhiwu Shenglixue Tongxun
0412-1961 Jinshu Xuebao
0412-2658 Chirugia Generale†
0412-2968 Christ in Our Home
0412-3131 Christian Librarian
0412-3921 Zhongxue Jiaoyu
0412-4154 Zhongguo Ertong
0412-4367 Zhongguo Yangfeng
0412-443X Zhongshan Daxue Shehui Kexue Xuebao *see* 1000-9639
0412-4553 Church Administration
0412-5568 Cineromanzo†
0412-5878 Cirugia, Ginecologia y Urologia *see* 0009-739X
0412-6300 Citrus Engineering Conference. Transactions
0412-7994 Clinical Medicine *changed to* Journal of Continuing Education in Rural and Community Medicine.
0413-7647 Colorado's Annual Highway Report†
0413-8384 Columbia University. Bureau of Applied Social Research. Bureau Reporter†
0413-9593 Comite du Folklore Champenois. Bulletin
0414-1105 Communes d'Europe
0414-2713 Concretezza†
0414-4406 Congres International Medical de Pays de Langue Francaise de l'Hemisphere Americain. Rapports et Communications
0414-7790 Contemporary Philosophy Series†
0414-8126 Contractor *changed to* A B C Today.
0414-8681 Enquette Restreinte sur les Salaries
0415-1798 Deine Gesundheit
0415-3049 Neue Zeitung
0415-3200 Musashino Electrical Communication Laboratories Technical Journal
0415-3693 Samling af Bekendtgoerelser *see* 0108-9102
0415-3944 Danish Plant Protection Service. Annual Report *changed to* Denmark. Plant Directorate. Annual Report.
0415-6102 Deutsche Ostkunde
0415-6412 Deutsche Zeitschrift fuer Akupunktur
0415-7435 Deutsches Musikleben (Year)
0415-7508 B D I Deutschland Liefert
0415-8407 Digest of Chiropractic Economics
0415-9241 Directory of Blood Transfusion Facilities and Services *see* 0419-2206
0415-9594 Directory of Leading Chain Stores (Year)
0415-9764 Directory of Oil Well Drilling Contractors *changed to* Drilling & Well Servicing Contractors.
0415-9772 Directory of Oil Well Supply Companies *changed to* Oil Well Supply Industry.
0416-0371 Discussione
0416-2706 Donaldson's Port Elizabeth, Uitenhage and Despatch Directory
0416-3540 Drobiarstwo
0416-5551 D M
0416-6906 Dansk Dendrologisk Aarsskrift
0416-6922 Danske Hedeselskabets. Forskningsvirksomheden. Beretning *see* 0903-5664
0416-6981 Dansk Teknisk Litteraturselskab. Skriftserie
0416-7341 Politechnika Gdanska. Zeszyty Naukowe. Chemia
0416-833X Decheniana-Beihefte (Bonn)
0416-928X Delpinoa
0416-9336 Delta Pi Epsilon. Research Bulletin
0416-9565 Democrazia e Diritto
0417-0164 Denmark. Danmarks Statistik. Detailpriser
0417-0296 Denryoku to Tetsudo
0417-0792 Dermatologia i Venerologia
0417-0946 Desert Locust Newsletter *see* 1014-2193
0417-2051 Deutsche Gesellschaft fuer Musik des Orients. Mitteilungen
0417-2957 Z D
0417-3635 Deutsches Soldatenjahrbuch
0417-3937 Dharmayug
0417-5190 Dirasat Arabiyat
0417-5271 Direct Line
0417-5522 Directory of American Horticulture *changed to* North American Horticulture: A Reference Guide.
0417-5662 British Commonwealth Collections of Micro-Organisms. Directory of Collections and List of Species Maintained in Australia†
0417-5751 Directory of Conventions
0417-5905 Directory of Geophysical and Oil Companies Who Use Geophysical Service†
0417-5964 Directory of Indian Engineering Exporters
0417-6383 Directory of Professional Electrologists
0417-6766 Diritto e Pratica nell'Assicurazione
0417-9382 Dominica. Ministry of Finance and Development. Annual Overseas Trade Report
0417-9927 Doriana
0417-9994 Dortmunder Beitraege zur Zeitungsforschung
0418-1263 Duesseldorf in Zahlen
0418-1379 Dukes County Intelligencer
0418-2057 Dwarf Iris Society Portfolio
0418-2642 Quaternary Research
0418-2693 Daily Labor Report
0418-3304 Danish Films
0418-3746 University of Dar es Salaam. Economic Research Bureau. Papers
0418-3770 Dar es Salaam University Law Journal
0418-3975 Geography Publications at Dartmouth†
0418-4297 Daugavas Vanagu Menesraksts
0418-5013 Defense Indicators†
0418-5021 Defense Industry Bulletin *see* 0011-7595
0418-5633 I.A.M.R. Reports
0418-582X Documentation List: Africa
0418-6303 Denki Kagaku Newsletter *see* 0366-9297
0418-6435 Risoe-M
0418-6443 Denmark. Atomenergikomissionens Forsoegsanslaeg, Risoe. Risoe Report *changed to* Denmark. Forskningscenter Risoe. Risoe-R.
0418-6559 Groenlands Geologiske Undersoegelse. Rapport
0418-6745 Denmark Review
0418-694X Dental Outlook†

ISSN

ISSN INDEX 5737

0418-7598 Desert Bighorn Council. Transactions

0418-761X Desert Locust Control Organization for Eastern Africa. Annual Report

0418-7717 Designed in Finland *see* 0782-4327

0418-7830 Detalle

0418-8233 Deutsche Bibliographie. Fuenfjahres-Verzeichnis *changed to* Deutsche Nationalbibliographie. Fuenfjahres-Verzeichnis.

0418-8314 Deutsche Bundesbank. Monatsberichte. Statistische Beihefte. Reihe 2: Wertpapierstatistik

0418-8322 Deutsche Bundesbank. Monatsberichte. Statistische Beihefte. Reihe 3: Zahlungsbilanzstatistik

0418-8330 Deutsche Bundesbank. Monatsberichte. Statistische Beihefte. Reihe 4: Saisonbereinigte Wirtschaftszahlen

0418-8381 Das Deutsche Firmen-Alphabet

0418-842X Deutsche Forschungsgemeinschaft. Mexiko-Projekt

0418-8802 Der Deutsche Lehrer im Ausland

0418-9140 Deutsche Studien†

0418-9426 Deutscher Germanisten-Verband. Mitteilungen

0418-9698 Baghdader Mitteilungen

0418-9701 Istanbuler Mitteilungen. Beihefte

0418-9779 Germanische Denkmaeler der Voelkerwanderungszeit

0418-9906 Dokumente zur Aussenpolitik der Deutschen Demokratischen Republik†

0419-005X Deutschsprachige Zeitschriften Deutschland - Oesterreich - Schweiz *changed to* Deutschsprachige Zeitschriften.

0419-0254 Developments in Geotectonics

0419-0432 Hukerikar Memorial Lecture Series

0419-0505 Diabetikeren

0419-0637 Dialog der Gesellschaft

0419-0890 Dianoia

0419-1137 Dictionary of International Biography

0419-1153 Dictionnaire Vidal

0419-1188 Didaskalos†

0419-1218 Didattica delle Scienze e Informatica nella Scuola

0419-1285 Digest of Commercial Laws of the World

0419-1293 Digest of Current Industrial and Labour Law

0419-1544 Dinamika i Prochnost' Mashin

0419-182X Standard Rate and Data Service. Direct Mail List Rates and Data

0419-1854 Direction (Washington)†

0419-2052 Directors Guild of America. Directory of Members

0419-2109 Directory of Alcoholism Treatment Facilities, Domiciliary Houses and State and Provincial Alcoholism *see* 0092-3826

0419-2206 Directory of Blood Banking and Transfusion Facilities and Services†

0419-2281 C I B Directory of Building Research Information and Development Organizations *changed to* International Directory of Building Research, Information and Development Organizations.

0419-2370 Directory of Collections and List of Species Maintained in Canada†

0419-2400 Directory of Communicators in Agriculture†

0419-2443 Directory of Cooperative Organisations in South-East Asia†

0419-2508 Directory of Department Stores (Year)

0419-2559 Directory of Educational Opportunities in Georgia *changed to* Georgia Post-Secondary School Directory: A Guide to Colleges, Vocational-Technical Schools & Special Purpose Institutions.

0419-2648 Directory of Fire Research in the United States *changed to* Directory of Fire Research.

0419-2818 Directory of Jewish Health and Welfare Agencies†

0419-2923 Directory of Mailing List Companies

0419-3040 Directory of Music Faculties in American Colleges and Universities *see* 0098-664X

0419-3253 Directory of Physics and Astronomy Facilities in North American Colleges and Universities *see* 0361-2228

0419-3733 Directory of the Cultural Organizations of the Republic of China

0419-3806 Directory of the Turf *changed to* The Turf Directory.

0419-3857 Directory of Washington State Manufacturers, Products, Industry, Location *see* 0148-5687

0419-3865 Directory of Water Pollution Research Laboratories†

0419-3903 Direktor

0419-3911 Dirigente Municipal

0419-4187 Dispatch (Springfield)

0419-4209 Dissertation Abstracts International. Section A: Humanities and Social Sciences

0419-4217 Dissertation Abstracts International. Section B: Physical Sciences and Engineering

0419-4241 Dissertationes Archaeologicae Gandenses†

0419-4357 Distribution of Physicians, Hospital, Hospital Beds in the U S *see* 0731-0315

0419-4632 Dizionario Bibliografico delle Riviste Giuridiche Italiane

0419-5345 Documentation on Asia

0419-5361 Documentation Photographique

0419-537X Documentation sur l'Europe Centrale†

0419-5728 Documents pour la Carte de la Vegetation des Alpes *changed to* Revue d'Ecologie Alpine.

0419-5736 Documents pour Servir a l'Histoire de l'Afrique Equatoriale Francaise. Deuxieme Serie. Brazza et la Fondation du Congo Francaise†

0419-7305 Saechsische Bibliographie

0419-747X Droit de l'Espace†

0419-764X Drug Topics Health & Beauty Aids Directory†

0419-7674 Drum

0419-7682 Drum (Nigerian Edition)

0419-7925 Dubrovacki Horizonti

0419-8050 Duke Endowment. Annual Report

0419-8093 Duke University. Council on Aging and Human Development. Proceedings of Seminars†

0419-8719 Dvigateli Vnutrennego Sgoraniya

0419-8735 Dwon Lwak

0419-8816 Dzieje Lublina

0419-8824 Dzieje Najnowsze

0419-9014 Deutsche Bundesbank. Monatsberichte. Statistische Beihefte. Reihe 1: Bankenstatistik nach Bankengruppen

0419-9081 Diagramm

0419-9154 Directory of Textile Plant Processes†

0419-9472 Danmarks 500 Stoerste Virksomheder *changed to* Danmarks 15000 Stoerste Virksomheder.

0419-9855 Delta (Palmerston North) *see* 0110-4748

0420-0098 Design Automation Workshop. Proceedings *see* 0738-100X

0420-0152 Deutsche Bibliothek

0420-0195 Deutsche Physikalische Gesellschaft. Verhandlungen

0420-0632 Directory of Law Enforcement Professors†

0420-073X Dissertation Abstracts. Section B: the Sciences and Engineering *see* 0419-4217

0420-0918 Doshisha American Studies

0420-0942 Test Yourself for Science†

0420-1132 Dansk Geologisk Forening. Aarsskrift

0420-2155 Directory of Engineers and Land Surveyors Registered in South Carolina

0420-2384 Dydaktyka Szkoly Wyzszej

0420-2392 Dziko

0420-3690 Eastern Indiana Farmer *changed to* FarmWeek (Knightstown).

0420-8870 Einst und Jetzt†

0420-9397 Electric Power Industry in Japan

0420-9885 Der Elektrofachmann

0421-0670 Elternhaus und Schule

0421-1715 Energetica

0421-2835 Entisaikain Helsinki

0421-2991 Entscheidungen der Finanzgerichte

0421-3750 Erkennungsblaetter

0421-4226 E S O P E

0421-4935 Est Industriel et Commercial†

0421-4986 Estadisticas de la Aviacion Civil en Espana

0421-5370 Estudios Internacionales *see* 0185-1616

0421-6423 Europe Service†

0421-7527 European Congress of Cardiology. Abstracts of Papers

0421-8094 Evangelical Magazine of Wales

0421-9090 Exile

0421-9724 Extension *see* 0020-4919

0421-9910 Analysis of Public Utility Financing

0422-017X ERB-Dom†

0422-0943 East Anglia Life

0422-1001 East-European Spokesman

0422-1494 Eastern Europe Agricultural Situation *changed to* World Agriculture Regional Supplement: Eastern Europe.

0422-1540 Eastern Industrial World *changed to* Northeastern Industrial World.

0422-2482 Echoes from the East Tennessee Historical Society *changed to* Newsline (Knoxville).

0422-2504 Echos des Communications†

0422-2555 Eco

0422-2628 Eco Motori

0422-2733 Economia Colombiana

0422-2784 Economia Industrial

0422-2954 Economic Research Institute. Economic Bulletin†

0422-5740 Edinburgh Tatler

0422-6186 Editur

0422-6690 Educational Council for Foreign Medical Graduates. Annual Report *see* 0145-2037

0422-6739 Educational Quest†

0422-7727 Ehime Daigaku Kyoikugakubu Kiyo. Dai-3-bu. Shizen Kagaku

0422-8707 Electrical Distributor

0422-9053 Electronic Industry Telephone Directory (Year)

0422-9576 Elelmiszervizsgalati Kozlemenyek

0422-9878 Elsevier Lexica†

0422-9932 Elu Local

0423-104X Endokrynologia Polska

0423-1163 Energiewirtschaft

0423-3174 Ertong Shidai

0423-4243 Espresso

0423-4596 Financial Estate Planners Quarterly

0423-4847 Estudios de Deusto

0423-5037 Estudios Turisticos

0423-5509 Etnoloski Pregled

0423-5673 Etudes Eburneennes

0423-5975 Eulenspiegel

0423-6645 E A A S Newsletter

0423-6777 European Bureau of Adult Education. Notes & Studies†

0423-6831 European Coal and Steel Community. Consultative Committee. Yearbook

0423-6955 Commission of the European Communities. Collection du Droit du Travail†

0423-7242 European Congress of Cardiology. (Proceedings)

0423-7269 European Cotton Industry Statistics†

0423-7781 European Organization for Nuclear Research. Repertoire des Communications Scientifiques. Index of Scientific Publications *see* 0304-2871

0423-7846 European Parliament. Bulletin

0423-8044 European Purchasing Conference. (Proceedings)

0423-8346 Evangelisch-Lutherische Landeskirche Sachsens. Amtsblatt

0423-8710 Everybody's Money

0424-0227 E U M E N Action†

0424-0928 East African Studies

0424-107X East Kentuckian

0424-1088 East Midland Archaeological Bulletin *changed to* East Midlands Archaeology.

0424-1401 East Pakistan Medical Journal *see* 0301-035X

0424-1851 Eastern Nigerian School Libraries Association. Bulletin *see* 0331-8109

0424-2033 Eau Pure

0424-2238 Ecole des Parents

0424-2483 Economia Politica

0424-2513 Economic Affairs

0424-2769 Economic Education Bulletin

0424-2815 Government College. Economic Journal

0424-3145 Economie Agricole

0424-3331 E I U World Outlook

0424-3374 Economista Mexicano†

0424-480X Year-End Summary of the Electric Power Situation in the United States *changed to* Electric Power Annual Report.

0424-4923 Editor & Publisher International Year Book

0424-5059 Edmund's Used Car Prices

0424-5393 Education des Adultes *see* 0018-8891

0424-5407 Education Development Center. Annual Report

0424-5504 Education in the Americas Information Series; Bulletin†

0424-5512 Education in the North

0424-6241 Educators Guide to Free Health, Physical Education & Recreation Materials

0424-6268 E D U C O M Bulletin *changed to* E D U C O M Review.

0424-7086 Japanese Journal of Sanitary Zoology

0424-7116 Eiszeitalter und Gegenwart

0424-7558 Ekonomski Pregled

0424-7701 Electra

0424-7760 Electrical Engineering in Japan

0424-8201 Electron Microscopy Society of America. Proceedings

0424-8287 Electronic Production Aids Catalog *changed to* Electronic Packaging and Production Vendor Selection Issue.

0424-8368 Electronics and Communications in Japan

0424-8384 Electronics Hobbyist†

0424-8562 Das Elektrofach

0424-8775 Elements de Bibliographie†

0424-8848 Elet es Irodalom

0424-9283 Empirical Research in Accounting, Selected Studies *changed to* Journal of Accounting Research. Supplement.

0424-9402 Commercial Bank of Greece. Report of the Chairman of the Board of Directors

0424-9674 Encuentro

0424-9844 Energeticheskoe Mashinostroenie

0425-0494 English in Education

0425-0508 English in Texas

0425-0575 English Miscellany†

0425-1067 Entomological Society of Nigeria. Bulletin *see* 0331-0094

0425-1288 Entscheidungen der Oberlandesgerichte in Zivilsachen

0425-1466 Ephemerides Mariologicae

0425-1482 Epidemiologija, Mikrobiologija i Infekciozni Bolesti

0425-1644 Equine Veterinary Journal

0425-1741 Erdkundliches Wissen

0425-2772 Espanol Actual

0425-340X Estudio Agustiniano

0425-3442 Estudios Agrarios

0425-3485 Revista de Estudios Cooperativos

0425-3698 Estudios Empresariales

0425-3752 Estudios Lulianos *changed to* Studia Lulliana.

0425-4082 Estudos Universitarios

0425-4309 Ethiopia. Customs Head Office. External Trade Statistics

0425-4414 Ethiopian Journal of Education

0425-4597 Ethnologia Europaea

0425-4791 Revue des Lettres Modernes. Etudes Bernanosiennes

ISSN

5738 ISSN INDEX

0425-4937 Commission of the European Communities. Collection Physiologie et Psychologie du Travail†

0425-497X Conseil Oecumenique des Eglises. Etudes†

0425-5054 Etudes et Sports Sous-Marins *changed to* Subaqua.

0425-5089 F A O Nutrition Meeting for Europe. Report.†

0425-5291 F I S Bulletin

0425-5860 Fact Finder *see* 0260-6429

0425-676X Family Economics Review

0425-7111 Far East Film News *see* 0047-8288

0425-7170 Far East Reporter *changed to* Far East Traveler.

0425-9076 Federation des Industries Chimiques de Belgique. Annuaire

0426-2700 Shobo Kenkyujo Hokoku

0426-3383 Fizyka w Szkole

0426-7230 Fontes Iuris Gentium. Section 2

0426-8261 Footprints (Fort Worth)

0426-844X For Men Only†

0426-9373 Forestal

0426-9918 Forschungsgesellschaft fuer das Strassenwesen. Arbeitsgruppe Asphalt- und Teerstrassen. Schriftenreihe *changed to* Forschungsgesellschaft fuer Strassen- und Verkehrswesen. Arbeitsgruppe Asphalt- und Teerstrassen. Schriftenreihe.

0427-0576 Foto

0427-2218 Institut Geographique National. Bulletin d'Information

0427-5217 Freie Welt†

0427-7058 Fujian Jiaoyu

0427-7074 Fujian Zhongyi Yao

0427-7082 Fujian Nongxueyuan Xuebao

0427-7104 Fudan Xuebao (Ziran Kexue Ban)

0427-7112 Fudao Yuan

0427-7554 Fundacao Getulio Vargas. Boletim Informativo *changed to* Fundacao Getulio Vargas. Informativo.

0427-7783 Der Fuss

0427-7945 Fynske Minder

0427-8070 F A O Regional Conference for Asia and the Far East. Report *changed to* F A O Regional Conference for Asia and the Pacific. Report.

0427-8089 F A O Regional Conference for the Near East. Report

0427-8321 F I F A Official Bulletin *changed to* F I F A News.

0427-8879 Facts

0427-8968 Yugoslav Facts and Views

0427-9107 Faerg och Fernissa

0427-9522 Familiengeschichtliche Blaetter und Mitteilungen

0427-959X Family Fare†

0427-9638 Family Law Newsletter *see* 0163-710X

0427-9824 Fantasmagie

0428-0296 Farmatsia

0428-061X Fauna Japonica†

0428-1039 Federacion Sudamericana de Asociaciones Cristianas de Jovenes. Noticias *changed to* Confederacion Latinoamericana de Asociaciones Cristianas de Jovenes. Carta.

0428-1128 Federal Economic Review *see* 0254-9204

0428-1276 Economic Commentary

0428-1365 Federal Savings and Loan Insurance Corporation. List of Member Institutions *changed to* Federal Home Loan Bank System. List of Member Institutions.

0428-1659 Federation Internationale de Gymnastique. Bulletin

0428-1845 Federation of Kenya Employers. Newsletter *changed to* Kenya Employer.

0428-2779 Feuillets de Biologie

0428-304X Field Studies

0428-3279 Fiji. Geological Survey. Economic Investigation *changed to* Fiji. Mineral Resources Department. Economic Investigation.

0428-3341 Filatelia

0428-4666 Fire Control Notes†

0428-4836 First Days

0428-4879 Citibank. Foreign Information Service. Annual Summary of Exchange and Foreign Trade Regulations†

0428-5018 Fischwirt†

0428-5190 Fishing Guidebook

0428-5387 Museum of Northern Arizona Glen Canyon Series†

0428-5395 Museum of Northern Arizona Technical Series†

0428-5573 Flashback

0428-5670 Flexographic Technical Association. Report of the Proceedings: Annual Meeting and Technical Forum *changed to* Foundation of Flexographic Technical Association. Report of the Proceedings: Annual Meeting and Technical Forum.

0428-5735 Flight Safety Foundation News

0428-6294 Florida. Department of Agriculture and Consumer Services. Division of Plant Industry. Bulletin Series

0428-6766 Florida State University. Publications of the Faculty

0428-7738 Fluid Power Handbook & Directory

0428-819X Foldrajzi Monografiak

0428-8211 Folger Shakespeare Library Annual Report†

0428-8254 Folia Antropologica

0428-8386 Folison†

0428-903X Fontes Iuris Gentium *see* 0426-7230

0428-9269 F A O Fisheries Papers *see* 0429-9345

0428-9374 Food and Agriculture Organization of the United Nations. Forestry Occasional Paper†

0428-9390 Food and Agriculture Organization of the United Nations. Index of Agricultural Institutions in Europe†

0428-9447 Nutrition Newsletter *see* 0304-8942

0428-9552 Food and Agriculture Organization of the United Nations. Animal Health Branch. Animal Health Monograph†

0428-9625 F A O Papers on Demand Analysis†

0428-9749 Food and Agricultural Organization of the United Nations. Plant Protection Committee for Southeast Asia and Pacific Region. Quarterly Newsletter *changed to* Food and Agriculture Organization of the United Nations. Asia and Pacific Plant Protection Commission. Quarterly Newsletter.

0428-9765 Food and Agricultural Organization of the United Nations. Plant Protection Committee for Southeast Asia and Pacific Region. Technical Document *changed to* Food and Agriculture Organization of the United Nations. Asia and Pacific Plant Protection Commission. Technical Document.

0429-0208 Footwear News Fact Book

0429-0550 Forefront: News from New Zealand†

0429-0917 Forest Products News†

0429-1050 Form & Zweck

0429-1573 Forschungen zur Innsbrucker Universitaetsgeschichte

0429-1816 Forschungsgesellschaft fuer das Strassenwesen. Arbeitsgruppe Betonstrassen. Schriftenreihe *changed to* Forschungsgesellschaft fuer Strassen- und Verkehrswesen. Arbeitsgruppe Betonstrassen. Schriftenreihe.

0429-2405 P I D C Journal *changed to* Civil Aviation in Pakistan: Half-Yearly Newsletter.

0429-2871 Fragmenta Coleopterologica

0429-288X Fragmenta Entomologica

0429-3843 France. Direction du Gaz et de l'Electricite. Statistiques Officielles de l'Industrie Gaziere en France *changed to* Statistiques de l'Industrie Gaziere en France.

0429-4092 Bulletin Mensuel de Statistiques Industrielles†

0429-5412 France-Horizon

0429-7539 Frodskaparrit; Annales Societatis Scientiarum Faeroensis. Supplementa

0429-7725 Frontiers in Physics

0429-7830 Fruchthandel

0429-7857 Fruits et Abeilles

0429-8020 Fujian Huabao

0429-8047 Fujian Nongye

0429-8284 Fuji Electric Review

0429-8357 Fujikura Technical Review

0429-8764 Centro de Estudios Sociales de la Santa Cruz del Valle de los Caidos. Boletin *see* 0303-9889

0429-8918 Fundamenty

0429-8950 Fundidor

0429-9159 Furukawa Review

0429-9329 F A O Fisheries Circulars

0429-9337 F A O Fisheries Reports

0429-9345 F A O Fisheries Technical Paper

0429-9353 F A O Regional Conference for Africa

0429-9388 F A O - W H O Expert Panel on Veterinary Education. Report of the Meeting†

0429-9442 F D A Clinical Experience Abstracts†

0429-9574 Faba

0429-9639 Fabulous Mexico

0429-9655 Fachbibliographischer Dienst Bibliothekswesen†

0430-0440 Familienkundliches Jahrbuch Schleswig-Holstein

0430-0610 Far East Scouting Bulletin *changed to* Asia - Pacific Scouting.

0430-0750 Farm Chemicals Handbook

0430-084X Farm Management Notes for Asia and the Far East

0430-1188 Faulkner Facts and Fiddlings

0430-1536 Federacion Latinoamericana de Bancos. Revista *changed to* Revista FeLaBan.

0430-1692 Federal Employees' News Digest

0430-1919 Federal Reserve Bank of Chicago. Seventh District Statistics†

0430-1943 Federal Reserve Bank Reviews†

0430-2222 Congress F A T I P E C

0430-2419 Federation Internationale des Syndicats Chretiens d'Ouvriers Agricoles. Travailleur de la Terre†

0430-2583 Federation of Insurance Counsel Quarterly *see* 0887-0942

0430-2990 Femina

0430-327X Fertiliser Association of India. Fertiliser Statistics

0430-3288 Fertiliser Association of India. Annual Review of Fertiliser. Consumption and Production *see* 0015-0266

0430-3873 Figurentheater

0430-4055 Fikr-o-Nazar

0430-4497 Filmoteca Ultramarina Portuguesa. Boletim

0430-4578 Il Filo Metallico

0430-4748 Financial Aid News†

0430-5205 Finland. Kansanelakelaitos. Julkaisuja. Sarja A

0430-5272 Finland. Tilastokeskus. Liikennetilastollinen Vuosikirja

0430-5280 Finland. Tyovoimaministerio. Tyovoimakatsaus†

0430-5299 Finland. Laakintohallitus. Laakarit, Hammaslaakarit, Sairaalat *changed to* Finland. Laakintohallitus. Laakarit, Hammaslaakarit - Lakare, Tandlaekare.

0430-5329 Finland. National Board of Agriculture. Statistics. Monthly Review of Agricultural Statistics

0430-5566 Finland. Tilastokeskus. Kuntien Finanssitilasto *see* 0359-081X

0430-5604 Finland. Tilastokeskus. Talonrakennustilasto

0430-5612 Finland. Tilastokeskus. Vaestonmuutokset *changed to* Finland. Tilastokeskus. Vaestoe.

0430-5809 Schriften aus dem Finnland-Institut Koeln

0430-5817 Finsk Palstidskrift

0430-6155 Fitopatologia

0430-6252 Fiziko-Khimicheskaya Mekhanika Materialov

0430-635X Museum of Northern Arizona Ceramic Series†

0430-6457 Fleet Street Patent Law Reports *changed to* Fleet Street Reports.

0430-666X Flore de la Nouvelle Caledonie et Dependances

0430-6953 Florida Tourist Study *changed to* Florida's Visitors.

0430-7291 Florida State University. Slavic Papers *changed to* Florida State University. Center for Yugoslav-American Studies, Research, and Exchanges. Proceedings and Reports of Seminars and Research.

0430-7313 Florida State University. Educational Media Center. Educational Motion Pictures *changed to* Florida State University. Instructional Support Center. Film and Video.

0430-7658 Florida Economic Indicators†

0430-7690 Florida F L Reporter†

0430-7801 Florida Public Documents

0430-7941 Flour Milling and Baking Research Association Abstracts

0430-8247 Focus (Waterloo)†

0430-8603 Folia Entomologica Mexicana

0430-8751 Folk Dance Scene

0430-8778 Folk Life: Journal of Ethnological Studies

0430-8913 G B Journal

0430-9928 Galloway Journal

0431-1930 GeoChile

0431-1981 Geografia nelle Scuole

0431-2155 Geological Society of China. Proceedings

0431-5480 Germany (Federal Republic, 1949-). Bundeskriminalamt. Polizeiliche Kriminalstatistik (Year)

0431-6045 Economic Situation in the Federal Republic of Germany

0431-8315 Ghana. Meteorological Department. Monthly Summary of Rainfall

0431-8323 Ghana. Meteorological Department. Monthly Weather Report

0431-8943 Gioventu al Lavoro

0431-915X Glades Star

0431-9168 Gladio Grams

0432-1251 Arstryck

0432-2924 R E M E Journal

0432-6105 Greece

0432-7454 Grundlagen und Fortschritte der Lebensmitteluntersuchung *see* 0341-0498

0432-9120 Guida Nazionale del Commercio Con l'Estero

0433-0730 Gaceta Bibliotecaria del Peru

0433-0854 Gaceta Indigenista

0433-0919 Garden Life

0433-230X Gdanskie Towarzystwo Naukowe. Wydzial 1. Nauk Spolecznych i Humanistycznych. Seria Monografii

0433-2733 Gelderse Bloem

0433-3179 Genealogical Forum of Portland, Oregon. Quarterly Bulletin *changed to* Genealogical Forum of Oregon. Bulletin.

0433-3519 General Fisheries Council for the Mediterranean. Studies and Reviews

0433-4035 Nuclear Engineering

0433-4515 Geographical Outlook *see* 0046-5712

0433-5015 Australia. Bureau of Mineral Resource, Geology and Geophysics. Geophysical Observatory Group. Report *changed to* Australian Geomagnetism Report.

0433-5473 Georgia Geological Survey. Information Circular

0433-6305 German Business Weekly *changed to* German American Trade.

0433-681X Nautisches Jahrbuch†

0433-6844 Statistisches Taschenbuch der D D R

0433-6933 Zentralinstitut fuer Bibliothekswesen. Mitteilungen und Materialien†

ISSN

ISSN INDEX 5739

ISSN	Title
0433-7344	Germany (Federal Republic, 1949-). Bundesministerium fuer Ernaehrung, Landwirtschaft und Forsten. Statistischer Monatsbericht
0433-7484	Wirtschaftliche Lage in der Bundesrepublik Deutschland
0433-7603	Weltwirtschaft am Jahreswechsel changed to Weltwirtschaftslage am Jahreswechsel.
0433-7646	Entscheidungen des Bundesverfassungsgerichts
0433-8251	Deutscher Wetterdienst. Jahresbericht
0433-860X	Gesellschaft fuer Bibliothekswesen und Dokumentation des Landbaues. Mitteilungen
0433-969X	Ghana Year Book†
0434-0035	Giessener Schriftenreihe Tierzucht und Haustiergenetik
0434-0094	Gifu Pharmaceutical University. Annual Proceedings
0434-0299	Giornale†
0434-040X	Giurisprudenza Agraria Italiana
0434-0760	Politechnika Slaska. Zeszyty Naukowe. Automatyka
0434-0779	Politechnika Slaska. Zeszyty Naukowe. Budownictwo
0434-0817	Politechnika Slaska. Zeszyty Naukowe. Mechanika
0434-1066	Glyndebourne Festival Programme Book
0434-2151	Gospodarka i Administracja Terenowa changed to Rada Narodowa, Gospodarka, Administracja.
0434-2410	Goeteborgs Universitet. Nationalekonomiska Institutionen. Ekonomiska Studier
0434-2593	Government Contracts Citator
0434-3336	Le Grand Baton
0434-3581	Grands Naturalistes Francais†
0434-3883	Steiermaerkisches Landesarchiv. Mitteilungen
0434-5975	Greater Minneapolis changed to Guide to Leading Twin Cities Companies.
0434-6785	Instituut voor Bodemvruchtbaarheid. Jaarverslag
0434-8850	Guide to Employment Abroad†
0434-9067	Guide to U S Government Statistics
0434-9245	Guild of Book Workers Journal
0435-1096	Gamma Field Symposia
0435-1312	Gas Turbine International see 0149-4147
0435-1339	Gastroenterologia Japonica
0435-1568	Rocznik Kulturalny Ziemi Gdanskiej changed to Gdanski Rocznik Kulturalny.
0435-1754	Gekkan Shakaito
0435-1924	Geltende Seekriegsrecht in Einzeldarstellungen changed to Das Geltende Seevoelkerrecht in Einzeldarstellungen.
0435-2033	Bulletin des Recherches Agronomiques de Gembloux
0435-219X	Gendai no Me
0435-284X	Genetik
0435-2866	Studies on Voltaire and the Eighteenth Century
0435-2874	I I L S Bulletin see 0378-5408
0435-2939	Observatoire de Geneve. Publications. Serie B
0435-3048	Universita degli Studi di Genova, Facolta di Giurisprudenza. Annali
0435-3676	Geografiska Annaler. Series A. Physical Geography
0435-3684	Geografiska Annaler. Series B. Human Geography
0435-3730	Geographia Medica Hungarica see 0300-807X
0435-382X	Aardrijkskunde - Geographie changed to Aardrijkskunde.
0435-3838	Geographische Gesellschaft zu Hannover. Jahrbuch changed to Hannoversche Geographische Arbeiten.
0435-3870	Geologia Applicata e Idrogeologia
0435-401X	Geological Society of Jamaica. Journal
0435-4311	Geonews
0435-5113	University of Georgia. Geography Curriculum Project Publications†
0435-5253	Georgia Advocate
0435-5261	Georgia Alert
0435-5385	Georgia Genealogical Magazine
0435-5482	Georgia Manufacturing Directory
0435-5601	Geos
0435-7124	Entscheidungen des Bundesgerichtshofes in Zivilsachen
0435-7183	Bundesinstitut fuer Ostwissenschaftliche und Internationale Studien. Berichte
0435-7329	Germany (Federal Republic, 1949-). Bundesministerium fuer das Post- und Fernmeldewesen. Jahresrechnung, Nachweisung ueber die Einnahmen und Ausgaben der Deutschen Bundespost changed to Germany (Federal Republic, 1949-). Bundesministerium fuer das Post- und Fernmeldewesen. Haushaltsrechnung, Nachweisung ueber die Einnahmen und Ausgaben der Deutschen Bundespost.
0435-7442	Gesamtstatistik der Kraftfahrtversicherung
0435-7965	Deutscher Wetterdienst. Monatlicher Witterungsbericht
0435-8406	Gesher
0435-852X	Gesundheitstechnik changed to Umwelttechnik.
0435-8600	Gewerblicher Rechtsschutz und Urheberrecht. Internationaler Teil
0435-8805	External Trade Statistics of Ghana
0435-8864	Ghana. Central Bureau of Statistics. Quarterly Digest of Statistics changed to Ghana. Statistical Service. Quarterly Digest of Statistics.
0435-9348	Ghana Commercial Bank. Annual Report
0435-9380	Ghana Journal of Sociology
0435-9437	Ghana Radio and Television Times changed to G B C Radio and T V Times.
0435-950X	Rijksuniversiteit te Gent. Centrum voor Onkruidonderzoek. Mededeling
0436-0257	Giving U S A
0436-0265	Gizi Indonesia
0436-029X	Gladius
0436-046X	Glasnik Arhiva i Drustva Arhivskih Radnika Bosne i Hercegovine
0436-0524	Glasshouse Crops Research Institute. Annual Report†
0436-0605	Glenbow Foundation. Archives Series changed to Glenbow Museum. Archives Series.
0436-0664	Globusfreund
0436-1024	Godesberger Heimatblaetter
0436-1121	Goeteborg Studies in Educational Sciences
0436-113X	Goeteborgs Kungliga Vetenskaps- och Vitterhets-Samhaelle. Aarsbok
0436-1202	Universitaet Goettingen. Jahresbericht changed to Universitaet Goettingen. Jahresforschungsbericht.
0436-1326	Gokhale Institute Mimeograph Series
0436-1474	Golf Course Superintendents Association of America. Membership Directory
0436-1563	Good News (Wilmore)
0436-1571	Good Tidings changed to East Asian Pastoral Review.
0436-2020	Etnografiska Museet, Goteborg. Aarstyck see 0280-3887
0436-2225	U S - R & D
0436-2616	Gradina
0436-2624	Gradinarska i Lozarska Nauka
0436-7316	Handbook of the Indian Cotton Textile Industry
0437-133X	Heating and Ventilating Research Association. Technical Notes see 0309-0248
0437-2468	Helsingin Laakarilehti
0437-3014	Herbergen der Christenheit†
0437-5602	Hispania Antiqua Epigraphica†
0437-6315	Deutscher Hochschulverband. Mitteilungen
0437-6633	Hokenjo Un'ei Hokoku Nenpo see 0911-8411
0437-7168	Die Holzzunft
0438-0460	Xiamen Daxue Xuebao (Zhexue Shehui Kexue Ban)
0438-0479	Xiamen Daxue Xuebao (Ziran Kexue Ban)
0438-1033	Xueshu Luntan
0438-1629	Human Factors Society Bulletin
0438-2013	Hungarian Travel Magazine†
0438-2242	Budapest Statisztikai Zsebkonyv
0438-4385	Martin-Luther-Universitaet Halle-Wittenberg. Wissenschaftliche Zeitschrift
0438-4415	Universitaets- und Landesbibliothek Sachsen-Anhalt. Arbeiten
0438-4555	Protokolle zur Fischereitechnik
0438-5004	Handakten fuer die Standesamtliche Arbeit†
0438-5403	Handel Wewnetrzny
0438-8887	Heating and Ventilating Research Association. Laboratory Reports see 0305-5973
0438-895X	Hebrew Abstracts see 0146-4094
0438-9050	Heilongjiang Jiaoyu
0439-0687	Hessische Floristische Briefe
0439-1292	Highway
0439-1365	Hikaku Ho Kenkyu
0439-1551	Das Himmelsjahr
0439-1705	Hirosaki University. Faculty of Literature and Science. Science Reports see 0367-6439
0439-1721	Hirosaki Medical Journal
0439-2116	Historia Junior changed to Gister en Vandag.
0439-2183	Historian Aitta
0439-2248	Historic Nantucket
0439-2345	Historical News
0439-237X	Michigan Historical Review (Mt. Pleasant)
0439-2795	Hitachi Zosen News
0439-3465	Hokkaido University. Research Institute of Applied Electricity. Monograph Series†
0439-3511	Hokkaido University. Faculty of Fisheries. Data Record of Oceanographic Observations and Exploratory Fishing
0439-3538	Low Temperature Science. Series A. Physical Science
0439-3546	Low Temperature Science. Series B. Biological Science†
0439-3600	Japan. Hokuriku National Agricultural Experiment Station. Bulletin
0439-3678	Holiday Time in Thailand†
0439-4208	Homiletica
0439-4216	Homme
0439-4291	Homo Faber
0439-5530	Horisont
0439-5956	National Institute of Radiological Sciences. Annual Report
0439-6162	Hospitalisation Privee
0439-755X	Xinli Xuebao
0439-7843	Xueqian Jiaoyu
0439-8041	Xueshu Yuekan
0439-8106	Hunan Wenxue
0439-9056	Hungarian Co-operation
0439-9080	Hungarian P.E.N.
0439-9285	Hungary. Kozponti Statisztikai Hivatal. Haztartasstatisztika
0439-9714	Husserliana
0440-0607	Haematologie und Bluttransfusion
0440-0771	Tuinbouwcijfers
0440-1352	Hallmark†
0440-1417	Altonaer Museum in Hamburg. Nordeutsches Landesmuseum. Jahrbuch
0440-1719	Hamburger Mittel-Ostdeutsche Forschungen
0440-1875	Handboek van de Nederlandse Pers en Publiciteit
0440-193X	Handbook on International Study: for Foreign Nationals changed to Handbook on U.S. Study for Foreign Nationals.
0440-1948	Handbook on International Study for U.S. Nationals see 0364-1449
0440-2103	Handbuch des Oeffentlichen Lebens in Oesterreich
0440-2278	Handjuawg
0440-2316	Hanging Loose
0440-2510	Korean Journal of Zoology
0440-2863	Hans - Pfitzner - Gesellschaft. Mitteilungen
0440-3428	Harvard Germanic Studies†
0440-3452	Harvard Monographs in Applied Science†
0440-4122	Haskins & Sells. Selected Papers†
0440-4947	Directory of State, County, and Federal Officials
0440-5145	Hawaiian Journal of History
0440-5234	Hawkeye Heritage
0440-5323	Haydn - Studien
0440-548X	Health Education Abstracts†
0440-5609	Health Organizations of the U.S., Canada and the World
0440-5730	Heartbeat†
0440-5749	Heat Transfer - Soviet Research
0440-5757	Heather Society. Yearbook
0440-5757	Heather Society. Bulletin
0440-5927	Hegel - Studien Beihefte
0440-601X	Universitaet Heidelberg. Suedasien-Institut. Schriftenreihe
0440-6230	Heimatgruss
0440-6826	Hemijski Pregled
0440-7059	Herion - Informationen
0440-7180	Hermeneutische Untersuchungen zur Theologie
0440-7881	Higher Education in New England changed to Connection (Boston).
0440-8152	Hillside Hospital Journal see 0193-5216
0440-9043	Historia Hospitalium
0440-9078	Acta Universitatis Upsaliensis. Historia Litterarum
0440-9205	Historica
0440-9213	Historical Archaeology
0440-9221	Historical Arms Series
0440-9264	Historical Association of Tanzania. Papers
0440-9426	Chronicle (Ann Arbor)
0440-9515	Historicke Studie
0440-9558	Historische Forschungen
0440-9728	Historisches Jahrbuch der Stadt Graz
0440-9736	Historisches Jahrbuch der Stadt Linz
0440-9809	Historisk-Topografisk Selskab for Gladsaxe Kommune. Arsskrift
0440-9884	History of Economic Thought Newsletter
0441-0017	Shizen Kagaku Kenkyu (Tokyo)
0441-067X	Hokkaido University. Faculty of Science. Journal. Series 7: Geophysics
0441-0734	Japan. Government Industrial Development Laboratory, Hokkaido. Reports
0441-0785	Chika Shigen Chosajo Hokoku
0441-084X	Hokkaidoritsu Suisan Shikenjo Hokoku see 0914-6830
0441-1196	Almanakh Gomonu Ukrainy
0441-1900	University of Hong Kong. Centre of Asian Studies. Bibliographies and Research Guides
0441-2044	Honolulu
0441-2370	Hornbill
0441-2516	Radioactivity Survey Data in Japan
0441-2745	Hospital Medicine
0441-3679	Xin Tiyu
0441-3776	Huaxue Tongbao
0441-389X	Hudson's Washington News Media Contacts Directory
0441-4004	University of Hull. Department of Geography. Miscellaneous Series in Geography changed to University of Hull. School of Geography and Earth Resources. Miscellaneous Series in Geography.
0441-4128	Affirmation†
0441-4144	Humanidad

5740 ISSN INDEX

0441-4195 Humanistic Judaism
0441-4411 Hungarian Law Review†
0441-4438 Hungarian Medical Bibliography
0441-4446 Hungarian Musical Guide†
0441-4675 Hungary. Kozponti Statisztikai Hivatal. Mezogazdasagi Adatok†
0441-4683 Hungary. Kozponti Statisztikai Hivatal. Mezogazdasagi Statisztikao Zsebkonyu *see* 0238-7891
0441-4713 Hungary. Kozponti Statisztikai Hivatal. Nemzetkozi Statisztikai Evkonyv
0441-5302 Hydronymia Germaniae
0441-537X Hyogo-ken Gan Senta Nenpo *changed to* Hyogo Cancer Hospital. Bulletin.
0441-5833 Hi Fi Aarbogen
0441-5973 Hungarian Music News *see* 0238-9401
0441-6058 Hacettepe Bulletin of Social Sciences and Humanities†
0441-6619 Heraldry in Canada
0441-6651 Herpetological Association of Africa. Journal
0441-6813 Hofmannsthal-Blaetter
0441-6910 Huguenot Trails
0441-7410 Hokudai Economic Papers *see* 0916-4650
0441-7445 Home Study†
0441-7461 Horticultural Research International
0441-7895 Honolulu's Annual Area Manpower Review *changed to* Hawaii. Department of Labor and Industrial Relations. Labor Market Review.
0441-7933 Health and Physical Education Bulletin for Teachers in Secondary Schools *changed to* Physical Education and Health.
0441-9057 International Recreation Association. Bulletin *changed to* World Leisure and Recreation.
0442-3054 Illustrierter Motorsport†
0442-6827 Indian Forest Records Wood Anatomy
0442-736X Indian Silk and Rayon *changed to* Indian Synthetic & Rayon.
0442-8102 Indiana Rural News *see* 0745-4651
0443-1243 Information fuer die Truppe
0443-2460 Insel-Almanach
0443-3173 Institut Geographique du Zaire. Rapport Annuel
0443-9058 International Correspondence Society of Obstetrics and Gynecology. Collected Letters
0443-9155 Fiches d'Identification du Zooplancton *see* 0109-2529
0444-0978 International Office of Cocoa and Chocolate and the International Sugar Confectionery Manufacturers' Association. Periodic Bulletin *changed to* International Office of Cocoa, Chocolate and Sugar Confectionery. Annual Statistical Bulletin.
0444-1419 World Road Statistics
0444-1583 International Conference of Social Security Actuaries and Statisticians. Reports
0444-4566 Iowa Documents†
0444-4663 Iowa English Bulletin
0444-4736 Iowa School Board Bulletin *see* 0021-0668
0444-5147 Ireland. Central Statistics Office. Particulars of Vehicles Registered and Licensed for the First Time
0444-6801 Israel. Meteorological Service. Series C: Miscellaneous Papers†
0445-0485 I C E A News *see* 0887-8625
0445-0698 I F C A T I Directory *changed to* I T M F Directory.
0445-1333 International Union of Biological Sciences. General Assemblies. Proceedings
0445-1821 Ich Schreibe
0445-2216 Ideas and Action Bulletin
0445-2429 Igaku Toshokan
0445-2577 Kleine Ikonenbuecherei†
0445-3387 Illinois. State Museum. Handbook of Collections
0445-3395 Illinois. State Museum. Scientific Papers Series
0445-4529 Imagen y Sonida *see* 0210-4261
0445-5150 Incontri Con la Pubblicita†
0445-6289 Trade Unions in India
0445-6653 Press in India
0445-6831 India. Parliament. Public Accounts Committee. Report on the Accounts
0445-7706 Indian Journal of Occupational Therapy
0445-7722 Indian Journal of Sericulture
0445-7854 Indian Machine Tools Journal
0445-7897 Indian Minerals Year Book
0445-801X Indian Press
0445-8192 Indian Tobacco *changed to* Tobacco News.
0445-8206 Town and Country Planning Association Quarterly Journal†
0445-9121 I P N L†
0446-0243 Industria dei Farmaci†
0446-1266 Industries of Japan
0446-2378 Ingenieria
0446-2424 Ingenieria Sanitaria
0446-2491 Ingenioeren Indkoebsbog
0446-3161 Installation Specialist *see* 0192-1657
0446-3943 Jahrbuch fuer Fraenkische Landesforschung
0446-4648 Geological Society of Egypt. Annual Meeting. Abstracts of Papers
0446-5059 Japan Meteorological Agency. Seismological Bulletin
0446-5458 Japan. Norin-sho Nenpo
0446-5849 Somu-cho. Tokei-kyoku Kenkyu Iho
0446-6217 Japan Hotel Guide
0446-6667 Japan's Bicycle Guide
0446-7310 Jersey at Home
0446-7965 Jezyki Obce w Szkole
0446-9283 Jordan Medical Journal
0446-9577 Joseph Haas Gesellschaft. Mitteilungensblatt
0446-9739 Journal du Fermier et du Metayer
0447-2276 J L C News *changed to* Jewish Labor Committee Review.
0447-2500 Jagriti
0447-2624 Jahrbuch der Wittheit zu Bremen
0447-2713 Jahrbuch fuer die Gefluegelwirtschaft†
0447-3086 Jamaica. Department of Statistics. Quarterly Abstract of Statistics†
0447-3280 Jamaica Annual
0447-3728 Japan. Maritime Safety Agency. Hydrographic Department. Notices to Mariners
0447-3868 Japan Meteorological Agency. Technical Report
0447-3892 Japan Meteorological Agency. Volcanological Bulletin
0447-4074 Japan. Ministry of Health and Welfare. Statistics and Information Department. Report on Basic Survey of Health and Welfare Administration†
0447-4740 Japan. Finance Department. Quarterly Bulletin of Financial Statistics *see* 0289-1522
0447-5240 Japan Agricultural Coop News *changed to* Zenchu Farm News.
0447-5321 Japan Cotton Statistics and Related Data
0447-5933 Japanese Society of Grassland Science. Journal
0447-6425 Jelenkor
0447-6441 Jemna Mechanika a Optika
0447-6573 Renmin Yinyue
0447-662X Renwen Zazhi
0447-6719 Jerusalem Chamber of Commerce. Bulletin†
0447-7049 Jewish Action
0447-7227 Jibi to Rinsho *changed to* Otologia Fukuoka - Jibi to Rinsho.
0447-8053 Joho Shori
0447-8452 Joint Meeting of the Members of the Consultative Assembly of the Council of Europe and of the Members of the European Parliamentary Assembly. Official Report of Debates†
0447-8819 Jornal do Exercito
0447-9181 Transportation Telephone Tickler
0447-922X Journal of Economic Behavior
0447-953X Journal of Sports Philately
0447-9645 Journalismus†
0447-9823 Association Internationale pour l'Histoire du Verre. Bulletin
0448-0147 Prirodoslovna Istrazivanja: Acta Biologica
0448-0155 Prirodoslovna Istrazivanja: Acta Geologica
0448-021X News - Jugoslavija Film†
0448-1054 Jabalpur Law Journal
0448-1143 Jadavpur Journal of Comparative Literature
0448-116X Jaderna Energie
0448-1445 Jahrbuch des Sports
0448-150X Jahrbuch fuer den Kreis Pinneberg
0448-1518 Jahrbuch fuer Geologie†
0448-1526 Jahrbuch fuer Geschichte
0448-1631 Jahresring†
0448-1690 Rajasthan University Studies in English
0448-1712 University of Rajasthan. Studies in Sanskrit and Hindi
0448-2174 Jamaica Library Association. Annual Bulletin *changed to* Jamaica Library Association. Bulletin.
0448-2433 Jammu and Kashmir. Legislative Council. Committee on Privileges. Report
0448-3294 Annual Statistics of Maritime Safety
0448-374X Japan. Meteorological Agency. Monthly Report
0448-3758 Japan Meteorological Agency. Annual Report
0448-3952 Japan. Ministry of Health and Welfare. Statistics and Information Department. Statistical Report on Public Health Administration and Services
0448-3960 Japan. Ministry of Health and Welfare. Statistics and Information Department. Report on Survey of Socio-Economic Aspects on Vital Events
0448-4002 Japan. Ministry of Health and Welfare. Statistics and Information Department. Report on Survey of Public Assistance
0448-4010 Japan. Ministry of Health and Welfare. Statistics and Information Department. Statistical Report on Social Welfare Administration and Services
0448-4029 Japan. Ministry of Health and Welfare. Statistics and Information Department. Report on Survey of Social Welfare Institutions
0448-4703 Science Council of Japan. Annual Report†
0448-6072 Finance
0448-7109 Family Saving Survey (Year)
0448-7141 Japan Statistical Association. Annual Report on the Unincorporated Enterprise Survey
0448-858X Japan Chemical Review†
0448-8709 Japan Science Review: Economic Sciences
0448-8806 Japanese Annual of International Law
0448-8938 Japanese Railway Engineering
0448-8954 Japanese Religions
0448-9144 Jaszkunsag
0448-9179 Jauna Gaita
0448-9241 Jazykovedne Studie
0448-9365 Renmin Jiaoyu
0448-9373 Renmin Huabao
0448-9497 Jena Review†
0449-0193 Local Government Review *see* 0288-7622
0449-0312 Jinmin Chugoku
0449-0436 Jizni Morava
0449-0495 Job Scope†
0449-0576 Joekull
0449-0738 Johari za Kiswahili†
0449-0754 John Birch Society. Bulletin
0449-122X Joint F A O - W H O Codex Alimentarius Commission. Report of the Session
0449-1343 J I L A Information Center. Report *changed to* J I L A Data Center. Report.
0449-1483 Jordan. Department of Statistics. External Trade Statistics and Shipping Activities in Aqaba Port†
0449-1491 Jordan Economy in Figures†
0449-1513 Jordan. Department of Statistics. National Accounts
0449-1602 Jordan Lectures in Comparative Religion†
0449-1750 Jornal Portugues de Economia e Financas
0449-1971 Journal des Agreges†
0449-2099 Journal Mondial de Pharmacie *see* 1010-0423
0449-2145 Journal of African and Asian Studies†
0449-2153 Journal of Alabama Archaeology
0449-2285 Egyptian Journal of Chemistry
0449-2544 Journal of Foot Surgery
0449-2560 Journal of Geosciences
0449-2722 Journal of Long Island History†
0449-2730 Journal of Macromolecular Chemistry *see* 1060-1325
0449-2730 Journal of Macromolecular Chemistry *see* 0022-2348
0449-2994 Journal of Polymer Science. Part C - Polymer Symposia *see* 0360-8905
0449-3060 Japan Radiation Research Society. Journal *changed to* Journal of Radiation Research.
0449-3109 Journal of Schizophrenia *changed to* Journal of Orthomolecular Medicine.
0449-3168 Journal of Social Sciences
0449-3362 Journalism Scholarship Guide *changed to* Journalism Career and Scholarship Guide.
0449-3540 Judaisme Sephardi†
0449-3648 Jugoslavenska Akademija Znanosti i Umjetnosti. Historijski Institut, Dubrovnik. Anali.
0449-3672 Institut Jugoslavenske Akademije Znanosti i Umjetnosti. Radovi *see* 0351-6709
0449-4156 Japanese Society of Lubrication Engineers. Journal *see* 0915-1168
0449-4342 Juristische Abhandlungen
0449-4555 Juventud Tecnica
0449-4733 Journal de l'Annee
0449-4741 Journal of Contemporary Revolutions†
0449-4830 Japan Atomic Energy Commission. Annual Report†
0449-4881 Jerusalem Historical Medical Publications *changed to* Koroth (Jerusalem).
0449-5225 Jahrbuch der Wirtschaft Osteuropas
0449-5314 Japan. Statistics Bureau. News Bulletin
0449-5705 Journal of Bioenergetics *see* 0145-479X
0449-5721 Journal of Plant and Machinery
0449-749X Gangtie
0449-752X Kango Gijutsu
0449-7554 Kansai University Economic Review
0449-7732 Kansas. Department of Health and Environment. Monthly Summary of Vital Statistics†
0449-7953 Kansas. State Department of Public Instruction. Bulletin *changed to* Kansas. State Department of Education. Bulletin.
0449-9069 Kaseigaku Zasshi *see* 0913-5227
0450-0261 Kemps Harrow and District Local Directory†
0450-2167 Chirurgia
0450-3171 Kirkehistoriske Samlinger†
0450-609X Kobe University of Mercantile Marine. Review. Part 2. Maritime Studies, and Science and Engineering
0450-6219 Kochi University. Faculty of Agriculture. Memoirs
0450-6235 Kochpraxis und Gemeinschaftsverpflegung
0450-660X Kokai
0450-6669 Koku Joho
0450-7169 Kommunalwirtschaft
0451-0712 Gong Lu
0451-0887 Kunsterziehung

ISSN

ISSN	Title
0451-1476	Kyoto Daigaku Shokuryo Kagaku Kenkyusho Hokoku
0451-1611	Kyushu Hematological Society. Journal
0451-1646	K Mitteilungen
0451-1980	National Research Institute of Police Science. Report see 0285-7960
0451-1999	Kagaku Keisatsu Kenkyujo Hokoku Bohan Shonen Hen
0451-2006	Kagaku Keisatsu Kenkyujo Hokoku Kotsu Ken
0451-2030	Kagaku Kojo†
0451-243X	K V Convertible Fact Finder Service†
0451-3118	Gansu Huabao
0451-3371	Kansa Taisteli - Miehet Kertovat†
0451-3991	Kansas City Genealogist
0451-4041	Kansas Farmer-Stockman changed to Kansas Farmer.
0451-4874	Kasseler Statistik
0451-5560	Kauppalehti
0451-5978	Keiei Kagaku - Management Science see 0030-3674
0451-6001	Keikinzoku Kogyo Tokei Nenpo
0451-6109	National Research Laboratory of Metrology. Bulletin
0451-6222	Keizai Riron - Economic Theory changed to Wakayama Economic Review.
0451-6338	Kelsey Review
0451-7059	Kentucky Economic Outlook changed to University of Kentucky. Center for Business and Economic Research. Review & Perspective.
0451-9396	Kikai Gijutsu
0451-9930	Kirkia
0452-2370	Kobe University. Faculty of Agriculture. Science Reports
0452-2486	Kochi Joshi Daigaku Kiyo. Shizen Kagaku Hen
0452-2834	Kogyo Zairyo
0452-2907	Testimonia Siciliae Antiqua
0452-3318	Kyoiku Kenkyu
0452-3385	Japan Commercial Arbitration Association. Quarterly
0452-3458	Kokyo to Junkan
0452-3687	Norway. Komite for Romforskning. N.S.C. Report changed to Space Research in Norway.
0452-4160	Konan Daigaku Kiyo. Rigaku Hen
0452-4918	Konstanzer Blaetter fuer Hochschulfragen†
0452-5914	Korean Stamps
0452-599X	Koroze a Ochrana Materialu
0452-621X	Kosmos Bibliothek†
0452-6457	Akademia Gorniczo-Hutnicza im. Stanislawa Staszica. Zeszyty Naukowe. Geodezja
0452-7208	Kristofer Lehmkuhl Forelesning
0452-7739	Die Kueste
0452-8255	Kunchong Zhishi
0452-8778	Guoji Zhanwang
0452-8832	Guoji Wenti Yanjiu
0452-9081	Kurtrierisches Jahrbuch
0452-9650	Kyoiku Shinrigaku Nenpo
0452-9995	Kyoto University. Research Institute for Food Science. Memoirs†
0453-0047	Kyoto Technical University. Faculty of Industrial Arts. Memoirs: Science and Technology see 0911-0305
0453-0314	Kyushu Daigaku Nogakubu Suisangakka Gyosekishu
0453-0349	Kyushu Institute of Technology. Bulletin: Humanities, Social Sciences
0453-0357	Kyushu Institute of Technology. Bulletin: Science and Technology
0453-0535	Japan. Norin-sho Kachiku Eisei Shikenjo Nenpo†
0453-0578	Kacic
0453-0667	Kagaku Keisatsu Kenkyujo Nenpo
0453-0675	Kagaku Keisatsu Kenkyujo Shiryo†
0453-0691	Japan Association for Philosophy of Science. Annals
0453-0853	Kagoshima University. Faculty of Agriculture. Memoirs
0453-1388	Kalmia
0453-1515	Kami Parupu Tokei Nenpo
0453-1906	Kanagawa-kenritsu Hakubutsukan Kenkyu Hokoku. Shizen Kagaku
0453-1981	Kanazawa University. Faculty of Law and Literature. Studies and Essays
0453-2198	Kansai University Technology Reports
0453-2384	Kansas. State Conservation Commission. Conservation in Kansas see 0094-1670
0453-2406	Library School Review changed to Great Plains Libraries.
0453-2805	Kansas Sportsman
0453-2899	Kaogu
0453-2902	Kaogu Xuebao
0453-3283	Karlsruher Juristische Bibliographie
0453-3402	Karstenia
0453-3429	Karthago
0453-3585	Kataliz i Katalizatory
0453-3623	Katalog Fauny Polski
0453-4387	Keats - Shelley Journal
0453-4395	Keats - Shelley Memorial Bulletin changed to Keats - Shelley Review.
0453-4484	Keidanren Geppo
0453-4514	Operations Research Society of Japan. Journal
0453-4557	Keio Business Review
0453-4611	Keiryo Kokugogaku
0453-4662	Keisoku to Seigyo
0453-4778	Keizaigaku Ronsan
0453-4867	Kellogg World changed to Kelloggram.
0453-4972	B R I Research Papers
0453-512X	Kennedy Quarterly†
0453-5146	Kensetsu Kogaku Kenkyujo Hokoku
0453-5677	Kentucky City
0453-5723	Kentucky Genealogist
0453-5944	Kenya. Dairy Board. Annual Report
0453-6002	Kenya Statistical Digest
0453-6525	Kenya, Uganda, Tanzania, Zambia, Malawi and Ethiopia Directory; Trade and Commercial Index changed to Kenya, Uganda, Tanzania, East African Community Directory; Trade Commerce Index.
0453-7440	Kerala; an Economic Review
0453-767X	Kernkraft Zentrale, Gundremmingen. Jahresberichte†
0453-7831	Kevo Subarctic Research Institute. Reports
0453-7998	Elektroenergetika i Avtomatizatsiya Energoustanovok
0453-8129	Sudan Research Information Bulletin
0453-8854	Kingston Law Review†
0453-9222	National Research Institute for Metals. Transactions
0453-9249	Kiplinger California Letter
0453-9478	Kiruna Geophysical Data
0453-9842	Klaus Groth Gesellschaft. Jahresgaben
0454-0816	Gequ
0454-0905	Kexue Huabao
0454-1111	Kobe University Economic Review
0454-1383	Koepfe des 20. Jahrhunderts
0454-1723	Kokugakuin University. Faculty of Law and Politics. Journal
0454-191X	Foreign Aero-Space Literature†
0454-1944	National Diet Library. Monthly List of Foreign Scientific and Technical Publications
0454-1960	Toshokan Kenkyu Sirizu
0454-2029	Kokuritsu Tama Kenkyujo Nenpo
0454-2134	Journal of Social Science
0454-2150	Asian Cultural Studies
0454-3491	Konyvtari es Dokumentacios Szakirodalom†
0454-4196	Korean Trade Unions
0454-448X	Kosmosophie
0454-4544	Kotai Butsuri
0454-4617	Za Casopis: Kovcezic
0454-4773	Akademia Gorniczo-Hutnicza im. Stanislawa Staszica. Zeszyty Naukowe. Automatyka
0454-4811	Akademia Gorniczo-Hutnicza im. Stanislawa Staszica. Zeszyty Naukowe. Zagadnienia Techniczno-Ekonomiczne
0454-4862	Politechnika Krakowska. Zeszyty Naukowe. Budownictwo Ladowe changed to Politechnika Krakowska. Zeszyty Naukowe. Inzynieria Ladowa.
0454-5230	Krigshistorisk Tidsskrift
0454-5265	Kriminalwissenschaftliche Abhandlungen
0454-5478	K R S Jugoslavije
0454-5508	Krugozor
0454-5524	Krystalinikum
0454-5648	Guisuanyan Xuebao
0454-577X	Kulkereskedelem see 0324-4202
0454-6059	Cultuurpatronen†
0454-6148	Kumamoto Daigaku Kyoikugakubu Kiyo. Shizen Kagaku
0454-6245	Kuml†
0454-6296	Kunchong Xuebao
0454-6520	Kunst og Museum
0454-6539	Kunst und Handwerk
0454-675X	National Palace Museum Quarterly see 1011-9094
0454-7330	Kwartalnik Historii Ruchu Zawodowego see 0860-9357
0454-7543	Korea (Republic). Economic Planning Board. Annual Report on the Economically Active Population Survey changed to Korea (Republic). National Statistical Office. Annual Report on the Economically Active Population Survey.
0454-7586	Mutual Aid Association. Medical Journal
0454-7659	Kyoto University. Abuyama Seismological Observatory. Seismological Bulletin
0454-7675	Kyoto University. Disaster Prevention Research Institute. Bulletin
0454-7802	Kyoto University. Faculty of Science. Memoirs. Series of Biology
0454-7810	Kyoto University. Faculty of Science. Memoirs. Series of Geology and Mineralogy
0454-7845	Kyoto University. Research Institute for Mathematical Sciences. Publications: Series A see 0034-5318
0454-7985	Kyoto University African Studies†
0454-8086	Kytoesavut
0454-8132	Kyushu American Literature
0454-8221	Kyushu Institute of Technology. Bulletin: Mathematics, Natural Science
0454-8302	Kanagawa Shigaku
0454-8973	Knight Letter
0454-9244	Kyoto University. Research Reactor Institute. Annual Reports
0454-949X	Kenya Newsletter
0454-9910	Kibernetika i Vychislitel'naya Tekhnika
0455-0374	Kernenergie Forschungsschiff "Otto Hahn". Jahresbericht†
0455-0420	Kieler Diskussionsbeitraege
0455-0463	Knjizevna Smotra
0455-2342	Landarbeit und Technik†
0455-2741	Landsbladet
0456-0434	Light
0456-3271	Living with Children
0456-3867	Canadian Hardware, Electrical & Building Supply Directory
0456-4804	Ramsay Society of Chemical Engineers. Journal
0456-5339	Look Japan
0456-7463	Louisiana English Journal
0456-9814	Laboratorio changed to Il Nuovo Laboratorio.
0457-0715	Landeskundliche Luftbildauswertung im Mitteileuropaeischen Raum see 0176-1633
0457-1320	Langues et Styles
0457-1673	Universidad Nacional de la Plata. Instituto de la Produccion. Serie Contribuciones
0457-3633	Legislative Trends
0457-3897	Neujahrsgabe der Deutschen Buecherei
0457-3919	Deutsche Hochschule fuer Koerperkultur. Wissenschaftliche Zeitschrift changed to Leipziger Sportwissenschaftliche Beitraege.
0457-4184	Lejeunia
0457-5792	Letecky Obzor
0457-6039	Levante Agricola
0457-6047	Leveltari Szemle
0457-6241	Lishi Jiaoxue
0457-6306	Liaoning Huabao
0457-7019	County Newsletter†
0457-7817	South Staffordshire Archaeological and Historical Society. Transactions
0457-8910	Lilly Endowment. Report†
0457-9976	Liste des Societes Savantes et Litteraires†
0458-063X	Liturgy
0458-1520	Muzeum Archeologiczne i Etnograficzne, Lodz. Prace i Materialy. Seria Archeologiczna
0458-1547	Politechnika Lodzka. Zeszyty Naukowe. Zeszyt Specjalny†
0458-1555	Politechnika Lodzka. Zeszyty Naukowe. Chemia
0458-1563	Politechnika Lodzka. Zeszyty Naukowe. Mechanika
0458-1822	Lok Magazin
0458-4201	Lower Cape Fear Historical Society. Bulletin†
0458-4317	Annales Universitatis Mariae Curie-Sklodowska. Sectio G. Ius
0458-4767	Lund Universitet. Historiska Museum. Meddelanden
0458-497X	Lutheran Digest
0458-5143	Lutte de Classe
0458-5674	L P V-Listos para Vencer†
0458-5747	Labo - Pharma Problems et Techniques see 1157-1489
0458-5860	France. Laboratoires des Ponts et Chaussees. Bulletin de Liaison
0458-595X	Laboratory Guide to Instruments, Equipment and Chemicals changed to Analytical Chemistry. Labguide (Year).
0458-6026	Labour Law Cases†
0458-6123	Ladenbau changed to Architektur und Ladenbau.
0458-6506	Lalit Kala
0458-6573	Washington Energy Memo see 0300-7243
0458-6859	Landbauforschung Voelkenrode
0458-6905	Landeskundliche Vierteljahrsblaetter
0458-6972	Landmark (New Berlin)
0458-7014	Landscape Research News see 0142-6397
0458-7073	Skrifter fra Landslaget for Bygde- og Byhistorie see 0802-0434
0458-7367	Language Research in Progress†
0458-7871	Laser and Unconventional Optics Journal
0458-7944	Lateinamerika
0458-8460	Law and Legislation in the German Democratic Republic
0458-8592	Law in Society
0458-8630	Law Office Economics & Management
0458-8711	Law Society of Scotland. Journal (Year)
0458-8983	Leads see 0892-4546
0458-9564	Legal Bulletin
0458-9599	Legal - Legislative Reporter. News Bulletin
0458-998X	Leidse Historische Reeks†
0459-0007	Leidse Wijsgerige Reeks†
0459-004X	Deutsche Buecherei. Jahrbuch†
0459-0805	Leningradskii Universitet. Uchenye Zapiski. Seriya Geologicheskikh Nauk
0459-0953	Lens and Speaker†
0459-1623	Letture Classensi
0459-1801	Rijksmuseum van Natuurlijke Historie. Zoologische Bijdragen changed to Nationaal Natuurhistorisch Museum. Zoologische Bijdragen.
0459-1879	Lixue Xuebao
0459-1909	Lishi Yanjiu
0459-2182	Liberia. Ministry of Planning and Economic Affairs. Annual Report to the Session of the Legislature of the Republic of Liberia changed to Liberia. Ministry of Planning and Economic Affairs. Annual Report to the People's Redemption Council.
0459-2298	Liberian Naturalist changed to U L Science and Technology Magazine.
0459-2476	Y L G News†
0459-2980	Libya Antiqua

ISSN INDEX

0459-3030 Libycat
0459-3650 American Council of Life Insurance. Economic and Investment Reportt
0459-3774 Life Sciencest
0459-3871 Ligue Internationale Contre la Concurrence Deloyale. Annuaire
0459-388X Ligue Internationale Contre la Concurrence Deloyale. Communication
0459-441X Linye Kexue
0459-4487 Lincolnshire History and Archaeology
0459-4541 Lines Review
0459-4835 Lipunan Journalt
0459-4851 Repertorio das Publicacoes Periodicas Portuguesast
0459-5009 List of Current Periodical Publications in Ethiopiat
0459-5084 Liszt Society, London. Newsletter see 0141-0792
0459-6137 Living Bird see 0732-9210
0459-6404 University E. Kardelja in Ljubljana. Biotechnical Faculty. Research Reports changed to University in Ljubljana. Biotechnical Faculty. Research Reports.
0459-6730 Lock Haven Reviewt
0459-6803 Locusta
0459-682X Politechnika Lodzka. Zeszyty Naukowe. Elektryka
0459-6854 Societe des Sciences et des Lettres de Lodz. Bulletin
0459-7222 Military Balance
0459-7230 Strategic Survey
0459-7354 University of London Classical Studiest
0459-7400 Bartlett Society. Transactionst
0459-8113 Contributions in Science
0459-8474 Louisiana. Geological Survey. Water Resources Bulletin
0459-8881 Louisiana Bar Journal
0459-889X Louisiana Cancer Reporter
0459-8962 Louisiana Folklore Miscellany
0459-9586 Annales Universitatis Mariae Curie-Sklodowska. Sectio H. Oeconomia
0459-9756 Lucknow Law Times
0460-007X Lute Society Journal see 0952-0759
0460-024X Lutheran Church in America. Western Canada Synod. Minutes of the Annual Conventiont
0460-0274 Lutheran Historical Conference Newsletter
0460-1297 Little Lamp
0460-1327 Locator (Silver Spring) changed to Locator of Used Machinery, Equipment & Plant Services.
0460-1424 Denmark. Landoekonomiske Driftsbureau. Meddelelse see 0106-2689
0460-2099 Lesotho. Ministry of Foreign Affairs. Diplomatic and Consular List
0460-2374 Luftverunreinigung
0460-2390 M & B Pharmaceutical Bulletint
0460-3060 Resultados das Observacoes Meteorologicas de Macau
0460-5047 Das Magazin
0460-6736 Maine Geological Survey. Mineral Resources Index Seriest
0461-0040 Manual of Excellent Managementt
0461-2531 Masinstvo
0461-5298 Rigsbibliotekaren. Meddelelser changed to Kongelige Bibliotek. Magasin.
0461-6308 Medicinsk Aarbog
0461-6375 Medico
0461-6529 Medizinstudent see 0344-5933
0461-6855 Meishu Yanjiu
0461-7185 Melodiast
0461-7398 Men and Women of Hawaii
0462-1069 Mexico News
0462-3134 Advocacy Institute. Proceedings (Year)
0462-4874 Military Digest
0462-9086 Heimatkundliches Beiblatt changed to Heimat im Weinland.
0463-1536 Monitor de la Farmacia y de la Terapeutica
0463-1935 Monographien zur Rheinisch-Westfaelischen Kunst der Gegenwartt
0463-6457 Motor Club News
0463-6635 Motor Vehicle Statistics of Japan
0463-9847 Universidad de Murcia. Ciencias. Anales see 0213-5469
0463-9863 Universidad de Murcia. Filosofia y Letras. Anales see 0212-9698
0463-9863 Universidad de Murcia. Filosofia y Letras. Anales changed to Universidad de Murcia. Anales de Letras.
0463-9863 Universidad de Murcia. Filosofia y Letras. Anales see 0212-8322
0463-9863 Universidad de Murcia. Filosofia y Letras. Anales see 0212-9728
0463-9863 Univerisdad de Murcia. Filosofia y Letras. Anales see 0213-5477
0463-9863 Universidad de Murcia. Filosofia y Letras. Anales see 0213-5485
0463-9863 Universidad de Murcia. Filosofia y Letras. Anales see 0213-392X
0464-1973 M P S A Newsletter
0464-2147 Ma'arachot
0464-3755 Escuela Diplomatica. Cuadernost
0464-476X Parttorteneti Kozlemenyekt
0464-5030 Maharaja Sayajirao University of Baroda. Department of History Series
0464-5820 Maine Historical Society. Newsletter see 0163-1152
0464-591X Mainly Marketing
0464-7734 Malet

0464-7777 Der Maler und Lackierermeister
0464-8072 Mammillaria Journal
0464-882X Manual Azucarero Mexicano
0464-9567 March of the Nationt
0464-9605 Marche Financier de Paris
0464-9680 Marian Studies
0464-9974 Market Bulletin
0465-031X Marriage Guidancet
0465-1499 Commerce Digestt
0465-2592 Maszyny i Ciagniki Rolnicze
0465-2746 Materiales de Construccion
0465-3750 Mathematik in der Schule
0465-3769 Mathematisch-Naturwissenschaftliche Bibliothekt
0465-4773 Universidad de Medellin. Facultad de Ciencias Administrativas. Revista
0465-5893 Medycyna Pracy
0465-7004 N R A News see 0890-5584
0465-7772 Nagoya-shiritsu Daigaku Kyoyobu Kiyo. Shizen Kagaku Hen
0466-1478 Official National Collegiate Athletic Association Baseball Guide see 0736-5209
0466-1761 N.C.A.I. News Bulletin changed to Sentinel: Bulletin - N C A I News.
0466-3276 National Institute of Sciences of India. Mathematical Tables changed to Indian National Science Academy. Mathematical Tables.
0466-499X Safety Newsletter: Occupational Health Nursing Section changed to Occupational Health Nursing Newsletter.
0466-5007 Safety Newsletter: Public Utilities Section changed to Public Utilities Newsletter.
0466-6054 Nature in Walest
0466-6089 Neicha Sutadi
0466-7530 Netherlands Federation of Trade Unions. Information Bulletin changed to F N V News.
0467-006X Rijksdienst voor het Oudheidkundig Bodemonderzoek te Amersfoort. Berichten
0467-1872 New Caduceant
0467-6769 New York (State). Insurance Department. Loss and Expense Ratiost
0468-1746 Der Niedergelassene Arzt
0468-1835 Nielsen Newscast
0468-3390 Norddeutsche Familienkunde changed to Nordeutsche Familienkunde in Verbindung mit der Zeitschrift fuer Niederdeutsche Familienkunde.
0468-5067 Groundwater Bulletint
0468-656X Nordrhein-Westfalen. Statistisches Jahrbuch
0468-6853 Northeastern Tour Book changed to Tourbook: Connecticut, Massachusetts, Rhode Island.
0468-6853 Northeastern Tour Book changed to Tourbook: Maine, New Hampshire, Vermont.
0468-8147 Norway. Statistisk Sentralbyraa. Samferdselsstatistikk
0468-8155 Norway. Statistisk Sentralbyraa. Skogstatstikk
0469-0281 Nova Trgovina
0469-2071 Nukada Institute for Medical and Biological Research. Reports
0469-2225 Nongcun Qingnian
0469-2454 Nuova Rivista Pedagogica
0469-323X N A S B I C News
0469-337X N B S Publications Newslettert
0469-4007 N U S A S Newsletter changed to Dissent.
0469-4236 Nachrichten aus dem Karten- und Vermessungswesen. Reihe I: Originalbeitraege
0469-4244 Nachrichten aus dem Karten- und Vermessungswesen. Reihe II: Uebersetzungen
0469-4759 Nagoya University. Research Institute of Environmental Medicine. Annual Report see 0287-0517
0469-4783 Nagoya Port Statistics Annual
0469-5097 Nanjing Daxue Xuebao (Ziran Kexue Ban)
0469-5550 Nara Igaku Zasshi
0469-8029 National Automotive Directoryt
0469-8592 National Collegiate Athletic Association. Official Skiing Rules see 0741-9279
0469-9130 National Council for Geographic Education. Do It This Wayt
0470-0384 National Forest Products Association. Fingertip Facts & Figurest
0470-0929 National Geographer
0470-1321 National Institute of Agricultural Botany, Cambridge, England. Vegetable Growers Leaflets
0470-1380 National Institute of Sciences of India. N I S I Monographs changed to Indian National Science Academy. Monographs.
0470-2824 Safety Newsletter: Aerospace Section changed to Aerospace Newsletter.
0470-2832 Air Transport Section changed to International Air Transport Newsletter.
0470-2840 Safety Newsletter: Public Employee Section changed to Public Employee Newsletter.
0470-3219 National Stripper Well Survey
0470-3901 Naturkundliches Jahrbuch der Stadt Linz

0470-5017 Naukove Tovarystvo Imeni Shevchenka. Proceedings of the Section of Mathematics, Natural Science and Medicine changed to Naukove Tovarystvo Imeni Shevchenka. Proceedings of the Section of Mathematics and Physics.
0470-5017 Naukove Tovarystvo Imeni Shevchenka. Proceedings of the Section of Mathematics, Natural Sciences and Medicine changed to Naukove Tovarystvo Imeni Shevchenka. Proceedings of the Section of Chemistry, Biology and Medicine.
0470-5106 Navajo Times changed to Navajo Times.
0470-5661 Nebraska Optometric Association. Journal changed to N O A Journal.
0470-6021 Nederlandse Chemische Industriet
0470-6684 Netherlands. Centraal Bureau voor de Statistiek. Maandstatistiek van de Industrie
0470-6978 Netherlands. Centraal Bureau voor de Statistiek. Sociale Maandstatistiek see 0168-549X
0470-7427 Synoptic and Upper Air Observations in the Netherlandst
0470-8105 Shinkei Geka
0471-0320 Odziez
0471-122X Offenbacher Geschichtsblaetter
0471-1424 Office Equipment Exporter
0471-380X Oil & Gas Directory
0471-3850 Oil Directory of Alaskat
0471-3877 Oil Directory of Houston, Texas changed to Houston Petroleum Industry.
0471-492X Oklahoma Employment Security Reviewt
0471-7376 Orafo Italiano
0471-7708 Ordine dei Medici. Bollettino changed to Piemonte Medico.
0471-8356 State Board of Accountancy. Roster of Accountants Authorized to Conduct Municipal Audits changed to Oregon. State Board of Accountancy. Certified Public Accountants, Public Accountants, and Accountants Authorized to Conduct Municipal Audits in Oregon.
0471-9174 Oregon Cattleman changed to Oregon Beef Producer.
0471-9336 Oregon Psychological Association. Newsletter changed to Oregon Psychology.
0472-0490 Orient
0472-0601 Orientacion Medica
0472-0784 Orientamenti Pastorali
0472-0989 Orissa, India. Finance Department. White Paper on Departmental Activities, Government of Orissa changed to Orissa, India. Finance Department. White Paper on the Economic Conditions and the Developmental Activities in Orissa.
0472-190X Ostdeutsche Familienkunde
0472-2191 Oswiata Doroslycht
0472-2744 Ouranos
0472-397X Ob-Gyn Collected Letters see 0443-9058
0472-4313 Obrobka Plastyczna see 0867-2628
0472-5182 Odra
0472-5263 Oeil
0472-5859 Oesterreichisches Forschungsinstitut fuer Sparkassenwesen. Schriftenreihe
0472-6480 Ohinemuri
0472-6685 Ohio. Division of Geological Survey. Educational Leaflet
0472-6979 Ohio State University. Institute of Polar Studies. Contribution Series changed to Ohio State University. Byrd Polar Research Center. Contribution Series.
0472-7584 Oil and Australiat
0472-7630 Oil and Gas Reporter
0472-7711 Oil Directory of Companies Outside the U.S. and Canada changed to International Petroleum Industry.
0472-8637 Olam Hadash
0472-8807 Oleo
0472-8874 Nestekide
0472-948X Ondas
0472-9986 Ontario. Labour Relations Board. Decisions see 0383-4778
0473-0062 Ontario Cancer Treatment and Research Foundation. Clinical Conference. Proceedingst
0473-0496 Operations Research - Management Science Yearbook
0473-0658 Instituto de Botanica "Dr. Goncalo Sampaio". Publicacoes. 3 Seriet
0473-0917 Optiquet
0473-1034 Opuscula Zoologica
0473-1174 Orafo Italiano nel Mondo
0473-1425 Die Orchidee
0473-3657 Organization of African Unity. Health, Sanitation and Nutrition Commission. Proceedings and Reportt
0473-4351 Ortnamnssallskapet i Uppsala. Aarsskrift
0473-4378 Ortopedia i Traumatologia
0473-4548 Osaka Daigaku Keizaigaku
0473-4580 Osaka University. Laboratory of Nuclear Studies. Annual Report
0473-4629 Osaka Daigaku Shigaku Zasshi

ISSN INDEX 5743

0473-4637 University of Osaka Prefecture. Bulletin. Series D: Sciences of Economy, Commerce and Law *changed to* University of Osaka Prefecture. Bulletin. Series D: Economics, Business Administration and Law.
0473-5277 Frankfurter Abhandlungen zur Slavistik†
0473-5587 Automation
0473-5609 Otorinolaringologija
0473-6303 Universidad de Oviedo. Facultad de Ciencias, Revista. Serie Biologia *see* 0212-8977
0473-6788 O E C D. Reviews of Manpower and Social Policies
0473-7490 Occasional Papers in Political Science†
0473-7733 Ochrona przed Korozja
0473-8063 Osterbotten
0473-8322 Oesterreichische Papier *changed to* Papier aus Oesterreich.
0473-8624 Oesterreichisches Volksliedwerk. Jahrbuch
0473-8837 Studies on Current Health Problems
0473-9442 Game Research in Ohio *see* 0085-4468
0473-9604 Ohio State University. Working Papers in Linguistics
0473-9787 O C W R U Quarterly Report†
0474-0114 Oil Directory of Canada *changed to* Canada Petroleum Industry.
0474-0157 Oita Daigaku Keizai Ronshu
0474-0696 Oklahoma Anthropological Society. Memoir
0474-070X Oklahoma Economic Indicators†
0474-0742 Oklahoma Genealogical Society Quarterly
0474-0750 Oklahoma Ornithological Society. Bulletin
0474-1382 On View†
0474-1560 Ontario. Ministry of Agriculture and Food. Seasonal Fruit and Vegetable Report
0474-2125 O L A Newsletter *changed to* Focus (Toronto).
0474-2389 Open Places
0474-2893 Opolskie Roczniki Ekonomiczne
0474-2966 Wyzsza Szkola Pedagogiczna, Opole. Zeszyty Naukowe. Seria A. Ekonomia
0474-2974 Wyzsza Szkola Pedagogiczna, Opole. Zeszyty Naukowe. Seria A. Filologia Rosyjska
0474-2982 Wyzsza Szkola Pedagogiczna, Opole. Zeszyty Naukowe. Seria A. Pedagogika
0474-3253 Oral History Association. Newsletter
0474-3326 Orbit (New York)†
0474-3342 Orchadian
0474-4039 Public Welfare in Oregon *changed to* Adult and Family Services in Oregon.
0474-4535 Oregon Historical Society. News
0474-4616 Oregon Recreation Briefs†
0474-4829 Organisation of European Aluminum Smelters. Economic Situation of the Aluminum Smelters in Europe *changed to* Secondary Aluminium.
0474-5086 O E C D. Catalogue of Publications
0474-5124 O E C D. Economic Surveys: Austria
0474-5132 O E C D. Economic Surveys: Belgium - Luxembourg
0474-5140 O E C D. Economic Surveys: Canada
0474-5159 O E C D. Economic Surveys: Denmark
0474-5167 O E C D. Economic Surveys: France
0474-5175 O E C D. Economic Surveys: Germany
0474-5183 O E C D. Economic Surveys: Greece
0474-5191 O E C D. Economic Surveys: Iceland
0474-5205 O E C D. Economic Surveys: Ireland
0474-5213 O E C D. Economic Surveys: Italy
0474-5221 O E C D. Economic Surveys: Japan
0474-523X O E C D. Economic Surveys: Netherlands
0474-5248 O E C D. Economic Surveys: Norway
0474-5256 O E C D. Economic Surveys: Portugal
0474-5264 O E C D. Economic Surveys: Yugoslavia
0474-5272 O E C D. Economic Surveys: Spain
0474-5280 O E C D. Economic Surveys: Sweden
0474-5299 O E C D. Economic Surveys: Switzerland
0474-5302 O E C D. Economic Surveys: Turkey
0474-5310 O E C D. Economic Surveys: United Kingdom
0474-5329 O E C D. Economic Surveys: United States
0474-5337 Organization for Economic Cooperation and Development. Employment of Special Groups†
0474-5353 O E C D. Survey of Electric Power Equipment†
0474-537X Food Consumption in the O E C D *changed to* O E C D. Food Consumption Statistics.
0474-5388 O E C D. Monthly Statistics of Foreign Trade Series A
0474-5396 O E C D. Statistics of Foreign Trade. Series B: Tables by Reporting Countries†
0474-540X O E C D. Foreign Trade by Commodities. Series C
0474-5434 Geographical Distribution of Financial Flows to Less Developed Countries. (Disbursements) *changed to* Geographical Distribution of Financial Flows to Developing Countries. Disbursements - Commitments - Economic Indicators.
0474-5442 Organization for Economic Cooperation and Development. Historical Statistics. Statistiques Retrospectives *changed to* O E C D. Main Economic Indicators. Historical Statistics.
0474-5450 O E C D. Industrial Production†
0474-5469 O E C D. Industrial Statistics†
0474-5477 O E C D. Electricity Supply Industry†
0474-5485 Pulp and Paper Industry in O E C D Member Countries and Finland - Industrie des Pates et Papiers dans les Pays Membres de l'O C D E et la Finlande *changed to* Pulp and Paper Industry in O E C D Member Countries.
0474-5493 O E C D. Cement Industry†
0474-5515 O E C D. Labour Force Statistics
0474-5523 O E C D. Main Economic Indicators
0474-5574 O E C D Economic Outlook
0474-5620 O E C D. Wages and Labour Mobility Supplement†
0474-5655 O E C D. Code of Liberalization of Capital Movements
0474-5663 O E C D. Development Cooperation
0474-585X Hides, Skins and Footwear Indusrty in O E C D Countries - Industrie des Cuirs et Peaux et de la Chaussure dans les Pays de l'O C D E *changed to* Footwear, Raw Hides and Skins, and Leatther Industry in O E C D Countries.
0474-5868 O E C D. Library. Special Annotated Bibliography: Automation
0474-5876 O E C D. Engineering Industries in O E C D Countries†
0474-5884 O E C D. Maritime Transport Committee. Maritime Transport
0474-5892 O E C D. Social Affairs Division. Developing Job Opportunities†
0474-5922 Organization for Economic Cooperation and Development. Social Affairs Division. Employment of Special Groups†
0474-5973 O E C D. Iron and Steel Industry
0474-6007 O E C D. Oil Statistics. Supply and Disposal
0474-6023 Textile Industry in O E C D Countries†
0474-6171 Organization of African Unity. Scientific Technical and Research Commission. Publication
0474-6279 Organization of the Petroleum Exporting Countries. Bulletin
0474-6317 Organization of the Petroleum Exporting Countries. Annual Review and Record *changed to* Organization of the Petroleum Exporting Countries. Annual Report.
0474-635X Organizzarsi
0474-6376 Organo
0474-6767 Origin Technical Journal
0474-7534 Annals of Dyslexia
0474-781X Osaka University. College of General Education. Science Reports
0474-7844 University of Osaka Prefecture. Bulletin. Series A: Engineering and Natural Sciences
0474-7852 University of Osaka Prefecture. Bulletin. Series B: Agriculture and Biology
0474-7879 Osaka (Prefecture). Radiation Research Institute. Annual Report *see* 0917-1630
0474-8042 Norsk Polarinstitutt. Polarhaandbok
0474-8158 Osnabruecker Mitteilungen
0474-8328 Osteuropastudien der Hochschulen des Landes Hessen. Reihe 2†
0474-8603 Otago Museum. Records. Anthropology†
0474-8611 Otago Museum. Records. Zoology†
0474-8662 Otbor i Peredacha Informatsii *see* 0135-3071
0474-9030 Our Heritage
0474-9588 Trabajos de Geologia
0474-9847 Oyo Kikai Kogaku
0475-0071 Okayama University. School of Engineering. Memoirs†
0475-0608 Organization of the Petroleum Exporting Countries. Annual Statistical Bulletin
0475-0926 Oklahoma. Attorney General's Office. Opinions of the Attorney General
0475-0942 Ontario. Ministry of the Environment. Water Resources Branch. Water Resources Report
0475-1310 Offshore Contractors and Equipment Directory *changed to* Offshore Contractors and Equipment Worldwide Directory.
0475-1388 Old Athlone Society Journal
0475-1671 Oyez
0475-171X Oceans
0475-1876 Old Car Value Guide *changed to* Classic Old Car Value Guide.
0475-1906 Optimum
0475-2015 Organizational Directory of the Government of Thailand
0475-2058 Osaka Dental University. Journal
0475-2112 Owner Operator
0475-2953 P S, The Preventive Maintenance Monthly
0475-4816 La Palabra Diaria
0475-9141 Patre
0476-0069 Pediatria Internazionale†
0476-0247 Beijing Zhongyi
0476-0255 Beijing University of Iron and Steel Technology. Journal
0476-0301 Beijing Shifan Daxue Xuebao (Ziran Kexue Ban)
0476-031X Beifang Wenxue
0476-1103 Pennsylvania Statistical Abstract†
0476-3475 Die Personalvertretung
0476-8612 Pionierleiter†
0476-9465 Planat†
0477-2008 Police & Constabulary Almanac
0477-244X Politica dei Trasporti
0477-5449 Poodle Review
0477-6763 Universidade Federal do Rio Grande do Sul. Faculdade de Odontologia. Revista *changed to* Faculdade de Odontologia de Porto Alegre. Revista.
0477-6801 Ports and Dredging and Oil Report *see* 0166-5766
0477-7166 Boletim Actinometrico *see* 0870-4740
0477-7255 Portugal Illustrado
0477-8685 Pozemni Stavby†
0478-1376 Presenza
0478-1392 Preservation Progress (Charleston)
0478-1546 Presse
0478-1805 Previdenza Sociale nell'Agricoltura
0478-3166 Pro Austria Romana
0478-4049 Asbestos Producer
0478-4251 Products Finishing Directory
0478-6378 Proyeccion
0478-6726 Przemysl Drzewny
0478-6866 Psychobiologie
0478-9997 P - D News
0479-0790 Pacific Hotel Directory and Travel Guide *see* 0894-1734
0479-1290 Padova
0479-1363 Beihefte Paedagogik
0479-2327 Pakistan Cotton Bulletin *see* 0030-9699
0479-4346 Panorama Economico
0479-480X Magyar Grafika
0479-4826 Papua New Guinea. National Statistical Office. Building Statistics
0479-7337 Pays de Bruxelles *changed to* Action Bruxelloise et le Pays de Bruxelles.
0479-7876 Pediatria
0479-8007 Beijing Nongye Daxue Xuebao
0479-8023 Beijing Daxue Xuebao (Ziran Kexue Ban)
0479-8244 Pembrokeshire Historian†
0479-8775 Pennsylvania. Department of Public Welfare. Public Welfare Report *see* 0098-8510
0479-947X P H S News
0479-9534 Pennsylvania Osteopathic Medical Association. Journal
0479-9828 Pentecostes *see* 0210-0851
0480-0257 Performing Arts Magazine (San Francisco Edition)†
0480-0516 Permanent International Association of Navigation Congresses. Bulletin
0480-2160 Petroleum Intelligence Weekly
0480-2780 Philadelphia Association for Psychoanalysis. Bulletin *see* 0094-1476
0480-2853 Philanthropic Digest
0480-3981 Series of Philippine Scientific Bibliographies†
0480-7898 Quill (Greencastle)
0480-9653 Queensland. Department of Forestry. Annual Report *changed to* Queensland Forest Service. Department of Primary Industries. Annual Report.
0481-0023 Quellen zur Geschichte des Islamischen Aegyptens
0481-0112 Quelques Donnees Statistiques sur l'Industrie Francaise des Pates, Papiers, Cartons *changed to* Statistiques de l'Industrie Francaise des Pates. Papiers et Cartons.
0481-1275 Quantum Physics and Its Applications†
0481-2018 Quarterly Economic Review of U S A *see* 0269-6185
0481-2085 Quarterly Journal of Engineering Geology
0481-2158 Quarterly Medical Review
0481-2786 Quebec (Province) Department of Tourism, Fish and Game. Annual Report *see* 0229-3811
0481-2875 Quebec (Province). Liquor Board. Annual Report *changed to* Societe des Alcools du Quebec. Rapport Annuel.
0481-3219 Queensland. Department of Forestry. Research Note *see* 1035-9788
0481-3375 Queensland. Registrar of Co-Operative and Other Societies. Report
0481-4118 Quimica e Derivados
0481-5084 R F D News
0481-5475 Rachunkowosc
0481-6684 Revista de Chirurgie, Oncologie, Radiologie, O.R.L., Oftalmologie, Stomatologie. Radiologie
0481-6722 Radionic Quarterly
0481-9306 Recht der Jugend *see* 0034-1312
0482-0819 Reform Judaism
0482-1319 Register of Registrars *changed to* Annual Registrars Service.
0482-2803 Report on Credit Unions
0482-430X Retreader's Journal *see* 1046-7157
0482-5020 Revista Cailor Ferate Romane†
0482-5276 Revista de Ciencias Sociales
0482-5527 Revista de Educacao e Cultura
0482-5772 Revista de Ingenieria
0482-5985 Revista de Ortopedia y Traumatologia

ISSN

5744 ISSN INDEX

ISSN	Title
0482-6019	Revista de Psiquiatria y Psicologia Medica de Europa y America Latinas
0482-640X	Revista Nacional de Oncologia†
0482-6876	Revista Mexicana de Seguridad Social†
0482-7171	Revista Portuguesa de Medicina Militar
0482-7678	Revue de Droit Familial *changed to* Cahiers de Droit Familial.
0482-8062	Revue du Travail
0482-9905	Rhododendron und Immergruene Laubgehoelze
0483-142X	Rivista del Lavoro
0483-2027	Robotnik
0483-3686	Rose Annual *changed to* The Rose.
0483-7738	R P A Bulletin *changed to* Regional Plan News.
0483-9218	Rajshahi University Studies
0483-9420	Random Lengths
0483-9889	Rating and Valuation *changed to* R R V Monthly.
0484-0305	Readaptation
0484-0828	Recent Researches in the Music of the Baroque Era
0484-1506	Recording for the Blind. Catalog of Recorded Books
0484-1689	Redbook of Used Gun Values†
0484-2286	Referativnyi Zhurnal. Kommunal'noe, Bytovoe i Torgovoe Oborudovanie
0484-2480	Referativnyi Zhurnal. Stroitel'nye i Dorozhnye Mashiny
0484-2502	Referativnyi Zhurnal. Teploenergetika†
0484-2545	Referativnyi Zhurnal. Vodnyi Transport
0484-2561	Referativnyi Zhurnal. Vozdushnyi Transport
0484-2596	Referativnyi Zhurnal. Zheleznodorozhnyi Transport
0484-2650	Reflection (Spokane)
0484-6796	Revista de Ciencias Economicas: Economia, Financas, Administracao, Estatistica *changed to* Ciencias Economicas.
0484-6923	Revista de Derecho Social Ecuatoriano
0484-8365	Revolution et Travail
0484-8578	Revue de Mycologie *see* 0181-1584
0484-8594	Revue de Podologie
0484-8764	Revue Francaise de Comptabilite
0484-8934	Revue Metapsychique
0484-8942	Revue Numismatique
0484-9019	Rit Fiskideildar
0485-1412	Japanese Journal of Clinical Nutrition
0485-1420	Rinsho Kensa
0485-2400	Rivista di Istochimica Normale e Patologica *see* 0391-7258
0485-2435	Rivista Giuridica dell'Edilizia
0485-2877	Rocket News
0485-3091	Rocznik Pilski *see* 0557-2088
0485-3504	Rodzina i Szkola
0485-5175	Roving Commissions
0485-6724	Old Sturbridge Visitor
0485-8182	R I S S; National Magazine for Residents, Interns, and Senior Students *see* 0018-5795
0485-8255	Regional Science Research Institute. Discussion Paper Series†
0485-893X	Radiologia Iugoslavica
0485-8972	Radiotekhnika (Kharkov)
0485-9561	Rajasthan Medical Journal
0485-9790	Rand Corporation. Index of Selected Publications *see* 0037-1343
0485-9960	Random Lengths Yearbook
0486-0306	Rassegna Geriatrica
0486-0349	Rassegna Italiana di Sociologia
0486-0748	Reactive Intermediates in Organic Chemistry†
0486-0845	University of Reading. Department of Agricultural Economics & Management. Miscellaneous Studies
0486-1019	Realidade†
0486-106X	Realites Gabonaises
0486-123X	Recent Researches in the Music of the Renaissance
0486-1345	Recherches Internationales a la Lumiere du Marxisme *see* 0294-3069
0486-1426	Recherches Voltaiques†
0486-1469	Recht der Landwirtschaft
0486-1493	Recht und Geschichte
0486-2236	Referativnyi Zhurnal. Astronomiya
0486-2252	Referativnyi Zhurnal. Avtomobil'nye Dorogi
0486-2260	Referativnyi Zhurnal. Biologicheskaya Khimiya *see* 0034-2300
0486-2279	Referativnyi Zhurnal. Dvigateli Vnutrennego Sgoraniya
0486-2287	Referativnyi Zhurnal. Elektronika i ee Primenenie *see* 0206-5452
0486-2309	Referativnyi Zhurnal. Geologiya
0486-2325	Referativnyi Zhurnal. Khimiya
0486-2333	Referativnyi Zhurnal. Kibernetika *changed to* Referativnyi Zhurnal. Tekhnicheskaya Kibernetika.
0486-235X	Referativnyi Zhurnal. Informatika
0486-252X	Reformed Journal *see* 0888-5281
0486-2902	Regional Science Association. Papers *see* 1056-8190
0486-3720	Renaissance and Modern Studies
0486-3739	Renaissance Drama
0486-3887	Renewal of Town and Village†
0486-400X	Rentgenologija i Radiologija
0486-4271	Repertorium Plantarum Succulentarum
0486-4514	Diplomatic Corps and Consular and Other Representatives in Canada
0486-4689	Res Facta
0486-4700	Res Publica
0486-4867	Research Corporation Quarterly Bulletin *see* 0276-0401
0486-5111	Research Progress in Organic, Biological and Medicinal Chemistry†
0486-5383	Reserve Bank of Malawi. Report and Accounts
0486-5588	Responsa Meridiana
0486-5642	Restoration Quarterly
0486-6096	Review of International Affairs
0486-6118	Review of Medical Microbiology *changed to* Jawetz, Melnick & Adelberg's Medical Microbiology.
0486-6134	Review of Radical Political Economics
0486-6460	Revista Camoniana
0486-6525	Revista Colombiana de Antropologia
0486-8161	Sacramento Newsletter
0486-8234	Saechsische Heimatblaetter
0486-8323	Safe Driver
0487-1596	I C A P Lista de Nuevas Adquisiciones†
0487-2088	St. Hedwigsblatt†
0487-3750	Guida Sardegna d'Oggi
0487-4013	Saskatchewan. Geodata Statistics and Research Branch. Weekly Drilling and Land Report *see* 0707-9788
0487-6598	Schoenhengster Jahrbuch
0487-6830	School Sister of Notre Dame†
0487-8965	Scientific Meetings
0488-1281	Seishin Igaku
0488-2644	Sempex Pharmaceutique *changed to* Sempex.
0488-3721	Servex
0488-3896	Service Station Management
0488-5368	Shanxi Nongye
0488-5406	Shanghai Jiaoyu (Chengren Jiaoyu Ban)
0488-6054	Shengwuxue Jiaoxue
0488-6291	Shiga Daigaku Kyoikugakubu Kiyo. Shizen Kagaku
0488-6720	Shipmate
0488-7115	Show Business Who's Where *see* 0508-6795
0488-728X	Free Albanian
0488-7387	Shuxue Jiaoxue
0488-7395	Shuxue Tongxun
0488-7557	Svetlosc
0488-8812	Simplicity School Catalog†
0489-1376	Literarny Almanach Slovaka V Amerike†
0489-2089	Norsk Etnologisk Gransking. Smaaskrifter†
0489-2313	Smithsonian Institution. Annual Symposia Publications†
0489-5606	Engineering Know-How in Engine Design†
0489-5967	Socijalizam
0489-6432	Sophia (Tokyo, 1952)
0489-8567	South African Licensee's Guardian
0489-9563	South of the Mountains
0490-0200	Southern Illinois Labor Tribune *changed to* St. Louis - Southern Illinois Labor Tribune.
0490-1274	Soviet Export *changed to* Business Contact.
0490-1606	Soziale Arbeit
0490-1657	Sozialgerichtsbarkeit
0490-2270	Instituto de Aclimatacion. Archives†
0490-3323	Spain. Ministerio de la Vivienda. Boletin Oficial
0490-334X	Spain. Ministerio de Obras Publicas. Boletin de Informacion *changed to* Obras Publicas.
0490-4176	Spex Speaker
0490-4788	Spoletium
0490-5113	Sport Universitario
0490-5326	Sports Afield Gun Annual†
0490-5474	Sports Turf Bulletin
0490-5687	Sportaube
0490-6381	Sri Lanka
0490-6659	Srpska Akademija Nauka i Umetnosti. Odeljenje Likovne i Muzicke Umetnosti. Muzicka Izdanja
0490-6748	Sichuan Daxue Xuebao (Shehui Kexue Ban)
0490-6756	Sichuan Daxue Xuebao (Ziran Kexue Ban)
0490-9348	Steirischer Burgenverein. Mitteilungen
0491-0869	Stockholm Studies in History of Literature
0491-0877	Stockholm Studies in Philosophy
0491-0982	Stomatologija
0491-1245	Strafvollzug in der Schweiz
0491-1520	Street and Smith's Baseball Yearbook *see* 0161-2018
0491-2705	Studia Ethnographica Upsaliensia
0491-2853	Studia Tehologica Lundensia
0491-3310	Studies in Public Opinion†
0491-3418	Studii de Muzicologie†
0491-421X	Suchtgefahren *see* 0939-5911
0491-4481	Sudan Medical Journal
0491-6204	Surmach
0491-6441	Svarochnoe Proizvodstvo
0492-004X	Transportarbetaren
0492-0716	T V Star Annual†
0492-0929	Dazhong Dianying
0492-1127	Tabor
0492-1283	Tag des Herrn
0492-1712	Taiwan Sugar
0492-1755	Tajekoztato a Kulfoldi Kozgazdasagi Irodalomrol *see* 0237-0840
0492-1755	Tajekoztato a Kulfoldi Kozgazdasagi Irodalomrol *see* 0237-0859
0492-2700	Tarif- und Verkehrs-Anzeiger†
0492-3901	Taylor Talk
0492-4851	Technik Wlokienniczy *changed to* Przeglad Wlokienniczy plus Technik Wlokienniczy.
0492-5408	Teen Talk†
0492-5882	Tekstil
0492-6471	Temas Sociales
0492-6749	Tempo Medico
0492-746X	Tennessee Magazine
0492-7958	Terres Lointaines
0492-8679	Guide to Texas State Agencies†
0493-2099	Tianjin Jiaoyu
0493-2137	Tianjin Daxue Xuebao
0493-2218	Dianxin Kexue
0493-2374	Dianying Gushi
0493-4091	Tokyo Keizai University. Journal
0493-4253	University of Electro-Communications. Report
0493-4334	Misaki Marine Biological Station. Contributions†
0493-4342	Area and Culture Studies
0493-4474	Tokyo Shosen Daigaku Kenkyu Hokoku. Shizen Kagaku
0493-5284	Torch: U.S.
0493-5306	Torino Motori *see* 0393-7666
0493-6779	Trade Times
0493-8348	Trelleborgs Nyheter†
0494-075X	Caizheng Yanjiu
0494-0911	Cehui Tongbao
0494-1101	Zuopin
0494-1225	Tushuguanxue Tongxun
0494-2884	Turkey Today†
0494-3880	T A C Attack
0494-4372	Dazhong Sheying
0494-464X	Taegliche Praxis
0494-4739	Korean Journal of Dermatology
0494-5263	Taiwan Agricultural Research Institute. Annual Report
0494-5336	Taiwan Exports
0494-612X	Taminga *changed to* South Australian Geographer.
0494-6162	Tankuang Gongcheng
0494-6944	Tap Roots
0494-7061	Tareas
0494-8203	Source References for Facts and Figures on Government Finance†
0494-8343	Taxation in Australia
0494-8440	Te Reo
0494-9390	Technische Mitteilungen Krupp
0494-9501	Tecnica e Metodologia Economale *changed to* Sintesi.
0494-9846	Tehnologija Mesa
0494-9870	Tehran Economist
0495-0127	Tele (English Edition)
0495-0216	Telenorma Nachrichten
0495-0615	Temas Economicos
0495-0658	Temi Romana
0495-0887	Tendenzen
0495-1328	Tennessee Lawyer *see* 0497-2325
0495-145X	Industrial Development in the T V A Area *see* 0882-9454
0495-1549	Teologia Espiritual
0495-257X	Texas Vital Statistics
0495-2634	University of Texas, Austin. Bureau of Business Research. Publications
0495-2944	Texas Archeological Society. Special Publication
0495-369X	Textile World Buyer's Guide - Fact File†
0495-5692	Dianying Wenxue
0495-5773	Tierras de Leon
0495-6753	T M A Tobacco Trade Barometer
0495-7199	Tohogaku
0495-730X	Tohoku Nogyo Shikenjo Kenkyu Sokuho *see* 0387-172X
0495-7318	Tohoku Nogyo Shikenjo Kenkyu Hokoku
0495-7601	Tokushima Daigaku Gakugei Kiyo
0495-7725	Maison Franco-Japonaise. Bulletin
0495-7814	University of Tokyo. Institute for Nuclear Study. INS-J
0495-7822	University of Tokyo. Institute for Nuclear Study. Report
0495-8012	Jinbun Shizen Kagaku Ronshu
0495-8020	Tokyo Institute of Technology. Bulletin†
0495-8055	Tokyo Institute of Technology. Research Laboratory of Resources Utilization. Report
0495-8667	Toomey J Gazette *see* 0361-4166
0495-9701	Tower
0495-9728	Town & Country Planning Association. Planning Bulletin
0496-1021	Transportes
0496-1102	Transvaal Museum. Bulletin
0496-1803	Tri-City Genealogical Society. Bulletin
0496-3326	Caoyuan
0496-3490	Zuowu Xuebao
0496-3547	Tsuda Review
0496-4225	Tongji Yanjiu
0496-4845	Turista†
0496-6201	Two and a Bud
0496-6457	T.A.
0496-6597	T R U Mathematics *changed to* S U T Journal of Mathematics.
0496-7046	Taiwan Financial Statistics Monthly *changed to* Financial Statistics Monthly, Taiwan District, Republic of China.
0496-7631	Tall Timbers Research Station. Bulletin
0496-764X	Tall Timbers Research Station. Miscellaneous Publication
0496-8018	Universite de Madagascar. Centre d'Etudes des Coutumes. Cahiers *changed to* Cahiers d'Histoire Juridique et Politique.
0496-8026	Tane

ISSN INDEX 5745

0496-8360 C A F R A D News†
0496-8492 Appropriation Accounts, Revenue Statements, Accounts of the Funds and Other Public Accounts of Tanzania†
0496-8859 Taraxacum†
0496-8913 Tar Heel Junior Historian
0496-9472 Tata Institute of Fundamental Research. Lectures on Mathematics and Physics. Physics changed to Tata Institute Lectures on Mathematics.
0496-9936 Teachers and Writers Collaborative Newsletter see 0146-3381
0496-9944 Teacher's Arts & Crafts Workshop†
0496-9987 T E S O L Newsletter see 1051-8886
0497-0292 Boletin Informativo Techint
0497-0489 Technical Translation Bulletin†
0497-0527 Technicon International Congress. Papers†
0497-0594 Technikus†
0497-1000 University of Teheran. Central Library. Library Bulletin
0497-1035 Tehnika Podmazivanja i Primjena Goriva see 0350-350X
0497-1140 Monthly Report of the Iron and Steel Statistics
0497-137X Telecommunication Journal
0497-1388 Telecommunications
0497-1507 Television Digest see 0497-1515
0497-1515 Television Digest with Consumer Electronics
0497-1817 Temenos (Turku)
0497-2007 France. Institut National de la Statistique et des Etudes Economiques. Tendances de la Conjoncture
0497-2325 Tennessee Bar Journal
0497-2384 Tennessee Studies in Literature
0497-2627 Teoreticheskaya i Eksperimental'naya Khimiya
0497-9400 Asian Bibliography
0497-9478 Steel Market
0498-2002 U.S. Agricultural Marketing Service. Dairy Division. Federal Milk Order Market Statistics
0498-7667 Wholesale Prices and Price Indexes changed to Producer Price Indexes.
0498-7845 U.S. Bureau of Mines. Mineral Industry Surveys
0498-8442 Current Construction Reports: Housing Starts
0498-8450 Current Housing Reports: Housing Characteristics
0498-8469 Current Housing Reports: Housing Vacancies
0498-8477 Current Industrial Reports
0498-8485 Current Population Reports: Special Studies
0499-0994 U.S. Department of Commerce. Publications. Supplement see 0277-7207
0499-9320 U.S. National Aeronautics and Space Administration. Technical Memorandum
0500-1951 U.S. Office of Naval Research. Annual Task Summary: Contract Research Program
0500-5922 Universitas Belgica. Communication - Mededeling changed to Universitas Belgica.
0500-6260 Unabhaengige Brandschutzzeitschrift
0500-7720 Utah Vital Statistics Annual Report
0500-8476 Uusi Nainen
0501-0659 Ulkopolitiikka
0501-1213 International Conference of Building Officials. Uniform Housing Code
0501-1590 Union of European Football Associations. Bulletin
0501-3054 Agricultural Review for Europe
0501-3062 Statistics of World Trade in Steel
0501-3615 Race Question in Modern Science†
0501-4697 U S D A-D H I A Cow Performance Index List†
0501-7041 U.S. Bureau of Labor Statistics. National Survey of Professional, Administrative, Technical and Clerical Pay
0501-7467 U.S. Bureau of Reclamation. Engineering and Research Center. Research Reports changed to U.S. Bureau of Reclamation. Denver Office. Research Reports.
0501-7718 Current Governments Reports: Quarterly Summary of State and Local Tax Revenue changed to Current Governments Reports: Quarterly Summary of Federal, State, and Local Tax Revenue.
0501-8390 U.S. Centers for Disease Control. Malaria Surveillance Report
0501-9117 Agricultural Finance Outlook changed to U.S. Department of Agriculture. Agricultural Income and Finance Situation and Outlook.
0501-9257 Agricultural Situation in the Western Hemisphere changed to World Agriculture Regional Supplement: Western Hemisphere.
0501-9664 Employees of Diplomatic Missions
0501-9966 Background Notes on the Countries of the World
0502-0034 International Boundary Study
0502-3238 World Marketing†
0502-4994 U.S. Forest Service. Research Note R M

0502-5001 U.S. Forest Service. Research Paper R M
0502-5842 United States - Italy Trade Directory
0502-6660 Latinamericanist†
0502-6938 Unsere Heimat (Vienna)
0502-7179 Up-To-Date changed to Milton Chronicles.
0502-7527 Uppsala University. Department of Sociology. Research Reports
0502-9392 U A W Ammunition changed to U A W Ammo.
0502-949X Universidad Nacional de Colombia. Direccion de Divulgacion Cultural. Revista
0502-9554 Unesco Source Books on Curricula and Methods
0502-9767 U S Oil Week
0503-1001 Ukrainian Academy of Arts and Sciences in the U S. Annals
0503-1036 Komitet' Ukrainstsiv Kanady. Biuleten' changed to Ukrainian Canadian Congress. Bulletin.
0503-1265 Ukrainskii Fizicheskii Zhurnal
0503-146X Haumah
0503-1540 La Mer
0503-1575 Umjetnost i Dijete
0503-1966 Uniform Commercial Code Law Letter
0503-1982 Uniformed Services Almanac
0503-2032 Unima France changed to U N I M A - France Marionnettes.
0503-2334 Union Mondiale des Organisations Syndicales sur Bases Economique et Sociale Liberales. Conferences: Rapport
0503-2407 Collection of Documents for the Study of International Non-Governmental Relations
0503-2628 Unit Trust Yearbook
0503-3551 United Methodist Church. General Minutes of the Annual Conferences
0503-356X United Methodist Directory†
0503-3772 Half-Yearly Bulletin of Electric Energy Statistics for Europe†
0503-3934 United Nations. Regional Centre for Demographic Training and Research in Latin America. Serie A
0503-3942 United Nations. Regional Centre for Demographic Training and Research in Latin America. Serie C
0503-3950 United Nations. Regional Centre for Demographic Training and Research in Latin America. Serie D
0503-4108 United Nations. Conference on Trade and Development. Trade and Development Board. Official Records
0503-440X Selected List of Catalogues for Short Films and Filmstrips†
0503-4434 Unesco. Regional Office for Science and Technology for Africa. Bulletin
0503-4442 Unesco. Regional Centre for the Training of Educational Planners, Administrators and Supervisors in Asia. Publication†
0503-4450 Unesco. Regional Office for Education in Asia. Bulletin. changed to Unesco. Principal Regional Office for Asia and the Pacific. Bulletin.
0503-4469 Unesco. Regional Office for Education in Asia. Regional Conference Reports changed to Population Education in Asia and the Pacific Newsletter and Forum.
0503-4663 United Schools International. Documents of the Biennial Conference
0503-5422 Appalachian Regional Commission. Annual Report
0504-0779 Veterans' Voices
0504-4251 Virginia Engineer
0504-426X Virginia English Bulletin
0504-6556 La Voix des Jeunes
0504-7250 Voordrachten Gehouden voor de Gelderse Leergangen te Arnhem†
0505-0146 Vanidades Continental
0505-0332 Vasi Szemle
0505-0448 Vector
0505-2904 V D E W die Oeffentliche Elektrizitaetsversorgung
0505-3838 Vesitalous
0505-4605 Vida Nueva
0505-4753 Vidya
0505-4885 Vie Economique
0505-5164 Naturhistorisches Museum in Wien. Veroeffentlichungen. Neue Folge
0505-5849 Vilagossag
0505-7523 Vishva Jyoti
0505-8813 Voice of the Tennessee Walking Horse
0505-9259 Volksarmee
0505-9461 Voluntad Hidraulica
0506-2772 Vatrechni Bolesti
0506-306X V D G S A News
0506-337X Vaabenhistorisk Tidsskrift
0506-3590 Yearbook of Population Research in Finland
0506-3876 Finnish State Railways†
0506-3973 Vancouver Historical Journal†
0506-4252 Varstvo Narave
0506-4406 Veckans Affaerer
0506-4414 Vector Genetics Information Service†
0506-5283 Venezuelan Petroleum Industry
0506-5291 Venezuela. Division de Estadistica Vital. Informe Especial changed to Venezuela. Departamento de Estadistica Vital. Informe Especial.
0506-6913 Verde Olivo
0506-7286 Verfassung und Recht in Uebersee

0506-7294 Vergilius
0506-7472 Vermont Labor Force changed to Vermont Labor Market.
0506-7553 Vermont Geological Survey. Special Bulletin changed to Vermont Division of Geology and Mineral Resources. Special Bulletin.
0506-7847 Vertebratologicke Zpravy see 0862-9609
0506-7936 Verzeichnis der Orientalischen Handschriften in Deutschland
0506-7944 Verzeichnis der Orientalischen Handschriften in Deutschland. Supplementbaende
0506-8347 Via
0506-8509 Victoria, Australia. Statutory Rules
0506-872X Vida Escolart
0507-0252 Viola da Gamba Society of America. Journal
0507-102X Virginia State Publications in Print
0507-1259 Virginia Polytechnic Institute and State University. Department of Geological Sciences. Geological Guidebooks
0507-1305 Virginia Social Science Journal
0507-1410 Vishveshvaranand Indological Journal
0507-1577 Vista changed to Vista U S A.
0507-1690 Vita Evangelica
0507-1887 Vizgazdalkodas changed to Magyar Vizgazdalkodas.
0507-1925 Vjesnik Bibliotekara Hrvatske
0507-2298 Voice of P S E A changed to Voice for Education.
0507-3758 Voprosy Onkologii
0507-3952 Voprosy Teatra
0507-4088 Voprosy Virusologii
0507-4150 Vorgaenge
0507-570X Universidad Central de Venezuela. Instituto de Ciencias Penales y Criminologicas. Anuario.
0507-6714 Verein Deutscher Zementwerke. Forschungsinstitut der Zementindustrie. Taetigkeitsbericht
0507-6773 Vertebrate Pest Conference. Proceedings
0507-6986 Vajra Bodhi Sea
0507-7184 Vida Pastoral
0507-7206 Hochschule fuer Welthandel in Wien. Dissertationen see 0259-0719
0507-9683 Waseda Daigaku Daigakuin Rikogaku Kenkyu Iho
0508-0924 Washington Report on Legislation for Children and What You Can do About It changed to Washington Report on Federal Legislation for Children.
0508-1254 Wasserrecht und Wasserwirtschaft
0508-2404 Weinberg und Keller
0508-6213 Wetterauer Geschichtsblaetter
0508-6795 Who's Where†
0508-7104 Wiadomosci Tytoniowe
0508-8445 Wir vom Konsum
0509-0652 Wochenpost
0509-089X Women's Circle
0509-3007 World Meteorological Organization. Regional Association II (Asia). Abridged Final Report of the (No.) Session
0509-3015 World Meteorological Organization. Regional Association VI (Europe). Abridged Final Report of the (No.) Session
0509-397X Wuhan Daxue Ziran Kexue Xuebao see 0253-9888
0509-4003 Wuli Jiaoxue
0509-4038 Wuli Tongbao
0509-5166 W.C.J. Meredith Memorial Lectures
0509-5190 W E M A Directory changed to American Electronics Association Directory.
0509-5832 Waksman Foundation of Japan. Report
0509-6057 Walter E. Edge Lectures†
0509-6413 Bibliografia Bibliografii i Nauki o Ksiazce†
0509-6510 Centralny Instytut Ochrony Pracy. Prace
0509-6529 Centralny Osrodek Badan i Rozwoju Techniki Drogowej. Prace changed to Instytut Badawczy Drog i Mostow. Prace.
0509-6839 Biuletyn Warzywniczy
0509-6936 Muzeum Narodowe w Warszawie. Rocznik†
0509-7053 Przemyslowy Instytut Elektroniki. Prace
0509-7134 Szkola Glowna Gospodarstwa Wiejskiego. Zeszyty Naukowe. Zootechnika changed to Warsaw Agricultural University. S G G W. Annals. Animal Science.
0509-769X Environmental Radiation Surveillance in Washington State. Annual Report
0509-7703 Washington (State). Department of Institutions. Jail Inspection Report see 0091-7265
0509-7967 Washington State Traffic Accident Facts†
0509-8262 Manufacturers and Distributors Directory of the Washington, D.C. Area†
0509-8858 Das Wassertriebwerk
0509-9498 Weekly Crusader see 0195-265X
0509-9773 Hochschule fuer Architektur und Bauwesen Weimar. Wissenschaftliche Zeitschrift
0510-0054 N Z O I Miscellaneous Publications†
0510-1492 West Virginia Geological Survey. Educational Series changed to West Virginia Geologic Education Series.

5746 ISSN INDEX
ISSN

0510-2014 Western Australia. Geological Survey. Mineral Resources Bulletin
0510-2332 Western Express
0510-243X Western Material Handling - Packaging - Shipping
0510-3517 Kihara Institute for Biological Research. Wheat Information Service
0510-372X White River Valley Historical Quarterly
0510-3746 Belaruski Instytut Navukii Mastatstva. Zapisy
0510-4130 Who's Who in the Egg and Poultry Industries
0510-4262 Wiadomosci Melioracyjne
0510-4270 Wiadomosci Naftowe†
0510-4882 William Nelson Cromwell Foundation. Legal Studies†
0510-5366 Wirtschaft und Boerse
0510-5528 Bilanz
0510-5609 Wirtschaftszahl
0510-7148 Women Ai Kexue
0510-7350 Women's Comfort†
0510-7385 Women's Household
0510-8055 World Branches Conference of the English Speaking Unions. Principal Addresses and Summary of the Proceedings†
0510-8225 World Congress in Public Park Administration. Reports *changed to* Congress in Park and Recreation Administration. Reports.
0510-8233 World Congress in Public Park Administration. Programme *changed to* Congress in Park and Recreation Administration. Programme.
0510-8284 World Congress of Sodalities of Our Lady. Proceedings†
0510-8292 World Congress of the Deaf. Proceedings.
0510-8837 World Health Organization. Regional Office for Africa. Report of the Regional Director
0510-906X World Meteorological Organization. Commission for Aeronautical Meteorology. Abridged Final Report of the (No.) Session
0510-9078 World Meteorological Organization. Commission for Agricultural Meteorology. Abridged Final Report of the (No.) Session
0510-9116 World Meteorological Organization. Commission of Synoptic Meteorology. Abridged Final Report of the (No.) Session *see* 0251-8953
0510-9124 World Meteorological Organization. Regional Association I (Africa). Abridged Final Report of the (No.) Session
0510-9132 World Meteorological Organization. Regional Association III (South America). Abridged Final Report of the (No.) Session
0510-9744 Wspolczesnosc *changed to* Literatura.
0510-9752 Wuhan Yixueyuan Xuebao *see* 0257-716X
0510-9833 Wuerzburger Geographische Arbeiten
0510-9868 Wychowanie Fizyczne i Higiena Szkolna
0510-9884 Wychowanie Techniczne w Szkole
0511-0440 Wyoming Trucker
0511-0653 Waelzlagertechnik *see* 0934-8875
0511-0726 A A G Bijdragen
0511-0831 Wakayama Daigaku Kyoikugakubu Kiyo. Shizen Kagaku
0511-084X Wakayama Medical Reports
0511-1145 Warehouse Distributor News†
0511-1196 Ruch Wydawniczy w Liczbach
0511-1927 Waseda University. Report of Castings Research Laboratory *changed to* Waseda University. Report of Materials Science and Technology.
0511-196X Waseda Political Studies
0511-2141 Washington (State) Department of Fisheries. Information Booklet†
0511-2400 Washington Economic Indicators†
0511-2834 University of Washington. College of Business Administration. Occasional Paper†
0511-3040 University Resources in the United States for Linguistics and the Teaching of English as a Foreign Language *changed to* Directory of Programs in Linguistics.
0511-3172 Washington Financial Reports *see* 0891-0634
0511-3180 Washington Highway News *changed to* Transpo News.
0511-3202 Washington Library Letter†
0511-3520 Wasser - Kalender
0511-3555 Water and Pollution Control Directory *changed to* Water & Pollution Control. Directory and Buyers' Guide.
0511-392X Selected List of Biomedical Serials in Metropolitan Detroit *changed to* Union List of Selected Serials of Michigan.
0511-4063 Wedgwood Society. Proceedings
0511-411X Weed Control Manual and Herbicide Guide
0511-4144 Weed Society of America. Abstracts *changed to* Weed Science Society of America. Abstracts.
0511-4187 U.S. Office of the Federal Register. Weekly Compilation of Presidential Documents
0511-4365 Welding Data Book *see* 0278-7067
0511-4683 Wenxue Pinglun
0511-4721 Wen Shi Zhe
0511-4772 Wenwu
0511-4934 Wesleyan Poetry Program
0511-5493 West Bengal. Bureau of Applied Economics and Statistics. Statistical Handbook
0511-568X West-European Symposia on Clinical Chemistry†
0511-6147 West Pakistan Cooperative Review *changed to* Punjab Cooperative Union. Review.
0511-6775 West Virginia Statistical Handbook†
0511-6848 Western Association of Graduate Schools. Proceedings of the Annual Meeting
0511-6910 Western Australia. Major Investment Projects, Public and Private, Current and Proposed†
0511-6996 Western Australia. Geological Survey. Annual Report†
0511-750X Western Forest Fire Committee. Proceedings *changed to* Western Forestry Conference. Proceedings.
0511-7518 Western Forest Pest Committee. Proceedings *changed to* Western Forestry Conference. Proceedings.
0511-7526 Western Reforestation Coordinating Committee. Proceedings *changed to* Western Forestry Conference. Proceedings.
0511-7542 Western Foundation of Vertebrate Zoology. Occasional Papers
0511-7550 Western Foundation of Vertebrate Zoology. Proceedings
0511-7666 W I C H E Reports
0511-7704 Western Lumber Facts
0511-8255 Barometer (Portland)
0511-8298 Western Wood Products Association. Monthly F.O.B. Price Summary, Past Sales. Coast Mills
0511-8484 Westpreussen - Jahrbuch
0511-8654 What's New in Chemical Processing Equipment *see* 0009-2630
0511-8662 What's New in Forensic Sciences *see* 0022-1198
0511-8719 Where to Retire on a Small Income
0511-8794 Whitmark Directory
0511-8832 Whittier Newsletter
0511-8891 Who's Who Among Students in American Junior Colleges
0511-8905 Who's Who in Advertising
0511-8948 Who's Who in California
0511-8964 Who's Who in Floriculture
0511-9022 Who's Who in Public Relations (International)
0511-9162 Wiadomosci Historyczne
0511-9510 Wildlife Review†
0511-9618 Willdenowia
0511-9715 William L. Bryant Foundation American Studies. Report†
0511-9723 William L. Hutcheson Memorial Forest. Bulletin
0512-0624 Wisconsin. Division of Highways. System Planning Section. Highway Traffic in Wisconsin Cities *see* 0084-0580
0512-0640 Wisconsin. Geological and Natural History Survey. Information Circulars
0512-0659 Wisconsin. Geological and Natural History Survey. Special Report
0512-0918 University of Wisconsin. Bureau of Business Research and Service. Monographs *see* 0084-0513
0512-1175 Wisconsin Academy Review
0512-1213 Wisconsin English Journal
0512-1523 Universitaet Frankfurt. Wissenschaftliche Gesellschaft. Sitzungsberichte
0512-1604 Wissenschaftliche Untersuchungen zum Neuen Testament
0512-1825 Women of Vietnam
0512-2368 World Airline Record Newsletter *see* 0002-2748
0512-2457 World Bank Atlas
0512-2511 World Confederation of Organizations of the Teaching Profession. Occasional Papers†
0512-252X W C O T P Theme Study†
0512-2589 Faith and Order Papers
0512-2740 World Directory of Mathematicians
0512-2953 World Fertilizer Atlas
0512-3011 Vaccination Certificate Requirements for International Travel *changed to* International Travel and Health: Vaccination Requirements and Health Advice.
0512-3038 World Health Organization. Monograph Series
0512-3054 W H O Technical Report Series
0512-3070 World Health Organization. Regional Office for Africa. Report of the Regional Committee. Minutes of the Plenary Session *changed to* World Health Organization. Regional Office for Africa. Report of the Regional Committee.
0512-3089 World Health Organization. Regional Office for the Eastern Mediterranean. Annual Report of the Regional Director *changed to* World Health Organization. Regional Office for the Eastern Mediterranean. Annual Report of the Regional Director.
0512-3135 World Hospitals
0512-3186 World Land Use Survey. Occasional Papers†
0512-3194 World Land Use Survey. Regional Monograph†
0512-3453 World Peace Through Law Center. Report of the Director-General†
0512-350X Estatistica Brasileira de Energia
0512-3739 World Trade Annual
0512-3747 World Trade Annual Supplement
0512-3844 World Wheat Statistics *changed to* World Grain Statistics Yearbook.
0512-4077 Wrangler
0512-4204 Wudao
0512-4255 Wychowanie Muzyczne w Szkole
0512-4263 Wychowanie Obywatelskie *changed to* Spoleczenstwo Otwarte.
0512-4395 Wyoming Statistical Review†
0512-4409 Wyoming Labor Force Trends
0512-4638 W.A. Cargill Memorial Lectures in Fine Art†
0512-4646 Akademia Rolnicza, Warsaw. Zeszyty Naukowe. Rozprawy Naukowe *see* 0239-8613
0512-4743 West Virginia Union List of Serials
0512-4921 World Health Organization. Regional Office for the Western Pacific. Annual Report of the Regional Director to the Regional Committee for the Western Pacific
0512-5030 Wasser und Abwasser in Forschung und Praxis
0512-5235 Western Catholic Reporter
0512-5278 What's Happening on the Chinese Mainland
0512-5405 Wire Journal Directory Catalog *see* 0277-4275
0512-5456 Wisconsin Studies in Vocational Rehabilitation. Monographs†
0512-5472 Works in Progress†
0512-5804 What They Said
0512-5898 Eutrophication Abstracts *see* 0094-3347
0512-5901 Woman's Day Christmas Ideas for Children†
0512-6355 Occupational Opportunities Information for Wisconsin†
0512-7920 Yinyue Shenghuo
0512-7955 Yingyang Xuebao
0512-9575 Youth Planbook *changed to* Curriculum Plans.
0512-9664 Yuhua
0513-0794 Yugoslavia. Savezni Zavod za Statistiku. Saobracaj i Veze
0513-0832 Yugoslavia. Savezni Zavod za Statistiku. Ucenici u Privredi
0513-0883 Yugoslavia. Savezni Zavod za Statistiku. Zaposleno Osoblje
0513-0891 Yugoslavia. Savezni Zavod za Statistiku. Zaposlenost
0513-1545 Western Historical Series†
0513-1693 Yamaguchi Daigaku Kyoikugakubu Kenkyu Ronso. Dai-2-bu. Shizen Kagaku
0513-1715 Yamaguchi University. Faculty of Agriculture. Bulletin
0513-1812 Yamaguchi University. School of Medicine. Bulletin
0513-2088 Yearly Digest of Criminal Cases†
0513-2592 Yokohama National University. Faculty of Engineering. Bulletin
0513-2622 Yokosuka-shi Hakubutsukan Kenkyu Hokoku. Shizen Kagaku
0513-2711 York Pioneer
0513-2762 Yorkshire Dialect Society. Summer Bulletin
0513-3297 Youth *see* 0013-1482
0513-353X Yuanyi Xuebao
0513-417X Yadoriga
0513-4242 Pharmaceutical Society of Korea. Journal
0513-4412 Yale Linguistic Series *changed to* Yale Language Series.
0513-4501 Yale Southeast Asia Studies. Monograph Series
0513-4757 Yamaguchi-ken Eisei Kenkyujo Gyoseki Hokoku *see* 0915-0498
0513-5117 Year Book of Neurology & Neurosurgery
0513-5303 Yeni Yayinlar
0513-5389 Yessis Review of Soviet Physical Education and Sports *see* 0275-598X
0513-5613 Yokohama National University. Science Reports. Section 2: Biological Sciences *changed to* Yokohama National University. Science Reports. Section 2: Biological and Geological Sciences.
0513-5621 Yokohama Kokuritsu Daigaku Jinbun Kiyo Dai-1-rui, Tetsugaku, Shakai Kagaku
0513-5656 Yokohama National University. Educational Sciences
0513-5710 Yonago Acta Medica
0513-5796 Yonsei Medical Journal
0513-5982 Young Fabian Pamphlet
0513-6032 World Alliance of Y M C A's Directory
0513-6121 Young Socialist Forum *see* 0044-0884
0513-6261 Yrke och Framtid
0513-6547 Yugoslavia. Savezni Zavod za Statistiku. Metodoloski Materijali
0513-6555 Yugoslavia. Savezni Zavod za Statistiku. Studije, Analize i Prikazi

ISSN INDEX 5747

0513-7926 Zahntechnik†
0513-8809 Zdrowie i Trzezwosc
0513-9147 Zeitschrift fuer Theologie und Kirche
0513-9295 Zeleznicni Technika
0513-9325 Zemedelske Aktuality *changed to* Zemedelske - Polnohospodarske Aktuality.
0513-9481 Zena
0513-9856 Zhinochyi Svit
0514-0668 Eidgenoessische Technische Hochschule Zuerich. Bibliothek. Schriftenreihe
0514-2253 Japanese Periodicals Index. Science and Technology
0514-2482 Zeal
0514-2571 Zeitschrift fuer Beamtenrecht
0514-2733 Zeitschrift fuer Philosophische Forschung. Beihefte
0514-275X Zeitschrift fuer Rechtsvergleichung *changed to* Zeitschrift fuer Rechtsvergleichung, Internationales Privatrecht und Europarecht.
0514-2776 Zeitschrift fuer Sozialreform
0514-2938 Zement - Taschenbuch
0514-3292 Genealogisches Jahrbuch
0514-342X Zeszyty "Argumentow"
0514-3446 Zeszyty Gliwickie
0514-3993 Zoo Review *see* 0736-2676
0514-4795 Zygos
0514-5090 Zavod za Slavensku Filologiju. Radovi†
0514-5236 Zambezia: A Journal of Social Studies in Southern and Central Africa *see* 0379-0622
0514-5392 Zambia. Central Statistical Office. Transport Statistics
0514-5430 Zambia. Department of Cooperatives. Annual Report *changed to* Zambia. Ministry of Cooperatives. Annual Report.
0514-5457 Zambia. Educational and Occupational Assessment Service. Annual Report
0514-5724 Zane Grey Collector†
0514-6151 Zbornik za Istoriju Skolstva i Prosvete
0514-616X Zbornik Zastite Spomenika Kulture
0514-6321 Zeitschrift fuer Allgemeine und Textile Marktwirtschaft†
0514-6364 Zeitschrift fuer Bibliothekswesen und Bibliographie. Sonderhefte
0514-6496 Zeitschrift fuer Rechtspolitik
0514-650X Zeitschrift fuer Religions- und Geistesgeschichte. Beihefte
0514-6658 Acta Biologica Iugoslavica. Serija A: Zemljiste i Biljka
0514-7115 Zentralblatt fuer Mineralogie. Teil I: Kristallographie, Mineralogie
0514-7123 Zentralblatt fuer Mineralogie. Teil II: Petrographie, Technische Mineralogie, Geochemie und Lagerstaettenkunde
0514-7166 Zentralblatt fuer Veterinaermedizin. Series B *see* 0931-1793
0514-7352 Zeri i Rinise
0514-7441 Zivotnovadni Nauki
0514-7905 Zoning Bulletin
0514-7972 Zoonosis†
0514-809X Z M P D. Kwartalny Biuletyn Informacyjny
0514-8294 Zur Politik und Zeitgeschichte
0514-8413 Zwischen Eider und Wiedau
0514-8561 Zeitschrift fuer Hohenzollerische Geschichte
0514-857X Zentralasiatische Studien
0514-8731 Zambia. Central Statistical Office. Fisheries Statistics (Natural Waters)
0514-8782 Zeitschrift fuer Militaermedizin
0514-8790 Akademie der Wissenschaften der D.D.R. Zentralinstitut fuer Physik der Erde. Veroeffentlichungen
0514-8863 American Crystallographic Association. Monographs
0514-9045 A D A Legislative Newsletter†
0514-9061 A D L Nachrichten *see* 0340-1545
0514-9142 A E G Newsletter *see* 0888-305X
0514-9193 Arte Fotografico
0514-9797 A N A P
0514-9886 A O K Gesundheitsblatt *changed to* Gesundheitsblatt A O K Aktuell.
0515-0272 A S L A Newsletter
0515-0361 Astin Bulletin
0515-2003 Academy of American Poets. Lamont Poetry Selections *changed to* Academy of American Poets. Lamont Poetry Selection and Walt Whitman Selection.
0515-2089 Academy Reporter *see* 0360-3679
0515-2178 Accademia Italiana di Scienze Forestali. Annali
0515-2690 Acta Agraria et Silvestria. Seria Rolnicza *see* 0065-0919
0515-2712 Acta Albertina Ratisbonensia
0515-2720 Acta Anaesthesiologica Scandinavica. Supplementum
0515-2925 Acta Medica et Sociologica
0515-3085 Acta Politecnica Mexicana
0515-3700 Actualites Pharmaceutiques
0515-4510 Advance
0515-4987 The Advocate (Boise)
0515-6327 Afro-Asian Publications
0515-6610 Aggiornamenti su Malattie Infettive ed Immunologia
0515-6831 Agrarmeteorologische Bibliographie
0515-6912 Agricoltore Bresciano
0515-698X Agricultura†
0515-779X Aichi Gakugei Daigaku Kenkyu Hokoku. Shizen Kagaku *see* 0365-3722
0515-7935 Aile et Roue
0515-8125 Air Freight Directory of Points in the United States Served Directly by Air and by Pick-up and Delivery Service and by Connecting Motor Carriers *see* 0092-2870
0516-3145 Akademiska Dzive
0516-4303 Alaska. Department of Fish and Game. Informational Leaflet
0516-4850 Alaska Farm Production *see* 0065-5694
0516-5504 Albuquerque Bar Journal†
0516-5644 Alemannisches Jahrbuch†
0516-5849 Alexandria Medical Journal
0516-6950 Cotton Textile Statistics†
0516-8635 Amateur Hockey Association of the United States. Official Guide *changed to* U S A Hockey.
0516-866X Amateur Skating Union of the United States. Official Handbook *changed to* Amateur Speedskating Union of the United States. Official Handbook.
0516-8856 American Academy of Orthopaedic Surgeons. Directory
0516-9313 American Association of Colleges for Teacher Education. Directory
0516-9445 Reference Book of Highway Personnel *changed to* A A S H T O Reference Book of Member Department Personnel and Committees.
0516-9518 A A V S O Bulletin *changed to* A A V S O Bulletin: Predicted Dates of Maxima and Minima of Long Period Variable Stars.
0516-9550 American Astrology Digest
0516-9593 American Astronautical Society. Proceedings of the Annual Meeting
0516-9623 American Atheist
0516-9674 Tourbook: Florida
0516-9968 A B A Washington Letter
0517-0648 American College Public Relations Association. Newsletter†
0517-0680 American College Testing Program. Annual Report *changed to* American College Testing. Annual Report.
0517-0745 American Concrete Institute. Compilation
0517-1024 Facts About States for the Dentist Seeking a Location
0517-3833 American Montessori Society. Proceedings of the National Seminar†
0517-3868 Anthropological Handbook†
0517-404X Numismatic Studies
0517-4252 American Perfumer and Aromatics *see* 0361-4387
0517-4376 America Pioneers: Tackett-Tacket-Tackitt Families of America *see* 1052-7753
0517-4856 American Shore and Beach Preservation Association. Newsletter
0517-5178 American Society of Clinical Hypnosis. Directory
0517-5208 American Society of Clinical Pathologists. Summary Report†
0517-564X American Trade Schools Directory
0517-5666 Truck Taxes by States†
0517-6298 Ammo House Bulletin *changed to* C.A.C. Sporting Bulletin.
0517-659X Anhui Huabao
0517-6611 Anhui Nongye Kexue
0517-6735 Analecta Praemonstratensia
0517-6816 Anales de Medicina. Cirugia *see* 0210-7465
0517-6824 Anales de Medicina. Medicina *see* 0210-7465
0517-6832 Anales de Medicina. Especialidades *see* 0210-7465
0517-6956 Analisis de la Situacion Agricola de Sinaloa *changed to* Analisis de la Agricultura Sinaloense.
0517-7731 Anglican
0517-8045 Ancient Iranian Cultural Society. Publication
0517-855X Annales des Antilles
0517-8991 Annuaire des Fournisseurs de Laboratoires Pharmaceutiques *see* 0396-0625
0517-9130 Annuaire Professionnel de l'Horticulture et des Pepinieres *changed to* Annuaire Federal de l'Horticulture et des Pepinieres.
0518-0147 Handbuch Holz
0518-0937 Anuario dos Criadores
0518-1259 L'Apicoltore Moderno
0518-1852 Arab World†
0518-2220 Arbeitsgemeinschaft der Parlaments- und Behoerdenbibliotheken. Arbeitshefte
0518-2840 Arche
0518-3138 Politechnika Gdanska. Zeszyty Naukowe. Architektura
0518-3618 Archivo
0518-3979 Arena, Auditorium, Stadium Guide *changed to* AudArena Stadium International Guide.
0518-4614 Argentina. Direccion General de Parques Nacionales. Anales de Parques Nacionales *see* 0302-5705
0518-4673 Argentina. Direccion Nacional de Estadistica y Censos. Boletin Mensual de Estadistica *see* 0326-6214
0518-5327 Arhiv za Rudarstvo i Geologiju
0518-6242 Arizona Statistical Review†
0518-6374 Water Resources Summary
0518-6544 University of Arkansas. Industrial Research and Extension Center. Annual Report *changed to* University of Arkansas. Arkansas Institute for Economic Advancement. Annual Report for the Vice Chancellor and Provost.
0518-6617 Arkansas Amateur
0518-7648 Art et Poesie
0518-794X Arthritis Foundation. Conference Series†
0518-8857 Asian Conference on Occupational Health. Proceedings†
0518-8881 Asian News Sheet
0518-8989 Asian Textile Workers Conference. Proceedings†
0518-9519 Asociacion Latinoamericana de Libre Comercio. Informe de las Actividades†
0519-1572 Bank Holding Company Facts
0519-2048 Associazione Italiana Biblioteche. Quaderni del Bollettino d'Informazioni†
0519-3125 Atlantic Mail†
0519-3273 Atlas Histoire *changed to* Atlas - Air France.
0519-3346 A E†
0519-3389 Atomic Energy Clearinghouse
0519-4997 Australia. Bureau of Statistics. Installment Credit for Retail Sales, Australia†
0519-5659 Commonwealth Scientific and Industrial Research Organization. Division of Fisheries and Oceanography *see* 0726-4275
0519-5950 Australia. Department of Foreign Affairs. Select Documents on International Affairs *changed to* Australia. Department of Foreign Affairs and Trade. Select Documents on International Affairs.
0519-6035 Australia. Department of the Treasury. Taxation Branch. Taxation Statistics
0519-7201 Biblioteca Romanica Hispanica. Estudios y Ensayos *changed to* Biblioteca Romanica Hispanica.
0519-8356 Biblioteka Matematyczna
0519-8631 Biblioteka Pisarzow Polskich. Seria A
0519-8658 Biblioteka Pisarzy Reformacyjnych
0519-9514 Bibliotekovedenie i Bibliografiya za Rubezhom
0519-9603 Bibliotheca Archaeologica
0519-9700 Bibliotheca Historica Lundensis
0520-1373 Bildnerisches Volksschaffen
0520-1810 Biological Journal of Okayama University†
0520-1985 Biophysical Society. Symposium Proceedings *see* 0067-8910
0520-2795 Bliss Classification Bulletin
0520-3015 Bluebell News
0520-3325 Bodhi Leaves
0520-4895 Bollettino delle Ricerche Sociali†
0520-5441 Bombay Cooperator†
0520-626X Borsodi Szemle
0520-6790 Bourne Society Local History Records
0520-6804 Bouwmarkt
0520-7002 Brabantica†
0520-7010 Braby's Bloemfontein Directory
0520-7037 Braby's Pietermaritzburg Directory
0520-9048 Begriffsbestimmungen fuer die Bundesstatistiken der Oesterreichische Elektrizitaetswirtschaft
0520-9404 Brevet†
0520-9455 Breviora Geologica Asturica
0521-0348 British Columbia. Ministry of Municipal Affairs. Municipal Statistics *changed to* British Columbia. Ministry of Municipal Affairs, Recreation and Culture. Municipal Statistics, Including Regional Districts.
0521-1573 British Schools Exploring Society. Report
0521-2359 Acta Musei Moraviae - Scientiae Naturales
0521-4211 Marx Karoly Kozgazdasagtudomanyi Egyetem: Doktori Ertekezesek *changed to* Budapesti Kozgazdasagtudomanyi Egyetem: Doktori Ertekezesek.
0521-4602 Temadokumentacios Kiadvanyok†
0521-4882 Budapest Statisztikai Evkonyve
0521-517X Hospital de Ninos. Revista
0521-6680 Bulgarski Tiutiun
0521-7032 Musees et Monuments Lyonnais. Bulletin
0521-7091 Federation Belgo-Luxembourgeoise des Industries du Tabac. Bulletin F E D E T A B
0521-713X Bulletin Historique et Artistique du Calais
0521-7237 Bulletin of Brewing Science†
0521-7903 Journal of Cultural Sciences
0521-8195 Burgense
0521-9477 British Broadcasting Corporation. B B C Lunchtime Lectures†
0521-9590 Library Association of Trinidad and Tobago. Bulletin
0521-9744 Babel
0521-9884 Kommission fuer Geschichtliche Landeskunde in Baden-Wuerttemberg. Veroeffentlichungen. Reihe B: Forschungen
0522-0033 Der Baer von Berlin
0522-0629 Ball and Roller Bearing Engineering *changed to* Ball and Roller Bearing Engineering - Industrial Engineering.
0522-0653 Ballet Review

ISSN

0522-0777 Banaras Hindu University. Darshana Series†
0522-0939 Banco Central de Bolivia. Boletin Estadistico
0522-098X Banco Central de Costa Rica. Estadisticas Economicas
0522-1153 Banco Central de Venezuela. Seccion A.L.A.L.C. Algunas Estadisticas de los Paises de A.L.A.L.C.†
0522-1315 Banco de Bilbao. Informe Economico
0522-1986 Banco Nacional de Panama. Cuadernos†
0522-2079 Banco Regional de Desenvolvimento do Extremo Sul. Relatorio da Directoria *changed to* Banco Regional de Desenvolvimento do Extremo Sul. Annual Report.
0522-246X Bank of Sudan. Foreign Trade Statistical Digest
0522-2478 Bank Auditing & Accounting Report
0522-2494 Bank Director's Report†
0522-2508 Bank Executive's Report†
0522-2818 Bank of New South Wales Review *see* 0812-3470
0522-2931 Banker
0522-3199 Banque de France. Direction de la Conjoncture. Structure et Evolution Financiere des Regions de Province *changed to* Banque de France. Direction de la Conjoncture. Situation Financiere des Regions En (Year).
0522-327X Banque Marocaine du Commerce Exterieur. Monthly Bulletin of Information *changed to* B M C E Information Review.
0522-3806 Boletin Estadistico Coyuntural *see* 0210-1580
0522-3822 Colegio de Agentes de Cambio y Bolsa de Barcelona. Servicio de Estudios e Informacion. Boletin Financiero†
0522-4314 Burqab†
0522-4497 International Peace Research Institute. Basic Social Science Monographs†
0522-4810 Battelle Research Outlook *see* 0145-8477
0522-4942 Bauen mit Aluminium
0522-4950 Bauingenieur-Praxis†
0522-5078 Letopis. Reihe B. Geschichte
0522-5086 Letopis. Reihe C. Volkskunde
0522-5337 Bayerische Verwaltungsblaetter
0522-5949 Beethoven-Jahrbuch
0522-604X Behoerden und Organisationen der Land- Forst- und Ernaehrungswirtschaft
0522-6201 Beitraege zum Buechereiwesen. Reihe B: Quellen und Texte†
0522-6562 Beitraege zur Geschichte der Universitaet Erfurt (1392-1816) *see* 0233-2930
0522-6570 Beitraege zur Geschichte der Wissenschaft und der Technik
0522-6643 Beitraege zur Geschichte des Parlementarismus und der Politischen Parteien
0522-6759 Beitraege zur Japanologie
0522-6848 Beitraege zur Kolonial und Ueberseegeschichte
0522-7216 Beitraege zur Wirtschaftspolitik
0522-7232 Bekesi Elet
0522-7291 Museu Paraense Emilio Goeldi. Boletim. Nova Serie: Antropologia *changed to* Museu Paraense Emilio Goeldi. Boletim. Serie Antropologia.
0522-7496 Belgium. Commission Royale des Monuments et des Sites. Bulletin
0522-7690 Annuaire Statistique de la Sante Publique
0522-8557 Zavod za Fiziku. Radovi *see* 0350-0594
0522-8603 Belize. Weekly Newsletter†
0522-8670 Bellman Memorial Lecture *changed to* Bellman Lecture.
0522-8883 Benedictine Yearbook
0522-8948 Benelux Economic Union. Conseil Consultatif Economique et Social Rapport du Secretaire Concernant les Activites du Conseil *changed to* B E N E L U X Economic Union. Conseil Central de l'Economie. Rapport du Secretaire sur l'Activite du Conseil.
0522-8980 Patrika *changed to* Bamla Ekademi Gabeshana Patrika.
0522-9170 Bergen. Universitetet. Aarbok†
0522-9804 Archiv der Hauptstadt der Deutschen Demokratischen Republik. Beitraege Dokumente, Informationen *changed to* Berliner Geschichte.
0522-9898 Humboldt - Universitaet zu Berlin. Universitaetsbibliothek. Schriftenreihe
0523-0144 Berliner Forum†
0523-1051 Better Beef Business
0523-1159 Bevolking en Gezin
0523-1469 Bisdeh Hemed
0523-1639 Bibliografi Nasional Indonesia
0523-1698 Bibliografia Argentina de Psicologia
0523-1760 Bibliografia Espanola (Annual)
0523-1833 Bibliografia Kombetare e Repulikes Popullore te Shqiperise. Artikujt e Periodikut Shqip *changed to* Bibliografia Kombetare e Periodikeve Shqip.
0523-1841 Bibliografia Kombetare e Repulikos Popullore te Shqiperise. Libri Shqip *changed to* Bibliografia Kombetare e Librit Shqip.
0523-218X Prirodne i Primenjene Nauke. Clanci i Prilozi u Casopisima, Listovima i Zbornicima *see* 0352-5945
0523-2201 Bibliografija Jugoslavije. Knjige, Brosure i Muzikalije
0523-2392 Bibliographie de l'Algerie
0523-2465 Bibliographie der Franzoesischen Literaturwissenschaft
0523-2678 Bibliographie Paedagogik
0523-2767 Bibliographien zur Deutschen Literatur des Mittelalters
0523-2988 Bibliography of Seismology
0523-302X Bibliography on Irrigation, Drainage, River Training and Flood Control
0523-5154 Biblische Untersuchungen
0523-5774 Bijdrage tot de Geschiedenis van het Zeewezen†
0523-6150 Bilten za Hematologiju i Transfuziju
0523-7238 Black Panther†
0523-7688 Blue Shield (Chicago)†
0523-7785 Boarding School Directory of the United States†
0523-7904 Bocagiana
0523-8080 Boei Daigakko Kyokan Kenkyu Yoroku
0523-8153 Boeki Kuremu to Chusai *see* 0386-3042
0523-8226 Boethius
0523-8587 Bohemia: Zeitschrift fuer Geschichte und Kultur der Bohemischen Laender
0523-9095 Boletin del Cemento Portland
0523-9141 C E N D E S Boletin Industrial
0523-9478 Museo Risorgimento. Bollettino
0524-0166 Bomaby Civic Journal *changed to* Brihanmumbai Mahanagarpalika Patrika.
0524-0182 Bombay Hospital Journal
0524-045X Bonner Mathematische Schriften
0524-0476 Bonplandia
0524-0581 Book Review Index
0524-0581 Book Review Index: Annual Clothbound Cumulations
0524-0654 Books and Articles on Oriental Subjects Published in Japan
0524-0913 Borthwick Institute of Historical Research. Borthwick Papers
0524-1014 Bosques *changed to* Bosques y Fauna.
0524-112X Boston College Studies in Philosophy
0524-1561 Bottin Europe†
0524-1685 Bovine Practitioner
0524-2053 Brasilia Medica
0524-2444 Braunschweiger Geographische Studien
0524-2533 Brazil. Comissao Central de Levantamento e Fiscalizacao das Safras Triticolas. Annuario Estatistico do Trigo: Producao Nacional
0524-4714 Briefs (Lexington)†
0524-4994 British Arachnological Society. Bulletin
0524-5141 British Ceramic Society. Proceedings
0524-5168 British Club Year Book
0524-5370 British Columbia. Department of Economic Development. Monthly Bulletin of Business Activity *see* 0821-0020
0524-5508 Schedule of Wells Drilled for Oil and Natural Gas in British Columbia
0524-5672 British Columbia Energy Board. Annual Report *changed to* British Columbia. Utilities Commission. Annual Report.
0524-5826 British Fern Gazette *see* 0308-0838
0524-6431 British Museum (Natural History). Bulletin. Entomology
0524-6474 British Museum (Natural History) Bulletin *changed to* British Museum (Natural History) Report.
0524-7403 Acta Universitatis Agriculturae. Ser. Facultas Agronomica
0524-7438 Acta Universitatis Agriculturae. Ser. Facultas Silviculturae
0524-7446 Acta Universitatis Agriculturae. Ser. Facultas Agroeconomica
0524-7624 Bibliotheque Royale Albert 1er. Acquisitions Majeures†
0524-7632 Bibliotheque Royale de Belgique. Bulletin *see* 0770-4372
0524-7764 Belgium. Institut Royal Meteorologique. Annuaire: Magnetisme Terrestre
0524-7780 Belgium. Institut Royal Meteorologique. Annuaire: Rayonnement Solaire
0524-8655 Eotvos Lorand Geophysical Institute of Hungary. Annual Report
0524-8868 Orszagos Szechenyi Konyvtar Evkonyve
0524-8906 Petofi Irodalmi Muzeum Evkonyve
0524-904X Acta Facultatis Politico-Juridicae Universitatis Scientiarum Budapestiensis de Rolando Eotvos Nominatae
0524-9481 Museo Argentino de Ciencias Naturales "Bernardino Rivadavia." Instituto Nacional de Investigacion de las Ciencias Naturales. Revista. Ecologia
0524-949X Museo Argentino de Ciencias Naturales "Bernardino Rivadavia." Instituto Nacional de Investigacion de las Ciencias Naturales. Revista. Entomologia
0524-9503 Museo Argentino de Ciencias Naturales "Bernardino Rivadavia." Instituto Nacional de Investigacion de las Ciencias Naturales. Revista. Hidrobiologia
0524-9511 Museo Argentino de Ciencias Naturales "Bernardino Rivadavia." Instituto Nacional de Investigacion de las Ciencias Naturales. Revista. Paleontologia
0524-952X Museo Argentino de Ciencias Naturales "Bernardino Rivadavia." Instituto Nacional de Investigacion de las Ciencias Naturales. Revista. Parasitologia
0524-9864 Buenos Aires (Province). Archivo Historico. Publicaciones. Sexta Serie
0525-0110 B O C A Basic Housing - Property Maintenance Code *see* 1055-6192
0525-0846 Etudes Historiques
0525-1443 Bulletin of Epizootic Diseases of Africa *see* 0378-9721
0525-1524 Bulletin of Volcanic Eruptions
0525-1931 Bunseki Kagaku
0525-2156 Bulletin to Management
0525-2539 Burundi. Ministere du Plan. Departement des Statistiques. Bulletin de Statistique *changed to* Burundi. Departement des Etudes et Statistiques. Bulletin Trimestriel.
0525-2989 Buss Handbuch Europaeischer Produktenboersen†
0525-3063 Butterworths Budget Tax Tables
0525-3306 Byzantinische Forschungen
0525-3675 Bibliografia Espanola (Monthly)
0525-3772 University of Birmingham. Faculty of Commerce and Social Science. Discussion Papers: Series F: Birmingham Society and Politics†
0525-4205 British National Committee on Large Dams. News and Views
0525-4507 Byzantina Neerlandica
0525-4515 Baad-Revyen
0525-4620 Biennial Survey of Bank Officer Salaries†
0525-4663 Basketball Case Book
0525-4736 Beitraege zur Landesentwicklung
0525-4752 Belgium. Administration des Mines. Service: Statistiques. Siderurgie, Houille, Agglomeres, Cokes *changed to* Belgium. Administration des Mines. Statistiques: Houille, Cokes, Agglomeres Metallurgie, Carrieres.
0525-5090 Botswana Notes and Records
0525-6402 Cooperative News Digest
0525-8693 Accidentes de Transito en Costa Rica†
0525-9282 Report on the Activities of the Council of Europe†
0526-4375 Current and Forthcoming Offprints on Archaeology in Great Britain and Ireland *see* 0269-1906
0526-5053 Analysis of Cyprus Foreign Trade†
0526-5096 Cyprus. Department of Statistics and Research. Statistical Summary†
0526-6122 C A T C Electronic News†
0526-6513 C.I.C.A.E. Bulletin d'Information
0526-717X Cactaceas y Suculentas Mexicanas
0526-7994 Cahiers de la Resistance
0526-8133 Cahiers des Explorateurs
0526-8443 Cahiers Percherons
0526-9288 California State Plan for Hospitals and Related Health Facilities *changed to* California State Health Plan.
0526-9970 California. Division of Forestry. Conservation Camp Program†
0527-0014 California. Division of Mines and Geology. Special Report
0527-2181 California. Agricultural Statistics Service. Fruit and Nut Acreage
0527-3277 California Tomato Grower
0527-446X Camping Journal (New York)†
0527-4834 Canada. Statistics Canada. Boatbuilding and Repair†
0527-4869 Canada. Statistics Canada. Breweries†
0527-4893 Canada. Statistics Canada. Carpet, Mat and Rug Industry *see* 0319-891X
0527-4915 Canada. Statistics Canada. Coffin and Casket Industry†
0527-494X Canada. Statistics Canada. Communications Equipment Manufacturers - Fabricants d'Equipement de Telecommunication *see* 0828-9824
0527-4974 Canada. Statistics Canada. Construction in Canada
0527-4990 Canada. Statistics Canada. Cordage and Twine Industry†
0527-5016 Canada. Statistics Canada. Cotton Yarn and Cloth Mills†
0527-5024 Canada. Statistics Canada. Distilleries†
0527-5148 Canada. Statistics Canada. Federal Government Employment in Metropolitan Areas†
0527-5318 Canada. Statistics Canada. Gas Utilities, Transport and Distribution Systems
0527-5504 Canada. Statistics Canada. Manufacturers of Electric Wire and Cable - Fabricants de Fils et de Cables Electriques *see* 0833-2002
0527-5539 Canada. Statistics Canada. Manufacturers of Industrial Chemicals†
0527-5679 Canada. Statistics Canada. Men's Clothing Industries *see* 0835-006X
0527-5822 Canada. Statistics Canada. Motor Vehicle, Part 1, Rates and Regulations†

ISSN INDEX 5749

ISSN	Title
0527-5830	Canada. Statistics Canada. Motor Vehicle. Part 2. Motive Fuel Sales *see* 0703-654X
0527-5849	Canada. Statistics Canada. Motor Vehicle, Part 4, Revenues†
0527-5865	Canada. Statistics Canada. Motor Vehicle Traffic Accidents†
0527-5881	Canada. Statistics Canada. New Manufacturing Establishments in Canada†
0527-5911	Canada. Statistics Canada. Oils and Fats
0527-5997	Canada. Statistics Canada. Ornamental and Architectural Metal Industry *see* 0835-0124
0527-608X	Canada. Statistics Canada. Provincial Government Employment *see* 0825-9224
0527-6144	Canada. Statistics Canada. Shipbuilding and Repair†
0527-6160	Canada. Statistics Canada. Shipping Statistics†
0527-6179	Canada. Statistics Canada. Shorn Wool Production†
0527-6411	Canada. Statistics Canada. Vending Machine Operators
0527-6497	Canadian Civil Aircraft Register
0527-6624	Marketing Boards in Canada†
0527-687X	Canada. Department of Finance. Small Business Loans Act. Annual Report *changed to* Canada. Department of Regional Industrial Expansion. Small Businesses Loans Act. Annual Report.
0527-7892	Martin's Annual Criminal Code
0527-9275	Directory of Canadian Chartered Accountants
0528-1458	Carl Newell Jackson Lectures
0528-1725	Carolina Journal of Pharmacy
0528-1865	Carta Economica del Ecuador
0528-2152	Case Studies of International Conflict†
0528-2195	Casopis pro Pestovani Matematiky
0528-2438	Guia del Comercio y de la Industria de Madrid *changed to* Guia del Comercio y de la Industria (Year).
0528-2594	Catalogus Translationem et Commentatorium
0528-2772	Catequetica
0528-2950	Catholic International Education Office. Bulletin Documentaire†
0528-3280	Revista Caucho
0528-4252	Centralna Rada Zwiazkow Zawodowych w Polsce. Biuro Historyczne. Biuletyn *see* 0860-9357
0528-4465	Centre d'Etudes et de Recherches Scientifiques de Biarritz. Bulletin
0528-4759	Centre International de Liaison des Ecoles de Cinema et de Television. Bulletin d'Informations *changed to* C I L E C T Newsletter.
0528-5984	Cerberus Alarm *changed to* Alarm.
0528-757X	Ceylon Economist
0528-7618	Ceylon Journal of Social Work
0528-7820	National Research Institute of Tea. Bulletin *changed to* National Research Institute of Vegetables, Ornamental Plants and Tea. Bulletin. Series B.
0528-8231	Chambre Francaise de Commerce et d'Industrie du Maroc. Revue Conjoncture
0528-838X	Changjiang Wenyi
0528-8592	Char-Koosta News
0528-9017	Zhejiang Nongye Kexue
0528-9254	Politechnika Lodzka. Zeszyty Naukowe. Technologia I. Chemia Spozywcza
0528-9432	Chemicke Vlakna
0528-953X	Chemmunique†
0529-0279	Jilin Daxue Ziran Kexue Xuebao
0529-0325	Ji You
0529-0414	Jiangsu Zhongyi
0529-0775	Institute of Gas Technology. Technical Reports†
0529-0937	University of Chicago. Industrial Relations Center. Occasional Papers *changed to* University of Chicago. Human Resources Center. Occasional Papers.
0529-1399	Jianzhu Xuebao
0529-1526	Zhiwu Fenlei Xuebao
0529-1542	Zhiwu Baohu
0529-1607	Current Publications: Serials *changed to* Catalogue of Japanese Periodicals.
0529-1674	Child Welfare League of America. Directory of Member Agencies and Associates *changed to* Child Welfare League of America. Directory of Member And Associate Agencies.
0529-2794	Jinrong Yanjiu
0529-3766	Qiu Shi
0529-4975	Chroniques de Port-Royal
0529-5548	Zhongji Yikan
0529-6013	Zhongguo Fangzhi
0529-6579	Zhongshan Daxue Xuebao *see* 1000-9639
0529-6579	Zhongshan Daxue Xuebao *see* 0253-4088
0529-7028	Church Recreation *see* 0162-4652
0529-7451	Cina
0529-8016	Cites Unies
0529-9160	Classroom Teacher Series in Health, Education, Recreation and Safety†
0529-9675	Clinical Trends in Ophthalmology, Otolaryngology, Allergy†
0529-9853	Club Filatelico de Caracas. Revista *changed to* Club Filatelico de Caracas. Gaceta Mensual.
0530-0495	Coir
0530-0657	Colecao de Estudos Juridicos
0530-749X	Commission of the European Communities. Collection d'Hygiene et de Medecine du Travail†
0530-8836	Collection Panorama†
0530-9751	Collegiate Baseball
0530-9794	Collegium Carolinum. Veroeffentlichungen
0530-9867	Istituto Internazionale di Studi Liguri. Collezione di Monografie Preistoriche e Archeologiche
0531-0008	Colligite†
0531-030X	Universitaet zu Koeln. Institut fuer Handelsforschung. Mitteilungen
0531-0318	Universitaet zu Koeln. Institut fuer Handelsforschung. Mitteilungen. Sonderhefte
0531-1926	Etudes Orientales
0531-1934	Etudes Philosophiques et Litteraires *changed to* Interdisciplinarite Etudes Philosophiques et Litteraires.
0531-1950	Etudes Preliminaires aux Religions Orientales dans l'Empire Romain
0531-2051	Etudes Togolaises
0531-206X	Etudes Vietnamiennes
0531-2159	Eulenspiegel-Jahrbuch
0531-2248	Eurocontrol†
0531-2485	Europarecht
0531-2612	European Academy of Allergy. Proceedings
0531-2663	European Aspects, Social Studies Series
0531-2671	European Aspects, Law Series
0531-2701	E A A A Newsletter
0531-3015	Commission of the European Communities. Collection d'Economie du Travail†
0531-3023	Commission of the European Communities. Collection d'Economie et Politique Regionale†
0531-304X	Commission of the European Communities. Conjoncture Energetique dans la Communaute *changed to* Commission of the European Communities. Energy Situation in the Community.
0531-3120	Fontes et Aciers†
0531-3198	Commission of the European Communities. Collection Objectifs Generaux Acier†
0531-3724	Commission of the European Communities. Expose sur l'Evolution Sociale dans la Communaute *changed to* Commission of the European Communities. Report on the Social Developments.
0531-4119	E F T A Trade
0531-4127	European Free Trade Association. Annual Report
0531-4283	C E R N School of Physics. Proceedings
0531-4321	European Parliament News *see* 0250-5754
0531-4496	European Southern Observatory. Annual Report
0531-4518	European Space Research Organization. General Report†
0531-4526	European Space Research Organization. Report†
0531-4798	Evangelische Mission Jahrbuch *see* 0931-248X
0531-495X	Everyman's Science
0531-5131	International Congress Series
0531-5174	European Council of Jewish Community Services. Exchange Information Service *changed to* European Council of Jewish Community Services. Exchange.
0531-531X	Exercise Exchange
0531-5360	Exhibits Schedule *changed to* Trade Shows & Exhibits Schedule.
0531-5565	Experimental Gerontology
0531-5824	Herold Export - Adressbuch von Oesterreich *changed to* Austria Export Herold.
0531-5980	Chemicals and Allied Products Export Promotion Council. Exporters Directory
0531-6723	Egyptian Library Journal
0531-6863	E A S C O N. Electronics and Aerospace Systems Convention. Record *changed to* I E E E - A E S C O N. Aerospace and Electronics System Conference. Record.
0531-7436	European League for Economic Cooperation. Report of the Secretary General on the Activities of E.L.E.C.
0531-7444	European Organisation for Civil Aviation Equipment. General Assembly. Annual Report
0531-7452	European Space Research Organization. Scientific Memorandum†
0531-7460	European Space Research Organization. Scientific Note†
0531-7479	Europhysics News
0531-755X	Explotacion Agraria†
0531-786X	Ecumene†
0531-7886	Edmund's Foreign Car Prices
0531-8203	Economia Politica
0531-8262	Vermont Geological Survey. Economic Geology *changed to* Vermont Division of Geology and Mineral Resources. Economic Geology.
0531-8327	Educating the Disadvantaged *see* 0270-1448
0531-8432	Ecology *see* 0096-7807
0531-8955	Economic Review
0531-9110	Acta Biologica Iugoslavica. Serija D: Ekologija
0531-9153	Ele e Ela
0531-9218	Der Elektroniker
0531-9315	E R I C Clearinghouse for Junior Colleges. Topical Paper Series†
0531-9323	Statistische Studien
0531-9455	Etudes Baudelairiennes
0531-9684	Folk Music Journal
0531-9870	Fondazione Luigi Einaudi. Annali
0532-0194	Food and Agriculture Organization of the United Nations. Agricultural Planning Studies†
0532-0208	Food and Agriculture Organization of the United Nations. Basic Texts
0532-0283	F A O Forestry Studies†
0532-0291	F A O Library List of Recent Accessions†
0532-0305	F A O Nutrition Special Reports†
0532-0313	F A O Terminology Bulletin
0532-0348	Food and Agriculture Organization of the United Nations. Interamerican Meeting on Animal Production and Health. Report†
0532-0402	Meeting of International Organizations for the Joint Study of Programs and Activities in the Field of Agriculture in Europe. Report.†
0532-0437	Food and Agriculture Organization of the United Nations. Soils Bulletins
0532-0488	Food and Agriculture Organization of the United Nations. World Soil Resources Reports
0532-0623	F A O African Regional Meeting on Animal Production and Health. Report of the Meeting.†
0532-0666	Food and Agriculture Organization of the United Nations. Forest Tree Seed Directory†
0532-0690	Food and Agriculture Organization of the United Nations. Forestry and Forest Products Division. World Forest Products Statistics†
0532-0747	Forestry Newsletter of the Asia-Pacific Region
0532-0941	Food Quality Control *changed to* F D C Control Newsletter.
0532-0968	Food Science
0532-1042	Footwear and Leather Abstracts†
0532-1360	Udenrigs Handelskalenderen for Danmark
0532-1700	Form
0532-2189	Forschungen zur Kunstgeschichte und Christlichen Archaeologie
0532-2731	Fortschritte der Verfahrenstechnik†
0532-3010	Fotomuveszet
0532-3215	Four Seasons (Berkeley)
0532-5781	Francis Thompson Society. Journal *changed to* Eighteen Nineties Society. Journal.
0532-579X	Franciscan
0532-5854	Deutsche Bibliographie. Halbjahres-Verzeichnis *changed to* Deutsche Nationalbibliographie. Halbjahres-Verzeichnis.
0532-596X	Johann-Wolfgang-Goethe Universitaet, Frankfurt. Ostasiatische Seminar. Veroeffentlichungen. Reihe A. Suedostasienkunde†
0532-6370	Freedom from Hunger Campaign. F F H C Report†
0532-7091	F C L Newsletter
0532-7334	From the Sourdough Crock†
0532-7466	Frontiers in Neuroendocrinology
0532-7776	Real Estate Research
0532-811X	Fukuoka Kyoiku Daigaku Kiyo. Dai-3-Bunsatsu. Sugaku, Rika, Gijutsuka Hen
0532-8632	Fundheft fuer Steuerrecht
0532-8721	Funkcialaj Ekvacioj, Serio Internacia
0532-8942	Furniture Production†
0532-9140	F F Dabei
0532-9175	A.A.'s Far East Businessman's Directory
0532-9396	E I F A C Newsletter†
0532-940X	Food and Agriculture Organization of the United Nations. European Inland Fisheries Advisory Commission. Technical Papers
0532-9817	Fertilizacion
0532-9841	Film Special
0533-005X	Foundry Catalog File *changed to* Foundry Databook & Catalog File.
0533-0327	Federacion Panamericana de Asociaciones de Facultades de Medicina. Boletin
0533-0386	Universita degli Studi di Ferrara. Annali. Sezione 14. Fisica Sperimentale e Teorica
0533-0653	All of Mexico at Low Cost
0533-070X	Forum foer Ekonomi och Teknik
0533-0793	France. Institut National de la Statistique et des Etudes Economiques. Collections. Serie C, Comptes et Planification†

5750 ISSN INDEX

0533-0807 France. Institut National de la Statistique et des Etudes Economiques. Collections. Serie D, Demographie et Emploi†
0533-0815 France. Institut National de la Statistique et des Etudes Economiques. Collections. Serie E, Enterprises†
0533-0823 France. Institut National de la Statistique et des Etudes Economiques. Collections. Serie M, Menages†
0533-0831 France. Institut National de la Statistique et des Etudes Economiques. Collections. Serie R, Regions†
0533-0866 France - Pays Arabes
0533-0939 Family Findings
0533-0963 Federal Aviation Regulations for Pilots *changed to* Aim - Far (Year).
0533-1072 Barron's Profiles of American Colleges. Vol. 2: Index of College Major Areas of Study
0533-1153 Fiziologicheski Aktivnye Veshchestva
0533-196X Great Lakes Commission. Report to the States†
0533-2869 Greyfriar-Siena Studies in Literature
0533-3164 Group Analysis: International Panel and Correspondence *changed to* Group Analysis.
0533-3180 Colloques A M P E R E†
0533-3407 Grundlagen und Praxis des Wirtschaftsrechts
0533-3431 Grundschule
0533-4179 Instituto de Nutricion de Centro America y Panama (INCAP). Informe Anual
0533-4500 Guia de la Industria del Caucho
0533-4675 Turismo, Guia Peuser *changed to* Guia Peuser de Turismo Argentina y Sudamericana.
0533-473X Guia Quatro Rodas. Brazil
0533-5248 Guide to American Directories
0533-5388 Guide to Microreproduction Equipment *see* 0360-8654
0533-540X Guide to Radio Electronics and Components Trade and Industry in India *changed to* Guide to Electronics Industry in India.
0533-5426 Guide to Scientific Instruments *changed to* Guide to Biotechnology Products and Instruments.
0533-5450 Guide to Hotels in South Africa *changed to* C V R Hotel Guide to Southern Africa.
0533-5469 Guide to the Mexican Markets
0533-5485 Guide to Traffic Safety Literature†
0533-5620 Guides to Jewish Subjects in Social and Humanistic Research†
0533-5701 Journal Officiel de Guinee
0533-649X Gujarat State Financial Corporation. Annual Report
0533-6627 Gunma University, Faculty of Education. Annual Report: Art, Technology, Health & Physical Education, and Science of Human Living Series
0533-6724 Gunma Symposia on Endocrinology
0533-7291 Generation (Windsor)
0533-7712 Giornale Italiano di Dermatologia e Venereologia
0533-8301 Geological Society of Iraq. Journal
0533-8387 Georgia Welcome Center. Research Report†
0533-8646 University of Ghana. Institute of African Studies. Local Studies Series
0533-8859 Govor†
0533-9235 Gaudeamus Information. English Edition
0533-9286 Geografia Urbana
0533-9529 Gifu Daigaku Kyoikugakubu Kenkyu Hokoku. Shizen Kagaku
0533-9685 Great Britain. Royal Commission on Historical Manuscripts. Secretary's Report to the Commissioners
0533-991X Guyana. Statistical Bureau. Annual Account Relating to External Trade
0534-0012 Acta Biologica Iugoslavica. Serija F: Genetika
0534-042X Laerarhoegskolan i Goeteborg. Pedagogiska Institutionen. Rapport *see* 0348-2219
0534-0489 G R I Newsletter†
0534-0500 Great Britain. Department of Employment. Changes in Rates of Wages and Hours of Work *changed to* Great Britain. Department of Employment. Statistics Division. Time Rates of Wages and Hours of Work.
0534-2104 Chartered Institute of Public Finance and Accountancy. Crematoria Statistics. Actuals *see* 0263-2969
0534-3313 Spain. Instituto de Relaciones Agrarias. Boletin de Informacion Extranjera *see* 0213-0602
0534-3364 Instituto de Estudios Tarraconenses Ramon Berenguer IV. Publicacion
0534-3844 Spain. Instituto Nacional de Industria. Direccion Financiera. Boletin de Informacion Financiera†
0534-4050 Kjeller Report†
0534-4697 Inter-African Conference on Co-Operative Societies Meeting. Reunion
0534-4700 Inter-African Conference on Food and Nutrition. Programa e Informacoes
0534-4727 Inter-African Conference on Industrial Commercial and Agricultural Education Meeting
0534-4735 Inter-African Conference on Medical Co-Operation. Meeting
0534-4751 Inter-African Conference on Social Science Meeting
0534-476X Inter-African Conference on Social Science Rapports
0534-4794 Inter-African Conference of the Mechanisation of Agriculture Meeting
0534-4816 Inter-African Conference on the Treatment of Offenders. Meetings. Reunion
0534-4824 Inter-African Forestry Conference. Conference Forestiere Interafricaine (Communications)
0534-607X Intercity Truck Tonnage *changed to* Motor Carrier Statistical Summary.
0534-6509 Federation Aeronautique International. General Conference Minutes (of the) Business Meetings *changed to* Federation Aeronautique International. Annual Information Bulletin.
0534-655X International African Seminar. Studies Presented and Discussed†
0534-6622 International Amateur Basketball Federation. Official Report of the World Congress *changed to* International Basketball Federation. Official Report of the World Congress.
0534-669X International Association for Dental Research. Abstracts of the General Meeting
0534-7319 I A E A Library Film Catalog
0534-7793 International Cargo Handling Coordination Association. Rapports des Comites Nationaux†
0534-8064 I C A O. Air Navigation Plan. North Atlantic Region *see* 0074-2325
0534-8072 I C A O. Air Navigation Plan. Pacific Region *see* 0074-2325
0534-8242 International Commission of Jurists. Bulletin *see* 0020-6393
0534-8293 International Commission on Large Dams. Bulletin
0534-8587 International Conference of Human Genetics. (Rapports et des Communications)†
0534-8676 International Conference on Electron and Ion Beam Science and Technology. Abstracts†
0534-8803 International Conference on Science and World Affairs. Proceedings
0534-8811 International Conference on Shielding Around High Energy Accelerators. Papers†
0534-9044 International Congress of Graphoanalysts. Proceedings†
0534-9257 International Congress on Canned Foods. Texts of Papers Presented and Resolutions
0534-9869 International Egg Marketing Conference. Proceedings
0534-9907 International Electrotechnical Commission. Central Office Report *see* 0074-4697
0535-0182 International Federation of Fruit Juice Producers. Proceedings. Berichte. Rapports *changed to* International Federation of Fruit Juice Producers. Rapport Annuel d'Activite.
0535-0492 International Financial Statistics. Supplement†
0535-1405 International Medical News
0535-1588 International North Pacific Fisheries Commission. Statistical Yearbook†
0535-1626 International Office of Cocoa and Chocolate and the International Sugar Confectionery Manufacturers' Association. Report of the General Assembly *changed to* International Office of Cocoa, Chocolate and Sugar Confectionery. Report of the General Assembly.
0535-1774 World List of Family Planning Agencies
0535-2479 International Skating Union. Minutes of Congress
0535-3076 International Symposium on Nervous Inhibition. Proceedings†
0535-3114 International Symposium on Submarine and Space Medicine. Proceedings†
0535-4358 Internationales Handbuch fuer Rundfunk und Fernsehen
0535-4455 Interphila
0535-4676 Interstate Commission on the Potomac River Basin. Proceedings
0535-5079 Inventare Nichtstaatlicher Archive
0535-5133 Investigacion Clinica
0535-5729 Iowa Archeological Society. Journal
0535-899X Istruzione Tecnica e Professionale
0535-9821 Italy. Istituto Centrale di Statistica. Statistica Mensile del Commercio con L'Estero *changed to* Italy. Istituto Centrale di Statistica. Statistica Trimestrale del Commercio con L'Estero.
0536-1095 I A G A News
0536-1184 I B M Medical Symposium. Proceedings†
0536-1222 I C C Bulletin
0536-132X I C S U Bulletin *changed to* I C S U Newsletter.
0536-1362 I D
0536-1486 I E E E International Conference on Communications. Conference Record
0536-1966 I R C D Bulletin†
0536-2008 I S A Aerospace Instrumentation Symposium. Proceedings *see* 0277-7576
0536-2067 I S O Memento
0536-2113 I T C Information Booklets†
0536-2121 I T V Guide to Independent Television *see* 0262-6470
0536-2180 I to Cho
0536-2512 Ibero-American Bureau of Education. Information and Publications Department Series V: Technical Seminars and Meetings†
0536-2571 I C A C H
0536-2733 Idaho Employment
0536-3403 International Latitude Observatory of Mizusawa. Proceedings†
0536-3535 Igeret Lechinuch
0536-3683 Japanese Journal of Breeding
0536-3713 Illinois. Administrative Office of Illinois Courts. Annual Report to the Supreme Court of Illinois
0536-4604 University of Illinois at Urbana-Champaign. Graduate School of Library Science. Allerton Park Institute. Papers *changed to* University of Illinois at Urbana-Champaign. Graduate School of Library and Information Science. Allerton Park Institute. Papers.
0536-5139 Illinois Teacher for Contemporary Roles *see* 0739-148X
0536-5465 Image (Rochester, 1952)
0536-647X Index of Economic Articles in Journals and Collective Volumes
0536-6518 Index of Reviews in Organic Chemistry
0536-7506 India. Office of the Comptroller and Auditor-General. Report: Union Government (Posts and Telegraphs)†
0536-8014 Quarterly Statistics of the Working of Capital Issues Control
0536-8502 India. Ministry of Agriculture. Bulletin on Food Statistics
0536-9061 Import Trade Control Policy
0536-9290 India. Ministry of Finance. Budget *changed to* India. Finance Department. Budget of the Central Government.
0536-9657 Bulletin for Metalliferous Mines in India†
0536-9983 Import Trade Control: Handbook of Rules and Procedures
0537-0035 India. Office of the Registrar General. Newsletter *changed to* India. Ministry of Home Affairs. Vital Statistics Division. Sample Registration Bulletin.
0537-0744 India. Zoological Survey. Annual Report
0537-0922 India Today
0537-1120 Survey of India's Exports
0537-1546 Indian Ephemeris and Nautical Almanac *changed to* Indian Astronomical Ephemeris.
0537-166X Indian Foreign Affairs
0537-197X Indian Journal of Agronomy
0537-1996 Indian Journal of Extension Education
0537-2003 Indian Journal of Fisheries
0537-202X Indian Journal of Homoeopathy *see* 0019-5243
0537-2410 Indian Phytopathological Society. Bulletin
0537-2429 Indian Police Journal
0537-2666 Indian Textile Annual & Directory
0537-2704 Indian Yearbook of International Affairs
0537-3131 Folklore Institute. Journal *see* 0737-7037
0537-3468 Fundacion de Investigaciones Economicas Latinoamericanas. Indicadores de Coyuntura
0537-3522 Indice Historico Espanol
0537-3638 Indo-Iranian Reprints†
0537-3654 Indo-Pacific Fisheries Council. Regional Studies†
0537-4715 Indus
0537-5126 Industrial Development in Arizona: Manufacturing *see* 0146-2997
0537-5215 Industrial Hygiene Foundation. Chemical-Toxicological Series. Bulletin *see* 0073-7488
0537-5223 Industrial Hygiene News Report†
0537-5355 Industrial Relations Aspects of Manpower Policy†
0537-5452 Industrial Review of Japan *changed to* Japan Economic Almanac.
0537-5819 Industries et Techniques Francaises
0537-6149 Information and Systems Theory†
0537-6173 Information Circular on Insecticide Resistance. Insect Behaviour and Vector Genetics†
0537-6211 Societe Saint-Jean-Baptiste de Montreal. Information Nationale
0537-6246 Information Processing in Japan†
0537-6297 Documentation Europeenne - Serie Agricole
0537-667X Informator Nauki Polskiej
0537-7137 Journal of Humanistic Studies
0537-779X Institut Francais d'Archeologie d'Istanbul. Bibliotheque Archeologique et Historique†

ISSN

ISSN INDEX 5751

0537-7919 Institut fuer Europaeische Geschichte, Mainz. Veroeffentlichungen. Abteilung Universitaetsgeschichte und Abteilung fuer Abendlaendische Religionsphilosophie *changed to* Institut fuer Europaeische Geschichte, Mainz. Veroeffentlichungen. Abteilung Universalgeschichte und Abteilung fuer Abendlaendische Religionsgeschichte.
0537-7927 Institut fuer Europaeische Geschichte, Mainz. Vortraege. Abteilung Universalgeschichte und Abteilung fuer Abendlaendische Religionsphilosophie *changed to* Institut fuer Europaeische Geschichte, Mainz. Vortraege. Abteilung Universalgeschichte und Abteilung fuer Abendlaendische Religionsgeschichte.
0537-9202 I D E Occasional Papers Series
0537-9679 Institute of Town Planners, India. Journal
0537-9768 University of Miami, Coral Gables. Law Center. Annual Institute on Estate Planning
0537-9989 I E E Conference Publication Series
0538-0022 British Institution of Radio Engineers. Journal *see* 0954-0695
0538-0057 Institution of Engineers, Malaysia. Journal
0538-009X Institution of Surveyors. Journal *changed to* Indian Surveyor.
0538-0391 Instituto Colombiano Agropecuario. Boletin Tecnico
0538-0898 Instituto de Investigacion de Recursos Naturales. Publicacion
0538-1126 Instituto Forestal Latinoamericano de Investigacion y Capitacion. Boletin *see* 0798-2437
0538-1347 Instituto Latinoamericano de Mercadeo Agricola. I L M A - RR†
0538-1355 Instituto Latinoamericano de Mercadeo Agricola. Information Bulletin†
0538-1428 Instituto Mexicano del Petroleo. Revista
0538-2351 Instrument Maintenance Management†
0538-2629 Insurance Marketplace
0538-2785 Inter-African Conference on Food and Nutrition. Report
0538-2807 Inter-African Labour Conference Reports, Recommendations and Conclusions
0538-2912 Inter-American Commission of Women. News Bulletin
0538-2920 Inter-American Commission of Women. Noticiero
0538-3048 Inter-American Council of Commerce and Production. Uruguayan Section. Publicaciones
0538-3110 Inter-American Development Bank. Institute for Latin American Integration. Annual Report
0538-3277 Inter-American Institute of Agricultural Sciences. Informe Anual *changed to* Inter-American Institute for Cooperation on Agriculture. Informe Anual.
0538-3579 Inter-American Statistical Institute. Committee on Improvement of National Statistics. Report
0538-3609 Inter-American Tropical Tuna Commission. Data Report
0538-3641 Interbank
0538-4028 Intermediate Technology Development Group. Bulletin *see* 0305-0920
0538-4141 I A A World Directory of Marketing Communications Periodicals†
0538-4168 International Advertising Association. United Kingdom Chapter. Concise Guide to International Markets†
0538-4281 International Animated Film Association. Bulletin *see* 0775-9746
0538-4400 International Association for Shell Structures. Bulletin *see* 0304-3622
0538-4427 International Association for the Exchange of Students for Technical Experience. Annual Report
0538-4524 International Association of Law Libraries. Bulletin *see* 0731-1265
0538-4680 International Association of Theoretical and Applied Limnology. Communications
0538-4850 International Atomic Energy Agency. Radiation Data for Medical Use; Catalogue *changed to* Radiation Dosimetry Data: Catalogue.
0538-4893 International Atomic Energy Agency. Law Library. Books and Articles in the I A E A Law Library. List†
0538-4915 International Audiology *see* 0020-6091
0538-5105 International Bibliography of the History of Religions†
0538-5342 International Centre for African Social and Economic Documentation. (Bibliographical Index Cards)†
0538-5415 International Centre for Theoretical Physics. Report *see* 0304-7091
0538-5466 International Chamber of Commerce. United States Council. Report *changed to* United States Council for International Business. Newsletter.
0538-5482 International Children's Center. Courrier†
0538-5490 International Children's Centre. Paris. Report of the Director-General to the Executive Board
0538-5504 International China Painting Teachers Organizations. News
0538-5520 International Christian Democratic Study and Documentation Center. Bulletin International *changed to* C D - Info.
0538-5539 International Christian Democratic Study and Documentation Center. Cahiers d'Etudes *changed to* Christian Democratic Study and Documentation Center. Cahiers d'Etudes.
0538-5555 International Christian Democratic Study and Documentation Center. Informations *changed to* Panorama Democrate Chretien.
0538-5644 International Colloquium on Rapid Mixing and Sampling Techniques Applicable to the Study of Biochemical Reactions. Proceedings†
0538-5687 International Commission for the Scientific Exploration of the Mediterranean Sea. Bulletin de Liaison des Laboratoires†
0538-5768 International Commission on Irrigation and Drainage. Report
0538-5865 International Committee on Urgent Anthropological and Ethnological Research. Bulletin
0538-5946 International Confederation of Free Trade Unions. Features†
0538-6012 International Conference of Orientalists in Japan. Transactions
0538-6039 International Conference of Social Work. Japanese National Committee. Progress Report *changed to* Japanese Report to the International Council on Social Welfare.
0538-611X International Conference on Liquefied Natural Gas. Proceedings *changed to* International Conference on Liquefied Natural Gas. Papers.
0538-6128 International Conference on Lighthouses and Other Aids to Navigation. Reports
0538-6349 International Congress Calendar
0538-6381 International Congress for the Study of Pre-Columbian Cultures of the Lesser Antilles. Proceedings
0538-6527 International Congress of Libraries and Museums of the Performing Arts. Acts
0538-6586 International Congress of Radiation Research. Proceedings†
0538-6772 International Congress Science Series
0538-6829 International Cotton Industry Statistics
0538-6918 C O D A T A Newsletter
0538-7043 International Crop Improvement Association. Production Publication *changed to* Association of Official Seed Certifying Agencies. Report of Acres Applied for Certification by Seed Certifying Agencies.
0538-7051 International Cryogenics Monograph Series
0538-7078 International Dairy Federation. Annual Memento
0538-7086 International Dairy Federation. Catalogue of I D F Publications
0538-7094 International Dairy Federation. International Standard
0538-7191 International Directory of Prisoners Aid Agencies
0538-7302 F I D Publications Catalogue†
0538-7353 I A G Communications†
0538-740X International Federation of Film Archives. Annuaire. Yearbook†
0538-7442 International Federation of Operational Research Societies. Airline Group (A G I F O R S) Proceedings
0538-7477 International Federation of Plantation, Agricultural and Allied Workers. Report of the Secretariat to the I F P A A W World Congress
0538-7590 Gas and Liquid Chromatography Abstracts *see* 0268-6287
0538-7639 International Geographical Union. Newsletter *see* 0018-9804
0538-7736 International Histological Classification of Tumours†
0538-7779 Internationale Hydrologische Dekade: Yearbook of the Federal Republic of Germany *see* 0344-5259
0538-7965 Worldwide Bibliography of Space Law and Related Matters†
0538-8066 International Journal of Chemical Kinetics
0538-8228 International Journal of Slavic Linguistics and Poetics
0538-8295 Cost of Social Security
0538-8325 Labour-Management Relations Series
0538-8333 International Labour Office. Special Report of the Director-General on the Application of the Declaration Concerning the Policy of Apartheid of the Republic of South Africa
0538-8643 International Maritime Committee. Documentation *changed to* C M I News Letter.
0538-8643 International Maritime Committee. Documentation *changed to* C M I Year Book.
0538-8732 International Military Sports Council Academy. Technical Brochure *changed to* International Military Sports Council. Technical Brochure.
0538-8759 International Monetary Fund. Pamphlet Series
0538-8783 I M Z Information *changed to* Music in the Media - I M Z Bulletin.
0538-8791 International Music Council. German Committee. Referate Informationen *changed to* Musikforum - Referate und Informationen des Deutschen Musikrates.
0538-8821 International Narcotic Enforcement Officers Association. Annual Conference Report *changed to* Narc Officer.
0538-8880 International Oceanographic Tables
0538-8988 International Organization of Consumers Unions. Proceedings
0538-9089 Family Planning in Five Continents†
0538-9143 International Plant Propagators' Society. Combined Proceedings of Annual Meetings
0538-933X International Reading Association. Annual Report†
0538-9461 International Rescue Committee Annual Report
0538-9550 International Rice Commission. Newsletter
0538-978X International Seismological Centre. P-Nodal Solutions for Earthquakes†
0538-9887 International Series on Civil Engineering†
0538-9968 International Series on Cerebrovisceral and Behavioral Psychology and Conditioned Reflexes†
0538-9992 International Series on Electromagnetic Waves†
0539-0168 International Skating Union. Ice Dancing Regulations
0539-0184 Social Science Information
0539-0230 I E S A Information
0539-0281 International Society for Rock Mechanics. News
0539-032X International Society of Criminology. Bulletin
0539-0338 International Society of Food Service Consultants. Directory†
0539-0346 International Society of Plant Morphologists. Yearbook
0539-0613 International Symposium on Rarefied Gas Dynamics. Proceedings†
0539-0761 International Television Almanac *changed to* International Television & Video Almanac.
0539-0788 International Textile Bulletin Dyeing - Finishing Edition
0539-0796 International Textile Bulletin Spinning Edition *changed to* International Textile Bulletin Yarn Forming Edition.
0539-080X International Textile Bulletin Weaving Edition
0539-0893 I T C Publications. Series B. Photo-Interpretation†
0539-0915 International Transport Workers' Federation Report on Activities
0539-0990 Commission on Crystallographic Apparatus†
0539-1016 International Union of Geodesy and Geophysics. Monograph
0539-113X International Union of Public Transport. Transports Publics dans les Principales Villes du Monde *see* 0378-1968
0539-1148 International Union of Pure and Applied Chemistry. Information Bulletin *see* 0193-6484
0539-1296 International Wheat Council. Report for Crop Year *changed to* International Wheat Council. Report for Crop Year.
0539-130X International Wheat Council. Record of Operations of Member Countries *changed to* International Wheat Council. Record of Shipments Wheat and Wheat Flour (Year).
0539-1318 International Wheat Council. Review of the World Grains Situation *changed to* International Wheat Council. Report for Crop Year.
0539-1326 International Wheat Council. Secretariat Papers
0539-1342 International Who's Who in Poetry†
0539-1512 Internationale Gesellschaft fuer Urheberrecht. Yearbook
0539-1539 Zahlentafeln der Physikalisch-Chemischen Untersuchungen des Rheins sowie der Mosel *see* 0173-6507
0539-2047 Potomac River Water Quality Network *changed to* Potomac River Basin Water Quality Reports.
0539-2063 Legal Report of Oil and Gas Conservation Activities†
0539-2306 Inventaria Archaeologica Roumanie†
0539-242X Academia Nacional de la Historia. Investigaciones y Ensayos
0539-2896 Memminger Geschichtsblaetter
0539-3027 Museo Municipal de Historia Natural de San Rafael. Instituto de Ciencias Naturales. Notas
0539-323X Meng Ya
0539-3728 Mercado Mundial
0539-3876 Merchandise Mart Directory *changed to* Merchandise Mart Resource Guide.
0539-3973 Mereni a Regulace†

ISSN

5752 ISSN INDEX

0539-421X Meshek Haofote
0539-6115 Hospital Infantil de Mexico. Boletin Medico
0539-6387 Mexico (City). Universidad Nacional. Observatorio Astronomico, Tacubaya. Boletin de los Observatorios Tonantzintla y Tacubaya *changed to* Instituto Nacional de Astrofisica, Optica y Electronica. Boletin.
0539-7413 Michigan Health Statistics
0539-8452 University of Michigan. Mental Health Research Institute. Annual Report†
0539-8703 Michigan Aviation
0539-8908 Michigan Sportsman
0539-998X Mie Prefectural University. Faculty of Fisheries. Bulletin *changed to* Mie University. Faculty of Fisheries. Journal.
0540-049X Universita Cattolica del Sacro Cuore. Facolta di Agraria. Annali
0540-0694 Milford Historical Society Newsletter
0540-0961 Milton Society of America. Proceedings
0540-1151 Minjian Wenxue
0540-1186 Minjian Wenyi Jikan *changed to* Chinese Folk Culture.
0540-1224 Minzu Huabao
0540-3847 Mississippi State University Abstracts of Theses *changed to* Mississippi State University Abstracts of Theses and Dissertations.
0540-3995 Mississippi Genealogical Exchange
0540-410X Mississippi's Health†
0540-4193 Missouri's New and Expanding Industry
0540-4517 Missouri Veterinarian *changed to* Veterinary Medical Review.
0540-4568 Misul Charyo
0540-469X Mitsubishi Technical Bulletin
0540-4746 Mitteilungen fuer die Archivpflege in Bayern
0540-4924 Miyazaki University. Faculty of Engineering. Memoirs
0540-5203 Modell
0540-5556 Modern Surgical Monographs†
0540-6471 Mongol Nyelvemlektar *see* 0230-8452
0540-6722 Monografie Parazytologiczne
0540-8962 Mortgage Market†
0541-2404 Muehlviertler Heimatblaetter
0541-2439 Muemlekvedelem
0541-3869 Mushroom News
0541-4385 Musizi
0541-4393 Muskeg Research Conference. Proceedings†
0541-4873 Mwana Shaba
0541-4938 Mycological Society of America Newsletter
0541-5357 M B I's Indian Industries Annual
0541-5462 M.I.I. Series
0541-5489 M L A News (Chicago)
0541-5632 Mitzion Tetzeh Torah. M.T.T.
0541-5896 Maccabi News Bulletin *changed to* Maccabi World Union. Newsletter.
0541-6159 McGill Journal of Business *changed to* Purple Report.
0541-623X Keith Callard Lecture Series†
0541-6256 Canadian Meteorological and Oceanographic Society. Climatological Bulletin
0541-6299 McGill University. Marine Sciences Centre. Annual Report *changed to* McGill University. Institute of Oceanography. Biennial Report.
0541-6388 Machine Building Industry
0541-6434 Machine Tool Engineer†
0541-6507 Mackinac History†
0541-7406 Majalah Perusahaan Gula
0541-8607 Universidad de Madrid. Revista *changed to* Universidad Complutense de Madrid. Revista.
0541-8836 Magazin Polovnika
0541-9093 Magyar Bibliografiak Bibliografiaja†
0541-9220 Magyar Kulpolitikai Evkonyv
0541-9344 Magyar Szo Naptara
0541-9417 Research Institute for Agricultural Economics. Bulletin
0541-9492 Magyar Tudomanyos Akademia Konyvtara Kezirattaranak Katalogusai
0541-9522 Nepi Kultura - Nepi Tarsadalom
0542-0938 Mahasagar
0542-0997 Mail-Coach
0542-1136 Maine Geological Survey. Special Economic Studies Series†
0542-1462 Mainstream
0542-1470 Maintenant†
0542-1551 Mainzer Romanistische Arbeiten
0542-1594 Maison de Marie Claire
0542-1748 Al-Majallah al-Ihsa'iyyah al-Misriyyah
0542-2108 Makedonski Folklor
0542-335X Malaya Law Review *see* 0218-2173
0542-3570 Malaysia. Department of Statistics. Annual Bulletin of Statistics *see* 0127-2624
0542-3686 Monthly Statistical Bulletin of West Malaysia *changed to* Malaysia. Department of Statistics. Monthly Statistical Bulletin, Malaysia.
0542-397X Malaysian Chinese Association. Annual Report
0542-4550 Malta Yearbook
0542-5395 Manitoba Crop Insurance Corporation. Annual Report
0542-5794 Manpower Information Service *see* 0146-9673
0542-5808 Manpower Journal
0542-6243 Map Collectors Circle†
0542-626X Maps†
0542-6375 Universidad del Zulia. Facultad de Medicina. Revista
0542-6480 Marburger Abhandlungen zur Politischen Wissenschaft†
0542-6669 Marche Romane
0542-6685 Marches Publics
0542-6758 Mare Balticum
0542-6766 International Association of Geodesy. Commission Permanente des Marees Terrestres. Marees Terrestres Bulletin d'Information
0542-6820 Lolland-Falsters Stiftsmuseums Aarskrift
0542-6987 Marine Invertebrates of Scandinavia
0542-7029 Marine Resources of the Atlantic Coast†
0542-7363 Marketing Forum *see* 0307-7667
0542-7770 Marxistische Blaetter
0542-8343 Maryland English Journal
0542-8351 Maryland Genealogical Society Bulletin
0542-836X Maryland Lawyer's Manual
0542-9943 Mishua
0542-9951 Informatyka
0542-9986 Matematicheskaya Fizika *see* 0233-7568
0543-0313 Materials Management Journal of India
0543-0941 Mathematics and Its Applications
0543-100X Mathematik fuer Naturwissenschaft und Technik
0543-1042 Mathematische Monographien
0543-1077 Iseljenicki Kalendar
0543-1433 Mauritania. Direction de la Statistique et des Etudes Economiques. Bulletin Mensuel Statistique
0543-1565 Mauritius. Director of Audit. Report
0543-1719 Max Freiherr von Oppenheim-Stiftung. Schriften
0543-1735 Veroeffentlichungen des Max-Reger-Institutes
0543-1786 Ma'yanot
0543-1972 Measurement Techniques
0543-2146 Med-Events†
0543-2243 Medecine de l'Homme
0543-2499 Medical Anthropology Newsletter *see* 0745-5194
0543-2774 M L A Directory (Year)
0543-3770 Meeting on Soil Correlation for North America. (Report)†
0543-3789 Meeting on Soil Survey Correlation and Interpretation for Latin America. Report†
0543-3916 Meiji Daigaku Kagaku Gijutsu Kenkyujo Nenpo
0543-4726 Der Mensch als Soziales und Personales Wesen
0543-5056 Merchant Explorer
0543-5099 Mercurius†
0543-5846 Metalurgija
0543-5900 Meteor Forschungsergebnisse. Reihe A. Allgemeines, Physik und Chemie des Meeres *see* 0721-8761
0543-5927 "Meteor" Forschungsergebnisse. Reihe C. Geologie und Geophysik†
0543-5935 "Meteor" Forschungsergebnisse. Reihe D. Biologie†
0543-6095 Methodology and Science
0543-615X Metmenys
0543-6206 Metodistkyrkans i Sverige Aarsbok
0543-6915 Principales Indicadores Economicos de Mexico
0543-758X Anuario de Letras
0543-7741 Mexico†
0543-8497 Michigan. Geological Survey Division. Bulletin
0543-9833 Michigan Jewish History
0543-9930 Michigan Slavic Materials
0544-0327 Mid-Atlantic Industrial Waste Conference Proceedings
0544-0424 Middle East Economic Survey
0544-1005 Mie University Forests. Bulletin
0544-1153 Migraine News
0544-1188 Migration Today
0544-1374 Fondazione Giangiacomo Feltrinelli. Annali
0544-2206 Minzu Tuanjie
0544-2524 Mineraloel - Mineraloelrundschau
0544-2540 Mineralogical Journal
0544-3083 Minnesota. Geological Survey. Educational Series
0544-3105 Minnesota. Geological Survey. Information Circulars
0544-3512 Minnesota Economic Data: Countries and Regions†
0544-3520 Minnesota English Newsletter
0544-358X Minnesota History News
0544-4020 Singapore Mirror *changed to* Mirror.
0544-408X Miscelanea de Estudios Arabes y Hebraicos
0544-4136 Miscellanea Musicologica
0544-439X Missions Digest and Year Book *see* 0317-266X
0544-5396 U M R Journal†
0544-5779 Mitsubishi Electric Engineer†
0544-6511 Modern Concepts of Medical Virology, Oncology and Cytology†
0544-7526 Momento
0544-8417 Monographs in Semiconductor Physics†
0544-8433 Monographs in the Economics of Development
0544-845X Monographs on American Art
0544-8794 Directory of Montana Manufacturers *see* 1057-6681
0544-9189 Biblioteca Nacional de Uruguay. Revista
0545-0152 Moody's Bank and Finance Manual
0545-0209 Moody's Handbook of Corporate Managements *changed to* Reference Book of Corporate Managements.
0545-0217 Moody's Industrial Manual
0545-0233 Moody's Municipal and Government Manual
0545-0241 Moody's Public Utility Manual
0545-025X Moody's Transportation Manual
0545-1604 New Hampshire Archeological Society Newsletter
0545-2252 New Jersey. Division of Water Resources. Water Resources Circulars†
0545-3631 New South Wales. Department of Agriculture. Soil Survey Unit. Bulletin *see* 0727-9078
0545-6061 New York City Trade Union Handbook *see* 1053-7007
0545-7041 New Zealand. Dairy Production and Marketing Board. Annual Report and Statement of Accounts *changed to* New Zealand. Dairy Board. Annual Report and Statement of Accounts.
0545-7157 New Zealand. Department of Statistics. External Trade. Country Analyses†
0545-7297 New Zealand. Lottery Board of Control. Report *changed to* New Zealand Lottery Board. Report.
0545-7572 New Zealand Current Taxation
0545-7785 New Zealand News Review†
0545-7866 New Zealand Shipping Directory
0545-7904 New Zealand Soil News
0545-9249 Universidad Nacional Autonoma de Nicaragua. Biblioteca Central. Boletin†
0545-9516 Niger. Service de la Statistique. Bulletin Trimestriel de Statistique *changed to* Niger. Direction de la Statistique et des Comptes Nationaux. Bulletin Trimestriel de Statistique.
0545-9532 Niger: Fraternite - Travail - Progres
0545-9923 Nigeria. Meteorological Service. Agrometeorological Bulletin
0546-0719 Nihon Insatsu Nenkan
0546-0786 Commodity Classification for Foreign Trade Statistics: Japan *changed to* Export Statistical Schedule of Japan (Year).
0546-0786 Commodity Classification for Foreign Trade Statistics: Japan *changed to* Import Statistical Schedule of Japan (Year).
0546-0921 Tenki
0546-093X Japanese National Railways. Facts and Figures
0546-109X Science Council of Japan. Annual Report of the Development of Agriculture in Japan - Nihon Nogaku Shinpo Nenpo *see* 0911-8012
0546-126X Nihon Seikosho Giho
0546-1324 Shakai Jigyo no Shomondai
0546-2347 Noise and Smog News
0546-2851 Nordisk Arkivnyt
0546-3432 Norman Ford's Florida
0546-4552 E S E Notes
0546-5001 North Dakota. Geological Survey. Bulletin
0546-5370 Northeast Folklore Society Newsletter
0546-5559 Northern Dog News *see* 0164-4483
0546-6210 Northwest Ruralite *changed to* Ruralite.
0546-8051 Nove Obzory
0546-8191 Plant Production
0546-9112 Nuernberger Wirtschafts-und Sozialgeographische Arbeiten
0546-9414 Numismaticky Sbornik
0546-9503 Nongcun Gongzuo Tongxun
0546-9538 Nongye Jixie
0546-9937 Nutmeg Shelf *changed to* Provisioner.
0547-034X N A S S P Newsletter *see* 0278-0569
0547-051X N E C Research and Development
0547-0730 N P A News
0547-0749 N R C - Nouvelle Revue Canadienne†
0547-1435 Collected Papers on Sciences of Atmosphere and Hydrosphere
0547-1567 Nagoya University. Institute of Plasma Physics. Annual Review
0547-1788 University of Nairobi. Institute for Development Studies. Discussion Papers
0547-1796 University College, Nairobi. Institute for Development Studies. Occasional Papers *changed to* University of Nairobi. Institute for Development Studies. Occasional Paper.
0547-2075 Napjaink
0547-2407 Nara Kyoiku Daigaku Kiyo. Shizen Kagaku
0547-2504 Narodna Umjetnost
0547-3101 Nase Gospodarstvo
0547-3128 Nase Snahy
0547-3144 Nase Teme
0547-3578 I E E E National Aerospace and Electronics Conference. Proceedings
0547-3616 National Agricultural Society of Ceylon. Journal *changed to* National Agricultural Society of Sri Lanka. Journal.
0547-4175 National Association of Schools of Music. Directory

ISSN

ISSN INDEX 5753

0547-4205 National Association of Secondary School Principals. Curriculum Report. *changed to* N A S S P Curriculum Report.
0547-4728 National Business Education Yearbook
0547-485X National Catholic Educational Association. Calendar of Meetings of National and Regional Educational Associations†
0547-5090 National Committee for the Defence of Peace in the Socialist Republic of Rumania. Information Bulletin *changed to* Alliance for Peace in Rumania. Information Bulletin.
0547-5554 National Cooperative Highway Research Program Research Results Digest
0547-5570 National Cooperative Highway Research Program Synthesis of Highway Practice
0547-5619 C O S E R V Newsletter (National Council for Community Services to International Visitors) *changed to* N C I V Newsletter.
0547-616X National Directory of College Athletics (Men's Edition)
0547-6232 National Directory of Newsletters and Reporting Services *changed to* Newsletters in Print.
0547-6658 National Endowment for the Arts. Guide to Programs *changed to* Guide to National Endowment for the Arts.
0547-6844 Birth Defects Original Article Series†
0547-7115 National Guild of Catholic Psychiatrists. Bulletin†
0547-7204 Consumer Attitudes and Buying Plans *changed to* Consumer Confidence Survey.
0547-7212 Consumer Market Indicators†
0547-7301 Conference Board. Investment Statistics. Utility Appropriations *see* 0896-2510
0547-7557 National Institute of Sciences of India. Biographical Memoirs of Fellows *changed to* Indian National Science Academy. Biographical Memoirs of Fellows.
0547-7573 National Institute of Sciences of India. Yearbook *see* 0073-6619
0547-7794 Legal Bulletin (Washington) *changed to* Legislative Update (Washington).
0547-8804 Financial and Operating Results of Department and Specialty Stores
0547-8847 N R E C A Legal Reporting Service *see* 0362-8833
0547-888X Fleet Safety Newsletter
0547-9665 Nature and Resources
0547-9789 Naturwissenschaftlicher Verein Wuppertal. Jahresberichte
0548-0019 Nauchno-Tekhnicheskaya Informatsiya. Seriya 1. Organizatsiya i Metodika Informatsionnoi Raboty
0548-0442 Politechnika Krakowska. Zeszyty Naukowe. Nauki Ekonomiczne
0548-0523 Nautologia
0548-1163 Nederlandse Entomologische Vereniging. Monographs
0548-1384 Need a Lift?
0548-1406 Neftepererabotka i Neftekhimiya
0548-1422 Negocios
0548-1600 Nentori
0548-1643 Annual of Advertising Art in Japan *changed to* Tokyo Art Directors Annual.
0548-1910 Netherlands. Centraal Bureau voor de Statistiek. Maandcijfers van de Invoer, Uitvoer en Assemblage van Motorrijtuigen.†
0548-2674 Neue Arzneimittel und Spezialitaeten *see* 0724-567X
0548-2682 Neue Ausgrabungen und Forschungen aus Niedersachsens Urgeschichte
0548-2801 Neue Heimat
0548-2836 Neue Landschaft
0548-3093 Neues von Rohde und Schwarz
0548-3794 Nevrologia, Psihiatria i Nevrohirurgija
0548-4065 New Brunswick Development Corporation. Annual Report†
0548-4162 New Canadian Film†
0548-4340 New Directions in Psychology†
0548-4448 New England Economic Indicators
0548-4537 New Era *changed to* Nave Parva.
0548-4987 New Haven Colony Historical Society. Journal
0548-5924 New Management
0548-5967 New Mexico State University. Agricultural Experiment Station. Research Report
0548-5975 New Mexico. Bureau of Mines and Mineral Resources. Memoir
0548-6599 New River News
0548-6793 New South Wales District Court Reports†
0548-6831 University of New South Wales, Kensington. Research and Publications
0548-7269 Foundation Center. Report *see* 0190-3357
0548-7390 New York Stock Exchange Monthly Review *see* 0275-4479
0548-7900 School Business Management Handbook†
0548-9040 New York State English Council. Monograph Series
0548-9067 New York State Industrial Directory *see* 0740-2953
0548-9415 Cancer Data: Deaths and Cases Reported *changed to* New Zealand. Health Statistical Services. Cancer Data: New Registrations and Deaths.
0548-9911 New Zealand. Health Statistical Services. Mortality and Demographic Data
0548-992X New Zealand. Health Statistical Services. Mental Health Data
0548-9938 New Zealand. Health Statistical Services. Hospital and Selected Morbidity Data
0548-9962 New Zealand. Customs Department. Customs Bulletin *see* 0113-3292
0549-0014 New Zealand. Road Research Unit. Newsletter *see* 1170-4683
0549-0030 New Zealand. Road Research Unit. Bulletin†
0549-0219 New Zealand Concrete Construction
0549-0294 New Zealand Federation of Labour. Bulletin†
0549-0502 New Zealand Marine News
0549-0618 New Zealand Universities Law Review
0549-110X News from the Ukraine
0549-2351 Nigeria. Federal Ministry of Labour. Quarterly Review *changed to* Nigeria. Federal Ministry of Employment, Labour and Productivity. Annual Report.
0549-2513 Nigeria. Federal Department of Petroleum Resources. Monthly Petroleum Information *changed to* Nigerian National Petroleum Corporation. Monthly Petroleum Information.
0549-2629 Nigeria and the Classics *changed to* Museum Africum.
0549-2734 Nigerian Industrial Development Bank. Annual Report and Accounts
0549-2998 Nihon University. Research Institute of Science and Technology. Report
0549-317X Bank of Japan. Japan's Balance of Payments. Summary Report *changed to* Bank of Japan. Balance of Payments Monthly.
0549-3811 Japan Society for Aeronautical and Space Sciences. Transactions
0549-4192 Japanese Political Science Association. Yearbook†
0549-4540 Mathematical Society of Japan. Publications
0549-4680 Monthly Statistics of Japan
0549-4826 Niigata Daigaku Nogakubu Kiyo
0549-5245 Nippon Dental University. Annual Publications
0549-5725 Japan. Ministry of Agriculture, Forestry and Fisheries. National Research Institute of Agricultural Engineering. Bulletin
0549-6179 Norddeutsche Studentenzeitung
0549-6330 Scandinavian Institute of African Studies. Newsletter *see* 1100-6749
0549-6896 Norsk Skogbruksmuseum. Aarbok
0549-7000 Norske Veritas Classification and Registry of Shipping. Publication†
0549-7078 North American Mentor Magazine†
0549-7175 N A T O Handbook
0549-7191 A G A R D Conference Proceedings†
0549-7728 North Carolina State Library Newsletter *see* 0193-4309
0549-799X W R R I News
0549-8333 North Dakota Securities Bulletin
0549-8368 North Dakota Growth Indicators†
0549-8899 Northeast Asia Journal of Theology†
0550-0494 Norway. Statistisk Sentralbyraa. Nasjonalregnskapsstatistikk
0550-0532 Norway. Statistisk Sentralbyraa. Sivilrettsstatistikk†
0550-0567 Norway. Statistisk Sentralbyraa. Statistisk Ukehefte
0550-0842 Notatki Ornitologiczne
0550-0850 Ukrainian Art Digest
0550-0923 Notes et Documents Voltaiques
0550-0958 Notes from Eastman *see* 0147-345X
0550-0990 Notes on Cardiovascular Diseases†
0550-1067 Noticias de Galapagos
0550-1091 Noticias Sobre Reforma Agraria†
0550-1105 Noticiero del Cafe
0550-1156 Notiziario Chimico e Farmaceutico
0550-1326 Nouveau Commerce
0550-1555 Nova Americana†
0550-1741 Nova Scotia. Department of Labour. Economics and Research Division. Wage Rates, Salaries and Hours of Labour in Nova Scotia†
0550-2241 Prirodni Vedy. Rada Biologicka *see* 0139-5106
0550-225X Prirodni Vedy. Rada Chemicke *see* 0139-5351
0550-3205 Nuclear Physics†
0550-3213 Nuclear Physics, Section B
0550-3248 Nuclear Science Abstracts of Japan *changed to* Nuclear Science Information of Japan. Oral Presentation.
0550-404X Nutrition
0550-4082 Nuttall Ornithological Club. Publications
0550-4112 Nya Perspektiv
0550-4333 National Association of Real Estate Investment Funds N A R E I F Handbook of Member Trusts *see* 0092-4865
0550-4376 N.C.A.I. Sentinel *changed to* Sentinel (Washington, D.C.).
0550-4791 N E I W P C C Aqua News *changed to* N E I W P C C Water Connection.
0550-5054 New York University Education Quarterly†
0550-5666 National Braille Association. Bulletin
0550-5682 N C E A Notes
0550-5755 Classroom Practices in Teaching English†
0550-6565 New York Botanical Garden Newsletter†
0550-6638 New York (State). Department of Labor. Statistics on Operations. Annual Report.
0550-6743 New Zealand National Society for Earthquake Engineering. Bulletin
0550-6891 Niger
0550-712X Northian Newsletter†
0550-7138 Northland Newsletter†
0550-7170 Norway. Statistisk Sentralbyraa. Folkmengde Etter Alder og Ekteskapelig Status - Norway. Central Bureau of Statistics. Population by Age and Marital Status *see* 0801-6690
0550-7421 National Association of Independent Schools. Annual Report
0550-7448 National Bibliography of Cases in Business Administration†
0550-824X Trends in Health and Health Services *changed to* Contemporary Health Issues.
0550-8398 Non-Ionizing Radiation†
0550-8401 Non-Profit Organization Tax Letter
0550-8452 A G A R D Annual Meeting†
0550-8525 North of Scotland College of Agriculture, Aberdeen. Annual Report *see* 0143-8654
0550-8754 Ny Teknik
0550-8843 N A F A Conference Brochure and Reference Book *changed to* N A F A Annual Reference Book.
0550-9483 New Mexico Labor Market Trends *changed to* New Mexico Labor Market Review.
0550-9955 Nova Scotia Labour-Management Study Conference. Proceedings†
0551-0503 Plastics Age
0551-0910 Plunkett Foundation for Co-Operative Studies. Occasional Papers†
0551-2050 Pokolenia
0551-3464 Politisk Revy†
0551-3707 Polonistyka
0551-3790 Biblioteka Kornicka. Pamietnik
0551-4193 Studia Naturae. Seria B. Wydawnictwa Popularno-Naukowe
0551-4932 University of Poona Science and Technology. Journal†
0551-651X Politechnika Poznanska. Zeszyty Naukowe. Bibliografia†
0551-6625 Uniwersytet im. Adama Mickiewicza w Poznaniu. Wydzial Matematyki, Fizyki i Chemii. Prace. Seria Matematyka *changed to* Matematyka (Poznan).
0551-9039 Pravnicke Studie
0551-9101 Prawo i Zycie
0551-9276 Predi-Briefs
0552-2005 Problems of the Baltic†
0552-2080 Problemy Gematologii i Perelivaniya Krovi *see* 0234-5730
0552-2188 Problemy Opiekunczo-Wychowawcze
0552-2234 Problemy Rodziny
0552-4199 Przeglad Kolejowy Przewozowy *see* 0137-219X
0552-4245 Przeglad Zachodniopomorski
0552-4466 Psychologische Achtergrondent†
0552-5276 Census of Manufacturing Industries of Puerto Rico
0552-5934 Pulsen†
0552-6426 Pure Life Society. Annual Report
0552-6450 Push Pin Graphic†
0552-6981 Publizistikwissenschaftlicher Referatedienst†
0552-7252 Pacific Coast Archaeological Society Quarterly
0552-7325 Pacific Dairyman *see* 1041-1666
0552-7333 Pacific Geology
0552-7635 Packaging Machinery Catalog *changed to* Package Engineering Annual Buyers Guide.
0552-7775 Pedagogische Studien
0552-8100 World Peace Through Law Center. Bulletin†
0552-9034 Pakistan Journal of Agricultural Sciences
0552-9050 Pakistan Journal of Scientific Research
0552-9115 Pakistan Petroleum Limited. Annual Report
0552-9352 Palaeontologia Jugoslavica
0552-9395 Palante
0552-9506 Osservatorio Regionale per le Malattie della Vite. Osservazioni di Meteorologia, Fenologia e Patologia della Vite
0552-9638 Palingenesia
0552-9913 Pan American Development Foundation. Annual Report
0553-0067 Pan American Highway Congress. Boletin Informativo†
0553-013X Pan American Institute of Geography and History. Commission on History. Bulletin†
0553-0237 Studies in Export Promotion†

ISSN

ISSN INDEX

0553-027X Pan American Union. Department of Educational Affairs. Bulletin of Information *changed to* Organization of American States. Department of Educational Affairs. Bulletin of Information.
0553-0296 Pan American Union. Department of Educational Affairs. Resena Analitica *changed to* Organization of American States. Department of Educational Affairs. Resena Analitica.
0553-0326 Pan American Associations in the United States; A Directory with Supplementary Lists of Other Associations. Inter-American and General†
0553-0334 Pan American Union. Department of Scientific Affairs. Report of Activities. *changed to* Organization of American States. Department of Scientific Affairs. Report of Activities.
0553-0342 Organization of American States. Department of Scientific Affairs. Serie de Biologia: Monografias
0553-0377 Organization of American States. Department of Scientific Affairs. Serie de Quimica: Monografias
0553-0385 Estudio Social de America Latina†
0553-0407 Pan American Union. Department of Social Affairs. Studies and Monographs†
0553-058X Inter-American Briefs†
0553-0601 Pan Am World Guide
0553-0644 Pan T'ai Hsueh Pao
0553-0946 Panchayati Raj (New Delhi) *see* 0023-5660
0553-2159 Parents
0553-2361 Materiaux pour le Manuel de l'Histoire des Song†
0553-237X Ecole Pratique des Hautes Etudes, Paris. Section des Sciences Economiques et Sociales. Memoires et Travaux *changed to* Ecole des Hautes Etudes en Sciences Sociales. Section des Sciences Economiques et Sociales. Memoires et Travaux.
0553-2507 Musee de l'Homme, Paris. Catalogues. Serie B: Afrique Blanche et Levant†
0553-2515 Musee de l'Homme, Paris. Catalogues. Serie G: Arctiques†
0553-3066 Park News *see* 0840-6189
0553-3104 Parking Progress *see* 0362-3122
0553-3864 Southwestern Legal Foundation. Patent Law Annual†
0553-4054 Patterson's Schools Classified
0553-4283 Peace Research Reviews
0553-4917 Penguin Modern Poets†
0553-5743 Foreign Policy Research Institute. Research Monograph Series *changed to* Philadelphia Papers.
0553-5816 University of Pennsylvania. Population Studies Center. Analytical and Technical Report†
0553-6065 Pennsylvania State Industrial Directory *see* 0740-4298
0553-6499 Percussionist *see* 0553-6502
0553-6502 Percussive Notes
0553-6626 Periodica Polytechnica. Civil Engineering
0553-6707 Peristil
0553-6812 Permanent International Committee of Linguists. Committee on Linguistic Statistics. Publication†
0553-6855 General Treaty for Central American Economic Integration. Permanent Secretariat. Carta Informativa
0553-6863 Convenios Centroamericanos de Integracion Economica
0553-6898 General Treaty for Central American Economic Integration. Permanent Secretariat. Newsletter
0553-6979 Peparimi
0553-7371 Perspective (Cincinnati)†
0553-738X Perspective†
0553-8467 Pesquisas: Publicacoes de Antropologia
0553-8475 Pesquisas: Publicacoes de Botanica
0553-8491 Pesquisas: Publicacoes de Historia
0553-8505 Pesquisas: Publicacoes de Zoologia
0553-8521 Pesticide Handbook (Entoma)†
0553-8572 Pet Dealer
0553-9323 Pharmacien Biologiste *see* 0999-5749
0553-9978 Philippine Atomic Energy Commission. Annual Report *changed to* Philippine Nuclear Research Institute. Annual Report.
0554-2308 Pivarstvo
0554-2537 Planiranje i Analiza Poslovanja
0554-2626 Planning News†
0554-2693 Plant Engineering Directory and Specifications Catalog *changed to* Plant Engineering Product Supplier Guide.
0554-291X Plasticos†
0554-2952 Plastics Focus (Amherst)
0554-3037 Play Index
0554-3045 Plays. A Classified Guide to Play Selection
0554-341X Pochvoznanie i Agrokhimiia *changed to* Pochvoznanie, Agrokhimiia i Rastitelna Zashtita.
0554-3983 Poetry Pilot
0554-4084 Poeziya (Kiev) *changed to* Boyan.
0554-4246 Pointer (Washington) *see* 1045-988X
0554-498X Polish Yearbook of International Law
0554-5196 Political Science Review
0554-5455 Politische Bildung†
0554-5749 Polska Akademia Nauk. Instytut Geografii. Prace Geograficzne *see* 0373-6547
0554-579X Polska Akademia Nauk. Oddzial w Krakowie. Komisja Historycznoliteracka. Prace
0554-6222 Poluprovodnikovaya Tekhnika i Mikroelektronika†
0554-7040 Poreditsa Balkani
0554-7342 Porta Linguarum Orientalium
0554-7555 Ports and Harbors
0554-7598 Portsmouth Papers
0554-8039 Akustyka
0554-811X Biologia
0554-8128 Geografia
0554-8136 Zoologia
0554-8144 Filologia Angielska
0554-8160 Filologia Klasyczna
0554-8179 Filologia Polska
0554-8195 Archeologia (Poznan)
0554-8233 Astronomia
0554-8241 Chemia
0554-825X Fizyka
0554-873X Pount
0554-890X Power Transmission and Bearing Handbook *changed to* Power Transmission Design Handbook.
0554-9221 Rocenka Povetrnostnich Pozorovani Observatore Karlov†
0554-9256 Naprstkovo Muzeum Asijskych, Africkych a Americkych Kultur. Annals
0554-9264 Acta Faunistica Entomologica
0554-9884 Prajna
0554-9906 Prakit Jain Institute Research Publication Series
0555-0025 Zeszyty Prasoznawcze
0555-1099 Prikladnaya Biokhimiya i Mikrobiologya
0555-1501 Princeton University. Center of International Studies. Research Monograph Series†
0555-1838 Prispevki za Zgodovino Delavskega Gibanja *see* 0353-0329
0555-2656 Problemy Bioniki
0555-3121 Producteur Agricole Francais *changed to* Le Nouvel Agriculteur.
0555-3407 Professional Pilot Magazine
0555-3989 Progress in Industrial Microbiology
0555-4276 Progress in Solid Mechanics†
0555-4349 Progress of Medical Parasitology in Japan†
0555-4810 Prospettive dell'Industria Italiana†
0555-5027 Protokolle
0555-5264 Przemysl Fermentacyjny i Rolny *see* 0137-2645
0555-5299 Psichiatria Generale e dell'Eta Evolutiva
0555-5620 Psychological Research Bulletin
0555-5795 Psychopathology and Pictorial Expression†
0555-5914 Public Affairs
0555-6015 Public Health Papers
0555-6023 Public Library Abstracts†
0555-6031 Public Library Reporters†
0555-6392 Publishing, Entertainment and Advertising and Allied Fields Law Quarterly†
0555-6511 Puerto Rico. Division of Demographic Registry and Vital Statistics. Annual Vital Statistics Report *changed to* Puerto Rico. Department of Health. Office of Planning, Evaluation and Reports. Division of Statistics and Reports. Annual Vital Statistics Report.
0555-6562 Puerto Rico. Planning Board. Statistics Coordination Section. Programas Estadisticos†
0555-6635 Empleo y Desempleo en Puerto Rico
0555-6945 Pulse
0555-7631 Panjab University Research Bulletin (Sciences)
0555-7666 University of the Punjab. Journal of Research: Humanities
0555-7860 Puranam
0555-8158 Pushto
0555-8581 Pacific Southwest Directory
0555-8786 Pakistan. Ministry of Finance. Estimates of Foreign Assistance *changed to* Pakistan. Finance Division. Estimates of Foreign Assistance.
0556-0136 Philosophia Aarhusiensis *see* 0108-1632
0556-0152 Phyllis Schlafly Report
0556-056X Police Research Bulletin†
0556-0691 Pomorania Antiqua
0556-1183 Universita Karlova. Pedagogicky Fakulta. Sbornik. Historie
0556-1442 Pressure Research Notes†
0556-1515 Printing Historical Society Newsletter *see* 0144-7505
0556-171X Problemy Prochnosti
0556-1906 Progress of Science in India†
0556-2791 Physical Review A (General Physics)
0556-2805 Physical Review B (Solid State) *see* 0163-1829
0556-2813 Physical Review C (Nuclear Physics)
0556-2821 Physical Review D (Particles and Fields)
0556-3100 Problems in Education and Nation Building†
0556-3321 Pakistan Journal of Botany
0556-3488 Partio
0556-350X Pasquim
0556-3585 Exports by Pennsylvania Manufacturers†
0556-3593 Pennsylvania. Department of Commerce. Bureau of Statistics. Statistics by Industry and Size of Establishment†
0556-3615 Pennsylvania. Department of Commerce. Bureau of Statistics, Research and Planning. Statistics for Manufacturing Industries†
0556-3860 Photochemistry (Cambridge)
0556-431X Psychosocial Process *see* 0738-0151
0556-5006 Photofact Annual Index *changed to* (Year) Annual Index: Photofact, Computerfact, V C R Fact, Radio, T V & Selected Original Manufacturer's Service Data.
0556-5367 Antique Trader Price Guide to Antiques and Collectors' Items
0556-543X Produktschap voor Siergewassen. Statistiek *changed to* Produktschap voor Siergewassen. Jaarverslag - Statistiek.
0556-5693 Revista de Derecho
0556-5987 Revista de Historia de las Ideas
0556-5995 Revista de Historia de Rosario
0556-6177 Revista de Medicina
0556-655X Revista Espanola de Micropaleontologia
0556-6630 Revista Geografica
0556-6703 Revista Interamericana de Ciencias Sociales†
0556-6835 Revista Mexicana de Fianzas
0556-6908 Revista Paraguaya de Microbiologia
0556-6916 Revista Paranaense de Desenvolvimento†
0556-7238 Revue Bibliographique des Ouvrages de Droit, de Jurisprudence, d'Economie Politique, de Science Financiere, de Sociologie, d'Histoire et de Philosophie†
0556-7262 Revue Camerounaise de Pedagogie *changed to* Syllabus.
0556-7297 Revue d'Economie et de Droit Immobilier†
0556-7335 Revue Annuelle d'Histoire du Quatorzieme Arrondissement de Paris
0556-7343 Revue d'Histoire et de Civilisation du Maghreb
0556-7734 Acta Technica Belgica. Revue E P E: Energie Primaire
0556-7793 Revue Francaise de Dietetique
0556-7807 Revue Francaise de Pedagogie
0556-7939 Revue Internationale des Droits de l'Antiquite
0556-7963 Revue Juridique Themis
0556-8099 Revue Roumaine de Geologie, Geophysique et Geographie. Geographie *changed to* Revue Roumaine de Geographie.
0556-8102 Revue Roumaine de Geologie, Geophysique et Geographie *changed to* Revue Roumaine de Geologie.
0556-8110 Revue Romaine de Geologie, Geophysique et Geographie. Geophysique *changed to* Revue Roumaine de Geophysique.
0556-8218 Rheinisch-Westfaelische Zeitschrift fuer Volkskunde
0556-8587 Rhode Island Audubon Report *changed to* Audubon Society of Rhode Island. Report.
0556-8595 Rhode Island Bar Journal
0556-8609 Rhode Island Jewish Historical Notes
0556-8641 Rhodes University. Department of Philosophy. Philosophical Papers
0556-8692 Zimbabwe. Registrar of Insurance. Report
0556-8706 Zimbabwe. Central Statistical Office. Monthly Digest of Statistics
0556-9605 Rhodesiana *changed to* Heritage of Zimbabwe.
0557-0220 Rikagaku Kenkyujo Kenkyu Nenpo
0557-0352 Japan. Government Forest Experiment Station, Tokyo. Annual Report *changed to* Japan. Forestry and Forest Products Research Institute. Annual Report.
0557-0395 Japan. Government Forest Experiment Station. Kyushu Branch. Annual Report
0557-0506 Bolsa de Valores do Rio de Janeiro. Resumo Anual
0557-109X Economic Studies Quarterly
0557-1391 Rivista Italiana di Diritto e Procedura Penale
0557-1413 Rivista Italiana di Piscicultura e Ittiopatologia
0557-1464 Rivista Trimestrale di Diritto Pubblico
0557-1480 Revon Lebankaut - Banking Quarterly *changed to* Riveon Lebankaut.
0557-1693 Rocenka Odborara
0557-2088 Rocznik Nadnotecki†
0557-2282 Rodna Gruda
0557-2614 Romanfuehrer
0557-3122 Universita degli Studi di Roma. Seminario di Archeologia e Storia dell'Arte Greca e Romana. Studi Miscellanei
0557-319X Central Building Research Institute. Building Digest *changed to* Central Building Research Institute. Building Research Note.

ISSN INDEX 5755

0557-322X Central Building Research Institute. List of Publications
0557-3254 University of Roorkee Research Journal†
0557-4161 Royal Society of New Zealand. Proceedings
0557-4242 Royal Western Australian Historical Society. Newsletter
0557-4250 Rozhlad
0557-4404 Rueckert Studien
0557-465X Institutul Agronomic Cluj-Napoca. Buletinul. Seria Agricultura
0557-4668 Institutul Agronomic Cluj-Napoca. Buletinul. Seria Zootehnie si Medicina Veterinara
0557-532X Russian Orthodox Greek Catholic Church of America. Yearbook and Church Directory *see* 0145-7950
0557-5486 Rutgers University. Bureau of Engineering Research. Annual Report
0557-6377 Regensburger Universitaetszeitung
0557-6601 Royal New Zealand Institute of Horticulture. Journal *see* 1170-1803
0557-661X R Y A News
0557-6911 University of Reading. Department of Agricultural Economics & Management. Farm Business Data
0557-6989 Recherches Anglaises et Americaines
0557-7527 Review of Plant Protection Research†
0557-7705 Revue Archeologique Narbonnaise
0557-7713 Revue d'Acoustique†
0557-7853 Rheinische Ausgrabungen
0557-8019 Rivista di Studi Salernitani†
0557-8051 Rocky Mountain Mineral Law Newsletter *changed to* Rocky Mountain Mineral Law Foundation. Newsletter.
0557-8280 Readings in Development Economics *changed to* Lectures in Development Economics.
0557-8558 Revista Interamericana de Sociologia
0557-8639 University of Rhode Island. Law of the Sea Institute. Special Publications†
0557-9147 Record Exchanger
0557-9325 Review of Progress in Coloration and Related Topics
0557-9414 Revue Libanaise des Sciences Politiques†
0557-9430 Riabilitazione
0558-0293 S I A M Series in Applied Mathematics†
0558-1257 Safn til Soegu Islands og Islenzkra Bokmennta
0558-1613 Shakhs
0558-1931 St. Lawrence County Historical Association. Quarterly
0558-2431 Mathematics, Physics and Chemistry *see* 0289-0739
0558-244X Saitama University. Science Reports. Series B: Biology and Earth Sciences†
0558-3918 San Diego Economic Bulletin *changed to* Economic Bulletin (San Diego).
0558-4477 San Marino (Repubblica). Segreteria di Stato per gli Affari Esteri. Notiziario *changed to* San Marino (Repubblica). Dipartimento Affari Esteri. Notizia.
0558-4639 Suomen Kielen Seuran Vuosikirja *changed to* Sananjalka.
0558-4779 Industry and Commerce†
0558-6208 Saobracaj
0558-6976 Saskatchewan Economic Review
0558-7220 Saudi Arabian Monetary Agency. Annual Report
0558-9274 Schriften zur Phonetik, Sprachwissenschaft und Kommunikationsforschung
0558-9746 Schriftenreihe fuer Raumforschung und Raumplanung.†
0559-1414 Scientia et Praxis
0559-1422 Scientia Juridica
0559-1791 Scottish Fisheries Bulletin
0559-2674 Sedar
0559-3840 Semaine Internationale d'Etudes Superieures des Methodes Physiques d'Analyse. (Papers)
0559-4065 Seminar of African Christian Students in Europe. Report
0559-5258 Serial Slants *see* 0024-2527
0559-698X Social Development Research Institute. Organization and Activities
0559-717X Shanxi Huabao
0559-7218 Shanhua
0559-7277 Shanghai Xiju
0559-7412 Shaonian Wenyi
0559-7765 Shengli Kexue Jinzhan
0559-8540 Shinrin Boeki Nyusu *changed to* Forest Pests.
0559-8621 Shinshu University. Faculty of Textile Science and Technology. Journal. Series C: Chemistry
0559-9091 Shopping Center Newsletter
0559-9342 Shuili Fadian
0559-9822 Sieboldia Acta Biologica
0560-0391 Silence
0560-0871 Sind University Journal of Education
0560-1894 Skalk
0560-3110 Slovensko Kemijsko Drustvo. Vestnik
0560-3617 Soccer Journal
0560-3641 Sociaal-Economische Raad. Jaarverslag
0560-4168 Boletin de la Sociedad Cientifica del Paraguay y del Museo Etnografico†
0560-5296 Societe des Etudes Juives. Memoires†
0560-5466 Societe Geologique et Mineralogique de Bretagne. Bulletin, Serie C *see* 0982-3816
0560-6152 Society of Archer-Antiquaries. Journal
0560-8325 Songwriter's Annual Directory†
0560-9208 South Africa. Geological Survey. Handbook
0560-9941 Textile and Fibre Programme. Division of Processing and Chemical Manufacturing Technology. Annual Report *changed to* South Africa. Division of Textile Technology. Annual Report.
0561-015X Checklist of South Carolina State Publications†
0561-1784 Southwestern Legal Foundation. Annual Report
0561-3590 Instituto de Estudios Giennenses Boletin
0561-3663 Anejos de Archivo Espanol de Arqueologia
0561-4619 Spain. Ministerio de Educacion y Ciencia. Junta Nacional Contra el Analfabetismo. Boletin†
0561-4902 Spain. Ministerio de la Vivienda. Estadistica de la Industria de la Construccion
0561-5062 Evolucion de la Economia Espanola†
0561-5313 Spain - U.S. Trade Bulletin *changed to* The Business Link.
0561-6832 Sports Turf Research Institute. Journal
0561-7383 Srpska Akademija Nauka i Umetnosti. Predavanja†
0561-7650 Sixiang Zhanxian
0561-7855 Stahlbau - Rundschau
0561-7979 Stamford Genealogical Society. Bulletin *see* 0197-2103
0561-8630 State Administrative Officials: Classified by Function
0561-8738 State Bank of Pakistan. State Bank News
0561-922X Statistical Notes of Japan
0561-9998 University of Stellenbosch. Bureau for Economic Research. Opinion Survey *see* 0258-9338
0562-0031 Stepping Stones
0562-0953 Statens Geotekniska Institut. Saertryck och Preliminaera Rapporter *see* 0348-0755
0562-1887 Strojarstvo
0562-2719 Studia Anglistica Upsalienses
0562-2786 Studia i Materialy do Historii Wojskowosci
0562-3022 Studia Romanica Upsaliensia
0562-4649 Subsidia Scientifica Franciscalia
0562-5033 Sudan Cotton Bulletin
0562-5068 Sudan Cotton Review
0562-5092 Sudan News Agency. English Daily Bulletin *changed to* S U N A.
0562-5130 Sudan Society
0562-5297 Suedostdeutsche Vierteljahresblaetter
0562-6048 Sunrise
0562-7087 Survivre *see* 0384-7810
0562-7192 Savremenna Medicina
0562-7451 Svenska Arkivsamfundets Skrifterie *see* 0349-0505
0562-8490 Sweden. Fisheries Board. Series Hydrography. Reports *see* 0346-8666
0562-861X Arbetsskador
0562-9020 Nouvelles Economiques de Suisse†
0563-0355 Systemation Letter†
0563-0592 Acta Universitatis de Attila Jozsef Nominatae. Acta Biologica
0563-0606 Acta Universitatis de Attila Jozsef Nominatae. Acta Iuridica et Politica
0563-0614 Acta Universitatis de Attila Jozsef Nominatae. Acta Climatologica
0563-0622 Acta Universitatis Szegediensis de Attila Jozsef Nominatae. Sectio Oeconomico-Politica
0563-0657 Acta Universitatis Szegediensis de Attila Jozsef Nominatae. Sectio Scientiae Socialismi
0563-0924 S C A U L Newsletter *see* 0189-6709
0563-1491 Universitaet des Saarlandes. Geographisches Institut. Arbeiten
0563-1637 Terre Malgache
0563-1874 Test Collection Bulletin *see* 0271-8472
0563-2153 Teva Va-Aretz
0563-2595 University of Texas. Humanities Research Center. Tower Bibliographical Series†
0563-2625 Texas Biannual of Electronics Research *changed to* Texas Annual of Electronics Research.
0563-3400 Thai Chamber of Commerce. Business Directory *changed to* Thai Chamber of Commerce. Handbook (Year).
0563-3737 Thailand Year Book†
0563-4040 Theatre News (Washington)†
0563-4245 Au Coeur de l'Afrique
0563-4407 Theorie des Systemes†
0563-4660 Things *see* 0440-2316
0563-4725 33 Magazine *see* 0149-1210
0563-4784 This is Malawi
0563-4806 This Week in Public Health†
0563-5020 Dizhi Kexue
0563-5446 Timber Tax Journal†
0563-5489 Timeless Fellowship
0563-5780 Studime Filologjike
0563-5799 Studime Historike
0563-587X Tiscia
0563-6140 Tobacco Bibliography†
0563-6191 Tax Burden on Tobacco
0563-6523 Tohoku University. Science Reports. Series 7: Geography†
0563-6590 Tohoku University. Research Institute for Strength and Fracture of Materials. Reports
0563-6760 Tokai Daigaku Kiyo. Bungakubu
0563-6795 Tokai University. Faculty of Science. Proceedings
0563-6981 Tokushima Daigaku Kyoyobu Kiyo. Shizen Kagaku
0563-7848 University of Tokyo. Institute for Nuclear Study. INS-PT
0563-7856 University of Tokyo. Institute for Nuclear Study. INS-TCA†
0563-7864 University of Tokyo. Institute for Nuclear Study. INS-TCB†
0563-7872 University of Tokyo. Institute for Nuclear Study. INS-TH
0563-7880 University of Tokyo. Institute for Nuclear Study. INS-TL
0563-7902 Strong-Motion Earthquake Records in Japan
0563-7929 Tokyo Daigaku Kogakubu. Denki Kogaku, Denshi Kogaku Iho
0563-7937 University of Tokyo. Faculty of Engineering. Journal: Series B
0563-8038 University of Tokyo. Department of Astronomy. Contributions
0563-8054 University of Tokyo. Institute of Social Science. Annals
0563-8186 Institute for Comparative Studies of Culture. Annals
0563-8313 Tokyo University of Agriculture and Technology. Annual Report
0563-8372 Tokyo University of Fisheries. Report
0563-8887 Tools and Tillage
0563-8895 Top Companies
0563-9093 Tops
0563-9425 Torreia
0563-9727 Universite des Sciences Sociales de Toulouse. Annales
0563-9743 Homo
0563-9751 Litteratures
0563-9786 Via Domitia†
0563-9794 Universite de Toulouse II (le Mirail). Institut d'Art Prehistorique. Travaux†
0564-0334 Trabajo
0564-0342 Trabalho
0564-0482 Trade Directories of the World
0564-0490 Trade Directory and Guide Book to Ethiopia
0564-089X Training Research Abstracts *see* 1055-9760
0564-108X Ch'indaba *changed to* Transition (New York).
0564-1373 Transports
0564-1632 Travel Market Yearbook *changed to* Travel Market Yearbook (1980).
0564-2159 Tribal Research and Development Institute. Bulletin
0564-2477 Universita degli Studi di Trieste. Istituto di Storia dell'Arte (Pubblicazioni)
0564-2612 Trinidad and Tobago. Central Statistical Office. Continuous Sample Survey of Population
0564-3287 Trooper
0564-3295 Tropical Ecology
0564-3325 Tropical Stored Products Information *see* 0041-3291
0564-3392 Truck Data Book
0564-3783 Tsitologiya i Genetika
0564-3910 Turang
0564-3929 Turang Xuebao
0564-4070 Universidad Nacional de Tucuman. Facultad de Filosofia y Letras. Cuadernos de Humanitas
0564-4232 Tuebinger Geographische Studien
0564-4402 Tulane Tax Institute
0564-4437 Tulsa Annals
0564-5093 Turk Kulturu Arastirmalari
0564-5409 Handelshoegeskolan vid Aabo Akademi. Ekonomisk-Geografiska Institutionen. Meddelanden *changed to* Aabo Akademi. Ekonomisk-Geografiska Institutionen. Meddelanden.
0564-5654 Twentieth Century Series†
0564-6103 Tavkozlesi Kutato Intezet Evkonyve†
0564-6170 Teplofizika i Teplotekhnika *see* 0204-3602
0564-6197 Texas Tech Law Review
0564-6294 Topics in Astrophysics and Space Physics†
0564-6545 Tanzania. Central Statistical Bureau. Survey of Industrial Production *changed to* Tanzania. Bureau of Statistics. Survey of Industrial Production.
0564-6723 Tea Research Association. Tocklai Experimental Station. Scientific Annual Report
0564-6758 Tecnologia de Alimentos
0564-6855 University of Texas. Humanities Research Center. Bibliographical Monograph Series†
0564-6898 University of Tokyo. Ocean Research Institute. Bulletin
0564-7169 T A I U S†
0564-724X Tanzania Directory of Trades
0564-7975 C E R E S Cahiers. Serie Linguistique
0564-836X Report on Tourism Statistics in Tanzania
0564-8602 Memphis State University. Anthropological Research Center. Occasional Papers

ISSN

ISSN INDEX

0564-8742 University of Tokyo. Computer Center. Report†
0564-9048 25 Weekend Build-It Projects†
0565-0704 U.S. Fish and Wildlife Service. Investigations in Fish Control
0565-0828 U.S. Bureau of the Census. Census Bureau Methodological Research†
0565-0909 Monthly Retail Trade *changed to* Current Business Reports: Monthly Retail Trade, Sales and Inventories.
0565-0917 Current Population Reports: Federal-State Cooperative Program for Population Estimates *changed to* Current Population Reports: Local Population Estimates.
0565-0933 U.S. Bureau of the Census. Guide to Foreign Trade Statistics
0565-0941 Foreign Trade Reports. Highlights of U.S. Export and Import Trade *changed to* Foreign Trade Reports. U.S. Export and Import Merchandise Trade and Supplement.
0565-1034 Current Business Reports: Monthly Department Store Sales for Selected Areas†
0565-1190 Foreign Trade Reports. U.S. Imports for Consumption and General Imports; Tariff Schedules Annotated by Country *changed to* Foreign Trade Reports. U.S. Imports for Consumption and General Imports-TSUSA Commodity by Country of Origin: Annual (Year).
0565-1204 Foreign Trade Reports. U.S. Trade with Puerto Rico and U.S. Possessions
0565-1530 U.S. Coast Guard Boating Statistics *changed to* Boating Statistics.
0565-1603 U.S. Coastal Engineering Research Center. Bulletin and Progress Reports†
0565-1980 Poultry Market Statistics
0565-2820 U.S. Department of Housing and Urban Development. Annual Report
0565-4866 Flight Standards Information Manual†
0565-5560 U.S. Foreign Broadcast Information Service. Daily Reports: Soviet Union
0565-6311 U S I T T Newsletter *changed to* Sightlines (New York).
0565-6567 U.S. Law Enforcement Assistance Administration. Annual Report†
0565-7024 National Advisory Council on the Education of Disadvantaged Children. Annual Report to the President and the Congress
0565-7199 Management (Baltimore)
0565-744X U.S. Department of Education. National Center for Education Statistics. Earned Degrees Conferred *changed to* U.S. Department of Education. National Center for Education Statistics. Completions in Institutions of Higher Education.
0565-7717 U.S. National Highway Traffic Safety Administration. Motor Vehicle Safety Defect Recall Campaigns
0565-811X Medical Subject Headings (Black Book)
0565-825X U.S. National Science Foundation. Grants and Awards *changed to* U.S. National Science Foundation. Fiscal Year Awards.
0565-8454 Where to Write for Divorce Records: U.S. and Outlying Areas†
0565-8462 Where to Write for Marriage Records *see* 0162-0916
0565-8543 Gulfstream *changed to* U.S. Department of Commerce. National Oceanic and Atmospheric Administration. Oceanographic Monthly Summary.
0565-8721 U.S. Forest Service. Research Paper N C
0565-873X U.S. Forest Service. Resource Bulletin N C
0565-9442 U.S. Office of Water Resources Research. Annual Report *changed to* U.S. Office of Water Research and Technology. Annual Report.
0565-9582 Directory of Registered Patent Attorneys and Agents *see* 0361-3844
0566-0327 U.S. Social Security Administration. O R S I P Notes†
0566-0963 United Steelworkers of America. Information
0566-201X Universite de Yaounde. Faculte des Sciences. Annales
0566-2389 University of Richmond Law Review
0566-2540 Unnatkrishi
0566-2621 Unsere Jagd†
0566-263X Unsere Kunstdenkmaeler
0566-2680 Untei
0566-3628 Monthly Price Review
0566-4152 Utah. Juvenile Court. Annual Report
0566-7038 U.S. National Institute of Mental Health. Report Series on Mental Health Statistics. Series C: Methodology Reports†
0566-7631 Census of Traffic on Main International Traffic Arteries *changed to* Census of Motor Traffic on Main International Traffic Arteries.
0566-8549 Selected United States Government Publications†
0566-8654 Univers des Sciences et Techniques†
0566-8700 U F A W News-Sheet

0566-8719 University of Kentucky Research Foundation. Annual Report *changed to* Odyssey (Lexington).
0566-9197 Music News Bulletin *changed to* Union of Bulgarian Composers. News Bulletin.
0567-168X Austrian Trade Bulletin *changed to* Made in Austria.
0567-1795 Auto Ja Tie
0567-2317 Automotive Rebuilder
0567-2392 Autopista
0567-2848 Avicultura Tecnica
0567-4069 A Ph A Newsletter *see* 1042-0991
0567-4263 A T A Professional Services Directory *changed to* Translation Services Directory.
0567-428X A U C A†
0567-4492 Alborg-Bogen
0567-4565 Aarets Fotboll
0567-4573 Aarets Idrott
0567-4840 Kano Studies†
0567-4980 Abhandlungen fuer die Kunde des Morgenlandes
0567-4999 Abhandlungen zur Kunst-, Musik- und Literaturwissenschaft
0567-5782 Academia de Ciencias de Cuba. Instituto de Oceanologia. Serie Oceanologica†
0567-5871 Academia Dominicana de la Historia. Publicaciones
0567-6029 Academia Provincial de la Historia. Boletin
0567-6304 Revista Istorica
0567-6312 Studii si Materiale de Istorie Medie
0567-6320 Studii si Materiale de Istorie Moderna
0567-6541 Academie des Sciences. Comptes Rendus Hebdomadaires des Seances. Series C: Sciences Chimiques *see* 0764-4450
0567-655X Academie des Sciences. Comptes Rendus Hebdomadaires des Seances. Series D: Sciences Naturelles *see* 0764-4469
0567-6576 Academie et Societe Lorraines de Sciences. Bulletin
0567-6584 Academie Royale de Langue et de Litterature Francaises. Annuaires
0567-6592 Academie Royale des Sciences d'Outre Mer. Revue Bibliographique†
0567-6630 Academy of American Franciscan History. Bibliographical Series
0567-672X Acarologie
0567-7246 Acta Universitatis de Attila Jozsef Nominatae. Acta Antiqua et Archaeologica
0567-7254 Acta Asiatica
0567-7289 Acta Baltica
0567-7351 Huaxue Xuebao
0567-7394 Acta Crystallographica. Section A: Crystal Physics, Diffraction, Theoretical and General Crystallography *see* 0108-7673
0567-7408 Acta Crystallographica. Section B: Structural Crystallography and Crystal Chemistry *see* 0108-7681
0567-7416 Acta Embryologiae et Morphologiae Experimentalis *changed to* Animal Biology.
0567-7505 Acta Geologica Hispanica
0567-7513 Acta Geologica Lilloana
0567-753X Acta Herediana
0567-7572 Acta Horticulturae
0567-7599 Acta Humboldtiana. Series Historica
0567-7661 Academia Scientiarum Hungarica. Acta Litteraria
0567-7718 Acta Mechanica Sinica
0567-7734 Acta Medica et Biologica
0567-7785 Acta Mexicana de Ciencia y Tecnologia
0567-784X Acta Neophilologica
0567-7874 Acta Organologica
0567-7920 Acta Palaeontologica Polonica
0567-8056 Acta Radiologica. Series 1: Diagnosis *changed to* Acta Radiologica.
0567-8064 Acta Radiologica. Series 2: Therapy, Physics, Biology *see* 0349-652X
0567-8099 Acta Universitatis de Attila Jozsef Nominatae. Acta Romanica
0567-8250 Acta Universitatis Carolinae: Medica
0567-8293 Universita Karlova. Acta Universitatis Carolinae. Philosophica et Historica Action *see* 0746-8911
0567-8412
0567-8587 Organization of American States. Department of Educational Affairs. Actualidades†
0567-932X Adelphi Papers
0567-9494 Administrative Law News
0567-9907 Advances in Electrochemistry and Electrochemical Engineering†
0568-0204 Advances in Test Measurement. Proceedings *see* 0277-7576
0568-0301 World Advertising Expenditures
0568-0352 Advertising Research Foundation. Conference Proceedings†
0568-0476 Aegyptologische Abhandlungen
0568-0530 Aero West†
0568-0581 University of Illinois at Urbana-Champaign. Department of Electrical Engineering. Aeronomy Laboratory. Aeronomy Report†
0568-062X Aerosol Review
0568-0743 Berliner Aerztekammer *changed to* Berliner Aerzte.
0568-1278 African Christian Student Seminar in Europe. Papers

0568-1308 African Development Bank. Report by the Board of Directors
0568-1332 African Historian
0568-1499 African Student Christian Seminar (Report)†
0568-2517 Agricultura Tecnica en Mexico
0568-2622 Agricultural Digest *changed to* Salt and Trace Minerals Report.
0568-2800 Index of Current Research on Pigs
0568-3114 Agrotecnia de Cuba
0568-3343 Ailleurs
0568-3424 Air Canada. Annual Report
0568-3653 Air Quality Monograph Series†
0568-3785 Aircraft Owners and Pilots Association. Handbook for Pilots *see* 1056-7704
0568-3866 Airplane, Missile and Spacecraft Structure Series†
0568-3939 Aisthesis
0568-4447 Akademie der Wissenschaften und der Literatur, Mainz. Orientalische Kommission. Veroeffentlichungen
0568-465X Rastenievadni Nauki
0568-5230 Academy of Sciences of the U S S R. Division of Chemical Sciences. Bulletin
0568-6245 Rezul'taty Issledovanii po Mezhdunarodnym Geofizicheskim Proektam. Glyatsiologicheskie Issledovaniya
0568-6776 Akademiya Nauk S.S.S.R. Sibirskoe Otdelenie. Ural'skii Nauchnyi Tsentr. Institut Elektrokhimii. Trudy†
0568-6989 Geofizicheskii Sbornik *see* 0203-3100
0568-7276 Der Akademiker in Wirtschaft und Verwaltung
0568-7306 Achshav
0568-7594 Aktuelle Fragen des Landbaues†
0568-7632 Aktuelle Schaufenster *see* 0173-1882
0568-8604 University of Alaska. Biological Papers
0568-8876 Economia Alavesa
0568-9074 University of Alberta. Faculty of Agriculture. Agriculture Bulletin *see* 0705-3983
0568-9848 Revue Algerienne du Travail
0569-0196 All India Central Land Development Bank Cooperative Union. Journal *changed to* Land Bank Journal.
0569-0838 Almanac for Geodetic Engineers
0569-1346 Altamura
0569-163X Am Veadamato
0569-1796 Amateur Wrestling News
0569-1966 America by Car
0569-2032 American Academy of Actuaries. Yearbook
0569-2229 American Antiquarian Society. News-Letter
0569-2245 American Assembly. Report
0569-230X School Nursing Monographs†
0569-2393 American Association for the Advancement of Science. Committee on Desert and Arid Zone Research. Contributions†
0569-2423 A A B G A Newsletter
0569-2482 Report of Credit Given by Educational Institutions *see* 0194-0988
0569-2628 A A F M Proceedings of Annual Meeting
0569-2679 American Association of Medical Clinics. Directory *see* 0098-2377
0569-2733 American Association of Psychiatric Clinics for Children. Newsletter *see* 0027-6022
0569-2857 Eastern Canada Tour Book *see* 0363-1788
0569-292X American Bank Directory
0569-2954 American Bankers Association. Committee on Uniform Security Identification Procedures. C U S I P Directory *changed to* C U S I P Master Directory.
0569-3098 American Bar Association. Section of Administrative Law. Annual Reports of Divisions and Committees *see* 0090-3647
0569-3160 Docket Call (Chicago) *see* 0741-9066
0569-3314 Public Contract Newsletter
0569-3349 American Bar Association. Utility Section. Newsletter
0569-3357 American Bar Association. Section of Real Property, Probate and Trust Law. Newsletter *see* 0164-0372
0569-3667 American Chamber of Commerce in Italy. Directory
0569-3845 American Christmas Tree Journal
0569-3993 A C T Research Report
0569-4043 Industrial Ventilation; a Manual of Recommended Practice
0569-4108 American Council of Polish Cultural Clubs. Quarterly Review *see* 0735-9209
0569-4221 American Crystallographic Association. Program & Abstracts
0569-4353 American Educational Research Association. Directory of Members†
0569-4450 American Entomological Institute. Contributions
0569-4833 American Foundation for the Study of Man. Publications†
0569-5341 A I A Emerging Techniques†
0569-5376 Research Problems in Biology†
0569-5457 A I Ch E Workshop Series†

0569-5473 A I Ch E Equipment Testing Procedures
0569-5503 Electronic Components Conference. Proceedings
0569-5554 A I I E Transactions *changed to* I I E Transactions.
0569-5716 Physics Manpower - Education and Employment Statistics†
0569-5961 American Italian Historical Association. Newsletter
0569-6275 Financial Assistance for Library Education
0569-6356 American Motor Carrier Directory: National Edition *changed to* American Motor Carrier Directory: North American Edition.
0569-6364 American Motor Carrier Directory: Specialized Services Edition *changed to* American Motor Carrier Directory: North American Edition.
0569-6666 American Musicological Society. Greater New York Chapter. Publications†
0569-6720 American Numismatic Society. Annual Report
0569-6763 A O A News Review *see* 0091-6269
0569-6852 American Petroleum Institute. Division of Statistics and Economics. Annual Statistical Review *changed to* Basic Petroleum Data Book.
0569-6909 American Petroleum Institute. Division of Refining. Proceedings. *see* 0163-495X
0569-6992 American Phytopathological Society. Monographs
0569-7344 American Review of Art and Science†
0569-7468 Symposium on the Art of Scientific Glassblowing Proceedings
0569-776X American Society for Training and Development. Membership Directory *see* 0092-4598
0569-7832 American Society of Animal Science. Western Section Proceedings
0569-7840 A S A Monograph (Washington)†
0569-7859 American Society of Appraisers. Appraisal and Valuation Manual†
0569-7891 Transportation Engineering Journal *see* 0733-947X
0569-7948 American Society of Civil Engineers. Construction Division. Journal *see* 0733-9364
0569-8030 American Society of Civil Engineers. Power Division. Journal *see* 0733-9402
0569-8057 Reinforced Concrete Research Council. Bulletins
0569-8073 American Society of Civil Engineers. Surveying and Mapping Division. Journal *see* 0733-9453
0569-8081 American Society of Civil Engineers. Urban Planning and Development Division. Journal *see* 0733-9488
0569-8197 A S L E Transactions *changed to* S T L E Tribology Transactions.
0569-8219 American Society of Mammalogists. Special Publications
0569-8243 Reports on Diesel and Gas Engines Power Costs†
0569-8553 A S H A Reports *changed to* American Speech - Language - Hearing Association Reports.
0569-8561 A S H A Directory *changed to* American Speech - Language - Hearing Association. Directory.
0569-9053 American Wedgwoodian†
0569-9460 Amministrazione della Difesa†
0569-9479 Amministrazione Tributi e Finanze†
0569-9495 Amnesty International Annual Report *changed to* Amnesty International Report.
0569-9665 Netherlands. Rijksmuseum Amsterdam. Bulletin
0569-9789 Analecta Calasanctiana
0569-9827 Analecta Musicologica
0569-986X Analecta Romanica
0569-9878 Anales Cervantinos
0569-9894 Anales de Anatomia
0569-9908 Anales del Desarrollo
0570-023X Ancient Peoples and Places†
0570-0655 Andhra Pradesh
0570-0833 Angewandte Chemie: International Edition
0570-1538 Annales Agriculturae Fenniae†
0570-1597 Annales de l'Abeille *see* 0044-8435
0570-1619 Invertebres *see* 0753-3969
0570-1627 Annales de Paleontologie: Vertebres *see* 0753-3969
0570-1716 Annales Islamologiques
0570-1724 Annales Malgaches. Droit *changed to* Universite de Madagascar. Annales. Serie Droit.
0570-1791 Annals of Arid Zone
0570-1864 Annals of Regional Science
0570-1937 Annee Africaine
0570-2070 Union of European Football Associations. Handbook of U E F A
0570-2194 Geneva International Year Book†
0570-2658 Annual Survey of Commonwealth Law†
0570-2666 Annual Survey of Indian Law
0570-2674 Annual Survey of Massachusetts Law†
0570-2976 Anthropological Studies†
0570-3697 Antropologia Social†
0570-393X Anuario Bibliografico Colombiano
0570-3956 Anuario Brasileiro de Propaganda
0570-3980 Anuario Comercial Iberoamericano
0570-4006 Anuario Cultural del Peru
0570-4022 Anuario da Provincia de Mocambique *changed to* Anuario do Estado de Mocambique.
0570-4200 Anuario del Desarrollo de la Educacion, la Ciencia y la Cultura en America Latina†
0570-4251 Anuario Ecuatoriano de Derecho Internacional
0570-426X Anuario Estadistico Centroamericano de Comercio Exterior
0570-4324 Anuario Iberoamericano
0570-4359 Anuario Latinoamericano
0570-4723 Die Apothekenhelferin *see* 0939-3331
0570-4839 Applied Economic Papers
0570-4898 Journal of Applied Polymer Science. Symposia
0570-4928 Applied Spectroscopy Reviews
0570-4979 Approach
0570-5029 Approdo Letterario†
0570-507X Aqlam Journal
0570-5169 Aquilo. Serie Botanica
0570-5177 Aquilo. Serie Zoologica
0570-5258 Arab Observer†
0570-5398 Arabica
0570-5886 Arbeitsmethoden der Medizinischen und Naturwissenschaftlichen Kriminalistik
0570-6068 Archaeologia Zambiana
0570-6084 Archaeological Reports *issued with* 0075-4269
0570-622X Archaiologikon Deltion
0570-6262 Archenhold-Sternwarte. Vortraege und Schriften
0570-6270 Archeologia
0570-6483 Architectural Index
0570-6602 Architektur Aktuell
0570-6769 Archiv fuer Musikwissenschaft. Beihefte
0570-6793 Archiv fuer Vergleichende Kulturwissenschaft†
0570-6955 Archives Medicales de l'Ouest†
0570-7242 Archivum Bibliographicum Carmelitanum *changed to* Archivum Bibliographicum Carmeli Teresiani.
0570-7293 Arco
0570-734X Arctos; Acta Philologica Fennica
0570-7439 Arena†
0570-751X Areopag
0570-8346 Instituto Nacional de Antropologia. Cuadernos *changed to* Instituto Nacional de Antropologia y Pensamiento Latinoamericano. Cuadernos.
0570-8621 Argentine Republic. Mercado Nacional de Hacienda. Memoria *changed to* Argentina. Mercado Nacional de Hacienda. Anuario.
0570-8834 Argentina. Instituto Forestal Nacional. Anuario de Estadistica Forestal
0570-8869 Argo
0570-8915 L'Argus de la Legislation Libanaise
0570-8966 Arheoloski Vestnik
0570-9008 Arhivski Vjesnik
0570-9520 Arizona. Oil & Gas Conservation Commission. Oil, Gas & Helium Production
0570-9601 Arizona State University. Faculty of Industrial Engineering. Industrial Engineering Research Bulletin†
0571-0111 Arizona Political Almanac†
0571-0189 Arkansas. Agricultural Experiment Station. Special Reports
0571-0278 Arkansas. Geological Commission. Water Resources Circulars
0571-0456 Arkansas Almanac
0571-0472 Arkansas Family Historian
0571-0731 Arkivinformation
0571-1223 Arquivo de Bibliografia Portuguesa
0571-1371 Ars Orientalis
0571-1509 Art de Basse Normandie
0571-1525 Art Dentaire Liberal
0571-1924 Artes Textiles: Bijragen tot de Geschiedenis van de Tapijt
0571-205X Artificial Satellites *see* 0208-841X
0571-205X Artificial Satellites *see* 0208-8428
0571-2378 Asahi Janaru
0571-2742 Asian and African Studies
0571-2912 A.P.D.S.A. Journal†
0571-2920 Asian Pacific Anti-Communist League, China. Pamphlet
0571-2939 Asian Peoples' Anti-Communist League. Charts About Chinese Communists on the Mainland
0571-3005 Asian Productivity Organization. Review of Activities of National Productivity Organizations *changed to* Directory of the National Productivity Organizations in A P O Member Countries.
0571-3161 Asiatic Society, Calcutta. Journal
0571-320X Asiatische Forschungen
0571-3218 Asilomar Conference on Circuits and Systems. Conference Record *changed to* Asilomar Conference on Signals, Systems and Computers. Conference Record.
0571-3609 Asociacion de Investigacion Textil Algodonera. Coleccion de Manuales Tecnicos†
0571-3692 Asociacion Espanola de Orientalistas. Boletin
0571-3846 Anuario de los Paises de A L A L C *see* 0066-5118
0571-3854 Asociacion Latinoamericana de Libre Comercio. Boletin Bibliografico†
0571-3870 Asociacion Latinoamericana de Libre Comercio. Comercio Exterior. Argentina. Exportacion *changed to* Asociacion Latinoamericana de Libre Comercio. Estadisticas de Comercio Exterior - Serie A: Exportaciones.
0571-3889 Asociacion Latinoamericana de Libre Comercio. Comercio Exterior Argentina. Importacion *changed to* Asociacion Latinoamericana de Libre Comercio. Estadisticas de Comercio Exterior-Serie B-Importaciones.
0571-3919 Asociacion Latinoamericana de Libre Comercio. Documentacion A L A L C†
0571-3927 Asociacion Latinoamericana de Libre Comercio. Indice Alfabetico de Mercaderias†
0571-3935 Asociacion Latinoamericana de Libre Comercio. Lista Consolidada de Concesiones†
0571-396X Asociacion Latinoamericana de Libre Comercio. Lista Nacional de Brasil†
0571-3978 Asociacion Latinoamericana de Libre Comercio. Lista Nacional de Chile†
0571-3986 Asociacion Latinoamericana de Libre Comercio. Lista Nacional de Colombia†
0571-3994 Asociacion Latinoamericana de Libre Comercio. Lista Nacional de Ecuador†
0571-4001 Asociacion Latinoamericana de Libre Comercio. Lista Nacional de la Republica Argentina *changed to* Asociacion Latinoamericana de Libre Comercio. Lista Nacional de Argentina.
0571-401X Asociacion Latinoamericana de Libre Comercio. Lista Nacional de Mexico†
0571-4028 Asociacion Latinoamericana de Libre Comercio. Lista Nacional de Paraguay†
0571-4036 Asociacion Latinoamericana de Libre Comercio. Lista Nacional de Peru†
0571-4044 Asociacion Latinoamericana de Libre Comercio. Lista Nacional de Uruguay†
0571-4052 Asociacion Latinoamericana de Libre Comercio. Listas de Concesiones Arancelarias para Ecuador y Paraguay†
0571-4079 Asociacion Latinoamericana de Libre Comercio. Serie Estadistica†
0571-4087 Asociacion Latinoamericana de Libre Comercio. Serie Instrumentos†
0571-5520 Association for Asian Studies. Committee on East Asian Libraries. Newsletter *see* 0148-6225
0571-5644 A R E Journal†
0571-5857 International Association for Byzantine Studies. Bulletin d'Information et de Coordination
0571-5865 International Association of French Studies. Cahiers
0571-5873 Association Internationale du Droit Commercial. Et du Droit Affaires. Groupe Francais. Travaux *see* 0074-6738
0571-5962 Association of American Geographers. Handbook-Directory *changed to* Association of American Geographers. Directory.
0571-6241 Association of Commonwealth Universities. Report of the Council Together with the Accounts of the Association *see* 0307-2274
0571-625X Compendium of University Entrance Requirements for First Degree Courses in the United Kingdom†
0571-6322 Association of Institutes for European Studies. Annuaire
0571-6330 Association of Institutes for European Studies. Year-Book
0571-6357 A I L/Doc†
0571-6373 Abstracts of Supreme Court Decisions Interpreting the Interstate Commerce Act†
0571-6519 Academic Library Statistics *see* 0147-2135
0571-7760 Crisis Papers†
0571-7795 Atlantic Papers†
0571-7817 Atlantic Provinces Checklist†
0571-7868 Atlantic Series†
0571-8236 Attakapas Gazette
0571-8279 Attorney - C P A
0571-8597 Attack†
0571-8619 Audio-Digest General Practice *see* 0271-1362
0571-8678 Audio-Technik†
0571-8724 Audiology *see* 0303-8106
0571-8759 Audio-Visual Equipment Directory *see* 0884-2124
0571-9291 Australasian Conference on Hydraulics and Fluid Mechanics. Proceedings
0571-9518 Australia. Bureau of Statistics. Life Insurance, Australia†
0571-964X Australia. Bureau of Statistics. Seasonally Adjusted Indicators†
0571-9844 Australia. Bureau of Statistics. Tasmanian Office. Wool Production Statistics *changed to* Australia. Bureau of Statistics. Tasmanian Office. Wool Production and Disposal.
0572-0125 Geological Survey of South Australia. Explanatory Notes
0572-0400 Australia. Department of Civil Aviation. Civil Aviation Report *see* 0311-628X

0572-0451 Australia. Department of Primary Industry. Wheat Industry Research, A.C.T. Annual Report *see* 0819-5854
0572-0494 Australia. Department of Territory of Norfolk Island. Report *changed to* Australia. Department of Home Affairs. Norfolk Island Annual Report.
0572-1431 Australian Road Research Board. Proceedings
0572-144X Australian Road Research Board. Special Report
0572-192X Oberoesterreichisches Landesarchiv. Mitteilungen†
0572-2691 Avtomatika
0572-2969 Cuaderno Literario Azor
0572-2993 Aarets Storsta Handelser i Bilder
0572-3221 Agricultural Science Hong Kong *changed to* Agriculture Hong Kong.
0572-3590 American Bar Association. Section of Individual Rights and Responsibilities. Newsletter *changed to* American Bar Association. I.R.R. Section Newsletter.
0572-4171 Asian Industrial Development News *see* 0252-4481
0572-4198 Asian Institute of Technology. Research Summary *changed to* Asian Institute of Technology. Annual Research and Activities Report.
0572-4295 Association of American Geographers. Proceedings†
0572-4325 Association of Southeast Asian Institutions of Higher Learning. Newsletter
0572-4562 Aarbok for Hadeland
0572-4953 American Association of Law Libraries. Newsletter
0572-5534 Brazil. Superintendencia da Borracha. Annuario Estatistico. Mercado Estrangeiro
0572-5860 Baas Becking Geobiological Laboratory. Annual Report†
0572-5933 Bank Automation Newsletter†
0572-5941 National Income of Iran
0572-595X Bank Marketing Management *see* 0888-3149
0572-5968 Bank of Jamaica. Statistical Digest
0572-6042 Barbados Nursing Journal
0572-6557 Biology and Behavior Series†
0572-6565 Biotechnology & Bioengineering Symposia†
0572-6654 Bochumer Schriften zur Entwicklungsforschung und Entwicklungspolitik†
0572-6921 Brigham Young University. Center for Thermochemical Studies. Contributions
0572-7146 Bruecke-Archiv
0572-7529 Bureau International des Societes Gerant les Droits d'Enregistrement et de Reproduction Mecanique. Bulletin
0572-7545 Business Asia
0572-7669 Colorado School Law Review
0572-7820 Columbia College Today
0572-9327 Comite International de Dachau. Bulletin
0572-9750 Common Market Reports
0572-9912 Trade Regulation Reports
0573-0473 Committee of the Professional Photographers of Europe. General Assembly. Report of Proceedings
0573-0872 Commonwealth Space-Flight Symposium. Proceedings†
0573-0910 Communes de France
0573-2646 International Art Treasures Exhibition
0573-3022 Conference Internationale sur les Phenomenes d'Ionisation dans les Gaz. Comptes Rendus
0573-4347 Conferencia de Facultades Latinoamericanas de Derecho. (Documentos Oficiales)
0573-4843 Congres International Aeronautique. Compte Rendu des Travaux
0573-5661 Congress of International Congress Organizers and Technicians. Proceedings
0573-665X Connecticut Market Data
0573-715X Conservation Topics†
0573-8555 Contributions to Economic Analysis
0573-8636 Control de Publicidad y Ventas *changed to* Control.
0573-9195 Analyse Economique et Fonctionelle du Budget de l'Etat des Pays du Benelux
0573-9209 Analyse Economique et Fonctionelle des Depenses de l'Etat en Belgique, aux Pays Bas et au Luxembourg
0573-9233 Etude Comparative des Budgets Belges, Neerlandais et Luxembourgeois
0573-9543 Cooperation Mediterraneenne pour l'Energie Solaire. Bulletin *changed to* Revue Internationale d'Heliotechnique.
0573-9799 Koebenhavn Boligkommissionen. Aarsberetning
0573-9985 Computer Aided Design i Danmark†
0574-0045 Koebenhavns Universitet. Oekonomiske Institut. Memo
0574-0681 Cornell University. Modern Indonesia Project. Translations†
0574-1181 Corporate Diagrams and Administrative Personnel of the Chemical Industry†
0574-1602 Corriere Nuova Europa
0574-2315 Cotton and Allied Textile Industries *changed to* International Textile Manufacturing.
0574-2323 Cotton Farming
0574-2374 Cotton Statistics Monthly†
0574-248X Calendar of Regional Congresses of Medical Sciences *see* 0301-2891
0574-3370 Courrier Consulaire du Burkina Faso
0574-3680 Covered Wagon
0574-3842 Anthropologia Hungarica
0574-475X Cronache e Opinioni
0574-5101 Cruzada Espanol
0574-6086 Bibliografia Cubana
0574-6132 Anuario Estadistico de Cuba
0574-7120 Curious Naturalist†
0574-8135 Cycle (New York, 1952) *see* 0011-4286
0574-8259 Cyprus. Geological Survey Department. Memoirs
0574-8267 Cyprus. Geological Survey Department. Annual Report
0574-8305 Cyprus. Loan Commissioners. Accounts and Statistics for the Year
0574-8399 Cyprus. Department of Statistics and Research. Motor Vehicles and Road Accidents†
0574-9069 Politechnika Czestochowska. Zeszyty Naukowe. Nauki Podstawowe†
0574-9077 Politechnika Czestochowska. Zeszyty Naukowe. Nauki Spoleczno-Ekonomiczne
0574-9468 C I A Revue
0574-9549 C I S
0575-0075 Cadernos de Folclore
0575-0385 Cahiers Alsaciens d'Archeologie d'Art et d'Histoire
0575-0415 Cahiers Charles du Bos
0575-0466 Cahiers d'Analyse Textuelle†
0575-0547 Cahiers d'Histoire des Prix
0575-0563 Cahiers de Biotherapie
0575-0571 Cahiers de Bruges†
0575-0970 Cahiers du Sart Tilman†
0575-108X Cahiers Ligures de Prehistoire et d'Archeologie *changed to* Cahiers Ligures de Prehistoire et de Protohistoire.
0575-1330 Institut Dominicain d'Etudes Orientales du Caire. Melanges
0575-1632 Caisse Centrale de Cooperation Economique. Rapport d'Activite *changed to* Caisse Centrale de Cooperation Economique. Rapport Annuel.
0575-206X University of Calgary. Department of Mathematics and Computing Science. Research Papers *changed to* University of Calgary. Department of Mathematics and Statistics. Research Papers.
0575-2124 Caliban
0575-2221 California State Plan for Hospitals *changed to* California State Health Plan.
0575-2426 California Economic Indicators
0575-2906 Characteristics of the California Youth Authority Parole Caseload†
0575-3317 California Cooperative Oceanic Fisheries Investigations Reports
0575-3368 Administrative Law Bulletin†
0575-4208 Giannini Foundation of Agricultural Economics. Monograph
0575-4941 California Water Resources Center. Contribution
0575-4968 California. Water Resources Center. Annual Report
0575-5298 California Agricultural Directory (Year)
0575-6316 California Trial Lawyers Journal *see* 0889-7751
0575-6863 Cambridge South Asian Studies
0575-6871 Cambridge Studies in the History and Theory of Politics
0575-7258 Activites Minieres au Cameroun
0575-7894 Canada. Statistics Canada. Annual Report of Notifiable Diseases/Rapport Annuel sur les Maladies a Declaration Obligatoire†
0575-7975 Canada. Statistics Canada. Building Permits. Annual Summary
0575-8254 Canada. Statistics Canada. Consolidated Government Finance: Fiscal Year Ended Nearest to December 31†
0575-8262 Canada. Statistics Canada. Corporation Financial Statistics
0575-8440 Canada. Statistics Canada. Estimates of Production and Disappearance of Meats/Estimation de la Production et de la Disparition des Viandes†
0575-8491 Canada. Statistics Canada. Federal Government Employment†
0575-8521 Canada. Statistics Canada. Federal Government Finance: Revenue and Expenditure, Assets and Liabilities†
0575-8548 Canada. Statistics Canada. Field Crop Reporting Series
0575-8645 Canada. Statistics Canada. General Review of the Mineral Industries, Mines, Quarries and Oil Wells
0575-8661 Canada. Statistics Canada. Glass and Glass Products Manufacturers-Fabricants de Verre et d'Articles en Verre *see* 0835-0167
0575-8807 Canada. Statistics Canada. Industrial Research and Development Expenditures in Canada/Depenses au Titre de la Recherche et du Developpement Industriels au Canada†
0575-8823 Inter-Corporate Ownership
0575-884X Canada. Statistics Canada. Iron and Steel Mills/Siderurgie†
0575-9021 Canada. Statistics Canada. Miscellaneous Manufacturing Industries *see* 0835-0191
0575-9048 Canada. Statistics Canada. Miscellaneous Metal Mines/Mines Metalliques Diverses.†
0575-9072 Canada. Statistics Canada. Motor Carriers Freight Quarterly/ Entrepreneurs en Camionnage†
0575-9137 Canada. Statistics Canada. Moving and Storage Household Goods†
0575-917X Canada. Statistics Canada. Murder Statistics *see* 0825-432X
0575-9331 Canada. Statistics Canada. Police Administration Statistics/Statistique de l'Administration Policiere†
0575-934X Population Estimates by Marital Status, Age & Sex, Canada and Provinces/ Estimations de la Population Suivant l'Etat Matrimonial, l'Age et le Sexe, Canada et Provinces *see* 0227-1796
0575-9412 Canada. Statistics Canada. Printing, Publishing and Allied Industries
0575-9455 Canada. Statistics Canada. Products Shipped by Canadian Manufacturers
0575-9463 Canada. Statistics Canada. Provincial Government Enterprise Finance: Income and Expenditure, Assets, Liabilities and Net Worth
0575-9501 Canada. Statistics Canada. Provincial Government Finance, Revenue and Expenditure (Estimates) /Finances Publiques Provinciales, Revenus et Defenses (Previsions)†
0575-9560 Canada. Statistics Canada. Radio and Television Broadcasting
0575-9633 Sales of Toilet Preparations in Canada†
0575-9757 Canada. Statistics Canada. Shipping Report. Part 4: Origin and Destination for Selected Ports/Transport Maritime. Partie 4: Orgine et Destination pour Certains Ports†
0575-979X Sporting Goods and Toy Industries *see* 0835-0191
0575-9846 Canada. Statistics Canada. Stone Quarries/Carrieres†
0575-996X Canada. Statistics Canada. Training Schools/Etablissements de Protection de la Jeunesse†
0575-9978 Canada. Statistics Canada. Trusteed Pension Plans - Financial Statistics *see* 0835-4634
0576-0046 Canada. Statistics Canada. Urban Transit/Transport Urbain†
0576-0070 Canada. Statistics Canada. Wooden Box Factories/Fabriques de Boites en Bois†
0576-0097 Canada. Statistics Canada. Mechanical Contracting Industry *see* 0835-1031
0576-0100 Canada. Statistics Canada. Credit Unions
0576-0119 Canada. Statistics Canada. Corporation Taxation Statistics
0576-016X Canada. Statistics Canada. Health Manpower Section. Annual Salaries of Hospital Nursing Personnel/ Traitements Annuels du Personnel Infirmier des Hopitaux†
0576-1174 Canada. Department of Manpower and Immigration. Quarterly Immigration Bulletin†
0576-1999 Gazetteer of Canada
0576-2286 Canada. Immigration Division. Immigration Statistics *changed to* Canada. Immigration and Demographic Policy Group. Immigration Statistics.
0576-4157 Unemployment Insurance Canada. Annual Report *changed to* Employment and Immigration Canada. Annual Report.
0576-4300 Canada Council Annual Report and Supplement
0576-470X Canadian Book Prices Current
0576-5161 Canadian Electrical Association. Engineering and Operating Division. Transactions
0576-5234 Canadian Folk Music Society Newsletter *see* 0829-5344
0576-5269 Canadian Gas Utilities Directory *changed to* Directory of Natural Gas Company Operations.
0576-5528 Canadian Jewish Archives (New Series)
0576-5803 Canadian Notes & Queries
0576-6176 Canadian Symposium on Water Pollution Research. Water Pollution Research in Canada. Proceedings *see* 0197-9140
0576-6370 Canadian Wildlife Service. Occasional Papers
0576-6478 Canado-Americain
0576-6621 Cancer Cytology†
0576-6885 University of Cape Town. Libraries. Statistical Report
0576-6931 Capilla Alfonsina. Boletin†
0576-7172 Carbohydrate Chemistry *changed to* Carbohydrate Chemistry. Part 1: Mono-Di-Tri-saccharides & Their Derivatives.
0576-7172 Carbohydrate Chemistry *changed to* Carbohydrate Chemistry. Part 2: Macromolecules.
0576-7296 Career Index *see* 0276-0355

0576-7547 Caribbean Congress of Labour. Report
0576-7598 Caribbean Monthly Bulletin
0576-7954 Carnegie Quarterly
0576-808X Carolina Comments
0576-8519 Casa, Arredamento e Giardino *changed to* Casa & Giardino.
0576-8861 Catalogo Bolaffi d'Arte Moderna *changed to* Catalogo dell'Arte Moderna Italiana.
0576-8888 Catalogo Bolaffi del Cacciatore e delle Armi†
0576-8942 Catalogo de Filmes Brasileiros *changed to* Brasil Cinema.
0576-9280 Catgut Acoustical Society Newsletter *see* 1053-7694
0576-9787 Cellulose Chemistry and Technology
0576-9922 C R I Abstracts
0577-0335 C E N T O Newsletter†
0577-036X Central Africa Historical Association. Local Series Pamphlets *changed to* Historical Association of Zimbabwe. Local Series Pamphlets.
0577-0653 Central Bank of Malta. Annual Report
0577-084X Central Marine Fisheries Research Institute. Bulletin
0577-1056 C E B E D E A U. Tribune *changed to* Tribune d'Eau.
0577-1331 Centre d'Etudes Ethnologiques. Publications *changed to* Centre d'Etudes Ethnologiques Bandundu. Publications.
0577-1730 Centre International d'Etude des Problems Humains. Bulletins
0577-1765 Universite Catholique de Louvain. Centre International de Dialectologie Generale. Travaux
0577-179X Centre Interuniversitaire d'Histoire Contemporaine. Cahiers
0577-1935 Centrepoint
0577-2168 Centro Camuno di Studi Preistorici. Bollettino
0577-2176 Centro Camuno di Studi Preistorici. Publicazioni†
0577-2451 Centro de Estudios Monetarios Latinoamericanos. Ensayos
0577-2907 Centro Interamericano de Investigacion y Documentacion sobre Formacion Profesional. Boletin
0577-2915 C I N T E R F O R - Documentacion
0577-2931 C I N T E R F O R Estudios y Monografias
0577-3334 Ceramica de Cultura Maya†
0577-3490 Ceska Bibliografie
0577-3725 Sbornik Historicky
0577-4691 Ceylon Historical Journal
0577-4772 Ceylon Rationalist Ambassador
0577-5000 Annuaire Statistique du Tchad
0577-5132 Challenge (Armonk)
0577-5183 Analysis of Workmen's Compensation Laws *see* 0191-118X
0577-5574 Charioteer
0577-571X Capital Investments of the World Petroleum Industry
0577-5728 Chase's Calendar of Annual Events *see* 0740-5286
0577-5825 Nongcun Kexue Shiyan
0577-6619 Qixiang Xuebao
0577-6686 Jixie Gongcheng Xuebao
0577-6848 Chiba University. Faculty of Engineering. Journal
0577-7240 Chicago Linguistic Society. Papers from the Regional Meetings
0577-7259 Chicago Mercantile Exchange Yearbook†
0577-7496 Zhiwu Xuebao
0577-750X Plant Protection Bulletin (Taiwan)
0577-781X Children's Books in Print
0577-800X Chile. Instituto Nacional de Estadisticas. Sintesis Estadistica *changed to* Chile. Instituto Nacional de Estadisticas. Informativo Estadistico.
0577-8131 Chile. Servicio de Impuestos Internos. Memoria†
0577-8832 China Informatie *see* 0920-203X
0577-893X China's Screen *changed to* China Screen.
0577-8948 China Sports
0577-9065 Chinese Historical Society of America. Bulletin
0577-9081 Chinese Journal of Physics†
0577-9154 Jingji Yanjiu
0577-9235 Ch'ing-shih Wen-t'i *see* 0884-3236
0577-9294 Chip Chats
0577-9316 Malacological Society of Japan. Newsletter *changed to* Chiribotan.
0577-9774 Chosen Gakujutsu Tsuho
0578-0152 Christian Science Monitor. Cumulated Index *see* 0893-245X
0578-0160 Christiana Albertina
0578-0594 Chrzescijanskie Stowarzyszenie Spoleczne. Information Bulletin
0578-0608 Qu Yi
0578-0659 Juben
0578-1485 Zhongguo Jinrong
0578-1736 Chinese Agricultural Chemical Society. Journal
0578-1752 Zhongguo Nongye Kexue
0578-1949 Zhongguo Yuwen
0578-2228 Chuo Daigaku Rikogakubu Kiyo
0578-3097 Circle K Magazine *see* 0745-1962
0578-3224 Cistercian Studies Quarterly
0578-3283 Citizen (Jackson)†
0578-3364 Citizens Conference on State Legislatures. Research Memorandum†
0578-3747 Civil Engineering in Japan
0578-3917 Civilisation Malgache
0578-4131 Clanky v Slovenskych Casopisoch *changed to* Slovenska Narodna Bibliografia. Rozpisovy Rad Clanky.
0578-4182 Claretianum
0578-4247 Clark University (Worcester, Mass.) Dissertations and Theses *changed to* Clark University Bulletin (Worcester, Mass.).
0578-4565 Classification Society Bulletin†
0578-4573 Classified Bibliography on Graph Theory†
0578-5294 Clothing Institute Journal *see* 0263-1008
0578-5464 Studia Universitatis "Babes-Bolyai". Iurisprudentia
0578-5472 Studia Universitatis "Babes-Bolyai." Oeconomica.
0578-5480 Studia Universitatis "Babes-Bolyai". Philosophia
0578-5502 Studia Universitatis Babes-Bolyai. Psychologia-Pedagogia *see* 0578-5480
0578-5634 Coastal Engineering in Japan
0578-5677 Coastal Research Notes *see* 0271-5376
0578-6371 University of Iowa. Center for Labor and Management. Research Series.†
0578-6533 Iowa Advocate
0578-655X Iowa Archeological Society. Newsletter
0578-6959 Iran. Ministry of Economy. Report on Commencement and Operation Permits for Industrial Establishments
0578-6967 Iran
0578-7483 Irish Journal of Agricultural Research *changed to* Irish Journal of Agricultural and Food Research.
0578-8056 Islamic Education
0578-8072 Islamic Studies
0578-8250 Israel. Department of Customs and Excise. Yalkut *changed to* Israel. Department of Customs and V A T. Yalkut.
0578-8420 Israel. Central Bureau of Statistics. Industry and Crafts Survey
0578-9230 Israel Academy of Sciences and Humanities. Section of Humanities. Proceedings
0578-9427 Israels Aussenhandel
0578-9761 Sarkiyat Mecmuasi
0578-9923 Istituto Italiano di Numismatica. Annali
0578-9931 Istituto Italiano per gli Studi Storici. Annali
0579-174X Itogi Nauki: Stratigrafiya. Paleontologiya *changed to* Itogi Nauki i Tekhniki: Stratigrafiya, Paleontologiya.
0579-1766 Itogi Nauki: Tekhnologiya Organicheskikh Veshchestv *see* 0303-2361
0579-2290 Al Ittihad†
0579-2428 Max-Planck-Institut fuer Europaische Rechtsgeschichte. Veroeffentlichungen. Ius Commune
0579-2983 Izvestiya Vysshikh Uchebnykh Zavedenii. Seriya Energetika
0579-3068 Ibaraki University. Faculty of Science. Bulletin. Series A: Mathematics
0579-3238 India. Department of Labour and Employment. Annual Report *changed to* India. Ministry of Labour. Annual Report.
0579-3599 Instituto Argentino de Ciencias Genealogicas. Boletin Interno
0579-3718 Sociedad Interamericana de Planificacion. Correo Informativo *changed to* Revista Interamericana de Planificacion. Correo Informativo.
0579-3742 International Association for Mass Communications Research. Letter from the President *see* 0925-7950
0579-3769 International Conference of Building Officials. Code Changes Committee. Annual Report
0579-3866 International Federation of Catholic Universities. General Assembly. Report
0579-3912 International Organization for Medical Cooperation. General Assembly. Report *changed to* International Organization for Cooperation in Health Care. General Assembly. Report.
0579-3920 International Pacific Halibut Commission (U S and Canada). Technical Reports
0579-4005 Introduktsiya ta Akklimatyzatsiya Rozlyn na Ukrayini *see* 0235-0904
0579-4234 I E E E International Symposium on Circuit Theory. Symposium Digest. Summaries of Papers *see* 0277-674X
0579-4374 Immigration History Newsletter
0579-4757 Indian Agricultural Index†
0579-5109 Institut Maurice Thorez. Conferences†
0579-5192 Instituto Latinoamericano de Mercadeo Agricola. Actividades del I L M A†
0579-5206 Instituto Latinoamericano de Mercadeo Agricola. Informes Sobre Comercializacion†
0579-5214 Instituto Latinoamericano de Mercadeo Agricola. Sistemas de Mercadeo de Productos Agricolas en Medellin†
0579-529X Insurance Stock Review *see* 0736-0126
0579-5362 International Association of Volcanology and Chemistry of the Earth's Interior. Newsletter†
0579-5400 International Cellular Plastics Conference. Proceedings†
0579-5427 I C I D Bulletin
0579-5486 Management Datamatics *see* 0378-7206
0579-5567 International Police Association. Meeting of the International Executive Council†
0579-5613 I S O Information *changed to* Organ Building Periodical.
0579-5621 U.I.A.M.S. Bulletin Trimestriel
0579-6059 Index to the Science Fiction Magazines *changed to* N E S F A Index to Short Science Fiction.
0579-6105 India. Ministry of Education and Social Welfare. Provisional Statistics of Education in the States
0579-6407 Ingenieur Digest *changed to* Innovation.
0579-6695 Inter American Press Association. Committee on Freedom on the Press. Report
0579-6733 International Association of Hydrogeologists. Memoires
0579-6881 International Police Association. Travel Scholarships†
0579-6903 I P T C Newsletter *changed to* I P T C News.
0579-692X International Union of Official Travel Organizations. Technical Bulletin *changed to* World Tourism Organization. Collection of Technical Bulletins.
0579-6938 Internationaler Weltkongress der U F O-Forscher. Dokumentarbericht
0579-7152 Acta Biologica Iugoslavica. Serija E: Ichthyologia
0579-7195 University of Ife. Faculty of Agriculture. Annual Research Report *changed to* Ife Journal of Agriculture.
0579-7772 Universitaet Innsbruck. Medizinische Fakultaet. Arbeiten
0579-7780 Universitaet Innsbruck. Theologische Fakultaet. Studien und Arbeiten
0579-7918 International Institute for the Unification of Private Law. Rapport sur l'Activite de l'Institute†
0579-7926 Tunisia. Institut National Scientifique et Technique d'Oceanographie et de Peche. Bulletin
0579-8108 International Conference on World Politics. Conference Papers
0579-8299 International Union of Food and Allied Workers' Associations. Meeting of the Executive Committee. I. Documents of the Secretariat. II. Summary Report
0579-8302 International Union of Food and Allied Workers' Associations. Tobacco Workers' Trade Group Board. Meeting†
0579-8337 Inter-Parliamentary Union. Series: "Reports and Documents"
0579-8353 Intervalle
0579-8388 Inventor
0579-9406 Moskovskii Universitet. Vestnik. Seriya 4: Geologiya
0579-9422 Moskovskii Universitet. Vestnik. Seriya 6: Biologiya, Pochvovedenie
0580-0412 Motion Picture, T V & Theatre Directory
0580-0420 Motive†
0580-0714 Mountain-Plains in Books *see* 0145-6180
0580-0943 Mowia Wieki
0580-1400 Muenchener Theologische Zeitschrift
0580-1540 Westfaelische Wilhelms-Universitaet Muenster. Slavisch-Baltisches Seminar†
0580-1737 Multiple Sclerosis Abstracts *see* 0360-0017
0580-2652 Museums Calendar *see* 0307-7675
0580-289X Music Library Association. Newsletter
0580-2954 Musica Britannica
0580-308X Musical America Annual Directory Issue *see* 0735-7788
0580-3403 Musteranlagen der Energiewirtschaft
0580-3713 Muzica
0580-373X Muzikoloski Zbornik
0580-3896 Myotis
0580-4396 Mysore Orientalist
0580-4485 Minoseg es Megbizhatosag
0580-468X Universidad Complutense de Madrid. Departamento de Botanica y Fisiologia Vegetal. Trabajos *see* 0214-4565
0580-4787 Magyar Tudomanyos Akademia Fold-es Banyaszati Tudomanyok Osztalyanak Kozlemenyei†
0580-4795 Gazdasag es Jogtudomany *see* 0231-2522
0580-4981 Makedonska Akademija na Naukite i Umetnostite. Letopis
0580-535X Agassiz Center for Water Studies. Research Report
0580-6712 Universidad de Murcia. Monteagudo
0580-6755 M I M S Medical Specialities
0580-7247 M L O
0580-7727 Massachusetts. Division of Employment Security. Quarterly Survey of Unfilled Job Openings - Boston *changed to* Massachusetts. Division of Employment Security. Survey of Unfilled Job Openings - Boston.
0580-8162 Modern Photography Annual†

ISSN

0580-8421 M D†
0580-8537 Reporter
0580-8650 Universidad de Madrid. Seminario de Metafisica. Anales
0580-8898 Manager and Entrepreneur†
0580-9320 Medicina Termale e Climatologia
0580-9746 Michigan State University. Institute of Water Research. Technical Reports
0581-0000 Mineral Statistics of India
0581-0086 Minnesota Genealogist
0581-0205 M L A Newsletter *see* 0884-2205
0581-0558 Musicologica Slovaca
0581-0833 Makedonska Akademija na Naukite i Umetnostite. Oddelenie za Prirodno-Matematicki Nauki. Prilozi. *see* 0351-3246
0581-0892 Malawi Housing Corporation. Annual Report and Accounts
0581-0906 Malawi. National Library. Annual Report *changed to* Malawi. National Library Service Board. Annual Report.
0581-1023 Marketing
0581-1058 Marxist Miscellany†
0581-1155 Mathematical Chronicle *changed to* New Zealand Journal of Mathematics.
0581-1538 Acta Biologica Iugoslavica. Serija B: Mikrobiologija
0581-2011 Mujeres
0581-2739 Safety†
0581-2801 Saga Daigaku Nogakubu Iho
0581-295X Saguenayensia
0581-2984 Sahifat al-Takhtit al-Tarbawi fi al-Bilad al-Arabiyah
0581-3018 Sahitya Sahakar†
0581-3115 Sailboat Directory *see* 0148-8732
0581-3263 Information Veterinaire†
0581-3298 Saint Lawrence Seaway Authority. Annual Report
0581-3441 St. Mary's Law Journal
0581-3662 Saitama Daigaku Kiyo. Shizen Kagaku Hen
0581-3808 Universidad de Salamanca. Seminario de Derecho Politico. Boletin Informativo†
0581-3999 Salt Research & Industry *changed to* Salt Inorganic and Bio-inorganic Chemistry.
0581-4111 El Salvador. Ministerio de Planificacion y Coordinacion del Desarrollo Economico y Social. Indicadores Economicos y Sociales
0581-4448 Sami Aellin†
0581-4480 Samiske Samlinger
0581-4758 Sanskriti
0581-4766 Samuel H. Kress Foundation. Annual Report
0581-4790 Samvadadhvam
0581-5207 Universidad Autonoma de San Luis Potosi. Instituto de Geologia. Folleto Tecnico
0581-572X Sankhya. Series A
0581-5738 Sankhya. Series B
0581-5908 Sericultural Experiment Station. Annual Report†
0581-6076 Universidade Federal de Santa Catarina. Museu de Antropologia. Anais
0581-6106 Santa Clara Lawyer *see* 0146-0315
0581-6866 Universidade de Sao Paulo. Faculdade de Odontologia. Revista *changed to* Universidade de Sao Paulo. Revista de Odontologia.
0581-7501 Zemaljski Muzej Bosne i Hercegovine. Glasnik. Arheologija
0581-751X Zemaljski Muzej Bosne i Hercegovine. Glasnik. Etnologija
0581-7528 Zemaljski Muzej Bosne i Hercegovine. Glasnik. Prirodne Nauke
0581-8079 Travel on Saskatchewan Highways
0581-8109 Saskatchewan. Department of Mineral Resources. Annual Report *changed to* Saskatchewan Energy & Mines. Annual Report.
0581-8389 Saskatchewan Fur Marketing Service. Annual Report
0581-8435 Saskatchewan Municipal Directory
0581-8443 Saskatchewan Natural History Society Newsletter *changed to* Blue Jay News.
0581-8532 Satapitaka. Indo-Asian Literatures
0581-8672 Saudi Arabian Monetary Agency. Statistical Summary
0581-8761 Savings and Loan Fact Book *changed to* Savings and Loan Yearbook.
0581-8761 Savings and Loan Fact Book *changed to* Savings Institutions Sourcebook.
0581-8850 Savremena Poljoprivreda
0581-9172 Sbornik Geologickych Ved: Geologie
0581-9180 Sbornik Geologickych Ved: Loziskova Geologie, Mineralogie
0581-9423 Scandinavian Building Research†
0581-9792 A D A C Handbuch: Schmerzensgeld-Betraege
0581-9911 School Activities and the Library†
0582-0421 Beitraege zur Politischen Wissenschaft†
0582-138X Schrifttumnachweis Bau-, Wohnungs- und Siedlungswesen†
0582-1487 Schwann Artist Issue *see* 0893-7486
0582-1592 Societe Suisse des Americanistes. Bulletin
0582-1673 Biblische Beitraege
0582-2343 Scientia Agriculturae Bohemoslovaca
0582-2351 Scientia Paedagogica Experimentalis
0582-2637 Scissortail
0582-3226 Scripta Instituti Donneriani Aboensis
0582-3234 Scripta Islandica
0582-3250 Scripta Scientifica Medica
0582-3471 Sea Chest
0582-3692 Secondary Education *see* 0013-1482
0582-3978 Segnalazioni Assofarma
0582-4001 Seguridad Social
0582-4192 Seikei Ronso - Faculty of Politics, Law and Economics. Journal *see* 0288-6340
0582-4206 Japan Society of Precision Engineering. Bulletin *see* 0916-782X
0582-4524 Seiyo Kotengaku Kenkyu
0582-4532 Sekai
0582-4656 Japan Petroleum Institute. Bulletin
0582-4761 Selbstbedienung und Supermarkt *see* 0722-6950
0582-4788 Selden Society, London. Supplementary Series
0582-4877 Selecta
0582-5164 Sel'skaya Nov'
0582-6152 Seminario de Filologia Vasca Julio de Urquijo. Anuario
0582-6314 Seminarium
0582-6802 Seoul Journal of Medicine
0582-7094 Cerro Tololo Interamerican Observatory (La Serena, Chile). Contributions†
0582-8198 Astrometriya i Astrofizika†
0582-8759 Sestante†
0582-8929 Universidad de Sevilla. Instituto Garcia Oviedo. Publicaciones
0582-9348 Shaker Quarterly
0582-9399 Shakespeare Studies
0582-9402 Shakespeare Studies
0582-9542 Shanghai Wenxue
0582-9836 Shamativ
0582-9860 Victorious
0582-9879 Shengwu Huaxue yu Shengwu Wuli Xuebao
0582-9887 Shepard's Law Review Citations
0582-9909 Shepard's United States Administrative Citations
0582-9917 Shepard's United States Patents and Trademarks Citations
0583-0176 Shijie Zhishi
0583-0206 Shijie Wenxue
0583-0214 Shixue Yuekan
0583-0230 Shikan
0583-0362 Shimane Law Review
0583-0516 Japanese Journal of Medical Mycology
0583-063X Shinshu University. Faculty of Science. Journal
0583-0648 Shinshu University. Faculty of Textile Science and Technology. Journal. Series A: Biology
0583-0664 Shinshu University. Faculty of Textile Science and Technology. Journal. Series D: Arts
0583-0923 Shizuoka University. Faculty of Science. Reports
0583-1024 The Shock and Vibration Digest
0583-1164 Food, Its Science and Technology
0583-1180 Shoni Igaku
0583-1288 Shou Huo
0583-1296 Shout
0583-1431 Shuxue Xuebao
0583-1776 Siberian Husky Club of America Newsletter
0583-1881 Side Effects of Drugs Annual
0583-2268 Sierra Leone. Library Board. Report
0583-239X Sierra Leone Geographical Journal
0583-2594 Signpost for Northwest Hikers *see* 8750-1600
0583-3132 Silvicultura Em Sao Paulo†
0583-3655 Singapore Yearbook of Statistics
0583-421X Korean Journal of Botany
0583-4279 Sino-British Trade Review *changed to* China - Britain Trade Review.
0583-4449 Siskiyou Pioneer and Yearbook
0583-4570 Sixties *changed to* Eighties.
0583-4597 Al-Siassa al-Dawlya
0583-4961 Institut za Nacionalna Istorija, Skopje. Glasnik
0583-5356 Universitatis Debreceniensis de Ludovico Kossuth Nominatae. Instituti Philologiae Slavicae. Annales. Slavica
0583-5429 Slavistische Beitraege
0583-5445 Slavistische Studienbuecher. Neue Folge
0583-5623 Slovakia
0583-564X Slovanske Studie
0583-6050 Acta Carsologica
0583-6263 Slovo na Storozhi
0583-7065 Social Work Forum
0583-712X Denmark. Socialforskningsinstitutt. Publikation†
0583-7405 Societat d'Historia Natural de Balears. Bolleti
0583-7480 Sociedad Espanola de Historia de la Medicina. Boletin
0583-7693 Sociedad Quimica de Mexico. Revista
0583-7731 Sociedad Venezolana de Espeleologia. Boletin
0583-774X Guacharo
0583-7774 Sociedad Venezolana de Planificacion. Cuadernos
0583-8045 Limba si Literatura
0583-8177 Societe Botanique de Geneve. Travaux *see* 0373-2525
0583-8193 Societe d'Archeologie et d'Histoire de la Manche. Departement de la Manche. Revue.
0583-8266 Societe d'Histoire de la Guadeloupe. Bulletin
0583-8452 Societe des Amis de Marcel Proust et des Amis de Combray. Bulletin
0583-8894 Analytical Sciences Monographs†
0583-8975 S C E H Newsletter
0583-9009 Society for Developmental Biology. Symposium
0583-9181 Society for the Preservation of Long Island Antiquities. Newsletter
0583-9246 Water Treatment and Examination†
0583-9270 S.A.W.E. Journal *changed to* Weight Engineering.
0583-9750 Sociologia
0584-0007 Narodna Biblioteka Kiril i Metodii. Izvestiya
0584-0252 Sofiiski Universitet. Fakultet po Zapadni Filologii. Godisnik *changed to* Sofiiski Universitet. Fakultet po Klasiceski i Novi Filologii. Godisnik.
0584-0651 Solar Energy Progress in Australia and New Zealand†
0584-0821 O Solo
0584-1070 Something
0584-1739 Textile Information Sources and Resources†
0584-195X South Africa. Department of Statistics. Road Traffic Accidents *changed to* South Africa. Central Statistical Service. Road Traffic Collisions.
0584-2166 South Africa. Department of Coloured Relations and Rehoboth Affairs. Annual Report†
0584-2352 South Africa. Geological Survey. Annals *changed to* South Africa. Geological Survey. Annual Technical Report.
0584-2360 Bibliography and Subject Index of South African Geology
0584-3073 South African Reserve Bank. Monthly Release of Money and Banking Statistics
0584-3170 South Asian Studies
0584-3219 Quarterly Geological Notes
0584-4088 Southeast Asia Treaty Organization. Secretary General. S E A T O Report†
0584-4118 S E C A C Review and Newsletter *changed to* Southeastern College Art Conference Review.
0584-4266 S E W R P C Newsletter
0584-455X American Office Dealer†
0584-4738 Southern Theatre
0584-5025 S M R C Newsletter
0584-6374 Instituto de Estudios Madrilenos. Anales
0584-6544 Spain. Direccion General de Aduanas. Informe Mensual sobre el Comercio Exterior
0584-7109 Documentacion Iberoamericana
0584-8016 Span
0584-8024 Span (Slough)†
0584-8067 Spanner (London, 1974)
0584-8539 Spectrochimica Acta. Part A: Molecular Spectroscopy
0584-8547 Spectrochimica Acta. Part B: Atomic Spectroscopy
0584-8555 Spectroscopic Properties of Inorganic & Organometallic Compounds
0584-8652 Speculum Juris
0584-9217 Sport Parachutist
0584-9365 Spotlight on Africa
0584-9667 Springs
0585-0282 Stal' in English *see* 0038-9218
0585-0428 Newspaper Circulation Analysis *changed to* Circulation 91.
0585-0444 Standard Trade Index of Japan
0585-0576 Stanford Lawyer
0585-086X Stapp Car Crash Conference Proceedings
0585-0967 Stat a Pravo
0585-0991 State Bank of India. Report of the Central Board of Directors *changed to* State Bank of India. Annual Report.
0585-1009 State Bank of Pakistan. Export Receipts
0585-1173 State Directory of Kentucky
0585-1289 State of South Africa†
0585-1432 Statistical Compendium of the Americas†
0585-1580 Statistical Office of the European Communities. Quarterly Bulletin of Energy Statistics. *changed to* Statistical Office of the European Communities. Energy Statistics Monthly Bulletin.
0585-1777 Statistical Pocket Book of Ceylon *changed to* Statistical Pocket Book of the Democratic Socialist Republic of Sri Lanka.
0585-1815 Statistical Pocket-Book of Yugoslavia
0585-1920 Statisticki Godisnjak Jugoslavije
0585-198X Statistics Sources
0585-2471 Stephen Wilson Annual Pharmacy Seminar. Report†
0585-2544 Stereophile
0585-2730 Great Britain. Warren Spring Laboratory. Investigation of Air Pollution: National Survey, Smoke and Sulphur Dioxide *changed to* Great Britain. Warren Spring Laboratory. U K Smoke and Sulphur Dioxide Monitoring Networks.
0585-3214 Medelhavsmuseet. Bulletin
0585-3273 Studia Missionalia Upsaliensia†
0585-3400 Sweden. Statens Raad foer Byggnadsforskning. Informationsblad†
0585-3680 The Brown Chart. Provincial Results

ISSN INDEX 5761

0585-3923 Straits Times Annual *changed to* Times Annual.
0585-3931 Straits Times Directory of Malaysia and Singapore *changed to* N S T Directory of Malaysia.
0585-3931 Straits Times Directory of Malaysia and Singapore *see* 0217-6009
0585-4172 Stredocesky Sbornik Historicky†
0585-4393 Struktura i Rol' Vody v Zhivom Organizme *changed to* Molekulyarnaya Fizika i Biofizika Vodnykh Sistem.
0585-4555 Student Aid Annual *changed to* Chronicle Financial Aid Guide.
0585-4768 Studi di Letteratura Francese
0585-4911 Studi Genuensi
0585-492X Studi Ispanici
0585-5098 Studia Entomologica†
0585-5462 Studia Philologica Jyvaskylaensia
0585-5543 Studia Slovenica
0585-5578 Studia Sumiro-Hungarica
0585-5721 Studiecentrum voor Jeugdmisdadigheid. Publikatie†
0585-5853 Studien zu den Bogazkoey-Texten
0585-6094 Studien zur Japanologie
0585-6175 Studien zur Publizistik. Bremer Reihe *changed to* Deutsche Presseforschung.
0585-6515 Studies in Anglesey History
0585-6523 Studies in Anthropological Method†
0585-6833 Studies in Judaica†
0585-6884 Studies in Managerial Economics†
0585-6914 Studies in Medieval and Reformation Thought
0585-6965 Studies in Philosophy & the History of Philosophy
0585-7023 Studies in Pre-Columbian Art and Archaeology
0585-7031 Studies in Public Communication†
0585-718X Studies in Speleology
0585-7260 Studies in the History of Religions *see* 0169-8834
0585-7325 Studies of Broadcasting
0585-7449 Studies on the Left *see* 0161-1801
0585-749X Studii si Articole de Istorie
0585-7694 Study Centre for Yugoslav Affairs. Review†
0585-7856 Universitaet Stuttgart. Institut fuer Geologie und Palaeontologie Arbeiten Neue Folge
0585-8127 National University of Singapore. Economics and Statistics Society. Journal *changed to* National University of Singapore. Economics & Statistics Society. Annual Journal - Suara Ekonomi.
0585-8364 Sucasnist
0585-8488 Sudan. Department of Statistics. Foreign Trade Statistics
0585-8631 Sudan Law Journal and Reports
0585-9328 Sunday School Senior Adults
0585-9581 Suomen Obligaatiorkirja *see* 0781-4437
0585-9794 Supreme Court Monthly Review
0585-9840 Surfaces (Paris)
0585-9980 Surrey Archaeological Society. Bulletin
0586-0431 Svensk Tidskriftsfoerteckning
0586-0709 Svenskt Musikhistoriskt Arkiv. Bulletin
0586-1179 Swasth Hind
0586-1357 Swaziland. Central Statistical Office. Annual Statistical Bulletin
0586-1691 Sweden. Sjukvaardens och Socialvaardens Planerings- och Rationaliseringsinstitut. S P R I Rapport
0586-1926 Sweden. Televerket. Annual Report *changed to* Swedish Telecom. Annual Report.
0586-2000 Swedish Archaeological Bibliography *changed to* Swedish Archaeology.
0586-3031 U S Symposium on Rock Mechanics. Proceedings
0586-3260 Synteza *changed to* Ekonomika Prace.
0586-3414 Syracuse University. Program of East African Studies. East African Bibliographic Series†
0586-3422 Syracuse University. Program of East African Studies. Occasional Bibliographies†
0586-3430 Syracuse University. Program of East African Studies. Occasional Papers†
0586-3708 Acta Universitatis de Attila Jozsef Nominatae. Acta Historiae Litterarum Hungaricarum
0586-3724 Acta Universitatis Szegediensis. Sectio Philosophica *see* 0231-2670
0586-3732 Acta Universitatis Szegediensis de Attila Jozsef Nominatae. Dissertationes Slavicae *changed to* Acta Universitatis Szegediensis de Attila Jozsef Nominatae. Dissertationes Slavicae. Sectio Linguistica.
0586-3732 Acta Universitatis Szegediensis de Attila Jozsef Nominatae. Dissertationes Slavicae *changed to* Acta Universitatis Szegediensis de Attila Jozsef Nominatae. Dissertationes Slavicae. Sectio Historiae Litterarum.
0586-3783 Szep Versek
0586-4496 Sieg's Moentkatalog. Danmark (Year)
0586-4534 Sinteticheskie Almazy *see* 0203-3119
0586-4607 Slovak Academy of Sciences. Geophysical Institute. Contributions
0586-4925 Statistical Office of the European Communities. Foreign Trade: Analytical Tables *changed to* Statistical Office of the European Communities. External Trade. Analytical Tables: Import - Export.
0586-4941 University of Stellenbosch. Bureau for Economic Research. Building and Construction
0586-500X Strictly Wholesaling†
0586-5050 Studies in Accounting Research
0586-5107 Studies in Urban Geography†
0586-5344 Sadakichi Hartmann Newsletter†
0586-5360 Saga och Sed
0586-5395 Saisons de la Danse
0586-5581 Scanning Electron Microscopy *see* 0891-7035
0586-5751 Scientific Directory of Hong Kong†
0586-6235 Social Studies Professional
0586-6766 Sweden. Statens Raad foer Byggnadsforskning. Document
0586-6928 Studies in Language and Linguistics†
0586-7282 Salt Lake City Messenger
0586-7606 Schema et Schematisation *see* 0982-6548
0586-7614 Schizophrenia Bulletin
0586-7746 Scientific and Technical Societies of Canada
0586-8440 Forest Products Research Institute. Annual Report
0586-8491 Southern Wholesalers' Guide *changed to* National Hardware Wholesalers' Guide.
0586-9145 Symposia Otorhinolaryngologica Iugoslavica
0586-965X Schulreport
0586-9668 Science and Archaeology
0586-9781 S A L A L M Bibliography Series *changed to* S A L A L M Bibliography and Reference Series.
0586-9889 Serie Vie Locale
0586-9919 Universidad Hispalense. Anales. Serie: Medicina *changed to* Universidad de Sevilla. Serie: Medicina.
0586-9943 Shimane Daigaku Kyoikugakubu Kiyo. Shizen Kagaku
0587-0054 Sineast
0587-0631 Southeast Asia Treaty Organization. Secretary General. Record of Progress *see* 0584-4088
0587-1131 Storia dell'Arte
0587-1514 Szamitastechnika
0587-1689 Arbeitsmarkt Politik
0587-1719 Archaeological Society of New Mexico. Papers
0587-1948 Association for Institutional Research. Annual Forum on Institutional Research. Proceedings *changed to* A I R.
0587-1956 A R S C Bulletin *see* 0004-5438
0587-2006 Journalists' International Association for Studying Problems of Overseas Peoples. Annuaire†
0587-2138 Australasian Tax Reports
0587-2871 American Animal Hospital Association Journal
0587-2936 American Bar Association. Section of Local Government Law. Committee Reports.†
0587-3053 A N A in Action *see* 0098-1486
0587-3452 Arch Plus
0587-3460 Archaeographie†
0587-3533 Arkansas Archeological Survey. Publications on Archeology. Popular Series
0587-3584 Art - Language
0587-3606 Asia Foundation. President's Review *changed to* Asia Foundation. Annual Report.
0587-3746 Assure Social
0587-3908 Australian Orthodontic Journal
0587-4076 Aarbok for Telemark
0587-4246 Acta Physica Polonica. Series A: General Physics, Physics of Condensed Matter, Optics and Quantum Electronics, Atomic and Molecular Physics, Applied Physics
0587-4254 Acta Physica Polonica. Series B: Elementary Particle Physics, Nuclear Physics, Theory of Relativity, Field Theory
0587-4300 Actualidad Pastoral
0587-4394 Advances in Metabolic Disorders. Supplements *see* 0065-2903
0587-4793 All India Architects Directory *see* 0256-4017
0587-503X American Peanut Research and Education Association. Journal *see* 0197-8748
0587-5196 Anuario del Cuento Costarricense†
0587-5234 Angewandte Sozialforschung
0587-5277 Archiv der Deutschen Jugendbewegung. Jahrbuch
0587-5447 Arte y Arqueologia
0587-5455 Arti Musices
0587-5471 Asian Pacific Congress of Cardiology. Symposia
0587-5560 Bulletin de l'ANECLA†
0587-565X Astronomie und Raumfahrt†
0587-5757 Australia. Bureau of Statistics. Divorces (Canberra) *see* 1031-2188
0587-5846 Australian Conservation Foundation. Annual Report
0587-5943 Pesticide Residues in Food
0587-5994 Coexistence
0587-6435 Colecao de Estudos Filologicos
0588-2583 Collectionneur Francais
0588-2990 Colleges Classified†
0588-3237 Australian & New Zealand Society for Theological Studies. Colloquium
0588-3253 Colloquium Geographicum
0588-4462 Colorado Fisheries Research Review†
0588-4543 Colorado. State Department of Public Health. Annual Progress Report. State Migrant Plan for Public Health Services†
0588-5094 Colour Society. Journal
0588-621X Comite International des Poids et Mesures. Comite Consultatif de Photometrie. (Rapport et Annexes) *changed to* Comite International des Poids et Mesures. Comite Consultatif de Photometrie et Radiometrie. (Rapport et Annexes).
0588-6228 Comite International des Poids et Mesures. Comite Consultatif pour la Definition de la Seconde. (Rapport et Annexes)
0588-6244 Comite International des Poids et Mesures. Comite Consultatif pour les Etalons des Mesure des Radiations Ionisantes (Rapport et Annexes) *see* 0255-3147
0588-6414 Commentationes Balticae†
0588-649X Euromarket News†
0588-6694 Commercial Bank of Ethiopia. Annual Report
0588-6783 Commission for Technical Co-Operation in Africa. Joint Project†
0588-6953 Commission of the European Communities. Expose Annuel sur les Activities d'Orientation Professionnelle dans la Communaute†
0588-702X Mines Safety and Health Commission. Report
0588-7356 C O R D News *see* 0149-7677
0588-7445 Common Market Law Reports
0588-7712 Abstracts of Papers on Geology of the United Kingdom *changed to* Abstracts of Current Information on Geology and Mineral Resources.
0588-7720 Commonwealth Geological Liaison Office. Liaison Report†
0588-7739 Commonwealth Geological Liaison Office. Newsletter *changed to* Earth Sciences Programme Newsletter.
0588-7755 Commonwealth Geological Liaison Office. Report (on) Resources of the British Commonwealth†
0588-7933 Commonwealth Trade†
0588-8018 Communications
0588-8093 Communicator†
0588-8360 Community
0588-8611 Easter Commemoration Digest†
0588-9049 Comparative Education Society in Europe. Proceedings of the General Meeting *changed to* Aims of Education and Development of Personality. Comparative Aspects. Proceedings of the CESE Conference.
0588-912X Compendio Estadistico Centroamericano†
0588-9278 Comprehensive Education
0588-9405 Computer Programs for Chemistry†
0588-9545 Comunicaciones - Revista Tecnica†
0588-9804 C O N C I L I U M
0588-9979 Confederacao Nacional do Comercio. Divisao de Divulgacao. Carta Mensal *see* 0101-4315
0589-1019 Alliance for Engineering in Medicine and Biology. Proceedings of the Annual Conference
0589-2813 Congreso Latinamericano de Siderurgia. Memoria Tecnica
0589-3267 Congresso Europeo di Storia Ospitaliera. Atti
0589-3305 Congresso Latinoamericano de Hidraulica (Papers)
0589-3496 Connaissance de l'Orient. Collection Unesco d'Oeuvres Representatives
0589-400X Connecticut Water Resources Bulletin
0589-4069 Conscientia
0589-4301 Consejo Superior Universitario Centroamericano. Actas de la Reunion Ordinaria
0589-4360 Consejo Superior Universitario Centroamericano. Publicaciones†
0589-4522 Conservative Journal
0589-4735 Construction-Amenagement
0589-4859 Consultants and Consulting Organizations *see* 0196-1292
0589-4867 Consultation on Church. Digest *changed to* Consultation on Church Union. Digest.
0589-5065 Contact Lens Society of America Journal *see* 0096-2716
0589-5081 Contacto
0589-5286 Contemporary Music Newsletter†
0589-574X Contrast *changed to* New Contrast.
0589-6355 Cooperative Housing Journal
0589-6665 Denmark. Statens Byggeforskningsinstitut. Landbrugsbyggeri†
0589-6681 University of Copenhagen. Institute of Phonetics. Annual Report

ISSN

5762 ISSN INDEX

0589-686X Corax
0589-7300 Cornell University. Modern Indonesia Project Publications. Monographs, Translations, Bibliographies, Interim Reports
0589-7351 Cornell University. Library. Wason Collection. Southeast Asia Accessions List *changed to* Cornell University. Library. John M. Echols Collection on Southeast Asia. Accessions List.
0589-7688 Ecuador. Comision de Valores. Corporacion Financiera Nacional. Memoria *changed to* Ecuador. Corporacion Financiera Nacional. Memoria.
0589-7742 Corporacion Nacional de Fertilizantes. Memoria Anual
0589-7920 Corporate Report Fact Book
0589-8056 Corpus Hispanorum de Pace
0589-8218 Correctional Psychologist *see* 0093-8548
0589-8366 Corriere Africano
0589-8447 Cosmetic World
0589-8544 Costa Rica. Direccion General de Estadistica y Censos. Inventario de las Estadisticas Nacionales
0589-8617 Costa Rica. Ministerio de Transportes. Memoria *changed to* Costa Rica. Ministerio de Obras Publicas y Transportes. Memorias.
0589-8765 Costruttori Italiani nel Mondo
0589-9028 C B A Annual Report
0589-915X Calendar of International Congresses of Medical Sciences *see* 0301-2891
0589-9362 Council of Europe. Exchange of Information Between the Member States on Their Legislative Activity and Regulations (New Series)†
0589-9478 Council of Europe. Council for Cultural Cooperation. Annual Report†
0589-9508 Council of Europe. Concise Handbook†
0589-9575 European Co-Operation
0589-9591 Council of Europe Film Weeks†
0589-9788 State Headlines†
0590-0239 Courrier des Pays de l'Est
0590-0727 Creditanstalt-Bankverein. Wirtschaftsberichte†
0590-1111 Cronache Meridionali†
0590-1243 Crop Protection Courier (International)
0590-1545 Cuadernos Bibliograficos†
0590-1871 Cuadernos de Etnologia y Etnografia de Navarra
0590-1979 Cuadernos de Informacion Economica
0590-2568 Cuadernos Uruguayos de Filosofia†
0590-2916 Cuba Azucar
0590-3343 Universidad de Oriente. Instituto Oceanografico Biblioteca. Boletin Bibliografico
0590-3351 Universidad de Oriente. Instituto Oceanografico. Cuadernos Oceanograficos
0590-4102 Current Primate References
0590-417X Current Research in British Studies by American and Canadian Scholars
0590-4846 Cyprus. Department of Statistics and Research. Demographic Report
0590-4854 Cyprus. Department of Statistics and Research. Annual Industrial Production Survey *changed to* Cyprus. Department of Statistics and Research. Industrial Production Survey.
0590-5001 Czechoslovak Economic Papers
0590-501X C T K Dokumentacni Prehled
0590-5702 Canada. Statistics Canada. Direct Selling in Canada
0590-580X Canada. Department of Indian Affairs and Northern Development. Mines and Minerals, Activities *changed to* Canada. Indian and Northern Affairs Canada. Mines and Mineral Activities (Year).
0590-5966 Casopis za Zgodovino in Narodopisje
0590-6008 Catholic International Education Office. Etudes et Documents†
0590-6105 Informes Latinoamericanos de Fisica†
0590-6334 Cicindela
0590-6342 Cimbebasia. Series A: Natural History
0590-6563 Commission of the European Communities. Community Law
0590-6571 Commission of the European Communities. Financial Report
0590-6776 Cord Sportfacts Guns Guide†
0590-711X C P D A News
0590-7225 Cours et Documents de Biologie†
0590-7233 Bibliographie de Jurisprudence Europeenne Concernant les Decisions Judiciaires Relatives aux Traites Institutant les Communautes Europeennes†
0590-7853 Canada West *see* 0829-5026
0590-8191 C R C Critical Reviews in Clinical Laboratory Sciences *see* 1040-8363
0590-8434 Cleveland and Teesside Local History Society. Bulletin
0590-8760 Consumer Communique *changed to* Consumer Contact.
0590-8876 Costume
0590-9325 Canada. Statistics Canada. Market Research Handbook
0590-9597 Casopis za Suvremenu Povijest
0590-966X Centro Cultural Portugues. Arquivos *changed to* Centre Culturel Portugais. Archives.
0590-9775 British Shipping Statistics†
0590-9783 Charities Digest (Year)
0590-9945 Coin Bulletin
0591-0110 Commission of the European Communities. Expose Annuel sur les Activities des Services de Main-d'Ouvre des Etats Membres de la Communaute†
0591-0129 Committee for Economic Development of Australia. C E D A Occasional Papers†
0591-017X Concern
0591-0188 Comentarios Economico†
0591-0358 Universite de Copenhague. Institut du Moyen-Age Grec et Latin. Cahiers
0591-0471 Courrier de l'Extreme-Orient
0591-0633 Cahiers Marxistes
0591-0986 Catalogue of Little Press Books in Print Published in the UK
0591-1036 Centrale Nucleare Garigliano. Relazione Annuale†
0591-1044 Centrale Elletronucleare Latina. Relazione Annuale†
0591-1133 Geschied- en Oudheidkundige Kring van Ronse en het Tenement van Inde. Annalen
0591-1281 Chips and Ships†
0591-1710 Commerce Yearbook of Public Sector
0591-1737 Commission of the European Communities. Etudes: Serie Industrie *changed to* Commission of the European Communities. Studies: Industry Series.
0591-1745 Commission of the European Communities, Directory
0591-2237 Country Music People
0591-2296 Crux of the News
0591-2334 Custom Car
0591-2369 Zycie Literackie
0591-2377 Zycie Szkoly Wyzszej†
0591-2385 Zygon
0591-2628 Panorama
0640-3603 Zeitschrift fuer Unfallchirurgie, Versicherungsmedizin und Berufskrankheiten *changed to* Zeitschrift fuer Unfallchirurgie und Versicherungsmedizin.
0700-0278 Canada. Statistics Canada. Canvas Products and Cotton and Jute Bag Industries/Industrie des Articles en Grosse Toile et des Sacs de Coton et de Jute†
0700-0731 Canada. Statistics Canada. Felt and Fibre Processing Mills/Industrie du Feutre et du Traitement des Fibres†
0700-138X Canada. Statistics Canada. Therapeutic Abortions†
0700-141X Canada. Statistics Canada. Continuing Education: Universities/Education Permanente: Universites†
0700-1444 Canada. Statistics Canada. Continuing Education: Elementary-Secondary/ Education Permanente: Niveau Elementaire-Secondaire†
0700-1517 Capacity Utilization Rates in Canadian Manufacturing
0700-1681 Quebec (Province) Ministere du Travail et de la Main d'Oeuvre. Jurisprudence en Droit du Travail: Tribunal du Travail†
0700-1770 ForesTalk(1978)†
0700-2033 Industry Price Indexes
0700-205X Canada. Statistics Canada. Quarterly Estimates of Trusteed Pension Funds
0700-2092 Public Sector
0700-2181 Canada. Statistics Canada. University Financial Statistics/Universites Statistiques Financieres†
0700-2211 Canada. Statistics Canada. Railway Transport. Service Bulletin *see* 0828-2897
0700-2408 Metric Monitor/Moniteur Metrique *changed to* Metric.
0700-2645 Alberta. Department of Energy and Natural Resources. Annual Report†
0700-2661 A Guide to National Associations, Service Organizations and Unions Operating in the Arts *see* 0832-865X
0700-284X Coal in Canada, Supply and Demand *changed to* Statistical Review of Coal in Canada.
0700-2866 Canada Grains Council. Annual Report
0700-2971 Manitoba Statistical Review
0700-3048 Dialogue (Ottawa)†
0700-3226 Korean Journal
0700-3269 Kodaly Institute of Canada. Notes *see* 1180-1344
0700-3617 Overview
0700-365X Estuaire
0700-3684 Manitoba Library Association. Newsline
0700-3722 Information-Status of Women†
0700-3749 Quebec (Province) Ministere des Terres et Forets. Conseil Consultatif des Reserves Ecologiques. Rapport Annuel *changed to* Quebec (Province). Conseil de la Conservation et de l'Environnement. Rapport Annuel.
0700-3838 Music Research News
0700-3862 Labour
0700-3900 A l'Ecoute
0700-3978 Canadian Journal of Applied Sport Science *see* 0833-1235
0700-3986 U S Activities Report *changed to* Wood Leader.
0700-4192 Missions des Franciscains
0700-432X Equipement et Methodes
0700-4400 International View†
0700-4532 Metropolitan Toronto Library Board. Annual Report
0700-463X Intralogue†
0700-4745 Musicanada†
0700-480X Sources Directory
0700-4982 London Community Services Directory
0700-5008 Marquee
0700-5032 Angler and Hunter in Ontario *changed to* Angler and Hunter.
0700-5040 Habitabec Montreal
0700-5105 Laurier Campus
0700-5156 Imperial Oil Review
0700-5199 Szamadas
0700-5202 Slavna Nadeje
0700-5245 Conseil Canadien de Protection des Animaux. Ressource
0700-5296 Book Trade in Canada
0700-5318 Opus
0700-5350 World Literacy of Canada. Newsletter *see* 0820-6686
0700-5369 Literacy
0700-5482 Quest for a Common Denominator *see* 0702-7575
0700-5539 Investment Reporter
0700-558X Eureka *see* 0705-0348
0700-5768 Aerospace Canada *changed to* Aviation & Aerospace.
0700-5989 Association of Ontario Land Surveyors. Annual Report
0700-6004 Reseau
0700-6365 Glenbow Foundation. Occasional Paper *see* 0072-467X
0700-6500 Revue Notre Dame du Cap
0700-6802 Scarboro Missions
0700-7388 Boating News
0700-7426 Sphere†
0700-8007 Purchasing Management Digest *changed to* Purchasing Management.
0700-9070 Federation of C.P.T.A. Associations of Ontario. Newsletter
0700-9216 Canadian Electrical Engineering Journal *see* 0840-8688
0700-9224 Applied Mathematics Notes†
0700-9275 Sea Pen
0700-9283 Records of Early English Drama Newsletter
0700-9445 Name Gleaner
0700-9712 Community Information Service. Newsletter
0700-9771 A R C Arabic Journal
0700-9801 Journal of Psychology and Judaism
0700-9828 Canadian Red Cross Society. Manitoba Division. News and Views
0700-9844 Ontario Safety League. News *changed to* Safety Update.
0700-9895 Outdoor Crest Newsletter *see* 0700-9909
0700-9909 Outdoor Crest
0700-9976 Gastown and Vancouver Today†
0700-9992 Upstream
0701-001X Coach *see* 0705-7504
0701-0028 Gestion
0701-0184 Culture & Tradition
0701-0214 Draudzes Vestis
0701-0281 The Cairn
0701-0419 Bookings†
0701-0427 Canadian Society of Military Medals and Insignia. Journal
0701-0524 University of Toronto. Centre of Criminology Library. Acquisitions List
0701-0605 Black Dial Directory
0701-0710 C I M Reporter
0701-0745 Grand Slam†
0701-0788 Catholic New Times
0701-080X Engineering Forum†
0701-0826 Periodical Writers Association Newsletter *see* 0845-8499
0701-1008 Etudes Inuit Studies
0701-1156 About Women (Regina) *changed to* A. E. & M. Network.
0701-1245 Equipment Trader†
0701-130X Curling News *see* 0701-1318
0701-1318 British Columbia Curling News
0701-1369 Wings Magazine of Canada *changed to* Wings.
0701-1539 Employee Benefit Costs in Canada
0701-1547 Action (Winnipeg)
0701-158X Annals of Air and Space Law
0701-161X Committee on Canadian Labour History. Journal†
0701-1687 Produits pour l'Industrie Quebecoise
0701-1733 Canadian Cases on the Law of Torts (2nd Series)
0701-1776 Alberta Archaeological Review
0701-1784 Canadian Water Resources Journal
0701-1792 Journal of Ukrainian Graduate Studies *see* 0228-1635
0701-1865 Antenne
0701-192X T R A C E Newsletter *see* 0704-6421
0701-1989 Revue 2
0701-2748 Periodics†
0701-4309 Canadian Council of Churches. Record of Proceedings
0701-4945 Phenomena†
0701-5208 National Research Council, Canada. Division of Building Research. Special Technical Publication *changed to* National Research Council, Canada. Institute for Research in Construction. Special Technical Publication.

ISSN

ISSN INDEX 5763

0701-5216 National Research Council, Canada. Division of Building Research. Building Practice Note *changed to* National Research Council, Canada. Institute for Research in Construction. Building Practice Note.
0701-5372 British Columbia. Department of Health. Annual Report *see* 0706-4810
0701-5488 Canada. Statistics Canada. Pension Plans in Canada
0701-5666 Quebec (Province) Regie de l'Assurance-Depots du Quebec. Rapport Annuel
0701-6557 Quebec (Province) Ministere de l'Agriculture. Rapport Annuel: Merite Agricole
0701-6786 Canada. Hydrographic Service. Activity Report
0701-6794 Study of Saskatchewan Collective Bargaining Agreements *see* 0830-0763
0701-6956 Prince Edward Island. Department of Community Affairs. Annual Report *changed to* Prince Edward Island. Department of Community and Cultural Affairs. Annual Report.
0701-7243 Inter-National†
0701-7391 Canada. Ministry of State for Science and Technology. Federal Science Programs *see* 0706-2206
0701-7502 Agricultural Real Estate Values in Alberta
0701-760X Index of Current B C Regulations
0701-7758 Ontario Science Centre. Centre News *see* 0228-4642
0701-7928 Air Carrier Traffic at Canadian Airports
0701-8002 Natural Life†
0701-8185 Hunter Training and Conservation. Instructor Newsletter†
0701-8517 Protegez-Vous
0701-8525 Protect Yourself†
0701-8533 Ontario Business News†
0701-8681 C I P S Review
0701-8746 Lutte Ouvriere
0701-8878 Relatively Speaking
0701-8894 Dalhousie University. School of Library Service. Y-A Hotline *changed to* Dalhousie University. School of Library and Information Studies. Y-A Hotline.
0701-8983 Canadian Industrial Health and Safety News *see* 0709-5252
0701-9548 Museum Methods Manuals†
0701-9556 Heritage Record Series
0701-9637 Environment Views
0701-9858 British Colombia. Ministry of Agriculture. Grape Production Guide *changed to* British Columbia. Ministry of Agriculture Fisheries and Food. Grape Production Guide.
0701-9890 Society of the Seven Sages Newsletter
0702-0007 Memorial University of Newfoundland. Occasional Papers in Biology
0702-0333 Canada - Japan, the Export - Import Picture
0702-0465 Canada. Statistics Canada. Quarterly Report on Energy Supply. Demand in Canada
0702-0481 International Journal of Mini and Microcomputers
0702-0538 Ontario. Human Rights Commission. Annual Report
0702-0627 Monitor (Ottawa)†
0702-0759 Labour Directory (Victoria) *see* 0715-2574
0702-0988 Statistics Relating to Regional and Municipal Governments in British Columbia
0702-0996 Quebec (Province). Commission des Transports du Quebec. Rapport Annuel
0702-1003 B.C. Regular Baptist *changed to* B.C. Fellowship Baptist.
0702-1437 Bakka Magazine†
0702-2441 Canadian Automobile Association. Statement of Policy
0702-2735 Independent Forester†
0702-3138 Alberta Disaster Services News and Notes *changed to* Alberta Public Safety Services. Agency Insight.
0702-3162 Canadian Coin News
0702-3855 Hrvatski Put
0702-4894 Wee Giant†
0702-5378 Association of Canadian Community Colleges. Journal†
0702-5459 On-Site
0702-5785 In the Driver's Seat
0702-6005 Foreign Investment Review†
0702-634X Basilian Historical Bulletins†
0702-6587 Canada. Statistics Canada. Security Transactions with Non-Residents
0702-6633 Economic Council of Canada. Bulletin *see* 0226-224X
0702-6641 British Columbia. Ministry of Municipal Affairs. Municipal Statistics, Including Regional Districts *changed to* British Columbia. Ministry of Municipal Affairs, Recreation and Culture. Municipal Statistics, Including Regional Districts.
0702-6803 Magook
0702-6846 Canada. Statistics Canada. Crude Petroleum and Natural Gas Production
0702-6943 Quebec at a Glance†
0702-7001 Atlantic Issues†
0702-701X Ski Canada
0702-7060 Industrial Management†
0702-7206 Municipal and Planning Law Reports (2nd Series)
0702-7222 Progressive Conservative Party of Canada. Leader's Report
0702-732X N.S. Conservation
0702-7354 Alberta Square and Round Dance Federation. Newsletter†
0702-7524 Boating Business *see* 0260-9452
0702-7532 New Literature and Ideology
0702-7575 Mamashee†
0702-7583 C S A Information Update *changed to* Canadian Standards Association. Info Update.
0702-7818 Atlantis
0702-7842 Ontario. Ministere des Affaires Culturelles et des Lois de l'Ontario. Rapport Annuel
0702-7915 Nunatsiag News
0702-7958 C.S.P. World News
0702-8075 B.C. Market News *changed to* Talking Business.
0702-8083 Canada. Statistics Canada. Electrical Contracting Industry *see* 0835-104X
0702-8091 Canada. Statistics Canada. Law Enforcement, Judicial and Correctional Statistics Service Bulletin/La Statistique Policiere, Judiciaire, et Correctionnelle, Bulletin de Service†
0702-8210 Ottawa Letter
0702-8318 Automotive Marketer†
0702-8318 Automotive Marketer Annual Buyer's Guide
0702-8393 Fugue
0702-8431 McGill University, Montreal. Centre for Developing-Area Studies. Occasional Monograph Series†
0702-844X End-Time News
0702-8458 Edmonton Revival Centre. News *see* 0702-844X
0702-8466 Psychiatric Journal of the University of Ottawa *see* 1180-4882
0702-8520 Dime Bag: Fiction Issue†
0702-8571 Revue Independantiste
0702-858X Monde des Loisirs
0702-8733 Canadian Highway Carriers Guide†
0702-8865 Alternate Routes
0702-8881 Sheep Canada
0702-9012 Music McGill
0702-9071 Western Rider
0702-9179 Moving to Toronto *see* 0713-8377
0702-9187 Moving to Vancouver - Victoria *see* 0713-8407
0702-9225 Moving to Montreal
0702-9233 Jewish Historical Society of Canada. Journal *see* 0706-3547
0702-9284 Recreation Research Review *see* 0843-9117
0702-9292 Nova Scotia School Boards Association Newsletter
0702-9446 Vital Statistics of the Province of British Columbia *see* 1188-3642
0702-9659 Alberta. Alberta Culture. Annual Report *changed to* Alberta. Alberta Culture and Multiculturalism. Annual Report.
0702-9829 Nova Scotia. Department of Labour and Manpower. Bulletin†
0702-9861 British Columbia. Ministry of Forests and Lands. Land Management Reports *changed to* British Columbia. Ministry of Forests. Land Management Reports.
0702-987X Collective Agreement Settlements in Nova Scotia†
0702-9888 Selected Labour Statistics for Nova Scotia†
0703-0169 Saskatchewan. Department of Labour. Policy Planning & Research Division. Wage Adjustments in Collective Bargaining Agreements†
0703-0312 EnRoute
0703-0320 Canada Institute for Scientific and Technical Information. Annual Report
0703-0428 Urban History Review
0703-0606 New Brunswick Museum. Journal†
0703-0665 British Columbia. Ministry of Labour. Negotiated Working Conditions *changed to* British Columbia. Ministry of Labour and Consumer Services. Negotiated Working Conditions.
0703-0762 Quebec (Province). Commission des Services Juridiques. Rapport Annuel
0703-0827 Manitoba. Lotteries Commission. Annual Report *changed to* Manitoba Lotteries Foundation. Annual Report.
0703-086X British Columbia. Energy Commission. Annual Report *changed to* British Columbia. Utilities Commission. Annual Report.
0703-0940 Quebec (Province). Department of Natural Resources. Report *changed to* Quebec (Province). Department of Energy and Resources. Report.
0703-1157 Chem Thirteen News
0703-1319 Weekly Criminal Bulletin
0703-1440 Big Country Cariboo Magazine
0703-1459 Canadian Journal of Irish Studies
0703-1491 Drochaid
0703-1599 Canadiana Germanica
0703-1831 Cicada†
0703-184X Ukulele Yes!†
0703-1866 Ploughshares Monitor
0703-1874 Europa: a Journal of Interdisciplinary Studies†
0703-1890 Bois Ouvre†
0703-1920 Conference Board of Canada. Survey of Business Attitudes and Investment Spending Intentions *changed to* Conference Board of Canada. Index of Business Confidence.
0703-1963 Canadian Canon Law Society
0703-2048 Saskatchewan Reporter†
0703-2129 Canadian Lawyer
0703-2226 Wage Changes in Collective Agreement Settlements in Nova Scotia†
0703-2633 Canada. Statistics Canada. Annual Report
0703-2684 Canada. Statistics Canada. Historical Labour Force Statistics, Actual Data, Seasonal Factors, Seasonally Adjusted Data
0703-2692 Canada. Statistics Canada. Air Passenger Origin and Destination. Domestic Report
0703-2749 Canada. Statistics Canada. Local Government Finance: Revenue and Expenditure, Assets and Liabilities, Actual†
0703-3052 Studies in Music
0703-3060 British Columbia Law Reports (3rd Series)
0703-3117 Alberta Law Reports (2nd Series)
0703-3249 Canadian Conference on Information Science. Proceedings *see* 0380-9218
0703-4288 A L S News
0703-4520 Forge
0703-4563 Review Ottawa†
0703-4598 Centre
0703-4660 National Museum of Natural Sciences. Natural History Notebook Series†
0703-4687 Real Property Reports
0703-4857 Canada. Statistics Canada. Farm Income and Prices Section. Farm Cash Receipts/Recettes Monetaires Agricoles†
0703-4873 Canada. Statistics Canada. Employment, Earnings and Hours. Seasonally-Adjusted Series/Emploi, Remunerations et Heures; Series Desaisonnalisees†
0703-489X Material History Bulletin - Bulletin d'Histoire de la Culture Materielle *see* 1183-1073
0703-5330 International Review of Slavic Linguistics
0703-5357 Atlantic Co-Operator
0703-5365 Postal History Society of Canada. Journal *see* 0714-8305
0703-5411 International Atlantic Salmon Foundation. Newsletter *changed to* Salar.
0703-5500 Victorian Studies Association of Western Canada. Newsletter *see* 0848-1512
0703-5527 P C L A Newsletter†
0703-5551 Business Law Reports (2nd Series)
0703-5608 Aviation Quebec
0703-5624 C P H A Health Digest
0703-5640 Theatre Canada. Special Bulletin
0703-5748 Antiques and Art *see* 0833-0891
0703-5764 Diabetes Dialogue
0703-5861 Canadians for a Democratic Workplace. Newsletter
0703-5888 Niagara Anglican
0703-6078 Canada Council. Touring Office. Bulletin†
0703-6337 Revue d'Integration Europeenne
0703-6507 Dawson and Hind†
0703-6523 Canada. Atmospheric Environment Service. Daily Soil Temperature Data/ Donnees Quotidiennes sur la Temperature du Sol†
0703-654X Canada. Statistics Canada. Road Motor Vehicles, Fuel Sales
0703-6566 New Brunswick. Department of Tourism. Annual Report *see* 0839-6434
0703-6752 Living with Christ - Complete Edition
0703-6760 Living with Christ - Sunday Edition
0703-6892 E & M Newsletter†
0703-7007 Link (Mississauga) *changed to* Check it Out!
0703-7090 R T A C Forum *see* 0826-8193
0703-7139 Possibles
0703-7163 MoneyLetter
0703-7228 Katimavik†
0703-7244 Canada. Statistics Canada. Cable Television - Teledistribution *changed to* Canada. Statistics Canada. Cable Television.
0703-7252 Canada. Statistics Canada. Telecommunications Statistics
0703-7295 Canada. Statistics Canada. Non-Residential General Building Contracting Industry *see* 0835-1066
0703-7333 Canada. Statistics Canada. Stocks of Frozen Meat Products†
0703-7368 Canada. Statistics Canada. Family Incomes, Census Families
0703-7384 Corpus Administrative Index
0703-7406 Canada. Statistics Canada. Silver-Cobalt Mines and Silver-Lead-Zinc Mines/Mines d'Argent-Cobalt et Mines d'Argent-Plomb-Zinc†
0703-766X A G M Reporter
0703-7732 Benefits Canada
0703-7945 Farm Cash Receipts

ISSN

0703-8240 International Journal of Women's Studies†
0703-8372 Canadian Association of Pathologists. Newsletter
0703-8380 Cadenza
0703-8763 Edmonton Area Series Report *changed to* Alberta - Edmonton Series Report.
0703-895X Canadian Token
0703-8968 Briarpatch
0703-8984 Electronics Today *changed to* Electronics & Technology Today.
0703-900X Canadian Journal of Law & Jurisprudence
0703-9018 Arab Review†
0703-9077 Canadian Band Journal
0703-9085 A I B C Forum†
0703-9115 Promises *see* 0831-0254
0703-9158 Dairy Goat Gazette and Lively Vivid Escapades *see* 0708-6164
0703-9328 Canada. Statistics Canada. Financial Statistics of Education
0703-9352 Consumer Price Index (Ottawa)
0703-9409 New Brunswick Anglican
0703-9468 Artisan News *see* 0229-4435
0703-9476 Best Canadian Stories
0703-9484 Auxiliaire *see* 0822-8558
0703-9492 Scientific Policy, Research and Development in Canada†
0703-9514 Furniture Production and Design Meubles *changed to* Canadian Wood Processing.
0703-9905 Marketing Voyages
0704-0024 Photographic Canadiana
0704-0059 Antiques *see* 0704-0067
0704-0067 Antique News (Toronto)†
0704-0288 Advocates Quarterly
0704-0393 Clic's Legal Materials Letter†
0704-0407 Hospital Trustee *changed to* Leadership in Health Services.
0704-0547 Silangan
0704-0598 N G R C Forum†
0704-061X Cineclube†
0704-0628 Plug-In
0704-0652 Maritimer
0704-0717 Canadian Workshop
0704-0733 Trot
0704-0857 Canadian Community Law Journal†
0704-0873 Bulletin sur les Relations du Travail
0704-0970 New Brunswick. Forest Products Commission. Progress Report†
0704-1217 L A R U Studies†
0704-1349 Palliser Wheat Growers Association. Newsletter *see* 0829-4763
0704-173X Your Home†
0704-2582 Ontario Geological Survey. Geological Report, Geoscience Report *changed to* Ontario Geological Survey. Report.
0704-2590 Ontario Geological Survey. Study
0704-2671 Education Manitoba
0704-2701 Ocean Dumping Report†
0704-2728 Information C.B. *changed to* Actualites S D M.
0704-2752 Ontario Geological Survey. Miscellaneous Paper
0704-2965 Horizons (Montreal)
0704-3015 Canada. Earth Physics Branch. Geomagnetic Series *see* 0068-7650
0704-3139 Canada. Hydrographic Service. Annual Report *see* 0701-6786
0704-3147 Canada. Service Hydrographique. Rapport Annuel *see* 0701-6786
0704-3694 Canadian Industry Report of Fisheries and Aquatic Sciences
0704-3724 Canadian Occupational Safety & Health Law
0704-4062 E C O - L O G Information Services†
0704-4550 Gazette des Femmes
0704-4771 N A F O Meeting Proceedings†
0704-4798 N A F O Annual Report
0704-4836 Northern Development *see* 0824-4952
0704-4860 Hearsay, for Dalhousie Law Graduates *changed to* Hearsay.
0704-5263 Perception
0704-5352 Voix Sepharade
0704-5387 Canada. Statistics Canada. Public Warehousing/Entreposage Public†
0704-5522 Concerned Canadian
0704-5646 Canadian Poetry (London, Ont.)
0704-5697 Y E R Monograph Series
0704-5700 Yeats Eliot Review
0704-576X National Museum of Natural Sciences. Syllogeus *changed to* Canadian Museum of Nature. Syllogeus.
0704-5824 Occasional
0704-5905 Targumic and Cognate Studies. Newsletter
0704-6138 A C M E Newsletter *changed to* Canada Country.
0704-6278 B C Manufacturer's Directory
0704-6286 Germination
0704-6359 L'Hospitalite
0704-6383 Image des Laurentides†
0704-6391 Canadian Firefighter
0704-6421 T R A C E S
0704-6588 Crosscurrents
0704-6596 Canada. Statistics Canada. Elementary - Secondary School Enrolment
0704-6766 Construction Safety Journal
0704-6804 Airforce
0704-6839 Northern Titles: K W I C Index
0704-7002 Polyphony
0704-7223 Taxipresse
0704-7339 Toronto International Auto Show Program
0704-7509 B C Journal of Special Education
0704-7517 Apprentissage et Socialisation *changed to* Apprentissage et Socialisation.
0704-7576 Grande Replique
0704-7584 International Development Research Centre. Annual Report
0704-7673 Canada. Northern Forestry Centre. Information Report
0704-769X Canada. Maritimes Forest Research Centre, Fredericton, New Brunswick. Information Report M-X *changed to* Canada. Forestry Canada - Maritimes Region, Fredericton, New Brunswick. Information Report M-X.
0704-7886 Lundi
0704-7916 Arts Atlantic
0704-7924 Cahiers de Recherches en Sciences de la Religion†
0704-7940 Repertoire des Produits Fabriques au Quebec *changed to* Repertoire des Produits Disponibles au Quebec.
0704-7975 Gardenland†
0704-8017 Edmonton Chamber of Commerce. Commerce News
0704-8025 Reports on Separatism†
0704-8475 Virus Montreal
0704-8874 Labour Topics
0704-9056 Alberta Art Foundation. Annual Report *changed to* Alberta Foundation for the Arts. Annual Report.
0704-9145 Alberta Genealogical Society. Surnames Register *changed to* Alberta Genealogical Society. Ancestor Index.
0704-9153 Ovo Magazine
0704-9226 Halton Farm News
0704-9471 Hamilton-Burlington Month
0704-9528 Administrateur Hospitalier†
0704-9536 Freeze Frame
0704-9641 Ontario. Advisory Committee on Confederation. Report†
0704-9722 Canadian Journal of Criminology
0705-0038 Childrens Book News
0705-0348 Crux Mathematicorum
0705-0518 Australia. Bureau of Statistics. Overseas Trade, Australia, Part 1: Exports and Imports *changed to* Australia. Bureau of Statistics. Foreign Trade, Australia, Part 1: Exports and Imports.
0705-0534 Australia. Bureau of Statistics. Australian Exports, Country by Commodity†
0705-0542 Australia. Bureau of Statistics. Australian Imports, Country by Commodity†
0705-0585 Decor a Coeur†
0705-064X Development Directions†
0705-0852 Journal de la Majorite *changed to* Quebec Etudiant.
0705-0992 Adsum
0705-1026 Federation des Associations de Parents et Instituteurs Langues Francaise de l'Ontario. Liaison
0705-1093 Decoration Chez-Soi
0705-1123 Echo (Ottawa)†
0705-1212 S T O P Press
0705-1298 Car Costs
0705-1328 Journal of Canadian Poetry
0705-1360 All Canada Weekly Summaries - National
0705-1379 Freelance
0705-1433 Canadian Footwear Journal
0705-1530 Canadian Stereo Guide *see* 0833-9570
0705-1549 Activities Digest
0705-1727 Canadian Weightlifting Journal - Journal Canadien d'Halterophilie *see* 0832-8196
0705-176X Canadian Wrestler
0705-1840 Sanford Evans Gold Book of Motorcycle Data & Used Prices
0705-1859 Journal des Affaires *see* 0229-3404
0705-1867 Vani
0705-1883 Books in Finnish†
0705-1905 Saint John Today *see* 1184-731X
0705-1913 Review of Architecture and Landscape Architecture†
0705-1980 Shearwater Warrior *see* 0707-8056
0705-2006 Canadian Journal of Archaeology
0705-2030 Motorcycle Dealer and Trade
0705-2103 Committee for Justice and Liberty. Newsletter *see* 0824-2062
0705-212X Lawn & Garden Trade
0705-2146 Australia. Bureau of Statistics. Western Australian Office. Fisheries, Western Australia
0705-2162 Canadian Federation of Film Societies. Newsletter†
0705-2170 Toronto Stock Exchange Daily Record
0705-2294 Books in Dutch†
0705-2316 Going On *see* 0311-0737
0705-2332 Books in Danish†
0705-2367 Coal Miner†
0705-243X Quebec Yachting *see* 0833-918X
0705-2553 Standardbred *see* 0834-0110
0705-2669 Manitoba Archaeological Quarterly
0705-2855 Archivist
0705-288X Water Pollution Research in Canada *see* 0197-9140
0705-3002 Canadian Journal of Italian Studies
0705-3010 Canadian Apparel Manufacture
0705-3045 Eastern Ontario Construction Industry Directory and Purchasing Guide†
0705-3193 Canadian Controls & Instruments *changed to* Canadian Controls & Instrumentation (1983).
0705-3215 C'est Pour Quand
0705-3355 Northwest Travel Guide - Alaska - Yukon *changed to* Northwest Travel Guide - Alaska - Yukon - British Columbia.
0705-3371 Northwest Travel Guide - British Columbia *changed to* Northwest Travel Guide - Alaska - Yukon - British Columbia.
0705-3428 Tam Ti Delam *changed to* Fetes et Festivals.
0705-3436 Loisir et Societe
0705-3657 Canadian Journal of Communication
0705-369X Injured Athlete
0705-372X Directory of Social Services in the A.C.T.†
0705-3754 Crescent International
0705-3797 Episodes (Herndon)
0705-3851 Femmes d'Ici
0705-386X Canadian Council of Teachers of English. Newsletter
0705-3878 Agri-Book Magazine. Farm Equipment Review
0705-3878 Agri-Book Magazine. Drainage Contractor
0705-3878 Agri-Book Magazine. Potatoes in Canada
0705-3878 Agri-Book Magazine. Top Crop Manager
0705-3878 Agri-Book Magazine. Corn in Canada
0705-3878 Agri-Book Magazine. Beans in Canada
0705-3878 Agri-Book Magazine. Farm Equipment Directory
0705-3886 Nash on Magistrates' Courts - Victoria
0705-3894 Free Throw†
0705-3932 Canadian Renewable Energy News *changed to* Renewable Energy News.
0705-3983 University of Alberta. Agriculture and Forestry Bulletin†
0705-4009 Music Magazine
0705-4157 Alumi-News
0705-4165 Incidences (1979)†
0705-4297 Canada. Statistics Canada. International Air Charter Statistics *see* 0828-8208
0705-4319 Canada. Statistics Canada. Control and Sale of Alcoholic Beverages in Canada†
0705-4343 Canada. Statistics Canada. Air Passenger Origin and Destination. Canada - United States Report
0705-436X Canada. Statistics Canada. Coal Mines
0705-4572 Chinook
0705-4580 Canadian Journal of Regional Science
0705-470X British Columbia. Ministry of Agriculture. Tree Fruit Production Guide for Interior Districts *changed to* British Columbia. Ministry of Agriculture Fisheries and Food. Tree Fruit Production Guide.
0705-4831 Nova Scotia Trappers Newsletter
0705-4890 Letter of the L A A
0705-503X Canada. Great Lakes Forest Research Centre. Survey Bulletin *changed to* Canada. Forestry Canada. Ontario Region. Survey Bulletin.
0705-5064 Checklist of Canadian Theatres *see* 0226-5125
0705-5137 Canadian Report
0705-517X Ontario. Ministry of Labour. Library. Library Bulletin *see* 0836-1525
0705-5196 C A N M E T Reports
0705-520X Canada. Great Lakes Forest Research Centre. Forestry Research Newsletter *changed to* Canada. Forestry Canada. Ontario Region. Forestry Newsletter.
0705-5242 Canada. Statistics Canada. Report on Livestock Surveys: Cattle, Sheep/ Rapport des Enquetes sur le Betail: Bovins, Moutons†
0705-5331 Canada: Official Handbook of Present Conditions and Recent Progress†
0705-548X Canadian Film Series
0705-5587 Canada Addictions Foundation. Directory
0705-5595 New Motor Vehicle Sales
0705-5617 Coaching Review†
0705-5757 British Columbia. Ministry of Agriculture Fisheries and Food. Nursery Production Guide *see* 0840-8068
0705-5765 Canada. Statistics Canada. Canadian Statistical Review. Annual Supplement to Section 1†
0705-5773 Australia. Bureau of Statistics. Tasmanian Office. Divorces Tasmania
0705-5838 Australian Geomechanics News
0705-5870 German Journal of Psychology
0705-5900 Atmosphere - Ocean
0705-5935 Gay Counselling *changed to* Lesbian and Gay Counselling News.
0705-596X Alberta. Office of the Superintendent of Insurance and Real Estate. Annual Report *changed to* Superintendent of Insurance Annual Report.
0705-6028 Canadian Advisory Council on the Status of Women. Annual Report - Rapport Annuel
0705-6087 Alberta Library News†
0705-6095 Sport and Recreation Index - Index de la Litterature des Sports et des Loisirs *see* 0882-553X
0705-6109 Misleading Advertising Bulletin

ISSN

ISSN INDEX 5765

0705-6249 Directory of Canadian Orchestras and Youth Orchestras
0705-6257 Australia. Bureau of Statistics. Victorian Office. Estimated Population in Local Government Areas, Victoria *see* 0819-6575
0705-6311 Physician's Management Manuals
0705-6494 Books in Hungarian†
0705-6591 Canadian Society for the Prevention of Cruelty to Children. Journal *see* 0825-7531
0705-6605 Televiews†
0705-6672 Court Judgement Report
0705-6680 Canadian Perspective†
0705-6702 Newfoundland Medical Association Journal†
0705-6710 Canadian Paper Analyst
0705-6923 Quebec Vert
0705-6931 Leadline
0705-7040 L'Echo du Transport
0705-7091 Financial Post Survey of Energy Resources *see* 0227-1656
0705-7113 A J A S: Australasian Journal of American Studies
0705-7156 Books in Spanish†
0705-7172 Books in Arabic†
0705-7199 Geographie Physique et Quaternaire
0705-7377 Criminal Law in New South Wales. Volume 1: Indictable Offences
0705-7385 Criminal Law in New South Wales. Volume 2: Summary Offences
0705-7423 University of Wollongong. Handbook for Undergraduates†
0705-7504 Canadian Soccer Association. Technical Manual†
0705-7520 Gite
0705-7814 Wise Owl News (Toronto)†
0705-7822 Nayer Dor†
0705-7970 Liban au Canada
0705-7989 Association for Canadian Theatre History. Newsletter *changed to* Association for Canadian Theatre Research. Newsletter.
0705-8063 Vandance
0705-8160 Directory of Courses: Tourism, Hospitality, Recreation†
0705-8209 Books in Armenian†
0705-825X Books in Urdu†
0705-8292 Conseil de la Jeunesse Scientifique. Bottin
0705-8314 Guide du Camping
0705-8330 Canadian Business Economics†
0705-8365 Cuvantul Romanesc
0705-8373 Books in Hindi†
0705-8454 A S T I S Current Awareness Bulletin
0705-856X Facts
0705-8594 Middle East Focus
0705-8616 Algonkian's *see* 0707-3143
0705-8748 Farm Gate
0705-8764 Great Barrier Reef Marine Park Authority Bulletin *changed to* Great Barrier Reef Marine Park Authority Newsletter.
0705-8802 British Columbia School Counsellors' Association. Newsletter
0705-8810 Canadian Police College. Journal
0705-8829 World Literacy of Canada, News and Views *see* 0820-6686
0705-887X City of Toronto Planning Board. City Planning *changed to* City of Toronto Planning and Development Department. City Planning.
0705-8993 Marine Trades
0705-9019 British Columbia Music Educator
0705-906X Western Grocer Magazine
0705-9094 Canadian Association for the Prevention of Crime. Bulletin - Societe Canadienne pour la Prevention du Crime. Bulletin *see* 0823-9436
0705-9191 Ryerson Rambler
0705-9213 Australian Road Research in Progress
0705-9272 Environment Systems and Industries *see* 0017-9418
0705-9388 Occupational Health in Ontario
0705-9698 British Columbia. Ministry of Labour. Annual Report *changed to* British Columbia. Ministry of Labour and Consumer Services. Annual Report.
0706-0092 Ontario Education Relations Commission. Annual Report
0706-0203 About Arts and Craft - Art et l'Artisanat *see* 0822-7217
0706-0262 Insight (Regina) *see* 0843-7092
0706-0300 Bicycling News Canada†
0706-0661 Canadian Journal of Plant Pathology
0706-067X Canada. Statistics Canada. Road Motor Vehicles, Registrations
0706-0726 Health Care in Canada *see* 0226-5788
0706-0955 Northward Journal
0706-098X Musees
0706-1005 Concordia University Magazine
0706-1021 Annuaire Franco-Ontarien
0706-1064 Book Times *see* 0705-0038
0706-1293 Canadian Nuclear Association. Annual International Conference. Summaries *changed to* Canadian Nuclear Association. Annual International Conference Proceedings.
0706-1382 C A F C Dialogue
0706-1420 Alberta Electric Industry, Annual Statistics
0706-1706 Labour, Capital and Society
0706-1870 Alert (Adelaide)
0706-1889 Writing
0706-1897 Passing Show†
0706-2168 Canadian Geographic
0706-2176 Western Australian Economic Review
0706-2192 C H C G Pulse
0706-2206 Canada. Ministry of State for Science and Technology. Federal Science Activities†
0706-2249 Quebec (Province). Centrale des Bibliotheques. Choix: Documentation Imprimee *changed to* Quebec (Province). Services Documentaires Multimedia. Choix: Documentation Imprimee.
0706-2257 Quebec (Province). Centrale des Bibliotheques. Choix: Documentation Audiovisuelle *changed to* Quebec (Province). Services Documentaires Multimedia. Choix: Documentation Audiovisuelle.
0706-2265 Quebec (Province) Centrale des Bibliotheques. Choix Jeunesse: Documentation Imprimee *changed to* Quebec (Province) Services Documentation Multimedia. Choix Jeunesse: Documentation Imprimee.
0706-2273 Documentation Audiovisuelle *changed to* Quebec (Province). Services Documentaires Multimedia. Choix: Documentation Audiovisuelle.
0706-2338 Directory of Canadian Universities (Year)
0706-2346 Canada. Hydrographic Service. Water Levels. Vol. 2: Tidal Highs and Lows†
0706-2354 Canada. Hydrographic Service. Water Levels. Vol. 1: Daily Means†
0706-2362 Photoworld Buyer's Guide. Cameras†
0706-2419 Parlure†
0706-2451 Canada. Statistics Canada. Highway, Road, Street and Bridge Contracting Industry *see* 0835-1058
0706-246X Institute of Man and Resources Reports†
0706-2788 Canada. Statistics Canada. Homicide Statistics *see* 0825-432X
0706-280X Canadian Jewish Herald
0706-2893 British Columbia Police Journal†
0706-2907 School Library Association Newsletter *see* 0706-2915
0706-2915 School Library Newsletter†
0706-2966 Canada. Statistics Canada. Annual Review of Science Statistics†
0706-3105 Canada. Statistics Canada. Road and Street Length and Financing†
0706-3202 Australian Institute of Pharmacy Management Newsletter
0706-3253 Action (Hull, Que.)†
0706-3369 Alberta. Horticultural Research Center. Annual Report†
0706-3547 Canadian Jewish Historical Society Journal
0706-3601 B.C. Economic Development†
0706-3679 Canada. Statistics Canada. Education in Canada
0706-3792 Manitoba. Municipal Employees Benefits Board. Annual Report
0706-3857 Fireweed
0706-3962 Transpo†
0706-4152 C C I Technical Bulletins
0706-425X Agricultural Research Institute of Ontario. Annual Report
0706-4284 Physio-Quebec
0706-4306 Ministry of Agriculture. Berry Production Guide *changed to* British Columbia. Ministry of Agriculture and Food. Berry Production Guide.
0706-4403 Prince Edward Island. Department of Municipal Affairs. Annual Report†
0706-4551 Ontario Geological Survey. Mineral Deposits Circular
0706-4713 U - Choose: A Guide to Canadian Universities
0706-4810 British Columbia. Ministry of Health. Annual Report
0706-4845 Canadian Journal of Anthropology†
0706-4926 Saskatchewan. Department of Labour. Wages and Working Conditions by Occupation
0706-5000 College Media Director Newsletter†
0706-5019 Occupational Health and Safety Law
0706-5043 Occupational Health and Safety Topics
0706-506X Automotive Review
0706-5086 N F A Journal
0706-5132 Diver Magazine
0706-5159 British Columbia Housing Quarterly†
0706-5205 L'Echange
0706-5213 Highlights of Agricultural Research in Ontario *changed to* Highlights of Agricultural and Food Research in Ontario.
0706-5264 Producteur Agricole
0706-5302 Vancouver Gastronomic
0706-5310 Calgary Gastronomic†
0706-5337 Chaos
0706-5388 Carswell's Practice Cases. (3rd Series)
0706-5426 British Columbia. Human Rights Commission. Annual Report *changed to* Human Rights Act of British Columbia.
0706-5469 E C S Newsletter†
0706-5531 Nicola Valley Archives Association Newsletter *changed to* Nicola Valley Archives Association. Historical Quarterly.
0706-5582 Canadian Journal of Life Insurance
0706-5590 Mission Magazine *see* 0225-7068
0706-5604 Thalia
0706-5639 Debacle†
0706-5655 Estates & Trusts Reports
0706-568X National Research Council, Canada. Division of Electrical Engineering. Bulletin†
0706-585X Ravings†
0706-5914 Impact (North Fitzroy)
0706-5965 University of Western Ontario. Computing Centre Newsletter†
0706-6007 Canada. Treasury Board Secretariat. Federal Expenditure Plan *changed to* Canada. Treasury Board Secretariat. Estimates. Part I: Government Expenditures Plan.
0706-6031 Law and Accounting Practice Management Manual†
0706-6449 Journal of Studies in the Bhagavadgita
0706-6457 Canadian Technical Report of Fisheries and Aquatic Sciences
0706-6473 Canadian Manuscript Report of Fisheries and Aquatic Sciences
0706-6481 Canadian Special Publication of Fisheries and Aquatic Sciences
0706-6503 Canadian Bulletin of Fisheries and Aquatic Sciences
0706-652X Canadian Journal of Fisheries and Aquatic Sciences
0706-666X Directory of the Australian Gas Industry *see* 0727-3541
0706-6678 Australian Music Directory
0706-6902 Australian Video and Communications *changed to* What's on Video and Cinema.
0706-6910 Atlantic Provinces Linguistic Association Journal
0706-7054 Earthcare Information Centre. Newsletter
0706-7372 En Avant†
0706-7402 Echo des Cantons
0706-7410 SonEcran
0706-7437 Canadian Journal of Psychiatry
0706-7534 Footwear Forum
0706-7623 Canadian Bluegrass Review
0706-7658 Transit Fact Book & Membership Directory *see* 0821-2996
0706-7666 Family Law Reports
0706-7682 Great Expeditions
0706-7747 Forest Times
0706-7798 Manitoba. Public Library Services. Newsletter
0706-7852 Benefits for Saskatchewan Industry from Resource Development
0706-7860 Direction (Regina)†
0706-7909 Canada & Arab World
0706-7917 Arab Directory
0706-795X Livres et des Jeunes
0706-8018 Contact (Willowdale)
0706-8042 Animals Canada†
0706-8069 Crosstalk *see* 0845-4795
0706-8085 Reaching the Manitoba Market
0706-8093 From an Island *see* 0826-5909
0706-8204 Canadian Women's Studies *see* 0713-3235
0706-8328 Annuaire de l'Eglise du Quebec
0706-8441 Labour History†
0706-8913 Council for Exceptional Children, Manitoba Branch. Magazine
0706-8921 NorAct
0706-8956 Dunhill Insurance Law Report *changed to* Dunhill Personal Injury & Death Reports.
0706-8964 Dunhill Liability Loss Report
0706-9006 Stoney Monday
0706-9014 Borealis†
0706-9278 Canadian Emergency Services News *see* 0847-947X
0706-9308 British Columbia. Ministry of Agriculture Fisheries and Food D.A.T.E. Program Report
0706-9391 Saskatchewan Research Council. Physics Division. Annual Climatic Summary *changed to* Saskatchewan Research Council. Climatological Reference Station. Annual Summary.
0706-9758 Canadian Student Traveller
0706-9820 Unican†
0706-9847 University of Manitoba Alumni Journal
0706-9928 Apostolat
0707-0047 Directory of Lifestyle Change Services†
0707-0152 Saskatchewan. Prescription Drug Plan. Annual Report
0707-0195 Provincial Council of Women of British Columbia. Newsletter†
0707-0306 Alberta Government Libraries' Newsletter
0707-0349 National P C President
0707-0365 Saskatchewan Motor Transport Guide *changed to* Saskatchewan Trucking - Ship by Truck Directory.
0707-0403 General Safety Digest
0707-0780 Heritage Seekers
0707-090X Copper Toadstool
0707-0926 Open Interest†
0707-0934 M S Ontario
0707-0942 Directory of Co-Operative Naturalists' Projects in Ontario.
0707-1000 Energy and Natural Resources Library Journals†
0707-1027 Of Steam and Stone *changed to* Steam and Stone.

ISSN

ISSN INDEX

ISSN	Title
0707-1434	Alberta. Health and Social Services Disciplines Committee. Annual Report
0707-1442	Ontario Tourism News
0707-1868	Pentecostal Assemblies of Canada. Cell Pak see 0832-9354
0707-1922	Probe Post†
0707-1949	Business & Government News†
0707-1965	Maintenance Management see 0710-362X
0707-2031	Videorecordings Available in the Public Libraries of Metropolitan Toronto†
0707-2279	Worldwind
0707-2287	Eidos
0707-2392	Common Cents Magazine†
0707-2422	Geosciences in Canada
0707-2430	Aspects of the Geosciences in Canada see 0707-2422
0707-2511	Vie Pedagogique
0707-2554	Highland Heritage
0707-2562	Saskatchewan Mineral Resources. Petroleum and Natural Gas Reservoir Annual changed to Saskatchewan Energy & Mines. Petroleum and Natural Gas Reservoir Annual.
0707-2570	Saskatchewan. Department of Mineral Resources. Statistical Yearbook changed to Saskatchewan Energy & Mines. Mineral Statistics Yearbook.
0707-2783	Alberta. Fish and Wildlife Division. Fisheries Pollution Report
0707-2791	Alberta. Fish and Wildlife Division. Pollution Report see 0707-2783
0707-2899	Economics in Canadian Schools†
0707-2937	Monthly Collector
0707-2945	Canadian Muslim
0707-2996	Canada. Geological Survey. Index of Publications of the Geological Survey of Canada
0707-3062	C E C Newsletter
0707-3135	Microlog Index see 0839-1289
0707-3143	Ontario Indian†
0707-3151	Algoma Outdoors
0707-3178	Ontario Out of Doors
0707-3232	Canadian Genealogist†
0707-3240	B.C. Runner
0707-3291	B C I T: The Career Campus changed to B C I T Annual Report.
0707-3356	Bottin des Organismes Franco-Ontariens see 0706-1021
0707-3364	Northland Today
0707-3372	Arab News of Toronto
0707-3380	Asian Tribune
0707-3542	Rollcall
0707-3674	Bibliotheca Medica Canadiana
0707-3739	British Columbia. Ministry of the Environment. Northeast Coal Study Preliminary Environmental Report†
0707-3747	C O N S E R Microfiche
0707-3836	Hilborn Family Journal
0707-3844	Canadian Association of Geographers. Directory
0707-3887	Natural History Contributions
0707-4409	Calgary Magazine†
0707-4611	Chickadee
0707-4808	Canadian Agricultural Economics Society. Proceedings of the Workshop changed to Canadian Agricultural Economics and Farm Management Society. Workshop and Annual Meeting Proceedings.
0707-4875	Current Law Notes see 0707-4883
0707-4883	Current Law Newsletter†
0707-4891	Aikamme
0707-5006	Log Home Guide for Builders and Buyers see 0844-3459
0707-5014	British Columbia Motor Transport Directory
0707-5065	Socialist Albania
0707-5103	Con Brio†
0707-5324	Lusitano
0707-5332	International History Review
0707-5405	Newfoundland and Labrador Recreation Advisory Council for Special Groups. Newsletter†
0707-5456	Directory of Canadian Plays and Playwrights changed to Playwrights Union of Canada Catalogue of Canadian Plays.
0707-5553	Canadian Distributor & Retailer†
0707-5588	Ascent (Ontario)
0707-5723	Analysist
0707-5766	Current Economic and Industrial Relations Indicators†
0707-624X	Canadian Automobile Association. Annual Report
0707-6894	Southeast Regional Library (Saskatchewan) Library Directory†
0707-7106	Swamp Gas Journal
0707-7114	B.C. Agent
0707-7130	Connections (Pointe Claire)
0707-7165	Envol
0707-7300	CanAsian Multicultural Scene
0707-7327	Alberta Council of College Librarians. Newsletter see 0829-4321
0707-7351	Management Consulting Institute. Bulletin†
0707-7459	Igalaaq
0707-7629	Canadian Locations of Journals Indexed for MEDLINE
0707-7718	Canada. Parks Canada. (Western Region). Library Information Bulletin†
0707-7793	Agricultural Science Bulletin†
0707-7807	Journal of Practical Approaches to Developmental Handicap
0707-7874	Canadian Environmental Law Report. New Series
0707-7904	Dairy Industry Research Report changed to Guelph Dairy Research Report.
0707-7920	Confluent Education Newsletter changed to M A C E Newsletter.
0707-7955	Canadian Association of University Research Administrators. Bulletin
0707-8013	Ingot
0707-8021	Point de Mire
0707-803X	Outwest Magazine
0707-8048	Canadian Federation for the Humanities. Bulletin
0707-8056	Warrior
0707-8064	Calgary Commerce
0707-820X	Blackwell Newsletter†
0707-8412	Resources for Feminist Research
0707-8501	Justice (Sainte-Foy)
0707-8552	Studies in Political Economy. Socialist Review.
0707-8897	Kaleidoscope Canada changed to Projection (Montreal).
0707-9087	Teaching of Adults Series†
0707-9184	Snowmobile Accidents, Manitoba†
0707-9389	24 Images
0707-9532	Arts Bulletin
0707-9559	Canada. Statistics Canada. Private and Public Investment in Canada, Mid-Year Review see 0823-0668
0707-9664	Astro-Directory News
0707-9680	Canadian Library Handbook changed to Directory of Libraries in Canada.
0707-9699	Revue Internationale d'Action Communautaire
0707-9753	Canada. Statistics Canada. Telephone Statistics
0707-9788	Monthly Summary Report of Saskatchewan Minerals†
0707-9834	Nova Scotia. Commission on Drug Dependency. Annual Report
0707-9850	Canada. Environment Canada. Land see 0840-4666
0707-994X	Alberta Authors Bulletin changed to Working Title.
0708-0131	Conseil de Presse du Quebec. Rapport Annuel
0708-0263	At a Glance
0708-028X	Saskatchewan Rail Committee. News Bulletin changed to Transport 2000 Canada. News Bulletin.
0708-0719	B.C. Technologist†
0708-0727	Canadian Shipping Project Newsletter changed to Maritime History Group Newsletter.
0708-0743	Recreation Saskatchewan see 0821-0160
0708-076X	International Sivananda Yoga Life and Yoga Vacations changed to Yoga Life.
0708-0840	B.C. News see 0708-0859
0708-0859	B.C. Peace News
0708-1006	Physioquebec
0708-1073	Construction Sightlines
0708-1332	Export Canada†
0708-1375	New Brunswick Construction Products Directory changed to New Brunswick Construction Directory.
0708-1510	Repertoire de la Vie Francaise en Amerique
0708-1723	Pest Control for the Home Garden see 0832-6509
0708-1936	Bio-Joule Newsletter changed to Bio-Joule.
0708-1987	Etape
0708-2061	Ontario Geological Survey. Aggregate Resources Inventory Paper
0708-2169	Hiballer Forest Magazine
0708-2177	Restoration
0708-2193	Directory of University Correspondence Courses changed to Canadian University Distance Education Directory.
0708-2398	Etudes Creoles
0708-2495	36 Manieres†
0708-2533	Devindex†
0708-2673	Alberta Health Education Programs†
0708-2762	Canada. Statistics Canada. Radio Broadcasting†
0708-3017	Directory of Alberta's Agricultural Processing Industry
0708-3025	Agricultural Processing and Manufacturing Guide see 0708-3017
0708-3041	Small Business News†
0708-3106	Alberta. Department of Education. Early Childhood Services Program Highlights†
0708-319X	Etienne Gilson Series
0708-3483	Manitoba Beekeeper
0708-3629	Nova Scotia Fisherman†
0708-3637	New Brunswick. Department of Social Services. Quarterly Statistical Bulletin†
0708-3793	Spectrum†
0708-3882	Saskatchewan. Department of Social Welfare. Annual Report changed to Saskatchewan. Department of Social Services. Annual Report.
0708-3963	Consumer Bulletin - Bulletin aux Consommateurs see 0834-2423
0708-4226	Canada's Atlantic Folklore and Folklife Series
0708-4331	High Flight
0708-4366	E P & T
0708-448X	Datum†
0708-4625	Free! The Newsletter of Free Materials and Services see 0836-0073
0708-4927	Flare
0708-501X	Pulp & Paper Canada Directory
0708-5052	Baha'i Studies
0708-5206	Agricultural Development Corporation of Saskatchewan. Annual Report†
0708-5354	Art Education
0708-5397	C I P Forum†
0708-5435	Photo Communique†
0708-5583	Ontario Genealogical Society. Ottawa Branch. Publication changed to Ontario Genealogical Society. Ottawa Branch News.
0708-5591	Canadian Psychology
0708-6024	Sales and Marketing Management in Canada changed to Sales & Marketing Manager Canada.
0708-6113	Directory of Sports, Recreation and Physical Education
0708-6164	Dairy Goat Gazette†
0708-6172	Forintek Canada Corp., Western Laboratory. Technical Reports†
0708-6180	About Women (Winnipeg)
0708-6431	Les Cahiers Nicoletains†
0708-6474	C O N A Journal
0708-6954	British Columbia. Provincial Archaeologist's Office. Annual Report changed to British Columbia. Heritage Conservation Branch. Annual Research Report.
0708-7012	Canada. Statistics Canada. Estimates of Population for Canada and the Provinces - Estimations de la Population du Canada et des Provinces†
0708-7632	Temps de Vivre see 0835-8702
0708-9031	Canada. Department of National Revenue. Excise News
0708-9066	Ex Libris†
0708-918X	Planetary Association for Clean Energy. Newsletter
0708-9422	Connexions Digest
0708-9494	Indo Canadian Times
0708-9511	Federation of Canadian Municipalities. Annual Conference Proceedings†
0708-9635	Canadian Musician
0709-003X	Business Journal changed to Metropolitan Toronto Business Journal.
0709-0412	Government of Canada Publications Quarterly Catalogue
0709-0471	Copie Zero see 0843-6827
0709-0528	Alberta Teachers' Association. Industrial Education Council. News & Notes
0709-0536	Serials Holdings in Newfoundland Libraries
0709-0579	Money Reporter
0709-0706	Children's Aid Society of Ottawa. Information Bulletin see 0705-1123
0709-082X	Nuclear Free Press†
0709-0854	Saskatchewan Business
0709-1141	Background
0709-1370	National (Ottawa, 1970)
0709-1532	Western Sportsman
0709-2016	Le Temps
0709-2334	Dimensions (Montreal)
0709-2423	Manitoba Business Magazine
0709-2431	Alberta Construction
0709-2563	Pulp & Paper Canada's Annual & Directory
0709-2652	Arctic Seas†
0709-2679	Coup d'Oeil sur le Saguenay-Lac-Saint-Jean
0709-325X	Saskatchewan FarmStart Corporation. Annual Report changed to Agricultural Credit Corporation of Saskatchewan. Annual Report.
0709-3373	Poetry Canada Review changed to Poetry Canada.
0709-3403	Canadian Security
0709-3519	Journal of Comparative Sociology and Religion changed to Journal of Comparative Sociology and Ethics.
0709-3756	Bibliographical Society of Canada. Bulletin
0709-3845	Le Communiste†
0709-4035	Wott
0709-4272	Pyramid changed to Truxpress.
0709-4515	Survey of Wage Rates from Collective Agreement Settlements in Nova Scotia†
0709-4604	A C A Bulletin
0709-4671	Ontario Geological Survey. Northern Ontario Engineering Geology Terrain Study
0709-4698	Victorian Periodicals Review
0709-4779	Canada. Statistics Canada. International Vessel Statistics see 0714-1955
0709-5112	Eclipset
0709-5201	Florilegium
0709-5228	O E and M, Office Equipment and Methods changed to Office Systems & Technology.
0709-5236	Canadian Secretary†
0709-5252	Canadian Occupational Health & Safety News
0709-5341	Motor Vehicle Reports
0709-5368	Transpotech†
0709-549X	Ultimate Reality and Meaning
0709-5562	Historic Guelph
0709-5600	Supreme Court of Canada Decisions. Civil and Criminal changed to Supreme Court of Canada Decisions.
0709-6941	Participation

ISSN INDEX 5767

ISSN	Title
0709-6968	Cases to be Heard by the Supreme Court of Canada†
0709-7115	Select Home Designs: Cottage Country†
0709-7123	Select Home Designs: Home Design and Decor see 0713-8075
0709-7727	Creative Source
0709-7751	Language and Society
0709-776X	B.C. Sea Angling Guide†
0709-7778	B.C. Fresh Water Fishing Guide†
0709-8006	F A P U Q Nouvelles Universitaires
0709-8146	Saskatchewan Educational Administrator
0709-8227	Kino - Nouvelles
0709-8383	British Columbia. Ministry of Education. Annual Report
0709-8413	Art Gallery of Ontario. The Gallery see 0829-4437
0709-8502	Annales de Biochimie Clinique du Quebec
0709-874X	Collection Choix
0709-8855	Imagine
0709-8987	University of Toronto. Library Automation Systems. New Publications Awareness List†
0709-9010	Indian Book Review Digest†
0709-9177	Hibou
0709-9487	Rencontre
0709-9762	Canada: Travel Information†
0709-9797	Broadcast Technology
0709-9800	B C T F Newsletter see 0841-9574
0709-9959	Canada. Northern Forestry Centre. Forestry Report†
0710-0167	Revue Quebecoise de Linguistique
0710-0353	Canadian University Music Review
0710-0469	Pappus
0710-0477	C G S News changed to Geotechnical News.
0710-068X	Cross-Cultural Psychology Bulletin
0710-0841	Windsor Yearbook of Access to Justice
0710-0868	Universite de Sherbrooke. Department de Geographie. Bulletin de Recherche
0710-1023	Canada. Statistics Canada. Provincial Government Finance: Assets, Liabilities, Source and Application of Funds†
0710-1163	A R Q: Architecture-Quebec
0710-1244	Hands Magazine
0710-1309	Holstein Journal
0710-1457	Phoenix Rising
0710-1481	Canadian Journal of Native Education
0710-1511	Personal Financial Planning Letter
0710-1678	Time Out†
0710-1805	Martin's Related Criminal Statutes
0710-2240	C C T A Cable Communique
0710-2259	C C T A Communique see 0710-2240
0710-2852	M G S News see 0226-6105
0710-300X	Magazine C E Q see 0710-5568
0710-3034	Pig Paper
0710-3360	Northwest Travel Guide - Northwest Territories†
0710-3417	M A L T Newsletter
0710-362X	P E M: Plant Engineering & Maintenance
0710-362X	P E M: Plant Engineering and Maintenance Sourcebook
0710-3697	Glenbow
0710-4251	Canada. Petawawa National Forestry Institute. Program Review
0710-4340	Canadian Journal of Educational Communication
0710-5118	Communiqu'elles†
0710-5185	Pasquin
0710-538X	Ombudsman Journal
0710-5568	Nouvelles C E Q
0710-6076	Rock Express changed to Music Express.
0710-622X	Canadian Oil & Gas Handbook†
0710-6629	Who's Who in Canadian Law
0710-6874	Alberta Energy Resource Industries. Monthly Statistics
0710-8575	Canadian Recycling Market†
0710-8702	Great Lakes Science Advisory Board. Report
0710-8974	Resource Technology see 0824-4952
0710-9326	Canadian R V Dealer
0710-9628	Key to Kingston
0710-9911	Equinox
0711-0030	Canada's Furniture Magazine
0711-0049	Quarterly Report on Transportation see 0834-9797
0711-0111	Law Reform Commission of Saskatchewan. Yearly Review see 0839-4539
0711-0162	Nouvel Introspec see 1181-8409
0711-026X	Revue Jonathan changed to Information Proche-Orient.
0711-0782	Canada. Department of Fisheries and Oceans. Annual Report
0711-0855	Focus on Great Lakes Water Quality see 0832-6673
0711-1150	Maritime Sediments and Atlantic Geology changed to Atlantic Geology.
0711-1215	Yukon Water Studies†
0711-124X	Badminton Canada
0711-1320	Canada. Environment Canada. Annual Report
0711-222X	Journal of Leisurability
0711-2866	Canada. National Museums of Canada. Annual Bulletin†
0711-3048	Choosing Life†
0711-3226	Score
0711-3277	Mining Review
0711-3366	Energy Newsletter see 0843-4379
0711-3374	Diesel Magazine
0711-3560	Ordre des Comptables Agrees du Quebec. Journal see 0828-6833
0711-3765	Dismantler
0711-382X	Algonquian and Iroquoian Linguistics
0711-3927	Foresight
0711-4370	Cannon†
0711-4818	Cahiers des Arts Visuels au Quebec
0711-5075	Journal of Strategic and Systemic Therapies
0711-5210	Moving to Los Angeles & Orange Counties†
0711-5229	Moving to Greater San Diego†
0711-5342	Nexus
0711-5377	Canadian Leader
0711-5539	Oldtimers' Sports News changed to Oldtimers' Hockey News.
0711-5601	Corpus Agribusiness Report†
0711-561X	Corpus Plastics Report†
0711-5652	Highlights changed to Hospital Highlights (Year).
0711-5725	C - F A R see 0826-4228
0711-5784	Energy Pricing News
0711-589X	Edmonton
0711-5946	P.W.A.C. Newsletter see 0845-8499
0711-6136	Group Travel
0711-642X	Radio Guide changed to National Radio Guide.
0711-6454	Snow Goer
0711-6659	Canadian Acoustics
0711-6683	S I M Now
0711-6780	Environments
0711-6829	L'Alliance (Montreal)
0711-6896	Ontario Universities Benefits Survey
0711-7051	Academic and Administrative Officers at Canadian Universities (Year) see 0847-3536
0711-7108	Globehopper Magazine
0711-7140	Hazardous Waste Management Handbook
0711-7388	Human: Life Issues for Canadians†
0711-7884	D P Market Facts
0711-7914	Videomania
0711-7957	Sentier Chasse - Peche
0711-818X	Canada. Livestock Feed Board of Canada. Annual Report†
0711-8244	British Columbia Export-Import Opportunities
0711-8422	Manitoba. Environmental Council. Topics
0711-849X	Ontario. Labour Relations Board. Annual Report
0711-852X	Gross Domestic Product by Industry
0711-8635	Canadian Directory of Awards for Graduate Study (Year)†
0712-1261	Travel Destination Canada see 0834-017X
0712-1318	Pundit
0712-1326	Now
0712-1539	Strike!†
0712-2349	Export U.S.A. see 0713-0341
0712-2683	Truck News
0712-2748	Cooperatives et Developpement
0712-3094	Tallyboard
0712-3183	N A C Memo see 0831-3377
0712-435X	Science Express X
0712-4384	Literary Markets†
0712-4635	E D U Q
0712-4724	Coulee Continue
0712-4767	Renaissance Universal Journal
0712-4813	Spectroscopy: an International Journal
0712-4996	Greenhouse Canada
0712-5828	Population Studies Centre. Highlights
0712-6115	LibSat
0712-6506	Health Management Forum†
0712-6662	Canada Tax Letter†
0712-6778	Canadian Operating Room Nursing Journal
0712-6875	Canadian Clinical Laboratory
0712-7243	Resource-Mag
0712-7456	Training Resources Tourism, Hospitality, Recreation†
0712-7561	Etudes Strategiques et Militaires (Collection)
0712-7685	Integrity International
0712-8231	Quebec (Province). Regie des Rentes du Quebec. Statistical Outlook†
0712-8290	The Record
0712-8487	Videotex Canada see 0823-8294
0712-8657	Teoros
0712-8762	Canada. Statistics Canada. System of National Accounts, Provincial Gross Domestic Product by Industry†
0712-9041	Adnews
0712-9238	Vista
0712-9343	Alberta Insurance Directory
0712-9467	Technology Today
0712-9939	Technical University of Nova Scotia. Newsletter†
0713-0341	Export News
0713-0376	Export Digest see 0713-0341
0713-0406	Conference Board of Canada. Quarterly Canadian Forecast see 0829-8416
0713-1844	Saskatchewan. Agriculture and Food. Annual Report
0713-2840	Travel-log
0713-3235	Canadian Woman Studies
0713-3286	Canadian MoneySaver
0713-3391	Worldview
0713-3421	C S S E Contact
0713-3545	Gamut
0713-357X	Canadian Institute of Chartered Accountants. Uniform Final Examination Report
0713-391X	C F B Gagetown Gazette
0713-3936	Canadian Journal of Community Mental Health
0713-4118	Jeux et Jouets
0713-4517	Canadian Police Chief Newsletter
0713-5424	Graphics Interface. Proceedings - Comptes Rendus
0713-5807	Pulp & Paper Journal
0713-6315	Antique Showcase
0713-6919	Information Construction
0713-7907	Weekly Digest of Family Law
0713-7931	Bank of Canada. Technical Reports
0713-7958	Revue de l'Histoire du Quebec et du Canada Francais†
0713-8075	Select Homes
0713-8369	Moving to & Around Alberta
0713-8377	Moving to & Around Toronto & Area
0713-8407	Moving to & Around Vancouver & B.C.
0713-8776	Manitoba Ship by Truck Directory
0713-8865	British Columbia Weekly Law Digest
0713-892X	Alberta Weekly Law Digest
0714-0045	Survey Methodology
0714-0339	Ethos
0714-0541	Northern Ontario Directory
0714-0983	National Museums, Ottawa: Publications in Natural Science
0714-1181	Canada. Northern Forestry Centre. Forest Management Note
0714-122X	Ontario Mineral Score
0714-1734	Forest Pest Management Institute Newsletter
0714-1904	Health and Social Service Manpower in Alberta changed to Inventory of Health & Social Service Personnel.
0714-1955	Canada. Statistics Canada. International Seaborne Shipping Statistics†
0714-2579	A C S Newsletter
0714-2870	Inkstone
0714-3192	Contact
0714-3508	Toronto South Asian Review
0714-3605	Gay Archivist
0714-3672	Nova Scotia Genealogist
0714-4067	Je Me Petit Debrouille changed to Les Debrouillards.
0714-4210	Small Business changed to Profit.
0714-4369	Reggae†
0714-4571	Highlights of Industrial Relations Literature†
0714-5896	Living Safety
0714-5918	Resources
0714-6140	Revue Canadienne de Biologie et Biologie Experimentale changed to Experimental Biology.
0714-6736	Ontario Historical Society. Bulletin
0714-6914	Mercer Bulletin
0714-7023	Directory of Museums, Art Galleries and Archives of British Columbia
0714-7058	Aurora
0714-7074	C N S Bulletin
0714-7511	Canadian Journal of Biochemistry and Cell Biology - Revue Canadien de Biochimie et Biologie Cellulaire see 0829-8211
0714-7724	Canadian Catholic Review
0714-8100	TransAction
0714-816X	Explore
0714-8305	P H S C Journal
0714-8356	Country Music News
0714-8992	Insight see 0833-4447
0714-900X	Infoage†
0714-9158	Quebec Farmers Advocate
0714-9476	Continuite
0714-9670	C E C M Bulletin d'Information
0714-9786	Women's Education
0714-9808	Canadian Journal on Aging
0715-1489	Landmarks†
0715-2574	B.C. Labour Directory
0715-271X	Juristat
0715-3155	Alberta, Saskatchewan, Manitoba - Criminal Conviction Cases
0715-3759	Briefly Speaking
0715-4275	West Coast Environmental Law Research Foundation Newsletter
0715-4356	Prolife News
0715-4623	Teaching Electronics and Computing see 0823-9940
0715-4747	Cassiopeia
0715-4798	British Columbia Decisions - Statute Citator
0715-4860	Canadian Rights Reporter
0715-5689	City & Country Home
0715-5808	British Columbia Decisions - Labour Relations Board Decisions changed to British Columbia Decisions - Industrial Relations Council.
0715-5883	Journal of Child Care see 0840-982X
0715-5948	Hi-Rise
0715-6626	Studio Magazine
0715-7045	Currents
0715-7320	Thought for Food Newsletter†
0715-755X	Touring Artists Directory of the Performing Arts in Canada changed to Tourarts.
0715-7657	Statistics on Alcohol and Drug Use in Canada and Other Countries†
0715-7983	Northern Decisions
0715-8114	Moving to & Around Southwestern Ontario

5768 ISSN INDEX

0715-8602	Journal: News of the Blood Programme in Canada
0715-8610	Rubicon†
0715-8661	C I S T I News
0715-8726	Vox Benedictina
0715-8920	Texte
0715-8947	Pets Magazine
0715-9684	Psychotropes
0716-0003	C E N I D Notas Informativas†
0716-0046	Cuadernos de Economia
0716-0054	Nucleotecnica
0716-0062	Mensaje
0716-0151	Resumenes Analiticos en Educacion
0716-0194	Carta Geologica de Chile
0716-0208	Revista Geologica de Chile
0716-0224	Museo Nacional de Historia Natural. Publicacion Ocasional
0716-0240	Estudios Internacionales
0716-0313	Creces
0716-0321	Estudios Sociales
0716-033X	Revista Catolica
0716-0348	Apuntes de Ingenieria
0716-0356	Trilogia
0716-0364	Informaciones Geograficas
0716-0496	Cuadernos de Educacion
0716-050X	Estudios Pedagogicos
0716-0526	Academia
0716-0631	C I E P L A N Coleccion Estudios
0716-0658	Informatica
0716-0720	Parasitologia al Dia
0716-0763	Boletin Antartico Chileno
0716-0798	Taller de Letras
0716-0909	Acta Literaria
0716-0917	Proyecciones
0716-0925	Estudios Atacamenos
0716-0976	Chile. Servicio Nacional de Pesca. Anuario Estadistico de Pesca
0716-1042	Mineria Chilena
0716-1069	Revista Investigaciones Marinas
0716-1115	Estudios Publicos
0716-1123	Centro de Estudios Publicos. Documento de Trabajo
0716-1190	Chile Forestal
0716-1255	Estrategia
0716-1344	Chilean Forestry News
0716-1387	Instituto de Salud Publica de Chile. Boletin
0716-1417	Revista de Ciencia Politica†
0716-145X	Chile. Servicio de Impuestos Internos. Boletin
0716-1468	Estudios Norteamericanos
0716-1484	Dimension Historica de Chile
0716-1530	Museo Chileno de Arte Precolombino. Boletin
0716-176X	Direccion de Bibliotecas Archivos y Museos. Bibliografia Chilena
0716-1832	Cuadernos de Historia
0716-1840	Atenea (Year)
0716-2138	Byzantion Nea Hellas
0716-2219	Deuda Externa de Chile
0716-2367	Banco Central de Chile. Boletin Mensual
0716-2405	Indicadores de Comercio Exterior
0716-2421	Economic and Financial Report
0716-243X	Informe Economico y Financiero
0716-2448	Banco Central de Chile, Santiago. Memoria Anual
0716-2456	Sintesis Estadistica de Chile
0716-2464	Statistical Synthesis of Chile
0716-2642	Revista Trabajo Social
0716-2790	Revista Musical Chilena
0716-2820	Chile. Superintendencia de Bancos e Instituciones Financieras. Informacion Financiera
0716-2901	Banco Central de Chile. Annual Report
0716-3312	Revista Chilena de Antropologia
0716-3460	Hoy
0716-4084	Revista de Otorrinolaringologia y Cirugia de Cabeza y Cuello
0716-4440	Apuntes
0716-4513	Opciones
0716-4610	Ingenieros
0716-4777	Microbyte
0716-4858	Computacion Personal
0716-4866	Fuerza Aerea
0716-5331	Investigacion y Progreso Agropecuario La Platina
0716-5927	Revista de Analisis Economico
0716-5951	Investigacion y Progreso Agropecuario Remehue
0716-6052	Investigacion y Progreso Agropecuario Quilamapu
0716-6346	Nueva Revista del Pacifico
0716-6478	Instituto de la Patagonia. Anales. Social Sciences
0716-730X	Persona y Sociedad
0716-7555	Carta Hidrogeologica de Chile
0716-8136	Siglo XXI Ciencia and Tecnologia
0720-0056	Bruckmanns Pantheon
0720-0218	Stadtansichten†
0720-0447	Forum Kritische Psychologie
0720-0463	Rind und Schlegel
0720-048X	European Journal of Radiology
0720-051X	Eisenbahn-Journal
0720-0528	Drechseln
0720-065X	Die Schilddruese
0720-0706	Lunge und Atmung
0720-0722	Infusions-Journal
0720-0730	Herz und Gefaesse
0720-0773	Seawater and Desalting
0720-0862	Deutsche Schafzucht
0720-0986	Sugia
0720-0994	Balkan-Archiv Neue Folge Beiheft
0720-101X	Elektronik-Applikation†
0720-1028	Apotheker Journal
0720-1168	Hispanorama
0720-1206	Der Deutsche Lebensmittel-Einzelhandel im Spiegel der Statistik (Year)
0720-1214	Q Z Qualitaet und Zuverlaessigkeit *changed to* Qualitaet und Zuverlaessigkeit (1980).
0720-1249	Dragoco Report: Flavoring Information Service
0720-1303	Tex: Mitteilungen Rund Ums Technikum
0720-1516	Sportartikel Wirtschaft
0720-1605	Strafverteidiger
0720-1753	Neue Zeitschrift fuer Strafrecht
0720-1842	Zoophysiology
0720-2032	Dokumentationsdienst Afrika. Kurzbibliographie
0720-213X	Zoomorphology
0720-2245	Phila-Report
0720-2520	Gauke's Jahrbuch
0720-2695	Neuerwerbung Suedasien
0720-2741	Neuerwerbungen Vorderer Orient
0720-2849	Alles fuer die Katz
0720-3098	Allmende
0720-3322	Radiologie
0720-3373	Krankenhaus-Hygiene & Infektionsverhuetung
0720-3438	Waermetechnik
0720-3462	Chirurgischen Arbeitsgemeinschaft. Verhandlung†
0720-3489	Aerzteblatt Baden-Wuerttemberg
0720-3519	Media Plakat
0720-3551	Aktion Jugendschutz. Informationen
0720-3659	Geschichte in Koeln
0720-3683	Welthandel
0720-3705	Naturwissenschaftlicher Verein fuer Schwaben. Berichte
0720-3772	Neuerwerbung Theologie und Allgemeine Religionswissenschaft
0720-3853	Gastronomie und Hotel Impulse
0720-390X	Rheuma
0720-3926	Wind - Energie Jahrbuch
0720-3934	Messergebnisse des Zentralen Immissionsmessnetzes. Monatsbericht
0720-3977	Krankenhaus Technik
0720-4116	Blinker
0720-4280	Pharmacopsychiatria *see* 0176-3679
0720-4299	Fortschritte der Neurologie - Psychiatrie *changed to* Fortschritte der Neurologie, Psychiatrie.
0720-4361	Zeitschrift fuer Sozialisationsforschung und Erziehungssoziologie
0720-4442	M C
0720-4507	Busverkehr
0720-4523	Jaeger
0720-454X	Geooekodynamik
0720-4612	V D I Informationsdienst. Drahtherstellung u. Drahterzeugnisse
0720-4868	Ostseejahrbuch
0720-5104	Reiten und Fahren
0720-5120	Integration
0720-5260	Fotogeschichte
0720-5775	Rhetorik
0720-5953	Konstruktion
0720-597X	Made in Europe - Medical Equipment and Supply Guide
0720-5988	Mexicon
0720-6003	Aerztezeitschrift fuer Naturheilverfahren
0720-6240	Energiewirtschaftliche Tagesfragen
0720-6259	Pastoraltheologie - Monatsschrift fuer Wissenschaft und Praxis in Kirche und Gesellschaft
0720-6542	Niespulver
0720-6593	Tapetenzeitung *changed to* B T H - Tapetenzeitung.
0720-6615	Nepal Research Centre. Journal
0720-6666	Jidische Schtudies
0720-6763	A B I Technik
0720-678X	Springer Series in Information Sciences
0720-728X	Mathematische Semesterberichte
0720-7301	Hochzeit
0720-7522	A I D Verbraucherdienst
0720-7883	Museen in Schleswig-Holstein
0720-8103	Marine-Rundschau International†
0720-8243	Disaster Medicine†
0720-8316	Lernen Foerdern
0720-8545	Radfahren
0720-8634	SchulPraxis
0720-8642	Log In
0720-8782	Ibykus
0720-8863	Geology of Petroleum
0720-9061	Aegypten und Altes Testament
0720-910X	P A E - Mitteilungen
0720-9118	Arbeitshilfen fuer die Erwachsenenbildung
0720-9150	Trakehner Hefte
0720-9258	Impressum
0720-9282	Karpatenland
0720-9339	Auszuege aus den Europaeischen Patentschriften. Teil 1. Grund- und Rohstoffindustrie, Chemie und Huetten-Wesen, Bauwesen und Bergbau
0720-9355	Haemostaseologie
0720-941X	Henkel - Referate
0720-969X	Deutsche Bibliotheksstatistik Teil B: Wissenschaftliche Bibliotheken
0720-9738	Bremer Beitraege zur Geographie und Raumplanung
0720-9746	Universitaet Bremen - Schwerpunkt Geographie. Materialien und Manuskripte
0720-9762	Zeitschrift fuer Physikalische Medizin, Balneologie und Medizinische Klimatologie
0720-9835	Denkmalpflege in Niedersachsen. Berichte
0720-9878	V D I Informationsdienst. Neue Fertigungsverfahren
0720-9886	V D I Informationsdienst. Mechanische Verbindungstechnik
0720-9916	Dienst am Wort - Gedanken zur Sonntagspredigt†
0720-9983	Kreolische Bibliothek
0720-9991	Wissenschaftsmagazin
0721-0035	C I B E D O - Beitraege zum Gespraech Zwischen Christen und Muslimen
0721-0086	Studien zur Bevoelkerungsoekonomie
0721-0094	Sonne
0721-0442	Archivum Calderonianum
0721-0477	Handelspartner
0721-0493	Am Erker
0721-0949	Psyche und Soma
0721-1295	Informationsdienst zur Auslaenderarbeit
0721-1392	American University Studies. Series 1. Germanic Languages and Literature
0721-1465	Hochdruck
0721-1600	Focus
0721-1821	Baden - Wuerttemberg in Wort und Zahl
0721-1872	Zeitschriftenbibliographie Gerontologie
0721-1902	D B - Deutsche Bauzeitung
0721-1937	Anzeiger fuer die Seelsorge
0721-2089	Scandica Magazin†
0721-2097	Im Gespraech
0721-2178	Entwicklung und Zusammenarbeit
0721-2402	Materialdienst
0721-2488	African Linguistic Bibliographies
0721-2585	Holz- und Kunststoffverarbeitung *changed to* Holz- und Moebelindustrie.
0721-2631	Statistics and Decisions
0721-2720	A U M A Kalender Ausland *see* 0934-9790
0721-2747	A U M A Kalender Regional *changed to* A U M A Handbook Regional.
0721-2887	Migration
0721-3115	Propellants, Explosives, Pyrotechnics
0721-3468	Beitraege zur Naturkunde der Wetterau
0721-3719	Japanese Studies in German Language and Literature
0721-3808	Zeitschrift fuer Wirtschaftspolitik
0721-393X	Cor & Coronarien†
0721-4235	Daidalos
0721-4332	Jahrbuch der Milchwirtschaft
0721-4340	Kuschitische Sprachstudien
0721-4383	Bayreuther Beitraege zur Sprachwissenschaft
0721-4405	Der Innovations-Berater†
0721-4553	Chemical Plants and Processing *see* 0009-2800
0721-4561	Internationale Germanistische Bibliographie†
0721-4588	Reno
0721-4626	Zusammen
0721-4863	Northeimer Heimatblaetter *see* 0936-8345
0721-5088	Informationsdienst Suedliches Afrika
0721-5096	Die Kontaktlinse
0721-5118	Ernaehrungsrundbrief
0721-5169	Arabische Pferde
0721-5231	Asien
0721-5398	Konzert Almanach
0721-5665	Pharma-Marketing Journal
0721-5681	Siemens Power Engineering Product News *changed to* Siemens Energy and Automation with Product News.
0721-5746	Zeitschrift fuer Auslaenderrecht und Auslaenderpolitik
0721-5894	Fluessiggas
0721-5932	Didaktik der Berufs- und Arbeitswelt
0721-6076	Medizin in Berlin (West)
0721-6203	Quellen und Untersuchungen zur Lateinischen Philologie des Mittelalters
0721-6513	Andrias
0721-667X	Endokrinologie - Informationen
0721-6742	Exil
0721-6823	Muenzautomat
0721-6831	Signal
0721-6858	L I B E R News Sheet *changed to* European Research Library Cooperation.
0721-6874	Hessische Faunistische Briefe
0721-6890	Wistra†
0721-6912	Food Composition and Nutrition Tables
0721-6971	Frau in der Offenen Gesellschaft *changed to* Frau in Unserer Zeit.
0721-7072	Etage
0721-7234	Verhaltenstherapie und Psychosoziale Praxis
0721-7242	V D I Informationsdienst. Strangpressen von Metallen
0721-7250	Applied Physics. A: Solids and Surfaces
0721-7269	Applied Physics. B: Photophysics and Laser Chemistry
0721-7587	Koelner Arbeiten zum Bibliotheks- und Dokumentationswesen
0721-7595	Journal of Plant Growth Regulation
0721-7714	Plant Cell Reports
0721-7854	Baustoff-Technik
0721-8206	D B B Nachrichten fuer den Oeffentlichen Dienst
0721-8222	Rheuma Schmerz und Entzuendung
0721-832X	Graefe's Archive for Clinical and Experimental Ophthalmology
0721-8400	Praxis Deutsch
0721-8486	Kinder Jugend Film Korrespondenz

ISSN

0721-8516 Z U M A - Nachrichten
0721-8672 Student und Praktikant
0721-8753 Texte und Studien zum Antiken Judentum
0721-8761 "Meteor" Forschungsergebnisse. Reihe A - B: Allgemeines, Physik und Chemie des Meeres Maritime Meteorologie†
0721-880X Neue Zeitschrift fuer Verwaltungsrecht
0721-8923 Bayreuther Beitraege zur Sprachwissenschaft. Dialektologie
0721-8982 Natuerlich und Gesund
0721-9067 Zeitschrift fuer Sprachwissenschaft
0721-9075 Human Neurobiology†
0721-9105 Arbeitsgemeinschaft der Bibliotheken und Dokumentationsstellen der Osteuropa-, Suedosteuropa- und DDR-Forschung. Mitteilungen *changed to* Arbeitsgemeinschaft der Bibliotheken und Dokumentationsstellen der Ost-, Ostmittel- und Suedosteuropaforschung. Mitteilungen.
0721-9121 Fruehfoerderung Interdisziplinaer
0721-9156 Progress in Sensory Physiology
0721-9318 Angio
0721-9431 Russia Mediaevalis
0721-9539 Schachmagazin 64 *changed to* Schachmagazin 64 - Schach-Echo.
0721-9628 Arbeitshefte Kinderpsychoanalyse
0721-9679 Giesserei-Literaturschau
0721-9741 Emma
0721-9903 Hobby
0721-9954 Informationen zur Deutschdidaktik
0722-0014 Digest fuer Jugend und Bildungseinrichtungen
0722-0057 Referateorgan: Messen Mechanischer Groessen
0722-0111 Entwicklungslaender-Studien
0722-0170 D G E G-Nachrichten
0722-0227 Konjunkturindikatoren
0722-0332 Alemannisch Dunkt Ues Guet
0722-0340 Jahrbuch Elektrotechnik
0722-0421 Beam
0722-0448 Diaet - Therapie†
0722-0456 K F A Intern
0722-0537 Trochilus
0722-060X Literaturinformationdienst Schrifttum Bauwesen: Gesamtausgabe
0722-0723 Catena Supplement
0722-0812 Deutscher Forschungsdienst. Berichte aus der Wissenschaft (Auslandausgabe)
0722-0820 Deutscher Forschungsdienst. Sonderdienst Angewandte Wissenschaft (Auslandausgabe)
0722-0847 Deutscher Forschungsdienst. Applied Science
0722-0855 Novedades Cientificas Alemanas
0722-0863 Novedades Cientificas Alemanas - Ciencia Aplicada
0722-0987 Computer Persoenlich
0722-1029 P T A in der Apotheke
0722-1258 Deutsches Textilforum *changed to* Textilforum.
0722-1509 B I B Mitteilungen
0722-1533 Psychologischer Index
0722-1541 Nervenheilkunde
0722-1789 Koeln Sarasvati Series
0722-1819 Handchirurgie - Mikrochirurgie - Plastische Chirurgie
0722-1843 Lernen Konkret
0722-2181 Afrikanisches Recht. Jahrbuch
0722-219X Tumordiagnostik & Therapie
0722-2408 Puppen und Spielzeug
0722-2416 German Yearbook on Business History
0722-2912 D I N Mitteilungen & Elektronorm
0722-2947 Seevoegel
0722-3056 Zentralblatt Rechtsmedizin
0722-3064 Zentralblatt Neurologie - Psychiatrie
0722-3072 Zentralblatt Radiologie
0722-3218 Packaging Science and Technology Abstracts
0722-3226 Military Technology *changed to* Military Technology: Miltech.
0722-3234 Zuversicht und Staerke
0722-3250 Deutsche Bank Bulletin
0722-3269 Advances in Physical Geochemistry
0722-3277 Zeitschrift fuer Physik. Section B: Condensed Matter
0722-3358 Wirtschafts und Steuer Hefte
0722-348X Zeitschrift fuer Phytotherapie
0722-3587 Assistenz
0722-3676 Quantitative Structure-Activity Relationships
0722-3773 Neue Entomologische Nachrichten
0722-4028 International Society for Reef Studies. Journal *changed to* Coral Reefs.
0722-4060 Polar Biology
0722-4192 Acta Biologica
0722-4303 Arab Tech†
0722-4397 Z K G: Ausgabe A
0722-4400 Z K G: Ausgabe B
0722-4516 Mitteldeutscher Kurier
0722-4532 Muenstersche Beitraege zur Antiken Handelsgeschichte
0722-4605 Kaelte Klima Aktuell
0722-477X P M D - Praxis Medizinischer Dokumentation
0722-480X Suedost-Europa. Zeitschrift fuer Gegenwartsforschung
0722-494X Tuexenia
0722-5067 Zeitschrift fuer Chemotherapie
0722-5091 Clinical Neuropathology
0722-5229 Deutscher Forschungsdienst. Sonderdienst Angewandte Wissenschaft
0722-5318 Deutscher Forschungsdienst. Berichte aus der Wissenschaft
0722-5369 Jahrbuch fuer Neue Politische Oekonomie
0722-5474 Alternative Kommunalpolitik
0722-5679 Archiv fuer Rechts und Sozialphilosophy. Supplementa
0722-5733 Z F L - Internationale Zeitschrift fuer Lebensmittel-Technologie und -Verfahrenstechnik *changed to* Z F L - Internationale Zeitschrift fuer Lebensmittel-Technik, Marketing, Verpackung und Analytik.
0722-6012 Productronic
0722-6179 I E E - Industrie, Elektrik und Elektronik
0722-6241 Tunnel
0722-6268 Ballett International
0722-6349 Research†
0722-6675 German Mining *changed to* Mining & Energy.
0722-6691 Messenger
0722-6713 Portugal - Nachrichten *see* 0932-2272
0722-6764 Chemie fuer Labor und Betrieb *changed to* Chemie in Labor und Biotechnik.
0722-6934 B R A K - Mitteilungen
0722-6942 Steyler Missionschronik
0722-6950 Dynamik im Handel
0722-6985 Zentralorgan Chirurgie
0722-706X Fischwaid *see* 0015-2838
0722-7108 Schiffs Modell
0722-7159 Braunschweiger Veroeffentlichungen zur Geschichte der Pharmazie und Naturwissenschaften
0722-7337 D I N - Handbooks
0722-7353 Sozialist
0722-740X Das Achtzehnte Jahrhundert
0722-7485 Zeitschrift Fuehrung und Organisation
0722-7531 Rottenburger Jahrbuch fuer Kirchengeschichte
0722-7647 Forum (Aachen)†
0722-7671 Rheinisch-Bergischer Kalender
0722-7795 Natur- und Landschaftkunde
0722-7833 Spiel
0722-7841 K F Z Betrieb *changed to* K F Z Betrieb Unternehmermagazin.
0722-7949 Raum und Zeit
0722-7973 Aufriss
0722-8058 Blues Forum†
0722-8120 Frau und Mutter
0722-8147 Quellen und Forschungen zur Geschichte des Ersten Weltkriees *changed to* Quellen und Studien zu den Friedensversuchen des Ersten Weltkrieges.
0722-821X Die Asphaltstrasse
0722-8244 Mikrowellen and Military Electronics *see* 0722-9488
0722-8252 Himmel & Erde
0722-8481 Universitaet-Gesamthochschule Duisburg. Universitaets-Report
0722-849X Gesellschaft fuer Kanada-Studien. Zeitschrift†
0722-8562 Umschau, das Wissenschafts Magazin†
0722-8589 Drachenflieger *changed to* Drachenflieger Magazin.
0722-8600 Lehrer Journal *changed to* Lehrerjournal Grundschulmagazin.
0722-8600 Lehrer Journal *changed to* Lehrerjournal Hauptschulmagazin.
0722-866X Aerztliches Mitteilungsblatt Mittelfranken
0722-8821 Suedostasien Aktuell
0722-883X German Comments
0722-8899 Kleist-Jahrbuch
0722-8910 Zeitschrift fuer Wasserrecht
0722-8953 Zentralblatt Kinderheilkunde
0722-8988 Schwarzer Faden
0722-9003 Laser und Optoelektronik
0722-9119 M M Branchen Handbuch
0722-9151 Zeitschrift fuer Religionspaedagogik *changed to* Religion Heute: Supplement.
0722-9399 Berliner Verkehrsblaetter
0722-9488 Mikrowellen and H F - Magazin
0722-964X Argument-Beiheft†
0722-9674 Berichte Pathologie
0722-9852 Berichte Gynaekologie und Geburtshilfe Sowie Deren Grenzgebiete *changed to* Berichte Gynaekologie - Geburtshilfe.
0722-9860 Zentralblatt Praktische Innere Medizin *see* 0931-4695
0722-9917 Kuechenplaner
0722-9933 Zentralblatt Ophthalmologie
0723-0095 R W P
0723-0192 Kunststoffe - German Plastics
0723-0206 Anglo-American Spotlight
0723-0338 R E A L. Yearbook
0723-0788 Schriftenreihe der Hochschule der Kuenste Berlin†
0723-0818 Video Magazin
0723-0834 Geowissenschaften in Unserer Zeit *see* 0933-0704
0723-0869 Expositiones Mathematicae
0723-0877 Einhorn-Jahrbuch
0723-0931 Neuropsychiatria Clinica†
0723-1172 TheaterZeitSchrift
0723-1237 Zeitschrift fuer Personenzentrierte Psychologie und Psychotherapie†
0723-1296 Jugoslavija-Wirtschaft
0723-1350 Weinwirtschaft - Markt
0723-1369 Weinwirtschaft Technik
0723-1407 Beitraege zur Theorie und Praxis des Tennisunterrichts und -trainings
0723-1520 Brauwissenschaft *changed to* Monatsschrift fuer Brauwissenschaft.
0723-1679 Geographische Hochschulmanuskripte. Diskussionspapiere
0723-175X Geographische Hochschulmanuskripte
0723-2020 Systematic and Applied Microbiology
0723-2047 Materialien zur Heimerziehung
0723-2098 Geschichtsblaetter des Kreises Coesfeld
0723-2446 Arbeitsgemeinschaft Neue Religioese Gruppen. Forum
0723-2454 Neues Glas
0723-2470 Bryologische Beitraege
0723-2500 Das Neue Unternehmen
0723-2632 Rock Mechanics and Rock Engineering
0723-2977 Arbitrium
0723-3078 M & A Infodienst†
0723-3264 Historische und Paedagogische Studien
0723-3280 Neue Didaktische Modelle†
0723-3299 Beitraege zur Zeitgeschichte
0723-3353 International Journal of Mycology and Lichenology
0723-3361 M und A Report
0723-3590 Bibliographie der Buch- und Bibliotheksgeschichte
0723-3604 Produkthaftpflicht International
0723-3655 Synform†
0723-3841 Miniaturbahnen M I B A
0723-3868 Personalfuehrung
0723-4007 Ostsprachige Fachliteratur: Ausgabe Japan Technik†
0723-4015 Ostsprachige Fachliteratur: Ausgabe Japan Naturwissenschaften†
0723-4066 D A T Z
0723-4295 Deutsche Umschau
0723-4384 Europaeische Integration - Dokumentation†
0723-4856 Holzbau - Report
0723-4864 Experiments in Fluids
0723-4899 Grundlagenstudien aus Kybernetik und Geisteswissenschaft
0723-4929 Information fuer den G M B H - Geschaeftsfuehrer
0723-5003 Medizinische Klinik
0723-5038 Natur
0723-5062 Baumarkt Tip
0723-5070 Paraplegiker
0723-5100 Arab Medico
0723-5119 Trickster
0723-5208 Handbuch der Modernen Datenverarbeitung *changed to* H M D - Theorie und Praxis der Wirtschaftsinformatik.
0723-5259 Vorschau-Monats-Tabelle *changed to* Messe- und Kongress-Vorschau.
0723-5321 Bundesforschungsanstalt fuer Landwirtschaft. Mitteilungen und Informationen
0723-5437 Feuerwehr und Modell
0723-5453 Beitraege zur Wirtschafts und Sozialgeschichte
0723-5607 Z A Information
0723-5658 Bau Trichter. Ausgabe B†
0723-5984 Die Mitbestimmung
0723-6050 Latein und Griechisch in Berlin
0723-6131 B Z Bauzentralblatt
0723-6174 Souvenir & Geschenk
0723-6204 Die Weltmission
0723-6212 Biologische Tiermedizin
0723-6506 Bau Trichter. Ausgabe A†
0723-6638 Kurt-Schwitters-Almanach
0723-6689 VerkehrsWirtschaft
0723-6913 Arzneimitteltherapie
0723-6980 Development and Cooperation
0723-7006 Desarrollo y Cooperacion
0723-7022 Bayerische Buergermeister
0723-7049 Magazin fuer Technik und Unterricht
0723-7065 Der Nuklearmediziner
0723-712X C S Q - Computational Statistics Quarterly *changed to* Computational Statistics.
0723-7197 Paedagogische Arbeitsstelle fuer Erwachsenenbildung. Schriften
0723-7286 Das Muehlrad
0723-7553 Wartturm
0723-7561 Die B G
0723-7669 Kommune
0723-7766 Journal fuer U F O - Forschung
0723-7839 Der Modellhut
0723-7901 D H F - Deutsche Hebe- und Foerdertechnik
0723-7928 Lehrer im Berufsfeld Koerperpflege
0723-8002 Deutsche Gesellschaft fuer Orthopaedie und Traumatologie. Mitteilungsblatt
0723-8010 Aerztliches Mitteilungsblatt Schwaben
0723-8029 Deutsche Gesellschaft fuer Gynaekologie und Geburtshilfe. Mitteilungen
0723-8045 Fortschritte der Ophthalmologie
0723-8061 WerWasWo? im Taschenbuch
0723-8177 Turmschreiber Kalender
0723-8398 East Asia
0723-8630 Funde und Ausgrabungen im Bezirk Trier
0723-8673 Hermetika†
0723-8886 Medizinrecht
0723-9297 Budo und Transkulturelle Bewegungsforschung
0723-9416 Zeitschrift fuer Wirtschaftsrecht - Z I P
0723-9432 Europaeische Wehrkunde - Wehrwissenschaftliche Rundschau *changed to* Europaeische Sicherheit.

ISSN INDEX

ISSN	Title
0723-9505	Zeitschrift fuer Systemische Therapie
0723-9653	Ostsprachige Fachliteratur: Ausgabe Osteuropa Bauwesen†
0723-9688	Ostsprachige Fachliteratur: Ausgabe Osteuropa, Chemie, Chemische Technik, Kunststoff†
0723-970X	Ostsprachige Fachliteratur: Ausgabe Osteuropa Elektrotechnik, Energietechnik†
0723-9726	Ostsprachige Fachliteratur: Ausgabe Osteuropa Geowissenschaften, Bergbau†
0723-9734	Ostsprachige Fachliteratur: Ausgabe Osteuropa Huettenwesen, Werkstoffkunde†
0723-9769	International Joseph Martin Kraus-Gesellschaft. Mitteilungen
0723-9793	Ostsprachige Fachliteratur: Ausgabe Osteuropa Mathematik, Physik†
0723-9815	Ostsprachige Fachliteratur: Ausgabe Osteuropa Umweltprobleme†
0723-9874	Universitaet Kiel. Geographisches Institut. Schriften
0724-0031	C A L: Computer Applications in the Laboratory see 0889-8308
0724-0155	Die Bromelie
0724-0252	Der Dialysepatient
0724-0279	Horizont (Cologne)
0724-0457	A U M A Zahlenspiegel Regional changed to A U M A Handbook Regional.
0724-0554	A U M A Zahlenspiegel Messeplatz Deutschland see 0933-6206
0724-0708	Passauer Pegasus
0724-0775	Fachhochschule fuer Bibliotehks- und Dokumentationswesen in Koeln. Amtliche Mitteilungen
0724-1062	Tanzen
0724-1070	Kontrolle
0724-1194	Flugasche
0724-1348	Heterocera Sumatrana
0724-1429	Locke
0724-1445	American University Studies. Series 3. Comparative Literature
0724-1453	American University Studies see 0741-0700
0724-1569	Teppe und Gelaendert
0724-1631	Bagatelle
0724-1712	Roboter
0724-1976	Verein Deutscher Ingenieure. Informationsdienst. Instandhaltung
0724-2034	Arcus†
0724-2247	Recht & Psychiatrie
0724-2263	Islamic Book Review Index
0724-2557	Schriften des Werksarchivs
0724-2573	Diabetes Mellitus†
0724-2603	Horvath Blaetter†
0724-2654	Deutsche Jagd-Zeitung
0724-2689	Delfin
0724-2735	Aktuelle Fragen†
0724-2778	Una Voce Korrespondenz
0724-3103	Sprachwissenschaft - Computerlinguistik
0724-3111	Berliner Botanischer Verein. Verhandlung
0724-3219	Europaeischer Molkerei und Kaeserei Adresskalender
0724-3227	Norddeutscher Molkerei und Kaeserei Adresskalender
0724-3235	Sueddeutscher Molkerei und Kaeserei Adresskalender
0724-343X	Kulturchronik
0724-3464	Sozialwissenschaften und Berufspraxis
0724-3472	Tribologie und Schmierungstechnik
0724-3499	Grundschulmagazin changed to Lehrerjournal Grundschulmagazin.
0724-3529	Militaria
0724-360X	Das Personal A B C
0724-3618	Kindergesundheit
0724-3766	Zwischenschritte
0724-3820	Leben und Weg
0724-4177	Agrargeographie
0724-4223	Bombus
0724-4266	Deutsche Getraenke Wirtschaft
0724-4320	Dokumentation Sprachwissenschaftliche Forschungsvorhaben
0724-4339	G M D-Spiegel
0724-4371	Datenschutz und Datensicherung Zugleich der Datenschutzbeauftragte changed to Datenschutz und Datensicherung.
0724-438X	International Journal of Biological Research in Pregnancy and Perinatology changed to Biological Research in Pregnancy and Perinatology.
0724-4401	Dokumentationsdienst Bildung und Kultur
0724-441X	Fortschritte der Medizinischen Mikrobiologie
0724-4509	Export-Markt, Euro-Revue†
0724-4533	Der Bruederbote
0724-4606	Raps
0724-4681	I C-Wissen Buerokommunikation
0724-469X	Personal Computer
0724-4703	Freiburger Fernoestliche Forschungen
0724-472X	Wolfenbuettler Arbeiten zur Barockforschung
0724-4770	Schwebstaubmessungen in Hessen. Bericht im Messjahr
0724-4983	World Journal of Urology
0724-4991	Oralprophylaxe
0724-5092	Zelte Planen Markisen changed to Technisches Textil Forum.
0724-5238	Asthma Bronchitis Emphysem
0724-5246	Orientierungen zur Gesellschafts- und Wirtschaftspolitik
0724-553X	Deutsche Steuer-Zeitung. Eildienst changed to Steuer-Eildienst.
0724-5572	Selbsthilfe
0724-5637	Deutsche Steuer-Zeitung
0724-5661	Produktionsmenge und Produktionswert der Verpackungsindustrie in der Bundesrepublik
0724-567X	Neue Arzneimittel
0724-5890	Lecture Notes on Coastal and Estuarine Studies
0724-603X	Reinigung & Service
0724-6137	Berliner Theologische Zeitschrift
0724-6145	Advances in Biochemical Engineering - Biotechnology
0724-6153	Getraenkefachgrosshandel
0724-6226	Contactologia-Bucherei
0724-6234	Trialog
0724-6331	Palaeo Ichthyologica
0724-6358	Gemeinsame Koerperschaftsdatei
0724-6471	Holz Aktuell
0724-6706	Einstein Quarterly Journal of Biology and Medicine
0724-6722	Abacus (New York)†
0724-6803	J M C I: Journal of Molecular and Cellular Immunology
0724-6811	M.D. Computing (New York)
0724-6870	EntsorgungsPraxis
0724-696X	Brauwelt
0724-696X	Brauwelt International
0724-6978	Discret
0724-6994	Arbeitsgestaltung fuer Behindertet
0724-7001	Buchwissenschaftliche Beitraege aus dem Deutschen Bucharchiv Muenchen
0724-7087	Universite de Neuchatel. Centre d'Hydrogeologie. Bulletin
0724-7125	Deutsches Meteorologisches Jahrbuch, Bundesrepublik Deutschland
0724-7206	Moto Cross & Enduro
0724-7265	Thyssen Edelstahl Technische Berichte
0724-7281	GaFa - Garten - Fachhandel Saatgutwirtschaft
0724-7435	D C G Informationen
0724-7443	112 - Magazin der Feuerwehr
0724-7567	Mediterranean Language Review
0724-7591	Digitale Bilddiagnostik see 0939-267X
0724-7613	Kaufmaennische Schule
0724-7656	Zelluloid
0724-7664	Omnibusspiegel
0724-7699	Architektenhandbuch Schleswig-Holstein
0724-7729	European Patent Office. Annual Report
0724-7885	Staatsanzeiger fuer das Land Hessen
0724-7931	Baupraxis-Zeitung
0724-8016	I L C O Praxis
0724-8156	Jahrbuch fuer Opernforschung
0724-8164	Besprechungen Annotationen
0724-8172	Medical Focus
0724-8199	Speedway International†
0724-8415	Bibliography of Chinese Studies
0724-844X	Forensia
0724-8482	Jahrbuch Stahl
0724-8555	Erdoel-Erdgas see 0179-3187
0724-8741	Pharmaceutical Research
0724-8822	Archivum Eurasiae Medii Aevi
0724-8849	Altenhilfe
0724-8857	Bayerisches Bienen-Blatt
0724-9179	Gastro-Entero-Hepatologie changed to Gastro-Verdauungs- und Stoffwechselerkrankungen.
0724-9187	Kardio
0724-956X	Wolfenbuettler Abhandlungen zur Renaissanceforschung
0724-9578	Repertorien zur Erforschung der Freuhen Neuzeit
0724-9586	Wolfenbuettler Schriften zur Geschichte des Buchwesens
0724-9594	Wolfenbuettler Forschungen
0724-9616	Informationen Deutsch als Fremdsprache
0724-9624	Das Abendland
0724-9713	Linguistik und Didaktik (Munich) changed to Sprache und Literatur in Wissenschaft und Unterricht.
0724-9780	Forum Loccum
0725-0037	Acquisition, Bibliography, Cataloguing News
0725-0045	Trees and Victoria's Resources see 0814-4680
0725-0096	Scripsi
0725-0142	Commonwealth Scientific and Industrial Research Organization of Energy and Earth Resources. Division of Mineral Physics. Biennial Report changed to Commonwealth Scientific and Industrial Research Organization. Division of Exploration Geoscience. Annual Report.
0725-0150	Australian Weeds see 0815-2195
0725-0207	S L A N T News†
0725-0290	Labour Resource†
0725-0320	Reserve Bank of Australia. Bulletin
0725-0371	Commonwealth Taxation Board of Review Decisions†
0725-0509	Copyright Reporter
0725-0665	Australian Credit Unions Magazine
0725-0673	Australasian Arts and Educations
0725-0711	Queensland Bookbinders' Guild. Newsletter
0725-086X	Australasian Textiles
0725-1122	Health in Schools†
0725-1394	Australian Sound & Broadcast
0725-1424	Herpetofauna
0725-1688	Healthright†
0725-2285	I A S AAustralian Branch Newsletter see 0818-5646
0725-2293	Australia. Australian Water Resources Council. Occasional Papers Series†
0725-2323	Philas News
0725-2455	Diary of Social Legislation and Policy
0725-2803	Social Sciences Bibliography Series†
0725-2919	Technical Aid to the Disabled Journal
0725-2986	Journal of Electrical and Electronics Engineering, Australia
0725-3109	Australian Business Index
0725-3141	Communicable Diseases Intelligence
0725-3338	Farm
0725-3427	Australia. Bureau of Statistics. Commonwealth Government Finance, Australia
0725-3850	Investment Projects in the Hunter Region
0725-3931	Your Computer
0725-394X	Australia. Bureau of Statistics. Queensland Office. Tourist Accommodation, Queensland
0725-4385	Australian Jewish Times changed to Australian Jewish News (Darlinghurst).
0725-4598	Commonwealth Scientific and Industrial Research Organization. Marine Laboratories. Report
0725-4644	Insurance Record of Australia & New Zealand
0725-4709	M I M S Annual
0725-4857	Australia. Bureau of Statistics. Queensland Office. Hospital Morbidity, Queensland
0725-4946	This Australia†
0725-5039	New South Wales in Brief
0725-5136	Thesis Eleven
0725-5365	Toowoomba and Golden West Visitors' Guide
0725-5454	Agricultural Trends
0725-5462	Australian Serials in Print see 1030-2476
0725-5489	Infocab
0725-5543	Brave New Word
0725-556X	Clinical Reproduction and Fertility
0725-5756	Australian National Commission for Unesco Newsletter changed to Unesco Australia.
0725-5810	Australian Transport Literature Information System. Bulletin†
0725-6140	S.U. News
0725-6361	New South Wales. Department of Agriculture. Plant Disease Survey changed to New South Wales. Agriculture and Fisheries. Plant Disease Survey.
0725-6590	Ghalib
0725-6639	Tension
0725-6701	Horticultural Trends†
0725-6809	Hunter Region Quarterly Economic Indicators see 1030-0856
0725-6892	Law of Stamp Duties in Queensland
0725-7090	International Clinical Nutrition Review
0725-8186	Parents and Children Magazine see 1036-0921
0725-8526	Commonwealth Scientific and Industrial Research Organization. Division of Soils. Divisional Report
0725-8739	Merigal
0725-8895	Western Transport
0725-8968	Hostelling
0725-900X	Scitech
0725-9107	Guide to Collections of Manuscripts Relating to Australia
0725-9131	Mining Monthly changed to Australia's Mining Monthly.
0725-9565	Fibre Forum see 0818-6308
0725-9573	Child Accident Prevention Foundation of Australia. Quarterly Journal changed to Safeguard.
0726-0458	Nelen Yubu
0726-0644	A B N News
0726-0717	University of Wollongong. Undergraduate Handbook changed to University of Wollongong. Undergraduate Calendar.
0726-0725	Western Australia. Department of Fisheries and Wildlife. Wildlife Research Bulletin†
0726-0733	Western Australia. Department of Fisheries and Wildlife. Report changed to Western Australia. Fisheries Department. Report.
0726-0741	F.I.N.S.†
0726-0784	Queensland Law Reporter
0726-0822	Australian Society of Sugar Cane Technologists. Proceedings.
0726-125X	Traverse
0726-1276	A B N Authorities
0726-1292	Australian Songs. Series
0726-1306	Songs of New South Wales. Series
0726-1314	Songs of Victoria. Series
0726-1322	Songs of South Australia. Series
0726-1330	Songs of Queensland. Series
0726-1349	Songs of Western Australia. Series
0726-1357	Songs of Tasmania. Series
0726-1365	Songs of Northern Territory. Series
0726-1527	South Australia. Department of Mines and Energy. Special Publications

ISSN INDEX 5771

0726-1586 University of Wollongong. Faculties Sector Postgraduate Handbook *changed to* University of Wollongong. Postgraduate Calendar.
0726-1772 Commonwealth Scientific and Industrial Research Organization. Institute of Energy and Earth Resources. Technical Communication.
0726-1780 Commonwealth Scientific and Industrial Research Organization. Institute of Energy and Earth Resources. Investigation Report.
0726-1861 Australia. Bureau of Statistics. Queensland Office. Number of New Dwelligns Commenced in Queensland *see* 0814-8023
0726-1926 South Australia. Department of Environment and Planning. Adelaide Statistical Division. Land Monitoring Report. Land Sales, Prices, Land Division and Land Stocks Statistics
0726-2019 Australia. Bureau of Statistics. Queensland Office. Brisbane City Statistical Summary
0726-2469 Western Australian Nature Reserve Management Plan†
0726-2566 Australian Beauty Counter
0726-2639 Ed Notes: Australian Union of Students Research Briefs
0726-2655 Education and Society Journal
0726-2809 Wild
0726-3139 Australian Clinical Review
0726-3252 Australian Communication Review
0726-3589 Creative Source Australia
0726-3716 Australian Robot Association. Newsletter
0726-3724 Asia-Pacific Work and Patrol Boat *changed to* Work Boat World.
0726-3759 Queensland Reports
0726-3864 Australia and New Zealand Journal of Developmental Disabilities
0726-4097 Victorian Baptist Witness
0726-4143 Editor's Clip Sheets
0726-416X Curriculum and Teaching
0726-4240 Australian Journal on Ageing
0726-4275 Commonwealth Scientific and Industrial Research Organization. Marine Laboratories. Circular†
0726-4283 Commonwealth Scientific and Industrial Research Organization. Marine Laboratories. Microfiche Report†
0726-4291 Commonwealth Scientific and Industrial Research Organization. Marine Laboratories. Research Report *see* 1031-9964
0726-4291 Commonwealth Scientific and Industrial Research Organization. Marine Laboratories. Research Report *see* 1031-9956
0726-4305 Lutheran Church of Australia. Yearbook
0726-4399 Primitiae
0726-4550 Australian Alcohol - Drug Review *see* 0959-5236
0726-4690 This is Newcastle and the Hunter Region
0726-4844 University of Wollongong. Legislation†
0726-4941 Australian Folk Directory
0726-5247 Periodontology
0726-5816 Administrative Law Decisions
0726-5883 Australian Industrial Law Review
0726-6065 Australian Company Law & Practicel
0726-626X Leaping
0726-6286 Discovery *see* 0311-0737
0726-6472 Maritime Studies
0726-6510 Commonwealth Scientific and Industrial Research Organization. Division of Geomechanics. Geomechanics of Coal Mining Report
0726-657X C S I R O Net News
0726-6715 Historic Environment
0726-6758 Crafts N.S.W.
0726-6987 Australian Waste Disposal Catalogue
0726-7002 Victoria, Australia. Department of Education. Education Nationally and Internationally†
0726-7126 Parent and Citizen
0726-7215 Flinders Journal of History and Politics
0726-7819 Australian Coal Miner
0726-7827 Australian Electrical World *changed to* Australian, Asian & Pacific Electrical World.
0726-8254 Turf Monthly
0726-8416 University of New England. Animal Genetics and Breeding Unit. Occasional Report
0726-8602 Australian Journal of Linguistics
0726-9072 Mask
0726-9366 Western Australia. Department of Agriculture. Annual Report
0726-9501 Western Australia. Department of Industrial Development. Building Investment†
0726-951X Western Australia Products Directory†
0726-9587 Joint Serials Catalogue of Western Australian Academic Librariest
0726-9609 Western Australian Naturalist Scientific Journal *changed to* Western Australian Naturalist.
0727-0003 A.A.P.A. Asphalt Review
0727-0119 Green Pages: Directory of Non-Government Environmental Groups in Australia
0727-1115 Metal Worker
0727-1239 Artlink
0727-1255 Classroom
0727-1417 Australia. Bureau of Statistics. Catalogue of Publications, Australia *see* 1032-805X
0727-145X Pocket Year Book, Australia
0727-1492 Australia. Bureau of Statistics. Overseas Trade, Australia. Part 2: Comparative and Summary Tables *see* 1031-1394
0727-1638 Australia. Bureau of Statistics. Motor Vehicle Registrations, Australia
0727-1689 Australia. Bureau of Statistics. Monthly Summary of Statistics, Australia
0727-1808 Australia. Bureau of Statistics. Queensland Office. Local Authority Areas Statistical Summary, Queensland *see* 1030-4789
0727-2200 Australia. Bureau of Statistics. Western Australian Office. Census of Manufacturing Establishments. Summary of Operations by Group, Western Australia†
0727-2367 Australia. Bureau of Statistics. Western Australian Office. Monthly Summary of Statistics
0727-2405 Annual Summary of Australian Notices to Mariners *see* 1035-6878
0727-2596 Australian Energy Statistics
0727-260X Major Energy Statistics†
0727-2723 Australia. Air Transport Statistics. International Air Transpore *changed to* Australia. Air Transport Statistics. International Scheduled Air Transport.
0727-2731 Australia. Air Transport Statistics. Airline Aircraft Utilisation†
0727-274X Australia. Air Transport Statistics. Commuter Air Transport *see* 1037-5937
0727-2758 Australia. Air Transport Statistics. Aerial Agriculture Operations†
0727-2766 Australia. Air Transport Statistics. Survey of Hours Flown
0727-2774 Australia. Air Transport Statistics. Flight Crew Licences†
0727-2782 Australia. Air Transport Statistics. Domestic Airlines (Quarterly)
0727-2790 Australia. Air Transport Statistics. Monthly Provisional Statistics of International Scheduled Air Transport
0727-2804 Australia. Land Transport Statistics. Non-Government Railways *changed to* Australian Non-Government Railways Operating Statistics (Years).
0727-2979 Business Indicators
0727-2987 Australia. China Council Annual Report
0727-338X Air Pilot
0727-3541 The Australian Gas Industry Directory (Year)
0727-3606 Australian Grapegrower & Winemaker
0727-3851 Australian Medliner
0727-3959 Photoworld
0727-3967 Photoworld Annual *changed to* Focus on Photography.
0727-3983 Photoworld Buyer's Guide. Photoguide†
0727-4076 Annual Survey of Australian Law
0727-419X Australian Journal of Coal Mining Technology and Research†
0727-4211 Collection of Australian Stamps
0727-4327 Sydney for Kids
0727-4335 F R V Kapala Cruise Report
0727-4386 Australian Association of Adult Education. Newsletter
0727-4459 Stereo Buyer's Guide. Amplifiers, FM Tuners and Receivers *see* 0819-0194
0727-5366 Environment Victoria
0727-5447 C A R T *changed to* Truck Australia.
0727-5803 Victorian Consultative Committee on Social Development. Annual Review†
0727-5854 Letterstick
0727-6001 South Australia. Department of Agriculture. Technical Paper
0727-6125 Australia. Sea Transport Statistics. Stevedoring Industrial Disputes. Nature of Issue and Extent†
0727-6346 Property Law and Practice in Queensland
0727-6672 Australia. Air Transport Statistics. Australian Air Distances
0727-6745 Vogue Entertaining Guide
0727-6753 Directory of C S I R O Research Programs
0727-6982 Review of Australia's Demographic Trends†
0727-7121 Photoworld Buyer's Guide. Lenses†
0727-7342 Local Government Management
0727-7369 Institution of Engineers, Australia. Transactions. Mechanical Engineering
0727-758X Business Review Weekly
0727-7687 Australasian Office News *changed to* Office News.
0727-7830 Local Government Law & Practice (New South Wales)
0727-7881 Scales of Costs, Charges and Fees N.S.W.
0727-7903 Scales of Cost Queensland
0727-7911 Building, Planning and Development Service (New South Wales) *see* 0727-792X
0727-792X Planning and Development Service (New South Wales)
0727-7938 Hannan's Local and District Criminal Courts Practice
0727-7946 Jacobs' County Court Practice†
0727-7954 Jackson and Byron Local Courts (Civil Claims) Practice
0727-7970 Stamp Duties N.S.W. & A.C.T.
0727-7989 Local Government Index (New South Wales)
0727-7997 Local Government Ordinance 70 "Building" (New South Wales)
0727-8004 Local Government Ordinances Services (New South Wales)
0727-8047 Baalman & Well's Land Titles Office Practice
0727-8063 Queensland Magistrates Courts
0727-8101 Light Railways
0727-8683 Music Teachers' Association of N.S.W. Quarterly Magazine
0727-8926 A P A I S: Australian Public Affairs Information Service
0727-9078 New South Wales. Department of Agriculture. Soil Survey Bulletin
0727-9256 New South Wales. Department of Mineral Resources. Annual Report *changed to* New South Wales. Department of Mineral Resources. Annual Report.
0727-9264 New South Wales. Department of Mineral Resources. Annual Report. Statistical Supplement†
0727-9418 New South Wales. Geological Survey. Mine Data Sheets and Metallogenic Study *changed to* New South Wales. Geological Survey. Mineral Deposit Data Sheets and Metallogenic Study.
0727-9620 Cunninghamia
0728-0351 Christophany
0728-0734 Trends in Animal Industries†
0728-0858 Q.P.A. News
0728-0874 Government Equipment News
0728-0912 Vox Reformata
0728-1188 Royal United Services Institute of Australia. Journal
0728-1307 Neville Coleman's Underwater *see* 1032-5212
0728-1897 Melbourne Citymission. Annual Report
0728-294X Australia. Bureau of Statistics. Queensland Office. Health and Welfare Establishments, Queensland
0728-3008 Consuming Interest
0728-3210 Paul's Police Offences
0728-3636 P A C E
0728-3873 What's New in Electronics
0728-4276 Australia. Northern Territory Information Service. Territory Digest *changed to* Australia. Northern Territory Protocol and Public Relations Branch. Territory Digest.
0728-4330 Indian Ocean Newsletter *see* 1031-2331
0728-4543 Australia. Bureau of Statistics. Child Care Arrangements, Australia, Preliminary†
0728-4551 Australia. Bureau of Stastistics. Child Care, Preliminary *see* 0728-4543
0728-4632 Australian Pharmacist
0728-4713 Journal of Food and Nutrition *see* 1032-1322
0728-490X Australian Rehabilitation Digest
0728-4969 A F M Explanatory Series (No.)
0728-5132 Australia. Bureau of Statistics. Queensland Office. Census of Mining Establishments: Details of Operations by Industry Sub-division, Queensland
0728-5493 Missionary Society of Saint Paul. Link *changed to* The Link.
0728-5531 Australian Children's Folklore Newsletter
0728-554X Teacher's Tax Guide
0728-5582 Council and Community
0728-5639 Lighting in Australia
0728-5671 Aboriginal Law Bulletin *see* 0817-3516
0728-5701 Image
0728-5884 Monash University. Centre of Policy Studies. Discussion Paper Series
0728-5914 Meridian
0728-5965 Animal Production in Australia
0728-5981 Martin and Morley Motor Vehicle Law (Queensland)
0728-6309 Australian Planning Appeal Decisions
0728-6368 Australia. Bureau of Statistics. Child Care Arrangements, Australia
0728-6376 Australia. Bureau of Statistics. Child Care (Canberra) *see* 0728-6368
0728-6414 A N A R E News
0728-6422 Heritage Australia
0728-6481 Dixson Library Report
0728-6503 In Unity
0728-6546 Australia. Bureau of Statistics. Queensland Office. Building Approvals: Small Area Statistics, Queensland
0728-6856 Australia. Department of Industry, Technology and Commerce. Annual Report
0728-6864 Australia. Office of the Life Insurance Commissioner. Half Yearly Financial & Statistical Bulletin
0728-6910 Australia. National Health and Medical Research Council. Department of Health. Report
0728-6929 Australia. Department of Primary Industry. Poultry Industry Assistance. Annual Report
0728-7275 Owner Builder Magazine

ISSN

5772 ISSN INDEX

0728-7291 Australian Chiropractor's Association. Membership Directory *see* 1037-8839
0728-7429 Libraries and Resources Centres in the Northern Territory. List *see* 1037-6399
0728-7569 Contact (Goodna, Qld.)†
0728-7615 Commonwealth Scientific and Industrial Research Organization. Division of Fossil Fuels. Report of Research *changed to* Commonwealth Scientific and Industrial Research Organization. Division of Coal and Energy Technology. Annual Report.
0728-8387 Australian Teacher
0728-8417 Industrial Reports
0728-8425 Australian Advances in Veterinary Science *changed to* Australian Veterinary Association Conference Handbook.
0728-8433 Australian Cultural History
0728-8948 Muse News
0728-9006 Secondary Journal (Sydney)†
0728-9359 Majalah Ikawiria
0728-9383 Mingay's Retailer & Merchandiser
0728-9413 Factory Equipment News
0728-988X Tandarra
0729-0012 Western Australia. Department of Agriculture. Bulletin
0729-0403 Ebb and Flow†
0729-0446 Social Accounting Monitor
0729-056X Commonwealth Scientific and Industrial Research Organization. Institute of Energy and Earth Resources. Annual Report
0729-0691 Australia. Department of Foreign Affairs. Development Assistance Bureau. Annual Review†
0729-1167 Video Week
0729-1221 Australian Company Secretary's Letter
0729-1531 Australia. Bureau of Statistics. Queensland Office. Census of Manufacturing Establishments: Small Area Statistics by Industry, Queensland *see* 0818-979X
0729-1957 Videoworld†
0729-1965 Videoworld Buyer's Guide Annual†
0729-199X Public Libraries in Western Australia. Statistical Bulletin
0729-218X Antibiotic Guidelines
0729-2368 New Zealand and Dependencies Stamp Catalogue†
0729-2384 Auditopics
0729-2473 War and Society
0729-2562 N U C O M 5
0729-2570 Cameron: Supreme and District Courts Practice N.S.W.
0729-2716 Human Rights: Newsletter of the Human Rights Commission
0729-2759 Breastfeeding Review
0729-2775 Companies and Securities Law Journal
0729-2910 Promissory Note Survey
0729-3356 Australian Journal of Law and Society
0729-3445 Western Australian Egg Marketing Board. Newsletter
0729-3542 Presbyterian Banner
0729-3682 Australian Planner
0729-3828 Superfunds
0729-4042 Christians Writing *changed to* Studio.
0729-4271 Directory of Australian Public Libraries
0729-4336 Commonwealth Scientific and Industrial Research Organization. Division of Soils. Research Report *see* 1032-5441
0729-4352 Australian Aboriginal Studies
0729-4360 Higher Education Research and Development. Research Papers
0729-5030 Hunter Valley Research Foundation. Working Papers
0729-5154 Southern Courier
0729-5464 New South Wales Official Publications Received in the State Library of New South Wales
0729-5472 State Library of New South Wales. Library Deposit List
0729-5529 Scuba Diver
0729-5545 Prime Time
0729-5588 Rural Merchant Magazine *changed to* Rural Business.
0729-5936 Domestic Travel in Queensland†
0729-5944 International Travel in Queensland†
0729-5987 New South Wales Statutes Annotation and References†
0729-5995 Institute of Art Education. Journal *see* 1032-1942
0729-6096 Australia. Air Transport Statistics. Airport Traffic Data
0729-6274 Journal of the Australian War Memorial
0729-6436 Solar Progress
0729-6509 State Trends†
0729-6533 A N A R E Research Notes
0729-6568 Directory of Company Histories of the Book Industries
0729-6924 Australian Science Magazine *changed to* Australasian Science Magazine.
0729-7823 Epiletter
0729-7920 Data Extract
0729-8463 A C R O D Newsletter
0729-8528 Education Guidelines
0729-8579 International Journal of Eclectic Psychotherapy *changed to* Journal of Integrative and Eclectic Psychotherapy.
0729-8595 Australian Society
0729-8714 Architecture Bulletin
0729-8757 Rural Quarterly
0729-8773 Ringing Towers
0729-9389 Sonics
0729-9745 Medical Practice†
0730-0050 Journal of Acoustic Emission
0730-0069 Center Journal (Notre Dame)†
0730-0077 Clinical and Experimental Hypertension. Part A: Theory and Practice
0730-0085 Clinical and Experimental Hypertension. Part B: Hypertension in Pregnancy
0730-0107 Occasional Papers - Reprint Series in Contemporary Asian Studies
0730-0131 Industrial Real Estate Market Survey *changed to* Comparative Statistics of Industrial Office Real Estate Markets.
0730-0158 Keyboard
0730-0212 Mortgage Banking
0730-0220 Literatura Chilena
0730-0263 TeleServices Report *changed to* Information & Interactive Services Report.
0730-028X Swedish-American Historical Quarterly
0730-0301 A C M Transactions on Graphics
0730-0808 Mirror (Washington)
0730-0832 Neonatal Network
0730-0913 American College of Toxicology. Journal. Part A
0730-0980 Peterson's Guide to Engineering, Science and Computer Jobs (Year) *see* 1048-342X
0730-1014 Semiconductor Industry & Business Survey Newsletter
0730-1022 Scott Report on Computer Law *see* 0893-2859
0730-1049 T'ai Chi
0730-1081 Discourse
0730-1162 Sports and Athletes†
0730-1189 Electronics Retailing†
0730-1219 G-Gram: Newsletter for Nurse Managers and Educators†
0730-1251 Coalition Close-Up *changed to* Coalition Close-Up.
0730-1316 Biography and Genealogy Master Index
0730-1367 California Periodicals Index
0730-1383 Teaching History: A Journal of Methods
0730-1502 Offshoots of Orgonomy
0730-1510 Europe on Thirty Dollars a Day *changed to* Europe on Forty Dollars a Day.
0730-1529 Urgent Tasks
0730-1618 News & Clues
0730-1677 National Data Book of Foundations
0730-1707 I E E E International Symposium on Electromagnetic Compatibility Symposium Record. *see* 0190-1494
0730-1715 I E E E Electromagnetic Compatibility Symposium Record *see* 0190-1494
0730-174X International U F O Reporter
0730-1766 Alternative Media Magazine†
0730-1790 International Congress on Instrumentation in Aerospace Simulation Facilities. Proceedings *see* 0730-2010
0730-188X TransAfrica Forum Issues Briefs
0730-1898 Progress in Pesticide Biochemistry and Toxicology
0730-1898 Progress in Pesticide Biochemistry *see* 0730-1898
0730-1928 Psycscan: Learning Disabilities - Mental Retardation *changed to* PsycScan: Learning and Communication Disorders and Mental Retardation.
0730-1936 Shepard's Bankruptcy Citations
0730-2010 International Congress on Instrumentation in Aerospace Simulation Facilities. Record
0730-2134 Discount America Guide†
0730-2150 Skiers Directory†
0730-2177 Southeastern Political Review
0730-2185 Restoration†
0730-2207 Plant Breeding Reviews
0730-2223 S P E X
0730-224X Newsreal
0730-2290 Discontinued I C's D.A.T.A. Book *changed to* Digital & Audio-Video Discontinued Devices D.A.T.A. Book.
0730-2304 Critical Texts: A Review of Theory and Criticism
0730-2312 Journal of Cellular Biochemistry
0730-2347 Texas Heart Institute Journal
0730-2355 The Intellectual Activist
0730-2363 Religion and Life Letters
0730-2371 S S C Booknews
0730-2444 Dean and Director *changed to* Program Trends for Business & Industry.
0730-2487 Kitchen & Bath Business
0730-2533 Directory of Auto Supply Chains *see* 0736-0452
0730-2568 Drinking Driving Law Letter
0730-2584 Mexican Forum†
0730-2606 Annual Editions: Marketing
0730-2614 Journal of Halacha and Contemporary Society
0730-2703 Directory of Drug Store and H B A Chains (Year)
0730-272X Michigan Economy†
0730-2894 Money Fund Safety Ratings *see* 0891-1215
0730-2908 Insiders
0730-2916 Comic Book Price Guide *see* 0891-8872
0730-2967 Dallas Review
0730-3009 Institute on Planning, Zoning and Eminent Domain. Proceedings
0730-305X Sulfur
0730-3084 Journal of Physical Education, Recreation and Dance
0730-3114 Advocate (Athens) *see* 0895-1381
0730-3157 C O M P S A C
0730-3238 Studies in American Indian Literatures
0730-3262 Media Monitor (Ardsley)†
0730-3300 Textures and Microstructures
0730-3319 Fact (New York)
0730-3327 Translator Referral and Translation Services Directory†
0730-3335 Reference Sources for the Social Sciences and Humanities
0730-3416 Bibliognost *see* 0196-5654
0730-3475 Oro Madre
0730-3491 Practical Diabetology
0730-3564 A A S History Series
0730-3785 Library Compensation Review†
0730-3815 Of Counsel
0730-4625 Dimensions of Critical Care Nursing
0730-4633 Shepard's Federal Citations
0730-465X Shepard's Code of Federal Regulations Citations
0730-4684 Shepard's Federal Labor Law Citations
0730-479X Tocqueville Review†
0730-4838 Discontinued Thyristors D.A.T.A. Book *changed to* Thyristor Discontinued Devices D.A.T.A. Book.
0730-4846 Transistor Discontinued Devices D.A.T.A. Book†
0730-4862 Computerized Radiology *see* 0895-6111
0730-4919 California Trial Lawyers Association. Journal *see* 0889-7751
0730-4943 Discontinued Type Locator D.A.T.A. Book *changed to* International Directory of Discontinued I Cs & Semiconductors D.A.T.A. Book.
0730-4978 Burnett Family Newsletter
0730-4986 Scott Scanner†
0730-5001 Carillon News
0730-5028 Federal Financial Regulatory Digest
0730-5036 Gilcrease Magazine of American History and Art
0730-5087 Justice Reporter†
0730-5125 O C L C Annual Report
0730-5141 Minority - Ethnic Media Guide†
0730-515X New Southern Literary Messenger†
0730-5168 Rota Gene
0730-5176 Western Wood Products Association. Export Report
0730-5214 Mennonite Family History
0730-5257 International Media Guide. Consumer Magazines Worldwide
0730-5303 High Speed Diesel Report *see* 1041-5416
0730-532X National Lawyers Guild Practitioner
0730-5419 Food Microstructure *see* 1046-705X
0730-5435 Perceptions (Indianapolis)
0730-5478 Journal of U F O Studies
0730-5710 New York State Archaeological Association. Bulletin and Journal *see* 1046-2368
0730-5796 Security Industry Yearbook *changed to* Securities Industry Yearbook.
0730-613X Islamic Revolution
0730-6148 Journal of American Indian Family Research
0730-6156 Telemarketing
0730-6172 Plains Poetry Journal
0730-6199 Compumath Citation Index
0730-6202 Cable T V Tax Letter
0730-6229 Shepard's Professional and Judicial Conduct Citations
0730-6237 Taft Foundation Reporter
0730-630X Northeastern Environmental Science *see* 0194-1453
0730-6318 Top Farmer Intelligence†
0730-6326 Top Farmer Market Insight *changed to* Brock Report.
0730-6466 Handicraft - Hobby Index
0730-6474 Minerals Exploration Alert†
0730-6490 Sugar Processing Research Conference. Proceedings
0730-6520 Herald (Conroe)
0730-6636 InforMed†
0730-6679 Advances in Polymer Technology
0730-6687 Electronic Games *changed to* Computer Entertainment.
0730-6725 Pediatrics for Parents
0730-6741 Publishing Trade *see* 0899-7039
0730-675X Sculptors International *see* 0889-728X
0730-6776 Master Type Locator D.A.T.A. Book *see* 1048-6607
0730-6784 Air Force Magazine
0730-6792 Animal Rights Law Reporter†
0730-6857 Stanford Italian Review
0730-689X Banking Expansion Reporter
0730-692X Get Rich Investment Guide - Money Maker *changed to* Your Money.
0730-6962 Annual Editions: Social Psychology†
0730-7004 American Health
0730-7039 Shepard's Federal Circuit Table
0730-7071 Datapro Directory of On-Line Services†
0730-711X Catalyst (Des Moines)
0730-7128 American Association on Mental Deficiency. Monographs *see* 0895-8009
0730-7152 Nondestructive Testing Monograms and Tracts

ISSN INDEX 5773

0730-7160 Art Libraries Society of North America. Occasional Papers
0730-7187 Art Documentation
0730-7241 BodyShop Business
0730-725X Magnetic Resonance Imaging
0730-7268 Environmental Toxicology and Chemistry
0730-7322 Progress (Muscle Shoals)†
0730-7594 American Politics Yearbook†
0730-7608 Pest Control Technology
0730-7616 Radio Electronics Special Projects *see* 1042-170X
0730-7624 Highlights of State Unemployment Compensations Laws
0730-7659 Birth
0730-7764 Nickel Topics†
0730-7780 American Journal of Pharmacy (1981)
0730-7799 Communication Briefings
0730-7802 Llama Newsletter *changed to* Llama World Magazine.
0730-7810 Medical Abstracts Newsletter
0730-7829 Music Perception
0730-7853 Sharing Barbara's Mail *see* 0741-5729
0730-8000 Journal of Shellfish Research
0730-8124 Hydrolysis and Wood Chemistry U.S.S.R.
0730-8132 Silver Institute Letter
0730-8213 Structural Engineering Practice: Analysis, Design, Management†
0730-823X Journal of Bioelectricity
0730-8396 Journal of Cardiovascular Ultrasonography *see* 1043-4356
0730-840X Clinical Sociology Review
0730-8418 Respiratory Care
0730-8450 Executive Skills†
0730-8485 Journal of Experimental Pathology†
0730-8604 Tax Notes Microfiche Data Base
0730-8612 Bibliophilos
0730-8639 Mathematics and Computer Education
0730-8647 Runzheimer on Cars & Living Costs
0730-8655 Runzheimer Reports on Transportation *changed to* Runzheimer Reports on Fleet Management.
0730-8663 Runzheimer Reports on Travel Management
0730-868X Thoreau Quarterly†
0730-8779 Datapro Directory of Software
0730-8787 Datapro Reports on Data Communications *changed to* Data Networking.
0730-8795 Datapro Directory of Microcomputer Software
0730-8809 Datapro Reports on Banking Automation
0730-8817 Datapro Reports on Retail Automation
0730-8825 Datapro Office Products Evaluation Service
0730-8876 Transafrica Forum
0730-8884 Work and Occupations
0730-8930 Readings in Health *see* 0278-4653
0730-8949 Novoye Russkoye Slovo
0730-9023 ArtSearch
0730-904X Explorations in Ethnic Studies
0730-9058 C W - P S Special Studies†
0730-9066 World University. International Newsletter *changed to* Liftoff.
0730-9082 Georgetowner
0730-9112 Global Report
0730-9139 Studies in Latin American Popular Culture
0730-9147 Seminars in Urology
0730-9163 Molysulfide Newsletter
0730-918X Food Products Formulary Series†
0730-9198 I F T Basic Symposium Series†
0730-9244 I E E E International Conference on Plasma Science. I E E E Conference Record-Abstracts
0730-9287 Tax Notes - Digest Bulletin *changed to* Index - Digest Bulletin.
0730-9295 Information Technology and Libraries
0730-9317 International Conference on Very Large Data Bases. Proceedings
0730-9384 Politics and the Life Sciences
0730-9481 Arts & Architecture†
0730-9503 Cultural Democracy
0730-9511 Guide to Federal Budget†
0730-952X Legal Briefs for the Construction Industry†
0730-9538 Control and Computers
0730-9791 Jazz Educators Journal
0730-9813 Impact of Travel on State Economies
0730-9872 Telecommunications Sourcebook
0730-9937 Catalog Marketer
0731-0056 Marketing Letter (English Edition)†
0731-0064 Marketing Letter (Spanish Edition)†
0731-0234 Social Questions Bulletin
0731-0250 Cable T V Investor
0731-0269 Cable T V Franchising
0731-0277 Assessment Digest
0731-0285 Property Tax Journal
0731-0307 Union Labor Report's - On The Line
0731-0315 Physician Characteristics & Distribution in the U S
0731-0323 Malcriado
0731-0331 Directory of Religious Broadcasting
0731-034X New Socialist†
0731-0358 International Symposium on Quantum Biology and Quantum Pharmacology. Proceedings
0731-0366 Purrrrr!†
0731-0382 Embers
0731-0455 Places (New York)
0731-0641 Annual Review of Jazz Studies†
0731-0668 Ground Water Energy Newsletter†
0731-0714 Pre-Text
0731-0781 Glory Songs
0731-0862 CraftsWoman†
0731-0897 Xin Tang - New China *changed to* Xinya.
0731-0935 Savings and Loan Sourcebook *changed to* Savings Institutions Sourcebook.
0731-1036 Canadian Mathematical Society. Conference Proceedings
0731-1125 Global Church Growth
0731-1214 Sociological Perspectives
0731-1222 Telltale Compass†
0731-1230 Photonics Spectra
0731-1265 International Journal of Legal Information
0731-1273 Journal of Group Psychotherapy, Psychodrama & Sociometry
0731-1281 Journal of Cash Management
0731-129X Criminal Justice Ethics
0731-1303 Retail Technology†
0731-1362 Digest of Emergency Medical Care *see* 0884-4712
0731-1478 Single Adult Bible Study
0731-163X Michigan Occasional Papers *see* 1055-856X
0731-1745 Educational Measurement: Issues and Practice
0731-1788 Laughing Matters
0731-1850 Educational Computer Magazine†
0731-1974 Creditweek
0731-2032 Clan Ross Newsletter
0731-2148 Journal of Religion & Psychical Research
0731-2180 Sextant†
0731-2199 Advances in Health Economics and Health Services Research
0731-2342 A M S Studies in the Seventeenth Century
0731-2350 Ask!
0731-2369 Worldwide Synthetic Fuels and Alternate Energy Directory†
0731-2377 C M P Bulletin†
0731-2385 Notes (New York)
0731-2474 Colorado Historical Society. Monograph Series *see* 0899-0409
0731-2504 Kinesiology for Dance Newsletter *changed to* Kinesiology and Medicine for Dance.
0731-2547 Orthodox Observer
0731-2652 International Life
0731-2784 Kentucky Geological Survey. Annual Report *changed to* Kentucky Geological Survey. Series 11. Annual Report.
0731-2911 Inter-Society Color Council News
0731-2946 Missouri Folklore Society. Journal
0731-2989 Art and Crafts Catalyst
0731-3071 International Symposium on Fault-Tolerant Computing. Digest of Papers
0731-3233 Index: Foreign Broadcast Information Service Daily Reports: South Asia *changed to* Index: Foreign Broadcast Information Service Daily Reports: Africa Sub-Sahara.
0731-3276 Index: Foreign Broadcast Information Service Daily Reports: Soviet Union
0731-3284 Ohio Arts Council. Biennial Report
0731-3292 Geographical Bulletin
0731-3322 Directory of Computerized Datafiles and Related Technical Reports *changed to* Directory of U.S. Government Software for Mainframes and Microcomputers.
0731-3381 Health Care Supervisor
0731-339X Annual Guide to Public Policy Experts
0731-3403 Medieval and Renaissance Drama in England
0731-3411 C A B Air Carrier Traffic Statistics
0731-3500 Linguistics of the Tibeto-Burman Area
0731-356X Electric Machines and Power Systems
0731-3616 Desktop Computing†
0731-3632 Magnetic Separation News *see* 1055-6915
0731-3667 Journal of Developmental Reading *see* 0022-4103
0731-3675 Media Spectrum
0731-3764 Journal of Undergraduate Research in Physics
0731-3799 Food & Beverage Marketing
0731-3810 Journal of Toxicology: Clinical Toxicology
0731-3829 Journal of Toxicology: Cutaneous and Ocular Toxicology
0731-3837 Journal of Toxicology: Toxin Reviews
0731-3896 Delaware Genealogical Society. Journal
0731-4019 Virrasztó†
0731-4094 Granite and Marble Directory *changed to* A M A Product Directory.
0731-4116 Index: Foreign Broadcast Information Service Daily Reports: Eastern Europe
0731-4213 Collegiate Microcomputer
0731-4221 Mississippi. Department of Wildlife Conservation. Annual Report to the Regular Session of the Mississippi Legislature *see* 0733-2017
0731-4361 Journal of Obesity and Weight Regulation†
0731-437X Aviation Accident Investigator†
0731-4388 Book Report
0731-4396 P S I Monitor
0731-4442 Frommer's Dollarwise Guide to Germany *see* 1044-2405
0731-4523 New Plays U S A†
0731-4531 International Society of Certified Employee Benefits Specialists. Newsbriefs
0731-454X Business and Technology Videolog†
0731-4612 Labor Relations Forms and Agreements
0731-4639 International Property Investment Journal†
0731-4655 Mideast Press Report
0731-4663 Passaic Review
0731-4728 World Affairs Journal†
0731-4817 Rackham Journal of the Arts and Humanities
0731-4833 Dispute Resolution Program Directory (Year)
0731-4841 Gypsy Lore Society. Newsletter
0731-5082 Stanford Journal of International Law
0731-5090 Journal of Guidance, Control, and Dynamics
0731-5112 Southeastern Campbook
0731-5163 Drug Newsletter
0731-5171 Ferroelectrics Letters
0731-518X I D Handbook of Foodservice Distribution (Year)
0731-5198 Independent Film and Video Monthly
0731-5236 Poetics Journal
0731-5244 Contemporary Education Review (Washington)†
0731-5384 Cornell Journal of Architecture
0731-5414 International Demographics *see* 0893-3561
0731-5465 Occasional Papers on Religion in Eastern Europe
0731-549X Freelance Writer's Report
0731-5589 Trends Update
0731-5600 Better Homes and Gardens Kitchen & Bath Ideas
0731-5627 Weather Almanac
0731-5651 Interstate Tax Report
0731-566X People with Special Needs - Down Syndrome Report
0731-5708 Progressive Media *changed to* C M J New Music Report.
0731-5724 American College of Nutrition. Journal
0731-5732 Environmental Forum
0731-5759 Tax Sheltered Investments Law Report *see* 0893-1364
0731-5767 Immigration Law Report
0731-5775 Bulletins on Science and Technology for the Handicapped†
0731-5783 Licensing Law Handbook
0731-5813 Trademark Law Handbook
0731-5821 Tax Sheltered Investments Handbook *changed to* Investment Limited Partnerships Handbook.
0731-5945 Health Sciences Videolog†
0731-602X American Association of Colleges for Teacher Education. Briefs
0731-6143 Gallup Report *see* 1051-2616
0731-6291 Energygrams†
0731-6305 Middle East Business Intelligence
0731-6321 University of California, Berkeley. Institute of International Studies. Policy Papers in International Affairs
0731-633X Directory of Special Libraries and Information Centers in the U S and Canada *changed to* Directory of Special Libraries and Information Centers.
0731-6399 Book Production Magazine *see* 0273-8724
0731-6445 Hydro-Abstracts
0731-6526 Woodall's Retirement Directory†
0731-6704 MacRae's Arizona State Industrial Directory *see* 0739-8476
0731-6720 MacRae's Nebraska State Industrial Directory *see* 0740-428X
0731-6739 MacRae's Maine State Industrial Directory *see* 0740-2945
0731-6763 American Arab Affairs *changed to* Middle East Policy.
0731-6844 Journal of Reinforced Plastics & Composites
0731-6925 Directory of General Merchandise, Variety Chains and Specialty Stores (Year) *changed to* Directory of General Merchandise, Variety & Specialty Stores (Year).
0731-6933 Slick
0731-6941 Economic Development and Law Center Report
0731-6984 Critical Reviews in Bioengineering *changed to* Critical Reviews in Biomedical Engineering.
0731-7085 Journal of Pharmaceutical and Biomedical Analysis
0731-7107 Child & Family Behavior Therapy
0731-7115 Clinical Gerontologist
0731-7123 Residential Group Care and Treatment *see* 0886-571X
0731-7131 Technical Services Quarterly
0731-714X Topics in Strategic Planning for Health Care *see* 0735-9683
0731-7158 Psychotherapy in Private Practice
0731-7174 Texas Vision†
0731-7239 Systems Research
0731-7247 Journal of African Earth Sciences *see* 0899-5362
0731-7441 Better Homes and Gardens Decorating Ideas *changed to* Better Homes and Gardens Decorating.
0731-7700 China Business and Trade
0731-7727 Soviet Business and Trade

ISSN

0731-7824 Herbarium News
0731-7840 Occultism Update†
0731-7840 Encyclopedia of Occultism and Parapsychology
0731-7867 Dictionary of Literary Biography Yearbook
0731-7875 Carnahan Conference on Security Technology. Proceedings *changed to* Carnahan Conference on Security Technology. Proceedings.
0731-7883 S U N Y L A Newsletter
0731-7891 Worldwide Videotex Update
0731-7948 Abundant Life Magazine
0731-7956 Ringling Museums *changed to* John & Mable Ringling Museum of Art.
0731-7980 Cumberland Poetry Review
0731-7999 Research in Real Estate
0731-8006 Photoplay Magazine *see* 0031-885X
0731-8014 Heisey News
0731-8081 Directory of Unpublished Experimental Mental Measures
0731-8103 Southwestern Campbook
0731-8111 Boletin Anglohispano†
0731-812X Batter Performance Handbook
0731-8138 Pitcher Performance Handbook
0731-8146 Insiders Baseball Fact-Book Extra†
0731-8162 Insiders Baseball Fact-Book
0731-8189 Current Treaty Index
0731-8235 Clinical Reviews in Allergy
0731-8294 Radio Only *changed to* Radio Magazine.
0731-8332 Journal of Prison and Jail Health
0731-8359 American Academy of Otolaryngology - Head and Neck Surgery. Bulletin
0731-8367 On-Line (Durham)
0731-8375 Cornsilk from DeKalb County, Il.
0731-8413 Special Aspects of Education
0731-843X Disc Collector
0731-8464 Statistics of Virginia Public Libraries and Institutional Libraries
0731-8499 Snow Surveys and Water Supply Outlook for Alaska *changed to* Alaska Snow Surveys - Basin Outlook Reports.
0731-8510 Directory of Multihospital Systems†
0731-8529 Dallas Opera Magazine†
0731-8545 Chicago Architectural Journal
0731-860X Progress in Solar Energy *changed to* American Solar Energy Society. Annual Meeting.
0731-8618 Advances in Solar Energy: An Annual Review of Research and Development
0731-8626 Progress in Passive Solar Energy Systems *changed to* American Solar Energy Society. Passive Conference. Annual Meeting.
0731-8634 Cook's Index
0731-8650 Occupational Programs in California Public Community Colleges
0731-8758 C B C Quarterly†
0731-8774 Chemical Business
0731-8863 American Paper Institute. Statistics of Paper, Paperboard and Wood Pulp
0731-8898 Journal of Environmental Pathology, Toxicology and Oncology
0731-8979 Johnson Reporter
0731-8987 Atavist†
0731-9053 Advances in Econometrics
0731-9096 Oregon International Trade Directory
0731-9126 Michigan Audubon *see* 0021-3845
0731-9150 Runzheimer Reports on Relocation
0731-9169 International Journal for Biosocial Research *see* 1044-811X
0731-9177 Financial Planning Strategist†
0731-9185 National Five Digit Zip Code and Post Office Directory
0731-9207 S. Klein Newsletter on Computer Graphics
0731-9258 Journal of Computers in Mathematics and Science Teaching
0731-9290 Wordwatching
0731-9371 Middle East Insight
0731-938X Veridian
0731-9398 Classroom Computer News *see* 1053-6728
0731-9444 Jenks Southeastern Business Letter†
0731-9487 Learning Disability Quarterly
0731-9541 Soccer Rulebook
0731-9622 Fleet Owner *changed to* Fleet Owner.
0731-9649 Research: Virginia Tech
0731-9711 L R E Report
0731-9770 Sports Medicine Digest
0731-9991 Teen Bag†
0732-0051 Public Press Newsletter†
0732-006X Collectibles Illustrated†
0732-0078 Center for Peace and Conflict Studies. Occasional Papers
0732-0124 Billboard's International Talent and Touring Directory
0732-0159 Exporters' Encyclopaedia
0732-0167 Nutrition & the M.D.
0732-0175 International Symposium on Computer-Aided Seismic Analysis and Discrimination. Proceedings†
0732-0205 McCarville - Hill Report
0732-0469 Bond Buyer
0732-0485 Everybody's Money Complaint Directory for Consumers†
0732-0515 Asian and Pacific Census Forum *see* 0891-2823
0732-0523 Table Rock Sentinel
0732-0531 East-West Population Institute. Working Papers *changed to* East-West Population Institute. Papers.
0732-0574 Actinomycetes
0732-0582 Annual Review of Immunology
0732-0590 Canadian County Connections†
0732-0671 Advances in Library Administration and Organization
0732-071X Colorado City Retail Sales by Standard Industrial Classification
0732-0760 Drug and Cosmetic Catalog
0732-085X Contributions to the Study of Aging
0732-0868 Psychiatric Medicine
0732-0876 Orion Nature Quarterly
0732-0914 Heritage (Waltham)
0732-0922 Lawyer's Microcomputer *see* 0740-0942
0732-0965 Probation and Parole Directory
0732-0973 Design for Arts in Education
0732-0981 Origin to Destination
0732-099X Salaries (Year)†
0732-1007 Eaglet
0732-1031 American Judicature Society. Annual Report
0732-1112 MacRae's Massachusetts State Industrial Directory *see* 0740-4689
0732-1139 Topics in Geriatrics†
0732-118X New Ideas in Psychology
0732-1228 Political and Legal Anthropology
0732-1295 Cognitive Science Series (Cambridge)
0732-1317 Research in Public Policy Analysis and Management
0732-1341 A F B Directory of Agencies Serving the Visually Handicapped in the U S *see* 0899-2533
0732-1511 Picture†
0732-1562 Women's Studies Quarterly
0732-1597 Numbers News
0732-1813 Federal Reserve Bank of Atlanta. Economic Review
0732-183X Journal of Clinical Oncology
0732-1856 National Cooperative Transit Research and Development Program Synthesis of Transit Practice
0732-1864 Nineteenth-Century Literary Criticism
0732-1872 Homily Service
0732-1880 Entertainment and Sports Lawyer
0732-1902 Sporting News Pro Football Guide
0732-1910 American Bar Association. Forum Committee on Franchising. Journal *see* 8756-7962
0732-1929 Literature and Belief
0732-2224 Beckett Circle
0732-2283 Kagan Census of Cable and Pay TV
0732-2305 Electric Power Monthly
0732-233X Facts About Store Development
0732-2364 Workers Under Communism†
0732-2399 Marketing Science
0732-2402 Impulse
0732-2569 Country Living (New York)
0732-2607 International Symposium on Urban Hydrology, Hydraulic Infrastructures and Water Quality Control. Proceedings†
0732-2631 Supply and Demand for Scientists and Engineers *changed to* Technological Marketplace: Supply and Demand for Scientists and Engineers.
0732-2666 Risk Management for Executive Women
0732-2674 Working Papers in Irish Studies
0732-2755 Directory of Graduate Programs in the Communication Arts and Sciences†
0732-2844 Softball Rule Book
0732-2852 Art Com: Contemporary Art Communications
0732-2895 M F A Bulletin *see* 0739-5736
0732-2941 Co-Op Development Report†
0732-295X Electrical Engineering Problems in the Rubber and Plastics Industry Technical Conference. Record *see* 0272-4685
0732-2968 Memphis State Review
0732-2992 Muqarnas
0732-300X Theatre Times†
0732-3034 Guide to the Evaluation of Educational Experiences in the Armed Services
0732-3085 Asia Foundation. President's Review and Annual Report *changed to* Asia Foundation. Annual Report.
0732-3093 Official New Mexico Blue Book
0732-3123 Journal of Mathematical Behavior
0732-3336 Pyramid Guide†
0732-3395 Meyer's Directory of Genealogical Societies in the U S A & Canada
0732-3565 Advances in Law and Child Development
0732-3581 Your Public Lands†
0732-3867 South Asia Bulletin
0732-4073 Memo (Washington, 1947)
0732-4170 MacRae's Iowa State Industrial Directory *see* 0740-428X
0732-4189 MacRae's Montana State Industrial Directory *see* 0740-6088
0732-4197 MacRae's Colorado State Industrial Directory *see* 0740-6126
0732-4200 MacRae's Idaho State Industrial Directory *see* 0740-6088
0732-4235 Discontinued Optoelectronics D.A.T.A. Book *changed to* Optoelectronics Discontinued Devices D.A.T.A. Book.
0732-4308 Essays in Contemporary Economic Problems†
0732-4375 Photovoltaics
0732-4383 Current Topics in Chinese Science. Section A: Physics
0732-4391 Current Topics in Chinese Science. Section B: Chemistry
0732-4405 Current Topics in Chinese Science. Section C: Mathematics
0732-4413 Current Topics in Chinese Science. Section D: Biology
0732-4421 Current Topics in Chinese Science. Section E: Astronomy
0732-443X Current Topics in Chinese Science. Section F: Earth Science
0732-4448 Current Topics in Chinese Science. Section G: Medical Science
0732-4456 Contributions to the Study of Mass Media and Communications
0732-4464 Contributions in Criminology and Penology
0732-4499 A L P S Newsletter *see* 0740-235X
0732-4529 Legal Writing Journal
0732-4642 Entrepreneurial Woman Newsletter†
0732-4650 A: a Journal of Contemporary Literature
0732-4677 Agricultural Education
0732-4766 Research Perspectives
0732-4839 National Cooperative Transit Research and Development Program Report
0732-4928 Society of Christian Ethics. Annual
0732-4944 Contemporary Philosophy
0732-5215 Directory of Financial Aids for Women†
0732-5223 Clinical Supervisor
0732-524X Office Systems Ergonomics Report†
0732-5258 P I P College "H E L P S" Newsletter
0732-5282 Compensation (Washington, 1982)
0732-5371 A C E I Exchange *see* 0009-4056
0732-538X Photoplay (1916) *see* 0031-885X
0732-5452 Kentucky Libraries
0732-5509 Noncovalent Interactions in Macromolecules†
0732-5517 From the Dragon's Den
0732-5533 Technology Update (Cleveland)
0732-5541 Planning Update†
0732-555X Marketing Update
0732-5568 Chemical Industry Update (North American Report)
0732-5576 Chemical Industry Update (Overseas Report)
0732-5584 Facility Capacities Update†
0732-5592 Process Engineering Update†
0732-5800 Review of Books and Religion *see* 0890-0841
0732-5819 E F L Gazette
0732-5983 Directory of Major Malls
0732-6092 Thyristor D.A.T.A. Book *see* 1040-0222
0732-6181 Annual Allerton Conference on Communication, Control and Computing
0732-6203 Transistor D.A.T.A. Book *see* 1040-0230
0732-6416 Afroasiatic Dialects
0732-6424 Sources from the Ancient Near East
0732-6432 American Research Center in Egypt. Reports
0732-6440 Bibliotheca Mesopotamica
0732-6475 Occasional Papers on the Near East
0732-6483 Syro-Mesopotamian Studies
0732-6491 Monographs on the Ancient Near East
0732-6505 Aids and Research Tools in Ancient Near Eastern Studies
0732-6572 Directory of Incentive Travel International
0732-6580 Journal of Biological Response Modifiers *see* 1053-8550
0732-6599 Buy Books Where, Sell Books Where
0732-6602 MS Outdoors *see* 1041-9306
0732-6610 Freedom in the World†
0732-6629 Natural Gas Production and Consumption *changed to* Natural Gas Annual.
0732-6637 Literary Magazine Review
0732-6653 Producer's MasterGuide
0732-667X Glitches†
0732-6696 Sourcefinder†
0732-6718 Machine - Mediated Learning
0732-6726 Inversion and Imaging†
0732-6734 Commonwealth Novel in English
0732-6750 Inti
0732-6882 Sea Letter
0732-6920 Intake (New Hyde Park) *changed to* Nutrition Action Healthletter.
0732-6971 Statistical Services Directory†
0732-703X American Academy of Osteopathy Yearbook
0732-7196 Broadcasting - Cable Yearbook *changed to* Broadcasting & Cable Market Place (Year).
0732-7218 Modern Methods in Pharmacology
0732-7269 Black Caucus Journal†
0732-7277 Urban Research Review
0732-7315 Northeastern Campbook
0732-7366 Guide to the Energy Industry†
0732-7382 Technology N Y Newsletter *see* 1058-2282
0732-7420 Children & Teens Today
0732-7455 Contemporary Issues Criticism
0732-7471 Flexible Automation†
0732-7501 Portable Companion
0732-7536 Legal Times of Washington *changed to* Legal Times.
0732-7595 Logsdon Connections
0732-7668 Satellite Orbit
0732-7714 Shepard's Federal Tax Citations
0732-7722 Shepard's Federal Occupational Safety and Health Citations
0732-7730 Tulsa Studies in Women's Literature
0732-7757 Cable T V Investor Charts
0732-7773 Dynamath

0732-7781 Gist
0732-7919 Hughes Report *see* 0745-4880
0732-7927 Environmental Analyst†
0732-8001 Lector
0732-8117 Ice Hockey Rule Book
0732-815X Means Square Foot Costs (Year)
0732-8265 Urban Outlook
0732-8281 C F A News (Washington)
0732-8303 Journal of Carbohydrate Chemistry
0732-8311 Nucleosides & Nucleotides
0732-8346 Computer Business
0732-8397 Coal Transportation Report
0732-8435 The C P A Journal
0732-8508 Shasta Abbey. Journal *see* 0891-1177
0732-8516 Financial Review (Champaign)
0732-8583 Abstracting and Indexing Services Directory
0732-8648 Television and Cable Factbook
0732-8672 MacRae's State Industrial Directory: Connecticut *see* 0740-2937
0732-8699 Crystal Lattice Defects and Amorphous Materials
0732-8818 Experimental Techniques
0732-8869 New Directions in Funding†
0732-8877 American Export Marketer†
0732-8893 Diagnostic Microbiology and Infectious Disease
0732-8923 Bifrost†
0732-894X Hennepin County Library Cataloging Bulletin
0732-8958 Taft Corporate Directory *see* 1055-0623
0732-9016 E E M
0732-9059 N C A A Lacrosse Guide *see* 0736-7775
0732-9113 Journal of Legal Pluralism and Unofficial Law
0732-9121 New York State Dairy Statistics
0732-913X Mid-American Review of Sociology
0732-9210 Living Bird Quarterly
0732-927X Subject Directory of Special Libraries and Information Centers
0732-9334 Mid-Atlantic Journal of Business
0732-9407 Fiber Optics and Communications Weekly News Service *see* 1051-189X
0732-9415 Telehints†
0732-944X Preschool Bible Teacher B
0732-9458 Preschool Bible Teacher C
0732-9466 Johnson Survey *changed to* America's Fastest Growing Companies.
0732-9482 Cancer Drug Delivery *see* 1043-0733
0732-9512 Micro Discovery†
0732-9539 Masson Monographs in Diagnostic Cytopathology
0732-9598 Advances in Infancy Research
0732-9636 Medical Liability Monitor
0732-9695 MacRae's Maryland State Industrial Directory *changed to* MacRae's State Industrial Directory: Maryland - District of Columbia - Delaware.
0732-9709 Brooklyn College Alumni Literary Review†
0732-9792 Fatal Accident Reporting System
0732-9814 Rutgers University Studies in Classical Humanities
0732-9881 Disciplina
0732-989X Geophysics: The Leading Edge of Exploration
0732-992X Women Organizing†
0732-9938 Social Responsibility: Business, Journalism, Law, Medicine
0732-9962 Family Life Educator
0733-0073 Black Willow Poetry†
0733-0103 Buying Strategy Forecast
0733-012X Chain Marketing and Management *changed to* Restaurant Management Insider.
0733-0138 Early Warning Forecast
0733-0154 Advanced Solar Energy Technology Newsletter†
0733-0200 Congressional Activities
0733-0219 Oliphant Washington Service. Energy Summary
0733-0227 Digest of Activities of Congress
0733-026X O T C Handbook
0733-0308 Bamboo Ridge
0733-0324 Fordyce Letter
0733-0332 H R Planning Newsletter
0733-0367 Siegrunen
0733-0405 B N A's Weekly Tax Report *see* 0884-6057
0733-0448 A C C Basketball Handbook
0733-0456 Eugene O'Neill Newsletter *see* 1040-9483
0733-0464 Seafood Business Report *see* 0889-3217
0733-0529 Golden Years Magazine
0733-0553 Petroleum Supply Monthly
0733-0677 Waterfront World
0733-0707 Restoration and Management Notes
0733-0928 Offshore Rig Location Report *changed to* Offshore Rig Locator.
0733-0960 Museum Studies Journal†
0733-1142 Research Materials in Microform Available in the Harvard University Library†
0733-1231 All About Issues
0733-1266 Office Guide to Orlando
0733-1274 Software Protection
0733-1290 American Journal of Forensic Psychology
0733-1320 Personal Wealth Digest†
0733-1339 Horse Digest *changed to* International Saddlery and Apparel Journal.
0733-1355 College Catalog Collection
0733-1398 In Vivo
0733-1428 Journal of Existential Psychiatry *see* 0014-4673
0733-1436 Referee
0733-1533 Africus†
0733-1606 Dramatists Sourcebook
0733-1614 Electronics Insight†
0733-172X Noise Pollution Publications Abstracts†
0733-1738 PrintNews†
0733-1746 Public Law Reporter†
0733-1754 Water Flying
0733-1924 Soviet Journal of Friction and Wear
0733-2017 Mississippi. Department of Wildlife Conservation. Annual Report
0733-2033 Theatre History Studies
0733-2076 Aquariculture and Aquatic Sciences. Journal
0733-2130 Collector Editions
0733-2149 Year's Work in Comic Indexing
0733-2165 Literary Criticism Register
0733-2173 Softalk for the I B M Personal Computer†
0733-222X Bio-Technology
0733-2238 Dolls
0733-2262 Doctor's Office
0733-2327 Clinical Nutrition†
0733-2378 World Food Trade and U.S. Agriculture
0733-2386 Display and Imaging Technology *see* 1058-7284
0733-2408 Business Forum (Los Angeles)
0733-2459 Journal of Clinical Apheresis
0733-2467 Neurourology and Urodynamics
0733-2491 Journal of Law & Commerce
0733-2599 Abstracts of Research in Pastoral Care and Counseling
0733-2629 Nuclear Magnetic Resonance Literature-Abstracts & Index†
0733-2637 Options Handbook†
0733-2823 Sporting News College Football Yearbook
0733-2831 Soviet Journal of Chemical Physics
0733-2947 MacRae's Delaware State Industrial Directory *changed to* MacRae's State Industrial Directory: Maryland - District of Columbia - Delaware.
0733-2998 Left Index
0733-3005 Book Alert (Bridgewater)
0733-3013 Mothering
0733-3021 Journal of Applied Meteorology
0733-303X Lasers & Optronics
0733-3048 American Society of Indexers. Newsletter
0733-3056 Equipment Management
0733-3129 Classroom Computer News Directory of Educational Computering Resources *changed to* Classroom Computer Learning Directory of Educational Computing Resources.
0733-3188 Zoo Biology
0733-3196 Footloose Librarian†
0733-3234 MacRae's Louisiana State Industrial Directory†
0733-3242 Postcard Dealer and Collector†
0733-3285 National and Federal Legal Employment Report
0733-3315 Popular Communications
0733-3323 Explorations in Sights and Sounds
0733-3382 Research Review of Equal Education†
0733-3390 Irish Literary Supplement
0733-3536 Computer-Aided Engineering
0733-3552 Greater New York Industrial Directory *see* 0740-2953
0733-3684 MacRae's State Industrial Directory: New Jersey
0733-3692 MacRae's West Virginia State Industrial Directory *see* 0740-4328
0733-401X U C L A Journal of Environmental Law and Policy
0733-4176 MacRae's Ohio State Industrial Directory†
0733-4265 Masson Monographs in Diagnostic Pathology
0733-4273 Journal of Psychology and Christianity
0733-4281 Linxletter†
0733-4311 Auslegung
0733-432X Newsletter Digest
0733-4346 American Journal of Videology†
0733-4443 Current Awareness in Biological Sciences
0733-4451 MacRae's Rhode Island State Industrial Directory *see* 0740-4689
0733-4540 Comparative Civilizations Review
0733-4559 Our Heritage
0733-4567 AirCal Magazine *changed to* AirCal.
0733-4605 Sound Advice *changed to* Wes English's Sound Advice.
0733-463X Traveling Exhibition Information Service. Newsletter
0733-4648 Journal of Applied Gerontology
0733-4664 Harris Ohio Marketers Industrial Directory *see* 0888-8140
0733-4680 Journal of Trace and Microprobe Techniques
0733-4745 Recreational Vehicle Blue Book
0733-4753 Handicapped Funding Directory
0733-4923 Garden Design
0733-4931 MacRae's South Carolina State Industrial Directory†
0733-4958 MacRae's Michigan State Industrial Directory†
0733-4974 MacRae's New Hampshire State Industrial Directory *see* 0740-2945
0733-4982 MacRae's Georgia State Industrial Directory *see* 0740-2910
0733-5016 MacRae's Alabama State Industrial Directory†
0733-5113 Journal of Arts Management and Law
0733-5121 Advances in World Archaeology†
0733-5172 Pension Planning Strategist†
0733-5180 Retirement Planning Strategist†
0733-5210 Journal of Cereal Science
0733-5237 Pennsylvania Directory of Manufacturers
0733-5253 Musician
0733-5342 Leonard's Annual Index of Art Auctions
0733-5350 Middle East Annual†
0733-5369 Divine Slave Gita
0733-5385 Arab Perspectives†
0733-5512 Executive Update
0733-558X Research in the Sociology of Organizations
0733-5644 Journal of V L S I and Computer Systems *see* 0888-224X
0733-5660 Showforth†
0733-5695 Playguy
0733-5709 Biotechnology Research Abstracts
0733-5768 Marketing Science Institute. Newsletter
0733-5776 Studies in Mayan Linguistics
0733-5792 Computational Seismology
0733-5865 Torso
0733-5881 Songsmith Journal†
0733-5946 David McCalden Revisionist Newsletter†
0733-5989 Ecotass (English Edition)
0733-6020 The Independent Study Catalog: N U C E A's Guide to Independent Study Through Correspondence Instruction
0733-6039 Electronic Games Hotline†
0733-6047 Sporting News Pro College Basketball Yearbook *see* 0895-0601
0733-6098 Eastern Mineral Law Foundation. Annual Institute
0733-6136 Teacher Brothers Modern-Day Almanac†
0733-6314 Abrams Planetarium Sky Calendar
0733-6349 Phila City Paper
0733-6357 Faulkner Newsletter & Yoknapatawpha Review
0733-6373 Interscience Conference on Antimicrobial Agents and Chemotherapy. Program and Abstracts
0733-6403 Residential - Light Commercial Cost Data *see* 0738-1239
0733-642X Economic Review of Travel in America
0733-6446 Reclamation Era (Denver)†
0733-6497 Mobile - Manufactured Home Blue Book
0733-6519 Romanticism Past and Present
0733-6527 W A R M Journal†
0733-6535 Journal of Volunteer Administration
0733-6551 Today's Delinquent
0733-6594 Desarrollo de Base
0733-6608 Grassroots Development
0733-6616 Hambone
0733-6683 Clearwater Journal†
0733-6764 Borgo Family Histories
0733-8015 Fiddlehead Forum
0733-8058 Catastrophism and Ancient History
0733-8074 Access (Research Triangle Park)
0733-8104 Washington Report on Africa
0733-8112 Basin Bulletin†
0733-8228 Textbook News†
0733-8244 Inside Textiles
0733-8252 New Product Development†
0733-8309 Rand McNally Campground and Trailer Park Guide. Eastern.
0733-8317 Practicing Midwife *see* 0890-3255
0733-835X North Central Tour Book *changed to* Tourbook: North Central.
0733-8619 Neurologic Clinics
0733-8627 Emergency Medicine Clinics of North America
0733-8635 Dermatologic Clinics
0733-8651 Cardiology Clinics
0733-866X Spencer Museum of Art. Register
0733-8678 Space Press
0733-8716 I E E E Journal on Selected Areas in Communications
0733-8724 Journal of Lightwave Technology
0733-8759 Country Heritage
0733-8813 SurView
0733-8899 Vanity Fair
0733-8902 C L A O Journal
0733-8910 I E C A Report
0733-8929 I W I Monthly *changed to* I W I Newsletter.
0733-8937 Kindex
0733-8961 Information Report
0733-9003 Progress and Topics in Cytogenetics
0733-9011 Composites Technology Review *see* 0884-6804
0733-9097 Calli's Tales
0733-9100 Geothermal Report†
0733-9178 Masson Monographs in Dermatopathology
0733-9305 Infoperspectives
0733-9364 Journal of Construction Engineering and Management
0733-9372 Journal of Environmental Engineering
0733-9380 Journal of Professional Issues in Engineering *see* 1052-3928
0733-9399 Journal of Engineering Mechanics
0733-9402 Journal of Energy Engineering
0733-9410 Journal of Geotechnical Engineering

5776 ISSN INDEX
ISSN

0733-9429 Journal of Hydraulic Engineering (New York)
0733-9437 Journal of Irrigation and Drainage
0733-9445 Journal of Structural Engineering
0733-9453 Journal of Surveying Engineering
0733-9461 Journal of Technical Topics in Civil Engineering†
0733-947X Journal of Transportation Engineering
0733-9488 Journal of Urban Planning and Development
0733-9496 Journal of Water Resources Planning and Management
0733-950X Journal of Waterway, Port, Coastal, and Ocean Engineering
0733-9526 Illinois Writers Review
0733-9542 New Vico Studies
0733-9577 Index to Micrographics Equipment Evaluations *changed to* Micrographics and Optical Storage Equipment Review.
0733-9739 D B S News *see* 0161-3448
0733-9836 Dental Asepsis Review
0734-0052 Marriage Encounter *changed to* Marriage Magazine.
0734-0133 S Q†
0734-0141 On Campus with Women
0734-015X MacRae's Nevada State Industrial Directory *see* 0740-6126
0734-0168 Criminal Justice Review
0734-0222 New Criterion
0734-0265 New York Alive
0734-0311 Soviet Progress in Virology
0734-032X Missouri Population Estimates
0734-0451 Seminars in Hearing
0734-0478 Seminars in Speech and Language
0734-0486 C M R E Monographs
0734-0508 N C A A Men's Water Polo Rules
0734-0575 Japan Economic Daily
0734-0591 Revista Hispanica de Semiotica Literaria *changed to* Revista Americana de Estudios Semioticos y Culturales.
0734-0605 Directory of American Poets and Fiction Writers
0734-0648 Urban Transportation Abstracts
0734-0664 Gerodontology†
0734-0680 Shavings
0734-0699 Loonfeather
0734-0788 Notes on Translation
0734-0842 From the State Capitals. Alcoholic Beverage Control
0734-0869 From the State Capitals. Disaster and Emergency Planning *see* 0749-2782
0734-0877 From the State Capitals. Drug Abuse Control
0734-0885 From the State Capitals. Prison Administration *see* 0749-2790
0734-0907 From the State Capitals. School Financing
0734-0931 From the State Capitals. Workers Compensation *see* 0734-1105
0734-0990 L R E Project Exchange
0734-1024 Soviet Energy Technology *see* 1052-6196
0734-1032 Conductors' Guild. Journal
0734-1059 From the State Capitals. Fire Administration *see* 0749-2782
0734-1067 From the State Capitals. Fish and Game Regulations *see* 0734-113X
0734-1105 From the State Capitals. Labor Relations
0734-1113 From the State Capitals. Milk Control†
0734-1121 From the State Capitals. Taxes - Property
0734-113X From the State Capitals. Parks and Recreation Trends
0734-1148 From the State Capitals. Police Administration *see* 0749-2782
0734-1156 From the State Capitals. Public Health
0734-1164 From the State Capitals. School Construction *changed to* From the State Capitals. Construction Policies.
0734-1199 From the State Capitals. Tourist Business Promotion
0734-1202 From the State Capitals. Federal Action Affecting the States
0734-1229 From the State Capitals. Wage Hour Regulations *see* 0734-1105
0734-1237 From the State Capitals. Water Supply
0734-1245 From the State Capitals. Unemployment Compensation *see* 0734-1105
0734-1415 T A P P I Journal
0734-1415 Technical Association of the Pulp and Paper Industry. Directory
0734-1423 Chilton's Commercial Carrier Journal
0734-1431 Program Plans: Nursing Basic Series
0734-1482 Prototype Modeler
0734-1490 Northern Illinois University Law Review
0734-1504 Scientific and Applied Photography and Cinematography
0734-1512 History and Technology
0734-1520 Physics, Chemistry and Mechanics of Surfaces
0734-1601 From the State Capitals. Public Assistance and Welfare Trends
0734-1628 From the State Capitals. Economic Development
0734-1636 From the State Capitals. Airport Construction and Financing *changed to* From the State Capitals. Construction Policies.
0734-1644 Chemical Engineering: Concepts and Reviews
0734-1679 Soviet Journal of Water Chemistry and Technology
0734-1717 National Logo Exchange *see* 0888-6970
0734-175X E E's Electronic Distributor *changed to* Electronics Distribution Today.
0734-1776 Organize Your Luck!
0734-1784 Plastics Business News
0734-1865 Bibliotheca Americana
0734-189X Computer Vision, Graphics, and Image Processing *see* 1049-9652
0734-189X Computer Vision, Graphics, and Image Processing *see* 1049-9660
0734-1938 Law Review Journal
0734-1962 A S C E Publications Information
0734-1970 Medical Utilization Review
0734-1997 Annals of Sports Medicine†
0734-2047 Transactions on Office Information Systems *changed to* Transactions on Information Systems.
0734-2055 Rainey Times
0734-2071 Transactions on Computer Systems
0734-2101 Journal of Vacuum Science and Technology. Part A. Vacuum, Surfaces and Films
0734-211X Journal of Vacuum Science and Technology. Part B. Microelectronics Processing and Phenomena
0734-2128 Ear (New York) *see* 0893-9500
0734-2306 Boston Review
0734-242X Waste Management and Research
0734-2705 Mideastern Campbook
0734-2799 Partnership Strategist *changed to* Tax Shelter Insider.
0734-2802 New Canaan Historical Society Annual
0734-2829 Journal of Psychoeducational Assessment
0734-2837 Alliance†
0734-2845 Dun's Business Rankings
0734-2861 Dun and Bradstreet Million Dollar Directory *changed to* Million Dollar Directory Series.
0734-2926 Family Studies Review Yearbook†
0734-2934 Bellingham Review
0734-3027 Prophetic Voices
0734-3035 Library Issues
0734-306X Journal of Labor Economics
0734-3078 Shelter Sense
0734-3086 American Library Association. Memorandum *changed to* O I F Memorandum.
0734-3116 W U U A Newsletter
0734-3124 Birth Psychology Bulletin
0734-3256 Harris Illinois Industrial Directory (Year)
0734-3299 Year Book of Critical Care Medicine
0734-3302 Today's Supervisor
0734-3310 Research Strategies
0734-3329 Goethe Yearbook
0734-3434 Desert Plants
0734-3469 Congress and the Presidency
0734-3671 Confederate Historical Institute Journal†
0734-3698 Library Company of Philadelphia. Occasional Miscellany
0734-371X Review of Public Personnel Administration *changed to* Public Administration.
0734-3795 Nibble
0734-3825 Idaho. Geological Survey. Bulletin
0734-4015 Review of Litigation
0734-4031 Henry George Newsletter
0734-4066 Original New England Guide
0734-4074 U.S. Chamber Watch on Small Business Legislation & Regulation
0734-4155 Ohio Business *changed to* Corporate Cleveland.
0734-4171 Clearinghouse Report on Science and Human Rights *see* 0895-5999
0734-4295 Leg Show
0734-4309 Juggs
0734-4325 Packaging and Manufacturing Electronics Data Service†
0734-4392 American Music
0734-4473 Totline (Everett) *changed to* Totline Newsletter.
0734-449X Cormosea Bulletin
0734-4503 Western European Specialists Section Newsletter
0734-452X Midwest Arts & Literature†
0734-4589 Jeffries Report
0734-4651 Federal - State Executive Directory†
0734-4856 C O R D Newsletter
0734-4937 Studies of Israeli Society
0734-4961 Lawrence Review of Natural Products Monograph System *changed to* Lawrence Review of Natural Products Newsletter.
0734-497X River City Review
0734-4988 Ancestors West
0734-5054 U S A 23 Milliones
0734-5089 Virginia Historical Abstracts†
0734-5097 Online Micro-Software Guide & Directory (Year)†
0734-5119 C B A S S E Newsletter
0734-5348 Annual of Urdu Studies†
0734-5399 S M A T V News
0734-5402 Computers for Design & Construction†
0734-5410 Journal of Craniomandibular Practice *changed to* Cranio: Journal of Craniomandibular Practice.
0734-5437 Circle Track
0734-5453 California Homes and Lifestyles
0734-5496 Grand Street
0734-5534 International Chinese Snuff Bottle Society. Journal
0734-5542 E A R for Children†
0734-5712 Valley Forge Journal
0734-578X Southeastern Archaeology
0734-5798 U C E A Review
0734-5801 American Single Shot Rifle News
0734-5836 Nuclear Times
0734-5844 Quality Assurance News for the Clinical Laboratory†
0734-5860 Investing in Real Estate
0734-5895 Speleonews
0734-5917 Bus Facts *see* 0278-1565
0734-5992 Bike Tech†
0734-600X Neurochemical Pathology *see* 1044-7393
0734-6018 Representations
0734-6166 Drug Law Report
0734-6506 Mid-Week Report†
0734-6514 F-D-C Reports: The Pink Sheet *changed to* Prescription and O T C Pharmaceuticals: The Pink Sheet.
0734-6549 China Guidebook
0734-6603 Virginia Country
0734-6670 Journal of College Admissions
0734-6735 Independent Higher Education†
0734-6786 Directory of U.S. Labor Organizations (Year)
0734-6794 Openers†
0734-6816 Cable T V Finance *see* 0893-2131
0734-6891 Baseball Research Journal
0734-6905 National Pastime
0734-6980 Flexographic Technical Journal *see* 1051-7324
0734-7073 Culinary Arts News†
0734-7138 Inkling *see* 0891-8759
0734-7146 Advanced Materials
0734-7219 N E A Today
0734-7324 Alcoholism Treatment Quarterly
0734-7332 Journal of Psychosocial Oncology
0734-7367 Music Therapy
0734-743X International Journal of Impact Engineering
0734-7537 Minnesota Tax Journal†
0734-7545 American Language Journal *see* 0899-885X
0734-757X Contributions to the Study of Computer Science
0734-7618 A M S Ars Poetica
0734-7642 National Union Catalog. U.S. Books†
0734-7650 National Union Catalog. Books
0734-8169 Children's Media Market Place
0734-8401 U Turn†
0734-841X Specialized Subject Bibliographies Series†
0734-8428 Cache Review†
0734-8479 Means Site Work Cost Data *changed to* Means Site Work and Landscape Cost Data (year).
0734-8495 Topeka Genealogical Society Quarterly
0734-8509 Society for Scholarly Publishing. Proceedings of Annual Meetings
0734-8541 Harris Pennsylvania Marketing Directory *changed to* Harris Pennsylvania Industrial Directory (Year).
0734-8584 Rhetorica
0734-8592 Scriptwriters Market
0734-8630 Reproductive Endocrinology *see* 0882-5815
0734-8665 Brecht Yearbook†
0734-8673 C A Selects. New Plastics
0734-8681 C A Selects. Plastics Additives
0734-869X C A Selects. Fiber-Reinforced Plastics
0734-8703 C A Selects. Polyesters
0734-8711 C A Selects. Paper Additives
0734-872X C A Selects. Novel Natural Products
0734-8738 C A Selects. Lubricants, Greases, & Lubrication
0734-8746 C A Selects. Enhanced Petroleum Recovery
0734-8754 C A Selects. Emulsifiers and Demulsifiers
0734-8762 C A Selects. Paint Additives
0734-8770 C A Selects. Electrochemical Organic Synthesis
0734-8789 C A Selects. Colorants and Dyes
0734-8797 C A Selects. Chelating Agents
0734-8800 C A Selects. Catalyst Regeneration
0734-8819 C A Selects. Novel Polymers from Patents
0734-8827 C A Selects. Polymer Blends
0734-8835 C A Selects. Polymer Degradation
0734-8843 C A Selects. Initiation of Polymerization
0734-8851 C A Selects. Block & Graft Polymers
0734-9033 Whole Again Resource Guide
0734-9041 Journal of Fire Sciences
0734-905X Maneapa
0734-9068 Encyclopedia of Information Systems and Services *changed to* Information Industry Directory.
0734-9149 Public Administration Quarterly
0734-9165 I A I A Bulletin *changed to* Impact Assessment Bulletin.
0734-9343 Coal Preparation
0734-9351 Soviet Scientific Reviews. Section D: Physiochemical Biology Reviews
0734-9378 Weekly Statistical Fishery Report *see* 1055-2766
0734-9513 Federal Court Procurement Decisions
0734-9556 Maine Agricultural Experiment Station. Technical Bulletin
0734-9564 Maine Agricultural Experiment Station. Miscellaneous Report.

ISSN INDEX 5777

0734-9637 Information Sources (Year)
0734-970X Beer Marketing Management†
0734-9750 Biotechnology Advances
0734-9831 History of Psychoanalysist†
0734-9874 Entomography
0734-9890 Emotions and Behavior. Monograph
0734-9963 Cutbank
0734-9998 Mutual Aid
0735-0007 Contemporary Policy Issues
0735-0015 Journal of Business and Economic Statistics
0735-0082 Superintendent's Digest†
0735-0147 World Aquaculture
0735-0198 Rhetoric Review
0735-0287 Genealogical Computer Pioneer
0735-0295 Bookmark (Moscow)
0735-0317 Photron†
0735-0368 N C A A Men's Soccer Rules *changed to* N C A A Men's and Women's Soccer Rules.
0735-0414 Alcohol & Alcoholism
0735-0503 Geothermal Hotline
0735-0651 Genetic Analysis Techniques *see* 1050-3862
0735-066X Lumber Price Index. P N W Coast Index
0735-0686 Symposium on Surface Mining, Hydrology, Sedimentology and Reclamation. Proceedings *changed to* National Symposium on Mining. Proceedings.
0735-0732 Healthcare Financial Management
0735-0791 Reliability Physics
0735-0864 Anselm Studies
0735-1097 American College of Cardiology. Journal
0735-1232 Journal of Pascal and Ada *see* 0747-1351
0735-1240 Mark
0735-1267 Arena Review†
0735-1283 American Review of Diagnostics
0735-1313 Molecular Biology and Medicine
0735-1321 Satsang
0735-1348 Ancient T L
0735-1364 Tibet Society. Journal
0735-1399 Society for Commercial Archeology. News Journal
0735-1402 Non-Profit Executive *see* 0882-5521
0735-1550 Saul Bellow Journal
0735-1623 Lone Star *changed to* Lone Star Humor.
0735-1631 American Journal of Perinatology
0735-1690 Psychoanalytic Inquiry
0735-1755 Horizons (Washington, 1981)†
0735-1844 Integrated Service Digital Network
0735-1887 All Area
0735-1895 Theaterwork
0735-1909 Vitae Scholasticae
0735-1917 Water Supply
0735-1925 Microcomputer Market Place†
0735-1933 International Communications in Heat and Mass Transfer
0735-1968 Journal of Park and Recreation Administration
0735-2026 Art Directors Annual
0735-2166 Journal of Urban Affairs
0735-2387 Hillsdale Review†
0735-2417 Indiana Manufacturers Directory
0735-245X Nuclear Tracks and Radiation Measurements *changed to* International Journal of Radiation Applications and Instrumentation. Part D: Nuclear Tracks and Radiation Measurements.
0735-2476 Alabama Business and Economic Reports *changed to* Southern Business & Economic Journal.
0735-2484 Direct Energy Conversion (Oak Ridge, 1982)†
0735-2492 Nuclear Reactor Safety
0735-2506 Nuclear Fuel Cycle
0735-2522 Foundation Grants Index Bimonthly†
0735-2689 C R C Critical Reviews in Plant Sciences *changed to* Critical Reviews in Plant Sciences.
0735-2700 Soviet Agricultural Sciences
0735-2719 Soviet Journal of Contemporary Mathematical Analysis
0735-2751 Sociological Theory
0735-2794 Terrebonne Life Lines
0735-3073 Deep Sky†
0735-3081 Resource Recovery Report
0735-309X Pioneer Wagon
0735-3103 J D: Journalism Directory *see* 0895-6545
0735-3170 Journal of Childhood Communication Disorders
0735-3677 Data Base Newsletter
0735-3677 Data Management Update
0735-3707 Directory of Outplacement Firms
0735-3723 E T C†
0735-3847 Integrative Psychiatry
0735-388X Telecommunications Counselor†
0735-3928 Crime and Justice†
0735-3936 Behavioral Sciences and the Law
0735-3995 World S F Newsletter
0735-4037 Perspectives in Psychotherapy
0735-4134 Peace Newsletter
0735-4355 Dirt Rider Magazine
0735-4398 Celibate Woman†
0735-4576 Hyst'ry Myst'ry Magazine†
0735-4592 Guthrie Bulletin *see* 0882-696X
0735-4665 Sagetrieb
0735-469X Home Video and Cable Yearbook†
0735-4703 Public Administrator and the Courts†
0735-4738 Employee Relations Report
0735-4754 Mason Memories†
0735-4789 Steppingstones†
0735-4797 American Federation of Astrologers Bulletin
0735-4843 Law Office Management & Administration Report
0735-5467 Missouri Archaeological Society. Special Publications
0735-5475 N C A A Football
0735-5513 Official International Business Directory of the Spanish Speaking World *changed to* Official International Business Directory of the Latin American World.
0735-5572 Archive (Tucson)
0735-5688 Sightsaving†
0735-5920 Quarterly Review of Doublespeak
0735-6161 Wood and Fiber Science
0735-6250 International Journal of Entomology†
0735-6315 Perspectives for Teachers of the Hearing Impaired *see* 1051-6204
0735-6323 National Centurion
0735-6331 Journal of Educational Computing Research
0735-6358 Choices: A Core Collection for Young Reluctant Readers
0735-648X Journal of Crime & Justice
0735-6501 Critique (West Vancouver)
0735-6544 Street Pharmacologist
0735-6552 Language Planning Newsletter†
0735-665X Publishers' Catalogs Annual
0735-6676 Outdoor Power Equipment Official Guide
0735-6722 Journal of Health Administration Education
0735-6757 American Journal of Emergency Medicine
0735-6846 Journal of Humanistic Education and Development
0735-6870 Southern Echoes
0735-7028 Professional Psychology: Research and Practice
0735-7036 Journal of Comparative Psychology
0735-7044 Behavioral Neuroscience
0735-7133 Sun Dog: The Southeast Review
0735-777X Musical America†
0735-7788 Musical America International Directory of the Performing Arts
0735-7877 ImportCar & Truck
0735-7885 Kalliope
0735-7907 Cancer Investigation
0735-7915 Clinical Research Practices and Drug Regulatory Affairs *changed to* Clinical Research and Regulatory Affairs.
0735-7923 Journal of Industrial Irradiation Technology†
0735-7931 Polymer Process Engineering *see* 0360-2559
0735-8032 Allertonia
0735-8202 Another Season†
0735-8237 China Spring
0735-8253 Steam Coal Watch†
0735-8296 S C O P E†
0735-8318 U S Catholic Historian
0735-8342 Southern Studies: an Interdisciplinary Journal of the South
0735-8393 Performing Arts Journal
0735-8407 L I N K Line
0735-8423 Electronic Office
0735-8458 Datapro Reports on Telecommunications†
0735-8490 Editors Only
0735-8547 American Journal of Police
0735-8571 New Library Scene
0735-8644 Southern Neighborhoods *changed to* Southern Communities.
0735-8652 Agave
0735-8660 Keraulophon
0735-8776 Daily Guide to Richer Living†
0735-8873 Fund-Raising Review *see* 0899-3793
0735-8938 Rutgers Computer & Technology Law Journal
0735-9020 Yachtsman's Guide to the Virgin Islands & Puerto Rico
0735-9055 Swallow's Tale Magazine†
0735-9144 Taylor Quarterly (Alexandria)
0735-9195 N C A A Men's Ice Hockey Rules and Interpretations
0735-9209 Polish Heritage
0735-9225 Investing & Trading with Spanish Speaking Countries†
0735-9276 Simulation Series
0735-9306 Clinical Ecology
0735-9314 Commercial Space Report†
0735-9330 Code News (Cleveland)
0735-9349 Polish Genealogical Society Newsletter
0735-9381 Processed World
0735-939X Journal of Agricultural Entomology
0735-9543 U C L A Symposium Series on Molecular and Cellular Biology
0735-9551 Ob-Gyn Litigation Reporter†
0735-9640 Plant Molecular Biology Reporter
0735-9683 Health Marketing Quarterly
0735-9691 N A T a T's Reporter
0735-9713 Painting and Wallcovering Contractor
0735-9799 King Saud University. College of Science. Journal *see* 1018-3647
0735-9950 Private Placements *changed to* Private Placement Letter.
0735-9969 School Microcomputing Bulletin *changed to* Educational Computing Chronicle.
0735-9977 Data Base Management
0735-9985 Systems Development Management
0735-9993 Data Processing Management *changed to* Information Management: Strategies, Systems, and Technologies.
0736-0002 Data Communications Management
0736-0010 Foodlines
0736-0037 Nutrition Research Newsletter
0736-0053 Opera Quarterly
0736-0061 Poland Watch *see* 0892-2519
0736-007X Al Hanson's Economic Newsletter
0736-0096 Nutrition Week
0736-0118 Medical Oncology & Tumor Pharmacotherapy
0736-0126 Insurance and Financial Review
0736-0142 C L S Quarterly
0736-0258 Journal of Clinical Neurophysiology
0736-0266 Journal of Orthopaedic Research
0736-0274 Catalyst Media Review†
0736-0312 N S S L H A Journal
0736-038X Oilfield Service, Supply, and Manufacturers Worldwide Directory *changed to* U S A Oilfield Service, Supply, and Manufacturers Directory.
0736-0401 Security Letter Source Book
0736-0452 Directory of Automotive Aftermarket Suppliers (Year)
0736-0460 Indo-Pacific Fishes
0736-0509 Contributions from the New York Botanical Garden
0736-0517 Commercial Lease Law Insider
0736-055X Scholastic News: News Ranger
0736-0576 Scholastic News Trails
0736-0592 Scholastic News: News Explorer
0736-0614 Scholastic News: News Citizen *changed to* Scholastic News: Citizen.
0736-0622 Scholastic News: Newstime
0736-0673 Notes on Linguistics
0736-0703 Cost of Doing Business for Retail Sporting Goods Stores
0736-0711 Plays in Process
0736-0770 Visual Arts Research
0736-0789 Space Journal *changed to* Space R & D Alert.
0736-0878 Co-op Source Directory
0736-0886 Kershner Kinfolk
0736-0894 P C Retailing
0736-0908 Modern Packaging Encyclopedia *changed to* Packaging Line Planning Guide.
0736-0983 Planning for Higher Education
0736-0991 Solar Utilization News (Estes Park)†
0736-1122 Barnhart Dictionary Companion
0736-1149 Threshold
0736-167X Telemarketing Update
0736-1688 Refunding Update
0736-1696 Continuing Education Alternatives Update
0736-170X Almost Free Cookbooks & Recipes Update
0736-1718 Family Systems Medicine
0736-1831 International Industrial Sensor Directory *changed to* International Industrial Sensor Products Database.
0736-1858 Family Records Today
0736-1874 A P R Oach *see* 8750-6106
0736-1890 Recycling Update
0736-1904 Barter Update
0736-1912 Self-Employment Update
0736-1920 Career Planning & Adult Development Journal
0736-198X W.W. 1 Aero
0736-2048 E L T Documents
0736-2056 Avicultura Profesional
0736-2102 Crawford Families Exchange *see* 1043-7401
0736-217X Reporting from the Russell Sage Foundation
0736-2188 Group Members Only *see* 1042-7953
0736-2196 Family Practice Survey†
0736-220X Beverage Alcohol Market Report
0736-2277 Wisconsin Natural Resources
0736-234X Foreign Trade Reports. U.S. General Imports and Imports for Consumption. Schedule A - Commodity by Country *see* 1057-9680
0736-2498 Mar-Marr-Marrs-Mars Exchange†
0736-2501 Noise Control Engineering Journal
0736-2536 Aerospace Engineering Magazine
0736-2544 Patients' Rights in California *changed to* Patients' Rights Reporter.
0736-2579 New England Review and Bread Loaf Quarterly *see* 1053-1297
0736-265X Indian - Artifact Magazine
0736-2676 Wildlife Publications Review†
0736-2684 Answer Man Newsletter†
0736-2692 Book of Apple Software†
0736-2706 Book of Atari Software†
0736-2714 Contributions in Psychology
0736-2773 Intelligence Report (Washington) *changed to* National Security Law Report.
0736-2803 Clinical Rheumatology in Practice†
0736-2854 Dodd Diggings
0736-2862 Oracle Science Fiction and Fantasy Anthology Magazine *changed to* Oracle Science Fiction and Fantasy Magazine.
0736-2870 Michigan Purchasing Directory†
0736-2889 Michigan Manufacturers Directory
0736-2900 Coastal Plains Farmer†
0736-2951 Bits'n Bytes Gazette†
0736-2994 Stochastic Analysis and Applications

ISSN

0736-3001 Journal of Environmental Science and Health. Part C: Environmental Carcinogenesis Review *see* 0882-8164
0736-3044 Center for Self-Sufficiency Update
0736-3427 Foreign Broadcast Information Service Daily Reports: Middle East and North Africa *changed to* Index: Foreign Broadcast Information Service Daily Reports: Near East and South Asia.
0736-3443 Health Lawyer
0736-3559 Almanac of Seapower
0736-3583 Bulletin of Clinical Neurosciences†
0736-3605 Focus on Critical Care†
0736-3621 Computer Programming Management†
0736-3648 Data Center Operations Management
0736-3680 Planetary Report
0736-3745 Facets Features
0736-3761 Journal of Consumer Marketing
0736-3796 Autoharpoholic
0736-3877 ComputerTalk Directory of Pharmacy Systems *changed to* ComputerTalk Pharmacy Systems Buyers Guide.
0736-3885 ComputerTalk for the Physician†
0736-3893 ComputerTalk for the Pharmacist
0736-3907 Mosasaur
0736-3966 Poetry Index Annual
0736-3974 Text (New York)
0736-3982 C U N Y English Forum†
0736-4075 New York Law School Journal of International and Comparative Law
0736-4083 Unique (Denville)
0736-4121 Strategic Moves
0736-4148 Latin America and Caribbean Contemporary Record
0736-4156 Telecommunications Product Review *changed to* Telecommunications Product Review and C P E Strategies.
0736-4202 Stimuli for Writers†
0736-4261 Fort Smith Historical Society. Journal
0736-427X High Tech Investor (Barrington)
0736-4377 Chiropractic History
0736-4393 Journal of Clinical Immunoassay
0736-4547 Protein Abnormalities†
0736-4555 Beckman Center News *changed to* Beckman Center News and Other Library News.
0736-458X Physical Bioinorganic Chemistry Series†
0736-4628 Quarry West
0736-4644 Bacon's Media Alerts
0736-4660 N A F S A Directory of Institutions and Individuals in International Educational Exchange
0736-4679 Journal of Emergency Medicine
0736-4709 Corporate Aviation Safety Seminar. Proceedings
0736-4725 Illuminations
0736-4733 Creative Woman
0736-4822 Metropolitan Life Foundation. Statistical Bulletin *see* 0741-9767
0736-4873 People's Medical Society Newsletter
0736-489X Cable T V Law and Finance *changed to* Cable T V and New Media Law & Finance.
0736-4903 L C Folk Archive Finding Aid
0736-4911 L C Folk Archive Reference Aid
0736-4962 Dairy World
0736-4970 Adrift
0736-5020 Personal Computer News *changed to* Computer Trader.
0736-5039 Isotope Effects in Chemical Reactions†
0736-5047 T and D Health and Safety Report *see* 0737-5743
0736-5071 A I Trends
0736-508X Dynamic Psychotherapy *changed to* Psychoanalysis and Psychotherapy.
0736-511X N C A A Wrestling Rules
0736-5128 N C A A Men's and Women's Swimming and Diving Rules
0736-5160 N C A A Football Rules and Interpretations
0736-5179 N C A A Illustrated Men's Rules *changed to* N C A A Men's and Women's Illustrated Basketball Rules.
0736-5187 N C A A Men's Basketball Rules and Interpretations *changed to* N C A A Men's and Women's Basketball Rules and Interpretations.
0736-5195 N C A A Men's Read-Easy Basketball Rules
0736-5209 N C A A Baseball Rules
0736-5225 Management Technology†
0736-5233 N A R D Home Health Care Pharmacy Bulletin†
0736-5268 Models of Scientific Thought
0736-5314 Seybold Report on Professonal Computing *changed to* Seybold Outlook on Professional Computing.
0736-5470 Eyas
0736-5527 Journal of Buyouts and Acquisitions *see* 0898-8390
0736-5659 Banking Literature Index
0736-5705 Electronic Business Forecast
0736-5713 Guide to United States Treaties in Force
0736-5721 International Gas Research Conference. Proceedings
0736-573X Environmental Statutes
0736-5748 International Journal of Developmental Neuroscience
0736-5764 Service Business *changed to* Cleaning Business.
0736-5810 Journal of Defense and Diplomacy *see* 1044-3177
0736-5829 Adapted Physical Activity Quarterly
0736-5845 Robotics and Computer-Integrated Manufacturing
0736-5853 Telematics and Informatics
0736-6051 Money Market Directory of Pension Funds and Their Investment Managers
0736-6094 Wildlife Disease Review
0736-6108 Clinical Progress in Pacing and Electrophysiology *see* 0892-1059
0736-6124 Older Car Red Book
0736-6132 Come - All - Ye
0736-6205 BioTechniques
0736-6213 Bioengineering Abstracts *changed to* Bioengineering and Biotechnology Abstracts.
0736-6256 No-Load Fund Investor
0736-6264 Handbook for No-Load Fund Investors
0736-6272 Urban Insights Monograph Series†
0736-6299 Solvent Extraction and Ion Exchange
0736-6396 I L R Report
0736-6477 Wilderness
0736-6531 Strategy and Tactics
0736-6574 Journal of Macromolecular Science: Part C - Reviews in Macromolecular Chemistry and Physics
0736-6620 Geothermal Energy Technology *changed to* Geothermal Energy.
0736-6701 Children's Defense Budget *see* 1055-9213
0736-6825 Facial Plastic Surgery
0736-6884 International Astronomical Union. Minor Planet Center. Minor Planet Circulars - Minor Planets and Comets
0736-6892 S I G U C C S Newsletter
0736-6906 S I G C H I Bulletin
0736-6922 International Comet Quarterly
0736-6957 Small Business Computer News†
0736-6981 E D P A C S
0736-7023 Cryptozoology
0736-7139 List of Serials Indexed for Online Users
0736-7163 Georgetown University Center for Strategic and International Studies. Significant Issues Series *changed to* Center for Strategic and International Studies. Significant Issues Series.
0736-7171 Better Rep Management†
0736-718X Minerva
0736-721X A C M Ada Letters
0736-7236 Journal of Social and Clinical Psychology
0736-7244 Somatosensory Research *see* 0899-0220
0736-7252 A P P A Newsletter
0736-7260 Seybold Report on Publishing Systems
0736-7317 Officer Review
0736-7392 Method: Journal of Lonergan Studies
0736-7430 Independence (Baltimore)†
0736-7457 Professional Publishing *see* 1060-2208
0736-7511 State Education Leader
0736-7635 Employee Communication *changed to* Williams Report.
0736-7643 Astute Investor (Kingston)
0736-7694 Cardozo Arts & Entertainment Law Journal
0736-7716 Population Trends and Public Policy
0736-7740 Music Reference Collection
0736-7759 Directory of Free Programs, Performing Talent and Attractions
0736-7775 N C A A Men's Lacrosse Rules
0736-7783 N C A A Men's and Women's Cross Country and Track & Field Rules
0736-7929 Healthline
0736-7953 Red Book Used Car Guide
0736-7988 Wisconsin Auto Valuation Guide
0736-8003 Ohio State University. Agricultural Research and Development Center. Special Circular
0736-8038 Zero to Three
0736-8046 Pediatric Dermatology
0736-8054 International Society for British Genealogy and Family History. Newsletter
0736-8089 Telephone Cost and Call Management *changed to* Telecommunications World.
0736-8143 Cable T V Financial Databook
0736-8151 The Federalist
0736-8194 Two - Sixteen Magazine *see* 0743-4278
0736-8232 P T C Newsletter
0736-8259 Master Production Scheduling†
0736-8283 Journal of Nutrition, Growth and Cancer
0736-8305 Execution and Control Systems†
0736-8313 Manufacturing Resource Planning†
0736-8321 Material Requirements Planning†
0736-8348 Smarts Insurance Bulletin
0736-8496 Oregon Wine Review *see* 0892-8363
0736-8518 Alef
0736-8534 Development News for Libraries†
0736-8593 Computers in Nursing
0736-8607 CoED Journal *changed to* Computers in Education Journal.
0736-8879 Footnotes (Chicago)
0736-895X A S E E Computers in Education Division. Application Notes *changed to* Computers in Education Journal.
0736-9050 Business of Herbs
0736-9069 Broadcast Investor Charts
0736-9077 Capell's Circulation Report
0736-9115 Ancestor Hunt
0736-9123 Papers in Comparative Studies
0736-9166 Work Times
0736-9182 Free Inquiry in Creative Sociology
0736-9212 Yellow Silk
0736-9220 The Hook
0736-9239 The Exporter
0736-9271 Black Fly Review
0736-928X Trivia
0736-931X Directory of Discount Department Stores *see* 0897-5442
0736-9417 Laser Medicine and Surgery News *see* 1044-5471
0736-9433 W L D F News
0736-9492 Color Computer Magazine†
0736-9522 Conservation (Year)†
0736-9549 Reed Organ Society Bulletin
0736-9557 Hayes of America Herald
0736-9603 Environmental Opportunities
0736-9662 Jubilee International *changed to* Jubilee International.
0736-9689 Pest Alerts†
0736-9719 Nursing Report
0736-9735 Psychoanalytic Psychology
0736-9743 Better Beagling
0736-9921 Supreme Court Economic Review
0736-9999 Index to USA Today *see* 0893-2409
0737-0008 Cognition and Instruction
0737-0016 Journal of Community Health Nursing
0737-0024 Human - Computer Interaction (Hillsdale)
0737-0032 Musical Woman
0737-0040 America's Textile *see* 0890-9970
0737-0083 Research Publications. Report†
0737-0172 Theatre Directory of the Bay Area (Year)
0737-0318 Growing Child Research Review
0737-0334 Computer Book Review
0737-0342 Western Humor and Irony Membership Serial Yearbook *see* 0933-1719
0737-0350 Sipiscope
0737-0393 Mississippi Kite
0737-0407 Aristos
0737-0415 Industrial Communications
0737-0466 Coyote†
0737-0482 Monthly Rent†
0737-0555 Langston Hughes Review
0737-0652 Journal of Energetic Materials
0737-0660 N F A I S Trainers' Circuit Newsletter†
0737-0679 Walt Whitman Quarterly Review
0737-0806 Journal of Equine Veterinary Science
0737-0881 Timex Sinclair User†
0737-089X Law & Inequality
0737-0903 Distribution Management†
0737-0911 Sporting News Draft Guide†
0737-0938 Psychotherapy Newsletter†
0737-0946 Business Computer Digest
0737-0954 Oxcart
0737-0989 North Jersey Regional Industrial Purchasing Guide *changed to* North Jersey Regional Industrial Buying Guide.
0737-0997 Dance Notation Journal†
0737-1020 High Volume Printing
0737-1055 I C P Data Processing Management†
0737-1071 Research on Technological Innovation, Management and Policy
0737-1160 Conference on Crime Countermeasures and Security. Proceedings *changed to* Carnahan Conference on Security Technology. Proceedings.
0737-1187 Personal Computer Buyers Guide†
0737-1195 Journal of Polymorphous Perversity
0737-1209 Public Health Nursing
0737-1217 Defense (Year)
0737-1292 E R I C - A A H E Research Reports *see* 0884-0040
0737-1306 Starmont Studies in Literary Criticism
0737-1314 New York State Directory
0737-139X Cuyahoga Review
0737-1411 Ethnic American Voluntary Organizations
0737-1454 International Journal of Cell Cloning
0737-1667 Beatniks from Space†
0737-187X Today's Education - Educational Support Edition *changed to* N E A Today: Educational Support Edition.
0737-1888 Today's Education (Annual Edition) *see* 0734-7219
0737-2094 Chapter I Handbook: Understanding and Implementing the Program
0737-2108 Science Citation Index. Abridged Edition†
0737-2124 Personal Communications *see* 0885-6710
0737-2140 Computer Classified Bluebook†
0737-2159 Banking Law Anthology
0737-2175 Biology (Year)†
0737-2191 Japan, Inc.
0737-2205 Snews
0737-2426 Conference on Electrical Insulation. Annual Report *see* 0084-9162
0737-2477 Diagnostique
0737-2590 Law School Journal
0737-2612 Best of Newspaper Design
0737-2620 National Travel Survey
0737-268X Alaska Quarterly Review
0737-2698 History of Higher Education Annual
0737-2817 Insulation Guide
0737-285X N Y C
0737-2884 International Journal of Satellite Communications
0737-2906 Personal Computer Age†

ISSN INDEX 5779

0737-2914 Perspectives in Clinical Pharmacology *changed to* Perspectives in Clinical Pharmacy.
0737-3082 Hypnotica†
0737-3112 Probate Law Journal
0737-3139 Medicom Drug Information Newsletter
0737-3147 Washington Business Journal
0737-3155 A P L News
0737-3163 Guide to Four-Year Colleges *see* 0894-9336
0737-318X Calligraphy Idea Exchange *see* 0895-7819
0737-3244 Communicator's Journal†
0737-3252 Journal of Health Care Marketing
0737-3368 Wharton Annual†
0737-3457 Abridged Catholic Periodical and Literature Index†
0737-3481 Fiscal Policy Forum†
0737-3627 Social Service Organizations and Agencies Directory
0737-3635 American Poetry†
0737-3716 Compute's Gazette†
0737-3724 New International
0737-3732 Outlook (Seattle)
0737-3740 Country Home
0737-3759 Quebec Studies
0737-3813 NewsBank (New Canaan)
0737-3929 International Television†
0737-3937 Drying Technology
0737-3945 Pediatric and Adolescent Gynecology†
0737-3953 Monographs in Neuroscience
0737-3988 NewsBank Review of the Arts: Film and Television
0737-3996 NewsBank Review of the Arts: Performing Arts
0737-4003 NewsBank Review of the Arts: Fine Arts and Architecture
0737-4011 Newsbank Review of the Arts: Literature
0737-402X Alternative Methods in Toxicology Series
0737-4038 Molecular Biology and Evolution
0737-4135 Standard & Poor's Stock Guide
0737-4143 Southwest Journal of Linguistics
0737-4178 Fedlink Technical Notes
0737-4208 Reading Today
0737-4313 Computers (Year)†
0737-4445 Ward's Directory of 49,000 Private U.S. Companies†
0737-4453 Source: Notes in the History of Art
0737-4461 Index to International Statistics
0737-4607 Journal of Accounting Literature
0737-4704 Fine Madness
0737-4720 Linguistic Notes from La Jolla
0737-4747 Poetry Flash
0737-481X Estes Trails
0737-4828 Journal of Evolutionary Psychology
0737-4836 Translation Review
0737-4844 Telephone Equipment Selection Guide *changed to* Telecommunications World.
0737-4984 L H R T Newsletter
0737-500X Computers, Reading and Language Arts†
0737-5034 T'ang Studies
0737-5077 Mobile Phone News
0737-5123 Parenting Studies
0737-5131 Paedovita
0737-514X Paedoperisse
0737-5158 Paedonoson
0737-5166 Acta Paedologica
0737-5174 Trisomy 21
0737-5182 Chiaroscuro†
0737-5255 Government Programs and Projects Directory
0737-5298 Luna Tack†
0737-5328 Teacher Education Quarterly
0737-5336 E P B: Electronic Publishing and Bookselling *see* 0888-0948
0737-5344 Design Book Review
0737-5379 New York Spectator
0737-5387 New Observations
0737-545X Surveys, Polls, Censuses and Forecasts Directory†
0737-5506 Salthouse†
0737-5700 Robotics Update†
0737-5743 Transmission - Distribution Health & Safety Report
0737-5778 Social Work and Christianity
0737-5840 Mystics Quarterly
0737-5875 Washington Tax Review *see* 0887-2562
0737-5883 Creative
0737-5905 American Prometheus†
0737-5980 Biotechnology Education Report†
0737-5999 Central Nervous System Trauma *see* 0897-7151
0737-6006 A I D S Research *see* 0889-2229
0737-6146 Advances in Anesthesia
0737-6227 Hunter Safety Instructor *changed to* Hunter Education Instructor.
0737-6413 Banking World
0737-6553 Electronic Imaging†
0737-660X C A D - C A M Technology *changed to* C I M Technology.
0737-6650 American Asian Review
0737-6707 Notes on Literacy
0737-6766 Occultation Newsletter
0737-6782 Journal of Product Innovation Management
0737-6812 A N S News
0737-6839 Personal Property Section News
0737-6855 Muppet Magazine†
0737-688X Engel-Poh Family History Newsletter
0737-7002 Slavic and European Arts
0737-7037 Journal of Folklore Research
0737-7169 Hemlocks and Balsams†
0737-7258 Heydon - Hayden - Hyden Families Quarterly
0737-7266 Liquid Fuels Technology *see* 0884-3759
0737-7363 Journal of Continuing Higher Education
0737-7371 Ohio C P A *changed to* Ohio C P A Journal.
0737-738X Patristic and Byzantine Review
0737-7436 Print World. Journal
0737-7495 Ohio Manufacturers Directory
0737-7576 Light Impressions Review†
0737-7592 O A - F A Update†
0737-7622 Communications Lawyer
0737-7630 Passport to Legal Understanding
0737-769X Journal of Chinese Religions
0737-772X Recent Transportation Literature for Planning and Engineering Librarians†
0737-7746 Aviation Litigation Reporter
0737-7762 Social Concept
0737-7770 Information Intelligence Online Libraries and Microcomputers *changed to* Online Libraries and Microcomputers.
0737-7797 Resource Sharing & Information Networks
0737-7843 Periodical Title Abbreviations
0737-7851 Current Issues in Psychoanalytic Practice. Journal *changed to* Current Issues in Psychoanalytic Practice. Monographs.
0737-7908 Robotics World
0737-7908 Robotics World Directory
0737-7932 Itawamba Settlers
0737-7940 Iowa Manufacturers Register
0737-8076 Hot Off the Computer
0737-8092 Center for Holocaust Studies Newsletter
0737-8122 Officemation Reports *see* 0161-8768
0737-8173 Lighted Pathway†
0737-8181 International Dredging Review
0737-8211 Systematic Botany Monographs
0737-8246 Quaker Yeomen
0737-8262 Current Psychological Research and Reviews *see* 1046-1310
0737-8289 Living Abroad *changed to* International Assignment.
0737-8335 Kahawai†
0737-8483 Membrane & Separation Technology News
0737-8505 Personal Robotics News†
0737-8513 Toxic Chemicals Litigation Reporter
0737-8548 World Spaceflight News
0737-8742 Discurso Literario *changed to* Discurso.
0737-8823 Euphorbia Journal
0737-8831 Library Hi Tech Journal
0737-8939 P C World
0737-8947 Boston University International Law Journal
0737-8998 Office Systems Research Journal
0737-9005 Zoobooks
0737-9021 E M I E Bulletin
0737-903X Hospital Management Review
0737-9080 Film Review Annual
0737-9218 White House Weekly
0737-9242 Roots and Branches
0737-9269 Blind Alleys
0737-9285 National Center for the Study of Collective Bargaining in Higher Education and the Professions. Newsletter
0737-948X Federal Reserve Bank of Minneapolis. Agricultural Credit Conditions Survey
0737-9501 Software Publishing Report†
0737-951X DataBase Alert
0737-9587 C R C Critical Reviews in Oncology - Hematology *see* 1040-8428
0738-0070 Wisconsin Manufacturers Register
0738-0089 International Hazardous Materials Transport *changed to* International Hazardous Materials Transport Manual.
0738-0097 Biography Almanac *changed to* Almanac of Famous People.
0738-0119 Starmont Contemporary Writers Series *see* 0163-2469
0738-0127 Starmont Reference Guides
0738-0143 Winning Sweepstakes Newsletter
0738-0151 Child and Adolescent Social Work Journal
0738-0186 Leader's Legal Tech Newsletter
0738-0194 P C Tech Journal†
0738-0208 Jobless Newsletter†
0738-0232 Hazardous Waste Consultant
0738-0313 Technical Association of the Pulp and Paper Industry. Paper Finishing and Converting Conference. Proceedings (Year) *see* 1050-4265
0738-0453 MicroWorld *changed to* Faulkner Report on Microcomputers and Software.
0738-0461 Aerospace Defense Markets & Technology†
0738-050X Southeast Asia Chronicle†
0738-0518 Consumer Sourcebook
0738-0569 Computers in the Schools
0738-0577 Occupational Therapy in Health Care
0738-0585 Forest Planning *see* 1057-2724
0738-0593 International Journal of Educational Development
0738-0623 Police Misconduct and Civil Rights Law Report
0738-064X A M S Studies in Anthropology
0738-0658 Puerto Rico Health Sciences Journal
0738-0666 Journal of Mechanisms, Transmissions and Automation in Design *see* 1050-0472
0738-0674 New Relationships†
0738-0690 Preview (Northbrook)
0738-0739 Holocaust Studies Annual
0738-0755 Studies in Black American Literature
0738-0763 Essays in Graham Greene
0738-0771 Smart Machines†
0738-081X Clinics in Dermatology
0738-0895 Journal of Architectural and Planning Research
0738-0925 Recent Publications in Natural History
0738-0941 5 Great Romances†
0738-095X World's Greatest Love Stories†
0738-0968 Space Age Times
0738-100X A C M - I E E E Design Automation Conference. Proceedings
0738-1018 Anesthesiology Malpractice Reporter
0738-1026 Malpractice Reporter
0738-1069 Cognitive Rehabilitation *changed to* Journal of Cognitive Rehabilitation.
0738-1085 Microsurgery
0738-1093 Overland Journal
0738-1131 Architecture California
0738-114X Planning & Zoning News
0738-1239 Means Residential Cost Data
0738-1247 Parascope
0738-1360 Journal of Marine Resource Economics *changed to* Marine Resource Economics.
0738-1379 Latin American Jewish Studies Newsletter
0738-1387 Robot - X News
0738-1395 C O A Review *changed to* Perrin & Treggett's Review.
0738-1409 English Leadership Quarterly
0738-1425 International Development Resource Books
0738-1433 Women's Review of Books
0738-1441 Lens Research†
0738-1514 Minnesota Manufacturers Register
0738-1522 Information America†
0738-1530 Fellowship Communique *changed to* Jubilee International.
0738-1719 Ethnic Information Sources of the U S
0738-1727 Journal of Modern Greek Studies
0738-1735 Journal of the Strong Arm
0738-1743 Polymer Science Yearbook
0738-1751 Antimicrobic Newsletter
0738-1859 Small Farm Advocate
0738-1891 Oregon Genealogical Society Quarterly
0738-1913 Collective Bargaining in Higher Education and the Professions. Annual Bibliography
0738-1956 Malpractice Reporter. Hospitals Edition
0738-2022 Journal of Forth Application and Research
0738-2103 National Center for the Study of Collective Bargaining in Higher Education. Newsletter *see* 0737-9285
0738-2170 B O M A Experience Exchange Report
0738-2170 Experience Exchange Report
0738-2227 New Products Marketplace†
0738-2278 Advances in Orthopaedic Surgery
0738-2294 Gesar
0738-2324 Guide to the High Technology and Industries†
0738-2421 Holly Society Journal
0738-2472 Coastal Ocean Pollution Assessment News†
0738-2480 Law and History Review
0738-2502 Precious Metals Performance Digest†
0738-2588 S C A Radio Subcarrier Report *see* 0882-5726
0738-260X National Fact Book of Savings Banking *see* 8756-9043
0738-2685 American Bus Association. Annual Report *see* 0278-1565
0738-2766 Consumer Health Reporter†
0738-2812 New Haven Studies in International Law and World Public Order
0738-2898 Journal of Environmental Horticulture
0738-2928 Journal of Hospital Supply, Processing and Distribution *see* 0889-2482
0738-3045 Telecommunications Systems and Services Directory *see* 1055-8454
0738-3053 Magnolia (Hammond)
0738-3096 Government Tender Report
0738-310X Government Traffic Bulletin
0738-3169 American Foreign Policy Newsletter
0738-3215 University Research in Business and Economics: a Bibliography of (Year) Publications
0738-3223 El Salvador Bulletin *see* 0893-7699
0738-3231 Instrumentation Symposium for the Process Industries *changed to* Instrumentation for the Process Industries.
0738-3312 Government Union Critique
0738-3355 Technical Analysis of Stocks & Commodities
0738-3371 New-Radio Cable Audio & Pay Radio Report†
0738-3398 I B C D: International Business Conditions Digest
0738-3401 Administration and Policy Journal
0738-341X Inter-Connection *see* 0271-5430
0738-3568 Database Update *see* 0737-0946
0738-3576 Digit Magazine
0738-3614 Computers in Psychiatry - Psychology†

ISSN

5780 ISSN INDEX

0738-3711 Ohio Directory of Manufacturers *see* 0737-7495
0738-3789 Food Service Marketing for Independent Operators *see* 0894-4466
0738-3835 Association of Physical Plant Administrators of Universities and Colleges. Proceedings of the Annual Meeting
0738-3843 Online Data Access *changed to* Access to Wang.
0738-386X Indiana Review
0738-3932 Recipes For Sale
0738-3991 Patient Education and Counseling
0738-4173 Sylvia Porter's Personal Finance Magazine†
0738-4203 For Your Eyes Only
0738-4211 Selling Direct†
0738-4254 Food Service Marketing for Independent Restaurants *see* 0894-4466
0738-4262 Com - S A C
0738-4270 COM - A N D
0738-4300 Government Computer News
0738-4351 Securities Traders' Monthly
0738-4548 Indochina Issues
0738-4556 M D S News
0738-4599 MacRae's Directory of Manufacturers' Representatives *changed to* MacRae's Verified Directory of Manufacturers' Representatives.
0738-4602 A I Magazine
0738-4610 Directory of Computerized Data Files *changed to* Directory of U.S. Government Software for Mainframes and Microcomputers.
0738-467X Caring (Washington)
0738-4718 Make it with Leather *see* 1056-4225
0738-4866 Gunn Salute
0738-4912 T A I C H Directory†
0738-4920 Smoking and Health Reporter *changed to* Tobacco-Free Young America Reporter.
0738-4947 Alabama Medicine
0738-517X Puerto del Sol
0738-5226 Genealogical Aids Bulletin
0738-5285 Tax Management Primary Sources
0738-5390 Saint Louis University Public Law Forum *see* 0898-8404
0738-5560 Chismearte Magazine
0738-5579 Bond Fund Survey
0738-5625 Hispanic American Arts
0738-565X Wheels of Time
0738-5676 Power Line
0738-5692 C A D - C A M Alert *see* 8756-842X
0738-5714 F C C Week
0738-5765 Busby Papers
0738-5919 Antitrust Law Handbook
0738-5927 Public Citizen
0738-5935 GO West
0738-5943 Rice World & Soybean News
0738-6001 Creation - Evolution
0738-601X Latin America Update
0738-6044 Workplace Democracy
0738-6079 Family Computing *see* 0899-7373
0738-6087 Teaching and Computers
0738-6168 Hazardous Waste *see* 0882-5696
0738-6176 Psychotherapy Patient
0738-6184 Journal of Religion and Aging *see* 1050-2289
0738-6192 Emergency Health Services Review *see* 0886-9723
0738-6206 Pace Environmental Law Review
0738-6354 Micro Software Marketing
0738-6370 Hospital Capital Formation and Reorganization Report *changed to* Hospital Capital Formation Management Letter.
0738-6494 Just Compensation
0738-6508 International Policy Report
0738-6532 Renewable Resources Journal
0738-6583 Executive Housekeeping Today
0738-6613 Printout Magazine *see* 0887-7556
0738-6648 Jacksoniana†
0738-6656 Ranger Rick
0738-6729 The Behavior Analyst
0738-6753 Midwest Agricultural Law Journal *changed to* Rural Practice Law Journal.
0738-6761 Midwest Labor & Employment Law Journal†
0738-677X Illinois Journal of Family Law†
0738-6826 T R News
0738-6869 Business News (San Diego)
0738-6923 Timesharing Law Reporter
0738-6931 D.C. Real Estate Reporter
0738-694X California in Print
0738-6958 Private Security Case Law Reporter
0738-6974 Administrative Radiology
0738-6982 Executive Compensation Reports
0738-7008 Crab Creek Review
0738-7016 Portable 100-200-600 *see* 0888-0131
0738-7024 Business Ideas
0738-7075 Career Center Bulletin
0738-7105 Institute of Modern Russian Culture Newsletter
0738-7113 Latin America in Books
0738-713X Microcontamination
0738-7148 Boy Meets Girl†
0738-7156 Microbanker
0738-7237 Mirror (Lancaster)
0738-7245 Nautical Research Journal
0738-7253 Business & Acquisition Newsletter
0738-7261 Jewelry Newsletter International
0738-7288 Bowser Report
0738-7326 Investor's Guide to High Technology Corporations†
0738-7334 New Issues in High Technology *changed to* Directory of High Technology Corporations. Supplement.
0738-7342 High Technology Outlook†
0738-7369 Directory of Public High Technology Corporations *changed to* Directory of Public High Technology and Medical Corporations.
0738-7393 High Technology Overviews†
0738-7415 How to Be Your Own Publisher Update
0738-7512 High Technology Growth Trends†
0738-7555 G P N Newsletter
0738-7563 Video Networks
0738-761X Folding Carton†
0738-7644 Texas Optometry
0738-7687 Living Off the Land
0738-7695 Waste Paper *changed to* Cycle (New York, 1970).
0738-7717 Rockin' 50's
0738-7776 ChemEcology
0738-7806 Generations (San Francisco)
0738-7857 Personal Fitness
0738-7911 Talkin' Union†
0738-7954 Augsburg Media Messenger
0738-7962 Parish Teacher
0738-7989 Journal of Materials Education
0738-7997 Journal of Northeast Asian Studies
0738-8012 Word from Washington
0738-8020 Pottery Southwest
0738-8063 W.A.S. Newsletter
0738-811X HealthFacts
0738-8128 Documentation Newsletter
0738-8144 Corrections Compendium
0738-825X Reynolds Family Newsletter†
0738-8268 Goodlet Family Newsletter†
0738-8357 Folk Art Finder
0738-8381 Rocky Mountain Quarter Horse Magazine
0738-839X Directory of Computer and Software Retailers *changed to* Directory of Computer & Software Storefront Dealers (Year).
0738-8446 Exchange (Washington)†
0738-8489 Evangelist (Albany)
0738-8497 Roundup (Washington)†
0738-8535 Washington State Genealogical and Historical Review *changed to* Washington Heritage.
0738-8543 List†
0738-8551 C R C Critical Reviews in Biotechnology *changed to* Critical Reviews in Biotechnology.
0738-8578 Single Source Newsletter
0738-8586 Victor Valley Magazine†
0738-8608 Western Boatman†
0738-8624 Notes Plus
0738-8632 Federal Tax Coordinator 2d
0738-8640 Knowledge
0738-8675 American Radio
0738-8705 Panhandler
0738-8756 Penny Stock Performance Digest†
0738-8772 Laboratory Computer Letter
0738-8845 C M C News
0738-8853 Beverage Digest
0738-8861 Progressive Platter Music Review
0738-8888 International Currency Report
0738-8896 Communications International *see* 0748-8920
0738-8942 Conflict Management and Peace Science
0738-8993 Spoon River Quarterly
0738-9000 Creative Black Book
0738-9035 Pacific Rim Intelligence Report†
0738-9094 Travelwriter Marketletter
0738-9116 Impartial Citizen
0738-9124 Land Mobile Product News†
0738-9159 National Council News
0738-9183 La Prensa San Diego
0738-9191 International Terrorism Newsletter
0738-9213 Computer Buyer's Guide and Handbook
0738-9264 Futurific
0738-9299 Frank
0738-9302 Ligature
0738-9310 Science of Food and Agriculture
0738-9345 Contributions to the Study of World Literature
0738-9361 Arts & Sciences (Evanston)†
0738-937X Guitar for the Practicing Musician
0738-9396 Mid-Atlantic Archivist
0738-9469 M S S Magazine
0738-9477 N E C N P Newsletter†
0738-9515 Travel Industry World Yearbook
0738-9523 Forum for Reading
0738-9604 Carefree Enterprise Magazine
0738-9639 The Older American
0738-9655 John Donne Journal: Studies in the Age of Donne
0738-9663 Illinois Issues
0738-9671 New Mexico Humanities Review
0738-968X I P M Practitioner
0738-9701 Journal of Developmental Education
0738-9728 International Lawyers' Newsletter
0738-9736 Kanhistique
0738-9744 Dental Computer Newsletter
0738-9752 Q J I†
0738-9760 Journal of Applied Rabbit Research
0738-9779 Tribune
0738-9787 Arts Insight *see* 0897-859X
0738-985X Natchez Trace Traveler
0738-9884 Space Business News
0738-9906 Predicasts Basebook
0738-9981 Collectrix
0738-999X Florida Field Naturalist
0739-0025 Luren
0739-0033 Fillers for Publications
0739-0041 Florida Geographer
0739-005X North Lousiana Historical Association. Journal
0739-0068 Near East Archaeological Society Bulletin
0739-0203 Pontiac - Oakland and County Legal News
0739-0211 Medical Dosimetry
0739-0270 A A M I News
0739-0289 Morticians of the Southwest
0739-0297 Librarian's World
0739-0351 A N A R C Newsletter†
0739-036X Closed Loop
0739-0408 Tennessee Education
0739-0416 Global Electronics Information Newsletter *changed to* Global Electronics.
0739-0491 Textile Business Outlook
0739-0572 Journal of Atmospheric and Oceanic Technology
0739-0653 Peek 65
0739-0696 International Bowhunter
0739-0718 Hue Points†
0739-0769 Fielding's Bermuda and the Bahamas
0739-0785 Fielding's Economy Europe *changed to* Fielding's Budget Europe.
0739-0793 Fielding's Mexico
0739-084X Grand River Valley Review
0739-0874 Computer Economics Report
0739-0882 Family Therapy Networker
0739-0939 Airpost Journal
0739-0971 TraNet
0739-0998 Jail and Prisoner Law Bulletin
0739-1048 Star Tech Journal
0739-1056 College Media Review
0739-1064 3 L Llama Magazine *see* 0887-9923
0739-1137 I A S S I S T Quarterly
0739-1153 O L A C Newsletter
0739-1161 Performing Arts Forum *changed to* International Society of Performing Arts Administrators. Forum.
0739-1188 New England Classical Newsletter *changed to* New England Classical Newsletter & Journal.
0739-1218 Philosophy and the Arts†
0739-1226 National Directory of College Athletics (Women's Edition)
0739-1242 Noninvasive Medical Imaging†
0739-1277 Willow Springs
0739-134X Landers Landing†
0739-1382 U.S. National Advisory Council on Continuing Education. Annual Report
0739-1390 International Council for Traditional Music. Bulletin
0739-148X Illinois Teacher of Home Economics†
0739-1544 N C E C A Journal
0739-1552 N C E C A Newsletter *changed to* N C E C A News.
0739-1587 Corporate & Incentive Travel
0739-1692 Cancer Update†
0739-1706 Lawyer Hiring & Training Report
0739-1714 Southern Partisan
0739-1749 Daughters of Sarah
0739-1781 Journal of Weather Modification
0739-1803 Lesbian News
0739-182X Society for Spanish and Portuguese Historical Studies. Bulletin
0739-1854 Harvard International Review
0739-1862 Predicasts Company Thesaurus
0739-1897 Entertainment, Publishing and the Arts Handbook
0739-1935 Satellite Audio Report†
0739-1943 Journal of Southwest Georgia History
0739-1951 National Legal Bibliography *see* 1049-796X
0739-196X Real Life Magazine
0739-2036 Human Ethology Newsletter
0739-2044 Medicine & Computer†
0739-2060 Radiator Reporter
0739-2184 Smith Funding Report
0739-2214 N P T A Management News
0739-2265 Computer Executive Letter *see* 0890-4316
0739-2281 Searching Together
0739-229X Sonus
0739-2311 Utah Holiday
0739-2354 Crosscurrents
0739-2451 Annual Review of Banking Law
0739-2486 Genealogy Today *see* 8755-7584
0739-2494 Barrister (Philadelphia)
0739-2532 Catalyst for Change
0739-2907 Electronic Publishing Abstracts *see* 0960-653X
0739-2931 Association of Part-Time Professionals. National Newsletter *changed to* Part-Time Professional.
0739-2958 All About Mail Order†
0739-2966 Teleconferencing Resources Directory *see* 0190-3705
0739-2974 Northern Lights Studies in Creativity
0739-2990 Managing International Development†
0739-3016 B N A's Employee Relations Weekly
0739-3024 Association of American University Presses Directory
0739-3067 Sporting News Official N B A Register
0739-3075 Energy Statistics
0739-3148 New Political Science
0739-3156 Office Professional
0739-3164 University R & D

ISSN

0739-3172 Issues in Accounting Education
0739-3180 Critical Studies in Mass Communication
0739-3202 Texas Books in Review
0739-3253 High-Tech New Issues Advisory†
0739-3369 Journal of Vocational Education Research
0739-344X Tradeswomen
0739-3474 Carrier Pidgin
0739-3482 Virginia Appalachian Notes
0739-3490 National Association of Railroad Passengers News
0739-3520 Commodity Trading Digest†
0739-3563 Fed Tracker - Reality Theory Newsletter
0739-3571 Line of March†
0739-358X Research Alert (New York)
0739-3601 Paralegal
0739-361X National Association of Academies of Science. Directory and Proceedings *changed to* National Association of Academies of Science. Directory, Proceedings and Handbook.
0739-3679 Energy Information Abstracts Annual
0739-3717 Journal of Vibration, Acoustics, Stress and Reliability in Design *see* 1048-9002
0739-3733 Atterbury Letter - Wine, Dining & Travel
0739-3784 Road Race Management Newsletter
0739-3830 North Carolina Plumbing - Heating - Cooling Forum
0739-3865 P O B - Point of Beginning
0739-3873 Business Mailers Review
0739-3881 Affaire de Coeur
0739-392X N A C A A News
0739-3938 Southern Political Report
0739-3946 Design Cost and Data for Management of Building Design *changed to* Design Cost & Data.
0739-4020 Surface Mining Reporter *see* 1040-8223
0739-4098 Mediation Quarterly
0739-4144 Textile Pricing Outlook
0739-4179 Alan Guttmacher Institute. Washington Memo
0739-4241 Provenance
0739-4268 I M C Newsletter *see* 0019-0012
0739-4314 Digital Review
0739-4322 Counterspy *changed to* National Reporter.
0739-4330 County Agents Directory
0739-439X University of California, Los Angeles. Institute of Industrial Relations. Monograph and Research Series
0739-4462 Archives of Insect Biochemistry and Physiology
0739-4497 Walking! Journal
0739-456X Journal of Planning Education and Research
0739-4586 V A H P E R D Journal
0739-4640 Global Risk Assessments
0739-4667 Book on Starting Pitchers
0739-4683 D I N Newservice *changed to* Preview (Tempe).
0739-4691 Texas Blue Book of Life Insurance Statistics
0739-4713 Freshman English News *changed to* Composition Studies - Freshman English News.
0739-4810 Current Hematology and Oncology†
0739-4853 Against the Current
0739-4942 Warren Family Historian
0739-4969 Outerbridge
0739-5043 Career Opportunities News
0739-506X A L I S E Statistics Report *changed to* Library and Information Science Education Statistical Report.
0739-5086 Judaica Librarianship
0739-5175 I E E E Engineering in Medicine and Biology Magazine
0739-5272 Motheroot Journal†
0739-5299 Federal Reserve Bank of Kansas City. Financial Letter *see* 1049-5339
0739-5388 Advanced Vehicle News†
0739-540X Current References in Fish Research
0739-5418 A Friendly Letter
0739-5515 Advantage *see* 1052-4215
0739-5523 Selected Readings in Plastic Surgery
0739-5531 Television Index
0739-5558 Children's Folklore Review
0739-5566 Economic News from Italy†
0739-5574 T V Pro-Log *changed to* Network Futures & ProLog.
0739-5612 Archaeological Society of Connecticut. Bulletin
0739-5639 Bulletin of Historical Research in Musical Education
0739-5663 Field Notes (Concord) *changed to* Fish & Game Highlights of New Hampshire.
0739-5728 Helicopter Annual
0739-5736 Museum of Fine Arts, Boston. Bulletin†
0739-5795 Goucher *changed to* Goucher Quarterly.
0739-5876 Radioactive Waste Management and the Nuclear Fuel Cycle
0739-5914 Mind: The Meetings Index
0739-5922 UNIX World
0739-5930 Year Book of Digestive Diseases
0739-6074 Nationwide Directory of Sporting Goods Buyers
0739-618X Business Publications Index and Abstracts†
0739-6198 Philateli-Graphics
0739-6201 ComputerTalk Directory of Medical Computer Systems
0739-621X Rain
0739-6236 Service Dealer's Newsletter
0739-6244 Asia - Pacific Currency Report†
0739-6260 Micron and Microscopica Acta
0739-6279 Baseline Data Report
0739-6376 Land Development Law Reporter
0739-6392 American University Studies. Series 5. Philosophy
0739-6406 American University Studies. Series 6. Foreign Language Instruction
0739-6422 Christian Life Communities Harvest
0739-6449 Investment Column Quarterly
0739-6538 Washington Remote Sensing Letter
0739-6546 American Clay Exchange
0739-6554 Medical Documentation Update
0739-6562 Drug Abuse Update
0739-6686 Annual Review of Nursing Research
0739-6694 Beginning (Iowa City)†
0739-6732 Quality Control Scanner
0739-6767 N C T V News
0739-6791 The Food and Fiber Letter
0739-6813 Americans for Legal Reform *changed to* Legal Reformer.
0739-6821 Exhibitor Magazine
0739-6937 Gotherman's Ohio Municipal Service
0739-6961 Almanac for Farmers and City Folk
0739-697X Newsletter of Engineering Analysis Software
0739-7046 Faith and Philosophy
0739-7089 Videodisc Monitor *changed to* Multimedia and Videodisc Monitor.
0739-7097 Special Libraries Association. Washington D.C. Chapter. Chapter Notes
0739-7100 U M T R I Research Review
0739-7194 Bus Industry Magazine
0739-7240 Domestic Animal Endocrinology
0739-7348 Infectious Disease Alert
0739-7437 Collision
0739-7453 G L A D News
0739-747X Nor'westing
0739-7704 E E R C News
0739-7712 School Library Media Annual
0739-7771 Computer Law Reporter
0739-7801 Hemingway Newsletter
0739-7828 Currents (Des Moines)
0739-7860 California Regulatory Law Reporter
0739-7895 Book Arts Review
0739-8042 California Today
0739-8069 Middle States Council for the Social Studies. Journal
0739-8077 Practical Winery & Vineyard
0739-8093 Fayette Connection†
0739-8123 Personal Electronics†
0739-814X A S F A Aquaculture Abstracts
0739-8158 Fram: The Journal of Polar Studies
0739-8182 Impact: Office Automation†
0739-828X Emotional First Aid
0739-8298 Concrete and Masonry Cost Data *changed to* Means Concrete Cost Data (Year).
0739-8328 Problems in General Surgery
0739-8417 Cybernetics and Computing Technology
0739-8425 Soviet Journal of Superhard Materials
0739-8433 Soviet Immunology†
0739-845X MacRae's North Carolina State Industrial Directory *changed to* MacRae's State Industrial Directory: North Carolina South Carolina - Virginia.
0739-8468 MacRae's North Dakota - South Dakota State Industrial Directory†
0739-8476 MacRae's Arizona - New Mexico State Industrial Directory†
0739-8484 MacRae's Texas State Industrial Directory†
0739-8506 Catalyst (Seattle)
0739-8565 Dutchess County Historical Society. Yearbook
0739-862X N A R F Legal Review
0739-8689 Securities & Syndication Review
0739-8743 Automated Office Systems
0739-876X Satellite Dealer *changed to* Satellite Direct.
0739-8972 Occasional Papers in Slavic Languages and Literature
0739-8999 Soviet Machine Science *see* 1052-6188
0739-9014 Journal of Information Systems Management
0739-9022 Automated Materials Handling and Storage†
0739-9065 Equine Veterinary Data
0739-9170 American Dane
0739-9189 C A L C Report
0739-9227 Community Services Catalyst
0739-9243 Frat
0739-9294 Public Employee (Boston)
0739-9332 Health Care for Women, International
0739-9405 Programmer's Market†
0739-9413 Business and Health
0739-9502 Gallup Monthly Report on Eating Out†
0739-9529 Seminars in Interventional Radiology
0739-9537 Northwest Edition *see* 0888-5346
0739-9553 Computer-Using Educators Newsletter *changed to* C U E Newsletter.
0739-9561 Hospital Pharmacy Service Instant Up-Date
0739-957X Hospital Pharmacy Director's Monthly Management Series
0739-9588 Vital Signs Pharmacy Services Newsletter
0739-9723 Merchant Magazine
0739-9766 P A H A Newsletter
0739-9820 Special Services in the Schools
0739-9847 Medical Month†
0739-9863 Hispanic Journal of Behavioral Sciences
0739-988X Link-Up
0739-9928 Computer Negotiations Report
0739-9936 Bank Acquisition Report†
0740-0004 Central America and the Caribbean: Development Assistance Abroad†
0740-0020 Food Microbiology
0740-0055 Used Cars Today *changed to* Used Cars Insider.
0740-0063 El Interprete: Maestros
0740-0101 InCider *see* 1054-6456
0740-011X Virginia Forests
0740-0179 T A C D A Update *changed to* T A C D A Alert.
0740-0187 Construction Bargaineer
0740-0195 Focus (Washington, 1970)
0740-0225 Our Life
0740-0403 Museum Year
0740-0411 Supervisor's Newsletter†
0740-0438 Personal Software Magazine *changed to* Personal Computing.
0740-0446 American University Studies. Series 7. Theology and Religion
0740-0454 American University Studies. Series 8. Psychology
0740-0462 American University Studies. Series 9. History
0740-0470 American University Studies. Series 10. Political Science
0740-0489 American University Studies. Series 11. Anthropology and Sociology
0740-0497 American University Studies. Series 12. Slavic Languages and Literature
0740-0519 Lawyers Letter
0740-0527 California Cable Letter
0740-0535 Washington Federal Science Newsletter
0740-0578 Lifelong Learning *see* 1045-1595
0740-0624 Perspectives on Local Public Finance and Public Policy
0740-0640 Radiation Protection Management
0740-0659 Faith and Mission
0740-0675 History of Philosophy Quarterly
0740-0683 C A Selects. Automated Chemical Analysis
0740-0691 C A Selects. Natural Product Synthesis
0740-0705 C A Selects. Polyurethanes
0740-0713 C A Selects. Fermentation Chemicals
0740-0721 C A Selects. Crosslinking Reactions
0740-073X C A Selects. Water Treatment
0740-0748 C A Selects. Controlled Release Technology
0740-0756 C A Selects. Carbohydrates (Chemical Aspects)
0740-0780 Carrousel Art
0740-0802 Spotlight on Youth Sports
0740-0853 Saybrook Review
0740-090X Law and Legal Information Directory
0740-0942 Lawyer's P C
0740-1035 Alcohol Clinical Update
0740-1086 Healthwise *changed to* Dr. Alexander Grant's Health Gazette.
0740-1116 Hunger Notes
0740-1205 Mr. Cogito
0740-1221 BioTech Market News & Strategies
0740-1248 Quarterly Review of Wines
0740-137X Protection of Assets Bulletin
0740-1388 Excess Express
0740-1434 Ag-Pilot International
0740-1469 Computer Industry Litigation Reporter
0740-1477 Ellis Cousins Newsletter
0740-1558 Yearbook for Traditional Music
0740-1590 A Plus *see* 1054-6456
0740-1604 P C Week
0740-1809 Wire Rope News and Sling Technology
0740-1825 Faxon News†
0740-1892 Media Profiles: Health Sciences Edition
0740-1922 The Electron
0740-1957 Madness Network News†
0740-1965 Schatzkammer
0740-1973 Florida Specifier
0740-2007 Ancient Philosophy
0740-2074 Draft Review and Preview†
0740-2082 International Journal of Sport Biomechanics
0740-2155 Software Supermarket†
0740-218X On the Beam
0740-2252 Acid Precipitation Digest
0740-235X A L P S Monthly†
0740-2368 Mole†
0740-2376 B M E Tax Newsletter *changed to* Ruxton Report.
0740-2384 New York Sports†
0740-2392 Agada
0740-2430 Quarterly Index: Information Access for the Small Animal Practitioner†
0740-2511 Laser Focus Including Electro-Optics Magazine *see* 1043-8092
0740-252X Technology Network†
0740-2546 Corporate Finance Bluebook
0740-2570 Seminars in Diagnostic Pathology
0740-2619 Synapse (San Francisco)
0740-2678 U S Association Executive
0740-2732 Great Plains National Instructional Television Library. Recorded Visual Instruction *changed to* G P N Educational Video Catalog. Elementary - Secondary.

0740-2732 Great Plains National Instructional Television Library. Recorded Visual Instruction *changed to* G P N Educational Video Catalog. College - Adult.
0740-2732 Great Plains National Instructional Television Library. Recorded Visual Instruction *changed to* G P N Educational Media. Crossover.
0740-2740 Sellers Letters†
0740-2775 World Policy Journal
0740-2791 Seminars, Workshops & Classes
0740-283X Creative Black Book. Portfolio Edition
0740-2856 Boca Raton Magazine
0740-2899 Business Journal Serving Greater Milwaukee
0740-2902 MacRae's Virginia State Industrial Directory
0740-2910 MacRae's State Industrial Directory: Georgia†
0740-2937 MacRae's State Industrial Directory: Connecticut - Rhode Island
0740-2945 MacRae's State Industrial Directory: Maine - New Hampshire - Vermont
0740-2953 MacRae's State Industrial Directory: New York State
0740-2961 A S T M Standards Infobriefs
0740-3119 Catalog Age
0740-3194 Magnetic Resonance in Medicine
0740-3224 Optical Society of America. Journal Part B
0740-3232 Optical Society of America. Journal Part A
0740-3291 Cultural Survival Quarterly
0740-3313 DNotes†
0740-3437 L A Parent
0740-3534 Automation in Housing and Manufactured Home Dealer *see* 0899-5540
0740-3550 New from Japan
0740-3569 New from Europe
0740-3577 New from U S
0740-3585 World Electronic Developments
0740-3593 Sex over Forty
0740-3666 Investing in Crisis
0740-3739 Fine Chemicals Directory†
0740-3763 Popular Magazine Review *see* 1041-1151
0740-3968 Computer User (Cerritos)†
0740-3984 D.C. Directory†
0740-4018 America's Corporate Families and International Affiliates
0740-4050 A B A - B N A Lawyers' Manual on Professional Conduct
0740-4085 Computer Publishers & Publications
0740-4093 Quilt Digest
0740-4182 Credences: A Journal of Twentieth Century Poets and Poetics†
0740-4247 Video Marketing Surveys and Forecasts†
0740-4271 Secondary Mortgage Markets
0740-428X MacRae's Iowa - Nebraska State Industrial Directory†
0740-4298 MacRae's State Industrial Directory: Pennsylvania
0740-431X Alabama State Industrial Directory *see* 0733-5016
0740-4328 MacRae's Kentucky - West Virginia State Industrial Directory†
0740-4336 MacRae's Illinois State Industrial Directory†
0740-4409 Under Construction
0740-445X Computers in Human Services
0740-4549 Source Book: Social and Health Services in the Greater New York Area
0740-4557 American University Studies. Series 13. Linguistics
0740-4565 American University Studies. Series 14. Education
0740-4603 Unity (Oakland)†
0740-4638 MacRae's State Industrial Directory: California†
0740-4646 MacRae's State Industrial Directory: Tennessee†
0740-4654 MacRae's Mississippi State Industrial Directory†
0740-4662 MacRae's Oklahoma State Industrial Directory†
0740-4670 MacRae's Arkansas State Industrial Directory†
0740-4689 MacRae's State Industrial Directory: Massachusetts - Rhode Island
0740-4697 MacRae's Florida State Industrial Directory†
0740-4816 Supermicro†
0740-4824 Brooklyn Journal of International Law
0740-4832 Grassroots Fundraising Journal
0740-4840 Publishing Northwest Newsletter†
0740-4859 Hyatt's P C News Report†
0740-4921 Details
0740-4956 Focus: Library Service to Older Adults, People with Disabilities
0740-4980 F T Systems
0740-4999 Trail Tracer
0740-5006 Iredell County Tracks (NC)
0740-5022 Software Publishers' Catalogs Annual†
0740-5065 Military Living
0740-5073 Military Living's R & R Report
0740-5103 Investment Decisions†
0740-5111 American University Studies. Series 15. Communications
0740-5138 International Journal of Reviews in Library and Information Science†
0740-5162 International Coal Testing Conference
0740-5197 B A S H Magazine
0740-5200 Data Based Advisor
0740-5286 Chase's Annual Events
0740-5294 Rehabfilm Newsletter†
0740-5324 Perspective on A T & T and Boc Products and Marketing†
0740-5375 International Journal of Islamic and Arabic Studies
0740-5383 Grant Advisor
0740-5391 Columbia Review (Columbia)
0740-5405 Cyrano's Journal
0740-5464 Bottomline (Washington)
0740-5472 Journal of Substance Abuse Treatment
0740-5502 Information and Behavior
0740-5537 Journal of Civil Defense
0740-557X United Mutual Fund Selector
0740-5618 Friendly Woman
0740-5901 Jews for Jesus Newsletter
0740-5928 Jersey Jazz
0740-5960 Academic Journal
0740-5995 N A I A News
0740-6045 MacRae's Indiana State Industrial Directory†
0740-6053 MacRae's Wisconsin State Industrial Directory†
0740-6061 MacRae's Minnesota State Industrial Directory†
0740-607X MacRae's Missouri State Industrial Directory†
0740-6088 MacRae's Idaho - Montana - Wyoming State Industrial Directory†
0740-610X MacRae's Oregon State Industrial Directory†
0740-6118 MacRae's Kansas State Industrial Directory†
0740-6126 MacRae's Colorado - Utah - Nevada State Industrial Directory†
0740-6134 MacRae's Washington State Industrial Directory†
0740-6169 Society for Historians of American Foreign Relations. Newsletter
0740-6215 Yankee Magazine's Travel Guide to New England *see* 1055-226X
0740-6231 Computer Publishing and Advertising Report
0740-624X Government Information Quarterly
0740-669X International Report (Irvine)
0740-672X Mutual Magazine
0740-6738 Astro Talk *changed to* Astrotalk Bulletin.
0740-6754 The Word
0740-6797 Society for Computer Simulation. Transactions
0740-6800 Data Base Product Reports
0740-6819 Automated Law Office Consultant†
0740-6851 Long-Distance Letter
0740-6932 LocalNetter Designer's Handbook *changed to* L A N Component Directory.
0740-6959 Profession
0740-6967 Cataract; International Journal of Cataract Surgery†
0740-6983 Practice Marketing and Management. Veterinary Edition *changed to* Veterinary Management Update.
0740-7130 A C C R A Inter-City Cost of Living Index *see* 1048-2830
0740-722X Aerospace America
0740-7262 Health Literature Review
0740-7270 Computers in Accounting
0740-7289 Dun's Employment Opportunities Directory *see* 0891-0596
0740-736X Library Hotline
0740-7459 I E E E Software
0740-7467 I E E E - A S S P Magazine *see* 1053-5888
0740-7475 I E E E Design & Test of Computers
0740-7513 International Publishing Newsletter *see* 0145-9457
0740-7548 Self-Help Group Directory *see* 8756-1425
0740-7556 Artificial Intelligence Report *see* 0885-9957
0740-7610 Zoos and Aquariums in the Americas *changed to* Zoological Parks & Aquariums in the Americas.
0740-7629 Parapsychology Abstracts International *see* 1053-4768
0740-770X Women & Performance: A Journal of Feminist Theory
0740-7769 Journal of In Vitro Fertilization and Embryo Transfer *changed to* Journal of Assisted Reproduction and Genetics.
0740-7785 Exhibit Reporter†
0740-7793 Washington Report on Health Legislation and Regulation *see* 0899-8965
0740-7815 Exquisite Corpse
0740-7890 Permafrost
0740-7998 Biblical Evangelist
0740-8013 Oak Leaves
0740-8161 Mushroom
0740-8188 Library & Information Science Research
0740-820X M.D. Anderson Hospital and Tumor Institute at Houston. Cancer Bulletin *changed to* University of Texas. M.D. Anderson Cancer Center. Cancer Bulletin.
0740-8293 Buried Treasure from Aceto Genealogical Files†
0740-8307 Eidos
0740-834X Eagle Wing Press *changed to* Eagle (Naugatuck).
0740-8439 The Book
0740-8498 The Wellness Newsletter
0740-8528 American Council for Judaism. Special Interest Report
0740-8625 Studies in Contemporary Jewry
0740-8668 Midwest Technology *see* 0882-6382
0740-8684 Nutrition Report
0740-8714 Nelson's Directory of Wall Street Research *see* 0896-0135
0740-8765 P M T
0740-8870 Stephen Wright's Mystery Notebook *changed to* Mystery Notebook.
0740-8900 Mechanisms of Inorganic and Organometallic Reactions
0740-8943 Communications from the International Brecht Society
0740-896X Tri-State Packet
0740-8978 American Public Opinion Index
0740-8994 New England Journal on Criminal and Civil Confinement
0740-9087 Employers' Health Costs Savings Letter
0740-9125 The Plough (Farmington)
0740-9133 Northeast African Studies
0740-9214 Arts Quarterly
0740-9222 Milk Facts
0740-9257 American University Studies. Series 2. Romance Languages and Literature
0740-9303 Ophthalmic Plastic and Reconstructive Surgery
0740-9311 Clockwatch Review
0740-9451 Microcirculation, Endothelium and Lymphatics
0740-946X Siglo XX
0740-9567 Africa Research and Publications Project. Working Papers Series†
0740-9583 Genetic Epistemologist
0740-9613 Let's Pray Together†
0740-9680 Times of Restoration
0740-9699 The Mohawk
0740-9702 The Saratoga
0740-9710 Food and Foodways
0740-9737 Genewatch
0740-9745 Benchmark Sites News†
0740-9893 Excellence in Teaching
0740-9982 Hospital Manager†
0741-0042 C A D - C A M: Management Strategies†
0741-0050 Executive Computing
0741-0069 Communications Concepts
0741-0131 International Review of Mental Imagery†
0741-0204 Global Perspectives†
0741-0271 Sunrust
0741-028X Tae Kwan Do Times
0741-0298 Brasilians Journal
0741-0344 California State Library Foundation Bulletin
0741-0360 The Pied Cow
0741-0379 M A C Newsletter
0741-0395 Genetic Epidemiology
0741-0506 New Brewer
0741-0522 Chronicle (Austin) *see* 0892-2829
0741-0549 Religion and Intellectual Life *changed to* Cross Currents: Religion and Intellectual Life.
0741-0581 Journal of Electron Microscopy Technique *see* 1059-910X
0741-0700 American University Studies. Series 4. English Language and Literature
0741-0786 Fiction Monthly *changed to* Short Story Review.
0741-0794 Ceilidh
0741-0808 High-Tech Materials Alert
0741-0883 Written Communication
0741-1111 American Politics
0741-1162 Pre Law Journal
0741-1170 Law School Administrator's Journal
0741-1189 Legal Bibliography Journal
0741-1197 Law Teacher's Journal
0741-1200 Bridge (Salem)
0741-1235 Sociology of Sport Journal
0741-1278 Mutual Fund Specialist
0741-1286 Hermes Americanus
0741-1294 Masonry Society Journal
0741-1308 Urban Resources†
0741-1316 Nebo
0741-1413 International Electrochemical Progress
0741-143X Southern Social Studies Quarterly *changed to* Southern Social Studies Journal.
0741-160X Radiology and Imaging Letter
0741-1618 Current Advances in Biochemistry *see* 0965-0504
0741-1626 Current Advances in Cell and Developmental Biology
0741-1634 Current Advances in Endocrinology†
0741-1642 Current Advances in Genetics and Molecular Biology
0741-1650 Current Advances in Immunology *see* 0964-8747
0741-1669 Current Advances in Microbiology *see* 0964-8712
0741-1677 Current Advances in Neuroscience
0741-1685 Current Advances in Pharmacology and Toxicology *see* 0965-0512
0741-1693 Current Advances in Physiology *see* 0964-8720
0741-1707 Gold Skills†
0741-1715 Sound & Video Contractor
0741-1731 Space Calendar
0741-1790 Avalon to Camelot
0741-1804 N A
0741-1952 Hideaways Guide
0741-1995 Concerned Investors Guide

0741-2029 S A E Technical Literature Abstracts
0741-2037 Crossroads (DeKalb)
0741-2045 Kates Kin
0741-2088 Belli Law Journal†
0741-2150 American University Studies. Series 16. Economics
0741-2223 Journal of Robotic Systems
0741-2347 Apple Index
0741-2355 I B M - P C Index
0741-2363 Business Computer Index
0741-2460 Wavelength (New Orleans)
0741-2851 Open Systems Communication
0741-2878 C I S Federal Register Index
0741-2894 Senior Voice
0741-2940 I S C A Quarterly
0741-3017 Health Letter (New York)†
0741-3106 I E E E Electron Device Letters
0741-3149 Midway Review†
0741-3157 Party Mail†
0741-3165 American Poetry Index *see* 1040-5461
0741-3173 Local - State Funding Report
0741-3335 Plasma Physics and Controlled Fusion
0741-3343 Oil Industry Outlook for the U S A
0741-3351 Artist's Magazine
0741-336X Standard for Auditing Computer Applications†
0741-3432 San Antonio Living
0741-3440 South Florida Living (North Edition) *changed to* South Florida Home Buyer's Guide.
0741-3467 From the State Capitals. Consumer Protection†
0741-3475 From the State Capitals. General Trends
0741-3483 From the State Capitals. Urban Development
0741-3491 From the State Capitals. Construction: Institutional *changed to* From the State Capitals. Construction Policies.
0741-3505 From the State Capitals. Family Relations
0741-3513 From the State Capitals. Parking Regulations *see* 0749-2774
0741-3521 From the State Capitals. Public Employee Policy
0741-353X From the State Capitals. Civil Rights
0741-3548 From the State Capitals. Banking *see* 0749-2812
0741-3564 From the State Capitals. Urban Transit *see* 0749-2774
0741-3572 From the State Capitals. Women and the Law
0741-3599 Minnesota Genealogical Journal
0741-3610 C P A Digest
0741-3629 Energy Design Update
0741-3653 Journal of Educational Public Relations
0741-367X Annual Report on Industrial Robots†
0741-3696 Sports - Nutrition News
0741-3750 Opportunity Magazine
0741-4129 Paperboard Packaging's International Container Directory†
0741-4188 Library Currents
0741-4218 Clinical Cardiology Alert
0741-4234 Neurology Alert
0741-4242 Long Story
0741-4269 International Tax and Business Lawyer
0741-4285 Run
0741-4498 Growing Edge†
0741-4501 Software Maintenance News
0741-4579 Arts Review†
0741-4587 U S S E A Update
0741-4609 International Association of Assessing Officers. News Bulletin *changed to* I A A O Update.
0741-4617 Contractor Profit News
0741-4641 Business Computing†
0741-465X American Council for Judaism. Issues
0741-482X Security and Special Police Legal Update
0741-4927 Paper Collector's Marketplace
0741-501X Assessor's Data Exchange†
0741-5028 Bluefish
0741-5044 Agenda (Westport) *changed to* Animals' Agenda.
0741-5095 Hospitality Education and Research Journal
0741-5141 Mental Health Law Reporter
0741-5192 K Power†
0741-5206 Plastic Surgical Nursing
0741-5214 Journal of Vascular Surgery
0741-5222 Laser Research†
0741-5230 Acid Precipitation
0741-5249 Solar Thermal Energy Technology
0741-5257 Coal Preparation and Pollution Control†
0741-5273 Dunrobin Piper
0741-5281 Index to the Boston Globe
0741-5362 I S C Newsletter
0741-5397 Journal of Medical Technology†
0741-5400 Journal of Leukocyte Biology
0741-5478 Austin Living *changed to* Home Finders Guidebook.
0741-5486 Living (Houston Edition) *changed to* Houston Living Housing Guide.
0741-5494 Living (Dallas - Fort Worth Edition) *changed to* Dallas - Fort Worth Home Buyer's Guide.
0741-5508 Living (Denver Edition) *changed to* Denver Housing Guide.
0741-5516 Living (Phoenix Edition)†
0741-5672 Society for American Archaeology. Bulletin
0741-5702 Formations
0741-5729 National Home-Business Report
0741-5737 American Salon Eighty-Five *changed to* American Salon.
0741-5745 Human Intelligence International Newsletter†
0741-5753 Society for German - American Studies. Newsletter
0741-5788 Bulwark
0741-5796 W O H R C News†
0741-580X Modem Notes
0741-5818 Travel Smart for Business†
0741-5826 Travel Smart
0741-5834 Lightwave
0741-5842 Shaw Annual
0741-5869 Optical Memory News
0741-5931 S P I E Optical Engineering Reports *see* 1048-6879
0741-5958 Third Rail
0741-5974 Aerostation
0741-6016 Microcomputer Industry Update
0741-6024 Fiction Network Magazine†
0741-6075 Journal of Christian Jurisprudence
0741-6091 Kovels on Antiques and Collectibles
0741-6105 Texarkana U S A Quarterly
0741-6113 Colposcopy and Gynecologic Laser Surgery *see* 1042-4067
0741-6148 Book Research Quarterly *see* 1053-8801
0741-6156 Theory and Practice
0741-6164 Phonetician
0741-6180 In Context
0741-6202 Kafka Society of America. Newsletter *see* 0894-6388
0741-6210 Croton Review†
0741-6229 Zetetic Scholar
0741-6245 Mayo Clinic Health Letter
0741-6253 Diabetes Self-Management
0741-6261 Rand Journal of Economics
0741-6423 American Productivity & Quality Center. Case Study
0741-6458 Productivity Perspectives *changed to* American Productivity & Quality Center. Perspectives (Year).
0741-6466 Productivity Digest *changed to* American Productivity & Quality Center. Digest (Year).
0741-6474 Productivity Letter *changed to* American Productivity & Quality Center. Letter.
0741-6512 D R G Monitor†
0741-6555 Feminist Bookstore News
0741-6563 The Primary Source
0741-6601 Sales & Marketing Digest (Boca Raton) †
0741-6776 Entrepreneurial Economy *see* 0899-7721
0741-6857 American Homeopathy - Consumer Edition *see* 0747-606X
0741-6865 American Homeopathy - Professional Edition *see* 0747-606X
0741-6873 American Homeopathy - Affiliate Edition *see* 0747-606X
0741-6997 H R Reporter
0741-7004 Foundation Giving Watch
0741-7136 Adult Education Quarterly
0741-7160 Export Graficas U S A *see* 1054-2434
0741-7284 Knox County Illinois Genealogical Society. Quarterly
0741-7357 New Jersey. Geological Survey. Report Series
0741-739X C S C Reports
0741-7403 Familia Latina†
0741-7497 Northern California Review of Business and Economics†
0741-7527 Annali d'Italianistica
0741-756X Poetry North Review†
0741-7586 Pacific Maritime Magazine
0741-7594 Young Authors Magazine
0741-7659 Double Reed
0741-7713 Coal-Based Synfuels†
0741-7721 Unconventional Petroleum†
0741-7748 Consuming Passions
0741-7772 Legal Assistant Today *see* 1051-3663
0741-7780 Sheet Music Exchange
0741-7950 Newspaper Guild. Proceedings of the Annual Convention
0741-8132 Business Book Review
0741-8264 Circuit Rider (Springfield)
0741-8280 Advances in Economic Botany
0741-8329 Alcohol
0741-8337 Blue Chip Economic WorldScan *changed to* Currency Forecasters' Digest.
0741-8345 Blue Chip Financial Forecasts
0741-8361 Report on A T & T
0741-837X School Finance News†
0741-8388 State Telephone Regulation Report
0741-8450 Simon Wiesenthal Center Annual
0741-8477 Boston University Journal of Tax Law
0741-8485 Urban Institute. Policy and Research Report
0741-8507 I G W M C Ground Water Modeling Newsletter
0741-8531 Wrap Up on Latin American Agriculture, Food, Fishing & Livestock†
0741-854X Wrap Up on Latin American Banking & Finance†
0741-8558 Wrap Up on Latin American Chemicals, Cosmetics, Pharmaceuticals & Medical Equipment†
0741-8566 Wrap Up on Latin American Construction, Housing & Real Estate†
0741-8574 Wrap Up on Latin American Mining & Forestry†
0741-8582 Wrap Up on Latin American Textile & Leather, Rubber & Plastic Industries†
0741-8590 Wrap Up on Latin American Machinery, Electronics & Communications†
0741-8604 Wrap Up on Latin American Energy†
0741-8620 Journal of Dental Practice Administration
0741-8639 Sage: A Scholarly Journal on Black Women
0741-8647 MacWorld
0741-8655 Author Biographies Master Index
0741-8736 G M U Law Review
0741-8760 Locomotive
0741-8787 Journal of the Senses *changed to* Elysium: Journal of the Senses.
0741-8795 Esoteric Review
0741-8809 Computer Law Monitor
0741-8825 Justice Quarterly
0741-8841 Packaging Patents Newsletter†
0741-885X Plastics Processing Patents Newsletter†
0741-8868 Plastics Materials Patents Newsletter†
0741-8876 Washington Journalism Review
0741-9031 Kentucky Manufacturers Register
0741-9058 Library Hi Tech News
0741-9066 Compleat Lawyer
0741-9147 National Women's Health Report
0741-9155 Chattahoochee Review
0741-9163 Sacred Art Journal
0741-918X Keystone *changed to* Orange Seed Technical Bulletin.
0741-9279 N C A A Men's and Women's Skiing Rules
0741-9309 American University Studies. Series 17. Classical Language and Literature
0741-9325 R A S E
0741-9333 Cogitations on Law and Government
0741-9384 Hora
0741-9422 N Y P C Newsletter *changed to* N Y P C Magazine.
0741-9430 Electric Utility Instrumentation†
0741-9449 Minnesota Journal†
0741-9457 Yale Journal on Regulation
0741-9597 Newsletter for Leonardisti
0741-9643 Petroleum Marketing Monthly
0741-9767 Metropolitan Life Insurance Company. Statistical Bulletin S B
0741-9783 Advances (Kalamazoo)
0741-9791 SoftNews†
0741-9821 Writers West†
0741-983X Solar and Wind Technology *see* 0960-1481
0741-9872 Concord
0741-9910 North American Lily Society. Yearbook
0741-9945 Polish Music History Series
0741-9953 International Book Collectors Almanac. Newsletter†
0742-0005 I B M P C Update *changed to* Macintosh Update.
0742-0013 Prism (Fort Lauderdale)
0742-0021 Real Estate Finance Today
0742-0242 Sponsored Research in the History of Art
0742-0250 Education Computer News *see* 1061-5008
0742-0269 International Journal of Applied Engineering Education
0742-0277 Black Issues in Higher Education
0742-0293 Word Processing News (Burbank)†
0742-0366 A B M S Directory of Certified Emergency Physicians
0742-0374 A B M S Directory of Certified Urologists
0742-0463 Volcanology & Seismology
0742-0498 State Budget and Tax News
0742-0501 Publishers Directory
0742-051X Teaching & Teacher Education
0742-0528 Chronobiology International
0742-0552 Blueprints
0742-0587 Sports Afield Fishing Annual *changed to* Sports Afield Fishing.
0742-0595 Sports Afield Fishing Secrets†
0742-0609 Sports Afield Bass *changed to* Sports Afield Bass & Panfish.
0742-0668 Clinics in Podiatry *see* 0891-8422
0742-0676 Software Digest Ratings Newsletter *see* 0893-6455
0742-0692 Tucson Weekly
0742-0714 Journal of Gambling Behavior *see* 1050-5350
0742-0757 Tennessee Tax Guide
0742-0935 Mature Outlook
0742-096X Allegheny Review
0742-1036 Professional Computing†
0742-1095 Want's Federal - State Court Directory (Year)
0742-1117 Bibliotheca Afroasiatica
0742-1125 Islamic Art and Architecture
0742-1133 Invited Lectures on the Middle East at the University of Texas at Austin
0742-1141 Byzantina Kai Metabyzantina
0742-115X Humana Civilitas
0742-1168 Studies in Near Eastern Culture and Society
0742-1184 Other Realities
0742-1206 U-News†
0742-1214 Business Software Magazine *changed to* P C Accounting.
0742-1222 Journal of Management Information Systems
0742-1419 Family History Capers
0742-1427 Data Sets: Cuneiform Texts

0742-1478 Health Care Strategic Management
0742-1494 Vintage '45†
0742-1532 Electronic Display World
0742-1648 Interior Landscape Industry
0742-1656 Art Therapy
0742-1702 County Executive Directory
0742-1710 Municipal Executive Directory
0742-1729 Federal Regional Executive Directory
0742-1737 Small Group Letter *see* 0273-5865
0742-1753 A S C E Annual Combined Index
0742-1877 Grito del Sol *see* 1045-8875
0742-1923 American University Studies. Series 18. African Literature
0742-1931 International Journal of Adult Orthodontics and Orthognathic Surgery
0742-194X Year Book of Podiatric Medicine and Surgery
0742-1974 Engineering Index Monthly
0742-2008 Washington Credit Letter *changed to* Consumer Credit Letter.
0742-2024 Industry News *changed to* Sports Industry News.
0742-2032 Ultrasport†
0742-2075 Hudson Valley Regional Review
0742-2091 Cell Biology and Toxicology
0742-2113 Stories
0742-2121 C T A Action
0742-2334 Computer Aided Research in Near Eastern Studies
0742-2393 Trinity University Monograph Series in Religion†
0742-2466 Florida Review
0742-2490 Indiana Directory of Music Teachers
0742-2644 Real Estate Quarterly†
0742-2733 Philosophy in Context
0742-2741 Telecommunications Patents Newsletter†
0742-2768 Rag Mag
0742-2792 Trumpeter Swan Society Newsletter
0742-2822 Echocardiography
0742-3071 Diabetic Medicine
0742-3098 Journal of Pineal Research
0742-3101 Engineering Geology Abstracts†
0742-3136 UNIX Review
0742-3225 Family Medicine
0742-3438 Aging Network News
0742-3446 Merritt Risk Management Review
0742-3470 Afro-American Journal of Philosophy
0742-3551 Channel 9000†
0742-3578 Techniques†
0742-3632 C I N C O M: Courses in Communications
0742-3640 International Journal on World Peace
0742-3667 National Center for the Study of Collective Bargaining in Higher Education and the Professions. Annual Conference Proceedings
0742-3675 United States Trade Fair
0742-3713 Economic Development Review
0742-3772 Sourceview *changed to* Sourceview Journal of Software Evaluations, Reviews & Ratings.
0742-3780 Michie's Texas Tort Reporter†
0742-390X Current Ornithology
0742-3918 Track Technique: Official Technical Publication
0742-3977 Woodall's Tenting Directory *changed to* Woodall's Tent Camping Guide.
0742-3985 International Periodicals and Reference Works
0742-406X Gates Researcher†
0742-4108 Receptors and Ligands in Intercellular Communication Series
0742-4221 Diabetes - Metabolism Reviews
0742-4299 U S F L Guide and Register†
0742-4337 Energy Meetings & Trade Shows Directory†
0742-4434 Raw
0742-4469 Compute's PC & PC jr.†
0742-4477 Agribusiness (New York)
0742-4485 Golf Digest Almanac (Year)†
0742-4507 Netback
0742-4515 Good Money
0742-454X Red Fox Review at Mohegan Community College†
0742-4574 Boxes and Arrows
0742-4612 Mississippi Rag
0742-4639 The Word Among Us
0742-4647 Mealey's Litigation Report: Asbestos
0742-4655 Mealey's Litigation Report: Iranian Claims†
0742-4671 Journal of Film and Video
0742-468X F - M Automation Newsletter (Facilities Management) *see* 1043-6146
0742-4779 Warren County Genealogical Society Quarterly *changed to* Heir Lines.
0742-4787 Journal of Tribology
0742-4795 Journal of Engineering for Gas Turbines and Power
0742-4817 Los Angeles Times Index
0742-4868 Nuclear Plant Safety *see* 0892-2055
0742-4876 Interpreter (Sacramento)
0742-4914 B C T V: Bibliography on Cable Television
0742-4949 Peterson's Guide to Colleges in the Midwest (Year)
0742-4957 Peterson's Guide to Colleges in the Middle Atlantic States (Year)
0742-4965 Peterson's Guide to Colleges in New York (Year)
0742-4973 Peterson's Guide to Colleges in New England (Year)
0742-5031 Kol ha-T'nuah
0742-5120 Licensing, Countersigning and Surplus Line Laws
0742-5244 Insight *changed to* Franklin's Insight.
0742-5260 Scientists Center for Animal Welfare. Newsletter
0742-5279 Election Politics†
0742-5325 Public Justice Report
0742-5333 International Documentary
0742-5341 Report on I B M
0742-535X World Right-to-Die Newsletter
0742-5376 Hemlock Quarterly
0742-5384 Telecommunications Alert
0742-5406 Corporate Responsibility Monitor
0742-5414 Plant Shutdowns Monitor *see* 0742-5406
0742-5457 Asian Theatre Journal
0742-5473 Dickens Quarterly
0742-552X Detention Reporter
0742-5538 Historical Guides to the World's Periodicals and Newspapers
0742-5562 Midwest Modern Language Association. Journal
0742-5619 Disability Income and Health Insurance
0742-5627 Innovative Higher Education
0742-5635 Wild and Free†
0742-5686 Comput-A-Cal†
0742-5694 Building Products Digest
0742-5708 Hospital Capital Finance†
0742-5732 Videodisc and Optical Disk Update *see* 1054-9706
0742-5740 Videodisc and Optical Disk *see* 1054-9692
0742-5759 Library Software Review
0742-5783 Radio P C Report†
0742-5821 International Directory of Nuclear Utilities
0742-5902 Computer User (Minneapolis)
0742-5953 I F A C Proceedings *see* 0962-9505
0742-597X Journal of Management in Engineering
0742-5996 Ring Systems Handbook
0742-6046 Psychology & Marketing
0742-6089 Used Computer Guide
0742-6224 Yeats
0742-6348 Northern Journal of Applied Forestry
0742-6410 Hazard Monthly
0742-6429 Shortwave Guide *changed to* World Radio Report.
0742-6445 Telecom Insider
0742-6453 Office Automation Reporting Service†
0742-6496 Computers in Banking
0742-6534 Catalyst (Montpelier)
0742-6542 Administrator's Update†
0742-6550 Business Journal (Portland)
0742-6569 News Baskett†
0742-6704 P C Accounting Trends *changed to* C P A Micro Report.
0742-6712 Studies in the Humanities (New York)
0742-6747 Hi-Res
0742-6763 American Journal of Islamic Social Sciences
0742-678X T I M I X Buyer's Guide
0742-6801 Bibliographies and Indexes in World Literature
0742-681X Bibliographies and Indexes in Psychology
0742-6828 Bibliographies and Indexes in American History
0742-6836 Bibliographies and Indexes in Religious Studies
0742-6844 Bibliographies and Indexes in Anthropology
0742-6852 Bibliographies and Indexes in World History
0742-6860 Bibliographies and Indexes in American Literature
0742-6879 Bibliographies and Indexes in Library and Information Science
0742-6887 Bibliographies and Indexes in Philosophy
0742-6895 Bibliographies and Indexes in Sociology
0742-6909 Bibliographies and Indexes in Law and Political Science
0742-6917 Bibliographies and Indexes in Education
0742-6925 Bibliographies and Indexes in Afro-American and African Studies
0742-6933 Bibliographies and Indexes in the Performing Arts
0742-6941 Bibliographies and Indexes in Women's Studies
0742-695X Bio-Bibliographies in American Literature
0742-6968 Bio-Bibliographies in Music
0742-6984 Religion & Society Report
0742-7018 W I T S: I
0742-7026 W I T S: II
0742-7115 Constitutional Commentary
0742-7123 New Books on Women & Feminism
0742-7387 Art Material Directory and Buyers' Guide *see* 0004-3265
0742-7425 Virginia Polytechnic Institute and State University. College of Agriculture and Life Sciences. Information Series *changed to* Virginia Polytechnic Institute and State University. Virginia Agricultural Experiment Station. Information Series.
0742-7433 Feminist Periodicals
0742-7441 Feminist Collections
0742-7514 New Book of Popular Science Annual
0742-7778 C A L I C O Journal
0742-7840 Update: Mideast
0742-7859 Practical Supervision
0742-7972 Lapidus Letter
0742-8014 Rahavard *changed to* Rahavard Persian Journal.
0742-8065 Hosiery News
0742-8081 Health Exchange
0742-8111 Video Movies *changed to* Video Times (Skokie).
0742-812X Collectible Automobile
0742-8219 HortIdeas
0742-8308 Bicycle Paper
0742-8413 Comparative Biochemistry and Physiology. Part C: Comparative Pharmacology & Toxicology
0742-843X The States and Small Business: A Directory of Programs and Activities
0742-8472 Overholser Family Association. Bulletin
0742-8480 College Band Directors National Association Journal
0742-8820 White Light†
0742-8839 Motion Picture Investor
0742-8936 South Dakota Authors' Catalog†
0742-8944 Matrimonial, Overseas Jobs and Real Estate International Newsletter *changed to* 100 Livelihood Occupations.
0742-8987 Campbell's List
0742-9045 National Directory of Local Researchers
0742-9290 A S A Newsletter
0742-9312 Tom Mann's Outdoors†
0742-9355 Freight Cars Journal
0742-938X V D T News
0742-9398 Micro Money Newsletter
0742-9517 American Society of C L U. Journal†
0742-955X Digital Bypass Report *see* 0271-5430
0742-9568 Entertainment Magazine
0742-9576 Arab American Almanac
0742-9614 Micro Communications†
0742-9622 Cardio
0742-9630 Black Sheep Review†
0742-9665 Lebanon News (English Edition)
0742-9681 Reader (Houghton)
0742-969X Hospice Journal
0742-9703 Journal of Psychotherapy and the Family *see* 0897-5353
0742-9711 Physical Therapy in Health Care
0742-972X S A E Update
0742-9770 Pryor Report
0742-9789 Using Personal Computers in Nonprofit Agencies†
0742-9797 Mexican Studies
0742-9800 Coding Clinic for ICD-9-CM
0742-9916 Outlook on I B M†
0742-9940 Practice, the journal of politics, economics, psychology, sociology and culture *changed to* Practice (New York).
0743-0159 Financial Computing†
0743-0167 Journal of Rural Studies
0743-0175 Defense Analysis
0743-0183 A I Ch E Applications Software Survey of Personal Computers
0743-0221 Hands On! (Cambridge)
0743-0272 Corporate Control Alert
0743-0302 Microcomputers for Libraries
0743-0310 Benchmark (Richmond)
0743-0361 Satellite Business†
0743-040X Arlis - N A Update
0743-0671 Communications Product Report
0743-0701 Robot Insider†
0743-0744 Florida Tourism Hotline
0743-0795 Multinational P R Report
0743-0809 Prudent Speculator
0743-0825 Jack Anderson Confidential *changed to* Jack Anderson First Alert.
0743-0841 Animal Welfare Institute. Quarterly
0743-085X Muslin Scientist *changed to* International Journal of Science and Technology.
0743-0876 Ocean-Air Interactions
0743-0884 American International Journal of Arts, Sciences, Engineering and Medicine
0743-0957 Bonnet-t-e's and Kin
0743-1066 Journal of Logic Programming
0743-1104 National Storytelling Journal *see* 1048-1354
0743-1120 Writer's Journal
0743-1163 Texas Manufacturers Register
0743-1341 North Suburban Genealogical Society. Newsletter
0743-1384 Talk of the Month
0743-1759 North Carolina Journal of International Law and Commercial Regulation
0743-1848 La Voix des Prairies
0743-1872 Crime Laboratory Digest
0743-216X Day Researcher†
0743-2178 Marketing New Media
0743-2208 Bowker's Electronic News†
0743-2240 The Eye (Wilmington)
0743-2283 TeleSpan
0743-2356 Woman of Power
0743-2399 World Christian
0743-2437 This Week in Washington
0743-2445 Logo and Education Computing Journal†
0743-2453 South Carolina Appellate Digest
0743-2461 Best-Selling Home Plans
0743-247X Equitable Distribution Journal
0743-2534 P C Abstracts†
0743-2542 Strategy and Executive Action
0743-2550 Journal of Christian Nursing
0743-2720 Wrestling Ringside
0743-2755 Amelia
0743-2836 Computer Graphics Directory *see* 0895-2760

0743-2860 Dorm Magazine *changed to* Student Life.
0743-2879 Studies in History and Culture
0743-2909 Limberlost Review
0743-2917 Blue Moon†
0743-2933 Desktop Publishing Users' Report
0743-2941 Washington (Seattle)
0743-2968 Hands On Electronics *see* 1042-170X
0743-2984 Engineering Software Exchange
0743-3069 Space Enterprise Today†
0743-3115 Pizza Today
0743-3204 Bomb
0743-3263 Western Electronics†
0743-3271 Industrial West
0743-3301 Journal of the U S Utopian Movement and the International Kibbutz Movement *changed to* Utopia 2.
0743-3387 Manager's Notebook *changed to* American Productivity & Quality Center. Notebook.
0743-345X P R N Forum *see* 0885-3924
0743-3492 Index to Electric Utility Week
0743-3522 Art Deco News
0743-3808 Behavior Research Methods, Instruments, and Computers
0743-3832 Meeting Planners Alert
0743-412X Trial Advocate Quarterly
0743-4154 Research in the History of Economic Thought and Methodology
0743-4170 International Directory of Special Events and Festivals *see* 0894-0649
0743-4200 Dvorak Developments†
0743-4235 Butson Family Newsletter†
0743-4243 Virginian
0743-4251 Abstracts in Maryland Archeology
0743-4278 Advanced Computing Magazine
0743-4294 High-Tech Marketing†
0743-4324 Survey of Press Freedom in Latin America
0743-4456 Prostaglandins Bibliography†
0743-4561 Comprehensive Directory of Sports Addresses *changed to* Sports Address Bible.
0743-4634 Annual Review of Cell Biology
0743-4642 Christian Computing *changed to* Christian Computing and Communications.
0743-4685 Semiconductors - I Cs Patents Newsletter†
0743-4758 A T C C Quarterly Newsletter
0743-4812 Common Carrier Week
0743-4820 Space Commerce Bulletin *changed to* Space Commerce Week.
0743-4839 Library Times International
0743-4863 Critical Reviews in Therapeutic Drug Carrier Systems
0743-4871 Japan High Tech Review *changed to* East Asia High Tech Review.
0743-5053 Public Scrutiny *changed to* Health Freedom News.
0743-5088 Pride Institute Journal of Long Term Health Care *changed to* Pride Institute Journal of Long Term Home Health Care.
0743-5150 Image: Journal of Nursing Scholarship
0743-5223 Itinerary (Bayonne)
0743-524X Eucharistic Minister
0743-5258 Mass Market Retailers *changed to* M M R.
0743-5266 Art and the Law *see* 0888-4226
0743-5363 World Currency Yearbook
0743-5398 International Business Monthly
0743-5436 A.I.D. Highlights
0743-5495 Bicycle Sport†
0743-5584 Journal of Adolescent Research
0743-5606 Great Activities Newspaper
0743-5614 International Partners in Prayer Trumpeting News
0743-5649 Recreation and Parks Law Reporter
0743-5657 Arizona Labor Market Newsletter *changed to* Arizona Labor Market Information Newsletter.
0743-5738 Vista Magazine Miami Metro Guide *changed to* Vista Magazine.
0743-5797 Analytical Instrumentation
0743-5800 Endocrine Research
0743-5878 Access: Apple
0743-5886 Access: I B M
0743-5983 Office Guide to Miami *changed to* South Florida Office Guide.
0743-605X Cato Policy Report
0743-6122 Who's Who in America's Restaurants
0743-619X Digital Audio and Compact Disc Review *see* 1044-1700
0743-6211 Municipal - County Executive Directory Annual
0743-6238 Anabiosis: The Journal for Near-Death Studies *see* 0891-4494
0743-6246 Seaport: New York's History Magazine
0743-6262 Computing & Management
0743-6351 Federal Reserve Bank of Kansas City. Banking Studies
0743-636X Mississippi Arts and Letters†
0743-6408 Daily Planetary Guide
0743-6610 Pasadena Journal of Business†
0743-6629 Travel South *see* 1041-3642
0743-6637 Trauma Quarterly
0743-6645 American University Studies. Series 19. General Literature
0743-6661 Journal of Insurance Medicine
0743-670X N E A Almanac of Higher Education
0743-6750 Petroleum Software Directory
0743-6831 South Central Review
0743-684X Journal of Reconstructive Microsurgery
0743-6858 Gear Technology
0743-6882 Newsletter Inago
0743-7129 Auto Racing Memories
0743-7188 Mignot-Luccote Historical Review†
0743-7250 Goldthwait Polar Library Accessions List
0743-7277 Buildings Design Journal†
0743-7285 Today's Living *changed to* Better Nutrition for Today's Living.
0743-7315 Journal of Parallel and Distributed Computing
0743-7439 Southern Friend
0743-7463 Langmuir
0743-7471 Graywolf Annual
0743-751X Ophthalmology Annual†
0743-7528 Material Culture Directories
0743-7560 Bibliographies and Indexes in Gerontology
0743-7579 Iroquois Stalker
0743-7617 Image File
0743-7625 Direct Line
0743-7633 M300 and P C Report *see* 1055-4769
0743-7641 Missouri Archaeological Society. Quarterly
0743-7749 Journal of Modern Hellenism
0743-7757 Echad
0743-779X Alabama Business and Economic Journal *changed to* Southern Business & Economic Journal.
0743-7803 Archer Quarterly
0743-7889 Studies in Romantic and Modern Literature†
0743-7897 Military Space
0743-7927 National Insurance Law Review
0743-7951 Wisconsin International Law Journal
0743-8001 Sensus†
0743-8036 Current Literature in Nephrology *changed to* Current Literature in Nephrology, Hypertension and Transplantation.
0743-8044 Views (Boston)
0743-8079 Medical Benefits
0743-8095 Magazine of Virginia Genealogy
0743-8125 Bow Waves Boating *see* 1045-8131
0743-8125 Bow Waves Boating *see* 1045-814X
0743-8133 Eastern Boating *see* 1045-8131
0743-8133 Eastern Boating *see* 1045-814X
0743-8176 Primary Care & Cancer
0743-8346 Journal of Perinatology
0743-8354 Ob-Gyn Clinical Alert
0743-8400 Agrichemical Briefing
0743-8443 Telegen Reporter *see* 0000-118X
0743-846X S A F E Symposium Proceedings
0743-8494 C S P A Stateside
0743-8508 Gold Mining Stock Report
0743-8591 Edwards Journal
0743-8613 Information Strategy
0743-863X South Florida Home and Garden *see* 0898-9494
0743-8826 Hazard Prevention
0743-8907 Prairie Wool Companion *see* 1042-7643
0743-8915 University of Kentucky Libraries. Occasional Papers
0743-894X Wood
0743-8958 Bridge Builder
0743-8974 Social Science News Letter *see* 0886-280X
0743-913X Light Year
0743-9156 Journal of Marketing and Public Policy *changed to* Journal of Public Policy & Marketing.
0743-9180 United Nations Issues Conference. Report
0743-9199 Classics of Soviet Mathematics
0743-9229 Medical Heritage†
0743-9245 State, Culture and Society†
0743-9261 Year Book of Infectious Diseases
0743-9288 Videosat News†
0743-9296 Journal of Management Case Studies†
0743-9466 I B M Compatibles Plus†
0743-9474 Burroughs World *see* 0892-2845
0743-9482 N C R Independent User Monthly *changed to* N C R Connection.
0743-9490 Honeywell Monthly *see* 0895-0326
0743-9504 Business Microworld *changed to* Network Computing News.
0743-9512 T I Professional Computing *see* 0892-2837
0743-9539 Annual Review of Chronopharmacology
0743-9547 Journal of South-East Asian Earth Sciences
0743-9628 Borgo Bioviews
0743-9636 International Journal of Micrographics and Video Technology *see* 0958-9961
0743-9644 U F S I Reports
0743-9679 Home and Educational Computing *see* 0194-357X
0743-9873 Children's Magazine Guide
0743-9989 Small Farmer's Journal
0743-9997 Arizona Business Reports
0744-0049 National Strength & Conditioning Association Journal
0744-0073 Diesel Progress North American *see* 1040-8878
0744-0081 Computer Industry Update
0744-0154 N E A Now
0744-0219 Daylily Journal
0744-0359 American Sunbeam†
0744-0405 Fast Service/Family Restaurants†
0744-057X Ecphorizer
0744-060X New York Native
0744-074X MotorHome
0744-0820 Woodstove, Wood, Coal and Solar Equipment Directory *see* 1045-8069
0744-0898 Epidemiology Monitor
0744-0901 Doll Reader
0744-0987 Texas Gardener
0744-1088 Associations Report
0744-1177 Focus Quarterly†
0744-1193 Builder (Washington)
0744-1223 I I A Today
0744-1339 Radio Free Europe Research Reports *see* 0937-7441
0744-1347 N C G A News
0744-1355 Speech Technology
0744-138X Upholstering Today†
0744-1444 Herzl Institute Bulletin
0744-1584 Computer-Electronic Service News *see* 1046-1965
0744-1649 Stitch 'n Sew Quilts
0744-1657 Test & Measurement World
0744-1657 Test & Measurement World Buyer's Guide
0744-1673 Data Sources
0744-1738 Hobby Merchandiser
0744-1908 Hairstylist *changed to* Salon Talk.
0744-1916 Foodservice Technology Int'l. (Kitchen Planning)†
0744-1932 Earth Shelter Living *changed to* Earth Shelter Living. Newsletter.
0744-2149 Construction Times
0744-2238 Lakota Times
0744-2319 Craft and Needlework Age - World of Miniatures *changed to* Craft and Needlework Age.
0744-2386 Commline
0744-2416 National Masters News
0744-2475 Peelings II†
0744-2513 Modern Jeweler National
0744-2548 Rural Telecommunications
0744-2602 I C P Business Software Review *see* 0885-8055
0744-2629 A O P A General Aviation National Report†
0744-267X Catholic Sun
0744-2688 Bankers News Weekly *see* 0746-3367
0744-2750 Corporate Design *changed to* Today's Facility Manager.
0744-2785 Predicasts F & S Index of Corporate Change
0744-2815 Today's Office *changed to* Office Technology Management.
0744-2823 Drugs & Drug Abuse Education. Newsletter
0744-2890 U.S. Department of Agriculture. Cotton and Wool Outlook and Situation *changed to* U.S. Department of Agriculture. Cotton and Wool Situation and Outlook.
0744-2955 Detective (Falls Church)
0744-3056 Side-Saddle News
0744-3064 Shreveport†
0744-3102 Magazine & Bookseller
0744-3161 Press Magazine
0744-3420 Chart Your Course *changed to* Creative Kids.
0744-3501 Electric Utility Fleet Management *changed to* Utility Fleet Management.
0744-351X Drives and Controls International *see* 0885-0259
0744-3587 Philadelphia Business Journal
0744-3609 Ultrarunning
0744-3625 Supervisor's Bulletin: Office Edition
0744-3633 Performance Horseman *see* 0018-5159
0744-3676 Employee Services Management
0744-3692 Louisiana Game and Fish
0744-3749 Antique Angler
0744-3773 Shotgun Sports
0744-3854 Instant Printer *changed to* Instant & Small Commercial Printer.
0744-3897 Hotels and Restaurants International *see* 1047-2975
0744-3943 Jonquil
0744-396X Kentucky Dental Association. Journal
0744-4052 Christian Missions in Many Lands
0744-4060 Christian Index (Memphis)
0744-4117 Education for the Handicapped Law Report
0744-415X Victorian Homes
0744-4168 Hazardous Waste Training Bulletin for Supervisors *changed to* O S H A Training Bulletin for Supervisors.
0744-4230 Pennsylvania Magazine
0744-4249 Byline
0744-4389 American National CattleWomen Newsletter *see* 1042-5233
0744-446X Computer Update *changed to* B C S Update.
0744-4540 Barr's Post Card News
0744-4567 Microcomputing†
0744-4583 Voice of North Carolina School Boards Association
0744-4664 Seafood Leader
0744-4680 Northwest Arts†
0744-4710 Resource Recycling
0744-4788 Rowing U S A *see* 0888-1154
0744-4869 Winston Cup Illustrated
0744-4923 Home Healthcare Business *see* 0884-741X
0744-5105 Muscle & Fitness
0744-5121 Shape
0744-5296 PlasticsBrief: Reinforced Plastic Edition

ISSN

0744-530X Better Buildings
0744-5326 International Railway Journal and Rapid Transit Review
0744-5474 Arizona Land and People
0744-5598 Agri-News
0744-561X Long Island Life†
0744-5709 National Leader†
0744-5733 Verdicts and Settlements†
0744-5881 Oil and Gas Investor
0744-5989 Collectors' Showcase
0744-6012 Business Digest of Central Massachusetts
0744-6020 Orthopaedic Nursing Journal
0744-6063 Forum (Tallahassee)
0744-6179 Blade Magazine
0744-6217 Midwest Art *see* 0899-1782
0744-6241 Defense Science and Electronics *changed to* Aerospace & Defense Science.
0744-625X Alimentos Procesados
0744-6314 Nursing Management
0744-6349 FirstHand Magazine
0744-6357 Pest Management
0744-6403 Apparel News South
0744-642X Real Estate Business
0744-6470 Hospital Employee Health
0744-6489 J E I Report
0744-6594 Nasinec
0744-6608 Sheltie Pacesetter
0744-6616 American Printer (Chicago, 1982)
0744-6640 Home Shop Machinist
0744-6667 Computer Gaming World
0744-6713 Journal of State Taxation
0744-673X Computer Retail News *see* 0893-8377
0744-6853 Plywood and Panel World *changed to* Panel World.
0744-6861 New England Bride
0744-7078 Administrator (Madison)
0744-7108 Interface. Administrative & Accounting†
0744-7132 Journal of Ophthalmic Nursing & Technology
0744-7140 National Ad Search
0744-7167 Construction Supervision & Safety Letter
0744-7418 River Cities†
0744-7434 First Teacher
0744-7477 Arizona Capitol Times
0744-7590 Long Island's Nightlife *changed to* New York's Nightlife.
0744-7612 Communication World
0744-7671 Bankruptcy Law Letter
0744-7698 Interface. Manufacturing and Engineering†
0744-7701 Fur Rancher
0744-7779 Employee Relations and Human Resources Bulletin
0744-7841 Satellite T V Week
0744-7868 80 Micro†
0744-7884 Voice of Universarius†
0744-7892 National O T C Stock Exchange *see* 0745-7049
0744-7981 Texas Public Utility News
0744-8120 Camperways
0744-8155 Pacific Automotive News
0744-8163 Diversity
0744-8279 Pastoral Renewal *changed to* Faith & Renewal.
0744-8295 Breakout
0744-8317 Oregon Coast
0744-8341 In Touch for Men
0744-8376 Ohio State Bar Association Report
0744-8481 Journal of American College Health
0744-8589 New Covenant
0744-8600 Californiai Magyarsag
0744-8635 Interiorscape
0744-8686 California Tomorrow
0744-8724 Commodore Magazine†
0744-8732 Nursing and Allied Health Index *see* 0146-5554
0744-8821 University of Washington. Academic Computing Services. Newsletter†
0744-8864 Warehousing Supervisor's Bulletin
0744-8899 Ohio State Alumni Magazine
0744-8988 Greenhouse Manager
0744-9062 Financial Managers' Statement†
0744-9070 Gulf Coast Oil Reporter *see* 0884-7967
0744-9100 Daily Devotions for the Deaf
0744-9143 Apartment Management Newsletter
0744-916X Scholastic News: News Pilot
0744-9194 Lakeland Boating
0744-9216 D E C Professional
0744-933X Pilot
0744-9372 3rd Coast†
0744-9488 Champion
0744-9585 Catholic Voice
0744-9593 North Carolina Farm Bureau News
0744-9631 A C F A Bulletin
0744-9666 Sun (Chapel Hill)
0744-9704 Defense Science 2000-Plus *changed to* Defense Science 2004-Plus.
0744-9798 County News
0744-9836 Working Papers Magazine *changed to* Modern Times.
0744-9860 Sproutletter
0744-9879 Collectors Mart
0744-9917 A.N.A.L.O.G. Computing
0744-9984 Journal of Chiropractic
0745-0168 PlasticsBrief: Marketing Edition *changed to* PlasticsBrief: Thermoplastics Marketing Edition.
0745-0214 Aviation Equipment Maintenance
0745-0257 Southern Cross
0745-0265 Current Consumer & Lifestudies
0745-0273 Maine United Methodist
0745-0311 Electronic Media
0745-032X Exploring 1
0745-0346 Exploring 1 for Leaders
0745-0354 Exploring 2 for Leaders
0745-0389 R V Trade Digest
0745-0419 Interface. Insurance Industry *see* 1054-0733
0745-0427 The Witness (Dubuque)
0745-0486 Evangelical Visitor
0745-0516 A.H.A. Perspectives *changed to* Perspectives (Washington).
0745-0532 Legal Administration *see* 1043-7355
0745-0575 Women's Household Crochet
0745-0745 Business Computer Systems†
0745-0753 Multi Level Marketing News
0745-080X 73: Amateur Radio's Technical Journal *see* 1052-2522
0745-0850 Systems & Software†
0745-0877 C P A Personnel Report
0745-0893 N Y Habitat
0745-0958 Delta Epsilon Sigma Journal
0745-0990 Pharmaceutical and Cosmetic Equipment *changed to* Pharmaceutical Processing.
0745-1032 Candy Industry
0745-1075 Computers in Healthcare
0745-113X Electronics West†
0745-1148 Hospital Security and Safety Management
0745-1172 Between Times†
0745-1199 Communications Industry Report†
0745-1237 Missouri Schools
0745-1253 Brookings Review
0745-1342 C P A Computer Report†
0745-1369 Attorneys Marketing Report
0745-1385 Black Powder Times
0745-1458 Computers & Electronics†
0745-1474 Tennessee Business
0745-1490 Stamp Review†
0745-1539 Illinois Advance
0745-1636 Corporate Meetings & Incentives
0745-1687 Builder (Scottdale)
0745-1784 Grower
0745-1962 Circle K
0745-2152 Remodeling World *see* 0885-8039
0745-2209 G F W C Clubwoman
0745-225X Pennsylvania Outdoors *changed to* Pennsylvania Game & Fish.
0745-2292 Jorgensen Report
0745-2349 Action Films†
0745-2357 Scholastic Editor's Trends in Publications *changed to* Trends in College Media.
0745-2357 Scholastic Editor's Trends in Publications *changed to* Trends in High School Media.
0745-242X Financier
0745-2489 Success (New York)
0745-2500 P C: The Independent Guide to I B M Personal Computers *see* 0888-8507
0745-2527 Antic: the Atari Resource†
0745-2578 I S O World *see* 0746-6765
0745-2594 Record (New York, 1967)
0745-2616 Human Services (Woodhaven)†
0745-2802 Cable T V Business†
0745-2810 Collage (Wheeling)
0745-2896 Makai
0745-2993 Microwaves & R F
0745-3027 Perspectives (Bloomington)
0745-3043 Automotive Products Report†
0745-3116 Country Handcrafts
0745-3167 Adopted Child
0745-3213 U C Clip Sheet†
0745-3256 Alliance Witness *see* 1040-6794
0745-3299 Roze Maryi
0745-3345 Kansas Alumni Magazine
0745-3353 Silver Circle
0745-3469 Nut Grower
0745-3590 The Seed Pod
0745-3612 Today's Catholic (San Antonio)
0745-3639 Stallion
0745-368X Agenda for Citizen Involvement *see* 1044-3134
0745-3787 Pork (Year)
0745-3795 Landscape & Irrigation
0745-3949 Dancscene
0745-3981 Stanford Magazine
0745-4058 Journal of Educational Communication *see* 0741-3653
0745-4171 Lifelines: The Software Magazine†
0745-421X Attorneys Computer Report†
0745-4295 V M & S D
0745-4309 Electri-Onics *see* 0895-3708
0745-4309 Electri-Onics Desk Manual *changed to* Electronic Manufacturing Desk Manual.
0745-4325 Office Administration and Automation *see* 0884-5905
0745-4384 Arizona Bar Briefs†
0745-449X Die Casting Management
0745-4503 Food Institute Report
0745-452X Agri-Practice
0745-4554 Physicians' Travel & Meeting Guide
0745-4570 Comics Buyers Guide
0745-4651 Electric Consumer
0745-4678 Health Industry Today
0745-4783 Executive Communications†
0745-4880 Management Report
0745-4929 Restaurant - Hotel Design International
0745-4937 Spotlight (Mamaroneck)
0745-4996 Piloting Careers *see* 1048-8898
0745-5070 Geriatric Guide to Pertinent Publications *changed to* Geriatric Directory of Geriatric Publications.
0745-5089 Newspaper Marketing
0745-5100 Air Cargo World
0745-5119 Corporate Accounting†
0745-5178 American Folklore Society Newsletter
0745-5194 Medical Anthropology Quarterly
0745-5305 Growing Without Schooling
0745-5356 Jewish Week
0745-5399 Dairymen's Digest
0745-5720 U S A - National Art Museum and Gallery Guide *changed to* Art Now Gallery Guide: International Edition.
0745-5747 Tulsa Business Chronicle
0745-5801 South Dakota Legion News
0745-5917 Triathlon *see* 0898-3410
0745-5925 Shepard's Uniform Commercial Code Citations
0745-5933 Business Marketing
0745-5941 High-Performance Pontiac
0745-6050 Catholic Times
0745-6069 Productivity Improvement Bulletin†
0745-6077 Hot Boat Magazine *see* 0892-8320
0745-6093 Security Management - Protecting Property, People & Assets
0745-6298 Challenge (Carthage)
0745-6352 Spiritual Fitness in Business†
0745-6506 Amazing Heroes
0745-6522 Nebraska Farm Bureau News
0745-6921 Management of World Wastes
0745-6999 Journal of Resource Management and Technology
0745-7049 National O T C Stock Journal
0745-7065 Scholastic Update
0745-7138 Journal of Microcomputer Applications
0745-7189 Teddy Bear and Friends
0745-7243 Screen Actor News *see* 0036-956X
0745-7324 Greenhouse Grower
0745-7472 Hearing Journal
0745-7510 Wire Technology International
0745-7553 Farmshine
0745-7790 Employment Relations Today
0745-7839 Journal American Rhododendron Society
0745-7847 Islands
0745-8088 Industrial News (Montrose)
0745-8126 Bicycle Business Journal
0745-8304 Senior High Class†
0745-841X F P G Weekly News Update *see* 0430-1692
0745-8509 Star (New York, 1945)
0745-8649 Black Beat
0745-8711 Private Cable *changed to* Private Cable Plus Wireless Cable.
0745-8738 Midwest Poetry Review
0745-8746 Psychic Guide *changed to* Body, Mind & Spirit Magazine.
0745-8754 Drafting and Repro Digest *see* 1042-8534
0745-8851 Alaska Native Magazine
0745-9009 Georgetown Magazine
0745-9033 Dairymen's Digest: North Central Region Edition
0745-9130 Whisker's Summer Weekly Reader *changed to* Weekly Reader. Summer Edition B. Grades 2-6.
0745-9149 Weekly Reader. Summer Edition. Grades 3-5 *see* 0899-6121
0745-9157 Weekly Reader. Summer Edition. Grade K *changed to* Weekly Reader. Summer Edition A. Pre K - Grade 1.
0745-9416 Eastern Horse World *changed to* America's Equestrian.
0745-9645 Greek Press
0745-9726 C I M E†
0745-9807 Houston Magazine†
0745-9858 Moneypaper
0745-9874 N T S B Reporter
0745-9963 Journal of Information and Image Management (Short title: J I I M) *see* 0892-3876
0745-9971 Amerikan Uutiset
0746-0023 Business Facilities
0746-004X Canal Zone Philatelist
0746-0066 Contemporary Christian *changed to* Contemporary Christian Music.
0746-0104 Bible Advocate
0746-0201 N.Y. Civil Liberties
0746-0252 L C - Liquid Chromatography and H P L C Magazine *see* 0888-9090
0746-0325 Movie Collectors World
0746-0554 Architecture
0746-0635 Message of the Cross
0746-1062 Pennsylvania C P A Journal
0746-1070 Ophthalmology Management†
0746-1089 Wood Digest
0746-1291 Missouri Jewish Post and Opinion†
0746-1321 Savings Institutions
0746-133X A H E P A N
0746-1380 Pipe Smoker *changed to* Smokers Pipeline.
0746-1402 Centerviews
0746-1461 Michigan Workers' Comp Digest
0746-147X Software Merchandising *changed to* Home Computer & Software Merchandising.
0746-1739 Nursing Economics
0746-1887 Independent Restaurants *see* 0894-4466
0746-1984 Institute of Certified Financial Planners. Journal *see* 1040-3981
0746-2018 Schooldays
0746-2255 Kentucky Engineer

ISSN

0746-2271 South Florida Business Journal
0746-2360 Business Systems Product Update *changed to* Macintosh Update.
0746-2379 Business Systems Update†
0746-2395 Chilton's I and C S *changed to* Instrumentation and Control Systems.
0746-2441 Fastener Technology International
0746-2468 Futures (Cedar Falls)
0746-2506 Emergency Medicine Reports
0746-2603 Economic Democrat *see* 0890-3956
0746-2743 I C A S News *see* 0888-5265
0746-2964 Denver Business
0746-3014 Editors' Forum
0746-3111 Roads *see* 8750-9229
0746-312X Shepard's Federal Energy Law Citations
0746-3138 Shepard's Immigration and Naturalization Citations
0746-3286 Videopro
0746-3367 A B A Bankers News Weekly
0746-3472 Queen City Heritage
0746-3537 Technology Teacher
0746-3545 Student Activities *changed to* Leadership (Reston).
0746-3618 New Age Journal
0746-3626 GraphiCommunicator
0746-3677 G S D News
0746-3685 National Squares
0746-3766 Jojoba Happenings
0746-3820 Packaging
0746-3839 Modern Office Technology
0746-3928 Portuguese Times
0746-4029 Water Conditioning and Purification
0746-4118 AntiqueWeek - Tri-State Trader *changed to* AntiqueWeek - Central.
0746-4134 Gas Turbine World
0746-4177 A T L A Advocate
0746-4185 El Heraldo Catolico
0746-4223 Classroom Computer Learning *see* 1053-6728
0746-4541 Recreational Skier
0746-469X Clinical Laser Monthly
0746-4703 Prospective Payment Survival
0746-4797 Rainbow (Prospect)
0746-4851 World Farming Agrimanagement *changed to* Agribusiness Worldwide.
0746-4975 Boston Business Journal
0746-5076 M *changed to* M.
0746-5335 Changes (Detroit) *see* 0739-4853
0746-5467 Office Products Industry Report
0746-5726 Synchro
0746-5963 Georgia Journal *changed to* Georgia Journal - Living.
0746-6013 Oklahoma Game & Fish
0746-6072 Telecommunication Products Plus Technology *changed to* Networking Management.
0746-6102 Postcard Collector
0746-6110 D & B Reports
0746-6129 Library Administrator's Digest
0746-6250 North American Whitetail
0746-6498 Innkeeping World
0746-6641 Certified Engineering Technician
0746-6765 Micro Marketworld
0746-7141 Converting Magazine
0746-7265 E D P Auditing
0746-7281 Data Security Management
0746-729X World Mining Equipment
0746-7400 W E S: Voice of the Window Treatment Industry *see* 0886-9669
0746-746X Pinellas County Review
0746-7656 MusicLine *changed to* C C M Update.
0746-7672 Rubberstampmadness
0746-7680 Videolog
0746-7761 Chief - Civil Service Leader
0746-7915 Financial Planning (Atlanta)
0746-7966 Baseball Card News
0746-7982 Singles Scene (Allardt)
0746-8121 Communications Week International
0746-813X C E R L Forum†
0746-8245 Farmstead†
0746-8288 Indiana Medicine
0746-8342 College Mathematics Journal
0746-8482 South Texas Business Journal
0746-8504 Auto Club News
0746-8601 Sea
0746-8652 Corporate Board
0746-8687 Collectors Motor News *see* 0888-1944
0746-8709 Iowa Medicine
0746-8830 Countdown
0746-8911 Business Radio
0746-9012 C P I Purchasing Chemicals Directory
0746-9012 C P I Purchasing
0746-9039 TeenAge
0746-9152 Lawn Servicing†
0746-9179 Research & Development
0746-9241 Worldwide Challenge
0746-9306 Sports Medicine Bulletin
0746-9403 George Street Journal†
0746-9438 Nemo: The Classic Comics Library†
0746-9462 Sensors
0746-9489 Back Pain Monitor
0746-9586 Fire Command *see* 1054-8793
0746-9640 Wildlife Art News
0746-9683 Employment Relations Bulletin
0746-9691 Tu
0746-9810 Today - the Videotex - Computer Magazine *changed to* CompuServe.
0746-9888 Baker Valley News
0746-990X Backstreets
0747-007X InSights (Herndon)
0747-0088 A B A Journal
0747-0258 Amit Woman
0747-0398 Chemical Product News *see* 0009-2630
0747-0460 P C M
0747-055X Home Computer Magazine
0747-0592 Country Living (Columbus)
0747-0711 Empire State Report
0747-0827 Club Magazine
0747-0843 American Traveler†
0747-0878 Noticias (New York)
0747-0932 National Geographic Traveler
0747-1289 A I P E Facilities Management, Operations and Engineering *see* 1054-7541
0747-1335 A V Video
0747-1351 Journal of Pascal, Ada, & Modula-2
0747-1424 Modern Horse Breeding
0747-1599 Hybrid Circuit Technology
0747-1637 Milton Caniff's Steve Canyon Magazine
0747-167X Memphis Business Journal
0747-1971 Pickups & Mini-Trucks†
0747-217X Magazine of Positive Thinking *changed to* Plus: Magazine of Positive Thinking.
0747-234X Fantasy Review *changed to* Science Fiction and Fantasy Book Review Annual.
0747-2420 Blood Bank Week
0747-2528 Petroleum Independent
0747-2536 Prepared Foods
0747-2536 Prepared Foods Buyers' Guide *changed to* Prepared Foods Food Industry Sourcebook.
0747-2544 Fleet Equipment
0747-2722 P - P M Technology†
0747-3044 Personal Investor *changed to* Worth.
0747-3079 Perfusion Life
0747-315X Athletic Business
0747-3168 Advertising & Graphic Arts Techniques
0747-3192 Spirits, Wine & Beer Marketing in Missouri
0747-3206 Spirits, Wine & Beer Marketing in Minnesota, North & South Dakota
0747-3214 Spirits, Wine and Beer Marketing in Iowa *changed to* Beverage Alcohol Business Scene.
0747-3397 The Fish Sniffer
0747-3540 Telefood *see* 1052-4630
0747-3583 Journal of Imaging Technology
0747-3680 Law Enforcement Technology
0747-3818 Contact (Berkeley)†
0747-3826 Class Magazine
0747-3869 Danske Pioneer
0747-4032 Radioactive *changed to* Radio Week.
0747-4059 On Sat - America's Weekly Guide to Satellite TV *changed to* ONSAT - America's Weekly Satellite Guide.
0747-4261 Glass Magazine
0747-4288 Brethren Evangelist
0747-4350 Arizona Solo *changed to* Single Scene (Scottsdale).
0747-444X Greater Phoenix Jewish News
0747-4458 Programmable Controls Technical Directory†
0747-4482 Silver Magazine *see* 0899-6105
0747-4504 Columbia University Record
0747-4857 Data Book of Social Studies Materials and Resources†
0747-489X Imagine (Boston)
0747-4938 Econometric Reviews
0747-4946 Sequential Analysis
0747-4954 R A P R A New Trade Names in the Rubber and Plastics Industries
0747-5020 Transition (Cincinnati)†
0747-525X Looking Ahead
0747-5276 Reinsurance Directory
0747-5284 Sculpture Review
0747-5322 Folklife Annual
0747-5403 Speedway Scene
0747-5411 Serials Perspective
0747-5438 B N A Online†
0747-5446 Early Childhood Music *changed to* Ultimate Early Childhood Music Resource.
0747-5500 A W E A Wind Energy Weekly
0747-5527 National Stampagraphic
0747-5535 Quarterly Journal of Business and Economics
0747-5543 Cross Sections
0747-5551 P A†
0747-5632 Computers in Human Behavior
0747-5659 Joe Scott's the Political Animal
0747-5667 Missouri State Genealogical Association Journal
0747-5675 Hughes Family Letter
0747-5810 Eswau Huppeday
0747-587X Micro Cornucopia†
0747-5993 Journal of Swimming Research
0747-606X American Homeopathy
0747-6078 Shells and Sea Life *changed to* The Opisthobranch.
0747-6086 Community Service Business†
0747-6175 A J L Newsletter
0747-6213 Inside Drug Law†
0747-6221 I F M A News
0747-623X S O L Etter
0747-6353 Advances in Forensic Psychology and Psychiatry†
0747-6388 F M R
0747-640X Expanding Horizons†
0747-6558 Die Pommerschen Leute
0747-6582 Fidelity and Surety News
0747-6663 Latah County Genealogical Society. Quarterly
0747-6817 Center for Sports Sponsorship's Sponsor Quest
0747-7171 Journal of Symbolic Computation
0747-7236 Cheap Investor
0747-7287 Streletz
0747-735X Michigan Environmental Report
0747-7368 Journal of Gastronomy
0747-7449 Air and Space Lawyer
0747-7503 Community Development Executive
0747-7767 Advances in Cyclic Nucleotide Research and Protein Phosphorylation Research *changed to* Advances in Second Messenger and Phosphoprotein Research.
0747-7805 Western Maryland Genealogy
0747-8003 Corporate Giving Watch
0747-8127 Washington Weekly
0747-8216 Microcosm - Lyrical Ways
0747-8291 Ultrapure Water
0747-8445 Huxford Genealogical Society. Magazine
0747-847X BookNotes: Resource Information for the Small and Self-Publisher
0747-8534 User's Guide to C P-M Systems and Software *changed to* Users Guide to Low Cost Computing.
0747-8607 Tax Management Compensation Planning Journal
0747-8631 Pulse (Wheaton)
0747-8739 News from the Northwest
0747-8887 Hot Wire
0747-8895 Mid-American Review
0747-8917 Bankruptcy Strategist
0747-8933 Computer Law Strategist
0747-8941 Human Resource Developments in the Middle East and North Africa *see* 1047-711X
0747-900X American Buddhist
0747-9026 Knitters
0747-9131 Benefits Today
0747-9182 Minerals and Metallurgical Processing
0747-9190 Partnership *see* 0897-5469
0747-9239 Seismic Instruments
0747-9255 Colorado Monthly Magazine
0747-9298 Legal Information Management Index
0747-9301 Society for Armenian Studies. Journal
0747-931X Unveiling
0747-9360 Design Issues
0747-9395 Fordham International Law Journal
0747-9409 Sites
0747-9514 Bible Book Study for Adults. Korean Edition
0747-9549 Data Entry Awareness Report
0747-9573 Packaged Software Reports
0747-962X Identification Journal†
0747-9662 Journal of Economic & Social Measurement
0747-9670 Computer Graphics Today†
0747-9697 Prickly Pear Tucson†
0747-9700 Federal Contract Disputes
0747-9727 Thirteen (Portlandville)
0747-9735 Waterworld News
0747-9840 Champ Channels
0747-9891 N E H G S Nexus
0748-0008 Texas Economic Forecast
0748-0016 Personal Engineering & Instrumentation News
0748-0024 Tribal Arts Review *see* 0893-0120
0748-0059 Image Understanding
0748-0067 Advances in Teacher Education
0748-0105 Governmental Accounting Procedures and Practices *see* 0883-6779
0748-0164 Cross Currents†
0748-0172 International Trade Reporter Current Reports
0748-0466 Carolina ChemTips
0748-0474 Computer-Integrated Manufacturing Review†
0748-0512 Journal of Veterinary Oncology†
0748-0571 Report of a Vantage Conference
0748-061X Compensation & Benefits Management
0748-0636 Contemporary Authors Autobiography Series
0748-0695 International Trade Reporter Reference File *see* 1043-5662
0748-0709 International Trade Reporter Decisions
0748-0725 Peacework
0748-075X Journal of Health Care Technology†
0748-0784 San Bernardino County Studies *see* 1041-4037
0748-0792 Cable Advertising, Merchandising & Programming Report†
0748-0814 Journal of Law and Religion
0748-0822 Home Video Publisher *changed to* Video Marketing News.
0748-0873 Quarterly Review of Literature Poetry Series
0748-0903 Turbomachinery International Handbook
0748-0970 Foothills Inquirer
0748-1012 Licking Lantern
0748-1071 Lancaster County Connections
0748-1179 District Council Journal
0748-1187 Death Studies
0748-1195 December Rose†
0748-1489 Oceanic Abstracts
0748-1543 Directory of Computer Software
0748-1624 Robomatix Reporter *see* 0000-1139
0748-1691 Lawson Letters
0748-1756 Measurement and Evaluation in Counseling and Development
0748-1780 Image Magazine
0748-1845 Financial Advertising Review

0748-1853 Brickman Letter *changed to* Seniors' Money Alert.
0748-1896 Fusion Technology
0748-1942 Surgery Alert
0748-1977 Journal of Clinical Monitoring
0748-1985 Journal of Rational-Emotive Therapy *see* 0894-9085
0748-2051 Micropsych Network
0748-206X International Information Report
0748-223X Worldwide Directory of East Indians *changed to* How to Start Your Own Business with 2000 to 5000 Dollars.
0748-2272 I S K C O N Report†
0748-2280 I S K C O N World Review
0748-2302 Minorities in America. Annual Bibliography†
0748-237X Clipper Studies in the Theater
0748-2418 Fabbro *see* 0899-5966
0748-2469 Official Directory of New Jersey Libraries and Media Centers Including Buyer's Guide *changed to* Official Directory of New Jersey Libraries and Media Centers.
0748-2477 Directory of Long Island Libraries and Media Centers Including Finding *changed to* Directory of Long Island Libraries and Media Centers.
0748-2485 Roots & Leaves
0748-2493 Rutland Historical Society Quarterly
0748-2531 Aqualine Abstracts
0748-2558 Shakespeare Bulletin
0748-2574 Directory of Connecticut Libraries and Media Centers Including Finding *changed to* Directory of Connecticut Libraries and Media Centers.
0748-2604 American Arts Project
0748-2655 National Prison Project Journal
0748-2698 Mechanical Cost Data *changed to* Means Mechanical Cost Data (Year).
0748-2809 U S - Japan Relations *changed to* U S - Third World Policy Perspectives.
0748-2841 Foreign Policy (San Diego)
0748-285X Death and Dying
0748-2868 Criminal Justice (San Diego)
0748-2876 Nuclear Arms
0748-2906 Bet-Nahrain
0748-2914 Horror Show
0748-2922 Economic Trends (Cleveland)
0748-3007 Cladistics: The International Journal of the Willi Hennig Society
0748-3015 Hibiscus†
0748-3058 Esto America
0748-3066 East Village Eye *changed to* International Eye.
0748-3155 Exercise Physiology: Current Selected Research
0748-3163 Real Estate Leasing Report
0748-318X Real Estate Finance
0748-321X Journal of Veterinary Medical Education
0748-3252 Electronics Week *see* 0883-4989
0748-3392 Q 38 Technical Journal *changed to* Midrange.
0748-3406 Venture Inward
0748-3430 New York Jury Verdict Reporter
0748-4054 Preschool Perspectives†
0748-4089 Asia - Pacific - Africa - Middle East Petroleum
0748-4135 Workers' Compensation Laws of California
0748-4216 Business Outlook for West Michigan
0748-4321 Legacy (University Park)
0748-433X United Nations of the Next Decade Conference. Report
0748-4356 Africa Insider
0748-4364 Higher Education Abstracts
0748-450X Journal of Clinical Hypertension *see* 0895-7061
0748-4518 Journal of Quantitative Criminology
0748-4526 Negotiation Journal
0748-4623 Journal of Professional Services Marketing
0748-4631 Interflo
0748-4658 Journal of Propulsion and Power
0748-4739 Runzheimer International Letter†
0748-4755 Pricing Advisor
0748-4763 Emerson's Professional Service Review
0748-478X Currents (Washington)
0748-4895 Strategic Planning Management†
0748-4976 V I Newspapers - Substantive Index†
0748-5190 Annotated Bibliographies of Serials: A Subject Approach
0748-5204 Critical Reviews in Biocompatibility
0748-5212 Advances in Plastic and Reconstructive Surgery
0748-5247 Freedonia Gazette
0748-5328 Journal of Nephrology Nursing†
0748-5360 Sunday School Lessons Special Ministries
0748-5409 Bible Study Special Ministries
0748-5476 A M S Asian Studies
0748-5484 Research in Word Processing Newsletter
0748-5492 Issues in Science and Technology
0748-5514 Journal of Free Radicals in Biology *see* 0891-5849
0748-5735 International League of Women Composers. Newsletter
0748-5743 Interactive Learning International
0748-5751 Journal of Accounting Education
0748-5786 Journal of Education for Library and Information Science
0748-5786 Association for Library and Information Science Education. Directory
0748-5883 Town Crier
0748-6006 U S A Gymnastics
0748-6022 Farmer's Market
0748-6111 Radiopharmacy and Radiopharmacology Yearbook Series
0748-6170 Ohio Attorney General Opinions
0748-6464 Center Magazine
0748-6472 Manhattan Inc. *changed to* M.
0748-6480 Seminars in Adolescent Medicine†
0748-6499 Cultic Studies Journal
0748-6510 Pomona
0748-657X Communication Booknotes
0748-6618 Today's Man†
0748-6642 Physiological Chemistry and Physics and Medical N M R
0748-6677 Aglow†
0748-6723 Vantage Point†
0748-6901 Quality of Life and Cardiovascular Care†
0748-7002 Means Electrical Cost Data (Year)
0748-7304 Journal of Biological Rhythms
0748-7347 TransitPulse
0748-7401 Transworld Skateboarding
0748-7630 Journal of Reading, Writing, and Learning Disabilities International
0748-7649 Culture Sculpture†
0748-7711 Journal of Rehabilitation Research and Development
0748-7878 Worker's Compensation Law Bulletin
0748-7975 Accountants' Index
0748-7983 European Journal of Surgical Oncology
0748-7991 Journal of Molecular Electronics *see* 1057-9257
0748-8009 Medicine and War
0748-8017 Quality and Reliability Engineering International
0748-8025 Communications in Applied Numerical Methods
0748-805X Yacht†
0748-8068 American Journal of Cosmetic Surgery
0748-8122 Virginia Journal of Natural Resources Law *see* 1045-5183
0748-8149 Illinois Historical Journal
0748-8157 Frontiers of Health Services Management
0748-8165 Nutrition Forum
0748-8203 California Inns *see* 0895-2965
0748-822X Agricultural Biotechnology News *see* 0899-3998
0748-8343 American Breweriana Journal
0748-8378 S P A C E S
0748-8386 Stress Medicine
0748-8394 Outpost Exchange
0748-8408 Inn Review Newsletter *changed to* Inn Business Review Newsletter.
0748-8475 Thought & Action
0748-8491 Education and Treatment of Children
0748-8513 Key (Lansdale)†
0748-8548 Chicago Geographic Directory†
0748-8572 Advances in Applied Developmental Psychology
0748-8580 Current Research in Film
0748-8599 Annual Review of Political Science
0748-8602 Advances in Human - Computer Interaction
0748-8653 Biological Membranes
0748-8742 Kaleidoscope (Akron)
0748-8769 Environmental Law (Washington)
0748-8785 Parnassus Literary Journal
0748-8807 Macintosh Connection†
0748-8815 Kettering Review
0748-8831 One-Person Library
0748-8890 International Employment Hotline
0748-8920 International Communications News†
0748-8939 Telecom Trade Reporter†
0748-8947 Audio-Digest Emergency Medicine
0748-9056 West's International Law Bulletin†
0748-9080 Kentucky Attorney General Opinions
0748-9188 Canine Collectors Companion†
0748-9196 I E E E ElectroTechnology Review†
0748-9234 University of California, Berkeley. Wellness Letter
0748-9250 C I M Strategies
0748-9269 Computers and the Social Sciences *see* 0894-4393
0748-9331 The Computer Journal
0748-9463 Alternative Press Annual†
0748-948X Manufacturing Systems
0748-9528 Second Opinion (San Francisco)†
0748-9536 L'An ha-Erev
0748-9579 Timeline
0748-9633 Journal of Counseling & Development
0748-9641 Strategy for Peace U.S. Foreign Policy Conference. Report
0748-9668 International University Collegiate Sports Report
0748-9676 International University Poetry Quarterly
0748-9706 Shofar
0749-0003 Employee Assistance Quarterly
0749-0151 Stereo T V Report†
0749-016X New England Journal of Public Policy
0749-0194 Change (Swarthmore)†
0749-0208 Journal of Coastal Research
0749-0291 James Dickey Newsletter
0749-0356 Documents to the People of New York State
0749-0372 Biotechnology Software
0749-064X Contemporary Theatre, Film & Television
0749-0658 King's Coal Export Week *changed to* King's Coal Export Report.
0749-0674 N A T O - Warsaw and Strategies *changed to* Western Policies.
0749-0690 Clinics in Geriatric Medicine
0749-0704 Critical Care Clinics
0749-0712 Hand Clinics
0749-0720 Veterinary Clinics of North America: Food Animal Practice
0749-0739 Veterinary Clinics of North America: Equine Practice
0749-0755 Sound Post
0749-0771 Slipstream (Niagara Falls)
0749-078X Tenant Communications *see* 0271-5430
0749-1069 World Environment Handbook†
0749-1093 MacRae's Directory of Firms Marketing through Manufacturers' Representatives†
0749-1190 Monographs in Psychobiology
0749-1263 Barnard Alumnae
0749-1301 Behavioral Counseling and Community Interventions†
0749-1352 Trail Walker
0749-1387 Faces
0749-1395 Scientific Sleuthing Newsletter *changed to* Scientific Sleuthing Review.
0749-1409 Women's Studies in Communication
0749-1484 Data Processing and Communications Security *changed to* Computing & Communications Protection.
0749-1492 Ohio Report†
0749-1557 Engineering Office Management and Administration Report *see* 1057-2864
0749-1565 American Journal of Hospice Care
0749-1573 Impact (Athens)
0749-1581 Magnetic Resonance in Chemistry
0749-159X Numerical Methods for Partial Differential Equations: An International Journal
0749-1670 S R R T Newsletter
0749-1697 King's Southern Coal
0749-1700 King's Western Coal
0749-1719 King's Northern Coal
0749-1727 King's Tennessee Valley News
0749-1786 Bibliographies and Indexes in Economics and Economic History
0749-1794 Underwater U S A
0749-1948 Coal Mining *see* 1040-7820
0749-1980 U S Water News
0749-2006 Marlin
0749-2014 Writers Connection
0749-2022 Top Shelf (Madison)
0749-2081 Seminars in Oncology Nursing
0749-2308 African Special Bibliographic Series
0749-2332 Agency Sales
0749-2375 California Municipal Bond Advisor
0749-2448 Population Today
0749-2472 Resound
0749-2510 Christian Retailing
0749-2561 Canada (Year)
0749-260X Dog River Review
0749-2758 Waste Disposal and Pollution Control *changed to* From the State Capitals. Waste Disposal and Pollution Control.
0749-2766 Construction Policies *changed to* From the State Capitals. Construction Policies.
0749-2774 From the State Capitals. Transportation Policies
0749-2782 From the State Capitals: Public Safety
0749-2790 From the State Capitals. Justice Policies
0749-2812 From the State Capitals. Banking Policies†
0749-2820 From the State Capitals. Taxation and Revenue Policies
0749-2839 Computer Language
0749-2871 Crescent Review
0749-2898 Psi Research†
0749-2928 Accounting Office Management & Administration Report
0749-2936 Broadcast Stats
0749-2960 High Technology Careers
0749-310X Family Safety & Health
0749-3223 American Biotechnology Laboratory
0749-341X American Liszt Society. Newsletter
0749-3495 Malpractice Reporter. Podiatry Edition
0749-3509 Vibrant Life (Hagerstown)
0749-3517 Hilton Head Islander *see* 1051-7898
0749-3584 Bible of Weather Forecasting
0749-3797 American Journal of Preventive Medicine
0749-3851 2600
0749-3878 Mapping Sciences & Remote Sensing
0749-3908 Acts (San Francisco)
0749-3940 Everyone's Backyard
0749-3959 Action Bulletin *see* 0749-3940
0749-3967 Marble & Ivy Review
0749-4025 Journal of Classroom Interaction
0749-4041 Year Book of Vascular Surgery
0749-4122 Multihulls
0749-4149 University Studies in Medieval and Renaissance Literature
0749-4300 Neurochemistry
0749-4351 Jokesmith
0749-4467 Contemporary Music Review
0749-4513 Journal of Partnership Taxation
0749-4521 He-Man and the Masters of the Universe†
0749-4645 Freddie Mac Reports†
0749-470X Bibliographies of Modern Authors
0749-4823 General Physics Advance Abstracts
0749-4831 Documents in Imperial History
0749-4874 Advanced Technology in Washington State

ISSN INDEX 5789

0749-4971 Antique Maps, Sea Charts, City Views, Celestial Charts and Battle Plans, Price Record and Handbook for...
0749-5021 Peterson's Guide to Business and Management Jobs (Year) *see* 1048-3411
0749-503X Yeast
0749-5056 Whole Earth Review
0749-5153 Strategic Health Care Marketing
0749-5161 Pediatric Emergency Care
0749-517X Around the Bend
0749-5250 Laser Disc Newsletter
0749-5285 Hoop - N B A Today
0749-5307 National Legal Bibliography. Subject Lists†
0749-5579 Chilton's Labor Guide and Parts Manual. Motor Age Professional Mechanics Edition
0749-5684 Certified Copy
0749-5900 Peace & Democracy News
0749-5927 Ancestry Newsletter
0749-5951 Immigrant Communities & Ethnic Minorities in the United States & Canada
0749-596X Journal of Memory and Language
0749-5978 Organizational Behavior and Human Decision Processes
0749-5986 MacRae's Industrial Directory *changed to* MacRae's Blue Book.
0749-6001 Censorship News
0749-6036 Superlattices and Microstructures
0749-6214 Central America Writers Bulletin†
0749-6419 International Journal of Plasticity
0749-6427 Wicazo Sa Review
0749-6524 Infections in Medicine
0749-6532 Working Smart
0749-6575 Space Daily *see* 1048-2652
0749-6664 Vealer
0749-6680 DataBase Directory
0749-6737 Insecta Mundi
0749-6753 International Journal of Health Planning and Management
0749-6761 Patriot
0749-6818 Wisconsin Counties
0749-6885 Alternative Library Literature
0749-6931 A S A Footnotes
0749-7296 C A Selects. Corrosion-Inhibiting Coatings
0749-730X C A Selects. Drilling Muds
0749-7318 C A Selects. Novel Pesticides & Herbicides
0749-7326 C A Selects. Photosensitive Polymers
0749-7334 C A Selects. Plasma & Reactive Ion Etching
0749-7342 C A Selects. Radiation Curing
0749-7350 C A Selects. Selenium & Tellurium Chemistry
0749-7369 C A Selects. Water-Based Coatings
0749-7474 C P C Annual
0749-7644 Gestus
0749-7652 Cable T V Law Reporter
0749-7709 Eastern Mineral Law Foundation. Case Update
0749-7946 Impact Yearbook†
0749-7962 Northwest Environmental Journal
0749-7989 Alcohol in History: A Multidisciplinary Newsletter *see* 0887-2783
0749-8004 Journal of Entomological Science
0749-8020 Endocrinology Abstracts *see* 0141-7711
0749-8047 Clinical Journal of Pain
0749-8055 Convulsive Therapy
0749-8063 Arthroscopy
0749-839X A B M S Directory of Certified Plastic Surgeons
0749-856X Vital Signs (Farmington)†
0749-8578 P C Netline *see* 0892-9467
0749-8586 Disability Rag
0749-8659 Children's Album
0749-8667 Insurance Review (New York)
0749-8942 Aerobics and Fitness *changed to* American Fitness.
0749-9043 King's International Coal Trade
0749-9078 Lex Collegii
0749-9108 Bethel Courier
0749-9132 Foreign Intelligence Literary Scene
0749-9213 Carpatho - Rusyn American
0749-9310 Texas Lone Star
0749-9361 Showboat Centennials Newsletter
0749-9418 Business First
0749-9779 Stockowners' News†
0749-9825 Food First News
0749-9973 Medical & Health Information Directory
0750-067X Cahiers de l'Afrique Occidentale Francaise *see* 0754-7625
0750-0688 Cahiers de l'Afrique Occidentale et de l'Afrique Equatoriale *see* 0754-7625
0750-0750 Reunion. Institut National de la Statistique et des Etudes Economiques. Indicateurs Conjoncturels†
0750-0769 L'Economie de la Reunion
0750-1331 Commission Departementale des Monuments Historiques du Pas-de-Calais. Bulletin *see* 0758-2722
0750-1455 Le Supplement
0750-1552 C.F.P. Chaud - Froid - Plomberie
0750-2036 Langues et Cultures du Pacifique
0750-3695 Letter from Taize
0750-3725 Vogue Hommes
0750-3806 Jeannette
0750-4152 Guide de France
0750-4160 Cap Levant
0750-4764 Filiere Maille
0750-6244 Archives of Otolaryngology
0750-6848 Societe Linneenne de Bordeaux. Bulletin
0750-7046 Catalogue Afnor (Normes Francaises)
0750-7186 Revue Francaise des Sciences de l'Eau *see* 0298-6663
0750-7240 Journal de Mecanique Theorique et Appliquee *see* 0997-7538
0750-7240 Journal de Mecanique Theorique et Appliquee *see* 0997-7546
0750-7321 Biologia Gallo-Hellenica
0750-747X Societe Zoologique de France. Memoires
0750-7569 S N E C M A Informations
0750-7658 Annales Francaises d'Anesthesie et de Reanimation
0750-7674 B.O.P.I. Brevets d'Invention - Abreges et Listes
0750-7682 Societe des Sciences Veterinaires et de Medecine Comparee de Lyon. Bulletin *changed to* Sciences Veterinaires - Medecine Comparee. Bulletin.
0750-7933 Societe des Sciences Naturelles. Miscellanea Entomologia†
0750-8158 Enfants S'amusent
0750-8743 I S T P M Rapports Techniques†
0750-8964 Travail et Maitrise (Edition Generale) *see* 1157-6049
0750-8980 Travail et Maitrise (Edition Siderurgie) *see* 1157-6057
0750-9189 Planedenn
0750-9278 Revue de Deux Mondes: Litterature, Histoire, Arts et Sciences
0751-0357 Zeszyty Literackie
0751-4239 Universite de Provence. Centre d'Aix. Cahiers d'Etudes Germaniques
0751-4875 Lacito Documents Asie - Austronesie
0751-4883 Lacito Documents Eurasie
0751-5405 Voiles et Voiliers
0751-5464 Publi 10
0751-5596 France Aviation
0751-5685 Louveteau
0751-5723 Pionnier
0751-5731 Scout
0751-5766 Hospitalisation Nouvelle
0751-5804 Revue des Sciences Morales et Politiques
0751-5812 Demain
0751-5839 Universite Syndicaliste
0751-5871 Activite Economique†
0751-588X Entreprises Rhone Alpes
0751-5944 Travaux Publics et Batiment du Midi
0751-5987 Pour la Verite
0751-6037 Circuits Culture
0751-6320 Courrier du Meuble
0751-6460 Ange Gardien
0751-6614 O F C E Observations et Diagnostics Economiques. Revue
0751-6649 Annuaire General de la Publicite
0751-6657 Tourisme
0751-7599 Institut National de la Statistique et des Etudes Economiques. Service Departemental de la Guyane. Bulletin Trimestriel de Statistiques
0751-7718 Consultation
0751-8145 F E N - Hebdo
0751-8447 Ekaina
0751-9907 Sauvagine et Sa Chasse
0751-994X Officiel du Cycle et du Motocycle
0752-4072 R A I R O - T S I Technique et Sciences Informatiques
0752-4250 L'Officiel Jardin-Motoculture
0752-4412 C E D E J Egypte - Monde Arabe
0752-4676 I C A Executive Search Newsletter
0752-4978 Robots
0752-5222 L'Ecrit-Voir
0752-5508 Mediagaz
0752-5702 Histoire Economie et Societe
0752-5729 Recherche en Dance
0752-7535 Annuaire de l'Alimentation Animale
0753-1621 Software in Healthcare†
0753-2830 Journal de Toxicologie Clinique et Experimentale
0753-311X France. Direction du Tourisme. Economie du Tourisme†
0753-3322 Biomedicine and Pharmacotherapy
0753-3454 Relais†
0753-3918 Actualites Biologiques
0753-3918 Cahier Technique du Biologiste
0753-3969 Annales de Paleontologie (Vert - Invert)
0753-4590 Cahiers Henri Bosco
0753-4655 Societe d'Histoire Naturelle du Doubs. Bulletin
0753-9053 Annales de Chirurgie de la Main *see* 1153-2424
0754-0264 Genetique, Selection, Evolution *see* 0999-193X
0754-054X Ouvertures
0754-121X Tracteurs et Machines Agricoles
0754-1996 Industrie de l'Information
0754-2143 P C M L-Flash *changed to* Flash Alternative.
0754-2275 Roman†
0754-2445 Lacito Documents Afrique
0754-2623 Ondes Courtes Informations
0754-281X Travailleurs
0754-3786 Nouvelles du Vietnam
0754-4618 Officiel des Transporteurs *changed to* Officiel des Transports.
0754-5215 Lettre Afrique Energies
0754-7625 A.F.P. Cahiers de l'Afrique Occidentale et de l'Afrique Equatoriale
0754-927X Luvah
0754-9725 Ge Magazine
0755-0251 Gai Pied Hebdo
0755-0960 Fabula†
0755-1088 Chronique du Transporteur
0755-110X L'Expert Automobile
0755-1150 Thesindex Pharmaceutique†
0755-1908 Series: Graph-Agri (Regions)
0755-1959 Classiques Francais du Moyen Age
0755-2025 Chambre Syndicale de la Siderurgie Francaise. Bulletin Statistique. Serie Rouge. Production *changed to* Comptoir Francais des Produits Siderurgiques. Bulletin Statistique. Serie Rouge. Production.
0755-219X Mesures
0755-2807 Recherches Iberiques Strasbourg II *changed to* Recherches Iberiques et Cinematographiques.
0755-3110 Annuaire Sucrier
0755-3218 France. Ministere de l'Agriculture. Series "S". Production Vegetale et Forestieres *changed to* France. Ministere de l'Agriculture et de la Foret. Donnees Chiffrees. I A A.
0755-3579 Soft & Micro
0755-3951 Journee de Medecine Physique et de Reeducation
0755-4168 France. Institut National de la Sante et de la Recherche Medicale. INSERM Actualites
0755-4982 La Presse Medicale
0755-5016 Eau et l'Industrie *changed to* L'Eau, l'Industrie, les Nuisances.
0755-5202 Energie Magazine†
0755-5350 Energie Nucleaire Magazine *see* 0755-5202
0755-561X Petrole Informations International (Edition Bilingue)
0755-6365 France. Bureau de Recherches Geologiques et Minieres. Agence Francaise pour la Maitrise de l'Energie. Geothermie-Actualites†
0755-7205 Croire et Servir
0755-7469 Nord Genealogie
0755-7647 Comite Francais de Cartographie. Bulletin
0755-7752 Nouvelle Revue d'Onomastique
0755-7809 Espaces - Populations - Societes
0755-883X Ar Falz
0755-8848 Skol Vreizh- l'Ecole Bretonne. Nouvelle Serie
0755-9208 Cahiers d'Economie et Sociologie Rurales
0755-9291 Applications et Transferts de la S E L A F
0755-9305 Langues et Cultures Africaines
0755-9313 Europe de Tradition Orale
0755-964X Sphinx Women's International Literary Art Review
0756-3205 Cite
0756-3825 Journees de la Societe de Legislation Comparee
0756-4392 I C C Business World†
0756-5860 Les Dossiers de l'Art Public
0756-7138 Universite de Lille III. Lexique
0756-7677 Inriatheque
0756-8037 Lettre Confidentielle des Transports
0756-8371 Petrole Informations (International Edition) *see* 0762-0357
0756-8630 France. Ministere du Travail. Dossiers Statistiques du Travail et de l'Emploi
0756-967X References *see* 0983-1924
0757-0090 Vogue Sport†
0757-0139 Harmonie - Panorama Musique
0757-2271 Beaux Arts Magazine
0757-3529 Actualite Religieuse dans le Monde
0757-3960 Antilla
0757-4673 Viti *changed to* Cultivar.
0757-6714 Etat du Monde
0757-7699 Etudes Ethno-Linguistiques Maghreb-Sahara
0757-8237 Reimpression
0757-9888 New Caledonia. Institut Territorial de la Statistique et des Etudes Economiques. Bulletin de Conjoncture
0758-0266 Centre I N F F O. Bulletin de Liason *changed to* Bulletin Officiel du Travail et de l'Emploi.
0758-0339 New Caledonia. Institut Territorial de la Statistique et des Etudes Economiques. Indices des Prix la Consommation
0758-0347 New Caledonia. Institut Territorial de la Statistique et des Etudes Economiques. Indices et Index du B T P
0758-1688 P H M, Revue Horticole
0758-1874 Machine - Outil Produire
0758-1998 France. Ministere des Affaires Sociales et de la Solidarite Nationale. Secretariat d'Etat Charge de la Sante. Bulletin Officiel *changed to* France. Ministere des Affaires Sociales et de l'Integration. Bulletin Officiel.
0758-2714 Cahiers d'Anthropologie et Biometrie Humaine
0758-2722 Commission Departementale d'Histoire et d'Archeologie. Bulletin
0758-4008 Travail et Maitrise (Edition Chimie - Techniciens) *see* 1157-6065
0758-4016 Travail et Maitrise (Edition Chimie) *see* 1157-6065
0758-413X Art et Metiers du Livre
0758-4164 Boulangerie Francaise
0758-4431 Monde Alpin et Rhodanien
0758-5055 Toute l'Alimentation
0758-5683 Anthropologie - Maritime
0758-573X Point Economique

ISSN

5790 ISSN INDEX

0758-5756 Inform'optique
0758-6531 Donnees Sociales
0758-6639 Annuaire Nautisme
0758-6760 Cahiers Lorrains
0758-6922 S T P Pharma *see* 1157-1489
0758-6922 S T P Pharma *see* 1157-1497
0758-6957 Automobile Magazine
0758-7244 Reunion. Service de Statistique Agricole. Bulletin de Statistique Agricole *see* 1150-1448
0758-7686 Proxima
0758-7724 I N S E E Premiers Resultats†
0758-802X Praxis Juridique et Religion
0758-8240 A I M Monastic Bulletin
0758-8526 F E L Actualites
0759-0083 France. Ministere des Affaires Sociales et de la Solidarite Nationale. Ministere Charge de l'Emploi. Conventions Collectives
0759-125X Comedie Francaise
0759-2280 Medecine et Chirurgie du Pied
0759-3686 Dictionnaire - Annuaire de l'Agriculture *changed to* Dictionnaire - Annuaire de l'Agriculture et de l'Agro-Alimentaire.
0759-3694 French Company Handbook
0759-6065 Automobiles Classiques
0759-7673 Investir
0759-8661 Cahiers de l'I L S E R
0759-9161 Bulletin on Applied Research for the Protection of Man at Work†
0760-0909 E T I
0760-1263 Africasia (Year)
0760-1999 Boissons de France - Jean Primus
0760-5641 Valenciennes
0760-579X Cahiers de la Recherche - Developpement
0760-629X Consequences
0760-6516 S.V.M. Science et Vie Micro
0760-8675 Echange-Sante
0760-9620 Philosophie Imaginaire
0761-0076 Revue de l'Artisan Electricien Electronicien
0761-022X Actes Semiotiques
0761-1102 Histoire des Sciences et des Techniques
0761-165X P A S C A L Thema. T 215: Biotechnologies (Editions Francaise)
0761-1668 P A S C A L Thema. T 230: Energie
0761-1676 P A S C A L Thema. T 235: Medecine Tropicale
0761-1684 P A S C A L Thema. T 240: Metaux. Metallurgie
0761-1692 P A S C A L Thema. T 245: Soudage, Brasage et Techniques Connexes†
0761-1714 P A S C A L Thema. T 260: Zoologie Fondamentale et Appliquee des Invertebres (Milieu Terrestre, Eaux Douces)
0761-1722 P A S C A L Thema. T 295: Batiment. Travaux Publics *see* 1146-5093
0761-1730 P A S C A L Folio. F 10: Mecanique et Acoustique *changed to* P A S C A L Folio. F 10: Mecanique et Acoustique et Transfert de Chaleur.
0761-1749 P A S C A L Folio. F 16: Chimie Analytique Minerale et Organique
0761-1757 P A S C A L Folio. F 17: Chimie Generale, Minerale et Organique
0761-1773 P A S C A L Folio. F 21: Electrotechnique
0761-1781 P A S C A L Folio. F 23: Genie Chimique. Industries Chimique et Parachimique
0761-179X P A S C A L Folio. F 24: Polymeres. Peintures. Bois
0761-1803 P A S C A L Folio. F 25: Transports Terrestres et Maritimes
0761-1811 P A S C A L Folio. F 40: Mineralogie. Geochimie. Geologie Extraterrestre
0761-182X P A S C A L Folio. F 41: Gisements Metalliques et Non-Metalliques. Economie Miniere
0761-1838 P A S C A L Folio. F 42: Roches Cristallines
0761-1846 P A S C A L Folio. F 43: Roches Sedimentaires. Geologie Marine
0761-1854 P A S C A L Folio. F 44: Stratigraphie. Geologie Regionale. Geologie Generale
0761-1862 P A S C A L Folio. F 45: Tectonique. Geophysique Interne
0761-1870 P A S C A L Folio. F 46: Hydrologie. Geologie de l'Ingenieur. Formations Superficielles
0761-1889 P A S C A L Folio. F 47: Paleontologie
0761-1897 P A S C A L Folio. F 52: Biochimie. Biophysique Moleculaire. Biologie Moleculaire et Cellulaire
0761-1900 P A S C A L Folio. F 53: Anatomie et Physiologie des Vertebres
0761-1919 P A S C A L Folio. F 54: Reproduction des Vertebres. Embryologie des Vertebres et des Invertebres
0761-1927 P A S C A L Folio. F 55: Biologie Vegetale
0761-1943 P A S C A L Folio. F 70: Pharmacologie. Traitements Medicamenteux
0761-1951 P A S C A L Explore. E 11: Physique Atomique et Moleculaire. Plasmas
0761-196X P A S C A L Explore. E 12: Etat Condense
0761-1978 P A S C A L Explore. E 13: Structure des Liquides et des Solides. Cristallographie
0761-2028 P A S C A L Explore. E 30: Microscopie Electronique et Diffraction Electronique
0761-2044 P A S C A L Explore. E 32: Metrologie et Appareillage en Physique et Physicochimie
0761-2052 P A S C A L Explore. E 33. Informatique
0761-2060 P A S C A L Explore. E 34: Robotique. Automatique et Automatisation des Processus Industriels
0761-2095 Petrole et Gaz
0761-2109 P A S C A L Explore. E 48: Environnement Cosmique Terrestre, Astronomie et Geologie Extraterrestre
0761-2117 P A S C A L Explore. E 49: Meteorologie
0761-2133 P A S C A L Explore. E 61: Microbiologie: Bacteriologie, Virologie, Mycologie, Protozoaires Pathogenes
0761-2141 P A S C A L Explore. E 62: Immunologie
0761-215X P A S C A L Explore. E 63: Toxicologie
0761-2168 P A S C A L Explore. E 64: Endocrinologie Humaine et Experimentale. Endocrinopathies
0761-2176 P A S C A L Explore. E 65: Psychologie, Psychopathologie, Psychiatrie
0761-2184 P A S C A L Explore. E 71: Ophtalmologie
0761-2192 P A S C A L Explore. E 72: Otorhinolaryngologie. Stomatologie. Pathologie Cervicofaciale
0761-2206 P A S C A L Explore. E 73: Dermatologie. Maladies Sexuellement Transmissibles
0761-2214 P A S C A L Explore. E 74: Pneumologie
0761-2222 P A S C A L Explore. E 75: Cardiologie et Appareil Circulatoire
0761-2230 P A S C A L Explore. E 76: Gastroenterologie, Foie, Pancreas, Abdomen
0761-2249 P A S C A L Explore. E 77: Nephrologie. Voies Urinaires
0761-2257 P A S C A L Explore. E 78: Neurologie
0761-2265 P A S C A L Explore. E 79: Pathologie et Physiologie Osteoarticulaires
0761-2273 P A S C A L Explore. E 80: Hematologie
0761-2281 P A S C A L Explore. E 81: Maladies Metaboliques
0761-229X P A S C A L Explore. E 82: Gynecologie. Obstetrique. Andrologie
0761-2303 P A S C A L Explore. E 83: Anesthesie et Reanimation
0761-2311 P A S C A L Explore. E 84: Genie Biomedical. Informatique Biomedicale
0761-2397 Mondes Hispanophone et Lusophone *changed to* Etudes sur les Mondes Hispanophones.
0761-3067 Gaussenia
0761-3369 G A P H Y O R. Base de Donnees
0761-3938 France. IFREMER. Centre de Brest. Publications. Serie: Rapports Economiques et Juridiques
0761-3962 France. IFREMER. Centre de Brest. Colloques. Actes
0761-3970 France. IFREMER. Centre de Brest. Publications. Serie: Rapports Scientifiques et Techniques
0761-3989 France. I.F.Re.Mer. Centre de Brest. Publications. Serie: Resultat des Campagnes a la Mer *changed to* Campagnes Oceanographiques Francaises.
0761-4241 Reperes
0761-7143 Territoires *see* 0981-1761
0761-7267 Dossiers de la Bible
0761-7593 Actu'A G F
0761-8417 Revue de Pneumologie Clinique
0761-8425 Revue des Maladies Respiratoires
0761-9553 Clarinette Magazine
0761-9634 S M F A
0761-9871 Cahiers de Sociologie Economique et Culturelle
0762-0357 Petrole Informations International (English Edition)
0762-0969 La Vie des Science
0762-140X Institut de Recherche du Cafe et du Cacao. Rapport d'Activite *see* 0762-1418
0762-1418 Institut de Recherche du Cafe, du Cacao et Autres Plantes Stimulantes. Rapport d'Activite
0762-3151 Journal de la Marine Marchande *see* 0983-0537
0762-400X Geste et Image
0762-6819 Nouvelle Revue d'Ethnopsychiatrie
0762-7203 Temps Micro
0762-7378 Neptune Yachting
0762-8374 Intelligence Newsletter
0762-915X Journal de Traumatologie du Sport
0763-0018 Composites et Nouveaux Materiaux (Paris, 1980)
0763-062X Club des Hebraisants
0763-1529 Cahiers Raymond Abellio
0763-1901 Centre International de Documentation Arachnologique. Bulletin d'Information et de Liaison. *changed to* Arachnologia - Bulletin d'Information et de Liaison du C I D A.
0763-5184 Equipes St Vincent
0763-7098 France. Institut National de la Sante et de la Recherche Medicale. Colloques
0764-0382 Degres†
0764-2873 Avant-Scene Opera
0764-2997 Astrolettre
0764-4442 Academie des Sciences. Comptes Rendus. Serie 1: Mathematiques
0764-4450 Academie des Sciences. Comptes Rendus des Sciences. Series 2: Mecanique, Physique, Chimie, Sciences de la Terre, Sciences de l'Univers
0764-4469 Academie des Sciences. Comptes Rendus des Seances. Series 3: Sciences de la Vie
0764-4493 Solidarite Sante Etudes Statistiques
0764-5066 Activite Immobiliere
0764-583X R A I R O - M 2 A N Mathematical Modelling and Numerical Analysis
0764-7557 Espace Rural
0764-7581 Detours d'Ecriture
0764-8111 Argus du Livre de Collection et de l'Autographe *changed to* Argus du Livre de Collection.
0764-8138 Annee Politique, Economique et Sociale
0764-8928 Gradhiva
0765-0019 Traitement du Signal
0765-0027 Science et Vie Economie
0765-0213 Cultures et Societe de l'Est
0765-0531 Histoire et Defense
0765-0817 Atlas Historique des Villes de France
0765-104X Delegation Archeologique Francaise en Iran. Cahiers
0765-1112 Plurial
0765-1376 Kouakou
0765-1597 Science et Sports
0765-1635 Travaux de Didactique du Francaise Langue Etrangere
0765-1937 C R E D I F Bulletin Bibliographique
0765-2046 European Biotechnology Newsletter
0765-3204 Flexo-Europe
0765-328X Bulletin Annuel d'Information et de Liaison entre C.L.P.L.M. *see* 1156-5977
0765-3697 Societes
0765-4847 Facultes de Droit et de la Science Juridique. Revue d'Histoire
0765-4944 Cahiers de Praxematique
0765-5290 Reanimation, Soins Intensifs, Medecine d'Urgence
0765-5320 Equinoxe
0765-5762 Entreprises Formation
0765-8702 Abeilles et Fleurs
0766-0502 Cahiers de Paleontologie
0766-0863 Energie et Creativite *see* 0982-6238
0766-1207 Industrie Minerale Mines et Carrieres. Techniques
0766-1827 Histoire et ses Representations
0766-1924 Polyphonies
0766-3269 Update Tahiti *changed to* Tahiti Sun Press.
0766-4214 Cahiers de Semiotique Textuelle
0766-4516 Bulletin d'Histoire de la Revolution Francaise
0766-5075 Cahiers d'Etudes Mongoles et Siberiennes *changed to* Etudes Mongoles et Siberiennes.
0766-5105 Geodynamique
0766-5210 Revue Pratique de Controle Industriel
0766-5229 Bureau et Informatique†
0766-5350 Dires
0766-5466 Lyon Mediterranee Medical - Medecine du Sud Est
0766-5598 Revue des Etudes Byzantines
0766-5725 Technique et Biologie
0766-6268 Note de Conjoncture de l'I N S E E
0766-6330 Etudiant
0766-916X Lettre du Musicien
0767-094X Revue de la Navigation Fluviale Europeenne, Ports et Industries
0767-0974 Medecine - Sciences
0767-2640 Documentation Touristique: Bibliographie Analytique Internationale†
0767-2659 Touristic Analysis Review†
0767-2667 Cahiers du Tourisme. Serie E: Legislation
0767-3701 Recherche et Applications en Marketing
0767-3981 Fundamental and Clinical Pharmacology
0767-399X Psychiatry and Psychobiology *see* 0924-9338
0767-4910 Lettre de l'Intelligence Artificielle
0767-6468 Cahiers de l'Orient
0767-6891 Sciences Orgonomiques
0767-709X Revue Archeologique de l'Ouest
0767-7529 Cahiers de l'Institut d'Etudes Germaniques
0767-807X Picsou
0767-8088 Journal de Mickey
0767-8444 Alsace Automobile
0767-869X Gazette des Armes
0768-0279 Cahiers du Tourisme. Serie C: Recherche Fondamentale et Appliquee - Methodologie
0768-3162 Cahiers du Tourisme. Serie B: Etranger
0768-7559 Annales de Psychiatrie
0768-858X Qualite Magazine *changed to* Qualite en Mouvement.
0768-9179 Pharmacien Hospitalier
0768-9403 Muntu
0768-9454 Technologie
0768-9659 Revue de Droit Francais Commercial Maritime et Fiscal
0768-9829 Cahiers des Sciences Humaines

ISSN

ISSN INDEX

ISSN	Title
0769-0088	Hor Yezh
0769-0509	Scribeco
0769-0770	Cahiers de l'Universite de Perpignan
0769-0878	Observations et Travaux
0769-0886	Recherches sur Diderot et sur l'Encyclopedie
0769-1025	Satellites de Saturne I to VIII
0769-1033	Satellites Galileens de Jupiter
0769-1041	Ephemerides of the Faint Satellites of Jupiter and Saturn
0769-184X	Fortuna
0769-2609	Institut Pasteur. Annales. Microbiologie see 0923-2508
0769-2617	Institut Pasteur. Annales. Virologie see 0923-2516
0769-2625	Institut Pasteur. Annales. Immunologie see 0923-2494
0769-3206	Materiaux pour l'Histoire de notre Temps
0769-3397	Lithiques
0769-3478	Dossiers de l'Outre-Mer†
0769-4679	Pas Tant
0769-489X	France. Institut National de la Statistique et des Etudes Economiques. Annales d'Economie et de Statistique
0769-6248	Entreprise changed to L'Entreprise - A pour Affaires.
0769-6833	Grand Froid
0770-0075	Critique Regionale
0770-0369	Belgium. Institut National de Statistique. Annuaire de Statistiques Regionales
0770-0415	Annuaire Statistique de la Belgique
0770-0717	Revue Belge de Geographie
0770-0725	C R I C Rapport de Recherche
0770-0911	Travaux Geographiques de Liege†
0770-0962	Universite de Bruxelles. Revue
0770-1055	Universite Libre de Bruxelles. Institut de Sociologie. Revue
0770-1640	Cinemaniac see 0773-2279
0770-1683	O I E C Bulletin
0770-1713	Cerevisia changed to Cerevisia and Biotechnology.
0770-1748	Natuurwetenschappelijk Tijdschrift
0770-1861	Centre d'Ecologie Forestiere et Rurale. Notes Techniques. A: Forestieres see 0775-3446
0770-237X	Belgium. Institut National de Statistique. Statistique des Accidents de la Circulation sur la Voie Publique avec Tues et Blesses
0770-2477	Lumen Vitae
0770-2515	Lait et Nous
0770-3058	Informations du Commerce Exterieur
0770-4372	Bibliotheque Royal Albert 1er. Bulletin Trimestriel d'Information
0770-4437	Alternatives changed to Presse-Inter.
0770-4518	Recherches Economiques de Louvain
0770-4526	Bibliotheque Royale Albert 1er. Rapport Annuel
0770-4720	Interface
0770-6081	Cahier du Grif see 0770-6138
0770-6138	G R I F†
0770-6472	Annales de Droit
0770-7223	Cooperation:
0770-7436	Presence de l'Histoire†
0770-7576	Societe Geographique de Liege. Bulletin†
0770-7762	Koninklijke Academie voor Nederlandse Taal- en Letterkunde. Jaarboek
0770-786X	Koninklijke Academie voor Nederlandse Taal- en Letterkunde. Verslagen en Mededelingen
0770-8378	Degres
0770-8602	Revue Generale
0770-9021	Courrier de Gand
0770-9412	Tractionel News changed to Tractebel News.
0770-9595	Tractionel. Annual Report see 0774-3998
0771-0410	Nationaal Instituut voor de Statistiek. Weekbericht
0771-0518	Cine & Media
0771-2022	I U S S P Newsletter
0771-2588	Operatie Veiligheid
0771-2634	Objectif Prevention
0771-2642	Belgische Brandtijdschrift changed to N V B B Magazine.
0771-2782	Promosafe
0771-2987	F E B Bulletin
0771-3371	Zakenidee†
0771-4025	Technivisie/Tecnopole
0771-4033	Revue Belge du Feu changed to A N P I Magazine - Protection Incendie et Vol.
0771-4084	Administration Publique
0771-4653	Cahiers Theatre Louvain
0771-4963	Universite Libre de Bruxelles. Institut de Philosophie. Annales
0771-5137	A C P States Yearbook†
0771-517X	Nationale Maatschappij van Belgische Spoorwegen. Documentatiebulletin
0771-5323	Universite Libre de Bruxelles. Institut de Sociologie. Annales†
0771-5579	Belgium. Ministerie van Economische Zaken. Algemene Directie voor Studien en Documentatie. Conjunctuurbrief
0771-5641	L'Economie Belge en (Year)
0771-5692	Cercle Royal d'Histoire et d'Archeologie d'Ath et de la Region et Musees Athois. Etudes et Documents
0771-6273	Banque Bruxelles Lambert. Bulletin Financier
0771-6303	Soundtrack! Incorporating CinemaScore
0771-6435	Bijdragen tot de Geschiedenis van de Tweede Wereldoorlog
0771-6443	Centre International d'Etudes Poetiques. Courrier
0771-6494	Le Museon
0771-6524	Institut de Linguistique de Louvain. Cahiers
0771-677X	Recherches Sociologiques
0771-6826	Technologia
0771-6842	Vie Consacree
0771-7016	Musica Antiqua
0771-713X	Genealogie and Computer
0771-7385	Belgische Economie in (Year)
0771-7415	Technologia Bruxellensis see 0771-6826
0771-7520	Fiskoloog International
0771-761X	Artefactum
0771-7865	Directory of European Community Trade and Professional Associations
0771-7873	Societe Belge de Photogrammetrie - Teledetection et Cartographie. Bulletin Trimestriel
0771-7911	European Communities and Other European Organizations Who's Who changed to Euro - Who's Who.
0771-7962	Yearbook of the European Communities and of the Other European Organizations
0771-937X	Travel Journalist
0772-0831	Belgium. Ministere des Affaires Economiques. Direction Generale des Etudes et de la Documentation. Lettre de Conjoncture
0772-1099	Ami des Fleurs
0772-120X	Centre de Recherches et d'Etudes Historiques de la Seconde Guerre Mondiale. Bulletin
0772-1838	Belgium. Institut National de Statistique. Comptes Nationaux de la Belgique
0772-3318	Kredietbank. Weekberichten
0772-3776	Bibliotheque Royale Albert 1er. Publications Annoncees
0772-4802	Social Trends changed to Personeel.
0772-4837	Fiskoloog
0772-4853	Balans
0772-4942	Industrie Magazine
0772-6112	Enquetes et Documents d'Histoire Africaine
0772-6287	Echo du Meuble
0772-652X	Fondation Auschwitz. Bulletin
0772-6694	Belgium. Institut National de Statistique. Statistiques du Commerce Exter
0772-7054	Boer en de Tuinder
0772-7151	Gentse Bijdragen tot de Kunstgeschiedenis en Oudheidkunde
0772-7402	Zonnekind
0772-7488	Archaelogia Belgica†
0772-7674	Tijdschrift voor Economie en Management
0772-7704	Belgium. Institut National de Statistique. Statistiques Industrielles
0772-7720	Belgium. Institut National de Statistique. Statistiques de la Construction et du Logement
0772-7739	Belgium. Institut National de Statistique. Statistique du Trafic International und Ports
0772-7852	Studia Iranica
0772-8050	Revue de Droit Commercial Belge
0772-876X	Avianews International
0772-9464	Societe Belge de Geologie. Bulletin
0772-9898	Zonnestraal
0773-0004	Vie Professionnelle
0773-0179	Doremi
0773-0292	Dauphin
0773-0306	Bonjour!
0773-0543	Gestion 2000
0773-0748	Budget Hebdo
0773-090X	Federation Professionnelle des Producteurs et Distributeurs d'Electricite de Belgique. Annuaire Statistique
0773-1027	Vlaamse Filmpjes
0773-1051	Top
0773-1213	Reseaux
0773-2279	Cine-Fiches de Grand Angle
0773-2805	Belgium. Institut National de Statistique. Statistique de la Navigation Interieure
0773-3070	Belgium. Institut National de Statistique. Statistique des Vehicules a Moteur Neufs Mis en Circulation
0773-3429	Science et Culture
0773-3666	Belgium. Ministerie van Economische Zaken. Algemene Directie voor Studien en Documentatie. Kwartaaloverzicht van de Economie
0773-4034	Decors New Editions
0773-4093	Bibliographies Analytiques sur l'Afrique Centrale†
0773-4182	C C A I
0773-4255	Belgium. Institut National de Statistique. Statistiques du Commerce Interieur et des Transports
0773-4409	Otica
0773-5820	Belgium. Ministere de l'Education Nationale. Etudes et Documents
0773-5901	Het Spoor
0773-6177	Belgian Journal of Food Chemistry and Biotechnology changed to Cerevisia and Biotechnology.
0773-6940	European Aquaculture Society Quarterly Newsletter changed to Aquaculture Europe Magazine.
0773-7688	Dialectes de Wallonie
0773-7777	Reseau Automatique Belge de la Pollution Atmospherique
0773-9559	Stad Antwerpen. Cultureel Jaarboek
0773-9664	Belgium. Ministere des Affaires Economiques. Direction Generale des Etudes et de la Documentation. Apercu Economique Trimestriel
0773-9826	Centre d'Etudes et de Documentation Africaines. Bulletin Bibliographique†
0774-0115	Revue Belge du Cinema
0774-0689	European Aquaculture Society. Special Publications
0774-1324	Auto
0774-1847	Tijdschrift voor de Studie van de Verlichting en van het Vrije Denken
0774-2908	Humanistica Lovaniensia
0774-3998	Tractebel. Annual Report
0774-4056	Technisch Management
0774-4919	Citeaux
0774-5427	Geschied- en Oudheidkundige Kring voor Leuven en Omgeving. Mededelingen see 0774-5435
0774-5435	Geschied- en Oudheidkundige Kring voor Leuven en Omgeving. Jaarboek
0774-8396	Commission Royale de Toponymie et de Dialectologie. Bulletin
0775-1435	Belgium: Economy and Technique
0775-1443	Belgium: Economic and Commercial Information
0775-2962	Ingenieur et Industrie
0775-3411	Thorikos
0775-3446	Centre de Recherche et de Promotion Forestieres. Documents
0775-8545	Kampeertoerist
0775-8553	Surf and Fun
0775-9746	A S I F A News
0776-0698	Stars
0776-1392	Musees Royaux des Arts Decoratifs et Industriels. Bulletin see 0776-1414
0776-1406	Musees Royaux du Cinquantenaire. Bulletin see 0776-1414
0776-1414	Musees Royaux d'Art et d'Histoire. Bulletin
0776-2143	Revue de l'Agriculture - Landbouwtijdschrift
0776-6912	Visserijblad
0776-7595	Business Aviation & Regional Transport
0777-0820	Recherche en Education
0777-2734	European Journal of Mechanical Engineering
0777-5466	Centre Genevois d'Anthropologie. Bulletin
0777-6276	Belgian Journal of Zoology
0777-6306	V R B - Informatie
0777-6349	Entreprise
0777-785X	Collection de la Revue des Etudes Juives
0777-8112	Subsidia Hagiographica
0778-2837	Archeologie in Vlaanderen
0778-631X	Federation Professionnelle des Producteurs et Distributeurs d'Electricite de Belgique. Repertoire des Centrales Electriques
0778-6336	Federation Professionnelle des Producteurs et Distributeurs d'Electricite de Belgique. Distribution de l'Energie
0780-0096	Helsingin Sanomat, Kuukausiliite
0780-1335	Finland. Kehittaemis ja Koerakentamistiedotek changed to Finland. Rakennushallitus. Tutkimus-ja Kehitystoiminnan. Tiedote.
0780-4199	Visio
0780-4288	Rotary Norden
0780-6884	Finnview†
0780-7295	Meteorological Yearbook of Finland. Part 3. Statistics of Radiosonde Observations 1961-1980
0780-8399	Surveying Science in Finland
0780-8763	Slaekt och Bygd
0780-9352	Finland. Tilastokeskus. Tulo- ja Varallisuustilasto
0781-2078	MikroBitti
0781-2442	Yhdistyneiden Kansankuntien Yleiskokous (Year)
0781-2477	P E P S Y
0781-2698	Acta Polytechnica Scandinavica. Chemical Technology and Metallurgy Series
0781-4437	Suomen Joukkovelkakirjalainat
0781-5611	Finland. Tilastokeskus. Tyovoimatutkimus
0781-6758	Metsaeteollissus†
0781-7177	J P
0781-7347	Assa
0781-8602	I.D.E.A. changed to Uusi Elektroniikka.
0781-8904	Rakennustieto
0782-0496	Riskienhallinta changed to Sampovisio.
0782-226X	Arctic Medical Research
0782-2952	Energy
0782-2979	S C I M P
0782-3789	Terveys 2000
0782-4327	Design in Finland
0782-4386	Journal of Agricultural Science in Finland
0782-6087	Finnish Meteorological Institute. Geophysical Publications
0782-6095	Finnish Meteorological Institute. Publications on Air Quality

5792 ISSN INDEX

ISSN

0782-6109 Ilmatieteen Laitos. Meteorologisia Julkaisuja
0782-6117 Finnish Meteorological Institute. Contributions
0782-6648 Dimensio
0782-7784 International Peat Journal
0782-8454 Suomi - Finland U S A
0783-0041 Avec Arctia
0783-0556 Meteorological Yearbook of Finland. Part 4: 2 Measurements of Sunshine Duration
0783-103X Meteorological Yearbook of Finland. Part 4: 1 Measurements of Solar Radiation
0783-3660 Arkkitehti
0783-4365 Finnish Game Research
0783-4632 Kodintekniikka
0783-5167 Kehittyvae Kauppa
0783-5876 Societas Scientiarum Fennica. Arsbok Vuosikirja Series A
0783-5892 Societas Scientiarum Fennica. Arsbok Vuosikirja Series B. Sphinx
0783-6244 Children in Finland
0783-6864 Karlebynejden
0783-8921 C - Lehti
0784-1736 Meijeriteollisuus†
0784-5480 Marina
0784-6509 Bank of Finland. Bulletin
0784-7726 B N
0784-8374 Finland. Tilastokeskus. Tilastotiedotus. Palkat Loner
0784-8382 Finland. Tilastokeskus. Rahoitus
0784-8420 Finland. Tilastokeskus. Tulot ja Kulutus
0784-8463 Finland. Tilastokeskus. Tilastotiedotus. Yritykset Foretag
0785-1324 Markkinointiviestinta
0785-2517 Kosmoskyna
0785-3165 Finland. Kauppa - Jateollisuusministerioe. Energiatilastot
0785-3572 Bank of Finland Discussions Papers
0785-6695 Sporttit†
0785-8736 Helsingin Kaupungin Tilastollinen Vuosikirja
0785-8760 Entomologica Fennica
0785-997X Tekniikka & Talous
0785-9988 Mikro P C
0786-0188 Lapsen Mailma
0786-1443 Asu Hyvin
0786-3012 Science Studies
0786-3683 Macmaailma
0786-5546 3000 Largest Companies in Finland (Year)
0788-5717 Commentationes Physico-Mathematicae et Chemico-Medicae
0788-6381 Tietoverkko
0788-6632 T V - Veckan och Radio
0788-6659 Vaasan Korkeakoulu. Julkaisuja. Opetusmonisteita
0788-6667 Vaasan Yliopisto. Julkaisuja. Tutkimuksia
0788-8430 Muovi - Plast
0789-600X Agricultural Science in Finland
0789-6093 Terassi
0790-004X Treoir
0790-0260 Geological Survey of Ireland. Guide Series
0790-0279 Geological Survey of Ireland. Report Series
0790-0422 National Botanic Gardens. Occasional Papers
0790-0627 International Journal of Water Resources Development
0790-066X Irish Bank Officials Association Newsheet
0790-0848 Irish Journal of Psychotherapy and Psychosomatic Medicine *see* 0790-9667
0790-0864 Micro News and Market *see* 0332-0197
0790-1186 Irish Journal of Psychiatry
0790-1216 Salesian Bulletin
0790-1267 New Democrat (Dublin) *changed to* Fine Gael News.
0790-150X Software Abstracts for Engineers
0790-1631 Salmon
0790-1712 Labour Comment (Cork)
0790-1763 Irish Journal of Earth Sciences
0790-178X Irish Arts Review
0790-2026 Irish Printer
0790-2360 R I A I Bulletin *changed to* Irish Architect.
0790-2743 Irish Council for Civil Liberties. Rights
0790-3030 Angling News
0790-3855 Modern Woman
0790-388X Trinity College. Friends of the Library. Newsletter
0790-3979 Central Bank of Ireland. Statistical Supplement *see* 0791-1785
0790-4568 Irish Cooperative Organization Society. Annual Report
0790-4657 Early Irish Law Series
0790-486X Consumer Choice
0790-4940 Focus (Dublin)
0790-505X Credit Union Review
0790-5068 Liberty News†
0790-5130 Ireland. Central Statistics Office. Industrial Production Index
0790-5750 International Structural Engineering Abstracts *changed to* International Building Science & Construction Abstracts.
0790-5769 International Building Science & Construction Abstracts *changed to* International Building Science & Construction Abstracts.
0790-5866 Ireland. Central Statistics Office. Labour Force Survey. First Results *see* 0791-0533
0790-6080 Ireland. Central Statistics Office. Census of Industrial Production
0790-6099 Ireland. Central Statistics Office. Census of Industrial Production. Overall Results for Industrial Establishments
0790-6277 Postal and Telecommunications Journal *changed to* Communications Worker.
0790-6862 In Dublin
0790-7184 Irish Political Studies
0790-732X Dairy Executive
0790-7508 Electrical Mail
0790-7710 Report on Vital Statistics
0790-7729 Ireland. Central Statistics Office. Distribution of Cattle and Pigs by Size of Herd
0790-7850 Irish Review
0790-8318 Language, Culture and Curriculum
0790-8334 Ireland. Stationery Office. Statistical Bulletin
0790-8407 Ireland. Stationery Office. Economic Series
0790-8482 Advanced Manufacturing Technology
0790-8830 Build
0790-8970 Ireland. Stationery Office. Statistical Abstract
0790-9136 Tuarascail
0790-9381 Trade Statistics
0790-9667 Irish Journal of Psychological Medicine
0790-9853 School of Celtic Studies. Newsletter
0790-9934 Ireland. Central Statistics Office. Road Freight Transport Survey
0791-0533 Ireland. Central Statistics Office. Labour Force Survey
0791-0770 Making Sense
0791-0878 Irish Building Services News
0791-1386 Banking Ireland
0791-1785 Central Bank of Ireland. Monthly Statistics
0791-2560 Employment Law Reports
0791-2765 Bank Marketing International
0791-2889 Ireland. Central Statistics Office. Industrial Turnover Index
0791-2897 Ireland. Central Statistics Office. Census of Industrial Production. Overall Results for Industrial Enterprises
0791-2900 Ireland. Central Statistics Office. Industrial Earnings and Hours Worked
0791-2919 Ireland. Central Statistics Office. Industrial Employment
0791-2927 Ireland. Central Statistics Office. Industrial Employment Earnings and Hours Worked: Details for Supplementary N A C E Sub-Sectors
0791-2943 Ireland. Central Statistics Office. Building and Construction. Monthly Index of Employment in Private Firms with 5 or More Persons Engaged
0791-2951 Ireland. Central Statistics Office. Building and Construction: Average Earnings and Hours Worked
0791-296X Ireland. Central Statistics Office. Census of Building and Construction. Results for Private Firms with 20 or More Persons Engaged
0791-2978 Ireland. Central Statistics Office. Building and Construction Planning Permissions
0791-3001 Ireland (Eire) Central Statistics Office. Estimated Output, Input and Income Arising in Agriculture
0791-301X Ireland. Central Statistics Office. Advance Estimate of Output, Input and Income Arising in Agriculture
0791-3028 Ireland. Central Statistics Office. Preliminary Estimate of Output, Input and Income in Agriculture
0791-3036 Ireland. Central Statistics Office. Production of Milk and Milk Products
0791-3044 Ireland. Central Statistics Office. Number and Weight of Pigs Slaughtered at Bacon Factories
0791-3079 Ireland. Central Statistics Office. Pig Survey
0791-3095 Ireland. Central Statistics Office. Pig Survey - August
0791-3133 Ireland (Eire) Central Statistics Office. December Livestock Survey
0791-3141 Ireland. Central Statistics Office. Agriculture - June Survey - Provisional Results
0791-315X Ireland. Central Statistics Office. Retail Sales Index
0791-3168 Ireland. Central Statistics Office. Banking, Insurance and Building Societies. Employment and Earnings
0791-3176 Ireland. Central Statistics Office. Labour Force, Preliminary Estimates
0791-3184 Ireland. Central Statistics Office. Labour Force. Mid-April Estimates
0791-3192 Ireland. Central Statistics Office. Live Register, Monthly Flow Analysis
0791-3206 Ireland. Central Statistics Office. Live Register Area Analysis
0791-329X Ireland. Central Statistics Office. Industrial Disputes
0791-3303 Ireland. Central Statistics Office. Consumer Price Index
0791-3311 Ireland. Central Statistics Office. Wholesale Price Index
0791-3346 Ireland. Central Statistics Office. Agricultural Input Price Index
0791-3354 Ireland. Central Statistics Office. Agriculture Output Price Index
0791-3370 Ireland. Central Statistics Office. Balance of International Payments
0791-3389 Ireland. Central Statistics Office. Hire Purchase and Credit Sales Inquiry
0791-3427 Ireland. Central Statistics Office. Particulars of Vehicles Registered and Licensed for First Time
0791-3435 Ireland. Central Statistics Office. Motor Registrations - Provisional Results
0791-3451 Ireland. Central Statistics Office. Analysis of External Trade by Ports
0791-346X Ireland. Central Statistics Office. Statistics of Port Traffic
0791-3478 Ireland. Central Statistics Office. External Trade Provisional Figures
0791-3516 Ireland (Eire) Central Statistics Office. Business of Advertising Agencies. Results for Respondents to Inquiry
0791-3524 Ireland (Eire) Central Statistics Office. Agriculture - June Survey - Final Estimates
0791-3656 Ireland. Central Statistics Office. Tourism and Travel Quarterly
0791-394X Ireland. Central Statistics Office. Live Register Age by Duration Analysis
0791-4857 Quantity Surveyors Inquiry
0791-539X Irish Criminal Law Journal
0791-5403 Irish European Law Journal
0791-5950 Bord Iascaigh Mhara. Tuarascail Agus Cuntaisi
0792-0032 Environmental Policy Review: The Soviet Union and East Europe
0792-044X Yiddishkeit
0792-0474 Mishkan
0792-0490 Adam Veavoda
0792-0598 Tel Aviv - Yafo. Center for Economic and Social Research. Statistical Yearbook
0792-0601 Tel Aviv - Yafo. Center for Economic and Social Research. Research and Surveys Series
0792-0679 In English *changed to* In English Magazine.
0792-0776 Technion - Israel Institute of Technology. Research Reports
0792-0814 Our Review
0792-0873 Likutim
0792-0970 Mashabei Einosh
0792-1268 Adrichalut Yisraelit
0792-1322 Taasiot
0792-156X Israeli Journal of Aquaculture - Bamidgeh
0792-1683 Tel Aviv Review
0792-2035 Knowhow†
0792-2337 Ya'ad
0792-318X Israeli Map Collectors Society. Journal
0792-3244 Technion Magazine
0792-3252 Hebrew Computational Linguistics
0792-3279 Od Meida
0792-3465 I C E N
0792-3910 Jewish Bible Quarterly
0792-4224 Readings in Glass History
0792-4275 Israel Chemist
0792-4569 Israel Journal of Obstetrics & Gynecology
0792-4615 The Other Israel
0792-4739 Biblical Polemics
0792-4836 Knafaim
0792-559X Jewish Linguistic Studies
0792-6049 Jerusalem Report
0792-6073 C M S News
0792-7355 Technion - Israel Institute of Technology. Abstracts of Research Theses
0794-2877 Nigeria Business Guide Annual
0794-3008 N P A Bulletin
0794-3415 Heritage (Lagos, 1984)
0794-3733 Medipharm Medical Journal
0794-3865 Nigeria Periodicals Review
0794-4055 Nigeria. Federal Office of Statistics. Report on General Household Survey
0794-439X New Horizon
0794-4810 Thisweek
0794-5655 Editors' Forum
0794-6406 Nigerian Periodicals Index
0794-6414 Nigerian Stored Products Research Institute. Annual Report
0794-7046 T C N N Research Bulletin
0794-7054 Nigerian Packaging News
0794-7968 Insight Magazine
0795-2864 Saiwa
0795-6762 African Journal of Genetics
0795-6770 Global Science Journal
0795-896X Weekly Probes
0795-9931 Nigeria. National Universities Commission. University System News
0796-0174 Family Planning Association of Gambia. Newsletter
0797-0064 S U M A
0797-0072 C I D A E
0797-0129 Archivos de la Biblioteca Nacional
0797-132X Uruguay. Instituto Nacional de Carnes. Anuario Estadistico de Faena y Exportacion
0797-9754 Relaciones
0798-1228 Educacion Superior y Sociedad

ISSN INDEX 5793

ISSN	Title
0798-1759	Revista Internacional de Sociologia sobre Agricultura y Alimentos
0798-1945	Bibliografia Forestal Latinoamericana
0798-2437	Revista Forestal Latinoamericana
0798-278X	Paramillo
0800-000X	N U P I Rapport
0800-0018	N U P I Notat
0800-014X	Loevetann
0800-0395	Polar Research
0800-0484	Kriminal Journalen
0800-0549	R - O - C - K
0800-0638	Europe's 15000 Largest Companies
0800-0646	Speideren
0800-0816	A M S - Skrifter
0800-0824	Invandrerinformasjon see 0802-3182
0800-0999	Valdres Historielag. Aarbok
0800-1200	Where to Build - Where to Repair
0800-1235	Skandinaviske Skipsrederier
0800-1936	Bonytt
0800-2169	Norway. Statistisk Sentralbyraa. Utdanningsstatistikk
0800-2177	Norway. Televerket. Statistikk
0800-2509	Gerontologisk Magasin see 0801-9991
0800-2606	Norwegica Pharmaceutica Acta see 1100-1801
0800-2789	European Paediatric Haematology and Oncology see 0888-0018
0800-336X	Nytt Norsk Tidsskrift
0800-403X	Norway. Statistisk Sentralbyraa. Helsepersonellstatistikk
0800-4129	Norway. Riksbibliotektjenesten. Skrifter
0800-4153	Norway. Riksbibliotektjenesten. Aarsmelding
0800-4412	N D R E Publications
0800-4684	Namn og Nemne
0800-532X	Teknisk Ukeblad Data see 0332-8171
0800-580X	Norway. Statistisk Sentralbyraa. Industristatistikk. Vol.1
0800-5818	Norway. Statistisk Sentralbyraa. Industristatistikk. Vol.2
0800-5850	Bil
0800-5923	Barne og Ungdomslitteratur. Utvalg av Boker Utkommet changed to Veiledende Liste for Barne og Ungdomslitteratur. Utvalg av Boker Utkommet.
0800-6016	Vaapenjournalen
0800-6032	4H - Klubben
0800-6113	Universitet i Oslo. Pedagogisk Forskningsinstitutt. Rapport
0800-658X	Stafo-Nytt
0800-6733	Eksport Aktuelt
0800-6865	Sommerfeltia
0800-7896	Norsk Energi
0800-8159	Praktisk Oekonomi changed to Praktisk Oekonomi & Ledelse.
0801-0986	Paa Hjul
0801-1087	Norwegian Music Information Center. Bulletin
0801-1400	Norsk Maskin-Tidende Styrmansblad changed to Norsk Skibsfoerertidende. Maskin-Tidende Styrmansblad.
0801-1621	Norway. Arbeidsdirektoratet. Aarsmelding
0801-1699	N I B R Rapport
0801-1745	Norsk Statsvitenskapelig Tidsskrift
0801-2202	Gaardbrukeren
0801-2334	Norges Landbrukshoegskole. Institutt for Jordskifte og Arealplanlegging. Melding
0801-3500	Normat: Nordisk Matematisk Tidsskrift
0801-3799	Astma Allergi
0801-4086	World Bulk Trades
0801-423X	Norsk Sjoefartsmuseum. Aarsberetning
0801-5007	World Bulk Fleet
0801-5333	Norsk Landbruksforsking
0801-5341	Norwegian Journal of Agricultural Sciences
0801-5384	Moderne Bil Transport see 0802-5193
0801-5589	Fearnleys Review
0801-5880	FerieForum
0801-5961	N G U Special Publication
0801-6690	Norway. Statistisk Sentralbyraa. Befolknings Statistisk Hefte 2
0801-6763	Brann og Sikkerhet
0801-6828	Bioingenioeren
0801-7093	Kulde
0801-9606	Overflate Teknikk
0801-9991	Aldring og Eldre. Gerontologisk Magasin
0802-0434	Skrifter - Landslaget for Lokalhistorie
0802-0442	Esperanto - Nytt
0802-2100	Renholdsnytt
0802-2836	Universitetsbiblioteket i Trondheim. Rapport
0802-2992	Universitetet i Trondheim. Vitenskapsmuseet. Rapport. Botanisk Serie
0802-3182	Mosaikk
0802-3212	El Entrepenoeren
0802-5193	Moderne Transport
0802-5428	Glass & Porselen
0802-7188	Norges Bank. Skriftserie
0802-7293	Racing
0802-8400	Norges Apotekerforenings Tidsskrift
0802-8524	Norges Landbrukshoegskole. Institutt for Tekniske Fag. Proevemeldinger
0802-8532	Norges Landbrukshoegskole. Institutt for Tekniske Fag. Rapporter
0802-8559	Elektronikk Bransjen
0802-8931	Lokalhistorisk Magasin
0802-9067	Norway. Statistisk Sentralbyraa. Stortingsvalg
0802-9474	Euroil
0802-9776	Journalen Sykepleien
0803-2394	Norsk Tidsskrift for Arbejdsmedisin
0803-2505	Universitetet i Oslo. Slavisk-Baltisk Avdeling. Meddelelser
0803-2858	Skogforsk. Rapport
0803-2866	Skogforsk. Meddelelser
0803-4087	Politi- og Lensmannsetaten
0803-5253	Acta Paediatrica, International Journal of Paediatrics
0803-5326	Acta Paediatrica, International Journal of Paediatrics, Supplement
0810-0039	Australia. Bureau of Statistics. Estimated Resident Population by Sex and Age: States and Territories of Australia
0810-0055	Australia New Zealand Foundation. Annual Report (Year)
0810-0713	Australian Journal of Clinical Hypnotherapy and Hypnosis
0810-1167	Safety in Australia changed to Health and Safety at Work.
0810-1442	Confederation of Western Australian Industry. Confederation Report
0810-1868	Australian Journal of Historical Archaeology
0810-2201	Australian and New Zealand Booksellers changed to Australian and New Zealand Booksellers and Publishers.
0810-2236	See Australia changed to See Australia Regional Information Series.
0810-2333	Marc N U C O M
0810-249X	T V Week
0810-2686	Australian Journalism Review
0810-2740	Matilda Literary and Art Magazine changed to Matilda Magazine: Literary and Art Magazine.
0810-2872	Bike Australia
0810-4115	Dairy Industry Leader
0810-4123	Australasian Drama Studies
0810-4395	University of Tasmania. Environmental Studies. Occasional Paper
0810-4468	Australian Short Stories
0810-4476	Victoria. State Film Centre. New Films and Videotapes see 1036-1839
0810-4972	Victoria. Housing Commision. Annual Report changed to Victoria. Department of Planning and Housing. Annual Report. Housing and Construction Victoria.
0810-5030	Western Australian Institute of Technology. Library. Western Library Studies changed to Curtin University of Technology. Library. Western Library Studies.
0810-5200	Sinatra International
0810-5294	University of Wollongong. Institute Sector Handbook changed to University of Wollongong. Undergraduate Calendar.
0810-5391	Accounting and Finance
0810-5537	Poverty Watch
0810-5596	Australian Master Tax Guide
0810-574X	Textile and Apparel Manufacturer see 0816-3588
0810-5928	Australian Shooters Journal changed to Australian Sporting Shooter.
0810-6029	Design World
0810-6142	Mathematics Students' Gazette†
0810-6150	Mathmag†
0810-6398	Hyper Activities
0810-6681	West Australian Nut and Tree Crop Association Yearbook
0810-669X	B & T Year Book
0810-6797	Australia. Bureau of Agricultural Economics. Situation and Outlook (Year). Farm Inputs†
0810-6800	Australia. Bureau of Agricultural Economics. Situation and Outlook (Year). Fish Products†
0810-6959	Victoria, Australia. Geological Survey. Reports
0810-719X	Queensland Government Statistician. Queensland Official Year Book see 1030-7389
0810-736X	Water Research in Australia changed to Water Research in Australia: Current Projects.
0810-7440	Australian Dental Association. News Bulletin
0810-7688	Ascent
0810-7742	Australia. Bureau of Statistics. Queensland Office. Value of Agricultural Commodities Produced, Queensland
0810-7750	Australia. Bureau of Statistics. Queensland Office. Value of Primary Industry Commodities Produced, Excluding Mining, Queensland see 0810-7742
0810-8021	Opera Australia Libretto Series
0810-8064	Rawlinsons Australian Construction Handbook (Year)
0810-820X	On the Beach
0810-8633	Australia. Bureau of Statistics. Year Book Australia
0810-8889	Association of Australasian Palaeontologists. Memoirs
0810-9028	Prometheus
0810-9176	Australia. Bureau of Statistics. Tasmanian Office. Livestock and Livestock Products changed to Australia. Bureau of Statistics. Tasmanian Office. Agricultural Statistics, Tasmania.
0810-9265	A L I S A
0810-9338	New South Wales Year Book
0810-9451	Modern Office†
0810-9796	Zadok Perspectives
0810-9958	Australian Motoring Year
0811-0026	Papers in Pidgin and Creole Linguistics
0811-0174	Bibliography of Education Theses in Australia
0811-0662	Australia - New Zealand Building Materials and Equipment see 1031-3745
0811-0670	Australia - New Zealand Building Construction Materials and Equipment see 1031-3745
0811-0859	Photofile
0811-0875	V A T Journal changed to V A T - C H A T.
0811-0905	Insurance in Australia and New Zealand changed to Insurance in Australia.
0811-0964	National Trust of Australia (New South Wales) National Trust Magazine see 1036-9880
0811-112X	Australasian College Libraries (South Australia)†
0811-1146	Urban Policy & Research
0811-1197	Maffra & District Historical Society. Bulletin
0811-1235	Film and Video Acquisitions
0811-1324	Australian and New Zealand Wine Industry Directory
0811-1863	Australia. Department of Employment and Industrial Relations. Employee Participation News†
0811-191X	Storylines†
0811-2045	Current Developments see 0728-6481
0811-2169	Outrage
0811-2274	Jewellery World
0811-2304	Trinity Occasional Papers
0811-2762	What's New in Computing
0811-3149	Sounds Australian Journal
0811-3394	Queensland Family Historian
0811-3513	Market Facts (Adelaide) see 0818-1152
0811-353X	Market Facts (Perth) see 0818-1152
0811-3556	Market Facts (Melbourne) see 0818-1152
0811-3564	Market Facts (Brisbane) see 0818-1152
0811-3661	Australian Family Bulletin changed to The Australian Family.
0811-3688	Australian Transport Information Directory†
0811-3696	Australasian Arachnology
0811-3742	Talking Electronics
0811-3963	Brandywine Bibliography
0811-3971	Brandywine Documents on the History of Books & Printing
0811-4188	Insight†
0811-4269	Peace Studies see 0817-895X
0811-4684	Tactual Mapping Newsletter
0811-4692	A.C.F.O.A. News
0811-5141	Australia. Bureau of Statistics. Queensland Office. Seleted Agricultural Commodities, Queensland, Preliminary
0811-5397	Australian Water Resources Council. Water Resources Series
0811-5400	Liane Newsletter
0811-546X	The Great Race
0811-5478	Victorian Arts Centre Magazine see 1033-3975
0811-5680	Small Business Review†
0811-5796	Law in Context
0811-580X	University of Tasmania. Centre for Environmental Studies. Project Report
0811-5931	Water and Mineral Development see 1037-3535
0811-594X	Quorum
0811-5982	New England Monographs in Continuing Education (No.)
0811-6199	Australia. National Health and Medical Research Council. Department of Health. Medical Research
0811-6202	Australian Journal of Communication
0811-6407	Defender
0811-6504	South Australian Geographical Papers
0811-7098	Armidale College of Advanced Education. Annual Report†
0811-7497	N M A
0811-7586	University of New South Wales. Faculty Handbooks: Applied Science
0811-7594	University of New South Wales. Faculty Handbooks: Architecture
0811-7608	University of New South Wales. Faculty Handbooks: Arts
0811-7616	University of New South Wales. Faculty Handbooks: Commerce
0811-7624	University of New South Wales. Faculty Handbooks: Engineering
0811-7632	University of New South Wales. Faculty Handbooks: Law
0811-7640	University of New South Wales. Faculty Handbooks: Sciences
0811-8655	Australia. Bureau of Statistics. Queensland Office. Causes of Death, Queensland see 0816-0465
0811-8698	Hoofbeats

5794 ISSN INDEX

0811-8892 Media Ownership in Australia
0811-9066 Eyespy
0811-9260 Australian International Law News
0811-9929 Scan
0812-0056 Fireman
0812-0099 Australian Journal of Earth Sciences
0812-0137 Australia. Bureau of Statistics. Award Rates of Pay Indexes, Australia
0812-0145 Australia. Bureau of Statistics. Wage Rates, Indexes, Australia, Preliminary *see* 0812-0137
0812-0153 Australia. Bureau of Statistics. Wage Rates, Australia *see* 0812-0137
0812-017X Soils News
0812-0293 Minfo
0812-0382 Australia. Bureau of Statistics. Wage Rates Indexes, Preliminary *see* 0812-0137
0812-0439 Economic Society of Australia Economic Papers
0812-0811 Australian Lectionary (Year)
0812-0927 Transport Indicators *see* 1033-9752
0812-1311 Western Australia. Ministry of Education. Education Statistics Bulletin
0812-1621 Australian Children's Television Foundation. Information Papers†
0812-163X Australian Nautical News *see* 1035-3852
0812-1648 Work and Patrol Boat World *changed to* Work Boat World.
0812-1729 Rural Industry Directory
0812-2024 Intellectual Property Reports
0812-2040 What's On in Victoria
0812-2237 Commonwealth Scientific and Industrial Research Organization. Division of Wildlife and Rangelands Research. Technical Paper *changed to* Commonwealth Scientific and Industrial Research Organization. Division of Wildlife and Ecology. Technical Paper.
0812-2288 Tenders Australia
0812-230X Melbourne College of Advanced Education. Handbook *changed to* Institute of Education. Handbook.
0812-2598 Australia. Bureau of Statistics. Livestock and Livestock Products, Australia
0812-2970 Victorian Tasmanian Retail Directory
0812-3136 Family Local History Sources in Victoria
0812-3152 Australia. Bureau of Statistics. Queensland Office. Fruit, Queensland
0812-3195 Australia. Bureau of Statistics. Queensland Office. Livestock and Livestock Products, Queensland
0812-3314 Institution of Engineers, Australia. Transactions. Multi-Disciplinary Engineering
0812-3330 Open Door Poetry Journal
0812-3470 Westpac Banking Corporation. Review†
0812-3594 Australian Electrical Contractor
0812-3705 National Thomson's Liquor Guide *see* 0816-0430
0812-3896 Australasian Health & Healing
0812-3985 Exploration Geophysics
0812-4663 Disability Aids Directory
0812-4930 Range Management Newsletter
0812-5074 Consumer Views
0812-5090 Australian Hydrographic Newsletter
0812-5767 Australia. Bureau of Statistics. Queensland Office. Livestock Products - Meat, Queensland
0812-5864 Blackall Leader
0812-6267 A A C O B S Annual Report†
0812-6453 Mingay's Product Service - Appliances *changed to* Mingay's Retail Guide.
0812-6461 Mingay's Product Service - Home Entertainment *changed to* Mingay's Retail Guide.
0812-6585 Australian Stationers and Office Suppliers Reference Book *changed to* Australian Stationers & Newsagent Buyer's Guide (Year) for Office Products & Stationers.
0812-6763 Tasmania. Major Economic Indicators†
0812-695X Australian Tax Forum
0812-7077 Medical Careers in Australia
0812-7131 J A I A
0812-7336 Commonwealth Scientific and Industrial Research Organization. Division of Animal Health. Research Report *see* 1031-1580
0812-7352 Riverina Library Review *see* 1034-8042
0812-7387 Australian Museum, Sydney. Records Supplements
0812-7417 Threshold†
0812-7573 P S A Reporter
0812-7735 Australia. Department of Resources and Energy. Streamline Update *changed to* Australia. Department of Primary Industries and Energy. Streamline Update.
0812-7859 Research in Mathematics Education in Australia *see* 1033-2170
0812-7883 Museums Australia
0812-8014 R A O U Newsletter
0812-8227 Australian Well Being
0812-8332 Australia. Bureau of Statistics. Queensland Office. Building Activity, Queensland
0812-843X Ecofile†
0812-857X A M P L A Yearbook
0812-8685 C C J P Issues†
0812-9169 Australian Veterinary Association. Year Book *changed to* Australian Veterinary Association. Annual Report.
0812-9258 National Union Catalogue of Serials
0812-9428 A P S E C S Eighteenth-Century News *changed to* A P S E C S Newsletter.
0812-9495 Australian Garden Journal
0812-955X Australian Small Farms Directory *changed to* Australian Small Farms Handbook.
0813-0051 Aust-Asian Robotics Journal
0813-006X Badminton Sidelines
0813-0183 International Journal of Management
0813-0426 Rock Art Research
0813-0493 Commonwealth Scientific and Industrial Research Organization. Division of Wildlife and Rangelands Research. Technical Memorandum *changed to* Commonwealth Scientific and Industrial Research Organization. Division of Wildlife and Ecology. Technical Memorandum.
0813-0523 Australian Sea Heritage
0813-0531 Australian Journal of Advanced Nursing
0813-1295 Royal Historical Society of Victoria. Journal *see* 1030-7710
0813-1317 Australia. Bureau of Statistics. Catalogue of Small Area Statistics
0813-1384 Australian P C World
0813-1600 Cinedossier
0813-1724 New South Wales Association for Mental Health. Newsletter *changed to* N S W A M H News.
0813-1759 V I S E. Occasional Papers†
0813-1988 S P U M S Journal
0813-2194 Australian Institute of Psychic Research Bulletin *see* 1035-9621
0813-2283 A C H P E R National Journal
0813-2402 Special Education Journal†
0813-2844 Asia Today
0813-295X Computerworld Australia
0813-2992 Personal Investment
0813-300X Environmental and Planning Law Journal
0813-3085 Australian College of Education. New South Wales Chapter Newsletter
0813-3409 Australian Imports *see* 1032-2116
0813-3573 Chorten
0813-4235 Education for Librarianship: Australia
0813-4537 Australian Disability Review
0813-4545 Photoworld Buyer's Directory
0813-4626 My Baby
0813-4634 Studio Collections
0813-4650 Solo
0813-474X Commonwealth Scientific and Industrial Research Organization. Division of Water Resources Research. Natural Resources Series†
0813-4758 D P Index and Software Register *see* 1036-0352
0813-4782 Travelweek Hotel, Motel Directory *see* 0813-4790
0813-4790 Travelweek Hotel, Motel Index†
0813-4820 Indonesian Studies
0813-4952 Australian Off-Road Year†
0813-5150 Viewprints†
0813-5207 Rawlinsons New Zealand Construction Handbook
0813-5231 Australian Seed Industry Magazine
0813-524X H E R D S A Green Guide
0813-5436 C C J P Occasional Papers†
0813-5886 Outrider
0813-5959 Australian Digest Annual Supplement *see* 0067-1843
0813-6289 Australian Journal of Science and Medicine in Sport
0813-6394 A M A Victoria Branch News
0813-6440 Qualm
0813-6491 Interest Rates Survey
0813-6580 Tasmanian Teacher *changed to* Teacher.
0813-6645 Albury & District Historical Society. Bulletin
0813-6734 Craft A.C.T.
0813-6785 A I M News *see* 0817-5713
0813-6998 Information Bulletin of Australian Criminology *changed to* Cinch. Australian Criminology Database.
0813-7196 Gayzette
0813-7455 Jobson's Quarterly
0813-7471 Hospital and Healthcare Australia
0813-7544 Australian Hotelier
0813-779X Administrative Appeal Reports
0813-7803 Federal Court Reports (North Ryde)
0813-782X Motor Vehicle Reports
0813-7951 Word of Salvation
0813-796X Trowel and Sword
0813-815X Royal Australian Historical Society. Newsletter *changed to* Royal Australian Historical Society. History Magazine.
0813-877X A F I T Bulletin†
0813-9091 Women Australia
0813-9474 Australia. National Institute of Economic & Industry Research. National Economic Review
0813-9806 Nowa Epoka†
0814-043X Stiletto Magazine
0814-0545 New South Wales. Department of Agriculture. Fisheries Bulletin *changed to* New South Wales. Department of Fisheries. Fisheries Bulletin.
0814-107X Australiana
0814-1185 Inside Indonesia
0814-138X Australia. Bureau of Statistics. Shipping and Air Cargo Commodity Statistics, Australia
0814-1819 Museum of Victoria. Occasional Papers
0814-1827 Museum of Victoria. Memoirs
0814-2556 Australia. Bureau of Statistics. Queensland Office. Agricultural Land Use and Selected Inputs, Queensland
0814-2610 A A M R Journal *see* 0818-6286
0814-2769 Video & Audio Marketing†
0814-303X Issues
0814-3609 Australia. Bureau of Statistics. Queensland Office. Estimated Resident Population and Area for Local Authority Areas, Queensland, Preliminary *see* 1030-911X
0814-3668 Australian Table Tennis
0814-3951 Australia. Bureau of Statistics. Population Estimates, Australia
0814-401X Community Quarterly
0814-4125 Youth Affairs in Australia†
0814-4273 Business Council of Australia Bulletin
0814-4540 Town and Country Farmer
0814-4680 Trees and Natural Resources
0814-480X Postmark News
0814-4990 Rutherglen Research Institute. Research Report
0814-5288 Elagu
0814-5296 Mansfield Historical Society's Magazine
0814-5482 Irish Link
0814-5490 Crafts Industry Guide N.S.W.: Printout
0814-5504 Economic Growth of the Australian States†
0814-561X Simmental Annual
0814-5733 Australian and New Zealand Citator to UK Reports. Cumulative Supplement
0814-5857 Musicology Australia
0814-6012 Australian Dr Weekly
0814-6039 Acoustics Australia
0814-6489 C C H Tax Action Digest
0814-6586 Craft Arts International Magazine
0814-673X Australian Journal of Educational Technology
0814-6764 Ex Nihilo Technical Journal *see* 1036-2916
0814-6802 Education Links
0814-6888 National Film and Sound Archive Newsletter
0814-6942 Ad News
0814-7078 V - Line News†
0814-7094 Prospect
0814-723X Australian and New Zealand Journal of Family Therapy
0814-7663 Australian Hereford Quarterly
0814-771X P L News†
0814-7752 Coaching Director
0814-7817 Australian Transport Research in Progress†
0814-7833 Gallery
0814-7965 South Pacific Smallholder Project. Research Notes
0814-7973 South Pacific Smallholder Project. Occasional Papers
0814-8023 Australia. Bureau of Statistics. Queensland Office. Dwelling Commencements Reported by Approving Authorities, Queensland
0814-8074 Chartac Accounting Report *changed to* Chartac Accountancy News.
0814-8112 Chartac Computer Report†
0814-8120 Chartac Taxation Report *changed to* Chartac Tax Planning News.
0814-8562 Australia. Bureau of Statistics. Foreign Trade, Australia, Part 2: Comparative and Summary Tables *see* 1031-1394
0814-8589 Australian Bar Review
0814-8805 Metaphysical Review
0814-883X Artswest†
0814-9089 Panorama (Melbourne)
0814-9267 Wheat Australia International
0814-9321 C I S Policy Report *see* 1032-6634
0814-9356 Australian Macworld
0814-9372 University of New England. Department of Accounting & Financial Management. Working Papers
0814-9488 Western Contractor
0814-9593 Australia. Bureau of Statistics. Tasmanian Office. Labour Force Statistics†
0814-9674 University of New England. Computer Centre Annual Report
0814-9682 University of New England. Computer Centre Handbook
0814-9690 University of New England. Computer Centre Newsletter
0814-9704 University of New England Library Publications
0814-9763 Australian and New Zealand Journal of Ophthalmology
0814-9933 S.A. Crafts News *see* 0819-2936
0815-0052 Log
0815-0249 Nuclear Spectrum†
0815-0303 A B N Catalogue†
0815-0478 Indonesian Economy
0815-0486 Streetwize Comics
0815-1210 Communications Update
0815-1458 Australia. Bureau of Agricultural Economics. Occasional Papers *changed to* Australia. Australian Bureau of Agricultural and Resource Economics. Occasional Papers.
0815-1652 A M B A News

ISSN

0815-1881 Australia. Department of the Treasury. Round-Up of Economic Statistics *changed to* Australia. Department of the Treasury. Economic Round-Up.
0815-2195 Plant Protection Quarterly
0815-2276 Independent Living
0815-2292 Inventors†
0815-2500 Australian Studies Bulletin *see* 1033-131X
0815-2969 Music Business *see* 1033-4831
0815-3191 Australasian Plant Pathology
0815-3205 Electrical and Computer Engineering in Australia†
0815-3337 Australian Meat and Livestock Corporation. Meat Producer and Exporter *changed to* A M L C News.
0815-3523 Australian Capital Territory at a Glance
0815-3701 Australian T A F E Teacher
0815-3752 Technology in Education†
0815-3809 Northern Territory at a Glance
0815-4171 Australian Science and Technology Newsletter
0815-4392 Aviation Heritage
0815-4465 Western Australia. Department of Conservation and Land Management. Landscope
0815-452X Carrionflower Writ
0815-4597 Australasian Family History Gazette†
0815-4627 Scout Magazine
0815-4678 Curriculum Australia†
0815-4740 Smash Hits Yearbook
0815-5046 Australian Electronics Monthly†
0815-5232 Directory of Australian Composers
0815-5992 Adelaide Review
0815-6050 Building and Construction Law
0815-6077 Simmental News
0815-6301 Australian National University. National Centre for Development Studies. History of Development Studies
0815-6344 Asia Pacific Context†
0815-6409 Journal of Occupational Health and Safety: Australia and New Zealand
0815-6794 Dawsons Venue Directory
0815-6816 Pelangi
0815-6883 Coal Journal
0815-709X Surface Coatings Australia
0815-7138 Macquarie University French Monographs
0815-7596 Australian National University. National Centre for Development Studies. Working Papers. Series: N C D S Working Papers
0815-8150 TalentEd
0815-8681 Australia. Bureau of Statistics. Queensland Office. Births, Queensland *see* 1036-2649
0815-9076 Australia Investment Quarterly
0815-9297 Australian Poultry Digest *see* 1032-3767
0815-9319 Journal of Gastroenterology and Hepatology
0815-9424 Development Dossier
0815-953X Meanjin
0815-9769 Dairy Goat Society of Australia. Victorian Branch Newsletter
0815-9777 British Alpine Breeders Group of Australia. Newsletter
0815-9904 Herald
0816-0031 Salt
0816-0430 National Liquor News
0816-0465 Australia. Bureau of Statistics. Queensland Office. Deaths, Queensland
0816-0627 Australia. Bureau of Statistics. Digest of Current Economic Statistics†
0816-0783 Australia. Bureau of Statistics. Queensland Office. Divorces, Queensland *see* 1036-2649
0816-1089 Australian Journal of Experimental Agriculture
0816-1321 Australia. Department of Housing and Construction. Technical Bulletin *changed to* Australia. Department of Administrative Services. Australian Construction Services. Technical Bulletin.
0816-1356 National Schools Statistics Collection, Australia, Preliminary *see* 1034-5671
0816-1623 Agricultural and Veterinary Product Index
0816-1631 Enterprise (Brisbane)
0816-1909 Photo Retailer *changed to* Photo & Video Retailer.
0816-2018 Australian Journal of T A F E Research and Development
0816-2271 Western Australian Resource Developement Services Directory
0816-2425 Rock (Prahran)
0816-2735 Sir Robert Madgwick Lecture Series (No.)
0816-2751 Natural Health
0816-2905 Truck & Bus Road Tests†
0816-3065 Prints
0816-3391 Australia. Bureau of Statistics. Projections of the Populations of Australia, States and Territories
0816-3537 Australia. Bureau of Statistics. Queensland Office. Demographic Summary, Queensland *see* 1036-2649
0816-3588 Australian Apparel Manufacturer
0816-3596 Australian Paint and Panel
0816-360X Crafts Competitions and Prizes†
0816-3634 Food Manufacturing News
0816-3642 Lucky
0816-3960 Information for Overseas Students and Their Families
0816-4290 Melbourne Star Observer
0816-4460 Australian Prosthodontic Society. Bulletin *see* 0819-0887
0816-4622 Clinical and Experimental Optometry
0816-4649 Australian Feminist Studies
0816-4746 Audit Guide
0816-486X Animal Liberation Magazine
0816-5041 University of New England. Faculty of Economic Studies. Occasional Papers in Economic Development (No.)
0816-5157 Third Degree
0816-5165 Australian National University. National Centre for Development Studies. Working Papers. Series: Islands - Australia Working Papers
0816-5173 Rural Development Working Papers†
0816-5890 Australian Communications
0816-6013 Commonwealth Scientific and Industrial Research Organization. Division of Geomechanics. Geomechanics Computer Programs
0816-6153 Home Loan Affordability in Australia
0816-6269 New Media Marketing Newsletter *changed to* Telecommunications.
0816-651X Australian Cricket Journal
0816-6668 Organic Growing (Ulverstone)
0816-6706 Jewellers Association of Australia. Federal Newsletter *changed to* Jewellers Association of Australia. National Newsletter.
0816-6757 Western Australia. Department of Conservation and Land Management. Technical Report
0816-6773 Education Department of Victoria. Textbooks†
0816-6919 Fremantle Arts Review
0816-7141 Australian Jewish Historical Society. Newsletter
0816-7656 D O G S Newsletter
0816-7885 Fishing News
0816-8474 Commonwealth Scientific and Industrial Research Organization. Division of Tropical Crops and Pastures. Annual Report
0816-8717 Chemicals Today *see* 1031-3761
0816-875X Conservation North Queensland
0816-9098 Manufacturers' Bulletin *see* 1035-3941
0816-9330 AudioVision & Prosound
0816-939X Studio Bambini
0816-942X A M R E P Database Bulletin
0816-956X Online Currents
0816-9594 South Australian Volunteering
0816-9675 Western Australia. Department of Conservation and Land Management. Bulletin *see* 1032-8106
0816-9799 Victorian Statutes - Annotations
0817-0088 Magpies
0817-024X New South Wales & Australian Capital Territory Retail Directory
0817-0398 Hospitality Industry Suppliers Index
0817-0444 Australian National University. National Centre for Development Studies. Pacific Policy Papers
0817-0975 Education Victoria†
0817-1203 British Soccer Week
0817-1300 A A A News
0817-1351 Access (Toorak)
0817-1904 Communications World
0817-2285 Sydney Organ Journal
0817-2420 Pregnancy, Birth and the Next 6 Months *see* 1035-5448
0817-2455 Your Pharmacy†
0817-2668 A I M M Bulletin and Proceedings *see* 1034-6775
0817-2773 Sailboard Extra
0817-2811 Ski Extra
0817-3052 Drugs: Australia†
0817-3516 Legal Service Bulletin
0817-3524 Social Security Reporter
0817-3532 Freedom of Information Review
0817-4075 Tasmanian Numismatist
0817-458X Linq
0817-4628 Xpress
0817-4792 Excel
0817-4830 A.C.C. - Westpac Economic Discussion Papers
0817-5675 Hospital Brief
0817-5713 A I M
0817-5829 Interest Rates Service
0817-5837 Comcise
0817-587X Directory of Women in Business, Professions & Management
0817-6191 Lipscombe Report
0817-623X Australian Journal of Family Law
0817-6337 Australian Plumbing Industry
0817-6345 Australian Institute of Family Studies. Working Paper†
0817-6353 Who's Pegging
0817-6418 Tasmanian Development Authority Annual Report
0817-6604 Australian Croquet Gazette
0817-6795 Custom Rodder
0817-6825 Australia. Department of Primary Industry. Domestic and Overseas Fish Market Notes *changed to* Australia. Department of Primary Industries and Energy. Domestic and Overseas Fish Market Notes.
0817-7724 Australian Oyster
0817-8038 Australian National University. National Centre for Development Studies. Pacific Economic Bulletin
0817-8445 Look Magazine
0817-8526 Australia. Bureau of Statistics. Queensland Office. Summary of Social Statistics, Queensland
0817-8585 Club Marine
0817-8771 University of Sydney. Department of Agricultural Economics. Research Report.
0817-895X Peace Magazine Australia†
0817-9263 Australia. Bureau of Mineral Resources, Geology and Geophysics. Australian Petroleum Accumulations Report
0817-9646 Australian Journal of Mining
0817-9751 United Nations Review
0818-0148 Gazette of Law Journalism
0818-0164 Invertebrate Taxonomy
0818-0229 Australian Institute of Family Studies. Newsletter *see* 1030-2646
0818-0261 Australian Woodworker
0818-044X Trade Practices Commission Bulletin
0818-0512 Australian National University. National Centre for Development Studies. Report (Year)
0818-0563 International Journal of Educology
0818-0954 Hrvatska Sloboda
0818-1152 Market Facts
0818-1233 R A I A Memo
0818-1764 Sheet Metal Australia
0818-1993 Australia. Bureau of Statistics. Queensland Office. Pre-schools and Child Care Centres, Queensland†
0818-2019 A.C.T. Science Teacher
0818-2132 Australia. Bureau of Statistics. Queensland Office. Schools, Queensland, Preliminary†
0818-2183 A F D J
0818-2469 Peace Research Centre Newsletter *see* 1031-9379
0818-2493 Good Government
0818-2582 Australia. Bureau of Statistics. Queensland Office. Schools, Queensland†
0818-2833 Garden Scene *see* 1035-655X
0818-2884 Service Station
0818-3597 Materials Australasia
0818-4127 National Trotguide
0818-4380 Queensland Hosteller *changed to* On the Go.
0818-4445 Prescription Products Guide
0818-4453 Non-Prescription Products Guide *see* 0818-4445
0818-4674 South Australia in Business
0818-4984 World Goodwill Newsletter
0818-5093 Dun's Gazette
0818-5166 Occasional Papers in Commerce
0818-5204 Transit Australia
0818-5352 Australian Institute of Family Studies. Policy Background Paper (No.)†
0818-545X Queensland Researcher
0818-5549 Motor News
0818-5646 Australasian Sound Archive
0818-5670 Environmental Health Review, Australia†
0818-6278 Australia. Bureau of Mineral Resouces, Geology and Geophysics. Resource Report *changed to* Australia. Bureau of Mineral Resources, Geology and Geophysics. Mineral Resource Report.
0818-6286 Interaction (Canberra)
0818-6308 Textile-Fibre Forum
0818-6316 International Monetary Agreements Acts. Annual Report
0818-6510 Australian Orienteer
0818-6618 Australian Prisoners
0818-7169 South Australian Dairyfarmer's Journal
0818-7185 Australia. Bureau of Statistics. Queensland Office. Manufacturing Establishments: Details of Operations, Queensland *see* 1036-2762
0818-8068 Australian Universities' Review
0818-8122 Auditing Discussion Paper
0818-8149 Australian Slavonic and East European Studies
0818-8238 Curtin University of Technology. Mulga Research Centre Journal
0818-8491 Electric Vehicle News
0818-917X Yearbook of South Australian Crafts (Year)†
0818-9404 Australian Accounting Research Foundation. Discussion Paper (Accounting)
0818-9412 Accounting Theory Monograph
0818-9641 Immunology and Cell Biology
0818-979X Australia. Bureau of Statistics. Queensland Office. Manufacturing Establishments: Small Area Statistics, Queensland†
0818-9846 Entertainment Worker
0818-9889 Q M A A News
0818-9935 Asian-Pacific Economic Literature
0819-0194 Stereo Buyer's Guide. Loudspeakers, Amplifiers and Tuners
0819-0208 Stereo Buyer's Guide. C D Players, Turntables and Cassettes Decks
0819-0216 Stereo Buyer's Guide. Audio Yearbook
0819-0852 Australian Folklore
0819-0887 Australian Prosthodontic Journal
0819-114X Australia. Bureau of Statistics. Balance of Payments, Australia (Quarterly)
0819-1239 C S I R O Tropical Crops and Pastures. Annual Report *see* 0816-8474

5796 ISSN INDEX

0819-1247 Kingia†
0819-1530 Creation Ex Nihilo
0819-1565 Press Press Magazine
0819-1794 Australian Official Journal of Patents
0819-1808 Australian Official Journal of Trade Marks
0819-2006 Foreword *changed to* A S U National.
0819-2421 Australian and New Zealand Wine Industry Journal
0819-243X W.A. Business World *changed to* Business News.
0819-2898 A F M Information Systems Series (No.)
0819-2928 Australia. Bureau of Statistics. Queensland Office. Economic Indicators, Queensland
0819-2936 S.A. Crafts
0819-2995 Australian Rural Science Annual
0819-3320 Investment Action Newsletter *changed to* Trendex.
0819-3355 Australian Journal of Biotechnology†
0819-3363 Australasian Cycling & Triathalon News
0819-4076 Australian Society for Historical Archaeology. Research Bulletin
0819-419X Flight Deck
0819-4610 World Council of Enterostomal Therapists Journal
0819-4823 Recent Advances in Animal Nutrition in Australia (Year)
0819-5218 C'oz
0819-5323 Australia. Bureau of Statistics. National Schools Statistics Collection *see* 1035-3461
0819-5447 What's New in Process Engineering
0819-5501 Commonwealth Scientific and Industrial Research Organization. Division of Protein Chemistry. Biennial Report *changed to* Commonwealth Scientific and Industrial Research Organization. Division of Biomolecular Engineering. Annual Report.
0819-5838 Art Monthly Australia
0819-5854 Australia. Department of Primary Industries and Energy. Wheat Research Council. Annual Report
0819-5862 Clumber Spaniel Correspondence
0819-5943 Australian Technology Review†
0819-6508 Australian Mineralogist
0819-6575 Australia. Bureau of Statistics. Victorian Office. Estimated Resident Population in Statistical Local Areas, Victoria
0819-6648 Adbrief Register: Agencies & Marketers
0819-677X Contemporary Art Centre of South Australia. Broadsheet
0819-6826 Tasmanian Naturalist
0819-7458 Offshore Yacht Racing and Cruising *changed to* Offshore Australian Yachting.
0819-7482 University of Queensland. Student Handbook *changed to* University of Queensland. Calendar. Volume 2. Student Handbook: Metropolitan Campuses.
0819-7806 Australian Correspondence Chess Quarterly
0819-808X A C C Agenda for Reform Papers
0819-923X Australian Art Auction Records
0819-9558 I A A H Newsletter
0819-9825 Labor Times
0819-9981 New Idea
0820-005X Perspectives Universitaires
0820-0165 Muse (Ottawa)
0820-0416 Music Directory Canada
0820-0467 Lottery and Gaming *see* 8750-801X
0820-0521 Library and Information Science Update
0820-0750 Microcomputer Applications
0820-0858 Offshore Resources
0820-2737 Nova Scotia Business Journal
0820-2893 Heritage Link
0820-2923 University of British Columbia. Faculty of Forestry. Research and Publications *changed to* University of British Columbia. Faculty of Forestry. Research Review.
0820-506X Anglican Magazine
0820-5450 C A Dalyst
0820-554X Canadian Messenger of the Sacred Heart
0820-5582 Southern Africa Report
0820-5728 Action (Toronto) *changed to* Action Now.
0820-5930 Canadian Journal of Medical Radiation Technology
0820-5949 A C F D Forum
0820-6244 European Studies Journal
0820-6686 Worldlit
0820-6759 Industrial Product Ideas
0820-683X Toronto Field Naturalist
0820-6848 Prairie Landscape Magazine
0820-7356 C L E M†
0820-7364 N A P O News
0820-8093 National Library of Canada. Technical News *see* 0825-9658
0820-8204 Atlantic Provinces Linguistic Association. Annual Meeting. Papers
0820-8336 Canadian Museum of Flight & Transportation. Museum Newsletter
0820-8344 Canadian Biker Magazine
0820-9006 Arthritis News
0820-9030 Cereals and Oilseeds Review
0820-909X Canadian Social Work Review
0820-9111 Goodwin's†
0820-9189 Phenomenology & Pedagogy
0820-926X Coda Magazine
0820-957X Journal of Small Business - Canada
0820-988X Boreal Institute for Northern Studies. Report of Activities *changed to* Canadian Circumpolar Library. Report of Activities.
0821-0020 B.C. Economic Bulletin†
0821-0160 Take Five†
0821-0306 Investment in Canadian High Technology Companies *changed to* Canadian High Growth Investment Letter.
0821-0314 Persuasions
0821-0705 Education Express
0821-1108 Chorus
0821-1124 Prairie Fire
0821-1272 C U S O Journal†
0821-1310 M H L A Newsletter *see* 0848-9009
0821-1450 C M: Canadian Materials for Schools and Libraries *changed to* C M: A Reviewing Journal of Canadian Materials for Young People.
0821-1809 Torpet
0821-1841 Forintek Review†
0821-2015 HospitAlta
0821-2635 Labour Arbitration
0821-2996 Urban Transit Facts in Canada. Membership Directory
0821-3127 C A S L I S, Calgary Chapter. Newsletter
0821-3275 Markwick Midden
0821-3704 Taxletter
0821-3747 Lemon Aid Bulletin - Auto Conseils *see* 0834-2423
0821-3925 Health News (Toronto)
0821-4425 Essays in Theatre
0821-4689 Egg Producer
0821-5073 Horse Sense *see* 0840-6200
0821-5278 Lethbridge Magazine
0821-5308 Videocom†
0821-5359 Generations (Fredericton)
0821-5758 Doctor's Review
0821-5774 Canada Century Home *see* 0838-9330
0821-5839 Briercrest Echo
0821-5855 Gardening and Leisure Living†
0821-5871 V C C Voice *see* 0822-7896
0821-6320 Ontario Veterinary Association. Update
0821-6371 Truth on Fire *changed to* Hallelujah!
0821-6452 McGill Studies in International Development†
0821-6673 Canadian General Aviation News
0821-6827 Vice Versa Magazine
0821-6916 Pensions and Benefits†
0821-719X Canadian Charter of Rights Decisions
0821-7270 Hellenic News
0821-7610 Inn Business
0822-0603 C A D - C A M & Robotics
0822-0638 Communicating Together
0822-1081 National Banking Review *changed to* National Banking Law Review.
0822-109X Canadian Journal of Insurance Law
0822-207X C I J Bulletin *see* 1184-0641
0822-2363 WindScript
0822-2509 A O S T R A Journal of Research
0822-2517 Yorkview†
0822-2584 National Insolvency Review
0822-3033 Coup de Pouce
0822-4277 Mental Retardation and Learning Disability Bulletin *see* 1184-0412
0822-4706 P.W.A.C. National Newsletter *see* 0845-8499
0822-4749 Choirs Ontario
0822-4838 Operational Geographer
0822-5109 Inform-Action
0822-5435 La Nouvelle Voix de l'Ancait†
0822-5486 Human Communication Canada *see* 0848-1970
0822-5672 En Passant
0822-5745 Ontario Lawyers Weekly *see* 0830-0151
0822-5931 Museum Quarterly
0822-6016 Culture Communique
0822-6377 Our Times Magazine
0822-6709 Canadian Computer Law Reporter
0822-6830 Canadian Banker
0822-6849 Le Banquier
0822-7098 Coulicou
0822-7217 Inuit Arts and Craft†
0822-7284 Franc - Vert
0822-7500 Prairie Sounds
0822-7896 Voice
0822-7942 Nomadic Peoples
0822-8094 Hay Roe's Paper Tree Letter *changed to* Paper Tree Letter.
0822-8426 C H A C Info
0822-8450 Getting There
0822-8523 Trouvez un Nom *see* 0822-8531
0822-8531 En Tete
0822-8558 L'Infirmiere Auxiliaire
0822-8574 Who's Who in Computing
0822-8981 Edmonton Metropolitan Regional Planning Commission. Regional Update *see* 0829-9153
0822-9058 Physiology Canada
0822-9228 Travel Scoop
0823-0269 Sciences et Techniques de l'Eau
0823-0498 Monde du Rock
0823-0552 Fungi Canadenses
0823-065X Canada. Statistics Canada. Private and Public Investment in Canada, Intentions
0823-0668 Canada. Statistics Canada. Private and Public Investment in Canada. Revised Intentions
0823-1133 Corpus Almanac & Canadian Sourcebook
0823-1257 Geology in British Columbia†
0823-1265 Mining in British Columbia *changed to* Engineering and Inspection Annual Report.
0823-1346 Jewellery World
0823-1745 P E G G
0823-1931 International Skyline
0823-2059 Exploration in British Columbia
0823-2105 Canadian Bulletin of Medical History
0823-2229 Quebec Economique International
0823-2490 Nuit Blanche
0823-2601 International Education Forum - Forum de l'Education International *see* 0827-0678
0823-2911 Manitoba Naturalists Society Bulletin
0823-4604 Maine - Anjou International
0823-4744 Current Canadian Ophthalmic Practice *see* 0832-9869
0823-5228 Canadian Chemical News
0823-5651 Mouvements *see* 0710-5568
0823-5708 Temps Libre
0823-5740 C U S O Forum
0823-5872 Financial Position of Ontario Universities
0823-6143 Ontario Recycling Update
0823-6437 Computing Now!
0823-6526 Kick it Over
0823-6542 Thunder Bay Magazine
0823-6720 Alberta Farmagazine *see* 0845-5007
0823-6798 Hospital Products & Technology†
0823-695X In the Middle
0823-6976 International Fur Fashion Review
0823-7689 Central America Update
0823-7867 Nursery Trades B.C. *see* 0847-9763
0823-8294 Videotex World†
0823-8367 Kindred Spirits
0823-8669 Conscience Canada Newsletter
0823-9150 Contemporary Accounting Research
0823-9266 Great Expectations
0823-9304 Protection Officer
0823-9436 Justice Report
0823-9452 T.O.: The Magazine of Toronto
0823-9746 Artsboard
0823-9940 Computers in Education
0824-0469 Marine Mammal Science
0824-0868 2 x 4
0824-1333 Allergy Alert
0824-1600 Biosphere
0824-1767 Charolais Banner
0824-1961 A Friend Indeed
0824-2062 Catalyst (Toronto)
0824-2100 Angles
0824-2119 Forintek Canada Corp., Western Laboratory. Special Publications
0824-2577 Informal Logic
0824-2585 Canadian Cases on the Law of Insurance (2nd Series)
0824-2593 Construction Law Reports
0824-2607 Canadian Cases on Employment Law Reports *changed to* Canadian Cases on Employment Law.
0824-2615 Administrative Law Reports
0824-2623 Canadian Intellectual Property Reports†
0824-2682 Dartmouth Business News
0824-2992 Green's Magazine
0824-3085 Folklore
0824-3298 Man and Nature
0824-3336 Risk Abstracts
0824-3433 Northwest Territories Reports
0824-3441 Optical Prism
0824-3492 Zest
0824-3514 Information Solutions
0824-457X Exchange (Kitchener)
0824-4766 Canada A-Z
0824-4790 Computer Law
0824-4936 L'Estuaire Genealogique
0824-4952 Oil & Gas Report
0824-5053 Journal of Mennonite Studies
0824-5134 University of Alberta. Centre for Criminological Research. Discussion Papers
0824-5487 World of Wheels
0824-5665 R M S News
0824-5991 Ukrainian Cultural and Educational Centre. Visti - News
0824-6017 Footprint
0824-6149 Northwest Prospector Miners and Developers Bulletin *see* 1181-6414
0824-7064 Intellectual Property Journal
0824-717X British Columbia Decisions - Civil Cases
0824-7188 British Columbia Decisions - Municipal Law Cases
0824-7196 British Columbia Decisions - Family Law Cases
0824-720X British Columbia Decisions - Insurance Law Cases
0824-7226 Freewheeler
0824-7242 British Columbia Decisions - Criminal Cases *changed to* British Columbia Decisions - Criminal Conviction and Sentence Cases.
0824-7269 Ontarion Decisions - Criminal Cases *changed to* Ontario Decisions - Criminal Conviction and Sentence Cases.
0824-7277 Alberta Decisions. Rules and Statute Citator
0824-7285 Saskatchewan Decisions - Rules and Statute Citator *changed to* Saskatchewan Decisions Citator.

ISSN

ISSN INDEX 5797

ISSN	Title
0824-7293	Manitoba Decisions - Rules and Statute Citator
0824-734X	Marine Engineering Digest
0824-7528	Eco-Log Canadian Pollution Legislation
0824-7579	Tidepool
0824-7714	Carleton Papers in Applied Language Studies
0824-7749	Special Libraries Association. Eastern Canada Chapter. Bulletin
0824-7870	Der Shmaiser†
0824-7935	Computational Intelligence
0824-8001	C.D. Howe Institute Commentary
0824-801X	Inflation Monitor†
0824-8028	Perspective (Toronto)†
0824-8192	B I N S Bibliographic Series†
0824-8206	British Colombia. Ministry of Agriculture. Greenhouse - Ornamental Production Guide see 1183-5710
0824-8672	Salus†
0824-8818	Realisations Recentes a Petawawa
0824-8907	Canadian Jewish Congress. National Archives Newsletter
0824-9075	Ottawa Magazine
0825-0049	Echec Plus
0825-0170	Canada. National Energy Board. Information Bulletins
0825-0367	T P U G Magazine†
0825-0383	Canadian Journal of Administrative Sciences
0825-0456	International Semiotic Spectrum
0825-1215	Revue d'Entomologie du Quebec
0825-1746	L'Incunable†
0825-1770	Canada. Great Lakes Forestry Centre. Forestry Newsletter changed to Canada. Forestry Canada. Ontario Region. Forestry Newsletter.
0825-1908	Arms Control Chronicle changed to Barometer.
0825-2432	Moving to & Around Winnipeg & Manitoba
0825-2777	Cultures du Canada Francais
0825-3021	Canadian Communications Network Letter
0825-3706	International Business Perspectives changed to Global Business Issues.
0825-3781	Canada. Statistics Canada. Regimes de Pensions en Fiducie - Statistisques Financieres see 0835-4634
0825-3854	Canadian Art
0825-432X	Canada. Statistics Canada. Homicide in Canada: a Statistical Perspective†
0825-4672	Canadian Law Information Council. Dossier†
0825-4729	Classroom†
0825-4982	Business & the Law
0825-5318	Heartwood
0825-592X	Policy Commentary†
0825-6446	British Columbia. Ministry of Energy, Mines and Petroleum Resources. Mineral Resources Branch. Summary of Operations see 0825-6896
0825-6896	British Columbia. Ministry of Energy, Mines and Petroleum Resources. Mineral Resources Division. Summary of Operations
0825-7256	Canadian Intellectual Property Review
0825-7531	Empathic Parenting
0825-754X	Canadian Vet Supplies
0825-799X	Spring Wind see 1181-8360
0825-8422	Dig Time Music Magazine†
0825-8570	Farm Builder of Canada see 0838-9357
0825-8597	Journal of Palliative Care
0825-9224	Canada. Statistics Canada. Provincial and Territorial Government Employment†
0825-9658	Bibliotech†
0825-9895	A E C Q Chantiers
0826-0265	Ottawa Newcomer†
0826-0532	Forest Pest Management Institute. Technical Note Series†
0826-1210	Tribute Goes to the Movies
0826-2713	Aeroscope
0826-3035	County Magazine
0826-3515	Magazine Ressources Humaines see 0846-5274
0826-3663	Canadian Journal of Latin American and Caribbean Studies
0826-4228	C - F A R Newsletter
0826-4392	Plans de Maisons du Quebec
0826-4716	Canadian Journal for Exceptional Children†
0826-4805	Interchange
0826-4864	Association Canadienne-Francaise pour l'Avancement des Sciences. Interface
0826-5003	Windsport
0826-502X	Condominium Magazine see 0849-6714
0826-581X	Environmental Law Centre Newsletter†
0826-5909	Raddle Moon
0826-595X	Building Renovation†
0826-6026	Canadian Civil Aviation
0826-6220	Journal of Pulp & Paper Science
0826-6778	Canadian Critical Care Nursing Journal
0826-6972	Last Issue†
0826-7049	Reclamation Newsletter
0826-7464	Anacrusis
0826-7537	Sport and Fitness Index see 0882-553X
0826-7731	En Ville
0826-7871	Ontario Government Libraries Council. Exchange
0826-791X	Ontario Geological Survey. Exploration Technology Development Fund Grants changed to Ontario Geological Survey. Exploration Technology Development Fund, Summary of Research.
0826-8134	Dictionary of Old English. Publications
0826-8185	International Journal of Robotics and Automation
0826-8193	Transportation Forum†
0826-8207	Montreal Business Forum
0826-8355	Ottawa's Senior Executives Guide changed to Canadian Federal Government Handbook.
0826-8371	Maritime Industries
0826-8754	Administrative Law Journal†
0826-8770	Canadian Industrial Transportation League. Transport Info
0826-8800	Collective Bargaining Information Monthly
0826-8983	Research and Development in the Canadian Corporate Sector changed to R & D Outlook.
0826-9343	C S N D T Journal
0826-9521	Peace Magazine
0826-967X	Border - Lines
0826-9696	Kids Toronto
0826-9726	National Gallery of Canada. Catalogue. Canadian Art. Volume One, A - F
0826-9831	Toronto Journal of Theology
0826-9874	Quebec Pharmacie
0826-9939	C.D. Howe Institute. Policy Review and Outlook
0826-9947	Observation
0827-0074	A M A Newsletter
0827-0325	British Columbia Energy Supply and Requirements Forecast Technical Report see 0832-820X
0827-0333	British Columbia Energy Suppy and Requirements Forecast Summary Report see 0832-820X
0827-0465	The Daily
0827-0678	International Education Magazine
0827-1038	Clinical Biofeedback and Health†
0827-1356	Feuillets du Naturaliste
0827-1364	Cercles des Jeunes Naturalistes. Bulletin de Nouvelles see 0836-0928
0827-1496	Horticulteur changed to Le Producteur Horticole.
0827-150X	Fleur Design
0827-1569	Intercultural Horizons
0827-1704	Canadian Catholic Historical Studies
0827-1755	Maple Orchard
0827-1828	What
0827-1844	Apprentissage et Socialisation en Piste changed to Apprentissage et Socialisation.
0827-2042	B.C. Sport Fishing Magazine
0827-2115	Marketing & Advertising Law Reporter changed to Marketing Law Reporting Service.
0827-2123	Pollution Law Reporting Service
0827-2530	Transactor
0827-2557	Free Flight
0827-262X	Computek
0827-2638	Bowbender
0827-2808	Autoparts Distributor
0827-2824	Island Grower
0827-2921	Prairie Journal
0827-3049	Teaching Today
0827-3480	Construction Law Letter
0827-3669	Carleton-Ottawa Mathematical Lecture Note Series changed to Lecture Notes in Mathematics.
0827-3677	Tax Profile
0827-3715	Canadian Library Yearbook changed to Directory of Libraries in Canada.
0827-4061	Renewable Energy Alerting Data Service†
0827-4266	Weekly Digest of Civil Procedure (2nd Series)
0827-4576	O H & S Canada
0827-4711	Info Presse Canada changed to Info Presse Communications.
0827-4789	Initiative
0827-4916	Shalom Magazine
0827-4932	Online - Onward
0827-5033	Direct Access
0827-522X	York Gazette
0827-5513	Trade Law Topics†
0827-5564	A L A I Servicio Mensual de Informacion y Documentacion Maintainer†
0827-5637	B.C. Fishing Directory & Atlas
0827-570X	Provincial Outlook
0827-5785	Conference Board of Canada. Consumer Attitudes and Buying Intentions changed to Conference Board of Canada. Index of Consumer Attitudes.
0827-5831	
0827-5955	G C N A Bulletin
0827-6277	Conference Board of Canada. Business Attitudes and Investment Spending Intentions changed to Conference Board of Canada. Index of Business Confidence.
0827-6307	Rudnyckiana
0827-6374	Formula 2000 see 0848-8630
0827-7230	Greater Vancouver Japanese Canadian Citizens Association Bulletin
0827-7893	Fraser Forum
0827-7982	Guide Ressources
0827-8911	Eastern Woods & Waters
0828-0584	C I D A Annual Report
0828-0851	Canada. Statistics Canada. Current Economic Indicators see 0835-9148
0828-086X	Canada. Statistics Canada. Quarterly Economic Summary see 0835-9148
0828-0878	Canada. Statistics Canada. Quarterly Economic Summary. Statistical Supplement see 0835-9148
0828-1289	The Idler
0828-1556	Summary of Canadian International Trade
0828-184X	Lonergan Studies Newsletter
0828-1890	10†
0828-1998	Preliminary Statement of Canadian International Trade
0828-203X	Health Career Post
0828-2773	Museum News and Views from the Nova Scotia Museum Complex
0828-282X	Canadian Journal of Cardiology
0828-2897	Canada. Statistics Canada. Surface and Marine Transport.
0828-2919	British Columbia Population Forecast
0828-301X	Connections
0828-3192	Archivy
0828-3907	Saskatchewan Indian Federated College Journal
0828-4083	Grail
0828-4253	Up Here
0828-4466	Hilborn's Family Newsletter Directory
0828-4474	Canada Tomorrow
0828-4539	Table Tennis Technical†
0828-4679	Horse Industry Directory of Canada
0828-4989	Monde Juridique
0828-525X	Info Outlook (Year)
0828-5721	Invest Canada
0828-5748	Catholic Health Association of Canada. Directory
0828-5802	Rites
0828-6094	British Columbia Exploration Review see 0846-0051
0828-6116	Aftermarket Canada
0828-6299	What they Say about Forestry on the Hill changed to Forestry on the Hill.
0828-6833	Ordre des Comptables Agrees du Quebec. Bilans
0828-6868	I S E R Research and Policy Papers
0828-6914	Canadian Pharmaceutical Journal
0828-7090	Humane Medicine
0828-7198	Indicator
0828-7252	Canadian Human Rights Advocate†
0828-7600	Charolais Connection
0828-797X	Interculture
0828-7988	Greenpeace Examiner see 0899-0190
0828-8089	Magazine P M E
0828-8208	Canada. Statistics Canada. Air Charter Statistics
0828-8259	Canadian Horticultural History
0828-8496	Next Exit
0828-864X	Equinews
0828-8666	Humanomics
0828-8720	Le Depanneur see 0002-5410
0828-8755	Calgary STAMPede
0828-9344	Aviation Today
0828-9522	Resource: The Canadian Journal of Real Estate†
0828-9824	Canada. Statistics Canada. Communications and Other Electronic Industries†
0828-9832	Jewellery and Precious Metal Industries see 0835-0191
0828-9867	Canada. Statistics Canada. Sawmills and Planing Mill and Shingle Mill Products Industries see 0835-0078
0828-9913	Canada. Statistics Canada. Wire and Wire Products Industries see 0835-0124
0828-9921	Canada. Statistics Canada. Ornamental and Architectural Metal Products Industry see 0835-0124
0828-9999	Revue Quebecois de Droit International
0829-0067	Rumors†
0829-0547	Western Canadian Anthropologist
0829-075X	Canadian Co-operative Wool Growers Magazine
0829-0784	Artpost Magazine
0829-0857	Periodical Writers Association of Canada. Directory of Members
0829-0865	Periodical Writers Association of Canada. Magazine Markets and Fees
0829-0938	L'Agent 03 see 1183-0824
0829-1055	C A H P E R Keeps In Touch see 0848-1733
0829-1411	Le Producteur Laitier
0829-1756	Canada. Statistics Canada. Passenger Bus and Urban Transit Statistics
0829-2019	National Creditor - Debtor Review
0829-2132	Canadian Aviation News
0829-254X	C A A T Tracks
0829-2558	Metropolitan Toronto Business and Market Guide
0829-2906	C Magazine
0829-2930	Corinthian Horse Sport
0829-3120	Weekly Stock Charts - Canadian Industrial Companies see 0830-1972
0829-3139	Weekly Stock Charts - Canadian Resource Companies
0829-3163	Canada. Statistics Canada. Honey Production and Value, Production Forecast†
0829-318X	Tree Physiology
0829-3198	Quebec Yachting et Voile see 0833-918X
0829-3201	Canadian Journal of Law and Society

ISSN INDEX

ISSN	Title
0829-3279	Sea Kayaker
0829-3309	Campus Canada
0829-3384	Xtra!
0829-352X	Wastewater Technology Centre Newsletter
0829-3716	Sports Business
0829-4003	Canadian Treasury Management Review
0829-4321	Alberta Association of College Librarians. Newsletter
0829-4437	A G O News
0829-4488	Asia Pacific Business
0829-4666	Gospel Herald
0829-4747	Face to Face with Talent
0829-4763	Wheatgrower
0829-4801	Agenda
0829-4836	Canadian Journal of Marketing Research
0829-4887	Canadian Programmable Control Conference and Exhibition. Conference Proceedings
0829-4909	University of Toronto. Institute for Policy Analysis. Working Paper Series
0829-4976	From My Bookshelf
0829-5026	Canadian West
0829-5247	A Fleur de Pot†
0829-5344	Canadian Folk Music Bulletin
0829-5425	University Computing and Information Services Newsletter
0829-5476	Juriste
0829-559X	B.S.D.A. News
0829-5654	Wedding Bells Magazine
0829-609X	Contributions to Natural Science
0829-6340	Ontario Nursing Home Journal see 0847-5520
0829-7010	Tyro Magazine†
0829-7274	Canadian Video Marketing see 0836-6055
0829-772X	Civic Public Works
0829-7762	Verve changed to You - Living With Verve.
0829-7975	British Columbia. Provincial Government. Provincial Report see 1180-0429
0829-7983	Cap-aux-Diamants
0829-8033	Les Laurentides
0829-8157	Trade Asia Magazine
0829-8203	Ontario Geological Survey. Summary of Field Work
0829-8211	Biochemistry and Cell Biology
0829-8297	Geroniont†
0829-8351	Nickel
0829-8416	Canadian Outlook
0829-8564	Compleat Mother
0829-8629	Canadian Government Buyer changed to Government Business.
0829-8726	Bead Forum
0829-8777	Canadian Magazine Index
0829-8815	Entourage
0829-9153	Edmonton Metropolitan Regional Planning Commission. Metro Planning Review
0829-9242	Applied Arts Quarterly changed to Applied Arts.
0829-948X	University of Waterloo Bibliography Series
0829-9552	Canadian Women's Periodicals: Title Word Index changed to Canadian Women's Periodicals Index.
0829-9676	Habitat 2000
0829-982X	Azure Magazine
0829-9889	Housewares Canada
0830-0151	The Lawyers Weekly
0830-0348	World Review of Doulton†
0830-0445	Journal of Distance Education
0830-0593	Canadian Thoroughbred
0830-0739	Okanagan History
0830-0763	Non-Wage Provisions in Saskatchewan Collective Agreements
0830-0895	Chef du Service Alimentaire
0830-1417	Network (Calgary)
0830-1808	Atlantic Trucking
0830-1972	Weekly Stock Charts - Canadian and U S Industrial Companies
0830-8284	Wilderness Alberta
0830-8535	Greater Winnipeg Business Magazine
0830-8721	Guitar Canada
0830-8810	Industrial Maintenance Repair and Overhaul News
0830-887X	Journal des Pates et Papiers
0830-9000	Canadian Journal of Veterinary Research
0830-9434	Epson Today†
0830-9442	Ontario Advisory Council on Women's Issues. Annual Report
0830-9507	Corporate & Commercial Aviation see 0828-9344
0831-0041	Telecom Bulletin changed to Clarkson, Tetrault Regulatory Reporter - Telecom.
0831-0114	Quebec ce Mois-ci
0831-0122	Journal Industriel du Quebec
0831-019X	Alberta Oil & Gas Directory
0831-0254	Network (Toronto)†
0831-067X	En Voyage
0831-0785	Son Hi-Fi Video
0831-0998	Practical Allergy & Immunology
0831-1161	Parcs Industriels Municipaux
0831-1846	Peace & Security
0831-1919	Breakthrough!
0831-2338	Prairie Farmers Catalogue
0831-2478	R R T: the Canadian Journal of Respiratory Therapy
0831-2559	Border Crossings
0831-2796	Genome
0831-2893	Canadian Academy of Sport Medicine Review see 1050-642X
0831-3016	Saskatchewan Library Association. Forum
0831-3040	M S O S Journal
0831-3377	Feminist Action
0831-3482	Securities and Corporate Regulation Review
0831-3881	C M A
0831-4020	Canadian Environmental Mediation Newsletter
0831-4039	Ven'd'Est
0831-4160	Toronto Business Magazine
0831-4268	International Conservative Insight†
0831-4306	Environmental Notes from the National Capital†
0831-4411	J A S M U
0831-4446	Eastern Synod Lutheran
0831-4462	Canadian Bulletin of Cardiovascular Nursing see 0843-6096
0831-4527	Canadian Free Trader
0831-4535	Canadian Employment and Equality Rights
0831-4853	OptionProfits†
0831-4926	C C S Focus
0831-5000	Geotechnical Science Laboratories. Publications, Reports, and Theses
0831-5175	Film Canada Yearbook
0831-5183	Directory of the Canadian Horse Industry
0831-5477	Bottom Line
0831-5671	Algonquian Conference. Papers
0831-5698	Canadian Social Trends
0831-6279	C M T Newsletter
0831-6309	Who's Who in Canadian Film and Television (Year)
0831-6503	Blue Chart Report
0831-6708	Inuit Art Quarterly
0831-7313	Canada. Statistics Canada. List of Canadian Hospitals†
0831-7445	Perspectives (Toronto)
0831-7496	City of Ottawa. Corporate Financial and Statistical Information
0831-7682	Canadian Paediatric Society. News Bulletin
0831-8093	Saint Mary's University. Atlantic Region Geographical Studies
0831-8107	Saint Mary's University. Occasional Papers in Geography
0831-8530	Health and Nutrition Update
0831-8603	Machinery & Equipment M R O
0831-9138	Canadian Travel Press Weekly
0831-9227	Amnesty International. Canadian Section (English Speaking). Bulletin
0831-9502	Contemporary Verse Two
0832-0136	Counterplay
0832-1191	Faith Today
0832-1418	Action Bulletin see 0831-3377
0832-1515	Electronic Times changed to Canadian Electronics.
0832-1590	Canadian Bible Society Quarterly Newsletter
0832-1655	Forest Planning Canada
0832-1922	Lang Van
0832-235X	Commercial Law Digest†
0832-2546	Ottawa Business News
0832-512X	Masthead
0832-5189	Clansman (Halifax)
0832-5332	O S M T Update
0832-5642	Nouveau Masculin see 0843-6665
0832-6002	Flabbergast†
0832-6096	Manitoba Medicine
0832-610X	Canadian Journal of Anaesthesia
0832-6215	Canada. Grain Commission. Economics and Statistics Division. Exports of Canadian Grain and Wheat Flour
0832-6266	Saint Mary's University. Studies in Marine and Coastal Geography
0832-638X	Information - Logiciel see 0847-4915
0832-6509	Gardener's Guide to Pest Prevention and Control in the Home and Garden
0832-655X	Canadian Statistics Index
0832-6614	New Biotech†
0832-6657	Canada. Statistics Canada. Community Colleges and Related Institutions, Postsecondary Enrollment and Graduates
0832-6673	Focus on International Joint Commission Activities
0832-6770	Sante
0832-6983	Canadian Family Law Quarterly
0832-7009	Herpetoculturist
0832-705X	Farm Business†
0832-722X	Canadian Aquaculture changed to Northern Aquaculture.
0832-7424	University of Ottawa. Alumni and Development. Alumni News
0832-7475	Bulletin I R P
0832-7556	Contact (Quebec)
0832-7580	Leaking Underground Storage Tank Newsletter†
0832-7688	Commercial Insolvency Reporter
0832-7912	Policy Study
0832-8196	Performance†
0832-820X	British Columbia Energy Supply and Requirements Forecast Update
0832-8609	Contributions to Human History
0832-865X	Directory of the Arts
0832-8722	Banking and Finance Law Review
0832-8781	Canadian Journal of Women and the Law
0832-9028	Canada's Office Automation Magazine changed to Office Systems & Technology.
0832-932X	New Canadian Review
0832-9354	Resource
0832-9656	Fusion Magazine
0832-9869	Ophthalmic Practice
0832-9966	Le Beffroi
0833-0026	M T L Montreal
0833-0123	Focus on Canadian Municipal Assessment and Taxation
0833-0247	Sans Frontieres - Les Forces Psychologiques
0833-031X	Houseplant Forum see 1061-4079
0833-0530	L'Orientation
0833-0689	Timberlines
0833-076X	Infection Control Canada†
0833-0816	Community Action
0833-0867	Alberta's Fishing & Hunting Magazine
0833-0891	Fine Art & Auction Review
0833-093X	Native Press changed to Press Independent.
0833-1103	Select Home Designs
0833-1146	Creative Leap International Newsletter
0833-1235	Canadian Journal of Sport Sciences
0833-1278	Without Prejudice
0833-1677	Research Money
0833-1731	Ontario. Ministry of Municipal Affairs. Annual Report
0833-174X	Canadian Food Trade Directory & Buyers Guide
0833-2002	Canada. Statistics Canada. Communications and Energy Wire and Cable Industry†
0833-3831	Dannzha
0833-4447	Insight on Collectables
0833-448X	EcoAlert
0833-4536	University of Toronto Alumni Magazine see 0840-562X
0833-5540	Forest Pest Management Institute. Information Report Series
0833-7594	Health Promotion
0833-823X	Earthkeeping see 1183-630X
0833-8264	Canadian Dental Assistants Association. Journal
0833-8388	Association de la Construction de Montreal et du Quebec. Bulletin
0833-918X	Quebec Yachting, Voile et Moteur
0833-921X	Journal Barreau
0833-9406	Contract Magazine
0833-9570	Stereo - Video Guide
0834-0110	Standardbred News
0834-0161	Travel Destination Canada, Meetings and Conventions see 0834-017X
0834-017X	Destination Canada Meetings and Conventions†
0834-020X	Business News
0834-0242	Outlook
0834-0471	Agent Canada
0834-1494	Canadian Dental Hygienists Association. Probe
0834-1508	C H W Letter
0834-1516	Canadian Journal of Program Evaluation
0834-1648	University of Toronto. Computer Systems Research Institute. Technical Reports
0834-1915	Canadian Association for Health, Physical Education and Recreation. Journal
0834-2008	Ontario Forestry Association. Newsletter
0834-213X	Alberta Home Economics Association Newsletter
0834-2423	Lemon Aid Magazine
0834-2466	Catalyst (Vancouver)
0834-2520	Costume Society of Ontario. Newsletter
0834-258X	Travel China Newsletter
0834-292X	Worklife Report
0834-3136	Nova Scotia Craft News
0834-3160	Dietetique en Action
0834-325X	Canadian Camping†
0834-3357	Canadian Property Management
0834-3365	Food Store Magazine†
0834-3543	Lifelines (Toronto)
0834-3586	Leads
0834-406X	Canada. Canadian Forestry Service - Maritimes, Fredericton, New Brunswick. Information Report M-X changed to Canada. Forestry Canada - Maritimes Region, Fredericton, New Brunswick. Information Report M-X.
0834-4612	Computer Dealer News
0834-809X	Performance Racing News
0834-9096	Canadian Aberdeen-Angus News see 0849-6188
0834-969X	New Catalyst
0834-9789	I C A E News
0834-9797	Cargo Express
0835-0000	Canada. Statistics Canada. Food Industries
0835-0019	Canada. Statistics Canada. Beverage and Tobacco Products Industries
0835-0027	Canada. Statistics Canada. Rubber and Plastic Products Industries
0835-006X	Canada. Statistics Canada. Clothing Industries
0835-0078	Canada. Statistics Canada. Wood Industries
0835-0094	Canada. Statistics Canada. Paper and Allied Products Industries
0835-0116	Canada. Statistics Canada. Primary Metal Industries
0835-0124	Canada. Statistics Canada. Fabricated Metal Products Industries

ISSN INDEX 5799

ISSN	Title
0835-0167	Canada. Statistics Canada. Non-Metallic Mineral Products Industries
0835-0191	Canada. Statistics Canada. Other Manufacturing Industries
0835-0213	Ontario. Ministry of Housing. Annual Report
0835-0264	Zymergy†
0835-0310	Paddler
0835-0620	Markham - York Region Business Journal *see* 1183-2231
0835-0663	Toronto Office Guide
0835-0752	Forest Resource Development Agreement Report
0835-0760	British Colombia. Ministry of Agriculture Fisheries and Food. Greenhouse Vegetable Production Guide *see* 0840-8068
0835-0892	Jurisfemme
0835-0906	Canada. Statistics Canada. Farm Products Price Index
0835-0949	Heritage Communicator
0835-1031	Canada. Statistics Canada. Mechanical Trade Contractors
0835-104X	Canada. Statistics Canada. Electrical Trade Contractors
0835-1058	Canada. Statistics Canada. Highway, Road, Street and Bridge Contractors
0835-1066	Canada. Statistics Canada. Non-Residential General Contractors and Developers
0835-1473	Real Travel
0835-1740	Octane
0835-1791	Global Plastics Report†
0835-2003	Caravan
0835-2372	Main Street: the Municipal and Regional Development Magazine
0835-2399	Review of International Business Law *changed to* Canada - U S Business Law Review.
0835-2445	Kola
0835-2526	Designs
0835-2933	Stone and Cox Life Insurance Tables
0835-3069	Medical Psychotherapy
0835-3271	T L C...For Plants
0835-3336	Asia Horizon Azie†
0835-3565	Clik
0835-359X	Cosmetics Beauty Guide
0835-3743	Les Expos†
0835-3808	Immigration Law Reporter. Second Series
0835-3859	A I B C Newsletter *changed to* A A B C Newsletter.
0835-3913	Career Options
0835-4014	Play and Parenting Connections
0835-412X	Christian Week
0835-4162	Passion Magazine
0835-4170	Hotel Amenities in Canada
0835-4251	Small Business World Magazine
0835-4375	Profile *changed to* Canadian Ski Pro Canadien.
0835-4545	Contemporary Radiology†
0835-4634	Canada. Statistics Canada. Trusteed Pension Funds - Financial Statistics
0835-4685	Alberta Film and Literary Arts Bulletin *changed to* Working Title.
0835-5134	Industrial Specialties News
0835-5509	Equine Research Centre Newsletter
0835-5533	Canada. Statistics Canada. Shipping in Canada
0835-5592	Market & Waterfront
0835-6203	Bedside Specialist *see* 0843-9966
0835-636X	Ontario Family Law Reporter
0835-6378	U - Choose: A Guide to Homes for Seniors in Canada (Ontario Edition)
0835-6386	U - Choose: A Guide to Homes for Seniors in Canada (Eastern - Atlantic Province Edition)
0835-6394	U - Choose: A Guide to Homes for Seniors in Canada (Western Edition)
0835-6742	Canadian Journal of Administrative Law & Practice
0835-6955	International Newsletter of Maritime History
0835-6963	Canadian Maritime Bibliography
0835-7099	Journal of Pre-Raphaelite & Aesthetic Studies†
0835-7447	Bowbender Magazine's Hunting Annual (Year)†
0835-7560	American & World Intellectual Property Report
0835-7641	Etc. Montreal
0835-7900	Canadian Journal of Gastroenterology
0835-7919	Safarir
0835-8044	Hockey Coaching Journal
0835-8087	National Labour Review†
0835-8672	A Rayons Ouverts
0835-8702	Le Belle Age
0835-9148	Canada. Statistics Canada. Canadian Economic Observer
0835-9245	Canadian Corporate Law Reporter†
0835-9423	New Weekly Magazine
0835-9628	Persuasions, Occasional Papers
0835-9768	Canadian Current Law
0835-9776	Canadian Citations
0836-0073	Free Materials for Schools and Libraries
0836-0472	New Times
0836-057X	National Property Review *changed to* National Real Property Review.
0836-0618	Leslie L. Schaffer Lectureship in Forest Science
0836-0782	Canadian Telecom
0836-0820	Trade Monitor†
0836-0839	Intersections (Montreal, 1987)
0836-0928	Les Naturalistes†
0836-0960	Canadian Shareowner
0836-1002	Film - Video Canadiana
0836-1355	Equine Employment and Education Guide
0836-1398	Physics Essays
0836-1509	Alberta Transportation and Utilities
0836-1525	Ontario. Ministry of Labour. Library. Infolink
0836-1630	Autopinion
0836-205X	Tourisme Plus, le Journal des Voyages
0836-3102	Au Pays de Matane
0836-320X	Alpine Garden Club of British Columbia. Monthly Bulletin
0836-3463	A C M C Forum
0836-3587	Micro-Gazette
0836-3803	Interior Design Ontario
0836-3862	Luggage, Leathergoods & Accessories
0836-4796	B.C. Woman to Woman Magazine
0836-4958	Directory of Trade and Professional Associations in Metropolitan Toronto *changed to* Directory of Trade and Professional Associations in the Toronto Region.
0836-6055	Video Marketing
0836-6527	Canada Computes!†
0836-6632	University of New Brunswick Law Journal
0836-6853	Logibase
0836-6942	Magazine Affaires Plus
0836-7094	Socialist Worker
0836-7221	Pro - Choice News
0836-7272	Emergency Prehospital Medicine
0836-7353	Travel a la Carte
0836-7515	Match News
0837-5771	Emergency Preparedness Digest
0837-6239	Welcome to the Best of Toronto & Ontario Guide
0838-0007	Canadian Automobile Association. Public Policy Newsletter *changed to* Canadian Automobile Association. C A A Public Policy.
0838-0015	Guide de la Route: La Floride
0838-0023	Guide de la Route: L'Ontario
0838-0163	Transactor for the Amiga
0838-018X	Contact (Montreal)
0838-0341	New Freeman
0838-0430	Journal of Baha'i Studies
0838-1313	Dance Connection
0838-1658	Gallerie: Women Artists Monographs
0838-1674	Option Serre
0838-1895	Beautiful British Columbia Magazine's Guidebook†
0838-1925	Allergy & Clinical Immunology News
0838-1933	British Columbia. Ministry of Environment and Parks. Annual Report *see* 1181-8336
0838-200X	Poetry Halifax Dartmouth
0838-228X	Canadian H R Reporter
0838-2395	Cottage Life
0838-2638	Nova Scotia Medical Journal
0838-2875	Education and Law Journal
0838-2913	Leisure Ontario *changed to* Leisure World.
0838-2948	Canadian Journal of Nursing Administration
0838-360X	Library Footnotes
0838-3693	New Brunswick. Department of Health and Community Services. Annual Report
0838-3715	Family Expenditure in Canada
0838-3871	Nuclear Sector Focus†
0838-3898	Family Food Expenditure in Canada
0838-391X	Alpha Beat Soup
0838-3952	Canada. Statistics Canada. International Travel
0838-4061	Sport & Leisure†
0838-4096	Winter Cities
0838-4185	Woodworking
0838-438X	Business ComputerNews
0838-4401	Sommets
0838-4479	Recherches Feministes
0838-4517	Paideusis
0838-4525	Scrutiny
0838-4711	Journal of Indigenous Studies
0838-5416	Expediteur
0838-5467	Canada West Travel News
0838-5505	Island Parent Magazine
0838-5610	Vehicule des Conducteurs Proprietaires
0838-5769	Timely Disclosure
0838-5777	New Biotech Business
0838-5785	New Bioresources *changed to* Canadian Plant Biotech News.
0838-603X	Fuse Magazine
0838-6536	Y Triangle
0838-6749	Underpass
0838-6838	Le Magazine Voyages Plus†
0838-6900	Avenir *see* 0846-5274
0838-7176	Voices
0838-7249	Lethbridge Historical Society Newletter
0838-9330	Century Home
0838-9357	Rural Construction†
0838-9446	Femme Plus
0838-9535	Electronic Composition & Imaging
0838-9624	Paragraph
0839-1041	Experts
0839-1289	Microlog: Canadian Research Index
0839-1335	Visitor's Magazine
0839-1416	Le Monde
0839-2188	Financial Times of Canada
0839-4539	Law Reform Commission of Saskatchewan. Annual Report and Review
0839-4555	Centre d'Etudes de l'Asie de l'Est. Cahiers
0839-458X	Revue Andre Malraux Review
0839-6434	New Brunswick. Department of Tourism, Recreation and Heritage. Annual Report†
0839-9506	Canada. Investment Canada. Annual Report
0840-3929	Computer Paper
0840-4313	Visual Media
0840-4348	Home Builder Magazine
0840-4445	The Edge
0840-4496	Fifty-Five Plus
0840-4666	Canada. Environment Canada. Sustainable Development†
0840-5425	John Deutsch Institute for the Study of Economic Policy. Discussion Paper Series
0840-5492	Okanagan Life Magazine
0840-562X	University of Toronto Magazine
0840-5662	North American Environment†
0840-6014	Canada, A Portrait
0840-612X	On Balance
0840-6154	C I R P A Newsletter
0840-6189	Borealis
0840-6200	Canadian Horseman
0840-6235	University Computing Systems Dispatch
0840-6286	Eighteenth-Century Fiction
0840-6529	Health Reports
0840-657X	Actif
0840-6715	Horsepower
0840-7061	C C R Business Review
0840-707X	Plowman
0840-7428	Bulletin d'Information sur l'Entretien et l'Amenagement des Espaces Verts *see* 0846-5339
0840-7681	Royal British Columbia Museum. Special Publications
0840-7738	Bridging the Gap
0840-7754	Journal of Motor Vehicle Law
0840-8068	British Columbia. Ministry of Agriculture Fisheries and Food. Nursery Greenhouse Vegetable and Ornamental Production Guide for Commercial Growers
0840-8130	Idees de ma Maison
0840-8173	Computer Words
0840-8289	AgriScience
0840-8688	Canadian Journal of Electrical and Computer Engineering
0840-8750	Perspectives on Labour and Income
0840-9137	Investment Executive
0840-9153	Cablecaster
0840-9269	Education Forum
0840-9331	Association of Canadian Map Libraries and Archives. Bulletin
0840-9455	Directory of Gas Distribution, Transmission and Production Companies *changed to* Directory of Natural Gas Company Operations.
0840-9803	Proem Canada
0840-982X	Journal of Child and Youth Care
0841-1956	Corporate Ethics Monitor†
0841-209X	Canola Guide
0841-2650	Streetsound
0841-8233	C I S M Journal A C S G
0841-9574	Teacher (Vancouver)
0842-1935	Secretaire Moderne
0842-1951	Direction Informatique
0842-5132	Wildflower
0842-9707	Metropolitan Toronto Reference Library. News
0842-9960	Maitres
0843-140X	Corpo Clip
0843-1566	Outbound
0843-1736	Chastity and Holiness Magazine
0843-2635	Physical Education Digest
0843-4247	Canadian Journal of Dermatology
0843-4255	Canadian Journal of Ob-Gyn *see* 1183-2517
0843-4263	Canadian Journal of Pediatrics
0843-4379	Energy Studies Review
0843-445X	Dreams & Visions
0843-4557	T G - Voices of Today's Generation
0843-459X	Landmark
0843-462X	Am-Can Report
0843-5049	Australian and New Zealand Studies in Canada
0843-5081	Ontario Today *changed to* Education Today.
0843-5383	Royal British Columbia Museum Memoirs
0843-5499	Beads
0843-5634	Crest
0843-5812	University of Toronto Dental Journal
0843-5901	O H L A Newsletter *changed to* O H L A Newsline.
0843-5995	Forum
0843-6096	Canadian Journal of Cardiovascular Nursing
0843-6142	Index to Statistics Canada Surveys and Questionnaires
0843-6509	Canada. Canadian International Trade Tribunal Bulletin
0843-6533	Ontario. Ministry of Agriculture and Food. Grain Letter
0843-6665	Votre Succes
0843-6673	Canadian Area Development
0843-6681	Montreal Office Guide
0843-6827	Revue de la Cinematheque
0843-6924	Shem Tov
0843-7076	Law Office Management Journal
0843-7092	Third Degree (Regina)

0843-7165 Hearts
0843-7343 Electricity Today
0843-7394 Yule Log
0843-7602 Christian Vision
0843-7777 Ateliers
0843-7815 Above & Beyond
0843-8021 B C Dairy Directory
0843-803X Vision Interface Conference Proceedings - Compte Rendu
0843-8048 Queen's Alumni Review
0843-8439 Canadian Criminal Justice Association. Bulletin
0843-8714 International Journal of Maritime History
0843-8838 Site Sound
0843-9117 Journal of Applied Recreation Research
0843-9214 Moving to Greater Hamilton and the Golden Triangle *changed to* Moving to Greater Hamilton, C.T.T., Brantford & Niagara.
0843-9303 Hazardous Materials Management
0843-9583 Canadian Conference of the Arts. Arts News
0843-9613 Canadian Cattle Buyer
0843-9753 Algorithm
0843-9966 Care Connection
0844-2487 Habitabec Quebec
0844-3459 Muir's Original Log Home Guide for Builders & Buyers
0844-3718 S I E C C A N Journal
0844-3955 Stat
0844-479X Musicien Quebecois
0844-5303 Ontario Sheep News
0844-5753 Happenings
0844-5982 Retirement Lifestyle Publication
0844-8353 Canada. Statistics Canada. Imports, Merchandise Trade H S Based
0844-8361 Canada. Statistics Canada. Exports, Merchandise Trade H S Based
0845-4213 Plant - Canada's Industrial Newsletter
0845-4531 Radiocomm in Canada
0845-471X Ontario's Common Ground Magazine
0845-4795 Crosstalk and Anglican Journal Episcopal
0845-5007 Alberta Farm and Ranch Magazine
0845-5341 Renew
0845-8081 Tableau
0845-8499 P.W.A.Contact
0845-8901 Prime Life Magazine
0845-9320 J D Q: Journal Dentaire du Quebec
0845-972X Fraser Valley Magazine
0845-9738 Coquitlam Magazine
0845-9762 Richmond Magazine
0845-9770 Victoria Magazine
0846-0051 British Columbia Mineral Exploration Review
0846-5274 Magazine Avenir
0846-5339 Espaces Verts
0846-6629 Canada. Canadian International Trade Tribunal. Annual Report
0847-0510 Canada and International Relations
0847-0529 Pacific Maritime Studies Series
0847-0537 Pioneers of British Columbia
0847-1525 B C Economic and Statistical Review
0847-1541 Environmental Eye
0847-1622 Semiotic Review of Books
0847-1762 Windhorse Review
0847-1797 D W D Newsletter
0847-2157 Diagnostic Cardiology
0847-2165 Logibase: Directory of Quebec Software
0847-2386 Business World
0847-2645 Papetieres du Quebec
0847-2823 Who's Succeeding†
0847-2831 Report on Business Canada Company Handbook
0847-3234 Child Care Focus
0847-3390 Spirit
0847-3463 Canadian Gardening
0847-3471 International Journal of Indian Studies
0847-3536 Universities Telephone Directory (Year)
0847-3668 Directory of Services for Victims of Crime
0847-4915 Info-Log Magazine
0847-5083 Law Times
0847-527X Directory of Certified Appliances and Accessories
0847-5520 Canadian Nursing Home Journal
0847-8538 Blue Line Magazine
0847-9097 Adbusters Quarterly
0847-9283 Canadian R V Trade†
0847-947X Canadian Emergency News
0847-9763 Hort West
0847-978X Anglican Journal
0847-9984 Horse Chronicle
0848-1512 Victorian Review
0848-1733 In Touch (Glouchester)
0848-1741 Servant Magazine
0848-1970 Journal of Speech Language Pathology and Audiology
0848-323X Designer's Choice *see* 1180-4971
0848-600X N B C - N F C News
0848-8002 Canadian Laboratory *see* 0712-6875
0848-8142 World of Beef *changed to* Alberta Beef.
0848-8630 Formula
0848-8851 N B I A News
0848-9009 M H L A News
0849-035X V O, Vie Ouvriere
0849-0767 Canadian Printer
0849-0899 McMaster Journal of Theology
0849-1089 Education et Francophonie
0849-1836 Ottawa Business Magazine *changed to* Ottawa Business Quarterly.
0849-3154 P T I C Bulletin
0849-3383 Nurse to Nurse
0849-5009 Veterinarian Magazine
0849-5696 Georgian Bay Today
0849-5858 Association of Manitoba Museums. Newsletter
0849-6188 Angus Times
0849-6714 Condominium
0850-010X Senegal. Archives du Senegal. Rapport Annuel
0850-1602 Senegal. Centre de Recherche Oceanographique. Document Scientifique
0850-1807 Politicien
0850-3907 Africa Development
0850-4008 Register Development Research Projects Africa
0850-430X West African Archivist†
0850-8194 Vivre Autrement
0850-8518 African Environment
0850-8526 African Environment. Occasional Papers - Etudes et Recherches
0851-0016 Index Documentation - Economie - Science - Technique
0851-0458 Economie et Socialisme
0851-0865 Morocco. Direction de la Statistique. Etudes Economiques et Statistiques
0851-089X Annuaire Statistique du Maroc
0851-092X Morocco. Direction de la Statistique. Population Active Urbaine, Rapport de Synthese
0851-0954 Morocco. Direction de la Statistique. Indice des Prix a la Production Industrielle, Energetique et Miniere
0851-0962 Morocco. Direction de la Statistique. Indice du Cout de la Vie
0851-0970 Morocco. Direction de la Statistique. Indice des Prix de Gros
0851-0989 Conjoncture Economique au Maroc *see* 0851-9722
0851-1128 Islam Today
0851-1934 Banque Nationale pour le Developpement Economique. Rapport Annuel
0851-5921 Conjoncture Economique *see* 0851-9722
0851-6804 Morocco. Direction de la Statistique. Population Active Urbaine, Resultats Detailles
0851-9722 Etudes de Conjoncture: Evolutions et Tendances
0852-0321 Pusat Penelitian Perkebunan Gula Indonesia. Berita
0852-0747 Edisi Chusus Bulletin Koperasi
0852-596X Foto Media
0853-0300 Nova
0855-0174 A A U Newsletter
0855-0328 Ghana Medical Journal
0855-0417 Ghana Commercial Bank. Quarterly Economic Review
0856-0005 Educational Abstracts for Tanzania
0856-003X Tanzania National Bibliography
0856-0048 Africa Theological Journal
0856-0056 African Review
0856-0080 T P R I Bulletin
0856-0129 Mulika
0856-017X Tanzania News Review
0856-0323 Gazette of the United Republic of Tanzania
0856-0366 Home Builders Journal†
0856-0374 Tanzania. Bureau of Standards. Announcer
0856-0382 Rasilimali
0856-0455 East Africana Accessions Bulletin
0856-048X Kiswahili
0856-0498 Mapinduzi Katika Uandishi *see* 0856-1982
0856-0560 Studies in Adult Education
0856-065X Tanzanian Mathematical Bulletin
0856-101X Bank of Tanzania. Economic Bulletin
0856-1109 Journal of Adult Education
0856-1222 Ngao
0856-1435 Uongori: Journal of Management Development
0856-1621 Tanzania Library Service. Occasional Paper
0856-1761 Tanzania Journal of Science
0856-1982 Kipepeo
0856-2172 Tanzania Industrial Studies and Consulting Organisation. Annual Report and Accounts
0856-2423 Tanzania Investment Bank. Annual Report
0856-2539 Tanzania. Bureau of Standards. Director's Annual Report
0856-3152 Uhandisi
0856-3349 Azania News
0857-0361 S E A M E O Quarterly
0857-0760 Peace Progress
0857-1155 Thai Industrial Directory
0857-1163 Secretaries Year Book
0857-1554 Buffalo Journal
0857-2143 Journal of Demography
0857-2410 Agrometeorological Report
0857-2984 Thailand Industrial Buyer's Guide
0857-4499 A I T Reports and Publications on Renewable Energy Resources. Abstracts *see* 0857-6181
0857-6173 R E R I C International Energy Journal
0857-6181 A I T Reports and Publications on Energy. Abstracts
0857-7277 Thailand Company Information (Year)
0857-9067 Statistical Yearbook of Thailand
0857-9164 Thailand. National Statistical Office. Annotated Statistical Bibliography
0857-9466 Statistical Handbook of Thailand
0857-9482 Thailand. National Statistical Office. Quarterly Bulletin of Statistics
0858-0391 Survey of Migration in Bangkok Metropolis
0858-1088 Phuket Marine Biological Center. Research Bulletin
0858-1630 Directory of Scientific and Technical Libraries in Thailand
0858-1886 Statistical Budget and Activities in Thailand
0858-2696 Thailand. National Statistical Office. Annual Report
0860-0007 Fasciculi Archaeologiae Historicae
0860-0023 Poznan Fair Magazine
0860-0066 Lituano-Slavica Posnaniensia
0860-0074 Politechnika Slaska. Zeszyty Naukowe. Architektura
0860-0082 Politechnika Lodzka. Zeszyty Naukowe. Informatyka
0860-0260 Akademia Gorniczo-Hutnicza im. Stanislawa Staszica. Zeszyty Naukowe. Fizyka
0860-0783 Politechnika Krakowska. Zeszyty Naukowe. Transport *changed to* Politechnika Krakowska. Zeszyty Naukowe. Inzynieria Transportowa i Elektryczna.
0860-1046 Wyzsza Szkola Pedagogiczna im. Komisji Edukacji Narodowej w Krakowie. Rocznik Naukowo-Dydaktyczny. Prace z Historii Oswiaty i Wychowania
0860-1100 Akademia Gorniczo-Hutnicza im. Stanislawa Staszica. Zeszyty Naukowe. Chemia
0860-1119 Acta Universitatis Lodziensis: Turyzm
0860-1194 Politechnika Wroclawska. Instytut Historii Architektury, Sztuki i Techniki. Prace Naukowe. Konferencje
0860-1615 Politechnika Wroclawska. Centrum Obliczeniowe. Prace Naukowe. Konferencje
0860-1623 Politechnika Wroclawska. Centrum Obliczeniowe. Prace Naukowe. Studia i Materialy
0860-1844 Archiwum Historii i Filozofii Medycyny
0860-1860 Akademia Gorniczo-Hutnicza im. Stanislawa Staszica. Zeszyty Naukowe. Wiertnictwo Nafta Gas
0860-2085 Studia Phonetica Posnaniensia
0860-2212 Szczecinskie Roczniki Naukowe
0860-2220 Kraje Socjalistyczne
0860-2328 Wyzsza Szkola Pedagogiczna, Opole. Zeszyty Naukowe. Seria A. Filogogia Angielska
0860-2441 Uniwersytet Slaski w Katowicach. Prace Naukowe. Acta Biologica Silesiana
0860-2603 Acta Academiae Agriculturae ac Technicae Olstenensis. Zootechnica - Zootechnics
0860-2611 Acta Academiae Agriculturae ac Technicae Olstenensis. Protectio Aquarum et Piscatoria - Water Conservation and Inland Fisheries
0860-262X Acta Academiae Agriculturae ac Technicae Olstenensis. Geodaesia et Ruris Regulatio - Geodesy and Agricultural Arrangement
0860-2727 Akademia Gorniczo-Hutnicza im. Stanislawa Staszica. Zeszyty Naukowe. Opuscula Mathematica
0860-276X Wyzsza Szkola Pedagogiczna im. Komisji Edukacji Narodowej w Krakowie. Rocznik Naukowe-Dydaktyczny. Prace Techniczne
0860-2832 Acta Academiae Agriculturae ac Technicae Olstenensis. Agricultura - Agriculture
0860-2840 Acta Academiae Agriculturae ac Technicae Olstenensis. Veterinaria - Veterinary Medicine
0860-2859 Acta Academiae Agriculturae ac Technicae Olstenensis. Technologia Alimentorum - Food Technology
0860-2948 Acta Academiae Agriculturae ac Technicae Olstenensis. Oeconomica - Economics
0860-2956 Acta Academiae Agriculturae ac Technicae Olstenensis. Aedificatio et Mechanica
0860-3111 Acta Universitatis Lodziensis: Folia Physiologica Cytologica et Genetica
0860-3200 Politechnika Wroclawska. Instytut Nauk Ekonomiczno-Spolecznych. Prace Naukowe. Konferencje
0860-3324 Maszyny Przeplywowe
0860-3359 Studies in the Developing Countries
0860-3456 Gdanskie Studia Jezykoznawcze
0860-3731 Uniwersytet Gdanski. Wydzial Prawa i Administracji. Zeszyty Naukowe. Studia Prawno-Ustrojowe
0860-374X Uniwersytet Gdanski. Wydzial Prawa i Administracji. Zeszyty Naukowe. Studia Iuridica Maritima
0860-4045 Polski Klub Ekologiczny Okregu Malopolska. Prace Naukowe
0860-4053 Acta Agraria et Silvestria. Series Silvestris
0860-407X Biuletyn Informacyjny. Budownictwo. Gospodarka Mieszkaniowa *see* 0867-4485
0860-4096 Bialostocczyzna
0860-410X Kalendarz Slowa Bozego

ISSN INDEX 5801

ISSN	Title
0860-4592	Res Publica
0860-4673	Organizacja - Metody - Technika w Administracji Panstwowej
0860-5629	Wyzsza Szkola Pedagogiczna im. Komisji Edukacji Narodowej w Krakowie. Rocznik Naukowo-Dydaktyczny. Prace Jezykoznawcze
0860-5742	University of Warsaw. Department of Economy. Economic Paper
0860-5882	Polish-AngloSaxon Studies
0860-6307	Akademia Gorniczo-Hutnicza im. Stanislawa Staszica. Zeszyty Naukowe. Folia Malacologica
0860-6536	Polish Journal of Occupational Medicine changed to Polish Journal of Occupational Medicine and Environmental Health.
0860-6730	Poland. Glowny Urzad Statystyczny. Statystyka Polski. Seria: Materialy Statystyczne. Ceny Detaliczne
0860-6994	Wyzsza Szkola Pedagogiczna im. Komisji Edukacji Narodowej w Krakowie. Rocznik Naukowo-Dydaktyczny. Prace z Rachunku Prawdopodobienstwa i Jego Dydaktyki
0860-7109	Akademia Gorniczo-Hutnicza im. Stanislawa Staszica. Zeszyty Naukowe. Geofizyka Stosowana
0860-7214	Politechnika Czestochowska. Zeszyty Naukowe. Budownictwo
0860-7222	Turbulence
0860-7311	Politechnika Wroclawska. Centrum Obliczeniowe. Prace Naukowe. Monografie
0860-7443	Acta Universitatis Lodziensis: Folia Scientiae Artium et Litterarum
0860-7591	Warsaw Voice
0860-7613	Gazeta Bankowa
0860-8091	Autograft
0860-9063	Wyzsza Szkola Pedagogiczna im. Komisji Edukacji Narodowej w Krakowie. Rocznik Naukowo-Dydaktyczny. Prace Fizjologiczne
0860-9071	Wyzsza Szkola Pedagogiczna im. Komisji Edukacji Narodowej w Krakowie. Rocznik Naukowo-Dydaktyczny. Prace z Wychowania Plastycznego
0860-911X	Music in Poland
0860-9357	Kwartalnik Historii i Teorii Ruchu Zawodowego
0860-9594	Studia Societatis Scientiarum Torunensis. Sectio H. Medicina
0861-038X	Central Committee of the Bulgarian Communist Party. Information Bulletin
0861-0568	Oxidation Communications
0861-0843	Abstracts of Bulgarian Scientific Literature. Linguistics and Literature
0861-4881	Bibliotekoznanie, Bibliografia, Knigoznanie
0861-7333	Signal A
0862-0598	Ochrana a Tvorba Zivotniho Prostredi v Zemedelstvi a Lesnictvi
0862-1179	Marxismus-Leninismus. Politika†
0862-1187	Prehledy Informativni Literatury†
0862-1195	Acta Musei Moraviae. Supplementum: Folia Numismatica
0862-1209	Acta Musei Moraviae. Supplementum: Folia Ethnographica
0862-2000	Zemedelska Informatika
0862-2264	Zemedelska Literatura
0862-2310	Zemedelska Aktuality ze Sveta changed to Zemedelske - Polnohospodarske Aktuality.
0862-2833	Okresni Archiv v Olomouci. Vyrocni Zprava
0862-3090	Historicka Ekologie
0862-3171	Studie z Dejin Techniky
0862-4372	Kaktusy
0862-7487	Narodni Knihovna
0862-7509	Online Kontakt
0862-7940	Applications of Mathematics
0862-8459	Casopis Pro Moderni Filologii
0862-8505	Opus Musicum
0862-8580	Bibliograficky Katalog C S F R: Ceske Hudebniny, Gramofonove Desky a C D
0862-8599	Bibliograficky Katalog C S F R: Ceske Knihy. Ceske Disertace a Autoreferaty
0862-8823	Slovenske Narodne Noviny
0862-9218	Bibliograficky Katalog C S F R: Ceske Knihy
0862-9226	Bibliograficky Katalog C S F R: Ceske Knihy. Ceska Grafika a Mapy v Roce
0862-9234	Bibliograficky Katalog C S F R: Ceske Knihy. Soupis Ceskych Bibliografii
0862-9269	Bibliograficky Katalog C S F R: Clanky v Ceskych Casopisech
0862-9358	Drevarske Informacie
0862-9382	I'91
0862-9609	U S E B Zpravy
0863-0070	Teachers of the World
0863-0445	Journal of New Generation Computer Systems
0863-0453	Journal of Information Recording Materials
0863-0593	Journal of Information Processing and Cybernetics
0863-0682	S L B Kurier
0863-0925	Technische Universitaet Otto von Guericke. Wissenschaftliche Zeitschrift Contributions to Plasma Physics
0863-1611	Journal fuer Unterhaltungskunst
0863-1743	Gastroenterologisches Journal
0863-1808	Archiv fuer Agraroekonomie und Betriebswirtschaft
0863-1840	Internationale-Agrar-Industriezeitschrift†
0863-2162	Z I S - Report†
0863-2790	Innovation & Management
0863-3045	Neu Leben†
0863-3746	Lava
0863-4076	Neues Wohnen
0863-4084	Handelswoche
0863-4106	Zentralblatt fuer Pathologie
0863-4300	Research in Informatics
0863-4645	Experimentelle Medizin. Mitteilungsblatt
0863-4807	Der Wald
0863-4831	Ing
0863-4912	Der Bueropraktiker
0863-4947	Gardens West
0863-5412	Aerzteblatt Thueringen
0864-0130	Economia del Trabajo changed to Hombre y Trabajo.
0864-0173	Pro Pesca changed to Revista Cubana de Construccion Naval.
0864-0254	Juprecu
0864-0262	Su Voz
0864-0270	Heraldo Cristiano
0864-0289	Revista Cubana de Hematologia, Inmunologia y Hematerapia
0864-0297	Revista Cubana de Oncologia
0864-0300	Revista Cubana de Investigaciones Biomedicas
0864-0319	Revista Cubana de Enfermeria
0864-0327	Muchacha
0864-1307	Cuba en el Ballet
0864-1315	Revolucion y Cultura
0864-1331	Caribe
0864-1382	Indice General de Publicaciones Periodicas Cubanas
0864-1420	Cuba: Economia Planificada
0864-1439	Actualidades de la Economia Socialista†
0864-165X	Revista Cubano de Derecho
0864-2125	Revista Cubana de Medicina General Integral
0864-2362	Militante Comunista
0864-3466	Revista Cubana de Salud Publica
0864-3873	Ciencia y Tecnologia Pesquera
0864-4616	Granma Internacional (Spanish Edition)
0864-4624	Granma International (English Edition)
0864-4632	Granma Internacional (Portuguese Edition)
0864-4640	Granma International (French Edition)
0864-8786	Uj Periodikumok
0864-9219	Auto Extra
0864-9227	Denise
0864-991X	Health Information and Libraries
0865-0047	Csaladi Haz
0865-0497	Izotoptechnika, Diagnosztika
0865-0926	Hungary. Kozponti Statisztikai Hivatal. A Kiskereskedem es a Fogyasztasi Szolgalt see 0866-1146
0865-1329	Konyvtari Levelezo
0865-1906	Magyar Neprajzi Bibliografia
0865-4093	Beszelo
0865-5227	Magyar Egyhaztorteneti Vazlatok
0865-6746	Investors' Guide to Hungary
0865-8986	Magyar Kiadas - Business Week
0865-9788	Alaplap
0866-1146	Hungary. Kozponti Statisztikai Hivatal. Belkereskedelm
0866-5192	Kutatasszervezesi Tajekoztato
0866-6083	Hungarian Journal of Viticulture and Enology
0866-9791	Mloda Polska
0867-0420	Przysposobienie Obronne w Szkole
0867-0609	Annales Universitatis Mariae Curie-Sklodowska. Sectio DDD. Pharmacia
0867-0633	Teksty Drugie
0867-1125	Kresy
0867-1184	Fontes Praehistorici see 0071-6863
0867-1966	Upper Silesian Museum in Bytom. Annals. Entomology
0867-2121	Archiwum Informatyki Teoretycznej i Stosowanej
0867-2237	Nie
0867-2628	Obrobka Plastyczna Metali
0867-3055	Medyk
0867-3594	Wyzsza Szkola Pedagogiczna im. Komisji Edukacji Narodowej w Krakowie. Rocznik Naukowo-Dydaktyczny. Prace Fizyczne
0867-4485	Budownictwo i Gospodarka Miejska. Biuletyn Informacyjny
0867-5880	Polish Building Market
0867-6038	Politechnika Slaska. Zeszyty Naukowe. Inzynieria Srodowiska
0868-409X	Tallinna Tehnikaulikool. Statisticheskie Metody Analiza Effektivnosti Proizvodstva
0868-4103	Tallinna Tehnikaulikool. Neustanovivsheesya Protsessy v Sistemakh Vodosnabzheniya i Vodootvedeniya
0868-4138	Tallinna Tehnikaulikool. Teoriya i Raschet Tonkostennykh i Prostranstvennykh Konstruktsii
0868-4162	Tallinna Tehnikaulikool. Trenie i Iznos v Mashinakh
0868-4189	Tallinna Tehnikaulikool. Problemy Razrabotki Mestorozdenii Poleznykh Iskopaemykh Estonii
0868-4197	Tallinna Tehnikaulikool. Sintez i Primenenie Polikondensatsionnykh Kleev
0868-4200	Tallinna Tehnikaulikool. Postroenie Translyatorov, Obrabotka Dannykh, Voprosy Programmirovaniya changed to Tallinna Tehnikaulikool. Data Processing, Compiler Writing, Programming.
0868-4219	Tallinna Tehnikaulikool. Issledovaniya po Prikladnoi Kvantovoi Elektronike
0868-4251	Tallinna Tehnikaulikool. Metody Stokhasticheskogo Upravleniya Rezhimami Energeticheskikh Sistem
0868-426X	Tallinna Tehnikaulikool. Gibkie Avtomatizirovannye Proizvodstvennye Sistemy i ikh Elementy dlya Liteinogo Proizvodstva
0868-4278	Tallinna Tehnikaulikool. Issledovanie Elektromagnitnykh i Elektromashinnykh Ustroistv Upravleniya i Kontrolya Spetsial'nogo Naznacheniya
0868-4308	Tallinna Tehnikaulikool. Fizicheskaya Khimiya Soedinenii A2B6 i A4B6
0868-4375	Tallinna Tehnikaulikool. Avtomatizatsiya Tekhnologicheskogo Proektirovaniya Protsessov Mekhanicheskoi Obrabotki
0868-4405	Autorevuu
0868-4448	Obshchestvennye Nauki za Rubezhom. Sotsiologiya
0868-5894	Eesti Teaduste Akadeemia. Toimetised. Okoloogia
0868-5975	Moya Moskva
0868-698X	Stolitsa
0868-7196	Vatan
0868-8230	Sotsium
0868-8400	Moscow Magazine
0868-9520	Vyzov
0868-9547	Mir Puteshestvii
0870-0001	Garcia de Orta: Serie de Zoologia
0870-001X	Estudos Ensaios e Documentos
0870-0028	Instituto de Investigacao Cientifica Tropical. Centro de Estudos de Historia e Cartografia Antiga. Studia
0870-0036	Instituto de Investigacao Cientifica Tropical. Memorias
0870-0044	Leba
0870-0133	Evphrosyne
0870-0141	Classica
0870-015X	Instituto de Investigacao Cientifica Tropical. Estudos de Historia e Cartografia Antiga - Memorias
0870-0168	Garcia de Orta: Serie de Antropobiologia
0870-0214	Associacao de Empresas de Construcao e Obras Publicas do Sul. Industria da Construcao
0870-0435	Instituto Nacional de Investigacao das Pescas. Publicacoes Avulsas
0870-0974	Bibliotecas, Arquivos e Museus
0870-0990	Antropologia Portuguesa
0870-1059	Instituto dos Produtos Florestais - Cortica. Boletim†
0870-1245	Portugal. Instituto Nacional de Investigacao das Pescas. Boletim
0870-1970	Expresso
0870-2594	Estado das Culturas e Previsao de Colheitas
0870-273X	Revista A C P
0870-2950	Anuario Climatologico
0870-3043	Planeamento
0870-3205	Portugal. Instituto Nacional de Estatistica. Estatisticas das Sociedades. Continente e Ilhas Adjacentes changed to Portugal. Instituto Nacional de Estatistica. Estatisticas das Sociedades: Continente, Acores e Madeira.
0870-3531	Economia
0870-3701	Cruz Vermelha Portugesa. Boletim de Informacao†
0870-3841	Coloquio: Artes
0870-3876	Museu Municipal do Funchal. Boletim
0870-4104	Clio (Lisbon)
0870-4112	Biblos
0870-4406	Portugal. Instituto Nacional de Estatistica. Estatisticas de Proteccao Social, Associacoes Sindicais e Patronais
0870-4457	Estudos de Antropologia Cultural e Social
0870-4546	Cultura, Historia y Filosofia
0870-4686	Boletim Meteorologico
0870-4694	Boletim Meteorologico para a Agricultura
0870-4716	Centro de Fisica da Atmosfera de Lisboa. Boletim
0870-4724	Projecto I2 do PIDDAC. Boletim
0870-4732	Resumos Meteorologicos para a Aeronautica†
0870-4740	Boletim Actinometrico de Portugal
0870-4759	Portugal. Instituto Nacional de Meteorologia e Geofisica. Revista†
0870-4783	Jornal de Psicologia
0870-5259	Livros de Portugal
0870-5283	Revista Portuguesa de Filosofia
0870-5291	Seara Nova (Lisbon Codex)
0870-5364	Electricidade
0870-6026	Economia e Sociologia
0870-6182	Ler Historia
0870-6506	Portugal. Instituto Nacional de Estatistica. Estatisticas de Seguranca Social, Associacoes Sindicais e Patronais. Continente, Acores e Madeira see 0870-4406
0870-6565	Infancia e Juventude

0870-6735 Instituto de Investigacao Cientifica Tropical. Centro de Estudos de Historia e Cartografia Antiga. Serie Separatas
0870-6891 Estudos de Antropologia Cultural *see* 0870-4457
0870-7235 Broteria Genetica
0870-7618 Broteria
0870-8231 Analise Psicologica
0870-8355 Arqueologia Industrial
0870-8487 Revista de Legislacao e de Jurisprudencia
0870-8789 Jornal de Contabilidade
0870-8924 Atlantis
0870-8932 Eles e Elas - a Revista *changed to* Eles & Elas.
0870-8932 Eles e Elas - a Revista *changed to* A Revista.
0870-8967 Diacritica
0870-9149 Laboratorio Nacional de Engeharia Civil. Boletim de Informacao Tecnica
0870-9912 Risco
0871-1747 Instituto de Investigacao Cientifica Tropical. Comunicacoes. Serie de Ciencias da Engenharia Geografica
0871-1755 Instituto de Investigacao Cientifica Tropical. Comunicacoes. Serie de Ciencias Biologicas
0871-1763 Instituto de Investigacao Cientifica Tropical. Comunicacoes. Serie de Ciencias Agrarias
0871-1771 Instituto de Investigacao Cientifica Tropical. Comunicacoes. Serie de Ciencias Historicas, Economicas e Sociologicas
0871-178X Instituto de Investigacao Cientifica Tropical. Comunicacoes. Serie de Ciencias Etnologicas e Etnomuseologicas
0871-1798 Instituto de Investigacao Cientifica Tropical. Comunicacoes. Serie de Ciencias da Terra
0871-2344 Revista Internacional de Estudos Africanos
0871-3316 Portugal. Comissao para a Igualdade e Direitos das Mulheres. Noticias
0871-4304 Arquivos de Reumatologia e Doencas Osted Articulares
0871-4614 Portugal em Numeros; Situacao Socio-Economica
0871-8725 Portugal em Numeros
0871-8741 Portugal. Instituto Nacional de Estatistica. Anuario Estatistico. Continente, Acores e Madeira
0871-875X Portugal. Instituto Nacional de Estatistica. Gabinete de Estudos Demograficos. Estudos Demograficos
0871-9799 Portugal. Comissao para a Igualdade e Direitos das Mulheres. Informacao Bibliografica
0882-0082 Bowker's Complete Sourcebook of Personal Computing†
0882-0104 Data General Micro World†
0882-0139 Immunological Investigations
0882-0147 Fertilizer Technology†
0882-018X Rundy's Journal and Confederation Courier
0882-0201 Early Keyboard Studies Newsletter
0882-0228 Selections (Los Angeles)
0882-0236 D O S S U Journal
0882-0287 Communications in Statistics. Part C: Stochastic Models
0882-0317 Utopian Psychology *changed to* RockHead.
0882-0384 Texas League Savings Account†
0882-0422 Genealogical Clearinghouse Quarterly†
0882-0481 Fitness Management
0882-049X Magazine Design and Production
0882-0511 Seminars in Veterinary Medicine and Surgery: Small Animal
0882-052X Seminars in Orthopaedics
0882-0538 Seminars in Ophthalmology
0882-0546 Seminars in Respiratory Infections
0882-0554 New England Sampler
0882-0589 Orange County Report
0882-0627 Journal of Nursing Staff Development
0882-0635 Tennessee Ancestors
0882-066X Widener Review
0882-0775 Unlisted Market Guide *changed to* Market Guide Over-the-Counter Stock Edition.
0882-0783 Journal of Police and Criminal Psychology
0882-0813 Vajradhatu Sun *changed to* Shambhala Sun.
0882-0880 Advances in Dermatology
0882-0910 Women and Work (Newbury Park)
0882-0929 California Chamber of Commerce Alert
0882-0937 V I T A News†
0882-0945 Buddhist - Christian Studies
0882-0953 Radiological Respiratory Protection Newsletter *changed to* Respiratory Protection Newsletter.
0882-1046 Journal of Contemporary Health Law and Policy
0882-1100 S P E Monograph Series
0882-1127 American Journalism
0882-1135 Women's Quarterly Review†
0882-116X L F L Reports:
0882-1232 Journal of Curriculum and Supervision
0882-1240 Dimensions: A Journal of Holocaust Studies
0882-1267 French Politics & Society
0882-1305 L B L Research Review
0882-133X Physician's Legal Alert†
0882-1348 Scifant
0882-1399 Dance Exercise Today *changed to* I D E A Today.
0882-1402 Acid Rain Abstracts *see* 0093-3287
0882-1410 Artificial Intelligence Abstracts
0882-1429 Telecommunications Abstracts†
0882-1437 C A D - C A M Abstracts
0882-1445 Public Technology†
0882-1461 Telephone Selling Report
0882-147X Morning Coffee Chapbook Series†
0882-1496 Market Moves
0882-1526 Design Horizons†
0882-1577 Health Progress
0882-1593 Black Elected Officials
0882-1658 Zone (Waverly)†
0882-1666 Systems and Computers in Japan
0882-178X Option Magazine
0882-1798 Issues Management Letter *changed to* Executive Trend Watch.
0882-1852 Biological Therapies in Dentistry
0882-1879 Island Properties Report
0882-1925 Flash (Chicago)†
0882-1933 Olschwanger Journal
0882-195X Annual Index to Poetry in Periodicals *see* 1040-5461
0882-1968 North American Culture
0882-200X Computer & Electronics Graduate†
0882-2042 Chicora Foundation Research Series
0882-2050 Merlyn's Pen
0882-2123 Ambassador Report
0882-2131 Executive Health Report *changed to* Executive Health's Good Health Report.
0882-2158 Traces (Glasgow)
0882-2190 Schabacker Investment Management. Weekly Advisory Bulletin†
0882-2212 Catgut Acoustical Society. Journal *see* 1053-7694
0882-228X Organization of American Historians Magazine of History
0882-231X Faxletter *see* 1048-3403
0882-2360 Current Contents Address Directory - Science & Technology†
0882-2476 Rehabilitation Technology Review *changed to* R E S N A News.
0882-2514 Frost on the Vine
0882-2522 American Native Press†
0882-2549 Duplex Planet
0882-2557 Texas Instruments Engineering Journal *see* 0893-7877
0882-2573 Kane's Beverage Week
0882-2611 Technology Reimbursement Reports: The Beige Sheet†
0882-2689 Journal of Psychopathology and Behavioral Assessment
0882-2700 Product Directory & Buyers'Guide†
0882-2743 Contents of Periodicals on Latin America
0882-2751 I A S News
0882-276X D A R Systems International's White Paper Series in Computer Programming†
0882-2786 International Journal of Oral & Maxillofacial Implants
0882-2816 Poodle Variety
0882-2832 A B M S Directory of Certified Neurological Surgeons
0882-2840 A L A N Review
0882-2867 Nontoxic and Natural News *see* 0889-8421
0882-3014 Systems Research and Information Science
0882-3030 Folio (Brockport)
0882-3049 Cultura Ludens
0882-309X Peterson's Guide to Colleges in the Southeast (Year)
0882-3103 Peterson's Guide to Colleges in the Southwest (Year)
0882-3111 MediaSource†
0882-3154 Western Reserve Historical Society News
0882-3189 Pitts Choice†
0882-3227 Corporate 1000 *see* 1058-2908
0882-326X Database End-User *see* 0891-6713
0882-3316 Emerging Patterns of Work and Communications in an Information Age
0882-3332 Pipe & Quill
0882-3340 Atari Explorer
0882-3391 Lifestyles: Family and Economic Issues *changed to* Journal of Family and Economic Issues.
0882-3456 Quorum Report
0882-3472 Attitude
0882-3499 Soft.letter
0882-3537 Energy Policy Studies
0882-3588 Arc†
0882-3693 Central Texas Archeologist
0882-3715 Finest Hour
0882-3723 Fourth World Journal
0882-3731 The Right of Aesthetic Realism to Be Known
0882-3758 Thermology
0882-3766 Government Research Directory
0882-3790 Potpourii Party-Line *see* 1062-855X
0882-3804 Letter Exchange
0882-3812 Natural Resources & Environment
0882-3820 Clean Yield
0882-3863 Equity and Choice
0882-3944 Monitor (Arlington)†
0882-4010 Microbial Pathogenesis
0882-4088 World Communication
0882-4096 Communication Research Reports
0882-410X Federal Reserve Bank of Minneapolis. District Economic Conditions *see* 1045-3334
0882-4126 Higher Education
0882-4142 Ivy Journal
0882-4150 Hamersky & Allied Families Newsletter
0882-4312 Berkeley Women's Law Journal
0882-4347 Applied Orgonometry
0882-4371 Cultural Critique
0882-438X A M S Studies in Education
0882-4401 Nautical Brass
0882-4428 Bean Home Newsletter
0882-4606 Kosmon Voice
0882-4665 MedicalDisc Reporter *see* 1048-0501
0882-4681 Corporate Times
0882-4711 Export Today (Washington)
0882-4738 Utah. Division of Administrative Rules. Utah State Bulletin
0882-4746 Good Stuff
0882-4754 Marketing Trends *changed to* A I M - Age of Information Marketing.
0882-4843 Feminist Teacher
0882-486X Doris Lessing Newsletter
0882-4908 Jukebox Collector Newsletter *see* 1053-6884
0882-4959 I E E E Translation Journal on Magnetics in Japan
0882-4967 I E E E Journal of Robotics and Automation *see* 1042-296X
0882-4983 Geotechnical Fabrics Report
0882-5017 C E A Voice
0882-5181 Caquelin Chronicle†
0882-5246 Japanese Technical Abstracts *changed to* Japan Technology Series.
0882-5297 Afro-American Culture and Society Monograph Series
0882-5300 C A A S Special Publication Series
0882-5351 American Magazine and Historical Chronicle
0882-536X Directory of Hardware and Housewares Distributors *changed to* Directory of Hardlines Distributors (Year).
0882-5424 Tapori
0882-5475 Humanities Education
0882-5491 Arkansas Archeological Survey. Publications on Archeology. Research Series
0882-5505 The Franchise Handbook
0882-5521 Taft Nonprofit Executive†
0882-553X SportSearch
0882-5572 Arizona Wildlife Views
0882-5637 Federal Career Insights†
0882-5645 Topics in Pain Management
0882-5696 Hazardous Waste & Hazardous Materials
0882-570X Soviet Journal of Automation & Information Sciences
0882-5726 Data Broadcasting Report
0882-5734 Flavour & Fragrance Journal
0882-5785 Analysis Instrumentation
0882-5793 Federation Review†
0882-5807 Economic Trends (Chicago)
0882-5815 Seminars in Reproductive Endrocrinology
0882-584X Urban Wildlife Manager's Notebook
0882-5858 Urban Wildlife News
0882-5874 Durch die Fensterscheibe
0882-5882 Heller Helper
0882-5890 Schartzer - Schertzer Connection
0882-5904 Schneider Connections
0882-5939 Sloane Report
0882-5955 Constitution (Washington)†
0882-5963 Journal of Pediatric Nursing
0882-5971 Georgia Trend
0882-598X Health Letter (Washington)
0882-5998 Year Book of Hematology
0882-6072 Hypnosis Reports
0882-6099 Luna City Press†
0882-617X Independent Report on Martin Marietta *changed to* S D I Intelligence Report.
0882-6188 Ground Water Monitor
0882-6196 Reading Plus
0882-6250 Employment Alert
0882-6277 Impact (New York, 1983) *see* 1044-8772
0882-6323 Ober Income Letter†
0882-6366 Workers' Advocate Supplement
0882-6382 New & Emerging Technology
0882-6420 Florida International Law Journal
0882-6447 Caduceus: A Museum Quarterly for the Health Sciences *changed to* Caduceus: A Museum Journal for the Health Sciences.
0882-6455 Monographs in Nuclear Medicine *see* 0896-0607
0882-6471 Patient Pleasers! Dental Edition†
0882-6471 Patient Pleasers! Health Care Edition†
0882-648X Bogg
0882-6498 Journal of Medical Humanities and Bioethics *see* 1041-3545
0882-6501 Avotaynu
0882-651X Bugeye Times
0882-6528 St. Clair County Genealogical Society Quarterly
0882-6587 Government Microcomputer Letter
0882-6757 Reaper†
0882-6773 Newkirk Notes†
0882-6846 C R I A R L Newsletter
0882-6951 Cutting Edge Quarterly (Ann Arbor)†
0882-696X Guthrie Journal
0882-6994 Soviet Economy
0882-701X Direct Response Marketing to Schools Newsletter *changed to* School Marketing Newsletter.
0882-7036 Preaching

0882-7044 Bio-Bibliographies in Afro-American and African Studies
0882-7052 Bio-Bibliographies in Law and Political Science
0882-7079 German Politics & Society
0882-7095 D D R Studien
0882-7133 Annual DeGarmo Lectures
0882-7141 Society of Professors of Education. Occasional Papers
0882-715X Preservation Law Reporter
0882-7176 Taft Corporate Giving Directory *see* 1055-0623
0882-7206 Wine Spectator Wine Maps *changed to* Wine Country Guide to California.
0882-7214 United Church News
0882-7249 Facilities Manager
0882-7397 World Association for Emergency and Disaster Medicine. Journal *see* 1049-023X
0882-7400 Published†
0882-7419 Powertechnics Magazine
0882-7508 Mineral Processing and Extractive Metallurgy Review
0882-7516 Active and Passive Electronic Components
0882-7524 Topics in Geriatric Rehabilitation
0882-7591 Directory of Corporate Financing *changed to* Handbook of Corporate Finance.
0882-7737 European Travel & Life
0882-7893 Journal of Interpretation (Rockville)†
0882-7907 Hurricane Alice
0882-7958 Advanced Materials & Processes
0882-7974 Psychology and Aging
0882-7982 Yarn Market News†
0882-8016 Ward's Business Directory of Major International Companies†
0882-8024 A S H S Newsletter
0882-8032 Applied Industrial Hygiene *see* 1047-322X
0882-8067 New Accountant
0882-8075 Node
0882-8083 Hematology Reviews and Communications
0882-8091 Speedx
0882-8105 M S M - The Magazine for Computer Service Managers *see* 0898-5499
0882-8121 Mathematical Geology
0882-8156 Weather and Forecasting
0882-8164 Journal of Environmental Science and Health. Part C: Environmental Carcinogenesis and Ecotoxicology Reviews
0882-8202 Barron Family Newsletter
0882-8210 Sports Participation in (Year): Series 1
0882-8245 Viral Immunology
0882-827X Magazine Publishing Career Directory
0882-8377 G A S Lites
0882-8415 Software Developer's Monthly
0882-8431 A R P E News†
0882-8458 Women's Travel Connection†
0882-8466 Lacan Study Notes†
0882-8512 Freethought Today
0882-8520 Youth Law News
0882-8555 Medical Malpractice Litigation Reporter *see* 1056-4098
0882-8598 Get - Two - Gether
0882-8644 Philippine Report†
0882-8652 Hypnotherapy Today
0882-8679 Quarterly Report†
0882-8709 Corporate Travel
0882-8768 Play It Safe
0882-889X Metabolic, Pediatric and Systemic Ophthalmology
0882-8938 Overseas Living
0882-9047 National Forum of Educational Administration and Supervision *see* 0888-8132
0882-908X F L I C C Newsletter
0882-9136 Compilation of State and Federal Privacy Laws
0882-9225 Pediatric Reviews and Communications
0882-9233 Surgical Research Communications
0882-9268 College Marketing Alert
0882-9284 Agricultural Computing†
0882-9403 Senior Citizens Advocate *changed to* Action Memo & Senior Citizens Advocate.
0882-9438 Florida Manufacturers Register
0882-9454 Industrial Development in the Tennessee Valley Region†
0882-9640 Silent Sports
0882-9659 New Ways (Evanston)†
0882-9667 N S I Advisory
0882-9691 Wheat Grower
0882-987X Chamberlain Association News
0882-990X Bulletin Board Systems *see* 1041-7915
0883-0061 Keeper's Log
0883-0126 Red Bass
0883-0185 International Reviews in Immunology
0883-0231 Europe for Travelers!†
0883-0258 Dimensional Stone Magazine
0883-0266 Monthly Prescribing Reference
0883-0347 U S Swimming News
0883-0355 International Journal of Educational Research
0883-0444 Refractive & Corneal Surgery
0883-0452 HealthSpan
0883-0487 Letter of Credit Update
0883-0568 Alaska Law Review
0883-072X American Intelligence Journal
0883-0738 Journal of Child Neurology
0883-0746 Landlord vs Tenant - N Y C
0883-0754 Experimental Musical Instruments
0883-0762 Health Care Instrumentation†
0883-0940 Cloud Family Journal
0883-0991 American Spacemodeling
0883-1130 Creative Crafters Journal *see* 0894-0924
0883-1157 Romance Quarterly
0883-1173 About Alfords
0883-1181 Chapman Chatter†
0883-119X The Wise Woman
0883-1203 A B M S Directory of Certified Pathologists
0883-1211 A B M S Directory of Certified Orthopaedic Surgeons
0883-122X A B M S Directory of Certified Anesthesiologists
0883-1238 A B M S Directory of Certified Radiologists
0883-1270 Soviet-American Debate
0883-1289 Human Sexuality
0883-1297 Legal Information Alert
0883-1300 S C P Journal
0883-1319 S C P Newsletter
0883-1335 Tax Features
0883-1351 Palaios
0883-136X John Naisbitt's Trend Letter
0883-1394 Journal of Inferential and Deductive Biology
0883-1416 Changing Work *changed to* G E O: Grassroots Economic Organizing Newsletter.
0883-1424 Computer Aided Publishing Report†
0883-1440 Current Christian Abstracts *see* 1054-8688
0883-1475 Sida: Botanical Miscellany
0883-1483 Government Accountants Journal
0883-1505 International Logo Exchange *see* 0888-6970
0883-1513 Heritage (Cooperstown)
0883-153X Polymer Contents
0883-1548 New York State Museum. Biennial Report
0883-1580 Sports Periodicals Index
0883-1599 Temblor
0883-1688 S H H H Journal
0883-1696 Trends Magazine
0883-1718 Character II (Chicago)†
0883-1874 Pediatric Asthma, Allergy & Immunology
0883-1904 Jewish Vegetarians of New York *changed to* Jewish Vegetarians.
0883-1963 Consumer Health and Nutrition Index
0883-2102 A P I Account
0883-2234 Retail Security Management Letter *changed to* Retail Loss Prevention Letter.
0883-2285 Hemochromatosis Awareness
0883-2293 Person-Centered Review†
0883-2323 Journal of Education for Business
0883-2331 Old Westbury Review†
0883-234X 73 for Radio Amateurs *see* 1052-2522
0883-2382 Pleasure Hunt Magazine *see* 1052-4592
0883-2390 AmigaWorld
0883-2412 Lawyer's Register by Specialties and Fields of Law
0883-2587 Salt
0883-265X Stanford Business School Magazine
0883-2668 Shoe Tree
0883-2781 Collage (New Cumberland)
0883-2811 Educators Guide to Free Home Economics Materials
0883-282X Spectrum (Olathe)
0883-2889 International Journal of Radiation Applications and Instrumentation. Part A: Applied Radiation and Isotopes
0883-2897 International Journal of Radiation Applications and Instrumentation. Part B: Nuclear Medicine and Biology
0883-2919 World Englishes
0883-2927 Applied Geochemistry
0883-2935 Journal of Applied Cardiology†
0883-2978 A B M S Directory of Certified Preventive Medicine Specialists
0883-2986 A B M S Directory of Certified Physical Medicine & Rehabilitation Physicians
0883-2994 A B M S Directory of Certified Allergists and Immunologists
0883-3001 A B M S Directory of Certified Otolaryngologists
0883-3087 G D G Report
0883-3095 Pre- and Peri-Natal Psychology Journal
0883-3125 Star Trek: The Official Fan Club Magazine
0883-315X Information Center†
0883-3419 Future Reflections
0883-3559 Historians of Early Modern Europe
0883-3605 Morgan Migrations
0883-3648 Notre Dame Journal of Law, Ethics & Public Policy
0883-3664 Odysseus
0883-3680 Material Culture
0883-4202 Cybernetic
0883-4237 Statistical Science
0883-4296 MicroEconomics *changed to* B C S Professional.
0883-4326 Clothed with the Sun *changed to* N: Nude and Natural.
0883-4687 Foreign Trade Fairs New Products Newsletter
0883-4725 Current Titles in Ocean, Coastal, Lake & Waterway Sciences†
0883-475X Choices (New York)
0883-4989 Electronics
0883-5330 Directory of Biomedical and Health Care Grants
0883-5365 Oral Tradition
0883-5381 Healthcare Executive
0883-5403 Journal of Arthroplasty
0883-5470 Poet's Market
0883-5527 World Biolicensing Report
0883-5551 Advanced Ceramic Materials†
0883-556X Madden Family Newsletter
0883-5594 Recognition Technologies Today *changed to* Remittance and Document Processing Today.
0883-5667 Church
0883-5683 Computer Pictures
0883-5691 Topics in Clinical Nutrition
0883-5705 Kit Car
0883-5713 Attorneys Office Management Report *changed to* Professional Office Manager.
0883-5721 V A Practitioner
0883-573X Voice (East Lansing)
0883-5772 Information Industry Bulletin
0883-5799 Washington Trooper
0883-5810 A T H A Newsletter†
0883-5845 News About Library Services for the Blind and Physically Handicapped
0883-5853 New Resources for State Government and Agencies *changed to* New Resources.
0883-587X Chesapeake and Ohio Historical Newsletter *see* 0886-6287
0883-5926 Allees All Around
0883-5977 Computer Industry Digest†
0883-5985 Cogeneration Journal
0883-6000 Emory Vico Studies
0883-6027 Urban Analysis and Public Management *changed to* Journal of Urban Analysis and Public Management.
0883-6078 A I P L A Quarterly Journal
0883-6086 Perspectives (Norwood)†
0883-6159 California Broker
0883-623X Leningrad University Mechanics Bulletin
0883-6264 California Facts
0883-6272 Space Power
0883-6337 Notebook (Barstow)
0883-6353 Geoarchaeology
0883-6493 Technotes *see* 1047-1367
0883-6590 Pulteney St. Survey
0883-6612 Annals of Behavioral Medicine
0883-6671 Health Insurance Medical Records Risk Management Report†
0883-6728 Colorado Episcopalian
0883-6752 Pages
0883-6760 State Revenue Newsletter
0883-6779 Financial Reporting for American Cities and Counties†
0883-6884 Contributions in Military Studies
0883-6922 Children's Video Report
0883-6949 Mannlicher Collector
0883-6973 In House Graphics
0883-7066 System Dynamics Review
0883-7090 Adult Video News
0883-7120 Institute Today *see* 1058-4455
0883-721X India - West
0883-7252 Journal of Applied Econometrics
0883-7279 Pratt Journal of Architecture
0883-7287 Nelson's Official Research Guide *see* 1044-0267
0883-7325 MidContinent Oil World
0883-735X Rotkin Review
0883-7392 A R E A Magazine *changed to* Alabama Living.
0883-7481 F E: The Magazine for Financial Executives *see* 0895-4186
0883-7554 I E E E Electrical Insulation Magazine
0883-7562 Journal of Independent Social Work
0883-7570 Journal of Hospital Marketing
0883-7589 Psychotherapy Marketing and Practice Development Reports *see* 1049-5142
0883-7597 Journal of Pharmaceutical Marketing and Management
0883-7619 Impact Valves *see* 1056-1544
0883-7627 Impact Pumps, Pumps-Compressors *see* 1056-1536
0883-7635 Orim: A Jewish Journal at Yale†
0883-7694 M R S Bulletin
0883-7708 Lamb's Pastures
0883-7724 Darnall, Darnell - Dawn to Dusk
0883-7732 Tibet Society Bulletin
0883-7767 Allergy Relief Newsletter†
0883-7783 North Carolina Law Monitor
0883-7805 Manley Family Newsletter
0883-7902 Mental and Physical Disability Law Reporter
0883-8038 Thoroughbred Business
0883-8046 Rocky Mountain High Technology Directory
0883-8100 World Resources Institute. Journal†
0883-8127 Open Shop Building Construction Cost Data (Year) *changed to* Means Open Shop Building Construction Cost Data (Year).
0883-8135 World Today Series: Canada
0883-8151 Journal of Broadcasting and Electronic Media
0883-8216 Health Science
0883-8259 Snowmobile Business
0883-8283 Ferroelectrics and Polar Materials
0883-8291 Reviews of Magnetic Resonance in Medicine
0883-8305 Paleoceanography

0883-8364 In Vitro Cellular and Developmental Biology *changed to* In Vitro Cellular & Developmental Biology - Animal.
0883-8364 In Vitro Cellular and Developmental Biology *see* 1054-5476
0883-8402 Utility Supervision
0883-8518 Oink! *see* 0893-7842
0883-8526 Alaska Native Language Center Research Papers
0883-8534 Journal of Multicultural Counseling and Development
0883-8542 Applied Engineering in Agriculture
0883-8550 Daugherty Family Newsletter†
0883-8577 Palestine Focus
0883-8690 Government Assistance Almanac
0883-8712 Urgent Care Business Report *see* 1052-8733
0883-8798 Penthouse Letters
0883-8909 Association for Asian Studies. Southeast Conference. Annals
0883-8992 Western Art Digest *see* 0192-4214
0883-9026 Journal of Business Venturing
0883-9115 Journal of Bioactive and Compatible Polymers
0883-9123 Shakespearean Criticism
0883-9131 Beloit Fiction Journal
0883-9166 Fessenden Review†
0883-9174 Celebration
0883-9182 Annual Review of Biophysics and Biophysical Chemistry *see* 1056-8700
0883-9212 Journal of Cardiopulmonary Rehabilitation
0883-9298 Written Communication Annual
0883-9301 Computer Industry Forecast *see* 0894-6213
0883-931X Computer Industry Abstracts *see* 0894-6213
0883-9417 Archives of Psychiatric Nursing
0883-9425 Informatics in Pathology†
0883-9433 Journal of Post Anesthesia Nursing
0883-9441 Journal of Critical Care
0883-9492 Molecular Biology and Toxicology *changed to* Molecular Toxicology.
0883-9506 Vibration Engineering†
0883-9514 Applied Artificial Intelligence
0883-9522 Metabolic Ophthalmology, Pediatric and Systemic *see* 0882-889X
0883-9549 American Association for the Advancement of Slavic Studies. Newsletter
0883-9611 Broomstick
0883-9697 Journal of Middle Atlantic Archaeology
0883-9719 Environ
0883-9727 Directions (New York)
0883-9735 Coal & Synfuels Technology
0883-9778 Burrelle's New Jersey Media Directory (Year)
0883-9808 Micrographics Newsletter
0883-9824 Argonaut
0883-9859 Inventors' Digest
0883-9875 Nuclear Resister
0883-9891 Willett House Quarterly†
0883-993X Resources (Washington, 1980) *see* 0013-922X
0883-9956 In Dance
0883-9980 C S L Bulletin
0883-9999 Burrelle's New England Media Directory (Year)
0884-0016 Advanced Studies in Contemporary Mathematics
0884-0024 Military Police Journal *see* 0895-4208
0884-0032 Civil R I C O Report
0884-0040 A S H E - E R I C Higher Education Report Series
0884-0075 The California Prisoner
0884-030X Inside Alabama Politics
0884-0318 Journal of Wind Energy Technology
0884-0431 Journal of Bone and Mineral Research
0884-0490 A S H R A E Technical Data Bulletin
0884-0504 Group's Jr. High Ministry Magazine *changed to* Jr. High Ministry Magazine.
0884-0709 Computers and Translation *see* 0922-6567
0884-0806 Food Protection Report
0884-0822 Forth Dimensions
0884-0830 Capital P C Monitor
0884-0873 Desktop Publishing *see* 0897-6007
0884-089X Directory of Periodicals Online: News, Law & Business†
0884-0911 Directory of Periodicals Online: Science & Technology†
0884-0946 Journal of Natural Hygiene
0884-0989 Choices†
0884-0997 MacUser
0884-1012 Robot Experimenter. Supplement†
0884-1020 She-Ra Princess of Power Magazine†
0884-1136 Ensign
0884-1179 Georgia Economic Outlook
0884-1209 Mexico (Year)
0884-1217 Georgia Law Letter
0884-1225 Journal of Hyperbaric Medicine
0884-1233 Journal of Teaching in Social Work
0884-1241 Journal of Marketing for Higher Education
0884-1357 V M E Bus Systems
0884-139X Defense News
0884-1403 Alcoholism and Addiction Magazine *changed to* Addiction & Recovery Magazine.
0884-1454 A B M S Directory of Certified Nuclear Medicine Specialists
0884-1462 A B M S Directory of Certified Thoracic Surgeons
0884-1470 A B M S Directory of Certified Colon & Rectal Surgeons
0884-1489 A B M S Directory of Certified Dermatologists
0884-1497 A B M S Directory of Certified Pediatricians
0884-1500 A B M S Directory of Certified Neurologists
0884-1519 A B M S Directory of Certified Psychiatrists
0884-1527 A B M S Directory of Certified Surgeons
0884-1535 A B M S Directory of Certified Obstetricians & Gynecologists
0884-1543 A B M S Compendium of Certified Medical Specialists
0884-1616 Pratt's Guide to Venture Capital Sources
0884-1667 M S B A in Brief
0884-1829 Minority Engineer
0884-1837 Progress in Analytical Spectroscopy *see* 0958-319X
0884-1918 Museum & Arts Washington†
0884-1934 Square One
0884-1977 Business Lawyer Update
0884-1985 Performance & Instruction
0884-2108 Terrell Trails
0884-2124 Equipment Directory of Audio-Visual, Computer and Video Products
0884-2159 Petroleum Market Shares: Report on Retail Sales of Gasoline†
0884-2175 J O G N N
0884-2205 Mo Info
0884-2264 Compressor News *changed to* Compressor News and Patents.
0884-2272 Communications Technology
0884-2280 Children's Business
0884-2558 Advanced Materials and Manufacturing Processes *see* 1042-6914
0884-2604 Data Training
0884-2884 Drug Design and Delivery *see* 1055-9612
0884-2914 Journal of Materials Research
0884-2930 Wyoming
0884-2949 Faulkner Journal
0884-2957 Belles Lettres
0884-2981 Euthanasia Review†
0884-3031 Richard C. Young's Intelligence Report
0884-3090 Publisher's Report
0884-3198 U C L A Journal of Dance Ethnology
0884-3228 Fourth Circuit Review†
0884-3236 Late Imperial China
0884-3244 Immigration Journal
0884-3252 Rodale's Organic Gardening
0884-3260 Star Wars Intelligence Report *changed to* S D I Intelligence Report.
0884-3279 Western New York Index
0884-3309 Pioneer America Society Transactions
0884-3457 Cream City Review
0884-3554 Refugee Reports
0884-3597 I E E E International Conference on Cybernetics and Society. Proceedings *changed to* I E E E International Conference on Systems, Man, and Cybernetics. Proceedings.
0884-3635 Brilliant Star
0884-3716 Family History World. Research News
0884-3740 R A L Report†
0884-3759 Fuel Science and Technology International
0884-3848 Paint & Coatings Industry
0884-3910 News for You
0884-3929 Nibble Mac *changed to* Macintosh Hands On.
0884-3988 Holistic Medicine *changed to* Journal of Interprofessional Care.
0884-3996 Journal of Bioluminescence and Chemiluminescence
0884-4089 Greener Pastures Gazette
0884-4097 Monosson on D E C *see* 1040-0966
0884-4194 Current Concepts of Cerebrovascular Disease: Stroke†
0884-4240 Irish America Magazine
0884-4356 The American Voice
0884-450X Rare Books and Manuscripts Librarianship
0884-4550 Petroleum Management†
0884-4674 Competitive Edge (Tempe)†
0884-4712 Emergency Medical Care Digest†
0884-4720 Electronic Musician
0884-4739 Bassin'
0884-4747 Artilleryman
0884-4755 Aviation Digest
0884-4771 Northeast Oil World
0884-4828 Electronic Warfare Digest
0884-4887 Economic Road Maps†
0884-4925 Insight (Chatsworth)
0884-495X World Trade Report†
0884-4984 Catering Today
0884-5107 Crime Victims Digest
0884-5123 International Telemetering Conference
0884-5166 New England Living Magazine†
0884-5336 Nutrition in Clinical Practice
0884-5352 Journal of Career Planning & Employment
0884-5506 Christian Education Today
0884-5581 Behavioral Residential Treatment
0884-5808 Hakomi Forum
0884-5816 Age of Johnson
0884-5905 Administrative Management (New York)
0884-5913 Kinematics and Physics of Celestial Bodies
0884-593X Wired Librarian's Newsletter
0884-6057 Tax Management Weekly Report
0884-6146 Photocopy Authorizations Report *see* 1044-2332
0884-6154 Socialist
0884-6197 Church Media Library Magazine
0884-6219 Southwest Oil World
0884-6227 Update U S S R
0884-626X Motorcycle Industry Magazine
0884-6278 N S G A Sports Retailer *see* 1045-2087
0884-6391 U.S. Department of Agriculture. Wheat Outlook and Situation *see* 0895-1454
0884-6421 Utah State Digest
0884-643X A B M S Directory of Certified Family Physicians
0884-6448 A B M S Directory of Certified Internists
0884-6510 Bennett Exchange
0884-660X Leather Today
0884-6677 Y E S Quarterly
0884-6685 Voice Processing
0884-6693 Competition and Strategy *changed to* U S Telecommunications.
0884-6804 Journal of Composites Technology and Research
0884-6898 G M D A Bulletin
0884-6952 Studies in Judaica & the Holocaust
0884-7010 Consecrated Life
0884-7185 Food Broker Quarterly
0884-7231 Van Conversion Blue Book
0884-7355 Women's Health Magazine†
0884-738X Totally Gospel
0884-7398 Admissions Marketing Report
0884-741X Home Healthcare Nurse
0884-7452 C A S BioTech Updates. Environmental Biotechnology
0884-7460 C A S BioTech Updates. Genetic Engineering
0884-7479 C A S BioTech Updates. Biosensors
0884-7487 C A S BioTech Updates. Pharmaceutical Applications
0884-7622 Andrew Harper's Hideaway Report
0884-7827 Texas Real Estate†
0884-7967 Gulf Coast Oil World
0884-8009 Vocational Education Journal
0884-8092 Combined Cumulative Index to Obstetrics and Gynecology
0884-8106 N A T S Journal
0884-8114 Chamber Executive
0884-8173 International Journal of Intelligent Systems
0884-8181 Toxicity Assessment *see* 1053-4725
0884-8297 International Journal of Psychosomatics
0884-8300 Directory of Value Added Resellers (Year)
0884-8335 Economics & Business
0884-8394 Interstate Information Report
0884-8408 Molecular Crystals and Liquid Crystals Bulletin *see* 1056-7046
0884-8424 Association of Children's Prosthetic-Orthotic Clinics. Journal
0884-8432 Modern Greek Studies Yearbook
0884-8475 S R C Green Book of 5-Trend 35-Year Charts
0884-8521 Hospital Home Health
0884-8548 Florida Shipper
0884-8688 Journal of Aging and Judaism *see* 0700-9801
0884-8696 Georgia State Literary Studies
0884-870X Stress in Modern Society
0884-8726 Information Marketing Newsletter
0884-8734 Journal of General Internal Medicine
0884-8815 Brookgreen Journal
0884-8823 Popular Woodworking
0884-8858 Sinsemilla Tips
0884-8947 Trucks
0884-8971 Sociological Forum
0884-8998 Drug Utilization Review
0884-903X C D C - A I D S Weekly
0884-9072 Golden State Report
0884-9196 Peace Corps Times
0884-9382 National Interest
0884-9390 American Visions
0884-9404 Advances in Pediatric Infectious Diseases
0884-9420 Work Dynamics
0884-9471 Advanced Military Computing *see* 1056-747X
0884-948X Chemically Modified Surfaces
0884-9498 Public Computing†
0884-9501 Baseball History†
0884-951X Personal Publishing *see* 1060-2208
0884-9536 National Directory of Bulletin Board Systems
0884-9641 Free Venice Beachhead
0884-9749 T V - T S Tapestry
0884-9757 Electronic Chemicals & Materials News†
0884-9862 Printed Circuit Design *changed to* Printed Circuit Design.
0884-9889 Friends (Warren)
0885-0003 Industries in Transition
0885-0097 C A Selects. Acid Rain & Acid Air
0885-0100 C A Selects. Ceramic Materials (Patents)
0885-0119 C A Selects. Chemical Vapor Deposition
0885-0127 C A Selects. Color Science
0885-0135 C A Selects. Conductive Polymers
0885-0143 C A Selects. Electrically Conductive Organics

ISSN

ISSN INDEX 5805

0885-0151 C A Selects. Electronic Chemicals & Materials
0885-0178 C A Selects. Laser-Induced Chemical Reactions
0885-0186 C A Selects. Organic Optical Materials
0885-0194 C A Selects. Phase Transfer Catalysis
0885-0208 C A Selects. Photochemical Organic Synthesis
0885-0216 C A Selects. Photoresists
0885-0224 C A Selects. Polymerization Kinetics & Process Control
0885-0232 C A Selects. Spectrochemical Analysis
0885-0259 Powerconversion & Intelligent Motion
0885-0429 Children's Literature Association Quarterly
0885-0445 E D P Auditor *changed to* E D P Auditor Journal.
0885-0607 International Journal of Intelligence and Counterintelligence
0885-0615 Human Research Report
0885-064X Journal of Complexity
0885-0658 Starmont Pulp & Paper Dime Novel Studies
0885-0666 Journal of Intensive Care Medicine
0885-0690 Good Food†
0885-0704 Food & Justice†
0885-0720 South Florida Poetry Review *changed to* South Florida Poetry Institute Presents the Review.
0885-0763 Sports Fitness *see* 0893-4460
0885-1123 Rehabilitation Report†
0885-114X Occupational Medicine
0885-1158 Medical Problems of Performing Artists
0885-1174 Human Stress: Current Selected Research
0885-1328 Hudson's State Capitals
0885-1522 Tanning Trends
0885-1603 Private Schools of the United States†
0885-1751 Hazardous Substances†
0885-176X U S - Mexico Report†
0885-1808 Professional Stained Glass
0885-1972 Military Forum†
0885-1980 Current Advances in Clinical Chemistry
0885-1999 Fairfax†
0885-2006 Early Childhood Research Quarterly
0885-2014 Cognitive Development
0885-2030 Outlaw Biker
0885-2049 Boston College Magazine
0885-2111 Research in Consumer Behavior
0885-2138 High Spots
0885-2200 Third World in Perspective
0885-2308 Computer Speech & Language
0885-2316 Annual Third World Conference Proceedings
0885-2332 Maat†
0885-2340 T V Program Investor
0885-2367 Hinman Heritage
0885-2413 A G A Monthly *changed to* A G A American Gas.
0885-2499 North Dakota R E C Magazine
0885-2510 Micro Ticker Report *see* 1047-2908
0885-257X Healthcare Forum *see* 0899-9287
0885-2685 Texas Review
0885-2707 Dollmaking
0885-2715 High Technology Law Journal
0885-3010 I E E E Transactions on Ultrasonics, Ferroelectrics and Frequency Control
0885-307X Maine Seine
0885-3177 Pancreas
0885-3185 Movement Disorders
0885-3258 The Oregon State
0885-3282 Journal of Biomaterials Applications
0885-3290 Washington Book Review (Washington, 1985)†
0885-3312 Marketing Research Review
0885-3363 International Advertiser
0885-3371 Poultry Times
0885-3460 Council of Exceptional Children. Division for Early Childhood. Journal *changed to* Journal of Early Intervention.
0885-3800 Joint A S M E - I E E E Railroad Conference. I E E E Technical Papers *see* 1054-0253
0885-3819 Joint A S M E - I E E E - A A R Railroad Conference. I E E E Technical Papers *see* 1054-0253
0885-386X Kurdish Times
0885-3886 Phenomenological Inquiry
0885-3894 Public Garden
0885-3908 International Trade Journal
0885-3916 Society of Logistics Engineers. Annals
0885-3924 Journal of Pain and Symptom Management
0885-3975 Guild: a Sourcebook of American Craft Artists *changed to* Guild: A Sourcebook of Artists and Artisans.
0885-4017 Open-Apple *changed to* A2 - Central.
0885-4122 Journal of Planning Literature
0885-4262 Photomarket
0885-4270 Photobulletin
0885-4300 Socialism and Democracy
0885-4327 Mineral News
0885-4483 Comments on Condensed Matter Physics
0885-4505 Biochemical Medicine and Metabolic Biology
0885-4513 Biotechnology and Applied Biochemistry
0885-4521 Who's Who in U S Writers, Editors and Poets *see* 1049-8621
0885-4572 Adult Day Care Letter
0885-4580 Heidegger Studies
0885-467X McNeese Review
0885-470X M R Magazine *changed to* Men's Report.
0885-4718 The Capital
0885-4726 Journal of Health Care Chaplaincy
0885-4734 Journal of Chemical Dependency Treatment
0885-4750 Fabulous Mustangs and Exotic Fords
0885-4769 Jacksonville Today
0885-4777 100 Highest Yields
0885-4823 Haynes Family Association. Chronicle
0885-4831 Connecticut Historical Society. Bulletin
0885-4858 Optimal Health†
0885-4890 Brilliant Ideas For Publishers
0885-4947 Pilgrim Journal
0885-5013 Saguaro
0885-5625 Bioprocessing Technology *see* 1056-7194
0885-5684 Advanced Manufacturing Technology
0885-5706 Nicaraguan Perspectives
0885-5722 Rock & Ice
0885-5749 Patterson Post
0885-5765 Physiological and Molecular Plant Pathology
0885-579X Journal of Personality Disorders
0885-5811 King's Gulf Grain Guide
0885-5935 Gas Daily
0885-5943 Florida State Collection of Arthropods. Occasional Papers
0885-5951 Soviet Biological Research Abstracts
0885-6087 Hydrological Processes: An International Journal
0885-6095 Western Journal of Applied Forestry
0885-6117 Hot Shots (San Diego)
0885-6125 Machine Learning
0885-6133 Common Ground (Alexandria)
0885-615X Bear News
0885-6168 Executive A I D S Watch†
0885-6206 Nielsen Researcher
0885-6214 Publishing and New Media Technology Newsletter†
0885-6222 Human Psychopharmacology: Clinical and Experimental
0885-6230 International Journal of Geriatric Psychiatry
0885-6249 Social Behaviour *see* 1052-9284
0885-6257 European Journal of Special Needs Education
0885-6362 Geobyte
0885-6370 Publication Design Annual
0885-6435 Seacoast Life *changed to* New Hampshire Life.
0885-6583 Ohio Chess Bulletin
0885-6648 The Single Scene (Gahanna)
0885-6699 Pragmatist
0885-6710 Personal Communications Technology†
0885-6729 S I N E T
0885-6745 S T V Guide†
0885-6788 I C A's Newsletter
0885-6842 Something about the Author. Autobiography Series
0885-6877 Foodservice East
0885-6990 BIOSIS CAS Selects: Antiviral Agents *see* 1047-8078
0885-7113 Balungan
0885-713X Quality Assurance and Utilization Review
0885-7156 Powder Diffraction
0885-7172 Fair Employment Compliance
0885-7202 Employee Communication (New York)
0885-7229 In Depth (New York)
0885-7237 Econews
0885-7253 Metaphor and Symbolic Activity
0885-7261 Brown University Child and Adolescent Behavior Letter
0885-7288 Career Development for Exceptional Individuals
0885-7385 La Posta
0885-7423 Psychology and Sociology of Sport: Current Selected Research
0885-7458 International Journal of Parallel Programming
0885-7466 Social Justice Research
0885-7474 Journal of Scientific Computing
0885-7482 Journal of Family Violence
0885-7490 Metabolic Brain Disease
0885-7555 Reference Guides to Archives and Manuscript Collections on Immigrant Culture
0885-7636 Vegetarian Journal
0885-7741 Recorder (New York)
0885-7776 General Council of the Assemblies of God. Memos
0885-7946 World Food & Drink Report
0885-7962 C O D A Newsletter
0885-8020 Professional Builder *changed to* Professional Builder & Remodeler.
0885-8039 Remodeling
0885-8055 Business Software Review†
0885-8160 Kayhan International
0885-8187 Kayhan Arabi
0885-8195 Journal of Cancer Education
0885-8276 American Journal of Physiologic Imaging
0885-8330 Transportation Energy Research
0885-8411 Access Control - Fence Industry *see* 0894-6639
0885-8411 Access Control Buyers' Guide
0885-8462 Contemporary Graphic Artists
0885-8500 Common Boundary
0885-8543 Triad†
0885-856X Tort & Insurance Law Journal
0885-8608 Natural Areas Journal
0885-8616 Merger Management Report
0885-8624 Journal of Business & Industrial Marketing
0885-8659 Shmate†
0885-8950 I E E E Transactions on Power Systems
0885-8969 I E E E Transactions on Energy Conversion
0885-8977 I E E E Transactions on Power Delivery
0885-8985 I E E E Aerospace and Electronic Systems Magazine
0885-8993 I E E E Transactions on Power Electronics
0885-9000 I E E E Expert
0885-9027 Washington Crossing Card Collectors Club Newsletter
0885-9124 Faxnet†
0885-9159 Contributions to the Study of World History
0885-9191 T M J Update: A Current Review of Temporomandibular Joint Developments
0885-9205 Manhattan Poetry Review
0885-9221 S P E Production Engineering
0885-923X S P E Formation Evaluation
0885-9248 S P E Reservoir Engineering
0885-9256 P S (Wynantskill)
0885-9264 Contact Lens Update
0885-9337 Boulevard
0885-9361 ArtToday
0885-940X City & State
0885-9477 Sparrow Poverty Pamphlets *changed to* Sparrow (West Lafayette).
0885-9507 Microcomputers in Civil Engineering
0885-9612 Shelterforce
0885-968X Emblematica
0885-9698 Techniques in Orthopaedics
0885-9701 Journal of Head Trauma Rehabilitation
0885-971X Topics in Acute Care and Trauma Rehabilitation†
0885-9744 S P E Drilling Engineering
0885-9779 China Clipper
0885-9809 R E T S Digest†
0885-9884 Association of Teachers of Japanese. Journal
0885-9914 Indian Health Trends and Services
0885-9922 Lutheran Partners
0885-9930 Building Economic Alternatives *changed to* Co-op America Quarterly.
0885-9949 Marine Textiles
0885-9957 Spang Robinson Report
0885-9973 Maine Bar Journal
0886-0009 Biotech Update†
0886-005X Champs-Elysees
0886-0076 Directory of American Research and Technology
0886-0092 Readers' Guide Abstracts. Microfiche Edition
0886-0114 International Arbitration Report
0886-0122 Mealey's Litigation Report: Tobacco
0886-0130 International Journal of Radiation Applications and Instrumentation. Part E: Nuclear Geophysics
0886-0149 Ocean Navigator
0886-0165 Non-Credit Learning News
0886-019X Optical Information Systems Update: Library and Information Center Applications *see* 0893-9934
0886-022X Renal Failure
0886-0238 Hematologic Pathology
0886-0246 Reading Research and Instruction
0886-0262 Heritage Quest
0886-0335 American Machinist and Automated Manufacturing *see* 1041-7958
0886-036X Reality Change
0886-0408 Law Books in Review
0886-0440 Journal of Cardiac Surgery
0886-0459 Letters of Credit Report
0886-0467 Lasers in the Life Sciences
0886-0475 B N A's Corporate Counsel Weekly
0886-0483 How
0886-0505 Children's Environments Quarterly†
0886-0521 Nelson's Research Monthly *see* 1044-0267
0886-0556 Computer Shopper
0886-0572 Maryland Medical Journal
0886-0599 Beckett Baseball Card Monthly
0886-0637 Wildfowl
0886-0653 Medical Ethics Advisor
0886-067X Southeastern Front
0886-0807 Washington Summary
0886-0912 Pay Dirt. Rocky Mountain Edition
0886-0920 Pay Dirt. Southwestern Edition
0886-0963 Shoe Retailing Today
0886-103X Technology Management Action
0886-1080 Orienteering North America
0886-1099 Affilia
0886-1102 P S L S
0886-1196 America's Spirit
0886-1269 Tennessee Wildlife
0886-1285 Seeker Magazine *see* 0890-538X
0886-1293 Company
0886-1315 Infant Screening
0886-1463 N C S Integrated Manufacturing
0886-1501 Sharing Ideas
0886-1528 International Review of Industrial and Organizational Psychology
0886-1544 Cell Motility and the Cytoskeleton
0886-1609 Radio Control Car Action
0886-1633 Evaluation Practice
0886-1641 Journal of Social Behavior and Personality
0886-1714 News in Physiological Sciences
0886-1811 Catholic War Veteran
0886-1862 Hogaku†
0886-1935 Closing the Gap

ISSN

0886-1943 Iowa Journal of Speech Communication
0886-1994 The Competitive Advantage
0886-2044 Community Murals†
0886-2060 Works and Days
0886-2087 VoiceNews
0886-2095 Health Care Competition Week
0886-2109 Historic New Orleans Collection Newsletter
0886-2249 Rolling Stock
0886-2257 Air & Space - Smithsonian
0886-229X National Communications Forum. Proceedings
0886-2362 Token Perspectives Newsletter
0886-2397 LocalNetter Newsletter
0886-2400 Datacom Reader
0886-2419 Linkup *see* 0893-8075
0886-2435 Change Exchange
0886-2451 New Pathways
0886-2478 France Magazine
0886-2508 School Law Bulletin (Chapel Hill)
0886-2605 Journal of Interpersonal Violence
0886-2648 Suffolk Transnational Law Journal
0886-2664 Upwellings
0886-2729 Florida Market Update
0886-2796 Dorot
0886-280X Social Science (Chapel Hill)†
0886-2818 Wind Energy News
0886-2958 Mystery Time *changed to* Mystery Time Anthology.
0886-3024 Business Alabama *see* 1050-091X
0886-3032 Spin
0886-3083 Activewear *see* 0896-1417
0886-3156 Spiritual Mothering Journal
0886-3210 California Western International Law Journal
0886-3342 Official Guide to U.S. Law Schools
0886-3350 Journal of Cataract and Refractive Surgery
0886-3458 Wildlife Harvest
0886-3474 Underwater Medicine: Abstracts from the Literature *changed to* Underwater and Hyperbaric Medicine: Abstracts from the Literature.
0886-3490 Arms Control Reporter
0886-3520 Copyright Society of the U.S.A. Journal
0886-3547 Tax Management Estates, Gifts and Trusts Journal
0886-3601 Hooks Family Chronicles†
0886-3717 U S - Arab Commerce†
0886-3741 Candy Marketer (Cleveland)
0886-3768 Western Investor Newsletter†
0886-3784 Readings
0886-3806 Cypris
0886-3849 Journal of Tumor Marker Oncology
0886-3881 National Directory of Minority - Owned Business Firms
0886-389X National Directory of Woman - Owned Business Firms
0886-3954 Dance Research Annual†
0886-3970 C A R D Report (Ames, 1986)
0886-4047 Abacus (Elmwood)
0886-4144 Loadstar
0886-4152 Softdisk
0886-4179 Serials Directory
0886-4187 Blue Pitcher
0886-4217 U S Aviation Reports
0886-4268 Precious Fibers
0886-4276 World Chronology Series
0886-4411 Power and Motoryacht
0886-4446 Cooking Light
0886-4454 Biocatalysis
0886-4470 Archives of Otolaryngology - Head & Neck Surgery
0886-4616 New Frontier
0886-4659 Ops: The Data Center Newsletter†
0886-4772 K C M S Bulletin
0886-4780 Potato Country
0886-4802 Young Viewers†
0886-4969 Heard Journal†
0886-5051 Cotton Boll
0886-5078 Staton's Money Advisory
0886-5140 Comments on Toxicology
0886-5159 American Presbyterians: Journal of Presbyterian History
0886-5272 Historical Footnotes (Stonington)
0886-5302 Petite
0886-537X Telephone Bypass News†
0886-5388 Shared Tenant Service News†
0886-5396 Pay Phone News†
0886-5418 Chevron U S A Odyssey
0886-5477 Journal of Pastoral Psychotherapy *see* 1045-5876
0886-5582 Private Label International
0886-5604 Cruise Digest Reports
0886-5612 Copycat Magazine
0886-5620 A S E T Newsletter
0886-5647 Nationwide Overnight Stabling Directory *changed to* Nationwide Overnight Stabling Directory & Equestrian Vacation Guide.
0886-5655 Journal of Borderland Studies
0886-5663 Produce Business
0886-5671 Electronic Chemicals News
0886-571X Residential Treatment for Children & Youth
0886-5779 Horticultural News
0886-5809 Optical Information Systems *see* 1054-9692
0886-5922 Business Journal (San Jose)
0886-5949 Exteriors†
0886-5957 Manna
0886-6015 Civilian - Based Defense: News and Opinion
0886-6104 Pro Motion
0886-6163 What to Buy for Business (US Edition)
0886-618X Surface Mount Technology Today
0886-6198 Global Affairs
0886-6236 Global Biogeochemical Cycles
0886-6287 Chesapeake and Ohio Historical Magazine
0886-6465 Diplomate *changed to* Environmental Engineering.
0886-6481 Thoughts for All Seasons
0886-6511 News About the A - V Scene
0886-6570 Cinematograph
0886-6597 Valley Business Perspectives
0886-6643 Electronic House
0886-6651 Southeast Asia Business *see* 1055-2073
0886-666X Stanford Literature Review
0886-6678 Legal Plan Letter
0886-6686 United Nations Resolutions. Series 1. Resolutions Adopted by the General Assembly
0886-6694 Preventing Sexual Abuse
0886-6708 Violence and Victims
0886-6716 Chemical Design Automation News
0886-6724 Collection of Bibliographic and Research Resources
0886-6791 The Gate
0886-6848 Human Nutrition
0886-6880 Claremont Reading Conference. Yearbook
0886-6910 Iskcon Review
0886-7062 Connexions (Oakland)
0886-7097 Studies in American Drama, 1945 - Present
0886-7151 Noticias del Puerto de Monterey
0886-7186 Clinical Oncology Alert
0886-7194 Computer Marketing Newsletter
0886-7267 Spirit (Princeton)†
0886-7356 Cultural Anthropology
0886-7402 Handbook of Living Will Laws *changed to* Refusal of Treatment Legislation (Year).
0886-747X Rocky Mountain Mineral Law Institute. Proceedings
0886-7607 S D I Monitor
0886-7682 Step-by-Step Graphics
0886-7755 Advances in Trauma *changed to* Advances in Trauma and Critical Care.
0886-7763 Searching Illinois Ancestors *changed to* Searching Illinois Ancestors - Travel Illinois.
0886-7771 Radius
0886-7798 Tunnelling and Underground Space Technology
0886-7976 Midland Review
0886-8018 Key Neurology and Neurosurgery
0886-8026 Key Ophthalmology
0886-8034 Soma: Engineering for the Human Body†
0886-8093 Q E X A R R L Experimenters' Exchange and A M S A T Satellite Journal *changed to* Q E X A R R L Experimenters' Exchange.
0886-814X News C A S T
0886-8166 Business Age
0886-8174 Puget Sound Computer User
0886-8204 Commercial Lending Review
0886-8220 Contributions in Medical Studies
0886-8239 Contributions in Labor Studies
0886-845X Entry
0886-8484 Working Classics
0886-8557 Tennessee Employment Law Update
0886-8573 Candle (Naselle)†
0886-8611 Rural Development News
0886-8743 2 A M Magazine
0886-876X Minute-a-Day Health Newsletter†
0886-8832 Military Club & Hospitality
0886-8859 Phoenix Metro *see* 1045-1773
0886-9103 Howard Historian
0886-9154 Rocky Mountain Council on Latin American Studies. Proceedings
0886-9162 Workers' Compensation Journal of Ohio
0886-9197 River Runner *changed to* Paddler.
0886-9375 Regulated Rivers: Research and Management
0886-9383 Journal of Chemometrics
0886-943X Cook's†
0886-9448 Sea Frontiers *see* 0897-2249
0886-9553 Computers & Mathematics with Applications. Part A *see* 0898-1221
0886-9561 Computers & Mathematics with Applications. Part B *see* 0898-1221
0886-9669 Window Fashions
0886-9693 Empire State Farmer
0886-9723 Journal of Ambulatory Care Marketing
0886-9812 Excellence (Louisville)
0886-9863 Resort & Hotel Management†
0886-9901 Cleaning and Restoration
0886-9979 National Education Association Rhode Island. Newsline
0886-9995 New Jersey Success†
0887-0004 N D Banner
0887-011X Wellsprings
0887-0144 Convenience Care Update†
0887-0152 Peterson's Competitive Colleges (Year)
0887-0187 A B A Bank Compliance
0887-0217 Teaching Thinking & Problem Solving Newsletter
0887-0241 Johns Hopkins University. Population Information Program. Population Reports. English Edition.
0887-025X Johns Hopkins University. Population Information Program. Population Reports. French Edition
0887-0268 Johns Hopkins University. Population Information Program. Population Reports. Spanish Edition
0887-0276 Johns Hopkins University. Population Information Program. Population Reports. Portuguese Edition
0887-0292 A I D S Alert
0887-0306 Orphan Disease Update
0887-0365 Parent and Preschooler Newsletter
0887-0373 Public Affairs Quarterly
0887-0411 Zone (New York)
0887-042X Creative Classroom
0887-0446 Psychology & Health
0887-0470 Monitor's Retail Tenant Directory
0887-0500 Soviet - East European Survey†
0887-0527 American Cities Chronologies Series
0887-0535 Food & Nutrition Quarterly Index†
0887-0551 Directory of Grants in the Humanities
0887-056X Accomplishments in Oncology†
0887-0594 Central America NewsPak
0887-0624 Energy & Fuels
0887-0896 For Poets Only
0887-0942 Federation of Insurance and Corporate Counsel Quarterly
0887-0950 M D N Motorcycle Dealer News *see* 0888-4234
0887-1027 Gym Dandies†
0887-1043 I R F Newsletter†
0887-106X National Legal Bibliography. Part 2. Government Documents from Official and Commercial Sources *see* 1049-7978
0887-1132 Charter Connections
0887-1167 Single Adult Ministry Information
0887-1175 Computing Information Directory
0887-1183 Legal Handbook for Architects, Engineers and Contractors
0887-1191 Civil Rights Litigation and Attorney Fees Annual Handbook
0887-1264 Cole Chronicle
0887-1280 Pate Pioneers
0887-1299 Elkins Eagle
0887-137X E B R I Issue Brief
0887-1388 Employee Benefit Notes
0887-1418 Hand Papermaking
0887-1493 A I D S Policy and Law
0887-1574 Index to Book Reviews in Religion
0887-1612 Conditioned Response
0887-1620 Metropolitan Indianapolis Realtor *changed to* Realtor Voice.
0887-1639 C M J S Centerpieces
0887-1655 Van Wert County Genealogical Quarterly†
0887-168X Heliogram (Bridgeport)
0887-1701 T V Technology
0887-171X Polling Report
0887-1876 Electronic Publishing & Printing
0887-1892 Founder Sounder
0887-1922 John T. Reed's Real Estate Investor's Monthly
0887-1930 Corporate Technology Directory
0887-1949 Materials and Processing Report
0887-1973 Metro Handbook and Directory of Members (Year)†
0887-2007 High-Scope Resource
0887-2015 Attorney's Medical Advisory Letter *see* 0899-0255
0887-2023 Vedic Globe
0887-2074 South Coast Poetry Journal
0887-2082 Journal of Biochemical Toxicology
0887-2104 Operations Forum
0887-2120 Woman Engineer
0887-2139 Frederick Forerunners
0887-2147 Au Courant Newsmagazine
0887-2155 Duckburg Times
0887-2171 Seminars in Ultrasound, C T and M R
0887-2198 Ad Nurse *see* 1042-9565
0887-2201 Private Funding Advisor†
0887-221X Expert System Strategies *changed to* Intelligent Software.
0887-2236 Biological and Cultural Tests for Control of Plant Diseases
0887-2244 Thoroughbred Times
0887-2252 Fairfield County Business Journal
0887-2279 Alaska Business Newsletter†
0887-2287 Installation News
0887-2333 Toxicology in Vitro
0887-2376 Science Scope
0887-2392 Soviet Medical Reviews. Section B: Physicochemical Aspects of Medicine Reviews
0887-2406 Curly Cues
0887-2465 Military & Commercial Fiber Business
0887-252X Journal of Theoretical Psychology
0887-2562 Tax Management Washington Tax Review
0887-2570 Journal of Heart Transplantation *see* 1053-2498
0887-2597 Heartland Journal (Madison)†
0887-2716 Apple Library Users Group Newsletter
0887-2783 Social History of Alcohol Review
0887-283X Dickinson Journal of International Law
0887-2856 Lest We Forget
0887-2929 Publishers' Physician Fee Catalog *changed to* Catalog of Publisher Information.
0887-2937 Clothing and Textile Arts Index
0887-302X Clothing & Textiles Research Journal
0887-3046 Zingsheim Times
0887-3054 UNIX in the Office
0887-3135 Holston Pastfinder
0887-3208 Florida Real Estate and Development Update
0887-3267 The Humanistic Psychologist

ISSN INDEX 5807

0887-3453 Spotlight (Robbinsville)
0887-3488 Soviet Medical Reviews. Section D: Immunology Reviews
0887-3496 Soviet Medical Reviews. Section E: Virology Reviews
0887-3518 Chinese Physics - Lasers†
0887-3534 Drug Therapy for the Elderly†
0887-3569 Contemporary Social Issues: A Bibliographic Series
0887-3577 Social Theory: A Bibliographic Series
0887-3585 Proteins: Structure, Function, and Genetics
0887-3615 I C L A Bulletin
0887-3682 Pennsylvania Manufacturers Register
0887-3690 Creative Quilting
0887-3712 H L B Newsletter
0887-3763 Reference and Research Book News
0887-3771 Utah Centennial Series
0887-378X Milbank Quarterly
0887-3801 Journal of Computing in Civil Engineering
0887-381X Journal of Cold Regions Engineering
0887-3828 Journal of Performance of Constructed Facilities
0887-3844 New Directions in Information Management
0887-3852 A I D S & Public Policy Journal
0887-3860 Wandering Wolfs
0887-3887 Mobile Graduate News and Notes *changed to* Health Professions News and Notes.
0887-4042 Directory of Primes
0887-4050 Small Business Preferential Subcontracts Opportunities Monthly
0887-4085 Government Primecontracts Monthly
0887-4107 Government Production Prime Contractors Directory
0887-4115 Bellowing Ark
0887-414X Beauty Age
0887-4220 Sea Grant Abstracts
0887-4247 Harris West Virginia Manufacturing Directory (Year)
0887-4255 Harris Kentucky Industrial Directory (Year)
0887-428X Washington Spectator
0887-4301 Northrop University Law Journal of Aerospace, Business and Taxation
0887-4328 Lighthouse (Auburn)
0887-4336 Electronic Representatives Directory (Year)
0887-4417 Journal of Computer Information Systems
0887-4468 Public Innovation Abroad
0887-4492 Lake Effect
0887-4514 A D L A
0887-4700 C-Store Week *see* 0502-9767
0887-4743 New West Virginia Hillbilly
0887-4778 Commercial Investment Real Estate Journal
0887-4905 Attorney's Directory of Forensic Psychologists†
0887-493X Alabama Heritage
0887-5049 Prism (New Brighton)
0887-5057 Erotic Fiction Quarterly
0887-5073 Valve News
0887-5081 Pump News
0887-5162 Optical Information Systems Update *see* 1054-9706
0887-5170 Hayden's Ferry Review
0887-5227 Virginia's Press
0887-5308 CrazyQuilt
0887-5332 On Achieving Excellence
0887-5367 Hypatia
0887-543X Lycoming County Historical Society Journal
0887-5480 Relationship & Family Communications
0887-5499 Hungry Mind Review
0887-5693 Emerick Family Newsletter
0887-5707 Magnets in Your Future
0887-5715 Redneck Review
0887-5731 Chronicles
0887-5812 Journal of Real Estate Development†
0887-5847 T V Collector
0887-5863 New York Mets Inside Pitch
0887-588X Northwest Georgia Historical & Genealogical Quarterly
0887-5901 Who's Who in Technology
0887-6045 Journal of Services Marketing
0887-6061 Balloon Life
0887-6134 Biomedical and Environmental Mass Spectrometry *see* 1052-9306
0887-6169 Clinical Vision Sciences
0887-6177 Archives of Clinical Neuropsychology
0887-6185 Journal of Anxiety Disorders
0887-6207 BioScan
0887-6223 Great Lakes Travel & Living
0887-624X Journal of Polymer Science. Part A: Polymer Chemistry
0887-6258 Journal of Polymer Science. Part C: Polymer Letters *see* 0887-6266
0887-6258 Journal of Polymer Science. Part C: Polymer Letters *see* 0887-624X
0887-6266 Journal of Polymer Science. Part B: Polymer Physics
0887-6274 Clinical Nurse Specialist
0887-6290 Georgist Journal
0887-6312 Frary Family Newsletter
0887-6320 Frary Family Journal
0887-638X Deaf Artists of America News *changed to* Uncharted.
0887-6398 Counter-Terrorism *changed to* Security Intelligence Report.
0887-6509 Journal of Compliance in Health Care†
0887-6576 Table Tennis Topics
0887-6622 Ferroelectrics Bulletin *see* 1056-7046
0887-6665 Masterkey†
0887-6681 Xavier Review
0887-6703 Spectroscopy
0887-6819 Great Britain Correspondence Club. Quarterly Newsletter *changed to* Great Britain Collectors Club. Quarterly Newsletter.
0887-6827 Offshore Service Vessels†
0887-6835 Offshore Tugs†
0887-6851 Video Librarian
0887-686X Hydrological Science and Technology
0887-6878 Exhibit Builder
0887-6916 Advances in Otolaryngology - Head and Neck Surgery
0887-6924 Leukemia
0887-6959 Whitman County Genealogical Society. Newsletter
0887-6991 Latest Jokes
0887-736X For Formulation Chemists Only
0887-7386 Apis
0887-7394 Toxics Law Reporter
0887-7408 RateGram
0887-7416 American Brewer Magazine
0887-7505 Bed & Breakfast Update†
0887-7521 The Agricultural Credit Letter
0887-7556 Printout
0887-7629 Political Risk Letter
0887-7637 Political Climate for International Business *see* 1041-3553
0887-7661 Network World
0887-7777 Lawyer Referral Network
0887-7785 Criminal Justice (Chicago)
0887-7793 Corporate Officers and Directors Liability Litigation Reporter
0887-7807 Failed Bank and Thrift Litigation Reporter
0887-7815 Pharmaceutical Litigation Reporter
0887-7823 General Aviation Accident Report
0887-7831 Tobacco Industry Litigation Reporter
0887-784X Commodities Litigation Reporter
0887-7858 Insurance Industry Litigation Reporter
0887-7866 Andrews School Asbestos Alert†
0887-7874 Racketeering Litigation Reporter *changed to* Civil R I C O Litigation Reporter.
0887-7963 Transfusion Medicine Reviews
0887-7971 American Journal of Cardiac Imaging
0887-8013 Journal of Clinical Laboratory Analysis
0887-8048 New Jersey Folklife
0887-8056 New York, New Jersey, Connecticut Real Estate†
0887-8064 Washington Information Directory (Year)
0887-8145 Addictions Alert *see* 1040-6328
0887-8161 F A C S
0887-817X Fitness in Business†
0887-8218 Forum for Applied Research and Public Policy
0887-8226 Providence Business News
0887-8250 Journal of Sensory Studies
0887-8358 Peterson's Guides. Annual Guides to Graduate Study. Book 1: Accredited Institutions Offering Graduate Work - An Overview *see* 0894-9344
0887-8374 Peterson's Guides. Annual Guides to Graduate Study. Book 2: Humanities and Social Sciences. *see* 0894-9352
0887-8412 Peterson's Guides. Annual Guides to Graduate Study. Book 3: Biological, Agricultural and Health Sciences *see* 0894-9360
0887-8439 Consumer Reports Travel Letter
0887-8447 National Gardening
0887-8579 Peterson's Guides. Annual Guides to Graduate Study. Book 4: Physical Sciences *see* 0894-9379
0887-8587 Physical Sciences and Mathematics *see* 0894-9379
0887-8609 Peterson's Guides. Annual Guides to Graduate Study. Book 5: Engineering and Applied Sciences *see* 0894-9387
0887-8625 International Journal of Childbirth Education
0887-8633 V L S
0887-8722 Journal of Thermophysics and Heat Transfer
0887-8781 Precis
0887-8897 Shaman's Drum
0887-8935 Station Relay
0887-896X A B A Juvenile and Child Welfare Law Reporter
0887-8978 American Institute for Conservation of Historic and Artistic Works. Book & Paper Group Annual
0887-8986 Applied Artificial Intelligence Reporter *see* 0897-3466
0887-9060 Casting World
0887-9087 G H A A News *see* 1050-9038
0887-9109 Family Therapy Today†
0887-9117 Yearbook on Socialist Legal Systems†
0887-9133 AgVenture
0887-9141 Cadence (Austin)
0887-9206 Notes on Computing
0887-9222 Kresge Art Museum Bulletin
0887-9249 South Carolina Out-of-Doors
0887-9257 Taproot
0887-9273 Mensest
0887-9346 The World & I
0887-9354 Lybarger Linkages
0887-9397 Shooting Sports Retailer
0887-9486 Teaching and Learning: The Journal of Natural Inquiry
0887-9559 World Status Map *changed to* Pinkerton World Status Map.
0887-9613 Pantera International News
0887-9672 P C I Journal
0887-9753 Environmental Manager's Compliance Advisor
0887-980X Computers in Personnel†
0887-9818 Craft & Needlework Age Annual Trade Directory
0887-9842 Neurosurgery (Philadelphia)†
0887-9850 Cardiac Surgery
0887-9869 Spine (Philadelphia, 1986)
0887-9923 Llamas Magazine
0887-9982 Tikkun Magazine
0887-9990 W E P Z A Newsletter
0888-000X Zone 3
0888-0018 Pediatric Hematology & Oncology
0888-0050 Dairy Foods
0888-0050 Dairy Foods Market Directory
0888-0131 Portable 100
0888-0166 Directory of Home Furnishings Retailers (Year)
0888-028X Animal Health and Nutrition *changed to* Large Animal Veterinarian.
0888-031X Karate - Kung Fu Illustrated
0888-0379 National Jewish Post and Opinion
0888-0387 Interior Construction
0888-0395 Journal of Neuroscience Nursing
0888-0417 Civil Liberties Review
0888-0433 Guide to the American Occult
0888-045X Bottom Line (New York)
0888-0573 N S B E Journal *changed to* N S B E Magazine.
0888-0611 I E E E Control Systems Magazine
0888-0697 Soviet Medical Reviews. Section A: Cardiology Reviews
0888-0700 Soviet Medical Reviews. Section F: Oncology Reviews
0888-0727 Soviet Medical Reviews Supplement Series. Section A: Cardiology
0888-076X Decorative Arts Digest
0888-0786 Serodiagnosis and Immunotherapy
0888-0794 Postal Employees' Newsletter†
0888-0808 Elle
0888-0832 Windham Phoenix
0888-0840 Adweek: New England
0888-0948 Electronic Publishing Business†
0888-0972 MalLife
0888-1006 Rodale's Practical Homeowner *see* 1042-4601
0888-1022 Mid-Atlantic Country Magazine
0888-1057 S T World
0888-1065 Caribbean Trend Watch
0888-1081 Avalon Hill General
0888-1103 Wheel
0888-1154 American Rowing
0888-1197 Wrongful Termination Litigation Reporter *changed to* Employment Litigation Reporter.
0888-1227 Composites & Adhesives Newsletter
0888-1286 Language of Dance
0888-1340 Virginia Business
0888-1375 East West: The Journal of Natural Health and Living
0888-1391 National Alliance (New York)
0888-1413 Business Organizations, Agencies, and Publications Directory
0888-1472 Farm Woman *see* 0892-8525
0888-1596 News Computing Journal
0888-1715 California Grower
0888-1812 T A C Bulletin†
0888-1839 A M A Educators' Proceedings
0888-1871 Atlantic Communicator
0888-188X Ball State University Forum†
0888-191X Na'Amat Woman
0888-1928 Gambit
0888-1944 Collector Car News
0888-1979 Nonwovens World†
0888-2061 Whole Life†
0888-2088 Computer Software Engineering Series
0888-2096 Principles of Computer Science Series
0888-2118 Digital System Design Series
0888-2126 Swarthmore College Bulletin
0888-2134 Electrical Engineering Communications and Signal Processing *changed to* Electrical Engineering, Telecommunications and Signal Processing.
0888-2177 Computers in Education Series†
0888-2193 Computers and Math Series†
0888-2207 Advances in Satellite Communications Series†
0888-2215 Advances in Biomedical Computing Series†
0888-2223 Advances in Telecommunications Networks Series†
0888-2231 Applications of Computer Science Series
0888-224X Advances in V L S I and Computer Systems†
0888-2274 Augustinian Heritage
0888-2452 Interim (Las Vegas)
0888-2460 Mideast Monitor
0888-2517 Voice *changed to* Hearing Health.
0888-255X Secured Lender
0888-2673 Length of Stay by Operation, United States, Northeastern Region *changed to* Length of Stay by Diagnosis & Operation, United States, Northeastern Region.
0888-2746 Housing and Society

ISSN

5808 ISSN INDEX

0888-2819 Wallenberg Papers on International Finance
0888-2843 Parent Care†
0888-3009 Pre-K Today
0888-3033 T C Interface
0888-305X A E G News
0888-3068 Hospital Materials Management
0888-3076 Dr. Dobb's Journal of Software Tools *see* 1044-789X
0888-3106 Strings
0888-3114 National Tort Reform *see* 1055-307X
0888-3149 Bank Marketing
0888-3173 Editors' Notes
0888-319X In Vitro Toxicology
0888-322X Pegasus (Nevada)
0888-3254 East European Politics & Societies
0888-3262 Personal Computing Series†
0888-3270 Mechanical Systems & Signal Processing
0888-3327 Marketers Forum Magazine
0888-3335 Single Impact†
0888-3432 Institute of Noetic Sciences. Newsletter *see* 0897-1013
0888-3440 Ultimate Issues
0888-3459 Westchester Commerce
0888-3467 Performance Materials
0888-3475 Aboriginal S F *changed to* Aboriginal Science Fiction.
0888-3483 Nutrition Clinics
0888-3521 Howling Dog
0888-367X Extra Income
0888-3742 Best American Essays
0888-3785 A I Expert
0888-3807 Robeson County Register
0888-3882 University of Cincinnati Studies in Historical and Contemporary Europe
0888-3890 Literature and the Visual Arts: New Foundations
0888-3904 Studies in Modern German Literature
0888-3920 Soviet Medical Reviews. Section C: Hematology Reviews
0888-3955 Follow Up File
0888-4080 Applied Cognitive Psychology
0888-4110 Executive Speeches
0888-4153 High Plains Literary Review
0888-4226 Columbia - V L A Journal of Law & the Arts
0888-4234 DealerNews
0888-4250 G H A A Journal†
0888-4285 New York Facts
0888-434X Delaware Corporation Law Update
0888-4390 Journal of Neurologic Rehabilitation
0888-4404 BioChromatography
0888-4412 Obsidian II: Black Literature in Review
0888-4463 Library Administration and Management
0888-448X Radiation Effects Bulletin
0888-4498 Audio Publishing Report *see* 0145-9457
0888-4501 Dealerscope Merchandising
0888-4536 Advances in Soviet Power Systems. Part 1: Thermal and Mechanical†
0888-4544 Advances in Soviet Power Systems. Part 2: Electrical Generation and Distribution†
0888-4552 Practicing Anthropology
0888-4595 Individual Psychology Reporter
0888-4625 Barnett Source
0888-4633 Home Education Magazine
0888-4641 M and M Rapper
0888-4692 Calliopes Corner
0888-4722 Expo Info†
0888-4773 Journal of Sport Management
0888-4781 The Sport Psychologist
0888-479X Applied Mathematics
0888-4803 Soviet Scientific Reviews. Section F: Physiology and General Biology Reviews
0888-4811 Kosher Gourmet Magazine
0888-4846 Peninsula
0888-4889 Bonanza Report
0888-4897 American Journal of Alzheimer's Care and Related Disorders *changed to* American Journal of Alzheimer's Care and Related Disorders and Research.
0888-4935 Insurance Times
0888-5109 The Consultant Pharmacist
0888-5257 Vstrechi
0888-5265 World Airshow News
0888-5281 Perspectives (Grand Rapids)
0888-529X Blades
0888-5346 Northwest Living!
0888-5354 Working Papers on Women in International Development
0888-5427 Realtors Land Institute
0888-5451 AntiqueWeek *changed to* AntiqueWeek - Central.
0888-5591 Privatization Review†
0888-5613 Latin American Indian Literatures Journal
0888-5621 Journal of Women and Religion
0888-5648 Federation Exchange
0888-5656 F S M B Handbook
0888-5664 F S M B Newsletter *see* 0014-9306
0888-5672 Gourd
0888-5680 Photo Design
0888-5702 Japan - U S Business Report
0888-5729 Nucleus (Cambridge)
0888-5753 Studies in Popular Culture
0888-5842 Y M
0888-5869 Asian Religious Studies Information†
0888-5885 Industrial & Engineering Chemistry Research
0888-5893 Trainer's Workshop
0888-5931 Who's Who in Electronics & Computer Science†
0888-594X Who's Who in Mechanical Engineering & Materials Science†
0888-5958 Who's Who in Chemistry & Plastics†
0888-5966 Who's Who in Civil Engineering, Earth Sciences & Energy†
0888-5974 Who's Who in Physics & Optics†
0888-5982 Who's Who in Biotechnology†
0888-6008 Breast Diseases (New York)
0888-6032 Topics in Total Compensation
0888-6067 Development (Arlington)
0888-6075 Laser Nursing
0888-613X International Journal of Approximate Reasoning
0888-627X American Kennel Club Awards
0888-6288 Nursing Scan in Administration
0888-6296 Journal of Cardiothoracic Anesthesia *see* 1053-0770
0888-6504 Journal of Research on Computing in Education *changed to* Journal of Research on Computing in Teacher Education.
0888-6512 Astrophysical Letters and Communications
0888-6520 Backbone†
0888-658X Medical Malpractice Verdicts, Settlements & Experts
0888-6601 Journal of Pan African Studies
0888-661X Hudson Valley G R E E N Times
0888-6768 Guide to the Essentials of a Modern Medical Practice Act
0888-6792 Model for the Preparation of a Guidebook on Medical Discipline
0888-6814 Appalachian Roots
0888-6830 Aging Research & Training News
0888-6881 Academy of Sciences of the U S S R. High Temperature Institute. I V T A N Reviews†
0888-689X Soviet Materials Science Reviews†
0888-6903 Property Data Update†
0888-6911 International Centre for Heat & Mass Transfer. Bulletin†
0888-692X Forensic Reports
0888-6970 Logo Exchange
0888-6989 M A P Netter
0888-6997 O S I Netter Newsletter
0888-7039 Health Facilities in Southern New York: A Guide to Inpatient, Outpatient, and Long-Term Care
0888-7128 European Clinical Laboratory
0888-7225 International Biotechnology Laboratory
0888-7233 Comparative Economic Studies
0888-7292 Telecom - Eye - Bee - Em
0888-7314 Journal of Decorative and Propaganda Arts†
0888-7322 Radiation Effects Express
0888-7330 Health World
0888-7357 Physical Medicine & Rehabilitation
0888-7373 Korea High Tech Review *changed to* East Asia High Tech Review.
0888-7411 Stall
0888-7446 Privatization
0888-7462 International Journal of Powder Metallurgy
0888-7543 Genomics
0888-7551 Bibliographies and Indexes in Science and Technology
0888-7586 Contraband (Lake Charles)
0888-7624 Directory of Nursing Home Facilities
0888-7772 W I D Forum
0888-7829 Modern Food Service News
0888-787X Quarterly Domestic & Global Forecasts of Key Economic Indicators
0888-7926 U S Statistics
0888-7950 Clinical Laboratory Management Review
0888-7993 Accounting Horizons
0888-8027 Linguistics and Language Behavior Abstracts
0888-8124 S A B R Review of Books†
0888-8132 National Forum of Education Administration and Supervision Journal
0888-8140 Harris Ohio Industrial Directory (Year)
0888-8159 Peterson's Guide to Colleges in the West (Year)
0888-8167 Harris Michigan Industrial Directory (Year)
0888-8175 Harris Indiana Industrial Directory (Year)
0888-8183 Energy Report
0888-8191 Circulation Management
0888-8264 Ultrasound Annual
0888-8418 Cardiology Board Review
0888-8469 Innovator (University Park)
0888-8507 P C Magazine: The Independent Guide to I B M - Standard Personal Computing
0888-8582 Right to Know Compliance Advisor *changed to* O S H A Compliance Advisor.
0888-8590 State Government (Washington)
0888-8612 Winds of Change
0888-8647 Governors' Weekly Bulletin
0888-8663 France Today
0888-8671 Callahan's Credit Union Directory
0888-868X Metropolitan Education
0888-8701 American Handel Society. Newsletter
0888-8752 Middlebury Studies in Russian Language and Literature
0888-8809 Molecular Endocrinology
0888-8817 Forensic Engineering†
0888-8833 Open Hands
0888-8884 Alaska Wilderness Milepost
0888-8892 Conservation Biology
0888-8957 J C P S Congressional District Fact Book
0888-9007 Jusur
0888-9015 Cue Sheet
0888-904X Japan Electronics (Gardena)
0888-9066 Practice Personel Bulletin *see* 1042-2625
0888-9074 Baptist Trumpet
0888-9090 L C - G C
0888-9171 Progressive Builder *see* 0895-2493
0888-9287 Advances in Motor Development Research
0888-9341 O H A I Bulletin
0888-9376 Classmate†
0888-9384 Chrysalis
0888-9449 King's Midwest Gas *changed to* King's North American Gas.
0888-9465 Health Professions Report
0888-9511 Hi-Tech Alert for the Professional Communicator *see* 0195-7791
0888-9538 Video Monitor *see* 0195-7791
0888-9546 Illinois. Natural History Survey. Special Publication
0888-9570 S O P A Newsletter
0888-9589 Sport Place International
0888-9600 Florida Living
0888-9724 In the Mainstream
0888-983X Harvard Review
0889-0064 Mutual Fund Trends
0889-0072 Waste Recovery Report
0889-0145 New German Review
0889-0153 Drew
0889-017X Mental Health Law News
0889-0196 Electronics Purchasing
0889-020X Soviet Spaceflight Report†
0889-0226 Management Solutions *changed to* Supervisory Management (New York).
0889-0234 D W I Journal: Law & Science
0889-0242 Pressure (Bethesda)
0889-0277 Shaw Historical Library. Journal
0889-0293 International Journal of Social Education
0889-0331 Health and Health Care in New York City: Local, State, and National Perspectives
0889-0358 Houston Medicine
0889-0382 Directory of New England Manufacturers
0889-0390 George D. Hall's Directory of Central Atlantic States Manufacturers
0889-0404 Defense Daily
0889-0498 Land Opportunity Review†
0889-0579 N A A C O G Newsletter
0889-0625 Security Law Newsletter
0889-0633 Chemical Waste Litigation Reporter
0889-065X Personalist Forum
0889-0692 Thrasher Magazine
0889-0722 Third Woman†
0889-0749 National School Bus Report
0889-0781 Wherever
0889-0803 Notus New Writing†
0889-082X Computer Industry Report
0889-0846 T A H P E R D Journal
0889-0870 Strongest Funds *see* 0889-0064
0889-0889 Transportation in America
0889-0897 Professional Investor
0889-0919 International Directory of News Libraries Including Finding
0889-0935 Valley Forge
0889-0951 Media Sports Business
0889-096X Hazardous Waste Hotline *see* 1040-1725
0889-0986 L I M R A's Marketfacts
0889-1575 Journal of Food Composition and Analysis
0889-1583 Journal of the Japanese and International Economies
0889-1591 Brain, Behavior, and Immunity
0889-1605 Journal of Ultrastructure and Molecular Structure Research *see* 1047-8477
0889-1613 Grants for Graduate Students (Year) *see* 1040-1091
0889-163X Eleven Meter Times & Journal
0889-1680 Anson Newsletter
0889-1699 Turnarounds & Workouts
0889-1761 Brazil Service
0889-177X Anvil's Ring
0889-1893 American Journal of Alternative Agriculture
0889-2148 Afghanistan Forum
0889-2202 Progressive Review
0889-2210 Decorating Digest
0889-2229 A I D S Research and Human Retroviruses
0889-2288 Carlsonreport for Shopping Center Management
0889-2326 Riverside Quarterly
0889-2393 Photofinishing News Letter
0889-2423 Independent Florida Alligator
0889-2474 Advokate *see* 1053-3362
0889-2482 Journal of Healthcare Materiel Management
0889-2504 Cavallino Magazine
0889-2644 Broadcast Banker - Broker
0889-2725 Political Risk Yearbook. Volume 4: Sub-Saharan Africa
0889-2776 Metro California Media
0889-2857 Ketch Pen
0889-2865 Voices of Youth
0889-289X Bicycle Guide
0889-2911 Paradox User's Journal
0889-2970 Rural Heritage

ISSN

0889-2997 Sabermetric Review†
0889-3012 Assemblage
0889-3047 Review of Austrian Economics
0889-3098 Star Date
0889-311X Crystallography Reviews
0889-3128 Studies in Gender and Culture
0889-3136 Best of Long Range Planning
0889-3144 R A P R A Review Reports
0889-3217 Seafood Business
0889-3241 A C I Structural Journal
0889-325X A C I Materials Journal
0889-3268 Journal of Business & Psychology
0889-3322 Florida Game & Fish
0889-3365 N B E R Macroeconomics Annual
0889-3403 Business Journal of New Jersey
0889-3411 Nuclear Monitor
0889-3454 Hazardous Materials Newsletter
0889-3519 Alcoholic Beverage Executives' Newsletter
0889-3586 Restaurant Reporter†
0889-3594 N D G S Newsletter
0889-3640 Miami Meanderings
0889-3667 International Journal of Comparative Psychology
0889-3675 Journal of Poetry Therapy
0889-3764 A P I S
0889-3888 Truck Identification Book
0889-3918 Automotive Week
0889-3950 Official Industrial Equipment Guide
0889-3969 Advances in Pathology *changed to* Advances in Pathology and Laboratory Medicine.
0889-3977 Advances in Sports Medicine and Fitness†
0889-3985 More Light Update
0889-4000 I B F A N News
0889-4019 Career Development Quarterly
0889-4094 Sailing World
0889-4159 Message of the Open Bible
0889-4175 Talent Education Journal†
0889-4256 Wine Investor: Executive Edition
0889-4299 America's Economy
0889-4302 Apple Assembly Line†
0889-4310 Entrepreneur's Franchise Yearbook *changed to* Entrepreneur's Guide to Franchise & Business Opportunities.
0889-4337 Today's C P A
0889-4396 Quarterly Pension Investment Report
0889-4434 Critical Reviews in Poultry Biology *see* 0964-6604
0889-4469 Liability & Insurance Bulletin†
0889-4477 Esthetic Dentistry Update†
0889-4507 Verbum
0889-4515 Gourmet Today (1986) *see* 1052-4630
0889-4523 Corporate Television†
0889-4558 Child Care Center†
0889-4590 Newspaper Financial Executives Journal
0889-4639 American Libraries (Year)†
0889-4647 Journal of Nursing Quality Assurance
0889-4655 Journal of Cardiovascular Nursing
0889-4663 Environmental Management Report *changed to* Environmental Management Review.
0889-468X Continuing the Conversation
0889-4698 Problems in Anesthesia
0889-4701 Problems in Critical Care
0889-471X Problems in Urology
0889-4752 Popular Lures†
0889-4817 O E A Communique *see* 1043-0695
0889-485X Jonesreport for Shopping Center Marketing
0889-4906 English for Specific Purposes
0889-4973 Videomaker
0889-504X Journal of Turbomachinery
0889-5074 Advances in Cardiovascular Surgery *changed to* Advances in Cardiac Surgery.
0889-5201 Bebop and Beyond
0889-5236 PsycScan: Psychoanalysis
0889-5244 Pilipinas
0889-5252 Heartsong Review
0889-5309 73 Amateur Radio Magazine *see* 1052-2522
0889-5333 Target Marketing
0889-5341 Monitoring Times
0889-5406 American Journal of Orthodontics and Dentofacial Orthopedics
0889-5414 Hospitality Law
0889-5422 Employee Testing & the Law
0889-5481 Arizona Trend†
0889-5589 Animator†
0889-5597 Credit Union Newswatch
0889-5643 Montessori Observer
0889-5694 Computer Crime Digest†
0889-5708 Narcotics Control Digest
0889-5716 Organized Crime Digest
0889-5724 Criminal Justice Digest
0889-5732 Training Aids Digest
0889-5740 Fire Control Digest
0889-5767 Community Crime Prevention Digest
0889-5791 Rip
0889-5805 Creative Selling *see* 1043-4364
0889-5813 Journal of Clinical Research and Drug Development *see* 1047-0336
0889-5899 Ostomy - Wound Management
0889-5902 Frozen Food Digest
0889-5996 Circus Report
0889-6038 U S Fire Sprinkler Reporter
0889-6054 Space Today
0889-6089 Amateur Satellite Report *changed to* A M S A T Journal.
0889-6143 Writing Center Journal
0889-6194 Computer Use in Social Services Network. Newsletter *see* 0740-445X
0889-6208 In Motion (Annapolis)
0889-6216 Start (San Francisco) *issued with* 0745-2527
0889-6216 Start (San Francisco)†
0889-6259 Master Teacher
0889-6283 Urology Annual
0889-6313 Psychobiology
0889-6321 Maeventec Software Review†
0889-6348 Proteus
0889-6402 Organization Development Journal
0889-6410 Lake Street Review†
0889-6445 Bugle (Missoula)
0889-647X Kentucky Poetry Review†
0889-6488 A T E A Journal
0889-6518 Magazines in Special Media
0889-6607 R I D I M - R C M I Inventory of Music Iconography
0889-6674 Business Executives' Expectations†
0889-6720 Montessori News
0889-6828 Boys Town Quarterly
0889-6976 Chiropractic Sports Medicine
0889-6984 Del-Gen-Data Bank†
0889-7018 Rehabilitation Education
0889-7042 Michaels on Etiquette†
0889-7077 Substance Abuse
0889-7085 Specialty Travel Index
0889-7107 Mexico West
0889-7166 Subnotes *see* 1055-0348
0889-7174 Changing Men
0889-7182 Scholarly Inquiry for Nursing Practice: An International Journal
0889-7190 A S A I O Transactions
0889-7204 Progress in Cardiovascular Nursing
0889-7247 Morrell, Morrill Families Association Newsletter†
0889-728X Sculpture
0889-7352 Alaska Oil and Industry News†
0889-7433 Aura Literary Arts Review
0889-745X Oklahoma Baptist Chronicle
0889-7468 Alabama Development News
0889-7581 Sigma Alpha Iota Quarterly: Pan Pipes
0889-759X Jean Rhys Review
0889-7611 Design Firm Directory
0889-7743 Yale Journal of International Law
0889-7751 C T L A Forum
0889-7840 Market Vane's Bullish Consensus
0889-7867 Wildfire
0889-7891 South American Explorer
0889-8022 E R I C - C U E Trends and Issues
0889-8030 E R I C - C U E Urban Diversity Series
0889-8049 E R I C Clearinghouse on Urban Education. Digest
0889-8138 Midwest Living
0889-8189 China Painter
0889-8197 Exploratorium Quarterly
0889-8227 Applied Management Newsletter
0889-8308 Intelligent Instruments & Computers
0889-8391 Journal of Cognitive Psychotherapy
0889-8421 Everything Natural†
0889-8464 N T I S Tech Notes
0889-8472 Upscale†
0889-8480 Mathematical Population Studies
0889-8529 Endocrinology and Metabolism Clinics
0889-8537 Anesthesiology Clinics *see* 0950-3501
0889-8545 Obstetrics and Gynecology Clinics
0889-8553 Gastroenterology Clinics
0889-8561 Immunology and Allergy Clinics of North America
0889-857X Rheumatic Diseases Clinics *see* 0950-3579
0889-8588 Hematology - Oncology Clinics of North America
0889-860X Precision Machinery and Robotics *see* 1045-4160
0889-8685 Creative Loafing
0889-8731 Al-Arabiyya
0889-8804 Double Talk (Amelia)
0889-8839 Teaching Opportunities Overseas - Bulletin
0889-8928 Media Arts†
0889-8936 P R R C: Emerging Trends
0889-9002 China Daily News†
0889-9118 Silver Wings
0889-9185 Latter - Day Woman†
0889-9223 Fed Tracker *changed to* Fed Tracker Special Report.
0889-9304 Southern Magazine†
0889-9312 B N A Criminal Practice Manual
0889-9363 N A F S A Government Affairs Bulletin
0889-9371 School Library Media Activities Monthly
0889-9428 North American Society of Adlerian Psychology. Newsletter
0889-9479 Blois Voice†
0889-9487 A A A S S Directory of Programs in Soviet & East European Studies
0889-9495 Radiance
0889-9525 Technical Trends
0889-9533 MicroPublishing Report
0889-9576 Air Alaska
0889-9614 Skywatchers Almanac (Year)
0889-9630 Comparative Ephemeris (Year)
0889-9657 Education and Self Management of the Psychiatric Patient†
0889-9681 Wine Investor: Buyers' Guide
0889-9746 Journal of Fluids and Structures
0889-9762 Seybold Report on Desktop Publishing
0889-9797 Casino Chronicle
0889-9878 Manhattan Cooperator
0889-9932 Microsoft Systems Journal
0889-9991 UPstate Magazine
0890-0078 Radio Control Boat Modeler
0890-0132 Journal of Interdisciplinary Studies
0890-0159 Advances in Behavioral Economics
0890-0167 Sportsturf *changed to* Sportsturf.
0890-0213 C D Review Digest *see* 1045-0114
0890-0213 C D Review Digest *see* 1045-0122
0890-0256 Thundercats Magazine†
0890-0299 Wine & Spirits
0890-0337 San Francisco Business Times
0890-0361 Families of Yancey Co.
0890-0396 Air & Water Pollution Control
0890-0426 Center for Applied Research in the Apostolate Seminary Forum
0890-0442 C B M C Contact
0890-0477 Louisiana Literature
0890-0485 Ninnau
0890-0523 Journal of Mass Media Ethics
0890-0566 Minnesota Literature
0890-0582 A I Ch E M I Modular Instruction. Series G: Design of Equipment
0890-0590 El Lider Bautista
0890-0604 Artificial Intelligence for Engineering Design, Analysis and Manufacturing
0890-0612 Hilliard History†
0890-0639 Connections: Kimball Family Association Newsletter
0890-068X National Tombstone Epitaph
0890-0833 Cuisinart Cook *see* 1040-1903
0890-0841 Books and Religion
0890-0876 Western & Eastern Treasures
0890-0914 George Odiorne Letter
0890-0973 N C L C Reports: Deceptive Acts & Warranties
0890-099X Orthodox America
0890-1155 Home Shopping Investor
0890-1171 American Journal of Health Promotion
0890-118X Across Frontiers
0890-1260 Satellite Times†
0890-135X Licensing Journal
0890-1392 Minergia†
0890-1406 Japan Computer Technology and Applications Abstracts†
0890-1465 Pennsylvania Portfolio
0890-1538 Interp Central Clearinghouse Newsletter
0890-1554 Alabama Literary Review
0890-1562 Transworld Identity Series
0890-1570 Second Opinion (Chicago)
0890-1619 New Options
0890-1759 Spy
0890-1767 Maintenance (Newsletter for Professional Truck Equipment Executives) *changed to* Maintenance.
0890-1775 Maintenance (Newsletter for Professional Truck Equipment Managers) *changed to* Maintenance.
0890-1783 Maintenance (Newsletter for Professional Truck Equipment Supervisors) *changed to* Maintenance.
0890-1791 Maintenance (Newsletter for Professional Truck Driver-Owner) *changed to* Maintenance.
0890-1813 C A Selects. Artificial Sweeteners
0890-1821 C A Selects. Memory & Recording Devices & Materials
0890-183X C A Selects. Asymmetric Synthesis & Induction
0890-1848 C A Selects. Antibacterial Agents
0890-1856 C A Selects. Carbon & Graphite Fibers
0890-1864 C A Selects. Catalytic & Kinetic Analysis
0890-1872 C A Selects. Fiber Optics and Optical Communication
0890-1880 C A Selects. Formulation Chemistry
0890-1899 C A Selects. Ion Chromatography
0890-1902 C A Selects. Pharmaceutical Analysis
0890-1910 C A Selects. Pharmaceutical Chemistry (Journals)
0890-1929 C A Selects. Pharmaceutical Chemistry (Patents)
0890-1937 C A Selects. Platinum and Palladium Chemistry
0890-1945 C A Selects. Polyacrylates (Journals)
0890-1953 C A Selects. Quaternary Ammonium Compounds
0890-1961 C A Selects. Silicas & Silicates
0890-2070 European Journal of Personality
0890-2097 Rapa Nui Notes *see* 1040-1385
0890-2143 Computer Entertainer
0890-2194 Recreation Executive Report
0890-2208 Nolo News
0890-2224 On Our Backs
0890-2240 Yale Daily News
0890-2267 Clinical Report on Aging†
0890-2305 International Employment Opportunities Digest
0890-2321 Access (Year) *changed to* Access to Wang.
0890-233X Horse Industry Directory
0890-2372 Gilbert Gallery
0890-2402 Cellular Marketing
0890-247X Parenting
0890-2518 A P V A Newsletter
0890-2526 Gateway (Ann Arbor) *see* 1052-701X
0890-2534 Anvil
0890-2577 Journal of Manufacturing and Operations Management
0890-2593 Groce Family Newsletter†
0890-2607 N C L C Reports: Debt Collection & Repossessions
0890-2615 N C L C Reports: Consumer Credit & Usury

5810 ISSN INDEX

ISSN

0890-2623 N C L C Reports: Consumer Bankruptcy and Foreclosures Edition *see* 1054-3775
0890-2631 Oswald Outlines
0890-2720 International Journal of Supercomputer Applications
0890-2739 Journal of Craniomandibular Disorders
0890-278X A G H E Exchange
0890-2828 N S F R E News
0890-2852 Tours & Resorts
0890-2909 G.I. Joe Magazine†
0890-2941 New Law Books Reviewer
0890-2968 Redwood Researcher
0890-2984 Utility Reporter: Fuels Energy & Power
0890-2992 For Your Information (New York)
0890-300X Innovator's Digest
0890-3018 Industrial Health & Hazards Update
0890-3050 Lake Superior Magazine
0890-3069 Arid Soil Research and Rehabilitation
0890-3077 Twins
0890-3085 Peterson's Applying to Colleges and Universities in the United States: A Handbook for International Students†
0890-3093 Exploradores
0890-3107 The Tartan
0890-3115 Estudios Biblicos para Ninos: Alumnos
0890-3123 Estudios Biblicos para Ninos: Maestros
0890-3158 Historias Biblicas para Preescolares: Maestros
0890-3166 Weekly Reader, Edition K
0890-3174 Weekly Reader, Pre-K Edition
0890-3204 Weekly Reader, Edition 3
0890-3212 Weekly Reader, Edition 2
0890-3220 Weekly Reader, Edition 1
0890-3239 Weekly Reader, Senior Edition
0890-3247 Historias Biblicas para Preescolares: Alumnos
0890-3255 Birth Gazette
0890-3263 Food Industry Skirmisher
0890-3271 Reports of Interest to Lawyers†
0890-3344 Journal of Human Lactation
0890-3360 Gossage Regan Manager's Memo
0890-3387 Christian Film & Video†
0890-3417 N C A H F Newsletter
0890-3433 Puckerbrush Review
0890-3484 Financial Accounting Reporter *see* 1044-8136
0890-3557 Lollipops
0890-3670 The Scientist
0890-3689 I D Strategist†
0890-3735 Nature Society News
0890-3743 Glass News *changed to* Glass Factory Directory.
0890-3816 A P G Quarterly *changed to* Association of Professional Genealogists Quarterly.
0890-3921 New Jersey Home and Garden *see* 0273-270X
0890-3921 New Jersey Home and Garden *see* 1044-3576
0890-3956 Campaign California Report
0890-3972 Podiatric Products
0890-3980 Computer Reseller Monthly†
0890-4014 Arnold Ancestry
0890-4022 Gillet Gillette Gillett Pride "n" Joy
0890-4049 Michigan Distributors Directory
0890-4065 Journal of Aging Studies
0890-4073 Advances in Health Education: Current Research
0890-4081 International Christian Digest†
0890-409X Clinical Connection
0890-412X American University Studies. Series 20. Fine Arts
0890-4162 Teddy Bear Review
0890-4197 Nathaniel Hawthorne Review
0890-4227 Current Packaging Abstracts
0890-4251 International Trade and Investment Letter
0890-426X Eximbank Letter
0890-4294 Differentia
0890-4316 D P Budget
0890-4332 Heat Recovery Systems & C H P
0890-4359 Paper Air†
0890-4448 Cherokee One Feather
0890-4456 Dewitt County Genealogical Society. Quarterly
0890-4464 Asia Institute. Bulletin
0890-4480 World Book Health and Medical Annual
0890-4596 Scream Magazine
0890-4634 Center Quarterly
0890-4685 Network Monitor
0890-4847 Studies in African and Afro-American Culture
0890-4863 P C Life
0890-4901 Smithsonian Studies in American Art *changed to* American Art.
0890-4928 Political Risk Database *see* 1041-3553
0890-4944 Arthurian Interpretations
0890-4952 Country Database *see* 1041-3553
0890-5010 Sub Rosa†
0890-5037 Law and Mental Health†
0890-507X G I G Newsletter
0890-5096 Annals of Vascular Surgery
0890-524X Wordstar Scroll
0890-5339 Journal of Orthopaedic Trauma
0890-5355 Tennessee Family Law Letter
0890-5363 Geothermal Science and Technology
0890-538X Emerging
0890-5401 Information and Computation
0890-541X Directory of Grants in the Physical Sciences†
0890-5436 Food Biotechnology
0890-5444 Membrane Separation Engineering†
0890-5452 Mechanics of Structures and Machines
0890-5460 Ocean Physics and Engineering†
0890-5487 China Ocean Engineering
0890-5509 Waste Minimization & Recycling Report
0890-5525 Directory of Directories: Publishers Volume†
0890-5533 Biomaterials, Medical Devices, and Artificial Organs *see* 1055-7172
0890-5541 Avaloka
0890-5568 Living Prayer
0890-5584 Restaurants U S A
0890-5592 Catastrophism and Ancient History. Proceedings
0890-5649 A P B A Journal
0890-5746 Children's Book Review
0890-5762 Review: Latin American Literature and Arts
0890-5908 C A C News *changed to* Chicago Artists' News.
0890-5924 Texas Weekly
0890-6076 Ski Patrol Magazine
0890-6130 Nature, Society, and Thought
0890-6149 Alaska History
0890-6165 A F L - C I O. Department of International Affairs. Bulletin
0890-622X Peregrine
0890-6238 Reproductive Toxicology
0890-6246 P I C O Laptops & Portables Magazine†
0890-6270 Starmont Popular Culture Studies
0890-6327 International Journal of Adaptive Control and Signal Processing
0890-6343 Clock Radio†
0890-6408 Apalachee Quarterly
0890-6432 Orbus *see* 0279-1323
0890-6440 Jazzletter
0890-6467 Oncogene Research
0890-6491 Weavings
0890-653X Fiberoptic Product News
0890-6548 Imagen
0890-6599 Journal of Neurological and Orthopaedic Medicine & Surgery
0890-6793 Christian Challenge
0890-6823 Factsheet Five
0890-684X Caribbean Action
0890-6858 Western New York Genealogical Society Journal
0890-6866 Universe in a Classroom
0890-6912 Sales and Marketing Training
0890-6955 International Journal of Machine Tools & Manufacture
0890-6998 Revue C E L F A N - C E L F A N Review
0890-7005 Le Mercenaire Intelligence Newsletter†
0890-7064 Journal of Psychology & Human Sexuality
0890-7129 Towpaths
0890-7137 Canal Society of Ohio. Newsletter
0890-7153 Mutual Fund Values *changed to* Morningstar Mutual Funds.
0890-720X Food Industry Newsletter
0890-7218 L A S A Forum
0890-7269 Caliban
0890-7315 Inside Litigation
0890-734X Soviet Biotechnology
0890-7358 Soviet Journal of Contemporary Engineering Mechanics
0890-7366 Minute-a-Day Drug Letter *see* 0886-876X
0890-7471 A A A Today Magazine
0890-7528 C A S BioTech Updates. Agriculture
0890-7587 M D R Watch
0890-7595 Medallion
0890-7625 Land Letter
0890-765X Journal of Rural Health
0890-7714 Winslow Homer: An Annual
0890-7722 Magill Book Reviews†
0890-7749 Translation and Textlinguistics. Occasional Papers *changed to* Journal of Translation and Textlinguistics.
0890-7757 Retirement Housing Report
0890-782X Official Video Directory & Buyer's Guide
0890-7889 Technology and Learning†
0890-7900 S M T Trends
0890-7951 G L C Voice
0890-796X Caribbean Treasures
0890-7986 Progressive Grocer's Directory of Mass Merchandisers
0890-8028 Whole Gay Catalog†
0890-8044 I E E E Network
0890-815X Privatization Report†
0890-8184 Chimera Connections†
0890-8192 Man from Mainz and His Descendants
0890-8206 Scouter's Digest
0890-8214 China Spring Digest†
0890-8265 Access to Energy
0890-8273 Council on Undergraduate Research Newsletter
0890-8362 Kentucky Explorer
0890-8389 British Accounting Review
0890-8478 First D I B S
0890-8508 Molecular and Cellular Probes
0890-8567 American Academy of Child and Adolescent Psychiatry. Journal
0890-8583 Reformed Worship
0890-8621 Laboratory Decisions Online†
0890-8648 U S A
0890-8702 Peace Institute Reporter *see* 1049-0779
0890-8745 Sports Trend
0890-8788 Bible Story Time Teacher
0890-8796 Bible Story Time Younger Pupil
0890-880X Bible Story Time Older Pupil
0890-8885 Cross Timbers Review
0890-9024 West Hills Review
0890-9059 Technology for Nursing *see* 1055-9620
0890-9075 Preparative Chromatography
0890-9083 I S I Atlas of Science: Pharmacology *changed to* Research Reviews in Pharmacology.
0890-913X Journal of Private Enterprise
0890-9156 Korea Automotive Review
0890-9199 Consumer Companion: The Quarterly Digest of Consumer Product Reviews†
0890-9369 Genes & Development
0890-9377 Contributions to the Study of Anthropology
0890-9423 Virginia, West Virginia Queries
0890-9458 Fisher Families
0890-9490 German Queries
0890-9504 Writer's Nook News
0890-9512 Morgan Report on Directory Publishing
0890-9520 Journal of Rural and Small Schools
0890-9555 Revue Francophone de Louisiane
0890-958X Habitat World
0890-9598 Harper's Bazaar en Espanol
0890-9695 WomenWise
0890-9768 Automatic I D News
0890-9776 NorthwestLetter
0890-9792 Perspectives (Columbus)
0890-9814 Architect's Office Management and Administration Report *see* 1057-2864
0890-9849 Forecast (New York)
0890-989X Pencil Press Quarterly†
0890-9903 Chinese Journal of Infrared and Millimeter Waves
0890-9911 Exchange Book
0890-9970 America's Textiles International
0890-9997 Historical Studies in the Physical and Biological Sciences
0891-0022 Triangle Business Journal
0891-0073 New Connections: Studies in Interdisciplinarity
0891-0146 Book of Days *changed to* Read More About It - Book of Days.
0891-0154 Food & Service
0891-0162 American Association of Occupational Health Nurses Journal
0891-0200 Federation of American Health Systems. Review *see* 1055-7466
0891-0278 Exercise Standards and Malpractice Reporter
0891-0316 Soviet Castings Technology
0891-0324 Soviet Forest Sciences
0891-0545 Raft
0891-0553 Gest Library Journal
0891-0596 The Career Guide
0891-060X Microbial Ecology in Health & Disease
0891-0618 Journal of Chemical Neuroanatomy
0891-0634 B N A's Banking Report
0891-0685 PsycScan: Applied Experimental and Engineering Psychology
0891-0707 The Wrestling News
0891-0758 Carto-Philatelist
0891-0766 Cancer Victors Journal
0891-0847 A P L I C Communicator
0891-0960 Downeast Ancestry
0891-1002 Music News (Washington)
0891-1029 Center City Report
0891-1150 Cleveland Clinic Journal of Medicine
0891-1177 Order of Buddhist Contemplatives. Journal
0891-1207 Professional Communicator
0891-1215 Income & Safety
0891-1223 Pediatric Length of Stay by Diagnosis and Operation, United States
0891-1231 Ridge Review
0891-124X Grenade
0891-1371 Witness (Farmington Hills)
0891-141X Equipment Today
0891-1436 Chinese United Journal
0891-1525 C A P Today
0891-1533 Today's Catholic (Fort Wayne)
0891-1622 Sales Promotion Monitor†
0891-1681 Promotion Digest†
0891-1703 National Air and Space Museum. Research Report†
0891-1762 Journal of Global Marketing
0891-1770 Vision Monday
0891-1797 Safety & Health
0891-1800 Surgical Rounds for Orthopaedics†
0891-1827 National Museum of Women in the Arts News *changed to* Women in the Arts.
0891-1835 Finding the Source
0891-1851 Kitplanes
0891-1886 C P I Digest
0891-1908 Conference on Editorial Problems: University of Toronto
0891-1916 International Journal of Political Economy
0891-1924 Health Technology†
0891-2017 Computational Linguistics
0891-2114 Length of Stay by Diagnosis, Canada†
0891-2122 Length of Stay by Diagnosis, United States, Northeastern Region *changed to* Length of Stay by Diagnosis & Operation, United States, Northeastern Region.
0891-2130 Length of Stay by Diagnosis, United States, Southern Region *changed to* Length of Stay by Diagnosis & Operation, United States, Southern Region.

ISSN INDEX 5811

0891-2149 Length of Stay by Diagnosis, United States *changed to* Length of Stay by Diagnosis & Operation, United States.
0891-2157 Length of Stay by Diagnosis, United States, Western Region *changed to* Length of Stay by Diagnosis & Operation, United States, Western Region.
0891-2165 Length of Stay by Diagnosis, United States, North Central Region *changed to* Length of Stay by Diagnosis & Operation, United States, North Central Region.
0891-2173 Geriatric Length of Stay by Diagnosis and Operation, United States
0891-2181 Length of Stay by Operation, Canada†
0891-219X Length of Stay by Operation, United States, Southern Region *changed to* Length of Stay by Diagnosis & Operation, United States, Southern Region.
0891-2203 Length of Stay by Operation, United States *changed to* Length of Stay by Diagnosis & Operation, United States.
0891-2211 Length of Stay by Operation, United States, Western Region *changed to* Length of Stay by Diagnosis & Operation, United States, Western Region.
0891-222X Length of Stay by Operation, United States, North Central Region *changed to* Length of Stay by Diagnosis & Operation, United States, North Central Region.
0891-2378 S P S M & H
0891-2386 Cicada
0891-2416 Journal of Contemporary Ethnography
0891-2424 Economic Development Quarterly
0891-2432 Gender and Society
0891-2521 Journal of Educational Techniques and Technologies
0891-2548 Crystal Gazing†
0891-2556 Carbonates and Evaporites
0891-2572 Kennedy's Career Strategist
0891-2599 Professional Apartment Management
0891-2610 Public History News
0891-2653 For the Record (Springfield)
0891-2661 Quarterdeck
0891-2688 Inter-hemispheric Education Resource Center. Bulletin
0891-2742 Library Personnel News
0891-2769 Fed in Print
0891-2823 Asian and Pacific Population Forum
0891-2831 Ten Million Flies Can't Be Wrong†
0891-2920 Archeomaterials
0891-2947 Secondary Marketing Executive
0891-2955 Bits & Bytes Review
0891-2963 Historical Biology
0891-2971 Crystal Rainbow
0891-3161 Biotech Investor
0891-3188 C D - R O M Review†
0891-3250 Health Management Quarterly
0891-3277 American Comparative Literature Association Newsletter
0891-334X Soviet Forging and Sheet Metal Stamping Technology†
0891-3374 Hope Health Letter
0891-3668 The Pediatric Infectious Disease Journal
0891-3706 Twigs Magazine†
0891-3749 Bibliographic Guide to Microform Publications
0891-3811 Critical Review
0891-382X California Planning and Development Report
0891-3846 Evangelizing Today's Child
0891-3978 Idea Factory
0891-4028 Obesity Newsletter *see* 1044-1522
0891-4036 Metalworking News†
0891-4044 C I O Letter†
0891-4052 Fundamentals of Test Measurement *see* 0277-7576
0891-4087 Lang Classical Studies
0891-4109 North American Studies in Nineteeth-Century German Literature
0891-4117 Reviews in Aquatic Sciences
0891-4141 Labor Relations Week
0891-415X Soviet Progress in Biochemistry *changed to* Ukrainian Biochemistry.
0891-4168 Molecular Genetics, Microbiology and Virology
0891-4176 Earthquake Research in China
0891-4214 Read, America!
0891-4222 Research in Developmental Disabilities
0891-4435 World Nuclear Performance
0891-4451 Systems Research in Psychology
0891-446X American Purpose†
0891-4478 International Journal of Technology & Aging
0891-4486 International Journal of Politics, Culture, and Society
0891-4494 Journal of Near-Death Studies
0891-4621 Robotics and Expert Systems
0891-4672 Online Today *changed to* CompuServe.
0891-4915 Guide to U S G S Geologic and Hydrologic Maps
0891-4990 Artquest Newsletter & Artquest Update
0891-5016 Healthcare Marketing Abstracts
0891-5121 1-2-3 User's Journal
0891-5148 Aviation Ground Equipment Market
0891-5202 Careers and the Handicapped *changed to* Careers & the Disabled.
0891-5237 Professional Quilter
0891-5245 Journal of Pediatric Health Care (St. Louis)
0891-5326 Re: View
0891-5393 James White Review
0891-5415 Contemporary Music Studies
0891-544X American Academy of Tropical Medicine & Surgery. Journal
0891-5571 U S S R Academy of Sciences. Transactions (Doklady). Earth Science Sections
0891-5628 Post (Port Washington)
0891-5644 Global Investing†
0891-5709 National Report on Substance Abuse
0891-5725 Ministries Today
0891-5741 Dossier (Washington, D.C.)†
0891-575X P C Digest
0891-5849 Free Radical Biology & Medicine
0891-5857 Selling Space *changed to* Selling.
0891-5865 Journal of Documentation Project Management
0891-5881 Dialogue & Alliance
0891-6004 InfoDB
0891-6055 Index Chemicus
0891-6063 Newsbreak (San Francisco)
0891-608X S P S C Letter
0891-6136 Poets & Writers Magazine
0891-6144 Himalayan Institute Quarterly Guide
0891-6152 Experimental Heat Transfer
0891-6209 A M C Journal
0891-625X Journal of Speculative Philosophy
0891-6330 American Journal of Family Law
0891-6365 Literary Research: A Journal of Scholarly Method and Technique
0891-6381 Choreography and Dance
0891-639X Wind Energy and Diesel Installations International (Year)†
0891-6403 Wind Farm Project Report
0891-6527 Hein Annual Checklist Statutes *changed to* Hein Checklist of Statutes.
0891-6578 Business Week Careers†
0891-6608 A H A News
0891-6624 H M O Practice
0891-6632 Journal of Diabetic Complications *see* 1056-8727
0891-6640 Journal of Veterinary Internal Medicine
0891-6659 Miami Jewish Tribune
0891-6683 Asia - Pacific Population & Policy
0891-6713 Database Searcher
0891-6780 East - West Film Journal
0891-6926 Sign of the Times
0891-6934 Autoimmunity
0891-6942 Magnesium Newsletter
0891-6969 Common Lives - Lesbian Lives
0891-6985 Chicano Periodical Index *changed to* Chicano Index.
0891-7035 Scanning Microscopy
0891-7043 Emory University Journal of Medicine
0891-7086 Alcohol, Drugs and Driving
0891-7140 Journal of Gay & Lesbian Psychotherapy
0891-7183 Public Risk
0891-7213 Aegean Review: Contemporary Greek Arts and Letters *changed to* Aegean Review: Greek Arts and Letters.
0891-7248 Paragraph
0891-7264 Music Technology
0891-7299 Printed Circuit News *see* 1058-9317
0891-7647 Locomotive & Railway Preservation
0891-7655 International Railway Traveler
0891-7698 Mercer County Board of Realtors. Newsline
0891-7701 Midwifery Today *changed to* Midwifery Today and Childbirth Education.
0891-771X Bird Talk
0891-7760 Adhesives Abstracts
0891-7779 Anxiety Research
0891-7795 Health, Society and Culture
0891-7973 Mapics the Magazine
0891-8066 U.S. Railroad Retirement Board. Annual Report
0891-8198 C D - R O Ms in Print
0891-8252 Seminole Tribune
0891-8287 A B C Forum
0891-8422 Clinics in Podiatric Medicine & Surgery
0891-8546 Antitrust Freedom of Information Log
0891-8759 Writers' Journal (N. St. Paul)
0891-8767 Alive Now
0891-8775 A B C News Index
0891-8791 A Positive Approach
0891-8813 Book Marketing Update
0891-8872 Overstreet Comic Book Price Guide
0891-8880 Reforma Newsletter
0891-8899 Weber Studies: An Interdisciplinary Humanities Journal
0891-902X Dakota Outdoors
0891-9070 Art Times
0891-9097 California Agricultural Export Directory
0891-9100 Crossosoma
0891-9194 Maine Organic Farmer and Gardener
0891-9267 Healthcare Management Team Letter
0891-9275 Elderly Health Services Letter
0891-9321 Journal of Black Sacred Music *see* 1043-9455
0891-9356 Nineteenth-Century Literature (Berkeley)
0891-947X Directory of Audio-Visual Programs for the Health Sciences and Related Fields
0891-9496 Caribbean Travel and Life
0891-9526 E N R
0891-9585 Woodstock Series
0891-9593 Essays on Fantastic Literature
0891-9607 Borgo Reference Guides
0891-9615 Borgo Cataloging Guides
0891-9623 Borgo Literary Guides
0891-9631 Black Political Studies
0891-9666 Christian History Magazine
0891-9801 Magnetohydrodynamics†
0891-9852 Real Estate Financing Update
0891-9895 University of Pennsylvania Journal of International Business Law
0891-9925 Trophoblast Research
0891-9941 Hospital Management Quarterly *see* 0891-3250
0891-9976 Engineered Systems
0892-0087 Quality Review†
0892-0109 Directory of Graduate Medical Education Programs Accredited by the Accreditation Council for Graduate Medical Education *changed to* Directory of Graduate Medical Education.
0892-0125 A T I N: A I D S Targeted Information Newsletter
0892-0249 N J A O P S Journal
0892-029X Journal of Packaging Technology
0892-032X Philatelic Exhibitor
0892-0354 Electron Microscopy Reviews
0892-0362 Neurotoxicology and Teratology
0892-0532 International Society of Bassists. Journal
0892-0575 P C Resource *see* 0737-8939
0892-0591 Journal of Direct Marketing
0892-0605 C L R Reports
0892-0613 International Construction & Development
0892-0753 Coastal Management
0892-077X Colorado Collections
0892-0788 Colorado Genealogical Chronicles
0892-080X Historic Documents
0892-0818 Resources in Aging
0892-0842 Big Two-Hearted†
0892-0850 Andrewsreport
0892-0869 Futures Factors - The Futures Portfolio Advisor *changed to* Options & Futures Factors - The Futures Portfolio Advisor.
0892-0915 Critical Reviews in Neurobiology
0892-094X I S I Online News†
0892-0966 Naseeha
0892-0990 Hawaii Magazine
0892-1008 R P C Voice *changed to* WorldView Magazine.
0892-1016 Journal of Raptor Research
0892-1024 Art Culinaire
0892-1032 International Tax Treaties of All Nations. Series A
0892-1040 International Tax Treaties of All Nations. Series B
0892-1059 Journal of Electrophysiology†
0892-1148 Capper's
0892-1202 Art Lover's Art and Craft Fair Bulletin
0892-130X Darshan
0892-1334 St. Louis Metropolitan Medicine
0892-1369 Hispanic Times Magazine
0892-1385 American Publishing Who's Who in New York
0892-1407 Shooting Star Review
0892-1458 Insurance Marketing Insider
0892-1466 Houston Sarmatian *changed to* Sarmatian Review.
0892-1474 Nutrition Funding Report
0892-1490 Emerge!
0892-1571 Martyrdom and Resistance
0892-1636 Gale Directory of Publications *see* 1048-7972
0892-1709 Passages (Anchorage)
0892-1733 N A S I G Newsletter
0892-1822 C B A Record
0892-1830 Lefsetz Letter
0892-189X Pring Market Review
0892-1903 BioVenture View
0892-1938 Southeast Asia High Tech Review *changed to* East Asia High Tech Review.
0892-1997 Journal of Voice
0892-2047 Construction Index
0892-2055 Nuclear Plant Journal
0892-208X Durkee Family Newsletter
0892-2098 Marshall Islands Journal
0892-2101 Comments on Agricultural and Food Chemistry
0892-211X Water Quality International
0892-2144 Ewing Exchange
0892-2152 Carroll Cables
0892-2160 Film History†
0892-2179 Archival Informatics Newsletter *see* 1042-1467
0892-2187 Clinical Chemistry and Enzymology Communications
0892-2284 American Fisheries Society. Symposium
0892-2306 How-to Video†
0892-2349 California Business Law Practitioner
0892-2357 Disc Golf World News
0892-2365 Intellectual Property Law
0892-2489 Northwest Association of Schools and Colleges. Convention Proceedings
0892-2519 Poland Watch Reports†
0892-2616 Nostalgia (Orangeburg)
0892-2632 O T C Growth Stock Watch
0892-2667 Fiction Review
0892-2675 Perspectives on Science and Christian Faith
0892-2683 Cellular Sales & Marketing
0892-2691 Family in America
0892-2721 Music of the Spheres
0892-2764 Contemporary Family Therapy
0892-2772 Medical Humanities Review

ISSN

0892-2799 Unisys World Software Directory *see* 0892-2845
0892-2802 Convergent World *changed to* Network Computing News.
0892-2810 H P Design & Manfacturing *changed to* Workstation.
0892-2829 H P Chronicle
0892-2837 T I Computing†
0892-2845 Unisys World
0892-2853 Educational Oasis
0892-290X Challenged American *see* 1056-7240
0892-2942 Pecan Press
0892-2977 Hippocrates
0892-2985 Superfund
0892-3116 W R E E - View of Women
0892-3272 Market Cycle Investing
0892-3310 Journal of Scientific Exploration
0892-3345 Atlanta Jewish Times
0892-3566 Freight Marketing Report *changed to* Freight Management Report.
0892-3582 A S A Artisan
0892-3612 Survival News for Cities and Towns *changed to* Financing Local Government.
0892-3647 American Journal of Distance Education
0892-371X Psychedelic Monographs and Essays
0892-3744 Rodale's Runner's World *see* 0897-1706
0892-3795 Iowa County
0892-3817 N C R Monthly *changed to* N C R Connection.
0892-3876 Inform (Silver Spring)
0892-3973 Immunopharmacology and Immunotoxicology
0892-399X Transnational Data and Communications Report
0892-4023 Unmanned Systems
0892-4090 Business Month†
0892-4171 Quality Cities
0892-418X Lynn - Linn Lineage Quarterly
0892-4198 Distressed Real Estate Law Alert
0892-4201 A M S Studies in the Emblem
0892-4228 Corrosion Engineering
0892-4236 Airline, Ship & Catering Onboard Services Magazine
0892-4295 Control Data World†
0892-4368 Activewear Business *see* 0896-1417
0892-4414 Today's Insurance Woman
0892-4422 Insurance Law Anthology
0892-4430 Tax Law Anthology†
0892-4449 Labor and Employment Law Anthology
0892-4546 International Leads
0892-4554 New Families *see* 0893-7621
0892-4562 Strategies (Reston)
0892-4619 Construction Consultant†
0892-4635 L I S P and Symbolic Computation
0892-4643 Health and Beauty Formulary *see* 0887-736X
0892-4694 Academic Computing†
0892-4708 Christian Management Review†
0892-4805 Partner's Report, a Monthly Brief for Law Firm Owners
0892-4872 Instruction Delivery Systems
0892-4880 Journal of Land Use and Environmental Law
0892-4945 Noah's Ark
0892-497X U S S R Technology Update†
0892-4996 Visitor Behavior
0892-5011 Learning Disabilities Focus *changed to* Learning Disabilities Research and Practice.
0892-502X Learning Disabilities Research *changed to* Learning Disabilities Research and Practice.
0892-5038 Running Journal
0892-5046 Consulting - Specifying Engineer
0892-5100 Slowo i Liturgia
0892-5135 High-Scope Extensions
0892-5178 Portu-Info
0892-5194 Fayette County (Ky.) Genealogical Society Quarterly
0892-5208 Oregon Postal History Journal
0892-5232 Corporate Jobs Outlook!
0892-5267 Mildred
0892-5429 Mutable Dilemma
0892-5437 Violexchange
0892-5461 Energy Books Quarterly
0892-547X Immigration Policy & Law
0892-5488 Work in America
0892-5534 Wildbird
0892-5542 Trading Systems Technology
0892-5550 Bio-Bibliographies in the Performing Arts
0892-5569 Comparative Urban and Community Research
0892-5658 Finger Lakes Magazine
0892-5747 Transpacific
0892-578X Onion World
0892-5798 Current Comments
0892-581X Righting Words
0892-5836 Normal
0892-5887 Insurance and Risk Management
0892-5984 Of a Like Mind
0892-6018 I R A - Individual Retirement Account Stocks
0892-6034 Business Information from Your Public Library
0892-6077 Meat and Poultry
0892-6085 Farm & Power Equipment Dealer
0892-6107 Orange County Business First
0892-6115 Journal of Hispanic Policy
0892-6174 Quality Care Advocate
0892-6271 Lone Star Horse Report
0892-628X H E R S Newsletter
0892-6301 Small Farm Today
0892-6387 American Pheasant and Waterfowl Society Magazine
0892-6433 Vanguard (Columbia)
0892-6484 Association for the Advancement of Automotive Medicine. Proceedings
0892-6514 Cat Fancy
0892-6522 Dog Fancy
0892-6581 Successful Magazine Publishing *see* 0895-2124
0892-662X Wine East
0892-6638 F A S E B Journal
0892-6719 Interfaith Women's News & Network†
0892-6735 Five Owls
0892-676X I D Systems
0892-6778 Banking Software Review
0892-6794 Ethics and International Affairs (Newsletter)
0892-6808 Soviet Technology Reviews. Section B: Thermal Physics Reviews
0892-6875 Minerals Engineering
0892-6883 Annual Review of Numerical Fluid Mechanics and Heat Transfer†
0892-6921 Later Years
0892-6948 Equipment Maintenance and Qualification Newsletter *changed to* Nuclear Plant Maintenance Newsletter.
0892-6956 Rohwedder
0892-6999 Soviet Agricultural Biology. Part 1: Plant Biology†
0892-7006 Soviet Agricultural Biology. Part 2: Animal Biology†
0892-7014 Biofouling
0892-7022 Molecular Simulation
0892-7049 Antibody, Immunoconjugates, and Radiopharmaceuticals
0892-7057 Journal of Thermoplastic Composite Materials
0892-7081 Clinical Decisions in Obstetrics & Gynecology†
0892-7103 Focus on Geriatrics and Rehabilitation
0892-7138 Stanford Environmental Law Journal
0892-7146 Techpak
0892-7162 Antique Comb Collector
0892-7200 Soviet Psychiatry and Psychology Today *changed to* Soviet Journal of Psychology.
0892-7219 Journal of Offshore Mechanics and Arctic Engineering
0892-7278 T W I C E
0892-7308 11th Circuit Law Letter
0892-7332 Technology for Laboratory Medicine
0892-7340 Technology for Imaging & Radiology
0892-7367 Finding
0892-7375 Visibilities†
0892-7383 Fee Income Report
0892-743X L D B Interior Textiles
0892-7537 Journal of World Prehistory
0892-7545 Employee Responsibilities and Rights Journal
0892-7553 Journal of Insect Behavior
0892-7561 Journal of the Multihandicapped Person *changed to* Journal of Developmental and Physical Disabilities.
0892-757X Food Service Forum†
0892-7626 Journal of Applied Business Research
0892-7782 Lunar Entrepreneurs Directory†
0892-7790 Journal of Endourology
0892-7812 Financial Sourcebooks' Source
0892-7847 Skylines (Washington)
0892-7855 C U P A News
0892-791X Junk Journal†
0892-7936 Anthrozoos
0892-7979 Tennessee Anthropologist
0892-8185 Medicenter Management†
0892-8193 Sales Motivation†
0892-8223 Women's Circle Country Needlecraft *see* 1048-3659
0892-8274 Adweek's Marketing Week
0892-8320 Hot Boat
0892-8355 Sports and Recreation *changed to* Outdoor Sports and Recreation.
0892-8363 Northwest Palate
0892-8525 Country Woman
0892-8533 Insurance Software Review *see* 1054-0733
0892-8649 Tax Policy and the Economy
0892-8762 Aging: Immunology & Infectious Disease
0892-8789 Southern Vermont Magazine
0892-8967 International Contact Lens Clinic
0892-9025 Gulf Coast Historical Review
0892-9084 Alabama County Data Book
0892-9092 Youth Theatre Journal
0892-922X Ellis Island Series: Immigration and the Pluralist Society
0892-9270 Space Technology
0892-9289 Respiratory Management
0892-9289 Respiratory Management Directory†
0892-9300 Christian Conquest
0892-9319 Corporate Fitness†
0892-9327 Cardiology Management†
0892-9343 P R Activity Report
0892-9351 Health and Safety Science Abstracts
0892-9386 Audio-Digest Gastroenterology
0892-9459 Spectrum Magazine (Bloomsburg)
0892-9467 Netline
0892-953X Scanning Microscopy Supplement
0892-9548 Rockwell Water Journal *changed to* Sensus Water Journal.
0892-9580 Gifted Child Today
0892-9696 Z Miscellaneous†
0892-970X MidCoaster
0892-9793 Interleaf
0892-9807 WittyWorld
0892-984X Low Priced Stocks
0892-9882 Science and Global Security
0892-9904 Association of Avian Veterinarians. Journal
0892-9912 Journal of Technology Transfer
0892-9955 Write Age†
0893-0120 EthnoArts Index
0893-0139 Index to Reproductions in Art Periodicals
0893-0147 Current Neuro-Ophthalmology
0893-0201 U: For University and College Students *see* 0743-2399
0893-0252 Drood Review of Mystery
0893-0260 Lurzer's International Archive
0893-0317 Optical-Electronic Publishing Directory *see* 0896-9841
0893-0325 Interactivity Report *changed to* Information & Interactive Services Report.
0893-0333 Electronic Shopping News *changed to* Information & Interactive Services Report.
0893-0341 Alzheimer Disease and Associated Disorders
0893-0430 Schwann C D†
0893-0449 Schwann†
0893-0465 City & Society (Washington)
0893-0511 Study in the United Kingdom and Ireland†
0893-052X Federal Computer Week
0893-0538 Activities of Daily Living Update
0893-0570 Ada Strategies
0893-0619 Defense Media Review
0893-0627 Hippocrates News
0893-0694 California Connections
0893-0708 Report from the Hill
0893-0732 Bank of Hawaii Business Trends
0893-0848 Child and Youth Care Quarterly *see* 1053-1890
0893-0872 Messenger (Worcester)
0893-0880 Signal (Streamwood)
0893-1003 Air Safety Law and Technology *see* 1044-727X
0893-1011 Mealey's Litigation Report: Bad Faith
0893-102X Sports Training, Medicine and Rehabilitation *see* 1057-8315
0893-1054 Radiology Today (Thorofare)
0893-1089 New England Getaways
0893-1151 La Jolla Magazine
0893-1208 Car Book (Year)
0893-1216 Comparative Guide to American Colleges
0893-1224 O N
0893-1240 Cruise Industry News
0893-1259 T M S - Letter
0893-1321 Journal of Aerospace Engineering
0893-133X Neuropsychopharmacology
0893-1364 Investment Limited Partnerships Law Report
0893-1526 A I D S Literature & News Review
0893-1550 The Caribbean Writer
0893-1585 Neurocomputers *changed to* Sixth Generation Systems.
0893-1593 Ohio Genealogical Society. Wood County Chapter. Newsletter
0893-1607 Jubilee
0893-164X Psychology of Addictive Behaviors
0893-1704 B N A's Alternative Dispute Resolution Report†
0893-181X Rhode Island Queries†
0893-1879 Hooked on Crochet!
0893-1909 Computers in Science†
0893-1925 Imaging on Campus
0893-195X Outdoors, Recreation & Leisure
0893-2034 Journal of Current Podiatric Medicine
0893-2069 Tree Shaker
0893-2107 U K & U S A
0893-2115 Libertarian E-Mail Directory†
0893-2131 Cable T V Banker - Broker
0893-2174 International Journal of Prosthodontics
0893-2182 Jazziminds Magazine
0893-2190 N C I Monographs *see* 1052-6773
0893-2190 Journal of Perinatal and Neonatal Nursing
0893-2204 International Obesity Newsletter *see* 1044-1522
0893-2212 Big Blue Disk
0893-228X Chemical Research in Toxicology
0893-2298 Indiana Facts
0893-2301 Central and Inner Asian Studies
0893-2395 Hispanic Issues
0893-2409 U S A Today Index
0893-2417 St. Louis Post-Dispatch Index
0893-2425 San Francisco Chronicle Index
0893-2433 Detroit News Index
0893-2441 Denver Post Index
0893-245X Christian Science Monitor Index
0893-2476 Houston Post Index
0893-2484 New Orleans Times-Picayune Index
0893-2514 M A Weapons *see* 0898-4786
0893-2565 E S D: The Electronic System Design Magazine†
0893-2573 Public and Local Acts of the Legislature of the State of Michigan
0893-2581 Alternative Fiction & Poetry†
0893-2654 Risk & Benefits Management
0893-2662 Tradeshow and Exhibit Manager
0893-2662 Tradeshow Directory
0893-2670 The Texas Philatelist
0893-2697 San Antonio Homes & Gardens†

0893-2700 Kegan Media Index
0893-2719 Midwest Real Estate News
0893-276X Columbiana
0893-2778 Chevy Outdoors
0893-2816 Missouri Manufacturers Register
0893-2824 West Virginia Manufacturers Register
0893-2859 International Computer Law Adviser
0893-2905 Psychiatric Times
0893-2921 Jewish Genealogical Society of Philadelphia. Chronicles
0893-293X A L F Newsletter
0893-2956 New Mexico Library Association Newsletter
0893-2972 Journal of Cardiovascular and Pulmonary Technology
0893-2980 Casualty Actuarial Society. Proceedings
0893-3030 Traffic Law Reports
0893-3057 Saline
0893-3081 F B O
0893-3103 The Quarterly (New York)
0893-312X Bishop Museum Bulletins in Zoology
0893-3138 Bishop Museum Bulletins in Botany
0893-3146 Bishop Museum Bulletins in Entomology
0893-3162 Gathering Gibsons
0893-3189 Management Communication Quarterly
0893-3200 Journal of Family Psychology
0893-326X Worldwide Chamber of Commerce Directory *see* 1048-2849
0893-3278 Computers and Philosophy Newsletter *changed to* Computers & Philosophy.
0893-3359 Stanly County Genealogical Society. Journal
0893-3375 Windfall
0893-3383 Lowfat Lifeline†
0893-3391 Cooperative Business Journal
0893-3472 N
0893-3499 Society of Logistics Engineers. Proceedings
0893-3561 Consumer Markets Abroad†
0893-357X Journal of Pesticide Reform
0893-3669 Paris Post-Intelligencer
0893-3766 Nineteenth Century Theatre
0893-3863 Military Vehicles
0893-3871 Journal of Osteopathic Sports Medicine
0893-3901 Art Calendar
0893-3952 Modern Pathology
0893-3960 International Journal of Engineering Fluid Mechanics
0893-4118 AppleWorks Forum
0893-4126 School and College Product News *see* 1045-3970
0893-4231 Protecting Children
0893-4274 InvesText Advisor
0893-4282 Journal of Agricultural Ethics *changed to* Journal of Agricultural and Environmental Ethics.
0893-4452 Environmental Nutrition
0893-4460 Men's Fitness
0893-4533 Asbestos Control Report
0893-4568 West Virginia Research League. Statistical Handbook
0893-4614 Star Tech
0893-4673 Resource Recovery Yearbook
0893-4762 A S A I O Primers in Artificial Organs†
0893-4800 Business N H *see* 1046-9575
0893-4835 PhotoStatic Magazine†
0893-4843 C D Computing News
0893-4851 Vera Lex
0893-4908 Archives of Soviet Science Series: Physical Sciences Section
0893-4983 Differential and Integral Equations
0893-5009 Reflections Quarterly Resource Directory
0893-5017 Excel Magazine
0893-5041 Flipping Flippins
0893-505X Alaska Association of Small Presses Newsletter†
0893-5068 A I D S Patient Care
0893-5076 Miller Family Newsletter†
0893-5084 A I D S Report
0893-5165 Current Contents - Health Services Administration†
0893-5289 Ohio School Boards Association. Journal
0893-5300 Immunodeficiency Reviews
0893-5343 P C R 2
0893-536X Hearts Aflame
0893-5378 Yale Journal of Criticism
0893-5386 Journal Holdings in the National Capital Area
0893-5440 Multi - Images
0893-5483 Progress in Self Psychology
0893-5556 BedTimes
0893-5580 Antipodes
0893-5599 Forced Exposure
0893-5602 Means Heavy Construction Cost Data
0893-5610 Photojournalist (Newark)
0893-567X Bad Haircut Quarterly *see* 1043-3732
0893-5696 Rethinking Marxism
0893-5769 Wisconsin Outdoor Journal
0893-5785 Pigment Cell Research
0893-5823 Allen Family Newsletter†
0893-5831 Baker Family Newsletter†
0893-584X Brown Family Newsletter†
0893-5858 Davis Family Newsletter†
0893-5866 Jones Family Newsletter†
0893-5874 Murphy Family Newsletter†
0893-5882 Wilson Family Newsletter†
0893-5939 Diabetes in the News
0893-5947 Computer P R Update†
0893-5963 Currents in Comparative Romance Languages and Literatures
0893-6005 New Studies in Aesthetics
0893-603X International Journal of Personal Construct Psychology
0893-6080 Neural Networks
0893-6188 Journal of Nuclear Materials Management
0893-620X Lip Service
0893-6218 Pediatric Therapeutics & Toxicology
0893-6242 Health & Environment Digest
0893-6250 Medical Product Manufacturing News
0893-6447 Harley Women
0893-6455 Software Digest Ratings Report
0893-6471 Bookends
0893-6552 A I Today
0893-6560 Wildlife Journal
0893-6609 Neuroscience Research Communicatons
0893-6633 Dysmorphology and Clinical Genetics
0893-665X Dental Watch *changed to* Clinical Dental Briefings.
0893-6684 Polymer Blends, Alloys and Interpenetrating Polymer Networks Abstracts
0893-6692 Environmental and Molecular Mutagenesis
0893-6862 Culture of European Cities
0893-6870 Asian Thought and Culture
0893-6889 Sexuality and Literature
0893-6897 Studies in Modern European History
0893-6900 Seventeenth - Century Texts and Studies
0893-6919 Studies in Contemporary Continental Philosophy
0893-6935 Berkeley Insights in Linguistics and Semiotics
0893-6943 Muffler Digest *changed to* Undercar Digest.
0893-7060 Financial Planning News
0893-7095 Slant: A Journal of Poetry
0893-7400 American Academy of Physician Assistants. Journal
0893-7451 Quirk's Marketing Research Review
0893-7486 Artist Issue
0893-7524 Arthritis Care and Research
0893-7621 Home Business Advisor†
0893-7648 Molecular Neurobiology
0893-7656 Newsletter Directory *changed to* Newsletters in Print.
0893-7664 The Tombstone
0893-7680 Northcoast View
0893-7699 Central America Bulletin†
0893-7702 Aquaphyte
0893-7842 New American Writing
0893-7850 New Perspectives Quarterly
0893-7877 Texas Instruments Technical Journal
0893-7931 Nineteenth-Century Studies
0893-7974 Facet†
0893-8067 Living Physics†
0893-8075 P C Netter Newsletter
0893-8083 Listen Real Loud
0893-8091 Cheer News Today
0893-8148 Psych It
0893-8210 Sports, Parks and Recreation Law Reporter
0893-8229 Medical Malpractice Defense Reporter
0893-8253 Alhope Business Observer
0893-8261 Compute's P C Magazine†
0893-827X Turbo Technix
0893-8326 Small Business Bulletin (Worcester)
0893-8342 Gannett Center Journal *see* 1057-7416
0893-8377 Computer Reseller News
0893-8415 Federal Managers Quarterly
0893-8458 Wrongful Discharge Case Law Reporter *see* 1053-0274
0893-8466 Ohio Health Law Insider *see* 1043-6081
0893-8504 Bio-Bibliographies in Sociology
0893-8512 Clinical Microbiology Reviews
0893-8520 A A R C Times
0893-8563 New Dog
0893-8571 Christian Contender
0893-858X Asbestos Abatement Report
0893-861X Condensed Matter Theories
0893-8660 Glass Collector's Digest
0893-8865 Balcones†
0893-889X Recorder (Searcy)
0893-8911 Manhattan Lawyer†
0893-8989 Police
0893-9136 CommonWealth Letters
0893-9349 Inside Word
0893-9381 Summerfield Journal†
0893-9403 Preservation Forum
0893-9454 Review of Financial Studies
0893-9462 Smart Card Monthly
0893-9500 Ear: Magazine of New Music
0893-9535 Humane Innovations and Alternatives in Animal Experimentation: A Notebook *changed to* Humane Innovations and Alternatives.
0893-9659 Applied Mathematics Letters
0893-9675 Critical Reviews in Oncogenesis
0893-9721 River Rat Review
0893-973X Coaldat Productivity Report
0893-9837 Primary Care Reports
0893-9888 Sign Business
0893-9934 C D - R O M Librarian
0894-0061 Journal of Cutaneous Aging & Cosmetic Dermatology
0894-0223 Caribbean Newsletter
0894-024X Ideas & Action
0894-0282 Molecular Plant - Microbe Interactions
0894-0347 American Mathematical Society. Journal
0894-0355 Log Homes Design, Construction & Finance Issue†
0894-0436 Architectural Lighting
0894-0479 Ink & Gall
0894-0525 Acta Meteorologica Sinica
0894-0606 Waterbury Chess Club Bulletin
0894-0622 American Society of Corporate Secretaries. Los Angeles Chapter. Newsletter
0894-0630 J A P C A *see* 1047-3289
0894-0649 I E G Directory of Sponsorship Marketing
0894-0681 Equity & Excellence
0894-069X Naval Research Logistics: An International Journal
0894-0703 Women's Pages Arizona *changed to* Women's Yellow Pages Arizona.
0894-0711 P C A I Magazine
0894-072X Soya International
0894-0754 Proletarian Revolution
0894-0789 New Technology Week
0894-0797 Card News
0894-0800 Northwesterner
0894-0886 Synchrotron Radiation News
0894-0924 Handmade Accents
0894-0932 Ethnic Affairs†
0894-1068 Admitting Management Journal *see* 1057-3526
0894-1122 Pediatric Trauma and Acute Care *see* 1059-0870
0894-1130 Journal of Hand Therapy
0894-1238 Music and Sound Retailer
0894-1270 Auto Age
0894-1289 E A A Experimenter
0894-1300 Drug Enforcement Report
0894-1351 Mythos: Seeking Truth Through Story†
0894-1386 Blum's Farmers & Planters Almanac and Turner's Carolina Almanac
0894-1408 Liberty (Port Townsend)
0894-1416 Lambda Rising Book Report *see* 1048-9487
0894-1491 Glia
0894-1513 Airport Pocket Guide
0894-1521 Worldwide Government Directory
0894-153X Walker's Manual of Western Corporations
0894-1564 Unpublished and Unnumbered Treaties Index *see* 0731-8189
0894-1564 Unpublished and Unnumbered Treaties Index *changed to* United States International Treaties Today.
0894-170X Connections (Fullerton, 1987)†
0894-1718 O A G Travel Planner Hotel & Motel Redbook. European Edition
0894-1726 O A G Travel Planner Hotel and Motel Guide Redbook. North American Edition *see* 1053-0002
0894-1734 O A G Travel Planner Hotel & Motel Redbook. Pacific Asia Edition
0894-1750 Newsletter of the Freudian Field
0894-1777 Experimental Thermal and Fluid Science
0894-1785 Book Marketing Opportunities: A Directory *changed to* Book Publishing Resource Guide.
0894-1793 Italian Journal
0894-1815 C P A Managing Partner Report
0894-184X Food Marketers' Handbook†
0894-1866 Computers in Physics
0894-1912 Journal of Continuing Education in the Health Profession†
0894-1920 Society and Natural Resources
0894-1939 Journal of Investigative Surgery
0894-2056 Densal
0894-2226 Serlin Report on Parallel Processing
0894-2242 Mankato Poetry Review
0894-2277 Current Surgical Diagnosis & Treatment
0894-2323 Bio-Bibliographies in World Literature
0894-234X Asian Art
0894-2366 Advances in Criminological Theory
0894-2498 Journal of Youth Services in Libraries
0894-251X Liberty and the Publick Good
0894-2528 Theoretical Parapsychology
0894-2536 China Center of Advanced Science and Technology Series
0894-2617 Scavenger's Newsletter
0894-2625 Alexandria Archaeology Volunteer News
0894-2633 Aerial
0894-2641 Profit Center
0894-265X Open Magazine†
0894-2684 Journal of Aerosol Medicine
0894-2757 Year Book of Geriatrics and Gerontology
0894-2986 Greenwood Library Management Collection
0894-3036 Links: Health and Development Report
0894-3044 Treetop Panorama†
0894-3052 Adweek's Winners†
0894-3087 World Leather
0894-3184 Nursing Science Quarterly†
0894-3214 Packaging, Technology and Science
0894-3222 International Journal of Digital and Analog Cabled Systems *changed to* International Journal of Digital & Analog Communication Systems.
0894-3230 Journal of Physical Organic Chemistry
0894-3257 Journal of Behavioral Decision Making
0894-3265 Federation of Genealogical Societies Newsletter *changed to* Federation of Genealogical Societies Forum.
0894-329X New York University School of Law. Linden Studies in Legal History

ISSN

5814 ISSN INDEX

0894-3303	New York University School of Law. Ingram Documents in American Legal History
0894-3346	Focus on the Family
0894-3362	Northern Review
0894-3370	International Journal of Numerical Modelling: Electronic Networks, Devices and Fields
0894-3427	Massachusetts Facts
0894-3443	Car Stereo Review
0894-346X	Directory Marketplace
0894-3486	S E R B Official Reporter
0894-3494	Island
0894-3540	Markets Abroad
0894-3575	Corporate Design *changed to* Today's Facility Manager.
0894-3583	Automobile (New York)
0894-3605	Locomotive Engineers Journal
0894-3737	Ricochet
0894-3745	I S I Atlas of Science: Immunology *changed to* Research Reviews in Immunology.
0894-3753	I S I Atlas of Science: Biochemistry *changed to* Research Reviews in Biochemistry.
0894-3761	I S I Atlas of Science: Animal and Plant Sciences *changed to* Research Reviews in Animal and Plant Sciences.
0894-3796	Journal of Organizational Behaviour
0894-3826	Corporate Security Digest
0894-3842	Governing
0894-3850	Pennsylvania Facts
0894-3907	Review of Research in Developmental Education
0894-3923	Selective Electrode Reviews
0894-3958	Bank Accounting & Finance
0894-3966	Minister's Manual (Year)
0894-3982	Electronic Publishing
0894-3990	Baby Connection News Journal
0894-4008	Forehead
0894-4024	Boston Bulletin on Chemicals and Disease
0894-4059	Midwestern Folklore
0894-4105	Neuropsychology
0894-4113	G R
0894-4156	Emerging Automotive Industries Review†
0894-4202	Guide to State and Federal Resources for Economic Development
0894-4210	American Coach†
0894-4237	Coaching Volleyball†
0894-4245	Coaching Women's Basketball†
0894-4253	Play & Culture
0894-4342	Means Assemblies Cost Data (Year)
0894-4385	Advances in Urology
0894-4393	Social Science Computer Review
0894-444X	Northwest Labor Press
0894-4466	Restaurant Management†
0894-4520	Sensory Systems
0894-4555	New Orleans Magazine *see* 0897-8174
0894-4652	Mexico Magazine
0894-4830	Recreation: Current Selected Research
0894-4849	Dance: Current Selected Research
0894-4857	Merton Annual: Studies in Thomas Merton, Religion, Culture, Literature, and Social Concerns
0894-4865	Family Business Review
0894-4911	Bill Nelson Newsletter
0894-492X	Runzheimer Reports on Fleet Maintenance & Safety
0894-5055	Toy Farmer
0894-508X	Greater Kansas City Medical Bulletin
0894-511X	Watermarks
0894-5152	School Intervention Report
0894-5179	Mustang & Fords
0894-5187	Drag Racing†
0894-5209	Boardwatch Magazine
0894-539X	Science and Technology (San Diego, 1987)
0894-5403	Woodshop News
0894-5446	Carolina Piedmont†
0894-5586	Family Digest *changed to* Real People.
0894-5594	S I O R Reports†
0894-5640	Chicago Times†
0894-5667	S P A Water Landing Directory
0894-5713	Maritime Personal Injury Report
0894-5748	Exec-U-Tary
0894-5780	Nightingale
0894-5810	High Performance Optometry
0894-5837	Writing Teacher (San Antonio)
0894-5861	Marketing to Women *see* 1047-1677
0894-587X	Administration and Policy in Mental Health
0894-5888	Journal of Advancement in Medicine
0894-590X	Travel Fit
0894-5926	ConneXions (Mountain View)
0894-5993	Legal Studies Forum
0894-6019	Urban Anthropology and Studies of Cultural Systems and World Economic Development
0894-6078	New Press
0894-6116	Podiatry Tracts
0894-6159	Gnosis
0894-6213	Computer Industry Forecasts
0894-6264	P S R Reports
0894-6388	Kafka Society of America. Journal
0894-6418	C S R Hotline
0894-6507	I E E E Semiconductor Manufacturing. Transactions
0894-6566	Journal of Elder Abuse & Neglect
0894-6620	I F R
0894-6639	Access Control
0894-6698	Maritime Advisor Arbitration Award Digest
0894-6795	Trends in Communications Policy
0894-6809	I C Master
0894-6817	Corporate Finance
0894-6825	Business and Economic History
0894-6981	Ancient Truth
0894-7260	Financial Services Report
0894-7295	Traders Magazine
0894-7317	American Society of Echocardiography. Journal
0894-7414	Specialty Automotive Magazine
0894-7597	Response to the Victimization of Women and Children
0894-7627	Financial 1000 *see* 1058-2878
0894-7635	Superconductor Week
0894-7651	Distribution Center Management
0894-783X	Santa Rosa News
0894-7872	National Notary Yearbook
0894-7899	Oak Square
0894-7902	Inner Circle Letter
0894-7910	Inverted - A Horn
0894-7929	Explorer (Falls Church)
0894-7937	D N A and Protein Engineering Techniques
0894-7953	Modern Dental Practice†
0894-7988	Child
0894-8097	Mexican American Grocers Association. MAGAzine
0894-8119	Gun List
0894-8135	Greene County Historical Journal
0894-8151	Inpatient Hospital Use in New York City (Year)
0894-8208	American Federation of Teachers. Action
0894-8291	American Journal of Electromedicine *changed to* Medical Electronics.
0894-8321	AeroMedical Journal *changed to* Journal of Air Medical Transport.
0894-833X	Talking Leaves
0894-8410	Journal of the Southwest
0894-8453	Journal of Career Development
0894-8542	Stars and Stripes - The National Tribune
0894-8550	Comments on Theoretical Biology
0894-8569	H P B Surgery
0894-8577	Journal of Contemplative Psychotherapy
0894-8631	Libraries & Culture
0894-8666	Film Producers, Studios, Agents and Casting Directors Guide *see* 1058-2630
0894-8674	Cinematographers, Production Designers, Costume Designers & Film Editors Guide
0894-8755	Journal of Climate
0894-8771	Ultrasound Quarterly
0894-878X	Neuropsychiatry, Neuropsychology and Behavioral Neurology
0894-8852	Spear Shaker Review
0894-8879	Journal of Law and Ethics in Dentistry†
0894-8941	Computers and Computing Information Resources Directory
0894-8984	Center Voice
0894-9085	Journal of Rational-Emotive and Cognitive-Behavior Therapy
0894-9093	Vacations
0894-9115	American Journal of Physical Medicine and Rehabilitation
0894-9158	Library Workstation and P C Report *see* 1055-4769
0894-9166	Acta Mechanica Solida Sinica
0894-9212	E D I News
0894-9255	Journal of Acquired Immune Deficiency Syndromes
0894-9301	C I O
0894-931X	A I D S: A Quarterly Bibliography from All Fields of Periodical Literature†
0894-9328	Peterson's Guide to Two-Year Colleges (Year)
0894-9336	Peterson's Guide to Four-Year Colleges (Year)
0894-9344	Peterson's Guide to Graduate and Professional Programs: An Overview (Year) (Book 1)
0894-9352	Peterson's Guide to Graduate Programs in the Humanities and Social Sciences (Year) (Book 2)
0894-9360	Peterson's Guide to Graduate Programs in the Biological and Agricultural Sciences (Year) (Book 3)
0894-9379	Peterson's Guide to Graduate Programs in the Physical Sciences and Mathematics (Year) (Book 4)
0894-9387	Peterson's Guide to Graduate Programs in Engineering and Applied Sciences (Year) (Book 5)
0894-9395	Peterson's College Money Handbook (Year)
0894-9409	Peterson's Guide to Independent Secondary Schools (Year)
0894-9417	Peterson's Summer Opportunities for Kids and Teenagers (Year)
0894-9425	Peterson's Engineering, Science, and Computer Jobs (Year) *see* 1048-342X
0894-9433	Peterson's Business and Management Jobs (Year) *see* 1048-3411
0894-9468	Visual Anthropology
0894-9492	Amityville Historical Society Dispatch
0894-9565	Phobia Practice and Research Journal†
0894-9573	Dirty Bum: A Magazine†
0894-9581	Telepublishing Report
0894-959X	Clinical Laboratory Science
0894-962X	Truckstop World
0894-9654	Alabama's Treasured Forests
0894-9697	Bill Shipp's Georgia
0894-9824	Journal of Afroasiatic Languages
0894-9832	Genders
0894-9840	Journal of Theoretical Probability
0894-9859	Systems Practice
0894-9867	Journal of Traumatic Stress
0894-9875	Foundations of Physics Letters
0894-9921	Patricia Seybold's Office Computing Report *see* 1057-8889
0894-9980	Healthcare Community Relations & Marketing Letter
0894-9999	American Waldensian Aid Society. Newsletter *changed to* American Waldensian Society. Newsletter.
0895-0016	Defense Counsel Journal
0895-0024	North Force
0895-0040	Felix Letter
0895-0083	Colorado History News
0895-0156	I E E E Computer Applications in Power
0895-0172	Journal of Neuropsychiatry and Clinical Neurosciences
0895-0180	Pen in Hand
0895-0202	Skinner Kinsmen Update
0895-0318	News (Marlin) *see* 0896-2111
0895-0326	The Bulletin (Austin)
0895-0334	Unisys World - Europe
0895-0342	H P Chronicle - Europe
0895-0377	Country (Greendale)
0895-0385	Journal of Spinal Disorders
0895-0407	Advanced Composite
0895-0482	American University Studies. Series 21. Regional Studies
0895-0490	American University Studies. Series 22. Latin American Studies
0895-0512	American University Studies. Series 24. American Literature
0895-0520	Contemporary Existentialism
0895-0601	Sporting News Pro Basketball Yearbook
0895-061X	Family Group Sheets of the World†
0895-0628	Word Processing Quality Clinic
0895-0695	Seismological Research Letters
0895-0792	Heritage (Carson)
0895-0814	Massage Therapy Journal
0895-0857	Past, Present, and Future
0895-0865	Potter County Historical Society. Quarterly Bulletin
0895-0997	Classic Toy Trains
0895-1012	Glasnost News and Review†
0895-1039	Teller Vision
0895-1071	Directory of Consumer Electronics, Photography and Major Appliance Retailers and Distributors (Year) *changed to* Directory of Consumer Electronics (Year).
0895-1101	Advising Quarterly
0895-1179	Library Outreach Reporter
0895-1195	Globecom. I E E E Global Telecommunications Conference. Conference Record
0895-125X	Artifex
0895-1268	Archaeus
0895-1306	Richard C. Young's International Gold Report
0895-1381	The New Advocate
0895-139X	Directory of Book, Catalog, and Magazine Printers *changed to* Directory of Book Printers.
0895-1454	U.S. Department of Agriculture. Wheat Situation and Outlook
0895-1489	Montana AgResearch
0895-1497	New Alchemy Quarterly†
0895-1527	Windplayer
0895-1543	Musi - Key
0895-1616	Progress *changed to* Dealer Progress.
0895-1640	Louisiana Banker
0895-1721	Compassion Magazine†
0895-1772	Mid-American Journal of Business
0895-1780	Black Congressional Monitor
0895-1799	Marketing Treasures
0895-1942	Fungal Genetics Newsletter
0895-2108	C A S E Outlook
0895-2124	MagazineWeek
0895-2175	American HomeArts Needlecraft for Today *changed to* Creative Ideas Needle and Craft.
0895-2183	Income Stocks
0895-2248	Library Video Magazine
0895-2256	Free Spirit (Minneapolis)
0895-2329	Vermont Woman†
0895-2469	Harris Missouri Directory of Manufacturers
0895-2485	C D S Connection
0895-2493	Custom Builder
0895-254X	Specialty Booksellers Directory†
0895-2604	Bowdoin Magazine
0895-2760	Computer Graphics World Buyers Guide
0895-2779	Journal of Sport and Exercise Psychology
0895-2787	The Controller's Report
0895-2809	Nursing Connections
0895-2833	Journal of Feminist Family Therapy
0895-2841	Journal of Women and Aging
0895-2876	Southern Roots & Shoots
0895-2892	Video Marketplace *changed to* Movie Marketplace.
0895-2914	Gymnastics Today†
0895-2965	The Inn Guide

ISSN

ISSN INDEX 5815

0895-3090 Food First Development Reports†
0895-3120 S M Y A L News
0895-3139 Right Here†
0895-3163 Key International Guide
0895-3171 Hotline (Stony Brook)
0895-3201 A I D S Research Today†
0895-3228 Private Practice News
0895-3260 Hazardous Materials Control
0895-3384 Chapter One (New York, 1987)
0895-3465 L.A. Style
0895-3481 Women's Health Nursing Scan *see* 1055-3533
0895-3503 Latin American Report
0895-3619 F E W's News and Views
0895-3678 Workamper News
0895-3708 Electronic Manufacturing†
0895-3716 Electrical Manufacturing
0895-3856 Truck Parts & Service
0895-3872 Patterson's Beverage Journal
0895-3880 National Forum of Applied Educational Research Journal
0895-3988 Biomedical and Environmental Sciences
0895-3996 Journal of X-Ray Science and Technology
0895-4143 Perfect Vision
0895-4151 Microcad News *changed to* Design Net.
0895-4186 Financial Executive
0895-4208 Military Police
0895-4313 Medical Office Report
0895-4321 National Directory of Magazines
0895-4356 Journal of Clinical Epidemiology
0895-4372 Workshop
0895-4437 Community Transportation Reporter
0895-4445 Chemtracts: Organic Chemistry
0895-4488 Perkins Family Newsletter
0895-4496 Mason Family Newsletter
0895-450X Fenestration
0895-4518 Database Programming & Design
0895-4550 Media Mergers & Acquisitions
0895-4615 Business Starts Record†
0895-4623 Rand McNally Bankers Directory
0895-4682 Places: A Directory of Public Places for Private Events and Private Places for Public Functions
0895-4690 Chinese American Forum
0895-4712 Political Pix
0895-4798 S I A M Journal on Matrix Analysis and Applications
0895-4801 S I A M Journal on Discrete Mathematics
0895-4836 Business View *changed to* Florida Business - Southwest.
0895-4844 Lawrence-Leiter Digest†
0895-4852 Academic Questions
0895-4895 Fastener Age†
0895-4909 Duke University Libraries
0895-500X Lewis County Historical Society Journal
0895-5018 Third World Legal Studies (Year)
0895-5093 New Research Reports†
0895-5220 L R A's Economic Notes
0895-5239 Ninth Street Center Journal
0895-5271 Foghorn *changed to* Foghorn - Foglight.
0895-528X Fog Light *changed to* Foghorn - Foglight.
0895-5352 South Florida
0895-5409 University of North Dakota. Alumni Review
0895-5441 L C - G C International
0895-5565 Reproductive and Genetic Engineering *see* 0958-6415
0895-5581 Dogs U S A
0895-559X Albany Review
0895-5603 Quattro *see* 1053-1467
0895-562X Journal of Productivity Analysis
0895-5638 Journal of Real Estate Finance and Economics
0895-5646 Journal of Risk and Uncertainty
0895-5662 New England Economic Indicators Monthly Update†
0895-5700 Renewable Energy *changed to* Renewable Energy News Digest.
0895-5735 C H F Newsbriefs
0895-5751 Mainframe Journal *see* 1053-6566
0895-5786 Blueprint for Social Justice
0895-5808 C A Selects. Enzyme Assays
0895-5816 C A Selects. Structure-Activity Relationships
0895-5824 C A Selects. Solid State N M R
0895-5832 C A Selects. Siloxanes & Silicones
0895-5840 C A Selects. Polyimides
0895-5859 C A Selects. Organometallics in Organic Synthesis
0895-5867 C A Selects. Nonlinear Optical Materials
0895-5875 C A Selects. New Antibiotics
0895-5883 C A Selects. Isomerization & Catalysts
0895-5891 C A Selects. Hot-Melt Adhesives
0895-5905 C A Selects. Free Radicals (Biochemical Aspects)
0895-5913 C A Selects. Food & Feed Analysis
0895-5921 C A Selects. Fluoropolymers
0895-593X C A Selects. Enzyme Applications
0895-5948 C A Selects. Ceramic Materials (Journals)
0895-5956 C A Selects. Carbon Fiber Composites
0895-5964 C A Selects. Alkylation & Catalysts
0895-5972 C A Selects. Free Radicals (Organic Aspects)
0895-5980 C A Selects. Air Pollution (Books & Reviews)
0895-5999 Report on Science and Human Rights
0895-6014 On the Issues
0895-6022 Casualty Actuarial Society. Yearbook
0895-6030 Frame-Work
0895-6049 Southwest Profile
0895-6103 Santa Clara County Connections
0895-6111 Computerized Medical Imaging and Graphics
0895-6200 The Art of Eating
0895-6286 Surviving Together: A Journal on Soviet-American Relations *changed to* Surviving Together: A Journal on Relations with the Former Soviet Union.
0895-6308 Research Technology Management
0895-6316 Neural Technology Update
0895-6324 Soviet Engineering Geology
0895-6332 Site San Diego
0895-6340 Computing Systems
0895-6359 Financial Services Yearbook†
0895-6464 Vista de Mexico
0895-6499 C A S BioTech Updates. Antibody Conjugates
0895-6510 New Writer's Magazine
0895-6529 T & E News
0895-6545 Journalism and Mass Communication Directory
0895-6618 C A S BioTech Updates. D N A Formation & Repair
0895-6626 C A S BioTech Updates. Biochemical Immobilization & Biocatalytic Reactors
0895-6669 Birth to Three. Newsletter *changed to* Birth to Three and Beyond.
0895-6685 Japan Manufacturing†
0895-6693 Japan Transportation†
0895-6707 Japan Materials†
0895-6715 Japan Computers†
0895-6723 Japan Electronics (Washington)†
0895-6731 Japan Business†
0895-674X Japan Chemistry†
0895-6766 Japan Telecommunications†
0895-6774 Japan Energy†
0895-6790 Design Systems Strategies
0895-688X State of New York City's Municipal Hospital System
0895-6928 E C B Newsletter *changed to* G A T F World.
0895-6936 Cymbiosis
0895-7002 Stained Glass
0895-7061 American Journal of Hypertension
0895-7126 Swenson Center News
0895-7169 Hospital Hazardous Materials Management *changed to* Healthcare Hazardous Materials Management.
0895-7177 Mathematical and Computer Modelling
0895-724X Journal of Social, Political and Economic Studies Monograph Series
0895-7258 Journal of Indo-European Studies Monograph Series
0895-7347 Applied Measurement in Education
0895-7371 A S T C Newsletter
0895-738X Epicurean Revue
0895-7428 Children's Choir
0895-7452 World Outlook
0895-7479 Second Messengers and Phosphoproteins
0895-7517 Spectrum Review†
0895-7533 Laboratory Robotics and Automation
0895-7541 E W Design Engineers' Handbook *changed to* E W Design Engineers' Handbook and Manufacturers Directory.
0895-755X Spotlight on A I D S
0895-7576 Nancy's Magazine
0895-7606 Native Peoples
0895-7673 Journal of Training & Practice in Professional Psychology
0895-769X A N Q: A Quarterly Journal of Short Articles, Notes and Reviews
0895-7703 Veterinary Medicine Report†
0895-7746 S Select *changed to* Infocus (Philadelphia).
0895-7754 N P U G News
0895-7762 Ironic Blood
0895-7819 Calligraphy Review
0895-786X Peelings (Washington)
0895-7886 Directory of Testing Laboratories
0895-7959 High Pressure Research
0895-7967 Seminars in Vascular Surgery
0895-8009 American Association on Mental Retardation. Monographs
0895-8017 American Journal on Mental Retardation
0895-8033 American Association on Mental Retardation. News and Notes
0895-8084 Florida Facts
0895-8092 Iowa Facts
0895-8106 North Carolina Facts
0895-8114 New Hampshire Facts
0895-8254 Longevity
0895-8262 Biological Therapies in Psychiatry *see* 1044-422X
0895-8270 Spectrum (Paxton)
0895-8378 Inhalation Toxicology
0895-8432 High Technology Business†
0895-8491 Western Sahara Campaign News
0895-8505 New West Notes
0895-853X Journal of Bank Accounting & Auditing
0895-8548 Transportation & Distribution
0895-8696 Journal of Molecular Neuroscience
0895-8718 Cosmetech *see* 0887-736X
0895-8777 Monitor (Stamford)
0895-8815 International Journal of Value-Based Management
0895-8939 Calvert County Genealogy Newsletter
0895-8947 Space Station News
0895-898X Writer's N W
0895-9048 Educational Policy
0895-9242 Military Avionics *see* 0887-2465
0895-9285 Human Performance
0895-9307 Green Mountains Review
0895-9331 A I D S Bibliography
0895-9374 Advances in Dental Research
0895-9390 Maui Update
0895-9420 Journal of Aging & Social Policy
0895-9471 U S Kids
0895-9595 Compute's Apple Applications†
0895-9706 Pinter Review: Annual Essays
0895-9722 National Dipper
0895-9773 Long Shot
0895-9803 Current Advances in Cancer Research
0895-9811 Journal of South American Earth Sciences
0895-9897 International Museum of Cultures. Publication
0896-0011 Classical and Medieval Literature Criticism
0896-0038 Co-Laborer
0896-0135 Nelson's Directory of Investment Research
0896-0143 Nelson's Directory of Investment Managers
0896-0194 Black Law Journal *changed to* National Black Law Journal.
0896-0267 Brain Topography
0896-0348 Military Robotics Newsletter
0896-0437 Super Automotive Service
0896-0453 Texas Economic Indicators
0896-0542 Diamonds in the Rough *see* 1048-2938
0896-0607 Nuclear Medicine
0896-0615 World Watch
0896-0631 Athena
0896-064X Tampa Review
0896-0801 Hinduism Today
0896-0828 Political Science Teacher *see* 1049-0965
0896-0844 British Journal of Serials Librarianship *see* 1048-5287
0896-0941 Employee Assistance Program Management Letter
0896-095X India Currents
0896-0968 International Choral Bulletin
0896-0976 Electronic Photography News
0896-100X Imaging Abstracts
0896-1018 American Romanian Academy of Arts and Sciences. Journal
0896-1107 Journal of Superconductivity
0896-114X Harriman Institute Forum
0896-1204 Health Care Marketer *see* 1052-8733
0896-1263 Nephrology News & Issues
0896-1301 Iris: A Journal About Women
0896-131X Handicap News
0896-1328 Zeta Magazine *see* 1056-5507
0896-1344 Asylum
0896-1379 Historical Roller Skating Overview
0896-1417 Activewear Business Magazine
0896-1441 Ideas (Reston)
0896-1468 Parentguide News
0896-1530 Journal of International Consumer Marketing
0896-1611 Manufacturing Review
0896-162X San Francisco Bay Area Gay and Lesbian Historical Society. Newsletter *see* 1053-296X
0896-1638 Sewanee Mediaeval Studies
0896-1646 Sea History Gazette
0896-1670 Snack World
0896-1727 La Palabra Entre Nosotros
0896-1794 Florida Water Resources Journal
0896-1883 Farm Chronicle
0896-193X Nails
0896-1956 Theater Week
0896-1964 Agincourt Irregular†
0896-2022 Turtle Quarterly Magazine
0896-209X Lutheran Woman Today
0896-2111 Wang in the News
0896-212X Workstation Magazine
0896-2138 Digest of the Arab Press†
0896-2146 Arab Press Bulletin†
0896-2154 Living World
0896-2162 Directory of Single Unit Supermarket Operators (Year)
0896-2189 Western Legal History
0896-226X Essays in Economic and Business History
0896-2278 South Carolina Port News
0896-2294 International Journal on the Unity of the Sciences
0896-2332 Fast Forward†
0896-2375 Mediactive *changed to* Immediate Impact.
0896-2413 God's Special People
0896-243X Harmony (San Francisco)
0896-2472 Ohio State University. Byrd Polar Research Center. Report Series
0896-2480 Music Technology *see* 0896-7172
0896-2510 Conference Board. Utility Investment Report†
0896-2529 Manufacturing Investment Outlook†
0896-2537 Regional Economies and Markets
0896-2545 World Economic Monitor†
0896-2553 Conference Board's Management Briefing: Business Finance†
0896-2561 Conference Board's Management Briefings: Marketing *changed to* Conference Board's Marketing Briefing.

ISSN

0896-257X Conference Board's Management Briefing: Human Resources *changed to* Conference Board's Human Resources Briefing.
0896-2618 Mulberry Tree Papers
0896-2685 Sprinkler Age
0896-2693 Now and Then
0896-2707 Forward (Oakland)†
0896-2898 Pan-Erotic Review
0896-2944 Peterson's Higher Education Directory (Year) *see* 1046-2406
0896-2960 Critical Reviews in Physical & Rehabilitation Medicine
0896-2979 Chinese Geography and Environment†
0896-2987 Treasury Manager
0896-3002 National Report on Work & Family
0896-3010 International Securities Regulation Report
0896-3053 O-blek
0896-3126 New Jersey Journal of School Psychology
0896-3134 A D A Today
0896-3142 TeleSpan's Business T V
0896-3150 New Heaven - New Earth†
0896-3169 E C A Magazine
0896-3193 Stern's Performing Arts Directory
0896-3215 Techline
0896-3223 Nielsen's International Investment Letter
0896-341X Thymus Update
0896-3517 Black Mountain Review
0896-3533 Codex Filatelica
0896-3568 Journal of Business & Finance Librarianship
0896-3576 Acquisitions Librarian
0896-3584 Budget and the Region
0896-3592 National Writing Project. Center for the Study of Writing Quarterly
0896-3614 Automotive Parts International
0896-3630 Talladega County Historical Association. Newsletter
0896-3649 National Gay and Lesbian Task Force. Task Force Reports
0896-3703 Business Perspectives
0896-372X Close Up Magazine
0896-3746 Infants and Young Children
0896-3827 Environmental Engineering Selection Guide
0896-3851 Nelson's Directory of Wall Street Research *see* 0896-0135
0896-3878 Timbuktu†
0896-3908 M L S
0896-3932 N C R T E Colloquy *see* 1054-7673
0896-3975 Atlanta History
0896-3991 Bobbin
0896-4009 Georgia Manufacturers Register
0896-4068 SilverPlatter Exchange
0896-4122 New York Education Law Report
0896-4157 InvesTech Market Analyst
0896-4165 InvesTech Mutual Fund Advisor
0896-4181 Global Finance
0896-422X Advanced Coatings & Surface Technology
0896-4300 Gardener Share
0896-4327 Journal of Interventional Cardiology
0896-4343 Ettore Majorana International Science Series. Life Sciences
0896-436X Neural Network Review†
0896-4386 Software Success
0896-4408 South Suburban Genealogical & Historical Society. Newsletter
0896-4416 United States Population Data Sheet
0896-4424 Train Rider Magazine
0896-4432 First Strike *see* 0029-6090
0896-4440 Rail Travel News
0896-4505 The Foodservice Distributor
0896-4521 Bookwatch *changed to* Wisconsin Bookwatch.
0896-4572 Breastfeeding Abstracts
0896-4602 Luther Family Newsletter
0896-4610 Cross-Bias
0896-4831 Medical Interface
0896-4858 Wildflower, Journal of the National Wildflower Research Center
0896-4904 Blue Chip Stocks
0896-4912 Newsletter for Information Executives†
0896-4955 Old Abe's News
0896-4971 Art Review *changed to* The 13th Street Journal.
0896-5048 Nonprofit Times
0896-5056 Applied Esthetiques *see* 0887-736X
0896-5080 Cancer Therapy and Control
0896-5099 Comments on Developmental Neurobiology
0896-548X The Journal of Trace Elements in Experimental Medicine
0896-5617 Prairie Gold Rush
0896-5633 American Academy of Psychiatry and the Law. Newsletter
0896-5641 9N - 2N - 8N Newsletter
0896-5706 Camping and R V Magazine
0896-5730 Ohio Writer
0896-5749 Fundamental News Service
0896-5773 Gayspring
0896-5781 T I P S Y *see* 1046-8366
0896-5803 Journal of Real Estate Research
0896-5846 Journal of Intravenous Nursing
0896-5900 Solid State and Superconductivity Abstracts
0896-5919 Virology and A I D S Abstracts
0896-5951 Turnstile
0896-6001 Gun Show Calendar
0896-601X Soviet Medical Reviews Supplement Series. Section B: Immunology
0896-6028 Family and Home Office Computing *see* 0899-7373
0896-6052 Automation *changed to* Controls and Systems.
0896-6095 StarLight
0896-6273 Neuron
0896-6281 Fine Gardening
0896-629X National Political Science Review
0896-6338 California State Poetry Quarterly
0896-6354 What Is to Be Read
0896-6362 Dreiser Studies
0896-6389 Film Threat
0896-6478 New Mexico Progress
0896-6508 International Association of Book Trade Consultants Report
0896-6532 Q D T Yearbook *see* 1060-1341
0896-6567 Managed Care Outlook
0896-6575 Airliners
0896-6591 Bibliographies and Indexes in Medical Studies
0896-6621 Journal of Research in Pharmaceutical Economics
0896-6834 Yard and Garden
0896-6915 Nursing Homes and Senior Citizen Care
0896-6966 Journal of Pharmacoepidemiology
0896-6974 Journal of Epilepsy
0896-7032 Looking Forward
0896-7067 Today's Chemist
0896-7113 I S M E C: Mechanical Engineering Abstracts
0896-7121 Gmac Quest†
0896-7148 American Literary History
0896-7164 Human Ecology Balancing Scientist *see* 1045-2729
0896-7172 Home & Studio Recording
0896-7199 New York Family
0896-7202 Political Woman†
0896-7210 Journal Watch
0896-7229 Procomm Enterprises Magazine
0896-7245 Apple Blossom Connection†
0896-7253 Pesticides and You
0896-7261 Roller Coaster!
0896-7385 N C I Cancer Weekly
0896-7423 Catalyst (Atlanta)
0896-7431 Generator
0896-7563 Baseball Card Price Guide Monthly
0896-7571 Soviet Scientific Reviews. Section G: Geology Reviews
0896-758X Snow Country
0896-7601 Means Light Commercial Cost Data (Year)
0896-7636 Cycles (Sharon)†
0896-7717 Word for Word
0896-7725 The Expert
0896-7733 Out - Look
0896-775X Corporate Restructuring†
0896-7768 Journal of Adolescent Chemical Dependency
0896-7784 Special Education Leadership
0896-7849 B - P A A Communicator
0896-792X P A I S Foreign Language Index *see* 1051-4015
0896-7946 Writer's Northwest Handbook
0896-7962 Home Fashions Magazine
0896-7970 Diehard
0896-8063 Tattoo Advocate†
0896-8071 Clarion Call
0896-8098 Bibliographic Guide to Computer Science
0896-8101 Bibliographic Guide to Anthropology and Archaeology
0896-8160 New England Gardener
0896-8195 Inside Chess
0896-8209 P C Publishing and Presentations
0896-8217 A A A A News
0896-8306 Soviet Medical Reviews. Section G: Neuropharmacology Reviews
0896-8322 Discoveries (Port Townsend)
0896-8381 Iowa Academy of Science. Journal
0896-839X Defense Computing *see* 0278-3479
0896-8411 Journal of Autoimmunity
0896-8438 Journal of Object-Oriented Programming
0896-8586 Technology Update (Palo Alto)
0896-8594 Indoor Pollution News
0896-8608 Peritoneal Dialysis International
0896-8683 Great Britain (Year)
0896-8705 Lactuca
0896-8713 Briefly†
0896-8756 Learning Edge
0896-8802 Gore Zone
0896-8926 P A M A News
0896-8934 Vox Pop Newsletter
0896-8942 Mountain Record
0896-8950 SunTechnology *see* 1046-5456
0896-8969 Texas Oil Marketer
0896-8985 Circuit Cellar Ink
0896-9035 Cancer in Puerto Rico
0896-9132 Pain Management
0896-9205 Critical Sociology
0896-9426 Cooperative Partners
0896-9442 Home Energy
0896-9590 Colton Clarion
0896-9841 Optical Publishing Directory
0896-9965 Horns of Plenty
0897-0106 Ethics: Easier Said than Done
0897-0149 Lear's
0897-0157 Passport to World Band Radio
0897-0181 Business Credit
0897-0238 Dreams and Nightmares
0897-0297 The E M S Leader
0897-0386 Best Recipes
0897-0459 E - S A *see* 0164-5528
0897-0475 Journal of Confederate History
0897-0491 Marine Log
0897-0696 Issues in Writing
0897-0750 Bible Book Study for Adults. Chinese Edition
0897-0823 Airpower Journal
0897-0963 MuscleCars
0897-0998 Connecticut River Review
0897-1005 Noetic Sciences Review
0897-1013 Institute of Noetic Sciences. Quarterly Bulletin
0897-1471 A C O G Current Journal Review
0897-1501 Asbestos Issues†
0897-1706 Runner's World
0897-1765 Directory of Discount Department Stores, Catalog Showrooms (Year) *see* 0897-5442
0897-1862 Journal of Economic Growth†
0897-1870 Endometriosis Association Newsletter
0897-1897 Applied Nursing Research
0897-1986 Knowledge and Policy
0897-2044 Quarterly Report on Money Fund Expense Ratios *changed to* I B C's Quarterly Report on Money Fund Performance.
0897-215X Massey Collectors News - Wild Harvest
0897-2176 American Libertarian†
0897-2249 Sea Frontiers
0897-2273 Salers Stockman - Salers Source
0897-229X Inner Horizons
0897-2354 Northeast Indian Quarterly *changed to* Akwe Kon Journal.
0897-2400 Journal of Contemporary Art
0897-2524 Alkaline Paper Advocate
0897-2540 Old Allis News
0897-2648 Organica
0897-2672 A A S C Newsletter *see* 1053-4202
0897-2680 Software Law Bulletin
0897-2826 I B E W Journal
0897-2834 Baseball Card Show Calendar *changed to* Baseball Card Shows.
0897-2842 Old Cars Show *changed to* Car Shows and Auctions.
0897-2907 B D A A Newsletter
0897-2915 Enhanced Services Outlook
0897-3067 Brazil Watch
0897-3261 Ice Cream Reporter
0897-3296 C D - R O M Databases
0897-330X S U N Y Research (Year) *see* 1041-9764
0897-3318 Catalyst (Menlo Park)
0897-3350 Doughty Tree
0897-3407 Mealey's Litigation Report: Superfund
0897-3466 I S R: Intelligent Systems Report
0897-3482 Bowman's Accounting Report
0897-3806 Clinical Anatomy
0897-3954 Matter of Fact: A Digest of Current Facts, with Citations to Sources *changed to* Matter of Fact: Statements Containing Statistics on Current Social, Economic and Political Issues.
0897-3962 Pacific World
0897-4020 Postcard Classics
0897-411X International Computer Update
0897-4179 Corvette Quarterly
0897-4268 Global Climate Change Digest
0897-4365 Iron Age
0897-4381 Celebrity Plus†
0897-4438 Journal of International Food & Agribusiness Marketing
0897-4446 Journal of Couples Therapy
0897-4454 Women & Criminal Justice
0897-4667 World Military Expenditures and Arms Transfers
0897-4721 Wow!
0897-4756 Chemistry of Materials
0897-4810 Federal Data Base Finder
0897-4888 Envoi
0897-4926 City & Country Club Life
0897-506X International Freedom Review *see* 1056-8018
0897-5094 New Waves (College Station)
0897-5159 Equipment Echoes
0897-5175 Gardener's Index
0897-5264 Journal of College Student Development
0897-5353 Journal of Family Psychotherapy
0897-5388 Investment Decisions Directory of Wall Street Research *see* 0896-0135
0897-5442 Directory of Discount Department Stores (Year)
0897-5469 Marriage Partnership
0897-5493 Sensualist
0897-5507 G I S World
0897-5515 B-City
0897-554X Ambulatory Medicine Letter
0897-5590 Christian Outlook†
0897-5736 501(C)(3) Monthly Letter
0897-5795 New England Antiques Journal
0897-5809 Bulletin on the 15 T F P S†
0897-5930 Journal of Teaching in International Business
0897-5973 Confetti (Elk Grove Village)
0897-6007 Publish!
0897-6015 Civil War
0897-6023 Peterson's Guide to Graduate Programs in Business, Education, Health, and Law (Year) (Book 6)
0897-6058 Chiropractic
0897-6104 Minerva's Bulletin Board
0897-6139 Access Faxon *changed to* Faxon Guide to C D - R O M.
0897-6201 Modern Baking
0897-621X Homestyles Home Plans

0897-6228 Designers' Collection Home Plans
0897-6236 Distinguished Home Plans
0897-6279 Superconductivity†
0897-6368 Tinnitus Today
0897-6376 University of Nevada. Desert Research Institute. Technical Report
0897-6481 Lucidity
0897-6511 Treasure Hunting Research Bulletin
0897-6538 Nelson's Guide to "Neglected" Stocks†
0897-6546 Law and Social Inquiry
0897-6554 Opera Monthly
0897-6627 Powder and Bulk Engineering
0897-6708 Immigration Briefings
0897-6716 Lyra
0897-6759 C C F A Foundation Focus
0897-7135 Contractor
0897-7151 Journal of Neurotrauma
0897-7186 Journal of Health & Social Policy
0897-7194 Growth Factors
0897-7216 Colonial Williamsburg Historic Trades
0897-7275 Goldbecks' True Food
0897-7305 Chess International†
0897-7321 The Drug Educator
0897-733X Suffolk University Magazine
0897-7356 Brussels Sprout
0897-7437 Nurse Anesthesia
0897-7550 Biological Monitoring
0897-7577 Waybill
0897-7682 Orthodox Southwest *changed to* Desert Voice.
0897-7690 St. Peter the Aleut Orthodox Educational Series
0897-7704 Yo-Yo Times
0897-7828 Studies in Biblical Greek
0897-7836 Renaissance and Baroque: Studies and Texts
0897-7844 Twentieth - Century American Jewish Writers
0897-7941 Pangloss Papers†
0897-7992 Benefits Law Journal
0897-800X S Corporations (New York)†
0897-8018 Journal of Home Health Care Practice
0897-8077 Transportation Executive Update
0897-8085 Software Magazine
0897-8093 Joliecoeur's Business N H *see* 1046-9575
0897-814X Treasure Chest
0897-8166 New Orleans *see* 0897-8174
0897-8174 New Orleans Magazine
0897-8271 Contemporanea
0897-8298 Northern California Monthly†
0897-831X Rotor: By the Industry - For the Industry
0897-8514 Political Risk Yearbook. Volume 7: Eastern Europe *changed to* Political Risk Yearbook. Volume 7: Europe - Outside the E C.
0897-8522 Political Risk Yearbook. Volume 6: Western Europe *changed to* Political Risk Yearbook. Volume 6: Europe - Countries of the E C.
0897-8530 Political Risk Yearbook. Volume 2: Middle East & North Africa
0897-8549 Political Risk Yearbook. Volume 3: South America
0897-8557 Political Risk Yearbook. Volume 1: North & Central America
0897-8565 Political Risk Yearbook. Volume 5: Asia & the Pacific
0897-8581 Science Illustrated
0897-859X Arts Indiana
0897-862X Environmental Health Report
0897-8778 Gas Buyers Guide
0897-8786 Churchman's Human Quest *changed to* Human Quest.
0897-8913 P C Disk Quarterly
0897-8921 Magazette
0897-893X P C Games
0897-9057 Birth of Tragedy Magazine
0897-9243 Studies in the Romantic Age
0897-9251 Healthways
0897-926X Worcester Polytechnic Institute - Studies in Science, Technology and Culture
0897-9286 Marion Zimmer Bradley's Fantasy Magazine
0897-9340 Sports Medicine Research Today†
0897-9375 A P S S Newsletter
0897-9421 The Blue Seal
0897-9472 World Monitor
0897-9545 Pax Christi U S A
0897-9561 Living Among Nature Daringly!
0897-9618 Olympic Travel Guide *changed to* Ferry Travel Guide.
0897-9642 Public Television Transcripts Index
0897-9650 T E D I Times
0897-9669 Uncaptive Minds
0897-9677 Problems in Respiratory Care
0897-9685 Journal of Child and Adolescent Psychiatric and Mental Health Nursing
0897-9707 Grue Magazine
0897-9790 Children's Writer's and Illustrator's Market
0897-9812 Novel & Short Story Writer's Market
0897-9979 Business Tax Report†
0898-0004 Society for Historical Archaeology. Special Publication Series
0898-0012 L A N
0898-0020 Whole Chile Pepper *changed to* Chile Pepper.
0898-0039 Fiery Foods Front†
0898-0071 Federal Budget Report
0898-011X Review of Futures Markets
0898-0209 Real Estate Finance Journal
0898-0233 Five Fingers Review
0898-0241 Her Own Words
0898-0284 Traditional Building
0898-0306 Journal of Policy History
0898-0403 Cellular Investor
0898-0454 Eurasian Language Archives
0898-0489 Open: O S I Product and Equipment News
0898-0721 Columbia Business Law Review
0898-0756 Scrap Processing and Recycling
0898-1140 La Nuez
0898-1191 Northern California Home & Garden
0898-1213 Distributor
0898-1221 Computers & Mathematics with Applications
0898-1353 Career Planning and Adult Development Network Newsletter
0898-1418 Kauai Update
0898-1485 Soap Opera Update
0898-1507 Lasers in Engineering
0898-154X Merveilles & Contes
0898-1574 Perkins Press
0898-1655 Decubitus
0898-1663 A I L A Monthly Mailing
0898-1698 Real Property Law Reporter
0898-1841 Business and Tax Planning Quarterly *changed to* Cost Management Update.
0898-2104 Journal of Liposome Research
0898-2112 Quality Engineering
0898-2155 Automotive Investor
0898-2201 P A I S Bulletin *see* 1051-4015
0898-2392 Muse (Burlington)†
0898-2503 PhillySport
0898-2562 Brown University Child Behavior and Development Letter *see* 0885-7261
0898-2643 Journal of Aging and Health
0898-2805 Humboldt Society Newsletter
0898-2848 Biotechnology Therapeutics
0898-2864 Mountain
0898-2929 United Nations Resolutions. Series 2. Resolutions and Decisions of the Security Council
0898-2961 New York Apartment Law Insider
0898-2996 Buzzworm
0898-302X P R C News
0898-3038 Hemisphere
0898-3127 Mind-Body-Health Digest†
0898-3283 Australian & New Zealand Journal of Serials Librarianship
0898-3410 Triathlete
0898-3569 Health & You
0898-3720 Car Audio & Electronics
0898-4204 World War II
0898-4212 Abraham Lincoln Association. Journal
0898-4271 Political Resource Director
0898-4298 N C S L Federal Update
0898-4387 Florida Leader
0898-4425 Aerospace Facts and Figures
0898-4484 Journal of Applied Corporate Finance
0898-4557 Gettysburg Review
0898-4646 A J N Guide
0898-4786 M A Training
0898-4808 Getty Conservation Institute Newsletter
0898-4921 Journal of Neurosurgical Anesthesiology
0898-4980 Model†
0898-5030 A I D S - H I V Treatment Directory
0898-5073 Weird Tales
0898-5111 Chinese Journal of Contemporary Mathematics
0898-512X Chinese Journal of Biochemistry and Biophysics
0898-5138 Chinese Journal of Genetics
0898-5146 Chinese Journal of Arid Land Research
0898-5154 Big Time *see* 0093-5832
0898-5162 Running & FitNews
0898-5170 Insurance Anti-Trust and Tort Reform Report *see* 1055-307X
0898-5197 Plum Creek Almanac
0898-5405 New Jersey Facts
0898-5413 Georgia Queries†
0898-5421 Wade World
0898-543X Hastings Herald
0898-5448 Robertson Report
0898-5456 Parker Papers
0898-5464 English Enquiries†
0898-5472 Tennessee Queries
0898-5499 M S M - The Magazine of Computer Service Management
0898-5502 Kindred Spirit *see* 1046-8897
0898-5529 Tetrahedron Computer Methodology†
0898-5561 Today's Distributor
0898-557X Long Island Monthly†
0898-560X Country Inns, Bed & Breakfast
0898-5626 Entrepreneurship & Regional Development
0898-5650 Toy Shop
0898-5669 Pediatric Physical Therapy
0898-5685 HazMat World
0898-5693 Japanese Technology Review *see* 1058-7292
0898-5693 Japanese Technology Review *see* 1058-7330
0898-5693 Japanese Technology Review *see* 1058-7306
0898-5693 Japanese Technology Review *see* 1058-7322
0898-5693 Japanese Technology Review *see* 1058-7314
0898-5715 Flight Safety Digest
0898-5723 Human Factors & Aviation Medicine
0898-574X Airport Operations
0898-5758 Cabin Crew Safety
0898-5774 Accident Prevention
0898-5812 Land Degradation and Rehabilitation
0898-5820 Legend Series: Muscle Cars of the '60s - '70s
0898-5839 Within and Beyond
0898-5898 Linguistics and Education
0898-5901 Laser Therapy
0898-5952 Performance Improvement Quarterly
0898-5987 American Viola Society. Journal
0898-6029 Holistic Medicine
0898-6088 Magazine of Masonry Construction
0898-6126 Woman's Enterprise†
0898-6185 Beethoven Newsletter
0898-6398 Clinical Pharmacology
0898-6401 New York Doctor
0898-6509 Data Conversion Newsletter *see* 1055-8098
0898-6525 Skin Inc
0898-6568 Cellular Signalling
0898-6894 H P V News
0898-6908 Human Power
0898-6959 Horn Speaker
0898-7084 Long Island Historical Journal
0898-7106 Rental
0898-7270 Hospimedica
0898-7297 State Legislative Sourcebook
0898-7521 Hot Tips†
0898-7564 Journal of Veterinary Dentistry
0898-7645 Lender Liability News
0898-784X Independent Publishers Trade Report†
0898-8048 Rivers
0898-8056 Locus (Denton)
0898-8064 Military History of the Southwest
0898-8145 Helicopter Safety
0898-8161 Radioactive Waste Management Handbook
0898-8277 Great American Orators
0898-8390 Corporate Growth Magazine
0898-8404 Saint Louis University Public Law Review
0898-8498 C B T Directions
0898-851X Black Music Research Newsletter *see* 0898-8536
0898-8536 Black Music Research Bulletin†
0898-8587 Historical Performance
0898-8684 Talisman
0898-8803 Wildflower, Newsletter of the National Research Center
0898-9052 Luso - Americano
0898-9095 Masters Abstracts International
0898-9184 Memories†
0898-929X Journal of Cognitive Neuroscience
0898-9494 Florida Home & Garden
0898-9583 Sugaku Expositions
0898-9591 Chinese Journal of Geophysics
0898-9621 Accountability in Research
0898-9745 The Real Calvin Coolidge
0898-9753 Executive Report on Managed Care
0898-9761 Japanese Investment in U S Real Estate Review
0898-9788 C Users Journal
0898-9842 Encyclopedia of Physical Science & Technology Yearbook
0899-0042 Chirality
0899-0115 Music Locator *changed to* Christian Music Directories: Printed Music.
0899-0123 Recording Locator *see* 1048-6844
0899-014X Recreational & Educational Computing
0899-0166 Research Guides in Military Studies
0899-0182 Chief Information Officer Journal
0899-0190 Greenpeace
0899-0204 California Chiropractic Association Journal
0899-0220 Somatosensory and Motor Research
0899-0255 Medico-Legal Advisor
0899-0409 Essays and Monographs in Colorado History
0899-045X Aquarium Fish Magazine
0899-1022 Swimming Pool - Spa Age
0899-1022 Swimming Pool - Spa Age Data & Reference Annual
0899-1073 Perspectives in Healthcare Risk Management
0899-1111 Ranch Dog Trainer
0899-1154 Emerge (New York)
0899-126X Computer Protocols
0899-1332 Quaker Queries
0899-1340 New Jersey Queries
0899-1359 Kentucky Queries
0899-1367 Barrett Branches
0899-1375 Cain Connections
0899-1405 Wary Canary
0899-1413 Out West
0899-1421 Musclecar Classics
0899-1464 A I D S Litigation Reporter
0899-1472 Public Officials Liability Litigation Reporter *see* 1055-5862
0899-1502 Journal of Sugar Beet Research
0899-1510 Review (Washington)
0899-1553 Reader's Guide Abstracts. Print Edition
0899-1561 Journal of Materials in Civil Engineering: Properties, Applications, Durability
0899-1596 Stafford Data
0899-160X Talbott Tree
0899-1618 Simonson Miscellaneous Research Data
0899-1626 Freeman Footnotes
0899-1634 Wiley World
0899-1782 U S Art
0899-188X Focus on Basics†
0899-1928 Aviation Tradescan
0899-1944 State Child Care Fact Book (Year)†
0899-1987 Molecular Carcinogenesis
0899-1995 Adult Residential Care Journal†

0899-2193 Texas Tech University. Interdepartmental Committee on Comparative Literature. Studies in Comparative Literature
0899-2207 State Yellow Book
0899-2339 Bonner County Genealogical Society Quarterly†
0899-2355 Student Successs Tutor Directory - Sarasota County *changed to* Student Success Tutor Directory - Sarasota and Manatee County.
0899-2363 Public Culture
0899-2371 Recent American History
0899-2398 The Diabetic Traveler
0899-2428 History of Mathematics
0899-2517 Journal of Musculoskeletal Medicine
0899-2525 Field Artillery
0899-2533 A F B Directory of Services for Blind and Visually Impaired Persons in the United States
0899-255X International Directories in Print *see* 0275-5580
0899-2673 H L I Reports
0899-2681 Boundary Waters Journal
0899-2851 Middle East Report
0899-3009 Brief (Houston)
0899-3114 James Joyce Literary Supplement
0899-3130 The Quarter Racing Journal
0899-3289 Journal of Substance Abuse
0899-336X Frommer's Dollarwise Guide to Italy *see* 1044-2170
0899-3408 Computer Science Education
0899-3459 Topics in Magnetic Resonance Imaging
0899-3467 Chiropractic Technique
0899-3483 Identity
0899-3521 Groundwater Pollution News
0899-3718 Journal of Military History
0899-3750 Avec
0899-3793 Giving U S A Update
0899-3815 SportCare & Fitness
0899-3998 AgBiotechnology News
0899-4137 Health of America's Children
0899-4153 Sea Fans
0899-4161 Final Frontier
0899-417X Turf News
0899-420X Human Life International. Special Report
0899-4307 Continuum: Problems in French Literature from the Renaissance to the Early Enlightenment
0899-434X Pacific Telecommunications
0899-4358 Chinese Journal of Numerical Mathematics and Applications
0899-4366 Home Plans to Build
0899-4560 Morgan Directory Reviews
0899-4579 Data Entry Services Directory
0899-4595 C P R - J
0899-4862 Ohio News
0899-4897 Studies in Moral Philosophy
0899-4927 The Merton Seasonal: A Quarterly Review
0899-5044 Read Me†
0899-5052 N C S L Conference Report
0899-5079 Multinational Environmental Outlook *changed to* Greenhouse Effect Report.
0899-5141 Journal of Cost Management for the Manufacturing Industry *changed to* Journal of Cost Management.
0899-5192 American Airgunner
0899-529X Skipping Stones
0899-5362 Journal of African Earth Sciences (and the Middle East)
0899-5397 Teaching Genealogy†
0899-5400 Immigration Digest
0899-5427 Student Action in Engineering
0899-5443 Drum
0899-5508 Women's Fastpitch World
0899-5540 Automated Builder
0899-5591 Adolescent Pregnancy Prevention Clearinghouse *see* 1055-9221
0899-5605 Military Psychology
0899-5648 HerbalGram
0899-5680 Applied Networks Report
0899-5702 Biotech Business
0899-5729 Maintenance Technology
0899-577X Current Mammalogy
0899-5869 Children's Hospital Quarterly
0899-5877 Directions for Utah Libraries
0899-5893 Stitches
0899-594X Southern Folklore
0899-5966 Limestone
0899-5982 Construction Claims Training Guide
0899-6008 Party & Paper Retailer
0899-6040 American University Studies. Series 25. Geography
0899-6059 Monk
0899-6091 Weekly Reader. Summer Edition A. Grade K *changed to* Weekly Reader. Summer Edition A. Pre K - Grade 1.
0899-6105 Silver
0899-6113 Weekly Reader. Summer Edition B. Grades 1-2 *changed to* Weekly Reader. Summer Edition B. Grades 2-6.
0899-6121 Weekly Reader. Summer Edition C. Grades 3-5†
0899-6172 National Directory of Art & Antiques Buyers & Specialists
0899-6210 Health Facilities Management
0899-6253 Index to Periodical Articles By and About Blacks *changed to* Index to Black Periodicals.
0899-630X F A R C E
0899-6369 Petroleum - C-Store Products
0899-6407 Kurt Weill Newsletter
0899-644X Long Cane News
0899-6458 Missouri Libraries
0899-6555 Federal Reserve Bank of Atlanta. Economics Update
0899-6563 Federal Reserve Bank of Atlanta. Financial Update
0899-6571 Federal Reserve Bank of Atlanta. Regional Update
0899-6741 Conference Board Briefing
0899-7039 Magazine Issues
0899-7071 Clinical Imaging
0899-708X Northland Quarterly
0899-7217 Trains Illustrated†
0899-725X Macintosh Business Review
0899-7292 Christian New Age Quarterly
0899-7349 Texas Facts
0899-7357 Rice
0899-7373 Home Office Computing
0899-7403 American Journal of Knee Surgery
0899-7411 American Journal of Asthma & Allergy for Pediatricians
0899-7446 U W L A Law Review
0899-7578 Motorist (Seattle)
0899-7640 Nonprofit and Voluntary Sector Quarterly
0899-7659 Journal of Aquatic Animal Health
0899-7667 Neural Computation
0899-7721 Entrepreneurial Economy Review
0899-7756 Fighting Blindness News
0899-7829 Chemtracts: Macromolecular Chemistry
0899-7993 Marketing Strategist *see* 1057-5316
0899-8019 Key Cardiology†
0899-8035 Year Book of Occupational Medicine
0899-8086 Temple Law Review
0899-8132 Early Keyboard Journal
0899-8159 Cryptosystems Journal
0899-8205 Biomedical Instrumentation & Technology
0899-8213 Physics of Fluids A: Fluid Dynamics
0899-8221 Physics of Fluids B: Plasma Physics
0899-823X Infection Control & Hospital Epidemiology
0899-8248 Impact of Computing in Science and Engineering
0899-8256 Games and Economic Behavior
0899-8329 Discovery Five Hundred†
0899-837X Contemporary Dialysis & Nephrology
0899-8418 International Journal of Climatology
0899-8434 Nevada Farm Bureau's Agriculture & Livestock Journal
0899-8493 Pediatric Exercise Science
0899-8531 High Reliability & Military Components Guide
0899-8671 Concrete Producers News
0899-8779 Briefs†
0899-8833 Employee Ownership Report
0899-8841 Inventor's Gazette
0899-885X Journal of Intensive English Studies
0899-8922 S A S Bulletin
0899-8930 Kalis' Shopping Center Leasing Directory
0899-8957 Hospital Patient Relations Report
0899-8965 Health Legislation and Regulation
0899-9112 Addictions Nursing Network
0899-9147 Fleet's Guide: Commercial Real Estate Financing Sourcebook
0899-9228 American Deafness & Rehabilitation Association. Journal
0899-9287 Healthcare Forum Journal
0899-9333 Ours (Minneapolis)
0899-9341 Microprocessor Report
0899-9392 Smash Hits *changed to* Hot!
0899-9422 Magnetic Resonance Quarterly
0899-9457 International Journal of Imaging Systems and Technology
0899-9546 A I D S Education and Prevention
0899-9554 I S D N News
0899-9570 I Love Cats
0899-9708 P E T A News
0899-9732 DX Monitor
0899-9775 Water Scooter
0899-9791 H V A C ProfitMaker
0899-9821 Preview (Ann Arbor)
0899-9848 Santa Monica Review
0899-9856 Hermeneutics of Art
0899-9872 Studies in Old Germanic Languages and Literatures
0899-9880 American University Studies. Series 26. Theater Arts
0899-9899 German Life and Civilization
0899-9902 Comparative Literary and Film Studies: Europe, Japan, and the Third World
0899-9910 Conflict and Consciousness: Studies in War, Peace and Social Thought
0899-9929 Studia Classica
0899-9937 Revisioning Philosophy
0899-9953 Sassy (New York, 1988)
0899-9988 Chinese Journal of Semiconductors†
0899-9996 High Energy Physics and Nuclear Physics
0900-002X Folk og Minder fra Koebenhavn
0900-0119 Teaterbladet
0900-0178 Skat
0900-0186 Vegetarisk Koekkenkalender
0900-0267 N H P Rapport
0900-0275 Normtalsundersoegelsen for Isenkrambranchen
0900-0283 Normtalsundersoegelse for Sportsbranchen
0900-0380 Landsforeningen af Kronisk Syge. Medlemsblad
0900-050X Limousine Nyt
0900-0542 Danmarks Biblioteksskole. Bibliotek. Biblioteks Tilvaeksliste *see* 0900-0550
0900-0550 Danmarks Biblioteksskole. Nye Boeger, Nye Blade, Nye Baand
0900-064X Jazz Festivals and Related Major Jazz Events. Directory
0900-078X Globalia Nyt†
0900-0801 Tidsskrift for Biavl
0900-081X Magistrenes Universitetslaererforeningen. Beskrivelse *see* 0902-2619
0900-1131 Foeroyar
0900-114X Gerontologi og Samfund
0900-1166 Nyere Dansk Faglitteratur
0900-1174 Logos†
0900-1204 Musik Nyt†
0900-1301 Herning Kunstmuseums Bulletin†
0900-1395 Ungdomsuddannelser
0900-1409 Moentsamleren
0900-1433 Kirkens Undervisning
0900-1484 Kommunal Aarbog
0900-1573 Almanak for Teologi og Litteratur†
0900-1581 Dagdryp†
0900-162X Om Forsoegsarbejdet
0900-1646 Denmark. Miljoestyrelsen Kemikaliekontrol. Aarsberetning *changed to* Denmark. Miljoministeriet. Danmarks Miljoundersogelser. Afdeling for Miljokemi.
0900-1972 Tique
0900-1980 Social Administration
0900-1999 Danmarks Transport. Tidendes Destinationregister†
0900-2006 Skole og Edb†
0900-2030 Social Sikring†
0900-2049 Familien Danmarks Forbruger. Haandbog†
0900-2073 Kvinder†
0900-2103 Sydthy Aarbog
0900-2219 Dansk Selskab for Mykopatologi. Meddeleser
0900-2278 Theses and Other Publications of the University of Copenhagen
0900-2367 Botanisk Centralbibliotek. Fortegnelse over Loebende Periodica
0900-2472 Handelshoejskolen i Koebenhavn. Center for Uddannelses Forskning. Arbejdsnote
0900-2499 Levevilkaar i Danmark
0900-2510 Denmark. Ministeriet for Groenland. Statistike Meddelelser *changed to* Groenlandsdepartementet. Statistike Meddelelser.
0900-2537 Flygtninge Nyt
0900-2596 Hoeje-Tastrup Kommunes Lokalhistoriske Arkiv. Aarskrift
0900-2650 Amatoerfiskeren
0900-2685 Nyhedsbrev for Social og Sundhedssektor†
0900-2723 Arbejderbevaegelsens Bibliotek og Arkiv. Aarsskrift
0900-274X Koebenhavns Universitet. Institut for Samfundsfag og Forvaltning. Forskningrapport
0900-2758 Denmark. Lovinformation fra Miljoestyrelsen
0900-2855 Konkylien
0900-2863 Vanfoeres Jul *changed to* Julehaeftet, Vanfoeres Jul.
0900-2871 Danske Selskab. Nyt *changed to* Danske Kulturinstitut. Nyt.
0900-288X Faellesudvalget til Kaninavlens Fremme Beretning
0900-2995 Frankrig Information. Nyhedsbrev
0900-3002 Tidskrift for Sygeplejeforskning
0900-3037 Folkesagn i Tekst og Billed fra Noerreherred†
0900-3053 Faglig Solidaritet
0900-3096 Amtskommunale Enkeltfagskurser†
0900-3126 Lokalhistorisk Arkiv for Fredericia og Omegn. Aarsskrift
0900-3134 Bag Kulisserne†
0900-3142 Afhaenging
0900-3339 Retorik
0900-3347 Tools
0900-3355 Paa Vej *changed to* Nu Pa Vej.
0900-338X Argos
0900-3401 Tidsskrift for Kaninavl
0900-3452 Musikbladet†
0900-3460 Skalmejen
0900-3479 Uddannelse og Erhverv Katalog
0900-3517 Design Denmark
0900-3665 D S B Bladet
0900-372X Dansk Curling
0900-3738 Denmark. Betaenkning fra Miljoestyrelsen
0900-3746 Miljoepolitik
0900-3754 Break 19
0900-3762 Technical Product Update
0900-3819 Arkitektur *see* 0004-2013
0900-4041 Dansk Kirurgisk Selskab. Nyhedsbrev
0900-419X Energylab Newsletter†
0900-4262 Astma Allergi Bladet
0900-4645 Danmarks Tekniske Bibliotek. Katalog
0900-470X Sidesporet†
0900-4858 Medicintakst
0900-5072 M S Biblioteksnyt
0900-5129 R U N Commodore - Magasin
0900-5269 Mikro-Bladet
0900-5293 Oversigt over Landsforsoegene
0900-5323 Europeisk Nyhedsbrev
0900-5579 Dantec Information
0900-5587 Polio-Nyt *changed to* P T U Nyt.

ISSN INDEX

ISSN	Title
0900-5781	Danmarks Laererhoejskole. Institut for Informatik. Arbejdspapir
0900-579X	Tidsskrift for Miljoeteknikt
0900-5846	Stambog over Shetland Ponyer
0900-6028	Maanedsmagasinet Erhverv - Nordjylland
0900-6230	Mikronyt i Specialundervisningen see 0903-9821
0900-6257	Danmarks Geologiske Undersoegelse. Serie D
0900-6354	Operabladet Ascolta
0900-6362	Danmarks Geologiske Undersoegelse. Serie C
0900-6559	Dats†
0900-6664	Foreningen af Filmlaerer i Gymnasiet. Meddelelser see 0903-8981
0900-6788	Denmark. Redegoerelse fra Miljoestyrelsen
0900-6885	Denmark. Direktoratet for Arbejdstilsynet. Arbejdstilsynets Aarsberetning
0900-7105	Tennis Avisen
0900-7350	Dramapaedagogik i Nordisk Perspektiv†
0900-7679	Emigrantent
0900-8012	Handbog for Kvaeghold
0900-8063	Energi og Planlaegning
0900-8187	Om Statsregnskabet
0900-8284	Independent Computer Commodore Magazine changed to Det Nye Computer.
0900-8322	Oekonomistryring og Informatik
0900-8373	D E H Bladet
0900-8632	Idraetshistorisk Aarbog
0900-8659	Bil Testent
0900-8675	North Western European Language Evolution
0900-8691	Guide Nyt
0900-8764	Molsbibliotekets Lokalhistorisk Arkiv
0900-8772	Nordisk Psykologisk Litteratur
0900-8829	Antal Modtagere, Adresseloese Postforsendelser
0900-9310	Sieg's Moentkatalog - Norden (year)
0900-9507	Prepublications
0900-9787	Fiskeriaarbogen
0900-9825	Fredningsstyrelsen Rapport
0900-9876	Koebenhavns Universitet. Sociologisk Institut. Arbejdspapir
0900-9922	Kobenhavns Universitet. Sociologisk Institut. Afhandling
0901-0025	Micro Publications. Social Science Series
0901-0106	Teater for Boern og Unge changed to Boerneteateravisen.
0901-0114	Sko og Laedervarer
0901-0270	Danmarks Geologiske Undersoegelse. Serie A
0901-0289	Danmarks Geologiske Undersoegelse. Serie B
0901-036X	Gacela - Gazela. Tidsskrift for Latinamerikastudier changed to Gacela - Gazela. Revista de Estudios Latinoamericanos.
0901-0602	Handbog i Socialiovgivning†
0901-067X	C A S Nyt
0901-0815	Arkeologiske Udgravninger i Danmark
0901-0963	Statens Vejlaboratorium. Nye Publikationer†
0901-1056	Ulricks Strikkeideer
0901-1374	Arabisk Verden. Maanedsoversigt changed to Mellemoest Information. Maanedsoversigt.
0901-1811	Spotlight
0901-1943	Goedskingrapport
0901-201X	Para - nyt
0901-2273	Actualitates de Interlingua
0901-2281	Kollegie Nyt
0901-229X	Danmarks 10000 Stoerste Virksomheder - Denmark's 10000 Largest Companies changed to Danmarks 15000 Stoerste Virksomheder.
0901-2508	Pilbladet
0901-2605	International Horisont
0901-2737	Frisoerfagene changed to Frisoerfaget.
0901-2745	Frit Koebmandskab
0901-2982	Monthly Journal of Scientology†
0901-3032	Turist- og Rutebilbladet
0901-3067	Hobby Bladet
0901-313X	Bartenderen
0901-3229	Bilruten
0901-3652	Diabetes
0901-3741	D J I F Fritid
0901-3768	Energy in Denmark
0901-3946	Chauffoeren
0901-4233	Info-Text
0901-4241	Goer det Selv
0901-4306	Blindes Jul
0901-4497	Aarhus Universitet. Teologiske Fakultet. Bibliografi
0901-4500	Cystisk Fibrose
0901-4632	D O P S Nyt
0901-5000	Ministerialtidende for Kongeriget Danmark. Afdeling A see 0085-3461
0901-5027	International Journal of Oral & Maxillofacial Surgery
0901-5213	Aarhus Universitet. Institut for Statskundskab. Arbejdspapir†
0901-5469	Punkt 95†
0901-6120	Bilismen i Danmark
0901-6139	Statistik over Registrering af Nye Automobiler i Danmark
0901-6171	I F U Annual Report
0901-6635	A F A Skandinavien Frimaerkekatalog
0901-6643	A F A Oesteuropa Frimaerkekatalog
0901-6996	A F A Danmark Fireblokke
0901-7003	A F A Danmark Frimaerkekatalog
0901-702X	A F A Vesteuropa Frimaerkekatalog
0901-747X	Miljoe & Teknologi
0901-7496	Kongelige Bibliotek og Universitetsbiblioteket. Magasin changed to Kongelige Bibliotek. Magasin.
0901-800X	Setting up in Denmark
0901-8077	Kolding Bogen
0901-8328	Scandanavian Journal of the Old Testament
0901-8735	Firmengruendung in Daenemark†
0901-8883	Passage
0901-9413	Brorfelde Geomagnetic Observatory Magnetic Results (Year)
0901-9685	Sex og Sundhed
0901-9901	Arte Nyt
0901-9928	Pharmacology & Toxicology
0901-9936	Pharmacology & Toxicology. Supplementum
0902-0055	Oral Microbiology and Immunology
0902-0063	Clinical Transplantation
0902-0071	Comprehensive Gerontology. Serie A: Clinical Laboratory Sciences changed to Comprehensive Gerontology. Section A: Clinical and Laboratory Sciences.
0902-008X	Comprehensive Gerontology. Serie B: Behavioural, Social and Applied Sciences changed to Comprehensive Gerontology. Section B: Behavioural, Social and Applied Sciences.
0902-0098	Comprehensive Gerontology. Serie C: Interdisciplinary Topics changed to Comprehensive Gerontology. Section C: Interdisciplinary Topics.
0902-1612	S F. Status
0902-2341	U F O Vision
0902-2619	Universitetslaereren. Beskrivelse
0902-3046	Hvidovre Lokalhistorie
0902-347X	Pan Bladet
0902-3704	Ledelse og Erhvervsoekonomi
0902-4441	European Journal of Haematology
0902-4506	European Journal of Haematology. Supplementum
0902-5057	Plus Proces
0902-5456	Dansk V V S
0902-6681	Statens Laantagning og Gaeld
0902-7270	Kort Sagt
0902-7513	Aalborg Universitetscenter. Institutet for Bygningsteknik. Rapport
0902-7521	Culture & History
0902-8005	Aalborg Universitetscenter. Institutet for Bygningsteknik. Note
0902-8927	Golf
0902-9958	Aalborg Universitetscenter. Institut for Sprog og Internationale Kulturstudier. Arbeijdspapirer
0903-0727	Groen Viden
0903-112X	D M I Update see 0905-3549
0903-1731	Fugle og Dyr i Nordjylland
0903-1936	European Respiratory Journal
0903-2444	Dansk Filatelistisk Tidsskrift
0903-2606	Techniques in Marine Environmental Sciences
0903-3424	Skanderborg Museum. Aarbog
0903-3440	Nordisk Filatelistisk Tidsskrift
0903-3483	Current Titles in Dentistry
0903-3955	Glas-Porcelaen-Brugskunst - Koekkentoej
0903-4641	A P M I S
0903-5079	Odense University. Department of Commercial Law and Political Science. Publications†
0903-5524	Brydning
0903-5664	Det Danske Hedeselskab. Forsoegsvirksomheden. Beretning
0903-5907	Denmark. Miljoe Danmark
0903-6083	Dok see 0905-9539
0903-6342	Nyt fra Nyhavn
0903-6814	Denmark. Socialforskningsinstuttet. Rapporter
0903-6962	Danish Illustration (year)
0903-7195	Bogmarkedet
0903-7543	Samfundsforskning
0903-7845	Udenrigs
0903-8086	Virksomheden ved Sygehuse
0903-8302	Rigsbibliotekarembedet. Retningslinier see 0905-555X
0903-8825	Dansk Moenstertidende
0903-8981	Medielaererforeningen for Gymnasien og H F. Meddelelser
0903-9287	Kiosk og Service
0903-9295	Henry - D R U Nytt
0903-9759	North European Food and Dairy Journal changed to S D I - Scandinavian Dairy Information.
0903-9821	Via Datch
0903-9961	International Studies. Nordic Seminar on Human Rights. Proceedings
0904-0919	L O - Ungdoms Blad
0904-1796	Dansk Turisme
0904-1966	Medicinsk Foedselsstatistik og Misdannelsesstatistik
0904-1990	Kriminalforsorgens Aarsberetning
0904-213X	Acta Chemica Scandinavica
0904-2253	Denmark. Statens Byggeforskningsinstitut. Projektresumeert
0904-2334	Museet for Fotokunst. Katalog
0904-2431	Studies in Central and East Asian Religions
0904-2512	Journal of Oral Pathology & Medicine
0904-275X	Patentdirektoratet Orienterer
0904-3764	Kost og Allergi Nyt
0904-3853	Over Broen
0904-4159	Klip
0904-4191	P C World
0904-4337	N I A S - Nytt
0904-4361	Denmark. Finanstilsynet. Forsikringsselskaber og Pensionskasser m.v. see 0905-0965
0904-437X	Denmark. Finanstilsynet. Fondsboersen of Boersmaeglerselskaber see 0905-0965
0904-5198	L S T Nyt
0904-597X	N I A S Report
0904-6089	Mellemamerika Nyt
0904-6267	Historisk Arbog for Thy og Vester Hanherred
0904-7824	Lys
0904-8081	Handicap - Nyt
0904-8987	Tordenskjold
0904-9363	Dansk Landbrug
0904-9398	Denmark. Socialforskningsinstituttet. Arbejdsnotater
0905-0221	Datch Information
0905-0957	Denmark. Socialforskningsinstituttet. Pjecer
0905-0965	Denmark. Finanstilsynet. Beretning. Bilag 5: Investeringsforeninger
0905-0965	Denmark. Finanstilsynet. Beretning
0905-1449	De Private Skoler i de Enkelte Kommuner
0905-1503	Ung og Fri
0905-1678	Julegaven
0905-295X	Dansk Skovbrugs Tidsskrift
0905-3549	D M I News
0905-4367	F S R's Skattelove med Noter
0905-4383	Photodermatology, Photoimmunology & Photomedicine
0905-4650	B 70
0905-5010	Arbejdsmiljoe
0905-5142	Agriculture in Denmark
0905-5193	Fiskeriundersoegelser i Groenland. Aarsberetning
0905-5215	Kalaallit Nunaani Aalisakkanik Misissuinerit. Ukiumoortumik Nalunaarusiaq
0905-5525	D S U'eren
0905-555X	Denmark. Statens Bibliotekstjeneste. Retningslinier
0905-5908	Dansk Sociologi
0905-6300	Dansk Musik Aarbog (Year)
0905-6440	Danske Malermestre
0905-6955	Aarhus School of Business. Centre for Labour Economics. Working Papers
0905-7188	Scandinavian Journal of Medicine & Science in Sports
0905-7749	Aslan
0905-8478	Denmark. Kgl. Veterinaer- og Landbohoejskole. Forskningsrapport
0905-8958	Aktuel Astronomi
0905-8966	Ledelse i Dag
0905-9415	Finans & Samfund
0905-9539	Arbejdsmiljoet - Netop Nu
0905-975X	Specialisten
0906-0294	Koebenhavns Universitet. Geologisk Centralinstitut. Aarsberetning
0906-0308	European Studies
0906-060X	I C E S Marine Science Symposia
0906-0820	Alt om Mad
0906-0952	Ide-Nyt: Til Villa, Raekkehuse og Jordbrugere
0906-1061	Strings and Squares
0906-1592	Under Paraplyen
0906-1614	Journalen. Lokal- og Kulturhistorisk Tidsskrift
0906-1770	Denmark. Landbrugsministeriet, Forskningssekretariatet. Kortlaegning
0906-1894	Denmark. Landbrugsministeriet, Forskningssekretariatet. Rammeplaner
0906-219X	Psykologisk Paedagogisk Raadgivning
0906-2483	Psykologisk Set
0906-5369	Danish Literary Magazine
0906-5504	Inuit Tusaataat
0906-5822	Denmark. Forskningsafdelingen. Forskning
0906-7043	Jord og Viden
0906-7590	Ecography
0910-0040	Japanese Association of Refrigeration. Transactions
0910-0156	Kokusai Kenkyu
0910-0377	Hirosaki Daigaku Igakubu Eiseigaku Kyoshitsu Gyosekishu
0910-0717	Meidai Uchusan Kenkyushitsu Kiji
0910-075X	Quarterly Forecast of Japan's Economy by the S.A. Method changed to Quarterly Forecast of Japanese Economy.
0910-1780	Diamond's Japan Business Directory (Year)
0910-2043	Japan Journal of Applied Mathematics
0910-2078	Tansuigyo changed to Tansuigyo-Hogo.
0910-223X	Arthroscopy
0910-3023	Hermes
0910-3732	This is N E C (Year)
0910-4100	Tochigi-kenritsu Hakubutsukan Kenkyu Hokokusho
0910-4208	Yobo Jiho
0910-4496	Marine Parks Journal
0910-4534	Japan Insurance News
0910-4607	P H P Intersect

ISSN INDEX

ISSN	Title
0910-4828	Tokyo Daigaku Sogo Kenkyu Shiryokan Gyosekishu
0910-5050	Japanese Journal of Cancer Research
0910-5190	Shizen Hakubutsuen Kiyot
0910-5476	Journal of International Studies
0910-5719	Statistics of Life Insurance Business in Japan
0910-5727	Statistics of Japanese Non-Life Insurance Business
0910-5999	Bank of Japan. Economic Statistics of Japan see 0910-6006
0910-6006	Bank of Japan. Economic Statistics Annual
0910-6030	Iryo (Year)
0910-6227	Nishinippon Kogyo Daigaku Kiyo. Rikogaku Hen
0910-6340	Analytical Sciences
0910-6510	Abstracts on Science and Technology in Japan: Electronics and Communication
0910-6529	Kodo Ryoho Kenkyu
0910-6987	Watakushitachi no Shizen
0910-7177	Tohoku no Shizen
0910-7800	Wing
0910-7878	Japan Dairy Technical Association. Bulletin
0910-7908	Japan English Publications in Print
0910-8327	Heart and Vessels
0910-8505	Nihon Boseki Geppo
0910-8629	Chubu University. College of Engineering. Memoirs
0910-8874	Chubu University. College of Business Administration and Information Science. Journal
0910-8882	Chubu University. College of International Studies. Journal
0910-9684	Jidosha Hoyu Sharyosu
0911-0119	Graphs and Combinatorics
0911-0151	Nihon Kagaku Gijutsu Kankei Chikuji Kankobutsu Mokuroku see 0916-1198
0911-0305	Kyoto Institute of Technology. Faculty of Engineering and Design. Memoirs
0911-0402	Phonetic Society of Japan. Bulletin
0911-0704	Control
0911-0755	J O I C F P News
0911-0844	Japanese Nursing Association Research Report
0911-1018	Nikkei New Materials
0911-209X	Osaka no Kagakusha
0911-3363	Hoppo Sangyo Eisei
0911-4041	Token Bijutsu
0911-4572	Nissan Kagaku Shinko Zaidan Kenkyu Hokokusho
0911-5064	Nagoya University. Cosmic-Ray Research Laboratory. Report changed to Nagoya University. Solar-Terrestrial Environment Laboratory. Cosmic Ray Section. Report.
0911-5137	Okinawa-ken Kachiku Eisei Shikenjo Nenpo
0911-5242	Nobeyama Uchu Denpa Kansokujo Nyusu
0911-5501	N R O
0911-551X	Journal of Space Technology and Science
0911-5625	Cross and Talk
0911-5870	Nobeyama Newsletter
0911-6044	Journal of Neurolinguistics
0911-6052	Japan Society of Plant Taxonomists. Proceedings
0911-6230	Hyogo Kyoiku Daigaku Kenkyu Kiyo. Dai-3-Bunsatsu. Shizenkei Kyoiku, Seikatsu Kenkokei Kyoiku
0911-6494	Houjyou
0911-6567	New Cicada
0911-6575	Japan. National Institute of Agrobiological Resources. Bulletin
0911-6664	Hokkaido University. Catalysis Research Center. Annual Report changed to Hokkaido University. Catalysis Research Center. Annual Report.
0911-6915	Sangyo Anzen Kenkyujo Hokoku see 0911-6923
0911-6923	Sangyo Anzen Kenkyujo Kenkyu Hokoku
0911-7008	Tokyo Business Today
0911-7237	Keio Gijuku Daigaku Hiyoshi Kiyo. Shizen Kagaku
0911-7652	Sky Watcher
0911-8004	Japanese Annual Bibliography of Economicst
0911-8012	Science Council of Japan. Annual Report on the Progress of Agriculturet
0911-8063	Sangyo Anzen Kenkyujo Gijutsu Shishin
0911-8233	Kwansei Gakuin Daigaku Rigakubu Tsushin
0911-8403	Japan. Ministry of Health and Welfare. Statistics and Information Department. Handbook of Health and Welfare Statistics
0911-8411	Japan. Ministry of Health and Welfare. Statistics and Information Department. Report on Activities of Public Health Centers
0911-8454	Japan. Ministry of Health and Welfare. Statistics and Information Department. Report on Survey of National Medical Care Insurance Services
0911-8489	Japan. Ministry of Health and Welfare. Statistics and Information Department. Statistical Report on Communicable Diseases
0911-8497	Japan. Ministry of Health and Welfare. Statistics and Information Department. Statistical Report on Food Poisonings
0911-8527	Japan. Ministry of Health and Welfare. Statistics and Information Department. Report on Survey of Occupational Statistics on Vital Events
0911-8764	News from Nisshin Steel
0911-9450	Nogyo Kankyo Gijutsu Kenkyujo Hokoku
0911-9639	Joetsu Kyoiku Daigaku Kenkyu Kiyo. Dai-3-Bunsatsu. Shizenkei Kyoiku, Seikatsu Kenkokei Kyoiku
0911-971X	Naito Zaidan Jiho
0911-9892	Hakubutsukan Kenkyu
0911-9973	Nippon Dojo Hiryogaku Zasshi
0912-0076	New Era of Telecommunications in Japan
0912-0599	Tokushima Kagakushi Zasshi
0912-1420	Hoken Kanri Senta Dayori
0912-1897	Kushiro-shiritsu Hakubutsukan Kiyo
0912-2036	Japanese Journal of Psychiatry and Neurology
0912-2311	Abstracts on Science and Technology in Japan: Energy Technology
0912-2346	Daito Bunka Daigaku Kiyo. Shizen Kagaku
0912-2354	Zaidan Nyusu
0912-2370	Research Reports on Information Sciences. Series A, Mathematical Science
0912-2389	Research Reports on Information Sciences. Series B, Operations Research
0912-2397	Research Reports on Information Sciences. Series C, Computer Sciences
0912-2826	Yokohama City Institute of Health. Annual Report
0912-3474	Japan Update
0912-3741	J J N Supesharu
0912-3814	Ecological Research
0912-4071	Okayama no Shizen
0912-4160	Media Info: International Media Directory Japan (Year)
0912-5434	Optoelectronics
0912-5604	Nagoya Daigaku Sogo Kenkyu Shiryoukan Houkoku - Nagoya University Museum. Bulletin see 0916-6319
0912-5833	DataNet
0912-6112	Tokei Suri
0912-6317	Japan Free Press
0912-6449	Kyodo to Kagaku
0912-7437	Umi to Anzen
0912-7569	Sugaku Ochikobore Tsushin
0912-7798	Hobetsu-choritsu Hakubutsukan Kenkyu Hokoku
0913-0101	Mitsubishi Densen Kogyo Jiho
0913-0195	Waseda Daigaku Kyoikugakubu Gakujutsu Kenkyu. Sugaku Hen
0913-025X	Materials on Asia - Accession List and Review
0913-1558	Kurashiki-shiritsu Shizenshi Hakubutsukanpo
0913-1566	Kurashiki-shiritsu Shizenshi Hakubutsukan Kenkyu Hokoku
0913-1620	Sophia University. Institute of Comparative Culture. Business Series
0913-185X	J S M E International Journal
0913-221X	Tohoku - Hokuriku Sugaku Kyoiku Kisoteki Kenkyu Hokoku
0913-3801	Japan. Information Science and Technology Association. Journal
0913-4182	Journal of Groundwater Hydrology
0913-4751	Osaka University. Research Institute for Microbial Diseases. Annual Reports
0913-5227	Nihon Kasei Gakkaishi
0913-5480	J A M R I Report
0913-5537	Koshien University. Department of Nutrition. Bulletin
0913-5545	Koshien University. College of Business Administration and Information Science. Bulletin.
0913-5693	Institute of Electronics, Information and Communications Engineers. Journal
0913-5707	Institute of Electronics, Information and Communication Engineers. Transactions (Section A)
0913-5715	Institute of Electronics Information and Communication Engineers. Transactions (Section B) see 0915-1877
0913-5723	Institute of Electronics Information and Communication Engineers. Transactions (Section C) see 0915-1893
0913-5731	Institute of Electronics, Information and Communication Engineers. Transactions (Section D) see 0915-1915
0913-5731	Institute of Electronics, Information and Communication Engineers. Transactions (Section D) see 0915-1923
0913-574X	I E I C E Transactions - Denshi Joho Tsushin Gakkai Ronbunshi (E) see 0917-1673
0913-6134	Journal of Communication between Rural Communities and Towns
0913-6681	Hospice Letter
0913-7785	Jinrui Dotai Gakkai Kaiho
0913-7912	Niigata Kogyo Tanki Daigaku Kenkyu Kiyo
0913-8102	Living in Japan
0913-9036	Japan Society for Comparative Endocrinology. Proceedings
0913-9664	Yokohama-shiritsu Daigaku Kiyo. Shizen Kagaku Hen
0914-0026	Business Tokyo
0914-0255	Japan Medical Review
0914-031X	Yamaguchi-ken Kogai Senta Nenpo see 0915-048X
0914-1340	Nissan Kagaku Shinko Zaidan Jigyo Hokokusho
0914-1707	Naito Kinen Kagaku Shinko Zaidan Kenkyu Hokokushu
0914-2029	N I P R Symposium on Antarctic Geosciences. Proceedings
0914-2037	N I P R Symposium on Polar Meteorology and Glaciology. Proceedings
0914-2045	Rejisumeito
0914-2401	Sapporo-shi Seishonen Kagakukan Kiyo
0914-3106	Journal of Tosoh Research
0914-3378	Jochi Daigaku Sugaku Kokyuroku
0914-3491	Jibi Inkoka, Tokeibu Geka
0914-3505	Congenital Anomalies
0914-4897	Abstracts of Scientific and Technological Publications
0914-5400	Seramikkusu Kyokai Shi
0914-5613	N I P R Symposium on Upper Atmosphere Physics. Proceedings
0914-5621	N I P R Symposium on Antarctic Meteorites. Proceedings
0914-563X	N I P R Symposium on Polar Biology. Proceedings
0914-5753	Kaijo Hoan-cho. Suiro-bu Kansoku Hokoku. Eisei Sokuchi Hen
0914-580X	Oita Daigaku Kyoikugakubu Kenkyu Kiyo
0914-627X	Mito Kagaku Gijutsu
0914-6385	Shizen Kagaku Kenkyu (Tokushima)
0914-6601	C D N L A O Newsletter
0914-675X	Kumamoto Journal of Mathematics
0914-6830	Hokkaidoritsu Suisan Shikenjo Kenkyu Hokoku
0914-6849	Hokusuishi Dayori
0914-7020	Kenkyu Gijutsu Keikaku
0914-8426	Primary Care
0914-8744	Kanagawa-kenritsu Shizen Hogo Senta Hokoku
0914-8833	Aera
0914-8930	Keisanki Tokeigaku
0914-9260	Communications Research Laboratory. Journal
0914-9279	Tsushin Sogo Kenkyujo Kiho
0914-9465	Archives of Histology and Cytology
0914-9775	Josai Daigaku Kenkyu Nenpo. Shizen Kagaku Hen
0914-9783	Journal of Mineralogy, Petrology and Economic Geology
0915-0021	National Astronomical Observatory. Reprints
0915-048X	Yamaguchi-ken Eisei Kogai Kenkyu Senta Nenpo
0915-0498	Yamaguchi-ken Eisei Kogai Kenkyu Senta Gyoseki Hokoku
0915-0862	University of Tokyo. Earthquake Research Institute. Special Bulletin
0915-1168	Tribologist
0915-1559	I S I J International
0915-163X	J A P I C Weekly Bulletin
0915-1702	Car Graphic
0915-1869	Hyomen Gijutsu
0915-1877	Institute of Electronics, Information and Communication Engineers. Transactions (Section B-I)
0915-1885	Institute of Electronics, Information and Communication Engineers. Transactions (Section B-II)
0915-1893	Institute of Electronics, Information and Communication Engineers. Transactions (Section C-I)
0915-1907	Institute of Electronics, Information and Communication Engineers. Transactions (Section C-II)
0915-1915	Institute of Electronics, Information and Communication Engineers. Transactions (Section D-I)
0915-1923	Institute of Electronics, Information and Communication Engineers. Transactions (Section D-II)
0915-2210	Passenger & In-Flight Servicet
0915-2334	N T T Review
0915-2652	Sanshi Konchu Nogyo Gijutsu Kenkyujo Hokoku
0915-2679	Sanshi. Konchunogyo Gijutsu Kenkyu Shiryo
0915-3640	National Astronomical Observatory. Publications
0915-3780	National Astronomical Observatory. Mizusawa Astrogeodynamics Observatory. Mizusawa Kansoku Center. Technical Report
0915-4116	Super C G
0915-5228	Tohoku Daigaku Iden Seitai Kenkyu Senta
0915-6321	National Astronomical Observatory. Report
0915-6348	National Institute for Fusion Science. Research Report
0915-6690	Speaking Out
0915-7352	Trends in Glycoscience and Glycotechnology
0915-8863	Kokuritsu Tenmondai Nyusu
0915-9444	Natural History Research
0915-9452	Natural History Museum and Institute, Chiba. Journal

0915-9517 Aiki News
0916-0701 Meikai University School of Dentistry. Journal
0916-1198 Nihon Kagaku Gijutsu Kankei Chikuji Kankobutsu Soran
0916-1740 Shigen Sozai
0916-1821 Materials Transactions, J I M
0916-2259 Kyushu Daigaku Rigakubu Shimabara Jishin Kazan Kansokujo Kenkyu Hokoku
0916-2623 Japan Petroleum and Energy Trends
0916-295X N.S.K. News Bulletin
0916-3158 Ryugin Keizai Report
0916-4650 Hokkaido University. Economic Journal
0916-6009 Toyama University. Mathematics Journal
0916-619X Rikagaku Kenkyujo Nyusu
0916-6211 Kawasaki Steel Bulletin
0916-6319 Nagoya Daigaku Furukawa Sogo Kenkyu Shiryokan Hokoku
0916-6688 Japanese Bulletin of Art Therapy
0916-7250 Journal of Veterinary Medical Science
0916-782X Japan Society for Precision Engineering. International Journal
0916-8370 Journal of Oceanography
0917-0480 Zairyo to Kankyo
0917-0537 Scientific Report of Cetacean Research
0917-0863 Road Home
0917-1630 University of Osaka Prefecture. Research Institute for Advanced Science and Technology. Annual Report
0917-1673 I E I C E Transactions on Communications Electronics Information and Systems
0917-7574 Shinku Tanku Nenpo
0917-7825 Japan Pharmaceutical Reference
0918-0753 Tokyo Rika Daigaku Kenkyu Ronbunshu
0920-0401 Manuscripts of the Middle East
0920-0517 Tijdschrift voor Sociale Gezondheidszorg
0920-0649 Tijdschrift voor Oude Muziek
0920-1009 Nederlandse Vereniging van Vrienden van de Ceramiek. Mededelingenblad
0920-1211 Epilepsy Research
0920-1319 Nieuws Berichten Informatie
0920-1580 Netherlands Journal of Housing and Environmental Research
0920-1610 Maritime Information Review
0920-1637 Clinical Neuropsychologist
0920-1742 Fish Physiology & Biochemistry
0920-1998 Orchid Monographs
0920-203X China Information
0920-2250 Palaeontology, Geology, Physics, and Chemistry. Proceedings *see* 0924-8323
0920-2307 Materials Science Reports
0920-234X I C C A Journal
0920-2412 Dier - En - Arts
0920-2706 Trends in Telecommunications
0920-3036 K - Theory
0920-3060 Critical Theory
0920-3079 Pragmatics and Beyond Companion Series *see* 0922-842X
0920-3206 Cardiovascular Drugs and Therapy
0920-3265 Lasers in Opthalmology *see* 0922-5307
0920-3273 Verpleegkunde
0920-3745 Informatierecht
0920-3796 Fusion Engineering and Design
0920-3958 Terugblik 40-45
0920-4105 Journal of Petroleum Science and Engineering
0920-427X Argumentation
0920-4369 V M *see* 0923-7674
0920-4741 Water Resources Management
0920-4776 Rijksmuseum van Oudheden, Leiden. Oudheidkundige Mededelingen
0920-4849 S E R Bulletin
0920-4989 Mesozoic Research†
0920-5047 Soviet Journal of Physical Oceanography
0920-5063 Journal of Biomaterials Science. Polymer Edition
0920-5071 Journal of Electromagnetic Waves and Applications
0920-525X Journal of Personnel Evaluation in Education
0920-5268 Applied Cardiopulmonary Pathophysiology
0920-5489 Computer Standards and Interfaces
0920-5497 Journal of Medical Imaging *see* 0720-048X
0920-5632 Nuclear Physics, Section B, Proceedings Supplements
0920-5691 International Journal of Computer Vision
0920-5861 Catalysis Today
0920-623X Vigiliae Christianae. Supplement
0920-6299 International Journal of Flexible Manufacturing Systems
0920-6434 Trade Facilitation *see* 0955-1255
0920-654X Journal of Computer-Aided Molecular Design
0920-7104 Bibliographia de Interlingua
0920-7430 Tentoonstellingsboekje
0920-8119 International Journal of Surface Mining *changed to* International Journal of Surface Mining and Reclamation.
0920-8437 Eurotrade (Dutch Edition)†
0920-8445 Eurotrade (French Edition)†
0920-8453 Eurotrade (English Edition)†
0920-8461 Eurotrade (German Edition)†
0920-8534 F E M S. Microbiology Immunology
0920-8542 Journal of Supercomputing
0920-8550 Journal of Financial Services Research
0920-8569 Virus Genes
0920-8607 Brill's Studies in Intellectual History
0920-8720 Regel & Recht Nieuws
0920-9026 Creole Language Library
0920-9034 Journal of Pidgin and Creole Languages
0920-9069 Cytotechnology
0920-9786 Catalogus van Nederlandse Zeekaarten en Andere Hydrografische Publikaties
0920-9964 Schizophrenia Research
0921-0296 Journal of Intelligent and Robotic Systems
0921-030X Natural Hazards
0921-0326 Muqarnas, Supplements
0921-0334 Iconography of Religions. Section 9, South America
0921-0717 Selected Works of Juan Luis Vives
0921-089X Instituut voor Cultuurtechniek en Waterhuishouding. Rapporten. Nieuwe Serie *see* 0924-3070
0921-2302 Fenomeno
0921-2523 Teoria Literaria: Texto y Teoria
0921-2566 I P O Annual Progress Report
0921-2574 Vangnet
0921-2639 Water Treatment
0921-2701 I N F
0921-2728 Journal of Paleolimnology
0921-2736 Computer Science in Economics and Management
0921-2787 Electric Word
0921-2973 Landscape Ecology
0921-2981 Surplus
0921-299X Biotherapy
0921-3449 Resources, Conservation and Recycling
0921-352X Annual on Terrorism (Year)
0921-3619 Dynamisch Oost-Nederland
0921-3732 European Cancer News
0921-3740 Cultural Dynamics
0921-3775 Frontiers of Medical and Biological Engineering
0921-3996 Blauwe Wegwijzer
0921-4097 Bedrijfsuitkomsten in de Landbouw
0921-4100 Financiele Positie van de Landbouw
0921-4135 Van Bedrijfsuitkomsten tot Financiele Positie
0921-4275 Bedrijfsuitkomsten in de Nederlandse Particuliere Bosbouw
0921-4283 Visserij in Cijfers
0921-4429 Museum Journaal *see* 0924-5251
0921-4488 Small Ruminant Research
0921-4496 Excerpta Medica. Section 130: Clinical Pharmacology†
0921-4526 Physica B - Physics of Condensed Matter
0921-4534 Physica C - Superconductivity
0921-4771 Probus
0921-4798 Aerosport - Info *changed to* Aeronovum.
0921-481X Tijdschrift voor Sociaal Wetenschappelijk Onderzoek van de Landbouw
0921-500X Contributions to the History of Labor and Society
0921-5093 Materials Science and Engineering A: Structural Materials: Properties, Microstructures and Processing
0921-5107 Materials Science & Engineering B: Solid-State Materials for Advanced Technology
0921-5166 Cardiac Imaging Video Journal
0921-5174 Zen
0921-5239 Handbuch der Orientalistik. 5. Abteilung. Japan
0921-531X A G F - Magazine
0921-5506 Prophyta
0921-5891 Hobbes Studies
0921-5956 Industrial Metrology
0921-6154 Literatuurinformatie Personeelsbeleid en Organisatie
0921-6200 Rijkspolitie Magazine *changed to* Politie Magazine.
0921-7126 Artificial Intelligence Communications
0921-7134 Asymptotic Analysis
0921-8009 Ecological Economics
0921-8017 Sportparachutist
0921-8068 Excerpta Medica. Section 36: Health Policy, Economics and Management
0921-8106 Industrial Crisis Quarterly
0921-8181 Global and Planetary Change
0921-8211 Normalisatie Magazine
0921-822X Excerpta Medica Abstract Journals
0921-8246 Brain Research
0921-8246 Brain Research *issued with* 0165-3806
0921-8246 Brain Research *issued with* 0165-0173
0921-8246 Brain Research *issued with* 0169-328X
0921-8254 F E M S. Microbiology
0921-8262 Mutation Research
0921-8319 Journal of Lipid Mediators
0921-8327 Open Systems Information Systems†
0921-8734 Mutation Research - D N Aging
0921-8777 Mutation Research - D N A Repair
0921-8831 Advanced Powder Technology
0921-884X Electroencephalography and Clinical Neurophysiology Including Evoked Potentials and Electromyography and Motor Control
0921-8890 Robotics and Autonomous Systems
0921-8912 Analytical Cellular Pathology
0921-8971 Journal of Applied Phycology
0921-898X Small Business Economics
0921-9668 Plant Foods for Human Nutrition
0921-9986 Wall Street Journal - Europe
0922-0895 Opleiding & Ontwikkeling
0922-1026 Financieel Overheidsmanagement
0922-1328 Grafisch Nederland
0922-1425 Japan and the World Economy
0922-1476 M A S T
0922-1808 Export Opportunities
0922-1891 Vereeniging Nederlandsch Historisch Scheepvaart Museum te Amsterdam. Jaarverslag
0922-2170 H B Modelbouw Magaziné
0922-2472 Neem Mijnou
0922-2979 Armex
0922-2995 Journal of Quantitative Anthropology
0922-3061 Advances in Suicidology
0922-3207 N F M Programmakrant *changed to* N F M - Programma.
0922-3282 Rapport I V V O
0922-3371 Cell Differentiation and Development *see* 0925-4773
0922-338X Journal of Fermentation and Bioengineering
0922-4106 European Journal of Pharmacology. Molecular Pharmacology Section
0922-4114 Renovatie en Onderhoud
0922-4270 Sportaccom
0922-4718 Wie Levert (Year)
0922-4777 Reading and Writing
0922-4939 Koninklijk Instituut voor de Tropen. Landenreeks
0922-5072 Semiotic Crossroads
0922-5307 Lasers and Light in Ophthalmology
0922-5366 C W I Quarterly
0922-5773 Journal of V L S I Signal Processing
0922-6001 Philosophy of History and Culture
0922-6028 Restorative Neurology and Neuroscience
0922-615X Produktwijzer - Elektres
0922-6168 Research on Chemical Intermediates
0922-6184 De Nederlandsche Bank N.V. Quarterly Bulletin
0922-6435 Experimental Astronomy
0922-6443 Real-Time Systems
0922-6532 Excerpta Medica. Section 54: A I D S†
0922-6567 Machine Translation
0922-680X Journal of Regulatory Economics
0922-7148 Port of Rotterdam Magazine
0922-7210 N I D I. Rapport - Report - Bericht - Rapporto
0922-7822 Gids bij de Prijscourant
0922-7911 Royal Tropical Institute. Bulletin
0922-842X Pragmatics and Beyond New Series
0922-8829 Beschrijvende Rassenlijst voor Siergewassen (Year)
0922-9744 Comparative Studies in Overseas History
0923-0211 Tijdschrift voor Revalidatiewetenschappen
0923-0408 Information & Decision Technologies
0923-0645 Marketing Letters
0923-0750 Journal of Inclusion Phenomena & Molecular Recognition in Chemistry
0923-1137 Reactive Polymers
0923-1722 Tijdschrift voor Oppervlaktetechnieken en Corrosiebestrijding
0923-1730 Oilfield Review
0923-179X Bioseparation
0923-1811 Journal of Dermatological Science
0923-182X Language International
0923-1919 De Ingenieurskrant
0923-2494 Research in Immunology
0923-2508 Research in Microbiology
0923-2516 Research in Virology
0923-2524 Urgences Medicales
0923-2532 Immuno-analyse et Biologie Specialisee
0923-2958 Celestial Mechanics and Dynamical Astronomy
0923-3660 Gaaf Goed
0923-4241 International Union of Consumers Unions Newsletter *changed to* World Consumer.
0923-4748 Journal of Engineering and Technology Management
0923-4861 Wetlands Ecology and Management
0923-5574 Het Houtblad
0923-5582 List of Journals Abstracted (Year)
0923-5957 Marketing and Research Today
0923-5965 Signal Processing: Image Communication
0923-6082 Multidimensional Systems and Signal Processing
0923-6511 Blind†
0923-6600 Od
0923-666X H S B International
0923-6805 China Earth Sciences
0923-7135 Incognita
0923-7143 Akkerbouw (The Hague)
0923-7534 Annals of Oncology
0923-7577 Lancet (Edition Francaise)
0923-7674 R O M Magazine
0923-7992 Open Economies Review
0923-8174 Journal of Electronic Testing
0923-9790 Delineavit et Sculpsit
0923-9820 Biodegradation
0924-0136 Journal of Materials Processing Technology
0924-0160 Dienst Landbouwkundig Onderzoek. Staring Centrum, Instituut voor Onderzoek van het Landelijke Gebied. Jaarverslag
0924-0314 Brill's Studies in Epistemology, Psychology and Psychiatry

ISSN

5822 ISSN INDEX

0924-0608 European Review of Latin American and Caribbean Studies
0924-090X Nonlinear Dynamics
0924-1884 Target
0924-2031 Vibrational Spectroscopy
0924-2244 Trends in Food Science and Technology
0924-2287 International Journal of Health Sciences
0924-2716 I S P R S Journal of Photogrammetry and Remote Sensing
0924-3046 Advanced Composite Materials
0924-3054 Artificial Organs Today
0924-3062 Agricultural Research Department. Winand Staring Centre for Integrated Land, Soil and Water Research. Reports
0924-3070 Dienst Landbouwkundig Onderzoek. Staring Centrum, Instituut voor Onderzoek van het Landelijk Gebied. Rapporten
0924-3089 Process Control and Quality
0924-3453 School Effectiveness and School Improvement
0924-3860 European Journal of Morphology
0924-3992 Mechatronics Systems Engineering
0924-4204 Institut Pasteur. Annales. Actualites
0924-4212 Bulletin du Cancer - Radiotherapie
0924-4247 Sensors and Actuators: A Physical
0924-4816 N G Gemeentelijk Magazine
0924-4824 Jurisprudentie voor Gemeenten
0924-5251 Kunst en Museumjournaal
0924-560X Entr'acte
0924-5723 Excerpta Medica. Section 17: Public Health, Social Medicine & Epidemiology
0924-6460 Environmental Resource Economics
0924-6479 International Journal of Risk and Safety in Medicine
0924-6495 Mind and Machines
0924-6533 Cancer Therapy Update
0924-669X Applied Intelligence
0924-6703 Discrete Event Dynamic Systems: Theory & Applications
0924-7963 Journal of Marine Systems
0924-8323 Royal Netherlands Academy of Sciences. Proceedings
0924-8455 Geriatric Nephrology and Urology
0924-8463 Artificial Intelligence and the Law
0924-8579 International Journal of Antimicrobial Agents
0924-8625 Space Communication
0924-865X Review of Quantitative Finance and Accounting
0924-8986 Indian Thought
0924-9265 Discrete Mathematics and Applications
0924-9338 European Psychiatry
0924-9370 Scoop
0924-9389 Studies in Christian Mission
0924-9745 Koninklijk Instituut vor de Tropen. Annotated Bibliographies Series
0924-977X European Neuropsychopharmacology
0924-980X Electromyography and Motor Control
0924-9826 Wonen en Milieu - Vakmatig
0924-9834 Personeel en Organisatie - Vakmatig
0924-9907 Journal of Mathematical Imaging and Vision
0925-0166 Fichte-Studien
0925-1014 Journal of Aquatic Ecosystem Health
0925-1022 Design, Codes and Cryptography
0925-1030 Analog Integrated Circuits and Signal Processing
0925-1375 International Humanist
0925-1413 Scan
0925-1421 Studies in Ancient Medicine
0925-1618 International Journal of Pharmacognosy
0925-1669 Economic and Social History in the Netherlands
0925-1944 Nederlandse Cystic Fibrosis Stichting. C F Nieuws
0925-2096 International Journal of Applied Electromagnetics in Materials
0925-2312 Neurocomputing
0925-2657 Schriftenreihe zur Philosophie Karl L. Poppers und des Kritischen Rationalismus
0925-2738 Journal of Biomolecular N M R
0925-2762 Agriloper
0925-2908 Arab History and Civilization
0925-2916 Brill's Indological Library
0925-2924 Energie & Milieutechnologie
0925-3467 Optical Materials
0925-4005 Sensors and Actuators: B Chemical
0925-4439 B B A - Molecular Basis of Disease
0925-4560 Journal for General Philosophy of Science
0925-4668 Dynamics and Control
0925-4676 Journal of Systems Integration
0925-4692 Inflammopharmacology
0925-4757 Reinardus
0925-4773 Mechanisms of Development
0925-4862 Onderwijs & Welzijn - Vakmatig
0925-4927 Psychiatry Research: Neuroimaging Section
0925-4986 Transputer and Occam Engineering Series
0925-5001 Journal of Global Optimization
0925-5052 Informatization and the Public Sector
0925-5060 European Water Pollution Control
0925-5125 Molecular Engineering
0925-5206 Advances in Echo-Contrast
0925-5214 Postharvest Biology and Technology
0925-5273 International Journal of Production Economics
0925-5281 Laboratory Information Management
0925-5710 International Journal of Hematology
0925-5893 Kan Anders
0925-5958 Excerpta Medica. Section 40: Drug Dependence, Alcohol Abuse and Alcoholism
0925-6164 Screening
0925-6806 Studia Copernicana - Brill Series
0925-7535 Safety Science
0925-7543 Tabak Plus Benelux
0925-7683 Medieval and Renaissance Authors and Texts
0925-7721 Computational Geometry
0925-7950 I A M C R Newsletter
0925-8175 Mixture
0925-8191 Lier en Boog
0925-8388 Journal of Alloys and Compounds
0925-8574 Ecological Engineering
0925-9635 Diamond and Related Materials
0926-2040 Solid State Nuclear Magnetic Resonance
0926-2245 Differential Geometry and Its Applications
0926-2261 Brill's Series in Jewish Studies
0926-227X Journal of Computer Security
0926-3373 Applied Catalysis B: Environmental
0926-3543 Amoeba
0926-4957 Geneva Papers on Risk and Insurance Theory
0926-5074 Geotechnika
0926-5473 I F I P Transactions A: Computer Science and Technology
0926-5481 I F I P Transactions B: Applications in Technology
0926-549X I F I P Transactions C: Communications Systems
0926-5805 Automation in Construction
0926-6070 Education and Society in the Middle Ages and the Renaissance
0926-6364 Random Operators and Stochastic Equations
0926-6410 Cognitive Brain Research
0926-6690 Industrial Crops and Products
0926-6801 Journal of High Speed Networks
0926-6917 European Journal of Pharmacology. Environmental Toxicology and Pharmacology Section
0926-7859 Beveiliging
0926-9851 Journal of Applied Geophysics
0926-9959 European Academy of Dermatology and Venereology. Journal
0927-0248 Solar Energy Materials and Solar Cells
0927-0256 Computational Materials Science
0927-0353 Centrum voor Onderzoek en Voorlichting voor de Pluimveehouderij "Het Spelderholt". Jaarsverlag
0927-1791 Alledaagse Dingen
0927-2011 Informatie en Automatisering - Vakmatig
0927-202X Lokaal & Mondial - Vakmatig
0927-2771 Excerpta Medica. Section 4: Microbiology: Bacteriology, Mycology, Parasitology and Virology
0927-278X Excerpta Medica. Section 29: Clinical and Experimental Biochemistry
0927-2798 Excerpta Medica. Section 30: Clinical and Experimental Pharmacology
0927-3034 Languages of Design
0927-6505 Astroparticle Physics
0930-0007 ZauberZeit
0930-021X Plattdeutsche Bibliographie
0930-0279 Walthari
0930-035X Roux's Archives of Developmental Biology
0930-0597 Bilanz- und Buchhaltung
0930-0708 Mineralogy and Petrology
0930-0716 Rosa Flieder
0930-0724 Tranvia
0930-0775 Kinderschutz Aktuell
0930-0791 Deutscher Tischtennis Sport
0930-0856 Wildtiere in Gehegen†
0930-1127 Muenchener Beitraege zur Mediaevistik und Renaissance-Forschung
0930-1143 Neue Gespraeche
0930-1151 Zeitschrift fuer Physik. Section A. Atomic Nuclei
0930-1186 Pony†
0930-1208 Heidelberger Althistorische Beitraege und Epigraphische Studien
0930-1240 Katastrophenschutz Aktuell *see* 0937-2555
0930-1313 Unterwegs (Munich)
0930-1437 Albanische Hefte
0930-1461 Forensic Science Progress
0930-2034 Stadt Remscheid Statistisches Jahrbuch
0930-2115 Die Offizin
0930-2255 N G Z Service Manager
0930-2492 Science Fiction Media
0930-2778 Literatur-Telegramm
0930-2786 Chinesische Medizin
0930-2794 Surgical Endoscopy, Ultrasound and Interventional Techniques
0930-2980 Blatt fuer Patent, Muster- und Zeichenwesen
0930-312X Surgical and Radiologic Anatomy
0930-3227 Computerbildung
0930-3308 Seitenwechsel
0930-343X European Journal of Plastic Surgery
0930-3618 Mittelstaendische Unternehmen
0930-3642 Tuebinger Blaetter
0930-3650 Braunviehzuchter
0930-3693 Password
0930-3782 Statistischer Vierteljahresbericht Hannover
0930-3839 Bundesforschungsanstalt fuer Landeskunde und Raumordnung. Seminare - Symposien - Arbeitspapiere
0930-3847 European Coatings Journal
0930-3855 Beilage Wirtschaftsrechtliche Blaetter *see* 0022-6912
0930-4010 Der Literatur Bote
0930-4177 Psychosoziale Umschau
0930-4207 Aphasie
0930-4274 Bochum. Amt fuer Statistik, Stadtforschung und Wahlen. Sonderberichte
0930-4282 Spektrum der Augenheilkunde
0930-4487 Werbeberater - Ideenservice fuer Erfolgreiche Werbung und Oeffentlichekeitsarbeit
0930-4584 Polen und Wir
0930-4622 M T A - Fachzeitschrift fuer Technische Assistenten der Medizin
0930-4827 Vitamine, Mineralstoffe, Spurenelemente
0930-4975 Data Welt *see* 0934-7178
0930-5467 E D V und Handwerk
0930-5580 Rheuma Praxis-Aktuell†
0930-5718 Christen Heute
0930-5874 Forum Modernes Theater
0930-6269 Fremdenverkehr - Tourismus und Kongress *changed to* European Tourism & Congress - Der Fremdenverkehr.
0930-6404 Historische Grundwissenschaften in Einzeldarstellungen
0930-6692 Hausbesitzer A B C
0930-6749 Der Garten Drinnen und Draussen
0930-6803 Informationszentrum Haut†
0930-6897 Zeitschrift fuer Ostkirchliche Kunst Hermeneia
0930-6900 Aerztebuch
0930-696X Lehrermagazin Sonderschulmagazin
0930-6994 Rock & Pop L P - Preiskatalog
0930-7109 Hautnah
0930-7133 Profitips fuer Selbermacher
0930-732X Tutzinger Blaetter
0930-7338 Moslemische Revue
0930-7370 Zeitschrift fuer Binnenschiffahrt und Wasserstrassen
0930-7516 Chemical Engineering and Technology
0930-7575 Climate Dynamics
0930-7656 Steuer Telex International
0930-777X International Polymer Processing
0930-7818 Muecke
0930-7834 Logistik im Unternehmen
0930-7842 D J I - Bulletin
0930-7923 Reports in Applied Measurement
0930-7974 Barett
0930-8040 Ultraschall in Klinik und Praxis
0930-8148 Biologische Anstalt Helgoland. Berichte.
0930-8199 A F B Info
0930-8253 Einblicke
0930-830X Friedensforschung Aktuell
0930-8318 Jatros H N O
0930-8326 Jatros Orthopaedie
0930-8350 Suchtreport
0930-8458 Einkaeufer im Markt
0930-8490 P P S Report
0930-8571 Geheim
0930-858X Deutsche Briefmarken - Revue
0930-861X Zeitschrift fuer Auslaendisches und Internationales Arbeits- und Sozialrecht
0930-8644 Messtechnische Briefe
0930-8679 Catholic Media Council. Information Bulletin
0930-8768 A U M A Kalender Messeplatz Deutschland *see* 0933-6206
0930-8792 Estonia
0930-8857 Purna Yoga†
0930-8873 Der Evangelische Buchberater
0930-8946 Stader Jahrbuch
0930-8954 Musik - Almanach
0930-9152 Jahrbuch fuer Biotechnologie
0930-9195 Surfen
0930-9225 Zeitschrift fuer Herz, Thorax- und Gefaesschirurgie
0930-9241 International Welding Engineering
0930-925X Fortschritte in der Arthroskopie
0930-9381 Zeitschrift fuer Internationale Erziehungs- und Sozialwissenschaftliche Forschung
0930-9950 Laurentius Sonderhefte
0930-9977 1999
0931-0029 Berufsbildungsbericht Duisburg (Year)
0931-0037 Deutsche Zeitschrift fuer Onkologie
0931-0053 A D A C Handbuch - Geschaeftswagen *see* 0937-3381
0931-0223 Christen Drueben
0931-041X Pediatric Nephrology
0931-0428 Fundamenta Psychiatrica
0931-0509 Nephrology, Dialysis and Transplantation
0931-0622 R W I Handwerksberichte
0931-0681 Der Geldscheinsammler
0931-0746 Universitaet Erlangen - Nuernberg. Vorlesungsverzeichnis
0931-119X Bond und Share
0931-1513 Natura Med
0931-1521 Pso Magazin
0931-1556 Cieslik's Puppenmagazin
0931-1688 Informationdienst Verkehr
0931-1785 Journal of Phytopathology
0931-1793 Journal of Veterinary Medicine. Series B
0931-184X Journal of Veterinary Medicine. Series A
0931-1890 Trees

ISSN

ISSN	Title
0931-1920	Canon Jahrbuch fuer Videofilmer
0931-1955	Stochastic Hydrology and Hydraulics
0931-2250	Journal of Agronomy and Crop Science
0931-2358	Information Medizin
0931-248X	Jahrbuch Mission
0931-2714	Mikroelektronik
0931-2811	Semitica Viva
0931-282X	Aetas Manjurica
0931-2838	Journal of Trace Elements and Electrolytes in Health and Disease
0931-2854	Juni
0931-2862	Bau-Berufsgenossenschaft Hannover. Mitteilungsblatt
0931-2889	Waeller Heimat
0931-2900	Bochum. Amt fuer Statistik, Stadtforschung und Wahlen. Verwaltungsbericht
0931-3079	Editio
0931-3117	K und L Magazin
0931-3125	C I M - Praxis
0931-3230	Japaninfo
0931-3265	Media Daten: Zeitungen
0931-3311	Musik - Konzepte
0931-3397	Germany (Federal Republic, 1949-). Deutscher Bundestag. Wissenschaftliche Dienste. Neuerwerbungen der Bibliothek
0931-3583	Afghanistanblaetter†
0931-3613	A L f A - Rundbrief
0931-380X	Kalender fuer den Biogarten
0931-3818	Esoterik-Almanach†
0931-3850	Triathlon und Sportwissenschaft
0931-3931	Plattduetsch Land un Waterkant
0931-4032	Wolfenbuetteler Bibliotheks - Informationen
0931-427X	Zavt
0931-4458	Katholische Oeffentliche Buecherei
0931-4695	Zentralblatt Innere Medizin†
0931-4733	Tele-Satellit
0931-4857	Museumsverband fuer Niedersachsen und Bremen. Mitteilungsblatt
0931-4873	D G A A E Nachrichten
0931-4938	Jahrbuch der Bundesrepublik Deutschland
0931-5020	Empirische Paedagogik
0931-5101	V M E-bus
0931-5179	Holiday Inn Live
0931-5187	Impressionen
0931-5233	Europaeische Gegenwart
0931-5381	Sportshop
0931-539X	Globus - Begleithefte
0931-5470	T V Programm fuer Nobel Hotels
0931-5527	German Journal of Homeopathy
0931-5551	Deutsche Gesellschaft fuer Angiologie. Mitteilungen
0931-5594	Medizin†
0931-573X	Golfclub Magazin
0931-5985	Fett - Wissenschaft Technologie
0931-6183	Rechtsprechung
0931-6418	Babylon
0931-6779	Berufsverband Aerzte fuer Orthopaedie. Informationen
0931-6965	Praktische Kieferorthopaedie
0931-7031	Sozial- und Zeitgeschichte des Sports
0931-704X	Journal of Materials Shaping Technology
0931-7058	Journal of Materials Engineering
0931-7317	Defense Update
0931-7597	ChemInform
0931-7775	S H - Technik†
0931-8224	Rehab-Report†
0931-8305	De Natura Rerum
0931-8593	Germany (Federal Republic, 1949-). Deutscher Bundestag. Wissenschaftliche Dienste. Neue Aufsaetze in der Bibliothek
0931-8623	Wuerzburger Geographische Manuskript
0931-8658	Journal of Economics - Zeitschrift fuer Nationaloekonomie
0931-8739	Muenchner Geowissenschaftliche Abhandlungen. Reihe B: Allgemeine und Angewandte Geologie
0931-8747	Muenchner Geowissenschaftliche Abhandlungen. Reihe C: Geographie
0931-8887	Lebendige Zelle
0931-8895	Berufliche Rehabilitation
0931-9069	Physis
0931-9077	K R P
0931-9085	Tageszeitung
0931-9158	Purana Research Publications, Tuebingen
0931-9190	Reinraumtechnik
0931-9344	Betrieb und Energie
0931-9360	Westermann's†
0931-9506	Protein Sequences & Data Analysis
0931-9522	Top Medizin
0931-9530	Applied Microgravity Technology see 0938-0108
0931-9808	MedienConcret
0932-0067	Archives of Gynecology and Obstetrics
0932-0075	Oldtimer Adressen Lexikon
0932-0113	Parasitology Research
0932-0180	Unitarische Blaetter
0932-0393	Professional Production
0932-0520	Europa
0932-0547	Zentralverband fuer Logopaedie. Forum der Mitglieder
0932-0555	Sportverletzung - Sportschaden
0932-0776	Zeitschrift fuer Naturforschung. Section B: Chemical Sciences
0932-0784	Zeitschrift fuer Naturforschung. Section A: Physical Sciences
0932-0814	Veterinary and Comparative Orthopaedics and Traumatology
0932-1055	K K H Journal
0932-1543	Reden-Berater
0932-2272	Portugal - Magazin
0932-2353	Springer Series in Biophysics
0932-2558	Technologie und Management
0932-2655	Alte Uhren und Moderne Zeitmessung
0932-268X	Bunken
0932-2698	D V und O R G A Brief changed to Tel-Com D V und Orga-Brief.
0932-2728	Near and Middle East Monographs
0932-2744	Food Marketing & Technology
0932-2876	Arbeitsmedizin
0932-2884	Gesundheitsfoerderung
0932-2892	Umweltmedizin
0932-2973	Deutsch-Amerikanische Geschaeftsbeziehungen
0932-2981	Das Grosse Leben
0932-318X	Lichtenrader Rundschau
0932-3201	Yarmouk University. Institute of Archaeology and Anthropology. Series
0932-3317	M und A - Messeplaner International
0932-3333	Art Buyer's Handbook
0932-3414	Tenside Surfactants Detergents
0932-3473	Code
0932-3481	W Z B Forschung
0932-3503	Natur und Heilen
0932-3635	Jahrbuch der Buerokommuniktation
0932-3708	A W T
0932-3724	Design-Report
0932-3902	Kerntechnik
0932-3961	Gablers - Magazin
0932-4089	Zeitschrift fuer Arbeits- und Organisationspsychologie
0932-4186	Reise und Preise
0932-4240	Suchtinformation
0932-433X	Der Schmerz
0932-4461	Zeitschrift fuer Althebraistik
0932-4488	Prodent
0932-4569	Journal of Institutional and Theoretical Economics
0932-4623	Literatur um 11
0932-4631	Profitravel
0932-464X	Goldschmiede und Uhrmacher Zeitung - European Jeweler
0932-4739	European Journal of Protistology
0932-4755	Muecki
0932-4879	Koeln-Duesseldorf von Hinten changed to Koeln - Rheinland von Hinten.
0932-4887	Berlin von Hinten changed to Berlin & Ex-DDR von Hinten.
0932-4895	Muenchen von Hinten changed to Muenchen & Bayern von Hinten.
0932-4909	Frankfurt von Hinten changed to Frankfurt - Rhein Main Neckar Saar von Hinten.
0932-4917	Hamburg und Sylt von Hinten changed to Hamburg - Norddeutschland von Hinten.
0932-4925	Schwule Maenner
0932-5026	Statistical Papers
0932-5034	Sozialmedizin
0932-5387	Dokumentation Sozialmedizin, Oeffentlicher Gesundheitsdienst, Gesundheitserziehung
0932-5409	Buergerrechte & Polizei
0932-5441	A T M - Forum
0932-5492	Betreff
0932-5565	Connection
0932-6162	Diesseits
0932-6251	Jahrbuch der Werbung
0932-6510	Methodika
0932-660X	Junge Freiheit
0932-710X	Nordrhein-Westfaelische Verwaltungsblaetter
0932-7118	Musicals
0932-7177	Compaq Magazin
0932-7231	Brennpunkt
0932-7398	Beauty
0932-7479	Deutsche Krebsgesellschaft. Mitteilungen
0932-7509	Zeichnen Fachzeitschrift fuer Konstruieren und Gestalten
0932-7541	Battelle Information
0932-7592	Paneuropa-Jugend in Paneuropa Deutschland changed to Paneuropa Deutschland.
0932-7754	D K I Literatur-Schnelldienst Kunststoffe Kautschuk Fasern
0932-7797	Entwicklungszusammenarbeit im Sport
0932-7886	Medien und Publicum
0932-7959	Lernhilfen fuer Bildende Kunst
0932-8092	Machine Vision & Applications
0932-8114	Zeitschrift fuer Sexualforschung
0932-8122	Die Hebamme
0932-822X	Jahrbuch des Schwalm-Eder-Kreises (Year)
0932-8297	H V V Rundschreiben
0932-8300	H V V Extra†
0932-8351	Bautechnik
0932-8408	Tel Aviver Jahrbuch fuer Deutsche Geschichte
0932-8610	Adolescent and Pediatric Gynecology
0932-8629	Botanica Acta
0932-8661	Jatros Dermatologie
0932-8823	Brennpunkte der Sportwissenschaft
0932-8955	Stadt Duisburg. Verwaltungsbericht
0932-9153	Limicola
0932-9196	Praxis der Anaesthesiologie und Intensivmedizin
0932-9315	Forst und Holz
0932-934X	G W G - Zeitschrift
0932-9358	Interview
0932-9692	Praxis Ergotherapie
0932-9714	Matatu
0932-9757	Heimat Dortmund
0932-9951	Kirchliche Zeitgeschichte
0933-002X	Cortison Spiegel
0933-0097	Klang & Ton
0933-0127	Bergbau-Berufsgenossenschaft. Jahresbericht
0933-016X	Schaufenster & Shop Design
0933-0585	TanzAktuell
0933-0615	Beamte Heute
0933-0682	Milchstrasset
0933-0704	Die Geowissenschaften
0933-0747	Clio
0933-0771	Diaconia Christi
0933-1093	Experimentelle und Klinische Hypnose
0933-1263	Buehnenkunst
0933-1409	A T M
0933-1433	Journal of Population Economics
0933-1557	D O S International
0933-1719	Humor
0933-1875	Kuenstliche Intelligenz
0933-1883	Sociolinguistica
0933-1905	Internationale Jahresbibliographie der Kongressberichte
0933-1980	Hoerakustik
0933-2286	I A B Aktuell
0933-2367	Neue Keramik
0933-2480	Chance
0933-257X	Koelner Museums Bulletin
0933-2731	Bundestag Report
0933-2871	Biomedizinische Forschung - Informationen
0933-3053	System Familie
0933-3096	Geschichte Lernen
0933-3169	Hoppenstedt Stock Guide Germany
0933-3282	Niemandslandt
0933-3347	Luzifer-Amor
0933-3630	Soil Technology
0933-3657	Artificial Intelligence in Medicine
0933-3983	Siebenbuergische Semesterblaetter
0933-4165	Packaging Production International
0933-4173	Journal of Planar Chromatography - Modern T L C
0933-4351	Nyankpala Agricultural Research Report
0933-4440	Touren-Fahrer
0933-4548	Versicherungsmedizin
0933-4580	Holz-Kunststoff
0933-4718	A V A - Arbeitsmaterialien zur Verwaltungs- und Hochschulausbildung†
0933-4769	Text und Kontext
0933-4807	Pteridines
0933-5137	Materialwissenschaft und Werkstofftechnik
0933-5315	Bios
0933-5358	Heimat Ostbayern
0933-5374	Praxis Geschichte
0933-5420	Historische Bibliographie
0933-5498	Herr Schmidt
0933-5846	Archive for Mathematical Logic
0933-5854	Biology of Metals
0933-6117	Die Voelker Rufen
0933-6168	Tabula Rasa
0933-6206	A U M A Handbook Germany - Trade Fair Country
0933-6230	Gutenberg - Gesellschaft. Kleine Drucke
0933-6265	Jugendpost see 0936-871X
0933-632X	Koelner Statistische Nachrichten
0933-632X	Koelner Statistische Nachrichten. Sonderhefte
0933-6346	Heimatpflege in Westfalen
0933-6389	Paedagogische Korrespondenz
0933-6540	Fernwaerme International
0933-6680	Feinschmecker fuer Aerzte
0933-6958	Parlaments- und Parteistiftungsarchivare Berichten
0933-7024	Schwaedds
0933-7075	Club Magazin
0933-7253	Passagen
0933-7334	Elbinger Nachrichten
0933-7385	Hautfreund
0933-758X	Mitteilungen zur Altenhilfe
0933-7598	Dampf und Reise
0933-7660	Prakla Seismos Report†
0933-7741	Forum Mathematicum
0933-7776	Kultus und Unterricht
0933-7792	Cross Magazin
0933-7814	Deutscher Forschungsdienst. Special Science Reports
0933-7849	Incentive Journal
0933-7857	Evangelischer Bund
0933-7954	Social Psychiatry and Psychiatric Epidemiology
0933-8055	Energiedepesche
0933-808X	Schuhtechnik International
0933-811X	Endoskopie Heute
0933-8241	Mensch und Buero
0933-8330	Schmiede Journal
0933-8357	Aussendienst Informationen
0933-842X	Praxis der Klinischen Verhaltensmedizin und Rehabilitation
0933-8586	Orthodoxes Forum
0933-8667	Design und Elektronik
0933-8721	Hefte fuer Ostasiatische Literatur
0933-8799	Spuren Suchen
0933-8810	M - Moderne Metalltechnik
0933-8934	Literaturschau "Stahl und Eisen"
0933-8985	Spirita
0933-9094	Rueckert zu Ehren
0933-9264	Brillen Special
0933-9280	HighTech†

5824 ISSN INDEX

ISSN	Title
0933-9345	Western Horse
0933-9663	Abstracts and Reviews from Zentralblatt fuer Mathematik
0933-968X	Briefmarken-Magazin
0933-9728	Media-Daten Annuals
0933-9760	Demeter Kongress Kalender Medizin
0933-9949	Bibelreport
0934-0378	Film und Fakten
0934-0696	Zeitschrift fuer Tuerkeistudien
0934-0815	C V World Report see 0940-8770
0934-0866	Particle & Particle Systems Characterization
0934-0874	Transplant International
0934-0939	Forum Politische Bildung
0934-1129	A I D S
0934-1234	Forschungen zur Brandenburgischen und Preussischen Geschichte
0934-1307	Neue Zeitschrift fuer Verkehrsrecht
0934-1749	AutoCAD Magazin
0934-1773	Bauen mit Kunststoffen
0934-1854	Classical Homoeopathy Quarterly
0934-2192	Religionswissenschaftliche Reihe
0934-3148	Med - Report
0934-3164	Hausarzt in Hessen
0934-3180	T V It
0934-3237	S T - Magazin
0934-3342	Textilkunst
0934-3407	Natuerlich
0934-3482	Muellmagazin
0934-361X	Dachau Review
0934-3814	Bausteine Grundschule
0934-3938	Aluminium Intern: Aluminium und Automobil
0934-4217	Media Selection
0934-4365	Scientific Drilling
0934-4535	Allgemeine Zeitschrift fuer Paranormologie
0934-4632	Unabhaengige Bauernstimme
0934-4640	Deutsche Gesellschaft fuer Pharmakologie und Toxikologie. Mitteilungen
0934-4713	Neue Kronstaedter Zeitung
0934-5043	Formal Aspects of Computing
0934-5140	Check-in
0934-5175	Indienrundbrief
0934-5191	Anzeiger des Germanischen Nationalmuseums und Berichte aus dem Forschungsinstitut fuer Realienkunde
0934-5256	Praxis Spiel und Gruppe
0934-5272	Themenzentrierte Interaktion
0934-5418	Xiang Qit
0934-5841	Software Kurier
0934-5906	Wireworld
0934-5914	Element und Bau
0934-5930	Eisenbahn Ingenieur Kalender (Year)
0934-5965	World Steel & Materials Fachberichte
0934-6082	C G
0934-6155	Zwischen Orient und Okzident
0934-6430	F I R und I A W Mitteilungen
0934-6449	Folk-Michel
0934-6465	Bayerisches Staatsministerium des Innern. Allgemeines Ministerialblatt
0934-649X	Marxismus heute
0934-6643	Mertensiella
0934-666X	Zeitschrift fuer Kulturtechnik und Landentwicklung
0934-6694	Operative Orthopaedie und Traumatologie
0934-7062	Geschmacksmusterblatt
0934-7100	Arbeitsrecht-Blattei (A R)
0934-7178	P C Praxis
0934-7348	Powder Handling & Processing
0934-7909	Natur- und Ganzheitsmedizin, Wissenschaft und Praxis
0934-8379	Infektions Klinik
0934-8387	Pneumologie
0934-8395	Thermo Med
0934-8417	A F E T - Mitglieder - Rundbrief
0934-8441	Boerse Online
0934-845X	Macintosh Magazin
0934-8468	P C Magazin Plus
0934-8522	Materialdienst des Konfessionskundlichen Instituts
0934-8549	Abgesaegtt
0934-8603	N V w Z Rechtsprechungs Report Verwaltungsrecht
0934-8654	Pocket & Laptop Computer
0934-8662	Elternforum
0934-8778	Computerreport der Neue Juristischen Wochenschrift
0934-8786	Vanessas Zeitgeist
0934-8832	Matrix
0934-8840	Zentralblatt fuer Bakteriologie
0934-8859	Zentralblatt fuer Hygiene und Umweltmedizin
0934-8875	Waelzlagertechnik - Industrietechnik
0934-8913	Nikephoros
0934-8964	Amtsblatt der Stadt Moenchengladbach
0934-9014	Parkett Magazin
0934-9235	Biometrie and Informatik
0934-926X	Technique du Roulement - Technique Industrielle
0934-9278	Tecnica de los Rodamientos - Tecnica Industrial
0934-9383	Nationaltheater Mannheim Theaterzeitung
0934-9391	Sieg Tech
0934-9456	Germany (Federal Republic, 1949-). Bundesanstalt fuer Materialforschung und -pruefung. Jahresbericht
0934-9472	Mannheimer Berichte
0934-9669	Thrombotic and Haemorrhagic Disorders
0934-9723	European Journal of Clinical Microbiology & Infectious Diseases
0934-9758	Vakuum in der Praxis
0934-9790	A U M A Handbook International
0934-9820	Eicosanoids
0934-9871	Tool
0934-9995	Japanische Fachtexte
0935-0179	Psychologie und Geschichtet
0935-0276	B T S - Buero Technik Systeme
0935-0373	C-Magazin
0935-0381	Controlling
0935-0411	Regional Cancer Treatment
0935-0454	A Z U R Camping Magazin
0935-0659	Die Wachenburg
0935-0721	Fantasywelt
0935-0853	Zeitschrift fuer Klassische Homoeopathie
0935-0993	Interkulturell
0935-1108	Leonardo
0935-1175	Continuum Mechanics and Thermodynamics
0935-1183	Structured Programming
0935-1221	European Journal of Mineralogy
0935-123X	Berichte der Deutschen Mineralogischen Gesellschaft
0935-137X	M T Dialog
0935-1523	Geo - Informations - Systeme
0935-1582	Weltmarkt
0935-1809	D E S W O S - Brief
0935-1965	Zeitschrift fuer Transplantationsmedizin
0935-2023	Industriebau
0935-2066	D G I P - Intern
0935-2147	Cryptogamic Botany
0935-2767	Arzneimittel Zeitung
0935-3097	Weiterbildung
0935-3194	Therapeutikon
0935-3208	T W Gynaekologie
0935-3216	T W Paediatrie
0935-3224	T W Neurologie - Psychiatrie
0935-3356	Outdoor
0935-3372	Rotpunkt
0935-3518	Historische Sprachforschung
0935-364X	Heimatblaettle
0935-3658	Essener Universitaetsberichte
0935-414X	Fotografie Draussen
0935-4344	Blick ins Hessenland
0935-4441	Verbindungstechnik in der Elektronik
0935-4964	Theoretical and Computational Fluid Dynamics
0935-5405	Das Gruene Jahrbuch
0935-5596	Trendletter Megatrends Aktuell
0935-5936	Media Daten: Radio - T V
0935-6274	Page
0935-6282	MACup
0935-6339	Journal of Manual Medicine
0935-6347	Vliesstoff Nonwoven International
0935-6398	Opernglas
0935-6436	Kultur Vorschau International
0935-6576	Heidelberger Studien zur Naturkunde der Fruehen Neuzeit
0935-6592	D A G - Journal
0935-6991	Bildschirmtext Aktuell
0935-7149	Porentief
0935-7238	Research & Development
0935-7262	C P & T International
0935-7335	Ethik in der Medizin
0935-7505	Tibetan and Indo-Tibetan Studies
0935-7602	Oekowerkmagazin
0935-7653	Artikel 5
0935-7688	Entsorgungs-Technik
0935-7866	Neumann - Handbuch fuer den Pressevertrieb
0935-7939	Logistik Spektrum
0935-798X	Der Merkurstab
0935-8005	Meine Geschichte
0935-8013	Bonner Aerztliche Nachrichten
0935-8080	M T U Heutet
0935-8234	Haeusliche Pflege
0935-8315	Toolbox
0935-8447	Dental Equipment and Supply Guide
0935-8641	Der GourmeTip
0935-865X	Lebensmittelreport
0935-8838	Maenner Aktuell
0935-8927	Jugendmagazin see 0940-4961
0935-8943	Laryngo- Rhino- Otologie
0935-8994	Frankfurt Magazin
0935-9060	Krieg und Literatur
0935-9400	P.M. Perspektive
0935-9451	Bilag Brief
0935-9648	Advanced Materials
0935-994X	Physis Computer changed to Physis Medizin Computer.
0936-014X	Instrumentenbau Report
0936-0352	Deutschen Kunststoff-Institut. Mitteilungen
0936-0492	P T B Berichte
0936-0689	Sound Check
0936-0700	V I T Informationstechnik
0936-1421	Rote Fahne
0936-1928	Euro-Focus
0936-2479	Bluegrass - Buehne
0936-2517	Ophthalmo Chirurgie
0936-2568	Soil Technology Series
0936-2665	Billard-Sport Magazin
0936-2800	Zeitschrift fuer Bankrecht und Bankwirtschaft
0936-2835	Exceptionality
0936-2940	Hochschule fuer Musik Koeln. Journal
0936-2975	Advances in Feed Technology
0936-3602	Der Elektriker
0936-3637	Tourist auf Reisen
0936-3734	Gaertnerboerse und Gartenwelt
0936-3971	Blaue Jungs
0936-4609	Museums - Eisenbahn
0936-5117	Wirtschaftsprueferkammer. Mitteilungen
0936-5133	Kassel Kulturell
0936-5184	Internationale Beziehungen
0936-5214	Chemoecology
0936-546X	Info3 Extra
0936-5761	Nachbarsprache Niederlaendisch
0936-577X	Climate Research
0936-5796	Historische Mitteilungen
0936-5818	Wetterkarte
0936-5869	Historischer Verein Eichstaett. Sammelblatt
0936-5877	Palstete
0936-5885	Wirtschaft im Suedwesten (Freiburg)
0936-5885	Wirtschaft im Suedwesten (Villingen)
0936-5907	Cognitive Linguistics
0936-6121	Der Schuhmacher
0936-6156	D O K: Politik - Praxis Recht
0936-627X	Reisen und Leben
0936-6318	European Dairy Magazine
0936-6520	Was Uns Betrifft
0936-6547	Kiel
0936-6652	RoeFo. Fortschritte auf dem Gebiete der Roentgenstrahlen und der Neuen Bildgebenden Verfahren
0936-6768	Reproduction in Domestic Animals
0936-6903	Biologie Heute
0936-6911	Elektronenmikroskopie
0936-6970	Praxis Schule 5-10
0936-7136	Zum Weitergeben
0936-7152	Geriatrie Praxis
0936-7160	PerinatalMedizin
0936-7578	Spuren und Motive
0936-7586	Die Philosophin
0936-7780	Medienpsychologie
0936-7802	Stripspiegel
0936-8299	Urspring Nachrichten
0936-8302	Top Agrar: Ausgabe B
0936-8310	Top Agrar: Ausgabe R
0936-8329	Top Agrar: Ausgabe S
0936-8345	Northeimer Jahrbuch
0936-8515	Haeckel Buecherei
0936-871X	Rasant
0936-8760	Werkzeuge
0936-8787	Zeitschrift fuer Planung
0936-8833	Desktop Dialog
0936-8965	Reihe der Villa Vigoni
0936-9090	Magnus
0936-9171	Dokumentationsdienst Asien und Suedpazifik. Ausgewaehlte Neuer Literatur
0936-9198	Sozialverisicherungs-Berater
0936-949X	Zentrum fuer Meeres- und Klimaforschung. Berichte
0936-9732	Urologie Poster
0936-9856	H V - Journal
0936-9902	Ichthyological Exploration of Freshwaters
0936-9933	Journal of Evolutionary Economics
0937-0005	Schleswig-Holstein. Ministerin fuer Bildung, Wissenschaft, Jugend und Kultur. Nachrichtenblatt
0937-0412	Biotech Europe see 0938-7501
0937-0420	D L R - Nachrichten
0937-0773	Interdisziplinaere Beitraege zur Kriminologischen Forschung
0937-0811	B G W Mitteilungen
0937-0927	Prisma (Hamburg)
0937-1508	Unsere Heimat
0937-1729	Evangelische Jugend in Bayern. Nachrichten
0937-2008	Izumi
0937-2105	Khoj
0937-2148	Chemistry of Plant Protection
0937-2555	Schutz Aktuell
0937-2644	Schleswig-Holstein. Jahrbuch - Heimatkalender
0937-2733	Fabrik 2000
0937-2768	Moderne Hotel Technik
0937-2873	Forschung an der Universitaet Bielefeld
0937-289X	Krankenhauspsychiatrie
0937-3225	Philosophy and Artificial Intelligence
0937-3381	Autokosten und Steuern Aktuell
0937-3756	B B R
0937-3926	Getraenke Gastronomie
0937-4167	Konstruktionspraxis
0937-4183	Materialwirtschaft und Logistik im Unternehmen
0937-5457	Gambit Revue
0937-5724	Wolfenbuetteler Mittelalter Studien
0937-583X	Musik in Bayern
0937-5929	Dokumentationsdienst Asien und Suedpazifik. Reihe A
0937-5937	Dokumentationsdienst Vorderer Orient. Ausgewaehlte Neuere Literatur
0937-5945	Dokumentationsdienst Vorderer Orient. Reihe A
0937-6178	Das Kloecknerhaus
0937-6186	Kloeckner Werke Heute
0937-6356	Schoenhengster Heimat
0937-6429	Wirtschaftsinformatik
0937-6488	Numismatisches Nachrichtenblatt
0937-6496	UniPress
0937-6569	Auszeit
0937-6755	Informationen Jugendliteratur und Medien-Jugendschriften-Warte
0937-700X	Food Technologie Magazin
0937-7123	Landschaftsverband Westfalen-Lippe. Mitteilungen des Landesjugendamtes
0937-7204	Europaeische Zeitschrift fuer Wirtschaftsrecht
0937-7247	Schleswig-Holstein
0937-7417	Medien Memot
0937-7425	Nachrichten - Paritaet

ISSN INDEX 5825

0937-7441 Report on Eastern Europe
0937-7549 Zyma
0937-7646 Das Betriebsrestaurant
0937-8243 EuroPean Journal for Fluid Power
0937-8316 Forum (Essen)
0937-8766 Themenhefte Gemeindearbeit
0937-9053 Sportstaetten und Schwimmbaeder
0937-907X Acta Demographica
0937-9258 Cokemaking International
0937-9347 Applied Magnetic Resonance
0937-938X Ethik und Sozialwissenschaften
0937-941X Osteoporosis International
0937-9509 Brucker Szene
0937-9819 Rechtsmedizin
0937-9827 International Journal of Legal Medicine
0937-9835 Kleine Historische Reihe
0938-0051 Travaux du Groupe de Recherches et d'Etudes Semitiques Anciennes
0938-0108 Microgravity - Science and Technology
0938-0124 Informationen fuer Einelternfamilien
0938-0213 Modellbahn Start
0938-0914 Steppke
0938-0922 InVitro Diagnostika Nachrichten
0938-1279 Applicable Algebra in Engineering, Communication and Computing
0938-1287 Shock Waves
0938-152X Jahrbuch Arbeit und Technik
0938-1643 Schiff und Hafen
0938-1694 Bauplan - Bauorga
0938-1759 Botanicus Brief
0938-1767 Literatur zum Angewoehnen
0938-1910 Tischtennis Lehre
0938-1953 Surveys on Mathematics for Industry
0938-2194 D L R - Jahresbericht
0938-2259 Economic Theory
0938-2569 Universitaet Augsburg. Personen- und Studienverzeichnis
0938-2623 Evolution and Cognition
0938-2666 Dokumentationsdienst Vorderer Orient. Kurzbibliographie
0938-2836 Deutsche Geodaetische Kommission. Veroeffentlichungen: Reihe A. Theoretische Geodaesie
0938-3190 Im Heiligen Dienst
0938-3506 Tibet und Buddhismus
0938-3638 Dokumentationsdienst Asien und Suedpazifik. Kurzbibliographie
0938-3697 Nordelbische Stimmen
0938-3808 Zeitschrift fuer Geriatrie
0938-4022 C B Funk
0938-4731 Hochtaunusblaetter
0938-5428 European Journal of International Law
0938-5495 Advances in Knowledge Organization
0938-5851 Kommission fuer Oekologie. Rundgespraeche
0938-619X Kultur Journal
0938-6300 Wissenschaft in den Medien
0938-6408 Friede Ueber Israel
0938-6467 GynComp
0938-6629 Harmonika International
0938-7390 Notfallvorsorge und Zivile Verteidigung
0938-7412 Herzschrittmachertherapie und Elektrophysiologie
0938-7463 Frauenaerztliches Seminar
0938-7501 Biotech Forum Europe
0938-765X Lasermedizin
0938-7994 European Radiology
0938-8184 Uro-Imaging
0938-8303 Wasser, Luft und Boden
0938-846X Deutsche Geodaetische Kommission. Jahresbericht
0938-8478 Aerzteblatt Sachsen
0938-8486 Zahnaerzteblatt Sachsen
0938-863X Villa Vigoni. Jahrbuch
0938-8702 E B
0938-8818 Deutsche Landwirt
0938-8974 Journal of Nonlinear Science
0938-8990 Mammalian Genome
0938-9016 Pain Digest
0938-9261 Offizielles Aerzteblatt fuer Sachsen-Anhalt
0938-9377 COBOL Journal
0938-9407 Fortschritte der Diagnostik
0938-9563 Modelling of Geo-Biosphere Process
0938-9806 Tile & Brick International
0938-9849 Kunststoffe Europe
0939-0073 Der Selbstaendige in der Binnenschiffahrt
0939-0081 Der Selbstaendige
0939-0286 Stil und Etikette *changed to* Handbuch Stil und Etikette.
0939-0367 Softwarefuehrer UNIX
0939-0367 Netzwerkfuehrer: Lokale Netze
0939-1142 Computer Produkte Software
0939-1649 Telcom-Brief *changed to* Tel-Com D V und Orga-Brief.
0939-205X Engineering und Automation
0939-219X Mit Rheuma Leben
0939-2335 R W I Konjunkturbrief
0939-2661 Anaesthesie - Intensivtherapie - Notfallmedizin - Schmerztherapie
0939-267X Aktuelle Radiologie
0939-2904 Neue Beitraege zur Juelicher Geschichte
0939-2947 Roter Morgen
0939-3072 E T E P
0939-3099 Aktuelle Ostinformationen
0939-3234 Greenpeace Magazin
0939-3331 Apothekenhelferin Heute
0939-334X Geschichte der Pharmazie
0939-3390 Astro
0939-3498 Brief Berater
0939-3625 Economic Systems
0939-3684 Material und Markt
0939-3986 Brandenburgischen Landeshochschule Potsdam. Wissenschaftliche Zeitschrift†
0939-4044 Siehste!
0939-4400 Verwaltungsjahrbuch fuer die Deutsche Bundespost
0939-4451 Amino Acids
0939-4508 E C Public Contract Law
0939-4648 Bielefelder Universitaetszeitung
0939-4664 Fermate
0939-4702 Deutsche Behindertenzeitschrift
0939-4761 Kirchenmusikalische Nachrichten
0939-4826 Unicum
0939-4966 Geldanlage Berater
0939-4974 European Journal of Clinical Chemistry and Clinical Biochemistry
0939-5059 Rheology (Year)
0939-5296 Aufwind
0939-5458 B L Journal
0939-5474 Unterschiede
0939-5555 Annals of Hematology
0939-5687 Thueringer Zahnaerzteblatt
0939-5911 Sucht
0939-6071 Politics and the Individual
0939-6292 Medizin ohne Nebenwirkungen
0939-6330 Zeitschrift fuer Fischkunde
0939-6365 European Journal of Pain
0939-6411 European Journal of Pharmaceutics and Biopharmaceutics
0939-6640 Mineralien Welt
0939-6675 NetWorks
0939-7116 Klinische Neuroradiologie
0939-7248 European Journal of Pediatric Surgery
0939-7256 Forum (Munich)
0939-7507 Erzieherbrief
0939-7795 Management & Seminar
0939-7825 Finanzierungs Berater
0939-7965 Fracht - Dienst
0939-8619 International Contact - Photo, Video, Lab Technology
0939-9275 K L A G E
0939-9437 European Journal of Hospital Pharmacy
0939-978X Phlebologie
0940-0001 Deutsche Industriebank. Geschaeftsbereich Volkswirtschaft. I K B - Mitteilungen
0940-0141 Muenchner Uni Magazin
0940-0265 Santag
0940-0834 Geologisches Landesamt Baden - Wuerttemberg. Informationen
0940-1849 Metro Man
0940-2330 InterCamara
0940-2500 Med. Dent. Magazin
0940-2675 Federn - Ketten - Biegeteile
0940-2691 Draht und Kabel Panorama
0940-2993 Experimental and Toxicologic Pathology
0940-3256 Ornithologischer Anzeiger
0940-4325 Suelchgau
0940-4783 Deutscher Forschungsdienst. Berichte aus der Wissenschaft - Auswahl Medizin
0940-4821 J O I C E
0940-4961 J U M A
0940-5178 Zeitschrift fuer Oekologie und Naturschutz
0940-533X Berliner Kongresskalender
0940-5925 Video Professional
0940-6689 Physikalische Medizin Rehabilitationsmedizin Kurortmedizin
0940-6697 Auto und Modell
0940-8428 Praxis Handbuch Personal
0940-8762 G V Manager
0940-8770 C V
0940-8789 J O T
0941-0155 Freie Universitaet Berlin. Studienhandbuch
0941-2131 Klinisches Labor
0941-2239 Bauernzeitung
0941-3480 Hp 1 Modellbahn
0941-6617 Kleine Bibliographische Reihe
0941-6781 Justuf
0943-612X 3-D Education†
0950-0170 Work, Employment & Society
0950-0189 Scottish Libraries
0950-0197 Bathrooms
0950-0308 British Leisure Centre Directory
0950-0332 Q Xt†
0950-0340 Journal of Modern Optics
0950-0502 Adrenergic Receptors
0950-0510 Heat Shock Proteins
0950-0529 Luminescence†
0950-0537 Methyl Transferases†
0950-0553 Neuroimmunoendocrinology†
0950-0561 Oncogenes
0950-057X Oxygen Radicals
0950-0588 Proteases and Inhibitors
0950-0596 Protein Secretion†
0950-0618 Construction and Building Materials
0950-0634 Strandlight
0950-0650 Africa and the World
0950-0693 International Journal of Science Education
0950-0707 Science, Technology & Development
0950-0715 Sheppard's Book Dealers in British Isles
0950-0731 Arab Affairs
0950-0782 Language and Education
0950-0790 Evaluation and Research in Education
0950-0804 Journal of Economic Surveys
0950-0839 Philosophical Magazine Letters
0950-091X Basin Research
0950-0928 Professional Horticulture
0950-1029 World Oil Trade
0950-1045 Oil and Energy Trends
0950-107X I E E Proceedings Part H: Microwaves, Antennas & Propagation
0950-110X Quarry and Mining News *changed to* New Quarrying & Mining.
0950-1487 Power International†
0950-1533 Artificial Intelligence Abstracts†
0950-1568 Restoration
0950-1584 Leadscan
0950-1592 Zincscan
0950-1630 Staffordshire Studies
0950-1657 Hortus
0950-1711 Natural Product Updates
0950-1991 Development
0950-2092 Micronutrient Analysis†
0950-2114 Image Technology Journal of the B K S T S
0950-2238 A S S I A
0950-2262 World Copper Databook
0950-236X Textual Practice
0950-2378 New Formations
0950-2386 Cultural Studies
0950-2513 Patent World
0950-2548 Iron Ore Databook
0950-2645 Insolvency Intelligence
0950-2688 Epidemiology and Infection
0950-2742 Sourozh
0950-2858 Numbers
0950-3005 British Review of Bulimia and Anorexia Nervosa
0950-3110 Al-Masaq
0950-3153 Practice
0950-317X Which P C?
0950-3188 Putting Your Amstrad to Work
0950-3285 Texas Oil and Gas Law Journal
0950-3293 Food Quality and Preference
0950-3358 Inside Housing
0950-3366 Power Engineering Journal
0950-3439 Royalty
0950-3471 Historical Research
0950-3501 Bailliere's Clinical Anaesthesiology
0950-3579 Bailliere's Clinical Rheumatology
0950-365X International Franchising and Distribution Law
0950-3668 Insurance Statistics (Years)
0950-3730 Milk Products
0950-382X Molecular Microbiology
0950-3846 International Journal of Lexicography
0950-3870 Performance Chemicals
0950-4044 P & I International
0950-4109 International Journal of Law and the Family
0950-4117 I A T U L Quarterly
0950-4125 Reference Reviews
0950-4214 Gas Separation and Purification
0950-4222 Industry and Higher Education
0950-4230 Journal of Loss Prevention in the Process Industries
0950-429X Classical Guitar
0950-4303 New Dance†
0950-4478 Paper European Data Book
0950-4508 Primary Education Directory
0950-4559 Lighting Journal
0950-4753 Key Abstracts - Advanced Materials
0950-4761 Key Abstracts - Antennas & Propagation
0950-477X Key Abstracts - Artificial Intelligence
0950-4788 Key Abstracts - Computer Communications and Storage
0950-4796 Key Abstracts - Computing in Electronics & Power
0950-480X Key Abstracts - Electronic Instrumentation
0950-4818 Key Abstracts - Measurements in Physics
0950-4826 Key Abstracts - Optoelectronics
0950-4834 Key Abstracts - Power Systems & Applications
0950-4842 Key Abstracts - Robotics & Control
0950-4850 Key Abstracts - Semiconductor Devices
0950-4869 Key Abstracts - Software Engineering
0950-4877 Key Abstracts - Telecommunications
0950-5024 The Stocklist
0950-5032 Stocklists Colour Magazine
0950-5040 Currency Management *see* 0955-5323
0950-5091 Margin
0950-5121 Princess Grace Irish Library Lectures
0950-5199 Surface Treatment Technology Abstracts
0950-5202 Surface Treatment *changed to* Surface Treatment Plant and Processes.
0950-5326 National Acquisitions Group. Newsletter
0950-5423 International Journal of Food Science and Technology
0950-5431 Science as Culture
0950-5458 Adviser
0950-5490 Drives and Controls
0950-5628 Institute of Mathematics and its Applications. Bulletin
0950-575X British Journal of Russian Philately
0950-5814 New Comparison
0950-5830 Rescue News
0950-5849 Information and Software Technology
0950-5911 Gastroenterology International
0950-6098 Mineral Resources Engineering†
0950-6128 Keesing's Record of World Events
0950-6144 Chemical Business Update
0950-6160 Kelly's Automated Office & Business Equipment Directory†
0950-6195 Investment International
0950-656X European Directory of Marketing Information Sources
0950-6608 International Materials Review

ISSN

0950-6659	Physiotherapy Index
0950-6667	Complementary Medicine Index
0950-6675	Occupational Therapy Index
0950-6764	Development Policy Review
0950-7035	Geography Review
0950-7043	Commonwealth Today†
0950-7051	Knowledge-Based Systems
0950-7086	National Library of Scotland News
0950-7116	Welding International
0950-7140	Separation
0950-7191	Come Learn Beginners
0950-7205	Come Learn Primaries
0950-7213	Come Learn Juniors
0950-7221	Go Teach Beginners
0950-7248	Go Teach Juniors
0950-7256	Go Teach Young Teens
0950-7264	Outposts Poetry Quarterly
0950-7434	Air-Britain Digest
0950-7442	Air-Britain News
0950-7493	Talking Folklore
0950-771X	Feed Compounder
0950-7981	V & A Album†
0950-8163	Noise & Vibration in Industry
0950-8171	Acoustical Summaries for Architects†
0950-8198	Raw Materials for the Refactories Industry
0950-821X	European Journal of Vascular Surgery
0950-8368	Band of Hope Chronicle
0950-8376	Orthodox Outlook
0950-8392	Computers and Libraries *see* 0957-4085
0950-8473	Al Dia
0950-8732	Cirplan
0950-8864	Cogito
0950-8945	Sheffield & South Yorkshire Chambers of Commerce Directory
0950-902X	Africa Analysis
0950-9038	Industrial Marketing Digest
0950-9089	Bookquest†
0950-9178	Condition Monitoring Journal
0950-9216	Steel Construction Today
0950-9224	Contemporary Record
0950-9232	Oncogene
0950-9240	Journal of Human Hypertension
0950-9534	Trafalgar Forum *see* 0956-4462
0950-9550	Hockey Digest
0950-9585	Simplified Spelling Society. Journal
0950-9593	Great Britain. Overseas Development Administration. Report on Research and Development
0950-9623	Food Science and Technology Today
0950-9720	Focus on Christian - Muslim Relations
0950-9747	Journals in Translation
0950-9879	Information World Review
0951-001X	Ancient Monuments Society Transactions
0951-0079	Abstracts of Working Papers in Economics
0951-032X	Diplomat
0951-0346	Construction Repair *see* 0959-5090
0951-0370	Belfast Gazette
0951-0427	Inkshed - Poetry and Fiction
0951-0443	Scottish Civil Law Reports
0951-0478	Nordic Times International *changed to* Anglo - Nordic Times.
0951-0524	Great Britain. Advisory Conciliation Arbitration Service. Work Research Unit. Information Service News and Abstracts *see* 0960-2615
0951-0605	Children & Society
0951-0621	Biodeterioration Abstracts
0951-0869	Metallurgical Journal
0951-0907	Programmed Learning and Educational Technology *see* 0954-7304
0951-1121	Arts Festivals in Britain and Ireland†
0951-1172	Human Life Matters†
0951-1237	Statistics of Education in Wales: Schools
0951-1245	Statistics of Education in Wales: Higher & Further Education
0951-1288	Fingerprint World
0951-1318	P O M P I
0951-1326	Folk Roots
0951-1334	House Builder
0951-1474	Literary and Linguistic Computing
0951-1512	Business Education Today
0951-1555	International Popular Bridge Monthly
0951-158X	Automotive Industry Data Newsletter
0951-1792	Business Executive
0951-1806	Escape: The Career Change Magazine
0951-1830	Journal of Ambulatory Monitoring
0951-1865	Agricultural Administration Research Extension Network. Newsletter
0951-192X	International Journal of Computer Integrated Manufacturing
0951-208X	Biotechnology Techniques
0951-2187	I L P Magazine
0951-2195	World Magazine
0951-2233	World Aluminium
0951-2500	Ammonite
0951-2616	German Studies Library Group Newsletter
0951-2640	Heavy Horse World
0951-2748	Pacific Review
0951-3019	Country Homes & Interiors
0951-3051	International Analyst†
0951-3094	Imperial War Museum Review
0951-3124	Jane's High-Speed Marine Craft and Air Cushion Vehicles *changed to* Jane's High-Speed Marine Craft.
0951-3140	Connexions
0951-3507	Training and Management Development Methods
0951-3531	Transport Marketing†
0951-354X	International Journal of Educational Management
0951-3558	International Journal of Public Sector Management
0951-3574	Accounting, Auditing and Accountability
0951-3752	Freshwater Fisheries Laboratory Pitlochry. Annual Review
0951-385X	Department of Town and Country Planning. Working Paper Series
0951-4066	Raven
0951-418X	Phytotherapy Research
0951-4198	Rapid Communications in Mass Spectrometry
0951-4546	Panurge
0951-4554	Food, Cosmetics and Drugs Packaging
0951-4600	Occupational Health Review
0951-4635	S R I S Newsletter
0951-4848	Health Services Management Research
0951-4864	Joe Soap's Canoe
0951-4937	Contemporary Wales
0951-497X	Theosophical History†
0951-5038	Journal of British Music Therapy
0951-5062	Institute of Administrative Management. Journal
0951-5070	Counselling Psychology Quarterly
0951-5089	Philosophical Psychology
0951-5127	Cut†
0951-5135	Music Journal
0951-5143	Jocks
0951-5151	British Society for the History of Philosophy Newsletter
0951-5208	British Performing Arts Yearbook
0951-5216	Geriatric Cardiovascular Medicine†
0951-5224	Higher Education Quarterly
0951-5232	Advanced Manufacturing Engineering *see* 0951-5240
0951-5240	Computer-Integrated Manufacturing Systems
0951-5283	Maple Leaves
0951-5305	N E R C News
0951-547X	New Mexico Real Estate Law Reporter
0951-5631	Profile of the Worldwide Semiconductor Industry
0951-5666	A I & Society
0951-5690	E D A
0951-5704	Draughting & Design
0951-5720	Butterworths Law Digest *see* 0961-5563
0951-5747	World Electronics Companies File
0951-5860	Anglo-Japanese Economic Journal
0951-5879	World Directory of Liner Shipping Agents
0951-5941	Skier
0951-5984	S.I.S. Chronology & Catastrophism Workshop
0951-6026	New Paradigms Newsletter
0951-614X	Hotlines
0951-6220	Incorporated Society of Musicians Yearbook
0951-6239	Register of Professional Private Music Teachers
0951-6298	Journal of Theoretical Politics
0951-631X	Social History of Medicine
0951-6328	Journal of Refugee Studies
0951-6379	Caribbean Times
0951-6425	Urban Wildlife
0951-6433	Biofactors
0951-645X	Ridge Detail in Nature
0951-6549	Journal of Roman Studies Monograph Series
0951-6573	N E M A Journal *see* 0960-6297
0951-6646	Great Britain. British Geological Survey. Overseas Memoirs
0951-6751	Torquay Pottery Collectors Society. Magazine
0951-6816	Sound on Sound
0951-6859	Benchmark
0951-6905	A B C Air Europe, Middle East and North Africa *changed to* A B C Executive Flight Planner: Europe, Middle East & Africa.
0951-7197	Advances in Cement Research
0951-726X	Yes
0951-7359	Institution of Water and Environmental Management. Journal
0951-7367	Current Opinion in Psychiatry
0951-7375	Current Opinion in Infectious Diseases
0951-7383	Current Opinion in Neurology & Neurosurgery
0951-7391	Latin and Greek Texts
0951-7588	Countertrade & Barter†
0951-7618	Longman Tax Digest
0951-7715	Nonlinearity
0951-7855	N U T Education Review
0951-7871	Engineering Services Management
0951-8045	Huna London
0951-8053	M O D News
0951-8088	Atrium
0951-8126	Discover North America
0951-8134	Discover North America Travel Industry Directory
0951-824X	Groupwork
0951-8266	Africa Health Marketletter
0951-8312	Ocean and Shoreline Management *changed to* Ocean and Coastal Management.
0951-8320	Reliability Engineering and System Safety
0951-8339	Marine Structures, Design, Construction and Safety
0951-8347	Living Stones
0951-838X	Books and Periodicals Online
0951-8398	International Journal of Qualitative Studies in Education
0951-8452	Borax Review
0951-855X	Great Britain. Department of Energy. Publications
0951-8673	World Airline Fleets News
0951-8681	U S Executive Report†
0951-872X	Gabbitas, Truman & Thring Guide to Boarding Schools & Colleges
0951-886X	Railway Philately
0951-8916	Monographs in Regional and Local History
0951-8932	In Cornwall Magazine
0951-8940	High Magazine *see* 0962-2667
0951-8967	Mediterranean Historical Review
0951-8975	Average Prices of U S A Academic Books
0951-8983	Public Library Statistics
0951-9084	Yorkshire Artscene
0951-9297	Contemporary France
0951-9327	Database Technology
0951-9521	National Genealogical Directory
0951-953X	Advanced Composites Bulletin
0951-9580	Journal of Orthopaedic Rheumatology
0951-9637	Hereford's Worldwide
0951-9653	Power Technology International
0951-9718	Office at Home
0951-9785	Exchange
0951-9882	Salmon Farming
0951-9904	HeliData *changed to* HeliData News.
0951-9955	Baton
0951-9971	Business Library Management†
0951-9998	Engineered Materials Abstracts
0952-0287	Welding Abstracts
0952-0309	Carbohydrate Antigens†
0952-0317	Drug Targeting
0952-0325	Human Genome†
0952-0333	Leishmaniasis†
0952-0341	Malaria†
0952-035X	Multi Drug Resistance†
0952-0368	Photochemotherapy†
0952-0376	Transcription Regulation†
0952-0384	Bioelectronics and Biosensors
0952-0392	Signal Transduction *see* 0964-7589
0952-0406	Proteins: Post-Translational Processing
0952-0414	Ribosomes and Translation
0952-0422	Membrane Lipids
0952-0430	Employment Initiatives
0952-0481	British Journal of Addiction
0952-0562	Annual of Cardiac Surgery
0952-0627	Current Practice in Surgery
0952-0643	Gullet
0952-0686	The Wire
0952-0732	Merseyside Economic and Business Prospect
0952-0759	The Lute
0952-083X	Which School?
0952-0899	Travel Management International
0952-1240	Archaeology Today†
0952-1453	Agroforestry Abstracts
0952-1666	Booksellers Association of Great Britain and Ireland. Directory of Members
0952-1895	Governance
0952-1909	Journal of Historical Sociology
0952-1917	Ratio Juris
0952-1976	Engineering Applications of Artificial Intelligence
0952-2190	Focus on Physical Distribution and Logistics Management
0952-2271	Health Service Journal
0952-231X	Occupational Pensions
0952-2603	Centre for Housing Research. Discussion Paper
0952-2697	Music & Musicians International†
0952-2700	Geosources
0952-2727	Fire & Flammability Bulletin
0952-2875	Cat World
0952-3170	World Wildlife News *changed to* W W F News.
0952-3197	Framing, Fine Art and Wall Decor *see* 0957-929X
0952-3243	Italian Politics
0952-3278	Prostaglandins, Leukotrienes and Medicine
0952-3359	Unigram.X
0952-3367	International Journal of the History of Sport
0952-3383	British Journal of Special Education
0952-3480	N M R in Biomedicine
0952-3499	Journal of Molecular Recognition
0952-3820	Euromarketing
0952-3855	Plants Today†
0952-3863	Plant Varieties and Seeds
0952-3871	Journal of Human Nutrition and Dietetics
0952-391X	European Journal of Intercultural Studies
0952-3979	Foolscap
0952-3987	Educational Media International
0952-4339	Journal of Educational Therapy
0952-4444	Viewfinder
0952-4452	Progress in Marketing†
0952-4541	Squills International Pigeon Racing Year Book
0952-4592	Geophysical Journal International
0952-4614	Management Services & Production Abstracts
0952-4622	Bioacoustics
0952-4649	Journal of Design History
0952-4711	M & Q Environment†
0952-4746	Journal of Radiological Protection
0952-4762	Solid Mechanics Archives
0952-4894	Di C T A Journal
0952-5106	Camping & Walking
0952-5211	Materials Edge
0952-522X	Wiccan Workshop News

0952-5238 Visual Neuroscience
0952-5335 N W R National Newsletter
0952-5394 Lloyd's Nautical Year Book
0952-5424 Progress in Tourism, Recreation and Hospitality Management
0952-5432 International Journal of Optoelectronics
0952-5467 Henley Centre for Forecasting. Director's Report
0952-5505 U K Iron and Steel Industry. Annual Statistics
0952-5556 Year Book of Co-Operative Enterprise
0952-5734 World Trade Steel
0952-5742 World Trade - Stainless, High Speed & Other Alloy Steel
0952-5793 Surveying Technician
0952-5807 Structural Engineering Review
0952-5831 International Steel Statistics - Australia
0952-584X International Steel Statistics - Austria
0952-5858 International Steel Statistics - Belgium, Luxembourg
0952-5866 International Steel Statistics - Brazil
0952-5874 International Steel Statistics - Canada
0952-5882 International Steel Statistics - Denmark and Greece *see* 0960-2372
0952-5890 International Steel Statistics - Finland
0952-5904 International Steel Statistics - France
0952-5912 International Steel Statistics - Germany, Federal Republic
0952-5920 International Steel Statistics - Irish Republic
0952-5939 International Steel Statistics - Italy
0952-5947 International Steel Statistics - Japan
0952-5955 Surface Topography
0952-6005 International Steel Statistics - Netherlands
0952-6013 International Steel Statistics - Norway
0952-6021 International Steel Statistics - South Africa, Rep.†
0952-603X International Steel Statistics - Korea (South)
0952-6048 International Steel Statistics - Sweden
0952-6056 International Steel Statistics - Eastern European Countries, Turkey and Yugoslavia
0952-6099 International Steel Statistics - Switzerland
0952-6102 International Steel Statistics - Selected Central and South American Countries
0952-6110 International Steel Statistics - Selected Asian Countries *see* 0958-515X
0952-6129 International Steel Statistics - Spain and Portugal *see* 0958-4943
0952-6145 Al-Hilal Al-Dawli
0952-6196 New Materials - Korea†
0952-620X Thomas Cook European Timetable
0952-6269 21st Century Christian *changed to* Alpha (New Malden).
0952-6277 Leadership Today *changed to* Alpha (New Malden).
0952-6293 Annual of Gastrointestinal Endoscopy
0952-6307 Clinician's Manual on Hypertension (Year)
0952-634X Distribution Maps of Pests
0952-6463 British Plant Growth Regulator Group. Monographs *changed to* British Society for Plant Growth Regulation. Monographs.
0952-6757 Phonology
0952-6803 International Steel Statistics - Summary Tables
0952-6811 International Steel Statistics - U S A
0952-6846 Multiphase Update
0952-6862 International Journal of Health Care Quality Assurance
0952-6900 Engineering Plastics
0952-6919 Composite Polymers
0952-6951 History of the Human Sciences
0952-7001 What's New in Business Information
0952-7052 Key Abstracts - Machine Vision
0952-7060 Key Abstracts - Microelectronics & Printed Circuits
0952-7079 Key Abstracts - Microwave Technology
0952-7095 Public Domain
0952-7117 University of London King's College. Age Concern Institute of Gerontology. Working Paper†
0952-7222 Rowett Research Institute Report
0952-7419 I V C A Magazine
0952-7427 A I D S Letter
0952-7516 Asian Communications
0952-7524 Southscan
0952-7532 Quiddity
0952-7613 World Intellectual Property Report
0952-7729 India Post
0952-7788 U K Pesticide Guide
0952-7907 Current Opinion in Anaesthesiology
0952-7915 Current Opinion in Immunology
0952-7974 Hot Air
0952-8059 International Journal for the Semiotics of Law
0952-8067 Asia Pacific International Journal of Business Logistics
0952-8075 Current A I D S Literature
0952-8091 International Journal of Computer Applications in Technology
0952-813X Journal of Experimental & Theoretical Artificial Intelligence
0952-8148 Quiz Trivia†
0952-8156 Housing Abstracts (H A B S)
0952-8172 Molecular Biotherapy
0952-8180 Journal of Clinical Anesthesia
0952-8199 Family Court Reporter
0952-8229 The Psychologist
0952-8245 Great Britain. Overseas Development Natural Resources Institute. Bulletin *changed to* Great Britain. Natural Resources Institute. Bulletin.
0952-8369 Journal of Zoology
0952-8512 Squash World
0952-8636 Care Weekly
0952-8652 Montessori Today
0952-8733 Higher Education Policy
0952-8776 Risk
0952-8784 London Directory for Trade & Industry
0952-8806 West Midlands Directory for Trade & Industry
0952-8873 Journal of Environmental Law
0952-892X British Library. Document Supply Centre. Document Supply News
0952-8962 Organic Farming Index†
0952-908X Defence Minister and Chief of Staff†
0952-9136 Child Abuse Review
0952-9500 Journal of Drug Development
0952-9543 Consumer U S A (Year)
0952-9608 Mental Handicap Research
0952-9616 Science and Technology Policy
0952-9632 Operating Systems and Networks *see* 0953-8402
0952-9691 Advanced Composites Manufacturing Centre Newsletter
0952-9705 National Library for the Handicapped Child. Newsletter
0952-9748 Education Bulletin
0953-0061 I M A Journal of Mathematics Applied in Business and Industry
0953-0223 International Financing Review
0953-024X National Galleries of Scotland. Bulletin
0953-0398 Whitaker's Books in Print
0953-041X Whitaker's Book List
0953-0460 Serials
0953-0509 Printed Circuits and Electronics Coatings Abstracts
0953-0592 Practical Wargamer
0953-0614 Commodore Disk User†
0953-0681 Design and Applied Arts Index
0953-0738 Theta
0953-0754 George Eliot - George Henry Lewes Newsletter *changed to* George Eliot - George Henry Lewes Studies.
0953-0975 Waste Management Today. News Journal *issued with* 0954-495X
0953-0975 Waste Management Today. News Journal
0953-1211 Institute of Hospital Engineering. Journal *see* 0957-7742
0953-1262 Key Abstracts - High-Temperature Superconductors
0953-1475 Choices†
0953-1580 A I D S Information
0953-1602 Great Britain. Overseas Development Natural Resources Institute *changed to* Great Britain. Natural Resources Institute. Annual Report.
0953-203X Off Road and 4 Wheel Drive
0953-2048 Superconductor Science & Technology
0953-2137 Logistics World *see* 0957-6053
0953-2188 Fruit Grower
0953-2226 B K S
0953-2293 C.A.B. Prompts Series: Groundnut Prompts
0953-2307 C.A.B. Prompts Series: Chickpea and Pigeon Peas Prompts
0953-2412 Steel Technology International
0953-2455 B S H R Institute of Horticultural Research. Annual Report *see* 0963-3235
0953-2579 Accounting World
0953-2617 Learning Languages in Europe
0953-3230 Executive Development
0953-3443 Baking Update
0953-3494 Labour & Trade Union Review
0953-3699 Communicator
0953-4075 Journal of Physics B: Atomic, Molecular and Optical Physics
0953-4180 Behavioral Neurology
0953-4199 Creativity and Innovation Yearbook
0953-4385 Christian Herald
0953-4431 Clinical Eye and Vision Care
0953-4458 Information Technology Notes
0953-4466 Aquatic Environment Protection
0953-461X Ulster Place-Name Society. Bulletin
0953-4814 Journal of Organizational Change Management
0953-4822 German Teaching
0953-5004 Lloyds Bank Annual Review
0953-5187 Top Management Digest†
0953-5217 Update On Computer Audit, Control and Security *see* 0960-2593
0953-5233 Gender and History
0953-5241 Stamp Mail
0953-5268 Grocery Update
0953-5314 Economic Systems Research
0953-5330 Register of Musicians in Education
0953-5365 Biological Sciences Review
0953-539X Mobile Communications
0953-5411 Gulf States Newsletter
0953-542X Britannia Monograph Series
0953-5438 Interacting with Computers
0953-5470 Norwich and Norfolk Chamber of Commerce and Industry. Directory
0953-5543 O R Insight
0953-556X International Journal of Information and Library Research
0953-5640 ReActions
0953-5713 Anbar Management Bibliography *changed to* Management Bibliographies & Reviews.
0953-6035 Foundryman
0953-6043 Golf Course *changed to* English Amateur Golf.
0953-6086 College of Speech and Language Therapists. Bulletin
0953-6132 Owen's Africa Business Company *changed to* Owen's Africa Business Directory.
0953-6167 V W Motoring
0953-6337 Essentials
0953-6442 Local Studies *see* 0959-8812
0953-6477 Equities International *changed to* Equities.
0953-6612 Practice Nurse
0953-6639 Professional Engineering
0953-6779 Terminal Care Index *see* 0961-4591
0953-6825 University of London. Institute of Latin American Studies. Occasional Papers *see* 0957-7947
0953-6833 Community Eye Health
0953-6906 Western Europe (Year)
0953-6949 Dial Electrical - Electronics
0953-6973 R I B A Journal
0953-7104 Platelets (Edinburgh)
0953-7112 Current Anaesthesia and Critical Care
0953-721X Ferro Alloy Directory and Databook
0953-7228 Stainless Steel Databook
0953-7252 Parallelogram International
0953-7287 Production Planning & Control
0953-7295 Institute for Grassland and Animal Production, England (Berkshire) *see* 0961-6071
0953-7325 Technology Analysis & Strategic Management
0953-7457 China Media Book
0953-7511 British Society for Music Therapy. Bulletin
0953-7562 Mycological Research
0953-7597 Pims European Trade & Technical Directory
0953-7899 Publishers Reports
0953-8070 British Goat Society. Monthly Journal
0953-8119 British Philatelic Bulletin
0953-816X European Journal of Neuroscience
0953-8178 International Immunology
0953-8186 International Journal of Refugee Law
0953-8194 Journal of Neuroendocrinology
0953-8208 Utilitas
0953-8259 Review of Political Economy
0953-8267 Fetal Medicine Review
0953-8348 Great Britain. Sea Fish Industry Authority. Key Indicators
0953-8364 University College London Calendar
0953-8399 European Banker
0953-8402 Network Monitor
0953-8429 British Telecom World
0953-8453 Investment Trust Directory (Year)†
0953-8534 Health Services Management
0953-8585 Physics World
0953-8704 Trading Standards Review
0953-8712 Advanced Information Report *see* 0961-7612
0953-8720 B W I Study Circle Bulletin
0953-8771 Interactive Update
0953-895X Topic
0953-8984 Journal of Physics: Condensed Matter
0953-9050 Laings' Review of Private Healthcare (Year)
0953-9085 Fleet Operators Handbook
0953-9182 Contemporary Reviews in Obstetrics and Gynaecology
0953-9263 Business Information Yearbook
0953-9301 Derby Diocesan News
0953-9336 New Worldwide Tanker Nominal Freight Scale
0953-9468 Studies in Christian Ethics
0953-9492 On Air - Off Air†
0953-9611 Geographical Abstracts: Human Geography
0953-9743 Hospital Management International
0953-9859 Journal of Wilderness Medicine
0953-9875 Clinical Sports Medicine
0953-9964 Education and the Law
0954-0075 Lubrication Science
0954-0083 High Performance Polymers
0954-0091 Connection Science
0954-0105 Food and Agricultural Immunology
0954-0113 Communist Economies *changed to* Communist Economies and Economic Transformation.
0954-0121 A I D S Care
0954-0172 Yearbook of World Electronics Data Vol. 2: America, Japan, Asia-Pacific
0954-0253 Gender and Education
0954-0261 International Review of Psychiatry
0954-027X Journal of Hard Materials
0954-0350 British Association of Psychotherapists. Journal
0954-0369 Getting About Britain
0954-0377 Music File
0954-0393 Electronic Payments International
0954-0423 Museum Reporter
0954-0431 Food & Drink from Britain Buyers' Guide
0954-0504 Geographical Abstracts: Physical Geography
0954-0512 Geological Abstracts
0954-0628 Offshore Investment
0954-0652 Building Today
0954-0695 Electronics & Communication Engineering Journal
0954-075X United Kingdom Freedom Bulletin
0954-0822 Special Educational Needs Abstracts
0954-0881 Vigil

5828 ISSN INDEX

0954-092X Royal Air Force Yearbook
0954-0954 Australian Studies
0954-0962 Public Money and Management
0954-0970 Bunyan Studies
0954-1004 Forum (London 1969) *see* 0956-4462
0954-1020 Antarctic Science
0954-1098 Living Earth
0954-1136 Middle East Strategic Studies Quarterly
0954-1179 Bulletin of Judaeo-Greek Studies
0954-1314 Journal of International Financial Management and Accounting
0954-1381 Lithium
0954-139X Reviews in Medical Microbiology
0954-1438 International Textiles Interior *changed to* Interior.
0954-1446 European Cognitive Psychology *changed to* European Journal of Cognitive Psychology.
0954-1470 Open Market
0954-1683 Institute of Grocery Distribution. Economic Commentary. Bulletin
0954-1748 Journal of International Development: Policy, Economics, & International Relations
0954-1802 British Music Worldwide
0954-1810 Artificial Intelligence in Engineering
0954-1985 Economics & Politics
0954-206X Social Inventions
0954-2094 Distribution
0954-2116 New Welsh Review
0954-2191 Theological Book Review
0954-2205 Bartlett Review
0954-2264 Optical Computing and Processing
0954-2299 Chemical Speciation and Bioavailability
0954-2361 New Statesman & Society
0954-237X R A D A R Bulletin
0954-2485 Investment Fund Index - Investment Trusts
0954-254X Journal of Soviet Military Studies
0954-2582 Vascular Medicine Review
0954-2620 Broadcasting Press Digest
0954-2809 Law for Business
0954-2833 P C - Business Software
0954-2892 International Journal of Public Opinion Research
0954-2957 Asia Pacific International Management Review *changed to* Asia Pacific International Management Forum.
0954-3317 Interventional Radiology†
0954-3333 Pulmonary Pharmacology (Sheffield)
0954-3392 Ulster Editions and Monographs
0954-3473 Mediafile
0954-349X Structural Change and Economic Dynamics
0954-3589 Current Military and Political Literature
0954-3899 Journal of Physics G: Nuclear and Particle Physics
0954-3902 Works
0954-3945 Language Variation and Change
0954-3988 Fast Ferry International
0954-4011 EuroBrief†
0954-4046 Institution of Mechanical Engineers. Proceedings. Part A: Journal of Power Engineering *changed to* Institution of Mechanical Engineers. Proceedings. Part A: Journal of Power and Energy.
0954-4054 Institution of Mechanical Engineers. Proceedings. Part B: Journal of Engineering Manufacture
0954-4070 Institution of Mechanical Engineers. Proceedings. Part D: Journal of Automobile Engineering
0954-4089 Institution of Mechanical Engineers. Proceedings. Part E: Journal of Process Mechanical Engineering
0954-4097 Institution of Mechanical Engineers. Proceedings. Part F: Journal of Rail and Rapid Transit
0954-4100 Institution of Mechanical Engineers. Proceedings. Part G: Journal of Aerospace Engineering
0954-4119 Institution of Mechanical Engineers. Proceedings. Part H: Journal of Engineering in Medicine
0954-4127 Total Quality Management
0954-416X African Languages and Cultures
0954-4194 Science and Christian Belief
0954-4224 Nutrition Research Reviews
0954-478X The T Q M Magazine
0954-4828 Journal of Engineering Design
0954-4860 Milling Flour and Feed
0954-4879 Terra Nova
0954-4887 Terra Abstracts
0954-4917 Process Industry International†
0954-495X Waste Management Today
0954-4968 Long Ashton Research Station Report *see* 0955-9051
0954-5271 ReSources Pharmaceutical and Healthcare Information News†
0954-5468 Profitable Machine Knitting
0954-5581 Diamond Insight
0954-5611 Look Hear
0954-562X Good News (Exeter)
0954-5735 Liberal Democrat News
0954-5735 Liberal Democrat News
0954-576X Journal of Health and Safety
0954-5794 Development and Psychopathology
0954-5824 Environmental Engineering
0954-5832 Aerospace Composites & Materials
0954-5867 Cambridge Opera Journal
0954-5913 Retail Marketing and Management *changed to* Retail Marketing & Management.
0954-5964 International Cargo Handling Coordination Association. Buyers' Guide to Manufacturers
0954-5972 Health and Safety Officer's Handbook
0954-6111 Respiratory Medicine
0954-6219 Holstein Friesian Journal
0954-6324 Wildfowl
0954-6421 Practioners' Child Law Bulletin
0954-6499 Samizdat
0954-6529 Mechanical Incorporated Engineer
0954-6537 Tax Partner *see* 0143-294X
0954-6545 Revolutionary Russia
0954-6553 Terrorism and Political Violence
0954-6561 Multi - User Computing
0954-6634 Journal of Dermatological Treatment
0954-6650 Journal of the History of Collections
0954-6685 London Society. Journal
0954-6693 British Journal of Physical Education
0954-6782 African Review of Business and Technology
0954-6820 Journal of Internal Medicine
0954-691X European Journal of Gastroenterology and Hepatology
0954-6928 Coronary Artery Disease
0954-7118 International Journal of Global Energy Issues
0954-7207 Chartered Building Societies Institute. Journal
0954-7304 Educational and Training Technology International
0954-7479 Trend Monitor *changed to* Trend Monitor Reports.
0954-7495 Clinical Cancer Monographs
0954-7517 Asia Pacific International Journal of Marketing
0954-7525 Asia Pacific International Journal of Business Research†
0954-7533 Asia Pacific International Journal of Management Development†
0954-7541 International Journal of Wine Marketing
0954-7649 Jane's Airport Review
0954-7746 B R A D Direct Marketing
0954-7894 Clinical and Experimental Allergy
0954-8017 Fear†
0954-8106 Accountants Record *changed to* Company Accountant.
0954-8521 Phillips' International Paper Directory (Paper)
0954-853X Gas Industry Directory (Year)
0954-8548 Benn's Guide (Year)
0954-8580 Inter Architecture
0954-8718 Shooting News and Weekly *changed to* Shooting News and Country Weekly.
0954-8750 British G Q
0954-8769 Scottish Book Collector
0954-8823 D I Y Week
0954-8874 Dean Archaeology
0954-8963 Cultural Trends
0954-898X Network - Computation in Neural Systems
0954-8998 Quantum Optics *changed to* Quantum Optics: Journal of European Optical Society, Part B.
0954-9021 Headlines (London)
0954-9072 Knowledge-Based Systems Management Review
0954-9145 Networks†
0954-9196 C A B L I S†
0954-9234 Journal of Contemporary Hospitality Management
0954-9765 Ski Special
0954-9897 AgBiotech News and Information
0955-0569 Institute of Development Studies. Development Bibliography Series
0955-0631 Learning Resources News
0955-0674 Current Opinion in Cell Biology
0955-0690 Staffordshire Polytechnic. Department of Sociology. Occasional Papers
0955-0801 Social Care Education
0955-0933 The Gate
0955-0984 Rehabilitation Index
0955-114X Starburst
0955-1247 Jane's Soviet Intelligence Review *changed to* Jane's Intelligence Review.
0955-1255 E D I World†
0955-1328 Automobile
0955-1484 Asia Pacific Top Management Digest†
0955-1581 Pims European Newspapers Directory
0955-1646 Dolls & Dolls' House†
0955-1662 Security Journal
0955-1689 Modelling and Miniature Crafts†
0955-2065 Health Manpower Management
0955-2138 Dealing with Technology
0955-2170 N C V O News
0955-2197 Intellectual Property in Business (Briefing and Review)
0955-2219 European Ceramic Society. Journal
0955-2235 Progress in Growth Factor Research
0955-2308 Adults Learning
0955-2340 Journal of Islamic Studies
0955-2359 Twentieth Century British History
0955-2367 Asian Philosophy
0955-2847 Minerals Industry International
0955-2855 Great Britain. Ministry of Agriculture, Fisheries and Food. Directorate of Fisheries Research. Fisheries Spotlight
0955-2863 Journal of Nutritional Biochemistry
0955-2979 Restaurateur
0955-3045 Climber and Hillwalker
0955-3541 Cancer Communications *see* 0965-0407
0955-355X Computer Optics†
0955-3681 European Journal of Implant and Refractive Surgery
0955-3800 Housing Finance
0955-3819 Bound Spiral
0955-3835 Technical Diagnostics and Nondestructive Testing in Welding *changed to* Technical Diagnostics and Nondestructive Testing.
0955-3843 Contemporary European Affairs
0955-3886 Transfusion Science
0955-3991 Housebuilding Today
0955-4025 British Outdoor Amenities Directory
0955-419X Geophysical Journal of the R A S, D G G and E G S *see* 0952-4592
0955-4262 Care of the Elderly
0955-4270 A C I S
0955-4319 Computer-Aided Process Control Abstracts
0955-4335 Dial Engineering
0955-4343 Consumer Marketing Magazine
0955-4386 Coin News
0955-4408 Scandanavian and European Shipping Review
0955-4416 European Food and Drink Review
0955-4475 Journal of Child Law
0955-4645 Libraries Yearbook *changed to* Libraries Directory.
0955-4718 Warwick Papers in Management *changed to* Warwick Business School Research Papers.
0955-4815 Human Potential Magazine
0955-498X International Tax Digest
0955-5080 International Leather Guide
0955-5099 Dial Computing
0955-5102 Tumour Marker Update
0955-5188 R E View
0955-5323 Currency Confidential
0955-534X European Business Review
0955-5404 Eurofood
0955-5439 Electricity International
0955-548X MinTech
0955-5803 Japan Forum
0955-5870 Savings and Loan Monthly *changed to* Mortgage Finance Monthly.
0955-5889 Autocar & Motor
0955-5986 Flow Measurement and Instrumentation
0955-615X Professional Translator and Interpreter
0955-6176 Econews
0955-6214 International Journal of Career Management
0955-6222 International Journal of Clothing Science and Technology
0955-6281 P S A News
0955-6400 Postscript Language Journal - International Edition *changed to* Postscript Review.
0955-6419 Business Strategy Review
0955-6621 Biotechnology Education
0955-663X Annual Review of Addictions Research and Treatment
0955-6648 Current Advances in Ecological and Environmental Sciences
0955-6656 Currency and Interest Rate Outlook
0955-6664 Journal of Nutritional Medicine
0955-7040 Industrial Corrosion Abstracts
0955-7059 Mixing and Separation Technology Abstracts
0955-7091 Air Forces Monthly
0955-7113 Kelly's London Business Link
0955-7369 Drilling News
0955-7717 Biomedical Materials
0955-792X Journal of Logic and Computation
0955-7997 Engineering Analysis with Boundary Elements
0955-8071 Hornsey Historical Society. Bulletin
0955-808X The European Business Journal
0955-8225 Ski Survey
0955-8276 Mesemb Study Bulletin
0955-8543 Hypermedia
0955-8586 Organometallic Chemistry in the U S S R
0955-8772 Rubber and Polyurethane Directory B.R.M.A.
0955-8810 Behavioural Pharmacology
0955-8829 Psychiatric Genetics
0955-8950 English Review
0955-9051 A F R C Institute of Arable Crops Research. Report
0955-9116 Motorcycle Sport
0955-9531 Instrumentation and Control Engineering in Japan *see* 0959-8286
0955-9647 Sunk Island Review
0955-9701 Biomedical Science
0955-9760 1992 Single Market Communications Review
0956-019X On Board Surf Magazine
0956-0521 Computing Systems in Engineering
0956-053X Waste Management: Nuclear, Chemical, Biological, Municipal
0956-0602 Pesticides Disc†
0956-0629 Geoactive
0956-0726 Modern History Review
0956-0904 The U S A and Canada (Year)
0956-0939 Pig Veterinary Journal
0956-0955 South East Asia Digest†
0956-0998 The International Directory of Government
0956-1234 Nonwovens Abstracts
0956-1250 Pesticide Outlook
0956-1498 Business Banker International
0956-2265 Thermal Analysis Reviews & Abstracts
0956-2273 Europa World Year Book
0956-2400 Falling Leaf

ISSN

ISSN INDEX 5829

0956-2478 Environment and Urbanization
0956-2486 Me Magazine
0956-2648 Today (New Malden) *changed to* Alpha (New Malden).
0956-2710 Take-Home Drinks†
0956-2737 H E C Forum
0956-2745 Photo Pro
0956-277X Primary Geographer
0956-2826 United States Air Forces Europe Yearbook
0956-2842 Young People Now
0956-2893 Hambro Corporate Register *changed to* Abthul Andersen Corporate Register.
0956-3091 Homes Abroad
0956-3113 Children and War Newsletter
0956-3202 Antiviral Chemistry & Chemotherapy
0956-3229 Ginger
0956-3385 Computing & Control Engineering Journal
0956-3393 J F I T News
0956-3709 Floodlight
0956-375X I E E Proceedings Part F: Radar and Signal Processing
0956-3768 I E E Proceedings Part G: Circuits, Devices and Systems
0956-3776 I E E Proceedings Part I: Communications, Speech and Vision
0956-3784 Asian Review of Business and Technology
0956-3954 Fiscal Press *see* 0143-294X
0956-4225 International Journal of Information Resource Management
0956-4241 A S I Journal
0956-4462 Trafalgar House News
0956-4624 International Journal of S T D & A I D S
0956-5000 Royal Society of Chemistry. Journal: Faraday Transactions
0956-5035 Heavyside Building Materials
0956-523X Growth Regulation
0956-5353 Wideworld G C S E Geography Review
0956-5361 Ancient MesoAmerica
0956-5388 Technology and People *see* 0959-3845
0956-5477 Angling Guide
0956-5507 Cytopathology
0956-5515 Journal of Intelligent Manufacturing
0956-5558 Cards International
0956-5663 Biosensors and Bioelectronics
0956-5698 Records Management Journal
0956-6163 Environmental Management & Health
0956-6333 Europetroleum
0956-666X Lipid Technology
0956-7135 Food Control
0956-7143 Composites Manufacturing
0956-7151 Acta Metallurgica et Materialia
0956-716X Scripta Metallurgica et Materialia
0956-7925 European Journal of Applied Mathematics
0956-7933 Rural History: Economy, Society, Culture
0956-7968 Journal of Functional Programming
0956-7976 Psychological Science
0956-8220 Handbook of Medicinal Feed Additives
0956-8700 World Tunnelling
0956-9006 Latin American Studies in the Universities and Polytechnics of the United Kingdom
0956-9014 Theses in Latin American Studies at British Universities in Progress and Completed *changed to* Research on Latin America in the Humanities and Social Sciences in the Universities and Polytechnics of the United Kingdom.
0956-9081 New Builder
0956-9146 Catering Buyer
0956-9170 European Security Industry Buyer's Guide (Year)
0956-9189 Construction Weekly
0956-9294 Volkswagen Audi Car
0956-960X Human Antibodies and Hybridomas
0956-9618 Separations Technology
0956-9758 World Architecture
0956-9820 Spectroscopy World
0957-0039 European Business Intelligence Briefing
0957-0144 History and Computing
0957-0233 Measurement Science and Technology
0957-0241 Great Britain. Royal Commission on the Historical Monuments of England. Newsletter
0957-0411 Arbitration International
0957-0438 E T I: Electronics Today International
0957-1035 Black Country Business Directory *see* 0963-1348
0957-1035 Black Country Business Directory *see* 0963-133X
0957-1043 Hemel Hempstead Business Directory
0957-1051 Milton Keynes Business Directory
0957-106X Northampton Business Directory
0957-1078 Peterborough Business Directory
0957-1086 Reading Business Directory
0957-1094 Redditch Business Directory
0957-1116 Telford Business Directory
0957-1124 Watford Business Directory
0957-1264 Journal of Wine Research
0957-1272 Atmospheric Environment. Part B: Urban Atmosphere
0957-1280 Mathematics Review
0957-1329 Small Enterprise Development
0957-154X History of Psychiatry
0957-1558 French Cultural Studies
0957-1663 Women in B H I
0957-171X Spon's Civil Engineering and Highway Works Price Book
0957-1728 Which? Way to Health
0957-1736 Language Learning Journal
0957-1744 Francophonie
0957-1752 Tuttitalia
0957-1760 Rusistika
0957-1787 Utilities Policy
0957-2384 India Energy†
0957-2899 Computational Mechanics Communications†
0957-2902 Boundary Elements Abstracts Journal & Newsletter
0957-297X Welsh Journal of Education
0957-3224 Automated Office Abstracts
0957-3518 Endothelium
0957-3526 Gene Expression
0957-3577 Writers News
0957-3704 Right Start
0957-381X Patterns Galore
0957-3844 T V Zone
0957-4042 Women: A Cultural Review
0957-4085 C & L Applications
0957-4107 Child Safety Review
0957-4115 Development Journal
0957-4158 Mechatronics
0957-4166 Tetrahedron: Asymmetry
0957-4174 Expert Systems with Applications
0957-4190 Papillomavirus Report
0957-4212 Manager Update
0957-4239 Arabic Sciences and Philosophy
0957-4271 Journal of Vestibular Research: Equilibrium and Orientation
0957-4344 International Journal of Continuing Engineering Education
0957-4352 International Journal of Environment and Pollution
0957-4360 Micronutrient News and Information
0957-4484 Nanotechnology
0957-4522 Journal of Materials Science: Materials in Electronics
0957-4530 Journal of Materials Science: Materials in Medicine
0957-4565 Noise and Vibration Worldwide
0957-4573 Depression Briefing
0957-4611 Telecomms Abstracts
0957-4697 United Kingdom Minerals Yearbook
0957-476X International Journal of Radioactive Materials Transport
0957-4832 Journal of Public Health Medicine
0957-4883 C I I Journal
0957-4964 International Journal of Cognitive Education & Mediated Learning
0957-5022 Sugar Industry Abstracts
0957-5073 Polar and Glaciological Abstracts
0957-5111 Local Government Employment†
0957-5138 Dental Laboratory
0957-5146 Early Years
0957-5170 Green Anarchist
0957-5235 Blood Coagulation and Fibrinolysis
0957-5243 Cancer Causes & Control
0957-5820 Process Safety and Environmental Protection
0957-5839 Current Paediatrics
0957-5847 Current Obstetrics and Gynaecology
0957-5936 Professional Secretary†
0957-6053 Logistics Information Management
0957-6061 Integrated Manufacturing Systems
0957-6215 Allons
0957-6517 Streetwise
0957-6525 Your Classic
0957-6584 Currencies and Interest Rates: The Outlook for 1991 and Beyond
0957-6673 Modern Machine Knitting
0957-6754 British Health & Fitness Club Directory
0957-6762 Review of Agricultural Entomology
0957-6770 Review of Medical and Veterinary Entomology
0957-6789 Helminthological Abstracts
0957-6797 Nematological Abstracts
0957-6851 Journal of Asian Pacific Communication
0957-6908 Pims U S A Consumer Directory
0957-6916 Pims European Consumer Directory
0957-7327 Family Sites Guide
0957-7505 Postharvest News and Information
0957-7572 International Journal of Technology and Design Education
0957-7696 International Cruise and Ferry Review
0957-7734 Equine Veterinary Education
0957-7742 Health Estate Journal
0957-7912 Library and Information Assistant
0957-7947 University of London. Institute of Latin American Studies. Research Papers
0957-8536 Law and Critique
0957-8625 Dairy Markets Weekly
0957-8730 British Leisure & Swimming Pool Directory
0957-8765 Voluntas
0957-8811 European Journal of Development Research
0957-8870 Amenity Management
0957-8897 World Ceramic Abstracts
0957-8935 Greater World Newsletter
0957-9133 Intelligent Tutoring Media
0957-9249 Batteries International
0957-9265 Discourse & Society
0957-929X Framing and Art
0957-9370 World Climate Change Report†
0957-9508 Sound Engineer and Producer
0957-9559 Advanced Materials Abstracts†
0957-9575 Education Libraries Journal
0957-9656 Logos
0957-9664 Criminal Behaviour and Mental Health
0957-9672 Current Opinion in Lipidology
0957-9710 Administrative Law Reports
0957-9729 Advanced Metals Technology
0957-9737 Electronic Materials and Processing
0957-9818 Doctor Who Magazine
0957-9869 Business Research Guides
0958-0328 Vachers Parliamentary Companion
0958-0336 Vacher's European Companion
0958-0344 Phytochemical Analysis
0958-0433 R S A Journal
0958-0441 Times Law Reports
0958-0581 Journal of Pharmaceutical Medicine
0958-0611 International Journal of Refractory Metals & Hard Materials
0958-0670 Experimental Physiology
0958-0980 For Him
0958-126X Jane's NATO Handbook
0958-1316 P H L S H I V Bulletin
0958-1413 Computer Security and Privacy Abstracts
0958-1499 C A D - C A M Abstracts
0958-1537 New Europe (London, 1989)
0958-1545 Moneta International
0958-1650 Clinician's Manual on Hyperlipidemia (Year)
0958-1669 Current Opinion in Biotechnology
0958-1804 Dressage Magazine
0958-1812 Pony Club Monthly
0958-1820 Carriage Driving
0958-2010 Business Travel International
0958-2029 Research Evaluation
0958-2118 Membrane Technology Newsletter
0958-2126 Environment & Industry Digest
0958-2584 Rheumatology Review
0958-2592 The Foot
0958-2630 Christian Music
0958-2770 United Society for the Propagation of the Gospel. Newsbrief
0958-2789 United Society for the Propagation of the Gospel. Issues
0958-2797 Encounter (London, 1990)
0958-2800 Together (London, 1990)
0958-3017 Design & Technology Teaching
0958-3076 Foreign Investment in the U S
0958-3157 Biocontrol Science and Technology
0958-3165 Nanobiology
0958-319X Spectrochimica Acta Reviews
0958-3467 Search (York)
0958-3548 The Manual
0958-3629 Catalyst G C S E Science Review
0958-3637 Hindsight G C S E Modern History Review
0958-3858 Christian Puzzler
0958-4013 Yorkshire Auto Trader
0958-4021 Inlogov Informs
0958-4234 Young India
0958-4277 North West Auto Trader
0958-4609 Legal Business
0958-465X Software Systems and Techniques Abstracts
0958-4668 Micro Abstracts
0958-4684 Shellfish Farming
0958-482X Journal of Management and Communication *changed to* Institute News.
0958-4935 Contemporary South Asia
0958-4943 International Steel Statistics - Spain
0958-4951 International Steel Statistics - Portugal
0958-5036 Microgravity Quarterly
0958-5125 Videographic
0958-5133 Profitable Gifts
0958-5141 Meat Industry
0958-515X International Steel Statistics - Selected Asian and African Countries
0958-5192 International Journal of Human Resources Management
0958-5206 Accounting, Business and Financial History
0958-5214 International Company and Commercial Law Review
0958-5222 I P M S Bulletin
0958-5389 Womanswear Resources
0958-5664 British Music
0958-5702 P O P S I
0958-6342 Guitar International
0958-6415 Issues in Reproductive and Genetic Engineering
0958-6571 Plant Hire Review
0958-6709 Summit G C S E Mathematics Review
0958-6946 International Dairy Journal
0958-7322 Centre Rankings
0958-7578 Transfusion Medicine
0958-7918 Business East Midlands
0958-7942 Business West Midlands
0958-823X Research Highlights in Animal Nutrition†
0958-868X Journal of Property Finance
0958-8787 Tanker Charter Record
0958-9155 Single Market Mobile and Satellite Review
0958-9309 Asiamoney *changed to* Asia Money & Finance.
0958-9600 London Weekly Advertiser
0958-9961 International Journal of Micrographics & Optical Technology
0959-020X Genetic Engineer and Biotechnologist
0959-051X Migration and Intercultural Education in Europe
0959-0552 International Journal of Retail & Distribution Management
0959-0684 New Technology in the Human Services
0959-0846 World Aerospace Technology
0959-1079 Dorset Life
0959-1362 Horizons

ISSN

5830 ISSN INDEX

0959-146X Recruitment and Development Report
0959-1524 Journal of Process Control
0959-1656 Rare Books Newsletter
0959-2288 Technical Analysis of Currencies
0959-2296 Diplomacy & Statecraft
0959-230X Regional Politics and Policy
0959-2318 Small Wars and Insurgencies
0959-2431 Journal of Smoking-Related Disorders
0959-2598 Reviews in Clinical Gerontology
0959-2601 South East Asia Monitor
0959-2695 Journal of French Language Studies
0959-2709 Bird Conservation International
0959-2822 Progress in Underwater Science†
0959-289X International Journal of Obstetric Anesthesia
0959-2903 Medical Audit News
0959-2946 Public Health News
0959-2954 Journal of Information Systems
0959-2989 Bio-Medical Materials and Engineering
0959-3020 Isokinetics and Exercise Science
0959-3071 Geophysics Abstracts†
0959-308X Superconductivity Abstracts†
0959-311X For a Change
0959-3268 Quality Forum
0959-3314 Gastroenterology and Rheumatology in Practice *changed to* Gastroenterology in Practice.
0959-3527 Euro III - Vs *see* 0961-1290
0959-3535 Feminism & Psychology
0959-3543 Theory & Psychology
0959-3756 Quality News
0959-3780 Global Environmental Change
0959-3799 Entertainment Law Review
0959-3845 Information Technology and People
0959-3969 International Review of Retail, Distribution and Consumer Research
0959-3985 Physiotherapy Theory and Practice
0959-3993 World Journal of Microbiology and Biotechnology
0959-4299 Postgraduate Education for General Practice
0959-437X Current Opinion in Genetics & Development
0959-4388 Current Opinion in Neurobiology
0959-440X Current Opinion in Structural Biology
0959-4558 Exuberance
0959-4655 Morgannwg
0959-4752 Learning and Instruction
0959-4906 British Library. Document Supply Centre. Index of Conference Proceedings
0959-4914 British Library. Document Supply Centre. Science Reference and Information Service. Current Serials Received
0959-4922 British Reports, Translations and Theses
0959-4957 Immunology and Infectious Diseases
0959-4965 NeuroReport
0959-4973 Ani-Cancer Drugs
0959-5031 Third Way - Beyond Capitalism and Communism
0959-5090 International Journal of Construction Maintenance & Repair
0959-5236 Drug and Alcohol Review
0959-5244 Molecular Neuropharmacology
0959-5740 Aktuell
0959-5937 Fingerprint News
0959-6038 International Cement Review
0959-6089 Tank Container World
0959-6127 World Ceramics & Refractories
0959-6402 International Journal of Sign Linguistics
0959-6658 Glycobiology
0959-6739 Ornithological Society of the Middle East Bulletin
0959-6828 Positive Teaching
0959-6879 British Journal of Phytotherapy
0959-6941 European Business Law Review
0959-7042 Environment Business
0959-7174 Waves in Random Media
0959-7697 Audiophile
0959-7743 Cambridge Archaeological Journal
0959-7808 Tees Valley Writer
0959-8006 Skeleton Crew
0959-8022 Accounting, Management and Information Technologies
0959-8030 Annual Review of Fish Diseases
0959-8103 Polymer International
0959-8111 Plastics, Rubber and Composites Processing and Applications
0959-8219 Latin American Mining Letter
0959-8278 European Journal of Cancer Prevention
0959-8286 Instrumentation and Control Engineering
0959-8464 Chemistry Review
0959-8472 Physics Review
0959-8480 Politics Review
0959-8499 Sociology Review
0959-8812 Northern Ireland Bibliography
0959-9428 Journal of Materials Chemistry
0959-9436 Mendeleev Communications
0959-9517 Surface Mount International†
0959-9592 Seed Pathology and Microbiology
0959-9673 International Journal of Experimental Pathology
0959-9851 Clinical Autonomic Research
0959-9916 Journal of Research Property
0959-9959 Ground Engineering Yearbook
0960-0035 International Journal of Physical Distribution & Logistics Management
0960-0175 Moscow Physical Society. Journal
0960-0760 Journal of Steroid Biochemistry and Molecular Biology
0960-0779 Chaos, Solitons and Fractals
0960-0833 Journal of Software Testing, Verification and Reliability
0960-085X European Journal of Information Systems
0960-0884 Soviet Lightwave Communications
0960-0906 Software Management
0960-0949 World Arbitration & Mediation Report
0960-1295 Mathematical Structures in Computer Science
0960-1317 Journal of Micromechanics and Microengineering
0960-1325 Games Master International†
0960-1422 Chess Post
0960-1449 Medium Companies of Europe
0960-1473 Japan Digest
0960-1481 Renewable Energy (Tarrytown)
0960-1511 International Current Awareness Services. Anthropology
0960-152X International Current Awareness Services. Economics
0960-1538 International Current Awareness Services. Political Science
0960-1546 International Current Awareness Services. Sociology
0960-1627 Mathematical Finance
0960-1643 British Journal of General Practice.
0960-1686 Atmospheric Environment. Part A: General Topics
0960-2003 European Work and Organizational Psychologist
0960-2011 Neuropsychological Rehabilitation
0960-233X Parks
0960-2348 History of Nursing Journal
0960-2372 International Steel Statistics - Denmark
0960-2380 International Steel Statistics - Greece
0960-250X Primary Health Care Management
0960-2585 Seed Science Research
0960-2593 Computer Audit Update
0960-2615 Great Britain. Advisory Conciliation Arbitration Service. Work Research Unit. News and Abstracts
0960-2720 European Journal of Theology
0960-2739 Asia Pacific Chemicals
0960-2976 Phosphorus in Agriculture
0960-2992 Writers Forum
0960-3069 Turkey Briefing
0960-3085 Food and Bioproducts Processing
0960-3107 Applied Financial Economics
0960-3115 Biodiversity and Conservation
0960-3123 International Journal of Environmental Health Research
0960-3131 Journal of Electronics Manufacturing
0960-314X Pharmacogenetics
0960-3158 Processing of Advanced Materials
0960-3166 Reviews in Fish Biology and Fisheries
0960-3174 Statistics and Computing
0960-3182 Geotechnical and Geological Engineering
0960-3212 Cytokines *see* 0964-7554
0960-3395 Journal of Strategic I T
0960-3409 Materials at High Temperature
0960-3999 Broadcasting Standards Council. Annual Review
0960-4529 Managing Service Quality
0960-4634 E D I in Finance Newsletter
0960-5088 Opportunities Briefing
0960-5290 Contemporary Hypnosis
0960-5398 E L F
0960-5428 Advances in Neuroimmunology
0960-5754 Scene Out
0960-6025 Studies in Hogg and His World
0960-6068 Ukrainian Journal of Physics
0960-6076 Technical University of Kosice. Transactions
0960-6130 European Research in Regional Science
0960-6297 Leading Notes
0960-6440 Bristol Medico - Chirurgical Journal *changed to* West England Medical Journal.
0960-6491 Industrial and Corporate Change
0960-653X World Publishing Monitor
0960-6556 Art Newspaper
0960-6572 Key Abstracts - Factory Automation
0960-720X Junior Friends†
0960-7412 Plant Journal for Cell and Molecular Biology
0960-7420 European Journal of Immunogenetics
0960-7439 International Journal of Paediatric Dentistry
0960-748X Changes (London, 1990)
0960-7560 Homeostasis in Health & Disease
0960-7609 General Studies Review
0960-7692 Ultrasound in Obstetrics & Gynecology
0960-7722 Cell Proliferation
0960-7773 Contemporary European History
0960-7935 O I O C Newsletter
0960-7943 Eurofood Monitor
0960-7986 Awards for Postgraduate Study at Commonwealth Universities
0960-832X Million
0960-8508 A N S A Journal
0960-8524 Bioresource Technology
0960-8567 Curriculum Journal
0960-8702 Latin American Economy and Business
0960-8710 Negocios Al Dia
0960-877X Watchwords G C S E English Review
0960-8796 Green Engineering
0960-8869 International Environmental Outlook
0960-8893 Practical Diabetes Digest
0960-8923 Obesity Surgery
0960-8931 Melanoma Research
0960-894X Bioorganic & Medicinal Chemistry Letters
0960-8966 Neuromuscular Disorders
0960-8974 Progress in Crystal Growth and Characterization of Materials
0960-9253 Printmaking Today
0960-9555 Lincolnshire Past and Present
0960-9768 Cancer Care
0960-9776 The Breast
0960-9784 International Food Safety News
0960-9822 Current Biology
0961-0006 Journal of Librarianship and Information Science
0961-0464 Fruit and Vegetable Markets
0961-0472 World Markets Service *changed to* Global Trends.
0961-088X Biomedical Letters
0961-1053 British Journal of Clinical Research
0961-1215 Leonardo Music Journal
0961-1290 III - Vs Review
0961-1444 Nonrenewable Resources
0961-2025 Women's History Review
0961-205X Social Development
0961-2076 Meat Focus International
0961-2149 Oxford Studies in Comparative Education
0961-2599 The Plant Finder
0961-2696 Classical Music
0961-2882 Social Intelligence
0961-3218 Building Research and Information
0961-3501 Small Animals
0961-3501 Lentils
0961-351X Tropical Oil Seeds
0961-3528 Cotton and Tropical Fibres
0961-3544 Recorder Magazine
0961-3552 Advances in Engineering Software and Workstations *see* 0965-9978
0961-3692 European Journal of Clinical Research
0961-4591 Palliative Care Index
0961-463X Time and Society
0961-4745 Impact AgBioBusiness *changed to* Impact AgBioIndustry.
0961-5202 Retail Newsagent Tobacconist Confectioner
0961-5261 Treasury Today
0961-5342 Financial Technology Insight
0961-5563 Mallal's Monthly Digest
0961-5628 Geoscientist
0961-5652 Labour History Review
0961-5822 Sports & Leisure News
0961-6071 A F R C Institute of Grassland and Environmental Research (UK). Annual Report
0961-6497 Art Business Today
0961-6608 Scotland's What's On
0961-7299 Books on the Environment and Related Topics
0961-754X Common Knowledge
0961-7612 Information Management Report
0961-8171 The Bondholder
0961-8368 Protein Science
0961-9305 Plastics and Rubbers Materials Disc
0961-9364 Somerset Magazine
0961-9526 Composites Engineering
0961-9534 Biomass & Bioenergy
0961-978X Feeds and Feeding
0962-0214 International Studies in Sociology of Education
0962-029X Journal of Information Technology for Teacher Education
0962-0648 Early Modern History Review
0962-1032 The European Communities Encyclopedia and Directory (Year)
0962-1040 Eastern Europe and the U S S R (Year) *changed to* Eastern Europe and the Commonwealth of Independent States (Year).
0962-1377 Journal of Celtic Linguistics
0962-1385 Insurance Law & Practice
0962-1423 British Journal of Medical Economics
0962-1792 Theatre Record
0962-1849 Applied and Preventive Psychology
0962-2152 Woman Alive
0962-225X Ravi
0962-2667 High Mountain Sports
0962-2764 Sheppard's Bookdealers in Australia and New Zealand
0962-2780 Economic & Financial Computing
0962-2918 New Zealand Outlook
0962-3507 In Common
0962-3752 Oil & Gas Finance and Accounting
0962-3841 Communications Africa
0962-4244 E D I T
0962-4694 Journal of Design Manufacturing
0962-7162 Fluid Abstracts: Process Engineering
0962-7170 Fluid Abstracts: Civil Engineering
0962-7189 Tribology & Corrosion Abstracts
0962-8428 Royal Society of London. Philosophical Transactions. Series A. Physical Sciences and Engineering
0962-8479 Tubercle and Lung Disease
0962-8770 Business Ethics
0962-8789 Primary Life
0962-8797 Review of European Community and International Environmental Law
0962-8819 Transgenic Research
0962-8827 Clinical Dysmorphology
0962-8924 Trends in Cell Biology
0962-9343 Quality of Life Research
0962-9351 Mediators of Inflammation
0962-9505 I F A C Symposia Series
0962-9580 Law, Computers, and Artificial Intelligence
0963-0171 Sheppard's Bookdealers in Europe
0963-0252 Plasma Sources Science and Technology

ISSN

ISSN	Title
0963-0805	New Moon
0963-116X	Defence Helicopter
0963-133X	Black Country Business Directory (South)
0963-1348	Black Country Business Directory (North)
0963-1690	Creativity and Innovation Management
0963-1798	Journal of Occupational and Organizational Psychology
0963-2638	Selection and Development Review
0963-2700	J C M T - U K I R T Newsletter
0963-3235	Horticultural Research International
0963-4894	World Food Regulation Review
0963-5483	Combinatorics, Probability & Computing
0963-5548	Employment News
0963-6412	Security Studies
0963-6633	Laissez - Faire
0963-6749	British Society for Plant Growth Regulation. Annual Bulletin
0963-6897	Cell Transplantation
0963-6927	T W I Journal
0963-6935	Advanced Composites Letters
0963-7001	British Society for Plant Growth Regulation. Newsletter
0963-7109	Automotive Materials
0963-7214	Current Directions in Psychological Science
0963-7273	European Journal of Disorders of Communication
0963-7338	Motorhome Magazine
0963-7354	U K O L N Newsletter
0963-7494	Religion, State and Society
0963-8008	Financial Markets, Institutions and Instruments
0963-8024	Journal of African Economies
0963-8237	Journal of Mental Health
0963-8253	Forum
0963-8288	Disability and Rehabilitation
0963-8601	Prep School
0963-9284	Accounting Education
0963-9292	Ecotoxicology
0963-9306	Journal of Programming Language Design and Implementation
0963-9314	Software Quality Journal
0963-9969	Food Research International
0964-0150	Key Abstracts - Human-Computer Interaction
0964-0169	Key Abstracts - Neural Networks
0964-0304	Acumen Magazine
0964-0568	Journal of Environmental Planning and Management
0964-0932	Admarine
0964-0940	Furniture Components & Production International
0964-0959	Pine News International
0964-1793	Shopping Centre
0964-1807	Applied Superconductivity
0964-1815	Complexity
0964-1823	Exploration & Mining Geology
0964-1890	Far Point
0964-1947	European Journal of Cancer Part A
0964-1955	European Journal of Cancer Part B: Oral Oncology
0964-2323	The Modern Review
0964-2706	Awards for University Teachers and Research Workers
0964-2714	Awards for University Administrators and Librarians
0964-3400	Alphanumeric Reports Publications Index
0964-3427	Mountain
0964-4008	German Politics
0964-4016	Environmental Politics
0964-4024	Russian Affairs
0964-4164	Food Safety and Security
0964-4563	Tobacco Control: An International Journal
0964-5993	Technical Textiles International
0964-6604	Poultry Science Reviews
0964-6639	Social and Legal Studies
0964-6779	Fabrication & Glazing Industries
0964-6841	Software Development Monitor
0964-7104	British Archaeological Bibliography
0964-7554	Growth Factors & Cytokines
0964-7562	Microbial Biotechnology
0964-7570	Parasitology (Sheffield)
0964-7589	Signal Transduction & Cyclic Nucleotides
0964-7597	Cholesterol & Lipoproteins
0964-7600	Mammary Gland
0964-7627	Library Technology News
0964-8070	Cub
0964-8712	Current Advances in Applied Microbiology & Biotechnology
0964-8720	Current Advances in Endocrinology & Metabolism
0964-8747	Current Advances in Immunology & Infectious Diseases
0964-8941	Primary D A T A
0964-9875	P R S Members Handbook
0965-0407	Oncology Research
0965-0504	Current Advances in Protein Biochemistry
0965-0512	Current Advances in Toxicology
0965-0660	Nottingham Law Journal
0965-1748	Insect Biochemistry and Molecular Biology
0965-3813	Environment Risk
0965-4380	Association for Global Strategic Information. Journal
0965-7738	Mela
0965-7746	Dan Haul
0965-9773	Nanostructured Materials
0965-9978	Advances in Engineering Software
0965-9986	F D I Dental World
0969-8027	Pakistan Management Review
0970-0048	International Library Movement
0970-0056	Invention Intelligence
0970-0137	Journal of Structural Engineering
0970-0153	Annals of Biology
0970-0188	N I S S A T Newsletter
0970-0277	Osmania Papers in Linguistics
0970-0285	Shipping and Marine Industries Journal
0970-0293	Social Scientist
0970-0307	Ganita Bharati
0970-034X	Dataquest
0970-0358	Indian Journal of Plastic Surgery
0970-0366	Aquaworld†
0970-0374	Journal of Optics
0970-0420	Environment and Ecology
0970-0447	Management Professionals Association. Events Diary
0970-0447	Management Professionals Association. Journal
0970-0560	Economic and Commercial News
0970-0595	Himachal Journal of Agricultural Research
0970-0765	Bulletin of Pure & Applied Sciences. Section A: Zoology
0970-0838	Journal of Polymer Materials
0970-0846	Journal of Aquaculture in the Tropics
0970-0870	Indian Textile Bulletin
0970-0889	Bio-Science Research Bulletin
0970-0897	Indian Journal of Behaviour
0970-0919	Madhuprapancha
0970-0927	Indian Anthropologist
0970-0935	Indian Journal of Colo-Proctology
0970-0943	C L I S Observer
0970-0951	Journal of Himalayan Geology
0970-096X	Akavita
0970-0978	Yuva Kavi
0970-0986	Samkaleen Kala Aur Kavita
0970-0994	Aligarh Journal of Oriental Studies
0970-1001	Art and Poetry Today
0970-1044	International Journal of Development Banking
0970-1052	Library Progress
0970-1060	Administrative Tribunals Cases
0970-1079	Vidyajyoti Journal of Theological Reflection
0970-1095	Indian Journal of Marketing Geography
0970-1117	Jeevadhara
0970-1206	Journal of Personality and Clinical Studies
0970-1257	Tibetan Medicine
0970-1311	Steel India
0970-1354	Indian Journal of Geology
0970-1370	Journal of Soil Biology and Ecology
0970-1397	Vayu Mandal
0970-1400	Indian Journal of Acarology changed to Journal of Acarology.
0970-1427	Glory of India
0970-1435	M L B D Newsletter
0970-1524	Indian Journal of Animal Production and Management
0970-1532	Indian Journal of Quantitative Economics
0970-1540	B H E L Journal
0970-1605	School of Economics. Quarterly Journal
0970-1664	Institution of Electronics and Telecommunication Engineers. Students' Journal
0970-1672	M A A S Journal of Islamic Studies changed to M A A S Journal of Islamic Science.
0970-1710	Frontline
0970-1737	Yoga and Total Health
0970-1761	Inside - Outside
0970-1788	Iron & Steel Newsletter
0970-1818	Cashew Causerie see 0970-2423
0970-1850	International Information, Communication and Education
0970-1923	Purabhilekh - Puratatva
0970-1958	Poultry Adviser
0970-1982	Indian Journal of Forensic Sciences
0970-2059	International Journal of Microbiology†
0970-2288	Biblebhashyam
0970-2318	Electricity Conservation Quarterly
0970-2326	Himalayan Plant Journal
0970-2334	Indian Vacuum Society. Bulletin
0970-2377	Applied Botany Abstracts
0970-2385	Abhigyan
0970-2423	The Cashew
0970-2431	Indian Journal of Natural Rubber Research
0970-244X	Soviet Journal on Concrete and Reinforced Concrete
0970-2458	Soviet Mining Journal†
0970-2466	S E S I Journal
0970-2512	Indian Defence Review
0970-2571	Light of Life
0970-258X	National Medical Journal of India
0970-2598	Highway Research Record
0970-2628	Standards India
0970-2733	Indian Journal of Home Science
0970-2776	Journal of Oilseeds Research
0970-2814	Institute of Asian Studies. Journal
0970-2849	Pratibha India
0970-2962	Agricultural Engineering Today†
0970-2970	Indian Journal of Mushrooms
0970-3004	Livestock Adviser
0970-3209	Indian Journal of Animal Nutrition
0970-3357	Journal of Rural Development
0970-3403	Universal Military Abstracts
0970-3411	Human Science
0970-3438	Dairy Guide
0970-3446	Energy Environment Monitor
0970-3454	Energy Digest see 0971-085X
0970-3497	India. Directorate of Jute Development. Jute Development Journal
0970-3578	Aviation & Space Journal
0970-3594	Journal of Hydrobiology
0970-3764	South Asian Social Scientist
0970-3799	Journal of Natural & Physical Sciences
0970-3810	Journal of Aphidology
0970-3853	Indian Energy Abstracts see 0971-085X
0970-3861	Annual Bibliography of Christianity in India†
0970-3888	Pacific and Asian Journal of Energy
0970-3918	Indian Society of Desert Technology. Transactions
0970-4019	Agricultural Research Abstracts and Newsletter
0970-4035	Diabetic Association of India. Journal
0970-4094	Oil Technologists' Association of India. Journal
0970-4205	Journal of Financial Management and Analysis
0970-4221	St. John's Journal of Medicine
0970-423X	Metals Materials and Processes
0970-4256	Indian Science Cruiser
0970-4477	W R I Journal
0970-454X	Demography India
0970-4612	Bulletin of Pure & Applied Sciences. Section B: Botany
0970-4620	Bulletin of Pure & Applied Sciences. Section C: Chemistry
0970-4639	Bulletin of Pure & Applied Sciences. Section F: Geology
0970-4698	Henry Martyn Institute of Islamic Studies. Bulletin
0970-471X	Health Action
0970-4736	Journal of Transport Management
0970-4868	South Asia Journal
0970-4914	Plant Disease Research
0970-4981	Indian Tobacco Journal†
0970-5120	Indian Academy of Mathematics. Journal
0970-5368	The Tibet Journal
0970-5392	Plus: The Total Computer Magazine
0970-5562	Studies in History of Medicine and Science
0970-5600	N C B Quest
0970-566X	Journal of General Medicine
0970-5686	Texincon
0970-5953	Physics Education
0970-6038	Homoeopathic Heritage
0970-6097	Psychological Research Journal
0970-6143	C I C F R I Newsletter
0970-616X	Central Inland Capture Fisheries Research Institute. Bulletin
0970-6186	Export Gazette
0970-6194	Beverage and Food World
0970-6267	Central Inland Capture Fisheries Research Institute. Annual Report
0970-6569	Bulletin of Pure & Applied Sciences. Section D: Physics
0970-6577	Bulletin of Pure & Applied Sciences. Section E: Mathematics
0970-6607	Awishkara
0970-6623	M D I Management Journal
0970-6666	Indian Journal of Aerospace Medicine
0970-6739	Sasmira's Bulletin†
0970-6852	Architects India
0970-6879	Indian Fisheries Abstracts
0970-695X	Mycorrhiza News
0970-714X	Journal of Library and Information Science
0970-7182	Poetry
0970-7654	Arthik Prasanga
0970-7727	Diamond World
0970-7867	Indian Journal of Rural Technology
0970-7891	C R I Current Contents
0970-7913	North-East India Council for Social Science Research. Journal
0970-8111	Personality Study and Group Behaviour
0970-812X	Itihas
0970-8235	Indian Potato Association. Journal
0970-8324	Sevartham
0970-8405	Personnel Today
0970-8413	Indian and World Arts & Crafts
0970-8626	Association of Scientific Workers of India. Bulletin
0970-8650	Krishak Jagat
0970-8863	Socialist Perspective
0970-9142	Chess Mate
0970-9223	Popular Electronics
0970-9258	River Behaviour and Control
0970-9266	Directory of Periodicals Published in India
0970-9274	Journal of Human Ecology
0970-9703	Tisglow
0970-9738	Indian Poultry Industry Yearbook
0970-9800	India. Textiles Committee. Consumer Purchases of Textiles
0970-9819	International Journal of Translation
0970-9843	Institution of Engineers (India). Interdisciplinary Panels Journal
0970-9851	Institute of Indian Geographers. Transactions
0970-9932	Dairy India Yearbook
0971-0043	Current Tax Reporter
0971-0388	Aligarh Journal of Statistics
0971-0701	Journal of Veterinary and Animal Sciences
0971-085X	T I D E
0971-0949	Hearing Aid Journal

0971-1384 Confederation of Engineering Industry. Handbook of Statistics *changed to* Confederation of Indian Industry. Handbook of Statistics.
0971-1562 Perspectives in Psychological Researches
0971-1589 Indian Books in Print
0971-1678 Aspect of Plant Sciences
0971-1686 Glimpses in Plant Research
0971-1708 Recent Researches in Ecology, Environment and Pollution
0971-1716 International Bioscience Series
0971-1937 Indian Journal of Veterinary Anatomy
0971-2038 Urja Oil and Gas International
0980-1367 Industrie du Cuir
0980-1472 Revue Internationale de Systemique
0980-2371 Bivouac
0980-2797 La Revue des Revues
0980-3483 Cahiers de l'Audition
0980-3637 Institut d'Etudes Slaves Informations
0980-9465 L'Atelier
0981-0455 Lettre Ada
0981-1095 Lille Medical
0981-1761 Cahiers Territoires
0981-1907 Texte et l'Idee
0981-1974 French Journal of Orthopaedic Surgery *changed to* Journal of Orthopaedic Surgery.
0981-6003 Biologiste *see* 0999-5749
0981-6402 Info P C
0981-9185 J'Ecris
0981-9428 Plant Physiology and Biochemistry
0982-1783 Histoire et Mesure
0982-3816 Hercynica
0982-5339 Ecole du Grand Paris
0982-6238 Energie et Creation
0982-6548 Societe de Bibliologie et de Schematisation. Almanach
0982-6548 Revue de Bibliologie
0982-7757 Chardon *see* 0996-9640
0982-9873 Le Grand Huit
0983-0537 Journal de la Marine Marchande et du Transport Multimondal
0983-0979 Cultivar 2000, Grandes Cultures, Elevages *changed to* Cultivar.
0983-1509 Arabies
0983-1592 Air and Cosmos Monthly *changed to* Aerospace World.
0983-1924 References de la Poste
0983-2424 Universite de Nantes. Centre de Recherches sur l'Histoire du Monde Atlantique. Enquetes et Documents
0983-4532 Cardiologie
0983-8651 Military Powers' Encyclopedia
0984-2292 Guerres Mondiales et Conflits Contemporains
0984-2594 New Caledonia. Institut Territorial de la Statistique et des Etudes Economiques. Indice et Index du B T P
0984-4724 Ile de France a la Page
0984-7685 Islam et Societes au Sud du Sahara
0984-7979 Verre...Bulletin d'Information
0984-8541 Documentation - Refugies
0984-8673 Institut International d'Administration Publique. Annee Administrative *changed to* Institut International d'Administration Publique. Dossiers et Debats.
0985-0503 France Composites
0985-0791 Centre d'Information des Utilisateurs de Progiciel. Catalogue
0985-1798 Unir
0985-1976 Propriete Agricole
0985-2220 F T S
0985-2654 Flash Japon
0985-2662 Flash Etats-Unis
0985-5734 Seve Eglise Aujourd'hui
0985-5939 Sociocriticism
0985-9195 Faiences Patriotiques
0986-1653 L'Enseignement Philosophique
0986-6426 Revue Languedocienne de Sociologie Ethnologie†
0987-0717 Sciences & Nature
0987-2213 Cahiers pour Croire Aujourd'hui
0987-4119 Telecoms International
0987-4216 Antiane
0987-6030 Repertoire
0987-7053 Neurophysiologie Clinique
0987-710X Tertiaire
0987-7401 Repertoire des Banques de Donnees Teletel Pour l'Entreprise
0987-741X Maison de la Chasse et de la Nature. Bulletin d'Information *changed to* Maison de la Chasse et de la Nature. Revue.
0987-7622 Standpoints
0987-7738 Langues Orientales Anciennes Philologie et Linguistique
0987-8238 C D - R O M International
0987-8467 Al-Handasah
0987-8947 Revue de l'Aide-Soignante
0987-903X Minute, le Chardon *see* 0996-9640
0988-1808 Vieux Marly
0988-1956 Aviron
0988-3215 New Caledonia. Institut Territorial de la Statistique et des Etudes Economiques. Indice des Prix a la Consommation
0988-3452 Computer Data Storage Newsletter
0988-3525 Opto
0988-3754 R A I R O Informatique Theorique et Appliquee - Theoretical Informatics and Applications
0988-4319 Journal d'Acoustique
0988-5226 Lignes
0988-5757 Famille Magazine
0988-5986 Universite de Toulouse - Le Mirail. Papiers
0988-6729 Revue Francaise d'Esperanto
0989-3105 Ophtalmologie
0989-6236 Astronomie et Sciences Humaines
0989-6988 Academie d'Agriculture de France. Comptes Rendus
0989-7577 Mineurs de France: Edition Centre-Midi
0989-8735 Information du Technicien Biologiste
0989-8972 Biological Structures and Morphogenesis
0989-9200 Societe des Sciences Historiques et Naturelles de Semur en Auxois et des Fouilles d'Alesia. Bulletin
0990-0063 Annuaire des Arachnologistes Mondiaux
0990-0632 Productions Animales
0990-1159 Locaguide
0990-1930 Top Echecs
0990-2562 Regards sur l'Ile-de-France
0990-5243 R N I S
0990-5413 Education Economie
0990-736X Elex
0990-7440 Aquatic Living Resources
0990-9141 Centre de Recherches Historiques. Cahiers
0990-9435 Note de Conjoncture Internationale
0991-532X Boulite
0991-8086 Revue des Etudes Georgiennes et Caucasiennes
0991-949X Acteurs
0991-9953 Langouste
0992-0692 I N I S T - Info
0992-0757 Levant
0992-1893 Cycnos
0992-2660 Serpent a Plumes
0992-3039 Journal de Medecine Nucleaire et Biophysique
0992-4361 European Journal of Solid State and Inorganic Chemistry
0992-5120 S V M Macintosh *changed to* S V M Mac.
0992-5899 Science et Vie Junior
0992-5945 Option - Bio
0992-5996 Plan de Classement P A S C A L
0992-6739 Guide Annuel des S A M U et S M U R de France
0992-6801 Association de l'Ecole Nationale Superieure des Bibliothecaires. Infos
0993-4871 Anthropologie Visuelle
0993-538X Atelier A S E M I
0993-5835 Groupe Interdisciplinaire du Theatre Antique. Textes et Documents
0993-5878 Institut des Hautes Etudes de l'Amerique Latine. Collection des Travaux et Memoires
0993-9857 Journal Europeen des Urgences
0994-415X Tableau Economique de la Reunion
0994-7736 Cahiers du L A C I T O - Revue d'Ethnolinguistique
0995-0583 Vendredi
0995-1180 Revue du Pediatre
0995-2721 European Sponsorship Newsletter†
0995-3671 Centre National de Documentation sur les Toxicomanies. Bulletin de Liaison
0996-5637 Retrovirus
0996-7109 Septieme Artifice
0996-9640 Minute
0997-1327 Revue du Monde Musulman de la Mediterranee
0997-3192 I N S E E. Premiere
0997-7538 European Journal of Mechanics A - Solids
0997-7546 European Journal of Mechanics B - Fluids
0998-4178 France. Ministere de l'Agriculture et de la Foret. Analyses et Etudes. Cahiers
0998-4186 France. Ministere de l'Agriculture et de la Foret. Analyses et Etudes. Etudes
0998-4194 Moniteur Architecture - A M C
0998-433X Diagnostic & Interventional Radiology
0998-4402 I N S E E - Infos
0998-4577 Le Moniteur - Materiels et Chantiers
0998-4771 Horizon. Bulletin Bibliographique O R S T O M Science de la Terre
0998-478X Horizon. Bulletin Bibliographique O R S T O M Sante
0998-4828 I N S E E. Cadrage et I N S E E Resultats Economie Generale
0998-4836 I N S E E. Cadrage et I N S E E Resultats Systeme Productif
0998-4844 I N S E E. Cadrage et I N S E E Resultats Emplois Revenus
0998-4852 I N S E E. Cadrage et I N S E E Resultats Consommations et Modes de Vie
0998-4860 I N S E E. Cadrage et I N S E E Resultats Demographie et Societe
0998-495X Motoculture Magazine
0998-6316 Courrier-Expression
0999-193X Genetics, Selection, Evolution
0999-5404 Piano
0999-5749 Eurobiologiste
0999-7385 Sang Thrombose Vaisseaux
0999-792X Approche Neuropsychologique des Apprentissages chez l'Enfant
1000-0003 Xizang Yanjiu
1000-0011 Zhiwu Shengtaixue yu Dizhiwuxue Xuebao
1000-002X Shandi Yanjiu
1000-0038 Ziran Ziyuan
1000-0097 Shijie Tushu
1000-0100 Waiyu Xuekan
1000-0119 Hangkong Zhishi
1000-0127 Yesheng Dongwu
1000-0135 Qingbao Xuebao
1000-0151 Dianshi Dianying Wenxue
1000-0186 Kecheng - Jiaocai - Jiaofa
1000-0194 Wenwu Tiandi
1000-0208 Zhengfa Luntan
1000-0224 Ziran Kexue Shi Yanjiu
1000-0232 Nanfang Jianzhu
1000-0240 Bingchuan Dongtu
1000-0267 Nongye Huanjing Baohu
1000-0305 Shoudu Yixueyuan Xuebao
1000-0348 Meiguo Yixuehui Yanke Zazhi
1000-0356 Hang Hai
1000-0372 Tiedao Zhishi
1000-0380 Zidonghua Yibiao
1000-0399 Anhui Yixue
1000-0437 Wenxian
1000-0453 Duzhe Wenzhai
1000-0496 Shandong Yike Daxue Xuebao
1000-0526 Qixiang
1000-0569 Yanshi Xuebao
1000-0577 Xitong Kexue yu Shuxue
1000-0585 Dili Yanjiu
1000-0593 Guangpuxue yu Guangpu Fenxi
1000-0615 Shuichan Xuebao
1000-0623 Zhongguo Linye
1000-0631 Zhiwu Zazhi
1000-064X Gang Ao Jingji
1000-0674 Weiti Gushengwu Xuebao
1000-0690 Dili Kexue
1000-0739 Dongwu Fenlei Xuebao
1000-0755 Dianzi Jishu
1000-078X Dili Jiaoxue
1000-0798 Zhongguo Keji Shiliao
1000-081X Gaodeng Xuexiao Jisuan Shuxue Xuebao
1000-0860 Shuili Shuidian Jishu
1000-0879 Lixue yu Shijian
1000-0887 Yingyong Shuxue yu Lixue
1000-0895 Qigong yu Kexue
1000-0909 Neiranji Xuebao
1000-0933 Shengtai Xuebao
1000-0941 Zhongguo Shuitu Baochi
1000-0976 Tianranqi Gongye
1000-0984 Shuxue de Shijian yu Renshi
1000-0992 Lixue Jinzhan
1000-1034 Shengwu Fangzhi Tongbao
1000-1050 Shoulei Xuebao
1000-1107 Zhongguo Xiaofang
1000-1115 Zhongguo Pengren
1000-1174 Zhongguo Gangchangbing Zazhi
1000-1182 Huaxi Kouqiang Yixue Zazhi
1000-1190 Huazhong Shifan Daxue Xuebao (Ziran Kexue Ban)
1000-1239 Jisuanji Yanjiu yu Fazhan
1000-1247 Dianxin Jishu
1000-1301 Dizhen Gongcheng yu Gongcheng Zhendong
1000-1328 Yuhang Xuebao
1000-1344 Dian Shijie
1000-1379 Renmin Huang He
1000-1441 Shiyou Wutan
1000-145X Dianli Jishu
1000-1476 Zhongguo Fangzhi Daxue Xuebao
1000-1492 Anhui Yike Daxue Xuebao
1000-1506 Beifang Jiaotong Daxue Xuebao
1000-1514 Beijing Nongye Gongcheng Daxue Xuebao
1000-1522 Beijing Linye Daxue Xuebao
1000-1530 Beijing Yike Daxue Xuebao
1000-1557 Tianjin Fangzhi Gongxueyuan Xuebao
1000-1565 Hebei Daxue Xuebao
1000-1573 Hebei Nongye Daxue Xuebao
1000-1581 Hebei Yixue Yuan Xuebao
1000-1603 Shanxi Kuangye Xueyuan Xuebao
1000-1611 Taiyuan Gongye Daxue Xuebao
1000-162X Shanxi Nongye Daxue Xuebao
1000-1638 Nei Menggu Daxue Xuebao (Ziran Kexue Ban)
1000-1719 Liaoning Zhongyi Zazhi
1000-176X Caijing Wenti Yanjiu
1000-1794 Changchun Youdian Xueyuan Xuebao
1000-1832 Dongbei Shida Xuebao (Ziran Kexue Ban)
1000-1875 Harbin Chuanbo Gongcheng Xueyuan Xuebao
1000-1913 Shanghai Tiedao Xueyuan Xuebao
1000-193X Shanghai Nongxueyuan Xuebao
1000-1956 Nanjing Hangkong Xueyuan Xuebao
1000-1972 Nanjing Youdian Xueyuan Xuebao
1000-1980 Hehai Daxue Xuebao
1000-1999 Suzhou Sichou Gongxueyuan Xuebao
1000-2030 Nanjing Nongye Daxue Xuebao
1000-2057 Nantong Yixueyuan Xuebao
1000-2065 Xuzhou Yixueyuan Xuebao
1000-2073 Qizhong Yunshu Jixie
1000-209X Zhejiang Gongxueyuan Xuebao
1000-2103 Zhejiang Sichou Gongxueyuan Xuebao
1000-2111 Zhejiang Nongye Daxue Xuebao
1000-2138 Wenzhou Yixueyuan Xuebao
1000-2154 Shangye Jingji yu Guanli
1000-2162 Anhui Daxue Xuebao (Ziran Kexue Ban)
1000-2189 Anhui Gongxueyuan Xuebao
1000-2219 Anhui Zhongyi Xueyuan Xuebao
1000-2243 Fuzhou Daxue Xuebao (Ziran Kexue Ban)
1000-2278 Jingdezhen Taoci Xueyuan Xuebao
1000-2359 Henan Shifan Daxue Xuebao (Shehui Kexue Ban)
1000-2367 Henan Shifan Daxue Xuebao (Ziran Kexue Ban)
1000-2456 Huazhong Shifan Daxue Xuebao (Shehui Kexue Ban)

ISSN

ISSN INDEX

ISSN	Title
1000-2472	Henan Daxue Xuebao (Ziran Kexue Ban)
1000-2529	Hunan Shifan Daxue Xuebao (Shehui Kexue Ban)
1000-2537	Hunan Shifan Daxue Xuebao (Ziran Kexue Ban)
1000-2561	Redai Zuowu Xuebao
1000-2618	Shenzhen Daxue Xuebao (Renwen Sheke Ban)
1000-2677	Xinan Shifan Daxue Xuebao (Shehui Kexue Ban)
1000-2731	Xibei Daxue Xuebao. Shehui Kexue Ban
1000-2871	Boli yu Tangci
1000-2928	Wenhua Yule
1000-2952	Zhongguo Shehui Kexueyuan Yanjiushengyuan Xuebao
1000-2979	Yuwen Yanjiu
1000-2987	Jinyang Xuekan
1000-2995	Keyan Guanli
1000-3029	Chinese Journal of Metal Science & Technology
1000-3037	Ziran Ziyuan Xuebao
1000-3045	Zhongguo Kexueyuan Yuankan
1000-3053	Redai Haiyang
1000-3061	Shengwu Gongcheng Xuebao
1000-307X	Nongcun Kexue - Science in Countryside see 1001-4284
1000-3088	Kexue Bolant
1000-3096	Haiyang Kexue
1000-310X	Yingyong Shengxue
1000-3118	Gujizhui Dongwu Xuebao
1000-3126	Zhongguo Kexue A
1000-3134	Zhongguo Kexue B
1000-3177	Yaogan Xinxi
1000-3185	Huashi
1000-3193	Renleixue Xuebao
1000-3207	Shuisheng Shengwu Xuebao
1000-3223	Bingduxue Zazhi
1000-3231	Ganguang Kexue yu Guanghuaxue
1000-324X	Wuji Cailiao Xuebao
1000-3258	Diwen Wuli Xuebao
1000-3266	Shuzhi Jisuan yu Jisuanji Yingyong
1000-3274	Dizhen
1000-3282	Shengwu Huaxue yu Shengwu Wuli Jinzhan
1000-3290	Wuli Xuebao
1000-3304	Gaofenzi Xuebao
1000-3312	Huanjing Yaogan
1000-3355	Zhengzhixue Yanjiu
1000-3363	Chengshi Guihua Huikan
1000-3398	Kexue yu Wenhua
1000-3401	Jisuan Jiegou Lixue Jiqi Yingyong
1000-3428	Jisuanji Gongcheng
1000-3436	Fushe Yanjiu yu Fushe Gongyi Xuebao
1000-3444	Ticao
1000-3452	Pingpang Shijie
1000-3460	Lanqiu
1000-3479	Qiaopai
1000-3487	Zhongguo Diaoyu
1000-3495	Youyong
1000-3509	Tianjing
1000-3517	Zuqiu Shijie
1000-3525	Zhonghua Wushu
1000-3541	Beifang Luncong
1000-355X	Xiandai Riben Jingji
1000-3568	Fazhi Jianshe
1000-3576	Xi'ou Yanjiu
1000-3584	Xiuci Xuexi
1000-3630	Shengxue Jishu
1000-3649	Sichuan Zhongyi
1000-3657	Zhongguo Dizhi
1000-3673	Dianwang Jishu
1000-3703	Qiche Jishu
1000-372X	Yingyong Jiguang
1000-3738	Jixie Gongcheng Cailiao
1000-3819	Guti Dianzixue Yanjiu yu Jinzhan
1000-3835	Zhendong yu Chongji
1000-3843	Xinyao yu Linchuang
1000-386X	Jisuanji Yingyong yu Ruanjian
1000-3878	Zaochuan Jishu
1000-3886	Dianqi Zidonghua
1000-3916	Fangzhi Wenzhai
1000-3975	Shanghai Huanjing Kexue
1000-4009	Guoji Hangkong
1000-4017	Yin Ran
1000-4041	Daziran Tansuo
1000-4068	Redai Qixiang
1000-4076	Xibei Shi-Di
1000-4106	Dunhuang Yanjiu
1000-4149	Renkou yu Jingji
1000-4157	Zhiyin
1000-4165	Dang'an yu Lishi
1000-4173	Bolan Qunshu
1000-4181	Zhongguo Jingji Wenti
1000-419X	Zhongxue Yuwen
1000-4211	Shanghai Jingji
1000-422X	Zhongguo Shehui Jingjishi Yanjiu
1000-4262	Xinjiang Shehui Kexue
1000-4270	Yinyue Yishu
1000-4289	Shijie Zongjiao Yanjiu
1000-4300	Xiandai Jiating
1000-4319	Weile Haizi
1000-4378	Banhua Yishu
1000-4394	Shanghai Gaojiao Yanjiu
1000-4416	Meiqi yu Reli
1000-4432	Eye Science
1000-4440	Jiangsu Nongye Xuebao
1000-4459	Zhongguo Nong-Shi
1000-4467	Keji Qingbao Gongzuo
1000-4483	Shiyong Meishu
1000-4491	Minguo Dang'an
1000-4505	Shijie Zongjiao Ziliao
1000-4513	Xiandai Lingdao
1000-4548	Yantu Gongcheng Xuebao
1000-4602	Zhongguo Geshui Paishui
1000-4653	Zhongguo Hanghai
1000-467X	Aizheng
1000-4688	Hanghai Keji Dongtai
1000-4696	Jiaotongbu Shanghai Chuanbo Yunshu Kexue Yanjiusuo Xuebao
1000-4718	Zhongguo Bingli Shengli Zazhi
1000-4726	Jianzhu Jishu
1000-4742	Diandu yu Huanbao
1000-4769	Shehui Kexue Yanjiu
1000-4785	Guowai Shehui Kexue Kuaibao
1000-4793	Shu Lin
1000-4807	Qingnian Yidai
1000-4815	Hualang
1000-4823	Huang He
1000-4831	Shanghai Gushi
1000-4874	Journal of Hydrodynamics
1000-4890	Shengtaixue Zazhi
1000-4963	Linchuang Pifuke Zazhi
1000-4971	Zhongguo Yiyao Xuebao
1000-4998	Jixie Zhizao
1000-5005	Nanjing Zhongyi Xueyuan Xuebao
1000-5013	Huaqiao Daxue Xuebao (Ziran Kexue Ban)
1000-503X	Zhongguo Yixue Kexueyuan Xuebao
1000-5072	Jinan Xuebao (Zhexue Shehui Kexue Ban)
1000-5102	Qinghai Shifan Daxue Xuebao (Shehui Kexue Ban)
1000-5145	Beijing Youdian Xueyuan Xuebao
1000-517X	Zhengzhou Gongxueyuan Xuebao
1000-5218	Nei Menggu Daxue Xuebao (Shehui Kexue Ban)
1000-5226	Shenyang Shifan Xueyuan Xuebao. Shehui Kexue Ban
1000-5234	Zhongnan Zhengfa Xueyuan Xuebao
1000-5242	Henan Daxue Xuebao (Shehui Kexue Ban)
1000-5285	Fujian Shifan Daxue Xuebao (Shehui Kexue Ban)
1000-5315	Sichuan Shifan Daxue Xuebao (Shehui Kexue Ban)
1000-5323	Shandong Gongye Daxue Xuebao (Shehui Kexue Ban)
1000-5331	Nanjing Yixueyuan Xuebao
1000-5374	Wuhan Daxue Xuebao (Shehui Kexue Ban)
1000-5382	Dongbei Linye Daxue Xuebao
1000-5420	Zhongguo Renmin Daxue Xuebao
1000-5439	Zhongnan Minzu Xueyuan Xuebao (Shehui Kexue Ban)
1000-5455	Huanan Shifan Daxue Xuebao (Shehui Kexue Ban)
1000-5463	Huanan Shifan Daxue Xuebao (Ziran Kexue Ban)
1000-5471	Xinan Shifan Daxue Xuebao (Ziran Kexue Ban)
1000-5560	Huadong Shifan Daxue Xuebao (Jiaoyu Ban)
1000-5579	Huadong Shifan Daxue Xuebao (Zhexue Shehui Kexue Ban)
1000-5587	Hebei Shifan Daxue Xuebao (Shehui Kexue Ban)
1000-5595	Shandong Yike Daxue Xuebao (Shehui Kexue Ban)
1000-5617	Harbin Shifan Daxue Ziran Kexue Xuebao
1000-5641	Huadong Shifan Daxue Xuebao (Ziran Kexue Ban)
1000-565X	Huanan Ligong Daxue Xuebao (Ziran Kexue Ban)
1000-5676	Dalian Yixueyuan Xuebao
1000-5684	Jilin Nongye Daxue Xuebao
1000-5692	Zhejiang Linxueyuan Xuebao
1000-5749	Suzhou Yixueyuan Xuebao
1000-5765	Zhenjiang Chuanbo Xueyuan Xuebao
1000-579X	Jiangxi Shifan Daxue Xuebao (Shehui Kexue Ban)
1000-5803	Jiangxi Gongye Daxue Xuebao
1000-582X	Chongqing Daxue Xuebao
1000-5854	Hebei Shifan Daxue Xuebao (Ziran Kexue Ban)
1000-5862	Jiangxi Shifan Daxue Xuebao (Ziran Kexue Ban)
1000-5870	Shiyou Daxue Xuebao (Ziran Kexue Ban)
1000-5897	Harbin Kexue Jishu Daxue Xuebao
1000-5919	Beijing Daxue Xuebao (Zhexue Shehui Kexue Ban)
1000-5935	Shanxi Daxue Xuebao (Shehui Kexue Ban)
1000-5994	Nanjing Huagong Xueyuan Xuebao
1000-6001	Jianghai Xuekan (Jingji Shehui Ban) see 1000-856X
1000-601X	Jianghai Xuekan (Wen-Shi-Zhe Ban) see 1000-856X
1000-6028	Duo Yun
1000-6036	Shufa
1000-6044	Shufa Yishu
1000-6052	Yatai Jingji
1000-6087	Renkou Yanjiu
1000-6125	Cishu Yanjiu
1000-6192	Xiandai Guoji Guanxi
1000-6214	Shu yu Hua
1000-6222	Wenhua Yicong
1000-6230	Zhongguo Laodong Kexue
1000-6257	Shuichan Wenzhai
1000-6265	Shanxi Dizhen
1000-6273	Liaoning Dizhi
1000-629X	Zhongguo Mafeng Zazhi
1000-6346	Zhongguo Shucai
1000-6362	Zhongguo Nongye Qixiang
1000-6370	Nongye Jishu Jingji
1000-6389	Nongye Jingji Wenti
1000-6400	Nongye Keji Tongxun
1000-6427	Guowai Nongxue - Nongye Qixiang
1000-6451	Tiancai Tangye
1000-6559	Xiandai Tongxin
1000-6648	Xinli Kexue Tongxun
1000-6680	Zhonghua Chuanranbing Zazhi
1000-6699	Zhonghua Neifenmi Daixie Zazhi
1000-6710	Zhongguo Yundong Yixue Zazhi
1000-6729	Zhongguo Xinli Weisheng Zazhi
1000-6753	Diangong Jishu Xuebao
1000-6761	Dongli Gongcheng
1000-677X	Tiyu Kexue
1000-6796	Qiche zhi You
1000-680X	Qiche Gongcheng
1000-6834	Zhongguo Yingyong Shenglixue Zazhi
1000-6885	Hangkong Moxing
1000-6893	Hangkong Xuebao
1000-6915	Yanshi Lixue yu Gongcheng Xuebao
1000-6931	Yuanzineng Kexue Jishu
1000-694X	Zhongguo Shamo
1000-6966	Beijing Nongye
1000-6982	Chuanbo Gongcheng
1000-7032	Faguang Xuebao
1000-7091	Huabei Nongxue Bao
1000-7121	Fujian Sheng Nongkeyuan Xuebao
1000-7148	Jianchuan Zhishi
1000-7156	Shanxi Zhongyi
1000-7199	Huang Bohai Haiyang
1000-7210	Shiyou Dili Wuli Kantan
1000-7237	Gujian Yuanlin Jishu
1000-7245	Zhongwen Zixiu
1000-7253	Luyou
1000-727X	Fumu Bidu
1000-7296	Dong Xi Nan Bei
1000-7318	Wulin
1000-7326	Xueshu Yanjiu
1000-7407	Maopi Dongwu Siyang
1000-7423	Zhongguo Jishengchongxue yu Jishengchongbing Zazhi
1000-7466	Petrochemical Equipment
1000-7474	Hangtian
1000-7490	Qingbao Lilun yu Shijian
1000-7504	Qiu Shi Wenxuan
1000-7563	Guowai Naihuo Cailiao
1000-758X	Zhongguo Kongjian Kexue Jishu
1000-7598	Yantu Lixue
1000-7628	Rencai Kaifa
1000-7636	Jingji yu Guanli Yanjiu
1000-7679	Beifang Qiyi
1000-7695	Keji Guanli Yanjiu
1000-7725	Shanghai Xumu Shouyi Tongxun
1000-7741	Nongmin Wenzhai
1000-7776	Shaonian Kexue Huabao
1000-7792	Silu
1000-7806	Zhonghua Zhengxing Shaoshang Waike Zazhi
1000-7830	Kaogu yu Wenwu
1000-7857	Keji Daobao
1000-7873	Manyu Yanjiu
1000-789X	Huacheng
1000-7903	Suibi
1000-7911	Chongqing Yiyao
1000-7946	Dangdai Xiaoshuo
1000-7954	Wen Bo
1000-7989	Jingji Gaige
1000-7997	Beijing Jiaoyu
1000-8047	Zhongguo Guoshu
1000-8071	Zhongzi Shijie
1000-8144	Shiyou Huagong
1000-8160	Taiwan Haixia
1000-8179	Zhongguo Zhongliu Linchuang
1000-8217	Zhongguo Kexue Jijin
1000-825X	Qigong
1000-8268	Zhongguo Qigong
1000-8306	Caijing Kexue
1000-8330	Jingji yu Shehui Fazhan
1000-8349	Tianwenxue Jinzhan
1000-8373	Shijie Jianzhu Daobao
1000-839X	Linye Yuekan
1000-8438	Daxue Huaxue
1000-8462	Jingji Dili
1000-8470	Dazhong Yixue
1000-8489	Qingbao Kexue
1000-8500	Cailiao Kexue Jinzhan
1000-8527	Xiandai Dizhi
1000-8543	Shengwu Huaxue Zazhi
1000-856X	Jianghai Xuekan
1000-8586	Cehui Yicong
1000-8608	Dalian Ligong Daxue Xuebao
1000-8616	Huazhong Ligong Daxue Xuebao
1000-8659	Fujian Luntan (Wen Shi Zhe Ban)
1000-8667	Zhongyang Minzu Xueyuan Xuebao
1000-8683	Shijie Meishu
1000-8691	Yunnan Shehui Kexue
1000-8705	Guizhou Wenshi Congkan
1000-8713	Se Pu
1000-873X	Zhongguo Fanyi
1000-8756	Aeronautical Manufacturing Technology
1000-8780	Fujian Luntan (Jingji Ban)
1000-8799	Shuiyun Guanli
1000-8802	Zhongguo Wuli Wenzhai
1000-8829	Cekong Jishu
1000-8888	Shanghai Fushi
1000-8896	Zhongguo Xibu Wenxue
1000-890X	Xiangjiao Gongye
1000-8918	Wutan yu Huatan
1000-8993	Gongye Jianzhu
1000-9000	Chinese Journal of Computer Science and Technology
1000-9027	Journal of Chemical Industry and Engineering
1000-9094	Zhongguo Jingji Xinwen
1000-9116	Acta Seismologica Sinica
1000-9132	Litterature Chinoise

1000-9140 Beijing Review
1000-9213 Chemical Journal of Chinese Universities
1000-9221 Approximation Theory and its Applications
1000-9264 China im Bild
1000-9272 La Chine
1000-9280 China Revista Ilustrada
1000-9299 China
1000-9302 China Gazeta la Picha
1000-9310 La Cina
1000-9329 Kina
1000-9337 Chugoku Gaho
1000-9345 Chinese Journal of Mechanical Engineering
1000-9361 Chinese Journal of Aeronautics
1000-9396 People's Republic of China Year Book
1000-940X Journal of Partial Differential Equations
1000-9426 Chinese Journal of Geochemistry
1000-9442 Acta Metallurgica Sinica. Series A: Physical Metallurgy & Materials Science
1000-9450 Acta Metallurgica Sinica. Series B: Process Metallurgy & Miscellaneous
1000-9515 Acta Geologica Sinica
1000-9574 Acta Mathematica Sinica, New Series
1000-9590 Systems Science and Mathematical Sciences
1000-9604 Chinese Journal of Cancer Research
1000-9639 Zhongshan Daxue Xuebao (Zhexue Shehui Kexue Ban)
1000-9647 Zhongguo Nianjian
1000-9663 Hebei Wenxue
1000-968X Qiye Jishu Jinbu
1000-971X Shandong Jingji
1000-9892 Taoci Yanjiu
1000-9906 Heilongjiang Zhongyiyao
1000-9930 Xiangtan Kuangye Xueyuan Xuebao
1000-9957 Dalian Shuichan Xueyuan Xuebao
1000-9973 Zhongguo Tiaoweipin
1000-999X Zhongguo Zixingche
1001-0009 Beifang Yuanyi
1001-0025 Zhongri Youhao Yiyuan Xuebao
1001-005X Senlin Caiyun Kexue
1001-0084 Siliao Bolan
1001-0092 Malingshu Zazhi
1001-0114 Guoji Rencai Jiaoliu
1001-0157 Haiyang Wenzhai
1001-0165 Sihai
1001-0181 Jinshu Kexue yu Gongyi
1001-019X Jianzhu Guanli Xiandaihua
1001-0203 Jiating Yixue
1001-0211 Youse Jinshu
1001-0238 Yindu Xuekan
1001-0270 Yingxiang Jishu
1001-0297 Xinxi Shijie
1001-0327 Jianghan Kaogu
1001-0408 Zhongguo Yaofang
1001-0432 Heilongjiang Jingrong
1001-0440 Shaanxi Huabao
1001-0459 Jingtan Fengyun
1001-0483 Beifang Wenwu
1001-0505 Dongnan Daxue Xuebao
1001-0513 Jixie Kexue yu Jishu
1001-0521 Rare Metals
1001-0572 Zhongguo Gonggong Weisheng Xuebao
1001-0580 Zhongguo Gonggong Weisheng
1001-0602 Cell Research†
1001-0610 Xiandai Wuli Zhishi
1001-0637 Zhongguo Haiguan
1001-0645 Beijing Ligong Daxue Xuebao
1001-0661 Hanzi Wenhua
1001-0718 Chinese Journal of Botany
1001-0742 Journal of Environmental Sciences
1001-0831 Shiyong Waike Zazhi
1001-084X Shiyong Neike Zazhi
1001-0858 Shiyong Fuke yu Chanke Zazhi
1001-0866 Shiyong Erke Zazhi
1001-0882 Zhongguo Shaoshu Minzu
1001-0920 Kongzhi yu Juece
1001-1072 Guowai Yixue (Jishengbing Fence)
1001-1269 Yejin Shebei
1001-1285 Baiyi Keji
1001-1315 Zhongguo Yixue Wenzhai (Jihua Shengyu, Fuchan Kexue)
1001-1374 Shanghai Dianqi Jishu
1001-1382 Hanjie
1001-1390 Diance yu Yibiao
1001-1412 Dizhi Zhaokuang Luncong
1001-1528 Zhong Cheng Yao
1001-1587 Wujin Keji
1001-1617 Yejin Nengyuan
1001-1625 Guisuanyan Tongbao
1001-1633 Jiepouxue Zazhi
1001-1641 Qidong Shiyan yu Celiang Kongzhi
1001-1692 Shiyong Zhongliu Zazhi
1001-1714 Liaoning Linye Keji
1001-1730 Zhili
1001-1757 Dangdai Waiguo Wenxue
1001-1765 Hangkong Zhizao Gongcheng
1001-179X Dongnan Wenhua
1001-182X Gongye Kongzhi Jisuanji
1001-1862 Ocean University of Qingdao. Journal
1001-1889 Zhongguo Difangbing Fangzhi Zazhi
1001-1897 Yilin
1001-1900 Zhongguo Shengwuxue Wenzhai
1001-1919 Zhongguo Shuxue Wenzhai
1001-1935 Naihuo Cailiao
1001-1978 Zhongguo Yaolixue Tongbao
1001-1994 Shuichan Keji Qingbao
1001-201X Dang'anxue Tongxun
1001-2044 Shanghai Fangzhi Keji
1001-2060 Reneng Dongli Gongcheng
1001-2079 Zhongguo Minhang Bao
1001-2095 Dianqi Chuandong
1001-2125 Shanghai Jinshu (Youse Fence)
1001-2141 Chongqing Huanjing Kexue
1001-2206 Shiyou Gongcheng Jianshe
1001-2230 Zhongguo Rupin Gongye
1001-2281 Chilun
1001-2346 Zhonghua Shenjing Waike Zazhi
1001-2362 Xinxi Xitong Gongcheng
1001-2370 Zouxiang Shijie
1001-2397 Xiandai Faxue
1001-2435 Anhui Shida Xuebao (Shehui Kexue Ban)
1001-2443 Anhui Shida Xuebao
1001-2451 Yuye Jixie Yiqi
1001-2672 Zhongguo Xiandai Shi
1001-2680 Chuban Gongzuo
1001-2710 Zhexue Yuanli
1001-277X "Hongloumeng" Yanjiu
1001-280X Zhongxue Yuwen Jiaoxue
1001-2885 Waiguo Wenxue Yanjiu
1001-2907 Zhongguo Xiandai, Dangdai Wenxue Yanjiu
1001-3210 Kexue Shehui Zhuyi
1001-3237 Gongren Zuzhi yu Huodong
1001-3261 Yuyan Wenzi Xue
1001-3377 Shijie Jingji
1001-3490 Guowai Yixue (Jihua Shengyu Fence)
1001-3571 Xuanmei Jishu
1001-358X Kuangshan Celiang
1001-3644 Sichuan Huanjing
1001-3709 Ranliao yu Huagong
1001-3768 Juzuojia
1001-3776 Zhejiang Linye Keji
1001-3822 Ziyuan yu Kaifa
1001-3849 Diandu yu Jingshi
1001-3865 Huanjing Wuran yu Fangzhi
1001-389X Fujian Linxueyuan Xuebao
1001-3911 Guowai Zaozhi
1001-3946 Kancha Kexue Jishu
1001-3962 Shuili Shuiyun Kexue Yanjiu
1001-3970 Fujian Dizhi
1001-4039 Baijia Zuowen Zhidao
1001-4047 Qingdao Yixueyuan Xuebao
1001-4055 Tuijin Jishu
1001-4071 Yandi Bing
1001-4136 Zhongguo Yixue Wenzhai (Neike Xue)
1001-4144 Shijie Daodan yu Hangtian *see* 1002-7742
1001-4160 Jisuanji yu Yingyong Huaxue
1001-4179 Renmin Chang Jiang
1001-4187 Zhongguo Tiancai
1001-4284 Kexue Zhifu Yu Shenghuo
1001-4306 Gushengwu Xue Wenzhai
1001-4357 Chaiyou Ji
1001-4381 Cailiao Gongcheng
1001-4446 Jinshu Zaisheng
1001-4462 Linye Jixie
1001-4489 Zhongguo Baoxian
1001-4500 Zhongguo Haiyang Pingtai
1001-456X Tianjin Qing Gongye Xueyuan Xuebao
1001-4586 Jilin Caimao Xueyuan Xuebao
1001-4608 Nanjing Shifan Daxue Xuebao (Shehui Kexue Ban)
1001-4624 Chuanbo Sheji Tongxun
1001-4632 Zhongguo Tiedao Kexue
1001-4667 Nankai Xuebao. Zhexue Shehui Kexue Ban
1001-4683 Zhongguo Dizhen
1001-4691 Nankai Jingji Yanjiu
1001-4802 Shijie Dianxin
1001-4810 Zhongguo Yanrong
1001-487X Bao Po
1001-4888 Shiyan Lixue
1001-4934 Mo Ju
1001-5000 Zhongguo Minhang Xueyuan Xuebao
1001-5019 Anhui Daxue Xuebao (Shehui Kexue Ban)
1001-5035 Zhejiang Shifan Daxue Xuebao (Shehui Kexue Ban)
1001-5043 Haiyang Shijie
1001-506X Journal of Systems Engineering and Electronics
1001-5116 Anhui Jiaoyu Xueyuan Xuebao (Shehui Kexue Ban)
1001-5124 Ningbo Daxue Xuebao (Shehui Kexue Ban)
1001-5132 Ningbo Daxue Xuebao (Ziran Kexue Ban)
1001-5159 Huadong Gongxueyuan Xuebao
1001-5221 Redai Dili
1001-5264 Sichuan Dang'an
1001-5272 Keji Chuban
1001-5329 Zhongguo Yiyuan Guanli
1001-5388 Jiangsu Chuanbo
1001-5396 Xiandaihua
1001-540X Tongxin Jishu yu Fazhan
1001-5450 Guoji Shichang
1001-5469 Jiaocai Tongxun
1001-5485 Changjiang Kexueyuan Yuanbao
1001-5493 Lizi Jiaohuan yu Xifu
1001-5515 Shengwu Yixue Gongchengxue Zazhi
1001-5523 Nengyuan Yanjiu yu Liyong
1001-5531 Diya Dianqi
1001-554X Jianzhu Jixie
1001-5558 Xibei Minzu Yanjiu
1001-5582 Dianying Zuopin
1001-5590 Shao Nu
1001-5604 Heilongjiang Tushuguan
1001-5620 Zuanjing Ye yu Wanjing Ye
1001-5663 Kuangchan yu Dizhi
1001-568X Zhongguo Chuji Weisheng Baojian
1001-5698 Beifang Guoshu
1001-571X Zuowen Chenggong zhi Lu
1001-5728 Zhongguo Fayixue Zazhi
1001-5736 Yuefu Xin Sheng
1001-5795 Waiyu Dianhua Jiaoxue
1001-5809 Kuangshan Jishu
1001-5825 Guowai Youqi Kantan
1001-5841 Zhongguo Jinrong Nianjian
1001-5876 Zhongguo Shebei Guanli
1001-5884 Qilunji Jishu
1001-5892 Kuangshan Dizhi
1001-5914 Huanjing yu Jiankang Zazhi
1001-5965 Beijing Hangkong Hangtian Daxue Xuebao
1001-599X Chengshi Gongyong Shiye
1001-6031 Chinese Journal of Nuclear Physics
1001-604X Chinese Journal of Chemistry
1001-6066 Heilongjiang Shangxueyuan Xuebao
1001-6104 Yan He
1001-6112 Shiyou Shiyan Dizhi
1001-6171 Shuini Jishu
1001-618X Faxue Zazhi
1001-6198 Shehui Kexue Jikan
1001-621X Chun Feng
1001-6279 International Silt Research
1001-6309 Zhi he Zaozhi
1001-6341 Ming Ri
1001-6376 Lushi yu Fazhi
1001-6384 Yingxiang Yixue
1001-6392 Haiyang Tongbao
1001-6511 Science in China. Series A: Mathematics, Physics, Astronomy & Technological Sciences
1001-652X Science in China. Series B: Chemistry, Life Sciences & Earth Sciences
1001-6538 Chinese Science Bulletin
1001-6546 Xiandai Qiyejia
1001-6635 Renwu
1001-6651 Xinhua Wenzhai
1001-666X Xinhua Yuebao
1001-6678 Gongye Weishengwu
1001-6694 Jiangnan
1001-683X Zhongguo Tielu
1001-6856 Guowai Yiyao - Zhiwuyao Fence
1001-6880 Tianran Chanwu Yanjiu yu Kaifa
1001-6910 Zhongyi Yanjiu
1001-6937 Dongli Jixue Wenzhai
1001-6953 Zhongxuesheng Shu-Li-Hua (Gaozhong Ban)
1001-697X Youtian Dimian Gongcheng
1001-6988 Gongye Lu
1001-7003 Sichou
1001-7011 Heilongjiang Daxue Ziran Kexue Xuebao
1001-7151 Zhongguo Dianti
1001-7178 Minzu Jiaoyu Yanjiu
1001-7216 Zhongguo Shuidao Kexue
1001-7224 Shuidao Wenzhai
1001-7275 Nanjing Tiedao Yixueyuan Xuebao
1001-7283 Zuowu Zazhi
1001-7313 Yingyong Qixiang Xueta
1001-7321 Jiamusi Yixueyuan Xuebao
1001-7348 Keji Jinbu yu Duice
1001-7372 Zhongguo Gonglu Xuebao
1001-7380 Jiangsu Linye Keji
1001-7399 Linchuang yu Shiyan Binglixue Zazhi
1001-7410 Disiji Yanjiu
1001-7437 Guilin Dianzi Gongye Xueyuan Xuebao
1001-747X Xi'an Tiyu Xueyuan Xuebao
1001-7550 Mudanjiang Yixueyuan Xuebao
1001-7585 Yixue Lilun yu Shijian
1001-7623 Nei Menggu Shifan Daxue Xuebao (Ziran Kexue Ban)
1001-7631 Huaxue Fanying Gongcheng yu Gongyi
1001-7658 Zhongguo Xiaoduxue Zazhi
1001-7666 Motuoche Jishu
1001-7682 Zhongguo Haishang Youqi (Gongcheng)
1001-8107 Dilixue yu Guotu Yanjiu
1001-8131 Harbin Yiyao
1001-814X Gongqi Yikan
1001-8212 Zhengzhou Daxue Xuebao (Ziran Kexue Ban)
1001-8220 Sichuan Shifan Xueyuan Xuebao (Ziran Kexue Ban)
1001-8255 Zhongguo Yiyao Gongye Zazhi
1001-8263 Nanjing Shehui Kexue
1001-8328 Zhongguo Xiuchuan
1001-8409 Ruan Kexue
1001-8417 Chinese Chemical Letters
1001-859X Zhongyao Yaoli yu Linchuang
1001-8689 Zhongguo Kangshengsu Zazhi
1001-8751 Guowai Yiyao (Kangshengsu Fence)
1001-8859 Zhongguo Chuban Nianjian
1001-8913 Yunnan Minzu Xueyuan Xuebao
1001-9294 Chinese Medical Sciences Journal
1001-960X Xuewei yu Yanjiusheng Jiaoyu
1001-9871 Zhongyang Yinyue Xueyuan Xuebao
1002-0063 Chinese Geographical Science
1002-0071 Progress in Natural Science
1002-0160 Pedosphere
1002-0179 Huaxi Yixue
1002-0721 Journal of Rare Earths
1002-087X Dianyuan Jishu
1002-1221 Jinzhan: Guoji Maoyi yu Keji Jiaoliu
1002-1299 Ke Xue
1002-1329 Chengshi Guihua
1002-1906 Xiangqi Yanjiu
1002-2554 Gushi Lin
1002-283X Jishu Kaifa yu Yinjin
1002-297X Jiankang
1002-3348 Beijing Fangzhi
1002-4417 Zhongguo Gaodeng Jiaoyu
1002-4557 Zhongguo Tongji
1002-4646 Dangdai Dianying
1002-4670 Guoji Maoyi Wenti
1002-5049 Zhongguo Shenji

ISSN INDEX 5835

1002-5626 Jiayong Dianqi
1002-5766 Zhongguo Jingji Nianjian
1002-5766 Jingji Guanli
1002-591X Zhongguo Shangye Nianjian
1002-5928 Zhongguo Gongye Jingji Yanjiu
1002-5952 Zhongguo Minzu Jiaoyu
1002-6592 China Aerospace Abstracts
1002-6614 Guowai Hangkong Wenzhai
1002-686X Huaxi
1002-7564 Zhongguo Gushi
1002-7742 Zhongguo Hangtian
1002-803X Fei Tian
1002-8447 China City Planning Review
1002-8528 Jianzhu Kexue
1002-865X Zhongguo Jingji Tizhi Gaige
1002-9591 Zhongguo Xizang
1003-0271 Shijie Bolan
1003-028X Shijie Zhishi Huabao
1003-0905 China Today
1003-1669 Qingnian Zuojia
1003-2029 Haiyang Jishu
1003-2452 Sichuan Kuaiji
1003-2681 Xiju yu Dianying
1003-2738 Chuanqi Wenxue Xuankan
1003-3521 Zhongguo Yaoxue Wenzhai
1003-4013 Wanpi Wawa
1003-4099 Yalujiang
1003-4331 Fujian Xumu Shouyi
1003-5230 Zhongnan Caijing Daxue Xuebao
1003-5605 Meiyuan
1003-5680 Kexue Jishu yu Bianzhengfa
1003-5702 Dufu Yanjiu Xuekan
1003-6008 China Aero Information
1003-7071 Hebei Xuekan
1003-7225 Guo Moruo Xuekan
1003-7527 Yang Guan
1003-7942 Xueyu Wenhua
1003-9082 Zhongwen Xinxi
1003-9384 Jingxi Shiyou Huagong
1004-1257 Zhiye yu Jiankang
1004-1265 Sichuan Sichou
1004-1508 Nanya Yanjiu Jikan
1004-2083 Sichuan Pengren
1004-2164 Xiaoshuo Pinglun
1004-2490 Haiyang Yuye
1004-5414 Guanli yu Xiaoyi
1010-0423 International Pharmacy Journal
1010-061X Journal of Evolutionary Biology
1010-0652 Zeitschrift fuer Paedagogische Psychologie
1010-0709 Al-Majallah al-Arabiyyah lil-Idarah
1010-0725 Chuanxi Lu *changed to* Philosophical Research.
1010-0733 Soochow Journal of Humanities
1010-1039 World Food Report *changed to* World Food Programme Report.
1010-1160 Cyprus. Department of Statistics and Research. Industrial Statistics
1010-1179 International Crude Oil and Product Prices
1010-1365 F A O Agricultural Services Bulletin
1010-1764 Statistical Office of the European Communities. Quarterly National Accounts
1010-2302 Madoqua. Series 2 *see* 1011-5498
1010-2582 Mintek Research Digest
1010-2760 Revista Ciencias Tecnicas Agropecuarias
1010-2973 Repertorio de Servicios IberoAmericanos de Documentacion e Informacion Educativa
1010-3023 World Bank Research Program *see* 0253-9535
1010-3538 Veterinary Drug Registration Newsletter
1010-3562 Pakistan Seafood Digest
1010-3597 Blaetter der Rilke-Gesellschaft
1010-3686 Magazin Sammeln *changed to* Troedler- und Magazin Sammeln.
1010-3724 Archeion Euvoikon Meleton
1010-3740 Libyan Journal of Agriculture
1010-3783 Rural Demography
1010-3848 A R N A H I S
1010-4208 Sri Lanka Journal of Tea Science
1010-4283 Tumor Biology
1010-447X International Trade Statistics Yearbook
1010-5182 Journal of Cranio-Maxillo-Facial Surgery
1010-5220 Opuscula Zoologica Fluminensia
1010-5247 S T I Review
1010-528X Cuadernos de Sociologia
1010-531X Flood Control Journal *see* 0377-8053
1010-5700 B T - L M & S
1010-5719 Business
1010-5735 News Advertiser
1010-5743 Sportswatch
1010-576X Kenya Medical Research Institute. Proceedings of the Annual Medical Scientific Conference
1010-5786 Casa†
1010-5808 Schweizer Bank
1010-5832 Ethnic Studies Report
1010-6030 Journal of Photochemistry and Photobiology, A: Chemistry
1010-6049 Geocarto International
1010-609X Tinplate World
1010-6146 Bundesanstalt fuer Alpenlaendische Landwirtschaft. Veroeffentlichungen
1010-6324 Alexandria Faculty of Medicine Bulletin
1010-7053 Safety and Health at Work
1010-7061 Securite et Sante au Travail
1010-7304 Journal of Ethical Studies
1010-7347 Journal of International Marketing & Marketing Research
1010-7576 Doga Turkish Journal of Biology
1010-7584 Doga Turkish Journal of Medical Sciences
1010-7592 Doga Turkish Journal of Veterinary and Animal Sciences
1010-7606 Doga Turkish Journal of Engineering and Environmental Science
1010-7614 Doga Turkish Journal of Chemistry
1010-7622 Doga Turkish Journal of Mathematics
1010-7630 Doga Turkish Journal of Physics
1010-7649 Doga Turkish Journal of Agriculture and Forestry
1010-7940 European Journal of Cardio-Thoracic Surgery
1010-8149 European Safety and Reliability Association. Bulletin
1010-8238 Revue Juridique du Rwanda
1010-8262 Journal of Comparative Physical and Education Sport
1010-8289 Seoul National University Forests. Research Bulletin
1010-8378 Durch
1010-8386 Imagination
1010-8408 Issues in Biomedicine
1010-8424 Hong Kong Medical Association. Journal
1010-8947 Cooperation Technique. Bulletin
1010-9021 F A O Animal Production and Health Series
1010-9099 World Food Programme Journal
1010-9501 U D T Newsletter
1010-9609 W H O Drug Information
1010-9617 Statistical Reflection of the Islamic Republic of Iran
1011-0135 Aurum
1011-0240 Rights
1011-0267 Progress in Basic and Clinical Pharmacology
1011-0275 Uniciencia
1011-0283 Skin Pharmacology
1011-0410 Revista Peruana de Ciencias Sociales
1011-0488 Farmer
1011-0887 Doga Turkish Journal of Botany
1011-0895 Doga Turkish Journal of Zoology
1011-1344 Journal of Photochemistry and Photobiology, B: Biology
1011-1638 Hellenic Photography Selections
1011-1727 Sunjet
1011-1816 Research Bulletin: Journal for the S A P R H S *see* 1017-6136
1011-1913 R S A: Dialogue with the Future *changed to* R S A 2000: Dialogue with the Future.
1011-1980 Southern Africa Freedom Bulletin
1011-226X Quest
1011-2359 China Current Laws
1011-2855 Institutului Politehnic Din Iasi. Buletinul. Sectia IV: Constructii de Masini
1011-288X Douleur et Analgesie
1011-2898 China Economic Express (Japanese Edition)
1011-2901 Geriatrie fuer die Taegliche Praxis
1011-291X Pharmacology and the Skin
1011-2928 Lithium Therapy Monographs†
1011-3010 Gregorios o Palamas
1011-3029 Journal of Pacific Studies
1011-3053 South African Journal of Cultural and Art History *changed to* South African Journal of Cultural History.
1011-3207 World Meteorological Organization. Commission for Marine Meteorology. Abridged Final Report of the (No.) Session
1011-3223 World Meteorological Organization. Commission of Aerology. Abridged Final Report of the (No.) Session *see* 0250-9172
1011-3231 World Meteorological Organization. Executive Council Session. Abridged Final Reports with Resolutions
1011-3495 Daneshmand
1011-3649 I P Asia
1011-372X Catalysis Letters
1011-3738 Teaching and Training in Geriatric Medicine
1011-3835 Egyptian Journal of Botany
1011-3878 Ethics & Perspectives!†
1011-3924 Chemical Society of Ethiopia. Bulletin
1011-4009 Maajan - Die Quelle
1011-4203 Schweizer Monatsschrift fuer Zahnmedizin
1011-4246 E P A Newsletter
1011-4386 Pharmaklinik *see* 1131-5253
1011-4548 World Competition
1011-4858 Foreign Trade Statistics of Asia and the Pacific
1011-4866 Carindex: Science & Technology
1011-4874 Etudes Rwandaises. Sciences Naturelles et Appliquees
1011-4955 Plus
1011-5021 Psychology and Human Development *see* 0301-2212
1011-5080 P I C Newsletter
1011-5110 South Pacific Periodicals Index
1011-5129 University of the South Pacific. Publications
1011-5145 South Pacific Research Register
1011-5196 Terra Grischuna - Graubuenden
1011-5498 Madoqua
1011-5528 Medical Technology S A
1011-5536 Quarterly Countdown
1011-5544 South African Institute of Race Relations. Update
1011-5765 Caribbean Affairs
1011-5773 W H O AIDS Series
1011-596X Asian Hospital
1011-5978 Asian Water & Sewage
1011-5986 Dental Update
1011-601X Pakistan Journal of Pharmaceutical Sciences
1011-6060 Cracker *changed to* The Clipper.
1011-6125 Stereotactic and Functional Neurosurgery
1011-6273 Asociacion Venezolana de Psicologia Social. Boletin
1011-6311 Central Bank of Trinidad and Tobago. Annual Economic Survey
1011-6338 Central Bank of Trinidad and Tobago. Monthly Statistical Digest
1011-6346 Central Bank of Trinidad and Tobago. Quarterly Economic Bulletin
1011-6362 Central Bank of Trinidad and Tobago. Quarterly Statistical Digest
1011-6370 Development
1011-6524 Renal Physiology and Biochemistry
1011-6559 Optoelektronika i Poluprovodnikovaya Tekhnika
1011-6672 New Trends in Lipid Mediators Research
1011-6761 Chukung
1011-6877 Zeitschrift fuer Gerontopsychologie und Psychiatrie
1011-6966 Infusionstherapie
1011-6974 Beitraege zu Infusionstherapie
1011-6982 Animal Models of Psychiatric Disorders
1011-7512 Fiji. Mineral Resources Department. Hydrogeological Report
1011-7571 Medical Principles and Practice
1011-7601 Journal for the Study of Religion
1011-7768 Travel Business Analyst
1011-7881 Syntarsus
1011-792X O E C D. Main Science and Technology Indicators
1011-7989 Escritura: Teoria y Critica Literarias
1011-8012 Artes Natales
1011-8063 South African Journal of Linguistics
1011-8101 Areopagus
1011-8519 Packaging (Year)
1011-8594 Diarrhoeal Diseases
1011-8624 Immunizations
1011-8713 International Sharing
1011-8721 I I R R Report
1011-873X Rural Reconstruction Review
1011-8748 Vorarlberger Landesmuseumsverein. Jahrbuch
1011-8780 F A O Quarterly Bulletin of Statistics
1011-8829 International Cataloguing and Bibliographic Control
1011-8993 Athenian
1011-9019 C R E - Action
1011-9027 International Dairy Federation. Newsletter
1011-906X National Palace Museum Bulletin
1011-9078 National Palace Museum. Monthly of Chinese Art
1011-9086 National Palace Museum. Newsletter
1011-9094 National Palace Museum Research Quarterly
1011-9108 Economy and Law
1011-9124 Eidgenoessische Anstalt fuer das Forstliche Versuchswesen. Jahresbericht
1011-9477 Studii Istorice Sud-Est Europene†
1012-0254 Nomina Africana
1012-0793 U N C T A D Commodity Yearbook
1012-1080 Journal of Social Development in Africa
1012-1935 Supplements of Women of Europe
1012-2435 I M A C S Annals on Computing and Applied Mathematics
1012-2443 Annals of Mathematics and Artificial Intelligence
1012-2478 Estudios
1012-2508 Universidad Central de Venezuela. Centro de Estudios del Desarrollo. Cuadernos del C E N D E S
1012-2532 Biopolitics
1012-2710 Commercial Crime International
1012-2737 Cuadernos para la Historia de la Evangelizacion en America Latina
1012-2796 Suid-Afrikaanse Argiefblad
1012-2850 South African Journal of Music Therapy
1012-3253 Real Estate Times
1012-327X U B C I M Occasional Paper
1012-3288 Power and Ski *see* 1018-1385
1012-3369 Journal of Petroleum Research
1012-3377 Journal of Iraqi Dissertation Abstracts. Part A: Humanities and Social Sciences
1012-3385 Journal of Electronics and Computer Research
1012-3393 General Index to Iraqi Periodical Literature. Part A: Sciences and Engineering
1012-3415 General Index to Iraqi Periodical Literature. Part B: Humanities and Social Sciences
1012-3423 Journal of Building Research
1012-3431 Journal of Space Astronomy Research
1012-344X Journal of Biological Science Research
1012-3458 Research Abstracts in Scientific Research Council
1012-3466 Journal of Agriculture and Water Resources Research. Animal Production
1012-3474 Journal of Agriculture and Water Research. Plant Production
1012-3482 Journal of Agriculture and Water Resources Research. Soil and Water Resources

ISSN

1012-3490 Journal of Iraqi Dissertation Abstracts. Part B: Science and Engineering
1012-3547 Estadistica Panamena. Situacion Economica. Seccion 334. Comunicaciones
1012-3555 Estadistica Panamena. Situacion Economica. Seccion 333. Transporte
1012-4195 Academia Sinica. Institute of History and Philology. Bulletin
1012-4543 Pro Mundi Vita Studies†
1012-4926 Cimbebasia
1012-4934 U N I D I R Newsletter
1012-5329 Disease Information
1012-5507 Nande Reko
1012-5558 Egyptian Journal of Biomedical Engineering
1012-5655 Bildgebung
1012-5930 Grace and Truth
1012-5973 Assiut Veterinary Medical Journal
1012-6244 Asiaweek
1012-6694 Child Nephrology and Urology
1012-6821 China, Republic. Central Geological Survey. Bulletin
1012-7410 Pasturas Tropicales
1012-7577 Food and Beverages (Year)
1012-7666 Bahrain Medical Bulletin
1012-7720 I F P R A Bulletin
1012-7887 H K Staff
1012-8204 Complement and Inflammation†
1012-8263 Transition
1012-8336 P C Week Asia
1012-8662 Asian Printing
1012-9790 Revista de Historia
1012-9871 New Issues in Neurosciences
1013-0845 World Health Organization A I D S Technical Bulletin
1013-090X Journal of Educational Media and Library Sciences
1013-0942 Republic of China Yearbook (Year)
1013-0950 Agenda
1013-1108 Strategic Review for Southern Africa
1013-1191 Peake Studies
1013-1205 L M S - Laboratory Marketing Spectrum
1013-2511 Issues & Studies
1013-2716 Chung-Kuo Ta-Lu Yen-Chiu
1013-2791 Taniguchi Symposia on Brain Sciences
1013-3119 A B B Review
1013-3178 United Nations Childrens Fund. Programme Division. Staff Working Papers Series
1013-3186 United Nations Children's Fund. Programme Division. Conference Reports Series
1013-3194 U N I C E F Policy Review Series
1013-3356 S A Golf Journal
1013-3453 Narcotic Drugs: Estimated World Requirements for (Year)
1013-4069 Estudios del Desarrollo
1013-4468 International Council of Kinetography Laban. Proceedings†
1013-4514 World Trade Materials
1013-4549 Ministries and Communities†
1013-5278 Iasi Polytechnic Magazine
1013-5332 Banque de la Republique du Burundi. Bulletin Mensuel
1013-5340 Banque de la Republique du Burundi. Bulletin Trimestriel
1013-5359 Banque de la Republique du Burundi. Rapport Annuel
1013-5375 China Economic Express (Korean Edition)
1013-5545 Acta Cancerologica
1013-5987 Psychoscope
1013-7394 Our Planet
1013-7424 Dementia
1013-7432 Arbitration Materials
1013-7459 Baseler Beitraege zur Chirurgie
1013-7467 Recent Achievements in Restorative Neurology
1013-7521 Digging Stick
1013-7785 A I D S Health Promotion Exchange
1013-8056 Nutrition de Sante Publique
1013-8129 Diagnostic Oncology
1013-8285 Public Health Nutrition
1013-8293 Nutricion en Salud Publica
1013-8374 Industrial Property, Statistics B. Part 1 - Patents
1013-8382 Industrial Property, Statistics B. Part 2 - Trademarks and Service Marks, Utility Models, Industrial Designs, Varieties of Plants, Microorganisms
1013-851X Higher Education Management
1013-8919 Tiroler Heimat
1013-9087 Annals of Dermatology
1013-9095 Economy
1013-9214 Conmilit
1013-9222 International Symposia on the Pharmacology of Thermoregulation
1013-9362 O E C D. Quarterly Oil Statistics and Energy Balances
1013-9478 Gusto
1013-9486 Oesterreichisches Recht der Wirtschaft
1013-9591 Agroforestry Today
1013-9656 Chinese Journal of Psychology
1013-9915 South Pacific Commission. Information Circular
1013-9982 Cytokines
1014-0034 International Civil Aviation Organization. Air Navigation Plan. Middle East and Asia Regions
1014-0077 International Civil Aviation Organization. Digests of Statistics. Series T. Traffic, Commercial Air Traffic
1014-0085 International Civil Aviation Organization. Digests of Statistics. Series T. Airline Traffic *see* 1014-0077
1014-0093 International Civil Aviation Organization. Digests of Statistics. Series TF. Traffic by Flight Stage
1014-0697 Anuario Estadistico de America Latina y el Caribe
1014-1235 Refugees Magazine
1014-1472 Studies in the Processing, Marketing and Distribution of Commodities
1014-2193 Migrant Pest Newsletter
1014-2207 Locust Newsletter *see* 1014-2193
1014-3181 F A O Food and Nutrition Series
1014-4986 Human Rights Newsletter
1014-7071 International Labour Office. Labour Law Documents
1014-7411 Trade Policy Review
1014-8132 The World Bank and the Environment
1014-8329 Construction Alert
1014-8361 U N R I S D News
1014-8507 Directory of the World's Largest Service Companies
1014-8906 Global Economics Prospects and the Developing Countries
1014-9635 Development Hotline
1014-9643 Meridian
1015-0021 Fu Jen Studies
1015-0099 South African Mercantile Law Journal
1015-0145 Chemical Immunology
1015-0676 East African Development Bank. Annual Report
1015-0730 China, Republic. Telecommunication Laboratories. T L Technical Journal
1015-0803 Soil Science Society of Sri Lanka. Journal
1015-0935 Natal Museum Journal of Humanities
1015-1184 Sigmund Freud House Bulletin
1015-1370 South African Sociological Review
1015-1451 Outdoor Living and Sports Goods (Year)
1015-1516 Bank Archiv
1015-1621 Aquatic Sciences
1015-1702 Comparative Physiology
1015-2008 Pathobiology
1015-2253 Intermodal Asia
1015-227X Lloyd's Maritime Asia
1015-230X Chemicals, Adhesives and Pharmaceuticals (Year)
1015-2369 National Ceramics Quarterly
1015-2377 South African Medical Research Council. Biennial Research Report†
1015-2431 Frauezitig
1015-2881 The Cyprus Review
1015-3055 Pakistan Journal of Agriculture, Agricultural Engineering and Veterinary Sciences
1015-3128 Asian Meetings and Incentives
1015-3276 Transfusion Today
1015-3802 Urban Forum
1015-3837 Fetal Diagnosis and Therapy
1015-3845 Magnesium and Trace Elements
1015-4248 Balance Financiero
1015-4442 Arab Gulf Journal of Scientific Research
1015-4523 Raydan
1015-4817 Korean Neuropsychiatric Association. Journal
1015-5007 Cardioscience
1015-5015 Yazhou Zhoukan
1015-5023 Asiamac Journal
1015-5090 Mediterranean Social Sciences Network Newsletter *changed to* Mediterranean Social Sciences Network Journal.
1015-5104 Aegypten und Levante
1015-5376 Fichier Afrique
1015-5546 Kobus
1015-5562 Asia Law & Practice
1015-5945 Human Rights Worldwide
1015-6070 China Steel Technical Report
1015-6488 Sea Rescue
1015-7891 Journal of Parametrics
1015-7999 South African Computer Journal
1015-8138 A T A Journal
1015-8154 Devenir
1015-8367 Xiangjian Xiaolu
1015-8383 Universitas
1015-8529 Umfeld
1015-8987 Cellular Physiology and Biochemistry
1015-9355 Chung Kung Yen Chiu
1015-9770 Cerebrovascular Diseases
1016-0922 Biological Signals
1016-1384 South African Panorama (Chinese Edition)†
1016-1902 Endangered Wildlife
1016-2054 Jamaican Journal of Science and Technology
1016-2135 Fiji. Mineral Resources Department. Information Notes
1016-2291 Pediatric Neurosurgery
1016-2399 Zack
1016-2550 South African National Museum of Military History. Review *see* 0026-4016
1016-2658 The Korea Letter
1016-3158 Eidgenoessenschaft Forschungsanstalt fuer Wald, Schnee und Landschaft. Mitteilungen
1016-3263 I U F R O World Series
1016-3328 Computational Complexity
1016-3360 Islamic Academy of Sciences. Journal
1016-359X World Link
1016-3778 Comite Consultatif pour la Masse et les Grandeurs Apparentees
1016-4162 Kaleidoscope
1016-4170 Artist
1016-4367 Deutschunterricht im Suedlichen Afrika
1016-443X Geometric and Functional Analysis
1016-4723 International Society for Applied Cardiovascular Biology
1016-4901 Indoor Environment
1016-4995 Droit Nucleaire
1016-524X Aloe, Cactus & Succulent Society of Zimbabwe. Ingens Bulletin
1016-5584 Journal of Coptic Studies
1016-5983 Conference Generale des Poids et Mesures. Comptes Rendus des Seances
1016-6262 Verhaltenstherapie
1016-6734 O F S Philatelic Magazine
1016-7250 Forum
1016-8206 Media Focus
1016-8397 S E B E S
1016-8699 International Child Health: A Digest of Current Information
1016-8834 B I R D
1016-9229 Cahiers Psychiatriques Genevois
1016-927X Species
1016-9717 Wajibu
1016-9970 Pacific Impact
1017-0448 Routes du Monde†
1017-1398 Numerical Algorithms
1017-141X Perspectives
1017-1711 South African Paediatrics Magazine
1017-1819 International Journal of Information and Management Sciences
1017-2777 Buhardilla
1017-2785 C E D H U
1017-2793 Mbya Guarani
1017-2807 Menores
1017-2815 La Puerta
1017-2823 Galeria Michele Malingue. Catalogo
1017-2874 Changer
1017-3102 World Animal Health
1017-3498 A B C
1017-3501 Afangar
1017-3528 Bondinn†
1017-3536 Fiskifrettir
1017-3544 Frjals Verzlun
1017-3552 Gestgjafinn
1017-3560 Grodur og Gardar
1017-3579 Ithrottabladid
1017-3587 Mannlif
1017-3595 Nytt Lif
1017-3609 Sjavarfrettir
1017-3625 A Veidum
1017-3803 Computer Spectrum
1017-3900 Women's News
1017-415X Kilk - Mahnamah-i Adabi va Hunari
1017-4214 Plant Protection News
1017-4249 Mining and Engineering & Electronics Industries (Year)
1017-4613 E A R S L Advances in Remote Sensing
1017-4753 Jamaican Geographer
1017-4966 Technobrief
1017-5199 China Telecommunication Construction
1017-5989 Pediatric and Adolescent Medicine
1017-6047 Centro de Documentacion y Estudios. Informativo Campesino
1017-6055 Centro de Documentacion y Estudios. Informativo Laboral
1017-6063 Centro de Documentacion y Estudios. Informativo Mujer
1017-6071 Cuaderno de Historia Obrera
1017-6136 Human Sciences Research Council. Bulletin. News for the Human Sciences
1017-6136 Bulletin - News for the Human Science Researcher
1017-6195 I C E S Cooperative Research Report
1017-6268 Quarantine Advisory Leaflet
1017-6276 Pest Advisory Leaflet
1017-639X Papua New Guinea. National Statistical Office. Gross Domestic Product and Expenditure
1017-6403 Papua New Guinea. National Statistical Office. Domestic Factor Incomes, by Region and Province
1017-6411 Papua New Guinea. National Statistical Office. Government Finance Statistics
1017-6470 Papua New Guinea. National Statistical Office. Statistical Bulletin: Census of Retail Sales and Selected Services
1017-6497 Papua New Guinea. National Statistical Office. Production Statistics
1017-6500 Papua New Guinea. National Statistical Office. Consumer Price Index
1017-6519 Papua New Guinea. National Statistical Office. International Trade - Exports
1017-6527 Papua New Guinea. National Statistical Office. Export Price Indexes
1017-6535 Papua New Guinea. National Statistical Office. International Trade - Imports
1017-6543 Papua New Guinea. National Statistical Office. Import Price Indexes
1017-6551 Papua New Guinea International Arrivals and Departures
1017-6683 Statistical Abstract of Iceland
1017-6721 European Journal of Physical Medicine and Rehabilitation
1017-6748 Asian Libraries
1017-6861 I I P Monitor
1017-6950 X I I I Magazine
1017-7124 Republic of China. National Science Council. Proceedings. Part D: Mathematics, Science, and Technology Education

ISSN INDEX 5837

1017-9259 Deep Sea Fisheries Development Project Reports
1017-9267 South Pacific Conference. Report
1017-9402 O E C D. Nuclear Energy Agency. Nuclear Energy Data
1018-0400 Viata Armatei
1018-0893 South Pacific Epidemiological and Health Information Service Annual Report
1018-094X Regional Tuna Bulletin
1018-0958 South Pacific Economies: Statistical Summary
1018-0966 South Pacific Foods Leaflet
1018-0974 Tuna and Billfish Assessment Programme Technical Report
1018-1172 Journal of Vascular Research
1018-1253 Join Us...Costa Rica Awaits You
1018-1261 Jamaica Naturalist
1018-1385 Power Boat and Ski
1018-1520 Sub-Saharan Monitor
1018-1571 I C E S Fisheries Statistics
1018-161X Academia Economic Papers
1018-2098 Cinebulletin
1018-2179 TransPort
1018-2438 International Archives of Allergy and Immunology
1018-2926 Caribbean Review of Books
1018-3310 Informat (International Edition)
1018-3337 Marine Ornithology
1018-3493 S A Barometer
1018-3582 King Saud University. Journal. Administrative Sciences
1018-3590 King Saud University. Journal. Agricultural Sciences
1018-3604 King Saud University. Journal. Architecture and Planning
1018-3612 King Saud University. Journal. Arts
1018-3620 King Saud University. Journal. Educational Sciences
1018-3639 King Saud University. Journal. Engineering Sciences
1018-3647 King Saud University. Journal. Sciences
1018-3779 Oesterreichische Zeitschrift fuer Rechnungswesen
1018-4252 Pacific Arts
1018-4295 S A B S Catalogue
1018-4430 Salud y Familia
1018-4473 Republic of China. National Science Council. Proceedings. Part C: Humanities and Social Sciences
1018-4619 Fresenius Environmental Bulletin
1018-4627 Medical Microbiology Letters
1018-4783 I S S N Compact
1018-4864 Telecommunication Systems
1018-5321 Revista Boliviana de Nefrologia
1018-533X Veterinary Biotechnology Newsletter
1018-7286 The Baltic Independent
1018-7324 Journal of Taiwan Fisheries Research
1018-7626 Directory of South African Publishers
1018-8371 Automotive Industries (Year)
1018-838X Building, Hardware and Housewares (Year)
1018-9599 Second Supplement to the S A Joint Catalogue of Monographs on Microfiche. Author Index
1018-9602 Second Supplement to the S A Joint Catalogue of Monographs on Microfiche. Title Index
1030-0155 Access (Elizabeth)
1030-0236 Australian Early Childhood Newsletter
1030-0287 Junior Clubhouse
1030-0295 Today (Lawson)
1030-0309 Today's Young Life
1030-0392 Garden Peskem
1030-0481 South Australian Geographical Journal
1030-0562 A C C Touche Ross Tax Legislation Fact Papers
1030-0724 Australia. Bureau of Statistics. Victorian Office. Local Government Finance, Victoria
1030-0740 Red Tape
1030-0759 Commercial Vessel Yearbook
1030-0775 A C C Submission Papers
1030-0856 Hunter Region Economic Indicators
1030-0988 Australia. Bureau of Statistics. Quarterly Estimates of National Income and Expenditure, Australia *see* 1031-5128
1030-147X A C C Research Papers
1030-178X A.D. Magazine†
1030-1798 A.D. Youthleader†
1030-1887 Australian Systematic Botany
1030-1917 Australian Home Builder and Improver†
1030-1925 Australian Building News
1030-1968 Parents Shopping Guide
1030-1976 Australian National University. National Centre for Development Studies. Indian Ocean Policy Papers
1030-1992 Prime Beef
1030-2166 Space Association News
1030-2379 Insurance Law Journal
1030-2425 National Marina Survey
1030-2433 Museum of Fine Arts, Boston. Journal
1030-2476 Australian Periodicals in Print
1030-2581 Construct in Steel
1030-2638 Australia. Bureau of Statistics. Queensland Office. Marriages, Queensland *see* 1036-2649
1030-2646 Family Matters
1030-360X Australian National University. National Centre for Development Studies. Working Papers. Series: China Working Papers
1030-3782 Modern Medicine of Australia
1030-3928 Successful Selling
1030-3987 New Parent
1030-407X Journal of Teaching Practice
1030-4134 University of New England. Centre for Water Policy Research. Occasional Papers (No.)
1030-4169 Institute of Public Affairs. Review *see* 1030-4177
1030-4177 I P A Review
1030-4320 South Australia. Department of Environment and Planning. Forecast Production and Usage of Residential Allotments for Private Purposes
1030-4479 Guide to Craft Supplies in New South Wales and the Australian Capital Territory
1030-4703 A S A Accounting and Business Index *see* 1036-689X
1030-4789 Australia. Bureau of Statistics. Queensland Office. Local Government Areas Statistical Summary, Queensland
1030-4916 Sounds Australian Update
1030-4924 Health and Safety Concepts *changed to* Health and Safety at Work.
1030-5025 Darwin Gay Informer *changed to* Darwin Gay and Lesbian Newsletter.
1030-5033 Australasian Public Libraries and Information Services
1030-5289 National A I D S Bulletin
1030-536X The Labour Force, Victoria
1030-5459 Lonely Planet Update†
1030-5467 Third Opinion
1030-570X Pacifica
1030-5882 Exposure Draft (Accounting Standards)
1030-5890 Proposed Statement of Accounting Concepts
1030-5920 Australian Regional Impact Analysis Series (No.)†
1030-5947 University of Technology. Sydney Calendar
1030-603X Proposed Statement of Auditing Practice *changed to* Exposure Draft (Auditing Practice).
1030-617X Australian Journal of Liturgy
1030-6196 W.H.A.T.†
1030-6560 Australian Economic Brief†
1030-6641 National Guide to Government
1030-7052 Contact (Blackburn South)
1030-7222 Australian Journal of Labour Law
1030-7230 Journal of Contract Law
1030-7257 Skin and Psoriasis Newsletter
1030-7370 Queensland Government Statistician. Official Year Book of Queensland *see* 1030-7389
1030-7389 Australia. Bureau of Statistics. Queensland Office. Queensland Year Book
1030-7451 Activnews
1030-763X Recreation and Sport in the Holidays†
1030-7699 Virgats
1030-7710 Victorian Historical Journal
1030-7745 Australia. Nuclear Science and Technology Organisation. A N S T O
1030-7915 Australian Nugget Journal
1030-8474 A U S - Meat Feedback
1030-8768 Tell
1030-8873 Victoria. Health Department. Annual Report
1030-911X Australia. Bureau of Statistics. Queensland Office. Estimated Resident Population and Area, Queensland, Preliminary
1030-9160 Printing Trades Journal
1030-9268 Australia. Bureau of Statistics. Queensland Office. Law and Order, Queensland, Summary
1030-9683 Australia. Bureau of Statistics. Queensland Office. Dwelling Unit Commencements: Small Area Statistics, Queensland
1030-9853 Summer Institute of Linguistics. Australian Aborigines and Islanders Branch. Work Papers. Series A *see* 1036-1243
1030-9861 Summer Institute of Linguistics. Australian Aborigines and Islanders Branch. Work Papers. Series B *see* 1036-1243
1031-0053 Australia. Bureau of Statistics. Perinatal Deaths, Australia
1031-010X A H A Special Monographs
1031-0150 Australia. Bureau of Statistics. Births, Australia
1031-0223 Australia. Bureau of Statistics. Deaths, Australia
1031-0231 Australia. Bureau of Statistics. Distribution and Composition of Employee Earnings and Hours, Australia, Preliminary
1031-024X Australian Bureau of Statistics. Distribution and Composition of Employee Earnings and Hours, Australia
1031-0282 Australia. Bureau of Statistics. Expenditure on Education, Australia
1031-0452 Australia. Bureau of Statistics. Marriages, Australia
1031-0533 Australia. Bureau of Statistics. Apparent Consumption of Foodstuffs and Nutrients
1031-0541 Australia at a Glance
1031-055X Australian Demographic Statistics
1031-0673 Australia. Bureau of Statistics. Publications Issued in (Month)
1031-0789 Australia. Bureau of Statistics. Value of Agricultural Commodities Produced, Australia
1031-1084 Australia. Bureau of Statistics. Road Traffic Accidents Involving Fatalities, Australia†
1031-1394 Australia. Bureau of Statistics. Foreign Trade, Australia: Comparative and Summary Tables
1031-1556 Bookman's Monthly *see* 1034-0785
1031-1580 Commonwealth Scientific and Industrial Research Organization. Division of Animal Health. Report
1031-1718 New England News
1031-198X Australia. Bureau of Statistics. Queensland Office. Building Approvals, Queensland
1031-2005 Australia. Bureau of Statistics. Causes of Death, Australia
1031-2145 Australia. Bureau of Statistics. Queensland Office. Crops and Pastures, Queensland
1031-217X Small Area Summary, Queensland *see* 1036-2649
1031-2188 Australia. Bureau of Statistics. Divorces, Australia
1031-2269 Australia. Bureau of Statistics. Queensland Office. Government Finance, Queensland
1031-2277 Australia. Bureau of Statistics. Queensland Office. Health and Welfare Establishments, Queensland, Preliminary†
1031-2331 Indian Ocean Review
1031-2528 Australia. Bureau of Statistics. Queensland Office. Local Government, Queensland
1031-2714 Australia. Bureau of Statistics. Queensland Office. Mineral Production, Queensland†
1031-2730 Australia. Bureau of Statistics. Queensland Office. Motor Vehicle Registrations, Queensland
1031-279X Queensland in Relation to Australia†
1031-2803 Australia. Bureau of Statistics. Queensland Office. Road Traffic Accidents, Queensland (Quarterly)†
1031-2927 Australia. Bureau of Statistics. Victorian Office. Value of Agricultural Commodities Produced, Victoria *changed to* Australia. Bureau of Statistics. Victorian Office. Value of Agricultural Production, Victoria.
1031-296X Manufacturing Report†
1031-3001 Terror Australis: The Australian Horror & Fantasy Magazine
1031-3109 Accounting Guidance Release
1031-3117 Auditing Guidance Release
1031-3516 Australia and the Sea
1031-3613 Reproduction, Fertility and Development
1031-3745 Building Construction Materials & Equipment
1031-3761 Farm Chemicals Today
1031-3893 Australia. Bureau of Statistics. Queensland Office. Road Traffic Accidents, Queensland (Annual)†
1031-4148 H W W Retail Banking Products Survey *see* 1032-870X
1031-4148 H W W Retail Banking Products Survey *see* 1032-8718
1031-4148 H W W Retail Banking Products Survey *see* 1032-8726
1031-4148 H W W Retail Banking Products Survey *see* 1032-8734
1031-4148 H W W Retail Banking Products Survey *see* 1032-8742
1031-4377 Filmviews Catalogue *changed to* Australian Catalogue of New Films and Videos.
1031-461X Australian Historical Studies
1031-4873 Accent
1031-4903 Cinch in Print *changed to* Cinch. Australian Criminology Database.
1031-5020 S I L - A A I B Bibliography
1031-5128 Australian National Accounts: National Income and Expenditure (Quarterly)
1031-5187 Australian Libraries: The Essential Directory
1031-5217 Australian Practice Management†
1031-5837 Church News
1031-6264 Australia. Bureau of Statistics. Queensland Office. Estimated Resident Population: Components of Change, Queensland
1031-6280 Donkey Digest
1031-6965 Natural Therapist
1031-7074 A I M L S Self Assessment Programmes Series *changed to* A I M S Self Assessment Programmes Series.
1031-7104 Australia. Bureau of Statistics. Government Finance Statistics, Australia
1031-7295 Australia. Bureau of Statistic. Queensland Office. Sand, Gravel and Quarry Production, Queensland†
1031-735X Studio for Men
1031-7767 Australia. Bureau of Statistics. Victorian Office. Schools, Victoria†
1031-7872 New South Wales Statutes Annotations
1031-8097 Australia. Bureau of Statistics. Queesland Office. Transport, Queensland†

ISSN

1031-8100 Australia. Bureau of Statistics. Queensland Office. Estimated Resident Population and Area, Queensland
1031-8283 Tightrope†
1031-8305 Australian Chemistry Resource Book
1031-8364 C C H Journal of Asian Pacific Taxation
1031-8690 University of Technology, Sydney. Annual Report
1031-8720 University of Technology, Sydney. General Information of Postgraduate Studies
1031-9115 Studio Brides
1031-9379 Pacific Research
1031-9425 National Union Catalogue of Non-Book Materials
1031-9956 C.S.I.R.O. Division of Fisheries. Research Report
1031-9964 C.S.I.R.O. Division of Oceanography. Research Report
1032-0229 Pride (Collingwood)
1032-0253 H W W Weekly Rates Update *see* 1032-9439
1032-0253 H W W Weekly Rates Update *see* 1032-9447
1032-0512 Australian Bureau of Statistics. Publications to be Released in (Year)
1032-0741 University of Wollongong. Research Report
1032-0776 Resources - Quarry Mine & Construction News
1032-1322 Australian Journal of Nutrition and Dietetics
1032-1810 C C H Journal of Australian Taxation
1032-1942 Australian Art Education
1032-2116 Australian Exports and Imports
1032-2205 A C S J C Occasional Papers
1032-240X Australian Building Construction and Housing
1032-2426 Australian Journal of Soil and Water Conservation
1032-2663 Graduate Careers in Engineering
1032-285X Taiwan Australia Business Discussion Papers
1032-3449 Ships & Ports
1032-3627 Asia Pacific Human Resource Management
1032-3759 Pork Journal
1032-3767 Poultry Digest
1032-4003 Australian Family and Society Abstracts
1032-4054 Australia. Department of Primary Industries and Energy. Annual Report
1032-4070 Eyecare Australia†
1032-4674 Defense and Aerospace Notes
1032-5212 Neville Coleman's Underwater Geographic
1032-5298 Food Australia
1032-5352 Australia. Bureau of Statistics. Queensland Office. Employment Injuries, Queensland
1032-5360 Boats, Boats, Boats...†
1032-5441 Commonwealth Scientific and Industrial Research Organization. Division of Soils. Annual Report
1032-5662 Sport Health
1032-5824 Bulk Grain
1032-6448 Showcast Casting Directory
1032-6456 Contacts & Facilities in the Australian Entertainment Industry
1032-6499 Americar Australia†
1032-6529 Fire Australia
1032-660X Invitation to Comment *see* 1030-5882
1032-6634 Policy
1032-6693 Queensland University of Technology Law Journal
1032-707X Australian Collector's Quarterly
1032-7290 International Tree Crops
1032-805X Australia. Bureau of Statistics. Catalogue of Publications and Products
1032-8068 Australian and New Zealand Biotechnology Directory
1032-8106 Western Australia. Department of Conservation and Land Management. Research Bulletin
1032-8149 National Union Catalogue of Library Materials for People with Disabilities
1032-8408 Directory of Small Area Statistics, Queensland
1032-8599 Access (Glenside)
1032-870X Retail Banking Products Survey: At Call Deposits
1032-8718 Retail Banking Products Survey: Term Deposits
1032-8726 Retail Banking Products Survey: Continuing Credit
1032-8734 Retail Banking Products Survey: Term Loans
1032-8742 Retail Banking Products Survey: Credit Cards
1032-8793 South Australia. Department of Environment and Planning. State and Regional Projections. Bulletin
1032-903X Estimated Resident Population and Area for Local Authority Areas, Queensland *see* 1031-8100
1032-9218 Gould League of Victoria. Newsletter
1032-9234 Anglican Encounter
1032-9315 Focus
1032-9439 Weekly Rates Update: At Call Deposits
1032-9447 Weekly Rates Update: Term Deposits
1032-948X Gould League Club Newsletter
1032-9552 University of New England. Department of Agricultural Economics and Business Management. Dairy Economics Research Report (No.)
1032-9625 Birth
1032-9684 University of Western Australia. Asian Studies Centre. Monographs†
1032-9722 Australia. Australian Bureau of Agricultural and Resource Economics. Agriculture and Resources Quarterly
1033-0003 Early Morn African Violet Group Newsletter
1033-0186 Lifestyles Season
1033-0313 Butterworths Australian Tax Handbook
1033-0526 C A M S Manual of Motor Sport
1033-0542 Australia. Bureau of Statistics. Actual and Expected Private Mineral Exploration
1033-1050 R.C.I.A. Resource
1033-1247 Fishing Boat World
1033-131X Australian Studies
1033-1425 Health at Work
1033-1522 Australian Printer Magazine
1033-1662 AustPlan
1033-1913 Action Africa
1033-2170 Mathematics Education Research Journal
1033-2235 Frontier News
1033-2243 World Mission Partners
1033-2405 Corporate and Business Law Journal
1033-2472 C.S.I.R.O. Division of Coal Technology and Division of Fuel Technolgy. Annual Reports *changed to* Commonwealth Scientific and Industrial Research Organization. Division of Coal and Energy Technology. Annual Report.
1033-2480 Lupus Association of New South Wales. Newsletter
1033-2618 Australia. Bureau of Statistics. Australian National Accounts: Gross Product, Employment and Hours Worked†
1033-2626 Australasian Religion Index
1033-2863 Index of Veterinary Specialties
1033-3088 Cramb Insight *see* 1035-4107
1033-3363 The Real Estate Price Guide
1033-3665 Australia. Bureau of Statistics. Victorian Office. Summary of Statistics (Year)
1033-3975 Stages
1033-4688 Signals
1033-4777 Criminology Australia
1033-4831 Video & Music Business
1033-6257 Soviet Review *see* 1034-7437
1033-6273 Information, Theory and Society
1033-6303 Nursing and Health Science Education
1033-6885 Thomson's Print Production Directory
1033-7466 Australian Corporations and Securities Reports
1033-7814 Hands On
1033-7903 New Life
1033-808X Critical Pedagogy Networker
1033-8810 Analgesic Guidelines
1033-9094 Survey of Victorian Manufacturing
1033-9183 Proposed Statement on Applicability *changed to* Exposure Draft (Auditing Practice).
1033-9191 Proposed Approved Accounting Standard and Proposed Australian Accounting Standard *see* 1030-5882
1033-9752 Transport and Communications Indicators
1034-0408 Corporate Management
1034-0785 Australian Book Collector
1034-0815 Vocational Education and Training Database
1034-1471 Australian National University. National Centre for Development Studies. Reprint Series
1034-2060 A A R F Report
1034-2109 New South Wales Coal Yearbook (Year)
1034-2516 Radio (Year)
1034-3016 Australian Cyclist
1034-3024 Public Law Review
1034-3032 Intellectual Property Journal
1034-3040 Journal of Banking and Finance - Law and Practice
1034-3059 Australian Dispute Resolution Journal
1034-327X A M P L A Bulletin
1034-3415 Proposed Australian Accounting Standard *see* 1030-5882
1034-3423 Audit Monograph
1034-3717 Australian Accounting Standard
1034-4284 New Perspectives†
1034-4810 Journal of Paediatrics and Child Health
1034-5132 Australia. Bureau of Statistics. Queensland Office. Child Care Arrangements, Queensland
1034-5329 Current Issues in Criminal Justice
1034-5671 Australia. Bureau of Statistics. Schools, Australia, Preliminary
1034-6244 The Literature Base
1034-6260 Australian Poultry Science Symposium
1034-652X Australian Journal of Marriage and Family
1034-6775 Aus I M M Bulletin
1034-6902 Technology Design Education
1034-7046 Sydney Residential Auction Market Survey *changed to* Sydney Residential Auction Market Study.
1034-7437 Soviet Society
1034-7658 What's New in Scientific & Laboratory Technology
1034-7860 Australian Concrete Construction
1034-8042 Australian Library Review
1034-8298 Supplementary Statement to Statement of Auditing Practice
1034-859X Statement of Auditing Practice
1034-8603 Statement of Auditing Standards
1034-8719 Encapsulator
1034-8883 Link Disability Journal
1034-9219 A A H L Biennial Report
1034-9243 Papers: Explorations into Children's Literature
1034-9596 C S R Construction News
1035-0462 Australian Journal of Adult & Community Education
1035-0748 Charter
1035-0780 Weekly Rates Update: Continuing Credit
1035-0799 Weekly Rates Update: Term Loans
1035-0802 MediaFax *see* 1037-3381
1035-0977 Facet Talk
1035-0993 Carmelite
1035-1035 The Pioneer
1035-1116 Smart Start
1035-1132 Australian National University. Australian Development Studies Network. Development Bulletin
1035-1264 SewTrade
1035-1396 Progress
1035-1914 Australian Farm Manager
1035-3097 Small Business, Marketing and Society
1035-3461 Australia. Bureau of Statistics. Schools, Australia
1035-3615 Pensioners Voice
1035-3631 Statement of Accounting Concepts
1035-3712 Wildlife Research
1035-3852 Australian Yachting
1035-3941 A C M Bulletin (N.S.W. Edition)
1035-395X A C M Bulletin (Victorian Edition)
1035-4107 Industry Review
1035-4247 Museum of Victoria. Memoirs - Anthropology and History
1035-4611 Australian Clay Journal & Ceramic News
1035-4670 Sydney Residential Auction Market Report
1035-4697 M U C G - Raker
1035-4832 Victorian Public Libraries. Annual Survey
1035-5014 Tasmania. Department of Education and the Arts. Gazette *see* 1037-2040
1035-5405 Directory of Postgraduate Study
1035-5448 Pregnancy
1035-5693 M I M S Disease Index
1035-5707 M I M S Services Directory
1035-5715 M I M S Drugs and Sport
1035-5723 M I M S Bi-Monthly
1035-6355 Songs of New Zealand
1035-655X Gardens & Backyards
1035-6576 Australian Meteorological and Oceanographic Society. Bulletin
1035-6622 Wilderness *changed to* Wilderness News.
1035-6878 Annual Australian Notices to Mariners
1035-7262 Sydney Eats Out
1035-7319 Australian Journal of Public Health
1035-753X National Library of Australia News
1035-7599 C S I R O Division of Materials Science & Technology Report
1035-7718 Australian Journal of International Affairs
1035-7823 Asian Studies Review
1035-915X Sports & Leisure Retailer
1035-9176 Toy & Hobby Retailer
1035-9338 Aus-Geo News
1035-9621 Australian Parapsychological Review
1035-9761 Mean Streets
1035-977X Queensland Forest Service. Advisory Leaflet
1035-9788 Queensland Forest Service. Research Note
1035-9796 Queensland Forest Service. Research Paper
1035-9818 Queensland Forest Service. Technical Note
1035-9826 Queensland Forest Service. Technical Paper
1036-0220 Commonwealth Scientific and Industrial Research Organization. Division of Tropical Crops and Pastures. Biennial Research Report
1036-0352 Information Technology Index
1036-0646 University of Technology, Sydney. Faculty of Business Handbook
1036-0654 University of Technology, Sydney. Faculty of Design Architecture and Building Handbook
1036-0662 University of Technology, Sydney. Faculty of Education Handbook
1036-0670 University of Technology, Sydney. Faculty of Engineering Handbook
1036-0689 University of Technology, Sydney. Faculty of Law & Legal Practice Handbook
1036-0697 University of Technology, Sydney. Faculty of Mathematical & Computing Sciences Handbook
1036-0700 University of Technology, Sydney. Faculty of Nursing Handbook
1036-0719 University of Technology, Sydney. Faculty of Science Handbook
1036-0727 University of Technology, Sydney. Faculty of Social Sciences Handbook
1036-0913 Chiropractic Journal of Australia
1036-0921 Australia's Parents
1036-1146 Australian Journal of Political Science

ISSN INDEX 5841

ISSN	Title
1042-3249	Monthly Planet
1042-3281	Canales
1042-3346	Independent Investor†
1042-346X	Journal of Laser Applications
1042-3494	The Catholic World
1042-3672	C V: The College Magazine†
1042-3680	Oral and Maxillofacial Surgery Clinics
1042-3737	E P S I G News
1042-3923	Desktop Communications
1042-3931	Journal of Invasive Cardiology
1042-4032	International Journal of Humanities and Peace
1042-4067	Journal of Gynecologic Surgery
1042-4091	Managed Care Law Outlook
1042-4105	Superconductor Industry
1042-4172	Directory of State Court Clerks & County Courthouses (Year)
1042-4199	Black Heritage Unveiled Newsletter
1042-4229	Washington View
1042-4296	Intelligence: The Future of Computing
1042-4326	Newspaper Investor
1042-4334	I H N News
1042-4431	Journal of International Financial Markets, Institutions & Money
1042-444X	Journal of Multinational Financial Management
1042-4458	Journal of Interlibrary Loan & Information Supply
1042-4601	The Practical Homeowner
1042-461X	Virginia Employment Law Letter
1042-4628	Classics in the History and Philosophy of Science
1042-4636	Research and Bibliographical Guides in Criminal Justice
1042-4695	L A N Technology
1042-4741	Public Budgeting and Financial Management
1042-4784	A I D S Update (Washington)
1042-4822	P S A
1042-508X	Compoundings
1042-5152	WordPerfect Magazine
1042-5179	Journal of D N A Sequencing and Mapping
1042-5233	American CattleWoman
1042-5268	Journal of Vascular Medicine and Biology
1042-5381	Heaven Bone
1042-5675	Professional Lawyer
1042-5683	Classic Auto Restorer
1042-5756	Delaware Corporate Litigation Reporter
1042-5764	Lender Liability Litigation Reporter
1042-5772	Stockholders and Creditors News Service Concerning L T V Corporation, et al
1042-5780	Stockholders and Creditors News Service Concerning the Johns-Manville Corporation, et al
1042-5799	Stockholders and Creditors News Service Concerning the Public Service Company of New Hampshire†
1042-5934	Domestic Relations Journal of Ohio
1042-5942	Criminal Law Journal of Ohio
1042-5985	American University Studies. Series 27. Feminist Studies
1042-606X	News Network International
1042-6116	Inbound - Outbound
1042-6167	Catalog Handbook
1042-6205	Auto Price Almanac
1042-6213	The America's Review
1042-6302	Foxtalk
1042-6329	Audiotex Directory & Buyer's Guide
1042-6388	Student Assistance Journal
1042-6418	Business Review
1042-6442	Cleanfax Magazine
1042-6450	Gun Tests
1042-6485	Radiation Effects and Defects in Solids Express
1042-6493	Radiation Effects and Defects in Solids Bulletin
1042-6507	Phosphorus, Sulphur and Silicon and the Related Elements
1042-654X	H B S Catalog of Teaching Materials
1042-6566	New Age Retailer
1042-6590	Partnerships in Education Journal
1042-6604	Southern Reader
1042-6647	Ex Libris (Portsmouth)
1042-6884	Will - Grundy Counties Genealogical Society News
1042-6914	Materials & Manufacturing Processes
1042-6922	Lens and Eye Toxicity Research
1042-6930	Intelligent Network News
1042-7015	B N A Special Report Series on Work & Family
1042-7082	Jacaranda Review
1042-7139	Bread Pudding Update
1042-7147	Polymers for Advanced Technologies
1042-7163	Heteroatom Chemistry
1042-7228	Cable World
1042-7260	Journal of Zoo and Wildlife Medicine
1042-7279	Dissertation Abstracts International. Section C: Worldwide
1042-7341	"Check the Oil!" Magazine
1042-735X	Trikone
1042-749X	Chinese Journal of Biotechnology
1042-7511	Business of New Hampshire see 1046-9575
1042-752X	North American Review of Economics and Finance
1042-7570	Professional Counselor Magazine
1042-7589	Adolescent Counselor Magazine
1042-7597	Vietnam Generation
1042-7643	Weavers
1042-7732	Backwoods
1042-7880	Swashbuckler
1042-7899	Unknown
1042-7902	Owlhooters
1042-7953	Teenage†
1042-7961	Journal of Women's History
1042-8011	World Resource Review
1042-8038	Oahu Update†
1042-8046	Hawaii: The Big Island Update
1042-8143	Knowledge Acquisition
1042-816X	Ward's Business Directory of U S Private and Public Companies. Vol.1; Over 11.5 Million Dollars in Sales see 1048-8707
1042-8194	Leukemia and Lymphoma
1042-8216	Primary Sources & Original Works
1042-8224	Journal of Multicultural Social Work
1042-8232	Journal of Progressive Human Services
1042-8399	England on Fifty Dollars a Day
1042-8534	Design Management
1042-8623	C D - R O M EndUser
1042-8704	Business for Central New Jersey
1042-8836	C B M R Monographs
1042-8933	C I T A Exam Reviews see 0887-736X
1042-895X	Gastroenterology Nursing
1042-9115	Corporate Real Estate Executive
1042-9123	Food Arts
1042-9190	Ward's Business Directory of U S Private and Public Companies. Vol.2; From .5 to 11.5 Million Dollars see 1048-8707
1042-9204	Ward's Business Directory of U S Private and Public Companies. Vol.3; Ranked by Sales within Industry see 1048-8707
1042-9220	C W R U: The Magazine of Case Western Reserve University
1042-9247	E M J: Engineering Management Journal
1042-928X	Accounting Department Management & Administration Report
1042-9379	Peanut Grower
1042-9565	Advancing Clinical Care†
1042-9573	Journal of Financial Intermediation
1042-9611	D I C P - The Annals of Pharmacotherapy
1042-9646	Contemporary Internal Medicine
1042-9662	Sports Car International
1042-9670	Academic Psychiatry
1042-9689	New England Real Estate News
1042-9697	Aquatics changed to Aquatics International.
1042-9719	Washington History
1042-9808	Latin American Art
1042-9832	Random Structures & Algorithms
1042-993X	Bare Knuckles†
1042-9948	Comstock Quarterly†
1042-9972	Weekend Gardener†
1043-0075	Blk
1043-0083	P J G
1043-0121	American Association for Laboratory Accreditation Annual Report
1043-0261	V I P Address Book
1043-0342	Human Gene Therapy
1043-0660	Clinical Consultations in Obstetrics and Gynecology
1043-0695	Communique (Columbus, 1967)
1043-0709	Student Traveler†
1043-0717	Defence Economics
1043-0725	Missionary Tidings
1043-0733	Selective Cancer Therapeutics
1043-0768	Acknowledge the Window Letter
1043-0792	Compute's Amiga Resource†
1043-0806	Buried Treasure
1043-0814	Poetics
1043-0946	Search (Devon)
1043-0989	Conference on Artificial Intelligence Applications. Proceedings
1043-1020	Journal of Artificial Intelligence in Education
1043-1039	Live Animal Trade & Transport Magazine
1043-1047	Taekwondo World
1043-1055	Journal of Computing in Childhood Education
1043-1195	Official Guide to American Historic Inns
1043-1209	Report on Disability Programs
1043-1217	Network Management Systems & Strategies
1043-125X	Renewal News
1043-1306	Healthcare Productivity Report see 1058-7829
1043-1314	P C LapTop Computers
1043-1489	Seminars in Colon and Rectal Surgery
1043-1497	Sycamore Review
1043-1543	A I D S Clinical Care
1043-1659	Arizona Facts
1043-1667	The Estimate
1043-1691	Archaeological Method and Theory
1043-1802	Bioconjugate Chemistry
1043-1918	V A S Newsletter
1043-2043	Directory of World Leaders & Factbook (Year)
1043-2051	Professional Licensing Report
1043-2094	Against the Grain
1043-2167	National Forum of Special Education Journal
1043-2280	Mature Traveler
1043-2299	Micropendium
1043-237X	Library Talk
1043-240X	Humor and Cartoon Markets
1043-2418	Super Group Magazine (English Edition)
1043-2450	North American Fisherman
1043-2485	Fire Protection Contractor
1043-254X	Journal of Dental Hygiene
1043-2620	News Media Yellow Book of Washington and New York
1043-2701	Rugging Room Bulletin
1043-2760	Trends in Endocrinology and Metabolism
1043-2833	Bricker Bulletin on Executive Education
1043-2841	PreShipment Testing
1043-285X	I B C's Money Market Insight
1043-2906	Growing Edge Magazine
1043-3031	Clinical Abstracts - Current Therapeutic Findings
1043-3074	Head & Neck
1043-3120	Arm Bender
1043-3198	Clinical Practice of Gynecology
1043-3309	Journal of Agricultural Economics Research
1043-3325	Parting Gifts
1043-3333	Evergreen Chronicles
1043-3473	Mystery Readers Journal
1043-3503	Haunts
1043-3546	Dairy, Food and Environmental Sanitation
1043-3732	Bad Haircut
1043-3740	Fair News
1043-3848	Ars Lyrica: Journal of Lyrica
1043-3856	Report on Guatemala
1043-3996	Contemporary Topics in Pure and Applied Condensed Matter Science
1043-4046	Advances in Physiology Education
1043-4054	Transportation Builder
1043-4062	Constitutional Political Economy
1043-4070	Journal of the History of Sexuality
1043-4186	Sorrow's Reward†
1043-4356	Journal of Cardiovascular Technology
1043-4364	Peak Performance Selling
1043-4631	Rationality and Society
1043-4666	Cytokine
1043-4674	The New Biologist†
1043-4879	Van & Truck Digest
1043-5085	Aspen Magazine
1043-5093	Stamping Quarterly
1043-5468	Beautiful Glass for Home & Office†
1043-5492	Bowhunting World
1043-5506	Labor Relations Reference Manual
1043-5506	Labor - Management Relations Analysis
1043-5565	Noise Regulation Report
1043-5662	International Trade Reporter Import Reference Manual
1043-5670	International Trade Reporter Export Reference Manual
1043-5727	Sociocriticism: Literature, Society, and History
1043-5735	Hermeneutic Commentaries
1043-5743	Irish Studies
1043-5751	Studies in Gerard Manley Hopkins
1043-576X	The Enlightenment: German and Interdisciplinary Studies
1043-5778	Ars Interpretandi
1043-5786	Studies in European Thought
1043-5794	Studies in Italian Culture: Literature in History
1043-5808	New German-American Studies
1043-5816	Emory Studies in Early Christianity
1043-5824	Allstate Motor Club R V Sales, Rental and Service Directory
1043-5913	Lebanon News (Arabic Edition)
1043-6030	Florida Technology Review
1043-6057	Insect World
1043-6073	O P A S T C O Roundtable
1043-6081	Health Law Journal of Ohio
1043-609X	Journal of N I H Research
1043-6138	Travel Publishing News see 1053-0177
1043-6146	Harlow Report: Geographic Information Systems
1043-6235	Pennsylvania Agriculture News
1043-6367	Discrete Semiconductors Direct Alternate Sources & Replacements
1043-6375	Southern Links
1043-6383	Bridge Today
1043-6405	New Jersey Lake Survey Map Guide see 1054-4623
1043-6464	Journal of Microcomputer Systems Management
1043-6596	Journal of Transcultural Nursing
1043-6618	Pharmacological Research
1043-6650	London Stage 1800-1900: A Documentary Record and Calendar of Performances
1043-6685	Hawaii Annual Economic Report
1043-6774	Westchester Family
1043-6790	Particle World
1043-6820	Economic and Tax Report
1043-6898	Ballot Access News
1043-6928	L I T: Literature Interpretation Theory
1043-7053	Service Quarterly
1043-7290	Cause. Proceedings of National Conference
1043-7320	Independent Energy
1043-7355	Legal Management
1043-7401	Crawford Exchange
1043-7428	Partner's Report, The Monthly Update for CPA Firm Owners
1043-7533	Pet Veterinarian
1043-7657	Kansas Review
1043-7789	Federal Credit Union
1043-786X	Environmental Manager
1043-7916	Journal of Soviet Nationalities
1043-7991	Performance Aftermarket Magazine changed to P & S A News.
1043-8033	Chinese Journal of Engineering Thermophysics

ISSN INDEX

ISSN	Title
1043-8092	Laser Focus World
1043-8130	Pacifica†
1043-8289	Who's Who Among International Students in American Universities and Colleges
1043-8378	Student Guide to the S A T
1043-8416	Mealey's Litigation Report: Insurance Insolvency
1043-8483	Courts, Health Science & the Law
1043-8491	Cancer Prevention
1043-8572	Narcotics Demand Reduction Digest
1043-8580	Studies of World Literature in English
1043-8599	Economics of Innovation and New Technology
1043-8637	Coping
1043-8688	Folio's Publishing News
1043-884X	Onthebus
1043-8858	Farm Chemicals International
1043-8947	Amaranth Review
1043-8963	Oncogenes and Growth Factors Abstracts
1043-8971	A S F A Marine Biotechnology Abstracts
1043-898X	Contemporary Pacific
1043-9196	Bank Card Credit Report
1043-934X	Space Commerce
1043-9366	Yale Journal of Law and Feminism
1043-9420	Euro TV Investor
1043-9455	Black Sacred Music
1043-9463	Policing and Society
1043-9501	Stiletto
1043-951X	China Economic Review
1043-9579	Videos for Business and Training
1043-9617	A S I C & E D A
1043-9668	Government Technology
1043-9676	Iowa Pork Today
1043-9692	Club Business International
1043-9714	Stockholders and Creditors News Service Concerning Eastern - Continental Airlines, Inc.
1043-979X	Women with Wheels
1043-9978	Big Allis
1044-002X	Journal of European Business
1044-0038	Journal of Staffing and Recruitment
1044-0046	Journal of Sustainable Agriculture
1044-0054	Journal of Pharmacy Teaching
1044-0151	V I C A Journal
1044-016X	Air Power History
1044-0267	Nelson's Global Research
1044-0275	S E N G A
1044-0305	American Society for Mass Spectrometry. Journal
1044-033X	Environmental and Urban Issues
1044-0445	A V Market Place
1044-0666	Recruitment & Retention Report
1044-0682	T V Entertainment Monthly changed to Cable Guide.
1044-0755	Journal of Computing and Society†
1044-0798	Tennessee Tax Review
1044-0801	U S Roller Skating
1044-1042	Old Time Country
1044-1085	Chinese Journal of Low Temperature Physics†
1044-1190	Mobile Product News
1044-1239	Systems 3X and A S World see 1055-7768
1044-1395	Physicians' Desk Reference for Nonprescription Drugs
1044-1417	Patterson's Elementary Education
1044-1425	Photonics Directory
1044-1433	Daily Food & Drink Report
1044-145X	Branch Automation News
1044-1476	Network (New York)
1044-1514	PsycBOOKS
1044-1522	Obesity & Health
1044-1549	American Journal of Respiratory Cell and Molecular Biology
1044-1638	Performance Practice Review
1044-1700	C D Review
1044-1859	Molecular Crystals and Liquid Crystals Incorporating Nonlinear Optics see 1058-725X
1044-1859	Molecular Crystals and Liquid Crystals Incorporating Nonlinear Optics see 1058-7268
1044-1891	Aramco World
1044-2006	Ambergris
1044-2049	American College of Toxicology. Journal. Part B
1044-2057	Diaspora: A Journal of Transnational Studies
1044-2073	Journal of Disability Policy Studies
1044-2103	Psychoanalytic Books
1044-2111	Harvard Business School. Publishing Division. Core Collection, An Author and Subject Guide
1044-2138	A I D S Information Sourcebook
1044-2170	Frommer's Italy
1044-2197	Contemporary Musicians
1044-226X	Frommer's Egypt
1044-2286	Frommer's New England see 1056-5787
1044-2324	Georgia Environmental Law Letter
1044-2332	Copyright Clearance Center. Report
1044-2405	Frommer's Germany
1044-2618	Wildlife Rehabilitation Today
1044-2626	Arthritis and Rheumatism Primary Care Review changed to Primary Care Rheumatology.
1044-2782	New Times (Seattle)
1044-2790	Journal of Health & Healing
1044-2944	British - American Deal Review
1044-2960	The 1992 M & A Monthly
1044-2979	Journal of Asian and African Affairs
1044-3002	Gay Community News (Honolulu) changed to Hawaii's National Gay Community News.
1044-3061	Garbage
1044-307X	Ob G Management
1044-310X	Wigwag†
1044-3134	N Y P I R G Agenda
1044-3150	Electronic Music Educator†
1044-3177	Defense & Diplomacy†
1044-3193	Consumer Reports Health Letter changed to Consumer Reports on Health.
1044-3495	Cool Traveler
1044-3509	International Educator
1044-3576	Garden State Home and Garden see 0273-270X
1044-3576	Garden State Home & Garden†
1044-3584	Business Interiors changed to Today's Facility Manager.
1044-3797	Emergency Pediatrics
1044-3894	Families in Society
1044-3975	Defense Marketing International
1044-3983	Epidemiology
1044-4068	International Journal of Conflict Management
1044-4149	Dionysos
1044-422X	Biological Therapies in Psychiatry Newsletter
1044-4238	South Carolina Lawyer
1044-4300	Journal of Applied Fire Science
1044-4319	Hotline on Object-Oriented Technology
1044-4343	Personal Financial Planning
1044-4386	Stanford Law and Policy Review
1044-4629	Price Guide Presents
1044-4807	Oriental Rug Review
1044-4890	Year Book of Perinatal - Neonatal Medicine
1044-498X	Business Studies on the U.S.S.R.
1044-4998	Principal's Report
1044-5005	Management Accounting Research
1044-5102	International Archives of Heat and Mass Transfer†
1044-5110	Atomization and Sprays
1044-5129	Moscow Aviation Institute. Journal†
1044-5137	Power Energy Ecology†
1044-5145	Strength and Fracture
1044-5323	Seminars in Immunology Series
1044-5331	Hellas
1044-5463	Journal of Child and Adolescent Psychopharmacology
1044-5471	Journal of Clinical Laser Medicine & Surgery
1044-5498	D N A and Cell Biology
1044-5714	Accounting Today
1044-5757	John Macmurray Studies
1044-5765	Seminars in Neurosciences Series
1044-5781	Seminars in Developmental Biology
1044-579X	Seminars in Cancer Biology Series
1044-5803	Materials Characterization
1044-5846	Christians in Crisis
1044-6141	Kayhan-i Hava'i
1044-6184	Singles Almanac (Boston)
1044-6222	Community Leader Briefings
1044-6303	Mexico Service
1044-6354	Video News International
1044-646X	Graphic Arts Blue Book. Northeastern Edition
1044-6672	Developmental Immunology
1044-6699	Our World
1044-6710	The (something)†
1044-6737	Morasha
1044-6753	Pennsylvania Academy of Science. Journal
1044-677X	National Institute of Standards and Technology. Journal of Research
1044-6826	In-Fisherman Angling Adventures see 1048-4892
1044-7032	Selected Readings in Oral and Maxillofacial Surgery
1044-7261	Tax Management Tax Practice Series
1044-727X	Air Safety Week
1044-7288	Video Magazine
1044-7318	International Journal of Human-Computer Interaction
1044-7377	Headway
1044-7385	Advancing the Consumer Interest
1044-7393	Molecular and Chemical Neuropathology
1044-7431	Molecular and Cellular Neurosciences
1044-7474	B N A's Bankruptcy Law Reporter
1044-7490	Impetus
1044-7512	The Door
1044-775X	Basically Buckles
1044-7768	Western Retailer
1044-7857	Chorus!
1044-789X	Dr. Dobb's Journal
1044-7903	Sport Truck
1044-7946	Wounds
1044-7962	Bio-Bibliographies in Education
1044-7970	Graphic Arts Blue Book. Delaware Valley-Ohio Edition
1044-7989	Graphic Arts Blue Book. Southeastern Edition
1044-7997	Advances in Software Science and Technology
1044-8004	Human Resource Development Quarterly
1044-8012	Aircraft Technician
1044-8039	Public Productivity and Management Review
1044-811X	International Journal of Biosocial and Medical Research
1044-8136	Journal of Corporate Accounting and Finance
1044-8179	C E Computing Review
1044-825X	Annual Directory of World Leaders
1044-8349	Bibliographies and Indexes in Geography
1044-8357	Journal of Chinese Physics†
1044-8403	Chinese Journal of Population Science
1044-8527	Graphic Arts Blue Book. Metro New York - New Jersey Edition
1044-8535	Graphic Arts Blue Book. Midwestern Edition
1044-856X	Broyles Family Newsletter
1044-8632	Neutron News
1044-8756	L A M P Lighter
1044-8772	The U S Non-Alcoholic Beverage Market: Impact Databank Review and Forecast†
1044-8780	U S Market for California Varietal Wine: Impact Databank Review and Forecast†
1044-8888	Chess in Indiana
1044-890X	China and Pacific Rim Letter
1044-8950	MacTech Quarterly see 1052-9128
1044-9078	Washington Facts
1044-9086	Georgia Facts
1044-9094	Legislative Information Alert see 1054-5859
1044-9116	Malcolm X Lovers Network
1044-9159	Dive Boat Calendar and Travel Guide: Pacific Coast Edition changed to Dive Boat Calendar & Travel Guide: International Edition.
1044-937X	Journal of American Drama and Theatre
1044-9493	Water Environment & Technology
1044-9507	H D T V World Review see 1055-6931
1044-9647	Radio - Chicago
1044-9663	PlasticsWeek
1044-9752	News & Notes (Washington)
1044-9779	Infectious Diseases in Children
1044-9892	Electronic Messaging News
1045-0114	C D Review Digest - Classical
1045-0122	C D Review Digest - Jazz, Popular, etc.
1045-0343	World Dredging - Mining & Construction
1045-0491	We're Living in Funny Times
1045-0513	Angola Peace Monitor
1045-0602	Hobbyist Sourcebook
1045-0629	I F M T Magazine
1045-0769	Plastics D.A.T.A. Digest
1045-0815	Creator
1045-0831	Story
1045-084X	Journal (Columbus)
1045-0955	Electronic Materials Technology News
1045-1005	Bread for the World Newsletter
1045-103X	Original Donna Kossy's Kooks Magazine changed to Kooks Magazine.
1045-1056	Biologicals
1045-1064	Journal of Technology Education
1045-1129	Stochastics and Stochastics Reports
1045-1188	Pen World
1045-1498	Voice Technology News
1045-1595	Adult Learning
1045-1773	Phoenix (Phoenix)
1045-179X	The Pilot Log
1045-1854	Plastic Canvas! Magazine
1045-1889	Innovations in Polymers - Engineering Plastics†
1045-1978	Autoparts Report
1045-1986	C A S E Strategies
1045-2001	Progress in Neuroendocrin Immunology
1045-2087	N S G A Retail Focus
1045-2249	Behavioral Ecology
1045-2265	Context South
1045-2354	Critical Perspectives on Accounting
1045-2397	High Tech Ceramics News
1045-2508	Leasing Sourcebook
1045-2605	Edward Howell Family Association. Newsletter
1045-2664	Alabama Manufacturers Register
1045-2680	Chemtracts: Biochemistry and Molecular Biology
1045-2699	International Journal of Human Factors in Manufacturing
1045-2729	Human Ecology & Energy Balancing Scientist
1045-2958	Chips Off the Writer's Block
1045-3172	British Journal of Management
1045-3334	Fedgazette: Federal Reserve Bank of Minneapolis Regional Business & Economics Newspaper
1045-3393	Video Rating Guide for Libraries
1045-3539	The Angling Report
1045-3555	Marine Fish Monthly
1045-3660	Underground Forest - Selva Subterranea
1045-3695	Journal of Managerial Issues
1045-3717	Emigre
1045-3830	School Psychology Quarterly
1045-3849	Fellowship Today
1045-3857	The European Community
1045-3873	Journal of Cardiovascular Electrophysiology
1045-3881	Asia Pacific Travel
1045-389X	Journal of Intelligent Material Systems and Stuctures
1045-3954	Used Equipment Directory
1045-3962	P T Distributor
1045-3970	School and College
1045-4055	Grand Rapids Business Journal
1045-4160	Precision Machinery
1045-4268	Massage Magazine
1045-4322	Community Economics
1045-4330	A A S C Quarterly see 1053-4202

1045-4365 Bilingualism Today
1045-4373 Rug Hooking
1045-4403 Critical Reviews in Eukaryotic Gene Expression
1045-4411 Critical Reviews in Oral Biology and Medicine
1045-4438 Journal of Applied Aquaculture
1045-4446 Journal of Food Products Marketing
1045-4470 Human Genome Abstracts
1045-4497 The Age of Revolution and Romanticism: Interdisciplinary Studies
1045-4500 New Perspectives in Philosophical Scholarship: Texts and Issues
1045-4519 Stone Through the Ages†
1045-4527 Seminars in Arthroplasty
1045-4594 Historic Brass Society Newsletter
1045-4616 Historic Brass Society Journal
1045-4853 Teaching Elementary Physical Education
1045-4861 Journal of Applied Biomaterials
1045-4969 Agenda New York
1045-5027 Glass Audio
1045-5108 Singles Almanac of New York
1045-5183 Virginia Environmental Law Journal
1045-5388 Mandeville's Used Book Price Guide
1045-5418 Pediatric A I D S and H I V Infection: Fetus to Adolescent
1045-5485 Nurse Practitioner Forum
1045-5493 Junior High Magazine Abstracts
1045-5515 Story Time Stories That Rhyme Newsletter
1045-5523 Basic and Clinical Biostatistics
1045-5566 Washington Journal
1045-5736 Journal of Democracy
1045-5752 Capitalism, Nature, Socialism
1045-5760 Auto Finance Update
1045-5795 Audiotex Update
1045-585X International Congress on Technology and Technology Exchange. Proceedings
1045-5876 Journal of Religion in Psychotherapy
1045-5914 Decorative Products World†
1045-5965 Quick & Easy Quilting
1045-599X Environmental Law Journal of Ohio
1045-6007 Journal of World History
1045-6015 Jewish Law in Context
1045-6031 Aquatic Sciences & Fisheries Abstracts. Part 3: Aquatic Pollution and Environmental Quality
1045-618X T A P P I Test Methods
1045-6201 Directory of Major Mailers & What They Mail (Year)
1045-6481 Journal Michigan Pharmacist
1045-6562 Telecom Outlook
1045-6570 Optical Materials and Engineering News
1045-6635 Latin American Antiquity
1045-6643 Quick Response News
1045-6686 Legal Professional *see* 1051-3663
1045-6732 Geographic Information, Mapping, and Positioning Newsletter
1045-6740 Permafrost and Periglacial Processes
1045-6767 Human Nature
1045-6775 Inside Turbo Pascal
1045-6791 Inside Turbo C *changed to* Inside Turbo C Plus Plus.
1045-7011 Creating Excellence
1045-7089 Facilities Planning News
1045-7097 Perspectives on Political Science
1045-7194 Design Management Journal
1045-7208 Current Topics in Remote Sensing
1045-7216 Car Corral†
1045-7259 Palm Beach Society
1045-7313 Lab Report
1045-7585 P R O U T Press
1045-7658 Small Business Advocate (Washington)
1045-7682 Swamp Root
1045-7704 Women & Guns
1045-7771 Cape Cod Home & Garden
1045-7798 Business Library Review
1045-7828 Japanese Journal of Tribology
1045-7909 Manoa
1045-8069 Winter Living†
1045-8115 School Board News
1045-8131 Eastern, Southeast Boating Newspaper (Eastern Edition)
1045-814X Eastern, Southeast Boating Newspaper (Southeast Edition)
1045-8352 Directory of Portable Databases
1045-8506 C A Selects. Adsorption
1045-8514 C A Selects. Activated Carbon
1045-8530 C A Selects. Drug Analysis Biological Fluids & Tissues
1045-8549 C A Selects. Polyacrylates (Patents)
1045-8557 C A Selects. Elastomers
1045-8565 C A S BioTech Updates. Commercial Fermentation
1045-8573 C A Selects. Polymerization Catalysts
1045-8581 C A S BioTech Updates. D N A & R N A Probes
1045-859X C A S BioTech Updates. Nucleic Acid & Protein Sequences
1045-8611 Environmental Business Journal
1045-8816 Decorative Rug
1045-8875 T Q S News
1045-8913 Art in California
1045-893X Women and International Development Annual
1045-9073 N C O A Networks
1045-9081 Law Practice Management
1045-9219 I E E E Transactions on Parallel and Distributed Systems
1045-9227 I E E E Transactions on Neural Networks
1045-9243 I E E E Antennas and Propagation Magazine
1045-926X Journal of Visual Languages and Computing
1045-9367 Home Improvement Center
1045-9456 Shakespeare Yearbook
1045-9723 Link (St. Louis)
1045-9871 Cather Studies
1045-988X Preventing School Failure
1045-9979 Animal Activist Alert
1045-9987 Sims Seeker
1046-0012 Blue Light Red Light
1046-0020 Senior Edition U S A
1046-039X High Tech Separations News
1046-042X Valley Genealogist
1046-0454 Valley Magazine (Selinsgrove)
1046-0470 American Amateur Journalist
1046-0616 Aldus Magazine
1046-0756 Journal of Muscle Foods
1046-0764 Current Opinion in Dentistry
1046-0896 Constitution (New York)
1046-0985 Rockford Review
1046-0993 A E R O Sun Times
1046-1043 DobEdition
1046-1094 Fiction Forum
1046-1183 C P C Career & Job Fair Finder
1046-1310 Current Psychology (New Brunswick)
1046-154X Lawn and Landscape Maintenance
1046-1647 Hospital Editors' Idea Exchange
1046-168X Business Digest of Greater Waterbury
1046-1736 Income Plus
1046-1744 Computers in Music Research
1046-1809 Soviet Studies
1046-1868 Fletcher Forum of World Affairs
1046-1957 Elle Decor
1046-1965 Service News (Yarmouth)
1046-2023 Methods: A Companion to Methods in Enzymology
1046-2066 Third World without Superpowers: Collected Documents of the Group of 77
1046-2074 Third World without Superpowers: Collected Documents of the Non-Aligned Countries
1046-2112 Pet Focus
1046-2252 Collections (Columbia)
1046-2333 Interstate Oil Compact Commission. Compact & Committee Bulletin
1046-2368 New York State Archaeological Association. Bulletin
1046-2406 Peterson's Register of Higher Education (Year)
1046-2511 Military
1046-2708 The Santa Fean Magazine
1046-2724 Ledge Poetry and Prose Magazine *changed to* Ledge Poetry & Fiction Magazine.
1046-2813 Bermuda Post
1046-2821 American Entomologist
1046-283X Computational Mathematics and Modeling
1046-2899 America's Civil War
1046-3046 Plastic Waste Strategies
1046-3089 Washington Flyer Magazine
1046-3267 Sandlapper
1046-3283 European Review of Social Psychology
1046-333X Pfeiffer & Company. Annual
1046-3348 Colorado Review
1046-3356 Oncology Issues
1046-3364 Research and Teaching in Developmental Education
1046-3410 Newsletter on Serials Pricing Issues
1046-3550 Multimedia Review
1046-3887 National Symposium on Mining, Hydrology, Sedimentology and Reclamation. Proceedings *changed to* National Symposium on Mining. Proceedings.
1046-3925 Expo (Kansas City)
1046-3976 Endocrine Pathology
1046-4166 T A P P I Proceedings
1046-4166 Technical Association of the Pulp and Paper Industry. Corrugated Containers Conference. Proceedings (Year) *see* 1058-0883
1046-4166 Technical Association of the Pulp and Paper Industry. International Process & Product Quality Conference Proceedings (Year)
1046-4204 Phillips County Historical Review
1046-4220 Descendants of Richard Risley Senior
1046-4239 Declassified Documents Catalog
1046-4255 College Media Directory
1046-4336 Ohio Libraries
1046-4352 P I M A Magazine
1046-4387 Stearns Newsletter
1046-4565 Zoo Life
1046-4573 Auction Results Quarterly†
1046-4611 Transworld Snowboarding
1046-462X Colored Stone
1046-4638 Vietnam
1046-4778 World M & A Network
1046-4964 Small Group Research
1046-4980 Information Please Sports Almanac (Year)
1046-5022 Drama - Theatre Teacher
1046-5030 Rola Boza
1046-5057 Business Travel Management
1046-5081 Actuarial Review
1046-526X Studies in Historiography
1046-5286 Mobile Satellite News (Potomac)
1046-5294 Environmental Topics
1046-5448 International Brain Dominance Review
1046-5456 SunTech Journal
1046-5480 All about Business in Hawaii
1046-5545 Seneca Searchers
1046-5596 Mosaic (Cambridge)
1046-5626 Corporate Risk Management
1046-5634 Mas
1046-5774 Guide to Accredited Camps (Year)
1046-5901 Charbonneau Connection
1046-5928 Protein Expression and Purification
1046-5944 C A S E Trends
1046-6029 FireHeart
1046-6193 Teacher
1046-6312 Beautiful Homes
1046-6568 Pennsylvania Environmental Law Letter
1046-6673 American Society of Nephrology. Journal
1046-669X Journal of Marketing Channels
1046-6940 Space News (Springfield)
1046-6967 War, Literature, and the Arts
1046-7009 Forest & Conservation History
1046-705X Food Structure
1046-7157 Retreading - Repair Journal
1046-719X Crochet Home
1046-7211 International New Product Newsletter
1046-7459 Nursing Diagnosis
1046-7874 The Formalist
1046-7882 Bibliographies and Indexes in Ethnic Studies
1046-7890 Journal of Clinical Ethics
1046-8021 E
1046-8110 Hudson's Subscription Newsletter Directory
1046-8250 Jobson's Liquor Handbook
1046-8331 Wisconsin Facts
1046-834X Kentucky Facts
1046-8366 The International Permaculture Solutions Journal
1046-8374 Criminal Law Forum
1046-8390 University of Kansas. Paleontological Contributions. New Series
1046-8471 Art Issues
1046-8595 Printing News - East
1046-8765 Bibliographic Guide to East Asian Studies
1046-8773 Mutual Fund Performance Report
1046-8781 Simulation & Gaming
1046-8897 Chiron Review
1046-8986 American Photo
1046-9095 Journal of Air Medical Transport
1046-9109 Michigan Employment Law Letter
1046-9125 Fantasy Baseball
1046-9184 Guidelines Magazine *see* 1053-1793
1046-9192 Michigan Environmental Law Letter
1046-9206 Ohio Employment Law Letter
1046-9214 Texas Employment Law Letter
1046-9354 Allergy Proceedings
1046-9443 Scripps Institution of Oceanography. Annual Report
1046-9508 C U P A Journal
1046-9575 Business New Hampshire Magazine
1046-9648 Inside Microsoft Works
1046-9656 Inside WordPerfect
1046-9699 Craft Marketing News
1046-9966 Real Estate - Environmental Liability News
1046-9974 Times: in harness
1046-9990 Liturgy 90
1047-0158 Hubbub
1047-0166 Tennessee Pharmacist
1047-0336 Journal of Clinical Research and Pharmacoepidemiology
1047-0476 Joe Franklin's Nostalgia
1047-0530 Tokyo Business Month†
1047-0549 In Health *see* 0279-3547
1047-0719 Focus (San Francisco)
1047-1006 Comparative State Politics
1047-1073 Canadian - America Public Policy
1047-1359 M I N Fax
1047-1367 TechNotes - dBASE IV
1047-1375 TechNotes - Framework III
1047-1383 TechNotes - Graphics
1047-1391 TechNotes - Word Publishing
1047-1413 Charlotte County Florida Land Owner
1047-1499 Tattoo Review
1047-1634 Quiltmaker
1047-1669 Competition Angler
1047-1677 Marketing to Women
1047-1707 Promo
1047-1715 Who's Where in the American Theatre
1047-1758 Defense Contract Litigation Reporter
1047-191X Future Choices
1047-2061 Autoglass
1047-2207 Rhododendron
1047-2258 Birmingham Poetry Review
1047-2312 Jobber Executive†
1047-2355 Opus
1047-2363 Inmusic†
1047-2371 Spectrum (Boston)
1047-2398 Nova (New Berlin)
1047-2436 Stocks, Bonds, Bills and Inflation (Year) Yearbook
1047-2444 Billiards: The (Year) Official B C A Rules & Records Book
1047-2452 Computer-Assisted Composition Journal
1047-2525 Fisheries Product News
1047-2622 Straight Ahead†
1047-2789 Carolina Literary Companion
1047-2797 Annals of Epidemiology
1047-2908 Inside Market Data
1047-2924 V L A News
1047-2932 University of Nevada. Basque Studies Program Newsletter
1047-2975 Hotels

1047-3033 Technical Association of the Pulp and Paper Industry. Polymers, Laminations & Coatings Conference. Proceedings (Year)
1047-305X Technical Association of the Pulp and Paper Industry. Coating Conference. Proceedings (Year)
1047-3068 Old News
1047-3084 Cubs Vine Line
1047-3203 Journal of Visual Communication and Image Representation
1047-3211 Cerebral Cortex
1047-322X Applied Occupational & Environmental Hygiene
1047-3289 Air & Waste Management Association. Journal
1047-3297 Arts and Culture Funding Report
1047-3300 Minority Funding Report
1047-3378 Cruise Industry News Annual
1047-3394 State and Local Statistics Sources
1047-353X Defense Technology Business
1047-3572 American Enterprise
1047-3610 Pacific *changed to* Monterey Bay Magazine.
1047-3971 The Second Stone
1047-4013 Personal Workstation†
1047-4064 Lithuanian Physics Journal
1047-4137 Entertainment Litigation Reporter
1047-417X News Library News
1047-4196 Circle Network News
1047-4250 Tawagoto
1047-4366 Truck Trader - Centerline
1047-4374 Industrial Machine Trader
1047-4382 Hot Line Construction Equipment Monthly Update
1047-4404 Car Trader
1047-4412 Journal of Educational and Psychological Consultation
1047-4447 Workplace Trends
1047-4463 Gauntlet
1047-451X 24 Hours
1047-4528 Puncture
1047-4552 Mediterranean Quarterly
1047-4633 North Carolina Environmental Law Letter
1047-4641 Florida Environmental & Land Use Letter
1047-4757 N A S Newsletter
1047-4811 Galilean Electrodynamics
1047-482X International Journal of Osteoarchaeology
1047-4838 J O M
1047-4862 Abstracts in Social Gerontology: Current Literature on Aging
1047-4951 Vineyard and Winery Management
1047-496X BoCoEx Index
1047-5117 Optical & Magnetic Report
1047-5125 Autonomic Nervous System
1047-5141 First Things
1047-515X Black Ice
1047-5249 I: The First Person†
1047-5303 Player
1047-5346 I I C S Reporter
1047-5370 Interrace Magazine
1047-5400 Ohio Archivist
1047-5419 Ohio Civil Practice Journal
1047-5567 Circuit Design *changed to* Printed Circuit Design.
1047-5583 U S Electronic Industry Directory
1047-5672 World Shrimp Farming
1047-5699 Family and Conciliation Courts Review
1047-594X Liberation! *see* 1051-7871
1047-5982 Modern Logic
1047-5990 Conservative Review
1047-6067 Inside Microsoft BASIC
1047-6075 Inside Microsoft C
1047-6083 The Clayton-Fillmore Report
1047-6229 Small College Creativity
1047-6334 Southern California Psychiatrist
1047-6377 Scholarly Research and Review
1047-6385 Mealey's Litigation Report: S and L Bailout *see* 1057-1000
1047-6393 Companies and Their Brands
1047-6415 Flight Training
1047-6458 Computers in H R Management
1047-6474 National Croquet Calendar
1047-6482 Law Office Technology Review
1047-6504 Defense Housing
1047-6598 People Searching News
1047-6628 Washington (Marietta)
1047-6709 Who's Who in Electronics *see* 1047-5583
1047-6903 Hospital Blue Book (Official National Edition)
1047-6911 Hospital Blue Book (Official Southern Edition)
1047-6938 Optics & Photonics News
1047-7039 Organization Science
1047-708X Indiana Historical Society News
1047-711X Arab World Almanac
1047-7144 Youth Record
1047-7195 Earth First!
1047-725X Hot Line Farm Equipment Guide
1047-7667 Texas Trees
1047-7845 Journal of Religious & Theological Information
1047-7918 International Review of Strategic Management
1047-7926 Manage I T
1047-8043 Science Watch
1047-8078 C A Selects. Virucides & Virustats
1047-8086 C A Selects. Leukotrienes
1047-8094 C A Selects. Monoclonal Antibodies
1047-8108 C A Selects. Nitrogen Fixation
1047-8116 C A Selects. Nutritional Aspects of Cancer
1047-8124 C A Selects. Occupational Exposure & Hazards
1047-8132 C A Selects. Osteoporosis & Related Bone Loss
1047-8140 C A Selects. Pesticide Analysis
1047-8159 C A Selects. Ulcer Inhibitors
1047-8167 C A Selects. Antifungal & Antimycotic Agents
1047-8175 C A Selects. Anticonvulsants & Antiepileptics
1047-8183 C A Selects. Alzheimer's Disease & Related Memory Dysfunctions
1047-8191 C A Selects. Allergy and Antiallergic Agents
1047-8205 C A Selects. Drug Interactions
1047-8213 C A Selects. Indoor Air Pollution
1047-8310 Journal of High Technology Management Research
1047-8388 Technical & Skills Training
1047-840X Psychological Inquiry
1047-8442 OutWeek†
1047-8477 Journal of Structural Biology
1047-8485 Metropolitan Universities
1047-8507 International Journal of Optical Computing
1047-854X Win (Van Nuys)
1047-8604 Columns (Seattle)
1047-8620 Equine Athlete
1047-8639 Veterinary Practice Staff
1047-871X Monoclonal Antibodies
1047-8779 International Counterterrorism & Security
1047-8833 Northeast Real Estate News
1047-8841 Retail Store Image
1047-8868 Art Cellar Exchange
1047-8876 Washington Report on the Medical Sciences *see* 1047-8922
1047-8922 McGraw-Hill's Washington Report on Medicine and Health
1047-9090 American Window Cleaner
1047-9120 Ocular Surgery News International Edition
1047-9244 I O M A's G I C - B I C Yields and Market Report (Guranteed Investment Contracts - Bank Investment Contracts) *changed to* I O M A's Report on Defined Contribution Plan Investing.
1047-9325 Graphic Arts Monthly
1047-9430 Journal of Database Administration
1047-949X A L C T S Newsletter
1047-9619 San Diego County Business Directory
1047-9775 Location Production Guide
1047-9791 Holt Advisory
1047-9805 Leather Craftsman *see* 1056-4225
1047-9821 Money & Markets
1047-9848 Psychotherapy Letter
1048-0056 Tampa Bay Life
1048-0323 Mobile Communications Handbook *changed to* R C R Cellular Handbook.
1048-0323 Mobile Communications Handbook *changed to* R C R Paging Handbook.
1048-0501 Interactive Healthcare Newsletter
1048-0706 Laboratory Regulation News
1048-0870 Generalist Papers
1048-0919 Minority Business Entrepreneur
1048-0935 Today's Refinery
1048-0986 The Celator
1048-1141 High - Tc Update
1048-1354 Storytelling Magazine
1048-1400 Music International
1048-1648 Journal for Corporate Growth
1048-1885 Psychoanalytic Dialogues
1048-1990 Journal of General Orthodontics
1048-2008 Reports in Molecular Theory†
1048-2180 Scherzo
1048-2253 Impact International Directory *changed to* Impact World Directory.
1048-2385 Educators' Guide to Corporate Support *changed to* Educators' Guide to Corporate and Voluntary Support.
1048-2598 Memory I Cs D.A.T.A. Digest
1048-2652 Space Fax Daily
1048-2822 Lafayette Business Digest
1048-2830 A C C R A Cost of Living Index
1048-2849 World Chamber of Commerce Directory
1048-2911 New Solutions
1048-2938 Distressed Property Investor's Monthly
1048-3055 Publishing & Production Executive
1048-3152 Huntsville Historical Review
1048-3160 Herb, Spice and Medicinal Plant Digest
1048-3403 Faxon Report
1048-3411 Peterson's Job Opportunities for Business and Liberal Arts Graduates (Year)
1048-342X Peterson's Job Opportunities For Engineering, Science, and Computer Graduates (Year)
1048-3659 Quick & Easy Crafts
1048-3667 Richard E. Band's Profitable Investing
1048-3748 Tulane Maritime Law Journal
1048-3896 School House Alert
1048-3950 Word of Mouth (San Antonio)
1048-406X C D - R O M Shoppers Guide
1048-4078 Federal Facilities Environmental Journal
1048-4493 Medical Waste News
1048-4507 Classical
1048-4892 In-Fisherman Angling Adventures Travel Guide
1048-4949 Wildlife Conservation
1048-4981 Washington C E O
1048-5104 G P S World
1048-5112 Entertainment Marketing Letter
1048-5120 Item Processing Report
1048-5201 Hospital Litigation Reporter
1048-5236 Strategic Planning for Energy and the Environment
1048-5252 Nonparametric Statistics
1048-5287 European Journal of Serials Librarianship
1048-5317 Today's F D A
1048-5341 Quick & Easy Plastic Canvas
1048-5538 F D C Newsletter (Federal Digital Cartography) *see* 1055-8357
1048-5554 Pittsburgh Singles' Lifestyles
1048-5791 Cortlandt Forum
1048-5848 Economic Growth Report *see* 1050-3250
1048-6097 Directory of Merger and Acquisition Firms and Professionals
1048-6259 Inter-American Tropical Tuna Commission. Quarterly Report/ Comision Interamericana del Atun Tropical. Informe Trimestral
1048-6607 International Semiconductor Directory I Cs & Discrete Semiconductors D.A.T.A. Digest: Master Type Locator
1048-6682 Nonprofit Management and Leadership
1048-6690 Medical Device Technology
1048-6798 Computers and the History of Art
1048-6801 Contemporary Theatre Review
1048-6844 Christian Music Directories: Recorded Music
1048-6879 O E Reports
1048-6976 Microcell Report
1048-6984 Eating Disorders Review
1048-7042 Science and Global Security Monograph Series
1048-7387 Current Politics of the Soviet Union *changed to* Current Politics of Russia.
1048-776X N I S T Special Publication
1048-7840 Chemtracts: Analytical, Physical and Inorganic Chemistry *see* 1051-7227
1048-7948 Corridor Real Estate Journal
1048-7972 Gale Directory of Publications and Broadcast Media
1048-7972 Gale Directory of Publications and Broadcast Media Update
1048-8030 The Raptor Report
1048-8111 Aqua Terra
1048-8464 Haworth Series in Marketing
1048-8545 New Athenaeum
1048-8553 Studies in Puritan American Spirituality
1048-8561 Synopsis (Lewiston)
1048-857X Medieval Folklore
1048-8588 Medieval and Renaissance Yearbook
1048-8596 The Edwardean
1048-860X Yearbook of Interdisciplinary Studies in the Fine Arts
1048-8618 Cather Yearbook
1048-8626 Yearbook of Women's Studies
1048-8707 Ward's Business Directory of U S Private and Public Companies
1048-874X C A Selects. Immunochemical Methods
1048-8758 Go: The Rider's Manual
1048-8820 Quantum (Washington)
1048-8898 Career Pilot
1048-8901 Descendants of Richard Risley in America
1048-891X International Journal of Gynecological Cancer
1048-9002 Journal of Vibration and Acoustics
1048-907X A S H Smoking and Health Review
1048-9207 Avionics Review
1048-9215 Tackle Test
1048-9223 Language Acquisition
1048-9401 Early Drama, Art, and Music Review
1048-9487 Lambda Book Report
1048-9495 Salmon Market Newsletter
1048-9843 Leadership Quarterly
1048-9924 Leningrad Mathematical Journal
1048-9940 Wolverine
1049-0000 Golf and Sportsturf *changed to* Sportsturf.
1049-0043 Bats
1049-0078 Journal of Asian Economics
1049-0140 World Music Connections
1049-023X Prehospital and Disaster Medicine
1049-0264 Yearbook of Educational Law
1049-0310 Horror Fiction Newsletter
1049-0574 Coal Local
1049-0760 M H L S News
1049-0779 Peace Reporter
1049-0795 Inside Word for Windows
1049-0809 Joyce Studies Annual
1049-0833 C D - R O M Professional
1049-085X Behavior, Health, and Aging
1049-0892 Dead of Night
1049-0965 P S: Political Science & Politics
1049-1015 Chemical Monitor
1049-1163 T V Entertainment *changed to* Cable Guide.
1049-121X C2C Currents: Japan - Materials
1049-1228 C2C Currents: Japan - Chemistry
1049-1236 C2C Currents: Japan - Electronics
1049-1244 C2C Currents: Japan - Computers
1049-1252 C2C Abstracts: Japan - Ceramics
1049-1260 C2C Abstracts: Japan - Analytical Chemistry
1049-1279 C2C Abstracts: Japan - Chemical Engineering
1049-1287 C2C Abstracts: Japan - Crystallography
1049-1295 C2C Abstracts: Japan - Hydrocarbons
1049-1309 C2C Abstracts: Japan - Inorganic Chemistry
1049-1317 C2C Abstracts: Japan - Materials Science

ISSN INDEX 5845

1049-1325 C2C Abstracts: Japan - Organic Chemistry
1049-1333 C2C Abstracts: Japan - Physical Chemistry
1049-1341 C2C Abstracts: Japan - Plastics
1049-135X C2C Abstracts: Japan - Polymer Chemistry
1049-1368 C2C Abstracts: Japan - Surface Chemistry
1049-1376 C2C Abstracts: Japan - Textiles
1049-1384 C2C Abstracts: Japan - Metals
1049-152X M A R Gospel Ministries
1049-1740 Advocate (Prattsville)
1049-1791 Calorie Control Commentary
1049-1821 Norton Notes
1049-1848 Ryan Ramblings
1049-2062 Massachusetts Employment Law Letter
1049-2089 Journal of Health Care for the Poor and Underserved
1049-2119 U S Mayor
1049-2135 A F S M International
1049-2194 Capacity Management Review
1049-2275 Journal of Craniofacial Surgery
1049-233X Helminthological Society of Washington. Journal
1049-2356 Not Guilty
1049-2372 Property Management Monthly
1049-2437 Idaho. Department of Education. News and Reports
1049-2445 Microprocessor I C's D.A.T.A. Digest
1049-2453 Additives for Plastics D.A.T.A. Digest
1049-2658 National Forum Teacher Education Journal
1049-2682 I C Alternate Sources & Replacements D.A.T.A. Digest
1049-2747 Green Consumer Letter
1049-2801 Mathematical Chemistry
1049-2976 Journal of Neural Network Computing†
1049-3158 Good Packaging Magazine
1049-3255 The Department Chair
1049-3271 Blackfire
1049-328X Kuumba
1049-3298 Black Lace
1049-3344 Nelson's Earnings Outlook
1049-3867 Women's Health Issues
1049-3921 B M W E Railway Journal
1049-3999 Handbook of Organizations Involved in Soviet-American Relations
1049-4316 The B B I Newsletter
1049-4332 Fundline
1049-4340 Look Back
1049-4456 Book Promotion Hotline
1049-4502 Lynx
1049-4618 Harrowsmith Country Life
1049-4782 Errant News
1049-4812 Linked Ring Letter
1049-4820 Interactive Learning Environments
1049-4987 Constitutional Law Journal
1049-510X Ethnicity & Disease
1049-5142 Journal of Nonprofit & Public Sector Marketing
1049-5150 Journal of Nutritional Immunology
1049-5290 Photonics: Technology and Applications†
1049-5320 Inside D O S
1049-5339 Regional Economic Digest
1049-5347 Mealey's Reinsurance Report *changed to* Mealey's Litigation Report: Reinsurance.
1049-5398 Animal Biotechnology
1049-5452 Quayle Quarterly
1049-5568 Food Business
1049-5614 Scripps Clinic Personal Health Letter
1049-5851 Instructor
1049-586X Rescue (Kansas City)
1049-5967 Service Quality
1049-6025 Northwestern University Cancer Center. Journal *changed to* Northwestern University. Robert H. Lurie Cancer Center. Journal.
1049-6092 D M A Statistical Fact Book
1049-6211 Travel 50 & Beyond
1049-6335 Journal of Ideas
1049-6343 Journal of Preventive Psychiatry and Allied Disciplines†
1049-6432 Georgia Living *changed to* Georgia Journal - Living.
1049-6475 Journal of Herbs, Spices & Medicinal Plants
1049-6483 Journal of Euromarketing
1049-6491 Journal of Promotion Management
1049-6505 Journal of Agricultural & Food Information
1049-6513 Contemporary Theatre Studies
1049-670X Grape Grower
1049-6734 Advances in Endocrinology and Metabolism
1049-6742 For the Record (Valley Forge)
1049-684X National Trial Lawyer
1049-7064 Adweek Client - Brand Directory
1049-7250 Education In Focus
1049-7285 American Prospect
1049-7315 Research on Social Work Practice
1049-7323 Qualitative Health Research
1049-7579 N I S T Building Science Series
1049-7730 Science Probe!
1049-7781 Wings West
1049-7838 S D A C C County Comment
1049-7927 Over-the-Counter 1000 Yellow Book *see* 1058-2886
1049-7935 Financial 1000 Yellow Book *see* 1058-2878
1049-7943 Corporate 1000 Yellow Book *see* 1058-2908
1049-7951 International Corporate 1000 Yellow Book *see* 1058-2894
1049-796X Catalog of Current Law Titles
1049-7978 Lawyers Monthly Catalog. Government Documents from Official and Commercial Sources
1049-7986 B N A's Medicare Report
1049-801X International Fiber Journal
1049-815X American Writing
1049-8583 New Car Prices - Buyer's Guide Reports
1049-8621 Who's Who in Writers, Editors & Poets in the United States & Canada
1049-8834 Arteriosclerosis and Thrombosis
1049-8850 Journal of Aquatic Food Product Technology
1049-8893 B N A's National Environment Watch
1049-8907 The Journal of Visualization and Computer Animation
1049-8915 Internetworking: Research and Experience
1049-8923 International Journal of Robust and Nonlinear Control
1049-8931 International Journal of Methods in Psychiatric Research
1049-9040 Europa 1992
1049-9083 Global Environmental Change Report
1049-913X Tech Specialist *changed to* Windows - D O S Developer's Journal.
1049-9172 Display & Design Ideas
1049-9261 Acoustic Guitar
1049-9326 Information Industry Alert†
1049-9334 California Employment Law Letter
1049-9342 Arizona Environmental Law Letter
1049-9350 Midwest Environmental Law Letter
1049-9369 Alabama Employment Law Letter
1049-9377 Maryland Employment Law Letter
1049-9385 Illinois Employment Law Letter
1049-9407 Critical Reviews in Surface Chemistry
1049-9466 Texas Child Care
1049-9571 Genealogy Bulletin
1049-9598 Literary Creations
1049-9644 Biological Control
1049-9652 C V G I P: Graphical Models and Image Processing
1049-9660 C V G I P: Image Understanding
1049-9695 Urban Profile
1049-9768 Bowhunting
1049-9776 Machiavelli Studies
1049-9849 Inventory Reduction Report
1049-9970 Balloons and Parties Today
1050-0073 Traditional Quilter
1050-0197 Problems in Plastic and Reconstructive Surgery
1050-0200 Economic Times
1050-0316 Gift Basket Review
1050-0332 BeFriending Creation
1050-0383 Opinions (Year)
1050-0391 Colorado Journal of International Environmental Law and Policy
1050-0413 EarthLight
1050-0421 Tome
1050-0472 Journal of Mechanical Design
1050-0782 F X Week
1050-091X Business Alabama Monthly
1050-1606 International Journal of Sport Nutrition
1050-1738 Trends in Cardiovascular Medicine
1050-1827 International Journal of Microwave and Millimeter-Wave Computer Aided Engineering
1050-2092 Traditional Dwellings and Settlements Review
1050-2114 Management Portfolio
1050-2122 Contingency Journal *see* 1053-6566
1050-2149 Aviation Employment Monthly
1050-219X Year Book of Speech, Language and Hearing†
1050-2289 Journal of Religious Gerontology
1050-2300 Daily Californian
1050-2343 Records Management Quarterly
1050-2408 Harvard University Library Notes
1050-2416 Home Power
1050-2440 Horizon Air Magazine
1050-2483 Advanced Recovery Week
1050-2548 Art Reference Services Quarterly
1050-2556 Journal of Divorce & Remarriage
1050-270X McMahon Heavy Construction Cost Guide
1050-2742 Religious Conference Manager
1050-2823 Washington Peace Letter
1050-2882 In-Side Harlem
1050-2955 Cornell East Asia Series
1050-3145 Alternative Energy Digests
1050-3153 Waste Information Digests
1050-3161 Senior Health Digest *see* 1051-6913
1050-3188 Aging Action Alert
1050-3196 Landlord - Tenant Relations Report
1050-3226 Mortgage Market Insight
1050-3234 Housing the Elderly Report
1050-3242 Federal Assistance Monitor
1050-3250 Community Development Digest
1050-3250 Senior Law Report
1050-3250 Community Health Funding Report
1050-3293 Communication Theory
1050-3307 Psychotherapy Research
1050-3331 National Mortgage News
1050-3439 Helping the Homeless *changed to* Public Assistance Report.
1050-3447 Public Assistance Success *changed to* Public Assistance Report.
1050-3463 Minorities in Business Insider
1050-3536 P3: Planet Three
1050-3730 Soviet Business Law Report *changed to* Russia and Commonwealth Business Law Report.
1050-3749 School Shop - Tech Directions
1050-3811 C D - Housing Register
1050-382X Selling to Seniors
1050-3862 Genetic Analysis: Techniques and Applications
1050-415X New Delta Review
1050-4265 Technical Association of the Pulp and Paper Industry. Finishing and Converting Conference. Proceedings (Year)
1050-4281 Journal of Chemical Education: Software. Series A
1050-429X Journal of Chemical Education: Software. Series B
1050-4303 Journal of Chemical Education: Software. Series C
1050-4435 Traditional Quiltworks
1050-4443 Year Book of Ultrasound
1050-4613 Connecticut Facts - Rhode Island Facts
1050-4648 Fish and Shellfish Immunology
1050-477X Yearbook of American Lutheran Church *changed to* Evangelical Lutheran Church in America (Year).
1050-4788 Writing Concepts
1050-4796 Doll Designs
1050-480X Good Old Days Specials
1050-4834 Office of Thrift Supervision
1050-4850 Current World Affairs
1050-4893 New Occasional Papers in Women's Studies *see* 1055-856X
1050-4974 Pensions & Investments
1050-5067 Public Perspective
1050-513X K C T S - Nine
1050-5156 Copyright Directory: Attorneys, Professors, Government Agencies, Congressional Committees, Searchers, Clearinghouses, Hotlines & Associations, (Year)
1050-5164 Annals of Applied Probability
1050-5253 Asthma Management
1050-5261 Antisense Research & Development
1050-527X Trainers' Forum
1050-5342 Probate Law Journal of Ohio
1050-5350 Journal of Gambling Studies
1050-5415 Used Car Prices - Buyer's Guide Reports
1050-5423 New and Used Foreign and Japanese Car Prices
1050-5504 Past Times: The Nostalgia Entertainment Newsletter
1050-5628 Metric Today
1050-5644 Campus Watch
1050-5725 A S C P Update
1050-5741 Bit and Bridle
1050-5873 Colby Quarterly
1050-6098 A R L
1050-6306 Sociological Practice Review
1050-6411 Journal of Electromyography and Kinesiology
1050-642X Clinical Journal of Sport Medicine
1050-6438 Neurosurgery Quarterly
1050-6519 Journal of Business and Technical Communication
1050-6667 Online Alert
1050-6802 Hippo
1050-6918 Optometry Clinics
1050-6942 Journal of Chemical Education: Software. Special Issue Series
1050-6993 Datek Imaging Supplies Monthly
1050-7019 Imaging Business Report
1050-7035 Wittenberg Review
1050-7051 Journal of Hospitality & Leisure Marketing
1050-7086 Calliope (Peterborough)
1050-7159 College Preview
1050-7256 Thyroid
1050-7272 Truck & Van Prices - Buyer's Guide Reports
1050-7280 Infinity Limited
1050-7310 Language of Defense
1050-7361 Yellowed Pages
1050-7671 American Trucking Associations. Current Economic Bulletin
1050-785X Bass Player
1050-7868 E Q
1050-7914 Reunion Talks on Risleys
1050-7922 Risley Record
1050-7930 Review of Books on the Book of Mormon
1050-8147 School of Library and Information Science. Occasional Papers Series
1050-8163 Zillions
1050-821X Kind News Jr.
1050-8376 International Directory of Brands and Their Companies
1050-8392 Journal of Research on Adolescence
1050-8414 International Journal of Aviation Psychology
1050-8422 Ethics & Behavior
1050-8430 Genome Analysis
1050-8481 International Economic Insights
1050-8619 International Journal for the Psychology of Religion
1050-8686 Transmission & Distribution International
1050-8953 Inform Special Reports
1050-897X Mealey's European Environmental Law Report†
1050-9011 Bob Nurock's Advisory
1050-9038 H M O Magazine

ISSN

5846 ISSN INDEX

1050-9070 International Spectrum
1050-9208 Quarterly Review of Film and Video
1050-9453 New York International Law Review
1050-9496 Advances in Telematics
1050-9518 Old Time Crochet
1050-9542 Kind News Sr.
1050-9577 Electronic Trade & Transport News
1050-9607 Contemporary Management in Internal Medicine†
1050-9615 Contemporary Management in Obstetrics and Gynecology
1050-9623 Contemporary Management in Critical Care
1050-9631 Hippocampus
1050-964X The Report of Pediatric Infectious Diseases
1050-9658 Laboratory Medicine Abstract and Comment
1050-9674 Journal of Offender Rehabilitation
1050-9712 Backwoods Home Magazine
1050-9720 New England Theatre Journal
1050-995X Year Book of Health Care Management
1051-0036 Briefly...
1051-0109 Recycling Today (Municipal Market Edition)
1051-0192 Preservation Progress (Crownsville, MD)
1051-0214 National Ground Water Association. Briefings
1051-0257 Washington International
1051-0567 Plastics & Environment
1051-0583 Water Farming Journal
1051-0613 Safe Cycling
1051-0621 Hawaiian Express Magazine
1051-063X Sailorman Star Magazine
1051-0761 Ecological Applications
1051-077X Current Obstetric Medicine
1051-0788 Willem Mengelberg Society. Newsletter
1051-0923 Surveillant
1051-1091 Recycling Today (Scrap Market Edition)
1051-1253 Journal of Criminal Justice Education
1051-1261 Independent Small Press Review
1051-127X Moksha Journal
1051-1377 Journal of Housing Economics
1051-1431 Argumentation & Advocacy
1051-144X Journal of Visual Literacy
1051-1482 Housing Policy Debate
1051-1695 Fish Drum
1051-1717 Exact Change
1051-1733 Northwestern Naturalist
1051-1814 Earthtreks Digest *changed to* Earthtreks Magazine.
1051-1822 Music Retailing
1051-1857 Calypso
1051-189X Fiber Optics Weekly Update
1051-1903 F D D I News
1051-192X Fiber to the Home
1051-1938 Cable Optics
1051-1946 Fiber Optic Sensor and Systems
1051-1954 Fiber Datacom
1051-1962 Local Area Networks
1051-1970 Primus
1051-2004 Digital Signal Processing
1051-2020 Biomedical Science and Technology
1051-208X B N A C Communicator
1051-2144 The Endocrinologist
1051-2187 Toy Trucker and Contractor
1051-2284 Journal of Neuroimaging
1051-2357 Mobile Robots and Unmanned Vehicles
1051-2373 Oh! Idaho
1051-2438 P S R Quarterly
1051-2446 Assisted Reproduction Reviews
1051-2454 Text Management Journal *see* 1058-0379
1051-2462 Defense - Aerospace Business Digest *see* 1057-0950
1051-2497 Pac-Rim Defense Marketing *see* 1044-3975
1051-2616 Gallup Poll Monthly
1051-2675 Bloc
1051-2691 Communications Systems Engineering: Postal Applications†
1051-2705 Journal of Hydraulic Engineering (Bristol)†
1051-2772 I C S A Newsletter
1051-2837 Environmental Management (Denver)
1051-2993 Thesaurus of E R I C Descriptors
1051-3124 Independent Telco News
1051-323X Back Home
1051-3299 Assistant Editor
1051-3310 Lingua Franca
1051-3345 Mission Today
1051-3434 Diablo
1051-3663 Legal Assistant Today
1051-3701 A A A Today (Cincinnati)
1051-3833 P C N News
1051-385X Police Technology and Management
1051-3884 C A Selects. Alkoxylated Oleochemicals
1051-3892 C A Selects. Antiarrhythmics
1051-3906 C A Selects. Calcium Channel Blockers
1051-3914 C A Selects. Food, Drugs, & Cosmetics - Legislative & Regulatory Aspects
1051-3922 C A Selects. Hypertension & Antihypertensives
1051-3930 C A Selects. Phospholipids (Chemical Aspects)
1051-3949 C A Selects. Photocatalysts
1051-4015 P A I S International in Print
1051-4023 New Hampshire Bar News
1051-404X Microscope Book
1051-4066 L A N Reporter
1051-4120 T P Q: The Tube & Pipe Quarterly
1051-4147 Mundo Hispanico
1051-4287 Political Report
1051-4546 In the Field
1051-4589 C A A S Report
1051-4775 B N A's Workers' Compensation Report
1051-4791 Research & Education Networking
1051-4805 Electronic Networking
1051-4813 American Short Fiction
1051-4880 Insight (Washington)
1051-4902 Home Equity Lines of Credit Report
1051-4961 Ladybug
1051-5011 Fantasy Commentator
1051-5062 American Literary Review
1051-5100 Marine Stores Merchandising
1051-5623 Facts About Alaska: Alaska Almanac
1051-5623 Alaska Almanac
1051-5658 Remediation
1051-5690 Elektor Electronics U S A
1051-5720 Cleaning Management
1051-5968 Lullwater Review
1051-600X Physician Assistant Programs Directory
1051-6050 Great American Video Business Newsletter
1051-6204 Perspectives in Education and Deafness
1051-6247 Worldwide Travel Information Contact Book
1051-628X Beverly Hills Bar Association Journal
1051-631X Airline Executive International
1051-6352 Flexo Espanol
1051-6573 Equipment Leasing & Asset-Based Borrowing Report
1051-6670 Theoretical Studies in Second Language Acquisition
1051-6794 Cells and Materials
1051-6913 Senior Care Professional
1051-6956 Skyways
1051-6964 G F O A Newsletter
1051-709X Texas Water Utilities Journal
1051-712X Journal of Business-to-Business Marketing
1051-7138 Kansas Facts
1051-7146 Michigan Facts
1051-7200 Surgical Laparoscopy and Endoscopy
1051-7227 Chemtracts: Inorganic Chemistry
1051-7235 Toxicology Methods
1051-7286 Alma Mariana
1051-7324 Flexo
1051-7375 Midway†
1051-7383 Compass Readings
1051-7707 Surface-Mounted Integrated Circuits D.A.T.A. Digest
1051-7715 Surface-Mounted Discretes D.A.T.A. Digest
1051-7723 Drugs Available Abroad
1051-7782 Comprehensive Mental Health Care
1051-7871 Liberation and Marxism
1051-7898 Islander
1051-7901 U.S. Department of Agriculture. Fruit and Tree Nuts Situation and Outlook Report
1051-8045 Russian Journal of Theoretical and Applied Mechanics
1051-8053 Russian Journal of Engineering Thermophysics
1051-8061 International Market Alert
1051-8207 I E E E Microwave and Guided Wave Letters
1051-8215 I E E E Transactions on Circuits and Systems for Video Technology
1051-8223 I E E E Transactions on Applied Superconductivity
1051-824X Mast
1051-8711 Visions (Beaverton)
1051-8886 T E S O L Matters
1051-8959 Between the Vines
1051-9076 FloraCulture International
1051-9084 Diamond Depositions
1051-919X Oklahoma Directory of Manufacturers and Processors
1051-9432 Measurement Chain *see* 1060-1902
1051-9440 Industrial Automation Outlook *see* 1060-2712
1051-9505 Fairs and Festivals in the Northeast *see* 1059-5929
1051-9513 Fairs and Festivals in the Southeast *see* 1059-5929
1051-953X Multimedia Computing & Presentations
1051-9718 Artists and Issues in the Theatre
1051-9815 Work (Reading)
1051-9971 Future Home Technology News
1051-9998 Plasma Devices and Operations
1052-0015 Journal of Small Fruit & Viticulture
1052-0139 CryoGas International
1052-0295 Biotechnic and Histochemistry
1052-0341 Upside
1052-0384 Nonviolent Sanctions
1052-0511 Theater Three†
1052-0600 Journal of Mathematical Systems, Estimation and Control
1052-0635 Defense Cleanup
1052-0775 Quser News
1052-1011 Latitudes South
1052-1062 Journal of Clean Technology and Environmental Sciences
1052-1151 Religion and American Culture
1052-1186 P C Novice
1052-1232 National Sports Daily†
1052-1372 P & T
1052-1380 Prince George's County Genealogical Society. Bulletin
1052-1453 Skull Base Surgery
1052-150X Business Ethics Quarterly
1052-1542 Supervisor's Environmental Alert *changed to* Environmental Safety Alert.
1052-1550 Pollution Prevention Review
1052-1577 Harvard Health Letter
1052-181X Martin Luther King, Jr. Memorial Studies in Religion, Culture and Social Development
1052-1976 C A Selects. Oleochemicals Containing Nitrogen
1052-1984 C A Selects. Omega-3 Fatty Acids & Fish Oil
1052-2131 European Packaging Newsletter and World Report
1052-214X Journal of Restaurant & Foodservice Marketing
1052-2174 Video Journal of Echocardiography
1052-2182 Video Journal of Color Flow Imaging
1052-2204 Rockwell Lecture Series
1052-2212 What do I Read Next?
1052-2263 Journal of Vocational Rehabilitation
1052-2433 Today in Mississippi
1052-2484 Urban Forests
1052-2522 73 Amateur Radio Today
1052-2581 Technical Support
1052-2662 Inside 1-2-3 Release 3
1052-2697 Small Press Book Review Annual†
1052-2727 Alaska's Wildlife
1052-2883 Institute of Environmental Sciences. Journal
1052-3049 Third World Libraries
1052-3154 Bakunin
1052-3162 Without Halos
1052-3189 Geborener Deutscher
1052-3243 Neil Sperry's Gardens
1052-3383 Space Exploration Technology
1052-3421 Wisconsin Women's Law Journal
1052-3545 Dowline
1052-3561 Midrange Computing
1052-3685 Harvard University Library Notes *see* 0017-8136
1052-3928 Journal of Professional Issues in Engineering and Practice
1052-3944 Postal Watch
1052-3952 French American Review
1052-4002 Current Problems in Geriatrics†
1052-4010 Current Problems in Urology
1052-4053 Disc Magazine
1052-4169 Beauty Education
1052-4207 A I D S Treatment News
1052-4215 Nashville Business and Lifestyles
1052-4231 Virginia Medical Quarterly
1052-4282 MarineFacts
1052-4355 Ohio Environmental Law Letter
1052-4363 Pennsylvania Employment Law Letter
1052-4371 Kentucky Employment Law Letter
1052-4592 Delaware Valley
1052-4630 Gourmet News
1052-4681 A Brief Relation
1052-469X Montana Land Magazine
1052-4703 Homes & Real Estate Magazine - Billings, Montana
1052-4711 Homes & Real Estate Magazine - Great Falls, Montana
1052-4746 The Hunting Report for Big Game Hunters
1052-486X Contemporary Doll
1052-4908 Plastics Recycling Update
1052-4916 Bottle - Can Recycling Update
1052-4959 Women's Caucus for Art. National Update
1052-5017 Transformations
1052-5173 G S A Today
1052-522X Albertsen's - International Edition†
1052-5238 U S and Foreign Diplomatic Contacts
1052-5335 1,000 Worldwide Newspapers
1052-5521 Quarterly Byte
1052-5629 Journal of Management Education
1052-5882 Cellular and Molecular Mechanisms of Inflammation
1052-6188 Journal of Machinery Manufacture and Reliability
1052-6196 Soviet Journal of Heavy Machinery
1052-6234 S I A M Journal on Optimization
1052-6242 Virtual Reality Report
1052-6471 FedWatch
1052-648X Short Story
1052-6692 Progress in Computer-Aided V L S I Design†
1052-6722 Northwest Mileposts
1052-6730 Ocean and Coastal Law Memo
1052-6773 National Cancer Institute. Journal. Monographs
1052-6846 Journal of School Leadership
1052-7001 Journal of Housing Research
1052-701X Open Systems Report
1052-7109 The M Street Journal
1052-7117 The M Street Radio Directory
1052-7206 Business and the Environment
1052-7249 Insurance Settlements Journal
1052-729X Urban Perspectives
1052-7346 Optometric Economics
1052-7354 Who's Who Among Hispanic Americans
1052-7613 Aquatic Conservation: Marine and Freshwater Ecosystems
1052-763X Game Player's Sega Genesis Strategy Guide
1052-7753 Tackett Journal
1052-7893 A S C P Washington Report on National and State Issues
1052-7958 American Psychoanalyst
1052-813X B N A California - Environment Reporter
1052-8555 Genesis (New York)
1052-8563 M Inc. *changed to* M.
1052-8571 Microsoft Networking Journal
1052-858X Ohio Genealogical Society Newsletter

ISSN INDEX 5847

1052-8725 Real-Time Systems Symposium. Proceedings
1052-8733 Hospital Revenue Report
1052-875X Star (Lantana)
1052-8814 Vox Magazine
1052-8822 Northern California Business Directory and Buyers Guide
1052-8857 Inside Michigan Politics
1052-9128 MacTech Journal
1052-9136 General Aviation News & Flyer
1052-9225 China Statistical Yearbook
1052-9241 Journal of Culinary Practice
1052-9268 International Video Journal of Engineering Research
1052-9276 Reviews in Medical Virology
1052-9284 Journal of Community and Applied Social Psychology
1052-9306 Biological Mass Spectrometry
1052-9411 Quality Assurance
1052-9438 New York Review of Science Fiction
1052-9632 Consumer Product Litigation Reporter
1052-9640 Pension Fund Litigation Reporter
1052-9896 Directory of Political Newsletters *see* 1057-0578
1052-9950 Journal of Analytic Social Work
1052-9985 Parking Security Report
1053-0002 O A G Business Travel Planner. North American Edition
1053-0010 North South Trader's Civil War
1053-0177 Romantic Traveling
1053-0215 Stockholders & Creditors News Service Re: Hillsborough Holding Corp.
1053-0223 Stockholders & Creditors News Service Re: Federated Department Stores, Inc.
1053-0231 Asbestos Abatement Litigation Reporter†
1053-024X Indoor Pollution Litigation Reporter
1053-0258 Utilities Industry Litigation Reporter
1053-0266 Securities Litigation Reporter
1053-0274 Wrongful Discharge Report
1053-0312 Nelson's Directory of Plan Sponsors and Tax Exempt Funds
1053-0347 Cash Flow Enhancement Report
1053-0452 Clinics in Applied Nutrition
1053-0460 Clearinghouse Directory
1053-0479 Journal of Psychotherapy Integration
1053-0487 Journal of Occupational Rehabilitation
1053-0495 Journal of Inorganic and Organometallic Polymers
1053-0509 Journal of Fluorescence
1053-0525 Recycling Related Newsletter, Publications, Periodicals
1053-055X T H - Ers Express
1053-0584 Aspects
1053-0754 Responsive Community
1053-0770 Journal of Cardiothoracic and Vascular Anesthesia
1053-0789 Journal of Social Distress and the Homeless
1053-0797 Dreaming
1053-0800 Journal of Child and Adolescent Group Therapy
1053-0819 Journal of Behavioral Education
1053-0908 Bowser Directory of Small Stocks
1053-1297 New England Review
1053-1467 Inside Quattro Pro
1053-1750 International Education Forum
1053-1793 Writers' Guidelines Magazine
1053-1866 Contributions in Asian Studies
1053-1890 Child and Youth Care Forum
1053-1998 Travel Review
1053-2013 Craft Related Newsletters, Periodicals & Publications
1053-2021 Bargain Hunters & Budgeteers Opportunity Newsletter
1053-203X Journal of the Freshman Year Experience
1053-2110 Master's Theses in the Natural and Technical Sciences
1053-2137 Journal of Human Muscle Performance
1053-2161 Stress and Emotion
1053-2293 Builders Trade Journal
1053-234X FAXreporter
1053-2404 Atlantic Trade Report & Global Defense Industry
1053-2498 Journal of Heart and Lung Transplantation
1053-2536 Nelson's Guide to Pension Fund Consultants
1053-2587 Innovating
1053-2838 Life & Health Insurance Sales
1053-296X Our Stories
1053-3362 Advocate (Saint Paul)
1053-3605 Buzz
1053-3648 Supermarket Strategic Alert
1053-377X Journal of Energy, Natural Resources and Environmental Law
1053-3834 Computer User's Survival Magazine
1053-3842 Punch in International Travel and Entertainment Magazine
1053-4202 Anthropology of Consciousness
1053-4245 Journal of Exposure Analysis and Environmental Epidemiology
1053-4261 Advanced Labanotation
1053-4466 Hunting Report: Edition II - For Birdshooters and Waterfowlers
1053-4628 Journal of Clinical Pediatric Dentistry
1053-4636 Bibliographies and Indexes in Science Fiction, Fantasy, and Horror
1053-4644 Motion Control
1053-4652 Federal Staffing Digest
1053-4660 International Merger Law: Events and Commentary
1053-4725 Environmental Toxicology and Water Quality
1053-4768 Exceptional Human Experience
1053-4792 Smarandache Function Journal
1053-4822 Human Resource Management Review
1053-4881 North American Pylon
1053-4911 Southwestern (Denton)
1053-4962 Full Disclosure
1053-4997 Japan Notebook
1053-5012 Provincetown Arts
1053-5020 Round Table (Beloit)
1053-5349 Controlling Benefits & Deferred Compensation
1053-5373 B N A's Employee Relations
1053-5381 International Journal of Offshore and Polar Engineering
1053-5454 Dancing U S A
1053-5500 Case Management Advisor
1053-5586 Infant - Toddler Intervention
1053-5594 Data Resource Management
1053-5845 Solid Value
1053-587X I E E E Transactions on Signal Processing
1053-5888 I E E E - Signal Processing Magazine
1053-6051 Robotics Abstracts Annual
1053-6183 Indiana Environmental Law Letter
1053-6191 Indiana Employment Law Letter
1053-6205 P C Techniques
1053-6256 Vizions
1053-637X Walkerana
1053-6388 Journal of Medical and Applied Malacology
1053-6418 Green 2000
1053-6426 Molecular Marine Biology and Biotechnology
1053-6477 University of Michigan. Museum of Zoology. Special Publications
1053-6493 T-Shirt Business Info Mapping Newsletter
1053-6507 Clothing for Less Newsletter
1053-6523 Coupon Treasure Hunt Newsletter
1053-654X Jobs in Recessionary Times Possibility Newsletter
1053-6566 Enterprise Systems Journal
1053-6728 Technology and Learning
1053-6736 Journal of Comparative and International Law
1053-6825 National Directory of Retirement Facilities
1053-6884 Jukebox Collector
1053-6949 L N G Observer
1053-6981 Journal of Narrative and Life History
1053-699X Journal of Jewish Thought and Philosophy
1053-7007 Trade Union Handbook
1053-7023 Labor News
1053-7031 Photographic Art Market: Auction Prices (Year)
1053-704X Black Employment and Education
1053-7090 Footnotes from the Arid Zone
1053-7104 Greenhouse Product News
1053-7163 Initial Public Offerings Annual†
1053-7201 Remark (New York)
1053-7287 Journal of Global Business
1053-749X Complications in Surgery
1053-7694 C A S Journal
1053-7899 M S W Management
1053-7937 Writing About Women: Feminist Literary Studies
1053-8100 Consciousness and Cognition
1053-8119 NeuroImage
1053-8127 Journal of Back and Musculoskeletal Rehabilitation
1053-8135 NeuroRehabilitation
1053-8186 Harvard Law Bulletin
1053-8259 Journal of Experiential Education (Boulder)
1053-8305 N R C A Membership Directory
1053-8321 MediaWatch
1053-8356 American Journal of Numismatics *changed to* American Journal of Numismatics. Series 2.
1053-8364 Journal of Philosophical Research
1053-8550 Journal of Immunotherapy
1053-8569 Pharmacoepidemiology and Drug Safety
1053-8712 Journal of Child Sexual Abuse
1053-8720 Journal of Gay & Lesbian Social Services
1053-8739 Journal of College & University Foodservice
1053-8747 Popular Culture in Libraries
1053-8755 Journal of Ministry in Addiction & Recovery
1053-8763 Africa Investment Monitor
1053-8801 Publishing Research Quarterly
1053-8860 Technical Brief
1053-8933 A J C U Higher Education Report
1053-8941 Association of Jesuit Colleges and Universities and Jesuit Secondary Education Association Directory
1053-8992 Louisiana Manufacturers Register
1053-9107 A B C Dialogue
1053-9115 Sensations
1053-9263 Central Business Review
1053-931X Landmark Studies
1053-9638 WordPerfect Report
1053-9662 Hawaii Health Messenger
1053-9719 R A M Research Cardtrak
1053-9751 Public Pulse
1053-9832 Nonwovens Markets and Fiber Structures Report
1053-9859 World Geophysical News
1053-9867 Federal Sentencing Reporter
1053-9905 Consolidated Treaties & International Agreements: United States Current Document Service
1053-993X Spectrum Report
1054-0040 A M S Montessori Life
1054-013X N I S T Technical Note
1054-0156 Pro Football Illustrated (Year)
1054-0164 Football Preview (Year)
1054-0253 A S M E - I E E E Joint Railroad Conference. I E E E Technical Papers
1054-0407 Circuits Assembly
1054-058X Austrian Literature
1054-0695 ShareDebate International
1054-0709 Archives Sharing Bulletin
1054-0725 Emergency Medicine News
1054-0733 Insurance and Technology
1054-0768 Food Free or Cheap Newsletter
1054-0792 Association for Past-Life Research and Therapy. Newsletter
1054-0830 Journal of Regression Therapy
1054-0970 Labmedica
1054-1136 Buyer's Guide Timber Frame Homes
1054-1144 Children's Ministry
1054-1209 Cal - O S H A Reporter
1054-1381 Icarus (New York)
1054-139X Journal of Adolescent Health
1054-1403 Cervantes and His Times
1054-1411 Alateen Talk
1054-142X Al-Anon in Institutions
1054-1438 Inside Al-Anon
1054-1446 Al-Anon Speaks Out
1054-1500 Chaos
1054-1721 Journal of Organizational Computing
1054-1756 Forging
1054-1802 Journal of Urban and Cultural Studies
1054-1934 Illustrated Buyers Guide to Exhibits
1054-2183 The Show
1054-2191 Don Heinrich's College Football
1054-2205 The National Sports Review
1054-2213 Dick Vitale's Basketball
1054-2221 Don Heinrich's Pro Preview
1054-2248 Bill Mazeroski's Baseball
1054-2264 Marketplace Magazine
1054-2353 Nurse Author and Editor
1054-2396 P P O Letter
1054-2434 Industria Grafica y Artes Graficas
1054-2523 Medicinal Chemistry Research
1054-2647 Inside I V H S
1054-2655 Mad River
1054-2663 Mexico Business Monthly
1054-2841 Kentucky Checklist of State Publications
1054-3031 Silver & Blue
1054-3120 Studies on the Shoah
1054-3139 I C E S Journal of Marine Science
1054-335X Aviation Heritage
1054-3376 E L F
1054-3406 Journal of Biopharmaceutical Statistics
1054-3430 Cross-Stitch Plus
1054-3465 Reflex Magazine
1054-3473 Experience
1054-3570 A C A Update
1054-3775 N C L C Reports: Bankruptcy & Foreclosures
1054-3902 Symantec
1054-3937 Exit 13 Magazine
1054-4054 Law Firms Yellow Book
1054-4062 Municipal Yellow Book
1054-4070 Associations Yellow Book
1054-4089 Best Bed & Breakfast in England, Scotland & Wales
1054-4232 Sanyo P C Hackers Newsletter
1054-4259 T V & Cable Publicity Outlets - Nationwide
1054-4267 Technology Alert
1054-4275 Management Matters
1054-4593 Selling to the Other Educational Markets
1054-4607 Amerikai Magyar Levelestar
1054-4623 New Jersey Lake Survey Fishing Maps Guide
1054-4682 Journal of Home & Consumer Horticulture
1054-4801 Rural Living
1054-5034 Tim Bell's Alaska Travel Guide
1054-5069 Credit Risk Management
1054-5123 Pig Tail Times
1054-5131 The Chemical Packaging Review
1054-5182 Atlanta's Business Makers and Shakers. Volume II - Atlanta's Top Networking Channels
1054-5212 Re: Arts and Letters
1054-5433 Video Digest
1054-5441 Aura of Fort Worth and Tarrant County
1054-5476 In Vitro Cellular & Developmental Biology - Plant
1054-5859 Government and Politics Alert
1054-5999 Appraiser News
1054-6006 Fisheries Oceanography
1054-6022 Seventeenth - Century Music
1054-6359 North Carolina Employment Law Letter
1054-6367 Minnesota Employment Law Letter
1054-6375 Missouri Employment Law Letter
1054-6456 InCider - A Plus
1054-6464 E & P Environment
1054-6480 Oakland University Magazine
1054-6588 Studies on Soviet Economic Development
1054-6596 Soviet Archives of Internal Medicine
1054-660X Laser Physics (Soviet)
1054-6618 Pattern Recognition and Image Analysis
1054-6626 Public Opinion in the Soviet Union: Statistics and Analysis

ISSN

5848 ISSN INDEX

1054-6634 Mathematical Modeling (Soviet)
1054-6707 Dream Network
1054-6790 Contributions in Latin American Studies
1054-6812 Sales & Use Tax Alert
1054-6863 Kennedy Institute of Ethics Journal
1054-7002 KidSports
1054-7126 Youth Ministry Quarterly (New Hampton)
1054-7436 Commuter Air International
1054-7460 Presence: Teleoperators and Virtual Environments
1054-7541 A I P E Facilities
1054-7614 Loyola Magazine
1054-7649 Stritch M.D.
1054-7673 N C R T L Special Report
1054-7681 Handbook of Comparative Economic Policies
1054-7711 Allure
1054-7738 Clinical Nursing Research
1054-7835 Bricker's International Directory, Volume 1: Long-Term University-Based Executive Programs (Year)
1054-7843 Bricker's International Directory, Volume 2: Short-Term University-Based Executive Programs (Year)
1054-8017 Environmental Finance
1054-8033 Home School Researcher
1054-8289 The Future of Children
1054-8351 Virginia Facts
1054-8378 Theatre Topics
1054-8386 Semiotics and the Human Sciences
1054-8408 Journal of Travel & Tourism Marketing
1054-8505 Clinics in Communication Disorders
1054-8513 Physical Therapy Practice
1054-853X International Journal of Energy - Environment - Economics
1054-8637 World Trade
1054-867X P C Advisor†
1054-8688 Current Thoughts & Trends
1054-8726 Family Dynamics of Addiction Quarterly
1054-8742 Global Trade White Pages
1054-8793 N F P A Journal
1054-8807 Cardiovascular Pathology
1054-8874 Chronicle of Latin American Economic Affairs
1054-8882 Central America Update
1054-8890 SourceMex
1054-8912 Muscle Mustangs & Fast Fords
1054-9102 Bibliographies and Indexes in Latin American and Caribbean Studies
1054-9110 Reference Guides to Archival and Manuscript Sources in World History
1054-9471 National Directory of Courts of Law
1054-948X Human Rights Watch World Report
1054-9609 Diagnostics Intelligence
1054-9676 Library Mosaics
1054-9692 Document Image Automation
1054-9706 Document Image Automation Update
1054-9714 Journal of Phase Equilibria
1054-979X TechScan Newsletter
1054-9803 P C R Methods and Applications
1054-9811 Journal of Sustainable Forestry
1054-9994 Cash Rich Companies
1055-0100 Baldwin's Ohio School Law Journal
1055-0259 Powder Coating
1055-0348 Waves
1055-0364 Decoy Magazine
1055-0496 American Journal on Addictions
1055-050X Journal of Psychotherapy Practice and Research
1055-0518 Child Assessment News
1055-0569 The D O S Authority
1055-0577 Inside QuickBasic
1055-0623 Corporate Giving Directory
1055-0658 Daily Graphs. American Stock Exchange - O.T.C.
1055-0860 Education in the Public Eye
1055-0887 Journal of Addictive Diseases
1055-0895 Random Lengths Yardstick
1055-0917 Movieline
1055-1018 Campbell Contacts in America
1055-1042 Soviet Perspectives
1055-1158 Research in Religion and Family: Black Perspectives
1055-1166 Wild Earth
1055-1247 Agenda (New York, 1991)
1055-128X Law Office Computing
1055-1344 Siberian Advances in Mathematics
1055-1379 Journal of Nutrition in Recipe & Menu Development
1055-1492 Quarry Farm Papers
1055-1670 Poet's Handbook
1055-1743 F Y I - I M
1055-176X Media Week
1055-1905 Women's Traveller
1055-1948 Writers Guild of America, West. Journal
1055-1964 N.A.D.A. Small Boat Appraisal Guide
1055-1972 N.A.D.A. Large Boat Appraisal Guide
1055-2073 Journal of Southeast Asia Business
1055-2251 Yankee Magazine's Travel Guide to New England and its Neighbors *see* 1055-226X
1055-226X Yankee Magazine's Travel Guide to New England, New York & Eastern Canada
1055-2286 Art and Design News
1055-2294 Beckett Football Card Monthly
1055-2340 Spray Technology & Marketing
1055-2456 Tax Penalties
1055-2464 Studies in Anthropology and History
1055-2766 N M F S Fisheries Market News Report
1055-2855 Chicora Foundation Research
1055-307X Mealey's Litigation Report: Punitive Damages and Tort Reform
1055-3169 Today's Family
1055-3177 Novon
1055-324X Journal of American Health Policy
1055-3290 Association of Nurses in A I D S Care. Journal
1055-3304 O'Dwyer's F A R A Report
1055-3398 Best of Health
1055-3495 Hazardous Waste Management & Business Opportunities Newsletter
1055-3533 N A A C O G's Women's Health Nursing Scan
1055-3568 Business Speaker's Digest
1055-3649 International Parallels
1055-3835 Journal of Addictions & Offender Counseling
1055-3908 Rural Southern Voice for Peace
1055-3916 Information Searcher
1055-3967 Hobo Times
1055-4181 Technology and Disability
1055-4319 Campus Security Report
1055-4394 Wallcoverings, Windows & Interior Fashion
1055-4653 Shackelford Newsletter†
1055-4742 Book Links
1055-4769 Academic and Library Computing
1055-4785 Disc Golf Journal
1055-484X Tricycle
1055-5145 Grand Rapids Magazine
1055-5153 Grand Rapids Parent
1055-5269 Surface Science Spectra
1055-5862 Municipal Liability Litigation Reporter†
1055-6087 Guide to Literary Agents and Art - Photo Reps
1055-615X International Journal of Intelligent Systems in Accounting, Finance & Management
1055-6192 B O C A National Property Maintenance Code
1055-6656 Cleft Palate - Craniofacial Journal
1055-6699 Journal of Health Education
1055-6796 Astronomical and Astrophysical Transactions
1055-6826 Bio-Bibliographies in Art and Architecture
1055-6850 Touring America
1055-6877 I E E E - L T S: The Magazine of Lightwave Telecommunications Systems
1055-6893 The Green Book: Environmental Resource Directory
1055-6915 Magnetic and Electrical Separation
1055-6931 H D World Review
1055-713X Progress in Neural Networks
1055-7148 International Journal of Network Management
1055-7172 Biomaterials, Artificial Cells and Immobilization Biotechnology
1055-7199 Hoover's Handbook of World Business
1055-744X Gulf Reconstruction Report
1055-7466 American Health Systems Review
1055-7512 Journal of Individual Employment Rights
1055-7571 Total Quality Environmental Management
1055-758X Journal of Environmental Regulation
1055-761X The Paradoxist Movement
1055-7628 American Salaries and Wages Survey
1055-7644 Temporary Culture
1055-7768 Systems 3X - 400
1055-7857 Wake Treasures
1055-789X Journal of Technology in Mathematics
1055-7903 Molecular Phylogenetics and Evolution
1055-7911 Yoga International
1055-808X Advances in Gastrointestinal Radiology
1055-8098 Imaging Service Bureau News
1055-8179 Beckett Basketball Monthly
1055-8217 Business Concepts
1055-8225 Credit & Finance
1055-8233 Motor World
1055-8241 Health Diet & Nutrition
1055-825X Government Programs
1055-8268 National Auctions & Sales
1055-8276 U S Immigration
1055-8284 Economic Home Owner
1055-8292 Current Employment
1055-8306 American Senior
1055-8314 Ideal Traveller
1055-8349 A A C N Nursing Scan In Critical Care
1055-8357 F G D Newsletter
1055-842X Nihilistic Review
1055-8454 Telecommunications Directory
1055-8462 International Journal of Systems Automation
1055-8470 International Journal in Computer Simulation
1055-856X Michigan Feminist Studies†
1055-8659 Whetstone (Barrington)
1055-8675 Financial Leadership Speaks
1055-8896 Journal of Educational Multimedia and Hypermedia
1055-9140 Drinking Water Research
1055-9175 Oil Spill U S Law Report
1055-9213 State of America's Children (Year)
1055-9221 Child, Youth, and Family Futures Clearinghouse
1055-923X National Consumers League Bulletin
1055-9272 Think
1055-9280 H D T V Report
1055-9299 InterAmerican Opportunities Briefing
1055-9477 Chapter 11 Update
1055-9493 Asbestos Regulatory Reporter - New York Edition
1055-9612 Drug Design and Discovery
1055-9620 Technology for Critical Care Nurses
1055-9671 Global Market Perspective
1055-9701 Color Publishing
1055-9744 Pharmacy Update
1055-9760 Training & Development
1055-9795 East-West Center. Views
1055-9809 In Depth (Washington)
1055-9922 Remote Sensing of Earth Resources: A Quarterly Bibliography
1056-0017 A P I C S the Performance Advantage
1056-0319 American Jails
1056-0327 Laughing Bear Newsletter
1056-0793 RadTech Report
1056-0815 Housewife - Writer's Forum
1056-1072 Contention
1056-1412 Integrated Messaging News
1056-1471 Contemporary Topics in Laboratory Animal Science
1056-148X Earth (Waukesha)
1056-1528 California Libraries
1056-1536 Impact Pump News Patents
1056-1544 Impact Valves News and Patents
1056-1595 Okay America
1056-1773 Engineering Department Management & Administration Report
1056-182X Comparison Report on Engineering Scanning Systems *see* 1061-9550
1056-2036 C Q Researcher
1056-2168 Alabama Facts
1056-2192 Greenwood Educators' Reference Collection
1056-2532 A A A Motorist
1056-2591 The Sagarin Review
1056-2850 C A Services Today
1056-3466 Annual Review of Energy and the Environment
1056-3482 National Enquirer
1056-3911 Journal of Algebraic Geometry
1056-4039 M E N C Soundpost
1056-4098 Medical Malpractice - Ob-Gyn Litigation Reporter
1056-4101 Access (Seattle)
1056-4225 Leather Crafters Journal
1056-4535 Women Writers of Italy
1056-490X Green Business Letter
1056-4926 Journal of Management Inquiry
1056-4950 Journal of Pharmaceutical Care in Pain & Symptom Control
1056-5132 Housing Market Statistics
1056-5140 Housing Economics
1056-5159 Forecast of Housing Activity
1056-5175 Man!
1056-5329 Lead Belly Letter
1056-5507 Z Magazine
1056-5515 Bibliographies of British Statesmen
1056-5523 Bibliographies of World Leaders
1056-5787 Frommer's Comprehensive Travel Guide. New England
1056-5876 South and Meso-American Indian Information Center (SIIC) Newsletter
1056-6090 Die Casting Buyers Guide
1056-6392 Journal of Veterinary Emergency and Critical Care
1056-6694 A L C T S Network News
1056-6716 Journal of Sport Rehabilitation
1056-6724 Sport Science Review
1056-6759 The Wacky World of Peafowl Report
1056-6848 Global Studies: Middle East
1056-6953 Blair County Genealogical Society. Newsletter
1056-697X Kiplinger's Personal Finance
1056-7011 State Executive Directory Annual
1056-7046 Condensed Matter News
1056-7119 A I N Report
1056-7127 G P S Report
1056-7143 Sotheby's Newsletter
1056-7194 Industrial Bioprocessing
1056-7240 Moving Forward
1056-7275 Federal Executive Directory Annual
1056-7321 Walker Footprints
1056-7410 Bibliographies of Battles and Leaders
1056-747X Defense & Aerospace Electronics
1056-7496 Academic Abstracts C D - R O M
1056-7542 Cross Stitch! Magazine
1056-7593 Current Politics and Economics of Japan
1056-7704 A O P A's Aviation U S A
1056-7860 Journal of Chemical Vapor Deposition
1056-7879 International Journal of Educational Reform
1056-7895 International Journal of Damage Mechanics
1056-7917 Medieval and Early Modern Mysticism
1056-7984 I O M A's Report on Reducing Benefits Costs
1056-800X National Geographic Research and Exploration
1056-8018 Terra Nova
1056-8190 Papers in Regional Science
1056-8484 Camera & Darkroom Photography
1056-8700 Annual Review of Biophysics and Biomolecular Structure
1056-8719 Journal of Pharmacological and Toxicological Methods
1056-8727 Journal of Diabetes and Its Complications
1056-9014 Natural Toxins
1056-9596 Missouri Facts
1056-960X South Carolina Facts
1056-9723 National Relocation and Real Estate Directory
1057-0071 Communications & Computer News
1057-0136 Gold Book Older Vehicles
1057-0314 Western Journal of Communication
1057-0535 Gold Book Contemporary Vehicles

ISSN

ISSN INDEX 5849

1057-0551 Studies in Transnational Legal Policy
1057-0578 Directory of Political Periodicals
1057-0586 State Reference Publications
1057-0594 Lobbying Resource Directory
1057-0810 Financial Services Review
1057-0829 Journal of Glaucoma
1057-0926 Congressional Quarterly's Editorial Research Reports *see* 1056-2036
1057-0942 Electronic Imaging Report
1057-0950 Aerospace Financial News
1057-1000 Mealey's Litigation Report: Banking Insolvency
1057-1035 Extropy
1057-1043 Unschoolers Network
1057-1426 Private Multifamily Manager
1057-204X Park & Grounds Management
1057-2082 A B U I Network News
1057-2279 Gas Storage Report
1057-2295 Political and Economic Spectrum of Russia
1057-2309 Current Politics and Economics of Europe
1057-2317 International Library and Information Review
1057-2341 Production & Inventory Managementt
1057-2368 Reminisce
1057-2414 International Journal of Nautical Archeology
1057-2724 Forest Watch
1057-2821 Wonder: Observing & Confronting the Enigmas that Surround Us
1057-2864 Design Firm Management & Administration Report
1057-2880 National Teaching and Learning Forum
1057-3291 Habilitative Mental Healthcare Newsletter
1057-3372 Countryside
1057-3445 Patterson People
1057-3526 N A H A M Management Journal
1057-3593 Early Development and Parenting
1057-3623 State Rankings
1057-4263 International Journal of Arts Medicine
1057-4522 Interface I Cs D.A.T.A. Digest
1057-4557 Guinness Book of Records
1057-493X Guidance and Control
1057-5235 International Communicator
1057-5316 Frohlinger's Marketing Report
1057-5375 Fiber Optics Business
1057-5383 Metropolitan Area Networks
1057-5391 Wireless Telecommunication
1057-5472 Best Bed and Breakfast in the World *see* 1054-4089
1057-5618 En Route Technology
1057-5642 America's Finest Companies
1057-5715 Radiation Curing - Journal of Radiation Curing
1057-6002 Telecom Calendar
1057-6010 Reynolds Records
1057-6029 Marquette Sports Law Journal
1057-6037 Language and Literature
1057-6193 Guide Lines (Red Rock)
1057-6614 Feline Practice
1057-6622 Canine Practice
1057-6649 American Feed Industry Association. Annual and Semiannual Meetings of the Nutrition Council. Proceedings
1057-6681 Montana Manufacturers Directory
1057-7122 I E E E Transactions on Circuits and Systems Part 1: Fundamental Theory and Applications
1057-7130 I E E E Transactions on Circuits and Systems Part 2: Analog and Digital Signal Processing
1057-7157 I E E E Journal of Microelectromechanical Systems
1057-7262 Equipment World
1057-736X Children's Voice
1057-7408 Journal of Consumer Psychology
1057-7416 Media Studies Journal
1057-7475 Keltic Fringe
1057-7769 Intercultural Communication Studies
1057-8153 Accident Reconstruction Journal
1057-8218 Graham Group
1057-8277 Designers World
1057-8315 Sports Medicine, Training and Rehabilitation
1057-834X Electronic Public Information Newsletter
1057-8374 Cognizer Report
1057-8501 Hunter & Sport Horse
1057-8803 P and I M Review *see* 1057-2341
1057-8889 Office Computing Report
1057-9192 Soap Opera Magazine
1057-9214 Journal of Multi-Criteria Decision Analysis
1057-9230 Health Economics
1057-9249 Psycho-Oncology
1057-9257 Advanced Materials for Optics and Electronics
1057-9265 Journal of Strategic Change
1057-9354 Medicine, Exercise, Nutrition and Health
1057-9680 U.S. Merchandise Trade: Exports, General Imports, and Imports for Consumption - Standard International Trade Classification Revision 3 - Commodity by Country
1057-9893 On the Air Magazine
1058-0271 Front Lines (Portland)
1058-0379 E D M S Journal
1058-0506 International Employment Gazette
1058-0603 Polk Bank Directory. International Edition
1058-0611 Polk Bank Directory. North American Edition
1058-0751 Amazing Stories
1058-0883 Corrugated Containers Conference (Year)
1058-0905 Technical Association of the Pulp and Paper Industry. Environmental Conference Proceedings (Year)
1058-093X Surface Modification Technology News
1058-0948 Flame Retardancy News
1058-1006 Transnational Law & Contemporary Problems
1058-1022 World Perspectives
1058-1103 Mental Health Weekly
1058-1324 Aid for Education Report
1058-1332 Municipal Environmental Journal
1058-1367 Journal of Environmental Permitting
1058-1561 Credit Union Newsletter for Directors
1058-1634 Issues and Concepts in the Postmodern Theory of Education
1058-2134 Washington Geology
1058-2282 Technology N Y Report
1058-2347 Biography Today
1058-2401 Comparative Medicine
1058-241X Drug Targeting and Delivery
1058-2428 U S Black Engineer
1058-2452 Journal of Musculoskeletal Pain
1058-2592 Advertising Options Plus
1058-2630 Film Producers, Studios, Agents and Casting Directors Guide
1058-269X Hispanic Engineer
1058-2878 Financial Yellow Book
1058-2886 N A S D Q Yellow Book
1058-2894 International Corporate Yellow Book
1058-2908 Corporate Yellow Book
1058-3300 Review of Financial Economics
1058-4021 Cooper Collection (Grawn)
1058-4226 Education Beat
1058-4455 C F P Today
1058-4587 Integrated Ferroelectrics
1058-5036 I C 2 Management and Management Science Series
1058-5133 California Genealogical Society Newsletter
1058-5397 Report on the Americas
1058-5427 Texas Journal of Women and the Law
1058-5605 Planning Commissioners Journal
1058-5834 Journal of Chemical and Biochemical Kinetics
1058-5842 Offshore International Newsletter
1058-5869 Offshore Field Development International
1058-5877 Offshore U S Oil Company Operating Personnel Directory
1058-5885 Gulf of Mexico Newsletter
1058-594X Greenkeeping
1058-5958 Beckett Hockey Monthly
1058-6008 International Offshore Rig Owners Directory
1058-6180 I E E E Annals of the History of Computing
1058-6326 Catharsis
1058-6350 Index to Dance Periodicals
1058-6369 Women's Studies Index (Year)
1058-644X Bibliographic Guide to Middle Eastern Studies
1058-6458 Journal of Experimental Mathematics
1058-6687 ImmunoMethods
1058-6695 Wireless - Satellite and Broadcasting
1058-6709 Wireless - Spectrum Management
1058-6717 Wireless Cellular
1058-6725 Wireless - Personal Communication Networks
1058-6741 NeuroProtocols
1058-675X American Petroleum Institute. Health and Environmental Sciences Department. Reports and Other Publications, Index and Abstracts
1058-6784 Forward Day By Day
1058-689X Corporate Giving Yellow Pages
1058-7012 Land Use Forum
1058-7063 Miniature Donkey Talk
1058-725X Molecular Crystals and Liquid Crystals Science and Technology. Section A: Molecular Crystals and Liquid Crystals
1058-7268 Molecular Crystals and Liquid Crystals Science and Technology. Section B: Nonlinear Optics
1058-7276 Molecular Crystals and Liquid Crystals Science and Technology. Section C: Molecular Materials
1058-7284 Molecular Crystals and Liquid Crystals Science and Technology. Section D: Display and Imaging
1058-7292 Japanese Technology Reviews: Electronics (Section A)
1058-7306 Japanese Technology Reviews: Computers and Communication (Section B)
1058-7314 Japanese Technology Reviews: New Materials (Section C)
1058-7322 Japanese Technology Reviews: Manufacturing Engineering (Section D)
1058-7330 Japanese Technology Reviews: Biotechnology (Section E)
1058-7365 B N A's Eastern Europe Reporter
1058-7373 B N A California - Employee Relations Report
1058-7691 Powys Notes
1058-7713 Advanced Wireless Communication
1058-7829 Strategies for Healthcare Excellence
1058-8167 Music Reference Services Quarterly
1058-8183 Veterinary Radiology & Ultrasound
1058-8388 Developmental Dynamics
1058-8396 Early Intervention
1058-8515 Video Letter
1058-8523 Innovative Products
1058-9236 MultiCultural Review
1058-9244 Scientific Programming
1058-9260 Contractor's Business Management Report
1058-9317 Circuit News (Webb City)
1058-9325 Circuit News Assembly
1058-9716 Bacon's Business - Financial Directory
1058-9813 Progress in Pediatric Cardiology
1058-9848 Rock Beatt
1058-9856 Teen Set
1058-997X Studies in Modern Art
1059-0145 Journal of Science Education and Technology
1059-0544 Broadband Networking News
1059-0552 Tactical Technology
1059-0587 Year Book of Dermatologic Surgery
1059-065X G L B Ames Newsletter
1059-0757 Beta Phi Mu Newsletter
1059-0803 Family Tree Quarterly
1059-0838 Green Library Journal
1059-0870 Pediatric Emergency & Critical Care
1059-096X Physical Therapy Products
1059-1001 Autocephalous Orthodox Churches
1059-1311 Seizure
1059-1621 H S U S News
1059-163X Directory of Executive Recruiters
1059-1664 Gleanings (Keokuk)
1059-2091 Innovations & Ideas
1059-2172 Game Player's Guide to Nintendo
1059-2180 Game Player's P C Entertainment
1059-2210 Sidewalks
1059-2741 I O M A's Report on Managing 401K Plans
1059-289X Energy News Brief
1059-2938 Video Games and Computer Entertainment
1059-3055 Cleveland Enterprise
1059-3071 National Housing Register
1059-3144 Opus Dei Awareness Network
1059-3195 Letter to Libraries Online
1059-3535 Major Concepts in Politics and Political Theory
1059-3659 American City & County Directory of Administrative Service
1059-3705 Morris Members
1059-3713 Murphy Mates
1059-4094 N O L P E School Law Reporter
1059-4124 Paeleoanthropology Annuals
1059-4132 MacArtist
1059-4485 Global Telcom Report
1059-4523 Oklahoma Directory of Manufacturers & Products
1059-4779 Raivaaja
1059-4957 C I S Soviet Travel Newsletter
1059-5155 Boating World
1059-5252 Today's Family Home Plans
1059-5325 Solstice: An Electronic Journal of Geography and Mathematics
1059-5856 Careers & Majors
1059-5929 Fairs and Festivals (Year): Northeast and Southeast
1059-5953 The Traditional MusicLine
1059-6011 Group & Organization Management
1059-6216 Walk Away
1059-6372 Freedom Writer
1059-6593 Life-Line
1059-7069 Journal of Technology and Teacher Education
1059-7123 Adaptive Behavior
1059-7468 Airborne Static Line
1059-8227 Inside U S A Volleyball
1059-8243 Cued Speech Journal
1059-8294 Security News (Salamanca)
1059-8375 St. Willibrord Studies in Philosophy and Religion
1059-8561 Consolidated Treaties & International Agreements: European Community Document Service
1059-8596 Journal of Fixed Income
1059-910X Journal of Microscopy Research and Technique
1059-9711 The Nugget
1059-9746 Archimage
1060-0337 Treasure State Lines
1060-0655 Domestic Affairs
1060-0698 Ethics Journal
1060-0876 Sociological Viewpoints
1060-1236 Cryptanthus Society. Journal
1060-1317 Auto C A D World
1060-1325 Journal of Macromolecular Science: Part A - Pure and Applied Chemistry
1060-1325 Macromolecular Reports
1060-1341 Q D T
1060-1902 Sensor Business Digest
1060-216X Skeptical Briefs
1060-2194 M P C World
1060-2208 Business Publishing
1060-233X Message Line
1060-2526 S F Weekly
1060-2615 Holistic Life
1060-2658 Editor's Choice
1060-2712 Manufacturing Automation
1060-2801 Beckett Focus on Future Stars
1060-2976 Daily Environment Report
1060-3158 Barclay Managed Futures Report
1060-3557 Cognizer Almanac
1060-4073 International Business
1060-4251 Sturza's Medical Investment Letter
1060-4936 Photo Electronic Imaging
1060-5649 Technos

ISSN

ISSN INDEX

ISSN	Title
1060-5924	I O M A's Report on Controlling Law Firms Costs
1060-6157	East Europe & The Republics
1060-6734	In Process
1060-7684	M U M P S Computing
1060-7870	E N N
1060-8338	Medical Device Approval Letter
1060-877X	Racquetball Magazine
1060-9148	Black Authors & Published Writers Directory
1060-9490	Military History
1061-0928	Nongame News
1061-1371	Ad Business Report
1061-138X	Commercial Inc.
1061-3153	Federal Regional Yellow Book
1061-4079	Houseplant Magazine
1061-4192	Medical Record Risks: Claims & Litigation
1061-4230	America's Censored Newsletter
1061-5008	Education Technology News
1061-6500	Bibliographies of the Presidents of the United States
1061-7639	The Public Manager
1061-9240	World Scanner Report
1061-9550	Engineering Document Management System Comparison Report
1062-0931	Praeger Series in Presidential Studies
1062-3868	G A N P A C Brief
1062-4236	Healthy Kids: 4-10 Years
1062-7863	Critique of Trade Union Rights in Countries Affiliated with the League of Arab States
1062-855X	Flora-Line
1062-9491	Inner Voice
1063-0945	Healthy Kids: Birth - 3
1080-8000	Christian Example
1100-052X	Fritidshandlaren Cykel och Sport
1100-1801	Acta Pharmaceutica Nordica
1100-2131	Nordiska Afrikainstitutet. Discussion Papers
1100-2808	Sweden. Socialstyrelsen. S O S - Rapport
1100-2859	Lund Studies in Art History
1100-3006	Best 'N' Most in D F S
1100-3847	Bibsamnytt
1100-4096	Nordic Journal of Freshwater Research
1100-4177	C E S I C Studies in International Conflict
1100-4290	Studies in Philosophy
1100-4843	Reader's Digest - Det Baesta
1100-5491	Soedokt
1100-5815	Sveriges Riksbank. Penning- och Valutapolitik
1100-620X	J U S E K
1100-6722	Salaries of Salaried Employees (Year)
1100-6749	Nordiska Afrikainstitutet. Annual Reportt
1100-7559	Nordic Economic Outlook
1100-9373	Sweden. Statistiska Centralbyraan. Statistiska Meddelanden. Subgroup S E (Service and Trade)
1100-9381	Statistics Sweden. Quarterly Foreign Trade Statistics S I T C
1100-956X	New Scandinavian Technology
1101-1939	Concern
1101-2633	Laerarnas Tidning
1101-413X	Roeda Korsets Tiding
1101-6345	Current Sweden
1101-7341	Enviro
1101-8399	N M I - Nordisk Mejeriinformation
1102-1101	Acta Chirurgica Scandinavica - European Journal of Surgery
1105-0225	Hiaka Khronika
1105-0519	Bank of Greece. Monthly Statistical Bulletin
1105-0969	Archailogike Hetaireia en Athenais. Praktika
1105-1213	Agrotics Synergatismos
1105-1280	4 Trochi
1105-1299	2 Trochi
1105-1302	Sound & Hi Fi
1105-1310	Ptisi
1105-1329	4 Trochoi Test
1105-1345	Stereophony and Music
1105-2155	Anthropos: Yearbook in Anthropology
1105-2414	Yevse
1105-2503	Epilogi
1105-2511	Balance Sheets
1105-252X	Economic Review of the Year - The Greek Economy
1110-0192	Egyptian Journal of Food Science
1110-0206	Egyptian Journal of Horticulture
1110-0214	Egyptian Journal of Physics
1110-0222	Egyptian Journal of Veterinary Science
1110-0230	Egyptian Journal of Phytopathology
1110-1148	Egyptian Orthopaedic Journal
1116-1027	Nigeria Industrial Directory
1120-0103	Cremona Produce - Cultura e Tradizione
1120-0375	Cremona Produce see 1120-0103
1120-0405	Giornale di Chirurgia Plastica Ricostruttiva ed Estetica
1120-0499	Giornale Internazionale di Dermatologia Pediatrica
1120-0634	Notiziario dell'Istituto Storico della Resistenza in Cuneo e Provincia
1120-0677	Storia delle Relazioni Internazionali
1120-1657	Difesa Oggi
1120-1665	Defence Today†
1120-1673	Force
1120-1681	Protec
1120-1770	Italian Journal of Food Science
1120-1789	Parts
1120-1797	Physica Medica
1120-1908	Alta Frequenza Rivista di Elettronica
1120-205X	A F T
1120-219X	Giornale dell'Installatore Telefonico
1120-2262	Gommone e la Nautica per Tutti
1120-2289	Elevatori
1120-2351	Constatto Elettrico
1120-236X	Habitat Ufficio
1120-2386	Office Furniture
1120-2394	Keramikos International Ceramics Magazine
1120-2513	O P D Restauro
1120-2521	A I B Notizie
1120-2726	Rivista di Linguistica
1120-2777	Arpel
1120-2785	Ars Week
1120-2890	Economia Politica
1120-3137	Journal of Sports Traumatology and Related Research
1120-3455	Otorinolaringologia Pediatrica
1120-3501	Arpel Fur
1120-3633	Attivita Fisica e Sport
1120-3641	Gastroenterologia Oggi
1120-365X	Ginecologia Oggi
1120-3749	Giornale Italiano di Farmacia Clinica
1120-3854	Methodologia
1120-3862	European Transactions on Telecommunications and Related Technologies
1120-3889	Agrinform
1120-3900	Camera di Commercio, Industria, Artigianato e Agricoltura di Ferrara. Listino dei Prezzi all'Ingrosso
1120-3919	Prezzi dei Materiali e delle Opere Edili in Ferrara
1120-3927	Rassegna Stampa
1120-3943	Camera di Commercio, Industria, Artigianato e Agricoltura di Ferrara. Notiziario Mensile
1120-396X	Ferrara Economica
1120-4079	Pro
1120-4249	Cina Notizie
1120-4605	Societa Italiana di Fitosociologia. Notiziario changed to Fitosociologia.
1120-4621	Cartellina
1120-4834	Surgery and Immunity
1120-4923	Erba d'Arno. Quaderni
1120-5407	Bagno e Cucina Architettura e Interior Design
1120-5741	Recercare
1120-5989	Urodinamica, Neurourology, Urodynamics and Continence
1120-6136	Rassegna dell'Imballaggio
1120-6195	Il Giornale della Musica
1120-6268	Italian Design Fashion
1120-6373	Giornale Italiano di Allergologia e Immunologia Clinica
1120-6721	European Journal of Ophthalmology
1120-6942	Detergo
1120-7000	Hip Pathology
1120-7094	Comparatistica
1120-7655	Auto In
1120-7752	Uomo Mare
1120-7760	Uomo Vogue
1120-7787	Vogue Bambini
1120-7795	Vogue Pelle
1120-7809	Vogue Sposa
1120-7817	Vogue Gioiello
1120-7876	S e C
1120-9178	Quaderni di Lingue e Letterature
1120-9402	Stomatologia Mediterranea
1120-9445	Fondazione Assi. Annali di Storia dell'Impresa
1120-9453	Banca Impresa Societa
1120-9461	Finanza Imprese e Mercati
1120-947X	Lavoro e Diritto
1120-9488	Polis
1120-9496	Politica Economica
1120-950X	Politica in Italia
1120-9518	Rapporto sull'Economia del Mezzogiorno
1120-9526	Ricerche di Storia Politica
1120-9534	Rivista Economica del Mezzogiorno
1120-9542	Rivista Giuridica del Mezzogiorno
1120-9550	Sistemi Intelligenti
1120-9569	Teatro e Storia
1120-9593	Economia Marche
1121-0036	Estetica (Bologna)
1121-063X	Stampi
1121-0656	Laser and Technology
1121-2098	Acta Tecnologiae et Legis Medicamenti
1130-0094	Revista de Actualidad Odonto Estomatologica Espanola
1130-0515	Hispania Antiqua
1130-0523	Progresos en Diagnostico Prenatal
1130-0558	Revista Espanola de Cirugia Oral y Maxilofacial
1130-099X	Indice Espanol de Humanidades. Series B: Historical Sciences
1130-1163	Indice Espanol de Humanidades. Series C: Linguistics and Literature
1130-1910	Archives of Dermatology (Edicion Espanola)
1130-2399	Enfermeria Intensiva
1130-3204	Etologia
1130-3700	Indice Espanol de Ciencias Sociales. Series E: Urban Planning
1130-3751	Express
1130-3948	XX Siglos
1130-4405	Revista de la Medicina Tradicional China
1130-4588	Revista Espanola de las Enfermedades Digestivas
1130-4618	Injuve
1130-4936	Anthropos. Documentos A
1130-5134	Archives of Ophthalmology (Edicion Espanola)
1130-6416	Medico Practico
1130-734X	Notas de Enfermeria
1130-7501	Cardiovascular Risk Factors
1130-9105	Indice Espanol de Humanidades. Series D: Philosophy
1131-5253	Ciencia Pharmaceutica
1131-6047	Calidad, Gestion y Tecnica
1131-799X	Revista Espanola de Ciencia y Tecnologia de Alimentos
1140-5104	Filiere Farine
1140-5252	I N S E E. Etudes
1140-5597	Formes et Structures
1140-7123	Annuaire de l'Administration des D.R.I.R.
1140-7131	Strategies Alimentaires
1141-1562	Semaine Religieuse du Diocese de Bourges see 0042-5362
1141-4588	Histoire des Sciences et des Techniques
1141-4804	Control
1141-5886	Revue du Gynecologue Obstetricien
1141-7161	Cahiers des Ameriques Latines
1142-2505	Horizon. Bulletin Bibliographique O R S T O M Oceanographie Hydrobiologie
1142-2513	Horizon. Bulletin Bibliographique O R S T O M Sciences Economiques et Sociales
1142-2521	Horizon. Bulletin Bibliographique O R S T O M Sciences du Monde Vegetal et Animal
1142-253X	Horizon. Bulletin Bibliographique O R S T O M Sciences et Techniques
1142-2904	Fondamentales Sciences de l'Ingenieur Quaternaire
1142-3080	I N S E E. Methodes
1142-3153	Diffusion Express
1143-3833	Du Sol a la Table
1143-3914	Ulysses International
1143-7375	Filieres Viande et Peche
1143-7391	Cutlivar 2000 changed to Cultivar.
1144-2549	Vocation see 0042-5362
1145-2447	M C It
1145-2668	F I E E Infos
1145-377X	Neo Restauration
1146-5093	P A S C A L. T 295: Batiment. Travaux Publics
1146-5360	P A S C A L. E 27: Methodes de Formation et Traitement des Images Courants
1146-5786	Acta Oecologica
1146-609X	Distributique Europe
1146-6456	Revue du Cardiologue Praticien
1146-6537	La Champagne Economique
1146-8599	Homme et l'Architecture
1147-7105	L'Archer
1148-3652	European Cytokine Network
1148-5493	Espace Bureau
1148-5566	Bulletin des Etudes Karaites
1148-6716	Bureaux d'Etudes
1147-7305	Kairos
1148-9227	Raisons Pratiques
1150-1367	Reunion. Direction de l'Agriculture et de la Foret. Agreste. Donnees, Bulletin de Statistique Agricole Reunion
1150-1448	Reunion. Direction de l'Agriculture et de la Foret. Agreste. Donnees, Annuaire de Statistique Agricole Reunion
1150-1456	B H A
1150-1588	Business in the U.S.S.R. (International Edition)
1150-4382	Maghreb Confidentiel
1150-4447	Federation Nationale de l'Industrie Laitiere. Bulletin d'Information
1150-5028	Journal International des Sciences de la Vigne et du Vin
1151-0285	Etudes et Documents d'Histoire Economique et Financiere
1151-9037	Parlanghe
1151-941X	Essor
1152-6963	Revue des Affaires Europeennes
1152-9172	Conjoncture in France
1152-9776	Paris le Journal
1153-026X	Annales de Chirurgie de la Main et du Membre Superieur
1153-2424	Societe d'Histoire et d'Archeologie de Vichy et des Environs. Bulletin
1153-3277	Journal de Therapie Comportamentale et Cognitive
1155-1704	Journal de Mycologie Medicale
1156-5233	Jericho
1156-5977	Recyclage Recuperation
1156-962X	S T P Pharma Sciences
1157-1489	S T P Pharma Techniques Pratiques Reglementations
1157-1497	Intertitres changed to Libertitres.
1157-2973	Tahiti Beach Press
1157-349X	Phenomena
1157-4704	Maitrise (Edition Generale)
1157-6049	Maitrise (Edition Siderurgie)
1157-6057	Maitrise (Edition Chimie)
1157-6065	Levage Actualite
1158-0038	Modal
1159-070X	Une Ville, Un Pays
1159-0769	Legendes et Rumeurs
1159-098X	Orient Express
1161-0344	Electricite de France. Direction des Etudes et Recherches. Collection de Notes Internes. Materiel Electrique Transport et Distribution d'Energie
1161-0581	

ISSN INDEX 5851

ISSN	Title
1161-059X	Electricite de France. Direction des Etudes et Recherches. Collection de Notes Internes. Mathematiques, Informatique, Telecommunications
1161-4951	Revue de Metrologie Pratique et Legale
1161-8043	Courrier de la Planete
1163-1961	Sein
1164-5679	Telescope
1170-1803	Horticulture in New Zealand (Lincoln)
1170-3229	Your Home
1170-327X	New Zealand General Practice, Business Management
1170-344X	Corporate Plan Reserve Bank of New Zealand
1170-4683	New Zealand. Transit New Zealand. Road Research Unit. Newsletter†
1170-4829	Monetary Policy Statement
1170-6244	Current
1170-7321	Transearch
1170-747X	New Zealand. Department of Statistics. Consumer Expenditure
1170-7607	Lincoln University. Agribusiness and Economics Research Unit. Discussion Paper
1170-7682	Lincoln University. Agribusiness and Economics Research Unit. Research Report
1170-7887	New Zealand Council of Trade Unions. Official Trade Union Directory
1170-8271	New Zealand. Department of Statistics. Incomes
1170-9758	Shadows
1171-0195	New Zealand Journal of Medical Laboratory Science
1180-0291	Vitality Magazine
1180-0429	British Columbia. Provincial Government. B C News†
1180-0453	Victims of Violence Report
1180-050X	Canadian Water Well
1180-0828	Canadian International Trade Directory
1180-0933	A R C
1180-0984	Ophthalmic Abstract Journal
1180-1344	Kodaly Society of Canada. Alla Breve
1180-1352	Canadian Cyclist
1180-1360	Velo Mag
1180-1670	Hole
1180-176X	Canadian Law Libraries
1180-2065	Canadian Automotive Technician
1180-2189	Long Term Care Monitor
1180-2936	Ontario. Ministry of Agriculture and Food. Agri-Food Outlook and Policy Review
1180-4009	Environmetrics
1180-4246	Materials & Energy Advantage†
1180-4467	Gloss
1180-4734	Synthesis
1180-4882	Journal of Psychiatry and Neuroscience
1180-4920	Canadian Nurses Association. Nursing Programs and Entrance Requirements at Canadian Universities.
1180-4971	D C
1180-5331	Encyclopedia Bananica
1180-5722	Recover
1180-5749	Nine to Five
1180-968X	Canadian Quaker History Journal
1181-6058	Practical Optometry
1181-6414	Prospector Exploration & Investment Bulletin
1181-6562	Pulp & Paper Canada Grade Directory
1181-6732	Canada. Statistics Canada. Exports by Commodity
1181-7267	Surrey Magazine changed to Surrey - Delta Magazine.
1181-7909	Canadian Railway Modeller
1181-7925	Classic Homestyles
1181-7933	Designer's Best Home Plans
1181-7941	A.P.C.R.I.Q. Bulletin d'Information
1181-8336	British Columbia. Ministry of Environment. Annual Report
1181-8360	Buddhism at the Crossroads
1181-8409	Uniscope
1181-8808	Sporting Times (Calgary)
1181-9456	Artistamp News
1182-0225	Japanese Canadian Citizens Association of Greater Vancouver. Bulletin
1182-0683	Burnaby Magazine
1182-0705	Where Victoria
1182-3798	Buildcore Product Review
1182-3968	Active Voice
1182-5405	Punch Digest for Canadian Doctors
1182-9699	Travel Courier
1183-0344	DX Ontario
1183-0824	Le Pont
1183-1073	Material History Review
1183-1243	Canadian Journal of Drama and Theatre
1183-1286	Greek Index Project Series
1183-1308	Educational Travel Planner
1183-1588	Ontario. Ministry of Agriculture and Food. Agri-Food Trade Update
1183-1677	Canadian R & D Directory
1183-2053	La Gauche
1183-2088	Canadian Free Trader International Supplement
1183-2231	York Region Business Journal
1183-2517	Canadian Journal of Ob-Gyn & Women's Health Care
1183-322X	Exceptionality Education Canada
1183-3246	McGoldrick's Canadian Customs Guide "Harmonized System"
1183-3777	Grey Book
1183-3963	Africa's Import - Export Trade Opportunities Directory
1183-4242	Futures and Options
1183-5362	Astronomie Quebec
1183-5710	British Columbia. Ministry of Agriculture Fisheries and Food. Greenhouse Floriculture Production Guide
1183-630X	Earthkeeping Ontario
1183-6350	International Society of Toronto for Hungarian Church History. Newsletter
1183-6652	Wood
1183-7780	Vision
1183-7918	Canada. Forestry Canada. Publications Digest - Abrege des Publications
1183-8000	Polonia Voice
1183-9082	National Research Council of Canada. Institute for Information Technology. Annual Report
1183-9597	Canadian Society of Plant Physiologists. Bulletin
1184-0412	Development Disability Bulletin
1184-0641	C A J Bulletin
1184-2164	British Columbia Agri Digest: Horse Issue
1184-6283	Dialogue (Kingston)
1184-731X	Saint John Business Today
1185-3638	Nursing B C
1185-4731	Waste Business West
1186-1797	Professional Sound
1187-1350	Where Ottawa - Hull
1187-3272	Rights and Liberties
1187-6484	Regroupement des Chercheurs-res en Histoire des Travailleurs et Travailleuses du Quebec. Bulletin
1188-0066	Imperial Quarterly
1188-0325	Canadian A I D S News
1188-1089	Ontario Genealogical Society. Kingston Branch. Kingston Relations
1188-181X	G R C News
1188-2654	C A C S W News
1188-2921	Neil Muscott's Success Newsletter
1188-3642	Selected Vital Statistics and Health Statistics Indicators. Annual Report
1188-5580	Presence
1188-6803	Inside Guide
1210-0250	Teorie Vedy
1215-2439	Hungarian Economic Review
1220-3009	Revista Romana de Proprietate Industriala
1220-3076	Biblioteconomie. Culegere de Traduceri Prelucrate
1220-3092	A B S I - Abstracte in Bibliologie si Stiinta Informarii
1220-4145	Institutul de Studii si Proiectari Energetice. Buletinul
1220-4560	Cronica
1220-5028	Romanian Panorama
1220-5079	Universitatea Tehnica Petrosani. Lucrari Stiintifice
1220-5710	Revista de Istorie Militara
1220-6105	Buletin Oficial de Proprietate Industrial
1235-0605	V T T Tiedotteita
1235-0613	V T T Julkaisuja
1235-0621	V T T Publications
1235-2136	Betoni
1508-1788	Prakriti see 0303-7967
1661-2434	Teamwork†
2209-7007	Communisme
2306-2525	Family Planning International Assistance Newsletter†
4001-4029	Cuadernos para el Debate Regional
6377-9137	Enhanced Recovery Week see 1050-2483
8750-0183	Earthwatch
8750-0191	Performance and Instruction Journal see 0884-1985
8750-0205	Turkey Hunter
8750-0256	Utne Reader
8750-037X	Avian - Exotic Practice†
8750-0434	Biometric Bulletin
8750-0477	Art & Style International
8750-0507	Contemporary Pediatrics
8750-0515	Georgia Advance Sheets
8750-0779	A N N A Journal
8750-1082	U K Magazine
8750-1090	Herb Basket†
8750-1104	Shepard's Corporation Law Citations
8750-1112	Shepard's Partnership Law Citations
8750-1139	Shepard's Products Liability Citations
8750-1147	Metropolitan Detroit see 0149-5976
8750-1244	D I T N: Diabetes in the News see 0893-5939
8750-1600	Signpost for Northwest Trails
8750-1627	Perfins Bulletin
8750-1643	Vegetarian Health Science see 0883-8216
8750-1813	California Physician
8750-1848	Adweek's Marketing Computers
8750-1880	Purebred Picture
8750-1961	Boston Jewish Times
8750-2011	Leaven (Franklin Park)
8750-2100	Mass High Tech
8750-216X	New England Monthly†
8750-2224	Prepress Bulletin
8750-2321	M D A Newsmagazine
8750-233X	Trapper and Predator Caller
8750-2348	Sandara
8750-2356	S R C Blue Book of 5-Trend Cycli-Graphs
8750-2410	Best Fares
8750-2461	S R C Red Book of 5-Trend Security Charts
8750-2577	Goldmine
8750-2798	Accountants I B Micro Report changed to Accountants Microcomputer News.
8750-2836	Hospital Practice
8750-3042	Horoscope Guide
8750-3085	Ocular Surgery News
8750-314X	Gourmet Today - Telefood see 1052-4630
8750-3204	Strategic Planning and Energy Management see 1048-5236
8750-3255	American Theatre
8750-331X	International Journal of Chinese Medicine†
8750-3360	Alumnus (Southern Illinois University at Carbondale)
8750-3530	Festival Quarterly
8750-3603	Bowling Digest
8750-3697	Culpepper Letter
8750-3727	Tiered Rate Watch changed to Rate Watch.
8750-3735	Hospital & Health Services Administration
8750-4081	Indoor Garden
8750-4170	Spokane, A Great Place, The Magazine†
8750-4219	Puller
8750-4278	Phillies Report
8750-4294	Southwest Journal of Business and Economics
8750-4502	Investment Coin Review
8750-4634	Southwest Hotel - Motel Review†
8750-488X	Opus see 0735-777X
8750-5126	Hotel - Motel Security and Safety Management
8750-5347	Sinfonian Magazine†
8750-5622	Focus Magazine (Hartford)
8750-5649	Home & Away
8750-5746	Kalamazoo College Quarterly
8750-5797	Pecan South Including Pecan Quarterly
8750-5851	Baseball Cards
8750-5886	Then and Now see 0745-1385
8750-6033	El Paso Economic Review
8750-6041	Plumbing & Mechanical
8750-6106	Progressive Rentals
8750-6238	Valley Catholic
8750-653X	Women's Sports and Fitness
8750-6629	Hunting Retriever
8750-6637	State Policy Reports
8750-6718	Pacific Banker
8750-6807	Florida Hotel & Motel Journal
8750-7218	Meeting Manager
8750-7234	Star Hits changed to Hot!
8750-7242	Bop
8750-7315	American Podiatric Medical Association. Journal
8750-7374	Limousine & Chauffeur
8750-7536	Shield & Diamond
8750-7587	Journal of Applied Physiology
8750-7595	Countryside and Small Stock Journal
8750-7668	United Methodist Christian Advocate
8750-7765	Christian Mission
8750-7811	E S D Technology
8750-7838	Modern Percussionist see 0194-4533
8750-7854	On Communications see 0887-7661
8750-7897	Shepherd
8750-7927	U S C Trojan Family
8750-7935	Microwave Systems News and Communications Technology changed to Microwave Systems News.
8750-7943	Veterinary Medicine
8750-801X	Lottery & Gaming Review
8750-8133	W & J Magazine
8750-8184	Wallcoverings Magazine see 1055-4394
8750-8206	Corporate Design and Realty changed to Today's Facility Manager.
8750-8257	Alpine Sun
8750-8281	Arizona Cattlelog
8750-8516	Masscitizen
8750-8613	Church Life
8750-8672	O A G Travel Planner and Hotel-Motel Guide. Pacific Area Edition see 0894-1734
8750-877X	S T L: The Art of Living in St. Louis
8750-8877	Crochet Fantasy
8750-8907	California Angler
8750-8915	Flex Magazine
8750-8923	Nostalgia (Milwaukee)
8750-8990	Veterinary Technician
8750-9024	Antique Market Report
8750-9067	Telemarketer
8750-9210	Stone Review
8750-9229	Roads & Bridges
8750-9261	Coach's Legal Report see 0094-0399
8750-9318	American Woodworker
8750-9334	Electronic Engineering Manager†
8750-9393	Pasta Journal
8750-9407	Physicians Financial News
8750-9415	Symphony User's Journal
8750-9482	Micro-Systems Journal see 1042-4695
8750-9490	American Clinical Laboratory
8750-9504	Kitchen and Bath Concepts see 0098-9207
8750-9555	Dental Lab Management Today
8750-9563	Welcome Home
8750-9628	V A X Professional
8750-9679	Alabama Churchman see 1041-3316
8750-9687	A A P S News
8750-9776	Afghan Hound Review
8750-9989	Red & Black (Middletown)

8755-0024 Applied Stochastic Models and Data Analysis
8755-0032 Advances in Neural and Behavioral Development
8755-0040 Current Topics in Human Intelligence
8755-0059 Kansas Medicine
8755-0199 Free Radical Research Communications
8755-0229 Medical Practice Management *changed to* Journal of Medical Practice Management.
8755-0237 Buildings Energy Conservation *changed to* Buildings Energy Technology.
8755-0245 Energy from Biomass *changed to* Energy from Biomass and Municipal Waste.
8755-0253 Professional Document Retrieval
8755-027X Africa Commentary†
8755-0423 Home Mechanix
8755-0474 Oceans Policy Study Series†
8755-0547 Sherbondy Beacon
8755-0555 Sound Management†
8755-0628 Tax Management Real Estate Journal
8755-0717 Beverage Industry Annual Manual
8755-0725 Chamber Music Magazine
8755-075X Geology of the Pacific Ocean
8755-0946 Veterinary Computing *see* 0362-8140
8755-0970 Topics in Ocular Pharmacology and Toxicology†
8755-1020 National Association of Document Examiners. Journal
8755-1039 Diagnostic Cytopathology
8755-1187 A S A E Standards
8755-1209 Reviews of Geophysics
8755-1225 Journal of Pharmacy Technology
8755-1616 Laser Focus - Electro Optics Buyers' Guide *changed to* Laser Focus World Buyers' Guide.
8755-1675 American Computer Law Digest
8755-1721 Johnson Journal†
8755-1748 Southern Genealogical Index
8755-1756 German Connection
8755-1853 Laser Focus *see* 1043-8092
8755-1985 Journal of Protective Coatings and Linings
8755-2019 Center (New York)
8755-2027 Swim Magazine
8755-2035 Porticus
8755-2094 Educational Media and Technology Yearbook
8755-2108 Library Science Annual *changed to* Library and Information Science Annual.
8755-2167 Waconda Roots and Branches
8755-2353 Dorchester County Genealogical Magazine
8755-2523 Chilton's Industrial Maintenance & Plant Operation
8755-254X Chilton's Hardware Age
8755-2566 Chilton's Industrial Safety & Hygiene News
8755-2582 Corporate Artnews
8755-2620 Leader in Action
8755-2655 The Cloth Doll
8755-2671 Who's Who in Direct Marketing Creative Services
8755-2841 Utah Directory of Business and Industry
8755-2914 The Columbia
8755-2922 Learning Resources Directory for Healthcare Executives†
8755-2930 Earthquake Spectra
8755-3023 Golden Roots of the Mother Lode
8755-3031 Social Science Microcomputer Review *see* 0894-4393
8755-3112 Nautica
8755-3139 Stamp Dealer Forum†
8755-3163 American Fireworks News
8755-321X Successful Marketing to Senior Citizens†
8755-3228 Llewellyn's Astrological Guide to California†
8755-3317 Futures Research Quarterly
8755-3406 Volume Reversal Survey
8755-3449 Journal of Third World Studies
8755-3457 Drinking Water & Backflow Prevention
8755-3511 B O C Week
8755-3651 El Gato Tuerto
8755-3732 C A A S News
8755-3759 Words on Tape *changed to* Words on Cassette (Year).
8755-3767 Wrestling Masters
8755-3929 Show Horse†
8755-3996 I E E E Circuits and Devices Magazine
8755-4151 Mutual Fund Source Book
8755-416X Legal Newsletters in Print
8755-4178 Journal of Feminist Studies in Religion
8755-4305 International Journal of Personal Property Appraising†
8755-4313 L C and You
8755-4348 Appraisers' Information Exchange
8755-4364 Freemen Digest *see* 0882-5955
8755-4372 Fireworks Business
8755-4380 T S R Hotline
8755-4550 Women and Language
8755-4585 Soviet Journal of Contemporary Physics
8755-4615 Computers and Composition
8755-464X Profiles (Solana Beach)†
8755-4682 Seiche
8755-4747 Pathways (Maynardville)
8755-4755 Takeover Target Weekly Forecast†
8755-4909 Call - A.P.P.L.E.
8755-4917 Washington Report on Middle East Affairs
8755-4941 Alternative Agriculture News
8755-5034 Africa International
8755-5093 Journal of Enzyme Inhibition
8755-5107 Educational Software Selector *changed to* The Latest and Best of T E S S.
8755-5123 Northeast Journal of Business and Economics *changed to* Journal of Business and Economic Studies.
8755-514X Nebraska Review
8755-5271 Heartline
8755-5298 I Know You Know
8755-5301 Lanthanide and Actinide Research
8755-5352 Lesbian Ethics
8755-5360 Studies in Social Welfare Policies and Programs
8755-5379 E R I S A Newsletter
8755-5689 Draw Magazine†
8755-5727 C D Data Report
8755-5735 Acquisition Mart
8755-5751 Printout *changed to* Update Newsletter.
8755-5786 Micro Software Report (Library Edition) †
8755-5794 Micro Software Evaluations†
8755-5824 Electrum†
8755-5832 Boombah Herald
8755-5875 People, Animals, Environment *changed to* People, Animals, Nature.
8755-5913 Phillips County Historical Quarterly *see* 1046-4204
8755-6073 Hardin County Historical Quarterly
8755-6103 Casino Digest
8755-612X Interbehaviorist
8755-6138 International Real Estate Journal
8755-6154 Record Collector's Monthly
8755-6189 Packaging Strategies
8755-6235 Licensing Letter
8755-6286 Information Today
8755-6316 Bible Review
8755-6340 Legerete *changed to* Europa.
8755-6863 Pediatric Pulmonology
8755-688X Who's Who in Animal Transportation *see* 1042-2633
8755-6898 Mammoth Trumpet
8755-6901 Christopher News Notes
8755-7142 Unlisted Drugs Index - Guide
8755-7169 Software Reviews on File
8755-7185 Independent Investor's Personal Investing Newsletter *see* 1042-3346
8755-7215 Military Electronics *see* 1056-747X
8755-7223 Journal of Professional Nursing
8755-724X National Geographic Research *see* 1056-800X
8755-7266 Matrix (Urbana)
8755-7282 S G P B Alert
8755-7339 Data Sources' Guide to V A Rs and Distributors
8755-741X Spitball
8755-7428 Nonviolent Activist
8755-7452 Weirdbook
8755-7460 Soft Sector†
8755-7479 Fantasy Mongers†
8755-7509 Reporter on the Legal Profession
8755-7525 Microcomputer Review *see* 0093-416X
8755-7541 Interior Cost Data (Year) *changed to* Means Interior Cost Data (Year).
8755-7584 Genealogy Tomorrow†
8755-7606 Creative Person†
8755-7614 Nonprofit World Report *changed to* Nonprofit World.
8755-7657 Takeoff
8755-7673 Heart Failure
8755-7878 The Human Ecologist
8755-8270 Industrial Accident Law Bulletin
8755-8289 Narcotics Law Bulletin
8755-8297 School Law Bulletin (Boston)
8755-8300 Arrest Law Bulletin
8755-8343 Roots Digest†
8755-8378 C P C National Directory
8755-8564 Journal of Fluid Control
8755-867X Network NewsNews
8755-8734 Hot Buttoneer
8755-8769 Teach
8755-8785 Magazine of Speculative Poetry
8755-8815 La Raza Law Journal
8755-8831 Third World Resources
8755-8912 Islam International
8755-8920 American Journal of Reproductive Immunology and Microbiology
8755-8939 Presidents' Journal
8755-898X Current Research in the Pleistocene
8755-9005 Mealey's Litigation Report: Insurance
8755-9013 Ecological Illness Law Report†
8755-9021 Lesbian - Gay Law Notes
8755-9129 Food Reviews International
8755-9137 Fast Folk Musical Magazine
8755-9218 Career Woman Magazine
8755-9250 Hawaii on 35 Dollars a Day *changed to* Hawaii on 60 Dollars a Day.
8755-9323 Green Bay Catholic Compass
8755-9358 Liaowang
8755-9404 Interfaith Action *changed to* Interfaith Impact.
8755-9412 Policy Notes†
8755-9447 Animal Air Transportation Association. International Conference. Proceedings *changed to* Animal Transportation Association. International Conference. Proceedings.
8755-9552 American Weather Observer
8755-9560 Show Music
8755-9633 Best Books By Consensus (Year)†
8755-965X Discovery Y M C A
8755-9668 Advances in Free Radical Biology and Medicine *see* 0891-5849
8755-9854 Tippah County Historical and Genealogical Society. News and Journal
8755-9889 Mutual Fund Forecaster
8755-9927 V C R Letter
8755-9978 Annual Report on High-Tech Materials†
8756-0038 Waterfront News
8756-0208 Guide to the American Left
8756-0216 Guide to the American Right
8756-0267 A B B W A Journal
8756-0275 International Journal of Small Group Research *see* 1046-4964
8756-0291 Creeping Bent
8756-0313 Flat Earth News
8756-0380 SingleLife Magazine
8756-0402 Ophthalmic Laser Therapy†
8756-0410 Current Problems in Obstetrics and Gynecology and Fertility
8756-0488 Development Anthropology Network
8756-0550 C E P A Newsletter
8756-0569 Southern Feminist†
8756-0577 AdaData
8756-0615 Michigan Yearbook of International Legal Studies *changed to* Michigan Journal of International Law.
8756-0666 Black Bear Review
8756-0674 C I M Magazine†
8756-0801 Journal of Urban & Contemporary Law
8756-0879 Journal of Plastic Film and Sheeting
8756-0909 Youth Policy
8756-0941 New Information Times *changed to* Information Times.
8756-1247 Crucible and Scientific Atheist *changed to* New Crucible.
8756-1263 Benefits Quarterly
8756-1271 Advances in Writing Research
8756-1336 Elisabeth Elliot Newsletter
8756-1360 Tax Management Financial Planning Journal
8756-1360 Tax Management Financial Planning
8756-1379 Jock
8756-1387 Apartment & Condominium News†
8756-1409 Hospital Outsidecare Advisory†
8756-1417 Journal of Ship Production
8756-1425 Self-Help Sourcebook
8756-1492 Trade Secret Law Reporter†
8756-1522 Loan Officers Legal Alert
8756-1530 Insecticide Product Guide
8756-1549 Mind in Motion
8756-1697 Turn-of-the-Century Women
8756-1700 Navy News & Undersea Technology
8756-1727 O C A W Reporter
8756-1964 Heavy-Ion Reactions†
8756-1972 Association for Business Communication. Bulletin
8756-1980 Prophet Newsline *see* 0894-6981
8756-2049 Fiber Optics News
8756-2057 Reporter on Human Reproduction & the Law
8756-2154 California Technology Stock Letter
8756-2243 National Psoriasis Foundation. Annual Report
8756-2294 Dynix Dataline
8756-2316 Florida Parishes Genealogical Newsletter
8756-2324 A T & T Technical Journal
8756-2332 Jumbo Rate News
8756-2367 Islamic Horizons
8756-2537 E M M S
8756-2855 Marketing Technology†
8756-288X Random Lengths Export
8756-2898 Gelosophist
8756-2995 Labor Lawyer
8756-3002 Regeneration Newsletter†
8756-3010 Afterwords
8756-3053 American Business Trend Synopsis
8756-3061 Accounting Practices & Regulation†
8756-310X Helping Out in the Outdoors
8756-3142 Iron Mountain†
8756-3150 Functional Orthodontist
8756-3185 Mongy Oak
8756-3207 Clinician's Research Digest
8756-324X Caribbean Update
8756-3282 Bone
8756-3320 Journal of Ocular Pharmacology
8756-3452 Year Book of Pulmonary Disease
8756-3460 Year Book of Rehabilitation†
8756-3479 Brookfield Zoo Bison
8756-3487 Rock and Soul†
8756-3592 Naturalist *changed to* New Crucible.
8756-3754 Doctor's Office Lab News
8756-3789 American Hockey Magazine
8756-3894 TechTrends
8756-3924 Cartographic Information *changed to* Cartographic Perspectives.
8756-3959 Mayflower Descendant
8756-4017 Sensor Technology
8756-4041 Truck Blue Book Lease Guide
8756-405X Addiction Letter
8756-4068 Catholic Health World
8756-4076 Connection Technology
8756-4092 Alaska Business Monthly
8756-4173 Alki
8756-4459 European Telecommunications
8756-4467 Center for Migration Studies Newsletter
8756-4513 Healthcare Advertising Review
8756-4521 Central State Business Review *see* 1053-9263
8756-4572 Drexel Polymer Notes†
8756-4610 Loss, Grief & Care

ISSN INDEX

ISSN	Title
8756-4629	Journal of Geriatric Drug Therapy
8756-4696	Other Voices
8756-4718	Nash Notations
8756-4726	Hayes Maze *see* 0736-9557
8756-4769	Favorably Positioned Stocks
8756-4793	Journal of Diagnostic Medical Sonography
8756-4807	Computer Smyth†
8756-4815	Underwater Equipment & Technology Review†
8756-4963	Type Reporter
8756-498X	New Orleans Menu
8756-5013	North American Association of Christians in Social Work. Practice Monograph Series
8756-5099	Long Pond Review
8756-5153	Bay Phil
8756-5161	Jay Schabacker's Mutual Fund Investing
8756-5188	ProEducation†
8756-5196	O C L C Micro
8756-520X	Quarante†
8756-5242	Heritage (Lawrenceville)
8756-5277	Worcester Review
8756-5285	International Water Color Guild Newsletter
8756-5293	Cornell East Asia Papers *see* 1050-2955
8756-5315	Tempo Magazine
8756-5323	Western Publisher
8756-5331	L 5 News†
8756-534X	GreenBook
8756-5366	National Safety and Health News *see* 0891-1797
8756-5382	Sidewinder Studies in History & Sociology
8756-5579	Serb World U.S.A.
8756-5609	Linington Lineup
8756-5633	Zyzzyva
8756-5641	Developmental Neuropsychology
8756-5668	Pennsylvania Review
8756-5676	Controllers Update
8756-5684	Controllers Quarterly†
8756-5714	Journal of Accounting and E D P *changed to* Financial & Accounting Systems.
8756-5811	Palaestra
8756-5900	Communicator (Reno) *changed to* Communicator Community News.
8756-5919	Nutrition News (Riverside)
8756-5927	Index to the Albany Times Union†
8756-5935	Drugs and Device Recall Bulletin
8756-5951	Architectural & Engineering Systems
8756-5978	Portable Lower East Side
8756-6060	Nutrition Legislation News
8756-6079	Banks in Insurance Report
8756-6095	American Association of Blood Banks. News Briefs
8756-6109	Artificial Intelligence Markets
8756-6176	Sound Choice
8756-6206	Journal of Pediatric & Perinatal Nutrition
8756-6222	Journal of Law, Economics, and Organization
8756-6265	Coinage of the Americas Conference. Proceedings
8756-6281	Interaction (Washington, 1981)
8756-6354	Calypso Log
8756-6362	Dolphin Log
8756-6389	Adweek: Southeast
8756-6508	Consultation†
8756-6540	Jazz Interactions
8756-6540	Jazzline
8756-6559	Adult Foster Care Journal *see* 0899-1995
8756-6575	Philosophy of Education
8756-6583	Holocaust and Genocide Studies
8756-6591	American Quilter
8756-6605	Garden State Report†
8756-6648	Soviet Journal of Communications Technology and Electronics
8756-6664	Image World
8756-6931	Will - Grundy Counties Genealogical Society Quarterly
8756-6990	Optoelectronics, Instrumentation and Data Processing
8756-7008	Soviet Surface Engineering and Applied Electrochemistry
8756-7016	Annual Review of Computer Science†
8756-7040	Microcomputer Index
8756-7067	Lapeer Legacy
8756-7075	Trails to Churchill County†
8756-7172	I F A R Reports
8756-7180	Electro-Optics Report††
8756-7202	Small Press Book Review
8756-7237	Ball Beginnings
8756-7245	Gypsy Lore Society. Publications
8756-7296	American Heritage of Invention & Technology
8756-7326	Touro Law Review
8756-7334	Lotus
8756-7385	Toronto Studies in Religion
8756-7407	Handbells
8756-7431	Telecommuting Review: The Gordon Report
8756-7474	Diagnostic Testing Alert *see* 0195-315X
8756-7482	Catholic Challenge
8756-7504	Cambridge Scientific Biochemistry Abstracts: Part 1. Biological Membranes
8756-7512	Cambridge Scientific Biochemistry Abstracts: Part 2. Nucleic Acids
8756-7520	Cambridge Scientific Biochemistry Abstracts: Part 3. Amino-Acids, Peptides & Proteins
8756-7547	Genetic, Social, and General Psychology Monographs
8756-7555	College Teaching
8756-758X	Fatigue & Fracture of Engineering Materials and Structures
8756-7644	Max
8756-7652	Old Toy Soldier
8756-7709	Anemone
8756-7717	1 - 1 Quarterly *changed to* 1 - 1 Journal.
8756-7741	Roberts Register
8756-775X	Evaluator
8756-7822	P C Letter
8756-7865	G. Stanley Hall Lecture Series
8756-7881	Common Sense Pest Control Quarterly
8756-7903	Revenews
8756-7911	Computeriter
8756-7938	Biotechnology Progress
8756-7962	Franchise Law Journal
8756-8047	O R Manager
8756-8160	Issues in Law and Medicine
8756-8187	Ceramic Source
8756-8217	Breathless Magazine
8756-8225	Journal of College Student Psychotherapy
8756-8233	Drugs & Society
8756-8357	American Brahms Society. Newsletter
8756-842X	C A D - C I M Alert
8756-8446	Fremont County Nostalgia News
8756-8519	Hospital Ethics
8756-8535	Espionage Magazine†
8756-8578	Technology for Anesthesia
8756-8586	Technology for Cardiology
8756-8594	Technology for Emergency Medicine *changed to* Technology for Emergency Care Nurses.
8756-8608	Technology for Materials Management
8756-8616	Technology for Respiratory Therapy
8756-8624	Technology for Surgery
8756-8667	Flutist Quarterly
8756-8705	Rural Special Education Quarterly
8756-8810	MacTutor
8756-890X	Movements in the Arts
8756-8926	New York Law School Journal of Human Rights
8756-9043	National Fact Book of Savings Institutions†
8756-9086	Connective Issues
8756-9094	Groundswell (Albany)†
8756-9116	Business Week Guide to Careers *see* 0891-6578
8756-9175	A B M S Directory of Certified Ophthalmologists
8756-923X	Machinery Outlook
8756-9248	Political Pulse
8756-9256	North Georgia Journal
8756-9302	Transportation Practitioners Journal
8756-9418	Herbertia
8756-9639	Business Media Week *changed to* Business Publisher.
8756-971X	American Mosquito Control Association. Journal
8756-9728	Project Management Journal
8756-9736	C Journal *see* 0898-9788
8756-9965	M O T C's Notebook
8756-9981	New Beginnings (Franklin Park)
9066-1605	International Directory of Published Market Research *changed to* Marketsearch.

Title Index

Page numbers in **boldface** refer to location of main entries, those in roman type refer to location of subject cross references. The symbol ▼ indicates a serial that began publication within the last three years. The symbol † indicates a ceased title.

A. (UK) **2986**
A A A A News. (American Association for Affirmative Action) (US ISSN 0896-8217) **3939**
A A A Annual Report. (American Arbitration Association) (US) **2592**
A A A C E Newsletter see Online with Adult and Continuing Educators **1686**
A A A Going Places. (Automobile Association of America) (US) **4750**
A A A Guide (Year). (American Anthropological Association) (US) **232**
A A A Letter. (American Association for Applied Linguistics) (US) **2799**
A A A Motorist. (American Automobile Association) (US ISSN 1056-2532) **4678**
A A A Motorist of Northeastern Pennsylvania. (US) **4750**
A A A News. (Allergy Association Australia - Victoria Inc.) (AT ISSN 0817-1300) **3182**
A A A S A Newsletter. (Association for the Advancement of Agricultural Sciences in Africa) (ET) **67**
A A A S Annual Meeting. Abstracts of Papers. (American Association for the Advancement of Science) (US) **4354**, 1
A A A S Miscellaneous Publication see A A A S Publications Catalog **4295**
A A A S Publications Catalog. (American Association for the Advancement of Science) (US ISSN 0271-2229) **4295**
A A A S Report: Research and Development. (American Association for the Advancement of Science) (US) **4295**
A A A A S S Directory of Programs in Soviet & East European Studies. (American Association for the Advancement of Slavic Studies) (US ISSN 0889-9487) **1988**
A A A S S Newsletter see American Association for the Advancement of Slavic Studies. Newsletter **1615**
A A A S Science Books and Films see Science Books & Films **4357**
A A A Today (Cincinnati). (American Automobile Association) (US ISSN 1051-3701) **4750**, 4678
A A A Today (Pottstown). (US) **4750**
A A A Today Magazine. (American Automobile Association) (US ISSN 0890-7471) **4678**, 4750
A A A Travel Topics. (US) **4750**

A A A Traveler (York). (US) **4750**, 4678
A A A World (Heathrow). (American Automobile Association) (US ISSN 0277-1403) **4678**, 4750
A A A World: Wisconsin Edition. (American Automobile Association) (US ISSN 0277-1004) **4750**, 4678
A A - B A Newsletter. (American Anorexia - Bulimia Association, Inc.) (US) **4007**, 4396, 4835
A A B Bulletin. (American Association of Bioanalysts) (US) **3256**
A A B C Newsletter. (American Association of Bible Colleges) (US ISSN 0094-260X) **1698**, 4227
A A B C Newsletter. (Archives Association of British Columbia) (CN) **2739**
A A B C Newsletter see Biofeedback Clinicians **3082**
A A B G A Newsletter. (American Association of Botanical Gardens & Arboreta, Inc.) (US ISSN 0569-2423) **2120**
A A B S Newsletter. (Association for the Advancement of Baltic Studies) (US ISSN 0162-976X) **2346**
A A C A News. (American Apparel Contractors Association) (US) **1282**
A A C: Augmentative and Alternative Communication. (CN) **3068**
A A C C Bulletin. (All Africa Conference of Churches) (KE) **4161**
A A C C Magazine. (All Africa Conference of Churches) (KE) **4161**
A A C C Newsletter. (American Automatic Control Council) (US) **1877**
A A C I North. (Association of Americans and Canadians) (IS) **2203**
A A C J C Guide to Community, Technical and Junior Colleges see Who's Who in Community, Technical & Junior Colleges **1698**
A A C J C Statistical Yearbook. (American Association of Community and Junior Colleges) (US ISSN 1673, 1691
▼A A C N Nursing Scan In Critical Care. (American Association of Critical Care Nurses) (US ISSN 1055-8349) **3165**, 1, 3274
A A C O G Newsletter see A A C O G Region **4083**
A A C O G Region. (Alamo Area Council of Governments) (US) **4083**

A A C O M Organizational Guide. (American Association of Colleges of Osteopathic Medicine) (US) **1724**, 3213
A A C P A Newsletter. (Asian American Certified Public Accountants) (US) **744**, 1988
A A C P News. (American Association of Colleges of Pharmacy) (US) **3714**
A A C R A O Data Dispenser. (American Association of Collegiate Registrars and Admissions Officers) (US ISSN 1040-8924) **1698**
A A C R A O Proceedings. (American Association of Collegiate Registrars and Admissions Officers) (US) **1698**
A A C R C Newsletter. (American Association of Children's Residential Centers) (US) **4007**, 1231, 1732
A A C S B Newsline. (American Assembly of Collegiate Schools of Business) (US ISSN 0360-697X) **1698**
A A C S Newsletter. (American Association of Christian Schools) (US) **1691**, 4227
A A D A News. (Associated Antique Dealers of America) (US) **254**, 1032
A.A.E.A. Byline. (American Agricultural Editors Association) (US ISSN 0001-0073) **67**
A A E Newsletter. (African Adult Education Association) (KE) **1681**
A A E News. (Association for Astronomy Education) (UK ISSN 0262-3099) **359**
A A - E V P News. (American Association - Electronic Voice Phenomena) (US) **3668**
A A F Communicator. (American Advertising Federation) (US) **25**, 1331, 2566
A A F M Proceedings of Annual Meeting. (American Association of Feed Microscopists) (US ISSN 0569-2628) **3390**, 559
A A F P Reporter. (American Academy of Family Physicians) (US) **3068**
A A Files. (Architectural Association) (UK ISSN 0261-6823) **291**
A A G Bijdragen. (Vakgroep Agrarische Geschiedenis) (NE ISSN 0511-0726) **2346**, 67
A A G International. (Adult Action Guide) (US) **3395**

A A G Newsletter. (Association of American Geographers) (US ISSN 0275-3995) **2240**
A A H E Bulletin. (American Association for Higher Education) (US ISSN 0162-7910) **1698**
A A H L Biennial Report. (Australian Animal Health Laboratory) (AT ISSN 1034-9219) **4804**
A A H L Newsletter. (Australian Animal Health Laboratory) (AT) **4804**
A A I I Journal. (American Association of Individual Investors) (US ISSN 0192-3315) **937**
A A I S Viewpoint. (American Association of Insurance Services) (US) **2525**
A A L A S Bulletin see Contemporary Topics in Laboratory Animal Science **3258**
A A L C Reporter. (African-American Labor Center, A F L - C I O) (US ISSN 0001-009X) **2579**
A A L L Publications Series. (American Association of Law Libraries) (US ISSN 0065-7255) **2592**, 2739
†A A M A. Technical Advisory Committee. Bulletin. (American Apparel Manufacturers Association) (US) **5127**
†A A M A. Technical Advisory Committee. Research Paper. (US) **5127**
†A A M A. Washington Letter. (US) **5127**
A A M A Committee Manual. (American Apparel Manufacturers Association) (US) **1282**
A A M A Industry Statistical Review and Forecast. (American Architectural Manufacturers Association) (US) **636**, 4560
▼A A M Briefings Series. (Anti-Apartheid Movement) (UK) **3939**
A A M C Curriculum Directory. (Association of American Medical Colleges) (US ISSN 0092-0371) **1742**, 3068
A A M C Directory of American Medical Education. (Association of American Medical Colleges) (US ISSN 0360-7437) **1724**, 1698, 3068
A A M I Annual Meeting. Proceedings. (Association for the Advancement of Medical Instrumentation) (US) **3068**
A A M I News. (Association for the Advancement of Medical Instrumentation) (US ISSN 0739-0270) **2521**, 3256

A A M O A Reports. (Afro-American Music Opportunities Association) (US ISSN 0360-7178) **3536**, 1988

A A M P Lifier. (American Association of Meat Processors) (US) **209**, 2592

A A M R Journal see Interaction (Canberra) **4409**

A A M R T Journal. (Alberta Association of Medical Radiation Technologists) (CN) **3356**

A A M V A Bulletin. (American Association of Motor Vehicle Administrators) (US ISSN 0001-0154) **4678**

A A N A Journal. (American Association of Nurse Anesthetists) (US ISSN 0094-6354) **3274**

A A N N Synapse. (American Association of Neuroscience Nurses) (US) **3274**

A A N Today. (American Association of Nurserymen) (US) **67**, 2120

A A O A Accents. (Auxiliary to the American Osteopathic Association) (US) **3213**

A A O A News. (American Academy of Otolaryngic Allergy) (US) **3182**, 3312

A A O H N Journal see American Association of Occupational Health Nurses Journal **3275**

▼A A O Newsletter. (American Academy of Osteopathy) (US) **3213**

A.A.P.A. Asphalt Review. (Australian Asphalt Pavement Association) (AT ISSN 0727-0003) **1861**

A.A.P.A. Newsletter. (Australian Asphalt Pavement Association) (AT ISSN 0155-3070) **1861**

A.A.P.A. Technitopics see A.A.P.A. Asphalt Review **1861**

A A P G Bulletin. (American Association of Petroleum Geologists) (US ISSN 0149-1423) **3680**, 1552

A A P G Explorer. (American Association of Petroleum Geologists) (US ISSN 0195-2986) **3680**, 1552, 1783

A A P G Studies in Geology Series. (American Association of Petroleum Geologists) (US ISSN 0271-8510) **3680**, 1552

A.A.P.M. Quarterly Bulletin see Medical Physics **3127**

A A P News. (American Academy of Pediatrics) (US) **3317**

A A P Policy Reference Guide. (American Academy of Pediatrics) (US) **3317**

A A P S News. (Association of American Physicians & Surgeons, Inc.) (US ISSN 8750-9687) **3068**

A A P S News Letter see A A P S News **3068**

A A P T Announcer. (American Association of Physics Teachers) (US ISSN 0275-5696) **3812**, 1742

A A R Academy Series. (American Academy of Religion) (US ISSN 0277-1071) **4161**

A A R C Times. (American Association for Respiratory Care) (US ISSN 0893-8520) **3364**

A A R Dissertation Series see A A R Academy Series **4161**

A.A.R.E. Newsletter see Australian Educational Researcher **1617**

A A R F Report. (Australian Accounting Research Foundation) (AT ISSN 1034-2060) **744**

A A R N A Pulse see C H C G Pulse **3276**

A.A.R.N. Newsletter. (Alberta Association of Registered Nurses) (CN ISSN 0001-0197) **3274**

A A R P Bulletin. (American Association of Retired Persons (Washington)) (US) **2269**

A A R P Environment Design. (Art and Archaeology Research Papers) (UK ISSN 0393-5183) **309**, 260

A A R P News Bulletin see A A R P Bulletin **2269**

A A R R O Newsletter. (Afro-Asian Rural Reconstruction Organization) (II) **925**, 67

A A R Studies in Religion. (American Academy of Religion) (US ISSN 0084-6287) **4161**

A A R Times see A A R C Times **3364**

A A S C Quarterly see Anthropology of Consciousness **234**

A A S C U Issues. (American Association of State Colleges and Universities) (US) **1698**

A A S C U Studies see A A S C U Issues **1698**

A.A.'s Far East Businessman's Directory. (Artists Associates) (HK ISSN 0532-9175) **1119**

A A S Goddard Memorial Symposium. Proceedings. (American Astronautical Society, Inc.) (US) **42**

A A S H T O Quarterly Magazine. (American Association of State Highway and Transportation Officials) (US ISSN 0147-4820) **1861**, 4717

A A S H T O Reference Book of Member Department Personnel and Committees. (American Association of State Highway and Transportation Officials) (US) **4646**

A A S History Series. (American Astronautical Society, Inc.) (US ISSN 0730-3564) **42**

A A S Job Register. (American Astronomical Society) (US) **359**

A A S Microfiche Series. (American Astronautical Society, Inc.) (US ISSN 0065-7417) **42**

A A S Newsletter see Space Times **63**

A A S R C News. (American Association of Small Research Companies) (US) **3672**

A A T A Newsletter. (American Association of Teachers of Arabic (Provo)) (US) **1742**, 2799

A.A.T.E. Guide to English Books see A.A.T.E. Guide to English Books and Resources **2980**

A.A.T.E. Guide to English Books and Resources. (Australian Association for the Teaching of English) (AT) **2980**, 1673

A A T E Newsletter. (American Alliance for Theatre & Education) (US) **4629**

A A T F National Bulletin. (American Association of Teachers of French) (US) **2799**

A A T G Newsletter. (American Association of Teachers of German, Inc.) (US ISSN 0001-0243) **2799**

A A T S E E L Newsletter. (American Association of Teachers of Slavic and East European Languages) (US ISSN 0001-0251) **2799**, 1612

A A U C G Insider. (Americans Against Union Control of Government) (US) **2579**

A A U Code see Amateur Athletic Union of the United States. Official Handbook of the A A U Code **4463**

A A U Newsletter. (Association of African Universities) (GH ISSN 0855-0174) **1698**

A A U Official Track and Field Handbook, Rules and Records. (Amateur Athletic Union of the United States) (US ISSN 0361-347X) **4463**

A A U W New York Division. Newsletter see A A U W New Yorker **1302**

A A U W New York Division Reports see A A U W New Yorker **1302**

A A U W New Yorker. (American Association of University Women) (US) **1302**, 1612

A A U W Outlook. (American Association of University Women) (US) **1698**

A A V S O Bulletin: Predicted Dates of Maxima and Minima of Long Period Variable Stars. (American Association of Variable Star Observers) (US) **359**

A A V S O Circular. (American Association of Variable Star Observers) (US) **359**

A A V S O Report see A A V S O Reports and Monographs **360**

A A V S O Reports and Monographs. (American Association of Variable Star Observers) (US) **360**

A A V Today see Association of Avian Veterinarians. Journal **4806**

A A W C J C Newsletter. (American Association of Women in Community and Junior Colleges) (US) **1698**, 4836

A A W H Quarterly. (American Association for World Health) (US) **4096**

A A Z P A Communique. (American Association of Zoological Parks and Aquariums) (US) **575**

A A Z P A Newsletter see A A Z P A Communique **575**

A & A see Aerospace and Aviation Documents Microfile **44**

A & B Computing. (UK ISSN 0264-4584) **1388**

A & D Business. (Architects & Designers) (US) **2556**

A & E Program Guide. (Arts & Entertainment Channel) (US) **1368**

A & H C I see Arts & Humanities Citation Index **351**

A & O see Zeitschrift fuer Arbeits- und Organisationspsychologie **4050**

A and S see Architect & Surveyor **292**

A & T Register. (Agricultural & Technical) (US) **1302**, 1988

A & U. (Architecture and Urbanism) (JA) **291**

A B A - B N A Lawyers' Manual on Professional Conduct. (American Bar Association) (US ISSN 0740-4050) **2592**

A B A Bank Card Letter see A B A Retail Banker **757**

A B A Bank Compliance. (American Bankers Association) (US ISSN 0887-0187) **757**, 2592

A B A Bankers News Weekly. (American Bankers Association) (US ISSN 0746-3367) **757**

A B A Banking Journal. (American Bankers Association) (US) **757**

A B A Business Briefs see Associations' Forum **938**

A B A Consumer Banking Digest. (American Bankers Association) (US) **757**, 1502

A B A Journal. (American Bar Association) (US ISSN 0747-0088) **2592**

A B A Juvenile and Child Welfare Law Reporter. (American Bar Association) (US ISSN 0887-896X) **1231**, 2592

A B A Management Update of Personal Trust & Private Banking. (US) **757**, 1000

A B A Newsletter. (American Bartenders' Association) (US) **377**, 2471

A B A Newsletter. (Association for Behavior Analysis) (US) **4007**

A B A Newswire. (American Booksellers Association) (US) **4119**

A B A Retail Banker. (American Bankers Association) (US) **757**

A B A Today. (African Businessmen's Association of Malawi) (MW) **643**

A B A - UNIX - Group Newsletter. (US) **2705**, 1475

A B A Washington Letter. (American Bar Association) (US ISSN 0516-9968) **2592**

A - B: Auto - Biography Studies. (US) **417**

A B B Review. (SZ ISSN 1013-3119) **1880**, 1926

A B B Technik see A B B Review **1880**

A B B Tidning see A B B Review **1880**

A B B W A Journal. (American Black Book Writers Association, Inc.) (US ISSN 8756-0267) **388**, 1988, 4119

A B Bookman's Weekly. (Antiquarian Bookman) (US ISSN 0001-0340) **4119**

A B Bookman's Yearbook. (Antiquarian Bookman) (US ISSN 0065-0005) **4119**

A B C see African Building Contractor **599**

A B C. (IC ISSN 1017-3498) **1248**

A B C/B J V. (Annuaire Belge de Chauffage et Climatisation) (BE) **2297**

A B C Air Cargo Guide. (UK ISSN 0141-6529) **4669**, 4646

A B C Air Travel Atlas. (UK) **4750**

A B C: Anuario Brasileiro da Construcao. (BL) **598**

A B C Blue Book: Canadian Daily Newspapers. (Audit Bureau of Circulations) (US) **40**

A B C Blue Book: Canadian Weekly Newspapers. (Audit Bureau of Circulations) (US) **40**

A B C Blue Book: Publisher's Statements. (US) **40**

A B C Blue Book: U S and Canadian Business Publications. (US) **4119**, 701

A B C Blue Book: U S and Canadian Magazines. (US) **4119**, 701

A B C Blue Book: U S and Canadian Magazines and Farm Publications see A B C Blue Book: U S and Canadian Magazines **4119**

A B C Blue Book: U S Daily Newspapers. (US) **40**

A B C Blue Book: U S Weekly Newspapers. (US) **40**

†A B C British Columbia Lumber Trade Directory and Year Book. (CN ISSN 0065-0013) **5127**

A B C C Newsletter. (Australian British Chamber of Commerce) (AT) **806**

A B C Car Ferry Guide. (UK) **4723**

†A B C Case Book. (US) **5127**

A B C Circulation Review. (UK) **2566**, 4119

A B C der Deutschen Wirtschaft. (GW) **1119**

A B C Dialogue. (Association of Bridal Consultants) (US ISSN 1053-9107) **3066**, 1112

A B C Enseignement de Droits de l'Homme see A B C Human Rights Teaching **1721**

A B C Europ Production - Europex. (GW ISSN 0065-003X) **899**

A B C Europe Production. (SI) **1119**

A B C Executive Flight Planner: Asia Planner. (UK) **4669**

A B C Executive Flight Planner: Europe, Middle East & Africa. (UK) **4669**, 4707

A B C Executive Flight Planner: North America. (UK) **4669**

A B C Film Review see Film Review (London, 1951) **3509**

A B C Freight Guide. (UK ISSN 0308-9304) **4742**

A B C Guide to International Travel. (UK ISSN 0141-6278) **4750**

A B C Guide to Party Booking see Guide to Party Booking **5202**

A B C Holiday Guide. (UK) **4750**

A B C Human Rights Teaching. (UN ISSN 0253-6455) **1721**

A B C Magazine International. (IS) **1295**

A B C Mladych Prirodovedcu. (CS) **1248**, 4295

A B C News Bulletin. (US) **40**

A B C News Index. (US ISSN 0891-8775) **1346**, 1, 1368, 2577

A B C Newsletter see Advance Band Magazine **3537**

A B C Newsmagazine see Advance Band Magazine **3537**

†A B C of Book Trade. (US ISSN 0065-0048) **5127**

A B C of Magic Sets. (GW) **2432**

A B C of Technics. see A B C Techniki **5127**

A B C Passenger Shipping Guide. (UK) **4723**

A B C Periodical F A S - F A X Reports. (Audit Bureau of Circulations) (US) **40**

A B C Pinpin Dudu Huabao/A B C Spelling and Reading Pictorial. (CC) **1613**, 1248

A B C Pol Sci. (US ISSN 0001-0456) **3936**, 1, 2697, 4078

†A B C Privrede Jugoslavije. (YU) **5127**

A B C Rail Guide. (UK ISSN 0001-0472) **4707**

A B C Revista. (PY) **2213**

A B C Spelling and Reading Pictorial. see A B C Pinpin Dudu Huabao **1613**

A B C Star Service. (UK) **4750**

†A B C Techniki/A B C of Technics. (PL) **5127**
A B C Today. (Associated Builders & Contractors, Inc.) (US) **598**
A B C Travel Directory. (UK) **4750**
A B C Truck Breakdown Guide *see* A B C Freight Guide **4742**
A B C U S Daily Newspaper F A S - F A X Reports. (Audit Bureau of Circulations) (US) **40**
A B C World Airways Guide. (UK ISSN 0309-6157) **4669**, **4750**
A B C Worldwide Hotel Guide *see* Hotel & Travel Index - A B C International Edition **2475**
A B C - Zeitung. (GW ISSN 0001-0375) **1248**
A.B.D. (Aviation Business Directory) (US ISSN 0001-0502) **42**
A B D *see* Asian - Pacific Book Development **4120**
A B E S P Boletim. (Associacao Brasileira de Endodontia, Seccao Sao Paulo) (BL) **3226**
A.B.E.U. Newsletter. (Australian Bank Employees Union) (AT) **757**, **970**
A B F By-Lines. (A B F Freight System, Inc.) (US) **4646**
A B F Freight System, Inc. By-Lines *see* A B F By-Lines **4646**
A B H B *see* Annual Bibliography of the History of the Printed Book and Library **4006**
A B I. (Aktuelle Berichte und Informationen fuer Architekten und Ingenieure) (GW) **291**
A B I - INFORM. (American Business Information) (US) **701**, **1**
A B I Technik. (GW ISSN 0720-6763) **2740**
A B M Metalurgia e Materiais. (Associacao Brasileira de Metalurgia e Materiais) (BL) **3401**, **1880**
A B M S Compendium of Certified Medical Specialists. (American Board of Medical Specialties) (US ISSN 0884-1543) **3068**
A B M S Directory of Certified Allergists and Immunologists. (American Board of Medical Specialties) (US ISSN 0883-2994) **3182**
A B M S Directory of Certified Anesthesiologists. (US ISSN 0883-122X) **3189**
A B M S Directory of Certified Colon & Rectal Surgeons. (US ISSN 0884-1470) **3266**
A B M S Directory of Certified Dermatologists. (US ISSN 0884-1489) **3245**
A B M S Directory of Certified Emergency Physicians. (US ISSN 0742-0366) **3068**
A B M S Directory of Certified Family Physicians. (US ISSN 0884-643X) **3068**
A B M S Directory of Certified Internists. (US ISSN 0884-6448) **3068**
A B M S Directory of Certified Neurological Surgeons. (US ISSN 0882-2832) **3327**, **3373**
A B M S Directory of Certified Neurologists. (US ISSN 0884-1500) **3327**
A B M S Directory of Certified Nuclear Medicine Specialists. (US ISSN 0884-1454) **3356**
A B M S Directory of Certified Obstetricians & Gynecologists. (US ISSN 0884-1535) **3288**
A B M S Directory of Certified Ophthalmologists. (US ISSN 8756-9175) **3297**
A B M S Directory of Certified Orthopaedic Surgeons. (US ISSN 0883-1211) **3306**
A B M S Directory of Certified Otolaryngologists. (US ISSN 0883-3001) **3312**
A B M S Directory of Certified Pathologists. (US ISSN 0883-1203) **3263**
A B M S Directory of Certified Pediatricians. (US ISSN 0884-1497) **3317**

A B M S Directory of Certified Physical Medicine & Rehabilitation Physicians. (US ISSN 0883-2986) **3068**
A B M S Directory of Certified Plastic Surgeons. (US ISSN 0749-839X) **3373**
A B M S Directory of Certified Preventive Medicine Specialists. (US ISSN 0883-2978) **3068**
A B M S Directory of Certified Psychiatrists. (US ISSN 0884-1519) **3327**
A B M S Directory of Certified Radiologists. (US ISSN 0883-1238) **3356**
A B M S Directory of Certified Surgeons. (US ISSN 0884-1527) **3373**
A B M S Directory of Certified Thoracic Surgeons. (US ISSN 0884-1462) **3068**, **3373**
A B M S Directory of Certified Urologists. (US ISSN 0742-0374) **3386**
A B M S Record. (American Board of Medical Specialties) (US) **3068**
A B N Authorities. (Australian Bibliographic Network) (AT ISSN 0726-1276) **388**
†A B N Catalogue. (Australian Bibliographic Network) (AT ISSN 0815-0303) **5127**
A B N Correspondence. (American Friends of the Anti-Bolshevik Bloc of Nations) (US ISSN 0001-0545) **3869**
A B N News. (Australian Bibliographic Network) (AT ISSN 0726-0644) **2740**
A.B.O.A. Newsletter (Australian Bank Officials Association) *see* A.B.E.U. Newsletter **757**
A B O I Catalogue. (Association of British Oceanic Industries) (UK) **4723**
A B Organisation Marine Portfolio. (AT) **4723**
A B P A Directory of Members. (Australian Book Publishers Association) (AT) **4120**
A B P - Association Belge des Paralyses. Bulletin/B V V - Belgische Vereniging voor Verlamden. Bulletin. (BE ISSN 0001-0553) **3327**, **4396**
A B P D A Journal *see* Collision Parts Journal **4688**
A B P R *see* American Book Publishing Record **4139**
†A B R A T E S. (Associacao Brasileira de Tradutores) (BL) **5127**
A B S E E S. (Abstracts Soviet and East European Series) (UK ISSN 0044-5622) **2327**, **2346**
A B S I - Abstracte in Bibliologie si Stiinta Informarii. (RM ISSN 1220-3092) **2792**, **1**
A B Stracts. (American Bonsai Society, Inc.) (US) **2141**, **1**
A.B. - The Samaritan News. (IS ISSN 0333-7286) **1988**
A B U I Network News. (Association of Banyan Users International) (US ISSN 1057-2082) **1426**
A B U Technical Review. (Asia - Pacific Broadcasting Union) (MY ISSN 0126-6209) **1368**
A B V Prepodavanie Prav Cheloveka *see* A B C Human Rights Teaching **1721**
A Bola. (US) **4463**
A C A Bulletin. (Association for Communication Administration) (US ISSN 0360-0939) **1331**, **1000**
A C A Bulletin. (Association of Canadian Archivists) (CN ISSN 0709-4604) **2305**
†A C A D S Quarterly. (AT) **5127**
A C A Index. (Americans for Constitutional Action) (US ISSN 0066-1228) **3936**
A C A Journal of Chiropractic *see* Journal of Chiropractic **3215**
A C A News. (American Compensation Association) (US) **1062**, **970**
A C A News. (Alberta Council on Aging) (CN) **2269**, **4396**

A C A R T S O D. Monograph Series. (African Centre for Applied Research and Training in Social Development) (LY) **925**
A C A R T S O D Newsletter. (African Centre for Applied Research and Training in Social Development) (LY) **4396**
A.C.A. Review. (Anglers Cooperative Association) (UK ISSN 0044-8257) **2035**, **1482**
A C A Update. (American Council for the Arts) (US ISSN 1054-3570) **309**, **2592**
A C B M Nouvelles. *see* C A M L Newsletter **3543**
A C C A Catalog of Technical Materials and Business Management Aids *see* A C C A Quality Contractor's Catalog of Materials, Products and Services **2304**
A C C A Docket. (American Corporate Counsel Association) (US) **643**, **2592**
A C C A Express. (Air Courier Conference of America) (US) **4669**
A C C A News. (Air Conditioning Contractors of America) (US) **2297**
A C C A Quality Contractor's Catalog of Materials, Products and Services. (Air Conditioning Contractors of America) (US) **2304**
A C C Agenda for Reform Papers. (Australian Chamber of Commerce) (AT ISSN 0819-808X) **806**
A C C Basketball Handbook. (Atlantic Coast Conference) (US ISSN 0733-0448) **4499**
A C C C Community. (Association of Canadian Community Colleges) (CN) **1698**
A C C C International. (Association of Canadian Community Colleges) (CN) **925**
A C C C National *see* The National Advocate **1712**
A C C E L. (American College of Cardiology) (US) **3203**
A C C E L for Physicians *see* A C C E L **3203**
A C C H Network. (Association for the Care of Children's Health) (US) **3317**, **1732**
A C C I Newsletter. (American Council on Consumer Interests) (US ISSN 0010-9975) **1502**
A C C J Directory. (American Chamber of Commerce in Japan) (JA) **1119**
A C C N Bulletin. (Associated Court and Commercial Newspapers) (US) **2566**, **2592**
A C C O Z News *see* Z N C C Newsletter **824**
A C C P Dialogue. *see* C A F C Dialogue **2031**
A C C R A Cost of Living Index. (American Chamber of Commerce Researchers Association) (US ISSN 1048-2830) **701**, **806**
A C C R A Inter-City Cost of Living Index *see* A C C R A Cost of Living Index **701**
A C C R A Newsletter. (American Chamber of Commerce Researchers Association (Louisville)) (US) **806**, **841**
A C C Research Papers. (Australian Chamber of Commerce) (AT ISSN 1030-147X) **806**
A C C Submission Papers. (Australian Chamber of Commerce) (AT ISSN 1030-0775) **806**
A C C Touche Ross Tax Legislation Fact Papers. (Australian Chamber of Commerce) (AT ISSN 1030-0562) **806**, **1087**
A.C.C. - Westpac Economic Discussion Papers. (Australian Chamber of Commerce) (AT ISSN 0817-4830) **806**
A C D F A Newsletter. (American College Dance Festival Association) (US) **1528**
A C D I Rapport Annuel. *see* C I D A Annual Report **927**
A C E. (Athletic Club Events) (US ISSN 0044-5932) **1295**
†A C E. (Accessories Components & Equipment) (UK) **5127**

A C E Action Newsletter. (Association of Collegiate Entrepreneurs) (US) **1113**, **1698**
A C E Bulletin. (Advisory Centre for Education (A C E) Ltd.) (UK ISSN 0266-6278) **1724**
A.C.E. Bulletin *see* Societe des Auteurs, Compositeurs, Editeurs pour la Gerance des Droits de Reproduction Mecanique. Bulletin **2679**
A C E C Newsletter *see* Last Word **1829**
A C E C Review. (Ateliers de Constructions Electriques de Charleroi) (BE ISSN 0001-0669) **1880**
A C E H I Journal/Association Canadienne des Educateurs des Deficients Auditifs. Revue. (Association of Canadian Educators of the Hearing Impaired) (CN ISSN 0382-7976) **2285**, **1733**
A C E I D Newsletter. (Asian Centre of Educational Innovation for Development) (UN) **1721**
A C E I Exchange *see* Childhood Education **1621**
A C E International. (A C E Publishing Ltd.) (UK) **1368**, **1466**, **1880**
A C E Lenkrad. (Auto Club Europa e.V.) (GW) **4678**, **4750**
A C E Newsletter *see* A C E Action Newsletter **1113**
A C E Publishing Ltd. International *see* A C E International **1368**
A C E R Newsletter. (Australian Council for Educational Research) (AT) **1698**
A C E S *see* El Faro **3752**
A C F. (UY) **3869**
A C F A Bulletin. (American Cat Fanciers Association, Inc.) (US ISSN 0744-9631) **3707**
A C F Bulletin. (American Checker Federation) (US) **4463**, **2432**
A C F D Forum. (Association of Canadian Faculties of Dentistry) (CN ISSN 0820-5949) **3226**
A C F Newsletter *see* Conservation News **1486**
A.C.F.O.A. News. (Australian Council for Overseas Aid) (AT ISSN 0811-4692) **925**, **1721**
A C Flyer. (Air Craft) (US ISSN 0194-8652) **4669**
A C G A Multilogue. (American Community Gardening Association) (US) **2120**
A C H A Action. (American College Health Association) (US ISSN 0002-7952) **3798**, **1698**
A C H Action *see* A C H A Action **3798**
A C H Newsletter. (Association for Computers and the Humanities) (US ISSN 0190-6631) **2520**
A C H P E R National Journal. (Australian Council for Health, Physical Education and Recreation) (AT ISSN 0813-2283) **1613**, **3798**, **4463**
A C I Bibliography. (American Concrete Institute) (US ISSN 0084-6325) **388**
A C I Informazioni. (Automobile Club d'Italia) (IT ISSN 0001-0715) **4678**
A C I M Newsletter. (American Committee on Italian Migration) (US) **3979**
A C I Manual of Concrete Practice. (American Concrete Institute) (US ISSN 0065-7875) **598**
A C I Materials Journal. (American Concrete Institute) (US ISSN 0889-325X) **598**
A C I News *see* Allergy & Clinical Immunology News **3183**
A C I S. (Association for Contemporary Iberian Studies) (UK ISSN 0955-4270) **2346**
A C I Structural Journal. (American Concrete Institute) (US ISSN 0889-3241) **598**
A C I Year Book. (Australian Cat Federation, Inc.) (AT) **3707**
A C J S Today. (Academy of Criminal Justice Sciences) (US) **1509**, **1613**

A C

A C L A L S Newsheet see Association for Commonwealth Literature and Language Studies. Bulletin **2896**

A C L D Newsbriefs (Association for Children and Adults with Learning Disabilities) see L D A Newsbriefs **1738**

A C L S Annual Report. (American Council of Learned Societies) (US ISSN 0065-7972) **2501**

A C L S Newsletter. (American Council of Learned Societies) (US) **2501**

A C L S Occasional Papers. (American Council of Learned Societies) (US) **2501**

A C L U News. (American Civil Liberties Union of Northern California) (US) **3939**

A C M see Another Chicago Magazine **2895**

A C M Ada Letters. (Association for Computing Machinery) (US ISSN 0736-721X) **1388**

A C M Administrative Directory of College and University Computer Science - Data Processing Programs and Computer Facilities. (US) **1388, 1448**

A C M Bulletin (N.S.W. Edition). (Australian Chamber of Manufactures) (AT ISSN 1035-3941) **1071**

A C M Bulletin (Victorian Edition). (Australian Chamber of Manufactures) (AT ISSN 1035-395X) **806**

A C M C Forum. (Association of Canadian Medical Colleges) (CN ISSN 0836-3463) **3068**

A C M Computing Surveys. (US ISSN 0360-0300) **1388**

A C M Guide to Computing Literature. (US ISSN 0149-1199) **1402**

A C M - I E E E Design Automation Conference. Proceedings. (US ISSN 0738-100X) **1416**

A C M Monograph Series. (Association for Computing Machinery) (US) **1388**

A C M R A News see News and Ideas **1353**

A C M S I G P L A N Notices. (US) **1429**

A C M Symposium on the Theory of Computing. (US) **1481**

A C M Transactions on Database Systems. (US ISSN 0362-5915) **1443**

A C M Transactions on Graphics. (US ISSN 0730-0301) **1420**

A C M Transactions on Information Systems see Transactions on Information Systems **828**

A C M Transactions on Mathematical Software. (US ISSN 0098-3500) **1475, 3063**

A C M Transactions on Programming Languages and Systems. (US ISSN 0164-0925) **1429, 1436**

A C O A Action News. (American Committee on Africa) (US) **3948**

A C O F A R. (Asociacion de Cooperativas Farmaceuticas) (SP) **3714**

A C O G Current Journal Review. (American College of Obstetricians and Gynecologists) (US ISSN 0897-1471) **3165, 3288**

A C O G Interactions: Programs in Clinical Decision Making. (American College of Obstetricians and Gynecologists) (CN) **3288**

A C O G Newsletter. (American College of Obstetricians and Gynecologists) (US) **3288**

A C O L A M Newsletter. (Advisory Committee on Latin American Materials) (UK ISSN 0263-6832) **2740**

A C O Newsletter. (American College of Orgonomy) (US) **3327, 3812**

A C O P Messenger. (Apostolic Church of Pentecost of Canada, Inc.) (CN) **4227**

A C O R N Journal. (Australian Confederation of Operating Room Nurses) (AT) **2458, 3274**

A C O S C A Eastern Regional Newsletter see A C O S C A News **757**

A C O S C A News. (Africa Co-operative Savings and Credit Association) (KE) **757**

A C O S News. (American College of Osteopathic Surgeons) (US ISSN 0001-0790) **3373**

A C O S S Quarterly see Australian Journal of Social Issues **4399**

A C P A. (Asociacion Cubana de Produccion Animal) (CU) **209**

†A.C.P.C. Forum. (Australian Crime Prevention Council) (AT ISSN 0155-8862) **5127**

A C P - E E C Council of Ministers. Annual Report (Year). (EI) **925**

A C P M News. (American College of Preventive Medicine) (US) **3068, 4096**

A C P Newslog. (Associated Church Press) (US) **4161**

†A C P States Yearbook. (BE ISSN 0771-5137) **5127**

A C P T C Newsletter see I T A A Newsletter **1285**

A C P T C Proceedings see I T A A Proceedings **1288**

A C P T C Special Publications see I T A A Special Publications **1285**

A C P U Bulletin. see C A U T Bulletin **1701**

A C R Bulletin. (American College of Radiology) (US ISSN 0098-6070) **3356**

A C R M D on the Record. (Association for Children with Retarded Mental Development) (US) **1733**

A C R O D Newsletter. (Australian Council for Rehabilitation of Disabled (ACROD)) (AT ISSN 0729-8463) **4396, 2290**

A C S A Faculty Directory. (Association of Collegiate Schools of Architecture, Inc.) (US) **291**

A C S A News. (Association of Collegiate Schools of Architecture, Inc.) (US ISSN 0149-2446) **291**

A C S Auto see Auto **4679**

A C S J C Occasional Papers. (Australian Catholic Social Justice Council) (AT ISSN 1032-2205) **3939**

A C S M Bulletin. (American Congress on Surveying and Mapping) (US ISSN 0097-6180) **2240**

A C S Monographs. (American Chemical Society) (US ISSN 0065-7719) **1168**

A C S Newsletter/A E C. Bulletin. (Association for Canadian Studies) (CN ISSN 0714-2579) **2501, 4364**

A C S Notebook see American Cryonics **3257**

A C S P Selection Sante see C P H A Health Digest **3800**

A C S Research Reports. (Agricultural Cooperative Service) (US) **145**

A C S S O Policy (Year). (Australian Council of State School Organisations) (AT) **1613**

A C S Symposium Series. (American Chemical Society) (US ISSN 0097-6156) **1168**

A C S U S Newsletter see American Review of Canadian Studies **3949**

A C S Victorian Bulletin. (Australian Computer Society Inc.) (AT) **1388**

A C S Zurich. (SZ) **4678**

A C T. (Ashram Community Trust) (UK) **4161**

A C T. (A T I R A Communications on Textile) (II) **4615**

A C T A C Newsletter. (Australian Children's Television Action Committee) (AT) **1248**

A C T A F L Football Record. (A C T Australian Football League) (AT) **4499**

A C T A Magazine see Interacta **1751**

A C T A News. (Art Craft Teachers Association of Victoria) (AT) **1742, 309**

A C T A Official Annual Directory. (Allied Canadian Travel Agents) (CN) **1120, 4750**

A C T Australian Football League Football Record see A C T A F L Football Record **4499**

A C T F L Foreign Language Education Series. (American Council on the Teaching of Foreign Languages) (US ISSN 0147-1236) **1742**

A C T F L Review of Foreign Languages Education see A C T F L Foreign Language Education Series **1742**

†A C T H and Related Peptides. (UK ISSN 0260-1117) **5127**

A C T Handbook for Financial Aid Administrators see American College Testing. Handbook for Financial Aid Administrators **1724**

A C T Research Report. (American College Testing) (US ISSN 0569-3993) **1698**

A C T Research Service Report see A C T Research Report **1698**

A.C.T. - S.T.A. Journal see A.C.T. Science Teacher **1743**

A.C.T. Science Teacher. (Science Teachers Association of the Australian Capital Territory) (AT ISSN 0818-2019) **1743**

†A C T U Bulletin. (Australian Council of Trade Unions) (AT ISSN 0314-2868) **5127**

†A C T U National Youth Brochure. (Australian Council of Trade Unions) (AT) **5127**

†A C T U Youth Book. (Australian Council of Trade Unions) (AT) **5127**

A C Tivity. (American College Testing) (US ISSN 0001-7620) **1613**

A C U Bulletin of Current Documentation (ABCD). (Association of Commonwealth Universities) (UK ISSN 0044-9563) **1698**

A C U C A A Bulletin see Association of Performing Arts Presenters Bulletin **4630**

A C U R I L Newsletter. see Association of Caribbean University Research and Institutional Libraries. Carta Informativa de A C U R I L **2745**

A C's Guide to the Commodore Amiga. (US) **1466**

A C's Tech for the Commodore Amiga. (US) **1466**

▼A D A A Reporter. (Anxiety Disorders Association of America) (US) **4007**

A D A B News see Grassroots **4406**

A D A B Sangbad see Adhuna **4397**

A D A C Atlas Deutschland - Europa. (Allgemeiner Deutscher Automobil Club e.V.) (GW) **4750, 4717**

A D A C Campingfuehrer. Band 1: Suedeuropa. (Allgemeiner Deutscher Automobil-Club e.V.) (GW ISSN 0179-6089) **4539, 4750**

A D A C Campingfuehrer. Band 2: Deutschland, Mittel- und Nordeuropa. (Allgemeiner Deutscher Automobil-Club e.V.) (GW) **4539, 4750**

A D A C Handbuch - Geschaeftswagen see Autokosten und Steuern Aktuell **4682**

A D A C Handbuch: Reiserecht Entscheidungen. (Allgemeiner Deutscher Automobil-Club e.V.) (GW) **2592, 4750**

A D A C Handbuch: Schadenersatz bei Verletzung. (Allgemeiner Deutscher Automobil-Club e.V.) (GW) **2592**

A D A C Handbuch: Schmerzensgeld-Betraege. (GW ISSN 0581-9792) **2719**

A D A C Handbuch: Unfall im Ausland - Schadensregulierung. (GW) **2592, 4750**

A D A C Handbuch: Unfall Ratgeber. (GW) **2592, 4750**

A D A C Motorwelt. (GW ISSN 0007-2842) **4678, 4750**

A D A C Signale. (GW) **4678**

A D A C SkiAtlas. (GW) **4750, 4539**

A D A C Special Auto. (GW) **4678**

A.D.A. Forecast see Diabetes Forecast **3251**

A.D.A. Journal see Defender **1273**

A D A M H A News. (Alcohol, Drug Abuse, and Mental Health Administration) (US) **1532, 4007**

A D A Magazine. (Art, Design, Architecture) (SA) **291, 309, 3788**

A D A News. (American Dental Association) (US ISSN 0001-0855) **3226**

A D A News Information see A D A Newsletter **3226**

A D A Newsletter. (Alberta Dental Association) (CN) **3226**

A D A P S O Data. (Association of Data Processing Service Organizations) (US) **1448**

A D A P S O Membership Directory see I T A A Membership Directory **1451**

A D A R A Newsletter. (American Deafness & Rehabilitation Association) (US) **2285**

A D A S P O, The Computer Software and Services Industry Association. Salary Study. (Association of Data Processing and Service Organizations) (US) **1475, 1448**

A D A S P O, The Computer Software and Services Industry Association. Technology Papers. (Association of Data Processing and Service Organizations) (US) **1475, 1448**

†A D A S Quarterly Review. (Agricultural Development and Advisory Service) (UK ISSN 0027-5670) **5127**

A D A Today. (Americans for Democratic Action) (US ISSN 0896-3134) **3869, 643, 1613, 1783**

A D A World see A D A Today **3869**

A D Action News and Notes. (Americans for Democratic Action) (US) **3869**

A.D. & D. Acquisitions, Dispositons & Distributions see A D & D: Tax Interpretations **5127**

†A D & D: Tax Interpretations. (US ISSN 0091-553X) **5127**

A D Architectural Digest, Edizione Italiana. (US) **291, 2547**

A D Architecture. (Architectural Digest) (US) **291, 2547**

A D B Business Opportunities. (Asian Development Bank) (PH) **643**

A D B News. (African Development Bank) (IV) **757**

A D B Quarterly Review. (Asian Development Bank) (PH) **925**

A D C I S Newsletter. (Association for the Development of Computer-Based Instructional Systems) (US) **1416**

A D C Nenkan. see Tokyo Art Directors Annual **39**

A D E Bulletin. (Association of Departments of English) (US ISSN 0001-0898) **2890**

A D E G - Kaufmann. (AU ISSN 0001-8112) **2090**

A D F L Bulletin. (Association of Departments of Foreign Languages) (US ISSN 0148-7639) **2799, 1698**

A D I News. (Association for Direct Instruction) (US) **1743, 1733**

A D I Quarterly News Letter. (Asian Development Institute) (UN) **925**

†A D I U Report. (Armament and Disarmament Information Unit) (UK ISSN 0264-0643) **5127**

†A.D.K. Booklet: Facts and Figures/ A.D.K. Schriftenreihe: Daten and Fakten. (Afrikaans Duitse Kultuurunie (SWA)) (SX) **5127**

A.D.K. Informationen. see A.D.K. Informations **2330**

A.D.K. Informations/A.D.K. Informationen. (Afrikaans-Duitse Kultuurunie (SWA)) (SX) **2330**

A.D.K. Schriftenreihe: Daten and Fakten. see A.D.K. Booklet: Facts and Figures **5127**

A D L A. (Art Directors Club of Los Angeles) (US ISSN 0887-4514) **309**

A D L Bulletin see A D L on the Front Line **3939**

A D L Law Report. (Anti-Defamation League of B'nai B'rith) (US) **2593, 1988**

A D L on the Front Line. (Anti-Defamation League of B'nai B'rith) (US) **3939**

A D M. (Asociacion Dental Mexicana, A.C.) (MX ISSN 0001-0944) **3227**

A D M A Bulletin. see Nashrat A D M A **3692**

A D M & T see Aerospace Defense Markets & Technology **5131**

†A.D. Magazine. (AT ISSN 1030-178X) 5127
A D N O C News/Akhbar A D N O C. (Abu Dhabi National Oil Company) (TS) 3680
A.D.O. see Animal Disease Occurrence 4805
†A D O P T. (Asian-Pacific and Worldwide Documents on Population Topics) (UN ISSN 0252-4422) 5127
A D P A Professional. (Alcohol and Drug Problems Association of North America) (US) 1532
†A D P Newsletter. (Automatic Data Processing) (US ISSN 0044-5649) 5127
A D R A Newsletter. (Automotive Dismantlers & Recyclers Association) (US) 4678
A D R D A Newsletter see Alzheimer's Association Newsletter 2270
A D R I D. (Adverse Drug Reactions & Interactions Database) (US) 3715
A D R I S see A D R I D 3715
A D R I S Newsletter. (Association for the Development of Religious Information Services) (US ISSN 0300-7022) 4161, 2740
A D - Solutions Report. (US) 1457
A D T A Newsletter. (American Dance Therapy Association, Inc.) (US) 1733, 3068
A D T Transmitter. (American District Telegraph Co.) (US ISSN 0001-0960) 2030
A D T V - Nachrichten. (Allgemeiner Deutscher Tanzlehrer Verband) (GW ISSN 0001-0979) 1528
A D U K. (Adresar Ukraintsiv u Vilnomu Sviti) (FR) 3948
A D V - Informationsdienst. (Arbeitsgemeinschaft Deutscher Verkehrsflughaefen) (GW ISSN 0001-0987) 4669
†A.D. Youthleader. (AT ISSN 1030-1798) 5127
A.D. 2000. (AT) 4161
†A E. (Atomenergi) (SW ISSN 0519-3346) 5127
A E A Advocate. (Arizona Education Association) (US ISSN 0194-8849) 1613
A E A M Newsletter Journal. (Adult Education Association in Massachusetts, Inc.) (US ISSN 0001-1002) 1681
A E A Newsletter. (American Education Association) (US) 1613
A E A Times. (United Kingdom Atomic Energy Authority) (UK) 1803
A E B see Annual Egyptological Bibliography 2327
A E B U. (Asociacion de Bancos del Uruguay) (UY ISSN 0001-1010) 757
A E C. Bulletin. see A C S Newsletter 2501
A - E - C Automation Newsletter. (Architecture, Engineering, Construction) (US ISSN 0277-1659) 1877, 309
A E C Canada. (Architectural Engineering and Construction) (CN) 291, 1877
A E C L Report Series. (Atomic Energy of Canada Ltd.) (CN ISSN 0067-0367) 1803, 1783
A E C Q Chantiers. (Association des Entrepreneurs en Construction du Quebec) (CN ISSN 0825-9895) 599
†A-E Concepts in Wood Design. (US ISSN 0099-1716) 5127
A E D S Journal see Journal of Research on Computing in Teacher Education 1691
†A E D S Monitor. (US ISSN 0001-1045) 5127
†A E D S Newsletter. (US) 5128
A E E Energy Insight. (Association of Energy Engineers) (US) 1783
A E F Newsletter. (American Economic Foundation) (US) 888, 970
A E G News. (Association of Engineering Geologists) (US ISSN 0888-305X) 1552
A E G - Schakels. (NE ISSN 0001-1053) 1880

†A E G-Telefunken. Wissenschaftliche Berichte. (Allgemeine Elektrizitaets Gesellschaft) (GW ISSN 0043-6801) 5128
A E G - Telefunken Ontladingen see Ontladingen 1904
†A E G - Telefunken Progress. (Allgemeine Elektrizitaets Gesellschaft) (GW ISSN 0001-107X) 5128
†A E I Economist. (American Enterprise Institute for Public Policy Research) (US ISSN 0149-9785) 5128
A.E.I.O.U. see Bivouac 1233
A.E.L.E. Law Enforcement Legal Defense Manual see Defense Manual 2702
A E L E Law Enforcement Legal Liability Reporter see Liability Reporter 2702
A E L E Liability Reporter see Liability Reporter 2702
A E Legal Newsletter. (Architects and Engineers) (US ISSN 0090-2411) 2593
A E M S Seminar (Papers). (American Engineering Model Society) (US) 1813, 599
A E N Activities en (Year) see O E C D Nuclear Energy Agency Activities in (Year) 1809
A E N Bulletin see N A E N Bulletin 1729
A E P Journal see Educational Psychology in Practice 4020
A E R O Sun Times. (Alternative Energy Resource Organization) (US ISSN 1046-0993) 1783, 67, 1941
A E R Report. (Association for Education and Rehabilitation of the Blind and Visually Impaired (AER)) (US) 2290
A E S. (Ambiente e Sicurezza) (IT ISSN 0391-7339) 1941
A E S D I see Revista Profesional del Gremio de Estaciones de Servicio 2588
A E S I S Quarterly. (Australian Earth Sciences Information System) (AT ISSN 0313-704X) 1549, 1, 3498
A E S Newsletter. (Abrasive Engineering Society) (US) 3401
A E Systems Report see Design Systems Strategies 309
A.E.T.F.A.T. Index. (Association pour l'Etude Taxonomique de la Flore d'Afrique Tropicale) (BE ISSN 0066-9784) 461, 1
A E T T Journal see A E T T Journal - E T T I 1743
A E T T Journal - E T T I. (Association for Educational and Training Technology) (UK) 1743
A E T T Journal - P L E T see A E T T Journal - E T T I 1743
A E U see Journal of Asia Electronics Union 1774
A E U Journal see A U E W E S Journal 1813
A E Ue. (Archiv fuer Elektronik und Uebertragungstechnik) (GW ISSN 0001-1096) 1331
†A en D. (Alcohol en Drugs) (NE ISSN 0006-4645) 5128
A F A A Bulletin d'Information. see A F A A Newsletter 67
A F A A Newsletter/A F A A Bulletin d'Information. (Association of Faculties of Agriculture in Africa) (MR) 67
A F A Danmark Fireblokke. (Aarhus Frimaerkehandel) (DK ISSN 0901-6996) 3748
A F A Danmark Frimaerkekatalog. (Aarhus Frimaerkehandel) (DK ISSN 0901-7003) 3748
A.F.A.E.P. Awards. (Association of Photographers) (UK) 3788
A F A Europa Frimaerkekatalog see A F A Vesteuropa Frimaerkekatalog 3748
A F A Europe Frimaerkekatalog see A F A Oesteuropa Frimaerkekatalog 3748
A F A Informationen. (Arbeitskreis fuer Arbeitsstudien) (GW ISSN 0001-1126) 2579
A F A N Newsletter. (Association for Astrological Networking) (US) 357

A F A News see Jack Knight Air Log & A F A News 3753
A F A Oesteuropa Frimaerkekatalog. (Aarhus Frimaerkehandel) (DK ISSN 0901-6643) 3748
A F A S Quarterly. (Automotive Fine Arts Society) (US) 309, 2432, 4678
A F A Skandinavien Frimaerkekatalog. (Aarhus Frimaerkehandel) (DK ISSN 0901-6635) 3748
A F A Vesteuropa Frimaerkekatalog. (Aarhus Frimaerkehandel) (DK ISSN 0901-702X) 3748
A F A's Resource Hotline Newsletter. (American Forestry Association) (US) 2094
A F B Action. (Association for Fitness in Business) (US) 3798, 643
A F B Directory of Services for Blind and Visually Impaired Persons in the United States. (American Foundation for the Blind, Inc.) (US ISSN 0899-2533) 2290
A F B Info. (Arbeitsstelle Friedensforschung Bonn) (GW ISSN 0930-8199) 3869, 4364
A F B News. (American Foundation for the Blind, Inc.) (US) 2290
A F D J. (Australian Farmers' Dealers' Journal) (AT ISSN 0818-2183) 161
A F E R. (African Ecclesial Review) (KE ISSN 0001-1134) 4161
A F E T - Mitglieder - Rundbrief. (Arbeitsgemeinschaft fuer Erziehungshilfe (AFET) e.V.) (GW ISSN 0934-8417) 4364, 1733
A F F I Letter. (American Frozen Food Institute) (US) 2060
A F H H A Insider. (American Federation of Home Health Agencies) (US) 3274, 3213
A F I A Safetygram. (American Feed Industry Association) (US) 209, 204
A F I P Atlas of Radiologic-Pathologic Correlation. (Armed Forces Institute of Pathology) (US) 3068
A F I Report. (Association of Federal Investigators) (US) 2593
†A F I T Bulletin. (Australian Families Income Transfer) (AT ISSN 0813-877X) 5128
A F L - C I O. Department of International Affairs. Bulletin. (American Federation of Labor - Congress of Industrial Organizations) (US ISSN 0890-6165) 2579, 3948
†A F L - C I O American Federationist. (American Federation of Labor - Congress of Industrial Organizations) (US ISSN 0149-2489) 5128
A F L - C I O Convention Proceedings. (US) 2579
A F L - C I O Education Update. (US) 970
†A F L - C I O Free Trade Union News. (US ISSN 0001-1177) 5128
A F L - C I O Library Acquisition List. (US ISSN 0001-1150) 2592
A F L - C I O News. (US ISSN 0001-1185) 2579
A F L - C I O Noticiario do Sindicalismo Livre see A F L - C I O Free Trade Union News 5128
A F L - C I O Noticiaro del Movimiento Sindical Libre see A F L - C I O Free Trade Union News 5128
A F M Explanatory Series (No.). (Department of Accounting and Financial Management) (AT ISSN 0728-4969) 744, 757, 1000
A F M Exploratory Series. (Department of Accounting & Financial Management) (AT ISSN 0155-1221) 744
A F M Information Systems Series (No.). (Department of Accounting and Financial Management) (AT ISSN 0819-2898) 1436, 1445
A F M Koinonia see Faith and Action 4177
A F Magazine. (CN) 2175
A F P - Auto. (Agence France-Presse) (FR) 4678, 3401, 3680

A.F.P. Cahiers de l'Afrique Occidentale et de l'Afrique Equatoriale. (Agence France-Presse) (FR ISSN 0754-7625) 3869
A F P Sciences. (Agence France-Presse) (FR) 3068, 4295, 4592
A F R A Advice Sheet. (Association for Rural Advancement) (SA) 3939, 2593
A F R A Boletin see A F R A Boletin Informativo 3748
A F R A Boletin Informativo. (Asociacion Filatelica de la Republica Argentina) (AG ISSN 0001-1193) 3748
A F R A Member Directory and Ancestral Surname Registry. (American Family Records Association) (US) 2143
A F R A Newsletter. (Association for Rural Advancement) (SA) 3939, 3979
A F R A Special Reports. (Association for Rural Advancement) (SA) 3939
A F R C Institute of Arable Crops Research. Report. (Agricultural & Food Research Council) (UK ISSN 0955-9051) 165
†A F R C Institute of Food Research Technical Bulletins. (UK) 5128
A F R C Institute of Grassland and Environmental Research (UK). Annual Report. (UK ISSN 0961-6071) 165
A F R E. (SP ISSN 0001-1207) 899
A F R I Liaison. (Association Francaise de Robotique Industrielle) (FR) 1406, 1411
A F R O Technical Papers. (UN ISSN 0250-8621) 4096
A F R O Technical Report Series. (UN ISSN 0250-8443) 4096
A F S M International. (Association for Services Management International) (US ISSN 1049-2135) 1423
A F T see Algemeen Fiscaal Tijdschrift 746
A F T. (Archivio Fotografico Toscano) (IT ISSN 1120-205X) 3788
A F T A see Crow 2863
†A F T in the News. (American Federation of Teachers) (US) 5128
A F T Issues Bulletin. (American Federation of Teachers) (US) 2579, 1613
A F T M A Trade Show Directory and Buyers' Guide. (American Fishing and Tackle Manufacturing Association) (US) 2035, 1032
A F T R A. (American Federation of Television and Radio Artists) (US) 2579, 1368
A F V A Evaluations. (American Film & Video Association, Inc.) (US) 1743, 2740, 3502
A F Z Fischmagazin see Fischmagazin 2040
A Fin L A Yearbook. (Association Finlandaise de Linguistique Appliquee) (FI ISSN 0356-8156) 2799
†A Fleur de Pot. (CN ISSN 0829-5247) 5128
A G see Die Aktiengesellschaft 1071
A G A. (Asociacion General de Agricultores) (GT ISSN 0001-1274) 67
A G A American Gas. (American Gas Association) (US) 3681
A G A Financial Quarterly Review. (American Gas Association) (US) 1783, 841
A G A Gas Energy Review. (American Gas Association) (US) 3681
A G A Gas Industry Training Directory. (US) 3704
A G A Gas Stats. (US) 3704
A G A Gas Stats Quarterly. (US) 3704
A G A Monthly see A G A American Gas 3681
A G A Rate Service. (US) 3681
A G A Synthetic Pipeline Gas Symposium. Proceedings. (US) 3681
A G A The Natural Resource Newsletter. (US) 3681
A G A Training Update. (US) 3681
A G B News Notes see A G B Notes 1698

A G B Notes. (Association of Governing Boards of Universities and Colleges) (US ISSN 0044-9601) **1698**

A G B Reports. (Association of Governing Boards of Universities and Colleges) (US ISSN 0044-961X) **1698**

A G B U Ararat. (Armenian General Benevolent Union) (US ISSN 0003-7583) **2891, 2501**

A G D Impact. (Academy of General Dentistry) (US ISSN 0194-729X) **3227**

A G E Current Awareness Service. (Asian Geotechnical Engineering Information Center) (TH ISSN 0301-4150) **1540, 1813**

A G E News. (Asian Geotechnical Engineering Information Center) (TH ISSN 0125-1767) **1540, 1813**

A G E Refdex. (Asian Geotechnical Engineering Information Center) (TH) **1549, 1, 1841**

A G E S. (Asociacion de Garajes y Estaciones de Servico) (AG) **4678**

A G F - Magazine. (Aardappelen, Groenten, Fruit) (NE ISSN 0921-531X) **165, 2090**

A G H E Exchange. (Association for Gerontology in Higher Education) (US ISSN 0890-278X) **2269, 1698, 3624**

A G H E Newsletter see A G H E Exchange **2269**

A G I E S. (IT ISSN 0001-1339) **806**

A G L L News. (American Genealogical Lending Library) (US) **2143**

A G M. (Arbeitsgemeinschaft Malta im Bund Deutscher Philatelisten e.V.) (GW) **3749, 1352**

A G M A Zine. (American Guild of Musical Artists) (US ISSN 0002-0990) **3536**

A G M Reporter. (CN ISSN 0703-766X) **1724**

A G M Service. (Agricultural and Garden Machinery) (UK ISSN 0308-9274) **161**

A G News. (Associated Grocers of Colorado Inc.) (US) **2090**

A G O News. (Art Gallery of Ontario) (CN ISSN 0829-4437) **3520**

A G P Mitteilungen see Das Neue Unternehmen **989**

A G Report. (National Association of Attorneys General) (US) **2593**

A G S Guides. (Alpine Garden Society) (UK) **2120**

A G S I Association for Global Strategic Information. Journal see Association for Global Strategic Information. Journal **804**

A G S Newsletter. (American Geographical Society) (US) **2240**

A.G.T. Dokumentation. (GW ISSN 0340-5745) **3015**

A G V A News see A G V A Newsletter **2579**

A G V A Newsletter. (American Guild of Variety Artists) (US) **2579**

A Granja. (BL) **209**

A H A F Journal. (American Handwriting Analysis Foundation) (US ISSN 1041-956X) **1613, 4007**

A H A Health Services Monographs see A H A Special Monographs **2458**

A H A! Hispanic Arts News. (Association of Hispanic Arts) (US) **309, 1988, 3536**

A H A Hospital Statistics (Year). (US) **2470, 4560**

A H A M Major Appliance Factory Shipment Report. (Association of Home Appliance Manufacturers) (US) **2556, 2297**

A H A M Major Appliance Industry Facts Book (Year). (Association of Home Appliance Manufacturers) (US) **2556, 2297**

A H A News. (American Hospital Association) (US ISSN 0891-6608) **2458**

A H A P Perspective. (Arthritis Health Professions Association) (US) **3368**

A H A Special Monographs. (Australian Hospital Association) (AT ISSN 1031-010X) **2458**

A H C A Notes. (American Health Care Association) (US) **4396, 4096**

A H C News. (American Horse Council, Inc.) (US) **4531**

A H D see Aussenhandelsdienst **938**

A H E A Action. (American Home Economics Association) (US ISSN 0194-7176) **2444**

A H E A Newsletter see Alberta Home Economics Association Newsletter **2444**

A H E P A N. (American Hellenic Educational Progressive Associations) (US ISSN 0746-133X) **1988, 1295**

A H I L Quarterly see Interface (Chicago) **2763**

A H P Newsletter see A H P Perspective **4007**

A H P Perspective. (Association for Humanistic Psychology) (US) **4007**

A H R A Announcement. (American Healthcare Radiology Administrators) (US) **3356**

A H R C Chronicle. (Association for the Help of Retarded Children) (US ISSN 0001-1436) **3327, 4396**

A H W Reporter. (US) **599**

A Het Turke. (IS) **2203**

A Hombros de Trabajadores. (SP) **2579**

A I. (Asian Insights) (US) **1988**

A I A A - A S M E Joint Fluid Mechanics, Plasma Dynamics, and Laser Conference. Proceedings. (American Institute of Aeronautics and Astronautics) (American Society of Mechanical Engineers) (US) **1926, 3812**

A I A A - A S M E - S A E Structures, Structural Dynamics, and Materials Conference. Proceedings. (American Institute of Aeronautics and Astronautics) (American Society of Mechanical Engineers) (US) **42**

A I A A - A S M E Thermophysics and Heat Transfer Conference. Proceedings. (American Institute of Aeronautics and Astronautics) (American Society of Mechanical Engineers) (US) **3840, 3842**

A I A A Atmospheric Flight Mechanics Conference Proceedings. (American Institute of Aeronautics and Astronautics, Inc.) (US) **42**

A I A A Communications Satellite Systems Conference. Technical Papers. (US) **42, 1331**

A I A A - I E E E Digital Avionics Systems Conference. Proceedings see I E E E - A I A A Digital Avionics Systems Conference. Proceedings **55**

A I A A Journal. (US ISSN 0001-1452) **42**

A I A A Roster. (US ISSN 0065-8693) **42**

A I A A Student Journal. (US ISSN 0001-1460) **42**

A I A A Symposium on the Aero-Hydronautics of Sailing. Proceedings see Ancient Interface **5135**

A I A Journal see J A I A **2202**

A I A Memo see Memo (Washington, 1947) **303**

A I A News see A I A Update **4678**

A I A Newsletter. (Alberta Institute of Agrologists) (CN) **67**

A I A P Quaderni. (Associazione Italiana Creativa Comunicazione Visiva) (IT) **25**

A I A Update. (Auto International Association) (US) **4678**

†A I A W Handbook - Directory. (Association for Intercollegiate Athletics for Women) (US ISSN 0361-5898) **5128**

A I & Society. (Artificial Intelligence) (UK ISSN 0951-5666) **1406, 1455, 3759**

†A I B C Bulletin. (American Institute of Biomedical Climatology) (US ISSN 1040-6018) **5128**

A I B C Newsletter see A A B C Newsletter **2739**

A I B Notizie. (Associazione Italiana Biblioteche) (IT ISSN 1120-2521) **2740, 388**

A I C A R C Bulletin. (Association Internationale de Critiques d'Art Recherche Centre) (SZ ISSN 0347-4240) **310**

A I C C M Bulletin. (Australian Institute for the Conservation of Cultural Material, Inc.) (AT ISSN 0313-5381) **1482**

†A I C C News. (US ISSN 0001-1517) **5128**

A I C F Report see Border Watch **3979**

A I C H Community Bulletin. (American Indian Community House) (US) **1988**

A I C Investment Bulletin. (US) **937**

A I C P A Professional Standards. (American Institute of Certified Public Accountants) (US) **744**

†A I C P A Washington Report. (American Institute of Certified Public Accountants) (US ISSN 0146-9770) **5128**

A I C Pizzaz see National News **1377**

A I C S Compass (Association of Independent Colleges and Schools) see Career Education **1682**

A I Ch E Applications Software Survey of Personal Computers. (American Institute of Chemical Engineers) (US ISSN 0743-0183) **1475, 1466**

A I Ch E Equipment Testing Procedures. (American Institute of Chemical Engineers) (US ISSN 0569-5473) **1847, 3256**

A I Ch E Journal. (American Institute of Chemical Engineers) (US ISSN 0001-1541) **1847**

A I Ch E M I Modular Instruction. Series A: Process Control. (American Institute of Chemical Engineers) (US ISSN 0270-6229) **1847**

A I Ch E M I Modular Instruction. Series B: Stagewise and Mass Transfer Operations. (US ISSN 0270-7624) **1847**

A I Ch E M I Modular Instruction. Series C: Transport. (US ISSN 0270-7632) **1847**

A I Ch E M I Modular Instruction. Series D: Thermodynamics. (US ISSN 0270-7640) **1847**

A I Ch E M I Modular Instruction. Series E: Kinetics. (US ISSN 0270-7659) **1847**

A I Ch E M I Modular Instruction. Series F: Material and Energy Balances. (US ISSN 0270-7667) **1847**

A I Ch E M I Modular Instruction. Series G: Design of Equipment. (US ISSN 0890-0582) **1847**

A I Ch E Monograph Series. (US ISSN 0065-8804) **1847**

†A I Ch E Symposium Series. (US ISSN 0065-8812) **5128**

A I Communications see Artificial Intelligence Communications **1407**

A I D A Bulletin see Business Council of Australia Bulletin **649**

A I D Bulletin. (Addiction Intervention with the Disabled) (US ISSN 0275-6692) **1532, 2283**

A.I.D. Highlights. (U.S. Agency for International Development) (US ISSN 0743-5436) **925, 3948**

A I D Newsletter see Automotive Industry Data Newsletter **4661**

A I D Research Abstracts see A I D Research and Development Abstracts **701**

A I D Research and Development Abstracts. (U.S. Agency for International Development) (US ISSN 0096-1507) **701, 1**

A I D S. (Acquired Immune Deficiency Syndrome) (US ISSN 0269-9370) **3068, 3216**

A I D S. (GW ISSN 0934-1129) **3216**

A I D S (Year). (US) **3165, 3216**

†A I D S: A Quarterly Bibliography from All Fields of Periodical Literature. (US ISSN 0894-931X) **5128**

A I D S Alert. (US ISSN 0887-0292) **3216, 3182**

†A I D S and Associated Diseases. (SZ) **5128**

A I D S & Florida Law. (US) **2593, 3216**

A I D S & Public Policy Journal. (US ISSN 0887-3852) **3216, 2593, 4096**

A I D S and Retroviruses Update see Current A I D S Literature **3169**

A I D S Bibliography. (US ISSN 0895-9331) **3165, 3216**

A I D S - Brief. (GW) **3216**

A I D S Bulletin. (US) **3216**

A I D S Care. (UK ISSN 0954-0121) **3216, 3327**

A I D S Clinical Care. (US ISSN 1043-1543) **3216**

A I D S Clinical Digest see Infectious Disease Alert **3220**

A I D S Education and Prevention. (US ISSN 0899-9546) **3216, 3798**

A I D S - H I V Treatment Directory. (US ISSN 0898-5030) **3216**

A I D S Health Promotion Exchange. (UN ISSN 1013-7785) **3216**

A I D S Information. (UK ISSN 0953-1580) **3165, 3216**

A I D S Information Exchange. (US) **3216, 3245, 4096**

A I D S Information Sourcebook. (US ISSN 1044-2138) **3216**

A I D S Law & Litigation Reporter. (US) **3216, 2593**

A I D S Letter. (UK ISSN 0952-7427) **3216**

A I D S Literature & News Review. (US ISSN 0893-1526) **3216**

A I D S Litigation Reporter. (US ISSN 0899-1464) **2593, 3216**

A I D S Medical Report see A I D S Alert **3216**

A I D S Newsletter. (UK ISSN 0268-8360) **3217**

A I D S Patient Care. (US ISSN 0893-5068) **3217**

A I D S Policy and Law. (US ISSN 0887-1493) **3217, 2593**

A I D S Report. (US ISSN 0893-5084) **3217**

A I D S Research see A I D S Research and Human Retroviruses **3217**

A I D S Research and Human Retroviruses. (US ISSN 0889-2229) **3217, 3182**

†A I D S Research Today. (US ISSN 0895-3201) **5128**

†A I D S Scan. (US) **5128**

A I D S Treatment News. (US ISSN 1052-4207) **3217**

A I D S Update. (CN) **3217**

A I D S Update (New York). (US) **3217, 2593, 4396**

A I D S Update (Washington). (US ISSN 1042-4784) **3217**

A I D S Weekly see C D C - A I D S Weekly **3218**

A I D Verbraucherdienst. (Auswertungs- und Informationsdienst fuer Ernaehrung, Landwirtschaft und Forsten e.V.) (GW ISSN 0720-7522) **3602, 1698, 2060**

A I E D A M see Artificial Intelligence for Engineering Design, Analysis and Manufacturing **1407**

A I Expert. (Artificial Intelligence) (US ISSN 0888-3785) **1406, 1411**

A I F L D Report. (American Institute for Free Labor Development) (US ISSN 0001-1576) **970**

A I G A Best Books Show see A I G A Graphic Design U S A **3997**

A I G A Graphic Design U S A. (American Institute of Graphic Arts) (US ISSN 0275-9470) **3997**

A I G A Journal of Graphic Design. (American Institute of Graphic Arts) (US) **3997**

A I H P Notes. (American Institute of the History of Pharmacy) (US) **3715, 2397**

A I I Journal. (Australian Insurance Institute) (AT ISSN 0314-8580) **2525**

A I I S Annual Report see American Institute of Indian Studies. Biennial Report **2336**

A I I S Quarterly Newsletter. (American Institute of Indian Studies) (II ISSN 0304-6214) **3632**

†A.I.J. Manual of Australasian Life Assurance. (Australasian Insurance Journal) (AT ISSN 0084-697X) **5128**

A I L A. (Agenzia Internazionale Letteraria Artistica) (IT ISSN 0001-1584) **2857**

A I L A Bulletin. (Association Internationale de Linguistique Appliquee) (IT ISSN 0044-9490) **2799**

A I L A Monthly Mailing. (American Immigration Lawyers Association) (US ISSN 0898-1663) **2593, 4427**

A I M. (Australian Institute of Management, N.S.W. Ltd.) (AT ISSN 0817-5713) **1000**

A I M. (Automotive Industry Matters Pty. Ltd.) (AT ISSN 0044-5681) **4678**

A I M. (Adventures in Mexico Newsletter) (MX) **4750**

A I M (American Investment Magazine) see Banner (St. Louis) **939**

A I M - Age of Information Marketing. (US) **1032**

A I M Bulletin see A I M Monastic Bulletin **4254**

A I M C Forum. (Association of International Management Consultants) (US) **1000**

A I M Career Exchange Clearinghouse. (Association for Information Management) (US) **3624**

A I M International. (Africa Inland Mission International) (US) **4161**

A I M L S Newsletter see A I M S Newsletter **3068**

A I M L S Self Assessment Programmes Series see A I M S Self Assessment Programmes Series **3256**

A I M M Bulletin and Proceedings see Aus I M M Bulletin **3478**

A I M M Symposia Series. (Australasian Institute of Mining and Metallurgy) (AT) **3477, 3401**

A I M Monastic Bulletin. (Aide Inter-Monasteres Secretariat) (FR ISSN 0758-8240) **4254**

A I M Network. (Association for Information Management) (US) **1000, 1032, 1443, 2740**

A I M News see A I M **1000**

A I M Newsletter - Incentive Report. (Association of Incentive Marketing) (US) **1032**

A I M Plus see Mature Health **5233**

A I M - R News. (Association of Industry Manufacturers Representatives) (US) **1071, 1000**

A I M R Newsletter. (Association for Investment Management and Research) (US) **758**

A I M Report. (Accuracy in Media, Inc.) (US) **2566**

A I M S Bulletin. (American Institute of Musical Studies) **3536**

A I M S Monograph Series. (Australian Institute of Marine Science) (AT) **1601**

A I M S Newsletter. (Australian Institute of Medical Scientists) (AT) **3068, 3256**

A I M S Self Assessment Programmes Series. (Australian Institute of Medical Scientists) (AT) **3256**

A I Magazine. (Artificial Intelligence) (US ISSN 0738-4602) **1406, 1411**

†A I N News. (Association of Interpretive Naturalists, Inc.) (US) **5128**

▼A I N Report. (Advanced Integrated Networks) (US ISSN 1056-7119) **1426**

A I O E Labour News. (All India Organisation of Employers) (II ISSN 0001-1630) **970**

A I O S P Bulletin see Educational and Vocational Guidance - Bulletin A I O S P, I A E V G, I V S B B **3626**

A I P Conference Proceedings. (American Institute of Physics) (US ISSN 0094-243X) **3812**

A I P E Facilities. (American Institute of Plant Engineers) (US ISSN 1054-7541) **1813**

A I P E Facilities Management, Operations and Engineering see A I P E Facilities **1813**

A I P E Newsletter see Facilities Forum **1822**

A I P E Newsline. (American Institute of Plant Engineers) (US) **1813, 599, 1783**

A I P L A Bulletin. (American Intellectual Property Law Association) (US) **2593, 3672**

A I P L A Quarterly Journal. (American Intellectual Property Law Association) (US ISSN 0883-6078) **2593**

A.I.P.P.I. Japanese Group. Journal (International Edition). (International Association for the Protection of Industrial Property) (JA ISSN 0385-8863) **3672**

A I P T Report. (Association for International Practical Training) (US) **1721**

A I Quarterly see Adrichalut Yisraelit **291**

▼A I R. (Alternative Information Record) (UK) **2857**

A I S C A T Informazioni. (Associazione Italiana Societa Concessionarie Autostrade e Trafori) (IT ISSN 0044-975X) **4717**

A I S E Yearbook. (Association of Iron and Steel Engineers) (US) **3401**

A I S I Journal of Genealogy. (Accelerated Indexing Systems International) (US) **2143**

A I S M. Bulletin/I A L A Bulletin. (Association Internationale de Signalisation Maritime) (FR ISSN 0373-9090) **4723**

A I S Newsletter. (Association for Integrative Studies (Oxford)) (US) **1613**

†A I S P Dialogue. (Association of Information Systems Professionals) (US) **5128**

A I S P Newsline see A I S P Dialogue **5128**

A I S 800 Report see Telemarketer **1055**

A I T. (Architektur, Innenarchitektur, Technischer Ausbau) (GW ISSN 0173-8046) **291, 2547**

A I T I M Boletin de Informacion Tecnica. (Asociacion de Investigacion Tecnica de las Industrias de la Madera) (SP ISSN 0044-9261) **2113, 639**

A I T Newsletter see Technos **1691**

A I T Reports and Publications on Energy. Abstracts. (Asian Institute of Technology) (TH ISSN 0857-6181) **1797**

A I T Reports and Publications on Renewable Energy Resources. Abstracts see A I T Reports and Publications on Energy. Abstracts **1797**

A I T Review. (Asian Institute of Technology) (TH) **1813**

A I Today. (US ISSN 0893-6552) **1406**

A I Trends. (US ISSN 0736-5071) **1406**

A I Week see I S R: Intelligent Systems Report **1408**

A I X Age. (US) **1457**

A I Z see Allgemeine Immobilien-Zeitung **4144**

A Is A. (US) **2857**

A Is A Newsletter see A Is A **2857**

A J A Benchmark. (American Judges Association) (US) **2593**

A J A S: Australasian Journal of American Studies. (AT ISSN 0705-7113) **2397**

†A J C Journal. (American Jewish Committee) (US) **5128**

A J C U Higher Education Report. (Association of Jesuit Colleges and Universities) (US ISSN 1053-8933) **1698**

A J D C: American Journal of Diseases of Children. (US ISSN 0002-922X) **3317**

A - J E I Newsletter. (Australia - Japan Economic Institute) (AT) **643**

A J H P see American Journal of Health Promotion **4097**

A J K S see American Journal of Knee Surgery **3374**

A J L I Newsline see Junior League Newsline **4411**

A J L Newsletter. (Association of Jewish Libraries) (US ISSN 0747-6175) **2740, 1988, 4221**

A J M E News. (Americans for Justice in the Middle East) (LE) **2427, 3949**

A J N Guide. (American Journal of Nursing Company) (US ISSN 0898-4646) **3274**

A J N R. (American Journal of Neuroradiology) (US ISSN 0195-6108) **3356**

A J P R S Reporter. (American Jewish Public Relations Society) (US) **26, 1988**

A J R. (American Journal of Roentgenology) (US ISSN 0361-803X) **3356**

A J S Informationen see Aktion Jugendschutz. Informationen **1232**

A J S Newsletter see Tomodachi **922**

A J S Review. (Association for Jewish Studies) (US ISSN 0364-0094) **1988, 4221**

A K F Nephrology Letter. (American Kidney Fund) (US) **3386**

A K F Newsletter. (American Kidney Fund) (US) **3386**

A K S B - Inform. (Verein zur Foerderung Katholisch-Soziaier Bildungswerke) (GW) **1681**

A K T. (Aktuelles Theater) (GW) **4629**

A - Kasse Information. (DK ISSN 0109-9167) **970**

A Kemia Ujabb Eredmenyei. (HU ISSN 0075-5397) **1168**

A L A. (AG ISSN 0002-4090) **2986**

A L A Handbook of Organization. (American Library Association) (US ISSN 0084-6406) **2740**

A L A I Servicio Mensual de Informacion y Documentacion. (Agence Latino-Americaine d'Information Inc.) (EC ISSN 0827-5564) **842**

A L A Lawn and Landscape Maintenance see Lawn and Landscape Maintenance **2133**

A L A M A R Informativo. (Asociacion Latinoamericana de Armadores) (UY) **4723**

A L A N Newsletter see A L A N Review **1743**

A L A N Review. (Assembly on Literature for Adolescents) (US ISSN 0882-2840) **1743, 2891**

A L A News. (American Lawyers Auxiliary) (US) **2593, 1743**

†A L A Sights to See Book. (Automobile Legal Association) (US ISSN 0090-8614) **5128**

A L A Social Responsibilities Round Table Newsletter see S R R T Newsletter **2882**

†A L A Studies in Librarianship. (American Library Association) (US ISSN 0065-907X) **5128**

A L A Vestis. (American Latvian Association in the United States, Inc.) (US) **1988**

A L A Washington Newsletter. (American Library Association) (US ISSN 0001-1746) **2740**

A L A Worldwide Directory and Fact Book. (American Logistics Association) (US) **3449, 1032, 1295, 2090**

†A L A Yearbook. (American Library Association) (US ISSN 0364-1597) **5128**

A l'Action. see Action Now **4836**

A L B A Bowls. (American Lawn Bowls Association) (US ISSN 0001-1754) **4499**

A L C - L C A Augsburg Adult Bible Studies. Adult Quarterly see Augsburg Adult Bible Studies. Participant Book **4229**

A L C - L C A Augsburg Adult Bible Studies. Home Bible Studies see Augsburg Home Bible Studies **4229**

A L C - L C A Augsburg Adult Bible Studies. Teacher's Guide see Augsburg Adult Bible Studies. Leader Guide **4229**

▼A L C T S Network News. (Association for Library Collections & Technical Services) (US ISSN 1056-6694) **2796**

A L C T S Newsletter. (Association for Library Collections and Technical Services) (US ISSN 1047-949X) **2740**

A L E B C I; Boletin Informativo. (Asociacion Latinoamericana de Escuelas de Bibliotecologia y Ciencias de la Informacion) (PN) **2740**

A L E C Report see Philippine Journal of Labor and Industrial Relations **991**

A L E S C O Newsletter see Arab League Educational, Scientific, and Cultural Organization. Information Newsletter **1616**

A l'Ecoute. (CN ISSN 0700-3900) **3536**

A L f A - Rundbrief. (Aktion Lebensrecht fuer Alle) (GW ISSN 0931-3613) **595**

A L F I News. (Auto, Life, Fire, Insurance) (US) **2525**

A L F Newsletter. (Association of Libertarian Feminists) (US ISSN 0893-293X) **3869, 4836**

A L H R T Newsletter see L H R T Newsletter **2767**

†A L I. (Allied Landscape Industry) (US) **5128**

A L I - A B A - C L E Review. (American Law Institute) (US ISSN 0044-7560) **2593**

A L I - A B A Course Materials Journal. (American Law Institute) (US ISSN 0145-6342) **2593**

A L I C O News. (American Life Insurance Co.) (US) **2525**

A L I Reporter. (American Law Institute) (US ISSN 0164-5757) **2593**

A L I S A. (Australian Library and Information Science Abstracts) (AT ISSN 0810-9265) **2792, 1**

A L L C Bulletin see Literary and Linguistic Computing **2856**

A L L C Journal see Literary and Linguistic Computing **2856**

A L L News. (American Life Lobby) (US) **595, 3979, 4161**

A L L-O-Grams. (Affiliated Leadership League of and for the Blind of America) (US ISSN 0195-363X) **2290**

A L M A Searchlight. (Adoptees' Liberty Movement Association) (US) **4396**

A L P A N Network Paper. (African Livestock Policy Analysis Network) (UN) **209**

A L P A N Newsletter. (African Livestock Policy Analysis Network) (UN) **209**

A L P C A Newsletter. (Automobile License Plate Collectors Association) (US) **2432, 4678**

A L P S P Bulletin see Learned Publishing: A L P S P Bulletin **4131**

A L R see Legal Reformer **3904**

A L R A Newsletter see Breaking Chains **2605**

A L R C Report Series. (Australia Law Reform Commission) (AT) **2593**

A L S A R. (Al Servicio de Una Agricultura Rentable) (SP) **67**

A L S C Newsletter. (Association for Library Service to Children) (US ISSN 0162-6612) **2740, 1248**

A L S News. (Alberta Land Surveyor Association) (CN ISSN 0703-4288) **1861**

A L S Projektwoche. (GW) **1743**

A L T A Newsletter. (American Literary Translators Association) (US) **2800**

A la Barre de l'Entreprise. (FR) **643**

A la Carte. (US) **2471**

A la Carte see Homes and Gardens **2552**

A la Premiere Personne. (FR) **417**

A Lampada. (BL ISSN 0001-1789) **3759**

A M. (Ave Maria) (BL ISSN 0005-1934) **4254**

A M A A News. (Armenian Missionary Association of America, Inc.) (US) **4279**

A M A - Agricultural Mechanization in Asia, Africa and Latin America. (JA ISSN 0084-5841) **161**

A M A - Agricultural Mechanization in Southeast Asia see A M A - Agricultural Mechanization in Asia, Africa and Latin America 161
A M A Council Reports see Management Review 1020
A M A Educators' Proceedings. (American Marketing Association) (US ISSN 0888-1839) 1032
A M A Management Briefings. (American Management Association) (US) 1001
A M A Newsletter. (Association of Manitoba Archivists) (CN ISSN 0827-0074) 2740
†A M A Product Directory. (American Monument Association) (US) 5128
A M A Survey Reports. (American Management Association) (US) 1001
A M A Victoria Branch News. (Australian Medical Association) (AT ISSN 0813-6394) 3068
A M B A C Noticiero. (Asociacion Mexicana de Bibliotecarios, A.C.) (MX ISSN 0001-186X) 2740
A M B A News. (Australian Multiple Birth Association Inc.) (AT ISSN 0815-1652) 1231, 1296, 4836
A M C see Moniteur Architecture - A M C 303
A M C CenterScope. (Animal Medical Center) (US) 3707
†A M C E E Monitor. (Association for Media-Based Continuing Education for Engineers) (US) 5128
A M C Journal. (American Mining Congress) (US ISSN 0891-6209) 3477, 1553, 3401
A M C News see Sounds Australian Update 3581
A M C R A Newsletter see A M C R A's Managed Care Monitor 2458
A M C R A's Managed Care Monitor. (American Managed Care & Review Association) (US) 2458, 2525, 3068
A M D E L Bulletin. (Australia Mineral Development Laboratories) (AT ISSN 0045-0707) 1553, 3477
A M D F: A R M S and Interc see Army Master Data File: Army Retrieval Microform Systems and Interc 3452
A M D I Bollettino. (Associazione Medici Dentisti Italiani) (IT ISSN 0001-1908) 3227
A.M.E. Christian Recorder. (African Methodist Episcopal Church) (US) 4227
A.M.E. Church Review. (African Methodist Episcopal Church) (US ISSN 0360-3725) 4227
A M E X Bank Review. (American Express Bank Ltd.) (UK) 758, 925
A M Engineering Data Base. (US) 1841
A M Engineering Data Base (for Microcomputers). (US) 1841
A M Engineering Data Base in Order by Frequency. (US) 1841
A M Engineering Data Base in Order by State. (US) 1841
A M Engineering Database in Order by Country and State. (US) 1841
A M F I Industry News. (Aviation Maintenance Foundation International) (US) 42
A M G B A Octagon. (American M G B Association) (US) 254, 4678
A M H C A Journal see Journal of Mental Health Counseling 4030
A M I see Asian Meetings and Incentives 3390
A M I C A Bulletin. (Automatic Musical Instrument Collectors' Association) (US) 3536
A M I News. (Association of Medical Illustrators) (US) 3068
†A M J Newsletter. (JA ISSN 0388-1423) 5128
A M J - S I Metricpac. (American Metric Journal Publishing Co.) (US) 3444
A M L C News. (Australian Meat and Livestock Corporation) (AT) 2060, 899
A M Magazine. (Aston Martin Owners' Club Ltd.) (UK) 4678

A M News - Southern Africa. (Addressograph-Multigraph (Pty.) Ltd.) (SA ISSN 0001-1932) 3788
A M O Perspectives. (Accredited Management Organization) (US) 4144
A M P A S Credits Bulletin see Annual Index to Motion Picture Credits 3503
A M P L A Bulletin. (Australian Mining and Petroleum Law Association Ltd.) (AT ISSN 1034-327X) 3477, 2593, 3681
A M P L A Yearbook. (Australian Mining and Petroleum Law Association Ltd.) (AT ISSN 0812-857X) 3477, 2593, 3681
A M P R A Review. (American Medical Peer Review Association) (US) 3068
A M P S see All Media & Product Survey 40
A M P S Black Radio and Television Diary. (All Media and Product Survey) (SA) 40, 4560
A M P S Broadcast Media see A M P S Black Radio and Television Diary 40
A M P S Broadcast Media see A M P S White - Coloured - Asian Radio Diary 1346
A M P S Meter Weekly Reports. (All Media and Product Survey) (SA) 40, 4560
A M P S White - Coloured - Asian Radio Diary. (All Media and Product Survey) (SA) 1346, 1354, 4561
A M Q U A Program and Abstracts. (American Quaternary Association) (US) 1549
A M Quarterly see A M Magazine 4678
A M R A Journal. (Australian Model Railway Association) (AT ISSN 0045-0715) 2432, 4707
A M R E P Database Bulletin. (Australian Mineral Resource Politics Pty. Ltd.) (AT ISSN 0816-942X) 3477, 3681
A M R Newsletter. (Association Marketing Roundtable) (US) 1032
A M R O see Journal of Health Information & Medical Records Officers 3116
A M R Report. (Advanced Manufacturing Research) (US) 1411, 937
A M S A A Newsletter. (Ambulance and Medical Service Association of America) (US) 2458
A M S A T Journal. (Amateur Satellite) (US) 1368
A M S Advisor. (Acquisition Management Service) (US) 2705
A M S Ars Poetica. (Abrahams Magazine Service) (US ISSN 0734-7618) 2986
A M S Asian Studies. (Abrahams Magazine Service) (US ISSN 0748-5476) 2336
A M S C O P E Newsletter. (American Miniature Schnauzer Club) (US) 3707
A M S Constructive Triangle see A M S Montessori Life 1743
A M S Data Processing Salaries Report see A M S Office, Professional and Data Processing Salaries Report 970
A M S E News. (International Association for the Advancement of Modelling and Simulation Techniques in Enterprises) (FR) 3063
A M S Management Salaries Report. (Administrative Management Society) (US) 970, 1001
A M S Montessori Life. (American Montessori Society) (US ISSN 1054-0040) 1743, 1231
A M S Newsletter (Boston). (American Meteorological Society) (US) 3431, 1596, 1601
A M S Newsletter (Philadelphia). (American Musicological Society) (US) 3536
A M S Office, Professional and Data Processing Salaries Report. (Administrative Management Society) (US) 970, 1001

A M S Office Salaries Report see A M S Office, Professional and Data Processing Salaries Report 970
A M S S - I I I T Newsbulletin. (Association of Muslim Social Scientists) (US) 4217
A M S - Skrifter. (Arkeologisk Museum i Stavanger) (NO ISSN 0800-0816) 260, 1941
A M S - Smaatrykk. (Arkeologisk Museum i Stavanger) (NO ISSN 0332-6411) 260, 1941
A M S Studies in Anthropology. (Abrahams Magazine Service) (US ISSN 0738-064X) 232
A M S Studies in Criminal Justice. (US ISSN 0270-2991) 1509, 2593
A M S Studies in Education. (US ISSN 0882-438X) 1613
A M S Studies in Library and Information Science. (US) 2740
A M S Studies in Modern Literature. (US ISSN 0270-2983) 2891, 2980
A M S Studies in Modern Society. (US ISSN 0275-8407) 4096, 4007, 4396
A M S Studies in Social History. (US ISSN 0270-6253) 2305
A M S Studies in the Eighteenth Century. (US ISSN 0196-6561) 2891, 2305, 2980
A M S Studies in the Emblem. (US ISSN 0892-4201) 2143, 310, 2305, 3449
A M S Studies in the Middle Ages. (US ISSN 0270-6261) 2305, 2891
A M S Studies in the Nineteenth Century. (US ISSN 0196-657X) 2891, 2980
A M S Studies in the Renaissance. (US ISSN 0195-8011) 2891, 2980, 4629
A M S Studies in the Seventeenth Century. (US ISSN 0731-2342) 2891, 2980
A M S - Varia. (Arkeologisk Museum i Stavanger) (NO ISSN 0332-6306) 260, 1941
A M T. (Auto Modell und Technik) (GW) 2432
A M T Chronicle. (Association of Medical Technologists) (US) 3256
A M T R I Library Bulletin see Standards and Technology Bulletin 2786
A M U. (Annuario Italiano Macchine Utensili e Complementari) (IT ISSN 0393-0483) 3015
A M U News. (American Malacological Union, Inc.) (US) 575, 2035, 3520, 3656
A M U S. Log. (Alpha Micro User Society) (US ISSN 0273-8708) 1466
A M W A Journal. (American Medical Writers Association) (US) 3069, 1331
A M Z. (Auto Motor Zubehoer) (GW ISSN 0001-1983) 4678
A N A B A D Boletin. (Asociacion Espanola de Archiveros Bibliotecarios, Museologos y Documentalistas) (SP ISSN 0210-4164) 2740
†A N A Communique. (American Numismatic Association) (US) 5128
A N A D: Working Together. (National Association of Anorexia Nervosa and Associated Disorders) (US) 4007, 1231, 3069, 4835
A N A E see Approche Neuropsychologique des Apprentissages chez l'Enfant 4011
A.N.A.L.O.G. Computing. (US ISSN 0744-9917) 1466, 1457
A N A P. (Asociacion Nacional de Agricultores Pequenos) (CU ISSN 0514-9797) 67
†A N A R C Newsletter. (Association of North American Radio Clubs) (US ISSN 0739-0351) 5128
A N A R E News. (Australian National Antarctic Research Expedition) (AT ISSN 0728-6414) 4295, 2240
A N A R E Report. (Australian National Antarctic Research Expeditions) (AT) 4295, 1540

A N A R E Research Notes. (Australian National Antarctic Research Expeditions) (AT ISSN 0729-6533) 4295
A N A R E Scientific Report see A N A R E Report 4295
†A N A Resource Directory. (American Numismatic Association) (US) 5128
A N: Artists Newsletter. (UK ISSN 0261-3425) 310
A N C O L D Bulletin. (Australian National Committee on Large Dams) (AT ISSN 0045-0731) 1861
A N C Showtime see Arts & Crafts ShowGuide 353
A N D E. (Associacao Nacional de Educacao) (BL) 1613
▼A N D I G. (Associazione Nazionale Docenti Informatica Giuridica) (IT) 2593
A N E C. (Asociacion Nacional de Enfermeras de Colombia) (CK ISSN 0044-930X) 3274
A N E P see European Petroleum Yearbook 3685
A N E R A Newsletter. (American Near East Refugee Aid, Inc.) (US) 3949
A N F I A Notiziario Statistico. (Associazione Nazionale fra le Industrie Automobilistiche) (IT ISSN 0001-2033) 4661
A N J E C Report. (Association of New Jersey Environmental Commissions) (US) 1482
A N J U P E C. (Asociacion Nacional de Jubilados y Pensionados de Comunicaciones) (CU) 3869
A N L A Bulletin. (Association of Newfoundland Labrador Archivists) (CN) 2740
A N N A Journal. (American Nephrology Nurses' Association) (US ISSN 8750-0779) 3274, 3386
A N N Y (Advertising News of New York) see Adweek (New York) 27
A N P H I Papers. (Academy of Nursing of the Philippines) (PH ISSN 0065-0676) 3275
A N P I Magazine - Protection Incendie et Vol. (BE) 2030
A N Q: A Quarterly Journal of Short Articles, Notes and Reviews. (US ISSN 0895-769X) 2891, 2052, 2397
A N R E D Alert. (Anorexia Nervosa & Related Eating Disorders, Inc.) (US) 4008, 3069, 4835
A N R E I Gram see A N R Educator 1743
A N R Educator. (Agricultural and Natural Resources) (US) 1743, 67
A N S A Journal. (Association of Nurses in Substance Abuse) (UK ISSN 0960-8508) 3275, 1532
A N S Bulletin. (American Name Society) (US) 2800
A N S I Reporter. (American National Standards Institute, Inc.) (US ISSN 0038-9676) 3444
†A N S L I C S News. (Aberdeen and North of Scotland Library and Information Co-operative Service) (UK) 5128
A N S News. (American Nuclear Society) (US ISSN 0737-6812) 1803
A N S Newsletter. (American Numismatic Society) (US) 3597
A N S S News see Nature Study 1964
A N S T O Nuclear News see A N S T O Technology 1803
A N S T O Technology. (Australian Nuclear Science and Technology Organisation) (AT) 1803
A N S Utility Quarterly. (American Nuclear Society) (US) 1803
†A N U Historical Journal. (Australian National University) (AT ISSN 0001-2068) 5128
A N U Reporter. (Australian National University) (AT) 1302, 4295
A N Z A A S Congress Papers. (Australian and New Zealand Association for the Advancement of Science) (AT ISSN 0312-8059) 4295
A N Z A News. (Australia - New Zealand Association) (CN ISSN 0045-0170) 2171

A.N.Z.A.S.A. Bulletin see A J A S: Australasian Journal of American Studies 2397
A N Z Bank Business Indicators see Business Indicators 848
A New Life. see Nueva Vida 3295
A O. (Aktuele Onderwerpen) (NE) 2211, 2290
A O A C International. Official Methods of Analysis. (US) 1203
A O A C International Journal. (US) 1203
A O A Yearbook and Directory of Osteopathic Physicians. (American Osteopathic Association) (US) 3213
A O C Newsletter see Court News 2731
A O C S News. (Airline Operational Control Society) (US) 4669
A O H A Annual Directory. (American Osteopathic Hospital Association) (US) 2458
A O H A Today. (American Osteopathic Hospital Association) (US) 2458
A O I Business Viewpoint. (Associated Oregon Industries, Inc.) (US) 643
A O J T News. (Association of Orthodox Jewish Teachers) (US) 1613, 4221
A O K Aktuell see Gesundheitsblatt A O K Aktuell 5199
A O M A Newsletter. (Apartment Owners and Managers Association of America) (US) 4144
A O N T A S Newsletter. (IE) 1681
A O Newsletter see C D N L A O Newsletter 2750
†A O P A General Aviation National Report. (Aircraft Owners and Pilots Association) (US ISSN 0744-2629) 5128
A.O.P.A. Magazine. (Aircraft Owners and Pilots Association of Australia) (AT ISSN 0002-2691) 42
A O P A Pilot. (Aircraft Owners and Pilots Association) (US ISSN 0001-2084) 42
A O P A's Airport U S A see A O P A's Aviation U S A 42
A O P A's Aviation U S A. (US ISSN 1056-7704) 42
A O P Bibliografija/Automatic Data Processing. Bibliography. (Automatska Obrada Podataka) (YU ISSN 0351-3548) 1403, 388
A O R N Journal. (Association of Operating Room Nurses, Inc.) (US ISSN 0001-2092) 3275
A O S Awards Quarterly. (American Orchid Society) (US) 2120
A O S T R A Journal of Research. (Alberta Oil Sands Technology and Research Authority) (CN ISSN 0822-2509) 3681
A P A C Inform. (Associazione Professionale Autonoma Cineoperatori) (IT ISSN 0044-9741) 3502
A P A Holiday. (Airline Passengers Association) (US) 4750, 4669
A P A I S: Australian Public Affairs Information Service. (AT ISSN 0727-8926) 4078, 1
A P a la Une. (Aeroports de Paris) (FR) 4669
A P A Magazine. (Advertising Photographers of America) (US) 3788
A P A Monitor. (American Psychological Association) (US ISSN 0001-2114) 4008
A P A Newsletter on Computer Use in Philosophy, Feminism and Philosophy, Law and Philosophy, Medicine and Philosophy, and Teaching Philosophy see A P A Newsletters on Computer Use in Philosophy, Feminism and Philosophy, Law and Philosophy, Medicine and Philosophy, Teaching Philosophy, and Philosophy and the Black Experience 3759

A P A Newsletters on Computer Use in Philosophy, Feminism and Philosophy, Law and Philosophy, Medicine and Philosophy, Teaching Philosophy, and Philosophy and the Black Experience. (American Philosophical Association) (US) 3759
A P A Planning Advisory Service Reports. (American Planning Association) (US ISSN 0160-8266) 2482
A P A Q see Adapted Physical Activity Quarterly 1733
A P A - Renga see Lynx 3640
A P A S News. (Association of Personal Assistants and Secretaries Ltd.) (UK) 2593
A.P.A.V.E. Revue Technique. (FR ISSN 0001-2122) 2297, 1880
A P B A Journal. (US ISSN 0890-5649) 4499
A P C see Asian Pacific Culture 3634
†A P C A Government Agencies Directory. (Air Pollution Control Associates) (US) 5128
A P C O Bulletin. (Associated Public-Safety Communications Officers Inc.) (US ISSN 0001-2165) 4096, 1331
▼A.P.C.R.I.Q. Bulletin d'Information. (CN ISSN 1181-7941) 4742
A P C T News Bulletin. (American Postal Chess Tournaments) (US) 4463, 1418
A P D U Newsletter. (Association of Public Data Users) (US) 4561, 1448, 3979
A P E C. (Analise e Perspectiva Economica) (BL ISSN 0001-2181) 842
A P E C see I E E E Applied Power Electronics Conference and Exposition. Conference Proceedings 1772
A P E X. (Association of Professional, Executive, Clerical and Computer Staff) (UK) 2579
A P F Newsletter. (Association of Professional Foresters) (UK) 2095
A P F Reporter. (Alicia Patterson Foundation) (US) 2566
A P G A Annual/A P K V Jaarblad. (Apricot, Peach and Pear Growers' Association) (SA) 2120
A P G Quarterly see Association of Professional Genealogists Quarterly 2144
A P H A Letter. (American Printing History Association) (US) 3997
A P H A Newsletter see A P H A Letter 3997
A P H Slate. (American Printing House for the Blind, Inc.) (US) 2290
A P I Abstracts - Catalysts and Catalysis see Literature Abstracts: Catalysts & Catalysis 1202
A P I Abstracts - Literature see Literature Abstracts 3706
A P I Abstracts - Oilfield Chemicals see Literature and Patent Abstracts: Oilfield Chemicals 3706
A P I Abstracts - Patents see Patents Abstracts 3706
A P I Account. (Accountants for the Public Interest) (US ISSN 0883-2102) 744, 4396
A P I C Bulletin see American Journal of Infection Control 3275
▼A P I C S the Performance Advantage. (American Production and Inventory Control Society) (US ISSN 1056-0017) 1001, 1071
A P I C Studies in Data Processing Series. (Automatic Programming Information Centre) (US) 1429
A P I S. (Apicultural Information and Issues) (US ISSN 0889-3764) 67
A P K V Jaarblad. see A P G A Annual 2120
A P L A Bulletin. (Atlantic Provinces Library Association) (CN ISSN 0001-2203) 2740
A P L I C Communicator. (Association for Population - Family Planning Library & Information Center International) (US ISSN 0891-0847) 2740, 3979

A P L Market News see A P L News 1429
A P L News. (A Programming Language) (US ISSN 0737-3155) 1429
A P L Quote Quad. (US ISSN 0163-6006) 1429, 1457, 1466
A P L Technical Digest see Johns Hopkins A P L Technical Digest 3821
†A P M A A Report (No.). (AT ISSN 0156-1766) 5128
A P M A News. (American Podiatric Medical Association) (US) 3069
A P M A Newsletter. (American Paper Machinery Association) (US) 3015
A P M Bulletin. (Air Power Museum) (US ISSN 0048-2358) 254, 42
A P M I S. (DK ISSN 0903-4641) 424, 3069
A P M Monograph Series. (Antique Phonograph Monthly) (US ISSN 0361-2147) 3536, 254
A P N R Newsletter. (American Professional Needlework Retailers, Inc.) (US) 352
A P O Annual Report. (Asian Productivity Organization) (JA ISSN 0066-846X) 1071, 925
A P O News. (Asian Productivity Organization) (JA ISSN 0044-9229) 1071, 925
A P P A Digest. (American Professional Practice Association) (US) 937, 2525
A P P A Newsletter. (Association of Physical Plant Administrators of Universities and Colleges) (US ISSN 0736-7252) 1724, 1001, 1813
A P P M Update. (Academy of Pharmacy Practice & Management) (US) 3715
A P R see Algemene Practische Rechtverzameling 2596
A P R. (Allgemeine Papier-Rundschau) (GW ISSN 0002-5917) 3661
A P R A News. (American Private Radio Association, Inc.) (US) 1354
A P R C Journal of Experimental Psychology. (Agra Psychological Research Cell) (II) 4008
A P R E S Proceedings. (American Peanut Research and Education Society) (US ISSN 0197-8748) 165
A P R I Journal. (African Peace Research Institute) (NR) 3949
A P R I Newsletter see A P R I Journal 3949
A P R T Newsletter see Association for Past-Life Research and Therapy. Newsletter 4012
A P S A Biographical Directory. (American Political Science Association) (US) 3869, 417
A P S A Departmental Services Program Survey of Departments. (American Political Science Association) (US ISSN 0094-7954) 3869
A P S A Directory of Department Chairmen see A P S A Directory of Department Chairpersons 3869
A P S A Directory of Department Chairpersons. (American Political Science Association) (US) 3869
A P S A Newsletter. (Australasian Political Studies Association) (AT) 3869, 3390, 4052
A P S Bulletin. (All Africa Press Service) (KE) 4161
A P S E C S Eighteenth-Century News see A P S E C S Newsletter 2336
A P S E C S Newsletter. (Australasian and Pacific Society for Eighteenth-Century Studies) (AT) 2336
A P S S Newsletter. (Association of Professional Sleep Societies) (US ISSN 0897-9375) 3327, 3364, 3390, 4096
A.P.S. Writers Unit Number Thirty News Bulletin see Philatelic Communicator 3756
A P T Communique. (Association for Preservation Technology) (CN ISSN 0319-4558) 1482, 291
A P U Life. (Azusa Pacific University) (US) 1302

A P U Press Alaskana Book Series. (Alaska Pacific University Press) (US) 2397, 232, 1613, 2891
A P U Press Alaskana Series see A P U Press Alaskana Book Series 2397
A P V A Newsletter. (Association for the Preservation of Virginia Antiquities) (US ISSN 0890-2518) 2397, 260, 291
A P V Tydskrif. see A S A Magazine 4707
A P W A News. (American Public Welfare Association) (US) 4396
A P W A Newsletter. (All Pakistan Women's Association) (PK ISSN 0001-2262) 4396
A P W A Reporter. (American Public Works Association) (US ISSN 0001-2270) 1861, 4083
A Plus see InCider - A Plus 1469
A Plus, Le Magazine Affaires Plus see Magazine Affaires Plus 954
A pour Affaires see L'Entreprise - A pour Affaires 1009
A Programming Language News see A P L News 1429
A Propos. see Candid Facts 3086
A Propos (Aurillac). (FR) 599
A Propos (Paris). (FR) 388
A Propos de Bain et Cuisine. (CN) 599, 2547
A Q P Report. (Association for Quality and Participation) (US) 1001, 970
A R see Albany Review 2857
A R see Arizona Review 5138
A R A see American Recovery Association. News and Views 758
A R A Bulletin see American Romanian Academy of Arts and Sciences. Journal 1699
A.R.A. Club News see Regatta 4528
A R A F Marketing Update. (Associated Regional Accounting Firms) (US) 744
A R A F Quarterly Report. (Associated Regional Accounting Firms) (US) 744
A R A Log. (American Radio Association) (US ISSN 0001-2289) 2579, 1354
▼A R C. (Architecture Research Criticism) (CN ISSN 1180-0933) 291
A R C. (Association for Retarded Citizens) (US ISSN 0199-9435) 4396, 1231, 3327
A R C Action. (Atlanta Regional Commission) (US) 2482, 4083
A R C Arabic Journal. (Arab Republic Community) (CN ISSN 0700-9771) 1988
A R D - Jahrbuch. (Arbeitsgemeinschaft der Oeffentlich-Rechtlichen Rundfunkanstalten der Bundesrepublik Deutschland) (GW ISSN 0066-5746) 1354
A R D R I News. (Agricultural and Rural Development Research Institute) (SA) 67
A R D U Publication. (Arussi Rural Development Unit) (ET) 67
A R E A Bulletin see American Railway Engineering Association Bulletin 4707
A R E A Magazine see Alabama Living 1502
A.R.E. Journal see Venture Inward 3597
A R E L S Brochure see A R E L S - F E L C O Brochure 1613
A R E L S - F E L C O Brochure. (Association of Recognised English Language Schools, Federation of English Language Course Organisations) (UK) 1613
A R E U E A Journal see American Real Estate and Urban Economics Association. Journal 4144
A R F Report. Annual see L A R F Report. Annual 677
A R G R Journal. (Association for Research in Growth Relationships) (US ISSN 0001-2300) 4008
A R I see Australasian Religion Index 4212
A R I E L. (A Review of International English Literature) (CN ISSN 0004-1327) 2891

A R I S. (Art Research in Scandinavia) (SW ISSN 0044-5711) 310, 291
A R K. (DK ISSN 0106-441X) 2800
A R L. (Association of Research Libraries) (US ISSN 1050-6098) 2740
A R L Annual Salary Survey. (US ISSN 0361-5669) 2740
A R L I S Newsletter see Art Libraries Journal 2744
A R L Minutes. (Association of Research Libraries) (US ISSN 0044-9652) 2740
A R L Newsletter see A R L 2740
A R L Statistics. (US ISSN 0147-2135) 2792
A R M A Records Management Quarterly see Records Management Quarterly 2781
A R M S Register. (Association of Retail Marketing Services) (US) 1032
A R N A B Newsletter. (African Research Network for Agricultural Byproducts) (UN) 67
A R N A H I S. (Archivo Nacional de Historia) (EC ISSN 1010-3848) 2397
A R N N Access. (Association of Registered Nurses of Newfoundland) (CN) 3275
A R N N News News News see A R N N Access 3275
A R N News. (Association of Rehabilitation Nurses) (US) 3275
A R P A Cahiers de Recherche Poetique. (Association de Recherche Poetique en Auvergne) (FR) 2986, 2891
A R P E L Boletin Informativo see A R P E L Hoy ·3681
A R P E L Boletin Tecnico. (Asistencia Reciproca Petrolera Estatal Latinoamericana) (UY ISSN 0253-6005) 3681
A R P E L Hoy. (Asistencia Reciproca Petrolera Estatal Latinoamericana) (UY) 3681
†A R P E News. (American Registry of Professional Entomologists) (US ISSN 0882-8431) 5128
A R P S Information Papers. (Association of Railway Preservation Societies Ltd.) (UK) 4707
A R Q: Architecture-Quebec. (CN ISSN 0710-1163) 291
A R R B Regional Symposium. (Australian Road Research Board) (AT ISSN 0314-2205) 4717
A R R L License Manual Series. (American Radio Relay League, Inc.) (US) 1354
A R R L Repeater Directory. (American Radio Relay League, Inc.) (US ISSN 0190-3632) 1354
A R S C Bulletin see A R S C Journal 4459
A R S C Journal. (Association for Recorded Sound Collections. Inc.) (US ISSN 0004-5438) 4459, 2740
A R S C Newsletter. (Association for Recorded Sound Collections, Inc.) (US) 4459, 2740
A R S Hai Sird. (Armenian Relief Society, Inc.) (US ISSN 0001-2335) 4396, 1988
A R S Journal see A I A A Journal 42
A R S Legislative Service see Arizona Legislative Service 2600
A R S - N C Agricultural Research Service. North Central Region see U.S. Agricultural Research Service. A R S - N C 126
A R S P see Archiv fuer Rechts- und Sozialphilosophie 3761
A R S Rosaceae see Rose Exhibitors Forum 2138
A R T B A Newsletter. (American Road & Transportation Builders Association) (US) 4717
A R T B A Officials and Engineers Directory, Transportation Agency Personnel. (American Road and Transportation Builders Association) (US ISSN 0360-6996) 4717, 599, 1861
A R T I News Letter. (Agrarian Research and Training Institute) (CE) 67, 1681, 4427

A R T I Reports. (Aeronautical Research and Test Institute) (CS) 42
A R T M E S see Aids and Research Tools in Middle Eastern Studies 2427
A R: The Complete Annual Report and Complete Image Planning Book. (US) 1001, 828
A R W Counterline. (Air-Conditioning & Refrigeration Wholesalers) (US) 2297
A R W Supplier. (US) 2297, 1071
A R W Wholesaler. (US) 2297, 643
A Rayons Ouverts. (CN ISSN 0835-8672) 2740
▼A Re A. (IT) 2482, 291
A Review of International English Literature see A R I E L 2891
A Revista. (PO) 2857, 643
A - Rivista Anarchica. (IT ISSN 0044-5592) 3869
A S see Arbeit und Sicherheit 3478
A S. (SP) 4463
A S A Accounting and Business Index see A S C P A Accounting and Business Index 701
A S A Artisan. (American Society of Artists, Inc.) (US ISSN 0892-3582) 310
A S A E. Management Conference. Proceedings see Sharing of Expertise and Experience 1027
A S A E Associate Member Update. (American Society of Association Executives) (US) 1001, 1032
A S A E Association Law and Policy. (American Society of Association Executives) (US) 1001, 2593
A S A E International News. (American Society of Association Executives) (US) 1001, 899, 3949
A S A E Monograph Series. (American Society of Agricultural Engineers) (US) 1813, 67
A S A E Standards. (American Society of Agricultural Engineers) (US ISSN 8755-1187) 165
A S A E Transactions. (American Society of Agricultural Engineers) (US ISSN 0001-2351) 165
A S A E Update see A S A E Associate Member Update 1001
A S A Employment Bulletin. (American Sociological Association) (US) 3624
A S A Footnotes. (American Sociological Association) (US ISSN 0749-6931) 4427
A S A I H L Seminar Reports. (Association of Southeast Asian Institutions of Higher Learning) (TH ISSN 0066-9695) 1698, 2336
†A S A I O Primers in Artificial Organs. (American Society of Artifical Internal Organs) (US ISSN 0893-4762) 5128
A S A I O Transactions. (American Society of Artificial Internal Organs) (US ISSN 0889-7190) 3069
A S A Journal see A S A Magazine 4707
A S A Magazine/A P V Tydskrif. (Artisan Staff Association) (SA) 4707
A S A Membership Directory. (American Supply Association) (US) 1120, 2297
†A S A Monograph (Washington). (American Society of Appraisers) (US ISSN 0569-7840) 5128
A S A Monographs (San Diego) see A S A Research Methods in Social Anthropology 232
A S A News. (African Studies Association) (US ISSN 0278-2219) 1988
A S A News. (American Supply Association) (US) 2297
A S A Newsletter. (American Studies Association) (US ISSN 0742-9290) 2397
A S A Papers. (African Studies Association) (US) 1988
A S A Refresher Courses in Anesthesiology. (American Society of Anesthesiologists) (US ISSN 0363-471X) 3189

A S A Research Methods in Social Anthropology. (Association of Social Anthropologists of the Commonwealth) (US) 232
A S A Special Publication. (American Society of Agronomy, Inc.) (US ISSN 0066-0566) 67
A S & T. (IT) 42
A S B A Today. (American Small Business Association) (US) 1113
A S B Bulletin. (Association of Southeastern Biologists, Inc.) (US ISSN 0001-2386) 424
A S B C Newsletter. (American Society of Brewing Chemists) (US ISSN 0149-7308) 377, 1168
A S B E Letter. (American Society of Bakery Engineers) (US ISSN 0001-2394) 2086
A S B O Accents. (Association of School Business Officials) (US) 1724
A S B S D Bulletin. (Associated School Boards of South Dakota) (US ISSN 0001-2408) 1724
A S C A Counselor. (American School Counselor Association) (US) 1733
A S C A Newsletter see A S C A Counselor 1733
A S C A P Biographical Dictionary. (American Society of Composers, Authors and Publishers) (US) 3536, 417, 2891
A S C A P in Action. (American Society of Composers, Authors and Publishers) (US) 3536
A S C Cybernetics Forum see Cybernetic 1440
A S C E Annual Combined Index. (American Society of Civil Engineers) (US ISSN 0742-1753) 1841
A S C E Publications Information. (American Society of Civil Engineers) (US ISSN 0734-1962) 1841, 1
A S C I I. (American Standard Code for Information Interchange) (JA) 1445
A S C I Journal of Management. (Administrative Staff College of India) (II ISSN 0257-8069) 1001
A S C Mini-File. (UK) 291, 599
A S C Newsletter (East Lansing). (African Studies Center) (US) 1988, 2330
A S C Newsletter (Washington). (Association of Systematics Collections) (US ISSN 0147-7889) 3520, 491, 575
A S C P A Accounting and Business Index. (Australian Society of Certified Practising Accountants) (AT ISSN 1036-689X) 701, 1, 744
A S C P Update. (American Society of Consultant Pharmacists) (US ISSN 1050-5725) 3715
A S C P Washington Report on National and State Issues. (American Society of Clinical Pathologists) (US ISSN 1052-7893) 3069, 2593
A S C U S Annual - A Job Search Handbook for Educators. (Association for School, College and University Staffing, Inc.) (US) 1724
A S C U S Annual - Teaching Opportunities for You see A S C U S Annual - A Job Search Handbook for Educators 1724
A S C U S Directory of Membership and Subject Field Index. (Association for School, College and University Staffing, Inc.) (US ISSN 0066-9164) 1724
A S C U S Staffer. (Association for School, College and University Staffing, Inc.) (US) 1692, 1698, 1724
A.S.D.A. Bulletin see A.S.D.A. Newsletter 3749
A S D A Handbook. (American Student Dental Association) (US ISSN 0277-3619) 3227
A S D A News (Year). (American Student Dental Association) (US ISSN 0277-3627) 3227
A.S.D.A. Newsletter. (American Stamp Dealers' Association, Inc.) (US) 3749
A S D M Newsletter see Sonorensis 4344
A S D Newsletter. (Association for the Study of Dreams) (US) 4008

A S D W A Update. (Association of State Drinking Water Administrators) (US) 4821
A S E A Action see Action (Lower Templestowe) 1743
A S E A Journal see A B B Review 1880
A S E A N Briefing. (Association of Southeast Asian Nations) (HK) 842, 3869
A S E A N Economic Bulletin. (Association of Southeast Asian Nations) (SI ISSN 0217-4472) 643
A S E C S News Circular. (American Society for Eighteenth-Century Studies) (US) 2305
A S E E Prism. (US) 1813, 1698
▼A S E E Prism. (American Society for Engineering Education) (US) 1813, 1698
A S E F I. (Annuario Servizi Finanziari) (IT) 758
A S E Journal. (Australasian Society of Engineers) (AT ISSN 0045-0103) 1813
A S E P News and Views. (American Society of Electroplated Plastics) (US) 3860
A S E S News see Solar Today 1812
A S E T Newsletter. (American Society of Electroneurodiagnostic Technologists, Inc.) (US ISSN 0886-5620) 3327
A S F A Aquaculture Abstracts. (Aquatic Sciences & Fisheries Abstracts) (US ISSN 0739-814X) 2050, 1
A S F A Marine Biotechnology Abstracts. (Aquatic Sciences & Fisheries Abstracts) (US ISSN 1043-8971) 1549, 461, 487, 1601
A S F E see Agenzia Stampa Filatelica Europea 3749
A S F Washington Letter. (American Ski Federation) (US) 4539
A S H A. (American Speech - Language - Hearing Association) (US ISSN 0001-2475) 2285, 3069
A S H A Directory see American Speech - Language - Hearing Association. Directory 3313
A S H A Reports see American Speech - Language - Hearing Association Reports 3313
A S H E - E R I C Higher Education Report Series. (Association for the Study of Higher Education) (US ISSN 0884-0040) 1698
A S H E - E R I C Higher Education Reports see A S H E - E R I C Higher Education Report Series 1698
A S H E - E R I C Higher Education Research Report Series see A S H E - E R I C Higher Education Report Series 1698
A S H E Notes. (Association for the Study of Higher Education (College Station)) (US) 1699
A S H E S Annual Conference. (American Society for Healthcare Environmental Services) (US) 2458, 1941
A S H Newsletter see A S H Smoking and Health Review 2593
A S H P Newsletter. (American Society of Hospital Pharmacists) (US ISSN 0001-2483) 3715
A S H R A E Handbook. (American Society of Heating, Refrigerating and Air-Conditioning Engineers, Inc.) (US ISSN 1041-2344) 2297
A S H R A E Journal. (American Society of Heating, Refrigerating and Air-Conditioning Engineers, Inc.) (US ISSN 0001-2491) 2297
A S H R A E Technical Data Bulletin. (American Society of Heating, Refrigerating and Air-Conditioning Engineers, Inc.) (US ISSN 0884-0490) 1926, 2297
A S H R A E Transactions. (American Society of Heating, Refrigerating and Air-Conditioning Engineers, Inc.) (US ISSN 0001-2505) 2297
A S H S Newsletter. (American Society for Horticultural Science) (US ISSN 0882-8024) 2120

A S H Smoking and Health Review. (Action on Smoking & Health) (US ISSN 1048-907X) **2593**, **3798**

A S I C & E D A. (Application Specific Integrated Circuits & Electronic Design Automation) (US ISSN 1043-9617) **1411**

A S I C Technology and News see A S I C & E D A **1411**

A S I D I C Newsletter. (Association of Information and Dissemination Centers) (US) **2740**

A S I D Report. (American Society of Interior Designers) (US) **2547**

A S I F A News. (Association Internationale du Film d'Animation) (BE ISSN 0775-9746) **3503**, **352**

A S I Journal. (Architects and Surveyors Institute) (UK ISSN 0956-4241) **291**

A S I L S International Law Journal see I L S A Journal of International Law **2633**

A S I Posten. (American Swedish Institute) (US) **3520**, **1988**

A S I S Handbook and Directory. (American Society for Information Science) (US ISSN 0066-0124) **2740**, **1120**

A S I S Key Papers Series. (American Society for Information Science) (US) **2740**

A S L A Members Handbook. (American Society of Landscape Architects) (US ISSN 0192-5067) **291**

A S L A Newsletter. (Arizona State Library Association) (US ISSN 0515-0272) **2740**

A S L A President's Newsletter see Interface (Chicago) **2763**

A S L E Transactions see S T L E Tribology Transactions **1860**

A S L H Newsletter. (American Society for Legal History) (US) **2593**, **2397**

A S L P Bulletin. (Association of Special Libraries of the Philippines) (PH ISSN 0001-2548) **2740**

A S L S Newsletter see Scotlit **2957**

A S M A News. (American Society of Marine Artists) (US) **310**

A S M E - I E E E Joint Railroad Conference. I E E E Technical Papers.(US ISSN 1054-0253) **4707**

A S M E News. (American Society of Mechanical Engineers) (US ISSN 0279-9316) **1926**

A S M E Solar Energy Conference. Proceedings. (American Society of Mechanical Engineers) (US) **1810**

A S M I C Newsletter. (American Society of Military Insignia Collectors, Inc. (ASMIC)) (US) **2432**

A S M, Ink. (Archaeological Society of Maryland, Inc.) (US) **260**

A S M News (Materials Park). (American Society for Metals) (US ISSN 0044-7889) **3401**

A S M News (Washington). (American Society for Microbiology) (US ISSN 0044-7897) **548**

A S M T Today. (American Society of Medical Technology, Inc.) (US) **3256**

A S M Z see Allgemeine Schweizerische Militaerzeitschrift **3450**

A S N E. Proceedings (Year). (American Society of Newspaper Editors) (US) **2566**

A S P C A Bulletin see A S P C A Report **229**

A S P C A Report. (American Society for the Prevention of Cruelty to Animals) (US) **229**

A S P Catalog. (Astronomical Society of the Pacific) (US) **360**

A S P E. (Agenzia di Stampa sui Problemi dell'Emarginazione) (IT ISSN 0394-6479) **4396**, **1941**, **2450**

A S P E C T. (Anti-Static Proposals & Electro-Conductive Technologies) (UK) **1881**

A S P I F Newsletter. (Association of Small Presses in Florida) (US) **4120**

A S P L O Newsletter. (Association of Small Public Libraries of Ontario) (CN) **2740**

†A S P N Newsletter. (American Society for Portuguese Numismatics) (US) **5128**

A.S.P.O. Genesis see Genesis (Washington) **3292**

A S P P Newsletter. (American Society of Plant Physiologists) (US) **491**, **3624**

A S P R Newsletter. (American Society for Psychical Research, Inc.) (US ISSN 0044-7919) **3668**

A S P Selectory see A S P Catalog **360**

†A S R. (Antrieb mit Steuerung und Regelung) (GW) **5129**

A S R A Journal. (Association for the Study of Reptilia and Amphibia) (UK ISSN 0142-5145) **575**

A S R C Newsletter see American Studies Research Centre. Newsletter **2398**

A S R C T Research News see T I S T R Research News **4346**

A S S A Proceedings see South African Sociological Review **4453**

A S S I A. (Applied Social Sciences Index & Abstracts) (UK ISSN 0950-2238) **4394**

A S S P Spectrum Estimation Workshop see A S S P Workshop on Spectrum Estimation and Modeling **3858**

A S S P Workshop on Spectrum Estimation and Modeling. (Acoustics, Speech and Signal Processing Society) (US) **3858**, **1881**

A S T A Newsletter. (American Seed Trade Association) (US) **2120**

A S T C Newsletter. (Association of Science-Technology Centers) (US ISSN 0895-7371) **3520**, **1613**, **4295**, **4592**

A S T D Buyers Guide and Consultants Directory. (American Society for Training and Development) (US) **1120**, **970**, **1062**

A S T D Journal see Training & Development **1070**

A S T D National Report see National Report for Training and Development **1022**

A S T I S Bibliography. (Arctic Science & Technology Information System) (CN ISSN 0226-1685) **1549**, **1**

A S T I S Current Awareness Bulletin. (Arctic Science & Technology Information System) (CN ISSN 0705-8454) **4613**, **4592**

A S T I S Occasional Publications. (Arctic Science & Technology Information System) (CN ISSN 0225-5170) **388**

A S T M Geotechnical Testing Journal see Geotechnical Testing Journal **1866**

A S T M Journal of Testing and Evaluation see Journal of Testing and Evaluation **1919**

A S T M S Journal. (Association of Scientific, Technical and Managerial Staffs) (UK ISSN 0001-2653) **1001**

A S T M Standardization News. (American Society for Testing and Materials) (US ISSN 0090-1210) **3444**, **1911**

A S T M Standards Infobriefs. (American Society for Testing and Materials) (US ISSN 0740-2961) **4592**

A S T R Newsletter. (American Society for Theatre Research) (US ISSN 0044-7927) **4629**

A S U C Journal of Music Scores see S C I Journal of Music Scores **3579**

A S U I Newsletter. (American Society of Utility Investors) (US) **937**, **1881**

A S U National. (Australian Services Union) (AT) **2579**

A S U Newsletter. (Association of Simula Users) (NO) **1429**

A S U Travel Guide. (Airline Service Unlimited) (US) **4750**, **4669**

A S W E A Journal for Social Work Education in Africa. (Association for Social Work Education in Africa) (ET) **4397**, **1743**

A S W Log. (US) **42**

A Sc W Journal see A S T M S Journal **1001**

A T. (Arkitekttidningen) (SW ISSN 0004-2005) **291**

A T see Automatisierungstechnik **1448**

A.T. see Auto Touring **4681**

A T A see Approximation Theory and its Applications **3030**

A T A Associazione Tecnica dell'Automobile. (IT ISSN 0001-2661) **4678**

A T A C. (Asociacion de Tecnicos Azucareros de Cuba) (CU) **166**

A T A Chronicle. (American Translators Association) (US) **2800**

▼A T A Journal. (HK ISSN 1015-8138) **4616**

A T A Newsletter see Tinnitus Today **3317**

A T A Professional Services Directory see Translation Services Directory **2856**

A T A V E Boletin Informativo. (Asociacion de Tecnicos Azucareros de Venezuela) (VE ISSN 0084-683X) **2060**

A T & T Standard Connection see N C R Connection **1471**

A T & T Technical Journal. (American Telephone and Telegraph) (US ISSN 8756-2324) **1361**

A T C C Microbes and Cells at Work. (American Type Culture Collection) (US) **548**, **522**

A T C C Quarterly Newsletter. (American Type Culture Collection) (US ISSN 0743-4758) **548**

A T C P Revista. (Asociacion Mexicana de Tecnicos de las Industrias de la Celulosa y del Papel, A.C.) (MX) **3661**

A T E A Journal. (American Technical Education Association, Inc.) (US ISSN 0889-6488) **1613**, **4592**

A T E Newsletter. (Association of Teacher Educators) (US ISSN 0001-2718) **1613**

A T F Annual Report. (Australian Teachers Union) (AT) **1613**, **2579**

A T F Monthly Report see A T F Annual Report **1613**

A T F Newsletter. (American Typecasting Fellowship) (US) **3997**

A T G Bulletin. (Accordion Teachers' Guild, Inc.) (US ISSN 0001-2734) **3536**, **1613**

A T IN: A I D S Targeted Information Newsletter. (US ISSN 0892-0125) **3165**, **3217**

A T I R A Communications on Textile see A C T **4615**

A T I R A Technical Digest see A C T **4615**

A T Index see Appropriate Technology Index **4614**

A T L see Annonsblad till Tidskrift foer Landtmaen **76**

A T L A Advocate. (Association of Trial Lawyers of America) (US ISSN 0746-4177) **2593**

A T L A Bibliography Series. (American Theological Library Association) (US) **4211**

A T L A Law Reporter. (Association of Trial Lawyers of America) (US ISSN 0364-8125) **2593**

A T L A Monograph Series. (American Theological Library Association) (US) **4161**

A T - L Newsletter see Advanced Technology Libraries **2741**

A T M. (GW ISSN 0933-1409) **3749**

A T M Directory. (Automated Teller Machines) (US) **1120**, **758**, **3015**

A T M - Forum. (GW ISSN 0932-5441) **3749**

A T M I Technology Directory. (Association for Technology in Music Instruction) (US) **3589**

A T M Reunion Registry. (Adoption Triangle Ministries) (US) **4397**, **2143**

A T O Palm. (Alpha Tau Omega Fraternity, Inc.) (US) **1302**

A T P. (AU) **4750**

A T P A S Bulletin see A T P A S Printing Education & Training Journal **3997**

A T P A S Printing Education & Training Journal. (Association of Teachers of Printing and Allied Subjects) (UK ISSN 0308-6895) **3997**

A T R. (Australian Telecommunication Research) (AT ISSN 0001-2777) **1331**

A T S News. (American Thoracic Society) (US) **3364**

A T S S Bulletin. (Association of Teachers of Social Studies in the City of New York) (US ISSN 0044-9687) **4364**, **1743**

†A T V News. (All Terrain Vehicle) (US) **5129**

†A T V Sports. (All Terrain Vehicle) (US) **5129**

A T W News. (GW ISSN 0341-4213) **1803**

A T W News of the Month see A T W News **1803**

A T Z. (Automobiltechnische Zeitschrift) (GW ISSN 0001-2785) **4678**

A U see Arredo Urbano **600**

A U A Decision Making. (American Urological Association) (CN) **3386**

A U A News. (American Underground-Space Association) (US) **291**, **1861**

A U A Today. (American Urological Association) (US) **3386**

A U B E R Bibliography see University Research in Business and Economics: a Bibliography of (Year) Publications **743**

A U bis Supplemento Tecnico. (Arredo Urbano) (IT) **599**, **291**

†A U C A. (Arquitectura, Urbanismo, Construccion y Arte) (CL ISSN 0567-428X) **5129**

A U D - Nyt. (Aalborg Universitetsdatacenter) (DK ISSN 0109-4157) **1388**

A U E W E S Journal. (Amalgamated Union of Engineering Workers, Engineering Section) (UK ISSN 0001-110X) **1813**

A U F Dive News see Diving Down Under **4471**

A U L Insights. (Americans United for Life) (US) **2593**, **3069**, **4836**

A U L L A. (Australian Universities Language and Literature Association) (AT) **2800**, **2891**

A U L Studies in Law, Medicine & Society. (Americans United for Life) (US) **2593**, **3069**, **4836**

A U M A Handbook Germany - Trade Fair Country. (Ausstellungs- und Messe-Ausschuss der Deutschen Wirtschaft e.V.) (GW ISSN 0933-6206) **1032**

A U M A Handbook International. (GW ISSN 0934-9790) **1032**, **3390**

A U M A Handbook Regional. (GW) **1032**, **3390**

A U M A Informationsblaetter. (GW) **26**, **1032**

A U M A Kalender Ausland see A U M A Handbook International **1032**

A U M A Kalender Messeplatz Deutschland see A U M A Handbook Germany - Trade Fair Country **1032**

A U M A Kalender Regional see A U M A Handbook Regional **1032**

A U M A - Mitteilungen. (GW) **26**, **1032**

A U M A Zahlenspiegel Messeplatz Deutschland see A U M A Handbook Germany - Trade Fair Country **1032**

A U M A Zahlenspiegel Regional see A U M A Handbook Regional **1032**

A U P E L F Bulletin de Nouvelles Breves see Universites **1719**

A U P E L F Revue see Perspectives Universitaires **1714**

A U R A Newsletter. (Association for Unity, Research and Awareness) (US) **3593**, **3759**

A U S - Meat Feedback. (Authority for Uniform Specifications Meat and Livestock (AUS-Meat)) (AT ISSN 1030-8474) **2060**, **209**

A U T Bulletin. (Association of University Teachers) (UK ISSN 0001-2823) **1699**

A und O Weg see Ihre Kette **32**

A V see Rivista di Avicoltura **225**

A-V see The A V Magazine 229
A V see Die Angestelltenversicherung 4053
A V A Advisor. (Asbestos Victims of America) (US) 3192, 2593
†A V A - Arbeitsmaterialien zur Verwaltungs- und Hochschulausbildung. (GW ISSN 0933-4718) 5129
A V A Magazine see Look Hear 1754
A V A Newsletter. (American Volkssport Association) (US) 1988, 1296, 3798
A-V Advisor. (US) 1368
A V - Branche (Year) see Corporate A V (Year) 1334
A V C Bulletin. (American Veterans Committee, Inc.) (US ISSN 0001-2874) 3449
A V C Communicator see A V C Visions 3503
A V C Development and Delivery. (US) 1331
A V C Visions. (Association of Visual Communicators) (US) 3503
A - V Communications. see A -V Kommunikacio 1613
A V D Auto Bordbuch. (GW) 4678, 4750
A V E A Newsletter. (American Veterinary Exhibitors Association) (US) 4804
A V E in Japan. (Audio-Visual Education) (JA ISSN 0065-0102) 1743
A V E P S O Fasciculo. (Asociacion Venezolana de Psicologia Social) (VE) 4008
A V Guide. (US ISSN 0091-360X) 1743, 3503
A V Guide Newsletter see A V Guide 1743
A V I D. (US) 1384
A V Information. (Gewerkschaft Auguste Victoria) (GW) 3477
A V K O Newsletter. (US) 1681, 1733, 1743
A V Kanal. (GW) 1368
A -V Kommunikacio/A - V Communications. (HU) 1613
A V M A R C see British Catalogue of Audio-Visual Materials 4462
The A V Magazine. (American Anti-Vivisection Society) (US ISSN 0274-7774) 229
A V Market Place. (US ISSN 1044-0445) 1743
A V N see Allgemeine Vermessungs-Nachrichten 1861
A - V Prof. (Audio - Visual) (NE) 1368
A V R. (Allgemeiner Vliestoff-Report) (GW ISSN 0170-4060) 4616
A V S Biomedical Bulletin see Biomedical Bulletin 5149
A V S C News. (Association for Voluntary Surgical Contraception, Inc.) (US) 595
A V S Journal see Pegasus 4814
A V S News see A V S C News 595
A V Video. (US ISSN 0747-1335) 1384, 1457, 1688
A Veidum. (IC ISSN 1017-3625) 4539
A Voice Without Sides. (US) 2986
A Voz do Trabalhador. (AO) 2579
A W A News. (Aviation - Space Writers Association) (US) 42
A W C News Forum. (American Women Composers, Inc.) (US) 3536, 4836
A W E A Update see A W E A Wind Energy Weekly 1812
A W E A Wind Energy Weekly. (American Wind Energy Association) (US ISSN 0747-5500) 1812
A W I S Magazine. (Association for Women in Science) (US) 4836, 4295
†A W im Blickpunkt. (Arbeiterwohlfahrt Kreisverband Koeln e.V.) (GW) 5129
A.W. Mellon Lectures in the Fine Arts. (US ISSN 0065-0129) 310
A W Mitteilungen see A W O Mitteilungen 4397
A W N Y Matters. (Advertising Women of New York) (US) 26, 4836
†A W N Y News. (Advertising Women of New York) (US) 5129
A W O Letter. (American Waterways Operators) (US) 4723
A W O Mitteilungen. (GW) 4397

A W O Weekly Letter see A W O Letter 4723
A W P Chronicle. (Associated Writing Programs) (US) 2566, 1743
A W P Newsletter see A W P Chronicle 2566
A W R Bulletin. (Association for the Study of the World Refugee Problems) (AU ISSN 0001-2947) 3949
A W S C P A. Newsletter. (American Women's Society of Certified Public Accountants) (US) 744, 4836
A W S Observer see Air Weather Service Observer 3432
A W T. (Abwassertechnik) (GW ISSN 0932-3708) 1941, 4821
A W T A O Annual Report. (Association of Water Transportation Accounting Officers) (US) 745, 4723
A W T A O Bulletin. (Association of Water Transportation Accounting Officers) (US) 745, 4723
A W W A Mainstream. (American Water Works Association) (US ISSN 0273-3218) 4821
A.X. Magazine. (US) 1466
†A Y Business. (Arthur /Young, Ed. & Pub.) (AT) 5129
A Y H Discovery Tours. (American Youth Hostels, Inc.) (US) 4750
A Y R S Airs. (Amateur Yacht Research Society) (UK ISSN 0144-1396) 4521
A - Ya. (FR ISSN 0241-8185) 310
A - Z de la Construccion y la Decoracion. (VE) 599
A Z - Nachrichten. (GW ISSN 0343-7647) 561
A - Z of U.K. Marketing Data. (UK ISSN 0260-6488) 1032
A Z U R Camping Magazin. (GW ISSN 0935-0454) 4750, 4539
A - Z: United Arab Emirates Business Locations Guide. (TS) 1120
A 2 L A (Year) Directory of Accredited Laboratories. (US ISSN 1040-9181) 1120, 3444
A 2 L A News. (American Association for Laboratory Accreditation) (US ISSN 1040-9157) 1120, 3444
A 2 L A Update see A 2 L A News 1120
Aabenraa Proevecenter for Ny Informationsteknologi Rapport see I N F A A Rapport 5210
†Aabo Akademi. Aarsskrift. (FI ISSN 0355-5798) 5129
Aabo Akademi. Ekonomisk-statsvetenskapliga Fakulteten. Meddelanden. (FI ISSN 0358-5654) 4364
Aabo Akademi. Statsvetenskapliga Fakulteten. Meddelanden see Aabo Akademi. Ekonomisk-statsvetenskapliga Fakulteten. Meddelanden 4364
Aachal. (BG) 4836
Aachen. Statistisches Amt. Statistische Kurzinformation. (GW) 4561
Aachener Beitraege zur Komparatistik. (GW) 2891
Aachener Geschichtsverein. Zeitschrift. (GW ISSN 0065-0137) 2346
Aakeri & Transport. (SW ISSN 0348-0356) 4742, 1861
Aakerifoeretagaren-Transportoeren see Aakeri & Transport 4742
Aalandsk Odling. (FI) 2346
Aalborg Universitetscenter. Institut for Elektroniske Systemer. Rapport. (DK ISSN 0106-0791) 1881, 1388
Aalborg Universitetscenter. Institut for Sprog og Internationale Kulturstudier. Arbejdspapirer. (DK ISSN 0902-9958) 2800, 2891
Aalborg Universitetscenter. Institutet for Bygningsteknik. Note. (DK ISSN 0902-8005) 599
Aalborg Universitetscenter. Institutet for Bygningsteknik. Rapport. (DK ISSN 0902-7513) 599
Aalborg Universitetscenter Kvindestudier ved A U C. Aarbog see Kvindestudier ved A U C. Aarbog 4846
Aalborg Universitetsdatacenter Nyt see A U D - Nyt 1388

Aalborg University. Papers on Language and Intercultural Studies see Aalborg Universitetscenter. Institut for Sprog og Internationale Kulturstudier. Arbejdspapirer 2800
Aalisakkanik Pinngortitamillu Avatangiisimik Kalaallit Nunanni see Kalaallit Nunaani Aalisakkanik Misissuinerit. Ukiumoortumik Nalunaarusiaq 2045
Aan de Schreve. (BE) 2346
De Aan- en Afvoer over Zee in de Nederlandse Zeehavens. (NE) 4723
†Aan- en Verkoopost. (NE) 5129
De Aandrijfkrant. (NE) 1861
Aandrijftechniek. (NE ISSN 0165-5108) 1926
Aarbog for Arbejderbevaegelsens Historie. (DK ISSN 0106-5912) 2346, 970
Aarbog for Folkeskolen. (DK ISSN 0106-0465) 1724
Aarbog for Svendborg & Omegns Museum. (DK ISSN 0106-2220) 2346
Aarbok for den Norske Kirke. (NO ISSN 0400-227X) 4161
Aarbok for Hadeland. (NO ISSN 0572-4562) 2346
Aarbok for Telemark. (NO ISSN 0587-4076) 2346
Aardappelen, Groenten, Fruit Magazine see A G F - Magazine 165
Aardappelwereld. (NE ISSN 0165-6031) 833, 67
Aarde en Kosmos see Aarde en Kosmos - D J O 4295
Aarde en Kosmos - D J O/Earth and Cosmos - D J O. (NE ISSN 0166-4786) 4295
Aardrijkskunde. (BE) 2240
Aardrijkskunde - Geographie see Aardrijkskunde 2240
Aardvark. (SA) 575
Aaret Fortalt i Billeder. (DK) 2346, 310
Aaret Rundt. (DK) 1813
Aaret Runt. (SW) 2218
Aaret som Gaatt. (SW) 970
†Aarets Bandy. (SW) 5129
Aarets Bedste Film see Film Aarbogen 3508
Aarets Fotboll. (SW ISSN 0567-4565) 4499
Aarets Idrott. (SW ISSN 0567-4573) 4463
Aarets Ishockey. (SW ISSN 0282-860X) 4463
Aarets Pressefoto. (DK ISSN 0109-4440) 3788, 2566
Aarhus Frimaerkehandel Danmark Fireblokke see A F A Danmark Fireblokke 3748
Aarhus Frimaerkehandel Danmark Frimaerkekatalog see A F A Danmark Frimaerkekatalog 3748
Aarhus Frimaerkehandel Oesteuropa Frimaerkekatalog see A F A Oesteuropa Frimaerkekatalog 3748
Aarhus Frimaerkehandel Skandinavien Frimaerkekatalog see A F A Skandinavien Frimaerkekatalog 3748
Aarhus Frimaerkehandel Vesteuropa Frimaerkekatalog see A F A Vesteuropa Frimaerkekatalog 3748
Aarhus Havn. (DK) 899
Aarhus Kommunes Statistiske Kontor. Information. (DK ISSN 0107-7120) 4561
Aarhus School of Business. Centre for Labour Economics. Working Papers. (DK ISSN 0905-6955) 970
†Aarhus Universitet. Center for Latinamerikastudier. Nyhedsbrev. (DK ISSN 0109-9035) 5129
†Aarhus Universitet. Geografisk Institut. Notat. (DK ISSN 0106-9047) 5129
Aarhus Universitet. Geologisk Institut. Geokompendier. (DK ISSN 0105-8258) 1553
Aarhus Universitet. Geologisk Institut. Georapporter. (DK ISSN 0105-8266) 1553
Aarhus Universitet. Geologisk Institut. Geoskrifter. (DK ISSN 0105-824X) 1553, 2240

Aarhus Universitet. Institut for Litteraturhistorie. Skrifter see Passage 2947
†Aarhus Universitet. Institut for Statskundskab. Arbejdspapir. (DK ISSN 0901-5213) 5129
Aarhus Universitet. Matematisk Institut. Datalogisk Afdeling. DAIMI FN. (DK ISSN 0105-8533) 3025
Aarhus Universitet. Matematisk Institut. Datalogisk Afdeling. DAIMI IR. (DK ISSN 0106-9969) 3025
Aarhus Universitet. Matematisk Institut. Datalogisk Afdeling. DAIMI MD. (DK ISSN 0105-8525) 3025
Aarhus Universitet. Matematisk Institut. Datalogisk Afdeling. DAIMI PB. (DK ISSN 0105-8517) 3025
Aarhus Universitet. Matematisk Institut. Elementaerafdeling. (DK ISSN 0106-8997) 3025
Aarhus Universitet. Matematisk Institut. Lecture Notes Series. (DK ISSN 0065-017X) 3025
Aarhus Universitet. Matematisk Institut. Memoirs. (DK) 3025
Aarhus Universitet. Matematisk Institut. Various Publications Series. (DK ISSN 0065-0188) 3026
Aarhus Universitet. Romansk Institut. Spansk Afdelingen. Information. (DK ISSN 0107-6531) 2800
Aarhus Universitet. Slavisk Institut. Arbejdspapirer. (DK ISSN 0105-4112) 2346
Aarhus Universitet. Teologiske Fakultet. Bibliografi. (DK ISSN 0901-4497) 4212
Aarhus University. Botanical Institute. Reports. (DK ISSN 0105-4236) 491
Aarni. (FI ISSN 0355-1644) 2346
Aarsberetning Vedkommende Norges Fiskerier. (NO ISSN 0365-8252) 2035
Aarsbok foer Skolan. (SW ISSN 0065-0196) 1613
Aarsbok foer Sveriges Kommuner. (SW ISSN 0065-020X) 4078
Aarsskrift for Sottrup Sogn. (DK ISSN 0108-2787) 2346
Aarsskrift for Toender Landbrugsskole. (DK ISSN 0107-0304) 67
Aarsveretninger. see National Agency of Industry and Trade. Annual Reports (Year) 1081
Aaspas. (II) 2198
Aawaz. (CN) 1988
Abacus. (UK ISSN 0001-3072) 745
Abacus. (NR ISSN 0001-3099) 3026
Abacus (Elmwood). (US ISSN 0886-4047) 2986
†Abacus (New York). (US ISSN 0724-6722) 5129
Abaka. (CN ISSN 0382-9251) 1988
Abanico. (CR) 4836
Abatis see Tampa Review 3007
Abattage et Conditionnement de la Viande. see Canada. Statistics Canada. Slaughtering and Meat Processors 5160
Abbey. (US) 2986
Abbey Newsletter. (US ISSN 0276-8291) 2741
Abbey Press Christian Family Catalog see Christian Family Catalog 2281
†Abbia. (CM ISSN 0001-3102) 5129
Abdominal Surgery see Journal of Abdominal Surgery 3379
Abe Bailey Institute of Inter-Racial Studies. Annual Report see Centre for Intergroup Studies. Annual Report 4431
Abeille de France et l'Apiculteur. (FR ISSN 0373-4625) 67
Abeilles et Fleurs. (FR ISSN 0765-8702) 67
Abel see Abel Value News 4629
Abel Value News. (US) 4629, 2471, 3503
Abendblatt see Come Out 2452
Das Abendland. (GW ISSN 0724-9624) 2501
Abenteuer & Reisen. (GW ISSN 0176-5388) 4750
Aber Bulletin. (US) 2143
Aberdeen and North East Scotland Family History Society. Journal. (UK) 2143

Aberdeen and North East Scotland Family History Society. Newsletter see Aberdeen and North East Scotland Family History Society. Journal **2143**

Aberdeen and North of Scotland Library and Information Co-operative Service News see A N S L I C S News **5128**

Aberdeen - Angus Herd Book. (UK) **209**

Aberdeen - Angus Review. (UK ISSN 0001-317X) **209**

Aberdeen Petroleum Quarterly see Europetroleum **3685**

Aberdeen Petroleum Report. (UK ISSN 0263-5054) **3681**

Aberdeen Port Handbook. (UK ISSN 0267-7377) **1120**, **3681**, **4723**

Aberdeen University Review. (UK) **1302**

Abertay Historical Society. Series of Monographs. (UK) **2346**

†Abgesaegt. (GW ISSN 0934-8549) **5129**

Abhandlungen aus dem Gebiet der Auslandskunde. Series B & C. (GW ISSN 0343-7051) **3632**, **2336**

Abhandlungen des Deutschen Palaestinavereins. (GW ISSN 0173-1904) **3632**

Abhandlungen fuer die Kunde des Morgenlandes. (GW ISSN 0567-4980) **3632**

Abhandlungen und Materialen zur Publizistik. (GW ISSN 0065-0323) **2566**

Abhandlungen zu den Wirtschaftlichen Staatswissenschaften. (GW) **888**

Abhandlungen zur Handels- und Sozialgeschichte. (GW ISSN 0065-0358) **2346**

Abhandlungen zur Kunst-, Musik- und Literaturwissenschaft. (GW ISSN 0567-4999) **310**, **2857**, **3536**

Abhandlungen zur Philosophie, Psychologie und Paedagogik. (GW ISSN 0065-0366) **3759**, **1613**

Al-Abhath. (LE ISSN 0002-3973) **3632**

Abhayaduta. (II) **2198**, **3869**

Abhigyan. (II ISSN 0970-2385) **4364**, **1062**, **4008**

Abhiyan. (II) **2198**

Abiko Quarterly Rag. (JA) **2891**

Abilities. (AT) **2285**, **2290**, **4397**

Abingdon Clergy Income Tax Guide. (US ISSN 0163-1241) **1087**, **4161**

Abitare. (IT ISSN 0001-3218) **291**, **2547**

Abitare con Arte. (IT) **310**

Ablex Series in Artificial Intelligence. (US) **1406**

▼Ablex Series in Computational Sciences. (US) **1388**

Ablex Series in Software Engineering. (US) **1417**

Aboard Aviateca. (US) **4801**

Aboard Dominicana. (US) **4801**

Aboard Ecuatoriana. (US) **4801**

Aboard L A B Airlines. (Lloyd Aero Boliviano) (US) **4801**

Aboard Lan-Chile. (US) **4801**

Aboard Taca. (US) **4801**

Aboard Tan Sahsa. (US) **4821**

Aboard Viasa. (US) **4801**

Abordage. (CN) **970**

Aboriginal and Islander Health Worker see Aboriginal and Islander Health Worker Journal **4096**

Aboriginal and Islander Health Worker Journal. (AT ISSN 1037-3403) **4096**

Aboriginal Child at School. (AT ISSN 0310-5822) **1613**, **1988**

The Aboriginal Circuit. (CN) **643**

Aboriginal Health Worker see Aboriginal and Islander Health Worker Journal **4096**

Aboriginal History. (AT ISSN 0314-8769) **232**, **2343**

Aboriginal Law Bulletin see Legal Service Bulletin **2648**

†Aboriginal Law Notes. (AT) **5129**

Aboriginal Medical Service. Newsletter. (AT ISSN 0310-8341) **3069**

Aboriginal S F see Aboriginal Science Fiction **3010**

Aboriginal Science Fiction. (US) **3010**

Abortion Bibliography. (US ISSN 0092-9522) **598**, **388**, **4835**

Abortion Research Notes. (US ISSN 0361-1116) **4835**, **595**

Abortion Review. (UK ISSN 0262-7299) **4835**, **595**

About Alfords. (US ISSN 0883-1173) **2143**

About Books for Children see Pick of the Year **1262**

About London. (UK) **4750**

About the House. (UK ISSN 0001-3242) **3536**, **1528**

About...Time. (US) **1988**

About U. (AT) **2579**

About Women (Winnipeg). (CN ISSN 0708-6180) **4836**

About Wool. (AT) **4616**

Above & Beyond. (CN ISSN 0843-7815) **1989**

Above Rubies. (AT) **2444**

Above the Bridge. (US) **2220**

Abr-Nahrain. (BE ISSN 0065-0382) **3632**

†Abr-Nahrain. Supplements. (NE ISSN 0065-0390) **5129**

Abracadabra. (US) **3997**, **310**

Abraham Lincoln Association. Journal. (US ISSN 0898-4212) **2305**, **3869**

Abraham Lincoln Association. Papers see Abraham Lincoln Association. Journal **2305**

Abrahams Magazine Service Ars Poetica see A M S Ars Poetica **2986**

Abrahams Magazine Service Asian Studies see A M S Asian Studies **2336**

Abrahams Magazine Service Studies in Anthropology see A M S Studies in Anthropology **232**

Abrams Planetarium Sky Calendar. (US ISSN 0733-6314) **360**

Abrasax. (US) **3668**

Abrasive Engineering Society. Conference Proceedings. (US ISSN 0363-8065) **1813**

Abrasive Engineering Society Magazine. (US ISSN 0195-0932) **3015**, **1926**

Abrasive Engineering Society Newsletter see A E S Newsletter **3401**

Abrasive Technology see Abrasive Engineering Society Magazine **3015**

Abraxas. (GW) **1692**

Abraxas. (US ISSN 0361-1663) **2986**

Abrego. (SP) **67**

Abricot. (FR) **1248**

†Abridged Catholic Periodical and Literature Index. (US ISSN 0737-3457) **5129**

Abridged Index Medicus. (US ISSN 0001-3331) **3165**, **1**

Abridged Magazine Index. (US) **4139**, **1**

Abridged Readers' Guide to Periodical Literature. (US ISSN 0001-334X) **1**

Abroad. (UK) **4750**

Abruzzo Notizie. (IT) **4052**

Absatzwirtschaft. (GW ISSN 0001-3374) **1032**

Absolute Reference. (US) **1457**, **1466**, **1475**

Absolute Sound. (US ISSN 0097-1138) **4459**

Absous. (FR) **3395**

Abstract Journal for Materials Handling and Packaging. see Anyagmozgatasi es Csomagolasi Szakirodalmi Tajekoztato **4661**

Abstract Journal for Textile and Clothing Industry. see Textil- es Textilruhazati Ipari Szakirodalmi Tajekoztato **5289**

Abstract Journal in Earthquake Engineering. (US ISSN 0363-5732) **1841**, **1**, **1549**

Abstract Journal: Non-Destructive Testing. see Referatorgan: Zerstoerungsfreie Pruefung **1846**

Abstract Newsletter: Administration and Management see N T I S Alerts: Administration and Management **4081**

Abstract Newsletter: Agriculture and Food see N T I S Alerts: Agriculture & Food **140**

Abstract Newsletter: Behavior and Society see N T I S Alerts: Behavior and Society **4458**

Abstract Newsletter: Biomedical Technology and Human Factors Engineering see N T I S Alerts: Biomedical Technology & Human Factors Engineering **3178**

Abstract Newsletter: Building Industry Technology see N T I S Alerts: Building Industry Technology **638**

Abstract Newsletter: Business and Economics see N T I S Alerts: Business & Economics **730**

Abstract Newsletter: Chemistry see N T I S Alerts: Chemistry **1202**

Abstract Newsletter: Civil Engineering see N T I S Alerts: Civil Engineering **1845**

Abstract Newsletter: Communication see N T I S Alerts: Communication **1349**

Abstract Newsletter: Computers, Control & Information Theory see N T I S Alerts: Computers, Control & Information Theory **1405**

Abstract Newsletter: Electrotechnology see N T I S Alerts: Electrotechnology **1776**

Abstract Newsletter: Energy see N T I S Alerts: Energy **1800**

Abstract Newsletter: Environmental Pollution and Control see N T I S Alerts: Environmental Pollution & Control **1974**

Abstract Newsletter: Foreign Technology see N T I S Alerts: Foreign Technology **4615**

Abstract Newsletter: Government Inventions for Licensing see N T I S Alerts: Government Inventions for Licensing **4615**

Abstract Newsletter: Health Care see N T I S Alerts: Health Care **3811**

†Abstract Newsletter: Industrial & Mechanical Engineering. (US) **5129**

Abstract Newsletter: Library and Information Sciences see N T I S Alerts: Library & Information Sciences **2794**

Abstract Newsletter: Manufacturing Technology see N T I S Alerts: Manufacturing Technology **4615**

Abstract Newsletter: Materials Sciences see N T I S Alerts: Materials Sciences **1845**

Abstract Newsletter: Medicine and Biology see N T I S Alerts: Medicine & Biology **466**

Abstract Newsletter: Natural Resources and Earth Sciences see N T I S Alerts: Natural Resources & Earth Sciences **1501**

Abstract Newsletter: Ocean Technology & Engineering see N T I S Alerts: Ocean Technology & Engineering **1551**

Abstract Newsletter: Physics see N T I S Alerts: Physics **3838**

Abstract Newsletter: Problem-Solving Information for State and Local Governments. (US) **4078**, **1**

Abstract Newsletter: Transportation see N T I S Alerts: Transportation **4665**

Abstract Newsletter: Urban and Regional Technology and Development. (US ISSN 0163-1535) **2499**, **1**, **4613**

Abstract of American Economic Trend Analysis. (CN) **701**

Abstract of International Economic Trend Analysis. (CN) **701**

Abstract of Statistics for Tamil Nadu. (II) **4561**

Abstract of Swedish Statistics. see Statistisk Aarsbok foer Sverige **4589**

Abstracta. (IT) **2857**

Abstracta Iranica. (BE ISSN 0240-8910) **2427**, **2327**

Abstracting and Indexing Bulletin for Agricultural and Animal Husbandry see Agricultural Abstracts for Tanzania **132**

Abstracting and Indexing Services Directory. (US ISSN 0732-8583) **1**

Abstracts and Abridgements of Patent Specifications. (UK) **3679**

Abstracts and Reviews from Zentralblatt fuer Mathematik. (GW ISSN 0933-9663) **3062**

Abstracts: Cellular Pathology. (UK ISSN 0268-4993) **3165**, **1**, **461**, **3256**

Abstracts for Social Workers see Social Work Research and Abstracts **4427**

Abstracts from Current Scientific and Technical Literature. (UK ISSN 0001-3439) **2084**, **1**, **3613**

Abstracts: Histopathology, Cytopathology see Abstracts: Cellular Pathology **3165**

Abstracts in Anthropology. (US ISSN 0001-3455) **253**, **1**

Abstracts in BioCommerce. (UK ISSN 0263-6778) **701**, **1**, **4613**

Abstracts in German Anthropology. (GW ISSN 0173-2986) **253**

▼Abstracts in Human - Computer Interaction. (US ISSN 1042-0193) **1403**, **1440**

Abstracts in Internal Medicine see Abstracts in Medicine and Key Word Index **3165**

Abstracts in Maryland Archeology. (US ISSN 0743-4251) **290**, **1**

Abstracts in Medicine and Key Word Index. (US) **3165**

Abstracts in Social Gerontology: Current Literature on Aging. (US ISSN 1047-4862) **2280**, **1**

Abstracts of Anesthesiology and Resuscitation. see Referatovy Vyber z Anestesiologie a Resuscitace **3180**

Abstracts of Bulgarian Scientific Literature. Agriculture and Forestry. Veterinary Medicine. (BU ISSN 0001-3463) **131**, **1**, **2111**

Abstracts of Bulgarian Scientific Literature. Biology. (BU) **461**, **1**

Abstracts of Bulgarian Scientific Literature. Biology and Biochemistry see Abstracts of Bulgarian Scientific Literature. Biology **461**

Abstracts of Bulgarian Scientific Literature. Economics and Law. (BU ISSN 0204-6083) **701**, **1**, **2697**

Abstracts of Bulgarian Scientific Literature. Geology and Geography see Abstracts of Bulgarian Scientific Literature. Geosciences **1550**

Abstracts of Bulgarian Scientific Literature. Geosciences. (BU ISSN 0204-9406) **1550**, **1**, **2267**

Abstracts of Bulgarian Scientific Literature. History, Archaeology and Ethnography. (BU ISSN 0205-3772) **2346**

Abstracts of Bulgarian Scientific Literature. Industry, Building and Transport. (BU ISSN 0204-577X) **701**, **1**, **636**

Abstracts of Bulgarian Scientific Literature. Linguistics and Literature. (BU ISSN 0861-0843) **2854**, **1**, **2980**

Abstracts of Bulgarian Scientific Literature. Mathematical and Physical Sciences. (BU ISSN 0204-9449) **3062**, **2**, **3836**

Abstracts of Bulgarian Scientific Literature. Mathematics, Physics, Astronomy, Geophysics, Geodesy see Abstracts of Bulgarian Scientific Literature. Mathematical and Physical Sciences **3062**

Abstracts of Bulgarian Scientific Literature. Philosophy, Psychology and Pedagogics see Abstracts of Bulgarian Scientific Literature. Philosophy, Sociology, Science of Sciences, Psychology and Pedagogics **1673**

Abstracts of Bulgarian Scientific Literature. Philosophy, Sociology, Science of Sciences, Psychology and Pedagogics. (BU) **1673**, **2**, **3787**

Abstracts of Bulgarian Scientific Medical Literature. (BU ISSN 0001-3536) **3165**, **2**

Abstracts of Cardiology and Physiology and Pathology of the Circulation System. see Referatovy Vyber z Kardiologie, Fysiologie a Patologie Obehoveho Ustroji **3180**

ABSTRACTS

Abstracts of Chinese Geological Literature. (CC ISSN 0258-6746) **1550**, 2, **1553**

Abstracts of Dermatology and Venerology. see Referatovy Vyber z Dermatovenerologie **3180**

Abstracts of Development Studies. (US) **701**

Abstracts of Educational Studies and Research. (NR) **1674**, 2

Abstracts of Endocrinology. see Referatovy Vyber z Endokrinologie **5268**

Abstracts of English Studies. (UK ISSN 0001-3560) **2980**, 2

Abstracts of Entomology. (US ISSN 0001-3579) **461**, 2

Abstracts of Gastroenterology. see Referatovy Vyber z Gastroenterologie **3180**

Abstracts of Gerontology and Geriatrics. see Referatovy Vyber z Gerontologie a Geriatrie **5268**

Abstracts of Health Legislature. see Bibliograficky Vyber: Zdravotnictvi a Pravo **5148**

Abstracts of Hungarian Economic Literature. (HU ISSN 0044-5800) **701**, 2

Abstracts of Infectious Diseases. see Referatovy Vyber z Chorob Infekcnich **3180**

Abstracts of Military Bibliography. (AG) **3476**, 2

Abstracts of Mycology. (US ISSN 0001-3617) **461**, 2

Abstracts of Neurology. see Referatovy Vyber z Neurologie **3180**

Abstracts of Obstetrics and Gynecology. see Referatovy Vyber z Porodnictvi a Gynekologie **3180**

Abstracts of Oncology. see Referatovy Vyber z Onkologie **5268**

Abstracts of Ophthalmology. see Referatovy Vyber z Oftalmologie **3180**

Abstracts of Orthopedics, Traumatology and Related Subjects. see Referatovy Vyber z Ortopedie, Traumatologie a Pribuznych Oboru **3180**

Abstracts of Otorhinolaryngology and Phoniatrics. see Referatovy Vyber z Otorhinolaryngologie a Foniatrie **5268**

Abstracts of Papers Presented at the Annual Meeting- American Institute for Conservation of Historic and Artistic Works see American Institute for Conservation of Historic and Artistic Works. Abstracts of Papers Presented at the Annual Meeting **311**

Abstracts of Pathology. see Referatovy Vyber z Patologicke Anatomie **5268**

Abstracts of Pediatrics. see Referatovy Vyber z Pediatrie **3180**

Abstracts of Pharmacy. see Referatovy Vyber z Lekarenstvi **3748**

Abstracts of Physiology. see Referatovy Vyber z Fysiologie **5268**

Abstracts of Pneumology and Tuberculosis. see Referatovy Vyber z Pneumologie a Tuberkulosy **3180**

Abstracts of Radiology. see Referatovy Vyber z Rentgenologie **3180**

Abstracts of Research in Pastoral Care and Counseling. (US ISSN 0733-2599) **4212**, 2

Abstracts of Rheumatology. see Referatovy Vyber z Revmatologie **3180**

Abstracts of Romanian Scientific and Technical Literature. (RM ISSN 0001-365X) **4354**, **4613**

Abstracts of Scientific and Technological Publications. (JA ISSN 0914-4897) **4613**, **4354**

Abstracts of Sports Medicine and Rehabilitation. see Referatovy Vyber ze Sportovni Mediciny a Lecebne Rehabilitace **3181**

Abstracts of Surgery. see Referatovy Vyber z Chirurgie **3180**

†Abstracts of the Current Literature on Respiratory Diseases and T B/ Kokyuki Shikkan Kekkaku Bunken no Shoroku Sokuho. (JA ISSN 0389-7389) **5129**

Abstracts of the Current Literature on T B and Other Respiratory Diseases see Abstracts of the Current Literature on Respiratory Diseases and T B **5129**

Abstracts of the Intermag Conference see International Magnetics Conference. Digests of the Intermag Conference **3820**

Abstracts of Think Tank Reports. see Shinku Tanku Nenpo **4358**

Abstracts of Uppsala Dissertations in Science. (SW ISSN 0001-3676) **4354**, 2

Abstracts of Urology. see Referatovy Vyber z Urologie **3181**

Abstracts of Working Papers in Economics. (UK ISSN 0951-0079) **701**, 2

Abstracts on Cassava. (CK ISSN 0120-288X) **131**, 2

Abstracts on Crime and Juvenile Delinquency see Criminal Justice Abstracts **1524**

Abstracts on Field Beans. (CK ISSN 0120-2928) **131**, 2

†Abstracts on Health Effects of Environmental Pollutants. (US ISSN 0044-5819) **5129**

Abstracts on Hygiene see Abstracts on Hygiene and Communicable Diseases **3165**

Abstracts on Hygiene and Communicable Diseases. (UK ISSN 0260-5511) **3165**

Abstracts on Rural Development in the Tropics. (NE ISSN 0169-605X) **701**, 2, **131**

Abstracts on Science and Technology in Japan: Electronics and Communication. (JA ISSN 0910-6510) **1346**, **1764**

Abstracts on Science and Technology in Japan: Energy Technology. (JA ISSN 0912-2311) **1797**

Abstracts on Tropical Agriculture. (NE ISSN 0304-5951) **132**, 2, **2084**

Abstracts Soviet and East European Series see A B S E E S **2327**

Abstracts Strengthening Research Library Resources Program. (US ISSN 0278-2820) **2741**

Abthul Andersen Corporate Register. (UK) **643**, **417**

Abu Dhabi. (TS) **806**

Abu Dhabi. Al-Jaridah al-Rasmiyyah/ Abu Dhabi. Official Gazette. (TS) **4052**

Abu Dhabi. Da'irat al-Takhtit. Al-Kitab al-Ihsa'i al-Sanawi. see Abu Dhabi. Department of Planning. Statistical Yearbook **4078**

Abu Dhabi. Da'irat al-Takhtit. Al-Nashrah al-Sanawiyyah li-As'ar al-Tajzi'ah/Abu Dhabi. Planning Administration. Annual Bulletin of Retail Prices. (TS) **702**

Abu Dhabi. Da'irat al-Takhtit. Al-Nashrah al-Shahriyyah li-As'ar al-Tajzi'ah/Abu Dhabi. Planning Administration. Monthly Bulletin of Retail Prices. (TS) **702**

Abu Dhabi. Department of Planning. Statistical Abstract and Yearbook see Abu Dhabi. Department of Planning. Statistical Yearbook **4078**

Abu Dhabi. Department of Planning. Statistical Yearbook/Abu Dhabi. Da'irat al-Takhtit. Al-Kitab al-Ihsa'i al-Sanawi. (TS) **4078**

Abu Dhabi. Foreign Trade Statistics/Abu Dhabi. Ihsa'iyyat al-Tijarah al-Kharijiyyah. (TS) **702**

Abu Dhabi. Ihsa'iyyat al-Tijarah al-Kharijiyyah. see Abu Dhabi. Foreign Trade Statistics **702**

Abu Dhabi. Official Gazette. see Abu Dhabi. Al-Jaridah al-Rasmiyyah **4052**

Abu Dhabi. Planning Administration. Annual Bulletin of Retail Prices. see Abu Dhabi. Da'irat al-Takhtit. Al-Nashrah al-Sanawiyyah li-As'ar al-Tajzi'ah **702**

Abu Dhabi. Planning Administration. Monthly Bulletin of Retail Prices. see Abu Dhabi. Da'irat al-Takhtit. Al-Nashrah al-Shahriyyah li-As'ar al-Tajzi'ah **702**

Abu Dhabi Chamber of Commerce and Industry. Annual Report/Ghurfat Tijarah wa-Sina'ah Abu Dhabi. Al-Taqrir al-Sanawi. (TS) **806**

Abu Dhabi Chamber of Commerce and Industry. Review see Abu Dhabi **806**

Abu Dhabi Fund for Arab Economic Development. Annual Report. see Sanduq Abu Dhabi lil-Inma' al-Iqtisadi al-Arabi. Al-Taqrir al-Sanawi **935**

Abu Dhabi National Oil Company News see A D N O C News **3680**

Abu Dhabi News. (TS) **4750**

Abu Dhabi Tourist Club. see Nadi Abu Dhabi al-Siyahi **1300**

Abundant Life Magazine. (US ISSN 0731-7948) **4227**

Abwassertechnik see A W T **1941**

Abyssinian. (AT) **3707**

Acacia Clarion. (US ISSN 0001-3730) **2525**

Ha-Acadamai. (IS) **1302**

Academe. (US ISSN 0190-2946) **1699**

Academia. (CL ISSN 0716-0526) **1613**

Academia. (AU) **2857**, **4161**, **4427**

Academia Alfonso X el Sabio. Cuadernos Bibliograficos. (SP) **388**

Academia Amazonense de Letras. Revista. (BL) **2891**

Academia Argentina de Letras. Boletin. (AG ISSN 0001-3757) **2800**, **2891**

Academia Boliviana de Ciencias Economicas. Revista. (BO) **842**

Academia Boliviana de la Lengua. Anales. (BO) **2800**

Academia Brasileira de Ciencias. Anais. (BL ISSN 0001-3765) **4295**

Academia Brasileira de Literatura. Revista. (BL) **2891**

Academia Campinense de Letras. Publicacoes. (BL ISSN 0065-0447) **2891**

Academia Chilena de Medicina. Boletin Anual. (CL) **3069**

Academia Colombiana. Boletin. (CK ISSN 0001-3773) **2800**, **2891**

Academia das Ciencias de Lisboa. Boletim. (PO ISSN 0001-3781) **4295**

Academia de Ciencias de Cuba. Instituto de Documentacion e Informacion Cientifica y Tecnica. Actualidades de la Informacion Cientifica y Tecnica. (CU ISSN 0138-7324) **2741**

Academia de Ciencias de Cuba. Instituto de Ecologia y Sistematica. Miscelanea Zoologica. (CU) **575**

Academia de Ciencias de Cuba. Instituto de Geologia. Resumenes, Comunicaciones y Notas del Consejo Cientifico. (CU) **1553**

Academia de Ciencias de Cuba. Instituto de Geologia. Resumenes del Consejo Cientifico see Academia de Ciencias de Cuba. Instituto de Geologia. Resumenes, Comunicaciones y Notas del Consejo Cientifico **1553**

Academia de Ciencias de Cuba. Instituto de Geologia. Serie Geologica. (CU) **1553**

Academia de Ciencias de Cuba. Instituto de Oceanologia. Informes Cientificos Tecnicos see Academia de Ciencias de Cuba. Instituto de Oceanologia. Reporte de Investigacion **1601**

Academia de Ciencias de Cuba. Instituto de Oceanologia. Reporte de Investigacion. (CU ISSN 0138-6328) **1601**

Academia de Ciencias de Cuba. Instituto de Oceanologia. Tablas de Mareas. (CU) **1601**

†Academia de Ciencias de Cuba. Instituto de Zoologia. Informe Cientifico-Tecnico. (CU) **5129**

Academia de Ciencias de Cuba. Instituto de Zoologia. Miscelanea Zoologica see Academia de Ciencias de Cuba. Instituto de Ecologia y Sistematica. Miscelanea Zoologica **575**

Academia de Ciencias de la Republica Dominicana. Anuario. (DR) **4295**

Academia de Ciencias Exactas, Fisico-Quimicas y Naturales. Revista. (SP) **4295**

Academia de Ciencias Fisicas Matematicas y Naturales. Boletin. (VE) **4295**, **3026**

Academia de Ciencias Politicas y Sociales. Boletin. (VE) **3869**, **4364**

Academia de Geografia e Historia de Guatemala. Anales. (GT ISSN 0252-337X) **2240**, **2397**

Academia de Stiinte Agricole si Silvice. Bulletin. (RM) **67**, **2095**

Academia Dominicana de la Historia. Publicaciones. (DR ISSN 0567-5871) **2397**

Academia Economic Papers. (CH ISSN 1018-161X) **643**

Academia Espanola, Madrid. Anejos del Boletin. (SP ISSN 0065-0455) **2891**

Academia Guatemalteca de Estudios Genealogicos, Heraldicos e Historicos. Revista. (GT ISSN 0065-0463) **2143**

Academia Hondurena de la Lengua. Boletin. (HO ISSN 0065-0471) **2800**

Academia Mexicana de la Historia. Memorias. (MX) **2397**

Academia Militar de Chorrillos. Revista. (PE ISSN 0001-3811) **3449**

Academia Nacional de Bellas Artes. Anuario. (AG) **310**

Academia Nacional de Ciencias Morales y Politicas. Anales. (AG) **3869**

Academia Nacional de la Historia. Boletin. (AG ISSN 0001-382X) **2305**

Academia Nacional de la Historia. Investigaciones y Ensayos. (AG ISSN 0539-242X) **2397**

Academia Nacional de Medicina. Boletim. (BL ISSN 0001-3838) **3069**

Academia Nacional de Medicina Revista see Academia Nacional de Medicina. Boletim **3069**

Academia Norteamericana de la Lengua Espanola. Boletin. (US) **2891**

Academia Paulista de Letras. Revista. (BL ISSN 0001-3846) **2891**, **2800**

Academia Pernambucana de Letras. Revista. (BL) **2891**

Academia Peruana de Cirugia Revista. (PE ISSN 0001-3854) **3373**

†Academia Portena del Lunfardo. Boletin. (AG ISSN 0001-3862) **5129**

Academia Portuguesa da Historia. Anais. (PO) **2346**

Academia Provincial de la Historia. Boletin. (AG ISSN 0567-6029) **2397**

Academia Scientiarum Fennica. Proceedings - Sitzungsberichte see Academia Scientiarum Fennica. Yearbook **4295**

Academia Scientiarum Fennica. Yearbook/Suomalainen Tiedeakatemia. Vuosikirja. (FI ISSN 0356-6927) **4295**

Academia Scientiarum Hungarica. Acta Agronomica see Acta Agronomica Hungarica **68**

Academia Scientiarum Hungarica. Acta Antiqua. (HU ISSN 0044-5975) **1274**, **2800**

Academia Scientiarum Hungarica. Acta Archaeologica. (HU ISSN 0001-5210) **260**

Academia Scientiarum Hungarica. Acta Biochimica et Biophysica see Acta Biochimica et Biophysica Hungarica **470**

Academia Scientiarum Hungarica. Acta Botanica see Acta Botanica Hungarica **492**

Academia Scientiarum Hungarica. Acta Chirurgica see Acta Chirurgica Hungarica **3374**

Academia Scientiarum Hungarica. Acta Ethnographica. (HU ISSN 0001-5628) **232**, **2052**

Academia Scientiarum Hungarica. Acta Geodaetica, Geophysica et Montanistica see Acta Geodaetica, Geophysica et Montanistica Hungarica **1586**

Academia Scientiarum Hungarica. Acta Historiae Artium. (HU ISSN 0001-5830) **310**
Academia Scientiarum Hungarica. Acta Historica. (HU ISSN 0001-5849) **2305**
Academia Scientiarum Hungarica. Acta Juridica. (HU ISSN 0001-592X) **2593**
Academia Scientiarum Hungarica. Acta Linguistica. (HU ISSN 0001-5946) **2800**
Academia Scientiarum Hungarica. Acta Litteraria. (HU ISSN 0567-7661) **2891**
Academia Scientiarum Hungarica. Acta Mathematica see Acta Mathematica Hungarica **3026**
Academia Scientiarum Hungarica. Acta Medica see Acta Medica Hungarica **3070**
Academia Scientiarum Hungarica. Acta Morphologica see Acta Morphologica Hungarica **3070**
Academia Scientiarum Hungarica. Acta Oeconomica. (HU ISSN 0001-6373) **643**
Academia Scientiarum Hungarica. Acta Orientalia. (HU ISSN 0001-6446) **3632**
Academia Scientiarum Hungarica. Acta Paediatrica see Acta Paediatrica Hungarica **3317**
Academia Scientiarum Hungarica. Acta Physica see Acta Physica Hungarica **3812**
Academia Scientiarum Hungarica. Acta Physiologica see Acta Physiologica Hungarica **568**
Academia Scientiarum Hungarica. Acta Phytopathologica see Academia Scientiarum Hungarica. Acta Phytopathologica et Entomologica Hungarica **491**
Academia Scientiarum Hungarica. Acta Phytopathologica et Entomologica Hungarica. (HU ISSN 0238-1249) **491**
Academia Scientiarum Hungarica. Acta Technica. (HU ISSN 0001-7035) **4592**
Academia Scientiarum Hungarica. Acta Veterinaria see Acta Veterinaria Hungarica **4804**
Academia Scientiarum Hungarica. Acta Zoologica see Acta Zoologica Hungarica **576**
Academia Sinica. Botanical Bulletin. (CH ISSN 0006-8063) **491**
Academia Sinica. Institute of Atmospheric Physics. Annual Report see Zhongguo Kexueyuan Daqi Wulisuo Nianbao **5309**
Academia Sinica. Institute of Chemistry. Bulletin. (CH ISSN 0001-3927) **1168**
Academia Sinica. Institute of Ethnology. Bulletin. (CH ISSN 0001-3935) **232**, 3632
Academia Sinica. Institute of History and Philology. Bulletin. (CH ISSN 1012-4195) **2336**, 260, 2800
Academia Sinica. Institute of Mathematics. Bulletin/Chung Yang Yen Chiu Yuan Shu Hsueh Yen Chiu So T'ung Pao. (CH) **3026**
Academia Sinica. Institute of Modern History. Bulletin/Chung Yang Yen Chiu Yuan. Chin Tai Shih Yen Chiu So Ch'i K'an. (CH) **2305**
Academia Sinica. Institute of Physics. Annual Report/Chung Yang Yen Chiu Yuan Wu Li Hsueh Yen Chiu So Nien Pao. (CH ISSN 0304-5293) **3812**
Academia Sinica. Institute of Zoology. Bulletin. (CH ISSN 0001-3943) **575**
Academia Venezolana de la Lengua. Correspondiente de la Espanola. Boletin. (VE) **2800**, 1743
Academiae Analecta. Mededelingen van de Koninklijke Academie voor Wetenschappen, Letteren en Schone Kunsten van Belgie. Series 1: Klasse der Wetenschappen. (BE) **4295**

Academiae Analecta. Mededelingen van de Koninklijke Academie voor Wetenschappen, Letteren en Schone Kunsten van Belgie. Series 2. Klasse der Letteren. (BE) **2502**
Academiae Analecta. Mededelingen van de Koninklijke Academie voor Wetenschappen, Letteren en Schone Kunsten van Belgie. Series 3: Klasse der Schone Kunsten. (BE) **310**
Academiae Medicae Gedanensis. Annales. (PL ISSN 0303-4135) **3069**
▼Academic Abstracts C D - R O M. (US ISSN 1056-7496) **2**
Academic and Administrative Officers at Canadian Universities (Year) see Universities Telephone Directory (Year) **1719**
Academic and Library Computing. (US ISSN 1055-4769) **2796**, 1457, 1466
Academic Collective Bargaining Information Service. Fact Sheet. Newsletter. (US) **1699**, 1724
Academic Collective Bargaining Information Service. Research Summary. (US) **1724**
Academic Collective Bargaining Information Service. Special Reports. (US) **1724**
†Academic Computing. (US ISSN 0892-4694) **5129**
Academic Degrees and Graduate Education. see Xuewei yu Yanjiusheng Jiaoyu **1720**
Academic Digest. (US) **1168**, 1699
Academic Index. (US) **2519**, 2, 1674
Academic Library Book Review. (US) **2741**, 4120
Academic Life. see Akademiska Dzive **1990**
Academic Medicine. (US ISSN 1040-2446) **3069**, 1699
Academic Monthly. see Xueshu Yuekan **3704**
Academic Press Geology Series. (US) **1553**
Academic Press Series in Cognition and Perception. (US) **4008**
Academic Psychiatry. (US ISSN 1042-9670) **3327**, 1699
Academic Psychology Bulletin. (US ISSN 0193-1709) **4008**, 1743
Academic Questions. (US ISSN 0895-4852) **1613**
Academic Research. see Xueshu Yanjiu **4392**
Academic Therapy see Intervention in School and Clinic **1737**
Academic Year Abroad. (US) **1721**
Academica Helvetica. (SZ) **1699**
The Academician. (US) **1613**
Academie Bulgare des Sciences. Comptes Rendus. (BU ISSN 0366-8681) **4296**
Academie d'Agriculture de France. Comptes Rendus. (FR ISSN 0989-6988) **67**
Academie d'Agriculture de France. Comptes Rendus des Seances see Academie d'Agriculture de France. Comptes Rendus **67**
Academie d'Architecture. (FR ISSN 0001-3994) **291**
Academie d'Architecture, Paris. Annuaire. (FR ISSN 0084-5876) **291**
Academie d'Histoire, Paris. Cahiers. (FR) **2346**
Academie de Droit International de la Haye. Recueil des Cours/Hague Academy of International Law. Collected Courses. (NE ISSN 0001-401X) **2719**
Academie de France a Rome. Correspondance des Directeurs. Nouvelle Serie. (IT) **2346**
Academie de Medicine. Memoirs see Academie Nationale de Medecine. Bulletin **3069**
Academie de Stiinte a R.S.S. Moldova. Buletinul. Economie se Sociologie/ Akademiya Nauk Moldavskoi S.S.R. Izvestiya. Ekonomika i Sotsiologiya. (MV ISSN 0236-3070) **842**, 4427

Academie de Stiinte a R.S.S. Moldova. Filosofie si Drept/Akademiya Nauk S.S.R. Moldova. Filosofiya i Pravo. (MV ISSN 0236-3062) **3759**, 2593
Academie des Inscriptions et Belles-Lettres. Etudes et Commentaires. (FR ISSN 0065-0544) **2800**, 260, 2305
Academie des Sciences. Annuaire. (FR ISSN 0065-0552) **4296**
Academie des Sciences. Comptes Rendus des Seances. Series 2: Mecanique, Physique, Chimie, Sciences de la Terre, Sciences de l'Univers. (FR ISSN 0764-4450) **4296**
Academie des Sciences. Comptes Rendus des Seances. Series 3: Sciences de la Vie. (FR ISSN 0764-4469) **425**, 4296
Academie des Sciences. Comptes Rendus. Serie 1: Mathematiques. (FR ISSN 0764-4442) **3026**
Academie des Sciences. Index Biographique des Membres et Correspondants. (FR ISSN 0065-0560) **4296**
Academie des Sciences d'Outre-Mer, Paris. Comptes Rendus des Seances see Mondes et Cultures **4324**
Academie des Sports, Paris. Annuaire. (FR ISSN 0065-0579) **4463**
Academie et Societe Lorraines de Sciences. Bulletin. (FR ISSN 0567-6576) **4296**
Academie Francaise. Annuaire. (FR ISSN 0065-0587) **2891**
Academie Internationale d'Histoire des Sciences. Collection des Travaux. (GW ISSN 0366-8258) **4296**, 2305
Academie Internationale d'Histoire des Sciences. Collection des Travaux. (NE ISSN 0169-7897) **4296**
Academie Internationale du Tourisme. Revue. (MC ISSN 0001-4060) **4750**
Academie Nationale de Medecine. Bulletin. (FR ISSN 0001-4079) **3069**
Academie Polonaise des Sciences. Bulletin. Serie des Sciences Biologiques see Polish Academy of Sciences. Bulletin. Biological Sciences **451**
Academie Polonaise des Sciences. Bulletin. Serie des Sciences Chimiques see Polish Academy of Sciences. Bulletin. Chemical Sciences **1185**
Academie Polonaise des Sciences. Bulletin. Serie des Sciences de la Terre see Polish Academy of Sciences. Bulletin. Earth Sciences **1577**
Academie Polonaise des Sciences. Bulletin. Serie des Sciences Mathematiques, Astronomiques et Physiques see Polish Academy of Sciences. Bulletin. Mathematical Sciences **3050**
Academie Polonaise des Sciences. Bulletin. Serie des Sciences Techniques see Polish Academy of Sciences. Bulletin. Technical Sciences **4606**
Academie Polonaise des Sciences. Centre d'Archeologie Mediterraneenne. Etudes et Travaux. (PL ISSN 0079-3566) **260**
†Academie Polonaise des Sciences. Centre Scientifique, Paris. Conferences. (PL ISSN 0079-3159) **5129**
Academie Royale d'Agriculture et de Sylviculture de Suede. Annales. see Kungliga Skogs- och Lantbruksakademiens Tidskrift **103**
Academie Royale de Langue et de Litterature Francaises. Annuaires. (BE ISSN 0567-6584) **2800**, 2857
Academie Royale de Langue et de Litterature Francaises. Bulletin. (BE) **2800**, 2891

ACADEMY 5869

Academie Royale de Marine de Belgique. Communications/ Koninklijke Belgische Marine Academie. Mededelingen. (BE) **4723**, 2346
Academie Royale de Medecine de Belgique. Bulletin et Memoires. (BE ISSN 0377-8231) **3069**
Academie Royale des Sciences Coloniales. Bulletin des Seances see Academie Royale des Sciences d'Outre-Mer. Bulletin des Seances **4296**
Academie Royale des Sciences d'Outre-Mer. Bulletin des Seances/Koninklijke Academie voor Overzeese Wetenschappen. Mededelingen der Zittingen. (BE ISSN 0001-4176) **4296**, 2346
Academie Royale des Sciences, des Lettres et des Beaux-Arts de Belgique. Annuaire. (BE) **2502**, 4296
Academie Royale des Sciences, des Lettres et des Beaux-Arts de Belgique. Classe des Beaux-Arts. Bulletin. (BE ISSN 0378-0716) **2502**
Academie Royale des Sciences, des Lettres et des Beaux-Arts de Belgique. Classe des Beaux-Arts. Memoires. (BE) **310**
Academie Royale des Sciences, des Lettres et des Beaux-Arts de Belgique. Classe des Lettres et des Sciences Morales et Politiques. Memoires. (BE) **2502**
Academie Royale des Sciences des Lettres et des Beaux-Arts de Belgique. Classe des Sciences. Bulletin. (BE ISSN 0001-4141) **4296**
Academie Royale des Sciences, des Lettres et des Beaux-Arts de Belgique. Classe des Sciences. Memoires. (BE) **4296**
Academie Royale des Sciences, des Lettres et des Beaux Arts de Belgique. Index Biographique des Membres, Correspondants et Associes. (BE ISSN 0065-0609) **417**
Academie Serbe des Sciences et des Arts. Classe des Sciences Mathematiques et Naturelles. Bulletin. Nouvelle Serie see Academie Serbe des Sciences et des Arts. Classe des Sciences Mathematiques et Naturelles. Bulletin. Sciences Mathematiques **3026**
Academie Serbe des Sciences et des Arts. Classe des Sciences Mathematiques et Naturelles. Bulletin. Sciences Mathematiques. (YU) **3026**, 360, 4296
Academie Serbe des Sciences et des Arts. Classe des Sciences Mathematiques et Naturelles. Bulletin. Sciences Naturelles. (YU ISSN 0352-5740) **4296**, 425, 1168
Academie Veterinaire de France. Bulletin. (FR ISSN 0001-4192) **4804**
Academus Poetry Magazine. (UK ISSN 0143-7488) **2987**
†Academy. (US ISSN 0362-708X) **5129**
Academy Awards for Distinguished Achievements. (US) **3503**
†Academy Bookman. (US ISSN 0001-4249) **5129**
Academy Computing Times. (US) **1388**
Academy Law Review. (II) **2593**
Academy of American Franciscan History. Bibliographical Series. (US ISSN 0567-6630) **4254**
Academy of American Franciscan History. Documentary Series. (US ISSN 0065-0633) **4254**
Academy of American Franciscan History. Monograph Series. (US ISSN 0065-0641) **4254**
Academy of American Franciscan History. Propaganda Fide Series. (US ISSN 0065-065X) **4254**

ACADEMY

Academy of American Poets. Lamont Poetry Selection and Walt Whitman Selection. (US) **2987**
Academy of American Poets. Lamont Poetry Selections *see* Academy of American Poets. Lamont Poetry Selection and Walt Whitman Selection **2987**
Academy of Criminal Justice Sciences Today *see* A C J S Today **1509**
Academy of General Dentistry Impact *see* A G D Impact **3227**
Academy of Management. Journal. (US ISSN 0001-4273) **1001**
Academy of Management. Proceedings.(US ISSN 0065-0668) **1001**
Academy of Management Executive. (US) **1001**
Academy of Management Newsletter. (US ISSN 0161-5998) **1001, 1062**
Academy of Management Review. (US ISSN 0363-7425) **1001**
Academy of Marketing Science. Journal.(US ISSN 0092-0703) **1032**
Academy of Medical Sciences of the U.S.S.R. All-Union Cardiology Research Center. Bulletin. *see* Akademiya Meditsinskikh Nauk S.S.S.R. Vsesoyuznyi Kardiologicheskii Nauchnyi Tsentr. Byulleten **3203**
Academy of Medical Sciences of the U.S.S.R. Annals. *see* Akademiya Meditsinskikh Nauk S.S.S.R. Vestnik **3073**
Academy of Medicine, Singapore. Annals. (SI ISSN 0304-4602) **3069**
Academy of Medicine, Toronto. Bulletin. (CN ISSN 0001-4311) **3069**
Academy of Natural Sciences of Philadelphia. Monographs. (US ISSN 0096-7750) **4296**
Academy of Natural Sciences of Philadelphia. Proceedings. (US ISSN 0097-3157) **4296**
Academy of Natural Sciences of Philadelphia. Special Publications. (US ISSN 0097-3254) **4296**
Academy of Nursing of the Philippines Papers *see* A N P H I Papers **3275**
Academy of Parish Clergy. News and Views *see* Sharing the Practice **4201**
Academy of Pharmacy Practice & Management Update *see* A P P M Update **3715**
Academy of Political Science. Proceedings. (US ISSN 0065-0684) **3869**
Academy of Rehabilitation Audiology. Journal. (US ISSN 0149-8886) **3312, 2285**
Academy of Religion and Psychical Research. Proceedings. (US) **3668, 4161**
Academy of Science of the U S S R. Lebedev Physics Institute. Proceedings. (US) **3851, 1803, 3812, 3842**
Academy of Sciences News. *see* Shinjleh Uhaany Akademiyn Medee **4342**
Academy of Sciences of the U S S R. Biology Bulletin. (English translation of: Akademiya Nauk S.S.S.R. Izvestiya. Seriya Biologicheskaya) (US ISSN 0098-2164) **425**
Academy of Sciences of the U S S R. Bulletin. Physical Series. (English translation of: Akademiya Nauk S.S.S.R. Izvestiya. Seriya Fizicheskaya) (US ISSN 0001-432X) **3812**
Academy of Sciences of the U S S R. Crimean Astrophysical Observatory. Bulletin. (US ISSN 0190-2717) **360**
Academy of Sciences of the U S S R. Division of Chemical Sciences. Bulletin. (English translation of: Akademiya Nauk S.S.S.R. Izvestiya. Seriya Khimicheskaya) (US ISSN 0568-5230) **1168**
†Academy of Sciences of the U S S R. High Temperature Institute. I V T A N Reviews. (US ISSN 0888-6881) **5129**
Academy of Sciences of the U S S R. Institute of General Physics. Proceedings. (English translation of: Akademiya Nauk S.S.S.R. Institut Obshchei Fiziki. Trudy) (US) **3812, 1601**
Academy of Sciences of the U S S R. Izvestiya. Atmospheric and Oceanic Physics. (English translation of: Akademiya Nauk S.S.S.R. Izvestiya. Seriya Fizika Atmosfery i Okeana) (US ISSN 0001-4338) **3431, 1601**
Academy of Sciences of the U S S R. Izvestiya. Physics of the Solid Earth. (English translation of: Akademiya Nauk S.S.S.R. Izvestiya. Seriya Fizika Zemli) (US ISSN 0001-4354) **1586**
Academy of Sciences of the U S S R. Mathematical Notes. (English translation of: Matematicheskie Zametki) (US ISSN 0001-4346) **3026**
Academy of Sciences of the U S S R. Oceanology. (English translation of: Okeanologiya) (US ISSN 0001-4370) **1601**
Academy of Sciences of the U S S R. Special Astrophysical Observatory-North Caucasus. Bulletin. (US ISSN 0190-2709) **360**
Academy of the Hebrew Language. Linguistic Studies *see* Academy of the Hebrew Language. Texts & Studies **2800**
Academy of the Hebrew Language. Specialized Dictionaries. (IS ISSN 0065-0692) **2800**
Academy of the Hebrew Language. Texts & Studies. (IS) **2800**
Academy of the Social Sciences in Australia. Annual Report. (AT) **4364**
Academy of Toledo and Lucas County. Bulletin *see* Toledo Medicine **3157**
Academy Players Directory. (US) **3503, 1368, 4629**
Academy Quarterly *see* Journal of Rural Development and Administration (PARD) **4065**
Acadia Bulletin. (CN ISSN 0044-5843) **1302**
Acadiana Profile. (US ISSN 0001-4397) **2220**
Acadiensis: Journal of the History of the Atlantic Region. (CN ISSN 0044-5851) **2397**
Acapulco (Year). (US) **4750**
Acarologia. (FR ISSN 0044-586X) **575**
Acarologie. (GW ISSN 0567-672X) **575**
Accademia dei Concordi Rovigo. Collana di Musiche. (IT) **3536**
Accademia dei Fisiocritici, Siena. Sezione Medico-Fisica *see* Accademia delle Scienze di Siena Detta de Fisiocritici. Atti **3069**
Accademia della Scienze Mediche. Atti. (IT) **3069**
Accademia delle Scienze di Siena Detta de Fisiocritici. Atti. (IT ISSN 0390-7783) **3069, 67**
Accademia delle Scienze di Torino. Atti. Part 1. Classe di Scienze Fisiche, Matematiche e Naturali. (IT ISSN 0001-4419) **4296, 3026**
Accademia delle Scienze di Torino. Atti. Part 2. Classe di Scienze Morali, Storiche e Filologiche. (IT) **2502**
Accademia delle Scienze di Torino. Memorie. Part 1. Classe di Scienze Fisiche, Matematiche e Naturali. (IT ISSN 0373-3033) **4296, 3026**
Accademia delle Scienze di Torino. Memorie. Part 2. Classe di Scienze Morali, Storiche e Filologiche. (IT) **2502**
Accademia Etrusca di Cortona. Annuario. (IT ISSN 0065-0730) **2346**
Accademia Italiana di Scienze Forestali. Annali. (IT ISSN 0515-2178) **2095**

Accademia Ligure di Scienze e Lettere. Atti. (IT ISSN 0392-2219) **4296, 2502**
Accademia Medica Lombarda. Atti. (IT ISSN 0001-4427) **3069**
Accademia Medica Pistoiese "Filippo Pacini". Bollettino. (IT) **3069**
Accademia Nazionale dei Lincei. Classe di Scienze Fisiche Matematiche e Naturali. Rendiconti. (IT ISSN 0392-7881) **3812, 3026, 4296**
Accademia Nazionale dei Lincei. Classe di Scienze Morali, Storiche e Filologique. Rendiconti. (IT ISSN 0391-8181) **2305**
Accademia Nazionale di San Luca. Annuario. (IT) **1699**
Accademia Nazionale Italiana di Entomologia. Rendiconti. (IT ISSN 0065-0757) **527**
Accademia Patavina di Scienze Lettere ed Arti. Collana Accademica. (IT ISSN 0065-0765) **4296**
Accademia Petrarca di Lettere, Arti e Scienza. Atti e Memorie. (US) **2502**
Accademia Polacca delle Scienze. Conferenze. (PL ISSN 0239-8605) **2502**
Accademia Toscana di Scienza e Lettere La Colombaria. Atti e Memorie. (IT) **4296**
Accademia Toscana di Scienza e Lettere La Colombaria. Studi. (IT ISSN 0065-0781) **4296**
Accademie e Biblioteche d'Italia. (IT ISSN 0001-4451) **2741**
Accao Socialista. (PO) **3869**
Accele *see* Cadet **1502**
Accelerated Indexing Systems International Journal of Genealogy *see* A I S I Journal of Genealogy **2143**
†Accelerator (Ottawa). (CN ISSN 0315-3339) **5129**
Accelerator (Saskatoon) *see* Accelerator Newsletter **4296**
Accelerator Newsletter. (US ISSN 0001-4478) **1168, 1847**
Accelerator Newsletter. (CN ISSN 0316-2893) **4296, 1613**
Accelerators and Storage Rings Series. (US ISSN 0272-5088) **3846**
Accent. (SW ISSN 0345-0406) **1532**
Accent. (AT ISSN 1031-4873) **3217**
Accent. (SI ISSN 0217-5851) **4751**
Accent (Birmingham). (US ISSN 0162-1955) **4227**
Accent (New York). (US ISSN 0192-7507) **2562**
Accent (Ogden). (US) **4669**
Accent on A C T F L *see* Foreign Language Annals **2814**
Accent on Living. (US ISSN 0001-4508) **1733, 3798**
Accent on Living Buyer's Guide. (US ISSN 0272-2461) **1733, 3798**
Accent on Worship. (US ISSN 0276-2358) **4161**
†Accent on Youth. (US ISSN 0001-4516) **5129**
Accent Unga Tankar *see* Accent **1532**
Accent West Amarillo. (US) **4751**
Acceptance Newsletter. (AT) **2450, 4161**
†Accepted Dental Therapeutics. (US ISSN 0065-079X) **5129**
Access (Chicago). (US) **3227**
Access (Don Mills). (CN) **1057, 825**
Access (Elizabeth). (AT ISSN 1030-0155) **2741**
Access (Glenside). (AT ISSN 1032-8599) **3477, 1681, 3681**
Access (Greenwood). (US) **758**
Access (Halifax) *see* Atlantic Silent News **2286**
Access (Melbourne). (AT) **310**
†Access (New York). (US) **5129**
Access (New York, 1979). (US) **1613**
Access (New York, 1983). (US) **1457**
Access (Research Triangle Park). (US ISSN 0733-8074) **4358, 1457, 1467**
Access (Rockville). (US) **1457**
Access (Seattle). (US ISSN 1056-4101) **310, 1120**
Access (Toorak). (AT ISSN 0817-1351) **3069**
Access (Toronto). (CN) **3069**

†Access (Washington, 1975). (US ISSN 0149-9262) **5129**
Access (Year) *see* Access to Wang **1445**
Access: Apple. (US ISSN 0743-5878) **1467, 1457**
Access Control. (US ISSN 0894-6639) **599**
Access Control Buyers' Guide. (US ISSN 0885-8411) **1120, 599**
Access Control - Fence Industry *see* Access Control **599**
Access Faxon *see* Faxon Guide to C D - R O M **2797**
Access: I B M. (US ISSN 0743-5886) **1467, 1458**
Access Magazine *see* Midland Cardowner **5237**
Access: The Supplementary Index to Periodicals. (US ISSN 0095-5698) **2**
Access to Canadian Income Tax. (CN) **1087**
Access to Energy. (US ISSN 0890-8265) **1783, 1941**
Access to Wang. (US) **1445, 1388, 1426, 1458**
Accessible *see* National Library News **2775**
Accessions List. South Asia *see* U.S. Library of Congress. Accessions List: South Asia **414**
Accessions List: Middle East *see* U.S. Library of Congress. Accessions List: Middle East **414**
Accessions List: Southeast Asia *see* U.S. Library of Congress. Accessions List: Southeast Asia **415**
Accessionskatalog over Utlaendsk Litteratur i Svenska Forskningsbibliotek/Union Catalogue of Foreign Literature in Swedish Research Libraries. (SW ISSN 0348-2480) **388**
Accessoirex. (FR) **3715**
Accessori Collezioni. (IT) **1289**
Accessories. (US) **1282, 1289**
Accessories. (GW ISSN 0343-4060) **1282**
Accessories Components & Equipment *see* A C E **5127**
Accessories Resources Directory. (US) **1282**
Accessories - Today. (US) **2548, 2280**
Accessory Merchandising. (US) **2548**
Acciaio. (IT ISSN 0001-4559) **599**
L'Acciaio Inossidabile. (IT ISSN 0001-4567) **3401**
Accident Analysis & Prevention. (US ISSN 0001-4575) **4097**
Accident Compensation Victoria. (AT) **2593**
Accident Facts. (US ISSN 0148-6039) **4097**
Accident - Incident Bulletin *see* U.S. Federal Railroad Administration. Office of Safety. Accident - Incident Bulletin **4716**
Accident Prevention. (US ISSN 0898-5774) **42**
Accident Prevention. (CN ISSN 0044-5878) **3614**
Accident Prevention Bulletin *see* Accident Prevention **42**
Accident Prevention Journal. *see* Yobo Jiho **2035**
Accident Reconstruction Journal. (US ISSN 1057-8153) **2593, 3264**
Accidents Claims Journal. (Il ISSN 0001-4583) **2594, 2525**
Accidents de la Circulation Routiere. *see* Canada. Statistics Canada. Motor Vehicle Traffic Accidents **5160**
Accidents in American Mountaineering *see* Accidents in North American Mountaineering **4539**
Accidents in North American Mountaineering. (US ISSN 0065-082X) **4539**
Accidents to Aircraft on the British Register. (UK ISSN 0306-3550) **4669**
Accion. (AG) **2857**
Accion. (PY ISSN 0001-4605) **4364, 4161**
Accion Critica. (PE) **4397**
Accion Empresarial. (SP ISSN 0044-5894) **1001**

Accion Indigenista see Mexico Indigena 2492
Accion Sindicalista. (SP) 2579
Accion y Critica. (CK) 2594
▼Accommodating Disabilities. (US) 2283
Accommodation Australia. (AT) 4751
Accommodation Directory. (AT) 4751
Accommodator. (CN) 2471, 4751
Accommodeur see Detaillant en Alimentation 5179
†Accomplishments in Oncology. (US ISSN 0887-056X) 5129
Accordion Teachers' Guild, Inc. Bulletin see A T G Bulletin 3536
Accordion Teachers' Guild Newsletter see A T G Bulletin 3536
Accountability in Research. (US ISSN 0898-9621) 4296
Accountancy. (UK ISSN 0001-4664) 745
Accountancy Age. (UK ISSN 0001-4672) 745
Accountancy, Business & Insurance Review. (UA ISSN 0001-4680) 745, 2525
Accountancy Ireland. (IE ISSN 0001-4699) 745
Accountancy Law Reports. (US) 745, 2594
Accountancy S A. (SA ISSN 0258-7254) 745
Accountancy Thema's. (BE) 1087
Accountant. (NE ISSN 0001-4729) 745
Accountant. (IE ISSN 0001-4710) 745
Accountant. (KE) 745
Accountants and Secretaries Educational Journal. (AT ISSN 0044-5916) 745
Accountants for the Public Interest Account see A P I Account 744
Accountants' Index. (US ISSN 0748-7975) 702, 2
Accountants' Journal. (NZ ISSN 0001-4745) 745
Accountants' Journal. (PH ISSN 0001-4753) 745
Accountants Magazine. (UK ISSN 0001-4761) 745
†Accountants Microcomputer News. (US) 5129
Accountants Record see Company Accountant 749
Accountants S E C Practice Manual. (US) 745, 937
Accounter see Management Accounter 753
Accounting and Auditing Update Service. (US) 745
Accounting and Business Research. (UK ISSN 0001-4788) 745
Accounting and Data Processing Abstracts see Accounting & Finance Abstracts 1403
Accounting and Finance. (AT ISSN 0810-5391) 745, 1699
Accounting & Finance Abstracts. (UK) 1403, 2, 702
†Accounting and Finance Tech Digest. (US) 5129
Accounting Articles. (US ISSN 0007-7992) 702, 2
Accounting, Auditing and Accountability.(UK ISSN 0951-3574) 745
▼Accounting, Business and Financial History. (UK ISSN 0958-5206) 643
Accounting Department Management & Administration Report. (US ISSN 1042-928X) 745
▼Accounting Education. (UK ISSN 0963-9284) 745, 1699
Accounting - Financial Report see Compensation in the Accounting - Financial Field 975
Accounting for Banks. (US) 745, 758, 2594
Accounting for Government Contracts: Cost Accounting Standards. (US) 745, 4052
Accounting for Government Contracts: Federal Acquisition Regulation. (US) 745, 4052
Accounting for Law Firms. (US) 746, 2594

Accounting for Public Utilities. (US) 746, 4052
Accounting Forum. (AT ISSN 0155-9982) 746, 1113
Accounting Guidance Release. (AT ISSN 1031-3109) 746
Accounting Historians Journal. (US ISSN 0148-4184) 746
Accounting Historians Notebook. (US) 746
Accounting Horizons. (US ISSN 0888-7993) 746
†Accounting Insight. (US) 5129
Accounting Journal. (MY ISSN 0126-625X) 746
▼Accounting, Management and Information Technologies. (US ISSN 0959-8022) 746, 825
†Accounting News (New York, 1981). (US) 5129
Accounting Office Management & Administration Report. (US ISSN 0749-2928) 746, 1001
Accounting, Organizations and Society. (US ISSN 0361-3682) 746
Accounting Review. (US ISSN 0001-4826) 746
Accounting Systems for Law Offices. (US) 746, 2594
Accounting Technician. (UK) 746, 1087
Accounting Theory Monograph. (AT ISSN 0818-9412) 746
Accounting Today. (US ISSN 1044-5714) 746
Accounting World. (UK ISSN 0953-2579) 746
Accounts of Chemical Research. (US ISSN 0001-4842) 1168
Accreditation. (US ISSN 0099-0256) 1699
Accreditation Council for Accountancy. Action Letter see Accreditation Council for Accountancy and Taxation. Action Letter 746
Accreditation Council for Accountancy and Taxation. Action Letter. (US) 746
Accreditation Fact Sheet. (US) 1692
Accredited Colleges of Pharmacy see Accredited Professional Programs of Colleges and Schools of Pharmacy 3715
Accredited Institutions of Postsecondary Education. (US ISSN 0270-1715) 1692
Accredited Professional Programs of Colleges and Schools of Pharmacy. (US) 3715
Accredited Programs in Architecture. (US) 291
Accueillir. (FR ISSN 0223-5420) 4397
Accuracy in Media, Inc. Report see A I M Report 2566
Ace. (UK) 1448
L'Acerba. (IT) 2891, 2987
Acervo. (BL ISSN 0102-700X) 2397
Achaab/People. (MR ISSN 0001-4869) 2857
Achabaka. (LE) 4836, 2444
Achademia Leonardi Vince: Journal of Leonardo Studies and Bibliography of Vinciana. (IT ISSN 0394-8501) 310, 388
Achats et Entretien - Equipement Industriel. (FR ISSN 0396-6666) 1032
Acheteurs. (FR ISSN 0001-4893) 1032
Achievement. (UK ISSN 0001-4907) 899
†Achievers. (CN) 5129
Achieving Health. (CN) 3602
Ha-Achote be-Yisrael/Nurse in Israel. (IS ISSN 0048-1165) 3275
Das Achtzehnte Jahrhundert. (GW ISSN 0722-740X) 2346
Das Achtzehnte Jahrhundert und Oesterreich. (AU) 2346
Acid Magazine see Enviro 1976
Acid News. (SW ISSN 0281-5087) 1941
Acid Precipitation. (US ISSN 0741-5230) 1941
Acid Precipitation Digest. (US ISSN 0740-2252) 1941
Acid Rain Abstracts see Environment Abstracts 1973

Acid Rain Abstracts Annual see Environment Abstracts Annual 1973
Acid Rain Annual Index see Environment Abstracts Annual 1973
†Acid Rain Fiche. (US) 5129
Acid Rain Resources Directory. (US) 1941
Acid Rain Update. (US) 1941, 2594
†Acid Rain Update. (UK ISSN 0267-6222) 5129
†Acidification Research in Sweden. (SW ISSN 0282-1540) 5129
Acier dans le Monde. (FR ISSN 0001-4931) 599, 3401
Acknowledge the Window Letter. (US ISSN 1043-0768) 1458, 1475
Acme. (IT ISSN 0001-494X) 2891, 2305, 3759
Acofar see A C O F A R 3714
Acompanhamento da Situacao Agropecuaria do Parana. (BL ISSN 0100-560X) 67
Aconteceu. (BL) 2741
Acoplasticos. (CK) 3860
Acopsis. (FR) 3069
Acorn see Acorn Storyteller 1248
Acorn Annual Art Auction Price Guide. (US) 310, 937
Acorn Storyteller. (US) 1248, 1613
Acorn User see B B C Acorn User 1467
▼Acoustic Guitar. (US ISSN 1049-9261) 3536
Acoustic Neuroma Association Notes. (US) 3312, 3192, 3373
Acoustical Imaging. (US) 3858, 3788
Acoustical Imaging: Recent Advances in Visualization and Characterization see Acoustical Imaging 3858
Acoustical Society of America. Journal. (US ISSN 0001-4966) 3858
Acoustical Society of India. Journal. (II ISSN 0253-7257) 3812
Acoustics Abstracts. (UK ISSN 0001-4974) 3836, 2
Acoustics Australia. (AT ISSN 0814-6039) 3858
Acoustics Bulletin. (UK ISSN 0308-437X) 3858
Acoustics Letters. (UK ISSN 0140-1599) 3858
Acoustique Canadienne. see Canadian Acoustics 3859
Acqua Aria. (IT ISSN 0391-5557) 1941
Acqua Industriale see Inquinamento 1958
Acquasport. (IT) 4539
▼Acquerello Italiano. (US) 2204
Acquired Immune Deficiency Syndrome see A I D S 3068
Acquisition, Bibliography, Cataloguing News. (AT ISSN 0725-0037) 2792
Acquisition Columbus. (US) 4144
Acquisition - Divestiture Weekly Report. (US ISSN 0279-4160) 937
Acquisition Management Service Advisor see A M S Advisor 2705
Acquisition Mart. (US ISSN 8755-5735) 937
Acquisition Newsletter International see Business & Acquisition Newsletter 769
Acquisition, Northeastern Ohio. (US) 4144
Acquisition of Greater Dayton see Dayton Business Reporter 658
Acquisitions, Dispositions & Distributions; Tax Interpretations see A D & D: Tax Interpretations 5127
Acquisitions Librarian. (US ISSN 0896-3576) 2741
Acquisitions Monthly. (UK) 937
AcreAGE Magazine. (US) 67
Acres U S A. (US) 67
Acrida. (FR ISSN 0300-4686) 527
Acrobatic see World Acrobatics 4496
Acrobatics and Magic. see Zaji yu Moshu 2444
Acronyms. (US ISSN 0163-6774) 1389
Acronyms, Initialisms and Abbreviations Dictionary. (US ISSN 0270-4404) 2800
Acropolis. (CN) 1989
Across Architecture. (UK ISSN 0266-6200) 291
Across Country. (AT) 3536

ACTA ALIMENTARIA 5871

Across from City Hall see Citizens Union Reports 4085
Across Frontiers. (US ISSN 0890-118X) 3949
Across the Board. (US ISSN 0147-1554) 1001
Across the Dial. (US) 1368, 1354
Across the Fence. (US) 3749
Across the Oceans. (MM) 1601
Across the Table. (US ISSN 0362-8493) 970, 4083
Act. (US ISSN 0001-5083) 4161
Acta (Binghamton) see State University of New York at Binghamton. Center for Medieval and Early Renaissance Studies. Acta 2323
Acta Academiae Aboensis, Series B: Mathematica et Physica. (FI ISSN 0001-5105) 3026, 1813, 4297
Acta Academiae Agriculturae ac Technicae Olstenensis. Aedificatio et Mechanica/Agricultural and Technical Academy in Olsztyn. Mechanics and Building Engineering. (PL ISSN 0860-2956) 1926, 599
Acta Academiae Agriculturae ac Technicae Olstenensis. Agricultura - Agriculture. (PL ISSN 0860-2832) 166
Acta Academiae Agriculturae ac Technicae Olstenensis. Geodaesia et Ruris Regulatio - Geodesy and Agricultural Arrangement. (PL ISSN 0860-262X) 68
Acta Academiae Agriculturae ac Technicae Olstenensis. Oeconomica - Economics. (PL ISSN 0860-2948) 145
Acta Academiae Agriculturae ac Technicae Olstenensis. Protectio Aquarum et Piscatoria - Water Conservation and Inland Fisheries. (PL ISSN 0860-2611) 4821, 2035
Acta Academiae Agriculturae ac Technicae Olstenensis. Technologia Alimentorum - Food Technology. (PL ISSN 0860-2859) 2060, 197
Acta Academiae Agriculturae ac Technicae Olstenensis. Veterinaria - Veterinary Medicine. (PL ISSN 0860-2840) 4804
Acta Academiae Agriculturae ac Technicae Olstenensis. Zootechnica - Zootechnics. (PL ISSN 0860-2603) 204, 209
Acta Academiae Medicinae Sinica. see Zhongguo Yixue Kexueyuan Xuebao 3165
Acta Academiae Medicinae Wuhan see Tongji Medical University. Journal 3158
Acta Academiae Regiae Gustavi Adolphi. (SW ISSN 0065-0897) 2052
Acta Ad Archaeologiam et Artium Historiam Pertinentia (Miscellaneous). (IT ISSN 0333-1512) 260
Acta Ad Archaeologiam et Artium Historiam Pertinentia (Monograph). (IT ISSN 0065-0900) 260
Acta Adriatica. (CI ISSN 0001-5113) 1601, 2035
Acta Aeronautica et Astronautica Sinica. see Hangkong Xuebao 54
Acta Agraria et Silvestria. Series Agraria. (PL ISSN 0065-0919) 166
Acta Agraria et Silvestria. Series Silvestris. (PL ISSN 0860-4053) 2095
Acta Agraria et Silvestria. Series Zootechnica. (PL ISSN 0065-0935) 209
Acta Agriculturae Scandinavica. (SW ISSN 0001-5121) 68
Acta Agrobotanica. (PL ISSN 0065-0951) 491, 68
Acta Agronomica. (CK ISSN 0120-2812) 166
Acta Agronomica Hungarica. (HU ISSN 0238-0161) 68
Acta Agronomica Sinica. see Zuowu Xuebao 197
Acta Albertina Ratisbonensia. (GW ISSN 0515-2712) 1540, 425, 1553
Acta Alimentaria Hungarica. (HU ISSN 0139-3006) 2060

ACTA ALIMENTARIA

Acta Alimentaria Polonica. (PL ISSN 0137-1495) **2060**
Acta Amazonica. (BL ISSN 0044-5967) **4297**
Acta Anaesthesiologica Belgica. (BE ISSN 0001-5164) **3189**
Acta Anaesthesiologica Italica. (IT ISSN 0374-4965) **3189**
Acta Anaesthesiologica Scandinavica. (DK ISSN 0001-5172) **3189**
Acta Anaesthesiologica Scandinavica. Supplementum. (DK ISSN 0515-2720) **3189**
Acta Anatomica. (SZ ISSN 0001-5180) **3069**, 522
Acta Anatomica Nipponica/Kaibogaku Zasshi. (JA ISSN 0022-7722) **425**, 232, 522, 3069
Acta Anthropogenetica. (II ISSN 0258-0357) **539**, 232
Acta Anthropologica Sinica. *see* Renleixue Xuebao **247**
Acta Apostolicae Sedis. Commentarium Officiale. (VC ISSN 0001-5199) **4254**
Acta Applicandae Mathematicae. (NE ISSN 0167-8019) **3026**
Acta Arachnologica. (JA ISSN 0001-5202) **575**
Acta Archaelogica Lundensia: Monographs of Lunds Universitets Historiska Museum. Series in 4. (SW ISSN 0065-1001) **260**
Acta Archaelogica Lundensia: Monographs of Lunds Universitets Historiska Museum. Series in 8. (SW ISSN 0065-0994) **260**
Acta Archaeologica. (DK ISSN 0065-101X) **260**
Acta Archaeologica. *see* Arheoloski Vestnik **265**
Acta Archaeologica Carpathica. (PL ISSN 0001-5229) **260**
Acta Archaeologica Lodziensia. (PL ISSN 0065-0986) **260**
Acta Archaeologica Lovaniensia. (BE) **260**
Acta Archaeologica Sinica. *see* Kaogu Xuebao **276**
Acta Arctica. (DK ISSN 0065-1028) **4297**
Acta Arithmetica. (PL ISSN 0065-1036) **3026**
Acta Asiatica. (JA ISSN 0567-7254) **3632**
Acta Astronautica. (US ISSN 0094-5765) **42**
Acta Astronomica. (PL ISSN 0001-5237) **360**
Acta Astronomica Sinica. *see* Tianwen Xuebao **370**
Acta Astrophysica Sinica. *see* Tianti Wuli Xuebao **370**
Acta Automatica Sinica. *see* Zidonghua Xuebao **1416**
Acta Baltica. (GW ISSN 0567-7289) **2346**
Acta Baltico - Slavica. (PL ISSN 0065-1044) **2346**
Acta Belgica - Medica Physica *see* European Journal of Physical Medicine and Rehabilitation **3097**
Acta Bernensia: Beitraege zur Praehistorischen, Klassischen und Juengeren Archaeologie. (SZ ISSN 0065-1052) **260**
Acta Bibliothecae Regiae Stockholmiensis. (SW ISSN 0065-1060) **2741**
Acta Bibliothecae Universitatis Gothoburgensis. (SW ISSN 0065-1079) **2741**
Acta Biochemica et Biophysica Sinica. *see* Shengwu Huaxue yu Shengwu Wuli Xuebao **482**
Acta Biochimica et Biophysica Hungarica. (HU ISSN 0237-6261) **470**, 484
Acta Biologiae Experimentalis *see* Acta Neurobiologiae Experimentalis **425**
Acta Biologica *see* Uniwersytet Slaski w Katowicach. Prace Naukowe. Acta Biologica Silesiana **459**
Acta Biologica. (GW ISSN 0722-4192) **3069**, 425, 3213
Acta Biologica Cracoviensia. Botanica. (PL ISSN 0001-5296) **492**
Acta Biologica Cracoviensia. Zoologia. (PL ISSN 0001-530X) **576**
Acta Biologica Hellenica *see* Biologia Gallo-Hellenica **431**
Acta Biologica Hungarica. (HU ISSN 0001-5288) **425**
Acta Biologica Iugoslavica. Serija A: Zemljiste i Biljka. (YU ISSN 0514-6658) **425**
Acta Biologica Iugoslavica. Serija B: Mikrobiologija. (YU ISSN 0581-1538) **548**
Acta Biologica Iugoslavica. Serija C: Iugoslavica Physiologica et Pharmacologica Acta. (YU ISSN 0021-3225) **425**, 3715
Acta Biologica Iugoslavica. Serija D: Ekologija. (YU ISSN 0531-9110) **425**
Acta Biologica Iugoslavica. Serija E: Ichthyologia. (YU ISSN 0579-7152) **576**
Acta Biologica Iugoslavica. Serija F: Genetika. (YU ISSN 0534-0012) **539**
Acta Biologica Iugoslavica. Serija G: Biosistematika. (YU ISSN 0350-2643) **425**
Acta Biologica Leopoldensia. (BL ISSN 0101-5354) **425**
Acta Biologica Paranaense. (BL ISSN 0301-2123) **425**
Acta Biologica Venezuelica. (VE ISSN 0001-5326) **425**
Acta Biologicae Experimentalis Sinica. *see* Shiyan Shengwu Xuebao **455**
Acta Biomedica Lovaniensia. (BE) **3069**
Acta Bioquimica Clinica Latinoamericana. (AG) **470**, 3069
Acta Biotechnologica. (GW ISSN 0138-4988) **487**
Acta Biotheoretica. (NE ISSN 0001-5342) **425**
Acta Botanica *see* Acta Botanica Slovaca **492**
Acta Botanica Barcinonensia. (SP ISSN 0210-7597) **492**
Acta Botanica Croatica. (CI ISSN 0365-0588) **492**, 548, 568, 1941
Acta Botanica Cubana. (CU ISSN 0138-6824) **492**
Acta Botanica Fennica. (FI ISSN 0001-5369) **492**
Acta Botanica Horti Bucurestiensis. (RM ISSN 0068-3329) **2120**, 492
Acta Botanica Hungarica. (HU ISSN 0236-6495) **492**
Acta Botanica Indica. (II ISSN 0379-508X) **492**
Acta Botanica Islandica/Timarit Um Islenzka Grasafraedi. (IC ISSN 0374-5066) **492**
Acta Botanica Malacitana. (SP ISSN 0210-9506) **492**, 166
Acta Botanica Neerlandica. (UK ISSN 0044-5983) **492**
Acta Botanica Sinica. *see* Zhiwu Xuebao **521**
Acta Botanica Slovaca. (CS) **492**
Acta Botanica Taiwanica *see* Taiwania **518**
Acta Botanica Venezuelica. (VE ISSN 0084-5906) **492**
Acta Botanica Yunnanica. *see* Yunnan Zhiwu Yanjiu **521**
Acta Campanologica. (DK ISSN 0105-6255) **3536**
Acta Cancerologica. (PE ISSN 1013-5545) **3192**
Acta Cardiologica. (BE ISSN 0001-5385) **3203**
Acta Cardiologica Mediteranea. (IT ISSN 0392-9698) **3203**
Acta Carsologica/Krasoslovni Zbornik. (XV ISSN 0583-6050) **1540**
Acta Chemica Scandinavica. (DK ISSN 0904-213X) **1224**, 1213
Acta Chemica Scandinavica. Series A: Physical and Inorganic Chemistry *see* Acta Chemica Scandinavica **1224**
Acta Chemica Scholarum Superiorum Sinensium. *see* Gaodeng Xuexiao Huaxue Xuebao **1177**
Acta Chimica Hungarica. (HU ISSN 0231-3146) **1168**
Acta Chimica Sinica. *see* Huaxue Xuebao **1178**
Acta Chimica Sinica (English Edition) *see* Chinese Journal of Chemistry **1175**
Acta Chirurgiae Orthopaedicae et Traumatologiae Cechoslovaca. (CS ISSN 0001-5415) **3306**
Acta Chirurgiae Plasticae. (CS ISSN 0001-5423) **3373**
Acta Chirurgica Austriaca. (AU ISSN 0001-544X) **3373**
Acta Chirurgica Belgica. (BE ISSN 0001-5458) **3374**
Acta Chirurgica Hungarica. (HU ISSN 0231-4614) **3374**
Acta Chirurgica Italica. (IT ISSN 0001-5466) **3374**
Acta Chirurgica Jugoslavica. (YU ISSN 0001-5474) **3374**
Acta Chirurgica Mediterranea. (IT ISSN 0393-6376) **3374**, 3288
Acta Chirurgica Scandinavica *see* Acta Chirurgica Scandinavica - European Journal of Surgery **3374**
Acta Chirurgica Scandinavica - European Journal of Surgery. (NO ISSN 1102-1101) **3374**
Acta Ciencia Indica. (II ISSN 0379-5411) **4297**
†Acta Cientifica. (AG ISSN 0001-5490) **5129**
Acta Cientifica Venezolana. (VE ISSN 0001-5504) **4297**
Acta Classica. (SA ISSN 0065-1141) **1274**
Acta Collegii Historiae Urbanae. (NE ISSN 0169-7293) **2346**
Acta Colloquii Didactici Classici. (BE) **2800**, 1613
Acta Comeniana. Archiv pro Badani o Zivote a Dile Jana Amose Komenskeho. (CS ISSN 0231-5955) **2347**
Acta Concilium Ophthalmologicum. (NE ISSN 0065-115X) **3297**
Acta Criminologiae et Medicae Legalis Japonica/Hanzaigaku Zasshi. (JA ISSN 0302-0029) **1509**, 3264
Acta Crystallographica. Section A: Foundations of Crystallography. (DK ISSN 0108-7673) **1210**
Acta Crystallographica. Section B: Structural Science. (DK ISSN 0108-7681) **1210**
Acta Crystallographica. Section C: Crystal Structure Communications. (DK ISSN 0108-2701) **1210**
Acta Cytologica. (US ISSN 0001-5547) **522**
Acta de Odontologia Pediatrica. (DR ISSN 0252-1032) **3227**, 3317
▼Acta Demographica. (GW ISSN 0937-907X) **3979**
Acta Dendrobiologica. (CS ISSN 0231-5335) **2095**
Acta Dermato-Venereologica. (SW ISSN 0001-5555) **3245**
Acta Dermatologica/Hifuka Kiyo. (JA ISSN 0065-1176) **3245**
Acta Dermatovenerologica Iugoslavica. (CI ISSN 0302-4466) **3245**
Acta Diabetologica Latina. (IT ISSN 0001-5563) **3250**
Acta Ecologica Sinica. *see* Shengtai Xuebao **1968**
Acta Editologica. *see* Bianji Xuebao **2567**
†Acta Electronica. (FR ISSN 0001-558X) **5129**
Acta Electronica Sinica. *see* Dianzi Xuebao **1765**
Acta Embryologiae et Morphologiae Experimentalis *see* Animal Biology **428**
Acta Endocrinologica. (NO) **3250**
Acta Endocrinologica Panamericana. (AG ISSN 0065-1192) **3250**
Acta Endoscopica. (FR ISSN 0240-642X) **3266**
Acta Energiae Solaris Sinica. *see* Taiyang Neng Xuebao **1812**
Acta Entomologica. (CS ISSN 0374-1036) **527**
Acta Entomologica Bohemoslovaca. (CS ISSN 0001-5601) **527**
Acta Entomologica Fennica *see* Entomologica Fennica **530**
Acta Entomologica Sinica. *see* Kunchong Xuebao **535**
Acta Facultatis Forestalis, Zvolen/Vysoka Skola Lesnicka a Drevarska vo Zvolene. Lesnicka Fakulta. Zbornik Vedeckych Prac. (CS) **2095**
Acta Facultatis Medicae Fluminensis. (CI ISSN 0065-1206) **3069**
Acta Facultatis Medicae Universitatis Brunensis. (CS) **3070**, 425
Acta Facultatis Medicae Zagrabiensis. *see* Sveuciliste u Zagrebu. Medicinski Fakultet. Radovi **3155**
Acta Facultatis Medicinae Skopiensis. *see* Medicinska Misla **3130**
Acta Facultatis Pharmaceuticae Bohemoslovenicae *see* Universitas Comeniana. Acta Facultatis Pharmaceuticae **3745**
Acta Facultatis Politico-Juridicae Universitatis Scientiarum Budapestiensis de Rolando Eotvos Nominatae. (HU ISSN 0524-904X) **2594**, 3869
Acta Faunistica Entomologica. (CS ISSN 0554-9264) **527**
Acta Forestalia Fennica. (FI ISSN 0001-5636) **2095**
Acta Gastro-Enterologica Belgica. (BE ISSN 0001-5644) **3266**
Acta Gastroenterologica Latinoamericana. (AG ISSN 0300-9033) **3266**
Acta Genetica Sinica. *see* Yichuan Xuebao **548**
Acta Geneticae Medicae et Gemellologiae: Twin Research. (IT ISSN 0001-5660) **3070**, 539
Acta Geobotanica Barcinonensia *see* Acta Botanica Barcinonensia **492**
Acta Geodaetica, Geophysica et Montanistica Hungarica. (HU ISSN 0374-1842) **1586**, 2240
Acta Geographica. (FR ISSN 0001-5687) **2241**
Acta Geographica *see* Fennia **2247**
Acta Geographica Lodziensia. (PL ISSN 0065-1249) **2241**
Acta Geographica Lovaniensia. (BE ISSN 0065-1257) **2241**
Acta Geographica Sinica. *see* Dili Xuebao **2246**
Acta Geologica Hispanica. (SP ISSN 0567-7505) **1553**
Acta Geologica Hungarica. (HU ISSN 0236-5278) **1553**
Acta Geologica Lilloana. (AG ISSN 0567-7513) **1553**
Acta Geologica Polonica. (PL ISSN 0001-5709) **1553**
Acta Geologica Sinica. (US ISSN 1000-9515) **1553**
Acta Geologica Taiwanica. (CH ISSN 0065-1265) **1553**
Acta Geophysica Polonica. (PL ISSN 0001-5725) **1586**
Acta Geophysica Sinica. *see* Diqiu Wuli Xuebao **1588**
Acta Germanica. (GW ISSN 0065-1273) **2800**
Acta Gerontologica. (IT ISSN 0001-5741) **2269**
Acta Ginecologica. (Spanish edition of: Journal of Gynaecology and Obstetrics) (SP) **3288**
Acta Haematologica. (SZ ISSN 0001-5792) **3270**
Acta Haematologica Japonica *see* International Journal of Hematology **3272**
Acta Haematologica Polonica. (PL ISSN 0001-5814) **3270**
Acta Herediana. (PE ISSN 0567-753X) **2213**
Acta Histochemica. (GW ISSN 0065-1281) **3070**
Acta Histochemica et Cytochemica/Nihon Soshiki Saibo Kagakkai Gakkaishi. (JA ISSN 0044-5991) **522**, 470
Acta Historiae Rerum Naturalium nec non Technicarum. (CS ISSN 0231-6005) **2347**, 1540
Acta Historica. (IT ISSN 0065-1303) **2347**
Acta Historica et Archaeologica Mediaevalia. (SP) **260**
Acta Historica Leopoldina. (GW ISSN 0001-5857) **4297**, 3070
Acta Historica Nova. (CI) **2347**
Acta Historica Scientiarum Naturalium et Medicinalium. (DK ISSN 0065-1311) **4297**
Acta Historico-Oeconomica Iugoslaviae. (CI ISSN 0350-3631) **888**

Acta Horticulturae. (NE ISSN 0567-7572) **2120**
Acta Horticulturae Sinica. *see* Yuanyi Xuebao **2141**
Acta Hospitalia. (BE ISSN 0044-6009) **2458**
Acta Humanistica et Scientifica Universitatis Sangio Kyotiensis. Natural Science Series. *see* Kyoto Sangyo Daigaku Ronshu. Shizen Kagaku Keiretsu **4322**
Acta Humboldtiana. (GW) **232**, 2241
Acta Humboldtiana. Series Geographica et Ethnographica *see* Acta Humboldtiana **232**
Acta Humboldtiana. Series Geologica, Palaeontologica et Biologica. (GW ISSN 0375-5452) **1553**, 425
Acta Humboldtiana. Series Historica. (GW ISSN 0567-7599) **2305**
Acta Hydrobiologica. (PL ISSN 0065-132X) **425**
Acta Hydrobiologica Sinica. *see* Shuisheng Shengwu Xuebao **455**
Acta Hydrochimica et Hydrobiologica. (GW ISSN 0323-4320) **1168**, 425
Acta Hydrophysica. (GW ISSN 0065-1338) **3842**
Acta I M E K O. (International Measurement Confederation) (HU ISSN 0237-028X) **3445**
†Acta Iberica Radiologica - Cancerologica. (SP ISSN 0001-589X) **5130**
Acta Ichthyologica et Piscatoria. (PL ISSN 0137-1592) **2035**, 576
Acta Industria Chimica *see* For Formulation Chemists Only **375**
Acta Informatica. (GW ISSN 0001-5903) **1455**
Acta Information. (US) **1455**
Acta Iranica. (NE ISSN 0378-4215) **2427**
Acta Juridica *see* Academia Scientiarum Hungarica. Acta Juridica **2593**
Acta Juridica. (SA ISSN 0065-1346) **2594**
Acta Jutlandica. (DK ISSN 0106-0937) **4161**
†Acta Leidensia. (NE ISSN 0065-1362) **5130**
Acta Leprologica. (SZ ISSN 0001-5938) **3217**
Acta Linguistica Hafniensia. (DK ISSN 0374-0463) **2800**
Acta Literaria. (CL ISSN 0716-0909) **2891**
Acta Magnetica. (PL ISSN 0209-3316) **3812**
Acta Manilana. (PH ISSN 0065-1370) **4297**
Acta Mathematica. (SW ISSN 0001-5962) **3026**
Acta Mathematica Hungarica. (HU ISSN 0236-5294) **3026**
Acta Mathematica Scientia *see* Shuxue Wuli Xuebao **3055**
Acta Mathematica Sinica, New Series. (CC ISSN 1000-9574) **3026**
Acta Mathematica Vietnamica. (VN ISSN 0251-4184) **3026**
Acta Mathematicae Applicatae Sinica/Chinese Journal of Applied Mathematics. (CC ISSN 0168-9673) **3026**
Acta Mechanica. (AU ISSN 0001-5970) **1926**, 3842
Acta Mechanica Sinica. (CC ISSN 0567-7718) **3842**
Acta Mechanica Solida Sinica. (US ISSN 0894-9166) **3842**
Acta Mediaevalia. (PL) **2347**, 4254
Acta Medica. (MX ISSN 0001-5997) **3070**
Acta Medica Austriaca. (AU ISSN 0303-8173) **3070**
Acta Medica Auxologica. (IT ISSN 0001-6004) **3250**, 1231, 3275, 3288
Acta Medica Colombiana *see* Colombia Medica **3090**
Acta Medica Costarricense. (CR ISSN 0001-6012) **3070**
Acta Medica Croatica. (CI) **3070**, 3256
Acta Medica Dominicana. (DR ISSN 0379-4857) **3070**

Acta Medica Empirica. *see* Erfahrungsheilkunde **3096**
Acta Medica et Biologica/Igaku Seibutsugaku Kenkyu Kiyo. (JA ISSN 0567-7734) **3070**, 425
Acta Medica et Sociologica. (BU ISSN 0515-2925) **4427**, 3798
Acta Medica Hungarica. (HU ISSN 0236-5286) **3070**
Acta Medica Iranica. (IR ISSN 0044-6025) **3070**
Acta Medica Kinki University. (JA ISSN 0386-6092) **3070**
Acta Medica Medianae. (YU ISSN 0365-4478) **3070**
Acta Medica Mediterranea. (IT ISSN 0393-6384) **3327**, 3368
Acta Medica Nagasakiensia. (JA ISSN 0001-6055) **3070**
Acta Medica Okayama. (JA ISSN 0386-300X) **3070**
Acta Medica Peruana. (PE) **3070**
Acta Medica Philippina. (PH ISSN 0001-6071) **3070**
Acta Medica Polona. (PL ISSN 0001-608X) **3070**
Acta Medica Romana. (IT ISSN 0001-6098) **3070**
Acta Medica Scandinavica *see* Journal of Internal Medicine **3116**
†Acta Medica Universitatis Kagoshimaensis. (JA ISSN 0001-611X) **5130**
Acta Medica Veterinaria. (IT ISSN 0001-6136) **4804**
Acta Medica Yugoslavica *see* Acta Medica Croatica **3070**
Acta Medicae Historiae Patavina. (IT ISSN 0065-1389) **3070**
Acta Medicinae Legalis et Socialis. (BE ISSN 0065-1397) **3264**
Acta Mediterranea di Patologia Infettiva e Tropicale. (IT ISSN 0392-9515) **3217**
Acta Metallurgica *see* Acta Metallurgica et Materialia **3401**
Acta Metallurgica et Materialia. (US ISSN 0956-7151) **3401**
Acta Metallurgica Sinica. Series A: Physical Metallurgy & Materials Science. (CC ISSN 1000-9442) **3401**
Acta Metallurgica Sinica. Series B: Process Metallurgy & Miscellaneous. (CC ISSN 1000-9450) **3401**
Acta Meteorologica Sinica. (CC ISSN 0894-0525) **3431**
Acta Mexicana de Ciencia y Tecnologia. (MX ISSN 0567-7785) **4297**
†Acta Mexicana de Ciencias Sociales. (MX) **5130**
Acta Microbiologica Bulgarica. (BU ISSN 0204-8809) **548**
Acta Microbiologica Hungarica. (HU ISSN 0231-4622) **548**
Acta Microbiologica Polonica. (PL ISSN 0001-6195) **548**, 539
Acta Microbiologica Sinica. *see* Weishengwu Xuebao **558**
Acta Micropalaeontologica Sinica. *see* Weiti Gushengwu Xuebao **559**
Acta Morfologica. (BU) **425**
Acta Morphologica Hungarica. (HU ISSN 0236-5391) **3070**, 425
Acta Morphologica Neelando-Scandinavica *see* European Journal of Morphology **3097**
Acta Mozartiana. (GW ISSN 0001-6233) **3536**
Acta Musealia *see* Oblastni Muzeum Jihovychodni Moravy. Acta Musealia **2378**
Acta Musei Apulensis *see* Apulum **2348**
Acta Musei Moraviae. Supplementum: Folia Ethnographica. (CS ISSN 0862-1209) **232**
Acta Musei Moraviae. Supplementum: Folia Mendeliana. (CS ISSN 0085-0748) **539**
Acta Musei Moraviae. Supplementum: Folia Numismatica. (CS ISSN 0862-1195) **3597**
Acta Musei Moraviae - Scientiae Naturales. (CS ISSN 0521-2359) **1540**
Acta Musei Moraviae - Scientiae Sociales. (CS) **2347**, 260

Acta Musei Nationalis Pragae. *see* Narodni Muzeum v Praze. Sbornik. Rada A: Historie **2318**
Acta Musei Nationalis Pragae. *see* Narodni Muzeum v Praze. Sbornik. Rada C: Literarni Historie **2775**
Acta Musei Nationalis Pragae. *see* Narodni Muzeum v Praze. Sbornik. Rada B: Prirodni Vedy **4326**
Acta Museorum Agriculturae. (CS) **68**
Acta Musicologica. (GW ISSN 0001-6241) **3536**
Acta Mycologica. (PL ISSN 0001-625X) **492**
Acta Mycologica Sinica. *see* Zhenjun Xuebao **521**
Acta Naturalia Islandica. (IC ISSN 0365-4850) **492**, 576, 1553
Acta Neonatologica Japonica. *see* Nihon Shinseiji Gakkai Zasshi **3323**
Acta Neophilologica. (XV ISSN 0567-784X) **2800**, 2891
Acta Neurobiologiae Experimentalis. (PL ISSN 0065-1400) **425**
Acta Neurochirurgica. (US ISSN 0001-6268) **3374**, 3327
Acta Neurochirurgica. Supplement *see* Acta Neurochirurgica. Supplementa **3327**
Acta Neurochirurgica. Supplementa. (US ISSN 0001-6268) **3327**, 3374
Acta Neurologica. (IT ISSN 0001-6276) **3327**
Acta Neurologica Belgica. (BE ISSN 0300-9009) **3327**
Acta Neurologica et Psychiatrica Belgica *see* Acta Neurologica Belgica **3327**
Acta Neurologica Scandinavica. (DK ISSN 0001-6314) **3328**
Acta Neurologica Scandinavica. Supplementum. (DK ISSN 0065-1427) **3328**
Acta Neuropathologica. (GW ISSN 0001-6322) **3328**
Acta Neuropathologica. Supplement. (GW ISSN 0065-1435) **3328**
Acta Nuntiaturae Gallicae. (VC ISSN 0065-1443) **4254**
Acta Nuntiaturae Polonae. (IT) **2347**
†Acta Obstetrica et Gynaecologica Japonica. (JA ISSN 0001-6330) **5130**
Acta Obstetrica et Gynecologica Scandinavica. (SW ISSN 0001-6349) **3288**
Acta Obstetrica et Gynecologica Scandinavica. Supplement. (SW ISSN 0300-8835) **3288**
Acta Oceanografica del Pacifico. (EC) **1601**
†Acta Oceanographica Argentina. (US ISSN 0325-5182) **5130**
Acta Oceanographica Taiwanica. (CH ISSN 0379-7481) **1601**
Acta Oceanologica Sinica. (CC ISSN 0253-505X) **1601**
Acta Odontologica Scandinavica. (NO ISSN 0001-6357) **3227**
Acta Oecologica. (FR ISSN 1146-609X) **426**
Acta Oncologica. (IT ISSN 0393-7542) **3192**
Acta Ophthalmologica. (DK ISSN 0001-639X) **3297**
Acta Ophthalmologica. Supplementum. (DK ISSN 0065-1451) **3297**
Acta Ophthalmologica Iugoslavica. (CI ISSN 0001-6403) **3297**
Acta Optica Sinica. *see* Guangxue Xuebao **3852**
Acta Ordinis Fratrum Minorum. (IT ISSN 0001-6411) **4254**
Acta Ordinis Sancti Augustini. (IT ISSN 0001-642X) **4254**
Acta Organologica. (GW ISSN 0567-7874) **3536**
Acta Orientalia. (DK ISSN 0001-6438) **3632**
Acta Ornithologica. (PL ISSN 0001-6454) **561**
Acta Orthopaedica Belgica. (BE ISSN 0001-6462) **3306**
Acta Orthopaedica Scandinavica. (DK ISSN 0001-6470) **3306**
Acta Orthopaedica Scandinavica. Supplementum. (DK ISSN 0300-8827) **3306**
Acta Oto-Laryngologica. (SW ISSN 0001-6489) **3312**

Acta Oto-Laryngologica. Supplement. (DK ISSN 0365-5237) **3312**
Acta Oto-Rhino-Laryngologica Belgica. (BE ISSN 0001-6497) **3312**
Acta Otorhinolaryngologica Italica. (IT ISSN 0392-100X) **3312**
Acta Otorrinolaringologica Espanola. (SP ISSN 0001-6519) **3312**
Acta Pacis Westphalicae. (GW ISSN 0065-146X) **2347**
Acta Paediatrica Belgica *see* European Journal of Pediatrics **3320**
Acta Paediatrica Hungarica. (HU ISSN 0231-441X) **3317**
Acta Paediatrica, International Journal of Paediatrics. (NO ISSN 0803-5253) **3317**
Acta Paediatrica, International Journal of Paediatrics, Supplement. (NO ISSN 0803-5326) **3317**
Acta Paediatrica Latina. (IT ISSN 0001-6551) **3317**
Acta Paediatrica Scandinavica *see* Acta Paediatrica, International Journal of Paediatrics **3317**
Acta Paediatrica Scandinavica, Supplement *see* Acta Paediatrica, International Journal of Paediatrics, Supplement **3317**
Acta Paediatrica Sinica. (CH ISSN 0001-6578) **3317**
Acta Paedologica. (US ISSN 0737-5166) **1231**, 4008
Acta Palaeobotanica. (PL ISSN 0001-6594) **492**, 3656
Acta Palaeontologica Polonica. (PL ISSN 0567-7920) **3656**
Acta Palaeontologica Sinica. *see* Gushengwu Xuebao **3657**
Acta Parasitologica Polonica. (PL ISSN 0065-1478) **548**
Acta Pathologica Japonica. (JA ISSN 0001-6632) **3071**
Acta Pathologica, Microbiologica et Immunologica Scandinavica. Section A: Pathology *see* A P M I S **424**
Acta Pediatrica Mediterranea. (IT ISSN 0393-6392) **3318**
Acta Pedologica Sinica. *see* Turang Xuebao **1549**
Acta Petrolei Sinica. *see* Shiyou Xuebao **3701**
Acta Petrologica Sinica. *see* Yanshi Xuebao **1586**
Acta Pharmaceutica Hungarica. (HU ISSN 0001-6659) **3715**
Acta Pharmaceutica Jugoslavica. (CI ISSN 0001-6667) **3715**
Acta Pharmaceutica Nordica. (SW ISSN 1100-1801) **3715**
Acta Pharmaceutica Sinica. *see* Yaoxue Xuebao **3746**
†Acta Pharmaceutica Suecica. (SW ISSN 0001-6675) **5130**
Acta Pharmaceutica Technologica *see* European Journal of Pharmaceutics and Biopharmaceutics **3725**
Acta Pharmaceutica Turcica. (TU) **3715**
Acta Pharmacologica et Toxicologica *see* Pharmacology & Toxicology **3739**
Acta Pharmacologica et Toxicologica. Supplementum *see* Pharmacology & Toxicology. Supplementum **1983**
Acta Pharmacologica Sinica. *see* Zhongguo Yaoli Xuebao **3746**
Acta Philologica. (IT ISSN 0065-1516) **2800**
Acta Philologica. (PL ISSN 0065-1524) **2800**
Acta Philologica Aenipontana. (AU ISSN 0065-1532) **2800**
†Acta Philologica Scandinavica. (DK ISSN 0001-6691) **5130**
Acta Philosophica et Theologica. (IT ISSN 0065-1540) **3759**, 4161
Acta Philosophica Gothoburgensia. (SW ISSN 0283-2380) **3759**
Acta Phoniatrica Latina. (IT ISSN 0392-3088) **3374**
Acta Physica Austriaca. Supplement. (US ISSN 0065-1559) **3812**
Acta Physica Hungarica. (HU ISSN 0231-4428) **3812**

Acta Physica Polonica see Acta Physica Polonica. Series A: General Physics, Physics of Condensed Matter, Optics and Quantum Electronics, Atomic and Molecular Physics, Applied Physics **3812**

Acta Physica Polonica see Acta Physica Polonica. Series B: Elementary Particle Physics, Nuclear Physics, Theory of Relativity, Field Theory **3812**

Acta Physica Polonica. Series A: General Physics, Physics of Condensed Matter, Optics and Quantum Electronics, Atomic and Molecular Physics, Applied Physics. (PL ISSN 0587-4246) **3812**

Acta Physica Polonica. Series B: Elementary Particle Physics, Nuclear Physics, Theory of Relativity, Field Theory. (PL ISSN 0587-4254) **3812**

Acta Physica Sinica. see Wuli Xuebao **3835**

Acta Physica Slovaca. (CS ISSN 0323-0465) **3812**

Acta Physiologiae Plantarum. (PL ISSN 0137-5881) **492**

Acta Physiologica et Pharmacologica Bulgarica. (BU ISSN 0323-9950) **568**, 3715

Acta Physiologica et Pharmacologica Latino Americana see Acta Physiologica Pharmacologica et Therapeutica Latinoamericana **568**

Acta Physiologica Hungarica. (HU ISSN 0231-424X) **568**, 470, 484

Acta Physiologica Pharmacologica et Therapeutica Latinoamericana. (AG) **568**, 3071

Acta Physiologica Scandinavica. (UK ISSN 0001-6772) **568**, 3071

Acta Physiologica Sinica. see Shengli Xuebao **574**

Acta Phytoecologica et Geobotanica Sinica. see Zhiwu Shengtaixue yu Dizhiwuxue Xuebao **521**

Acta Phytogeographica Suecica. (SW ISSN 0084-5914) **492**, 2241

Acta Phytomedica. (GW ISSN 0065-1567) **493**

Acta Phytopathologica Sinica. see Zhiwu Bingli Xuebao **521**

Acta Phytophylactica Sinica. see Zhiwu Baohu Xuebao **521**

Acta Phytophysiologica Sinica. see Zhiwu Shengli Xuebao **521**

Acta Phytotaxonomica et Geobotanica/ Shokubutsu Bunrui Chiri. (JA ISSN 0001-6799) **493**

Acta Phytotaxonomica Sinica. see Zhiwu Fenlei Xuebao **521**

Acta Poetica. (MX ISSN 0185-3082) **2987**

Acta Politecnica Mexicana. (MX ISSN 0515-3085) **4592**

Acta Politica. (NE ISSN 0001-6810) **3869**

Acta Poloniae Historica. (PL ISSN 0001-6829) **2347**

Acta Poloniae Pharmaceutica. (PL ISSN 0001-6837) **3715**

Acta Polymerica. (GW ISSN 0323-7648) **1168**

Acta Polymerica Sinica. see Gaofenzi Xuebao **1226**

Acta Polytechnica. Rada 1: Stavebni. (CS) **1861**

Acta Polytechnica. Rada 2: Strojni. (CS) **1926**

Acta Polytechnica. Rada 3: Elektrotechnicka. (CS) **1881**

Acta Polytechnica. Rada 4: Technicko-Teoreticka. (CS) **4593**

Acta Polytechnica. Rada 5: Spolecensko-Vedni. (CS) **4593**

Acta Polytechnica. Rada 6: Vseobecna. (CS) **4593**

Acta Polytechnica Scandinavica. Applied Physics Series. (FI ISSN 0355-2721) **3846**

Acta Polytechnica Scandinavica. Chemical Technology and Metallurgy Series. (FI ISSN 0781-2698) **1168**, 3401

Acta Polytechnica Scandinavica. Chemistry and Metallurgy Series see Acta Polytechnica Scandinavica. Chemical Technology and Metallurgy Series **1168**

Acta Polytechnica Scandinavica. Civil Engineering and Building Construction Series. (FI ISSN 0355-2705) **1861**, 599

Acta Polytechnica Scandinavica. Electrical Engineering Series. (FI ISSN 0001-6845) **1881**

Acta Polytechnica Scandinavica. Mathematics and Computer Science Series. (FI ISSN 0355-2713) **1389**, 3063

Acta Polytechnica Scandinavica. Mechanical Engineering Series. (FI ISSN 0001-687X) **1926**

†Acta Polytechnicae Wratislaviensis. (PL) **5130**

Acta Praehistorica et Archaeologica. (GW ISSN 0341-1184) **260**, 2347

Acta Protozoologica. (PL ISSN 0065-1583) **426**, 576

Acta Psiquiatrica y Psicologica de America Latina. (AG ISSN 0001-6896) **3328**

Acta Psychiatrica Scandinavica. (DK ISSN 0001-690X) **3328**

Acta Psychiatrica Scandinavica. Supplementum. (DK ISSN 0065-1591) **3328**

Acta Psychologica. (NE ISSN 0001-6918) **4008**

Acta Psychologica Fennica. (FI) **4008**

†Acta Psychologica - Gothoburgensia. (SW ISSN 0065-1605) **5130**

Acta Psychologica Sinica. see Xinli Xuebao **4050**

Acta Radiobotanica et Genetica/ Hoshasen Ikushujo Kenkyu Hokoku. (JA ISSN 0065-1621) **426**, 539

Acta Radiologica. (DK) **3356**

Acta Radiologica. Series 1: Diagnosis see Acta Radiologica **3356**

Acta Regiae Societatis Scientiarum et Litterarum Gothoburgensis. Botanica.(SW ISSN 0347-4917) **493**

Acta Regiae Societatis Scientiarum et Litterarum Gothoburgensis. Geophysica. (SW ISSN 0072-4815) **1586**

Acta Regiae Societatis Scientiarum et Litterarum Gothoburgensis. Humaniora. (SW ISSN 0072-4823) **2502**

Acta Regiae Societatis Scientiarum et Litterarum Gothoburgensis. Interdisciplinaria. (SW ISSN 0347-4925) **2502**, 4297

Acta Regiae Societatis Scientiarum et Litterarum Gothoburgensis. Zoologica. (SW ISSN 0072-4807) **576**

Acta Regiae Societatitis Humaniorum Litteratum Lundensis. (SW) **260**, 2305, 2800

Acta Rei Cretariae Romanae Fautorum. Supplementa. (GW) **260**

Acta Reproductiva Turcica. (TU) **3288**

Acta Reumatologica Portuguesa. (PO) **3368**

Acta Rheumatologica Scandinavica see Scandinavian Journal of Rheumatology **3370**

Acta Romanorum Pontificum. (VC) **4254**

Acta Sagittariana. (GW ISSN 0001-6942) **3536**

Acta Scholae Medicinalis Universitatis in Gifu. see Gifu University. School of Medicine. Archives **3100**

Acta Scientiae Circumstantiae. see Huanjing Kexue Xuebao **1957**

Acta Scientiarum Naturalium Academiae Scientiarum Bohemoslovacae Brno. see Ceskoslovenska Acedemie Ved. Ustav v Brne. Prirodovedne Prace **4304**

Acta Scientiarum Naturalium Universitatis Sunyatseni. see Zhongshan Daxue Xuebao (Ziran Kexue Ban) **4354**

Acta Scientiarum Socialium. (IT ISSN 0065-1656) **4427**

Acta Scientiarum Universitatis Amoiensis. see Xiamen Daxue Xuebao (Ziran Kexue Ban) **4352**

Acta Sedimentologica Sinica. see Chenji Xuebao **1557**

Acta Seismologica Sinica. (US ISSN 1000-9116) **1586**

Acta Seminarii Neotestamentici Upsaliensis see Coniectanea Biblica. New Testament Series **4172**

Acta Sericologica. see Sanshi Kenkyu **5273**

Acta Silesiaca. see Slezsky Sbornik **4448**

Acta Societatis Botanicorum Poloniae. (PL ISSN 0001-6977) **426**, 493

Acta Socio-Medica Scandinavica see Scandinavian Journal of Social Medicine **3151**

Acta Sociologica. (NO ISSN 0001-6993) **4427**

Acta Sociologica. Serie Promocion Social. (MX) **4427**

Acta Stereologica. (XV ISSN 0351-580X) **426**, 3026, 3071

Acta Stomatologica Belgica. (BE ISSN 0001-7000) **3227**

Acta Stomatologica Croatica. (CI ISSN 0001-7019) **3227**

Acta Stratigraphica Sinica see Dicengxue Zazhi **1559**

Acta Studentica. (AU) **2305**

▼Acta Tecnologiae et Legis Medicamenti. (IT ISSN 1121-2098) **3071**, 2594

Acta Theologica Danica. (NE ISSN 0065-1672) **4161**

Acta Theriologica. (PL ISSN 0001-7051) **576**

Acta Theriologica Sinica. see Shoulei Xuebao **591**

Acta Toxicologica et Therapeutica. (IT ISSN 0393-635X) **1980**, 3256, 3715

Acta Tropica. (NE ISSN 0001-706X) **3217**

Acta Universitatis Agriculturae. Ser. Facultas Agroeconomica. (CS ISSN 0524-7446) **68**

Acta Universitatis Agriculturae. Ser. Facultas Agronomica. (CS ISSN 0524-7403) **68**

Acta Universitatis Agriculturae. Ser. Facultas Horticulturae. (CS) **2120**

Acta Universitatis Agriculturae. Ser. Facultas Silviculturae. (CS ISSN 0524-7438) **2095**

Acta Universitatis Carolinae. Historia Universitatis Carolinas Pragensis. (CS ISSN 0323-0562) **2347**

Acta Universitatis Carolinae: Biologica. (CS ISSN 0001-7124) **426**

Acta Universitatis Carolinae: Geographica. (CS ISSN 0300-5402) **2241**

Acta Universitatis Carolinae: Geologica. (CS ISSN 0001-7132) **1553**

Acta Universitatis Carolinae: Mathematica et Physica. (CS ISSN 0001-7140) **3026**, 3812

Acta Universitatis Carolinae: Medica. (CS ISSN 0567-8250) **3071**

Acta Universitatis de Attila Jozsef Nominatae. Acta Antiqua et Archaeologica. (HU ISSN 0567-7246) **1274**, 260

Acta Universitatis de Attila Jozsef Nominatae. Acta Biologica. (HU ISSN 0563-0592) **426**

Acta Universitatis de Attila Jozsef Nominatae. Acta Climatologica. (HU ISSN 0563-0614) **3431**

Acta Universitatis de Attila Jozsef Nominatae. Acta Historiae Litterarum Hungaricarum. (HU ISSN 0586-3708) **2891**

Acta Universitatis de Attila Jozsef Nominatae. Acta Iuridica et Politica. (HU ISSN 0563-0606) **2594**, 3869

Acta Universitatis de Attila Jozsef Nominatae. Acta Mineralogica - Petrographica. (HU ISSN 0365-8066) **3477**, 3681

Acta Universitatis de Attila Jozsef Nominatae. Acta Romanica. (HU ISSN 0567-8099) **2800**, 2891

Acta Universitatis de Attila Jozsef Nominatae. Papers in English and American Studies. (HU ISSN 0230-2780) **2800**, 2891

Acta Universitatis Lodziensis: Folia Archaeologica. (PL ISSN 0208-6034) **260**, 1613

Acta Universitatis Lodziensis: Folia Biochimica et Biophysica. (PL ISSN 0208-614X) **470**, 484, 1613

Acta Universitatis Lodziensis: Folia Botanica. (PL ISSN 0208-6174) **493**, 1613

Acta Universitatis Lodziensis: Folia Chimica. (PL ISSN 0208-6182) **1168**, 1613

Acta Universitatis Lodziensis: Folia Ethnologica. (PL ISSN 0208-6042) **232**, 1613

Acta Universitatis Lodziensis: Folia Geographica. (PL ISSN 0208-6123) **2241**, 1613

Acta Universitatis Lodziensis: Folia Historica. (PL ISSN 0208-6050) **2305**, 1613

Acta Universitatis Lodziensis: Folia Iuridica. (PL ISSN 0208-6069) **2594**, 1613

Acta Universitatis Lodziensis: Folia Librorum. (PL) **2502**

Acta Universitatis Lodziensis: Folia Limnologica. (PL ISSN 0208-6158) **1596**, 1613

Acta Universitatis Lodziensis: Folia Linguistica. (PL ISSN 0208-6077) **2800**, 1613

Acta Universitatis Lodziensis: Folia Litteraria. (PL ISSN 0208-6085) **2891**, 1613

Acta Universitatis Lodziensis: Folia Mathematica. (PL ISSN 0208-6204) **3026**, 1613

Acta Universitatis Lodziensis: Folia Oeconomica. (PL ISSN 0208-6018) **643**, 1613

Acta Universitatis Lodziensis: Folia Paedagogica et Psychologica. (PL ISSN 0208-6093) **4008**, 1613

Acta Universitatis Lodziensis: Folia Philosophica. (PL ISSN 0208-6107) **3760**, 1613

Acta Universitatis Lodziensis: Folia Physica. (PL ISSN 0208-6190) **3812**, 1613

Acta Universitatis Lodziensis: Folia Physiologica Cytologica et Genetica. (PL ISSN 0860-3111) **493**

Acta Universitatis Lodziensis: Folia Scientiae Artium et Litterarum. (PL ISSN 0860-7443) **2502**, 1613

Acta Universitatis Lodziensis: Folia Scientiarum Artium et Librorum see Acta Universitatis Lodziensis: Folia Scientiae Artium et Litterarum **2502**

Acta Universitatis Lodziensis: Folia Scientiarum Artium et Librorum see Acta Universitatis Lodziensis: Folia Librorum **2502**

Acta Universitatis Lodziensis: Folia Sociologica. (PL ISSN 0208-600X) **4427**, 1614

Acta Universitatis Lodziensis: Folia Sozologica. (PL ISSN 0208-6131) **1482**

Acta Universitatis Lodziensis: Folia Zoologica et Anthropologica. (PL ISSN 0208-6166) **576**, 232, 1614

Acta Universitatis Lodziensis: Turyzm. (PL ISSN 0860-1119) **4751**

Acta Universitatis Nicolai Copernici. Archeologia. (PL ISSN 0137-6616) **260**

Acta Universitatis Nicolai Copernici. Biologia. (PL ISSN 0208-4449) **426**

Acta Universitatis Nicolai Copernici. Ekonomia. (PL ISSN 0208-5305) **644**

Acta Universitatis Nicolai Copernici. Filologia Germanska. (PL ISSN 0208-5259) **2801**

Acta Universitatis Nicolai Copernici. Filologia Polska. (PL ISSN 0208-5321) **2801**

Acta Universitatis Nicolai Copernici. Filozofia. (PL ISSN 0208-564X) **3760**

ACTUALITE ECONOMIQUE   5875

Acta Universitatis Nicolai Copernici. Geografia. (PL ISSN 0208-5291) **2241**
Acta Universitatis Nicolai Copernici. Historia. (PL ISSN 0137-5830) **2347**
Acta Universitatis Nicolai Copernici. Nauki Polityczne. (PL ISSN 0137-6667) **3869**
Acta Universitatis Nicolai Copernici. Prace Limnologiczne. (PL ISSN 0208-5348) **1596**
Acta Universitatis Nicolai Copernici. Prawo. (PL ISSN 0208-5283) **2594**
Acta Universitatis Nicolai Copernici. Socjologia Wychowania. (PL ISSN 0208-5267) **1614**
Acta Universitatis Nicolai Copernici. Zabytkoznawstwo i Konserwatorstwo.(PL ISSN 0208-533X) **1482**
Acta Universitatis Ouluensis, Series D. Medica. (FI ISSN 0355-3221) **3071**
Acta Universitatis Palackianae Olomucensis. Facultatis Medicae. (CS ISSN 0301-2514) **3071**
Acta Universitatis Szegediensis de Attila Jozsef Nominatae. Acta Bibliothecaria. (HU ISSN 0001-7175) **2741**, **1614**
Acta Universitatis Szegediensis de Attila Jozsef Nominatae. Acta Germanistica. (HU ISSN 0238-079X) **2801**
Acta Universitatis Szegediensis de Attila Jozsef Nominatae. Acta Historica. (HU ISSN 0324-6965) **2347**, 2397
Acta Universitatis Szegediensis de Attila Jozsef Nominatae. Acta Physica et Chemica. (HU ISSN 0001-6721) **3812**, 1168
Acta Universitatis Szegediensis de Attila Jozsef Nominatae. Acta Scientiarum Mathematicarum. (HU ISSN 0001-6969) **3026**
Acta Universitatis Szegediensis de Attila Jozsef Nominatae. Dissertationes Slavicae. Sectio Historiae Litterarum. (HU) **2892**, 3760
Acta Universitatis Szegediensis de Attila Jozsef Nominatae. Dissertationes Slavicae. Sectio Linguistica. (HU) **2801**, **2892**
Acta Universitatis Szegediensis de Attila Jozsef Nominatae. Sectio Ethnographica et Linguistica/Neprajz es Nyelvtudomany. (HU ISSN 0209-9543) **2801**
Acta Universitatis Szegediensis de Attila Jozsef Nominatae. Sectio Oeconomico-Politica/Politikai Gazdasagtan. (HU ISSN 0563-0622) **644**
Acta Universitatis Szegediensis de Attila Jozsef Nominatae. Sectio Philosophica/Filozofia. (HU ISSN 0231-2670) **3760**
Acta Universitatis Szegediensis de Attila Jozsef Nominatae. Sectio Paedagogica et Psychologica. (HU ISSN 0324-7260) **4008**, 1614
Acta Universitatis Szegediensis de Attila Jozsef Nominatae. Sectio Scientiae Socialismi/Tudomanyos Szocializmus.(HU ISSN 0563-0657) **3869**
Acta Universitatis Upsaliensis. (SW ISSN 0282-8928) **4297**, 3071
Acta Universitatis Upsaliensis. Historia Litterarum. (SW ISSN 0440-9078) **2892**
Acta Universitatis Upsaliensis. Studia Germanistsca Upsaliensis. (SW) **2892**
Acta Universitatis Wratislaviensis. Prace Pedagogiczne. (PL ISSN 0137-1096) **1614**
Acta Urologica Belgica. (BE ISSN 0001-7183) **3386**
Acta Urologica Japonica/Hinyokika Kiyo.(JA ISSN 0001-7191) **3386**
Acta Veterinaria. (CS ISSN 0001-7213) **4804**
Acta Veterinaria et Zootechnica Sinica. see Xumu Shouyi Xuebao **4820**

Acta Veterinaria Hungarica. (HU ISSN 0236-6290) **4804**
Acta Veterinaria Japonica. (JA ISSN 0001-7221) **4820**, 2
Acta Veterinaria Scandinavica. (DK ISSN 0044-605X) **4804**
Acta Veterinaria Scandinavica. Supplementum. (DK ISSN 0065-1699) **4804**
Acta Victoriana. (CN) **2892**
Acta Virologica. (UK ISSN 0001-723X) **548**, 3217
Acta Visbyensia. (SW ISSN 0065-1702) **2347**
†Acta Vitaminologica et Enzymologica. (IT ISSN 0300-8924) **5130**
Acta Wasaensia. (FI ISSN 0355-2667) **889**
Acta Wexionensia. Serie 1: History & Geography. (SW ISSN 0349-0564) **2241**, 2347
Acta Zoologica. (US ISSN 0001-7272) **576**
Acta Zoologica Bulgarica. (BU ISSN 0324-0770) **576**
Acta Zoologica Cracoviensia. (PL ISSN 0065-1710) **576**
Acta Zoologica et Pathologica Antverpiensia. (BE ISSN 0001-7280) **576**, 4804
Acta Zoologica Fennica. (FI ISSN 0001-7299) **576**
Acta Zoologica Hungarica. (HU ISSN 0236-7130) **576**
Acta Zoologica Lilloana. (AG ISSN 0065-1729) **576**
Acta Zoologica Sinica. see Dongwu Xuebao **581**
Acta Zootaxonomica Sinica. see Dongwu Fenlei Xuebao **581**
Actas del Cabildo Colonial de Guayaquil.(EC) **2397**
Actas Dermosifiolograficas. (SP ISSN 0001-7310) **3245**
Actas Luso Espanolas de Neurologia Psiquiatria y Ciencias Afines. (SP ISSN 0300-5062) **3328**
Actas Luso Espanolas de Neurologia y Psiquiatria see Actas Luso Espanolas de Neurologia Psiquiatria y Ciencias Afines **3328**
Actes "Cahiers d'Action Juridique". (FR ISSN 0339-6851) **2594**
Actes de la Recherche en Sciences Sociales. (FR ISSN 0335-5322) **4364**
Actes du Symposium. see I C E S Marine Science Symposia **1605**
Actes Semiotiques. (US ISSN 0761-022X) **2801**
Acteurs. (FR ISSN 0991-949X) **4629**
Actif. (CN ISSN 0840-657X) **2175**
Acting Out. (US) **4397**, 3328, 3939
Actinidia Enthusiasts Newsletter. (US) **2120**
Actinomycetes. (IT ISSN 0732-0574) **548**
Action see Barnett Action **768**
Action see P M A C News **1049**
Action see British Journal of Physical Education **1745**
Action see Spirit **4421**
Action (Clearwater). (US) **1614**
†Action (Concord). (US) **5130**
Action (Fitzroy). (AT ISSN 0300-4678) **4397**
Action (Horsham) see Action Research **5130**
Action (Louisville) see Update (Louisville) **823**
Action (Lower Templestowe). (AT) **1743**, 310
Action (New York, 1977) see Scholastic Action **1759**
†Action (Rensselaerville). (US ISSN 0001-7396) **5130**
Action (Toronto) see Action Now **4836**
Action (Washington) see P A D F News **933**
Action Africa. (AT ISSN 1033-1913) **4161**, 232, 925, 4227
Action Alert (New York). (US) **229**
Action Alert (Washington, 19??). (US) **4397**
Action Alert (Washington, 1980). (US) **2594**, 4836
Action Alert (Washington, 1986) see Bread for the World Newsletter **4400**

Action Alerts. (US) **1941**, 1482
Action & Resources for Quaker Peace and Service. (UK) **4279**
Action Automobile. (FR) **4678**
Action Automobile et Touristique see Action Automobile **4678**
Action Bulletin see Everyone's Backyard **1984**
Action Canada France. (CN ISSN 0318-7306) **806**
Action Catholique Generale Feminine En Equipe A C G F au Service de l'Evangile see En Equipe A C G F au Service de l'Evangile **4263**
Action Era Vehicle. (US ISSN 0044-6092) **254**, 4678
Action Feministe. see Feminist Action **4842**
†Action for Corporate Accountability. Action News. (US) **5130**
Action for Libraries. (US ISSN 0363-0250) **2741**
Action for Public Transport Newsletter. (AT ISSN 0155-8234) **2482**
Action Francaise Etudiante see Aspects de la France **3874**
Action in Teacher Education. (US ISSN 0162-6620) **1699**
Action Information. (US) **4227**, 4254
†Action Informatique. (CN) **5130**
Action Juridique (Paris, 1978). (FR ISSN 0181-2874) **2579**
Action Kit for Hospital Law. (US) **2594**, 2458
Action Kit for Hospital Trustees. (US) **2458**, 2594
Action Line (Baltimore). (US ISSN 0001-7442) **1614**
†Action Line (Memphis). (US ISSN 0162-5306) **5130**
Action Linkage Networker. (US) **2220**
†Action Memo & Senior Citizens Advocate. (US) **5130**
Action Municipale. (FR ISSN 0001-7450) **4083**, 2482
Action Nationale. (CN ISSN 0001-7469) **3869**
Action Newsletter. (UK ISSN 0143-3253) **4161**
Action Newsletter (Baton Rouge) see Baton Rouge's Commerce **808**
Action Now/A l'Action. (CN) **4836**
Action on Smoking & Health Smoking and Health Review see A S H Smoking and Health Review **2593**
Action Outdoor. (AT) **4539**
Action Poetique. (FR ISSN 0001-7477) **2987**
Action Populaire. (DM ISSN 0044-6106) **3869**
Action Pursuit Games. (US) **4463**
Action - Reaction see Pacific Theological Review **4246**
Action - Reflexion - Culture. (UV) **1614**
†Action Research. (UK) **5130**
Action Resources see Action & Resources for Quaker Peace and Service **4279**
Action Sante see Health News (Toronto) **3103**
Action Sociale. (SZ ISSN 0001-7507) **3870**, 4161
Action Sociale et Sante. (FR) **970**
Action Speaks see Excellence Education Journal **3893**
Action Sports Retailer. (US ISSN 0199-4972) **4463**
†Action Stations: The Directory of Social Action Programmes. (UK) **5130**
Action Universitaire. (FR ISSN 0065-177X) **1614**
Action Update see S G M A Today - Action Update **4486**
Action Veterinaire. (FR ISSN 0001-7523) **4804**
Action Wheels. (US) **4678**
Actiongram. (US) **209**
Activa. (US) **2857**
▼Active American. (US) **3799**, 2269
Active and Passive Electronic Components. (US ISSN 0882-7516) **1881**
Active Parenting Leader. (US) **1231**
Active Singles Life. (US) **4362**
Active Voice. (CN ISSN 1182-3968) **4120**
Activewear Business Magazine. (US ISSN 0896-1417) **1282**, 4463
†Actividad Economica. (NQ) **5130**

Actividad Minera. (AG ISSN 0326-6672) **3477**
Actividade Economica de Angola. (AO ISSN 0001-7566) **842**
†Actividades Petroleras. (VE ISSN 0001-7582) **5130**
Activitas Nervosa Superior see Homeostasis in Health & Disease **3338**
Activite Immobiliere. (FR ISSN 0764-5066) **4144**
Activite Immobiliere Commerciale et Industrielle see Activite Immobiliere **4144**
Activites Mineres au Cameroun. (CM ISSN 0575-7258) **3477**
Activities, Adaptation & Aging. (US ISSN 0192-4788) **2269**
Activities des Aerodromes Belges see Belgium. Institut National de Statistique. Statistiques du Commerce Interieur et des Transports **4662**
Activities Digest. (AT ISSN 0705-1549) **2269**
Activities of O E C D: Report by the Secretary General see O E C D. Activities of the O E C D: Report by the Secretary General **933**
Activity. (UK) **2086**, 2090
Activnews. (AT ISSN 1030-7451) **4397**
†Actor's Complete Summer Theater Guide. (US) **5130**
Acts (San Francisco). (US ISSN 0749-3908) **2987**
Acts and Cases by Popular Names, Federal and State. (US) **2594**
Acts & Facts. (US) **4279**
The Acts the Shelflife. (US) **2857**
Actu Eco. (NE) **644**, 1614
Actu'A G F. (FR ISSN 0761-7593) **2526**
Actual. (VE ISSN 0001-7639) **2892**
Actualidad Agraria. (SP) **209**
Actualidad Aseguradora. (SP) **2526**
Actualidad Bibliografica de Filosofia y Teologia. (SP ISSN 0211-4143) **3787**, 4212
Actualidad Bibliografica Iberoamericana.(SP ISSN 0210-0177) **388**
Actualidad Cultural. (CU) **2184**
Actualidad Economica. (SP ISSN 0001-7655) **842**
Actualidad Economica del Peru. (PE) **842**
Actualidad Electronica. (SP ISSN 0210-6302) **1881**
†Actualidad Estadistica. (CR) **5130**
Actualidad Juridica. (CK) **2594**
▼Actualidad Juridica Aranzadi. (SP) **2594**
Actualidad Panadera de Cataluna see Actualitat Flequera de Catalunya **2086**
Actualidad Pastoral. (AG ISSN 0587-4300) **4254**
Actualidad Tabaquera. (SP) **4643**
Actualidad Veterinaria. (MX) **4804**
Actualidades Biologicas. (CK ISSN 0304-3584) **426**
Actualidades de Japon. (AG ISSN 0001-768X) **2207**
†Actualidades de la Economia Socialista.(CU ISSN 0864-1439) **5130**
Actualitat Flequera de Catalunya. (SP) **2086**
Actualitates de Interlingua. (DK ISSN 0901-2273) **2801**
L'Actualite. (CN ISSN 0383-8714) **2176**
L'Actualite. (FR) **2556**, 2120
Actualite Chimique. (FR ISSN 0151-9093) **1168**
Actualite Chimique Canadienne. see Canadian Chemical News **1171**
Actualite Commerce. (FR) **833**
Actualite Comptable. (BE) **746**, 1087
Actualite de la Formation Permanente. (FR ISSN 0397-331X) **1743**
Actualite de la Medecine Officielle et Medecine Naturelle. (FR ISSN 0044-6149) **3071**
Actualite des Arts Plastiques. (FR) **310**
Actualite Diocesaine. (CN) **4254**
Actualite Economique. (CN ISSN 0001-771X) **644**

ACTUALITE FIDUCIAIRE

Actualite Fiduciaire. (FR ISSN 0044-6157) **2594**
L'Actualite Juridique: Droit Administratif.(FR) **2594**, 4144
Actualite Juridique: Edition Droit Administratif see L'Actualite Juridique: Droit Administratif **2594**
Actualite Juridique: Edition Propriete Immobiliere see L'Actualite Juridique: Droit Administratif **2594**
Actualite Juridique Propriete Immobiliere. (FR) **2594**
Actualite Legislative Dalloz. (FR) **2594**
Actualite Policiere. (FR) **1509**
Actualite Religieuse dans le Monde. (FR ISSN 0757-3529) **4254**
Actualite Rhumatologique Presentee au Praticien. (FR ISSN 0065-1818) **3368**
Actualite Semence see Seed Scoop **192**
Actualite Terminologique/Terminology Update. (CN ISSN 0001-7779) **2801**
Actualites Biologiques. (FR ISSN 0753-3918) **426**
Actualites Botaniques. (FR ISSN 0181-1789) **493**
Actualites C B see Actualites S D M **2741**
Actualites Communautaires. (FR) **2594**
Actualites de Rohde et Schwarz see Neues von Rohde und Schwarz **59**
Actualites Digestives. (FR) **3266**
Actualites Economiques. (FR) **758**
Actualites H L M. (Habitations a Loyer Modere) (FR) **2482**
Actualites Hepato-Gastro-Enterologiques de l'Hotel Dieu see Annales de Gastroenterologie et d'Hepatologie **3266**
Actualites I C I S T. see C I S T I News **4359**
Actualites Industrielles Lorraines. (FR ISSN 0044-6165) **3401**
Actualites Justice. see Justice Report **1517**
Actualites Nephrologiques. (FR ISSN 0073-3326) **3386**
Actualites Odonto-Stomatologiques. (FR ISSN 0001-7817) **3227**
Actualites Pharmaceutiques. (FR ISSN 0515-3700) **3715**
Actualites Psychiatriques. (FR ISSN 0300-8274) **3328**
Actualites S D M. (Services Documentaires Multimedia, Inc.) (CN) **2741**
Actualites Sociales des Transports. (FR) **4646**
Actualites Sociales Hebdomadaires. (FR ISSN 0400-471X) **4397**
▼Actualities. (UK) **3788**
Actualizacion de las Inversiones Azucareras. (CU) **937**, 166
Actuarial Digest. (US) **2526**
Actuarial Review. (US ISSN 1046-5081) **2545**, 4561
Actuarial Update. (US) **2526**, 746
Actuarieel Genootschap. Mededelingenblad. (NE) **2526**
Actuary. (US ISSN 0001-7825) **2526**
Actuel Developpement. (FR ISSN 0395-9481) **925**
Actuel Marx. (FR) **3870**, 889
Actuele Onderwerpen-Reeks see A O **2211**
Actuels. (FR ISSN 0399-5070) **310**
Actum Luce. (IT ISSN 0391-9994) **2347**
Acumen Magazine. (UK ISSN 0964-0304) **2987**
Acupuncture and Electro-Therapeutics Research. (US ISSN 0360-1293) **3071**
Acustica. (GW ISSN 0001-7884) **3858**
†Acute Care. (SZ ISSN 0254-0819) **5130**
Ad. (IT) **2556**
Ad Astra. (US ISSN 1041-102X) **42**
Ad Business Report. (US ISSN 1061-1371) **26**
Ad Change. (US ISSN 0001-7914) **26**
Ad - Com Magazine. (US) **26**
Ad Daily see Ad Day **5130**
Ad Dastour. (UK) **842**

Ad-Dawat. (BG) **2173**
†Ad Day. (US) **5130**
Ad Day - U S A see Ad Day **5130**
†Ad East. (US ISSN 0192-7922) **5130**
Ad Forum see Adweek's Marketing Week **27**
Ad Kaan. (US) **1989**
Ad - Mag. (US) **26**
Ad Magazine. (AT) **26**
Ad Marginem. (GW ISSN 0001-7965) **3536**, 2052, 4427
Ad Media. (NZ ISSN 0112-6997) **26**, 1032, 4120
Ad News. (AT ISSN 0814-6942) **26**
Ad News. (US) **26**
Ad News Handbook. (AT) **26**
Ad Nurse see Advancing Clinical Care **5131**
Ad Pages. (CN) **26**, 1120
†Ad-Pro. (US) **5130**
Ad Q. (PH) **26**
Ad Report. (US) **26**
Ad Sack. (US) **1502**
Ad Search: The Weekly National Want Ad Digest see National Ad Search **3629**
Ad-Tier Newsletter. (US) **26**, 1368
Ad Trends. (US) **26**, 758
Ad Verbum. (AG) **2285**
Ad-Viser. (CN) **68**
Ada Magazine see A D A Magazine **291**
Ada Strategies. (US ISSN 0893-0570) **1448**
Ada User. (UK ISSN 0268-652X) **1429**
▼Adabistan. (IR) **2892**
AdaData. (US ISSN 8756-0577) **1475**
†Adala. (IQ) **5130**
Al-Adalah/Justice. (TS) **2594**, 4217
Adalbert-Stifter-Institut des Landes Oberoesterreich. Vierteljahresschrift. (AU ISSN 0001-799X) **2892**
Adam. (GW) **2450**
Adam. (US ISSN 0001-8007) **3395**
Adam. (HU ISSN 0230-1911) **3395**
†Adam. (FR) **5130**
Adam and Eve. (II ISSN 0044-6181) **2857**, 2892
Adam Chofshe/Free Man. (IS ISSN 0334-5831) **3870**
Adam Erotomic. (US) **3395**, 2450
Adam Film World Guide see Adam Film World Guide Directory **3503**
Adam Film World Guide Directory. (US) **3503**, 1120
Adam Girls International. (US) **3395**
Adam International Review. (US ISSN 0001-8015) **2892**, 310, 3536, 4629
Adam Veavoda/Man and Work. (IS ISSN 0792-0490) **3624**, 1001, 1062
Adansonia see Museum National d'Histoire Naturelle. Bulletin - Section B - Adansonia (Botanique, Phytochimie) **510**
Adapt Japan: Employment Opportunities For You. (JA) **970**
Adaptation. (CN ISSN 0380-4194) **1733**
Adaptations Series. (US ISSN 0065-1877) **2892**
Adapted Physical Activity Quarterly. (US ISSN 0736-5829) **1733**, 3799
▼Adaptive Behavior. (US ISSN 1059-7123) **1406**
Adbrief. (AT ISSN 0311-2225) **26**
Adbrief Register: Agencies & Marketers.(AT ISSN 0819-6648) **1120**, 26
Adbusters Quarterly. (CN ISSN 0847-9097) **1368**
Adclubber. (US) **26**, 1296
Adcrafter. (US ISSN 0001-8066) **26**
†Add-On Buyer's Guide & Handbook. (US) **5130**
Addab Journal. (SJ ISSN 0302-8844) **2502**
Addendum see Research Update **2781**
Addiction & Recovery Magazine. (US) **1533**
Addiction and Substance Abuse Report see Substance Abuse Report **1539**
Addiction Intervention with the Disabled Bulletin see A I D Bulletin **1532**

Addiction Letter. (US ISSN 8756-405X) **1533**
Addiction Research Foundation. Journal.(CN) **1533**
Addiction Research Foundation of Ontario. Annual Report. (CN) **1533**
†Addiction Research Foundation of Ontario. Bibliographic Series. (CN ISSN 0065-1885) **5130**
Addictions Alert see Brown University Digest of Addiction Theory & Application Data **1534**
Addictions Nursing Network. (US ISSN 0899-9112) **3275**, 1533
Addictions Program Management see Alcoholism & Drug Abuse Weekly **1533**
Addictive Behaviors. (US ISSN 0306-4603) **1533**
Addis Ababa Chamber of Commerce. Chamber News. (ET) **806**
Addis Ababa Employment Survey. (ET) **970**
Addis Ababa University. College of Technology. Library Bulletin. (ET ISSN 0017-6680) **2741**, 291, 1813
Addis Ababa University. Educational Research Centre. News Bulletin see Addis Ababa University. Institute of Educational Research. News Bulletin **1614**
Addis Ababa University. Institute of Educational Research. News Bulletin. (ET) **1614**
Addis Ababa University. Library. Annual Report. (ET) **2741**
Addis Ababa University. University Testing Center. Technical Report. (ET ISSN 0072-9388) **1614**
Addison Report. (US) **937**
Additional Voluntary Contributions (Year). (UK) **937**
Additives for Plastics D.A.T.A. Digest. (US ISSN 1049-2453) **3860**
Additives for Polymers. (UK ISSN 0306-3747) **3861**, 1215
Address List, Regional and Subregional Libraries for the Blind and Physically Handicapped. (US) **2290**, 2741
Addressograph-Multigraph (Pty.) Ltd. News - Southern Africa see A M News - Southern Africa **3788**
Addvantage Magazine. (US) **4499**
Adelaar. (NE ISSN 0001-8139) **1302**
Adelaide. Institute of Medical and Veterinary Science. Annual Report of the Council. (AT ISSN 0065-1907) **3071**, 4804
Adelaide Botanic Gardens. Journal. (AT ISSN 0313-4083) **493**, 2120
Adelaide Church Guardian. (AT ISSN 0001-8147) **4228**
Adelaide City Council Municipal Reference Book. (AT) **4083**
Adelaide City Council Municipal Yearbook see Adelaide City Council Municipal Reference Book **4083**
Adelaide Law Review. (AT ISSN 0065-1915) **2594**
Adelaide Review. (AT ISSN 0815-5992) **2857**
Adelaide University Graduates's Union. Gazette see Lumen **1316**
▼Adelante (Alexandria). (US) **1989**
Adelante (Orlando). (US ISSN 0044-6238) **1989**
Adelphi Papers. (UK ISSN 0567-932X) **3949**
Adelphia Law Journal. (US) **2594**
Adem. (BE ISSN 0001-8171) **3536**
Adenosine Triphosphate ATPases see ATPases **471**
Adeverul. (IS) **2203**
Adgeziya Rasplavov i Paika Materialov. (KR ISSN 0136-1732) **3401**
Adhaesion. (GW ISSN 0001-8198) **3861**, 1168
Adhesifs see Assemblages Adhesifs **3016**
Adhesion. (UK ISSN 0260-4450) **3861**
Adhesion and Adhesives/Setchaku. (JA ISSN 0037-0495) **3861**
Adhesion Society of Japan. Journal/ Nihon Setchaku Kyokaishi. (JA ISSN 0001-8201) **3861**
Adhesive and Sealant Council. Newsletter. (US) **4290**, 3861

Adhesive and Sealant Council. Seminar Papers. (US) **4291**, 3861
Adhesive Trends. (US) **4291**, 3661, 3861
Adhesives Abstracts. (UK ISSN 0891-7760) **1191**, 2
Adhesives Age. (US ISSN 0001-821X) **1847**
Adhesives Age Directory. (US ISSN 0001-821X) **1847**
Adhesives & Sealants Newsletter. (US) **1847**
Adhesives D.A.T.A. Digest. (US) **1911**
Adhesives Directory. (UK ISSN 0305-3199) **1120**, 1847
Adhesives Euro-Guide see Guidebook to the European Adhesives Industry **1137**
Adhesives Red Book see Adhesives Age Directory **1847**
Adhuna see Adhuna Sahitya **2892**
Adhuna. (BG ISSN 0042-1057) **4397**
Adhuna Sahitya. (II ISSN 0001-8228) **2892**
Al-Adhwaa' (BA) **2173**
Adiestramento para el Desarrollo Agropecuario y Rural see Training for Agriculture and Rural Development **1687**
Adinah. (IR) **2892**
Adirondac. (US ISSN 0001-8236) **4539**, 1482
†Adirondack Bits'n Pieces. (US) **5130**
Adirondack Life. (US ISSN 0001-8252) **4539**, 4751
Adjo Direct. (NE) **1032**
Adjoints Techniques des Villes de France. (FR) **4052**
Adjusters' Reference Guide. (US) **2526**
Der Adler. (GW ISSN 0001-8279) **42**
Adler. (AU ISSN 0001-8260) **2143**
Adler Museum Bulletin. (SA ISSN 0379-6531) **3520**, 3071
Adline. (UK) **26**, 1032
Admap. (UK ISSN 0001-8295) **26**
Admarine. (UK ISSN 0964-0932) **4521**
Administracao do Porto de Lisboa. Relatorio see Administracao do Porto de Lisboa. Relatorio e Contas **4723**
Administracao do Porto de Lisboa. Relatorio e Contas. (PO) **4723**
Administracion. (AG) **1001**
Administracion Publica. (SP) **4052**
Administracion y Desarrollo. (CK ISSN 0120-3754) **3870**, 4052
Administrateur du Credit Agricole. (FR) **145**
Administratief en Gerechtelijk Jaarboek voor Belgie. see Annuaire Administratif et Judiciaire de Belgique **4053**
Administration. (II) **2857**
Administration. (IE ISSN 0001-8325) **4052**
Administration see Quarterly Journal of Administration **4072**
Administration and Development. see Al-Idarah wal-Tanmiyah **4063**
Administration & Management. (US) **3071**, 2458
Administration and Policy in Mental Health. (US ISSN 0894-587X) **3071**, 4097
Administration and Policy Journal. (US ISSN 0738-3401) **3870**, 4052
Administration and Political Sciences Review/Majallat al-Ulum al-Idariyyah wal-Siyasiyyah. (TS) **3870**, 4052
Administration and Society. (US ISSN 0095-3997) **4052**, 3870, 4427
†Administration for Development. (PP ISSN 0311-4511) **5130**
Administration Hospitaliere et Sociale. (CN ISSN 0317-3739) **2458**
Administration in Kenya see Kenya Institute of Administration. Journal **5223**
Administration in Mental Health see Administration and Policy in Mental Health **3071**
Administration in Social Work. (US ISSN 0364-3107) **4397**
Administration of Elementary and High School. see Zhongxiaoxue Guanli **1732**
Administration of Justice Memoranda. (US) **2594**

ADVANCED SERIES 5877

Administration of Juvenile Justice in California. (US) **2594**, 1231, 1509
Administration of the Employee Retirement Income Security Act *see* U.S. Department of Labor. Employee Retirement Income Security Act. Report to Congress **996**
Administration of the Marine Mammal Protection Act of 1972 *see* Marine Mammal Protection Act of 1972 Annual Report **1491**
Administration Publique. (BE ISSN 0771-4084) **2594**
Administration Publique du Canada. *see* Canadian Public Administration **4056**
Administrative Accountant *see* Accounting World **746**
Administrative Affairs in Bangladesh. (BG) **4052**
Administrative Appeal Reports. (AT ISSN 0813-779X) **2594**
Administrative Comments and Letters *see* Administration and Policy Journal **3870**
Administrative Compensation Survey. (US) **970**, 1699
Administrative Digest Business Directory *see* Office Product News Directory **1022**
Administrative Directory of College and University Computer Science Departments and Computer Centers *see* A C M Administrative Directory of College and University Computer Science - Data Processing Programs and Computer Facilities **1388**
Administrative Interpretations of the Uniform Consumer Credit Code. (US) **2594**
Administrative Judiciary News and Journal. (US) **2594**
Administrative Law. (US) **2594**
Administrative Law Decisions. (AT ISSN 0726-5816) **2594**
†Administrative Law Journal. (CN ISSN 0826-8754) **5130**
Administrative Law News. (US ISSN 0567-9494) **2595**
Administrative Law Reports. (CN ISSN 0824-2615) **2595**
Administrative Law Reports. (UK ISSN 0957-9710) **2595**
Administrative Law Review. (US ISSN 0001-8368) **2595**
Administrative Management/Jimu Kanri.(JA ISSN 0386-9962) **1001**
Administrative Management (New York) . (US ISSN 0884-5905) **1001**
Administrative Management (Orpington) *see* Institute of Administrative Management. Journal **1013**
Administrative Management Society Management Salaries Report *see* A M S Management Salaries Report **970**
Administrative Management Society Office, Professional and Data Processing Salaries Report *see* A M S Office, Professional and Data Processing Salaries Report **970**
Administrative News and Notes *see* County Care **3626**
Administrative Officials Classified by Functions *see* State Administrative Officials: Classified by Function **4074**
Administrative Radiology. (US ISSN 0738-6974) **3356**, 2458
Administrative Rulemaking. (US) **2595**
Administrative Scene. (CN ISSN 0044-6300) **1724**
Administrative Science Quarterly. (US ISSN 0001-8392) **4052**, 4427
Administrative Science Review *see* Bangladesh Journal of Public Administration **4054**
Administrative Sciences Association of Canada. Proceedings, Annual Conference. (CN) **1001**
Administrative Staff College of India Journal of Management *see* A S C I Journal of Management **1001**
Administrative Tribunals Cases. (II ISSN 0970-1060) **2595**
Administrative World. *see* Guanli Shijie **1011**
Administrator. (IO) **1724**

Administrator. (II) **4052**
Administrator. (UK ISSN 0263-3868) **4083**, 1433
Administrator (Madison). (US ISSN 0744-7078) **1724**, 1699
Administrators' Computer Letter. (US) **1724**, 4083
Administrators Newsletter. (US) **1724**
Administrators Notebook. (US ISSN 0001-8430) **1724**, 1743
†Administrator's Update. (US ISSN 0742-6542) **5130**
Administrer. (FR) **4144**
Admiralty Law Newsletter. (US) **2595**
Admission Requirements of American Dental Schools *see* Admission Requirements of U S and Canadian Dental Schools **3227**
Admission Requirements of U S and Canadian Dental Schools. (US ISSN 0091-729X) **3227**, 1692
Admissions Marketing Report. (US ISSN 0884-7398) **26**, 1724
Admitting Management Journal *see* N A H A M Management Journal **2467**
Adnews. (CN ISSN 0712-9041) **26**
Adobe Trails. (US) **2397**
Adolescence. (US ISSN 0001-8449) **1231**, 1614, 4008
Adolescent and Pediatric Gynecology. (US ISSN 0932-8610) **3318**, 3288
Adolescent Counselor Magazine. (US ISSN 1042-7589) **1232**, 1533
Adolescent Literature. *see* Wenxue Shaonian **2975**
▼Adolescent Medicine (Philadelphia). (US ISSN 1041-3499) **3318**
Adolescent Medicine (Washington). (US ISSN 0044-6335) **3071**
†Adolescent Mental Health Abstracts. (US) **5130**
Adolescent Pregnancy Prevention Clearinghouse *see* Child, Youth, and Family Futures Clearinghouse **4401**
Adolescent Psychiatry. (US ISSN 0065-2008) **3328**
Adolescent Studies. *see* Shaonian Ertong Yanjiu **1244**
†Adolinks. (US) **5130**
Adoptalk. (US ISSN 0273-6497) **4397**, 1232
Adopted Child. (US ISSN 0745-3167) **1232**, 4397
Adoptees' Liberty Movement Association Searchlight *see* A L M A Searchlight **4396**
Adoption. (US) **4397**, 2595
Adoption and Fostering. (UK ISSN 0308-5759) **4397**, 2595
Adoption Factbook. (US) **4397**, 2595
Adoption Reform Organizations. (US) **4397**, 2143
Adoption Triangle Ministries Reunion Registry *see* A T M Reunion Registry **4397**
Adoptologist. (US) **4427**, 1232
†Adrenal Glands. (UK ISSN 0142-8551) **5130**
Adrenergic Receptors. (UK ISSN 0950-0502) **3715**
Adresar Ukraintsiv u Vilnomu Sviti *see* A D U K **3948**
Adress Report. (GW) **26**
Adressbuch fuer den Deutschsprachigen Buchhandel. (GW ISSN 0065-2032) **4120**
Adresseloese Postforsendelser. (DK ISSN 0107-4350) **1352**
Adresserede Brevforsendelser. (DK ISSN 0107-4369) **1352**
Adrian Day's Investment Analyst. (US) **937**
Adrichalut. (IS ISSN 0334-794X) **291**
Adrichalut Yisraelit/Architecture of Israel. (IS ISSN 0792-1268) **291**, 2548
Adrift. (US ISSN 0736-4970) **2892**, 1989
Adroit Expression. (US) **2987**
Adsum. (CN ISSN 0705-0992) **3449**, 4463
Adult Action Guide International *see* A A G International **3395**
Adult & Community Education Organizations & Leaders Directory. (US) **1681**
Adult and Continuing Education Newsletter. (US) **1681**

Adult & Continuing Education Today. (US ISSN 0001-8473) **1681**
Adult and Family Services in Oregon. (US) **4397**
Adult Basic Education Journal. (US) **1681**
Adult Bible Studies. (US ISSN 0149-8347) **4228**
Adult Bible Study. (US ISSN 0162-4156) **4228**
Adult Bible Study. American Indian Edition. (US ISSN 1040-5186) **4228**
†Adult Bible Study. Pupil. French Edition. (US) **5130**
Adult Bible Study. Pupil. Vietnamese Edition *see* Adult Bible Study. Vietnamese Edition **4228**
Adult Bible Study. Vietnamese Edition. (US) **4228**
Adult Bible Teacher. (US ISSN 0162-4164) **4228**
†Adult Bible Teacher. Large Print Edition. (US ISSN 0162-4164) **5130**
Adult Cinema Review. (US) **3395**
Adult Day Care Letter. (US ISSN 0885-4572) **2269**, 1001, 2458
Adult Education *see* Adult Education Quarterly **1681**
†Adult Education. (UK ISSN 0001-849X) **5130**
Adult Education Association in Massachusetts, Inc. Newsletter Journal *see* A E A M Newsletter Journal **1681**
Adult Education College: An Grianan Programme. (IE) **1614**
Adult Education in Finland *see* L E I F - Life and Education in Finland **1685**
Adult Education Information Notes. (UN) **1681**
Adult Education Quarterly. (US ISSN 0741-7136) **1681**
Adult Leadership. (US ISSN 0162-4172) **4228**
†Adult Learner. **5130**
Adult Learning. (US ISSN 1045-1595) **1681**
Adult Literacy and Basic Education *see* Adult Basic Education Journal **1681**
†Adult Literacy & Technology: Guide to Literacy Software (Year). (US) **5130**
Adult Literacy & Technology Newsletter.(US) **1688**
Adult Literacy Contacts Victoria. (AT) **1681**
†Adult Planbook. (US ISSN 0149-998X) **5130**
Adult Quarterly. (US) **4161**, 2290
†Adult Residential Care Journal. (US ISSN 0899-1995) **5131**
Adult Students. (US) **1681**
Adult Study Guide. (US) **4228**
Adult Teacher. (US ISSN 0400-5880) **4228**
Adult Video News. (US ISSN 0883-7090) **1384**
Adult's Health Adviser. (US) **3071**
Adults Learning. (UK ISSN 0955-2308) **1681**
Advance. (UK ISSN 0265-1300) **26**, 1032, 4120
Advance. (DK ISSN 0109-1743) **4279**
Advance. (GH ISSN 0515-4510) **4397**
Advance (Chicago) *see* Anglican Advance **4229**
Advance (Liberty). (US) **3624**
Advance (Springfield). (US ISSN 0001-8589) **4279**
Advance Australia. (AT ISSN 0001-8619) **4161**
Advance Band Magazine. (US) **3537**, 3390
Advance for Radiologic Science Professionals. (US) **3356**
Advance for Respiratory Care Practitioners. (US) **3364**
Advance Locator for Capitol Hill. (US) **3870**, 4052
Advance News for Supermarketers. (US) **2090**, 1032
Advanced Agricultural Engineering. *see* Savremena Poljoprivredna Tehnika **118**
Advanced Battery Technology. (US ISSN 0001-8627) **1881**

Advanced Bible Study. (US ISSN 0162-4148) **4228**
Advanced Cardiac Life Support. (US) **3203**
▼Advanced Ceramics and Glass. (IT) **1160**
Advanced Ceramics Report. (UK ISSN 0268-9847) **1160**, 1847
Advanced Clinical Updates *see* Emergency Medicine Reports **3096**
Advanced Coatings & Surface Technology. (US ISSN 0896-422X) **1203**
Advanced Composite. (US ISSN 0895-0407) **1813**
▼Advanced Composite Materials. (NE ISSN 0924-3046) **1911**
Advanced Composites. (US) **3861**
Advanced Composites Bulletin. (UK ISSN 0951-953X) **3861**, 1160, 3401, 4616
▼Advanced Composites Letters. (UK ISSN 0963-6935) **3861**
Advanced Composites Manufacturing Centre Newsletter. (UK ISSN 0952-9691) **3861**, 1215
Advanced Composites Monthly. (US) **43**, 4669
Advanced Computing Magazine. (US ISSN 0743-4278) **1458**, 1467
Advanced Drug Delivery Reviews. (NE ISSN 0169-409X) **3715**, 426
Advanced Fossil Energy Technologies. (US) **1783**, 3681
Advanced Imaging. (US ISSN 1042-0711) **1349**, 3788
Advanced Industrial Technology *see* Industrial Technology **1824**
Advanced Information Report *see* Information Management Report **2797**
Advanced Information Systems. Proceedings. (US) **1406**
Advanced Integrated Networks Report *see* A I N Report **1426**
Advanced Labanotation. (US ISSN 1053-4261) **3256**
Advanced Management Journal. (US ISSN 0036-0805) **1002**
Advanced Manufacturing *see* Manufacturing Automation **1045**
Advanced Manufacturing Engineering *see* Computer-Integrated Manufacturing Systems **1877**
Advanced Manufacturing Research Report *see* A M R Report **1411**
Advanced Manufacturing Technology. (US ISSN 0885-5684) **1411**, 3015
Advanced Manufacturing Technology. (IE ISSN 0790-8482) **1881**, 1411
†Advanced Manufacturing Technology. (UK) **5131**
Advanced Materials. (US ISSN 0734-7146) **1911**
Advanced Materials. (GW ISSN 0935-9648) **1911**
†Advanced Materials Abstracts. (UK ISSN 0957-9559) **5131**
Advanced Materials and Manufacturing Processes *see* Materials & Manufacturing Processes **1935**
Advanced Materials & Processes. (US ISSN 0882-7958) **1911**
Advanced Materials for Optics and Electronics. (UK ISSN 1057-9257) **1211**, 3851
▼Advanced Metals Technology. (UK ISSN 0957-9729) **3401**
Advanced Military Computing *see* Defense & Aerospace Electronics **3456**
Advanced Office Technologies Report. (US) **1448**
Advanced Oil and Gas Recovery Technologies. (US) **3681**, 1783
▼Advanced Powder Technology. (NE ISSN 0921-8831) **1848**
Advanced Recovery Week. (US ISSN 1050-2483) **1783**
Advanced Robotics. (NE ISSN 0169-1864) **1406**, 1877
Advanced Series in Agricultural Sciences. (US ISSN 0172-4207) **68**
Advanced Series in Applied Physics. (SI) **3813**

5878 ADVANCED SERIES

Advanced Series in Astrophysics and Cosmology. (SI) 360
Advanced Series in Dynamical Systems. (SI) 3026
Advanced Series in Electrical and Computer Engineering. (SI) 1881, 1417
▼Advanced Series in Fluid Mechanics. (SI) 1911
Advanced Series in Management. (NE) 1002
Advanced Series in Mathematical Physics. (SI) 3813, 3026
Advanced Series in Neuroscience. (SI) 3328
▼Advanced Series in Nonlinear Dynamics. (SI) 3813
Advanced Series on Artificial Intelligence: Architectures, Languages and Algorithms. (SI) 1406
Advanced Series on Directions in High Energy Physics. (SI) 3813
Advanced Series on Ocean Engineering. (SI) 1813, 1601
Advanced Studies in Contemporary Mathematics. (UK ISSN 0884-0016) 3027
Advanced Studies in Pure Mathematics.(JA) 3027
†Advanced Studies in Pure Mathematics. (NE) 5131
Advanced Systems News. (US) 1071
Advanced Technology in Washington State. (US ISSN 0749-4874) 1120, 1475
Advanced Technology Libraries. (US ISSN 0044-636X) 2741
Advanced Textbooks in Economics. (NE) 889
Advanced Underwriting Service. (US) 2526
Advanced Water Conference. Proceedings. (US) 4821
▼Advanced Wireless Communication. (US ISSN 1058-7713) 1361, 1368
Advancement 2: Literature, Media Arts, Opera, Musical Theater, Visual Arts see N E A Grantmaking Programs: Challenge and Advancement 2940
Advances. (US) 3799, 3602
Advances (Kalamazoo). (US ISSN 0741-9783) 3071
Advances and Technical Standards in Neurosurgery. (US ISSN 0095-4829) 3328, 3374
Advances in Accounting. (US) 746
Advances in Aerosol Physics. (US) 3813
Advances in Agronomy. (US ISSN 0065-2113) 68
Advances in Agronomy and Crop Science/Fortschritte im Acker- und Pflanzenbau. (GW ISSN 0301-2735) 166
Advances in Alcohol and Substance Abuse see Journal of Addictive Diseases 1537
Advances in Anatomy, Embryology and Cell Biology. (US ISSN 0301-5556) 426, 522
Advances in Anesthesia. (US ISSN 0737-6146) 3189
Advances in Animal Breeding and Genetics/Fortschritte der Tierzuechtung und Zuechtungsbiologie. (GW ISSN 0344-208X) 539
Advances in Animal Physiology and Animal Nutrition/Fortschritte in der Tierphysiologie und Tierernaehrung. (GW ISSN 0301-2743) 576, 568
Advances in Animal Welfare Science. (NE) 229, 4804
Advances in Applied Business Strategy. (US) 1002
Advances in Applied Developmental Psychology. (US ISSN 0748-8572) 4008
Advances in Applied Mathematics. (US ISSN 0196-8858) 3027
Advances in Applied Mathematics and Mechanics in China. (UK) 3027, 1911
Advances in Applied Mechanics. (US ISSN 0065-2156) 3842, 1911
Advances in Applied Microbiology. (US ISSN 0065-2164) 548

Advances in Applied Microeconomics. (US ISSN 0278-0984) 889
Advances in Applied Probability. (UK ISSN 0001-8678) 3027
Advances in Applied Social Psychology. (US) 4008, 4427
Advances in Archaeological Method and Theory see Archaeological Method and Theory 263
Advances in Artificial Intelligence see Ablex Series in Artificial Intelligence 1406
Advances in Atmospheric Sciences. (CC ISSN 0256-1530) 3432
Advances in Atomic and Molecular Physics see Advances in Atomic, Molecular and Optical Physics 3846
Advances in Atomic, Molecular and Optical Physics. (US) 3846
Advances in Audiology. (SZ ISSN 0254-8747) 3312
Advances in Automation and Robotics. (US) 1406, 1411
Advances in Behavioral Biology. (US) 4008
Advances in Behavioral Economics. (US ISSN 0890-0159) 4008, 842
Advances in Behavioral Pediatrics see Advances in Developmental and Behavioral Pediatrics 3318
Advances in Behaviour Research and Therapy. (US ISSN 0146-6402) 4008
Advances in Biochemical Engineering see Advances in Biochemical Engineering - Biotechnology 487
Advances in Biochemical Engineering - Biotechnology. (US ISSN 0724-6145) 487, 468, 470
Advances in Biochemical Psychopharmacology. (US ISSN 0065-2229) 3715, 3328
Advances in Bioengineering. (US ISSN 0360-9960) 468, 1813
Advances in Bioinorganic Chemistry. (IS) 1213
Advances in Biological Psychiatry. (SZ ISSN 0378-7354) 3328
Advances in Biomaterials. (NE) 470
†Advances in Biomedical Computing Series. (US ISSN 0888-2215) 5131
Advances in Biophysics. (IE ISSN 0065-227X) 484
Advances in Botanical Research. (US ISSN 0065-2296) 493
Advances in Bryology. (GW) 493
Advances in Business Marketing. (US) 1032
Advances in Cancer Research. (US ISSN 0065-230X) 3192
Advances in Carbohydrate Chemistry and Biochemistry. (US ISSN 0065-2318) 1215, 470
Advances in Cardiac Surgery. (US) 3203, 3374
Advances in Cardiology. (SZ ISSN 0065-2326) 3203
Advances in Cardiovascular Disease. see Xinxueguanbingxue Jinzhan 3212
Advances in Cardiovascular Physics. (SZ ISSN 0378-6900) 3203
Advances in Cardiovascular Surgery see Advances in Cardiac Surgery 3203
Advances in Catalysis. (US ISSN 0360-0564) 1224
Advances in Cell Culture. (US ISSN 0275-6358) 522
Advances in Cement Research. (UK ISSN 0951-7197) 599
Advances in Chemical Engineering. (US ISSN 0065-2377) 1848
Advances in Chemical Physics. (US ISSN 0065-2385) 3813, 1224
Advances in Chemistry Series. (US ISSN 0065-2393) 1168
Advances in Child Development and Behavior. (US ISSN 0065-2407) 4008, 3318
Advances in Chromatography. (US ISSN 0065-2415) 1203
Advances in Clinical Chemistry. (US ISSN 0065-2423) 470, 3715
Advances in Clinical Child Psychology. (US ISSN 0149-4732) 4008
Advances in Clinical Enzymology. (SZ ISSN 0250-4197) 470
Advances in Clinical Rehabilitation. (US) 4397

Advances in Colloid and Interface Science. (NE ISSN 0001-8686) 1224, 426, 3813
▼Advances in Comparative Psychology.(US) 4008
†Advances in Computer Programming Management. (US ISSN 0196-870X) 5131
Advances in Computers. (US ISSN 0065-2458) 1389
Advances in Computing Research. (US) 1389
▼Advances in Connectionist and Neural Computation Theory. (US) 1406, 3224, 3328
Advances in Consumer Research. (US ISSN 0098-9258) 1032, 1502
Advances in Contraception. (NE ISSN 0267-4874) 595
Advances in Contraceptive Delivery Systems. (US) 595
▼Advances in Control Networks and Large Scale Parallel Distributed Processing Models. (US) 1406, 3224, 3328
Advances in Control Systems see Control and Dynamic Systems: Advances in Theory and Applications 50
Advances in Criminological Theory. (US ISSN 0894-2366) 1509
Advances in Cryogenic Engineering. (US ISSN 0065-2482) 3840, 1813
Advances in Cyclic Nucleotide Research and Protein Phosphorylation Research see Advances in Second Messenger and Phosphoprotein Research 470
†Advances in Cytopharmacology. (US ISSN 0084-5949) 5131
†Advances in Data Base Management. (US ISSN 0196-8718) 5131
Advances in Data Communications Management. (US ISSN 0197-1476) 1443
Advances in Data Processing Management. (US ISSN 0196-8696) 1448, 1443
Advances in Dental Research. (US ISSN 0895-9374) 3227
Advances in Dermatology. (US ISSN 0882-0880) 3245
Advances in Descriptive Psychology. (US ISSN 0276-9913) 4008
Advances in Desert and Arid Land Technology and Development Series. (US ISSN 0142-5889) 2241
Advances in Developmental and Behavioral Pediatrics. (UK) 3318
Advances in Developmental Psychology.(US ISSN 0275-3049) 4008
Advances in Discourse Processes. (US) 2801
Advances in Disordered Semiconductors. (SI) 3813
Advances in Distributed Processing Management. (US ISSN 0197-1433) 1443
Advances in Drug Research. (US ISSN 0065-2490) 3715
Advances in Drying. (US ISSN 0272-4790) 1926, 1848, 3661
Advances in Dynamic Stereochemistry. (UK) 1168
Advances in Early Education and Day Care. (US ISSN 0270-4021) 1614
Advances in Earth and Planetary Sciences. (NE) 1553
▼Advances in Echo-Contrast. (NE ISSN 0925-5206) 3071, 3224, 3356
Advances in Ecological Research. (US ISSN 0065-2504) 1941
Advances in Econometrics. (US ISSN 0731-9053) 842, 889
Advances in Economic Botany. (US ISSN 0741-8280) 493
Advances in Education. (II ISSN 0001-8694) 1614
†Advances in Electrochemistry and Electrochemical Engineering. (US ISSN 0567-9907) 5131
Advances in Electronics and Electron Physics. (US ISSN 0065-2539) 1881, 3813
▼Advances in Endocrinology and Metabolism. (US ISSN 1049-6734) 3250

Advances in Engineering. (US ISSN 0065-2555) 4679
Advances in Engineering Software. (UK ISSN 0965-9978) 1877, 1475
Advances in Engineering Software and Workstations see Advances in Engineering Software 1877
Advances in Environmental Psychology. (US) 4008, 1941
Advances in Environmental Science and Engineering. (US ISSN 0141-8106) 1941, 4593
†Advances in Environmental Science and Technology. (US ISSN 0065-2563) 5131
Advances in Enzyme Regulation. (US ISSN 0065-2571) 3071, 568
Advances in Enzymology and Related Areas of Molecular Biology. (US ISSN 0065-258X) 470
Advances in Epileptology. (US) 3328
Advances in Ethology/Fortschritte der Verhaltensforschung. (GW ISSN 0301-2808) 576
Advances in Experimental Medicine and Biology. (US ISSN 0065-2598) 426, 3071
Advances in Experimental Social Psychology. (US ISSN 0065-2601) 4427, 4008
Advances in Family Intervention, Assessment and Theory. (UK ISSN 0270-9228) 4009, 4427
Advances in Feed Technology. (GW ISSN 0936-2975) 204
Advances in Financial Planning and Forecasting. (US) 758
Advances in Food and Nutrition Research. (US ISSN 3602, 2060
Advances in Food Research see Advances in Food and Nutrition Research 3602
†Advances in Forensic Psychology and Psychiatry. (US ISSN 0747-6353) 5131
Advances in Free Radical Biology and Medicine see Free Radical Biology & Medicine 485
▼Advances in Free Radical Chemistry. (US) 1168
▼Advances in Gastrointestinal Radiology. (US ISSN 1055-808X) 3357, 3266
Advances in Genetics. (US ISSN 0065-2660) 539
Advances in Geophysical Data Processing. (US ISSN 1389, 1553
Advances in Geophysics. (US ISSN 0065-2687) 1586
Advances in Group Processes. (US) 4427
Advances in Health Economics and Health Services Research. (US ISSN 0731-2199) 3799
Advances in Health Education: Current Research. (US ISSN 0890-4073) 1743, 3799, 4009
Advances in Heat Transfer. (US ISSN 0065-2717) 3840
Advances in Heterocyclic Chemistry. (US ISSN 0065-2725) 1215
Advances in Horticultural Science. (IT ISSN 0394-6169) 2120
Advances in Host Defense Mechanisms.(US) 3217, 3182
Advances in Human - Computer Interaction. (US ISSN 0748-8602) 1411
Advances in Human Factors - Ergonomics. (NE) 4009, 3328
†Advances in Human Fertility & Reproductive Endocrinology. (US) 5131
Advances in Human Genetics. (US ISSN 0065-275X) 539
Advances in Human Psychopharmacology. (UK ISSN 0272-068X) 3715, 3328
Advances in Immunity and Cancer Therapy. (US) 3192
Advances in Immunology. (US ISSN 0065-2776) 3182
Advances in Inclusion Science. (NE) 1215
Advances in Industrial and Labor Relations. (US) 970
Advances in Industrial Engineering. (NE) 1925

Advances in Infancy Research. (US ISSN 0732-9598) **3318**, 4009
Advances in Inflammation Research. (US ISSN 0197-8322) **3071**
Advances in Information Processing in Organizations. (US) **1455**
Advances in Inorganic Biochemistry. (NE) **1213**
Advances in Inorganic Chemistry and Radiochemistry. (US ISSN 0065-2792) **1213**, 1168
Advances in Insect Physiology. (US ISSN 0065-2806) **527**
Advances in Instructional Psychology. (US ISSN 0163-5379) **4009**
Advances in Instrumentation. (US ISSN 0065-2814) **2521**
Advances in Internal Medicine. (US ISSN 0065-2822) **3071**
Advances in Internal Medicine and Pediatrics. see Ergebnisse der Inneren Medizin und Kinderheilkunde. New Series **3096**
Advances in International Comparative Management. (US) **899**, 1002
▼Advances in Knowledge Organization. (GW ISSN 0938-5495) **1455**
Advances in Large Scale Systems. (US) **1436**
Advances in Law and Child Development. (UK ISSN 0732-3565) **1232**, 2595
Advances in Learning and Behavioral Disabilities. (US) **1232**, 1733, 4009
Advances in Librarianship. (US ISSN 0065-2830) **2741**
Advances in Library Administration and Organization. (US ISSN 0732-0671) **2741**
Advances in Limnology. see Ergebnisse der Limnologie **1597**
Advances in Lipid Research. (US ISSN 0065-2849) **470**
▼Advances in Logic Programming and Automated Reasoning. (US) **1406**, 1411
Advances in Magnetic Resonance. (US ISSN 0065-2873) **3813**, 1881
Advances in Magnetic Resonance Imaging. (US) **1420**, 1881, 3813
Advances in Man - Machine Systems Research. (US) **1436**
Advances in Marine Biology. (US ISSN 0065-2881) **426**, 1601
Advances in Material Science. see Cailiao Kexue Jinzhan **3403**
Advances in Mathematical Programming and Financial Planning.(US) **3063**, 804
Advances in Mathematics. (US ISSN 0001-8708) **3027**
Advances in Meat Research Series. (UK) **209**
Advances in Mechanics. see Lixue Jinzhan **3844**
Advances in Medical Social Science. (US ISSN 0275-5742) **4364**, 3071
Advances in Metabolic Disorders. (US ISSN 0065-2903) **3250**
Advances in Metabolic Disorders. Supplements see Advances in Metabolic Disorders **3250**
Advances in Metal-Organic Chemistry. (US) **1215**
Advances in Microbial Ecology. (US ISSN 0147-4863) **548**
Advances in Microbial Physiology. (US ISSN 0065-2911) **548**
Advances in Microcirculation. (SZ ISSN 0065-2938) **3203**
Advances in Microwaves. (US ISSN 0065-2946) **1881**, 3813
Advances in Modelling & Analysis. (FR) **3064**
Advances in Molecular Biology. see Uspehi na Moleculiarnata Biologia **459**
Advances in Molten Salt Chemistry. (US ISSN 0065-2954) **1213**
Advances in Motivation and Achievement. (US) **4009**
Advances in Motor Development Research. (US ISSN 0888-9287) **3799**, 1232, 2269
Advances in Multiphoton Processes and Spectroscopy. (SI) **3851**
Advances in Nephrology. (US) **3386**

Advances in Nephrology from the Necker Hospital see Advances in Nephrology **3386**
Advances in Neural and Behavioral Development. (US ISSN 8755-0032) **4009**
Advances in Neurochemistry. (US ISSN 0098-6089) **470**, 3328
▼Advances in Neuroimmunology. (UK ISSN 0960-5428) **3182**
Advances in Neurological Sciences. see Shinkei Kenkyu no Shinpo **3354**
Advances in Neurology. (US ISSN 0091-3952) **3328**
▼Advances in Neuropsychiatry and Psychopharmacology. (US) **3328**, 3715
▼Advances in Neurosciences. (US) **3328**
Advances in Neurosurgery. (US ISSN 0302-2366) **3328**, 3374
Advances in Nonprofit Marketing. (US) **1032**
Advances in Nuclear Physics. (US ISSN 0065-2970) **3846**
Advances in Nuclear Science and Technology. (US ISSN 0065-2989) **3846**, 1813
Advances in Nursing Science. (US ISSN 0161-9268) **3275**
Advances in Nutritional Research. (US ISSN 0149-9483) **3602**
Advances in Ophthalmic Plastic & Reconstructive Surgery. (UK ISSN 0276-3508) **3297**
Advances in Optical and Electron Microscopy. (US ISSN 0065-3012) **3851**, 559
Advances in Organic Coatings Science and Technology. (US) **1215**, 3652
▼Advances in Organization Development. (US) **1002**
Advances in Organometallic Chemistry. (US ISSN 0065-3055) **1215**
Advances in Orthopaedic Surgery. (US ISSN 0738-2278) **3306**
Advances in Oto-Rhino-Laryngology. (SZ ISSN 0065-3071) **3312**
Advances in Otolaryngology - Head and Neck Surgery. (US ISSN 0887-6916) **3312**, 3374
Advances in Pain Research and Therapy. (US ISSN 0146-0722) **3328**, 3071
Advances in Parasitology. (US ISSN 0065-308X) **576**
Advances in Parenteral Sciences. (US) **3715**
Advances in Pathology see Advances in Pathology and Laboratory Medicine **3071**
Advances in Pathology and Laboratory Medicine. (US) **3071**
Advances in Pediatric Infectious Diseases. (US ISSN 0884-9404) **3217**, 3318
Advances in Pediatrics. (US ISSN 0065-3101) **3318**
Advances in Pedology. see Turang Xue Jinzhan **1549**
Advances in Personality Assessment. (US ISSN 0278-2367) **4009**, 3328
Advances in Petroleum Geochemistry. (US) **3681**, 1553
Advances in Pharmaceutical Sciences. (US ISSN 0065-3136) **3715**
Advances in Pharmacology. (US) **3715**
Advances in Pharmacology and Chemotherapy see Advances in Pharmacology **3715**
†Advances in Pharmacotherapy/ Fortschritte in der Pharmakotherapie.(SZ ISSN 0253-2093) **5131**
Advances in Photochemistry. (US ISSN 0065-3152) **1224**
Advances in Physical Geochemistry. (US ISSN 0722-3269) **1553**
Advances in Physical Organic Chemistry. (US ISSN 0065-3160) **1224**
Advances in Physics. (UK ISSN 0001-8732) **3813**
Advances in Physiology Education. (US ISSN 1043-4046) **568**, 1614
Advances in Plant Breeding/Fortschritte der Pflanzenzeuchtung. (GW ISSN 0301-2727) **166**, 493

Advances in Plant Pathology. (US) **493**
Advances in Plastic and Reconstructive Surgery. (US ISSN 0748-5212) **3374**
Advances in Plastics Technology see Advances in Polymer Technology **3861**
†Advances in Political Science. (US) **5131**
Advances in Pollen Spore Research. (II ISSN 0376-480X) **493**
†Advances in Polyamine Research. (US ISSN 0160-2179) **5131**
Advances in Polymer Science/ Fortschritte der Hochpolymeren-Forschung. (US ISSN 0065-3195) **1215**, 1848
Advances in Polymer Technology. (US ISSN 0730-6679) **3861**
Advances in Probability see Advances in Probability and Related Topics **3027**
Advances in Probability and Related Topics. (US) **3027**
Advances in Prostaglandin and Thromboxane Research see Advances in Prostaglandin, Thromboxane, and Leukotriene Research **3250**
Advances in Prostaglandin, Thromboxane, and Leukotriene Research. (US) **3250**
Advances in Protein Chemistry. (US ISSN 0065-3233) **470**
Advances in Protein Phosphatases. (BE) **3071**
Advances in Psychology. (NE) **4009**
Advances in Psychosomatic Medicine. (SZ ISSN 0065-3268) **3329**
Advances in Quantum Chemistry. (US ISSN 0065-3276) **1169**
Advances in Radiation Biology. (US ISSN 0065-3292) **484**
Advances in Radiological Protection see International Commission on Radiological Protection. Annals **3358**
Advances in Reading - Language Research. (US) **1614**
Advances in Regulation of Cell Growth Series. (US) **426**
Advances in Risk Analysis. (US) **4116**, 1972, 4561
†Advances in Satellite Communications Series. (US ISSN 0888-2207) **5131**
Advances in School Psychology. (US ISSN 0270-3920) **4009**
Advances in Second Messenger and Phosphoprotein Research. (US) **470**
Advances in Serials Management. (US ISSN 1040-4384) **2741**
Advances in Small Animal Medicine and Surgery. (US ISSN 1041-7826) **4804**
Advances in Software Engineering. (US) **1475**
Advances in Software Science and Technology. (US ISSN 1044-7997) **1475**
Advances in Soil Sciences. (US ISSN 0176-9340) **1540**, 166
Advances in Solar Energy: An Annual Review of Research and Development. (US ISSN 0731-8618) **1810**
Advances in Solid-State Chemistry. (US) **1169**
Advances in Solid State Technology. (NE) **3813**, 1224
†Advances in Soviet Power Systems. Part 1: Thermal and Mechanical. (English translation (in part) of: Elektricheskie Stantsii) (US ISSN 0888-4536) **5131**
†Advances in Soviet Power Systems. Part 2: Electrical Generation and Distribution. (English translation (in part) of: Electricheskie Stantsii) (US ISSN 0888-4544) **5131**
Advances in Space Research. (US ISSN 0273-1177) **43**
▼Advances in Spatial Reasoning. (US) **1406**
Advances in Special Education. (US ISSN 0270-4013) **1733**

ADVANCES SESSION   5879

Advances in Special Electrometallurgy. (English translation of: Problemy Spetsial'noi Elektrometallurgii) (UK ISSN 0267-4009) **3401**
†Advances in Sports Medicine and Fitness. (US ISSN 0889-3977) **5131**
Advances in Statistical Analysis and Statistical Computing. (US) **1389**, 4561
Advances in Strategic Management. (US) **1002**
Advances in Substance Abuse: Behavioral and Biological Research. (UK ISSN 0272-1740) **1533**
Advances in Suicidology. (NE ISSN 0922-3061) **3329**, 4427
Advances in Surgery. (US ISSN 0065-3411) **3374**
Advances in Teacher Education. (US ISSN 0748-0067) **1743**
†Advances in Telecommunications Networks Series. (US ISSN 0888-2223) **5131**
▼Advances in Telematics. (US ISSN 1050-9496) **1331**
Advances in Test Anxiety Research. (NE) **4009**, 1614
Advances in Thanatology. (US ISSN 0196-1934) **4009**
Advances in the Astronautical Sciences. (US ISSN 0065-3438) **43**
Advances in the Astronautical Sciences. Supplement see Science and Technology Series **61**
Advances in the Biosciences. (US ISSN 0065-3446) **426**, 3072
Advances in the Economics of Energy and Resources. (US ISSN 0192-558X) **1783**
▼Advances in the Implementation and Impact of Computer Systems. (US) **1436**
Advances in the Mechanics and Physics of Surfaces Series. (US ISSN 0272-0434) **3842**
Advances in the Psychology of Human Intelligence. (US ISSN 0278-2359) **4009**, 1743
Advances in the Study of Aggression. (US) **4009**
Advances in the Study of Behavior. (US ISSN 0065-3454) **4009**
Advances in the Study of Communication and Affect. (US) **4009**, 4427
Advances in the Study of Entrepreneurship, Innovation, and Economic Growth. (US) **842**, 889
▼Advances in the Theory of Computation and Computational Mathematics. (US) **3064**
†Advances in Transport Processes. (US ISSN 0271-2334) **5131**
Advances in Trauma see Advances in Trauma and Critical Care **3306**
Advances in Trauma and Critical Care. (US) **3306**
Advances in Urethane Science and Technology. (US ISSN 0044-6378) **1215**, 1848, 3861
Advances in Urology. (US ISSN 0894-4385) **3386**
†Advances in V L S I and Computer Systems. (Very Large Scale Integration) (US ISSN 0888-224X) **5131**
Advances in Vegetation Science. (NE) **493**
Advances in Veterinary Medicine/ Fortschritte der Veterinaermedizin. (GW ISSN 0301-2794) **4804**
Advances in Veterinary Science and Comparative Medicine. (US ISSN 0065-3519) **4804**
Advances in Viral Oncology. (US) **3192**
Advances in Virus Research. (US ISSN 0065-3527) **548**, 3217
Advances in Water Resources. (UK ISSN 0309-1708) **4821**, 1813
▼Advances in World Aquaculture. (US) **1601**
Advances in Writing Research. (US ISSN 8756-1271) **2892**
Advances in X-Ray Analysis. (US ISSN 0069-8490) **4593**, 1911, 3357, 3401, 4297
Advances Session Laws. (US) **2595**

ADVANCING CLINICAL

†Advancing Clinical Care. (US ISSN 1042-9565) **5131**
Advancing the Consumer Interest. (US ISSN 1044-7385) **1502**
Advantage see Nashville Business and Lifestyles **681**
The Advantage. (US) **2220**
Advantage Point. (US) **26**, 1113
Adveniat. (IT ISSN 0001-8740) **4254**
Advent. (US) **2450**, 4161
Advent. (II) **4217**, 3760
Advent. (NE ISSN 0165-8603) **4228**
Advent Christian Witness. (US) **4279**
Adventbode see Advent **4228**
Adventecho. (GW ISSN 0179-7999) **4228**
†Adventgemeinde. (GW ISSN 0232-6086) **5131**
Adventist Heritage. (US ISSN 0360-389X) **4280**
Adventist Life. (JA) **4228**
Adventist Review. (US ISSN 0161-1119) **4228**
Adventure (Nashville). (US ISSN 0001-8783) **4228**
Adventure Education see Adventure Education and Outdoor Leadership **1248**
Adventure Education and Outdoor Leadership. (UK) **1248**, 4539
Adventure Holidays. (UK ISSN 0143-389X) **4751**
Adventure King/Boken-O. (JA) **1248**
Adventure Road. (US ISSN 0001-8805) **4751**, 4539
Adventure Travel. (US) **4751**
Adventure Travel North America. (US) **4751**
†Adventures in Learning. (US) **5131**
Adventures in Mexico Newsletter see A I M **4750**
Adventures in Science see Living Physics **5228**
Adventuring in Conservation. (CN ISSN 0225-6533) **2095**
Adventus see Advent **2450**
Adverse Drug Reaction Bulletin. (UK ISSN 0044-6394) **3072**, 3716
Adverse Drug Reactions and Acute Poisoning Reviews see Adverse Drug Reactions and Toxicological Reviews **3072**
Adverse Drug Reactions & Interactions Database see A D R I D **3715**
Adverse Drug Reactions and Toxicological Reviews. (UK) **3072**, 1980, 3716
Advertentieblad. (NE ISSN 0001-8856) **26**
Advertentieblad van de Republiek Suriname see Surinam. Advertentieblad **39**
Advertiser. (AT) **2171**
Advertiser. (CN) **4120**
Advertiser & Agency List. (UK) **26**
Advertiser Post. (CN) **68**
Advertisers and their Agencies. (US) **26**
Advertiser's Annual. (UK ISSN 0065-3578) **26**
Advertisers Annual. see Jahrbuch der Werbung **3525**
Advertising Age. (US ISSN 0001-8899) **27**, 1032
†Advertising Age Yearbook. (US ISSN 0276-9751) **5131**
Advertising Agencies. (UK) **27**
Advertising Age's Creativity. (US) **27**
Advertising Age's Focus see Advertising Age **27**
Advertising & Graphic Arts Techniques. (US ISSN 0747-3168) **27**
Advertising and Marketing Law and Practice see Journal of Media Law and Practice **2640**
Advertising and Marketing News see National Business Review **875**
Advertising and Publicity Resources for Scholarly Books. (US) **27**
▼Advertising by Telemarketing Script - Presentations Newsletter. (US) **27**
Advertising Club of New York. Newsletter. (US) **27**
Advertising - Communications Times. (US ISSN 0193-4457) **27**
Advertising Compliance Service Newsletter. (US ISSN 0277-9943) **27**, 2595

Advertising Law and Practice see Journal of Media Law and Practice **2640**
Advertising Law Anthology. (US) **2595**, 27
Advertising News see Ad News **26**
▼Advertising Options Plus. (US ISSN 1058-2592) **27**
▼Advertising, P R, Marketing Currents.(US) **27**, 1032
Advertising Photographers of America Magazine see A P A Magazine **3788**
Advertising Research Foundation. Transcript Proceedings. (US) **27**
Advertising Specialty Register: Product Research and Source Data. (US) **27**
Advertising Women of New York Matters see A W N Y Matters **26**
Advertising Women of New York News see A W N Y News **5129**
Advertising World. see Guanggao Shijie **32**
Advertlink. (II ISSN 0001-8988) **27**, 1032
Advice and Results. see Raad och Roen **2216**
†Advice for Adults with Aging Parents or a Dependent Spouse. (US) **5131**
Adviser. (UK ISSN 0950-5458) **4397**, 2482
Advising Quarterly. (US ISSN 0895-1101) **1721**
†Advisor (Chicago). (US) **5131**
Advisor (Mitchell). (US) **4751**
Advisor (Weston) see Cult Observer **4433**
Advisor Newsletter. (US) **758**
Advisory Board for Arthritis and Musculoskeletal and Skin Diseases. Annual Report. (US) **3368**
Advisory Centre for Education (A C E) Ltd. Bulletin see A C E Bulletin **1724**
Advisory List of International Educational Travel and Exchange Programs. (US) **1721**
Advocacy Institute. Proceedings (Year). (US ISSN 0462-3134) **2595**
Advocacy: The Art of Pleading a Cause, 2-E. (US) **2595**
Advocate. (UK) **2290**
The Advocate. (AT) **4254**
Advocate (Athens) see The New Advocate **2941**
The Advocate (Boise). (US ISSN 0515-4987) **2595**
Advocate (Englewood). (US ISSN 1040-2225) **230**
The Advocate (Indianapolis). (US) **3939**, 2595, 4397
Advocate (Johnstown). (US) **1302**
Advocate (Kansas City). (US) **1302**
Advocate (Los Angeles, 1967). (US ISSN 0001-8996) **2450**
Advocate (Los Angeles, 1973). (US ISSN 0199-1876) **2595**
Advocate (New York). (US ISSN 0001-9003) **1989**
Advocate (Old Brookville). (US) **3707**
Advocate (Panhandle). (US) **3870**
Advocate (Prattsville). (US ISSN 1049-1740) **2892**, 2987
Advocate (Providence). (US) **2857**
Advocate (Saint Paul). (US ISSN 1053-3362) **1614**
Advocate (Scarborough) see Concerns **1535**
Advocate (Toronto). (CN ISSN 0382-456X) **2595**
Advocate (West Vancouver). (CN 0044-6416) **2595**
Advocate Men. (US) **3395**, 2450
Advocate Weekender. (AT) **2171**
Advocate's Advocate. (US) **3870**, 4052
Advocates for Animals. Annual Pictorial Review. (UK) **230**
Advocates for Animals. Annual Report. (UK) **576**
Advocates Quarterly. (CN ISSN 0704-0288) **2595**
Advocate's Voice. (US) **1614**
Advokatbladet see Advokaten **2595**
Advokatbladet. (NO) **2595**
Advokate see Advocate (Saint Paul) **1614**
Advokaten. (SW ISSN 0281-3505) **2595**

Advokaten. (DK) **2595**
Advokatska Komora Vojvodine. Glasnik. (YU ISSN 0017-0933) **2595**
Advokatura. (YU) **2595**
Advokatura Bosne i Hercegovine. (BN) **2595**
Al-Adwa' (MK) **644**
Adweek (Los Angeles). (US ISSN 0199-4743) **27**
Adweek (New York). (US ISSN 0199-2864) **27**
Adweek Agency Directory. (US) **27**, 1120
Adweek Client - Brand Directory. (US ISSN 1049-7064) **27**, 1120
Adweek: Midwest. (US) **27**
Adweek: National Marketing Edition see Adweek's Marketing Week **27**
Adweek: New England. (US ISSN 0888-0840) **27**
Adweek: Southeast. (US ISSN 8756-6389) **27**
Adweek: Southeast Advertising News see Adweek: Southeast **27**
Adweek: Southwest. (US ISSN **27**
Adweek: Southwest Advertising News see Adweek: Southwest **27**
Adweek's Computer and Electronics Marketing see Adweek's Marketing Computers **1423**
Adweek's Marketer's Guide to Media. (US) **27**
Adweek's Marketing Computers. (US ISSN 8750-1848) **1423**, 1032
Adweek's Marketing Week. (US ISSN 0892-8274) **27**
Adweek's Media Cost Guide see Adweek's Marketer's Guide to Media **27**
†Adweek's Winners. (US ISSN 0894-3052) **5131**
Adyar. (GW ISSN 0001-9011) **3760**
Adyar Library Bulletin see Brahmavidya **3635**
Adyatan. (FR) **3632**, 2801
Ae K - K V W L Aktuell. (Aerztkammer Westfalen-Lippe, Kassenaerztliche Vereinigung Westfalen-Lippe) (GW) **3072**, 2458, 2595
Aecoop. Boletin. (SP) **145**
Aegean Review: Contemporary Greek Arts and Letters see Aegean Review: Greek Arts and Letters **2892**
Aegean Review: Greek Arts and Letters.(US) **2892**
Aegir/Sea. (IC ISSN 0001-9038) **2050**
Aegypten und Altes Testament. (GW ISSN 0720-9061) **3632**
▼Aegypten und Levante. (AU ISSN 1015-5104) **261**
Aegyptica Helvetica. (SZ) **261**
Aegyptologische Abhandlungen. (GW ISSN 0568-0476) **3632**
Aegyptologische Forschungen. (US) **2427**, 261, 310
Aegyptus. (IT ISSN 0001-9046) **261**
Aeldre Danske Tingboeger. (DK ISSN 0065-3667) **2347**
Aeldre Sagen. (DK) **2269**
Aeon. (US) **2052**, 2347
Aequationes Mathematicae. (SZ ISSN 0001-9054) **3027**
Aera. (JA ISSN 0914-8833) **2207**
Aerei. (IT) **43**
Aerei Modellismo. (IT) **2432**, 43
Aerial. (US ISSN 0894-2633) **2987**, 310, 2857
Aerial Archaeology. (UK ISSN 0140-9220) **261**, 3788
Aerie. (US) **2987**
†Aero. (GW ISSN 0001-9100) **5131**
†Aero. (US ISSN 0001-9097) **5131**
Aero Fan/Koku Fan. (JA) **2433**
Aero Lloyd. (GW) **4669**
Aero Modeller. (UK ISSN 0001-9232) **2433**
Aero-Revue. (SZ ISSN 0001-9186) **43**
Aero Sun-Times. (US) **2987**
†AeroArt. (US) **5131**
Aerobic Beat. (US) **3799**, 1528
Aerobics and Fitness see American Fitness **3799**
Aerobics News. (US) **3799**
Aeroespacio/Aerospace. (AG ISSN 0001-9127) **43**
Aerofill News. (UK) **1224**
Aerogram. (UK ISSN 0265-8569) **43**

Aeroguide. (GW) **4669**
Aerokurier. (GW ISSN 0341-1281) **43**
Aerolog. (US) **43**
Aerological Data of Japan/Jo-Koso Geppo. (JA ISSN 0001-9216) **3432**
Aerological Report. see Aerologische Berichte **5131**
†Aerologische Berichte/Aerological Report. (AU ISSN 0001-9224) **5131**
Aeromedical & Training Digest. (US) **3072**, 43
AeroMedical Journal see Journal of Air Medical Transport **3114**
Aeromedical Reviews see U.S. Air Force. School of Aerospace Medicine. Standard Technical Report Series **3159**
▼AeroMexico Escala. (MX) **4801**
Aeromilitaria. (UK) **3449**, 43, 2305
Aeronautica and Air Label Collector. (US) **3749**
Aeronautica Meridiana. (SA ISSN 0257-8573) **43**
Aeronautical Engineering: A Continuing Biography with Indexes. (US ISSN 0163-4941) **66**
Aeronautical Engineering: A Special Biography with Indexes see Aeronautical Engineering: A Continuing Biography with Indexes **66**
Aeronautical Journal. (UK ISSN 0001-9240) **43**
Aeronautical Manufacturing Technology/ Hangkong Gongyi Jishu. (CC ISSN 1000-8756) **43**
Aeronautical Quarterly see Aeronautical Journal **43**
Aeronautical Research and Test Institute Reports see A R T I Reports **42**
Aeronautical Society of India. Journal. (II ISSN 0001-9267) **43**
Aeronautical Society of South Africa. Journal see Aeronautica Meridiana **43**
†Aeronautics and Flight. (UK) **5131**
Aeronautics Archives. see Hangkong Dang'an **54**
Aeronautique et l'Astronautique. (FR ISSN 0001-9275) **43**
Aeronavegacion Comercial Argentina. (AG ISSN 0325-9293) **43**
Aeronomica Acta. (BE ISSN 0065-3713) **43**
Aeronovum. (NE) **43**, 4539
Aerophile. (US ISSN 0147-7668) **2433**, 43, 3449
Aeroplane Monthly. (UK ISSN 0143-7240) **43**, 2305
Aeroports de Paris. Bulletin Mensuel de Statistiques. (FR ISSN 0245-8756) **4669**
Aeroports de Paris. Rapport du Conseil d'Administration. (FR ISSN 0065-3721) **4669**
Aeroports de Paris. Service Statistique. Statistique de Trafic. (FR ISSN 0078-947X) **4669**
Aeroports de Paris. Trafic des Principaux Aeroports Mondiaux. (FR) **4669**
Aeroports de Paris Une see A P a la Une **4669**
Aeroports Magazine. (FR ISSN 0336-626X) **4669**
Aeroscope. (CN ISSN 0826-2713) **43**
Aerosol Age see Spray Technology & Marketing **3652**
Aerosol Report see Aerosol Spray Report **3647**
Aerosol Review. (UK ISSN 0568-062X) **1120**
Aerosol Science and Technology. (US ISSN 0278-6826) **1169**
Aerosol Spray Report. (GW) **3647**
Aerospace. (UK ISSN 0305-0831) **43**
Aerospace. see Aeroespacio **43**
Aerospace. (SI) **43**
Aerospace America. (US ISSN 0740-722X) **44**
Aerospace and Aviation Documents Microfile. (UK) **44**
Aerospace & Defence Review. (UK) **44**

Aerospace and Defense International Product News see Aviation Week & Space Technology 48
Aerospace & Defense Science. (US) 3449, 44
Aerospace and Defense Technology see Aviation & Aerospace 47
Aerospace China. see Zhongguo Hangtian 66
Aerospace Composites & Materials. (UK ISSN 0954-5832) 44
Aerospace Computer Security Applications Conference see Computer Security Applications Conference 66
Aerospace Daily. (US) 44
†Aerospace Defense Markets & Technology. (US ISSN 0738-0461) 5131
Aerospace Design and Components. (UK) 44
Aerospace Dynamics. (UK ISSN 0263-2012) 44
Aerospace Engineering Magazine. (US ISSN 0736-2536) 44
Aerospace Europe. (UK) 44
Aerospace Facts and Figures. (US ISSN 0898-4425) 66, 4561
Aerospace Financial News. (US ISSN 1057-0950) 3449, 44
Aerospace Historian see Air Power History 45
Aerospace Industries Annual Report. (US) 44
Aerospace Industries Association of America. Newsletter. (US) 44
Aerospace Industry Yearbook. (JA) 44
†Aerospace Intelligence. (US) 5131
Aerospace Japan Weekly. (JA) 44
Aerospace Knowledge. see Hangkong Zhishi 54
▼Aerospace Management and Law. (US) 44, 2595
Aerospace Medicine and Biology. (US ISSN 0001-9410) 3166, 66, 426
Aerospace News. (CN) 44
Aerospace Newsletter. (US) 44, 3614
Aerospace Products. (US) 44
Aerospace Propulsion. (US ISSN 0363-8219) 44
Aerospace Safety see Flying Safety 53
Aerospace Testing Seminar. Proceedings. (US) 44, 1941, 4593
Aerospace U F O News. (JA) 44
Aerospace World. (SZ) 44
▼Aerospace Yearbook. (SI) 44
Aerosport - Info see Aeronovum 43
Aerostatical Notes, Anvil Firers Salutes, and Cannon Shooters Target. (US) 44, 2052
Aerostation. (US ISSN 0741-5974) 44
Aerotecnica, Missili e Spazio. (IT) 44
Aerovisao. (BL) 44
Aerovoz. (CU ISSN 0001-9461) 44, 2579
Aersceala. (IE ISSN 0001-9550) 44
Aerzte Zeitung. (GW ISSN 0175-5811) 3072, 3390
Aerzteblatt Baden-Wuerttemberg. (GW ISSN 0720-3489) 3072
Aerzteblatt Rheinland-Pfalz. (GW ISSN 0001-9488) 3072
Aerzteblatt Sachsen. (GW ISSN 0938-8478) 3072
▼Aerzteblatt Thueringen. (GW ISSN 0863-5412) 3072
Aerztebuch. (GW ISSN 0930-6900) 3072
Aerztezeitschrift fuer Naturheilverfahren.(GW ISSN 0720-6003) 3072
Aerztin. (GW ISSN 0341-2458) 3072
Aerztkammer Westfalen-Lippe Ae K - K V W L Aktuell see Ae K - K V W L Aktuell 3072
Aerztliche Jugendkunde. (GW ISSN 0001-9518) 3318
Aerztliche Kosmetologie see T W Dermatologie 3250
Aerztliche Laboratorium see Klinisches Labor 3260
Aerztliche Praxis. (GW ISSN 0001-9534) 3072
Aerztlicher Ratgeber fuer Werdende und Junge Muetter. (GW) 3288, 3318

Aerztliches Mitteilungsblatt Mittelfranken. (GW ISSN 0722-866X) 3072
Aerztliches Mitteilungsblatt Schwaben. (GW ISSN 0723-8010) 3072
Aeskan. (IC) 1248
†Aesop Institute Newsletter. (US) 5131
Aesthetic Golden Pages. see Khryses Selides Esthitikis 376
Aesthetic Plastic Surgery. (US ISSN 0364-216X) 3374
Aesthetics. see Estetika 325
Aesthetics in Music Series. (US) 3537
Aesthetics Magazine. see Revista de Estetica 342
Aesthetik und Kommunikation. (GW ISSN 0341-7212) 2188
Aetas Manjurica. (GW ISSN 0931-282X) 3632
Aethiopistische Forschungen. (GW ISSN 0170-3196) 3633
Aetinape. (Asociacion Espanola de Titulados Nautico-Pesqueros) (SP) 2035
Aetnalzer. (US ISSN 0001-9585) 2526
Aevum. (IT ISSN 0001-9593) 2801, 2305
Afangar. (IC ISSN 1017-3501) 4539, 4751
Afaq/Horizons. (TS) 1733
Afaq Amniya/Security Outlook. (BA) 1525
Afaq Arabiya. (IQ) 1989
Afaq Iqtisadiyyah/Economic Horizons. (TS) 644
Affaersekonomi Management. (SW) 1002
Affaersvaerlden. (SW ISSN 0345-3766) 937
Affaersvaerlden - Finanstidningen see Affaersvaerlden 937
Affaire de Coeur. (US ISSN 0739-3881) 2983
Les Affaires. (CN ISSN 0229-3404) 758
Affaires. (FR ISSN 0001-9615) 937
Affaires et Gens d'Affaires. (FR ISSN 0065-3799) 2347, 758
Affaires Universitaires. see University Affairs 1719
†Affairs of State. (US) 5131
Affari Sociali Internazionali. (IT) 4427, 3949
Affiches d'Alsace et de Lorraine - Moniteur des Soumissions et des Ventes de Bois de l'Est. (FR ISSN 0001-9666) 599, 2113
Affilia. (US ISSN 0886-1099) 4397, 4858
Affiliate (Chicago). (US ISSN 0360-5485) 2595
†Affiliated Advertising Agencies International. News. (US) 5131
Affiliated Leadership League of and for the Blind of America Grams see A L L-O-Grams 2290
Affinities. (US) 2892
Affinity. (US) 2450, 1614, 4280
Affirm. (US ISSN 0044-6467) 4228
†Affirmation. (CN ISSN 0441-4128) 5131
Affirmative Action Compliance Manual for Federal Contractors. (US ISSN 0148-8147) 970
Affirmative Action Register. (US ISSN 0146-2113) 3624, 970, 3939
Affirmative Action Statistics see California. Department of the Youth Authority. Affirmative Action Statistics 974
Affirmative Employment Statistics. (US) 702, 970, 4078
Affluent Markets Alert. (US ISSN 1041-7508) 1502
Afghan Hound Club of America. Bulletin.(US) 3707
Afghan Hound Review. (US ISSN 8750-9776) 3707
Afghan Military Review. (AF) 3450
Afghan Studies see South Asian Studies 2342
†Afghan World. (US) 5131
Afghanistan. (AF ISSN 0001-9682) 2336, 2801
Afghanistan. Ministry of Justice. Law Journal. (AF) 2595
Afghanistan. Ministry of Justice. Official Gazette/Rasmi Jaridah. (AF) 2595

Afghanistan Forum. (US ISSN 0889-2148) 2336
Afghanistan Republic Annual. (AF ISSN 0304-6133) 2336
Afghanistan Today. (AF) 2857
†Afghanistanblaetter. (GW ISSN 0931-3583) 5131
Afhaenging. (DK ISSN 0900-3142) 3716
Afinidad. (SP ISSN 0001-9704) 1169, 1848
AFinLA Yearbook see A Fin L A Yearbook 2799
Afkar. see Ideas 2869
†Afkar Inquiry. (UK ISSN 0266-2701) 5131
Afn Shvel. (US ISSN 0030-7718) 1989, 4397
Afram Communique. (US ISSN 1041-6854) 1989
Afram Drum. (US ISSN 1041-5076) 1989
Afram Newsletter. (FR ISSN 0243-7090) 2892, 1989
Africa. (IT ISSN 0001-9747) 2330, 2892, 3949
Africa. (BL ISSN 0100-8153) 2330, 232, 3949, 4427
Africa see Africa International 2331
Africa (Edinburgh). (UK ISSN 0001-9720) 2330
Africa Analysis. (UK ISSN 0950-902X) 842, 758, 3870
Africa and the World. (US ISSN 0950-0650) 3949
†Africa Bibliography. (UK ISSN 0266-6731) 5131
Africa Calls From Zimbabwe see Africa Calls Worldwide 4751
Africa Calls Worldwide. (RH) 4751
Africa Catalyst. (US) 842, 925
Africa Co-operative Savings and Credit Association News see A C O S C A News 757
Africa Confidential. (UK ISSN 0044-6483) 3870
Africa Contemporary Record. Annual Survey and Documents. (US ISSN 0065-3845) 2331
Africa Cooperative Savings and Credit Association. Annual Report see African Confederation of Savings and Credit Cooperatives. Annual Report 758
Africa Cooperative Savings and Credit Association. Newsletter see African Confederation of Savings and Credit Cooperatives. Newsletter 758
Africa Development. (SG ISSN 0850-3907) 925, 889
Africa Diary. (II ISSN 0001-978X) 3949
Africa Economic Digest. (UK ISSN 0144-8234) 842
†Africa Economica. (PO) 5131
Africa Energy and Mining. (FR) 3681, 3477
Africa Events. (UK ISSN 0267-6362) 2168
Africa Guide see Africa Review 842
Africa Health. (UK ISSN 0141-9536) 3072
Africa Health Marketletter. (UK ISSN 0951-8266) 3072
Africa Hoje. (PO) 2168
†Africa in the Modern World. (US) 5132
†Africa Index to Continental Periodical Literature. (UK) 5132
Africa Inland Mission International International see A I M International 4161
Africa Insider. (US ISSN 0748-4356) 3949
Africa Insight. (SA ISSN 0256-2804) 2331, 842
Africa International. (FR) 2331
Africa International. (NP ISSN 8755-5034) 3870
▼Africa Investment Monitor. (US ISSN 1053-8763) 937
Africa Letter. (II ISSN 0044-6491) 3870, 2331
Africa Link. (UK) 595
Africa Markets Monitor. (US) 899, 1071
Africa Media Monograph Series. (KE) 2566, 1331

AFRICAN CENTRE 5881

Africa Media Review. (KE ISSN 0258-4913) 1331
Africa Medicine and Health. (KE) 3072, 4097
Africa News. (US ISSN 0191-6521) 3870
Africa Press Clips. (AU ISSN 0259-5796) 2168
▼Africa Product Digest. (SA) 899
Africa Quarterly. (II ISSN 0001-9828) 3870
Africa Report. (US ISSN 0001-9836) 3949
Africa Research Bulletin. Series A: Political. (UK) 3870
Africa Research Bulletin. Series B: Economic. (UK) 842
Africa Review. (UK) 842, 3870
†Africa Seminar: Collected Papers. (SA ISSN 0250-0116) 5132
Africa Since Independence Stamp Catalogue. (UK ISSN 0142-9868) 3749
Africa South of the Sahara (Year). (UK ISSN 0065-3896) 3870, 842
Africa Tervuren. (BE ISSN 0001-9879) 4297, 232
Africa Theological Journal. (TZ ISSN 0856-0048) 4161
Africa Today. (US ISSN 0001-9887) 3870
Africa Update. (US ISSN 0194-4584) 4751
Africa Watch. (US) 3939
Africa Watch Report. (US) 3939
Africa ya Kesho. (KE) 2168
Africa 2000. (EG) 310
African see Odini 4271
African Administrative Studies. (MR ISSN 0007-9588) 4052
African Adult Education Association. Journal. (KE) 1681
African Adult Education Association Newsletter see A A E A Newsletter 1681
African Affairs. (UK ISSN 0001-9909) 3870
African Air Transport. (UK ISSN 0261-2313) 4669
†African-American Chamber of Commerce. News. (US) 5132
African-American Family History Association Newsletter. (US) 1989, 2143
African-American Issues Center Discussion Papers. (US) 4364
African-American Labor Center, A F L - C I O Reporter see A A L C Reporter 2579
African American Museums Association. Annual Meeting Report. (US) 3520
†African and Asian Water & Sewage. (UK) 5132
African Archaeological Review. (UK ISSN 0263-0338) 261, 2331
African Arts. (US ISSN 0001-9933) 310, 2892, 4629
African Association for Literacy and Adult Education. Journal. (KE) 1614, 1681
African Association for Literacy and Adult Education. Newsletter. (KE) 1743
African Bibliography Series. (US) 2327, 388
African Book Publishing Record. (UK ISSN 0306-0322) 4139
African Book World and Press: A Directory. (UK) 4120
African Books in Print. (UK ISSN 0306-9516) 388
African Books Newsletter. (II ISSN 0001-9941) 388
African Building Contractor. (SA) 599
African Business. (UK ISSN 0141-3929) 925
African Business and Chamber of Commerce Review. (SA) 806
African Business and Trade see Washington Report on Africa 3933
African Business News. (CN) 644
African Businessmen's Association of Malawi Today see A B A Today 643
African Buyers Guide. (SA) 1120
African Centre for Applied Research and Training in Social Development Monograph Series see A C A R T S O D. Monograph Series 925

5882 AFRICAN CENTRE

African Centre for Applied Research and Training in Social Development Newsletter *see* A C A R T S O D Newsletter **4396**
African Christian. (KE) **4161**
African Clarion. (SW) **3870**
African Coffee. *see* Cafe D'Afrique **2063**
African Communist. (SA ISSN 0001-9976) **3870, 3939**
African Concord. (UK ISSN 0268-0432) **2168**
African Confederation of Savings and Credit Cooperatives. Annual Report. (KE) **758**
African Confederation of Savings and Credit Cooperatives. Newsletter. (KE) **758**
African Crescent. (SL ISSN 0044-653X) **4217**
African Crusader. (NR) **2331**
†African Defence Journal. (FR ISSN 0244-0342) **5132**
African Development Bank. Annual Report *see* African Development Bank. Report by the Board of Directors **925**
African Development Bank. Annual Report/Fonds Africain de Developpement. Rapport Annuel. (IV) **925**
African Development Bank. Report by the Board of Directors/Banque Africaine de Developpement. Rapport du Conseil d'Administration. (IV ISSN 0568-1308) **925**
African Development Bank News *see* A D B News **757**
African Development Fund. Annual Report *see* African Development Bank. Annual Report **925**
African Documents Series. (US) **2331**
African Ecclesial Review *see* A F E R **4161**
African Economic Development News. (KE) **842**
African Economic History. (US ISSN 0145-2258) **889**
African Economic History Review *see* African Economic History **889**
African Enquirer. (US) **1989**
African Environment. (SG ISSN 0850-8518) **1941**
African Environment. Occasional Papers - Etudes et Recherches. (SG ISSN 0850-8526) **1942**
†African Environment Special Reports. (UK ISSN 0309-345X) **5132**
African Farming and Food Processing. (UK ISSN 0266-8017) **68, 2060**
African Geology. *see* Geologie Africaine **1564**
African Historian. (NR ISSN 0568-1332) **2331**
African Historical Dictionaries. (US) **2331**
African Historical Studies *see* International Journal of African Historical Studies **2333**
African Index. (US ISSN 0149-0796) **2331**
African Institute for Economic Development and Planning. Programme *see* African Institute for Economic Development and Planning. Prospectus **925**
African Institute for Economic Development and Planning. Prospectus. (SG) **925**
African Insurance & Finance Record. (SA) **2526**
African Insurance Record *see* African Insurance & Finance Record **2526**
African Interpreter. (GW) **644, 27, 2857**
African Journal of Academic Librarianship. (NR ISSN 0189-6709) **2741**
African Journal of Agricultural Sciences. (ET) **68**
African Journal of Biblical Studies. (NR) **4161, 4254**
†African Journal of Clinical and Experimental Immunology. (SA) **5132**
African Journal of Ecology. (UK ISSN 0141-6707) **1482, 576**
African Journal of Genetics. (NR ISSN 0795-6762) **539**

African Journal of Medicine & Medical Sciences. (UK ISSN 0309-3913) **3072**
African Journal of Pharmacy and Pharmaceutical Sciences. (NR ISSN 0044-6564) **3716**
African Journal of Plant Protection/Revue Africaine de la Protection des Vegetaux. (CM ISSN 0379-6930) **166, 527**
African Journal of Sociology. (KE) **4427**
African Kora/Kora Africaine. (UN) **1248, 310**
African Labour News. (LB ISSN 0002-0044) **2579**
African Languages and Cultures. (UK ISSN 0954-416X) **2801, 2892, 4427**
African Law Digest. (ET ISSN 0002-0052) **2595**
African Library Association of S.A. Newsletter. (SA) **2741**
African Linguistic Bibliographies. (GW ISSN 0721-2488) **2855**
African Literature Association. Bulletin. (CN) **2892**
African Livestock Policy Analysis Network Network Paper *see* A L P A N Network Paper **209**
African Livestock Policy Analysis Network Newsletter *see* A L P A N Newsletter **209**
African M I M S *see* M I M S Africa **3734**
African Methodist Episcopal Church Christian Recorder *see* A.M.E. Christian Recorder **4227**
African Methodist Episcopal Church Church Review *see* A.M.E. Church Review **4227**
African Mind *see* Journal of African Religion and Philosophy **4184**
African Missionary *see* S M A - the African Missionary **4274**
African Music. (SA ISSN 0065-4019) **3537**
African Musicology. (KE) **3537**
†African National Congress of South Africa. Newsbriefings. (UK ISSN 0263-1989) **5132**
African News Sheet. (SZ ISSN 0379-7074) **2526**
†African Newsletter. (UA) **5132**
African Notes. (NR ISSN 0002-0087) **1989**
African Peace Research Institute Journal *see* A P R I Journal **3949**
African Philosophical Journal. *see* Cahiers Philosophiques Africains **3763**
African Political Review *see* African Review **3870**
African Population Newsletter. (UN) **3979**
African Recorder. (II ISSN 0002-0133) **3870**
African Regional Trade Union Conference. Report. (BE ISSN 0065-4027) **2579**
African Research and Documentation. (UK ISSN 0305-862X) **1989**
African Research Network for Agricultural Byproducts Newsletter *see* A R N A B Newsletter **67**
African Research Studies. (US) **4364, 2331**
African Review. (TZ ISSN 0856-0056) **3870**
African Review of Business and Technology. (UK ISSN 0954-6782) **4593, 644**
African Review of Educational Sciences. *see* Revue Africaine des Sciences de l'Education **1659**
African Social Challenges *see* A C A R T S O D. Monograph Series **925**
African Social Research. (ZA ISSN 0002-0168) **4427**
African Social Security Series *see* African News Sheet **2526**
African Special Bibliographic Series. (US ISSN 0749-2308) **2327, 388**
African Studies. (SA ISSN 0002-0184) **232, 2801, 3870**
African Studies. (US) **1989**
African Studies. (CH) **2331**
African Studies Association News *see* A S A News **1988**

African Studies Association Papers *see* A S A Papers **1988**
African Studies Center Newsletter *see* University of California, Los Angeles. James S. Coleman African Studies Center. Newsletter **2335**
African Studies Journal. (GH) **2331**
African Studies Review. (US ISSN 0002-0206) **1989**
African Studies Series. (UK ISSN 0065-406X) **2331**
African Study Monographs. (JA ISSN 0285-1601) **232, 68, 2168**
African Study Monographs. Supplementary Issue. (JA ISSN 0286-9667) **232, 68**
African Tax Systems. (NE) **1087**
African Technical Review *see* African Review of Business and Technology **4593**
African Textiles. (UK ISSN 0144-7521) **4616**
African Trade/Commerce Africain. (UN) **899, 833**
African Trade Union News. (TG) **2579**
African Trader. (SA ISSN 0002-0249) **806**
African Trader - Commercant Africaine *see* African Trade **899**
African Urban Notes *see* African Urban Studies **1989**
African Urban Studies. (US) **1989, 2482**
African Violet Magazine. (US ISSN 0002-0265) **2120, 493**
African Water and Sewage *see* African and Asian Water & Sewage **5132**
African Wildlife. (SA ISSN 0002-0273) **1483**
African Wildlife News *see* Wildlife News **1500**
African Woman. (GH) **4836**
African Women *see* Rural Progress **935**
Africana Aantekeninge en Nuus. *see* Africana Notes and News **2331**
Africana Annual *see* Africana Journal **388**
Africana Bulletin. (PL ISSN 0002-029X) **4364**
Africana Gandensia. (BE) **232**
Africana i Nordiska Vetenskapliga. Bibliotek *see* Africana in the Library of the Scandinavian Institute of African Studies **388**
Africana in the Library of the Scandinavian Institute of African Studies. (SW ISSN 0348-8691) **388, 2331**
Africana Journal. (US) **388, 2741**
Africana Libraries Newsletter. (US) **2741**
Africana Marburgensia. (GW ISSN 0174-5603) **1989, 2331, 2801**
Africana Newsletter *see* C O D E S R I A Bulletin **2332**
Africana Notes and News/Africana Aantekeninge en Nuus. (SA ISSN 0002-032X) **2331**
Africana Research Bulletin. (SL) **4364, 1989**
Africana Society of Pretoria. Journal. (SA ISSN 0379-6574) **2331**
Africana Society of Pretoria. Yearbook/Africana Vereniging van Pretoria. Jaarboek. (SA) **2331**
Africana Vereniging van Pretoria. Jaarboek. *see* Africana Society of Pretoria. Yearbook **2331**
Africanus. (SA ISSN 0304-615X) **3870, 4052**
▼Africa's Import - Export Trade Opportunities Directory. (CN ISSN 1183-3963) **899**
Africom. (KE) **1331**
Afrika. (GW ISSN 0340-5796) **3949**
Afrika Bulletin. (SZ) **2567**
Afrika - Midden Oosten Bulletin. (NE) **828**
Afrika-Post. (GW) **1989**
Afrika Spectrum. (GW ISSN 0002-0397) **3871, 842, 4427**
Afrika Studien. (GW) **644**
Afrika und Uebersee. (GW ISSN 0002-0427) **2801**
Afrikaans Duitse Kultuurunie (SWA) Booklet: Facts and Figures *see* A.D.K. Booklet: Facts and Figures **5127**

Afrikaans-Duitse Kultuurunie (SWA) Informations *see* A.D.K. Informations **2330**
Afrikaans edition *see* South African Panorama (English Edition) **2217**
Afrikabulletinen. (SW ISSN 0346-9158) **3949**
Die Afrikaner. (SA) **3871, 68, 644**
Afrikaner Beesjoernaal. (SA) **209**
Afrikanisches Recht. Jahrbuch. (GW ISSN 0722-2181) **2595**
Afrique Contemporaine. (FR ISSN 0002-0478) **3949**
†Afrique Defense. (FR ISSN 0182-2322) **5132**
Afrique Economique. (SG) **644**
Afrique Entreprise. (FR) **899**
Afrique et l'Asie Modernes. (FR ISSN 0399-0370) **3871, 925**
Afrique et Philosophie. (ZR) **3760**
Afrique Expansion. (FR) **599, 644**
Afrique Industrie. (FR) **3477, 1783**
†Afrique Industrie. (FR) **5132**
Afrique Informations *see* Marches Africains **917**
Afrique Litteraire. (FR) **2892, 310**
Afrique Litteraire et Artistique *see* Afrique Litteraire **2892**
Afrique Medecine et Sante. (FR ISSN 0299-3007) **3072**
Afrique Medicale. (SG ISSN 0002-0516) **3072**
Afrique Mon Pays. (SG ISSN 0002-0524) **3871, 4427**
Afrique Noire Politique et Economique. (FR) **842, 3871**
Afrique Service. (FR ISSN 0002-0540) **926**
Afrique - Sports. (IV) **4463**
Afro-American Culture and Society Monograph Series. (US ISSN 0882-5297) **4364, 1989**
Afro-American Historical and Genealogical Society. Journal. (US) **2143, 1989, 2397**
Afro-American Historical and Genealogical Society. Newsletter. (US) **2143, 1989, 2397**
Afro-American Museum of Detroit. Newsletter *see* Museum of African-American History. Newsletter **2015**
Afro-American Music Opportunities Association. Resource Papers. (US) **3537**
Afro-American Music Opportunities Association Reports *see* A A M O A Reports **3536**
Afro-American Studies *see* Ethnic Groups **2001**
Afro-Americans in New York Life and History. (US ISSN 0364-2437) **1989, 2397**
Afro - Arave Revue. (ML) **1989**
Afro-Asia. (BL ISSN 0002-0591) **2305, 2331, 3633**
Afro Asian Economic Review. (UA ISSN 0002-0613) **926**
Afro-Asian Peoples' Conference. Proceedings. (UA ISSN 0065-4191) **2331, 2336**
Afro-Asian Peoples' Solidarity Organization. Council. Documents of the Session. (UA ISSN 0078-6233) **2331, 2336**
Afro-Asian Publications. (UA ISSN 0515-6327) **2331**
Afro-Asian Rural Reconstruction Organization Newsletter *see* A A R R O Newsletter **925**
Afro-Hispanic Review. (US ISSN 0278-8969) **1989**
Afro Image. (NR) **2892**
Afro Technical Papers *see* A F R O Technical Papers **4096**
Afroasiatic Dialects. (US ISSN 0732-6416) **2801**
Afroasiatic Linguistics. (US ISSN 0362-3637) **2801**
Afrolit News *see* African Association for Literacy and Adult Education. Newsletter **1743**
Afroscope. (KE) **4280**
Afrox News. (SA ISSN 0002-0672) **3429**
Afryka, Azja, Ameryka Lacinska. (PL) **2168**
Afskrivning m.v. *see* Skatten. Erhverv **1106**
After College. (US) **3624**

After Hours. (US) 3010
†After School. (UK) 5132
After the Battle. (UK ISSN 0306-154X) 3450, 2347
After Work Hours. see Ba Xiaoshi Yiwai 2180
After 9.00. (GW) 2188
Afterimage. (US ISSN 0300-7472) 3788
Aftermarket Business. (US) 4679
Aftermarket Business Buyer's Guide. (US) 1032, 4679
Aftermarket Canada. (CN ISSN 0828-6116) 4679
Afterwords. (US ISSN 8756-3010) 4009, 3329, 4427
Afurika Kenkyu. see Journal of African Studies 2333
Afya. (KE) 3072
Ag Alert. (US ISSN 0161-5408) 68
Ag-Chem Age/Noyaku Jidai. (JA ISSN 0029-5426) 68, 1169
Ag Chem and Commercial Fertilizer see Farm Chemicals 176
Ag Consultant. (US) 68
Ag Consultant and Fieldman see Ag Consultant 68
Ag Engineers Notebook. (US ISSN 0065-0072) 166
Ag Focus. (US) 68
Ag-Marketer see Potato Country 189
Ag News see Agricultural News 71
Ag-Pilot International. (US ISSN 0740-1434) 44, 68
Agada. (US ISSN 0740-2392) 1989, 2892, 4221
Against the Current. (US ISSN 0739-4853) 3871
Against the Grain. (US ISSN 1043-2094) 2741
†Agape. (UK ISSN 0261-5630) 5132
Agape (Franklin). (US) 4161
Agape (Los Angeles). (US) 3593, 4161
Agarte. (IT) 3520
Agave. (US ISSN 0735-8652) 493
AgBiotech News and Information. (UK ISSN 0954-9897) 461, 2, 487, 4613
AgBiotechnology News. (US ISSN 0899-3998) 487, 68, 4804
Ag'Chem Business. (FR) 166
Age. (US ISSN 0161-9152) 2269
Age and Ageing. (UK ISSN 0002-0729) 2269
Age d'Or Hebdo. (CN) 1296
Age d'Or - Vie Nouvelle. (CN ISSN 0226-6121) 2269, 1681, 4397
Age Discrimination. (US) 3939, 2269
Age News. (US) 2269
Age of Johnson. (US ISSN 0884-5816) 2892, 2305
The Age of Revolution and Romanticism: Interdisciplinary Studies. (US ISSN 1045-4497) 2347
Age of Tomorrow. (JA ISSN 0002-0753) 2207
Ageing and Society. (UK ISSN 0144-686X) 4364, 2269
Ageing International. (US ISSN 0163-5158) 2269
Agence France-Presse Auto see A F P - Auto 4678
Agence France-Presse Cahiers de l'Afrique Occidentale et de l'Afrique Equatoriale see A.F.P. Cahiers de l'Afrique Occidentale et de l'Afrique Equatoriale 3869
Agence France-Presse Sciences see A F P Sciences 3068
Agence Latino-Americaine d'Information Inc. Servicio Mensual de Informacion y Documentacion see A L A I Servicio Mensual de Informacion y Documentacion 842
Agence pour la Securite de la Navigation Aerienne en Afrique et a Madagascar. Direction de l'Exploitation Meteorologique. Publications. Serie 1. (SG ISSN 0065-4248) 3432
Agence pour la Securite de la Navigation Aerienne en Afrique et a Madagascar. Direction de l'Exploitation Meteorologique. Publications. Serie 2. (SG ISSN 0084-6015) 3432
Agence Telegraphique Juive. Bulletin. (FR ISSN 0242-3782) 3871
Agence Togolaise de Presse. Bulletin d'Information. (TG) 4052
Agences de l'Eau. (FR) 4821
Agencia de Noticias Fides. Notas. (BL) 3871
Agencies: What the Actor Needs to Know. (US) 1120, 1368, 3503, 4629
▼Agency. (US) 27
Agency Expertise. (US) 27
Agency Issues. (US) 1062
Agency News. (US) 2526
Agency News Items see Agency News 2526
Agency Sales. (US ISSN 0749-2332) 1032
Agency Sales Magazine see Agency Sales 1032
Agenda. (CN ISSN 0829-4801) 310, 1113, 3520, 3624
Agenda. (UK ISSN 0002-0796) 2987
Agenda. (IT) 4254
Agenda. (NE) 4629
Agenda. (SA ISSN 1013-0950) 4836
Agenda (New York) see Agenda in Brief 1989
▼Agenda (New York, 1991). (US ISSN 1055-1247) 1614, 1724
Agenda (Washington). (US ISSN 0146-020X) 1989
Agenda American Almanac (Year) see Agenda Canadian American Almanac 5132
†Agenda Canadian American Almanac. (CN) 5132
Agenda del Dirigente di Azienda. (IT ISSN 0065-4264) 644
▼Agenda del Rendito Fisso. (IT) 937
Agenda dello Sport. (IT) 4499
Agenda des Armees. (FR) 3450
Agenda dos Criadores e Agricultores. (BL) 209
Agenda Edizione Guida Monaci see Agenda Nazionale 1002
Agenda Estadistica. (MX ISSN 0186-0453) 4561
Agenda for Citizen Involvement see N Y P I R G Agenda 1506
Agenda in Brief. (US) 1989, 2567
Agenda Industriel du Quebec. (CN) 599
Agenda Nautica. (IT) 4723
Agenda Nazionale. (IT) 1002
Agenda New York. (US ISSN 1045-4969) 2220
Agenda World. (CN) 4751
Agenor. (BE ISSN 0002-080X) 3949
Agent. (US) 4616
▼Agent & Manager. (US) 1002, 27
Agent Canada. (CN ISSN 0834-0471) 4751
Agent Commercial. (FR ISSN 0002-0826) 833
Agent de Voyages. (FR) 3624, 4751
Agent Newsletter. (US) 145, 2526
Agent Ontario. (CN) 4751
Agent Orange Review. (US) 2595, 3450
Agent West Weekly see Agent Canada 4751
Agenten. (DK) 899
Agentinformasjon see Agentur 899
Agents and Actions. (SZ ISSN 0065-4299) 3716
Agent's Hotel Gazetteer: America. (UK) 2471, 4751
Agent's Hotel Gazetteer: Cities of Europe. (UK) 2471
Agent's Hotel Gazetteer: Resorts see Agent's Hotel Gazetteer: Resorts of Europe 2471
Agent's Hotel Gazetteer: Resorts of Europe. (UK ISSN 0002-0800) 2471, 4751
Agent's Hotel Gazetteer: Tourist Cities see Agent's Hotel Gazetteer: Cities of Europe 2471
Agents Information Service. (US) 2526
AgentTravel. (SP) 4751
Agentur. (NO) 899
Agenturen und Marken. (GW ISSN 0178-658X) 27
Agenzia di Stampa sui Problemi dell'Emarginazione see A S P E 4396
Agenzia di Viaggi. (IT ISSN 0002-0869) 4751

Agenzia Economica Finanziaria. (IT ISSN 0002-0877) 758
Agenzia Internazionale Letteraria Artistica see A I L A 2857
Agenzia Nazionale Informazioni Turistiche. (IT ISSN 0002-0893) 4751
Agenzia Stampa Filatelica Europea. (IT) 3749
†Ages 3-4 Church and Home Leaflets. (US ISSN 0275-9667) 5132
Ages 4-6 Church and Home Leaflets see Ages 5-6 Church and Home Leaflets 5132
†Ages 5-6 Church and Home Leaflets. (US) 5132
Aggiornamenti di Terapia Oftalmologica.(IT ISSN 0002-0915) 3297
Aggiornamenti Sociali. (IT ISSN 0002-094X) 4364
Aggiornamento del Medico. (IT ISSN 0392-3002) 3072
Aggiornamento Pediatrico. (IT ISSN 0002-0958) 3318
Aggressive Behavior. (US ISSN 0096-140X) 4009
Agham. (PH ISSN 0115-5679) 4297
Aghamtao. (PH) 232
AgImpact. (US) 68
†Agincourt Irregular. (US ISSN 0896-1964) 5132
Aging. (UK ISSN 0268-1544) 2269, 568
Aging (New York). (US ISSN 0361-0179) 2269
Aging (Washington). (US ISSN 0002-0966) 2269
Aging Action Alert. (US ISSN 1050-3188) 2269
Aging and Human Development see International Journal of Aging & Human Development 2274
Aging - Clinical and Experimental Research. (IT ISSN 0394-9532) 2269
Aging: Immunology & Infectious Disease. (US ISSN 0892-8762) 2269, 3182
Aging in the Jewish World. (IS ISSN 0334-9144) 2269, 1989
Aging Network News. (US ISSN 0742-3438) 2270
Aging News. (US) 2270
Aging Program Letter see Aging Network News 2270
Aging Research & Training News. (US ISSN 0888-6830) 2270
Aging Service News see Older Americans Report 4415
Aging Today. (US) 2270
AgLink Index see AgLink Index and Catalogue 132
AgLink Index and Catalogue. (NZ ISSN 0112-2320) 132
AgLink Leaflets. (NZ) 68, 493
†Aglow. (US ISSN 0748-6677) 5132
Agmazine see A G M A Zine 3536
Agnes Scott Alumnae Magazine. (US) 1302
Agni. (US) 2892
Agni Review see Agni 2892
▼Agog. (US) 2987
Agora. (CN) 1302
Agora. (GW ISSN 0177-9265) 1302
Agora. (US) 1989, 2892
Agora (Ravenna). (IT) 3760, 4427
†Agora (Rome). (IT ISSN 0392-8306) 5132
Agra Europe. (UK ISSN 0002-1024) 145
Agra Europe (London). Special Report. (UK ISSN 0142-422X) 145
Agra Psychological Research Cell Journal of Experimental Psychology see A P R C Journal of Experimental Psychology 4008
Agra University. Bulletin. (II ISSN 0044-6734) 1699
Agra University Journal of Research (Science). (II ISSN 0002-1032) 4297
Agradoot. (BG ISSN 0002-1040) 1232, 1296
Agrafile: Grain and Oilseeds. (UK) 204
Agrafile: Livestock and Meat. (UK) 209
†Agrar-Inform. (GW) 5132
Agrar-Praxis. (GW) 166

Agrar-Uebersicht. (GW) 68, 145, 161
Agrargewerbliche Wirtschaft. (GW) 161, 3015
Agrarian Advocate. (US) 68
Agrarian Development Studies. (UK ISSN 0065-4337) 145
Agrarian Research and Training Institute News Letter see A R T I News Letter 67
Agraringenieur see Agraringenieur und Agrarmanager 69
Agraringenieur und Agrarmanager. (GW ISSN 0341-2520) 69
Agrarirodalmi Szemle. (HU ISSN 0002-1067) 132, 2
Agrarisch Dagblad. (NE) 69
Agrarisch Weekoverzicht. (NE ISSN 0002-1075) 132, 204
Agrarische Rundschau. (AU ISSN 0002-0710) 69
Agrarische Voorlichting. (NE) 69
Agrarisches Informationszentrum. (AU) 69
Agrarmarkt-Studien. (GW ISSN 0065-4345) 145
Agrarmeteorologische Bibliographie. (GW ISSN 0515-6831) 132, 3444
Agrarmeteorologischer Wochenbericht fuer Norddeutschland. (GW ISSN 0344-0397) 166
Agrarmeteorologischer Wochenbericht fuer Nordrhein - Westfalen. (GW ISSN 0172-9403) 69, 3432
Agrarmeteorologischer Wochenhinweis fuer das Gebiet Bundesrepublik Deutschland. (GW ISSN 0172-0570) 69, 3432
Agrarrecht. (GW ISSN 0340-840X) 69, 2595
Agrarsoziale Gesellschaft. Geschaefts- und Arbeitsbericht. (GW ISSN 0065-437X) 4427, 69
Agrarsoziale Gesellschaft. Kleine Reihe. (GW ISSN 0170-7671) 4427, 69
Agrarsoziale Gesellschaft. Laendlicher Raum Rundbriefe. (GW ISSN 0179-7603) 4427, 69
Agrarsoziale Gesellschaft. Materialsammlung. (GW ISSN 0344-5712) 4427, 69
Agrarsoziale Gesellschaft. Rundbriefe see Agrarsoziale Gesellschaft. Laendlicher Raum Rundbriefe 4427
†Agrartechnik (Berlin). (GW ISSN 0323-3308) 5132
Agrartechnik (Wuerzburg). (GW) 69
Agrartechnik International see Agrartechnik (Wuerzburg) 69
Agrartorteneti Szemle/Agricultural History Review. (HU ISSN 0002-1105) 69
†Agrarvilag. (HU ISSN 0238-8197) 5132
Agrarwirtschaft. (GW ISSN 0002-1121) 69
Agregation. (FR ISSN 0044-6742) 1614
Agressologie. (FR ISSN 0002-1148) 3072, 426, 3716
Agri-Book Magazine. Beans in Canada. (CN ISSN 0705-3878) 69
Agri-Book Magazine. Corn in Canada. (CN ISSN 0705-3878) 69
Agri-Book Magazine. Drainage Contractor. (CN ISSN 0705-3878) 69
Agri-Book Magazine. Farm Equipment Directory. (CN ISSN 0705-3878) 161
Agri-Book Magazine. Farm Equipment Review. (CN ISSN 0705-3878) 161
Agri-Book Magazine. Potatoes in Canada. (CN ISSN 0705-3878) 69
Agri-Book Magazine. Top Crop Manager.(CN ISSN 0705-3878) 69
Agri-Business Monthly see Agri-Business Scotland 145
Agri-Business Scotland. (UK) 145
Agri-Com. (CN) 69
Agri-Equipment and Chemical. (US) 161
Agri Finance. (US ISSN 0002-1164) 145
Agri Horticultural Society of India. Horticultural Bulletin. (II) 2120

AGRI HORTIQUE

Agri Hortique Genetica. (SW ISSN 0002-1172) **493**, 166
Agri Infos. (NL) **69**
Agri-Mark Journal. (US) **1032**
Agri-Mark Monthly. (US) **197**
Agri Marketing. (US ISSN 0002-1180) **145**, 69
Agri-Naturalist. (US) **69**, 1302
Agri News. (US) **69**
Agri-News. (US ISSN 0744-5598) **69**
Agri-Pick-Up. (FR ISSN 0002-1199) **69**
Agri-Plastics Report. (US) **3861**, 69
Agri-Practice. (US ISSN 0745-452X) **4805**, 209
Agri-Safety Newsletter. (US) **69**
Agri-Service International. (BE) **69**
†Agri-Technology Buyers Guide. (UK) **5132**
Agri-Times Northwest. (US) **69**
Agri View (Iola). (US) **69**
Agribiological Research. (GW) **70**
Agribusiness (Des Moines). (US) **70**
Agribusiness (New York). (US ISSN 0742-4477) **145**
Agribusiness Fieldman. (US) **166**
Agribusiness Worldwide. (US) **146**
†Agrichemical Age. (US ISSN 0044-6769) **5132**
Agrichemical Briefing. (US ISSN 0743-8400) **166**
Agricola XXI. (SP) **161**
Agricola Vergel. (SP ISSN 0211-2728) **166**, 2120
†Agricolas. (BL) **5132**
Agricoltore (Perugia). (IT ISSN 0002-1202) **70**
Agricoltore Bresciano. (IT ISSN 0515-6912) **70**
Agricoltore Cuneense. (IT) **70**
Agricoltore di Terra di Lavoro. (IT ISSN 0400-7719) **70**
Agricoltore Laziale. (IT) **70**
Agricoltore Monregalese. (IT) **70**
Agricoltore Subalpino. (IT) **70**
Agricoltore Trevisano. (IT ISSN 0002-1229) **146**
Agricoltore Veronese. (IT) **70**
Agricoltura (Rome, 19??). (IT) **70**
Agricoltura Aretina. (IT ISSN 0002-1245) **70**
Agricoltura d'Italia. (IT ISSN 0002-127X) **70**
Agricoltura del Friuli-Venezia Giulia. (IT) **70**
Agricoltura delle Venezie. (IT ISSN 0002-1261) **70**
Agricoltura e Cooperazione. (IT) **70**
L'Agricoltura Italiana. (IT) **70**
Agricoltura Mantovana. (IT) **70**
Agricoltura Mediterranea. (IT ISSN 0394-0438) **70**
Agricoltura Nostra. (IT ISSN 0002-1288) **70**
Agricoltura Nuova (Rome). (IT) **70**
Agricoltura Romagnola. (IT ISSN 0002-1296) **70**
Agricom. (CN) **70**
Agriculteur de la Dordogne. (FR) **70**
Agriculteur du Sud-Est Magazine. (FR ISSN 0002-130X) **70**
Agriculteur Valdotain. (IT) **70**
Agriculteurs de France. (FR) **70**
†Agricultor. (BL ISSN 0002-1318) **5132**
Agricultor Practico y Ganadero. (SP ISSN 0213-196X) **209**
Agricultor Venezolano. (VE ISSN 0002-1326) **70**
Agricultura. (SP ISSN 0002-1334) **70**, 209
Agricultura. (DR) **70**
Agricultura. (MZ) **70**
Agricultura Biologico-Dinamica. Boletin. (SP) **70**, 426
Agricultura de las Americas. (US ISSN 0002-1350) **70**
Agricultura e Industrias Agropecuarias y Pesca see Agricultura y Pesca **2050**
Agricultura em Sao Paulo. (BL ISSN 0044-6793) **146**
Agricultura Espanola en (Year). (SP ISSN 0065-440X) **70**
Agricultura, la Pesca y la Alimentacion Espanolas. (SP) **2035**, 70
Agricultura Romaniei. (RM) **70**
Agricultura Tecnica en Mexico. (MX ISSN 0568-2517) **70**

Agricultura y Cooperacion. (SP) **70**
Agricultura y la Pesca Espanolas see Agricultura, la Pesca y la Alimentacion Espanolas **2035**
Agricultura y Pesca. (CL) **2050**
Agricultura y Sociedad. (SP ISSN 0211-8394) **70**
Agriculturae Conspectus Scientificus. see Poljoprivredna Znanstvena Smotra **114**
Agricultural Abstracts for Tanzania. (TZ ISSN 0251-2440) **132**, 2
Agricultural Administration Network. Newsletter see Agricultural Administration Research Extension Network. Newsletter **146**
Agricultural Administration Research Extension Network. Newsletter. (UK ISSN 0951-1865) **146**
Agricultural and Biological Chemistry see Bioscience, Biotechnology, and Biochemistry **433**
Agricultural and Biological Sciences see Arab Gulf Journal of Scientific Research **4299**
Agricultural & Food Research Council Institute of Arable Crops Research. Report see A F R C Institute of Arable Crops Research. Report **165**
Agricultural and Forest Meteorology. (NE ISSN 0168-1923) **3432**, 70
Agricultural and Garden Machinery Service see A G M Service **161**
Agricultural and Natural Resources Educator see A N R Educator **1743**
Agricultural and Sugar Review of Mauritius. see Revue Agricole et Sucriere de Maurice **191**
Agricultural and Technical Academy in Olsztyn. Mechanics and Building Engineering. see Acta Academiae Agriculturae ac Technicae Olstenensis. Aedificatio et Mechanica **1926**
Agricultural & Technical Register see A & T Register **1302**
Agricultural & Veterinary Chemicals. (UK) **166**, 161
Agricultural and Veterinary Chemicals and Agricultural Engineering see Agricultural & Veterinary Chemicals **166**
Agricultural and Veterinary Product Index. (AT ISSN 0816-1623) **132**, 2, 4820
Agricultural Archaeology. see Nongye Kaogu **280**
Agricultural Association of China. Journal/Chung Hua Nung Yeh Hui Hsueh Pao. (CH ISSN 0300-550X) **71**
Agricultural Aviation. (US) **44**, 71
Agricultural Banker. (Il) **146**
Agricultural Banker see A B A Bankers News Weekly **757**
Agricultural Biotechnology News see AgBiotechnology News **487**
Agricultural Books Information Journal. see Nongye Tushu Qingbao Xuekan **2776**
Agricultural Chemical Newsletter. (US) **1216**, 71
Agricultural Chemical Society of Japan. Journal see Nippon Nogeikaggaku Kaishi **491**
Agricultural Chemicals. see Agrochemia **73**
Agricultural Chemicals Monthly. see Kongetsu no Nogyo **184**
†Agricultural Computing. (US ISSN 0882-9284) **5132**
Agricultural Cooperative Service Research Reports see A C S Research Reports **145**
Agricultural Credit. (NP) **146**, 758
Agricultural Credit Corporation of Saskatchewan. Annual Report. (CN) **146**
The Agricultural Credit Letter. (US ISSN 0887-7521) **71**, 758
Agricultural Development and Advisory Service Quarterly Review see A D A S Quarterly Review **5127**
Agricultural Development and Marketing Corporation. Annual Report see Agricultural Development and Marketing Corporation. Annual Report and Statement of Accounts **146**

Agricultural Development and Marketing Corporation. Annual Report and Statement of Accounts. (MW) **146**
Agricultural Development Bank of Pakistan. Annual Report and Statement of Accounts. (PK ISSN 0065-4426) **146**, 758
Agricultural Development Corporation. Annual Report. (KE) **71**
Agricultural Development Corporation. Balance Sheet and Accounts see Agricultural Development and Marketing Corporation. Annual Report and Statement of Accounts **146**
†Agricultural Development Corporation of Saskatchewan. Annual Report. (CN ISSN 0708-5206) **5132**
Agricultural Development in Pakistan. (PK) **71**
Agricultural Digest see Salt and Trace Minerals Report **225**
Agricultural Division. see Nongye Quhua **110**
Agricultural Economic News. see Khao Setthakit Kan-Kaset **201**
Agricultural Economics. (NE ISSN 0169-5150) **146**
Agricultural Economics and Finance. see Economie et Finances Agricoles **149**
Agricultural Economics and Rural Sociology. Bulletins. (US) **146**, 4428
Agricultural Economics and Rural Sociology. Report Series. (US) **146**, 4428
Agricultural Economics and Rural Sociology. Southern Cooperative Series Bulletin. (US) **146**, 4428
Agricultural Economics and Rural Sociology. Special Reports. (US) **146**, 4428
Agricultural Economics Bulletin (No.). (AT ISSN 0313-377X) **146**
Agricultural Economics Miscellaneous Publication (No.) see University of New England. Department of Agricultural Economics and Business Management. Agricultural Economics Miscellaneous Publication (No.) **159**
Agricultural Economy. see Zemedelska Ekonomika **160**
Agricultural Education. (US ISSN 0732-4677) **71**, 1614
Agricultural Educators Directory. (US) **71**, 1699
†Agricultural Electronics. (US) **5132**
Agricultural Engineer. (UK ISSN 0308-5732) **71**
Agricultural Engineering. (CE) **71**
Agricultural Engineering. (US ISSN 0002-1458) **166**
Agricultural Engineering. Bulletins. (US) **166**, 161
Agricultural Engineering. Report Series. (US) **166**, 161
Agricultural Engineering. Special Reports. (US) **166**, 161
Agricultural Engineering Abstracts. (UK ISSN 0308-8863) **132**, 2, 1841
Agricultural Engineering Australia. (AT ISSN 0044-6807) **166**, 161
Agricultural Engineering in South Africa.(SA) **161**, 166
†Agricultural Engineering Today. (Il ISSN 0970-2962) **5132**
Agricultural Engineers Yearbook of Standards see A S A E Standards **165**
Agricultural Enterprise Studies in England and Wales. (UK) **146**
Agricultural Estate, Tax & Business Planning. (US) **758**, 71, 1087
Agricultural Experiment. see Nongcun Kexue Shiyan **110**
Agricultural Experiment Station Suriname. Annual Report. see Landbouwproefstation Suriname. Jaarverslag **104**
Agricultural Finance Review. (US ISSN 0002-1466) **146**
†Agricultural Genetics Report. (US ISSN 0278-9736) **5132**
Agricultural History. (US ISSN 0002-1482) **71**, 2305
Agricultural History of China. see Zhongguo Nong-Shi **131**
Agricultural History Review. see Agrartorteneti Szemle **69**

Agricultural History Review. (UK ISSN 0002-1490) **71**
Agricultural Knowledge. see Nongye Zhishi **110**
Agricultural Land Bulletin. (AT) **71**
Agricultural Law. (US) **2595**, 71
Agricultural Law Manual. (US) **2596**, 71
Agricultural Law Update. (US) **146**, 2596
Agricultural Letter. (US ISSN 0002-1512) **71**
Agricultural Libraries Information Notes.(US ISSN 0095-2699) **2741**, 71
Agricultural Literature of Czechoslovakia. (CS ISSN 0002-1520) **132**, 2, 2111, 4834
Agricultural Machinery. see Nongye Jixie **163**
Agricultural Machinery Dealers' Digest. (SA) **161**
Agricultural Machinery Experiment and Popularization. see Nongji Shiyan yu Tuiguang **163**
Agricultural Machinery News. see Noki Shinbun **163**
Agricultural Manpower. (UK ISSN 0260-2040) **71**
Agricultural Marketing. (Il ISSN 0002-1555) **71**
Agricultural Marketing/Taswiq Al-Ziraiy. (JO) **146**
Agricultural Markets: Places. (EI ISSN 0250-9601) **71**, 1032
Agricultural News. (US ISSN 0002-158X) **71**
Agricultural Pesticide Society. Annual Meeting. Proceedings see Canadian Pest Management Society Proceedings **172**
Agricultural Policy and Economics Issues. (US) **146**
Agricultural Prices in India see India. Ministry of Agriculture. Directorate of Economics and Statistics. Bulletin of Agriculture Prices **138**
Agricultural Processing and Manufacturing Guide see Directory of Alberta's Agricultural Processing Industry **149**
Agricultural Production Levels in Bangladesh. (BG) **146**
Agricultural Progress. (UK ISSN 0065-4493) **146**
Agricultural Real Estate Values in Alberta. (CN ISSN 0701-7502) **4144**, 71
Agricultural Regions of Cyprus. (CY) **71**
Agricultural Research. (US ISSN 0002-161X) **71**
Agricultural Research Abstracts and Newsletter. (Il ISSN 0970-4019) **132**
Agricultural Research Center. Proceedings of the Annual Meeting. (US) **71**
Agricultural Research Centres. (UK) **71**
Agricultural Research Council of Malawi. Annual Report see Malawi. Department of Agricultural Research. Annual Report **106**
Agricultural Research Department. Winand Staring Centre for Integrated Land, Soil and Water Research. Reports. (NE ISSN 0924-3062) **166**, 1942, 4821
Agricultural Research Guyana. (GY ISSN 0065-4523) **71**
Agricultural Research Index see Agricultural Research Centres **71**
Agricultural Research Institute of Ontario. Annual Report. (CN ISSN 0706-425X) **71**
Agricultural Research Journal of Kerala.(Il ISSN 0002-1628) **72**
Agricultural Research Organization. Scientific Activities. (IS) **72**, 4593
Agricultural Research Organization. Special Publications. (IS ISSN 0334-2484) **72**
Agricultural Research Organization. Yedion. (IS) **72**
Agricultural Review for Europe. (UN ISSN 0501-3054) **146**, 842
Agricultural Reviews. (Il ISSN 0253-1496) **72**

Agricultural Revolution Review. see Thawrah al-Ziraia **124**
Agricultural Science and Technology see AgLink Leaflets **68**
Agricultural Science and Technology Bulletin. see Nongye Keji Tongxun **110**
†Agricultural Science Bulletin. (CN ISSN 0707-7793) **5132**
Agricultural Science Digest. (II ISSN 0253-150X) **72**, **166**, **209**
▼Agricultural Science in Finland. (FI ISSN 0789-600X) **72**
Agricultural Science in the Netherlands. (NE ISSN 0169-4901) **72**
Agricultural Situation see Farmline Magazine **91**
Agricultural Situation in Eastern Europe see World Agriculture Regional Supplement: Eastern Europe **160**
Agricultural Situation in India. (II ISSN 0002-1679) **132**
Agricultural Situation in Western Europe see World Agriculture Regional Supplement: Western Europe **160**
Agricultural Society of Nigeria. Proceedings. (NR ISSN 0065-454X) **72**
Agricultural Spray Adjuvants. (US) **1216**, **72**
Agricultural Statistics. see Norway. Statistisk Sentralbyraa. Jordbruksstatistikk **141**
Agricultural Statistics, England. (UK ISSN 0262-2394) **72**
Agricultural Statistics, England and Wales see Agricultural Statistics, England **72**
Agricultural Statistics, Madhya Pradesh see Madhya Pradesh. Directorate of Agriculture. Agricultural Statistics **140**
Agricultural Statistics of Bangladesh see Yearbook of Agricultural Statistics of Bangladesh **130**
Agricultural Statistics of Greece. (GR ISSN 0065-4574) **132**, **4561**
Agricultural Statistics of Sabah. (MY) **132**
Agricultural Statistics of Sarawak. (MY) **132**
Agricultural Statistics Series No.1: Crop Production. (EI) **132**, **166**
Agricultural Statistics Series No.2: Animal Production. (EI) **132**
Agricultural Statistics Series No.3: European Communities Index of Agricultural Prices. (EI) **132**, **4561**
Agricultural Structure and Production. see Turkey. Devlet Istatistik Enstitusu. Tarimsal Yapi ve Uretim **125**
Agricultural Supply Industry. (UK ISSN 0140-4822) **72**
Agricultural Systems. (UK ISSN 0308-521X) **72**
Agricultural Technology. see Zemedelska Technika **130**
Agricultural Technology Marketing. see Nongji Tuiguang **110**
Agricultural Trade in Europe. (UN) **146**, **842**
Agricultural Trends. (AT ISSN 0725-5454) **72**
Agricultural University of Norway. Department of Agricultural Engineering. Research Reports. see Norges Landbrukshoegskole. Institutt for Tekniske Fag. Rapporter **111**
Agricultural University of Norway. Department of Building Technology in Agriculture. Annual Report. see Norges Landbrukshoegskole. Institutt for Bygningsteknikk. Aarsmelding **5248**
Agricultural University of Norway. Department of Land Use Planning. Serie. see Norges Landbrukshoegskole. Institutt for Jordskifte og Arealplanlegging. Melding **155**
Agricultural University of Norway, Department of Agricultural Engineering, Test Reports. see Norges Landbrukshoegskole. Institutt for Tekniske Fag. Proevemeldinger **111**
Agricultural Wages in India. (II ISSN 0084-6066) **146**, **970**

Agricultural Water Management. (NE ISSN 0378-3774) **167**, **4821**
Agricultural Working People of Korea. (KN) **72**, **3871**
Agricultural Zoology Reviews. (UK ISSN 0269-0543) **576**
Agriculture. (CN ISSN 0002-1687) **72**
Agriculture. (FR ISSN 0002-1709) **72**
Agriculture. (NR) **72**
Agriculture. see Polnohospodarstvo **114**
Agriculture Africaine. (FR) **146**
Agriculture and Agro-Industries Journal. (II ISSN 0002-1725) **72**
Agriculture and Better Farming. see Nogyo Fumin **186**
Agriculture and Economy. see Nogyo to Keizai **155**
Agriculture and Horticulture/Noko to Engei. (JA) **72**, **2120**
Agriculture and Veterinary Sciences International Who's Who. (UK) **72**
Agriculture Checklist. (II ISSN 0002-1733) **132**
Agriculture d'Eure et Loir see Horizons **96**
Agriculture dans le Monde - F I P A Nouvelles see World Agriculture - I F A P News **130**
Agriculture Decisions. (US ISSN 0002-1741) **2596**, **72**
Agriculture, Ecosystems and Environment. (NE ISSN 0167-8809) **72**, **1942**
Agriculture et Cooperation. (FR ISSN 0181-995X) **72**
Agriculture et Vie see Du Sol a la Table **1947**
Agriculture in Denmark. (DK ISSN 0905-5142) **132**
Agriculture in Jordan/Zira'at Fi El-Urdon.(JO) **72**
Agriculture in Northern Ireland. (UK ISSN 0002-175X) **72**
Agriculture in Scotland. (UK) **73**
Agriculture in the Arab World. see Al-Zira'a fil-Alam al-Arabi **131**
Agriculture International. (UK ISSN 0269-2457) **73**
Agriculture News Bulletin see Pennsylvania Agriculture News **156**
Agriculture Pratique see Agriculteurs de France **70**
†Agriculture Review. (US) **5132**
Agriculture Teachers Directory see Agricultural Educators Directory **71**
AGRIDEV Weekly Bulletin. (PH) **132**
Agrifack. (SW ISSN 0044-6831) **73**, **842**, **1942**
Agrikultura. (CS) **73**, **2347**
Agriloper. (NE ISSN 0925-2762) **73**
Agrindex. (UN ISSN 0254-8801) **73**, **2035**, **2060**, **2095**
Agrinform. (IT ISSN 1120-3889) **806**
Agripesca. (SP) **2036**
AgriScience. (CN ISSN 0840-8289) **73**
Agrishell. (SP ISSN 0211-030X) **73**
Agrisul. (BL ISSN 0002-1784) **73**
Agritrade. (UK) **146**
Agritrop. (FR ISSN 0399-1539) **73**
Agriweek. (CN ISSN 0228-5584) **73**
Agro-Chemicals News in Brief. (UN ISSN 0257-5035) **167**, **146**
Agro Chemie Koerier. (Dutch translation of: Pflanzenschutz Kurier) (NE) **167**
Agro-Environmental Protection. see Nongye Huanjing Baohu **1964**
Agro-Nouvelles. (CN ISSN 0065-4655) **73**
Agro-Service/Landbouw Service. (BE ISSN 0002-1814) **73**
Agro-Sintesis. (MX) **73**
Agro Sur. (CL ISSN 0304-8802) **73**, **426**, **4428**
†Agroanalysis. (BL ISSN 0100-4298) **5132**
Agroborealis. (US ISSN 0002-1822) **73**
Agrochemia/Agricultural Chemicals. (CS ISSN 0002-1830) **73**, **1169**
Agrochemia. (PL ISSN 0002-1849) **73**, **1169**
Agrochemicals Handbook. (UK) **73**, **1169**
Agrochimica. (IT ISSN 0002-1857) **73**, **1169**

Agrociencia. (MX ISSN 0185-0288) **73**
Agroconocimiento. (DR) **73**
Agrodiario. (CK) **73**
Agroekonomika. (YU ISSN 0350-5928) **146**, **4428**
Agroforesterie Aujourd'hui see Agroforestry Today **74**
Agroforestry Abstracts. (UK ISSN 0952-1453) **2111**, **132**, **461**
Agroforestry Review see Agroforestry Today **74**
Agroforestry Systems. (NE ISSN 0167-4366) **74**, **2095**
Agroforestry Today. (KE ISSN 1013-9591) **74**
†Agrohemija. (YU ISSN 0002-1865) **5132**
Agroindex - Automated Information System. (CS) **132**, **2**, **2111**, **4820**
Agroindustry: Latin American Industrial Report. (US) **147**
Agrokemia es Talajtan. (HU ISSN 0002-1873) **74**
Agrokhimiya. (RU ISSN 0002-1881) **74**
Agrologisk Tidsskrift Marken. (DK ISSN 0108-8459) **74**
†Agromatique. (FR) **5132**
Agrometeorological Report. (TH ISSN 0857-2410) **3432**
Agrometeorolosko Porocilo. (XV ISSN 0352-1818) **3432**
Agronews see AgriScience **73**
Agronomia Costarricense. (CR ISSN 0377-9424) **74**
Agronomia Lusitana. (PO ISSN 0002-1911) **167**
Agronomia Mocambicana. (MZ ISSN 0044-6858) **74**, **493**
Agronomia Sulriograndense. (BL ISSN 0400-8111) **74**, **426**
Agronomia Tropical. (VE ISSN 0002-192X) **167**
Agronomico. (BL ISSN 0365-2726) **74**
Agronomie. (FR ISSN 0249-5627) **167**, **147**
Agronomie Tropicale. (FR ISSN 0002-1946) **167**
Agronomiliitto. Yearbook. (FI) **74**
Agronomski Glasnik. (CI ISSN 0002-1954) **74**
Agronomy: a Series of Monographs. (US ISSN 0065-4663) **74**
Agronomy Abstracts. (US ISSN 0065-4671) **132**, **2**
Agronomy Institute. Annual Report. (RH) **74**
Agronomy Journal. (US ISSN 0002-1962) **74**
Agronomy News. (US) **74**
Agronomy Society of New Zealand. Proceedings. (NZ ISSN 0110-6589) **167**
Agropecuario (Venezuela). (VE) **74**
Agropromyshlennyi Kompleks Rossii see Khozyain (Moscow) **103**
Agros. (PO ISSN 0002-1970) **74**
Agroselekt. Reihe 1: Landtechnik. (GW ISSN 0233-2655) **132**, **2**
Agroselekt. Reihe 2: Pflanzenproduktion. (GW ISSN 0233-2701) **132**, **2**
Agroselekt. Reihe 3: Tierproduktion. (GW ISSN 0233-2752) **133**, **2**
Agroselekt. Reihe 4: Veterinaermedizin. (GW ISSN 0233-2809) **4820**, **2**
Agrosintesis. (CK ISSN 0044-6882) **74**
Agrotecnia de Cuba. (CU ISSN 0568-3114) **74**
Agrotehnicar. (CI ISSN 0002-1989) **74**
Agroticos Synergatismos. (GR ISSN 1105-1213) **828**
Agrotis/Countryman. (CY ISSN 0002-1997) **74**
Agrotropica. (BL ISSN 0103-3816) **75**
Agrow. (UK ISSN 0268-313X) **75**, **1213**
Agrupacion Astronomica de Sabadell. Circular Informativa. (SP) **360**
Agrupacion Sindical Nacional de Empresas de Financiacion. Censo. (SP) **758**
Agua. (VE ISSN 0044-6890) **1923**

Agua. see Water International **5303**
Ha-Agudah ha-Israelit le-Gerontologyah. Yedion. see Israel Gerontological Society. Information Bulletin **2274**
Agur. (FR) **1989**
AgVenture. (US ISSN 0887-9133) **75**
Agway Cooperator. (US ISSN 0002-2012) **75**
Agweek. (US) **75**
Aha. (GW) **4161**
†Aha! (SZ) **5132**
Ahad. (LE ISSN 0002-3981) **3871**, **1614**
Al-Ahad al-Gedid. (UA) **2185**
Aha'llono. (US ISSN 0098-9738) **2596**
Ahali. (UA) **2857**, **2185**
Ahang. (PK) **2213**
Ahang. (IR) **3537**
Ahara Vijnana. see Food Science **2070**
Al-Ahd. (QA) **2857**
AHEPAN see A H E P A N **1988**
Ahfad Journal. (SJ ISSN 0255-4070) **4858**, **3949**
Ahijuna. (AG ISSN 0002-2039) **2397**, **2892**
Ahimsa. (US) **3602**
Ahlan Wasahlan/Hello, Welcome. (SU) **4801**
Al-Ahly. (TS) **1296**, **4463**
Ahmadi. (BG) **2173**
Ahmadu Bello University. Centre for the Study of Nigerian Languages. Harsunan Nijeriya see Harsunan Nijeriya **2816**
Ahmadu Bello University. Centre of Islamic Legal Studies. Journal. (NR ISSN 0065-468X) **4217**
Ahmadu Bello University. Department of Geography. Occasional Paper. (NR ISSN 0065-4698) **2241**
Ahmadu Bello University. Institute for Agricultural Research. Annual Report.(NR ISSN 0065-471X) **75**
Ahmadu Bello University. Institute for Agricultural Research. Soil Survey Bulletin. (NR ISSN 0065-4728) **167**
Ahmadu Bello University. Institute of Education. Paper see Nigeria Educational Forum. Journal **1651**
Ahmadu Bello University. Northern History Research Scheme. Interim Report. (NR) **2331**
Ahmadu Bello University. Northern History Research Scheme. Papers see Ahmadu Bello University. Northern History Research Scheme. Interim Report **2331**
Ahmedabad Textile Industry's Research Association. Joint Technological Conferences. Proceedings. (II ISSN 0075-4005) **4616**
Ahnenlisten Kartei. (GW ISSN 0170-2653) **2143**
Ahora see Mas **2013**
Ahora. (DR ISSN 0002-2047) **2185**
Ahoy! (US) **1467**, **1458**
Ahoy! (AT) **4521**
Ahoy! Disk Magazine. (US) **1467**, **1458**
▼Al-Ahram al-Riyadi. (UA) **4463**
Ahram Index. (UA ISSN 0303-2728) **2577**, **2**
Al-Ahram al-Iqtisadi/Economic Al-Ahram.(UA) **2185**
Al-Ahram Medical Guide. see Dalil al-Ahram al-Tibbi **3092**
Ahsahta. (US) **2987**
Ahwaz University of Medical Sciences. Scientific Medical Journal/Majalleh Elmi Peseshki Daneshgahe Elome Pezeshki Ahwaz. (IR) **3072**
Ai Nostri Amici. (IT ISSN 0002-4066) **4254**
Aiastani Kensabanakan Andes. (AI ISSN 0017-8683) **4297**
Aichi Cancer Center Research Institute. Annual Report see Aichi Cancer Center Research Institute. Scientific Report **3192**
Aichi Cancer Center Research Institute. Scientific Report. (JA) **3192**
Aichi-Gakuin Journal of Dental Science. (JA ISSN 0044-6912) **3227**
Aichi-ken Kyodo Shiryo Sogo Mokuroku.(JA) **388**

5886 AICHI KYOIKU

Aichi Kyoiku Daigaku Kenkyu Hokoku. Geijutsu, Hoken Taiiku, Kasei, Gijutsu Kagaku. (JA ISSN 0388-7367) **4297**

Aichi Kyoiku Daigaku Kenkyu Hokoku. Shizen Kagaku/Aichi University of Education. Natural Science Bulletin. (JA ISSN 0365-3722) **4297**, 3027

Aichi Medical University Association. Journal. (JA ISSN 0301-0902) **3072**

Aichi University of Education. Natural Science Bulletin. see Aichi Kyoiku Daigaku Kenkyu Hokoku. Shizen Kagaku **4297**

▼Aid for Education Report. (US ISSN 1058-1324) **4052**, 1614

Aid Newsletter see A M S A A Newsletter **2458**

Aida Parker Newsletter. (SA) **3871**

Aidai-Echoes. (US ISSN 0002-208X) **1989**

Aidai Menesinis see Aidai-Echoes **1989**

Aide Inter-Monasteres Secretariat Monastic Bulletin see A I M Monastic Bulletin **4254**

Aide Juridique Nouveau Brunswick Rapport Annuel. see Legal Aid New Brunswick Annual Report **2734**

Aids and Research Tools in Ancient Near Eastern Studies. (US ISSN 0732-6505) **2427**

Aids and Research Tools in Middle Eastern Studies. (US) **2427**

Aids Index to How to do It Information see Index to How to Do It Information **14**

Aiguillon. see Hosteni **2570**

Aikakan Himiakan Amsagir/Armenian Chemical Journal. (AI ISSN 0002-2101) **1169**

†Aikamerkki. (FI ISSN 0044-6920) **5132**

Aiken No Tomo. see Friends of Dog **3710**

Aiki News/Aiki Nyusu. (JA ISSN 0915-9517) **4463**

Aiki Nyusu. see Aiki News **4463**

Aileron. (US) **2987**, 310, 3788

Ailes Magazine. (FR) **45**

Ailleurs et Demain; Classiques. (FR ISSN 0065-4787) **2892**

Aim. (II) **4280**

Aim. (CN ISSN 0382-4373) **4463**

Aim (Boston). (US) **2526**

Aim (Kansas City). (US) **3624**

Aim - Far (Year). (US) **45**

Aim Magazine (Chicago). (US) **1990**, 3939

Aims of Education and Development of Personality. Comparative Aspects. Proceedings of the CESE Conference.(BE) **1614**

Al-Ain. (TS) **4052**

Ain Agricole. (FR ISSN 0002-2136) **75**

Ain Shams Medical Journal. (UA ISSN 0002-2144) **3072**

Aiolika Grammata. (GR) **2892**

Air Accidents & the News Media. (US) **45**, 2567

Air Accidents and the Newswriter see Air Accidents & the News Media **45**

Air Actualites. (FR ISSN 0002-2152) **3450**, 45

Air Alaska. (US ISSN 0889-9576) **45**, 4669

Air Almanac. (UK ISSN 0002-2160) **45**

Air & Business Travel. (UK) **4669**

Air and Cosmos Monthly see Aerospace World **44**

Air and Space Lawyer. (US ISSN 0747-7449) **2596**, 45

Air & Space - Smithsonian. (US ISSN 0886-2257) **45**, 1743

Air & Waste Management Association. Journal. (US ISSN 1047-3289) **1942**

Air and Water News see Air - Water Pollution Report **1942**

Air & Water Pollution Control. (US ISSN 0890-0396) **1942**

Air-Britain Airline Fleets. (UK) **4669**

Air-Britain Digest. (UK ISSN 0950-7434) **45**

Air-Britain News. (UK ISSN 0950-7442) **45**

Air Cadet see Air Cadet Review **1248**

Air Cadet Review. (UK) **1248**, 45

Air California Magazine see AirCal **4751**

Air Canada. Annual Report. (CN ISSN 0568-3424) **45**

Air Cargo. (IT) **4669**

†Air Cargo. (FR) **5132**

Air Cargo Agents Association of India. News. (II) **4707**

Air Cargo News. (US) **4669**

Air Cargo World. (US ISSN 0745-5100) **4669**

Air Carrier, Aircraft Utilization and Propulsion Reliability Report. (US) **4669**

Air Carrier Financial Statements see Canadian Civil Aviation **4663**

Air Carrier Financial Statistics. (US ISSN 0002-2225) **4661**

Air Carrier Industry Schedule Service Traffic Statistics see Air Carrier Industry Schedule Service Traffic Statistics. Medium Regional Carriers **4669**

Air Carrier Industry Schedule Service Traffic Statistics. Medium Regional Carriers. (US) **4669**

Air Carrier Operations in Canada/Operations des Transporteurs. Aeriens au Canada. (CN ISSN 0008-2570) 66, 4561

Air Carrier Traffic at Canadian Airports. (CN ISSN 0701-7928) **4661**, 4561

Air Circle. see Meishu Jie **335**

Air Classics. (US ISSN 0002-2241) **45**

Air Combat. (US) **3450**

Air Comprime. (FR ISSN 0002-225X) **1926**

Air Conditioning & Heating Service & Repair - Domestic Cars, Light Trucks & Vans. (US) **4679**, 2297, 4742

Air Conditioning & Heating Service & Repair - Imported Cars & Trucks. (US) **4679**, 2297, 4742

Air-Conditioning & Refrigeration Wholesalers Counterline see A R W Counterline **2297**

Air Conditioning Contractors of America News see A C C A News **2297**

Air Conditioning Contractors of America Quality Contractor's Catalog of Materials, Products and Services see A C C A Quality Contractor's Catalog of Materials, Products and Services **2304**

Air Conditioning, Heating & Refrigeration News. (US ISSN 0002-2276) **2297**

Air Conservation. see Ochrana Ovzdusi **1978**

Air Courier Conference of America Express see A C C A Express **4669**

Air Craft Flyer see A C Flyer **4669**

Air Currents. (US ISSN 0400-8510) **1942**

Air Enthusiast see Air International **45**

Air et Cosmos. (FR ISSN 0044-6971) **1942**

Air Fan. (FR ISSN 0223-0038) **3450**, 2433

Air Force Civil Engineer see Air Force Engineering & Services Quarterly **1861**

Air Force Comptroller. (US ISSN 0002-2365) **3450**, 45

Air Force Engineering & Services Quarterly. (US ISSN 0362-188X) **1861**, 3450

Air Force Interchangeable and Substitution Report. (US) **3476**

Air Force Journal of Logistics. (US ISSN 0270-403X) **3450**

Air Force Law Review. (US ISSN 0094-8381) **2596**

Air Force List. (UK) **3450**

Air Force Magazine. (US ISSN 0730-6784) **3450**, 45

Air Force Times. (US ISSN 0002-2403) **3450**, 45

Air Forces Monthly. (UK ISSN 0955-7091) **3450**

†Air Forces of the World. (UK) **5132**

Air France Madame. (FR) **4801**, 4836

Air Freight Directory. (US ISSN 0092-2870) **4670**, 1120

Air Gazette. see Gaceta Aerea **53**

Air Gunner. (UK) **4463**

Air Industriel see Energie Fluide - L'Air Industriel **3017**

Air Infiltration Review. (UK ISSN 0143-6643) **2297**, 1783

Air International. (UK ISSN 0306-5634) **45**, 2433

Air Jobs Digest. (US) **3624**, 45

Air Law. (NE ISSN 0165-2079) **4670**

Air Line Employee. (US ISSN 0002-2411) **2579**

Air Line Pilot. (US ISSN 0002-242X) **45**, 2579, 4670

Air Market News. (US) **45**

Air Museum News see Museum of Flight News **59**

Air New Zealand. Annual Report. (NZ ISSN 0065-4817) **4670**

Air Pictorial. (UK ISSN 0002-2462) **45**

Air Pilot. (AT ISSN 0727-338X) **4670**

Air Pollution Advisory see Environmental Spectrum **1953**

▼The Air Pollution Consultant. (US) **1942**

▼Air Pollution Control (Novi). (US) **1942**

Air Pollution Control (Washington). (US ISSN 0196-7150) **1942**

Air Pollution Control Associates Government Agencies Directory see A P C A Government Agencies Directory **5128**

†Air Pollution Control Progress. (US) **5132**

Air Pollution Effects Surveillance Network Data Report see Air Quality Data for Arizona **1942**

Air Pollution Management. (US) **1942**

Air Pollution Titles. (US ISSN 0002-2497) **1972**, 2, 1975

Air Power History. (US ISSN 1044-016X) **45**, 2305

Air Power Museum Bulletin see A P M Bulletin **254**

Air Press. (IT) **45**

Air Progress. (US ISSN 0002-2500) **45**

Air Progress Warbirds International. (US) **45**

Air Quality Data for Arizona. (US) **1942**

Air Rhodesia Annual Report see Air Zimbabwe Annual Report **4670**

Air Safety Law and Technology see Air Safety Week **45**

Air Safety Week. (US ISSN 1044-727X) **45**, 2596

Air Toxics Reports. (US) **1942**

Air Traffic Control Association. Bulletin. (US ISSN 0400-1915) **4670**, 2596

Air Traffic Control Association. Fall Conference Proceedings. (US ISSN 0192-8740) **45**

Air Transport. (US) **4670**

Air Transport Association of Canada. Annual Report. (CN ISSN 0065-485X) **4670**

Air Transport Magazine see Aviation Magazine International **47**

†Air Transport Management. (CN) **5132**

Air Transport Newsletter see International Air Transport Newsletter **3618**

Air Transport World. (US ISSN 0002-2543) **45**, 4646

Air Transportation Annual (Bombay). (II) **4670**

Air Travel see Air & Business Travel **4669**

Air Travel and Interline News see Air & Business Travel **4669**

Air Travel Journal. (US) **4751**

Air University Library Index to Military Periodicals. (US ISSN 0002-2586) **3476**, 2

Air University Review see Airpower Journal **3450**

Air - Water Pollution Report. (US ISSN 0002-2608) **1942**

Air Weather Service Observer. (US ISSN 0002-2616) **3432**

Air Wisconsin - Air Destinations. (US) **4801**

Air Zimbabwe Annual Report. (RH) **4670**

Airborne A S W Log see A S W Log **42**

Airborne Magazine. (AT) **2433**, 4463

Airborne Static Line. (US ISSN 1059-7468) **3450**

Airbrush Action. (US ISSN 1040-8509) **310**, 1160, 2433

Airbrush Zeitung. (GW) **27**, 310

AirCal. (US) **4751**

AirCal Magazine see AirCal **4751**

Airconditioning and Refrigeration Business see Contracting Business **2298**

Aircraft see Aircraft & Aerospace **45**

Aircraft. see Samolyot **61**

Aircraft Accident Digest. (UN ISSN 0065-4876) **45**

Aircraft & Aerospace. (AT) **45**

†Aircraft Dealer. (US) **5132**

Aircraft Engineering see Aircraft Engineering and Aerospace Technology **45**

Aircraft Engineering. see Koku Gijutsu **58**

Aircraft Engineering and Aerospace Technology. (UK) **45**

Aircraft Illustrated. (UK ISSN 0002-2675) **45**

Aircraft Illustrated Annual see Civil Aviation Review **50**

Aircraft Industry Record. (UK ISSN 0002-2683) **45**

Aircraft Magazine see Aviation Digest **47**

Aircraft Owners and Pilots Association. Handbook for Pilots see A O P A's Aviation U S A **42**

Aircraft Owners and Pilots Association General Aviation National Report see A O P A General Aviation National Report **5128**

Aircraft Owners and Pilots Association of Australia Magazine see A.O.P.A. Magazine **42**

Aircraft Owners and Pilots Association Pilot see A O P A Pilot **42**

Aircraft Technician. (US ISSN 1044-8012) **4670**

Airedale Terrier Club of America. Newsletter. (US) **3707**

Aireings. (UK ISSN 0261-0124) **2892**, 2987

Aireview. see Koku Joho **2437**

Airfinance Annual. (UK ISSN 0266-2132) **938**

Airfinance Journal. (UK ISSN 0143-2257) **4670**, 758

†Airfix. (UK ISSN 0002-2705) **5132**

Airflow. (AT) **46**, 4539

Airforce. (CN ISSN 0704-6804) **46**

Airgun World. (UK) **4463**

Airline Business. (UK ISSN 0268-7615) **4670**, 1002

Airline Data News see World Airline Fleets News **4678**

Airline Executive see Airline Executive International **4670**

Airline Executive International. (US ISSN 1051-631X) **4670**, 1002

Airline Financial News. (US ISSN 1040-5410) **4670**, 644

Airline Fleet Record. (UK ISSN 0002-2721) **4670**

Airline Fleets see Air-Britain Airline Fleets **4669**

Airline Guide to Stewardess and Stewards Career see Official Guide to Flight Attendants Careers **3630**

Airline Handbook. (US ISSN 0095-4683) **4670**

Airline Industrial Relations Conference. Newsletter. (US) **4670**

Airline Newsletter. (US ISSN 0002-2748) **4670**

Airline Ninety Two. (SP) **4670**

Airline Operational Control Society News see A O C S News **4669**

Airline Passengers Association Holiday see A P A Holiday **4750**

Airline Service Unlimited Travel Guide see A S U Travel Guide **4750**

Airline, Ship & Catering Onboard Services Magazine. (US ISSN 0892-4236) **4670**, 2060

Airliners. (US ISSN 0896-6575) **4670**

Airman. (US ISSN 0002-2756) **3450**, 46

Airman's Information Manual see Aim - Far (Year) 45
Airman's Information Manual. Basic Flight Information and A T C Procedures see Airman's Information Manual. Official Guide to Basic Flight Information and A T C Procedures 46
Airman's Information Manual. Notices to Airmen see Notices to Airmen 60
Airman's Information Manual. Official Guide to Basic Flight Information and A T C Procedures. (US) 46
Airnews. (AT) 46
Airone. (IT) 426
Airport. (UK) 4670
Airport Executive Magazine. (US) 4670
Airport Forum. (GW ISSN 0002-2802) 599
Airport Forum News. (GW ISSN 0174-3279) 4670
Airport Highlights. (US) 4670
Airport Journal. (US) 4670
Airport News see B A A News 4671
Airport Operations. (US ISSN 0898-574X) 4670
Airport Operations Safety Bulletin see Airport Operations 4670
Airport Pocket Guide. (US ISSN 0894-1513) 4751, 4670
Airport Press. (US) 4670
†Airport Quarterly. (US) 5132
Airport Report. (US ISSN 0044-7021) 4670
Airport Services Management. (US ISSN 0002-2829) 46, 4646
Airport Support. (UK) 4670
Airports. (US) 4671
Airports International Magazine. (UK) 46, 4646
Airpost Journal. (US ISSN 0739-0939) 3749
Airpower. (US) 46
AirPower. (AT) 46
Airpower Journal. (US ISSN 0897-0823) 3450, 46
Airteam Circle. (JM) 4671
Airtech News. (US) 1942
Airtrade. (UK ISSN 0306-0349) 4671
AirTran News see N A T A News 4676
Airwave. (CN) 3364
Airwaves see Spectrum 1380
Airways see Plane and Pilot 60
Ais-Eiri see An Gael 2002
†Aisle View. (US) 5133
Aisthesis. (CL ISSN 0568-3939) 3760, 310, 1614
Aitia Magazine. (US) 2502
Aitvaras. (LI) 1248
Aizheng/Cancer. (CC ISSN 1000-467X) 3192
Aja. (FI ISSN 0355-9610) 4679
Ajedrez de Estilo. (AG) 4463
Ajedrez Universal. (CK) 4463
†Ajedrez 2000. (AG) 5133
Ajia Keizai. see Asian Economies 646
Ajia Keizai Shiryo-Geppo. see Institute of Developing Economies. Library Bulletin 2763
Ajia Shiryo Tsuho. see Materials on Asia - Accession List and Review 406
Ajman. (TS) 806
Ajman Chamber of Commerce and Industry. Magazine see Ajman 806
Ajuris. (BL) 2596
Ak Express. (GW) 2052, 2433
Akademac. (YU) 3450
Akademia Athenon. Kentron Erevnes tis Hellenikis Laographias. Epeteris. (GR) 2052, 2347
Akademia Athenon. Pragmateiai. (GR) 2347
Akademia Athenon. Praktika. (GR) 2347
Akademia Ekonomiczna, Krakow. Zeszyty Naukowe. (PL ISSN 0208-7944) 644
Akademia Ekonomiczna, Krakow. Zeszyty Naukowe. Seria Specjalna: Monografie. (PL ISSN 0209-1674) 644
Akademia Ekonomiczna, Poznan. Zeszyty Naukowe. Seria 1. (PL ISSN 0079-4546) 644
Akademia Ekonomiczna, Poznan. Zeszyty Naukowe. Seria 2. Prace Habilitacyjne i Doktorskie. (PL ISSN 0079-4554) 644

Akademia Ekonomiczna we Wroclawiu. Prace Naukowe. (PL) 644
Akademia Gorniczo-Hutnicza im. Stanislawa Staszica. Zeszyty Naukowe. Automatyka. (PL ISSN 0454-4773) 1881
Akademia Gorniczo-Hutnicza im. Stanislawa Staszica. Zeszyty Naukowe. Elektrotechnika/Stanislaw Staszic University of Mining and Metallurgy. Scientific Bulletins. Electrotechnics. (PL ISSN 0239-5312) 1881
Akademia Gorniczo-Hutnicza im. Stanislawa Staszica. Zeszyty Naukowe. Ceramika. (PL) 1160
Akademia Gorniczo-Hutnicza im. Stanislawa Staszica. Zeszyty Naukowe. Chemia. (PL ISSN 0860-1100) 1169
Akademia Gorniczo-Hutnicza im. Stanislawa Staszica. Zeszyty Naukowe. Fizyka. (PL ISSN 0860-0260) 3813
Akademia Gorniczo-Hutnicza im. Stanislawa Staszica. Zeszyty Naukowe. Geodezja. (PL ISSN 0452-6457) 3477
Akademia Gorniczo-Hutnicza im. Stanislawa Staszica. Zeszyty Naukowe. Geologia. (PL ISSN 0372-9427) 1553
Akademia Gorniczo-Hutnicza im. Stanislawa Staszica. Zeszyty Naukowe. Elektrotechnika. Kwartalnik. (PL ISSN 0239-5274) 1881
Akademia Gorniczo-Hutnicza im. Stanislawa Staszica. Zeszyty Naukowe. Folia Malacologica. (PL ISSN 0860-6307) 1540
Akademia Gorniczo-Hutnicza im. Stanislawa Staszica. Zeszyty Naukowe. Gornictwo. (PL ISSN 0372-9400) 3477
Akademia Gorniczo-Hutnicza im. Stanislawa Staszica. Zeszyty Naukowe. Geologia. Kwartalnik. (PL ISSN 0138-0974) 1553
Akademia Gorniczo-Hutnicza im. Stanislawa Staszica. Zeszyty Naukowe. Gornictwo. Kwartalnik. (PL ISSN 0138-0990) 3477
Akademia Gorniczo-Hutnicza im. Stanislawa Staszica. Zeszyty Naukowe. Geofizyka Stosowana. (PL ISSN 0860-7109) 1586
Akademia Gorniczo-Hutnicza im. Stanislawa Staszica. Zeszyty Naukowe. Mechanika/Stanislaw Staszic University of Mining and Metallurgy. Scientific Bulletins. Mechanics. (PL ISSN 0239-5320) 1927
Akademia Gorniczo-Hutnicza im. Stanislawa Staszica. Zeszyty Naukowe. Metalurgia i Odlewnictwo. (PL ISSN 0372-9443) 3401
Akademia Gorniczo-Hutnicza im. Stanislawa Staszica. Zeszyty Naukowe. Metalurgia i Odlewnictwo. Kwartalnik. (PL ISSN 0137-6535) 3401
Akademia Gorniczo-Hutnicza im. Stanislawa Staszica. Zeszyty Naukowe. Mechanika. Kwartalnik. (PL ISSN 0239-5282) 1927
Akademia Gorniczo-Hutnicza im. Stanislawa Staszica. Zeszyty Naukowe. Opuscula Mathematica. (PL ISSN 0860-2727) 3027
Akademia Gorniczo-Hutnicza im. Stanislawa Staszica. Zeszyty Naukowe. Sozologia i Sozotechnika. (PL ISSN 0138-0923) 426
Akademia Gorniczo-Hutnicza im. Stanislawa Staszica. Zeszyty Naukowe. Wiertnictwo Nafta Gas/Stanislaw Staszic University of Mining and Metallurgy. Scientific Bulletins. Drillign Oil Gas. (PL ISSN 0860-1860) 3681
Akademia Gorniczo-Hutnicza im. Stanislawa Staszica. Zeszyty Naukowe. Zagadnienia Spoleczno-Filozoficzne. (PL ISSN 0239-5622) 4365

Akademia Gorniczo-Hutnicza im. Stanislawa Staszica. Zeszyty Naukowe. Zagadnienia Techniczno-Ekonomiczne. (PL ISSN 0454-4811) 4593, 644
Akademia Medyczna w Bialymstoku. Roczniki/Annales Academiae Medicae Bialostocensis. (PL ISSN 0067-6489) 3073
†Akademia Medyczna we Wroclawiu. Prace Naukowe. (PL ISSN 0084-277X) 5133
Akademia Muzyczna. Prace Specjalne. (PL) 3537
Akademia Muzyczna. Skrypty. (PL) 3537
Akademia Muzyczna. Sprawozdania. (PL) 3537
Akademia Muzyczna. Wydawnictwa Okolicznosciowe. (PL) 3537
Akademia Rolnicza, Krakow. Rolnictwo. (PL) 75
Akademia Rolnicza, Poznan. Roczniki. Algorytmy Biometryczne i Statystyczne. (PL ISSN 0137-169X) 3027
Akademia Rolnicza, Poznan. Roczniki. Archeozoologia. (PL ISSN 0137-1703) 576
Akademia Rolnicza, Poznan. Roczniki. Chemiczna Technologia Drewna. (PL) 2113
Akademia Rolnicza, Poznan. Roczniki. Ekonomika i Organizacja Rolnictwa. (PL ISSN 0137-1711) 147
Akademia Rolnicza, Poznan. Roczniki. Fizyka, Chemia. (PL ISSN 0208-8940) 3813, 1169
Akademia Rolnicza, Poznan. Roczniki. Lesnictwo. (PL ISSN 0137-172X) 2095
Akademia Rolnicza, Poznan. Roczniki. Mechaniczna Technologia Drewna. (PL ISSN 0137-1800) 1927
Akademia Rolnicza, Poznan. Roczniki. Melioracje. (PL) 167
Akademia Rolnicza, Poznan. Roczniki. Melioracje Wodne see Akademia Rolnicza, Poznan. Roczniki. Melioracje 167
Akademia Rolnicza, Poznan. Roczniki. Ogrodnictwo. (PL ISSN 0137-1738) 2120
Akademia Rolnicza, Poznan. Roczniki. Ornitologia Stosowana. (PL ISSN 0137-1746) 561
Akademia Rolnicza, Poznan. Roczniki. Rolnictwo. (PL ISSN 0137-1754) 75
Akademia Rolnicza, Poznan. Roczniki. Rozprawy Naukowe. (PL ISSN 0208-8436) 75
Akademia Rolnicza, Poznan. Roczniki. Technologia Drewna see Akademia Rolnicza, Poznan. Roczniki. Chemiczna Technologia Drewna 2113
Akademia Rolnicza, Poznan. Roczniki. Technologia Rolno-Spozywcza see Akademia Rolnicza, Poznan. Roczniki. Technologia Zywnosci 2061
Akademia Rolnicza, Poznan. Roczniki. Technologia Zywnosci. (PL) 2061
Akademia Rolnicza, Poznan. Roczniki. Zootechnika. (PL ISSN 0137-1770) 576, 209
Akademia Rolnicza w Szczecinie. Informatory. (PL ISSN 0137-2149) 75
Akademia Rolnicza w Szczecinie. Rozprawy. (PL) 75
†Akademia Rolnicza w Szczecinie. Zeszyty Naukowe. Ekonomika, Organizacja i Kierowanie. (PL) 5133
Akademia Rolnicza w Szczecinie. Zeszyty Naukowe. Nauki Spoleczne i Ekonomiczne. (PL ISSN 0208-7669) 4365, 889
Akademia Rolnicza w Szczecinie. Zeszyty Naukowe. Rolnictwo. (PL ISSN 0137-1924) 167
†Akademia Rolnicza w Szczecinie. Zeszyty Naukowe. Rolnictwo. Seria Agrotechniczna. (PL) 5133
†Akademia Rolnicza w Szczecinie. Zeszyty Naukowe. Rolnictwo. Seria Przyrodnicza. (PL) 5133

†Akademia Rolnicza w Szczecinie. Zeszyty Naukowe. Rolnictwo. Seria Techniczna. (PL) 5133
Akademia Rolnicza w Szczecinie. Zeszyty Naukowe. Rybactwo Morskie i Technologia Zywnosci. (PL ISSN 0239-9180) 2036, 2061
Akademia Rolnicza w Szczecinie. Zeszyty Naukowe. Zootechnika. (PL ISSN 0137-1940) 209
Akademia Rolnicza w Szczecinie. Zeszyty Naukowe. Zootechnika. Teratologica Scripta. (PL) 209
Akademia Rolnicza, Warsaw. Zeszyty Naukowe. Ogrodnictwo see Warsaw Agricultural University. S G G W. Annals. Horticulture 2140
Akademia Rolnicza, Warsaw. Zeszyty Naukowe. Weterynaria see Warsaw Agricultural University. S G G W. Annals. Veterinary Medicine 4819
Akademia Rolnicza, Wroclaw. Rolnictwo.(PL) 75
Akademia Rolniczo-Techniczna. Zeszyty Naukowe. Ekonomika see Acta Academiae Agriculturae ac Technicae Olstenensis. Oeconomica - Economics 145
Akademia Rolniczo-Techniczna. Zeszyty Naukowe. Geodezja i Urzadzenia Rolne see Acta Academiae Agriculturae ac Technicae Olstenensis. Geodaesia et Ruris Regulatio - Geodesy and Agricultural Arrangement 68
Akademia Rolniczo-Techniczna. Zeszyty Naukowe. Ochrona Wod i Rybactwo Srodladowe see Acta Academiae Agriculturae ac Technicae Olstenensis. Protectio Aquarum et Piscatoria - Water Conservation and Inland Fisheries 4821
Akademia Rolniczo-Techniczna. Zeszyty Naukowe. Rolnictwo see Acta Academiae Agriculturae ac Technicae Olstenensis. Agricultura - Agriculture 166
Akademia Rolniczo-Techniczna. Zeszyty Naukowe. Technologia Zywnosci see Acta Academiae Agriculturae ac Technicae Olstenensis. Technologia Alimentorum - Food Technology 2060
Akademia Rolniczo-Techniczna. Zeszyty Naukowe. Weterynaria see Acta Academiae Agriculturae ac Technicae Olstenensis. Veterinaria - Veterinary Medicine 4804
Akademia Rolniczo-Techniczna. Zeszyty Naukowe. Zootechnika see Acta Academiae Agriculturae ac Technicae Olstenensis. Zootechnica - Zootechnics 204
Akademie der Wissenschaften. Berlin. Jahrbuch see Akademie der Wissenschaften der D.D.R. Jahrbuch 4297
Akademie der Wissenschaften, Berlin. Sektion fuer Vor- und Fruehgeschichte. Schriften see Schriften zur Ur- und Fruehgeschichte 2322
Akademie der Wissenschaften, Berlin. Volkskundliche Veroeffentlichungen see Veroeffentlichungen zur Volkskunde und Kulturgeschichte 2059
Akademie der Wissenschaften, Berlin. Zentralinstitut fuer Sprachwissenschaft. Schriften see Sprache und Gesellschaft 2843
Akademie der Wissenschaften der D.D.R. Abhandlungen. Abteilung Mathematik, Naturwissenschaften, Technik. (GW ISSN 0138-1059) 4365
Akademie der Wissenschaften der D.D.R. Institut fuer Geographie und Geooekologie. Wissenschaftliche Veroeffentlichungen see Beitraege zur Geographie 2243
Akademie der Wissenschaften der D.D.R. Jahrbuch. (GW ISSN 0304-2154) 4297
Akademie der Wissenschaften der D.D.R. Studien zur Geschichte. (GW ISSN 0138-4112) 4297

AKADEMIE

Akademie der Wissenschaften der D.D.R. Zentralinstitut fuer Geschichte. Schriften. (GW ISSN 0138-3566) **2347**

Akademie der Wissenschaften der D.D.R. Zentralinstitut fuer Physik der Erde. Veroeffentlichungen. (GW ISSN 0514-8790) **2241**

Akademie der Wissenschaften der D.D.R. Zentralinstitut fuer Wirtschaftswissenschaften. Schriften. (GW ISSN 0138-3469) **644**

Akademie der Wissenschaften in Goettingen. Abhandlungen. Mathematisch-Physikalische Klasse. Dritte Folge. (GW) **3027**, 3813

Akademie der Wissenschaften in Goettingen. Abhandlungen. Mathematisch-Physikalische Klasse. Dritte Folge Sonderhefte. (GW) **3027**

Akademie der Wissenschaften in Goettingen. Jahrbuch. (GW ISSN 0084-6082) **4297**

Akademie der Wissenschaften in Goettingen. Nachrichten 1. Philologisch-Historische Klasse. (GW ISSN 0065-5287) **2801**, 2305

Akademie der Wissenschaften in Goettingen. Nachrichten 2. Mathematisch-Physikalische Klasse. (GW ISSN 0065-5295) **3027**, 3813

Akademie der Wissenschaften und der Literatur. Geistes- und Sozialwissenschaftliche Klasse. Abhandlungen. (GW ISSN 0002-2977) **2502**

Akademie der Wissenschaften und der Literatur, Mainz. Jahrbuch. (GW ISSN 0084-6104) **4297**, 2502

Akademie der Wissenschaften und der Literatur, Mainz. Klasse der Literatur. Abhandlungen. (GW ISSN 0002-2985) **2892**

Akademie der Wissenschaften und der Literatur, Mainz. Mathematisch-Naturwissenschaftliche Klasse. Abhandlungen. (GW ISSN 0002-2993) **4297**

Akademie der Wissenschaften und der Literatur, Mainz. Orientalische Kommission. Veroeffentlichungen. (GW ISSN 0568-4447) **3633**

Akademie fuer Fuehrungskraefte der Wirtschaft. Taschenbuecher zur Betriebspraxis. (GW ISSN 0065-5384) **1002**

Akademie fuer Oeffentliches Gesundheitswesen. Schriftenreihe. (GW ISSN 0172-2131) **4097**

Akademie fuer Staatsmedizin, Duesseldorf. Jahrbuch see Akademie fuer Oeffentliches Gesundheitswesen. Schriftenreihe **4097**

Akademija Nauka i Umjetnosti Bosne i Hercegovine. Centar za Balkanoloska Ispitivanja. Godisnjak. (BN ISSN 0350-0020) **2347**

Akademija Nauka i Umjetnosti Bosne i Hercegovine. Odjeljenje Drustvenih Nauka. Djela. (BN) **2347**, 2801

Akademija Nauka i Umjetnosti Bosne i Hercegovine. Odjeljenje Drustvenih Nauka. Radovi. (BN ISSN 0350-0039) **4365**

Akademija Nauka i Umjetnosti Bosne i Hercegovine. Odjeljenje Istorijsko Filoloskih Nauka. Djela see Akademija Nauka i Umjetnosti Bosne i Hercegovine. Odjeljenje Drustvenih Nauka. Djela **2347**

Akademiker see Politische Perspektiven **3918**

Akademische Monatsblaetter. (GW ISSN 0002-3000) **4254**, 1302

Akademische Vortraege und Abhandlungen. (GW ISSN 0065-5538) **4297**

Akademiska Dzive/Academic Life. (US ISSN 0516-3145) **1990**, 2347

Akademiya Meditsinskikh Nauk S.S.S.R. Vestnik/Academy of Medical Sciences of the U.S.S.R. Annals. (RU ISSN 0002-3027) **3073**

Akademiya Meditsinskikh Nauk S.S.S.R. Vsesoyuznyi Kardiologicheskii Nauchnyi Tsentr. Byulleten/Academy of Medical Sciences of the U.S.S.R. All-Union Cardiology Research Center. Bulletin. (RU ISSN 0201-7369) **3203**

Akademiya Nauk Armyanskoi S.S.R. Doklady. (AI) **4297**

Akademiya Nauk Armyanskoi S.S.R. Izvestiya. Seriya Fizika. (AI ISSN 0002-3035) **3813**

Akademiya Nauk Armyanskoi S.S.R. Izvestiya. Seriya Matematika. (AI ISSN 0002-3043) **3027**

Akademiya Nauk Armyanskoi S.S.R. Izvestiya. Seriya Mekhanika. (AI ISSN 0002-3051) **1927**

Akademiya Nauk Armyanskoi S.S.R. Izvestiya. Seriya Tekhnicheskikh Nauk. (AI ISSN 0002-306X) **4593**, 4297

Akademiya Nauk Azerbaidzhanskoi S.S.R. Doklady. (AJ ISSN 0002-3078) **3027**, 3813

Akademiya Nauk Azerbaidzhanskoi S.S.R. Izvestiya. Seriya Biologicheskikh Nauk. (AJ ISSN 0002-3086) **426**

Akademiya Nauk Azerbaidzhanskoi S.S.R. Izvestiya. Seriya Ekonomicheskikh Nauk. (AJ ISSN 0002-3094) **644**

Akademiya Nauk Azerbaidzhanskoi S.S.R. Izvestiya. Seriya Fiziko-Tekhnicheskikh i Matematicheskikh Nauk. (AJ ISSN 0002-3108) **3813**, 3027, 4593

Akademiya Nauk Azerbaidzhanskoi S.S.R. Izvestiya. Seriya Istoriya, Filosofiya i Pravo. (AJ ISSN 0002-3116) **2305**, 2596, 3760

Akademiya Nauk Azerbaidzhanskoi S.S.R. Izvestiya. Seriya Nauki o Zemle. (AJ ISSN 0002-3124) **1553**

Akademiya Nauk Azerbaidzhanskoi S.S.R. Izvestiya. Seriya Yazykoznanie, Literatura i Iskusstvo. (AJ ISSN 0002-3132) **2801**, 310, 2892

Akademiya Nauk Azerbaidzhanskoi S.S.R. Muzei Istorii. Trudy. (AJ) **3537**

Akademiya Nauk Belarusskoi S.S.R. Doklady. (BW ISSN 0002-354X) **4297**

Akademiya Nauk C.S.S.R. Vostochno-Sibirskii Filial, Irkutsk. Institut Geokhimii. Geokhimiya Endogennych Protsessov. (RU) **1540**

Akademiya Nauk C.S.S.R. Vostochno-Sibirskii Filial, Irkutsk. Institut Geokhimii. Geokhimicheskie Metody Poiskov, Metody Analiza. (RU) **1540**

Akademiya Nauk Gruzinskoi S.S.R. Izvestiya. Seriya Biologicheskaya. (GS) **426**

Akademiya Nauk Gruzinskoi S.S.R. Izvestiya. Seriya Khimicheskaya. (GS ISSN 0132-6074) **1169**

Akademiya Nauk Gruzinskoi S.S.R. Soobshcheniya. (GS ISSN 0002-3167) **4297**

Akademiya Nauk Kazakhskoi S.S.R. Astrofizicheskii Institut. Trudy. (RU) **360**

Akademiya Nauk Kazakhskoi S.S.R. Institut Khimicheskikh Nauk. Trudy. (RU) **1216**

Akademiya Nauk Kazakhskoi S.S.R. Institut Metallurgii i Obogashcheniya. Trudy. (RU) **3401**

Akademiya Nauk Kazakhskoi S.S.R. Institut Organicheskogo Kataliza i Elektrokhimii. Trudy. (RU) **1212**

Akademiya Nauk Kazakhskoi S.S.R. Izvestiya/Qazaq S.S.R. Ghylym Akademiasynyng Khabarlary. (RU) **2347**

Akademiya Nauk Kazakhskoi S.S.R. Izvestiya. Seriya Biologicheskaya. (RU ISSN 0002-3183) **427**

Akademiya Nauk Kazakhskoi S.S.R. Izvestiya. Seriya Filologicheskaya. (RU) **2801**

Akademiya Nauk Kazakhskoi S.S.R. Izvestiya. Seriya Fiziko-Matematicheskaya. (RU ISSN 0002-3191) **3813**, 3027

Akademiya Nauk Kazakhskoi S.S.R. Izvestiya. Seriya Geologicheskaya. (RU ISSN 0002-3175) **1553**

Akademiya Nauk Kazakhskoi S.S.R. Izvestiya. Seriya Khimicheskaya. (RU ISSN 0002-3205) **1169**

Akademiya Nauk Kazakhskoi S.S.R. Vestnik. (RU ISSN 0002-3213) **4297**

Akademiya Nauk Kirgizskoi S.S.R. Izvestiya. (KG ISSN 0002-3221) **4298**

Akademiya Nauk Latviiskoi S.S.R. Izvestiya/Latvijas P.S.R. Zinatnu Akademijas. Vestis. (LV ISSN 0132-6422) **4298**, 427

Akademiya Nauk Latviiskoi S.S.R. Izvestiya. Seriya Fizicheskikh i Tekhnicheskikh Nauk. (LV ISSN 0321-1673) **3813**, 4593

Akademiya Nauk Latviiskoi S.S.R. Izvestiya. Seriya Khimicheskaya. (LV ISSN 0002-3248) **1169**

†Akademiya Nauk Litovskoi S.S.R. Trudy. Seriya A. Obshchestvennye Nauki/Lietuvos T.S.R. Mokslu Akademijos Darbai. A Serija. Visuomenes Mokslai. (UR ISSN 0131-3843) **5133**

†Akademiya Nauk Litovskoi S.S.R. Trudy. Seriya B. Khimiya, Tekhnika, Fizicheskaya Geografiya/Lietuvos T.S.R. Mokslu Akademijos Darbai. B Serija. Chemija, Technika, Fizine Geografija. (UR ISSN 0132-2729) **5133**

†Akademiya Nauk Litovskoi S.S.R. Trudy. Seriya C. Biologicheskie Nauki/Lietuvos T.S.R. Mokslu Akademijos Darbai. C Serija. Biologijos Mokslai. (UR ISSN 0131-3851) **5133**

Akademiya Nauk Moldavskoi S.S.R. Izvestiya. Ekonomika i Sotsiologiya. see Academie de Stiinte a R.S.S. Moldova. Buletinul. Economie se Sociologie **842**

Akademiya Nauk Moldavskoi S.S.R. Izvestiya. Seriya Biologicheskikh i Khimicheskikh Nauk. (MV) **427**, 1169

Akademiya Nauk Moldavskoi S.S.R. Izvestiya. Seriya Fiziko-Tekhnicheskikh i Matematicheskikh Nauk. (MV) **3813**, 3027, 4593

Akademiya Nauk Moldavskoi S.S.R. Izvestiya. Seriya Obshchestvennykh Nauk see Academie de Stiinte a R.S.S. Moldova. Buletinul. Economie se Sociologie **842**

Akademiya Nauk Moldavskoi S.S.R. Izvestiya. Seriya Obshchestvennykh Nauk see Revista de Istorie a Moldovei **2383**

Akademiya Nauk Moldavskoi S.S.R. Izvestiya. Seriya Obshchestvennykh Nauk see Academie de Stiinte a R.S.S. Moldova. Filosofie si Drept **3759**

Akademiya Nauk S.S.R. Moldova. Filosofiya i Pravo. see Academie de Stiinte a R.S.S. Moldova. Filosofie si Drept **3759**

▼Akademiya Nauk S.S.S.R. Dal'nevostochnoe Otdelenie. Vestnik/U.S.S.R Academy of Sciences. Far Eastern Branch. Bulletin. (RU ISSN 0235-8611) **4397**

Akademiya Nauk S.S.S.R. Doklady. (RU ISSN 0002-3264) **4298**

Akademiya Nauk S.S.S.R. Institut Arkheologii. Kratkie Soobshcheniya. (RU) **261**

Akademiya Nauk S.S.S.R. Institut Etnografii. Polevye Issledovaniya. (RU) **232**

Akademiya Nauk S.S.S.R. Institut Obshchei Fiziki. Trudy. (RU) **3813**, 1601

Akademiya Nauk S.S.S.R. Institut Okeanologii. Trudy. (RU ISSN 0002-3450) **1601**

Akademiya Nauk S.S.S.R. Institut Paleontologii. Trudy see Paleontologicheskii Zhurnal **3660**

Akademiya Nauk S.S.S.R. Izvestiya. Energetika i Transport. (RU ISSN 0002-3310) **1927**, 1881

Akademiya Nauk S.S.S.R. Izvestiya. Seriya Biologicheskaya. (RU ISSN 0002-3329) **427**

Akademiya Nauk S.S.S.R. Izvestiya. Seriya Fizika Atmosfery i Okeana. (RU ISSN 0002-3515) **3432**, 1601

Akademiya Nauk S.S.S.R. Izvestiya. Seriya Fizika Zemli. (RU ISSN 0002-3337) **1587**

Akademiya Nauk S.S.S.R. Izvestiya. Seriya Geologicheskaya. (RU ISSN 0002-3345) **1553**

Akademiya Nauk S.S.S.R. Izvestiya. Seriya Khimicheskaya. (RU ISSN 0002-3353) **1169**

Akademiya Nauk S.S.S.R. Izvestiya. Seriya Literatury i Yazyka. (RU) **2892**

Akademiya Nauk S.S.S.R. Izvestiya. Seriya Matematicheskaya. (RU ISSN 0002-3361) **3027**

Akademiya Nauk S.S.S.R. Izvestiya. Seriya Neorganicheskie Materialy. (RU ISSN 0002-337X) **1169**

Akademiya Nauk S.S.S.R. Izvestiya. Tekhnicheskaya Kibernetika. (RU ISSN 0002-3388) **1440**

Akademiya Nauk S.S.S.R. Sibirskoe Otdelenie. Izvestiya. Seriya Biologicheskikh i Meditsinskikh Nauk.(RU ISSN 0002-3418) **427**, 3073

Akademiya Nauk S.S.S.R. Sibirskoe Otdelenie. Izvestiya. Seriya Khimicheskikh Nauk. (RU ISSN 0002-3426) **1169**

Akademiya Nauk S.S.S.R. Sibirskoe Otdelenie. Izvestiya. Seriya Obshchestvennykh Nauk. (RU) **2347**

Akademiya Nauk S.S.S.R. Sibirskoe Otdelenie. Izvestiya. Seriya Tekhnicheskikh Nauk. (RU ISSN 0002-3434) **4593**

Akademiya Nauk S.S.S.R. Vestnik. (RU ISSN 0002-3442) **4298**

Akademiya Nauk Tadzhikskoi S.S.R. Doklady. (TK ISSN 0002-3469) **3027**, 360, 427, 3813

Akademiya Nauk Tadzhikskoi S.S.R. Izvestiya. Otdelenie Biologicheskikh Nauk. (TA ISSN 0002-3477) **427**

Akademiya Nauk Tadzhikskoi S.S.R. Izvestiya. Otdelenie Fiziko-Matematicheskikh i Geologo-Khimicheskikh Nauk. (TA ISSN 0002-3485) **3813**, 1169, 1553, 3027

Akademiya Nauk Tadzhikskoi S.S.R. Otdelenie Obshchestvennykh Nauk. Izvestiya. see Akademiyai Fanhoi R.S.S. Tojikiston. Shu'Bai Fanhoi Jam'iiati. Akhboroti **2347**

Akademiya Nauk Turkmenskoi S.S.R. Izvestiya. Seriya Biologicheskikh Nauk. (TK ISSN 0002-3493) **427**

Akademiya Nauk Turkmenskoi S.S.R. Izvestiya. Seriya Fiziko-Tekhnicheskikh, Khimicheskikh i Geologicheskikh Nauk. (TK ISSN 0002-3507) **3813**, 1169, 1553

Akademiya Nauk Turkmenskoi S.S.R. Izvestiya. Seriya Obshchestvennykh Nauk. (TK) **4365**

Akademiya Nauk Ukrainskoi S.S.R. Doklady. Seriya A. Fiziko-Matematicheskie i Tekhnicheskie Nauki. (KR ISSN 0201-8446) **3813**, 3027

Akademiya Nauk Ukrainskoi S.S.R. Doklady. Seriya B. Geologicheskie, Khimicheskie i Biologicheskie Nauki. (KR ISSN 0201-8454) **1553**, 427, 1169

Akademiya Nauk Ukrainskoi S.S.R. Dopovidi. Seria A. Fiziko-Matematichni ta Tekhnichni Nauki see Akademiya Nauk Ukrainskoi S.S.R. Doklady. Seriya A. Fiziko-Matematicheskie i Tekhnicheskie Nauki **3813**

ALABAMA 5889

Akademiya Nauk Ukrainskoi S.S.R. Dopovidi. Seriya B. Geologiya, Geofizika, Geokhimiya, Khimiya, Biologiya, Meditsina see Akademiya Nauk Ukrainskoi S.S.R. Doklady. Seriya B. Geologicheskie, Khimicheskie i Biologicheskie Nauki **1553**

Akademiya Nauk Ukrainskoi S.S.R. Visnyk. (KR ISSN 0372-6436) **4298**

Akademiya Nauk Uzbekskoi S.S.R. Izvestiya. Seriya Fiziko-Matematicheskikh Nauk. (UZ) **3813**, 3027

Akademiya Nauk Uzbekskoi S.S.R. Izvestiya. Seriya Tekhnicheskikh Nauk. (UZ) **4593**

Akademiya Navuk Belarusskai S.S.R. Vestsi. Seriya Biyalagichnykh Navuk. (BW ISSN 0002-3558) **427**

Akademiya Navuk Belarusskai S.S.R. Vestsi. Seriya Fizika-Energetychnykh Navuk. (BW ISSN 0374-4760) **3814**

Akademiya Navuk Belarusskai S.S.R. Vestsi. Seriya Fizika-Matematychnykh Navuk. (BW ISSN 0002-3574) **3814**, 3027

Akademiya Navuk Belarusskai S.S.R. Vestsi. Seriya Fizika-Tekhnichnykh Navuk. (BW ISSN 0002-3566) **3814**, 4593

Akademiya Navuk Belarusskai S.S.R. Vestsi. Seriya Gramadskikh Navuk. (BW ISSN 0321-1649) **4365**

Akademiya Navuk Belarusskai S.S.R. Vestsi. Seriya Khimichnykh Navuk. (BW ISSN 0002-3590) **1169**

Akademiya Navuk Belarusskai S.S.R. Vestsi. Seriya Sel'skogaspadarchykh Navuk. (BW ISSN 0321-1657) **75**

Akademiyai Fanhoi R.S.S. Tojikiston. Shu'Bai Fanhoi Jam'iiati. Akhboroti/Akademiya Nauk Tadzhikskoi S.S.R. Otdelenie Obshchestvennykh Nauk. Izvestiya. (TA ISSN 0321-1738) **2347**

Akaroa Mail. (NZ ISSN 0002-3612) **2212**

Akashi. (II ISSN 0002-3620) **1368**

†Akashvani. (II) **5133**

Akavita. (II ISSN 0970-096X) **2987**

Al-Akha. (IR) **2202**

Akhaden. (US) **3668**

Akhand Anand. (II ISSN 0002-3639) **2198**

Akhbar A D N O C. see A D N O C News **3680**

Akhbar al-Butrul wal-Sina'a/Petroleum and Industry News. (TS) **3681**

Akhbar al-Usbou/News of the Week. (JO) **2208**

Akhbar al-Usbu' (QA) **2210**

Akhbar al-Yawm. (UA) **2185**

Akhbar B A P C O. (Bahrain Petroleum Co. Ltd.) (BA) **3681**

†Akhbar Dubai. (TS) **5133**

Akhbar-e Pezeshki. (IR) **3073**

Akhbar-e-Watan Urdu Newsweekly see Watan Weekend **2028**

Akhbar el-Arab Fe Toronte. see Arab News of Toronto **1991**

Akher Saa. (UA ISSN 0002-3655) **2185**

Aki Yerushalayim. (IS) **1990**

Akim Review. (IS) **1733**

Akita Daigaku Kyoikugakubu Kenkyu Kiyo/Akita University. College of Education. Memoirs. (JA) **3027**

Akita Dog. (US) **3707**

Akita Journal of Rural Medicine/Akita-ken Noson Igakkai Zasshi. (JA ISSN 0002-368X) **3073**

Akita-ken Noson Igakkai Zasshi. see Akita Journal of Rural Medicine **3073**

Akita-kenritsu Hakubutsukan Kenkyu Hokoku/Akita Prefectural Museum. Annual Report. (JA ISSN 0385-1354) **3520**, 4298

Akita Magazine see Akita Dog **3707**

Akita Natural History Association. see Akita Shizenshi Kenkyu **4298**

Akita Prefectural College of Agriculture. Bulletin. (JA) **75**, 493, 1596

Akita Prefectural Museum. Annual Report. see Akita-kenritsu Hakubutsukan Kenkyu Hokoku **3520**

Akita Shizenshi Kenkyu/Akita Natural History Association. (JA ISSN 0285-0257) **4298**

Akita University. College of Education. Memoirs. see Akita Daigaku Kyoikugakubu Kenkyu Kiyo **3027**

Akita University. Faculty of Education. Memoirs see Akita Daigaku Kyoikugakubu Kenkyu Kiyo **3027**

Akita World. (US) **3707**

Akivon. (US) **1990**, 1248

Akiyoshidai Kagaku Hakubutsukan Hokoku/Akiyoshidai Museum of Natural History. Bulletin. (JA) **3521**

Akiyoshidai Museum of Natural History. Bulletin. see Akiyoshidai Kagaku Hakubutsukan Hokoku **3521**

Akkadica. (BE) **261**, 2331

Akkerbouw (Doetinchen). (NE) **75**

Akkerbouw (The Hague). (NE ISSN 0923-7143) **147**

Akkerbouwpraktijk. (NE) **75**

Akron. (US) **1303**

†Akron Business and Economic Review. (US ISSN 0044-7048) **5133**

Akron Dental Society. Bulletin. (US ISSN 0002-3701) **3227**

Akron Law Review. (US ISSN 0002-371X) **2596**

Akron Magazine see Akron **1303**

Akroterion. (SA ISSN 0303-1896) **1274**

Aks. (II) **2892**

Aksel see Specialisten **1665**

Aktie. (NE ISSN 0002-3744) **4161**, 1248

Die Aktiengesellschaft. (GW ISSN 0002-3752) **1071**

Aktiengesellschaften in der Schweiz/Societes Anonymes en Suisse. (SZ) **829**

Aktiespararen/Shareholder. (SW ISSN 0345-049X) **758**

Aktines/Beam. (GR) **4161**

Die Aktion. (GW) **2857**

Aktion. (GW) **4162**, 1248

Aktion Jugendschutz. Informationen. (GW ISSN 0720-3551) **1232**, 1533

Aktion Lebensrecht fuer Alle Rundbrief see A L f A - Rundbrief **595**

Aktiv. (SZ) **2113**, 599

Aktiv Islam. (SZ ISSN 0108-7290) **4218**

Aktiviteitensektor. Maandblad. (NE) **4397**, 2290

†Aktiviteten i Sygehusvaesenet. (DK ISSN 0107-7619) **5133**

Aktschen. (GW) **2188**

Aktualne Problemy Informacji i Dokumentacji. (PL ISSN 0002-3787) **2741**

†Aktual'nye Problemy Leksikologii i Slovoobrazovaniya. (UR ISSN 0320-734X) **5133**

Aktuel Astronomi. (DK ISSN 0905-8958) **360**

Aktuel Bilsport. (DK) **4679**, 4751

†Aktuel Data - E D B. (DK) **5133**

Aktuel Elektronik. (DK ISSN 0105-2373) **1881**

Aktuel Grafisk Information. (DK) **3997**

Aktuele Onderwerpen see A O **2211**

Aktueli. (UK ISSN 0959-5740) **2801**, 1614

Aktuell see Missio Aktuell **4269**

Aktuell Auf Deutsch see Aktuell **2801**

Aktuell Grafisk Information see Aktuel Grafisk Information **3997**

Aktuell Josefs - Gesellschaft. (GW) **4397**

Aktuell Nordisk Statistik. (DK ISSN 0109-8047) **4561**

Die Aktuelle. (GW) **2188**

Aktuelle Berichte und Informationen fuer Architekten und Ingenieure see A B I **291**

Aktuelle Chirurgie. (GW ISSN 0001-785X) **3374**

Aktuelle Dermatologie. (GW ISSN 0340-2541) **3245**

Aktuelle Endokrinologie und Stoffwechsel. (GW ISSN 0172-4606) **3250**

Aktuelle Ernaehrungsmedizin. (GW ISSN 0341-0501) **3602**, 3073

†Aktuelle Fragen. (GW ISSN 0724-2735) **5133**

Aktuelle Gerontologie see Zeitschrift fuer Gerontologie **2280**

Aktuelle Literaturinformationen aus dem Obstbau. (GW ISSN 0302-4601) **2141**, 167

Aktuelle Neurologie. (GW ISSN 0302-4350) **3329**

Aktuelle Ostinformationen. (GW ISSN 0939-3099) **3871**

Aktuelle Radiologie. (GW ISSN 0939-267X) **3357**

Aktuelle Rheumatologie. (GW ISSN 0341-051X) **3368**

Aktuelle Schaufenster see Apotheke Heute **3717**

Aktuelle Steuer-Informationen see Steuer Telex **1107**

Aktuelle Traumatologie. (GW ISSN 0044-6173) **3306**

Aktuelle Urologie. (GW ISSN 0001-7868) **3387**

Aktueller Informationsdienst Afrika. (GW ISSN 0342-0396) **2168**

Aktueller Informationsdienst Moderner Orient/Original News and Comments from Middle Eastern Newspapers. (GW ISSN 0342-0329) **3633**, 3949

Aktuelles Bauen see Schweizer Baumarkt **631**

Aktuelles fuer den Landwirt. (GW) **829**

Aktuelles Theater see A K T **4629**

Aktuellt For Kontor. (SW) **1057**

Aktuellt i Politiken. (SW ISSN 0345-0635) **3871**

Aktuellt Maaleri. (SW) **3652**

Aktuellt och Historiskt see Militaerhistorisk Tidskrift **2375**

Aktuelna Pitanja Socijalizma. (YU) **3871**

Aktuelnosti u Vaspitanju i Obrazovanju. (YU) **1743**, 1614

†Aktuelt om Byggelitteratur. (DK ISSN 0108-6669) **5133**

Aktuelt Perspektiv. (NO) **3871**

Aku Ankka. (FI ISSN 0355-2101) **1248**

Akuntansi & Administrasi. (IO ISSN 0002-3892) **746**

Akupunktur: Theorie und Praxis. (GW ISSN 0340-3130) **3073**

Der Akupunkturarzt - Aurikulotherapeut.(GW ISSN 0172-9322) **3073**

Akuserstvo i Ginekologija. (BU ISSN 0324-0959) **3288**

Akusherstvo i Ginekologiya/Obstetrics and Gynecology. (RU ISSN 0300-9092) **3289**

Akusticheskii Zhurnal. (RU ISSN 0002-3914) **3858**

Akustyka. (PL ISSN 0554-8039) **3858**

Akvariebladet. (DK ISSN 0108-2396) **2036**

Akvariet. (SW ISSN 0002-3922) **2433**

Akvarium a Terarium. (CS ISSN 0002-3930) **2036**

Akwansosem. (GH) **2192**

Akwe Kon Journal. (US) **1990**

Akwekon. (US) **2892**

Akwekon Literary Journal. (US) **2892**

Akwesasne Notes. (US ISSN 0002-3949) **1990**

Akzente. (GW ISSN 0002-3957) **2987**

Akzo Annual Report (Year). (NE) **1848**

Al El. (IS) **2203**

Al Hanson's Economic Newsletter. (US ISSN 0736-007X) **938**

Al Servicio de Una Agricultura Rentable see A L S A R **67**

Al Sukar al-Arabi see Al Sukaria **2082**

Ala-Arts see Alabama Arts **310**

Alabama. Commission on Higher Education. Annual Report. (US) **1699**

Alabama. Department of Revenue. Annual Report. (US) **4083**, 1087

Alabama. Public Library Service. Annual Report. (US) **2741**

Alabama. Public Library Service. Basic State Plan and Annual Program see Alabama. Public Library Service. Annual Report **2741**

Alabama Academy of Science. Journal. (US ISSN 0002-4112) **4298**

Alabama Agricultural Experiment Station. Research Report Series. (US) **75**, 2095, 2120

Alabama Alumni Bulletin see Alabama Alumni Magazine **1303**

Alabama Alumni Magazine. (US) **1303**

Alabama Alumni News see Alabama Alumni Magazine **1303**

Alabama & Gulf Coast Retailing News. (US ISSN 0191-9113) **1032**

Alabama Archaeological Society. Special Publication. (US) **261**

Alabama Arts. (US) **310**

Alabama Association for Counseling and Development Journal. (US) **3624**

†Alabama Association of Secondary School Principals. Bulletin. (US ISSN 0002-4139) **5133**

Alabama Baptist Historian. (US ISSN 0002-4147) **4228**, 2305

Alabama Book of Surprises. (US) **4751**

Alabama Builder. (US ISSN 0002-4155) **599**

Alabama Cattleman. (US) **209**

Alabama Churchman see The Apostle **4229**

Alabama Conservation. (US ISSN 0002-4171) **1483**, 4540

Alabama Contractor. (US ISSN 0002-418X) **2297**

Alabama County Data Book. (US ISSN 0892-9084) **4052**

Alabama Dental Association. Journal. (US ISSN 0002-4198) **3227**

Alabama Development News. (US ISSN 0889-7468) **842**

Alabama Directory of Mining and Manufacturing see Alabama Industrial Directory **1120**

Alabama Dogshoe Moustache. (US) **2987**

Alabama Economic Outlook. (US) **842**

▼Alabama Employment Law Letter. (US ISSN 1049-9369) **2596**, 970

▼Alabama Facts. (US ISSN 1056-2168) **1779**

Alabama Family History and Genealogy News. (US) **2143**

Alabama Farm Bureau Federation AlFa News see AlFa News **75**

Alabama Farm Bureau News see AlFa News **75**

Alabama Food Merchants Journal. (US ISSN 0002-421X) **2090**

Alabama Forest Products see Alabama Forests **2095**

Alabama Forests. (US ISSN 0275-6625) **2095**

Alabama Game & Fish. (US) **4540**

Alabama Genealogical Exchange Quarterly. (US) **2143**

Alabama Geographer. (US) **2241**

Alabama Geological Society. Guidebook for the Annual Field Trip. (US ISSN 0065-5635) **1553**

Alabama Heritage. (US ISSN 0887-493X) **2397**

Alabama Industrial Directory. (US) **1120**

Alabama Junior College Library Association Newsletter. (US) **2741**

Alabama Labor Market News. (US) **702**, 4561

Alabama Law Review. (US ISSN 0002-4279) **2596**

Alabama Lawyer. (US ISSN 0002-4287) **2596**

Alabama Liberty. (US) **3871**, 644

Alabama Librarian. (US ISSN 0002-4295) **2742**

Alabama Literary Review. (US ISSN 0890-1554) **2857**

Alabama Living. (US) **1502**

Alabama, Louisiana, Mississippi TourBook see Tourbook: Alabama, Louisiana, Mississippi **4790**

Alabama Magazine. (US) **2857**

Alabama Manufacturers Register. (US ISSN 1045-2664) **1120**

Alabama Medicine. (US ISSN 0738-4947) **3073**

Alabama - Mississippi Grocers' Digest. (US) **2090**

5890 ALABAMA MUNICIPAL

Alabama Municipal Journal. (US ISSN 0002-4309) **4083**
Alabama Personnel and Guidance Journal *see* Alabama Association for Counseling and Development Journal **3624**
Alabama Press Association. Rate and Data Guide. (US) **2742**
Alabama Propane Gas News. (US) **3681**
Alabama Purchasor. (US ISSN 0002-4325) **1032**
Alabama Review. (US ISSN 0002-4341) **2397**
Alabama School Journal. (US ISSN 0002-435X) **1614**
Alabama State Data Center Newsletter. (US) **3979**
†Alabama Sunrise. (US) **5133**
Alabama Today. (US) **806**, 2596
Alabama Tourist Guide. (US) **4751**
Alabama's Health. (US ISSN 0145-6857) **4097**
Alabama's Treasured Forests. (US ISSN 0894-9654) **2095**
Alabama's Vital Events. (US ISSN 0095-3431) **4078**, 4561
Alabamian. (US) **1303**
Alabo Shijie/Arab World. (CC) **2801**
Alahli Bank of Kuwait K.S.C. Annual Report and Balance Sheet. (KU) **758**
Alaluz. (US ISSN 0044-7064) **2892**
Alam al-Handasah/World of Engineering. (TS) **1813**
Alam Al-Idarah. *see* International Management (Arabic Edition) **5217**
Al-Alam al-Iqtisadiy. *see* Conjoncture **851**
Alam al-Siyaha. *see* World of Tourism **4798**
Alam Attijarat. (US ISSN 0002-4392) **842**
Alam Tub al-Assnan. *see* Arab Dental **3228**
Alamanc of China's Economy. *see* Zhongguo Jingji Nianjian **1673**
Alambre. (GW ISSN 0002-4406) **1881**, 1813, 3015, 3401
Alameda-Contra Costa Medical Association. Bulletin. (US ISSN 0002-4414) **3073**
Alamo Area Council of Governments Region *see* A A C O G Region **4083**
Alan Guttmacher Institute. Washington Memo. (US ISSN 0739-4179) **3289**, 2596, 4052
Alan Shawn Feinstein Insiders Report. (US ISSN 0095-2931) **938**, 3749
Al-Anon in Institutions. (US ISSN 1054-142X) **1533**
Al-Anon Speaks Out. (US ISSN 1054-1446) **1533**
Alaplap. (HU ISSN 0865-9788) **1389**
Alarm/Allarme/Alarme. (SZ) **2031**, 1509
Alarm Installer and Dealer *see* Security Sales **643**
Alarma. (MX) **2857**
Alarma. (VE) **3871**
Alarme. *see* Alarm **2031**
Alaska. (US ISSN 0002-4562) **2221**
Alaska. Agricultural Statistics Service. Agricultural Statistics. (US ISSN 0065-5694) **133**, 4561
Alaska. Agricultural Statistics Service. Crop Weather Report *see* Alaska Weekly Crop Weather **133**
Alaska. Department of Administration. Revenue Sources *see* Alaska. Department of Revenue. Revenue Sources **1087**
†Alaska. Department of Fish and Game. Commercial Operators. (US) **5133**
Alaska. Department of Fish and Game. Fishery Research Bulletin. (US) **1483**
Alaska. Department of Fish and Game. Informational Leaflet. (US ISSN 0516-4303) **1483**
Alaska. Department of Fish and Game. Technical Data Report *see* Alaska. Department of Fish and Game. Technical Fishery Report **2036**
Alaska. Department of Fish and Game. Technical Fishery Report. (US) **2036**

Alaska. Department of Fish and Game. Wildlife Booklet Series *see* Alaska. Department of Fish and Game. Wildlife Notebook Series **1483**
Alaska. Department of Fish and Game. Wildlife Notebook Series. (US) **1483**
Alaska. Department of Health and Social Services. Division of Alcoholism and Drug Abuse. Report. (US) **1533**
Alaska. Department of Health and Social Services. Office of Alcoholism. Report *see* Alaska. Department of Health and Social Services. Division of Alcoholism and Drug Abuse. Report **1533**
Alaska. Department of Revenue. Revenue Sources. (US) **1087**
Alaska. Department of Revenue. State Investment Portfolio. (US ISSN 0092-6736) **938**, 1087
Alaska. Division of Game. Annual Report of Survey - Inventory Activities *see* Alaska. Division of Wildlife Conservation. Annual Report of Survey - Inventory Activities **4540**
Alaska. Division of Geological and Geophysical Surveys. Geologic - Professional Report. (US) **1554**, 1587
Alaska. Division of Geological and Geophysical Surveys. Information Circular. (US ISSN 0065-5759) **1554**, 1587
Alaska. Division of Geological and Geophysical Surveys. Laboratory Report *see* Alaska. Division of Geological and Geophysical Surveys. Geologic - Professional Report **1554**
Alaska. Division of Geological and Geophysical Surveys. Open-File Report *see* Alaska. Division of Geological and Geophysical Surveys. Report of Investigations **1554**
Alaska. Division of Geological and Geophysical Surveys. Report of Investigations. (US) **1554**, 1587
Alaska. Division of Geological and Geophysical Surveys. Special Report. (US ISSN 0360-3881) **1554**, 1587
Alaska. Division of Wildlife Conservation. Annual Report of Survey - Inventory Activities. (US ISSN 0362-6962) **4540**
Alaska. Legislature. Budget and Audit Committee. Annual Report. (US ISSN 0095-3865) **4052**
Alaska. Office of Ombudsman. Report of the Ombudsman *see* Alaska Ombudsman Report **4052**
†Alaska. Office of the Governor. Performance Report. (US) **5133**
Alaska. State Building Authority. Annual Report *see* Alaska. State Housing Authority. Annual Report **2482**
Alaska. State Council on the Arts. Bulletin. (US) **310**
Alaska. State Housing Authority. Annual Report. (US) **2482**
Alaska. Violent Crimes Compensation Board. Annual Report. (US ISSN 0095-3415) **1509**
Alaska Action. (US) **806**
Alaska Adult Education. (US) **1681**
Alaska Airlines Magazine. (US) **4801**, 4671
Alaska Almanac. (US ISSN 1051-5623) **1779**, 2221, 4751
▼Alaska Area Airport Business Directory. (CN) **4671**
†Alaska Association of Small Presses Newsletter. (US ISSN 0893-505X) **5133**
Alaska Bar Brief *see* Alaska Bar Rag **2596**
Alaska Bar Rag. (US) **2596**
†Alaska Beverage Analyst. (US ISSN 0191-5320) **5133**
Alaska Blue Book. (US ISSN 0092-1858) **4052**
Alaska Business *see* Alaska Business Newsletter **5133**
Alaska Business Monthly. (US ISSN 8756-4092) **644**, 1113, 1120
†Alaska Business Newsletter. (US ISSN 0887-2279) **5133**
Alaska Center for the Environment. Center News. (US) **1483**

†Alaska Construction & Oil. (US) **5133**
Alaska Construction and Oil Report *see* Alaska Construction & Oil **5133**
Alaska Economic Report. (US) **842**
Alaska Economic Trends. (US ISSN 0160-3345) **842**
Alaska Employment and Earnings Report. (US) **702**
Alaska Environmental Notes *see* Northern Line **1964**
Alaska Farm Reporter. (US) **133**, 4561
Alaska Fish and Game *see* Alaska's Wildlife **2036**
Alaska Fisheries Commercial Operators. *see* Alaska. Department of Fish and Game. Commercial Operators **5133**
Alaska Fisherman's Journal. (US ISSN 0164-8330) **2036**
†Alaska Flying. (US) **5133**
Alaska Forest Products Newsletter. (US) **2113**
Alaska Geographic. (US ISSN 0361-1353) **4298**
Alaska History. (US ISSN 0890-6149) **2397**, 232
Alaska Journal of Commerce *see* Alaska Journal of Commerce & Pacific Rim Reporter **833**
Alaska Journal of Commerce & Pacific Rim Reporter. (US ISSN 0271-3276) **833**
Alaska Law Review. (US ISSN 0883-0568) **2596**
Alaska Legislative Digest. (US) **4052**
Alaska Library Directory. (US) **2742**
Alaska Medicine. (US ISSN 0002-4538) **3073**
Alaska Municipal Officials Directory. (US) **4083**
Alaska Native Language Center Research Papers. (US ISSN 0883-8526) **2801**, 232
Alaska Nurse. (US ISSN 0002-4546) **3275**
Alaska Ombudsman Report. (US) **4052**
Alaska Outdoors. (US ISSN 0274-8282) **4540**
Alaska Pacific University Press Press Alaskana Book Series *see* A P U Press Alaskana Book Series **2397**
Alaska Quarterly Review. (US ISSN 0737-268X) **2892**
Alaska Review of Business and Economic Conditions *see* Alaska Review of Social and Economic Conditions **842**
Alaska Review of Social and Economic Conditions. (US ISSN 0162-5403) **842**
Alaska Science Conference. Proceedings *see* Arctic Science Conference. Proceedings **4299**
Alaska Snow Surveys *see* Alaska Snow Surveys - Basin Outlook Reports **4821**
Alaska Snow Surveys - Basin Outlook Reports. (US) **4821**
Alaska Statistical Quarterly *see* Alaska Employment and Earnings Report **702**
Alaska Summary Report - Index. (US) **3681**
Alaska Travel Guide *see* Tim Bell's Alaska Travel Guide **4789**
Alaska Weekly Crop Weather. (US) **133**, 3444
Alaska Wilderness Milepost. (US ISSN 0888-8884) **4751**
▼Alaska Women. (US) **2857**, 4836
AlaskaMen U S A. (US ISSN 1041-4002) **4362**
Alaskan Gangline. (US) **3707**
Alaskan Malamute Club of America. Newsletter. (US) **3707**
Alaska's Wildlife. (US ISSN 1052-2727) **2036**, 4463
Alateen Talk. (US ISSN 1054-1411) **1248**
Alauda. (FR ISSN 0002-4619) **561**
Alawdah. (IS) **2203**
Alazan. (MX) **4531**
Alba Pompeia. (IT ISSN 0394-9427) **261**
Alba Regia. (HU ISSN 0324-542X) **3521**
Albania Oggi. (AA ISSN 0002-4643) **3949**

Albania Report. (US ISSN 0002-4651) **3871**, 842
Albania Socialista. (IT) **3949**
Albania Today *see* Shqiperia Sot **2883**
Albanian Catholic Bulletin/Buletini Katolik Shqiptar. (US ISSN 0272-7250) **4162**
Albanian Resistance. (FR) **3871**
Albanie Aujourd'hui. *see* Shqiperia Sot **2883**
Albanie Aujurd'hui *see* Shqiperia Sot **2883**
Albanische Hefte. (GW ISSN 0930-1437) **1990**
Albany. (US) **1303**
Albany County Agriculture News *see* Extension News - Albany - Rensselaer - Saratoga - Washington Counties **89**
Albany Institute of History & Art. Annual Report. (US) **2397**, 310
Albany Law Review. (US ISSN 0002-4678) **2596**
The Albany Report. (US) **842**
Albany Review. (US ISSN 0895-559X) **2857**, 310
Albarregas. (VE) **2502**, 1614
Albatros. (FR) **2987**
Albatros. (CN) **4499**
Albatross. (US) **2987**
Albemarle Almanac. (US) **1779**
Alberta. Alberta Culture and Multiculturalism. Annual Report. (CN) **4365**
Alberta. Alcohol and Drug Abuse Commission. Annual Report. (CN) **1533**
†Alberta. Department of Agriculture. Market Situation and Outlook. (CN) **5133**
Alberta. Department of Agriculture. Production Economics Branch. Economics of Milk Production in Alberta. (CN) **197**
Alberta. Department of Family and Social Services. Annual Report. (CN) **4397**, 4097
Alberta. Department of Social Services. Annual Report *see* Alberta. Department of Family and Social Services. Annual Report **4397**
Alberta. Department of the Environment. Annual Report. (CN ISSN 0383-3739) **1942**
Alberta. Department of Utilities. Annual Report *see* Alberta Transportation and Utilities **4646**
Alberta. Fish and Wildlife Division. Fisheries Pollution Report. (CN ISSN 0707-2783) **1942**, 2036
Alberta. Health and Social Services Disciplines Committee. Annual Report. (CN ISSN 0707-1434) **4398**, 4097
Alberta Agriculture. Annual Report. (CN) **75**
Alberta Archaeological Review. (CN ISSN 0701-1776) **261**, 232
Alberta Art Foundation. Annual Report *see* Alberta Foundation for the Arts. Annual Report **310**
Alberta Association of College Librarians. Newsletter. (CN ISSN 0829-4321) **2742**
Alberta Association of Medical Radiation Technologists Journal *see* A A M R T Journal **3356**
Alberta Association of Registered Nurses Newsletter *see* A.A.R.N. Newsletter **3274**
Alberta Association of Registered Nursing Assistants. Bulletin *see* C H C G Pulse **3276**
Alberta Beef. (CN) **209**
Alberta Business. (CN) **644**
Alberta Calls. (CN ISSN 0002-4740) **1361**
Alberta Catholic Directory. (CN ISSN 0316-473X) **4254**
Alberta Chamber of Commerce. Legislative Report. (CN) **806**
Alberta Coal Industry, Annual Statistics. (CN ISSN 0380-4321) **3498**
Alberta Construction. (CN ISSN 0709-2431) **599**
Alberta Construction Association Membership Roster and Buyers' Guide. (CN) **599**

Alberta Corporations Law Guide. (CN) **2596**
Alberta Council on Aging News see A C A News **2269**
Alberta Decisions. Rules and Statute Citator. (CN ISSN 0824-7277) **2596**
Alberta Decisions, Civil and Criminal Cases. (CN ISSN 0319-7980) **2596**
Alberta Dental Association Newsletter see A D A Newsletter **3226**
Alberta Drilling Progress and Pipeline Receipts. Weekly Report see Alberta Drilling Progress Weekly Report **3704**
Alberta Drilling Progress Weekly Report.(CN) **3704**
Alberta Economic Accounts. (CN ISSN 0319-4264) **702**, **4561**
Alberta - Edmonton Series Report. (CN) **3979**, **4428**
Alberta Electric Industry, Annual Statistics. (CN ISSN 0706-1420) **1801**
Alberta Energy Resource Industries. Monthly Statistics. (CN ISSN 0710-6874) **1797**
Alberta Family Law. (CN) **2596**
Alberta Farm and Ranch Magazine. (CN ISSN 0845-5007) **75**, **167**
Alberta Farmagazine see Alberta Farm and Ranch Magazine **75**
Alberta Film and Literary Arts Bulletin see Working Title **2976**
Alberta Fishing Guide. (CN ISSN 0318-4943) **4540**
Alberta Foundation for the Arts. Annual Report. (CN) **310**
Alberta Gazette. (CN ISSN 0002-4775) **2176**
Alberta Genealogical Society. Ancestor Index. (CN) **2143**
Alberta Government Libraries' Newsletter. (CN ISSN 0707-0306) **2742**
Alberta Hail and Crop Insurance Corporation. Annual Report. (CN ISSN 0319-3535) **167**, **2526**
Alberta History. (CN ISSN 0316-1552) **2397**
Alberta Home Economics Association Newsletter. (CN ISSN 0834-213X) **2444**
†Alberta Hotel Association. Membership Roster & Buyers Guide. (CN) **5133**
Alberta Institute of Agrologists Newsletter see A I A Newsletter **67**
Alberta Insurance Directory. (CN ISSN 0712-9343) **2526**
Alberta Insurance Report see Superintendent of Insurance Annual Report **2544**
Alberta Italian Times. (CN) **1990**
Alberta Journal of Educational Research. (CN ISSN 0002-4805) **1614**
Alberta - Judicially Considered see Statutes of Alberta - Judicially Considered **2682**
Alberta Junior Farm Quarterly. (CN) **1296**
Alberta Land Surveyor Association News see A L S News **1861**
Alberta Landrace Association. Newsletter. (CN ISSN 0044-7145) **209**
Alberta Law Reports (2nd Series). (CN ISSN 0703-3117) **2596**
Alberta Law Review. (CN ISSN 0002-4821) **2596**
†Alberta Library News. (CN ISSN 0705-6087) **5133**
Alberta Limitations Manual. (CN) **2596**
Alberta Motor Transport Directory see Truxbook **4749**
Alberta Motorist see Westworld Alberta Magazine **4706**
Alberta, N.W.T. & Yukon Tax Reports. (CN) **1087**
Alberta Naturalist. (CN ISSN 0318-5540) **1483**, **427**
Alberta Oil & Forestry Review. (CN) **3681**, **2095**
Alberta Oil & Gas Directory. (CN ISSN 0831-019X) **1120**, **3477**, **3681**

Alberta Oil Sands Technology and Research Authority Journal of Research see A O S T R A Journal of Research **3681**
Alberta Opportunity Company. Annual Report. (CN ISSN 0318-3971) **758**
†Alberta Parent Magazine. (CN) **5133**
Alberta Public Safety Services. Agency Insight. (CN) **4097**
Alberta Public Safety Services News and Notes see Alberta Public Safety Services. Agency Insight **4097**
†Alberta Regulations Service. (CN) **5133**
Alberta Report. (US) **2176**
Alberta Report - Western Report. (CN) **2176**
Alberta Reports. (CN) **2596**
Alberta Research Council. Annual Report. (CN ISSN 0080-1526) **4593**, **4298**
Alberta Research Council. Atmospheric Sciences Reports. (CN) **3432**
Alberta Research Council. Bulletins. (CN ISSN 0034-5172) **1540**
Alberta Research Council. Contribution Series. (CN ISSN 0080-1534) **4593**
Alberta Research Council. Earth Science Reports. (CN) **1540**
Alberta Research Council. Information Series. (CN ISSN 0034-5180) **4593**
Alberta Research Council. List of Publications. (CN ISSN 0080-1569) **2792**
Alberta Research Council. Reports. (CN) **4593**, **4298**
Alberta Research Council. River Engineering and Surface Hydrology Reports. (CN) **1861**, **1596**
Alberta, Saskatchewan, Manitoba - Criminal Conviction Cases. (CN ISSN 0715-3155) **2596**
Alberta Statistical Review. (CN ISSN 0317-3925) **4561**
†Alberta: Studies in the Arts and Sciences. (CN) **5133**
Alberta Teachers' Association. Industrial Education Council. News & Notes. (CN ISSN 0709-0528) **1743**
Alberta Transportation and Utilities. (CN ISSN 0836-1509) **4646**
Alberta Weekly Law Digest. (CN ISSN 0713-892X) **2596**
Alberta Wild Rose Quarter Horse Journal. (CN ISSN 0227-0579) **4531**
Alberta's Fishing & Hunting Magazine. (CN ISSN 0833-0867) **4540**
Alberta's Reserve of Gas: Complete Listing. (CN ISSN 0229-8546) **3681**, **1783**
†▼Albertsen's - International Edition. (US ISSN 1052-522X) **5133**
▼Albertsen's Singles Directory. (US) **4362**
Albina. (RM) **2215**
Albion. (US ISSN 0095-1390) **2347**
Albir. (SP) **2327**, **388**
Albricias. (US) **1296**
Albrightian. (US) **1303**
Album de Recuerdos. (PR) **1368**
Album of Concert Pieces for Bayan-Accordion see Concert Repertoire of Bayan Player **5171**
Album Page. (US) **3749**
Album Slavnych Sportovcov. (CS) **4463**
Album Tracking. (UK) **3749**
Albuquerque Archaeological Society Newsletter. (US ISSN 0002-4953) **261**
Albuquerque Monthly. (US) **2221**
Albury & District Historical Society. Bulletin. (AT ISSN 0813-6645) **2343**, **1483**, **2143**, **3521**
Albus. (YU ISSN 0002-4961) **1169**
Alcalde see Texas Alcalde **1326**
Alcan Facts - Australia (Year). (AT) **644**
Alcan Informiert. (GW) **3401**, **3647**
†Alcatraz. (US) **5133**
Alchemist. (CN ISSN 0384-8523) **2892**, **2987**
Alcheringa. (AT ISSN 0311-5518) **3656**
Alcohol. (US ISSN 0741-8329) **1533**

Alcohol Abuse and Alcoholism: A Directory of Community Services in California see Alcohol Recovery Services: Directory of Community Resources in California **1533**
Alcohol & Alcoholism. (US ISSN 0735-0414) **1533**
Alcohol and Drug Abuse Pulse Beats Newsletter. (US) **1533**
Alcohol and Drug Problems Association of North America Professional see A D P A Professional **1532**
Alcohol and Drug Research see Alcohol **1533**
Alcohol and Drugs. see Norway. Statistisk Sentralbyraa. Alkohol og Andre Rusmidler **5249**
Alcohol and Other Drugs. see Alkohol och Narkotika **1534**
Alcohol Clinical Update. (US ISSN 0740-1035) **1533**
Alcohol, Drugs and Driving. (US ISSN 0891-7086) **1533**, **3264**
Alcohol, Drugs and Driving: Abstracts and Reviews see Alcohol, Drugs and Driving **1533**
Alcohol en Drugs see A en D **5128**
Alcohol Fuels Program. Annual Report see S E R I. Ethanol Annual Report **1795**
Alcohol Health & Research World. (US ISSN 0090-838X) **1533**
Alcohol in History: A Multidisciplinary Newsletter see Social History of Alcohol Review **385**
Alcohol Issues Insights. (US) **377**, **1533**, **2596**
Alcohol Recovery Services: Directory of Community Resources in California. (US) **1533**
Alcohol, Tobacco and Firearms Bulletin. (US ISSN 0098-0757) **2596**, **4643**
Alcohol Week see New Fuels Report **1793**
Alcoholic Beverage Executives' Newsletter. (US ISSN 0889-3519) **377**
Alcoholism. (CI ISSN 0002-502X) **1533**
Alcoholism and Addiction Magazine see Addiction & Recovery Magazine **1533**
Alcoholism and Alcohol Education see Drugs & Drug Abuse Education. Newsletter **1536**
Alcoholism & Drug Abuse Weekly. (US ISSN 1042-1394) **1533**
Alcoholism Briefs. (US) **1534**
Alcoholism: Clinical and Experimental Research. (US ISSN 0145-6008) **1534**
Alcoholism - Codependency - Addiction Lifeline. (US) **1534**
Alcoholism Counseling and Treatment see Alcoholism Treatment Quarterly **1534**
Alcoholism Digest Annual. (US ISSN 0093-3279) **1534**
Alcoholism Treatment Quarterly. (US ISSN 0734-7324) **1534**
Alcool ou Sante. (FR ISSN 0002-5054) **1534**
Alcovit. (LU) **75**
Alcuin. (UK) **4162**
Aldebaran. (US) **2987**
Aldebaran Review. (US ISSN 0002-5089) **2987**
Aldrich Entomology Club. Newsletter. (US ISSN 0065-6143) **527**
Aldrichimica Acta. (US ISSN 0002-5100) **1216**
Aldring og Eldre. Gerontologisk Magasin. (NO ISSN 0801-9991) **2270**
Aldus Magazine. (US ISSN 1046-0616) **1475**
Alea see L'Ennemi **325**
Alef. (IS ISSN 0736-8518) **2203**
Alegria. (BL) **1248**
†Aleh. (SA ISSN 0002-5127) **5133**
Alei Esev. (IS) **75**
Alei Merchavim. (IS) **2203**
Alei Sefer. (IS ISSN 0334-4754) **2742**
Alei Siach. (IS ISSN 0334-4827) **2893**
Alejandria. (AG) **2893**

ALGEBRAIC CONFERENCE 5891

Alemannisch Dunkt Ues Guet. (GW ISSN 0722-0332) **2801**, **2052**
Alembic. (UK ISSN 0140-5136) **2987**
Aleph. (CK ISSN 0120-0216) **2857**
Alephenalia Beer News. (US) **377**
Alere Flammam. (IT) **3450**
Alergia. (MX ISSN 0002-5151) **3182**
Alero. (GT) **2893**, **4365**
Alert (Adelaide). (AT ISSN 0706-1870) **4398**
Alert (Los Angeles). (US) **4398**, **2596**, **3217**
Alert! (Seattle). (US) **1942**, **1483**
Alert (Washington, 1980). (US) **4836**
Alert!: Focus on Central America. (US) **3949**
Alerta Agrario. (PE) **75**
Alerta Biotecnologia. (BL) **133**, **388**, **461**
▼Alerta Ecologia e Ciencias do Ambiente. (BL) **1972**, **389**
Alerte Atomique. (FR ISSN 0002-5186) **3949**
Aletheia. (SZ ISSN 0149-2004) **3760**
Alexander Lectures. (CN ISSN 0065-616X) **2893**
Alexander Newsletter. (US) **2143**
Alexander Tree see Alexander Newsletter **2143**
Alexander von Humboldt Foundation. Annual Report. (GW ISSN 0342-6785) **2502**
Alexander von Humboldt-Stiftung. Jahresbericht see Alexander von Humboldt Foundation. Annual Report **2502**
Alexander von Humboldt-Stiftung. Mitteilungen. (GW ISSN 0344-0354) **2502**
Alexandra & Eildon Standard. (AT) **2857**
Alexandria Archaeology Volunteer News.(US ISSN 0894-2625) **261**
Alexandria Dental Journal/Magallat al-Iskandiriyyah li-Tibb al-Asnan. (UA) **3227**
Alexandria Faculty of Medicine Bulletin. (UA ISSN 1010-6324) **3073**
Alexandria Journal of Agricultural Research. (UA ISSN 0044-7250) **75**
Alexandria: Journal of National & International Library & Information Issues. (UK) **2742**
Alexandria Medical Journal. (UA ISSN 0516-5849) **3073**
Alexanor. (FR ISSN 0002-5208) **527**
†Alf. (US) **5133**
Alfa. (BL ISSN 0002-5216) **2801**, **2893**
Alfa-Gamma. (EC) **644**
AlFa News. (Alabama Farm Bureau Federation) (US) **75**
Alfa Owner. (US ISSN 0364-930X) **4679**
Alfa Romeo World. (US) **4679**
Alfalfa Hay, California Market Summary.(US) **147**
Al-Fateh University. Faculty of Education. Bulletin. (LY) **1614**
Al-Fateh University. Faculty of Engineering. Bulletin. (LY) **1813**
Al-Fateh University. Faculty of Petroleum. Bulletin. (LY) **3681**
Alfil Dama. (CK) **4463**
Alfold. (HU ISSN 0401-3174) **2893**
Alforja. (SP ISSN 0210-3168) **2061**, **1071**
Alfred Benzon Symposium. Proceedings.(DK ISSN 0105-3639) **3073**, **568**
Alfred Hitchcock's Mystery Magazine. (US ISSN 0002-5224) **2985**
The Alfred's Yachtsman. (AT) **4521**
Algebra and Logic. (English translation of: Algebra i Logika) (US ISSN 0002-5232) **3027**
Algebra i Analiz. (RU ISSN 0234-0852) **3027**
Algebra, Logic and Applications. (UK ISSN 1041-5394) **3027**
Algebra Universalis. (SZ ISSN 0002-5240) **3027**
Algebraic Conference. Proceedings. (YU) **3028**

Algemeen Arbeidsongeschiktheidsfonds. Jaarverslag see Arbeidsongeschiktheidsfonds en Algemeen Arbeidsongeschiktheidsfonds. Jaarverslag **2526**
Algemeen Fiscaal Tijdschrift. (BE) **746, 1087**
Algemeen Jaarboek der Schone Kunsten. see Jaarboek der Schone Kunsten **331**
Algemeen Maconniek Tijdschrift. (NE ISSN 0002-5267) **4162**
Algemeen Nederlands Tijdschrift voor Wijsbegeerte. (NE ISSN 0002-5275) **3760**
Algemeen Politieblad van het Koninkrijk der Nederlanden. (NE ISSN 0002-5283) **1509**
Algemeen Weekblad voor Kerk en Christendom see Wending **2212**
Algemeen Werkloosheidsfonds. Jaarverslag. (NE ISSN 0401-331X) **2526**
Algemene Practische Rechtverzameling.(BE) **2596**
Algeria. Direction des Douanes. Bulletin Comparatif Trimestriel. (AE) **1087**
Algeria. Direction des Statistiques et de la Comptabilite Nationale. Bulletin Trimestriel de Statistiques. (AE) **4561**
Algeria. Institut National Algerien du Commerce Exterieur. Annuaire des Exportateurs. (AE) **899**
Algeria. Office Nationale de la Geologie. Bulletin. (AE) **1554**
Algeria. Service Geologique. Bulletin see Algeria. Office Nationale de la Geologie. Bulletin **1554**
Algeria Monitor - Algeria Information see North Africa Monitor **5248**
Algerie Actualite. (AE) **2427**
Algerie Economique see Economie **862**
Algerie Medicale. (AE) **3073**
Algerie Selection. (FR) **842**
Algerien en Europe. (FR ISSN 0002-5313) **3871**
Algo see Algo 2000 **4298**
Algo 2000. (SP ISSN 0214-0381) **4298, 4593**
Algologia. (IT ISSN 0392-9116) **3073**
Algological Studies. (GW ISSN 0342-1120) **427, 493, 1596**
Algonquian and Iroquoian Linguistics. (CN ISSN 0711-382X) **2801**
Algonquian Conference. Papers. (CN ISSN 0831-5671) **233, 261, 2801**
Algonquin Times. (CN) **1303**
Algorithm. (CN ISSN 0843-9753) **1467, 1429, 1458, 1475**
Algorithmica. (US ISSN 0178-4617) **1389**
Algorithms and Combinatorics. (US) **3028**
Alhachuma. (IS) **829**
Alhambra. (SP ISSN 0401-3689) **3749**
Alhaperek. (IS) **4221, 1743**
Alhope Business Observer. (US ISSN 0893-8253) **1002**
†Alia. Royal Wings. (HK) **5133**
Alibi. (FI ISSN 0357-542X) **2596, 1509**
Alice Reports. (US) **3871, 2450**
Alicia Patterson Foundation Reporter see A P F Reporter **2566**
Alien see Chronicle **1307**
▼Aliens. (RU) **3010**
Alif. (UA) **2987, 2893**
Aligarh Journal of English Studies. (II ISSN 0258-0365) **2893**
Aligarh Journal of Oriental Studies. (II ISSN 0970-0994) **3633**
Aligarh Journal of Statistics. (II ISSN 0971-0388) **4561**
Aligarh Muslim University, Aligarh, India. Department of History. Publication. (II ISSN 0065-6259) **2336**
Alighieri. (IT) **2987**
Alim. (IS ISSN 0334-5084) **1614**
Alimarket. (SP) **2061, 75**
Alimarket Monografico. (SP) **2061, 75**
Alimentacion. (SP ISSN 0212-1689) **2061**
Alimentacion y Nutricion see Food and Nutrition **5195**
Alimentaria. (SP ISSN 0300-5755) **2061, 2471**
Alimentaria. (CK) **2061**
Alimentaria see Guia de la Industria Alimentaria **2072**
Alimentarista. (IT) **2061**
Alimentary Pharmacology and Therapeutics. (UK ISSN 0269-2813) **3266**
Alimentation au Quebec. (CN ISSN 0002-5410) **2090**
Alimentation et Distribution see Voedingsblad **2083**
Alimentation et la Vie see Alimentation et la Vie - Nouvelle Presentation **3602**
Alimentation et la Vie - Nouvelle Presentation. (FR) **3602**
Alimentation et Nutrition see Food and Nutrition **5195**
Alimentazione Nutrizione Metabolismo. (IT ISSN 0392-7512) **3602**
Alimentazione Oggi. (IT) **2061**
Alimentec. (SP ISSN 0212-6400) **3602**
Alimentos e Nutricao. (BL ISSN 0103-4235) **2061, 3602**
Alimentos Procesados. (US ISSN 0744-625X) **2061**
Aliments du Pacifique Sud see South Pacific Foods Leaflet **2082**
Aliso. (US ISSN 0065-6275) **493**
Alive. (II) **2857**
Alive. (CN ISSN 0228-586X) **3799, 3602**
†Alive & Kicking. (US ISSN 0147-5762) **5133**
Alive & W E L. (AT) **4836**
Alive and Well and Living in New York City Saint Patrick's Cathedral see Alive and Well Saint Patrick's Cathedral **4254**
Alive and Well Saint Patrick's Cathedral.(US) **4254**
Alive Now. (US ISSN 0891-8767) **4228**
Alive to God. (UK) **4228**
Aliyon. (US) **1990**
Alkaline Paper Advocate. (US ISSN 0897-2524) **3661, 4120**
Alkalizer see Miles Alkalizer **447**
Alkalmazott Matematikai Lapok. (HU ISSN 0133-3399) **3028, 3814**
Alkaloids. (US) **1216, 3716**
Alki. (US ISSN 8756-4173) **2742**
Alkmaarse Historische Reeks. (NE) **2347**
Alkohol-Industrie. (GW ISSN 0002-5496) **377**
Alkohol och Narkotika/Alcohol and Other Drugs. (SW ISSN 0345-0732) **1534**
Alkoholdebatt. (SW ISSN 0002-550X) **1534**
Alkoholfraagen see Alkohol och Narkotika **1534**
Alkohologia. (HU ISSN 0133-3356) **1534**
All About Arizona, the Healthful State. (US) **4751**
All About Beer. (US) **377**
All about Business in Hawaii. (US ISSN 1046-5480) **842**
All About Food and Cooking. see Allt Om Mat **2061**
All About Issues. (US ISSN 0733-1231) **595, 3979**
All About Kids. (US) **1232**
All About Medicare. (US) **2526**
All Abroad see Abroad **4750**
All Abroad with P & O European Ferries see Abroad **4750**
All Access Pass. (CN) **3537**
All Africa Conference of Churches. Refugee Department. Progress Report. (KE) **4162**
All Africa Conference of Churches. Refugee Department. Project List. (KE) **4162**
All Africa Conference of Churches Bulletin see A A C C Bulletin **4161**
All Africa Conference of Churches Magazine see A A C C Magazine **4161**
All Africa Press Service Bulletin see A P S Bulletin **4161**
All-American Man. (US) **3395, 2450**
All Area. (US ISSN 0735-1887) **310, 2857, 2987**
All Around the Editor's Desk see Editor's Desk **2992**
All-Asia Agency Guide. (HK) **28**
All-Asia Guide. (HK ISSN 0072-4939) **4751, 2241**
All Available Light. (US) **2987**
All Canada Weekly Summaries - National. (CN ISSN 0705-1360) **2596**
All Chevy. (US) **4679**
All-Church Press Newspapers. (US ISSN 0002-5542) **2567, 4162**
All England Law Reports. (UK ISSN 0002-5569) **2597**
All England Law Reports. Annual Review. (UK ISSN 0265-766X) **2597**
All Hands. (US ISSN 0002-5577) **3450**
All In. (UK) **2987**
▼All-In-One Business Contactbook (Year). (US) **1120**
All-India Anglo-Indian Association. Review. (II ISSN 0002-5585) **3949**
All India Appointment Gazette. (II) **2198**
All India Architects Directory see Indian Architects Directory **301**
All-India Conference of Linguists. Proceedings. (II) **2801**
All-India Conference of Linguists. Souvenir. (II) **2801**
All India Congress Committee. Congress Bulletin. (II) **3871**
All India Handloom Exporters Guide. (II) **4616**
All India Institute of Local Self Government. Quarterly Journal. (II ISSN 0024-5623) **4083**
All India Institute of Speech and Hearing. Journal. (II) **2285, 1733**
All India Magic Circle Bulletin. (II) **2433**
All India Ophthalmological Society. Proceedings. (II) **3297**
All India Organisation of Employers Labour News see A I O E Labour News **970**
All India Reporter. (II ISSN 0002-5593) **2597**
All India Services Law Journal. (II) **2597**
All India Textiles Directory. (II) **1120, 4616**
All Male. (US) **3395, 2450**
All Media & Product Survey. (SA) **40, 4561**
All Media and Product Survey Black Radio and Television Diary see A M P S Black Radio and Television Diary **40**
All Media and Product Survey Meter Weekly Reports see A M P S Meter Weekly Reports **40**
All Media and Product Survey White - Coloured - Asian Radio Diary see A M P S White - Coloured - Asian Radio Diary **1346**
All of Housing/Katei-Ban Hyakka Series.(JA) **2482, 599**
All of Mexico at Low Cost. (US ISSN 0533-0653) **4751**
All Ohio Scanner Club Newsletter. (US) **1354**
All Pakistan Legal Decisions. (PK ISSN 0030-9958) **2597**
All Pakistan Textile Mills Association. Annual Report see All Pakistan Textile Mills Association. Chairman's Review **1071**
All Pakistan Textile Mills Association. Chairman's Review. (PK) **1071, 4616**
All Pakistan Women's Association. Triennial Conference Report. (PK) **4836**
All Pakistan Women's Association Newsletter see A P W A Newsletter **4396**
All Reading Matters. see Ooru Yomimono **2945**
All Scenario Data Base. (US) **938**
▼All Sport Weekly. (UK) **4463**
All State. (US) **1303**
All State Sales Tax Reports. (US) **1087**
All States Tax Handbook (Year). (US) **1087**
All States Tourist Park Guide. (AT) **4751**
All T V Publicity Outlets - Nationwide see T V & Cable Publicity Outlets - Nationwide **1380**
All Terrain Vehicle News see A T V News **5129**
All Terrain Vehicle Sports see A T V Sports **5129**
All the World. (UK ISSN 0002-5623) **4228, 4398**
All Time Favorite Crochet. (US) **3590**
All Weather Fund Investor. (US) **938**
All Yomimono. (JA) **2893**
Alla Bottega. (IT ISSN 0002-5631) **2893, 310**
Allahabad Law Journal. (II) **2597**
Allam es Igazgatas. (HU ISSN 0324-7171) **2597, 4052**
Allam- es Jogtudomany/Political Science and Jurisprudence. (HU ISSN 0002-564X) **2597, 3871**
Allami Gazdasag/State Farming. (HU) **75**
Allarme. see Alarm **2031**
Allas Veckotidning. (SW ISSN 0345-0759) **2218**
Allattani Kozlemenyek/Zoological Proceedings. (HU ISSN 0002-5658) **576**
Allattenyeztes es Takarmanyozas/ Animal Breeding and Feeding. (HU ISSN 0230-1814) **209**
Alle Boerns Jul see Jul i Familien **1257**
Alle den Volcke. (NE ISSN 0002-5666) **4228**
Alle Hens. (NE ISSN 0002-5674) **3450**
Alle Risico's. (BE) **2526**
Alle Tiders Odsherred. (DK ISSN 0108-9846) **2347, 261**
Alleanza Monarchica. (IT) **2204**
▼Alledaagse Dingen. (NE ISSN 0927-1791) **2052**
Allees All Around. (US ISSN 0883-5926) **2143, 2052, 3979**
Allegany County Cooperative Extension News see News & Views (Belmont) **110**
Allegany Poetry see Uroboros **3008**
Allegheny Business News. (US) **644**
Allegheny County Medical Society. Bulletin. (US ISSN 0098-3772) **3073**
Allegheny County Pharmacist. (US ISSN 0002-5690) **3716**
Allegheny Lawyer. (US) **2597**
Allegheny Review. (US ISSN 0742-096X) **2893**
Allegheny Trucker. (US) **4742**
Alegoria. (IT) **2893**
Allegro. (US ISSN 0002-5704) **2580, 3537**
Allelographia Worldwide. (GR) **1296, 2433**
Allemagne d'Aujourd'hui. (FR ISSN 0002-5712) **1990, 2188**
Allen County Historical Society. Newsletter. (US) **2397**
Allen County Lines. (US) **2143**
Allen County Reporter. (US) **2397**
Allen Memorial Art Museum. Bulletin. (US ISSN 0002-5739) **3521**
Allensbacher Almanach. (GW) **2347**
Allensbacher Berichte. (GW ISSN 0176-9251) **4365**
Allensbacher Jahrbuch der Demoskopie.(GW ISSN 0175-9191) **4428**
Allensbacher Markt-Analyse - Werbetraeger-Analyse. (GW) **1033, 2526**
Allensbacher Werbetraeger-Analyse see Allensbacher Markt-Analyse - Werbetraeger-Analyse **1033**
Allergie et Immunologie. (FR) **3182**
Allergie und Immunologie. (GW ISSN 0323-4398) **3183**
Allergologia et Inmunopathologia. (SP ISSN 0301-0546) **3183**
Allergologicum; Transactions of the Collegium Internationale. (SZ ISSN 0065-6372) **3183**
Allergologie. (GW ISSN 0344-5062) **3183**
Allergothek. (GW) **3183**
Allergy. (DK ISSN 0105-4538) **3183**

Allergy. Supplementum. (DK ISSN 0108-1675) **3183**
Allergy Alert. (CN ISSN 0824-1333) **3183**
Allergy & Clinical Immunology News. (CN ISSN 0838-1925) **3183**
Allergy Association Australia - Victoria Inc. News see A A A News **3182**
Allergy Proceedings. (US ISSN 1046-9354) **3183**
†Allergy Relief Newsletter. (US ISSN 0883-7767) **5133**
Allers. (NO ISSN 0002-5771) **2212**
Allers. (SW ISSN 0002-578X) **2218**
Allertonia. (US ISSN 0735-8032) **493**, 2120
Alles fuer die Katz. (GW ISSN 0720-2849) **3707**
Alles Ueber Wein. (GW ISSN 0175-8314) **2061**, 4751
Allesoe, Broby, Naesby Lokalarkiv. (DK ISSN 0108-7142) **2348**
Allestire. (IT) **644**, 3390
Allevatore. (IT) **4805**
L'Allevatore Avicunicolo. (IT) **209**
Allgaeuer Geschichtsfreund. (GW ISSN 0178-6199) **2348**
Der Allgemeinarzt. (GW ISSN 0172-7249) **3073**
Allgemeine Baecker-Zeitung. (GW) **2086**
Allgemeine Bau-Zeitung. (AU ISSN 0002-5798) **599**
Allgemeine Bauzeitung. (GW ISSN 0002-5801) **599**
Allgemeine Deutsche Imkerzeitung. (GW ISSN 0002-5828) **75**
Allgemeine Deutsche Lehrerzeitung see Erziehung und Wissenschaft **1632**
Allgemeine Elektrizitaets Gesellschaft Telefunken. Wissenschaftliche Berichte see A E G-Telefunken. Wissenschaftliche Berichte **5128**
Allgemeine Elektrizitaets Gesellschaft Telefunken Progress see A E G - Telefunken Progress **5128**
Allgemeine Fleischer Zeitung. (GW ISSN 0170-9828) **2061**
Allgemeine Forst- und Jagdzeitung. (GW ISSN 0002-5852) **2095**
Allgemeine Forst Zeitschrift. (GW ISSN 0002-5860) **2095**
Allgemeine Forstzeitung see Oesterreichische Forstzeitung **2105**
Allgemeine Homoeopathische Zeitung. (GW ISSN 0175-7881) **3213**
Allgemeine Hotel- und Gaststaetten-Zeitung. (GW ISSN 0002-5895) **2471**
Allgemeine Immobilien-Zeitung. (GW) **4144**
Allgemeine Papier-Rundschau see A P R **3661**
Allgemeine Schweizerische Militaerzeitschrift. (SZ ISSN 0002-5925) **3450**
Allgemeine Sparkasse. Kurz Notiert. (AU) **758**
Allgemeine Sparkasse Linz. Kurz Notiert see Allgemeine Sparkasse. Kurz Notiert **758**
Allgemeine Vermessungs-Nachrichten. (GW ISSN 0002-5968) **1861**
Allgemeine Zeitschrift fuer Paranormologie. (GW ISSN 0934-4535) **3593**, 3668
Allgemeine Zeitschrift fuer Parapsychologie see Allgemeine Zeitschrift fuer Paranormologie **3593**
Allgemeine Zeitschrift fuer Philosophie. (GW ISSN 0340-7969) **3760**
Allgemeiner Anzeiger fuer Buchbindereien see Binderreport **4121**
Allgemeiner Caecilien-Verband. Schriftenreihe. (GW) **3537**, 4254
Allgemeiner Deutscher Automobil Club e.V. Atlas Deutschland - Europa see A D A C Atlas Deutschland - Europa **4750**
Allgemeiner Deutscher Automobil-Club e.V. Campingfuehrer. Band 1: Suedeuropa see A D A C Campingfuehrer. Band 1: Suedeuropa **4539**

Allgemeiner Deutscher Automobil-Club e.V. Campingfuehrer. Band 2: Deutschland, Mittel- und Nordeuropa see A D A C Campingfuehrer. Band 2: Deutschland, Mittel- und Nordeuropa **4539**
Allgemeiner Deutscher Automobil-Club e.V. Grosse A D A C Ski Atlas (Year) see Der Grosse A D A C Ski Atlas (Year) **4547**
Allgemeiner Deutscher Automobil-Club e.V. Handbuch: Reiserecht Entscheidungen see A D A C Handbuch: Reiserecht Entscheidungen **2592**
Allgemeiner Deutscher Automobil-Club e.V. Handbuch: Schadenersatz bei Verletzung see A D A C Handbuch: Schadenersatz bei Verletzung **2592**
Allgemeiner Deutscher Tanzlehrer Verband Nachrichten see A D T V - Nachrichten **1528**
Allgemeiner Muehlen-Markt. (AU ISSN 0002-5992) **204**
Allgemeiner Samen- und Pflanzen Anzeiger. (GW ISSN 0002-600X) **2120**
Allgemeiner Vliestoff-Report see A V R **4616**
Allgemeines Statistisches Archiv. (GW ISSN 0002-6018) **4561**
Allgemeinmedizin. (GW ISSN 0257-3199) **3073**
Alliance see Alliance News **3871**
Alliance (Charleston). (US) **1303**, 3073
L'Alliance (Montreal). (CN ISSN 0711-6829) **1614**, 2580
Alliance (Ottawa). (CN) **4053**, 2580
▼Alliance Alert. (US) **938**
Alliance Atlantique. Structure, Faits et Chiffres. see North Atlantic Treaty Organization. Facts and Figures **3967**
Alliance Autochtone du Quebec. (CN) **1990**
Alliance for Engineering in Medicine and Biology. Proceedings of the Annual Conference. (US ISSN 0589-1019) **3073**, 427, 1813
Alliance for Peace in Rumania. Information Bulletin. (RM) **3871**
Alliance Israelite Universelle en France. Cahiers. (FR ISSN 0002-6050) **4221**
Alliance Israelite Universelle en France Nouveaux Cahiers see A I U Les Nouveaux Cahiers **4225**
Alliance Life. (US ISSN 1040-6794) **4228**
Alliance News. (UK) **3871**
Alliance of Information and Referral Systems. Journal see Information and Referral **4408**
Alliance Pastorale. Bulletin. (FR) **209**
Alliance Review. (US ISSN 0002-6093) **1614**, 4162
Alliance Update. (US ISSN 0273-8023) **3799**, 1743, 4463
Alliance Witness see Alliance Life **4228**
Alliancer. see Zwiazkowiec **2030**
Allianz Zeitung. (GW) **2526**
Allicht. (NE ISSN 0168-3748) **1803**
Allied Artists of America. Exhibition Catalog. (US ISSN 0065-6410) **3521**
Allied Arts Newsletter. (US) **4083**, 291, 310, 2857
Allied Canadian Travel Agents Official Annual Directory see A C T A Official Annual Directory **1120**
Allied Dunbar Tax Guide. (UK) **1087**
Allied Health Education Directory. (US ISSN 0194-3766) **1692**, 3073
Allied Health Education Newsletter. (US) **1614**, 3073
Allied Health Trends see Trends (Washington, 1969) **4113**
Allied Industrial Worker. (US ISSN 0002-6107) **2580**
Allied Irish Bank Review. (IE) **758**
Allied Landscape Industry see A L I **5128**
Allied Trucking Publications. (US) **4743**
Allier Magazine. (FR) **4751**
Alligator. (US) **3537**, 3503, 4459
Alligator Times see Seminole Tribune **2022**

Allionia. (IT ISSN 0065-6429) **493**
Allmende. (GW ISSN 0720-3098) **2987**, 2857
Allo Paris. (FR) **4751**
Allo Dix-Huit. (FR ISSN 0044-7358) **2031**
Allons. (UK ISSN 0957-6215) **2802**, 1743
Alloy Digest. (US ISSN 0002-614X) **3401**
Alloys Index. (US ISSN 0094-8233) **3424**, 2
Allpanchis. (PE) **4365**
Allpanchis Phuturinga see Allpanchis **4365**
Allstate Motor Club National Park Guide see National Park Guide **4551**
Allstate Motor Club R V Park and Campground Directory. (US) **4540**
▼Allstate Motor Club R V Sales, Rental and Service Directory. (US ISSN 1043-5824) **4646**
Allt i Hemmet. (SW ISSN 0002-6182) **2556**, 2548
Allt om Hobby. (SW ISSN 0002-6190) **2433**
Allt om Husvagn och Camping. (SW ISSN 0346-9190) **4540**
Allt om M C. (MotorCyclar) (SW ISSN 0345-0813) **4515**
Allt Om Mat/All About Food and Cooking. (SW ISSN 0002-6204) **2061**
Alltag. (GW) **2893**, 3788
Alluminio. (IT ISSN 0365-3927) **3401**
Alluminio e Nuova Metallurgia see Alluminio **3401**
▼Allure. (US ISSN 1054-7711) **3799**, 1289
Alm und Bergbauer. (AU) **75**
Alm und Weide see Alm und Bergbauer **75**
Alma see Paz e Alegria **4272**
Alma Mariana. (US ISSN 1051-7286) **4254**
Alma Mater. (CU) **3871**
Almacenero. (AG) **2090**
†Almanac for Computers. (US ISSN 0191-3867) **5133**
Almanac for Farmers and City Folk. (US ISSN 0739-6961) **1780**, 75
Almanac for Geodetic Engineers. (PH ISSN 0569-0838) **360**
Almanac of Business and Industrial Financial Ratios. (US) **758**, 938
†Almanac of California Government and Politics. (US) **5133**
Almanac of China's Commerce. see Zhongguo Shangye Nianjian **841**
Almanac of China's Foreign Economic Relations and Trade. (HK) **926**, 899, 2719
Almanac of Current World Leaders see Current World Leaders **3889**
Almanac of Famous People. (US) **417**
Almanac of Seapower. (US ISSN 0736-3559) **3450**
Almanacco Calcistico Svizzero. (SZ) **4499**
Almanacco Caravan & Camper. (IT) **4540**
Almanacco di Fotografare. (IT) **3788**, 1368
Almanacco di Stereo. (IT) **1368**, 4459
Almanacco la Moto. (IT) **4515**
Almanacco Repubblicano. (IT) **1780**
Almanacco Roulotte. (IT) **4540**
Almanach de l'Auto. (CN) **4679**
Almanach du Peuple. (CN ISSN 0065-650X) **1780**, 417
Almanach du Vieux Geneve see Revue du Vieux Geneve **2383**
Almanach Sceny Polskiej. (PL ISSN 0065-6526) **4629**
Almanahul Cinema. (RM) **3503**
†Almanak for Teologi og Litteratur. (DK ISSN 0900-1573) **5133**
Almanak NUBIKA see Almanak Nuklir Biologi dan Kimia **1803**
Almanak Nuklir Biologi dan Kimia. (IO) **1803**, 427, 1169
Almanakh Gomonu Ukrainy. (CN ISSN 0441-1196) **1990**, 1780
Almanaque. (UY) **1601**
Almanaque Abril. (BL) **2175**
Almanaque Brazil see Almanaque Abril **2175**

Almanaque del Peru. (PE) **2397**
Almanaque Nautico Reducido para Uso con Maquinas de Calcular. (SP ISSN 0210-8046) **360**, 1780
Almanaque Puertorriqueno (Year). (PR) **1780**
†Almannaco Auto. (IT) **5133**
Almas. (MX ISSN 0002-628X) **4162**, 3760
Al-Masaq. (UK ISSN 0950-3110) **2428**, 4218
Der Almbauer. (GW ISSN 0002-6298) **75**, 2095
Almennyttige Boligafdelingers Regnskaber. (DK) **2483**
Almennyttige Boligselskabers Regnskaber see Almennyttige Boligafdelingers Regnskaber **2483**
Almindelige Danske Laegeforening see Laegeforeningens Vejviser **3121**
Almogaren see Institutum Canarium Yearbook. Almogaren **274**
Almond Facts. (US) **2120**
Almost Free Cookbooks & Recipes Update. (US ISSN 0736-170X) **2444**
Almshouses Gazette. (UK) **4398**, 2270
Aloe. (SA ISSN 0002-6301) **493**
Aloe, Cactus & Succulent Society of Zimbabwe. Ingens Bulletin. (RH ISSN 1016-524X) **493**, 2120
Aloha. (US ISSN 0147-5436) **4751**
Alokpaat. (II) **2198**
Alon Hanotea. (IS ISSN 0333-8886) **167**
Alon Lamorah Lesifrut. (IS ISSN 0334-5076) **1614**
Alon Lemoreh Habiologia. (IS) **1743**, 427
Alon Shvut. (IS) **4221**
Along the Towpath. (US) **1483**
Alpen/Alpes. (SZ ISSN 0002-6336) **4540**
Alpenhorn. (US) **3707**
Alpeninstitut. Schriftenreihe. (GW) **4298**
Alpenlaendische Bienenzeitung. (AU ISSN 0002-6352) **76**
Alpes. see Alpen **4540**
Alpha. (US ISSN 0162-5918) **1303**
Alpha. (II) **1331**
Alpha see Nueva Revista del Pacifico **2832**
Alpha. (CN) **2893**, 311, 4629
Alpha see Prisma **3946**
Alpha. (NE) **4228**, 1368
Alpha. (NZ ISSN 0111-1957) **4298**
Alpha (New Malden). (UK) **4228**
Alpha Beat Soup. (US ISSN 0838-391X) **2893**, 2987
Alpha Communications Monthly. (II) **1331**, 1699
Alpha Digest. (II) **2198**, 1303
Alpha Flore. (FR) **2120**
Alpha-Mathematische Schuelerzeitschrift. (GW ISSN 0002-6395) **3028**, 1614
Alpha Micro User Society Log see A M U S. Log **1466**
Alpha Omegan. (US ISSN 0002-6417) **3227**
Alpha Psi Omega: Playbill. (US) **4629**, 1303
Alpha Tau Omega Fraternity, Inc. Palm see A T O Palm **1302**
Alphabetic Subject Index to Petroleum Abstracts. (US ISSN 0002-6441) **3704**, 2
▼Alphanumeric Reports Publications Index. (UK ISSN 0964-3400) **389**
Alpi Venete. (IT ISSN 0002-6468) **4540**
Alpin jo, Mame! (IT) **3450**
Alpin-Magazin. (GW ISSN 0177-3542) **4540**
Alpine Garden Club of British Columbia. Monthly Bulletin. (CN ISSN 0836-320X) **2120**
Alpine Garden Society. Quarterly Bulletin. (UK ISSN 0002-6476) **2120**
Alpine Garden Society Guides see A G S Guides **2120**
Alpine Gardening see Alpine Garden Society. Quarterly Bulletin **2120**
Alpine Journal. (UK ISSN 0065-6569) **2241**

Alpine Sun. (US ISSN 8750-8257) 2221
Alpinist. see Gakujin 4547
Alpino. (IT ISSN 0002-6492) 2204
Alsace Automobile. (FR ISSN 0767-8444) 4751, 4679
Alsatian Studies. (US) 2348
Alsterverein Jahrbuch. (GW) 2348
Alt for Damerne. (DK ISSN 0002-6506) 4836
Alt-Katholik see Altkatholische Kirchenzeitung 4280
Alt-Offenbach. (GW ISSN 0174-8726) 2348
Alt om Data. (DK ISSN 0109-2847) 1448
Alt om Haandarbejde see Haandarbejde Trin for Trin 3591
▼Alt om Mad. (DK ISSN 0906-0820) 2061, 377
Alt-Thueringen. (GW ISSN 0065-6585) 2348, 233
Alt und Jung Metten. (GW) 4254
Alt- und Neu-Indische Studien. (GW ISSN 0170-3242) 2336
Alta Direccion. (SP ISSN 0002-6549) 1002
Alta Direccion. Monografias. (SP) 1002
Alta Fedelta. (IT ISSN 0393-0882) 4459, 3537
Alta Frequenza see European Transactions on Telecommunications and Related Technologies 1335
Alta Frequenza Rivista di Elettronica. (IT ISSN 1120-1908) 1331
Alta Nizza. (FR ISSN 0240-902X) 1990
Alta Tecnologia. (SP) 4593
Alta Val Tanaro. (IT) 2204
†Altadena Review. (US ISSN 0162-8208) 5133
Altamura. (IT ISSN 0569-1346) 3521
Al-Tawhid. (IR) 4218
Altbabylonische Briefe im Umschrift und Uebersetzung. (NE ISSN 0065-6593) 3633
Altdeutsche Textbibliothek. Ergaenzungsreihe. (GW ISSN 0065-6607) 2893
Altdorfer Sportspiegel. (GW) 4463
Alte Abenteuerliche Reiseberichte. (GW) 2893
Alte Musik Aktuell. (GW) 3537
Die Alte Stadt. (GW ISSN 0170-9364) 2483
Alte Uhren see Alte Uhren und Moderne Zeitmessung 2521
Alte Uhren und Moderne Zeitmessung. (GW ISSN 0932-2655) 2521
Altech. (II ISSN 0065-6623) 4593
Die Alten Sprachen im Unterricht. (GW ISSN 0179-387X) 2802, 1274
Altenburger Naturwissenschaftliche Forschungen. (GW ISSN 0232-5381) 427, 1554, 3656
Altenheim. (GW ISSN 0002-6573) 3275
Altenhilfe. (GW ISSN 0724-8849) 2270, 4398
Altenpflege. (GW ISSN 0341-0455) 3275
Alter-Alter. (IT) 2983
The Altered Mind. (US) 2987
†Alternate Energy Transportation Newsletter. (US ISSN 0271-9029) 5133
Alternate Roots Newsletter. (US) 4629, 3537
Alternate Routes. (CN ISSN 0702-8865) 4365, 233
Alternatif see Petite Caisse 1321
Alternativa Cultura. (AG) 2857
▼Alternativa 2000. (SP) 4162
Alternativas see Opciones 3967
Alternative. (MF) 3871, 4162
Alternative Agriculture News. (US ISSN 8755-4941) 76
Alternative Alternative. (UK ISSN 0260-0552) 4457, 598, 4354
Alternative America. (US) 1296
Alternative - Appropriate Technologies in Agriculture. (II) 76
Alternative Archivist. (CN) 2742, 2857
Alternative Economic Commentary. (US) 938
Alternative Energy. (US) 1783

Alternative Energy Digests. (US ISSN 1050-3145) 1783, 1797
Alternative Energy Resource Organization Sun Times see A E R O Sun Times 1783
Alternative Energy Retailer. (US ISSN 0273-8163) 1783
Alternative Energy Sourcebook. (US) 1783, 1942
Alternative England and Wales. (UK) 1780
†Alternative Fiction & Poetry. (US ISSN 0893-2581) 5133
Alternative Information Record see A I R 2857
Alternative Kommunalpolitik. (GW ISSN 0722-5474) 4053, 4083
Alternative Library Literature. (US ISSN 0749-6885) 2742
Alternative London see Alternative England and Wales 1780
†Alternative Media Magazine. (US ISSN 0730-1766) 5133
†Alternative Medicine. (NE ISSN 0168-8448) 5134
Alternative Methods in Toxicology Series. (US ISSN 0737-402X) 1980, 3716
Alternative Press. (US) 2987, 311
†Alternative Press Annual. (US ISSN 0748-9463) 5134
Alternative Press Index. (US ISSN 0002-662X) 2890, 2, 3936
Alternative Press Review see Alternative Media Magazine 5133
Alternative Research Newsletter. (CN) 2858, 4428
Alternative Times. (UK ISSN 0261-6033) 1783
Alternative Trading News. (US) 926, 829, 899, 3949
▼Alternative Transportation News. (US) 4646, 1942, 4679
Alternatives see Continuation Education 1683
Alternatives. (CN ISSN 0002-6638) 1942, 4365
Alternatives see Creative Mind 2862
Alternatives see Presse-Inter 3596
Alternatives. (US ISSN 0304-3754) 3949
†Alternatives (Ellenwood). (US) 5134
Alternatives (Hamilton). (US) 2858
Alternatives (Myrtle Beach). (US) 2221
Alternatives Économiques. (FR) 644
Alternatives in Education. (US) 1743, 1733
Alternatives Newsletter. (US) 2597
Alternatives to "A" Level. (UK) 1699
Alternatives to Laboratory Animals: A T L A. (UK ISSN 0261-1929) 3257
Das Altertum. (GW ISSN 0002-6646) 1274, 2305, 3633
Altes Handwerk. (GW) 2052
Altes Haus Modern. (GW) 599, 291
†Altfraenkische Bilder und Wappenkalender. (GW ISSN 0342-8699) 5134
Althaus Modernisierung see Modernisieren 625
Althochdeutsches Woerterbuch. (GW) 2802
Altkatholische Kirchenzeitung. (AU ISSN 0002-6514) 4280
Altman Weil Pensa Report to Legal Management. (US ISSN 0191-863X) 2705
Alto Gerencia. (CK) 1002
Alto Peinado. (MX) 371
Altonaer Museum in Hamburg. Nordeutsches Landesmuseum. Jahrbuch. (GW ISSN 0440-1417) 3521
Altorientalische Forschungen. (GW ISSN 0232-8461) 2428, 3633
L'Altra Europa. (IT) 311, 2893, 4162, 4428
Altri Termini. (IT) 2858
Altrimedia. (IT) 1368
†Altrive Chapbooks. (UK ISSN 0266-8521) 5134
†L'Altro Piemonte. (IT) 5134
▼Altroquando. (IT) 2893
Der Altsprachliche Unterricht. (GW ISSN 0002-6670) 2802, 1743
Alumi-Age. (JA) 3401
Alumi-News. (CN ISSN 0705-4157) 599
†Aluminium in Use. (AT) 5134

Aluminium Industry. (UK ISSN 0268-5280) 1813, 3401
†Aluminium Industry in the Soviet Union. (US) 5134
Aluminium Intern: Aluminium und Automobil. (GW ISSN 0934-3938) 3401
Aluminium-Kurier. (GW ISSN 0175-6273) 599
Aluminium Smelters see Secondary Aluminium 3495
Aluminium Today. (UK) 3401
Aluminum. (GW ISSN 0002-6689) 3402
†Aluminum Review. (SA) 5134
Aluminum Situation. (US) 3402
Aluminum Standards and Data. (US ISSN 0065-6658) 3402
Aluminum Standards and Data-Metric. (US) 3402
Aluminum Statistical Review. (US ISSN 0065-6666) 3402
Alumnews. (US) 1303
Alumni Columns. (US) 1303
Alumni Companion. (US) 1303
Alumni Happenings see M S M C Happenings 1316
Alumni News (North Carolina). (US) 1303
Alumni Publications: a Catalogue. (II) 389
Alumni Relations News - Carson-Newman College. (US) 1303
Alumni U B C Chronicle. (University of British Columbia) (CN ISSN 0041-4999) 1303
Alumni Update see Philadelphia College of Textiles & Science. Portfolio 1321
Alumnus see Morehouse College Bulletin 1318
Alumnus. (US) 3374, 1303
Alumnus (Southern Illinois University at Carbondale). (US ISSN 8750-3360) 1303
†Alura. (US) 5134
Alurama. (NE) 3402
Alverno Today. (US) 1303
Alvey News see J F I T News 1430
Alwan. see Colours 1308
Alzheimer Disease and Associated Disorders. (US ISSN 0893-0341) 2270, 3329
Alzheimer's Association Newsletter. (US) 2270, 3073, 4428
Am Albergo Moderno see In Design 5211
Am-Can Report. (CN ISSN 0843-462X) 1033, 4751
Am Erker. (GW ISSN 0721-0493) 2893, 2858
Am F A R Report. (American Foundation for A I D S Research) (US) 3217
Am, Olam u-Medinah. see Folk, Velt un Medine 2002
Am-Pol Eagle. (US) 1990
Am Veadamato. (IS ISSN 0569-163X) 2203
Amacadmy. (US) 311, 291, 2893
Amakusa Marine Biological Laboratory. Publications. (JA ISSN 0065-6682) 427
Al-Amal. (LY) 1248
†Amal. (BA) 5134
Amalgamated Union of Engineering Workers, Engineering Section Journal see A U E W E S Journal 1813
Amaltheia. (GR) 2348, 261
Amanah. (IO) 4218
Amandala. (BH) 4053
Amandla. (NE ISSN 0166-0373) 3871
Amanecer. (US) 4162
Amanecer. (NQ) 4254
Amanita Brandy. (US) 2987
Amar Chitra Katha. (II) 2893, 1248
Amar Deep. (UK ISSN 0264-1453) 1990
Amar-e Bazargani-Ye Khareji-Ye Iran. see Foreign Trade Statistics of Iran 717
Amaranth Review. (US ISSN 1043-8947) 2987
Amaranth Today. (US) 167, 2120
Amaru. (AG) 2893
Amaterska Scena. (CS ISSN 0002-6786) 4629

Amaterske Radio A. (CS ISSN 0322-9572) 1354
Amaterske Radio B. (CS) 1354
Amatersky Film a Video see Video plus Film 1387
Amateur Astronomer. see Tianwen Aihaozhe 370
Amateur Athlete. (US) 4463
Amateur Athletic Association. Handbook. (UK ISSN 0065-6690) 4463
Amateur Athletic Union of the United States. Official Handbook of the A A U Code. (US ISSN 0091-3405) 4463
Amateur Athletic Union of the United States Info A A U see Info A A U 4475
Amateur Athletic Union of the United States Official Track and Field Handbook, Rules and Records see A A U Official Track and Field Handbook, Rules and Records 4463
Amateur Baseball News. (US ISSN 0002-6816) 4499
†Amateur Boxer. (US ISSN 0160-7332) 5134
Amateur Chamber Music Players. Annual Newsletter. (US) 3537
Amateur Chamber Music Players. Directory. (US ISSN 0065-6704) 3537
Amateur Entomologists Society. Bulletin.(UK ISSN 0266-836X) 527
Amateur Film and Video Maker. (UK) 3503, 1384
Amateur Film Maker see Amateur Film and Video Maker 3503
Amateur Gardening. (UK ISSN 0002-6832) 2120
Amateur Golf Register. (US) 4499
Amateur Historian see Local Historian 2373
Amateur Hockey Association of the United States. Official Guide see U S A Hockey 4495
Amateur Hockey Association of the United States. Rule Book see U S A Hockey. Rule Book 4495
Amateur Master File. (US) 1346
Amateur Music Activities. (RU) 3537
Amateur Musician/Musicien Amateur. (CN) 3537
Amateur Photographer. (UK ISSN 0002-6840) 3788
Amateur Radio. (AT ISSN 0002-6859) 1354
Amateur Radio. (UK ISSN 0264-2557) 1354
Amateur Radio Service Master File Updates. (US) 1346, 1354
Amateur Rider. (US) 4531
Amateur Satellite Journal see A M S A T Journal 1368
Amateur Satellite Report see A M S A T Journal 1368
Amateur Skating Union of the United States. Official Handbook see Amateur Speedskating Union of the United States. Official Handbook 4463
Amateur Softball Association of America. Official Guide and Rule Book. (US ISSN 0065-6739) 4499
Amateur Speedskating Union of the United States. Official Handbook. (US) 4463
Amateur Stage. (UK ISSN 0002-6867) 4629
Amateur Swimming Association Handbook. (UK) 4463
Amateur Trapshooting Association. Official Trapshooting Rules. (US ISSN 0065-6747) 4540
Amateur Wrestling News. (US ISSN 0569-1796) 4463
Amateur Writer's Journal. (US) 2893
Amateur Yacht Research Society Airs see A Y R S Airs 4521
Amateurfilm Journal. (SZ) 3503
Amateurfotografie. (GW) 3788
Amateurtuinder. (NE ISSN 0002-6875) 2120
Amauta. (PE) 1615
Amax News. (US) 3477, 842, 1002
Amazing Cinema see Cinema News 3506

Amazing Computing for the Commodore Amiga. (US) **1467**
Amazing Heroes. (US ISSN 0745-6506) **311**, **4120**
Amazing Stories. (US ISSN 1058-0751) **3010**
†Amazonia - Bibliografia. (BL ISSN 0100-0977) **5134**
Amazonia Peruana. (PE ISSN 0252-886X) **233**, **2241**
Amazoniana; Limnologia et Oecologia Regionalis Systemae Fluminis Amazonas. (GW ISSN 0065-6755) **427**
Ambacher Schriften. (GW ISSN 0179-4922) **2893**
Ambacht & Industrie. (NE) **2061**
Ambassador Report. (US ISSN 0882-2123) **4162**
Ambergris. (US ISSN 1044-2006) **2893**, **311**
Ambient Assessment Air Portion *see* National Air Quality and Emissions Trends Report **1978**
Ambientare Home *see* Home **2551**
Ambiente. (GW) **2548**, **639**
L'Ambiente Cucina/Kitchen. (IT ISSN 0392-5730) **2548**
Ambiente e Sicurezza *see* A E S **1941**
Ambiente Naturale e Urbano *see* Pro Natura Genova **1966**
Ambiente Risorse Salute. (IT ISSN 0393-0521) **1942**, **4097**
▼Ambiente Storico. (IT) **2483**
Ambiente y Recursos Naturales. (AG) **3871**
Ambio. (US ISSN 0044-7447) **1942**
Ambit. (UK ISSN 0002-6972) **2893**
Ambito Empresarial. (UY) **899**, **926**
Ambito Financiero. (AG) **758**
Ambix. (UK ISSN 0002-6980) **1169**
Ambt en Plicht. (NE ISSN 0002-6999) **644**
Ambulance *see* Ambulance Service Journal **2458**
Ambulance and Medical Service Association of America Newsletter *see* A M S A A Newsletter **2458**
†Ambulance Bulletin. (UK) **5134**
Ambulance Industry Digest (A I D) *see* Ambulance Industry Journal **1120**
Ambulance Industry Journal. (US) **1120**, **3624**, **4097**, **4646**
Ambulance Service Journal. (UK) **2458**
Ambulanseforum. (NO) **4097**, **4398**
Ambulatory Medicine Letter. (US ISSN 0897-554X) **3073**
Ambulatory Pediatric Association Newsletter. (US ISSN 0002-7006) **3318**
Ambuli Ammavan. (II) **1248**
Ambulimama. (II) **2198**
AmCham. (BE) **806**, **833**
AmCham Journal *see* Business Journal **809**
AmCham Morocco. (MR ISSN 0065-7689) **806**
AmCham News Update *see* American Chamber of Commerce - Sao Paulo. Update **807**
AmCham Newsletter. (NE ISSN 0001-1878) **806**
AmCham W E U *see* American Chamber of Commerce of the Philippines. Weekly Executive Update **807**
AmCham Weekly News *see* Comments on Argentine Trade **813**
Ame Populaire. (FR) **4254**
Ameghiniana. (AG ISSN 0002-7014) **3656**
Amelia. (US ISSN 0743-2755) **2893**
Amenagement et Nature. (FR ISSN 0044-7463) **1483**, **291**, **2483**
Amenity Management. (UK ISSN 0957-8870) **2121**
Amentia. (BE ISSN 0002-7022) **4398**, **3799**
Amerasia Journal. (US ISSN 0044-7471) **4428**, **1990**, **2397**
America. (US ISSN 0002-7049) **4254**, **2221**
America (Knoxville) *see* Student Traveler **5284**
America by Car. (US ISSN 0569-1966) **4751**
America Cooperativa. (CK) **829**
America Desde Mexico. (MX) **2858**
America Economia. (US) **644**
America Entertains. (US) **2221**

America: History and Life. Annual Index.(US) **2327**, **2**
America: History and Life. Articles Abstract and Citations of Reviews and Dissertations Covering the United States and Canada. (US) **2327**, **2**
America Indigena. (MX ISSN 0002-7081) **233**
America Latina. Boletin. (PE) **4254**
America Latina 2001. (CK) **4298**
America Meridional. (UY) **2397**
America Pioneers: Tackett-Tacket-Tackitt Families of America *see* Tackett Journal **2165**
America - Problema. (PE ISSN 0065-6763) **4428**
America Votes. (US ISSN 0065-678X) **3871**
America West Airlines Magazine. (US) **4801**
Americaeconomia. (TC) **842**, **998**
American. (US) **1303**
American. (UK) **2193**
American - A S E A N Trade Council. Bulletin. (Association of South-East Asian Nations) (US) **899**
American Academy and Institute of Arts and Letters. Proceedings. (US ISSN 0145-8493) **2502**
American Academy for Jewish Research. Monograph Series. (US) **4221**, **2428**
American Academy for Jewish Research. Proceedings of the A A J R. (US ISSN 0065-6798) **4221**, **2428**
American Academy for Jewish Research. Text and Studies Series. (US) **4221**, **2428**
American Academy in Rome. Memoirs. (US ISSN 0065-6801) **311**, **291**
American Academy in Rome. Papers and Monographs. (US ISSN 0065-681X) **1274**
†American Academy of Actuaries. Journal. (US ISSN 0193-6581) **5134**
American Academy of Actuaries. Yearbook. (US ISSN 0569-2032) **2526**
American Academy of Allergy. Pollen and Mold Committee. Statistical Report. (US) **3183**
American Academy of Allergy and Immunology. Abstract Book. (US) **3166**, **3183**
American Academy of Arts and Letters. Proceedings *see* American Academy and Institute of Arts and Letters. Proceedings **2502**
American Academy of Arts and Sciences. Bulletin. (US ISSN 0002-712X) **2502**, **4298**
American Academy of Arts and Sciences. Proceedings *see* Daedalus (Cambridge) **2506**
American Academy of Audiology. Journal. (CN) **3313**
American Academy of Child and Adolescent Psychiatry. Journal. (US ISSN 0890-8567) **3329**
American Academy of Child Psychiatry. Journal *see* American Academy of Child and Adolescent Psychiatry. Journal **3329**
American Academy of Dermatology. Journal. (US ISSN 0190-9622) **3245**
American Academy of Environmental Engineers. Consultant Directory *see* Environmental Engineering Selection Guide **1951**
American Academy of Environmental Engineers. Roster *see* Who's Who in Environmental Engineering **1971**
American Academy of Family Physicians Reporter *see* A A F P Reporter **3068**
American Academy of Gold Foil Operators. Journal *see* Operative Dentistry **3239**
American Academy of Nurse Practitioners. Journal. (US ISSN 1041-2972) **3275**
American Academy of Orthopaedic Surgeons. Directory. (US ISSN 0516-8856) **3306**

American Academy of Osteopathy Newsletter *see* A A O Newsletter **3213**
American Academy of Osteopathy Yearbook. (US ISSN 0732-703X) **3213**
American Academy of Otolaryngic Allergy News *see* A A O A News **3182**
American Academy of Otolaryngology - Head and Neck Surgery. Bulletin. (US ISSN 0731-8359) **3313**
American Academy of Pediatrics. Committee on Infectious Diseases. Report (Year). (US ISSN 0065-6909) **3318**
American Academy of Pediatrics News *see* A A P News **3317**
American Academy of Pediatrics Policy Reference Guide *see* A A P Policy Reference Guide **3317**
American Academy of Physician Assistants. Journal. (US ISSN 0893-7400) **3073**
American Academy of Podiatric Sports Medicine Journal *see* American Academy of Podiatric Sports Medicine Newsletter **3370**
American Academy of Podiatric Sports Medicine Newsletter. (US) **3370**
American Academy of Podiatry Administration News-Letter. (US) **3374**
American Academy of Political and Social Science. Annals. (US ISSN 0002-7162) **3872**, **4365**
American Academy of Practice Management in Podiatry. News-Letter *see* American Academy of Podiatry Administration News-Letter **3374**
American Academy of Psychiatry and the Law. Bulletin. (US ISSN 0091-634X) **3329**, **2597**
American Academy of Psychiatry and the Law. Newsletter. (US ISSN 0896-5633) **2597**, **3329**, **4009**
American Academy of Psychoanalysis. Journal. (US ISSN 0090-3604) **4009**
American Academy of Religion. Annual Meeting. (US) **4162**
American Academy of Religion. Journal.(US ISSN 0002-7189) **4162**
American Academy of Religion Academy Series *see* A A R Academy Series **4161**
American Academy of Religion Studies in Religion *see* A A R Studies in Religion **4161**
American Academy of Tropical Medicine & Surgery. Journal. (US ISSN 0891-544X) **3217**
American Accounting Association. Newsletter. (US) **746**
American Accounting Association. Southeast Regional Group. Collected Papers of the Annual Meeting. (US ISSN 0360-8840) **746**
American Advertising. (US) **28**
American Advertising Federation. Annual Report to the Members. (US) **28**
American Advertising Federation Communicator *see* A A F Communicator **25**
American Agent and Broker. (US ISSN 0002-7200) **2526**
American Agricultural Economics Association. Handbook *see* American Agricultural Economics Association. Handbook-Directory **147**
American Agricultural Economics Association. Handbook-Directory. (US) **147**
American Agricultural Editors Association Byline *see* A.A.E.A. Byline **67**
American Agricultural Exporter Directory *see* American Food and Ag Exporter Directory **147**
American Agricultural Exporter Magazine *see* American Food and Ag Exporter Magazine **147**
American Agriculturist. (US ISSN 0161-8237) **76**
American Airgunner. (US ISSN 0899-5192) **4463**

AMERICAN ASIAN   5895

American Alliance for Theatre & Education Newsletter *see* A A T E Newsletter **4629**
American Alpine Journal. (US ISSN 0065-6925) **4540**
American Alpine News. (US ISSN 0147-9288) **4540**
American Amateur Journalist. (US ISSN 1046-0470) **2567**
American Angler. (US) **4540**
American Angler and Fly Tyer *see* American Angler **4540**
American Animal Hospital Association. Annual Meeting Scientific Proceedings. (US ISSN 0164-1999) **4805**, **2458**
American Animal Hospital Association Journal. (US ISSN 0587-2871) **4805**, **2458**
American Animal Hospital Association Trends Magazine *see* Trends Magazine **4816**
American Annals of the Deaf. (US ISSN 0002-726X) **2286**, **1733**
American Anorexia - Bulimia Association, Inc. Newsletter *see* A A - B A Newsletter **4007**
American Anthropological Association. Abstracts of Meetings. (US) **233**
American Anthropological Association. Newsletter *see* Anthropology Newsletter **234**
American Anthropological Association Guide (Year) *see* A A A Guide (Year) **232**
American Anthropologist. (US ISSN 0002-7294) **233**
American Anthropologist. Special Publication. (US ISSN 0065-6941) **233**
American Anti-Vivisection Society Magazine *see* The A V Magazine **229**
American Antiquarian Society. News-Letter. (US ISSN 0569-2229) **2742**, **2397**
American Antiquarian Society. Proceedings. (US ISSN 0044-751X) **2742**, **2397**
American Antiquity. (US ISSN 0002-7316) **261**
American Apparel Contractors Association News *see* A A C A News **1282**
American Apparel Manufacturers Association Committee Manual *see* A A M A Committee Manual **1282**
American Apparel Manufacturers Association Technical Advisory Committee. Bulletin *see* A A M A. Technical Advisory Committee. Bulletin **5127**
American Arab Affairs *see* Middle East Policy **3965**
American-Arab Association. Bulletin *see* American Mideast Business Association. Bulletin **5135**
American-Arab Message. (US) **1990**
American Arbitration Association Annual Report *see* A A A Annual Report **2592**
American Architectural Manufacturers Association Industry Statistical Review and Forecast *see* A A M A Industry Statistical Review and Forecast **636**
†American Archives of Rehabilitation Therapy. (US ISSN 0002-7324) **5134**
American Archivist. (US ISSN 0360-9081) **2397**
American Art. (US) **311**
American Art Directory. (US ISSN 0065-6968) **311**, **1120**
American Art Journal. (US ISSN 0002-7359) **311**, **2397**
American Art Therapy Association Newsletter. (US) **1733**, **311**, **4009**
American Artist. (US ISSN 0002-7375) **311**
American Artist Directory of Art Schools & Workshops. (US ISSN 0146-9606) **311**, **1615**
American Arts Pamphlet Series *see* Exeter Studies in American & Commonwealth Arts **2916**
American Asian Review. (US ISSN 0737-6650) **2336**

AMERICAN ASSEMBLY

American Assembly (Background Papers and Final Report) *see* American Assembly. Report **3872**

American Assembly. Report. (US ISSN 0569-2245) **3872**

American Assembly of Collegiate Schools of Business Newsline *see* A A C S B Newsline **1698**

American Association - Electronic Voice Phenomena News *see* A A - E V P News **3668**

American Association for Affirmative Action News *see* A A A A News **3939**

American Association for Applied Linguistics Letter *see* A A A Letter **2799**

American Association for Chinese Studies. Bulletin *see* Journal of Chinese Studies **3639**

American Association for Crystal Growth Newsletter. (US) **1210**, 1160, 1848

American Association for Dental Aesthetics Newsletter. (US) **3227**

American Association for Higher Education Bulletin *see* A A H E Bulletin **1698**

American Association for Laboratory Accreditation Annual Report. (US ISSN 1043-0121) **1120**, 3445

American Association for Laboratory Accreditation News *see* A 2 L A News **1120**

American Association for Marriage and Family Therapy Newsletter *see* Family Therapy News **4021**

American Association for Respiratory Care Times *see* A A R C Times **3364**

†American Association for the Advancement of Science. Committee on Desert and Arid Zone Research. Contributions. (US ISSN 0569-2393) **5134**

American Association for the Advancement of Science. Handbook; Officers, Organization, Activities. (US ISSN 0361-7874) **4298**

American Association for the Advancement of Science. Meeting Program. (US ISSN 0361-1833) **4298**

American Association for the Advancement of Science Annual Meeting. Abstracts of Papers *see* A A A S Annual Meeting. Abstracts of Papers **4354**

American Association for the Advancement of Science Publications Catalog *see* A A A S Publications Catalog **4295**

American Association for the Advancement of Science Report: Research and Development *see* A A A S Report: Research and Development **4295**

American Association for the Advancement of Slavic Studies. Newsletter. (US ISSN 0883-9549) **1615**

American Association for the Advancement of Slavic Studies Directory of Programs in Soviet & East European Studies *see* A A A S S Directory of Programs in Soviet & East European Studies **1988**

American Association for World Health Quarterly *see* A A W H Quarterly **4096**

American Association of Advertising Agencies. Bulletin. (US) **28**

American Association of Advertising Agencies. New York and Washington, DC Newsletter. (US) **28**

American Association of Bible Colleges Newsletter *see* A A B C Newsletter **1698**

American Association of Bicycle Importers. Newsletter. (US) **4515**, 899

American Association of Bioanalysts. Proficiency Testing Service. Test of the Month. (US) **3257**

American Association of Bioanalysts Bulletin *see* A A B Bulletin **3256**

American Association of Blood Banks. News Briefs. (US ISSN 8756-6095) **3073**, 2458

American Association of Botanical Gardens and Arboreta. Bulletin *see* Public Garden **2137**

American Association of Botanical Gardens & Arboreta, Inc. Newsletter *see* A A B G A Newsletter **2120**

American Association of Cereal Chemists. Monograph Series. (US ISSN 0065-7107) **2061**

American Association of Children's Residential Centers Newsletter *see* A A C R C Newsletter **4007**

American Association of Christian Schools. Directory. (US) **1692**, 4228

American Association of Christian Schools Newsletter *see* A A C S Newsletter **1691**

American Association of Colleges for Teacher Education. Briefs. (US ISSN 0731-602X) **1699**

American Association of Colleges for Teacher Education. Directory. (US ISSN 0516-9313) **1692**, 1699

American Association of Colleges for Teacher Education. Legislative Briefs *see* American Association of Colleges for Teacher Education. Briefs **1699**

American Association of Colleges of Osteopathic Medicine. Annual Statistical Report. (US) **1674**, 3166

American Association of Colleges of Osteopathic Medicine Organizational Guide *see* A A C O M Organizational Guide **1724**

American Association of Colleges of Pharmacy. Annual Survey of Faculty Salaries *see* American Association of Colleges of Pharmacy. (Year) Profile of Pharmacy Faculty **3716**

American Association of Colleges of Pharmacy. (Year) Profile of Pharmacy Faculty. (US) **3716**

American Association of Colleges of Pharmacy News *see* A A C P News **3714**

American Association of Collegiate Registrars and Admissions Officers. Monograph Series. (US) **1699**

American Association of Collegiate Registrars and Admissions Officers Data Dispenser *see* A A C R A O Data Dispenser **1698**

American Association of Collegiate Registrars and Admissions Officers Proceedings *see* A A C R A O Proceedings **1698**

American Association of Community and Junior Colleges Statistical Yearbook *see* A A C J C Statistical Yearbook **1673**

American Association of Cost Engineers. Transactions of the Annual Meeting. (US ISSN 0065-7158) **1814**

American Association of Critical Care Nurses Nursing Scan In Critical Care *see* A A C N Nursing Scan In Critical Care **3165**

American Association of Crop Insurers Agent Newsletter *see* American Association of Crop Insurers Washington Update **147**

American Association of Crop Insurers Washington Update. (US) **147**, 2526

American Association of Dental Examiners. Board Bulletin. (US ISSN 0002-7421) **3227**

American Association of Engineering Societies. Engineering Manpower Commission. Engineering and Technology Degrees. (US ISSN 0071-0393) **1814**

American Association of Engineering Societies. Engineering Manpower Commission. Engineering and Technology Enrollments (Year). (US ISSN 0071-0407) **1814**, 970

American Association of Engineering Societies. Engineering Manpower Commission. Engineers' Salaries: Special Industry Report (Year). (US ISSN 0071-0415) **1814**, 970

American Association of Engineering Societies. Engineering Manpower Commission. Professional Income of Engineers (Year). (US ISSN 0071-0423) **1814**, 970

American Association of Engineering Societies. Engineering Manpower Commission. Salaries of Engineers in Education (Year). (US) **1814**, 1699

American Association of Equine Practitioners. Proceedings of the Annual Convention. (US ISSN 0065-7182) **4805**

American Association of Feed Microscopists Proceedings of Annual Meeting *see* A A F M Proceedings of Annual Meeting **3390**

American Association of Feline Practitioners. Journal. (US) **4805**

American Association of Foot Specialists. Program Journal *see* American College of Foot Specialists. Annual Yearbook **3374**

American Association of Genito-Urinary Surgeons. Transactions. (US ISSN 0065-7204) **3266**, 3289

American Association of Housing Educators. Newsletter. (US) **2483**

American Association of Housing Educators. Proceedings. (US) **2483**

American Association of Individual Investors Journal *see* A A I I Journal **937**

American Association of Insurance Services Viewpoint *see* A A I S Viewpoint **2525**

American Association of Language Specialists. Yearbook. (US) **2802**

American Association of Law Libraries. Newsletter. (US ISSN 0572-4953) **2742**

American Association of Law Libraries Publications Series *see* A A L L Publications Series **2592**

American Association of Meat Processors. Directory of Suppliers and Wholesalers *see* American Association of Meat Processors. The Gold Book Members **1120**

American Association of Meat Processors. The Gold Book Members.(US) **1120**, 2061

American Association of Meat Processors Lifier *see* A A M P Lifier **209**

American Association of Medical Milk Commissions. Methods and Standards for the Production of Certified Milk. (US ISSN 0065-7263) **197**

American Association of Motor Vehicle Administrators. Annual Conference. Proceedings. (US ISSN 0065-7271) **4743**

American Association of Motor Vehicle Administrators Bulletin *see* A A M V A Bulletin **4678**

American Association of Nephrology Nurses and Technicians. Journal *see* A N N A Journal **3274**

American Association of Neuroscience Nurses Synapse *see* A A N N Synapse **3274**

American Association of Nurse Anesthetists Journal *see* A A N A Journal **3274**

American Association of Nurserymen Directory for the Nursery Industry and Related Associations *see* American Association of Nurserymen Who's Who in the Nursery Industry Member Directory **76**

American Association of Nurserymen Today *see* A A N Today **67**

American Association of Nurserymen Update. (US) **76**, 2121

American Association of Nurserymen Who's Who in the Nursery Industry Member Directory. (US) **76**, 2121

American Association of Obstetricians and Gynecologists. Transactions. (US ISSN 0065-728X) **3289**

American Association of Occupational Health Nurses Journal. (US ISSN 0891-0162) **3275**

American Association of Petroleum Geologists. Memoir. (US ISSN 0065-731X) **1554**, 3681

American Association of Petroleum Geologists Bulletin *see* A A P G Bulletin **3680**

American Association of Petroleum Geologists Explorer *see* A A P G Explorer **3680**

American Association of Petroleum Geologists Studies in Geology Series *see* A A P G Studies in Geology Series **3680**

American Association of Physics Teachers Announcer *see* A A P T Announcer **3812**

American Association of Retired Persons (Washington) Bulletin *see* A A R P Bulletin **2269**

American Association of Small Research Companies News *see* A A S R C News **3672**

American Association of State Colleges and Universities. Proceedings. (US) **1699**

American Association of State Colleges and Universities Issues *see* A A S C U Issues **1698**

American Association of State Highway and Transportation Officials. Proceedings. (US) **4717**

American Association of State Highway and Transportation Officials. Sub-Committee on Computer Technology. National Conference. Proceedings. (US ISSN 0091-5122) **4706**

American Association of State Highway and Transportation Officials Quarterly Magazine *see* A A S H T O Quarterly Magazine **1861**

American Association of State Highway and Transportation Officials Reference Book of Member Department Personnel and Committees *see* A A S H T O Reference Book of Member Department Personnel and Committees **4646**

American Association of Stratigraphic Palynologists. Abstracts of Papers Presented at the Annual Meetings. (US ISSN 0192-7272) **1550**, 2, 3661

American Association of Stratigraphic Palynologists. Contributions Series. (US ISSN 0160-8843) **3656**, 1554

American Association of Stratigraphic Palynologists. Newsletter. (CN ISSN 0192-7299) **1554**, 3656

American Association of Stratigraphic Palynologists Foundation. Field Trip Guide. (US ISSN 0192-737X) **3656**

American Association of Suicidology. Proceedings of the Annual Meeting. (US) **4009**

American Association of Teachers of Arabic (Provo) Newsletter *see* A A T A Newsletter **1742**

American Association of Teachers of Esperanto Quarterly Bulletin/Amerika Asocio de Instruistoj de Esperanto Kvaronjara Bulteno. (US ISSN 0002-7499) **1743**, 2802

American Association of Teachers of French National Bulletin *see* A A T F National Bulletin **2799**

American Association of Teachers of German, Inc. Newsletter *see* A A T G Newsletter **2799**

American Association of Teachers of Slavic and East European Languages Newsletter *see* A A T S E E L Newsletter **2799**

American Association of Textile Chemists and Colorists. Buyer's Guide. (US ISSN 0040-490X) **4616**

American Association of Textile Chemists and Colorists. National Technical Conference. Book of Papers. (US ISSN 0192-4699) **4616**

American Association of Textile Chemists and Colorists. Products Buyer's Guide *see* American Association of Textile Chemists and Colorists. Buyer's Guide **4616**

American Association of Textile Chemists and Colorists. Technical Manual. (US) **4616**

American Association of Theological Schools in the United States and Canada. Bulletin see Association of Theological Schools in the United States and Canada. Bulletin **4163**

American Association of Theological Schools in the United States and Canada. Directory see Association of Theological Schools in the United States and Canada. Directory **4163**

American Association of Tissue Banks Newsletter. (US ISSN 0270-2673) **3073**

American Association of University Women New Yorker see A A U W New Yorker **1302**

American Association of University Women Outlook see A A U W Outlook **1698**

American Association of Variable Star Observers. Journal. (US) **360**

American Association of Variable Star Observers. Solar Bulletin. (US) **360**

American Association of Variable Star Observers Bulletin: Predicted Dates of Maxima and Minima of Long Period Variable Stars see A A V S O Bulletin: Predicted Dates of Maxima and Minima of Long Period Variable Stars **359**

American Association of Variable Star Observers Circular see A A V S O Circular **359**

American Association of Variable Star Observers Reports and Monographs see A A V S O Reports and Monographs **360**

†American Association of Veterinary Laboratory Diagnosticians. Proceedings of Annual Meeting. (US ISSN 0098-3543) **5134**

American Association of Women Dentists. Chronicle. (US) **3227, 4836**

American Association of Women Dentists. Journal see American Association of Women Dentists. Chronicle **3227**

American Association of Women in Community and Junior Colleges Newsletter see A A W C J C Newsletter **1698**

American Association of Workers for the Blind with Association for Education of the Visually Handicapped. Alliance News see A E R Report **2290**

American Association of Zoological Parks and Aquariums. Proceedings. A A Z P A Annual Conference. (US ISSN 0090-4473) **577**

American Association of Zoological Parks and Aquariums Communique see A A Z P A Communique **575**

American Association on Mental Retardation. Monographs. (US ISSN 0895-8009) **4009**

American Association on Mental Retardation. News and Notes. (US ISSN 0895-8033) **3329**

American Astrology. (US ISSN 0002-7529) **357**

American Astrology Digest. (US ISSN 0516-9550) **357**

American Astronautical Society. Proceedings of the Annual Meeting. (US ISSN 0516-9593) **46**

American Astronautical Society, Inc. Goddard Memorial Symposium. Proceedings. see A A S Goddard Memorial Symposium. Proceedings **42**

American Astronautical Society, Inc. History Series see A A S History Series **42**

American Astronautical Society, Inc. Microfiche Series see A A S Microfiche Series **42**

American Astronomical Society. Bulletin.(US ISSN 0002-7537) **360**

American Astronomical Society Job Register see A A S Job Register **359**

American Atheist. (US ISSN 0516-9623) **3760**

American Atheist Newsletter. (US) **3760**

American Auditory Society. Journal see Ear and Hearing **3314**

American Austin Bantam Club News. (US) **254**

American Automatic Control Council Newsletter see A A C C Newsletter **1877**

American Automatic Merchandiser. (US ISSN 0002-7545) **1033**

American Automobile Association. Digest of Motor Laws. (US ISSN 0093-4062) **4679, 2597**

American Automobile Association Motorist see A A A Motorist **4678**

American Automobile Association Today (Cincinnati) see A A A Today (Cincinnati) **4750**

American Automobile Association Today Magazine see A A A Today Magazine **4678**

American Automobile Association World (Heathrow) see A A A World (Heathrow) **4678**

American Automobile Association World: Wisconsin Edition see A A A World: Wisconsin Edition **4750**

American Aviation Historical Society Journal. (US) **46**

American Baby. (US ISSN 0044-7544) **1232, 3799**

American Baby's Childbirth Educator see Childbirth Educator **5165**

American Baby's Healthy Kids see Healthy Kids: Birth - 3 **1238**

American Baby's Healthy Kids: Birth - 3 see Healthy Kids: Birth - 3 **1238**

American Baby's Healthy Kids: 4-10 Years see Healthy Kids: 4-10 Years **1238**

American Baha'i. (US) **4280**

American Bamboo Society. Journal. (US ISSN 0197-3789) **493, 2121**

American Bamboo Society Newsletter. (US) **493, 2121**

American Bank Directory. (US ISSN 0569-292X) **758**

American Banker. (US ISSN 0002-7561) **758**

American Banker - Bond Buyer Newsletter. (US) **758, 938**

American Banker Index see Index to the American Banker **721**

American Bankers Association. Banking Literature Index see Banking Literature Index **705**

American Bankers Association. Committee on Uniform Security Identification Procedures. C U S I P Directory see C U S I P Master Directory **941**

American Bankers Association. Committee on Uniform Security Identification Procedures. C U S I P Directory: Corporate Directory see C U S I P Corporate Directory **941**

American Bankers Association. National Operations & Automation Conference. Proceedings. (US ISSN 0095-5396) **804, 1448**

American Bankers Association. Operations and Automation Division. Results of the National Automation Survey see American Bankers Association. Operations and Automation Division. Results of the National Operations & Automation Survey **804**

American Bankers Association. Operations and Automation Division. Results of the National Operations & Automation Survey. (US ISSN 0363-2539) **804, 1448**

American Bankers Association Bank Compliance see A B A Bank Compliance **757**

American Bankers Association Bankers News Weekly see A B A Bankers News Weekly **757**

American Bankers Association Banking Journal see A B A Banking Journal **757**

American Bankers Association Consumer Banking Digest see A B A Consumer Banking Digest **757**

American Bankers Association Key to Routing Numbers. (US) **758**

American Bankers Association Master Directory see C U S I P Master Directory **941**

American Bankers Association Retail Banker see A B A Retail Banker **757**

▼American Banker's Banking Factbook.(US) **758**

American Bankruptcy Law Journal. (US ISSN 0027-9048) **2597**

American Bantam Association. Yearbook. (US ISSN 0065-745X) **209**

American Baptist. (US ISSN 0002-757X) **4228**

American Baptist Churches in the U S A Directory. (US ISSN 0091-9381) **4228**

American Baptist Churches in the U S A Yearbook. (US ISSN 0092-3478) **4228**

American Baptist Convention. Directory see American Baptist Churches in the U S A Directory **4228**

American Baptist Quarterly. (US) **4228, 2305**

American Baptist Woman. (US) **4162, 4836**

American Bar Association. Economics of Law Practice Section. Network see American Bar Association. Law Practice Management Section. Network **2597**

American Bar Association. Forum Committee on Franchising. Journal see Franchise Law Journal **2628**

American Bar Association. I.R.R. Section Newsletter. (Section of Individual Rights and Responsibilities) (US) **2597**

American Bar Association. Law Practice Management Section. Network. (US) **2597**

American Bar Association. Office of Policy Administration. Summary and Reports. (US) **2597**

American Bar Association. Section of Insurance, Negligence and Compensation Law. I N C L Brief see Brief (Chicago) **2605**

American Bar Association. Section of Taxation. Newsletter. (US ISSN 0277-2361) **2597, 1087**

American Bar Association. Special Committee on Environmental Law. Quarterly Newsletter see Environmental Law (Washington) **2623**

American Bar Association. Utility Section. Newsletter. (US ISSN 0569-3349) **2597, 4083**

American Bar Association Journal see A B A Journal **2592**

American Bar Association Juvenile and Child Welfare Law Reporter see A B A Juvenile and Child Welfare Law Reporter **1231**

American Bar Association Lawyers' Manual on Professional Conduct see A B A - B N A Lawyers' Manual on Professional Conduct **2592**

American Bar Association Washington Letter see A B A Washington Letter **2592**

American Bar Foundation Journal see Law and Social Inquiry **2644**

American Bar - The Canadian Bar - The International Bar. (US ISSN 0094-3584) **2597**

American Bartenders' Association Newsletter see A B A Newsletter **377**

American Bee Journal. (US ISSN 0002-7626) **76**

American Beekeeping Federation. Newsletter. (US ISSN 0014-9438) **76**

American Behavioral Scientist. (US ISSN 0002-7642) **4365, 4009**

American Bell Association. Directory. (US ISSN 0093-1330) **3537**

American Bench. (US) **2597**

American Benedictine Review. (US ISSN 0002-7650) **4254, 2305, 2893, 4365**

American Bible Society Record. (US ISSN 0006-0801) **4162**

American Bibliography of Russian and East European Studies see American Bibliography of Slavic and East European Studies **2327**

American Bibliography of Slavic and East European Studies. (US ISSN 0094-3770) **2327**

American Bicyclist & Motorcyclist. (US ISSN 0002-7677) **4515**

American Big Twin Dealer. (US) **4515**

American Biology Teacher. (US ISSN 0002-7685) **427, 1699**

American Biotechnology Laboratory. (US ISSN 0749-3223) **487, 3257**

American Birds. (US ISSN 0004-7686) **561**

American Black Book Writers Association, Inc. Journal see A B B W A Journal **388**

American Blue Book of Funeral Directors. (US ISSN 0065-7565) **1120, 2119**

American Board of Medical Specialties. Annual Report & Reference Handbook. (US ISSN 0272-9741) **3073**

American Board of Medical Specialties Compendium of Certified Medical Specialists see A B M S Compendium of Certified Medical Specialists **3068**

American Board of Medical Specialties Directory of Certified Allergists and Immunologists see A B M S Directory of Certified Allergists and Immunologists **3182**

American Board of Medical Specialties Record see A B M S Record **3068**

American Board of Nuclear Medicine. Information Policies and Procedures. (US) **3357**

American Board of Practice. Journal. (US) **3073**

American Boat Modeler see Radio Control Boat Modeler **2441**

American Bonsai Society, Inc. Stracts see A B Stracts **2141**

American Book Collector. (US ISSN 0196-5654) **4120, 2433**

American Book Prices Current. (US ISSN 0091-9357) **4139**

American Book Prices Current. Four Year Index. (US) **4139**

American Book Publishing Record. (US ISSN 0002-7707) **4139**

American Book Review. (US ISSN 0149-9408) **2858, 2502**

American Book Trade Directory. (US ISSN 0065-759X) **4120**

American Bookseller. (US ISSN 0148-5903) **4120**

American Booksellers Association Newswire see A B A Newswire **4119**

American Bottom Archaeology. (US) **261**

American Brahms Society. Newsletter. (US ISSN 8756-8357) **3537**

American Brewer Magazine. (US ISSN 0887-7416) **377**

American Breweriana Journal. (US ISSN 0748-8343) **377**

American Brittany. (US ISSN 0199-7297) **3707**

American Broncho-Esophagolaryngological Association. Transactions. (US ISSN 0065-7603) **3313**

American Buddhist. (US ISSN 0747-900X) **4213**

American Buddhist Newsletter see American Buddhist **4213**

American Bullmastiff Association. Bulletin. (US) **3707**

American Bungalow. (US) **2548**

American Bureau of Shipping. Record. (US) **4723**

American Burn Association. Annual Meeting. Proceeding. (US) **3306**

American Business. (US ISSN 0363-566X) **842**

American Business in Argentina. (AG) **1120**

American Business Information INFORM see A B I - INFORM **701**

American Business Law Journal. (US ISSN 0002-7766) **2597, 644**

American Buyer's Review see Candy World Illustrated **2087**

American Cage-Bird Magazine. (US ISSN 0002-7782) **561, 3707**

American Camellia Yearbook. (US ISSN 0065-762X) **2121**

American Canals. (US) **4723, 2397**

5898 AMERICAN CAR

American Car Prices *see* Car Prices 4687
American Carbon Society. Biennial Conference on Carbon - Extended Abstracts and Program. (US) 1848
American Carnival Glass News. (US) 1160
American Cartographer *see* Cartography and Geographic Information Systems 2244
American Cat Carwash Review. (US) 4679
American Cat Fanciers Association, Inc. Bulletin *see* A C F A Bulletin 3707
American Catholic Historical Society of Philadelphia. Records. (US ISSN 0002-7790) 4254, 2305
American Catholic Philosophical Association. Proceedings. (US ISSN 0065-7638) 3760, 4254
American Catholic Philosophical Quarterly. (US) 3760
American CattleWoman. (US ISSN 1042-5233) 209, 4836
▼American Caucus. (US) 3872
American Cement Directory. (US ISSN 0065-7646) 599
American Cemetery. (US ISSN 0002-7804) 2119
American Cemetery Association. Membership Directory. (US) 1120, 2119
American Ceramic Society. Bulletin. (US ISSN 0002-7812) 1161
American Ceramic Society. Journal. (US ISSN 0002-7820) 1161
American Ceramics. (US ISSN 0278-9507) 353
American Chamber of Commerce for Brazil. Annual Directory. (BL ISSN 0065-7662) 806
American Chamber of Commerce in France. Directory. (FR ISSN 0065-7670) 806
American Chamber of Commerce in Italy. Directory. (IT ISSN 0569-3667) 806
American Chamber of Commerce in Italy. Newsletter. (IT) 806
American Chamber of Commerce in Japan. Journal. (JA ISSN 0002-7847) 806
American Chamber of Commerce in Japan Directory *see* A C C J Directory 1119
American Chamber of Commerce in Morocco. Annual Review *see* AmCham Morocco 806
American Chamber of Commerce in Morocco. Bulletin. (MR) 806
American Chamber of Commerce in New Zealand. Annual Directory. (NZ ISSN 0113-9495) 806
American Chamber of Commerce in New Zealand. Newsletter. (NZ) 807
American Chamber of Commerce in Thailand. Handbook Directory. (TH) 807
American Chamber of Commerce of the Philippines. Weekly Business Letter *see* American Chamber of Commerce of the Philippines. Weekly Executive Update 807
American Chamber of Commerce of the Philippines. Weekly Executive Update.(PH) 807
American Chamber of Commerce of Venezuela. Yearbook and Membership Directory *see* Venezuelan - American Chamber of Commerce and Industry. Yearbook and Membership Directory 824
American Chamber of Commerce Researchers Association (Louisville) Newsletter *see* A C C R A Newsletter 806
American Chamber of Commerce Researchers Association Cost of Living Index *see* A C C R A Cost of Living Index 701
American Chamber of Commerce - Sao Paulo. Update. (BL) 807
American Checker Federation Bulletin *see* A C F Bulletin 4463
American Checkered Giant Rabbit Club. News Bulletin. (US) 3707
American Chemical Society *see* S C A L A C S 1187

American Chemical Society. Abstracts of Papers (at the National Meeting). (US ISSN 0065-7727) 1191
American Chemical Society. Abstracts of Papers (at the Regional Meetings). (US ISSN 0065-7735) 1191
American Chemical Society. Directory of Graduate Research. (US ISSN 0193-5011) 1692, 1169
American Chemical Society. Division of Environmental Chemistry. Preprints of Papers. (US ISSN 0093-3066) 1169
American Chemical Society. Journal. (US ISSN 0002-7863) 1169
American Chemical Society Monographs *see* A C S Monographs 1168
American Chemical Society Symposium on Analytical Calorimetry *see* Analytical Calorimetry 5135
American Chemical Society Symposium Series *see* A C S Symposium Series 1168
American Chesapeake Club. Bulletin. (US) 3707
American Chianina Journal. (US ISSN 0198-8816) 76
American Chiropractor. (US ISSN 0194-6536) 3213, 3602
American Choral Foundation. Research Memorandum Series. (US ISSN 0002-788X) 3537
American Choral Review. (US ISSN 0002-7898) 3537
American Chow Chow. (US) 3707
American Christmas Tree Journal. (US ISSN 0569-3845) 2121
American Cinematographer. (US ISSN 0002-7928) 3503, 3788
American Cinemeditor *see* On Production 3515
American Cities Chronologies Series. (US ISSN 0887-0527) 2483, 2397
†American Citizen. (US) 5134
American City & County. (US ISSN 0149-337X) 4084
American City & County Directory of Administrative Service. (US ISSN 1059-3659) 4084
American City & County Municipal Index. (US ISSN 0077-2151) 4084
American Civil Liberties Union of Northern California News *see* A C L U News 3939
American Classic House Plans. (US) 291, 599
American Classic Screen. (US ISSN 0195-8267) 3503
American Classical Review. (US ISSN 0044-7633) 1274, 2893
American Classical Studies. (US ISSN 0278-5943) 2802
American Clay Exchange. (US ISSN 0739-6546) 254, 1161
American Clean Car. (US ISSN 0095-1811) 4679
American Clinical and Climatological Association. Transactions. (US ISSN 0065-7778) 3073
American Clinical Laboratory. (US ISSN 8750-9490) 3257
American Clinical Products Review *see* American Clinical Laboratory 3257
†American Clipper. (US) 5134
†American Coach. (US ISSN 0894-4210) 5134
American Cocker Magazine. (US ISSN 0279-358X) 3708
American Coin-Op. (US ISSN 0092-2811) 1281
American Collector's Journal. (US) 254
American College Dance Festival Association Newsletter *see* A C D F A Newsletter 1528
American College Health Association. Journal *see* Journal of American College Health 3805
American College Health Association. Newsletter *see* A C H A Action 3798
American College Health Association Action *see* A C H A Action 3798
American College of Cardiology *see* A C E L 3203
American College of Cardiology. Abstracts. (US) 3166, 2, 3203
American College of Cardiology. Journal.

(US ISSN 0735-1097) 3203
American College of Cardiology. Symposia. (US) 3203
American College of Cardiology Annual Scientific Session News. (US) 3203
American College of Dentists. Journal. (US ISSN 0002-7979) 3227
American College of Foot Orthopedists Newsletter. (US ISSN 0002-7987) 3306
American College of Foot Specialists. Annual Yearbook. (US) 3374, 3306
American College of Healthcare Executives. Directory. (US) 2458
American College of Hospital Administrators. Directory *see* American College of Healthcare Executives. Directory 2458
American College of Laboratory Animal Medicine Series. (US) 3257
American College of Medical Quality Newsletter. (US) 3073
†American College of Neuropsychiatrists. Bulletin. (US ISSN 0002-7995) 5134
American College of Nursing Home Administrators. Newsletter *see* Long-Term Care Administrator 2467
American College of Nutrition. Journal. (US ISSN 0731-5724) 3603
American College of Obstetricians and Gynecologists Current Journal Review *see* A C O G Current Journal Review 3165
American College of Obstetricians and Gynecologists Interactions: Programs in Clinical Decision Making *see* A C O G Interactions: Programs in Clinical Decision Making 3288
American College of Obstetricians and Gynecologists Newsletter *see* A C O G Newsletter 3288
American College of Orgonomy Newsletter *see* A C O Newsletter 3327
American College of Osteopathic Surgeons News *see* A C O S News 3373
American College of Physicians Observer. (US ISSN 0279-9529) 3073
American College of Preventive Medicine News *see* A C P M News 3068
American College of Preventive Medicine Newsletter *see* A C P M News 3068
American College of Radiology Bulletin *see* A C R Bulletin 3356
American College of Sports Medicine. Career Services Bulletin. (US) 3370, 3624
American College of Surgeons. Bulletin. (US ISSN 0002-8045) 3374
American College of Toxicology. Journal. Part A. (US ISSN 0730-0913) 1980, 3073, 3716, 4097
American College of Toxicology. Journal. Part B. (US ISSN 1044-2049) 3716, 1980, 3074, 4097
American College of Utilization Review Physicians Newsletter *see* American College of Medical Quality Newsletter 3073
American College Testing. Annual Report. (US) 1699
American College Testing. Handbook for Financial Aid Administrators. (US) 1724
American College Testing Program. Annual Report *see* American College Testing. Annual Report 1699
American College Testing Program. Handbook for Financial Aid Administrators *see* American College Testing. Handbook for Financial Aid Administrators 1724
American College Testing Research Report *see* A C T Research Report 1698
American College Testing Tivity *see* A C Tivity 1613
American Collegiate Poets. (US) 2987
American Committee on Africa Action News *see* A C O A Action News 3948

American Committee on Italian Migration Newsletter *see* A C I M Newsletter 3979
American Community Gardening Association Multilogue *see* A C G A Multilogue 2120
American Comparative Literature Association Newsletter. (US ISSN 0891-3277) 2893
American Compensation Association News *see* A C A News 1062
American Concrete Institute. Compilation. (US ISSN 0517-0745) 600
American Concrete Institute. Journal *see* A C I Materials Journal 598
†American Concrete Institute. Proceedings. (US ISSN 0097-4145) 5134
American Concrete Institute. Special Publication. (US ISSN 0065-7891) 600
American Concrete Institute Bibliography *see* A C I Bibliography 388
American Concrete Institute Manual of Concrete Practice *see* A C I Manual of Concrete Practice 598
American Concrete Institute Materials Journal *see* A C I Materials Journal 598
American Concrete Institute Structural Journal *see* A C I Structural Journal 598
American Concrete Paving Association. Newsletter. (US) 1861
American Conference of Academic Deans. Proceedings. (US ISSN 0065-7905) 1699
American Conference of Governmental Industrial Hygienists. Transactions of the Annual Meeting. (US) 3614
American Congress on Surveying & Mapping. Proceedings. (US) 2241
American Congress on Surveying and Mapping. Technical Papers. (US ISSN 0277-2876) 2241
American Congress on Surveying and Mapping Bulletin *see* A C S M Bulletin 2240
American Conifer Society. Bulletin. (US) 2095, 2121
▼American Consulting Engineer. (US) 1814
American Control Conference. Conference Proceedings. (US) 1881
American Control Conference. Conference Records *see* American Control Conference. Conference Proceedings 1881
American Cookery. (US) 2444
American Cooner. (US ISSN 0002-807X) 4540
American Cooperation Yearbook. (US ISSN 0065-793X) 829
American Corporate Counsel Association Docket *see* A C C A Docket 643
American Correctional Association. The State of Corrections. Proceedings. (US) 1509
American Correctional Association. Winter Conference and Annual Congress of Correction. Proceedings *see* American Correctional Association. The State of Corrections. Proceedings 1509
American Corrective Therapy Journal *see* Clinical Kinesiology 3371
American Cotton Grower *see* Cotton Grower 174
American Council for Judaism. Issues. (US ISSN 0741-465X) 4221
American Council for Judaism. Special Interest Report. (US ISSN 0740-8528) 4221, 1990, 3872
American Council for the Arts Update *see* A C A Update 309
American Council for the Arts Vantage Point *see* Vantage Point 5300
American Council of Independent Laboratories. Directory. (US ISSN 0065-7964) 4298, 4593
American Council of Learned Societies Annual Report *see* A C L S Annual Report 2501
American Council of Learned Societies Newsletter *see* A C L S Newsletter 2501

American Council of Learned Societies Occasional Papers see A C L S Occasional Papers **2501**
American Council of Life Insurance. Council Review. (US) **2526**
American Council on Consumer Interests. Proceedings of the Annual Conference. (US ISSN 0275-1356) **1502**
American Council on Consumer Interests Newsletter see A C C I Newsletter **1502**
American Council on Education. Center for Adult Learning and Educational Credentials Update. (US) **1699, 3450**
American Council on Education. Office of Educational Credit and Credentials. News see American Council on Education. Center for Adult Learning and Educational Credentials Update **1699**
American Council on Industrial Arts Teacher Education. Yearbook see Council on Technology Teacher Education. Yearbook **1623**
American Council on the Teaching of Foreign Languages Foreign Language Education Series see A C T F L Foreign Language Education Series **1742**
▼American Counselor. (US) **1615, 4398**
†American Country. (US) **5134**
†American Court and Commercial Newspapers. Bulletin. (US) **5134**
†American Court and Commercial Newspapers. Convention Proceedings. (US) **5134**
†American Court and Commercial Newspapers. News Service. (US) **5134**
American Craft. (US ISSN 0194-8008) **353**
American Criminal Law Review. (US ISSN 0164-0364) **1509, 2597**
American Croat/Americki Hrvat. (US) **1990**
American Crosby Clipper see American Clipper **5134**
▼American Crossdresser. (US) **4009, 4428**
American Cryonics. (US) **3257**
American Crystallographic Association. Monographs. (US ISSN 0514-8863) **1210**
American Crystallographic Association. Program & Abstracts. (US ISSN 0569-4221) **1210, 3814**
American Crystallographic Association. Transactions. (US ISSN 0065-8006) **1210**
American Cultural Heritage Series. (US) **4428**
American Currents. (US) **577, 1483**
American Dahlia Society. Bulletin. (US ISSN 0002-8150) **2121**
American Dance Circle. (US) **1528, 2052**
American Dance Guild Newsletter. (US ISSN 0300-7448) **1528**
American Dance Therapy Association, Inc. Newsletter see A D T A Newsletter **1733**
American Dane. (US ISSN 0739-9170) **1990**
American Deafness & Rehabilitation Association. Journal. (US ISSN 0899-9228) **2286**
American Deafness & Rehabilitation Association Newsletter see A D A R A Newsletter **2285**
American Defense Annual (Year). (US) **3450**
American Deli-Bakery News. (US) **2090, 2086**
American Demographics. (US ISSN 0163-4089) **3979, 1502**
American Dental Association. Journal. (US ISSN 0002-8177) **3227**
American Dental Association. Transaction Series: Annual Reports and Resolutions, Supplements One and Two, Transactions. (US) **3227**
American Dental Association News see A D A News **3226**
American Dental Directory. (US ISSN 0065-8073) **3227**

American Dexter Cattle Association. Herd Book. (US ISSN 0065-8081) **209**
American Dialect Society. Newsletter. (US ISSN 0002-8193) **2802**
American Dialect Society. Publications. (US ISSN 0002-8207) **2802**
American Diamond Industry Association Newsletter. (US) **2562**
American Dietetic Association. Journal. (US ISSN 0002-8223) **3603**
American Dissertations on Foreign Education. (US) **1674, 389**
American District Telegraph Co. Transmitter see A D T Transmitter **2030**
American Doctoral Dissertations. (US ISSN 0065-809X) **1699**
American Dove Association. Monthly Bulletin see American Dove Association Newsletter **3708**
American Dove Association Newsletter. (US) **3708**
American Dowser. (US) **4821**
The American Dream. (US) **2556**
▼American Dream Cars. (US) **4679**
American Drop-Shippers Directory. (US ISSN 0065-8103) **1033, 1120**
American Drug Index. (US ISSN 0065-8111) **3747, 2**
American Druggist. (US ISSN 0190-5279) **3716**
American Druggist Blue Book. (US ISSN 0364-7471) **3716**
American Druggist Blue Price Book see American Druggist Blue Book **3716**
American Druggist Merchandising see American Druggist **3716**
American Drycleaner. (US ISSN 0002-8258) **1281**
American Dyestuff Reporter. (US ISSN 0002-8266) **1281, 4616**
American Economic Foundation Newsletter see A E F Newsletter **888**
American Economic Review. (US ISSN 0002-8282) **843, 889**
American Economist. (US ISSN 0002-8290) **843**
†American Education. (US ISSN 0002-8304) **5134**
American Education Association Newsletter see A E A Newsletter **1613**
American Educational Research Journal.(US ISSN 0002-8312) **1615**
American Educator. (US ISSN 0148-432X) **1615, 2580**
American Electronics Association Directory. (US) **1881**
American Engineering Model Society. Newsletter. (US) **1814**
American Engineering Model Society Seminar (Papers) see A E M S Seminar (Papers) **1813**
American Enterprise. (US ISSN 1047-3572) **3872, 4365**
†American Enterprise Institute for Public Policy Research. Memorandum. (US) **5134**
American Enterprise Institute for Public Policy Research Economist see A E I Economist **5128**
American Entomological Institute. Contributions. (US ISSN 0569-4450) **527**
American Entomological Institute. Memoirs. (US ISSN 0065-8162) **528**
American Entomological Society. Memoirs. (US ISSN 0065-8170) **528**
American Entomological Society. Transactions. (US ISSN 0002-8320) **528**
American Entomologist. (US ISSN 1046-2821) **528**
American Environment see North American Environment **5248**
American Environmental Laboratory. (US) **1942**
American Ephemeris and Nautical Almanac see Astronomical Almanac **361**
American Ethnologist. (US ISSN 0094-0496) **233**
American Exploration and Travel. (US ISSN 0065-8219) **2397**

American Export Register. (US ISSN 0272-1163) **900**
American Express Bank Ltd. Bank Review see A M E X Bank Review **758**
American Family (Latham). (US) **1232**
American Family (Washington). (US ISSN 0161-1178) **4428**
American Family Physician. (US ISSN 0002-838X) **3074**
American Family Records Association Member Directory and Ancestral Surname Registry see A F R A Member Directory and Ancestral Surname Registry **2143**
American Family Therapy Association Newsletter. (US) **4009, 4428**
American Fancy Rat and Mouse Association Yearbook. (US) **3708, 1296**
American Farmer Series. (US) **2893, 76**
American Farriers Journal. (US ISSN 0274-6565) **4531, 209**
American Fastener Jouranl. (US) **3647**
American Federation of Astrologers Bulletin. (US ISSN 0735-4797) **358**
American Federation of Home Health Agencies Insider see A F H H A Insider **3274**
American Federation of Labor - Congress of Industrial Organizations American Federationist see A F L - C I O American Federationist **5128**
American Federation of Labor - Congress of Industrial Organizations Department of International Affairs. Bulletin see A F L - C I O. Department of International Affairs. Bulletin **2579**
American Federation of Musicians Local 325. (US ISSN 0036-407X) **3537, 2580**
American Federation of Teachers. Action. (US ISSN 0894-8208) **2580, 1615**
American Federation of Teachers Issues Bulletin see A F T Issues Bulletin **2579**
American Federation of Teachers News see A F T in the News **5128**
American Federation of Television and Radio Artists see A F T R A **2579**
American Federation of Television and Radio Artists. A F T R A see A F T R A **2579**
American Feed Industry Association. Annual and Semiannual Meetings of the Nutrition Council. Proceedings. (US ISSN 1057-6649) **209, 204**
American Feed Industry Association. Production School Proceedings. (US) **210, 204**
American Feed Industry Association Safetygram see A F I A Safetygram **209**
American Feed Manufacturers Association. Annual Meeting of the Nutrition Council. Proceedings see American Feed Industry Association. Annual and Semiannual Meetings of the Nutrition Council. Proceedings **209**
American Fencing. (US ISSN 0002-8436) **4463**
American Fern Journal. (US ISSN 0002-8444) **494**
American Field. (US ISSN 0002-8452) **4540**
†American Film. (US) **5134**
American Film & Video Association, Inc. Evaluations see A F V A Evaluations **1743**
American Film and Video Festival Guide.(US) **3503, 1384**
American Film & Video Review. (US) **3503, 1384**
American Film Institute Monograph Series. (US) **3503**
American Film Institute Theater Brochure see Preview Theater Brochure **3515**
American Film Magazine (New York). (US) **3503**
American Film Magazine (Washington) see American Film **5134**
American Fire Journal. (US) **2031**

American Firearms Industry. (US ISSN 0164-8136) **4463**
American Fireworks News. (US ISSN 8755-3163) **1848, 644**
American Fisheries Society. Special Publication. (US ISSN 0097-0638) **2036**
American Fisheries Society. Symposium.(US ISSN 0892-2284) **2036**
American Fisheries Society. Transactions. (US ISSN 0002-8487) **2036**
American Fisheries Society Monograph. (US ISSN 0362-1715) **2036**
American Fishing and Tackle Manufacturing Association Trade Show Directory and Buyers' Guide see A F T M A Trade Show Directory and Buyers' Guide **2035**
American Fitness. (US) **3799**
American Fitness Quarterly. (US) **3799**
American Flint. (US ISSN 0002-8525) **2580**
American Folklore Society Newsletter. (US ISSN 0745-5178) **2052**
American Food and Ag Exporter Directory. (US) **147, 900**
American Food and Ag Exporter Magazine. (US) **147, 900**
American Forage and Grassland Council. Proceedings of the Research Industry Conference. (US) **204**
American Forces Network T V Guide. (GW) **3450, 1368**
American Foreign Law Association Newsletter. (US) **2597**
American Foreign Policy Library. (US) **3949, 2398**
American Forensic Association. Journal see Argumentation & Advocacy **1733**
American Forestry Association Resource Hotline Newsletter see A F A's Resource Hotline Newsletter **2094**
American Forests. (US ISSN 0002-8541) **2095**
American Forum. (US) **2858**
American Foundation for A I D S Research Am F A R Report see Am F A R Report **3217**
American Foundation for the Blind. Annual Report. (US ISSN 0065-8359) **2290, 4398**
American Foundation for the Blind, Inc. Directory of Services for Blind and Visually Impaired Persons in the United States see A F B Directory of Services for Blind and Visually Impaired Persons in the United States **2290**
American Foundation for the Blind, Inc. News see A F B News **2290**
American Foundation for the Blind News see A F B News **2290**
American Foundrymen's Society. Transactions. (US ISSN 0065-8375) **3402**
American Fox Terrier Club. Newsletter. (US) **3708**
American Freestyler. (US) **4515**
American Friend see Quaker Life **4287**
American Friends of Lafayette. Gazette. (US) **2398, 2348**
American Friends of the Anti-Bolshevik Bloc of Nations Correspondence see A B N Correspondence **3869**
American Friends Service Committee. Annual Report. (US ISSN 0071-9617) **4398**
American Frozen Food Institute. Membership Directory see American Frozen Food Institute. Membership Directory and Buyer's Guide **2061**
American Frozen Food Institute. Membership Directory and Buyer's Guide. (US ISSN 0361-0888) **2061**
American Frozen Food Institute. Weekly Report see A F F I Letter **2060**
American Frozen Food Institute Letter see A F F I Letter **2060**
American Fruit Grower. (US ISSN 0002-8568) **2121**
American Fuchsia Society. Monthly Bulletin. (US) **2121**
American Fund for Alternatives to Animal Research. News Abstracts. (US) **4805**

5900 AMERICAN FUNERAL

American Funeral Director. (US ISSN 0002-8576) **2119**
American Fur Industry. Newsletter. (US) **2735**, 1483
American Gas Association. Operating Section. Proceedings. (US ISSN 0362-4994) **3681**
American Gas Association American Gas see A G A American Gas **3681**
American Gas Association Financial Quarterly Review see A G A Financial Quarterly Review **1783**
American Gas Association Gas Energy Review see A G A Gas Energy Review **3681**
American Genealogical Lending Library News see A G L L News **2143**
American Genealogist. (US ISSN 0002-8592) **2143**
American Geographical Society Newsletter see A G S Newsletter **2240**
American Geophysical Union. Geophysical Monograph Book Series. (US) **1587**
American Geriatrics Society. Journal. (US ISSN 0002-8614) **2270**
American Geriatrics Society Newsletter. (US) **2270**
American-German Studies/Deutsch-Amerikanische Studien. (GW) **3949**
▼American Girl. (US) **1248**
American Glass Review. (US ISSN 0002-8649) **1161**
American Go Journal. (US ISSN 0148-0243) **4463**
American Goat Society. Year Book. (US ISSN 0065-8456) **210**
American Gold News see American Gold News and Western Prospector **3477**
American Gold News and Western Prospector. (US) **3477**, 3402
†American Golf Magazine. (US) **5134**
American Grocer. (US ISSN 0002-8665) **2090**
American Group Directory of Specialized Knowledge. (US) **746**
American Group of C P A Firms. Chronicle. (US) **746**
American Group Practice Association. Executive News Service. (US) **3074**, 2597
American Group Practice Association Directory. (US ISSN 0098-2377) **3074**
American Group Psychotherapy Monograph Series. (US) **4009**
American Guild of Musical Artists Zine see A G M A Zine **3536**
American Guild of Variety Artists Newsletter see A G V A Newsletter **2579**
American Gynecological and Obstetrical Society. Transactions of the A G O S. (US) **3289**
American Gynecological Society. Transactions of the A G S see American Gynecological and Obstetrical Society. Transactions of the A G O S **3289**
American Hampshire Herdsman. (US ISSN 0002-8681) **210**
†American Hampshire Sheep Association. Flock Book. (US) **5134**
American Handel Society. Newsletter. (US ISSN 0888-8701) **3537**
American Handgunner. (US ISSN 0145-4250) **2433**, 4463
American Handgunner Book of Combat.(US) **4464**, 2433
American Handgunner Book of the 10mm. (US) **4464**, 2433
American Handgunner's Annual Book of Handguns. (US) **4540**
American Handwriting Analysis Foundation Journal see A H A F Journal **1613**
American Harp Journal. (US ISSN 0002-869X) **3537**
American Health. (US ISSN 0730-7004) **3799**
American Health Care Association. Journal see American Health Care Association. Provider **4398**
American Health Care Association. Provider. (US) **4398**, 4097
American Health Care Association Notes see A H C A Notes **4396**

American Health Consultants. Press Report see G P **3233**
American Health Information Management Association. Journal. (US) **3074**
American Health Systems Review. (US ISSN 1055-7466) **2458**
American Healthcare Radiology Administrators Announcement see A H R A Announcement **3356**
American Heart Association. Monographs see American Heart Association. Supplements **3203**
American Heart Association. Scientific Sessions. Abstracts. (US ISSN 0065-8502) **3203**
American Heart Association. Supplements. (US) **3203**
American Heart Journal. (US ISSN 0002-8703) **3204**
American Heartworm Society. Bulletin. (US) **4805**
American Heartworm Society. Symposium Proceedings. (US) **4805**
American Helicopter Society. Annual Forum. Proceedings. (US) **46**
American Helicopter Society. Journal. (US ISSN 0002-8711) **46**
American Helicopter Society. Membergram. (US) **46**
American Helicopter Society. National Forum. Proceedings see American Helicopter Society. Annual Forum. Proceedings **46**
American - Hellenic Chamber of Commerce. Business Directory. Special Issue. (GR ISSN 0065-8537) **1120**
American-Hellenic Chamber of Greece. Business Directory/Ellinoamerikanikon Emborikon Epimelitirion. Business Directory. (GR ISSN 0065-8529) **807**
American Hellenic Educational Progressive Associations see A H E P A N **1988**
American Herb Association Newsletter. (US) **2121**, 3716
American Hereford Journal. (US ISSN 0002-872X) **210**
American Heritage. (US ISSN 0002-8738) **2398**
American Heritage Cumulative Index. (US) **2327**, 2
American Heritage Index see American Heritage Cumulative Index **2327**
American Heritage of Invention & Technology. (US ISSN 8756-7296) **4593**, 2398, 4298
American Hiker. (US ISSN 0279-9472) **4540**, 3799
American Hiker Newsletter. (US ISSN 0164-5722) **4540**, 3799
American Historical Association. Annual Report. (US ISSN 0065-8561) **2305**
American Historical Review. (US ISSN 0002-8762) **2305**
American Historical Society of Germans from Russia. Journal. (US ISSN 0162-8283) **1990**, 2348
American Historical Society of Germans from Russia. Work Paper see American Historical Society of Germans from Russia. Journal **1990**
American History. (US) **2327**, 389
American History Illustrated. (US ISSN 0002-8770) **2398**
American Hockey and Arena see American Hockey Magazine **4464**
American Hockey Magazine. (US ISSN 8756-3789) **4464**
American Holiday and Life. (US) **4752**
American Holistic Veterinary Medical Association. Journal. (US) **4805**
American Holistic Veterinary Medical Association. Newsletter see American Holistic Veterinary Medical Association. Journal **4805**
American Home see Colonial Homes **610**
American Home Economics Association Action see A H E A Action **2444**
American HomeArts Needlecraft for Today see Creative Ideas Needle and Craft **5174**

American Horse Council, Inc. News see A H C News **4531**
†American Horse Exchange. (US) **5134**
American Horse Protection Association Newsletter. (US) **4532**
American Horticulturist. (US ISSN 0096-4417) **2121**
American Horticulturist News Edition. (US) **2121**
†American Hospital Association. House of Delegates. Proceedings. (US ISSN 0360-5167) **5134**
American Hospital Association Guide to the Health Care Field. (US ISSN 0094-8969) **2470**, 4097
American Hospital Association News see A H A News **2458**
American Hospital Formulary Service Drug Information. (US) **3716**
†American Hosta Society. Newsletter. (US) **5134**
American Hosta Society Journal. (US) **2121**
American Hotel and Motel Association. Buyers Guide for Hotels & Motels. (US) **2471**
American Hotel and Motel Association. Product News. see American Hotel and Motel Association. Buyers Guide for Hotels & Motels **2471**
American Humanities Index. (US ISSN 0361-0144) **2519**, 2, 2980
American Hungarian Educator. (US ISSN 0163-0040) **1615**, 1990
American Hunter. (US ISSN 0092-1068) **4540**
American Imago. (US ISSN 0065-860X) **3329**, 2858, 2893, 4009
American Immigration Lawyers Association Monthly Mailing see A I L A Monthly Mailing **2593**
American Independent. (US) **3872**
American Indian Archaeological Institute. Occasional Paper. (US) **261**
American Indian Art Magazine. (US ISSN 0192-9968) **311**
American Indian Basketry and Other Native Arts. (US) **353**, 311, 1990, 2398
American Indian Bibliographic Series. (US) **2030**
American Indian Community House Community Bulletin see A I C H Community Bulletin **1988**
American Indian Culture and Research Journal. (US ISSN 0161-6463) **1990**
American Indian Horse News. (US) **4532**
American Indian Journal. (US ISSN 0145-7993) **2398**, 1615, 2597
American Indian Law Newsletter. (US ISSN 0002-8886) **1990**, 2597
American Indian Law Review. (US ISSN 0094-002X) **2597**, 1990
American Indian Libraries Newsletter. (US ISSN 0193-8207) **1990**, 2742
American Indian Quarterly. (US ISSN 0095-182X) **233**, 2052, 2398
American Indian Report. (US) **1990**
American Indian Studies. (US) **1990**, 2398
†American Indian Treaties Publications Series. (US) **5134**
American Industrial Hygiene Association. Conference Abstracts. (US) **3623**
American Industrial Hygiene Association Journal. (US ISSN 0002-8894) **3614**
American Industry. (US ISSN 0002-8908) **1071**
American Inkmaker. (US ISSN 0002-8916) **3997**
American Innovation see Innovations & Ideas **4315**
American Insects see Insecta Mundi **533**
American Institute for Cancer Research Newsletter. (US) **3192**
American Institute for Conservation of Historic and Artistic Works. Abstracts of Papers Presented at the Annual Meeting. (US) **311**, 1483

American Institute for Conservation of Historic and Artistic Works. Book & Paper Group Annual. (US ISSN 0887-8978) **4120**, 311
American Institute for Conservation of Historic and Artistic Works. Preprints of Papers Presented at the Annual Meeting see American Institute for Conservation of Historic and Artistic Works. Abstracts of Papers Presented at the Annual Meeting **311**
American Institute for Conservation of Historic & Artistic Works. Journal. (US ISSN 0197-1360) **311**, 1483
American Institute for Decision Sciences. National Conference Proceedings see Decision Sciences Institute. Annual Meeting Proceedings **1007**
American Institute for Decision Sciences. Southeast Section. Proceedings. (US ISSN 0360-7100) **1002**
American Institute for Economic Research. Research Reports. (US ISSN 0034-5407) **644**
American Institute for Free Labor Development Report see A I F L D Report **970**
American Institute for Shippers Associations. News. (US) **4723**
American Institute for the Study of Middle Eastern Civilization. Journal. (US) **2428**
†American Institute of Aeronautics and Astronautics. A I A A Los Angeles Section. Monographs. (US ISSN 0065-8685) **5134**
American Institute of Aeronautics and Astronautics, Inc. Atmospheric Flight Mechanics Conference Proceedings see A I A A Atmospheric Flight Mechanics Conference Proceedings **42**
American Institute of Aeronautics and Astronautics Joint Fluid Mechanics, Plasma Dynamics, and Laser Conference. Proceedings see A I A A - A S M E Joint Fluid Mechanics, Plasma Dynamics, and Laser Conference. Proceedings **1926**
American Institute of Aeronautics and Astronautics Structures, Structural Dynamics, and Materials Conference. Proceedings see A I A A - A S M E - S A E Structures, Structural Dynamics, and Materials Conference. Proceedings **42**
American Institute of Aeronautics and Astronautics Thermophysics and Heat Transfer Conference. Proceedings see A I A A - A S M E Thermophysics and Heat Transfer Conference. Proceedings **3840**
American Institute of Baking. Institute News see Bakers Way **2086**
American Institute of Baking. Technical Bulletin. (US) **2061**
American Institute of Banking. Leaders Letter. (US) **758**
American Institute of Biomedical Climatology Bulletin see A I B C Bulletin **5128**
American Institute of Certified Public Accountants. Public Oversight Board. Annual Report. (US) **747**
American Institute of Certified Public Accountants Client Bulletin see C P A Client Bulletin **748**
American Institute of Certified Public Accountants Professional Standards see A I C P A Professional Standards **744**
American Institute of Certified Public Accountants Washington Report see A I C P A Washington Report **5128**
American Institute of Chemical Engineers Ch E Applications Software Survey of Personal Computers see A I Ch E Applications Software Survey of Personal Computers **1475**
American Institute of Chemical Engineers Ch E Equipment Testing Procedures see A I Ch E Equipment Testing Procedures **1847**
American Institute of Chemical Engineers Ch E Journal see A I Ch E Journal **1847**

AMERICAN JOURNAL 5901

American Institute of Chemical Engineers Ch E M I Modular Instruction. Series A: Process Control see A I Ch E M I Modular Instruction. Series A: Process Control **1847**

American Institute of Chemists. Membership Directory see American Institute of Chemists. Professional Directory **1169**

American Institute of Chemists. Professional Directory. (US) **1169**

American Institute of Graphic Arts. Journal see A I G A Journal of Graphic Design **3997**

American Institute of Graphic Arts Graphic Design U S A see A I G A Graphic Design U S A **3997**

American Institute of Graphic Arts Journal of Graphic Design see A I G A Journal of Graphic Design **3997**

American Institute of Homeopathy. Journal. (US ISSN 0002-8967) **3213**

American Institute of Hydrology. Bulletin. (US) **4821**, 1596, 1942

American Institute of Indian Studies. Biennial Report. (US) **2336**

American Institute of Indian Studies Quarterly Newsletter see A I I S Quarterly Newsletter **3632**

American Institute of Industrial Engineers. Material Handling Institute. Proceedings. (US) **1925**

American Institute of Musical Studies Bulletin see A I M S Bulletin **3536**

American Institute of Musicology. Miscellanea. (GW ISSN 0065-8855) **3537**

American Institute of Physics. Center for History of Physics. Newsletter. (US) **3814**

American Institute of Physics. Symposium on Temperature. Proceedings see Temperature: Its Measurement and Control in Science and Industry **3842**

American Institute of Physics Conference Proceedings see A I P Conference Proceedings **3812**

American Institute of Plant Engineers Facilities see A I P E Facilities **1813**

American Institute of Plant Engineers Newsline see A I P E Newsline **1813**

American Institute of the History of Pharmacy Notes see A I H P Notes **3715**

American Institute of Ultrasound in Medicine. Annual Scientific Conference. Proceedings. (US) **3074**, 3858

American Institute of Ultrasound in Medicine. Annual Scientific Conference. Program see American Institute of Ultrasound in Medicine. Annual Scientific Conference. Proceedings **3074**

American Institute of Wine & Food. New York Area Chapter. News. (US) **2061**, 377

American Insurance Newsletter. (US) **2526**

American Intellectual Property Law Association Bulletin see A I P L A Bulletin **2593**

American Intellectual Property Law Association Quarterly Journal see A I P L A Quarterly Journal **2593**

American Intelligence Journal. (US ISSN 0883-072X) **3450**

American International Checkers Society Newsletter. (US) **4464**

American International Journal of Arts, Sciences, Engineering and Medicine. (NP ISSN 0743-0884) **311**, 1814, 3074

American Iron and Steel Institute. Annual Statistical Report. (US) **1841**, 636

American Iron Magazine. (US) **4515**

American Italian Historical Association. Newsletter. (US ISSN 0569-5961) **1990**

American Italian Historical Association. Proceedings. (US) **1990**

American Jails. (US ISSN 1056-0319) **1509**

American Jewelry Manufacturer. (US ISSN 0002-9041) **2562**

American Jewish Alternatives to Zionism. Report. (US) **3949**, 1990

American Jewish Archives. (US ISSN 0002-905X) **1990**, 2305, 4221

†American Jewish Committee. Domestic Affairs Department. Pertinent Papers.(US) **5134**

†American Jewish Committee. Recent Additions to the Library. (US) **5134**

American Jewish Committee. Recently Arrived in the Library. (IS) **2742**, 2, 1990

American Jewish Committee Journal see A J C Journal **5128**

American Jewish Communal History. (US ISSN 0065-8936) **2398**

American Jewish Congress. Congress Bi-Weekly see American Jewish Congress. Congress Monthly **1990**

American Jewish Congress. Congress Monthly. (US ISSN 0163-1365) **1990**, 4221

American Jewish History. (US ISSN 0164-0178) **1991**, 2398

American Jewish Press Association. Bulletin see Pittsburgh Jewish Chronicle **2574**

American Jewish Public Relations Society Reporter see A J P R S Reporter **26**

American Jewish World. (US ISSN 0002-9084) **1991**, 4221

American Jewish Year Book. (US ISSN 0065-8987) **4221**

American Journal of Acupuncture. (US ISSN 0091-3960) **3074**

American Journal of Agricultural Economics. (US ISSN 0002-9092) **147**

American Journal of Alternative Agriculture. (US ISSN 0889-1893) **76**

American Journal of Alzheimer's Care and Related Disorders see American Journal of Alzheimer's Care and Related Disorders and Research **3074**

American Journal of Alzheimer's Care and Related Disorders and Research.(US) **3074**

American Journal of Ancient History. (US ISSN 0362-8914) **2305**

American Journal of Archaeology. (US ISSN 0002-9114) **261**

American Journal of Art Therapy. (US ISSN 0007-4764) **1733**, 311, 353, 3329, 4009

American Journal of Asthma & Allergy for Pediatricians. (US ISSN 0899-7411) **3183**, 3318, 3364

▼American Journal of Audiology. (US) **3313**

American Journal of Botany. (US ISSN 0002-9122) **494**

American Journal of Cardiac Imaging. (US ISSN 0887-7971) **3204**, 3357

American Journal of Cardiology. (US ISSN 0002-9149) **3204**

American Journal of Chinese Medicine. (US ISSN 0192-415X) **3074**

†American Journal of Clinical Assessment. (US) **5134**

American Journal of Clinical Hypnosis. (US ISSN 0002-9157) **3274**

American Journal of Clinical Nutrition. (US ISSN 0002-9165) **3603**, 3074

American Journal of Clinical Oncology. (US ISSN 0277-3732) **3193**

American Journal of Clinical Pathology. (US ISSN 0002-9173) **3074**, 427

American Journal of Community Psychology. (US ISSN 0091-0562) **4428**, 4009

American Journal of Comparative Law. (US ISSN 0002-919X) **2719**

American Journal of Computational Linguistics see Computational Linguistics **2856**

▼American Journal of Contact Dermatitis. (US) **3245**

American Journal of Cosmetic Surgery. (US ISSN 0748-8068) **3374**

American Journal of Criminal Law. (US ISSN 0092-2315) **1510**, 2597

American Journal of Dance Therapy. (US ISSN 0146-3721) **1528**, 4009

American Journal of Dermatopathology. (US ISSN 0193-1091) **3245**

American Journal of Distance Education.(US ISSN 0892-3647) **1681**

American Journal of Drug and Alcohol Abuse. (US ISSN 0095-2990) **1534**

American Journal of E E G Technology. (US ISSN 0002-9238) **3329**

American Journal of Economics and Sociology. (US ISSN 0002-9246) **645**, 4365

American Journal of Education. (US ISSN 0195-6744) **1615**

American Journal of Electromedicine see Medical Electronics **3126**

American Journal of Emergency Medicine. (US ISSN 0735-6757) **3306**, 3257

American Journal of Enology and Viticulture. (US ISSN 0002-9254) **377**, 167

American Journal of Epidemiology. (US ISSN 0002-9262) **3074**

American Journal of Family Law. (US ISSN 0891-6330) **2597**

American Journal of Family Therapy. (US ISSN 0192-6187) **4010**, 4428

American Journal of Forensic Medicine and Pathology. (US ISSN 0195-7910) **3264**

American Journal of Forensic Psychiatry. (US ISSN 0163-1942) **3264**, 2597, 3329

American Journal of Forensic Psychology. (US ISSN 0733-1290) **4010**, 2597

American Journal of Gastroenterology. (US ISSN 0002-9270) **3266**

▼American Journal of Geriatric Cardiology. (US) **3204**, 2270

American Journal of Germanic Linguistics and Literatures. (US ISSN 1040-8207) **2802**, 2893

American Journal of Gynecologic Health.(US) **3289**

American Journal of Health Promotion. (US ISSN 0890-1171) **4097**, 3603, 3799

American Journal of Hematology. (US ISSN 0361-8609) **3270**

American Journal of Hospice Care. (US ISSN 0749-1565) **4398**, 2270

American Journal of Hospital Pharmacy.(US ISSN 0002-9289) **3716**, 2458

American Journal of Human Biology. (US ISSN 1042-0533) **427**

American Journal of Human Genetics. (US ISSN 0002-9297) **539**

American Journal of Hypertension. (US ISSN 0895-7061) **3204**, 3074

American Journal of Industrial Medicine.(US ISSN 0271-3586) **3614**

American Journal of Infection Control. (US ISSN 0196-6553) **3275**, 3217

American Journal of International Law. (US ISSN 0002-9300) **2719**

American Journal of Intravenous Therapy and Clinical Nutrition see Intravenous Therapy News **3209**

American Journal of Islamic Social Sciences. (US ISSN 0742-6763) **4365**, 4218

American Journal of Jurisprudence. (US ISSN 0065-8995) **2598**

American Journal of Kidney Diseases. (US ISSN 0272-6386) **3387**, 522, 3250, 3270

American Journal of Knee Surgery. (US ISSN 0899-7403) **3374**, 1733, 3370

American Journal of Law & Medicine. (US ISSN 0098-8588) **2598**, 3074

American Journal of Legal History. (US ISSN 0002-9319) **2598**, 2305

American Journal of Maternal Child Nursing see M C N: American Journal of Maternal Child Nursing **3282**

American Journal of Mathematical and Management Sciences. (US ISSN 0196-6324) **3028**, 4561

American Journal of Mathematics. (US ISSN 0002-9327) **3028**

American Journal of Medical Genetics. (US ISSN 0148-7299) **539**, 3074

American Journal of Medicine. (US ISSN 0002-9343) **3074**

American Journal of Mental Deficiency see American Journal on Mental Retardation **3329**

American Journal of Nephrology. (SZ ISSN 0250-8095) **3387**

American Journal of Neuroradiology see A J N R **3356**

American Journal of Noninvasive Cardiology. (SZ ISSN 0258-4425) **3204**, 3213

American Journal of Numismatics see American Journal of Numismatics. Series 2 **3598**

American Journal of Numismatics. Series 2. (US) **3598**

American Journal of Nursing. (US ISSN 0002-936X) **3275**

American Journal of Nursing Company Guide see A J N Guide **3274**

American Journal of Obstetrics and Gynecology. (US ISSN 0002-9378) **3289**

American Journal of Occupational Therapy. (US ISSN 0272-9490) **3074**

American Journal of Ophthalmology. (US ISSN 0002-9394) **3297**

†American Journal of Optometric Medicine. (US) **5134**

American Journal of Optometry and Physiological Optics see Optometry and Vision Science **3304**

American Journal of Orthodontics and Dentofacial Orthopedics. (US ISSN 0889-5406) **3227**

American Journal of Orthodontics and Dentofacial Orthopedics: Italian Edition. (IT) **3228**

American Journal of Orthopsychiatry. (US ISSN 0002-9432) **4010**, 1232, 4398

American Journal of Otolaryngology. (US ISSN 0196-0709) **3313**

American Journal of Otology. (CN ISSN 0192-9763) **3313**

American Journal of Pathology. (US ISSN 0002-9440) **3074**

American Journal of Pediatric Hematology - Oncology. (US ISSN 0192-8562) **3318**, 3193, 3270

American Journal of Perinatology. (US ISSN 0735-1631) **3289**

American Journal of Pharmaceutical Education. (US ISSN 0002-9459) **3716**, 1699

American Journal of Pharmacy (1981) .(US ISSN 0730-7780) **3716**, 4097

American Journal of Philology. (US ISSN 0002-9475) **2802**, 1274

American Journal of Physical Anthropology. (US ISSN 0002-9483) **233**

American Journal of Physical Medicine see American Journal of Physical Medicine and Rehabilitation **3075**

American Journal of Physical Medicine and Rehabilitation. (US ISSN 0894-9115) **3075**, 3370, 3799

American Journal of Physics. (US ISSN 0002-9505) **3814**

American Journal of Physiologic Imaging. (DK ISSN 0885-8276) **427**

American Journal of Physiology. (US ISSN 0002-9513) **569**, 3075

American Journal of Physiology: Cell Physiology. (US ISSN 0363-6143) **569**

American Journal of Physiology: Endocrinology and Metabolism. (US ISSN 0193-1849) **569**

American Journal of Physiology: Gastrointestinal and Liver Physiology.(US ISSN 0193-1857) **569**

American Journal of Physiology: Heart and Circulatory Physiology. (US ISSN 0363-6135) **3204**, 569

American Journal of Physiology: Lung Cellular and Molecular Physiology. (US ISSN 1040-0605) **569**

American Journal of Physiology: Regulatory, Integrative and Comparative Physiology. (US ISSN 0363-6119) **569**

American Journal of Physiology: Renal, Fluid and Electrolyte Physiology. (US ISSN 0363-6127) **569**

American Journal of Police. (US ISSN 0735-8547) **1510**

American Journal of Political Science. (US ISSN 0092-5853) **3872**

American Journal of Preventive Medicine. (US ISSN 0749-3797) **3075, 4097**

American Journal of Primatology. (US ISSN 0275-2565) **427**

American Journal of Proctology see American Journal of Proctology, Gastroenterology & Colon & Rectal Surgery **3266**

American Journal of Proctology, Gastroenterology & Colon & Rectal Surgery. (US ISSN 0162-6566) **3266**

American Journal of Psychiatry. (US ISSN 0002-953X) **3329**

American Journal of Psychoanalysis. (US ISSN 0002-9548) **4010**

American Journal of Psychology. (US ISSN 0002-9556) **4010**

American Journal of Psychotherapy. (US ISSN 0002-9564) **3329**

American Journal of Public Health. (US ISSN 0090-0036) **4097**

American Journal of Reproductive Immunology see American Journal of Reproductive Immunology and Microbiology **3183**

American Journal of Reproductive Immunology and Microbiology. (DK ISSN 8755-8920) **3183, 3289**

American Journal of Respiratory Cell and Molecular Biology. (US ISSN 1044-1549) **3364**

American Journal of Rhinology. (US) **3313**

American Journal of Roentgenology see A J R **3356**

American Journal of Science. (US ISSN 0002-9599) **1541**

American Journal of Semiotic and Cultural Studies. see Revista Americana de Estudios Semioticos y Culturales **2837**

American Journal of Semiotics. (US ISSN 0277-7126) **2502, 4365**

American Journal of Small Business see Entrepreneurship: Theory and Practice **1114**

American Journal of Sociology. (US ISSN 0002-9602) **4428**

▼American Journal of Speech - Language Pathology. (US) **3313, 3329**

American Journal of Sports Medicine. (US ISSN 0363-5465) **3370**

American Journal of Surgery. (US ISSN 0002-9610) **3374**

American Journal of Surgical Pathology.(US ISSN 0147-5185) **3374, 3075**

American Journal of the Anatomy see Developmental Dynamics **436**

American Journal of the Medical Sciences. (US ISSN 0002-9629) **3075**

American Journal of Theology & Philosophy. (US ISSN 0194-3448) **4162, 3760**

American Journal of Therapy. (US) **3075**

American Journal of Trial Advocacy. (US ISSN 0160-0281) **2598**

American Journal of Tropical Medicine and Hygiene. (US ISSN 0002-9637) **3217**

American Journal of Veterinary Research. (US ISSN 0002-9645) **4805**

▼American Journal on Addictions. (US ISSN 1055-0496) **3329**

American Journal on Mental Retardation. (US ISSN 0895-8017) **3329**

American Journalism. (US ISSN 0882-1127) **2567**

American Judges Association Benchmark see A J A Benchmark **2593**

American Judicature Society. Annual Report. (US ISSN 0732-1031) **2598**

American Kennel Club. Show, Obedience and Field Trial Awards see American Kennel Club Awards **3708**

American Kennel Club Awards. (US ISSN 0888-627X) **3708, 4464**

American Kennel Gazette see Pure-Bred Dogs, American Kennel Gazette **3713**

American Kidney Fund. Annual Report. (US) **3387**

American Kidney Fund Nephrology Letter see A K F Nephrology Letter **3386**

American Kidney Fund Newsletter see A K F Newsletter **3386**

American Killifish Association. Journal. (US ISSN 0002-967X) **2036**

American Labor. (US) **970**

American Laboratory. (US ISSN 0044-7749) **1203**

American Laboratory News. (US) **1203**

American Language Journal see Journal of Intensive English Studies **2821**

†American Laryngological, Rhinological and Otological Society Transactions. (US ISSN 0065-9037) **5134**

American Latvian Association in the United States, Inc. Vestis see A L A Vestis **1988**

American Laundry Digest. (US ISSN 0002-9718) **1281**

American Law Institute. Annual Meeting. Proceedings. (US ISSN 0065-9045) **2598**

American Law Institute Course Materials Journal see A L I - A B A Course Materials Journal **2593**

American Law Institute Reporter see A L I Reporter **2593**

American Law Institute Review see A L I - A B A - C L E Review **2593**

American Lawn Applicator see Lawn and Landscape Maintenance **2133**

American Lawn Bowls Association Bowls see A L B A Bowls **4499**

American Lawyer. (US ISSN 0162-3397) **2598**

American Lawyer Management Service. (US) **2598**

American Lawyers Auxiliary News see A L A News **2593**

American Leather Chemists Association. Journal. (US ISSN 0002-9726) **2735, 1169**

American Legion Auxiliary. National News. (US) **1296**

American Legion Magazine. (US ISSN 0002-9734) **1296, 3450**

American Legion News Service. (US) **3450**

American Legion Press Association News-Letter. (US ISSN 0002-9742) **2567, 1296**

American Leprosy Missions Annual Report. (US) **3217, 4162**

†American Libertarian. (US ISSN 0897-2176) **5134**

American Libraries. (US ISSN 0002-9769) **2742**

American Library Association. Annual Conference Program. (US) **2742, 3390**

American Library Association. Memorandum see O I F Memorandum **2777**

American Library Association Handbook of Organization see A L A Handbook of Organization **2740**

American Library Association Studies in Librarianship see A L A Studies in Librarianship **5128**

American Library Association Washington Newsletter see A L A Washington Newsletter **2740**

American Library Association Yearbook see A L A Yearbook **5128**

American Library Directory. (US ISSN 0065-910X) **2742**

†American Library Directory Updating Service. (US ISSN 0002-9793) **5134**

†American Library Laws. (US) **5135**

American Life Insurance Co. News see A L I C O News **2525**

American Life Lobby News see A L L News **595**

American Liszt Society. Newsletter. (US ISSN 0749-341X) **3537**

▼American Liszt Society Studies Series.(US) **3537**

American Literary History. (US ISSN 0896-7148) **2893**

American Literary Realism. (US ISSN 0002-9823) **2980**

▼American Literary Review. (US ISSN 1051-5062) **2987**

American Literary Scholarship. (US ISSN 0065-9142) **2893**

American Literary Translators Association Newsletter see A L T A Newsletter **2800**

American Literature. (US ISSN 0002-9831) **2893**

American Littoral Society. Special Publications. (US ISSN 0065-9150) **1483**

American Living Press. (US) **311, 3760**

American Logistics Association Worldwide Directory and Fact Book see A L A Worldwide Directory and Fact Book **3449**

American Lutherie. (US ISSN 1041-7176) **3537**

American M G B Association Octagon see A M G B A Octagon **254**

American Machinist (1988). (US ISSN 1041-7958) **1071, 3015**

American Machinist and Automated Manufacturing see American Machinist (1988) **1071**

American Magazine and Historical Chronicle. (US ISSN 0882-5351) **2742**

American Malacological Bulletin. (US) **577**

American Malacological Union, Inc. News see A M U News **575**

American Managed Care & Review Association Managed Care Monitor see A M C R A's Managed Care Monitor **2458**

American Management Association. Research Reports. (US ISSN 0065-9185) **1002**

American Management Association. Seminar Program. (US ISSN 0065-9193) **1002**

American Management Association Management Briefings see A M A Management Briefings **1001**

American Management Association Survey Reports see A M A Survey Reports **1001**

American Manchester Terrier Club. Newsletter. (US) **3708**

American Manufacturers Directory. (US ISSN 1042-1742) **1121**

American Marine Engineer. (US ISSN 0002-9866) **4723**

American Maritime Cases. (US ISSN 0002-9874) **2598, 2526**

American Maritime Officer. (US ISSN 0002-9882) **2580, 4723**

American Market. (Il) **900**

American Marketing Association. Annual Marketing Educators' Conference. Proceedings. (US) **1033**

†American Marketing Association. International Membership Directory and Marketing Services Guide. (US) **5135**

American Marketing Association. Proceedings see American Marketing Association. Annual Marketing Educators' Conference. Proceedings **1033**

American Marketing Association Educators' Proceedings see A M A Educators' Proceedings **1032**

American Marketplace. (US) **3979**

†American Material Culture and Folklife.(US) **5135**

American Mathematical Monthly. (US ISSN 0002-9890) **3028**

American Mathematical Society. Abstracts of Papers Presented. (US ISSN 0192-5857) **3028**

American Mathematical Society. Bulletin. see American Mathematical Society. Bulletin. New Series **3028**

American Mathematical Society. Bulletin. New Series. (US ISSN 0273-0979) **3028**

American Mathematical Society. C B M S Regional Conference Series in Mathematics. (US ISSN 0160-7642) **3028**

American Mathematical Society. Colloquium Publications. (US ISSN 0065-9258) **3028**

American Mathematical Society. Journal. (US ISSN 0894-0347) **3028**

American Mathematical Society. Memoirs. (US ISSN 0065-9266) **3028**

American Mathematical Society. Notices. (US ISSN 0002-9920) **3028**

American Mathematical Society. Proceedings. (US ISSN 0002-9939) **3028**

American Mathematical Society. Proceedings of Symposia in Pure Mathematics. (US ISSN 0082-0717) **3028**

American Mathematical Society. Symposia in Applied Mathematics. Proceedings. (US ISSN 0160-7634) **3028**

American Mathematical Society. Transactions. (US ISSN 0002-9947) **3028**

American Mathematical Society. Translations. Series 2. (US ISSN 0065-9290) **3028**

American Meat Science Association. Reciprocal Meat Conference. Proceedings. (US) **2061, 210**

American Medallic Sculpture Association. Members Exchange. (US) **311, 353**

American Medical Association. Council on Ethical and Judicial Affairs. Current Opinions. (US) **3075**

American Medical Directory. (US) **3075**

American Medical News. (US ISSN 0001-1843) **3075**

American Medical Peer Review Association Review see A M P R A Review **3068**

American Medical Record Association. Journal see American Health Information Management Association. Journal **3074**

American Medical Women's Association. Journal. (US ISSN 0098-8421) **3075, 4836**

American Medical Writers Association Journal see A M W A Journal **3069**

American Men and Women of Science. (US ISSN 0192-8570) **417, 4298**

American Merchant Marine Conference. Proceedings. (US ISSN 0364-7374) **4723**

American Merchant Marine Library Association. Annual Report. (US) **2742**

American Merchant Marine Library Association. Report see American Merchant Marine Library Association. Annual Report **2742**

American Metal Market. (US ISSN 0002-9998) **3402**

American Meteorological Society. Bulletin. (US ISSN 0003-0007) **3432, 1596, 1601**

American Meteorological Society. Meteorological Monographs. (US ISSN 0065-9401) **3432**

†American Meteorological Society and American Institute of Aeronautica and Astronautics. International Conference on the Environmental Impact of Aerospace Operations in the High Atmosphere. (Proceedings). (US) **5135**

American Meteorological Society Historical Monograph Series. (US) **3432**

American Meteorological Society Newsletter (Boston) see A M S Newsletter (Boston) **3431**

American Metric Journal Publishing Co. Metricpac see A M J - S I Metricpac **3444**

American Microscopical Society. Transactions. (US ISSN 0003-0023) **559**
†American Mideast Business Association. Bulletin. (US) **5135**
American Midland Naturalist. (US ISSN 0003-0031) **4298**
American Midland Naturalist Monograph Series. (US ISSN 0003-0031) **427**
American Mineralogist. (US ISSN 0003-004X) **3477**, 1210, 1224
American Mines Handbook. (CN) **3477**
American Miniature Schnauzer Club Newsletter see A M S C O P E Newsletter **3707**
American Mining Congress Journal see A M C Journal **3477**
American Mizrachi Woman see Amit Woman **1991**
American Monastic Newsletter. (US) **4254**
American Montessori Society Montessori Life see A M S Montessori Life **1743**
American Monument Association Product Directory see A M A Product Directory **5128**
American Morris Newsletter. (US) **1528**
American Mosquito Control Association. Journal. (US ISSN 8756-971X) **528**
American Motor Carrier Directory: North American Edition. (US) **4743**
American Motor Carrier Directory: Specialized Services Edition see American Motor Carrier Directory: North American Edition **4743**
American Motorcyclist. (US) **4515**
American Mover. (US) **4743**
American Museum Novitates. (US ISSN 0003-0082) **577**, 4298
American Museum of Natural History. Annual Report. (US) **3521**, 4298
American Museum of Natural History. Anthropological Papers. (US ISSN 0065-9452) **233**
American Museum of Natural History. Bulletin. (US ISSN 0003-0090) **577**, 3521, 4298
American Music. (US ISSN 0734-4392) **3537**
American Music Center. Newsletter. (US ISSN 0003-0104) **3538**
American Music Teacher. (US ISSN 0003-0112) **3538**
American Musical Instrument Society. Journal. (US ISSN 0362-3300) **3538**
American Musical Instrument Society. Newsletter. (US ISSN 0160-2365) **3538**
American Musicological Society. Journal.(US ISSN 0003-0139) **3538**
American Musicological Society. Studies and Documents. (US) **3538**
American Musicological Society Newsletter (Philadelphia) see A M S Newsletter (Philadelphia) **3536**
American Name Society Bulletin see A N S Bulletin **2800**
American National CattleWomen Newsletter see American CattleWoman **209**
American National Standards Institute, Inc. Reporter see A N S I Reporter **3444**
American Natural Hygiene Society. New Jersey Chapter. Newsletter see Natural Hygiene Society of New Jersey. Newsletter **3609**
American Naturalist. (US ISSN 0003-0147) **428**
American Near East Refugee Aid, Inc. Newsletter see A N E R A Newsletter **3949**
American Nephrology Nurses' Association Journal see A N N A Journal **3274**
American Neptune. (US ISSN 0003-0155) **2398**
American Newspaper Carrier. (US) **1248**
American Newspaper Markets Circulation. (US) **2567**
American Notary. (US ISSN 0044-7773) **2598**

†American Nuclear Society. Proceedings of the Executive Conference. (US) **5135**
†American Nuclear Society. Proceedings of the National Topical Meeting. (US) **5135**
American Nuclear Society. Proceedings of the Pacific Basin Conference on Nuclear Power Development. (US) **1803**
American Nuclear Society News see A N S News **1803**
American Nuclear Society Transactions. (US ISSN 0003-018X) **1803**, 1814
American Nuclear Society Utility Quarterly see A N S Utility Quarterly **1803**
American Numismatic Association Communique see A N A Communique **5128**
American Numismatic Association Resource Directory see A N A Resource Directory **5128**
American Numismatic Society. Annual Report. (US ISSN 0569-6720) **3598**
American Numismatic Society Newsletter see A N S Newsletter **3597**
The American Nurse. (US ISSN 0098-1486) **3275**
American Nurseryman. (US ISSN 0003-0198) **2121**
American O R T Federation. Yearbook. (US) **1991**, 1721, 3949
American O R T Federation Bulletin. (US) **1991**
†American Office Dealer. (US ISSN 0584-455X) **5135**
American Oil & Gas Reporter. (US ISSN 0145-9198) **3681**
American Oil Chemists' Society. Journal.(US ISSN 0003-021X) **1216**, 1848
American Ophthalmological Society. Transactions. (US ISSN 0065-9533) **3297**
American Optometric Association. Journal. (US ISSN 0003-0244) **3298**
American Optometric Association News. (US ISSN 0094-9620) **3298**
American Orchid Society Awards Quarterly see A O S Awards Quarterly **2120**
American Orchid Society Bulletin. (US ISSN 0003-0252) **2121**
American Organist. (US ISSN 0164-3150) **3538**
American Organization for Rehabilitation Through Training Federation Bulletin see O R T Bulletin **2018**
American Oriental Series. (US ISSN 0065-9541) **3633**
American Oriental Society. Journal. (US ISSN 0003-0279) **3633**
American Orthoptic Journal. (US ISSN 0065-955X) **3298**
American Orthotic and Prosthetic Association. Almanac. (US) **3306**
American Orthotics and Prosthetics Association Almanac see O & P Almanac **3310**
American Osteopathic Association Yearbook and Directory of Osteopathic Physicians see A O A Yearbook and Directory of Osteopathic Physicians **3213**
American Osteopathic College of Radiology. Newsletter. see Viewbox **3363**
American Osteopathic Hospital Association Annual Directory see A O H A Annual Directory **2458**
American Osteopathic Hospital Association Today see A O H A Today **2458**
American Otological Society. Transactions. (US) **3313**
American Oxonian. (US ISSN 0003-0295) **2858**, 2987
†American Package Express Carriers Association. Service Directory. (US) **5135**
American Paint & Coatings Journal. (US ISSN 0098-5430) **3652**

American Paint and Wallcoverings Dealer see Decorative Products World **5178**
American Painting Contractor. (US ISSN 0003-0325) **3652**
American Paper Institute. Capacity Survey. (US) **3661**
American Paper Institute. Paper, Paperboard, & Wood Pulp Monthly Statistical Summary. (US ISSN 0003-0341) **3667**
American Paper Institute. Paper Production Ratio Weekly Report. (US) **3667**
American Paper Institute. Statistics of Paper, Paperboard and Wood Pulp. (US ISSN 0731-8863) **3667**
†American Paper Institute. Wood Pulp and Fiber Statistics. (US) **5135**
American Paper Machinery Association Newsletter see A P M A Newsletter **3015**
American Papermaker. (CN) **3662**
American Patriot (Scottsdale). (US) **3872**
American Peanut Research and Education Society Proceedings see A P R E S Proceedings **165**
American Penstemon Society Bulletin. (US) **2121**
American Peony Society. Bulletin. (US) **2121**
American Petroleum Institute. Central Abstracting and Indexing Service. Thesaurus see American Petroleum Institute. Central Abstracting & Information Services. Thesaurus **3704**
American Petroleum Institute. Central Abstracting & Information Services. Thesaurus. (US) **3704**, 2742
American Petroleum Institute. Division of Statistics and Economics. Weekly Statistical Bulletin see American Petroleum Institute. Division of Statistics. Weekly Statistical Bulletin **3704**
American Petroleum Institute. Division of Statistics. Weekly Statistical Bulletin. (US) **3704**
American Petroleum Institute. Health and Environmental Sciences Department. Reports and Other Publications, Index and Abstracts. (US ISSN 1058-675X) **4116**, 3704, 4593
American Petroleum Institute. Health and Environmental Sciences Department. Research Reports see American Petroleum Institute. Health and Environmental Sciences Department. Reports and Other Publications, Index and Abstracts **4116**
American Petroleum Institute. Monthly Completion Report. (US) **3704**, 3681
American Petroleum Institute. Monthly Statistical Report. (US) **3704**, 4561
American Petroleum Institute. Quarterly Completion Report. (US) **3704**
American Petroleum Institute. Weekly Statistical Bulletin and Monthly Statistical Report see American Petroleum Institute. Division of Statistics. Weekly Statistical Bulletin **3704**
American Petroleum Institute Literature Abstracts see Literature Abstracts **3706**
American Petroleum Institute Literature Abstracts: Catalysts & Catalysis see Literature Abstracts: Catalysts & Catalysis **1202**
American Petroleum Institute Literature and Patent Abstracts: Oilfield Chemicals see Literature and Patent Abstracts: Oilfield Chemicals **3706**
American Petroleum Institute Patents Abstracts see Patents Abstracts **3706**
American Pharmacy. (US ISSN 0160-3450) **3716**
American Pheasant and Waterfowl Society Magazine. (US ISSN 0892-6387) **561**
American Philatelic Congress. Congress Book. (US) **3749**

American Philatelic Society Newsletter see C A C Newsletter **3750**
American Philatelist. (US ISSN 0003-0473) **3749**
American Philological Association. Directory of Members. (US ISSN 0044-779X) **2802**, 1274, 2893
American Philological Association. Transactions. (US ISSN 0360-5949) **2802**
American Philological Association. Transactions and Proceedings see American Philological Association. Transactions **2802**
†American Philosophical Association. Newsletter on Philosophy and Medicine. (US) **5135**
American Philosophical Association. Proceedings and Addresses. (US ISSN 0065-972X) **3760**
American Philosophical Association Newsletters on Computer Use in Philosophy, Feminism and Philosophy, Law and Philosophy, Medicine and Philosophy, Teaching Philosophy, and Philosophy and the Black Experience see A P A Newsletters on Computer Use in Philosophy, Feminism and Philosophy, Law and Philosophy, Medicine and Philosophy, Teaching Philosophy, and Philosophy and the Black Experience **3759**
American Philosophical Quarterly. (US ISSN 0003-0481) **3760**
American Philosophical Society. Memoirs. (US ISSN 0065-9738) **4298**, 2305, 3760
American Philosophical Society. Proceedings. (US ISSN 0003-049X) **2306**, 2502, 3760
American Philosophical Society. Transactions. (US ISSN 0065-9746) **4298**, 2306, 3760
American Philosophical Society. Yearbook. (US ISSN 0065-9762) **3760**
American Photo. (US ISSN 1046-8986) **3788**
American Photographer see American Photo **3788**
American Photographers. (US) **3788**
American Physical Society. Bulletin. (US ISSN 0003-0503) **3814**
American Physical Therapy Association. Progress Report. (US ISSN 0162-3907) **3075**
American Phytopathological Society. Monographs. (US ISSN 0569-6992) **494**
American Pigeon Journal. (US ISSN 0003-0511) **3708**, 561, 4464
American Planning Association. Journal.(US ISSN 0194-4363) **2483**
American Planning Association Planning Advisory Service Reports see A P A Planning Advisory Service Reports **2482**
American Podiatric Medical Association. Journal. (US ISSN 8750-7315) **3375**
American Podiatric Medical Association News see A P M A News **3069**
American Podiatric Medical Writers Association. Newsletter. (US) **2567**, 3375
†American Poetry. (US ISSN 0737-3635) **5135**
American Poetry and Poetics. (US ISSN 0095-1684) **2987**
American Poetry Anthology. (US) **2987**
American Poetry Review (Philadelphia). (US ISSN 0360-3709) **2987**
American Poetry Series. (US) **2987**
American Political Parties and Election Series. (US) **3872**
American Political Report. (US) **3872**
American Political Science Association Biographical Directory see A P S A Biographical Directory **3869**
American Political Science Association Departmental Services Program Survey of Departments see A P S A Departmental Services Program Survey of Departments **3869**

American Political Science Association Directory of Department Chairpersons see A P S A Directory of Department Chairpersons **3869**
American Political Science Review. (US ISSN 0003-0554) **3872**
American Politics. (US ISSN 0741-1111) **3872**
American Politics Quarterly. (US ISSN 0044-7803) **3872**
American Polygraph Association. Journal see Polygraph (Severna Park) **1521**
American Polygraph Association Newsletter. (US) **1510**, 3257, 4010
American Popular Culture. (US ISSN 0193-6859) **2398**
American Portuguese Society. Journal. (US ISSN 0098-4981) **4752**, 2348
American Postal Chess Tournaments News Bulletin see A P C T News Bulletin **4463**
American Postal Worker. (US ISSN 0044-7811) **1352**, 2580
American Potato Journal. (US ISSN 0003-0589) **167**
American Poultry Association. News and Views see Fancy Feathers. A P A News and Views **216**
American Power Boat Association. A P B A Rule Book see American Power Boat Association. A P B A Rule - Reference Book **4521**
American Power Boat Association. A P B A Rule - Reference Book. (US) **4521**
American Power Conference. Proceedings. (US ISSN 0097-2126) **1783**, 4593
American Premiere Magazine. (US ISSN 0279-0041) **3503**
American Presbyterians: Journal of Presbyterian History. (US ISSN 0886-5159) **4228**, 2306
American Primrose Society. Quarterly see Primroses **2137**
American Printer (Chicago, 1982). (US ISSN 0744-6616) **3997**
American Printing History Association Letter see A P H A Letter **3997**
American Printing House for the Blind. Department of Educational and Technical Research. Report of Research and Development Activities.(US) **2290**, 1733
American Printing House for the Blind. Department of Educational Research. Report of Research and Development Activities see American Printing House for the Blind. Department of Educational and Technical Research. Report of Research and Development Activities **2290**
American Printing House for the Blind, Inc. Slate see A P H Slate **2290**
American Private Radio Association, Inc. News see A P R A News **1354**
American Problems Studies. (US) **2398**
American Production and Inventory Control Society. Annual Conference Proceedings see American Production and Inventory Control Society. Annual International Conference Proceedings **1002**
American Production and Inventory Control Society. Annual International Conference Proceedings. (US) **1002**
American Production and Inventory Control Society Performance Advantage see A P I C S the Performance Advantage **1001**
American Productivity & Quality Center. Case Study. (US ISSN 0741-6423) **1002**
†American Productivity & Quality Center. Digest (Year). (US) **5135**
American Productivity & Quality Center. Letter. (US) **1002**, 1071
American Productivity & Quality Center. Notebook. (US) **1002**
American Productivity & Quality Center. Perspectives (Year). (US) **1002**
American Professional Needlework Retailers, Inc. Newsletter see A P N R Newsletter **352**

American Professional Practice Association Digest see A P P A Digest **937**
†American Prometheus. (US ISSN 0737-5905) **5135**
▼American Prospect. (US ISSN 1049-7285) **4053**
American Protection Review. (US) **1525**
American Protestant Health Association. Bulletin. (US) **2458**, 4228
American Protestant Hospital Association. Bulletin see American Protestant Health Association. Bulletin **2458**
American Psychiatric Association. Scientific Proceedings in Summary Form. (US ISSN 0090-1881) **3329**, 3166
American Psychiatric Association. Task Force Reports. (US) **3329**
American Psychiatric Association Gay Caucus. Newsletter see Association of Gay and Lesbian Psychiatrists. Newsletter **2451**
American Psychoanalyst. (US ISSN 1052-7958) **4010**
American Psychoanalytic Association. Journal. (US ISSN 0003-0651) **4010**, 3329
American Psychoanalytic Association. Journal. Monograph. (US ISSN 0065-9843) **4010**
American Psychoanalytic Association. Workshop Series. (US) **4010**
American Psychological Association. Directory. (US ISSN 0196-6545) **417**, 4010
American Psychological Association. Employment Bulletin see A P A Monitor **4008**
American Psychological Association Monitor see A P A Monitor **4008**
American Psychologist. (US ISSN 0003-066X) **4010**
American Psychopathological Association. Proceedings of the Annual Meeting. (US ISSN 0091-7389) **3329**
American Psychopathological Association Series. (US) **3329**
American Public Gas Association. Newsletter. (US) **3681**
American Public Opinion Data. (US) **2221**
American Public Opinion Index. (US ISSN 0740-8978) **4457**, 2
American Public Welfare Association. W - Memo. (US ISSN 0163-8300) **4398**
American Public Welfare Association News see A P W A News **4396**
American Public Works Association. Directory. (US ISSN 0360-6899) **4053**, 4593
American Public Works Association. Research Foundation. Special Reports. (US ISSN 0065-9932) **1861**
American Public Works Association Reporter see A P W A Reporter **1861**
American Publishing Who's Who in New York. (US ISSN 0892-1385) **4120**
†American Purpose. (US ISSN 0891-446X) **5135**
American Quarterly. (US ISSN 0003-0678) **2502**
American Quaternary Association Program and Abstracts see A M Q U A Program and Abstracts **1549**
American Quilter. (US ISSN 8756-6591) **3590**
American Racing Motorcycles. (US) **4515**
American Racing Pigeon News. (US ISSN 0003-0686) **4464**
American Radio. (US ISSN 0738-8675) **1346**, 1354, 4561
American Radio Association Log see A R A Log **2579**
American Radio Relay League, Inc. Experimenters' Exchange see Q E X A R R L Experimenters' Exchange **1378**
American Radio Relay League, Inc. License Manual Series see A R R L License Manual Series **1354**

American Radio Relay League, Inc. Repeater Directory see A R R L Repeater Directory **1354**
American Rag. (US ISSN 0163-8211) **311**
American Railway Bridge and Building Association. Proceedings. (US ISSN 0065-9940) **600**
American Railway Engineering Association. Proceedings. (US) **4707**
American Railway Engineering Association Bulletin. (US ISSN 0003-0694) **4707**
American Rambouillet Sheep Breeders Association. Newsletter. (US) **210**
American Rationalist. (US ISSN 0003-0708) **3760**
American Real Estate and Urban Economics Association. Journal. (US ISSN 0270-0484) **4144**, 2483
American Record Guide. (US ISSN 0003-0716) **3538**
American Recorder. (US ISSN 0003-0724) **3538**
American Recorder Society Members' Library. (US) **3538**
American Recorder Society Newsletter. (US) **3538**
American Recovery Association. News and Views. (US) **758**, 1121
American Red Angus. (US) **210**
American Red Cross. Annual Report. (US) **4398**
American Reference Books Annual. (US ISSN 0065-9959) **4120**
American Register of Exporters and Importers see American Export Register **900**
American Registry of Professional Entomologists News see A R P E News **5128**
American Rehabilitation. (US ISSN 0362-4048) **4398**, 3075
American Research Center in Egypt. Journal. (US ISSN 0065-9991) **261**, 311
American Research Center in Egypt. Reports. (US ISSN 0732-6432) **261**
†American Retailer. (US) **5135**
American Revenuer. (US ISSN 0163-1608) **3749**
American Review. (US) **311**, 2893, 3538
American Review. (JA ISSN 0387-2815) **3872**
American Review of Canadian Studies. (US ISSN 0272-2011) **3949**
American Review of Diagnostics. (US ISSN 0735-1283) **3204**
▼American Review of International Arbitration. (US) **2719**, 900
American Review of Management and Inventiveness Report see Management Review & Inventiveness Report **1020**
American Review of Public Administration. (US ISSN 0275-0740) **4053**
American Review of Respiratory Disease. (US ISSN 0003-0805) **3364**
American Rifleman. (US ISSN 0003-083X) **4464**
American Right to Read Newsletter. (US) **4120**
American Road & Transportation Builders Association Newsletter see A R T B A Newsletter **4717**
American Road and Transportation Builders Association Officials and Engineers Directory, Transportation Agency Personnel see A R T B A Officials and Engineers Directory, Transportation Agency Personnel **4717**
American Rock Garden Society Bulletin.(US ISSN 0003-0864) **2121**
American Rodder. (US) **4679**
American Romanian Academy of Arts and Sciences. Journal. (US ISSN 0896-1018) **1699**
American Romanian Academy of Arts and Sciences. Publications. (US) **1991**
†American Romanian Review. (US ISSN 0193-8118) **5135**

American Rose Annual. (US ISSN 0066-0000) **2121**
American Rose Magazine. (US ISSN 0003-0899) **2121**
American Rowing. (US ISSN 0888-1154) **4521**
†American Sailings. (US) **5135**
American Sailor. (US ISSN 0279-9553) **4522**
American Salaries and Wages Survey. (US ISSN 1055-7628) **702**, 3631, 4561
American Salesman. (US ISSN 0003-0902) **1033**
American Salon. (US) **372**
American Saluki Association. Newsletter.(US) **3708**
American Savings Directory. (US) **758**
American Scandinavian Review see Scandinavian Review **2022**
American Scene (Washington). (US) **1303**
American Scholar. (US ISSN 0003-0937) **2858**
American School and Hospital Maintenance. (US) **1724**, 2458
American School & University. (US ISSN 0003-0945) **1725**
American School Board Journal. (US ISSN 0003-0953) **1725**
American School Counselor Association Counselor see A S C A Counselor **1733**
American School of Prehistoric Research. Bulletins. (US ISSN 0066-0027) **261**
American Schools of Oriental Research. Annual. (US ISSN 0066-0035) **2428**, 261
American Schools of Oriental Research. Bulletin. (US ISSN 0003-097X) **3633**, 2428
American Schools of Oriental Research. Newsletter. (US ISSN 0361-6029) **3633**
American Scientific Affiliation. Journal: Evangelical Perspectives on Science and Christian Faith see Perspectives on Science and Christian Faith **4195**
American Scientist. (US ISSN 0003-0996) **4298**
American Secondary Education. (US ISSN 0003-1003) **1615**
American Seed Trade Association Newsletter see A S T A Newsletter **2120**
American Self-Protection Association World of A S P see The World of A S P **4497**
▼American Senior. (US ISSN 1055-8306) **2270**
American Sentinel. (US ISSN 0278-0585) **3872**
American Sephardi. (US ISSN 0003-102X) **1991**, 4221
American Series of Foreign Penal Codes. (US ISSN 0066-0051) **1510**
American Shetland Sheepdog Association. Bulletin see American Shetland Sheepdog Association. Bulletin Board **3708**
American Shetland Sheepdog Association. Bulletin Board. (US) **3708**
American Shipper. (US ISSN 0160-225X) **4723**
American Shoemaking. (US ISSN 0003-1038) **4360**, 2735
American Shoemaking Directory. (US) **4360**, 1121
American Shore and Beach Preservation Association. Newsletter. (US ISSN 0517-4856) **1942**, 1596, 1601, 4821
▼American Short Fiction. (US ISSN 1051-4813) **2893**
American Single Shot Rifle News. (US ISSN 0734-5801) **4464**
American Skating World. (US) **4464**
American Ski Federation Washington Letter see A S F Washington Letter **4539**
American Skier. (US) **4540**, 1502
American Small Business Association Today see A S B A Today **1113**
American Snowmobiler. (US) **4540**
American Social Experience. (US) **2398**

American Society for Abrasive Methods. Technical Conference. Proceedings see Abrasive Engineering Society. Conference Proceedings **1813**

American Society for Adolescent Psychiatry. Annals. see Adolescent Psychiatry **3328**

American Society for Adolescent Psychiatry. Newsletter. (US) **3329**

American Society for Concrete Construction. Hotline Summary. (US) **600**

American Society for Concrete Construction. Literature Roundup. (US) **600**

American Society for Concrete Construction. Management Report and Tax Alert. (US) **600**

American Society for Concrete Construction. Research Quarterly. (US) **600**

American Society for Conservation Archaeology. Proceedings. (US) **261**

American Society for Conservation Archaeology Newsletter see American Society for Conservation Archaeology Report **261**

American Society for Conservation Archaeology Report. (US) **261, 1483**

American Society for Cybernetics. Proceedings of the Annual Symposium. (US ISSN 0066-0086) **1440**

American Society for Eighteenth-Century Studies News Circular see A S E C S News Circular **2305**

American Society for Engineering Education. Annual Conference Proceedings. (US ISSN 0190-1052) **1814**

American Society for Engineering Education Prism see A S E E Prism **1813**

American Society for Geriatric Dentistry. Journal. (US ISSN 0003-1054) **3228, 2270**

American Society for Healthcare Environmental Services Annual Conference see A S H E S Annual Conference **2458**

American Society for Horticultural Science. Journal. (US ISSN 0003-1062) **2121, 494**

American Society for Horticultural Science Newsletter see A S H S Newsletter **2120**

American Society for Hospital Engineering Technical Document Series. (US) **2458, 1927**

American Society for Hospital Materials Management. Conference Proceedings. (US) **2459**

American Society for Hospital Materials Management. Perspectives. (US) **2459**

American Society for Information Science. Annual Meeting. Proceedings. (US ISSN 0160-0044) **2742**

American Society for Information Science. Bulletin. (US ISSN 0095-4403) **2742**

American Society for Information Science. Journal. (US ISSN 0002-8231) **2742, 1455**

American Society for Information Science. Proceedings see American Society for Information Science. Annual Meeting. Proceedings **2742**

American Society for Information Science. Western Canada Chapter. Annual Meeting Proceedings. (CN ISSN 0318-9937) **2742**

American Society for Information Science Handbook and Directory see A S I S Handbook and Directory **2740**

American Society for Information Science Key Papers Series see A S I S Key Papers Series **2740**

American Society for Legal History Newsletter see A S L H Newsletter **2593**

▼American Society for Mass Spectrometry. Journal. (US ISSN 1044-0305) **3851, 1203**

American Society for Metals News (Materials Park) see A S M News (Materials Park) **3401**

American Society for Microbiology. Abstracts of the Annual Meeting see American Society for Microbiology. Abstracts of the General Meeting **548**

American Society for Microbiology. Abstracts of the General Meeting. (US) **548**

American Society for Microbiology News (Washington) see A S M News (Washington) **548**

American Society for Netherlands Philately. Newsletter. (US) **3749**

American Society for Neurochemistry. Transactions. (US ISSN 0066-0132) **3330, 470**

American Society for Ophthalmology and Optometry. Archives. see Sociedad Americana de Oftalmologia y Optometria. Archivos **3305**

American Society for Photogrammetry and Remote Sensing. Technical Papers from the Annual Meeting. (US) **2241, 1814**

American Society for Photogrammetry and Remote Sensing Fall Convention. Technical Papers. (US) **3851,** 360

American Society for Portuguese Numismatics Newsletter see A S P N Newsletter **5128**

American Society for Psychical Research. Journal. (US ISSN 0003-1070) **3668**

American Society for Psychical Research, Inc. Newsletter see A S P R Newsletter **3668**

American Society for Public Administration. Section on International and Comparative Administration. Occasional Papers. (US) **4053**

American Society for Quality Control. Annual Technical Conference Transactions. (US ISSN 0360-6929) **3445**

American Society for Quality Control. Transactions of Annual Technical Conferences see American Society for Quality Control. Annual Technical Conference Transactions **3445**

American Society for Reformation Research. Newsletter see Historians of Early Modern Europe **2366**

American Society for Testing and Materials. Compilation of A S T M Standards in Building Codes. (US ISSN 0066-0523) **1911,** 600

American Society for Testing and Materials. Data Series Publications. (US ISSN 0066-0531) **1911**

American Society for Testing and Materials. Five-Year Index to A S T M Technical Papers and Reports. (US ISSN 0066-054X) **1911**

American Society for Testing and Materials. Special Technical Publications. (US ISSN 0066-0558) **1911**

American Society for Testing and Materials Annual Book of A S T M 1.1 see Annual Book of A S T M Standards. Volume 01.01. Steel-Piping, Tubing, Fittings **1911**

American Society for Testing and Materials Standardization News see A S T M Standardization News **3444**

American Society for Testing and Materials Standards Infobriefs see A S T M Standards Infobriefs **4592**

American Society for the Advancement of Anesthesia in Dentistry. Proceedings. (US) **3228**

American Society for the Advancement of General Anesthesia in Dentistry. Proceedings see Pain Control in Dentistry **3192**

American Society for the Defense of Tradition, Family and Property Bulletin on the 15 T F P S see Bulletin on the 15 T F P S **5154**

American Society for the Defense of Tradition, Family and Property Newsletter see T F P Newsletter **4454**

American Society for the Prevention of Cruelty to Animals Report see A S P C A Report **229**

American Society for Theatre Research Newsletter see A S T R Newsletter **4629**

American Society for Training and Development Buyers Guide and Consultants Directory see A S T D Buyers Guide and Consultants Directory **1120**

American Society for Veterinary Clinical Pathology. Journal see Veterinary Clinical Pathology **4817**

American Society of Agricultural Engineers. Annual Meeting Papers. (US) **76**

American Society of Agricultural Engineers Monograph Series see A S A E Monograph Series **1813**

American Society of Agricultural Engineers Standards see A S A E Standards **165**

American Society of Agricultural Engineers Transactions see A S A E Transactions **165**

American Society of Agronomy, Inc. Special Publication see A S A Special Publication **67**

American Society of Anesthesiologists Refresher Courses in Anesthesiology see A S A Refresher Courses in Anesthesiology **3189**

American Society of Animal Science. Western Section Proceedings. (US ISSN 0569-7832) **4805**

American Society of Appraisers. Newsline. (US) **4144,** 311, 758, 2526

American Society of Appraisers Monograph (Washington) see A S A Monograph (Washington) **5128**

American Society of Artifical Internal Organs Primers in Artificial Organs see A S A I O Primers in Artificial Organs **5128**

American Society of Artificial Internal Organs Transactions see A S A I O Transactions **3069**

American Society of Artists, Inc. Artisan see A S A Artisan **310**

American Society of Association Executives Associate Member Update see A S A E Associate Member Update **1001**

American Society of Association Executives Association Law and Policy see A S A E Association Law and Policy **1001**

American Society of Association Executives International News see A S A E International News **1001**

American Society of Association Executives Sharing of Expertise and Experience see Sharing of Expertise and Experience **1027**

American Society of Bakery Engineers. Proceedings of the Annual Meeting. (US ISSN 0066-0582) **2086**

American Society of Bakery Engineers Letter see A S B E Letter **2086**

American Society of Bookplate Collectors and Designers. Year Book. (US ISSN 0275-1569) **2433,** 311, 4120

American Society of Brewing Chemists. Journal. (US ISSN 0361-0470) **377,** 1169

American Society of Brewing Chemists Newsletter see A S B C Newsletter **377**

†American Society of C L U. Journal. (US ISSN 0742-9517) **5135**

American Society of Cartographers. Bulletin. (US ISSN 0044-7943) **2241**

American Society of Civil Engineers. Official Register. (US) **1861**

American Society of Civil Engineers. Proceedings. (US ISSN 0003-1119) **1861**

American Society of Civil Engineers. Transactions. (US ISSN 0066-0604) **1841**

American Society of Civil Engineers Annual Combined Index see A S C E Annual Combined Index **1841**

American Society of Civil Engineers Publications Information see A S C E Publications Information **1841**

American Society of Clinical Hypnosis. Directory. (US ISSN 0517-5178) **3274**

American Society of Clinical Pathologists Washington Report on National and State Issues see A S C P Washington Report on National and State Issues **3069**

American Society of Composers, Authors and Publishers Action see A S C A P in Action **3536**

American Society of Composers, Authors and Publishers Biographical Dictionary see A S C A P Biographical Dictionary **3536**

American Society of Consultant Pharmacists Update see A S C P Update **3715**

American Society of Corporate Secretaries. Los Angeles Chapter. Newsletter. (US ISSN 0894-0622) **1002,** 2598

American Society of Echocardiography. Journal. (US ISSN 0894-7317) **3204**

American Society of Electroneurodiagnostic Technologists, Inc. Newsletter see A S E T Newsletter **3327**

American Society of Electroplated Plastics News and Views see A S E P News and Views **3860**

American Society of Farm Managers and Rural Appraisers. Journal. (US ISSN 0003-116X) **76**

American Society of Heating, Refrigerating and Air-Conditioning Engineers, Inc. Handbook see A S H R A E Handbook **2297**

American Society of Heating, Refrigerating and Air-Conditioning Engineers, Inc. Journal see A S H R A E Journal **2297**

American Society of Heating, Refrigerating and Air-Conditioning Engineers, Inc. Transactions see A S H R A E Transactions **2297**

American Society of Heating, Refrigerating and Air-Conditioning Engineers, Inc. Technical Data Bulletin see A S H R A E Technical Data Bulletin **1926**

American Society of Hospital Pharmacists Newsletter see A S H P Newsletter **3715**

American Society of Hypertension. Symposium Series. (US) **3075**

American Society of Indexers. Newsletter. (US ISSN 0733-3048) **2792**

American Society of Interior Designers Report see A S I D Report **2547**

American Society of International Law. Letter to Members see American Society of International Law. Newsletter **2719**

American Society of International Law. Newsletter. (US ISSN 0066-0639) **2719**

American Society of International Law. Occasional Papers see Studies in Transnational Legal Policy **2729**

American Society of International Law. Proceedings of the Annual Meeting. (US ISSN 0272-5045) **2719**

American Society of Landscape Architects Members Handbook see A S L A Members Handbook **291**

American Society of Magazine Photographers. Bulletin. (US ISSN 0361-9168) **3788**

American Society of Mammalogists. Special Publications. (US ISSN 0569-8219) **577**

American Society of Marine Artists News see A S M A News **310**

American Society of Mechanical Engineers Joint Fluid Mechanics, Plasma Dynamics, and Laser Conference. Proceedings see A I A A - A S M E Joint Fluid Mechanics, Plasma Dynamics, and Laser Conference. Proceedings **1926**

American Society of Mechanical Engineers News see A S M E News **1926**

American Society of Mechanical Engineers Solar Energy Conference. Proceedings *see* A S M E Solar Energy Conference. Proceedings **1810**

American Society of Mechanical Engineers Structures, Structural Dynamics, and Materials Conference. Proceedings *see* A I A A - A S M E - S A E Structures, Structural Dynamics, and Materials Conference. Proceedings **42**

American Society of Mechanical Engineers Thermophysics and Heat Transfer Conference. Proceedings *see* A I A A - A S M E Thermophysics and Heat Transfer Conference. Proceedings **3840**

American Society of Medical Technology, Inc. Today *see* A S M T Today **3256**

American Society of Military Insignia Collectors, Inc. (ASMIC) Newsletter *see* A S M I C Newsletter **2432**

▼American Society of Nephrology. Journal. (US ISSN 1046-6673) **3387**

American Society of Newspaper Editors. Bulletin. (US ISSN 0003-1178) **2567**

American Society of Newspaper Editors Proceedings (Year) *see* A S N E. Proceedings (Year) **2566**

American Society of Papyrologists. Bulletin. (US ISSN 0003-1186) **261**

American Society of Photogrammetry. Technical Papers from the Annual Meeting *see* American Society for Photogrammetry and Remote Sensing. Technical Papers from the Annual Meeting **2241**

American Society of Planning Officials. A S P O Planning Advisory Service *see* A P A Planning Advisory Service Reports **2482**

American Society of Plant Physiologists. Proceedings of Annual Meeting *see* Plant Physiology. Supplement Abstracts of Annual Meeting **515**

American Society of Plant Physiologists Newsletter *see* A S P P Newsletter **491**

American Society of Psychosomatic Dentistry and Medicine. Journal *see* International Journal of Psychosomatics **3110**

American Society of Safety Engineers. Proceedings. Professional Conference *see* American Society of Safety Engineers. Proceedings. Professional Development Conference **1814**

American Society of Safety Engineers. Proceedings. Professional Development Conference. (US) **1814**

American Society of Sanitary Engineering. Year Book. (US ISSN 0066-068X) **4097**

American Society of Sephardic Studies Series *see* Sephardic Scholar **2023**

†American Society of Traffic and Transportation. Newsletter. (US) **5135**

American Society of University Composers Newsletter *see* Society of Composers Newsletter **3580**

American Society of Utility Investors Newsletter *see* A S U I Newsletter **937**

American Sociological Association. Proceedings of Annual Meeting. (US) **4428**

American Sociological Association Employment Bulletin *see* A S A Employment Bulletin **3624**

American Sociological Association Footnotes *see* A S A Footnotes **4427**

American Sociological Review. (US ISSN 0003-1224) **4428**

American Sociologist. (US ISSN 0003-1232) **4428**

American Sokol. (US ISSN 0003-1259) **1743**

American Solar Energy Society. Annual Meeting. (US) **1810**

American Solar Energy Society. Passive Conference. Annual Meeting. (US) **1810**

American Spacemodeling. (US ISSN 0883-0991) **2433**, **46**

American Spaniel Club. Bulletin. (US) **3708**

American Spectator. (US ISSN 0148-8414) **2858**

American Speech. (US ISSN 0003-1283) **2802**

American Speech - Language - Hearing Association *see* A S H A **2285**

American Speech - Language - Hearing Association. Directory. (US) **3313**, 1733, 2286

American Speech - Language - Hearing Association Reports. (US) **3313**, 1733, 2286

American SquareDance. (US ISSN 0091-3383) **1528**

American Stamp Dealers' Association, Inc. Newsletter *see* A.S.D.A. Newsletter **3749**

American Standard Chinchilla Rabbit Association. Newsletter. (US) **3708**, 210

American Standard Code for Information Interchange *see* A S C I I **1445**

American Statistical Association. Business and Economic Statistics Section. Proceedings. (US ISSN 0066-0736) **702**

American Statistical Association. Section on Statistical Education. Proceedings.(US) **1674**, 4561

American Statistical Association. Section on Statistical Graphics. Proceedings. (US) **4561**

American Statistical Association. Social Statistics Section. Proceedings. (US ISSN 0066-0752) **3989**

American Statistical Association. Statistical Computing Section. Proceedings (of the Annual Meeting) .(US ISSN 0149-9963) **4561**, 1403

American Statistical Association. Survey Research Methods. Proceedings. (US) **4561**

American Statistician. (US ISSN 0003-1305) **4561**

American Statistics Index. (US ISSN 0091-1658) **4561**

American Stock Exchange. AMEX Databook *see* American Stock Exchange. AMEX Fact Book **938**

American Stock Exchange. AMEX Fact Book. (US) **938**

American Stock Exchange. Annual Report. (US ISSN 0066-0779) **938**

American Stock Exchange Directory. (US) **938**

American Stock Exchange Guide. (US) **758**

American Stock Exchange Stock Reports. (US ISSN 0002-8347) **938**

American Stock Exchange Weekly Bulletin. (US) **938**

American String Teacher. (US ISSN 0003-1313) **3538**, 1615

American Student Dental Association Handbook *see* A S D A Handbook **3227**

American Student Dental Association News (Year) *see* A S D A News (Year) **3227**

American Studies. *see* Amerikastudien **2398**

American Studies. (US ISSN 0026-3079) **4365**, 2502

American Studies. (PL ISSN 0137-3536) **4365**

American Studies. *see* Meiguo Yanjiu **4379**

American Studies Association Newsletter *see* A S A Newsletter **2397**

American Studies in Scandinavia. (DK ISSN 0044-8060) **2398**

American Studies International. (US ISSN 0003-1321) **2502**, 2398

American Studies Library Newsletter. (UK ISSN 0265-3389) **2743**

American Studies Research Centre. Newsletter. (II ISSN 0066-0795) **2398**

†American Style. (US) **5135**

American Subsidiaries of German Firms.(US ISSN 0272-1953) **807**

American Supply Association. Operating Performance Report. (US) **2304**

American Supply Association Membership Directory *see* A S A Membership Directory **1120**

American Supply Association News *see* A S A News **2297**

American Surgeon. (US ISSN 0003-1348) **3375**

American Survival Guide. (US) **4540**

American Suzuki Journal. (US ISSN 0193-5372) **3538**

American Swedish Historical Museum Newsletter. (US) **3521**

American Swedish Institute Posten *see* A S I Posten **3520**

American Taxation Association. Journal. (US ISSN 0198-9073) **1087**

American Teacher. (US ISSN 0003-1380) **2580**, 1615

American Technical Education Association, Inc. Journal *see* A T E A Journal **1613**

American Telephone and Telegraph Technical Journal *see* A T & T Technical Journal **1361**

American Textile Directory. (US) **4616**

American Theatre. (US ISSN 8750-3255) **4629**

American Theological Library Association. Conference. Summary of Proceedings. (US ISSN 0066-0868) **2743**

American Theological Library Association. Newsletter. (US ISSN 0003-1399) **2743**

American Theological Library Association Bibliography Series *see* A T L A Bibliography Series **4211**

American Theological Library Association Monograph Series *see* A T L A Monograph Series **4161**

American Theosophist. (US ISSN 0003-1402) **3760**

American Thoracic Society News *see* A T S News **3364**

American Timberman and Trucker. (US) **2113**

American Tinnitus Association Tinnitus Today *see* Tinnitus Today **3317**

American Tool, Die and Stamping News *see* Diemaking, Stamping & EDMing **3017**

American Topical Association. Casey Jones Railroad Unit. Newsletter *see* Dispatcher (San Francisco, 1953) **3751**

American Trade Schools Directory. (US ISSN 0517-564X) **1692**

American Trail Series. (US ISSN 0066-0884) **2398**

American Translators Association. Annual Conference Proceedings. (US) **2802**

American Translators Association Chronicle *see* A T A Chronicle **2800**

American Transportation Builder *see* Transportation Builder **4722**

American Trapper. (US) **2735**

American Tree Farmer *see* Tree Farmer **2109**

American Trucker Magazine. (US) **4743**

▼American Trucking Associations. Current Economic Bulletin. (US ISSN 1050-7671) **4661**, 4743

American Trucking Trends (Year). (US) **4743**

American Trust for the British Library. Newsletter. (UK ISSN 0260-3667) **2743**

American Turf Monthly. (US ISSN 0003-1445) **4532**

American Type Culture Collection. Catalogue of Animal and Plant Viruses, Chlamydiae, Rickettsiae and Virus Antisera *see* American Type Culture Collection. Catalogue of Animal Viruses and Antisera, Chlamydiae, Rickettsiae and Virus Antisera **549**

American Type Culture Collection. Catalogue of Animal Viruses and Antisera, Chlamydiae, Rickettsiae and Virus Antisera. (US) **549**

American Type Culture Collection. Catalogue of Bacteria & Bacteriophages. (US) **549**

American Type Culture Collection. Catalogue of Cell Lines and Hybridomas. (US) **549**

American Type Culture Collection. Catalogue of Fungi - Yeasts. (US) **549**

American Type Culture Collection. Catalogue of Protists. Algae - Protozoa. (US) **549**

American Type Culture Collection. Catalogue of Recombinant D N A Collections *see* American Type Culture Collection. Catalogue of Recombinant D N A Materials **549**

American Type Culture Collection. Catalogue of Recombinant D N A Materials. (US) **549**

American Type Culture Collection. Catalogue of Strains 1 *see* American Type Culture Collection. Catalogue of Bacteria & Bacteriophages **549**

American Type Culture Collection. Catalogue of Strains 1: Algae, Bacteria, Bacteriophages, Plasmids, Fungi, Plant Viruses and Antisera and Protozoa *see* American Type Culture Collection. Catalogue of Fungi - Yeasts **549**

American Type Culture Collection. Catalogue of Strains 1: Algae, Bacteria, Bacteriophages, Plasmids, Fungi, Plant Viruses and Antisera and Protozoa *see* American Type Culture Collection. Catalogue of Protists. Algae - Protozoa **549**

American Type Culture Collection. Catalogue of Strains 2: Animal Cell Lines, Animal Viruses, Bacterial Viruses, Mycoviruses, Plant Viruses, Rickettsiae, Chlamydiae *see* American Type Culture Collection. Catalogue of Cell Lines and Hybridomas **549**

American Type Culture Collection Microbes and Cells at Work *see* A T C C Microbes and Cells at Work **548**

American Type Culture Collection Quarterly Newsletter *see* A T C C Quarterly Newsletter **548**

American Typecasting Fellowship Newsletter *see* A T F Newsletter **3997**

American Underground-Space Association News *see* A U A News **291**

American Universities and Colleges. (US ISSN 0066-0922) **1692**

American University in Cairo. News. (UA) **1699**

American University Law Review. (US ISSN 0003-1453) **2598**

American University Studies. Series 1. Germanic Languages and Literature. (US ISSN 0721-1392) **2802**

American University Studies. Series 2. Romance Languages and Literature. (US ISSN 0740-9257) **2893**

American University Studies. Series 3. Comparative Literature. (US ISSN 0724-1445) **2894**

American University Studies. Series 4. English Language and Literature. (US ISSN 0741-0700) **2894**

American University Studies. Series 5. Philosophy. (US ISSN 0739-6392) **3760**

American University Studies. Series 6. Foreign Language Instruction. (US ISSN 0739-6406) **2802**

American University Studies. Series 7. Theology and Religion. (US ISSN 0740-0446) **4162**, 2306

American University Studies. Series 8. Psychology. (US ISSN 0740-0454) **4010**

American University Studies. Series 9. History. (US ISSN 0740-0462) **2306**

American University Studies. Series 10. Political Science. (US ISSN 0740-0470) **2598**

American University Studies. Series 11. Anthropology and Sociology. (US ISSN 0740-0489) **4365**
American University Studies. Series 12. Slavic Languages and Literature. (US ISSN 0740-0497) **2802**
American University Studies. Series 13. Linguistics. (US ISSN 0740-4557) **2802**
American University Studies. Series 14. Education. (US ISSN 0740-4565) **1725**
American University Studies. Series 15. Communications. (US ISSN 0740-5111) **28**
American University Studies. Series 16. Economics. (US ISSN 0741-2150) **3979, 4428**
American University Studies. Series 17. Classical Language and Literature. (US ISSN 0741-9309) **1274, 2894**
American University Studies. Series 18. African Literature. (US ISSN 0742-1923) **2894**
American University Studies. Series 19. General Literature. (US ISSN 0743-6645) **2894**
American University Studies. Series 20. Fine Arts. (US ISSN 0890-412X) **311**
American University Studies. Series 21. Regional Studies. (US ISSN 0895-0482) **1991, 1483, 1942, 2052**
American University Studies. Series 22. Latin American Studies. (US ISSN 0895-0490) **2398**
American University Studies. Series 24. American Literature. (US ISSN 0895-0512) **2894**
▼American University Studies. Series 25. Geography. (US ISSN 0899-6040) **2241**
▼American University Studies. Series 26. Theater Arts. (US ISSN 0899-9880) **4629**
▼American University Studies. Series 27. Feminist Studies. (US ISSN 1042-5985) **4836**
American Urban Guidenotes. (US) **4752**
American Urological Association Decision Making see A U A Decision Making **3386**
American Urological Association Today see A U A Today **3386**
American Vegetable Grower. (US ISSN 0003-1461) **167**
American Venereal Disease Association. Journal see Sexually Transmitted Diseases **3249**
American Vernacular Music. (US) **3538**
American Veterans Committee, Inc. Bulletin see A V C Bulletin **3449**
American Veterinary Exhibitors Association Newsletter see A V E A Newsletter **4804**
American Veterinary Medical Association. Directory. (US ISSN 0066-1147) **4805**
American Veterinary Medical Association. Journal. (US ISSN 0003-1488) **4805**
American Viola Society. Journal. (US ISSN 0898-5987) **3538**
American Viola Society. Newsletter see American Viola Society. Journal **3538**
American Visions. (US ISSN 0884-9390) **1991, 2398**
The American Voice. (US ISSN 0884-4356) **2894**
American Volkssport Association Newsletter see A V A Newsletter **1988**
American Wagner Association. Newsletter. (US) **3538**
American Waldensian Society. Newsletter. (US) **4162**
American Wanderer. (US) **1991, 1296, 3799**
American Water Resources Association. Monographs. (US) **4821**
American Water Resources Symposia. Annual Proceedings. (US) **4821**

American Water Works Association. Journal. (US ISSN 0003-150X) **4821**
American Water Works Association. Proceedings, A W W A Annual Conference. (US ISSN 0360-814X) **4821**
American Water Works Association Mainstream see A W W A Mainstream **4821**
American Waterways Operators Letter see A W O Letter **4723**
American Weather Observer. (US ISSN 8755-9552) **3432**
American Welding Society Annual Meeting. Abstracts of Papers. (US) **3429**
†American West. (US ISSN 0003-1534) **5135**
American White Water. (US ISSN 0300-7626) **4522, 1483**
American Wind Energy Association Wind Energy Weekly see A W E A Wind Energy Weekly **1812**
American Window Cleaner. (US ISSN 1047-9090) **3614, 1113, 3624**
American Window Cleaner Newsletter see American Window Cleaner **3614**
American Wine Society. Bulletin. (US ISSN 0149-6778) **377, 2433**
American Wine Society Journal. (US ISSN 0364-698X) **377**
American Wine Society Manual. (US ISSN 0149-676X) **377**
American Wine Society News. (US) **377**
▼American Woman. (US) **4837**
American Woman Magazine see American Woman Motorsports **4464**
American Woman Motorsports. (US) **4464, 4837**
American Women Composers, Inc. News Forum see A W C News Forum **3536**
American Women's Society of Certified Public Accountants Newsletter see A W S C P A. Newsletter **744**
American Wood - Preservers' Association. Book of Standards. (US) **2113**
American Wood - Preservers' Association. Proceedings. (US) **2113**
American Woodworker. (US ISSN 8750-9318) **2500, 639**
American Worker. (US) **970, 3624**
▼American Writing. (US ISSN 1049-815X) **2894**
American Youth Hostels, Inc. Discovery Tours see A Y H Discovery Tours **4750**
American Youth Hostels Knapsack see Explorer (Washington) **4762**
American Zionist. (US ISSN 0003-1550) **3872, 1991**
†American Zionist Federation. News and Views. (US ISSN 0044-8079) **5135**
American Zoologist. (US ISSN 0003-1569) **577**
Americana. (US ISSN 0090-9114) **2221, 2398**
Americana Annual. (US ISSN 0196-0180) **1780, 2221**
Americana Philatelic News. (US) **3749**
Americans Before Columbus. (US ISSN 0066-121X) **2398**
Americans for Constitutional Action. Report. (US ISSN 0066-1236) **3872**
Americans for Constitutional Action Index see A C A Index **3936**
Americans for Democratic Action Action News and Notes see A D Action News and Notes **3869**
Americans for Democratic Action Today see A D A Today **3869**
Americans for Justice in the Middle East News see A J M E News **2427**
Americans for Legal Reform see Legal Reformer **3904**
Americans for the Universality of Unesco Newsletter. (US) **3949, 1721, 4298**
Americans United for Life Insights see A U L Insights **2593**

Americans United for Life Studies in Law, Medicine & Society see A U L Studies in Law, Medicine & Society **2593**
AmericanWay. (US ISSN 0003-1518) **4801**
†Americar Australia. (AT ISSN 1032-6499) **5135**
The Americas. (US ISSN 0003-1615) **2398**
Americas. (US ISSN 0379-0940) **2503, 3949**
Americas Boychoir - International Children's Choir Federation. Newsletter. (US) **3538, 1743**
▼America's Censored Newsletter. (US ISSN 1061-4230) **2567**
America's Civil War. (US ISSN 1046-2899) **2398, 3450**
America's Corporate Families and International Affiliates. (US ISSN 0740-4018) **1121**
America's Cup Challenge and Guide to Australia see America's Cup Defense **4464**
▼America's Cup Defense. (US) **4464, 4752**
America's Economy. (US ISSN 0889-4299) **833, 900, 998**
America's Equestrian. (US) **4532**
America's Fastest Growing Companies. (US) **938**
America's Favorite National Parks. (US) **4752**
▼America's Finest Companies. (US ISSN 1057-5642) **1121**
America's Future. (US ISSN 0003-1593) **3872, 645**
▼America's Pay-Per-Call Directory. (US) **1361**
Americas Review. (UK) **843, 3872**
The America's Review. (US ISSN 1042-6213) **2894, 1991**
Americas Review. (US) **2987**
America's Spirit. (US ISSN 0886-1196) **4398**
America's Textile see America's Textiles International **4616**
America's Textiles International. (US ISSN 0890-9970) **4616**
Americas Watch. (US) **3939**
Americas Watch Report. (US) **3939**
Americki Hrvat. see American Croat **1990**
Amerigold Newsletter. (US) **2121**
Amerika Asocio de Instruistoj de Esperanto Kvaronjara Bulteno. see American Association of Teachers of Esperanto Quarterly Bulletin **1743**
Amerika Woche. (US) **1991**
▼Amerikai Magyar Levelestar/ Hungarian Archives of America. (US ISSN 1054-4607) **2348, 2743**
Amerikai Magyar Szo/Hungarian Word. (US ISSN 0194-7990) **1991**
Amerikan Uutiset. (US ISSN 0745-9971) **1991**
Amerikanische Handelskammer in Oesterrich. Newsletter. (AU) **807**
Amerikastudien/American Studies. (GW ISSN 0340-2827) **2398**
Amerindia. (UY) **233**
Amerisure Safety News. (US) **4097, 2526, 3614**
Ameritech Industrial Yellow Pages. (US) **1121, 1071**
Ameron News. (US) **4593**
Ametrias. (MX) **2894**
Amex Fact Book see American Stock Exchange. AMEX Fact Book **938**
Amherst. (US) **1303**
Amherst Alumni News see Amherst **1303**
Ami de la Boulangerie see Nouvelles de la Boulangerie **2089**
Ami de la Nature. see Naturfreund **4779**
Ami des Fleurs. (BE ISSN 0772-1099) **2121**
Ami des Jardins et de la Maison. (FR ISSN 0044-8095) **2121, 2556**
Ami du Peuple/Volksfreund. (FR ISSN 0003-1704) **2186**
Ami du Professionnel en Alimentation. (FR ISSN 0296-8746) **2061**
▼Ami Pro Report. (US) **1475**
Amica. (IT) **4837**
Amicale Philatelique l'Ancre. Bulletin. (FR) **3749**

Amicales Regimentaires. (FR) **3450**
Amici. (US) **4254, 2743**
Amici della Pipa. (IT ISSN 0392-5773) **4643**
Amicizia. (IT ISSN 0003-1720) **1615**
Amicizia Ebraico-Cristiana di Firenze. Bollettino. (IT ISSN 0003-1739) **4162**
Amico del Coltivatore. (IT) **76**
L'Amico del Popolo. (IT) **2204**
Amico dell'Arte Cristiana. (IT ISSN 0003-1747) **311, 4162**
Amicus Journal. (US ISSN 0276-7201) **1943**
Amideast Counseling Quarterly see Advising Quarterly **1721**
Amiga. (BL ISSN 0003-1755) **4837**
Amiga Animation. (US) **1420**
Amiga Format. (UK) **1467**
Amiga Insider. (US) **1467**
Amiga Magazine. (IT) **1418**
Amiga Plus see AmigaWorld **1467**
†Amiga User. (US) **5135**
Amigahelp see Epson LifeBoat **1469**
AmigaWorld. (US ISSN 0883-2390) **1467, 825, 1458**
▼AmigaWorld Tech Journal. (US) **1467**
Amigo. (CN ISSN 0318-5729) **1248, 1615**
Amigo del Hogar. (DR) **4254**
Amigos Volando. (US) **4801**
Amina. (FR ISSN 0244-0008) **4837, 2168**
Amina. (SG) **4837**
▼Amino Acids. (AU ISSN 0939-4451) **470**
Amino Acids and Peptides. (UK) **470**
Amino Acids, Peptides and Proteins see Amino Acids and Peptides **470**
Amis-Coop see Delta (Paris) **1253**
Amis d'Andre Gide. Bulletin. (FR ISSN 0044-8133) **2894**
Les Amis de Curnonsky. (FR) **2052, 2306**
Amis de Han Ryner. Cahiers. (FR ISSN 0003-178X) **2858**
Amis de l'E.N.S.B.A.N.A. see Ecole Nationale Superieure de Biologie Appliquee a la Nutrition et a l'Alimentation. Cahiers **3605**
Amis de l'Histoire de la Perade. Collection "Nos Vieilles Familles". (CN) **2143**
Amis de l'Oeuvre et la Pensee de Georges Migot. Bulletin d'Information.(FR ISSN 0154-7283) **3538**
Amis de la Radiesthesie. (FR ISSN 0003-1798) **3668, 3799**
Amis de Milosz. (FR ISSN 0003-181X) **2894**
Amis de Napoleon 3rd. Bulletin Interne see Nouveaux Cahiers du Second Empire **2378**
Amis de Ramuz. Bulletin. (FR ISSN 0293-0773) **2894, 417**
Amis des Roses. (FR ISSN 0003-1844) **2121**
Amis du Chateau de Pau. Bulletin. (FR ISSN 0003-1852) **311, 2348**
Amis Suisses de la Ceramique. Bulletin. see Keramik-Freunde der Schweiz. Mitteilungsblatt **355**
Amisol. (CN ISSN 0318-5737) **1248, 1615**
Amistad. (MX) **2398, 311, 2598, 4752**
Amit Woman. (US ISSN 0747-0258) **1991**
L'Amitie/Friendship. (CS) **2802, 1743**
Amitie Charles Peguy. Bulletin d'Informations et de Recherches. (FR ISSN 0180-8567) **2894**
Amitie Charles Peguy. Feuillets see Amitie Charles Peguy. Bulletin d'Informations et de Recherches **2894**
Amitie Internationale. (UA) **2185**
Amities Catholiques Francaises. (FR ISSN 0003-1895) **4255, 3949**
Amities Spirituelles. Bulletin. (FR ISSN 0003-1909) **4162**
Amityville Historical Society Dispatch. (US ISSN 0894-9492) **2398**
Amman-al Masa'a. see Amman in the Evening **2208**

Amman Chamber of Industry. Bimonthly Industrial Bulletin. see Risalat al Sina'a **822**
Amman in the Evening/Amman-al Masa'a. (JO) **2208**
Ammattiautoilija. (FI ISSN 0355-7286) **4743**
Amministrare. (IT ISSN 0044-8141) **4053**
Amministratore Manager. (IT) **4084**
Amministrazione e Finanza. (IT) **758**
Amministrazione Italiana. (IT ISSN 0303-9722) **4053**
†Amministrazione Tributi e Finanze. (IT ISSN 0569-9479) **5135**
Ammochostos. (CY) **3872**
Ammonia Plant Safety and Related Facilities. (US ISSN 0360-7011) **1848**
Ammonite. (UK ISSN 0951-2500) **2987**, 3593
Ammonitore. (IT) **3015**
Al-Amn/Security. (TS) **1525**
Amnesty Action. (US ISSN 0003-1933) **3939**
Amnesty International. Canadian Section (English Speaking). Bulletin. (CN ISSN 0831-9227) **3939**, 2503
Amnesty International Australian Newsletter. (AT ISSN 0256-0771) **3939**, 1615
Amnesty International Newsletter. (UK ISSN 0308-6887) **3940**
Amnesty International Report. (UK) **3950**, 3940
Amoco Traveler. (US) **4752**
Amod. (BG) **2173**
Amoeba. (NE ISSN 0926-3543) **428**, 1483, 1943
Amon Hen. (UK ISSN 0306-8781) **2894**
Among Friends. (US ISSN 0003-195X) **2743**, 4120
Among Ourselves. (AT ISSN 0003-1968) **4646**
Amp. (US) **3075**
Amperland. (GW ISSN 0003-1992) **2348**, 311
Ampersand see Moving Up **5240**
†Ampersand's Entertainment Guide. (US) **5135**
Amphibia Reptilia. (NE ISSN 0173-5373) **577**
Amphibious Warfare Review. (US) **3450**
Amphora. (CN ISSN 0003-200X) **4120**
Ampleforth Journal. (UK ISSN 0003-2018) **4162**
Ampo. (JA ISSN 0003-2026) **2858**
Amptelike Suid-Afrikaanse Munisipale Jaarboek. see Official South African Municipal Yearbook **4093**
Ampurias. (SP) **261**
Ampute de Guerre. (FR ISSN 0044-815X) **3451**
†Amra. (US ISSN 0044-8168) **5135**
Amro Bank Netherlands Economic Report. (NE) **843**
Amro Beursnieuws/Amro Stock Market News. (NE) **938**
Amro Stock Market News. see Amro Beursnieuws **938**
Amruta/Cine Weekly. (II) **2198**
AmStat News. (US ISSN 0163-9617) **4561**
Amsterdam News see New York Amsterdam News **2016**
Amsterdam-Rotterdam Bank. Annual Report. (NE ISSN 0066-1309) **758**
Amsterdam Stock Exchange. (NE) **938**
Amsterdam Studies in the Theory and History of Linguistic Science. Series 2: Classics in Psycholinguistics. (US ISSN 0165-716X) **2802**, 4010
Amsterdam Studies in the Theory and History of Linguistic Science. Series 3: Studies in the History of the Language Sciences. (US ISSN 0304-0720) **2802**
Amsterdam Studies in the Theory and History of Linguistic Science. Series 4: Current Issues in Linguistic Theory. (US ISSN 0304-0763) **2802**

Amsterdam Studies in the Theory and History of Linguistic Science. Series 5: Library and Information Sources in Linguistics. (US ISSN 0165-7267) **2855**
Amsterdam Studies in the Theory and History of the Linguistic Science. Series 3: Studies in the History of Linguistics see Amsterdam Studies in the Theory and History of Linguistic Science. Series 3: Studies in the History of the Language Sciences **2802**
Amsterdam Studies in Theology. (NE ISSN 0169-0272) **4162**
Amsterdamer Beitraege zur Aelteren Germanistik. (NE ISSN 0165-7305) **2894**, 2348
Amsterdamer Beitraege zur Neueren Germanistik. (NE ISSN 0304-6257) **2894**, 2348
Amsterdamer Publikationen zur Sprache und Literatur. (NE ISSN 0169-0221) **2802**, 2894
Amsterdams Sociologisch Tijdschrift see Sociologisch Tijdschrift **4452**
Amstkommunernes Oekonomi. (DK ISSN 0109-7822) **4084**
Amt- og Kommune Bladet. (DK ISSN 0109-9418) **4084**
Amtliche Bekanntmachungen der Universitaet Gesamthochschule Essen. (GW) **2598**
Amtliche Spanische Handelskammer fuer Deutschland. Informationsblatt see InterCamara **817**
Amtlicher Anzeiger. (SZ ISSN 0003-2115) **4053**
Amtlicher Schulanzeiger fuer den Regierungsbezirk Unterfranken. (GW) **4084**
Amtliches Bekanntmachungsblatt fuer die Gemeinde Mettlach. (GW) **2188**
Amtliches Kreisblatt fuer den Kreis Herzogtum Lauenburg. (GW ISSN 0003-2131) **4084**
Amtliches Mitteilungsblatt der Marktgemeinde Leobersdorf. (AU) **4084**, 1615, 4398
Amtliches Schulblatt fuer den Regierungsbezirk Duesseldorf. (GW ISSN 0003-2190) **1615**, 2598
Amtliches Schulblatt fuer den Regierungsbezirk Muenster. (GW) **1725**
Amtliches Schulblatt fuer die Volks-, Real- und Berufsschulen fuer den Bezirksregierung Trier. (GW ISSN 0003-2204) **1725**
Amtliches Telefax- und Telebriefverzeichnis der Deutschen Bundespost Telecom. (GW) **1352**
Amtrak Annual Report. (US ISSN 0097-7039) **4707**
Amtrak Express. (US ISSN 1040-1776) **4801**, 4707
Amtsblatt der Deutschen Bundesbahn. (GW ISSN 0179-7824) **4707**
Amtsblatt der Gemeinde Wilhelmsfeld. (GW) **4084**
Amtsblatt der Landeshauptstadt Linz. (AU ISSN 0038-8971) **4084**
Amtsblatt der Landeshauptstadt Muenchen. (GW) **4084**
Amtsblatt der Oesterreichischen Justizverwaltung. (AU ISSN 0003-2220) **2598**
Amtsblatt der Regierung von Unterfranken. (GW) **4053**
Amtsblatt der Stadt Kapfenberg. (AU ISSN 0003-2239) **4084**
Amtsblatt der Stadt Koeln. (GW ISSN 0172-2522) **4084**
Amtsblatt der Stadt Korntal - Muenchingen. (GW) **4084**
Amtsblatt der Stadt Moenchengladbach.(GW ISSN 0934-8964) **4053**
Amtsblatt des Bistums Limburg. (GW) **2188**
Amtsblatt des Kreises Wesel. (GW) **4084**, 4097
Amtsblatt des Landkreises Dillingen an der Donau. (GW) **4053**
Amtsblatt des Landkreises Hof. (GW) **4053**
Amtsblatt fuer Berlin. (GW) **4084**
Amtsblatt fuer das Land Vorarlberg. (AU ISSN 0003-2271) **4084**

Amtsblatt fuer den Landkreis Rosenheim. (GW) **4084**
Amtsblatt fuer den Stadt- und Landkreis Heilbronn. (GW) **4084**
Amtsblatt fuer die Erzdioezese Bamberg. (GW ISSN 0003-2328) **4255**
Amtsblatt fuer Schleswig-Holstein. (GW) **4084**
Amtsblatt Grosse Kreisstadt Leinfelden. (GW) **4053**
Amtsblatt - Stadt Augsburg. (GW) **4084**
†Amtskommunale Enkeltfagskurser. (DK ISSN 0900-3096) **5135**
Der Amtsvormund. (GW ISSN 0003-2336) **2598**
Amudim. (IS) **829**, 3872
Amudim. (US) **1991**, 1303, 4221
Amusement Business. (US ISSN 0003-2344) **4629**, 843, 4540
Amusement Business's Directory North American Fairs see Directory of North American Fairs, Festivals and Expositions **4545**
Amusement Business's Funparks Directory see Directory of Funparks & Attractions **4759**
Amusement-Industrie. (GW ISSN 0171-7243) **4464**
Amusement Industry Buyers Guide. (US) **4540**
Amusement Rides and Game Buyers Guide see Amusement Industry Buyers Guide **4540**
Amy D. Wohl's Trends Letter. (US) **1467**, 1466
An Heiligen Quellen see Dienender Glaube **4174**
An Reabhloid/Revolution. (IE) **3940**
▼An Searud. (IE) **2894**, 4255
Anacrusis. (CN ISSN 0826-7464) **3538**
Anadolu Sanati Arastirmalari/ Researches on Anatolian Art. (TU ISSN 0066-1333) **311**
Anaesthesia (London). (UK ISSN 0003-2409) **3189**
†Anaesthesia (Sheffield). (UK ISSN 0261-4510) **5135**
Anaesthesia and Intensive Care. (AT) **3189**
Anaesthesia and Intensive Care in Italy. (IT) **3189**
Anaesthesia and Intensive Care Journal see Anaesthesia and Intensive Care **3189**
Anaesthesia Essays and Researches. (JO ISSN 0259-1162) **3190**
Anaesthesie - Intensivtherapie - Notfallmedizin see Anaesthesie - Intensivtherapie - Notfallmedizin - Schmerztherapie **3190**
Anaesthesie - Intensivtherapie - Notfallmedizin - Schmerztherapie. (GW ISSN 0939-2661) **3190**
Anaesthesiologie und Intensivmedizin. (GW ISSN 0170-5334) **3190**
Anaesthesiologie und Intensivmedizin/ Anaesthesiology and Intensive Care Medicine. (US ISSN 0171-1814) **3190**
Anaesthesiologische Informationen see Anaesthesiologie und Intensivmedizin **3190**
Anaesthesiology and Intensive Care Medicine. see Anaesthesiologie und Intensivmedizin **3190**
Anaesthesiology and Resuscitation see Anaesthesiologie und Intensivmedizin **3190**
Der Anaesthesist. (GW ISSN 0003-2417) **3190**
Anagnostika Hetaireia Kerkyras. Deltion.(GR) **2348**
Anahata Nada/Soundless Sound. (US) **4162**
Anais. (US) **2894**
Anais Brasileiros de Dermatologia. (BL ISSN 0365-0596) **3245**
Anais de Farmacia e Quimica de Sao Paulo. (BL ISSN 0003-2441) **3716**, 470, 1169
Anais Hidrograficos. (BL) **4821**
Anais Paulistas de Medicina e Cirurgia. (BL ISSN 0003-245X) **3375**
Analecta Augustiniana. (IT ISSN 0392-2855) **4255**

Analecta Biblica. (IT ISSN 0066-135X) **4255**
Analecta Bollandiana. (BE ISSN 0003-2468) **4162**, 2306
Analecta Calasanctiana. (SP ISSN 0569-9789) **2217**
Analecta Cartesiana. (NE) **3760**
Analecta Cartusiana. (AU) **4162**, 2348, 2894
Analecta Cisterciensia. (IT ISSN 0003-2476) **4255**, 2306
Analecta Gregoriana. (VC ISSN 0066-1376) **4255**
Analecta Husserliana. (NE) **3760**
Analecta Linguistica. (NE ISSN 0044-8176) **2855**
Analecta Musicologica. (GW ISSN 0569-9827) **3538**
Analecta Ordinis Carmelitarum. (IT ISSN 0394-7726) **4255**, 2306, 4162
Analecta Orientalia. (VC) **3633**
Analecta Praemonstratensia. (BE ISSN 0517-6735) **2348**
Analecta Romana Instituti Danici. (IT ISSN 0066-1392) **2348**
Analecta Romana Instituti Danici. Supplementum. (IT ISSN 0066-1406) **2348**
Analecta Romanica. (GW ISSN 0569-986X) **2802**, 2894
Analecta Sacri Ordinis Cisterciensis see Analecta Cisterciensia **4255**
Analecta Vaticano-Belgica. Deuxieme Serie. Section A: Nonciature de Flandre. (BE ISSN 0066-1414) **4255**
Analecta Vaticano-Belgica. Deuxieme Serie. Section B: Nonciature de Cologne. (BE ISSN 0066-1422) **4255**
Analecta Vaticano-Belgica. Deuxieme Serie. Section C: Nonciature de Bruxelles. (BE ISSN 0066-1430) **4255**
Analecta Vaticano-Belgica. Premiere Serie: Documents Relatifs aux Anciens Dioceses de Cambrai, Liege, Therouanne et Tournai. (BE ISSN 0066-1449) **4255**
Analecta Veterinaria. (AG) **4805**
Analecta Vlatadon. (GR) **4280**
Anales Cervantinos. (SP ISSN 0569-9878) **2802**
Anales Ciencias Politicas y Sociales. (AG) **3872**, 4365
Anales Cientificos. (PE ISSN 0003-2484) **4298**
Anales de Anatomia. (SP ISSN 0569-9894) **3075**
Anales de Antropologia. (MX ISSN 0020-3947) **233**
Anales de Arqueologia y Etnologia. (AG ISSN 0325-0288) **261**, 233
Anales de Arquitectura. (SP ISSN 0214-4727) **292**
Anales de Bromatologia. (SP ISSN 0003-2492) **2061**, 3603
Anales de Cirugia. (AG ISSN 0066-1465) **3375**
Anales de Edafologia y Agrobiologia see Suelo y Planta **194**
Anales de Estudios Economicos y Empresariales. (SP ISSN 0213-7569) **645**
Anales de Geografia. (MX) **2241**
†Anales de la Comunidad Israelita de Buenos Aires. (AG) **5135**
Anales de la Literatura Espanola Contemporanea. (US ISSN 0272-1635) **2894**
Anales de la Narrativa Espanola Contemporanea see Anales de la Literatura Espanola Contemporanea **2894**
Anales de Legislacion Argentina. (AG ISSN 0034-6985) **2598**
Anales de Literatura Hispanoamericana.(SP ISSN 0210-4547) **2894**
Anales de Mecanica y Electricidad. (SP ISSN 0003-2506) **1927**, 1881
Anales de Medicina. Cirugia see Annals de Medicina **3076**
Anales de Medicina. Especialidades see Annals de Medicina **3076**
Anales de Medicina. Medicina see Annals de Medicina **3076**

Anales de Moral Social y Economica. (SP ISSN 0066-1473) **4428**
Anales de Ortopedia y Traumatologia. (MX ISSN 0044-8184) **3306**
Anales de Veterinaria de Murcia. (SP ISSN 0213-5434) **4805**
Anales del Desarrollo. (SP ISSN 0569-9908) **428**
Anales del Instituto Corachan. (SP ISSN 0003-2530) **3075**
Anales del Instituto de Etnologia Americana *see* Anales de Arqueologia y Etnologia **261**
Anales Espanoles de Pediatria. (SP ISSN 0302-4342) **3318**
Anales Galdosianos. (US) **2894**
Anales Internacionales de Criminologia. *see* Annales Internationales de Criminologie **1510**
Anales Otorrinolaringologicos Ibero-Americanos. (SP ISSN 0303-8874) **3313**
Die An-Alfabeten. (GW) **1248**
Analgesic Guidelines. (AT ISSN 1033-8810) **3075**
Anali Bolnice "Dr. M. Stojanovic" *see* Anali Klinicke Bolnice "Dr. M. Stojanovic **3075**
Anali Klinicke Bolnice "Dr. M. Stojanovic". (CI ISSN 0301-2255) **3075**
Anali za Sumarstvo. *see* Annales Forestales **2095**
Analise e Perspectiva Economica *see* A P E C **842**
Analise Jurisprudencial *see* Instituto dos Advogados de S. Paulo. Revista **2635**
Analise Psicologica. (PO ISSN 0870-8231) **4010**
Analise Social. (PO ISSN 0003-2573) **4428**
Analisis. (CL) **2180**
Analisis. (PE) **3872**
Analisis Anual del Mercado del Azucar. (CU) **702**, 2, **900**
Analisis Clinicos. (SP ISSN 0212-4572) **3075**
Analisis - Confirmado. (AG ISSN 0003-2581) **2170**
Analisis de la Agricultura Sinaloense. (MX) **147**
Analisis de la Situacion Agricola de Sinaloa *see* Analisis de la Agricultura Sinaloense **147**
Analisis Geografico. (CK) **2241**
Analisis Semanal. (EC) **2185**
Analizy i Proby Technik Badawczych w Socjologii. (PL) **4428**
Analog Computing *see* A.N.A.L.O.G. Computing **1466**
Analog Dialogue. (US ISSN 0161-3626) **1417**, 1416, 1436
▼Analog Integrated Circuits and Signal Processing. (NE ISSN 0925-1030) **1881**
Analog Science Fiction & Fact. (US ISSN 0161-2328) **3010**, **4299**
Analogo-Diskretnye Preobrazovaniya Signalov. (LV ISSN 0135-1281) **1453**
Analusis. (FR ISSN 0365-4877) **1203**
Analyse. (NE ISSN 0166-7688) **3257**
Analyse & Kritik. (GW ISSN 0171-5860) **4365**
Analyse de Politiques. *see* Canadian Public Policy **849**
Analyse Musicale. (FR ISSN 0295-3722) **3538**
Analysen. (GW) **1615**, **4365**
Analyses de la S.E.D.E.I.S. (Societe d'Etudes et de Documentation Economiques, Industrielles et Sociales) (FR ISSN 0399-1245) **843**
Analyses of Natural Gases. (US) **3681**
Analyses of Natural Gases of the United States *see* Analyses of Natural Gases **3681**
Analyses of New Jersey Public Library Statistics for (Year). (US) **2743**
Analysis *see* Analysis of Jewish Policy Issues **1991**
Analysis. (GW ISSN 0174-4747) **3028**
Analysis. (UK ISSN 0003-2638) **3760**

†Analysis. (CN ISSN 0707-5723) **5135**
Analysis and Intervention in Developmental Disabilities *see* Research in Developmental Disabilities **3147**
Analysis Instrumentation. (US ISSN 0882-5785) **2521**
Analysis Mathematica. (HU ISSN 0133-3852) **3028**
Analysis of Jewish Policy Issues. (US ISSN 0164-2790) **1991**
Analysis of Official Pesticide Samples *see* Louisiana. Department of Agriculture. Analysis of Official Pesticide Samples. Annual Report **184**
Analysis of Oregon Personal Income *see* Oregon Personal Income Tax Statistics **733**
†Analysis of Organic Materials: an International Series of Monographs. (US) **5135**
Analysis of Public Utility Financing. (US ISSN 0421-9910) **759**
Analysis of School Finances, New York State School Districts. (US ISSN 0077-9342) **1725**
Analysis of Workers' Compensation Laws. (US ISSN 0191-118X) **970**, 2526, 2598
Analysis Politico. (CK) **3872**
Analysis: Quaderni di Anglistica. (IT) **2894**
Analyst. (JA ISSN 0003-2662) **1071**
Analyst. (UK ISSN 0003-2654) **1203**
Analysts Handbook. (US) **938**
Analytic Psychotherapy and Psychopathology. *see* Psichiatria e Psicoterapia Analitica **3350**
Analytica Chimica Acta. (NE ISSN 0003-2670) **1203**
Analytica Chimica Acta - Computer Technique and Optimization *see* Analytica Chimica Acta **1203**
Analytical Abstracts. (UK ISSN 0003-2689) **1191**, 2
Analytical & Enumerative Bibliography. (US ISSN 0161-0376) **389**, 2894
Analytical and Quantitative Cytology *see* Analytical and Quantitative Cytology and Histology **522**
Analytical and Quantitative Cytology and Histology. **522**
Analytical Biochemistry. (US ISSN 0003-2697) **471**, 1203
†Analytical Calorimetry. (US ISSN 0066-1538) **5135**
Analytical Cellular Pathology. (NE ISSN 0921-8912) **522**
Analytical Chemistry. (US ISSN 0003-2700) **1204**
Analytical Chemistry. *see* Fenxi Huaxue **1205**
Analytical Chemistry. Labguide (Year). (US) **1204**
Analytical Chemistry of the Elements Series. (UK) **1204**
Analytical Chemistry Symposia Series. (NE) **1204**
Analytical Instrument Industry Report. (UK ISSN 0265-3435) **2521**, 1204
Analytical Instrumentation. (US ISSN 0743-5797) **1204**, 3257
Analytical Letters *see* Analytical Letters: Chemical Analysis - Clinical and Biomedical Analysis **1204**
Analytical Letters: Chemical Analysis - Clinical and Biomedical Analysis. (US ISSN 0003-2719) **1204**
Analytical Proceedings. (UK ISSN 0144-557X) **1204**
Analytical Profiles of Drug Substances. (US ISSN 0099-5428) **3716**
Analytical Psychology Club of New York. Bulletin. (US) **4010**, 2858
Analytical Sciences. (JA ISSN 0910-6340) **1169**
Analytical Trilogy *see* Revista de Psicanalise Integral **4044**
Analytichem International. Annual International Symposium. Proceedings. (US) **1204**
Analytika *see* Chemsa **1851**
Analytische Psychologie. (SZ ISSN 0301-3006) **4010**
An-An. (JA) **1289**

Anand Digest. (II) **2444**
Ananda Acharya Universal Series. (II) **3760**, **2894**
Ananda Bichitra. (BG) **2173**
Ananda Patra. (BG) **2173**
Ananda Varta. (II) **3633**, 3760
Ananda Vikatan. (II) **2894**
Anandalok. (II) **3503**
Anandamela. (II) **1248**
Anaporc. (SP) **210**
Anapress. (AT ISSN 0044-8206) **2171**
Anarchismo. (IT) **3872**
Anashim Vemachshevim. *see* P C Plus **1472**
Anatolian Studies. (UK ISSN 0066-1546) **261**
Anatolica. (NE ISSN 0066-1554) **2336**, 261
Anatomia, Histologia, Embryologia. Series C. (GW ISSN 0340-2096) **4805**
Anatomical Record. (US ISSN 0003-276X) **428**, 3075
Anatomical Society of India. Journal. (II ISSN 0003-2778) **428**, 3075
Anatomische Gesellschaft. Verhandlungen. (GW ISSN 0066-1562) **3075**
Anatomischer Anzeiger. (GW ISSN 0003-2786) **3075**, 428
Anatomy and Embryology. (GW ISSN 0340-2061) **569**, 3075
Anatomy of Wonder. (US) **2980**, 389, 3010
Anba al-Jamiah. *see* Jordan University Newsletter **1709**
†Anbar Cumulative Joint Index. (UK) **5135**
Anbar Management Bibliography *see* Management Bibliographies & Reviews **728**
Anbar Management Services Abstracts *see* Personnel & Training Abstracts **734**
Anbar Management Services Abstracts *see* Top Management Abstracts **741**
Anbar Yearbook *see* Compleat Anbar **1006**
Anblick. (AU ISSN 0003-2824) **4540**, 1483
Ancestor. (AT ISSN 0044-8222) **2144**
Ancestor Hunt. (US ISSN 0736-9115) **2144**
Ancestoring. (US ISSN 0272-0426) **2144**
Ancestors - Descendants of Futral - Clifford, Watkins - Wood. (US) **2144**
Ancestors West. (US ISSN 0734-4988) **2144**
Ancestral Searcher. (AT ISSN 0313-251X) **2144**
Ancestry. (US) **2144**
Ancestry Newsletter. (US ISSN 0749-5927) **2144**
L'Ancetre. (CN ISSN 0316-0513) **2144**
▼Anche Noi. (IT) **2548**, 2270
Anch'io. (IT) **3075**
Anchor. (AT) **4228**
Anchor. (US) **4255**
Anchor. (US ISSN 0003-2840) **4398**
Anchor News. (US) **4724**
Anchor Watch. (US) **3451**, 2398
Anchora. (US) **1296**, 4837
†Anchorage Magazine. (US) **5135**
Anchorage Philatelist. (US) **3749**
Anciens Pays et Assemblees d'Etats. (BE ISSN 0066-1589) **3872**, 2306
Ancient and Medieval Philosophy. Series 1, Publications of De Wulf-Mansion Centre. (BE) **3761**
Ancient and Medieval Philosophy. Series 2, Henrici de Gandavo Opera. (BE) **3761**
Ancient Capital. *see* Yan Du **2343**
Ancient Ceylon. (CE) **262**
Ancient Coins in North American Collections. (US ISSN 0271-4019) **3598**
Ancient Controversy. (US ISSN 1042-2471) **3873**, 4428
Ancient Greek Cities Report. (GR) **2483**, 2306, 4428
Ancient History; Resources for Teachers. (AT) **2306**, 2348, 2428

ANDHRA PRADESH 5909

†Ancient Interface. (US ISSN 0097-8442) **5135**
Ancient Iranian Cultural Society. Publication/Anjoman-e Farhang-e Iran-e Bastan. Nashriyeh. (IR ISSN 0517-8045) **2894**
▼Ancient MesoAmerica. (UK ISSN 0956-5361) **2398**
Ancient Monuments Board for England. Annual Report. (UK ISSN 0072-5625) **2348**
Ancient Monuments Society Transactions. (UK ISSN 0951-001X) **292**, 262, 600
Ancient Near Eastern Society. Journal. (US) **3633**
Ancient Near Eastern Texts and Studies.(US) **2428**
Ancient Nepal. (NP) **3633**, 262
Ancient Philosophy. (US ISSN 0740-2007) **3761**
Ancient Science of Life. (II ISSN 0257-7941) **3075**
Ancient Skies. (US) **46**, 3593
Ancient Society. (BE ISSN 0066-1619) **2306**
Ancient Society; Resources for Teachers *see* Ancient History; Resources for Teachers **2306**
Ancient States in the Territory of the U.S.S.R. *see* Drevneishie Gosudarstva na Territorii S.S.S.R **271**
Ancient T L. (UK ISSN 0735-1348) **262**
Ancient Times. (US ISSN 0091-7176) **3538**, 2306
Ancient World. (US ISSN 0160-9645) **2306**, 262, 1274
Ancilla *see* Mirjam **4269**
And All That Jazz. (US) **3538**
The And Review. (US) **2987**
Anda. (IO) **4010**
Andalucia Islamica. Textos y Estudios. (SP ISSN 0212-159X) **2428**
Al-Andalus. (SP) **3761**
Andar per Ceramiche. (IT ISSN 0003-2891) **1161**
Ande Sopi. (SG) **3873**
Andean Report. (PE ISSN 0251-2491) **843**
Andelsbladet. (DK ISSN 0003-2913) **829**
Andere Sinema. (NE) **3503**
Anders And Co. (DK) **1248**
Anders And Ekstra. (DK) **1248**
Anderschume *see* Anderschume - Kontiki **2451**
Anderschume - Kontiki. (SZ ISSN 0259-5419) **2451**, 2858, 3395
Anderseniana. (DK ISSN 0084-6465) **2894**
Anderson College News *see* Signatures **1324**
The Anderson Monitor - Business & Politics. (US) **645**, 3873
The Anderson Report. (US ISSN 0197-7040) **1389**
Andes. (CL) **3873**
Andes. (BO ISSN 0003-2948) **3950**
Andhra Agricultural Journal. (II ISSN 0003-2956) **76**
Andhra Historical Research Society. Journal. (II) **2336**
Andhra Jyoti Sachitra Vara Patrika. (II) **2198**
Andhra Patrika. (II) **2198**
Andhra Patrika Panchangam. (II) **4217**
Andhra Prabha Illustrated Weekly. (II) **2198**
Andhra Pradesh. (II ISSN 0570-0655) **2336**
Andhra Pradesh, India. Department of Archaeology and Museums. Annual Report. (II) **262**
Andhra Pradesh, India. Department of Archaeology and Museums. Archaeological Series. (II) **262**, 311
Andhra Pradesh, India. Department of Archaeology and Museums. Archaeological Series: A.P. Journal of Archaeology. (II) **262**
Andhra Pradesh, India. Department of Archaeology and Museums. Art and Architectural Series *see* Andhra Pradesh, India. Department of Archaeology and Museums. Archaeological Series **262**

5910 ANDHRA PRADESH

Andhra Pradesh, India. Department of Archaeology and Museums. Epigraphy Series. (II) **262, 2336**
Andhra Pradesh, India. Department of Archaeology and Museums. Museum Series. (II) **3598, 2336**
Andhra Pradesh, India. Department of Archaeology and Museums. Museum Objects and Numismatics Series *see* Andhra Pradesh, India. Department of Archaeology and Museums. Museum Series **3598**
Andhra Pradesh, India. Department of Archaeology. Epigraphy Series *see* Andhra Pradesh, India. Department of Archaeology and Museums. Epigraphy Series **262**
Andhra Pradesh Productivity Council. Journal *see* Andhra Pradesh Productivity Council. Target **4053**
Andhra Pradesh Productivity Council. Target. (II ISSN 0003-2964) **4053, 76, 1071**
Andhra Pradesh State Financial Corporation. Report *see* Andhra Pradesh State Financial Corporation. Report and Accounts **1087**
Andhra Pradesh State Financial Corporation. Report and Accounts. (II) **1087**
Andhra Pradesh State Trading Corporation Limited. Annual Report. (II ISSN 0376-5512) **1033**
Andhra Sachitra Vara Patrika. (II) **2894**
Andhra University Memoirs in Oceanography. (II ISSN 0066-1686) **1601**
†Andhra Weekly Reporter. (II) **5135**
Andon. (NE ISSN 0168-2997) **311**
Andragogija *see* Theleme **1687**
Andre Gide. (FR ISSN 0180-9350) **2894**
Andreaner. (GW) **1615, 1725**
Andres Bello Biblioteca. Coleccion. (CL) **2894**
Andrew Harper's Hideaway Report. (US ISSN 0884-7622) **4752**
Andrew W. Mellon Foundation. Report. (US ISSN 0066-1694) **2503**
Andrews Advisor. (US) **2598, 2743**
†Andrews School Asbestos Alert. (US ISSN 0887-7866) **5135**
Andrews University. Monographs. (US ISSN 0066-1708) **4229**
Andrews University Seminary Studies. (US ISSN 0003-2980) **4162**
Andrewsreport. (US ISSN 0892-0850) **4144, 1002, 1033**
Andrias. (GW ISSN 0721-6513) **494, 1554**
Androgyne. (US) **2988**
Andrologia. (GW ISSN 0303-4569) **3075**
Andros Digest. (US) **4010**
Andvari. (IC) **2348**
Andy Awards Souvenir Journal. (US ISSN 0270-2525) **28**
Andy's Front Hall. (US) **3538**
Anees for Children. *see* Kochniano Anees **1258**
Anejos de Archivo Espanol de Arqueologia. (SP ISSN 0561-3663) **262**
†Aneks. (UK ISSN 0345-0295) **5135**
Anemone. (US ISSN 8756-7709) **312, 2894**
Anestesista. (IT) **3190**
Anesteziologiya i Reanimatologiya/Anesthesiology and Reanimatology. (RU ISSN 0201-7563) **3190, 3375**
Anesthesia and Analgesia. (US ISSN 0003-2999) **3190**
Anesthesia Malpractice Protector. (US) **3190, 2598**
Anesthesia Progress. (US ISSN 0003-3006) **3228, 3190**
Anesthesia Staff News *see* Anesthesiology News **3190**
Anesthesiology. (US ISSN 0003-3022) **3190**
Anesthesiology Alert *see* Anesthesia Malpractice Protector **3190**
Anesthesiology and Reanimatology. *see* Anesteziologiya i Reanimatologiya **3190**
Anesthesiology Clinics *see* Bailliere's Clinical Anaesthesiology **3190**
Anesthesiology Malpractice Reporter. (US ISSN 0738-1018) **3075, 2598**
Anesthesiology News. (US) **3190**
Anesthesiology Review. (US ISSN 0093-4437) **3190**
Anexartitos/Independent. (CY) **2184**
Anfora. (AG) **2894, 3761**
Ang Philipinas: Your Tourist Magazine. (PH) **4752**
Ang Tagamasid. (PH ISSN 0115-5032) **3432, 360**
Ang Tala. (PH ISSN 0115-5814) **3451**
Ange Gardien. (FR ISSN 0751-6460) **4162**
Angeiologie. (FR ISSN 0003-3049) **3204, 428**
Angela Luisa. (PR) **4837**
Angela Thirkell Society. Journal. (UK) **2895**
†Angeles. (US) **5135**
Angelic Warfare Dispatch. (US) **1232, 4255**
Angelicum. (VC ISSN 0003-3081) **3761, 4255**
†Angelstone. (US) **5135**
Angeltread. (US) **2895, 312**
Angestellten *see* D A G - Journal **2582**
Angestellten Magazin. (GW ISSN 0341-017X) **2580**
Die Angestelltenversicherung. (GW) **4053, 2526**
Angevines de Paris *see* Les Amis de Curnonsky **2052**
Angewandte Arbeitswissenschaft. (GW ISSN 0341-0900) **971, 3614**
Angewandte Botanik. (GW ISSN 0066-1759) **494**
Angewandte Chemie. (GW ISSN 0044-8249) **1170**
Angewandte Chemie: International Edition. (GW ISSN 0570-0833) **1170**
Angewandte Informatik *see* Wirtschaftsinformatik **1453**
Angewandte Kosmetik *see* Kosmetik Journal **376**
Angewandte Makromolekulare Chemie. (SZ ISSN 0003-3146) **1216, 1848**
Angewandte Ornithologie/Applied Ornithology. (GW ISSN 0003-3154) **561**
Angewandte Parasitologie. (GW ISSN 0003-3162) **3217**
Angewandte Sozialforschung. (AU ISSN 0587-5234) **4428**
Angewandte Statistik und Oekonometrie.(GW) **889**
Angio. (GW ISSN 0721-9318) **3270**
Angiologia. (SP ISSN 0003-3170) **3204**
Angiology. (US ISSN 0003-3197) **3204**
Angle. (JA) **2207**
Angle Orthodontist. (US ISSN 0003-3219) **3228**
Angler. (US) **4540**
Angler and Hunter. (CN) **4540**
Angler and Hunter in Ontario *see* Angler and Hunter **4540**
Angler Rinderzucht. (GW ISSN 0171-7383) **210**
Angler Tierzucht *see* Angler Rinderzucht **210**
Anglers Cooperative Association Review *see* A.C.A. Review **2035**
Angler's Mail. (UK ISSN 0003-3243) **4540**
Anglers Mail Annual. (UK) **4540**
Angles. (CN ISSN 0824-2100) **2451, 3940**
Anglesey Antiquarian Society Transactions. (UK ISSN 0306-5790) **262**
Anglia. (GW ISSN 0003-3251) **2803, 2895**
Anglia Farmer and Contractor. (UK) **76**
Anglica. (JA ISSN 0003-326X) **2803**
Anglica et Americana. (DK ISSN 0105-9963) **2803, 2306, 2895**
Anglica Germanica: Series 2. (UK) **2803, 4629**
Anglican. (CN ISSN 0517-7731) **4229**
Anglican Advance. (US) **4229**
Anglican and Episcopal History. (US) **4229**

Anglican Catholic. (UK) **4229**
Anglican Church of Canada. General Synod. Journal. (CN) **4229**
Anglican Crusader *see* Crusader (Toronto) **4235**
Anglican Digest. (US ISSN 0003-3278) **4229**
Anglican Encounter. (AT ISSN 1032-9234) **4229**
Anglican Gazette. (AT) **4229**
Anglican Journal/Journal Anglican. (CN ISSN 0847-978X) **4229**
Anglican Journal - Journal Episcopal *see* Anglican Journal **4229**
Anglican Magazine. (CN ISSN 0820-506X) **4229**
Anglican Messenger. (AT) **4229**
Anglican Pacifist *see* Challenge (London, 1961) **4232**
Anglican Theological Review. (US ISSN 0003-3286) **4162**
Anglican Year Book. (CN ISSN 0317-8765) **4229**
Angling America Magazine. (US) **4540**
Angling Guide. (UK ISSN 0956-5477) **4540**
Angling Holidays in Ireland. (IE) **4752**
Angling in China. *see* Zhongguo Diaoyu **4560**
The Angling Report. (US ISSN 1045-3539) **4540**
Angling Times. (UK ISSN 0003-3308) **4541**
Anglistica. (DK ISSN 0066-1805) **2895**
Anglistik und Englischunterricht. (GW ISSN 0344-8266) **2503, 1615**
Anglistische Forschungen. (GW) **2895**
Anglo-American Forum. (GW) **2895, 2306, 2803**
Anglo-American Law Review. (UK ISSN 0308-6569) **2598**
Anglo-American Spotlight. (GW ISSN 0723-0206) **2188**
Anglo - American Trade Directory. (UK) **807**
Anglo American Trade News *see* Atlantic **807**
Anglo-Catalan Society. Occasional Publications. (UK ISSN 0144-5863) **2348**
Anglo-German Review. (UK ISSN 0003-3340) **3950**
Anglo - Nordic Times. (UK) **900**
Anglo-Norman Studies. (US ISSN 0261-9857) **2348**
Anglo-Norwegian Trade Journal. (UK ISSN 0003-3375) **807**
Anglo Orthodoxy. (UK ISSN 0265-1580) **4280**
Anglo-Portuguese News. (PO) **1991**
Anglo-Saxon England. (UK ISSN 0263-6751) **2348, 2503**
Anglo-Soviet Journal. (UK ISSN 0044-8265) **3950**
Anglo-Spanish Quarterly Review. (UK ISSN 0003-3383) **3950**
Anglofile. (US) **2193**
Angola. Direccao dos Servicos de Estatistica. Anuario Estatistico. (AO ISSN 0066-5193) **4078, 4561**
Angola. Direccao dos Servicos de Estatistica. Boletim Mensal. (AO ISSN 0003-3413) **4561**
Angola. Direccao dos Servicos de Estatistica. Estatistica dos Veiculos Motorisados. (AO) **4661**
Angola. Direccao dos Servicos de Estatistica. Estatisticas do Comercio Externo. (AO ISSN 0066-1848) **702**
Angola. Direccao dos Servicos de Estatistica. Informacoes Estatisticas. (AO) **4078, 4561**
Angola. Direccao dos Servicos de Geologia e Minas. Boletim. (AO ISSN 0003-3456) **1554, 3477**
Angola. Secretaria Provincial de Saude, Trabalho. Previdencia e Assistencia. Sintese da Actividade dos Servicos e Organismos. (AO) **4097**
Angola in Arms. (TZ) **3873**
Angola Peace Monitor. (US ISSN 1045-0513) **3950, 900**
Angolite. (US ISSN 0402-4249) **1510**
†Angolo Acuto. (IT) **5135**

Angora Goat & Mohair Journal/Angorabok- en Sybokhaarblad. (SA ISSN 0003-3464) **210**
Angora Goat Exchange. (US) **210**
Angora Quarterly. (US) **210**
Angorabok- en Sybokhaarblad. *see* Angora Goat & Mohair Journal **210**
Angus. (US) **210**
Angus District Council. Housing Plans and Programmes. (UK ISSN 0261-5932) **2483**
Angus Journal. (US ISSN 0194-9543) **210**
Angus Times. (CN ISSN 0849-6188) **210**
Anhui Agricultural Science. *see* Anhui Nongye Kexue **76**
Anhui Daxue Xuebao (Shehui Kexue Ban)/Anhui University. Journal (Social Science Edition). (CC ISSN 1001-5019) **4365**
Anhui Daxue Xuebao (Ziran Kexue Ban)/Anhui University. Journal (Natural Science Edition). (CC ISSN 1000-2162) **4299**
Anhui Economic Yearbook *see* Anhui Nianjian **1780**
Anhui Gongxueyuan Xuebao/Anhui Institute of Technology. Journal. (CC ISSN 1000-2189) **1814**
Anhui Huabao/Anhui Pictorial. (CC ISSN 0517-659X) **2180, 3788**
Anhui Institute of Education. Journal (Social Science Edition). *see* Anhui Jiaoyu Xueyuan Xuebao (Shehui Kexue Ban) **1615**
Anhui Institute of Technology. Journal. *see* Anhui Gongxueyuan Xuebao **1814**
Anhui Institute of Traditional Chinese Medicine. Journal. *see* Anhui Zhongyi Xueyuan Xuebao **3076**
Anhui Jiaoyu Xueyuan Xuebao (Shehui Kexue Ban)/Anhui Institute of Education. Journal (Social Science Edition). (CC ISSN 1001-5116) **1615**
Anhui Medical Sciences. *see* Anhui Yixue **3075**
▼Anhui Nianjian/Anhui Yearbook. (CC) **1780**
Anhui Nongye Kexue/Anhui Agricultural Science. (CC ISSN 0517-6611) **76**
Anhui Normal University. Journal. *see* Anhui Shida Xuebao **4299**
Anhui Normal University. Journal (Social Science Edition). *see* Anhui Shida Xuebao (Shehui Kexue Ban) **4365**
Anhui Pictorial. *see* Anhui Huabao **2180**
Anhui Shida Xuebao/Anhui Normal University. Journal. (CC ISSN 1001-2443) **4299**
Anhui Shida Xuebao (Shehui Kexue Ban)/Anhui Normal University. Journal (Social Science Edition). (CC ISSN 1001-2435) **4365, 3761**
Anhui University. Journal (Natural Science Edition). *see* Anhui Daxue Xuebao (Ziran Kexue Ban) **4299**
Anhui University. Journal (Social Science Edition). *see* Anhui Daxue Xuebao (Shehui Kexue Ban) **4365**
Anhui University of Medical Sciences. Journal. *see* Anhui Yike Daxue Xuebao **3075**
Anhui Xin Xi. (CC) **4629**
Anhui Yearbook. *see* Anhui Nianjian **1780**
Anhui Yike Daxue Xuebao/Anhui University of Medical Sciences. Journal. (CC ISSN 1000-1492) **3075**
Anhui Yixue/Anhui Medical Sciences. (CC ISSN 1000-0399) **3075**
Anhui Zhongyi Xueyuan Xuebao/Anhui Institute of Traditional Chinese Medicine. Journal. (CC ISSN 1000-2219) **3076**
▼Ani-Cancer Drugs. (UK ISSN 0959-4973) **3193**
Anichti Orizontes-Angheliaforos. (GR) **4255**
Anima. (JA) **577**
Anima. (US ISSN 0097-1146) **3593, 2503, 4837**
Anima. (IT) **4010, 2503**
Animal Activist Alert. (US ISSN 1045-9979) **230**

Animal Air Transportation Association. International Conference. Proceedings see Animal Transportation Association. International Conference. Proceedings **4646**

Animal and Grassland Research Institute, Hurley, England (Berkshire) Technical Reports see A F R C Institute of Grassland and Environmental Research (UK). Annual Report **165**

Animal Anti-Cruelty League. Chairman's Report. (SA ISSN 0379-654X) **230**

Animal Behavior Abstracts. (US ISSN 0301-8695) **461, 2**

Animal Behaviour. (UK ISSN 0003-3472) **577, 4010, 4805**

Animal Biology. (IT) **428**

▼Animal Biotechnology. (US ISSN 1049-5398) **487, 210**

Animal Breeding Abstracts. (UK ISSN 0003-3499) **461, 2**

Animal Breeding and Feeding. see Allattenyeztes es Takarmanyozas **209**

Animal Concern. (UK) **230**

Animal Concern (Scotland). Annual Report. (UK) **230**

Animal de Compagnie see Pratique Medicale et Chirurgicale de l'Animal de Compagnie **4814**

Animal Defence League of Canada. News Bulletin. (CN ISSN 0044-829X) **230**

Animal Disease Occurrence. (UK ISSN 0144-3879) **4805**

†Animal Disease Occurrence - Data Tables. (UK ISSN 0144-3879) **5136**

Animal Feed Science and Technology. (NE ISSN 0377-8401) **204, 4593**

Animal Feeding and Nutrition. (US) **4805**

Animal Finders' Guide. (US) **210, 3708**

Animal Genetics. (UK ISSN 0268-9146) **539, 577**

Animal Health see Animal Health Trust. Annual Report **4805**

Animal Health and Nutrition see Large Animal Veterinarian **220**

Animal Health Research Centre. Annual Report. (UG) **4805**

Animal Health Trust. Annual Report. (UK ISSN 0142-6591) **4805**

Animal Health Yearbook. (UN ISSN 0066-1872) **4805**

Animal Husbandry. see Chikusan no Kenkyu **214**

Animal Husbandry and Breeding. (GR) **210, 4805**

Animal Keepers' Forum. (US ISSN 0164-9531) **577, 1483, 1615**

Animal Kingdom see Wildlife Conservation **593**

Animal Law Report. (US) **2598, 230**

Animal Learning & Behavior. (US ISSN 0090-4996) **4011**

Animal Legal Defense Fund. Newsletter see Animal's Advocate **230**

Animal Liberation Magazine. (AT ISSN 0816-486X) **230**

Animal Life. (UK) **230**

Animal Medical Center CenterScope see A M C CenterScope **3707**

Animal Models of Psychiatric Disorders.(SZ ISSN 1011-6982) **3330, 4805**

Animal Pharm. (UK ISSN 0262-2238) **4806**

Animal Production. see Zivocisna Vyroba **229**

Animal Production and Health Bulletin. (CE) **210**

Animal Production and Health Newsletter. (UN) **3357**

Animal Production in Australia. (AT ISSN 0728-5965) **210**

Animal Protection see A S P C A Report **229**

Animal Reproduction Science. (NE ISSN 0378-4320) **210**

Animal Reproduction Techniques/ Hanshoku Gijutsu. (JA ISSN 0017-7520) **210**

Animal Resources see Resources for Comparative Biomedical Research **3181**

Animal Science and Technology (Japan). (JA) **210**

Animal Science Journal of Pakistan see Bangladesh Journal of Animal Science **212**

†Animal Science Research Report. (US) **5136**

Animal Tales. (US) **2988**

Animal Talk. (CN) **230**

Animal Technology. (UK ISSN 0264-4754) **4806**

Animal Times. (SA) **230**

Animal Transportation Association. International Conference. Proceedings. (US) **4646**

Animal Welfare Institute. Quarterly. (US ISSN 0743-0841) **230**

Animal Welfare Institute Information Report see Animal Welfare Institute. Quarterly **230**

Animal World. (UK) **230**

†Animaland. (US ISSN 0019-3127) **5136**

Animaldom. (US ISSN 0003-360X) **3708**

Animalia. (SP ISSN 0214-3151) **577**

Animals. (US ISSN 0030-6835) **230**

Animal's Advocate. (US) **230**

Animals' Agenda. (US) **230**

Animals: Defender and Anti-Vivisection News see Campaigner & Animal's Defender **230**

Animals for Research see Animals for Research - A Directory of Sources **577**

Animals for Research - A Directory of Sources. (US) **577, 3076**

Animals International. (UK ISSN 0254-3923) **230**

Animals' Voice Magazine. (US) **230**

Animation et Education. (FR ISSN 0395-0840) **1615**

Animations. (UK ISSN 0140-7740) **4629**

Animator. (UK) **3503, 1368**

†Animator. (US ISSN 0889-5589) **5136**

Animatrix. (US) **3503**

Animaux Hebdo. (FR) **147**

Animazione ed Espressione - Tempo Sereno. (IT ISSN 0392-2804) **1615**

Animazione Sociale. (IT ISSN 0392-5870) **4428**

Animedia. (JA) **312**

Animer. (FR) **4464**

Animer mon Pays, mon Village see Animer **4464**

Animo. (NE ISSN 0003-3669) **1303**

Anjoman-e Farhang-e Iran-e Bastan. Nashriyeh. see Ancient Iranian Cultural Society. Publication **2894**

Anjoman-i Riyazi-i Iran. Buletan-i. see Iranian Mathematical Society. Bulletin **3039**

Anjou Economique. (FR) **807**

Ankara Universitesi. Tip Fakultesi. Mecmuasi. (TU ISSN 0365-8104) **3076**

Ankara Universitesi. Veteriner Fakultesi. Dergisi. (TU ISSN 0003-3685) **4806**

Anklagemyndighedens Aarsberetning. (DK ISSN 0108-7169) **2598**

Anlaegsgartneren see Groent Miljoe **2129**

Anlaegsteknik see Byggeri **608**

Anlagepraxis. (GW ISSN 0172-7419) **759**

Anleitung fuer die Chemische Laboratoriumspraxis see Anleitung fuer die Chemische Laboratoriumspraxis - Chemical Laboratory Practice **1170**

Anleitung fuer die Chemische Laboratoriumspraxis - Chemical Laboratory Practice. (US) **1170, 3257**

†Anmeldelser i Paedagogiske Tidsskrifter. (DK ISSN 0106-8172) **5136**

Ann Arbor Observer. (US ISSN 0192-5717) **2221**

Ann Arbor Scene Magazine. (US ISSN 0192-5725) **2221**

Anna. (FI ISSN 0355-3035) **4837**

Anna. (IT) **4837**

Anna Freud Centre. Bulletin. (UK ISSN 0267-3061) **3330, 3318**

Annabel. (UK ISSN 0003-3758) **4837**

Annabella. (IT ISSN 0003-3766) **4837**

Annabelle. (SZ) **4837**

Annabelle-Femina see Annabelle **4837**

Annale van die Natalse Museum. see Natal Museum. Annals **589**

Annalen der Gemeinwirtschaft see Annales de l'Economie Publique, Sociale et Cooperative **829**

Annalen der Meteorologie. Neue Folge. (GW ISSN 0072-4122) **3432**

Annalen der Mijnen van Belgie. see Annales des Mines de Belgique **3478**

Annalen der Physik. (GW ISSN 0003-3804) **3814**

Annalen fuer Ornithologie. (GW ISSN 0232-5519) **561**

Annales Academiae Medicae Bialostocensis. see Akademia Medyczna w Bialymstoku. Roczniki **3073**

Annales Academiae Medicae Cracoviensis. Index Dissertationum Editarum. (PL ISSN 0066-1937) **3166**

Annales Academiae Medicae Stetinensis/Roczniki Pomorskiej Akademii Medycznej w Szczecinie. (PL ISSN 0066-1945) **3076**

Annales Academiae Scientiarum Fennicae. Dissertationes Humanarum Litterarum. (FI ISSN 0355-113X) **2503**

Annales Academiae Scientiarum Fennicae. Series A, I: Mathematica. (FI ISSN 0066-1953) **3028**

Annales Academiae Scientiarum Fennicae. Series A, I: Mathematica Dissertationes. (FI ISSN 0355-0087) **3028**

Annales Academiae Scientiarum Fennicae. Series A, II: Chemica. (FI ISSN 0066-1961) **1170**

Annales Academiae Scientiarum Fennicae. Series A, III: Geologica-Geographica. (FI ISSN 0066-197X) **1554**

Annales Academiae Scientiarum Fennicae. Series A, V: Medica. (FI ISSN 0066-1996) **3076**

Annales Academiae Scientiarum Fennicae. Series A, VI: Physica. (FI ISSN 0066-2003) **3814**

Annales Academiae Scientiarum Fennicae. Series B. (FI ISSN 0066-2011) **2503**

Annales Aequatoria. (ZR ISSN 0254-4296) **233, 2803**

†Annales Agriculturae Fenniae. (FI ISSN 0570-1538) **5136**

Annales Benjamin Constant. (SZ ISSN 0263-7383) **2503**

Annales Botanici Fennici. (FI ISSN 0003-3847) **494**

Annales Canadiennes d'Histoire. see Canadian Journal of History **2308**

Annales Chirurgiae et Gynaecologiae. (FI ISSN 0355-9521) **3289**

Annales Collegii Medici Antverpiensis. (BE ISSN 0003-3863) **3076**

Annales d'Endocrinologie. (FR ISSN 0003-4266) **3250**

Annales d'Esthetique/Chronika Aisthetikis. (GR ISSN 0066-2119) **312, 3761**

†Annales d'Etudes Internationales. (BE ISSN 0066-2135) **5136**

Annales d'Histoire de l'Art Canadien. see Journal of Canadian Art History **331**

Annales d'Histoire Sociale et Economiques. see Roczniki Dziejow Spolecznych i Gospodarczych **2384**

Annales d'Oto-Laryngologie et de Chirurgie Cervico Faciale. (FR ISSN 0003-438X) **3313**

Annales d'Urologie. (FR ISSN 0003-4401) **3387**

Annales de Biochimie Clinique du Quebec. (CN ISSN 0709-8502) **3257, 1204**

Annales de Biologie Clinique. (FR ISSN 0003-3898) **428, 3076**

Annales de Bourgogne. (FR ISSN 0003-3901) **2348**

Annales de Bretagne see Annales de Bretagne et des Pays de l'Ouest (Anjou, Maine, Touraine) **2895**

Annales de Bretagne et des Pays de l'Ouest (Anjou, Maine, Touraine). (FR ISSN 0003-391X) **2895**

Annales de Cardiologie et d'Angeiologie.(FR ISSN 0003-3928) **3204**

Annales de Chimie: Science des Materiaux. (FR ISSN 0151-9107) **1170**

Annales de Chirurgie. (FR ISSN 0003-3944) **3375**

Annales de Chirurgie de la Main see Annales de Chirurgie de la Main et du Membre Superieur **3375**

Annales de Chirurgie de la Main et du Membre Superieur. (FR ISSN 1153-2424) **3375**

Annales de Chirurgie Plastique see Annales de Chirurgie Plastique et Esthetique **3375**

Annales de Chirurgie Plastique et Esthetique. (FR ISSN 0294-1260) **3375**

Annales de Chirurgie Thoracique et Cardio-Vasculaire. (FR ISSN 0066-2054) **3204, 3375**

Annales de Demographie Historique. (FR ISSN 0066-2062) **3979**

Annales de Dermatologie et de Syphiligraphie see Annales de Dermatologie et de Venereologie **3245**

Annales de Dermatologie et de Venereologie. (FR ISSN 0151-9638) **3245**

Annales de Droit. (BE ISSN 0770-6472) **2598**

Annales de Droit Aerien et Spatial. see Annals of Air and Space Law **46**

Annales de Gastroenterologie et d'Hepatologie. (FR ISSN 0066-2070) **3266**

Annales de Gembloux. (BE ISSN 0303-9099) **167**

Annales de Genetique. (FR ISSN 0003-3995) **539**

Annales de Geographie. (FR ISSN 0003-4010) **2241**

Annales de Geomorphologie. see Zeitschrift fuer Geomorphologie **1586**

Annales de Geomorphologie, Supplements. see Zeitschrift fuer Geomorphologie, Supplementbaende **2267**

Annales de Kinesitherapie. (FR ISSN 0302-427X) **3076, 3213, 3370**

Annales de l'Abeille see Apidologie **528**

Annales de l'Economie Publique, Sociale et Cooperative. (BE ISSN 0379-3699) **829**

Annales de l'Est. (FR ISSN 0365-2017) **2348, 4428**

Annales de l'Institut Fourier see Universite Scientifique et Medicale de Grenoble. Institut Fourier. Annales **3060**

Annales de l'Institut Pasteur - Actualites see Institut Pasteur. Annales. Actualites **552**

Annales de la Propagation de la Fois see Solidaires - Lumiere du Monde **4202**

Annales de la Recherche Urbaine. (FR ISSN 0180-930X) **2483**

Annales de la Voirie et de l'Environnement. (FR) **4646, 1943**

Annales de Limnologie. (FR ISSN 0003-4088) **1596**

Annales de Medecine des Accidents et du Trafic Traumatologie. (FR ISSN 0003-4126) **3306**

Annales de Medecine Interne. (FR ISSN 0003-410X) **3076**

Annales de Medecine Veterinaire. (BE ISSN 0003-4118) **4806**

Annales de Normandie. (FR ISSN 0003-4134) **2348**

Annales de Paleontologie (Vert - Invert) .(FR ISSN 0753-3969) **3656**

Annales de Paleontologie: Vertebres see Annales de Paleontologie (Vert - Invert) **3656**

ANNALES

Annales de Parasitologie Humaine et Comparee. (FR ISSN 0003-4150) **3218,** 549
Annales de Pathologie. (FR ISSN 0242-6498) **428,** 3076
Annales de Pediatrie. (FR ISSN 0037-1769) **3318**
Annales de Physique. (FR ISSN 0003-4169) **3814**
Annales de Psychiatrie. (FR ISSN 0768-7559) **3330**
Annales de Radiologie. (FR ISSN 0003-4185) **3357**
Annales de Readaptation et de Medecine Physique. (FR ISSN 0168-6054) **3076**
Annales de Recherches Veterinaires/Annals of Veterinary Research. (FR ISSN 0003-4193) **4806**
Annales de Zootechnie. (FR ISSN 0003-424X) **577,** 210
Annales des Composites. (FR ISSN 0292-627X) **1848**
Annales des Mines see Gerer et Comprendre **3484**
Annales des Mines see Realites Industrielles **3494**
Annales des Mines. Dossiers Documentaires see Realites Industrielles **3494**
Annales des Mines. Gerer et Comprendre see Gerer et Comprendre **3484**
Annales des Mines de Belgique/Annalen der Mijnen van Belgie. (BE ISSN 0003-4290) **3478**
Annales des Ponts et Chaussees. (FR ISSN 0152-9668) **1861**
Annales des Sciences Forestieres. (FR ISSN 0003-4312) **2095**
Annales des Sciences Naturelles. Botanique et Biologie Vegetale. (FR ISSN 0003-4320) **494**
Annales des Sciences Naturelles. Zoologie et Biologie Animale. (FR ISSN 0003-4339) **577**
Annales des Telecommunications. (SW ISSN 0003-4347) **1331**
Annales des Travaux Publics de Belgique. (BE) **1861**
Annales du Midi. (FR ISSN 0003-4398) **262,** 2306, 2803
Annales du Tabac Section 1. (FR ISSN 0399-0206) **4643**
Annales du Tabac Section 2. (FR ISSN 0399-0354) **4643**
Annales - Economies, Societes, Civilisations. (FR ISSN 0003-441X) **4428**
Annales Economiques de Clermont-Ferrand. (FR) **645**
Annales Entomologici Fennici see Entomologica Fennica **530**
Annales Forestales/Anali za Sumarstvo. (CI ISSN 0351-2045) **2095**
Annales Francaises d'Anesthesie et de Reanimation. (FR ISSN 0750-7658) **3190**
Annales Francaises de Chronometrie et de Microtechniques see Annales Francaises de Microtechniques et de Chronometrie **1927**
Annales Francaises de Microtechniques et de Chronometrie. (FR ISSN 0294-1228) **1927**
Annales Hindemith. see Hindemith - Jahrbuch **3554**
Annales Historiques de la Revolution Francaise. (FR ISSN 0003-4436) **2348**
Annales Hydrographiques. (FR ISSN 0373-3629) **1597**
Annales Internationales de Criminologie/International Annals of Criminology/Anales Internacionales de Criminologia. (FR ISSN 0003-4452) **1510**
Annales Islamologiques. (UA ISSN 0570-1716) **3633,** 4218
Annales Medico-Psychologiques. (FR ISSN 0003-4487) **4011,** 3076
†Annales Moreau de Tours. (FR ISSN 0066-2186) **5136**
Annales Musei Archaeologici Posnaniensis. see Fontes Archaeologici Posnanienses **272**
Annales Musei Goulandris. (GR ISSN 0302-1033) **3521**
Annales Paderewski. (SZ) **3538**

Annales Paediatrici Japonici/Shonika Kiyo. (JA ISSN 0003-4495) **3318**
Annales Pharmaceutiques Francaises. (FR ISSN 0003-4509) **3716**
Annales Polonici Mathematici. (PL ISSN 0066-2216) **3029**
Annales Scientrairum Stetinenses. see Szczecinskie Roczniki Naukowe **4346**
Annales Silesiae. (PL ISSN 0066-2224) **2348**
Annales Societatis Geologorum Poloniae. (PL ISSN 0208-9068) **1554**
Annales Societatis Mathematicae Polonae. Seria 1: Commentationes Mathematicae. (PL ISSN 0032-3799) **3029**
Annales Societatis Mathematicae Polonae. Seria 3: Matematyka Stosowana. (PL) **3029**
†Annales Societatis Mathematicae Polonae. Seria 4: Fundamenta Informaticae. (PL ISSN 0324-8429) **5136**
Annales Techniques. see Technika Chronika **4347**
Annales Tectonicae. (IT ISSN 0394-5596) **1587**
Annales Universitatis Mariae Curie-Sklodowska. Sectio A. Mathematica. (PL ISSN 0365-1029) **3029**
Annales Universitatis Mariae Curie-Sklodowska. Sectio AA. Chemia. (PL ISSN 0137-6853) **1170**
Annales Universitatis Mariae Curie-Sklodowska. Sectio AAA. Physica. (PL ISSN 0137-6861) **3814**
Annales Universitatis Mariae Curie-Sklodowska. Sectio B. Geographia, Geologia, Mineralogia et Petrographia. (PL ISSN 0137-1983) **2241,** 1554
Annales Universitatis Mariae Curie-Sklodowska. Sectio C. Biologia. (PL ISSN 0066-2232) **428**
Annales Universitatis Mariae Curie-Sklodowska. Sectio D. Medicina. (PL ISSN 0066-2240) **3076**
Annales Universitatis Mariae Curie-Sklodowska. Sectio DD. Medicina Veterinaria. (PL ISSN 0301-7737) **4806**
Annales Universitatis Mariae Curie-Sklodowska. Sectio DDD. Pharmacia. (PL ISSN 0867-0609) **3716**
Annales Universitatis Mariae Curie-Sklodowska. Sectio E. Agricultura. (PL ISSN 0365-1118) **76**
Annales Universitatis Mariae Curie-Sklodowska. Sectio EE. Zootechnika. (PL ISSN 0239-4243) **4806**
Annales Universitatis Mariae Curie-Sklodowska. Sectio F. Historia. (PL ISSN 0239-4251) **2306**
Annales Universitatis Mariae Curie-Sklodowska. Sectio F. Humaniora see Annales Universitatis Mariae Curie-Sklodowska. Sectio F. Historia **2306**
Annales Universitatis Mariae Curie-Sklodowska. Sectio FF. Philologiae. (PL ISSN 0239-426X) **2803**
Annales Universitatis Mariae Curie-Sklodowska. Sectio G. Ius. (PL ISSN 0458-4317) **2598**
Annales Universitatis Mariae Curie-Sklodowska. Sectio H. Oeconomia. (PL ISSN 0459-9586) **645**
Annales Universitatis Mariae Curie-Sklodowska. Sectio I. Philosophia-Sociologia. (PL ISSN 0137-2025) **3761,** 4428
Annales Universitatis Mariae Curie-Sklodowska. Sectio J. Paedagogia - Psychologia. (PL) **1615,** 4011
Annales Universitatis Mariae Curie-Sklodowska. Section AA. Physica et Chemica see Annales Universitatis Mariae Curie-Sklodowska. Sectio AAA. Physica **3814**
Annales Universitatis Saraviensis. Medicinae. (GW ISSN 0173-6973) **3076**
Annales Universitatis Saraviensis. Wirtschaftswissenschaftliche Abteilung. Schriftenreihe. (GW) **645**
Annales Zoologici. (PL ISSN 0003-4541) **577**

Annales Zoologici Fennici. (FI ISSN 0003-455X) **577**
Annali Alfieriani. (IT) **2895**
Annali Benacensi. (IT) **262**
Annali d'Italia. (IT) **2204**
Annali d'Italianistica. (US ISSN 0741-7527) **2895**
Annali dell'Architettura Italiana Contemporanea. (IT) **292**
Annali dell'Istituto Sperimentale Agronomico. (IT ISSN 0304-0615) **167**
Annali dell'Ospedale Maria Vittoria di Torino. (IT ISSN 0390-5454) **549**
Annali della Carita. (IT ISSN 0003-4568) **4398**
Annali della Pubblica Istuzione. (IT) **1725**
Annali della Sanita Pubblica. (IT ISSN 0021-3071) **4097**
Annali di Botanica. (IT) **494**
Annali di Chimica. (IT ISSN 0003-4592) **1170**
Annali di Matematica. (IT ISSN 0003-4622) **3029**
Annali di Medicina Navale. (IT ISSN 0003-4630) **3076**
Annali di Microbiologia ed Enzimologia. (IT ISSN 0003-4649) **549,** 471
Annali di Ostetricia Ginecologia Medicina Perinatale. (IT ISSN 0300-0087) **3289**
Annali di Ottamologia e Clinica Oculistica. (IT ISSN 0003-4665) **3298**
Annali di Ricerche e Studi di Geografia. (IT) **2241**
Annali di Storia Economica e Sociale see Quaderni Internazionali di Storia Economica e Sociale **2382**
†Annali di Studi Giuridici e Socio-Economici sui Servizii Sanitari Nazionale e Regionale. (IT) **5136**
Annali Italiani di Chirurgia. (IT ISSN 0003-469X) **2743,** 3375
Annali Italiani di Dermatologia Clinica e Sperimentale. (IT ISSN 0003-4703) **3245**
Annali Sclavo see Annali Sclavo Monograph **5136**
†Annali Sclavo Monograph. (IT) **5136**
Annali Universita per Stranieri. (IT) **1721**
Annals de Medicina. (SP ISSN 0210-7465) **3076,** 3375
Annals Magazine. (AT) **4255,** 1248
Annals of Air and Space Law/Annales de Droit Aerien et Spatial. (CN ISSN 0701-158X) **46,** 2598
Annals of Allergy. (US ISSN 0003-4738) **3183**
Annals of Animal Science. see Instytut Zootechniki. Roczniki Naukowe Zootechniki **219**
Annals of Applied Biology. (UK ISSN 0003-4746) **428**
▼Annals of Applied Probability. (US ISSN 1050-5164) **3029**
Annals of Arid Zone. (II ISSN 0570-1791) **168,** 1541
▼Annals of Balloon History and Museology. (US) **46**
Annals of Behavioral Medicine. (US ISSN 0883-6612) **3076**
Annals of Biology. (II ISSN 0970-0153) **428**
Annals of Biomedical Engineering. (US ISSN 0090-6964) **468,** 3076
Annals of Borno. (NR ISSN 0189-2207) **2331**
Annals of Botany. (UK ISSN 0305-7364) **494**
Annals of Carnegie Museum see Carnegie Museum of Natural History. Annals of Carnegie Museum **4304**
Annals of Child Development. (UK) **4011,** 1248
Annals of Clinical and Laboratory Science. (US ISSN 0091-7370) **3257**
Annals of Clinical Biochemistry. (UK ISSN 0004-5632) **471**
Annals of Clinical Psychiatry. (US ISSN 1040-1237) **3330**
Annals of Clinical Research see Annals of Medicine **3257**
Annals of Dentistry. (US ISSN 0003-4770) **3228**

Annals of Dermatology. (KO ISSN 1013-9087) **3245**
Annals of Dermatology and Venereology. see Vestnik Dermatologii i Venerologii **3250**
Annals of Discrete Mathematics. (NE) **3029**
Annals of Dyslexia. (US ISSN 0474-7534) **1733**
Annals of Emergency Medicine. (US ISSN 0196-0644) **3306,** 3076
▼Annals of Epidemiology. (US ISSN 1047-2797) **3076**
Annals of Geomorphology. see Zeitschrift fuer Geomorphologie **1586**
Annals of Geomorphology, Supplement Volumes. see Zeitschrift fuer Geomorphologie, Supplementbaende **2267**
Annals of Glaciology. (UK ISSN 0260-3055) **1554**
Annals of Global Analysis and Geometry. (GW ISSN 0232-704X) **3029**
Annals of Good St. Anne. (CN ISSN 0318-434X) **4255**
Annals of Hematology. (GW ISSN 0939-5555) **3270**
Annals of Human Biology. (UK ISSN 0301-4460) **428**
Annals of Human Genetics. (UK ISSN 0003-4800) **539**
Annals of Immunology see Immunologia Polska **3185**
Annals of Internal Medicine. (US ISSN 0003-4819) **3076**
Annals of International Studies see Annales d'Etudes Internationales **5136**
Annals of Iowa. (US ISSN 0003-4827) **2398**
Annals of Library Science and Documentation. (II ISSN 0003-4835) **3245,** 1455
Annals of Mathematics. (US ISSN 0003-486X) **3029**
▼Annals of Mathematics and Artificial Intelligence. (SZ ISSN 1012-2443) **1406,** 3029, 3064
Annals of Mathematics Studies. (US) **3029**
Annals of Medicine. (FI) **3257,** 3076
Annals of Neurology. (US ISSN 0364-5134) **3330**
Annals of Nuclear Energy. (US ISSN 0306-4549) **1803**
Annals of Nutrition and Metabolism. (SZ ISSN 0250-6807) **3603**
Annals of Occupational Hygiene. (US ISSN 0003-4878) **4097**
▼Annals of Oncology. (NE ISSN 0923-7534) **3193**
Annals of Operations Research. (SZ ISSN 0254-5330) **3064**
Annals of Ophthalmology. (US ISSN 0003-4886) **3298**
Annals of Ophthalmology. see Vestnik Oftal'mologii **3305**
Annals of Oriental Research. (II) **3633**
Annals of Otology, Rhinology and Laryngology. (US ISSN 0003-4894) **3313**
Annals of Otorhinolaryngology. see Vestnik Otorinolaringologii **3317**
Annals of Physics. (US ISSN 0003-4916) **3814**
Annals of Plastic Surgery. (US ISSN 0148-7043) **3375**
Annals of Probability. (US ISSN 0091-1798) **3029**
Annals of Public Administration. (US ISSN 0278-4289) **4053**
Annals of Public and Cooperative Economy see Annales de l'Economie Publique, Sociale et Cooperative **829**
Annals of Pure and Applied Logic. (NE ISSN 0168-0072) **3029,** 3761
Annals of Regional Science. (GW ISSN 0570-1864) **645,** 2241, 2483
Annals of Roentgenology and Radiology. see Vestnik Rentgenologii i Radiologii **3363**
Annals of Saudi Medicine. (SU ISSN 0256-4947) **3076**
Annals of Scholarship. (US ISSN 0192-2858) **2503**

Annals of Science. (UK ISSN 0003-3790) **4299**
†Annals of Sports Medicine. (US ISSN 0734-1997) **5136**
Annals of Statistics. (US ISSN 0090-5364) **4561**
Annals of Surgery. (US ISSN 0003-4932) **3375**
Annals of the College of Medicine, Mosul see Mosul University. College of Medicine. Annals **3132**
Annals of the History of Computing see I E E E Annals of the History of Computing **1396**
Annals of the I C R P see International Commission on Radiological Protection. Annals **3358**
Annals of the Rheumatic Diseases. (UK ISSN 0003-4967) **3368**
Annals of the South African Museum see South African Museum. Annals **457**
Annals of the Upper Silesian Museum in Bytom. Entomology see Upper Silesian Museum in Bytom. Annals. Entomology **538**
Annals of Theoretical Psychology. (US) **4011**
Annals of Thoracic Surgery. (US ISSN 0003-4975) **3375**
Annals of Tourism Research. (US ISSN 0160-7383) **4752**
Annals of Tropical Medicine and Parasitology. (UK ISSN 0003-4983) **3218**
Annals of Tropical Paediatrics. (UK ISSN 0272-4936) **3318**
Annals of Tropical Research. (PH ISSN 0116-0710) **76**
Annals of Vascular Surgery. (US ISSN 0890-5096) **3375**, **3204**
Annals of Veterinary Research. see Annales de Recherches Veterinaires **4806**
Annals of Wyoming. (US ISSN 0003-4991) **2398**
Annals of Zoology. (II ISSN 0003-5009) **577**
Annandale Campus Peashooter. (US) **1303**
Annapolitan. (US) **2221**
Annasach. (UK) **1303**
Annee Africaine. (FR ISSN 0570-1937) **2719**, **3940**
Annee Balzacienne. (FR ISSN 0084-6473) **2895**
Annee Bateaux Magazine see Mer & Bateaux **4526**
L'Annee Biologique. (FR ISSN 0003-5017) **428**
Annee du Cinema. (FR) **3503**
Annee du Cyclisme. (FR) **4515**
Annee du Football. (FR) **4499**
Annee du Rugby. (FR) **4499**
Annee du Tennis. (FR) **4499**
Annee Epigraphique; Revue des Publications Epigraphiques Relatives a l'Antiquite Romaine. (FR ISSN 0066-2348) **2803**
Annee Philologique. (FR ISSN 0184-6949) **1281**, **2855**
Annee Politique see Annee Politique, Economique et Sociale **3873**
Annee Politique Africaine. (SG ISSN 0066-2364) **3873**
Annee Politique, Economique et Sociale.(FR ISSN 0764-8138) **3873**
Annee Politique Suisse/Schweizerische Politik. (SZ ISSN 0066-2372) **3873**
Annee Psychologique. (FR ISSN 0003-5033) **4011**
Annee Sociologique. (FR ISSN 0066-2399) **4429**
Annee Sportive U.S.M.T. (Union Sportive Metropolitaine des Transports) (FR) **4464**, **1296**
Annee Technologique. (FR) **4613**
Annee Theologique Augustinienne see Revue des Etudes Augustiniennes **4199**
Annee Therapeutique en Ophtalmologie see Annee Therapeutique et Clinique en Ophtalmologie **3298**
Annee Therapeutique et Clinique en Ophtalmologie. (FR ISSN 0301-4495) **3298**
Annonces. (FR) **28**

Annonces de l'Industrie. (BE ISSN 0003-505X) **1002**
Annonsblad till Tidskrift foer Landtmaen. (SW) **76**
Annotated Accessions List of Studies and Reports in the Field of Science Statistics. (UN) **389**
Annotated Bibliographies of Serials: A Subject Approach. (US ISSN 0748-5190) **389**, **2743**
Annotated Bibliography and Index of the Geology of Zambia. (ZA ISSN 0066-2410) **1554**
Annotated Bibliography of Literature on Cooperative Movements in South-East Asia. (II) **389**, **829**
Annotated Bibliography of Literature Produced by the Cooperative Movements in South-East Asia see Annotated Bibliography of Literature on Cooperative Movements in South-East Asia **389**
†Annotated Guide to Taiwan Periodical Literature. (US ISSN 0066-2445) **5136**
Annotated Reference Tools in Music Series. (US) **3538**
Annotation. (US ISSN 0160-8460) **2398**, **2743**
Annotationes Zoologicae Japonenses see Zoological Science **594**
Annotations to the Acts and Regulations of the Australian Parliament see Federal Legislation Annotations **4060**
Announced... (US) **3538**
Annrinya. (II ISSN 0003-5203) **2858**
Annuaire Administratif et Judiciaire de Belgique/Administratief en Gerechtelijk Jaarboek voor Belgie. (BE ISSN 0066-2461) **4053**
Annuaire Belge de Chauffage et Climatisation see A B C **2297**
Annuaire Birkner France. (GW) **3662**
Annuaire Bureautique Informatique. (FR) **1057**
Annuaire Canadien de Droit International see Canadian Yearbook of International Law **2720**
Annuaire Canadien des Droits de la Personne. see Canadian Human Rights Yearbook **3940**
Annuaire Canadien des Orchestres et Orchestres des Jeunes. see Directory of Canadian Orchestras and Youth Orchestras **3549**
Annuaire Catholique de France. (FR ISSN 0066-2488) **4255**
Annuaire d'Etudes Europeennes. see Yearbook of European Studies **3978**
Annuaire d'Exportation de l'Autriche. see Austria Export Herold **1122**
Annuaire de l'Administration des D.R.I.R. (FR ISSN 1140-7123) **1783**, **3478**, **4053**
Annuaire de l'Administration des Mines see Annuaire de l'Administration des D.R.I.R **1783**
Annuaire de l'Afrique du Nord. (FR ISSN 0242-7540) **4365**
Annuaire de l'Alimentation Animale. (FR ISSN 0752-7535) **204**
Annuaire de l'Ameublement. (FR) **2556**
Annuaire de l'Ameublement et des Industries s'y Rattachant see Annuaire de l'Ameublement **2556**
Annuaire de l'Armement a la Peche. (FR ISSN 0066-2623) **2036**
Annuaire de l'Art International. (FR) **312**
Annuaire de l'Eclairage. (FR ISSN 0066-264X) **1881**
Annuaire de l'Eglise Catholique a Madagascar see Eglise Catholique a Madagascar **4263**
Annuaire de l'Eglise Catholique au Zaire.(ZR) **4255**
Annuaire de l'Enseignement Assiste par Ordinateur. (FR) **1615**
▼Annuaire de l'Equipement Vinicole: Materiels - Fournitures - Prestations. (FR) **161**, **1615**
Annuaire de l'Exportation du Danemark. see Udenrigs Handelskalenderen for Danmark **1156**
Annuaire de la Chaussure et des Cuirs. (FR ISSN 0066-2526) **2735**

Annuaire de la France Rurale dans le Marche Commun see Annuaire de la France Rurale et de l'Agro-Alimentaire dans le Marche Commun **76**
Annuaire de la France Rurale et de l'Agro-Alimentaire dans le Marche Commun. (FR) **76**
Annuaire de la Maree see Annuaire de la Maree et de l'Aquaculture **2036**
Annuaire de la Maree et de l'Aquaculture. (FR) **2036**
Annuaire de la Marine Marchande. (FR ISSN 0066-2550) **4724**
Annuaire de la Mecanographie, Materiel de Bureau, Informatique see Annuaire Bureautique Informatique **1057**
Annuaire de la Mercerie, Nouveautes, Bonneterie, Lingerie, Confections. (FR) **1282**
Annuaire de la Noblesse de France et d'Europe. (FR ISSN 0066-2569) **2144**
Annuaire de la Presse, de la Publicite et de la Communication (Year). (FR) **1121**, **1331**
Annuaire de la Presse et de la Publicite.(FR ISSN 0066-2585) **2567**
▼Annuaire de la Recherche Geographique Francophone. (FR) **2241**
Annuaire de Legislation Francaise et Etrangere. (FR ISSN 0066-2658) **76**
†Annuaire de Statistique Agricole. (FR ISSN 0243-6825) **5136**
Annuaire de Statistique Agricole du Departement de la Reunion see Reunion. Direction de l'Agriculture et de la Foret. Agreste. Donnees, Annuaire de Statistique Agricole Reunion **143**
Annuaire Dentaire. (FR ISSN 0066-2712) **3228**
Annuaire des Abonnes Telex du Danemark. see Telex Danmark **1367**
Annuaire des Administrateurs et des Societes. (FR) **645**
Annuaire des Agents Commerciaux Courtiers et Representants de Commerce-France et Marche Commun. (FR) **900**
Annuaire des Annuaires see Repertoire des Annuaires **410**
Annuaire des Arachnologistes Mondiaux.(FR ISSN 0990-0063) **528**, **577**
Annuaire des Assurances. (FR) **2526**
Annuaire des Assurances et l'Assureur-Conseil see Annuaire des Assurances **2526**
†Annuaire des Boissons et des Liquides Alimentaires/Jahrbuch der Getraenke und Fluessigen Nahrmittel. (FR ISSN 0066-2763) **5136**
Annuaire des Centrales et Groupements d'Achats. (FR) **1121**
Annuaire des Centres de Recherche Demographique/Directory of Demographic Research Centers. (FR) **3979**
Annuaire des Chambres de Commerce et d'Industrie. (FR ISSN 0066-2798) **807**
Annuaire des Chercheurs Francais du Fonds de Bourses de Recherche Scientifique et Technique de l'Organisation du Traite de l'Atlantique Nord. (FR ISSN 0066-2771) **1699**
Annuaire des Communautes d'Enfants. (FR ISSN 0069-7761) **1232**, **1615**
Annuaire des Departements de Sociologie, d'Anthropologie et d'Archeologie des Universites et des Musees du Canada. see Guide to Departments of Sociology, Anthropology and Archaeology in Universities and Museums in Canada **1707**
Annuaire des Employeurs des Nouveaux Diplomes de College see Employers of New University Graduates: Directory **1134**
Annuaire des Entreprises du Zaire. (ZR) **807**

ANNUAIRE 5913

Annuaire des Entreprises et Organismes d'Outre-Mer. (FR) **900**
Annuaire des Exportateurs de Cafes Africains/Exporter Directory of African Coffee. (IV) **900**, **2061**
Annuaire des Exportateurs Francais Commercant avec l'U.R.S.S. (FR) **1121**
Annuaire des Femmes de Montreal. see Montreal Women's Directory **1146**
Annuaire des Fournisseurs de Laboratoires de Recherches. (FR) **4299**
Annuaire des Fournisseurs de Laboratoires Pharmaceutiques see Annuaire des Fournisseurs de Laboratoires Pharmaceutiques et Cosmetiques **3717**
Annuaire des Fournisseurs de Laboratoires Pharmaceutiques et Cosmetiques. (FR ISSN 0396-0625) **3717**
Annuaire des Hopitaux du Canada. see Canadian Hospital Directory **2460**
Annuaire des Hypermarches. (FR) **1121**
Annuaire des Industries Avicoles. (FR) **210**
Annuaire des Industries Charcuteries. (FR) **210**
Annuaire des Industries de la Conserve. (FR) **2061**
Annuaire des Industries Laitieres. (FR) **197**
Annuaire des Instituts de Religieuses en France. (FR ISSN 0066-2860) **4162**
Annuaire des Laboratoires d'Analyses de Biologie Medicale de France. (FR) **3257**
Annuaire des Marees pour l'An. Tome 1. Ports de France. (FR ISSN 0180-989X) **1601**
Annuaire des Marees pour l'An. Tome 2. Ports d'Outre Mer. (FR ISSN 0180-9962) **1601**
Annuaire des Mineraux du Canada. see Canadian Minerals Yearbook **3480**
Annuaire des Notables Regionaux. (FR) **2241**
Annuaire des Organisations Internationales. see Yearbook of International Organizations **3978**
Annuaire des Pays de l'Ocean Indien. (FR ISSN 0247-400X) **4365**, **2241**
Annuaire des Produits Forestiers. see Yearbook of Forest Products **2119**
Annuaire des Professeurs de Droit. see Directory of Law Teachers **2619**
Annuaire des Professions au Liban. see Lebanese Industrial and Commercial Directory **1143**
Annuaire des Serveurs Temps Partage. (FR) **4613**
Annuaire des Societes Libanaises a Responsibilite Limitee. see Year-Book of the Lebanese Limited Liability Companies **970**
Annuaire des Societes Libanaises Par Action. see Year-Book of the Lebanese Joint-Stock Companies **969**
Annuaire des Statistiques du Commerce Exterieur du Togo. (TG) **702**, **4561**
Annuaire Desechaliers. (FR) **1121**
Annuaire Desfosses see Annuaire des Administrateurs et des Societes **645**
Annuaire Diplomatique et Consulaire de la Republique Francaise. (FR ISSN 0066-295X) **3950**
Annuaire du Canada see Canada Yearbook **5160**
Annuaire du CD-ROM. (FR) **1424**
Annuaire du Cinema et Television see Annuaire du Cinema, Television, Video **3503**
Annuaire du Cinema, Television, Video. (FR) **3503**, **1368**, **1384**
Annuaire du Commerce de la Norvege. see Norges Handels-Kalender **1148**
Annuaire du Commerce Exterieur d'Haiti: Importations, Exportations. (HT) **900**
Annuaire du Diocese de Lyon. (FR) **4255**
Annuaire du Marketing. (FR ISSN 0066-300X) **1033**

5914 ANNUAIRE

Annuaire du Quebec see Annuaire du Quebec Statistiques **4561**
Annuaire du Quebec Statistiques. (CN) **4561**
Annuaire du R N I S. (FR) **1426**
Annuaire du Spectacle. (FR ISSN 0066-3026) **4629**
Annuaire Economique de la Tunisie. (TI ISSN 0066-3042) **843**
Annuaire Economique des Pays Membres de l'Organisation de l'Unite Africaine/Economic Yearbook of Member States of the Organization of African Unity. (ET) **843**
Annuaire Europeen du Petrole. see European Petroleum Yearbook **3685**
Annuaire F F C A T. (Federation Francaise des Commissionnaires et Auxiliares de Transport Commissionnaires en Douane, Transitaires et Agents Aeriens) (FR) **1121, 4646**
Annuaire Federal de l'Horticulture et des Pepinieres. (FR) **2121**
Annuaire Fourni-Labo Pharmacie (Year) .(FR) **1121, 3717**
Annuaire Fourni-Labo Recherche (Year) .(FR) **1121, 3257**
Annuaire Francais d'Australie. (AT) **1121**
Annuaire Francais de Droit International.(FR ISSN 0066-3085) **2719**
Annuaire Franco-Italien. (FR ISSN 0066-3115) **807**
Annuaire Franco-Ontarien. (CN ISSN 0706-1021) **3873**
Annuaire Fructidor. (FR ISSN 0066-3131) **168**
Annuaire General de la Publicite. (FR ISSN 0751-6649) **28**
Annuaire General des Cooperatives et de leurs Fournisseurs: France, Outre-Mer et Marche Europeen. (FR) **833, 829**
Annuaire General des Cooperatives Francaises et de leurs Fournisseurs: France, Afrique et Marche Commun see Annuaire General des Cooperatives et de leurs Fournisseurs: France, Outre-Mer et Marche Europeen **833**
Annuaire H L M. (Habitations a Loyer Modere) (FR) **2483, 4398**
Annuaire Industriel. Repertoire General de la Production Francaise see La France de l'Industrie et ses Services **1135**
Annuaire International des Collectionneurs. (FR) **2433**
Annuaire International des Jus de Fruits/Internation Directory of Fruit Juices. (FR ISSN 0066-3255) **377**
Annuaire International des Ventes. (FR ISSN 0066-3263) **312**
Annuaire International du Monde Sous-Marin. see International Yearbook of the Underwater World **5218**
Annuaire Interprofessionnel de la Surgelation et de la Congelation. (FR) **2061**
Annuaire Magnetique. see Rocznik Magnetyczny **5271**
Annuaire Medical de l'Hospitalisation Francaise. (FR ISSN 0066-3298) **3076, 2459**
Annuaire Medical du Dr. Porcheron et Prof. G. Beltrami. (FR) **3077**
Annuaire Mondial des Corses. (FR) **417**
Annuaire National de l'Aviculture see Annuaire des Industries Avicoles **210**
Annuaire National de la Conserve see Annuaire des Industries de la Conserve **2061**
Annuaire National des Beaux-Arts. (FR ISSN 0066-3352) **312**
Annuaire National des Fournisseurs des Administrations Francaises. (FR ISSN 0066-3379) **1071**
Annuaire National des Lettres. (FR ISSN 0066-3387) **2895**
Annuaire National des Matieres Premieres de Recuperation et du Materiel d'Occasion. (FR) **3015**

Annuaire National des Specialistes Qualifies Exclusifs en Pediatrie. (FR ISSN 0066-3514) **3318**
Annuaire National des Transports. (FR ISSN 0066-3549) **4646**
Annuaire National du Lait see Annuaire des Industries Laitieres **197**
Annuaire National Officiel de la Republique Gabonaise. (GO) **4053**
Annuaire Nautisme. (FR ISSN 0758-6639) **4522**
Annuaire O.G.M. (Office General de la Musique) (FR ISSN 0066-3565) **3538, 1331, 4459**
Annuaire Officiel de la Charcuterie see Annuaire des Industries Charcuteries **210**
Annuaire Pluviometrique. (BD) **3432**
Annuaire Polonais de Droit International. see Polish Yearbook of International Law **2728**
Annuaire Protestant: la France Protestante et les Eglises de Langue Francaise see France Protestante et les Eglises de Langue Francaise **4238**
Annuaire Roumain d'Anthropologie. (RM) **233**
Annuaire Souvenir Normand. (DK) **2348, 4752**
Annuaire Statistique de Benin. (DM) **4562**
Annuaire Statistique de la Belgique. (BE ISSN 0770-0415) **4562**
Annuaire Statistique de la Belgique et du Congo Belge see Annuaire Statistique de la Belgique **4562**
Annuaire Statistique de la France. (FR ISSN 0066-3654) **4562**
Annuaire Statistique de la Sante Publique/Statistisch Jaarboek van Volksgezondheid. (BE ISSN 0522-7690) **4116**
Annuaire Statistique de la Suisse. see Statistisches Jahrbuch der Schweiz **4589**
Annuaire Statistique de la Tunisie. (TI ISSN 0066-3689) **4562**
Annuaire Statistique des Telecommunications du Secteur Public. see Yearbook of Common Carrier Telecommunication Statistics **1346**
Annuaire Statistique du Dahomey see Annuaire Statistique de Benin **4562**
Annuaire Statistique du Maroc. (MR ISSN 0851-089X) **4562**
Annuaire Statistique du Togo. (TG) **4562**
Annuaire Statistique pour l'Asie et le Pacifique. see Statistical Yearbook for Asia and the Pacific **4588**
Annuaire Sucrier. (FR ISSN 0755-3110) **2086**
Annuaire Suisse de l'Economie Forestiere et de l'Industrie du Bois. see Schweizerischen Wald- und Holzwirtschaft. Jahrbuch **2113**
Annuaire Suisse de Science Politique/ Schweizerisches Jahrbuch fuer Politische Wissenschaft/Swiss Political Science Yearbook. (SZ ISSN 0066-3727) **3873**
Annuaire Suisse du Monde et des Affaires. see Swiss Biographical Index of Prominent Persons **421**
▼Annuaire Telexport. (FR) **807, 645**
Annuaires Francais et Listes d'Adresses Susceptibles d'Interesser le Commerce et l'Industrie see Repertoire d'Annuaires Francais **821**
Annual Accounting Review. (US ISSN 0142-5897) **747**
Annual Advances in Bone and Mineral Research see Bone and Mineral Research Annual **3307**
Annual Advertising Art in Japan. (JA) **28**
Annual Agricultural Institute. (US) **2598, 76**
Annual Agricultural Outlook Conference Proceedings see Outlook (Year) Proceedings **156**
Annual Allerton Conference on Communication, Control and Computing. (US ISSN 0732-6181) **1881**
Annual Almanac of Records and Results. (AT) **4541**

Annual Art Sales Index: Oil Paintings, Drawings, Water Colours and Sculptures see Art Sales Index: Oil Paintings, Drawings, Water Colours and Sculpture **315**
Annual Australian Notices to Mariners. (AT ISSN 1035-6878) **4724**
Annual Automation Report to the Arizona Legislature. (US) **1411**
†Annual Bibliography of Christianity in India. (II ISSN 0970-3861) **5136**
Annual Bibliography of English Language and Literature. (UK ISSN 0066-3786) **2980**
†Annual Bibliography of Indian Archaeology. (NE ISSN 0066-3794) **5136**
Annual Bibliography of Modern Art. (US) **312, 389, 3521**
Annual Bibliography of Scottish Literature. (UK ISSN 0307-9864) **2980**
Annual Bibliography of the History of Natural History. (UK) **2327**
Annual Bibliography of the History of the Printed Book and Library. (NE) **4006**
Annual Bibliography of Victorian Studies.(CN ISSN 0227-1400) **2980, 389**
Annual Book of A S T M Standards. Part 1 see Annual Book of A S T M Standards. Volume 01.01. Steel-Piping, Tubing, Fittings **1911**
Annual Book of A S T M Standards. Part 5. Steel Bars, Chain, and Springs; Bearing Steel; Steel Forgings see Annual Book of A S T M Standards. Volume 01.05. Steel-Bars, Bearings, Forgings, Chain, Springs **1912**
Annual Book of A S T M Standards. Part 41. General Test Methods, Nonmetal; Statistical Methods; Space Simulation; Particle Size Measurement; Laboratory Apparatus; Durability of Nonmetallic Materials; Metric Practice; Solar Energy Conversion see Annual Book of A S T M Standards. Volume 15.03. Space Simulation; Aerospace Materials; High Modulus Fibers and Their Composites **1915**
Annual Book of A S T M Standards. Volume 03.03. Metallography; Nondestructive Testing see Annual Book of A S T M Standards. Volume 03.03. Nondestructive Tests **1912**
Annual Book of A S T M Standards. Volume 00.01. Index. (US ISSN 0066-0493) **1911**
Annual Book of A S T M Standards. Volume 01.01. Steel-Piping, Tubing, Fittings. (American Society for Testing and Materials) (US ISSN 0066-0183) **1911, 3402**
Annual Book of A S T M Standards. Volume 01.02. Ferrous Castings, Ferro Alloys. (US) **1911, 3402**
Annual Book of A S T M Standards. Volume 01.03. Steel Plate, Sheet, Strip Wire. (US) **1911, 3402**
Annual Book of A S T M Standards. Volume 01.04. Steel-Structural, Reinforcing, Pressure Vessel; Railway. (US) **1912, 3402**
Annual Book of A S T M Standards. Volume 01.05. Steel-Bars, Bearings, Forgings, Chain, Springs. (US) **1912, 3402**
Annual Book of A S T M Standards. Volume 01.06. Coated Steel Products. (US) **1912, 3402**
▼Annual Book of A S T M Standards. Volume 01.07. Shipbuilding. (US) **1912, 3402**
Annual Book of A S T M Standards. Volume 02.01. Copper and Copper Alloys. (US) **1912, 3402**
Annual Book of A S T M Standards. Volume 02.02. Die-Cast Metals; Aluminum and Magnesium Alloys. (US) **1912, 3402**
Annual Book of A S T M Standards. Volume 02.03. Electrical Conductors.(US) **1912, 1881**

Annual Book of A S T M Standards. Volume 02.04. Nonferrous Metals-Nickel, Lead, Tin Alloys, Precious, Primary, Reactive Metals. (US) **1912, 3402**
Annual Book of A S T M Standards. Volume 02.05. Metallic and Inorganic Coatings; Metal Powders, Sintered P-M Structural Parts. (US) **1912, 3402**
Annual Book of A S T M Standards. Volume 03.01. Metals - Mechanical Testing; Elevated and Low-Temperature Tests Metallography. (US) **1912, 3402**
Annual Book of A S T M Standards. Volume 03.02. Wear and Erosion; Metal Corrosion. (US) **1912, 3402**
Annual Book of A S T M Standards. Volume 03.03. Nondestructive Tests.(US) **1912, 3402**
Annual Book of A S T M Standards. Volume 03.04. Magnetic Properties; Metallic Materials for Thermostats, Electrical Resistance, Heating Contacts. (US) **1912**
Annual Book of A S T M Standards. Volume 03.05. Chemical Analysis of Metals; Metal Bearing Ores. (US ISSN 0066-0485) **1912, 1204, 3402**
Annual Book of A S T M Standards. Volume 03.06. Analytical Atomic Spectroscopy; Surface Analysis. (US) **1912**
Annual Book of A S T M Standards. Volume 04.01. Cement; Lime; Gypsum. (US) **1912, 600**
Annual Book of A S T M Standards. Volume 04.02. Concrete and Aggregates (Including Manual of Aggregate and Concrete Testing). (US) **1912, 600**
Annual Book of A S T M Standards. Volume 04.03. Road and Paving Materials; Pavement Management Technologies. (US) **1913**
Annual Book of A S T M Standards. Volume 04.04. Roofing, Waterproofing, and Bituminous Materials. (US) **1913**
Annual Book of A S T M Standards. Volume 04.05. Chemical-Resistant Materials; Vitrified Clay, Concrete; Fiber-Cement Products; Masonry; Mortars. (US) **1913, 600**
Annual Book of A S T M Standards. Volume 04.06. Thermal Insulation; Environmental Acoustics. (US) **1913, 600**
Annual Book of A S T M Standards. Volume 04.07. Building Seals and Sealants; Fire Standards; Building Constructions. (US) **1913**
Annual Book of A S T M Standards. Volume 04.08. Soil and Rock; Dimension Stone; Geosynthetics. (US) **1913, 168, 600**
Annual Book of A S T M Standards. Volume 04.09. Wood. (US) **1913, 2113, 3861**
Annual Book of A S T M Standards. Volume 05.01. Petroleum Products and Lubricants (1). (US) **1913, 3681**
Annual Book of A S T M Standards. Volume 05.02. Petroleum Products and Lubricants (2). (US) **1913, 3682**
Annual Book of A S T M Standards. Volume 05.03. Petroleum Products and Lubricants (3); Catalysts. (US) **1913, 3682**
Annual Book of A S T M Standards. Volume 05.04. Test Methods for Rating Motor, Diesel, and Aviation Fuels. (US) **1913**
Annual Book of A S T M Standards. Volume 05.05. Gaseous Fuels; Coal and Coke. (US) **1913, 3478, 3682**
Annual Book of A S T M Standards. Volume 06.01. Paint - Tests for Formulated Products and Applied Coatings. (US ISSN 0066-037X) **1913, 3652**

ANNUAL NATIONAL   5915

Annual Book of A S T M Standards. Volume 06.02. Paint - Pigments, Resins and Polymers. (US) **1913, 3652**

Annual Book of A S T M Standards. Volume 06.03. Paint - Fatty Oils and Acids, Solvents, Miscellaneous; Aromatic Hydrocarbons. (US) **1913, 1848, 3652**

Annual Book of A S T M Standards. Volume 07.01. Textiles - Yarn, Fabrics, and General Test Methods. (US ISSN 0066-040X) **1913, 4616**

Annual Book of A S T M Standards. Volume 07.02. Textiles - Fibers, Zippers. (US) **1914, 4616**

Annual Book of A S T M Standards. Volume 08.01. Plastics (1): C 177 to D 1600. (US) **1914, 3861**

Annual Book of A S T M Standards. Volume 08.02. Plastics (2): D 1601 to D 3099. (US) **1914, 3861**

Annual Book of A S T M Standards. Volume 08.03. Plastics (3): D 3100 to Latest. (US) **1914**

Annual Book of A S T M Standards. Volume 08.04. Plastic Pipe and Building Products. (US) **1914, 600, 3861**

Annual Book of A S T M Standards. Volume 09.01. Rubber, Natural and Synthetic - General Test Methods; Carbon Black. (US) **1914, 4291**

Annual Book of A S T M Standards. Volume 09.02. Rubber Products, Industrial - Specifications and Related Test Methods; Gaskets; Tires. (US) **1914, 4291**

Annual Book of A S T M Standards. Volume 10.01. Electrical Insulation, Composites, and Coatings - Solids. (US) **1914, 1882**

Annual Book of A S T M Standards. Volume 10.02. Electrical Insulation; Wire and Cable, Heating and Electrical Tests - Solids (2). (US) **1914**

Annual Book of A S T M Standards. Volume 10.03. Electrical Insulating Liquids and Gases; Electrical Protective Equipment. (US) **1914, 1882**

Annual Book of A S T M Standards. Volume 10.04. Electronics (1). (US) **1914, 1882**

Annual Book of A S T M Standards. Volume 10.05. Electronics (2). (US) **1914, 1882**

Annual Book of A S T M Standards. Volume 11.01. Water (1). (US) **1914, 1943**

Annual Book of A S T M Standards. Volume 11.02. Water (2). (US) **1914**

Annual Book of A S T M Standards. Volume 11.03. Atmospheric Analysis; Occupational Health and Safety. (US) **1914**

Annual Book of A S T M Standards. Volume 11.04. Pesticides; Resource Recovery; Hazardous Substances and Oil Spill Response; Waste Disposal; Biological Effects. (US) **1914**

Annual Book of A S T M Standards. Volume 12.01. Nuclear Energy (1). (US) **1914, 1814**

Annual Book of A S T M Standards. Volume 12.02. Nuclear Energy (2), Solar, and Geothermal Energy. (US) **1914, 1783**

Annual Book of A S T M Standards. Volume 13.01. Medical Devices. (US) **1914, 3077**

Annual Book of A S T M Standards. Volume 14.01. Analytical Methods - Spectroscopy; Chromatography; Temperature Measurement; Computerized Systems. (US) **1914, 1204**

Annual Book of A S T M Standards. Volume 14.02. General Test Methods, Nonmetal; Laboratory Apparatus; Statistical Methods; Appearance of Materials; Durability of Nonmetallic Materials. (US) **1915**

Annual Book of A S T M Standards. Volume 14.03. Temperature Measurement. (US) **1915**

Annual Book of A S T M Standards. Volume 15.01. Refractories, Manufactured Carbon and Graphite Products; Activated Carbon. (US) **1915, 1161**

Annual Book of A S T M Standards. Volume 15.02. Glass; Ceramic Whitewares. (US) **1915**

Annual Book of A S T M Standards. Volume 15.03. Space Simulation; Aerospace Materials; High Modulus Fibers and Their Composites. (US) **1915**

Annual Book of A S T M Standards. Volume 15.04. Soaps; Polishes; Cellulose; Leather; Resilient Floor Covering. (US) **1915**

Annual Book of A S T M Standards. Volume 15.05. Engine Coolants; Halogenated Organic Solvents; Industrial Chemicals. (US) **1915, 1848**

Annual Book of A S T M Standards. Volume 15.06. Adhesives. (US) **1915**

Annual Book of A S T M Standards. Volume 15.07. End Use Products. (US) **1915**

Annual Book of A S T M Standards. Volume 15.08. Fasteners. (US) **1915**

Annual Book of A S T M Standards. Volume 15.09. Paper; Packaging; Flexible Barrier Materials; Business Copy Products. (US) **1915, 3647, 3662**

Annual Bulletin of Coal Statistics for Europe. (SZ ISSN 0066-3808) **3498**

Annual Bulletin of Electric Energy Statistics for Europe. (UN ISSN 0066-3816) **1797, 1801**

Annual Bulletin of Gas Statistics for Europe/Bulletin Annuel de Statistiques de Gaz pour l'Europe. (UN ISSN 0066-3824) **3704**

Annual Bulletin of General Energy Statistics for Europe. (UN ISSN 0377-9165) **1797**

Annual Bulletin of Historical Literature. (UK ISSN 0066-3832) **2895**

Annual Bulletin of Housing and Building Statistics for Europe. (UN ISSN 0066-3840) **600**

Annual Bulletin of Steel Statistics for Europe. (UN ISSN 0250-9903) **3424, 4562**

Annual Bulletin of Trade in Chemical Products. (UN ISSN 0251-0081) **1071, 1170**

Annual Bulletin of Transport Statistics for Europe. (UN ISSN 0066-3859) **4661**

Annual Can Shipments Report. (US) **3647**

†Annual Canadian-American Seminar. Proceedings. (CN ISSN 0384-1103) **5136**

Annual Catalogue of Government Publications. (UK) **4053**

Annual Chart Summaries. (UK) **3539**

Annual Coal Production Report see Coal Production (Year) **3481**

Annual Conference Computer Security Applications. (US) **1433**

▼Annual Conference on A I, Simulation and Planning in High Autonomy Systems. (US) **1406**

Annual Conference on Activated Sludge Process Control. Proceedings. (US) **4097, 1814**

Annual Conference on Applications of X-Ray Analysis. Proceedings see Advances in X-Ray Analysis **4593**

Annual Conference on Fire Research see Summaries of B F R L Fire Research In-House and Grants (Year) **2035**

Annual Conference on Taxation. Proceedings see National Tax Association - Tax Institute of America. Proceedings of the Annual Conference **1101**

Annual DeGarmo Lectures. (US ISSN 0882-7133) **1699**

Annual Development Assistance Review, Memorandum of New Zealand see Development Co-operation: Review of N.Z. Official Development Assistance **5179**

†Annual Directory of Booksellers in the British Isles Specialising in Antiquarian and Out-Of-Print Books. (UK ISSN 0066-3913) **5136**

Annual Directory of Oklahoma Libraries.(US) **2743**

Annual Directory of World Leaders. (US ISSN 1044-825X) **3873, 3950**

Annual Directory through Press and Advertising. see Stamm Leitfaden Durch Presse und Werbung **412**

Annual Drug Data Report see Drug Data Report **3723**

Annual Economic Review. (RH) **843**

Annual Editions: Aging. (US ISSN 0272-3808) **2270**

Annual Editions: American Government. (US) **3873**

Annual Editions: American History. (US ISSN 0090-4511) **2398**

Annual Editions: Anthropology. (US) **233**

Annual Editions: Biology. (US) **428**

†Annual Editions: Business and Management. (US ISSN 0090-4309) **5136**

Annual Editions: Business Ethics. (US) **645, 3761**

▼Annual Editions: Canadian Politics. (US) **3873**

Annual Editions: Comparative Politics. (US) **3873**

Annual Editions: Criminal Justice. (US ISSN 0272-3816) **1510**

Annual Editions: Drugs, Society & Behavior. (US) **4429, 1534**

Annual Editions: Early Childhood Education. (US) **1615**

Annual Editions: Economics. (US) **645**

Annual Editions: Educating Exceptional Children. (US ISSN 0198-7518) **1733**

Annual Editions: Education. (US ISSN 0095-5787) **1615**

Annual Editions: Educational Psychology. (US) **4011, 1615**

Annual Editions: Environment. (US ISSN 0272-9008) **1943**

Annual Editions: Geography. (US) **2241**

Annual Editions: Global Issues. (US) **2241**

Annual Editions: Health. (US ISSN 0278-4653) **3799**

Annual Editions: Human Development. (US ISSN 0090-5348) **569, 3077, 4011**

Annual Editions: Human Resources. (US) **4429, 4365, 4398**

Annual Editions: Human Sexuality. (US) **428, 4011, 4429**

▼Annual Editions: International Business. (US) **900**

Annual Editions: Macroeconomics. (US) **998**

▼Annual Editions: Management. (US) **1002**

Annual Editions: Marketing. (US ISSN 0730-2606) **1033**

Annual Editions: Marriage and Family. (US ISSN 0272-7897) **3066, 4429**

▼Annual Editions: Microeconomics. (US) **889**

▼Annual Editions: Money and Banking. (US) **759**

Annual Editions: Nutrition. (US) **3603, 2061, 3799**

Annual Editions: Personal Growth and Behavior. (US ISSN 0198-912X) **4011**

Annual Editions: Psychology. (US ISSN 0272-3794) **4011**

▼Annual Editions: Public Administration. (US) **4053**

▼Annual Editions: Race & Ethnic Relations. (US) **4429, 1991**

Annual Editions: Social Problems. (US ISSN 0272-4464) **4398**

Annual Editions: Sociology. (US ISSN 0277-9315) **4429**

Annual Editions: State & Local Government. (US) **4053**

Annual Editions: Third World. (US) **2241, 926, 1071, 1087**

Annual Editions: Urban Society. (US ISSN 0160-9815) **4429**

▼Annual Editions: Violence and Terrorism. (US) **1510**

Annual Editions: Western Civilization. (US) **2306**

Annual Editions: World History. (US) **2306**

Annual Editions: World Politics. (US) **3950, 3873**

Annual Educational Summary, New York State. (US ISSN 0085-4077) **1615**

Annual Egyptological Bibliography/Bibliographie Egyptologique Annuelle/Jaehrliche Aegyptologische Bibliographie. (NE) **2327, 290, 3646**

Annual Epidemiological and Vital Statistics see World Health Statistics Annual **4119**

Annual Estimates of the Population of Scotland. (UK ISSN 0066-3964) **3979**

Annual Executive Compensation Report.(US) **1062**

Annual Executive Compensation Study see Annual Executive Compensation Report **1062**

Annual Fertilizer Review see F A O Fertilizer Yearbook **176**

Annual Financial Data (Year). see Anuario Financiero (Year) **843**

Annual Foreign Trade Statistics. see Turkey. Devlet Istatistik Enstitusu. Dis Ticaret Yillik Istatistik **741**

Annual Foreign Trade Statistics of Bangladesh see Foreign Trade Statistics of Bangladesh **717**

Annual Forestry Symposium. Proceedings see Louisiana State University. School of Forestry, Wildlife, and Fisheries. Annual Forestry Symposium. Proceedings **5229**

Annual Franchise Handbook Directory. (US) **1121, 3672**

Annual Frequency Control Symposium see Frequency Control Symposium **1771**

Annual Garden. (US) **2121**

Annual General Meeting of the Asiatic Society of Bangladesh: Report of the General Secretary. (BG) **3633**

Annual Guide to Public Policy Experts. (US ISSN 0731-339X) **4053**

Annual Hardwood Symposium. Proceedings. (US ISSN 0193-8495) **2113**

†Annual High Frequency Broadcasting Frequency List. (UN) **5136**

Annual Hospital Directory see Nursingworld Journal Nursing Job Guide **3285**

Annual Index to Motion Picture Credits. (US ISSN 0163-5123) **3503**

Annual Infectious Disease Symposia. Proceedings see Infectious Disease Reviews **5212**

Annual Institute on Securities Regulation. (US) **759, 2598**

Annual International Technical Conference and Exhibit see Abrasive Engineering Society. Conference Proceedings **1813**

Annual Investment File see Economic Development Briefing **945**

Annual Local Government Financial Report, State of Florida. Department of Banking & Finance. Annual Local Government Financial Report **1095**

Annual Meeting - American Association for the Advancement of Science see American Association for the Advancement of Science. Meeting Program **4298**

Annual Membrane Technology - Planning Conference Proceedings (Year). (US) **4593**

Annual Mosquito Review see New Jersey Mosquito Control Association. Proceedings **536**

Annual National Conference on Labor at New York University. Proceedings. (US ISSN 0193-3418) **971**

5916 **ANNUAL NEW**

Annual New Mexico Water Conference. Proceedings. (US ISSN 0161-4924) **4821**
Annual Obituary (Year). (US) **424**
Annual of Advertising Art in Japan *see* Tokyo Art Directors Annual **39**
Annual of Advertising, Editorial and Television Art and Design with the Annual Copy Awards *see* Art Directors Annual **314**
Annual of Animal Psychology. (JA ISSN 0003-5130) **4011**
Annual of Armenian Linguistics. (US ISSN 0271-9800) **2803**
Annual of Auction Prices for Posters. (US) **312**, 938
Annual of Cardiac Surgery. (US ISSN 0952-0562) **3166**, 3204, 3375
Annual of Czechoslovak Medical Literature. (CS) **3166**
Annual of Gastrointestinal Endoscopy. (US ISSN 0952-6293) **3166**, 3266
Annual of Indian Photography. (II) **3788**
†Annual of Psychoanalysis. (US ISSN 0092-5055) **5136**
†Annual of Urdu Studies. (US ISSN 0734-5348) **5136**
Annual on Terrorism (Year). (NE ISSN 0921-352X) **1510**, 2719, 3950
Annual Organ Handbook. (US) **3539**
Annual Planning Information: Bridgeport - Norwalk - Stamford - Valley Service Delivery Area. (US) **843**, 971
Annual Planning Information for Stamford Labor Market Area *see* Annual Planning Information: Bridgeport - Norwalk - Stamford - Valley Service Delivery Area **843**
Annual Planning Information: Sacramento Metropolitan Statistical Area. (US) **843**, 971
Annual Planning Information: Sacramento Standard Metropolitan Statistical Area *see* Annual Planning Information: Sacramento Metropolitan Statistical Area **843**
Annual Policy Review. (US) **1943**, 1783, 3873, 3950
Annual Program of the Five Year Development Plan. *see* Turkey. Devlet Planama Teskilati. Yili Programi Ucuncu Bes Yil **1086**
Annual Progress in Child Psychiatry and Child Development. (US ISSN 0066-4030) **3330**
Annual Progress Report - U.S. Army Medical Research Institute of Infectious Diseases *see* U.S. Army Medical Research Institute of Infectious Diseases. Annual Progress Report **3224**
Annual Record of Patent Office Proceedings. (AT) **3672**
Annual Record of Trade Marks Office Proceedings. (AT) **3672**
Annual Register. (US) **3950**, 2306
Annual Register of Grant Support. (US ISSN 0066-4049) **1699**
Annual Register of Pharmaceutical Chemists. (UK ISSN 0260-955X) **3717**
Annual Register World Events. (UK ISSN 0066-4057) **3873**
Annual Registrars Service. (UK) **4562**
Annual Report (Year). (US) **1071**
Annual Report and Accounts-Cameroon Development Corporation *see* Cameroon Development Corporation. Annual Report and Accounts **1073**
Annual Report - Andhra Pradesh State Trading Corporation Limited *see* Andhra Pradesh State Trading Corporation Limited. Annual Report **1033**
Annual Report - Association of American Publishers *see* Association of American Publishers. Annual Report **4121**
Annual Report - Central Sericultural Research and Training Institute *see* Central Sericultural Research and Training Institute. Annual Report **83**
Annual Report - Citizens Advisory Council (Harrisburg) *see* Pennsylvania. Citizens Advisory Council to the Department of Environmental Resources. Annual Report **1965**
Annual Report - Cotton Corporation of India *see* Cotton Corporation of India. Annual Report **149**
Annual Report - Criminal Injuries Compensation Commission *see* Hawaii. Criminal Injuries Compensation Commission. Annual Report **1515**
Annual Report, Damon Runyon - Walter Winchell Cancer Research Fund *see* Damon Runyon - Walter Winchell Cancer Research Fund. Annual Report **3196**
Annual Report - Department of Environmental Protection (Trenton) *see* New Jersey. Department of Environmental Protection. Annual Report **1964**
Annual Report - Department of Safety *see* Tennessee. Department of Safety. Annual Report **4721**
Annual Report - Educational Testing Service *see* Educational Testing Service Annual Report **1631**
Annual Report - Engineering Experiment Station (Madison) *see* University of Wisconsin, Madison. Engineering Experiment Station. Annual Report **3441**
Annual Report - Family Planning Association of Kenya *see* Family Planning Association of Kenya. Annual Report **596**
Annual Report - Federal Home Loan Bank of San Francisco *see* Federal Home Loan Bank of San Francisco. Annual Report **779**
Annual Report - Indian Council of Historical Research *see* Indian Council of Historical Research. Annual Report **2338**
Annual Report - Indian School of Mines *see* Indian School of Mines. Annual Report **3485**
Annual Report - Institute of Secretariat Training and Management *see* Institute of Secretariat Training and Management. Annual Report **1066**
Annual Report - Jammu & Kashmir Minerals Limited *see* Jammu & Kashmir Minerals Limited. Annual Report **3486**
Annual Report - Madhya Pradesh State Agro-Industries Development Corporation Ltd. *see* Madhya Pradesh State Agro-Industries Development Corporation Ltd. Annual Report **154**
Annual Report - Meghalaya Industrial Development Corporation *see* Meghalaya Industrial Development Corporation. Annual Report **679**
Annual Report - Mississippi Marine Resources Council *see* Mississippi Marine Resources Council. Annual Report **1608**
Annual Report - National Association of Independent Schools *see* National Association of Independent Schools. Annual Report **1649**
Annual Report - National Society to Prevent Blindness *see* National Society to Prevent Blindness. Report **2295**
Annual Report - Nebraska State Patrol *see* Nebraska. State Patrol. Annual Report **1519**
Annual Report - New Brunswick Development Corporation *see* New Brunswick Development Corporation. Annual Report **5245**
Annual Report - New York State Medical Care Facilities Finance Agency *see* New York (State). Medical Care Facilities Finance Agency. Annual Report **4109**
Annual Report of ACP-EEC Council of Ministers *see* A C P - E E C Council of Ministers. Annual Report (Year) **925**
Annual Report of Births, Deaths, Marriages and Divorces as Reported to the Bureau of Vital Statistics (Little Rock) *see* Arkansas. Bureau of Vital Statistics. Annual Report of Births, Deaths, Marriages and Divorces as Reported to the Bureau of Vital Statistics **3989**
Annual Report of Climatological Stations. *see* Kansokujo Kisho Nenpo **3438**
Annual Report of Community Services Administration *see* U.S. Community Services Administration. Annual Report **4422**
Annual Report of Educational Psychology in Japan. *see* Kyoiku Shinrigaku Nenpo **4034**
Annual Report of Fire and Disaster Prevention. *see* Saigai no Jittai to Shobo no Genkyo **2034**
Annual Report of Life Insurance, Republic of China *see* Life Insurance Business in Taiwan (Year) **2536**
Annual Report of Public Health, Saitama Prefecture. *see* Saitama-ken Eisei Tokei Nenpo **4112**
Annual Report of Survey - Inventory Activities *see* Alaska. Division of Wildlife Conservation. Annual Report of Survey - Inventory Activities **4540**
Annual Report of the Arizona Department of Health Services *see* Arizona. Department of Health Services. Annual Report **4098**
Annual Report of the Department of Environmental Quality *see* Wyoming. Department of Environmental Quality. Annual Report **1972**
Annual Report of the Department of Revenue and Taxation of the State of Wyoming *see* Wyoming. Department of Revenue and Taxation. Annual Report **1112**
Annual Report of the Division of Police (Cincinnati) *see* Cincinnati. Division of Police. Annual Report **1512**
Annual Report of the Federal Trade Commission *see* U.S. Federal Trade Commission. Annual Report **840**
Annual Report of the Idaho Department of Labor and Industrial Services *see* Idaho. Department of Labor and Industrial Services. Annual Report **5210**
Annual Report of the Oklahoma Water Resources Research Institute *see* Oklahoma Water Resources Research Institute. Annual Report **4827**
Annual Report of the Register of Copyrights *see* U.S. Copyright Office. Annual Report of the Register of Copyrights **3679**
Annual Report of the State Superintendent of Public Instruction Utah Public School System *see* Utah. State Office of Education. Annual Report of the State Superintendent of Public Instruction **1732**
Annual Report of the Superintendent of Public Instruction *see* Arizona. Department of Education. Annual Report of the Superintendent of Public Instruction **1616**
Annual Report of the Virginia State Water Control Board *see* Virginia. State Water Control Board. Annual Report **5301**
Annual Report of the Working and Affairs of Mysore Minerals Limited. (II) **3478**
Annual Report, Ohio Advisory Council on Vocational Education *see* Ohio. Council on Vocational Education. Annual Report **1739**
Annual Report - Ombudsman for Corrections (St. Paul) *see* Minnesota. Office of Ombudsman for Corrections. Annual Report **1518**
Annual Report on Advanced Dental Education. (US) **3228**, 1744
Annual Report on Allied Dental Health Education. (US) **3166**, 1674
Annual Report on Dental Auxillary Education *see* Annual Report on Allied Dental Health Education **3166**
Annual Report on Dental Education. (US ISSN 0065-8030) **3166**, 1674
Annual Report on Development Assistance to Mauritius. (UN) **926**
Annual Report on Highway Safety Improvement Programs *see* U.S. Department of Transportation. Highway Safety Stewardship Report **4722**
Annual Report on National Account. (JA) **843**
Annual Report on Privatization. (US) **4053**, 3873, 4398
Annual Report on the Administration of Prisons in Kenya. (KE) **1510**
Annual Report on the Consumer Price Index. (JA) **1509**, 4562
Annual Report on the Results of Treatment in Gynecological Cancer. (SW ISSN 0348-8799) **3193**
Annual Report on the Working and Affairs of Mysore Sales International Limited. (II) **833**
Annual Report on Tourism Statistics, Republic of China *see* Ministry of Communication. Tourism Bureau. Annual Report **4800**
Annual Report on Unemployment *see* Labour Statistics **726**
Annual Report on Work of Fabian Society *see* Fabian Society. Annual Report **3894**
Annual Report - Overseas Development Council *see* Overseas Development Council. Annual Report **933**
Annual Report - Overseas Private Investment Corporation *see* Overseas Private Investment Corporation. Annual Report **959**
Annual Report - Petroleum Division *see* Minnesota. Department of Revenue. Petroleum Division. Annual Report **3692**
Annual Report - Punjab National Bank *see* Punjab National Bank. Annual Report **796**
Annual Report - Rajasthan State Tanneries Limited *see* Rajasthan State Tanneries Limited. Annual Report **2738**
Annual Report - Republic Forge Company *see* Republic Forge Company. Annual Report **1084**
Annual Report - Robert Wood Johnson Foundation *see* Robert Wood Johnson Foundation. Annual Report **3150**
Annual Report - San Francisco Bay Area Rapid Transit District *see* San Francisco Bay Area Rapid Transit District. Annual Report **4656**
Annual Report - Southeast Michigan Council of Governments *see* Southeast Michigan Council of Governments. Annual Report **4074**
Annual Report - Southern California Rapid Transit District. *see* Southern California Rapid Transit District. Annual Report **4656**
Annual Report - State Consumer Protection Board *see* New York (State) Consumer Protection Board. Annual Report **1507**
Annual Report - State of Alaska. Violent Crimes Compensation Board *see* Alaska. Violent Crimes Compensation Board. Annual Report **1509**
Annual Report - State of Alaska, Legislative Budget and Audit Committee *see* Alaska. Legislature. Budget and Audit Committee. Annual Report **4052**
Annual Report - State of Connecticut, Council on Environmental Quality *see* Connecticut. Council on Environmental Quality. Annual Report **1946**
Annual Report - State of Hawaii. State Commission on the Status of Women *see* Hawaii. State Commission on the Status of Women. Annual Report **4844**
Annual Report: State of Idaho Johnson-O'Malley Program *see* Idaho. State Superintendent of Public Instruction. Annual Report. State of Idaho Johnson-O'Malley Program **1638**

Title

ANNUARIO STATISTICO 5917

Annual Report - State of New York, Division of Criminal Justice Services *see* New York (State). Division of Criminal Justice Service. Annual Report **1519**
Annual Report - Susquehanna River Basin Commission *see* Susquehanna River Basin Commission. Annual Report **4828**
Annual Report - The Asia Society *see* The Asia Society. Annual Report **2336**
Annual Report - the Institute for Certification of Computer Professionals *see* Institute for the Certification of Computer Professionals. Annual Report **1396**
Annual Report to Congress by the Task Force on Environmental Cancer and Heart and Lung Disease *see* Task Force on Environmental Cancer and Heart and Lung Disease. Annual Report to Congress **1983**
Annual Report to Congress on the Automotive Technology Development Program *see* U.S. Department of Energy. Annual Report to Congress on the Automotive Technology Development Program **4704**
Annual Report to Congress - Urban Initiatives Anti-Crime Program *see* U.S. Urban Initiatives Anti-Crime Program. Annual Report to Congress **1524**
Annual Report to the Congress by the Office of Technology Assessment *see* U.S. Office of Technology Assessment Annual Report to the Congress **4076**
Annual Report to the Governor and Legislature - Teacher's Retirement Board *see* California. Teachers Retirement Board. State Teacher's Retirement System; Annual Report to the Governor and the Legislature **1725**
Annual Report to the Supreme Court of Illinois *see* Illinois. Administrative Office of Illinois Courts. Annual Report to the Supreme Court of Illinois **2633**
Annual Report - University of Georgia, Institute of Ecology *see* University of Georgia. Institute of Ecology. Annual Report **1970**
Annual Report - Utah Juvenile Court *see* Utah. Juvenile Court. Annual Report **1245**
Annual Report - Vermont Industrial Development Authority *see* Vermont Industrial Development Authority. Annual Report **1086**
Annual Report - Western Society of Malacologists *see* Western Society of Malacologists. Annual Report **593**
Annual Report - Woodrow Wilson International Center for Scholars *see* Woodrow Wilson International Center for Scholars. Annual Report **1724**
Annual Reports in Medicinal Chemistry. (US ISSN 0065-7743) **3717**
Annual Reports in Organic Synthesis. (US ISSN 0066-409X) **1224**
Annual Reports on Competition in O E C D Member Countries *see* Competition Policy in O E C D Countries **927**
†Annual Reports on Fermentation Processes. (US ISSN 0140-9115) **5136**
Annual Reports on N M R Spectroscopy. (US ISSN 0066-4103) **3851**
Annual Review in Automatic Programming. (US ISSN 0066-4138) **1429**
▼Annual Review of Addictions Research and Treatment. (US ISSN 0955-663X) **1534**, 3330
Annual Review of Agriculture in Kinki District/Kinki Nogyo Josei Hokoku. (JA) **76**
Annual Review of Anthropology. (US ISSN 0084-6570) **233**
Annual Review of Applied Linguistics. (UK ISSN 0267-1905) **2803**
Annual Review of Astronomy and Astrophysics. (US ISSN 0066-4146) **360**, 3814
Annual Review of Banking Law. (US ISSN 0739-2451) **759**, 2598
Annual Review of Behavior Therapy: Theory and Practice *see* Review of Behavior Therapy: Theory & Practice **4044**
Annual Review of Biochemistry. (US ISSN 0066-4154) **471**
Annual Review of Biophysics and Biomolecular Structure. (US ISSN 1056-8700) **484**, 468, 1814
Annual Review of Biophysics and Biophysical Chemistry *see* Annual Review of Biophysics and Biomolecular Structure **484**
†Annual Review of Birth Defects. (US) **5136**
Annual Review of California - Alaska Oil and Gas Exploration. (US) **3682**
Annual Review of Cell Biology. (US ISSN 0743-4634) **522**
Annual Review of Chronopharmacology.(US ISSN 0743-9539) **3717**
†Annual Review of Computer Science. (US ISSN 8756-7016) **5136**
Annual Review of Criminal Law. (CN) **2598**
Annual Review of Earth and Planetary Sciences. (US ISSN 0084-6597) **1541**, 360
Annual Review of Ecology and Systematics. (US ISSN 0066-4162) **1943**
Annual Review of Energy *see* Annual Review of Energy and the Environment **1783**
Annual Review of Energy and the Environment. (US ISSN 1056-3466) **1783**
Annual Review of Engineering Industries and Automation. (UN ISSN 0255-9293) **1915**
Annual Review of Entomology. (US ISSN 0066-4170) **528**
▼Annual Review of European Community Affairs (Year). (BE) **3950**, 843
▼Annual Review of Fish Diseases. (US ISSN 0959-8030) **578**
Annual Review of Fluid Mechanics. (US ISSN 0066-4189) **3842**
Annual Review of Genetics. (US ISSN 0066-4197) **539**
Annual Review of Gerontology & Geriatrics. (US ISSN 0198-8794) **2270**
Annual Review of Global Education. (UK) **1615**, 4593
Annual Review of Immunology. (US ISSN 0732-0582) **3183**
Annual Review of Information Science and Technology. (NE ISSN 0066-4200) **2743**
†Annual Review of Jazz Studies. (US ISSN 0731-0641) **5136**
Annual Review of Major Residential Property Markets in Australia. (AT) **2499**
Annual Review of Materials Science. (US ISSN 0084-6600) **1915**
Annual Review of Medicine: Selected Topics in the Clinical Sciences. (US ISSN 0066-4219) **3077**
Annual Review of Microbiology. (US ISSN 0066-4227) **549**
Annual Review of N M R Spectroscopy *see* Annual Reports on N M R Spectroscopy **3851**
Annual Review of Neuroscience. (US ISSN 0147-006X) **3330**
Annual Review of Nuclear and Particle Science. (US ISSN 0163-8998) **3846**
†Annual Review of Numerical Fluid Mechanics and Heat Transfer. (US ISSN 0892-6883) **5136**
Annual Review of Nursing Research. (US ISSN 0739-6686) **3275**
Annual Review of Nutrition. (US ISSN 0199-9885) **3603**
Annual Review of Pharmacology and Toxicology. (US ISSN 0362-1642) **3717**, 1980
Annual Review of Physical Chemistry. (US ISSN 0066-426X) **1224**
Annual Review of Physiology. (US ISSN 0066-4278) **569**
Annual Review of Phytopathology. (US ISSN 0066-4286) **494**
Annual Review of Plant Physiology *see* Annual Review of Plant Physiology and Plant Molecular Biology **494**
Annual Review of Plant Physiology and Plant Molecular Biology. (US ISSN 1040-2519) **494**
Annual Review of Political Science. (US ISSN 0748-8599) **3873**
Annual Review of Poverty Law. (US) **2598**
Annual Review of Project Performance Results. (UN) **926**, 759, 3950
Annual Review of Psychology. (US ISSN 0066-4308) **4011**
Annual Review of Public Health. (US ISSN 0163-7525) **4097**
Annual Review of Rehabilitation *see* Advances in Clinical Rehabilitation **4397**
Annual Review of Sociology. (US ISSN 0360-0572) **4429**
Annual Review of the Chemical Industry. (UN ISSN 0255-4291) **1071**, 1170
Annual Review of the Residential Property Markets in Australia *see* Annual Review of Major Residential Property Markets in Australia **2499**
Annual Review of United Nations Affairs. (US ISSN 0066-4340) **3950**
Annual Review of World Press Freedom *see* World Press Freedom Review **2577**
†Annual Statement of the Overseas Trade of the United Kingdom. (UK ISSN 0072-5846) **5136**
Annual Statistical Report of the Colorado Judiciary. (US ISSN 0094-7504) **2697**
Annual Statistical Report on Profit, Sales & Marketing Trends for the Men's & Boy's Tailored Clothing Industry. (US) **1288**
Annual Statistical Survey of Cancer. *see* Etesia Statistike. Erevna tou Karkinou **3171**
Annual Statistics of Maritime Safety. (JA ISSN 0448-3294) **4724**
Annual Statistics of Water Works. *see* Suido Jigyo Nenpo **4835**
Annual Student Symposium on Marine Affairs. Proceedings. (US ISSN 0270-1480) **1615**, 428
Annual Summary of Australian Notices to Mariners *see* Annual Australian Notices to Mariners **4724**
Annual Summary of Business Statistics, New York State. (US ISSN 0066-4375) **702**
Annual Summary of Investigations Relating to Reading. (US ISSN 0197-5129) **1615**
Annual Summary of Merchant Ships Completed in the World. (UK ISSN 0261-2720) **4724**, 4661
Annual Summary of Merchant Ships Launched, Completed in the World *see* Annual Summary of Merchant Ships Completed in the World **4724**
Annual Summary of Progress in Gravitation Sciences. (US) **3814**
Annual Summary of Vital Statistics (Boise) *see* Idaho. Department of Health and Welfare. Annual Summary of Vital Statistics **4117**
Annual Survey of African Law. (UK ISSN 0066-4405) **2599**
Annual Survey of American Law. (US ISSN 0066-4413) **2599**
Annual Survey of Australian Law. (AT ISSN 0727-4076) **2599**
Annual Survey of Bankruptcy Law. (US) **2599**
Annual Survey of Clerical Employees. (CN) **807**
Annual Survey of Computer Users. (JA) **1389**
Annual Survey of Indian Law. (II ISSN 0570-2666) **2599**
Annual Survey on Current Rolling Stock Production. *see* Tetsudo Sharyoto Seisan Dotai Tokei Nenpo **4667**
Annual T N G Convention Officers' Report *see* Newspaper Guild. Annual T.N.G. Convention Officers' Report **2573**
Annual Task Summary, Contract Research Program *see* U.S. Office of Naval Research. Annual Task Summary: Contract Research Program **3474**
Annual Textile Industry Technical Conference (Publication) *see* Textile Industry Technical Conference (Publication) **4625**
Annual Third World Conference Proceedings. (US ISSN 0885-2316) **2306**, 926, 3873
Annual U S C O L D Lecture. (U S Committee on Large Dams) (US) **1861**
Annual Water Quality Report to Congress *see* Wisconsin. Department of Natural Resources. Annual Water Quality Report to Congress **4834**
†Annual World's Best S F. (US) **5136**
Annual Worldwide T V Survey *see* Movie - T V Marketing Annual Worldwide Television Survey **1377**
▼Annuario A N D I L (Year). (Associazione Nazionale degli Industriali dei Laterizi) (IT) **1161**, 3015
Annuario Aerospaziale. (IT) **46**
Annuario Amministrativo Italiano/Italian Administrative Directory. (IT ISSN 0084-6619) **4053**
Annuario Articoli Casalinghi e Articoli Regalo. (IT) **2556**, 1161
Annuario Audio & Video. (IT) **4459**, 1384
Annuario Brasileiro de Ceramica. (BL ISSN 0100-8633) **1161**
Annuario Cattolico d'Italia. (IT ISSN 0066-4464) **4255**
Annuario Ceramica. (IT ISSN 0066-4472) **1161**
Annuario de Ceramica *see* Tile Book (Year) **1155**
Annuario de Fornitori *see* Suppliers Ceramics Book **1154**
Annuario dei Fornitori per l'Industria del Vetro *see* Glass Book **1136**
Annuario dell'Agricoltura Italiana. (IT ISSN 0304-0666) **76**
Annuario dell'Industria Italiana della Gomma *see* Guida all'Industria Italiana della Gomma **4291**
Annuario dell'Industria Italiana della Magliera e della Calzetteria *see* Guida all'Industria Italiana della Maglieria e della Calzetteria **4619**
Annuario della Nautica. (IT) **4522**
Annuario delle Ceramiche Italiane per l'Edilizia *see* Tile Book **1155**
Annuario di Contabilita Nazionale Tomo 1. (IT ISSN 0390-654X) **4078**
Annuario di Contabilita Nazionale Tomo 2. (IT ISSN 0390-6531) **4078**
Annuario di Statistiche Giudiziarie - Tomo 2. (IT) **2697**, 4562
Annuario Diplomatico del Regno d'Italia *see* Annuario Diplomatico della Repubblica Italiana **3950**
Annuario Diplomatico della Repubblica Italiana. (IT) **3950**
Annuario Europeo dell'Ambiente. (IT) **1943**, 2483, 2599
Annuario Filosofico (Year). (IT) **3761**
Annuario Fotografico. (IT) **3788**
Annuario Generale delle Imprese di Viaggio e Turismo. (IT) **4752**
Annuario Generale Italiano. (IT ISSN 0084-6627) **833**
Annuario Illustrato del Tennis. (IT) **4499**
Annuario Italiano delle Imprese Assicuratrici. (IT ISSN 0084-6635) **2526**
Annuario Italiano Macchine Utensili e Complementari *see* A M U **3015**
†Annuario Italiano Pubblicita Marketing Relazioni Pubbliche. (IT) **5136**
Annuario Musicale Italiano. (IT) **3539**
Annuario Ottico Italiano. (IT) **1121**, 3298
Annuario Sanitario Italiano/Italian Sanitary Directory. (IT) **4097**
Annuario Servizi Finanziari *see* A S E F I **758**
Annuario Statistico dell'Attivita Edilizia e delle Opere Pubbliche. (IT ISSN 0075-1804) **636**

Title

Annuario Statistico dell'Istruzione - Tomo 1. (IT ISSN 0390-6582) **1674**
Annuario Statistico dell'Istruzione - Tomo 2. (IT ISSN 0390-6590) **1674**
†Annuario Statistico delle Biblioteche Lombarde. (IT) **5136**
Annuario Statistico Italiano. (IT ISSN 0066-4545) **4562**
Annuario Suono. (IT) **4459**
Annuarium Historiae Conciliorum. (GW ISSN 0003-5157) **4162**, 2306
Annuarium Statisticum Ecclesiae/Statistique de l'Eglise/Statistical Yearbook of the Church. (VC) **4212**, 4562
Annuel de Chasse ou Annuel de Peche. (CN) **4541**
Annunciatore Poligrafico. (IT ISSN 0003-5165) **3997**
Ano del Transporte. (SP) **4646**
Anocero. (AG) **3873**
Anomalous Phenomenon Review see Hidden History **3669**
Anon Nine. (US) **2895**
Anorexia Nervosa & Related Eating Disorders, Inc. Alert see A N R E D Alert **4008**
Another Chicago Magazine. (US ISSN 0272-4359) **2895**
†Another Place to Publish. (US) **5136**
†Another Season. (US ISSN 0735-8202) **5136**
Anregung. (GW ISSN 0402-5563) **1744**, 4464
Die Anregung. (GW ISSN 0003-519X) **4163**
Anritsu Technical Bulletin/Anritsu Tekunikaru. (JA ISSN 0003-5211) **1882**, 1331
Anritsu Tekunikaru. see Anritsu Technical Bulletin **1882**
Anruf. (GW) **4163**
†Ans Werk. (GW ISSN 0003-522X) **5136**
Ansaetze. (GW) **4163**
†Anschlaege. (GW ISSN 0344-2667) **5136**
Anschriften Deutscher Verlage und Auslaendischer Verlage mit Deutschen Auslieferungen see Deutschsprachige Verlage **4126**
Ansearchin' News see Tennessee Genealogical Magazine, "Ansearchin'" News **2165**
Anselm Studies. (US ISSN 0735-0864) **4163**
Ansgarsposten. (SW ISSN 0003-5262) **1248**
†Anson G. Phelps Lectureship on Early American History. (US ISSN 0066-4618) **5136**
Anson Newsletter. (US ISSN 0889-1680) **2144**
Anstoesse. (GW ISSN 0003-5270) **4163**, 2503
Answer. (US) **1361**
†Answer Man Newsletter. (US ISSN 0736-2684) **5136**
Answers. (US) **2743**
▼Ant Farm. (US) **2988**
Ant Spoim - Smash Apathy. (US) **2988**
Antaeus. (HU ISSN 0238-0218) **262**
Antaeus. (US ISSN 0003-5319) **2895**
Antal Modtagere, Adresseloese Postforsendelser. (DK ISSN 0900-8829) **1352**
Antarctic. (NZ ISSN 0003-5327) **2241**, 4752
Antarctic Bibliography. (US ISSN 0066-4626) **2242**
Antarctic Bulletin. see Antarktiese Bulletin **1541**
Antarctic Journal of the United States. (US ISSN 0003-5335) **4299**, 1541
Antarctic Meteorite Newsletter. (US) **360**
Antarctic Record. see Nankyoku Shiryo **2256**
Antarctic Research Book Series. (US) **2242**
Antarctic Science. (UK ISSN 0954-1020) **428**
Antarktiese Bulletin/Antarctic Bulletin. (SA ISSN 0003-5351) **1541**, 428, 3432

Antartida. (AG ISSN 0302-5691) **2242**
Antena. (XV ISSN 0003-536X) **2858**
Antenna. (UK ISSN 0140-1890) **528**
Antenna see Antenna - Eletronica Popular **1368**
Antenna. (IT ISSN 0003-5386) **1368**, 4459
Antenna see Sensor **2883**
Antenna - Eletronica Popular. (BL ISSN 0101-9112) **1368**, 1764
Antenna Survey System Tower File Report. (US) **1346**
Antenna Survey Tower File. (US) **1346**
Antenne see Antenne Aktuell **1615**
L'Antenne. (FR) **4724**, 833
Antenne Aktuell. (GW) **1615**, 1232
Antenne Medicale. (FR ISSN 0003-5394) **3375**
Anteprima Libri. (IT ISSN 0393-2664) **2858**
Anterem. (IT) **2895**
Antheon. (US) **2895**, 1303
Anthologia Medica Santoriana. (IT) **3077**
Anthology of Magazine Verse see Anthology of Magazine Verse and Yearbook of American Poetry **2855**
Anthology of Magazine Verse and Yearbook of American Poetry. (US ISSN 0196-2221) **2855**
The Anthonian. (US) **4255**
Anthony and Berryman's Magistrates' Court Guide. (UK ISSN 0262-3234) **2599**
Anthos. (SZ ISSN 0003-5424) **292**, 2121
Anthropologia Hungarica. (HU ISSN 0574-3842) **233**
Anthropologiai Kozlemenyek. (HU ISSN 0003-5440) **233**
Anthropologica. (CN ISSN 0003-5459) **233**, 262
Anthropologica. (SP ISSN 0301-6587) **233**
Anthropologica (Lima). (PE ISSN 0254-9212) **234**
Anthropological Forum. (AT ISSN 0066-4677) **234**
Anthropological Index to Current Periodicals in the Library of the Museum of Mankind Library. (UK) **253**, 2
Anthropological Linguistics. (US ISSN 0003-5483) **2803**, 234
Anthropological Literature. (US ISSN 0190-3373) **253**, 234
Anthropological Quarterly. (US ISSN 0003-5491) **234**
Anthropological Society of Nippon. Journal. (JA ISSN 0003-5505) **234**
Anthropological Society of Oxford. Journal. (UK ISSN 0044-8370) **234**
Anthropological Survey of India. Bulletin see Human Science **241**
L'Anthropologie. (FR ISSN 0003-5521) **234**
Anthropologie. (CS ISSN 0323-1119) **234**
Anthropologie. (GW ISSN 0066-4685) **234**
Anthropologie - Maritime. (FR ISSN 0758-5683) **578**, 234
Anthropologie Visuelle. (FR ISSN 0993-4871) **234**
Anthropologika. (GR ISSN 0253-5092) **262**
Anthropologische Gesellschaft, Vienna. Mitteilungen. (AU ISSN 0066-4693) **234**
Anthropologischer Anzeiger. (GW ISSN 0003-5548) **253**, 2
Anthropologist. (II ISSN 0003-5556) **234**
Anthropology and Archeology of Eurasia. (US) **234**, 262
Anthropology & Education Quarterly. (US ISSN 0161-7761) **234**, 1615
Anthropology and Humanism Quarterly. (US ISSN 0193-5615) **234**
Anthropology Newsletter. (US ISSN 0098-1605) **234**
Anthropology of America see Masterkey **5233**
Anthropology of Consciousness. (US ISSN 1053-4202) **234**, 3668

Anthropology Research Association. Research Bulletin. (II) **234**
Anthropology Today. (UK) **234**
Anthropology U C L A. (US ISSN 0003-5564) **234**
Anthropos. (SZ ISSN 0257-9774) **234**, 2803
Anthropos. (IT ISSN 0391-3163) **234**
Anthropos. (VE) **234**
Anthropos. (SP ISSN 0211-5611) **2503**, 2743
Anthropos. (GW ISSN 0066-4723) **3656**, 234
▼Anthropos. Documentos A. (SP ISSN 1130-4936) **2503**, 2743
Anthropos. Suplementos. (SP) **2503**, 2743
Anthropos: Yearbook in Anthropology. (GR ISSN 1105-2155) **234**
Anthroposophy Today. (UK ISSN 0269-3259) **4280**
Anthrozoos. (US ISSN 0892-7936) **235**, 578, 1943
Anti. (GR) **3873**
Anti-Apartheid Movement. Annual Report of Activities and Developments. (UK) **3940**
Anti-Apartheid Movement Briefings Series see A A M Briefings Series **3939**
Anti-Apartheid News. (UK ISSN 0003-5580) **3940**
Anti Apartheidskrant. (NE) **2331**
Anti-Cancer Drug Design. (UK ISSN 0266-9536) **3193**, 471
Anti-Censorship NewsLetter. (US) **4429**, 1232, 3940, 4398
Anti-Corrosion Handbook & Directory. (UK) **3402**
Anti-Corrosion Methods and Materials. (UK ISSN 0003-5599) **3402**
Anti-Defamation League of B'nai B'rith Front Line see A D L on the Front Line **3939**
Anti-Defamation League of B'nai B'rith Law Report see A D L Law Report **2593**
Anti-Draft. (US) **3451**, 3950
Anti-Isolation. (US) **2988**
Anti-Slavery Reporter. (UK) **3940**
Anti-Static Proposals & Electro-Conductive Technologies see A S P E C T **1881**
Antiane. (GP ISSN 0987-4216) **645**
Antibiotic Guidelines. (AT ISSN 0729-218X) **3077**
Antibiotics and Chemotherapy. see Antibiotiki i Khimioterapiya **3717**
Antibiotics and Chemotherapy. (SZ ISSN 0066-4758) **3717**
Antibiotiki i Khimioterapiya/Antibiotics and Chemotherapy. (RU ISSN 0235-2990) **3717**
Antibiotiki i Meditsinskaya Biotekhnologiya see Antibiotiki i Khimioterapiya **3717**
Antibody, Immunoconjugates, and Radiopharmaceuticals. (US ISSN 0892-7049) **3193**, 3183, 3717
†Antic: the Atari Resource. (US ISSN 0745-2527) **5136**
Anticancer Research. (GR ISSN 0250-7005) **3193**
Antichita, Archeologia, Storia dell'Arte. (IT) **312**, 262
Antichita Classica e Cristiana. (IT ISSN 0066-4766) **2306**, 2803, 3761
†Antichita Pisane. (IT) **5136**
Antichthon. (AT ISSN 0066-4774) **1274**
Anticipation see Church and Society Newsletter **4170**
Antiek. (NE ISSN 0003-5653) **254**, 312
Antiekrevue see Kunst & Antiekrevue **258**
Antietam Review. (US) **2895**, 2988
†Antigen Antibody Reactions. (UK ISSN 0142-8462) **5136**
Antigonish Review. (CN ISSN 0003-5661) **2895**
Antigua Commercial Bank. Annual Report. (AQ) **759**
Antik & Auktion. (SW ISSN 0346-9212) **254**, 312
Antik Tanulmanyok. (HU ISSN 0003-567X) **1274**
Antike Kunst. (SZ ISSN 0003-5688) **262**, 254, 312

Antike Kunst. Beihefte. (SZ ISSN 0066-4782) **262**, 254, 312
Antike und Abendland. (GW ISSN 0003-5696) **1274**
Antilia. (TR) **2858**
Antilla. (MQ ISSN 0757-3960) **2239**
Antilliaanse Nieuwsbrief. (NE ISSN 0003-5718) **2211**
Antimicrobial Agents and Chemotherapy. (US ISSN 0066-4804) **549**, 3717
Antimicrobial Agents Annual. (NE) **549**, 559
Antimicrobic Newsletter. (US ISSN 0738-1751) **3218**
Antimilitarismus Information. (GW ISSN 0342-5789) **3451**
Antioch Review. (US ISSN 0003-5769) **2858**
Antioquia. Secretaria de Educacion y Cultura. Revista Cultura. (CK) **2895**
Antioquia Medica. (CK ISSN 0044-8389) **3077**
Antipode. (US ISSN 0066-4812) **2242**
Antipodes. (US ISSN 0893-5580) **2895**
Antiqua. (IT) **262**, 254, 312
Antiquarian (Plattsburgh). (US) **2398**, 254, 312
Antiquarian Book Monthly Review. (UK ISSN 0306-7475) **4120**
Antiquarian Bookman Bookman's Weekly see A B Bookman's Weekly **4119**
Antiquarian Bookman Bookman's Yearbook see A B Bookman's Yearbook **4119**
Antiquarian Horology and the Proceedings of the Antiquarian Horological Society. (UK ISSN 0003-5785) **2562**
Antiquariato. (IT) **254**, 312
Antiquaries Journal. (UK ISSN 0003-5815) **262**
Antique Airplane Association News. (US ISSN 0003-5823) **46**, 254
Antique and Classic Boat see Classic Boating **4524**
Antique and Collectors Mart see Collectors Mart **256**
Antique Angler. (US ISSN 0744-3749) **4541**, 254
Antique Appraisal Association of America. Newsletter. (US) **254**
Antique Automobile. (US ISSN 0003-5831) **254**, 4679
Antique Car Times. (US) **254**
Antique Clocks. (UK) **2563**, 255
Antique Collecting. (UK ISSN 0003-584X) **255**
Antique Collector. (UK ISSN 0003-5858) **255**
Antique Comb Collector. (US ISSN 0892-7162) **255**, 2563
Antique Dealer and Collectors' Guide. (UK ISSN 0003-5866) **255**
Antique Finder see Antique Collecting **255**
Antique Label Collector Magazine. (US) **2433**
Antique Maps, Sea Charts, City Views, Celestial Charts and Battle Plans, Price-Record and Handbook for... (US ISSN 0749-4971) **255**, 2242
Antique Market Report. (US ISSN 8750-9024) **255**
Antique Monthly. (US ISSN 0003-5882) **255**
Antique Outboard Motor Club Newsletter. (US) **255**
Antique Outboarder. (US ISSN 0003-5904) **4522**, 255
Antique Phonograph Monthly. (US ISSN 0361-2147) **3539**, 255
Antique Phonograph Monthly Monograph Series see A P M Monograph Series **3536**
Antique Radio Classified. (US) **1355**
Antique Review. (US) **255**
†Antique Shops of Australia. (AT) **5136**
Antique Showcase. (CN ISSN 0713-6315) **255**
Antique Stove Association. Yearbook. (US) **255**, 2297

Antique Trader Price Guide to Antiques and Collectors' Items. (US ISSN 0556-5367) **255**
Antique Trader Weekly. (US ISSN 0161-8342) **255**
Antique Truck Registry. (US) **4743**
Antique Week. (US) **255**
†Antiques. (UK) **5136**
Antiques and Art Directory and Traveler's Guide see Antiques Directory and Traveler's Guide **255**
Antiques and Auction News. (US) **255**
Antiques & Collectibles Magazine. (US) **255**
Antiques & Collecting Hobbies. (US) **255, 2433**
Antiques & Fine Arts. (US) **255, 353**
Antiques Bulletin. (UK) **255**
Antiques Dealers' Association of America. Forum. (US) **255, 1033**
▼The Antiques Directory. (US) **255**
Antiques Directory and Traveler's Guide.(US) **255, 312**
Antiques Folio. (UK) **255, 312**
Antiques Investment Report see Art - Antiques Investment Report **313**
Antiques Trade Gazette. (UK ISSN 0306-1051) **255**
Antiques World see Antiques **5136**
AntiqueWeek see AntiqueWeek - Central **255**
AntiqueWeek - Central. (US) **255, 2144**
AntiqueWeek - Eastern. (US) **255, 2144**
Antiquitaeten-Zeitung. (GW) **255**
Antiquitas. Reihe 1. Abhandlungen zur Alten Geschichte. (GW ISSN 0066-4839) **2306**
Antiquitas. Reihe 2. Abhandlungen aus dem Gebiete der Vor- und Fruehgeschichte. (GW ISSN 0066-4847) **2306**
Antiquitas. Reihe 3. Abhandlungen zur Vor- und Fruehgeschichte, zur Klassischen und Provinzial-Roemischen Archaeologie und zur Geschichte des Altertums. (GW ISSN 0066-4855) **2306, 262**
Antiquitas. Reihe 4. Beitraege zur Historia-Augusta-Forschung. (GW ISSN 0066-4863) **2306**
Antiquites Africaines. (FR ISSN 0066-4871) **2331, 262**
Antiquity. (UK ISSN 0003-598X) **262**
▼Antisense Research & Development. (US ISSN 1050-5261) **539, 471**
The Antiseptic. (II ISSN 0003-5998) **3375**
Antisexism Newsletter. (US) **4837**
Antithetical Couplet - Folk Stories about Antithetical Couplet. see Duilian - Minjian Duilian Gushi **2912**
Antitrust. (US ISSN 0162-7996) **2599**
Antitrust Adviser, 3-E. (US) **2599**
Antitrust and American Business Abroad, 2-E. (US) **2599**
Antitrust & Commerce Report. (US) **2599, 645**
Antitrust & Trade Regulation Report. (US ISSN 0003-6021) **1072, 2599**
Antitrust Bulletin. (US ISSN 0003-603X) **2599**
Antitrust Counseling and Litigation Techniques. (US) **2599**
Antitrust Freedom of Information Log. (US ISSN 0891-8546) **900, 2599**
Antitrust Law and Economics Review. (US ISSN 0003-6048) **2599, 645**
Antitrust Law Handbook. (US ISSN 0738-5919) **2599**
Antitrust Law Journal. (US ISSN 0003-6056) **2599**
Antitrust Laws and Trade Regulation. (US) **2599**
Antitrust Laws and Trade Regulation: Desk Edition. (US) **2599**
Antitumor and Antiviral Agents - Experimental Therapeutics, Toxicology, Pharmacology see I C R D B Cancergram: Antitumor and Antiviral Agents - Experimental Therapeutics, Toxicology, Pharmacology **1982**

Antitumor and Antiviral Agents-- Mechanism of Action see I C R D B Cancergram: Antitumor and Antiviral Agents - Mechanism of Action **3175**
▼Antiviral Chemistry & Chemotherapy. (UK ISSN 0956-3202) **3717**
Antiviral Research. (NE ISSN 0166-3542) **549**
†Antoinette. (FR ISSN 0402-6233) **5136**
Antologia. (AG) **2895**
Antologia di Belle Arti. (IT) **312**
Antologia Medica Italiana see Rivista Internazionale di Chirurgia Vertebrale e dei Nervi Periferici **3150**
Antologia Poetica de Esteban Echevarria see Antologia Poetica del Partido de Esteban Echevarria **2988**
Antologia Poetica del Partido de Esteban Echevarria. (AG) **2988**
Antologia Vieusseux see Il Vieusseux **2888**
Antonianum. (VC ISSN 0003-6064) **4255**
Antonie van Leeuwenhoek International Journal of General and Molecular Microbiology. (NE) **549**
Antonie van Leeuwenhoek Journal of Microbiology see Antonie van Leeuwenhoek International Journal of General and Molecular Microbiology **549**
Antrieb. (GW) **4724**
Antrieb mit Steuerung und Regelung see A S R **5129**
Antriebstechnik. (GW ISSN 0003-6099) **4593**
Antrim County Library Quarterly Newssheet see Northern Eastern Education Library Board. Library Bulletin **2777**
Antropologi i Finland. see Suomen Antropologi **250**
Antropologia. (BO) **235**
Antropologia. (PL ISSN 0137-1460) **235**
Antropologia see Revista Chilena de Antropologia **248**
Antropologia Andina. (PE) **235**
Antropologia Contemporanea. (IT ISSN 0392-9035) **235**
Antropologia e Historia de Guatemala (I D A E H). (GT ISSN 0003-6102) **235, 262, 2306**
Antropologia Ecuatoriana. (EC) **235**
Antropologia Portuguesa. (PO ISSN 0870-0990) **235**
Antropologica. (VE ISSN 0003-6110) **235**
Antropologiska Studier. (SW) **235**
Antropolognytt see Antropologiska Studier **235**
Antropos. (AG ISSN 0003-6137) **2858**
Antroposofia. (IT ISSN 0003-6145) **3761**
Antwerp Bee-Argus. (US ISSN 0003-617X) **2221**
Antwerp Port Annual. (BE) **1121, 4724**
Antwerpens Oudheidkundige Kring. Jaarboek see Koninklijke Oudheidkundige Kring van Antwerpen. Jaarboek **277**
Die Antwort. (GW) **4717**
Anuari Verdaguer. (SP) **2988**
Anuario A B D I B. (Associacao Brasileira para o Desenvolvimento das Industrias de Base) (BL) **1072**
Anuario Aerospacial Brasileiro/Brazilian Aerospace Yearbook. (BL) **46**
Anuario Antropologico. (BL) **235**
†Anuario Avicola. (BL) **5136**
Anuario Avicola & Suinicola. (BL) **210**
Anuario Avicola e Anuario Suincola see Anuario Avicola & Suinicola **210**
Anuario Bibliografico Colombiano. (CK ISSN 0570-393X) **389**
Anuario Bibliografico Costaricense. (CR ISSN 0066-5010) **389**
Anuario Bibliografico Dominicano. (DR) **389**
Anuario Bibliografico Ecuatoriano. (EC) **389**
Anuario Bibliografico Uruguayo. (UY ISSN 0304-8861) **389**
Anuario Brasileiro de Media. (BL) **28, 1331**

Anuario Brasileiro de Propaganda. (BL ISSN 0570-3956) **28**
Anuario Brasileiro do Plastico. (BL) **3861**
Anuario Brasileiro de Otica Cine Foto Som. (BL) **3788**
Anuario - C B A - Yearbook. (US ISSN 0084-893X) **389**
Anuario Climatologico. (PO ISSN 0870-2950) **3432**
Anuario Colombiano de Historia Social y de la Cultura. (CK ISSN 0066-5045) **4365**
Anuario da Provincia de Mocambique see Anuario do Estado de Mocambique **2331**
Anuario das Estradas de Ferro. (BL) **4707**
Anuario das Industrias do Estado do Rio Grande do Sul. (BL) **1072**
†Anuario de Arquitectura Mexicana. (MX) **5136**
Anuario de Derecho Civil Uruguayo. (UY) **2599**
Anuario de Derecho Internacional. (SP) **2719**
Anuario de Derecho Publico y Estudios Politicos. (SP) **2599, 3873**
Anuario de Empresas Exportadoras. (SP) **1121**
Anuario de Estadisticas de Turismo see Spain. Ministerio de Transportes, Turismo y Comunicaciones. Secretaria General de Turismo. Anuario de Estadisticas de Turismo **4800**
Anuario de Estadisticas Estatales. (MX) **2267, 4562**
Anuario de Estudios Americanos. (SP ISSN 0210-5810) **235**
Anuario de Estudios Centroamericanos. (CR ISSN 0377-7316) **4365**
Anuario de Estudios Medievales. (SP ISSN 0066-5061) **2348**
Anuario de Exportacion de Austria. see Austria Export Herold **1122**
Anuario de Filologia. (SP ISSN 0210-1343) **2803, 2895**
Anuario de Historia Contemporanea. (SP) **2306**
Anuario de Historia Moderna y Contemporanea. (SP ISSN 0210-9603) **2306**
Anuario de Importacion - Exportacion del Uruguay. (UY) **900**
Anuario de Jurisprudencia Argentina see Jurisprudencia Argentina **2641**
Anuario de la Exportacion de Dinamarca. see Udenrigs Handelskalenderen for Danmark **1156**
Anuario de la Mineria de Chile. (CL ISSN 0066-5096) **3478, 1554**
Anuario de la Relojeria en Espana see Anuario de Relojeria y Arte en Metal para Espana e Hispanoamerica **2563**
Anuario de Letras. (MX ISSN 0543-758X) **2895**
Anuario de Linguistica Hispanica. (SP ISSN 0213-053X) **2803**
Anuario de Portos e Navios. (BL) **4724**
Anuario de Productos Forestales. see Yearbook of Forest Products **2119**
Anuario de Psicologia. (SP ISSN 0066-5126) **4011**
Anuario de Relojeria y Arte en Metal para Espana e Hispanoamerica. (SP ISSN 0066-510X) **2563**
†Anuario de Sociologia y Psicologia Juridicas. (SP ISSN 0210-1785) **5137**
Anuario del Arte Espanol. (SP ISSN 0302-6965) **312**
Anuario del Comercio Exterior de Venezuela. (VE) **702**
†Anuario del Comercio Exterior Latino-Americano. (AG ISSN 0066-5118) **5137**
†Anuario del Cuento Costarricense. (CR ISSN 0587-5196) **5137**
Anuario Delta Larousse. (BL) **1780**
Anuario do Estado de Mocambique. (MZ) **2331**
Anuario dos Criadores. (BL ISSN 0518-0937) **76**

ANUARIO MINERAL 5919

Anuario Ecuatoriano de Derecho Internacional. (EC ISSN 0570-4251) **2719**
Anuario Empresarial de Colombia. (CK) **1121**
Anuario Enfermedades de Notificacion Obligatoria. (CL) **3077**
Anuario Espanol de Seguros. (SP) **2526**
Anuario Estadistico Centroamericano de Comercio Exterior. (GT ISSN 0570-426X) **702**
Anuario Estadistico Centroamericano de Comercio Exterior. (GT) **702, 900**
Anuario Estadistico de America Latina y el Caribe/Statistical Yearbook for Latin America and the Caribbean. (UN ISSN 1014-0697) **4562**
Anuario Estadistico de Chiapas. (MX) **4562**
Anuario Estadistico de Comercio Exterior de los Estados Unidos Mexicanos. (MX) **702**
Anuario Estadistico de Cuba. (CU ISSN 0574-6132) **4562**
Anuario Estadistico de Estado de Chihuahua. (MX) **4562**
†Anuario Estadistico de los Andes: Venezuela. (VE ISSN 0066-5185) **5137**
Anuario Estadistico de los Estados Unidos Mexicanos. (MX) **4562**
Anuario Estadistico de Oaxaca. (MX) **4562**
Anuario Estadistico de Puebla. (MX) **3979**
Anuario Estadistico del Paraguay. (PY) **4562**
Anuario Estadistico del Transporte Aereo Espana - (Year). (SP) **4661, 4671**
Anuario Estatistico das Ferrovias do Brasil. (BL) **4707**
Anuario Estatistico de Energia Electrica. (BL) **1797, 1801**
Anuario Estatistico do Brasil/Statistical Yearbook of Brazil. (BL ISSN 0100-1299) **4562**
Anuario Estatistico do Estado de Sao Paulo. (BL ISSN 0100-8730) **4562**
Anuario Estatistico do Rio Grande do Sul. (BL ISSN 0102-0226) **4562**
Anuario Estatistico dos Transportes. (BL) **4646**
Anuario F.H.I. Argentina: Frutas y Hortalizas Industriarizadas y Frescas/ F.H.I. Annual: Fresh and Industrialized Fruits and Vegetables. (AG ISSN 0066-5207) **168**
Anuario Filosofico. (SP ISSN 0066-5215) **3761**
Anuario Financiero (Year)/Annual Financial Data (Year). (MX) **843**
Anuario Financiero y de Sociedades Anonimas de Espana. (SP ISSN 0301-7443) **1072, 759**
Anuario Geografico del Peru. (PE ISSN 0066-5223) **2399, 2242**
Anuario Hidrologico del Istmo Centroamericano. (UN) **1597**
Anuario Hispano. (US) **3624, 1991**
Anuario Hortofruticola Espanol. (SP ISSN 0210-637X) **147**
Anuario Iberoamericano. (SP ISSN 0570-4324) **4366**
Anuario Indigenista/Indianist Yearbook. (MX) **235**
Anuario Industrial de la Provincia. (SP) **807**
Anuario Industrial de Minas Gerais see Guia Economico e Industrial do Estado de Minas Gerais **3484**
Anuario Interamericano de Archivos. (AG ISSN 0325-3899) **2399, 2743**
Anuario Interamericano de Derechos Humanos/Inter-American Yearbook on Human Rights. (US) **2719**
Anuario Juridico. (MX ISSN 0185-3295) **2599**
Anuario L L. (Literatura Linguistica) (CU) **2895, 2803**
Anuario Latinoamericano de los Plasticos. (MX) **3861**
Anuario Mexicano de Historia del Derecho. (MX) **2599**
Anuario Mineral Brasileiro. (BL) **3478**

ANUARIO: MUENSTERANER

†Anuario: Muensteraner Beitraege zur Latein Amerika Forschung. (GW) 5137
Anuario Musical. (SP ISSN 0211-3538) 3539
Anuario Politico de America Latina. (MX) 3873
†Anuarios de Geomagnetismo (Year). (SP) 5137
Anuarul Arhivei de Folclor. (RM) 2052
Anuarul de Folclor see Anuarul Arhivei de Folclor 2052
Anubis. (AU) 3668, 3593
Anustup. (II) 2858
Anuvad/Translation. (II ISSN 0003-6218) 2803
Anvesak. (II ISSN 0378-4568) 645, 4429
Anvil. (US ISSN 0890-2534) 3402, 76
Anvil. (UK) 4229
Anvil's Ring. (US ISSN 0889-177X) 353
Anwaltsblatt. (GW ISSN 0171-7227) 2599
Anxiety Disorders Association of America Reporter see A D A A Reporter 4007
Anxiety Research. (US ISSN 0891-7779) 4011
Any. (JA) 4837
Anyagmozgatas-Csomagolas. (HU ISSN 0003-6242) 4724, 3647
Anyagmozgatasi es Csomagolasi Szakirodalmi Tajekoztato/Abstract Journal for Materials Handling and Packaging. (HU ISSN 0230-5348) 4661, 2, 3652
▼Anyone. (US) 312
Anzeigen Beobachter Moebel. (GW) 2556, 1033
Anzeiger des Germanischen Nationalmuseums see Anzeiger des Germanischen Nationalmuseums und Berichte aus dem Forschungsinstitut fuer Realienkunde 2348
Anzeiger des Germanischen Nationalmuseums und Berichte aus dem Forschungsinstitut fuer Realienkunde. (GW ISSN 0934-5191) 2348, 312
Anzeiger des Oesterreichischen Buchhandels. (AU ISSN 0003-6277) 4120
Anzeiger des Reiches der Gerechtigkeit.(GW ISSN 0003-6285) 4163
Anzeiger des Verbandes der Antiquare Oesterreichs. (AU ISSN 0042-3610) 4120
Anzeiger fuer die Altertumswissenschaft. (AU ISSN 0003-6293) 1274, 262, 2306
Anzeiger fuer die Seelsorge. (GW ISSN 0721-1937) 4255
Anzeiger fuer Schaedlingskunde, Pflanzen- und Umweltschutz see Anzeiger fuer Schaedlingskunde, Pflanzenschutz, Umweltschutz 528
Anzeiger fuer Schaedlingskunde, Pflanzenschutz, Umweltschutz. (GW ISSN 0340-7330) 528, 76, 1943
Anzeiger fuer Slavische Philologie. (AU ISSN 0066-5282) 2803
Anzeiger Solothurn-Lebern. (SZ ISSN 0003-6315) 2218
Anzen no Shihyo/Barometer of Occupational Safety. (JA) 3614
Aomori-ken Kisho Geppo. see Aomori Prefecture. Monthly Report of Meteorology 3432
Aomori-ken Nogyo Kisho Junpo. (JA ISSN 0003-6323) 3432
Aomori Prefecture. Monthly Report of Meteorology/Aomori-ken Kisho Geppo. (JA ISSN 0029-7399) 3432
†Aontas Review. (IE ISSN 0332-1568) 5137
Aouzou. (LY) 2503
Aoyama Journal of Social Sciences/ Aoyama Shakai Kagaku Kiyo. (JA) 4366, 2599
Aoyama Shakai Kagaku Kiyo. see Aoyama Journal of Social Sciences 4366
L'Apache. (US) 2895, 312
Apache (Douglas). (US) 1303
Apacheta. (PE) 2052
Apalachee Quarterly. (US ISSN 0890-6408) 2895
Apararea Patriei. (RM) 3451
Aparato Locomotor. (Spanish edition of: Rheumatology and Traumatology) (SP) 3368, 3306
Apartment Age. (US ISSN 0192-0030) 2483, 2599, 4144
Apartment and Office Management News see Property Management Monthly 4155
Apartment Construction News see Multi Housing News 5240
Apartment Gazetteer (Europe). (UK) 4752
Apartment Management Newsletter. (US ISSN 0744-9143) 4144
Apartment Management Report. (US) 4144
Apartment News see Apartment Owner - Builder 2483
Apartment Owner. (US ISSN 0191-8826) 4144
Apartment Owner - Builder. (US) 2483
Apartment Owners and Managers Association of America Newsletter see A O M A Newsletter 4144
Ape del Conca. (IT) 2204
Apeiron. (CN ISSN 0003-6390) 3761, 1274
Apercu Technique - Technisch Overzicht (A T O). (BE ISSN 0003-6412) 3424, 2
Apereyon. (IS ISSN 0334-0899) 2895, 2203
Aperiodicity and Order. (US) 3814, 3029
Aperitif. (SW) 2471, 377
Aperture. (US ISSN 0003-6420) 3788
Aperture Northwest see Media Inc 1047
†Apex. (UK ISSN 0003-6439) 5137
Aphasie. (GW ISSN 0930-4207) 1733, 3077
Aphasiology. (UK ISSN 0268-7038) 3330
Apiacta. (RM ISSN 0003-6455) 76
L'Apicoltore Moderno. (IT ISSN 0518-1259) 76, 528
Apicultura in Romania. (RM) 76
Apicultural Abstracts. (UK ISSN 0003-648X) 133, 2
Apicultural Information and Issues see A P I S 67
Apidologie. (FR ISSN 0044-8435) 528
Apis. (US ISSN 0887-7386) 4806, 210, 230
Apitalia. (IT ISSN 0391-5522) 578
Apka Swasthya. (II ISSN 0003-6498) 3799
Aplastic Anemia Foundation of America. Newsletter. (US) 3270
Aplikace Matematiky - Applied Mathematics see Applications of Mathematics 3029
Apocalypso. (US) 2858
Apogee - Lyrical Ways see Microcosm - Lyrical Ways 2874
Apollinaris. (VC) 4255
Apollo. (UK ISSN 0003-6536) 312, 255
Apollo. (NR) 1248
Apollo see Oeko.L 4331
Aportes. (CR) 3873
El Aposento Alto. (US ISSN 0003-6552) 4229
The Apostle. (US ISSN 1041-3316) 4229
Apostolat. (CN ISSN 0706-9928) 4255
Apostolic Church of Pentecost of Canada, Inc. Messenger see A C O P Messenger 4227
Apostolos Varnavas. (CY) 4280
Apotek - Teknikeren. (NO) 3717
Apotekstjaenstemannen. (SW) 3717
Apothecary. (US ISSN 0003-6560) 3717
Apotheke Heute. (GW ISSN 0173-1882) 3717
Apotheke und Krankenhaus. (GW ISSN 0177-9591) 3717, 2459
Apotheken Kurier. (GW) 3717
Apothekenhelferin Heute. (GW ISSN 0939-3331) 3717
Apotheker - Jahrbuch. (GW ISSN 0066-5347) 3717
Apotheker Journal. (GW ISSN 0720-1028) 3717
Apothekerkammer Niedersachsen. Mitteilungsblatt. (GW) 3717
Apothekerpraktikant und Pharmazeutisch-Technische Assistent see P T A Heute 3737
Apothekersblad. (BE ISSN 0003-6579) 3717
▼Apoyo a la Docencia. (MX ISSN 0188-3992) 312
Appalachia. (US ISSN 0003-6595) 1615
Appalachia Bulletin. (US) 4541
Appalachia Journal. (US ISSN 0003-6587) 4541
Appalachian Bibliography. (US) 389
Appalachian Families. (US) 2144
Appalachian Heritage. (US ISSN 0363-2318) 2221, 4752
Appalachian Journal. (US ISSN 0090-3779) 2399, 2895
Appalachian Outlook. (US ISSN 0003-6625) 2792, 2
Appalachian Regional Commission. Annual Report. (US ISSN 0503-5422) 4429
Appalachian Roots. (US ISSN 0888-6814) 2144
Appalachian Trailway News. (US ISSN 0003-6641) 4541
Appaloosa Journal. (US) 4532
Appaloosa World. (US ISSN 0273-6519) 4532
Apparat Upravleniya Sotsialisticheskogo Gosudarstva. (RU) 2895
Apparecchi Elettrodomestici Nella Casa Moderna. (IT ISSN 0003-6668) 1882
Apparel see Hong Kong Apparel 1285
Apparel. (NZ) 4616
Apparel Accessories. (CH) 1282
Apparel Buyers Guide Year Book. (NZ) 1121, 4616
Apparel Digest. (US) 4616
†Apparel Factory Outlet Stores Survey. (US) 5137
Apparel Guild. Journal. (US) 1283, 4398
Apparel Import Digest. (US) 1283, 900
Apparel Industry Magazine. (US ISSN 0192-1878) 1283
Apparel Industry Trends. (US) 1283
Apparel International. (UK ISSN 0263-1008) 1283, 4360
Apparel: Latin American Industrial Report. (US) 1283
Apparel Manufacturer see Bobbin 1283
Apparel Merchandising. (US) 1283
Apparel Needle Trades Digest see Apparel Digest 4616
Apparel News South. (US ISSN 0744-6403) 1283
Apparel Plant Wages and Personnel Policies see Personnel Policies and Benefits for the Apparel Industry 1069
Apparel Plant Wages and Personnel Policies see Apparel Plant Wages Survey 4616
Apparel Plant Wages Survey. (US ISSN 0275-8873) 4616, 1283
Apparel Production News. (JA) 1283, 28
Apparel Research Notes. (US) 1283
Apparel Sales - Marketing Compensation Survey. (US) 1283, 1033
Apparel World see Knitting Times 1286
Appeals to the Eleventh Circuit. (US) 2599
Appeals to the Fifth Circuit. (US) 2599
Appeals to the Third Circuit. (US) 2599
Appearances. (US) 2895
Appearances of Soviet Leaders see U.S. Central Intelligence Agency. Appearances of Soviet Leaders 3975
Appel de l'Afrique. (FR) 4163
Appel Service; Repertoire d'Adresses Utiles pour le Commerce et l'Industrie. (FR ISSN 0066-5398) 1121
Appeltjes van het Meetjesland. (BE) 2348, 2052
Appendix see Maritime Guide 4733
Appetite. (UK ISSN 0195-6663) 3603
Appetizer see Iowa Appetizer 2477
Appita. (AT ISSN 0003-6757) 3662
†Applause. (US) 5137
Applause Theatre Book Review & Catalog. (US) 2895, 2980, 4629
Apple. see Pom's 1473
Apple Blad 2 - Macintosh Blad see Apple Macintosh Blad 1467
†Apple Blossom Connection. (US ISSN 0896-7245) 5137
Apple Business. (UK) 1448
Apple Direct. (US) 1467
Apple Education News. (US) 1467, 1458, 1688
Apple IIGS Buyer's Guide. (US) 1467
Apple Index. (US ISSN 0741-2347) 1403, 2
Apple Library Users Group Newsletter. (US ISSN 0887-2716) 2796, 1467
Apple Macintosh Blad. (NE) 1467
Apple Time. (AU) 1467
Appleland Bulletin. (US) 2144
AppleWorks Forum. (US ISSN 0893-4118) 1458
Appliance. (US ISSN 0003-6781) 1882, 641
Appliance Engineer see Appliance 1882
Appliance Manufacturer. (US ISSN 0003-679X) 1882
Appliance Manufacturer Buyers Guide. (US) 1121
†Appliance New Product Digest. (US) 5137
Appliance Service News. (US ISSN 0003-6803) 1882
Appliances: Latin American Industrial Report. (US) 2548
Applica. (SZ) 3652
▼Applicable Algebra in Engineering, Communication and Computing. (GW ISSN 0938-1279) 3064
Applicable Analysis. (US ISSN 0003-6811) 3029
Application Notes Reference D.A.T.A. Digest. (US) 1882
Application Specific Integrated Circuits & Electronic Design Automation see A S I C & E D A 1411
Applicationes Mathematicae. see Zastosowania Matematyki 3062
Applications et Transferts de la S E L A F. (FR ISSN 0755-9291) 2803, 235
Applications of Atomic Energy in Agriculture. see Yuanzineng Nongye Yingyong 1810
Applications of Computer Science Series. (US ISSN 0888-2231) 4358
Applications of Electronic Technique. see Dianzi Jishu Yingyong 1765
Applications of Management Science. (US ISSN 0276-8976) 1002
Applications of Mathematics. (US ISSN 0862-7940) 3029
Applications of Mathematics. (US ISSN 0172-4568) 3029
Applications of Surface Science see Applied Surface Science 3402
Applications Software Reports. (US) 1475
Applicator. (US) 600
Applied Acoustics. (UK ISSN 0003-682X) 3858
Applied Acoustics. see Yingyong Shengxue 3860
Applied Agricultural Research. (US ISSN 0179-0374) 76
Applied and Environmental Microbiology. (US ISSN 0099-2240) 549
▼Applied and Preventive Psychology. (US ISSN 0962-1849) 4011
Applied Animal Behaviour Science. (NE ISSN 0168-1591) 578
Applied Artificial Intelligence. (US ISSN 0883-9514) 1406
Applied Artificial Intelligence Reporter see I S R: Intelligent Systems Report 1408
Applied Arts. (CN) 312
Applied Arts Quarterly see Applied Arts 312

Applied Biochemistry and Biotechnology.(US ISSN 0273-2289) **471**, 487

Applied Biochemistry and Microbiology. (English translation of: Prikladnaya Biokhimiya i Mikrobiologiya) (US ISSN 0003-6838) **471**, 549

Applied Botany Abstracts. (II ISSN 0970-2377) **461**, 2, 494

Applied Cardiopulmonary Pathophysiology. (NE ISSN 0920-5268) **569**, 3077

Applied Catalysis. (NE ISSN 0166-9834) **1848**

▼Applied Catalysis B: Environmental. (NE ISSN 0926-3373) **1848**, 1943

Applied Chemical News. (AT) **1848**

Applied Clay Science. (NE ISSN 0169-1317) **1554**, 1161, 1861, 1943

Applied Cognitive Psychology. (UK ISSN 0888-4080) **4011**

Applied Computer and Communications Law. (UK ISSN 0267-6621) **1389**, 1331, 2599

Applied Economic Papers. (II ISSN 0570-4839) **645**

Applied Economics. (UK ISSN 0003-6846) **645**

Applied Energy. (UK ISSN 0306-2619) **1783**, 1943, 3682

Applied Engineering in Agriculture. (US ISSN 0883-8542) **77**, 1814

Applied Entomology and Zoology. (JA ISSN 0003-6862) **528**, 578

Applied Ergonomics. (UK ISSN 0003-6870) **1814**, 4011, 4593

Applied Esthetiques *see* For Formulation Chemists Only **375**

▼Applied Financial Economics. (UK ISSN 0960-3107) **843**, 759

Applied Fine Art. *see* Shiyong Meishu **343**

Applied Genetics News. (US ISSN 0271-7107) **539**

Applied Geochemistry. (US ISSN 0883-2927) **1554**

Applied Geography. (UK ISSN 0143-6228) **2242**

Applied Geography and Development. (GW) **2242**

Applied Geography Conferences. (US ISSN 0192-8996) **2242**

Applied Health Physics Abstracts and Notes. (US ISSN 0305-7615) **3836**, 2, 4116

Applied Industrial Hygiene *see* Applied Occupational & Environmental Hygiene **4097**

Applied Industrial Psychology. *see* Psychologie v Ekonomicke Praxi **4041**

▼Applied Intelligence. (NE ISSN 0924-669X) **1406**

Applied Lasers. *see* Yingyong Jiguang **3858**

Applied Linguistics. (UK ISSN 0142-6001) **2803**

Applied Linguistics. *see* Jezykoznawstwo Stosowane **2820**

▼Applied Magnetic Resonance. (GW ISSN 0937-9347) **3814**

Applied Management Newsletter. (US ISSN 0889-8227) **1062**

Applied Marketing Research. (US) **1033**

Applied Mathematical Modelling. (US ISSN 0307-904X) **3064**

Applied Mathematical Sciences. (US ISSN 0066-5452) **3029**

Applied Mathematics. (UK ISSN 0888-479X) **3029**

Applied Mathematics. *see* Yingyong Shuxue **3061**

Applied Mathematics and Computation. (US ISSN 0096-3003) **3029**

Applied Mathematics and Mechanics. (US ISSN 0066-5479) **3029**, 3842

Applied Mathematics and Mechanics. (SZ ISSN 0253-4827) **3029**, 3842

Applied Mathematics and Mechanics. *see* Yingyong Shuxue yu Lixue **3061**

Applied Mathematics and Optimization. (US ISSN 0095-4616) **3029**

Applied Mathematics Letters. (US ISSN 0893-9659) **3029**

†Applied Mathematics Notes/Notes de Mathematiques Appliquees. (CN ISSN 0700-9224) **5137**

Applied Mathematics Problems. (AT) **3030**

Applied Measurement in Education. (US ISSN 0895-7347) **1616**

Applied Mechanics Reviews. (US ISSN 0003-6900) **1841**, 2

†Applied Mechanisms Conference Proceedings. (US) **5137**

Applied Microbiology and Biotechnology.(GW ISSN 0175-7598) **487**, 550

Applied Microgravity Technology *see* Microgravity - Science and Technology **58**

Applied Mineralogy - Technische Mineralogie. (US ISSN 0066-5487) **3478**

Applied Networks Report. (US ISSN 0899-5680) **1426**

Applied Neurophysiology *see* Stereotactic and Functional Neurosurgery **3355**

Applied Numerical Mathematics. (NE ISSN 0168-9274) **3064**

Applied Nursing Research. (US ISSN 0897-1897) **3275**

Applied Occupational & Environmental Hygiene. (US ISSN 1047-322X) **4097**

Applied Ocean Research. (UK ISSN 0141-1187) **1601**, 1814

Applied Optics. (US ISSN 0003-6935) **3851**

Applied Optics. Supplement. (US ISSN 0066-5495) **3851**

Applied Organometallic Chemistry. (UK ISSN 0268-2605) **1170**

Applied Orgonometry. (US ISSN 0882-4347) **4299**

Applied Ornithology. *see* Angewandte Ornithologie **561**

†Applied Pathology. (SZ ISSN 0252-1172) **5137**

Applied Physics *see* Applied Physics. A: Solids and Surfaces **3814**

Applied Physics *see* Applied Physics. B: Photophysics and Laser Chemistry **3814**

Applied Physics. A: Solids and Surfaces.(GW ISSN 0721-7250) **3814**, 1814

Applied Physics. B: Photophysics and Laser Chemistry. (GW ISSN 0721-7269) **3814**, 1814

Applied Physics and Engineering. (US ISSN 0066-5509) **3814**, 1814

Applied Physics Communications. (US ISSN 0277-9374) **3814**

Applied Physics Letters. (US ISSN 0003-6951) **3815**, 1814

Applied Polymer Symposia *see* Journal of Applied Polymer Science. Symposia **1855**

Applied Psycholinguistics. (UK ISSN 0142-7164) **2803**, 3330, 4011

Applied Psycholinguistics and Communication Disorders. (US) **2803**, 4011

Applied Psychological Measurement. (US ISSN 0146-6216) **4011**

Applied Psychology. (UK ISSN 0269-994X) **4011**

Applied Radiation and Isotopes *see* International Journal of Radiation Applications and Instrumentation. Part A: Applied Radiation and Isotopes **3847**

Applied Radiology. (US ISSN 0160-9963) **3357**

Applied Radiology and Nuclear Medicine *see* Applied Radiology **3357**

Applied Radiology Buyer's Guide *see* Applied Radiology Directory **5137**

†Applied Radiology Directory. (US ISSN 0160-9963) **5137**

Applied Research in Mental Retardation *see* Research in Developmental Disabilities **3147**

Applied Science and Technology Index. (US ISSN 0003-6986) **1841**, 2, 4354

Applied Sciences and Development *see* Applied Geography and Development **2242**

Applied Scientific Research. (NE ISSN 0003-6994) **4299**, 1814

Applied Social Psychology Annual *see* Social Psychological Applications to Social Issues **4047**

Applied Social Sciences Index & Abstracts *see* A S S I A **4394**

Applied Solar Energy. (English translation of: Geliotekhnika) (US ISSN 0003-701X) **1810**

Applied Solid State Science. (US ISSN 0066-5533) **1882**, 3815

Applied Spectroscopy. (US ISSN 0003-7028) **3852**, 1170

Applied Spectroscopy Reviews. (US ISSN 0570-4928) **3852**

Applied Stochastic Models and Data Analysis. (UK ISSN 8755-0024) **3030**, 3062

▼Applied Superconductivity. (UK ISSN 0964-1807) **1882**

Applied Surface Science. (NE ISSN 0169-4332) **3402**, 1212

Applied Virology Research. (US) **550**

Applying G A A P and G A A S. (US) **747**

Appointments Market Weekly. (II) **3624**

Apportionment of Liability in British Columbia. (CN) **2599**

Appraisal. (US ISSN 0003-7052) **4120**, 1232, 4299

Appraisal Digest. (US ISSN 0003-7060) **4144**

Appraisal Institute Digest. (CN ISSN 0003-7079) **4144**

Appraisal Journal. (US ISSN 0003-7087) **4144**

Appraisal Manual *see* Means Square Foot Costs (Year) **4152**

Appraisal Report. (US) **4145**

Appraisal Review. (US) **4145**

Appraisal Review and Mortgage Underwriting Journal. (US ISSN 0195-4407) **4145**

Appraiser *see* Appraiser News **4145**

Appraiser Gram. (US) **4145**

Appraiser News. (US ISSN 1054-5999) **4145**

Appraisers' Information Exchange. (US ISSN 8755-4348) **938**, 2526

Appraisers Standard. (US) **312**, 255, 3749

Apprentice. (US) **3521**

Apprenticeship News. (US ISSN 0003-7109) **971**

Apprentissage et Socialisation. (CN) **1733**, 1232

Apprentissage et Socialisation en Piste *see* Apprentissage et Socialisation **1733**

Approach. (US ISSN 0570-4979) **46**, 3451

Approach. (JA ISSN 0003-7117) **292**

Approaches; a Periodical of Poems by Kentuckians *see* Kentucky Poetry Review **5223**

Approche Neuropsychologique des Apprentissages chez l'Enfant. (FR ISSN 0999-792X) **4011**

Approches *see* Levant **2932**

Appropriate Technology. (UK ISSN 0305-0920) **147**, 1072

Appropriate Technology Documentation Bulletin. (II) **4593**

Appropriate Technology in Australia & New Zealand. (AT) **4613**

Appropriate Technology in Indian Periodicals. (AT) **4613**

Appropriate Technology Index. (AT) **4614**, 2

Appropriate Technology Newsletter. (SA) **4593**

Approved Courses for Accountancy Education. (UK ISSN 0263-1768) **747**, 1699

Approved Doctoral Dissertations in Progress in Music Education *see* Directory of International Music Education Dissertations in Progress **3549**

Approved Drug Products with Therapeutic Equivalence Evaluations. (US) **3717**

Approximation Theory and its Applications/Bijinlun. (CC ISSN 1000-9221) **3030**

Apres - Demain. (FR ISSN 0003-7176) **3873**

Apricot, Peach and Pear Growers' Association Annual *see* A P G A Annual **2120**

Apricot Quarterly Roundup. (US) **168**

Apropaa *see* Roeda Korsets Tiding **4418**

Apropos. (US) **4837**

Apu. (FI ISSN 0355-3051) **2186**

Apulum. (RM) **2348**

Apuntes. (PE ISSN 0252-1865) **4366**

Apuntes. (CL ISSN 0716-4440) **4629**

Apuntes de Abordo - Inflight Notes *see* El Mundo al Vuelo - Inflight Notes **4803**

Apuntes de Ingenieria. (CL ISSN 0716-0348) **1814**

Apuntes de Jardineria. (SP) **2122**

Apuntes de Medicina Deportiva *see* Apunts **3370**

Apunts. (SP ISSN 0212-4009) **3370**, 3306

Al-Aqidah. (MK) **4218**

Aqlam Journal/Pen. (IQ ISSN 0570-507X) **2895**, 2858

Al-Aqsa. (JO) **3451**

Aqua. (IT) **1597**, 1554, 1587, 1601

Aqua. (UK ISSN 0003-7214) **4821**

Aqua Buyers Guide *see* Aqua Industry Guide **3799**

Aqua Fennica. (FI ISSN 0356-7133) **4821**

Aqua Industry Guide. (US) **3799**, 1502

Aqua Pura *see* Australian Fluoridation News. Aqua-Pura **4822**

Aqua Review. (FR ISSN 0295-0448) **1601**

Aqua Terra. (US ISSN 1048-8111) **4822**

Aqua: The Business Magazine for the Spa and Pool Industry. (US) **3799**

Aquacultural Engineering. (UK ISSN 0144-8609) **1814**

Aquaculture. (NE ISSN 0044-8486) **2036**

Aquaculture. (CH ISSN 0254-6493) **2036**

Aquaculture. *see* Suisanzoshoku **2049**

Aquaculture and Fisheries Management.(UK ISSN 0266-996X) **2036**

Aquaculture Digest *see* World Shrimp Farming **2050**

Aquaculture Digest *see* Mollusk Farming U S A **5239**

Aquaculture Europe Magazine. (BE) **1602**

Aquaculture Magazine. (US ISSN 0199-1388) **2036**

Aquaculture Today. (CN) **2036**

Aqualert. (UK) **4834**, 2, 1972

Aqualine *see* Aqualine Abstracts **4834**

Aqualine Abstracts. (UK ISSN 0748-2531) **4834**, 2, 1972

Aquanotes. (US) **1602**

Aquaphyte. (US ISSN 0893-7702) **494**, 1602, 2036

Aquarama. (FR ISSN 0151-6981) **2433**

Aquarian *see* Aquarian Weekly **2858**

Aquarian Alchemist. (US) **3668**, 3603, 3761

Aquarian Arrow. (UK ISSN 0141-0121) **3668**

Aquarian Voices. (US) **358**, 3593

Aquarian Weekly. (US) **2858**

Aquariculture and Aquatic Sciences. Journal. (US ISSN 0733-2076) **429**, 4822

Aquarien Magazin *see* D A T Z **2039**

Aquarien Terrarien *see* D A T Z **2039**

Aquarimantima. (CK) **2988**

Aquario. (AG) **2988**

Aquarium. (NE ISSN 0003-729X) **2036**, 2433

Aquarium. (GW ISSN 0341-2709) **2037**

†Aquarium Digest International. (US) **5137**

Aquarium Fish Magazine. (US ISSN 0899-045X) **3708**

Aquarium Industry *see* Pet Business **3712**

Aquarium Society of New South Wales. Monthly Journal. (AT ISSN 0044-8508) **2037**

Aquarius. (UK ISSN 0003-7303) 2988
Aquas Vivas. (AG) 2170
Aquasphere. (US) 1943
Aquatechnic International. (UK ISSN 0261-5355) 4822
Aquaterra, Water Concepts for the Ecological Society. (US) 2988
Aquatic Botany. (NE ISSN 0304-3770) 494
▼Aquatic Conservation: Marine and Freshwater Ecosystems. (UK ISSN 1052-7613) 1483, 429, 1602
Aquatic Ecological Chemistry. see Seitai Kagaku 5275
Aquatic Environment Protection. (UK ISSN 0953-4466) 1943, 1483
Aquatic Farming Newsletter. (US) 2037
The Aquatic Gardener. (CN) 2122
Aquatic Insects. (NE ISSN 0165-0424) 528
Aquatic Living see Aquatic Living Resources 2037
Aquatic Living Resources. (FR ISSN 0990-7440) 2037
Aquatic Plant News. (US) 495, 2122
Aquatic Pollution and Environmental Quality see Aquatic Sciences & Fisheries Abstracts. Part 3: Aquatic Pollution and Environmental Quality 2051
Aquatic Sciences. (SZ ISSN 1015-1621) 1597
Aquatic Sciences & Fisheries Abstracts. Part 1: Biological Sciences and Living Resources. (US ISSN 0140-5373) 4834, 3, 1483, 2051
Aquatic Sciences & Fisheries Abstracts. Part 2: Ocean Technology, Policy and Non-Living Resources. (US ISSN 0140-5381) 4834, 3, 2051
▼Aquatic Sciences & Fisheries Abstracts. Part 3: Aquatic Pollution and Environmental Quality. (US ISSN 1045-6031) 2051, 3, 1972
Aquatic Sciences & Fisheries Abstracts Aquaculture Abstracts see A S F A Aquaculture Abstracts 2050
Aquatic Sciences & Fisheries Abstracts Marine Biotechnology Abstracts see A S F A Marine Biotechnology Abstracts 1549
Aquatic Toxicology. (NE ISSN 0166-445X) 1980, 471
†Aquatic Toxicology. (US) 5137
Aquatics see Aquatics International 4464
Aquatics Buyers' Guide see Aquatics International 4464
Aquatics International. (US) 4464, 1002
†Aquaworld. (II ISSN 0970-0366) 5137
Aqueduct. (US ISSN 0092-0622) 4822
Aqui. (UY ISSN 0066-5606) 2895
Aqui. (PY ISSN 0044-8524) 4429, 3873
Aqui (Phoenix). (US) 1991
Aqui (River Edge). (US) 3395, 1991
Aqui y Ahora. (HO) 4752
Aquilegia. (US) 2122
Aquileia Nostra. (IT) 262
Aquillon. (CN) 2176
Aquilo. Serie Botanica. (FI ISSN 0570-5169) 495, 569
Aquilo. Serie Zoologica. (FI ISSN 0570-5177) 578, 561
Aquinas. (VC ISSN 0003-7362) 3761, 4255
Aquinas Journal. (CE) 4255, 2306
Aquinas Law Journal. (CE) 2599
Aquinas Lecture Series. (US ISSN 0066-5614) 3761
Aquinian. (CN) 1303
Ar Falz. (FR ISSN 0755-883X) 2858
Ar Gwyr. see Cahiers Bretons 4367
Al-Arab. (QA) 2216
Al-Arab. (SU) 2428
Arab. (UK ISSN 0003-7389) 3950
Arab Affairs. (UK ISSN 0950-0731) 900, 3950
Arab Agriculture Yearbook. (BA) 77
Arab American Almanac. (US ISSN 0742-9576) 1991
Arab-Asian Affairs. (UK ISSN 0196-3538) 3873

Arab Bank for Economic Development in Africa. Annual Report. (SJ) 759, 926
Arab Bank for Economic Development in Africa. Quarterly Review. (SJ) 759
Arab Banker. (UK ISSN 0261-2925) 759
Arab Banking and Finance Directory. (BA) 759, 1361
Arab Banking and Finance Handbook see Arab Banking and Finance Directory 759
†Arab Banks. (FR) 5137
Arab Book Annual. see Al-Kitab al-Arabi Fi Aam 4141
Arab Book Guide International. (US) 4120, 2895
Arab Book World. (US) 2428, 645, 2858, 3950
Arab Buyers' Guide to British Industry. (UK) 1121
Arab Construction World. (CY ISSN 0255-8572) 600
Arab Defence. (LE) 3451
Arab Dental/Alam Tub al-Assnan. (GW) 3228
Arab Digest. (US) 2428
Arab Directory/Dalil el Arab. (CN ISSN 0706-7917) 1991
Arab Economic Union Journal. see Majallat al-Wahdah al-Iqtisadiyyah al-Arabiyyah 896
Arab Film and Television Center News. (LE ISSN 0003-7397) 3503, 1368
†Arab Food & Beverage. (GW) 5137
Arab Fund for Economic and Social Development. Annual Report. (KU ISSN 0304-6729) 926
Arab Future. see Al-Mustaqbal al-Arabi 4380
Arab Guide. (CN) 1991
Arab Gulf. see Al-Khalij al-Arabi 2430
Arab Gulf Journal of Scientific Research. (SU ISSN 1015-4442) 4299, 3030, 3815
Arab Gulf Journal of Scientific Research. Section A: Mathematical and Physical Sciences see Arab Gulf Journal of Scientific Research 4299
Arab Health. (CY ISSN 0257-3202) 4098
▼Arab Historical Review for Ottoman Studies. (TI ISSN 0330-8081) 2428, 2331
Arab History and Civilization. (NE ISSN 0925-2908) 2428, 3633
Arab Horse Society News. (UK ISSN 0402-7493) 4532
Arab Horse Stud Book. (UK) 4532
Arab Industry Review. (BA) 1072
Arab Journal of Administration. see Al-Majallah al-Arabiyyah lil-Idarah 4066
Arab Journal of Language Studies. (SJ) 2803, 1744
Arab Language Academy. Journal. see Majma' al-Lughah al-Arabiyyah. Majallah 2936
Arab Law Quarterly. (UK ISSN 0268-0556) 2719
Arab League Educational, Scientific, and Cultural Organization. Information Newsletter. (TI) 1616, 312, 4299
Arab Medical Bulletin. (SJ ISSN 0254-9492) 3077
Arab Medico. (GW ISSN 0723-5100) 3077
Arab Mining Journal. (JO ISSN 0250-9881) 3478
Arab News. (UK) 1991, 2210
Arab News International. (CN) 1991
Arab News of Toronto/Akhbar el-Arab Fe Toronte. (CN ISSN 0707-3372) 1991
Arab Oil & Gas. (FR ISSN 0031-6369) 3682
Arab Oil & Gas Directory. (FR ISSN 0304-8551) 3682
Arab Oil & Gas Magazine (Monthly). (FR) 3682
Arab Oil Review. (LY ISSN 0003-7435) 3682
Arab Palestinian Resistance. (SY) 2219
Arab Petroleum. (LY ISSN 0003-7443) 3682, 3478
Arab Postal Union. Review. see Ittihad al-Baridi al-Arabi 1353

†Arab Press Bulletin. (US ISSN 0896-2146) 5137
Arab Republic Community Arabic Journal see A R C Arabic Journal 1988
Arab Shipping see Seatrade Arab Shipping Guide 5275
Arab Struggle. (CS) 2428, 3633
Arab Studies. see Dirasat Arabiyat 3891
Arab Studies Quarterly. (US ISSN 0271-3519) 1991
†Arab Tech. (GW ISSN 0722-4303) 5137
Arab Trade Directory. (UK) 1121
Arab Travel Magazine see Travel & Tourism News International 4792
Arab Traveller. see Al-Musafir al-Arabi 4778
Arab Veterinary Medical Association. Journal. (UA ISSN 0003-746X) 4806
Arab Water World. (CY ISSN 0255-8580) 4822
Arab World. see Alabo Shijie 2801
Arab World. (LE) 3873
Arab World. (KE) 3950
†Arab World. (UK ISSN 0518-1852) 5137
Arab World Agribusiness. (BA) 77, 147, 645
Arab World Almanac. (US ISSN 1047-711X) 1744, 2428
Arabe see Carta Informativa 903
Arabesque. (US ISSN 0148-5865) 1528
Arabia Past & Present Series. (UK) 2428
Arabian Computer News. (UK) 1389, 1361
Arabian Gulf Research Review. (TS) 2428
Arabian Horse Country. (US) 4532
Arabian Horse Express. (US ISSN 0194-6803) 4532
Arabian Horse Times. (US) 4532
Arabian Horse World. (US ISSN 0003-7494) 4532
Arabian Journal for Science and Engineering. (SU ISSN 0377-9211) 1815, 4299
Arabian Studies. (UK ISSN 0305-036X) 2428, 3873
Arabian Studs and Stallions Magazine. (AT) 4532
Arabian Sun. (SU) 2216
Arabian Trade Digest see Arabian Year Book 843
Arabian Year Book. (KU ISSN 0378-8970) 843
Arabian Yearbook. (UK) 1121
▼Arabic Sciences and Philosophy. (UK ISSN 0957-4239) 4299, 3761
Arabica. (NE ISSN 0570-5398) 3633
Arabies. (FR ISSN 0983-1509) 1991
Arabische Pferde. (GW ISSN 0721-5169) 4532
Arabisk Verden. Maanedsoversigt see Mellemoest Information. Maanedsoversigt 3965
Arabism. see Al-Urubah 2211
Al-Arabiyya. (US ISSN 0889-8731) 2803, 2895
Arable Farmer see Arable Farming 168
Arable Farming. (UK ISSN 0300-2829) 168
Arabusiness International. (CN) 645
Arachim/Values. (IS) 3873
Arachne. (US) 2988
Arachnologia - Bulletin d'Information et de Liaison du C I D A. (FR) 528
Araksha. (II ISSN 0003-7540) 1510
Aral. (SP) 2090
Araldo della Scienza Cristiana see Herald of Christian Science 4283
Araldo di S. Antonio. (IT ISSN 0003-7559) 4255
Aramco World. (US ISSN 1044-1891) 1991, 3682
Aramco World Magazine see Aramco World 1991
Araneta Research Journal. (PH ISSN 0115-0820) 77, 2095, 4806
▼Aranzadi Social. (SP) 2599, 4366
Ararat see A G B U Ararat 2891
Arastirma Eserleri Serisi. (TU) 528, 550, 578
Arauto da Ciencia Crista see Herald of Christian Science 4283

O Arauto do Vendedor. (BL) 1033
Arba Sicula. (US ISSN 0271-0730) 1992
Arbeidervern. (NO ISSN 0332-7124) 3614
Arbeidrungdommen see Prausis 2588
Arbeidsblad see Revue du Travail 992
Arbeidslederen. (NO) 4593
Arbeidsmiljoe. (NO ISSN 0332-9127) 3614
Arbeidsomstandigheden/Working Environment. (NE) 3614
Arbeidsongeschiktheidsfonds en Algemeen Arbeidsongeschiktheidsfonds. Jaarverslag. (NE) 2526
Arbeidsveiligheid. (BE) 3614
Die Arbeit. (AU ISSN 0003-7605) 971
Arbeit, Beruf, und Arbeitslosenhilfe see Arbeit und Beruf 971
Arbeit und Arbeitsrecht. (GW ISSN 0323-4568) 971, 2599
Arbeit und Beruf. (GW) 971
Arbeit und Recht. (GW ISSN 0003-7648) 2599, 971
Arbeit und Sicherheit. (GW ISSN 0344-239X) 3478, 3614
Arbeit und Soziales. (GW ISSN 0171-8819) 971
Arbeit und Sozialpolitik. (GW ISSN 0340-8434) 971
Arbeit und Technik in der Schule. (GW) 1744
Arbeit und Wirtschaft. (AU ISSN 0003-7656) 2580
Arbeit und Wirtschaft in Bayern see Arbeit und Soziales 971
Arbeiten aus Anglistik und Amerikanistik. (GW ISSN 0171-5410) 2895, 2803
Arbeiten und Lernen see Arbeiten & Lernen: Technik und Wirtschaft 1744
Arbeiten & Lernen: Technik und Wirtschaft. (GW) 1744
Arbeiten und Text zur Slavistik. (GW ISSN 0173-2307) 2895
Arbeiten zur Angewandten Statistik. (GW ISSN 0066-5673) 4562
Arbeiten zur Geschichte der Antiken Judentums und des Urchristentums. (NE ISSN 0169-734X) 4221
Arbeiten zur Geschichte des Pietismus. (GW) 4163
Arbeiten zur Kirchlichen Zeitgeschichte. Reihe B. (GW) 4163
Arbeiten zur Literatur und Geschichte des Hellenistischen Judentums. (NE ISSN 0169-7390) 4221
Arbeiten zur Paedagogik. (GW ISSN 0066-569X) 1616
Arbeiten zur Pastoraltheologie. (GW) 4163
Arbeiten zur Rheinischen Landeskunde. (GW ISSN 0373-7187) 2242
Arbeiten zur Sozialwissenschaftlichen Psychologie. (GW) 4011, 4429
Arbeiten zur Theologie. Reihe 1. (GW ISSN 0066-5711) 4163
Arbeiterstimme. (GW) 3873
Arbeiterwohlfahrt Kreisverband Koeln e.V. Blickpunkt see A W im Blickpunkt 5129
Der Arbeitgeber. (GW ISSN 0402-7787) 971
Arbeitnehmer. (GW) 2580
Arbeits und Forschungsberichte zur Saechsischen Bodendenkmalpflege. (GW ISSN 0402-7817) 3521
Arbeitsblaetter fuer Restauratoren. (GW ISSN 0066-5738) 262, 3521
Arbeitsgemeinschaft der Bibliotheken und Dokumentationsstellen der Ost-, Ostmittel- und Suedosteuropaforschung. Mitteilungen. (GW) 2743, 2803, 2858
Arbeitsgemeinschaft der Bibliotheken und Dokumentationsstellen der Osteuropa-, Suedosteuropa- und DDR-Forschung. Mitteilungen see Arbeitsgemeinschaft der Bibliotheken und Dokumentationsstellen der Ost-, Ostmittel- und Suedosteuropaforschung. Mitteilungen 2743

Arbeitsgemeinschaft der Oeffentlich-Rechtlichen Rundfunkanstalten der Bundesrepublik Deutschland Jahrbuch see A R D - Jahrbuch 1354
Arbeitsgemeinschaft der Parlaments- und Behoerdenbibliotheken. Arbeitshefte. (GW ISSN 0518-2220) 2743
Arbeitsgemeinschaft der Parlaments- und Behoerdenbibliotheken. Mitteilungen. (GW ISSN 0170-5598) 2743
Arbeitsgemeinschaft der Sektion Geschichte der Akademie der Wissenschaften Geschichte der Buergerlichen Parteien in Deutschland. Mitteilungsblatt see Jenaer Beitraege zur Parteigeschichte 5220
Arbeitsgemeinschaft Deutsche Ostgebiete. Rundschreiben. (GW) 3749
Arbeitsgemeinschaft Deutscher Verkehrsflughaefen Informationsdienst see A D V - Informationsdienst 4669
Arbeitsgemeinschaft fuer Erziehungshilfe (AFET) e.V. Mitglieder - Rundbrief see A F E T - Mitglieder - Rundbrief 4364
Arbeitsgemeinschaft fuer Jugendhilfe. Mitteilungen see Forum Jugendhilfe 4406
Arbeitsgemeinschaft fuer Jugendpflege und Jugendfuersorge. Mitteilungen see Forum Jugendhilfe 4406
Arbeitsgemeinschaft fuer Juristisches Bibliotheks- und Dokumentationswesen. Mitteilungen. (GW ISSN 0300-0990) 2697
Arbeitsgemeinschaft fuer Klinische Nephrologie. Mitteilungen. (GW ISSN 0172-7311) 3330
Arbeitsgemeinschaft fuer Rheinische Musikgeschichte. Mitteilungen. (GW) 3539
Arbeitsgemeinschaft Katholisch-Theologischer Bibliotheken. Mitteilungsblatt. (GW ISSN 0177-8358) 2743
Arbeitsgemeinschaft Malta im Bund Deutscher Philatelisten e.V. see A G M 3749
Arbeitsgemeinschaft Neue Religioese Gruppen. Forum. (GW ISSN 0723-2446) 4163
Arbeitsgemeinschaft Oesterreichischer Entomologen. Zeitschrift. (AU ISSN 0375-5223) 528
Arbeitsgemeinschaft Saechsischer Botaniker. Berichte. (GW) 495
†Arbeitsgestaltung fuer Behinderte. (GW ISSN 0724-6994) 5137
Arbeitshefte Kinderpsychoanalyse. (GW ISSN 0721-9628) 4011
Arbeitshefte zur Sozialistischen Theorie und Praxis. (GW ISSN 0173-5403) 3873
Arbeitshilfen fuer die Erwachsenenbildung. (GW ISSN 0720-9118) 1682
†Arbeitshygienische Information Bauwesen. (GW ISSN 0232-7287) 5137
Arbeitsinformationen ueber Studienprojekte auf dem Gebiet der Geschichte des Deutschen Judentums und des Antisemitismus. (GW ISSN 0341-8340) 2349, 4221
Arbeitskosten in der Industrie Oesterreichs. (AU) 971
Arbeitskreis der Deutschen Afrika-Forschungs- und Dokumentationsstellen. Rundbrief. (GW) 2331
Arbeitskreis fuer Mammillarienfreunde. Mitteilungsblatt. (GW ISSN 0172-875X) 495
Arbeitskreis Musik in der Jugend Intervalle see Intervalle 3557
Arbeitskreis Zweiter Weltkrieg. Bulletin see Bulletin Faschismus - Zweite Weltkrieg 2354
Arbeitsmappe Sozial- und Wirtschaftskunde. (GW) 1780
Arbeitsmarkt in Hessen. (GW ISSN 0172-2751) 971

Arbeitsmarkt Politik. (AU ISSN 0587-1689) 971
Arbeitsmedizin. (GW ISSN 0932-2876) 3623, 3
Arbeitsmedizin, Sozialmedizin, Arbeitshygiene see Arbeitsmedizin, Sozialmedizin, Praeventivmedizin 4098
Arbeitsmedizin, Sozialmedizin, Praeventivmedizin. (GW ISSN 0300-581X) 4098, 3077
†Arbeitsmedizininformation. (GW ISSN 0232-5160) 5137
Arbeitsmethoden der Medizinischen und Naturwissenschaftlichen Kriminalistik. (GW ISSN 0570-5886) 3264
Arbeitsoekonomik see Sozialistische Arbeitswissenschaft 5281
Arbeitsrecht-Blattei (A R). (GW ISSN 0934-7100) 2599
Arbeitsrecht der Gegenwart. (GW ISSN 0066-586X) 971, 2600
Arbeitsrecht in Stichworten. (GW ISSN 0003-7761) 971, 2600
Arbeitsrecht und Arbeitslosenversicherung. (SZ ISSN 0003-777X) 971
Arbeitsschutz see Bundesarbeitsblatt 974
†Arbeitsschutz, Arbeitshygiene. (GW ISSN 0138-1555) 5137
Arbeitsstelle Friedensforschung Bonn Info see A F B Info 3869
Arbeitstechnische Merkhefte der Waldarbeit. (GW ISSN 0003-7796) 2095
Arbeitsvorbereitung. (GW ISSN 0003-780X) 4593
Arbejderbevaegelsen i Danmark. Historisk og Aktuelt. Tilvaekst. (DK ISSN 0105-2233) 971
Arbejderbevaegelsens Bibliotek og Arkiv. Aarsskrift. (DK ISSN 0900-2723) 702, 971
Arbejderbevaegelsens Bibliotek og Arkiv. Bibliografisk Serie. (DK ISSN 0107-4628) 971
Arbejderbevaegelsens Bibliotek og Arkiv. Liste over Loebende Tidsskrifter og Aarboeger paa A B A. (DK ISSN 0107-9018) 702, 971
Arbejderbevaegelsens Erhvervsraad. Beretning. (DK ISSN 0108-9625) 971
Arbejderbladet. (DK ISSN 0109-3851) 971
Arbejderbladet Deruda see Arbejderbladet 971
Arbejderhistorie. (DK) 971
†Arbejdermuseet. Aarbog. (DK ISSN 0109-1158) 5137
Arbejdsbetingede Lidelser. Yearbook. (DK) 3614
†Arbejdsdirektoratet Beretning om Arbejdsformidlingen og Arbejdsloeshedsforsikringen. (DK ISSN 0109-1514) 5137
Arbejdsgiveren. (DK ISSN 0003-7818) 971, 1062
Arbejdslederen. (DK ISSN 0003-7826) 1002
†Arbejdsmarkedet og Arbejdsmarkedspolotik/Labor Market and Labor Market Policy. (DK ISSN 0107-9735) 5137
Arbejdsmiljoe. (DK ISSN 0905-5010) 971
Arbejdsmiljoet - Netop Nu. (DK ISSN 0905-9539) 3623, 3
Arbejdsretlige Domme see Arbejdsretligt Tidsskrift 971
Arbejdsretlige Kendelser see Arbejdsretligt Tidsskrift 971
Arbejdsretligt Tidsskrift. (DK ISSN 0108-7150) 971, 2600
Arbejdsulykker. Aarsstatistik. (DK ISSN 0106-9683) 3623
Arbetaren. (SW) 2858
Arbetarhistoria. (SW ISSN 0281-7446) 971, 2349
Arbetarnas Kulturhistoriskap. Notiser see Arbetarroerelsens Aarsbok 971
Arbetarroerelsens Aarsbok. (SW ISSN 0347-2965) 971, 2349
Arbetsgivaren see S A F - Tidningen 1027
Arbetsledaren. (SW ISSN 0003-7842) 2580

Arbetsmiljoe. (SW ISSN 0003-7834) 4098
Arbido-B. (SZ ISSN 0258-0764) 2743, 4120
Arbido-R. (SZ ISSN 0258-0772) 2743, 4120
Arbitration & the Law. (US) 971, 833, 900
Arbitration in the Schools. (US ISSN 0003-7885) 971, 1616
Arbitration International. (UK ISSN 0957-0411) 971, 2600
Arbitration Journal. (US ISSN 0003-7893) 972, 2600
Arbitration Materials. (SZ ISSN 1013-7432) 900, 2719
Arbitration Services Reporter/Revue des Services d'Arbitrage. (CN) 972
Arbitration Times. (US) 972
Arbitrator. (US) 4724
Arbitrium. (GW ISSN 0723-2977) 2858, 389, 2895
Arbitro. (IT ISSN 0003-7907) 4499
Arbo Jaarboek. (NE) 3614
†Arbok Visindafelags Islendinga. (IC) 5137
Arbor. (SP ISSN 0210-1963) 4366
Arbor Age. (US ISSN 0279-0106) 495, 2095
Arbor Day. (US) 1483
Arbor Day News see Arbor Day 1483
Arboretum Kornickie. (PL ISSN 0066-5878) 495
Arboretum Leaves. (US) 495, 2122
Arboricultural Journal. (UK ISSN 0307-1375) 2095, 2122
Arboriculture Consultant. (US) 2122
Arboriculture Fruitiere. (FR ISSN 0003-794X) 168
Arbutus Society for Children. Annual Report. (CN) 2459
Arc. (IS) 2895, 2988
Arc see A R C 4396
†Arc. (US ISSN 0882-3588) 5137
Arc & Spark. (US) 256
Arc Arabic Journal. (CN) 1992
Arc-Boutant. (FR) 4398, 2580
Arca. (UK ISSN 0309-5541) 1275
Arcadia. (GW ISSN 0003-7982) 2896
Arcadia Bibliographica Virorum Eruditorum. (US ISSN 0195-7163) 389
▼Arcanum. (UK) 3010
Arch. (CN) 1303
Arch Notes see Ontario Archaeological Society. Arch Notes 281
Arch Plus. (GW ISSN 0587-3452) 600, 292
†Archaeologia Belgica. (BE ISSN 0772-7488) 5137
Archaelogica Venatoria. Mitteilungsblatt. (GW ISSN 0177-4840) 262
Archaeologische Forschungen. (GW) 262
Archaeo-Physika. (GW ISSN 0066-5886) 262
Archaeoastronomy. (US ISSN 0190-9940) 262, 360
Archaeoastronomy. (UK ISSN 0142-7253) 360, 262
†Archaeolog. (UK ISSN 0143-0661) 5137
Archaeologia. (UK ISSN 0261-3409) 262, 256, 312, 2144
Archaeologia Aeliana. (UK ISSN 0261-3417) 2349, 262
Archaeologia Austriaca. (AU ISSN 0003-8008) 263, 235
Archaeologia Cantiana. (UK ISSN 0066-5894) 263
Archaeologia Historica. (CS ISSN 0231-5823) 263
Archaeologia Japonica. (JA ISSN 0402-852X) 263
†Archaeologia Musicalis. (GW) 5137
Archaeologia Polona. (PL ISSN 0066-5924) 263
Archaeologia Transatlantica. (BE) 263
Archaeologia Zambiana. (ZA ISSN 0570-6068) 263
Archaeological Ertesito/Archaeological Bulletin. (HU ISSN 0003-8032) 263
Archaeological Bulletin. see Archaeologiai Ertesito 263

ARCHAEOLOGY ABROAD 5923

Archaeological Commission of Rome. Bulletin. see Commissione Archeologica Comunale di Roma. Bollettino 269
Archaeological Completion Report Series. (US) 2399, 263
Archaeological Excavation Reports see Israel. Antiquities Authority. Atiqot (English Series) 275
Archaeological Excavations. (IS) 263
Archaeological Exploration of Sardis. Monographs. (US ISSN 0066-5975) 263
Archaeological Institute of America. Abstracts of the General Meeting. (US) 290, 312
Archaeological Journal. (UK ISSN 0066-5983) 263
Archaeological Method and Theory. (US ISSN 1043-1691) 263
Archaeological Monuments. see Pamatky Archeologicke 281
Archaeological News. (US ISSN 0194-3413) 263, 1275
Archaeological Newsletter. (CN) 263
Archaeological Newsletter see Current Archaeology 270
Archaeological Reports. (UK ISSN 0141-8971) 263
Archaeological Research Tools. (US) 263
Archaeological Review. see Archeologicke Rozhledy 265
Archaeological Review from Cambridge. (UK ISSN 0261-4332) 263
Archaeological Society of Connecticut. Bulletin. (US ISSN 0739-5612) 263
Archaeological Society of Connecticut. Newsletter. (US) 263
Archaeological Society of Delaware. Bulletin. (US ISSN 0003-8067) 263
Archaeological Society of Delaware. Monograph. (US) 263
Archaeological Society of Japan. Journal/Kokogaku Zasshi. (JA ISSN 0003-8075) 263
Archaeological Society of Maryland, Inc. Ink see A S M, Ink 260
Archaeological Society of New Jersey Bulletin. (US ISSN 0196-8319) 263
Archaeological Society of New Mexico. Papers. (US ISSN 0587-1719) 263
Archaeological Survey of Israel. Survey Map Series. (IS) 263
†Archaeologicum Belgii Speculum. (BE) 5137
Archaeologie. Zeitschrift see Zeitschrift fuer Archaeologie 290
Archaeologie der Schweiz/Archeologie Suisse/Archeologia Svizzera. (SZ ISSN 0255-9005) 263
Archaeologie in Deutschland. (GW ISSN 0176-8522) 263
Archaeologie Oesterreichs. (AU) 263, 235, 2306
Archaeologische Ausgrabungen. (GW ISSN 0341-1222) 2349
Archaeologische Bibliographie. (GW) 290
Archaeologische Funde und Denkmaeler des Rheinlandes. (GW ISSN 0066-6009) 263
Archaeologische Informationen. Mitteilungen zur Ur- und Fruehgeschichte. (GW) 263
Archaeologische Mitteilungen aus Iran. Neue Folge. (GW ISSN 0066-6033) 264
Archaeologische Mitteilungen aus Nordwestdeutschland. (GW ISSN 0170-5776) 264
Archaeologische Gesellschaft Graz. Mitteilungen. (AU) 264
Archaeologischer Anzeiger. (GW ISSN 0003-8105) 264
Archaeologisches Korrespondenzblatt. (GW ISSN 0342-734X) 264
Archaeology. (US ISSN 0003-8113) 264
Archaeology. (IS) 264
Archaeology. see Kaogu 276
Archaeology Abroad Bulletin. (UK ISSN 0140-7880) 264

ARCHAEOLOGY

Archaeology and Art Magazine. see Arkeoloji ve Sanat Dergisi 265
Archaeology and Biblical Research. (US) 264, 4163
Archaeology and Cultural Relics. see Kaogu yu Wenwu 277
Archaeology and Physical Anthropology in Oceania see Archaeology in Oceania 235
Archaeology in Britain (Year). (UK ISSN 0308-8456) 264
†Archaeology in Korea. (KO) 5137
Archaeology in Montana. (US ISSN 0044-8591) 264, 235, 4366
Archaeology in New Zealand. (NZ ISSN 0113-7832) 264
Archaeology in Oceania. (AT) 235, 264
Archaeology in the United Arab Emirates. see Al-Athar fi Dawlat al-Imarat al-Arabiyyah al-Muttahidah 266
Archaeology of Eastern North America. (US ISSN 0360-1021) 264
Archaeology on Kaua'i. (US ISSN 0191-7730) 264
†Archaeology Today. (UK ISSN 0952-1240) 5137
Archaeometry. (UK ISSN 0003-813X) 264, 1815
Archaeonautica. (FR ISSN 0154-1854) 264, 1602
Archaeozoologia. (FR) 264
Archaeus. (US ISSN 0895-1268) 3668, 4011
Archailogike Hetaireia en Athenais. Praktika. (GR ISSN 1105-0969) 264
Archaiologike Ephemeris. (GR) 264
Archaiologikon Deltion. (GR ISSN 0570-622X) 264
Archdiocese of Baltimore. Directory see Catholic Directory of the Archdiocese of Baltimore 4259
Archdiocese of Cincinnati Almanac Directory and Buyer's Guide. (US) 4255
Arche. (FR ISSN 0518-2840) 4221
Archeia tes Pharmakeutikes (Athens). (GR ISSN 0003-8148) 3717, 1170
Archeion. (PL ISSN 0066-6041) 2349
Archeion Ekklesiastikou kai Kanonikou Dikaiou. (GR) 2349
Archeion Euvoikon Meleton. (GR ISSN 1010-3724) 2349, 264
Archeion Thessalikon Meleton. (GR) 2349, 264
Archenhold-Sternwarte. Vortraege und Schriften. (GW ISSN 0570-6262) 360
Archeo. (IT) 264
Archeoclub see Notiziario (Rome) 280
Archeografo Triestino. (IT ISSN 0392-0038) 264
Archeologia. (FR ISSN 0570-6270) 264
Archeologia (Poznan). (PL ISSN 0554-8195) 264
Archeologia (Wroclaw). (PL ISSN 0066-605X) 264
Archeologia Classica. (IT ISSN 0003-8172) 264, 1275
Archeologia Polski. (PL ISSN 0003-8180) 265
Archeologia Svizzera. see Archaeologie der Schweiz 263
Archeologia Viva. (IT ISSN 0392-9485) 265
Archeological Newsletter see American Schools of Oriental Research. Newsletter 3633
Archeological Society of North Carolina. Newsletter see North Carolina Archeological Society. Newsletter 280
Archeological Society of South Carolina. Occasional Papers. (US) 265
Archeological Society of Virginia. Quarterly Bulletin. (US ISSN 0003-8202) 265
Archeologicke Rozhledy/Archaeological Review. (CS ISSN 0323-1267) 265
Archeologicke Vyskumy a Nalezy na Slovensku. (CS) 265, 2349
Archeologie see Archeologie in Vlaanderen 265
Archeologie de la Moldavie. see Arheologia Moldovei 2350
Archeologie en Bretagne. (FR ISSN 0335-5233) 265
Archeologie in Vlaanderen. (BE ISSN 0778-2837) 265
Archeologie Mediterraneenne. (FR ISSN 0066-6084) 265
Archeologie Suisse. see Archaeologie der Schweiz 263
†Archeologische Kaarten van Belgie. (BE ISSN 0066-6025) 5137
Archeomaterials. (US ISSN 0891-2920) 3402, 265
L'Archer. (FR ISSN 1148-3652) 4464
Archer Quarterly. (US ISSN 0743-7803) 2144
Archery Business. (US) 4464
Archery World see Bowhunting World 4542
Archi-Cree. (FR ISSN 0294-8567) 2548
Archidiocesi di Monreale. Bollettino Ecclesiastico. (IT ISSN 0003-8296) 4255
Archidiocesis de Madrid-Alcala. Boletin Oficial. (SP) 4255
Archief- en Bibliotheekwezen in Belgie. see Archives et Bibliotheques de Belgique 2349
Archief voor de Geschiedenis van de Katholieke Kerk in Nederland see Trajecta 4277
†Archigram. (UK ISSN 0066-6092) 5137
Archimage. (US ISSN 1059-9746) 292, 2548
Archimede. (IT ISSN 0003-8369) 3030
Archimedes. (SA ISSN 0003-8385) 1249, 4299
Archipel. (FR ISSN 0044-8613) 3633
Archipelago. (PH) 4752, 2336
Archistra: Archives - Histoire - Traditions. (FR ISSN 0181-0197) 2349
De Architect. (NE ISSN 0044-8621) 292
Architect. (AT ISSN 0003-8393) 292, 2483, 2548
Architect. see Kenchiku Techo 302
Architect see R I B A Journal 306
Architect & Builder. (SA ISSN 0003-8407) 292, 600
Architect & Contractor. (US ISSN 0003-8423) 600, 292
Architect & Surveyor. (UK) 292, 1861
Architectes see Homme et l'Architecture 301
Architectes - Architecture see Homme et l'Architecture 301
Architectonika Themata. see Architecture in Greece 293
Architects see R I B A Directory of Practices 306
Architects & Designers Business see A & D Business 2556
Architects and Engineers Legal Newsletter see A E Legal Newsletter 2593
Architects and Surveyors Institute Journal see A S I Journal 291
Architects, Contractors & Engineers Guide to Construction Costs. (US ISSN 0066-6157) 600
†Architects Directory. (SA) 5137
Architects' Guide to Glass, Metal & Glazing. (US) 292, 1161
Architect's Handbook of Professional Practice. (US ISSN 0066-6173) 292
Architects India. (II ISSN 0970-6852) 292
Architects' Journal. (UK ISSN 0003-8466) 292, 600
Architect's Office Management and Administration Report see Design Firm Management & Administration Report 1007
Architects Standard Catalogues see A S C Mini-File 291
Architects Trade Journal see Architects India 292
Architectura. (GW ISSN 0044-863X) 292
Architectura. (HU ISSN 0066-6270) 292
Architectura. (DK ISSN 0106-3030) 292
Architectural & Building Directory of India. (II) 1121, 292, 600
†Architectural & Building Information Selector. (UK) 5137
Architectural & Engineering Systems. (US ISSN 8756-5951) 292, 1815
Architectural Annual Review see Construction and Architectural Specifiers Guide. Annual Review 297
Architectural Association Files see A A Files 291
Architectural Design. (UK ISSN 0003-8504) 292
Architectural Designs. (US) 292, 2548
Architectural Digest. (US ISSN 0003-8520) 292, 2548
Architectural Digest Architecture see A D Architecture 291
Architectural Engineering/Sekoh. (JA) 600
Architectural Engineering and Construction Canada see A E C Canada 291
Architectural Heritage I. (UK) 292
Architectural Heritage Society of Scotland. Journal and Annual Report see Architectural Heritage I 292
Architectural History. (UK ISSN 0066-622X) 292
Architectural Index. (US ISSN 0570-6483) 309, 3
Architectural Journal. see Jianzhu Xuebao 302
Architectural Lighting. (US ISSN 0894-0436) 292, 2548
Architectural Machinery. see Jianzhu Jixie 3018
Architectural Monographs. (UK) 292
Architectural Periodicals Index. (UK ISSN 0266-4380) 309, 2792
Architectural Psychology Newsletter. (UK ISSN 0260-4523) 4012, 292
Architectural Record. (US ISSN 0003-858X) 293
▼Architectural Record Review. (US) 293
Architectural Review. (UK ISSN 0003-861X) 293, 600
Architectural Science Review. (AT ISSN 0003-8628) 293
Architectural Services Books of Plans. (UK) 293
Architectural Structure. see Jianzhu Jiegou 301
Architectural Technology see Architecture 293
Architectural Technology see Atrium 295
Architectural Technology. see Jianzhu Jishu 622
Architecture. (US ISSN 0746-0554) 293, 600
Architecture. see Jianzhu 301
Architecture. (KE) 600, 293
Architecture & Behaviour/Architecture et Comportement. (SZ ISSN 0379-8585) 293, 4012
Architecture and Building Industry. (II ISSN 0003-8652) 293, 600
Architecture & Competitions. (GW) 293
†Architecture and Urban Design. (US) 5137
Architecture and Urbanism see A & U 291
Architecture and Urbanism. see Architektura a Urbanizmu 294
Architecture Australia. (AT) 293
Architecture - Building. see Architectuur - Bouwen 1861
Architecture Bulletin. (AT ISSN 0729-8714) 293
Architecture California. (US ISSN 0738-1131) 293
Architecture Concept. (CN ISSN 0003-8687) 293
Architecture Culture/Kenchiku Bunka. (JA ISSN 0003-8490) 293
Architecture d'Aujourd'hui (Paris, 1930). (FR ISSN 0003-8695) 293
Architecture, Engineering, Construction Automation Newsletter see A - E - C Automation Newsletter 1877
Architecture et Comportement. see Architecture & Behaviour 293
Architecture in Australia see Architecture Australia 293
Architecture in Greece/Architectonika Themata. (GR ISSN 0066-6262) 293
Architecture Minnesota. (US ISSN 0149-9106) 293
Architecture Mouvement Continuite see Moniteur Architecture - A M C 303
Architecture New Jersey. (US ISSN 0003-8733) 293
Architecture New Zealand. (NZ ISSN 0113-4566) 293
Architecture of Israel. see Adrichalut Yisraelit 291
Architecture Research Criticism see A R C 291
Architecture S.A. (Cape Town). (SA ISSN 0250-054X) 293
Architecture Schools: Special Programs.(US) 293
†Architecture Series: Bibliography. (US ISSN 0194-1356) 5137
†Architectures. (US) 5137
Architectuur - Bouwen/Architecture - Building. (NE) 1861
Architekt. (CS) 293
Der Architekt. (GW ISSN 0003-875X) 293
Der Architekt und der Bauingenieur. (GW ISSN 0003-8768) 293, 600
Architektenhandbuch Schleswig-Holstein. (GW ISSN 0724-7699) 293
Architektur. (GW ISSN 0323-3413) 294
Architektur Aktuell. (AU ISSN 0570-6602) 294
Architektur der D.D.R. see Architektur 294
Architektur, Innenarchitektur, Technischer Ausbau see A I T 291
Architektur und Bau. (AU) 294
Architektur und Kultiviertes Wohnen see Architektur und Wohnen 294
Architektur und Ladenbau. (SZ) 294, 2548
Architektur und Wettbewerbe see Architecture & Competitions 293
Architektur und Wohnen. (GW) 294
Architektur und Wohnwelt see A I T 291
Architektura. (PL ISSN 0003-8814) 294
Architektura. (CS) 294
Architektura a Urbanizmu/Architecture and Urbanism. (CS ISSN 0044-8680) 294
Architektura C S R see Architektura 294
Architetto. (IT) 294
Architettura (Milan). (IT ISSN 0003-8830) 294
Architettura (Venice). (IT) 294
Architettura Urbanistica: Metodi di Programmazione e Progetti. (IT) 294
Archithese see Werk - Bauen & Wohnen 308
Archiv. (AU ISSN 0003-8849) 972
Archiv der Deutschen Jugendbewegung. Jahrbuch. (GW ISSN 0587-5277) 2349
Archiv der Gegenwart. (GW ISSN 0003-8865) 3873, 843
Archiv der Geschichte der Naturwissenschaften. (AU ISSN 0253-7400) 2743
Archiv der Hauptstadt der Deutschen Demokratischen Republik. Beitraege Dokumente, Informationen see Berliner Geschichte 2352
Archiv der Mathematik/Archives of Mathematics/Archives Mathematiques. (SZ ISSN 0003-889X) 3030
Archiv der Pharmazie. (GW ISSN 0365-6233) 3717
Archiv des Oeffentlichen Rechts. (GW ISSN 0003-8911) 2600
Archiv des Voelkerrechts. (GW ISSN 0003-892X) 2600
Archiv for Pharmaci og Chemi see Farmaci 3726

Archiv fuer Acker- und Pflanzenbau und Bodenkunde/Archives of Agronomy and Soil Science. (GW ISSN 0365-0340) **168**
▼Archiv fuer Agraroekonomie und Betriebswirtschaft/Archives of Agricultural Economics and Farm Management. (GW ISSN 0863-1808) **147**
Archiv fuer Begriffsgeschichte. (GW ISSN 0003-8946) **3761**
Archiv fuer das Eisenhuettenwesen see Steel Research - Archiv fuer das Eisenhuettenwesen **3421**
Archiv fuer das Post - und Fernmeldewesen. (GW ISSN 0170-8988) **1331**
Archiv fuer das Studium der Neueren Sprachen und Literaturen. (GW ISSN 0003-8970) **2803**, 2896
Archiv fuer Dermatologische Forschung see Archives of Dermatological Research **3246**
Archiv fuer Deutsche Postgeschichte. (GW ISSN 0003-8989) **1352**, 1331, 3749
Archiv fuer die Civilistische Praxis. (GW ISSN 0003-8997) **2600**
Archiv fuer Diplomatik, Schriftgeschichte, Siegel- und Wappenkunde. (GW ISSN 0066-6297) **2349**
Archiv fuer Eisenbahntechnik. (GW ISSN 0341-0463) **4707**
Archiv fuer Elektronik und Uebertragungstechnik Ue see A E Ue **1331**
Archiv fuer Elektrotechnik/Archive of Electrical Engineering. (GW ISSN 0003-9039) **1882**
Archiv fuer Experimentelle Veterinaermedizin. (GW ISSN 0003-9055) **4806**
Archiv fuer Fischereiwissenschaft. (GW ISSN 0003-9063) **2037**
Archiv fuer Frankfurts Geschichte und Kunst. (GW ISSN 0341-8324) **2349**
Archiv fuer Gartenbau/Archives of Horticulture. (GW ISSN 0003-908X) **2122**
Archiv fuer Gefluegelkunde/Archives of Poultry Science/Archives de Science Avicole. (GW ISSN 0003-9098) **210**
Archiv fuer Geschichte der Philosophie. (GW ISSN 0003-9101) **3761**
Archiv fuer Geschichte des Buchwesens.(GW ISSN 0066-6327) **4120**
Archiv fuer Geschichte von Oberfranken.(GW ISSN 0066-6335) **2349**
†Archiv fuer Geschwulstforschung. (GW ISSN 0003-911X) **5137**
Archiv fuer Hessische Geschichte und Altertumskunde. (GW ISSN 0066-636X) **2349**
Archiv fuer Hydrobiologie. (GW ISSN 0003-9136) **429**, 495, 1597
Archiv fuer Indische Philosophie see Wiener Zeitschrift fuer die Kunde Suedasiens und Archiv fuer Indische Philosphie **3786**
Archiv fuer Japanische Chirurgie/Nihon Geka Hokan. (JA ISSN 0003-9152) **3375**
Archiv fuer Katholisches Kirchenrecht. (GW ISSN 0003-9160) **4255**
Archiv fuer Kinderheilkunde. Beihefte see Buecherei des Paediaters **3319**
Archiv fuer Klinische und Experimentelle Ohren-, Nasen- und Kehlkopfheilkunde see Archives of Oto-Rhino-Laryngology **3313**
Archiv fuer Kommunalwissenschaften. (GW ISSN 0003-9209) **4084**
Archiv fuer Kriminologie. (GW ISSN 0003-9225) **1510**
Archiv fuer Kulturgeschichte. (GW ISSN 0003-9233) **2306**
Archiv fuer Lebensmittel Hygiene, Fleisch-, Fisch- und Milchhygiene. (GW) **2061**
Archiv fuer Liturgiewissenschaft. (GW ISSN 0066-6386) **4163**
Archiv fuer Mathematische Logik und Grundlagenforschung see Archive for Mathematical Logic **3030**

Archiv fuer Mikrobiologie see Archives of Microbiology **550**
Archiv fuer Mittelrheinische Kirchengeschichte. (GW ISSN 0066-6432) **4163**
Archiv fuer Molluskenkunde. (GW ISSN 0003-9284) **578**
Archiv fuer Musikwissenschaft. (GW ISSN 0003-9292) **3539**
Archiv fuer Musikwissenschaft. Beihefte.(GW ISSN 0570-6769) **3539**
Archiv fuer Naturschutz und Landschaftsforschung/Archives of Nature Conservation and Landscape Research. (GW ISSN 0003-9306) **77**
Archiv fuer Oeffentliche und Freigemeinnuetzige Unternehmen. (GW ISSN 0003-9314) **1072**
Archiv fuer Ohren-, Nasen- und Kehlkopfheilkunde. see Archives of Oto-Rhino-Laryngology **3313**
Archiv fuer Orientforschung. (AU ISSN 0066-6440) **2428**
Archiv fuer Orthopaedische und Unfallchirurgie see Archives of Orthopaedic and Traumatic Surgery **3306**
Archiv fuer Papyrusforschung und Verwandte Gebiete. (GW ISSN 0066-6459) **2306**, 265
Archiv fuer Phytopathologie und Pflanzenschutz/Archives of Phytopathology and Plant Protection.(GW ISSN 0323-5408) **77**
Archiv fuer Presserecht. (GW ISSN 0341-5198) **2600**, 2567
Archiv fuer Protistenkunde. (GW ISSN 0003-9365) **429**
Archiv fuer Psychiatrie und Nervenkrankheiten see European Archives of Psychiatry and Neurological Sciences **3336**
Archiv fuer Psychologie. (GW ISSN 0066-6475) **4012**
Archiv fuer Rechts- und Sozialphilosophie/Archives de Philosophie du Droit et de Philosophie Sociale/Archives for Philosophy of Law and Social Philosophy. (GW ISSN 0001-2343) **3761**, 2600
Archiv fuer Rechts- und Sozialphilosophie. Beihefte. (GW ISSN 0341-079X) **3761**, 2600
Archiv fuer Rechts und Sozialphilosophy. Supplementa. (GW ISSN 0722-5679) **3761**
Archiv fuer Reformationsgeschichte./ Archive for Reformation History. (GW ISSN 0003-9381) **4163**
Archiv fuer Reformationsgeschichte. Literaturbericht. see Archive for Reformation History. Literature Review **4163**
Archiv fuer Religionspsychologie. (GW ISSN 0084-6724) **4163**, 4012
Archiv fuer Schlesische Kirchengeschichte. (GW ISSN 0066-6491) **4163**, 2306
†Archiv fuer Sippenforschung. (GW ISSN 0003-9403) **5138**
Archiv fuer Sozialgeschichte. (GW ISSN 0066-6505) **2349**
Archiv fuer Tierernaehrung. see Archives of Animal Nutrition **4806**
Archiv fuer Tierzucht/Archives of Animal Breeding. (GW ISSN 0003-9438) **210**
Archiv fuer Toxikologie see Archives of Toxicology **3718**
Archiv fuer Vaterlaendische Geschichte und Topographie. (AU ISSN 0003-9462) **2349**
Archiv fuer Voelkerkunde. (AU ISSN 0066-6513) **235**, 2052
Archiv fuer Wissenschaft und Praxis der Sozialen Arbeit. (GW ISSN 0340-3564) **4398**, 4366
Archiv fuer Zuechtungsforschung/ Archives of Breeding Research. (GW ISSN 0365-8406) **210**
Archiv Orientalni/Oriental Archives. (NE ISSN 0044-8699) **3633**, 2331, 2336
Archiv Ostdeutscher Familienforscher. (GW ISSN 0003-9470) **2144**

Archiv pro Badani o Zivote a Dile Jana Amose Komenskeho see Acta Comeniana. Archiv pro Badani o Zivote a Dile Jana Amose Komenskeho **2347**
Archiv und Wirtschaft. (GW ISSN 0342-6270) **645**
Archival Communications. see Leveltari Kozlemenyek **2317**
Archival Informatics Newsletter see Archives and Museum Informatics **1411**
Archival Informatics Technical Report see Archives and Museum Informatics Technical Report **2796**
Archivalische Zeitschrift. (GW ISSN 0003-9497) **2306**
Der Archivar. (GW ISSN 0003-9500) **2306**
Archivaria. (CN ISSN 0318-6954) **2399**
Archive (Air-Britain). (UK ISSN 0262-4923) **46**
Archive (Tucson). (US ISSN 0735-5572) **3788**
Archive for History of Exact Sciences. (GW ISSN 0003-9519) **4299**, 3030
Archive for Mathematical Logic. (GW ISSN 0933-5846) **3030**
Archive for New Poetry Newsletter. (US) **2988**
Archive for Rational Mechanics and Analysis. (GW ISSN 0003-9527) **3030**
Archive for Reformation History. see Archiv fuer Reformationsgeschichte **4163**
Archive for Reformation History. Literature Review/Archiv fuer Reformationsgeschichte. Literaturbericht. (US) **4163**, 2896
Archive Magazine see Lurzer's International Archive **34**
Archive of Applied Mechanics. see Ingenieur-Archiv **1825**
Archive of Electrical Engineering. see Archiv fuer Elektrotechnik **1882**
Archives. (UK ISSN 0003-9535) **2349**, 2743
Archives. (CN ISSN 0044-9423) **2743**, 2306
Archives and History. see Dang'an yu Lishi **2754**
Archives and Museum Informatics. (US ISSN 1042-1467) **1411**
Archives and Museum Informatics Technical Report. (US ISSN 1042-1459) **2796**
Archives and the User. (UK ISSN 0066-653X) **2743**
Archives Antillaises. see Caribbean Archives **2401**
Archives - Archaeology. see Purabhilekh - Puratatva **2341**
Archives Association of British Columbia Newsletter see A A B C Newsletter **2739**
Archives Bakounine/Bakunin-Archiv. (NE ISSN 0066-6548) **2349**
Archives Belges de Medecine Sociale et d'Hygiene. (BE) **3077**, 3614, 4098
Archives Claudeliennes. (FR ISSN 0066-6556) **2896**
Archives d'Anatomie, d'Histologie et d'Embryologie. (FR ISSN 0003-9586) **429**, 522, 3077
Archives d'Anatomie et de Cytologie Pathologiques. (FR ISSN 0395-501X) **3077**
Archives d'Anatomie Microscopique et de Morphologie Experimentale see Biological Structures and Morphogenesis **431**
Archives d'Anthropologie see Musee Royal de l'Afrique Centrale. Archives d'Anthropologie **245**
Archives d'Ethnologie Francaise see Ethnologie Francaise **239**
Archives d'Histoire Doctrinale et Litteraire du Moyen Age. (FR ISSN 0373-5478) **3761**
Archives de Medecine Generale et Tropicale see Archives Mediterraneennes de Medecine **3077**
Archives de Philosophie. (FR ISSN 0003-9632) **3761**

ARCHIVES 5925

Archives de Philosophie du Droit. (FR ISSN 0066-6564) **2600**
Archives de Philosophie du Droit et de Philosophie Sociale. see Archiv fuer Rechts- und Sozialphilosophie **3761**
Archives de Psychologie. (SZ ISSN 0003-9640) **4012**
Archives de Science Avicole. see Archiv fuer Gefluegelkunde **210**
Archives de Sciences Sociales des Religions. (FR ISSN 0335-5985) **4394**, 4212, 4457
Archives des Lettres Canadiennes. (CN ISSN 0066-6572) **2896**
Archives des Lettres Modernes. (FR ISSN 0003-9675) **2896**
Archives des Maladies du Coeur et des Vaisseaux. (FR ISSN 0003-9683) **3204**
Archives des Maladies Professionnelles de Medecine du Travail et de Securite Sociale. (FR ISSN 0003-9691) **3614**
Archives des Sciences. (SZ ISSN 0003-9705) **4299**
Archives du Fo Fi Fa. (MG) **77**
Archives et Bibliotheques de Belgique/ Archief- en Bibliotheekwezen in Belgie. (BE ISSN 0003-9748) **2349**, 2743, 3521
Archives Europeennes de Sociologie. see European Journal of Sociology **4435**
Archives for Clinical Ecology see Clinical Ecology **435**
Archives for Mother and Child Health. see Arhiv za Zastitu Majke i Djeteta **3319**
Archives for Philosophy of Law and Social Philosophy. see Archiv fuer Rechts- und Sozialphilosophie **3761**
Archives for Scandinavian Philology. see Arkiv for Nordisk Filologi **2804**
Archives Francaises de Pediatrie. (FR ISSN 0003-9764) **3318**
Archives Internationales Claude Bernard.(FR ISSN 0302-2358) **4299**
Archives Internationales d'Histoire des Idees/International Archives of the History of Ideas. (NE ISSN 0066-6610) **3761**
Archives Internationales d'Histoire des Sciences. (IT ISSN 0003-9810) **4299**
Archives Internationales de Pharmacodynamie et de Therapie/ International Archives of Pharmacology. (BE ISSN 0003-9780) **3718**
Archives Internationales de Physiologie, de Biochimie et de Biophysique. (BE) **569**, 471
Archives Internationales de Physiologie et de Biochimie see Archives Internationales de Physiologie, de Biochimie et de Biophysique **569**
Archives Italiennes de Biologie. (IT ISSN 0003-9829) **3330**, 569
Archives Juives. (FR ISSN 0003-9837) **4221**
Archives Mathematiques. see Archiv der Mathematik **3030**
Archives Mediterraneennes de Medecine. (FR ISSN 0003-9845) **3077**
Archives of A I D S Research. (US) **3218**
Archives of Acoustics. (PL ISSN 0137-5075) **3858**
Archives of Agricultural Economics and Farm Management. see Archiv fuer Agraroekonomie und Betriebswirtschaft **147**
Archives of Agronomy and Soil Science. see Archiv fuer Acker- und Pflanzenbau und Bodenkunde **168**
Archives of American Art Journal. (US ISSN 0003-9853) **312**
Archives of Anatomy, Histology and Embryology. see Arkhiv Anatomii, Gistologii i Embriologii **429**
Archives of Andrology. (US ISSN 0148-5016) **3077**
Archives of Animal Breeding. see Archiv fuer Tierzucht **210**
Archives of Animal Nutrition/Archiv fuer Tierernaehrung. (GW ISSN 0003-942X) **4806**, 211

ARCHIVES

Archives of Asian Art. (US ISSN 0066-6637) **312**
Archives of Biochemistry and Biophysics. (US ISSN 0003-9861) **471, 484**
Archives of Breeding Research. *see* Archiv fuer Zuechtungsforschung **210**
Archives of Child Health. (IL ISSN 0044-8710) **3318**
Archives of Clinical Neuropsychology. (US ISSN 0887-6177) **3330, 4012**
Archives of Croatia. Bulletin. *see* Arhiv Hrvatske. Bilten **2350**
Archives of Dermatological Research. (GW ISSN 0340-3696) **3246**
Archives of Dermatology. (US ISSN 0003-987X) **3246**
Archives of Dermatology (Edicion Espanola). (Spanish translation of: Archives of Dermatology (SP ISSN 1130-1910) **3246**
Archives of Diseases in Childhood. (UK ISSN 0003-9888) **3318**
Archives of Emergency Medicine. (UK ISSN 0264-4924) **3375**
Archives of Environmental Contamination and Toxicology. (US ISSN 0090-4341) **1980**
Archives of Environmental Health. (US ISSN 0003-9896) **3077, 1943**
Archives of Gastroenterohepatology. *see* Gastroenterohepatoloski Arhiv **3267**
Archives of General Psychiatry. (US ISSN 0003-990X) **3330**
Archives of Gerontology and Geriatrics. (NE ISSN 0167-4943) **2270**
Archives of Gynecology *see* Archives of Gynecology and Obstetrics **3289**
Archives of Gynecology and Obstetrics. (GW ISSN 0932-0067) **3289**
Archives of Histology and Cytology/Nihon Soshikigaku Kiroku. (JA ISSN 0914-9465) **522, 3077**
Archives of Horticulture. *see* Archiv fuer Gartenbau **2122**
Archives of Hydrotechnic. (PL) **4822**
Archives of Industrial Hygiene and Toxicology. *see* Arhiv za Higijenu Rada i Toksikologiju **1980**
Archives of Insect Biochemistry and Physiology. (US ISSN 0739-4462) **528**
Archives of Internal Medicine. (US ISSN 0003-9926) **3077**
Archives of Labor and Urban Affairs Newsletter. (US) **972**
Archives of Mathematics. *see* Archiv der Mathematik **3030**
Archives of Mechanics. (PL ISSN 0373-2029) **3842, 1927**
Archives of Medical Hydrology. (IT ISSN 0003-9934) **3077**
Archives of Metallurgy. (PL) **3402**
Archives of Microbiology. (GW ISSN 0302-8933) **550**
Archives of Mining Sciences. (PL) **3478**
Archives of National Economy. *see* Narodnostopanski Arkhiv **681**
Archives of Natural History. (UK ISSN 0260-9541) **4299**
Archives of Nature Conservation and Landscape Research. *see* Archiv fuer Naturschutz und Landschaftsforschung **77**
Archives of Neurology. (US ISSN 0003-9942) **3330**
Archives of Ophthalmology. (US ISSN 0003-9950) **3298**
Archives of Ophthalmology (Edicion Espanola). (Spanish translation of: Archives of Ophthalmology) (SP ISSN 1130-5134) **3298**
Archives of Oral Biology. (US ISSN 0003-9969) **3228, 578**
Archives of Orthopaedic and Traumatic Surgery. (GW ISSN 0344-8444) **3306**
Archives of Oto-Rhino-Laryngology/Archiv fuer Ohren-, Nasen- und Kehlkopfheilkunde. (GW ISSN 0302-9530) **3313**
Archives of Otolaryngology/Journal d'O.R.L. (FR ISSN 0750-6244) **3077**
Archives of Otolaryngology *see* Archives of Otolaryngology - Head & Neck Surgery **3313**
Archives of Otolaryngology - Head & Neck Surgery. (US ISSN 0886-4470) **3313**
Archives of Pathology. *see* Arkhiv Patologii **3078**
Archives of Pathology & Laboratory Medicine. (US ISSN 0363-0153) **3077, 3257**
Archives of Pharmacal Research. (KO ISSN 0253-6269) **3718**
Archives of Physical Medicine and Rehabilitation. (US ISSN 0003-9993) **3077**
Archives of Phytopathology and Plant Protection. *see* Archiv fuer Phytopathologie und Pflanzenschutz **77**
Archives of Poultry Science. *see* Archiv fuer Gefluegelkunde **210**
Archives of Practical Pharmacy *see* Journal of Pharmaceutical Science and Technology **3732**
Archives of Psychiatric Nursing. (US ISSN 0883-9417) **3275, 3330**
Archives of Sexual Behavior. (US ISSN 0004-0002) **3077**
Archives of Soviet Science Series: Physical Sciences Section. (US ISSN 0893-4908) **3846**
Archives of Surgery. (US ISSN 0004-0010) **3376**
Archives of the Republic of China. *see* Minguo Dang'an **2340**
Archives of Toxicology. (GW ISSN 0340-5761) **3718, 1980**
Archives of Toxicology. Supplement. (GW ISSN 0171-9750) **3718, 1980**
Archives of Virology. (US ISSN 0304-8608) **3218, 550**
Archives Parlementaires de 1787 a 1860. (FR) **3873**
Archives Quarterly Bulletin *see* Archives of American Art Journal **312**
Archives, Recherches et Cultures Lesbiennes. Bulletin. (FR) **2451**
Archives Roumaines de Pathologie Experimentale et de Microbiologie *see* Roumanian Archives of Microbiology and Immunology **3188**
Archives Science Bulletin. *see* Dang'anxue Tongxun **2754**
Archives Sharing Bulletin. (US ISSN 1054-0709) **1534**
Archivio Amministrativo ed Urbanistico Subalpino. (IT) **4084**
Archivio Botanico e Biogeografico Italiano. (IT ISSN 0004-0053) **495, 2242**
Archivio del Teatro Italiano. (IT ISSN 0066-6661) **4629**
Archivio della Corrispondenza degli Scienziati Italiani. (IT) **4299**
Archivio di Chirurgia Toracica e Cardiovascolare. (IT ISSN 0391-7029) **3376, 3204**
Archivio di Filosofia. (IT ISSN 0004-0088) **3761**
Archivio di Fisiologia. (IT ISSN 0004-0096) **569**
Archivio di Medicina Interna. (IT ISSN 0004-010X) **3078**
Archivio di Oceanografia e Limonologia. (IT ISSN 0066-667X) **1602, 1597**
Archivio di Ortopedia e Reumatologia. (IT ISSN 0390-7368) **3306, 3368**
Archivio di Ostetricia e Ginecologia. (IT ISSN 0004-0126) **3289**
Archivio di Psichiatria Generale. (IT) **3330**
Archivio di Psicologia, Neurologia e Psichiatria. (IT ISSN 0004-0150) **3330, 4012**
Archivio di Studi Urbani e Regionali. (IT ISSN 0004-0177) **2483**
Archivio di Tisiologia e delle Malattie dell'Aparato Respiratorio *see* Archivio Monaldi per le Malattie del Torace **3364**
Archivio E. Maragliano di Patologia e Clinica. (IT ISSN 0004-0193) **3078**
Archivio Fotografico Toscano *see* A F T **3788**
Archivio Giuridico. (IT ISSN 0391-5646) **2600**
Archivio Glottologico Italiano. (IT ISSN 0004-0207) **2803**
Archivio Italiano di Anatomia e di Embriologia. (IT ISSN 0004-0223) **429, 3078**
Archivio Italiano di Dermatologia, Sifilografia, Venereologia e Sessuologia *see* Archivio Italiano di Urologia e Nefrologia, Andrologia **3387**
Archivio Italiano di Patologia e Clinica dei Tumori. (IT ISSN 0004-0266) **3193**
Archivio Italiano di Urologia e Nefrologia, Andrologia. (IT) **3387**
Archivio Italiano per la Storia della Pieta. (IT ISSN 0066-6688) **4163**
Archivio Linguistico Veneto. Quaderni. (IT ISSN 0066-6696) **2804**
Archivio Monaldi per le Malattie del Torace. (IT) **3364, 522**
Archivio per l'Alto Adige. (IT) **2804, 312, 2052**
Archivio per l'Antropologia e la Etnologia. (IT) **235**
Archivio per la Storia del Movimento Sociale Cattolico in Italia. Bollettino. (IT ISSN 0390-8240) **4255**
Archivio per le Scienze Mediche *see* Gazzetta Medica Italiana Archivio per le Scienze Mediche **3100**
Archivio Piombinese di Studi Storici *see* Ricerche Storiche (Naples) **2321**
Archivio Putti di Chirurgia degli Organi di Movimento. (IT ISSN 0066-670X) **3376**
Archivio Sardo del Movimento Operaio Contadino e Antonomistico. (IT) **2349**
Archivio Siciliano di Medicina e Chirurgia (Sezione Chirurgica) *see* Acta Chirurgica Mediterranea **3374**
Archivio Siciliano di Medicina e Chirurgia (Sezione Medica) *see* Acta Medica Mediterranea **3327**
Archivio Siciliano di Medicina e Chirurgia (Sezione Pediatrica) *see* Acta Pediatrica Mediterranea **3318**
Archivio Storico Bergamasco. (IT) **2349**
Archivio Storico Civico e Biblioteca Trivulziana. Libri & Documenti. (IT ISSN 0390-1009) **389**
▼Archivio Storico del Sannio. (IT) **2306**
Archivio Storico Italiano. (IT ISSN 0391-7770) **2349**
Archivio Storico Italiano. Biblioteca. (IT ISSN 0066-6718) **2349**
Archivio Storico Lodigiano. (IT ISSN 0004-0347) **2349**
Archivio Storico per la Calabria e la Lucania. (IT ISSN 0004-0355) **2349**
Archivio Storico per la Sicilia Orientale. (IT ISSN 0004-0363) **2349**
Archivio Storico per le Province Parmensi. (IT) **2349**
Archivio Storico Sardo. (IT) **2349**
Archivio Storico Siracusano. (IT ISSN 0044-8737) **2349**
Archivio Storico Ticinese. (SZ ISSN 0004-0371) **2349, 265**
Archivio Trentino di Storia Contemporanea. Museo del Risorgimento e della Lotta per la Liberta. Bollettino. (IT) **2349**
Archivio Trimestrale. (IT ISSN 0390-0916) **3873**
Archivio Veterinario Italiano. (IT ISSN 0004-0479) **4806**
Archivist. (CN ISSN 0705-2855) **2399, 312, 3521**
Archivium Hibernicum. (IE ISSN 0044-8745) **2349**
Archivium Historicum Carmelitanum. (IT ISSN 0394-7734) **4256, 2306**
Archivmitteilungen. (GW ISSN 0004-038X) **2743, 2306**
Archivni Casopis. (CS ISSN 0004-0398) **2743**
Archivo de Ciencias Biologicas y Naturales, Teoricas y Aplicadas. (AG ISSN 0004-0401) **429**
Archivo Epistolar Colombiano. (CK ISSN 0066-6734) **2896**
Archivo Espanol de Arqueologia. (SP ISSN 0066-6742) **265**
Archivo Espanol de Arte. (SP ISSN 0004-0428) **312**
Archivo General de la Nacion. Revista. (AG ISSN 0325-2868) **2743**
Archivo Historico de Miraflores. Boletin. (VE ISSN 0004-0444) **2399**
Archivo Historico del Guayas. Coleccion Monografica. (EC) **2399**
Archivo Historico del Guayas. Revista. (EC) **2399**
Archivo Historico Diocesano de San Cristobal de las Casas. Boletin. (MX) **2399, 235**
▼Archivo Historico Diocesano de San Cristobal de las Casas. Serie Tecnica.(MX) **4079, 253**
Archivo Ibero-Americano. (SP ISSN 0004-0452) **2349, 4256**
Archivo Nacional de Historia *see* A R N A H I S **2397**
Archivos Argentinos de Dermatologia. (AG ISSN 0066-6750) **3246**
Archivos Argentinos de Tisiologia y Neumonologia. (AG ISSN 0004-0509) **3364**
Archivos Argentinos Enfermedades del Aparato Digestivo. (AG ISSN 0004-0517) **3266**
Archivos Bolivianos de Medicina. (BO ISSN 0004-0525) **3078**
Archivos de Biologia Andina. (PE) **429, 3078**
Archivos de Biologia y Medicina Experimentales. (CL ISSN 0004-0533) **429, 3257**
Archivos de Bronconeumologia. (SP ISSN 0300-2896) **3364**
Archivos de Criminologia, Neuro-Psiquiatria y Disciplinas Conexas. (EC ISSN 0004-0541) **3330, 1510**
Archivos de Farmacologia y Toxicologia.(SP ISSN 0304-8616) **3718, 1980**
Archivos de Historia Andina. (PE) **2399, 2052**
Archivos de Historia Potosina. (MX ISSN 0004-055X) **2399**
Archivos de Investigacion Medica. (MX ISSN 0066-6769) **3078**
Archivos de la Biblioteca Nacional. (UY ISSN 0797-0129) **2744, 2399**
Archivos de Medicina del Deporte. (SP ISSN 0212-8799) **3370**
Archivos de Neurobiologia. (SP ISSN 0004-0576) **3330**
Archivos de Odontoestomatologia. (SP ISSN 0213-4144) **3228, 3266**
Archivos de Odontoestomatologia Preventiva y Comunitaria. (SP) **3228**
Archivos de Oftalmologia de Buenos Aires. (AG ISSN 0066-6777) **3298**
Archivos de Pediatria. (SP ISSN 0402-9054) **3318**
Archivos de Pediatria del Uruguay. (UY ISSN 0004-0584) **3318**
Archivos de Tisiologia *see* Archivos Argentinos de Tisiologia y Neumonologia **3364**
Archivos de Zootecnia. (SP ISSN 0004-0592) **211, 197, 204, 4806**
Archivos del Caribe. *see* Caribbean Archives **2401**
Archivos Dominicanos de Pediatria. (DR ISSN 0004-0606) **3319**
Archivos Latinoamericanos de Nutricion.(GT ISSN 0004-0622) **3603**
Archivos Leoneses. (SP ISSN 0004-0630) **2349**
Archivos Venezolanos de Puericultura y Pediatria. (VE ISSN 0004-0649) **3319**
Archivs. (AT) **1992**
Archivum. (GW ISSN 0066-6793) **2744**
Archivum (Oviedo). (SP) **3761**
Archivum Bibliographicum Carmeli Teresiani. (VC) **4212**
Archivum Bibliographicum Carmelitanum *see* Archivum Bibliographicum Carmeli Teresiani **4212**
Archivum Calderonianum. (GW ISSN 0721-0442) **2804**
Archivum Eurasiae Medii Aevi. (GW ISSN 0724-8822) **3633**

ARGENTINA. SECRETARIA 5927

Archivum Franciscanum Historicum. (IT ISSN 0004-0665) **4256**, 2306
Archivum Fratrum Praedicatorum. (IT) **2349**
Archivum Histologicum Japonicum *see* Archives of Histology and Cytology **522**
Archivum Historiae Pontificae. (VC ISSN 0066-6785) **4256**
Archivum Historicum Societatis Iesu. (IT ISSN 0037-8887) **4256**, 2350
Archivum Immunologiae et Therapiae Experimentalis. (PL ISSN 0004-069X) **3078**, 3264
Archivum Iuridicum Cracoviense. (PL ISSN 0066-6882) **2600**
Archivum Mathematicum. (CS ISSN 0044-8753) **3030**
Archivum Musicum. (IT) **3539**
Archivum Ottomanicum. (GW ISSN 0378-2808) **2428**
Archivum Romanicum. Biblioteca. Serie 1: Storia Letteratura Paleografia. (IT ISSN 0066-6807) **2896**
Archivum Romanicum. Biblioteca. Serie 2: Linguistica. (IT ISSN 0066-6815) **2804**
Archivum Trebonense. (CS) **2350**, 645
Archivy. (CN ISSN 0828-3192) **2744**
Archiwa, Biblioteki i Muzea Koscielne. (PL) **2350**, 4256
Archiwista. (PL ISSN 0004-0711) **2350**
†Archiwum Akustyki. (PL ISSN 0066-6823) **5138**
Archiwum Automatyki i Robotyki. (PL) **1440**
Archiwum Automatyki i Telemechaniki *see* Archiwum Automatyki i Robotyki **1440**
Archiwum Combustionis. (PL ISSN 0208-4198) **1815**, 1170
Archiwum Dziejow Oswiaty. (PL ISSN 0066-6831) **1616**
Archiwum Energetyki. (PL ISSN 0066-684X) **1815**, 4299
Archiwum Filologiczne. (PL ISSN 0066-6866) **2804**, 1275
Archiwum Gornictwa *see* Archives of Mining Sciences **3478**
Archiwum Historii Filozofii i Mysli Spolecznej. (PL ISSN 0066-6874) **3761**, 4366
Archiwum Historii i Filozofii Medycyny. (PL ISSN 0860-1844) **3078**
Archiwum Hutnictwa *see* Archives of Metallurgy **3402**
Archiwum Hydrotechniki *see* Archives of Hydrotechnic **4822**
Archiwum Informatyki Teoretycznej i Stosowanej. (PL ISSN 0867-2121) **1389**
Archiwum Inzynierii Ladowej. (PL ISSN 0004-0797) **1861**
Archiwum Kryminologii. (PL ISSN 0066-6890) **1510**
Archiwum Literackie. (PL ISSN 0066-6904) **2896**
Archiwum Mechaniki Stosowanej *see* Archives of Mechanics **3842**
Archiwum Mineralogiczne. (PL ISSN 0066-6912) **1554**
Archiwum Nauki o Materialach. (PL ISSN 0138-032X) **1915**, 3402
Archiwum Ochrony Srodowiska. (PL ISSN 0324-8461) **1943**
Archiwum Procesow Spalania - Archives of Combustion Processes *see* Archiwum Combustionis **1815**
Archiwum Tlumaczen z Teorii Literatury i Metodologii Badan Literackich. (PL ISSN 0208-7596) **2804**, 2896
Archiwum Veterinarium Polonicum. *see* Polskie Archiwum Weterynaryjne **4814**
The Archway (Smithfield). (US) **1303**
Arcidiocesi di Reggio Calabria. Rivista Pastorale. (IT) **4256**
Arco. (CK ISSN 0570-7293) **2503**
Arctic. (CN ISSN 0004-0843) **4299**, 1587, 2242
Arctic and Alpine Research. (US ISSN 0004-0851) **4299**, 429, 1541, 2242
Arctic & Antarctic Regions (Cold Regions 1800 - Present). (US) **1550**, 3

Arctic Anthropology. (US ISSN 0066-6939) **235**
Arctic Medical Research. (FI ISSN 0782-226X) **3078**, 4098
Arctic Science & Technology Information System Bibliography *see* A S T I S Bibliography **1549**
Arctic Science & Technology Information System Current Awareness Bulletin *see* A S T I S Current Awareness Bulletin **4613**
Arctic Science & Technology Information System Occasional Publications *see* A S T I S Occasional Publications **388**
Arctic Science Conference. Proceedings.(US) **4299**
Arctos; Acta Philologica Fennica. (FI ISSN 0570-734X) **1275**, 2804
Ard. (SY) **3950**
Ardea. (NE ISSN 0373-2266) **562**
Al-Ardh. (LY) **2580**, 77
Ardhi: Journal of Land Development. (KE) **2483**
Ardrinews *see* A R D R I News **67**
Ardyn Armi/People's Army. (MP) **2858**
Ardyn Tor/People's State. (MP) **3873**
Are You Spoofing *see* Spoofing **2058**
Area. (IT) **312**, 294
Area. (UK ISSN 0004-0894) **2242**
Area and Culture Studies. (JA ISSN 0493-4342) **1700**
Area and Production of Principal Crops in India. Summary Tables. (II) **168**
Area Auto Racing News. (US) **4464**
Area Development in Japan. (JA) **2483**
Area Development Industrial Development Directory of Canada. (US) **1121**
Area Development Magazine. (US ISSN 0004-0908) **1002**, 600, 4145
Area Footprints. (US) **2144**
Areas of Concern. (US ISSN 0044-8788) **2221**
Areas of Critical Teacher Needs in Florida *see* Teacher Supply and Demand in Florida **1666**
Arecanut and Spices Bulletin *see* Indian Cocoa, Arecanut & Spices Journal **2072**
Arena. (AT ISSN 0004-0932) **3873**
Arena. (CI ISSN 0402-9283) **3873**, 3950
Arena *see* Stadion **4493**
†Arena. (UK ISSN 0142-5498) **5138**
Arena (Edinburgh). (UK) **4464**
Arena (London). (UK) **2193**
Arena News. (US ISSN 0164-8047) **4532**
†Arena Review. (US ISSN 0735-1267) **5138**
Arenaturist. (CU) **4752**
Arengo. (IT) **3874**
Areopag. (GW ISSN 0570-751X) **1331**
Areopago Cirals. (IT) **2858**
Areopagus. (HK ISSN 1011-8101) **4163**
Arerugi. *see* Japanese Journal of Allergology **3187**
Arerugia. (JA ISSN 0287-0185) **3183**, 3364
Ares. (BE) **3451**
Arete. (US ISSN 0363-2903) **4398**
Arethusa. (US ISSN 0004-0975) **1275**
Aretusa. (IT) **2204**
Arev. (UA ISSN 0334-326X) **578**
Argamon. (IS ISSN 0334-326X) **578**
Arge-Saar. Mitteilungsblatt. (GW) **3749**
Argent. (FR) **645**
Argentina. (AG ISSN 0004-0983) **2170**
Argentina. Central de Estadisticas Nacionales. Informe. (AG) **4562**
Argentina. Centro Nacional de Documentacion e Informacion Educativa. Boletin Bibliografico. (AG ISSN 0326-2944) **389**, 1616
†Argentina. Centro Nacional de Documentacion e Informacion Educativa. Informaciones y Documentos. (AG) **5138**
†Argentina. Comision Nacional de Valores. Boletin Informativo. (AG) **5138**
†Argentina. Comision Nacional de Valores. Informacion Estadistica. (AG) **5138**

Argentina. Congreso. Biblioteca. Boletin *see* Argentina. Congreso de la Nacion. Biblioteca. Boletin **389**
Argentina. Congreso de la Nacion. Biblioteca. Boletin. (AG) **389**
Argentina. Congreso de la Nacion. Biblioteca. Boletin Legislativo. (AG ISSN 0301-7818) **4053**
Argentina. Congreso de la Nacion. Biblioteca. Serie Bibliografica. (AG ISSN 0325-3147) **3936**
†Argentina. Consejo Nacional de Desarrollo. Recursos Humanos. (AG) **5138**
†Argentina. Consejo Nacional de Investigaciones Cientificas y Tecnicas. Informaciones. (AG ISSN 0010-6364) **5138**
Argentina. Departamento de Estadistica Educativa. Boletin Informativo. (AG ISSN 0066-7021) **1616**
Argentina. Departamento de Estudios Historicos Navales. Serie A: Cultura Nautica. (AG ISSN 0066-703X) **3451**
Argentina. Departamento de Estudios Historicos Navales. Serie B: Historia Naval Argentina. (AG ISSN 0066-7048) **3451**
Argentina. Departamento de Estudios Historicos Navales. Serie C: Biografias Navales Argentinas. (AG ISSN 0066-7056) **3451**, 417
Argentina. Departamento de Estudios Historicos Navales. Serie E: Documentos. (AG) **3451**, 2399
Argentina. Departamento de Estudios Historicos Navales. Serie J: Libros y Impresos Raros. (AG ISSN 0066-7080) **3476**
Argentina. Direccion General de Coordinacion e Informacion Energetica. Anuario de Combustibles. *see* Argentina. Direccion General de Evaluacion Energetica. Anuario de Combustibles **1882**
Argentina. Direccion General de Coordinacion e Informacion Energetica. Anuario Energia Electrica. *see* Argentina. Direccion General de Evaluacion Energetica. Anuario Energia Electrica **1882**
Argentina. Direccion General de Evaluacion Energetica. Anuario de Combustibles. (AG) **1882**
Argentina. Direccion General de Evaluacion Energetica. Anuario Energia Electrica. (AG) **1882**
Argentina. Direccion General de Parques Nacionales. Anales de Parques Nacionales *see* Argentina. Servicio Nacional de Parques Nacional. Anales **4053**
Argentina. Direccion General de Planificacion y Control Energetico. Anuario Estadistico. Combustibles. *see* Argentina. Direccion General de Evaluacion Energetica. Anuario de Combustibles **1882**
Argentina. Direccion Nacional de Asistencia Nacional. DAS. (AG ISSN 0004-1025) **2526**
Argentina. Direccion Nacional de Estadistica y Censos. Boletin de Estadistica *see* Argentina. Instituto Nacional de Estadistica y Censos. Boletin Estadistico Trimestral **4562**
Argentina. Empresa Nacional de Correos y Telegrafos. Boletin. (AG) **1352**
Argentina. Escuela de Defensa Nacional. Revista. (AG ISSN 0325-0792) **3950**, 3451
Argentina. Escuela Superior de Guerra. Revista *see* Argentina. Escuela de Defensa Nacional. Revista **3950**
Argentina. Instituto de Asuntos Tecnicos. Estadisticas. (AG) **4614**
Argentina. Instituto Forestal Nacional. Anuario de Estadistica Forestal. (AG ISSN 0570-8834) **2111**
Argentina. Instituto Nacional de Estadistica y Censos. Anuario Estadistico. (AG) **3989**, 4562
Argentina. Instituto Nacional de Estadistica y Censos. Boletin Estadistico Trimestral. (AG ISSN 0325-1969) **4562**

Argentina. Instituto Nacional de Estadistica y Censos. Estadistica Mensual. (AG ISSN 0326-6214) **4562**
†Argentina. Instituto Nacional de Tecnologia Industria. Boletin Tecnico. (AG ISSN 0325-6278) **5138**
Argentina. Junta Nacional de Carnes. Boletin Diario de Informaciones. (AG) **211**
Argentina. Junta Nacional de Carnes. Boletin Semanal Sobre Ganados, Carnes y Subproductos. (AG) **211**
Argentina. Junta Nacional de Carnes. Exportaciones de Productos Ganaderos. (AG) **211**, 900
Argentina. Junta Nacional de Carnes. Sintesis Estadistica. (AG ISSN 0066-7269) **133**
Argentina. Mercado Nacional de Hacienda. Anuario. (AG) **211**
Argentina. Ministeria de Salud y Accion Social. Programa Nacional de Estadisticas de Salud. (AG) **4116**
Argentina. Ministerio de Cultura y Educacion. Boletin Bibliografico. (AG) **1674**
Argentina. Ministerio de Cultura y Educacion. Estadisticas de la Educacion. (AG) **1674**
Argentina. Ministerio de Economia. Boletin Semanal *see* Argentina. Ministerio de Economia, Hacienda y Finanzas. Boletin Semanal de Economia **843**
Argentina. Ministerio de Economia. Economic Report. Summary. (AG) **843**
Argentina. Ministerio de Economia, Hacienda y Finanzas. Boletin Semanal de Economia. (AG ISSN 0325-383X) **843**
Argentina. Ministerio de Economia. Informe Economico. Resumen. (AG) **843**
Argentina. Ministerio de Hacienda y Finanzas. Economic Report. Summary *see* Argentina. Ministerio de Economia. Economic Report. Summary **843**
Argentina. Ministerio de Hacienda y Finanzas. Informe Economico. Resumen *see* Argentina. Ministerio de Economia. Informe Economico. Resumen **843**
Argentina. Ministerio de Relaciones Exteriores y Culto. Revista. (AG) **3950**
Argentina. Museo Provincial de Ciencias Naturales. Comunicaciones *see* Argentina. Museo Provincial de Ciencias Naturales. Comunicaciones. Nueva Serie **429**
Argentina. Museo Provincial de Ciencias Naturales. Comunicaciones. Nueva Serie. (AG ISSN 0325-3856) **429**, 3656
Argentina. Oficina Sectorial de Desarrollo de Energia. Anuarios Estadisticos. Energia Electrica *see* Argentina. Direccion General de Evaluacion Energetica. Anuario Energia Electrica **1882**
Argentina. Secretaria de Estado de Agricultura y Ganaderia. Area de Trabajo de Lecheria. Resena Estadistica. (AG) **133**
Argentina. Secretaria de Estado de Agricultura y Ganaderia. Comunicado de Prensa. (AG) **77**
Argentina. Secretaria de Estado de Comunicaciones. Boletin *see* Argentina. Empresa Nacional de Correos y Telegrafos. Boletin **1352**
Argentina. Secretaria de Estado de Hacienda. Memoria. (AG) **1087**
Argentina. Secretaria de Estado de Salud Publica. Programa Nacional de Estadisticas de Salud *see* Argentina. Ministeria de Salud y Accion Social. Programa Nacional de Estadisticas de Salud **4116**
Argentina. Secretaria de Guerra. Direccion de Estudios Historicos. Boletin Bibliografico. (AG ISSN 0066-7293) **2399**, 3451

Argentina. Servicio de Inteligencia Naval. Bibliotecas de la Armada. Boletin Bibliografico. (AG ISSN 0066-7331) **3476**
Argentina. Servicio Nacional de Economia y Sociologia Rural. Publicacion E S R. (AG) **77**
Argentina. Servicio Nacional de Parques Nacional. Anales. (AG ISSN 0302-5705) **4053**
Argentina. Servicio Nacional Minero Geologico. Anales. (AG ISSN 0066-7145) **1554**, **3478**
Argentina. Servicio Nacional Minero Geologico. Boletin. (AG ISSN 0066-7153) **1554**, **3478**
Argentina. Servicio Nacional Minero Geologico. Estadistica Minera. (AG ISSN 0066-7161) **3498**
Argentina. Servicio Nacional Minero Geologico. Informes Tecnicos. (AG) **1554**
Argentina. Servicio Nacional Minero Geologico. Revista. (AG ISSN 0066-717X) **1554**
Argentina Automotriz. (AG ISSN 0004-0991) **4679**
Argentina en Postivo. (AG) **2170**
Argentina Forestal. (AG) **2113**, **2095**
Argentina Grafica. (AG ISSN 0004-105X) **3997**
Argentina Tecnologica. (AG ISSN 0326-8101) **4593**
Argentine-American Business Review Directory. (US) **900**
Argentine Economic Development. (AG) **843**
Argentine Economic Legislation. see Legislacion Economica Argentina **2648**
Argentine Letter. (AG) **843**, **2242**, **3874**
Argentine Republic. Junta Nacional de Carnes. Resena see Argentina. Junta Nacional de Carnes. Sintesis Estadistica **133**
Argentine Republic. Mercado Nacional de Hacienda. Memoria see Argentina. Mercado Nacional de Hacienda. Anuario **211**
Argentine Science Fiction Review. (AG ISSN 0004-1084) **3010**
Argentine Society of Soil Science. Journal. see Ciencia del Suelo **173**
Argentinos Lietuviu Balsas/Voz de los Lituanos en la Argentina. (AG ISSN 0004-1106) **1992**
Arges. (RM) **2215**
Argo. (XV ISSN 0570-8869) **2350**, **3521**
Argo see Probe (Santa Barbara) **3946**
†Argo (Oxford). (UK ISSN 0143-0246) **5138**
Argo (Stirling). (UK) **1303**
▼Argomenti di Cardiologia. (IT) **3204**
▼Argomenti di Chemioantibioticoterapia. (IT) **3078**
▼Argomenti di Dermatologia. (IT) **3246**
Argomenti di Gastroenterologia Clinica. (IT) **3266**
Argomenti di Gerontologia. (IT) **2270**
▼Argomenti di Neurologia. (IT) **3330**
Argomenti Esso. (IT) **3682**
Argomenti Radicali. (IT) **3874**
Argonaut. (US ISSN 0883-9824) **2988**
Argonauta. (CN) **4724**, **2399**
Argonaute: Le Magazine de la Decouverte see Sciences & Nature **4341**
Argonne National Laboratory. Research Highlights. (US) **1815**, **1943**
Argos. (DK ISSN 0900-338X) **312**
Argos. (AG ISSN 0325-4194) **1275**
Argos (Milan). (IT) **4806**
Argos (Milan, 1987). (IT) **2168**
Argosy Weekly. (CN ISSN 0044-8818) **1303**
Das Argument. (GW ISSN 0004-1157) **4366**, **3761**
†Argument-Beiheft. (GW ISSN 0722-964X) **5138**
Argument for Frihet och Raett. (SW ISSN 0004-1149) **3874**
Argumentation. (NE ISSN 0920-427X) **3761**, **2804**, **2858**
Argumentation & Advocacy. (US ISSN 1051-1431) **1733**, **3264**

Argumente zur Wirtschaftspolitik. (GW) **843**
Arguments of the Philosophers. (UK) **3761**
Argus. (BE) **1033**
Argus. (FR ISSN 0004-1173) **2526**
Argus (Bloomington). (US ISSN 0004-1181) **1303**
Argus (Montreal). (CN ISSN 0315-9930) **2744**
Argus (San Francisco). (US) **3298**
Argus (Thunder Bay). (CN ISSN 0004-1165) **1303**
Argus de l'Automobile et des Locomotions. (FR) **4679**
L'Argus de l'Economie Libanaise. (LE) **645**
L'Argus de la Legislation Libanaise. (LE ISSN 0570-8915) **4053**, **2600**
Argus de la Miniature. (FR ISSN 0182-0230) **2433**
Argus de la Poesie Francaise. (FR ISSN 0066-734X) **2988**
†Argus des Collectivites. (FR ISSN 0004-119X) **5138**
Argus des Pharmaciens. (FR ISSN 0004-1203) **3718**
Argus du Bateau. (FR) **4522**
Argus du Bateau et de Tout le Materiel Nautique. (FR) **4522**
Argus du Livre de Collection. (FR) **2981**
Argus du Livre de Collection et de l'Autographe see Argus du Livre de Collection **2981**
†Argus du Petrole. (FR ISSN 0398-7515) **5138**
Argus F C and S Chart see National Underwriter Profiles **2538**
†L'Argus International. (FR ISSN 0153-3614) **5138**
Argus-Journal see Alliance (Ottawa) **4053**
Argus Magazine. (US) **2221**
Argus Pharma Report. (LE) **3718**
Arheografski Prilozi. (YU ISSN 0351-2819) **2350**
Arheologia Moldovei/Archeologie de la Moldavie. (RM ISSN 0066-7358) **2350**, **265**
Arheoloski Muzej u Zagrebu. Vjesnik. (CI ISSN 0350-7165) **265**
Arheoloski Vestnik/Acta Archaeologica. (XV ISSN 0570-8966) **265**
Arhitectura. (RM ISSN 0300-5356) **294**, **2483**
Arhitektura. (CI ISSN 0350-3666) **294**
Arhiv Hrvatske. Bilten/Archives of Croatia. Bulletin. (CI ISSN 0353-4960) **2350**
†Arhiv Jugoslavije. Bilten. (YU) **5138**
Arhiv za Farmaciju. (YU ISSN 0004-1963) **3718**
Arhiv za Higijenu Rada i Toksikologiju/Archives of Industrial Hygiene and Toxicology. (CI ISSN 0004-1254) **1980**, **3614**, **3718**
Arhiv za Poljoprivredne Nauke. (YU ISSN 0004-1262) **77**, **1815**
Arhiv za Pravne i Drustvene Nauke. (YU ISSN 0004-1270) **2600**, **4366**
Arhiv za Rudarstvo i Geologiju. (BN ISSN 0518-5327) **3478**, **1554**
Arhiv za Zastitu Majke i Djeteta/Archives for Mother and Child Health.(CI ISSN 0004-1289) **3319**, **3289**
Arhivist. (YU ISSN 0350-2856) **2350**
Arhivski Vjesnik. (CI ISSN 0570-9008) **2350**
Arhus Stifts Arboeger. (DK) **2350**
Aria Compressa. (IT ISSN 0004-1300) **1862**
Ariadne. (NE) **3590**
Ariadne. (GW ISSN 0178-1073) **4837**
Ariake Fisheries Experiment Station. Annual Report. (JA ISSN 0289-5242) **2037**
Arid Lands Newsletter. (US) **77**, **1541**, **4822**
Arid Soil Research and Rehabilitation. (UK ISSN 0890-3069) **168**, **1483**
Ariel. (UK ISSN 0004-1335) **1368**
Ariel. (IS ISSN 0004-1343) **2503**, **312**, **2896**
Ariel. (PK ISSN 0254-3028) **2896**

Ariel. (CN) **2988**
Ariel. (IT) **4629**
Aril Society International Newsletter. (US) **2122**
Aril Society International Yearbook. (US) **2122**
Arilds Lokaltidende. (DK ISSN 0108-3589) **2350**
Arion. (US ISSN 0095-5809) **1275**, **2503**
Aristocrat. (US) **3708**
Aristos. (US ISSN 0737-0407) **312**, **2896**, **3539**, **4629**
Aristoteles. (GR) **2350**
Aristotelian Society. Proceedings. (UK ISSN 0066-7374) **3762**
Aristotelian Society. Proceedings. Supplementary Volume. (UK ISSN 0309-7013) **3762**
Aristotelion Panepistemion Thessalonikes. Philosophike Schole. Epistemonike Epeteris. (GR) **2350**
Aristotelion Panepistemion Thessalonikes. Theologike Schole. Epistemonike Epeteris. (GR) **4163**, **2350**
Aristotle University of Thessaloniki. School of Philosophy. Philology Department. Scientific Yearbook. (GR) **2804**
Arithmetic Teacher. (US ISSN 0004-136X) **3030**, **1744**
Arithmetic Teacher. see Xiaoxue Shuxue Jiaoshi **3061**
Arizona. Commission on the Arizona Environment. Annual Report. (US) **1943**
Arizona. Commission on the Arizona Environment. Proceedings of Quarterly Conferences. (US) **1943**
Arizona. Department of Education. Annual Report of the Superintendent of Public Instruction. (US ISSN 0095-5310) **1616**
Arizona. Department of Health Services. Annual Report. (US ISSN 0362-1421) **4098**
Arizona. Department of Water Resources. Open-File Report. (US) **4822**
Arizona. Governor's Commission on Arizona Environment. Proceedings of Annual Summer Conference see Arizona. Commission on the Arizona Environment. Proceedings of Quarterly Conferences **1943**
Arizona. Oil & Gas Conservation Commission. Oil, Gas & Helium Production. (US ISSN 0570-9520) **3682**
†Arizona. Oil and Gas Conservation Commission. Report of Investigation. (US) **5138**
Arizona. Oil and Gas Conservation Commission. Special Publication. (US) **3682**, **1554**
Arizona. State Advisory Council for Vocational Technical Education. Annual Report see Arizona. State Council for Vocational Education. Biennial Report **1744**
Arizona. State Council for Vocational Education. Biennial Report. (US) **1744**
Arizona A A A Highroads. (US) **4752**, **4679**
Arizona Advocate. (US ISSN 0004-1386) **2600**
Arizona Alumnus. (US ISSN 0004-1394) **1303**
Arizona and the West see Journal of the Southwest **2411**
Arizona Appeal Reports. (US) **2600**
Arizona Archaeologist. (US) **265**
Arizona Artists Guild News. (US) **3521**, **312**
Arizona Attorney. (US ISSN 1040-4090) **2600**
Arizona Bank Ledger see Security News (Los Angeles) **799**
Arizona Bank News see Security News (Los Angeles) **799**
Arizona Bar Journal see Arizona Attorney **2600**
Arizona Beverage Analyst. (US) **377**
Arizona Beverage Guide. (US) **377**
Arizona Business & Development. (US) **1057**, **4145**

Arizona Business Gazette. (US ISSN 0273-6950) **645**
Arizona Business - Industry. (US ISSN 0193-7480) **843**, **1072**
Arizona Capitol Times. (US ISSN 0744-7477) **4053**, **3874**
Arizona Cattlelog. (US ISSN 8750-8281) **211**
Arizona Commission on the Arts. Report to the Governor. (US ISSN 0098-7387) **312**
Arizona Commission on the Arts and Humanities. Report to the Governor see Arizona Commission on the Arts. Report to the Governor **312**
Arizona Daily Wildcat. (US) **1303**
Arizona Directory of Manufacturers see Arizona Industrial Directory **1121**
Arizona Economic Indicators (Tucson). (US) **645**
Arizona Education Association Advocate see A E A Advocate **1613**
Arizona English Bulletin. (US ISSN 0004-1483) **1744**, **2804**
▼Arizona Environmental Law Letter. (US ISSN 1049-9342) **2600**, **1943**
Arizona Facts. (US ISSN 1043-1659) **1780**
Arizona Farm Bureau News. (US ISSN 0274-7014) **77**, **2600**
Arizona Farmer - Stockman. (US) **77**
Arizona Forestry Notes. (US ISSN 0066-7404) **2095**
Arizona Game and Fish Department Wildlife Bulletin. (US) **2037**, **578**, **4541**
Arizona Geological Society Digest. (US ISSN 0066-7412) **1554**
Arizona Geology. (US) **1554**, **1783**
Arizona Golf Journal. (US) **4499**
Arizona Great Outdoors. (US) **4541**
Arizona Grocer. (US ISSN 0004-1505) **2090**
Arizona High - Tech Times. (US) **645**
Arizona Highways. (US ISSN 0004-1521) **4752**
Arizona Historical Society. Historical Monographs. (US) **2399**
Arizona Historical Society. Museum Monograph Series. (US) **2399**
Arizona History Magazine. (US) **2399**
Arizona Horse Connection. (US) **4532**
Arizona Humanities Association Journal see International Journal of Humanities and Peace **2508**
Arizona Hunter and Angler. (US) **4541**
†Arizona Indian Monthly. (US) **5138**
Arizona Industrial Directory. (US) **1121**
Arizona Informant. (US) **1992**
Arizona Jewish Post. (US) **1992**
Arizona Labor Market Information Newsletter. (US) **972**, **843**
Arizona Labor Market Newsletter see Arizona Labor Market Information Newsletter **972**
Arizona Land and People. (US ISSN 0744-5474) **77**
Arizona Law Review. (US ISSN 0004-153X) **2600**
Arizona Legislative Review see Arizona Capitol Times **4053**
Arizona Legislative Service. (US ISSN 0094-4246) **2600**
Arizona Mobile Citizen. (US ISSN 0004-1564) **2483**
Arizona Modern Business and Industry see Arizona Business - Industry **843**
Arizona Music News. (US) **3539**
Arizona Networking News. (US) **3593**
Arizona-Nevada Academy of Science. Journal. (US ISSN 0193-8509) **4300**
Arizona, New Mexico TourBook see Tourbook: Arizona, New Mexico **4790**
Arizona Nurse. (US ISSN 0004-1599) **3275**
Arizona Pharmacist. (US) **3718**
Arizona Philatelist. (US) **3749**
Arizona Poison Control System Newsletter. (US) **3718**, **3078**
Arizona Post see Arizona Jewish Post **1992**
Arizona Producer see Arizona Farmer - Stockman **77**
Arizona Professional Engineer. (US ISSN 0194-7435) **5138**
†Arizona Progress. (US) **5138**

Arizona Quarterly. (US ISSN 0004-1610) **2858**, 2896
Arizona Radiation Regulatory Agency. Annual Report. (US) **1803**, 4098
Arizona Radiation Review. (US) **1803**, 1943
†Arizona Review. (US ISSN 0004-1629) **5138**
Arizona Review of Business and Public Administration *see* Arizona Review **5138**
Arizona Singles. (US) **4362**
Arizona Solo *see* Single Scene (Scottsdale) **4363**
Arizona-Sonora Desert Museum. Annual Report *see* Sonorensis. Annual Report **3533**
Arizona State Law Journal. (US ISSN 0164-4297) **2600**
Arizona State Library Association Newsletter *see* A S L A Newsletter **2740**
Arizona State Plan for the Education of Migratory Children. (US) **1616**
Arizona State University. Center for Asian Studies. Monograph Series. (US) **3633**, 2336, 2896
Arizona State University. Governmental Finance Institute. Proceedings *see* Papers in Public Administration **4069**
Arizona State University Anthropological Research Papers. (US ISSN 0271-0641) **235**
Arizona State University Directory of A S U Latin Americanists *see* Directory of A S U Latin Americanists **2404**
†Arizona Statistical Review. (US ISSN 0518-6242) **5138**
Arizona Times *see* New Times Weekly **2876**
†Arizona Trend. (US ISSN 0889-5481) **5138**
Arizona U S A International Trade Directory *see* Directory of Arizona Exporters **1128**
Arizona Wildlife Views. (US ISSN 0882-5572) **1483**, 1943, 2037
Arizona Women's Voice. (US) **4837**
Arizona's Economy. (US) **843**
Arizoo. (US) **578**, 1483
Ark. (UK ISSN 0004-167X) **230**
The Ark (Cambridge). (US) **2988**
Ark (Colorado Springs). (US) **3708**
Ark (Tiburon). (US) **2858**
Arka-Tech. (US ISSN 0004-1882) **1304**
Arkansas. (US) **645**
Arkansas. Agricultural Experiment Station. Bulletins. (US ISSN 0097-3491) **133**, 168
Arkansas. Agricultural Experiment Station. Bulletins: Cotton. (US) **168**
Arkansas. Agricultural Experiment Station. Bulletins: Dairy. (US) **197**
Arkansas. Agricultural Experiment Station. Bulletins: Fruit, Vegetables, Crops and Flowers. (US) **168**, 2122
Arkansas. Agricultural Experiment Station. Bulletins: Grain, Forage Crops and Legumes. (US) **204**, 168
Arkansas. Agricultural Experiment Station. Bulletins: Insects, Pests, Diseases and Bees. (US) **168**, 528
Arkansas. Agricultural Experiment Station. Bulletins: Livestock. (US) **211**
Arkansas. Agricultural Experiment Station. Bulletins: Poultry. (US) **211**
Arkansas. Agricultural Experiment Station. Bulletins: Rice. (US) **168**
Arkansas. Agricultural Experiment Station. Bulletins: Soils and Fertilizers.(US) **168**
Arkansas. Agricultural Experiment Station. Bulletins: Soybean. (US) **168**
Arkansas. Agricultural Experiment Station. Report Series. (US ISSN 0097-5370) **133**, 77
Arkansas. Agricultural Experiment Station. Report Series: Cotton. (US) **168**
Arkansas. Agricultural Experiment Station. Report Series: Fruit, Vegetable Crops and Flowers. (US) **168**, 2122

Arkansas. Agricultural Experiment Station. Report Series: Grain, Forage Crops and Legumes. (US) **204**, 168
Arkansas. Agricultural Experiment Station. Report Series: Insects, Pests, Diseases and Bees. (US) **168**, 528
Arkansas. Agricultural Experiment Station. Report Series: Livestock. (US) **211**
Arkansas. Agricultural Experiment Station. Report Series: Poultry. (US) **211**
Arkansas. Agricultural Experiment Station. Report Series: Rice. (US) **168**
Arkansas. Agricultural Experiment Station. Report Series: Soils and Fertilizers. (US) **168**
Arkansas. Agricultural Experiment Station. Report Series: Soybean. (US) **168**
Arkansas. Agricultural Experiment Station. Research Series. (US) **133**, 168
Arkansas. Agricultural Experiment Station. Research Series: Cotton. (US) **168**
Arkansas. Agricultural Experiment Station. Research Series: Fruit, Vegetable Crops and Flowers. (US) **169**, 2122
Arkansas. Agricultural Experiment Station. Research Series: Grain, Forage Crops and Legumes. (US) **204**, 169
Arkansas. Agricultural Experiment Station. Research Series: Insects, Pests, Diseases and Bees. (US) **169**, 528
Arkansas. Agricultural Experiment Station. Research Series: Livestock. (US) **211**
Arkansas. Agricultural Experiment Station. Research Series: Rice. (US) **169**
Arkansas. Agricultural Experiment Station. Research Series: Soils and Fertilizers. (US) **169**
Arkansas. Agricultural Experiment Station. Research Series: Soybean. (US) **169**
Arkansas. Agricultural Experiment Station. Special Reports. (US ISSN 0571-0189) **133**, 77
Arkansas. Agricultural Experiment Station. Special Reports: Cotton. (US) **169**
Arkansas. Agricultural Experiment Station. Special Reports: Dairy. (US) **197**
Arkansas. Agricultural Experiment Station. Special Reports: Fruit, Vegetable Crops and Flowers. (US) **169**, 2122
Arkansas. Agricultural Experiment Station. Special Reports: Grain, Forage and Legumes. (US) **205**, 169
Arkansas. Agricultural Experiment Station. Special Reports: Insects, Pests, Diseases and Bees. (US) **169**, 529
Arkansas. Agricultural Experiment Station. Special Reports: Livestock. (US) **211**
Arkansas. Agricultural Experiment Station. Special Reports: Poultry. (US) **211**
Arkansas. Agricultural Experiment Station. Special Reports: Rice. (US) **169**
Arkansas. Agricultural Experiment Station. Special Reports: Soils and Fertilizers. (US) **169**
Arkansas. Agricultural Experiment Station. Special Reports: Soybean. (US) **169**
Arkansas. Bureau of Vital Statistics. Annual Report of Births, Deaths, Marriages and Divorces as Reported to the Bureau of Vital Statistics. (US ISSN 0094-3576) **3989**
Arkansas. Department of Labor. Employment Security Division. Annual Report. (US) **3624**

Arkansas. Department of Labor. Employment Security Division. Statistical Review. (US) **702**, 3624, 4562
Arkansas. Division of Rehabilitation Services. Annual Report. (US) **1733**, 3078, 4398
Arkansas. Geological Commission. Information Circulars. (US) **1554**
Arkansas. Geological Commission. Miscellaneous Publications. (US) **1554**
Arkansas. Geological Commission. Water Resources Circulars. (US ISSN 0571-0278) **4822**
Arkansas Amateur. (US ISSN 0518-6617) **265**, 235
Arkansas Archeological Society. Field Notes. (US ISSN 0015-0711) **265**
Arkansas Archeological Survey. Publications on Archeology. Popular Series. (US ISSN 0587-3533) **265**
Arkansas Archeological Survey. Publications on Archeology. Research Reports. (US ISSN 0277-6308) **265**
Arkansas Archeological Survey. Publications on Archeology. Research Series. (US ISSN 0882-5491) **265**
Arkansas Archeological Survey. Publications on Archeology. Technical Papers. (US) **265**
Arkansas Archeologist. (US ISSN 0004-1718) **265**
Arkansas Banker. (US ISSN 0004-1726) **759**
Arkansas Bar Association. News Bulletin. (US) **2600**
Arkansas Business and Economic Review. (US ISSN 0004-1742) **645**
Arkansas Catholic. (US) **4256**
Arkansas Cattle Business. (US ISSN 0004-1750) **211**
Arkansas Country Dancer. (US) **1528**, 3539
Arkansas Covered Employment and Earnings. (US) **972**
Arkansas Dental Journal. (US ISSN 0004-1769) **3228**
Arkansas Directory of Manufacturers. (US) **1121**
Arkansas Educator. (US ISSN 0161-7753) **1616**
Arkansas Engineer. (US) **1815**
Arkansas Episcopalian. (US) **4229**
Arkansas Family Historian. (US ISSN 0571-0472) **2144**
Arkansas Farm and Country. (US) **77**
Arkansas Farm Research. (US ISSN 0004-1785) **77**
†Arkansas Football Magazine. (US) **5138**
Arkansas Game & Fish Magazine. (US ISSN 0004-1807) **1483**, 4541
Arkansas Grocer. (US ISSN 0004-1815) **2090**
Arkansas Grocers and Retail Merchants News. (US) **2090**
Arkansas Highways. (US ISSN 0403-1792) **4717**
Arkansas Historical Quarterly. (US ISSN 0004-1823) **2399**
Arkansas Homes & Lifestyles. (US) **2221**
Arkansas Hospital Association. President's Letter. (US) **2459**
Arkansas Journal. (US) **1072**
Arkansas, Kansas, Missouri, Oklahoma TourBook *see* Tourbook: Arkansas, Kansas, Missouri, Oklahoma **4790**
Arkansas L P News *see* Arkansas Propane Gas News **3682**
Arkansas Law Review. (US ISSN 0004-1831) **2600**
Arkansas Lawyer. (US) **2600**
Arkansas Libraries. (US ISSN 0004-184X) **2744**
Arkansas Medical Society. Journal. (US ISSN 0004-1858) **3078**
Arkansas Motor Carrier. (US) **4743**
Arkansas Municipalities *see* City & Town (North Little Rock) **4085**
Arkansas Oil and Gas Statistical Bulletin.(US ISSN 0004-1874) **3704**
Arkansas - Oklahoma Trucker *see* Fastline for Arkansas - Oklahoma Truckers **5191**

Arkansas Outdoors. (US) **1483**, 4541
Arkansas Philological Association. Publications. (US) **2804**
Arkansas Poultry Times. (US ISSN 0044-8907) **211**
Arkansas Propane Gas News. (US) **3682**
Arkansas Register. (US) **2600**
Arkansas Report. (US ISSN 0273-2742) **4053**, 2600, 3874
Arkansas Report - Weekly Legislative Edition. (US) **4053**, 2600
Arkansas Sportsman. (US) **4541**
Arkansas State Directory. (US) **4053**
Arkansas State Press. (US) **1992**
Arkansas Tech University. Department of History. Occasional Papers. (US) **2399**
Arkansas Times. (US ISSN 0164-6273) **2221**
Arkansas Travel and Tourism Report. (US) **4752**
Arkansas United Methodist. (US) **4229**
Arkansas Valley Journal. (US ISSN 0004-1890) **211**
Arkansas Vital Statistics. (US ISSN 0364-0728) **3989**, 3979
Arkansas Vital Statistics Report *see* Arkansas. Bureau of Vital Statistics. Annual Report of Births, Deaths, Marriages and Divorces as Reported to the Bureau of Vital Statistics **3989**
Arken. (DK ISSN 0107-363X) **4163**
Arken-Tryk. (DK ISSN 0107-4520) **4163**
Arkeoikuska. (SP) **265**
Arkeologisk Museum i Stavanger. Skrifter *see* A M S - Skrifter **260**
Arkeologisk Museum i Stavanger Skrifter *see* A M S - Skrifter **260**
Arkeologisk Museum i Stavanger Smaatrykk *see* A M S - Smaatrykk **260**
Arkeologisk Museum i Stavanger Varia *see* A M S - Varia **260**
Arkeologiske Udgravninger i Danmark. (DK ISSN 0901-0815) **265**
Arkeoloji ve Sanat Dergisi/Archaeology and Art Magazine. (TU) **265**
Arkham Sampler. (US) **3010**
Arkheograficheskii Ezhegodnik. (RU) **2306**, 265
Arkheologicheskie Raboty v Tadzhikistane. (TA) **265**
Arkheologiia. (BU ISSN 0324-1203) **265**
Arkheologiya. (KR ISSN 0320-9407) **265**
Arkheologiya i Etnografiya Udmurtii. (RU) **265**
Arkhimedes. (FI ISSN 0004-1920) **3030**, 3815
Arkhitektura. (BU ISSN 0003-8644) **294**
Arkhitektura S.S.S.R. (RU ISSN 0004-1939) **294**
Arkhiv Anatomii, Gistologii i Embriologii/ Archives of Anatomy, Histology and Embryology. (RU ISSN 0004-1947) **429**, 3078
Arkhiv Patologii/Archives of Pathology. (RU ISSN 0004-1955) **3078**
Arkhivy Ukrainy. (KR) **2350**, 2744
Arkhiyon ha-Merkazi le-Toldot ha-Am ha-Yehudi. Yediot. *see* Central Archives for the History of the Jewish People Newsletter **2429**
Arkia In-Flight Magazine. (IS) **4801**
Arkib Negara Malaysia. Laporan Tahunan. *see* National Archives of Malaysia. Annual Report **2340**
Arkitekt. (TU ISSN 0004-1971) **294**
Arkitektaevlingar - Architect Contest *see* A T **291**
Arkitekten. (DK ISSN 0004-198X) **294**
Arkitektnytt. *see* Arkkitehtiuutiset **294**
Arkitektnytt. (NO ISSN 0004-1998) **294**
Arkitekttidningen *see* A T **291**
Arkitektur. (SW ISSN 0004-2021) **294**
Arkitektur DK. (DK ISSN 0004-2013) **294**
Arkiv. (DK ISSN 0004-203X) **2306**, 2744
Arkiv foer Matematik. (SW ISSN 0004-2080) **3030**

ARKIV

Arkiv for det Fysiske Seminar i Trondheim see Theoretical Physics Seminar in Trondheim **3834**
Arkiv for Nordisk Filologi/Archives for Scandinavian Philology. (SW ISSN 0066-7668) **2804**
Arkiv for Studier i Arbetarrorelsens Historia. (SW) **972**, 2350
Arkiv, Samhaelle och Forskning. (SW ISSN 0349-0505) **2744**, 2306
Arkiver: Folkemindesamlinger og Museer i Faaborg Kommune see Faaborg-Aarbogen **2361**
Arkivet foer Folkets Historia. Meddelanden see Folkets Historia **2361**
Arkkitehti/Finnish Architectural Review/Finsk Arkitekturtidskrift. (FI ISSN 0783-3660) **294**
Arkkitehtiuutiset/Arkitektnytt. (FI ISSN 0044-8915) **294**
Arkkitehtuurikilpailuja - Architectural Competitions in Finland see Arkkitehti **294**
Arlington Catholic Herald. (US ISSN 0361-3712) **4256**
Arlington Historical Magazine. (US ISSN 0066-7684) **2399**
Arlis - N A Update. (US ISSN 0743-040X) **2744**, 312
Arlis News-Sheet. (UK ISSN 0308-809X) **2744**, 312
Arm Bender. (US ISSN 1043-3120) **4464**
Arma. (SA ISSN 0004-2145) **2144**
Armada International. (SZ ISSN 0252-9793) **46**, 3451
Armaghan. (IR ISSN 0378-2883) **2896**, 2428
Armament and Disarmament Information Unit Report see A D I U Report **5127**
Armament Data Sheets. (UK ISSN 0004-2153) **46**
Armamentaria. (NE ISSN 0168-1672) **3451**, 2350
Arman. (IR) **2202**
Armarium Codicum Insignium. (BE) **2350**, 4163
Armas e Trofeus. (PO) **2350**, 312, 2144
Armchair Archaeologist. (US) **265**, 2600
Armchair Detective. (US ISSN 0004-217X) **2985**
Armed Citizen News. (US ISSN 0044-8931) **3940**
Armed Forces. (SA ISSN 0379-6477) **3451**
†Armed Forces. (UK ISSN 0142-4696) **5138**
Armed Forces and Society. (US ISSN 0095-327X) **3451**, 3874, 4429
Armed Forces Comptroller. (US ISSN 0004-2188) **3451**
Armed Forces Institute of Pathology Atlas of Radiologic-Pathologic Correlation see A F I P Atlas of Radiologic-Pathologic Correlation **3068**
Armed Forces Journal International. (US ISSN 0196-3597) **3451**
Armed Forces News. (GH) **3451**
Armee du Peuple. (UV) **3451**
Armee-Motor. (SZ ISSN 0004-2269) **3451**
Armee-Rundschau. (GW ISSN 0004-2277) **3451**
Armees d'Aujourd'hui. (FR) **3451**
Armeiski Pregled. (BU ISSN 0004-2285) **3451**
Armement. (FR) **3451**
Armenia Today see Armenya Segodnia **3950**
Armenian Chemical Journal. see Aikakan Himiakan Amsagir **1169**
Armenian Church see Bema **4280**
Armenian Digest. (US ISSN 0004-2323) **1992**
Armenian General Benevolent Union Ararat see A G B U Ararat **2891**
Armenian Mirror - Spectator. (US ISSN 0004-234X) **1992**
Armenian Missionary Association of America, Inc. News see A M A A News **4279**
Armenian Observer. (US ISSN 0044-894X) **1992**

Armenian Relief Society, Inc. Hai Sird see A R S Hai Sird **4396**
Armenian Reporter. (US ISSN 0004-2358) **1992**, 2221
Armenian Review. (US ISSN 0004-2366) **2858**
Armenian Texts and Studies. (US) **2350**
Armenian Weekly. (US ISSN 0004-2374) **1992**
Armenian Welfare Association of New York News. (US ISSN 0004-2382) **4398**
Armenpfleger see Zeitschrift fuer Oeffentliche Fuersorge **4425**
Armenya Segodnia. (AI ISSN 0004-2293) **3950**
Armenytt. (SW ISSN 0004-2404) **3451**
Armex. (NE ISSN 0922-2979) **3451**
Armi e Pesca. (IT) **4541**
Armi e Tiro. (IT) **4541**
Armidale and District Historical Society. Journal and Proceedings. (AT ISSN 0084-6732) **2344**
†Armidale College of Advanced Education. Annual Report. (AT ISSN 0811-7098) **5138**
Armidale News. (AT) **1700**
Armieri see Armi e Pesca **4541**
Armiger's News. (US) **2144**
Armonia di Voci. (IT ISSN 0391-5425) **3539**, 1249, 4163
Armor. (FR ISSN 0044-8966) **2186**
Armor. (US ISSN 0004-2420) **3451**
Armorial Francais. (BE) **2144**
Arms and Armour Society Journal. (UK ISSN 0004-2439) **256**
Arms Collecting. (US ISSN 0380-982X) **256**
Arms Control. (UK ISSN 0144-0381) **3874**, 3451
Arms Control see Barometer **3951**
Arms Control Reporter. (US ISSN 0886-3490) **3950**, 3451
Arms Control Today. (US ISSN 0196-125X) **3874**, 3950
Armstrong Logic. (US ISSN 0044-8974) **2556**
Armstrong News. (UK ISSN 0265-2269) **1992**, 2052, 2144, 2350
Armstrong Oil Directories: Louisiana, Mississippi, Arkansas, Texas Gulf Coast and East Texas Edition. (US ISSN 0273-4931) **3682**
Armstrong Oil Directories: Mini Briefcase Edition. (US) **3682**
Armstrong Oil Directories: Rocky Mountain - Central United States Edition. (US ISSN 0273-5229) **3682**
Armstrong Oil Directories: Texas Including Southeast New Mexico Edition. (US ISSN 0277-2280) **3682**
†Armstrong's Monthly Bulletin. (UK) **5138**
Army. (AT) **3451**
Army. (US ISSN 0004-2455) **3451**
Army see Field Artillery **3458**
Army, Air Force & Naval Air Statistical Record. (UK ISSN 0004-2463) **3452**
Army Aviation. (US ISSN 0004-248X) **3452**, 46
Army Aviation Digest see United States Army Aviation Digest **64**
Army Communicator. (US ISSN 0362-5745) **3452**, 1331
Army Digest see Soldiers **3472**
Army Flier. (US) **3452**, 46
Army Lawyer. (US ISSN 0364-1287) **2600**, 3452
Army List. (UK) **3452**
Army Literature. see Kun Lun **2930**
Army Literature and Arts. see Van Nghe Quan Doi **2973**
Army Logistician. (US) **3452**
Army Manuals and Regulations Index (Consolidated Index of Army Publications). (US) **3476**
Army Master Data File: Army Retrieval Microform Systems and Interc. (US) **3452**
Army Medical Services Magazine. (UK) **3452**, 3078
Army Motors. (US ISSN 0195-5632) **2433**, 3452

†Army Museum. (UK) **5138**
Army - Navy Store & Outdoor Merchandiser. (US ISSN 0160-7278) **1283**, 4541
†Army Organizational Effectiveness Journal. (US) **5138**
Army Quarterly and Defence Journal. (UK ISSN 0004-2552) **3452**
Army R D and A see R, D & A **3469**
Army Reserve Magazine. (US ISSN 0004-2579) **3452**
Army Times. (US ISSN 0004-2595) **3452**
†Army's Life. (RM) **5138**
Arnamagnaean Institute. Bulletin see Arnamagnaean Institute and Dictionary. Bulletin **2896**
Arnamagnaean Institute and Dictionary. Bulletin. (DK ISSN 0107-1475) **2896**, 2804
Arnes Journal fuer Guten Geschmack. (GW ISSN 0342-7439) **2444**
Arnold Air Letter. (US ISSN 0004-2617) **46**
Arnold Ancestry. (US ISSN 0890-4014) **2144**
†Arnold Arboretum. Journal. (US ISSN 0004-2625) **5138**
Arnold Bennett Newsletter see Era of Arnold Bennett **5187**
Arnold Schoenberg Institute. Bulletin see Arnold Schoenberg Institute. Journal **3539**
Arnold Schoenberg Institute. Journal. (US ISSN 0146-5856) **3539**
Arnoldia. (US ISSN 0004-2633) **495**
Arnoldia Zimbabwe. (RH ISSN 0250-6386) **429**, 578, 1541
Arnoldian see Nineteenth-Century Prose **2943**
Arnolt-Bristol Registry. (US) **4679**
Arogya. (II ISSN 0253-682X) **3799**, 3078
Aroideana. (US) **2122**
Around & About K S U. (Kentucky State University) (US) **1304**, 2221
†Around Canterbury. (UK) **5138**
Around Film. see Yinmu Neiwai **3519**
Around Football. (UK) **4499**
†Around Hong Kong. (HK) **5138**
Around San Diego. (US) **2221**
Around the Bargaining Loop. (US) **3997**, 972
Around the Bend. (US ISSN 0749-517X) **2144**
Around the World - A Travers le Monde - Po Svetu see Po Svetu **2834**
Around Town Publication. (US) **2221**
Arpan. (NP) **2211**
Arpel. (IT ISSN 1120-2777) **2736**
Arpel Fur. (IT ISSN 1120-3501) **2736**, 1289
Arpenteur-Geometre. (CN ISSN 0228-6637) **2242**
Arqueologia. (PO) **265**
Arqueologia. (MX ISSN 0187-6074) **266**
Arqueologia Industrial. (PO ISSN 0870-8355) **266**, 4593
Arquitectura. (SP ISSN 0004-2706) **294**
Arquitectura Cuba. (CU) **294**
Arquitectura, Urbanismo, Construccion y Arte see A U C A **5129**
Arquitectura y Urbanismo. (CU) **294**, 2483
Arquitetura e Urbanismo. (BL ISSN 0102-8979) **294**
Arquitetura - R S. (BL) **294**
Arquitetura y Construcao. (BL) **295**, 600
Arquivo Brasileiro de Medicina Veterinaria e Zootecnia. (BL ISSN 0102-0935) **4806**
Arquivo de Anatomia e Antropologia. (PO ISSN 0066-7811) **570**
Arquivo de Patologia. (PO ISSN 0004-2714) **3078**
Arquivos Brasileiros de Cardiologia. (BL ISSN 0066-782X) **3204**
Arquivos Brasileiros de Endocrinologia e Metabologia. (BL ISSN 0004-2730) **3250**
Arquivos Brasileiros de Medicina. (BL ISSN 0365-0723) **3078**
Arquivos Brasileiros de Oftalmologia. (BL ISSN 0004-2749) **3298**
†Arquivos Brasileiros de Psicologia. (BL ISSN 0100-8692) **5138**

Arquivos Brasileiros de Tuberculose e Doencas do Torax. (BL ISSN 0004-2765) **3364**
Arquivos Catarinenses de Medicina. (BL ISSN 0004-2773) **3078**
Arquivos de Angola. (AO ISSN 0004-2781) **2331**
Arquivos de Biologia e Tecnologia. (BL ISSN 0365-0979) **429**, 487
Arquivos de Botanica do Estado de Sao Paulo see Hoehnea **505**
Arquivos de Ciencias do Mar. (BL ISSN 0374-5686) **1602**
Arquivos de Cirurgia Clinica e Experimental. (BL ISSN 0066-7846) **3376**, 3257
Arquivos de Gastroenterologia. (BL ISSN 0004-2803) **3266**
Arquivos de Neuro-Psiquiatria. (BL ISSN 0004-282X) **3331**
Arquivos de Patologia Geral e Anatomia Patologica. (PO ISSN 0066-7854) **3078**
Arquivos de Reumatologia e Doencas Osted Articulares. (PO ISSN 0871-4304) **3368**, 3306, 3357
Arquivos de Saude Mental do Estado de Sao Paulo. (BL ISSN 0103-0809) **3331**
Arquivos de Zoologia. (BL ISSN 0066-7870) **578**
Arquivos dos Hospitais e da Faculdade de Ciencias Medicas da Santa Casa de Sao Paulo. (BL ISSN 0018-5442) **2459**, 3078
Arredo Biancheria Casa see Arredo Tessili Complementi - Biancheria Casa **4616**
Arredo Tessili Complementi see Arredo Tessili Complementi - Biancheria Casa **4616**
Arredo Tessili Complementi - Biancheria Casa. (IT) **4616**
Arredo Urbano. (IT) **600**, 295
Arredo Urbano Supplemento Tecnico see A U bis Supplemento Tecnico **599**
Arredorama. (IT ISSN 0004-2854) **2556**
†Arredostile Middle East. (IT ISSN 0393-5132) **5138**
Arrest Law Bulletin. (US ISSN 8755-8300) **2600**
Arrets de la Cour de Cassation de Belgique see Belgium. Cour de Cassation. Bulletin des Arrets **2604**
Arringa. (IT) **2204**
▼Arrival. (HK) **4752**
Arrive see Walk **4723**
Arrive. (US) **4752**
Arrived. (US) **4802**
Arrow (Ashland). (US) **1992**
Arrow (Brooklyn)/Flecha. (US) **3950**
Arrow (Kenosha). (US ISSN 0001-3056) **1304**
Arrow (Rochester). (US) **4679**
Arrowhead. (UK ISSN 0144-7424) **4464**, 2433
Arrows see Inking **1314**
Arrow's Complete Guide to Mail Order Foods. (US) **1033**, 2061
Arrowsmith's Bristol Channel Tide Table.(UK) **4724**
Ars. (CS ISSN 0044-9008) **313**
Ars see D'Ars **323**
Ars Aequi. (NE ISSN 0004-2870) **2600**
Ars Buddhica/Bukkyo Geijutsu. (JA ISSN 0004-2889) **313**, 4213
Ars Combinatoria. (CN ISSN 0381-7032) **3030**
Ars Cvrandi Gastro. (BL) **3266**
Ars Decorativa/Iparmuveszet. (HU ISSN 0133-6673) **3521**
Ars Hungarica. (HU ISSN 0133-1531) **313**
Ars Interpretandi/Art of Interpretation. (US ISSN 1043-5778) **2896**
Ars Lyrica: Journal of Lyrica. (US ISSN 1043-3848) **3539**, 2804
Ars Medici. (SZ ISSN 0004-2897) **3078**
Ars Nova. (SA ISSN 0379-6485) **3539**
Ars Organi. (GW ISSN 0004-2919) **3539**
Ars Orientalis. (US ISSN 0571-1371) **3633**, 313

Ars Pharmaceutica. (SP ISSN 0004-2927) **3718**
Ars Quatuor Coronatorum. (UK ISSN 0066-7900) **1296**
Ars, Revista de Arte. (AG) **313**
Ars Suecica. (SW ISSN 0066-7919) **313**, 2350
Ars Sutoria. (IT ISSN 0004-265X) **4360**, 1289
Ars-Uomo. (IT) **2858**
Ars Veterinaria. (BL ISSN 0102-6380) **4806**
Ars Week. (IT ISSN 1120-2785) **2736**, 1289
Arsenal. (US) **313**, 2988
Arsenale. (IT ISSN 0393-8263) **2896**, 2988
Arson Reporter. (US) **2600**, 1510, 2031
Arstryck. (SW ISSN 0432-1251) **266**, 2052
Art. (UN ISSN 0004-5535) **313**
Art. (GW) **313**
Art. see Meishu **335**
Art. (BL ISSN 0102-3357) **3539**
†Art/Kunst. (SZ) **5138**
Art (New York). (US) **3521**
Art Alliance Bulletin. (US ISSN 0004-296X) **313**
Art Almanac. (AT ISSN 0313-220X) **313**, 353
Art & Antiques. (US ISSN 0195-8208) **256**, 313
Art and Archaeology Newsletter. (US ISSN 0004-2986) **266**, 1275
Art and Archaeology Research Papers Environment Design see A A R P Environment Design **309**
Art and Archaeology Technical Abstracts. (US ISSN 0004-2994) **351**, 3, 290
Art and Architecture Bibliographies. (US) **351**, 309
Art & Artists. (US) **313**, 3521
Art & Auction. (US ISSN 0197-1093) **313**
Art and Australia. (AT ISSN 0004-301X) **313**
†Art & Cinema. (US) **5138**
Art & Craft. (UK ISSN 0262-7035) **353**, 313, 1616
Art and Craft in Education see Art & Craft **353**
Art and Crafts Catalyst. (US ISSN 0731-2989) **353**, 313, 2433
Art and Crafts Market see Artist's Market **316**
Art and Culture. (BE) **313**, 2896, 3539, 4629
Art and Design. (UK ISSN 0267-3991) **313**, 295, 3521
Art and Design Education in the Region.(UK) **1700**, 313
Art and Design in the Region see Art and Design Education in the Region **1700**
Art and Design News. (US ISSN 1055-2286) **313**
Art and Life. (II ISSN 0004-3044) **313**
Art and Man. (US ISSN 0004-3052) **313**, 1744, 2503
Art and Philosophy. (US) **313**, 3762
Art and Poetry Today. (II ISSN 0970-1001) **313**, 2988
Art & Style International. (CN ISSN 8750-0477) **372**
Art and the Artist. (II) **313**
Art and the Law see Columbia - V L A Journal of Law & the Arts **322**
Art - Antiques Investment Report. (US ISSN 0161-1232) **313**, 256, 938
Art at Auction: the Year at Sotheby's and Parke-Bernet. (US ISSN 0084-6783) **256**
Art Aurea. (GW ISSN 0179-647X) **313**, 2563
Art Bulletin. (US ISSN 0004-3079) **313**
Art Bulletin of Victoria. (AT ISSN 0066-7935) **3521**
Art Business News. (US ISSN 0273-5652) **313**
▼Art Business Today. (UK ISSN 0961-6497) **313**
Art Buyer's Handbook. (GW ISSN 0932-3333) **3788**
Art Buyer's Index. (US) **313**

Art Calendar. (US ISSN 0893-3901) **313**, 1161, 3788
Art Cellar Exchange. (US ISSN 1047-8868) **313**, 3521
Art Chretien. (FR ISSN 0004-3087) **313**
Art Com: Contemporary Art Communications. (US ISSN 0732-2852) **314**
Art, Craft, Design & Textile Technology Directory. (UK) **1692**, 1289, 4616
Art Craft Teachers Association of Victoria News see A C T A News **1742**
Art Culinaire. (US ISSN 0892-1024) **2061**, 377
Art de Basse Normandie. (FR ISSN 0571-1509) **314**
Art Dealers Association of America. Directory. (US) **1121**, 3521
Art Dealers Association of America. Update. (US) **314**, 3521
Art Deco News. (US ISSN 0743-3522) **314**, 295
Art Dentaire Liberal. (FR ISSN 0571-1525) **3228**
Art, Design, Architecture Magazine see A D A Magazine **291**
Art Direction. (US ISSN 0004-3109) **28**
Art Directors Annual. (US ISSN 0735-2026) **314**
Art Directors Club Jahrbuch. (GW) **28**
Art Directors Club of Los Angeles see A D L A **309**
Art Documentation. (US ISSN 0730-7187) **2744**, 314
Art Dramatique Canadien. see Canadian Drama **5161**
Art e Dossier. (IT ISSN 0394-0179) **314**
Art Education. (US ISSN 0004-3125) **1616**, 314
Art Education. (CN ISSN 0708-5354) **1616**, 314
Art Enfantin see Creations **323**
Art et Curiosite. (FR ISSN 0004-315X) **256**
Art et Decoration. (FR ISSN 0004-3168) **2548**
Art et Image. (FR) **3788**
L'Art et la Mer. (FR) **314**, 3521, 4724
Art et les Grandes Civilisations. (FR) **314**
Art et Metiers du Livre. (FR ISSN 0758-413X) **4120**
Art et Nature see Art et les Grandes Civilisations **314**
Art et Poesie. (FR ISSN 0518-7648) **314**, 2988
Art et Valeurs. (FR) **2556**, 314
Art Forum see Artforum **316**
Art Gallery Exhibition Guide see Art Gallery Scene **3521**
Art Gallery News see Benalla Art Gallery Newsletter **318**
Art Gallery of Ontario. Annual Report. (CN ISSN 0082-5018) **3521**
Art Gallery of Ontario News see A G O News **3520**
Art Gallery Scene. (US) **3521**
Art Happenings of Houston. (US) **3521**
Art Hazards News. (US ISSN 0197-7903) **3614**, 314
Art History. (UK ISSN 0141-6790) **314**
Art History Series. (US) **314**
Art Impressions. (CN) **314**
Art in America. (US ISSN 0004-3214) **314**
Art in California. (US ISSN 1045-8913) **314**
Art in Israel. (IS) **314**
Art in Wisconsin. (US) **314**
Art Index. (US ISSN 0004-3222) **315**, 3
†Art Insight Southwest. (US) **5138**
Art Institute of Chicago. Museum Studies. (US ISSN 0069-3235) **3521**
Art International. (FR ISSN 0004-3230) **314**, 2896
Art Investment Report see Art - Antiques Investment Report **313**
Art Issues. (US ISSN 1046-8471) **314**
Art Journal (Year). (US) **314**

Art - Language. (UK ISSN 0587-3584) **2804**
Art Libraries Journal. (UK ISSN 0307-4722) **2744**, 314
Art Libraries Society of North America. Occasional Papers. (US ISSN 0730-7160) **2744**, 314
Art - Life. see Yishu - Shenghuo **357**
Art - Life. (US) **2896**
Art Line. (UK) **314**, 4120
Art Lover's Art and Craft Fair Bulletin. (US ISSN 0892-1202) **314**
†Art Magazine. (UK) **5138**
Art Mate-Aktuell. (GW) **28**, 314
Art Material Directory and Buyers' Guide see Art Material Trade News **314**
Art Material Trade News. (US ISSN 0004-3265) **314**, 645
Art Monthly. (UK ISSN 0142-6702) **314**, 3521
Art Monthly Australia. (AT ISSN 0819-5838) **314**
Art New England. (US ISSN 0274-7073) **314**
Art New Zealand. (NZ ISSN 0110-1102) **314**, 3788
Art News and Review see Arts Review **317**
Art News Directory of Corporate Art Collections see Art News International Directory of Corporate Art Collections **315**
Art News International Directory of Corporate Art Collections. (US) **315**, 3521
Art Newsletter see Artnewsletter **316**
▼Art Newspaper. (IT ISSN 0960-6556) **315**
Art Nexus. (CK ISSN 0120-713X) **315**
Art Now: Boston and New England Gallery Guide see Art Now Gallery Guide: Boston - New England Edition **3521**
Art Now: Chicago and Midwest Gallery Guide see Art Now Gallery Guide: Chicago - Midwest Edition **3521**
Art Now Gallery Guide: Boston - New England Edition. (US) **3521**
Art Now Gallery Guide: California - Northwest Edition see Art Now Gallery Guide: West Coast Edition **3522**
Art Now Gallery Guide: Chicago - Midwest Edition. (US) **3521**
Art Now Gallery Guide: International Edition. (US) **3521**
Art Now Gallery Guide: National Edition see Art Now Gallery Guide: International Edition **3521**
Art Now Gallery Guide: New York Edition. (US) **3521**
Art Now Gallery Guide: Philadelphia Edition. (US) **3521**
Art Now Gallery Guide: Southeast Edition. (US) **3521**
Art Now Gallery Guide: Southwest Edition. (US) **3522**
Art Now Gallery Guide: West Coast Edition. (US) **3522**
Art Now: New York Gallery Guide see Art Now Gallery Guide: New York Edition **3521**
Art Now: Philadelphia Gallery Guide see Art Now Gallery Guide: Philadelphia Edition **3521**
Art Now: Southeast Gallery Guide see Art Now Gallery Guide: Southeast Edition **3521**
Art Now: Southwest Gallery Guide see Art Now Gallery Guide: Southwest Edition **3522**
Art of Dancing. see Wudao Yishu **1532**
The Art of Eating. (US ISSN 0895-6200) **2444**
Art of Film and Drama. see Yingju Yishu **3519**
Art of Interpretation. see Ars Interpretandi **2896**
Art of Music. see Ongaku Geijutsu **3571**
Art of Music. see Yinyue Yishu **3587**
Art of Negotiating Newsletter. (US ISSN 0270-8388) **972**
Art of New Year Picture. see Nienhua Yishu **338**
Art of Pictorial Stories. see Lianhuanhua Yishu **334**
Art of Prints. see Banhua Yishu **318**

Art of Records, Discography Review. see Record Geijutsu **3576**
Art of the Orient. see Kunst des Orients **5225**
Art of the West. (US) **315**
†Art on the Line Series. (US ISSN 0277-7053) **5138**
Art Papers. (US ISSN 0278-1441) **315**
Art Police. (US) **315**, 1616
Art-Price Annual see Kunstpreis-Jahrbuch **333**
Art Product News see Art and Design News **313**
Art Reference Collection. (US ISSN 0193-6867) **315**
▼Art Reference Services Quarterly. (US ISSN 1050-2548) **315**
Art Research. see Meishu Yanjiu **335**
Art Research in Scandinavia see A R I S **310**
Art Research News see I F A R Reports **329**
Art Review see The 13th Street Journal **351**
Art Review and Criticism. see Wenyi Pinglun yu Piping **2889**
†Art Romanic. (SP) **5138**
Art Sales Index: Oil Paintings, Drawings, Water Colours and Sculpture. (US) **315**
Art Speculator. (US) **315**
Art Students League News. (US) **315**
Art Studies. see Wenyi Xuexi **349**
Art-Talk. (US) **315**
Art Therapy. (US ISSN 0742-1656) **1733**, 315, 4012
Art Times. (US ISSN 0891-9070) **353**
Art to Science in Tissue Culture. (US) **550**
Art West see Southwest Art **344**
Art Workers Guild. Annual Report. (UK) **315**
Art Workers News see Art & Artists **313**
Art - World. (US ISSN 0194-1070) **315**
Art World. (IT) **315**
Art World. see Yishu Shijie **350**
Arta. (RM ISSN 0004-3354) **315**
Arta Plastica Review see Arta **315**
ARTANES see Aids and Research Tools in Ancient Near Eastern Studies **2427**
Artbibliographies Current Titles. (UK ISSN 0095-1420) **351**, 3
Artbibliographies Modern. (UK ISSN 0300-466X) **351**, 3
Arte. (IT) **315**, 4593
De Arte. (SA ISSN 0004-3389) **315**
Arte al Dia. (AG ISSN 0326-4807) **315**
Arte Cristiana. (IT ISSN 0004-3400) **315**, 4163
Arte e Archeologia. (IT) **315**, 266
Arte & Cornice. (IT ISSN 0393-439X) **315**
Arte em Revista. (BL) **315**
Arte en Colombia Internacional see Art Nexus **315**
Arte Lombarda. (IT ISSN 0004-3443) **315**
Arte Naive. (IT) **315**
Arte Nuova. (IT) **315**
Arte Nuova Oggi see Arte Nuova **315**
Arte Nyt. (DK ISSN 0901-9901) **4629**
Arte Orientale in Italia. (IT) **3633**
Arte Regalo. (SP ISSN 0211-7959) **2280**
Arte Stampa. (IT) **315**
Arte Stampa Liguria see Arte Stampa **315**
Arte Tipografico see Graficas Mundiales **3999**
Arte U N E S P. (Universidade Estadual Paulista) (BL ISSN 0102-6550) **315**
Arte Veneta. (IT) **315**
Arte y Arqueologia. (BO ISSN 0587-5447) **315**, 266
Arte y Cemento. (SP) **600**
Artefact. (AT ISSN 0044-9075) **266**
Artefactum. (BE ISSN 0771-761X) **316**
Artemis see Artemis - Artists and Writers **2988**

Artemis - Artists and Writers. (US) 2988, 316, 4837
Artepiel. (SP) 2736
†Arterama. (IT ISSN 0004-3451) 5138
Artere. (CN) 2459, 3718
Arteregalo. (IT ISSN 0004-3478) 1161, 2280
Arteregalo - Oreficeria, Argenteria, Vetri d'Arte see Arteregalo Oro Argento 2563
Arteregalo Oro Argento. (IT) 2563
Arteres et Veines. (FR ISSN 0293-5090) 3205
Arterial Blood Gas Analysis. (CN) 3270
Arterien und Venen see Cerebro 3206
Arteriosclerosis see Arteriosclerosis and Thrombosis 3205
Arteriosclerosis and Thrombosis. (US ISSN 1049-8834) 3205
Artes. (BL ISSN 0004-3486) 316, 2896, 3539, 4629
Artes de la Comunicacion see Revista Artes de la Comunicacion 5269
Artes de Mexico. (MX ISSN 0300-4953) 316
Artes Graficas en Mexico. (MX ISSN 0004-3508) 3997
Artes Graficas U S A see Industria Grafica y Artes Graficas 4001
Artes Natales. (SA ISSN 1011-8012) 2744
Artes Populares. (HU ISSN 0139-4649) 2052
Artes Textiles: Bijragen tot de Geschiedenis van de Tapijt. (BE ISSN 0571-1924) 4616
Artesania y Folklore de Venezuela. (VE ISSN 0254-1572) 2052
Artesanias de America. (EC ISSN 0257-1625) 316
ARTEunesp see Arte U N E S P 315
Artforum. (US ISSN 0004-3532) 316
Artful Dodge. (US ISSN 0196-691X) 2896
†Artful Reporter. (UK) 5138
Artha. (II ISSN 0004-3540) 759, 843
Artha Vijnana. (II ISSN 0004-3559) 645
Artha Vijnana Reprint Series. (II) 645
Artha-Vikas. (II ISSN 0004-3567) 1072
Arthaniti. (II ISSN 0004-3575) 645
Arthik Prasanga. (II ISSN 0970-7654) 646
Arthika Sampat. (CE) 843
Arthika Vidya Nibandhana. (CE) 889
Arthika Vivaranaya. see Central Bank of Sri Lanka, Review of the Economy 5163
Arthritis Action. (AT) 3368
Arthritis and Rheumatism. (US ISSN 0004-3591) 3368
Arthritis and Rheumatism Council. Magazine. (UK) 3368
Arthritis and Rheumatism Primary Care Review see Primary Care Rheumatology 3369
Arthritis Care and Research. (US ISSN 0893-7524) 3368, 3275
Arthritis Foundation Annual Report. (US ISSN 0191-2836) 3368
Arthritis Health Professions Association Perspective see A H A P Perspective 3368
Arthritis News. (UK ISSN 0144-6339) 3368
Arthritis News. (CN ISSN 0820-9006) 3368
Arthritis News see Arthritis Action 3368
Arthritis Today. (US) 3368
Arthropods of Florida and Neighboring Land Areas. (US ISSN 0066-8036) 529
Arthroscopy. (US ISSN 0749-8063) 3307, 3376
Arthroscopy. (JA ISSN 0910-223X) 3307, 3368, 3376
Arthur. (CN ISSN 0044-9091) 1304
Arthur Holmes Society. Journal. (UK ISSN 0066-8044) 1541
Arthur Rimbaud. (FR ISSN 0180-9385) 2896

Arthurian Interpretations. (US ISSN 0890-4944) 2896
Arti e Mercature. (IT ISSN 0004-363X) 807
Arti Musices/Musicological Yearbook. (CI ISSN 0587-5455) 3539
Artibus Asiae. (SZ ISSN 0004-3648) 316, 266, 3633
Artibus Asiae Supplementa. (SZ) 316, 266, 3633
Artibus et Historiae. (AU ISSN 0391-9064) 316, 3503, 3788
Articles from Bulgarian Journals and Collections. see Letopis na Statiite ot Bulgarskite Spisaniia i Sbornitsi 405
Articles from Bulgarian Newspapers. see Letopis na Statiite ot Bulgarskite Vestnitsi 405
Articles in Hospitality and Tourism. (UK ISSN 0268-0858) 2482, 4798
†Articles of Interest in Current Periodicals. (US) 5138
Articoli Casalinghi see Articoli Casalinghi ed Elettrocasalinghi 2556
Articoli Casalinghi ed Elettrocasalinghi. (IT) 2556, 1161
Articulata. (GW ISSN 0171-4090) 429
Articulator. (US) 3228
Articulos en Linguistica y Campos Afines. (CK) 2804
Artifact. (US ISSN 0004-3680) 266
Artifact see Artsbeat 317
ArtiFacts (Columbia). (US) 316, 3522
Artifacts (Washington). (US) 266, 1992
Artifex. (US ISSN 0895-125X) 3668, 4012
Artificial Intelligence. (NE ISSN 0004-3702) 1407
Artificial Intelligence Abstracts. (US ISSN 0882-1410) 1403
Artificial Intelligence and Education see Interactive Learning Environments 1690
▼Artificial Intelligence and the Law. (NE ISSN 0924-8463) 2600, 1407
Artificial Intelligence Business see Expert Systems 1407
Artificial Intelligence Communications. (NE ISSN 0921-7126) 1407
Artificial Intelligence Expert see A I Expert 1406
Artificial Intelligence for Engineering Design, Analysis and Manufacturing. (UK ISSN 0890-0604) 1407
Artificial Intelligence in Engineering. (UK ISSN 0954-1810) 1407, 1475, 1877
Artificial Intelligence in Medicine. (NE ISSN 0933-3657) 3224, 1407
Artificial Intelligence Magazine see A I Magazine 1406
Artificial Intelligence Markets. (US ISSN 8756-6109) 1407
Artificial Intelligence Review. (UK ISSN 0269-2821) 1407
Artificial Intelligence Society see A I & Society 1406
Artificial Organs. (US ISSN 0160-564X) 3257
▼Artificial Organs Today. (NE ISSN 0924-3054) 3078
Artificial Satellites see Planetary Geodesy 60
Artificial Satellites see Space Physics 3832
Artigianato di Sicilia. (IT) 646
Artigianato Oggi. (IT) 353
Artigiano Modenese. (IT ISSN 0004-3737) 1113
Artigliere. (IT ISSN 0004-3745) 3452
Artikel 5. (GW ISSN 0935-7653) 4120, 3997
Artikler i Boeger/Danish National Bibliography. Articles in Books. (DK ISSN 0108-0261) 389
Der Artikulator. (GW) 3228
Artilleri-Tidskrift. (SW ISSN 0004-3788) 3452
Artillerie, Armee & Technik. (SZ ISSN 0004-3796) 3452

Artillery Journal. (II ISSN 0004-3826) 3452
Artilleryman. (US ISSN 0884-4747) 2399
Artis. (SZ ISSN 0004-3842) 316
Artisan Golfer. (UK) 4499
Artisan Staff Association Magazine see A S A Magazine 4707
Artisanat Batiment 34. (FR) 1113
Artisanat Francais. (FR) 1113
Artist see The Artist Incorporating Art & Artists 316
Artist. (CH ISSN 1016-4170) 316
Artist/Mei Shu Chia. (HK) 316
Artist. see Yishujia 350
Artist. (GW ISSN 0004-3885) 3539
The Artist Incorporating Art & Artists. (UK) 316
Artist Issue. (US ISSN 0893-7486) 3588
Artist of the Rockies and the Golden West see Southwest Art 344
Artist Update see M C A News 334
Artista. (IT) 316
Artistamp News. (US ISSN 1181-9456) 316, 1352, 3749
Artistes du Canada: Une Liste Collective des Dossiers d'Artistes. see Artists in Canada: A Union List of Artists Files 5139
Artistes et Varietes. (FR ISSN 0004-3907) 3539
Artists and Issues in the Theatre. (US ISSN 1051-9718) 4629
Artist's and Photographer's Market see Artist's Market 316
Artists Associates Far East Businessman's Directory see A.A.'s Far East Businessman's Directory 1119
Artists in Canada see Artists in Canada: A Union List of Artists Files 5139
†Artists in Canada: A Union List of Artists Files/Artistes du Canada: Une Liste Collective des Dossiers d'Artistes. (CN) 5139
Artists in Stained Glass. Bulletin. (CN) 1161, 316
Artist's Magazine. (US ISSN 0741-3351) 316
Artist's Market. (US ISSN 0161-0546) 316
Artists on Art Magazine see Re-View 5267
†Artists Resource Guide to New England Galleries, Grants and Services. (US) 5139
Artists Review Art. (US) 316, 3522
Artists View Art see Artists Review Art 316
Artletter. (US) 316
Artlink. (AT ISSN 0727-1239) 316, 1616
Artnews. (US ISSN 0004-3273) 316
Artnewsletter. (US ISSN 0145-7241) 316
Artpaper. (US) 316, 2896
†Artpark. (US ISSN 0164-1298) 5139
▼Artplus. (US) 316
Artpost Magazine. (CN ISSN 0829-0784) 316
Arts. (AT ISSN 0066-8095) 316
Arts. see Umeni 347
Arts (Minneapolis). (US) 316
Arts Address Book. (UK) 316, 1528, 3539
Arts Alive! (US) 4629, 316
Arts Amateurs/Huwat al-Funoun. (JO) 316
Arts and Activities. (US ISSN 0004-3931) 1744, 317
†Arts & Architecture. (US ISSN 0730-9481) 5139
†Arts & Business Council. Annual Report. (US) 5139
Arts & Crafts ShowGuide. (US) 353
Arts & Cultural Times. (US) 317, 4053
Arts and Culture Funding Report. (US ISSN 1047-3297) 317, 4084
Arts & Entertainment Channel Program Guide see A & E Program Guide 1368
Arts & Humanities Citation Index. (US ISSN 0162-8445) 351, 3, 2519
†Arts and Leisure Magazine. (US) 5139
Arts and Letters. see Van Nghe 2973

†Arts & Sciences (Evanston). (US ISSN 0738-9361) 5139
Arts & Sciences Journal. (PH ISSN 0115-6950) 2503, 4300
Arts and Sciences Newsletter. (US) 4300, 4593
Arts & the Islamic World. (UK ISSN 0264-1828) 317
Arts, Antiques et Auctions. (BE) 317, 256
Arts Asiatiques. (FR ISSN 0004-3958) 317, 295, 3633
Arts Atlantic. (CN ISSN 0704-7916) 317
Arts Bulletin. (CN ISSN 0707-9532) 317, 3539
†The Arts Business. (UK) 5139
Arts Club Theatre Encore. (CN) 4629
Arts Council of Australia. Annual Report. (AT) 317
Arts Council of Great Britain. Annual Report and Accounts. (UK ISSN 0066-8133) 317
†Arts Council of Great Britain. Education Bulletin. (UK ISSN 0143-4519) 5139
Arts de l'Ouest. (FR) 317
Arts en Auto. (NE ISSN 0004-3966) 4679
Arts et Industries. (FR ISSN 0004-3982) 1815
Arts et Manufactures. (FR ISSN 0004-3990) 4594
Arts et Metiers. (FR ISSN 0004-4008) 1927, 317
†Arts Festivals in Britain and Ireland. (UK ISSN 0951-1121) 5139
Arts in Alaska see Alaska. State Council on the Arts. Bulletin 310
The Arts in Psychotherapy. (US ISSN 0197-4556) 4012, 317
Arts in Virginia. (US ISSN 0004-4032) 317
Arts Indiana. (US ISSN 0897-859X) 317
Arts Insight see Arts Indiana 317
†Arts Journal. (US) 5139
Arts Letter see Washington International Arts Letter 349
Arts London Review. (UK ISSN 0260-6801) 317
Arts Magazine (New York). (US ISSN 0004-4059) 317
Arts Management. (US ISSN 0004-4067) 4629, 1528, 3539
Arts Manitoba see Border Crossings 319
Arts of Asia. (HK ISSN 0004-4083) 317
Arts of Himachal. (II) 317
Arts Patronage Series. (US ISSN 0066-8168) 317
Arts Quarterly. (US ISSN 0740-9214) 317
†Arts Report. (UK ISSN 0260-8723) 5139
Arts Review. (UK ISSN 0004-4091) 317
Arts Review. (JM) 317
†Arts Review. (US ISSN 0741-4579) 5139
Arts Review Yearbook. (UK) 317
Arts Support by Private Foundations and Business Corporations see National Directory of Arts and Education Support by Business Corporations 337
Arts Yorkshire see Yorkshire Artscene 350
Artsbeat. (CN) 317, 353
Artsboard. (CN ISSN 0823-9746) 4629, 1528, 3539
Artscope see Center of Attention 321
Artscribe. (UK ISSN 0309-2151) 317
ArtSearch. (US ISSN 0730-9023) 3624, 4629
Artsenpraktijk. (BE) 3078, 646
Artsfocus. (US) 3522, 317, 1161, 3539
Artsheaf see New Hampshire Arts 338
Artspace (Albuquerque). (US ISSN 0193-6956) 317
Artspace (Columbus). (US) 317, 3539, 4629
Artspeak. (US) 317
Artstudio. (FR) 317
†Artswest. (AT ISSN 0814-883X) 5139
ArtToday. (US ISSN 0885-9361) 317

Artus. (FR ISSN 0181-1835) **2503**
Artviews. (AT ISSN 0311-0095) **317**
†Artviews. (CN ISSN 0381-9515) **5139**
Artweek. (US ISSN 0004-4121) **317**
Artworkers News *see* Art & Artists **313**
Artworks. (AT) **317**
▼Artworld Europe. (US) **318**
Arun. (II) **2896**
Aruru. (JA) **2444**
Arusha Chamber of Commerce and Agriculture. Bulletin to Members. (TZ) **807**, 147
Arusia. Historiske Skrifter. (DK ISSN 0108-0075) **2350**
Arussi Rural Development Unit Publication *see* A R D U Publication **67**
Arut Perum Jothi. (II) **4217**, 3078
Arv. (SW ISSN 0066-8176) **2052**
Arv og Eje. (DK ISSN 0105-0192) **2350**
Arvernia Biologica: Botanique. (FR ISSN 0066-8184) **495**
Arx Tavastica. (FI ISSN 0358-3414) **2350**
Aryana. (AF ISSN 0004-4164) **2336**, 2804, 3633
Arznei-Telegramm. (GW ISSN 0066-8192) **3718**
Arzneimittel-Forschung/Drug Research. (GW ISSN 0004-4172) **3718**
Arzneimittel Zeitung. (GW ISSN 0935-2767) **3718**, 646
Der Arzneimittelbrief. (GW) **3718**
Arzneimitteltherapie. (GW ISSN 0723-6913) **3718**
Arzobispado de Santiago. Vicaria de la Solidaridad. Estudios. (CL) **4256**
Arzobispado de Sevilla. Boletin Oficial Eclesiastico. (SP) **4256**
Arzt in Niederoesterreich. (AU ISSN 0004-4180) **3078**, 4098
Arzt und Auto. (GW ISSN 0341-4434) **3078**, 4679
Arzt und Christ. (GW ISSN 0403-3884) **3078**, 3762
Die Arzthelferin. (GW) **3275**
Arzthelferin Aktuell. (GW ISSN 0176-1897) **3376**, 3275
Arztrecht. (GW ISSN 0343-5733) **3078**, 2600
As a Matter of Fact. (CN) **938**, 843
A's & B's of Academic Scholarship. (US) **1700**
A's and B's: Your Guide to Academic Scholarship *see* A's & B's of Academic Scholarship **1700**
†Asahi Ajia Rebyu/Asahi Asia Review. (JA ISSN 0387-2785) **5139**
Asahi Asia Review. *see* Asahi Ajia Rebyu **5139**
Asahi Camera. (JA ISSN 0044-9148) **3788**
Asahi Cosmos. *see* Asahi Kosumosu **5139**
Asahi Garasu Kenkyu Hokoku. *see* Asahi Glass Company. Research Center. Reports **1161**
Asahi Glass Company. Research Center. Reports/Asahi Garasu Kenkyu Hokoku. (JA) **1161**
Asahi Graph. (JA) **2207**
Asahi Graph Bessatsu *see* Asahi Graph Bessatu Bijutu **318**
Asahi Graph Bessatu Bijutu. (JA) **318**
Asahi Janaru/Asahi Journal. (JA ISSN 0571-2378) **2207**
Asahi Journal. *see* Asahi Janaru **2207**
†Asahi Kosumosu/Asahi Cosmos. (JA) **5139**
Asahi Pasokon/Asahi Personal Computers. (JA) **1467**
Asahi Personal Computers. *see* Asahi Pasokon **1467**
Asahi Shimbun Shukusatuban/Reduced Size Asahi Shimbun. (JA) **2207**
Asam Bani. (II) **2198**
Asbarez. (US ISSN 0004-4229) **2859**
†Asbestos Abatement Litigation Reporter. (US ISSN 1053-0231) **5139**
Asbestos Abatement Report. (US ISSN 0893-858X) **4098**
Asbestos Case Law Quarterly. (US) **2600**, 3614
Asbestos Control Report. (US ISSN 0893-4533) **1943**

†Asbestos Issues. (US ISSN 0897-1501) **5139**
Asbestos Litigation Reporter. (US ISSN 0273-3048) **2600**
▼Asbestos M D L 875 Update. (US) **2601**, 1943
Asbestos Producer/Producteur d'Amiante. (CN ISSN 0478-4049) **600**, 3478
Asbestos Property Litigation Reporter. (US ISSN 1041-5130) **2601**
▼Asbestos Regulatory Reporter - New York Edition. (US ISSN 1055-9493) **2601**, 1943
Asbestos Victims of America Advisor *see* A V A Advisor **3192**
Asbestos Watch. (CN) **1943**, 3614
Asbestos Worker. (US ISSN 0004-4245) **2580**, 600
Asbury Seminarian *see* Asbury Theological Journal **4229**
Asbury Theological Journal. (US) **4229**
Ascenders. (US) **3997**
Ascent *see* Focus (Warwickshire) **4178**
Ascent. (AT ISSN 0810-7688) **4594**, 4300
†Ascent. (US ISSN 0098-9363) **5139**
Ascent (Kootenay Bay). (CN ISSN 0315-8179) **3593**
Ascent (Ontario). (CN ISSN 0707-5588) **1803**, 1943
Aschaffenburger Stadtzeitung. (GW) **4084**
Aschaffenburg'she Monatsschrift *see* Monatsschrift fuer Kriminologie und Strafrechtsreform **1518**
▼Aschkenas. (AU) **1992**, 4221
Ascidian News. (US ISSN 0066-8222) **578**
Asclepio. (SP ISSN 0210-4466) **3078**, 235
Ascolta *see* Operabladet Ascolta **3572**
Aseguradores. (SP ISSN 0004-430X) **2526**
Asemka. (GH) **2896**
Asfalt. (DK ISSN 0004-4318) **1862**
Asfar. (NE) **4218**
Ash. (US) **2988**
†Ash at Work. (US) **5139**
Asharq Al-Awsat. (UK) **843**
Asheville Report. (US) **807**
Ashford Advertiser *see* Ashford Extra **2193**
Ashford Extra. (UK) **2193**
Ashland News. (US) **3682**
Ashram Community Trust *see* A C T **4161**
†Ashton-Tate Quarterly. (US) **5139**
Ashtree Echo. (US ISSN 0004-4377) **2144**
Ashur. (IR) **1992**
Asia - Africa World Trade Register. (II ISSN 0066-8230) **900**
†Asia and Middle East Food Trade. (GW) **5139**
Asia and Pacific *see* Asia & Pacific Review **843**
Asia & Pacific Review. (UK) **843**, 3874
Asia and the Far East Commission on Agricultural Statistics. Periodic Report *see* Food and Agriculture Organization of the United Nations. Asia and the Pacific Commission on Agricultural Statistics. Periodic Report **137**
Asia Cable. (US) **1368**
Asia Computer Weekly. (SI ISSN 0129-5896) **1389**
Asia Corporate Profile and National Finance. (HK) **844**
Asia Foundation. Annual Report. (US) **2336**
Asia Foundation. President's Review and Annual Report *see* Asia Foundation. Annual Report **2336**
†Asia Horizon Azie. (CN ISSN 0835-3336) **5139**
Asia Insights *see* Indochina Newsletter **3960**
Asia Institute. Bulletin. (US ISSN 0890-4464) **3633**
▼Asia Law & Practice. (HK ISSN 1015-5562) **2601**
Asia Letter. (HK ISSN 0004-4466) **844**
Asia Magazine. (HK ISSN 0004-4474) **2197**

Asia Money & Finance. (HK) **759**
Asia - Pacific - Africa - Middle East Petroleum. (US ISSN 0748-4089) **3682**
Asia - Pacific Agribusiness Report. (HK) **147**
Asia - Pacific Aviation and Engineering. (SI) **46**
Asia - Pacific Broadcasting. (SI) **1368**, 1355
Asia - Pacific Broadcasting Union Technical Review *see* A B U Technical Review **1368**
Asia Pacific Business. (CN ISSN 0829-4488) **646**
▼Asia Pacific Chemicals. (US ISSN 0960-2739) **1170**
†Asia Pacific Context. (AT ISSN 0815-6344) **5139**
†Asia - Pacific Currency Report. (US ISSN 0739-6244) **5139**
Asia - Pacific Defense Forum. (US) **3452**
▼Asia - Pacific Electro-Optics. (US) **1882**
▼Asia-Pacific Engineering Journal. (SI ISSN 0129-5411) **1815**
Asia Pacific Food Industry. (SI ISSN 0218-2734) **2062**
Asia Pacific Food Processing and Packaging *see* Asia Pacific Food Industry **2062**
▼Asia Pacific Foodservice Product News. (US) **2471**, 2062
Asia - Pacific Forecasting Service. (HK) **646**
Asia Pacific H R M *see* Asia Pacific Human Resource Management **1062**
Asia Pacific Human Resource Management. (AT ISSN 1032-3627) **1062**
Asia - Pacific in Figures. (UN) **4562**
†Asia - Pacific International and Strategic Studies Newsletter. (SI) **5139**
Asia Pacific International Journal of Business Logistics. (UK ISSN 0952-8067) **1033**
†Asia Pacific International Journal of Business Research. (UK ISSN 0954-7525) **5139**
†Asia Pacific International Journal of Management Development. (UK ISSN 0954-7533) **5139**
Asia Pacific International Journal of Marketing. (UK ISSN 0954-7517) **1033**
†Asia Pacific International Management Forum. (UK) **5139**
Asia Pacific International Management Review *see* Asia Pacific International Management Forum **5139**
Asia Pacific Journal of Management. (SI ISSN 0217-4561) **1002**
Asia Pacific Journal of Operational Research. (SI) **1389**
Asia Pacific Journal of Ophthalmology *see* Implants in Ophthalmology **3301**
Asia Pacific Journal of Pharmacology. (SI ISSN 0217-9687) **3718**
Asia Pacific Metalworking Equipment News. (SI ISSN 0129-5519) **3016**
Asia - Pacific Petroleum Directory *see* Asia - Pacific - Africa - Middle East Petroleum **3682**
Asia - Pacific Population & Policy. (US ISSN 0891-6683) **3979**
Asia - Pacific Population Journal. (UN ISSN 0259-238X) **3979**
Asia - Pacific Scouting. (PH) **1232**
Asia - Pacific Telecommunications. (SI) **1361**
†Asia Pacific Top Management Digest. (UK ISSN 0955-1484) **5139**
▼Asia Pacific Travel. (US ISSN 1045-3881) **4752**
Asia Serial Reports: Korea: Kulloja. (US) **3950**
Asia Serial Reports: Viet Nam: Top Chi Chong San. (US) **3950**
The Asia Society. Annual Report. (US ISSN 0098-1214) **2336**
Asia Technology. (HK) **4594**
Asia Textile and Apparel *see* A T A Journal **4616**
Asia Today. (AT ISSN 0813-2844) **646**, 938

Asia Travel Trade. (SI ISSN 0255-7320) **4752**
Asia Travel Trade Directory *see* Travel Directory **4792**
Asia Watch. (US) **3950**
Asia Watch Report. (US) **3940**
Asia Yearbook. (HK) **646**
AsiaBanking. (HK) **759**
AsiAm *see* Transpacific **2026**
Asiamac Journal. (HK ISSN 1015-5023) **3016**, 1002
Asiamoney *see* Asia Money & Finance **759**
Asiamoney. (UK) **759**
Asian Advertising and Marketing. (HK ISSN 0257-893X) **28**, 1033, 4120
Asian Affairs (New York) *see* Asian Affairs: An American Review **3950**
Asian Affairs: An American Review. (US ISSN 0092-7678) **3950**
Asian Agribusiness Buyers Guide *see* Agri-Technology Buyers Guide **5132**
Asian Almanac. (SI ISSN 0004-4520) **3936**, 3
Asian American Certified Public Accountants Newsletter *see* A A C P A Newsletter **744**
Asian American Trade Directory. (US) **807**, 1121
Asian and African Studies. (IS ISSN 0066-8281) **2336**, 2331
Asian and African Studies. (CS ISSN 0571-2742) **3634**, 2331, 2336
Asian and Pacific Council. Food and Fertilizer Technology Center. Extension - Technical Bulletin. (CH) **77**
Asian and Pacific Development Administration Centre. Occasional Papers Series *see* Asian and Pacific Development Centre Newsletter **844**
Asian and Pacific Development Centre Newsletter. (MY ISSN 0127-3337) **844**
Asian and Pacific Labour. (II) **2580**
Asian and Pacific Population Forum. (US ISSN 0891-2823) **3979**
Asian and Pacific Quarterly. (KO) **2804**
Asian and Pacific Women's Resource and Action Series. (MY) **4837**, 596, 3289
Asian Architect & Contractor. (HK) **295**, 600
Asian Architecture and Builder *see* Asian Architect & Contractor **295**
Asian Archives of Anaesthesiology and Resuscitation. (II ISSN 0301-0363) **3190**
Asian Art. (US ISSN 0894-234X) **3634**, 318
Asian Aviation. (SI ISSN 0129-9972) **46**
Asian Banking and Corporate Finance *see* AsiaBanking **759**
Asian Banking Guide *see* Banking Guides - Asia, Australia, New Zealand with Principal Hotels and Bank Holidays **766**
Asian Bibliography. (UN ISSN 0497-9400) **2327**
Asian Book Development *see* Asian - Pacific Book Development **4120**
†Asian Book Trade Directory. (II ISSN 0066-8362) **5139**
Asian Books Newsletter. (II ISSN 0004-4547) **389**
Asian Building & Construction. (UK ISSN 0264-8164) **600**, 295
Asian Building Products Catalogue. (UK) **600**
Asian Bulletin/Bulletin d'Asie. (CS) **2336**, 3634
Asian Bulletin. (CH) **3874**, 2336
†Asian Bureau Australia. Newsletter. (AT) **5139**
Asian Business. (HK ISSN 0254-3729) **1072**
Asian Centre of Educational Innovation for Development Newsletter *see* A C E I D Newsletter **1721**
Asian Cinema. (US) **3503**
Asian Communications. (UK ISSN 0952-7516) **1361**
Asian Company Handbook. (JA) **1121**
Asian Computer Directory. (HK) **1424**
†Asian Computer Monthly. (HK ISSN 0254-217X) **5139**
Asian Computerworld. (SI) **1389**

5934 ASIAN CULTURAL

Asian Cultural Centre for Unesco. Organization and Activities. (UN) **3634**
Asian Cultural Studies. (JA ISSN 0454-2150) **2336**, 3634
Asian Culture see Asian Pacific Culture **3634**
Asian Culture. (SI) **4429**
Asian Culture Quarterly see Asian Pacific Culture Quarterly **3634**
Asian Defence Journal. (MY ISSN 0126-6403) **3452**
Asian Development Bank. Annual Report. (PH ISSN 0066-8370) **759**, 926
Asian Development Bank. Board of Governors. Summary of Proceedings.(PH ISSN 0066-8389) **926**, 759
Asian Development Bank. Key Indicators of Asian and Pacific Countries. (PH) **759**, 926
Asian Development Bank. Key Indicators of Developing Member Countries of A D B see Asian Development Bank. Key Indicators of Asian and Pacific Countries **759**
†Asian Development Bank. Occasional Papers. (PH ISSN 0066-8397) **5139**
Asian Development Bank Business Opportunities see A D B Business Opportunities **643**
Asian Development Bank Quarterly Review see A D B Quarterly Review **925**
Asian Development Institute. Newsletter see A D I Quarterly News Letter **925**
Asian Development Outlook. (PH) **646**
Asian Development Review. (PH ISSN 0116-1105) **926**
Asian Economic and Social Review. (II) **4366**, 926
Asian Economies/Ajia Keizai. (JA ISSN 0002-2942) **646**, 926
Asian Electricity. (UK ISSN 0264-3340) **1882**
Asian Electronics Engineer. (SI) **1882**
Asian Environment. (PH ISSN 0116-2993) **1943**, 3614, 4098, 4822
†Asian Finance. (HK) **5139**
Asian Fisheries Science. (PH ISSN 0116-6514) **578**
Asian Folklore Studies. (JA ISSN 0385-2342) **2052**
†Asian Furniture. (SI) **5139**
Asian Geotechnical Engineering Abstracts see A G E Refdex **1549**
Asian Geotechnical Engineering Information Center Current Awareness Service see A G E Current Awareness Service **1540**
Asian Geotechnical Engineering Information Center News see A G E News **1540**
Asian Geotechnical Engineering Information Center Refdex see A G E Refdex **1549**
Asian Hospital. (HK ISSN 1011-596X) **3078**, 2459
Asian Hotel & Catering Times. (HK) **2471**
Asian Hotelkeeper and Catering Times see Asian Hotel & Catering Times **2471**
Asian Industrial Reporter. (US) **646**, 900
Asian Industrial World. (US) **1072**
Asian Insights see A I **1988**
Asian Institute of Technology. Annual Research and Activities Report. (TH) **4594**
Asian Institute of Technology. Newsletter see A I T Review **1813**
Asian Institute of Technology. Research Summary see Asian Institute of Technology. Annual Research and Activities Report **4594**
Asian Institute of Technology Reports and Publications on Energy. Abstracts see A I T Reports and Publications on Energy. Abstracts **1797**
Asian Institute of Technology Review see A I T Review **1813**
Asian Journal of Dairy Research. (II ISSN 0253-6595) **197**

Asian Journal of European Studies. (II ISSN 0378-7516) **2350**
Asian Journal of Physical Education. (CH) **3799**
Asian Journal of Psychology and Education. (II) **4012**, 1616
Asian Journal of Public Administration. (HK ISSN 0259-8272) **4054**, 646, 3874
Asian Labor Education Center. Labor Review. see Philippine Journal of Labor and Industrial Relations **991**
Asian Labour see Asian and Pacific Labour **2580**
†Asian Law Series. (US) **5139**
▼Asian Libraries. (HK ISSN 1017-6748) **2744**
Asian Literary Market Review. (II ISSN 0254-6183) **4120**
Asian Markets. (US) **900**, 1121
Asian Mass Communications Bulletin. (SI ISSN 0129-2056) **1332**
▼Asian Medical Education Index. (AT) **3166**, 3
Asian Medical News. (HK ISSN 0250-3328) **3078**
Asian Meetings and Incentives. (HK ISSN 1015-3128) **3390**, 646
Asian Music. (US ISSN 0044-9202) **3539**
Asian Music Publications. Series A: Bibliographic and Research Aids. (US ISSN 0081-1319) **3539**
Asian Music Publications. Series B. Translations. (US ISSN 0081-1327) **3539**
Asian Music Publications. Series C: Reprints. (US ISSN 0081-1335) **3539**
Asian Music Publications. Series D: Monographs. (US ISSN 0081-1343) **3539**
Asian News Sheet. (SZ ISSN 0518-8881) **2527**
Asian Oil and Gas. (JA) **3682**
Asian Oil and Gas. (HK) **3682**
Asian Outlook. (CH ISSN 0004-4628) **3874**
Asian - Pacific American Librarians Association Newsletter. (US ISSN 1040-8517) **2744**
Asian-Pacific and Worldwide Documents on Population Topics see A D O P T **5127**
Asian Pacific Anti-Communist League, China. Pamphlet. (CH ISSN 0571-2920) **3874**
Asian - Pacific Book Development. (UN) **4120**
Asian Pacific Congress of Cardiology. Symposia. (IO ISSN 0587-5471) **3205**
Asian Pacific Culture. (UN) **3634**
Asian Pacific Culture Quarterly. (CH) **3634**
Asian-Pacific Economic Literature. (UK ISSN 0818-9935) **702**, 926
Asian-Pacific Environment. (MY ISSN 0127-7170) **1943**, 1483, 2242
Asian Pacific Quarterly of Cultural and Social Affairs see Asian and Pacific Quarterly **2804**
†Asian Pacific Review. (AT) **5139**
Asian Parliamentarians' Union. Central Secretariat. Report on Meeting of APU Secretaries-General in Tokyo. (JA) **3950**
Asian Peoples' Anti-Communist League. Charts About Chinese Communists on the Mainland. (CH ISSN 0571-2939) **2336**
Asian Perspective. (KO) **3874**, 3950
Asian Perspectives. (US ISSN 0066-8435) **266**
▼Asian Philosophy. (US ISSN 0955-2367) **3762**, 3634
Asian Plastics News. (UK) **3861**
Asian Population Programme News see Population Headliners **3986**
Asian Press. (KO) **2567**
Asian Printing. (HK ISSN 1012-8662) **3997**
Asian Printing Directory. (HK ISSN 0258-218X) **3997**, 1121
Asian Productivity Organization Annual Report see A P O Annual Report **1071**
Asian Productivity Organization News see A P O News **1071**

Asian Profile. (HK ISSN 0304-8675) **3634**, 2336, 4366
†Asian Property. (HK) **5139**
Asian Recorder. (II ISSN 0004-4644) **2198**
Asian Regional Conference on Industrial Relations. Proceedings. (JA) **972**
Asian Regional Organisation of the International Textile, Garment and Leather Workers' Federation News see T W A R O News **4623**
†Asian Religious Studies Information. (US ISSN 0888-5869) **5139**
Asian Research Trends: a Humanities and Social Science Review. (JA) **3634**
Asian Review of Business and Technology. (UK ISSN 0956-3784) **4594**, 646
Asian Security. (JA) **3950**
Asian Security & Safety Journal. (HK ISSN 0259-059X) **1526**
Asian Shipping. (HK) **4724**
Asian Sources. (HK) **1502**
Asian Sources Computer Products. (US ISSN 0254-5586) **1423**
Asian Sources Electronics. (US ISSN 0254-1114) **1882**
Asian Sources Electronics Components. (US ISSN 0254-1122) **1882**
Asian Sources Fashion Accessories. (US ISSN 0254-1130) **1289**
Asian Sources Gifts & Home Products. (US ISSN 0254-1157) **2280**, 2556
Asian Sources Hardwares. (US ISSN 0254-1149) **641**
Asian Sources Timepieces. (US ISSN 0254-1173) **2563**
Asian Studies. (PH ISSN 0004-4679) **3634**
Asian Studies Association of Australia. Conference Papers. (AT ISSN 0156-0182) **3634**, 2336
Asian Studies Association of Australia. Newsletter see Asian Studies Review **2336**
Asian Studies Association of Australia. Review see Asian Studies Review **2336**
Asian Studies Center Backgrounder. (US) **3950**
Asian Studies Monographs Series. (CN) **2336**, 3634
Asian Studies Newsletter. (US) **3634**
Asian Studies Review. (AT ISSN 1035-7823) **2336**, 3634
†Asian Studies Series. (SZ) **5139**
Asian Survey. (US ISSN 0004-4687) **3874**, 3634
Asian Textile Record. (JA) **4616**
Asian Theatre Journal. (US ISSN 0742-5457) **4629**, 3634
Asian Thought and Culture. (US ISSN 0893-6870) **3634**
Asian Thought and Society: an International Review. (US ISSN 0361-3968) **4366**, 2503
†Asian Timber. (SI) **5139**
Asian Timber Trades Journal see Asian Timber **5139**
Asian Times. (UK) **1992**, 2193
Asian Trade and Industry. (MY) **1072**
Asian Trader. (UK) **1122**
Asian Tribune. (CN ISSN 0707-3380) **1992**
Asian Wall Street Journal Weekly. (HK ISSN 0191-0132) **759**
Asian Water & Sewage. (HK ISSN 1011-5978) **1943**, 4822
Asian Week. (US ISSN 0195-2056) **1992**
Asiana. (KO) **4802**
Asia's 7500 Largest Companies. (UK) **759**
Asiatic Society. Annual Report. (II ISSN 0403-4457) **2199**, 1992
Asiatic Society, Calcutta. Journal. (II ISSN 0571-3161) **3634**
Asiatic Society, Calcutta. Monograph Series. (II) **3634**
Asiatic Society, Calcutta. Seminar Series. (II) **3634**
Asiatic Society of Bangladesh. Journal. (BG) **3634**
Asiatic Society of Bangladesh. Journal: Science. (BG) **4300**, 3634
Asiatic Society of Bombay. Journal. (II ISSN 0004-4709) **3634**

Asiatic Society of Japan. Transactions. (JA ISSN 0287-6051) **3634**
Asiatische Forschungen. (GW ISSN 0571-320X) **3634**
Asiatische Studien/Etudes Asiatiques. (SZ ISSN 0004-4717) **3634**
Asiaweek. (HK ISSN 1012-6244) **2197**, 2336
Asie du Sud-Est et Monde Insulindien. (FR ISSN 0224-2680) **2804**, 235
Asie Nouvelle. (FR ISSN 0004-4725) **807**
Asien. (GW ISSN 0721-5231) **3634**
Asien, Afrika, Lateinamerika. (GW ISSN 0323-3790) **2336**, 2331, 2399
†Asien - Afrika - Lateinamerika. Jahrbuch. (GW ISSN 0232-8410) **5139**
Asien-Studier i Skandinavien see N I A S - Nytt **3641**
Asilomar Conference on Signals, Systems and Computers. Conference Record. (US) **1416**, 1389, 1436
†Asimetria. (SP ISSN 0213-7585) **5140**
Asimptoticheskie Metody v Teorii Sistem. (RU) **3030**
Asistencia Reciproca Petrolera Estatal Latinoamericana Boletin Tecnico see A R P E L Boletin Tecnico **3681**
Asistencia Reciproca Petrolera Estatal Latinoamericana Hoy see A R P E L Hoy **3681**
Ask! (US ISSN 0731-2350) **1002**
Ask. (DK ISSN 0109-4718) **2350**
Asklepios. (UK) **495**, 2122
Askov Laerlinge. (DK ISSN 0106-7478) **1616**
Aslan. (DK ISSN 0905-7749) **4163**, 2859
Aslib Annual Report. (UK) **2744**
Aslib Book Guide. (UK) **389**, 4354, 4614
Aslib Book List see Aslib Book Guide **389**
Aslib Information. (UK ISSN 0305-0033) **2744**
Aslib Proceedings. (UK ISSN 0001-253X) **2744**
Asmara Chamber of Commerce. Trade and Development Bulletin. (ET) **807**
Asocebu see Cebu **214**
Asociacao Medica Brasileira. Boletim. (BL) **3079**
Asociacion. (UY) **1232**, 4163
Asociacion Archivistica Argentina Boletin. (AG) **2399**, 2744
Asociacion Argentina Criadores de Cerdos. Revista. (AG ISSN 0004-4741) **211**
Asociacion Argentina de Actores. Memoria y Balance. (AG) **2580**, 4629
Asociacion Argentina de Mineralogia, Petrologia y Sedimentologia. Revista.(AG ISSN 0325-0253) **1541**
Asociacion Bioquimica Argentina. Revista. (AG ISSN 0004-4768) **471**
Asociacion Comercial Hispano-Sueca. Circula Informativa see Camara de Comercio Hispano-Sueca de Madrid. Info **810**
Asociacion Costarricense de Bibliotecarios. Boletin. (CR ISSN 0004-4784) **2744**
†Asociacion Cubana de la Naciones Unidas. Boletin. (CU) **5140**
Asociacion Cubana de Produccion Animal see A C P A **209**
Asociacion Cultural Humboldt. Boletin. (VE ISSN 0004-4792) **1296**
Asociacion de Bancos del Uruguay see A E B U **757**
Asociacion de Bibliotecarios de Instituciones de Ensenanza Superior e Investigacion. Archivos. (MX) **2744**
Asociacion de Ciencias Naturales del Litoral. Revista. (AG ISSN 0325-2809) **4300**
Asociacion de Comerciantes en Materiales para Construccion y Afines Revista A C O M A C see Revista A C O M A C **630**
Asociacion de Compositores Sinfonicos Espanoles. Boletin. (SP) **3539**

Asociacion de Cooperativas Farmaceuticas see A C O F A R 3714
Asociacion de Economistas Argentinos. Coleccion Instituto Superior. (AG) 646
Asociacion de Escribanos del Uruguay. Revista. (UY ISSN 0376-5024) 2601
Asociacion de Ex-Alumnos de la Escuela Nacional de Bibliotecarios. Boletin. (AG ISSN 0004-4806) 2744
Asociacion de Garajes y Estaciones de Servico see A G E S 4678
Asociacion de Hispanistas de las Americas. Coleccion Monografias. (US) 2988, 2804
Asociacion de Investigacion Tecnica de las Industrias de la Madera Boletin de Informacion Tecnica see A I T I M Boletin de Informacion Tecnica 2113
†Asociacion de Investigacion Textil Algodonera. Coleccion de Manuales Tecnicos. (SP ISSN 0571-3609) 5140
†Asociacion de Investigacion Textil Algodonera. Estudios y Documentos. (SP) 5140
Asociacion de Prensa Hondurena Revista A P H see Revista A P H 2180
Asociacion de Tecnicos Azucareros de Cuba see A T A C 166
Asociacion de Tecnicos Azucareros de Venezuela Boletin Informativo see A T A V E Boletin Informativo 2060
Asociacion del Congreso Panamericano de Ferrocarriles. Boletin. (AG) 4707
Asociacion Dental Mexicana, A.C. see A D M 3227
Asociacion Espanola Contra el Cancer. Memoria de la Assemblea General see Asociacion Espanola Contra el Cancer. Memoria Tecnico-Administrativa 3193
Asociacion Espanola Contra el Cancer. Memoria Tecnico-Administrativa. (SP) 3193
Asociacion Espanola de Archiveros Bibliotecarios, Museologos y Documentalistas Boletin see A N A B A D Boletin 2740
Asociacion Espanola de Farmaceuticos de Hospitales Boletin Informativo A E F H see Boletin Informativo A E F H 3719
Asociacion Espanola de Orientalistas. Boletin. (SP ISSN 0571-3692) 3634
Asociacion Espanola de Tecnicos de Maquinaria para la Construccion, Obras Publicas y Mineria Revista A T E M C O P see Revista A T E M C O P 1873
Asociacion Espanola de Titulados Nautico-Pesqueros Aetinape see Aetinape 2035
Asociacion Filatelica de la Republica Argentina Boletin Informativo see A F R A Boletin Informativo 3748
Asociacion Franco-Mexicana de Ingenieros y Tecnicos. Boletin. (MX ISSN 0004-4814) 1815
Asociacion General de Agricultores see A G A 67
Asociacion Geologica Argentina. Revista. (AG ISSN 0004-4822) 1555
Asociacion Interamericana de Bibliotecarios y Documentalistas Agricolas. Boletin Especial. (CR ISSN 0074-0748) 77, 2744
Asociacion Interamericana de Bibliotecarios y Documentalistas Agricolas. Boletin Informativo. (CR ISSN 0001-1495) 2744, 77
Asociacion Interamericana de Bibliotecarios y Documentalistas Agricolas Revista A I B D A see Revista A I B D A 2781
Asociacion Latinoamericana de Armadores Informativo see A L A M A R Informativo 4723
Asociacion Latinoamericana de Escuelas de Bibliotecologia y Ciencias de la Informacion Boletin Informativo see A L E B C I; Boletin Informativo 2740

Asociacion Latinoamericana de Integracion Ecos de A L A D I see Ecos de A L A D I 3892
Asociacion Latinoamericana de Integracion Sintesis - A L A D I see Sintesis - A L A D I 5277
Asociacion Latinoamericana de Produccion Animal. Memoria. (VE) 211
Asociacion Medica de Puerto Rico. Boletin. (PR ISSN 0004-4849) 3079
Asociacion Mexicana de Bibliotecarios, A.C. Noticiero see A M B A C Noticiero 2740
Asociacion Mexicana de Facultades y Escuelas de Medicina. Boletin. (MX ISSN 0004-4857) 3079
Asociacion Mexicana de Tecnicos de las Industrias de la Celulosa y del Papel, A.C. Revista see A T C P Revista 3661
Asociacion Nacional de Agricultores Pequenos see A N A P 67
Asociacion Nacional de Enfermeras de Colombia see A N E C 3274
Asociacion Nacional de Industriales. Revista Bimestral. (CK ISSN 0120-9515) 1072
Asociacion Nacional de Industriales. Revista Trimestral see Asociacion Nacional de Industriales. Revista Bimestral 1072
Asociacion Nacional de Instituciones Financieras. Carta Financiera. (CK) 844
Asociacion Nacional de Jubilados y Pensionados de Comunicaciones see A N J U P E C 3869
Asociacion Nacional de Promotores Constructores de Edificios Urbanos. Annual Report. (SP) 2483, 4145
Asociacion Nacional de Promotores Constructores de Edificios Urbanos. Promocion. (SP) 2483, 4145
Asociacion Nacional del Cafe. Departamento de Asuntos Agricolas. Annual Memory see Asociacion Nacional del Cafe. Departamento de Asuntos Agricolas. Informe Anual 377
Asociacion Nacional del Cafe. Departamento de Asuntos Agricolas. Informe Anual. (GT ISSN 0066-8567) 377
Asociacion Numismatica Argentina. Revista. (AG ISSN 0004-4873) 3598
Asociacion Odontologica Argentina. Revista. (AG ISSN 0004-4881) 3228
Asociacion para Evitar la Ceguera en Mexico. Archivos. (MX ISSN 0004-489X) 3079
Asociacion Peruana de Astronomia. Boletin. (PE ISSN 0044-9318) 360
Asociacion Quimica Argentina. Anales. (AG ISSN 0365-0375) 1170
Asociacion Rural del Uruguay. Revista. (UY ISSN 0044-9326) 77
Asociacion Salvadorena de Industriales Directorio de Asociados. (ES) 1122
Asociacion Venezolana de Archiveros. Coleccion Doctrina. (VE ISSN 0066-8591) 2744
Asociacion Venezolana de Psicologia Social. Boletin. (VE ISSN 1011-6273) 4012
Asociacion Venezolana de Psicologia Social Fasciculo see A V E P S O Fasciculo 4008
Asociacion Venezolano Britanica de Comercio e Industria. Anuario see Camara Venezolana Britanica de Comercio e Industria. Anuario 810
Asociation Euratom-Ital. Annual Report see Centre for Plant Breeding and Reproduction Research. Annual Report 83
Aspaklaria. (IS) 4221
Aspas de la Patata. (SP ISSN 0403-5542) 169
Aspect of Plant Sciences. (II ISSN 0971-1678) 495
Aspects. (UK ISSN 0143-537X) 318
Aspects. (US ISSN 1053-0584) 358
Aspects de la France. (FR) 3874

Aspects of Edenbridge. (UK ISSN 0261-8850) 2144
Aspects of Education. (UK ISSN 0066-8672) 1616
Aspects of Educational and Training Technology Series. (UK) 1744
Aspects of Educational Technology Series see Aspects of Educational and Training Technology Series 1744
Aspects of France. (AT) 1992, 4429
†Aspects of Greek and Roman Life. (US) 5140
Aspects of Homogeneous Catalysis: a Series of Advances. (NE) 1216
Aspects Statistiques de l'Ile de France see Regards sur l'Ile-de-France 4584
Aspen Airways - Air Destinations. (US) 4802
Aspen Magazine. (US ISSN 1043-5085) 2221
Aspen's Advisor for Nursing Executives. (US) 3276
Asphalt. (US ISSN 0004-4954) 4717
Asphalt Emulsion Manufacturers Association. Newsletter. (US) 4717, 3682
Asphalt Paving Technology see Association of Asphalt Paving Technologists. Proceedings 1862
Asphalt Roofing Manufacturers Association. Newsletter. (US) 3682
Die Asphaltstrasse. (GW ISSN 0722-821X) 1862
Aspis. (UK ISSN 0260-2474) 1122, 900
Asprenas. (IT ISSN 0004-4970) 4256, 2306
Assa. (FI ISSN 0781-7347) 829
Assam Directory & Tea Areas Handbook. (II) 1122, 377
Assam Directory of Tea Areas see Assam Directory & Tea Areas Handbook 1122
Assam Economic Journal. (II) 889
Assam Information. (II ISSN 0004-4989) 2199
Assam Review and Tea News. (II ISSN 0004-4997) 2062
Assaph. Section C. Studies in the Theatre. (IS ISSN 0334-5963) 4630
Assayad. (LE ISSN 0004-5012) 3874
†Assays. (US) 5140
Assemblage. (US ISSN 0889-3012) 295
Assemblages Adhesifs. (FR) 3016
Assemblee de l'Union de l'Europe Occidentale. Actes Officiels see Assembly of Western European Union. Proceedings 2719
Assemblee Nouvelle. (CN ISSN 0335-5012) 3539, 4163
Assemblees de Dieu de France. Annuaire. (FR ISSN 0083-6184) 4280
Assembling see Assembling Annual 2896
Assembling Annual. (US) 2896
Assembly. (US ISSN 1041-2581) 1700, 3452
Assembly Automation. (UK ISSN 0144-5154) 1411, 1927
Assembly Engineering. (US ISSN 0004-5063) 1815
Assembly of Western European Union. Proceedings. (FR ISSN 0083-8853) 2719
Assembly on Education Network. (US) 3079, 1700
Assembly Technology Buyer's Guide. (US) 1815
Assessment. (UK) 1087
Assessment and Evaluation in Higher Education. (UK ISSN 0260-2938) 1700
†Assessment and Valuation Legal Reporter. (US ISSN 0090-6352) 5140
Assessment Digest. (US ISSN 0731-0277) 4145, 1087
Assessment Report Index. (CN) 1797, 3
Assessment Update: Progress, Trends, and Practices in Higher Education. (US ISSN 1041-6099) 1700, 1744

Assessorato all'Urbanistica e Assetto del Territorio. Ad Arnum Quaderni. (IT) 2483
Asset. (US) 747
Asset. (II ISSN 0379-573X) 1783, 1797
Asset Allocation Review. (US) 759
†Asset-Backed Securities Report. (US) 5140
Asset Based Financing: A Transactional Guide. (US) 759, 2601
Asset Finance and Leasing Digest. (UK) 938, 844
Asset International. (US) 938, 759
Assets (Bryn Mawr). (US) 2527
Assets Protection. (US ISSN 0098-9169) 747, 1002
L'Assetu. (CN) 1304
Assia. (IS ISSN 0334-3871) 3079, 2601
Assia - Jewish Medical Ethics see Assia 3079
Assicurazioni. (IT ISSN 0004-511X) 2527
Assignation. (UK ISSN 0265-2587) 4366
Assignment Children. (UN) 1232, 4398
Assignment Guam. (GU) 3452
Assistance aux Maternites et Dispensaires en Afrique Centrale see Education Sanitaire et Nutritionnelle d'Afrique Centrale 3605
Assistance et le Prothesiste Dentaires. (FR) 3228
▼Assistant Editor. (US ISSN 1051-3299) 2896, 2744
Assistant Librarian. (UK ISSN 0004-5152) 2745
Assistant Masters & Mistresses Association. Report. (UK ISSN 0142-3134) 1616
▼Assisted Reproduction Reviews. (US ISSN 1051-2446) 3289
Assistente Ecclesiastico see Presenza Pastorale 4273
Assistenz. (GW ISSN 0722-3587) 1057, 1389
Assistenza Infermieristica del Nord America. (IT ISSN 0393-7550) 3276
Assistive Technology. (US ISSN 1040-0435) 1733, 3079
Assiut University. Faculty of Education. Journal. see Jami'at Assiut. Kulliyyat al-Tarbiyyah. Majallah 1641
Assiut University. Faculty of Engineering. Bulletin. (UA) 1815
Assiut Veterinary Medical Journal. (UA ISSN 1012-5973) 4806
Asso Cham Bulletin. (Associated Chambers of Commerce and Industry of India) (II) 807
Asso Cham Parliamentary Digest. (Associated Chambers of Commerce and Industry of India) (II) 807
Assocham Bulletin see Asso Cham Bulletin 807
Associacao Bahiana de Bibliotecarios. Informa. (BL ISSN 0004-5187) 2745
Associacao Brasileira de Endodontia, Seccao Sao Paulo Boletim see A B E S P Boletim 3226
Associacao Brasileira de Metalurgia e Materiais Metalurgia e Materiais see A B M Metalurgia e Materiais 3401
Associacao Brasileira de Psiquiatria e Asociacion Psiquiatrica de la America Latina. Revista. (BL ISSN 0102-7646) 3331
Associacao Brasileira de Tradutores see A B R A T E S 5127
Associacao Brasileira para o Desenvolvimento das Industrias de Base Anuario A B D I B see Anuario A B D I B 1072
Associacao Comercial do Amazonas. Boletim. (BL ISSN 0004-5217) 807
Associacao Comercial do Porto. Boletim.(PO) 646
Associacao de Empresas de Construcao e Obras Publicas do Sul. Industria da Construcao. (PO ISSN 0870-0214) 600
†Associacao Industrial Portuense. Boletim Informativo. (PO) 5140

ASSOCIACAO MEDICA

Associacao Medica Brasileira. Jornal. (BL ISSN 0004-5233) **3079**
Associacao Medica Brasileira. Revista. (BL ISSN 0004-5241) **3079**
Associacao Medica de Minas Gerais. Revista. (BL ISSN 0004-525X) **3079**
Associacao Medica do Rio Grande do Sul. Revista *see* Revista A M R I G S **3147**
Associacao Mineira de Acao Educacional. Revista. (BL ISSN 0102-0471) **1616, 1692**
Associacao Nacional de Educacao *see* A N D E **1613**
Associacao Paulista de Cirurgioes Dentistas. Journal. (BL) **3228**
Associacao Paulista de Cirurgioes Dentistas. Revista. (BL ISSN 0004-5276) **3228**
Associacao Portuguesa de Bibliotecarios Arquivistas e Documentalistas. Noticia. (PO ISSN 0251-4141) **2745**
Associacao Portuguesa de Empresas Cinematograficas. Jornal. (PO) **3503, 4630**
Associaco "Omnium Cultural." Butlleti Interior Informatiu. (SP) **2217**
Associate Degree Education for Nursing.(US) **3276, 1700**
Associate Reformed Presbyterian. (US ISSN 0362-0816) **4229**
Associated Accounting Firms International Newsletter. (US) **747**
Associated Antique Dealers of America News *see* A A D A News **254**
Associated British Ports Handbook. (UK ISSN 0262-1630) **4724, 1122**
Associated British Ports Holdings PLC. Annual Report and Accounts. (UK) **4724**
Associated Builders & Contractors, Inc. Today *see* A B C Today **598**
Associated Chambers of Commerce and Industry of India Asso Cham Bulletin *see* Asso Cham Bulletin **807**
Associated Chambers of Commerce and Industry of India Asso Cham Parliamentary Digest *see* Asso Cham Parliamentary Digest **807**
Associated Chambers of Commerce and Industry of Malawi. Industrial and Trade Directory. (MW) **1122**
Associated Chambers of Commerce and Industry of Malawi. Newsletter. (MW) **807**
Associated Chambers of Commerce of Zimbabwe. Commerce. (RH) **807**
Associated Chinese Chamber of Commerce. Trade Directory. (MY) **807**
Associated Chinese Chambers of Commerce and Industry of Malaysia. Quarterly Magazine. (MY) **807**
Associated Church Press. Directory. (US ISSN 0066-8710) **1122, 4212**
Associated Church Press Newslog *see* A C P Newslog **4161**
Associated Colleges of Illinois. Report. (US ISSN 0066-8729) **1700**
Associated Court and Commercial Newspapers Bulletin *see* A C C N Bulletin **2566**
Associated Equipment Distributors. Rental Rates Compilation. (US ISSN 0164-0593) **600, 3016**
Associated Grocers of Colorado Inc. News *see* A G News **2090**
Associated Oregon Industries, Inc. Business Viewpoint *see* A O I Business Viewpoint **643**
Associated Public-Safety Communications Officers Inc. Bulletin *see* A P C O Bulletin **4096**
Associated Public Schools Systems. Yearbook. (US ISSN 0066-8753) **1725**
Associated Regional Accounting Firms Marketing Update *see* A R A F Marketing Update **744**
Associated Regional Accounting Firms Quarterly Report *see* A R A F Quarterly Report **744**
Associated School Boards of South Dakota Bulletin *see* A S B S D Bulletin **1724**

Associated Scientific and Technical Societies of South Africa. Annual Proceedings. (SA ISSN 0373-4250) **4300, 4594**
Associated Society of Locomotive Engineers and Firemen. Annual Report and Balance Sheet. (UK) **4707**
Associated Students of the California Institute of Technology California Tech *see* California Tech **1306**
Associated Western Universities. Program Guide. (US) **1700**
Associated Western Universities. Program Report *see* Associated Western Universities. Program Guide **1700**
Associated Writing Programs Award for Creative Nonfiction. (US) **2896**
Associated Writing Programs Chronicle *see* A W P Chronicle **2566**
Associatie Memoriaal. (NE) **1616**
Association Aeronautique et Astronautique de France. Annuaire *see* Aeronautique et l'Astronautique **43**
Association Belge de Documentation. Cahiers de la Documentation. (BE ISSN 0007-9804) **2745**
Association Belge pour l'Etude, l'Essai et l'Emploi des Materiaux. Publication A.B.E.M. (BE ISSN 0066-8796) **1915**
Association Belge pour l'Etude, l'Essai et l'Emploi des Materiaux. Proces Verbal de l'Assemblee Generale Ordinaire. (BE ISSN 0066-8818) **1915**
Association Canadienne d'Education. Bulletin. (CN ISSN 0004-5306) **1616**
Association Canadienne d'Education de Langue Francaise. Revue *see* Education et Francophonie **1628**
Association Canadienne de Justice Penale. Bulletin. *see* Canadian Criminal Justice Association. Bulletin **1511**
Association Canadienne des Dietetistes. Revue. *see* Canadian Dietetic Association. Journal **3604**
Association Canadienne des Eaux Potables et Usees. Bulletin. *see* Canadian Water and Wastewater Association. Bulletin **4822**
Association Canadienne des Educateurs des Deficients Auditifs. Revue. *see* A C E H I Journal **2285**
Association Canadienne des Etudes Africaines. Bulletin. *see* Canadian Association of African Studies. Newsletter **1702**
Association Canadienne des Radiologistes. Journal. *see* Canadian Association of Radiologists. Journal **3357**
Association Canadienne des Technologistes de Laboratoire. Bulletin. *see* Canadian Society of Laboratory Technologists. Bulletin **3258**
Association Canadienne du Marketing Direct. Communicator *see* Direct Marketing Communicator **1037**
Association Canadienne-Francaise pour l'Avancement des Sciences. Annales. (CN ISSN 0066-8842) **4300**
Association Canadienne-Francaise pour l'Avancement des Sciences. Cahiers Scientifiques. (CN) **4300**
Association Canadienne-Francaise pour l'Avancement des Sciences. Interface.(CN ISSN 0826-4864) **4300**
Association Canadienne pour la Sante Mentale. Rapport Annuel. *see* Canadian Mental Health Association. Annual Report **4015**
Association Contact. (US) **1616**
Association d'Art des Universites du Canada. Journal. *see* Universities Art Association of Canada. Journal **348**
Association Dahomeene de Geographie. Bulletin de Liaison. (DM) **2242**
Association de Geographes Francais. Bulletin. (FR ISSN 0004-5322) **2242**

Association de l'Ecole Nationale Superieure des Bibliothecaires. Annuaire. (FR ISSN 0066-8877) **2745**
Association de l'Ecole Nationale Superieure des Bibliothecaires. Infos. (FR ISSN 0992-6801) **2745**
Association de la Construction de Montreal et du Quebec. Bulletin. (CN ISSN 0833-8388) **600**
Association de la Construction de Montreal et du Quebec. Nouvelles *see* Association de la Construction de Montreal et du Quebec. Bulletin **600**
Association de Recherche Poetique en Auvergne Cahiers de Recherche Poetique *see* A R P A Cahiers de Recherche Poetique **2986**
Association Dentaire Canadienne. Journal. *see* Canadian Dental Association. Journal **3229**
Association des Amis d'Alfred de Vigny. Bulletin. (FR ISSN 0066-8893) **2896**
Association des Amis de Pierre Teilhard de Chardin. Bulletin. (FR ISSN 0066-8907) **4163**
Association des Anatomistes. Bulletin. (FR ISSN 0066-8915) **3079, 429**
Association des Anciens Eleves de l'Ecole d'Ingenieurs de Geneve. Bulletin Technique. (SZ) **1815**
Association des Anciens Eleves des Ecoles Techniques Superieures de Geneve. Bulletin Technique *see* Association des Anciens Eleves de l'Ecole d'Ingenieurs de Geneve. Bulletin Technique **1815**
Association des Banques du Liban. Bilans des Banques. (LE) **759**
Association des Banques du Liban. Rapport Annuel *see* Association des Banques du Liban. Rapport du Conseil **844**
Association des Banques du Liban. Rapport du Conseil. (LE) **844**
Association des Bibliothecaires Francais. Bulletin d'Informations. (FR ISSN 0004-5365) **4120**
Association des Bibliotheques Ecclesiastiques de France. Bulletin de Liaison. (FR ISSN 0066-8958) **2745**
Association des Colleges du Quebec Annuaire. (CN ISSN 0228-7730) **1616**
Association des Comptables. Bulletin. (FR) **747**
Association des Eleves et Anciens Eleves de l'Ecole Nationale Superieure des Postes et Telecomunications. Cahiers d'Etudes et d'Information. (FR) **1352**
Association des Enseignantes et des Enseignants Francophones du Nouveau-Brunswick. Nouvelles. (CN) **1616**
Association des Entrepreneurs en Construction du Quebec Chantiers *see* A E C Q Chantiers **599**
Association des Ingenieurs et Techniciens Africains de Cote d'Ivoire. Annuaire. (IV) **1815**
Association des Institutions d'Enseignement Secondaire. Annuaire. (CN ISSN 0066-8990) **1616**
Association des Journalistes Agricoles. Annuaire. (FR) **77, 2567**
Association des Medecins de Langue Francaise du Canada. Bulletin. (CN ISSN 0004-539X) **3079**
Association des Medecins Israelites de France. Revue Medicale *see* J A M I F **3112**
Association des Medicins du Canada. Journal. *see* Canadian Medical Association Journal **3086**
Association des Naturalistes du Mali. Bulletin. (ML) **3289**
Association des Sages-Femmes de la Maternite de Nancy. Bulletin. (FR) **3289**
Association des Societes et Fonds Francais d'Investissement. Annuaire. (FR ISSN 0066-9008) **938**

Association des Traducteurs et Interpretes de l'Ontario. InformATIO/ Association of Translators and Interpreters of Ontario. InformATIO. (CN ISSN 0381-5781) **2804**
Association des Traducteurs et Interpretes de l'Ontario. Repertoire/ Association of Translators and Interpreters of Ontario. Directory. (CN ISSN 0066-9016) **2804**
Association Education Director. (US) **1003, 1682**
†Association Europeenne de Management et de Marketing Financiers. Bank and Management. (FR) **5140**
Association Europeenne des Graveurs et des Flexographes. Bulletin Professional. (GW) **3997**
Association Finlandaise de Linguistique Appliquee Fin L A Yearbook *see* A Fin L A Yearbook **2799**
Association for Advancement of Behavior Therapy. Newsletter *see* Behavior Therapist **4013**
Association for Applied Psychophysiology and Biofeedback. Proceedings of the Annual Meeting. (US) **4012, 3331**
Association for Asian Studies. Committee on East Asian Libraries. Bulletin. (US ISSN 0148-6225) **2745**
Association for Asian Studies. Monographs, Occasional Papers and Reference Series. (US) **2336**
Association for Asian Studies. Newsletter *see* Asian Studies Newsletter **3634**
Association for Asian Studies. Southeast Conference. Annals. (US ISSN 0883-8909) **3634**
Association for Astrological Networking Newsletter *see* A F A N Newsletter **357**
Association for Astronomy Education News *see* A A E News **359**
Association for Behavior Analysis Newsletter *see* A B A Newsletter **4007**
Association for Business Communication. Bulletin. (US ISSN 8756-1972) **1003, 1332**
Association for Canadian Studies Newsletter *see* A C S Newsletter **2501**
Association for Canadian Theatre History. Newsletter *see* Association for Canadian Theatre Research. Newsletter **4630**
Association for Canadian Theatre Research. Newsletter. (CN) **4630**
Association for Child Psychoanalysis. Newsletter. (US) **1232, 3331, 4012**
Association for Children with Retarded Mental Development Record *see* A C R M D on the Record **1733**
Association for Commonwealth Literature and Language Studies. Bulletin. (Il ISSN 0066-9083) **2896, 2804**
Association for Communication Administration Bulletin *see* A C A Bulletin **1331**
Association for Community Based Education Report *see* C B E Report **1619**
Association for Computers and the Humanities Newsletter *see* A C H Newsletter **2520**
Association for Computing Machinery. Communications. (US ISSN 0001-0782) **1446**
Association for Computing Machinery. Computer Service. (US) **3016**
Association for Computing Machinery. Conference Proceedings. (US) **3016**
Association for Computing Machinery. Journal. (US ISSN 0004-5411) **1389**
†Association for Computing Machinery. Proceedings of National Conference. (US ISSN 0066-9091) **5140**
Association for Computing Machinery. Special Interest Group for Business Processing and Management. Conference Proceedings. (US) **1443**

Association for Computing Machinery Ada Letters see A C M Ada Letters 1388

Association for Computing Machinery Monograph Series see A C M Monograph Series 1388

Association for Contemporary Iberian Studies see A C I S 2346

Association for Continuing Higher Education. Newsletter see Five Minutes with A C H E 1683

Association for Continuing Higher Education. Proceedings. (US) 1700

Association for Direct Instruction News see A D I News 1743

Association for Education and Rehabilitation of the Blind and Visually Impaired (AER) Report see A E R Report 2290

Association for Educational and Training Technology Journal - E T T I see A E T T Journal - E T T I 1743

†Association for Educational Data Systems. Annual Convention Proceedings. (US ISSN 0147-9296) 5140

Association for Fitness in Business Action see A F B Action 3798

Association for Gerontology in Higher Education Exchange see A G H E Exchange 2269

▼Association for Global Strategic Information. Journal. (A G S I) (UK ISSN 0965-4380) 804

Association for Gravestone Studies. Newsletter. (US ISSN 0146-5783) 318, 235, 2144

Association for Humanistic Psychology Perspective see A H P Perspective 4007

Association for Information Management Career Exchange Clearinghouse see A I M Career Exchange Clearinghouse 3624

Association for Information Management Network see A I M Network 1000

Association for Integrative Studies (Oxford) Newsletter see A I S Newsletter 1613

Association for Intercollegiate Athletics for Women Handbook - Directory see A I A W Handbook - Directory 5128

Association for International Practical Training Report see A I P T Report 1721

Association for Investment Management and Research. Seminar Proceedings. (US) 759

Association for Investment Management and Research Newsletter see A I M R Newsletter 758

Association for Jewish Studies Review see A J S Review 1988

Association for Library and Information Science Education. Directory. (US ISSN 0748-5786) 2745

Association for Media-Based Continuing Education for Engineers Monitor see A M C E E Monitor 5128

Association for Past-Life Research and Therapy. Newsletter. (US ISSN 1054-0792) 4012

Association for Persons with Severe Handicaps. Journal. (US) 2283

Association for Persons with Severe Handicaps. Newsletter. (US) 2283

Association for Population - Family Planning Library & Information Center International Communicator see A P L I C Communicator 2740

Association for Preservation Technology. Bulletin see Association for Preservation Technology International. Bulletin 295

Association for Preservation Technology Communique see A P T Communique 1482

Association for Preservation Technology International. Bulletin. (US) 295

Association for Professional Education for Ministry. Report of the Biennial Meeting. (US) 4163, 1700

Association for Psychoanalytic Medicine. Bulletin. (US ISSN 0004-542X) 4012, 3079

Association for Quality and Participation. Annual Conference and Resource Mart Transactions. (US) 1003, 972

Association for Quality and Participation Report see A Q P Report 1001

Association for Recorded Sound Collections, Inc. Journal see A R S C Journal 4459

Association for Recorded Sound Collections, Inc. Newsletter see A R S C Newsletter 4459

Association for Research in Growth Relationships Journal see A R G R Journal 4008

Association for Research in Nervous and Mental Disease. Research Publications. (US ISSN 0091-7443) 3331

Association for Retarded Citizens see A R C 4396

Association for Rural Advancement Advice Sheet see A F R A Advice Sheet 3939

Association for Rural Advancement Newsletter see A F R A Newsletter 3939

Association for Rural Advancement Special Reports see A F R A Special Reports 3939

Association for School, College and University Staffing, Inc. Annual - A Job Search Handbook for Educators see A S C U S Annual - A Job Search Handbook for Educators 1724

Association for School, College and University Staffing, Inc. Directory of Membership and Subject Field Index see A S C U S Directory of Membership and Subject Field Index 1724

Association for School, College and University Staffing, Inc. Staffer see A S C U S Staffer 1692

Association for Services Management International International see A F S M International 1423

Association for Social Anthropology in Oceania. Monograph Series. (US ISSN 0066-9172) 235

Association for Social Work Education in Africa. Bulletin see A S W E A Journal for Social Work Education in Africa 4397

Association for Social Work Education in Africa Journal for Social Work Education in Africa see A S W E A Journal for Social Work Education in Africa 4397

Association for Supervision and Curriculum Development. Curriculum Materials see Association for Supervision and Curriculum Development. Curriculum Materials Digest 1744

Association for Supervision and Curriculum Development. Curriculum Materials Digest. (US) 1744

Association for Supervision and Curriculum Development. Yearbook. (US ISSN 0066-9199) 1744

Association for Technology in Music Instruction Newsletter. (US) 3589

Association for Technology in Music Instruction Technology Directory see A T M I Technology Directory 3589

Association for the Advancement of Agricultural Sciences in Africa. Journal see African Journal of Agricultural Sciences 68

Association for the Advancement of Agricultural Sciences in Africa Newsletter see A A A S A Newsletter 67

Association for the Advancement of Automotive Medicine. Proceedings. (US ISSN 0892-6484) 3079, 4679

Association for the Advancement of Baltic Studies Newsletter see A A B S Newsletter 2346

Association for the Advancement of Medical Instrumentation Annual Meeting. Proceedings. see A A M I Annual Meeting. Proceedings 3068

Association for the Advancement of Medical Instrumentation News see A A M I News 2521

Association for the Care of Children's Health. Journal see Children's Health Care Journal 4402

Association for the Care of Children's Health Network see A C C H Network 3317

Association for the Development of Computer-Based Instructional Systems Newsletter see A D C I S Newsletter 1416

Association for the Development of Religious Information Services Newsletter see A D R I S Newsletter 4161

Association for the Help of Retarded Children Chronicle see A H R C Chronicle 3327

Association for the Preservation of Virginia Antiquities Newsletter see A P V A Newsletter 2397

Association for the Sociology of Religion. News and Announcements. (US) 4429

Association for the Study of Dreams Newsletter see A S D Newsletter 4008

Association for the Study of Higher Education (College Station) Notes see A S H E Notes 1699

Association for the Study of Higher Education Higher Education Report Series see A S H E - E R I C Higher Education Report Series 1698

Association for the Study of Play Newsletter. (US) 4012, 235, 4366, 4464

Association for the Study of Reptilia and Amphibia Journal see A S R A Journal 575

Association for the Study of the World Refugee Problems Bulletin see A W R Bulletin 3949

Association for Transpersonal Development. Newsletter see Association for Transpersonal Psychology. Newsletter 4012

Association for Transpersonal Psychology. Newsletter. (US) 4012

Association for Unity, Research and Awareness Newsletter see A U R A Newsletter 3593

Association for Voluntary Surgical Contraception, Inc. News see A V S C News 595

Association for Women in Mathematics. Newsletter. (US) 4837, 3030

Association for Women in Science. Newsletter see A W I S Magazine 4836

Association for Women in Science Magazine see A W I S Magazine 4836

Association Francaise d'Amitie et de Solidarite avec les Peuples d'Afrique. Bulletin d'Information see Aujourd'hui l'Afrique 3874

Association Francaise de Robotique Industrielle Liaison see A F R I Liaison 1406

Association Francaise des Amis d'Albert Schweitzer. Cahiers. (FR ISSN 0153-6133) 3762, 4398

Association Francaise des Experts de la Cooperation Technique Internationale. Annuaire. (FR ISSN 0066-9288) 4594

Association Francaise des Ingenieures et Techniciens de l'Aeronautique et de l'Espace. Annuaire see Aeronautique et l'Astronautique 43

Association Francaise des Ingenieurs du Caoutchouc et des Plastiques. Annuaire see Association Francaise des Ingenieurs et Cadres du Caoutchouc et des Plastiques. Annuaire 4291

Association Francaise des Ingenieurs et Cadres du Caoutchouc et des Plastiques. Annuaire. (FR) 4291, 3861

Association Francaise des Techniciens et Ingenieurs de Securite et des Medecins du Travail. Annuaire. (FR ISSN 0066-927X) 3615

Association Francaise pour l'Etude du Quaternaire. Bulletin see Quaternaire 1578

Association Francaise pour l'Etude du Sol. Science du Sol. Bulletin. (FR ISSN 0335-1653) 169

Association Francaise pour les Recherches et Etudes Camerounaises. Bulletin see Office National de Recherches Scientifiques du Cameroun. Recherches et Etudes Camerounaises 246

Association Generale des Conservateurs de Musees et Collections Publiques de France. Annuaire. (FR) 3522

Association Generale des Medecins de France. Bulletin. (FR ISSN 0004-5519) 3079

Association Guillaume Bude. Bulletin. (FR ISSN 0004-5527) 2804

Association Internationale d'Etudes du Sud-Est Europeen. Bulletin. (RM ISSN 0004-5551) 2350, 318, 2896, 4429

Association Internationale d'Etudes Patristiques. Bulletin d'Information et de Liaison. (IT) 4163, 2307

Association Internationale d'Histoire des Telecommunications et de l'Informatique. Bulletin. (FR) 1332

Association Internationale d'Orientation Scolaire et Professionelle Educational and Vocational Guidance - Bulletin A I O S P, I A E V G, I V S B B see Educational and Vocational Guidance - Bulletin A I O S P, I A E V G, I V S B B 3626

Association Internationale de Critiques d'Art Recherche Centre Bulletin see A I C A R C Bulletin 310

Association Internationale de Linguistique Appliquee Bulletin see A I L A Bulletin 2799

Association Internationale de Signalisation Maritime Bulletin see A I S M. Bulletin 4723

Association Internationale des Numismates Professionels. Bulletin-Circular. (FR ISSN 0004-5543) 3598

Association Internationale du Droit Commercial. Et du Droit Affaires. Groupe Francais. Travaux see International Law Association. Reports of Conferences 2725

Association Internationale du Film d'Animation News see A S I F A News 3503

Association Internationale Permanente des Congres de la Route. Bulletin see Routes - Roads 1873

Association Internationale pour l'Histoire du Verre. Bulletin. (NE ISSN 0447-9823) 1161

Association: Journal of Texas Osteopathic Medical Association see Texas D O 3156

Association Leader (Montvale). (US) 747

†Association Leader (Washington). (US) 5140

Association Management. (US ISSN 0004-5578) 1003

†Association Management. (UK ISSN 0144-9613) 5140

Association Marketing Roundtable Newsletter see A M R Newsletter 1032

Association Meetings. (US ISSN 1042-3141) 3391

Association Men see Yuvak 4211

Association Nationale d'Etude et de Lutte Contre les Fleaux Atmospheriques. Rapport de Campagne. (FR ISSN 0242-4002) 3432

Association Nationale des Communautes Educatives. Bulletin Hebdomadaire d'Informations. (FR) 1616

Association Nationale des Communautes Educatives. Bulletin Mensuel d'Informations. (FR) 1616

Association Nationale des Entreprises du Zaire. Circulaire d'Information. (ZR) 807

Association Nationale des Entreprises Zairoises. Circulaire d'Information see Association Nationale des Entreprises du Zaire. Circulaire d'Information 807

ASSOCIATION

Association of Advanced Rabbinical and Talmudic Schools. Accreditation Commission. Handbook. (US) **1700**, 1992

†Association of Adventist Forums Newsletter. (US) **5140**

Association of African Universities. Information Bulletin see A A U Newsletter **1698**

Association of African Universities. New Acquisitions List. (GH) **2745**, 1700

Association of African Universities. Report of the General Conference. (GH) **1700**

Association of African Universities Newsletter see A A U Newsletter **1698**

Association of American Feed Control Officials. Official Publication. (US) **205**

Association of American Geographers. Annals. (US ISSN 0004-5608) **2242**

†Association of American Geographers. Directory. (US) **5140**

Association of American Geographers. Handbook-Directory see Association of American Geographers. Directory **5140**

Association of American Geographers Newsletter see A A G Newsletter **2240**

Association of American Indian Physicians Newsletter. (US) **3079**

Association of American Law Schools. Newsletter. (US) **2601**, 1616

Association of American Law Schools. Proceedings. (US ISSN 0066-9407) **2601**

Association of American Medical Colleges Curriculum Directory see A A M C Curriculum Directory **1742**

Association of American Medical Colleges Directory of American Medical Education see A A M C Directory of American Medical Education **1724**

Association of American Pesticide Control Officials. Official Publication. (US ISSN 0066-9431) **169**

Association of American Physicians. Transactions. (US ISSN 0066-9458) **3079**

Association of American Physicians & Surgeons, Inc. News see A A P S News **3068**

Association of American Plant Food Control Officials. Official Publication. (US ISSN 0094-8764) **169**

Association of American Publishers. Annual Report. (US ISSN 0276-5349) **4121**

Association of American Publishers. Exhibits Directory. (US ISSN 0147-0310) **4121**

†Association of American Railroads. Data Systems Division. Papers. (US) **5140**

Association of American University Presses Directory. (US ISSN 0739-3024) **4121**

Association of Americans and Canadians in Israel. Central Region. Newsletter. (IS) **2203**

Association of Americans and Canadians North see A A C I North **2203**

Association of Art Historians. Bulletin. (UK ISSN 0307-9163) **318**

Association of Asphalt Paving Technologists. Proceedings. (US ISSN 0066-9466) **1862**

Association of Attenders and Alumni of the Hague Academy of International Law. Yearbook. (NE ISSN 0066-8923) **2719**

Association of Australasian Palaeontologists. Memoirs. (AT ISSN 0810-8889) **3656**

Association of Avian Veterinarians. Journal. (US ISSN 0892-9904) **4806**

Association of Banyan Users International Network News see A B U I Network News **1426**

Association of Birth Defect Children Newsletter. (US) **1733**, 1502

Association of Black Psychologists Newsletter see Psych Discourse **4039**

Association of Bridal Consultants Dialogue see A B C Dialogue **3066**

Association of British Oceanic Industries Catalogue see A B O I Catalogue **4723**

Association of British Theological and Philosophical Libraries. Bulletin. (UK ISSN 0305-781X) **2745**, 3762, 4163

Association of Canadian Archivists Bulletin see A C A Bulletin **2305**

†Association of Canadian Community Colleges. Journal. (CN ISSN 0702-5378) **5140**

Association of Canadian Community Colleges Community see A C C C Community **1698**

Association of Canadian Community Colleges International see A C C C International **925**

Association of Canadian Educators of the Hearing Impaired Journal see A C E H I Journal **2285**

Association of Canadian Faculties of Dentistry. Newsletter see A C F D Forum **3226**

Association of Canadian Faculties of Dentistry Forum see A C F D Forum **3226**

Association of Canadian Map Libraries. Annual Conference Proceedings see Association of Canadian Map Libraries and Archives. Bulletin **2242**

Association of Canadian Map Libraries. Bulletin see Association of Canadian Map Libraries and Archives. Bulletin **2242**

Association of Canadian Map Libraries and Archives. Bulletin. (CN ISSN 0840-9331) **2242**

Association of Canadian Medical Colleges Forum see A C M C Forum **3068**

Association of Caribbean Studies. Abstracts. (US) **2327**

Association of Caribbean University Research and Institutional Libraries. Carta Informativa de A C U R I L/A C U R I L Newsletter. (PR) **2745**

Association of Children's Prosthetic-Orthotic Clinics. Journal. (US ISSN 0884-8424) **3079**

Association of Clinical Biochemists. News Sheet. (UK ISSN 0141-8912) **471**

Association of College and University Concert Managers. Bulletin see Association of Performing Arts Presenters Bulletin **4630**

Association of College Honor Societies, Booklet of Information. (US) **1304**

Association of College Unions - International. Bulletin. (US ISSN 0004-5659) **1616**, 1304

Association of College Unions - International. Directory. (US) **1700**

Association of College Unions - International. Proceedings of the Annual Conference. (US ISSN 0147-1120) **1700**

Association of College Unions - International. Union Wire. (US ISSN 0004-5667) **1616**

Association of Colleges for Further and Higher Education. Handbook. (UK) **1700**, 1682

Association of Colleges for Further and Higher Education. Year Book see Association of Colleges for Further and Higher Education. Handbook **1700**

Association of Collegiate Entrepreneurs Action Newsletter see A C E Action Newsletter **1113**

Association of Collegiate Schools of Architecture. Proceedings of the Annual Meeting. (US ISSN 0194-410X) **295**

Association of Collegiate Schools of Architecture, Inc. Faculty Directory see A C S A Faculty Directory **291**

Association of Collegiate Schools of Architecture, Inc. News see A C S A News **291**

Association of Commonwealth Universities. Annual Report of the Council Together with the Accounts of the Association. (UK ISSN 0307-2274) **1700**

Association of Commonwealth Universities. Report of the Council Together with the Accounts of the Association see Association of Commonwealth Universities. Annual Report of the Council Together with the Accounts of the Association **1700**

Association of Commonwealth Universities Bulletin of Current Documentation (ABCD) see A C U Bulletin of Current Documentation (ABCD) **1698**

Association of Consulting Engineers of Canada. Directory of Member Firms and Their Services. (CN) **1815**

†Association of Consulting Engineers Who's Who & Year Book. (UK) **5140**

Association of Contemporary Historians. Bulletin. (UK) **2307**

Association of County Commissioners County Comment see S D A C C County Comment **4073**

Association of County Councils. Yearbook. (UK ISSN 0305-2044) **4054**

Association of Data Processing and Service Organizations The Computer Software and Services Industry Association. Salary Study see A D A S P O, The Computer Software and Services Industry Association. Salary Study **1475**

Association of Data Processing and Service Organizations The Computer Software and Services Industry Association. Technology Papers see A D A S P O, The Computer Software and Services Industry Association. Technology Papers **1475**

Association of Data Processing Service Organizations Data see A D A P S O Data **1448**

Association of Departments and Administrators in Speech Communication. Bulletin see A C A Bulletin **1331**

Association of Departments of English Bulletin see A D E Bulletin **2890**

Association of Departments of Foreign Languages Bulletin see A D F L Bulletin **2799**

Association of Development Agencies in Bangladesh Grassroots see Grassroots **4406**

Association of Economic Geographers. Annals. (JA ISSN 0004-5683) **646**

Association of Energy Engineers Energy Insight see A E E Energy Insight **1783**

Association of Engineering Geologists. Bulletin. (US ISSN 0004-5691) **1555**

Association of Engineering Geologists. Special Publications. (US) **1555**

Association of Engineering Geologists News see A E G News **1552**

Association of Engineers, India. Journal. (II ISSN 0044-9598) **1815**

Association of Engineers, Kerala P.W.D. News Letter. (II) **1815**

Association of Exploration Geochemists. Special Publications. (CN) **1541**

Association of Faculties of Agriculture in Africa Newsletter see A F A A Newsletter **67**

Association of Faculties of Pharmacy of Canada. Proceedings. (CN ISSN 0066-9555) **3718**

Association of Federal Investigators Report see A F I Report **2593**

Association of Food and Drug Officials. Journal. (US) **2062**, 2601

Association of Food and Drug Officials Quarterly Bulletin see Association of Food and Drug Officials. Journal **2062**

Association of Football Statisticians. Annual. (UK ISSN 0263-0354) **4499**

†Association of Free Community Papers. News Bulletin. (US) **5140**

Association of Gay and Lesbian Psychiatrists. Newsletter. (US) **2451**, 4398

Association of Governing Boards of Universities and Colleges Notes see A G B Notes **1698**

Association of Governing Boards of Universities and Colleges Reports see A G B Reports **1698**

Association of Hispanic Arts Hispanic Arts News see A H A! Hispanic Arts News **309**

Association of History Teachers in Nigeria. (NR) **1744**, 2331

▼Association of Home Appliance Manufacturers. Green Report. (US) **1943**, 2556

Association of Home Appliance Manufacturers. M A C A P Statistical Report. (Major Appliance Consumer Action Panel) (US) **2556**, 1072

Association of Home Appliance Manufacturers. Trends and Forecasts.(US) **1072**

Association of Home Appliance Manufacturers Major Appliance Factory Shipment Report see A H A M Major Appliance Factory Shipment Report **2556**

Association of Home Appliance Manufacturers Major Appliance Industry Facts Book (Year) see A H A M Major Appliance Industry Facts Book (Year) **2556**

Association of Human Resource Systems Professionals. Conference Highlights. (US) **1057**, 3391

Association of Human Resource Systems Professionals Review see H R S P Review **1065**

Association of Incentive Marketing Newsletter - Incentive Report see A I M Newsletter - Incentive Report **1032**

Association of Independent Museums Bulletin. (UK ISSN 0142-887X) **3522**

Association of Independent Television Stations, Inc. Newsletter see I N T V Newsletter **1374**

Association of Indian Engineering Industry. Handbook of Statistics see Confederation of Indian Industry. Handbook of Statistics **1842**

Association of Industry Manufacturers Representatives News see A I M - R News **1071**

Association of Information and Dissemination Centers Newsletter see A S I D I C Newsletter **2740**

Association of Information Systems Professionals Dialogue see A I S P Dialogue **5128**

Association of Insolvency Accountants Newsletter. (US) **747**

Association of Institutes for European Studies. Annuaire. (SZ ISSN 0571-6322) **2350**

Association of Institutes for European Studies. Year-Book. (SZ ISSN 0571-6330) **2350**

Association of International Colleges & Universities Directory. (US) **1700**, 1721

Association of International Colleges & Universities Newsletter. (US) **1700**, 1721

Association of International Education Administrators. Journal see International Education Forum **1728**

Association of International Management Consultants Forum see A I M C Forum **1000**

Association of Interpretive Naturalists, Inc. News see A I N News **5128**

Association of Iron and Steel Engineers. A I S E Proceedings see A I S E Yearbook **3401**

Association of Iron and Steel Engineers Yearbook see A I S E Yearbook **3401**

Association of Island Marine Laboratories of the Caribbean. Proceedings see Association of Marine Laboratories of the Caribbean. Proceedings **1602**

Association of Japanese Geographers. Special Publication. (JA ISSN 0066-958X) **2242**

Association of Jesuit Colleges and Universities and Jesuit Secondary Education Association Directory. (US ISSN 1053-8941) **1700**, 4256

Association of Jesuit Colleges and Universities Higher Education Report see A J C U Higher Education Report **1698**

Association of Jewish Libraries Newsletter see A J L Newsletter **2740**

Association of Jewish Sponsored Camps. Camp Directory. (US) **4541**, 1992

Association of Law Teachers. Journal see Law Teacher **2646**

Association of Learned and Professional Society Publishers Learned Publishing: A L P S P Bulletin see Learned Publishing: A L P S P Bulletin **4131**

Association of Libertarian Feminists Newsletter see A L F Newsletter **3869**

Association of Life Insurance Medical Directors of America. Transactions. (US ISSN 0066-9598) **2527**, 3079

Association of Lunar and Planetary Observers. Journal. (US ISSN 0039-2502) **360**

Association of M B A Address Book. (UK) **1003**

Association of Manitoba Archivists Newsletter see A M A Newsletter **2740**

Association of Manitoba Museums. Newsletter. (CN ISSN 0849-5858) **3522**

Association of Marine Laboratories of the Caribbean. Newsletter. (PR) **1602**, 429, 1170, 1555

Association of Marine Laboratories of the Caribbean. Proceedings. (PR) **1602**, 429, 1170, 1555

Association of Medical and Veterinary Technologists of Nigeria. Newsletter see Nigerian Journal of Medical Laboratory Technology **3262**

Association of Medical Illustrators News see A M I News **3068**

Association of Medical Rehabilitation Administrators. Journal. (US) **3079**

Association of Medical Rehabilitation Administrators. Newsletter. (US) **3079**

Association of Medical Rehabilitation Directors and Coordinators. Quarterly Bulletin see Association of Medical Rehabilitation Administrators. Journal **3079**

Association of Medical Technologists Chronicle see A M T Chronicle **3256**

Association of Medical Women in India. Journal. (II) **4835**, 3276, 4837

Association of Mental Health Administrators. Newsletter. (US) **4098**, 4398

Association of Midwest Fish and Wildlife Agencies. Proceedings. (US) **1483**

Association of Midwest Fish and Wildlife Commissioners. Proceedings see Association of Midwest Fish and Wildlife Agencies. Proceedings **1483**

Association of Military Dermatologists. Bulletin see Association of Military Dermatologists. Journal **3246**

Association of Military Dermatologists. Journal. (US ISSN 0360-4020) **3246**

Association of Municipal Electricity Undertakings of South Africa. Proceedings of Convention. (SA) **1882**

Association of Muslim Social Scientists Newsbulletin see A M S S - I I I T Newsbulletin **4217**

Association of National Health Service Supplies Officers. Reference Book & Buyer's Guide. (UK ISSN 0140-4563) **4098**

Association of New Brunswick Land Surveyors. Annual Report. (CN ISSN 0318-2126) **4145**

Association of New Jersey Environmental Commissions Report see A N J E C Report **1482**

Association of Newfoundland Labrador Archivists Bulletin see A N L A Bulletin **2740**

Association of Newspaper Classified Advertising Managers Exchanges. (US) **28**, 1003, 1332

Association of North American Radio Clubs Newsletter see A N A R C Newsletter **5128**

Association of Nova Scotia Land Surveyors see Nova Scotian Surveyor **1872**

Association of Nurses in A I D S Care. Journal. (US ISSN 1055-3290) **3218**, 3276

Association of Nurses in Substance Abuse Journal see A N S A Journal **3275**

Association of Obedience Clubs and Judges. Newsletter. (US) **3708**

Association of Official Analytical Chemists. Journal see A O A C International Journal **1203**

Association of Official Analytical Chemists. Official Methods of Analysis see A O A C International. Official Methods of Analysis **1203**

Association of Official Seed Analysts. News Letter. (US ISSN 0004-5764) **495**, 77

Association of Official Seed Certifying Agencies. Production Publication see Association of Official Seed Certifying Agencies. Report of Acres Applied for Certification by Seed Certifying Agencies **169**

Association of Official Seed Certifying Agencies. Report of Acres Applied for Certification by Seed Certifying Agencies. (US) **169**

Association of Ontario Land Surveyors. Annual Report. (CN ISSN 0700-5989) **1862**

Association of Operating Room Nurses, Inc. Journal see A O R N Journal **3275**

Association of Operative Millers. Bulletin.(US) **205**

Association of Orthodox Jewish Teachers News see A O J T News **1613**

Association of Pacific Coast Geographers. Yearbook. (US ISSN 0066-9628) **2242**

Association of Part-Time Professionals. National Newsletter see Part-Time Professional **3630**

Association of Performing Arts Presenters Bulletin. (US) **4630**, 318, 3539

Association of Personal Assistants and Secretaries Ltd. News see A P A S News **2593**

Association of Photographers Awards see A.F.A.E.P. Awards **3788**

Association of Physical Plant Administrators of Universities and Colleges. Proceedings of the Annual Meeting. (US ISSN 0738-3835) **1725**, 1003, 1062, 1783

Association of Physical Plant Administrators of Universities and Colleges Newsletter see A P P A Newsletter **1724**

Association of Physicians of India. Journal. (II ISSN 0004-5772) **3079**

Association of Private Postal Systems. Directory. (US) **1352**, 4707

Association of Private Postal Systems. Update. (US) **1352**, 4707

Association of Professional Engineers of Trinidad and Tobago. Journal. (TR) **1815**

Association of Professional, Executive, Clerical and Computer Staff see A P E X **2579**

Association of Professional Foresters Newsletter see A P F Newsletter **2095**

Association of Professional Genealogists. List of Professional Genealogists and Related Services see Directory of Professional Genealogists **2149**

Association of Professional Genealogists Quarterly. (US) **2144**

Association of Professional Sleep Societies Newsletter see A P S S Newsletter **3327**

Association of Public Analysts. Journal. (UK ISSN 0004-5780) **1204**

Association of Public Data Users Newsletter see A P D U Newsletter **4561**

Association of Railroad Advertising and Marketing. Newsletter. (US) **28**, 1033, 4707

Association of Railroad Editors. Proof. (US) **4707**

Association of Railway Preservation Societies. Journal. (UK) **4707**

Association of Railway Preservation Societies Ltd. Information Papers see A R P S Information Papers **4707**

Association of Recognised English Language Schools Brochure see A R E L S - F E L C O Brochure **1613**

Association of Registered Nurses of Newfoundland Access see A R N N Access **3275**

Association of Rehabilitation Nurses News see A R N News **3275**

Association of Research Libraries see A R L **2740**

Association of Research Libraries. Office of Management Studies. Occasional Paper. (US) **2745**

Association of Research Libraries Minutes see A R L Minutes **2740**

Association of Retail Marketing Services Register see A R M S Register **1032**

Association of Russian - American Scholars in the U S A. Transactions/Zapiski. (US ISSN 0066-9717) **1992**

Association of School Business Officials Accents see A S B O Accents **1724**

Association of Science-Technology Centers Newsletter see A S T C Newsletter **3520**

Association of Scientific, Technical and Managerial Staffs Journal see A S T M S Journal **1001**

Association of Scientific Workers of India. Bulletin. (II ISSN 0970-8626) **2580**

Association of Simula Users Newsletter see A S U Newsletter **1429**

Association of Small Presses in Florida Newsletter see A S P I F Newsletter **4120**

Association of Small Public Libraries of Ontario Newsletter see A S P L O Newsletter **2740**

Association of Social Anthropologists of the Commonwealth Research Methods in Social Anthropology see A S A Research Methods in Social Anthropology **232**

Association of South-East Asian Nations American - A S E A N Trade Council. Bulletin see American - A S E A N Trade Council. Bulletin **899**

Association of Southeast Asian Institutions of Higher Learning. Handbook: Southeast Asian Institutions of Higher Learning. (TH ISSN 0066-9687) **1700**

Association of Southeast Asian Institutions of Higher Learning. Newsletter. (TH ISSN 0572-4325) **1700**

Association of Southeast Asian Institutions of Higher Learning Seminar Reports see A S A I H L Seminar Reports **1698**

Association of Southeast Asian Nations Briefing see A S E A N Briefing **842**

Association of Southeast Asian Nations Economic Bulletin see A S E A N Economic Bulletin **643**

Association of Southeastern Biologists, Inc. Bulletin see A S B Bulletin **424**

Association of Special Libraries of the Philippines Bulletin see A S L P Bulletin **2740**

Association of Sports Museums and Halls of Fame. Newsletter see I A S M H F Newsletter **3525**

Association of State Drinking Water Administrators Update see A S D W A Update **4821**

Association of Surgeons of East Africa. Proceedings. (ZA) **3376**, 1616

Association of Systematics Collections Newsletter (Washington) see A S C Newsletter (Washington) **3520**

Association of Talent Agents. Newsletter. (US) **4630**, 1003, 3257, 3503

†Association of Teacher Educators. Publications. (US) **5140**

Association of Teacher Educators Newsletter see A T E Newsletter **1613**

Association of Teachers of English as a Foreign Language. Bulletin. (AT ISSN 0310-608X) **1744**

Association of Teachers of Italian. Journal see Tuttitalia **2848**

Association of Teachers of Japanese. Journal. (US ISSN 0885-9884) **2804**, 1744

Association of Teachers of Japanese. Journal-Newsletter see Association of Teachers of Japanese. Journal **2804**

Association of Teachers of Printing and Allied Subjects Printing Education & Training Journal see A T P A S Printing Education & Training Journal **3997**

Association of Teachers of Russian. Newsletter. (UK ISSN 0306-7432) **2804**

Association of Teachers of Social Studies in the City of New York Bulletin see A T S S Bulletin **4364**

Association of the Bar of the City of New York. Record. (US ISSN 0004-5837) **2601**

Association of the Concrete Industry of Finland. Publication. see Suomen Betoniteollisuuden Keskusjarejesto. Julkaisuja **633**

†Association of the Wall and Ceiling Industries International. Bulletin. (US) **5140**

Association of Theological Schools in the United States and Canada. Bulletin. (US ISSN 0362-1472) **4163**

Association of Theological Schools in the United States and Canada. Directory. (US) **4163**, 1692

Association of Translators and Interpreters of Ontario. Directory. see Association des Traducteurs et Interpretes de l'Ontario. Repertoire **2804**

Association of Translators and Interpreters of Ontario. InformATIO. see Association des Traducteurs et Interpretes de l'Ontario. InformATIO **2804**

Association of Trial Lawyers of America Advocate see A T L A Advocate **2593**

Association of Trial Lawyers of America Law Reporter see A T L A Law Reporter **2593**

Association of University Evening Colleges. Newsletter see Five Minutes with A C H E **1683**

Association of University Evening Colleges. Proceedings see Association for Continuing Higher Education. Proceedings **1700**

Association of University Summer Sessions. Summary Report. (US ISSN 0066-975X) **1700**

Association of University Teachers Bulletin see A U T Bulletin **1699**

Association of Urban Authorities. Annual Bulletin. (MF ISSN 0304-6451) **4084**

Association of Visual Communicators Visions see A V C Visions **3503**

Association of Water Transportation Accounting Officers Annual Report see A W T A O Annual Report **745**

Association of Water Transportation Accounting Officers Bulletin see A W T A O Bulletin **745**

Association of Wine Suppliers. Bankruptcy Update. (US) **377**, 759

Association of Women's Clubs. News. (RH) **4837**

Association Pharmaceutique d'Israel. Journal. see Israel Pharmaceutical Journal **3730**

ASSOCIATION

Association pour l'Avancement des Sciences et des Techniques de la Documentation. Nouvelles de l'ASTED. (CN ISSN 0316-0963) **2745**
Association pour l'Avancement des Sciences et des Techniques de la Documentation. Rapport Annuel. (CN ISSN 0316-0955) **2745**
Association pour l'Etude des Problemes d'Outre Mer. Documentation-Developpement. (FR ISSN 0153-3657) **3951, 900**
Association pour l'Etude Taxonomique de la Flore d'Afrique Tropicale Index see A.E.T.F.A.T. Index **461**
Association pour le Developpement International de l'Observatoire de Nice. Bulletin. (FR ISSN 0249-7522) **360**
Association pour le Developpement International de l'Observatoire de Nice. Bulletin d'Information see Association pour le Developpement International de l'Observatoire de Nice. Bulletin **360**
Association Professionelle des Opticiens de Belgique. Bulletin d'Information Mensuel see Opto Magazine **3304**
Association Senegalaise pour l'Etude du Quaternaire Africain. Bulletin de Liaison. (SG) **2331, 3874**
Association Senegalaise pour l'Etude du Quaternaire de l'Ouest African. Bulletin de Liaison see Association Senegalaise pour l'Etude du Quaternaire Africain. Bulletin de Liaison **2331**
Association Suisse des Electriciens. Bulletin. (SZ ISSN 0004-587X) **1882**
Association Suisse des Geologues et Ingenieurs du Petrole. Bulletin. see Vereinigung Schweizerischer Petroleum-Geologen und -Ingenieure. Bulletin **3703**
Association Suisse pour l'Energie Atomique. Bulletin see Schweizerische Vereinigung fuer Atomenergie. Bulletin **1809**
Association Technique de Fonderie. Annuaire. (FR) **3402**
Association Technique de Fonderie. Bulletin Mensuel d'Information see Hommes et Fonderie **3408**
Association Technique de l'Importation Charbonniere. Annual Report. (FR) **3478**
Association Technique de l'Importation Charbonniere. Monthly Statistics. (FR) **3498**
Association Technique de l'Industrie Papetiere. Feuillets Bibliographiques. see Centre Technique du Papier. Feuillets Bibliographiques **3662**
Association Technique de l'Industrie Papetiere. Revue. (FR ISSN 0004-5896) **3662**
Association Technique Maritime et Aeronautique, Paris. Bulletin. (FR ISSN 0066-9814) **4724, 46**
Associations' Forum. (US) **938, 759, 1003**
Associations Report. (US ISSN 0744-1088) **1003, 3391**
Associations Transnationales. see Transnational Associations **3974**
▼Associations Yellow Book. (US ISSN 1054-4070) **1122**
Associazione degli Industriali della Provincia di Arezzo. Notiziario see Notiziario (Arezzo) **1082**
Associazione Elettrotecnica Ed Elettronica Italiana. Rendiconti della Riunione Annuale. (IT ISSN 0066-9822) **1882**
Associazione fra Mutilati e Invalidi di Guerra. Bollettino. (IT) **4398, 3452**
Associazione Genetica Italiana. Atti. (IT ISSN 0066-9830) **540**
Associazione Italiana Biblioteche. Bollettino d'Informazioni. (IT ISSN 0004-5934) **2745, 389**
†Associazione Italiana Biblioteche. Quaderni del Bollettino d'Informazioni.(IT ISSN 0519-2048) **5140**
Associazione Italiana Biblioteche Notizie see A I B Notizie **2740**

Associazione Italiana Creativa Comunicazione Visiva Quaderni see A I A P Quaderni **25**
Associazione Italiana di Cartografia. A I C Bollettino. (IT ISSN 0044-9733) **2242**
Associazione Italiana Industriali Tintori, Stampatori e Finitori Tessili. Notiziario see Associazione Nobilitazione Tessile. Notiziario **4616**
Associazione Italiana Ingegneri del Traffico. Bolletino. (IT) **4707**
Associazione Italiana Laringectomizzati. Atti (del) Convegno Nazionale. (IT ISSN 0066-9865) **3313**
Associazione Italiana Societa Concessionarie Autostrade e Trafori Informazioni see A I S C A T Informazioni **4717**
Associazione Italiana Veterinari per Piccoli Animali. Bollettino. (IT ISSN 0004-5977) **4806**
Associazione Medici Dentisti Italiani Bollettino see A M D I Bollettino **3227**
Associazione Nazionale Autoservizi in Concessione. Informa. (IT) **4707**
Associazione Nazionale degli Industriali dei Laterizi Annuario A N D I L (Year) see Annuario A N D I L (Year) **1161**
Associazione Nazionale Docenti Informatica Giuridica see A N D I G **2593**
Associazione Nazionale Ex Internati. Bollettino Ufficiale. (IT ISSN 0004-5985) **3874**
Associazione Nazionale fra le Industrie Automobilistiche Notiziario Statistico see A N F I A Notiziario Statistico **4661**
Associazione Nazionale Mutilati e Invalidi di Guerra. Sezione di Roma. Notiziario. (IT ISSN 0004-5993) **3452, 4398**
Associazione Nazionale per la Tutela del Patrimonio Storico Artistico e Naturale della Nazione. Atti di Convegni. (IT) **2350**
Associazione Nazionale per la Tutela del Patrimonio Storico Artistico e Naturale della Nazione. Documenti. (IT) **2350**
Associazione Nazionale per la Tutela del Patrimonio Storico Artistico e Naturale della Nazione. Quaderni. (IT) **2350**
Associazione Nazionale per la Tutela del Patrimonio Storico Artistico e Naturale della Nazione. Studi. (IT) **2350**
Associazione Nobilitazione Tessile. Notiziario. (IT) **4616**
Associazione Pedagogica Italiana. Bollettino. (IT) **1721, 1725**
Associazione Professionale Autonoma Cineoperatori Inform see A P A C Inform **3502**
Associazione Romana di Entomologia. Bollettino. (IT ISSN 0004-6000) **529**
Associazione Volontari Italiani del Sangue (Turin) Corriere A V I S see Corriere A V I S **4099**
Associazioni Cristiane Lavoratori Italy Savona A C L I see Savona A C L I **3947**
AssoCom Review. (SA) **807**
Assogomma Notizie. (IT) **4291**
†As-Soukan. (MR) **5140**
Assur. (US ISSN 0145-6334) **2428**
Assurance Francaise. (FR ISSN 0004-6019) **2527**
Assurance Mutuelle. (FR) **2527**
Assurances. (CN ISSN 0004-6027) **2527**
Assurandoeren. (DK ISSN 0109-1875) **2527**
Assurantie Magazine. (NE ISSN 0167-3882) **2527**
Assure Social. (FR ISSN 0587-3746) **4429**
Assyrian Observer. (UK ISSN 0144-7122) **1992**
Assyrian Star. (US ISSN 0004-6051) **1992**
Assyriological Studies. (US ISSN 0066-9903) **2804**

Asta-Press. (GW ISSN 0076-1745) **1725**
Aste e Cornici see Arte & Cornice **315**
Aste Giudiziarie. (IT ISSN 0004-606X) **4054**
Asterisco. (PE) **318**
Asterisque. (FR ISSN 0303-1179) **3030**
Asthma and Allergy Advocate. (US) **3183, 3364**
Asthma Bronchitis Emphysem. (GW ISSN 0724-5238) **3364**
▼Asthma Management. (US ISSN 1050-5253) **3184**
▼Asthma Resources Directory. (US) **3183**
Asthma Welfarer. (AT ISSN 0044-9776) **3364**
Asti Informazioni Economiche. (IT ISSN 0004-6078) **807**
Astin Bulletin. (UK ISSN 0515-0361) **2527**
Astma Allergi. (NO ISSN 0801-3799) **3183**
Astma Allergi Bladet. (DK ISSN 0900-4262) **3183**
Aston Martin Owners' Club Ltd. Magazine see A M Magazine **4678**
Astra. (IT) **358**
Astra. (RM ISSN 0004-6108) **2859**
Astra. (FI ISSN 0004-6094) **4837**
Astrado. (FR ISSN 0004-6116) **2896, 2052, 2804**
Astral. (FR) **358**
Astralog. (US) **4646**
Astrapi. (FR) **1249**
Astres. (FR) **358**
Astro. (GW ISSN 0939-3390) **46, 360**
Astro Analytics. (US) **358**
Astro Annual see New Age Astrology Guide (Year) **359**
Astro-Directory News. (US ISSN 0707-9664) **360**
The Astro-Investor. (US) **938, 358**
Astro Signs. (US) **358**
Astro Stock Market Advisory see Whole Earth Forecaster **969**
Astro Talk see Astrotalk Bulletin **358**
Astrodynamics. (US) **47**
Astrofizicheskie Issledovaniia. (BU ISSN 0324-1459) **361**
Astroflash. (US) **358, 3593**
Astrograph. (US ISSN 0094-1417) **361**
Astrolab. (FR ISSN 0398-074X) **361**
Astrolabe. (FR) **3874**
†Astrolabe. (CN) **5140**
Astrolettre. (FR ISSN 0764-2997) **361**
Astrological Magazine. (II ISSN 0004-6140) **358**
Astrological Review. (US ISSN 0044-9784) **358**
Astrologischer Auskunftsbogen. (GW ISSN 0004-6175) **358**
Astrology. (UK ISSN 0004-6183) **358**
Astrology and Athrishta. (II ISSN 0044-9792) **358**
Astrology and Psychic News. (US) **358**
Astrology Annual. (US) **358**
Astrology Directory. (US) **358**
Astrology Guide. (US ISSN 0004-6191) **358**
Astrology: Your Daily Horoscope. (US) **358**
Astronautics. see Hangtian **54**
Astronautyka. (PL ISSN 0004-623X) **47**
Astronews. (US) **358**
Astronomi og Rumfart see Aktuel Astronomi **360**
Astronomia. (PL ISSN 0554-8233) **361**
L'Astronomia. (IT) **361**
Astronomia (Naples). (IT ISSN 0392-2308) **361**
Astronomical Almanac. (UK) **361**
Astronomical and Astrophysical Transactions. (US ISSN 1055-6796) **361**
Astronomical Ephemeris see Astronomical Almanac **361**
Astronomical Ephemeris of Geocentric Places of Planets. (II ISSN 0066-9970) **361**
Astronomical Herald. see Tenmon Geppo **370**

Astronomical Journal. (US ISSN 0004-6256) **361**
Astronomical Phenomena. (US ISSN 0083-2421) **361**
Astronomical Society of Australia. Proceedings. (AT ISSN 0066-9997) **361**
Astronomical Society of India. Bulletin. (II ISSN 0304-9523) **361**
Astronomical Society of Japan. Publications/Nihon Tenmon Gakkai Obun Kenkyu Hokoku. (JA ISSN 0004-6264) **361**
Astronomical Society of New York. Newsletter. (US) **361**
Astronomical Society of South Australia. Bulletin. (AT ISSN 0044-9806) **361**
Astronomical Society of Southern Africa. Monthly Notes. (SA ISSN 0024-8266) **361**
Astronomical Society of the Pacific. Publications. (US ISSN 0004-6280) **361**
Astronomical Society of the Pacific Catalog see A S P Catalog **360**
Astronomical Society of Victoria. Astronomical Yearbook. (AT ISSN 0067-0006) **361**
Astronomicheski Kalendar na Observatoriiata v Sofia. (BU ISSN 0068-3639) **361**
Astronomicheskii Vestnik. (RU ISSN 0320-930X) **361, 1587**
Astronomicheskii Zhurnal. (RU ISSN 0004-6299) **361**
Astronomie. (FR ISSN 0004-6302) **361**
Astronomie et Sciences Humaines. (FR ISSN 0989-6236) **361**
Astronomie in der Schule. (GW ISSN 0004-6310) **361, 1616**
Astronomie Quebec. (CN ISSN 1183-5362) **361**
†Astronomie und Raumfahrt. (GW ISSN 0587-565X) **5140**
Astronomische Grundlagen fuer den Kalender. (GW ISSN 0067-0014) **362**
Astronomische Nachrichten. (GW ISSN 0004-6337) **362**
Astronomischer Jaresbericht see Astronomy and Astrophysics Abstracts **371**
Astronomisk Tidsskrift. (DK ISSN 0004-6345) **362**
Astronomy. (US ISSN 0091-6358) **362**
Astronomy and Astrophysics. (GW ISSN 0004-6361) **362, 3815**
Astronomy and Astrophysics Abstracts. (US ISSN 0067-0022) **371, 3, 3836**
Astronomy and Astrophysics Review. (US) **362, 3815**
Astronomy and Astrophysics Supplement Series. (FR ISSN 0365-0138) **362**
Astronomy Quarterly see Vistas in Astronomy **371**
Astronomy Through Practical Investigation. (US) **362**
▼Astroparticle Physics. (NE ISSN 0927-6505) **362, 3815**
Astrophile. (US) **3749**
Astrophysical Journal. (US ISSN 0004-637X) **362, 3815**
Astrophysical Journal. Supplement Series. (US ISSN 0067-0049) **362, 3815**
Astrophysical Letters see Astrophysical Letters and Communications **362**
Astrophysical Letters and Communications. (US ISSN 0888-6512) **362, 3815**
Astrophysics. (English translation of: Astrofizika) (US ISSN 0004-6396) **362, 3815**
Astrophysics and Space Science. (NE ISSN 0004-640X) **362, 3815**
Astrophysics and Space Science Library.(NE ISSN 0067-0057) **362, 3815**
Astrotalk Bulletin. (US) **358, 1475**
Astrum. (SP ISSN 0210-4105) **362**
Asturiensia Medievalia. (SP) **2307**
Astute Investor (Kingston). (US ISSN 0736-7643) **938, 844**

Astute Investor (Paoli) see Bob Nurock's Advisory **939**
Asu Hyvin. (FI ISSN 0786-1443) **641**, **3016**
Asu no Tomo/Friend of Tomorrow. (JA) **2270**
Asunto. (VE) **1332**
Aswamedham. (US) **28**, **318**, **2896**, **3503**
Aswaq al-Khalij. (QA) **646**
Asyl. (SZ) **2719**
Asylum. (US ISSN 0896-1344) **2988**, **2859**
Asymptotic Analysis. (NE ISSN 0921-7134) **3030**
At Cooper Union. (US ISSN 0004-6434) **1304**
▼At Home. (US) **2548**
At the Centre/Au Centre. (CN ISSN 0226-9422) **3615**
†At the Centre. (AT) **5140**
At the L A T A Level. (US) **1361**
At the Library. (US) **2745**
At the Park. (US) **4752**
At the Polls Series. (US) **3874**
Atalanta. (GW ISSN 0171-0079) **529**
Atalanta. (IT) **2896**
Atalanta. (US) **4837**, **2451**
Atalaya. (SW) **3749**
Atari Connection see Atari Explorer **1458**
Atari Explorer. (US ISSN 0882-3340) **1458**, **1467**
Atarian. (US) **1418**, **1384**
†Atavist. (US ISSN 0731-8987) **5140**
†Ateizmus. (CS) **5140**
Atelier. (GW ISSN 0176-8530) **318**
L'Atelier. (FR ISSN 0980-9465) **2548**, **2433**
Atelier A S E M I. (FR ISSN 0993-538X) **235**
Atelier des Metiers d'Art see L'Atelier **2548**
Ateliers. (CN ISSN 0843-7777) **1249**, **429**, **1170**, **3815**
Ateliers de Constructions Electriques de Charleroi Review see A C E C Review **1880**
Ateliers Proteges. (FR) **4398**
Atem see Atem und Mensch **3799**
Atem und Mensch. (GW ISSN 0341-3403) **3799**
Atemwegs- und Lungenkrankheiten. (GW ISSN 0341-3055) **3364**
Atencion Medica. (MX ISSN 0185-6235) **3079**
Atene e Roma. (IT ISSN 0004-6493) **1275**
Atenea. (PR ISSN 0044-9849) **2859**
Atenea (Year). (CL ISSN 0716-1840) **2503**
Ateneo Bruzio. (IT) **2204**
Ateneo de El Salvador. Revista. (ES) **2859**
Ateneo de Medicina. (BO) **3079**
Ateneo Parmense. Acta Bio-Medica. (IT ISSN 0004-6531) **3079**, **429**
Ateneo Parmense. Acta Naturalia. (IT ISSN 0392-419X) **4300**
Ateneu. (RM) **2215**
Ateneu Angrense de Letras e Artes. Revista. (BL) **2896**
Atgimimas. (LI) **2209**
▼Athanor. (IT) **318**, **2896**
Al-Athar fi Dawlat al-Imarat al-Arabiyyah al-Muttahidah/Archaeology in the United Arab Emirates. (TS) **266**
Atheism and Dialogue see Atheism and Faith **4163**
Atheism and Faith. (VC) **4163**
Atheist. (US ISSN 0304-1409) **3762**, **4163**
Athena. (GR) **2350**
Athena. (US ISSN 0896-0631) **4837**, **1232**
†Athena Incognito Magazine. (US) **5140**
Athena Mediterranea. (IT) **2859**
Athenaeum. (IT ISSN 0004-6574) **1275**
Athenaeum. (CN) **1304**
Athenaeum Annotations. (US) **353**
Athenaeum Bookshelf. (US) **389**
Ta Athenaika. (GR) **2350**
L'Athenee. (BE ISSN 0004-6590) **1616**
Athenian. (GR ISSN 1011-8993) **4752**, **2804**

Athenisin Ethnikon kai Kapodistrakion Panepistemion. Theologike Schole. Epistemonike Epeteris. (GR) **4280**
Athens. Ethnikon kai Kapodistriakon Panepistemion. Philosophike Schole. Epistemonike Epeteris. (GR) **2350**
Athens Annals of Archaeology. (GR ISSN 0004-6604) **266**
Athens Center of Ekistics. Research Report. (GR ISSN 0067-0073) **2483**
Athens Chamber of Commerce and Industry. Monthly Bulletin. (GR ISSN 0004-6612) **807**
Athens College Bulletin. (GR) **1617**
Athens Magazine. (US) **2221**
Atherosclerosis. (IE ISSN 0021-9150) **3205**
†Atherosclerosis. (US) **5140**
Atherosclerosis Reviews. (US ISSN 0362-1650) **3205**
Athlerama. (FR) **4464**
Athletes in Action. (US) **4464**
Athlete's World see Athletics Today **4465**
Athletic Administration. (US ISSN 0044-9873) **4464**
Athletic Business. (US ISSN 0747-315X) **4464**
Athletic Club Events see A C E **1295**
Athletic Director. (US ISSN 0004-6647) **1744**
Athletic Director and Coach see Your School and the Law **1732**
Athletic Directory. (US) **1122**, **4464**
Athletic Echo. (AT ISSN 0300-4600) **4464**
Athletic Event see Running Review **5271**
Athletic Journal see Scholastic Coach **3808**
Athletic Management. (US) **1725**
Athletic Sports Magazine/Rikujo-Kyogi Magazine. (JA) **4464**
Athletic Training see Journal of Athletic Training **3371**
Athletics. (CN ISSN 0229-4966) **4464**
Athletics Arena see Athletics Arena International **4464**
Athletics Arena International. (UK) **4464**
Athletics Coach. (UK ISSN 0267-0267) **4465**
Athletics Employment Weekly. (US) **3624**, **4465**
Athletics Today. (UK) **4465**, **4541**
Athletics Weekly. (UK ISSN 0004-6671) **4465**
Athletik. (GW ISSN 0004-6698) **4465**
Atholl & Breadalbane Community Comment. (UK ISSN 0262-5113) **2859**
Heatid. (GW) **844**, **3874**
Atkinson Balloon see Atkinsonian **1304**
Atkinsonian. (CN) **1304**
Atlanta Business Chronicle. (US ISSN 0164-8071) **844**
Atlanta History. (US ISSN 0896-3975) **2399**
Atlanta Homes and Lifestyles. (US) **2548**
Atlanta Inquirer. (US) **2221**
Atlanta Jewish Times. (US ISSN 0892-3345) **1992**
Atlanta Magazine. (US ISSN 0004-6701) **2221**
Atlanta N O W News. (US) **4837**
Atlanta Parent. (US) **1232**
†Atlanta Professional. (US) **5140**
Atlanta Regional Commission Action see A R C Action **2482**
Atlanta Singles Magazine. (US) **4362**
Atlanta Skier. (US ISSN 0199-1574) **4541**
Atlanta Small Business Journal see Atlanta Small Business Monthly **1113**
Atlanta Small Business Monthly. (US) **1113**
Atlanta Sports South see Sports South **4492**
Atlanta University Bulletin. (US) **1304**
Atlanta Voice. (US) **1992**
▼Atlanta's Business Makers and Shakers. Volume II - Atlanta's Top Networking Channels. (US ISSN 1054-5182) **1122**

Atlanta's Top Business Makers & Skakers. Volume I - Atlanta's Top Decision Makers. (US) **1122**
Atlante. (IT ISSN 0004-6736) **2242**, **4300**, **4752**
Atlantic. (UK) **807**
The Atlantic. (US ISSN 0276-9077) **2859**
†Atlantic Advocate. (CN ISSN 0004-6744) **5140**
Atlantic Bakers News. (US) **2086**
Atlantic Baptist. (CN ISSN 0004-6752) **4229**
▼Atlantic Beef Quarterly. (CN) **211**
†Atlantic Business. (CN) **5140**
Atlantic Canada Economics Association. Annual Conference: A C E A Papers. (CN ISSN 0319-003X) **646**
†Atlantic Canada Shipping Project. Annual Conference. Proceedings. (CN) **5140**
Atlantic Chamber Journal. (CN) **646**
†Atlantic Chess News. (US) **5140**
Atlantic City Action. (US) **938**, **2471**, **4465**
Atlantic City Magazine. (US) **2221**, **4752**
Atlantic Co-Operator. (CN ISSN 0703-5357) **1682**
Atlantic Coast Conference Basketball Handbook see A C C Basketball Handbook **4499**
Atlantic Coast Conference Lindy's A C C Football Annual see Lindy's A C C Football Annual **4507**
Atlantic Communicator. (US ISSN 0888-1871) **197**, **147**
†Atlantic Community News. (US) **5140**
†Atlantic Community Quarterly. (US ISSN 0004-6760) **5140**
Atlantic Construction Journal. (CN) **600**
Atlantic Construction Magazine. (CN) **600**
Atlantic Control States Beverage Journal. (US ISSN 0044-9881) **377**
Atlantic County Historical Society Yearbook. (US) **2399**, **2144**
Atlantic Economic Journal. (US ISSN 0197-4254) **646**
Atlantic Firefighter. (CN) **2031**
Atlantic Fisherman. (CN) **2037**
Atlantic Food & Beverage News. (CN) **2062**, **377**
Atlantic Forestry Journal. (CN) **2096**
Atlantic Geology. (CN) **1555**
Atlantic Horse & Pony. (CN) **4532**
Atlantic Hospitality. (CN) **2471**
Atlantic Kaleidoscope. (CN) **2176**
▼Atlantic Lifestyle Business. (CN) **833**
Atlantic Mining Journal. (CN) **3478**
†Atlantic Papers. (UK ISSN 0571-7795) **5140**
Atlantic Post Calls. (CN) **4532**
Atlantic Provinces and Quebec; New Brunswick Newfoundland, Nova Scotia, Prince Edward Island, Quebec TourBook see Tourbook: Atlantic Provinces and Quebec **4790**
Atlantic Provinces Book Review. (CN ISSN 0316-5981) **4121**
Atlantic Provinces Economic Council. Annual Report. (CN ISSN 0067-0162) **844**
Atlantic Provinces Economic Council. Newsletter. (CN ISSN 0044-989X) **844**
Atlantic Provinces Library Association Bulletin see A P L A Bulletin **2740**
Atlantic Provinces Linguistic Association. Annual Meeting. Papers. (CN ISSN 0820-8204) **2804**
Atlantic Provinces Linguistic Association Journal. (CN ISSN 0706-6910) **2804**
Atlantic Provinces Numismatic Association. Newsletter. (CN ISSN 0044-9903) **3598**
Atlantic Provinces Reporters. (CN) **2601**
Atlantic Provinces Transportation Commission. Tips & Topics. (CN ISSN 0381-9345) **4646**
▼Atlantic Region Aviation Business Directory. (CN) **4671**
Atlantic Report. (CN ISSN 0004-6841) **844**

Atlantic Salmon Federation. Special Publication Series. (CN) **2037**, **1483**
Atlantic Salmon Journal. (CN ISSN 0044-992X) **2037**, **4541**
Atlantic Salmon Newsletter see Salar **2048**
Atlantic Science. (CN) **4300**
Atlantic Silent News. (CN) **2286**
Atlantic States Insurance. (US) **2527**
Atlantic Summary Report - Index. (US) **3682**, **1555**
Atlantic Sun. (US ISSN 0004-685X) **1304**
Atlantic Trade Report see Atlantic Trade Report & Global Defense Industry **900**
Atlantic Trade Report & Global Defense Industry. (US ISSN 1053-2404) **900**
Atlantic Transportation Journal. (CN) **4646**
Atlantic Triannual see Dolphin-Moon Press "Signatures" Series **2992**
Atlantic Truck Transport Review see Atlantic Trucking **4743**
Atlantic Trucking. (CN ISSN 0830-1808) **4743**
Atlantic Update. (US) **197**
Atlantic Woman. (CN) **4837**
Atlantica. (FR) **2186**
Atlantica. (IC) **4802**
Atlantida. (VE) **4366**
Atlantide Report. Scientific Results of the Danish Expedition to the Coasts of Tropical West Africa. (DK ISSN 0067-0227) **4300**
Atlantis. (PO ISSN 0870-8924) **4671**
Atlantis. (CN ISSN 0702-7818) **4858**
Atlantisch Perspektief. (NE ISSN 0167-1847) **3951**
Atlantische Tijdingen see Atlantisch Perspektief **3951**
Atlas. (UK ISSN 0267-484X) **318**
Atlas (Paris, 1960) see Atlas - Air France **4752**
Atlas - Air France. (FR) **4752**, **4671**
Atlas Bulletin. (US) **4679**
†Atlas Copco Comments. (CN) **5140**
Atlas de la Revolution Francaise. (FR) **2350**
†Atlas de Tecnicas de Bloqueios Regionais. (BL ISSN 0034-7094) **5140**
Atlas der Verbreitung Palaearktischer Voegel. (GW) **562**
Atlas des Usines de France. (FR) **1072**
Atlas Filmszene. (GW) **3503**
Atlas Florae Europaeae. (FI) **495**
Atlas Flory Polskiej i Ziem Osciennych/Florae Polonicae Terrarunique Adiacentium Sconographia. (PL ISSN 0067-0294) **495**
Atlas Historique des Villes de France. (FR ISSN 0765-0817) **2350**
Atlas Polskich Strojow Ludowych. (PL ISSN 0067-0316) **235**, **266**, **2052**
†Atlas Rozmieszczenia Drzew i Krzewow w Polsce. (PL ISSN 0067-0324) **5140**
Atlas World Press Review see World Press Review **2889**
Atletica. (IT) **4465**
Atleticastudi. (IT) **4465**
Atletiekwereld. (NE ISSN 0004-668X) **4465**
†Atletika. (CS ISSN 0323-1364) **5140**
Atma Jaya Research Centre. Annual Report. (IO) **1744**
Atma Jaya Research Centre. Education Development Research Report/Pusat Penelitian Atma Jaya. Studi Tentang Pengembangan Pendidikan. (IO) **1617**
Atma Jaya Research Centre. International Contract Labour. (IO) **972**, **2719**
Atma Jaya Research Centre. Library Bulletin. (IO ISSN 0126-1630) **2745**
Atma Jaya Research Centre. Newsletter. (IO ISSN 0126-1584) **1700**

Atma Jaya Research Centre. Socio-Medical Research Report/Pusat Penelitian Atma Jaya. Penelitian Tentang Kebutuhan Kesehatan Masyarakat dan Sistem Peleyanan Kesehatan di Kecamatan Penjaringan. (IO) **3079**, 4429
Atma Jaya Research Centre. Socio-Religious Research Report/Pusat Penelitian Atma Jaya. Laporan Penelitian Keagamaan. (IO) **4213**, 4429
Atmosferos Fizika/Atmospheric Physics.(LI ISSN 0135-1419) **3433**
Atmosphere. (US) **2221**
Atmosphere - Ocean. (CN ISSN 0705-5900) **3433**
Atmospheric Environment see Atmospheric Environment. Part A: General Topics **1976**
Atmospheric Environment see Atmospheric Environment. Part B: Urban Atmosphere. **1976**
Atmospheric Environment. Part A: General Topics. (US ISSN 0960-1686) **1976**, 1943
Atmospheric Environment. Part B: Urban Atmosphere. (US ISSN 0957-1272) **1976**, 1943
Atmospheric Optics. (English translation of: Optika Atmosfery) (US ISSN 0235-277X) **3852**
Atmospheric Physics. see Atmosferos Fizika **3433**
Atmospheric Research. (NE ISSN 0169-8095) **3433**
Atmospheric Science Paper see Colorado State University. Atmospheric Science Paper **3434**
Atmospheric Sciences Library. (NE) **1541**
Atoka. (NR ISSN 0004-7007) **2896**, 2052, 4630
Atom. (UK ISSN 0004-7015) **1783**, 1803
Atom Indonesia. (IO ISSN 0126-1568) **1803**
Atom-Informationen. (GW ISSN 0004-7031) **1803**
Atom News see A E A Times **1803**
†Atomedia. (PH ISSN 0115-3757) **5140**
Atomenergi see A E **5127**
Atomes see Recherche **4335**
Atomic Collision Research in Japan. Progress Report. (JA) **3846**
Atomic Data see Atomic Data and Nuclear Data Tables **3846**
Atomic Data and Nuclear Data Tables. (US ISSN 0092-640X) **3846**
Atomic Energy Clearinghouse. (US ISSN 0519-3389) **1803**, 1783
Atomic Energy Law Journal. (US ISSN 0004-7104) **1803**, 2601
Atomic Energy Law Reports see Nuclear Regulation Reports **2662**
Atomic Energy Levels and Grotrian Diagrams. (NE) **3846**
Atomic Energy of Canada. Annual Report. (CN ISSN 0067-0383) **1803**, 1783
Atomic Energy of Canada. List of Publications. (CN ISSN 0067-0405) **3836**, 1797
Atomic Energy of Canada Ltd. Report Series see A E C L Report Series **1803**
Atomic Energy Pocketbook. (JA) **1803**, 1783
Atomic Energy Society of Japan. Journal/Nihon Genshiryoku Gakkai Shi. (JA ISSN 0004-7120) **1803**
†Atomic Physics. (US ISSN 0090-6360) **5140**
Atomic Spectroscopy. (US ISSN 0195-5373) **1204**
Atomisation and Spray Technology see Aerosol Science and Technology **1169**
▼Atomization and Sprays. (US ISSN 1044-5110) **1848**, 2521
Atomkernergie - Kerntechnik see Kerntechnik **1806**
Atomnaya Energiya. (RU ISSN 0004-7163) **1803**
Atomo Petrolio Elettricita. (IT ISSN 0004-718X) **1783**, 1803, 1882, 3682

Atoms in Japan. (JA ISSN 0403-9319) **1803**
Atomu Fukushima. (JA ISSN 0386-1430) **1803**
Atomwirtschaft - Atomtechnik. (GW ISSN 0365-8414) **1804**
▼Atopos. (US) **3010**
Atout Cambresis. (FR) **807**
ATPases. (Adenosine Triphosphate) (UK ISSN 0261-4553) **471**
Atrashi Sumai-No Sekkai. see New Home Design **2493**
Atraves. (BL) **2896**
Atrial Natriuretic Factors. (UK ISSN 0268-1641) **3250**, 3718
Atrium. (UK ISSN 0951-8088) **295**
Atro-gramme. (IT) **1617**
The Atrocity. (US) **2859**
Atsuryoku Gijutsu/Journal of High Pressure Institute of Japan. (JA ISSN 0387-0154) **1815**
†Att.: (DK) **5140**
▼Attack. (SW) **1418**
Attadamon see Al-Tadamun **2195**
Attakapas Gazette. (US ISSN 0571-8236) **2399**
Attendance Centre News. (UK) **1510**
Attenderingsbulletin Staring-gebouw: Land, Bodem, Water. (NE) **1972**, 3, 169, 4822
Attent see Marktgilde Gids **917**
Atterbury Letter - Wine, Dining & Travel.(US ISSN 0739-3733) **4752**, 377
Atterraggio Forzato. (IT ISSN 0004-7279) **3452**, 47
Atti dello Psicodramma. (IT) **4630**, 4012
Atti e Memorie della Deputazione di Storia Patria per le Antiche Provincie Modenesi. (IT) **2350**
†Attic Press. (US ISSN 0147-7129) **5140**
Atticus Review. (US) **2988**, 318
Attila Jozsef University. Acta Cybernetica. (HU ISSN 0324-721X) **1440**
Attila Jozsef University. Acta Geographica. (HU ISSN 0324-5268) **2242**
Attitude. (US ISSN 0882-3472) **1528**
Attitudes and Arabesques. (US) **1528**
Attivita Dopolavoristiche. (IT) **4465**
▼Attivita Fisica e Sport. (IT ISSN 1120-3633) **3799**
Attorney - C P A. (US ISSN 0571-8279) **2706**, 747
Attorney Fee Awards. (US) **2601**
▼Attorney Fees in Washington. (US) **2601**
†Attorney Sanctions Newsletters. (US) **5140**
Attorneys and Agents Registered to Practice Before the U.S. Patent and Trademark Office. (US ISSN 0361-3844) **3672**
Attorneys and Agents Registered to Practice Before the U.S. Patent Office see Attorneys and Agents Registered to Practice Before the U.S. Patent and Trademark Office **3672**
†Attorneys Computer Report. (US ISSN 0745-421X) **5141**
†Attorney's Directory of Forensic Psychiatrists in the United States and Canada. (US ISSN 0278-0879) **5141**
†Attorney's Directory of Forensic Psychologists. (US ISSN 0887-4905) **5141**
Attorney's Fees in Florida. (US) **2601**
†Attorney's Guide to Law Office Automation. (US) **5141**
Attorney's Guide to Social Security Disability Claims. (US) **2734**, 2527
Attorney's Handbook of Accounting. (US) **2706**, 747
Attorneys Marketing Report. (US ISSN 0745-1369) **1033**, 2601
Attorney's Medical Advisory Letter see Medico-Legal Advisor **2703**
Attorneys Personnel Report. (US) **1062**, 2601, 3624
Attorney's Practical Guide to Accounting see Attorney's Handbook of Accounting **2706**
Attractions Australia. (AT) **4752**
Attraverso il Mondo. (IT) **4752**, 2242

Attrezzatura Alberghiera in Italia. (IT) **2482**
Attrezzature see Auto Attrezzature **4680**
Attualita Cinematografiche. (IT) **3503**
Attualita di Ostetricia e Ginecologia. (IT ISSN 0004-7317) **3289**
Attualita in Chirurgia. (IT ISSN 0390-5527) **3376**
Atualidades Veterinarias see Raizes **5267**
Atwood Ancestors. (US) **2144**
†Atze. (GW ISSN 0323-8903) **5141**
Au Centre. see At the Centre **3615**
Au Coeur de l'Afrique. (BD ISSN 0563-4245) **4164**, 2331
Au Courant. (CN) **646**
Au Fil des Evenements. (CN) **1617**
†Au Fil du Bois. (CN ISSN 0383-0047) **5141**
Au Fil du Rail. (CN ISSN 0004-7376) **4707**
Au Large/Go Ahead. (CM) **1249**
Au P C. (Publicite Club de Montreal) (CN) **28**, 1033
Au Pays de Matane. (CN ISSN 0836-3102) **2399**
Auario de Estadistica del Medio Ambiente. (CL) **1797**
Auberge de la Jeunesse. (FR ISSN 0004-7392) **4752**, 1249
Auburn Alumnews. (US) **1304**
Auburn Plainsman. (US) **1304**
Auburn University. Water Resources Research Institute. Annual Report. (US ISSN 0067-043X) **4822**
Auchmuty Library Publication. (AT ISSN 0158-6610) **389**, 2745
Auckland Institute and Museum. Bulletin. (NZ ISSN 0067-0456) **3522**
Auckland Institute and Museum. Records. (NZ ISSN 0067-0464) **3522**
Auckland University Law Review. (NZ ISSN 0067-0510) **2601**
Auckland-Waikato Historical Journal. (NZ ISSN 0111-7653) **2344**
Auction and Surplus. (US) **646**, 1122
Auction Bulletin. (US) **1033**
Auction Prices of American Artists. (US ISSN 0144-3690) **318**, 646
†Auction Results Quarterly. (US ISSN 1046-4573) **5141**
The Auctioneer. (US ISSN 0004-7465) **1033**
Auctus. (US) **1304**
AudArena Stadium Guide see AudArena Stadium International Guide **4630**
Audarena Stadium Guide and International Directory see AudArena Stadium International Guide **4630**
AudArena Stadium International Guide. (US) **4630**, 1122
Audecibel. (US ISSN 0004-7473) **2286**
Audenshaw Papers. (UK ISSN 0004-7481) **4164**
†Audi - Daily Mail Skier's Holiday Guide.(UK) **5141**
Audience and Programme Research. (SW ISSN 0044-9989) **1355**
Audio. (US) **3539**, 4459
Audio. (GW) **3859**
Audio Alert see Investor's Hotline **952**
Audio Amateur. (US ISSN 0004-7546) **4459**
Audio & Electronics. see Toranjisuta Gijutsu **1779**
†Audio & Electronics Digest. (US ISSN 0164-8985) **5141**
Audio Canada see Sound & Vision **1343**
Audio Critic. (US ISSN 0146-4701) **4459**
Audio-Digest Anesthesiology. (US ISSN 0271-1265) **3190**
Audio-Digest Emergency Medicine. (US ISSN 0748-8947) **3079**
Audio-Digest Family Practice. (US ISSN 0271-1362) **3079**
Audio-Digest Gastroenterology. (US ISSN 0892-9386) **3266**
Audio-Digest General Surgery. (US) **3376**
Audio-Digest Internal Medicine. (US ISSN 0271-1303) **3079**
Audio-Digest Obstetrics - Gynecology. (US ISSN 0271-129X) **3289**

Audio-Digest Ophthalmology. (US ISSN 0271-1281) **3298**
Audio-Digest Orthopaedics. (US ISSN 0271-132X) **3307**
Audio-Digest Otolaryngology - Head and Neck Surgery. (US ISSN 0271-1354) **3313**
Audio-Digest Otorhinolaryngology - Head and Neck Surgery see Audio-Digest Otolaryngology - Head and Neck Surgery **3313**
Audio-Digest Pediatrics. (US ISSN 0271-1346) **3319**
Audio-Digest Psychiatry. (US ISSN 0271-1311) **3331**
Audio-Digest Surgery see Audio-Digest General Surgery **3376**
Audio-Digest Urology. (US ISSN 0271-1338) **3387**
Audio Engineering Society. Journal. (US ISSN 0004-7554) **4459**
Audio Estate Planner. (US) **2714**, 4145
Audio Giornale. (IT) **4459**
Audio Journal. (FR) **2286**
Audio Lawyer. (US) **2601**
▼Audio Litigator. (US) **2601**
Audio Magazine see Audio Video Magazine **4459**
Audio Publishing Report see B P Report **4121**
Audio Real Estate Lawyer. (US) **2601**, 4145
Audio Review. (IT) **4459**
†Audio-Technik. (GW ISSN 0571-8678) **5141**
†Audio Times. (US) **5141**
Audio Universal. (AG) **4459**
Audio - Video Interiors. (US ISSN 1041-5378) **1764**, 2556
Audio Video Magazine. (FR ISSN 0246-2958) **4459**, 1384
Audio Video Market Place see A V Market Place **1743**
†Audio Video Review Digest. (US) **5141**
Audio Visual. (UK ISSN 0305-2249) **1744**, 3503
Audio-Visual Communications see A V C Development and Delivery **1331**
Audio Visual Directory. (UK) **1332**
Audio-Visual Education. see Shichokaku Kyoiku **1663**
Audio-Visual Education Japan see A V E in Japan **1743**
Audio-Visual Education Programs. see Dianhua Jiaoyu **1625**
Audio - Visual Prof see A - V Prof **1368**
Audio-Visual Teaching of Foreign Languages. see Waiyu Dianhua Jiaoxue **1763**
Audio-Visual World. see Yinxiang Shijie **3587**
Audio Visueel Magazine. (NE) **1744**
Audio-Vizualis Kozlemenyek - Audio-Visual Review see A -V Kommunikacio **1613**
Audio Week. (US) **4459**
Audiocassette Finder. (US) **1674**, 3
Audiocraft. (US) **4459**
Audiologia Italiana. (IT ISSN 0393-3393) **3313**
Audiological Acoustics. see Audiologisch Akustik **3859**
Audiologisch Akustik/Audiological Acoustics. (GW ISSN 0172-8261) **3859**, 3079
Audiology. (SZ ISSN 0020-6091) **3313**
Audiology Japan. (JA ISSN 0303-8106) **3314**, 570
Audiology Protesica. (SP) **3314**, 1733, 2286
Audiology Today. (CN) **3314**
Audiophile. (UK ISSN 0959-7697) **4459**
Audiophile with Hi-Fi Answers see Audiophile **4459**
Audioprothesiste Francais see Cahiers de l'Audition **2286**
Audioptica. (SP ISSN 0213-9014) **3718**, 3298
Audioreview see Audio Review **4459**
AudioScene Canada see Sound & Vision **1343**
Audiotex Directory & Buyer's Guide. (US ISSN 1042-6329) **1361**, 1122, 1349

Audiotex Update. (US ISSN 1045-5795) **1349, 1435**
Audiovideo International. (JA ISSN 0362-1162) **1764,** 1033
AudioVision & Prosound. (AT ISSN 0816-9330) **4459**
Audiovisivi. (IT ISSN 0004-7627) **1744, 3503**
Audiovisual Librarian. (UK ISSN 0302-3451) **2745**
Audiozine. (US) **318**
▼Audit & Accounting Guides. (US) **747**
Audit Bureau of Circulations. Annual Meeting. Proceedings. (US) **28**
Audit Bureau of Circulations. Annual Report. (US) **40, 4562**
Audit Bureau of Circulations. Bylaws and Rules. (US) **4121**
Audit Bureau of Circulations. Divisional Director's Newsletter. (US) **747**
Audit Bureau of Circulations. Fact Book. Canadian Daily - Weekly Newspaper Circulation. (US) **40**
Audit Bureau of Circulations. Supplemental Data Reports. (US) **40, 4562**
Audit Bureau of Circulations Blue Book: Canadian Daily Newspapers *see* A B C Blue Book: Canadian Daily Newspapers **40**
Audit Bureau of Circulations Blue Book: Canadian Weekly Newspapers *see* A B C Blue Book: Canadian Weekly Newspapers **40**
Audit Bureau of Circulations Daily Newspaper F A S - F A X Reports *see* A B C U S Daily Newspaper F A S - F A X Reports **40**
Audit Bureau of Circulations Periodical F A S - F A X Reports *see* A B C Periodical F A S - F A X Reports **40**
Audit en Revisoraat. (BE) **747**
Audit Guide. (AT ISSN 0816-4746) **747**
▼Audit Monograph. (AT ISSN 1034-3423) **747**
†Audit Procedure for Out-of-Home Media. (US) **5141**
Audit Reports. (US) **4121**
Auditing. (US) **747**
Auditing Discussion Paper. (AT ISSN 0818-8122) **747**
Auditing Guidance Release. (AT ISSN 1031-3117) **747**
Auditing in China. *see* Zhongguo Shenji **757**
Auditing Research Monographs. (US ISSN 0146-9819) **747**
Auditing Studies. *see* Shenji Yanjiu **756**
Auditing Theory and Practice. *see* Shenji Lilun yu Shijian **756**
Auditopics. (AT ISSN 0729-2384) **646,** 1003
Auditor. (IR) **747**
Auditor. (US ISSN 0004-7651) **4280**
Auditor. (DK) **4280**
Audrey Babington's Workbox. (UK ISSN 0268-5175) **3590**
Audrey Gostlin's Inside Fashion. (CN) **1289**
Audubon Activist. (US) **1943,** 1483
Audubon Field Notes *see* American Birds **561**
Audubon Leader. (US ISSN 0045-0014) **1483**
Audubon Magazine. (US ISSN 0004-7694) **1483**
Audubon Society of Rhode Island. Report. (US) **1483**
Auerbach Applications Software Reports *see* Applications Software Reports **1475**
†Auerbach D P Training. (US) **5141**
†Auerbach Data Communications Reports *see* Data Communications Reports **1446**
†Auerbach Distributed Data Processing Management. (US) **5141**
†Auerbach Financial - Retail Systems Reports. (US) **5141**
Auerbach Information Management Series. (US) **1455**
Auerbach Microform Reports *see* Auerbach Office Systems Reports **5141**
Auerbach Minicomputers Report *see* Minicomputers Reports **1463**

†Auerbach Office Systems Reports. (US) **5141**
Auerbach Peripherals and Data Handling Reports *see* Auerbach Plug-Compatible Peripherals Report **5141**
†Auerbach Plug-Compatible Peripherals Report. (US) **5141**
Auerbach Software Reports *see* Systems Software Reports **1481**
Auerbach Systems Software Reports *see* Systems Software Reports **1481**
Auf - Eine Frauenzeitschrift. (AU) **4837,** 2451, 4398
Auf Einen Blick. (GW) **2188**
Auf Nummer Sicher *see* S I H Magazin **2449**
Aufbau/Reconstruction. (US ISSN 0004-7813) **1992**
†Aufbau. (SZ ISSN 0004-7821) **5141**
Aufbau und Frieden *see* Prager Volkszeitung **2020**
Aufbereitungs-Technik - Mineral Processing. (GW ISSN 0004-783X) **3478,** 1072
Aufbruch. (GW ISSN 0004-7848) **4229**
Aufklaerung. (GW ISSN 0178-7128) **2351**
Aufklaerung - Vormaerz - Revolution. (GW) **2351**
Aufriss. (GW ISSN 0722-7973) **2351,** 4429
Aufrisse. (AU) **2351**
Der Aufschluss. (GW) **1555**
Auftrag. (SZ ISSN 0004-7880) **4229**
Auftrag. (GW) **4229,** 4256
Auftrag und Weg. (GW) **4164**
Auftrags-, Produktions-, Umsatz- und Lagerverhaeltnisse in der Industrie und im Bauhauptgewerbe/Les Commandes, la Production, les Chiffres d'Affaires et les Stocks dans l'Industrie et le Secteur Principal de la Construction. (SZ) **702**
Auftritt *see* Journal Frankfurt **2189**
Aufwaerts *see* Ran **3921**
Aufwaerts (Giessen). (GW) **4164**
Aufwind. (GW ISSN 0939-5296) **2433**
Augenaerztliche Fortbildung. (GW ISSN 0341-1486) **3298**
Der Augenarzt. (GW ISSN 0004-7902) **3298**
†Augenoptik. (GW ISSN 0004-7910) **5141**
Der Augenoptiker. (GW ISSN 0004-7929) **3298**
Der Augenspiegel. (GW ISSN 0004-7937) **3298**
Augsburg Adult Bible Studies. Leader Guide. (US) **4229**
Augsburg Adult Bible Studies. Participant Book. (US) **4229**
Augsburg Audiovisual Newsletter *see* Augsburg Media Messenger **1744**
Augsburg College Now. (US ISSN 0300-6964) **1304**
Augsburg Echo. (US ISSN 0004-7945) **1304**
Augsburg Home Bible Studies. (US) **4229**
Augsburg in Zahlen. (GW ISSN 0004-7953) **4562**
Augsburg Media Messenger. (US ISSN 0738-7954) **1744**
Augsburger Jahrbuch fuer Musikwissenschaft. (GW) **3539**
Augsburger Kulturnachrichten. (GW ISSN 0004-7961) **4752**
Augsburger Schriften zum Staats- und Voelkerrecht *see* Schriften zum Staats- und Voelkerrecht **2729**
Auguries. (UK) **3010**
August Derleth Society. Newsletter. (US) **2896,** 2985, 3010
August 1st Films. *see* Bayi Dianying **3504**
Augusta Historical Bulletin. (US) **2399**
Augusta Magazine. (US ISSN 0004-797X) **2221**
Augustan Age. (US) **1275**
Augustan Society Newsletter. (US) **2144**
Augustan Society Omnibus. (US) **2144,** 2307

†Augustana College Bulletin. (US ISSN 0004-7996) **5141**
Augustana College Library Publications *see* Augustana Library Publications **2503**
Augustana College Magazine. (US) **1304**
Augustana Historical Society, Rock Island, Illinois. Publications. (US ISSN 0067-0588) **2307**
Augustana Library Publications. (US ISSN 0067-057X) **2503**
Augustinian Heritage. (US ISSN 0888-2274) **4256**
Augustinian Studies. (US ISSN 0094-5323) **4256**
Augustiniana. (BE ISSN 0004-8003) **4256**
Augustinianum. (IT ISSN 0004-8011) **4256**
Augustinus. (SP ISSN 0004-802X) **4256**
Augustus. (US) **4398**
Aujourd'hui Credo. (CN ISSN 0383-2554) **2176**
Aujourd'hui Dimanche. (MQ) **4229**
Aujourd'hui l'Afrique. (FR ISSN 0339-9958) **3874**
Auk. (US ISSN 0004-8038) **562**
Aula. (DR) **4366,** 2896
Aula Abierta. (PE) **1617**
Aulisarnermit Nutarsiagssat/Groenlands Fiskeritende. (GL ISSN 0107-9417) **2037**
Aullwood Notes. (US) **1483**
Aum Namo Narayanay. (US) **3762,** 2336, 2896, 4280
Aunarte. (AG) **2859**
†Aunt Edna's Reading List. (US) **5141**
Aura. (PL ISSN 0197-7296) **1943**
Aura Literary Arts Review. (US ISSN 0889-7433) **2859**
Aura of Fort Worth *see* Aura of Fort Worth and Tarrant County **2221**
Aura of Fort Worth and Tarrant County. (US ISSN 1054-5441) **2221**
Aural News. (UK ISSN 0004-8054) **2286**
†Aurea Flamma. (US) **5141**
Aurealis. (AT) **3010**
Aurifex. (BE) **2563**
Auris. (SW ISSN 0045-0030) **2286**
Auris. Nasus. Larynx. (JA) **3314**
Aurora. (IT) **318**
Aurora. (IS ISSN 0334-8954) **2203**
Aurora. *see* Moethaukpan **2220**
Aurora. (AT ISSN 0004-8089) **2242,** 1296
Aurora. (CN ISSN 0714-7058) **2745**
Aurora. (GW ISSN 0341-1230) **2896,** 318
Aurora (Madison). (US ISSN 0275-3715) **3010,** 4837
Aurora (Richmond). (US) **2897**
Aurora A F X Road Racing Handbook. (US ISSN 0092-6256) **4465**
Aurora-Buchreihe. (GW ISSN 0171-6530) **2897,** 318
Aurora S F *see* Aurora (Madison) **3010**
Auroral Observatory. Magnetic Observations. (NO ISSN 0373-4854) **362,** 3815
Aus dem Antiquariat. (GW ISSN 0343-186X) **389,** 318
†Aus dem Schweizerischen Landesmuseum. (SZ ISSN 0067-0618) **5141**
Aus der Schatzkammer der Buecher *see* Buecher (Year) **4140**
Aus der Wehrheimer Geschichte. (GW) **2351**
Aus Forschung und Kunst. (GW ISSN 0067-0642) **318**
▼Aus-Geo News. (AT ISSN 1035-9338) **1541**
Aus I M M Bulletin. (Australasian Institute of Mining and Metallurgy) (AT ISSN 1034-6775) **3478**
Ausbau *see* Technik Heute **4610**
Der Ausbilder. (GW ISSN 0004-8100) **1682,** 3624
Ausbilder in der Chemischen Industrie. (GW) **1170,** 646
†Ausbilder-Informationen. (GW) **5141**
Ausbildung Pruefung Fortbildung. (GW) **4054**

Ausbildung und Beratung in Land- und Hauswirtschaft. (GW ISSN 0045-0049) **77**
Ausblick (Dusseldorf). (GW ISSN 0004-8119) **2580**
Ausblick (Luebeck). (GW) **3951**
Ausgabe. (GW) **2897,** 318
Ausgabe Technik *see* Bank und Markt und Technik **765**
Ausgrabungen und Funde. (GW ISSN 0004-8127) **266**
Ausinet Newsletter *see* Concatenation **2796**
Ausland - Maerkte. (SZ) **1033**
Auslandsoesterreicher *see* Rotweissrot **2173**
Auslegung. (US ISSN 0733-4311) **3762**
Die Auslese. (GW) **4164**
Aussendienst Informationen. (GW ISSN 0933-8357) **2527**
Aussenhandel. (GW) **900,** 844
Aussenhandel der Tschechoslowakei *see* Czechoslovak Foreign Trade **905**
Aussenhandelsblaetter. (GW) **900**
Aussenhandelsdienst *see* B F G: Aussenhandelsdienst **901**
Aussenhandelsdienst. (GW) **938,** 900
Aussenhandelsdienst der Industrie- und Handelskammern und Wirtschaftsverbaende. (GW ISSN 0001-1401) **900**
Aussenhandelsrundschreiben *see* Aussenwirtschaft Aktuell **808**
Aussenpolitik. (GW ISSN 0004-8194) **3951**
†Aussenpolitische Korrespondenz. (GW ISSN 0004-8208) **5141**
Aussenwirtschaft. (SZ ISSN 0004-8216) **900**
Aussenwirtschaft Aktuell. (GW) **808,** 900
Aussenwirtschaftsbrief. (GW ISSN 0178-8876) **900**
Aussenwirtschaftsrecht (Year). (GW) **900,** 2601
Ausstellungs- und Messe-Ausschuss der Deutschen Wirtschaft e.V. Handbook Germany - Trade Fair Country *see* A U M A Handbook Germany - Trade Fair Country **1032**
Austcare News. (AT) **3940**
Austin Book of Lists. (US) **4121,** 646
Austin Business Journal. (US) **646**
Austin Chronicle. (US) **3540,** 4630
Austin Dental News *see* Tenth Times **3243**
Austin Genealogical Society Quarterly. (US) **2144,** 417, 1682
Austin Greensheet. (US) **1502**
Austin Healey Year Book. (UK ISSN 0260-664X) **4679**
Austin Health & Fitness. (US) **3799**
†Austin Homes & Gardens. (US ISSN 0199-1531) **5141**
Austin Magazine. (US) **808**
▼Austin Minority Business Guide. (US) **646,** 1992
Austin Report. (US) **3874,** 4054
AustPlan. (AT ISSN 1033-1662) **295**
Austra-Link. (AT) **1534**
▼Australasian and New Zealand Medical Education Index. (AT) **3166,** 3
Australasian and Pacific Parliamentary Seminar. Summary Report of Proceedings *see* Australasian and Pacific Regional Parliamentary Seminar. Summary Report of Proceedings **2601**
Australasian and Pacific Regional Parliamentary Seminar. Summary Report of Proceedings. (AT) **2601**
Australasian and Pacific Society for Eighteenth-Century Studies Newsletter *see* A P S E C S Newsletter **2336**
Australasian Arts and Educations. (AT ISSN 0725-0673) **1617,** 318, 4594
Australasian Baker and Miller's Journal *see* Pastrycooks & Bakers News Monthly **2079**
Australasian Baking *see* Pastrycooks & Bakers News Monthly **2079**
Australasian Bandsman. (AT ISSN 0084-6953) **3540**
Australasian Beekeeper. (AT ISSN 0004-8313) **77**

5944 AUSTRALASIAN BUS

Australasian Bus and Coach. (AT) **4647**, 4752
Australasian Catholic Record. (AT ISSN 0004-8321) **4256**
†Australasian College Libraries (South Australia). (AT ISSN 0811-112X) **5141**
Australasian Commercial Teachers' Association. Journal. (AT ISSN 0084-6961) **1744**
Australasian Computerworld *see* Computerworld Australia **1449**
Australasian Conference on Hydraulics and Fluid Mechanics. Proceedings. (NZ ISSN 0571-9291) **1923**
Australasian Corrosion Association. Annual Conference Proceedings. (AT ISSN 0155-6002) **1212**
Australasian Cycling & Triatholon News.(AT ISSN 0819-3363) **4515**
Australasian Dirt Bike. (AT) **4515**
Australasian Drama Studies. (AT ISSN 0810-4123) **4630**
†Australasian Family History Gazette. (AT ISSN 0815-4597) **5141**
▼Australasian Federation of Family History. Newsletter. (AT) **2144**
Australasian Forest & Timber Bulletin. (AT) **2096**
Australasian Health & Healing. (AT ISSN 0812-3896) **3603**, 3079
Australasian Institute of Metals. Proceedings of the Annual Conference *see* Institute of Metals and Materials Australasia. Proceedings **3408**
Australasian Institute of Mining and Metallurgy Aus I M M Bulletin *see* Aus I M M Bulletin **3478**
Australasian Institute of Mining and Metallurgy Symposia Series *see* A I M M Symposia Series **3477**
†Australasian Insurance Journal. (AT ISSN 0045-0073) **5141**
Australasian Insurance Journal Manual of Australasian Life Assurance *see* A.I.J. Manual of Australasian Life Assurance **5128**
Australasian Journal of American Studies *see* A J A S: Australasian Journal of American Studies **2397**
Australasian Journal of Dermatology. (AT ISSN 0004-8380) **3246**
Australasian Journal of Philosophy. (AT ISSN 0004-8402) **3762**
†Australasian Journal of Philosophy. Monograph Series. (AT) **5141**
Australasian Marine Directory *see* Commercial Vessel Yearbook **2039**
Australasian Methodist Historical Society. Journal and Proceedings *see* Church Heritage **4234**
Australasian Physical & Engineering Sciences in Medicine. (AT ISSN 0158-9938) **3257**, 3815
Australasian Plant Pathology. (AT ISSN 0815-3191) **495**
Australasian Political Studies Association Newsletter *see* A P S A Newsletter **3869**
Australasian Post. (AT ISSN 0004-8437) **2171**
Australasian Printer Magazine *see* Australian Printer Magazine **3997**
Australasian Public Libraries and Information Services. (AT ISSN 1030-5033) **2745**
Australasian Radiology. (AT ISSN 0004-8461) **3357**
Australasian Religion Index. (AT ISSN 1033-2626) **4212**, 3
Australasian Science Magazine. (AT) **4300**, 1744, 1943, 4594
Australasian Shipping Record. (AT ISSN 0314-0377) **4724**
Australasian Society of Engineers Journal *see* A S E Journal **1813**
Australasian Solar Index and Buyers Guide. (AT) **1810**
Australasian Spartacist. (AT) **3874**
Australasian Sportsgoods and Toy Retailer *see* Sports & Leisure Retailer **4491**
Australasian Stamp Catalogue. (AT ISSN 0155-8498) **3749**
Australasian Stud and Stable *see* Stud and Stable **4538**
Australasian Studies in History and Philosophy *see* Australasian Studies in History and Philosophy of Science **4366**
Australasian Studies in History and Philosophy of Science. (NE) **4366**, 3762
Australasian Tax Reports. (AT ISSN 0587-2138) **1087**
Australasian Textiles. (AT ISSN 0725-086X) **4616**
Australasian Track and Field *see* Fun Runner **4472**
Australasian Tree Crops Sourcebook. (AT) **169**, 2062
Australasian Tuberous Sclerosis Society Inc. Today *see* T S Today **3156**
†Australia. Air Transport Statistics. Airline Aircraft Utilisation. (AT ISSN 0727-2731) **5141**
Australia. Air Transport Statistics. Airport Traffic Data. (AT ISSN 0729-6096) **4661**, 4562
Australia. Air Transport Statistics. Australian Air Distances. (AT ISSN 0727-6672) **4661**
Australia. Air Transport Statistics. Commuter Air Transport *see* Australia. Air Transport Statistics. Commuter Airlines **4661**
Australia. Air Transport Statistics. Commuter Airlines. (AT ISSN 1037-5937) **4661**, 4562
Australia. Air Transport Statistics. Domestic Air Transport *see* Australia. Air Transport Statistics. Domestic Airlines (Annual) **4661**
Australia. Air Transport Statistics. Domestic Airlines (Annual). (AT ISSN 1037-1273) **4661**, 4562
Australia. Air Transport Statistics. Domestic Airlines (Quarterly). (AT ISSN 0727-2782) **4661**, 4562
†Australia. Air Transport Statistics. Flight Crew Licences. (AT ISSN 0727-2774) **5141**
Australia. Air Transport Statistics. International Air Transpore *see* Australia. Air Transport Statistics. International Scheduled Air Transport **4661**
Australia. Air Transport Statistics. International Scheduled Air Transport.(AT) **4661**, 4562
Australia. Air Transport Statistics. Monthly Provisional Statistics of International Scheduled Air Transport.(AT ISSN 0727-2790) **4661**, 4562
Australia. Air Transport Statistics. Survey of Hours Flown. (AT ISSN 0727-2766) **4661**, 4562
Australia. Atomic Energy Commission. List of Report Publications *see* Australia. Nuclear Science and Technology Organisation. List of Report Publications **3836**
Australia. Atomic Energy Commission. Research Establishment. A A E C - E *see* Australia. Nuclear Science and Technology Organisation. A N S T O **1804**
Australia. Australian Bureau of Agricultural and Resource Economics. Agriculture and Resources Quarterly. (AT ISSN 1032-9722) **147**
Australia. Australian Bureau of Agricultural and Resource Economics. Crop Report. (AT) **147**, 169
Australia. Australian Bureau of Agricultural and Resource Economics. Occasional Papers. (AT) **147**
Australia. Australian Bureau of Agricultural and Resource Economics. Quarterly Review of the Rural Economy *see* Australia. Australian Bureau of Agricultural and Resource Economics. Agriculture and Resources Quarterly **147**
†Australia. Australian Water Resources Council. Hydrological Series. (AT ISSN 0067-219X) **5141**
Australia. Bureau of Agricultural and Resource Economics. Monthly Forest Products Trade Statistics. (AT) **2111**, 4562
Australia. Bureau of Agricultural Economics. Crop Report *see* Australia. Australian Bureau of Agricultural and Resource Economics. Crop Report **147**
Australia. Bureau of Agricultural Economics. Occasional Papers *see* Australia. Australian Bureau of Agricultural and Resource Economics. Occasional Papers **147**
Australia. Bureau of Industry Economics. Research Report. (AT ISSN 0156-3394) **646**
Australia. Bureau of Meteorology. Bulletin. (AT ISSN 0067-1312) **3433**
Australia. Bureau of Meteorology. Meteorological Study. (AT ISSN 0067-1320) **3433**
Australia. Bureau of Mineral Resouces, Geology and Geophysics. Resource Report *see* Australia. Bureau of Mineral Resources, Geology and Geophysics. Mineral Resource Report **3478**
Australia. Bureau of Mineral Resource, Geology and Geophysics. Geophysical Observatory Group. Report *see* Australian Geomagnetism Report **1587**
Australia. Bureau of Mineral Resources, Geology and Geophysics. Australian Petroleum Accumulations Report. (AT ISSN 0817-9263) **3682**, 1541
Australia. Bureau of Mineral Resources, Geology and Geophysics. Bulletin. (AT ISSN 0084-7089) **1541**
Australia. Bureau of Mineral Resources, Geology and Geophysics. Mineral Resource Report. (AT) **3478**, 1541
†Australia. Bureau of Mineral Resources, Geology, and Geophysics. Publications. (AT) **5141**
Australia. Bureau of Mineral Resources, Geology and Geophysics. Reports. (AT ISSN 0084-7100) **1541**
Australia. Bureau of Mineral Resources, Geology and Geophysics. Yearbook. (AT ISSN 0158-7285) **1541**
Australia. Bureau of Mineral Resources, Geology and Geophysics. 1: 250000 Geological Maps and Explanatory Notes Series. (AT) **1555**, 1541
†Australia. Bureau of Statistic. Queensland Office. Sand, Gravel and Quarry Production, Queensland. (AT ISSN 1031-7295) **5141**
Australia. Bureau of Statistics. Actual and Expected Private Mineral Exploration. (AT ISSN 1033-0542) **3498**
†Australia. Bureau of Statistics. Adoptions. (AT) **5141**
Australia. Bureau of Statistics. Apparent Consumption of Foodstuffs and Nutrients. (AT ISSN 1031-0533) **4079**
Australia. Bureau of Statistics. Apparent Consumption of Selected Foodstuffs, Australia, Preliminary. (AT ISSN 0158-2496) **4079**, 4563
†Australia. Bureau of Statistics. Australian Exports, Country by Commodity. (AT ISSN 0705-0534) **5141**
†Australia. Bureau of Statistics. Australian National Accounts: Gross Product, Employment and Hours Worked. (AT ISSN 1033-2618) **5141**
Australia. Bureau of Statistics. Award Rates of Pay Indexes, Australia. (AT ISSN 0812-0137) **702**
Australia. Bureau of Statistics. Balance of Payments, Australia (Annual). (AT) **702**, 4563
Australia. Bureau of Statistics. Balance of Payments, Australia (Quarterly). (AT ISSN 0819-114X) **702**, 4563
Australia. Bureau of Statistics. Balance of Payments (Canberra, 1976). (AT ISSN 0313-2773) **703**, 4563
†Australia. Bureau of Statistics. Banking, Australia. (AT) **5141**
Australia. Bureau of Statistics. Births, Australia. (AT ISSN 1031-0150) **3989**
Australia. Bureau of Statistics. Catalogue of Publications and Products. (AT ISSN 1032-805X) **4079**
Australia. Bureau of Statistics. Catalogue of Publications, Australia *see* Australia. Bureau of Statistics. Catalogue of Publications and Products **4079**
Australia. Bureau of Statistics. Catalogue of Small Area Statistics. (AT ISSN 0813-1317) **4563**
Australia. Bureau of Statistics. Causes of Death, Australia. (AT ISSN 1031-2005) **3989**
Australia. Bureau of Statistics. Child Care Arrangements, Australia. (AT ISSN 0728-6368) **4079**
†Australia. Bureau of Statistics. Child Care Arrangements, Australia, Preliminary. (AT ISSN 0728-4543) **5141**
Australia. Bureau of Statistics. Commonwealth Government Finance, Australia. (AT ISSN 0725-3427) **4079**
Australia. Bureau of Statistics. Deaths, Australia. (AT ISSN 1031-0223) **3990**
†Australia. Bureau of Statistics. Digest of Current Economic Statistics. (AT ISSN 0816-0627) **5141**
Australia. Bureau of Statistics. Distribution and Composition of Employee Earnings and Hours, Australia, Preliminary. (AT ISSN 1031-0231) **703**, 4563
Australia. Bureau of Statistics. Divorces, Australia. (AT ISSN 1031-2188) **3990**
Australia. Bureau of Statistics. Earnings and Hours of Employees, Distribution and Composition, Australia *see* Australian Bureau of Statistics. Distribution and Composition of Employee Earnings and Hours, Australia **704**
Australia. Bureau of Statistics. Estimated Resident Population by Sex and Age: States and Territories of Australia. (AT ISSN 0810-0039) **3990**
Australia. Bureau of Statistics. Expenditure on Education, Australia. (AT ISSN 1031-0282) **1674**
†Australia. Bureau of Statistics. Finance Companies, Australia. (AT) **5141**
Australia. Bureau of Statistics. Foreign Trade, Australia: Comparative and Summary Tables. (AT ISSN 1031-1394) **703**
†Australia. Bureau of Statistics. Foreign Trade, Australia, Part 1: Exports and Imports. (AT) **5141**
Australia. Bureau of Statistics. Government Finance Statistics, Australia. (AT ISSN 1031-7104) **703**
Australia. Bureau of Statistics. Government Financial Estimates, Australia. (AT ISSN 0159-3951) **703**
Australia. Bureau of Statistics. Labour Report *see* Australia. Bureau of Statistics. Labour Statistics, Australia **703**
Australia. Bureau of Statistics. Labour Statistics, Australia. (AT ISSN 0314-2779) **703**
Australia. Bureau of Statistics. Livestock and Livestock Products, Australia. (AT ISSN 0812-2598) **133**
Australia. Bureau of Statistics. Marriages, Australia. (AT ISSN 1031-0452) **3990**
Australia. Bureau of Statistics. Mineral Production, Australia. (AT ISSN 0311-8975) **3498**
Australia. Bureau of Statistics. Monthly Review of Business Statistics *see* Australia. Bureau of Statistics. Monthly Summary of Statistics, Australia **4563**
Australia. Bureau of Statistics. Monthly Summary of Statistics, Australia. (AT ISSN 0727-1689) **4563**
Australia. Bureau of Statistics. Motor Vehicle Registrations, Australia. (AT ISSN 0727-1638) **4661**, 4679

Title

Australia. Bureau of Statistics. New South Wales Office. Monthly Summary of Statistics. (AT) **3990**, 759
†Australia. Bureau of Statistics. New South Wales Office. Tertiary Education, New South Wales. (AT) **5142**
Australia. Bureau of Statistics. Northern Territory Statistical Summary. (AT ISSN 0067-0855) **4563**
Australia. Bureau of Statistics. Perinatal Deaths, Australia. (AT ISSN 1031-0053) **3990**
Australia. Bureau of Statistics. Population Estimates, Australia. (AT ISSN 0814-3951) **3990**
Australia. Bureau of Statistics. Private Mineral Exploration, Australia *see* Australia. Bureau of Statistics. Actual and Expected Private Mineral Exploration **3498**
Australia. Bureau of Statistics. Projections of the Populations of Australia, States and Territories. (AT ISSN 0816-3391) **3990**
Australia. Bureau of Statistics. Publications Advice. (AT ISSN 0156-4722) **4079**
Australia. Bureau of Statistics. Publications Issued in (Month). (AT ISSN 1031-0673) **4079**
Australia. Bureau of Statistics. Quarterly Estimates of National Income and Expenditure, Australia *see* Australian National Accounts: National Income and Expenditure (Quarterly) **704**
Australia. Bureau of Statistics. Queensland Office. Age and Sex Distribution of the Estimated Resident Population, Queensland. (AT ISSN 1037-3594) **3990**
Australia. Bureau of Statistics. Queensland Office. Agricultural Land Use and Selected Inputs, Queensland.(AT ISSN 0814-2556) **133**
Australia. Bureau of Statistics. Queensland Office. Births, Queensland *see* Australia. Bureau of Statistics. Queensland Office. Demography, Queensland **3990**
Australia. Bureau of Statistics. Queensland Office. Brisbane City Statistical Summary. (AT ISSN 0726-2019) **4563**
Australia. Bureau of Statistics. Queensland Office. Building Activity, Queensland. (AT ISSN 0812-8332) **2499**
†Australia. Bureau of Statistics. Queensland Office. Building Approvals: Preliminary Figures for Dwelling Units Approved. (AT) **5142**
Australia. Bureau of Statistics. Queensland Office. Building Approvals, Queensland. (AT ISSN 1031-198X) **2499**
Australia. Bureau of Statistics. Queensland Office. Building Approvals: Small Area Statistics, Queensland. (AT ISSN 0728-6546) **2499**
Australia. Bureau of Statistics. Queensland Office. Cattle Breeds, Queensland. (AT) **133**, 211
Australia. Bureau of Statistics. Queensland Office. Causes of Death, Queensland *see* Australia. Bureau of Statistics. Queensland Office. Deaths, Queensland **3990**
Australia. Bureau of Statistics. Queensland Office. Census of Mining Establishments: Details of Operations by Industry Sub-division, Queensland. (AT ISSN 0728-5132) **703**, 3498
†Australia. Bureau of Statistics. Queensland Office. Census of Population and Housing: Characteristics of Persons and Dwellings in Suburbs of Brisbane City and Local Authority Areas within Brisbane Statistical Division. (AT) **5142**
†Australia. Bureau of Statistics. Queensland Office. Census (Year) - Aboriginal and Torres Strait Islander People in Queensland. (AT) **5142**

†Australia. Bureau of Statistics. Queensland Office. Census (Year) - Families and Households. (AT) **5142**
Australia. Bureau of Statistics. Queensland Office. Child Care Arrangements, Queensland. (AT ISSN 1034-5132) **4425**
†Australia. Bureau of Statistics. Queensland Office. Community Crime Prevention Attitudes, Queensland. (AT) **5142**
Australia. Bureau of Statistics. Queensland Office. Crops and Pastures, Queensland. (AT ISSN 1031-2145) **133**
Australia. Bureau of Statistics. Queensland Office. Deaths, Queensland. (AT ISSN 0816-0465) **3990**
Australia. Bureau of Statistics. Queensland Office. Demographic Summary, Queensland *see* Australia. Bureau of Statistics. Queensland Office. Demography, Queensland **3990**
Australia. Bureau of Statistics. Queensland Office. Demography, Queensland. (AT ISSN 1036-2649) **3990**, 4563
Australia. Bureau of Statistics. Queensland Office. Divorces, Queensland *see* Australia. Bureau of Statistics. Queensland Office. Demography, Queensland **3990**
Australia. Bureau of Statistics. Queensland Office. Dwelling Commencements Reported by Approving Authorities, Queensland. (AT ISSN 0814-8023) **2499**
Australia. Bureau of Statistics. Queensland Office. Dwelling Unit Commencements: Small Area Statistics, Queensland. (AT ISSN 1030-9683) **2499**
Australia. Bureau of Statistics. Queensland Office. Economic Indicators, Queensland. (AT ISSN 0819-2928) **703**
Australia. Bureau of Statistics. Queensland Office. Employment Injuries, Queensland. (AT ISSN 1032-5352) **3623**
†Australia. Bureau of Statistics. Queensland Office. Establishment Size Statistics. (AT) **5142**
Australia. Bureau of Statistics. Queensland Office. Estimated Resident Population and Area, Queensland. (AT ISSN 1031-8100) **3990**
Australia. Bureau of Statistics. Queensland Office. Estimated Resident Population and Area, Queensland, Preliminary. (AT ISSN 1030-911X) **3990**, 4563
Australia. Bureau of Statistics. Queensland Office. Estimated Resident Population: Components of Change, Queensland. (AT ISSN 1031-6264) **3990**
Australia. Bureau of Statistics. Queensland Office. Estimated Resident Population, Queensland. (AT) **3990**, 4563
Australia. Bureau of Statistics. Queensland Office. Fertility Trends in Queensland. (AT) **3990**
Australia. Bureau of Statistics. Queensland Office. Fruit, Queensland. (AT ISSN 0812-3152) **133**, 169
Australia. Bureau of Statistics. Queensland Office. Government Finance, Queensland. (AT ISSN 1031-2269) **703**
Australia. Bureau of Statistics. Queensland Office. Health and Welfare Establishments, Queensland. (AT ISSN 0728-294X) **4425**, 4116
†Australia. Bureau of Statistics. Queensland Office. Health and Welfare Establishments, Queensland, Preliminary. (AT ISSN 1031-2277) **5142**
Australia. Bureau of Statistics. Queensland Office. Hospital Morbidity, Queensland. (AT ISSN 0725-4857) **3990**, 2470

†Australia. Bureau of Statistics. Queensland Office. Hospital Morbidity Rates, Queensland. (AT) **5142**
Australia. Bureau of Statistics. Queensland Office. Household Expenditure Survey, Queensland. (AT) **2450**
†Australia. Bureau of Statistics. Queensland Office. Indexes of Retail Prices of Food in Queensland Towns. (AT) **5142**
†Australia. Bureau of Statistics. Queensland Office. Interstate and Foreign Trade. (AT) **5142**
Australia. Bureau of Statistics. Queensland Office. Labour Force, Queensland. (AT ISSN 0313-1912) **703**, 972
Australia. Bureau of Statistics. Queensland Office. Law and Order, Queensland, Summary. (AT ISSN 1030-9268) **1524**
Australia. Bureau of Statistics. Queensland Office. Law and Order, Queensland. (AT ISSN 0155-3631) **1524**
†Australia. Bureau of Statistics. Queensland Office. List of Publications. (AT ISSN 0312-7397) **5142**
Australia. Bureau of Statistics. Queensland Office. Livestock and Livestock Products, Queensland. (AT ISSN 0812-3195) **133**, 211
Australia. Bureau of Statistics. Queensland Office. Livestock Products - Meat, Queensland. (AT ISSN 0812-5767) **133**, 211
Australia. Bureau of Statistics. Queensland Office. Local Government Areas Statistical Summary, Queensland. (AT ISSN 1030-4789) **4563**
Australia. Bureau of Statistics. Queensland Office. Local Government, Queensland. (AT ISSN 1031-2528) **4079**, 703
Australia. Bureau of Statistics. Queensland Office. Manufacturing Establishments: Details of Operations, Queensland *see* Australia. Bureau of Statistics. Queensland Office. Manufacturing Industry, Queensland **703**
†Australia. Bureau of Statistics. Queensland Office. Manufacturing Establishments: Employment Size Statistics. (AT) **5142**
†Australia. Bureau of Statistics. Queensland Office. Manufacturing Establishments: Small Area Statistics, Queensland. (AT ISSN 0818-979X) **5142**
†Australia. Bureau of Statistics. Queensland Office. Manufacturing Establishments: Summary of Operations. (AT) **5142**
Australia. Bureau of Statistics. Queensland Office. Manufacturing Industry, Queensland. (AT ISSN 1036-2762) **703**
Australia. Bureau of Statistics. Queensland Office. Marriages, Queensland *see* Australia. Bureau of Statistics. Queensland Office. Demography, Queensland **3990**
Australia. Bureau of Statistics. Queensland Office. Migration Patterns in Queensland. (AT) **3990**
†Australia. Bureau of Statistics. Queensland Office. Mineral Production, Queensland. (AT ISSN 1031-2714) **5142**
Australia. Bureau of Statistics. Queensland Office. Monthly Summary of Statistics, Queensland. (AT ISSN 0048-6396) **4563**
Australia. Bureau of Statistics. Queensland Office. Motor Vehicle Registrations, Queensland. (AT ISSN 1031-2730) **4661**
†Australia. Bureau of Statistics. Queensland Office. Pre-schools and Child Care Centres, Queensland. (AT ISSN 0818-1993) **5142**
Australia. Bureau of Statistics. Queensland Office. Queensland Year Book. (AT ISSN 1030-7389) **4563**

†Australia. Bureau of Statistics. Queensland Office. Retail Industry: Details of Operations. (AT) **5142**
Australia. Bureau of Statistics. Queensland Office. Retail Industry: Small Area Statistics, Queensland. (AT) **703**
†Australia. Bureau of Statistics. Queensland Office. Road Traffic Accidents, Queensland (Annual). (AT ISSN 1031-3893) **5142**
†Australia. Bureau of Statistics. Queensland Office. Road Traffic Accidents, Queensland (Quarterly). (AT ISSN 1031-2803) **5142**
†Australia. Bureau of Statistics. Queensland Office. Sawmill Statistics, Queensland. (AT ISSN 0314-3287) **5142**
†Australia. Bureau of Statistics. Queensland Office. Schools, Queensland. (AT ISSN 0818-2582) **5142**
†Australia. Bureau of Statistics. Queensland Office. Schools, Queensland, Preliminary. (AT ISSN 0818-2132) **5142**
†Australia. Bureau of Statistics. Queensland Office. Selected Accommodation Establishments, Queensland. (AT) **5142**
Australia. Bureau of Statistics. Queensland Office. Seleted Agricultural Commodities, Queensland, Preliminary. (AT ISSN 0811-5141) **133**
†Australia. Bureau of Statistics. Queensland Office. Smoking Behaviour. (AT) **5142**
Australia. Bureau of Statistics. Queensland Office. Summary of Social Statistics, Queensland. (AT ISSN 0817-8526) **4425**
†Australia. Bureau of Statistics. Queensland Office. The Labour Force: Regional Estimates. (AT) **5142**
Australia. Bureau of Statistics. Queensland Office. Tourist Accommodation, Queensland. (AT ISSN 0725-394X) **2482**
†Australia. Bureau of Statistics. Queensland Office. Type and Conditions of Part-time Employment. (AT) **5142**
†Australia. Bureau of Statistics. Queensland Office. Usage of Legal Services, Queensland. (AT) **5142**
Australia. Bureau of Statistics. Queensland Office. Value of Agricultural Commodities Produced, Queensland. (AT ISSN 0810-7742) **133**
†Australia. Bureau of Statistics. Queesland Office. Transport, Queensland. (AT ISSN 1031-8097) **5142**
†Australia. Bureau of Statistics. Road Traffic Accidents Involving Fatalities, Australia. (AT ISSN 1031-1084) **5142**
Australia. Bureau of Statistics. Schools, Australia. (AT ISSN 1035-3461) **4079**, 1674
Australia. Bureau of Statistics. Schools, Australia, Preliminary. (AT ISSN 1034-5671) **4079**, 1674
†Australia. Bureau of Statistics. Seasonally Adjusted Indicators. (AT ISSN 0571-964X) **5142**
Australia. Bureau of Statistics. Shipping and Air Cargo Commodity Statistics, Australia. (AT ISSN 0814-138X) **4661**, 703
Australia. Bureau of Statistics. Social Indicators, Australia. (AT) **4079**
Australia. Bureau of Statistics. South Australian Office. Births, South Australia *see* Australia. Bureau of Statistics. South Australian Office. Demography, South Australia **3990**
Australia. Bureau of Statistics. South Australian Office. Building Activity. (AT) **636**
Australia. Bureau of Statistics. South Australian Office. Deaths, South Australia. (AT ISSN 0067-0898) **3990**

5946 AUSTRALIA. BUREAU

Australia. Bureau of Statistics. South Australian Office. Demography, South Australia. (AT) 3990

Australia. Bureau of Statistics. South Australian Office. Divorces, South Australia. (AT ISSN 0067-0901) 3990

Australia. Bureau of Statistics. South Australian Office. Manufacturing Establishments see Australia. Bureau of Statistics. South Australian Office. Manufacturing Establishments: Details of Operations by Industry 703

Australia. Bureau of Statistics. South Australian Office. Manufacturing Establishments: Details of Operations by Industry. (AT) 703

Australia. Bureau of Statistics. South Australian Office. Monthly Summary of Statistics, South Australia. (AT ISSN 0047-8032) 4563

Australia. Bureau of Statistics. South Australian Office. The Labour Force, South Australia. (AT) 703

Australia. Bureau of Statistics. State and Local Government Finance, Australia see Australia. Bureau of Statistics. Government Finance Statistics, Australia 703

Australia. Bureau of Statistics. Tasmanian Office. Agricultural Statistics, Tasmania. (AT) 133

Australia. Bureau of Statistics. Tasmanian Office. Crops and Pastures see Australia. Bureau of Statistics. Tasmanian Office. Agricultural Statistics, Tasmania 133

Australia. Bureau of Statistics. Tasmanian Office. Divorces Tasmania.(AT ISSN 0705-5773) 3991

Australia. Bureau of Statistics. Tasmanian Office. Finance see Australia. Bureau of Statistics. Tasmanian Office. Government Finance Statistics 703

Australia. Bureau of Statistics. Tasmanian Office. Fruit Production see Australia. Bureau of Statistics. Tasmanian Office. Agricultural Statistics, Tasmania 133

Australia. Bureau of Statistics. Tasmanian Office. Government Finance Statistics. (AT) 703

Australia. Bureau of Statistics. Tasmanian Office. Livestock and Livestock Products see Australia. Bureau of Statistics. Tasmanian Office. Agricultural Statistics, Tasmania 133

Australia. Bureau of Statistics. Tasmanian Office. Local Government Finance see Australia. Bureau of Statistics. Tasmanian Office. Government Finance Statistics 703

Australia. Bureau of Statistics. Tasmanian Office. Mining Tasmania. (AT ISSN 0314-1888) 3499, 4563

Australia. Bureau of Statistics. Tasmanian Office. Monthly Summary of Statistics Tasmania see Australia. Bureau of Statistics. Tasmanian Office. Tasmanian Statistical Indicators 4563

Australia. Bureau of Statistics. Tasmanian Office. Tasmanian Statistical Indicators. (AT) 4563

Australia. Bureau of Statistics. Tasmanian Office. Tasmanian Year Book. (AT ISSN 0082-2116) 2344

†Australia. Bureau of Statistics. Technical Papers. (AT) 5142

†Australia. Bureau of Statistics. Tertiary Education. (AT) 5142

Australia. Bureau of Statistics. Time Series Data on Magnetic Tape and Microfiche see Australia. Bureau of Statistics. Time Series Service 5142

†Australia. Bureau of Statistics. Time Series Service. (AT) 5142

Australia. Bureau of Statistics. Trade Union Statistics, Australia. (AT ISSN 0312-1437) 2592

Australia. Bureau of Statistics. Value of Agricultural Commodities Produced, Australia. (AT ISSN 1031-0789) 134

Australia. Bureau of Statistics. Victorian Office. Estimated Resident Population in Statistical Local Areas, Victoria. (AT ISSN 0819-6575) 3991, 4563

Australia. Bureau of Statistics. Victorian Office. Local Government Finance, Victoria. (AT ISSN 1030-0724) 703, 4563

Australia. Bureau of Statistics. Victorian Office. Monthly Summary of Statistics, Victoria. (AT ISSN 0158-202X) 4563

†Australia. Bureau of Statistics. Victorian Office. Schools, Victoria. (AT ISSN 1031-7767) 5142

Australia. Bureau of Statistics. Victorian Office. Summary of Statistics (Year). (AT ISSN 1033-3665) 4563

Australia. Bureau of Statistics. Victorian Office. Value of Agricultural Commodities Produced, Victoria see Australia. Bureau of Statistics. Victorian Office. Value of Agricultural Production, Victoria 134

Australia. Bureau of Statistics. Victorian Office. Value of Agricultural Production, Victoria. (AT) 134, 4563

Australia. Bureau of Statistics. Victorian Office. Victorian Monthly Statistical Review see Australia. Bureau of Statistics. Victorian Office. Monthly Summary of Statistics, Victoria 4563

Australia. Bureau of Statistics. Victorian Office. Victorian Yearbook. (AT ISSN 0067-1223) 4563

Australia. Bureau of Statistics. Western Australian Office. Abstract of Statistics of Local Government Areas. see Australia. Bureau of Statistics. Western Australian Office. Local Government, Western Australia 4079

†Australia. Bureau of Statistics. Western Australian Office. Census of Manufacturing Establishments. Summary of Operations by Group, Western Australia. (AT ISSN 0727-2200) 5142

Australia. Bureau of Statistics. Western Australian Office. Fisheries, Western Australia. (AT ISSN 0705-2146) 2051, 4563

Australia. Bureau of Statistics. Western Australian Office. Industrial Accidents, Western Australia see Western Australia. Department of Occupational Health, Safety and Welfare. Industrial Accidents 5303

Australia. Bureau of Statistics. Western Australian Office. Local Government, Western Australia. (AT ISSN 0312-6072) 4079

Australia. Bureau of Statistics. Western Australian Office. Monthly Summary of Statistics. (AT ISSN 0727-2367) 4563

Australia. Bureau of Statistics. Western Australian Office. Monthly Statistical Summary see Australia. Bureau of Statistics. Western Australian Office. Monthly Summary of Statistics 4563

Australia. Bureau of Statistics. Year Book Australia. (AT ISSN 0810-8633) 4563

Australia. Chamber of Industries, Northern Territory. N.T. Business Journal. (AT) 808

Australia. Chamber of Industries, Northern Territory. Northern Territory Business Journal see Australia. Chamber of Industries, Northern Territory. N.T. Business Journal 808

Australia. China Council Annual Report. (AT ISSN 0727-2987) 3951

Australia. Commonwealth Department of Education. Annual Report see Australia. Department of Employment, Education and Training. Annual Report 1617

Australia. Commonwealth Department of Health. Annual Report see Australia. Department of Community Services and Health. Annual Report (Year) 4098

†Australia. Commonwealth Grants Commission. Grants Commission Report on Financial Assistance for Local Government. (AT) 5143

Australia. Department of Aboriginal Affairs. Report. (AT) 1992

†Australia. Department of Administrative Services. Australian Construction Services. Technical Bulletin. (AT) 5143

Australia. Department of Civil Aviation. Civil Aviation Report see Australian Transport 5144

Australia. Department of Community Services and Health. Annual Report (Year). (AT) 4098

Australia. Department of Employment and Industrial Relations. Annual Report. (AT) 972

†Australia. Department of Employment and Industrial Relations. Employee Participation News. (AT ISSN 0811-1863) 5143

Australia. Department of Employment, Education and Training. Annual Report. (AT) 1617

Australia. Department of Foreign Affairs and Trade. Select Documents on International Affairs. (AT) 3951

Australia. Department of Foreign Affairs. International Treaties and Conventions see Australia. Department of Foreign Affairs and Trade. Select Documents on International Affairs 3951

Australia. Department of Foreign Affairs. Select Documents on International Affairs see Australia. Department of Foreign Affairs and Trade. Select Documents on International Affairs 3951

Australia. Department of Home Affairs. Norfolk Island Annual Report. (AT) 2344

Australia. Department of Industry, Technology and Commerce. Annual Report. (AT ISSN 0728-6856) 1087

Australia. Department of Labour and National Service. Personnel Practice Bulletin see Work and People 1071

Australia. Department of Police and Customs. Review of Activities see Australia. Department of Industry, Technology and Commerce. Annual Report 1087

Australia. Department of Primary Industries and Energy. Annual Report. (AT ISSN 1032-4054) 844

Australia. Department of Primary Industries and Energy. Background Fisheries Statistics. (AT) 2051

Australia. Department of Primary Industries and Energy. Basic Fish Statistics see Australia. Department of Primary Industries and Energy. Background Fisheries Statistics 2051

Australia. Department of Primary Industries and Energy. Cotton Market News. (AT) 169

Australia. Department of Primary Industries and Energy. Raw Cotton Marketing Advisory Committee. Annual Report. (AT) 169

Australia. Department of Primary Industries and Energy. Recommended Marketing Names for Fish. (AT) 2037

†Australia. Department of Primary Industries and Energy. Streamline Update. (AT) 5143

Australia. Department of Primary Industries and Energy. Wheat Industry Research, A.C.T. Annual Report see Australia. Department of Primary Industries and Energy. Wheat Research Council. Annual Report 169

Australia. Department of Primary Industries and Energy. Wheat Research Council. Annual Report. (AT ISSN 0819-5854) 169

Australia. Department of Primary Industry. Annual Report see Australia. Department of Primary Industries and Energy. Annual Report 844

Australia. Department of Primary Industry. Australian Plague and Locust Commission. Annual Report. (AT ISSN 0313-2781) 147

†Australia. Department of Primary Industry. Conditions for Export of Experimental Shipments. (AT) 5143

†Australia. Department of Primary Industry. Conditions for Export of Grapes. (AT) 5143

†Australia. Department of Primary Industry. Conditions for Export of Primary Products. (AT) 5143

Australia. Department of Primary Industry. Cotton Market News see Australia. Department of Primary Industries and Energy. Cotton Market News 169

Australia. Department of Primary Industry. Monthly Forest Products Trade Statistics see Australia. Bureau of Agricultural and Resource Economics. Monthly Forest Products Trade Statistics 2111

Australia. Department of Primary Industry. Poultry Industry Assistance. Annual Report. (AT ISSN 0728-6929) 211

Australia. Department of Primary Industry. Raw Cotton Marketing Advisory Committee. Annual Report see Australia. Department of Primary Industries and Energy. Raw Cotton Marketing Advisory Committee. Annual Report 169

†Australia. Department of Primary Industry. Tobacco Industry Trust. Account Annual Report. (AT ISSN 0404-181X) 5143

Australia. Department of Resources and Energy. Streamline Update see Australia. Department of Primary Industries and Energy. Streamline Update 5143

Australia. Department of Social Security. Annual Report of the Director-General. (AT) 2527

Australia. Department of Territory of Norfolk Island. Report see Australia. Department of Home Affairs. Norfolk Island Annual Report 2344

Australia. Department of the Treasury. Economic Round-Up. (AT) 703

Australia. Department of the Treasury. Income Tax Statistics. (AT ISSN 0067-1444) 703

Australia. Department of the Treasury. Round-Up see Australia. Department of the Treasury. Economic Round-Up 703

Australia. Department of the Treasury. Taxation Branch. Taxation Statistics. (AT ISSN 0519-6035) 703

Australia. Department of the Treasury. Treasury Economic Paper. (AT) 1087

Australia. Designs Office. Annual Record of Designs Office Proceedings. (AT) 3672

†Australia. Education Research and Development Committee. Annual Report. (AT) 5143

Australia. Fishing Industry Research and Development Council. Annual Report.(AT) 2037

Australia. Fishing Industry Research Committee. Annual Report see Australia. Fishing Industry Research and Development Council. Annual Report 2037

Australia. Foreign Investment Review Board. Report. (AT) 938

†Australia. Industries Assistance Commission. Annual Report. (AT) 5143

Australia. Insurance Commissioner. Annual Report. (AT) 2527

Australia. Land Transport Statistics. Non-Government Railways see Australian Non-Government Railways Operating Statistics (Years) 4661

Australia. Law Reform Commission. Annual Report. (AT ISSN 0312-6994) 2601

Title

†Australia. Library Information Service. Catalogue of Serials. (AT ISSN 0156-9643) 5143
†Australia. National Capital Development Commission. Annual Report. (AT ISSN 0067-1517) 5143
†Australia. National Capital Development Commission. Technical Papers. (AT ISSN 0313-9948) 5143
Australia. National Drug Information Service. Technical Information Bulletin see Australia. National Information Service on Drug Abuse. Technical Information Bulletin 1534
Australia. National Health and Medical Research Council. Department of Health. Medical Research. (AT ISSN 0811-6199) 3079
Australia. National Health and Medical Research Council. Department of Health. Report. (AT ISSN 0728-6910) 3080
Australia. National Information Service on Drug Abuse. Technical Information Bulletin. (AT ISSN 0157-8200) 1534
†Australia. National Women's Advisory Council. Annual Report. (AT) 5143
Australia. Non-Government Railways Statistics see Australian Non-Government Railways Operating Statistics (Years) 4661
†Australia. Northern Territory Protocol and Public Relations Branch. Territory Digest. (AT) 5143
Australia. Northern Territory Protocol and Public Relations Service. Territory Digest see Australia. Northern Territory Protocol and Public Relations Branch. Territory Digest 5143
Australia. Nuclear Science and Technology Organisation. A N S T O. (AT ISSN 1030-7745) 1804, 1815
†Australia. Nuclear Science and Technology Organisation. A N S T O - M. (AT) 5143
Australia. Nuclear Science and Technology Organisation. List of Report Publications. (AT) 3836
Australia. Office of the Life Insurance Commissioner. Half Yearly Financial & Statistical Bulletin. (AT ISSN 0728-6864) 2527, 2545
Australia. Operation of the Fishing Industry, A.C.T. Annual Report. (AT ISSN 0067-1436) 2037
Australia. Patent Office. Annual Report of Activities see Australia. Patent, Trade Marks and Designs Offices. Activities Report 3672
Australia. Patent, Trade Marks and Designs Offices. Activities Report. (AT) 3672
Australia. Public Service Board. Annual Report. (AT) 4054
Australia. Public Service Board. Bulletin.(AT ISSN 0157-6178) 4054
†Australia. Stevedoring Statistics. Stevedoring Labour Review. (AT) 5143
Australia. Working Papers in Language and Linguistics. (AT ISSN 0312-5467) 2804
†Australia & New Zealand Jewish Year Book. (AT) 5143
Australia and New Zealand Journal of Developmental Disabilities. (AT ISSN 0726-3864) 3331, 1733
Australia & Pacific Islands Letter. (II) 3874
Australia and the Sea. (AT ISSN 1031-3516) 4724
Australia at a Glance. (AT ISSN 1031-0541) 4564
†Australia Bulletin. (US) 5143
Australia Camera Craft Photographer's Handbook. (AT) 3788
Australia Concise Stamp Catalogue. (UK) 3749
†Australia Handbook. (AT ISSN 0067-1495) 5143
Australia Indonesia Association of New South Wales. Bulletin see Kabar 3963

Australia Investment Quarterly. (AT ISSN 0815-9076) 938
Australia - Israel Review. (AT ISSN 0313-9727) 2859
Australia - Japan Economic Institute Newsletter see A - J E I Newsletter 643
Australia Law Reform Commission Report Series see A L R C Report Series 2593
Australia Mineral Development Laboratories Bulletin see A M D E L Bulletin 1553
Australia - New Zealand Association News see A N Z A News 2171
Australia-New Zealand Conference on Geomechanics Proceedings. (AT) 1862, 1587
Australia New Zealand Conference on Soil Mechanics and Foundation Engineering Proceedings see Australia-New Zealand Conference on Geomechanics Proceedings 1862
Australia New Zealand Foundation. Annual Report (Year). (AT ISSN 0810-0055) 3951, 4398
Australia Now. (US ISSN 0045-0197) 2171
Australia Parliamentary Seminar. Summary Report of Proceedings see Australasian and Pacific Regional Parliamentary Seminar. Summary Report of Proceedings 2601
Australian Aboriginal Studies. (AT ISSN 0729-4352) 235, 266, 318
Australian Academic and Research Libraries. (AT ISSN 0004-8623) 2745
Australian Academy of Science. Annual General Meeting Symposium. (AT) 4300
†Australian Academy of Science. National Committee for Antarctic Research. Australian Antarctic and Sub-Antarctic Research Programmes.(AT) 5143
Australian Academy of Science. Records see Historical Records of Australian Science 4312
Australian Academy of Science. Reports see Australian Academy of Science. Annual General Meeting Symposium 4300
Australian Academy of Science. Science and Industry Forum Reports. (AT ISSN 0067-1576) 4300
Australian Academy of Science. Year Book. (AT ISSN 0067-1584) 4300
Australian Academy of the Humanities. Proceedings. (AT ISSN 0067-1592) 2503
Australian Accommodation Guide. (AT) 4752, 2471
Australian Accountant. (AT ISSN 0004-8631) 747
Australian Accounting Research Foundation. Discussion Paper (Accounting). (AT ISSN 0818-9404) 747
Australian Accounting Research Foundation. Research Studies. (AT) 747
Australian Accounting Research Foundation Report see A A R F Report 744
Australian Accounting Standard. (AT ISSN 1034-3717) 747
Australian Accounts Preparation Manual. (AT) 747
Australian Acoustical Society. Bulletin see Acoustics Australia 3858
Australian Acupuncture Association. Newsletter. (AT) 3080
Australian Administrator. (AT ISSN 0158-7447) 1725
Australian Advances in Veterinary Science see Australian Veterinary Association Conference Handbook 4807
Australian Advertising Rate and Data Service. (AT ISSN 0067-1606) 28
Australian Agricultural Economics Society. Papers Presented at Annual Conference (Microfiche). (AT) 77, 646
Australian Agriculture, Fisheries and Forestry Directory see Rural Industry Directory 118
Australian Airsport. (AT) 47, 4465

Australian-American Business Review. (US) 900
Australian-American News N.S.W. Annual Edition. (AT) 3951, 4752
Australian and New Zealand Association for the Advancement of Science Congress Papers see A N Z A A S Congress Papers 4295
Australian and New Zealand Biotechnology Directory. (AT ISSN 1032-8068) 1122, 487
Australian and New Zealand Booksellers see Australian and New Zealand Booksellers and Publishers 4121
Australian and New Zealand Booksellers and Publishers. (AT) 4121
Australian and New Zealand Citator to UK Reports. Cumulative Supplement.(AT ISSN 0814-5733) 2601
Australian & New Zealand Conveyancing Report. (AT) 1087
Australian and New Zealand Equal Opportunity Law and Practice. (AT) 2601
Australian and New Zealand Hospitals and Health Services Yearbook see Australian Hospitals and Health Services Yearbook 2459
Australian and New Zealand Insurance Reporter. (AT) 2527, 2601
Australian and New Zealand Journal of Criminology. (AT ISSN 0004-8658) 1510
Australian and New Zealand Journal of Family Therapy. (AT ISSN 0814-723X) 4429, 4012, 4398
Australian and New Zealand Journal of Medicine. (AT ISSN 0004-8291) 3080
Australian and New Zealand Journal of Obstetrics and Gynecology. (AT ISSN 0004-8666) 3289
Australian and New Zealand Journal of Ophthalmology. (AT ISSN 0814-9763) 3298
Australian & New Zealand Journal of Psychiatry. (AT ISSN 0004-8674) 3331
▼Australian & New Zealand Journal of Serials Librarianship. (US ISSN 0898-3283) 2745
Australian & New Zealand Journal of Sociology. (AT ISSN 0004-8690) 4429
Australian and New Zealand Journal of Surgery. (AT ISSN 0004-8682) 3376
Australian & New Zealand Society for Theological Studies. Colloquium. (AT ISSN 0588-3237) 4164
Australian and New Zealand Studies in Canada. (CN ISSN 0843-5049) 2897
Australian and New Zealand Studies in German Language and Literature. (SZ) 2897, 2804
Australian and New Zealand Wine Industry Directory. (AT ISSN 0811-1324) 377, 1122
Australian and New Zealand Wine Industry Journal. (AT ISSN 0819-2421) 377
Australian Angler see The Australian Angler's Fishing World 4541
The Australian Angler's Fishing World. (AT ISSN 0158-572X) 4541, 2037
Australian Angora Mohair Journal see The Mohair Bulletin 4622
Australian Animal Health Laboratory Biennial Report see A A H L Biennial Report 4804
Australian Animal Health Laboratory Newsletter see A A H L Newsletter 4804
Australian Antique Collector. (AT ISSN 0004-8704) 256, 318
Australian Antique Trader. (AT) 256, 2548
†Australian Antiques Trade Gazette. (AT) 5143
Australian Apparel Manufacturer. (AT ISSN 0816-3588) 4616
Australian Arabian Horse News. (AT) 4532
Australian Archaeology. (AT ISSN 0312-2417) 266

Australian Art Auction Records. (AT ISSN 0819-923X) 318, 417
Australian Art Education. (AT ISSN 1032-1942) 318, 1617, 1744
Australian, Asian & Pacific Electrical World. (AT) 1882
Australian Asphalt Pavement Association Asphalt Review see A.A.P.A. Asphalt Review 1861
Australian Asphalt Pavement Association Newsletter see A.A.P.A. Newsletter 1861
Australian Association for Adolescent Health. Newsletter. (AT ISSN 0157-9789) 3080, 1249
Australian Association for the Teaching of English Guide to English Books and Resources see A.A.T.E. Guide to English Books and Resources 2980
Australian Association of Adult Education. Newsletter. (AT ISSN 0727-4386) 1682
Australian Association of Clinical Biochemists. Newsletter. (AT) 471
†Australian Association of Permanent Building Societies. National Newsletter. (AT ISSN 0310-1045) 5143
†Australian Audio-Visual Reference Book. (AT ISSN 0311-323X) 5143
Australian Author. (AT ISSN 0045-026X) 4121
Australian Bank Employees Union Newsletter see A.B.E.U. Newsletter 757
Australian Banker. (AT) 759
Australian Bankruptcy Bulletin see Australian Insolvency Bulletin 759
Australian Bankruptcy Legislation. (AT) 2601
†Australian Baptist. (AT ISSN 0004-8739) 5143
Australian Bar Review. (AT ISSN 0814-8589) 2601
Australian Beacon. (AT) 4164
Australian Beauty Counter. (AT ISSN 0726-2566) 375
Australian Beverage Review see Hospitality Beverage 381
Australian Biblical Review. (AT ISSN 0045-0308) 4164
Australian Bibliographic Network Authorities see A B N Authorities 388
Australian Bibliographic Network News see A B N News 2740
Australian Biochemical Society. Proceedings. (AT ISSN 0067-1703) 471
Australian Biochemical Society. Programme and Abstracts see Australian Biochemical Society. Proceedings 471
†Australian Biographical and Genealogical Record. Newsletter. (AT) 5143
Australian Birds. (AT ISSN 0311-8150) 562
Australian Birdwatcher. (AT ISSN 0045-0316) 562
Australian Book Collector. (AT ISSN 1034-0785) 2897, 2981
Australian Book Publishers Association Directory of Members see A B P A Directory of Members 4120
Australian Books. (AT ISSN 0067-1738) 389
Australian Books in Print. (AT ISSN 0067-172X) 389
Australian Books in Print on Microfiche. (AT) 389, 4139
Australian Bookseller and Publisher. (AT ISSN 0004-8763) 4121
Australian Booksellers see Australian and New Zealand Booksellers and Publishers 4121
Australian Bride Magazine see Mode Brides 3067
Australian Bridge. (AT ISSN 0045-0332) 4465
†Australian British Business Directory. (AT) 5143
Australian British Chamber of Commerce Newsletter see A B C C Newsletter 806
Australian Builder. (AT ISSN 0004-878X) 601

Australian Building Construction and Housing. (AT ISSN 1032-240X) **601**
Australian Building News. (AT ISSN 1030-1925) **601, 295**
Australian Bulletin of Labour. (AT ISSN 0311-6336) **972**
Australian Bureau of Statistics. Distribution and Composition of Employee Earnings and Hours, Australia. (AT ISSN 1031-024X) **704**
Australian Bureau of Statistics. List of Publications to be Released in (Year) *see* Australian Bureau of Statistics. Publications to be Released in (Year) **4564**
Australian Bureau of Statistics. Publications to be Released in (Year). (AT ISSN 1032-0512) **4564**
▼Australian Business Advisers Guide. (AT) **646**
†Australian Business and Assets Planning Reporter. (AT) **5143**
Australian Business Collector's Annual *see* Australian Collector's Quarterly **256**
Australian Business Education Directory.(AT) **646, 1682**
Australian Business Index. (AT ISSN 0725-3109) **704**
Australian Business Law Review. (AT ISSN 0310-1053) **2706, 2601**
Australian Business Monthly. (AT) **646**
Australian Business Profiles. (AT) **1072**
Australian Camera Craft. (AT ISSN 0158-2658) **3788**
Australian Canary Breeder. (AT) **3708**
Australian Canegrower. (AT ISSN 0157-3039) **78**
Australian Capital Gains Tax Planner. (AT) **1087**
Australian Capital Territory at a Glance.(AT ISSN 0815-3523) **4564**
Australian Capital Territory Statistical Summary. (AT ISSN 0067-1754) **4564**
Australian Caravan World and Camper Trailering *see* Australian Caravan World and Outdoor Life **4752**
Australian Caravan World and Outdoor Life. (AT) **4752, 4647**
Australian Case Citator. (AT) **2601**
Australian Cat Federation, Inc. Year Book *see* A C I Year Book **3707**
Australian Catalogue of New Films and Videos. (AT) **3503, 1384**
Australian Catholic Historical Society. Journal. (AT ISSN 0084-7259) **2344**
Australian Catholic Social Justice Council Occasional Papers *see* A C S J C Occasional Papers **3939**
Australian Centre for Maritime Studies. Occasional Papers in Maritime Affairs. (AT) **4724, 2037**
Australian Ceramic Society. Journal. (SZ ISSN 0004-881X) **1161**
Australian Chamber of Commerce Agenda for Reform Papers *see* A C C Agenda for Reform Papers **806**
Australian Chamber of Commerce Research Papers *see* A C C Research Papers **806**
Australian Chamber of Commerce Submission Papers *see* A C C Submission Papers **806**
Australian Chamber of Commerce Touche Ross Tax Legislation Fact Papers *see* A C C Touche Ross Tax Legislation Fact Papers **806**
Australian Chamber of Commerce Westpac Economic Discussion Papers *see* A.C.C. - Westpac Economic Discussion Papers **806**
Australian Chamber of Manufactures Bulletin (N.S.W. Edition) *see* A C M Bulletin (N.S.W. Edition) **1071**
Australian Chamber of Manufactures Bulletin (Victorian Edition) *see* A C M Bulletin (Victorian Edition) **806**
Australian Charter Guide. (AT) **4522**
Australian Chemical Processing and Engineering *see* P A C E **1857**
Australian Chemistry Resource Book. (AT ISSN 1031-8305) **1170**
Australian Chess Lore. (AT) **4465**

Australian Chicken Farmer. (AT) **211, 646**
Australian Children's Folklore Newsletter. (AT ISSN 0728-5531) **2052, 1232**
Australian Children's Television Action Committee Newsletter *see* A C T A C Newsletter **1248**
†Australian Children's Television Foundation. Information Papers. (AT ISSN 0812-1621) **5143**
Australian Chiropractors Association. Journal *see* Chiropractic Journal of Australia **3213**
Australian Chiropractor's Association. Membership Directory *see* Chiropractors' Association of Australia. Membership Directory **3214**
Australian Christian. (AT ISSN 0004-8852) **4229**
Australian Churches of Christ Historical Society. Digest. (AT) **2344, 417, 4164**
Australian Citizen Limited *see* Interaction (Canberra) **4409**
Australian Citrus News. (AT ISSN 0004-8283) **169**
Australian Clay Journal & Ceramic News. (AT ISSN 1035-4611) **601**
Australian Clay Target Shooting News. (AT) **4465, 2433**
Australian Clinical Review. (AT ISSN 0726-3139) **3080**
Australian Coal Industry Research Laboratories. Annual Report. (AT ISSN 0067-1762) **3478**
Australian Coal Miner. (AT ISSN 0726-7819) **3478**
Australian Coal Report. (AT ISSN 0157-4566) **3478, 1783**
Australian Coin Review. (AT ISSN 0004-8887) **3598**
Australian Collector's Quarterly. (AT ISSN 1032-707X) **256, 3522**
Australian College of Education. New South Wales Chapter Newsletter. (AT ISSN 0813-3085) **1617**
Australian College of Ophthalmologists Transactions. *see* Australian and New Zealand Journal of Ophthalmology **3298**
Australian Commerce Review *see* A.C.C. - Westpac Economic Discussion Papers **806**
Australian Commodore and Amiga Review. (AT) **1467**
Australian Commodore Review *see* Australian Commodore and Amiga Review **1467**
Australian Commonwealth Collectors Club of New South Wales. Bulletin. (AT) **3749**
Australian Communication Review. (AT ISSN 0726-3252) **1368, 2503**
Australian Communications. (AT ISSN 0816-5890) **1361**
Australian Communications Networks. (AT) **1332**
Australian Company Law *see* Australian Corporation Law **2601**
†Australian Company Law & Practice. (AT ISSN 0726-6065) **5143**
Australian Company Law Cases. (AT) **2706**
Australian Company Law Reports *see* Australian Corporations and Securities Reports **2706**
Australian Company Practice. (AT) **2601, 972**
Australian Company Secretary's Business Law Manual. (AT) **2706, 646**
Australian Company Secretary's Letter. (AT ISSN 0729-1221) **2706, 1087**
Australian Company Secretary's Practice Manual. (AT) **646**
Australian Compensation Review. (AT) **1062**
†Australian Composer. (AT ISSN 0311-2764) **5143**
Australian Computer Journal. (AT ISSN 0004-8917) **1389**
Australian Computer Society Inc. Victorian Bulletin *see* A C S Victorian Bulletin **1388**
Australian Computer Weekly *see* Pacific Computer Weekly **1399**

Australian Concrete Construction. (AT ISSN 1034-7860) **601**
Australian Confederation of Operating Room Nurses Journal *see* A C O R N Journal **2458**
Australian Conference on Chemical Engineering. Proceedings *see* Chemeca - Australasian Conference on Chemical Engineering. Proceedings **1849**
Australian Congress of Trade Unions. Decisions. (AT) **2580**
Australian Conservation Foundation. Annual Report. (AT ISSN 0587-5846) **1483**
Australian Conservation Foundation. Conservation Directory *see* Green Pages: Directory of Non-Government Environmental Groups in Australia **1488**
Australian Consumer Sales and Credit Law Reporter. (AT) **2601, 646**
Australian Contract Furnishing Cyclopaedia. (AT) **2556**
▼Australian Contract Law Reporter. (AT) **2601**
Australian Contract Yearbook *see* Australian Contract Furnishing Cyclopaedia **2556**
Australian Copyright Council. Bulletin. (AT ISSN 0311-2934) **3672**
Australian Corporate Affairs Reporter *see* Australian Company Law & Practice **5143**
Australian Corporation Law. (AT) **2601**
▼Australian Corporations & Securities Law Reporter. (AT) **2706**
Australian Corporations and Securities Reports. (AT ISSN 1033-7466) **2706**
Australian Correspondence Chess Quarterly. (AT ISSN 0819-7806) **4465**
Australian Cottongrower. (AT) **169**
Australian Council for Educational Research. Annual Report. (AT) **1617**
†Australian Council for Educational Research. Occasional Papers. (AT ISSN 0067-1835) **5143**
Australian Council for Educational Research. Research Monograph. (AT) **1617**
Australian Council for Educational Research. Research Series *see* Australian Council for Educational Research. Research Monograph **1617**
Australian Council for Educational Research Newsletter *see* A C E R Newsletter **1698**
Australian Council for Health, Physical Education and Recreation National Journal *see* A C H P E R National Journal **1613**
Australian Council for Overseas Aid News *see* A.C.F.O.A. News **925**
Australian Council for Rehabilitation of Disabled (ACROD) Newsletter *see* A C R O D Newsletter **4396**
Australian Council of State School Organisations Policy (Year) *see* A C S S O Policy (Year) **1613**
Australian Council of Trade Unions Bulletin *see* A C T U Bulletin **5127**
Australian Council of Trade Unions National Youth Brochure *see* A C T U National Youth Brochure **5127**
Australian Council of Trade Unions Youth Book *see* A C T U Youth Book **5127**
Australian Country Music Newsletter. (AT) **3540**
Australian Credit Unions Magazine. (AT ISSN 0725-0665) **759**
Australian Cricket. (AT) **4499**
Australian Cricket Journal. (AT ISSN 0816-651X) **4499, 4429**
Australian Cricket Newspaper *see* Australian Cricket **4499**
Australian Cricket Tour Guide. (AT) **4499**
Australian Cricket Yearbook *see* Australian Cricket Tour Guide **4499**
Australian Crime Prevention Council Forum *see* A.C.P.C. Forum **5127**
Australian Criminal Law - Federal Offences. (AT) **1510**

Australian Criminal Reports. (AT) **1510, 2601**
Australian Croquet Gazette. (AT ISSN 0817-6604) **4499**
Australian Cultural History. (AT ISSN 0728-8433) **2344**
Australian Current Law *see* Australian Current Law Legislation **2601**
Australian Current Law *see* Australian Current Law Reporter **2602**
Australian Current Law Legislation. (AT) **2601**
Australian Current Law Reporter. (AT) **2602**
▼Australian Customs Law and Practice.(AT) **2602, 900**
Australian Cyclist. (AT ISSN 1034-3016) **4515**
Australian Dairy Farmer. (AT) **197**
Australian De Facto Relationships Law. (AT) **2602**
Australian Defence Equipment Catalogue. (AT) **3452**
Australian Defence Force Journal. (AT) **3452, 2307**
Australian Demographic Statistics. (AT ISSN 1031-055X) **3991**
Australian Dental Association. Dental Bulletin. (AT) **3228**
Australian Dental Association. News Bulletin. (AT ISSN 0810-7440) **3228**
Australian Dental Journal. (AT ISSN 0045-0421) **3228**
Australian Department of Social Security. Social Security Journal. (AT) **4398**
Australian Department of Social Security. Social Security Quarterly *see* Australian Department of Social Security. Social Security Journal **4398**
Australian Design Series. (AT) **2548**
Australian Digest. (AT ISSN 0067-1843) **2602**
Australian Digest Annual Supplement *see* Australian Digest **2602**
†Australian Director. (AT) **5143**
Australian Directory of Conferences, Seminars and Short Courses *see* Australian Business Education Directory **646**
Australian Disability Review. (AT ISSN 0813-4537) **2283, 1733**
Australian Dispute Resolution Journal. (AT ISSN 1034-3059) **2602**
Australian Doll Digest. (AT) **256, 3522**
Australian Dr Weekly. (AT ISSN 0814-6012) **3080, 4098**
Australian Dried Fruit News. (AT) **2062**
Australian Drilling. (AT ISSN 1037-3535) **4822**
Australian Drug and Alcohol Review *see* Drug and Alcohol Review **1535**
Australian Early Childhood Association. Victorian Branch. Journal. (AT) **1617, 1232**
Australian Early Childhood Association. Victorian Branch. Newsletter *see* Australian Early Childhood Association. Victorian Branch. Journal **1617**
Australian Early Childhood Newsletter. (AT ISSN 1030-0236) **1232, 1744**
Australian Early Childhood Research Booklets *see* Australian Early Childhood Resource Booklets **1232**
Australian Early Childhood Resource Booklets. (AT) **1232, 1725, 1744, 4012**
Australian Earth Sciences Information System Quarterly *see* A E S I S Quarterly **1549**
†Australian Economic Brief. (AT ISSN 1030-6560) **5143**
Australian Economic History Review. (AT ISSN 0004-8992) **889**
Australian Economic Papers. (AT ISSN 0004-900X) **646**
Australian Economic Review. (AT ISSN 0004-9018) **646**
Australian Education Index. (AT ISSN 0004-9026) **1674, 3, 2745**
Australian Education Review. (AT ISSN 0311-6875) **1617**
Australian Educational Researcher. (AT ISSN 0311-6999) **1617**

Australian Electrical Contractor. (AT ISSN 0812-3594) **1882**
Australian Electrical World *see* Australian, Asian & Pacific Electrical World **1882**
Australian Electronics Directory. (AT ISSN 0159-2947) **1764**
Australian Electronics Engineering. (AT ISSN 0004-9042) **1764**
†Australian Electronics Monthly. (AT ISSN 0815-5046) **5143**
Australian Employment Law Guide. (AT) **2706**, **972**
Australian Employment Legislation. (AT) **2706**, **972**
Australian Energy Statistics. (AT ISSN 0727-2596) **1797**, **4564**
Australian Engineering Case Studies *see* Graduate Careers in Engineering **1917**
Australian Engineering Directory. (AT ISSN 0159-2955) **1815**
Australian Entomological Magazine. (AT ISSN 0311-1881) **529**
Australian Entomological Society. Journal. (AT ISSN 0004-9050) **529**
Australian Entomological Society. Miscellaneous Publications. (AT) **529**
Australian Entomological Society. News Bulletin. (AT) **529**
Australian Environment. (US) **1943**
Australian Esperantist. (AT) **2804**
Australian Expatriate. (US) **4752**
Australian Exports *see* Australian Exports and Imports **900**
Australian Exports and Imports. (AT ISSN 1032-2116) **900**, **1122**
▼Australian Faculty Directory. (AT) **1700**
Australian Families Income Transfer Bulletin *see* A F I T Bulletin **5128**
The Australian Family. (AT) **1232**, **2444**
Australian Family and Society Abstracts.(AT ISSN 1032-4003) **4457**, **3991**
Australian Family Bulletin *see* The Australian Family **1232**
Australian Family Circle. (AT ISSN 0310-1118) **2171**
Australian Family Law & Practice. (AT) **2716**
Australian Family Law - Court Handbook. (AT) **2716**
†Australian Family Law Guide. (AT) **5143**
Australian Family Law Service. (AT) **2716**
Australian Family Physician. (AT ISSN 0300-8495) **3080**
Australian Farm Management Society Newsletter *see* Australian Farm Manager **78**
Australian Farm Manager. (AT ISSN 1035-1914) **78**
Australian Farmers' Dealers' Journal *see* A F D J **161**
Australian Federal Tax Reporter. (AT ISSN 0310-7817) **1087**
Australian Federation of University Women. Newsletter. (AT) **4837**, **1700**
Australian Feminist Studies. (AT ISSN 0816-4649) **4837**, **4366**
Australian Film and Television School. Annual Report *see* Australian Film, Television and Radio School. Annual Report **1368**
Australian Film and Television School Handbook *see* Australian Film, Television and Radio School Handbook **1368**
Australian Film Institute Newsletter. (AT ISSN 0313-7031) **3503**
Australian Film, Television and Radio School. Annual Report. (AT) **1368**, **1355**, **3503**
Australian Film, Television and Radio School Handbook. (AT ISSN 0313-8461) **1368**, **1355**, **3503**
†Australian Films. (AT ISSN 0045-0448) **5143**
Australian Finance Availability Guide. (AT) **759**
Australian Financial Review. (AT) **759**
Australian Fisheries. (AT ISSN 0004-9115) **2037**

Australian Fisheries Newsletter *see* Australian Fisheries **2037**
Australian Fishing Industry Directory (Year). (AT ISSN 0157-9630) **2037**
Australian Fleet Magazine. (AT) **4679**, **4743**
Australian Fluoridation News. Aqua-Pura. (AT) **4822**, **4098**
Australian Flying. (AT ISSN 0004-9123) **47**
Australian Folklore. (AT ISSN 0819-0852) **2052**, **4429**
Australian Foreign Affairs and Trade: The Monthly Record. (AT) **3951**
Australian Foreign Affairs Record *see* Australian Foreign Affairs and Trade: The Monthly Record **3951**
Australian Forest Grower. (AT) **2096**
†Australian Forest Research. (AT ISSN 0004-914X) **5143**
Australian Forest Resources. (AT ISSN 0314-1438) **2096**
Australian Forestry. (AT ISSN 0004-9158) **2096**
Australian Fringe Benefits Tax Guide for Employers. (AT) **2706**, **1087**
Australian Fringe Benefits Tax Service. (AT) **1087**
Australian Furnishing Trade Journal. (AT ISSN 0045-0456) **2556**
Australian Gallup Polls *see* Morgan Gallup Polls **4443**
Australian Garden Journal. (AT ISSN 0812-9495) **2122**
Australian Gardener. (AT) **2122**
The Australian Gas Industry Directory (Year). (AT ISSN 0727-3541) **3682**, **1927**
The Australian Gas Journal. (AT ISSN 0004-9166) **3682**
Australian Gemmologist. (AT ISSN 0004-9174) **2563**
Australian Geographer. (AT ISSN 0004-9182) **2243**
Australian Geographical Studies. (AT ISSN 0004-9190) **2243**
Australian Geomagnetism Report. (AT) **1587**
Australian Geomechanics News. (AT ISSN 0705-5838) **3478**, **1915**
Australian Geranium Society. Journal. (AT) **2122**
Australian Giftguide Magazine. (AT ISSN 0312-5327) **2280**
Australian Gliding. (AT ISSN 0004-9204) **47**, **4465**
Australian Gliding Yearbook. (AT ISSN 0084-7364) **47**
Australian Goat World. (AT ISSN 0045-0472) **211**
Australian Golf (Year) *see* Australian Golf Digest **4499**
Australian Golf Digest. (AT) **4499**
Australian Gourmet Traveller. (AT ISSN 0155-3380) **2444**
Australian Government Directory *see* Commonwealth Government Directory **4057**
Australian Government Publications. (AT ISSN 0067-1878) **389**
Australian Graduate School of Management. Handbook. (AT ISSN 0313-7112) **1003**
Australian Grapegrower *see* Australian Grapegrower & Winemaker **169**
Australian Grapegrower & Winemaker. (AT ISSN 0727-3606) **169**
Australian Gymnast. (AT) **4465**
Australian Hardware Journal. (AT ISSN 0004-9255) **641**, **2280**
Australian Health and Medical Law Reporter. (AT) **2602**
Australian Health Review. (AT ISSN 0156-5788) **2459**
Australian Health Surveyor *see* Environmental Health Review, Australia **5187**
Australian Hereford Annual *see* Australian Hereford Quarterly **211**
Australian Hereford Quarterly. (AT ISSN 0814-7663) **211**
Australian Hi-Fi *see* Australian Hi-Fi and Music Review **4459**
Australian Hi-Fi and Music Review. (AT) **4459**
Australian Hi-Fi Annual. (AT ISSN 0310-8902) **4459**

Australian High Court and Federal Court Practice. (AT) **2602**
Australian Historical Association. Bulletin. (AT ISSN 0312-6986) **2344**, **1700**
Australian Historical Studies. (AT ISSN 1031-461X) **2307**
Australian Holiday *see* TraveLeisure **4794**
Australian Home Beautiful. (AT ISSN 0004-928X) **2548**, **295**
Australian Home Gardener's Handbook and Diary. (AT) **2122**, **495**
▼Australian Home Woodworker. (AT) **601**
Australian Honey Board. Annual Report.(AT ISSN 0067-1894) **2062**
Australian Horse Racing Annual. (AT ISSN 0084-7402) **4532**
Australian Horticulture. (AT) **2122**
Australian Hospital. (AT) **2459**
Australian Hospital Association Special Monographs *see* A H A Special Monographs **2458**
Australian Hospital Newsletter *see* Hospital Brief **2464**
Australian Hospitals and Health Services Yearbook. (AT ISSN 0312-5599) **2459**
Australian Hotelier. (AT ISSN 0813-7544) **2471**, **377**, **4753**
Australian House and Garden. (AT ISSN 0004-931X) **2548**
Australian Hydrographic Newsletter. (AT ISSN 0812-5090) **1597**
Australian Imports *see* Australian Exports and Imports **900**
Australian Income Tax Assessment Act and Regulations *see* Australian Income Tax Legislation **1087**
Australian Income Tax Guide. (AT) **1087**
Australian Income Tax Guide (North Ryde, 1938) *see* Butterworths Australian Tax Handbook **1089**
Australian Income Tax Legislation. (AT) **1087**
Australian Income Tax Rulings. (AT) **2602**, **1087**
Australian-Indonesian Association of Victoria *see* J A I A **2202**
Australian Industrial and Intellectual Property. (AT) **2602**, **1072**
▼Australian Industrial Law Index. (AT) **2697**, **3**
Australian Industrial Law Review. (AT ISSN 0726-5883) **2706**
Australian Industrial Safety, Health & Welfare. (AT) **3615**, **2602**
Australian Insolvency Bulletin. (AT) **759**
Australian Insolvency Management Practice. (AT) **647**
Australian Institute for the Conservation of Cultural Material, Inc. Bulletin *see* A I C C M Bulletin **1482**
Australian Institute of Aboriginal and Torres Strait Islander Studies. Annual Bibliography. (AT) **253**
Australian Institute of Aboriginal Studies. Annual Bibliography *see* Australian Institute of Aboriginal and Torres Strait Islander Studies. Annual Bibliography **253**
Australian Institute of Criminology. Reporter *see* Criminology Australia **1513**
Australian Institute of Family Studies. Annual Report. (AT) **3979**
Australian Institute of Family Studies. Newsletter *see* Family Matters **4435**
†Australian Institute of Family Studies. Policy Background Paper (No.). (AT ISSN 0818-5352) **5143**
†Australian Institute of Family Studies. Working Paper. (AT ISSN 0817-6345) **5144**
Australian Institute of Management, N.S.W. Ltd. *see* A I M **1000**
Australian Institute of Marine Science. Yearly Report. (AT) **1602**
Australian Institute of Marine Science Monograph Series *see* A I M S Monograph Series **1601**
Australian Institute of Medical Scientists Newsletter *see* A I M S Newsletter **3068**

Australian Institute of Medical Scientists Self Assessment Programmes Series *see* A I M S Self Assessment Programmes Series **3256**
Australian Institute of Metals. Proceedings of the Annual Conference *see* Institute of Metals and Materials Australasia. Proceedings **3408**
Australian Institute of Parapsychological Research Bulletin *see* Australian Parapsychological Review **3668**
Australian Institute of Petroleum. Annual Report. (AT ISSN 0314-3171) **3682**, **1555**
Australian Institute of Pharmacy Management Newsletter. (AT ISSN 0706-3202) **3718**
Australian Institute of Psychic Research Bulletin *see* Australian Parapsychological Review **3668**
Australian Insurance Institute Journal *see* A I I Journal **2525**
Australian International Law News. (AT ISSN 0811-9260) **2719**
Australian International Tax Agreements. (AT) **2602**, **900**, **1087**
Australian International U F O Flying Saucer Research. (AT ISSN 0156-742X) **47**
Australian Investment Planning Guide. (AT) **938**
Australian Jaguar Driver. (AT) **4679**
Australian Jaycee. (AT) **1296**
Australian Jaycees National Directory. (AT) **1296**
Australian Jewish Historical Society. Journal of Proceedings. (AT ISSN 0004-9360) **2344**, **4221**
Australian Jewish Historical Society. Newsletter. (AT ISSN 0816-7141) **2344**, **4221**
Australian Jewish News (Darlinghurst). (AT) **1992**
Australian Jewish Times *see* Australian Jewish News (Darlinghurst) **1992**
†Australian Jockey Club Thoroughbred Stallion Register. (AT ISSN 0155-6134) **5144**
Australian Journal for Health, Physical Education and Recreation *see* A C H P E R National Journal **1613**
Australian Journal of Adult & Community Education. (AT ISSN 1035-0462) **1682**
Australian Journal of Adult Education *see* Australian Journal of Adult & Community Education **1682**
Australian Journal of Advanced Nursing.(AT ISSN 0813-0531) **3276**
Australian Journal of Agricultural Economics. (AT ISSN 0004-9395) **147**
Australian Journal of Agricultural Research. (AT ISSN 0004-9409) **78**
Australian Journal of Art. (AT ISSN 0314-6464) **318**
Australian Journal of Biological Sciences *see* Reproduction, Fertility and Development **453**
†Australian Journal of Biotechnology. (AT ISSN 0819-3355) **5144**
Australian Journal of Botany. (AT ISSN 0067-1924) **495**
Australian Journal of Chemistry. (AT ISSN 0004-9425) **1170**
Australian Journal of Chinese Affairs. (AT ISSN 0156-7365) **3634**, **3874**, **4366**
Australian Journal of Clinical and Experimental Hypnosis. (AT ISSN 0156-0417) **3274**
Australian Journal of Clinical Hypnotherapy and Hypnosis. (AT ISSN 0810-0713) **3274**
Australian Journal of Communication. (AT ISSN 0811-6202) **1368**, **28**, **2567**
Australian Journal of Dairy Technology. (AT ISSN 0004-9433) **197**
Australian Journal of Early Childhood. (AT ISSN 0312-5033) **1617**
Australian Journal of Earth Sciences. (AT ISSN 0812-0099) **1555**
Australian Journal of Ecology. (AT ISSN 0307-692X) **429**

Australian Journal of Education. (AT ISSN 0004-9441) **1617**
Australian Journal of Educational Technology. (AT ISSN 0814-673X) **1744**
Australian Journal of Experimental Agriculture. (AT ISSN 0816-1089) **169, 4806**
Australian Journal of Experimental Agriculture and Animal Husbandry see Australian Journal of Experimental Agriculture **169**
Australian Journal of Experimental Biology and Medical Science see Immunology and Cell Biology **3186**
Australian Journal of Family Law. (AT ISSN 0817-623X) **2716**
Australian Journal of Family Therapy see Australian and New Zealand Journal of Family Therapy **4429**
Australian Journal of Forensic Sciences. (AT ISSN 0045-0618) **3264**
Australian Journal of French Studies. (AT ISSN 0004-9468) **2897, 2804**
Australian Journal of Geodesy, Photogrammetry & Surveying. (AT ISSN 0159-8910) **2243**
Australian Journal of Historical Archaeology. (AT ISSN 0810-1868) **266**
Australian Journal of Hospital Pharmacy. (AT ISSN 0310-6810) **3718, 2459**
Australian Journal of Instrumentation and Control. (AT ISSN 0045-0626) **2521**
Australian Journal of International Affairs. (AT ISSN 1035-7718) **3951**
Australian Journal of Labour Law. (AT ISSN 1030-7222) **2706, 972**
Australian Journal of Law and Society. (AT ISSN 0729-3356) **2602**
Australian Journal of Linguistics. (AT ISSN 0726-8602) **2804**
Australian Journal of Liturgy. (AT ISSN 1030-617X) **4164**
Australian Journal of Management. (AT ISSN 0312-8962) **1003**
Australian Journal of Marine and Freshwater Research. (AT ISSN 0067-1940) **1602, 429**
Australian Journal of Marriage and Family. (AT ISSN 1034-652X) **3066, 4012**
Australian Journal of Medical Science. (AT ISSN 0158-4960) **3080, 3257**
Australian Journal of Mining. (AT ISSN 0817-9646) **3478**
Australian Journal of Nutrition and Dietetics. (AT ISSN 1032-1322) **3603**
Australian Journal of Ophthalmology see Australian and New Zealand Journal of Ophthalmology **3298**
Australian Journal of Optometry see Clinical and Experimental Optometry **3299**
Australian Journal of Pharmacy. (AT ISSN 0004-8399) **3718**
Australian Journal of Physics. (AT ISSN 0004-9506) **3815, 362**
Australian Journal of Physiotherapy. (AT ISSN 0004-9514) **3080**
Australian Journal of Plant Physiology. (AT ISSN 0310-7841) **570**
Australian Journal of Political Science. (AT ISSN 1036-1146) **3874**
Australian Journal of Politics and History. (AT ISSN 0004-9522) **3874, 2344**
Australian Journal of Psychotherapy. (AT) **4012, 3080, 3331**
Australian Journal of Public Administration. (AT ISSN 0313-6647) **4054**
Australian Journal of Public Health. (AT ISSN 1035-7319) **4098, 3218**
Australian Journal of Reading. (AT ISSN 0156-0301) **1617, 1744**
Australian Journal of Remedial Education. (AT ISSN 0311-1954) **1733**
Australian Journal of Science see Search **4342**

Australian Journal of Science and Medicine in Sport. (AT ISSN 0813-6289) **3370**
Australian Journal of Sex, Marriage and Family see Australian Journal of Marriage and Family **3066**
Australian Journal of Social Issues. (AT ISSN 0004-9557) **4399**
Australian Journal of Soil and Water Conservation. (AT ISSN 1032-2426) **170**
Australian Journal of Soil Research. (AT ISSN 0004-9573) **170**
Australian Journal of Statistics. (AT ISSN 0004-9581) **4564**
Australian Journal of T A F E Research and Development. (Technical and Further Education) (AT ISSN 0816-2018) **1617**
Australian Journal of Zoology. (AT ISSN 0004-959X) **578**
Australian Journal on Ageing. (AT ISSN 0726-4240) **2270**
Australian Journalism Review. (AT ISSN 0810-2686) **2567**
Australian Key Business Directory. (AT ISSN 0311-2667) **1122**
Australian Labor Party. A.C.T. Branch. Magazine see Lobby **3905**
Australian Labour Law Reporter. (AT) **2706, 972**
Australian Ladies Golf Union. Official Yearbook. (AT) **4541**
Australian Latvian. see Australijas Latvietis **1992**
Australian Law Journal. (AT ISSN 0004-9611) **2602**
Australian Law Librarians' Group. Newsletter. (AT ISSN 0311-5984) **2745**
Australian Law News. (AT ISSN 0159-7531) **2602**
Australian Law Reports. (AT ISSN 0310-0014) **2602**
†Australian Leather Journal. (AT) **5144**
Australian Leather Journal, Boot and Shoe Recorder see Australian Leather Journal **5144**
Australian Leave and Holidays Practice Manual. (AT) **2602, 1062**
Australian Lectionary (Year). (AT ISSN 0812-0811) **4164, 4229**
Australian Left Review. (AT ISSN 0004-9638) **3874**
Australian Legal Directory. (AT ISSN 0155-297X) **1122, 2602**
Australian Legal Monthly Digest. (AT ISSN 0004-9646) **2602**
Australian Liberal Catholic see Communion **4281**
Australian Libraries: The Essential Directory. (AT ISSN 1031-5187) **2746**
Australian Library and Information Science Abstracts see A L I S A **2792**
Australian Library Journal. (AT ISSN 0004-9670) **2746**
Australian Library Review. (AT ISSN 1034-8042) **2746**
Australian Literary Studies. (AT ISSN 0004-9697) **2897**
Australian Lithographer see Australian Lithographer, Printer, and Packager **3997**
Australian Lithographer, Printer, and Packager. (AT ISSN 0159-2319) **3997, 3647, 3662**
Australian Littoral Society. Bulletin. (AT ISSN 0157-308X) **1483**
Australian Lutheran Almanac see Lutheran Church of Australia. Yearbook **4242**
Australian Machinery and Production Engineering see Production Machinery **3022**
Australian Macworld. (AT ISSN 0814-9356) **1467, 1458**
Australian Mammalogy. (AT ISSN 0310-0049) **578**
Australian Maps. (AT ISSN 0045-0677) **389, 2243**
Australian Marine Science Bulletin. (AT) **1602**
Australian Marine Sciences Association. Bulletin see Australian Marine Science Bulletin **1602**
Australian Market Guide. (US ISSN 0067-1959) **938, 1122**

Australian Marxist Review. (AT ISSN 0310-8252) **3874**
Australian Master Tax Guide. (AT ISSN 0810-5596) **1087**
Australian Master Tax Guide Updater. (AT) **1088**
Australian Mathematical Society. Bulletin. (AT ISSN 0004-9727) **3030**
Australian Mathematical Society. Journal. Series A. Pure Mathematics and Statistics. (AT ISSN 0263-6115) **3030**
Australian Mathematical Society. Journal. Series B. Applied Mathematics. (AT ISSN 0334-2700) **3030**
Australian Mathematical Society Gazette. (AT ISSN 0311-0729) **3030**
Australian Meat and Livestock Corporation. Meat Producer and Exporter see A M L C News **2060**
Australian Meat and Livestock Corporation News see A M L C News **2060**
Australian Meat Industry Bulletin. (AT ISSN 0156-2681) **2062**
Australian Meat Livestock Research and Development Corporation. Annual Report. (AT) **211, 2062**
Australian Meat Research Committee. Annual Report see Australian Meat Livestock Research and Development Corporation. Annual Report **211**
Australian Medical Association. Victoria Branch. Monthly Paper see A M A Victoria Branch News **3068**
Australian Medical Association Victoria Branch News see A M A Victoria Branch News **3068**
Australian Medliner. (AT ISSN 0727-3851) **3080**
Australian Meteorological and Oceanographic Society. Bulletin. (AT ISSN 1035-6576) **3433, 1602**
Australian Meteorological and Oceanographic Society. Newsletter see Australian Meteorological and Oceanographic Society. Bulletin **3433**
Australian Meteorological Magazine. (AT ISSN 0004-9743) **3433**
†Australian Micro C W. (AT) **5144**
†Australian Mineral Industry. Annual Review. (AT ISSN 0084-7488) **5144**
†Australian Mineral Industry. Quarterly. (AT ISSN 0155-9419) **5144**
Australian Mineral Resource Politics Pty. Ltd. Database Bulletin see A M R E P Database Bulletin **3477**
Australian Mineralogist. (AT ISSN 0819-6508) **1555, 3478**
Australian Mining. (AT ISSN 0004-976X) **3478**
Australian Mining and Petroleum Law Association Ltd. Bulletin see A M P L A Bulletin **3477**
Australian Mining and Petroleum Law Association Ltd. Yearbook see A M P L A Yearbook **3477**
Australian Mining Industry Council. Directory. (AT) **3478**
Australian Mining Product Register. (AT) **3478**
Australian Mining Year Book see Australian Mining Product Register **3478**
Australian Mission to the United Nations. United Nations General Assembly. Australian Delegation. Report see United Nations General Assembly: Report of the Australian Delegation **3975**
Australian Model Railroad Magazine see Australian Model Railway Magazine **2433**
Australian Model Railway Association Journal see A M R A Journal **2432**
Australian Model Railway Magazine. (AT) **2433, 4707**
Australian Motor Manual. (AT) **4679**
Australian Motor Racing Year. (AT ISSN 0158-4138) **4515**
Australian Motoring Year. (AT ISSN 0810-9958) **4679, 4465**
Australian Multiple Birth Association Inc. News see A M B A News **1231**

Australian Municipal Journal. (AT ISSN 0004-9808) **4084**
Australian Museum, Sydney. Memoirs see Australian Museum, Sydney. Records Supplements **3522**
Australian Museum, Sydney. Records. (AT ISSN 0067-1975) **3522**
Australian Museum, Sydney. Records Supplements. (AT ISSN 0812-7387) **3522**
Australian Music Industry: An Economic Evaluation. (AT) **3540**
Australian National Accounts: National Income and Expenditure (Annual). (AT ISSN 0067-1983) **704**
Australian National Accounts: National Income and Expenditure (Quarterly). (AT ISSN 1031-5128) **704**
Australian National Antarctic Research Expedition News see A N A R E News **4295**
Australian National Antarctic Research Expeditions Report see A N A R E Report **4295**
Australian National Antarctic Research Expeditions Research Notes see A N A R E Research Notes **4295**
Australian National Bibliography. (AT ISSN 0004-9816) **389**
Australian National Clay see Australian Clay Journal & Ceramic News **601**
Australian National Commission for Unesco Newsletter see Unesco Australia **936**
Australian National Committee on Large Dams Bulletin see A N C O L D Bulletin **1861**
Australian National Drycleaner. (AT ISSN 0045-074X) **1281**
Australian National Parks and Wildlife Service. Report. (AT) **1483**
Australian National Tourguide see Accommodation Australia **4751**
Australian National University. Australian Development Studies Network. Development Bulletin. (AT ISSN 1035-1132) **4366**
Australian National University. Development Studies Centre. Demography Teaching Notes see Australian National University. National Centre for Development Studies. Demography Teaching Notes **4366**
†Australian National University. Development Studies Centre. Monograph. (AT ISSN 0157-5767) **5144**
Australian National University. National Centre for Development Studies. Demography Teaching Notes. (AT) **4366**
Australian National University. National Centre for Development Studies. History of Development Studies. (AT ISSN 0815-6301) **926**
Australian National University. National Centre for Development Studies. Indian Ocean Policy Papers. (AT ISSN 1030-1976) **926**
Australian National University. National Centre for Development Studies. Newsletter see Australian National University. Australian Development Studies Network. Development Bulletin **4366**
Australian National University. National Centre for Development Studies. Proceedings. (AT) **926**
Australian National University. National Centre for Development Studies. Pacific Economic Bulletin. (AT ISSN 0817-8038) **844, 926**
Australian National University. National Centre for Development Studies. Pacific Policy Papers. (AT ISSN 0817-0444) **926**
Australian National University. National Centre for Development Studies. Reprint Series. (AT ISSN 1034-1471) **926**
Australian National University. National Centre for Development Studies. Report (Year). (AT ISSN 0818-0512) **926**

AUSTRALIAN SOCIETY

Australian National University. National Centre for Development Studies. Working Papers. Series: China Working Papers. (AT ISSN 1030-360X) **4366**

Australian National University. National Centre for Development Studies. Working Papers. Series: Islands - Australia Working Papers. (AT ISSN 0816-5165) **4366**

Australian National University. National Centre for Development Studies. Working Papers. Series: N C D S Working Papers. (AT ISSN 0815-7596) **4366**

Australian National University. Research School of Physical Sciences and Engineering. Annual Report. (AT) **3815**

Australian National University. Research School of Physical Sciences. Annual Report see Australian National University. Research School of Physical Sciences and Engineering. Annual Report. **3815**

Australian National University, Canberra. Department of Engineering Physics. Publication Ep-Rr. (AT ISSN 0084-7496) **1877**

Australian National University, Canberra. Department of Political Science. Occasional Paper. see Australian National University, Canberra. Research School of Social Sciences. Department of Political Science. Occasional Papers **3874**

Australian National University, Canberra. Geology Department. Annual Report. (AT) **1555**

Australian National University, Canberra. Geology Department. Publication see Australian National University, Canberra. Geology Department. Annual Report **1555**

Australian National University, Canberra. Research School of Physical Sciences. Research Paper. (AT ISSN 0084-7518) **3815**

Australian National University, Canberra. Research School of Social Sciences. Department of Political Science. Occasional Papers. (AT) **3874**

Australian National University Historical Journal see A N U Historical Journal **5128**

Australian National University Reporter see A N U Reporter **1302**

Australian Natural History. (AT ISSN 0004-9840) **4300**

Australian Nautical News see Australian Yachting **4522**

Australian Naval Institute. Journal. (AT ISSN 0312-5807) **3452**

Australian Newsagent and Stationer see Australian Stationer and Newsagent **1033**

Australian Newsletter see Australian Shell News **578**

Australian Non-Government Railways Operating Statistics (Years). (AT) **4661, 4564**

Australian Nuclear Science and Technology Organisation Technology see A N S T O Technology **1803**

Australian Nugget Journal. (AT ISSN 1030-7915) **3478, 938, 3598**

Australian Numismatic Journal. (AT ISSN 0004-9875) **3598**

Australian Nursery. (AT) **2122**

Australian Nurseryman see Australian Nursery **2122**

Australian Nurses' Journal. (AT ISSN 0045-0758) **3276**

Australian Occupational Therapy Journal. (AT ISSN 0045-0766) **3080**

†Australian Off-Road Year. (AT ISSN 0813-4952) **5144**

Australian Official Journal of Designs. (AT ISSN 1038-0671) **3672**

Australian Official Journal of Patents. (AT ISSN 0819-1794) **3672**

Australian Official Journal of Trade Marks. (AT ISSN 0819-1808) **3672**

Australian Orchid Review. (AT ISSN 0045-0782) **2122**

Australian Orienteer. (AT ISSN 0818-6510) **4541**

Australian Orthodontic Journal. (AT ISSN 0587-3908) **3228**

Australian Outdoors. (AT ISSN 0004-9905) **4541**

Australian Outlook. (UK ISSN 0301-5785) **2171**

Australian Outlook see Australian Journal of International Affairs **3951**

Australian Overseas Information Service. Science Newsletter see Australian Science and Technology Newsletter **4300**

Australian Oyster. (AT ISSN 0817-7724) **2037**

Australian P C World. (AT ISSN 0813-1384) **1467**

Australian Packaging. (AT ISSN 0004-9921) **3647**

Australian Paediatric Journal see Journal of Paediatrics and Child Health **3322**

Australian Paint and Panel. (AT ISSN 0816-3596) **3652**

Australian Parapsychological Review. (AT ISSN 1035-9621) **3668, 4012**

Australian Parks & Recreation. (AT ISSN 0311-8223) **1484, 4541**

Australian Parliamentary Handbook see Parliamentary Handbook of the Commonwealth of Australia **3913**

Australian Pay-Roll Tax Manual. (AT) **1088**

Australian Penthouse. (AT ISSN 0158-0655) **3395**

Australian Periodicals in Print. (AT ISSN 1030-2476) **390**

Australian Personal Computer. (AT) **1467, 1458**

Australian Personnel Management. (AT) **1062**

Australian Pharmacist. (AT ISSN 0728-4632) **3718**

Australian Photography. (AT ISSN 0004-9964) **3788**

Australian Photography Camera Test Reports. (AT) **3789**

Australian Photography Photo-Directory.(AT) **3789**

Australian Physicist. (AT ISSN 0004-9972) **3815**

Australian Physiological and Pharmacological Society. Proceedings. (AT ISSN 0067-2084) **570, 3718**

Australian Physiological Society. Proceedings see Australian Physiological and Pharmacological Society. Proceedings **570**

Australian Pipeliner. (AT ISSN 0310-1258) **1862**

Australian Planner. (AT ISSN 0729-3682) **2483**

Australian Planning Appeal Decisions. (AT ISSN 0728-6309) **2602, 2483**

Australian Plant Introduction Review. (AT ISSN 0313-3192) **170**

Australian Plants. (AT ISSN 0005-0008) **495, 2122**

Australian Playboy. (AT) **3395**

Australian Playwrights. (NE) **2897, 417**

Australian Plumbing Industry. (AT ISSN 0817-6337) **2297**

Australian Police Journal. (AT ISSN 0005-0024) **1510**

Australian Police World. (AT) **1510**

Australian Poll Dorset Journal. (AT) **211**

Australian Poll Hereford Magazine. (AT) **211**

▼Australian Pollution Law (Control). (AT) **2602, 1943**

▼Australian Pollution Law New South Wales. (AT) **2602, 1943**

▼Australian Pollution Law Victoria. (AT) **2602, 1943**

Australian Pork Journal see Pork Journal **223**

Australian Poultry Digest see Poultry Digest **223**

Australian Poultry Science Symposium. (AT ISSN 1034-6260) **211**

Australian Powerboat. (AT ISSN 0313-766X) **4522**

†Australian Practice Management. (AT ISSN 1031-5217) **5144**

Australian Presbyterian Life. (AT ISSN 0005-0059) **4229**

Australian Prescriber. (AT ISSN 0312-8008) **3718**

Australian Printer Magazine. (AT ISSN 1033-1522) **3997**

Australian Prisoners. (AT ISSN 0818-6618) **1510**

Australian Property News. (AT) **647**

Australian Prosthodontic Journal. (AT ISSN 0819-0887) **3228**

Australian Prosthodontic Society. Bulletin see Australian Prosthodontic Journal **3228**

Australian Psychologist. (AT ISSN 0005-0067) **4012**

Australian Public Affairs Information Service see A P A I S: Australian Public Affairs Information Service **4078**

Australian Purebred Pig Herd Book. (AT) **211**

Australian Quarterly. (AT ISSN 0005-0091) **3874**

Australian Racing Drivers Club Journal see Australian Racing Drivers Club Newsletter **4515**

Australian Racing Drivers Club Newsletter. (AT) **4515**

Australian Radio Times. (AT) **1355, 4164**

Australian Railway Historical Society. Bulletin. (AT ISSN 0005-0105) **4707, 2307**

Australian Railways Union. Federal Office News. (AT) **2580, 4707**

Australian Rationalist. (AT ISSN 1036-8191) **3762**

Australian Refrigeration, Air Conditioning and Heating. (AT ISSN 0005-0148) **2297**

†Australian Regional Impact Analysis Series (No.). (AT ISSN 1030-5920) **5144**

Australian Rehabilitation Digest. (AT ISSN 0728-490X) **3080**

Australian Rehabilitation Review see Australian Disability Review **2283**

Australian Research Grants Committee. Report see Australian Research Grants Scheme. Report on Grants Approved **1617**

Australian Research Grants Scheme. Report on Grants Approved. (AT) **1617**

Australian Retail Tobacconist. (AT ISSN 0045-0820) **4643**

Australian Revenue & Stamp Duties. (AT) **1088**

Australian Rhododendron Society. Journal see The Rhododendron **2138**

Australian Road Research see Road and Transport Research **1873**

Australian Road Research Board. Briefing. (AT) **4717**

Australian Road Research Board. Proceedings. (AT ISSN 0572-1431) **4717, 1862**

Australian Road Research Board. Research Report. (AT) **4717**

Australian Road Research Board. Special Report. (AT ISSN 0572-144X) **4717**

Australian Road Research Board. Technical Manuals. (AT ISSN 0313-895X) **4706, 4717**

Australian Road Research Board Regional Symposium see A R R B Regional Symposium **4717**

Australian Road Research in Progress. (AT ISSN 0705-9213) **1841, 3, 4661**

Australian Robot Association. Newsletter. (AT ISSN 0726-3716) **1407**

Australian Rowing. (AT) **4522**

Australian Runner. (AT) **4465**

Australian Rural Science Annual. (AT ISSN 0819-2995) **78**

Australian S F News. (Science Fiction) (AT ISSN 0155-8870) **3010, 3504**

Australian Sailing. (AT) **4522**

Australian Sales Tax Guide. (AT) **1088**

Australian Science and Technology Newsletter. (AT ISSN 0815-4171) **4300, 4594**

Australian Science Education Research Association. Research in Science Education. (AT ISSN 0157-244X) **1744**

Australian Science Magazine see Australasian Science Magazine **4300**

Australian Science Teachers' Journal. (AT ISSN 0045-0855) **1764**

Australian Sea Heritage. (AT ISSN 0813-0523) **3522, 4724**

Australian Sea Spray. (AT ISSN 0311-7839) **4522**

Australian Sea Spray Weekly see Australian Sea Spray **4522**

Australian Seacraft. (AT ISSN 0005-0237) **4522**

Australian Secretary. (AT) **1062**

▼Australian Securities Commission Releases. (AT) **2706**

Australian Securities Law Reporter. (AT ISSN 0311-0265) **2706, 938**

Australian Seed Industry Magazine. (AT ISSN 0813-5231) **170, 161**

Australian Serials in Print see Australian Periodicals in Print **390**

Australian Services Union National see A S U National **2579**

Australian Shell News. (AT ISSN 0310-1304) **578**

†Australian Shepherd Quarterly. (US) **5144**

†Australian Shipping and Shipbuilding. (AT) **5144**

Australian Shooters Journal see Australian Sporting Shooter **4541**

Australian Short Stories. (AT ISSN 0810-4468) **2897**

Australian Ski Yearbook. (AT ISSN 0084-7593) **4541**

Australian Slavonic and East European Studies. (AT ISSN 0818-8149) **2804, 2897**

Australian Small Farms Directory see Australian Small Farms Handbook **5144**

†Australian Small Farms Handbook. (AT) **5144**

†Australian Small Offset Inplant Printer. (AT) **5144**

Australian Social Security Guide. (AT) **4399**

Australian Social Welfare: Impact see Impact (Sydney) **4408**

Australian Social Work. (AT ISSN 0312-407X) **4399**

Australian Society. (AT ISSN 0729-8595) **2859**

Australian Society for Historical Archaeology. Research Bulletin. (AT ISSN 0819-4076) **266**

Australian Society for Medical Research Proceedings see Clinical and Experimental Pharmacology and Physiology **570**

Australian Society of Accountants. Annual Report see Australian Society of Certified Practising Accountants. Annual Report **747**

Australian Society of Animal Production. Proceedings see Animal Production in Australia **210**

Australian Society of Certified Practising Accountants. Annual Report. (AT) **747**

Australian Society of Certified Practising Accountants Accounting and Business Index see A S C P A Accounting and Business Index **701**

Australian Society of Endodontology. Newsletter. (AT ISSN 0313-7384) **3228**

Australian Society of Exploration Geophysicists. Bulletin see Exploration Geophysics **1588**

Australian Society of Hypnosis. Journal see Australian Journal of Clinical and Experimental Hypnosis **3274**

Australian Society of Indexers Newsletter. (AT ISSN 0314-3767) **2792, 3, 4139**

Australian Society of Otolaryngology Head and Neck Surgery. Journal see Journal of Otolaryngology **3315**

Australian Society of Sugar Cane Technologists. Proceedings. (AT ISSN 0726-0822) **2062**

AUSTRALIAN SONGS

Australian Songs. Series. (AT ISSN 0726-1292) **3540**
Australian Special Library News. (AT ISSN 0005-027X) **2746**
Australian Spectator. (AT) **2171**
Australian Speleo Abstracts. (AT) **1550**, 3
Australian Sporting Shooter. (AT) **4541**
Australian Stamp Bulletin. (AT) **3749**
Australian Stamp Duties see New South Wales and A.C.T. Stamp Duties **1102**
Australian Stamp Duties see Queensland Stamp Duties **1104**
Australian Stamp Duties see South Australia and Northern Territory Stamp Duties **1106**
Australian Stamp Duties see Victoria and Tasmania Stamp Duties **1111**
Australian Stamp Duties see Western Australia Stamp Duties **1112**
†Australian Stamp Duties. (AT) **5144**
Australian Stamp Duties Bulletin. (AT) **1088**
Australian Stamp Explorer. (AT) **3749**
Australian Stamp Monthly see Stamp News **3758**
Australian Standard. (AT ISSN 0158-3999) **3445**
Australian Stationer and Newsagent. (AT ISSN 1036-7969) **1033**, 1057
Australian Stationers & Newsagent Buyer's Guide (Year) for Office Products & Stationers. (AT) **1122**, 1057
Australian Stationers and Office Suppliers Reference Book see Australian Stationers & Newsagent Buyer's Guide (Year) for Office Products & Stationers **1122**
Australian Stock Exchange Journal. (AT ISSN 0045-0901) **938**
Australian Stock Horse Journal. (AT) **4532**
Australian String Teacher. (AT) **3540**
Australian Stud Pig Herd Book see Australian Purebred Pig Herd Book **211**
Australian Studies. (AT ISSN 1033-131X) **2171**
Australian Studies. (UK ISSN 0954-0954) **2344**
Australian Studies Bulletin see Australian Studies **2171**
Australian Studies in Health Service Administration. (AT ISSN 0067-2165) **4098**
†Australian Studies Newsletter. (AT) **5144**
Australian Sugar Year Book. (AT ISSN 0067-2173) **2062**
Australian Sunflower Annual. (AT) **2122**
Australian Superannuation and Employment Benefits Guide see Australian Superannuation Law and Practice **4399**
Australian Superannuation Law and Practice. (AT) **4399**, 2527
▼Australian Superannuation Source Materials. (AT) **4399**
Australian Surgeon. (AT) **3376**
Australian Surveyor. (AT ISSN 0005-0326) **1862**
Australian Systematic Botany. (AT ISSN 1030-1887) **495**
Australian T A F E Teacher. (Technical and Further Education Teacher's Association) (AT ISSN 0815-3701) **1744**
Australian Tax Cases. (AT) **1088**, 2602
Australian Tax Forum. (AT ISSN 0812-695X) **1088**, 2602
Australian Tax Review. (AT ISSN 0311-094X) **1088**, 2602
Australian Taxpayer's Association. Annual Taxation Summary. (AT) **1088**
Australian Teacher. (AT ISSN 0728-8387) **1617**, 2580
Australian Teacher see Teachers Guild of New South Wales. Proceedings **1667**
Australian Teacher of the Deaf. (AT ISSN 0005-0334) **2286**, 1617
Australian Teachers Union Annual Report see A T F Annual Report **1613**
Australian Technical Teacher see Australian T A F E Teacher **1744**
†Australian Technology Review. (AT ISSN 0819-5943) **5144**
Australian Telecommunication Monographs. (AT ISSN 0067-2181) **1361**
Australian Telecommunication Research see A T R **1331**
Australian Tempo Libero see Tempo Australia **4788**
Australian Tenancy Practice & Precedents. (AT) **2602**, 4145
Australian Tennis Magazine. (AT) **4499**
Australian Terrier Club of America Newsletter. (US) **3708**
Australian Thoroughbreds. (AT ISSN 0005-0350) **4532**
Australian Timberman. (AT) **2113**
Australian Torts Reporter. (AT) **2602**
Australian Tourist Commission. Annual Report. (AT) **4753**
Australian Trade Practices Reporter. (AT) **647**, 2602
Australian Trader. (AT ISSN 0045-0944) **900**
Australian Trail & Track Monthly. (AT) **4515**
†Australian Transport. (AT ISSN 0311-628X) **5144**
Australian Treaty List see Australian Treaty Series **2719**
Australian Treaty Series. (AT) **2719**
Australian Trotting Register. (AT ISSN 0005-0407) **4532**
Australian U F O Bulletin. (AT) **47**
Australian Universities Language and Literature Association see A U L L A **2800**
Australian Universities' Review. (AT ISSN 0818-8068) **1700**
Australian Urban Studies. (AT) **2483**
Australian Vegetarian. (AT) **3603**
Australian Veterinary Association. Annual Report. (AT) **4806**
Australian Veterinary Association. Year Book see Australian Veterinary Association. Annual Report **4806**
Australian Veterinary Association Conference Handbook. (AT) **4807**
Australian Veterinary Journal. (AT ISSN 0005-0423) **4807**
Australian Veterinary Practitioner. (AT ISSN 0310-138X) **4807**
Australian Video and Communications see What's on Video and Cinema **1388**
Australian Videography. (AT) **1384**
†Australian War Memorial Newsletter. (AT) **5144**
Australian Waste Disposal Catalogue. (AT ISSN 0726-6987) **1943**
Australian Water Resources Council. Water Resources Series. (AT ISSN 0811-5397) **4822**
Australian Way. (AT) **4671**, 4753
Australian Weed Control Handbook. (AT ISSN 0310-0405) **170**
Australian Welding Research Association. Bulletin see Welding Technology Institute of Australia. Bulletin **3431**
Australian Well Being. (AT ISSN 0812-8227) **3799**, 3603
Australian Wildlife Newsletter. (AT) **1484**
Australian Wildlife Research see Wildlife Research **1500**
Australian Wine Industry Journal see Australian and New Zealand Wine Industry Journal **377**
Australian Wine Research Institute Technical Review. (AT) **377**
Australian Women's Chess Bulletin. (AT ISSN 0155-7831) **4465**, 4837
Australian Women's Weekly. (AT ISSN 0005-0458) **4837**
Australian Woodworker. (AT ISSN 0818-0261) **639**
Australian Wool see Australian Wool Sale Statistics. Statistical Analysis. Part A & B & C **4628**
Australian Wool Compendium. (AT) **4616**
Australian Wool Corporation. Bi-Monthly Market Report see Australian Wool Corporation. Wool Market News: Monthly Perspective **4616**
Australian Wool Corporation. Wool Market News: Monthly Perspective. (AT) **4616**
Australian Wool Sale Statistics. Statistical Analysis. Part A & B & C. (AT ISSN 0311-9882) **4628**, 4564
Australian Worker. (AT ISSN 0045-0979) **2580**
Australian Workers Compensation Guide. (AT) **972**
†Australian Workers' Union. Official Report of the Annual Convention. (AT) **5144**
Australian Yachting. (AT ISSN 1035-3852) **4522**
Australian Youth Hostels Association Incorporated Hostels in Australia see Y H A Hostels in Australia **4798**
Australian Youth Hostels Handbook see Y H A Hostels in Australia **4798**
Australian Zoologist. (AT ISSN 0067-2238) **572**
Australiana. (AT ISSN 0814-107X) **2548**
Australia's Mining Monthly. (AT) **3478**
Australia's Overseas Development Assistance see Australia's Overseas Development Assistance. Budget Paper **3951**
Australia's Overseas Development Assistance. Budget Paper. (AT) **3951**
Australia's Parents. (AT ISSN 1036-0921) **1232**, 2444
Australia's Top 500 Companies. (AT) **1033**
Australien Kurier. (AT) **4753**
Australijas Latvietis/Australian Latvian. (AT ISSN 0005-0482) **1992**
Austria. Bundesamt fuer Eich- und Vermessungswesen. Amtsblatt fuer das Eichwesen. (AU) **3445**
Austria. Bundeskammer der Gewerblichen Wirtschaft. Fremdenverkehr in Zahlen. (AU) **4798**
Austria. Bundeskammer der Gewerblichen Wirtschaft. Statistik und Dokumnentation. Information see Austria. Bundeskammer der Gewerblichen Wirtschaft. Fremdenverkehr in Zahlen **4798**
†Austria. Bundesministerium fuer Bauten und Technik. Wohnbauforschung. (AU) **5144**
Austria. Bundesministerium fuer Land- und Forstwirtschaft. Taetigkeitsbericht. (AU ISSN 0067-2262) **78**
Austria. Bundesministerium fuer Soziale Verwaltung. Bericht ueber die Taetigkeit. (AU) **4366**
Austria. Bundesministerium fuer Wissenschaft und Forschung. Bericht der Bundesregierung an den Nationalrat. (AU ISSN 0300-2772) **4300**
Austria. Bundesministerium fuer Wissenschaft und Forschung. Hochschulbericht. (AU) **1700**
Austria. Entscheidungen des Obersten Gerichtshofes in Sozialrechtssachen (SSV-NF). (AU) **2734**
Austria. Hoehere Bundeslehr- und Versuchsanstalt fuer Wein- und Obstbau. Mitteilungen Klosterneuburg. (AU ISSN 0007-5922) **170**, 377
Austria. Oberlandesgericht Wien im Leistungsstreitverfahren Zweiter Instanz der Sozialversicherung (SSV). Entscheidungen see Austria. Entscheidungen des Obersten Gerichtshofes in Sozialrechtssachen (SSV-NF) **2734**
Austria. Statistisches Zentralamt. Aussenhandel Oesterreichs. (AU) **704**
Austria. Statistisches Zentralamt. Baustatistik. (AU) **636**
Austria. Statistisches Zentralamt. Demographisches Jahrbuch Oesterreiches. (AU) **3991**, 3979
Austria. Statistisches Zentralamt. Die Kindergaerten (Kindertagesheime). (AU) **1674**
Austria. Statistisches Zentralamt. Ergebnisse der Landwirtschaftlichen Statistik. (AU ISSN 0067-2327) **134**
Austria. Statistisches Zentralamt. Ergebnisse der Landwirtschatlichen Maschinenzaehlung see Austria. Statistisches Zentralamt. Landwirtschaftliche Maschinenzaehlung **134**
Austria. Statistisches Zentralamt. Erhebung der Land und Forstwirtschaftlichen Arbeitskraefte see Austria. Statistisches Zentralamt. Land- und Forstwirtschaftliche Arbeitskraefte **704**
Austria. Statistisches Zentralamt. Gewerbestatistik Part 2. (AU) **704**
Austria. Statistisches Zentralamt. Industrie und Gewerbestatistik Part 1. (AU) **704**, 4564
Austria. Statistisches Zentralamt. Jugendwohlfahrtspflege. (AU) **4399**
Austria. Statistisches Zentralamt. Land- und Forstwirtliche Arbeitskraefte. (AU) **704**
Austria. Statistisches Zentralamt. Landwirtschaftliche Maschinenzaehlung. (AU) **134**
Austria. Statistisches Zentralamt. Mikrozensus; Jahresergebnisse. (AU) **4564**
Austria. Statistisches Zentralamt. Publikationsangebot. (AU) **4564**
Austria. Statistisches Zentralamt. Sozialhilfe. (AU) **4425**
Austria. Statistisches Zentralamt. Statistik der Aktiengesellschaften in Oesterreich. (AU ISSN 0081-5233) **704**
Austria. Statistisches Zentralamt. Statistik der Rechtspflege. (AU) **2697**
Austria. Statistisches Zentralamt. Statistische Nachrichten. (AU) **4564**
Austria. Statistisches Zentralamt. Wohnungsdaten. (AU) **636**
Austria. Zentralanstalt fuer Meteorologie und Geodynamik. Jahrbuch. (AU ISSN 0067-2351) **3433**, 1587
Austria & Hungary Stamp Catalogue. (UK ISSN 0142-9760) **3749**
Austria Export. (AU ISSN 0005-0490) **901**
Austria Export Herold/Austrian Export Directory/Annuaire d'Exportation de l'Autriche/Anuario de Exportacion de Austria. (AU) **1122**
Austria Innovativ. (AU) **4594**
Austria-Philatelist. (AU ISSN 0005-0512) **3749**
Austria Today. (AU ISSN 0304-8713) **2173**
†Austrian Airlines. Flight Guide. (AU) **5144**
Austrian Airlines Skylines. (AU) **4802**
Austrian Business. (US) **808**
Austrian Economic News. (AU) **844**
Austrian Economics Newsletter. (US) **889**
Austrian Export Directory. see Austria Export Herold **1122**
Austrian History Newsletter see Austrian History Yearbook **2351**
Austrian History Yearbook. (US ISSN 0067-2378) **2351**
Austrian Information. (US ISSN 0005-0520) **3951**
Austrian Institute Calendar of Events. (US) **2173**
Austrian Institute Newsletter see Austrian Institute Calendar of Events **2173**
Austrian Journal of Public and International Law. see Oesterreichische Zeitschrift fuer Oeffentliches Recht und Voelkerrecht **2663**
Austrian Journalists Index. (AU) **2577**
Austrian Literature. (US ISSN 1054-058X) **2897**
Austroflug. (AU ISSN 0005-0555) **47**
Austropack. (AU ISSN 0005-0563) **3647**, 4717

Auswertungs- und Informationsdienst fuer Ernaehrung, Landwirtschaft und Forsten e.V. Verbraucherdienst see A I D Verbraucherdienst 3602
Auszeit. (GW ISSN 0937-6569) 1700, 1721
Ausztraliai Magyar Ujsaf. Hungarian Weekly. (AT) 1992
Auszuege aus den Europaeischen Patentanmeldungen. Teil 1. Grund- und Rohstoffindustrie, Chemie und Huettenwesen, Bauwesen, Bergbau. (GW) 3672
Auszuege aus den Europaeischen Patentanmeldungen. Teil 2. Elektrotechnik, Physik, Feinmechanik und Optik, Akustik. (GW ISSN 0177-963X) 3672
Auszuege aus den Europaeischen Patentanmeldungen. Teil 3. Uebrige Verarbeitungsindustrie und Arbeitsverfahren, Maschinen- und Fahrzeugbau, Ernaehrung, Landwirtschaft. (GW ISSN 0177-9648) 3672
Auszuege aus den Europaeischen Patentschriften. Teil 1. Grund- und Rohstoffindustrie, Chemie und Huetten-Wesen, Bauwesen und Bergbau. (GW ISSN 0720-9339) 3672
Auszuege aus den Europaeischen Patentschriften. Teil 2. Elektrotechnik, Physik, Feinmechanik und Optik, Akustik. (GW) 3672
Auszuege aus den Europaeischen Patentschriften. Teil 3. Uebrige Verarbeitungsindustrie und Arbeitsverfahren, Maschinen- und Fahrzeugbau, Ernaehrung, Landwirtschaft. (GW) 3673
Auszuege aus den Gebrauchsmustern. (GW ISSN 0005-0571) 3673
Auszuege aus den Offenlegungsschriften. Teil 1. Grund- und Rohstoffindustrie, Chemie und Huetten-wesen, Bauwesen und Bergbau. (GW ISSN 0340-0816) 3673
Auszuege aus den Offenlegungsschriften. Teil 2. Elektrotechnik, Physik, Feinmechanik und Optik, Akustik. (GW ISSN 0340-0867) 3673
Auszuege aus den Offenlegungsschriften. Teil 3. Uebrige Verarbeitungsindustrie und Arbeitsverfahren, Maschinen- und Fahrzeugbau, Ernaehrung, Landwirtschaft. (GW ISSN 0340-0913) 3673
Auszuege aus den Patentschriften. (GW ISSN 0178-4250) 3673
Auszuege aus Presseartikeln. (GW ISSN 0005-0598) 844
Aut Aut. (IT ISSN 0005-0601) 3762, 2859
Autark. (GW) 2270
Author. (UK ISSN 0005-0628) 2897
Author Biographies Master Index. (US ISSN 0741-8655) 417
Authority for Uniform Specifications Meat and Livestock (AUS-Meat) Meat Feedback see A U S - Meat Feedback 2060
Authority Report. (US) 939
Authors & Artists for Young Adults. (US) 1249, 318, 2567
Author's and Writer's Who's Who see International Authors and Writers Who's Who 419
Author's Choice. (US) 3010
Author's Choice Monthly see Author's Choice 3010
Authors Guild Bulletin. (US) 2897, 2602
†Authors in the News. (US ISSN 0145-1499) 5144
Authors Newsletter. (US) 4121
Authorship. (US ISSN 0005-0660) 2897
Authorware. (US) 1475
Auto. (SZ) 4679
Auto. (BE ISSN 0774-1324) 4679, 4717
Auto. (IT) 4679
Auto Age. (II ISSN 0005-0709) 4679
Auto Age. (US ISSN 0894-1270) 4679

Auto Age. (NZ) 4679
Auto Age Buyer's Guide. (US) 4680, 1122
Auto Aktuell. (GW ISSN 0179-4078) 4680
Auto and Flat Glass Journal. (US ISSN 0005-0717) 1161, 4680
Auto & Motor Techniek. (NE) 4680
†Auto and Service. (GW ISSN 0178-4811) 5144
Auto & Truck International. (US) 4680
Auto Attrezzature. (IT) 4680
Auto Bladet. (DK) 4680
Auto C A D World. (US ISSN 1060-1317) 1426
Auto Capital. (IT) 4680
Auto Caravan Notizie. (IT) 4753, 4541
Auto-Club. (SP) 4680
Auto Club Europa e.V. Lenkrad see A C E Lenkrad 4678
Auto Club News. (US ISSN 0746-8504) 4680
Auto Club News Pictorial see Auto Club News 4680
Auto d'Epoca. (IT) 4680
Auto Data Digest. (SA) 4680
Auto Dealers' Digest see Auto Dealers' Guide 4680
Auto Dealers' Guide. (SA) 4680
Auto Defense. (FR) 4680
Auto e Design. (IT ISSN 0393-8387) 4680
Auto Exklusiv. (SZ) 4680
Auto Exotica. (US) 4680
Auto Expertise. (FR ISSN 0150-7230) 4680
Auto-Express. (GR) 2196
Auto Extra. (HU ISSN 0864-9219) 4680
Auto Finance Update. (US ISSN 1045-5760) 4680
Auto Gids see Le Moniteur de l'Automobile 4695
Auto Glass Magazine. (US) 4680, 1161
Auto Hebdo. (CN) 4680
†Auto Illustrierte. (SZ) 5144
Auto In. (IT ISSN 1120-7655) 4680
Auto in Fuoristrada. (IT) 4680
Auto Index. (US ISSN 0145-6776) 4661, 3, 4680
Auto-Industria see Autoindustria 4682
Auto Industry Newsletter. (UK) 4680, 1411
Auto International Association Update see A I A Update 4678
Das Auto-International-in Zahlen/ International Auto Statistics. (GW ISSN 0175-9531) 4680
Auto Ja Tie/Automobiles and Highways in Finland (Year). (FI ISSN 0567-1795) 4661
Auto-Jahr. see Automobile Year 4682
Auto-Journal. (FR ISSN 0005-0768) 4680, 4753
Auto Journal. (BE) 4680
Auto-Katalog. (GW) 4680
Auto Katalog. (GW) 4680
Auto Laundry News. (US ISSN 0005-0776) 4680
Auto, Life, Fire, Insurance News see A L F I News 2525
Auto Magazin (Gross-Bieberau) see Suedhessisches Auto Magazin 4702
Auto Magazine. (GW 3452, 4680
Auto Mecanica. (SP) 4680
Auto Merchandising News. (US) 4680
Auto Modell und Technik see A M T 2432
Auto-Modelle see Auto-Katalog 4680
Auto Modeller. (UK) 2433
Auto-Moto-Revue. (BE) 4680
Auto-Motor. (HU ISSN 0005-0792) 4680
Auto Motor und Sport. (GW ISSN 0005-0806) 4681, 4465
Auto Motor und Sport Spezial. (GW) 4681, 4465
Auto Motor und Sport Testjahrbuch. (GW) 4681, 4465
Auto Motor Zubehoer see A M Z 4678
Auto Motorrad und Freizeit. (GW) 4681
†Auto Nyt. (DK ISSN 0106-0473) 5144
Auto Oggi. (IT) 4681
Auto Orienting see Aktuel Bilsport 4679

Auto Passion. (FR) 4681
Auto Price Almanac. (US ISSN 1042-6205) 4681, 1033
Auto Racing Digest. (US ISSN 0090-8029) 4465
Auto Racing Memories. (US ISSN 0743-7129) 4681
Auto Rental Fleet. (US) 1033, 4681
Auto Rental News. (US) 4681, 647
Auto Retail Report. (US) 4681
Auto Revista. (SP ISSN 0005-1691) 4681
Auto Revista. (US) 4681
Auto Revue. (AU) 4681
Auto Service Insider. (US) 4681
Auto Service Today. (US) 4681
Auto 70. (IT) 4681
Auto Sound & Security. (US) 4681, 1882
Auto Sport. (PO) 4681, 4465
Auto Sukces. (PL) 4681
Auto-Technik. (SZ ISSN 0005-0857) 4681
Auto-Technika Motoryzacyjna. (PL) 4594
Auto Touring. (AU ISSN 0001-2688) 4681, 4753
Auto Trim & Restyling News. (US) 4681
Auto Trim News see Auto Trim & Restyling News 4681
Auto und Modell. (GW ISSN 0940-6697) 2433
Auto und Reise. (GW ISSN 0045-1010) 4753
Auto und Verkehr. (GW) 4681, 1296
Auto und Wirtschaft. (AU) 4681
Auto Verte. (FR ISSN 0222-3996) 4681
Auto-Volt. (FR ISSN 0005-0881) 4681, 1882
Auto-X and Grassroots Motorsports see Grassroots Motorsports 4692
Auto y Camion Internacional see Auto & Truck International 4680
Auto Zeitung. (GW) 4681
Auto Zubehoer Markt. (GW) 4681
Auto 8. (FR) 2433
Auto 70. (IT) 4681
†Autobody. (US) 5144
Autobus. (IT) 4647, 4681
Autobus Oggi. (IT) 4707
Autobuses y Autocares. (SP) 4647
Autobuskroniek. (NE) 4647
AutoCAD Magazin. (GW ISSN 0934-1749) 1475
Autocar see Autocar & Motor 4681
Autocar & Motor. (UK ISSN 0955-5889) 4681
Autocarri e Autobus-Trans see Autobus 4647
Autocatalogue. (FR ISSN 0067-2424) 4681
▼Autocephalous Orthodox Churches. (US ISSN 1059-1001) 4216
Autoclub. (AG ISSN 0005-0946) 4681
Autoclub see Touring 4704
Autofachmann. (GW) 4681
Autoferrotranviere. (IT) 4647
Autogiornale. (IT) 4681
▼Autoglass. (US ISSN 1047-2061) 1161, 4681
†Autograf. (PL ISSN 0860-8091) 5144
Autografo. (IT) 2204
Autograph Collector's Magazine. (US) 2399
†Autoguide. (US) 5144
Autoharpoholic. (US ISSN 0736-3796) 3540
Autohaus. (GW ISSN 0005-0989) 4681
Autoimmune Diseases. (UK ISSN 0142-8365) 3183, 471, 3368
Autoimmunity. (US ISSN 0891-6934) 3080
AutoInc. (US ISSN 0199-6908) 4681
Autoindustria. (MX) 4682
Autokampioen. (NE ISSN 0005-0997) 4682, 4717
Autokaufmann. (GW) 4682
Autokosten und Steuern Aktuell. (GW ISSN 0937-3381) 4682
Autolla Ulkomaille. (FI ISSN 0355-2896) 4753
Automarques. (FR) 4682, 4515
Automat. (IT ISSN 0005-1012) 1411

Automated Builder. (US ISSN 0899-5540) 601
Automated Builder Annual Buyers' Guide. (US) 2483
Automated Office Abstracts. (UK ISSN 0957-3224) 1403, 704
Automated Office Profiles see Automated Office Abstracts 1403
Automated Payments Update. (US) 759, 747
Automated Teller Machines Directory see A T M Directory 1120
Automaten-Markt. (GW ISSN 0005-1039) 1033
Automatic Control and Computer Sciences. (English translation of: Avtomatika i Vychislitel'naya Tekhnika (Riga)) (US ISSN 0146-4116) 1411
Automatic Data Processing. Bibliography. see A O P Bibliografija 1403
Automatic Data Processing Newsletter see A D P Newsletter 5127
Automatic Documentation and Mathematical Linguistics. (English Translation of: Nauchno-Tekhnicheskaya Informatsiya. Seriya 2) (US ISSN 0005-1055) 2746, 2804, 4300
Automatic I D News. (US ISSN 0890-9768) 1411, 2567
Automatic Machining. (US ISSN 0005-1071) 3016
Automatic Musical Instrument Collectors' Association Bulletin see A M I C A Bulletin 3536
Automatic Programming Information Centre Studies in Data Processing Series see A P I C Studies in Data Processing Series 1429
Automatic Subject Citation Alert see Research Alert (Philadelphia) 22
Automatic Support Systems Symposium for Advanced Maintainability. Proceedings see Autotestcon 1883
Automatic Testing Conference Autotestcon see Autotestcon 1883
Automatica. (US ISSN 0005-1098) 1411
Automatica e Instrumentacion. (SP ISSN 0213-3113) 1411, 1927
Automatie. (NE ISSN 0005-1128) 1411
Automatik. (DK ISSN 0105-0168) 1815, 1411
Automatika. (CI ISSN 0005-1144) 1411
Automation. (UK ISSN 0005-1152) 1411
Automation. (JA ISSN 0473-5587) 1411
Automation. (SW) 1411, 1923
Automation. see Automatizace 1412
Automation see Controls and Systems 1818
Automation. see Automatizalas 1927
Automation and Control. (NZ ISSN 0110-6295) 1411
Automation and Remote Control. (English translation of: Avtomatika i Telemekhanika) (US ISSN 0005-1179) 1412
Automation, Computing. Computers & Measurement Abstracts. see Automatizalasi, Szamitastechnikai es Merestechnikai Szakirodalmi Tajekoztato 3836
▼Automation in Construction. (NE ISSN 0926-5805) 1416
Automation in Housing and Manufactured Home Dealer see Automated Builder 601
Automation in Housing and Manufactured Home Dealer Annual Buyers' Guide see Automated Builder Annual Buyers' Guide 2483
Automation Journal of Japan see A M J Newsletter 5128
Automation News. (US) 1412, 1815
Automation of Electric Power Systems. see Dianli Xitong Zidonghua 1885
Automation Products and Technology see Automation Systems 1412
Automation Systems. (CN) 1412
Automatisering. (NO ISSN 0333-3302) 1412, 1440
Automatisering Gids/Computer Weekly. (NE) 1448

AUTOMATISIERUNGSTECHNIK

Automatisierungstechnik. (GW ISSN 0178-2312) **1448**
Automatisierungstechnische Praxis. (GW ISSN 0178-2320) **2521**
Automatizace/Automation. (CS ISSN 0005-125X) **1412**
Automatizacija Poslovanja. (YU ISSN 0005-1268) **1412**
Automatizacion Integrada y Revista de Robotica. (SP) **1877**
Automatizalas/Automation. (HU ISSN 0133-1620) **1927**, 2521
Automatizalasi, Szamitastechnikai es Merestechnikai Szakirodalmi Tajekoztato/Automation, Computing, Computers & Measurement Abstracts. (HU ISSN 0231-0643) **3836**, 3, 2525
Automatska Obrada Podataka Bibliografija see A O P Bibliografija **1403**
†Automatyka Kolejowa. (PL ISSN 0137-2858) **5144**
Automazione e Strumentazione. (IT ISSN 0005-1284) **1412**
Automazione Integrata. (IT ISSN 0393-3911) **2521**
Automazione Navale. (IT ISSN 0392-2294) **4724**, 1412, 1602
Automazione Oggi. (IT ISSN 0392-8829) **1412**, 1407
Automedica. (US ISSN 0095-0963) **3225**
Automobiel Klassiek. (NE) **256**, 4682
Automobil. (SA ISSN 0304-8721) **4682**
Automobil/Automobile. (CS ISSN 0404-3529) **4682**
Automobil-Industrie. (GW ISSN 0005-1306) **4682**
Automobil Produktion. (GW) **4682**
Automobil Revue see Revue Automobile **4655**
Automobil Sport-Zeitschrift see Rallye Racing **4700**
Automobil- und Motorrad-Chronik. (GW) **4682**
L'Automobile. (CN ISSN 0005-1330) **4682**
Automobile. (IT ISSN 0005-1349) **4682**
Automobile. see Automobil **4682**
Automobile. (UK ISSN 0955-1328) **4682**
†Automobile. (AT) **5144**
Automobile (New York). (US ISSN 0894-3583) **4682**
Automobile & Tractor. (Il ISSN 0045-1053) **161**, 3016, 4682
Automobile Association Members Handbook. (UK) **4753**, 4682
Automobile Association of America Going Places see A A A Going Places **4750**
Automobile Association of Zimbabwe. Members' Handbook. (RH) **4682**
Automobile Club d'Italia Informazioni see A C I Informazioni **4678**
Automobile Club Torino. (IT) **4682**
Automobile Design Liability. (US) **2602**, 4682
Automobile Engineering. see Jidosha Kogaku **4693**
Automobile Facts and Figures see M V M A Motor Vehicle Facts and Figures **4695**
Automobile Finance Update see Auto Finance Update **4680**
Automobile in Cifre. (IT) **4661**
Automobile India. (Il ISSN 0005-1403) **4682**
Automobile Industry - Japan and Toyota. (JA) **4682**
Automobile Insurance Losses, Collision Coverages, Variations by Make and Series. (US ISSN 0093-0466) **2527**, 4682
†Automobile International. (FR) **5144**
Automobile International - Automovil Internacional see Auto & Truck International **4680**
Automobile Law Reports - Insurance Cases. (US) **2527**
Automobile Law Reports Insurance Decisions see Automobile Law Reports - Insurance Cases **2527**
Automobile Legal Association Sights to See Book see A L A Sights to See Book **5128**

Automobile License Plate Collectors Association Newsletter see A L P C A Newsletter **2432**
Automobile Magazine. (FR ISSN 0758-6957) **4753**, 4682
Automobile Quarterly. (US ISSN 0005-1438) **4682**
Automobile Technology. see Qiche Jishu **4700**
Automobile Year/L'Annee Automobile/Auto-Jahr. (SZ ISSN 0084-7674) **4682**
Automobiler. (US) **4682**
Automobiles and Highways in Finland (Year). see Auto Ja Tie **4661**
Automobiles Classiques. (FR ISSN 0759-6065) **4682**
Automobiles: Latin American Industrial Report. (US) **4682**
Automobilisme Ardennais. (FR) **4753**, 4682
Automobilismo. (IT) **4682**
Automobilista. (IT) **4682**
Automobiliste. (FR) **4682**
Automobiltechnische Zeitschrift see A T Z **4678**
Automondo see Automundo Deportivo **4465**
Automondo. (IT) **4682**
Automotive (Year) see Automotive Industries (Year) **4683**
Automotive Aftermarket News see Chilton's Automotive Marketing **4687**
Automotive Age see Auto Age **4679**
Automotive Age - Kelley Blue Book Reporter see Auto Age **4679**
Automotive and Ancillary Industry see Automotive Industry of India - Facts & Figures **4683**
Automotive and Machine Shop Section see Automotive, Tooling, Metalworking, and Associated Industries. Newsletter **3615**
Automotive Applications on Microprocessors see I E E E Workshop on Automotive Applications of Electronics (Publication) **4707**
Automotive Body Repair News. (US ISSN 0192-0995) **4682**
Automotive Body Repair News (Year) Buyers Guide and Fact Book. (US) **4682**
Automotive Booster of California. (US) **4682**
Automotive Buyer see Automotive Week **4683**
Automotive Contact. (US) **4682**
Automotive Contact Directory. Indiana. (US) **4683**
Automotive Cooling Journal. (US ISSN 0005-1497) **4683**
Automotive Dealers Digest. (US) **4683**, 647
Automotive Design Engineering see Automotive Engineer **4683**
Automotive Dismantlers & Recyclers Association Newsletter see A D R A Newsletter **4678**
Automotive Dismantlers and Recyclers Buyers Guide/Membership Roster. (US) **1122**
†Automotive Electronic News. (US) **5144**
Automotive Engineer. (AT) **4683**, 3682
Automotive Engineer. (UK ISSN 0307-6490) **4683**
Automotive Engineering. see Qiche Gongcheng **4700**
Automotive Engineering Magazine. (US ISSN 0098-2571) **4683**
Automotive Executive. (US ISSN 0195-1564) **4683**
Automotive Fine Arts Society Quarterly see A F A S Quarterly **309**
Automotive Fleet. (US ISSN 0005-1519) **4683**
Automotive Fuel Economy Program. Annual Report to the Congress. (US) **3682**
Automotive Herald. Facts and Info see Jan Corporation. Facts & Info **4693**
Automotive Independent see AutoInc **4681**
Automotive Industries. (US) **4683**
Automotive Industries (Year). (SA ISSN 1018-8371) **4683**, 1122

Automotive Industry Data Newsletter. (UK ISSN 0951-158X) **4661**
Automotive Industry Matters Pty. Ltd. see A I M **4678**
Automotive Industry of India - Facts & Figures. (Il) **4683**
Automotive Investor. (US ISSN 0898-2155) **4683**, 256, 939
Automotive Literature Index. (US) **4662**
Automotive Litigation Reporter. (US) **2602**, 4683
Automotive Manufacturers E D P Council Newsletter. (US) **1057**, 825
Automotive Market Report. (US) **4683**
Automotive Marketer Annual Buyer's Guide. (CN ISSN 0702-8318) **1122**
†Automotive Marketer. (CN ISSN 0702-8318) **5144**
†Automotive Marketing Retail Aftermarket Guide. (US) **5144**
Automotive Marketing Who's Who A P A Show Directory. (Automotive Parts and Accessories Association) **4683**, 1122
▼Automotive Materials. (UK ISSN 0963-7109) **4683**
Automotive Messenger. (US ISSN 0045-1088) **4683**
Automotive News. (US ISSN 0005-1551) **4683**
Automotive News Market Data Book. (US) **4683**
Automotive News of the Pacific Northwest. (US ISSN 0005-156X) **4683**
Automotive Parts and Accessories Association Automotive Marketing Who's Who A P A A Show Directory see Automotive Marketing Who's Who A P A A Show Directory **4683**
Automotive Parts International. (US ISSN 0896-3614) **4683**
†Automotive Products Report. (US ISSN 0745-3043) **5144**
Automotive Rebuilder. (US ISSN 0567-2317) **4683**
Automotive Recycling. (US) **4683**
Automotive Repair & Re-manufacture. (UK) **4683**, 4743
Automotive Retailer. (CN ISSN 0005-1578) **4683**
Automotive Service see Service Station **4701**
†Automotive Service Data Book. (CN ISSN 0068-9629) **5144**
Automotive Technology. see Qiche Gongyi **4700**
Automotive, Tooling, Metalworking, and Associated Industries. Newsletter. (US) **3615**, 4683
Automotive Week. (US ISSN 0889-3918) **4683**, 1033
Automoto Giornale. (IT) **4683**
Automotor. (AG ISSN 0005-1608) **4684**
Automovel Club de Portugal Revista A C P see Revista A C P **4700**
Automovil. (SP) **4684**
Automovil de Venezuela. (VE ISSN 0005-1616) **4684**
Automovilismo en Espana. (SP) **4684**
Automundo Deportivo. (MX) **4465**
Autonews. (KE) **4684**
Autonomi. (IT ISSN 0045-1118) **2859**
Autonomia Local. (SP) **4084**
Autonomic Nervous System. (US ISSN 1047-5125) **570**, 3080
†Autonomic Nervous System. (UK ISSN 0142-856X) **5144**
Autonomie Locali e Servizi Sociali. (IT ISSN 0392-2278) **4399**, 3874
Autoparts Distributor. (CN ISSN 0827-2808) **4684**
▼Autoparts Report. (US ISSN 1045-1978) **4684**
Autoperformance see Cars & Car Conversions **4687**
Autopinion. (CN ISSN 0836-1630) **4684**
Autopista. (SP ISSN 0567-2392) **4684**
Autoracer's Monthly. (US) **4465**
Autorama. (IT ISSN 0005-1683) **4684**, 4515
Autores. (PO) **4630**, 3540

Autores Africanos. (BL) **2897**
Autorevue. (AU ISSN 0005-0830) **4647**
AutoRevue. (LU) **4684**
▼Autorevuu. (ER ISSN 0868-4405) **4684**, 4515, 4717
Autoriparatore see Autoriparatore, il Gommista, Elettrauto **4684**
Autoriparatore, il Gommista, Elettrauto. (IT) **4684**
Autoriserede Laeger i Danmark. (DK) **3080**
Autoriserede Laeger, Tandlaeger, Dyrlaeger i Danmark see Autoriserede Laeger i Danmark **3080**
Autoroute. (CN) **4753**
Autoruote 4x4. (IT) **4684**
Autoservice Profit Report see Auto Retail Report **4681**
Autoservicios, Supermercados & Almaceneros. (AG) **2090**
Autoservicios y Almaceneros see Autoservicios, Supermercados & Almaceneros **2090**
†Autosound & Communications. (US) **5144**
Autospark. (Il ISSN 0005-0695) **4684**, 4743
Autosport. (YU ISSN 0005-173X) **4465**, 4684
Autosport. (UK) **4684**, 4465
Autosport. (IT) **4684**, 4465
Autosprint. (IT ISSN 0005-1748) **4684**
Autosprint Anno. (IT) **4684**
Autostrade. (IT ISSN 0005-1756) **1862**
Autotechnica. (BE) **4684**
Autotecnica. (AG) **4684**, 2580
Autotecnica. (IT) **4684**
Autotestcon. (Automatic Testing Conference) (US) **1883**
Autotouring see Touring Club Magazine **4790**
Autotrade. (UK) **4684**
Autoveicoli Circolanti in Italia. (IT) **4662**
Der Autovermieter. (GW) **4684**
Autoveteranen. (SW ISSN 0005-1799) **4684**
Autovisie. (NE ISSN 0005-0873) **4684**
AutoWeek. (US ISSN 0005-1802) **4684**
Autoweek and Competition Press see AutoWeek **4684**
Autoworld. (UK ISSN 0005-1829) **4684**
Autozeitung. (GW) **4684**
Autre Journal. (FR) **2859**
Autre Monde. (FR) **3668**
Autrement. (FR) **4366**
Autumn School of Studies on Alcohol & Drugs. Proceedings of Seminars. (AT) **1534**, 1249, 4399
Auvergne Economique. (FR ISSN 0045-1142) **844**
Auvergne Magazine. (FR) **2186**, 4753
Auxiliary to the American Osteopathic Association Accents see A A O A Accents **3213**
AV Video see A V Video **1384**
Avakash. (Il) **2199**
Avalanche News. (CN) **3433**
Avalanche Review. (US) **1541**, 3433
Avaloka. (US ISSN 0890-5541) **4164**, 3762
Avalon Dispatch. (US) **2988**
Avalon Hill General. (US ISSN 0888-1081) **3452**, 2433
Avalon to Camelot. (US ISSN 0741-1790) **2897**, 1249, 2052, 2307
Avance. (NQ) **3874**
Avance de Informacion Economica. Balanza Comercial. (MX ISSN 0187-4942) **704**, 901
Avance de Informacion Economica. Ciudad de Guadalajara: Encuesta sobre Establecimientos Comerciales. (MX ISSN 0187-6708) **704**, 833
Avance de Informacion Economica. Ciudad de Mexico: Encuesta sobre Establecimientos Comerciales. (MX ISSN 0187-4985) **704**, 833

Avance de Informacion Economica. Cuidad de Monterrey: Encuesta sobre Establecimientos Comerciales. (MX ISSN 0187-5000) **704**, 833
Avance de Informacion Economica. Empleo. (MX ISSN 0187-4969) **704**, 972
Avance de Informacion Economica. Indicadores de la Actividad Industrial.(MX) **704**, 1072
Avance de Informacion Economica. Indicadores del Sector Manufacturero.(MX ISSN 0187-4977) **704**, 1072
Avance de Informacion Economica. Industria de la Construccion. (MX ISSN 0187-4950) **637**
Avance de Informacion Economica. Industria Minerometalurgica. (MX ISSN 0187-5027) **3499**, **3424**
Avance de Informacion Economica. Producto Interno Bruto Trimestral. (MX) **704**, 844
Avance de Informacion Estadistica. Industria Maquiladora de Exportacion.(MX ISSN 0187-5019) **704**, 901
Avance Hispano. (US) **1992**, 647
†Avances en Obstetricia y Ginecologia. (SP ISSN 0210-7171) **5144**
Avances en Produccion Animal. (CL ISSN 0378-4509) **211**
Avances en Psicologia Clinica Latinoamericana. (CK ISSN 0120-3797) **4012**
†Avances en Terapeutica. (SP ISSN 0210-3397) **5144**
Avant Garde. (US ISSN 0005-1918) **2859**
Avant Garde. (NE) **2897**, 318
Avant Gardener. (US ISSN 0005-1926) **2122**
Avant-Scene Cinema. (FR ISSN 0045-1150) **3504**
Avant-Scene Opera. (FR ISSN 0764-2873) **3540**
Avant Scene Theatre. (FR ISSN 0045-1169) **4630**
Avant-Siecle. (FR ISSN 0067-2610) **2897**
Avante. (CU) **3452**
Avante. (PO) **3875**
Avanti Owners Association Newsletter. (US ISSN 0149-1911) **4684**
Avareyanut Vestiya Cheurati/Crime and Social Deviance. (IS ISSN 0334-4525) **4399**
Avatar. (IT) **2859**
Ave Maria see A M **4254**
Avec. (US ISSN 0899-3750) **2897**
Avec Arctia. (FI ISSN 0783-0041) **2471**
Avedik. (LE ISSN 0005-1950) **4256**
Avenir see Magazine Avenir **1685**
Avenir et Sante. (FR ISSN 0240-6411) **3276**
Avenirs. (FR ISSN 0005-1969) **3624**
Aventura Lifestyles. (US) **2221**
Avenue. (US) **2221**
Avenue. (NE ISSN 0005-1985) **4837**
Average Prices of British Academic Books. (UK ISSN 0261-0302) **2746**, 4121
Average Prices of U S A Academic Books. (UK ISSN 0951-8975) **2746**
†Average Wage Rates of Farm Workers in the Philippines. (PH) **5144**
Avery Index to Architectural Periodicals.(US) **309**, 3
Aves. (BE ISSN 0005-1993) **562**
Aves del Arca. (UY ISSN 0067-2637) **2897**
Avgherinos/Morning Star. (CY) **1249**
Avia. (IT ISSN 0005-2027) **47**
†Avia. (NE ISSN 0005-2035) **5144**
Aviacao em Revista. (BL) **47**
Aviacion. (PE ISSN 0005-2078) **3452**, 47
Aviacion y Astronautica. (AG ISSN 0045-1177) **47**
Aviaguide. (FR) **47**
Avian Diseases. (US ISSN 0005-2086) **4807**
†Avian - Exotic Practice. (US ISSN 8750-037X) **5144**
Avian Pathology. (UK ISSN 0307-9457) **4807**

Avianews see Avianews International **4671**
Avianews International. (BE ISSN 0772-876X) **4671**, 47
Aviary-Bird and Wildlife. (AT) **562**
Aviation & Aerospace. (CN) **47**
Aviation and Air Transport Abstracts. see Repulesi Szakirodalmi Tajekoztato **4666**
†Aviation and Computer Enthusiasts Newsletter. (US) **5144**
Aviation & Space Journal. (II ISSN 0970-3578) **4671**, 4753
Aviation Annual of Japan. (JA) **47**
Aviation Business Directory see A.B.D **42**
†Aviation - C L A P. (FR) **5145**
Aviation Canada. (CN) **47**
The Aviation Consumer. (US ISSN 0147-9911) **47**, 1502, 4671
Aviation Daily. (US) **47**
Aviation Digest. (US ISSN 0884-4755) **47**
Aviation Directory of Canada. (CN) **47**
Aviation Education News Bulletin. (US) **47**, 1682, 4671
Aviation Employment Monthly. (US ISSN 1050-2149) **47**, 3624
Aviation Equipment Maintenance. (US ISSN 0745-0214) **47**
Aviation et Pilote. (FR) **4671**
Aviation et Pilote Prive see Aviation et Pilote **4671**
Aviation Europe see Aerospace Europe **44**
Aviation Facilities Energy Association. Annual Report. (US) **47**, 1783
Aviation Facilities Energy Association. Energy Consumption Analysis Report.(US) **47**, 1783
Aviation Focus see International Air Show Guide **4674**
Aviation Ground Equipment Market. (US ISSN 0891-5148) **47**
Aviation Heritage. (AT ISSN 0815-4392) **47**
▼Aviation Heritage. (US ISSN 1054-335X) **47**, 2399
Aviation Historical Society of Australia. Journal see Aviation Heritage **47**
Aviation Historical Society of New Zealand. Journal. (NZ ISSN 0110-5493) **47**, 2344
Aviation International News. (US) **4671**
Aviation Law Reports. (US) **4671**, 2602
Aviation Litigation. (US) **2602**, 47
Aviation Litigation Reporter. (US ISSN 0737-7746) **2602**, 4671
Aviation Magazine International. (FR ISSN 0005-2132) **47**
Aviation Maintenance Foundation International. Industry Report. (US) **47**
Aviation Maintenance Foundation International Industry News see A M F I Industry News **42**
Aviation Master File. (US) **1346**, 47, 1355
Aviation Mechanics Bulletin. (US ISSN 0005-2140) **48**
Aviation Mechanics Journal see General Aviation Mechanics Journal **53**
Aviation Medical Education Series. (US ISSN 0067-2661) **48**, 3080
Aviation Medicine. (II ISSN 0250-5045) **3080**, 48, 4671
Aviation Monthly. (US ISSN 0145-1014) **48**
Aviation News see Aircraft & Aerospace **45**
Aviation News. (UK) **48**, 2433
Aviation Production Engineering. see Hangkong Zhizao Gongcheng **54**
Aviation Regulatory Digest Service. (US) **4671**
Aviation Reports. (UK ISSN 0005-2159) **48**
Aviation Review see Aerospace & Defence Review **44**
Aviation Safety. (US ISSN 0277-1764) **48**, 4671
†Aviation Safety Digest. (AT ISSN 0045-1207) **5145**
Aviation, Space, and Environmental Medicine. (US ISSN 0095-6562) **3080**
Aviation Space Writers Association. Yearbook and Directory. (US) **48**

Aviation - Space Writers Association News see A W A News **42**
Aviation - Space Writers Association Newsletter see A W A News **42**
Aviation Studies International. Official Price List. (UK ISSN 0005-2167) **48**
Aviation Today. (CN ISSN 0828-9344) **48**
Aviation Trade see Aviation Today **48**
Aviation Trade. (CN) **4671**
Aviation Tradescan. (US ISSN 0899-1928) **66**, 3
†Aviation U S A (Tuscaloosa). (US) **5145**
Aviation Week & Space Technology. (US ISSN 0005-2175) **48**
Aviation Week and Space Technology. Buyers Guide see World Aviation Directory **65**
Aviation Week and Space Technology. Marketing Directory see World Aviation Directory **65**
Aviation Week Video. (US) **48**, 1368
Aviation Week Video Magazine see Aviation Week Video **48**
Aviators Hot Line. (US ISSN 0195-0347) **48**, 1033
Aviatsiya i Kosmonavtika. (RU ISSN 0005-2183) **48**
Aviazione. (IT) **48**
Aviazione di Linea Difesa e Spazio see Aviazione **48**
Aviazione e Difesa News see Publi and Consult News **60**
Aviculteur. (FR) **212**
Avicultura Andina. (CK) **212**
Avicultura Colombiana. (CK) **212**
Avicultura Industrial. (BL ISSN 0009-0905) **212**
Avicultura Profesional. (US ISSN 0736-2056) **212**
Avicultural Magazine. (UK ISSN 0005-2256) **212**
†AViiON News. (US) **5145**
Avion. (II) **4671**
†Avion. (SP ISSN 0005-2272) **5145**
Avion Revue. (SP) **48**
Avionics. (US ISSN 0273-7639) **48**, 1883
Avionics Data Sheets see Directed Energy - Avionics Data Sheets .**51**
Avionics Maintenance Conference. Booklet. (US) **48**
Avionics Maintenance Conference. Conference Program. (US) **48**
Avionics Maintenance Conference. Conference Report. (US) **48**
Avionics News Magazine. (US) **48**, 1883
Avionics Newsletter. (US) **48**
Avionics Review. (US ISSN 1048-9207) **48**, 4671
Aviron. (FR ISSN 0988-1956) **4522**
Avis aux Navigateurs. (FR ISSN 0180-9938) **4724**
Avis et Decisions du Conseil de la Concurrence. (FR) **760**, 844
Avis - Personally Yours. (IE) **4753**
Aviso. (IS) **3522**
Avisos see In Touch (Austin) **2293**
Avisos a los Navegantes. (CU) **1597**
Avivamento. (PO) **4280**
Avoda Ubituach Leumi. see Labour and National Insurance **986**
Avon Contact. (UK) **375**
Avon Past. (UK ISSN 0260-2954) **266**, 2351
Avotakka. (FI ISSN 0355-2950) **2548**, 2556
Avotaynu. (US ISSN 0882-6501) **2144**, 1992
Avto. (XV) **4684**
Avtomaticheskaya Svarka. (KR ISSN 0005-2302) **3429**
Avtomatika. (KR ISSN 0572-2691) **1412**
Avtomatika i Telemekhanika. (RU ISSN 0005-2310) **1412**
Avtomatika i Vychislitel'naya Tekhnika (Minsk). (BW ISSN 0206-8214) **1412**
Avtomatika i Vychislitel'naya Tekhnika (Riga). (LV ISSN 0132-4160) **1412**
Avtomatika, Telemekhanika i Svyaz' (RU ISSN 0005-2329) **4707**, 1412

Avtomatizirovannye Sistemy Upravleniya. (RU) **1412**
Avtomobil'naya Promyshlennost' (RU ISSN 0005-2337) **4684**
Avtomobil'nye Dorogi. (RU ISSN 0005-2353) **1862**, 4684
Avtomobil'nyi Transport. (RU ISSN 0005-2345) **4684**
Avvenire Agricolo (Parma). (IT ISSN 0005-2361) **78**
L'Avvenire Medico. (IT) **3080**
Avventura. (IT) **4753**
Avventure nel Mondo. (IT) **4753**
Avvisatore. (IT) **647**
Awake. (US ISSN 0005-237X) **4280**
Awakened India. see Prabuddha Bharata **3777**
▼Awards Almanac. (US) **3391**
Awards for Commonwealth University Academic Staff see Awards for University Teachers and Research Workers **1701**
Awards for Postgraduate Study at Commonwealth Universities. (UK ISSN 0960-7986) **1701**
Awards for University Administrators and Librarians. (UK ISSN 0964-2714) **1701**
Awards for University Teachers and Research Workers. (UK ISSN 0964-2706) **1701**
Awards, Honors and Prizes. (US ISSN 0196-6316) **1780**
†Awards in the Visual Arts. (US) **5145**
Awards Specialist see Recognition & Promotions Business **2162**
Awards to Academic Institutions by the Department of Transportation see U.S. Department of Transportation. Office of University Research. Awards to Academic Institutions by the Department of Transportation **4660**
Aware. (UK) **4164**
Aware. (US ISSN 0162-6833) **4230**
Aware Harvester see Aware **4164**
Awareness List-Bulletin Signaletique-Boletin Descriptivo see International Bureau of Education. Bulletin **1677**
Awasis Journal. (CN) **1992**, 1744
Awasis Newsletter. (CN) **1992**, 1744
Awishkara. (II ISSN 0970-6607) **4300**, 3673, 4594
Awraq. (TS) **2897**
Awraq Yadida see Revista Awraq **2383**
Axbridge Archaeological and Local History Society. Journal. (UK) **2351**
Axe Factory Review. (US) **2897**, 2859, 3504
Axe Sud. (FR) **2859**
Axial. (VE ISSN 0005-2426) **2988**
Axios. (US ISSN 0278-551X) **4280**
Ayandeh. (IR) **3634**
Ayin l'Tzion. (IS) **1992**, 3951
Aylesbury News see Bucks Advertiser **2193**
Aylesford Carmelite Newsletter. (US) **4256**
Aylik Ekonomik Durum see Turkey. Monthly Economic Letter **696**
Ayrshire Cattle Society's Journal. (UK ISSN 0005-2442) **198**
Ayrshire Collections see Ayrshire Monographs **266**
Ayrshire Digest. (US ISSN 0005-2450) **198**
Ayrshire Monographs. (UK) **266**, 2052, 2307
Ayu. (II ISSN 0005-2469) **3080**
†Ayurveda-Bharati. (II ISSN 0005-2485) **5145**
Ayurveda Doot. (II ISSN 0005-2493) **3080**
Ayurveda Saukhyam Series. (II) **3213**, 3257
Al-Ayyam. (TS) **2859**
AZ. (US) **2221**
†Azabu Daigaku Juigakubu Kenkyu Hokoku/Azabu University. Veterinary Medicine. Bulletin. (JA ISSN 0389-1836) **5145**
Azabu University. Veterinary Medicine. Bulletin. see Azabu Daigaku Juigakubu Kenkyu Hokoku **5145**
Azad Mazdur. (II ISSN 0005-2515) **3875**, 4429
Azalea City News & Review. (US) **2221**
Azalean. (US) **2122**

5956 AZANIA

Azania. (KE ISSN 0067-270X) **2331**, 266

Azania News. (TZ ISSN 0856-3349) **2168**

Azerbaidzhan. Gosudarstvennyi Universitet. Nauchnye Trudy. Seriya Istoricheskikh i Filosofskikh Nauk. (AJ) **2351**

Azerbaidzhan Tibb Zhurnaly/ Azerbaidzhanskii Meditsinskii Zhurnal. (AJ ISSN 0005-2523) **3080**

Azerbaidzhanskii Khimicheskii Zhurnal. (AJ ISSN 0005-2531) **1170**

Azerbaidzhanskii Meditsinskii Zhurnal. *see* Azerbaidzhan Tibb Zhurnaly **3080**

Azeta Calzature. (IT) **4360**

Al-Azhar University. Arabic Language Faculty in Mansoura. Journal. *see* Jami'at al-Azhar. Kulliyyat al-Lughah al-Arabiyyah bil-Mansurah. Majallah **2820**

Al-Azhar University. Arabic Language Faculty in Menoufia. Journal. *see* Jami'at al-Azhar. Kulliyyat al-Lughah al-Arabiyyah bil-Manufiyyah. Majallah **2820**

Al-Azhar University. Arabic Language Faculty in Zagazig. Journal. *see* Jami'at al-Azhar. Kulliyyat al-Lughah al-Arabiyyah bil-Zagazig. Majallah **2820**

Al-Azhar University. Faculty of Islamic Theology in Tanta. Journal. *see* Jami'at al-Azhar. Kulliyyat Usul al-Din wal-Da'wah al-Islamiyyah bi-Tanta. Majallah **4219**

Azienda Pubblica. (IT) **1003**

Aziende & Dintorni. (IT) **647**

Azione Cooperativa. (IT ISSN 0005-2566) **4399**

Azione Nonviolenta. (IT) **1273**, **2602**

Aziya i Afrika Segodnya. (RU ISSN 0005-2574) **3875**

Azoan. (IT) **3718**

Azor *see* Cuaderno Literario Azor **2863**

Azorean Express. (US) **2897**

Aztag Shapatoriag-Troshag. (LE) **3875**

Aztec Press. (US) **1304**

Aztlan: A Journal of Chicano Studies. (US) **1993**, 318, 4366

Aztlan - International Journal of Chicano Studies Research *see* Aztlan: A Journal of Chicano Studies **1993**

Azucarera Cooperativa "Onesimo Redondo" Revista A C O R *see* Revista A C O R **190**

Azulejo. (SP ISSN 0211-7967) **1161**, 601

Azur et Or. (FR) **3452**

Azure Magazine. (CN ISSN 0829-982X) **2548**, 318, 353

Azusa Pacific University Life *see* A P U Life **1302**

A2 - Central. (US) **1467**, 1458

B A A *see* Uebersee-Museum, Bremen. Veroeffentlichungen. Reihe F: Bremer Afrika-Archiv **2335**

B A A F Discussion Series. (British Agencies for Adoption & Fostering) (UK ISSN 0260-082X) **4399**

B A A F News. (British Agencies for Adoption & Fostering) (UK ISSN 0260-3888) **4399**

B A A F Practice Series. (British Agencies for Adoption & Fostering) (UK ISSN 0260-0803) **4399**

B A A F Research Series. (British Agencies for Adoption & Fostering) (UK ISSN 0260-0811) **4399**

B A A News. (UK) **4671**

B A A R G Bulletin *see* B A A S Bulletin **266**

B A A S Bulletin. (Bristol and Avon Archaeological Society) (UK) **266**

B A & R T *see* Business Aviation & Regional Transport **49**

B A B A Trade Association for the British Biomass Industries. The Digest. (UK) **1784**, 429, 1815

B A C A Calendar of Cultural Events. (Brooklyn Arts and Culture Association, Inc.) (US ISSN 0045-3242) **3522**

B A C C Trade Bulletin. (British - American Chamber of Commerce) (US) **808**

B A C M I Review. (British Aggregate Construction Materials Industries) (UK) **601**

B A D E A Quarterly Review *see* Arab Bank for Economic Development in Africa. Quarterly Review **759**

B A G - Nachrichten. (Bundes Arbeitsgemeinschaft der Mittel- und Grossbetriebe des Einzelhandels e.V.) (GW ISSN 0005-2639) **833**, 1033

B A I E Membership and Services Directory (Year). (British Association of Industrial Editors) (UK) **1122**

B A I E Membership Directory *see* B A I E Membership and Services Directory (Year) **1122**

B A I E News. (British Association of Industrial Editors) (UK ISSN 0306-1000) **2567**

B A M A Annual Report. (British Aerosol Manufacturers Association) (UK) **1170**, 1072

B A Magazine. (Brooklyn Academy of Music) (US) **3540**

B A N Newsletter. (Blacks Against Nukes) (US) **1784**, 1804, 1944

B A P C O Daily News *see* B A P C O News **3682**

B A P C O News. (Bahrain Petroleum Co. B.S.C.) (BA) **3682**

B A P I P Bulletin. (UK ISSN 0140-2889) **3749**

B A P L A Journal. (British Association of Picture Libraries and Agencies) (UK) **3789**

B A R - B R I Bar Review. (US) **2602**

B A R - B R I Bar Review. Civil Procedure. (US ISSN 0099-1244) **2701**

B A R - B R I Bar Review. Community Property. (US) **2602**

B A R - B R I Bar Review. Constitutional Law. (US ISSN 0098-7638) **2705**

B A R - B R I Bar Review. Contracts. (US ISSN 0098-762X) **2602**

B A R - B R I Bar Review. Corporations.(US ISSN 0099-1236) **2706**

B A R - B R I Bar Review. Criminal Law.(US ISSN 0098-8049) **1510**

B A R - B R I Bar Review. Evidence. (US) **2602**

B A R - B R I Bar Review. Professional Responsibility. (US) **2603**

B A R - B R I Bar Review. Real Property. (US) **2603**

B A R - B R I Bar Review. Remedies. (US ISSN 0098-7999) **2603**

B A R - B R I Bar Review. Torts. (US ISSN 0098-7611) **1510**

B A R - B R I Bar Review. Trusts. (US) **1072**

B A R - B R I Bar Review. Wills. (US) **2715**

B A R C News. (British Automobile Racing Club) (UK ISSN 0005-2647) **4465**, 4684

B A R G Review *see* Bristol and Avon Archaeology **267**

B A S A *see* Bangladesh Agricultural Sciences Abstracts **134**

B A S A Adhesives & Sealants Yearbook and Directory. (British Adhesives and Sealants Association) (UK) **3652**

B A S C A News. (British Academy of Songwriters, Composers & Authors) (UK ISSN 0144-9621) **3540**

B A S H Magazine. (Bulimia Anorexia Self-Help) (US ISSN 0740-5197) **3331**, 3603, 4012, 4399

B A S H Monthly Newsletter *see* B A S H Magazine **3331**

B A S O R *see* American Schools of Oriental Research. Bulletin **3633**

B A S R A Journal. (British-American Scientific Research Association) (US ISSN 0141-6413) **4300**

B.A.S. Speaker. (Boston Audio Society) (US) **4459**

B A U D. (Big Apple Users Digest) (US) **1467**, 1426, 1458

B A W - Monatsbericht. (Bremer Ausschuss fuer Wirtschaftsforschung) (GW) **844**

B & B *see* Brickbats & Bouquets **2528**

B & B Review *see* Bits & Bytes Review **2520**

B & B Shoptalk. (Bed & Breakfast) (US) **4753**

B and C News *see* B C & T News **2580**

B and C Tests *see* Biological and Cultural Tests for Control of Plant Diseases **496**

B & H. (Bausoertiment & Holz und Ausbaubedarf) (GW) **647**

B & I Exhibition Calendar. (Business & Industrial Trade Fairs Ltd.) (HK) **28**

B & M Bulletin. (Boston & Maine Railroad Historical Society, Inc.) (US ISSN 0362-2711) **4707**

B & P A. (Business & Public Affairs) (US ISSN 0361-7653) **647**, 4054

B & Q Scottish Football League Review. (UK) **4500**

B & T. (AT ISSN 0005-268X) **28**, 1033

B & T Year Book. (AT ISSN 0810-669X) **28**

B B A *see* Biochimica et Biophysica Acta **473**

B B A - Bioenergetics. (NE ISSN 0005-2728) **484**, 471, 3799

B B A - Biomembranes. (NE ISSN 0005-2736) **471**, 484

†B B A - Enzymology. (NE ISSN 0005-2744) **5145**

B B A - Gene Structure and Expression. (NE ISSN 0167-4781) **540**, 3257

B B A - General Subjects. (NE ISSN 0304-4165) **471**, 484

†B B A Library. (NE ISSN 0067-2734) **5145**

B B A - Lipids & Lipid Metabolism. (NE ISSN 0005-2760) **471**, 484

B B A - Molecular Basis of Disease. (NE ISSN 0925-4439) **3080**, 471, 540

B B A - Molecular Cell Research. (NE ISSN 0167-4889) **484**, 522, 3257

B B A Planen und Bauen. (GW ISSN 0171-1555) **601**

B B A - Protein Structure and Molecular Enzymology. (NE ISSN 0167-4838) **472**, 484

†B B A Reviews on Bioenergetics. (NE ISSN 0304-4173) **5145**

B B A - Reviews on Biomembranes. (NE ISSN 0304-4157) **522**, 472

B B A - Reviews on Cancer. (NE ISSN 0304-419X) **3193**

B B C Acorn User. (UK) **1467**, 1458

†B B C Annual Report and Handbook. (British Broadcasting Corporation) (UK ISSN 0068-1377) **5145**

B B C Good Food. (British Broadcasting Corporation) (UK) **2444**

B B C Mail Bag *see* Mail Bag **565**

†B B C Music Guides. (British Broadcasting Corporation) (US ISSN 0084-8018) **5145**

B B C Wildlife. (UK ISSN 0265-3656) **578**, 1484

B B E Chef-Telegramm. (Betriebswirtschaftliche Beratungsstelle fuer den Einzelhandel) (GW) **1003**

B B I A Flashes. (Billiard and Bowling Institute of America) (US) **4500**, 833

B B I A Membership and Product Information Guide. (Billiard and Bowling Institute of America) (US) **1122**, 4500

The B B I Newsletter. (Biomedical Business International) (US ISSN 1049-4316) **3080**, 901

B B K Buchfuehrung, Bilanz, Kostenrechnung. (GW) **2603**

B B R *see* Back Brain Recluse **3010**

B B R. (Brunnenbau, Bau von Wasserwerk, Rohrleitungsbau) (GW ISSN 0937-3756) **4822**, 4594

▼B B S Callers Digest. (US) **1467**

B B U Info-Dienst. (Bundesverband Buergerinitiativen Umweltschutz) (GW) **1944**

B B W: Big Beautiful Woman Magazine. (US ISSN 0192-5938) **1289**, 4837

B B W Friendship Express. (Big Beautiful Woman) (US) **2221**

†B C. (Before College) (US) **5145**

B C A Break. (Billiard Congress of America) (US) **4500**

B C A News. (Business Committee for the Arts, Inc.) (US ISSN 0005-2841) **647**, 318

B.C. Agent. (CN ISSN 0707-7114) **2527**

B.C. and Alberta Grocer Magazine. (CN) **2090**

B C & T News. (Bakery, Confectionery and Tobacco Workers International Union) (US ISSN 0163-447X) **2580**

B.C. Broker. (British Columbia) (CN) **2527**

B C Business. (CN ISSN 0384-0581) **647**

B C Business Examiner. (CN) **647**

B C C Evening Reporter. (Bronx Community College) (US) **1304**

B C D N A News. (British Columbia Dietitians' and Nutritionists' Association) (CN) **3603**

B C Dairy Directory. (CN ISSN 0843-8021) **1122**

†B C Discovery. (CN) **5145**

B C E A Reporter. (Bergen County Education Association) (US) **1617**

B C Economic and Statistical Review. (CN ISSN 0847-1525) **844**

†B.C. Economic Bulletin. (CN ISSN 0821-0020) **5145**

†B.C. Economic Development. (CN ISSN 0706-3601) **5145**

B C F Newsletter. (British Chess Federation) (UK) **4465**

B.C. Farmer. (CN) **78**

B.C. Fellowship Baptist. (CN) **4230**

B.C. Fishing Directory & Atlas. (CN ISSN 0827-570X) **2037**

B C Gazette. Part 1. (CN) **2603**

B C Gazette. Part 2. (CN) **2603**

B.C. Grocer Magazine *see* B.C. and Alberta Grocer Magazine **2090**

†B.C. Health Management Review. (CN) **5145**

B.C. Hoteliex. (CN) **2472**

B.C. Hotelman *see* B.C. Hoteliex **2472**

B C I Magazine. (Bonsai Clubs International) (US) **2122**

B C I News. (Battery Council International) (US) **4684**, 4743

B C I R A Abstracts of International Foundry Literature *see* B C I R A Abstracts of International Literature on Metal Castings Production **3424**

B C I R A Abstracts of International Literature on Metal Castings Production. (British Cast Iron Research Association) (UK ISSN 0268-3393) **3424**, 3

B C I S Quarterly Review of Building Prices. (Building Cost Information Service) (UK ISSN 0260-6216) **601**

B C I T Annual Report. (British Columbia Institute of Technology) (CN) **4594**

B C I T Update. (British Columbia Institute of Technology) (CN) **4594**, 1701

B C Journal of Special Education. (CN ISSN 0704-7509) **1734**

B C L A Reporter. (British Columbia Library Association) (CN ISSN 0005-2876) **2746**

B.C. Labour Directory. (CN ISSN 0715-2574) **972**

B C M A News. (B C Medical Association) (CN) **3080**

B C Manufacturer's Directory. (CN ISSN 0704-6278) **833**

B C Medical Association News *see* B C M A News **3080**

B C Mine Rescue Manual. (CN) **3478**

B.C. Motorist *see* Going Places Magazine **4691**

B.C. Naturalist. (CN) **4300**

B C Outdoors. (CN ISSN 0045-3013) **4541**

B.C. Peace News. (CN ISSN 0708-0859) **3951**

†B C Pharmacist. (CN) **5145**

B C Power Engineer. (CN ISSN 0005-2892) **1923**

B.C. Professional Engineer. (CN ISSN 0005-2906) **1815**

B.C. Professional Forester. (CN) **2096**

B C R A Quarterly. (UK) **1797**

B C Report. (CN) **2176**
B.C. Research. Annual Report *see* B.C. Research. Annual Report & Brochure **4300**
B.C. Research. Annual Report & Brochure. (CN) **4300**
B.C. Research Newsletter. (CN) **4300**
B C S Enterprise *see* B C S Professional **825**
B C S F A-zine. (British Columbia Science Fiction Association) (CN) **1296**, 3010
B C S Newsletter. (Bucknell Computer Service) (US) **1389**
B C S P Newsletter. (Board of Certified Safety Professionals) (US) **3615**
B C S Professional. (Boston Computer Society) (US) **825**, 1458, 1467
B C S Update. (Boston Computer Society) (US) **1458**, 1467
B.C. Science Teacher *see* Catalyst (Vancouver) **1746**
B.C. Sport Fishing Magazine. (CN ISSN 0827-2042) **4541**
B C Studies. (CN ISSN 0005-2949) **4366**, 2503
B C T C - C A M R A S O - In-Site. (British Carpet Technical Centre) (UK) **1281**
B C T F Newsletter *see* Teacher (Vancouver) **1666**
B C T M *see* Bipolar Circuits and Technology Meeting. Proceedings **1764**
B C T V: Bibliography on Cable Television. (US ISSN 0742-4914) **1368**, 390
B.C. Teacher. (CN ISSN 0005-2957) **1617**
B C U N Briefing *see* Business Council for the U N Briefing **3952**
B.C. Voice. (CN ISSN 0045-3080) **4837**, 3951
B C Well Tape. (CN) **3704**
B-City. (US ISSN 0897-5515) **2897**, 2988
B D. (Centre d'Information des Banques de Donnees) (FR) **1443**
B D A A Newsletter. (Balalaika and Domra Association of America) (US ISSN 0897-2907) **3540**, 2052
B D Baumaschinendienst. (GW ISSN 0005-6723) **601**
B D E F - Jahrbuch. (Bund Deutscher Eisenbahn-Freunde) (GW) **4708**
B D G Nachrichten. (Bundesverbaende des Deutschen Gueterkraftverkehrs) (GW) **4743**
B D Guide. (Band Director) (US) **3540**, 1617
B D I Alemania Suministra. *see* B D I Deutschland Liefert **901**
B D I Deutschland Liefert/B D I Germany Supplies/B D I l'Allemagne Fournit/B D I Alemania Suministra. (Bundesverband der Deutschen Industrie) (GW ISSN 0415-7508) **901**
B D I Germany Supplies. *see* B D I Deutschland Liefert **901**
B D I l'Allemagne Fournit. *see* B D I Deutschland Liefert **901**
B D K - Mitteilungen. (Bund Deutscher Kunsterzieher) (GW) **1617**
B.D.M.A. News *see* B D M A Newsletter **28**
B D M A Newsletter. (British Direct Marketing Association) (UK) **28**, 1033
B E A Magazine de la Femme. (ZR) **4837**
†B E C A N. (Bioengineering Current Awareness Notification) (UK ISSN 0142-0674) **5145**
†B E C A N Biomechanics & Orthopaedics. (Bioengineering Current Awareness Notification) (UK ISSN 0262-7779) **5145**
†B E C A N Electrodes for Medicine and Biology. (Bioengineering Current Awareness Notification) (UK ISSN 0261-8281) **5145**
†B E C A N Equipment for the Disabled Population. (Bioengineering Current Awareness Notification) (UK ISSN 0262-7760) **5145**

†B E C A N Instrumentation and Techniques in Cardiology. (Bioengineering Current Awareness Notification) (UK ISSN 0261-8273) **5145**
B E E - Bulletin of Environmental Education *see* Streetwise **1969**
B E F A R. Publication. (Bibliotheque des Ecoles Francaises d'Athenes et de Rome) (FR) **266**, 2307
B E K - Bruecke *see* Barmer Bruecke **2527**
B E M A Bulletin. (Bristol & Western Engineering Manufacturers Association Ltd.) (UK ISSN 0005-304X) **1815**
B E M A Engineering Directory. (Bristol and Western Engineering Manufacturers Association Ltd.) (UK ISSN 0067-5709) **1815**
B E N E L U X Economic Union. Conseil Central de l'Economie. Rapport du Secretaire sur l'Activite du Conseil. (BE) **1072**
B E P *see* Estadistico del Petroleo. Boletin **3685**
B E T A News *see* Phi Pi Epsilon B E T A News **2588**
B & G. (Bank en Gemeenten) (NE ISSN 0166-8528) **1088**
B F B *see* Bibliotheksforum Bayern **2748**
B F C Flyer. (Boston Food Co-Operative) (US) **2090**, 1502
B F G: Aussenhandelsdienst. (Bank fuer Gemeinwirtschaft Aktiengesellschaft) (GW ISSN 0171-8789) **901**
B F G: Facts and Figures - Germany. (Bank fuer Gemeinwirtschaft Aktiengesellschaft) (GW) **844**
B F G: Wirtschaftsblaetter. (Bank fuer Gemeinwirtschaft Aktiengesellschaft) (GW) **844**
B F S S Members Handbook *see* Country Sports Directory **1127**
B F S S Reference Book *see* Country Sports Directory **1127**
B F Z - Info. (Berufsfoerderungszentrum Essen e.V.) (GW) **3624**
Die B G. (Hauptverband der Gewerblichen Berufsgenossenschaften e.V.) (GW ISSN 0723-7561) **2527**
B G F Bulletin. (Banana Growers Federation Co-operative Ltd.) (AT) **170**
B G L *see* Bibliothek der Griechischen Literatur **1275**
B G News. (US) **1304**
B.G. Rudolph Lectures in Judaic Studies. (US ISSN 0067-2742) **4221**
B G S. (Bundesgrenzschutz) (GW ISSN 0302-9468) **3951**, 3452
B G W Mitteilungen. (Berufsgenossenschaft fuer Gesundheitsdienst und Wohlfahrtspflege) (GW ISSN 0937-0811) **2527**, 3615
B G W Mitteilungsblatt *see* B G W Mitteilungen **2527**
B H A. (Bibliography of the History of Art) (US ISSN 1150-1588) **351**, 3
B H A B Information Handbook. (British Helicopter Advisory Board) (UK) **48**, 1122
B H & H P A Journal. (British Holiday & Home Parks Association Ltd.) (UK) **4753**
B H E L Journal. (Bharat Heavy Electricals Ltd.) (II ISSN 0970-1540) **1883**, 1784
B H F Directory. (British Hardware Federation) (UK) **1122**, 641
B H M. Berg- und Huettenmaennische Monatshefte. (AU ISSN 0005-8912) **3478**, 3402
B H R A Fluid Engineering Series. (UK) **1923**
B I. (Bauwirtschaftliche Informationen) (GW ISSN 0341-3896) **601**
B I A Certification Handbook *see* N M M A Certification Handbook **4526**
B I A Newsletter. (Bond Investors Association, Inc.) (US) **939**
B I B E Annual Summary. (International Bulletin of Bibliography on Education) (UN ISSN 0211-8335) **1674**

B I B E Quarterly Bulletin. (International Bulletin of Bibliography on Education) (UN ISSN 0211-8335) **1674**
B I B Mitteilungen. (Bundesinstitut fuer Bevoelkerungsforschung) (GW ISSN 0722-1509) **3979**
B I B - Report. (Bibliographischer Index Bildungswissenschaften) (GW ISSN 0342-0531) **1674**
B I C - Code. (Bureau International des Containers) (FR) **3647**, 4647
†B I C E R I Abstracts from Technical and Patent Publications. (British Internal Combustion Engine Research Institute Ltd.) (UK ISSN 0001-3447) **5145**
B I D S. Monograph. (BG) **4429**, 926
B I D S. Newsletter. (BG) **926**, 4429
B I D S. Research Reports. (BG) **4429**, 926
B I D S. Working Paper. (BG) **4429**, 926
B I D Service Weekly. (US ISSN 0194-6587) **601**
B I F O C A L. (Bar Associations in Focus on Aging and the Law) (US) **2603**, 2270
B I F U Report. (Banking Insurance & Finance Union) (UK) **760**, 2527
†B I H E P. (Bibliographic Index of Health Education Periodicals) (US ISSN 0278-2340) **5145**
B I K I *see* Byulleten' Inostrannoi Kommercheskoi Informatsii **902**
B I M C O Bulletin. (Baltic and International Maritime Conference) (DK) **4724**
B I M S. (Blaukreuz Information - Meinungen - Szene) (GW) **4230**, 1534
B I Middle East Marketing Conditions: Saudi Arabia *see* Saudi Arabia Market Conditions **5273**
B I N - Beverage Industry News. (US ISSN 0274-9041) **378**
†B I N California Goldbook. (Beverage Industry News) (US ISSN 0194-0406) **5145**
B I N D E Annual Report *see* Revista do B I N D E **798**
B I N Merchandiser. (US ISSN 0271-9894) **378**
B I N O P Bulletin *see* Orientation Scolaire et Professionnelle **4037**
B I N of California *see* B I N - Beverage Industry News **378**
B I O T A Bulletin. (Biological Institute of Tropical America) (US) **429**, 1484
B I O T A Newsletter. (Biological Institute of Tropical America) (US) **429**, 1484
B I P. (Bulletin de l'Industrie Petroliere) (FR ISSN 0300-4554) **3682**
B I - P E R S Annual Compensation Survey *see* B I - P E R S Executive Compensation Report **1003**
B I - P E R S Executive Compensation Report. (Business International) (SZ) **1003**
†B I P Plastics Review. (British Imperial Plastics) (UK ISSN 0144-5014) **5145**
B I R D. (Base d'Information Robert-Debre) (FR ISSN 1016-8834) **1247**
B I S F A Magazine *see* I V C A Magazine **3511**
B I T. (Buero und Informations Technik) (GW ISSN 0006-3843) **1057**, 825
B I T S. (Business Industry Technology Service) (US ISSN 0005-318X) **704**
†B I T S. (Bibliographic Index of the Tobacco Scene) (US) **5145**
B I - Turkey Monitor. (Business International Corp.) (US) **901**
B International. (HK) **2197**, 1289, 4465, 4753
B J S M *see* British Journal of Sexual Medicine **3084**
B J V. *see* A B C **2297**
B K I *see* Bijdragen tot de Taal-, Land- en Volkenkunde **236**
B K S. (Biotech Knowledge Sources) (UK ISSN 0953-2226) **461**
B K S T S Journal *see* Image Technology Journal of the B K S T S **3511**

B L A C. (Black Literature and Arts Congress) (SA) **1993**, 318, 2897
B L A Solicitor *see* Independent Solicitor **2634**
B L E S M A G. (British Limbless Ex-Servicemen's Association) (UK) **4399**
B L I B A D. (Bulletin de Liaison a l'Intention des Bibliothecaires, Archivistes et Documentalistes Africains) (SG) **2746**
▼B L Journal. (GW ISSN 0939-5458) **429**, 78
B L L D Announcement Bulletin *see* British Reports, Translations and Theses **4355**
B L L V Bayerische Schule. (Bayerischer Lehrer und Lehrerinnen Verband) (GW ISSN 0171-8495) **1617**
B L M. (Bonniers Litteraera Magasin) (SW ISSN 0005-3198) **2859**, 4121
B L N - Bayerische Luftsport-Nachrichten. (GW) **48**
B L S News Bulletin *see* Bangladesh Library Science News Bulletin **2746**
B L S Update. (Bureau of Labor Statistics) (US) **972**
B L V S *see* Literarischer Verein in Stuttgart. Bibliothek **2933**
B M A News Review. (British Medical Association) (UK ISSN 0306-5472) **3080**
B M C E. Monthly Information Review *see* B M C E Information Review **760**
B M C E Information Review. (Banque Marocaine du Commerce Exterieur) (MR) **760**
B M C I S Building Maintenance Price Book *see* B M I Building Maintenance Price Book **601**
B M C News. (Baptist Medical Centers) (US) **2459**
B M D - Beratungsdienst. (Bund der Mitteldeutschen e.V.) (GW) **3940**
B M D C A *see* Alpenhorn **3707**
B M - E. (Broadcast Management - Engineering) (US ISSN 0005-3201) **1369**, 4459
B M E *see* B M E's Television Engineering **5145**
B M E S Bulletin. (Biomedical Engineering Society) (US) **3081**, 1815
B M E Tax Newsletter *see* Ruxton Report **1105**
B M - E: The Source Issue. (Broadcast Management - Engineering) (US) **1122**, 1369
†B M E's Television Engineering. (Broadcast Management Engineering) (US) **5145**
B M E's World Broadcast News *see* World Broadcast News **1384**
B M F Rundschau. (Bundesverband Montagebau und Fertighauser) (GW) **601**
B M F T Journal. (Bundesministerium fuer Forschung und Technologie) (GW ISSN 0170-9615) **4594**, 4300
B M F T Risiko- und Sicherheitsforschung. (Bundesministerium fuer Forschung und Technologie) (GW) **4098**
B M I Building Maintenance Price Book. (Building Maintenance Information) (UK) **601**
B M I: Music World. (Broadcast Music Inc.) (US) **3540**
B.M.J. *see* Bangladesh Medical Journal **3081**
B M Magazine. (British Museum Society) (UK) **3522**
B M P Forecasts. (Building Material Producers) (UK ISSN 0144-9060) **601**
B M P Information. (Building Material Producers) (UK ISSN 0144-9052) **601**
B M P Monthly Statistical Bulletin. (Building Material Producers) (UK ISSN 0144-9036) **601**, 637
B M R - Correspondenz. (Bayerischer Musikrat e.V.) (GW) **3540**
B M R Journal of Australian Geology and Geophysics. (AT ISSN 0312-9608) **1555**, 1587

B M T. (Baumaschinentechnik) (GW) 601, 1862
B M T Abstracts. (British Maritime Technology Ltd.) (UK ISSN 0268-9650) 4662, 4724
†B M T Cortec Bibliographies. (British Maritime Technology Ltd.) (UK) 5145
B M V Car Club Magazine see B M W Magazine 5145
B M W Club Journal. (GW) 4684
B M W E Railway Journal. (Brotherhood of Maintenance of Way Employes) (US ISSN 1049-3921) 2580, 4708
B M W E Railway Journal see B M W E Railway Journal 2580
†B M W Magazine. (UK) 5145
B M X Action Bike. (UK) 4515
B M X Plus. (Bicycle Motocross) (US) 4515
B M Z - Materialien. (Bundesministerium fuer Wirtschaftliche Zusammenarbeit) (GW) 926
B N. (Blues News) (FI ISSN 0784-7726) 3540
B N A Administrative Practice Manual. (The Bureau of National Affairs, Inc.) (US) 2603
B N A Administrative Practice Manual. Supplement. (US) 2603
B N A C Communicator. (US ISSN 1051-208X) 647
▼B N A California - Employee Relations Report. (US ISSN 1058-7373) 1062
▼B N A California - Environment Reporter. (US ISSN 1052-813X) 1944, 2603
B N A Civil Trial Manual. (US) 2701
B N A Criminal Practice Manual. (US ISSN 0889-9312) 2712
B N A Informes Tecnicos. (SP) 212
B N A Labor Relations Reporter. (US ISSN 0148-7981) 972
B N A Labor Relations Reporter. Analysis & Expediter. (US) 972
B N A Labor Relations Reporter. Fair Employment Practices. (US) 972
B N A Labor Relations Reporter. Labor Arbitration. (US) 972
B N A Labor Relations Reporter. State Labor Laws. (US) 972, 2603
B N A Labor Relations Reporter. Wages and Hours. (US) 972
B N A Noise Regulation Reporter see Noise Regulation Reporter 2661
†B N A Online. (US ISSN 0747-5438) 5145
B N A Pension Reporter. (US ISSN 0095-7100) 973, 2527
B N A Policy and Practice Series. (US ISSN 0005-3228) 1063
B N A Policy and Practice Series. Compensation. (US ISSN 0279-5418) 973, 1063
B N A Policy and Practice Series. Fair Employment Practices. (US ISSN 0149-2683) 973
B N A Policy and Practice Series. Labor Relations. (US ISSN 0149-2713) 973
B N A Policy and Practice Series. Personnel Management. (US ISSN 0149-2675) 1063
B N A Policy and Practice Series. Wages and Hours. (US ISSN 0149-2691) 973
B N A Publicaciones Tecnicas. (SP) 212
B N A Special Report Series on Work & Family. (US ISSN 1042-7015) 4399
B N A Topics. (British North America Philatelic Society Ltd.) (CN ISSN 0045-3129) 3749
†B N A's Alternative Dispute Resolution Report. (US ISSN 0893-1704) 5145
▼B N A's Americans with Disabilities Act Manual. (US 2734, 1063
B N A's Banking Report. (US ISSN 0891-0634) 2603, 1088
B N A's Bankruptcy Law Reporter. (US ISSN 1044-7474) 2603
B N A's Corporate Counsel Weekly. (US ISSN 0886-0475) 1003, 2603

B N A's Directory of State Courts, Judges, and Clerks. (US) 1122, 2603
▼B N A's Eastern Europe Reporter. (US ISSN 1058-7365) 844
▼B N A's Employee Relations. (US ISSN 1053-5373) 1063
B N A's Employee Relations Weekly. (US ISSN 0739-3016) 973
▼B N A's Environmental Due Diligence Guide. (US) 2603, 1944, 4145
B N A's Law Reprints: Trade Regulation Series see Law Reprints: Trade Regulation Series 916
▼B N A's Medicare Report. (US ISSN 1049-7986) 3081, 2603
▼B N A's National Environment Watch. (US ISSN 1049-8893) 1944
B N A's Patent, Trademark & Copyright Journal. (US ISSN 0148-7965) 3673
B N A's Washington Memorandum see B N A's Corporate Counsel Weekly 1003
B N A's Weekly Tax Report see Tax Management Weekly Report 1109
▼B N A's Workers' Compensation Report. (US ISSN 1051-4775) 973, 2603
B N - Betriebswirtschaftliche Nachrichten fuer die Landwirtschaft. (GW) 148
B N D E Noticias. (Banco Nacional do Desenvolvimento Economico) (BL) 760
B N F L News. (UK) 1804, 1784
B N F Nutrition Bulletin. (British Nutrition Foundation) (UK ISSN 0141-9684) 3603, 2062
B N H see Business New Hampshire Magazine 834
B.N.I.A. see Build 604
B N News. (Burlington Northern Railroad) (US) 4708
B O A C News see British Airways News 4671
B O A T - U S Reports. (Boat Owners Association of the United States) (US) 4522
†B O C A A D. (Bulletin of Computer Aided Architectural Design) (UK ISSN 0264-4606) 5145
B O C A Basic Fire Prevention Code see B O C A National Fire Prevention Code 2031
B O C A Basic Mechanical Code see B O C A National Mechanical Code 601
B O C A Basic National Building Code see B O C A National Building Code 601
B O C A Basic Plumbing Code see B O C A National Plumbing Code 2297
B O C A National Building Code. (Building Officials and Code Administrators International) (US) 601, 2603
B O C A National Existing Structure Code see B O C A National Property Maintenance Code 601
B O C A National Fire Prevention Code. (Building Officials and Code Administrators International) (US) 2031
B O C A National Mechanical Code. (Building Officials and Code Administrators International) (US) 601, 2603
B O C A National Plumbing Code. (Building Officials and Code Administrators International) (US) 2297, 2603
B O C A National Property Maintenance Code. (Building Officials and Code Administrators International) (US ISSN 1055-6192) 601, 2603
B O C Week. (Bell Operating Companies) (US ISSN 8755-3511) 1361, 1033
B O M A Experience Exchange Report. (Building Owners and Managers Association International) (US ISSN 0738-2170) 4145, 1003
B O M A International Convention Directory. (Building Owners and Managers Association International) (US) 3391
B O M A News. (Building Owners & Managers Association of Australia Ltd.) (AT) 4145

B.O.P.I. Abreges see B.O.P.I. Brevets d'Invention - Abreges et Listes 3673
B.O.P.I. Brevets d'Invention - Abreges et Listes. (FR ISSN 0750-7674) 3673
B.O.P.I. Dessins & Modeles. (FR ISSN 0223-3398) 3679
B.O.P.I. Marques. (FR ISSN 0223-3401) 3673
B.O.P.I. Statistiques. (Bulletin Officiel de la Propriete Industrielle) (FR) 3673
B - P A A Communicator. (Business - Professional Advertising Association) (US ISSN 0896-7849) 28, 647, 1332
B - P A A Membership Directory and Yellow Pages. (Business - Professional Advertising Association) (US) 28, 1332
B P A Quarterly. (Black Psychiatrists of America) (US) 3331, 1993
B P Accelerator. (British Petroleum) (AT) 647
B P Fleet News see B P Shipping Review 3683
B P I C S Control see Control 1006
B P I Newsletter. (Business and Professional People for the Public Interest) (US) 1944
B.P.M. (Banco Popolare di Milano) (IT) 760
B P M A News. (British Promotional Merchandise Association) (UK) 1034
B P N see Building Products News 606
B P N see Butane - Propane News 3683
B P News. (British Petroleum Company p.l.c.) (UK) 3683
B P Report. (US ISSN 0145-9457) 4121
B P Reporter. (AT) 647
B P S - Report. (GW ISSN 0170-5067) 1232
B P Shield see Shield 3701
B P Shipping Review. (UK) 3683
B P Statistical Review of World Energy. (UK) 3705
B P Z see Baupraxis-Zeitung 603
B R see Baustoff, Recycling und Deponietechnik 1915
†B R. (Boletin Rodoviario) (BL ISSN 0006-6087) 5145
B R A D Advertiser and Agency List see Advertiser & Agency List 26
B R A D Direct Marketing. (British Rate and Data) (UK ISSN 0954-7746) 1034
B R A D Directories and Annuals see British Rate and Data 395
B R A D S. (Bollettino del Repertorio e dell'Atlante Demologico Sardo) (IT ISSN 0067-9860) 2052
B R A K - Mitteilungen. (GW ISSN 0722-6934) 2603
B R I A see Bill of Rights in Action 2705
B R I C S Bracs. (Black Resources Information Coordinating Services, Inc.) (US) 1993
B R I Research Papers. (JA ISSN 0453-4972) 601
B R S Bulletin. (US ISSN 0196-7223) 1455, 2796
B S A Annual Report. (Building Societies Association) (UK) 601, 4145
B S A Bulletin see Housing Finance 4150
B S B I Abstracts. (Botanical Society of the British Isles) (UK ISSN 0307-2657) 461, 3
†B S C Bulletin. (British Shipbuilders Council) (UK) 5145
B S C S: The Natural Selection. (US) 430, 1744
B.S.D.A. News. (Building Supply Dealers Association of British Columbia) (CN ISSN 0829-559X) 601
B S H R Institute of Horticultural Research. Annual Report see Horticultural Research International 179
B S H S Newsletter. (British Society for the History of Science) (UK ISSN 0144-6347) 4300
B S Handbook 3. Summaries of British Standards for Building. (UK) 601, 1862

B S I Catalogue. (UK) 3445
B S I News. (British Standards Institution) (UK ISSN 0005-3309) 3445
B S P Magazine/Ispat Vihangam. (Bhilai Steel Plant) (II ISSN 0005-3325) 3402
B S P S Journal see Poetry Halifax Dartmouth 3002
B S R. (Bohren, Sprengen, Raeumen) (GW ISSN 0005-3333) 1848
B S R I A Application Guides. (Building Services Research and Information Association) (UK ISSN 0305-5973) 2297
B S R I A Statistics Bulletin. (Building Services Research and Information Association) (UK ISSN 0308-6224) 2304, 4564
B S R I A Technical Notes. (Building Services Research and Information Association) (UK ISSN 0309-0248) 2297
B T see Bibliotheque de Travail 1249
B T A - Buerotechnik und Automation see Office Management 828
B T A Studycards. (British Trade Alphabet) (UK) 28
B T B. (Branchevejviser for Traelast og Byggemarkeder) (DK ISSN 0107-6779) 601
B T E Marketing-Berater. (Bundesverband des Deutschen Textileinzelhandels e.V.) (GW ISSN 0171-838X) 1034
B T H A Buyers Guide. (British Toy & Hobby Association) (UK) 2280, 1034, 2433
B T H Fussboden-Forum - Tapetenzeitung see B T H - Tapetenzeitung 2557
B T H - Tapetenzeitung. (Boden - Tapeten - Heimtextilien) (GW) 2557, 295
B T J see Bibliotheque de Travail Junior 1618
B T - L M & S. (Building Technology - Land Management & Safety) (XK ISSN 1010-5700) 601, 4098
B T O - Buerotechnik und Organisation see Office Management 828
B T O News. (British Trust for Ornithology) (UK ISSN 0005-3392) 562
B T S. (Buero, Technik, Systeme) (GW ISSN 0341-1370) 1057
B T S - Buero Technik Systeme. (GW ISSN 0935-0276) 1057
B T U Handbook. (British Thermal Unit) (US) 3683
B T U Weekly. (British Thermal Unit) (US) 3683
B T V Speigel. (Bremer Turnvereinigung von 1877 e.V.) (GW) 4465, 4500
B T 2 see Bibliotheque de Travail 2d Degre 1618
B U C New Boat Price Guide. (US) 4522, 1502
B U C Used Boat Price Guide see Used Boat Price Guide 4530
B U F V C Newsletter see Viewfinder 1763
B U G Newsletter. (Brevard Users Group) (US) 1467, 1458
B U K S. (Boerne- og Ungdomskultursammenslutningen) (DK ISSN 0108-8963) 1232
B U M. (Boerne og Ungdoms-Litteratur Magasinet) (DK ISSN 0108-4976) 1249, 2897
B U M P (Black Upwardly Mobile Professionals) see Excel Magazine 2001
B und B see Bautenschutz und Bausanierung 603
B V A Bulletin. (Blinded Veterans Association) (US ISSN 0005-3430) 2290
B V B A. (BE) 647, 747, 1072
B V - Euroletter. (Bayerische Vereinsbank AG) (GW) 760, 647
B V G Aktuell. (Berliner Verkehrs Betriebe) (GW) 4647
B V V - Belgische Vereniging voor Verlamden. Bulletin. see A B P - Association Belge des Paralyses. Bulletin 3327
B W I A Sunjet. (British West Indies Airways) (AQ) 4671, 2221, 4753

B W I Study Circle Bulletin. (British West Indies Study Circle) (UK ISSN 0953-8720) **3749**
B W K. (Brennstoff-Waerme-Kraft) (GW ISSN 0006-9612) **1784, 1883, 3815**
B W M T - Atlanta Newsletter. (US) **2221, 2451**
B W P A Gazette. (British Women Pilots Association) (UK) **48, 4837**
B W P A Magazine *see* B W P A Gazette **48**
B Y U Today. (Brigham Young University) (US) **1304**
B Z. (AU ISSN 0005-3465) **747**
B Z B. (Bayerisches Zahnaerzteblatt) (GW ISSN 0005-3473) **3228**
B Z B Sachmagazin. (GW) **1389**
B Z Bauzentralblatt. (GW ISSN 0723-6131) **602**
B 70. (DK ISSN 0905-4650) **2746**
†Ba Shiru. (US ISSN 0045-1282) **5145**
Ba Xiaoshi Yiwai/After Work Hours. (CC) **2180**
Baad-Revyen. (DK ISSN 0525-4515) **4522**
Baadnyt. (DK) **4522**
Baalaranjani. (II) **1249**
Baalman & Well's Land Titles Office Practice. (AT ISSN 0727-8047) **2603, 4145**
Baamleh. (IS) **1249**
Baatnytt/Boating News. (SW ISSN 0005-6308) **4522**
Baavir. (IS) **48**
Babel. (AT ISSN 0005-3503) **1744, 1617, 2804**
Babel. (NE ISSN 0521-9744) **2805, 2897**
Babesch *see* Bulletin Antieke Beschaving **2307**
Babiniya. *see* Building Centre of Israel Bulletin **605**
Babson Alumni Bulletin *see* Babson Bulletin **1304**
Babson Bulletin. (US) **1304**
Baby. (GW) **4837**
Baby! *see* Working Mother (New York) **4857**
Baby Age. (JA) **1232, 3799**
▼Baby and Child Care Quick Reference Encyclopedia. (CN) **4837**
Baby & Junior. (GW ISSN 0005-3554) **1283**
Baby Book. (UK) **1232**
Baby Connection News Journal. (US ISSN 0894-3990) **1232**
▼Baby on the Way. (US) **3289, 1232**
▼Baby on the Way: Basics. (US) **4837, 1232**
Baby Sue. (US) **2988**
Baby Talk Magazine. (US) **1232**
†Baby Times. (US) **5145**
Babylon. (GW ISSN 0931-6418) **4221, 2428**
Baca/Read. (IO ISSN 0125-9008) **2746**
Baccalaureate Education in Nursing: Key to a Professional Career in Nursing. (US ISSN 0069-5602) **3276, 1701**
Bacchus. (IT) **378**
Bach. (US ISSN 0005-3600) **3540**
Bach-Jahrbuch. (GW ISSN 0084-7682) **3540**
Back Bay View. (US) **2859**
Back Brain Recluse. (UK ISSN 0269-9990) **3010, 2897**
▼Back Home. (US ISSN 1051-323X) **2221, 2444**
Back Home in Kentucky. (US ISSN 0199-6290) **2222**
Back Nine. (US) **4500**
Back-Office Bulletin *see* End Point Express **777**
†Back Pain. (US) **5145**
Back Pain Monitor. (US ISSN 0746-9489) **3081**
Back Stage Film - Tape Syndication Directory *see* Shoot Commercial Production Directory **3517**
▼Back Stage - Shoot. (US) **3504, 1369**
Back Street Heroes. (UK ISSN 0267-9841) **4684, 1534, 4515**
Back to Godhead. (US ISSN 0005-3643) **3762**

Back to Health Magazine. (US) **3799, 3395, 4835**
Backboard. (US) **2988, 3540**
†Backbone. (US ISSN 0888-6520) **5145**
Backflow Prevention *see* Drinking Water & Backflow Prevention **1864**
Background. (CN ISSN 0709-1141) **4084**
Background Notes on the Countries of the World. (US ISSN 0501-9966) **2243**
Backgrounder. (US ISSN 0382-8352) **3951**
Backgrounder Series *see* C S G Backgrounder **5157**
Backgrounder Update. (US) **4054**
Backjournal. (GW) **2086**
Backlash Times. (US) **4837, 3940**
Backpacker. (US ISSN 0277-867X) **4541**
Backpacking Newsletter. (US) **4541**
Backpain *see* Back to Health Magazine **3799**
Backstage. (US) **4630, 1369**
Backstage Pass Magazine. (US) **3540**
†Backstage T V Film - Tape & Syndication Directory. (US ISSN 0098-5481) **5145**
Backstreets. (US ISSN 0746-990X) **3540**
Backstretch. (US ISSN 0005-366X) **4532**
Backtechnik *see* Brot- und Backwaren **2087**
Backtracker. (US ISSN 0094-6915) **2145**
†Backup. (GW) **5145**
Backwoods. (US ISSN 1042-7732) **78**
Backwoods Home Magazine. (US ISSN 1050-9712) **2222, 2444**
Backwoodsman. (US) **2399, 2444**
Baconiana. (UK) **2859**
▼Bacon's Business - Financial Directory.(US ISSN 1058-9716) **40**
Bacon's International Publicity Checker. (US ISSN 0161-4363) **28**
Bacon's Media Alerts. (US ISSN 0736-4644) **1122**
Bacon's Publicity Checker. (US ISSN 0162-3125) **40**
Bacon's Radio - T V Directory. (US) **1369, 1122, 1355**
†Bacterial Cell Surface. (UK ISSN 0263-7227) **5145**
Bacteriologia, Virusologia, Parazitologia, Epidemiologia *see* Revista de Igiena, Bacteriologie, Virusologie, Parazitologie, Pneumoftiziologie.
Bacteriologie, Virusologie, Parazitologie, Epidemiologie **557**
Bad *see* Der Deutsche Badebetrieb **3801**
Bad Aachen Sport. (GW) **4465**
Bad Abbacher Kur- und Geschaeftsanzeiger. (GW) **4753**
Bad Attitude. (US) **2451, 4837**
Bad Haircut. (US ISSN 1043-3732) **3875, 1944, 2859, 2988**
Bad Henry Review. (US) **2988**
Bad Heute und Morgen. *see* Il Bagno Oggi e Domani **2548**
Bad Seed. (US) **4429**
Badan Meteorologi dan Geofisika. Laporan Evaluasi Hujan dan Perkiraan Hujan. (IO ISSN 0126-0561) **3433**
Badania Fizjograficzne nad Polska Zachodnia. Seria A. Geografia Fizyczna. (PL ISSN 0067-2807) **2243**
Badania Fizjograficzne nad Polska Zachodnia. Seria B. Biologia *see* Badania Fizjograficzne nad Polska Zachodnia. Seria B. Botanika **495**
Badania Fizjograficzne nad Polska Zachodnia. Seria B. Botanika. (PL) **495**
Badania Fizjograficzne nad Polska Zachodnia. Seria C. Zoologia. (PL ISSN 0137-6683) **578**
Badania Oswiatowe *see* Edukacja **1631**
Badania z Dziejow Spolecznych i Gospodarczych. (PL ISSN 0067-2793) **2351**
Baden - Wuerttemberg. (GW ISSN 0404-6307) **4753**

Baden - Wuerttemberg. Statistisches Landesamt. Statistisch-Prognostischer Bericht. (GW ISSN 0408-1714) **4564, 4079**
Baden - Wuerttemberg. Statistisches Landesamt. Statistische Berichte. (GW) **4564, 4079**
Baden - Wuerttemberg in Wort und Zahl. (GW ISSN 0721-1821) **4564**
Baden - Wuerttembergische Verwaltungspraxis. (GW ISSN 0340-3505) **4054**
Baden - Wuerttembergische Wertpapierboerse zu Stuttgart. Amtliches Kursblatt. (GW) **939**
Baden - Wuerttembergisches Verwaltungsblat *see* Baden - Wuerttembergische Verwaltungspraxis **4054**
Badger Builder. (US) **602**
Badger Chess. (US) **4465**
Badger Common'tater. (US) **170**
Badger Farm Bureau News *see* AgVenture **75**
Badger Herald. (US ISSN 0045-1304) **1304**
Badger Legionnaire. (US ISSN 0005-3767) **3452, 2222**
Badger Sportsman. (US ISSN 0005-3775) **4541**
Badger Stone Chronicles. (US) **318**
Badger Trucker. (US) **4743**
Badia Greca di Grottaferrata. Bollettino. (IT ISSN 0005-3783) **4256**
Badische Biographien Neue Folge. (GW) **2351**
Badische Saengerzeitung. (GW) **3540**
Badische Winzer. (GW) **378**
Badischer Landesverein fuer Naturkunde und Naturschutz, Freiburg. Mitteilungen. Neue Folge. (GW ISSN 0067-2858) **430, 1555**
Badminton. (DK ISSN 0005-3791) **4465**
Badminton Association of England. Annual Handbook. (UK ISSN 0262-1940) **4465**
Badminton Association of England. Official Handbook *see* Badminton Association of England. Annual Handbook **4465**
Badminton Canada. (CN ISSN 0711-124X) **4500**
Badminton Magazine. (JA) **4465**
Badminton Now. (UK) **4465**
Badminton - Report. (GW ISSN 0175-825X) **4465**
Badminton Sidelines. (AT ISSN 0813-006X) **4465**
Badminton Sporting Diary. (UK) **4465**
Baecker Konditor Zeitung. (SZ) **2086**
Baecker und Konditor. (GW ISSN 0005-383X) **2086**
Baecker - Werk. (GW) **2086**
Baecker - Zeitung. (GW) **2086**
Der Baeckermeister. (GW) **2086**
Baeko Informationen. (GW) **2086**
Baeko Magazin. (GW) **2086**
Baender, Bleche, Rohre. (GW ISSN 0005-3848) **3402, 3016**
Der Baer von Berlin. (GW ISSN 0522-0033) **2351**
†Baereboelgen. (DK ISSN 0109-3088) **5146**
Baeretz Yisrael. (IS ISSN 0334-3170) **2203**
Baer's Garden Newsletter. (US) **2122**
Baessler Archiv. (GW ISSN 0005-3856) **235**
Baesta Ur Reader's Digest (Swedish Edition) *see* Reader's Digest - Det Baesta **2218**
Baetica. (SP) **318, 2243, 2351**
Baff. (GW) **4399**
The Baffler. (US) **2859**
†Bag Kulisserne. (DK ISSN 0900-3134) **5146**
Bagalil Haelyon. (IS) **2203**
Bagatelle. (GW ISSN 0724-1631) **1296**
Bagdala. (YU ISSN 0005-3880) **2897, 2859**
Baghdad Chamber of Commerce. Weekly Bulletin *see* Baghdad Chamber of Commerce & Industry. Monthly Bulletin **808**
Baghdad Chamber of Commerce & Industry. Monthly Bulletin. (IQ) **808**

Baghdad Observer. (IQ ISSN 0005-3902) **2202**
Baghdader Mitteilungen. (GW ISSN 0418-9698) **266**
Bagno e Accessori. (IT ISSN 0392-2723) **602**
Bagno e Accessori International *see* Bagno e Accessori **602**
Bagno e Cucina Architettura e Interior Design. (IT ISSN 1120-5407) **2548, 295**
Il Bagno Oggi e Domani/Bain Aujourd'hui et Demain/Bathroom Today and Tomorrow/Bad Heute und Morgen. (IT ISSN 0392-2715) **2548**
Bagnoguida. (IT) **2548**
Bagolah *see* Batnua **3875**
†Baha'i News. (US ISSN 0195-9212) **5146**
Baha'i Studies. (CN ISSN 0708-5052) **4164**
Baha'i World. (IS ISSN 0045-1320) **4164**
Bahamas. Chamber of Commerce. Annual Directory. (BF) **808**
Bahamas. Department of Statistics. Annual Review of Prices: Report. (BF) **704**
Bahamas. Department of Statistics. External Trade. (BF) **704**
Bahamas. Department of Statistics. Household Income Report. (BF) **704**
Bahamas. Department of Statistics. Labour Force and Income Distribution *see* Bahamas. Department of Statistics. Household Income Report **704**
Bahamas. Department of Statistics. Statistical Abstract. (BF) **4564**
Bahamas. Department of Statistics. Statistical Summary. (BF) **4564**
Bahamas. Department of Statistics. Summary of External Trade Statistics.(BF) **704**
Bahamas. Ministry of Education and Culture. Annual Report. (BF) **1617**
Bahamas. Ministry of Transport. Port and Marine Department. Annual Report. (BF) **4724**
Bahamas. Ministry of Works and Utilities. Annual Report. (BF) **1862**
Bahamas. Ministry of Works. Annual Report *see* Bahamas. Ministry of Works and Utilities. Annual Report **1862**
Bahamas (Year) Including Turks & Caicos. (US) **4753**
Bahamas Dateline. (US) **939, 844, 4753**
Bahamas Family Islands Travel Guide. (BF) **4753**
Bahamas Handbook and Businessman's Annual. (BF ISSN 0067-2912) **844**
Bahamas Pharmaceutical Association. Newsletter. (BF) **3719**
Bahamian Review. (BF ISSN 0005-397X) **844**
Bahana. (BX ISSN 0005-3988) **2897, 2805**
Bahia. (SP) **2988**
Bahia, Brazil (State). Centro de Estatistica e Informacoes. Indice de Preco ao Consumidor. (BL) **704, 4564**
Bahia, Brazil (State). Centro de Pesquisas e Desenvolvimento. Sumarios de Periodicos em Ciencia e Tecnologia. (BL) **4354, 4614**
Bahia, Brazil (State). Secretaria das Minas e Energia. Boletim Estatistico Mensal de Energia Eletrica. (BL) **1797, 1801**
Bahnengolfer. (GW ISSN 0178-2436) **4500**
Bahnsport Aktuell. (GW) **4516**
Al-Bahrain. (BA) **2428**
Bahrain. Educational Documentation Library. Acquisitions List. (BA) **1674, 3**
Bahrain. Educational Documentation Library. Bibliographic Lists. (BA) **1674, 3**
Bahrain. Ministry of Information. Official Gazette/Bahrain. Wizarat al-Isti'lamat. Al-Jaridah al-Rasmiyah. (BA) **4054**
Bahrain. Monetary Agency. Annual Report. (BA) **1088**

5960 BAHRAIN. MONETARY

Bahrain. Monetary Agency. Quarterly Statement of Affairs and Statistical Bulletin see Bahrain. Monetary Agency. Quarterly Statistical Bulletin 704
Bahrain. Monetary Agency. Quarterly Statistical Bulletin. (BA) 704, 4564
Bahrain. Wizarat al-Isti'lamat. Al-Jaridah al-Rasmiyah. see Bahrain. Ministry of Information. Official Gazette 4054
Bahrain al-Yaum. see Bahrain Today Magazine 2428
Bahrain Bibliography. (BA) 390
Bahrain Chamber of Commerce and Industry. Commerce Review/Al-Haya al-Tijariya. (BA) 808
Bahrain Medical Bulletin. (BA ISSN 1012-7666) 3081
Bahrain News - Akhbar al-Bahrain see Al-Bahrain 2428
Bahrain Petroleum Co. B.S.C. News see B A P C O News 3682
Bahrain Petroleum Co. Ltd. Akhbar B A P C O see Akhbar B A P C O 3681
Bahrain Today Magazine/Bahrain al-Yaum. (BA) 2428
Bahrain Tourism Directory. (BA) 4753
Bahrain Trade Directory. (BA ISSN 0408-215X) 1122
Bahubacana. (BG) 4630
Baiertaler. (GW) 1113, 4098
Baihua Yuan. (CC) 2897
Baihua Zhou. (CC) 2897
Baijia Zuowen Zhidao. (CC ISSN 1001-4039) 1617, 2897
Baike Zhishi/Encyclopedic Knowledge. (CC) 4301
Baileya. (US ISSN 0005-4003) 495, 2122
Bailliere's Clinical Anaesthesiology. (UK ISSN 0950-3501) 3190
Bailliere's Clinical Rheumatology. (UK ISSN 0950-3579) 3368
Bailliere's Handbook of First Aid. (UK) 3081
Bailliere's Midwives' Dictionary. (UK) 3289
Bailliere's Nurses' Dictionary. (UK) 3276
Bailliere's Pocket Book of Ward Information. (UK) 3276
Bailrigg Papers on International Security. (UK) 3951, 1526, 2719
Baily's Hunting Directory. (UK ISSN 0067-2947) 1122, 4541
Bain Aujourd'hui et Demain. see Il Bagno Oggi e Domani 2548
Baiqiu'en University of Medical Sciences. Journal. see Baiqiu'en Yike Daxue Xuebao 3081
Baiqiu'en Yike Daxue Xuebao/Baiqiu'en University of Medical Sciences. Journal. (CC ISSN 0253-3707) 3081
Bairnsdale Advertiser. (AT) 2859
Al-Bait. (LY) 2209
Bait al-Imarat/Emirates Home. (TS) 2557
Baiyi Keji. (CC ISSN 1001-1285) 529
▼Baja Explorer. (US) 4753
Baja Times. (US) 4753
Bajan see The New Bajan 2239
▼Bake. (CN) 2086
Baker and Miller's Journal see Pastrycooks & Bakers News Monthly 2079
†Baker Deer Hunting Annual. (US) 5146
Baker - Konditor. (NO ISSN 0005-4062) 2086
†Baker Series in Chemistry. (US) 5146
Baker Street Journal. (US ISSN 0005-4070) 2985, 2897
Baker Valley News. (US ISSN 0746-9888) 2222
Bakers Journal. (CN ISSN 0005-4097) 2086
Bakers Review. (UK ISSN 0005-4100) 2086
Bakers Way. (US) 2086
Bakersfield News Observer. (US) 1993
Bakery, Confectionery and Tobacco Workers International Union News see B C & T News 2580
Bakery Production and Marketing. (US ISSN 0005-4127) 2086
Bakery Production and Marketing Red Book. (US) 2086

Bakery World. (IE) 2086
Baking & Snack. (US) 2086
Baking and Snack Equipment see Baking & Snack 2086
Baking and Snack Systems see Baking & Snack 2086
Baking Buyer. (US) 2087
Baking Directory - Buyers Guide see Baking - Snack Directory. Buyers Guide 1122
Baking Equipment see Baking & Snack 2086
†Baking Industry. (US ISSN 0005-416X) 5146
Baking Industry Review. (AT) 2062
Baking Industry Review. see I P: Revista da Industria de Panificacao 2088
Baking - Snack Directory. Buyers Guide.(US) 1122, 205
Baking Update. (UK ISSN 0953-3443) 2087
Bakker see Bakkerij 2087
Bakkerij. (NE) 2087
Bakkerswereld. (NE ISSN 0026-5934) 2087
▼Bakunin. (US ISSN 1052-3154) 2988, 318
Bakunin-Archiv. see Archives Bakounine 2349
Bal Bharati. (II ISSN 0005-4194) 1249
Bal Sandesh. (II ISSN 0005-4208) 1249
Bala Jyoti. (II) 2199
Baladiah Ras al-Khaimah/Ras al-Khaimah Municipality. (TS) 4084
Al-Baladiat/Municipalities. (TS) 4084
Balafon. (FR ISSN 0378-469X) 2859
Balai Penyelidikan Perusahaan Perkebunan Gula. Warta Bulanan. (IO ISSN 0043-0382) 78
Balak. (II) 1249
Balalaika and Domra Association of America Newsletter see B D A A Newsletter 3540
Balance. (UK ISSN 0005-4216) 3250
Balance see Balance Report 3979
Balance Financiero. (PY ISSN 1015-4248) 760, 844
Balance of Payments of Barbados see Central Bank of Barbados. Balance of Payments 710
Balance of Payments of Jamaica. (JM) 901
Balance of Payments of Sierra Leone. (SL ISSN 0067-2998) 1088, 901
Balance of Payments of Trinidad and Tobago. (TR ISSN 0067-3005) 704, 901, 1088
Balance of Payments Statistical Yearbook. (EI) 704, 4564
Balance of Payments, Taiwan District, Republic of China. (CH) 760
Balance Report. (US) 3979
Balance Sheet. (US ISSN 0005-4232) 1617
Balance Sheet Analysis of Joint Stock Companies. (PK) 704, 760
Balance Sheets. (GR ISSN 1105-2511) 705, 647, 4564
Balance Suisse des Paiements see Zahlungsbilanz der Schweiz 1112
Balance Touristique de la Suisse. see Fremdenverkehrsbilanz der Schweiz 4799
Balance Wheel for Accreditation see Directory of Recognized Accrediting Bodies 1705
†Balances of London and Scottish Banks' Groups. (UK) 5146
Balanco Energetico Nacional. (BL ISSN 0101-6636) 1784
Balanco Financeiro. (BL) 939
Balans. (BE ISSN 0772-4853) 747
Balans. (NE ISSN 0005-4259) 1510
Balanza de Pagos de Espana. (SP ISSN 0067-3021) 1088, 901
Balarama. (II) 1249
Balatros Berichtet. (GW) 161
Balcanica. (YU) 2351
Balcanica. (IT ISSN 0392-7660) 2859, 1993
Balde Branco. (BL ISSN 0005-4275) 198
Baldwin Lectures. (US) 1617
Baldwin Lectures in Teacher Education see Baldwin Lectures 1617

Baldwin's Ohio Legislative Service. (US ISSN 0092-0959) 4054, 2603
Baldwin's Ohio School Law Journal. (US ISSN 1055-0100) 1617, 2603
Baldwin's Ohio School Service see Baldwin's Ohio School Law Journal 1617
Bale Catalogue of Israel Postage Stamps. (UK) 3749
Bale Catalogue of Palestine and Israel Stamps see Bale Catalogue of Israel Postage Stamps 3749
Balikatanews. (PH ISSN 0115-3994) 4838
Balita. (CN) 1993
Baljivan. (II ISSN 0005-4291) 1249
Balkan-Archiv Neue Folge. (GW ISSN 0170-8007) 2805
Balkan-Archiv Neue Folge Beiheft. (GW ISSN 0720-0994) 2805
Balkan Bibliography. (GR) 2327, 390
Balkan Studies. (GR ISSN 0005-4313) 2351, 4366
Balkanika Symmeikta. (GR) 2351
Balkanologische Veroeffentlichungen see Freie Universitaet Berlin. Osteuropa-Institut. Balkanologische Veroeffentlichungen 2815
Balkans Stamp Catalogue. (UK ISSN 0142-9779) 3749
Balkanskie Issledovaniya. (RU) 2351
Balkansko Izikoznanie. see Linguistique Balkanique 2827
Ball and Roller Bearing Engineering see Ball and Roller Bearing Engineering - Industrial Engineering 1925
Ball and Roller Bearing Engineering - Industrial Engineering. (GW) 1925
Ball Bearing Journal see Kullagertidningen 1934
Ball Beginnings. (US ISSN 8756-7237) 2145
Ball State Teachers College Forum see Ball State University Forum 5146
†Ball State University Forum. (US ISSN 0888-188X) 5146
Ballade. (NO) 3540
Ballantine and Sterling California Corporation Laws. (US) 2707
Ballast (Atlanta). (US) 48, 1784
Ballena Press Anthropological Papers. (US) 235
Ballet-Hoo. (CN ISSN 0045-1347) 1528, 4630
Ballet no Hon/Book on Ballet. (JA) 1528
Ballet Review. (US ISSN 0522-0653) 1529
Ballett Info see Ballett International 1529
Ballett International. (GW ISSN 0722-6268) 1529
Balletto Oggi. (IT) 1529
Ballon Kurier. (GW ISSN 0005-4364) 3749
Balloon. (JA) 1232
Balloon Life. (US ISSN 0887-6061) 4465, 48
Ballooning. (US) 48, 4465
Balloons and Parties Today. (US ISSN 1049-9970) 353
Balloons Today see Balloons and Parties Today 353
Ballot Access News. (US ISSN 1043-6898) 3940
Ballroom Dancing Across the U S A see Dancing U S A 1530
Ballroom Dancing Times. (UK ISSN 0005-4380) 1529
Ballroom Dancing Year Book see Dancing Year Book 1530
Balls & Strikes. (US) 4500
Ballsout. (CN ISSN 0005-4399) 2988
Balnearios. (MX) 4466
Balneologia Bohemica. (CS ISSN 0302-8070) 3081
Balneologia Polska. (PL ISSN 0005-4402) 3081
Balon. (MX ISSN 0005-4410) 4500
Balsa de la Medusa. (SP ISSN 0214-9982) 318, 2897, 3762
Balskrishnan - Neustadt Series. (US) 4594, 3030
Baltic and International Maritime Conference Bulletin see B I M C O Bulletin 4724
Baltic Bulletin. (US) 3951, 2351

▼The Baltic Independent. (ER ISSN 1018-7286) 3951, 844
Baltic Philology. see Filologia Baltycka 5192
Baltiiskie Shakhmaty. (LV) 4466
Baltimore. (US ISSN 0005-4453) 808
Baltimore Afro-American. (US) 1993
Baltimore - Annapolis (Year). (US) 2399
Baltimore Business Journal. (US) 647
Baltimore City Public Schools Staff Newsletter. (US) 1618
Baltimore City Public Schools Staff Newsletter and Community Newsletter see Baltimore City Public Schools Staff Newsletter 1618
†Baltimore Computer Digest. (US) 5146
Baltimore County Muster. (US) 2400
Baltimore Engineer. (US ISSN 0005-4496) 1815
Baltimore Gay Paper. (US) 2451
Baltimore Jewish Times. (US ISSN 0005-450X) 1993
Baltimore Sanyo User's Newsletter. (US) 1467, 1458
Baltimore Scene Magazine. (US) 2222
▼Baltimore Sports Focus. (US) 4466, 3370
Baltimore Vegetarians see Vegetarian Journal 3612
Baltische Briefe. (GW ISSN 0005-4526) 3875
Baltische Hefte. (GW ISSN 0005-4534) 2351
Baltische Studien. (GW ISSN 0067-3099) 2351
Baltisches Jahrbuch. (GW ISSN 0177-4859) 1993
Baltistica. (LI ISSN 0132-6503) 2805
Balungan. (US ISSN 0885-7113) 3540
Bam: The California Music Magazine. (US) 3540
Bamaaleh. (IS) 1249
Bamaarachot. (IS) 2580, 1815
Bama'arakha. (IS ISSN 0005-4542) 4429
Bamachane. (IS) 3452
Bamachane Gadna. (IS) 1233
Bamachane Nachal. (IS) 3452
Bamah. (IS) 3193
Bamah. (IS ISSN 0045-138X) 4630
Bambi. (FR) 1249
Bambini. (IT ISSN 0393-4209) 1233
Bambini Collezioni. (IT) 1289
Bamboo Ridge. (US ISSN 0733-0308) 2897
Bamerindus see Informativo Bamerindus 784
Bamla Ekademi Gabeshana Patrika. (BG) 2897, 2805
Bampton Lectures in America. (US ISSN 0067-3129) 4164, 318, 2400
Ban Yue Tan/Semi-Monthly Tribune. (CC) 2859
Banadesa see Guatemala. Banco Nacional de Desarrollo Agricola. Memoria 152
Banana Bulletin see B G F Bulletin 170
Banana Growers Federation Co-operative Ltd. Bulletin see B G F Bulletin 170
Banana Rag see Artistamp News 316
Banaras Metallurgist. (II) 3402
Banasthali Patrika. (II) 2898, 2859
Banativ Avir. (IS) 48
Banber Hayastani Arkhivneri/Vestnik Arkhivov Armenii. (AI) 2351
Banbury Reports. (US ISSN 0198-0068) 430
Banbury Reports Series see Banbury Reports 430
†Banc-Titre - Animation Stand. (FR ISSN 0184-8895) 5146
Banca Borsa e Titoli di Credito. (IT) 760
Banca d'Italia. Assemblea Generale Ordinaria dei Partecipanti. (IT ISSN 0067-3161) 760
Banca d'Italia. Bollettino del Servizio Studi Economici see Banca d'Italia. Bollettino Statistico. Nuova Serie 760
Banca d'Italia. Bollettino Economico. (IT) 844

BANCO NACIONAL 5961

Banca d'Italia. Bollettino Statistico. Nuova Serie. (IT) **760**
Banca d'Italia. Bollettino Statistico - Servizio Studi *see* Banca d'Italia. Bollettino Statistico. Nuova Serie **760**
Banca d'Italia. Contributi alla Analisi Economica. (IT) **844, 889**
Banca d'Italia. Contributi alla Ricerca Economica *see* Banca d'Italia. Contributi alla Analisi Economica **844**
Banca d'Italia. Economic Bulletin *see* Banca d'Italia. Bollettino Economico **844**
Banca d'Italia. Servizio Studi. Temi di Discussione. (IT) **760**
Banca Espanola. (SP ISSN 0210-1688) **760**
Banca Impresa Societa. (IT ISSN 1120-9453) **760**
†Banca Nazionale del Lavoro. Condensed Statement of Condition. (IT) **5146**
Banca Nazionale del Lavoro Quarterly Review. (IT ISSN 0005-4607) **760**
Banca Oggi. (IT) **760**
Banca Romana de Comert Exterior. Annual Bulletin. (RM) **760, 901**
Banca Santo Paulo di Brescia. Notiziario Economico. (IT) **760, 844, 889**
Banca y Comercio. (MX ISSN 0005-4615) **760**
Bancaria. (IT ISSN 0005-4623) **760**
Banche e Banchieri. (IT) **760**
Bancni Vestnik. (XV ISSN 0005-4631) **760**
Banco Agrario del Peru. Memoria. (PE) **148**
Banco Agricola y Pecuario. Informe *see* Instituto de Credito Agricola y Pecuario. Informe Annual **869**
Banco Agricola y Pecuario, Caracas. Boletin Mensual *see* Instituto de Credito Agricola y Pecuario. Boletin Mensual **139**
Banco Central. Boletin Informativo. (SP ISSN 0211-7142) **760**
Banco Central. Momento Economico. (SP) **760**
Banco Central. Momento Economico: Bolsa - Informacion de Valores. (SP) **760**
Banco Central. Momento Economico: Economia. (SP) **760**
Banco Central de Bolivia. Boletin Estadistico. (BO ISSN 0522-0939) **705**
Banco Central de Chile. Annual Report. (CL ISSN 0716-2901) **760**
Banco Central de Chile. Boletin Mensual. (CL ISSN 0716-2367) **760, 844**
Banco Central de Chile, Santiago. Memoria Anual. (CL ISSN 0716-2448) **760, 844**
Banco Central de Costa Rica. Anuario Estadistico de las Cuentas Monetarias. (CR) **705, 760, 4564**
Banco Central de Costa Rica. Balanza de Pagos. (CR) **844**
Banco Central de Costa Rica. Boletin Estadistico. (CR) **760**
Banco Central de Costa Rica. Departamento de Transacciones Internacionales. Informacion Estadistica Mensual. (CR) **761**
Banco Central de Costa Rica. Departamento Monetario. Credito y Cuentas Monetarias. (CR) **761**
Banco Central de Costa Rica. Estadisticas Economicas. (CR ISSN 0522-098X) **705**
Banco Central de Costa Rica. Informacion de Estadistica Mensual *see* Banco Central de Costa Rica. Boletin Estadistico **760**
Banco Central de Costa Rica. Informacion Economica Semanal. (CR ISSN 0408-3172) **844**
Banco Central de Costa Rica. Memoria Anual. (CR ISSN 0067-320X) **761**
Banco Central de Costa Rica. Serie: Comentarios sobre Asuntos Economicos. (CR) **844**
Banco Central de Ecuador. Informacion Estadistica Mensual *see* Banco Central del Ecuador. Informacion Estadistica Quincenal **705**

Banco Central de Honduras. Departamento de Estudios Economicos. Boletin Estadistico. (HO) **705**
Banco Central de Honduras. Division de Seguros. Boletin de Estadisticas de Seguros. (HO) **2545, 705**
Banco Central de Honduras. Informe Economico. (HO) **844**
Banco Central de Honduras. Memoria Anual (Year) *see* Banco Central de Honduras. Memoria (Year) **845**
Banco Central de Honduras. Memoria (Year). (HO) **845**
Banco Central de la Republica Argentina. Boletin Estadistico. (AG ISSN 0005-4674) **705**
Banco Central de la Republica Argentina. Centro de Estudios Monetarios y Bancarios. Discussion Paper. (AG) **761**
Banco Central de la Republica Argentina. Centro de Estudios Monetarios y Bancarios. Serie de Computacion. (AG) **761**
Banco Central de la Republica Argentina. Centro de Estudios Monetarios y Bancarios. Serie de Estudios Tecnicos. (AG) **761**
Banco Central de la Republica Argentina. Centro de Estudios Monetarios y Bancarios. Serie de Informacion Publica. (AG) **761**
Banco Central de la Republica Argentina. Ensayos Economicos. (AG) **889**
Banco Central de la Republica Dominicana. Boletin Mensual. (DR ISSN 0005-4682) **761**
Banco Central de la Republica Dominicana. Memoria. (DR) **761**
Banco Central de Nicaragua. Biblioteca y Servicios de Informacion. Barricada Indice Tematico y Onomastico. (NQ) **761**
Banco Central de Nicaragua. Boletin Anual. (NQ) **761**
Banco Central de Nicaragua. Boletin Semestral *see* Banco Central de Nicaragua. Boletin Anual **761**
Banco Central de Nicaragua. Carta Quincenal. (NQ) **761, 845**
Banco Central de Nicaragua. Comercio Exterior de Nicaragua Por Productos y Paises. (NQ) **901**
Banco Central de Nicaragua. Departmento de Estudios Economicos. Indicadores Economicos.(NQ) **845**
Banco Central de Nicaragua. Informe Anual. (NQ ISSN 0067-3226) **761**
Banco Central de Reserva de El Salvador. Boletin Economico. (ES) **761**
Banco Central de Reserva de El Salvador. Memoria. (ES) **761**
Banco Central de Reserva de El Salvador. Revista Mensual *see* Banco Central de Reserva de El Salvador. Revista Trimestral **761**
Banco Central de Reserva de El Salvador. Revista Trimestral. (ES) **761**
Banco Central de Reserva del Peru. Boletin. (PE ISSN 0005-4712) **761**
Banco Central de Reserva del Peru. Memoria. (PE) **761**
Banco Central de Venezuela. Anuario de Cuentas Nacionales. (VE) **761**
Banco Central de Venezuela. Boletin de Indicadores Semanales. (VE) **761**
Banco Central de Venezuela. Boletin Mensual. (VE) **761**
Banco Central de Venezuela. Boletin Trimestral. (VE) **845**
Banco Central de Venezuela. Informe Economico. (VE ISSN 0067-3250) **845**
Banco Central de Venezuela. Memoria. (VE ISSN 0067-3269) **761**
Banco Central de Venezuela. Revista. (VE) **761**
Banco Central del Ecuador. Acuerdos Internacionales de Comercio y Pagos.(EC) **901**
Banco Central del Ecuador. Balanza de Pagos. (EC) **705, 761**

Banco Central del Ecuador. Boletin. (EC ISSN 0005-4739) **761**
Banco Central del Ecuador. Boletin Anuario. (EC) **845**
Banco Central del Ecuador. Division Tecnica. Cuentas Nacionales. (EC) **845**
Banco Central del Ecuador. Informacion Estadistica Quincenal. (EC) **705**
Banco Central del Ecuador. Memoria del Gerente General. (EC ISSN 0067-3277) **761**
Banco Central del Paraguay. Memoria. (PY ISSN 0067-3285) **761**
Banco Central del Uruguay. Boletin Estadistico Mensual *see* Banco Central del Uruguay. Departamento de Estadisticas Economicas. Boletin Estadistico **705**
Banco Central del Uruguay. Departamento de Estadisticas Economicas. Boletin Estadistico. (UY) **705**
Banco Central del Uruguay. Departamento de Estadisticas Economicas. Producto e Ingreso Nacionales. (UY) **998**
Banco Central del Uruguay. Departamento de Investigaciones Economicas. Boletin Estadistico. *see* Banco Central del Uruguay. Departamento de Estadisticas Economicas. Boletin Estadistico **705**
Banco Central del Uruguay. Division Asesoria Economica y Estudios. Producto e Ingreso Nacionales. Actualizacion de las Principales Variables *see* Banco Central del Uruguay. Departamento de Estadisticas Economicas. Producto e Ingreso Nacionales **998**
Banco Central del Uruguay. Indicadores de la Actividad Economico-Financiera.(UY) **845**
Banco Central del Uruguay. Resena de la Actividad Economico-Financiera. (UY) **761**
Banco Central del Uruguay. Seleccion de Temas. (UY) **845**
Banco Central del Uruguay. Seleccion de Temas Economicos *see* Banco Central del Uruguay. Seleccion de Temas **845**
Banco Central do Brazil. Boletim. (BL ISSN 0005-4763) **761**
Banco Central do Brazil. Monthly Newsletter. (BL) **761**
Banco Centroamericano de Integracion Economica. Memoria Anual. (HO) **761**
†Banco de Bibliografias. (BL ISSN 0101-0697) **5146**
Banco de Bilbao. Agenda Financiera. (SP) **761**
Banco de Bilbao. Economic Report. (SP) **845**
Banco de Bilbao. Informacion Semanal de Valores. (SP ISSN 0213-2648) **939**
Banco de Bilbao. Informe Economico. (SP ISSN 0522-1315) **845**
Banco de Bilbao. Informe - Memoria. (SP) **761**
Banco de Bilbao. Memoria *see* Banco de Bilbao. Informe - Memoria **761**
Banco de Desenvolvimento do Parana. Information on Parana *see* Information on Parana **869**
Banco de Espana. Boletin Economico. (SP ISSN 0210-3737) **845**
Banco de Espana. Boletin Estadistico. (SP ISSN 0005-4798) **761, 705**
Banco de Espana. Estudios de Historia Economia. (SP) **889**
Banco de Espana. Estudios Economicos.(SP ISSN 0213-2699) **845**
Banco de Espana. Informe Anual. (SP ISSN 0067-3315) **761**
Banco de Guatemala. Boletin Estadistico. (GT ISSN 0005-481X) **762, 705**
Banco de Guatemala. Boletin Informativo. (GT) **762**
Banco de Guatemala. Estadisticas del Sector Externo. (GT) **845**
Banco de Guatemala. Estudio Economico y Memoria de Labores. (GT) **762**

Banco de Guatemala. Informe Economico. (GT ISSN 0045-1401) **845**
Banco de la Republica. Biblioteca Luis Angel Arango. Boletin Cultural y Bibliografico. (CK ISSN 0006-6184) **390, 2503**
Banco de la Republica. Revista. (CK ISSN 0005-4828) **762, 845**
Banco de la Republica Oriental del Uruguay. Boletin Mensual. Seleccion de Temas Economicos *see* Banco Central del Uruguay. Seleccion de Temas **845**
Banco de Mexico. Indicadores Economicos. (MX) **845**
Banco de Mexico. Informe Anual. (MX ISSN 0067-3374) **762, 845**
Banco de Mexico. Serie Documentos de Investigacion. (MX) **762**
Banco de Portugal. Estatistica e Estudos Economicos. (PO) **705, 762, 4564**
Banco de Venezuela. Informe Semestral.(VE) **762**
Banco do Brasil. Annual Report. (BL ISSN 0101-0646) **762**
†Banco do Brasil. Boletim. (BL ISSN 0005-4879) **5146**
Banco do Brasil. Boletim de Informacao Ao Pessoal. (BL) **762**
Banco do Estado de Pernambuco. BANDEPE Relatorio. (BL) **762**
Banco do Nordeste do Brasil. Serie Estudos Economicos e Sociais. (BL) **845**
Banco Hipotecario del Uruguay. Boletin Estadistico. (UY) **705**
Banco Minero de Bolivia. Memoria. (BO) **762**
Banco Nacional de Comercio Exterior, Mexico. Annual Report. (MX) **762**
Banco Nacional de Desarrollo Agricola. Memoria Anual. (HO) **762**
Banco Nacional de Fomento. Informe de Labores. (EC) **845**
Banco Nacional de Fomento Boletin B N F *see* Boletin B N F **768**
Banco Nacional de Fomento, Tegucigalpa. Memoria Anual *see* Banco Nacional de Desarrollo Agricola. Memoria Anual **762**
Banco Nacional de Panama. Asesoria Economica. Memoria Anual *see* Banco Nacional de Panama. Memoria Anual **762**
Banco Nacional de Panama. Asesoria Economica y Planificacion. Carta Economica *see* Banco Nacional de Panama. Grupo Gubernamental. Carta Economica **845**
Banco Nacional de Panama. Boletin Economico. (PN) **845**
Banco Nacional de Panama. Grupo Gubernamental. Carta Economica. (PN) **845**
Banco Nacional de Panama. Informacion Economica y Financiera de la Republica de Panama. (PN) **1088**
Banco Nacional de Panama. Informe del Gerente General. (PN) **762**
Banco Nacional de Panama. Memoria Anual. (PN) **762**
Banco Nacional do Desenvolvimento Economico. Annual Report. (BL) **762**
Banco Nacional do Desenvolvimento Economico. Boletim Bibliografico. (BL) **705, 390**
Banco Nacional do Desenvolvimento Economico. Plan of Action. *see* Banco Nacional do Desenvolvimento Economico. Plano de Acao **1072**
Banco Nacional do Desenvolvimento Economico. Plano de Acao/Banco Nacional do Desenvolvimento Economico. Plan of Action. (BL) **1072**
Banco Nacional do Desenvolvimento Economico. Relatorio Anual *see* Revista do B I N D E **798**
Banco Nacional do Desenvolvimento Economico. Relatorio das Atividades. (BL) **845**
Banco Nacional do Desenvolvimento Economico Noticias *see* B N D E Noticias **760**

5962 BANCO NACIONAL

Banco Nacional do Desenvolvimento Economico Revista do B I N D E see Revista do B I N D E 798
Banco Popolare di Milano see B.P.M 760
Banco Regional de Desenvolvimento do Extremo Sul. Annual Report. (BL) 845
Banco Regional de Desenvolvimento do Extremo Sul. Relatorio Annual see Banco Regional de Desenvolvimento do Extremo Sul. Annual Report 845
Banco Regional de Desenvolvimento do Extremo Sul. Relatorio da Directoria see Banco Regional de Desenvolvimento do Extremo Sul. Annual Report 845
Banco Sindical. Memoria y Balance General. (AG) 762
Bancos Centrales de los Paises del Acuerdo de Cartagena. Boletin Estadistico. (CK) 762, 705
Bancos y Bancarios de Colombia. (CK ISSN 0120-5226) 762
Bancoseguros see Seguros 2542
Bancroftiana. (US ISSN 0067-3412) 2746
Band see K B M - Kantoormarkt 1059
Das Band. (GW ISSN 0170-902X) 1734, 4399
Band Director Guide see B D Guide 3540
Band Fan. (US) 3540
Band Journal. (JA ISSN 0005-4933) 3540
Band Music Guide. (US ISSN 0084-7704) 3540
Band of Hope Chronicle. (UK ISSN 0950-8368) 4164
Band- und Flechtindustrie/Narrow Fabric and Braiding Industry. (GW ISSN 0005-4925) 4616
Bandaoti Xuebao. (English translation: Chinese Journal of Semiconductors) (CC ISSN 0253-4177) 1764
Bandari. (KE) 4647
Bandelette. (US) 3228
Bandersnatch. (UK ISSN 0306-8404) 2898
Bandersnatch (Quebec). (CN) 1304
Bandwagon. (US ISSN 0005-4968) 4630
Baner Ac Amserau Cymru see Y Faner 2866
Baner Kernewek. see Cornish Banner 1997
Bang Jin Mei Duo. (CC) 2052
Bangalore Theological Forum. (II ISSN 0253-9365) 4164, 3634
Bangiya Sahityakosha. (II) 390
Bangkok Bank. Monthly Review. (TH ISSN 0005-4984) 762
Bangkok Post Weekly Review. (TH) 2219
Bangkok, Thailand. College of Education. Thesis Abstract Series. (TH ISSN 0067-3498) 1674
Bangkok Weekly. (TH) 2219
Bangla Academy Journal. (BG) 2898
Bangladesh. (BG) 2174
Bangladesh. Directorate of Agricultural Marketing. Agricultural Marketing Series. (BG ISSN 0070-8143) 148
Bangladesh. Directorate of Agriculture. Season and Crop Report. (BG ISSN 0070-8151) 170
Bangladesh. Education Directorate. Report on Pilot Project on Adult Education. (BG ISSN 0070-8135) 1682
Bangladesh. Ministry of Foreign Affairs. List of the Diplomatic Corps and Other Foreign Representatives. (BG) 4054
Bangladesh. Planning Commission. Annual Development Programme. (BG) 845
Bangladesh Academy of Sciences. Journal. (BG ISSN 0378-8121) 4301
Bangladesh Agricultural Sciences Abstracts. (BG) 134, 3
Bangladesh Arthanaitika Jarip. (BG) 647
Bangladesh Association for Voluntary Sterilization. Annual Report. (BG) 596
Bangladesh Bank. Annual Report. (BG) 762

Bangladesh Bank. Bulletin. (BG) 845
Bangladesh Bank. Statistics Department. Annual Balance of Payments. (BG) 705, 901, 1088, 4564
Bangladesh Bank. Statistics Department. Annual Import Payments. (BG) 705
Bangladesh Bank. Statistics Department. Balance of Payments. (BG) 901, 1088
Bangladesh Bank. Statistics Department. Quarterly Scheduled Banks Statistics. (BG) 705
Bangladesh Development Studies. (BG ISSN 0304-095X) 845, 3979
Bangladesh Directory and Year Book. (II) 1123
Bangladesh Forest Industries Development Corporation. Annual Report. (BG) 2113
Bangladesh Gazette. (BG) 2174
Bangladesh Horticulture. (BG ISSN 0379-4288) 2122
Bangladesh Illustrated Weekly. (BG) 2174
Bangladesh in International Affairs. (BG) 2719
Bangladesh Institute of Development Studies. Annual Report. (BG) 845
Bangladesh Insurance Academy. Journal see Insurance Journal 2534
Bangladesh Itihas Samiti. Journal/Ithasa Samiti Patrika. (BG) 2337
Bangladesh Jatiya Ainjibi Samity. Annual Law Journal see Bangladesh Jatiya Ainjibi Samity Souvenir 2603
Bangladesh Jatiya Ainjibi Samity Souvenir. (BG) 2603
Bangladesh Journal of Agricultural Sciences. (BG ISSN 0379-4296) 78
Bangladesh Journal of Animal Science. (BG) 212, 4807
Bangladesh Journal of Biological and Agricultural Sciences see Bangladesh Journal of Biological Sciences 430
Bangladesh Journal of Biological Sciences. (BG) 430, 78
Bangladesh Journal of Botany. (BG ISSN 0253-5416) 495
Bangladesh Journal of Forest Science. (BG) 2096
Bangladesh Journal of Jute & Fibre Research. (BG) 4616
Bangladesh Journal of Nuclear Agriculture. (BG ISSN 0258-7130) 78
Bangladesh Journal of Psychology. (BG) 4012
Bangladesh Journal of Public Administration. (BG) 4054
Bangladesh Journal of Scientific and Industrial Research. (BG) 4301
Bangladesh Journal of Scientific Research. (BG) 4301
Bangladesh Journal of Soil Science. (BG) 170, 430, 4301
Bangladesh Journal of Zoology. (BG ISSN 0304-9027) 578
Bangladesh Lalit Kala. (BG) 3522, 266, 318
Bangladesh Library Science News Bulletin. (BG) 2746
Bangladesh Medical Journal. (BG ISSN 0301-035X) 3081
Bangladesh Medical Research Council Bulletin. (BG ISSN 0377-9238) 3081
Bangladesh National Bibliography. (BG) 390
Bangladesh News. (II) 1993, 845, 3875
Bangladesh Pharmaceutical Journal. (BG ISSN 0301-4606) 3719
Bangladesh Political Studies. (BG) 3875
Bangladesh Rice Research Institute. Annual Report. (BG) 170
Bangladesh Science Conference. Proceedings. (BG) 4301
Bangladesh: Selected Economic Indicators. (BG) 845
Bangladesh Small and Cottage Industries Corporation. Bulletin. (BG) 1113
Bangladesh Sugar Mills Corporation. Annual Report. (BG) 2062
Bangladesh Supreme Court Reports. (BG) 2603

Bangladesh Tea Research Institute. Annual Report. (BG) 78
Bangladesh University of Engineering and Technology, Dhaka. Technical Journal. (BG ISSN 0070-8186) 1815
Bangladesh Veterinary Journal. (BG) 4807
†Bangor Occasional Papers in Economics. (UK ISSN 0306-9338) 5146
Bangsbomuseet. Aarbog. (DK ISSN 0109-8489) 3522
Banhua Shijie/Print World. (CC) 318
Banhua Yishu/Art of Prints. (CC ISSN 1000-4378) 318
Banicke Listy/Folia Montana. (CS) 3479
Banif's Investment Bulletin. (SP ISSN 0005-4992) 939
Banjo Newsletter. US ISSN 0190-1559) 3540
Die Bank. (GW) 762
Bank Accounting & Finance. (US ISSN 0894-3958) 747, 762
Bank Administration see Bank Management 763
Bank Advertising News. (US ISSN 0274-7111) 762, 28
Bank al-Inma al-Sinai. Annual Report and Balance Sheet. see Industrial Development Bank. Annual Report and Balance Sheet 784
Bank Al-Maghrib. Rapport Annuel. (MR) 762
Bank al-Markazi al-Urduni. Annual Report. see Central Bank of Jordan. Annual Report 771
Bank and Quotation Record. (US ISSN 0005-5026) 939
Bank Archiv. (AU ISSN 1015-1516) 762
Bank Asset - Liability Management. (US) 762, 1003, 2603
Bank Auditing & Accounting Report. (US ISSN 0522-2478) 762, 747
†Bank Automation Newsletter. (US ISSN 0572-5933) 5146
Bank Bailout Litigation News. (US) 762, 2603
Bank-Betrieb see Die Bank 762
Bank Board Letter. (US ISSN 0005-5042) 762
Bank Board Watch see Thrift Regulator 801
Bank Brussel Lambert. Annual Reports. see Banque de Bruxelles Lambert. Rapports de l'Exercice 767
Bank Card Credit Report. (US ISSN 1043-9196) 762
▼Bank Director. (US) 762
Bank Director's Briefing. (US) 762
†Bank Director's Report. (US ISSN 0522-2494) 5146
Bank Directory of Canada see Canadian Payments Directories 770
Bank Directory of New England. (US) 763
Bank Eksport Import Indonesia. Annual Report. (IO ISSN 0302-6795) 763
Bank Employee. see Trapezikos 695
Bank Employment News. (US) 3624, 763
Bank- en Effectenbedrijf. (NE ISSN 0005-5018) 763
Bank en Gemeenten see B & G 1088
Bank Expansion Quarterly. (US ISSN 0160-130X) 763
Bank Facts. (CN) 763
Bank Financial Management International. (IE) 763
Bank Financial Quarterly (Hartland). (US) 763
Bank Financial Quarterly (Rockville). (US) 763
†Bank - Financial Services Marketing Report. (US) 5146
Bank for International Settlements. Annual Report. (SZ ISSN 0067-3560) 763
Bank Fraud Alert. (US) 763
Bank fuer Gemeinwirtschaft Aktiengesellschaft Aussenhandelsdienst see B F G: Aussenhandelsdienst 901
Bank fuer Gemeinwirtschaft Aktiengesellschaft Facts and Figures - Germany see B F G: Facts and Figures - Germany 844

Bank fuer Gemeinwirtschaft Aktiengesellschaft Wirtschaftsblaetter see B F G: Wirtschaftsblaetter 844
Bank Guide. (PK) 763
Bank ha-Sapanut le-Yisrael. Annual Report. see Maritime Bank of Israel. Annual Report 790
Bank Holding Company (Y-9). (US) 763
Bank Holding Company Compliance Manual. (US) 2603, 763
Bank Holding Company Facts. (US ISSN 0519-1572) 763
Bank Human Resouces Report. (US) 763, 1063
Bank Income Tax Return Manual. (US) 763, 1088, 2603
Bank Installment Lending Newsletter see Consumer Lending Report 773
Bank Investments and Funds Management Newsletter see Financial Manager 5192
Bank Karamchari. (II ISSN 0005-5077) 2580, 763
Bank Letter. (US) 763
Bank Leumi Economic Review see Leumi Review 872
Bank Leumi Israel Macroperspectives see Leumi Review 872
†Bank Loan Officers Report. (US ISSN 0162-7422) 5146
Bank Management. (US) 763
Bank Markazi Jomhouri Islami Iran. Bulletin. (IR) 763, 845
Bank Markazi Jomhouri Islami Iran. Survey of the Large Manufacturing Industries. (IR) 845
Bank Marketing. (US ISSN 0888-3149) 763, 1034
Bank Marketing International. (IE ISSN 0791-2765) 763
†Bank Marketing Report. (US ISSN 0162-7430) 5146
Bank Melli Iran. Bulletin/Bank Melli Iran. Nashrieh Dakheli. (IR ISSN 0045-1444) 763
Bank Melli Iran. Nashrieh Dakheli. see Bank Melli Iran. Bulletin 763
Bank Mergers and Acquisitions. (US) 763
Bank Negara Malaysia. Annual Report. (MY) 845
Bank Negara Malaysia. Bulletin Ekonomi Suku Tahunan - Quarterly Economic Bulletin. (MY) 845
Bank Negara Malaysia. Statistical Bulletin. (MY) 845
Bank Network News. (US) 804
Bank New Product News. (US) 763
Bank News. (US ISSN 0005-5123) 763
Bank Note Reporter. (US ISSN 0164-0828) 3598
Bank Notes. (AT ISSN 0005-5131) 763
Bank of Botswana. Bulletin. (BS) 763
Bank of Canada. Annual Report. (CN ISSN 0067-3587) 763
Bank of Canada. Review/Banque du Canada. Revue. (CN ISSN 0045-1460) 763
Bank of Canada. Technical Reports. (CN ISSN 0713-7931) 763
Bank of Canada. Weekly Financial Statistics. (CN ISSN 0005-5158) 705
Bank of Ceylon. Annual Report and Accounts. (CE) 763
Bank of Communications. Annual Report. (CH) 763
Bank of England. Discussion Papers. (UK) 764
Bank of England. Panel of Academic Consultants. Papers. (UK) 764
Bank of England. Report see Bank of England. Report and Accounts 764
Bank of England. Report and Accounts. (UK ISSN 0308-5279) 764
Bank of England. Technical Series. (UK) 764
Bank of England Quarterly Bulletin. (UK ISSN 0005-5166) 845
Bank of Finland. Annual Statement see Bank of Finland. Yearbook 764
Bank of Finland. Bulletin. (FI ISSN 0784-6509) 764
Bank of Finland. Monthly Bulletin see Bank of Finland. Bulletin 764

BANQUE COMMERCIALE 5963

Bank of Finland. Publications. Series A. see Suomen Pankki. Julkaisuja. Sarja A **693**

Bank of Finland. Publications. Series B. see Suomen Pankki. Julkaisuja. Sarja B **693**

Bank of Finland. Publications. Series C. see Suomen Pankki. Julkaisuja. Sarja C **693**

Bank of Finland. Publications. Series D. see Suomen Pankki. Julkaisuja. Sarja D **693**

Bank of Finland. Publications. Studies on Finland's Economic Growth see Suomen Pankki. Julkaisuja. Kasvututkimuksia **1085**

Bank of Finland. Statement. (FI) **764**

Bank of Finland. Yearbook. (FI ISSN 0081-9468) **764**

Bank of Finland Discussions Papers. (FI ISSN 0785-3572) **764**

Bank of Ghana. Quarterly Economic Bulletin. (GH ISSN 0005-5182) **846**

Bank of Greece. Monthly Statistical Bulletin. (GR ISSN 1105-0519) **764, 4564**

Bank of Hawaii. Review of Business and Economic Conditions see Bank of Hawaii Business Trends **846**

Bank of Hawaii Business Trends. (US ISSN 0893-0732) **846**

Bank of India. Bulletin. (II ISSN 0005-5212) **846, 764**

Bank of Israel. Annual Report. (IS ISSN 0067-365X) **764**

Bank of Israel. Annual Statistics of Israel's Banking System. (IS ISSN 0334-4541) **705, 764**

Bank of Israel. Bulletin see Bank of Israel. Economic Review **846**

Bank of Israel. Economic Review. (IS) **846, 764**

Bank of Israel. Recent Economic Developments. (IS) **846**

Bank of Jamaica. Bulletin. (JM ISSN 0005-5239) **764**

Bank of Jamaica. Monthly Review. (JM ISSN 0377-7553) **846**

Bank of Jamaica. Report and Statement of Accounts. (JM ISSN 0067-3668) **764**

Bank of Jamaica. Statistical Digest. (JM ISSN 0572-5968) **764**

†Bank of Japan. Annual Report. (JA) **5146**

Bank of Japan. Balance of Payments Monthly. (JA) **1088, 901**

†Bank of Japan. Business Report. (JA ISSN 0067-3684) **5146**

Bank of Japan. Commodities, Weights and Linked Indexes of 1985 Base Wholesale Price Indexes. (JA) **901**

Bank of Japan. Economic Statistics Annual/Nippon Ginko. Keizai Toket Nenpo. (JA ISSN 0910-6006) **705**

Bank of Japan. Economic Statistics Monthly. (JA ISSN 0005-5247) **705**

Bank of Japan. International Comparative Statistics Centering on the Japanese Economy. (JA) **705**

Bank of Japan. Japan's Balance of Payments. Summary Report see Bank of Japan. Balance of Payments Monthly **1088**

Bank of Japan. Price Indexes Annual. (JA) **901, 705**

Bank of Japan. Price Indexes Annual (Appendix) see Bank of Japan. Commodities, Weights and Linked Indexes of 1985 Base Wholesale Price Indexes **901**

Bank of Japan. Statistics Handbook. (JA) **705**

Bank of Japan Monthly Bulletin. see Nippon Ginko Geppo **793**

Bank of Libya. Annual Report of the Board of Directors. (LY ISSN 0067-3714) **846**

Bank of Libya. Balance of Payments. (LY ISSN 0075-921X) **1088, 901**

Bank of Libya. Economic Research Division. Economic Bulletin. (LY ISSN 0005-5271) **846**

Bank of Mauritius. Annual Report. (MF ISSN 0067-3722) **764**

Bank of Mauritius. Quarterly Review. (MF ISSN 0005-5301) **764**

Bank of Montreal Business Review. (CN ISSN 0005-531X) **764, 846**

Bank of Papua New Guinea. Quarterly Economic Bulletin. (PP) **764**

Bank of Papua New Guinea. Report and Financial Statements. (PP) **764**

Bank of Seoul and Trust Company. Economic Review. (KO) **764**

Bank of Sierra Leone. Annual Report see Bank of Sierra Leone. Annual Report and Statement of Accounts **764**

Bank of Sierra Leone. Annual Report and Statement of Accounts. (SL) **764**

Bank of Sierra Leone. Economic Review.(SL) **846**

Bank of Sierra Leone. Economic Trends.(SL) **846**

Bank of Sudan. Economic and Financial Statistics Review. (SJ) **846**

Bank of Sudan. Foreign Trade Statistical Digest. (SJ ISSN 0522-246X) **705**

Bank of Sudan. Report. (SJ ISSN 0067-3749) **764**

Bank of Taiwan Quarterly. (CH ISSN 0005-5344) **846, 764**

Bank of Tanzania. Economic and Operations Report (Year). (TZ ISSN 0067-3757) **846, 764**

Bank of Tanzania. Economic Bulletin. (TZ ISSN 0856-101X) **846**

Bank of Tanzania. Economic Report see Bank of Tanzania. Economic and Operations Report (Year) **846**

Bank of Thailand. Annual Economic Report. (TH) **846**

Bank of Thailand. Monthly Report. (TH ISSN 0125-1074) **846**

Bank of Thailand. Quarterly Bulletin. (TH ISSN 0125-605X) **846**

Bank of Tokyo Annual Report. (JA) **764**

Bank of Tokyo Weekly Review see Tokyo Financial Review **801**

Bank of Tonga. Annual Report. (TO) **764**

Bank of Zambia. Quarterly Financial and Statistical Review. (ZA) **764**

Bank of Zambia. Report and Statement of Accounts. (ZA) **764**

Bank Officers Handbook of Commercial Banking Law (Supplement). (US) **764, 2603**

Bank One. (US ISSN 0005-5387) **764**

Bank Operations Bulletin. (US) **804, 1448**

†Bank Operations Management Service. (US) **5146**

Bank Operations Report. (US ISSN 0045-1487) **764**

Bank Pembangunan Indonesia. Annual Report. (IO ISSN 0408-4632) **764**

Bank Pembangunan Indonesia. Bulletin Ekonomi Bapindo. (IO) **846**

Bank Pembangunan Indonesia. Newsletter. (IO ISSN 0045-1495) **764**

Bank Pembangunan Indonesia. Operations of BAPINDO. (IO) **764**

Bank Personnel News. (US ISSN 0272-3271) **765, 1063**

Bank Personnel Report see Bank Human Resouces Report **763**

Bank Portfolio Strategist. (US) **765, 939**

Bank President's Letter see The F E R C Report **778**

Bank Protection Bulletin see Banking Insurance and Protection Bulletin **766**

Bank Rate Monitor. (US) **765**

Bank Securities Monthly. (US) **765**

Bank Security Report. (US ISSN 0162-7457) **765**

▼Bank Stock Analyst. (US) **939**

Bank Street News - Reviews - Reporting see Street Scenes **1760**

Bank Structure File Tape. (US) **765**

Bank Systems & Technology. (US ISSN 0146-0900) **765, 825**

Bank Tax Report. (US ISSN 0162-7465) **765, 1088**

Bank Teller's Report. (US ISSN 0162-7473) **765**

Bank und Markt see Bank und Markt und Technik **765**

Bank und Markt und Technik. (GW) **765, 1003**

Bank Vaerlden. (SW) **765**

Bank Worker. (AT) **765**

Banka ve Ekonomik Yorumlar. (TU) **765**

Banka ve Ticaret Hukuku Dergisi. (TU) **2603, 765**

Bankcard Consumer News. (US) **765**

Banken-Jahrbuch. (GW) **765**

Banker. (UK ISSN 0005-5395) **765**

Banker. (Il ISSN 0522-2931) **765**

Banker and Businessman. (PK) **765**

Banker & Tradesman. (US ISSN 0005-5409) **4145, 765**

Bankers/Bunuk. (FR) **765, 939**

Bankers Almanac and Year Book. (UK ISSN 0067-379X) **765**

Bankers' Almanac World Ranking. (UK) **765**

Bankers Diary and Guide. (US) **765**

Bankers Digest. (US ISSN 0005-5425) **765**

Bankers Handbook for Asia. (HK) **765**

Banker's Letter of the Law. (US ISSN 0005-5433) **765, 2603**

Bankers Magazine. (US ISSN 0005-545X) **765**

Bankers' Magazine of Australasia see Australian Banker **759**

Bankers Monthly. (US) **765**

Bankers Research. (US) **765**

†Bankers Schools Directory (Year). (US ISSN 0084-9855) **5146**

Bankers' Training Institute (Sri Lanka). Bulletin see Institute of Bankers of Sri Lanka. Journal **3628**

Bankers' Who's Who. (Il ISSN 0067-3803) **765**

Bankfachklasse. (GW ISSN 0170-6659) **647**

Bankhistorisches Archiv. (SZ ISSN 0341-6208) **765**

Bankiga Dhexe ee Soomaaliya. Faafin. see Central Bank of Somalia. Bulletin **710**

Banking Abstracts. (IT) **765, 705**

Banking and Finance Law Review. (CN ISSN 0832-8722) **766, 2603**

Banking and Finance Studies. see Jinrong Yanjiu **787**

Banking & Financial Training. (UK ISSN 0265-7988) **766, 1682**

Banking Attorney. (US) **2603, 766**

Banking Expansion Reporter. (US ISSN 0730-689X) **766**

Banking Fintac Report. (IE) **747, 766**

Banking Guides - Asia, Australia, New Zealand with Principal Hotels and Bank Holidays. (US) **766**

Banking in the E E C. (UK) **766**

Banking Insurance & Finance Union Report see B I F U Report **760**

Banking Insurance and Protection Bulletin. (US) **766**

Banking Ireland. (IE ISSN 0791-1386) **766**

Banking Issues and Innovations in Products, Marketing and Technology.(US) **766**

Banking: Latin American Industrial Report. (US) **766**

Banking Law. (US) **2603, 766**

Banking Law Anthology. (US ISSN 0737-2159) **2603, 766**

Banking Law Briefs. (US) **766, 2603**

Banking Law in the United States. (US) **2603, 766**

Banking Law Journal. (US ISSN 0005-5506) **766, 2603**

Banking Law Journal Digest (Supplement). (US) **766, 2604**

Banking Law Manual: Legal Guide to Commercial Banks, Thrift Institutions and Credit Unions. (US) **2604, 766**

Banking Law Review. (US) **766, 2604**

Banking Literature Index. (US ISSN 0736-5659) **705**

Banking Reporter. (US) **766**

Banking Sector see Banks, Investment & Stockmarket **767**

Banking Software Review. (US ISSN 0892-6778) **805**

Banking Statistics of Pakistan. (PK ISSN 0067-3811) **766**

Banking Structures and Sources of Finance in the European Community see Banking in the E E C **766**

Banking Structures and Sources of Finance in the Far East. (UK) **766**

Banking Technology. (UK ISSN 0266-0865) **766**

Banking Today see Florida Banking **782**

Banking Week. (US) **766**

Banking World. (UK ISSN 0737-6413) **766**

Bankin'Ny Indostria. Rapport Annuel. (MG) **766**

Bankinsurance News. (PK ISSN 0005-5522) **766, 2527**

Bankkaufmann. (GW ISSN 0005-5085) **766**

BankNews. (US) **805, 1448**

Banknotes. (UK) **766**

Bankoekonomen. (NO) **766**

BankRisk. (US) **766**

Bankruptcy Court Decisions. (US ISSN 0098-7336) **2707, 766**

Bankruptcy Law Letter. (US ISSN 0744-7671) **766, 2604**

Bankruptcy Law Reports. (US ISSN 0005-5530) **2707**

Bankruptcy Law Review. (US) **2707, 747**

Bankruptcy Practice Deskbook. (US) **2707**

Bankruptcy Practice for the General Practitioner. (US) **2707**

Bankruptcy Practice Manual see Bankruptcy Practice Deskbook **2707**

Bankruptcy Service Current Awareness Alert. (US) **2707, 647**

Bankruptcy Strategist. (US ISSN 0747-8917) **766**

Banks in Insurance Report. (US ISSN 8756-6079) **766, 2527**

▼Banks, Investment & Stockmarket. (GR) **767, 647**

Bankstanden. (DK) **767**

Bankstown - Canterbury Torch. (AT) **2171**

Bankvaerlden. (SW ISSN 0005-5549) **767, 2580**

Bankverein-Heft see S B C Booklet **798**

Bankwirtschaftliche Forschungen. (SZ ISSN 0067-382X) **767**

Banner (Grand Rapids). (US ISSN 0005-5557) **4230**

Banner (St. Louis). (US) **939**

The Banner (Zanesville). (US) **4280**

Banner of Truth. (UK) **4164**

†Banneret. (NO ISSN 0005-5565) **5146**

Bano. (Il ISSN 0005-5573) **4838**

Bano Biggyan Patrika see Bangladesh Journal of Forest Science **2096**

Banque. (FR ISSN 0005-5581) **767**

Banque Africaine de Developpement. Rapport Annuel see African Development Bank. Report by the Board of Directors **925**

Banque Africaine de Developpement. Rapport du Conseil d'Administration. see African Development Bank. Report by the Board of Directors **925**

Banque Afrique. (FR ISSN 0184-9719) **901**

Banque Bruxelles Lambert. Bulletin Financier. (BE ISSN 0771-6273) **939**

Banque Centrale de Tunisie. Bulletin. (TI ISSN 0067-3854) **767**

Banque Centrale de Tunisie. Rapport d'Activite. (TI ISSN 0067-3862) **767**

Banque Centrale de Tunisie. Statistiques Financieres. (TI) **767**

Banque Centrale des Etats de l'Afrique de l'Ouest. Notes d'Information et Statistiques. (SG ISSN 0005-559X) **767**

Banque Centrale des Etats de l'Afrique de l'Ouest. Rapport Annuel. (SG ISSN 0067-3889) **767**

Banque Centrale des Etats de l'Afrique de l'Ouest. Rapport d'Activite. (SG ISSN 0067-3897) **767**

Banque Commerciale Zairoise. Rapports et Bilans Annuels/Banque Commerciale Zairoise. Reports and Balance Sheets. (ZR) **767**

BANQUE COMMERCIALE

Banque Commerciale Zairoise. Reports and Balance Sheets. *see* Banque Commerciale Zairoise. Rapports et Bilans Annuels **767**
Banque de Bruxelles. Rapport Annuel *see* Banque de Bruxelles Lambert. Rapports de l'Exercice **767**
Banque de Bruxelles Lambert. Rapports de l'Exercice/Bank Brussel Lambert. Annual Reports. (BE) **767**
Banque de Credit de Bujumbura. Rapports et Bilan. (BD) **767**
Banque de France. Bulletin de la Commission Bancaire. (FR) **767**
Banque de France. Bulletin Mensuel. (FR) **767**
Banque de France. Bulletin Trimestriel. (FR) **767**, **846**
Banque de France. Cahier des Titres de Creances Negociables. (FR) **705**
Banque de France. Centrale de Bilans. Fascicules de Resultats. (FR) **767**
Banque de France. Centrale de Bilans. Selection d'Indicateurs. (FR) **767**
Banque de France. Compte-Rendu. (FR ISSN 0067-3927) **767**
Banque de France. Comptes Annuels des Etablissements de Credit. (FR) **767**
Banque de France. Conseil National du Credit. Rapports des Groupes de Travail. (FR) **767**
Banque de France. Direction de la Conjoncture. Situation Financiere des Regions de Province en (Year). (FR) **846**
Banque de France. Direction de la Conjoncture. Situation Financiere des Regions En (Year). (FR) **846**
Banque de France. Enquete Financiere. (FR) **705**
Banque de France. Enquete Mensuelle de Conjoncture. (FR ISSN 0242-5815) **846**
Banque de France. Etudes et Analyses Comparatives les Resultats des Etablissements de Credit et des Maisons de Titres. (FR) **767**
Banque de France. La Zone Franc en (Year). (FR) **846**
Banque de France. Lettre Mensuelle Regionale. (FR) **767**
Banque de France. Moyens de Paiement et Circuits de Recouvrement. (FR) **705**
Banque de France. Note Financiere Annuelle. (FR) **767**
Banque de France. Notes d'Information. (FR) **767**
Banque de France. Rapport du Comite Consultatif. (FR) **767**
Banque de France. Rapport du Comite de la Reglementation Bancaire. (FR) **767**
Banque de France. Rapport du Comite des Etablissements de Credit. (FR) **767**
Banque de France. Recueil des Textes Applicables a l'Exercice des Activites Bancaires. (FR) **767**
Banque de France. Revue Annuelle de l'Evolution des Principales Branches d'Activite en (Year). (FR) **767**
Banque de France. Situation Economique a l'Etranger *see* Situation Economique a l'Etranger **884**
Banque de France. Statistiques Monetaires et Financieres Annuelles. (FR) **705**
Banque de l'Union Europeenne. Chiffres et Commentaires. (FR ISSN 0245-761X) **846**
Banque de l'Union Europeenne. Informations Economiques et Financieres. *see* Banque de l'Union Europeenne. Chiffres et Commentaires **846**
Banque de la Republique d'Haiti. Rapport Annuel. (HT) **767**
Banque de la Republique du Burundi. Bulletin Mensuel. (BD ISSN 1013-5332) **767**
Banque de la Republique du Burundi. Bulletin Trimestriel. (BD ISSN 1013-5340) **767**
Banque de la Republique du Burundi. Rapport Annuel. (BD ISSN 1013-5359) **768**
Banque de Port-Said. Revue Economique Trimestrielle. (UA ISSN 0005-5603) **846**
Banque des Etats de l'Afrique Centrale. Etudes et Statistiques. (CM ISSN 0014-2069) **705**
Banque des Etats de l'Afrique Centrale. Rapport d'Activite. (CM ISSN 0067-3900) **768**
Banque des Mots. (FR ISSN 0067-3951) **2746**
Banque du Canada. Revue. *see* Bank of Canada. Review **763**
Banque du Maroc. Rapport Annuel *see* Bank Al-Maghrib. Rapport Annuel **762**
Banque du Zaire. Bulletin Mensuel de la Statistique. (ZR) **706**
Banque du Zaire. Rapport Annuel. (ZR ISSN 0300-1172) **768**
Banque et Caisse d'Epargne de l'Etat, Luxembourg. Annual Report *see* Banque et Caisse d'Epargne de l'Etat, Luxembourg. Rapports et Bilans **768**
Banque et Caisse d'Epargne de l'Etat, Luxembourg. Rapports et Bilans. (LU) **768**
Banque et Informatique. (FR ISSN 0248-9708) **805**
Banque Francaise et Italienne. Etudes Economiques *see* Banque SudAmeris. Etudes Economiques **846**
Banque Internationale a Luxembourg. Cahiers Economiques. (LU) **846**
Banque Internationale pour l'Afrique Occidentale. Conseil d'Administration. Rapport et Resolutions, Rapport des Commissaires aux Comptes. (FR) **846**
Banque Marocaine du Commerce Exterieur. Annual Report. (MR) **768**
Banque Marocaine du Commerce Exterieur Information Review *see* B M C E Information Review **760**
Banque Nationale de Belgique. Bulletin. (BE ISSN 0005-5611) **768**, **846**
Banque Nationale de Belgique. Rapport sur les Operations. (BE ISSN 0067-3978) **768**
Banque Nationale de Developpement Economique du Burundi. Rapport Annuel. (BD) **768**
Banque Nationale de la Republique d'Haiti. Rapport du Departement Fiscal *see* Banque de la Republique d'Haiti. Rapport Annuel **767**
†Banque Nationale du Canada. Revue Economique. (CN ISSN 0225-2910) **5146**
Banque Nationale du Congo. Rapport Annuel *see* Banque du Zaire. Rapport Annuel **768**
Banque Nationale du Rwanda. Bulletin. (RW) **768**
Banque Nationale du Rwanda. Bulletin Trimestriel *see* Banque Nationale du Rwanda. Bulletin **768**
Banque Nationale du Rwanda. Rapport Annuel *see* Banque Nationale du Rwanda. Rapport sur l'Evolution Economique et Monetaire du Rwanda **768**
Banque Nationale du Rwanda. Rapport d'Activites *see* Banque Nationale du Rwanda. Rapport sur l'Evolution Economique et Monetaire du Rwanda **768**
Banque Nationale du Rwanda. Rapport sur l'Evolution Economique et Monetaire du Rwanda. (RW) **768**
Banque Nationale Malagasy de Developpement. Rapport d'Activite *see* Bankin'Ny Indostria. Rapport Annuel **766**
Banque Nationale pour le Developpement Economique. Rapport Annuel. (MR ISSN 0851-1934) **1072**
Banque Nationale pour le Developpement Rural. Rapport Annuel. (MG) **768**
Banque Populaire Suisse. Balance Sheet Prospectus. (SZ ISSN 0005-4240) **768**
Banque Populaire Suisse. Information. (SZ ISSN 0067-4028) **768**
Banque Populaire Suisse. Journal. (SZ) **768**
Banque Rwandaise de Developpement. Rapport Annuel. (RW) **768**
Banque SudAmeris. Etudes Economiques. (FR) **846**
Banque Togolaise de Developpement. Rapport Annuel *see* Banque Togolaise de Developpement. Rapport d'Activites **768**
Banque Togolaise de Developpement. Rapport d'Activites. (TG) **768**
Banques et Entreprises au Maroc. (MR) **768**, 647
Le Banquier. (CN ISSN 0822-6849) **768**
Bantam Standard. (US) **212**
Bantu Education Journal - Bantoe Onderwysblad *see* Educamus **1627**
Bantu Treasury *see* Black Writers Series **2899**
Banxquote Online. (US) **939**
Banyan Tree. (UK ISSN 0140-8623) **2145**
Banyaszati es Kohaszati Lapok - Kohaszat. (HU ISSN 0005-5670) **3403**
Banyaszati es Kohaszati Lapok - Ontode. (HU ISSN 0375-9504) **3403**
Banyaszati Szakirodalmi Tajekoztato/ Mining Abstracts. (HU ISSN 0231-0651) **3499**, 3, **3479**
Bao Po/Blasting. (CC ISSN 1001-487X) **1848**
Baogao Wenxue/Reportage Literature. (CC ISSN 0257-0149) **2567**, **2898**
Bapco News *see* B A P C O News **3682**
Baptist Adults. (US ISSN 0162-4180) **4230**
Baptist and Reflector. (US) **4230**
Baptist Bulletin. (US ISSN 0005-5689) **4230**
Baptist Challenge. (US ISSN 0005-5697) **4230**
Baptist Courier. (US) **4164**
Baptist Directory. (CN) **4230**
Baptist Herald. (US ISSN 0005-5700) **4230**
Baptist Heritage Update. (US) **4230**
Baptist History and Heritage. (US ISSN 0005-5719) **4230**, **2307**
Baptist Informer. (US) **4230**, 1993
Baptist Leader. (US ISSN 0005-5727) **1744**, **4230**
Baptist Medical Centers News *see* B M C News **2459**
Baptist Missionary Association of America. Directory and Handbook. (US ISSN 0091-2743) **4230**
Baptist Missionary Society, Didcot. Annual Report. (UK ISSN 0067-4060) **4230**
Baptist Missionary Society, London. Official Report and Directory of Missionaries. (UK ISSN 0067-4079) **4230**
Baptist Program. (US ISSN 0005-5743) **4230**
Baptist Progress. (US ISSN 0005-5751) **4230**
Baptist Public Relations Association Newsletter. (US) **4230**
Baptist Quarterly. (UK ISSN 0005-576X) **4230**, **2307**
Baptist Record. (US ISSN 0005-5778) **4230**
The Baptist Standard. (US) **4164**, **4280**
Baptist Student *see* The Student (Nashville) **4250**
Baptist Times. (UK ISSN 0005-5786) **4230**
Baptist True Union. (US ISSN 0025-4169) **4230**
Baptist Trumpet. (US ISSN 0888-9074) **4230**
Baptist Union Directory. (UK ISSN 0302-3184) **4230**
Baptist Union of Western Canada. Yearbook. (CN ISSN 0067-4087) **4230**
Baptist World. (US ISSN 0005-5808) **4230**
Baptist World Alliance. Congress Reports. (US ISSN 0067-4095) **4230**
Baptist Yearbook *see* Baptist Directory **4230**
Baptist Young Adults. (US ISSN 0195-136X) **4230**
Baptist Youth. (US ISSN 0162-4199) **4230**
Die Bar. (GW) **2472**
Bar. *see* Palestra **2665**
Bar Association of Sri Lanka. Newsletter. (CE) **2604**
Bar Associations in Focus on Aging and the Law *see* B I F O C A L **2603**
Bar Code News *see* I D Systems **827**
Bar Council of India. Journal *see* Indian Bar Review **2634**
Bar Directory of Maine. (US) **2604**
Bar Examiner. (US ISSN 0005-5824) **2604**
Bar Giornale. (IT ISSN 0392-2707) **2472**
Bar-Ilan: Annual of Bar-Ilan University. (IS ISSN 0067-4109) **4221**, 1993, **2503**
Bar-Ilan Law Studies. (IS ISSN 0334-0716) **2604**
Bar-Ilan University. Studies in Judaica and the Humanities *see* Bar-Ilan: Annual of Bar-Ilan University **4221**
Bar Leader. (US ISSN 0099-1031) **2604**
Bar News (Washington). (US) **2604**
Al-Bara'im. (MK) **2210**
Barakela. (ML) **2580**
Baran's Tech Letter. (US) **1458**
†Baranyai Konyvtaros. (HU ISSN 0237-0719) **5146**
Barataria. (IT) **2898**
Barbacane. (FR) **2898**, 318
Barbados. Board of Tourism. Annual Report. (BB) **4798**, **4753**
Barbados. Export Directory. (BB) **1123**
Barbados. Legislature. House of Assembly. Minutes of Proceedings. (BB ISSN 0377-144X) **4054**
Barbados. Legislature. Senate. Minutes of Proceedings. (BB ISSN 0377-1458) **4054**
Barbados. Ministry of Finance and Economic Affairs. Economic Report. (BB) **846**
Barbados. Ministry of Finance and Economic Affairs. Financial Statement and Budgetary Proposals. (BB) **1088**
Barbados. Ministry of Finance and Planning. Economic Report *see* Barbados. Ministry of Finance and Economic Affairs. Economic Report **846**
Barbados. Ministry of Finance and Planning. Financial Statement and Budgetary Proposals *see* Barbados. Ministry of Finance and Economic Affairs. Financial Statement and Budgetary Proposals **1088**
Barbados. Ministry of Health. Chief Medical Officer. Annual Report. (BB) **4098**
Barbados. Registration Office. Report on Vital Statistics & Registrations. (BB) **4079**, 3991
Barbados. Statistical Service. Bulletin. Overseas Trade. (BB) **706**, **4564**
Barbados. Statistical Service. Digest of Tourism Statistics. (BB) **4799**
Barbados. Statistical Service. Monthly Digest of Statistics. (BB ISSN 0378-8873) **4564**
Barbados. Statistical Service. Overseas Trade Report. (BB ISSN 0067-4125) **706**, 3
Barbados. Statistical Service. Survey of Accommodation Establishments. (BB) **4564**
Barbados Museum and Historical Society. Journal. (BB ISSN 0005-5891) **2400**, 318
Barbados National Bank. Annual Report & Statement of Accounts. (BB) **768**
Barbados Nursing Journal. (BB ISSN 0572-6042) **3276**
Barbados Official Gazette. (BB) **2239**
Barbados Tourist Board. Annual Report.(BB) **4753**
Barbara Brabec's National Home-Business Report *see* National Home-Business Report **1116**
Barbara Eden International Fan Club Newsletter. (US) **1296**, **3504**
Barbara Woodhouse Animal Annual. (UK) **3708**

Barbie. (US) **1249**
Barbie. (MX) **1249**
Barbinella. (IT) **2204**, **3875**
Barbizon Magazine. (CN) **2988**
Barbour Compendium Building Products. (UK ISSN 0260-9169) **2548**, **602**
Barbra Critiques see Heartland Critiques **2868**
Barcelona. Metropolis Mediterrania. (SP ISSN 0214-6215) **2483**, **318**, **2898**
Barcelona (Year). (SP) **4753**
Barcelona Port. (SP) **4724**
Barche e Catalogo. (IT) **4522**
▼Barclay Managed Futures Report. (US ISSN 1060-3158) **939**
Barclays Business Brief see Business Brief **848**
Barclays Country Reports. (UK ISSN 0307-4552) **846**
Barclays Law Monthly. (US ISSN 0164-3835) **2604**
Barclays Review. (UK) **768**
Barclays United States Eighth Circuit Service. (US) **2604**
Barclays United States Tenth Circuit Service. (US) **2604**
Barcos. (AG) **4522**, **4753**
Bard. (UK ISSN 0307-3408) **2898**
Bard Observer. (US) **1304**
Bardsey Observatory Report. (UK ISSN 0408-5655) **430**, **562**
Bare in Mind. (US) **3799**, **2738**
†Bare Knuckles. (US ISSN 1042-993X) **5146**
Bare Nibs. (UK ISSN 0264-6137) **4630**, **2988**
▼Barefoot Prints. (US) **2145**
Bareme des Coefficients. (FR) **602**
Bareme Social Periodique. (FR) **647**
Barett. (GW ISSN 0930-7974) **3452**
▼Bargain Hunters & Budgeteers Opportunity Newsletter. (US ISSN 1053-2021) **2444**, **1502**
Bargain Paradises of the World see Retirement Paradises of the World **4784**
Bargain Shopper's Guide to Melbourne. (AT ISSN 0159-6861) **1502**, **833**
Bargain Shoppers Guide to Sydney. (AT) **1502**, **833**
Bargaining Report. (UK ISSN 0143-2680) **973**
Bargfelder Bote. (GW ISSN 0342-8036) **2805**
Bariatrician. (US) **3603**, **3370**
Barid ash-Sharikat. (UA) **647**
Barid Hollanda. (NE ISSN 0005-5956) **901**
Bark Producers Report. (US) **2096**
Barkai. (IS ISSN 0334-1380) **4221**
Die Barke. (AU ISSN 0067-4206) **2898**, **1249**
Barker-Joslyn Family Tree Climber. (US) **2145**
Barks. (US) **3708**
Barletter see Kansas Bar Association. Journal **2642**
Barley Genetics Newsletter. (US) **495**
Barman. (IT) **378**
Die Barmer. (GW) **2527**
Barmer Bruecke. (GW) **2527**
Barmherzigkeit. (AU ISSN 0005-5999) **4399**
Barn i Hem-Skola-Samhaelle. (SW ISSN 0005-6006) **1618**
Barn och Kultur/Children and Culture. (SW ISSN 0037-6477) **2746**, **1618**
Barnard Alumnae. (US ISSN 0749-1263) **1304**
Barnard Bulletin. (US ISSN 0005-6014) **1304**
Barnardo News. (UK) **4399**, **1249**
Barnard's Retail Marketing Report. (US) **1034**
Barnboken. (SW ISSN 0347-772X) **4121**, **2898**
Barne og Ungdomslitteratur. Utvalg av Boker Utkommet see Veiledende Liste for Barne og Ungdomslitteratur. Utvalg av Boker Utkommet **1269**
Barnes Bulletin see Barnes Bulletin 2.0 **2145**
Barnes Bulletin 2.0. (US) **2145**
Barnet Marksman. (CN ISSN 0045-155X) **4466**
Barnett Action. (US) **768**

Barnett Source. (US ISSN 0888-4625) **2145**
Barney. (US) **2859**
Barnhart Dictionary Companion. (US ISSN 0736-1122) **2805**
▼The Barnstormer. (US) **48**
Barntradgarden see Foerskolan **1634**
Barnwood. (US) **2859**
Baroda Reporter. (II) **3979**
Barometer. (CN) **3951**, **3452**
Barometer (Portland). (US ISSN 0511-8255) **2113**
Barometer of Business. (US) **846**
Barometer of Occupational Safety. see Anzen no Shihyo **3614**
Barometre de Notoriete des Services Telematiques Grand Public. (FR) **1403**
Baromfiipar see Baromfitenyesztes es Feldolgozas **212**
Baromfitenyesztes es Feldolgozas. (HU ISSN 0133-011X) **212**
Baron. (CN) **1304**
Baroque. (FR ISSN 0067-4222) **2898**
Barque's Pakistan Trade Directory and Who's Who. (PK ISSN 0067-4230) **1123**
Barrett Branches. (US ISSN 0899-1367) **2145**
Barrett Correspondents' List and Registry Index. (CN) **2145**
Barricada Internacional. (NQ ISSN 0254-802X) **3875**
La Barrique. (CN ISSN 0228-5452) **378**
Barrister. (NR ISSN 0331-0086) **2604**
Barrister (Chicago). (US ISSN 0094-5277) **2604**
Barrister (Philadelphia). (US ISSN 0739-2494) **2604**
Barrister Bulletin see Los Angeles Lawyer **2650**
Barron Family Newsletter. (US ISSN 0882-8202) **2145**
Barron's Guide to Graduate Business Schools. (US) **1692**, **647**
Barron's Index. (US) **706**, **3**
Barron's National Business and Financial Weekly. (US ISSN 0005-6073) **939**
Barron's Profiles of American Colleges. Vol. 1: Descriptions of the Colleges. (US) **1692**
Barron's Profiles of American Colleges. Vol. 2: Index of College Major Areas of Study. (US ISSN 0533-1072) **1692**
Barrow and Silloth Docks Tidal Predictions. (UK) **4724**
Barr's Post Card News. (US ISSN 0744-4540) **2433**
Bars and Stripes. (US) **1510**
Barshika Bibarani Bayaska Siksha Parikshya Prakalpa Bangladesh see Bangladesh. Education Directorate. Report on Pilot Project on Adult Education **1682**
Barshika Unnayana Karmasuci see Bangladesh. Planning Commission. Annual Development Programme **845**
Barstow College Collegiate see The Viking Press **1329**
Bartender. (US) **378**
Bartender International. (UK) **3624**, **378**
Bartenderen. (DK ISSN 0901-313X) **3624**, **378**
Barter Communique. (US) **1123**, **28**
Barter Update. (US ISSN 0736-1904) **1113**
BarterNews. (US) **846**
Barthmess Family Association. (US) **2145**
Bartlett Letters. (US) **939**
Bartlett Review. (UK ISSN 0954-2205) **295**
Barton County Genealogical Society. Newsletter see Barton County Genealogical Society. Quarterly **2145**
Barton County Genealogical Society. Quarterly. (US) **2145**, **2400**
Bartonia. (US ISSN 0198-7356) **495**
Barts Journal. (UK) **2459**
Baruch Today. (US) **1304**
†Basal Facts. (US) **5146**

Base d'Information Robert-Debre see B I R D **1247**
Base Line. (US ISSN 0272-8532) **2243**, **1555**, **2746**
Base-100. (SP) **1034**
†Baseball (Year). (US) **5146**
Baseball Address List see The Sport Americana Baseball Address List **2442**
Baseball America. (US ISSN 0228-6033) **4500**
Baseball Bulletin. (US ISSN 0199-0128) **4500**
Baseball Card News. (US ISSN 0746-7966) **2433**, **4500**
Baseball Card Price Guide see The Sport Americana Baseball Card Price Guide **2442**
Baseball Card Price Guide Monthly. (US ISSN 0896-7563) **2433**, **4500**
Baseball Card Show Calendar see Baseball Card Shows **5146**
†Baseball Card Shows. (US) **5146**
Baseball Cards. (US ISSN 8750-5851) **2433**, **4500**
Baseball Case Book. (US ISSN 0270-4218) **4500**
Baseball Digest. (US ISSN 0005-609X) **4500**
Baseball Encyclopedia Update. (US) **4500**, **1780**
Baseball Fans. see Yakyo-to **4515**
Baseball Forecast (Year). (US) **4500**
Baseball Guide. (US ISSN 0067-4273) **4500**
Baseball Hobby News. (US ISSN 0199-946X) **4500**
Baseball Illustrated (Year). (US) **4500**
Baseball Insight. (US) **4500**
Baseball Magazine. (JA) **4500**
Baseball: Our Way. (US) **2988**
Baseball Preview (Year). (US) **4500**
Baseball Register see Official Baseball Register **4509**
Baseball Research Journal. (US ISSN 0734-6891) **4500**
Baseball - Revue du Baseball see Les Expos **5190**
Baseball Rulebook. (US) **4500**
Baseball Umpires Manual. (US) **4500**
Baseball Update. (US) **4500**
†Baseball Video Magazine. (US) **5146**
Basel Africa Bibliography. Newsletter. see Basler Afrika Bibliographien. Nachrichten **5146**
Basel Institute for Immunology. Annual Report. (SZ ISSN 0301-3782) **3183**
Basel Stock Exchange. Annual Report. see Basler Boerse. Jahresbericht **939**
Baseler Beitraege zur Chirurgie. (SZ ISSN 1013-7459) **3376**
Baseline. (US) **1944**
Baseline Data Report. (US ISSN 0739-6279) **4084**
Basenji. (US ISSN 0094-9744) **3708**
Basenji Club of America. Official Bulletin.(US) **3708**
Bases. (FR) **1443**
Bashkimi. (AA) **3875**
Basi Razionali della Terapia see G and B **3208**
Basic and Applied Histochemistry. (IT ISSN 0391-7258) **472**, **522**, **3081**
Basic and Applied Social Psychology. (US ISSN 0197-3533) **4012**, **4366**
▼Basic and Clinical Biostatistics. (US ISSN 1045-5523) **3031**, **3081**, **4564**
Basic and Clinical Cardiology Series. (US) **3205**
Basic & Clinical Endocrinology. (US) **3250**
Basic and Clinical Nutrition. (US) **3603**
†Basic Concepts in Psychology Series. (US) **5146**
Basic Economic Data for Idaho. (US ISSN 0094-1115) **847**
Basic Education. (US ISSN 0196-4984) **1618**
Basic Education. see Nayi Talim **1650**
Basic Facts about the United Nations. (UN ISSN 0067-4419) **3951**
Basic Life Sciences. (US ISSN 0090-5542) **430**

BASLER BEITRAEGE 5965

Basic Medical Science and Clinics. see Jichu Yixue yu Linchuang **3113**
Basic Oil Laws & Concession Contracts: Asia & Australasia. (US) **2719**, **3683**
Basic Oil Laws & Concession Contracts: Central America & Caribbean. (US) **2719**, **3683**
Basic Oil Laws & Concession Contracts: Europe. (US ISSN 0093-5018) **2720**, **3683**
Basic Oil Laws & Concession Contracts: Middle East. (US) **2720**, **3683**
Basic Oil Laws & Concession Contracts: North Africa. (US) **2720**, **3683**
Basic Oil Laws & Concession Contracts: South America. (US) **2720**, **3683**
Basic Oil Laws & Concession Contracts: South & Central Africa. (US) **2720**, **3683**
Basic Patterns in Union Contracts. (US) **2707**, **3257**
Basic Petroleum Data Book. (US) **3705**
Basic Port Statistics of India. (II) **4662**, **4724**
Basic Research in Cardiology. (GW ISSN 0300-8428) **3205**
Basic Road Statistics of India. (II ISSN 0067-6462) **4662**
Basic Software. (SZ) **1475**
Basic Statistics of the European Community. (EI) **706**
Basic Sugaku. (JA ISSN 0386-6319) **3031**
Basically Buckles. (US ISSN 1044-775X) **2433**
Basilicata. (IT ISSN 0005-6111) **3875**
Basim. (UK) **1249**
Basin Research. (UK ISSN 0950-091X) **1541**
Basis. (IO ISSN 0005-6138) **318**, **2503**, **2898**
Basis. (NE ISSN 0005-6146) **3453**, **4164**
Basistexte Personalwesen. (GW ISSN 0174-6200) **1063**
Basket Bits. (US) **353**
Basketball see Basketball Monthly **4500**
Basketball. (GW ISSN 0178-9279) **4500**
Basketball. see Lanqiu **4507**
Basketball Annual (Year). (US) **4500**
Basketball Card Price Guide and Alphabetical Checklist see The Sport Americana Basketball Card Price Guide and Alphabetical Checklist **2442**
Basketball Case Book. (US ISSN 0525-4663) **4500**
Basketball Clinic see Coaching Clinic **4502**
Basketball Digest. (US ISSN 0098-5988) **4500**
Basketball Forecast (Year). (US) **4500**
Basketball Guide. (US) **4500**
Basketball Hall of Fame Newsletter. (US) **4500**
Basketball Hall of Fame Yearbook. (US) **4500**
Basketball Handbook. (US) **4500**
Basketball Monthly. (UK) **4500**
Basketball Officials Manual. (US ISSN 0270-4226) **4500**
Basketball Rulebook. (US) **4500**
Basketball - Simplified & Illustrated Rules. (US) **4501**
Basketball Statisticians' Manual. (US) **4498**
Basketball Weekly. (US ISSN 0005-6170) **4501**
†Basler Afrika Bibliographien. Nachrichten/Basel Africa Bibliography. Newsletter. (SZ ISSN 0171-0087) **5146**
Basler Beitraege zur Ethnologie. (SZ ISSN 0067-4478) **235**
Basler Beitraege zur Geographie. (SZ ISSN 0067-4486) **2243**
Basler Beitraege zur Geographie und Ethnologie. Ethnologische Reihe see Basler Beitraege zur Ethnologie **235**
Basler Beitraege zur Geschichtswissenschaft. (SZ) **2307**
Basler Beitraege zur Physiogeographie. (SZ) **2243**

BASLER BOERSE

Basler Boerse. Jahresbericht/Basel Stock Exchange. Annual Report. (SZ) **939**
Basler Effektenboerse. Jahresbericht *see* Basler Boerse. Jahresbericht **939**
Basler Feldbuch. (SZ) **2243**
Basler Geomethodisches Colloquium. Veroeffentlichungen - Basel Geomethodological Meeting. Proceedings *see* Geomethodica **1544**
Basler Handelskammer. Info and Bulletin. (SZ) **808**
Basler Predigten. (SZ ISSN 0005-6189) **4164**
Basler Studien zur Deutschen Sprache und Literatur. (SZ ISSN 0067-4508) **2898**, 2805
Basler Studien zur Rechtswissenschaft. (SZ) **2604**
Basler Veroeffentlichungen zur Geschichte der Medizin und der Biologie. (SZ ISSN 0067-4524) **3081**, 430
Basler Zeitschrift fuer Geschichte und Altertumskunde. (SZ ISSN 0067-4540) **2351**
Basrah Natural History Museum. Bulletin. (IQ) **4301**
Basrah Natural History Museum. Publication. (IQ) **4301**
Bass and Freshwater Fishing. (US) **4541**
Bass Fishing *see* Field & Stream Bass Fishing Annual **4545**
Bass Magazine Hall of Fame Yearbook (Year). (US) **3540**
Bass Player. (US ISSN 1050-785X) **3540**
Basse Normandie Automobile. (FR ISSN 0005-6197) **4685**
Basserne. (DK) **1249**
Bassin' (US ISSN 0884-4739) **2037**, 4541
Bassmaster Classic Report. (US) **4541**, 4522
Bassmaster Magazine. (US) **4541**
Basta! (US) **3951**, 4164
Basteria. (NE ISSN 0005-6219) **578**
Bastions de Geneve. (SZ ISSN 0408-6392) **1701**
Bat Kol. (IS) **1734**, 2286
Bat Research News. (US ISSN 0005-6227) **578**
Batchat. (UK) **578**
Bateaux. (FR ISSN 0005-6235) **4522**
Bateman Datum. (US) **2145**
Bateria. (GW ISSN 0178-000X) **2859**
Bates. (US) **1304**
Batfutzot. (IS) **1993**, 4221
Bath & Kitchen Marketer. (CN) **2548**, 602, 1034
Bath and West Show Catalogue *see* Royal Bath & West Show Catalogue **117**
Bathroom Today and Tomorrow. *see* Il Bagno Oggi e Domani **2548**
Bathrooms. (UK ISSN 0950-0197) **2548**
†Bathrooms, Kitchen & Tiles. (UK) **5146**
Baths Service and Recreation Management *see* Recreation **4485**
Batiguide *see* Maison et Travaux **623**
Batiment/Building. (CN ISSN 0005-6278) **602**
Batiment Artisanal. (FR) **602**
Batiment - Entretien. (FR) **3615**, 1944
Batiment International, Building Research and Practice *see* Building Research and Information **607**
Batiprix. (FR) **602**
Batkivshchyna/Our Country. (CN) **1993**
Batnua. (US) **3875**, 1249
Bato Loc International. (FR) **4522**
Baton. (US ISSN 0951-9955) **3750**, 3540
Le Baton Rouge. (US) **2145**, 2400
Baton Rouge Business Report. (US) **847**
Baton Rouge's Commerce. (US) **808**
Bats. (US ISSN 1049-0043) **578**
Battaglia Letteraria. (IT ISSN 0005-6332) **2859**
Battelle Information. (GW ISSN 0932-7541) **4594**
Battelle Memorial Institute. Published Papers and Articles. (US ISSN 0084-7712) **4354**
Battelle Today. (US ISSN 0145-8477) **4594**
Batter Performance Handbook. (US ISSN 0731-812X) **4501**
Battered Women's Directory. (US) **4838**, 3940, 4835
Batteries International. (UK ISSN 0957-9249) **1883**, 4685
Battery & E V Technology News. (US ISSN 0271-7093) **1883**
Battery Council International. Convention Proceedings. (US) **4647**
Battery Council International News *see* B C I News **4684**
Battery Man. (US ISSN 0005-6359) **4685**, 1883
Battery Replacement Data Book. (US) **1883**
Batting the Breeze. (US ISSN 0005-6367) **3364**
Battle Action Force. (UK) **1249**
Battle Call. (US) **3453**, 2400
Battle Conference on Anglo-Norman Studies III *see* Anglo-Norman Studies **2348**
Battler Columns. (US) **1304**
Bau *see* Wuerttembergische Bau-Berufsgenossenschaft. Mitteilungen **636**
Bau. (GW ISSN 0341-096X) **3615**
Bau - Aktuell. (GW) **602**
Bau & Heimwerker Markt. (GW ISSN 0172-200X) **602**
Bau & Holz. (SZ) **602**
Bau-Berufsgenossenschaft Hannover. Mitteilungsblatt. (GW ISSN 0931-2862) **3615**
Bau; Fachzeitschrift fuer Baupraxis, Bautechnik, Baumaschinen, Betriebsfuehrung und Kalkulation. (SZ) **602**
Bau Information. (GW) **602**
Bau Magazin *see* Technopress Bau Magazin **634**
Bau Rundschau mit Bau-Flash. (SZ) **602**
†Bau Trichter. Ausgabe A. (GW ISSN 0723-6506) **5146**
Bau und Baustoff. (GW ISSN 0005-643X) **602**
Bau- und Moebelschreiner. (GW ISSN 0341-3659) **2557**
Bau-Zentralblatt *see* B Z Bauzentralblatt **602**
†Baubedarf Einkaufen, Beraten, Verkaufen. (GW) **5146**
Baubedarf Manager *see* Baubedarf Einkaufen, Beraten, Verkaufen **5146**
Baubeschlag Magazin. (GW) **641**
Baubeschlag Magazin mit Praktikus *see* Baubeschlag Magazin **641**
Baubeschlag-Taschenbuch. (GW ISSN 0067-4583) **641**
Bauelemente Bau. (GW) **602**
Bauen. (GW) **602**
Bauen fuer die Landwirtschaft. (GW ISSN 0171-7952) **602**, 78
Bauen in Stahl/Construire en Acier/Costruire in Acciaio. (SZ) **295**, 602, 1862
Bauen mit Aluminium. (GW ISSN 0522-4942) **602**
Bauen mit Holz. (GW ISSN 0005-6545) **639**
Bauen mit Kunststoffen. (GW ISSN 0934-1773) **602**, 3861, 4291
Bauen und Fertighaus. (GW ISSN 0005-6510) **602**
Bauen und Modernisieren *see* Bauen **602**
Der Bauer. (AU ISSN 0005-6561) **78**
Der Bauer. (BE) **78**
Bauern-Echo. (GW ISSN 0323-6471) **78**
Bauernblatt fuer Schleswig-Holstein. (GW) **78**
Bauernhaeuser aus Mitteleuropa. (GW) **295**, 235, 2307
Bauernhaeuser der Schweiz. (GW ISSN 0067-4591) **2052**
Bauernzeitung. (GW ISSN 0941-2239) **78**
Baufachblatt. (GW) **602**
Bauforum. (AU ISSN 0005-6596) **295**, 602
Baugeraetemarkt *see* Deutsches Baublatt **615**
Das Baugeruest. (GW ISSN 0005-6618) **4164**
Baugeschaeft und Bauunternehmer. (GW ISSN 0005-6626) **602**
Baugewerbe. (GW ISSN 0005-6634) **1862**
Baugewerbe - Mitteilungen Westfalen. (GW) **602**
Bauhandwerk. (GW ISSN 0173-5365) **602**
Bauhinia. (SZ ISSN 0067-4605) **495**
Bauindustriebrief. (GW) **602**, 647
†Bauinformation Wissenschaft und Technik. (GW ISSN 0323-8490) **5146**
Bauingenieur. (GW ISSN 0005-6650) **602**, 1862
Baukeramik. (GW) **1161**
Baukonjunkturspiegel. (GW) **602**, 647
Baum Bugle. (US ISSN 0005-6677) **2898**
Baum-Zeitung. (GW ISSN 0341-3624) **496**
Bauma-Trends. (GW ISSN 0041-2368) **1862**
Baumarkt. (GW ISSN 0341-2717) **602**
Baumarkt Tip. (GW ISSN 0723-5062) **602**
Baumaschine - Baugeraet - Baustelle. (AU) **602**
Baumaschine Baugeraet Baustoff *see* Baumaschine - Baugeraet - Baustelle **602**
Baumaschine und Bautechnik *see* B M T **601**
Baumaschinen- und Baugeraete-Handel.(GW ISSN 0005-6715) **602**
Baumaschinentechnik *see* B M T **601**
Baumeister. (GW ISSN 0005-674X) **295**, 602
Baumetall. (GW) **602**
Bauphysik. (GW ISSN 0171-5445) **602**, 3842
Bauplan - Bauorga. (GW ISSN 0938-1694) **603**, 295
Bauplanung - Bautechnik. (GW ISSN 0005-6758) **1862**
Baupraxis-Zeitung. (GW ISSN 0724-7931) **603**
BauR *see* Baurecht **603**
Baurecht. (GW ISSN 0340-7489) **603**, 2604
Baurecht/Droit de la Construction. (SZ) **2604**
Bausoertiment & Holz und Ausbaubedarf *see* B & H **647**
Bauspar-Journal. (GW ISSN 0174-3058) **603**, 2557
Baustatistisches Jahrbuch. (GW ISSN 0084-7739) **637**
Baustein. (GW ISSN 0005-6790) **1249**
Bausteine fuer Eine Soziale Zukunft. (GW) **4429**
Bausteine Grundschule. (GW ISSN 0934-3814) **1682**
Bausteine Kindergarten. (GW ISSN 0173-8585) **1745**, 1233, 1734
Bausteine zur Geschichte des Neuhochdeutschen *see* Bausteine zur Sprachgeschichte des Neuhochdeutschen **2805**
Bausteine zur Sprachgeschichte des Neuhochdeutschen. (GW) **2805**
Baustoff, Recycling und Deponietechnik.(GW ISSN 0178-1510) **1915**, 3016
Baustoff-Technik. (GW ISSN 0721-7854) **603**
Baustoff- und Baubedarfs-Grosshandel. (GW ISSN 0005-6804) **603**
Baustoffe Umschau. (GW) **603**
Baustoffindustrie. (GW ISSN 0232-2765) **603**
Baustoffindustrie. Ausgabe A. Primaerbaustoffe *see* Baustoffindustrie **603**
Baustoffmarkt. (GW ISSN 0005-6448) **603**
Bausubstanz. (GW ISSN 0179-2857) **603**
Bautaetigkeit und Bauvorhaben in der Schweiz/Constructions Executees et Constructions Projetees. (SZ) **637**
Bautechnik. (GW ISSN 0932-8351) **603**
Die Bautechnik. Ausgabe A. (GW ISSN 0341-1052) **1862**
Die Bautechnik. Ausgabe B. (GW ISSN 0340-5044) **1862**
Bautenschutz und Bausanierung. (GW ISSN 0170-9267) **603**, 266, 295
Die Bauverwaltung. (GW ISSN 0005-6847) **603**
Bauwelt. (GW ISSN 0005-6855) **295**
Bauwelt Katalog *see* Bertelsmann Baukatalog **603**
Bauwirtschaft. Ausgabe A. (GW ISSN 0341-3810) **603**
Bauwirtschaft. Ausgabe B. (GW ISSN 0005-6863) **603**
Bauwirtschaft im Zahlenbild. (GW) **603**, 647
Bauwirtschaftliche Informationen *see* B I **601**
Bauzeitung. (GW ISSN 0005-6871) **603**
Das Bauzentrum. (GW ISSN 0005-688X) **295**
Bawl Street Journal. (US) **2859**, 768
Bax Society Bulletin. (UK) **3540**
Baxter. (US) **1072**, 939
Bay and Delta Yachtsman. (US) **4522**
Bay Area Homestyle Resource Magazine. (US) **2548**
Bay Area Parent. (US) **1233**
Bay Area Reporter. (US) **2451**
Bay Area Review Course. Legal Ethics *see* B A R - B R I Bar Review. Professional Responsibility **2603**
Bay County Crier *see* Museum Record **2159**
Bay of Plenty Farmer. (NZ) **78**, 148, 2122
Bay Phil. (US ISSN 8756-5153) **3750**
▼Bay Sports Review. (US) **4466**
Bay State F L Bulletin *see* MA F L A Newsletter **2828**
Bay State Letter *see* Bay State Librarian **2746**
Bay State Librarian. (US ISSN 0005-6944) **2746**
Bay Window. (US) **2222**
Bay Windows. (US) **2451**
Bay Zikh. (IS ISSN 0302-8178) **2898**, 1993
Al-Bayan. (TS) **647**
Bayano. (PN) **3875**
Bayarri Internacional. (SP) **901**
†Bayavaya Uskalos. (CN ISSN 0005-6952) **5146**
Bayer Agrochem Courier. (GW) **170**
†Bayer Agrochem Courier. (UK) **5146**
Bayer Berichte/Bayer Reports. (GW ISSN 0005-6960) **3719**, 1170
Bayer Reports. *see* Bayer Berichte **3719**
Bayer-Symposien. (US ISSN 0067-4672) **3081**
Bayerisch-Schwaebische Wirtschaft. (GW) **808**
Bayerische Akademie der Wissenschaften. Historische Kommission. Schriftenreihe. (GW) **2307**
Bayerische Akademie der Wissenschaften. Jahrbuch. (GW ISSN 0084-6090) **4301**
Bayerische Akademie der Wissenschaften. Mathematisch-Naturwissenschaftliche Klasse. Abhandlungen. (GW ISSN 0005-6995) **4301**
Bayerische Akademie der Wissenschaften. Mathematisch-Naturwissenschaftliche Klasse. Sitzungberichte. (GW ISSN 0340-7586) **4301**, 3031
Bayerische Akademie der Wissenschaften. Philosophisch-Historische Klasse. Abhandlungen, N.F. (GW ISSN 0005-710X) **2503**, 4301
Bayerische Akademie der Wissenschaften. Philosophisch-Historische Klasse. Sitzungberichte. (GW ISSN 0342-5991) **2503**, 4301
Bayerische Blaetter fuer Stenographie. (GW ISSN 0005-7010) **1057**

Bayerische Boerse in Muenchen. Amtliches Kursblatt. (GW ISSN 0005-7029) **939**
Bayerische Botanische Gesellschaft. Berichte. (GW ISSN 0373-7640) **496**
Bayerische Buergermeister. (GW ISSN 0723-7022) **4054**
Bayerische Denkmalpflege. Jahrbuch. (GW ISSN 0341-9150) **318**
Bayerische Gemeindezeitung. (GW ISSN 0005-7045) **2188**
Bayerische Hausbesitzer-Zeitung. (GW) **4145**
Das Bayerische Inn-Oberland. (GW) **2351**
Bayerische Kommission fuer die Internationale Erdmessung. Veroeffentlichungen. (GW ISSN 0340-7691) **2243**
Das Bayerische Kraftfahrzeughandwerk. (GW ISSN 0005-7061) **4685**
Bayerische Krippenfreund. (GW ISSN 0005-707X) **4164**, **2052**
Bayerische Landjugend. (GW) **1233**
Die Bayerische Realschule. (GW) **1745**
Bayerische Staatsbibliothek. Jahresbericht. (GW ISSN 0342-0221) **2746**
Bayerische Staatsbibliothek. New Contents Slavistics. Inhaltsverzeichnisse Slavistischer Zeitschriften - ISZ. (GW ISSN 0173-6388) **390**, **2805**, **2898**
Bayerische Staatsbibliothek. Osteuropa-Neuerwerbungen. (GW) **390**
Bayerische Staatsgemaeldesammlungen. Jahresbericht. (GW) **318**
†Bayerische Staatsregierung. Grenzlandbericht. (GW) **5146**
Bayerische Staatssammlung fuer Palaeontologie und Historische Geologie. Mitteilungen. (GW ISSN 0077-2070) **3656**, **1555**
Bayerische Vereinsbank AG Euroletter see B V - Euroletter **760**
Bayerische Verwaltungsblaetter. (GW ISSN 0522-5337) **2604**, **4054**
Bayerische Vorgeschichtsblaetter. (GW ISSN 0341-3918) **2351**
Bayerischen Oberlandesgerichte. Entscheidungen in Strafsachen. (GW) **2604**
Bayerischen Oberlandesgerichte. Entscheidungen in Zivilsachen. (GW) **2701**
Bayerischer Einzelhandel. (GW) **833**
Bayerischer Landesverein fuer Familienkunde. Blaetter. (GW ISSN 0005-7118) **2145**
Bayerischer Lehrer und Lehrerinnen Verband Bayerische Schule see B L L V Bayerische Schule **1617**
Bayerischer Monatsspiegel. (GW) **3875**, **647**
Bayerischer Musikrat e.V. Correspondenz see B M R - Correspondenz **3540**
Bayerischer Waldbesitzerverband. (GW ISSN 0177-5375) **2096**
Bayerisches Aerzteblatt. (GW ISSN 0005-7126) **3081**
Bayerisches Bienen-Blatt. (GW ISSN 0724-8857) **78**
Bayerisches Forstdienst-Taschenbuch. (GW ISSN 0067-4710) **2096**
Bayerisches Jahrbuch. (GW) **4084**
Bayerisches Jahrbuch fuer Volkskunde. (GW ISSN 0067-4729) **2052**, **1993**
Bayerisches Justizministerialblatt. (GW ISSN 0005-7142) **2604**
Bayerisches Landesamt fuer Statistik und Datenverarbeitung. Zeitschrift - Bayern in Zahlen. (GW) **4564**
Bayerisches Landwirtschaftliches Jahrbuch. (GW ISSN 0005-7150) **78**
Bayerisches Landwirtschaftliches Wochenblatt. (GW ISSN 0005-7169) **78**
Bayerisches Raiffeisenblatt. (GW) **829**
Bayerisches Sonntagsblatt fuer die Katholische Familie. (GW ISSN 0005-7177) **4256**, **2052**, **2188**
Bayerisches Staatsministerium des Innern. Allgemeines Ministerialblatt. (GW ISSN 0934-6465) **4054**

Bayerisches Staatsministerium des Innern. Ministerialamtsblatt der Bayerischen Innern Verwaltung see Bayerisches Staatsministerium des Innern. Allgemeines Ministerialblatt **4054**
Bayerisches Staatsministerium fuer Unterricht und Kultus. Amtsblatt. (GW ISSN 0005-7207) **1618**
Bayerisches Zahnaerzteblatt see B Z B **3228**
Bayern in Zahlen see Bayerisches Landesamt fuer Statistik und Datenverarbeitung. Zeitschrift - Bayern in Zahlen **4564**
Bayern Metall. (GW) **1927**, **3403**
Bayern Tennis. (GW ISSN 0342-8915) **4501**
Bayern Zeitung. (GW) **4753**
Bayerns Pferde Zucht und Sport. (GW ISSN 0174-0512) **4532**
Bayernspiegel. (GW) **2188**
Bayernsport. (GW) **4466**
Bayernturner. (GW ISSN 0005-7231) **4466**
Bayerwald. (GW) **2351**
Bayi Dianying/August 1st Films. (CC) **3504**
Baylor Dental Journal. (US ISSN 0005-7258) **3229**
Baylor Geological Studies Bulletin. (US ISSN 0005-7266) **1555**
Baylor Law Review. (US ISSN 0005-7274) **2604**
Baylor Medicine. (US) **3081**
Baylor Progress. (US) **2459**, **3081**
Bayou Bengal. (US) **1304**
Bayou Talk. (US) **1993**
Bayreuther Beitraege zur Sprachwissenschaft. (GW ISSN 0721-4383) **2805**
Bayreuther Beitraege zur Sprachwissenschaft. Dialektologie. (GW ISSN 0721-8923) **2805**
Bayreuther Gemeindeblatt. (GW ISSN 0005-7282) **4230**
Bayreuther Pauke. (GW) **1249**
Baystate Business Magazine. (US) **647**
Bazak Guide to Spain. (IS) **4753**
Bazmavep. (IT) **2428**, **2805**, **2898**, **3762**
De Bazuin. (NE ISSN 0005-7312) **4164**
†Be Safe at Home/Wees Veilig Tuis. (SA) **5146**
▼Be Somebody, Be Yourself Letter. (US) **2988**
Beach Conservation. (AT ISSN 0313-7872) **1484**, **1602**, **1862**, **1944**
†Beach Culture. (US) **5146**
Beach 'N Waves. (US) **4542**
Beacon see Cityscape **1307**
Beacon. (GW ISSN 0005-7347) **2805**
Beacon. (CN ISSN 0382-6384) **4280**
Beacon (Georgia). (US) **1618**, **2805**
Beacon (Iowa). (US) **3213**
The Beacon (Miami Shores). (US) **3593**, **3668**, **3762**
Beacon (New York). (US ISSN 0005-7339) **3762**, **3668**, **4164**
Beacon House Bulletin see Mental Health Matters **4035**
The Beacon Review. (US) **2270**
Beaconette. (GW ISSN 0005-7363) **2805**
Bead Forum. (CN ISSN 0829-8726) **2563**, **235**, **266**, **2433**
Beads. (CN ISSN 0843-5499) **2563**, **236**, **266**, **2433**
Beads of Truth. (US) **4280**
Beaken. (NE ISSN 0005-738X) **2805**, **2351**, **2898**
Beale's Letter. (CN ISSN 0315-0917) **1072**
Beale's Resource Industry Newsletter see Beale's Letter **1072**
Beam. (GW ISSN 0722-0421) **1369**
Beam. see Aktines **4161**
Beam Modification of Materials. (NE) **3852**, **1927**, **3815**
Beamte Heute. (GW ISSN 0933-0615) **2580**
Beamte im Lande Bremen see D B B Nachrichten fuer den Oeffentlichen Dienst **4058**
Der Beamte in der Bundesanstalt fuer Arbeit. (GW) **2580**

Der Beamte in Rheinland-Pfalz. (GW ISSN 0005-741X) **4054**
†Bean Commission Journal. (US) **5146**
Bean Home Newsletter. (US ISSN 0882-4428) **2898**, **417**
Bean Improvement Cooperative. Annual Report. (US ISSN 0084-7747) **170**
Bean Newsletter see Hojas de Frijol **96**
Bean Program Annual Report. (CK) **78**
Bean Stalk. (US) **2145**
Beans see Bean Program Annual Report **78**
†Bear Flag Republic. (US) **5146**
Bear News. (US ISSN 0885-615X) **1484**, **1944**
Bear Report. (US) **4501**
Beards & Spurs. (US) **4542**
Beat (Highland). (US) **3540**
The Beat (Los Angeles). (US) **3540**, **1993**
Beat Scene. (UK) **2988**
Beatlefan. (US ISSN 0274-6905) **3541**
Beatles Book. (UK ISSN 0261-1600) **3541**
Beatles Visie. (NE) **3541**
Beato Angelo. (IT ISSN 0005-7436) **4256**
Beats Magazine. (US) **3541**
Beau. (US) **3395**, **2451**
Beaufortia. (NE ISSN 0067-4745) **579**
Beauties of Slovakia. see Krasy Slovenska **2184**
Beautiful British Columbia Magazine. (CN ISSN 0005-7460) **4753**
†Beautiful British Columbia Magazine's Guidebook. (CN ISSN 0838-1895) **5146**
Beautiful Doe. see Goo Maral **373**
†Beautiful Glass for Home & Office. (US ISSN 1043-5468) **5146**
Beautiful Homes. (US ISSN 1046-6312) **295**, **2548**
Beautiful Kimono. see Utsukushii-Kimono **1295**
Beauty. (GW ISSN 0932-7398) **375**
Beauty Age. (US ISSN 0887-414X) **375**
Beauty Care Supply Guide. (GW) **372**
Beauty Counter. (UK) **375**
Beauty Counter and Perfumery and Toiletries Buyer see Beauty Counter **375**
Beauty Education. (US ISSN 1052-4169) **372**
Beauty Fashion. (US) **372**
Beauty Handbook Magazine. (US) **372**
†Beauty Product Marketing. (US) **5146**
Beauty Salon see Health & Beauty Salon **373**
Beaux Arts Magazine. (FR ISSN 0757-2271) **318**
Beaver. (UK ISSN 0005-7525) **1304**
The Beaver. (CN ISSN 0005-7517) **2176**
Beaverbrook Art Gallery see Tableau **3533**
Beaverbrook Art Gallery. Annual Report.(CN) **3522**
Bebidas. (US ISSN 0005-7533) **378**
Beboerbladet. (DK) **2483**
Bebop Drawing Club Book. (US) **318**, **1993**, **2898**
Beckett Baseball Card Monthly. (US ISSN 0886-0599) **2433**, **4501**
Beckett Basketball Monthly. (US ISSN 1055-8179) **2433**, **4501**
Beckett Circle/Cercle de Beckett. (US ISSN 0732-2224) **2898**
Beckett Focus on Future Stars. (US ISSN 1060-2801) **2433**, **4466**
Beckett Football Card Monthly. (US ISSN 1055-2294) **2433**, **4501**
Beckett Hockey Monthly. (US ISSN 1058-5958) **2434**, **4466**
Beckman Center News see Beckman Center News and Other Library News **1170**
Beckman Center News and Other Library News. (US) **1170**, **2400**
Beckman Report. (GW ISSN 0005-755X) **2521**
Becoming. (AT) **4164**, **1993**
Bectis Bulletin. (UK ISSN 0308-8537) **2746**, **2792**
†Bed & Breakfast Guest. (US) **5146**

BEEHIVE HISTORY 5967

Bed and Breakfast Guestletter see Bed & Breakfast Guest **5146**
Bed and Breakfast in Britain. (UK ISSN 0267-3436) **4753**
Bed and Breakfast in South and Southwest England see Bed and Breakfast in Britain **4753**
Bed and Breakfast in Wales, Northern England and Scotland see Bed and Breakfast in Britain **4753**
Bed & Breakfast North America. (US) **4753**
Bed & Breakfast Shoptalk see B & B Shoptalk **4753**
Bed & Breakfast Stops. (UK ISSN 0267-3363) **4753**
Bed and Breakfast U S A. (US) **4753**
†Bed & Breakfast Update. (US ISSN 0887-7505) **5147**
Bed, Breakfast & Evening Meal. (UK) **4753**
Bedding see BedTimes **2557**
Bedford Historical Quarterly. (US) **2400**
Bedford Institute of Oceanography. Biennial Review see Bedford Institute of Oceanography. Science Review **1602**
Bedford Institute of Oceanography. Review see Bedford Institute of Oceanography. Science Review **1602**
Bedford Institute of Oceanography. Science Review. (CN) **1602**
Bedfordshire and Huntingdonshire Farmer. (UK) **78**
Bedfordshire County Bowling Association. Handbook. (UK) **4501**
Bedfordshire Historical Record Society. Publications. (UK ISSN 0067-4826) **2351**
†Bedfordshire Life. (UK) **5147**
Bedfordshire Magazine. (UK ISSN 0005-7592) **2351**
Bedriftsoekonomisk Informasjon see Oekonomisk Rapport **1082**
Bedrijf Industrial Digest. see Usine **1086**
Bedrijfschap voor de Lederwarenindustrie. Jaarverslag. (NE ISSN 0067-4834) **2736**
Bedrijfsdocumentaire. (NE) **1003**
Bedrijfsontwikkeling see Agrarische Voorlichting **69**
Bedrijfsontwikkeling. Editie Akkerbouw see Agrarische Voorlichting **69**
Bedrijfsontwikkeling. Editie Tuinbouw see Agrarische Voorlichting **69**
Bedrijfsontwikkeling. Editie Veehouderij see Agrarische Voorlichting **69**
Bedrijfsuitkomsten in de Landbouw. (NE ISSN 0921-4097) **148**
Bedrijfsuitkomsten in de Nederlandse Particuliere Bosbouw. (NE ISSN 0921-4275) **2096**
Bedroom. (US ISSN 0273-7469) **2557**, **1034**
Bedrooms & Baths. (US) **2548**
Bedside Specialist see Care Connection **3277**
†Bedsitter. (UK ISSN 0005-7673) **5147**
Det Bedste fra Reader's Digest (Danish Edition). (DK ISSN 0005-7681) **2185**
BedTimes. (US ISSN 0893-5556) **2557**
Beduin. (II ISSN 0005-769X) **2898**
Bee Craft. (UK ISSN 0005-7703) **78**
Bee World. (UK ISSN 0005-772X) **78**
Beebug. (UK ISSN 0263-7561) **1458**, **1467**
Beech Grove. (US) **2145**
Beecham Society Bulletin see Le Petit Baton **5257**
Beecham Society Newsletter see Le Petit Baton **5257**
Beef. (US ISSN 0005-7738) **212**
Beef Bulletin. (US) **212**
Beef Business Bulletin. (US) **212**
Beef Extra see Beef Today **212**
Beef in B C. (CN) **212**
Beef Roundup. (US) **212**
Beef Today. (US) **212**
Beefmaster Cowman. (US ISSN 0194-4282) **212**
†Beefmaster Times. (US) **5147**
Beefweek. (US) **212**
Beehive History. (US) **2400**

5968 BEEKEEPING

Beekeeping. (UK ISSN 0005-7754) 78
Beeldenaar. (NE ISSN 0165-8654) 3598
Beeline. (RH) 78
Beeline Books. (US) 3396
Be'emmet. (IS ISSN 0334-973X) 2898, 1249
Beer Can Collectors News Report. (US) 2434, 378
Beer Industry Update. (US) 378
Beer Marketer's Insights. (US ISSN 0300-7480) 378, 2604
†Beer Marketing Management. (US ISSN 0734-970X) 5147
Beer-Sheva. (IS ISSN 0334-2255) 4221, 2428
Beer Statistics News. (US) 378, 4564
Beer Wholesaler. (US ISSN 0005-7770) 378
Beermat Magazine. (UK ISSN 0306-7912) 2434
Beet Sugar Industries. see Tiancai Tangye 124
Beethoven-Jahrbuch. (GW ISSN 0522-5949) 3541
Beethoven Newsletter. (US ISSN 0898-6185) 3541
Beetle. (CN) 3541
Le Beffroi. (CN ISSN 0832-9966) 3762, 2898
Befolkningen i Koebenhavn i Januar. (DK ISSN 0107-5071) 4564
Befolkningen i Kommunerne/ Populations of Municipalities. (DK ISSN 0108-8076) 3991
†Befolkningens Forbrug af Psykiatriske Sengepladser. (DK ISSN 0107-4156) 5147
Before & After. (US) 3997
Before College see B C 5145
Before You Build. (SA) 603, 295
BeFriending Creation. (US ISSN 1050-0332) 4164, 1484
Bega District News. (AT) 2171, 28, 4466
Begegnen und Helfen. (GW ISSN 0171-9319) 4399
Begegnung und Austausch mit Franzosen. (GW) 3951, 1249
Beginners Please see Investing for Beginners 950
†Beginning (Iowa City). (US ISSN 0739-6694) 5147
Beginning (Nashville). (US ISSN 0198-6201) 4230
Beginnings (New York). (US) 3319, 4838
Beginnings (Raleigh). (US) 3276, 4838
Begonian. (US ISSN 0096-8684) 2122, 496
Begriffsbestimmungen fuer die Bundesstatistiken der Oesterreichische Elektrizitaetswirtschaft. (AU ISSN 0520-9048) 4054, 1883
Le Begue. (BE) 2898
Begum. (BG) 4838
Behandeling Verpakkingen. see Manutention Emballages 3649
The Behavior Analyst. (US ISSN 0738-6729) 4012
Behavior and Information Technology. (UK ISSN 0144-929X) 4012, 4458
Behavior and Philosophy. (US) 4012
Behavior Genetics. (US ISSN 0001-8244) 540, 3081
▼Behavior, Health, and Aging. (US ISSN 1049-085X) 2270
Behavior Improvement News. (US) 4012, 1003
Behavior Modification. (US ISSN 0145-4455) 4013
Behavior Research Methods, Instruments, and Computers. (US ISSN 0743-3808) 4013
Behavior Science Research. (US ISSN 0094-3673) 4366
Behavior Therapist. (US) 4013
Behavior Therapy. (US ISSN 0005-7894) 4013
Behavior Today. (US ISSN 0005-7924) 4013, 236, 4429
Behavioral and Brain Sciences. (UK ISSN 0140-525X) 4013, 430, 3331
Behavioral and Neural Biology. (US ISSN 0163-1047) 430, 4013
Behavioral & Social Sciences Librarian. (US ISSN 0163-9269) 2746
Behavioral Assessment. (US ISSN 0191-5401) 4013
Behavioral Brain Research. (NE ISSN 0166-4328) 3331
Behavioral Disorders Journal. (US ISSN 0198-7429) 1734
▼Behavioral Ecology. (US ISSN 1045-2249) 430
Behavioral Ecology and Sociobiology. (GW ISSN 0340-5443) 1944, 4013
Behavioral Educator. (US) 1745, 4013
Behavioral Medicine. (US) 4013, 3331
Behavioral Medicine Abstracts see Annals of Behavioral Medicine 3076
Behavioral Medicine Update see Annals of Behavioral Medicine 3076
Behavioral Neurology. (UK ISSN 0953-4180) 3331
Behavioral Neuropsychiatry. (US ISSN 0005-7932) 3331, 4013
Behavioral Neuroscience. (US ISSN 0735-7044) 4013, 3331
Behavioral Residential Treatment. (UK ISSN 0884-5581) 3331
Behavioral Science. (US ISSN 0005-7940) 4359
Behavioral Sciences and the Law. (UK ISSN 0735-3936) 4013, 2604
Behavioral Sciences Newsletter. (US ISSN 0361-4646) 4013, 1003
Behaviormetrika. (JA ISSN 0385-7417) 4051
Behaviorometric. (II) 4366
Behaviour. (NE ISSN 0005-7959) 579
†Behaviour. Supplements. (NE ISSN 0169-7544) 5147
Behaviour & Health. see Gedrag & Gezondheid 4022
Behaviour Research and Therapy. (US ISSN 0005-7967) 4013
†Behavioural Approaches with Children. (UK ISSN 0262-4109) 5147
▼Behavioural Pharmacology. (UK ISSN 0955-8810) 3719, 4013
Behavioural Processes. (NE ISSN 0376-6357) 3331
Behavioural Psychotherapist. (UK) 4013
Behavioural Psychotherapy. (UK ISSN 0141-3473) 4013
Beheer en Onderhoud. (NE) 4145
†Behind Small Business. (US) 5147
Behind the Headlines. (CN ISSN 0005-7983) 3951, 2307
Behind the Scenes. see Paraskino 2184
Behind the Scenes see The Theatre Listing 4641
Behinderte Kind see Deutsche Behindertenzeitschrift 3093
Behindertenhilfe Durch Erziehung, Unterricht und Therapie. (GW ISSN 0171-9718) 1734
Behindertenpaedagogik. (GW ISSN 0341-7301) 1734, 2283
Behindertenpaedagogik in Bayern. (GW) 1734
Behindertensport/Sport-Handicap. (SZ) 3370
Behindertenzeitschrift see Deutsche Behindertenzeitschrift 3093
Behoerden Spiegel. (GW) 4085
Behoerden und Organisationen der Land- Forst- und Ernaehrungswirtschaft. (GW ISSN 0522-604X) 78
Behring Institute Mitteilungen. (GW ISSN 0301-0457) 1170
Behuising in Suid-Afrika. see Housing in South Africa 2488
Behuisingsnavorsingsoorsig. see Housing Research Review 2488
Bei Uns. (AU ISSN 0005-8009) 973
Die Beiden Tuerme. (GW) 4164, 2351
Beiersdorf Journal. (GW) 1072
Beifang Guoshu/Northern Fruit Trees. (CC ISSN 1001-5698) 170
Beifang Huanjing/Northern Environment. (CC) 1944
Beifang Jiaotong Daxue Xuebao/North Communications University. Journal. (CC ISSN 1000-1506) 1332
Beifang Luncong/Northern Forum. (CC ISSN 1000-3541) 2503
Beifang Qiyi/Northern Chess. (CC ISSN 1000-7679) 4466
Beifang Wenwu/Relics of North China. (CC ISSN 1001-0483) 266
Beifang Wenxue/Northern Literature. (CC ISSN 0476-031X) 2898
Beifang Yinyue/Northern Music. (CC) 3541
Beifang Yuanyi/North Gardening. (CC ISSN 1001-0009) 2122
Beihefte der Bonner Jahrbuecher. (GW ISSN 0067-4893) 318
Beihefte Paedagogik. (GW ISSN 0479-1363) 1618
Beihefte zur Internationalen Wissenschaftlichen Korrespondenz zur Geschichte der Deutschen Arbeiterbewegung. (GW ISSN 0342-3875) 973
Beihefte zur Theologischen Zeitschrift see Sonderbaende zur Theologischen Zeitschrift 4202
Beihefte zur Wiener Zeitschrift fuer die Kunde des Morgenlandes. (AU ISSN 0259-0654) 3634, 2337
Beiji Guang/Northern Lights. (CC) 2898
Beijing Accounting. see Beijing Caikuai 747
Beijing Aeronautic and Astronautic University. Journal. see Beijing Hangkong Hangtian Daxue Xuebao 48
Beijing Agricultural Science. see Beijing Nongye Kexue 79
Beijing Agriculture. see Beijing Nongye 79
Beijing Caikuai/Beijing Accounting. (CC) 747
Beijing Caimao Xueyuan Xuebao/Beijing Institute of Finance and Trade. Journal. (CC) 647
Beijing Daxue Xuebao (Zhexue Shehui Kexue Ban)/Beijing University. Journal (Social Science Edition). (CC ISSN 1000-5919) 2503
Beijing Daxue Xuebao (Ziran Kexue Ban)/Beijing University. Journal (Natural Science Edition). (CC ISSN 0479-8023) 4301
Beijing Education. see Beijing Jiaoyu 1618
Beijing Fangdichan/Beijing Real Estate. (CC) 4145
Beijing Fangzhi/Beijing Textile. (CC ISSN 1002-3348) 4617
Beijing Film Studio Pictorial. see Beijing Huabao 3504
Beijing Gangtie Jishu Daxue Xuebao. see Beijing University of Iron and Steel Technology. Journal 3403
Beijing Golf Club News. (JA) 4501
Beijing Gongren/Beijing Workers. (CC) 2580
Beijing Gongshang Guanli/Beijing Industrial and Commercial Management. (CC) 1003
Beijing Hangkong Hangtian Daxue Xuebao/Beijing Aeronautic and Astronautic University. Journal. (CC ISSN 1001-5965) 48
Beijing Industrial and Commercial Management. see Beijing Gongshang Guanli 1003
Beijing Informa see Beijing Review 2181
Beijing Institute of Finance and Trade. Journal. see Beijing Caimao Xueyuan Xuebao 647
Beijing Institute of Posts and Telecommunications. Journal. see Beijing Youdian Xueyuan Xuebao 1332
Beijing Institute of Traditional Chinese Medicine. Journal. see Beijing Zhongyi Xueyuan Xuebao 3081
Beijing Jiaoyu/Beijing Education. (CC ISSN 1000-7997) 1618
Beijing Keji Daxue Xuebao/Beijing University of Science and Technology. Journal. (CC) 4301
Beijing Ligong Daxue Xuebao/Beijing University of Science and Engineering. Journal. (CC ISSN 1001-0645) 4301
Beijing Linye Daxue Xuebao/Beijing University of Forestry. Journal. (CC ISSN 1000-1522) 2096
Beijing Literature. see Beijing Wenxue 2898
Beijing Medical Sciences. see Beijing Yixue 3081
Beijing Nongye/Beijing Agriculture. (CC ISSN 1000-6966) 79
Beijing Nongye Daxue Xuebao/Beijing University of Agriculture. Journal. (CC ISSN 0479-8007) 79
Beijing Nongye Gongcheng Daxue Xuebao/Beijing University of Agricultural Engineering. Journal. (CC ISSN 1000-1514) 79
Beijing Nongye Kexue/Beijing Agricultural Science. (CC) 79
Beijing Normal Institute. Journal (Natural Science Edition). see Beijing Shifan Xueyuan Xuebao (Ziran Kexue Ban) 4301
Beijing Normal Institute. Journal (Social Science Edition). see Beijing Shifan Xueyuan Xuebao (Shehui Kexue Ban) 4367
Beijing Normal University. Journal (Natural Science Edition). see Beijing Shifan Daxue Xuebao (Ziran Kexue Ban) 4301
Beijing Normal University. Journal (Social Science Edition). see Beijing Shifan Daxue Xuebao (She Ke Ban) 4366
Beijing Real Estate. see Beijing Fangdichan 4145
Beijing Review. (CC ISSN 1000-9140) 2181
Beijing Rundschau see Beijing Review 2181
Beijing Shehui Kexue/Beijing Social Sciences. (CC) 4366
Beijing Shifan Daxue Xuebao (She Ke Ban)/Beijing Normal University. Journal (Social Science Edition). (CC) 4366
Beijing Shifan Daxue Xuebao (Ziran Kexue Ban)/Beijing Normal University. Journal (Natural Science Edition). (CC ISSN 0476-0301) 4301
Beijing Shifan Xueyuan Xuebao (Shehui Kexue Ban)/Beijing Normal Institute. Journal (Social Science Edition). (CC) 4367
Beijing Shifan Xueyuan Xuebao (Ziran Kexue Ban)/Beijing Normal Institute. Journal (Natural Science Edition). (CC) 4301
Beijing Social Sciences. see Beijing Shehui Kexue 4366
Beijing Textile. see Beijing Fangzhi 4617
Beijing Traditional Chinese Medicine. see Beijing Zhongyi 3081
Beijing University. Journal (Natural Science Edition). see Beijing Daxue Xuebao (Ziran Kexue Ban) 4301
Beijing University. Journal (Social Science Edition). see Beijing Daxue Xuebao (Zhexue Shehui Kexue Ban) 2503
Beijing University of Agricultural Engineering. Journal. see Beijing Nongye Gongcheng Daxue Xuebao 79
Beijing University of Agriculture. Journal. see Beijing Nongye Daxue Xuebao 79
Beijing University of Forestry. Journal. see Beijing Linye Daxue Xuebao 2096
Beijing University of Iron and Steel Technology. Journal/Beijing Gangtie Jishu Daxue Xuebao. (CC ISSN 0476-0255) 3403
Beijing University of Medical Sciences. Journal. see Beijing Yike Daxue Xuebao 3081
Beijing University of Science and Engineering. Journal. see Beijing Ligong Daxue Xuebao 4301
Beijing University of Science and Technology. Journal. see Beijing Keji Daxue Xuebao 4301

Beijing Wenxue/Beijing Literature. (CC ISSN 0257-0262) **2898**
Beijing Workers. *see* Beijing Gongren **2580**
Beijing Yike Daxue Xuebao/Beijing University of Medical Sciences. Journal. (CC ISSN 1000-1530) **3081**
Beijing Yixue/Beijing Medical Sciences. (CC ISSN 0253-9713) **3081**
Beijing Youdian Xueyuan Xuebao/Beijing Institute of Posts and Telecommunications. Journal. (CC ISSN 1000-5145) **1332**
Beijing Zhibu Shenghuo. (CC) **3875**
Beijing Zhongyi/Beijing Traditional Chinese Medicine. (CC ISSN 0476-0247) **3081**
Beijing Zhongyi Xueyuan Xuebao/Beijing Institute of Traditional Chinese Medicine. Journal. (CC ISSN 0258-8811) **3081**
Beijing Zhoubao *see* Beijing Review **2181**
Beilage Wirtschaftsrechtliche Blaetter *see* Juristische Blaetter **2641**
Beilsteins Handbuch der Organischen Chemie. Supplement. (US ISSN 0067-4915) **1216**
Being Parents. *see* Ser Padres **4852**
▼Beirut Review. (LE) **3951**, 847, 2428, 3634
Beiruter Texte und Studien. (GW ISSN 0067-4931) **2428**
Beispiele. (GW ISSN 0175-2723) **1745**
Beitraege Archaeologie des Romischen Rheinlands. (GW ISSN 0341-910X) **266**
Beitraege aus der Plasmaphysik *see* Contributions to Plasma Physics **3816**
Beitraege fuer die Forstwirtschaft. (GW ISSN 0323-4673) **2096**
Beitraege zu Infusionstherapie. (SZ ISSN 1011-6974) **3081**
Beitraege zu Infusionstherapie und Klin. Ernaehrung *see* Beitraege zu Infusionstherapie **3081**
Beitraege Zum Auslaendischen Oeffentlichen Recht und Voelkerrecht.(US ISSN 0172-4770) **2720**
Beitraege zum Buch- und Bibliothekswesen. (GW ISSN 0408-8107) **2746**
Beitraege zum Deutschstudium *see* Faustchen **2813**
Beitraege zum Universitaetsrecht. (AU) **2604**
Beitraege zur Aegyptischen Bauforschung und Altertumskunde. (GW ISSN 0170-3218) **2331**
Beitraege zur Afrikakunde. (SZ ISSN 0171-1660) **2331**, 236
Beitraege zur Alexander-von Humboldt-Forschung. (GW ISSN 0232-1556) **4301**
Beitraege zur Algebra und Geometrie. (GW ISSN 0138-4821) **3031**
Beitraege zur Arbeitsmarkt- und Berufsforschung. (GW ISSN 0173-6574) **3624**
Beitraege zur Archaeologie *see* Technische Beitraege zur Archaeologie **5288**
Beitraege zur Archaeologie des Mittelalters. (GW ISSN 0341-9185) **266**
Beitraege zur Bach-Forschung. (GW ISSN 0233-0105) **3541**
Beitraege zur Biologie der Pflanzen. (GW ISSN 0005-8041) **496**
Beitraege zur Deutschen Philologie. (GW) **2805**, 2898
Beitraege zur Entomologie/ Contributions to Entomology. (GW ISSN 0005-805X) **529**
Beitraege zur Erforschung der Deutschen Sprache *see* Beitraege zur Geschichte der Deutschen Sprache und Literatur **2805**
Beitraege zur Forschungstechnologie. (GW ISSN 0323-5130) **4301**, 4594
Beitraege zur Geographie. (GW ISSN 0138-4422) **2243**, 1944
Beitraege zur Gerichtlichen Medizin. (AU ISSN 0067-5016) **3264**

Beitraege zur Geschichte der Arbeiterbewegung. (GW ISSN 0005-8068) **3875**, 2307
Beitraege zur Geschichte der Carolo-Wilhelmina. (GW) **2351**
Beitraege zur Geschichte der Deutschen Sprache und Literatur. (GW ISSN 0005-8076) **2805**, 2898
Beitraege zur Geschichte der Pharmazie *see* Geschichte der Pharmazie **3727**
Beitraege zur Geschichte der Philosophie und Theologie des Mittelalters. Neue Folge. (GW ISSN 0067-5024) **3762**, 4164
Beitraege zur Geschichte der Reichskirche in der Neuzeit. (GW ISSN 0408-8344) **2351**
Beitraege zur Geschichte der Universitaet Erfurt (1392-1816) *see* Beitraege zur Hochschul- und Wissenschaftsgeschichte Erfurts **2351**
Beitraege zur Geschichte der Universitaet Mainz. (GW ISSN 0408-8379) **2351**
Beitraege zur Geschichte der Wissenschaft und der Technik. (GW ISSN 0522-6570) **4301**
Beitraege zur Geschichte des Alten Moenchtums und des Benediktinerordens. (GW ISSN 0342-1341) **4164**
Beitraege zur Geschichte des Bistums Regensburg. (GW) **4164**
Beitraege zur Geschichte des Parlamentarismus und der Politischen Parteien. (GW ISSN 0522-6643) **3875**
†Beitraege zur Geschichte des Rundfunks. (GW ISSN 0138-113X) **5147**
Beitraege zur Geschichte Thueringens. (GW) **4367**
Beitraege zur Geschichte und Kultur der Stadt Nuernberg. (GW ISSN 0078-2785) **2351**
Beitraege zur Gesellschafts- und Bildungspolitik. (GW) **4367**
Beitraege zur Harmonikalen Grundlagenforschung. (AU ISSN 0067-5067) **3541**
Beitraege zur Heimatkunde der Stadt Schwelm und ihrer Umgebung. (GW) **2351**
Beitraege zur Hochschul- und Wissenschaftsgeschichte Erfurts. (GW ISSN 0233-2930) **2351**
Beitraege zur Hochschulforschung. (GW ISSN 0171-645X) **1701**
Beitraege zur Hydrologie. (GW ISSN 0343-0987) **1597**, 1923, 2243, 4822
Beitraege zur Individualpsychologie. (GW) **4013**
Beitraege zur Inkunabelkunde. Dritte Folge. (GW ISSN 0067-5091) **4121**, 2746
Beitraege zur Intensiv- und Notfallmedizin. (SZ ISSN 0254-8275) **3081**
Beitraege zur Japanologie. (AU ISSN 0522-6759) **3634**, 2317
Beitraege zur Jazzforschung/Studies in Jazz Research. (AU) **3541**
Beitraege zur Kinderpsychotherapie. (GW ISSN 0067-5105) **3319**
Beitraege zur Klassischen Philologie. (GW) **2805**
Beitraege zur Kolonial und Ueberseegeschichte. (GW ISSN 0522-6848) **2351**
Beitraege zur Kommunikationswissenschaft und Medienforschung. (GW ISSN 1332-2567
†Beitraege zur Konfliktforschung. (GW ISSN 0045-169X) **5147**
†Beitraege zur Kritik der Buergerlichen Ideologie und des Revisionismus. (GW ISSN 0232-2803) **5147**
Beitraege zur Kryptogamenflora der Schweiz *see* Cryptogamica Helvetica **500**
Beitraege zur Kunst des Christlichen Ostens. (GW ISSN 0067-5121) **318**
Beitraege zur Landesentwicklung. (GW ISSN 0525-4736) **1484**

Beitraege zur Landeskunde. (GW ISSN 0408-8492) **2351**
Beitraege zur Literatur des 15.-18. Jahrhunderts. (GW ISSN 0170-3315) **2898**
Beitraege zur Luxemburgischen Sprach- und Volkskunde. (LU) **2805**
Beitraege zur Meereskunde/ Contributions to Marine Scientific Research. (GW ISSN 0067-5148) **1602**
Beitraege zur Mittelamerikanischen Voelkerkunde. (GW ISSN 0408-8514) **236**
Beitraege zur Namenforschung. (GW ISSN 0005-8114) **2805**
Beitraege zur Nationalsozialistischen Gesundheits- und Sozialpolitik. (GW) **3081**, 2307, 4429
Beitraege zur Naturkunde der Wetterau.(GW ISSN 0721-3468) **430**
Beitraege zur Naturkunde in Osthessen.(GW) **430**, 1555
Beitraege zur Naturkunde Niedersachsens. (GW ISSN 0340-4277) **430**
Beitraege zur Oberpfalzforschung. (GW ISSN 0067-5164) **2351**
Beitraege zur Oekonomischen Forschung. (GW) **647**
Beitraege zur Oekumenischen Theologie.(GW ISSN 0067-5172) **4164**
Beitraege zur Oesterreichischen Statistik. (AU ISSN 0067-2319) **4564**
Beitraege zur Onkologie. *see* Contributions to Oncology **3091**
†Beitraege zur Orthopaedie und Traumatologie. (GW ISSN 0005-8149) **5147**
Beitraege zur Paedagogischen Arbeit. (GW ISSN 0005-8157) **3762**, 1745
Beitraege zur Palaeontologie von Oesterreich. (AU) **3656**
Beitraege zur Phonetik und Linguistik. (GW ISSN 0178-1723) **2805**
Beitraege zur Physik der Atmosphaere. *see* Contributions to Atmospheric Physics **3434**
Beitraege zur Psychodiagnostik des Kindes. (GW ISSN 0340-0123) **4013**
Beitraege zur Psychologie und Soziologie des Kranken Menschen. (GW ISSN 0173-0967) **4013**, 3081, 4429
Beitraege zur Psychopathologie. (US ISSN 0175-5943) **4013**
Beitraege zur Romanischen Philologie des Mittelalters. (GW ISSN 0067-5202) **2898**, 2805
Beitraege zur Rudolf Steiner Gesamtausgabe. (SZ) **4280**
Beitraege zur Schleswiger Stadtgeschichte. (GW ISSN 0405-2161) **2352**
Beitraege zur Schul und Bildungspolitik *see* Blickpunkt Bildung **1725**
Beitraege zur Schwabischen Literatur- und Geistesgeschichte und Mitteilungen des Justinius Kerner-Vereins und Frauenvereins *see* Suevica - Beitraege zur Schwabischen Literatur- und Geistesgeschichte **2966**
Beitraege zur Sexualforschung. (GW ISSN 0067-5210) **4014**
Beitraege zur Sozial- und Wirtschaftsgeschichte. (GW) **2307**
Beitraege zur Sozialgeschichte Bremen. (GW) **2352**, 4367
Beitraege zur Sprachinselforschung. (AU ISSN 0259-0662) **2805**
Beitraege zur Strafvollzugswissenschaft.(GW ISSN 0067-5237) **1510**
Beitraege zur Suedasienforschung. (GW ISSN 0170-3137) **2337**
Beitraege zur Suedosteuropa-Forschung.(GW) **2352**
Beitraege zur Tabakforschung International. (GW ISSN 0173-783X) **4643**
Beitraege zur Theorie und Praxis des Tennisunterrichts und -trainings. (GW ISSN 0723-1407) **4501**

Beitraege zur Tropischen Landwirtschaft und Veterinaermedizin. (GW ISSN 0301-567X) **79**, 4807
Beitraege zur Umweltgestaltung. Reihe A. (GW ISSN 0340-9716) **1944**
Beitraege zur Ur- und Fruehgeschichte der Bezirke Rostock, Schwerin und Neubrandenburg. (GW ISSN 0138-4279) **3522**
Beitraege zur Ur- und Fruehgeschichtlichen Archaeologie des Mittelmeerkulturraumes. (GW ISSN 0067-5245) **266**
Beitraege zur Urgeschichte des Rheinlandes. (GW ISSN 0341-9193) **266**
Beitraege zur Urologie. (SZ ISSN 0250-3212) **3387**
Beitraege zur Vogelkunde. (GW ISSN 0005-8211) **562**
Beitraege zur Westfaelischen Familienforschung. (GW ISSN 0067-5261) **2145**
†Beitraege zur Wirkstofforschung. (GW) **5147**
Beitraege zur Wirtschafts und Sozialgeschichte. (GW ISSN 0723-5453) **2352**
Beitraege zur Wirtschaftspolitik. (SZ ISSN 0522-7216) **889**
Beitraege zur Zeitgeschichte. (GW ISSN 0723-3299) **2307**, 3875
Beiying Huabao/Beijing Film Studio Pictorial. (CC) **3504**
Beiyue Feng. (CC) **2898**
Bekendtgoerelser fra Plantenyhedsnaevnet *see* Meddelelser fra Sortsafproevningen **509**
Bekesi Elet. (HU ISSN 0522-7232) **2352**
Beklaednadsfolket. (SW ISSN 0005-8262) **2580**
Bekleidung und Maschenware. (GW ISSN 0005-8270) **4617**
Bekleidung und Waesche. (GW ISSN 0005-8289) **1283**
Bekleidungs-Industrie (Year). Jahrbuch. (GW) **1283**
Le Belle Age. (CN ISSN 0835-8702) **2270**
Belarus'. (BW ISSN 0320-7544) **2174**
Belaruskaja Carkva. (US ISSN 0005-8327) **4164**, 2307, 4429
Belaruski Dziarzhauny Universitet. Vesnik. Seryia 3; Historyia, Filosofiya, Navukovy Kamunism, Ekanomika, Prava/Belorusskii Gosudarstvennyi Universitet. Vestnik. Seriya 3; Istoriya, Filosofiya, Nauchnyi Kommunizm, Ekonomika, Pravo. (BW ISSN 0321-0359) **2352**
Belaruski Instytut Navukii Mastatstva. Zapisy/Byelorussian Institute of Arts and Sciences. Annals. (US ISSN 0510-3746) **2352**, 1993
Belarusskaya Linhvistika. (BW ISSN 0320-7552) **2805**
Belcher Bulletin. (US) **2145**, 417, 2400
Beleggen met van Lanschot. (NE) **939**
Beleggingsontleders Tydskrif. *see* Investment Analysts Journal **951**
Beleid en Maatschappij. (NE ISSN 0165-1625) **3875**
Beleidsanalyse. (NE ISSN 0166-9222) **4054**
Belfagor. (IT ISSN 0005-8351) **2859**
Belfast and Northern Ireland Directory. (UK ISSN 0067-5342) **1034**
Belfast Gazette. (UK ISSN 0951-0370) **2193**
Belgian - American Chamber of Commerce in the United States. Directory. (US ISSN 0196-7622) **1072**
Belgian American Trade Review. (US) **808**
Belgian Business *see* Belgian Business Magazine **1072**
Belgian Business Magazine. (BE) **1072**
Belgian Chamber of Commerce in Great Britain Journal *see* Belgo-Luxembourg Chamber of Commerce in Great Britain. Journal **808**
Belgian Entomology Journal. *see* Linneana Belgica **536**
Belgian Environmental Research Index. (BE ISSN 0379-1815) **1972**, 3

5970 BELGIAN JOURNAL

Belgian Journal of Food Chemistry and Biotechnology *see* Cerevisia and Biotechnology **489**
Belgian Journal of Zoology. (BE ISSN 0777-6276) **579**
Belgian Knitwear Association. Report. (BE) **2087**
Belgian Review of International Law. *see* Revue Belge de Droit International **2728**
Belgian Trade Review *see* Belgian American Trade Review **808**
Belgicatom. (BE ISSN 0005-8408) **1804,** 1883
Belgie. Ministerie van de Economie. Algemene Directie voor Studien en Documentatie. Centrale Bibliotheek Queteletfonds. Aanwinsten *see* Belgium. Ministere des Affaires Economiques. Bibliotheque Centrale (Fonds Quetelet). Accroissements **390**
Belgiophile. (US) **3750**
Belgisch Centrum voor Landelijke Geschiedenis. Publikaties. *see* Centre Belge d'Histoire Rurale. Publications **2355**
Belgisch Comite voor de Distributie. Speciale Uitgaven. *see* Comite Belge de la Distribution. Editions Speciales **1036**
Belgisch-Nederlands Tijdschrift voor Oppervlaktetechnieken van Metalen *see* Tijdschrift voor Oppervlaktetechnieken en Corrosiebestrijding **3422**
Belgisch Tijdschrift voor Geneeskunde *see* Tijdschrift voor Geneeskunde **3157**
Belgisch Tijdschrift voor Militaire Geschiedenis. *see* Revue Belge d'Histoire Militaire **3470**
Belgisch Tijdschrift voor Muziekwetenschap. *see* Revue Belge de Musicologie **3577**
Belgisch Tijdschrift voor Nieuwste Geschiedenis. *see* Revue Belge d'Histoire Contemporaine **2320**
Belgisch Tijdschrift voor Tandheelkunde *see* Revue Belge de Medecine Dentaire **3242**
Belgisch Ziekenhuis. *see* L'Hopital Belge **2463**
Belgische Bakker. *see* Boulanger Belge **2087**
Belgische Beenhouwerij *see* Boucherie Belge **2062**
Belgische Bibliografie. *see* Bibliographie de Belgique **392**
Belgische Brandtijdschrift *see* N V B B Magazine **2034**
Belgische Cementnijverheid. *see* Industrie Cimentiere Belge **620**
Belgische Economie in (Year). (BE ISSN 0771-7385) **847**
Belgische Fruitrevue. (BE ISSN 0005-8467) **2122**
Belgische Opticien. *see* Opticien Belge **5253**
Belgische Tuinbouw. (BE ISSN 0005-8483) **2122**
Belgische Vereiniging voor Tropische Geneeskunde. Annalen. *see* Societe Belge de Medecine Tropicale. Annales **3223**
Belgische Vereniging voor Geologie. Bulletin. *see* Societe Belge de Geologie. Bulletin **1580**
Belgische Verminkte *see* Invalide Belge **3460**
Belgische Visser *see* Pecheur Belge **2047**
Belgium. Administration de l'Energie. Bulletin Mensuel de l'Energie Electrique. (BE) **1883**
Belgium. Administration de la Marine et de la Navigation Interieure. Rapport Annuel sur l'Evoltuion de la Flotte de Peche *see* Belgium. Administration des Affaires Maritimes et de la Navigation. Rapport Annuel sur l'Evolution de la Flotte de Peche **4724**
Belgium. Administration des Affaires Maritimes et de la Navigation. Rapport Annuel sur l'Evolution de la Flotte de Peche. (BE) **4724**
Belgium. Administration des Eaux et Forets. Station de Recherche des Eaux et Forets. Travaux. Serie D. Hydrobiologie *see* Belgium. Station de Recherches Forestieres et Hydrobiologiques. Travaux. Serie D. Hydrobiologie **430**
Belgium. Administration des Mines. Service: Statistiques. Siderurgie, Houille, Agglomeres, Cokes *see* Belgium. Administration des Mines. Statistiques: Houille, Cokes, Agglomeres Metallurgie, Carrieres **3479**
Belgium. Administration des Mines. Statistiques: Houille, Cokes, Agglomeres Metallurgie, Carrieres. (BE) **3479**
Belgium. Administration Penitentiaire. Bulletin/Belgium. Bestuur Strafinrichtingen. (BE ISSN 0007-4306) **1510**
Belgium. Bestuur Strafinrichtingen. *see* Belgium. Administration Penitentiaire. Bulletin **1510**
Belgium. Centre d'Etude de la Population et de la Famille. Dossiers. (BE) **3979**
Belgium. Centre d'Etude de la Population et de la Famille. Population et Famille. (BE) **3979**
Belgium. Commission Royale des Monuments et des Sites. Bulletin. (BE ISSN 0522-7496) **295,** 266
Belgium. Conseil Superieur des Classes Moyennes. Rapport Annuel du Secretaire General. (BE ISSN 0067-5393) **1113**
Belgium. Cour de Cassation. Bulletin *see* Belgium. Cour de Cassation. Bulletin des Arrets **2604**
Belgium. Cour de Cassation. Bulletin des Arrets. (BE) **2604**
Belgium. Fonds National de la Recherche Scientifique. Listes des Beneficiaires d'une Subvention. *see* Belgium. Nationaal Fonds voor Wetenschappelijk Onderzoek. Lijst der Kredietgenieters **4301**
Belgium. Fonds National de la Recherche Scientifique. Rapport Annuel. *see* Belgium. Nationaal Fonds voor Wetenschappelijk Onderzoek. Jaarverslag **4301**
Belgium. Hoge Raad voor de Middenstand. Jaarverslag van de Secretaris Generaal. (BE) **4054,** 973
Belgium. Institut National d'Assurance Maladie Invalidite. I.N.A.M.I. Bulletin d'Information/Belgium. Rijksinstituut voor Ziekte- en Invaliditeitsverzekering. R.I.Z.I.V. Informatieblad. (BE ISSN 0046-9726) **2527**
Belgium. Institut National d'Assurances Sociales Pour Travailleurs Independants. Rapport Annuel. (BE) **2527**
Belgium. Institut National d'Assurances Sociales pour Travailleurs Independants. Statistiques des Beneficiaires de Prestations de Retraite et de Survie/Belgium. Rijksinstituut voor de Sociale Verzekeringen der Zelfstandigen. Statistiek van de Personen die een Rust- en Overlevingsprestatie Genieten. (BE) **2546**
Belgium. Institut National d'Assurances Sociales pour Travailleurs Independants. Statistique des Enfants Beneficiaires d'Allocations Familiales/Belgium. Rijksinstituut voor de Sociale Verzekeringen der Zelfstandigen. Statistiek van de Kinderen die Recht Geven Op Kinderbijslag. (BE) **2546**
Belgium. Institut National d'Assurances Sociales pour Travailleurs Independants. Statistiques des Personnes Assujetties au Statut Social des Travailleurs Independants/Belgium. Rijksinstituut voor de Sociale Verzekeringen der Zelfstandigen. Statistiek van de Personen die Onder de Toepassing Vallen van het Sociaal Statuut van de Zelfstandigen. (BE) **2546**
Belgium. Institut National de Statistique. Annuaire de Statistiques Regionales. (BE ISSN 0770-0369) **4564**
Belgium. Institut National de Statistique. Annuaire Statistique de Poche. (BE ISSN 0067-5431) **4564**
Belgium. Institut National de Statistique. Annuaire Statistique de l'Enseignement *see* Belgium. Ministere de l'Education Nationale. Etudes et Documents **1674**
Belgium. Institut National de Statistique. Bevolkingsstatistieken. (BE) **3991**
Belgium. Institut National de Statistique. Bulletin de Statistique. (BE ISSN 0045-1703) **4564**
Belgium. Institut National de Statistique. Comptes Nationaux de la Belgique. (BE ISSN 0772-1838) **706**
Belgium. Institut National de Statistique. Etudes Statistiques. (BE ISSN 0069-8075) **4564**
Belgium. Institut National de Statistique. Mouvement de la Population des Communes *see* Belgium. Institut National de Statistique. Statistiques Demographiques **3991**
Belgium. Institut National de Statistique. Statistique Annuelle du Trafic International des Ports *see* Belgium. Institut National de Statistique. Statistique du Trafic International des Ports **4662**
Belgium. Institut National de Statistique. Statistique de la Navigation du Rhin *see* Belgium. Institut National de Statistique. Statistique de la Navigation Interieure **4662**
Belgium. Institut National de Statistique. Statistique de la Navigation Interieure. (BE ISSN 0773-2805) **4662,** 4564
Belgium. Institut National de Statistique. Statistique des Accidents de la Circulation sur la Voie Publique avec Tues et Blesses. (BE ISSN 0770-237X) **4116,** 4564
Belgium. Institut National de Statistique. Statistique des Accidents de Roulage *see* Belgium. Institut National de Statistique. Statistique des Accidents de la Circulation sur la Voie Publique avec Tues et Blesses **4116**
Belgium. Institut National de Statistique. Statistique des Vehicules a Moteur Neufs Mis en Circulation. (BE ISSN 0773-3070) **4662,** 4564
Belgium. Institut National de Statistique. Statistique du Commerce. *see* Belgium. Institut National de Statistique. Statistiques du Commerce Interieur et des Transports **4662**
Belgium. Institut National de Statistique. Statistique du Tourisme et de l'Hotellerie. (BE ISSN 0067-5547) **4799,** 4564
Belgium. Institut National de Statistique. Statistique du Trafic International des Ports. (BE ISSN 0772-7739) **4662,** 4564
Belgium. Institut National de Statistique. Statistique Generale. (BE) **706**
Belgium. Institut National de Statistique. Statistiques Agricoles. (BE ISSN 0067-5466) **134,** 4565
Belgium. Institut National de Statistique. Statistiques de la Construction et du Logement. (BE ISSN 0772-7720) **637,** 4565
Belgium. Institut National de Statistique. Statistiques Demographiques. (BE ISSN 0067-5490) **3991,** 4565
Belgium. Institut National de Statistique. Statistiques des Causes de Deces. (BE) **3991**
Belgium. Institut National de Statistique. Statistiques des Transports. *see* Belgium. Institut National de Statistique. Statistiques du Commerce Interieur et des Transports **4662**
Belgium. Institut National de Statistique. Statistiques du Commerce Exter. (BE ISSN 0772-6694) **4662,** 4799
Belgium. Institut National de Statistique. Statistiques du Commerce Interieur et des Transports. (BE ISSN 0773-4255) **4662,** 4565
Belgium. Institut National de Statistique. Statistiques Financieres. (BE) **706**
Belgium. Institut National de Statistique. Statistiques Industrielles. (BE ISSN 0772-7704) **706,** 4565
Belgium. Institut National de Statistique. Statistiques Judiciaires. (BE) **2697**
Belgium. Institut National de Statistique. Statistiques Sociales. (BE ISSN 0067-5563) **4394**
Belgium. Institut Royal Meteorologique. Annuaire: Magnetisme Terrestre/Jaarboek: Aardmagnetisme. (BE ISSN 0524-7764) **3433,** 1555
Belgium. Institut Royal Meteorologique. Annuaire: Rayonnement Solaire/Jaarboek: Zonnestraling. (BE ISSN 0524-7780) **3433**
Belgium. Institut Royal Meteorologique. Bulletin Quotidien du Temps. (BE ISSN 0007-5280) **3433,** 362
Belgium. Institut Royal Meteorologique. Observations Climatologiques. (BE ISSN 0029-7682) **3433**
Belgium. Institut Royal Meteorologique. Observations d'Ozone. (BE ISSN 0029-7690) **3433**
Belgium. Institut Royal Meteorologique. Observations Geophysiques. (BE ISSN 0020-2525) **1587**
Belgium. Institut Royal Meteorologique. Observations Ionospheriques et du Rayonnement Cosmique. (BE ISSN 0020-2533) **3433,** 362, 3815
Belgium. Institut Royal Meteorologique. Observations Synoptiques. (BE ISSN 0020-2541) **3433**
Belgium. Institut Royal Meteorologique. Publications. (BE ISSN 0020-255X) **3433,** 1587
Belgium. Ministere de l'Education Nationale et de la Culture Francaise. Annuaire Statistique de l'Enseignenment *see* Belgium. Ministere de l'Education Nationale. Etudes et Documents **1674**
Belgium. Ministere de l'Education Nationale et de la Culture Francaise. Bulletin d'Information *see* Belgium. Ministere de l'Education Nationale. Revue **1618**
Belgium. Ministere de l'Education Nationale et de la Culture Francaise. Revue *see* Belgium. Ministere de l'Education Nationale. Revue **1618**
Belgium. Ministere de l'Education Nationale et de la Culture Francaise. Rapport Annuel *see* Belgium. Ministere de l'Education Nationale. Rapport Annuel **1618**
Belgium. Ministere de l'Education Nationale. Etudes et Documents. (BE ISSN 0773-5820) **1674,** 4565
Belgium. Ministere de l'Education Nationale. Rapport Annuel. (BE) **1618**
Belgium. Ministere de l'Education Nationale. Revue. (BE) **1618,** 4429
Belgium. Ministere de la Prevoyance Sociale. Rapport General sur la Securite Sociale. (BE ISSN 0067-558X) **4399,** 4054
Belgium. Ministere de la Sante Publique et de l'Environnement. Administration des Etablissements de Soins. Service d'Etudes. Annuaire Statistique des Etablissements de Soins/Belgium. Ministerie van Volksgezondheid en Leefmilieu. Bestuur voor de Verzorgingsinstellingen. Studiedienst. Statistisch Jaarboek van de Verzorginingsinstellingen. (BE) **4117,** 4565
Belgium. Ministere de la Sante Publique et de la Famille. Annuaire Statistique des Hopitaux *see* Belgium. Ministere de la Sante Publique et de l'Environnement. Administration des Etablissements de Soins. Service d'Etudes. Annuaire Statistique des Etablissements de Soins **4117**
Belgium. Ministere de la Sante Publique et de la Famille. Bulletin. (BE) **4098**
Belgium. Ministere de la Sante Publique et de la Famille. Rapport Annuel. (BE) **4399,** 4098

Title

Belgium. Ministere des Affaires Economiques. Bibliotheque Centrale (Fonds Quetelet). Accroissements. (BE ISSN 0005-8521) **390**
Belgium. Ministere des Affaires Economiques. Direction Generale des Etudes et de la Documentation. Apercu Economique Trimestriel. (BE ISSN 0773-9664) **847**, **901**
Belgium. Ministere des Affaires Economiques. Direction Generale des Etudes et de la Documentation. Lettre de Conjoncture. (BE ISSN 0772-0831) **847**
†Belgium. Ministere des Affaires Economiques. Rapport Annuel sur les Investissements Etrangers en Belique/Belgium. Ministerie van Economische Zaken. Jaarlijks Rapport over de Buitenlandse Investeringen. (BE) **5147**
Belgium. Ministere des Finances. Administration des Contributions. Bulletin des Contributions. (BE ISSN 0005-853X) **1088**
Belgium. Ministerie van Economische Zaken. Algemene Directie voor Studien en Documentatie. Conjunctuurbrief. (BE ISSN 0771-5579) **847**
Belgium. Ministerie van Economische Zaken. Algemene Directie voor Studien en Documentatie. Kwartaaloverzicht van de Economie. (BE ISSN 0773-3666) **847**, **901**
Belgium. Ministerie van Economische Zaken. Jaarlijks Rapport over de Buitenlandse Investeringen. see Belgium. Ministere des Affaires Economiques. Rapport Annuel sur les Investissements Etrangers en Belique **5147**
Belgium. Ministerie van Financien. Hoofdbestuur der Directe Belastingen. Bulletin der Belastingen see Belgium. Ministere des Finances. Administration des Contributions. Bulletin des Contributions **1088**
Belgium. Ministerie van Volksgezondheid en Leefmilieu. Bestuur voor de Verzorgingsinstellingen. Studiedienst. Statistisch Jaarboek van de Verzorginingsinstellingen. see Belgium. Ministere de la Sante Publique et de l'Environnement. Administration des Etablissements de Soins. Service d'Etudes. Annuaire Statistique des Etablissements de Soins **4117**
Belgium. Nationaal Fonds voor Wetenschappelijk Onderzoek. Jaarverslag/Belgium. Fonds National de la Recherche Scientifique. Rapport Annuel. (BE ISSN 0067-5407) **4301**
Belgium. Nationaal Fonds voor Wetenschappelijk Onderzoek. Lijst der Kredietgenieters/Belgium. Fonds National de la Recherche Scientifique. Listes des Beneficiaires d'une Subvention. (BE) **4301**
Belgium. Office Belge du Commerce Exterieur. Informations du Commerce Exterieur see Informations du Commerce Exterieur **912**
Belgium. Office National de l'Emploi. see Belgium. Office National de l'Emploi. Communique Mensuel **973**
Belgium. Office National de l'Emploi. Bulletin Mensuel. (BE) **973**
Belgium. Office National de l'Emploi. Communique Mensuel. (BE) **973**
Belgium. Office National de l'Emploi. Etudes Economiques et Sociales. (BE) **973**
Belgium. Office National de l'Emploi. Rapport Annuel see Belgium. Office National de l'Emploi. Etudes Economiques et Sociales **973**
Belgium. Regie des Postes. Rapport d'Activite. (BE) **1352**
Belgium. Rijksinstituut voor de Sociale Verzekeringen der Zelfstandigen. Jaarverslag see Belgium. Institut National d'Assurances Sociales Pour Travailleurs Independants. Rapport Annuel **2527**

Belgium. Rijksinstituut voor de Sociale Verzekeringen der Zelfstandigen. Statistiek van de Kinderen die Recht Geven Op Kinderbijslag. see Belgium. Institut National d'Assurances Sociales pour Travailleurs Independants. Statistique des Enfants Beneficiaires d'Allocations Familiales **2546**
Belgium. Rijksinstituut voor de Sociale Verzekeringen der Zelfstandigen. Statistiek van de Personen die een Rust- en Overlevingsprestatie Genieten. see Belgium. Institut National d'Assurances Sociales pour Travailleurs Independants. Statistiques des Beneficiaires de Prestations de Retraite et de Survie **2546**
Belgium. Rijksinstituut voor de Sociale Verzekeringen der Zelfstandigen. Statistiek van de Personen die Onder de Toepassing Vallen van het Sociaal Statuut van de Zelfstandigen. see Belgium. Institut National d'Assurances Sociales pour Travailleurs Independants. Statistiques des Personnes Assujetties au Statut Social des Travailleurs Independants **2546**
Belgium. Rijksinstituut voor Ziekte- en Invaliditeitsverzekering. R.I.Z.I.V. Informatieblad. see Belgium. Institut National d'Assurance Maladie Invalidite. I.N.A.M.I. Bulletin d'Information **2527**
Belgium. Rijksstation voor Landbouwtechniek. Mededelingen. (BE ISSN 0303-9056) **79**
†Belgium. Rijksstation voor Sierplantenteelt. Mededelingen. (BE ISSN 0303-903X) **5147**
Belgium. Rijksstation voor Zeevisserij. Mededelingen. (BE ISSN 0303-9072) **2037**
Belgium. Station de Recherches Forestieres et Hydrobiologiques. Travaux. Serie D. Hydrobiologie. (BE) **430**
Belgium: Economic and Commercial Information. (BE ISSN 0775-1443) **901**
Belgium: Economic and Technical Information see Belgium: Economic and Commercial Information **901**
Belgium: Economy and Technique. (BE ISSN 0775-1435) **901**
Belgium Micro. (BE) **1458**
Belgium Netherlands Luxembourg Benelux Publikatieblad see Benelux Publikatieblad **4054**
Belgo-Luxembourg Chamber of Commerce in Great Britain. Journal. (UK) **808**
Belicht. (NE) **3789**
Belisane. (FR ISSN 0339-8498) **3762**
Belize. Central Bank. Quarterly Review. (BH) **1088**
Belize. Department of Agriculture. Annual Report and Summmary of Statistics. (BH) **79**
Belize. Monetary Authority. Quarterly Review see Belize. Central Bank. Quarterly Review **1088**
Belize Collector. (US) **3750**
Belize External Trade Bulletin. (BH) **926**
Belize Times. (BH) **3875**
Belize Today. (BH) **2239**
Belizean Studies. (BH ISSN 0250-6831) **2400**
Bell/Cloche. (CN) **198**, **212**
Bell and Howell Newspaper Index to the American Banker see Index to the American Banker **721**
Bell & Howell Newspaper Index to the St. Louis Post-Dispatch see St. Louis Post-Dispatch Index **2579**
Bell and Howell Transdex see Transdex Index **2579**
Bell Chimes. (US ISSN 1041-231X) **2145**
Bell' Italia. (IT) **4754**
Bell of Freedom. see Die Freiheitsglocke **3942**
Bell of St. Francis. see Sv. Pranciskaus Varpelis **4276**

Bell Operating Companies Week see B O C Week **1361**
†Bell Telephone Magazine. (US ISSN 0096-8692) **5147**
Bell Tower. (US ISSN 0092-8666) **3541**
Bell - U C M S M Students' Magazine. (UK) **2459**
Bella. (GW) **4838**
Bella (Milan, 1947). (IT ISSN 0005-8602) **4838**
Bella (Milan, 1975). (IT ISSN 0399-2322) **4838**
La Bella Figura. (US) **1993**
Bellaire - S W. (US) **2222**
Belle. (AT ISSN 0310-1452) **2444**, **2548**
Belles Histoires de Pomme d'Api. (FR) **1249**
Belles Lettres. (US ISSN 0884-2957) **2898**, **4121**, **4858**
Belleza y Moda see Belleza y Moda - Votre Beaute **372**
Belleza y Moda - Votre Beaute. (SP) **372**, **1289**
Bellingham Review. (US ISSN 0734-2934) **2898**
Bellowing Ark. (US ISSN 0887-4115) **2898**
Belmonda Letero. (US) **4280**, **2805**
Belmont Vision. (US) **1304**
Belmontia. (NE ISSN 0169-4375) **496**
Beloit Fiction Journal. (US ISSN 0883-9131) **2898**
Beloit Magazine. (US) **1304**
Beloit Poetry Journal. (US ISSN 0005-8661) **2988**
Beloit Poetry Journal. Chapbook. (US ISSN 0067-5695) **2988**
Belorusskaya S.S.R. v Pechati S.S.S.R. i Drugikh Zarubezhnych Stran. (BW ISSN 0207-9003) **2174**
Belorusskii Gosudarstvennyi Universitet. Vestnik. Seriya 3; Istoriya, Filosofiya, Nauchnyi Kommunizm, Ekonomika, Pravo. see Belaruski Dziarzhauny Universitet. Vesnik. Seryia 3; Historiya, Filosofiya, Navukovy Kamunism, Ekanomika, Prava **2352**
Belser Kunstquartal. (GW) **3522**
Belt Line. (US) **1283**
Beltane Papers see T B P's Octava **4853**
Bem Lingua Portuguesa. (PO) **2805**
Bema. (US ISSN 0199-8765) **4280**
Bemoatza. (IS) **2580**
Ben Gurion University. Bulletin. (IS) **1701**
†Ben Gurion University. Institutes for Applied Research. Library Acquisitions. (IS) **5147**
Ben-Gurion University of the Negev. Institutes for Applied Research. Scientific Activities. (IS) **4301**
Ben-Gurion University of the Negev. Research and Development Authority. Applied Research Institute. Scientific Activities see Ben-Gurion University of the Negev. Institutes for Applied Research. Scientific Activities **4301**
Ben Liu/Torrent. (US) **2898**
Benalla Art Gallery Newsletter. (AT) **318**
▼Benbella and Lulu. (NR) **319**
Bench & Bar of Minnesota. (US ISSN 0276-1505) **2604**
†Bench Investment Letter. (US) **5147**
Benchmark. (UK ISSN 0951-6859) **1816**, **3445**
Benchmark (Richmond). (US ISSN 0743-0310) **2705**
Bend of the River. (US) **2400**, **2052**, **2145**
Bendel State. Ministry of Home Affairs and Information. Mid-Western State Estimates see Bendel State. Ministry of Information, Social Development and Sports. Estimate **4054**
Bendel State. Ministry of Information, Social Development and Sports. Estimate. (NR) **4054**
Bendel State Gazette. (NR) **3875**
Bender's Dictionary of 1040 Deductions. (US ISSN 0270-5206) **2604**
Benedict on Admiralty. (US) **2720**, **4724**

Benedictijns Tijdschrift. (NE ISSN 0005-8734) **4256**
Benedictina. (IT) **2352**, **4256**
Benedictine Almanac see Benedictine Yearbook **4256**
Benedictine Yearbook. (UK ISSN 0522-8883) **4256**
Benedictines. (US ISSN 0005-8726) **4256**
Benefits. (US) **973**
Benefits & Compensation International. (UK ISSN 0268-764X) **2528**, **973**
▼Benefits & Pensions Monitor. (CN) **1063**
Benefits Canada. (CN ISSN 0703-7732) **973**, **939**
Benefits Coordinator. (US) **1063**, **748**
Benefits for Saskatchewan Industry from Resource Development. (CN ISSN 0706-7852) **647**
Benefits International see Benefits & Compensation International **2528**
Benefits Law Journal. (US ISSN 0897-7992) **2734**, **1063**, **2528**
Benefits News Analysis. (US ISSN 0199-3100) **1063**
Benefits Quarterly. (US ISSN 8756-1263) **1063**
Benefits Today. (US ISSN 0747-9131) **973**
Benelux see Benelux Dossier **847**
Benelux Dossier/Dossier Benelux. (BE) **847**
Benelux Economic Union. Conseil Consultatif Economique et Social Rapport du Secretaire Concernant les Activites du Conseil see B E N E L U X Economic Union. Conseil Central de l'Economie. Rapport du Secretaire sur l'Activite du Conseil **1072**
Benelux Publikatieblad/Bulletin Benelux. (Belgium Netherlands Luxembourg) (BE ISSN 0005-8777) **4054**
Benelux Rail. (SW) **4708**
Benelux Stamp Catalogue. (UK ISSN 0142-9787) **3750**
Benelux Tijdschrift - Revue Benelux see Benelux Dossier **847**
†Benenson Restaurant Guide (Year). (US) **5147**
†Benetax Remuneration Planner. (AT) **5147**
Bengal Medical Journal. (II ISSN 0005-8793) **3081**
Bengal Motion Picture Diary and General Information see Indian Motion Picture Almanac **3512**
Bengal: Past and Present. (II ISSN 0005-8807) **2337**, **3875**
Bengali International. (II) **2988**
Bengali Literature. (II ISSN 0005-8815) **2898**
Beni Culturali e Ambiente. (IT) **2859**
Benibana. (JA) **353**
Benin - Magazine. (DM) **2168**
Benin - Presse Information. (DM) **2168**
Benin Review. (NR) **2859**
Benissimo. (IT) **1289**, **4838**
†Benissimo Speciale. (IT) **5147**
Benjamin F. Fairless Lectures. (US ISSN 0067-5717) **3875**
†Benjamin Publishing - Marketing Report. (US) **5147**
Benki ya Nyumba Tanzania. Ripoti ya Mwaka. see Tanzania Housing Bank. Annual Report and Statement of Accounts **800**
Bennett Exchange. (US ISSN 0884-6510) **2145**
Benn's Direct Marketing Service. (UK ISSN 0264-8970) **1034**
Benn's Guide (Year). (UK ISSN 0954-8548) **641**
Benn's Hardware Directory and D-I-Y Buyers Guide see Benn's Guide (Year) **641**
†Benn's Hardware Price List. (UK ISSN 0265-069X) **5147**
Benn's Media Directory. International Edition. (UK) **2567**, **2577**
Benn's Media Directory. Overseas Press see Benn's Media Directory. International Edition **2567**
Benn's Media Directory. U.K. Edition. (UK) **2567**, **2577**
Benn's Media Directory. U.K. Media see Benn's Media Directory. U.K. Edition **2567**

BEN'S BOOK

Ben's Book. (FR) **1369**, 1332
Bensiini Uutiset. (FI ISSN 0045-1738) **3683**
Benson and Hedges Cricket Year. (UK) **4501**
Benson & Hedges West Indies Cricket Annual (Year). (UK) **4501**
Bent. (CN ISSN 0067-5733) **2898**
Bent of Tau Beta Pi. (US ISSN 0005-884X) **1304**, 1816
Bentham Newsletter see Utilitas **1302**
Bentley Historical Library. (US) **2400**, 2746
Bentley Historical Library Annual Report. (US ISSN 0362-6881) **2746**
Bentley Observer. (US) **1304**
Benzin & Olie Bladet. (DK ISSN 0005-8858) **3683**
Der Benzolring. (GW) **1170**
Beograd. (YU) **1915**, 1862
Beogradski Univerzitet. Elektrotehnicki Fakultet. Publikacije. Serija: Elektronika, Telekomunikacije, Automatika. (YU ISSN 0351-2177) **1764**
Beogradski Univerzitet. Pravni Fakultet. Anali. (YU ISSN 0003-2565) **2604**
Beop Ryun. (KO) **4214**
Beratende Ingenieure. (GW ISSN 0005-8866) **1816**
Berckers Katholischer Taschenkalender. (GW) **4164**
Berckers Taschenkalender see Berckers Katholischer Taschenkalender **4164**
Berea Alumnus. (US ISSN 0005-8874) **1304**
Berea College Appalachian Center Newsletter. (US) **2400**
Berean Expositor. (UK) **4164**
Berean Searchlight. (US ISSN 0005-8890) **4165**
†Beretning for Psykiatriske Institutioner i Danmark. (DK ISSN 0108-7819) **5147**
Beretning over Arbejdsmiljoefondets Virksomhed. (DK ISSN 0106-7052) **973**
Berezil. (KR) **2859**
Berg (Year). (GW ISSN 0179-1419) **4542**
Bergakademie Freiberg. Bibliothek "Georgius Agricola". Veroeffentlichungen. (GW) **2746**
Bergakademie Freiberg. Wissenschaftliches Informationszentrum. Veroeffentlichungen see Bergakademie Freiberg. Bibliothek "Georgius Agricola". Veroeffentlichungen **2746**
Bergbau. (GW ISSN 0342-5681) **3479**, 1784
Bergbau-Berufsgenossenschaft. Jahresbericht. (GW ISSN 0933-0127) **2580**, 2528, 3479
Bergbau in der Bundesrepublik Deutschland. (GW) **3499**
Bergen County Dental Society. Newsletter. (US ISSN 0092-9832) **3229**
Bergen County Education Association Reporter see B C E A Reporter **1617**
Berger Building & Design Cost File. Unit Prices. Vol. 1: General Construction Trades. (US) **603**
Berger Building & Design Cost File. Unit Prices. Vol. 2: Mechanical and Electrical Trades. (US) **603**, 1883
Bergey's Manual of Determinative Bacteriology. (US) **550**
Bergische Handwerk. (GW ISSN 0343-1711) **319**, 639
Bergischer Geschichtsverein. Zeitschrift. (GW ISSN 0067-5792) **2352**
Das Bergmann-Echo. (AU ISSN 0005-8947) **3789**
Bergmannsfreund see Saarberg **3495**
Bergomun. (IT ISSN 0005-8955) **2352**, 319, 2805
Bergshanteringen. see Vuoriteollisus **3497**
Bergsmannen. (SW ISSN 0284-0448) **3479**, 3403
Bergsmannen med Jernkontorets Annaler see Bergsmannen **3479**
Der Bergsteiger. (GW ISSN 0005-8963) **4542**

Bergverks-Nytt. (NO ISSN 0005-8971) **3479**, 3403
Bergvriend. (NE ISSN 0005-898X) **4542**
Bericht der Bundesregierung an den Nationalrat see Austria. Bundesministerium fuer Wissenschaft und Forschung. Bericht der Bundesregierung an den Nationalrat **4300**
Bericht ueber die Lage der Oesterreichischen Landwirtschaft. (AU) **148**
Bericht ueber Schwebstaubmessungen in Hessen im Messjahr (Year) see Lufthygienischer Monatsbericht **1977**
Bericht zur Aktuellen Konjunkurlage im Bundesgebiet und in Bayern. (GW) **847**
†Berichte aus Namibia. (GW) **5147**
Berichte der Deutschen Mineralogischen Gesellschaft. (GW ISSN 0935-123X) **3479**, 1555
Berichte des Vereins Natur und Heimat und des Naturhistorischen Museums zu Luebeck. (GW ISSN 0067-5806) **4301**
Berichte Gynaekologie - Geburtshilfe/Gynecology - Obstetrics. (GW) **3166**, 3
Berichte Gynaekologie und Geburtshilfe Sowie Deren Grenzgebiete see Berichte Gynaekologie - Geburtshilfe **3166**
Berichte Naturwissenschaftlich-Medizinischen Vereins in Innsbruck. (AU) **430**, 3081
Berichte Pathologie/Trends in Pathology. (GW ISSN 0722-9674) **3166**, 3
Berichte ueber Landwirtschaft. (GW ISSN 0005-9080) **79**
Berichte ueber Landwirtschaft. Sonderhefte. (GW ISSN 0301-2689) **79**
Berichte und Informationen. (AU ISSN 0029-9863) **647**, 3875
Berichte zur Orts-, Regional- und Landesplanung. (SZ) **2483**
Berichte zur Raumforschung und Raumplanung. (AU ISSN 0005-9102) **2484**
Berichte zur Wissenschaftsgeschichte. (GW ISSN 0170-6233) **4301**
Berichten aan Zeevarenden. (NE ISSN 0166-932X) **2243**, 4522, 4724
†Berichten van de Afdeling Volkskredietwezen. (NE ISSN 0005-9110) **5147**
La Berio. (IT ISSN 0409-1132) **2746**
Berita Bibliografi. (IO ISSN 0216-1273) **4139**
Berita Hasil Hutan see Statistik Kehutanan Indonesia **2108**
Berita Idayu see Berita Bibliografi **4139**
Berita Idayu Bibliografi see Berita Bibliografi **4139**
Berita Ilmu Pengetahuan den Teknologi.(IO ISSN 0125-9156) **4301**
Berita Jururawat. see Nursing Journal of Singapore **3284**
Berita L.I.P.I. see Berita Ilmu Pengetahuan den Teknologi **4301**
Berita M M A/M M A Newsletter. (Malaysian Medical Association) (MY) **3081**
Berita Negara. (IO) **2202**
Berita Pas see Al-Harakah **3897**
Berita Selulosa. (IO ISSN 0005-9145) **2096**, 3662
Berita Shell. (SI ISSN 0005-9153) **3683**
Berita Topografi. (IO) **2243**
Berkala Bioanthropologi Indonesia. see Indonesian Journal of Bioanthropology **242**
Berkala Ilmu Kedokteran. see Journal of the Medical Sciences **3118**
Berkeley Insights in Linguistics and Semiotics. (US ISSN 0893-6935) **2805**
Berkeley Journal of Sociology. (US ISSN 0067-5830) **4429**
Berkeley Monthly. (US) **2860**
Berkeley Papers in History of Science. (US ISSN 0145-0379) **4354**

Berkeley Poetry Review. (US) **2988**
▼Berkeley Review of Books. (US) **4121**, 2898
†Berkeley Symposia on Mathematical Statistics and Probability. (US) **5147**
Berkeley Women's Law Journal. (US ISSN 0882-4312) **2604**, 4838
Berkeleyan and California Pelican see California Pelican **2860**
Berks, Bucks and Oxon Farmer. (UK) **79**
Berks County Business. (US) **647**
Berks County Genealogical Society. Journal. (US) **2145**
Berkshire Archaeological Committee. Publication see Berkshire Archaeological Trust. Publication **266**
Berkshire Archaeological Journal. (UK ISSN 0309-3093) **266**
Berkshire Archaeological Trust. Publication. (UK) **266**
Berkshire Magazine. (US) **2222**
Berkshire Restaurant & Entertainment Guide. (US) **4754**
Berlin. Freie Universitaet. Institut fuer Statistik und Versicherungsmathematik. Berichte see Arbeiten zur Angewandten Statistik **4562**
Berlin (West). Senatsverwaltung fuer Frauen, Jugend und Familie. Statistischer Dienst. (GW) **4425**, 1247
Berlin & Ex-DDR von Hinten. (GW) **2451**, 4754
Berlin - Brandenburgische Handwerk. (GW) **808**
Berlin - Brandenburgisches Sonntagsblatt. (GW) **4230**
Berlin-Flugplan. (GW ISSN 0005-9242) **4671**
Berlin in Zahlen see Statistisches Jahrbuch Berlin **4589**
Berlin Programm. (GW ISSN 0005-9250) **4754**
Berlin von Hinten see Berlin & Ex-DDR von Hinten **2451**
Berliner Aerzte. (GW) **3081**
Berliner Aerzteblatt. (GW) **3081**
Berliner Aerztekammer see Berliner Aerzte **3081**
Berliner Anwaltsblatt. (GW) **2604**
Berliner Baer. (GW ISSN 0005-9269) **1296**
Berliner Bank. Boersenbrief. (GW) **768**, 939
Berliner Bank. Konjunkturbrief. (GW) **847**
Berliner Bank. Wirtschaftsbericht. (GW ISSN 0005-9277) **847**
Berliner Bauwirtschaft. (GW ISSN 0045-1762) **603**
Berliner Behoerden Spiegel. (GW) **4085**
Berliner Beitraege zur Archaeometrie. (GW ISSN 0344-5089) **266**
Berliner Botanischer Verein. Verhandlung. (GW ISSN 0724-3111) **496**, 430
Berliner Byzantinistische Arbeiten. (GW ISSN 0067-6055) **2352**, 1275
†Berliner Forum. (GW ISSN 0523-0144) **5147**
Berliner Geschichte. (GW) **2352**
Berliner Handelsregister Verzeichnis. (GW ISSN 0067-6063) **1123**
Berliner Haus- und Grundbesitz. (GW) **4145**, 2484
Berliner Hausbesitzer-Magazin. (GW) **2484**
†Berliner Historische Kommission. Veroeffentlichungen. (GW) **5147**
Berliner Islamstudien. (GW ISSN 0174-2477) **4165**
▼Berliner Kongresskalender. (GW ISSN 0940-533X) **3391**
Berliner Kunstblatt see Kunstblatt **5225**
Berliner Liberale Zeitung. (GW ISSN 0005-9307) **2860**
Berliner Naturschutzblaetter. (GW ISSN 0173-7074) **430**, 1944
Berliner Sonntagsblatt see Berlin - Brandenburgisches Sonntagsblatt **4230**
Berliner Statistik. (GW ISSN 0005-9331) **4565**

Berliner Studentenzeitung. (GW ISSN 0005-934X) **1305**
Berliner Theologische Zeitschrift. (GW ISSN 0724-6137) **4230**
Berliner Tierpark-Buch. (GW ISSN 0067-6098) **579**
Berliner Turfantexte. (GW ISSN 0138-4228) **3634**
Berliner Turnzeitung. (GW ISSN 0005-9358) **4466**
Berliner und Muenchener Tieraerztliche Wochenschrift. (GW ISSN 0005-9366) **4807**
Berliner Verkehrs Betriebe Aktuell see B V G Aktuell **4647**
Berliner Verkehrsblaetter. (GW ISSN 0722-9399) **4647**
Berliner Wertpapierboerse. Amtliches Kursblatt. (GW ISSN 0003-214X) **939**
Die Berliner Wirtschaft. (GW ISSN 0405-5756) **808**
†Berliner Wirtschaftsdaten. (GW) **5147**
Berliner Wissenschaftlicher Gesellschaft. Jahrbuch. (GW ISSN 0171-3302) **4301**
Berlinische Reminiszenzen. (GW ISSN 0067-611X) **2352**
Berlitz Cruise Guides. (SZ) **4754**
Bermuda. Biological Station for Research. Special Publications. (BM) **1602**, 1944
Bermuda. Department of Agriculture and Fisheries. Report for the Year see Bermuda. Department of Agriculture, Fisheries and Parks. Report for the Year **79**
Bermuda. Department of Agriculture, Fisheries and Parks. Report for the Year. (BM) **79**, 2037
Bermuda (Year). (US) **4754**
Bermuda Beacon. (US) **2145**
Bermuda Monetary Authority. Quarterly Notice. (BM) **768**
Bermuda Monetary Authority. Quarterly Report and Accounts see Bermuda Monetary Authority. Quarterly Notice **768**
Bermuda Monetary Authority. Reports & Accounts. (BM) **768**
Bermuda National Bibliography. (BM ISSN 0255-0067) **390**
Bermuda Post. (US ISSN 1046-2813) **3750**, 1352
Bermuda Shorts. (US) **4754**
The Bermudian. (BM ISSN 0005-9382) **2175**
Bern Porter International. (US) **2898**
Bern Universitaet. Archaeologisches Seminar. Hefte see Bern Universitaet. Seminar fuer Klassische Archaeologie. Hefte **267**
Bern Universitaet. Seminar fuer Klassische Archaeologie. Hefte. (SZ) **267**
Bernard und Graefe Aktuell. (GW) **3453**
Bernards and Babani Press Radio & Electronics & Computer Books. (UK) **1355**, 1389, 1764
Bernards and Babani Press Radio and Electronics Books see Bernards and Babani Press Radio & Electronics & Computer Books **1355**
Berner Beitraege zur Nationaloekonomie. (SZ ISSN 0067-6128) **647**
†Berner Beitraege zur Soziologie. (SZ ISSN 0067-6136) **5147**
Berner Boersenverein. Jahresbericht. (SZ) **939**
Berner Briefmarken-Zeitung/Journal Philatelique de Berne. (SZ ISSN 0005-9404) **3750**
Berner Heimatbuecher. (SZ) **2352**
†Berner Kriminologische Untersuchungen. (SZ ISSN 0067-6144) **5147**
Berner Kunstmitteilungen. (SZ) **319**
†Berner Studien zum Fremdenverkehr. (SZ ISSN 0067-6152) **5147**
Berner Wochen Bulletin/This Week in Berne/Semaine a Berne. (SZ ISSN 0005-9412) **4754**
Berner Zeitschrift fuer Geschichte und Heimatkunde. (SZ ISSN 0005-9420) **2352**, 2145

Bernice P. Bishop Museum Bulletin see Bishop Museum Bulletins in Botany **496**
Bernice Pauahi Bishop Museum, Honolulu. Occasional Papers. (US ISSN 0067-6160) **4301**, 236
Bernice Pauahi Bishop Museum, Honolulu. Special Publications. (US ISSN 0067-6179) **4302**, 236
Bernie. (GW) **1249**, **4098**, **4399**
Beroepsleven. see Vie Professionnelle **2090**
Beroepsvervoer. (NE) **4708**
Bertelsmann Baukatalog. (GW) **603**
Bertelsmann Briefe. (GW ISSN 0005-9455) **4121**
Bertine Koperberg Conference (Proceedings). (SW) **3368**
Bertrand Russell Today see Philosophy and the Arts **5258**
Bertrand Vacances. (FR) **4145**, **4754**
Beruf und Gesinnung. (AU ISSN 0005-9471) **1618**
Beruf und Gesundheit - Occupational Health see Arbeitsmedizin **3623**
Berufliche Bildung see Gewerkschaftliche Bildungspolitik **1635**
Berufliche Rehabilitation. (GW ISSN 0931-8895) **3624**
Berufs-Dermatosen see Dermatosen in Beruf und Umwelt **3247**
Berufsausbildung (Year)/Formation Professionnelle (Year). (SZ) **1682**
Berufsausbildung Jugendarbeitslosigkeit.(GW) **4399**, 1618
Berufsberatung und Berufsbildung/ Orientation et Formation Professionnelles. (SZ ISSN 0005-9501) **1618**
Die Berufsbildende Schule. (GW ISSN 0005-951X) **1682**
Berufsbildung. (GW ISSN 0005-9536) **1618**
Berufsbildungsbericht Duisburg (Year). (GW ISSN 0931-0029) **1725**, 4565
Berufsbildungsbrief. (GW) **808**
Berufsfoerderungszentrum Essen e.V. Info see B F Z - Info **3624**
Berufsgenossenschaft see Die B G **2527**
Berufsgenossenschaft fuer Gesundheitsdienst und Wohlfahrtspflege Mitteilungen see B G W Mitteilungen **2527**
Berufsplanung fuer den Management Nachwuchs. (GW) **3624**
Berufsverband Aerzte fuer Orthopaedie. Informationen. (GW ISSN 0931-6779) **3307**
Berytus Archeological Studies. (LE ISSN 0067-6195) **267**
Berzsenyi Daniel Megyei Konyvtar. Evkonyve. (HU) **2746**
Beschaeftigungs- und Erwerbstaetigenstatistik/Statistique de l'Emploi et de la Population Active Occupee. (SZ) **847**
Beschaffung Aktuell. (GW ISSN 0341-4507) **1034**
Bescheid. (GW) **1249**, **2188**
Beschreibende Sortenliste Getreide, Mais, Oelfruechte, Leguminosen und Hackfruechte. (GW) **205**
Beschreibende Sortenliste Kartoffeln. (GW) **205**
Beschrijvende Rassenlijst voor Landbouwgewassen. (NE ISSN 0168-7484) **170**
Beschrijvende Rassenlijst voor Siergewassen (Year). (NE ISSN 0922-8829) **170**
Besprechungen Annotationen. (GW ISSN 0724-8164) **2746**
Bessatsu Bungei Shunju. (JA) **2898**
Bessatsu Daiyamondo. see Diamond **1007**
Bessatsu Saiensu. (JA ISSN 0285-1008) **4302**, 4594
Besser Verpacken see O V Z - Mitteilungen **3650**
Besseres Leben. (GW ISSN 0176-8816) **2188**
Besseres Obst. (AU ISSN 0005-9609) **2122**
Best. (FR) **3541**

Best American Essays. (US ISSN 0888-3742) **2898**
Best American Short Stories. (US ISSN 0067-6233) **2898**
Best Bed & Breakfast in England, Scotland & Wales. (US ISSN 1054-4089) **4754**
Best Bed and Breakfast in the World see Best Bed & Breakfast in England, Scotland & Wales **4754**
Best Bets. (NZ) **4532**
Best Bike see Best Motoring **2434**
Best Book Catalog in the World. (US) **390**
†Best Books By Consensus (Year). (US ISSN 8755-9633) **5147**
Best Books for Children. (US) **1233**
Best Boomerang. (IT) **2204**
Best Bottles Wineletter. (CN) **378**
Best Canadian Stories. (CN ISSN 0703-9476) **2899**
Best Car. (JA) **4685**
Best Detective Cases. (US) **2985**
Best Editorial Cartoons of the Year. (US ISSN 0091-2220) **2860**, 319
Best Fares. (US ISSN 8750-2410) **4754**, 4671
Best Fishing. (JA) **4542**
The Best for Less. (US) **1502**
Best Guide to Amsterdam and Benelux Venues see Best Guide to Amsterdam & the Benelux **2451**
Best Guide to Amsterdam & the Benelux. (NE) **2451**, 4754
Best Guide to Asia, Australasia, and South Pacific Islands. (NE) **2451**, 4754
▼Best Guide to Caribbean, Central and South American Lands. (NE) **2451**, 4754
▼Best Guide to France, Spain, and Portugal. (NE) **2451**, 4754
Best Guide to Great Britain. (NE) **2451**, 4754
▼Best Guide to Mediterranean Lands. (NE) **2451**, 4754
Best Guide to the North Pacific and Orient. (NE) **2451**, 4754
Best Hit. (JA) **3541**
Best in Advertising. (US) **28**
Best in Annual Reports. (US ISSN 0360-8743) **1003**
Best in Covers and Posters. (US) **4121**, 319
Best in Environmental Graphics. (US ISSN 0360-8271) **319**
Best in Packaging. (US ISSN 0360-8689) **3647**
Best Motoring. (JA) **2434**, 4516
Best 'N' Most in D F S. (SW ISSN 1100-3006) **901**, 378
Best Nest. (JA) **2145**
Best Newspaper Writing. (US ISSN 0195-895X) **2567**
Best of American Literature. (US) **2860**
†Best of Business International. (US) **5147**
†Best of Business Quarterly. (US) **5147**
Best of Club. (US) **3396**
Best of Club International. (US) **3396**
▼The Best of Cross Country Skiing. (US) **4542**
Best of E R I C on Educational Management. (US) **1725**
▼The Best of Europe. (US) **4754**
Best of Genesis. (US) **3396**
Best of Health. (US ISSN 1055-3398) **4835**, 1993
Best of Lafayette: The Southern Writer and Artist. (US) **2899**
Best of Lauderdale and the Gold Coast. (US) **4754**
Best of Long Range Planning. (US ISSN 0889-3136) **1003**
Best of Maui. (US) **4754**
Best of Newspaper Design. (US ISSN 0737-2612) **2567**
Best of Oui. (US) **3396**
▼Best of Packaging in Japan. (JA) **3647**
Best of Photojournalism. (US) **3789**
Best of Real Letters. (US) **3396**
Best of Sensuous Letters. (US) **3396**
▼Best of the Beach. (US) **4754**
Best One. (JA) **1249**

Best Performance Film and Video Directory see San Jose Film & Video Commission Directory **3517**
†Best Plays of ... (Year). (US) **5147**
Best Radio Plays of (Year). (UK) **1355**
Best Read Guide. (US) **4754**
Best Recipes. (US ISSN 0897-0386) **2444**, 2062
▼Best Report. (US) **2281**
Best Science Fiction of the Year. (US ISSN 0095-7119) **3010**
Best-Selling Home Plans. (US ISSN 0743-2461) **295**, 603, 2484
Best Selling Home Plans. (US) **2548**
Best Short Plays. (US ISSN 0067-6284) **2899**
Best Sports Stories. (US ISSN 0067-6292) **4466**
Best Wishes. (CN ISSN 0005-965X) **1233**
Best Works of Literature. see Mingzuo Xinshang **2938**
Bestand an Kraftfahrzeugen und Kraftfahrzeuganhaengern. (GW) **4743**
Bestattungsgewerbe. (GW) **2119**
Das Beste aus Reader's Digest (Swiss-German Edition). (SZ ISSN 0005-9676) **2219**
Det Beste fra Reader's Digest (Norwegian Edition). (NO ISSN 0005-9684) **2212**
Het Beste uit Reader's Digest (Belgian - Flemish Edition). (BE ISSN 0005-8386) **2174**
Het Beste uit Reader's Digest (Dutch Edition). (NE ISSN 0005-9692) **2211**
Bestelauto. (NE) **4647**
Bestia. (US ISSN 1041-2212) **2053**
Best's Agents Guide to Life Insurance Companies. (US ISSN 0094-9973) **2528**
Best's Directory of Recommended Insurance Adjusters. (US) **2528**
Best's Directory of Recommended Insurance Attorneys. (US ISSN 0277-1551) **2528**
Best's Insurance Management Reports: Life - Health Edition. (US) **2528**
Best's Insurance Management Reports: Property - Casualty Edition. (US) **2528**
Best's Insurance Report: Life - Health. (US) **2528**
Best's Insurance Report: Property - Casualty. (US ISSN 0148-3218) **2528**
Best's Insurance Report: Property - Liability see Best's Insurance Report: Property - Casualty **2528**
Best's Recommended Insurance Attorneys see Best's Directory of Recommended Insurance Attorneys **2528**
Best's Retirement Income Guide. (US) **2528**
Best's Review. Life - Health Insurance Edition. (US ISSN 0005-9706) **2528**
Best's Review. Property - Casualty Insurance Edition. (US ISSN 0161-7745) **2528**
Best's Review. Property - Liability Insurance Edition see Best's Review. Property - Casualty Insurance Edition **2528**
Best's Safety Directory. (US ISSN 0090-7480) **3615**
Bestseller. (AU) **29**, 1034
†Bestsellers. (US) **5147**
Bestuur en Beleid V Z W. (BE) **647**, 748, 1072
Bestuurswetenschappen. (NE ISSN 0165-7194) **4054**
Bestways Magazine see Bestways to Health **5147**
†Bestways to Health. (US) **5147**
Beszelo. (HU ISSN 0865-4093) **3875**
Bet Mikra. (IS ISSN 0005-979X) **4165**, 4221
Bet-Nahrain. (US ISSN 0748-2906) **2428**, 1993
†Beta Lactams. (UK ISSN 0263-7235) **5147**
†Beta Phi Mu Chapbook. (US ISSN 0067-6357) **5147**

Beta Phi Mu Monograph Series. (US) **2746**
Beta Phi Mu Newsletter. (US ISSN 1059-0757) **2747**
Betail. (FR ISSN 0005-9765) **212**
Betar Jagat. (II ISSN 0005-9773) **1355**
Beth Hatefutsoth. (IS) **3522**
Bethel College Bulletin. (US ISSN 0005-982X) **1305**
Bethel Courier. (US ISSN 0749-9108) **2400**
Bethel Focus. (US) **1305**
Bethelite Challenger. (US) **4165**
Bethlem and Maudsley Gazette. (UK ISSN 0263-9963) **3331**, 2459, 3276, 4014
Bethphage Messenger. (US) **1734**, 4399
Beto. (GW ISSN 0179-0315) **1993**
Beto na Beto. (ZR) **4466**
Beton. (GW ISSN 0005-9846) **603**
Beton. (BE) **603**
Beton i Zhelezobeton. (RU ISSN 0005-9889) **603**
Beton-Kalender. (GW) **603**
Beton-Landbau see Bauen fuer die Landwirtschaft **602**
†Beton-Litteratur Referater. (DK ISSN 0409-2694) **5147**
Beton- und Fertigteil-Jahrbuch. (GW ISSN 0067-6365) **1862**
Beton- und Stahlbetonbau. (GW ISSN 0005-9900) **603**
▼Betong. (SW) **603**
Betongprodukter. (NO) **603**
Betoni. (FI ISSN 1235-2136) **604**
Betoniek. (NE ISSN 0166-137X) **604**
Betonituote see Betoni **604**
Betonstein-Jahrbuch see Beton- und Fertigteil-Jahrbuch **1862**
Betonstein-Zeitung see Betonwerk und Fertigteil-Technik **604**
Betontechnik. (GW ISSN 0138-2101) **604**
Betontechnische Berichte. (GW ISSN 0409-2740) **604**
Betonwerk und Fertigteil-Technik. (GW ISSN 0373-4331) **604**
Betreff. (GW ISSN 0932-5492) **4054**, 1249
Der Betrieb. (GW ISSN 0005-9935) **2707**
Betrieb und Belegschaft. (GW) **1784**
Betrieb und Energie. (GW ISSN 0931-9344) **1784**
Betrieb und Meister. (GW ISSN 0341-4477) **1072**
Betrieb und Wirtschaft. (GW) **847**
Betriebliche Altersversorgung. (GW ISSN 0005-9951) **2528**
Betriebliche Ausbildungspraxis. (GW) **3403**, 1682
Betriebliches Vorschlagswesen. (GW ISSN 0340-9279) **1003**
Betriebs-Berater. (GW ISSN 0340-7918) **2604**, 1003
Betriebs-Management Service see Der Betriebsleiter **1003**
Betriebs- und Marktwirtschaft im Gartenbau. (GW ISSN 0303-1241) **2122**
Betriebs- und Wirtschaftsinformatik. (US) **825**
Betriebsergebnisse Buchfuehrender Betriebe. (GW) **647**
Die Betriebskrankenkasse. (GW ISSN 0342-0817) **2528**
Der Betriebsleiter. (GW ISSN 0344-5941) **1003**
Betriebspruefung. (GW ISSN 0174-5395) **1088**
▼Das Betriebsrestaurant. (GW ISSN 0937-7646) **2472**
Betriebssicherheit - B S see Neue B S **3619**
Betriebstechnik. (GW ISSN 0409-2791) **1816**, 3016
Die Betriebswirtschaft. (GW ISSN 0342-7064) **1003**
Betriebswirtschaftliche Beratungsstelle fuer den Einzelhandel Chef-Telegramm see B B E Chef-Telegramm **1003**

Betriebswirtschaftliche Blaetter fuer die Praxis der Sparkassen und Girozentralen see Betriebswirtschaftliche Blaetter fuer die Praxis der Sparkassen und Landesbanken - Girozentralen **1003**
Betriebswirtschaftliche Blaetter fuer die Praxis der Sparkassen und Landesbanken - Girozentralen. (GW) **1003**, **768**, **1057**
Betriebswirtschaftliche Forschung und Praxis. (GW ISSN 0340-5370) **1003**
Betriebswirtschaftliche Mitteilungen see Management Praxis **1019**
†Betriebswirtschaftliche O P W Z - Dokumentation. (Oesterreichisches Produktivitaets- und Wirtschaftlichkeits-Zentrum (OPWZ) (AU) **5147**
Betriebswirtschafts-Magazin see Gablers - Magazin **1011**
Betrifft Justiz. (GW ISSN 0179-2776) **2604**
Betrifft Sport. (GW ISSN 0176-8700) **3799**, **1529**
Better Beagling. (US ISSN 0736-9743) **3708**
Better Breeding. (UK ISSN 0006-0046) **212**, **198**
Better Buildings. (US ISSN 0744-530X) **604**
Better Business. (US) **1113**
Better Business see New Zealand Business **1148**
†Better Business Bureau. (US) **5147**
Better Business Bureau of Metropolitan Toronto. Directory & Consumer Guide. (CN) **1502**
Better Business by Telephone. (US) **1003**, **1361**
Better Buys for Business see What to Buy for Business **1056**
A Better Channel. (US) **805**
Better Crops with Plant Food. (US ISSN 0006-0089) **170**
†Better Health & Living. (US) **5148**
Better Homemaking see Planning for Living **2449**
Better Homes & Dykes. (US) **2451**, **4838**
Better Homes and Gardens. (US ISSN 0006-0151) **2548**, **295**, **2444**
Better Homes and Gardens Baking Ideas see Better Homes and Gardens Holiday Cooking **2087**
Better Homes and Gardens Bedroom and Bath Ideas. (US) **2548**
Better Homes and Gardens Building Ideas. (US ISSN 0093-0938) **295**
▼Better Homes and Gardens Bunnies, Bears and Cats. (US) **353**
Better Homes and Gardens Christmas Cookies. (US) **2444**
▼Better Homes and Gardens Christmas Cross Stitch. (US) **353**
Better Homes and Gardens Christmas Ideas. (US ISSN 0405-6590) **2444**, **2434**
▼Better Homes and Gardens Christmas Ornaments. (US) **353**
Better Homes and Gardens Country Crafts. (US) **353**
Better Homes and Gardens Country Kitchen Ideas. (US) **2444**
Better Homes and Gardens Decorating. (US) **2549**
Better Homes and Gardens Decorating Ideas see Better Homes and Gardens Decorating **2549**
▼Better Homes and Gardens Decorative Woodcrafts. (US) **353**, **639**
Better Homes and Gardens Do-It-Yourself. (US) **2444**
▼Better Homes and Gardens Dollmaker. (US) **353**
▼Better Homes and Gardens Garden, Deck and Landscape Planner. (US) **2122**, **604**
Better Homes and Gardens Garden Ideas and Outdoor Living. (US) **2122**, **2444**
▼Better Homes and Gardens Garden Products and Planning Guide. (US) **2123**
▼Better Homes and Gardens Guide to Children's Products. (US) **1233**, **2281**

Better Homes and Gardens Holiday Appetizers. (US) **2444**
Better Homes and Gardens Holiday Cooking. (US) **2087**
Better Homes and Gardens Holiday Crafts. (US ISSN 0278-7490) **353**
Better Homes and Gardens Holiday Desserts. (US) **2062**, **2444**
▼Better Homes and Gardens Home Furnishings Products Guide. (US) **2557**
Better Homes and Gardens Home Improvement Ideas see Better Homes & Gardens Remodeling Ideas **295**
Better Homes and Gardens Home Plan Ideas. (US) **2444**, **2123**
Better Homes and Gardens Home Products Guide. (US) **604**, **2500**
Better Homes and Gardens Kitchen & Bath Ideas. (US ISSN 0731-5600) **2549**
▼Better Homes and Gardens Kitchen and Bath Products Guide. (US) **2557**
Better Homes and Gardens Low-Calorie Recipes. (US) **3603**
†Better Homes and Gardens Microwave Recipes. (US) **5148**
▼Better Homes and Gardens Needlework & Craft Ideas. (US) **5148**
▼Better Homes and Gardens Prizewinning Remodeling. (US) **2549**, **2500**
Better Homes & Gardens Remodeling Ideas. (US) **295**, **604**
▼Better Homes and Gardens Santa Claus. (US) **353**
Better Homes and Gardens Traditional Home see Traditional Home **2555**
Better Homes and Gardens Window & Wall Ideas. (US ISSN 0277-836X) **2549**
Better Homes and Gardens Wood. (US) **2500**
Better Investing. (US ISSN 0006-016X) **939**
Better Living. (US ISSN 0273-6160) **2222**
Better Management. (UK ISSN 0006-0186) **198**, **1003**
Better Nutrition see Better Nutrition for Today's Living **3603**
Better Nutrition for Today's Living. (US) **3603**
Better Radio and Television. (US ISSN 0006-0194) **1355**, **1369**
†Better Rep Management. (US ISSN 0736-7171) **5148**
Better Roads. (US ISSN 0006-0208) **1862**, **4717**
Better Schools (Chicago) see Gas Industries Magazine **3687**
Better Transit Bulletin see Notes from Underground **4654**
Better World. (US) **3593**, **3762**
Betteravier. (BE) **170**
Betteravier Francais. (FR ISSN 0405-6701) **170**
Betuman. (IS) **604**
†Between C and D. (US) **5148**
Between Friends. (US) **2286**, **2270**
Between the Chains. (SA) **2331**
Between the Lakes Newsletter. (US) **2400**
Between the Leaves. (AT) **2096**
†Between the Lines (Los Angeles). (US) **5148**
Between the Lines (Syracuse). (US) **4501**
Between the Lines (Washington). (US) **3875**, **2567**
Between the Lions. (US) **3522**
Between the Vines. (US ISSN 1051-8959) **2123**
¡Between Times. (US ISSN 0745-1172) **5148**
Beursbengel. (NE ISSN 0006-0313) **2528**
Beursklanken see Expovisie **3392**
Bev Dobson's Rose Letter. (US) **2123**
Beveiliging. (NE ISSN 0926-7859) **3615**, **604**
▼Beverage Aisle. (US) **2090**
Beverage Alcohol Business Scene. (US) **378**
Beverage Alcohol Market Report. (US ISSN 0736-220X) **378**

Beverage and Food World. (II ISSN 0970-6194) **378**, **2062**
Beverage Beacon - Ledger. (US) **378**
Beverage Bulletin. (US ISSN 0006-0356) **378**
Beverage Canada. (CN ISSN 0381-6745) **378**
Beverage Communicator. (US) **378**
Beverage Digest. (US ISSN 0738-8853) **378**, **2062**, **3647**
Beverage Dynamics. (US) **378**
Beverage Industry. (US ISSN 0148-6187) **378**
Beverage Industry Annual Manual. (US ISSN 8755-0717) **378**
Beverage Industry News California Goldbook see B I N California Goldbook **5145**
Beverage Ledger see Beverage Beacon - Ledger **378**
Beverage Marketing Directory (Year). (US) **378**
Beverage Media. (US ISSN 0006-0372) **378**
†Beverage Profit Ideas. (US) **5148**
Beverage Record. (US) **378**
Beverage Register. (US) **378**
†Beverage Retailer Weekly. (US) **5148**
Beverage World (English Edition). (US ISSN 0098-2318) **378**, **2062**
Beverage World En Espanol. (US) **379**, **2062**
Beverage World International. (US) **379**
Beverage World's Daily Desk Reference Living Directory see Beverage World's Databank **379**
Beverage World's Databank. (US) **379**
Beverages. (US ISSN 0006-0399) **379**
Beverages: Latin American Industrial Report. (US) **379**
Beverly Hills (213). (US) **2222**
Beverly Hills Bar Association Journal. (US ISSN 1051-628X) **2604**
▼Beverly Hills 90210. (US) **1369**
Beverly Review. (US ISSN 0006-0410) **2222**
Bevoelkerungsbewegung in der Schweiz/Mouvement de la Population en Suisse. (SZ) **3979**
Bevoelkerungsschutz-Magazin. (GW) **1273**
Bevolking en Gezin. (BE ISSN 0523-1159) **3979**
Bewaehrungs: Fachzeitschrift fuer Bewaehrungs, Gerichts, und Straffaelligheit. (GW ISSN 0405-6779) **1484**
Bewusster Leben. (LH ISSN 0006-0429) **3799**
†Beyond Avalon. (US) **5148**
Beyond Reality. (US) **3668**
†Beyond S F Anthology. (GW) **5148**
Beyond Science Fiction. (US) **3010**
Beyond Words. (AT) **4165**, **2805**
▼Beyond Z. (US) **1618**
Bezalel in Brief. (IS) **1305**
Bezirkshauptmannschaft Amstetten. Heimatkundliche Beilage zum Amstblatt. (AU) **2307**
Bezirkshauptmannschaft Melk. Heimatkundliche Beilage zum Amtsblatt. (AU) **2307**
Bezirkshauptmannschaft Tulln. Heimatkundliches Beiblatt zum Amtsblatt. (AU) **2307**
Bezopasnost' Truda v Promyshlennosti/Labour Safety in Industry. (RU) **3615**
Bezpecna Praca. (CS) **3615**
Bezpecnost a Hygiena Prace/Safety and Hygiene of Work. (CS ISSN 0006-0453) **2580**, **4098**
Bhabha Atomic Research Centre. Nuclear Physics Division. Annual Report. (II) **3846**
Bhagalpur University Journal. (II) **4367**, **4302**
Bhagirath. (II ISSN 0006-0461) **4822**
Bhagyavati Panchanga. (II) **362**
Bhandarkar Oriental Research Institute. Annals. (II) **3635**
Bharat Darshan. (CN) **1993**
Bharat Heavy Electricals Ltd. Journal see B H E L Journal **1883**
†Bharat Krishak Samaj. Year Book. (II ISSN 0067-6454) **5148**

Bharat Sevak. (II ISSN 0006-0488) **847**
Bharata Varsha. (II) **3875**
Bharatha Darshana. (II ISSN 0006-0496) **3762**
Bharathi. (II) **2199**
Bharati Research Institute. Journal. (II) **2337**
Bharati Te Videshi Sahita. (II ISSN 0006-050X) **2899**
Bharatiya Purabhilekha Patrika. see Studies in Indian Epigraphy **2845**
Bharatiya Sthalanama Patrika. see Studies in Indian Place Names **2845**
Bharatya Vidya. (II) **3635**, **3762**, **4217**
Bhartiya Krishi Anusandhan Patrika. (II ISSN 0303-3821) **79**, **579**
†Bhashavimarsa. (II ISSN 0250-975X) **5148**
Bhau Vishnu Ashetar Vedic Research Series. (II) **2805**, **4217**
Bhavan's Journal. (II ISSN 0006-0518) **2899**, **2503**
Bhilai Darshan see Steel Bulletin **3420**
Bhugola Samayiki. (BG) **2243**
Bhushan's World Trade Enquiries. (II ISSN 0006-0542) **901**
Bi-Lifestyle. (US) **3396**, **4838**
Bi-Monthly. (US) **2451**
Bi-Monthly Theatrical Calendar. (US) **4630**
Bi-Weekly Theatrical Calendar see Bi-Monthly Theatrical Calendar **4630**
Biaf - Israel Aviation and Space Magazine. (IS ISSN 0302-8194) **49**
Bialostocczyzna. (PL ISSN 0860-4096) **2352**
Bialostockie Towarzystwo Naukowe. Prace. (PL ISSN 0067-6470) **2352**
Bianco e Nero. (IT ISSN 0006-0577) **3504**, **1369**
Bianji Xuebao/Acta Editologica. (CC) **2567**
Bianji zhi You/Compilers' Friend. (CC) **4121**, **2567**, **2604**
Biannual of Electronics Research see Texas Annual of Electronics Research **1779**
Bianyaqi/Converter. (CC) **1883**
Biatas - the Tillage Farmer. (IE) **170**
Bibbia e Oriente. (IT ISSN 0006-0585) **4165**, **267**, **2307**
La Bibbia nella Storia. (IT) **4256**
Bibel Heute. (GW ISSN 0006-0593) **4256**
Bibel im Jahr. (GW) **4165**
Bibel-Journalen. (SW ISSN 0006-0607) **4165**
Bibel und Gemeinde. (GW ISSN 0006-0615) **4165**
Bibel und Kirche. (GW ISSN 0006-0623) **4165**
Bibel und Liturgie. (GW ISSN 0006-064X) **4165**
Bibelreport. (GW ISSN 0933-9949) **4165**
Bibeltrogna Vaenners Missionstidning. (SW ISSN 0006-0658) **4165**
Bibione Vacanze. (IT) **4754**
Bible Advocate. (US ISSN 0746-0104) **4165**
Bible Book Study for Adult Teachers. (US ISSN 0162-4202) **4231**
Bible Book Study for Adults. (US ISSN 0162-4849) **4231**
Bible Book Study for Adults. Chinese Edition. (US ISSN 0897-0750) **4231**
Bible Book Study for Adults. Korean Edition. (US ISSN 0747-9514) **4231**
Bible Book Study for Adults. Large Print Edition. (US ISSN 0162-4849) **4231**
Bible Book Study for Youth. (US ISSN 0162-4822) **4231**
Bible Book Study for Youth Teachers. (US ISSN 0162-4830) **4231**
Bible Discoverers. (US ISSN 0162-4695) **4231**
Bible Discoverers Teacher. (US ISSN 0162-4687) **4231**
Bible et Terre Sainte see Monde de la Bible **279**

Bible Exploration Material and Annual Project. (UK) **4165**
Bible Exploration Material and Annual Scripture Project *see* Bible Exploration Material and Annual Project **4165**
Bible Friend. (US ISSN 0006-0739) **4165**
Bible-in-Life Friends. (US) **4165**
Bible-in-Life Pix. (US ISSN 0039-5250) **1249**
Bible Lands. (UK ISSN 0006-0763) **4231**
Bible Learners. (US ISSN 0162-4679) **4231**
Bible Learners. Teacher. (US ISSN 0162-4660) **4231**
Bible Lesson Digest. (US ISSN 0162-4857) **4231**
Bible of Weather Forecasting. (US ISSN 0749-3584) **3433**
Bible Researcher. (SW ISSN 0347-2787) **4165**, **2352**
Bible Review. (US ISSN 8755-6316) **4165**
Bible Science Newsletter. (US) **4165**
Bible Searchers. (US ISSN 0006-078X) **4231**
Bible Searchers Teacher. (US ISSN 0006-0798) **4231**
Bible Society News *see* Word in Action **4210**
Bible Standard and Herald of Christ's Kingdom. (US ISSN 0006-081X) **4165**
Bible Story Time Older Pupil. (US ISSN 0890-880X) **4231**
Bible Story Time Teacher. (US ISSN 0890-8788) **4231**
Bible Story Time Younger Pupil. (US ISSN 0890-8796) **4231**
Bible Study Leaflet. (US ISSN 0162-475X) **4231**
Bible Study Monthly. (UK) **4165**
Bible Study Pocket Commentary. (US ISSN 0162-4741) **4231**
Bible Study Special Ministries. (US ISSN 0748-5409) **4231**
Bible Teacher and Leader. (US) **4280**
Bible-Time. (US ISSN 0006-0828) **1249**, **4165**
Bible Today. (US ISSN 0006-0836) **4165**
Biblebhashyam. (II ISSN 0970-2288) **4256**
Bibles for the World News. (US) **4165**
Biblia. (JA ISSN 0006-0860) **2792**
Biblia - Gente. (BL) **4256**
Biblia Revuo. (IT ISSN 0006-0879) **4165**
Biblica. (VC ISSN 0006-0887) **4256**
Biblica et Orientalia. (VC) **4256**, **3635**
Biblical Archaeologist. (US ISSN 0006-0895) **267**, **3635**, **4165**
Biblical Archaeology Review. (US ISSN 0098-9444) **267**, **4165**
Biblical Errancy. (US) **4165**
Biblical Evangelist. (US ISSN 0740-7998) **4231**
Biblical Illustrator. (US ISSN 0195-1351) **4231**
Biblical Missions. (US ISSN 0006-0909) **4231**
Biblical Polemics. (IS ISSN 0792-4739) **4165**
Biblical Recorder. (US ISSN 0279-8182) **4231**
Biblical Research. (US ISSN 0067-6535) **4165**
Biblical Scholarship in North America. (US ISSN 0277-0474) **4165**
Biblical Theology. (IE ISSN 0006-0917) **4165**
Biblical Theology Bulletin. (US ISSN 0146-1079) **4165**
Biblical Viewpoint. (US ISSN 0006-0925) **4166**
Biblicum. (SW ISSN 0345-1453) **4166**
Biblio-Files *see* At the Library **2745**
Bibliofilia. (IT ISSN 0006-0941) **4140**
Bibliografi Nasional Indonesia/Indonesian National Bibliography. (IO ISSN 0523-1639) **390**
Bibliografi Negara Malaysia. *see* Malaysian National Bibliography **2329**

Bibliografi over Danmarks Offentlige Publikationer. (DK ISSN 0067-6543) **390**
Bibliografi over Dansk Kunst. (DK) **351**
Bibliografi over Europaeiske Kunstneres Ex Libris/Europaeische Ex Libris/European Book Plates/Ex Libris d'Europe. (DK) **352**
Bibliografia Agricola Chilena. (CL) **134**
Bibliografia Agrometeorologii/Bibliography of Agrometeorology. (PL ISSN 0239-958X) **3444**, **134**, **390**
Bibliografia Analityczna Bibliotekoznawstwa i Informacji Naukowej. (PL ISSN 0033-233X) **2792**, **390**
Bibliografia Argentina de Psicologia. (AG ISSN 0523-1698) **4051**
Bibliografia Bibliotecologica Argentina. (AG ISSN 0067-656X) **2792**
Bibliografia Brasileira. (BL) **2792**
†Bibliografia Brasileira de Agricultura (Year). (BL) **5148**
†Bibliografia Brasileira de Ciencias Sociais. (BL ISSN 0067-6608) **5148**
†Bibliografia Brasileira de Direito. (BL ISSN 0067-6616) **5148**
†Bibliografia Brasileira de Documentacao. (BL ISSN 0067-6624) **5148**
Bibliografia Brasileira de Educacao. (BL ISSN 0067-6632) **1674**
Bibliografia Brasileira de Energia Nuclear. (BL ISSN 0102-3500) **1797**, **1804**
†Bibliografia Brasileira de Engenharia. (BL ISSN 0100-0705) **5148**
†Bibliografia Brasileira de Fisica. (BL ISSN 0067-6640) **5148**
†Bibliografia Brasileira de Matematica. (BL ISSN 0067-6667) **5148**
†Bibliografia Brasileira de Medicina. (BL ISSN 0067-6675) **5148**
Bibliografia Brasileira de Odontologia. (BL ISSN 0100-6266) **3166**
Bibliografia Brasileira de Quimica *see* Bibliografia Brasileira de Quimica e Quimica Tecnologica **5148**
†Bibliografia Brasileira de Quimica e Quimica Tecnologica. (BL ISSN 0100-0756) **5148**
Bibliografia Brasileira de Quimica Tecnologia *see* Bibliografia Brasileira de Quimica e Quimica Tecnologica **5148**
†Bibliografia Brasileira de Zoologia. (BL ISSN 0067-6691) **5148**
Bibliografia Classificada. (BL ISSN 0006-0992) **390**
Bibliografia Cubana. (CU ISSN 0574-6086) **390**
Bibliografia de la Literatura Hispanica. (SP) **2981**, **390**
Bibliografia de Politica Industrial. (BL ISSN 0103-2038) **706**, **973**, **3936**
†Bibliografia de Publicacoes Oficiais Brasileiras. (BL ISSN 0100-722X) **5148**
Bibliografia Dobrogei. (RM) **390**
Bibliografia e Storia della Critica. (IT) **2981**
Bibliografia Erityssiryhmien Liikunnan Tutkimuksesta/Bibliography on Research in Physical Education and Sport for the Handicapped. (FI ISSN 0357-2498) **1674**, **1734**
Bibliografia Espanola (Annual). (SP ISSN 0523-1760) **390**
Bibliografia Espanola (Monthly). (SP ISSN 0525-3675) **390**
Bibliografia Espanola. Suplemento de Cartografia. (SP ISSN 0214-4441) **390**
Bibliografia Espanola. Suplemento de Musica Impresa. (SP) **390**
Bibliografia Espanola. Suplemento de Publicaciones Periodicas. (SP ISSN 0210-8372) **390**
Bibliografia Forestal Latinoamericana. (VE ISSN 0798-1945) **2111**
Bibliografia Geologiczna Polski. (PL ISSN 0373-1987) **1550**, **390**, **1555**

Bibliografia Gospodarki i Inzynierii Wodnej/Bibliography of Water Management and Engineering. (PL ISSN 0239-622X) **4834**, **390**, **1841**
Bibliografia Historica Mexicana. (MX ISSN 0185-1578) **2327**
Bibliografia Historii Polskiej. (PL ISSN 0067-6721) **2327**
Bibliografia Hydrologii i Oceanologii/Bibliography of Hydrology and Oceanology. (PL ISSN 0239-6246) **1550**, **390**
Bibliografia Italiana di Idraulica. (IT ISSN 0006-1042) **1841**
Bibliografia Kombetare e Librit Shqip. (AA) **390**
Bibliografia Kombetare e Periodikeve Shqip. (AA) **390**
Bibliografia Kombetare e Republikes Popullore Socialiste te Shqiperise. Artikujt e Periodikut Shqip. *see* Bibliografia Kombetare e Periodikeve Shqip **390**
Bibliografia Kombetare e Republikos Popullore Socialiste te Shquperise. Librit Shqip *see* Bibliografia Kombetare e Librit Shqip **390**
Bibliografia Latinoamericana: Part I. (MX ISSN 0185-2884) **3**
Bibliografia Latinoamericana: Part II. (MX ISSN 0185-2930) **3**, **390**
†Bibliografia Linguistica Italiana. (IT) **5148**
Bibliografia Meteorologii/Bibliography of Meteorology. (PL ISSN 0239-6270) **3444**, **390**
Bibliografia Mexicana. (MX ISSN 0006-1069) **391**
Bibliografia Missionaria. (VC ISSN 0394-9869) **4212**
Bibliografia Muzyczna Polskich Czasopism Niemuzycznych. (PL) **3588**
Bibliografia na Bulgarskata Bibliografiia/Bibliography of Bulgarian Bibliographies. (BU ISSN 0204-7373) **391**
Bibliografia Nazionale Italiana. (IT ISSN 0006-1077) **391**, **4140**
Bibliografia Polskich Czasopism Muzycznych. (PL) **3588**
Bibliografia Pomorza Zachodniego. Pismiennictwo Polskie/Bibliography of West Pomerania. Polish Literature.(PL ISSN 0409-3453) **391**
▼Bibliografia Pomorza Zachodniego - Pismiennictwo Zagraniczne/Bibliography of West Pomerania - Foreign Literature. (PL ISSN 0138-0702) **391**
Bibliografia Portuguesa de Construcao Civil *see* Bibliografia Portuguesa de Engenharia Civil **1841**
Bibliografia Portuguesa de Engenharia Civil. (PO) **1841**
Bibliografia Prac Magisterskich, Doktorskich i Habilitacyjnych Przyjetych w S G G W w Warszawie. (PL ISSN 0208-4252) **134**
Bibliografia Publikacji Pracownikow Naukowych Akademii Ekonomicznej w Krakowie. (PL) **706**
Bibliografia Publikacji Pracownikow w S G G W w Warszawie. (PL ISSN 0208-4260) **134**
Bibliografia sobre la Economica Mexicana. Libros. (MX ISSN 0188-6673) **706**
Bibliografia Tematica sobre Judaismo Argentino. (AG) **4222**, **391**
Bibliografia Teologica Comentada del Area Iberoamericana. (AG ISSN 0326-6680) **4212**, **391**
†Bibliografia Ticinese. (SZ ISSN 0067-6772) **5148**
Bibliografia Venezolana. (VE ISSN 0006-1085) **2747**
Bibliografia Wydawnictw Ciaglych/Bibliography of Polish Serials. (PL ISSN 0239-4421) **391**
Bibliografia z Zakresu Meteorologii Rolniczej i Lesnej *see* Bibliografia Agrometeorologii **3444**
Bibliografia Zawartosci Czasopism. (PL ISSN 0006-1093) **391**
Bibliografica Folclorica. (BL) **2053**, **236**

BIBLIOGRAFIJA JUGOSLAVIJE 5975

Bibliograficheskie Posobiya Belorusskoi S.S.R. (BW ISSN 0203-3941) **391**
Bibliograficky Katalog C S F R. Ceske Knihy. Ceska Grafika a Mapy v Roce.(CS ISSN 0862-9226) **391**
Bibliograficky Katalog C S F R. Ceske Knihy. Soupis Ceskych Bibliografii. (CS ISSN 0862-9234) **391**
Bibliograficky Katalog C S F R: Ceske Hudebniny, Gramofonove Desky a C D. (CS ISSN 0862-8580) **391**, **3541**
Bibliograficky Katalog C S F R: Ceske Knihy. (CS ISSN 0862-9218) **391**
Bibliograficky Katalog C S F R: Ceske Knihy. Ceske Disertace a Autoreferaty. (CS ISSN 0862-8599) **391**
Bibliograficky Katalog C S F R: Clanky v Ceskych Casopisech. (CS ISSN 0862-9269) **391**
Bibliograficky Katalog C S S R. Ceske Knihy. Ceska Grafika a Mapy za Rok (Year) *see* Bibliograficky Katalog C S F R. Ceske Knihy. Ceska Grafika a Mapy v Roce **391**
Bibliograficky Katalog C S S R. Ceske Knihy. Zvlastni Sesit. Bibliografie A V T I *see* Bibliografie Ceskeho Knihovnictvi, Bibliografie a V T I **391**
Bibliograficky Katalog C S S R: Ceske Hudebniny a Gramofonove Desky *see* Bibliograficky Katalog C S F R: Ceske Hudebniny, Gramofonove Desky a C D **391**
Bibliograficky Katalog C S S R. Ceske Knihy. Ceske Disertace *see* Bibliograficky Katalog C S F R: Ceske Knihy. Ceske Disertace a Autoreferaty **391**
†Bibliograficky Vyber: Zdravotnictvi a Pravo/Abstracts of Health Legislature. (CS) **5148**
Bibliograficky Zbornik. (CS ISSN 0067-6780) **391**
Bibliografie Ceskeho Knihovnictvi, Bibliografie a V T I. (CS ISSN 0139-8539) **391**
Bibliografie Nederlandse Sociale Wetenschappen. (NE) **4425**, **391**
Bibliografie Nederlandse Sociologie *see* Bibliografie Nederlandse Sociale Wetenschappen **4425**
Bibliografie van de Nederlandse Taal- en Literatuur Wetenschap. (NE ISSN 0045-186X) **2855**
Bibliografie van Nederlandse Proefschriften/Dutch Theses. (NE ISSN 0166-9966) **391**
Bibliografie van Regionale Onderzoekingen op Sociaalwetenschappelijk Terrein/Bibliography of Regional Studies in the Social Sciences. (NE ISSN 0168-5988) **4394**
Bibliografija Domacih i Stranih Knjiga. (YU ISSN 0350-1450) **2981**
Bibliografija Jugoslavije. Clanci i Prilozi u Serijskim Publikacijama. Serija A: Drustvene Nauke. (YU ISSN 0352-5899) **4394**, **391**
Bibliografija Jugoslavije. Clanci i Prilozi u Serijskim Publikacijama. Serija B: Prirodne, Primenjene, Medicinske i Tehnicke Nauke. (YU ISSN 0352-5945) **4354**, **391**
Bibliografija Jugoslavije. Clanci i Prilozi u Serijskim Publikacijama. Serija C: Umetnost, Sport, Filologija, Knjizevnost. (YU ISSN 0352-5996) **391**
Bibliografija Jugoslavije. Knjige, Brosure i Muzikalije. (YU ISSN 0523-2201) **391**
Bibliografija Jugoslavije. Naucni i Strucni Radovi u Serijskim Publikacijama. Serija B: Prirodne, Primenjene, Medicinske i Tehnicke Nauke *see* Bibliografija Jugoslavije. Clanci i Prilozi u Serijskim Publikacijama. Serija B: Prirodne, Primenjene, Medicinske i Tehnicke Nauke **4354**
Bibliografija Jugoslavije. Serija A: Drustvene Nauke. Clanci i Prilozi u Casopisima, Listovima i Zbornicima *see* Bibliografija Jugoslavije. Clanci i Prilozi u Serijskim Publikacijama. Serija A: Drustvene Nauke **4394**

Bibliografija Jugoslavije. Serijske Publikacije. (YU ISSN 0350-0349) **391**

Bibliografija Medicinske Periodike Jugoslavije/Index Medicus Iugoslavicus. (CI ISSN 0067-6799) **3166**

Bibliografija Prevoda U S F R J. (YU ISSN 0350-9974) **391**

†Bibliografija Prinovljenih Domacih Publikacija. (YU) **5148**

Bibliografija Prispelih Knjiga Clanaka iz Strucnih Casopisa i Drugih Dokumenata. (YU ISSN 0006-1166) **392**

Bibliografija Recenzija iz Domacih Listova i Casopisa. (YU) **2860**

Bibliografija Roto Stampe i Stripova. (YU ISSN 0351-1537) **2981**, 392

Bibliografija Zvanicnih Publikacija S F R J. (YU ISSN 0351-2843) **392**

Bibliografisch Repertorium van de Wijsbegeerte. *see* Repertoire Bibliographique de la Philosophie **3788**

Bibliografski Vjesnik. (YU ISSN 0409-3739) **2747**, 2352

Bibliographia Africana. (II ISSN 0006-1190) **392**

Bibliographia Asiatica. (II ISSN 0006-1212) **3646**

Bibliographia Belgica. (BE ISSN 0409-3747) **392**

Bibliographia Cartographica. (GW ISSN 0340-0409) **2267**, 392

Bibliographia de Interlingua. (NE ISSN 0920-7104) **2855**, 392

Bibliographia Franciscana. (IT) **4212**, 424

Bibliographia Geodaetica. (GW ISSN 0006-1239) **1550**

Bibliographia Humboldtiana. (GW) **2503**

Bibliographia Internationalis Spiritualitatis. (VC ISSN 0084-7836) **3787**

Bibliographia Medica Cechoslovaca. (CS ISSN 0067-6802) **3166**

Bibliographia Missionaria *see* Bibliografia Missionaria **4212**

Bibliographia Musicologica. (NE ISSN 0084-7844) **3588**

Bibliographia Phytosociologica Syntaxonomica. (GW) **461**, 496

Bibliographia Scientiae Naturalis Helvetica. (SZ ISSN 0067-6829) **4354**

Bibliographic Guide to Anthropology and Archaeology. (US ISSN 0896-8101) **253**, 290, 392

Bibliographic Guide to Art and Architecture. (US ISSN 0360-2699) **309**, 392

Bibliographic Guide to Black Studies. (US ISSN 0360-2710) **2030**, 392

Bibliographic Guide to Business and Economics. (US ISSN 0360-2702) **706**

Bibliographic Guide to Computer Science. (US ISSN 0896-8098) **1403**

Bibliographic Guide to Conference Publications. (US ISSN 0360-2729) **392**

Bibliographic Guide to Dance. (US ISSN 0360-2737) **1532**, 392

▼Bibliographic Guide to East Asian Studies. (US ISSN 1046-8765) **3646**, 392, 4394

Bibliographic Guide to Education. (US) **1674**, 392

Bibliographic Guide to Government Publications - Foreign. (US ISSN 0360-280X) **392**

Bibliographic Guide to Government Publications - U S. (US ISSN 0360-2796) **392**

Bibliographic Guide to Latin American Studies. (US ISSN 0162-5314) **392**, 4394

Bibliographic Guide to Law. (US ISSN 0360-2745) **2697**, 392

Bibliographic Guide to Maps and Atlases. (US) **2267**, 392

Bibliographic Guide to Microform Publications. (US ISSN 0891-3749) **392**

▼Bibliographic Guide to Middle Eastern Studies. (US ISSN 1058-644X) **3646**, 392

Bibliographic Guide to Music. (US ISSN 0360-2753) **3588**, 392

Bibliographic Guide to North American History. (US ISSN 0147-6491) **2327**, 392

Bibliographic Guide to Psychology. (US ISSN 0360-277X) **4051**, 392

Bibliographic Guide to Soviet and European Studies. (US ISSN 0162-5322) **2352**

Bibliographic Guide to Technology. (US ISSN 0360-2761) **392**, 4594

Bibliographic Guide to Theatre Arts. (US ISSN 0360-2788) **4643**

Bibliographic Index. (US ISSN 0006-1255) **392**

Bibliographic Index of Health Education Periodicals *see* B I H E P **5145**

Bibliographic Index of the Tobacco Scene *see* B I T S **5145**

Bibliographica Judaica. (US ISSN 0067-6853) **4212**

†Bibliographical Series on Coconut. (CE ISSN 0379-1564) **5148**

Bibliographical Services Throughout the World. (UN) **392**

Bibliographical Society of America. Papers. (US ISSN 0006-128X) **4121**, 2747

Bibliographical Society of Australia and New Zealand. Bulletin. (AT ISSN 0084-7852) **2792**

Bibliographical Society of Canada. Bulletin. (CN ISSN 0709-3756) **392**

Bibliographical Society of Canada. Facsimile Series. (CN ISSN 0067-687X) **392**

Bibliographical Society of Canada. Monographs. (CN ISSN 0067-6888) **392**

Bibliographical Society of Canada. Papers. (CN ISSN 0067-6896) **392**

†Bibliographie Aktuell. (GW ISSN 0138-2225) **5148**

Bibliographie Analytique de l'Afrique Antique. (FR) **2327**

Bibliographie Annuelle de l'Histoire de France. (FR ISSN 0067-6918) **2327**

Bibliographie Annuelle de Madagascar. (MG ISSN 0067-6926) **392**

Bibliographie Bildende Kunst. (GW ISSN 0232-5810) **352**

†Bibliographie Courante d'Articles de Periodiques Posterieurs a 1944 sur les Problemes Politiques, Economiques et Sociaux/Index to Post-1944 Periodical Articles on Political, Economic and Social Problems. (US) **5148**

Bibliographie d'Histoire Luxembourgeoise. (LU ISSN 0067-7043) **2327**

Bibliographie de Belgique/Belgische Bibliografie. (BE ISSN 0006-1336) **392**

Bibliographie de l'Algerie/Al-Bibliyugrafya al-Djazairiyah. (AE ISSN 0523-2392) **392**, 3

Bibliographie de l'Histoire Bernoise. *see* Bibliographie der Berner Geschichte **2327**

Bibliographie de la C I I D. Irrigation, Drainage et Maitrise des Crues. *see* Bibliography on Irrigation, Drainage, River Training and Flood Control **4834**

Bibliographie de la Cote d'Ivoire. (IV ISSN 0084-7860) **392**

Bibliographie de la France. Publications Officielles. (FR ISSN 0150-5955) **392**

Bibliographie de la France. Supplement 1: Publications en Serie. (FR ISSN 0150-1399) **392**

Bibliographie de la France. Supplement 3: Musique. (FR ISSN 0150-5971) **3588**

Bibliographie de la France. Supplement 4: Atlas, Cartes et Plans. (FR ISSN 0150-5998) **2267**

Bibliographie de la Philosophie/Bibliography of Philosophy. (FR ISSN 0006-1352) **3787**

Bibliographie de la Protection des Plantes. *see* Bibliographie der Pflanzenschutzliteratur **134**

Bibliographie der Antiquariats-, Auktions- und Kunstkataloge. (GW) **352**, 2792

Bibliographie der Berner Geschichte/Bibliographie de l'Histoire Bernoise. (SZ ISSN 0250-5673) **2327**, 392

Bibliographie der Bibliographien. (GW ISSN 0301-4614) **393**

Bibliographie der Buch- und Bibliotheksgeschichte. (GW ISSN 0723-3590) **2792**, 393

Bibliographie der Deutschen Literaturwissenschaft *see* Bibliographie der Deutschen Sprach- und Literaturwissenschaft **2981**

Bibliographie der Deutschen Sprach- und Literaturwissenschaft. (GW ISSN 0341-9363) **2981**

Bibliographie der Deutschsprachigen Psychologischen Literatur. (GW ISSN 0303-5999) **4051**

Bibliographie der Franzoesischen Literaturwissenschaft. (GW ISSN 0523-2465) **2981**

Bibliographie der Paedagogischen Veroeffentlichungen in der Deutschen Demokratischen Republik. (GW ISSN 0067-6969) **1674**

Bibliographie der Pflanzenschutzliteratur/Bibliography of Plant Protection/Bibliographie de la Protection des Plantes. (GW ISSN 0006-1387) **134**, 393

Bibliographie der Uebersetzungen Deutschsprachiger Werke. (GW ISSN 0006-1409) **393**

Bibliographie der Wirtschaftspresse. (GW ISSN 0006-1417) **706**

Bibliographie der Wirtschaftswissenschaften. (GW ISSN 0340-6121) **393**, 647

Bibliographie des Schweizerischen Rechts. (SZ) **2697**, 393

†Bibliographie des Travaux en Langue Francaise sur l'Afrique au Sud du Sahara, Sciences Humaines et Sociales. (FR) **5148**

Bibliographie du Quebec. (CN ISSN 0006-1441) **393**

Bibliographie du Senegal. (SG ISSN 0378-9942) **393**

Bibliographie Egyptologique Annuelle. *see* Annual Egyptological Bibliography **2327**

Bibliographie en Langue Francaise d'Histoire du Droit de 987 a 1914. (FR) **2697**

Bibliographie Ethnographique de l'Afrique Sud-Saharienne. (BE) **4394**

Bibliographie Europeene des Travaux sur l'URSS et l'Europe de l'Est. *see* European Bibliography of Soviet, East European and Slavonic Studies **2328**

Bibliographie Fremdsprachiger Germanica. (GW ISSN 0323-3154) **2855**

Bibliographie Geographique Internationale. (FR ISSN 0067-6993) **2267**, 393

Bibliographie Geschichte der Technik. (GW ISSN 0323-4355) **4614**, 2327

Bibliographie International de l'Histoire des Religions. *see* International Bibliography of the History of Religions **5215**

Bibliographie Internationale D'Ethnologie. *see* Internationale Volkskundliche Bibliographie **2060**

Bibliographie Internationale de l'Humanisme et de la Renaissance. (SZ ISSN 0067-7000) **2519**

Bibliographie Internationale de la Demographie Historique. *see* International Bibliography of Historical Demography **3992**

Bibliographie Internationale des Industries Agro-Alimentaires. (FR ISSN 0245-985X) **134**, 393, 2084

Bibliographie Juridique. *see* Rechtsbibliographie **2700**

Bibliographie Linguistique. *see* Linguistic Bibliography **2855**

Bibliographie Linguistischer Literatur. (GW ISSN 0172-3960) **2981**, 2855

Bibliographie Luxembourgeoise. (LU) **393**, 2352

Bibliographie Moderner Fremdsprachenunterricht. (GW) **2805**

Bibliographie Musik. (GW ISSN 0232-7678) **3588**

Bibliographie "Nahrung und Ernaehrung der Menschen": Ernaehrung *see* Bibliographie Nutris, Series: Ernaehrungswissenschaft **3613**

Bibliographie "Nahrung und Ernaehrung der Menschen": Lebensmittelwissenschaft *see* Bibliographie Nutris, Series: Lebensmittelwissenschaft **3613**

Bibliographie Nichtmarxistischer Philosophischer Zeitschriften *see* Bibliographie Philosophie **5148**

Bibliographie Nutris, Series: Ernaehrungswissenschaft. (GW) **3613**

Bibliographie Nutris, Series: Lebensmittelwissenschaft. (GW) **3613**

Bibliographie Paedagogik/Educational Bibliography. (GW ISSN 0523-2678) **393**, 1618

Bibliographie Papyrologique sur Fiches. (BE) **290**, 393

†Bibliographie Philosophie. (GW ISSN 0034-2262) **5148**

†Bibliographie Politikwissenschaft und Voelkerrecht. (GW) **5148**

Bibliographie Programmierter Unterricht *see* Bibliographie Paedagogik **393**

Bibliographie Rechtswissenschaft. (GW) **2697**

Bibliographie Romane. *see* Romanische Bibliographie **2856**

†Bibliographie Sozialisation und Sozialpaedagogik. (GW ISSN 0342-3964) **5148**

†Bibliographie Soziologie. (GW ISSN 0138-5038) **5148**

Bibliographie Staat und Recht *see* Bibliographie Rechtswissenschaft **2697**

Bibliographie Universelle de Securite Sociale. *see* World Bibliography of Social Security **744**

Bibliographie Unselbstaendiger Literatur-Linguistik *see* Bibliographie Linguistischer Literatur **2981**

Bibliographie Voelkerrecht und Internationale Beziehungen *see* Bibliographie Politikwissenschaft und Voelkerrecht **5148**

†Bibliographie zur Archaeo-Zoologie und Geschichte der Haustiere. (GW ISSN 0232-4865) **5148**

Bibliographie zur Deutschsprachigen Schweizerliteratur. (SZ) **2981**

Bibliographie zur Geschichte der Deutschen Arbeiterbewegung. (GW ISSN 0343-4117) **2352**, 973

Bibliographie zur Kunstgeschichtlichen Literatur in Ost- und Suedosteuropaeischen Zeitschriften. (GW ISSN 0173-1637) **352**, 309

Bibliographie zur Symbolik, Ikonographie und Mythologie. (GW ISSN 0067-706X) **253**, 2060

Bibliographien zur Deutschen Literatur des Mittelalters. (GW ISSN 0523-2767) **2981**, 2899

Bibliographien zur Philosophie. (GW ISSN 0173-1831) **3762**, 393

Bibliographien zur Romanistik. (GW ISSN 0171-0125) **2981**

Bibliographies and A L I N. (US) **134**, 79

Bibliographies and Indexes in Afro-American and African Studies. (US ISSN 0742-6925) **2327**

Bibliographies and Indexes in American History. (US ISSN 0742-6828) **2328**

Bibliographies and Indexes in American Literature. (US ISSN 0742-6860) **2981**

Bibliographies and Indexes in Anthropology. (US ISSN 0742-6844) **253**

Bibliographies and Indexes in Economics and Economic History. (US ISSN 0749-1786) **706**, 393
Bibliographies and Indexes in Education.(US ISSN 0742-6917) **1674**
Bibliographies and Indexes in Ethnic Studies. (US ISSN 1046-7882) **2030**
Bibliographies and Indexes in Geography. (US ISSN 1044-8349) **2267**
Bibliographies and Indexes in Gerontology. (US ISSN 0743-7560) **2280**
▼Bibliographies and Indexes in Latin American and Caribbean Studies. (US ISSN 1054-9102) **2328**, 4394
Bibliographies and Indexes in Law and Political Science. (US ISSN 0742-6909) **2697**, 3936
Bibliographies and Indexes in Library and Information Science. (US ISSN 0742-6879) **2792**
Bibliographies and Indexes in Medical Studies. (US ISSN 0896-6591) **3166**, 3
Bibliographies and Indexes in Military Studies. (US ISSN 1040-7995) **3476**
Bibliographies and Indexes in Philosophy. (US ISSN 0742-6887) **3787**
Bibliographies and Indexes in Psychology. (US ISSN 0742-681X) **4051**
Bibliographies and Indexes in Religious Studies. (US ISSN 0742-6836) **4212**
Bibliographies and Indexes in Science and Technology. (US ISSN 0888-7551) **4354**, 3
Bibliographies and Indexes in Science Fiction, Fantasy, and Horror. (US ISSN 1053-4636) **2981**, 393, 3010
Bibliographies and Indexes in Sociology.(US ISSN 0742-6895) **4457**
Bibliographies and Indexes in the Performing Arts. (US ISSN 0742-6933) **4643**, 1532
Bibliographies and Indexes in Women's Studies. (US ISSN 0742-6941) **4861**, 393
Bibliographies and Indexes in World History. (US ISSN 0742-6852) **2328**
Bibliographies and Indexes in World Literature. (US ISSN 0742-6801) **2981**
Bibliographies and Literature of Agriculture see Bibliographies and A L I N **134**
Bibliographies Commentees. (IV) **706**, 4394
Bibliographies in American Music. (US) **3588**
Bibliographies in the History of Psychology and Psychiatry. (US) **4051**, 3166, 3331
▼Bibliographies of American Notables. (US) **393**
▼Bibliographies of Battles and Leaders.(US ISSN 1056-7410) **3476**
Bibliographies of British Statesmen. (US ISSN 1056-5515) **3936**
Bibliographies of Modern Authors. (US ISSN 0749-470X) **393**, 2981
Bibliographies of the Presidents of the United States. (US ISSN 1061-6500) **3936**, 2328
Bibliographies of World Leaders. (US ISSN 1056-5523) **3936**, 2328
Bibliographies on the History of Science and Technology. (US) **4354**, 4614
Bibliographische Informationen zu Migration und Ethnizitaet. (GW) **4457**, 2030
Bibliographischer Index Bildungswissenschaften Report see B I B - Report **1674**
†Bibliographischer Informationsdienst der Deutschen Buecherei. (GW ISSN 0070-3931) **5148**
Bibliography and Index of Geology. (US ISSN 0098-2784) **1550**, 3

Bibliography and Index of Micropaleontology. (US ISSN 0300-7227) **3661**
Bibliography and Subject Index of South African Geology. (SA ISSN 0584-2360) **1550**, 393
Bibliography Newsletter. (US ISSN 0145-3084) **2747**, 3997, 4121
Bibliography of Agriculture. (US ISSN 0006-1530) **134**, 79, 393
Bibliography of Agrometeorology. see Bibliografia Agrometeorologii **3444**
Bibliography of Articles in Turkish Periodicals/Turkiye Makaleler Bibliyografyasi. (TU ISSN 0041-4344) **393**
Bibliography of Asian Studies. (US ISSN 0067-7159) **2328**
Bibliography of Bioethics. (US ISSN 0363-0161) **3166**
†Bibliography of Books for Children. (US ISSN 0147-250X) **5148**
Bibliography of Bulgarian Bibliographies. see Bibliografia na Bulgarskata Bibliografiia **391**
Bibliography of Chinese Studies. (GW ISSN 0724-8415) **393**
Bibliography of Developmental Medicine and Child Neurology. Books and Articles Received. (UK ISSN 0067-7183) **3166**
Bibliography of Doctoral Dissertations: Natural and Applied Sciences. (II) **4354**, 393
Bibliography of Doctoral Dissertations: Social Sciences and Humanities. (II) **4394**, 393
Bibliography of Economic and Social Development Sri Lanka. (CE) **706**, 393, 1003
Bibliography of Economic and Statistical Publications on Tanzania. (TZ) **706**, 393, 4565
Bibliography of Economic Geology. (UK) **3479**
Bibliography of Education Theses in Australia. (AT ISSN 0811-0174) **1674**, 2792, 4051, 4394
Bibliography of Fossil Vertebrates. (US ISSN 0272-8869) **3656**
†Bibliography of Germfree Research. (US) **5148**
Bibliography of Government Publications. see T C Devlet Yayinlari Bibliyografyasi **413**
Bibliography of Hydrology and Oceanology. see Bibliografia Hydrologii i Oceanologii **1550**
Bibliography of Icelandic Sound Recordings. see Islensk Hljodritaskra **403**
Bibliography of Indian Writing in English Series. (II) **2981**
Bibliography of Italian Publications Published or Distributed in Great Britain. (UK) **393**
†Bibliography of Maritime and Naval History Periodical Articles. (US) **5148**
Bibliography of Mediaeval Latin Lexicology. (US) **393**, 2805
Bibliography of Meteorology. see Bibliografia Meteorologii **3444**
Bibliography of Modern Hebrew Literature in Translation. (IS ISSN 0334-309X) **2981**
Bibliography of Old Norse-Icelandic Studies. (DK ISSN 0067-7213) **2328**
Bibliography of Periodical Articles Relating to the South Pacific see South Pacific Periodicals Index **412**
Bibliography of Philosophy. see Bibliographie de la Philosophie **3787**
Bibliography of Plant Protection. see Bibliographie der Pflanzenschutzliteratur **134**
Bibliography of Polish Serials. see Bibliografia Wydawnictw Ciaglych **391**
Bibliography of Publications from Economic Research Centres in India. (II) **706**

Bibliography of Publications of University Bureaus of Business and Economic Research see University Research in Business and Economics: a Bibliography of (Year) Publications **743**
Bibliography of Regional Studies in the Social Sciences. see Bibliografie van Regionale Onderzoekingen op Sociaal-wetenschappelijk Terrein **4394**
Bibliography of Reproduction. (UK ISSN 0006-1565) **461**, 3166
Bibliography of Seismology. (UK ISSN 0523-2988) **1550**, 393
Bibliography of Skiing Studies. (US) **4498**, 393
†Bibliography of South African Government Publications. (SA ISSN 0067-7256) **5148**
†Bibliography of Surgery of the Hand. (US ISSN 0067-7264) **5149**
Bibliography of Systematic Mycology. (UK ISSN 0006-1573) **461**, 496
Bibliography of the Geology of Fiji. (FJ ISSN 0252-8398) **1550**, 1555
Bibliography of the Geology of Missouri.(US ISSN 0067-7272) **1550**
Bibliography of the History of Art see B H A **351**
Bibliography of the History of Medicine. (US ISSN 0067-7280) **3166**
Bibliography of the Middle East. (SY ISSN 0067-7302) **393**
Bibliography of Tourism and Travel Research Studies, Reports and Articles. (US) **4799**
Bibliography of Wales. (UK) **393**
Bibliography of Water Management and Engineering. see Bibliografia Gospodarki i Inzynierii Wodnej **4834**
Bibliography of West Pomerania. Polish Literature. see Bibliografia Pomorza Zachodniego. Pismiennictwo Polskie **391**
Bibliography of West Pomerania - Foreign Literature. see Bibliografia Pomorza Zachodniego - Pismiennictwo Zagraniczne **391**
Bibliography of Works by Polish Scholars and Scientists Published Outside Poland in Languages Other Than Polish. (UK ISSN 0067-7310) **393**
Bibliography on Cold Regions Science & Technology. (US) **1841**, 393, 1550
Bibliography on Foreign and Comparative Law: Books and Articles in English. (US ISSN 0067-7329) **2698**
Bibliography on High Pressure Research. (US ISSN 0045-1932) **1191**, 3836
Bibliography on Irrigation, Drainage, River Training and Flood Control/ Bibliographie de la C I I D. Irrigation, Drainage et Maitrise des Crues. (II ISSN 0523-302X) **4834**
Bibliography on Logistics and Physical Distribution Management. (US) **706**, 1034
Bibliography on Philippine Geology, Mining and Mineral Resources. (PH) **3479**
Bibliography on Physical Distribution Management see Bibliography on Logistics and Physical Distribution Management **706**
Bibliography on Research in Physical Education and Sport for the Handicapped. see Bibliografia Eritysiryhmien Liikunnan Tutkimuksesta **1674**
Bibliography on Satellite Geodesy and Related Subjects see International Association of Geodesy. Central Bureau for Satellite Geodesy. Bibliography **2268**
Bibliography on Smoking and Health. (US ISSN 0067-7361) **3811**
Bibliography Quarterly. see Shu Mo Chi Kan **2795**
Bibliologia. (BE) **4121**, 2352, 2899
Biblionews and Australian Notes and Queries. (AT ISSN 0157-3276) **4121**, 393
Bibliophilia. (GR) **2352**, 3997

BIBLIOTECA NACIONAL 5977

Biblioscan H-L. (US ISSN 0148-9011) **393**
Biblioscan Q-Z. (US ISSN 0148-8996) **393**
Biblioteca. (AG ISSN 0006-1611) **2170**
Biblioteca Alfa-Omega de Poesia Brasileira: Serie 1. (BL) **2988**
Biblioteca Apostolica Vaticana. Cataloghi e Norme di Catalogazione. (VC) **4257**
Biblioteca Apostolica Vaticana. Edizioni Illustrate. (VC) **4257**
Biblioteca Apostolica Vaticana. Studi e Testi. (VC) **4257**
Biblioteca Azuaya. (EC) **2400**
Biblioteca Clasica Gredos. (SP) **1275**
Biblioteca Clasicos Colorados. (PY) **4367**
Biblioteca Colombiana. (CK) **2899**
Biblioteca de Arheologie. (RM ISSN 0067-7388) **267**
Biblioteca de Autores Espanoles. Publicacion. (SP) **2899**
Biblioteca de Ciencias Sociales. (AG) **4367**
Biblioteca de Cultura Andina. Ediciones. (PE) **236**
Biblioteca de Economia, Politica, Sociedad. Serie Mayor. (AG) **4367**
Biblioteca de Economia, Politica, Sociedad. Serie Menor. (AG) **4367**
Biblioteca de Educacao. (BL) **1618**
Biblioteca de Estudios Paraguayos. (PY) **2400**, 2503
Biblioteca de la Tradicion Oral Andina. (PE) **2400**, 2053
Biblioteca de Linguistica. (SP) **2805**
Biblioteca de Menendez Pelayo. Boletin. (SP ISSN 0006-1646) **2860**, 2307, 2899
▼Biblioteca de Mexico. (MX ISSN 0188-476X) **2899**
Biblioteca de Temas y Autores de Anzoategui. (VE) **2400**
Biblioteca de Teologia. (SP ISSN 0067-740X) **4166**
Biblioteca degli Studi Classici e Orientali.(IT) **1275**, 3635
Biblioteca della Liberta. (IT ISSN 0006-1654) **3875**
Biblioteca di Bibliografia Italiana. (IT ISSN 0067-7418) **393**
Biblioteca di Labeo. (IT ISSN 0067-7434) **2503**
Biblioteca di Letteratura e Arte. (IT) **2899**
Biblioteca di Storia della Scienza. (IT) **4302**
Biblioteca di Storia Toscana Moderna e Contemporanea. Studi e Documenti. (IT ISSN 0067-7442) **2352**
Biblioteca di Studi Antichi. (IT) **1275**
Biblioteca di Studi Etruschi. (IT ISSN 0067-7450) **2805**
Biblioteca do Educador Profissional. (PO ISSN 0067-7469) **2503**
Biblioteca do Sejur. Boletim. (BL ISSN 0006-1662) **2698**, 2792
Biblioteca Filologica. Ensayos. (SP) **2805**
Biblioteca Filologica. Manuales. (SP) **2805**
Biblioteca Historica Lundensis. (SW) **2307**
Biblioteca Istorica. (RM ISSN 0067-7493) **2352**
Biblioteca "Jose Artigas". Boletin. (UY ISSN 0006-1697) **393**, 2747
Biblioteca "Jose Artigas". Lista de Adquisiciones see Biblioteca "Jose Artigas". Boletin **393**
Biblioteca Jose Jeronimo Triana (Serial). (CK) **4302**
†Biblioteca Labronica Notiziario. (IT ISSN 0006-1700) **5149**
Biblioteca Municipale A. Panizzi. Contributi. (IT) **2747**
Biblioteca N T. (SP) **2504**
Biblioteca Nacional. Boletin see Universidad Nacional Autonoma de Mexico. Instituto de Investigaciones Bibliograficas. Boletin **415**
Biblioteca Nacional de Brasil. Anais. (BL ISSN 0100-1922) **2747**
Biblioteca Nacional de Brasil. Boletim Bibliografico see Bibliografia Brasileira **2792**

BIBLIOTECA NACIONAL

Biblioteca Nacional de Peru. Anuario Bibliografico Peruano. (PE) **393**
Biblioteca Nacional de Portugal. Revista. (PO ISSN 0251-1711) **2747**
Biblioteca Nacional de Uruguay. Revista.(UY ISSN 0544-9189) **2747**
Biblioteca Nacional del Peru. Boletin. (PE ISSN 0031-6067) **2747**
Biblioteca Nacional Jose Marti. Boletin Bibliografico. Literatura. (CU) **2981**
Biblioteca Nacional Jose Marti. Departamento de Informacion y Documentacion de la Cultura. Serie Teatro y Danza. (CU) **4630**, 1529
Biblioteca Nacional Jose Marti. Revista. (CU ISSN 0006-1727) **2519**
Biblioteca Napoletana di Storia e Arte. (IT) **2352**, 319
Biblioteca Paraguaya de Antropologia. (PY) **236**
Biblioteca Popular. Serie A: Capacitacion. (PE) **3875**
†Biblioteca Prehistorica Hispana. (SP ISSN 0067-7507) **5149**
Biblioteca Romanica Hispanica. (SP) **2899**
Biblioteca Statale. Fonti e Sussidi. (IT) **393**
Biblioteca Statale e Libreria Civica di Cremona. Annali. (IT ISSN 0392-0550) **2352**
Biblioteca Statale e Libreria Civica di Cremona. Mostre. (IT) **393**
Biblioteca Storica Toscana. Serie I. (IT) **2352**
Biblioteca Storica Toscana. Serie II. (IT) **2352**
Biblioteca Teatrale. (IT ISSN 0045-1959) **4630**
Biblioteca Theologiae Practicae. (SW) **4166**
†Biblioteca Universitaria y Provincial, Barcelona. Boletin de Noticias. (SP) **5149**
Il Bibliotecario. (IT) **2747**
Bibliotecas. (CU ISSN 0006-176X) **2747**
Bibliotecas, Arquivos e Museus. (PO ISSN 0870-0974) **2747**, 4302, 4594
Bibliotecas Universitarias. (NQ) **2747**
†Bibliotecas y Archivos. (MX ISSN 0185-0083) **5149**
†Bibliotech. (CN ISSN 0825-9658) **5149**
Biblioteche Oggi. (IT ISSN 0392-8586) **2747**
Bibliotecologia y Documentacion Paraguaya. (PY ISSN 0258-6436) **2747**
Biblioteconomia e Bibliografia. Saggi e Studi. (IT ISSN 0067-7531) **2747**
Biblioteconomie. Culegere de Traduceri Prelucrate. (RM ISSN 1220-3076) **2792**
Biblioteek voor Hedendaagse Dokumentatie. Bulletin. (BE ISSN 0250-9725) **2796**
Bibliotek for Laeger. (DK ISSN 0006-1786) **2747**, 3081
Bibliotek 70 see B 70 **2746**
Biblioteka Archeologiczna. (PL ISSN 0067-7639) **267**
Biblioteka Bulteno. (UK) **2747**, 2805
Biblioteka Chopinowska. (PL) **3541**
Biblioteka Etnografii Polskiej. (PL ISSN 0067-7655) **4430**
Biblioteka Fizyki. (PL ISSN 0137-5059) **3815**
Biblioteka Kornicka. Pamietnik. (PL ISSN 0551-3790) **2747**
Biblioteka Krakowska. (PL ISSN 0067-7698) **319**, 2352
Biblioteka Matematyczna. (PL ISSN 0519-8356) **3031**
Biblioteka Mechaniki Stosowanej. (PL ISSN 0067-7701) **1915**
Biblioteka Pediatry. (PL) **3319**
Biblioteka Pisarzow Polskich see Biblioteka Pisarzow Polskich. Seria A **2899**
Biblioteka Pisarzow Polskich. Seria A. (PL ISSN 0519-8631) **2899**
Biblioteka Pisarzy Reformacyjnych. (PL ISSN 0519-8658) **4166**

Biblioteka Polonijna/Polonia Library. (PL ISSN 0138-094X) **3875**, 2307
Biblioteka Res Facta. (PL ISSN 0208-9963) **3541**
Biblioteka Sluchacza Koncertowego. Seria Wprowadzajaca. (PL ISSN 0067-7779) **3541**
Biblioteka Wiadomosci Statystycznych. (PL ISSN 0067-7795) **3991**
Bibliotekar. (BU ISSN 0204-7438) **2747**
Bibliotekar' (RU ISSN 0006-1808) **2747**
Bibliotekar. (YU ISSN 0006-1816) **2747**
Bibliotekariesamfundet Meddelar. (SW ISSN 0345-1097) **2747**
Bibliotekarstvo/Librarianship. (BN ISSN 0006-1832) **2747**
Bibliotekarz. (PL ISSN 0208-4333) **2747**
Bibliotekarz Zachodniopomorski/ Librarian of West Pomerania. (PL ISSN 0406-1578) **2747**
Bibliotekovedenie, Bibliografiya i Informatika. (RU) **2747**
Bibliotekovedenie i Bibliografiya za Rubezhom. (RU ISSN 0519-9514) **2747**
▼Bibliotekoznanie, Bibliografia, Knigoznanie. (BU ISSN 0861-4881) **2747**
Bibliotekoznanie, Bibliografiia, Knigoznanie, Nauchna Informatsiia. (BU ISSN 0324-1858) **2747**
Biblioteksaarbog. (DK ISSN 0084-957X) **2747**
Biblioteksbladet/Library Journal. (SW ISSN 0006-1867) **2747**
Bibliotekshistorie. (DK ISSN 0109-923X) **2747**
Biblioteksvejviser/Guide to Danish Libraries. (DK) **2748**
Biblioten see Over Broen **2778**
Bibliotheca Aegyptiaca. (BE ISSN 0067-7817) **267**, 2428
Bibliotheca Afroasiatica. (US ISSN 0742-1117) **2805**
Bibliotheca Anatomica. (SZ ISSN 0067-7833) **3081**, 430
Bibliotheca Archaeologica. (SP ISSN 0519-9603) **267**
Bibliotheca Archaeologica. (IT) **267**
Bibliotheca Arnamagnaeana. (DK ISSN 0067-7841) **2806**, 2899
Bibliotheca Arnamagnaeana. Supplementum. (DK ISSN 0067-785X) **2806**, 2899
Bibliotheca Athena. (IT ISSN 0067-7868) **2806**
Bibliotheca Australiana. (NE ISSN 0067-7876) **2344**
Bibliotheca Bibliographica Aureliana. (GW ISSN 0067-7884) **394**
Bibliotheca Bibliographica Neerlandica. (NE) **394**
Bibliotheca Botanica. (GW ISSN 0067-7892) **496**
Bibliotheca Cardiologica. (SZ ISSN 0067-7906) **3205**
Bibliotheca Cartographica see Bibliographia Cartographica **2267**
Bibliotheca Celtica see Bibliography of Wales **393**
Bibliotheca del Planeamiento Educativo.(AG ISSN 0067-7922) **1725**
Bibliotheca Diatomologica. (GW) **496**
Bibliotheca Dissidentium. (GW) **394**, 4166
Bibliotheca Ephemeridum Theologicarum Lovaniensium. (BE) **4166**
Bibliotheca Germanica. Handbuecher, Texte und Monographien aus dem Gebiete der Germanischen Philologie.(SZ ISSN 0067-7477) **2806**
Bibliotheca Helvetica Romana. (SZ ISSN 0067-7965) **1275**
Bibliotheca Hertziana. Roemisches Jahrbuch. (GW) **319**
Bibliotheca Historica Lundensis. (SW ISSN 0519-9700) **2307**
Bibliotheca Historica Romaniae. Monographies. (RM ISSN 0067-799X) **2352**

Bibliotheca Historica Romaniae. Studies.(RM ISSN 0067-7981) **2352**
Bibliotheca Historico-Ecclesiastica Lundensis. (SW ISSN 0346-5438) **4231**, 2307
Bibliotheca Historico Militaris. (UK) **3453**
Bibliotheca Humanistica & Reformatorica. (NE) **4166**
Bibliotheca Hungarica Antiqua. (HU ISSN 0067-8007) **4121**, 3997
Bibliotheca Ibero-Americana. (GW ISSN 0067-8015) **3936**
Bibliotheca Indonesica. (NE ISSN 0067-8023) **236**
Bibliotheca Instituti Historici Societatis Iesu. (IT) **4257**
Bibliotheca Islamica. (GW ISSN 0170-3102) **4218**, 3635
Bibliotheca Latina Medii et Recentiori Aevi. (PL ISSN 0067-8031) **2352**, 267
Bibliotheca Lichenologica. (GW) **496**
Bibliotheca Medica Canadiana. (CN ISSN 0707-3674) **2748**, 3081
Bibliotheca Mesopotamica. (US ISSN 0732-6440) **2428**
Bibliotheca Mycologica. (GW ISSN 0067-8066) **496**
Bibliotheca Nostratica. (US ISSN 0342-4871) **2806**
Bibliotheca Nutritio et Dieta. (SZ ISSN 0067-8198) **3604**
Bibliotheca Oeconomica. (RM ISSN 0067-8082) **648**
Bibliotheca Orientalis. (NE ISSN 0006-1913) **2328**, 2428, 3635
Bibliotheca Orientalis Hungarica. (HU ISSN 0067-8104) **3635**
Bibliotheca Phycologica. (GW ISSN 0067-8112) **496**
Bibliotheca Psychiatrica. (SZ ISSN 0067-8147) **3331**
Bibliotheca Romanica. (GW ISSN 0067-7515) **2806**
Bibliotheca Russica. (GW ISSN 0341-3217) **2806**, 2899
Bibliotheca Sacra. (US ISSN 0006-1921) **4231**
Bibliotheca Seraphico-Capuccina. Sectio Historica. (IT ISSN 0067-8163) **4257**
Bibliotheca Unitariorum. (NE) **4231**
Bibliotheca Vita Humana see Contributions to Human Development **3091**
Bibliotheck. (UK ISSN 0006-193X) **394**
Bibliotheek- en Archiefgids. (BE) **2748**
Bibliotheek en Samenleving. (NE ISSN 0165-1048) **2748**
▼Bibliotheek Nederlandse Muziek. (NE) **3541**
Bibliothek der Aufklaerung. (GW) **2328**
Bibliothek der Griechischen Literatur. (GW ISSN 0340-7853) **1275**
Bibliothek der Klassischen Altertumswissenschaften. Neue Folge.(GW ISSN 0067-8201) **2307**
Bibliothek des Buchwesens (B B). (GW ISSN 0340-8051) **2748**
Bibliothek Forschung und Praxis. (GW ISSN 0341-4183) **2748**
Bibliothek fuer Alle. (GW ISSN 0176-2397) **2748**
Bibliothek fuer Zeitgeschichte, Stuttgart. Jahresbibliographie. (GW ISSN 0081-8992) **2328**
Bibliothek fuer Zeitgeschichte, Stuttgart. Schriften. (GW ISSN 0081-900X) **2307**
Bibliothek und Wissenschaft. (GW ISSN 0067-8236) **2748**
†Der Bibliothekar. (GW ISSN 0006-1964) **5149**
Bibliothekar-Lehrinstitut des Landes Nordrhein-Westfalen. Arbeiten aus dem B L I see Koelner Arbeiten zum Bibliotheks- und Dokumentationswesen **2767**
Bibliothekar-Lehrinstitut des Landes Nordrhein-Westfalen. Bibliographische Hefte see Koelner Arbeiten zum Bibliotheks- und Dokumentationswesen **2767**
Bibliotheken der Bundesrepublik Deutschland. Datierte Handschriften. (GW ISSN 0175-6796) **2748**

Bibliotheks Taschenbuch. (GW) **2748**
Bibliotheksdienst. (GW ISSN 0006-1972) **2748**
Bibliotheksforum Bayern. (GW ISSN 0340-000X) **2748**
Bibliothekspraxis. (GW ISSN 0300-287X) **2748**
†Bibliotheksstudien. (GW) **5149**
Bibliotheque Africaine. Liste des Acquisitions. (BE) **394**, 1993
Bibliotheque d'Etudes Balkaniques. (FR ISSN 0067-8325) **2806**, 2899
Bibliotheque d'Histoire Antillaise. (GP) **2400**
Bibliotheque d'Humanisme et Renaissance. (SZ ISSN 0006-1999) **2352**, 2899
Bibliotheque de l'Ecole des Chartes. (SZ ISSN 0006-1980) **2307**, 2806
Bibliotheque de la Mer. (FR ISSN 0067-8260) **4498**
Bibliotheque de la Revue d'Histoire Ecclesiastique. (BE ISSN 0067-8279) **4257**
Bibliotheque de la S E L A F. (Societe d'Etudes Linguistiques et Anthropologiques de France (SELAF)) (FR ISSN 0081-1238) **2806**
Bibliotheque de Travail. (FR ISSN 0005-335X) **1249**, 1618
Bibliotheque de Travail Junior. (FR ISSN 0005-3120) **1618**, 1233
Bibliotheque de Travail 2d Degre. (FR ISSN 0005-3414) **1618**
Bibliotheque des Cahiers Archeologiques see Cahiers Archeologiques **268**
Bibliotheque des Ecoles Francaises d'Athenes et de Rome Publication see B E F A R. Publication **266**
Bibliotheque du Museon see Universite Catholique de Louvain. Institut Orientaliste. Publications **2342**
Bibliotheque Francaise et Romane. Serie A: Manuels et Etudes Linguistiques. (FR ISSN 0067-8341) **2806**
Bibliotheque Francaise et Romane. Serie B: Editions Critiques de Textes. (FR ISSN 0067-835X) **2899**
Bibliotheque Francaise et Romane. Serie C: Etudes Litteraires. (FR ISSN 0067-8368) **2899**
Bibliotheque Francaise et Romane. Serie D: Initiation, Textes et Documents. (FR ISSN 0067-8376) **2899**
Bibliotheque Francaise et Romane. Serie E: Langue et Litterature Francaises au Canada. (FR ISSN 0067-8384) **2806**, 2899
Bibliotheque Historique. (FR) **2307**
Bibliotheque Historique Vaudoise. (SZ ISSN 0067-8406) **2352**
Bibliotheque Introuvable. (FR ISSN 0067-8422) **2899**
Bibliotheque Nationale. Bibliographie Nationale. (ZR) **394**
Bibliotheque Nationale. Nouvelles. see National Library News **2775**
Bibliotheque Nationale. Revue. (FR ISSN 0249-7344) **2748**
Bibliotheque Royal Albert 1er. Bulletin Bimestriel d'Information see Bibliotheque Royal Albert 1er. Bulletin Trimestriel d'Information **2748**
Bibliotheque Royal Albert 1er. Bulletin Trimestriel d'Information. (BE ISSN 0770-4372) **2748**
Bibliotheque Royale Albert 1er. Publications Annoncees/Koninklijke Bibliotheek Albert I. Aangekondigde Publikaties. (BE ISSN 0772-3776) **2748**
Bibliotheque Royale Albert 1er. Rapport Annuel. (BE ISSN 0770-4526) **2748**
Bibliotheques de Droit Canadiennes. see Canadian Law Libraries **2751**
Bibliotheques et Musees. (SZ) **2352**, 3522
Bibliotheques Suisses. see Schweizerische Bibliotheken **2783**
Biblische Beitraege. (SZ ISSN 0582-1673) **4166**
Biblische Untersuchungen. (GW ISSN 0523-5154) **4166**
Biblische Zeitschrift. (GW ISSN 0006-2014) **4166**
Biblisches Seminar. (GW) **4166**

Al-Bibliyugrafya al-Djazairiyah. see Bibliographie de l'Algerie 392
Biblos/Biburosu. (JA ISSN 0006-2030) 2748
Biblos. (PO ISSN 0870-4112) 2899, 2243, 2307, 2806
Biblos. (AU ISSN 0006-2022) 4140, 2792
▼Bibsamnytt. (SW ISSN 1100-3847) 2748
Biburosu. see Biblos 2748
Bicentennial Reflections on the French Revolution. (US) 2352
Bichitra. (BG) 2174
Bichon Frise Reporter. (US) 3708
La Bici. (SP) 2217
Bicicleta. (CL) 319
Bicycle Action. (UK) 4516
†Bicycle Action. (UK) 5149
Bicycle Business Journal. (US ISSN 0745-8126) 4516
Bicycle Dealer Showcase. (US ISSN 0361-381X) 4516
Bicycle Dealer Showcase Buyers Guide. (US ISSN 0361-381X) 4516
Bicycle Forum. (US) 4516
Bicycle Guide. (US ISSN 0889-289X) 4516
†Bicycle Guide's Complete Cycling Fitness. (US) 5149
Bicycle Handbook. (CN) 4516
Bicycle Motocross Plus see B M X Plus 4515
Bicycle Ontario see Cycle Ontario 4517
Bicycle Paper. (US ISSN 0742-8308) 4516
▼Bicycle Retailer and Industry News. (US) 4516, 1034
Bicycle Rider (Agoura). (US) 4516
Bicycle U S A. (US ISSN 0199-2139) 4516
Bicycles. (UK) 4516
Bicycling. (US ISSN 0006-2073) 4516, 4542
†Bid Data on Current Municipal Public Works. (US) 5149
Bide-A-Wee News. (US) 3708
BidNet Link. (US) 1034, 939
†Bidrag til H. C. Andersens Bibliografi. (DK ISSN 0067-8473) 5149
Bidrag till Kaennedom av Finlands Natur och Folk. (FI ISSN 0067-8481) 4367, 2504
Bielarus. (US ISSN 0006-209X) 1993
Bielaruskaya Dumka. (US) 1993
Bielaruski Holas/Byelorussian Voice/Voix Bielarusienne. (CN) 1993
Bielefelder Beitraege zur Sprachlehrforschung. (GW ISSN 0172-3510) 2806
Bielefelder Katalog - Jazz. (GW) 3541
Bielefelder Katalog - Klassik. (GW) 3541
Bielefelder Universitaetszeitung. (GW ISSN 0939-4648) 1305
Die Biene. (GW ISSN 0006-212X) 79
Das Bienenmuetterchen. (GW) 79
Bienenvater. (AU ISSN 0006-2146) 79
Bienenwelt. (AU ISSN 0006-2154) 79
Bienenzucht see Neue Bienenzucht 109
Biennale Internationale de la Tapisserie see Catalogue Biennale Internationale de Lausanne 321
Biennial Report-Educational Communications Board see Wisconsin. Educational Communications Board. Biennial Report 1672
Biennial Report for the Department of Industrial Relations see California. Department of Industrial Relations. Biennial Report 974
Biennial Report of the Michigan State Advisory Council for Vocational Education see Michigan Council on Vocational Eduation. Biennial Evaluation Report (Year) 1738
Biennial Report - State of Minnesota, Department of Revenue see Minnesota. Department of Revenue. Biennial Report 1101
Biennial Survey of Advertising Expenditures Around the World see World Advertising Expenditures 39

†Biennial Survey of Bank Officer Salaries. (US ISSN 0525-4620) 5149
†Biennial Survey of Bank Personnel Policies and Practices. (US) 5149
Bienvenidos a Miami. (US) 4802
Bienvenidos Puerto Rico. (US) 4754
▼Bier & Getraenke. (GW) 379
Der Biergrosshandel. (GW) 379
Bierzo 7. (SP) 2217
Bifidobacteria and Microflora. (JA ISSN 0286-9306) 430, 496
Bifocal see B I F O C A L 2603
▼Big Allis. (US ISSN 1043-9978) 2899
Big Apple Blues. (US) 3541
†Big Apple Dyke News. (US) 5149
Big Apple Parents' Paper. (US) 1233, 3396, 4838
▼Big Apple Press. (US) 2222
Big Apple Users Digest see B A U D 1467
Big Beans. (US) 2222
Big Beautiful Woman Friendship Express see B B W Friendship Express 2221
Big Blue Disk. (US ISSN 0893-2212) 1475, 1467
▼Big Bond Book. (US) 939
Big Bopper. (US) 1249, 3541
Big Businesses Directory. (US) 1123
Big Butt. (US) 3396
Big Car Life. see Kuruma no Techo 4694
Big Cigars. (US) 2988
Big E. (US) 1296
Big Eight Review see Emerson's Professional Service Review 750
Big Fin Outdoor Report. (CN) 4542
†Big Fish Country Fishing Guide. (CN) 5149
▼Big Game Guide. (US) 4542
Big Game Hunting. (US) 4542
Big Hammer. (US) 2989
Big League. (AT ISSN 0311-175X) 4501
Big Little Times. (US) 4121
Big Picture. (US) 1249, 1745
Big Reel. (US) 3504
Big Scream. (US) 2860
Big Ten Football Media Guide. (US) 4501, 1305
Big Ten Football Yearbook see Big Ten Football Media Guide 4501
Big Time see Farmland News 91
†Big Two-Hearted. (US ISSN 0892-0842) 5149
Biggest Greatest Cracked Annual. (US) 2860
Bigre. (FR ISSN 0221-5225) 1389, 1429, 1436
Bihar Industries. (II ISSN 0006-2219) 1113
Bihar Law Journal Reports. (II) 2605
Bij de Haard see Eigen Aard 4840
†Bijbellessen voor de Kinderen. (NE ISSN 0006-2235) 5149
Bijbellessen voor de Sabbatschool. (NE ISSN 0006-2243) 4280
Bijblad bij de Industriele Eigendom. (NE ISSN 0006-2251) 3673, 2605
Bijblijven. (NE ISSN 0006-226X) 1233
Bijdragen. (NE ISSN 0006-2278) 4166, 3762
Bijdragen en Mededelingen Betreffende de Geschiedenis der Nederlanden. (NE ISSN 0165-0505) 2353
Bijdragen tot de Bibliotheekwetenschap/Contributions to Library Science. (BE ISSN 0067-8538) 2748
Bijdragen tot de Dierkunde/Contributions to Zoology - Amsterdam. (NE ISSN 0067-8546) 579
Bijdragen tot de Geschiedenis. (BE ISSN 0006-2286) 2307
Bijdragen tot de Geschiedenis der Stad Deinze en van Het Land aan Leie en Schelde. (BE) 2307
Bijdragen tot de Geschiedenis van Arnhem. (NE ISSN 0067-8554) 2353
Bijdragen tot de Geschiedenis van de Tweede Wereldoorlog/Cahiers d'Histoire de Seconde Guerre Mondiale. (BE ISSN 0771-6435) 2353

Bijdragen tot de Taal-, Land- en Volkenkunde. (NE ISSN 0006-2294) 236, 2806, 2899
Bijeen. (NE ISSN 0006-2308) 4166, 926
Bijenteelt. (NE ISSN 0166-6444) 79
Bijinesu Rebyu. see Business Review 652
Bijinlun. see Approximation Theory and its Applications 3030
†Bijou Magazine. (CN ISSN 0006-2316) 5149
Bijoutier. (FR) 2563
De Bijstaander. (NE) 4399
Bijutsu Kenkyu. see Journal of Art Studies 331
Bijutsu Shi. see Journal of Art History 331
Bijutsu Techo. (JA) 319
Bijvoorbeeld. (NE) 3590
Bike. (UK ISSN 0140-4547) 4516
Bike. (GW) 4516
Bike Australia. (AT ISSN 0810-2872) 4516
Bike Buyer. (UK) 4516
Bike Journal. (US) 4516
Bike S.A. (SA) 4516
†Bike Tech. (US ISSN 0734-5992) 5149
Biker. (US) 4516
†Biker Parties. (US) 5149
BikeReport. (US) 4516, 4754
†Bikini. (US) 5149
Bikini Girl. (US) 2860
Bikmaus. (PP) 2899
Bikoret. (IS) 748
Bikoret Veparshanut/Criticism and Interpretation. (IS ISSN 0084-9456) 2504, 2899
Bil. (NO ISSN 0800-5850) 4685, 4717
Bil og Motor. (DK ISSN 0006-2332) 4685
Bil-Revyen. (DK ISSN 0107-0924) 4685
†Bil Testen. (DK ISSN 0900-8659) 5149
Bilabladid Billinn see Billinn 4685
▼Biladi. (TS) 2220
Bilag Brief. (GW ISSN 0935-9451) 3615
Bilan see Balans 747
Bilan. (SZ) 847
Bilans Hebdomadaires. (FR) 648, 3875
Bilanz. (SZ ISSN 0510-5528) 847
Bilanz- und Buchhaltung. (GW ISSN 0930-0597) 748
Bilanz- und Buchhaltungspraxis see Bilanz- und Buchhaltung 748
Bilbao Maritimo see Singuladuras 4739
Bilbransjen see Bilbransjen - Bilteknisk Fagblad 4685
Bilbransjen - Bilteknisk Fagblad. (NO ISSN 0006-2367) 4685
Bild Am Sonntag. (GW) 2188
Bild der Frau. (GW) 1289
Bild der Wissenschaft. (GW ISSN 0006-2375) 4302
Bild und Funk. (GW) 2188
†Bild und Ton. (GW ISSN 0006-2383) 5149
Bildende Kunst. (GW ISSN 0006-2391) 319
Bildgebung/Imaging. (SZ ISSN 1012-5655) 3357
Bildmessung und Luftbildwesen see Z P F - Photogrammetrie und Fernerkundung 2267
Bildnerisches Volksschaffen. (GW ISSN 0520-1373) 319
Bildor see Building Business and Apartment Management Bildor 605
Bildschirmtext Aktuell. (GW ISSN 0935-6991) 1369
Bildschirmtext fuer Einsteiger. (GW) 1369
†Bildung im Geschichtsmuseum. (GW) 5149
Bildung Konkret. (GW) 1618
Bildung und Erziehung. (GW ISSN 0006-2456) 1618
Bildung und Wissenschaft. (GW ISSN 0172-0171) 1618
Bildungs-Kurier. (AU) 2860
Bildungsimpuls. (AU) 1682
Bildwoche. (GW) 2188
Bilekonomi see Vi Bilaegare 4705

Bilen. (DK) 4685, 4466
Bilen, Motor og Sport see Bilen 4685
Bilen og Baaden see Bilen 4685
†Bilens Aarsrevy. (DK ISSN 0108-5018) 5149
†Biliary Tract. (UK ISSN 0261-4561) 5149
Bilingual Family Newsletter. (UK) 2806, 1993
Bilingual Review/Revista Bilingue. (US ISSN 0094-5366) 2806, 1618, 1993, 2899
Bilingualism Today. (US ISSN 1045-4365) 2806
Bilismen i Danmark. (DK ISSN 0901-6120) 4685
Bilismen i Sverige see Motor Traffic in Sweden 4696
Bill Dale Marcinko's A F T A see Crow 2863
Bill Mazeroski's Baseball. (US ISSN 1054-2248) 4501
Bill Nelson Newsletter. (US ISSN 0894-4911) 2434
Bill of Fare. (US) 2062, 2472
Bill of Health. (US) 3081, 1063
Bill of Rights in Action. (US ISSN 0160-7731) 2705, 1618, 3875
Bill of Rights Journal. (US) 3940
Bill Shipp's Georgia. (US ISSN 0894-9697) 4054, 648
Billard-Sport Magazin. (GW ISSN 0936-2665) 4466
Billboard (Chambersburg). (US) 1305
Billboard (New York). (US ISSN 0006-2510) 3541, 4459
▼Billboard History of Rock 'N Roll. (US) 3541
Billboard International Manufacturing and Packaging Directory see Tape - Disc Directory (Year) 1386
Billboard's Country Music Sourcebook see Country Music Sourcebook 3548
Billboard's International Buyer's Guide of the Music-Record-Tape Industry. (US ISSN 0067-8600) 3541
Billboard's International Directory of Manufacturing and Packaging see Billboard's Tape - Disc Directory 1123
Billboard's International Recording Equipment & Studio Directory. (US ISSN 0160-7790) 4459
Billboard's International Talent and Touring Directory. (US ISSN 0732-0124) 3541
Billboard's Tape - Disc Directory. (US) 1123, 4459
Billboard's Year-End Awards Issue. (US) 3541
Billboard's Year-End Issue Talent in Action see Billboard's Year-End Awards Issue 3541
Billed Bladet. (DK ISSN 0006-2537) 2185
Billiard and Bowling Institute of America Flashes see B B I A Flashes 4500
Billiard and Bowling Institute of America Membership and Product Information Guide see B B I A Membership and Product Information Guide 1122
Billiard Congress of America Break see B C A Break 4500
Billiards Digest. (US ISSN 0164-761X) 4501
Billiards: The (Year) Official B C A Rules & Records Book. (US ISSN 1047-2444) 4501
Billie Jo Williams International Fan Club.(US) 3541, 1296
Billiken. (AG ISSN 0006-2553) 1249
Billinn. (IC) 4685
Billion see Asia Money & Finance 759
Bill's Bulletin see Genealogy Bulletin 2152
Billy Blue. (AT) 2899
Billy James Hargis' Christian Crusade. (US ISSN 0195-265X) 4166
Bilruten. (DK ISSN 0901-3229) 4647
Bilsport. (SW) 4685
Bilten Ahriva Hrvatske see Arhiv Hrvatske. Bilten 2350
Bilten Dokumentacije. Elektroprivreda/Bulletin of Documentation. Electrical Energy. (YU ISSN 0351-238X) 1797, 1801

Bilten Dokumentacije. Elektrotehnika i Elektronika. Proizvodnja Elektricnih Masina i Aparata. Ptt Usluge/Bulletin of Documentation. Electrotechnics and Electronics. Manufacture of Electrical Machinery and Apparatus. Postal Services. (YU) **1883**, 1764

Bilten Dokumentacije. Gradjevinarstvo - Visokogradnja i Završni Radovi u Gradjevinarstvu/Bulletin of Documentation. Civil Engineering - Superstructures and Final Work. (YU ISSN 0352-1028) **1841**, 3, 309

Bilten Dokumentacije. Metalopreradjivacka Delatnost. Proizvodnja Raznovrsnih Proizvoda/ Bulletin of Documentation. Manufacture of Fabricated Metal Products. Manufacture of Miscellaneous Products. (YU ISSN 0351-8906) **1927**

Bilten Dokumentacije. Metalurgija/ Bulletin of Documentation. Metallurgy. (YU ISSN 0006-2642) **3424**, 3

Bilten Dokumentacije. Poljoprivreda. Biljna Proizvodnja/Bulletin of Documentation. Agricultural-Plant Production. (YU ISSN 0351-2312) **134**, 3, 461

Bilten Dokumentacije. Poljoprivreda- Stocna Proizvodnja/Bulletin of Documentation. Agricultural- Stockbreeding. (YU ISSN 0351-2320) **134**, 3

Bilten Dokumentacije. Prerada Nemetalnih Minerala-Proizvodnja Gradjevinskog Materijala/Bulletin of Documentation. Manufacture of Non-Metalic Mineral Products-Manufacture of Construction Materials. (YU ISSN 0351-2509) **1167**, 3

Bilten Dokumentacije. Proizvodnja Prehrambenih Proizvoda. Proizvodnja Pica/Bulletin of Documentation. Manufacture of Food Products. Manufacture of Beverages. (YU ISSN 0351-2479) **2084**, 3

Bilten Dokumentacije. Rudarstvo i Geologija/Bulletin of Documentation. Mining and Geology. (YU ISSN 0351-7543) **3499**, 3

Bilten Dokumentacije. Savremena Organizacaija i Ekonomija Radnih Organizacija see Bilten Dokumentacije. Savremena Organizacija i Ekonomija Organizacija Udruzenog Rada **706**

Bilten Dokumentacije. Savremena Organizacija i Ekonomija Organizacija Udruzenog Rada. (YU ISSN 0351-4048) **706**, 3

Bilten Dokumentacije. Serija D1. Hemija i Hemijska Industrija/Bulletin of Documentation. Series D1. Chemistry and Chemical Industry. (YU ISSN 0351-756X) **1191**, 3

Bilten Dokumentacije. Serija D6. Analiticka Hemija/Bulletin of Documentation. Series D6. Analytical Chemistry. (YU ISSN 0352-633X) **1191**, 3

Bilten Dokumentacije. Serija I1. Informatika/Bulletin of Documentation. Series I1. Informatics. (YU ISSN 0352-6437) **2748**

Bilten Dokumentacije. Serija S1. Saobracaj/Bulletin of Documentation. Series S1. Traffic. (YU ISSN 0352-6402) **4662**, 3

Bilten Dokumentacije. Urbanizam i Arhitektura/Bulletin of Documentation. Town Planning and Architecture. (YU ISSN 0351-2592) **295**, 309

Bilten Dokumentacije. Zastita Covekove Okoline i Iskoriscenje Otpadaka/ Bulletin of Documentation. Environmental Protection and Waste Utilization. (YU ISSN 0352-1036) **1501**, 1484

Bilten Dokumentacije. Zastita na Radu/ Bulletin of Documentation. Safety Precautions. (YU ISSN 0350-0306) **4117**, 3

Bilten Drustva Ekologa Bosne i Hercegovine. Serija B - Naucni Skupovi i Savjetovanja. (BN ISSN 0352-0811) **496**, 1944

Bilten Pravne Sluzbe J N A. (YU ISSN 0006-2731) **2605**

Bilten Recenzija iz Damacih Listova i Casopisa see Bibliografija Recenzija iz Domacih Listova i Casopisa **2860**

Bilten za Hematologiju i Transfuziju. (YU ISSN 0523-6150) **3270**

Bilten za Hmelj, Sirak i Lekovito Bilje. (YU ISSN 0351-9430) **148**, 496, 540

Bim. (BB ISSN 0006-2766) **2899**, 2989

Bimarihaye Guiahi. see Iranian Journal of Plant Pathology **506**

Bimbo. (GW ISSN 0342-8095) **579**, 1249

Bimestre. (AG ISSN 0326-1980) **3875**, 847

▼Bimonthly Review of Law Books. (US) **2605**, 2748

BiN see Bibliography Newsletter **2747**

Binah: Studies in Jewish History, Culture, and Thought. (US) **4222**

Binario. (PO ISSN 0006-2804) **295**

Binary: Computing in Microbiology. (UK ISSN 0266-304X) **550**, 1453, 1475

Binden en Bouwen. (NE ISSN 0006-2812) **1305**

Bindereport. (GW ISSN 0342-3573) **4121**

Bindestube see Der Junge Florist **2142**

Bindetechnik/Reliure. (SZ) **4121**

Bingara Advocate. (AT) **2171**

Bingchong Cebao/Plant Disease and Insect Forecast. (CC) **170**

Bingchuan Dongtu/Journal of Glaciology and Geocryology. (CC ISSN 1000-0240) **1587**

Bingduxue Zazhi/Virologica Sinica. (CC ISSN 1000-3223) **550**

Bingo. (FR ISSN 0005-6499) **2168**

Bingo Bugle. (US) **4466**

Bingo Caller News. (CN) **4466**

Bingo Hi-Lites and Gaming News see Bingo News & Gaming Hi-Lites **1502**

Bingo News & Gaming Hi-Lites. (CN) **1502**, 1123

Bingwa. (ZR) **4466**

Bingxue Yundong. (CC) **4542**

Binian Deir. (IS) **2549**

Die Binnengewaesser. (GW ISSN 0067-8643) **1597**, 430

Binnenschiffahrts-Nachrichten. (GW ISSN 0179-7743) **4647**

Binnenvaart. (BE) **4708**

Binsted's Directory of Food Trade Marks and Brand Names. (UK ISSN 0067-8651) **2062**

Ha-Binui Be-Yisrael. see Israel. Central Bureau of Statistics. Construction in Israel **621**

Bio. (FR ISSN 0291-2430) **487**

†Bio. (GW) **5149**

Bio-Bibliografia Boliviana. (BO) **394**

Bio-Bibliographies in Afro-American and African Studies. (US ISSN 0882-7044) **2030**

Bio-Bibliographies in American Literature. (US ISSN 0742-695X) **2981**

▼Bio-Bibliographies in Art and Architecture. (US ISSN 1055-6826) **352**, 309

▼Bio-Bibliographies in Economics. (US) **706**

Bio-Bibliographies in Education. (US ISSN 1044-7962) **1674**

Bio-Bibliographies in Law and Political Science. (US ISSN 0882-7052) **2698**

Bio-Bibliographies in Music. (US ISSN 0742-6968) **3588**

Bio-Bibliographies in Sociology. (US ISSN 0893-8504) **4457**

Bio-Bibliographies in the Performing Arts. (US ISSN 0892-5550) **4643**, 1532, 3519

Bio-Bibliographies in World Literature. (US ISSN 0894-2323) **2981**

Bio-Engineering. (GW ISSN 0178-2029) **468**

Bio Engineering News. (US) **468**

†Bio Garten. (GW ISSN 0176-2494) **5149**

Bio-Joule. (CN) **3683**, 430, 1784

Bio-land. (GW ISSN 0173-9832) **2123**

▼Bio-Medical Materials and Engineering. (US ISSN 0959-2989) **468**, 1816, 3081

Bio Nachrichten. (GW) **170**, 3604

Bio-Nyt. (DK ISSN 0107-4415) **430**, 1944, 3081

Bio Options. (US) **472**

Bio Science Abstracts. (SW ISSN 0284-9321) **461**, 3

Bio-Science Research Bulletin. (II ISSN 0970-0889) **430**

Bio Spezial Magazin. (GW) **3799**

Bio-Technology. (US ISSN 0733-222X) **487**, 1170, 3081, 4594

Bioacoustics. (UK ISSN 0952-4622) **3859**, 579

Biocatalysis. (US ISSN 0886-4454) **472**

Biochemia Clinica Bohemoslovaca. (CS) **472**

Biochemical and Biophysical Research Communications. (US ISSN 0006-291X) **472**, 484

Biochemical Education. (US ISSN 0307-4412) **472**

Biochemical Genetics. (US ISSN 0006-2928) **472**, 540

Biochemical Journal. (UK ISSN 0264-6021) **472**

Biochemical Medicine see Biochemical Medicine and Metabolic Biology **472**

Biochemical Medicine and Metabolic Biology. (US ISSN 0885-4505) **472**, 3081

Biochemical Pharmacology. (US ISSN 0006-2952) **3719**, 472, 1216

Biochemical Reviews. (II ISSN 0365-9429) **472**

Biochemical Society. Transactions. (UK) **472**

Biochemical Society, London. Transactions see Biochemical Society. Transactions **472**

Biochemical Systematics and Ecology. (US ISSN 0305-1978) **472**, 430

Biochemie und Physiologie der Pflanzen (B P P). (GW ISSN 0015-3796) **496**, 472, 570

Biochemistry. (US ISSN 0006-2960) **472**

Biochemistry. (English translation of: Biokhimiya) (US ISSN 0006-2979) **473**

Biochemistry Abstracts. Part 3: Amino-Acids, Peptides and Proteins see Cambridge Scientific Biochemistry Abstracts: Part 3. Amino-Acids, Peptides & Proteins **464**

Biochemistry and Cell Biology/Biochimie et Biologie Cellulaire. (CN ISSN 0829-8211) **473**

Biochemistry International. (AT ISSN 0158-5231) **473**

Biochemistry of Disease. (US ISSN 0067-8678) **473**, 3081

Biochemistry of the Elements. (US) **473**

Biochemistry: Series of Monographs. (US ISSN 0194-0538) **473**

Biochimica et Biophysica Acta. (NE ISSN 0006-3002) **473**, 484

Biochimie. (FR ISSN 0300-9084) **473**, 487

Biochimie et Biologie Cellulaire. see Biochemistry and Cell Biology **473**

BioChromatography. (US ISSN 0888-4404) **473**, 1204

†Biocompatible Materials. (UK ISSN 0266-6316) **5149**

▼Bioconjugate Chemistry. (US ISSN 1043-1802) **473**

Biocontrol News and Information. (UK ISSN 0143-1404) **430**, 79

▼Biocontrol Science and Technology. (UK ISSN 0958-3157) **170**, 529

BioCycle. (US ISSN 0276-5055) **1984**, 1944

▼Biodegradation. (NE ISSN 0923-9820) **430**

Biodeterioration Abstracts. (UK ISSN 0951-0621) **461**, 1972

Biodex see U S Sci-Tech **483**

▼Biodiversity and Conservation. (UK ISSN 0960-3115) **1484**, 430

BioDynamics. (US ISSN 0006-2863) **170**

Bioelectrochemistry and Bioenergetics. (SZ ISSN 0302-4598) **473**, 484

Bioelectromagnetics. (US ISSN 0197-8462) **3082**, 3357

Bioelectromagnetics Society Newsletter. (US) **484**, 3815

Bioelectronics see Bioelectronics and Biosensors **484**

Bioelectronics and Biosensors. (UK ISSN 0952-0384) **484**, 3257

Bioengineering Abstracts see Bioengineering and Biotechnology Abstracts **1841**

Bioengineering and Biotechnology Abstracts. (US) **1841**, 3, 468, 487

Bioengineering and the Skin see Skin Pharmacology **3743**

Bioengineering Current Awareness Notification see B E C A N **5145**

Bioengineering Current Awareness Notification Biomechanics & Orthopaedics see B E C A N Biomechanics & Orthopaedics **5145**

Bioengineering Current Awareness Notification Electrodes for Medicine and Biology see B E C A N Electrodes for Medicine and Biology **5145**

Bioengineering Current Awareness Notification Equipment for the Disabled Population see B E C A N Equipment for the Disabled Population **5145**

Bioengineering Current Awareness Notification Instrumentation and Techniques in Cardiology see B E C A N Instrumentation and Techniques in Cardiology **5145**

BioEngineering News. (US ISSN 0275-4207) **468**, 3082

BioEssays. (UK ISSN 0265-9247) **431**

Bioethics. (UK ISSN 0269-9702) **3762**, 540, 3082

Bioethics Literature Review. (US) **3166**, 3, 2698

Biofactors. (UK ISSN 0951-6433) **473**

Biofeedback. (US) **4014**, 3331

Biofeedback & Self Regulation. (US ISSN 0363-3586) **4014**, 3593

Biofeedback Clinicians. (US) **3082**

Biofeedback Society of America. Proceedings of the Annual Meeting see Association for Applied Psychophysiology and Biofeedback. Proceedings of the Annual Meeting **4012**

Biofizika. (RU ISSN 0006-3029) **484**

Biofizika Zhivoi Kletki. (RU ISSN 0301-2425) **522**

Bioforum. (GW) **550**

Biofouling. (US ISSN 0892-7014) **1980**

Biofuels Program Summary see Conservation and Renewable Energy Technologies for Transportation Technologies **1785**

Biofutur. (FR ISSN 0294-3506) **487**

Biogenic Amines. (NE ISSN 0168-8561) **473**

Biogeochemistry. (NE ISSN 0168-2563) **473**

Biograficke Studie. (CS ISSN 0067-8724) **417**

Biographical Dictionaries and Related Works. (US) **394**, 417

Biographical Dictionaries Master Index see Biography and Genealogy Master Index **424**

Biographical Literature. see Zhuanji Wenxue **2980**

†Biographien Hervorragender Naturwissenschaftler, Techniker und Mediziner. (GW ISSN 0232-3516) **5149**

Biography (Honolulu). (US ISSN 0162-4962) **417**

Biography Almanac see Almanac of Famous People **417**

Biography and Genealogy Master Index.(US ISSN 0730-1316) **424**, 3

Biography Index. (US ISSN 0006-3053) **424**, 3

▼Biography Today. (US ISSN 1058-2347) **417**

†BioIndonesia. (IO ISSN 0126-0758) **5149**
Bioingenioeren. (NO ISSN 0801-6828) **1224**
Biokhimiya. (RU ISSN 0006-307X) **473**
Biokhimiya Zhivotnykh i Cheloveka. (KR ISSN 0136-9377) **473**
BioLaw: A Legal and Ethical Reporter on Medicine, Health Care, and Bioengineering. (US) **468**, 2605
Biologi Italiani. (IT ISSN 0392-2510) **431**
Biologia. (HU ISSN 0133-3844) **431**
Biologia. (PK ISSN 0006-3096) **431**, 579
Biologia see Biologia. C: General Biology **431**
Biologia. (MX) **431**
Biologia. (PL ISSN 0554-811X) **431**
Biologia see Biologia. D: Biochemistry and Molecular Biology **474**
Biologia see Biologia. A: Botany **496**
Biologia see Biologia. B: Zoology **579**
Biologia. A: Botany. (CS) **496**
Biologia. B: Zoology. (CS) **579**
Biologia. C: General Biology. (CS) **431**
Biologia. D: Biochemistry and Molecular Biology. (CS) **474**
Biologia e Etologia. (IT) **431**
Biologia Gabonica. (FR ISSN 0006-3118) **431**
Biologia Gallo-Hellenica. (GR ISSN 0750-7321) **431**
Biologia Pesquera. (CL ISSN 0067-8767) **2037**
Biologia Plantarum. (CS ISSN 0006-3134) **496**
Biologia w Szkole. (PL ISSN 0137-8031) **431**
Biologiai Kozlemenyek - Biological Publications see Biologia **431**
Biological Abstracts. (US ISSN 0006-3169) **462**, 3
Biological Abstracts Cumulative Indexes.(US ISSN 0006-3169) **462**, 3
Biological Abstracts - R R M. (US ISSN 0192-6985) **462**, 4
Biological Abstracts - R R M Cumulative Index. (US ISSN 0192-6985) **462**, 4
Biological Agriculture and Horticulture. (UK ISSN 0144-8765) **79**, 2123
Biological & Agricultural Index. (US ISSN 0006-3177) **462**, 4, 134
Biological and Chemical Factors in Animal Production - Veterinaria. see Biologizace a Chemizace Zivocisne Vyroby - Veterinaria **4807**
Biological and Cultural Tests for Control of Plant Diseases. (US ISSN 0887-2236) **496**
Biological Bulletin/Shengwuxue Tongbao. (CC ISSN 0006-3193) **431**
Biological Bulletin. (US ISSN 0006-3185) **431**
Biological Chemistry Hoppe-Seyler. (GW) **474**, 570
Biological Conservation. (UK ISSN 0006-3207) **1484**, 431
▼Biological Control. (US ISSN 1049-9644) **431**
Biological Cybernetics. (GW ISSN 0340-1200) **1440**, 4359
Biological Farming News. (US) **79**
Biological Institute of Tropical America Bulletin see B I O T A Bulletin **429**
Biological Institute of Tropical America Newsletter see B I O T A Newsletter **429**
Biological Journal of the Linnean Society see Linnean Society. Biological Journal **446**
Biological Magnetic Resonance. (US) **3815**, 474
Biological Mass Spectrometry. (UK ISSN 1052-9306) **1204**
Biological Membranes. (US ISSN 0748-8653) **484**
▼Biological Monitoring. (US ISSN 0897-7550) **474**, 431
†Biological Oceanography Journal. (US ISSN 0196-5581) **5149**
Biological Psychiatry. (US ISSN 0006-3223) **3332**, 431, 474
Biological Psychology. (NE ISSN 0301-0511) **4014**, 431

Biological Regulation & Development. (US ISSN 0271-9355) **474**
Biological Research in Norwich. (UK) **540**, 550, 1216
Biological Research Reports from the University of Jyvaskyla. (FI ISSN 0356-1062) **431**
Biological Review. see Biologicke Listy **432**
Biological Rhythms. (UK ISSN 0142-8004) **570**, 3082
Biological Science/Seibutsu Kagaku. (JA ISSN 0045-2033) **431**
Biological Sciences Review. (UK ISSN 0953-5365) **431**
▼Biological Signals. (SZ ISSN 1016-0922) **474**
Biological Society of Washington. Proceedings. (US ISSN 0006-324X) **431**, 496, 579
Biological Structure and Function. (UK ISSN 0308-5384) **570**
Biological Structures and Morphogenesis. (FR ISSN 0989-8972) **431**, 559, 3082
Biological Substances. (UN) **431**
Biological Therapies in Dentistry. (US ISSN 0882-1852) **3229**, 3082
Biological Therapies in Psychiatry see Biological Therapies in Psychiatry Newsletter **3332**
Biological Therapies in Psychiatry Newsletter. (US ISSN 1044-422X) **3332**
Biological Trace Element Research. (US ISSN 0163-4984) **474**, 3604
Biological Wastes see Bioresource Technology **487**
Biologicals. (UK ISSN 1045-1056) **431**
Biologicheskie Nauki. (KZ) **432**
Biologicheskii Zhurnal Armenii. (AI ISSN 0002-2969) **432**
Biologicke Listy/Biological Review. (CS ISSN 0366-0486) **432**
Biologico. (BL ISSN 0029-6953) **4807**
†Biologie du Comportement/Biology of Behaviour. (FR ISSN 0397-7153) **5149**
Biologie et Ecologie Mediterraneene. (FR ISSN 0397-2836) **432**
Biologie Heute. (GW ISSN 0936-6903) **432**
Biologie in der Schule. (GW ISSN 0406-3317) **432**
Biologie in Unserer Zeit. (GW ISSN 0045-205X) **432**
Biologisation und Chemisation der Tiererzeugung - Veterinaria. see Biologizace a Chemizace Zivocisne Vyroby - Veterinaria **4807**
Biologische Abhandlungen. (GW ISSN 0006-3282) **432**
Biologische Anstalt Helgoland. Berichte. (GW ISSN 0930-8148) **1602**
Biologische Bundesanstalt fuer Land- und Forstwirtschaft, Berlin-Dahlem. Mitteilungen. (GW ISSN 0067-5849) **79**, 2096
Biologische Medizin. (GW ISSN 0340-8671) **3213**
†Biologische Rundschau. (GW ISSN 0006-3290) **5149**
Biologische Tiermedizin. (GW ISSN 0723-6212) **4807**, 432
Biologische Zeitschrift. (GW ISSN 0179-5295) **529**, 579, 1944
Biologisches Zentralblatt. (GW ISSN 0006-3304) **432**
Biologist. (UK ISSN 0006-3347) **432**
Biologiste see Eurobiologiste **476**
Biologiya Laboratornykh Zhivotnykh. (RU) **3257**
Biologiya Morya/Marine Biology. (RU ISSN 0134-3475) **432**, 1602
Biologizace a Chemizace Zivocisne Vyroby - Veterinaria/Biological and Chemical Factors in Animal Production - Veterinaria/Biologisation und Chemisation der Tiererzeugung - Veterinaria/Facteurs Biologiques et Chimiques dans la Production des Animaux - Veterinaria/Factores Biologicos y Quimicos de la Production Animal - Veterinaria. (CS ISSN 0139-8571) **4807**, 3719
Biology. see Saengmulhak **454**

Biology and Fertility of Soils. (GW ISSN 0178-2762) **170**, 432
Biology and Philosophy. (NE ISSN 0169-3867) **432**
†Biology and Society. (UK ISSN 0266-3880) **5149**
Biology Bulletin see Academy of Sciences of the U S S R. Biology Bulletin **425**
Biology Bulletin Monthly. (US) **432**
Biology Digest. (US ISSN 0095-2958) **462**, 4
Biology Forum. see Rivista di Biologia **454**
Biology International: I U B S Newsmagazine. (International Union of Biological Sciences) (FR ISSN 0253-2069) **432**
Biology of Behaviour. see Biologie du Comportement **5149**
Biology of Metals. (US ISSN 0933-5854) **3403**
Biology of Reproduction. (US ISSN 0006-3363) **540**
Biology of the Cell. (FR ISSN 0248-4900) **559**, 522
Biology of the Neonate. (SZ ISSN 0006-3126) **3289**, 432
†Biology Series (Seattle). (US) **5149**
Biology Teaching. see Shengwuxue Jiaoxue **455**
Biomass see Bioresource Technology **487**
▼Biomass & Bioenergy. (UK ISSN 0961-9534) **1784**
Biomass Bulletin. (UK) **1784**, 3815
Biomassa. (BL) **1224**
Biomaterials. (UK ISSN 0142-9612) **3082**, 1915
Biomaterials, Artificial Cells and Artificial Organs see Biomaterials, Artificial Cells and Immobilization Biotechnology **3257**
Biomaterials, Artificial Cells and Immobilization Biotechnology. (US ISSN 1055-7172) **3257**, 487
Biomaterials Forum. (US) **474**
Biomaterials, Medical Devices, and Artificial Organs see Biomaterials, Artificial Cells and Immobilization Biotechnology **3257**
Biomathematics. (US ISSN 0067-8821) **432**, 3031
Biomathematics Review. see Revue de Bio-Mathematique **3052**
Biomechanics. see Biomekhanika **3842**
Biomedica Biochimica Acta. (GW ISSN 0232-766X) **432**, 3082
Biomedical and Environmental Mass Spectrometry see Biological Mass Spectrometry **1204**
Biomedical and Environmental Sciences.(CC ISSN 0895-3988) **3082**, 3719
†Biomedical Bulletin. (US) **5149**
Biomedical Business International Newsletter see The B B I Newsletter **3080**
Biomedical Chromatography. (UK ISSN 0269-3879) **3257**
Biomedical Engineering. see Biomedizinische Technik **3082**
Biomedical Engineering. (English translation of: Meditsinskaya Tekhnika) (US ISSN 0006-3398) **3082**
Biomedical Engineering see Journal of Medical Engineering & Technology **3117**
Biomedical Engineering and Computation Series. (US ISSN 0194-2778) **468**
†Biomedical Engineering and Health Systems: A Wiley-Interscience Series. (US) **5149**
Biomedical Engineering and Instrumentation Series. (US) **468**, 1816, 3082
Biomedical Engineering Society Bulletin see B M E S Bulletin **3081**
Biomedical Instrumentation & Technology. (US ISSN 0899-8205) **3082**
Biomedical Letters. (UK ISSN 0961-088X) **522**, 3082
Biomedical Materials. (UK ISSN 0955-7717) **3082**, 3861
Biomedical Polymers see Biomedical Materials **3082**

BIOPSYCHE 5981

Biomedical Products. (US ISSN 0192-1266) **3082**, 3257
Biomedical Research Technology Program see Biomedical Research Technology Resources **462**
Biomedical Research Technology Resources. (US) **462**, 432
▼Biomedical Science. (UK ISSN 0955-9701) **3082**, 432
▼Biomedical Science and Technology. (US ISSN 1051-2020) **3082**, 432, 4594
Biomedical Sciences Instrumentation. (US ISSN 0067-8856) **3082**, 2521
Biomedical Technology Information Service. (US ISSN 0147-2682) **3082**
Biomedicina Iugoslavica. (XV ISSN 0352-8685) **3166**, 4
Biomedicine see Biomedicine and Pharmacotherapy **3082**
Biomedicine and Pharmacotherapy. (FR ISSN 0753-3322) **3082**, 432
Biomedizinische Technik/Biomedical Engineering. (GW ISSN 0013-5585) **3082**
Biomedizinsche Forschung - Informationen. (GW ISSN 0933-2871) **3082**, 432
Biomekhanika/Biomechanics. (BU ISSN 0204-7594) **3842**, 484
Biomembranes. (US ISSN 0067-8864) **522**
Biometeorology; Proceedings. (GW ISSN 0067-8902) **3433**
Biometric Bulletin. (US ISSN 8750-0434) **4565**, 432
Biometrical Journal. (GW ISSN 0323-3847) **432**
Biometrics. (US ISSN 0006-341X) **4565**, 432, 3031
Biometrie and Informatik. (GW ISSN 0934-9235) **3083**, 432
Biometrie-Praximetrie. (BE ISSN 0006-3436) **4565**, 432
Biometrika. (UK ISSN 0006-3444) **462**, 4565
Biometrische Zeitschrift see Biometrical Journal **432**
▼Biomimetics. (US) **468**, 487
Bionews. (GR) **3875**
Bionics. (US) **3257**, 939
BioNieuws. (NE) **432**
Bionika. (KR ISSN 0374-6569) **484**
Bionomica. (GW ISSN 0006-3487) **3800**
▼Bioorganic & Medicinal Chemistry Letters. (UK ISSN 0960-894X) **1216**, 3083
Bioorganic Chemistry. (US ISSN 0045-2068) **1216**
Bioorganicheskaya Khimiya. (RU) **1216**, 474
Biopharm. (US ISSN 1040-8304) **3719**
Biopharm Manufacturing see Biopharm **3719**
Biopharmaceutics & Drug Disposition. (UK ISSN 0142-2782) **3719**
Biophysical Chemistry. (NE ISSN 0301-4622) **484**, 474
Biophysical Journal. (US ISSN 0006-3495) **484**
Biophysical Society. Abstracts. (US ISSN 0067-8910) **462**, 4, 484
Biophysics. (English translation of: Biofizika) (US ISSN 0006-3509) **484**
Biopolimery i Kletka. (KR) **433**
Biopolitics. (GR ISSN 1012-2532) **3875**, 3940
Biopolitics International Organization Report see Biopolitics **3875**
Biopolymer Sequences see C A S BioTech Updates. Nucleic Acid & Protein Sequences **463**
Biopolymers. (US ISSN 0006-3525) **1216**
Bioprocess Engineering. (GW ISSN 0178-515X) **487**, 1816
Bioprocess Technology Series. (US) **433**, 4594
Bioprocessing Technology see Industrial Bioprocessing **1218**
Biopsy Interpretation Series. (US) **3258**
Biopsyche. (IT) **4014**, 1618, 3083

BIORECOVERY

Biorecovery. (UK ISSN 0269-7572) 3403, 487
†Bioresearch Today: Addiction. (US ISSN 0149-1008) 5149
†Bioresearch Today: Bio Engineering & Instrumentation. (US ISSN 0149-0990) 5149
†Bioresearch Today: Birth Defects. (US ISSN 0149-0982) 5149
†Bioresearch Today: Cancer A - Carcinogenesis. (US ISSN 0149-1016) 5149
†Bioresearch Today: Cancer B - Anticancer Agents. (US ISSN 0149-1024) 5149
†Bioresearch Today: Cancer C - Immunology. (US ISSN 0149-1032) 5149
†Bioresearch Today: Food Additives & Residues. (US ISSN 0149-0958) 5149
†Bioresearch Today: Food Microbiology. (US ISSN 0149-0974) 5149
†Bioresearch Today: Human & Animal Aging. (US ISSN 0149-0966) 5149
†Bioresearch Today: Human and Animal Parasitology. (US ISSN 0149-094X) 5150
†Bioresearch Today: Human Ecology. (US ISSN 0149-0931) 5150
†Bioresearch Today: Industrial Health & Toxicology. (US ISSN 0149-0923) 5150
†Bioresearch Today: Pesticides. (US ISSN 0149-0907) 5150
†Bioresearch Today: Population, Fertility & Birth Control. (US ISSN 0149-0915) 5150
Bioresource Technology. (UK ISSN 0960-8524) 487, 79, 1170, 1784
Biorheology. (US ISSN 0006-355X) 485
Bios. (FR ISSN 0366-2284) 379
Bios. (GW ISSN 0933-5315) 417
Bios. (US ISSN 0005-3155) 433
BioScan. (US ISSN 0887-6207) 1123
BioScene. (US) 462, 4, 2796
BioScience. (US ISSN 0006-3568) 433
Bioscience, Biotechnology, and Biochemistry. (JA) 433, 474, 487
Bioscience Reports. (US ISSN 0144-8463) 474
BioSearch. (US) 462, 4, 1455
Biosensors see Biosensors and Bioelectronics 485
Biosensors and Bioelectronics. (UK ISSN 0956-5663) 485
▼Bioseparation. (NE ISSN 0923-179X) 487
†BIOSIS CAS Selects: Antiarrythmic Drugs. (US) 5150
BIOSIS CAS Selects: Antifungal Agents see C A Selects. Antifungal & Antimycotic Agents 463
†BIOSIS CAS Selects: Bacterial & Viral Genetics. (US) 5150
†BIOSIS CAS Selects: Biochemistry of Dairy Products. (US) 5150
†BIOSIS CAS Selects: Biochemistry of Fermented Foods. (US ISSN 0276-3109) 5150
†BIOSIS CAS Selects: Biochemistry of Fruits & Vegetables. (US) 5150
†BIOSIS CAS Selects: Biological Clocks. (US ISSN 0276-3117) 5150
BIOSIS CAS Selects: Cancer and Nutrition see C A Selects. Nutritional Aspects of Cancer 3167
†BIOSIS CAS Selects: Cancer Immunology. (US ISSN 0276-3125) 5150
BIOSIS CAS Selects: Drug Interactions see C A Selects. Drug Interactions 3167
†BIOSIS CAS Selects: Endorphins. (US ISSN 0276-3133) 5150
†BIOSIS CAS Selects: Enzyme Methods. (US) 5150
†BIOSIS CAS Selects: Food and Drug Legislation. (US) 5150
†BIOSIS CAS Selects: Genetic Manipulation in Plants. (US) 5150
†BIOSIS CAS Selects: Histochemistry and Cytochemistry. (US ISSN 0276-315X) 5150

†BIOSIS CAS Selects: Hormone & Hormone Receptor Interactions. (US) 5150
†BIOSIS CAS Selects: Hormones & Gene Expression. (US) 5150
BIOSIS CAS Selects: Indoor Air Pollution see C A Selects. Indoor Air Pollution 4117
†BIOSIS CAS Selects: Interferon. (US ISSN 0276-3176) 5150
BIOSIS CAS Selects: Leukotrienes and Slow-Reacting Substances see C A Selects. Leukotrienes 1195
†BIOSIS CAS Selects: Lymphokines. (US) 5150
†BIOSIS CAS Selects: Mammalian Birth Defects. (US ISSN 0276-3184) 5150
†BIOSIS CAS Selects: Neuroreceptors. (US) 5150
BIOSIS CAS Selects: Nitrogen Fixation see C A Selects. Nitrogen Fixation 1196
†BIOSIS CAS Selects: Nutrition & Immunology. (US) 5150
BIOSIS CAS Selects: Occupational Exposure see C A Selects. Occupational Exposure & Hazards 3623
†BIOSIS CAS Selects: Peptide and Protein Sequences. (US) 5150
BIOSIS CAS Selects: Pesticide Analysis see C A Selects. Pesticide Analysis 463
†BIOSIS CAS Selects: Plant Genetics. (US ISSN 0276-3206) 5150
†BIOSIS CAS Selects: Schizophrenia. (US ISSN 0276-3214) 5150
†BIOSIS CAS Selects: Transplantation. (US ISSN 0276-3222) 5150
BIOSIS Previews Search Guide (Year). (US) 462, 4
Biosistematika see Acta Biologica Iugoslavica. Serija G: Biosistematika 425
Habiosphera. (IS) 1944, 1484
Biosphere. (CN ISSN 0824-1600) 1484
Biosphere en Bref see Biosphere 1484
Biostatistica. (US ISSN 1041-7648) 462, 4, 3062
Biosynthetic Products for Cancer Chemotherapy. (NE) 3193, 3719
Biosystems. (IE ISSN 0303-2647) 433
Biotech Business. (US ISSN 0899-5702) 540, 805
Biotech Buyer's Guide. (US) 488, 1816
Biotech Europe see Biotech Forum Europe 488
Biotech Forum Europe. (GW ISSN 0938-7501) 488
Biotech-Info see Biotechnology Information 462
Biotech Investor. (US ISSN 0891-3161) 939, 550
Biotech Knowledge Sources see B K S 461
BioTech Market News & Strategies. (US ISSN 0740-1221) 488, 648
Biotech News. (UK ISSN 0263-8029) 488
Biotechnic and Histochemistry. (US ISSN 1052-0295) 559, 488, 522
BioTechniques. (US ISSN 0736-6205) 488, 468, 540, 550
Biotechnology. see Shengwu Gongcheng Xuebao 491
Biotechnology Advances. (US ISSN 0734-9750) 488, 468, 3083
Biotechnology and Applied Biochemistry.(US ISSN 0885-4513) 488, 474
Biotechnology and Bioengineering. (US ISSN 0006-3592) 488, 469, 474
†Biotechnology & Bioengineering Symposia. (US ISSN 0572-6565) 5150
Biotechnology and Genetic Engineering Reviews. (UK ISSN 0264-8725) 488, 79, 469, 3083
Biotechnology Directory (Year). (UK) 1123, 488
▼Biotechnology Education. (US ISSN 0955-6621) 488, 1618
Biotechnology in Agriculture and Forestry. (US) 488, 79, 2096

Biotechnology in Japan Newsservice. (US) 488
Biotechnology Information. (HU ISSN 0237-0115) 462, 488
Biotechnology Information Package. (US) 488
Biotechnology Insight. (UK ISSN 0268-7291) 488
Biotechnology Investment Opportunities.(US) 939, 488, 540
Biotechnology Law Report. (US ISSN 0278-9728) 488, 2605
Biotechnology Letters. (UK ISSN 0141-5492) 488
Biotechnology News. (US ISSN 0273-3226) 488
Biotechnology Progress. (US ISSN 8756-7938) 488
Biotechnology Research Abstracts. (US ISSN 0733-5709) 462, 4, 488
Biotechnology Resources see Biomedical Research Technology Resources 462
Biotechnology Software. (US ISSN 0749-0372) 488, 1475, 3258
Biotechnology Software Report see Biotechnology Software 488
Biotechnology Techniques. (UK ISSN 0951-208X) 489
Biotechnology Therapeutics. (US ISSN 0898-2848) 489, 3719
†Biotechnology Week. (US) 5150
Biotherapy. (NE ISSN 0921-299X) 3193, 433, 3083
†Biotica. (MX ISSN 0185-0326) 5150
Biotransformations. (UK) 474
Biotronics. (JA ISSN 0289-0011) 489, 469, 1944
Biotropica. (US ISSN 0006-3606) 433
BioVenture View. (US ISSN 0892-1903) 489
Biovisie - Biovision see BioNieuws 432
BioWorld see BioWorld Online 433
▼BioWorld Online. (US) 433
BioWorld Today. (US) 433
Biplav. (BG) 2174
Bipolar Circuits and Technology Meeting. Proceedings. (US) 1764, 3815
Birbal. (II ISSN 0006-3614) 1249
Bird Behaviour. (US ISSN 0156-1383) 562, 4014
▼Bird Conservation International. (UK ISSN 0959-2703) 562
Bird Effort. (US) 2860
Bird Keeping in Australia. (AT ISSN 0045-2076) 562, 212
Bird Life. (UK ISSN 0006-3649) 562, 1249
Bird Research. (UK) 562
Bird Study. (UK ISSN 0006-3657) 562
Bird Talk. (US ISSN 0891-771X) 3708, 562
Bird Watcher's Digest. (US ISSN 0164-3037) 562
Bird World. (US ISSN 0199-5979) 562, 3708
Birder's World. (US) 562
†Birdfinding in Canada. (CN ISSN 0229-5024) 5150
Birding. (US ISSN 0161-1836) 562
Birding in Southern Africa. (SA) 562
Birdkeeper. (UK) 3708
Birds. (UK ISSN 0006-3665) 562
Birds see Australian Birds 562
†Birds and Country. (UK ISSN 0006-3673) 5150
▼Birds U S A. (US) 3708
Birdsall Bulletin. (US) 2145
Birdscope. (US ISSN 1041-6676) 562
Birdwatcher's Yearbook see Birdwatcher's Yearbook and Diary 562
Birdwatcher's Yearbook and Diary. (UK) 562, 1484
Birkbeck College Discussion Papers in Economics. (UK) 648
†Birkner Eurolignum. (GW) 5150
Birmingham. (US ISSN 0006-369X) 808, 2222
Birmingham & Warwickshire Archaeological Society. Transactions. (UK ISSN 0140-4202) 267

Birmingham & West Midlands Chambers of Commerce Directory. (UK ISSN 0307-0158) 808
Birmingham and West Midlands Chambers of Commerce Journal see Midlands Industry and Commerce 819
Birmingham Bar Association. Bulletin. (US ISSN 0006-3711) 2605
▼Birmingham Bugle. (UK) 2145
Birmingham Business. (US) 808
▼Birmingham Commercial Real Estate Review & Forecast Annual. (US) 4145
▼Birmingham Healthcare Review & Forecast Annual. (US) 2459, 3083
†Birmingham Historical Society. Journal.(US) 5150
†Birmingham International Trade Directory. (US) 5150
Birmingham Poetry Review. (US ISSN 1047-2258) 2989
Birmingham Post and Mail Year Book and Who's Who see Birmingham Post Year Book and Who's Who 417
Birmingham Post Year Book and Who's Who. (UK) 417
Birmingham Times. (US) 1993
Birmingham World. (US ISSN 0006-3754) 2222
Birombo. (IT) 2204, 4516
Birra e Malto. (IT ISSN 0006-3770) 379
Birritu. (ET) 847
Birth. (US ISSN 0730-7659) 3289, 3276
Birth. (AT ISSN 1032-9625) 3290
Birth Defects Institute. Symposia. (US) 3083
†Birth Defects Original Article Series. (US ISSN 0547-6844) 5150
Birth Gazette. (US ISSN 0890-3255) 3290
Birth Notes. (US) 3290, 4838
Birth of Tragedy Magazine. (US ISSN 0897-9057) 2860, 3396
Birth Psychology Bulletin. (US ISSN 0734-3124) 3290, 4014
Birth to Three. Newsletter see Birth to Three and Beyond 1233
Birth to Three and Beyond. (US) 1233
Bisdeh Hemed. (IS ISSN 0523-1469) 1618
Biserica Ortodoxa Romana. (RM) 4257
Biserica Romaneasca. (IT) 4257
Bishop Get-Together Newsletter. (US) 2145
Bishop Museum Bulletins in Anthropology. (US) 236
Bishop Museum Bulletins in Botany. (US ISSN 0893-3138) 496
Bishop Museum Bulletins in Entomology. (US ISSN 0893-3146) 529
Bishop Museum Bulletins in Zoology. (US ISSN 0893-312X) 579
Bishvilei Harefuah. (IS) 4222, 3083
Bismarckschule. (GW) 1618
Bismoi. (II ISSN 0006-3827) 2199
Bismuth Institute. Bulletin. (BE ISSN 0379-0401) 3403, 1883
Bisra see Belizean Studies 2400
Bistandshaandbogen see Haandbog for Social og Sundhedssektor 4407
Bisuteria y Bisuteros. (SP) 2563
Biswin Sadi. (II) 2199
Bit. (DK ISSN 0006-3835) 1389
Bit. (JA ISSN 0385-6984) 1429, 1448
Bit. (IT ISSN 0392-8837) 1458, 1475
Bit. (SP) 1458, 1475
Bit and Bridle. (US ISSN 1050-5741) 4532
Bit Dropper. (US) 1436
Bit International. (CI) 1369
Bitacora Colombo Suizo. (CK) 808
†Bitaon Chel Rifuah. (IS) 5150
Bitaon Heyl ha-Avir/Israel Air Force Magazine. (IS ISSN 0006-3878) 49, 3453
Bitechut. (IS) 3615
Bithell Series of Dissertations see University of London. Institute of Germanic Studies. Bithell Series of Dissertations 2972
Bitidningen. (SW ISSN 0006-3886) 79

Bitki Koruma Bulteni. *see* Plant Protection Bulletin **189**
Bitlupe. (GW) **1475**, 1429
Biton Lemorim Le'Aravit. (IS ISSN 0334-9985) **2806**, 1745
Al-Bitrul. (UA) **3683**
Bits and Bytes. (NZ) **1389**
Bits & Bytes Review. (US ISSN 0891-2955) **2520**
Bits 'n Chips. (US) **639**
†Bitterroot. (US ISSN 0006-3908) **5150**
Bitumen. (GW ISSN 0006-3916) **1862**
Bitumen, Teere, Asphalte, Peche *see* Strassen- und Tiefbau Vereinigt mit Strasse-Bruecke-Tunnel, Bitumen-Teere-Asphalts-Peche **1874**
Bitzaron: A Quarterly of Hebrew Letters.(US) **2860**, 1993, 4222
Biuletyn/Bulletin of Polonia. (AT) **1993**
Biuletyn Historii Sztuki. (PL ISSN 0006-3967) **319**
Biuletyn Informacyjny. Budownictwo. Gospodarka Mieszkaniowa *see* Budownictwo i Gospodarka Miejska. Biuletyn Informacyjny **604**
Biuletyn Informacyjny Biblioteki Narodowej. (PL ISSN 0006-3983) **2748**
Biuletyn Informacyjny Cointe. (PL) **833**
Biuletyn Instytutu Hodowli i Aklimatyzacji Roslin *see* Instytut Hodowli i Aklimatyzacji Roslin. Biuletyn **181**
Biuletyn Instytutu Roslin Leczniczych *see* Herba Polonica **504**
Biuletyn Meteorologiczny. (PL) **3433**
Biuletyn Numizmatyczny/Numismatic Bulletin. (PL ISSN 0006-4017) **3598**
Biuletyn Peryglacjalny. (PL ISSN 0067-9038) **1587**
Biuletyn Polonistyczny. (PL ISSN 0067-902X) **2806**, 2899
Biuletyn Warzywniczy. (PL ISSN 0509-6839) **170**
Bivoie. (CN ISSN 0315-2138) **1618**
Bivouac. (FR ISSN 0980-2371) **1233**
Biweekly List of Papers on Radiation Chemistry and Photochemistry. (US ISSN 0164-5315) **1191**, 4
Biza Neira (Bise Noire). (FR ISSN 0398-9453) **2353**, 319, 2899
Bjelovarski List. (CI ISSN 0006-4068) **2860**
Bjerg-Posten. Medlemsblad. (DK ISSN 0107-072X) **2353**
B'kitzur/Briefs. (US) **4222**
Blaa Stjaernan. (SW ISSN 0006-4076) **3708**, 4807
†Blaaklint - Livlinan. (SW ISSN 0345-1593) **5150**
Blac-Tress. (US) **372**, 1993
Blacfax. (US) **1993**
Black American *see* New American (New York) **2016**
▼Black American History Rhyme. (US) **1993**
Black American Literature Forum. (US ISSN 0148-6179) **1993**, 2899
Black Americans Information Directory (Year). (US) **1993**
Black & Decker Build It. (US) **2500**, 2434, 2444
Black and Magenta. (US) **1305**
Black and Red. (US) **1305**
Black Art *see* International Review of African American Art **331**
Black Arts Annual. (US) **319**, 1993
Black Arts National Diaspora. Newsletter. (US) **1993**
▼Black Authors & Published Writers Directory. (US ISSN 1060-9148) **417**, 1993, 2899
Black Bag. (UK ISSN 0045-2084) **3083**
Black Bear Review. (US ISSN 8756-0666) **2989**, 319
Black Beat. (US ISSN 0745-8649) **1249**, 3541
Black Beauty & Hair. (UK ISSN 0263-3213) **372**, 375
Black Beauty Handbook. (US) **372**, 1993
Black Belt Magazine. (US ISSN 0006-4106) **4466**
Black Book Auction Report. (US) **3016**
▼Black BottomLine. (US) **1993**

Black Buzzard Review. (US) **2989**
Black Careers. (US ISSN 0006-4122) **3624**
Black Child Advocate. (US) **1233**, 1993, 4399
†Black Coal in Australia. (AT) **5150**
Black College Sports Review. (US) **4466**
Black Collegian. (US ISSN 0192-3757) **1305**, 1993
Black Communicators *see* Black Press Periodical Directory **2030**
Black Congressional Monitor. (US ISSN 0895-1780) **3875**, 1993
Black Country. (UK) **2053**
Black Country Bugle. (UK) **2145**
Black Country Bugle Annual. (UK) **2053**
Black Country Business Directory *see* Black Country Business Directory (North) **1123**
Black Country Business Directory *see* Black Country Business Directory (South) **1123**
Black Country Business Directory (North). (UK ISSN 0963-1348) **1123**
Black Country Business Directory (South). (UK ISSN 0963-133X) **1123**
Black Country Geologist. (UK ISSN 0260-714X) **1555**
Black Country Ghosts and Mysteries. (UK) **2053**, 3010
Black Data Processing Associates. Data News. (US) **1448**, 1993
Black Data Processing Associates. National Journal. (US) **1448**, 1993
Black Elected Officials. (US ISSN 0882-1593) **4054**, 1994
Black Elegance. (US) **1994**
▼Black Employment and Education. (US ISSN 1053-704X) **1994**, 1618, 3624
Black Enterprise. (US ISSN 0006-4165) **648**, 1994
Black Experience in Children's Books. (US ISSN 0067-9070) **1247**
Black Family. (US ISSN 0279-0718) **1994**
Black Farmer *see* African Business and Chamber of Commerce Review **806**
Black Film Review. (US) **3504**, 1994
Black Flag. (UK ISSN 0045-2157) **3875**
Black Fly Review. (US ISSN 0736-9271) **2899**
Black Hair Today - Beauty & Lifestyles. (US) **372**, 1994
Black Health. (US) **1994**, 3083, 3800
▼Black Heritage Unveiled Newsletter. (US ISSN 1042-4199) **1994**, 3940
Black Hills Anemone *see* Black Hills State Today **1305**
Black Hills State Today. (US) **1305**
Black Ice. (US ISSN 1047-515X) **2899**
Black Issues in Higher Education. (US ISSN 0742-0277) **1701**, 1994
Black Jack & Valley Grapevine. (US) **2989**
▼Black Lace. (US ISSN 1049-3298) **2451**, 1994
Black Law Journal *see* National Black Law Journal **2656**
Black Lechwe. (ZA ISSN 0045-219X) **1484**
Black Liberation Journal. (US) **3940**
Black Literature and Arts Congress *see* B L A C **1993**
Black Manufacturer *see* African Business and Chamber of Commerce Review **806**
Black Messiah. (US) **1994**
Black Ministries. (US) **1994**, 4231
Black Mountain Review. (US ISSN 0896-3517) **2860**, 2899
Black Mullet Review. (US) **2989**
Black Music and Jazz Review *see* Blues & Soul Music Review **3542**
†Black Music Research Bulletin. (US ISSN 0898-8536) **5150**
Black Music Research Journal. (US ISSN 0276-3605) **3541**, 1994
Black Music Research Newsletter *see* Black Music Research Bulletin **5150**
†Black Nation. (US) **5150**

Black New York Magazine. (US) **1994**
Black News Digest. (US ISSN 0045-2238) **973**, 1994
Black Orpheus. (NR ISSN 0067-9100) **2899**, 1994
Black Pages. (US) **1123**, 1994
Black Pages Pamphlet Series. (US) **1994**
†Black Papers. (US) **5150**
†Black Perspective in Music. (US ISSN 0090-7790) **5150**
▼Black Political Studies. (US ISSN 0891-9631) **3876**
†Black Position. (US ISSN 0084-7909) **5150**
Black Powder Times. (US ISSN 0745-1385) **4466**
Black Press Periodical Directory. (US) **2030**
Black Psychiatrists of America Quarterly *see* B P A Quarterly **3331**
Black Resource Guide. (US) **1994**
Black Resources Information Coordinating Services, Inc. Bracs *see* B R I C S Bracs **1993**
Black River Review. (US) **2989**
Black Rose. (US) **3876**
Black Sacred Music. (US ISSN 1043-9455) **3541**, 1994
Black Sash *see* Sash **3947**
Black Scholar. (US ISSN 0006-4246) **1994**, 3876, 4367
Black Sheep Newsletter. (US) **4617**, 212
Black Spots. (US) **1994**
†Black Star. (US) **5150**
Black Studies. (US) **1994**
Black Studies Series. (US) **1994**
Black Swamp Magazine *see* Miscellany Magazine **1318**
▼Black Tail. (US) **3396**
Black Teen *see* Spice (New York) **2024**
Black Tennis. (US) **4501**
Black View *see* Ofari's Bi-Monthly **2018**
Black Warrior Review. (US ISSN 0193-6301) **2899**
Black Welsh Mountain Sheep Breeders' Association. Annual Flock Book. (UK) **212**
†Black Who's Who of Southern Africa. (SA ISSN 0250-0817) **5150**
Black Women's Voice. (US) **4838**, 1994
Black Writer. (US) **1994**, 2899
Black Writers Series. (SA) **2899**
Blackall Leader. (AT ISSN 0812-5864) **2171**
†Blackberry. (US) **5150**
Blackboard Bulletin. (CN ISSN 0006-4327) **4280**
Blackcountryman. (UK ISSN 0006-4335) **2353**, 4430
Blackface Sheep Breeders' Association Journal. (UK) **212**
Blackfire. (US ISSN 1049-3271) **2451**, 1994
Blackfish. (CN ISSN 0045-2270) **2989**
Blackfriars *see* New Blackfriars **4270**
Blackjack Forum. (US) **4466**, 3031
Blacklist. (US) **2989**
Blackpool Hotel & Guest House Association. Journal. (UK ISSN 0006-4351) **2472**
Blacks Against Nukes Newsletter *see* B A N Newsletter **1784**
Black's Broker - Tenant Guide: South Florida - Treasure Coast. (US) **4145**
Black's Broker - Tenant Guide: Tampa Bay - Southwest Florida. (US) **4145**
Black's Broker - Tenant Guide: Washington - Baltimore. (US) **4145**
Black's Guide to the Office Space Market: Connecticut - New York Suburbs. (US) **4145**
Black's Guide to the Office Space Market: Dallas - Fort Worth. (US) **4145**
Black's Guide to the Office Space Market: Denver. (US) **4145**
Black's Guide to the Office Space Market: Greater Los Angeles Area. (US) **4145**
Black's Guide to the Office Space Market: Houston. (US) **4145**
Black's Guide to the Office Space Market: Northern New Jersey. (US) **4145**

Black's Guide to the Office Space Market: Philadelphia and Suburbs *see* Black's Guide to the Office Space Market: Philadelphia - South New Jersey - Delaware **4145**
Black's Guide to the Office Space Market: Philadelphia - South New Jersey - Delaware. (US) **4145**
Black's Guide to the Office Space Market: San Francisco Bay Area. (US) **4145**
Black's Guide to the Office Space Market - Washington - Baltimore *see* Black's Broker - Tenant Guide: Washington - Baltimore **4145**
Blacks in Law Enforcement. (US) **1510**, 1994
Blacks in the New World. (US) **1994**
Black's Medical Dictionary. (UK) **3083**
Black's Veterinary Dictionary. (UK) **4807**
Blacksmith's Gazette *see* Black Powder Times **4466**
Blade Magazine. (US ISSN 0744-6179) **256**
Blades. (US ISSN 0888-529X) **2989**, 319
Bladsmutten. (DK ISSN 0109-257X) **562**
Blaetter aus dem Henriettenstift. (GW) **2459**, 2270, 3276
Blaetter der Freien Volksbuehne Berlin. (GW ISSN 0006-4378) **4630**, 319, 3541
Blaetter der Rilke-Gesellschaft. (GW ISSN 1010-3597) **2899**
Blaetter der Wohlfahrtspflege. (GW) **4399**
†Blaetter fuer den Deutschlehrer. (GW ISSN 0006-4394) **5150**
Blaetter fuer Deutsche Landesgeschichte. (GW ISSN 0006-4408) **2353**
Blaetter fuer Deutsche und Internationale Politik. (GW ISSN 0006-4416) **3876**
†Blaetter fuer Grundstuecks, Bau- und Wohnungsrecht. (GW ISSN 0006-4440) **5150**
Blaetter fuer Heimatkunde. (AU ISSN 0006-4459) **2307**, 319, 2053
†Blaetter fuer Lehrerfortbildung. (GW) **5151**
Blaetter fuer Oberdeutsche Namenforschung. (GW ISSN 0172-0872) **2806**
Blaetter fuer Pfaelzische Kirchengeschichte und Religioese Volkskunde. (GW ISSN 0341-9452) **4231**
†Blaetter fuer Steuerrecht, Sozial Versicherung und Arbeitsrecht. (GW ISSN 0006-4475) **5151**
Blaetter fuer Technikgeschichte. (US ISSN 0067-9127) **4594**
Blaetter fuer Volksliteratur. (AU ISSN 0006-4483) **2899**
Blaetter fuer Vorgesetzte. (GW) **1072**
Blaetter fuer Wuerttembergische Kirchengeschichte. (GW ISSN 0341-9479) **4166**, 2353
Blaetter fuer Zuercherische Rechtsprechung. (SZ ISSN 0006-4491) **2605**
Blaetter zur Geschichte des Coburger Landes. (GW) **4085**
†Blagues. (FR ISSN 0006-4513) **5151**
Blair County Genealogical Society. Newsletter. (US ISSN 1056-6953) **2145**
Blaireau. (FR) **1250**
Blake: An Illustrated Quarterly. (US ISSN 0160-628X) **2899**
Blakes Boating Abroad. (UK) **4754**, 4522
Blakes Boating Holiday Books. (UK) **4522**
Blakes Boating Holidays *see* Blakes Boating in Britain **4754**
Blakes Boating Holidays *see* Blakes Boating Abroad **4754**
Blakes Boating in Britain. (UK) **4754**, 4522
Blakes Report - Intellectual Property. (CN) **2605**, 3673
▼Blank Gun Silence. (US) **2989**
Blank Tape *see* Bikini Girl **2860**
Blanket Statements. (US) **3590**

Blantyre Handbook. (MW) **2209**
Blantyre Water Board. Annual Report and Statement of Accounts. (MW ISSN 0084-7925) **4822**
Die Blasmusik. (GW) **3541**
Blasting. see Bao Po **1848**
Blastpipe. (UK ISSN 0263-0125) **4708**
Blatt fuer Patent, Muster- und Zeichenwesen. (GW ISSN 0930-2980) **3673**
Blatt fuer Sortenwesen. (GW ISSN 0300-4627) **134**, 4
Blattsalat - Literaturmagazin. (AU) **1250**
Blau Gelb. (GW) **4466**
Blaue, Alpwirtschaftliche Monatsblaetter.(SZ ISSN 0006-4610) **79**
Blaue Datei der Krankenhauslieferanten.(GW) **2459**
Blaue Datei der Krankenhauslieferanten mit Krankenhausverzeichnis see Blaue Datei der Krankenhauslieferanten **2459**
Blaue Feder. (GW) **4430**
Das Blaue Jahrbuch. (GW) **3708**
Blaue Jungs. (GW ISSN 0936-3971) **3453**
Blaue Kreuz. (SZ ISSN 0006-4629) **4098**
Der Blaue Peter. (GW ISSN 0006-4637) **4522**, 4542
Blaues Kreuz. (GW) **4166**
Blaukreuz Information - Meinungen - Szene see B I M S **4230**
Blauwe Kruis see Blauwe Wegwijzer **1534**
Blauwe Wegwijzer. (NE ISSN 0921-3996) **1534**, 4430
Blauwe Wimpel. (NE ISSN 0006-4661) **4724**
Blazes. (IE ISSN 0332-253X) **2860**
Blech see Blech-Rohre-Profile **3403**
Blech-Rohre-Profile. (GW ISSN 0006-4688) **3403**, 1816, 3016
Bleib Gesund. (GW) **2528**
Blessings of Liberty. (US ISSN 0006-4696) **4166**
Bleter far Geszichte. (PL ISSN 0006-470X) **1994**
Bleu et Rouge. (FR ISSN 0045-2289) **4466**
Blicheregnens Museumsforening. Aarsskrift. (DK ISSN 0107-6094) **2353**
Blick. (GW) **2062**
Blick hinter die Fassade. (GW ISSN 0067-9178) **4399**
Blick in die Kirche. (GW) **4231**
Blick ins Fleischer-Fachgeschaeft see Blick **2062**
Blick ins Hessenland. (GW ISSN 0935-4344) **79**, 2096
Blick Ins Land. (AU ISSN 0006-4742) **79**
Blick vom Hochhaus. (GW ISSN 0006-4750) **1170**
Blickpunkt. (GW ISSN 0006-4769) **1250**
Blickpunkt Bildung. (GW) **1725**
Blickpunkt: Film. (GW) **3504**
Blickpunkt Gemeinde. (GW) **4231**
Blickpunkt Strassenbahn. (GW ISSN 0173-0290) **4647**
Blickpunkt Wirtschaft. (GW) **808**
Blickpunkte. (GW) **4231**
Blimp. (AU) **3504**
†Blind. (NE ISSN 0923-6511) **5151**
Blind Advocate see Advocate **2290**
Blind Alleys. (US ISSN 0737-9269) **2989**
Blind Citizen. (IE ISSN 0006-4815) **2290**, 2202
Blind Donkey. (US) **4214**
†Blind Justice. (US) **5151**
Blind - Sehbehindert. (GW ISSN 0176-7836) **2291**
Blind Welfare. (II ISSN 0006-4823) **2291**
Blindaba. (SA) **2291**, 2216
Blinded Veterans Association Bulletin see B V A Bulletin **2290**
Der Blindenhelfer. (GW) **2291**
Die Blindenselbsthilfe. (GW) **2291**
Blindenwelt see Die Blindenselbsthilfe **2291**
Blindes Jul. (DK ISSN 0901-4306) **2291**

Blindmaker see Blinds and Shutters **2557**
†Blindoc. (GW) **5151**
Blinds and Shutters. (UK ISSN 0305-733X) **2557**
Blinker. (GW ISSN 0720-4116) **4542**
Bliss Classification Bulletin. (UK ISSN 0520-2795) **2748**
Blitz. (II ISSN 0006-4882) **2199**
Blitz. (US) **3542**
Blitz Chess. (US) **4466**
Blitz Magazin see Blitz-Terminal **2188**
Blitz Magazine. (UK ISSN 0263-2543) **319**, 1289, 3789
Blitz News Magazine. (II) **2199**
Blitz-Terminal. (GW) **2188**
Blk. (US ISSN 1043-0075) **2451**, 1994
Bloc. (US ISSN 1051-2675) **901**
Bloc. (FR ISSN 0006-4890) **1862**
Bloc-Notes de l'Observatoire Economique de Paris. (FR ISSN 0180-9105) **706**
Block. (UK ISSN 0143-3245) **319**
Block. (NE) **3542**
Block Aid. (VI) **2484**
†Blockbuster. (US) **5151**
Bloem en Blad. (NE) **2141**
Bloembollencultuur. (NE) **2123**
Bloemenvak. (NE) **2141**
Bloemenvriend. (BE ISSN 0006-4920) **2123**
Bloemfontein Agricultural Show Catalogue. (SA) **79**
Bloemfontein Newsletter. see Bloemfontein Nuusbrief **4085**
Bloemfontein Nuusbrief/Bloemfontein Newsletter. (SA ISSN 0006-4939) **4085**
Bloemheuwel-Nuus. (SA ISSN 0006-4947) **4231**
†Blois Voice. (US ISSN 0889-9479) **5151**
Blomster. (DK ISSN 0006-4955) **2141**
Blomster-Branschen. (SW ISSN 0006-4963) **2141**
Blomsterbinderen see Blomster **2141**
Blonde on Blonde see Siren Magazine **2883**
Blood. (US ISSN 0006-4971) **3271**, 474, 522
Blood and Its Products. (AT) **3083**
Blood Bank Week. (US ISSN 0747-2420) **3083**
Blood Cells. (US ISSN 0340-4684) **3271**
†Blood Coagulation. (UK ISSN 0142-8586) **5151**
▼Blood Coagulation and Fibrinolysis. (UK ISSN 0957-5235) **3271**
Blood Coagulation Factors. (UK ISSN 0266-6294) **3271**, 3205
The Blood-Horse. (US ISSN 0006-4998) **4532**
†Blood Proteins. (UK ISSN 0142-8594) **5151**
Blood Purification. (SZ ISSN 0253-5068) **3271**
Blood Reviews. (UK ISSN 0268-960X) **3271**
Blood Therapy Journal see Blood Therapy Journal International **3271**
Blood Therapy Journal International. (II) **3271**
Blood Transfusion. (UK ISSN 0261-4596) **3271**, 3307, 3376
†Blood Vessel Walls. (UK ISSN 0268-1536) **5151**
Blood Vessels see Journal of Vascular Research **479**
Bloodhound Bulletin. (US) **3708**
Bloodlines. (US) **3708**
Bloodroot (Madison) see Madison Review **2997**
Bloodstock Breeders' Review. (UK ISSN 0067-9224) **4532**, 212
Bloodstock Sales Review and Stud Register. (UK) **4532**
Bloom Magazine see Bloomsburg Literary Journal **1305**
Blooming Grove Courier. (US) **2400**
Bloomington Monthly. (US) **2222**
Bloomsburg Literary Journal. (US) **1305**
Bloomsbury Geographer. (UK ISSN 0067-9232) **2243**
Bloomsbury Review. (US ISSN 0276-1564) **2899**

Blu and Blu. (IT) **3542**
Blue and Gold Triangle of Lambda Kappa Sigma. (US ISSN 0006-503X) **3719**
Blue and Gray. (US) **1305**
Blue and White see Westminster Magazine **1330**
Blue Banner. (US) **1305**
The Blue Beret. (CY) **2184**
Blue Bill. (CN ISSN 0382-5655) **562**, 496, 1484
Blue Book Digest of H M O's. (US) **3083**
Blue Book Digest of P P O's. (Preferred Provided Organization) (US) **3083**
Blue Book Dolls and Values. (US) **2434**, 2281
Blue Book of British Broadcasting. (UK) **1369**
Blue Book of C B S Stock Reports see Blue.Book of Stock Reports **939**
Blue Book of Canadian Business. (CN ISSN 0381-7245) **847**
Blue Book of College Athletics see Blue Book of College Athletics of Senior, Junior and Community Colleges **4466**
Blue Book of College Athletics of Senior, Junior and Community Colleges. (US) **4466**
Blue Book of Food Store Operators & Wholesalers. (CN ISSN 0316-9537) **2084**, 4565
Blue Book of Fur Farming. (US) **2736**
Blue Book of Junior and Community College Athletics see Blue Book of College Athletics of Senior, Junior and Community Colleges **4466**
Blue Book of Major Home Builders. (US ISSN 0195-8461) **604**
Blue Book of Materials, Compounding Ingredients and Machinery for Rubber. (US) **4291**
Blue Book of Occupational Education see Occupational Education **1713**
Blue Book of Optometrists. (US ISSN 0067-9283) **3298**
Blue Book of S.A. Business see Business Blue Book of S.A **649**
Blue Book of Stock Reports. (CN) **939**
▼Blue Book: The Buyer's Guide for Pharmaceutical Packagers. (US) **3719**
Blue Buildings. (US) **2989**
Blue Bulletin see National Association of Regulatory Utility Commissioners. Bulletin **4068**
Blue Chart Report. (CN ISSN 0831-6503) **2528**
Blue Chip Companies Directory see Big Businesses Directory **1123**
Blue Chip Economic Indicators. (US ISSN 0193-4600) **847**
Blue Chip Economic WorldScan see Currency Forecasters' Digest **859**
Blue Chip Financial Forecasts. (US ISSN 0741-8345) **939**
Blue Chip Stocks. (US ISSN 0896-4904) **939**
Blue Cross Illustrated. (UK) **230**
Blue Goose Flyer. (US) **1484**
Blue Guitar. (US) **2989**
†Blue Guitar. (IT) **5151**
Blue Horse. (US) **2899**
Blue Jay. (CN ISSN 0006-5099) **4302**
Blue Jay News. (CN) **4302**, 1944
Blue Jeans. (UK) **1250**
Blue Life. (KO) **2271**, 4466
Blue Light Red Light. (US ISSN 1046-0012) **2900**
Blue Light Review. (US) **2900**
Blue Line Magazine. (CN ISSN 0847-8538) **1510**
†Blue Moon. (US ISSN 0743-2917) **5151**
Blue Mountains Gazette. (AT) **2171**
Blue Pig. (US) **2989**
Blue Pitcher. (US ISSN 0886-4187) **2989**, 3789
Blue Ridge Country. (US) **2222**
The Blue Seal. (US ISSN 0897-9421) **4685**
Blue Sky Bulletin see Update (Lansing) **5299**
Blue Sky Compliance Manual. (US) **2605**
Blue Sky Law Reports. (US) **2605**
Blue Sky News. (US) **4054**

Blue Smoke. (US **2900**, 2053
Blue Unicorn. (US ISSN 0197-7016) **2989**
Blue Water see Boating Safety **4523**
Blue Wings. (FI ISSN 0358-7703) **4802**
Bluebell News. (UK ISSN 0520-3015) **2434**
Blueboy. (US) **2451**
Bluefield. (US) **1305**
Bluegrass - Buehne. (GW ISSN 0936-2479) **3542**
Bluegrass Bulletin. (US) **2806**, 1745
Bluegrass Directory. (US) **3542**
Bluegrass Music News. (US ISSN 0006-5129) **3542**, 1745
Bluegrass Trucker see Fastline for Kentucky Truckers **4744**
Bluegrass Unlimited. (US ISSN 0006-5137) **3542**
Blueline. (US ISSN 0198-9901) **2900**
Blueline. (GR) **3951**
Bluemont Muse. (US) **3542**
Bluenose Rambler. (CN) **2900**
Blueprint. (UK) **1511**
Blueprint for Social Justice. (US ISSN 0895-5786) **3940**, 4367
Blueprints. (US ISSN 0742-0552) **295**, 604
II Blues. (IT) **3542**
Blues Access. (US) **3542**
Blues & Rhythm. (UK) **3542**
Blues & Soul Music Review. (UK ISSN 0045-2297) **3542**
Blues at the Foundation. (US) **3542**
Blues Life. (AU ISSN 0250-4421) **3542**
Blues News see B N **3540**
Blues Research. (US) **3542**
Blues Unlimited. (UK ISSN 0006-5153) **3542**, 2053
†Blues World. (UK ISSN 0006-5161) **5151**
▼Bluff City. (US) **2900**
Blumea. (NE ISSN 0006-5196) **496**
Blumen Einzelhandel. (GW ISSN 0341-2075) **2141**
Blumenau em Cadernos. (BL ISSN 0006-5218) **2400**
Blumenfreundin Blumenpost. (GW ISSN 0006-5226) **2123**
Blum's Farmers & Planters Almanac and Turner's Carolina Almanac. (US ISSN 0894-1386) **2222**
Blushing Bride. (US) **3066**, 1994
Blut see Annals of Hematology **3270**
Blutalkohol. (GW ISSN 0006-5250) **1534**
Blyton Handi Read Centre Newsletter see National Library for the Handicapped Child. Newsletter **1739**
Blyttia. (NO ISSN 0006-5269) **496**
B'nai B'rith International Jewish Monthly.(US ISSN 0279-3415) **1994**
B'nai B'rith Messenger. (US ISSN 0006-5277) **1994**
Bo Bedre. (DK) **2549**
Bo Ji/Technique of Self-Defense. (CC) **4466**
Bo Kun Hak Non Zip. see Korean Journal of Public Health **4106**
Boa Semente. (PO) **1250**, 4166
Board and Administrator. (US) **1003**
Board & Sail Magazine. (US ISSN 0163-7452) **4522**
Board Converting News. (US) **3647**, 3662
Board Converting News Espanol see Mari-Board Converting News Espanol **3649**
Board Converting News International. (US) **3647**, 3662
Board for International Broadcasting. Annual Report. (US) **1369**
Board Manufacture & Processing. (UK ISSN 0306-4123) **2113**
Board Manufacture Practice see Board Manufacture & Processing **2113**
Board of Celtic Studies. Bulletin. (UK ISSN 0142-3363) **2900**, 2353, 2806
Board of Certified Safety Professionals Directory see C S P Directory **3615**
Board of Certified Safety Professionals Newsletter see B C S P Newsletter **3615**

BOLETIM ALAGOANO 5985

Board of Contract Appeals Bid Protest Decisions. (US) **2605**, 847
Board Report for Graphic Artists. (US) **29**, **3997**
Boarderline Magazine. (US) **3708**, 1113
Boardman see Boardmember **1725**
Boardmember. (US) **1725**
Boardroom. (UK) **648**, 1003
Boardroom. (SA ISSN 0378-9144) **1057**
Boardroom Reports. (US ISSN 0045-2300) **1004**
Boards. (UK) **4522**
Boardwatch Magazine. (US ISSN 0894-5209) **1443**
†Boat. (US) **5151**
Boat & Motor Dealer. (US ISSN 0006-5366) **4522**, 1123
Boat and Motor Dealer's Market see Boat & Motor Dealer's Market Manual **4522**
Boat & Motor Dealer's Market Manual. (US) **4522**
Boat Guide. (CN) **4522**, 1123
Boat Journal see Boating World **4523**
Boat Mart International. (UK) **4522**
Boat Owners Association of the United States Reports see B O A T - U S Reports **4522**
Boat Pennsylvania. (US) **4522**
Boat World. (CN) **4522**
Boatbuilder. (US) **4523**
Boatbuilder's International Directory. (US) **4523**, 4724
Boating. (US ISSN 0006-5374) **4523**
Boating Almanac, Volume 1: Rhode Island, Massachusetts, Maine, New Hampshire. (US) **4523**
Boating Almanac, Volume 2: Long Island, Connecticut, Rhode Island, Southern Massachusetts. (US) **4523**
Boating Almanac, Volume 3: New Jersey, Delaware Bay, Hudson River, Lake Champlain, Erie Canal. (US) **4523**
Boating Almanac, Volume 4: Chesapeake Bay, Delaware, Maryland, District of Columbia, Virginia. (US) **4523**
Boating Business. (CN) **4523**
Boating Business and Marine Trade News. (UK ISSN 0260-9452) **4523**
†Boating Digest. (US) **5151**
Boating in the San Juan Islands. (US) **4523**, 4754
Boating Industry. (US ISSN 0006-5404) **4523**
Boating Industry Marine Buyers' Guide. (US ISSN 0006-5404) **1123**, 4523, 4724
Boating Industry's O E M Business. (US) **4523**
†Boating Information. (US) **5151**
Boating News. see Baatnytt **4522**
Boating News. (CN ISSN 0700-7388) **4523**
†Boating Product News. (US ISSN 0190-4507) **5151**
Boating Registration Statistics. (US ISSN 0163-7207) **4498**
Boating Safety. (NZ) **4523**
Boating Statistics. (US) **4498**
Boating World. (US ISSN 1059-5155) **4523**
Boating World see Sea Spray **4529**
†Boatracing. (US) **5151**
†Boats & Gear. (US) **5151**
Boats & Harbors. (US) **4523**
†Boats, Boats, Boats... (AT ISSN 1032-5360) **5151**
Bob Brinker's Marketimer. (US) **939**
Bob Damron's Address Book. (US) **4754**, 2451
Bob Ellsberg's Hunter & Fisherman's Planning Yearbook. (US) **4542**
†Bob Jennings Confidential Report. (US) **5151**
Bob Larson's Junior and Collegiate Tennis. (US) **4501**
Bob Larson's Tennis Junior see Bob Larson's Junior and Collegiate Tennis **4501**
Bob Nurock's Advisory. (US ISSN 1050-9011) **939**
Bob Watkins Sports 24 Magazine. (US) **4466**

Bob Zwirz' Fishing Annual see Fishing and Boating Illustrated **5193**
Bobbin. (US ISSN 0896-3991) **1283**
Bobina see La Bobina - Notivest **1283**
La Bobina - Notivest. (US ISSN 0194-7249) **1283**, 4617
Bobo. (IO) **1250**
Boca Raton Magazine. (US ISSN 0740-2856) **2222**, 4754
Bocagiana. (PO ISSN 0523-7904) **579**, 496
Bochum. Amt fuer Statistik, Stadtforschung und Wahlen. Reihe "Wahlen in Bochum". (GW) **3936**, 4079
Bochum. Amt fuer Statistik, Stadtforschung und Wahlen. Sonderberichte. (GW ISSN 0930-4274) **2499**, 4079
Bochum. Amt fuer Statistik, Stadtforschung und Wahlen. Statistical Yearbook. (GW ISSN 0067-9437) **2499**, 3991, 4079
Bochum. Amt fuer Statistik, Stadtforschung und Wahlen. Verwaltungsbericht. (GW ISSN 0931-2900) **2499**, 4079
Bochum. Amt fuer Statistik, Stadtforschung und Wahlen. Zur Stadtentwicklung. (GW) **2499**, 4079
Bochum Studies in English. see Bochumer Anglistische Studien **2900**
Bochumer Anglistische Studien/Bochum Studies in English. (NE ISSN 0169-6165) **2900**
Bochumer Jahrbuch zur Ostasienforschung. (GW ISSN 0170-0006) **3635**, 2337
†Bochumer Materialen zur Entwicklungsforschung und Entwicklungspolitik. (GW ISSN 0170-1916) **5151**
†Bochumer Schriften zur Entwicklungsforschung und Entwicklungspolitik. (GW ISSN 0572-6654) **5151**
Bochumer Studien zur Philosophie. (NE) **3762**
BoCoEx Index. (US ISSN 1047-496X) **1423**, 1458
Bode des Heils see Bode van het Heil in Christus **4166**
Bode van het Heil in Christus. (NE ISSN 0006-5439) **4166**
Boden - Tapeten - Heimtextilien Tapetenzeitung see B T H - Tapetenzeitung **2557**
†Boden und Gesundheit. (GW ISSN 0006-5455) **5151**
Boden, Wand, Decke. (GW ISSN 0006-5463) **2549**, 604
Bodendenkmalpflege in Mecklenburg. (GW ISSN 0067-9461) **3522**
Die Bodenkultur. (AU ISSN 0006-5471) **80**
Bodensee Hefte. (SZ ISSN 0006-548X) **2243**, 319, 2900
Bodhi Baum. (AU) **4214**
Bodhi Leaves. (CE ISSN 0520-3325) **4214**
Bodine Motorgram. (US ISSN 0006-5498) **3016**
Bodleian Library Record. (UK ISSN 0067-9488) **2748**
Body. (UK ISSN 0006-5501) **4685**
Body Boarding see Surfing **4557**
Body Bulletin Newsletter. (US) **3615**, 3800
Body Cast. (CN) **3307**
Body Copy. (US) **29**
Body Engineering. (US) **4685**
Body Fashions see Body Fashions - Intimate Apparel **1283**
Body Fashions Directory and Source of Supply see Body Fashions - Intimate Apparel Directory **1283**
Body Fashions - Intimate Apparel. (US ISSN 0360-3520) **1283**
Body Fashions - Intimate Apparel Directory. (US ISSN 0362-2452) **1283**
†Body Forum. (US ISSN 0145-6210) **5151**
Body Language. (US) **4685**
Body, Mind and Spirit see Body, Mind & Spirit Magazine **3593**

Body, Mind & Spirit Magazine. (US) **3593**, 3668
▼Bodybuilding Lifestyles. (US) **3800**
†Bodybuilding Woman. (US) **5151**
Bodyshop. (CN ISSN 0045-2319) **4685**
BodyShop Business. (US ISSN 0730-7241) **4685**
▼Bodywise. (US) **3800**
Boecksteiner Montana. (AU) **3479**
Boei Daigakko Kiyo. Rikogaku Hen. see National Defense Academy. Memoirs. Mathematics, Physics, Chemistry, and Engineering **4334**
Boei Daigakko Kyokan Kenkyu Yoroku/ National Defense Academy. Digest of Researches by Faculty Members. (JA ISSN 0523-8080) **3476**
Boei Daigakko Rikogaku Kenkyu Hokoku/National Defense Academy. Scientific and Engineering Reports. (JA ISSN 0385-7301) **1816**, 3453
Boei Eisei. see National Defense Medical Journal **3134**
Boek der Boeken see Schrift **4275**
Boekblad. (NE ISSN 0167-4765) **4121**
Boekparade. see Book Parade **2749**
Boer see Boer en de Tuinder **80**
Boer en de Tuinder. (BE ISSN 0772-7054) **80**
Boer en Tuinder. (NE ISSN 0006-5609) **80**
Boerderij. (NE ISSN 0006-5617) **80**
Boerderij Stierenboek. (NE) **212**
Boerenbrief see Ekoland **88**
Boerenleenbank see Rabobank **796**
Boern i Tiden see Boerns Trivsel i Tiden **4399**
Boern og Boeger. (DK ISSN 0006-7792) **4121**, 2748
Boern & Unge. (DK ISSN 0006-5633) **1618**, 1250
Boerne og Ungdoms-Litteratur Magasinet see B U M **1249**
Boerne- og Ungdomskultursammenslutningen see B U K S **1232**
Boerne- og Ungdomstandplejen i Danmark. (DK) **3229**, 1233
Boernebibliotekskatalog. Boeger & Tidsskrifter. Emnekatalog. (DK ISSN 0106-9713) **394**
Boernebibliotekskatalog. Boeger & Tidsskrifter. Forfatterkatalog. (DK ISSN 0106-9691) **394**
Boernebibliotekskatalog. Boeger & Tidsskrifter. Titelkatalog. (DK ISSN 0106-9705) **394**
Boernebibliotekskatalog. Grammofonplader, Kassettebaand. (DK ISSN 0106-729X) **3588**
Boernebibliotekskatalog. Lydboeger, Bog & Baand. (DK ISSN 0109-193X) **1247**
Boernebladet. (DK) **4231**, 1250
Boernebladet (Ringkoebing) see Helses Boerneblad **5204**
Boernebladets Jul see Jul i Familien **1257**
Boernebogsserier Tegneserier. (DK ISSN 0106-8199) **1250**
Boernefilmkataloget. (DK ISSN 0105-1377) **1250**, 3504
Boernefilmkataloget. Supplement. (DK ISSN 0106-7990) **1250**
Boernesagspaedagogen see Socialpaedagogen **4421**
Boernetandplejen i Danmark see Boerne- og Ungdomstandplejen i Danmark **3229**
Boerneteateravisen. (DK) **4630**
Boerns Trivsel i Tiden. (DK) **4399**
Boerse. (AU) **940**, 768
Boerse Online. (GW ISSN 0934-8441) **940**, 768
Boersen. (DK) **648**
Boersen-Kurier. (AU) **940**
Boersenblatt fuer den Deutschen Buchhandel see BuchWoche **5153**
Boersenblatt fuer den Deutschen Buchhandel. Frankfurter Ausgabe. (GW ISSN 0340-7373) **394**
Boersens Nyhedsmagasin. (DK) **1004**
Boethius. (GW ISSN 0523-8226) **4302**
Bof see Le Declin **1310**

Bog og Baand. (DK ISSN 0107-5187) **4121**
Bogazici Universitesi Dergisi: Ey Oneticilik, Ekonomi, ve Sosyal Bilimler. see Bogazici University Journal: Management, Economic and Social Sciences **4367**
Bogazici University Journal: Engineering.(TU) **1816**
Bogazici University Journal: Management, Economic and Social Sciences/Bogazici Universitesi Dergisi: Ey Oneticilik, Ekonomi, ve Sosyal Bilimler. (TU) **4367**
Bogazici University Journal: Sciences. (TU) **4302**
Bogens Verden. (DK ISSN 0006-5692) **2748**, 2900
Bogg. (US ISSN 0882-648X) **2989**, 2900
Boggs Newsletter Quarterly. (US) **2145**
Bogmarkedet. (DK ISSN 0903-7195) **4121**
Bogong. (AT) **1484**, 1944
Bogormen. (DK ISSN 0006-5706) **4121**
Bogoslovlje. (YU ISSN 0006-5714) **4166**
Bogoslovni Vestnik. (XV ISSN 0006-5722) **4257**
Bogtrykkerbladet see De Grafiske Fag **4000**
Bogtrykkerne - Distriktsbladene. (DK) **3997**
Bogvennen. (DK ISSN 0006-5749) **4122**, 3997
▼Bohannon's New Mexico Environmental Law Handbook. (US) **2605**, 1944
Bohemia. (CU) **2184**
Bohemia Venezuela. (VE) **2238**
Bohemia: Zeitschrift fuer Geschichte und Kultur der Bohemischen Laender.(GW ISSN 0523-8587) **2353**
Bohman Ocean Shipping News Summary. (US) **4724**
Bohman Traffic News Summary. (US) **4717**
Bohren, Sprengen, Raeumen see B S R **1848**
Boi. (BG ISSN 0006-5773) **4122**
†Boian News Service. (US ISSN 0045-2351) **5151**
Boilermakers - Blacksmiths Reporter. (US) **2580**
Boing see Offspring - Boing **1262**
Bois. see Wood **2118**
Bois et Forets des Tropiques. (FR ISSN 0006-579X) **2096**
Bois Hebdo. (FR) **2113**
Bois National (Edition Rouge) see Officiel du Bois (Edition Rouge) **640**
Bois National (Edition Verte) see Officiel du Bois (Edition Verte) **2105**
Boise Cascade Insight. (US) **3662**, 2096
Boise Cascade Quarterly see Boise Cascade Insight **3662**
Boissons de France - Jean Primus. (FR ISSN 0760-1999) **379**
Boissons de France "Saines et Legeres" see Boissons de France - Jean Primus **379**
Bok og Bibliotek. (NO ISSN 0006-5811) **2748**
Bok og Samfunn. (NO) **4140**
Boken-O. see Adventure King **1248**
Boken Report. (JA) **4617**
Bokmakierie see Birding in Southern Africa **562**
†Bokrevy. (SW ISSN 0005-2833) **5151**
Bokult. (GW) **3522**
Bol og By see Landbohistorisk Tidsskrift **2372**
Bola. (IO) **4466**
BolaffiArte Antiquariato see Antiquariato **254**
Bolan Qunshu. (CC ISSN 1000-4173) **2900**
Bolchevique. (US) **3876**, 973
Bold Gay Life Style. (US) **2451**, 3396
Bold Print. (US) **2989**
Bolebu. (UY) **808**
Boletim Actinometrico de Portugal. (PO ISSN 0870-4740) **3433**
Boletim Alagoano de Folclore. (BL) **2053**

Boletim Climatologico. (BL ISSN 0067-9585) **3433**
Boletim da Republica. (MZ) **2211**
Boletim de Analise e Logica Matematica. (BL) **3031**
Boletim de Bibliografia Portuguesa. Documentos nao Textuais. (PO ISSN 0253-343X) **2792**
Boletim de Bibliografia Portuguesa. Monografias. (PO ISSN 0253-3413) **2792**
Boletim de Bibliografia Portuguesa. Publicacoes em Serie. (PO ISSN 0253-3421) **2792**
Boletim de Ciencias do Mar. (BL ISSN 0067-9593) **433**
Boletim de Custos. (BL ISSN 0006-5900) **604**
†Boletim de Engenharia de Producao. (BL ISSN 0067-9607) **5151**
†Boletim de Estudos de Pesca. (BL ISSN 0006-5927) **5151**
Boletim de Filologia. (PO) **2806**
Boletim de Geociencias da Petrobras. (BL ISSN 0102-9304) **3683**
Boletim de Geografia Teoretica. (BL ISSN 0100-9761) **1541**, **2243**
†Boletim de Indicadores Energeticos. (BL) **5151**
Boletim de Industria Animal. (BL ISSN 0067-9615) **212**
Boletim de Materiais Dentarios. (BL ISSN 0045-2378) **3229**
Boletim de Minas. (PO ISSN 0006-5935) **3479**
Boletim de Pesquisa. (BL ISSN 0101-5117) **80**
Boletim de Zoologia. (BL ISSN 0101-3580) **433**
Boletim de Zoologia e Biologia Marinha. Nova Serie *see* Boletim de Zoologia **433**
Boletim do Curso de Educacao Fisica *see* Boletim Tecnico de Educacao Fisica e Desportos **1745**
Boletim do Porto de Lisboa. (PO ISSN 0006-596X) **4724**
Boletim Eclesial. (MH) **4166**
Boletim Epidemiologico. (BL) **4098**
Boletim I G *see* Boletim I G - U S P. Serie Cientifica **1541**
Boletim I G *see* Boletim I G - U S P. Serie Didatica **1541**
Boletim I G *see* Boletim I G - U S P. Publicacao Especial **1541**
Boletim I G - U S P. Publicacao Especial. (Universidade de Sao Paulo, Instituto de Geociencias) (BL ISSN 0102-6275) **1541**, **362**
Boletim I G - U S P. Serie Cientifica. (Universidade de Sao Paulo, Instituto de Geociencias) (BL ISSN 0102-6283) **1541**, **362**
Boletim I G - U S P. Serie Didatica. (Universidade de Sao Paulo, Instituto de Geociencias) (BL ISSN 0102-6291) **1541**, **362**
Boletim Mensal das Estatisticas do Comercio Externo. (PO ISSN 0377-2160) **706**
†Boletim Mensuel des Seismes Proches.(PO) **5151**
Boletim Meteorologico. (PO ISSN 0870-4686) **3433**
Boletim Meteorologico para a Agricultura. (PO ISSN 0870-4694) **3433**, **80**
Boletim Oficial. (MH) **4054**
Boletim Oficial da Republica de Cabo Verde. (CV) **2168**
Boletim Oficial de Angola. (AO ISSN 0067-9631) **2332**
Boletim Paulista de Geografia. (BL ISSN 0006-6079) **2243**
Boletim Sorocaba. (BL) **2243**
Boletim Tecnico da Petrobras *see* Boletim de Geociencias da Petrobras **3683**
Boletim Tecnico de Educacao Fisica e Desportos. (BL) **1745**
Boletim U E R J. (Universidade do Estado do Rio de Janeiro) (BL) **1618**
Boletin Aceprensa. (SP) **2504**
Boletin Antartico Chileno. (CL ISSN 0716-0763) **2344**
Boletin B N F. (Banco Nacional de Fomento) (EC) **768**
Boletin Bibliografico *see* Albir **2327**

Boletin Bibliografico Boliviano. (BO ISSN 0006-6141) **394**, **4140**
Boletin Bibliografico C E R L A L *see* C E R L A L C: El Libro en America Latina y el Caribe **4124**
Boletin Bibliografico I S B N. (CK ISSN 0121-2400) **394**
Boletin Bibliografico Mexicano. (MX ISSN 0185-2027) **394**, **4140**
Boletin Botanico Latinoamericano. (US) **496**
Boletin Bursatil. (PE) **940**
Boletin Cefnomex *see* El Correo Fronterizo **2245**
Boletin Chileno de Parasitologia. (CL ISSN 0006-6176) **3218**, **550**
Boletin Cientifico-Tecnico I N D E R - Cuba. (Instituto Nacional de Deportes, Educacion Fisica y Recreacion) (CU) **3800**
Boletin Comercial. (UY) **833**
Boletin D U P *see* U A P Newsletter **2788**
Boletin de America Latina. *see* Latin American Bulletin **2217**
Boletin de Antropologia Americana. (MX ISSN 0252-841X) **253**
Boletin de Arqueologia Medieval. (SP) **267**
Boletin de Arte. (PR ISSN 0006-6206) **319**
Boletin de Asuntos Economicos. (CK) **648**
Boletin de Biotecnologia. (CR ISSN 0255-7924) **489**, **3083**
Boletin de Cardiologia y Cirugia Cardiovascular *see* Revista Cubana Cardiologia y Cirugia Cardiovascular **3211**
Boletin de Ciencias Politicas y Sociales *see* Anales Ciencias Politicas y Sociales **3872**
Boletin de Comercio Exterior *see* Boletin de Asuntos Economicos **648**
Boletin de Coyuntura y Estadistica del Pais Vasco. (SP ISSN 0211-1268) **808**
Boletin de Derecho Publico. (CL) **2605**
†Boletin de Economia Internacional. (MX) **5151**
Boletin de Estadistica y Coyuntura. (SP ISSN 0210-1580) **4565**
Boletin de Estadisticas Bancarias. (GT) **706**, **768**
Boletin de Estudios Economicos. (SP ISSN 0006-6249) **648**
Boletin de Estudios Latinoamericanos y del Caribe *see* European Review of Latin American and Caribbean Studies **4371**
Boletin de Estudios Medicos y Biologicos. (MX ISSN 0067-9666) **3083**, **433**
Boletin de Estupefacientes *see* Bulletin on Narcotics **1535**
Boletin de Eventos Cientifico-Tecnicos. (CU) **4302**
Boletin de Filologia. (CL ISSN 0067-9674) **2806**
Boletin de Formacion Cooperativa. (SP ISSN 0006-6273) **829**
Boletin de Geociencias. (VE ISSN 0257-8611) **1555**
Boletin de Historia y Antiguedades. (CK ISSN 0006-6303) **2400**
Boletin de Indicadores de Coyuntura *see* Venezuela. Oficina Central de Estadistica e Informatica. Coyuntura Economica **743**
Boletin de Informacion Oportuna del Sector Alimentario. (MX ISSN 0186-9027) **2084**
Boletin de Informacion Yugoslavo *see* Yugoslav Information Bulletin **3935**
Boletin de Informaciones y de Estudios Sociales y Economicos *see* Instituto Ecuatoriano de Seguridad Social. Boletin. Normas Resoluciones y Jurisprudencias **2533**
Boletin de la Propiedad Industrial. (VE ISSN 0006-6338) **3673**
†Boletin de la Sociedad Cientifica del Paraguay y del Museo Etnografico. (PY ISSN 0560-4168) **5151**
Boletin de Legislacion e Informacion Juridica. (EC) **2605**
Boletin de Legislacion Extranjera. (SP) **2720**

Boletin de Lima. (PE ISSN 0253-0015) **2213**
Boletin de Mediciana Tradicional Grupo "Juan Tomas Roig". (CU) **3083**
Boletin de Medio Ambiente y Urbanizacion. (AG ISSN 0326-7857) **2484**, **1944**
Boletin de Musica y Danza. (PE) **3542**, **1529**
Boletin de Poblacion de las Naciones Unidas *see* Population Bulletin of the United Nations **3986**
Boletin de Politica Informatica. (MX ISSN 0186-0461) **3876**
Boletin de Prehistoria de Chile *see* Revista Chilena de Antropologia **248**
Boletin de Prensa Latinoamericana. *see* Spiegel der Lateinamerikanischen Presse **3972**
Boletin de Promecafe. (GT) **171**, **2062**
Boletin de Psicologia. (CU) **4014**
Boletin de Resumenes Analiticos. (VE) **1701**, **1682**
Boletin de Salud Publica. (VE) **4098**
Boletin de Telecomunicaciones *see* Telecommunication Journal **1343**
Boletin de Teoria de Numeros y Temas Conexos. *see* Bulletin of Number Theory and Related Topics **3031**
Boletin de Traducciones. (SP ISSN 0211-4046) **4354**, **4**, **4614**
Boletin del Archivo de la Paz. (BO) **2400**
Boletin del Cemento Portland. (AG ISSN 0523-9095) **604**
Boletin del F M I *see* I M F Survey **720**
Boletin del Registro de Variedades. (SP) **171**, **2123**
Boletin Eclesiastico de Fillipinas. (PH) **4257**
Boletin Economico de la Construccion. (SP ISSN 0210-1947) **847**
Boletin Epidemiologico. (MX) **4098**
Boletin Epidemiologico Anual *see* Boletin Epidemiologico **4098**
Boletin Epidemiologico Nacional. (CK) **4098**, **3218**
Boletin Estadistico de Trafico Aereo Internacional. (EC) **4662**, **4671**
Boletin Galego de Literatura. (SP ISSN 0214-9117) **2900**
Boletin Genetico. (AG ISSN 0067-9720) **540**
Boletin Geologico. (CK ISSN 0120-1425) **1555**
Boletin Geologico y Minero. (SP ISSN 0366-0176) **1555**, **3479**
Boletin Geologico y Minero. Publicaciones Especiales. (SP) **1555**, **3479**
Boletin Hemerografico *see* Sintesis Bibliografica **738**
Boletin Hidrologico. (CR ISSN 0067-9747) **1597**
Boletin Historico *see* Boletin Historico del Ejercito **2307**
Boletin Historico del Ejercito. (UY) **2307**
Boletin I I E. (Instituto de Investigaciones Electricas) (MX ISSN 0185-0059) **1883**
Boletin Informativo. *see* I C M C Newsletter **5208**
Boletin Informativo A E F H. (Asociacion Espanola de Farmaceuticos de Hospitales) (SP) **3719**, **2459**
▼Boletin Informativo Crefal - Reduc. (MX) **1682**
Boletin Informativo de Ciencia Politica. (SP) **3876**
Boletin Informativo Techint. (AG ISSN 0497-0292) **4367**
Boletin Ingenieria Comercial. (CL) **1816**
Boletin Interamericano de Contabilidad. (AG) **748**
Boletin Internacional de Opportunidades.(CK) **808**
Boletin Intimo de Compania *see* Evangelio y Mision **4177**
Boletin Juridico Militar. (MX ISSN 0006-6419) **3453**, **2605**
Boletin Maritimo de la Exportacion Argentina. (AG) **4725**
Boletin Medico. (CR) **596**, **3979**
Boletin Medico de I P P F *see* I P P F Medical Bulletin **597**

Boletin Merksa de Estudios de Mercado.(SP ISSN 0210-1831) **1034**
Boletin Mexicano de Derecho Comparado. (MX ISSN 0041-8633) **2605**
Boletin Naval. (PY ISSN 0006-646X) **3453**
Boletin Nicaraguense de Bibliografia y Documentacion. (NQ) **2328**
Boletin Oficial de la Jurisdiccion Eclesiastica Castrense *see* Boletin Oficial Eclesiastico del Arzobispado Castrense de Espana **4166**
Boletin Oficial de la Propiedad Industrial. Informacion Tecnologica de Patentes *see* Boletin Oficial de la Propiedad Industrial. 4: Resumenes de Patentes **3673**
Boletin Oficial de la Propiedad Industrial. 1: Marcas y Otros Signos Distintivos. (SP ISSN 0211-0105) **3673**
Boletin Oficial de la Propiedad Industrial. 2: Patentes, Modelos y Dibujos *see* Boletin Oficial de la Propiedad Industrial. 2: Patentes y Modelos de Utilidad **3673**
Boletin Oficial de la Propiedad Industrial. 2: Patentes, Modelos y Dibujos *see* Boletin Oficial de la Propiedad Industrial. 3: Modelos y Dibujos Industriales y Artisticos **3673**
Boletin Oficial de la Propiedad Industrial. 2: Patentes y Modelos de Utilidad. (SP ISSN 0211-0121) **3673**
Boletin Oficial de la Propiedad Industrial. 3: Modelos y Dibujos Industriales y Artisticos. (SP ISSN 0211-013X) **3673**
Boletin Oficial de la Propiedad Industrial. 4: Resumenes de Patentes. (SP) **3673**
Boletin Oficial de las Cortes Espanoles. (SP) **2605**
Boletin Oficial del Registro Mercantil *see* Spain. Registro Mercantil. Boletin Oficial **692**
Boletin Oficial Eclesiastico del Arzobispado Castrense de Espana. (SP) **4166**
Boletin Rodoviario *see* B R **5145**
Boletin S I N I C Y T. (Sistema Nacional de Informacion Cientifica y Tecnologia) (EC ISSN 0253-5033) **4302**, **4594**
Boletin Semanal *see* Weekly Bulletin **2198**
Boletin Tecnico Pulpa y Papel. (CU ISSN 0138-8940) **3662**
Boletin Tecnico Sartorial. (SP) **1283**
Boletin Trimestral de Informacion Economica. (EC) **648**
Boletin Trimestral F A O de Estadisticas. *see* F A O Quarterly Bulletin of Statistics **137**
Boletin Uruguayo de Sociologia. (UY ISSN 0006-6508) **4430**
Bolgarskii Fizicheskii Zhurnal. *see* Bulgarian Journal of Physics **3815**
Boli yu Tangci. (CC ISSN 1000-2871) **1161**
Boligen. (DK) **2484**, **295**
Bolivar. (CK) **2528**
Bolivia. (BO ISSN 0006-6540) **4754**
Bolivia. Academia Nacional de Ciencias. Instituto de Energia. Revista. (BO) **1784**
Bolivia. Instituto Nacional de Estadistica. Anuario de Comercio Exterior. (BO) **706**, **4565**
Bolivia. Instituto Nacional de Estadistica. Anuario de Estadisticas Industriales. (BO) **706**, **4565**
†Bolivia. Instituto Nacional de Estadistica. Boletin Estadistico Mensual. (BO) **5151**
†Bolivia. Instituto Nacional de Estadistica. Boletin Estadistico Trimestral. (BO) **5151**
Bolivia. Instituto Nacional de Estadistica. Estadisticas Regionales Departamentales. (BO) **4079**, **4565**
Bolivia. Instituto Nacional de Estadistica. Indice de Precios al Consumidor. (BO) **706**
Bolivia. Servicio Geologico. Boletin. (BO ISSN 0067-9828) **1541**

Bolivia. Servicio Geologico. Circulare. (BO ISSN 0067-9836) **1541**
Bolivia. Servicio Geologico. Informe. (BO ISSN 0067-9844) **1541**
Bolivia. Servicio Geologico. Serie Mineralogica. Contribucione. (BO ISSN 0067-9852) **3479**, 1541
Bolivia. Superintendencia Nacional de Seguros y Reaseguros. Coleccion Estudios. (BO) **2528**
Bolivia en Cifras. (BO) **4565**
Bolivia en el Deporte. (BO) **4466**
Bolivia: Guia Eclesiastica. (BO) **4257**
Bolivia Sago Informationsblatt. (GW) **2175**
Bolletino Svizzero di Mineralogia e Petrografia. see Schweizerische Mineralogische und Petrographische Mitteilungen **3495**
Bollettino Bibliografico per le Scienze Morali e Sociale. (IT ISSN 0006-6621) **3787**
Bollettino Bibliografico Sardo e Archivio Tradizioni Popolari. (IT ISSN 0045-2432) **2060**
Bollettino Ceciliano. (IT ISSN 0006-663X) **3542**
Bollettino Chimico Farmaceutico. (IT ISSN 0006-6648) **3719**
Bollettino d'Arte. (IT ISSN 0391-9854) **319**
Bollettino d'Informazione degli Sloveni in Italia see Sloveni in Italia **2023**
Bollettino d'Oculistica. (IT ISSN 0006-677X) **3298**
Bollettino dei Brevetti per Invenzioni, Modelli e Marchi. (IT ISSN 0006-6664) **3673**
Bollettino dei Classici. (IT ISSN 0391-8270) **1275**
Bollettino dei Medici Svizzeri. see Schweizerische Aerztezeitung **3151**
Bollettino dei Protesi. (IT) **808**
Bollettino del Lavoro see Bollettino del Lavoro e dei Tributi **2605**
Bollettino del Lavoro e dei Tributi. (IT ISSN 0394-6592) **2605**
Bollettino del Repertorio e dell'Atlante Demologico Sardo see B R A D S **2052**
Bollettino dell'Agricoltura. (IT) **80**, 148, 198, 4807
Bollettino dell'Atlante Linguistico Italiano. (IT) **2806**, 1994
Bollettino dell'Attivita di Inanellamento/ Bulletin of Bird Ringing Activity. (IT) **562**
Bollettino delle Accessioni di Periodici e Libri. (IT ISSN 0006-6680) **394**
Bollettino delle Scienze Mediche. (IT ISSN 0007-5787) **3083**
Bollettino di Collegamento. (IT ISSN 0300-4589) **4166**
▼Bollettino di Farmacosorveglianza. (IT) **3719**
Bollettino di Geodesia e Scienze Affini. (IT ISSN 0006-6710) **1541**
Bollettino di Geofisica, Teorica ed Applicata. (IT ISSN 0006-6729) **1587**
†Bollettino di Italianistica. (NE ISSN 0168-7298) **5151**
Bollettino di Libri Antichi e Moderni di Varia Cultura Esauriti e Rari. (IT ISSN 0006-6745) **256**
Bollettino di Microbiologia ed Indagini di Laboratorio. (IT ISSN 0394-9877) **550**, 3083
Bollettino di Oceanologia. (IT ISSN 0393-196X) **1602**
Bollettino di Pesca see Bollettino di Pesca, Piscicoltura e Idrobiologia **5151**
†Bollettino di Pesca, Piscicoltura e Idrobiologia. (IT) **5151**
Bollettino di Psichiatria Biologica/ Psychiatric News. (IT ISSN 0393-4853) **3332**, 433
Bollettino di Psicologia Applicata. (IT ISSN 0006-6761) **4014**
Bollettino di S. Nicola. (IT ISSN 0404-9462) **4257**
Bollettino di Storia delle Scienze Matematiche. (IT ISSN 0392-4432) **3031**
Bollettino di Studi Latini. (IT ISSN 0006-6583) **1275**
Bollettino di Zoologia. (IT ISSN 0373-4137) **579**

Bollettino di Zoologia Agraria e di Bachicoltura. (IT ISSN 0366-2403) **529**
Bollettino Ecclesiastico see Arcidiocesi di Reggio Calabria. Rivista Pastorale **4256**
Bollettino Economico. (IT ISSN 0006-6796) **808**
Bollettino Emerografico di Economia Internazionale. (IT ISSN 0006-680X) **889**
Bollettino Italiano di Audiologia e Foniatria see Audiologia Italiana **3313**
Bollettino Ligustico per la Storia e la Cultura Regionale. (IT) **2353**, 319
Bollettino Malacologico. (IT ISSN 0394-7149) **579**
Bollettino Nazionale A I S O see Giovane Odontoiatria **3234**
Bollettino per le Farmacodipendenze e l'Alcoolismo. (UN) **1534**, 1511
Bollettino per le Religiose Domenicane in Italia. (IT) **4257**
Bollettino Prefilatelico e Storico-Postale.(IT) **3750**
Bollettino Salesiano. (IT) **4257**
Bollettino Storico-Bibliografico Subalpino.(IT) **2353**
Bollettino Storico della Svizzera Italiana. (SZ ISSN 0006-6869) **2353**
Bollettino Storico Piacentino. (IT ISSN 0006-6591) **2353**
Bollettino Storico Pisano. (IT) **2353**
Bollettino sul Risparmio d'Energia. see Courrier de l'Antigaspillage **1486**
Bollettino Tecnico Geloso. (IT ISSN 0006-6877) **1369**, 1355
Bollettino Termomeccanica. (IT ISSN 0006-6885) **1927**, 3840
Bollettino Ufficiale delle Ferrovie Dello Stato. Parte Prima e Seconda. (IT) **4708**
Bollettino Ufficiale delle Ferrovie Dello Stato. Parte Terza. (IT) **4708**
Bollettino Vincenziano. (IT ISSN 0006-6907) **4257**
Bollingen Series. (US) **3762**, 4166
Bologna. (IT) **4085**
Bologna Agricola. (IT) **80**
†Bologna Incontri. (IT) **5151**
Bolovsrol/Education. (MP) **1618**
Bolsa. (AG) **808**
Bolsa de Barcelona. Memoria. (SP) **940**
†Bolsa de Cereales. Revista Institucional. (AG ISSN 0045-2467) **5151**
Bolsa de Cereales. Revista Institucional. Numero Estadistico. (AG ISSN 0084-7968) **80**
Bolsa de Comercio de Buenos Aires. Boletin see Bolsa **808**
Bolsa de Comercio de Mendoza. Centro de Informaciones. Boletin. (AG) **808**
Bolsa de Comercio de Rosario. Revista. (AG ISSN 0006-6931) **808**
Bolsa De Valores de Caracas. Anuario Bursatil/Caracas Stock Exchange. Annual Report. (VE) **940**
Bolsa de Valores de Caracas. Monthly Bulletin. (VE) **940**
Bolsa de Valores de Caracas. Revista Trimestral/Caracas Stock Exchange. Quarterly Bulletin. (VE) **940**
Bolsa de Valores de Caracas. Weekly Bulletin. (VE) **940**
Bolsa de Valores de Lima. Memoria. (PE) **940**
Bolsa de Valores de Mexico. Monthly Newspaper. (MX) **940**
Bolsa de Valores de Montevideo. Boletin Bimestral. (UY) **940**
Bolsa de Valores de Montevideo. Estudio Estadisticos. Boletin Trimestral. (UY) **940**
Bolsa de Valores de Montevideo. Estudios Estadisticos. (UY) **768**
Bolsa de Valores de Quito. Informes y Memoria Anual. (EC) **940**
Bolsa de Valores de Sao Paulo. Relatorio see Profile of the Sao Paulo Stock Exchange **5262**
Bolsa de Valores do Rio de Janeiro. Resumo Anual. (BL ISSN 0557-0506) **940**
Bolsa Mexicana de Valores. Daily Bulletin. (MX) **940**

Bolsa Mexicana de Valores. Weekly Bulletin. (MX ISSN 0006-6915) **940**
Il Bolscevico. (IT ISSN 0392-3886) **3876**
Bolsilibros. (UY ISSN 0067-9909) **2900**, 2400
Bolton Landing Conference. Proceedings. (US) **1816**
Bolwerk. (NE ISSN 0006-6958) **80**
Boma Lathu. (MW) **847**
†Boma Magazine. (AT) **5151**
Bomaby Civic Journal see Brihanmumbai Mahanagarpalika Patrika **4085**
Bomb. (US ISSN 0743-3204) **319**, 2900, 3504, 4630
Bomb. (JA) **1250**
Bomb Summary see U.S. Federal Bureau of Investigation. Bomb Summary **1524**
†Bombast. (US) **5151**
Bombay. (II) **2199**
Bombay Art Society's Art Journal. (II) **319**, 3542
Bombay Chartered Accountant Journal. (II) **748**
Bombay Hospital Journal. (II ISSN 0524-0182) **3083**, 2459
Bombay Labour Journal. (II ISSN 0067-9917) **973**
Bombay Law Reporter. (II) **2605**
Bombay Market. (II ISSN 0006-6974) **847**
Bombay Natural History Society. Journal. (II ISSN 0006-6982) **4302**
Bombay Technologist. (II ISSN 0067-9925) **1170**, 4594
Bombus. (GW ISSN 0724-4223) **529**, 579
Bome in Suid-Afrika. see Trees in South Africa **2140**
Bomp. (US) **3542**
Bomsel. (II) **2860**
Bon a Tirer. (FR) **3997**
Bon Appetit. (US ISSN 0006-6990) **2444**, 2062
Bon Cultivateur de l'Est. (FR) **80**
Bon Vivant. (US) **4754**, 379
Bona. (SA ISSN 0006-7016) **2216**
Bona Espero. (SA ISSN 0006-7024) **2806**, 2216
Bonanza. (JA) **3479**
Bonanza Report. (US ISSN 0888-4889) **940**
Bond. (US ISSN 0279-9111) **4231**, 2528
Bond Buyer. (US ISSN 0732-0469) **940**
Bond Fund Survey. (US ISSN 0738-5579) **940**
Bond Information Database Service. (US) **1448**, 940
Bond Investors Association, Inc. Newsletter see B I A Newsletter **939**
Bond Market: Analysis and Outlook. (US) **940**
Bond Market in Luxembourg Francs and in E C U. (LU) **706**, 940
Bond Market Manager see Courageous Contrarian **943**
Bond Market Research, Currencies and International Interest Rates. (US) **940**
Bond Teller. (US) **1088**
Bond und Share. (GW ISSN 0931-119X) **256**
Bond World. (US) **940**
Bondebladet. (NO ISSN 0332-8414) **80**
Bondevennen. (NO) **80**
The Bondholder. (UK ISSN 0961-8171) **940**
Bondholder's Register see The Bondholder **940**
Bondi Junction Cityscope. (AT) **4159**
Bondi Spectator see Australian Spectator **2171**
Bondi Weekly-Courier see Weekly Southern Courier **2172**
Bondings. (US) **2451**, 4257
†Bondinn. (IC ISSN 1017-3528) **5151**
Bondsspaarbanken see De Spaarbank **800**
Bondweek (1981). (US) **940**
Bone. (US ISSN 8756-3282) **3229**, 3307

BOOK 5987

Bone & Flesh. (US) **2989**
Bone and Mineral. (NE ISSN 0169-6009) **3251**
Bone and Mineral Research Annual. (NE) **3307**, 3083, 3719
Bone Marrow Transplantation. (UK ISSN 0268-3369) **3258**
Bong Crier. (LB) **2168**
Bonheur - la Revue des Familles. (FR) **2444**
Bonifatiusblatt. (GW ISSN 0006-7113) **4257**
Bonifica e l'Assetto Territoriale. (IT) **80**
Boning Up On Osteoporosis. (US) **3083**
Bonjour! (BE ISSN 0773-0306) **1250**
Bonjour. (UK ISSN 0006-7121) **2806**, 1745
Bonn Journal see Esprit **3892**
Bonne Cuisine. (FR ISSN 0006-713X) **2444**
Bonne Nouvelle. (CN ISSN 0225-0233) **4257**
Bonne Nouvelle pour le Transporteur see Transporteur **4251**
Bonne Soiree Tele. (FR) **4838**
Bonne Table et Tourisme. (FR) **2062**, 4754
Bonner Aerztliche Nachrichten. (GW ISSN 0935-8013) **3083**
Bonner Akademische Reden. (GW ISSN 0344-1857) **3762**
Bonner Arbeiten zur Deutschen Literatur. (GW ISSN 0068-001X) **2900**
Bonner Behoerden Spiegel. (GW) **4085**
Bonner Beitraege zur Bibliotheks- und Buecherkunde. (GW ISSN 0068-0028) **2748**
Bonner Beitraege zur Kunstwissenschaft. (GW ISSN 0068-0036) **319**
†Bonner Beitraege zur Soziologie. (GW ISSN 0068-0044) **5151**
†Bonner County Genealogical Society Quarterly. (US ISSN 0899-2339) **5151**
Bonner Energie-Report see Bonner Umwelt und Energie Report **1784**
Bonner Geographische Abhandlungen. (GW ISSN 0373-0468) **2243**
Bonner Geschichtsblaetter. (GW ISSN 0068-0052) **2353**
Bonner Jahrbuecher. (GW ISSN 0067-9976) **2353**
Bonner Mathematische Schriften. (GW ISSN 0524-045X) **3031**
Bonner Meteorologische Abhandlungen. (GW ISSN 0006-7156) **3433**
Bonner Monatszahlen. (GW) **4565**
Bonner Romanistische Arbeiten. (GW ISSN 0170-821X) **2806**
Bonner Umwelt und Energie Report. (GW) **1784**
Bonner Zoologische Beitraege. (GW ISSN 0006-7172) **579**
Bonner Zoologische Monographien. (GW ISSN 0302-671X) **579**
Bonnet-t-e's and Kin. (US ISSN 0743-0957) **2145**
Bonneville Racing News. (US) **4466**
Bonniers Litteraera Magasin see B L M **2859**
Bonnvue: Tips fuer Schulabgaenger. (GW) **1250**
Bonny Moor Hen. (UK ISSN 0142-7660) **2353**
Bonplandia. (AG ISSN 0524-0476) **496**
Bonsai Bulletin. (US ISSN 0006-7180) **496**
Bonsai Canada. Yearbook. (CN) **2123**
Bonsai Clubs International Magazine see B C I Magazine **2122**
†Bonsai in Australia. (AT ISSN 0045-2483) **5151**
Bonsai Journal. (US) **2123**
Bontebok. (SA) **1944**
Bonytt/Design for Living. (NO ISSN 0800-1936) **2549**, 295
Boodschap. (NE) **4280**, 3762
Boogie Woogie and Blues Collector. (NE ISSN 0166-1426) **3542**, 4122
The Book. (US ISSN 0740-8439) **4122**
Book Alert (Bridgewater). (US ISSN 0733-3005) **4122**
Book and Library. see Konyv es Konyvtar **2767**

BOOK

Book and Magazine Collector. (UK) 4122
▼Book & Media. (GR) 4122
Book Arts Review. (US ISSN 0739-7895) 3997
Book Auction Records. (UK ISSN 0068-0095) 4122
Book Business Mart see Lee Howard Newsletter 4131
Book Buyer see Publishing News 4135
Book Club of California. Quarterly News-Letter. (US ISSN 0006-7202) 4122
Book Collecting World. (US ISSN 0006-7229) 2434, 4122
Book Collector. (UK ISSN 0006-7237) 2444, 4140
Book Collectors' Handbook of Values. (US) 4122
Book Dealers World. (US) 4122
Book Exchange. (UK ISSN 0006-7245) 4140
Book Forest. see Shu Lin 4137
Book Forum. (US ISSN 0094-9426) 4122, 2504, 2900
†Book - Guide: Mystery, Detective and Suspense Stories. (US ISSN 0000-0280) 5151
Book Industry Study Group. Research Report see Book Industry Trends 4122
Book Industry Trends. (US ISSN 0160-970X) 4122
Book Information Hotline see Book Promotion Hotline 4122
Book Information Knowledge. see Tushu Qingbao Zhishi 2787
▼Book Links. (US ISSN 1055-4742) 1233
Book Mark. (US) 1233, 1745, 4122
Book Market see Australian Book Collector 2897
Book Marketing News. (UK ISSN 0264-3219) 4122
Book Marketing Opportunities: A Directory see Book Publishing Resource Guide 4122
Book Marketing Update. (US ISSN 0891-8813) 4122, 1034
†Book Markets in the Americas, Africa, Asia and Australasia. (UK) 5151
†Book Markets in Western and Eastern Europe. (UK) 5151
Book Marks. (US) 2748
Book News from Wales. see Llais Llyfrau 4142
Book News Letter. (US ISSN 0006-7296) 4122
Book Newsletter. (US) 4122
†Book Notes. (US) 5152
Book of Bantams. (US ISSN 0068-0117) 212
Book of Baseball Records. (US) 4501
Book of Days see Read More About It - Book of Days 2420
Book of Papers, National Technical Conference see American Association of Textile Chemists and Colorists. National Technical Conference. Book of Papers 4616
Book-Of-The-Month Club News. (US ISSN 0006-730X) 4122
Book of the States. (US ISSN 0068-0125) 4055, 4565
Book on Ballet. see Ballet no Hon 1528
Book on Starting Pitchers. (US ISSN 0739-4667) 4501
Book Page. (US) 4122
Book Parade/Boekparade. (SA ISSN 0258-7149) 2749, 4122
Book People. (SZ ISSN 0256-159X) 2900
Book Promotion Hotline. (US ISSN 1049-4456) 4122
Book Publishers see Britain's Book Publishing Industry 4123
Book Publishing Resource Guide. (US) 4122, 1034, 1123
The Book Reader. (US) 4122
Book Report. (US ISSN 0731-4388) 2749
Book Report see The Euromonitor Book Report (Year) 4127
Book Research Quarterly see Publishing Research Quarterly 4135
Book Review Digest. (US ISSN 0006-7326) 4140, 4

Book Review Index. (US ISSN 0524-0581) 4140, 4, 2981
Book Review Index: Africa. (II) 4394
Book Review Index: Annual Clothbound Cumulations. (US ISSN 0524-0581) 4140, 4, 2981
†Book Review Newsletter. (US) 5152
†Book Reviewers Guide. (US) 5152
Book Talk. (US ISSN 0145-627X) 4122
Book Trade in Canada/Industrie du Livre au Canada. (CN ISSN 0700-5296) 4122
Book Trolley see Health and Welfare Libraries Quarterly 2760
Book World. (US ISSN 0006-7369) 4122
Bookbinding Industry. see Seihonkai 4137
Bookbird. (AU ISSN 0006-7377) 1250, 4122
Bookdealer. (UK) 4122
Bookdealers in India, Pakistan and Sri Lanka see Sheppard's Book Dealers in India and the Orient 4137
Bookdealers in North America see Sheppard's Bookdealers in North America 4137
Booked for Brunch? see A Different Light Review 2452
Bookends. (US ISSN 0893-6471) 2749, 2860, 2989, 4122
Booker Food Magazine. (UK) 2062
Booklegger. (US ISSN 0092-7686) 4122, 2749
Booklegger Magazine see Booklegger 4122
Booklist. (US ISSN 0006-7385) 4140
BookLover. (US) 4122
Bookman. (BG) 4122
Bookman's Guide to Americana. (US ISSN 0068-0133) 4123
Bookman's Monthly see Australian Book Collector 2897
Bookman's Price Index. (US ISSN 0068-0141) 4123
Bookmark. (CN ISSN 0381-6028) 1618, 2749
Bookmark. (UK ISSN 0260-0315) 2900
Bookmark (Albany). (US ISSN 0006-7407) 2749
Bookmark (Chapel Hill). (US ISSN 0006-7393) 2749
Bookmark (Moscow). (US ISSN 0735-0295) 2749
Booknews. (UK ISSN 0266-4208) 2900, 4123
BookNotes: Resource Information for the Small and Self-Publisher. (US ISSN 0747-847X) 4123
Bookplate Journal. (UK ISSN 0264-3693) 4123, 394
Bookplate Society Newsletter. (UK ISSN 0309-7935) 4123
Bookplates in the News. (US ISSN 0045-2521) 2434
†Bookquest. (UK ISSN 0950-9089) 5152
Books see Booknews 2900
Books. (UK) 4123
Books About Birds. (US) 462
Books About Malaysia see Books about Singapore 4799
Books about Singapore. (SI ISSN 0068-0176) 4799, 2328
Books and Articles on Oriental Subjects Published in Japan. (JA ISSN 0524-0654) 3646, 2328, 2981, 4212
Books and Bookmen see Books Magazine 4123
Books and Essays/Tosho. (JA) 4123
Books and Journals Wanted List. (UK) 4123
Books and Libraries at the University of Kansas. (US ISSN 0006-7458) 2749, 4123
Books and Periodicals Online. (US ISSN 0951-838X) 394, 1389
Books and Religion. (US ISSN 0890-0841) 4123, 4166
Books Are Everything. (US) 2900, 2985, 3010
Books at Boston Spa. (UK ISSN 0268-6538) 394
Books at Brown. (US ISSN 0147-0787) 394

Books at Iowa. (US ISSN 0006-7474) 2749, 4123
Books Bohemian. (US) 2900, 2451
Books for Everybody. (CN) 4123
Books for Keeps. (UK ISSN 0143-909X) 4123
Books for the Teen Age. (US ISSN 0068-0192) 2792
†Books for World Explorers Series. (US) 5152
Books for Young Explorers Series. (US) 1250, 2243
Books for Young People see Quill and Quire 4135
Books for Your Children. (UK ISSN 0006-7482) 4123, 1250
Books from Finland. (FI ISSN 0006-7490) 4140
Books from Korea. (KO) 394, 4140
Books from Pakistan. (PK ISSN 0068-0206) 394
†Books in Arabic. (CN ISSN 0705-7172) 5152
†Books in Armenian. (CN ISSN 0705-8209) 5152
†Books in Bengali. (CN ISSN 0316-7437) 5152
Books in Canada. (CN ISSN 0045-2564) 4123
†Books in Chinese. (CN) 5152
†Books in Danish. (CN ISSN 0705-2332) 5152
†Books in Dutch. (CN ISSN 0705-2294) 5152
Books in English. (UK ISSN 0045-2572) 394
†Books in Finnish. (CN ISSN 0705-1883) 5152
†Books in Hindi. (CN ISSN 0705-8373) 5152
†Books in Hungarian. (CN ISSN 0705-6494) 5152
Books in Library and Information Science Series. (US) 2792
Books in Polish or Relating to Poland. (UK ISSN 0006-7512) 4140, 2214, 2328
Books in Print. (US ISSN 0068-0214) 394
Books in Print on Microfiche. (US) 394
Books in Print Plus. (US) 394
Books in Print Supplement. (US ISSN 0000-0310) 394
Books in Scotland. (UK ISSN 0143-1285) 4123
Books in Series. (US ISSN 0000-0906) 394
Books in Soils and the Environment Series. (US ISSN 0081-1890) 171
†Books in Spanish. (CN ISSN 0705-7156) 5152
Books in the Earth Sciences. (UK ISSN 0140-7805) 395, 1555
†Books in Urdu. (CN ISSN 0705-825X) 5152
Books Ireland. (IE ISSN 0376-6039) 4123
Books Kids Will Sit Still For. (US) 395, 1250
Books Magazine. (UK) 4123
Books of Oral Tradition. (US) 4166
Books of the Southwest. (US ISSN 0006-7520) 4140
Books on Tape see Words on Cassette (Year) 416
▼Books on the Environment and Related Topics. (UK ISSN 0961-7299) 1972
Books Out-of-Print. (US ISSN 0000-0736) 395
Books Out-of-Print Plus. (US) 395
Books - 100 Reviews. (US ISSN 0095-3555) 4123
Bookseller. (PK ISSN 0006-7547) 4123
Bookseller. (UK ISSN 0006-7539) 4123
†Bookseller Pustak Vikreta Baroda. (II ISSN 0006-7555) 5152
Booksellers Association of Great Britain and Ireland. Charter Group. Economic Survey. (UK ISSN 0141-917X) 4123, 1034
Booksellers Association of Great Britain and Ireland. Directory of Members. (UK ISSN 0952-1666) 4123

Booksellers Association of Great Britain and Ireland. List of Members see Booksellers Association of Great Britain and Ireland. Directory of Members 4123
Bookselling News. (UK ISSN 0268-246X) 4123
Booksellers Association of Great Britain. List of Charter Members see Booksellers Association of Great Britain and Ireland. Directory of Members 4123
Bookslinger Bibliofile. (US) 395
Bookslinger News. (US) 395
Bookslinger Update. (US) 395
Bookstore Journal. (US ISSN 0006-7563) 4123, 4166
Booktraders Bulletin see Indian Publisher and Bookseller 4129
Bookwatch see Wisconsin Bookwatch 416
Bookwoman. (US ISSN 0163-1128) 4123, 4838
Boom-Pers Combinatie. (NE ISSN 0006-7571) 2211
Boombah Herald. (US ISSN 8755-5832) 3542
▼Boomerang! (US) 1250
Boone and Crockett Club Associates Newsletter. (US) 4542, 1484
Boor. (NE ISSN 0006-758X) 171
Boosey and Hawkes Newsletter. (US ISSN 0006-7598) 3542
Boost. (UK ISSN 0006-7601) 3683
Boot Cove Economic Forecast. (US) 847
Bootblack. (US ISSN 1040-7405) 417
Boote. (GW ISSN 0006-7636) 4523
Boots News. (UK) 3719
Bootswirtschaft. (GW ISSN 0006-7644) 4523
Bop. (US ISSN 8750-7242) 1250, 3542
Bopuxue Zazhi/Journal of Spectrum. (CC) 3852
Bor- es Cipotechnika. (HU ISSN 0006-7652) 2736, 4360
Borax Review. (UK ISSN 0951-8452) 1171
Bor'ba s Gazom v Ugol'nykh Shakhtakh.(RU) 3479
Borbin Informator. (YU) 4123
Bord Iascaigh Mhara. Tuarascail Agus Cuntaisi/Irish Sea Fisheries Board. Annual Report. (IE ISSN 0791-5950) 2037
Bordbuch/Logbook. (SZ) 4754
Border Agricultural Show Prize List. (SA) 212
Border Crossings. (CN ISSN 0831-2559) 319, 4630
Border Health/Salud Fronteriza. (US) 4098
Border Issues and Public Policy. Research Papers. (US) 3876, 2400
Border Leicester Flock Book. (UK) 212
Border - Lines. (CN ISSN 0826-967X) 319, 1332
Border Perspectives. Research Papers. (US) 3876, 2400
Border States. (US ISSN 0092-4571) 2400
Border Watch. (US) 3979
Border Watch. (AT) 3998, 2567
▼Borderlands. (US) 2989
Borderlands Journal. (US ISSN 0276-9220) 2504
Borderline. (US) 3708
Bordtennis Aarbogen. (DK ISSN 0109-6761) 4501
Bore Da. (UK ISSN 0006-7709) 1250, 1618, 2806
Boreal see Boreal International 2989
Boreal Institute, Edmonton. Miscellaneous Publications see Canadian Circumpolar Library. Miscellaneous Publications 5160
Boreal Institute for Northern Studies. Library Bulletin see Canadian Circumpolar Library. Bulletin 2267
Boreal Institute for Northern Studies. Occasional Publications see Canadian Circumpolar Library. Occasional Publications Series 2401

Boreal Institute for Northern Studies. Report of Activities see Canadian Circumpolar Library. Report of Activities **2401**
Boreal International. (CN) **2989**
Borealis. (CN ISSN 0840-6189) **1484**
Borealis. (US) **2123**
Boreas. (GW) **267**
Boreas. (NO ISSN 0300-9483) **1555, 3656**
Borgazdasag. (HU ISSN 0006-7741) **80, 379**
Borghese. (IT ISSN 0006-775X) **3396**
Borgo Bioviews. (US ISSN 0743-9628) **417, 2900**
Borgo Cataloging Guides. (US ISSN 0891-9615) **2749**
Borgo Family Histories. (US ISSN 0733-6764) **2145**
▼Borgo Literary Guides. (US ISSN 0891-9623) **2900, 2981**
Borgo Political Scenarios. (US ISSN 0278-9752) **3876, 2900**
Borgo Reference Guides. (US ISSN 0891-9607) **2307, 395, 2900, 3876**
Borgo Reference Library see Borgo Reference Guides **2307**
Borgyogyaszati es Venerologiai Szemle. (HU ISSN 0006-7768) **3246**
Born to Die. (AT) **4516**
Borneo Research Bulletin. (US ISSN 0006-7806) **236**
Bornholms Tidende. (DK) **2185**
Bornholmske Samlinger. (DK ISSN 0084-7976) **2353**
Boro Park Voice/Kol Boro Park. (US) **1994**
†Boron in Glass. (UK ISSN 0006-7822) **5152**
Borough Architects Yearbook. (UK) **295**
Borough of Twickenham Local History Society. Papers. (UK ISSN 0084-7984) **2353**
Borsa dei Noli. (IT ISSN 0006-7849) **4647**
Borsa Marmi. (IT ISSN 0006-7857) **1072, 604**
Borsa Recuperi Industriali. (IT) **2472**
Borsodi Szemle. (HU ISSN 0520-626X) **2353**
Borthwick Institute of Historical Research. Borthwick Papers. (UK ISSN 0524-0913) **2353**
Borussen-Echo. (AU ISSN 0006-7865) **1305, 1296**
Borzoi International. (US) **3708**
Borzoi Quarterly. (US) **3708**
Bosai. see Disaster Prevention **4100**
Bosbouw see Nederlands Bosbouw Tijdschrift **2105**
Bosch Technische Berichte. (GW ISSN 0006-789X) **1883, 1816**
Bose Institute. Transactions. (II ISSN 0006-7903) **4302**
Boshoku Gijutsu see Zairyo to Kankyo **3424**
Bosom Friend. see Zhiyin **4858**
Boss. (GW) **1057**
†Boss - Oesterreich. (AU) **5152**
Boston (Year). (US) **4754**
Boston & Maine Railroad Historical Society, Inc. Bulletin see B & M Bulletin **4707**
Boston Audio Society Speaker see B.A.S. Speaker **4459**
Boston Bar Journal. (US) **2605**
Boston Bruins Yearbook. (US) **4466**
Boston Bulletin. (US) **3708**
Boston Bulletin on Chemicals and Disease. (US ISSN 0894-4024) **3083**
Boston Business Journal. (US ISSN 0746-4975) **847**
†Boston Business Magazine. (US) **5152**
Boston Celtics Yearbook. (US) **4501**
Boston City Record. (US ISSN 0006-7946) **4085**
Boston College Environmental Affairs Law Review. (US ISSN 0190-7034) **1944, 2605**
Boston College International and Comparative Law Review. (US ISSN 0277-5778) **2720**

Boston College Law Review. (US ISSN 0161-6587) **2605**
Boston College Magazine. (US ISSN 0885-2049) **1305**
Boston College Studies in Philosophy. (NE ISSN 0524-112X) **3762**
Boston Computer Society Professional see B C S Professional **825**
Boston Computer Society Update see B C S Update **1458**
Boston ComputerNews. (US) **1389, 1458, 1467**
Boston Cyclist. (US) **4516, 1502, 4098**
Boston Food Co-Operative Flyer see B F C Flyer **2090**
Boston Jewish Times. (US ISSN 8750-1961) **1994**
Boston Literary Review. (US) **2900**
Boston Magazine. (US ISSN 0006-7989) **2222**
Boston Marathon. (US) **4466**
Boston Marine Guide see New England Journal of Transportation **4654**
Boston Metro Business. (US) **648**
Boston Museum of Fine Arts. Museum Year. Annual Report see Museum Year **3529**
Boston N O W see N O W News (Boston) **4849**
Boston Organ Club Newsletter. (US) **3542**
Boston Parents' Paper. (US) **1233**
Boston Phoenix. (US ISSN 0163-3015) **2222**
Boston Quarterly. (US) **3709**
Boston Review. (US ISSN 0734-2306) **4123, 2900**
Boston Sea and Air Port Handbook. (UK ISSN 0267-2243) **1123, 4671, 4725**
Boston Seniority. (US) **2271**
Boston Society of Architects. ChapterLetter. (US) **295**
▼Boston Spa Conferences on C D - R O M. (UK) **395**
Boston Spa Serials on C D - R O M. (UK) **395**
Boston Stock Exchange Guide. (US) **940**
Boston Studies in the Philosophy of Science. (NE ISSN 0068-0346) **3762, 4302**
Boston Symphony Orchestra Program. (US) **3542**
Boston Symphony Orchestra Program Book-Notes see Boston Symphony Orchestra Program **3542**
Boston Third World Law Journal. (US ISSN 0276-3583) **2720, 926, 3635**
Boston University Africana Libraries. Newsletter see Africana Libraries Newsletter **2741**
Boston University International Law Journal. (US ISSN 0737-8947) **2720**
Boston University Journal of Tax Law. (US ISSN 0741-8477) **1088, 2605**
Boston University Law Review. (US ISSN 0006-8047) **2605**
Boston University Papers on Africa. (US) **4367, 2332**
Boston University Studies in Philosophy and Religion. (US) **4166, 3762**
Boston Woman. (US) **4838**
Bostonia. (US ISSN 0164-1441) **2222**
†Bostonian Society. Proceedings. (US ISSN 0190-3586) **5152**
Bostwick Paper. (US ISSN 0068-0354) **648**
Botanica. (II ISSN 0045-2629) **496**
Botanica Acta. (GW ISSN 0932-8629) **497**
Botanica Complutensis. (SP ISSN 0214-4565) **497**
Botanica Gothoburgensia. (SW ISSN 0068-0370) **497**
Botanica Helvetica. (SZ ISSN 0253-1453) **497**
Botanica Marina. (GW ISSN 0006-8055) **497**
Botanical Bulletin. see Zhiwuxue Tongbao **521**
Botanical Gazette see International Journal of Plant Sciences **506**

Botanical Journal of the Linnean Society see Linnean Society. Botanical Journal **508**
Botanical Magazine, Tokyo. (JA) **497**
Botanical Proceedings. see Botanikai Kozlemenyek **497**
Botanical Review. (US ISSN 0006-8101) **497**
Botanical Society of Bengal. Bulletin. (II ISSN 0006-811X) **497**
Botanical Society of Edinburgh. Transactions and Proceedings see Botanical Society of Edinburgh Transactions **497**
Botanical Society of Edinburgh Transactions. (UK ISSN 0374-6607) **497**
Botanical Society of South Africa. Journal see Veld & Flora **520**
Botanical Society of the British Isles Abstracts see B S B I Abstracts **461**
Botanical Survey of India. Bulletin. (II ISSN 0006-8128) **497**
Botanical Survey of India. Occasional Publications. (II) **497**
Botanical Survey of South Africa. Memoirs. (SA) **497**
Botanicheskii Zhurnal. (RU ISSN 0006-8136) **497**
Botanicus Brief. (GW ISSN 0938-1759) **497**
Botanikai Kozlemenyek/Botanical Proceedings. (HU ISSN 0006-8144) **497**
Botanische Jahrbuecher fuer Systematik, Pflanzengeschichte und Pflanzengeographie. (GW ISSN 0006-8152) **497**
Botanische Staatssammlung Muenchen. Mitteilungen. (GW ISSN 0006-8179) **497**
Botanisk Centralbibliotek. Fortegnelse over Loebende Periodica. (DK ISSN 0900-2367) **462**
Botanisk Tidsskrift see Nordic Journal of Botany **511**
Botaniska Notiser see Nordic Journal of Botany **511**
Botaniste see Revue de Cytologie et de Biologie Vegetales - Le Botaniste **516**
Botany as a Profession see Careers in Botany **499**
Bote. (CN ISSN 0006-8209) **4280**
Der Bote aus dem Wehrgeschichtlichen Museum. (GW) **3453, 2307**
Bote fuer Tirol. (AU ISSN 0006-8225) **4085**
Both Sides Now. (US ISSN 8233) **3593**
Bothalia. (SA ISSN 0006-8241) **497**
Botschaft. (GW) **4231**
Botschaft des Alten Testaments. (GW ISSN 0068-0443) **4166**
Botschaft Heute. (GW ISSN 0176-8573) **4166**
†Botschaft und Dienst. (GW) **5152**
Botswana. Annual Statements of Accounts. (BS ISSN 0068-0451) **1088**
Botswana. Central Statistical Office. Statistical Newsletter see Botswana. Central Statistics Office. Statistical Bulletin **706**
Botswana. Central Statistics Office. Employment Survey. (BS) **706**
Botswana. Central Statistics Office. Statistical Bulletin. (BS) **706, 4565**
Botswana. Central Statistics Office. Tourist Statistics. (BS) **4799**
Botswana. Commissioner of the Police. Annual Report. (BS ISSN 0068-046X) **1511**
Botswana. Department of Health. Report see Botswana. Ministry of Health. Report **4098**
Botswana. Department of Income Tax. Annual Report. (BS) **1088**
Botswana. Department of Mines. Air Pollution Control. Annual Report. (BS) **1976, 1944**
Botswana. Forest Department. Report. (BS ISSN 0068-0486) **2096**
Botswana. Geological Survey and Mines Department. Annual Reports see Botswana. Geological Survey Department. Annual Reports **1555**

Botswana. Geological Survey Department. Annual Reports. (BS) **1555**
Botswana. Ministry of Agriculture. Annual Report. (BS ISSN 0068-0478) **80**
Botswana. Ministry of Agriculture. Division of Arable Crops Research. Annual Report. (BS) **171**
Botswana. Ministry of Agriculture. Division of Co-Operative Development. Annual Report (Year). (BS) **829**
Botswana. Ministry of Agriculture. Farm Management Survey Results. (BS) **148, 171**
Botswana. Ministry of Agriculture. Livestock Management Survey Results. (BS) **212**
Botswana. Ministry of Agriculture. Review of Crop Experiments, Bechunland Protectorate see Botswana. Ministry of Agriculture. Division of Arable Crops Research. Annual Report **171**
Botswana. Ministry of Commerce and Industry. Farm Management Survey Results see Botswana. Ministry of Agriculture. Farm Management Survey Results **148**
Botswana. Ministry of Health. Report. (BS) **4098**
Botswana. National Archives. Report on the National Archives. (BS) **2749**
Botswana. National Library Service. Report. (BS) **2749**
Botswana Development Corporation. Annual Report. (BS) **940, 1072**
Botswana Handbook. (BS ISSN 0301-9020) **2168**
Botswana in Pictures. (BS) **2168**
Botswana Notes and Records. (BS ISSN 0525-5090) **2332**
Botswana Society. Symposium Proceedings. (BS) **2332**
Bottega del Colore. (IT) **3652**
Bottin Administratif. (FR) **4055**
Bottin Bleu. (CN) **1883**
Bottin Communes. (FR) **4085**
Bottin des Organismes Franco-Ontariens see Annuaire Franco-Ontarien **3873**
Bottin Entreprises. (FR) **1123**
Bottin Mondain. (FR) **417**
Bottin Professions see Bottin Entreprises **1123**
Bottin Telephonique des Universites (year). see Universities Telephone Directory (Year) **1719**
▼Bottle - Can Recycling Update. (US ISSN 1052-4916) **1984, 2605, 3647**
Bottle Shipwright. (US) **2434**
Bottled Water Reporter. (US) **379**
Bottom Dog. (IE) **3940**
Bottom Line. (CN ISSN 0831-5477) **648**
Bottom Line (Lansing). (US ISSN 0161-1267) **1540, 4**
Bottom Line (Louisville). (US) **748**
Bottom Line (New York). (US ISSN 0888-045X) **2749**
Bottom Line (New York, 1969) see B P A Quarterly **3331**
Bottom Line Communicator. (US) **1332**
Bottom Line - Personal. (US ISSN 0274-4805) **648**
Bottom Line Publications. (US) **2890, 2989**
Bottomfish. (US) **2900**
Bottomline (Austin). (US ISSN 0279-1889) **748, 1004, 1389, 2472**
Bottomline (Washington). (US ISSN 0740-5464) **768**
Boucher - Charcutier. see Metzger und Wurster **2077**
Boucherie Belge. (BE) **2062**
Boucherie Francaise. (FR ISSN 0006-8284) **2062**
Bouilleur de France. (FR) **379**
Boulanger Belge/Belgische Bakker. (BE) **2087**
Boulanger Region Nord Pas de Calais. (BE) **2087**
Boulangerie Francaise. (FR ISSN 0758-4164) **2087**
Boulevard. (US ISSN 0885-9337) **2900**
Boulite. (FR ISSN 0991-532X) **2053, 1994, 4430**

BOULOGNE INFORMATIONS

Boulogne Informations. (FR) **808**
Boum see Allons **2802**
Boumi Temple News. (US ISSN 0006-8306) **1296**
Bound Brook Diamond see O C D Diamond **4605**
Bound Spiral. (UK ISSN 0955-3819) **2900**
Boundary Elements Abstracts Journal & Newsletter. (UK ISSN 0957-2902) **1842**, **4**
Boundary Historical Society. Report. (CN ISSN 0068-0524) **2400**
Boundary-Layer Meteorology. (NE ISSN 0006-8314) **3434**, **433**
Boundary Waters Journal. (US ISSN 0899-2681) **1484**
Boundary 2. (US ISSN 0190-3659) **2900**, **2989**
Bounty DiabetesCare Guide. (US) **3251**
▼Bounty Infant Care Guide. (CN) **3319**, **1233**
▼Bounty Pregnancy Guide. (CN) **3290**
†Bouquet. (FR) **5152**
Bouquet see Vous **5302**
Bourland Bulletin - Loving Letter see Bourland - Loving Bulletin **2145**
Bourland - Loving Bulletin. (US) **2145**
Bourne Society Local History Records. (UK ISSN 0520-6790) **2353**
Bourse. (IR) **768**
Bourse de Paris. Statistiques Mensuelles. (FR ISSN 0039-0623) **940**
Bourse des Valeurs de Casablanca. Bulletin Mensuel d'Information. (MR) **940**
Bourse Monthly. (IR) **768**
Bourse Revue. (BE) **940**
Bouteille a la Mer. (FR) **2900**
Boutiques de France see Boutiques de France International **1283**
Boutiques de France International. (FR) **1283**
Bouw. (NE ISSN 0366-2330) **604**, **295**
Bouw en Beheer. (NE) **604**
Bouwadviseur. (NE) **604**, **1816**
Bouwbedrijf see Construction **611**
Bouwbelangen. (NE ISSN 0006-8330) **604**
De Bouwbrief. (NE) **3542**
Bouwen aan de Nieuwe Aarde. (NE ISSN 0006-8349) **4257**
Bouwen met Staal. (NE) **604**
Bouwkosten. (NE) **604**
Bouwkroniek. (BE) **604**
Bouwmachines. (NE ISSN 0006-8373) **604**
Bouwmarkt. (NE ISSN 0520-6804) **604**
Bouwondernemer. (NE ISSN 0006-8381) **2484**
Bouwrevue. (NE) **604**
BouwWereld. (NE ISSN 0026-5942) **604**
Bovagblad. (NE ISSN 0006-839X) **4685**, **3016**
Bove & Rhodes Inside Report. (US) **1458**
Bovilogisk Tidsskrift Kvaeget. (DK) **198**, **171**, **205**
Bovine Practice see Agri-Practice **4805**
Bovine Practitioner. (US ISSN 0524-1685) **4807**
Bow and Arrow Hunting. (US ISSN 0006-8403) **4542**
Bow & Arrow Magazine's Bowhunter's Annual. (US) **4542**
Bow & Swing. (US) **1529**
Bow Valley This Week. (CN) **1369**
Bow Waves Boating see Eastern, Southeast Boating Newspaper (Eastern Edition) **4524**
Bow Waves Boating see Eastern, Southeast Boating Newspaper (Southeast Edition) **4524**
Bowbender. (CN ISSN 0827-2638) **4466**
†Bowbender Magazine's Hunting Annual (Year). (CN ISSN 0835-7447) **5152**
Bowdoin Alumni Magazine see Bowdoin Magazine **1305**
Bowdoin College. Museum of Art. Occasional Papers. (US ISSN 0084-7992) **3522**
Bowdoin Magazine. (US ISSN 0895-2604) **1305**
Bowen Independent. (AT) **2171**
Bowhunter. (US ISSN 0273-7434) **4542**
Bowhunter's Annual see Bow & Arrow Magazine's Bowhunter's Annual **4542**
Bowhunting. (US ISSN 1049-9768) **4542**
Bowhunting World. (US ISSN 1043-5492) **4542**
Bowker Annual see The Bowker Annual Library and Book Trade Almanac **2749**
The Bowker Annual Library and Book Trade Almanac. (US ISSN 0068-0540) **2749**, **4123**
Bowker Buying Guide Series. (US) **395**
▼Bowker's Complete Video Directory. (US) **1384**
Bowker's Law Books and Serials in Print. (US ISSN 0000-0752) **1123**, **395**, **2698**
Bowker's Law Books and Serials in Print Supplement. (US ISSN 0000-1031) **2698**, **395**
Bowlaren. (SW) **4501**
Bowler. (UK) **4501**
Bowlers Journal. (US ISSN 0164-9183) **4466**
Bowlers' World. (UK) **4501**
Bowling Digest. (US ISSN 8750-3603) **4466**
†Bowling Green Studies in Applied Philosophy. (US) **5152**
Bowling Magazine. (US ISSN 0162-0274) **4501**
Bowling News. (US) **4501**
Bowling Notizie. (IT ISSN 0006-8438) **4501**
Bowling Proprietor. (US ISSN 0006-8446) **4501**
Bowling Times see World Bowls Magazine **4515**
Bowls. (AT) **4501**
Bowls in N.S.W. see Bowls **4501**
Bowls International. (UK ISSN 0262-6942) **4501**
Bowls - News and Views. (AT) **4501**
Bowman's Accounting Report. (US ISSN 0897-3482) **748**, **1004**
Bows and Arrows see For Parents **1237**
▼Bowser Directory of Small Stocks. (US ISSN 1053-0908) **940**
Bowser Report. (US ISSN 0738-7288) **940**
Box y Lucha. (MX ISSN 0006-8470) **4466**
Boxboard Containers. (US ISSN 0006-8489) **3647**
Boxe Ring. (IT ISSN 0006-8497) **4466**
Boxer Review. (US) **3709**
Boxes and Arrows. (US ISSN 0742-4574) **1443**
Boxing. (SW) **4466**
Boxing and Football Illustrated. (GH) **4467**
†Boxing Beat. (US) **5152**
Boxing Magazine. (JA) **4467**
Boxing Monthly. (UK) **4467**
Boxing News. (UK ISSN 0006-8519) **4467**
Boxing U S A. (US) **4467**
Boxoffice. (US ISSN 0006-8527) **3504**
†Boxring. (GW ISSN 0138-1245) **5152**
Boxspring see Norwottuck **2944**
Boxwood Bulletin. (US ISSN 0006-8535) **2123**
Boxwood Buyer's Guide. (US) **2123**, **1123**
Boy Scouts of America. Annual Report to Congress. (US) **1296**, **1233**
Boy Scouts of Canada. Provincial Council for Ontario. Provincial Notes. (CN) **1233**
Boy Scouts World Bureau see World Scout Organization Report **1246**
Boyan. (KR) **2989**
Boyce Thompson Institute for Plant Research. Annual Report. (US) **497**
Boyce's Service Station Manual. (AT) **4685**
Boycott Law Bulletin. (US ISSN 0162-1726) **2605**
Boycott Report. (US) **901**
Boyle Family Letter. (US) **2145**
Boys and Girls. see Shaonan Shaonu **2959**
Boys & Girls Clubs of America Bulletin. (US) **1233**
Boys Brigade Gazette. (UK ISSN 0006-8578) **1250**
Boys' Brigade, London. Annual Report. (UK ISSN 0068-0605) **1250**
Boys Club Bulletin see Boys & Girls Clubs of America Bulletin **1233**
Boys Gymnastics Rulebook. (US ISSN 0160-3280) **4467**
Boys' Life (Braille Edition). (US) **2291**, **1250**, **1296**
Boys' Life (Inkprint Edition). (US ISSN 0006-8608) **1250**, **1296**
Boys Town Quarterly. (US ISSN 0889-6828) **4399**
Boys Village Report see Dellcrest News **5178**
Bozje Okolje. (XV) **4257**
Bozze. (IT ISSN 0391-6723) **4166**
Brabant see Brabant Tourisme **4754**
Brabant Tourisme. (BE ISSN 0006-8616) **4754**
Brabantia. (NE ISSN 0006-8624) **2504**, **319**
Brabantse Folklore see Folklore Brabancon **2054**
De Brabantse Leeuw. (NE ISSN 0006-8632) **2145**
Braby's Bloemfontein Directory. (SA ISSN 0520-7010) **1123**
Braby's Business Directory of Johannesburg see Johannesburg - West Rand Directory **1141**
Braby's Cape Province Directory. (SA ISSN 0378-9179) **1123**
Braby's Commercial Directory of South, East and Central Africa see Braby's Commercial Directory of Southern Africa **1123**
Braby's Commercial Directory of Southern Africa. (SA) **1123**
Braby's East London Directory. (SA ISSN 0378-9217) **1123**
Braby's Natal Directory. (SA) **1123**
Braby's Orange Free State Directory see Braby's Orange Free State - Northern Cape Directory **1123**
Braby's Orange Free State - Northern Cape Directory. (SA) **1123**
Braby's Pietermaritzburg Directory. (SA ISSN 0520-7037) **1123**
Braby's Transvaal Directory. (SA ISSN 0068-0621) **1123**
Bracara Augusta. (PO ISSN 0006-8640) **2353**, **267**
Bracket Racing, U S A. (US) **4685**
Brackety - Ack. (US ISSN 0006-8667) **1305**
Brackishwater Aquaculture Development Centre. Bulletin. (IO ISSN 0126-1924) **2037**
Braddock's Federal-State-Local Government Directory. (US ISSN 1041-6722) **4055**
Bradea. (BL ISSN 0084-800X) **497**
Bradfield College Chronicle. (UK ISSN 0006-8675) **1305**
Bradford Occasional Papers. (UK ISSN 0261-0353) **2900**
Bradford Poetry. (UK) **2989**
Bradford Poetry Quarterly see Bradford Poetry **2989**
Bradford-Tioga-Sullivan-Potter-Wyoming Farm and Home News. (US ISSN 0192-4176) **80**
Bradford's Directory of Marketing Research Agencies and Management Consultants in the United States and the World. (US ISSN 0068-063X) **1034**
Bradleya. (UK ISSN 0265-086X) **497**
Bradshaw - Bratcher Letter see Bradshaw - Bratcher Quarterly **2145**
Bradshaw - Bratcher Quarterly. (US) **2145**
Bradstreet Gazette see Dun's Gazette **1008**
Bragantia. (BL ISSN 0006-8705) **80**, **433**, **1171**, **1555**
Bragi. (AU) **2900**
Brahman Journal. (US ISSN 0192-6764) **212**
Brahman News. (AT) **212**
Brahmavadin. (II ISSN 0006-8721) **4217**, **3762**
Brahmavidya. (II ISSN 0001-902X) **3635**, **4217**
Brahms Studien. (GW) **3542**
Braille Book Review (Large Print Edition). (US ISSN 0006-873X) **2291**, **2749**, **2900**, **4123**
Braille Books (Large Print Edition). (US ISSN 0277-5247) **2285**, **395**, **1674**, **2291**
Braille Chess Magazine. (UK ISSN 0006-8756) **2291**, **4467**
Braille Evangelism Bulletin. (US) **2291**, **4231**
Braille Forum. (US ISSN 0006-8772) **2291**
Braille Journal of Physiotherapy. (UK ISSN 0006-8780) **2291**, **3083**
Braille Mainichi Weekly. (JA) **2291**
Braille Mirror. (US ISSN 0006-8810) **2291**, **2860**
Braille Monitor (Inkprint Edition). (US ISSN 0006-8829) **2291**
Braille Music Magazine. (UK ISSN 0006-8837) **2291**, **3542**
Braille Musical Magazine see Braille Music Magazine **2291**
†Braille Pilot. (US) **5152**
Braille Radio Times. (UK ISSN 0006-887X) **2291**, **1355**
Braille Rainbow see Rainbow **2295**
Braille Science Journal. (UK ISSN 0006-8896) **2291**
Braille Scores Catalog - Choral see Music & Musicians: Braille Scores Catalog - Choral (Large Print Edition) **2285**
Braille Scores Catalog - Organ see Music & Musicians: Braille Scores Catalog - Organ (Large Print Edition) **2285**
Braille Scores Catalog - Piano see Music & Musicians: Braille Scores Catalog - Piano (Large Print Edition) **2285**
Braille Sporting Record. (UK ISSN 0006-890X) **2291**, **4399**
Braille Star Theosophist. (US ISSN 0006-8918) **2291**, **4280**
Braille Technical Tables Bank Catalog. (US) **2291**
Braille Television Times. (UK) **2291**, **1369**
Braillorama. (SA) **2291**
Braillorette. Supplement. (SA) **2291**
Brain/Burein. (JA) **29**, **1034**
Brain. (UK ISSN 0006-8950) **3332**
Brain and Cognition. (US ISSN 0278-2626) **4014**
Brain and Development. (JA ISSN 0387-7604) **3332**, **3319**
Brain and Development - No to Hattatsu see No to Hattatsu **3349**
Brain and Language. (US ISSN 0093-934X) **4014**, **2806**
Brain and Nerve/No to Shinkei. (JA ISSN 0006-8969) **3332**
Brain, Behavior and Evolution. (SZ ISSN 0006-8977) **3332**
Brain, Behavior, and Immunity. (US ISSN 0889-1591) **3184**
Brain Dysfunction. (SZ ISSN 0259-1278) **3332**, **3083**
Brain Injury. (UK ISSN 0269-9052) **3332**
Brain - Mind Bulletin see New Sense Bulletin **3349**
Brain News. (II ISSN 0006-8985) **3332**
Brain Research. (NE ISSN 0921-8246) **3332**
Brain Research Bulletin. (US ISSN 0361-9230) **3332**
Brain Research Foundation Annual Report. (US) **3332**
Brain Research Reviews. (NE ISSN 0165-0173) **3332**
Brain Topography. (US ISSN 0896-0267) **3332**
Braives. (BE) **267**
Brake and Front End. (US ISSN 0193-726X) **4685**
Branch Automation News. (US ISSN 1044-145X) **805**
†Branch Banker's Report. (US ISSN 0162-7481) **5152**

Branch Line News. (UK) **4708**
Branch Redd Review. (US) **2989**
Branches of Berks. (US) **2145**
Branchevejviser for Traelast og Byggemarkeder *see* B T B **601**
Branching Out. (US) **2749**
Brand *see* Brand en Brandweer **2031**
Brand Aus. (AU ISSN 0006-9035) **2031**
Brand Book. (US) **2400**
Brand en Brandweer. (NE) **2031**
Brand & Raeddning. (SW ISSN 0283-1155) **2031**
Brandeis Quarterly *see* Brandeis Review **1305**
Brandeis Review. (US) **1305**
Brandeis University. Bigel Institute for Health Policy. Research News. (US) **3083**, **2605**
Brandenburg - Berlinisches Woerterbuch. (GW) **2806**
†Brandenburgischen Landeshochschule Potsdam. Wissenschaftliche Zeitschrift. (GW ISSN 0939-3986) **5152**
Brandfare og Brandvaern *see* Brandvaern **2031**
Die Brandhilfe. (GW ISSN 0006-906X) **2031**
Branding Iron. (US ISSN 0006-9078) **2400**
Brandmanden. (DK ISSN 0106-8725) **2031**
Brandon's Shipper & Forwarder *see* American Sailings **5135**
Brands and Their Companies. (US) **3673**
Brands and Their Companies Supplement. (US) **3673**
Brandschutz. (GW ISSN 0006-9094) **2031**, **2307**
Brandvaern. (DK ISSN 0106-6072) **2031**
Brandvaern. *see* Palontorjunta **2034**
Brandverhuetung. (AU ISSN 0029-8956) **2031**
Brandwacht. (GW ISSN 0006-9116) **2031**
Brandywine Bibliography. (AT ISSN 0811-3963) **4006**, **4140**
Brandywine Documents on Printing and Printing History *see* Brandywine Documents on the History of Books & Printing **3998**
Brandywine Documents on the History of Books & Printing. (AT ISSN 0811-3971) **3998**, **2344**, **4123**
Brandywine Keepsake. (AT ISSN 0157-5619) **3998**, **2344**, **4123**
Brangus Journal. (US ISSN 0006-9132) **212**
†Braniff Destination. (US) **5152**
Brann og Sikkerhet. (NO ISSN 0801-6763) **2031**
Brannmannen. (NO ISSN 0045-2696) **2031**
Die Branntweinwirtschaft. (GW ISSN 0006-9159) **379**
Brasil - Brazil. (US) **2860**
Brasil Comercio e Industria *see* Brazil Comercio e Industria **901**
Brasil Dia-a-Dia. (BL) **2400**
Brasil em Exame *see* Exame **1075**
†Brasil Florestal. (BL ISSN 0045-270X) **5152**
Brasil Madeira. (BL) **2096**, **2113**
Brasil-Medico. (BL ISSN 0006-9205) **3083**
Brasil Vogue. (BL) **1289**, **4838**
Brasilia. Departamento de Estradas de Rodagem do Distrito Federal. Diretoria Geral. Relatorio Anual. *see* Brasilia. Departamento de Estradas de Rodagem do Distrito Federal. Diretoria Geral. Relatorio de Atividades **4717**
Brasilia. Departamento de Estradas de Rodagem do Distrito Federal. Diretoria Geral. Relatorio de Atividades. (BL) **4717**
Brasilia. Fundacao do Servico Social do Distrito Federal. Relatorio Anual das Atividades. (BL) **4399**
Brasilia Medica. (BL ISSN 0524-2053) **3083**
Brasilians Journal. (US ISSN 0741-0298) **1994**, **901**, **4754**
Brasilien Handel und Industrie *see* Brazil Comercio e Industria **901**

Brasilien Nachrichten. (GW ISSN 0173-6582) **2175**
Brasilturis Journal. (BL) **4754**
Brass Band News *see* British Bandsman **3542**
Brass Bulletin. (SZ ISSN 0303-3848) **3542**
Brass Players Guide (Year). (US) **3542**
Brass Research Series. (US ISSN 0363-454X) **3542**
Brasserie Malterie Europe. (BE) **379**
Brasseries. *see* Canada. Statistics Canada. Breweries **5159**
Brassey's Annual - the Armed Forces Year-Book *see* R U S I and Brassey's Defence Yearbook **3469**
Bratislava. (CS) **2484**, **926**
Bratislava-Studia. (CS) **267**
Bratislavske Lekarske Listy. (CS ISSN 0006-9248) **3083**
Bratrsky Vestnik/Fraternal Herald. (US ISSN 0006-9256) **2528**
Bratstvo. (CN ISSN 0006-9264) **1994**
Bratstvo. (YU ISSN 0006-9272) **2175**
Bratstvo/Brotherhood. (US) **4257**
Bratstvo Fraternity. (CN) **3876**, **1994**
Brau und Brunnen Bote. (GW) **2062**
Brauer und Maelzer *see* Brauindustrie **379**
Brauerei-Forum. (GW ISSN 0179-2466) **379**
Brauerei Journal. (GW ISSN 0172-0589) **379**
Brauerei und Getraenke-Rundschau/ Revue de la Brasserie et des Boissons/Rivista delle Birrerie e delle Bevande. (SZ) **379**
Brauereibesitzer und Braumeister *see* Brauerei Journal **379**
Brauereien und Maelzereien in Europa. (GW ISSN 0068-0710) **379**
Brauindustrie. (GW ISSN 0341-7115) **379**
Braun's Systems. (US) **940**
Braunauer Rundbrief. (GW) **2353**, **4257**
Braunkohle. (GW ISSN 0341-1060) **3479**
Braunkohle Waerme und Energie *see* Braunkohle **3479**
Braunschweiger Geographische Studien.(GW ISSN 0524-2444) **2243**
Braunschweiger Naturkundliche Schriften. (GW ISSN 0174-3384) **579**, **497**
Braunschweiger Veroeffentlichungen zur Geschichte der Pharmazie und Naturwissenschaften. (GW ISSN 0722-7159) **3719**
Braunschweigische Heimat. (GW) **2353**, **319**
Braunschweigische Wissenschaftliche Gesellschaft. Abhandlungen. (GW) **4302**
Braunschweigisches Jahrbuch. (GW ISSN 0068-0745) **2353**
Braunviehzuchter. (GW ISSN 0930-3650) **212**
Braut und Braeutigam. (GW) **4838**, **2444**, **3396**
Braut und Braeutigam mit Trachtenmode *see* Braut und Braeutigam **4838**
Brauwelt. (GW ISSN 0724-696X) **379**
Brauwelt International. (GW ISSN 0724-696X) **379**
Brauwissenschaft *see* Monatsschrift fuer Brauwissenschaft **388**
Brava *see* Brava-Casa **3590**
Brava-Casa. (IT) **3590**
Bravado *see* Rangel's Reports **3969**
Brave New Word. (AT ISSN 0725-5543) **2900**, **2989**
Bravo. (CN) **319**
Bravo. (US ISSN 0275-6080) **2989**, **1994**
Bravo. (GW) **3504**, **3542**
Bravo Girl. (GW) **1250**
Bravura Studies in Music. (UK) **3588**, **3542**
Bray People. (IE) **2202**
Brayer. (US) **4532**
Brazil. Arquivo Nacional. Serie de Publicacoes. (BL) **2400**

Brazil. Centro Nacional de Pesquisa de Mandioca e Fruticultura. Circular Tecnica. (BL ISSN 0100-8064) **80**
Brazil. Centro Nacional de Pesquisa de Mandioca e Fruticultura. Comunicado Tecnico. (BL ISSN 0100-8854) **80**
Brazil. Comissao de Financiamento da Producao. Anuario Estatistico. (BL) **706**, **4565**
Brazil. Companhia de Financiamento da Producao. Relatorio anual da C F P. (Comissao de Financiamento da Producao) (BL) **148**
Brazil. Conselho Federal de Cultura. Boletim. (BL) **2504**
Brazil. Conselho Federal de Farmacia. Relatorio. (BL) **3719**
Brazil. Conselho Nacional de Desenvolvimento Cientifico e Tecnologico. Boletim. (BL) **4302**, **4594**
Brazil. Conselho Nacional de Desenvolvimento Cientifico e Tecnologico. Programa do Tropica Semi-Arido (Publicacion). (BL) **4302**
Brazil. Conselho Nacional de Desenvolvimento Cientifico e Tecnologico. Relatorio de Atividades. (BL) **4302**
†Brazil. Conselho Nacional do Petroleo. Atualidades. (BL) **5152**
Brazil. Coordenacao de Assistencia Medica e Hospitalar. Cadastro de Estabelecimentos de Saude. (BL) **2459**
Brazil. Coordenacao de Assistencia Medica e Hospitalar. Cadastro Hospitalar Brasileiro *see* Brazil. Coordenacao de Assistencia Medica e Hospitalar. Cadastro de Estabelecimentos de Saude **2459**
Brazil. Departamento de Assuntos Universitarios. Coordenacao de Avaliacao e Controle. Atividades das Instituicoes Federais de Ensino Superior. (BL) **1701**
Brazil. Departamento de Assuntos Universitarios. Coordenacao de Availiacao e Controle. Catalogo Geral das Instituicoes de Ensino Superior. (BL) **1701**
Brazil. Departamento Nacional da Producao Mineral. Avulso. (BL) **3479**
Brazil. Departamento Nacional da Producao Mineral. Boletim. (BL) **3479**
Brazil. Departamento Nacional da Producao Mineral. Programacao. (BL) **3479**
Brazil. Departamento Nacional de Obras Contra as Secas. Boletim Tecnico. (BL ISSN 0374-6658) **2037**
Brazil. Departamento Nacional de Obras Contra as Secas. Relatorio. (BL ISSN 0101-5680) **4055**
Brazil. Departamento Nacional do Servico Social do Comercio. Centro de Estudos e Informacao. Boletim Bibliografico. (BL) **926**
Brazil. Diretoria do Patrimonio Historico e Artistico Nacional. Revista *see* Brazil. Patrimonio Historico e Artistico Nacional. Revista **5152**
Brazil. Divisao de Pesquisas Ictiologicas. Serie Circular *see* Brazil. Departamento Nacional de Obras Contra as Secas. Boletim Tecnico **2037**
Brazil. Fundacao Instituto Brasileiro de Geografia e Estatistica. Boletim Bibliografico. (BL ISSN 0406-9765) **2267**, **395**, **4565**
Brazil. Fundacao Nacional do Indio. Informativo. (BL) **1994**
†Brazil. Fundacao Nacional do Livro Infantil e Juvenil. Boletim Informativo.(BL ISSN 0100-7238) **5152**
Brazil. Instituto de Zootecnia. Zootecnia.(BL ISSN 0044-5320) **212**
Brazil. Instituto Nacional de Estudos e Pesquisas Educacionais. Informativo. (BL) **1618**
Brazil. Instituto Nacional do Livro. Relatorio de Atividades. (BL) **2749**

Brazil. Ministerio da Agricultura. Commissao de Financiamento da Producao. Relatorio Anual da C F P *see* Brazil. Companhia de Financiamento da Producao. Relatorio anual da C F P **148**
Brazil. Ministerio da Agricultura. Escritorio de Estatistica. Cadastro das Empresas Produtoras de Oleos, Gorduras Vegetais e Sabprodutos. (BL) **134**
Brazil. Ministerio da Agricultura. Escritorio de Estatistica. Oleos e Gorduras Vegetais. (BL) **80**
Brazil. Ministerio da Agricultura. Escritorio de Estatistica. Pecuaria, Avicultura, Apicultura, Sericicultura. (BL) **134**
Brazil. Ministerio da Educacao. Servico de Estatistica da Educacao e Cultura. Sinopse Estatistica da Educacao Pre-Escolar. (BL) **1674**
Brazil. Ministerio da Fazenda. Boletim Informativo da Secao de Documentacao. (BL) **4079**
Brazil. Ministerio da Fazenda. Nucleo Regional de Administracao. Boletim Informativo *see* Brazil. Ministerio da Fazenda. Boletim Informativo da Secao de Documentacao **4079**
Brazil. Ministerio de Educacao. Departamento de Educacao Fisica e Desportos. Caderno Cultural. (BL) **1745**
Brazil. Ministerio do Trabalho, Industria e Comercio. Boletim. (BL) **973**
Brazil. Museu do Indio. Boletim. Antropologia. (BL ISSN 0101-0433) **236**
Brazil. Museu do Indio. Boletim. Documentacao. (BL ISSN 0101-0484) **2400**, **3522**
Brazil. Museu do Indio. Boletim. Etno-Historia. (BL ISSN 0100-7475) **2400**
Brazil. Museu do Indio. Boletim. Linguistica. (BL ISSN 0101-0530) **2806**
†Brazil. Patrimonio Historico e Artistico Nacional. Revista. (BL) **5152**
Brazil. S U D E N E. Departamento de Agricultura e Abastecimento. (Superintendencia do Desenvolvimento do Nordeste) (BL) **80**
Brazil. Servico de Estatistica da Educacao e Cultura. Sinopse Estatistica do Ensino Primario. *see* Brazil. Ministerio da Educacao. Servico de Estatistica da Educacao e Cultura. Sinopse Estatistica da Educacao Pre-Escolar **1674**
Brazil. Servico de Estatistica da Educacao e Cultura. Sinopse Estatistica do Ensino Superior. (BL) **1674**
Brazil. Servico de Estatistica da Educacao. Sinopse Estatistica do Ensino Regular de 1o Grau. (BL) **1674**
Brazil. Servico Nacional de Aprendizagem Comercial. Boletim Tecnico. (BL) **1618**, **4367**
Brazil. Servico Social do Comercio. Administracao Regional do Estado de Sao Paulo. Relatoria Annual. (BL) **4399**
Brazil. Servico Social do Comercio. Anuario Estatistico. (BL) **4079**, **4565**
Brazil. Servico Social do Comercio. Boletim Bibliografico. (BL) **4425**
Brazil. Servico Social do Comercio. Boletim de Intercambio *see* Intercambio **4409**
†Brazil. Servico Social do Comercio. Colecao Bibliografica. (BL) **5152**
Brazil. Superintendencia do Desenvolvimento da Amazonia. S U D A M Documenta. (BL ISSN 0045-2742) **1073**
Brazil. Superintendencia do Desenvolvimento do Nordeste. Departamento de Agricultura e Abastecimento. Programa de Trabalho para a Agricultura Nordestina. (BL) **148**

†Brazil. Superintendencia do Desenvolvimento do Nordeste. Nordeste, Oportunidades de Investimentos. (BL) **5152**
Brazil. Superintendencia do Desenvolvimento do Nordeste. Relatorio Anual. (BL) **847**
†Brazil. Superintendencia do Desenvolvimento do Nordeste. Relatorio Sintetico, Andamento do Programa de Irrigacao do Nordeste. (BL) **5152**
Brazil. Superintendencia do Desenvolvimento do Nordeste. S U D E N E Plano de Acao. (BL) **2484**
Brazil. Supremo Tribunal Federal. Indices de Legislacao Federal. (BL) **2605**
Brazil. Supremo Tribunal Federal. Relatorio dos Trabalhos Realizados. (BL) **2605**
Brazil. Tribunal Regional do Trabalho. Tercera Regiao. Revista. (BL ISSN 0076-8855) **2605**
Brazil Acucareiro. (BL ISSN 0006-9167) **2062**
Brazil Comercio e Industria. (BL ISSN 0101-3645) **901**
Brazil Development Series/Series Desenvolvimento Brasileiro. (BL) **1073**
Brazil Journal *see* Brazil News Update **4754**
Brazil News Update. (UK) **4754**
Brazil Service. (UK ISSN 0889-1761) **648**
Brazil Trade and Industry *see* Brazil Comercio e Industria **901**
Brazil - U.S. Business Listing. (US) **1123**, 901
Brazil Watch. (US ISSN 0897-3067) **847**, 3951
Brazilian Aerospace Yearbook. *see* Anuario Aerospacial Brasileiro **46**
Brazilian American Chamber of Commerce News Bulletin. (US) **808**
Brazilian Chess Magazine. *see* Preto & Branco **4484**
Brazilian Energy Statistics. *see* Estatistica Brasileira de Energia **1799**
Brazilian Export Market. (BL) **901**, 1123
Brazilian Geographic Journal. *see* Revista Brasileira de Geografia **2261**
Brazilian Journal of Agricultural Research. *see* Pesquisa Agropecuaria Brasileira **114**
Brazilian Journal of Botany. *see* Revista Brasileira de Botanica **516**
Brazilian Journal of Cassava. *see* Revista Brasiliera de Mandioca **190**
Brazilian Journal of Genetics/Revista Brasileira de Genetica. (BL ISSN 0100-8455) **540**, 522
Brazilian Journal of Medical and Biological Research. *see* Revista Brasileira de Pesquisas Medicas e Biologicas **3147**
Brazilian Journal of Plant Physiology. *see* Revista Brasileira de Fisiologia Vegetal **516**
Brazilian Seed Journal/Revista Brasileira de Sementes. (BL) **171**
Brazilian Statistical Journal. *see* Revista Brasileira de Estatistica **4584**
Brazing and Soldering *see* Soldering & Surface Mount Technology **3430**
Bread *see* Bread for the World Newsletter **4400**
Bread Caterers' Directory. *see* Pan Directorio de Proveedores **2089**
Bread for the World Newsletter. (US ISSN 1045-1005) **4400**
Bread Pudding Update. (US ISSN 1042-7139) **2444**, 2062
Break-In. (NZ ISSN 0006-9523) **1355**
Breaker. (NE) **1355**
Breaker's Guide. (US) **4754**, 1305
Breaking Chains. (UK ISSN 0309-7978) **2605**, 596, 4835
Breakthrough! (CN ISSN 0831-1919) **2176**
Breakthrough. (UK) **3332**
Breakthrough (Faber) *see* Hemi-Sync Journal **3859**
Breakthrough (Nashville). (US) **4014**

†Breakthrough (New York). (US) **5152**
Breakthrough (New York, 1986). (US) **1721**
Breakthrough (San Francisco). (US) **3876**
Breakthrough (Wheaton). (US) **4280**
†Breakthroughs in Health & Science. (US) **5152**
▼The Breast. (UK ISSN 0960-9776) **3290**
Breast Cancer--Diagnosis, Treatment, Preclinical Biology *see* I C R D B Cancergram: Breast Cancer - Diagnosis, Treatment, Preclinical Biology **3175**
Breast Cancer Research and Treatment.(NE ISSN 0167-6806) **3193**
Breast Diseases (New York). (US ISSN 0888-6008) **3083**
▼Breast Diseases (St. Louis). (US) **3166**, 4
Breast Feeding. (UK) **3319**
Breastfeeding Abstracts. (US ISSN 0896-4572) **3166**, 4, 1247
Breastfeeding Review. (AT ISSN 0729-2759) **3604**
Breathline. (US) **3190**, 3276
Brecha. (UY) **2238**
Breche. (SZ) **3876**
†Brecht Yearbook. (US ISSN 0734-8665) **5152**
†Brecon and Radnor Farmer. (UK ISSN 0006-954X) **5152**
Breeder & Feeder. (CN) **212**
Breeders Journal. (US) **213**
Breeding of Fur-Bearing Animals. *see* Maopi Dongwu Siyang **2737**
Breeze (Harrisonburg). (US) **1305**
Bref Rhone Alpes. (FR ISSN 0006-9566) **847**
Bref til Storkaupmanna. (Felag Islenzkra Storkaupmanna) (IC) **1123**
Brefskaktidindi. (IC) **4467**
Breifne. (IE ISSN 0068-0877) **2353**, 267
Bremer Aerzteblatt. (GW ISSN 0340-5362) **3083**
Bremer Afrika-Archiv *see* Uebersee-Museum, Bremen. Veroeffentlichungen. Reihe F: Bremer Afrika-Archiv **2335**
†Bremer Archaeologische Blaetter. (GW ISSN 0068-0907) **5152**
Bremer Ausschuss fuer Wirtschaftsforschung Monatsbericht *see* B A W - Monatsbericht **844**
Bremer Beitraege zur Geographie und Raumplanung. (GW ISSN 0720-9738) **2243**
Bremer Kirchenzeitung. (GW) **4231**
†Bremer Missionsschiff. (GW ISSN 0006-9574) **5152**
Bremer Schulblatt. (GW ISSN 0006-9582) **1725**
Bremer Suedpazifik-Archiv *see* Uebersee-Museum, Bremen. Veroeffentlichungen. Reihe G: Bremer Suedpazifik-Archiv **2346**
Bremer Turnvereinigung von 1877 e.V. Speigel *see* B T V Speigel **4465**
Bremische Hausbesitzerzeitung. (GW) **4145**
Bremisches Jahrbuch. (GW ISSN 0341-9622) **2353**
Brenesia. (CR ISSN 0304-3711) **4302**
Brennan Reports on Sophisticated Tax and Investment Planning *see* Ernst & Young Financial Planning Reporter **945**
Brennessel. (GW) **3762**
Brennpunkt. (GW ISSN 0932-7231) **3789**
Brennpunkt Seelsorge. (GW) **4166**
Brennpunkte der Sportwissenschaft. (GW ISSN 0932-8823). **4467**
Brennstoff-Waerme-Kraft *see* B W K **1784**
Brennstoffchemie *see* Erdoel und Kohle, Erdgas, Petrochemie **3685**
Brennstoffspiegel. (GW ISSN 0342-6580) **3683**

Brennstoffstatistik der Waermekraftwerke fuer die Oeffentliche Elektrizitaetsversorgung in Oesterreich *see* Begriffsbestimmungen fuer die Bundesstatistiken der Oesterreichische Elektrizitaetswirtschaft **4054**
Brentford and Chiswick Local History Society. Journal. (UK ISSN 0144-672X) **2353**
Bres' (NE) **3762**
Bres-Planete *see* Bres **3762**
Bresil Commerce et Industrie *see* Brazil Comercio e Industria **901**
Bretagne Immobiliere. (FR) **4145**
Bretagne Reelle. (FR ISSN 0006-9647) **3876**, 2307
Brethren Evangelist. (US ISSN 0747-4288) **4231**
Brethren Journal. (US) **4166**
Brethren Life and Thought. (US ISSN 0006-9663) **4280**
Brethren Missionary Herald. (US ISSN 0161-5238) **4280**
Breton News *see* Carn **3952**
Brevard Users Group Newsletter *see* B U G Newsletter **1467**
Breve, il Gruppo, la Cultura, l'Idee. (IT ISSN 0006-968X) **2900**
†Breves de Solagral. (FR) **5152**
Brevetti & Invenzioni. (IT ISSN 0393-5981) **3673**
Breviora. (US ISSN 0006-9698) **579**
Breviora Geologica Asturica. (SP ISSN 0520-9455) **1555**
Brewer. (UK ISSN 0006-9736) **379**
Brewer - Distiller and Bottler *see* Beverage and Food World **378**
Brewers Almanac. (US) **379**
Brewers Digest. (US ISSN 0006-971X) **379**
Brewers Digest Annual Buyers Guide and Brewery Directory. (US ISSN 0006-971X) **379**, 1123
Brewers' Guild Journal *see* Brewer **379**
Brewery Manual & Who's Who. (UK) **379**, 1123
Brewing and Beverage Industry International. (GW) **379**
Brewing and Malting Barley Research Institute. Annual Report. (CN ISSN 0068-094X) **379**
Brewing Industry News. (US) **379**
Brewing Research Convention. Current Awareness Monthly. (NE) **388**
Brewing Research Foundation. Current Awareness Monthly *see* Brewing Research Convention. Current Awareness Monthly **388**
Briarpatch. (CN ISSN 0703-8968) **3876**
Brick. (CN ISSN 0382-8565) **2860**
Brickbats & Bouquets. (US ISSN 0006-9779) **2528**
Bricker Bulletin on Executive Education. (US ISSN 1043-2833) **1701**
Bricker's International Directory *see* Bricker's International Directory, Volume 1: Long-Term University-Based Executive Programs (Year) **1004**
Bricker's International Directory *see* Bricker's International Directory, Volume 2: Short-Term University-Based Executive Programs (Year) **1004**
Bricker's International Directory, Volume 1: Long-Term University-Based Executive Programs (Year). (US ISSN 1054-7835) **1004**, 1692
Bricker's International Directory, Volume 2: Short-Term University-Based Executive Programs (Year). (US ISSN 1054-7843) **1004**, 1692
Bricker's Short Term Executive Programs *see* Bricker's International Directory, Volume 2: Short-Term University-Based Executive Programs (Year) **1004**
Bricklayer. (CN) **1305**
Bricklayers', Masons' and Plasterers' International Union of America. Journal *see* International Union of Bricklayers and Allied Craftsmen. Journal **2585**
Brickman Letter *see* Seniors' Money Alert **5275**
Bricolage Service. (FR) **2500**, 641

Bridal Apparel News. (US) **1289**, 3066
▼Bridal Crafts. (US) **3066**, 353
Bridal Fair *see* Bridal Trends **3066**
Bridal Guide. (US) **3066**
Bridal Trends. (US) **3066**
Bride and Groom. (US) **3066**, 3396
Bride & Groom Magazine. (CN) **3066**
Bride's *see* Bride's & Your New Home **3066**
Brides & Setting Up Home. (UK ISSN 0006-9787) **3066**, 2444
Bride's & Your New Home. (US) **3066**, 1289
Brides of Britain Series. (UK) **3066**, 1289
▼Brides Today. (US) **3066**, 1994
Bridge. (AT) **1511**, 4400
Bridge. *see* Drochaid **1999**
Bridge. *see* Most **2940**
Bridge. (SW ISSN 0345-1798) **3980**
Bridge. (NE ISSN 0006-9825) **4467**
Bridge. (UK) **4467**
Bridge. *see* Qiaopai **4484**
Bridge (Kingston-upon-Thames). (UK) **4257**
▼The Bridge (Oak Park). (US) **2989**
Bridge (Salem). (US ISSN 0741-1200) **1994**, 2053, 2400
Bridge Builder. (US ISSN 0743-8958) **2146**
Bridge International *see* Bridge **4467**
Bridge of Eta Kappa Nu. (US ISSN 0006-9809) **1883**
Bridge S A. (SA) **4467**
Bridge Today. (US ISSN 1043-6383) **4467**
Bridge World. (US ISSN 0006-9876) **4467**
†Bridgeport News. (US ISSN 0006-9892) **5152**
Bridges (Brooklyn). (US) **1994**
†Bridges (Columbia). (US ISSN 1042-2234) **5152**
Bridges in Japan. *see* Hashi **1866**
Bridgeur. (FR ISSN 0006-9914) **4467**
Bridgewater. (US) **1305**
Bridging the Gap. (CN ISSN 0840-7738) **2146**
Bridging the Gap: What's Happening Now. (US) **1250**
Brief *see* Design Brief **1128**
Brief *see* American Council for Judaism. Issues **4221**
Brief (Chicago). (US ISSN 0273-0995) **2605**, 2528
Brief (Houston). (US ISSN 0899-3009) **1004**, 1073
Brief aus Wahlwies. (GW ISSN 0006-9949) **1233**, 1618, 3750, 4400
▼Brief Berater. (GW ISSN 0939-3498) **2567**
†Brief Information on the Co-operative Movement in Czechoslovakia. (CS) **5153**
A Brief Relation. (US ISSN 1052-4681) **2400**
†Briefe an den Mitmenschen. (SZ ISSN 0006-999X) **5153**
Briefe fuer junge Steuerfachleute. (GW ISSN 0007-0009) **1088**
Briefing. *see* Enimerossi **2184**
Briefing (New York). (US) **2472**
Briefing Paper on Southern Africa. (SA ISSN 0262-3781) **3940**
Briefing Papers. (US ISSN 0007-0025) **847**, 2605
Briefing Sessions on Collective Bargaining and Employee Relations. (US) **973**, 2580
Briefing: Weekly Inside Perspective on Turkish Political, Economic and Business Affairs. (TU) **3876**, 847, 1994
Briefings (Dublin, Ohio) *see* National Ground Water Association. Briefings **1599**
▼Briefly... (US ISSN 1051-0036) **2605**, 1004, 1034, 1475
†Briefly. (US ISSN 0896-8713) **5153**
Briefly Speaking. (CN ISSN 0715-3759) **2605**, 1296
Briefmarke. (AU ISSN 0007-0033) **3750**
Briefmarken-Magazin. (GW ISSN 0933-968X) **3750**

Briefmarken-Spiegel. (GW ISSN 0007-0041) **3750**
Briefmarkenwelt. (GW ISSN 0171-1970) **3750**
Briefs. *see* B'kitzur **4222**
†Briefs. (US ISSN 0899-8779) **5153**
Briercrest Echo. (CN ISSN 0821-5839) **1305**
Brieven aan Gezinnen. (BE) **4430**
Brieven aan Jonge Gezinnen *see* Brieven aan Gezinnen **4430**
Brieven van Paulus. (NE) **2353**
Brig. (UK) **1305**
Brigade *see* Church Lads' and Church Girls' Brigade. Annual Report **1235**
Brigadier. (UK) **1305**, **3453**
Brigantia. (PO) **2504**
Brigham Young University. Center for Thermochemical Studies. Contributions. (US ISSN 0572-6921) **1224**
Brigham Young University. Department of Geology. Geology Studies *see* Brigham Young University Geology Studies **1555**
Brigham Young University Geology Studies. (US) **1555**
Brigham Young University Law Review. (US ISSN 0360-151X) **2605**
Brigham Young University Research Studies. Geology Series *see* Brigham Young University Geology Studies **1555**
Brigham Young University Studies. (US ISSN 0007-0106) **2504**
Brigham Young University Today *see* B Y U Today **1304**
Brighton Newsletter. (AT) **2344**
Brighton Park Life. (US ISSN 0007-0149) **2222**
Brighton Voice. (UK) **2860**
Brightonian. (UK ISSN 0007-0157) **1305**
Brigitte. (GW) **4838**
Brigitte (Austria). (AU) **1289**
Brigitte (Switzerland). (SZ) **1289**
Brihanmumbai Mahanagarpalika Patrika. (II) **4085**
Brillen Special. (GW ISSN 0933-9264) **3298**
Brilliant Ideas For Publishers. (US ISSN 0885-4890) **2567**, **2291**, **4123**
Brilliant Star. (US ISSN 0884-3635) **1250**, **4280**
Brill's Indological Library. (NE ISSN 0925-2916) **3635**
Brill's Japanese Studies Library. (NE) **3635**
Brill's Series in Jewish Studies. (NE ISSN 0926-2261) **4222**, **2307**
Brill's Series in Judaic Studies. (NE) **4222**
Brill's Studies in Epistemology, Psychology and Psychiatry. (NE ISSN 0924-0314) **3762**, **3332**
Brill's Studies in Intellectual History. (NE ISSN 0920-8607) **2504**
Brimleyana. (US ISSN 0193-4406) **579**, **3522**, **3656**
Bringin' Home the Bacon. (US) **2146**
Bringing Religion Home. (US) **4257**
Brio. (UK ISSN 0007-0173) **2749**, **3542**
Brio. (US) **4754**
Briquet. *see* Lighter **5227**
†Brisas Alfonsinas. (SP) **5153**
Brisbane Cityscope. (AT) **4160**
The Brisbane to Gladstone Yacht Race Programme Annual. (AT) **4523**
†Bristlecone. (US) **5153**
Bristol and Avon Archaeological Society Bulletin *see* B A A S Bulletin **266**
Bristol and Avon Archaeology. (UK ISSN 0263-1091) **267**
Bristol and Avon Family History Society. Journal. (UK ISSN 0308-4183) **2146**
Bristol and Gloucestershire Archaeological Society, Bristol, England. Transactions. (UK ISSN 0068-1032) **267**, **2353**
Bristol and West Country Illustrated *see* This is Bristol and Bath **2196**
Bristol & Western Engineering Manufacturers Association Ltd. Bulletin *see* B E M A Bulletin **1815**

Bristol and Western Engineering Manufacturers Association Ltd. Engineering Directory *see* B E M A Engineering Directory **1815**
Bristol Chamber of Commerce and Industry Directory. (UK) **808**
Bristol Diocesan News. (UK) **4232**
Bristol Medico - Chirurgical Journal *see* West England Medical Journal **3162**
Bristol-Meyers Cancer Symposia. Proceedings. (US) **3193**
Bristol-Myers - Squibb Symposium on Pain Research Series. (US) **3190**
Bristol-Myers - Zimmer Orthopaedic Symposium Series. (US) **3307**
Bristol Naturalists' Society. Proceedings. (UK ISSN 0068-1040) **4302**
Bristol Papers. (UK) **4367**
The Bristol Port Company. (UK) **4725**
Bristow's Book of Motor Cruisers *see* Bristow's Book of Yachts **4523**
Bristow's Book of Sailing Cruisers *see* Bristow's Book of Yachts **4523**
Bristow's Book of Yachts. (UK ISSN 0309-1252) **4523**
La Brita Esperantisto. (UK ISSN 0007-067X) **2806**
Britain: An Official Handbook. (UK ISSN 0068-1075) **2353**
Britain and Europe During (Year). (UK) **3951**
Britain & Holland Marina Guide. (UK) **4523**
Britain and Overseas. (UK ISSN 0045-2866) **901**
Britain and the Netherlands. (NE) **2353**
Britain by Britrail. (US) **4754**, **4708**
Britain: Hotels & Restaurants. (UK) **4754**
†Britain in Brief. (UK) **5153**
†Britain Welcomes Coaches. (UK) **5153**
Britain's Best Holidays - A Quick Reference Guide. (UK ISSN 0267-1468) **4754**
Britain's Book Publishing Industry. (UK) **4123**, **1034**
Britain's Catering Industry. (UK) **2472**, **1034**
Britain's Computer Industry *see* Britain's Top Computer Companies **1423**
Britain's D I Y Industry. (UK) **1453**, **1034**
Britain's Data Communications Equipment Suppliers *see* Britain's Top Computer Companies **1423**
Britain's Defence Service Industry *see* Britain's Top 500 Defence Companies **3453**
Britain's Direct Marketing Industry (Year). (UK) **1123**, **833**, **1034**
Britain's Drinks Industry. (UK) **380**, **1034**
Britain's Fire Protection Industry. (UK) **2031**, **1034**
Britain's Franchising Industry. (UK) **1123**, **833**
Britain's Freight-Forwarding Industry *see* Britain's Top 500 Transport Companies **4647**
†Britain's P.C. Manufacturers. (UK) **5153**
Britain's Paint Industry. (UK) **1123**, **833**
Britain's Security Industry. (UK) **1124**, **940**
Britain's Sporting Goods Industry: Into the 1990's. (UK) **1124**, **833**
Britain's Sports Industry Equipment, Clothing and Footwear *see* Britain's Sporting Goods Industry: Into the 1990's **1124**
Britain's Top Computer Companies. (UK) **1423**
Britain's Top Japanese-Owned Companies. (UK) **1124**, **901**
Britain's Top Private Companies. The First and Second Thousand *see* Britain's Top 10,000 Privately Owned Companies **1124**
Britain's Top 10,000 Privately Owned Companies. (UK) **1124**
Britain's Top 1000 Foreign-Owned Companies *see* Britain's Top 2500 Foreign-Owned Companies **1124**
Britain's Top 1000 Motor Distributors. (UK) **1124**, **833**

Britain's Top 2500 Foreign-Owned Companies. (UK) **1124**
Britain's Top 300 Motor Distributors *see* Britain's Top 1000 Motor Distributors **1124**
Britain's Top 300 Printers. (UK) **1124**, **833**, **3998**
Britain's Top 500 Defence Companies. (UK) **3453**
Britain's Top 500 Electrical & Electronic Companies. (UK ISSN 0263-2446) **1124**, **1883**
Britain's Top 500 Transport Companies. (UK) **4647**, **1034**
Britain's Wine Industry *see* Britain's Drinks Industry **380**
Britannia. (UK ISSN 0068-113X) **2354**
Britannia Monograph Series. (UK ISSN 0953-542X) **1275**
Britannica Atlas. (US ISSN 0068-1148) **2243**
Britannica Book of the Year. (US ISSN 0068-1156) **1780**
Britannica World Data Annual *see* Britannica Book of the Year **1780**
Britannica Yearbook of Science and the Future *see* Yearbook of Science and the Future **4353**
Britischer Export. *see* British Exports **1124**
British Academy. Proceedings. (UK) **2354**
British Academy of Songwriters, Composers & Authors News *see* B A S C A News **3540**
British Accounting Review. (UK ISSN 0890-8389) **748**
British Adhesives and Sealants Association Adhesives & Sealants Yearbook and Directory *see* B A S A Adhesives & Sealants Yearbook and Directory **3652**
British Advent Messenger *see* Messenger (Grantham) **4243**
British Aerosol Manufacturers Association Annual Report *see* B A M A Annual Report **1170**
British Agencies for Adoption & Fostering Discussion Series *see* B A A F Discussion Series **4399**
British Agencies for Adoption & Fostering News *see* B A A F News **4399**
British Agencies for Adoption & Fostering Practice Series *see* B A A F Practice Series **4399**
British Agencies for Adoption & Fostering Research Series *see* B A A F Research Series **4399**
British Agents Review *see* British Commercial Agents Review **1034**
British Aggregate Construction Materials Industries Review *see* B A C M I Review **601**
British Aid Statistics; Statistics of U.K. Economic Aid to Developing Countries. (UK ISSN 0068-1210) **706**
British Airways Executive. (UK ISSN 0306-7041) **4671**, **4754**
British Airways News. (UK) **4671**
British Alpine Breeders Group of Australia. Newsletter. (AT ISSN 0815-9777) **198**
British Alternative Theatre Directory. (UK ISSN 0142-5218) **4630**, **1124**
British Amateur Journalist. (UK ISSN 0007-0238) **2567**, **2900**
British Amateur Scientific Research Association *see* B A S R A Journal **4300**
British - American Chamber of Commerce Trade Bulletin *see* B A C C Trade Bulletin **808**
British - American Deal Review. (US ISSN 1044-2944) **648**
British-American Scientific Research Association Journal *see* B A S R A Journal **4300**
British - American Trade News. (US) **808**
British and European Geranium Society. Gazette. (UK) **2123**
British & European Geranium Society. Yearbook. (UK) **2123**
British and Irish Authors: Introductory Critical Studies. (UK) **2900**

BRITISH BIRDS 5993

British Antarctic Survey. Annual Report. (UK ISSN 0141-3325) **4302**
British Antique Dealers' Association Handbook. (UK) **256**
British Arachnological Society. Bulletin. (UK ISSN 0524-4994) **579**
British Archaeological Abstracts *see* British Archaeological Bibliography **290**
British Archaeological Association. Conference Transactions. (UK) **267**, **295**, **319**
British Archaeological Association. Journal. (UK ISSN 0068-1288) **267**, **295**, **319**
British Archaeological Bibliography. (UK ISSN 0964-7104) **290**, **4**
British Archaeological News. (UK ISSN 0269-1906) **267**
British Archer. (UK ISSN 0007-0289) **4467**
British Association for American Studies. Newsletter *see* Journal of American Studies **2411**
British Association for Behavioural Psychotherapy. Newsletter *see* Behavioural Psychotherapist **4013**
British Association for Canadian Studies. Newsletter. (UK) **4430**, **2400**
British Association for Immediate Care. Journal. (UK ISSN 0267-3258) **3307**
British Association for Psychopharmacology. Journal *see* Journal of Psychopharmacology **3733**
British Association of Colliery Management. National News Letter. (UK ISSN 0027-9773) **3479**
British Association of Friends of Museums Yearbook. (UK) **3522**
British Association of Industrial Editors. B A I E Directory of Members *see* B A I E Membership and Services Directory (Year) **1122**
British Association of Industrial Editors Membership and Services Directory (Year) *see* B A I E Membership and Services Directory (Year) **1122**
British Association of Industrial Editors News *see* B A I E News **2567**
British Association of Picture Libraries and Agencies Journal *see* B A P L A Journal **3789**
British Association of Psychotherapists. Bulletin *see* British Association of Psychotherapists. Journal **4014**
British Association of Psychotherapists. Journal. (UK ISSN 0954-0350) **4014**
British Association of Social Workers. Annual Report. (UK) **4400**
British Association of Sport and Medicine. Bulletin *see* British Journal of Sports Medicine **3371**
British Association of Teachers of the Deaf. Journal. (UK) **2286**, **1734**
British Astronomical Association. Handbook. (UK ISSN 0068-130X) **362**
British Astronomical Association. Journal. (UK ISSN 0007-0297) **363**
British Authors Series *see* British and Irish Authors: Introductory Critical Studies **2900**
British Automobile Racing Club News *see* B A R C News **4465**
†British Aviation Year Book. (UK ISSN 0068-1342) **5153**
British Baker. (UK ISSN 0007-0300) **2087**
British Baker Directory and Buyers Guide. (UK) **2087**
British Baking Industries Research Association. Abstracts *see* Flour Milling and Baking Research Association Abstracts **2085**
British Baking Industries Research Association. Annual Report *see* Flour Milling and Baking Research Association. Annual Report and Accounts **2067**
British Bandsman. (UK ISSN 0007-0319) **3542**
British Bee Journal. (UK ISSN 0007-0327) **80**
British Birds. (UK ISSN 0007-0335) **562**

British Book News. (UK ISSN 0007-0343) 395, 4124
British Book News Children's Books see Books for Keeps 4123
British Books in Print see Whitaker's Books in Print 416
British Boot and Shoe Institution. Journal see Apparel International 1283
†British Boxing Yearbook. (UK) 5153
British Broadcasting Corporation Annual Report and Handbook see B B C Annual Report and Handbook 5145
British Broadcasting Corporation Good Food see B B C Good Food 2444
British Broadcasting Corporation Music Guides see B B C Music Guides 5145
British Bulletin of Publications on Latin America, the Caribbean, Portugal and Spain. (UK ISSN 0268-2400) 395
British Bulletin of Publications on Latin America, the West Indies, Portugal and Spain see British Bulletin of Publications on Latin America, the Caribbean, Portugal and Spain 395
†British Business. (UK ISSN 0143-9111) 5153
British Business Rankings. (UK) 648
British Cactus & Succulent Journal. (UK ISSN 0264-3405) 2123
British Car. (US) 4685, 4516
British Car and Bike see British Car 4685
British Caribbean Philatelic Journal. (CN ISSN 0045-2890) 3750
British Carpet Technical Centre In-Site see B C T C - C A M R A S O - In-Site 1281
British Cast Iron Research Association Abstracts of International Literature on Metal Castings Production see B C I R A Abstracts of International Literature on Metal Castings Production 3424
British Catalogue of Audio-Visual Materials. (UK) 4462, 1674, 3798
British Catalogue of Music. (UK ISSN 0068-1407) 3542
British Cave Research Association. Transactions see Cave Science: Transactions of the British Cave Research Association 1557
British Ceramic Abstracts see World Ceramic Abstracts 1167
British Ceramic Manufacturers' Federation. Annual Report. (UK) 1161
British Ceramic Research. Special Publications. (UK ISSN 0144-2147) 1161
British Ceramic Review. (UK ISSN 0306-7076) 1161
British Ceramic Society. Proceedings. (UK ISSN 0524-5141) 1161
British Ceramic Society. Transactions and Journal. (UK ISSN 0307-7357) 1167, 4
British Chamber of Commerce. Monthly Information Service. (TH) 809
British Chamber of Commerce in Brazil. News & Views. (BL) 809
British Chamber of Commerce in France. Year Book see Franco - British Chamber of Commerce and Industry. Year Book 816
British Chamber of Commerce in the Argentine Republic. Bulletin. (AG) 809
British Chamber of Commerce of Turkey. Trade Journal. (TU ISSN 0007-0416) 809
British Chemicals and Their Manufacturers see Chemicals 1173
British Chess Federation Newsletter see B C F Newsletter 4465
British Chess Magazine. (UK ISSN 0007-0440) 4467
British Clayworker see Ceramic Industries International 1162
The British Clothing Industry Yearbook. (UK) 1283
†British Clothing Manufacturer. (UK ISSN 0007-0467) 5153
British Coal Guide to Steam Trains in the British Isles. (UK) 4708
British Columbia. Council of Human Rights. Annual Report. (CN) 3940

British Columbia. Housing Management Commission. Annual Report. (CN ISSN 0225-509X) 2484
British Columbia. Industrial Relations Council. Annual Report. (CN) 973
British Columbia. Labour Relations Board. Annual Report see British Columbia. Industrial Relations Council. Annual Report 973
British Columbia. Law Reform Commission. Annual Report. (CN ISSN 0381-2510) 2605
British Columbia. Law Reform Commission. Reports. (CN) 2605
British Columbia. Legislative Assembly. Debates (Hansard Daily). (CN) 4055
British Columbia. Legislative Assembly. Debates (Hansard Paperbound). (CN) 4055
British Columbia. Legislative Assembly. Journals. (CN) 4055
British Columbia. Legislative Assembly. Third Reading Bills. (CN) 4055
†British Columbia. Ministry of Agriculture and Food. Agricultural Aid to Developing Countries. (CN ISSN 0227-3802) 5153
British Columbia. Ministry of Agriculture and Food D.A.T.E. Program Report see British Columbia. Ministry of Agriculture Fisheries and Food D.A.T.E. Program Report 80
British Columbia. Ministry of Agriculture and Food. Field Crop Production Guide see British Columbia. Ministry of Agriculture Fisheries and Food. Field Crop Production Guide 171
British Columbia. Ministry of Agriculture and Food. Grape Production Guide. see British Columbia. Ministry of Agriculture Fisheries and Food. Grape Production Guide 171
British Columbia. Ministry of Agriculture and Food. Tree Fruit see British Columbia. Ministry of Agriculture Fisheries and Food. Tree Fruit Production Guide 171
British Columbia. Ministry of Agriculture and Food. Vegetable Production Guide see British Columbia. Ministry of Agriculture Fisheries and Food. Vegetable Production Guide 171
British Columbia. Ministry of Agriculture Fisheries and Food D.A.T.E. Program Report. (CN ISSN 0706-9308) 80
British Columbia. Ministry of Agriculture Fisheries and Food. Field Crop Production Guide. (CN) 171
British Columbia. Ministry of Agriculture Fisheries and Food. Grape Production Guide. (CN) 171
British Columbia. Ministry of Agriculture Fisheries and Food. Greenhouse Floriculture Production Guide. (CN ISSN 1183-5710) 171
British Columbia. Ministry of Agriculture Fisheries and Food. Greenhouse - Ornamental Production Guide see British Columbia. Ministry of Agriculture Fisheries and Food. Greenhouse Floriculture Production Guide 171
British Columbia. Ministry of Agriculture Fisheries and Food. Nursery Greenhouse Vegetable and Ornamental Production Guide for Commercial Growers. (CN ISSN 0840-8068) 171
British Columbia. Ministry of Agriculture Fisheries and Food. Nursery Production Guide see British Columbia. Ministry of Agriculture Fisheries and Food. Nursery Greenhouse Vegetable and Ornamental Production Guide for Commercial Growers 171
British Columbia. Ministry of Agriculture Fisheries and Food. Tree Fruit Production Guide. (CN) 171
British Columbia. Ministry of Agriculture Fisheries and Food. Vegetable Production Guide. (CN) 171
British Columbia. Ministry of Agriculture. Tree Fruit Production Guide for Interior Districts see British Columbia. Ministry of Agriculture Fisheries and Food. Tree Fruit Production Guide 171

British Columbia. Ministry of Education. Annual Report. (CN ISSN 0709-8383) 1618
British Columbia. Ministry of Energy, Mines and Petroleum Resources. Annual Report. (CN ISSN 0365-9356) 3479, 3683
British Columbia. Ministry of Energy, Mines and Petroleum Resources. Mineral Market Update. (CN) 3479
British Columbia. Ministry of Energy, Mines and Petroleum Resources. Mineral Resources Branch. Summary of Operations see British Columbia. Ministry of Energy, Mines and Petroleum Resources. Mineral Resources Division. Summary of Operations 3499
British Columbia. Ministry of Energy, Mines and Petroleum Resources. Mineral Resources Division. Summary of Operations. (CN ISSN 0825-6896) 3499
British Columbia. Ministry of Energy, Mines and Petroleum Resources. Paper Series. (CN ISSN 0226-9430) 1555
British Columbia. Ministry of Energy, Mines and Petroleum Resources. Bulletin. (CN ISSN 0068-144X) 1555, 3683
British Columbia. Ministry of Environment and Parks. Annual Report see British Columbia. Ministry of Environment. Annual Report 1484
British Columbia. Ministry of Environment. Annual Report. (CN ISSN 1181-8336) 1484, 4822
British Columbia. Ministry of Finance and Corporate Relations. Current Statistics. (CN) 4565
British Columbia. Ministry of Finance and Corporate Relations. Facts and Statistics see B C Economic and Statistical Review 844
British Columbia. Ministry of Finance and Corporate Relations. Financial and Economic Review see B C Economic and Statistical Review 844
British Columbia. Ministry of Forests and Lands. Annual Report see British Columbia. Ministry of Forests. Annual Report 2096
British Columbia. Ministry of Forests and Lands. Land Management Handbooks see British Columbia. Ministry of Forests. Land Management Handbooks 2096
British Columbia. Ministry of Forests and Lands. Land Management Reports see British Columbia. Ministry of Forests. Land Management Reports 2096
British Columbia. Ministry of Forests. Annual Report. (CN) 2096
British Columbia. Ministry of Forests. Land Management Handbooks. (CN ISSN 0229-1622) 2096
British Columbia. Ministry of Forests. Land Management Reports. (CN) 2096
British Columbia. Ministry of Forests. Research Notes. (CN ISSN 0226-9368) 2096
British Columbia. Ministry of Forests. Special Report Series. (CN) 2096, 2123
British Columbia. Ministry of Health. Annual Report. (CN ISSN 0706-4810) 4098
British Columbia. Ministry of Human Resources. Services for People see British Columbia. Ministry of Social Services and Housing. Services for People. Annual Report (Year) 4400
British Columbia. Ministry of Labour and Consumer Services. Annual Report. (CN) 974
British Columbia. Ministry of Labour and Consumer Services. Negotiated Working Conditions. (CN) 974, 3615
British Columbia. Ministry of Labour. Annual Report see British Columbia. Ministry of Labour and Consumer Services. Annual Report 974

British Columbia. Ministry of Labour. Negotiated Working Conditions see British Columbia. Ministry of Labour and Consumer Services. Negotiated Working Conditions 974
British Columbia. Ministry of Municipal Affairs. Municipal Statistics, Including Regional Districts see British Columbia. Ministry of Municipal Affairs, Recreation and Culture. Municipal Statistics, Including Regional Districts 2484
British Columbia. Ministry of Municipal Affairs, Recreation and Culture. Municipal Manual. (CN) 4085
British Columbia. Ministry of Municipal Affairs, Recreation and Culture. Municipal Statistics, Including Regional Districts. (CN) 2484
British Columbia. Ministry of Social Services and Housing. Services for People. Annual Report (Year). (CN) 4400
British Columbia. Office of the Ombudsman. Public Report Series. (CN) 4055
†British Columbia. Provincial Government. B C News. (CN ISSN 1180-0429) 5153
British Columbia. Provincial Government. Provincial Report see British Columbia. Provincial Government. B C News 5153
British Columbia. Utilities Commission. Annual Report. (CN) 1784
British Columbia. Workers' Compensation Board. Workers' Compensation Reporter. (CN) 2528
British Columbia Agri Digest: Dairy Issue. (CN) 198
▼British Columbia Agri Digest: Farm Business Issue. (CN) 148
▼British Columbia Agri Digest: Forage Issue. (CN) 205
▼British Columbia Agri Digest: Horse Issue. (CN ISSN 1184-2164) 4532
British Columbia Agri Digest: Horticulture. (CN) 2123
British Columbia Agri Digest: Poultry & Swine Issue. (CN) 213
British Columbia & Alberta Grocer Magazine. (CN) 2090
British Columbia & Yukon Hotelier. (CN) 2472
British Columbia and Yukon Hotelman see British Columbia & Yukon Hotelier 2472
British Columbia & Yukon Hotels Association. Membership Directory & Buyers Guide. (CN) 2472
British Columbia Annotated Industrial Relations Act. (CN) 2606, 974
British Columbia Annual Practice. (CN) 2606
British Columbia Art Teachers' Association. Journal. (CN ISSN 0316-1544) 1745, 319
British Columbia Broker see B.C. Broker 2527
British Columbia Business see B C Business 647
British Columbia Business Indicators. (CN) 707
British Columbia Cancer Research Centre. Annual Report. (CN) 3193
British Columbia Catholic. (CN ISSN 0007-0483) 4257
British Columbia Commercial Catch Statistics: By Species, Gear, Month and Area. (CN) 2051
British Columbia Commercial Catch Statistics: Herring, Groundfish, Shellfish and Other Fish see British Columbia Commercial Catch Statistics: By Species, Gear, Month and Area 2051
British Columbia Construction Association Membership Directory & Buyers' Guide. (CN) 604
British Columbia Corporations Law Guide. (CN) 2606
British Columbia Court Forms. (CN) 2606
British Columbia Decisions - Civil Cases.(CN ISSN 0824-717X) 2701

British Columbia Decisions - Criminal Cases see British Columbia Decisions - Criminal Conviction and Sentence Cases **2712**

British Columbia Decisions - Criminal Conviction and Sentence Cases. (CN) **2712**

British Columbia Decisions - Family Law Cases. (CN ISSN 0824-7196) **2716**

British Columbia Decisions - Industrial Relations Council. (CN) **2707, 974**

British Columbia Decisions - Insurance Law Cases. (CN ISSN 0824-720X) **2606, 2528**

British Columbia Decisions, Labour Arbitration. (CN) **974, 2606**

British Columbia Decisions - Labour Relations Board Decisions see British Columbia Decisions - Industrial Relations Council **2707**

British Columbia Decisions - Municipal Law Cases. (CN ISSN 0824-7188) **2606, 4085**

British Columbia Decisions - Statute Citator. (CN ISSN 0715-4798) **2606**

British Columbia Dietitians' and Nutritionists' Association News see B C D N A News **3603**

British Columbia Economic Activity see Economic Review and Outlook **5184**

British Columbia Employment and Labour Law Reporter see Employment and Labour Law Reporter **978**

British Columbia Energy Supply and Requirements Forecast Technical Report see British Columbia Energy Supply and Requirements Forecast Update **1784**

British Columbia Energy Supply and Requirements Forecast Update. (CN ISSN 0832-820X) **1784**

British Columbia Energy Suppy and Requirements Forecast Summary Report see British Columbia Energy Supply and Requirements Forecast Update **1784**

British Columbia English Teachers' Association. Journal. (CN ISSN 0316-0173) **1745, 2806**

British Columbia Export-Import Opportunities. (CN ISSN 0711-8244) **901**

British Columbia Family Law. (CN) **2716**

†British Columbia Family Law Quantum Service. (CN) **5153**

British Columbia Fruit Growers Association. Horticultural Forum Proceedings. (CN) **2123**

British Columbia Fruit Growers Association. Minutes of the Proceedings of the Annual Convention. (CN ISSN 0068-1563) **2123**

British Columbia Genealogical Society. Newsletter. (CN ISSN 0229-527X) **2146**

British Columbia Genealogist. (CN ISSN 0315-3835) **2146**

British Columbia Geographical Series: Occasional Papers in Geography. (CN ISSN 0068-1571) **2243**

British Columbia Golf Guide see Golf Guide **4505**

British Columbia Historical News. (CN ISSN 0045-2963) **2400**

British Columbia Institute of Technology Annual Report see B C I T Annual Report **4594**

British Columbia Institute of Technology Update see B C I T Update **4594**

British Columbia Insurance Directory. Insurance Companies, Agents and Adjusters. (CN ISSN 0068-1598) **2528**

British Columbia Labour Code see British Columbia Annotated Industrial Relations Act **2606**

British Columbia Law Reports (3rd Series). (CN ISSN 0703-3060) **2606**

British Columbia Library Association Reporter see B C L A Reporter **2746**

British Columbia List. (CN) **4055**

†British Columbia Lumberman. (CN ISSN 0007-0548) **5153**

British Columbia Medical Association. News. (CN) **3083**

British Columbia Medical Journal. (CN ISSN 0007-0556) **3083**

British Columbia Mineral Exploration Review. (CN ISSN 0846-0051) **3479**

British Columbia Monthly. (CN ISSN 0382-5272) **2989**

British Columbia Motor Transport Directory. (CN ISSN 0707-5014) **4743**

British Columbia Mountaineer. (CN ISSN 0045-2998) **4542**

British Columbia Museums Association. Museum Round Up. (CN ISSN 0045-3005) **3522**

British Columbia Music Educator. (CN ISSN 0705-9019) **3543**

British Columbia Orchardist. (CN ISSN 0007-0572) **2123**

British Columbia Origin Exports. (CN) **707**

British Columbia Population Forecast. (CN ISSN 0828-2919) **3980, 4145**

British Columbia Ports Handbook 1984. (UK ISSN 0265-8178) **4725, 1124**

British Columbia Practice. (CN) **2606**

British Columbia Public Libraries, Statistics. (CN) **2792**

British Columbia Real Estate Law Guide.(CN) **4145, 2606**

British Columbia Regional Index. (CN) **707, 3991**

British Columbia Report. (CN) **2176**

British Columbia Rules Citator. (CN) **2606**

British Columbia School Counsellors' Association. Newsletter. (CN ISSN 0705-8802) **1618**

British Columbia School Trustees Association. Newsletter see Education Leader **1727**

British Columbia Science Fiction Association see B C S F A-zine **1296**

British Columbia Snow Survey Bulletin. (CN ISSN 0045-303X) **3434**

British Columbia Tax Reports. (CN ISSN 0045-3056) **1088**

British Columbia Teachers' Federation. Arguments Bulletin see British Columbia Teachers' Federation. Effective Bargaining Committee. Information Report **5153**

†British Columbia Teachers' Federation. Effective Bargaining Committee. Information Report. (CN) **5153**

British Columbia Teachers' Federation. Newsletter see Teacher (Vancouver) **1666**

†British Columbia Water and Waste Association. Proceedings of the Annual Conference. (CN) **5153**

British Columbia Weekly Law Digest. (CN ISSN 0713-8865) **2606**

British Commercial Agents Review. (UK) **1034**

†British Computer Society. Microform Specialist Group. Annual Proceedings. (UK) **5153**

British Construction Equipment and Cranes. Directory. (UK) **1124**

British Corrosion Journal. (UK ISSN 0007-0599) **3403**

British Council Annual Report and Accounts (Year). (UK) **1701, 926, 3951**

British Cycling Federation. Handbook. (UK ISSN 0068-1938) **4467**

British Cycling Federation. Racing Handbook see British Cycling Federation. Handbook **4467**

British Deaf News. (UK ISSN 0007-0602) **2286**

British Decorator. (UK) **2549**

British Decorators Association. Members Reference Handbook. (UK) **3653**

British Defence Directory. (UK ISSN 0272-4782) **3453**

British Dental Journal. (UK ISSN 0007-0610) **3229**

British Dental Surgery Assistant. (UK ISSN 0007-0629) **3229, 3376**

British Design & Art Direction Annual. (UK) **3998**

British Direct Marketing Association Newsletter see B D M A Newsletter **28**

British Economy Survey. (UK ISSN 0263-3523) **648**

British Education Index. (UK ISSN 0007-0637) **1675, 4**

British Educational Research Journal. (UK ISSN 0141-1926) **1619**

British Electricity Ambulance Bulletin see Ambulance Bulletin **5134**

British Electrotechnical Approvals Board. Annual List of Approved Electrotechnical Equipment. (UK ISSN 0140-766X) **4594**

British Equestrian Directory. (UK ISSN 0144-7203) **4532**

British Exporters see Sell's British Exporters **920**

British Exports/Exportations Britanniques/Britischer Export/ Exportaciones Britanicas. (UK) **1124, 902**

British Exports. Export Services. see British Exports **1124**

▼British Exports to Europe. (UK) **1124, 902**

▼British Exports to North America. (UK) **1124, 902**

British Federation of Festivals. Yearbook. (UK) **3543**

British Federation of Music Festivals. Yearbook see British Federation of Festivals. Yearbook **3543**

British Field Archer see British Archer **4467**

British Field Sports Society. Annual Journal see Country Sports Directory **1127**

British Fire Services Association. Journal. (UK) **2031**

British Fleet. (UK) **3683**

British Fleet List see Fleet List **3686**

British Fleet News see British Fleet **3683**

British Food Journal. (UK ISSN 0007-070X) **2062, 3604**

British Footwear Manufacturers Federation. Statistics. (UK) **4362**

British Foundryman see Foundryman **3407**

British Friesian Journal see Holstein Friesian Journal **217**

British G Q. (UK ISSN 0954-8750) **1289, 3396**

British Gas. Annual Report and Accounts. (UK) **3683**

British Gas. Monitor. (UK) **3683, 1784, 1883**

British Gas. Report and Accounts see British Gas. Annual Report and Accounts **3683**

British Gas Corporation. Monitor see British Gas. Monitor **3683**

British Gas Corporation. Report and Accounts see British Gas. Annual Report and Accounts **3683**

British Geological Literature. (UK ISSN 0140-7813) **1550, 4**

British Geologist see Geoscientist **1566**

†British Geomorphological Research Group. Technical Bulletin. (UK ISSN 0306-3380) **5153**

British Glass Industry Research Association. Annual Report see British Glass Manufacturers Confederation. Annual Review **1161**

British Glass Industry Research Association Review see British Glass Manufacturers Confederation. Digest of Information and Patent Review **1161**

British Glass Manufacturers Confederation. Annual Review. (UK) **1161**

British Glass Manufacturers Confederation. Digest of Information and Patent Review. (UK) **1161, 3673**

British Goat Society. Herd Book. (UK ISSN 0068-2039) **213**

British Goat Society. Monthly Journal. (UK ISSN 0953-8070) **213**

British Goat Society. Year Book. (UK ISSN 0068-2047) **213**

British Grassland Society. Journal see Grass and Forage Science **94**

British Hardware Federation Directory see B H F Directory **1122**

▼British Health & Fitness Club Directory. (UK ISSN 0957-6754) **1124, 4467**

British Health and Safety Society. Newsletter see Journal of Health and Safety **3618**

British Health and Safety Society. Reviews Bulletin see Journal of Health and Safety **3618**

British Heart Journal. (UK ISSN 0007-0769) **3205**

British Helicopter Advisory Board Handbook see European Helicopter Association Handbook **4673**

British Helicopter Advisory Board Information Handbook see B H A B Information Handbook **48**

British Heritage. (US ISSN 0195-2633) **2354, 4754**

British Herpetological Society. Bulletin. (UK ISSN 0260-5805) **579**

British Herpetological Society. Newsletter see British Herpetological Society. Bulletin **579**

British History Illustrated see British Heritage **2354**

British Holiday & Home Parks Association Ltd. Journal see B H & H P A Journal **4753**

British Holstein Society Journal. (UK) **198**

British Homing World. (UK ISSN 0007-0777) **4467**

British Homoeopathic Journal. (UK ISSN 0007-0785) **3213**

†British Horse Society Diary. (UK) **5153**

British Horse Society Year Book & Event Guide. (UK) **4532**

British Hospitals Contributory Schemes Association. Directory of Convalescent Homes Serving the Provinces. (UK ISSN 0068-208X) **2459**

British Hospitals Contributory Schemes Association. Directory of Hospitals Contributory Scheme Benefits. (UK ISSN 0068-2098) **2459**

British Hotel Industry. (UK ISSN 0263-368X) **1124, 2472**

British Hotelier and Restauranteur see Voice of the British Hospitality Association **2481**

British Humanities Index. (UK ISSN 0007-0815) **2519, 4**

British Hydromechanics Research Association. Proceedings of Hydrotransport. (UK ISSN 0306-6916) **1923**

British Hydromechanics Research Association. Proceedings of Pneumotransport. (UK ISSN 0140-1785) **1923**

British Imperial Calendar and Civil Service List see Civil Service Year Book **4057**

British Imperial Plastics Plastics Review see B I P Plastics Review **5145**

British Independent Steel Companies and Their Products. (UK) **3403**

British Industrial and Scientific International Translations Service see Materials Information Translations Service **3413**

British Industry. (HK) **902**

British Industry and Engineering. (UK ISSN 0007-0823) **4594, 1925**

British Ink Maker see Ink & Print International **4001**

British Institute in Eastern Africa. Annual Report. (KE ISSN 0068-2152) **2332**

British Institute in Eastern Africa. Memoirs. (KE) **2332**

British Institute of History and Archaeology in East Africa. Report see British Institute in Eastern Africa. Annual Report **2332**

British Institute of Interior Design Members' Reference Book. (UK ISSN 0263-2047) **2549**

British Institute of International and Comparative Law. Quarterly Newsletter. (UK) **2720**

BRITISH INSTITUTE

▼British Institute of Management Databases on C D - R O M. (UK) **1004**
British Institute of Mental Handicap. Current Awareness Service. (UK ISSN 0143-0289) **1675, 1734, 2285**
British Insurance Broker see Broker **2528**
British Internal Combustion Engine Research Institute Ltd. Abstracts from Technical and Patent Publications. see B I C E R I Abstracts from Technical and Patent Publications **5145**
British International Freight Association. Yearbook. (UK) **4708**
British Interplanetary Society Journal. (UK ISSN 0007-084X) **49**
British Invisible Exports Council. Annual Report. (UK) **902**
British-Israel Trade. (UK ISSN 0260-3985) **809**
British Italian Trade Review. (IT ISSN 0007-0858) **809**
British Ivy Society. Journal. (UK) **2123**
British Ivy Society. Occasional Papers. (UK) **2123**
British Jeweller see British Jeweller & Watch Buyer **2563**
British Jeweller. Yearbook see British Jeweller & Watch Buyer. Yearbook **2563**
British Jeweller & Watch Buyer. (UK) **2563**
British Jeweller & Watch Buyer. Yearbook. (UK) **2563**
British Journal for Eighteenth-Century Studies. (UK) **2504**
British Journal for the History of Science. (UK ISSN 0007-0874) **4302**
British Journal for the Philosophy of Science. (UK ISSN 0007-0882) **4302, 3763**
British Journal of Academic Librarianship. (UK ISSN 0269-0497) **2749**
†British Journal of Accident & Emergency Medicine. (UK) **5153**
British Journal of Acupuncture. (UK ISSN 0143-4977) **3084**
British Journal of Addiction. (UK ISSN 0952-0481) **1534**
British Journal of Administrative Management see Institute of Administrative Management. Journal **1013**
British Journal of Aesthetics. (UK ISSN 0007-0904) **319, 3763**
British Journal of Anaesthesia. (UK ISSN 0007-0912) **3190**
British Journal of Audiology. (UK ISSN 0300-5364) **2286**
British Journal of Canadian Studies. (UK ISSN 0269-9222) **4430, 2400**
British Journal of Cancer. (UK ISSN 0007-0920) **3193**
British Journal of Clinical Pharmacology.(UK ISSN 0306-5251) **3719**
British Journal of Clinical Practice. (UK ISSN 0007-0947) **3084**
British Journal of Clinical Psychology. (UK ISSN 0144-6657) **4014**
▼British Journal of Clinical Research. (UK ISSN 0961-1053) **3084, 3719**
British Journal of Criminology. (UK ISSN 0007-0955) **1511**
British Journal of Dermatology. (UK ISSN 0007-0963) **3246**
British Journal of Dermatology. Supplement. (UK ISSN 0366-077X) **3246**
British Journal of Developmental Psychology. (UK ISSN 0261-510X) **4014**
British Journal of Diseases of the Chest see Respiratory Medicine **3367**
British Journal of Disorders of Communication see European Journal of Disorders of Communication **1735**
British Journal of Education and Work. (UK ISSN 0269-0004) **1745, 1063, 2105**
British Journal of Educational Studies. (UK ISSN 0007-1005) **1619**

British Journal of Educational Technology. (UK ISSN 0007-1013) **1745**
British Journal of Experimental and Clinical Hypnosis see Contemporary Hypnosis **4017**
British Journal of Experimental Pathology see International Journal of Experimental Pathology **3110**
British Journal of Family Planning. (UK ISSN 0144-8625) **596**
British Journal of General Practice. (UK ISSN 0960-1643) **3084**
British Journal of Guidance and Counselling. (UK ISSN 0306-9885) **3624**
British Journal of Haematology. (UK ISSN 0007-1048) **3271**
British Journal of Healthcare Computing. (UK ISSN 0265-5217) **3225**
British Journal of Hospital Medicine. (UK ISSN 0007-1064) **3084, 2459**
British Journal of In-Service Education. (UK ISSN 0305-7631) **1701**
British Journal of Industrial Medicine. (UK ISSN 0007-1072) **3615**
British Journal of Industrial Relations. (UK ISSN 0007-1080) **974**
British Journal of Language Teaching see Language Learning Journal **2824**
British Journal of Law and Society see Journal of Law and Society **2639**
▼British Journal of Management. (UK ISSN 1045-3172) **1004**
British Journal of Mathematical and Statistical Psychology. (UK ISSN 0007-1102) **4014**
▼British Journal of Medical Economics. (UK ISSN 0962-1423) **3084, 2459**
British Journal of Medical Psychology. (UK ISSN 0007-1129) **4014, 3332**
British Journal of Mental Subnormality. (UK ISSN 0374-633X) **1734, 4014**
British Journal of Middle East Studies. (UK) **2428**
British Journal of Music Education. (UK ISSN 0265-0517) **3543**
British Journal of Music Therapy see Journal of British Music Therapy **1737**
British Journal of Neurosurgery. (UK ISSN 0268-8697) **3376**
British Journal of Non-Destructive Testing. (UK ISSN 0007-1137) **3403**
British Journal of Nutrition. (UK ISSN 0007-1145) **3604**
British Journal of Obstetrics & Gynaecology. (UK ISSN 0306-5456) **3290**
British Journal of Occupational Therapy.(UK ISSN 0308-0226) **3084**
British Journal of Ophthalmology. (UK ISSN 0007-1161) **3298**
British Journal of Oral and Maxillofacial Surgery. (UK ISSN 0266-4356) **3229, 3376**
British Journal of Oral Surgery see British Journal of Oral and Maxillofacial Surgery **3229**
British Journal of Orthodontics. (UK ISSN 0301-228X) **3229**
British Journal of Parenteral Therapy see Intensive Therapy & Clinical Monitoring **5215**
†British Journal of Pharmaceutical Practice. (UK ISSN 0144-8803) **5153**
British Journal of Pharmacology. (UK ISSN 0007-1188) **3719**
British Journal of Pharmacology and Chemotherapy see British Journal of Pharmacology **3719**
British Journal of Photography. (UK ISSN 0007-1196) **3789**
British Journal of Photography Annual. (UK ISSN 0068-2217) **3789**
British Journal of Physical Education. (UK ISSN 0954-6693) **1745, 3811**
British Journal of Physiological Optics see Ophthalmic and Physiological Optics **3303**

▼British Journal of Phytotherapy. (UK ISSN 0959-6879) **3213**
British Journal of Plastic Surgery. (UK ISSN 0007-1226) **3376**
British Journal of Political Science. (UK ISSN 0007-1234) **3876**
British Journal of Projective Psychology.(UK ISSN 0309-7757) **4014, 3332**
British Journal of Projective Psychology and Personality Study see British Journal of Projective Psychology **4014**
British Journal of Psychiatry. (UK ISSN 0007-1250) **3333**
British Journal of Psychology. (UK ISSN 0007-1269) **4014**
British Journal of Psychotherapy. (UK ISSN 0265-9883) **3333**
British Journal of Radiology. (UK ISSN 0007-1285) **3357**
British Journal of Religious Education. (UK ISSN 0141-6200) **4166**
British Journal of Rheumatology. (UK ISSN 0263-7103) **3084, 3368**
British Journal of Russian Philately. (NE ISSN 0950-575X) **3750**
British Journal of Serials Librarianship see European Journal of Serials Librarianship **2757**
British Journal of Sexual Medicine. (UK ISSN 0301-5572) **3084**
British Journal of Social and Clinical Psychology see British Journal of Social Psychology **4014**
British Journal of Social Psychology. (UK ISSN 0144-6665) **4014**
British Journal of Social Work. (UK ISSN 0045-3102) **4400**
British Journal of Sociology. (UK ISSN 0007-1315) **4430**
British Journal of Sociology of Education. (UK ISSN 0142-5692) **1619, 4430**
British Journal of Special Education. (UK ISSN 0952-3383) **1734, 3084**
British Journal of Sports Medicine. (UK ISSN 0306-3674) **3371**
British Journal of Surgery. (UK ISSN 0007-1323) **3376**
British Journal of Surgery (Edicion Espanola). (SP ISSN 0214-2376) **3376**
British Journal of Urology. (UK ISSN 0007-1331) **3387**
British Journal of Visual Impairment. (UK ISSN 0264-6196) **2291, 1619**
British Kinematograph Sound and Television Society Image Technology Journal of the B K S T S see Image Technology Journal of the B K S T S **3511**
British Kinematography, Sound and Television see Image Technology Journal of the B K S T S **3511**
▼British Leisure & Swimming Pool Directory. (UK ISSN 0957-8730) **1124, 2738, 4467**
British Leisure Centre Directory. (UK ISSN 0950-0308) **1124, 2738, 4467**
British Librarianship and Information Science see British Librarianship & Information Work **2749**
British Librarianship & Information Work. (UK) **2749**
British Library. Annual Report. (UK ISSN 0305-7887) **2749**
British Library. Bibliographic Services. Newsletter see Select: National Bibliographic Service Newsletter **2784**
British Library. Document Supply Centre. Document Supply News. (UK ISSN 0952-892X) **2749**
British Library. Document Supply Centre. Index of Conference Proceedings. (UK ISSN 0959-4906) **3395, 4**
British Library. Document Supply Centre. Newsletter see British Library. Document Supply Centre. Document Supply News **2749**
British Library. Document Supply Centre. Science Reference and Information Service. Current Serials Received. (UK ISSN 0959-4914) **395**

British Library. Lending Division. Current Serials Received see British Library. Document Supply Centre. Science Reference and Information Service. Current Serials Received **395**
British Library. Lending Division. Index of Conference Proceedings Received see British Library. Document Supply Centre. Index of Conference Proceedings **3395**
British Library. Name Authority List. (UK) **2792, 4**
British Library. Newspaper Library. Newsletter. (UK) **2749**
British Library. Reference Division Newspaper Library. Newsletter see British Library. Newspaper Library. Newsletter **2749**
†British Library. Subject Authority Fiche.(UK) **5153**
British Library Journal. (UK ISSN 0305-5167) **2749**
British Library News. (UK ISSN 0307-9481) **2749**
†British Library of Political and Economic Science. Quarterly List of Additions in Russian and East European Languages. (UK ISSN 0140-4113) **5153**
British Library Research Reviews. (UK ISSN 0261-2178) **2749**
British Lichen Society Bulletin. (UK ISSN 0300-4562) **498**
British Limbless Ex-Servicemen's Association see B L E S M A G **4399**
British Marine Industries Federation Handbook. (UK) **4725**
British Maritime Technology Ltd. Abstracts see B M T Abstracts **4662**
British Maritime Technology Ltd. Cortec Bibliographies see B M T Cortec Bibliographies **5145**
British Maritime Technology News. (UK) **4725**
British Medical Association News Review see B M A News Review **3080**
British Medical Bulletin. (UK ISSN 0007-1420) **3084**
British Medical Journal. (UK ISSN 0007-1447) **3084**
British Medical Journal. Edicion Espanola. (SP ISSN 0213-3954) **3084**
†British Medicine. (US ISSN 0140-2722) **5153**
British Micro Software News. (UK ISSN 0264-1283) **1475**
British Mining. (UK ISSN 0308-2199) **3479**
British Model Soldier Society. Bulletin. (UK ISSN 0306-7947) **2434**
British Mouthpiece. (UK ISSN 0007-1463) **3543**
British Museum (Natural History) Bulletin see British Museum (Natural History) Report **433**
British Museum (Natural History) Bulletin. Botany. (UK ISSN 0068-2292) **498**
British Museum (Natural History). Bulletin. Entomology. (UK ISSN 0524-6431) **529**
British Museum (Natural History). Bulletin. Geology. (UK ISSN 0007-1471) **1556**
†British Museum (Natural History) Bulletin. Historical. (UK ISSN 0068-2306) **5153**
British Museum (Natural History) Bulletin. Zoology. (UK ISSN 0007-1498) **579**
British Museum (Natural History) Report. (UK) **433**
British Museum Society. Bulletin see B M Magazine **3522**
British Museum Society Magazine see B M Magazine **3522**
British Music. (UK ISSN 0958-5664) **3543**
British Music Education Yearbook. (UK ISSN 0266-2329) **3543**
British Music Society. Journal see British Music **3543**
British Music Worldwide. (UK ISSN 0954-1802) **3543**

British Music Yearbook. (UK ISSN 0306-5928) **3543**
British Mycological Society. Bulletin *see* Mycologist **510**
British Mycological Society. Transactions *see* Mycological Research **510**
British National Bibliography. (UK ISSN 0007-1544) **4140**
British National Committee on Large Dams. News and Views. (UK ISSN 0525-4205) **1862**
British National Film Catalogue. (UK ISSN 0007-1552) **3519**
British National Formulary. (UK ISSN 0260-535X) **3719**
British Naturalist. (UK ISSN 0144-9761) **1541**
British Naturism. (UK ISSN 0264-0406) **3800**
British Newspaper and Magazines Industry. (UK) **1124**, **2567**
British Newspaper Industry *see* British Newspaper and Magazines Industry **1124**
British North America Philatelic Society Ltd. Topics *see* B N A Topics **3749**
British-North American Committee Publications. (UK) **648**
British-North American Research Association. Committee Publications *see* British-North American Committee Publications **648**
British-North American Research Association. Occasional Papers. (UK) **648**
British Numismatic Journal. (UK) **3598**
British Nutrition Foundation Briefing Papers. (UK) **3604**
British Nutrition Foundation Monograph.(UK) **3604**
British Nutrition Foundation Newsletter *see* British Nutrition Foundation Monograph **3604**
British Nutrition Foundation Nutrition Bulletin *see* B N F Nutrition Bulletin **3603**
British Nutrition Foundation Task Force Reports. (UK) **3604**
British Olympic Association Diary. (UK) **4467**
British Olympic Association Year Book and Diary *see* British Olympic Association Diary **4467**
British Ornithologists' Club. Bulletin. (UK ISSN 0007-1595) **563**
British Orthoptic Journal. (UK ISSN 0068-2314) **3298**
British Osteopathic Journal *see* Clinical Biomechanics **3214**
British Outdoor Amenities Directory. (UK ISSN 0955-4025) **1124**, **4467**
British Overseas Development. (UK) **926**
†British Paper. (UK) **5153**
British Paper and Board Industry Federation. Technical Association. Fundamental Research International Symposia *see* Paper Industry Technical Association. Fundamental Research International Symposia **3664**
British Paper and Board Industry Federation. Technical Association. Technical Papers. (UK ISSN 0068-2330) **3662**
British Pelargonium & Geranium Society. Yearbook. (UK) **2123**
British Performing Arts Yearbook. (UK ISSN 0951-5208) **1529**, **3543**, **4630**
British Petroleum Accelerator *see* B P Accelerator **647**
British Petroleum Company p.l.c. News *see* B P News **3683**
British Pharmacological Society. Symposia. (UK) **3719**
British Pharmacopoeia (Veterinary). (UK) **4807**, 3719
British Philatelic Bulletin. (UK ISSN 0953-8119) **3750**
British Philatelic Federation. Congress Handbook. (UK) **3750**
British Phycological Bulletin *see* British Phycological Journal **498**
British Phycological Journal. (UK ISSN 0007-1617) **498**
British Pig Association Herd Book. (UK) **213**

British Pirandello Society. Yearbook *see* Society for Pirandello Studies. Yearbook **2961**
British Plant Growth Regulator Group. Monographs *see* British Society for Plant Growth Regulation. Monographs **171**
British Plastics and Rubber Magazine. (UK ISSN 0307-6164) **3861**, **4291**
British Plumbing and Heating *see* Plumb and Heat **2302**
British Polio Fellowship. Bulletin. (UK ISSN 0007-1633) **3333**, **4400**
British-Portuguese Chamber of Commerce. Monthly Magazine *see* Camara de Comercio Luso-Britanica. Bi-monthly Magazine **810**
British Postmark Society. Quarterly Bulletin. (UK) **3750**
British Poultry Science. (UK ISSN 0007-1668) **213**
British Premium Merchandise Association News *see* B P M A News **1034**
British Printer. (UK ISSN 0007-1684) **3998**
British Privately Owned Companies: The Third 2000 *see* Britain's Top 10,000 Privately Owned Companies **1124**
British Promotional Merchandise Association News *see* B P M A News **1034**
British Protestant *see* Gospel Magazine **4239**
British Psychological Society. Annual Report. (UK ISSN 0309-7773) **4014**
British Psychological Society. Bulletin *see* The Psychologist **4042**
British Psychological Society. Division of Criminological & Legal Psychology. Occasional Papers. (UK) **4015**
British Psychological Society. Education Section. Review. (UK ISSN 0262-4087) **1619**
British Psychology Society. Division of Educational and Child Psychology. Papers *see* Educational & Child Psychology **4019**
British Pteridological Society. Bulletin. (UK ISSN 0301-9195) **498**
†British Pump Manufacturers Association. Technical Conference Proceedings. (UK ISSN 0140-2145) **5153**
British Pump Market. (UK) **3683**
British Puppet and Model Theatre Guild. (Newsletter). (UK) **4630**
British Qualifications. (UK ISSN 0141-5972) **1619**
British Rabbit Council Year Book. (UK) **213**
British Racehorse *see* European Racehorse **4534**
British Racing News. (UK ISSN 0045-3137) **4467**, **4685**
British Railways Board. Annual Report and Accounts. (UK ISSN 0305-1420) **4708**
British Railways Board. Report and Statement of Accounts *see* British Railways Board. Annual Report and Accounts **4708**
British Rate and Data. (UK ISSN 0263-3515) **395**, 29
British Rate and Data Direct Marketing *see* B R A D Direct Marketing **1034**
British Regional Geology. (UK ISSN 0367-3928) **1556**
British Reports, Translations and Theses. (UK ISSN 0959-4922) **4355**, 4, **4614**
British Review of Bulimia and Anorexia Nervosa. (UK ISSN 0950-3005) **4015**, **4835**
British Review of Economic Issues. (UK ISSN 0141-4739) **889**, 848
British Rowing Almanack *see* British Rowing Almanack. A R A Yearbook **4523**
British Rowing Almanack. A R A Yearbook. (UK) **4523**
British Rubber Industry Directory *see* Rubber and Polyurethane Directory B.R.M.A **4293**

British Rubber Manufacturers' Association Ltd. Rubber and Polyurethane Directory B.R.M.A. *see* Rubber and Polyurethane Directory B.R.M.A **4293**
British School at Athens. Annual. (UK ISSN 0068-2454) **267**
British School at Rome. Papers. Archaeology, History, History of Art. (UK) **267**, **2354**, **3522**
British School at Rome. Papers. Archeology *see* British School at Rome. Papers. Archaeology, History, History of Art **267**
British Scientific Instrument Research Association. Annual Report *see* Sira Spotlight **2525**
British Security Companies *see* Britain's Security Industry **1124**
British Security Industry Buyer's Guide (Year) *see* European Security Industry Buyer's Guide (Year) **1526**
British Ship Research Association. B.S.R.A. Bibliographies *see* B M T Cortec Bibliographies **5145**
British Shipbuilders Council Bulletin *see* B S C Bulletin **5145**
British Shipper *see* British Shipper and Forwarder **4647**
British Shipper and Forwarder. (UK) **4647**
British Ski Magazine *see* Skier **4556**
British Soccer Week. (AT ISSN 0817-1203) **4501**
British Society for Cell Biology. Symposia. (UK) **522**
British Society for Developmental Biology. Symposia. (UK) **570**
British Society for Middle Eastern Studies. Bulletin *see* British Journal of Middle East Studies **2428**
British Society for Music Therapy. Bulletin. (UK ISSN 0953-7511) **3543**, **4015**
British Society for Phenomenology. Journal. (UK ISSN 0007-1773) **3763**
British Society for Plant Growth Regulation. Annual Bulletin. (UK ISSN 0963-6749) **498**, 171
British Society for Plant Growth Regulation. Monographs. (UK) **171**, 498
British Society for Plant Growth Regulation. News Bulletin *see* British Society for Plant Growth Regulation. Annual Bulletin **498**
British Society for Plant Growth Regulation. Newsletter. (UK ISSN 0963-7001) **171**, 498
British Society for the History of Pharmacy. Transactions. (UK ISSN 0068-2519) **3719**
British Society for the History of Philosophy Newsletter. (UK ISSN 0951-5151) **3763**
British Society for the History of Science Newsletter *see* B S H S Newsletter **4300**
British Society of Commerce. Review *see* Business Administration **833**
British Society of Dental and Maxillofacial Radiology. Proceedings. (UK) **3229**
British Society of Dowsers. Journal. (UK ISSN 0007-179X) **3668**
British Society of Master Glass Painters Journal *see* Journal of Stained Glass **355**
British Society of Rheology. Bulletin. (UK ISSN 0045-3145) **3842**
British-Soviet Friendship. (UK ISSN 0007-1803) **3951**
British Speleological Association. Bulletin *see* Caves & Caving **1557**
†British Stamp Values. (UK) **5153**
British Standards Institution News *see* B S I News **3445**
British Standards Microfile. (UK) **1816**, **4594**
British Standards Year Book *see* B S I Catalogue **3445**
British Steel Corporation. Annual Report and Accounts *see* British Steel Plc. Annual Report and Accounts **3403**
British Steel Plc. Annual Report and Accounts. (UK) **3403**
British Sugar Beet Review. (UK ISSN 0007-1854) **171**

British Tax Guide. (US ISSN 0007-1862) **1088**
British Tax Review. (UK ISSN 0007-1870) **1088**
British Telecom Journal *see* British Telecom World **1361**
British Telecom Technology Journal. (UK ISSN 0265-0193) **1332**
British Telecom World. (UK ISSN 0953-8429) **1361**
British Telecommunications Engineering.(UK ISSN 0262-401X) **1361**, 1352
British Thermal Unit Handbook *see* B T U Handbook **3683**
British Thermal Unit Weekly *see* B T U Weekly **3683**
British Tourist Authority. Digest of Tourist Statistics. (UK ISSN 0068-2616) **4754**
British Toy & Hobby Association Buyers Guide *see* B T H A Buyers Guide **2280**
British Toys & Hobbies Briefing. (UK) **2281**, **2434**
British Trade Alphabet Studycards *see* B T A Studycards **28**
British Trust for Ornithology. Annual Report. (UK ISSN 0068-2675) **563**
British Trust for Ornithology News *see* B T O News **562**
British Universities' Guide to Graduate Study. (UK) **1692**
British Veterinary Journal. (UK ISSN 0007-1935) **4807**
British Virgin Islands. Statistics Office. Balance of Payments. (VB) **707**, **4565**
British Virgin Islands. Statistics Office. National Income and Expenditure. (VB) **707**, **4565**
British Virgin Islands Welcome Tourist Guide. (VB) **4755**
British Vogue. (UK) **1289**
British Waterways Board. Annual Report and Accounts. (UK ISSN 0068-2683) **4725**, **4755**
British Weekly and Christian Record *see* Church of England Newspaper **4234**
British West Indies Airways Sunjet *see* B W I A Sunjet **4671**
British West Indies Study Circle Study Circle Bulletin *see* B W I Study Circle Bulletin **3749**
British Women Pilots Association Gazette *see* B W P A Gazette **48**
British Year Book of International Law. (UK ISSN 0068-2691) **2720**
Britoil. Annual Report. (UK) **3683**
Brittany World. (US) **3709**
Brittonia. (US ISSN 0007-196X) **498**
Britts: Comparable Verdicts in Personal Injury Claims. (AT) **2606**
Brivais Vards. (AT) **1994**
Broadband Networking. (US) **1349**
▼Broadband Networking News. (US ISSN 1059-0544) **1446**
Broadcast. (UK ISSN 0040-2788) **1369**
Broadcast *see* Encore **1373**
Broadcast Banker - Broker. (US ISSN 0889-2644) **768**, **1355**, **1369**
Broadcast Banking *see* Broadcast Banker - Broker **768**
Broadcast Cable Financial Journal. (US) **1369**, 768
Broadcast Engineering. (US ISSN 0007-1994) **1369**
Broadcast Engineering (Spanish Language Edition). (US) **1369**, 1355
Broadcast Engineering Equipment Reference Manual. (US) **1369**, 1355
Broadcast Engineering News. (AT) **1369**
†Broadcast Engineering Notes. (UK ISSN 0141-9471) **5153**
Broadcast Engineering Spec Book *see* Broadcast Engineering Equipment Reference Manual **1369**
Broadcast Equipment Exchange *see* Radio World **1359**
Broadcast Investor. (US ISSN 0146-0110) **940**, **1355**, **1369**
Broadcast Investor Charts. (US ISSN 0736-9069) **1369**, 940

BROADCAST MANAGEMENT

Broadcast Management - Engineering see B M - E **1369**
Broadcast Management Engineering Television Engineering see B M E's Television Engineering **5145**
Broadcast Management - Engineering The Source Issue see B M - E: The Source Issue **1122**
Broadcast Music Inc. Music World see B M I: Music World **3540**
Broadcast Production Guide. (UK) **1124**
Broadcast Stats. (US ISSN 0749-2936) **1346**, 940, 1355, 1369
Broadcast Systems Engineering see Broadcast Systems International **4460**
Broadcast Systems International. (UK) **4460**
Broadcast Technology. (CN ISSN 0709-9797) **1332**
Broadcast Week. (CN) **1332**
Broadcast Yearbook and Diary. (UK) **1369**
Broadcaster. (CE) **1332**
Broadcaster. (CN ISSN 0008-3038) **1369**, 1355
Broadcaster see Sower **1741**
Broadcasting see B & T **28**
Broadcasting (Washington). (US ISSN 0007-2028) **1369**, 1355
Broadcasting Abroad. (US) **1369**, 1355
Broadcasting & Cable Market Place (Year). (US) **1369**, 1355
Broadcasting and Television Year Book see B & T Year Book **28**
Broadcasting and the Law. (US ISSN 0161-5823) **1370**, 2606
Broadcasting - Cable Yearbook see Broadcasting & Cable Market Place (Year) **1369**
Broadcasting Law and Practice. (AT) **1370**, 2606
Broadcasting Press Digest. (UK ISSN 0954-2620) **1370**
Broadcasting Standards Council. Annual Review. (UK ISSN 0960-3999) **1332**
Broadcasting Yearbook see Broadcasting & Cable Market Place (Year) **1369**
Broadman Comments; International Sunday School Lessons. (US ISSN 0068-2721) **4166**
Broadsheet. (UK) **2062**
Broadsheet. (AT ISSN 0007-2036) **4367**, 3763
Broadsheet. (NZ ISSN 0110-8603) **4838**
Broadside (Bend). (US) **1305**
Broadside (Houston) see H A N O W Herald **4844**
Broadside (New York, 1940). (US ISSN 0068-2748) **4630**
Broadway, Bill of Fare see City Guide - Broadway Magazine **4757**
Brock Report. (US) **148**
†Broder New York Tort Reporter. (US) **5153**
Brodogradnja. (CI ISSN 0007-215X) **4725**
Broed. (SW) **2087**
Broed-Konditorn see Broed **2087**
Broken Spoke. (CN ISSN 0045-3226) **4685**, 4467
Broken Streets. (US) **2989**
Broken Strings see Strings and Squares **3582**
Broker. (UK) **2528**
The Broker. (US) **2528**
Broker-Dealers and Securities Markets. (US) **2606**, 4145
Broker Report Index. (AT) **941**
Broker World. (US ISSN 0273-6551) **2528**
Brokers' Monthly & Insurance Adviser. (UK ISSN 0260-2385) **2528**
Bromatologia i Chemia Toksykologiczna.(PL ISSN 0365-9445) **3719**
Bromberg. (GW ISSN 0171-1644) **2188**
Brome County Historical Society. Publication. (CN ISSN 0381-6206) **2400**
†Bromeliad Hobbyist. (US) **5153**
Bromeliad Society. Journal. (US ISSN 0090-8738) **498**

Bromeliads. (UK ISSN 0084-8107) **498**
Die Bromelie. (GW ISSN 0724-0155) **498**
Bromides in Agriculture. (IS ISSN 0007-2192) **80**, 1171
Bronca. (AG) **1250**
Bronchial Mucology Series. (US) **3364**
Brong's Business Success News. (US) **648**
Bronte Newsletter. (US) **2900**
Bronte Society Transactions. (UK ISSN 0309-7765) **2900**
Bronx Community College Evening Reporter see B C C Evening Reporter **1304**
Bronx County Historical Society. Journal.(US ISSN 0007-2249) **2400**
Bronx County Medical Society. Bulletin see Bronx Medicine **3084**
Bronx Medicine. (US) **3084**
Bronx Realtor News. (US) **4145**, 604
The Bronx Report. (US) **4055**
Bronze Swagman Book of Bush Verse. (AT ISSN 0310-2467) **2989**
Brook. see Xiao Xi Liu **1271**
Brookdale Hospital Medical Center News see Brookdale Hospital Medical Center News-Scope **2459**
Brookdale Hospital Medical Center News-Scope. (US) **2459**
Brookdale Institute. Annual Report see J D C - Brookdale Institute of Gerontology and Human Development in Israel. Annual Report **2274**
Brookdale Institute of Gerontology. Discussion Papers see J D C - Brookdale Institute of Gerontology and Human Development in Israel. Discussion Papers **2274**
Brookdale Institute of Gerontology. International Forum see J D C - Brookdale Institute of Gerontology and Human Development in Israel. International Forum **2274**
Brookdale Institute of Gerontology. Special Series see J D C - Brookdale Institute of Gerontology and Human Development in Israel. Special Series **2274**
Brookfield Bandarlog. (US ISSN 0068-2780) **579**
Brookfield Bison see Brookfield Zoo Bison **579**
Brookfield Zoo Bison. (US ISSN 8756-3479) **579**
Brookgreen Bulletin see Brookgreen Journal **2123**
Brookgreen Journal. (US ISSN 0884-8815) **2123**, 319
Brookhaven Highlights. (US ISSN 0092-1548) **1804**
Brookhaven Lecture Series. (US) **1804**
Brookhaven Symposia in Biology. (US ISSN 0068-2799) **433**
Brookings Dialogues in Public Policy see Dialogues in Public Policy **4058**
Brookings Pamphlet Series see Brookings Reprint Series **4367**
Brookings Papers on Economic Activity. (US ISSN 0007-2303) **889**
Brookings Papers on Economic Activity: Microeconomics. (US) **889**
Brookings Reprint Series. (US) **4367**
Brookings Review. (US ISSN 0745-1253) **648**
Brooklyn Academy of Music Magazine see B A Magazine **3540**
Brooklyn Arts and Culture Association, Inc. Calendar of Cultural Events see B A C A Calendar of Cultural Events **3522**
Brooklyn Barrister. (US ISSN 0007-232X) **2606**
Brooklyn Business Journal. (US) **648**
†Brooklyn College Alumni Literary Review. (US ISSN 0732-9709) **5153**
Brooklyn Engineer. (US ISSN 0271-6437) **1816**
Brooklyn Heights Press. (US ISSN 0007-2346) **2222**
Brooklyn Home Journal. (US) **2444**, 2549
Brooklyn Insurance Brokers Association. Bulletin see Messenger Reporter **2538**

Brooklyn Journal of Arts & Urban Affairs. (US) **319**
Brooklyn Journal of International Law. (US ISSN 0740-4824) **2720**
Brooklyn Law Review. (US ISSN 0007-2362) **2606**
Brooklyn Literary Review see Brooklyn College Alumni Literary Review **5153**
Brooklyn Longshoreman see 1814 Union News **2592**
Brooklyn Public Library Bulletin. (US ISSN 0007-2397) **2749**
Brooklyn Public Library Service to Business and Industry - B P L see Service to Business and Industry - B P L **737**
Brooklyn Review. (US) **2989**
Brookmire Investment Reports. (US) **768**
Brooks Family Query Exchange. (US) **2146**
Brooks Memorial Art Gallery. Newsletter see Memphis Brooks Museum of Art. Newsletter **3527**
Brookside Columns. (US) **2400**
Broom and Broom Corn News see Broom, Brush & Mop **2557**
Broom, Brush & Mop. (US) **2557**
Broome County Historical Society Newsletter. (US) **2401**
Broome County Public Library. Annual Report. (US) **2749**
Broomstick. (US ISSN 0883-9611) **4838**
Brorfelde Geomagnetic Observatory Magnetic Results (Year). (DK ISSN 0901-9413) **1587**
Brossapress-Nachrichtenblatt fuer die Buersten- und Pinselindustrie. (GW) **3653**
Brot- und Backwaren. (GW) **2087**
Broteria. (PO ISSN 0870-7618) **2504**
Broteria Genetica. (PO ISSN 0870-7235) **540**
Brotherhood. (US ISSN 0007-2435) **4222**
Brotherhood. see Bratstvo **4257**
Brotherhood of Maintenance of Way Employes Railway Journal see B M W E Railway Journal **2580**
Brots de Collcerola. (SP) **1296**
Brottning. (SW) **4467**
Broward Jewish World. (US) **1994**, 4222
Broward Review. (US) **648**, 2606
Brown Alumni Monthly. (US ISSN 0007-2478) **1305**
Brown Boveri Symposia. Proceedings. (US) **1883**
Brown Boveri Technik see A B B Review **1880**
Brown Chart see The Brown Chart. Provincial Results **2528**
The Brown Chart. Provincial Results. (CN ISSN 0585-3680) **2528**
Brown Family see Brown Family News & Geneological Society **2146**
Brown Family News & Geneological Society. (US) **2146**
Brown Gold. (US ISSN 0007-2494) **4166**
Brown Lines. (US) **320**
Brown Swiss Bulletin. (US ISSN 0007-2516) **198**
Brown Thrasher Books. (US) **2401**
Brown University. Program in Judaic Studies. Annual Report. (US) **1995**
Brown University Child and Adolescent Behavior Letter. (US ISSN 0885-7261) **4015**, 4400
Brown University Child Behavior and Development Letter see Brown University Child and Adolescent Behavior Letter **4015**
Brown University Digest of Addiction Theory & Application Data. (US ISSN 1040-6328) **1534**
Brown University Family Therapy Letter.(US) **1534**
Brown University Long-Term Care Letter. (US ISSN 1042-1386) **1534**
Brown University S T D Update see C D C - A I D S Weekly **3218**
Brownie. (UK ISSN 0007-2524) **1250**
Browning Deer Hunting. (US) **4542**

†Browning Institute Studies. (US ISSN 0092-4725) **5153**
Browning Newsletter. (US) **3434**, 941
Browning Society Notes. (UK) **2989**
Brown's Business Reporter. (US) **833**, 1113
Brown's Directory of North American and International Gas Companies. (US ISSN 0197-8098) **3683**
Browns Mills Review. (US) **2900**
Brown's Nautical Almanac. (UK ISSN 0068-290X) **4523**
Brownstone Chapbook Series see Brownstone Mystery Guides **2985**
Brownstone Mystery Guides. **2985**, 2900
Browse. (CN) **213**, 198
Broyles Family Newsletter. (US ISSN 1044-856X) **2146**
Bruce County Historical Society. Year Book. (CN ISSN 0084-8115) **2401**
Bruce Gould on Commodities. (US) **941**
Bruce Jenner's Better Health and Living see Better Health & Living **5148**
Bruce Trail News. (CN ISSN 0383-9249) **4542**
Brucellosis Surveillance; Annual Summary see U.S. Centers for Disease Control. Brucellosis Surveillance: Annual Summary **4114**
Brucka. (SA ISSN 0259-0115) **2216**, 1995
Brucker Szene. (GW ISSN 0937-9509) **2860**, 2188
Bruckmanns Pantheon. (GW ISSN 0720-0056) **320**
Brud Nevez. (FR ISSN 0399-7014) **2900**
Das Bruderhaus. (GW) **1734**, 2286, 2291
Bruderus Post. (GW) **1073**
Die Bruecke. (AU) **2860**, 320
Bruecke (Cologne) see Wir (Cologne) **2545**
†Bruecke (Neustadt). (GW ISSN 0007-2605) **5153**
Bruecke-Archiv. (GW ISSN 0572-7146) **320**
▼Brueckenschlag. (GW) **4166**
Der Bruederbote. (GW ISSN 0724-4533) **4280**
Bruehl. (GW ISSN 0007-2664) **2736**
Brug. (BE) **1619**
Brug. (NE ISSN 0007-2648) **2211**
Bruges Quarterly. see Cahiers de Bruges **5158**
Brugsch Handelsblad. (BE) **2174**
Brujula. (AG) **2528**
Brujula see Universidad de San Carlos. Facultad de Ingeneria. Escuela Regional de Ingenieria Sanitaria. Carta Periodica **4114**
Brukshunden. (SW) **3709**
Brulot. (FR ISSN 0007-2672) **3940**, 2900
Brunei Darussalam Newsletter. (BX) **1332**
Brunei Museum. Special Publication/ Muzium Brunei. Penerbitan Khas. (BX ISSN 0084-8131) **3522**
Brunei Museum Journal. (BX ISSN 0068-2918) **3522**
Brunnen Journal. (GW) **2901**
Brunnenbau, Bau von Wasserwerk, Rohrleitungsbau see B B R **4822**
Brunnenbau, Bau von Wasserwerk, Rohrleitungsbau see B B R **4822**
Brunonia see Australian Systematic Botany **495**
Brunswick Business Journal. (CN) **648**
Brunswick Monthly. (US) **3662**
Brunswick Week see Brunswick Monthly **3662**
Brunswickan. (CN ISSN 0007-2699) **1305**
Brush and Allied Trades Directory. (UK) **1124**, 641
Brushes International. (UK) **641**
Brushmaking International see Brushes International **641**
Brushstrokes. (US) **320**, 1250
Brushware. (US ISSN 0007-2710) **641**, 2557, 3653
Brussels. Chamber of Commerce Bulletin see Entreprendre **815**
Brussels Griffon Quarterly. (US) **3709**
Brussels Hilton Magazine. (NE) **2472**

BUILDING ECONOMIC 5999

Brussels Sprout. (US ISSN 0897-7356) **2989**
Brutus. (JA) **3396**
Bryan County Heritage Association Quarterly. (US) **2146**
†Bryan Newsletter. (US) **5153**
†Bryant Backtrails. (US ISSN 0146-1990) **5153**
Brydning/Wrestling. (Dansk Atlet Union) (DK ISSN 0903-5524) **4467**
Bryggan. (SW ISSN 0345-178X) **3980**, 2354
Bryn Mawr Alumnae Bulletin. (US) **1305**
Bryn Mawr-Haverford College News. (US) **1305**
Bryologische Beitraege. (GW ISSN 0723-2470) **498**
Bryologist. (US ISSN 0007-2745) **498**
Bryophytorum Bibliotheca. (GW) **498**
Bryozoa. (US ISSN 0108-0325) **579**
B'sdeh Habniya. (IS ISSN 0334-0430) **604**
Buana Minggu. (IO) **2202**
▼Bubble and Chewing Gum World. (US) **2087**
†Buccaneer. (CJ) **5153**
Das Buch der Jugend. (GW ISSN 0068-3043) **395**
Buch der Zeit. (GW ISSN 0007-2761) **4124**
Buch und Buchhandel in Zahlen. (GW ISSN 0068-3051) **4124**
Buchanan Banner. (US) **1995**
Buchhaendler Heute. (GW ISSN 0007-2796) **4124**
Buchhaltungsergebnisse Schweizerische Unternehmungen/Resultats Comptables des Entrepises Suisse. (SZ) **707**
Buchhandelsgeschichte. Zweite Folge. (GW ISSN 0170-5105) **4124**
Buchjournal. (GW ISSN 0178-7241) **2901**
Buchreport. (GW ISSN 0176-8220) **2901**
Buchwissenschaftliche Beitraege see Buchwissenschaftliche Beitraege aus dem Deutschen Bucharchiv Muenchen **4124**
Buchwissenschaftliche Beitraege aus dem Deutschen Bucharchiv Muenchen. (GW ISSN 0724-7001) **4124**
†BuchWoche. (GW) **5153**
Buck Rogers. (US) **1250**
Buckeye Business Journal see Columbus Business Journal **656**
Buckeye Farm News. (US ISSN 0007-2834) **80**
Buckeye Review. (US ISSN 0045-3285) **1995**, 2222
Buckeye Trucker. (US) **4743**
Buckhead Life. (US) **2472**
Buckley on the Companies Acts. (UK) **2606**
Buckmasters Whitetail. (US) **4542**
Bucknell Computer Service Newsletter see B C S Newsletter **1389**
Bucknell Engineer. (US) **1816**
Bucknell Review. (US ISSN 0007-2869) **4302**, 2504
Bucknell World. (US) **1305**
Bucks Advertiser. (UK ISSN 0144-784X) **2193**
Bucks County Genealogical Society. Newsletter. (US) **2146**, 2401
Bucks County Law Reporter. (US ISSN 0407-5501) **2606**
Bucks County Planning Commission. Planning Progress. (US) **2484**
Budapest. (HU ISSN 0007-2885) **2197**
Budapest Statisztikai Evkonyve. (HU ISSN 0521-4882) **4565**
Budapest Statisztikai Zsebkonyve. (HU ISSN 0438-2242) **4565**
Budapest Studies in Arabic. (HU) **2806**
Budapester Rundschau. (HU ISSN 0007-2893) **2197**
Budapesti Kozgazdasagtudomanyi Egyetem: Doktori Ertekezesek. (HU) **707**
Budapesti Kozgazdasagtudomanyi Egyetem Folyoirata. Aula. (HU) **648**
Budapesti Kozgazdasagtudomanyi Egyetem Oktatoinak Szakirodalmi Munkassaga. (HU) **707**, 395

Budapesti Oriental Reprints, Series A-2. (HU ISSN 0139-4614) **3635**
Budapesti Statisztikai Tajekoztato. (HU ISSN 0133-2449) **4565**
†Budavox Telecommunication Review. (HU ISSN 0007-2907) **5153**
Buddha World. (US) **4214**, 3763
Buddhism at the Crossroads. (CN ISSN 1181-8360) **4214**
Buddhist - Christian Studies. (US ISSN 0882-0945) **4214**, 4167
Buddhist Publication Society Newsletter.(CE) **4214**
Buddhist Research Information see Asian Religious Studies Information **5139**
Buddhist Studies. (II) **4214**
Buddhist Studies Review. (UK ISSN 0265-2897) **4214**
Buddhist Text Information. (US ISSN 0360-6112) **4212**, 4214
Buddhists For Peace see Dharmaduta **4214**
Buddy. (US) **3543**
Buddy's Weekly Reader see Weekly Reader, Edition 1 **1270**
Budgerigar Bulletin. (UK ISSN 0045-3323) **563**, 3709
Budgerigar World. (UK) **3709**, 579
Budget and Droits. (BE) **1502**
Budget and the Region. (US ISSN 0896-3584) **4055**, 3876
Budget Hebdo. (BE ISSN 0773-0748) **1502**
Budget in Brief - Department of Transportation (Washington) see U.S. Department of Transportation. Fiscal Year Budget in Brief **4660**
Budget of the Government of Liberia. (LB) **4055**
Budget of the Government of Pakistan. Demands for Grants and Appropriations. (PK) **1088**
Budget Representations to the Chancellor. (UK ISSN 0268-2265) **1088**
Budget Wise Home Plans. (US) **2549**
Budgets des Menages. see Haushaltsrechnungen **719**
Budkavlen. (FI ISSN 0302-2447) **2354**
Budo Echo see Judo **4477**
Budo Koerier. (NE) **4467**
Budo und Transkulturelle Bewegungsforschung. (GW ISSN 0723-9297) **4467**
Budoka y Su Revista de las Artes Marciales. (SP) **4467**
Budowa Geologiczna Polski. (PL) **1556**, 3656
Budownictwo i Gospodarka Miejska. Biuletyn Informacyjny. (PL ISSN 0867-4485) **604**
Budownictwo Okretowe. (PL ISSN 0007-2990) **4725**
†Budownictwo Weglowe. Projekty - Problemy. (PL ISSN 0239-9679) **5153**
Budstikken. (US) **2053**
Buecher (Year). (AU) **4140**
Buecher fuer das Studium - Geisteswissenschaften. (GW) **1675**
Buecher fuer das Studium - Medizin. (GW) **3167**, 1675
Buecher fuer das Studium - Naturwissenschaften. (GW) **4355**, 1675
Buecher fuer Sie see Buecher (Year) **4140**
Buecherei des Augenarztes. (GW ISSN 0068-3361) **3298**
Buecherei des Frauenarztes. (GW ISSN 0068-337X) **3290**
Buecherei des Orthopaeden. (GW ISSN 0068-3388) **3307**
Buecherei des Paediaters. (GW ISSN 0373-3165) **3319**
Buechereidienst see Bibliotheksdienst **2748**
Buechergilde. (GW ISSN 0007-3032) **4124**
Buecherkarren. (GW) **2860**
Buecherpick. (SZ) **4124**
Buecherschau. (AU ISSN 0007-3040) **2750**, 4124
Der Buechsenmacher. (GW ISSN 0007-3067) **2434**, 3453
Der Buechsenmacher und Messer und Schere. (GW) **641**

Buehne. (AU ISSN 0007-3075) **4630**, 3543
Die Buehnengenossenschaft. (GW ISSN 0007-3083) **4630**
Buehnenkunst. (GW ISSN 0933-1263) **4630**, 1529
Buehnentechnische Rundschau. (SZ ISSN 0007-3091) **4630**
Buena Salud. (PR) **3800**, 1995
Buena Vista Today. (US) **1305**
Buenhogar. (US) **2444**
Buenos Aires. Camara de Comercio. Informativo Mensual. (AG) **809**
†Buenos Aires. Centro de Investigacion de Biologia Marina. Contribucion Cientificia. (AG ISSN 0068-340X) **5153**
†Buenos Aires. Instituto de Fitotecnia. Boletin Informativo. (AG ISSN 0068-3418) **5154**
Buenos Aires (Province). Archivo Historico. Publicaciones. Sexta Serie. (AG ISSN 0524-9864) **2401**
Der Buerger im Staat. (GW ISSN 0007-3121) **3876**
Buergerblatt der Gemeinde Rohrdorf. (GW) **4085**
Buergerrechte & Polizei. (GW ISSN 0932-5409) **1511**, 2712, 3876, 3940
Das Buero. (GW) **2291**, 1734
Buero Revue see Computer Produkte Software **1058**
Buero, Technik, Systeme see B T S **1057**
Buero und Computer Report. (AU) **825**
Buero und Informations Technik see B I T **1057**
†Buero und Verkauf. (SZ) **5154**
Buero-Wirtschaft see Bueromarkt **1057**
Bueromarkt. (GW ISSN 0007-3148) **1057**
Bueromaschinen-Lexicon see Buerotechnik im Test **1057**
Der Bueropraktiker. (GW ISSN 0863-4912) **1619**
Bueroreport see Buero und Computer Report **825**
Buerotechnik see Sysdata **1401**
Buerotechnik Automation und Organisation see Office Management **828**
Buerotechnik im Test. (GW) **1057**, 825
Buerotechnische Sammlung see B T S - Buero Technik Systeme **1057**
Buffalo. (CN ISSN 0045-334X) **1233**, 1296
Buffalo and Erie County Public Library Bulletin. (US ISSN 0020-966X) **2750**
Buffalo Area Chamber of Commerce Directory-Metropolitan Buffalo see Greater Buffalo Business Directory **1137**
Buffalo Business Journal. (US) **648**
Buffalo Journal. (TH ISSN 0857-1554) **80**
Buffalo Law Review. (US ISSN 0023-9356) **2606**
Buffalo Magazine see Western New York Magazine **824**
Buffalo Society of Natural Sciences. Bulletin. (US ISSN 0096-4131) **4302**, 433, 1541
Buffalo Society of Natural Sciences. Occasional Papers. (US) **4302**
Buffalo Spree. (US ISSN 0300-7499) **2222**
Buffalo State Record. (US) **1305**
Bug Report. (US) **1467**, 1458
Bug Tar. (US) **2860**
Bugeye Times. (US ISSN 0882-651X) **3522**
Bugle (Missoula). (US ISSN 0889-6445) **4542**, 1484
▼Buhardilla. (PY ISSN 1017-2777) **3593**
†Buhiti. (PR ISSN 0045-3374) **5154**
Buhuth. (SJ) **4367**
Buick Bugle. (US) **256**
Build. (IE ISSN 0790-8830) **604**
Build. (AT) **604**
▼Build It! (US) **605**
Build Kenya see Architecture **600**
†Build Your Dream Home Designs. (US) **5154**
Buildcore Index. (CN ISSN 0227-0595) **605**, 296, 641

Buildcore Product Review. (CN ISSN 1182-3798) **605**, 296
Builder see Building **296**
Builder see Builder & Remodeler **605**
Builder see LifeLine (Kingston) **2537**
Builder (Columbus). (US ISSN 0007-3261) **2528**
Builder (Scottdale). (US ISSN 0745-1687) **4280**
Builder (Washington). (US ISSN 0744-1193) **605**
Builder and Contractor see A B C Today **598**
Builder & Remodeler. (US) **605**
Builder Architect. (US) **605**
Builder Architect-Contractor Engineer see Builder Architect **605**
Builder-Dealer. (US ISSN 0279-6368) **605**
Builder-Dealer Magazine. (UA) **605**
Builder Insider. (US) **296**, 605
Builder N.S.W. see Australian Building Construction and Housing **601**
Builder Profile. (US) **605**
Builders and Timber Merchant see Builders Merchants Journal **605**
Builders Association News. (US) **605**
Builders' Association of India. Bulletin see Indian Construction **620**
▼Builder's Best Home Designs. (US) **605**, 2549
Builder's Calendar. see Rakentajain Kalenteri **629**
Builders' Computer Newsletter. (US) **605**, 825, 1458
Builders Databank. (PH) **605**
Builders' Merchant News. (UK) **605**
†Builders' Merchants Information Selector. (UK) **5154**
Builders Merchants Journal. (UK) **605**
Builders Merchants Review. (UK) **605**
Builders of Indian Anthropology. (II) **4367**, 417
Builder's Quarterly. (US) **605**
Builders Trade Journal. (US ISSN 1053-2293) **639**, 605
Building. (UK ISSN 0007-3318) **296**, 605
Building. (SA ISSN 0258-2228) **296**, 605
Building. see Batiment **602**
Building and Architectural Science. see Epites- Epiteszettudomany **617**
▼Building and Construction Contracts in Australia. (AT) **605**, 2606
Building and Construction Law. (AT ISSN 0815-6050) **605**, 2606
Building & Construction Market Forecast. (US) **605**, 941
Building & Construction News. (SI ISSN 0217-5541) **605**, 296
▼Building & Construction Trades Today. (CN) **605**
Building and Environment. (US ISSN 0360-1323) **605**
Building and Estate Management Society. Proceedings. (SI) **4146**
Building and Technic. (SW ISSN 0281-658X) **605**, 296
Building and Wood. (SZ) **2580**, 605
▼Building Blocks in Total Compensation. (US) **1063**
Building Business and Apartment Management Bildor. (US) **605**
Building Business & Management. (US) **605**
Building Centre of Israel Bulletin/Babiniya. (IS) **605**
Building Concerns. (US) **606**, 1995
Building, Construction and Real Estate Sectors. Survey. (HK) **637**, 4160
Building Construction Cost Data (Year). (US ISSN 0068-3531) **606**
Building Construction Materials & Equipment. (AT ISSN 1031-3745) **606**
Building Construction News. (US ISSN 0192-7907) **606**
Building Contracts & Practice. (UK) **2606**, 606
Building Cost Index. see Finland. Tilastokeskus. Indeksitiedotus RK. Rakennuskustannusindeksi **637**
Building Design. (UK ISSN 0007-3423) **296**, 606
Building Design & Construction. (US ISSN 0007-3407) **606**
Building Economic Alternatives see Co-op America Quarterly **852**

6000 BUILDING ECONOMIST

Building Economist. (AT ISSN 0007-3431) **606**
Building Equipment & Materials. (SA) **606**
Building Equipment and Materials for South Africa see Building Equipment & Materials **606**
Building Fire and Security Design. (UK) **3615, 1526**
Building, Hardware and Housewares (Year). (SA ISSN 1018-838X) **606, 641, 1124**
Building History. (US) **606**
Building Homes & Renovation. (CN) **606**
Building Ideas see Better Homes and Gardens Building Ideas **295**
Building in Australia (Year). (AT) **606, 648**
Building Industries Federation. Annual Report. (SA ISSN 0378-9020) **606**
Building Industry Digest see B I D Service Weekly **601**
Building Industry Digest of Hawaii. (US) **606**
Building Industry Management. see Shigong Qiye Guanli **1027**
Building Industry Prospects. (AT) **606, 648**
Building Inspectors' Association of Nova Scotia. Reporter. (CN) **606**
Building Journal China see Building Journal Hong Kong China **606**
Building Journal Hong Kong China. (HK) **606**
Building Law Monthly. (UK) **2606, 606**
Building Law Reports. (UK ISSN 0141-5875) **2606, 606**
Building Maintenance and Modernization see Building Operating Management **606**
Building Maintenance Information Building Maintenance Price Book see B M I Building Maintenance Price Book **601**
Building Market Report. (UK ISSN 0267-2561) **606, 1034**
Building Material Producers Forecasts see B M P Forecasts **601**
Building Material Producers Information see B M P Information **601**
Building Material Producers Monthly Statistical Bulletin see B M P Monthly Statistical Bulletin **601**
Building Materials. see Stavivo **633**
Building News see Australian Building News **601**
Building News. (NZ) **606**
Building News. see Byggnadstidningen **608**
Building Official and Code Administrator.(US ISSN 0007-3547) **4085, 606**
Building Officials and Code Administrators International National Building Code see B O C A National Building Code **601**
Building Officials and Code Administrators International National Fire Prevention Code see B O C A National Fire Prevention Code **2031**
Building Officials and Code Administrators International National Mechanical Code see B O C A National Mechanical Code **601**
Building Officials and Code Administrators International National Plumbing Code see B O C A National Plumbing Code **2297**
Building Officials and Code Administrators International National Property Maintenance Code see B O C A National Property Maintenance Code **601**
Building Oklahoma. (US) **606**
Building Operating Management. (US ISSN 0007-3490) **606**
Building Owner and Property Manager. (CN) **4146, 606, 2484**
Building Owners and Managers Association International Experience Exchange Report see B O M A Experience Exchange Report **4145**
Building Owners and Managers Association International International Convention Directory see B O M A International Convention Directory **3391**
Building Owners & Managers Association of Australia Ltd. News see B O M A News **4145**
Building Permit Activity in Florida. (US ISSN 0007-3555) **606, 4055**
Building Permit Values. (US ISSN 0007-3563) **637**
Building Planned List. (US) **606**
Building, Planning and Development Service (New South Wales) see Planning and Development Service (New South Wales) **2666**
Building Products. (UK ISSN 0261-8761) **606**
▼Building Products. (US) **606**
Building Products Digest. (US ISSN 0742-5694) **606, 2113**
Building Products File. (US) **1124, 606**
†Building Products Index (Sydney). (AT) **5154**
Building Products News. (SA) **606, 296**
Building Products News (Chippendale). (AT ISSN 0007-358X) **606**
†Building Products Report. (US) **5154**
†Building Products Selector. (SA) **5154**
Building Refurbishment. (UK) **607**
Building Refurbishment and Maintenance see Building Refurbishment **607**
†Building Renovation. (CN ISSN 0826-595X) **5154**
Building Research and Information. (UK ISSN 0961-3218) **607**
†Building Research News. (CN ISSN 0007-361X) **5154**
Building Review. see Przeglad Budowlany **629**
Building Science. see Jianzhu Kexue **1868**
Building Sciences. (US) **607**
Building Service. (AT) **607, 1944, 2606**
Building Services. (UK) **2297, 607**
Building Services & Environmental Engineer. (UK) **1816**
Building Services Contractor. (US ISSN 0007-3644) **607**
Building Services Engineer see Building Services **2297**
Building Services Engineering Research & Technology. (UK ISSN 0143-6244) **607, 4594**
Building Services Journal see Building Services **2297**
Building Services Research and Information Association Application Guides see B S R I A Application Guides **2297**
Building Services Research and Information Association Statistics Bulletin see B S R I A Statistics Bulletin **2304**
Building Services Research and Information Association Technical Notes see B S R I A Technical Notes **2297**
Building Societies. Year Book. (UK ISSN 0068-3566) **768**
Building Societies Association. Annual Report see B S A Annual Report **601**
Building Societies Association. Monthly Figures Press Release. (UK ISSN 0261-6416) **4146, 607, 707, 768**
Building Societies Association Annual Report see B S A Annual Report **601**
Building Societies Association of Jamaica Factbook. (JM) **607**
Building Societies' Gazette see Mortgage Finance Gazette **791**
Building Societies Institute. Journal see Chartered Building Societies Institute. Journal **771**
Building Society Fact Book (Year) see Housing Finance Fact Book (Year) **4150**
Building Standards. (US ISSN 0270-1197) **607**

Building Standards Newsletter. (US) **607**
Building Stone Magazine. (US) **607**
Building Stone News see Building Stone Magazine **607**
Building Supply Dealers Association of British Columbia. Buyer's Guide and Product Source Directory. (CN) **607, 1124**
Building Supply Dealers Association of British Columbia News see B.S.D.A. News **601**
Building Supply Home Centers. (US) **607**
Building Supply Home Centers Directory Products and Services. (US) **607**
Building Technology and Management see Chartered Builder **610**
Building Technology - Land Management & Safety see B T - L M & S **601**
Building Today. (UK ISSN 0954-0652) **607, 296**
Building Trades Employers' Association of the City of New York. News and Opinion see Building Trades Employers' Association of the City of New York. Update **607**
Building Trades Employers' Association of the City of New York. Update. (US) **607**
Building Trades Journal see Building Today **607**
Building Tradesman. (US ISSN 0007-3717) **2581, 607**
BuildingBlocks. (US) **1995**
Buildings. (US ISSN 0007-3725) **607, 1004**
Buildings Energy Conservation see Buildings Energy Technology **607**
Buildings Energy Technology. (US) **607, 1484, 1784**
†Buildings for Health and Welfare Services. (SA) **5154**
Buisness Examiner - Mid-North Island Edition. (CN) **648**
The Business Link. (US) **902, 809**
Buitenlandse Handel van de B.L.E.U. met de Industrielanden (Niet E.E.G.- en E.V.A.- Lidstaten). see Commerce Exterieur de l'U.E.B.L. avec les Pays Industrialises (Autre Que les Pays de la C.E.E. et l'A.E.L.E.) **5168**
Buitenlandse Handel van de B.L.E.U. Met de Landen van Azie. see Commerce Exterieur de l'U.E.B.L. Avec les Pays d'Asie **5167**
Buitenlandse Handel van de B.L.E.U. Met de Landen van Latijns Amerika. see Commerce Exterieur de l'U.E.B.L. Avec les Pays d'Amerique Latine **5167**
Buitenlandse Handel van de B.L.E.U. Met de Oostlanden. see Commerce Exterieur de l'U.E.B.L. Avec les Pays de l'Est **5167**
Buitenspoor. (NE ISSN 0007-3768) **4542, 4755**
Buitlandse Handel van de B.L.E.U. Met de E.E.G.-Lidstaten. see Commerce Exterieur de l'U.E.B.L. Avec les Pays de la C.E.E **5168**
Bujqesia Socialiste. (AA) **80**
Bukhgalterskii Uchet. (RU ISSN 0007-3776) **748**
Bukkyo Geijutsu. see Ars Buddhica **313**
Buko Kampagne Stoppt den Ruestungsexport. Rundbrief. (GW) **3876**
Buku Saku Statistik Indonesia. see Statistical Pocketbook of Indonesia **4588**
Bulawayo This Month. (RH) **4755, 3504**
Buletin de Informare in Bibliologie see A B S I - Abstracte in Bibliologie si Stiinta Informarii **2792**
Buletin de Informare Pedagogica see Probleme de Pedagogie Contemporana **1656**
Buletin Oficial de Proprietate Industrial/ Official Bulletin for Industrial Property. (RM ISSN 1220-6105) **3673**
Buletini i Shkencave Bujqesore/Bulletin des Sciences Agricoles. (AA) **80**
Buletini i Shkencave Gjeologjike. (AA ISSN 0254-5276) **1556, 3479**

Buletini i Shkencave Mjekesore/Bulletin des Sciences Medicales. (AA) **3084**
Buletini i Shkencave Natyres/Bulletin des Sciences Naturelles. (AA) **1541**
Buletini i Shkencave Teknike/Bulletin des Sciences Techniques. (AA) **4302**
Buletini Katolik Shqiptar. see Albanian Catholic Bulletin **4162**
Buletinul de Informare pentru Inventii si Marci - Bulletin for Inventions and Trademarks see Buletin Oficial de Proprietate Industrial **3673**
Bulgaria - Economic Development (Year). (BU) **648**
†Bulgaria in Figures. (BU) **5154**
Bulgaria in Foreign Literature. see Bulgaria v Chuzhdata Literatura **395**
Bulgaria Today. (BU ISSN 0007-3903) **2175**
Bulgaria v Chuzhdata Literatura/ Bulgaria in Foreign Literature. (BU ISSN 0323-9969) **395**
Bulgarian Academic Books. (BU) **395**
Bulgarian Federation of Agricultural Workers' Independent Unions. Bulletin. (BU) **2581, 2062**
Bulgarian Films. (BU ISSN 0007-3911) **3504**
Bulgarian Foreign Trade. (BU ISSN 0204-8892) **809**
Bulgarian Historical Review/Revue Bulgare d'Histoire. (BU ISSN 0204-8906) **2354**
Bulgarian Journal of Physics/Bolgarskii Fizicheskii Zhurnal. (BU ISSN 0323-9217) **3815**
Bulgarian Journalist. see Bulgarski Zhurnalist **2567**
Bulgarian Periodicals. see Bulgarski Periodichen Pechat **395**
Bulgarian Review. (BL ISSN 0007-3946) **2354**
Bulgarian Trade Unions. (BU ISSN 0007-3954) **2581**
Bulgaro-Suvetska Druzhba. (BU ISSN 0204-8213) **3876**
Bulgarska Akademiia na Naukite. Arkheologicheski Institut Izvestiia. (BU ISSN 0068-3620) **267**
Bulgarska Akademiia na Naukite. Geologicheski Institut. Izvestiia see Inzenerna Geologiia i Khidrogeologiia **1546**
Bulgarska Akademiia na Naukite. Geologicheski Institut. Izvestiia see Paleontologiia, Stratigrafiia i Litologiia **3660**
Bulgarska Akademiia na Naukite. Institut po Khidrologiia i Meteorologiia. Izvestiia see Hydrology and Meteorology **3436**
Bulgarska Akademiia na Naukite. Institut po Vodni Problemi. Izvestiia see Vodni Problemi **4830**
Bulgarska Akademiia na Naukite. Institut za Bulgarski Ezik. Izvestiia. (BU ISSN 0068-3787) **2806**
Bulgarska Akademiia na Naukite. Institut za Istoriia. Izvestiia. (BU ISSN 0323-9985) **2354**
Bulgarska Akademiia na Naukite. Spisanie. (BU ISSN 0007-3989) **4303**
Bulgarska Akademiia na Naukite, Sofia. Zoologicheski Institut S Muzei. Izvestiia see Acta Zoologica Bulgarica **576**
Bulgarska Akademiia na Naukite, Sofia, Institut po Fiziologiia. Izvestiia see Acta Physiologica et Pharmacologica Bulgarica **568**
Bulgarska Etnografiia. (BU ISSN 0323-9268) **236**
Bulgarska Musika. (BU) **3543**
Bulgarski Disertacii. (BU ISSN 0323-9411) **395**
Bulgarski Ezik. (BU ISSN 0005-4283) **2807**
Bulgarski Folklor. (BU ISSN 0323-9861) **2053**
Bulgarski Gramofonni Plochi. (BU ISSN 0323-9365) **3588**
Bulgarski Knigopis see Bulgarski Knigopis. Seriia 1: Knigi, Notni, Graficheski i Kartografski **4140**
Bulgarski Knigopis. Seriia 1: Knigi, Notni, Graficheski i Kartografski. (BU) **4140**

Bulgarski Knigopis. Seriia 2: Sluzhebni Izdaniia i Disertatsii. (BU ISSN 0323-9667) **395**
Bulgarski Periodichen Pechat/Bulgarian Periodicals. (BU ISSN 0323-9764) **395**
Bulgarski Tiutiun. (BU ISSN 0521-6680) **4643**
Bulgarski Voenen Knigopis. (BU) **3453**
Bulgarski Voin see Signal A **3471**
Bulgarski Zhurnalist/Bulgarian Journalist. (BU ISSN 0323-956X) **2567**, 1332, 2354
Bulgarsko Foto. (BU ISSN 0007-4012) **3789**
Bulgarsko Geologichesko Druzhestvo. Spisanie. (BU ISSN 0007-3938) **1556**
Bulimia Anorexia Self-Help Magazine see B A S H Magazine **3331**
Bulk Carrier Register. (UK ISSN 0305-0122) **3683**, 4725
Bulk Grain. (AT ISSN 1032-5824) **205**
†Bulk Handling & Transport. (UK) **5154**
Bulk Handling: Storage, Movement, Control. (UK) **1927**
Bulk Solids Handling. (GW ISSN 0173-9980) **1848**, 1927
Bulk: Storage, Movement, Control see Bulk Handling: Storage, Movement, Control **1927**
Bulk Systems International see CoalTrans **4726**
Bulk Wheat see Bulk Grain **205**
Bull & Bear Financial Newspaper. (US ISSN 0319-1362) **941**
Bull Sheet. (US) **3709**
Bulldog Reporter. (US) **29**
Bulldog Weekly. (US) **1305**, 1619, 2567
Bulldogger. (US) **3709**
Bulldok Bauschaeden. (GW ISSN 0177-8285) **309**
Bullet. (Il ISSN 0045-348X) **2581**
Bullet (Fredericksburg). (US) **1305**
The Bullet (Nashville). (US) **1370**, 3504
The Bulletin (Austin). (US ISSN 0895-0326) **1458**, 825, 1453, 1475
Bulletin A B Q. see Q L A Bulletin **2780**
Bulletin A I O S P-I A E V G-I V S B B see Educational and Vocational Guidance - Bulletin A I O S P, I A E V G, I V S B B **3626**
Bulletin A R F see Bulletin L A R F **769**
Bulletin Agricole du Rwanda/Rwanda Agricultural Bulletin. (RW) **80**
Bulletin Analytique de Documentation Politique, Economique et Sociale Contemporaine. (FR ISSN 0007-4071) **3876**, 648, 4367
Bulletin Analytique de la Litterature Scientifique et Technique Roumaine. (RM) **4355**, 4614
Bulletin Analytique de Lexicologie see Bulletin Analytique de Linguistique Francaise **2807**
Bulletin Analytique de Linguistique Francaise. (FR ISSN 0007-408X) **2807**
Bulletin Analytique sur le Developpement. see Development Information Abstracts **713**
Bulletin Annote des Lois et Decrets. (FR ISSN 0007-411X) **2606**
Bulletin Annuel d'Information et de Liaison entre C.L.P.L.M. see Jericho **4130**
Bulletin Annuel de Statistiques de Gaz pour l'Europe. see Annual Bulletin of Gas Statistics for Europe **3704**
Bulletin Annuel des Transports et Parc Auto. (CF) **4647**
Bulletin Antieke Beschaving. (NE ISSN 0165-9367) **2307**
Bulletin Archeologique Polonais. see Wiadomosci Archeologiczne **289**
Bulletin Argus see Corpo Clip **2753**
Bulletin Baudelairien. (US ISSN 0007-4128) **2901**
Bulletin Benelux. see Benelux Publikatieblad **4054**
†Bulletin Bibliographique. (FR) **5154**
†Bulletin Bibliographique des Laboratoires Professionnels Francais et Belge. (BE) **5154**

†Bulletin Bibliographique International du Machinisme Agricole/International Farm Machinery Abstracts. (FR ISSN 0007-4160) **5154**
Bulletin Bibliographique Speleologique. see Speleological Abstracts **1552**
Bulletin Bibliographique Thematique. (FR ISSN 0076-0137) **395**
Bulletin Board see International Frozen Food Association. Bulletin Board **5217**
Bulletin Board Systems see Computers in Libraries **1459**
Bulletin C I L A. (SZ ISSN 0251-7256) **2807**
Bulletin C I S see Securite et Sante au Travail **3623**
Bulletin - California Museum of Photography see C M P Bulletin **5157**
Bulletin Canadien d'Histoire de la Medecine. see Canadian Bulletin of Medical History **3085**
Bulletin Canadien de Mathematiques. see Canadian Mathematical Bulletin **3031**
Bulletin Celinien. (BE ISSN 0252-1121) **2901**
Bulletin Colfra. (FR) **3750**
Bulletin Comptable & Financier. (FR ISSN 0220-2352) **748**
Bulletin - Connecticut River Valley Covered Bridge Society see Connecticut River Valley Covered Bridge Society. Bulletin **5171**
Bulletin Critique des Annales Islamologiques. (UA ISSN 0259-7373) **4218**, 3635
Bulletin Critique du Livre Francais. (FR ISSN 0007-4209) **4144**
Bulletin d'Analyses de la Litterature Scientifique Bulgare. Linguistique et Litterature see Abstracts of Bulgarian Scientific Literature. Linguistics and Literature **2854**
Bulletin d'Arabe Chretien. Bibliographie des Auteurs Arabes Chretiens. (BE) **2328**, 395, 3646
Bulletin d'Archeologie Marocaine. (MR ISSN 0068-4015) **267**
Bulletin d'Archeologie Sud-Est Europeenne. (RM) **267**
Bulletin d'Asie. see Asian Bulletin **2336**
Bulletin d'Etudes Politiques see Etudes Politiques **3893**
Bulletin d'Histoire de la Revolution Francaise. (FR ISSN 0766-4516) **2354**
▼Bulletin d'Information Archeologique. (UA) **267**
Bulletin d'Information de la Region Parisienne see Informations d'Ile de France **5213**
†Bulletin d'Information des Riziculteurs de France. (FR) **5154**
Bulletin d'Information Protestant. (FR) **4232**
Bulletin d'Information Statistique pour l'Afrique. see Statistical Information Bulletin for Africa **739**
Bulletin d'Information sur l'Entretien et l'Amenagement des Espaces Verts see Espaces Verts **2125**
Bulletin d'Information Yougoslave see Yugoslav Information Bulletin **3935**
Bulletin d'Informations Proustiennes. (FR ISSN 0338-0548) **2901**
Bulletin de Correspondance Hellenique. (FR ISSN 0007-4217) **1275**, 267
Bulletin de Documentation Pratique de Securite Sociale et de Legislation du Travail see Bulletin Social **974**
Bulletin de Droit Nucleaire see Droit Nucleaire **1804**
†Bulletin de Droit Tchecoslovaque. (CS) **5154**
Bulletin de l'A.I.S.M. see A I S M. Bulletin **4723**
Bulletin de l'Afrique Noire. (FR ISSN 0045-3501) **3876**, 926, 1995
Bulletin de l'Antiquaire et du Brocanteur.(FR) **256**
Bulletin de l'Hopital Sadiki see La Tunisie Medicale **3158**
Bulletin de l'Industrie Petroliere see B I P **3682**
Bulletin de l'Oeuvre Apostolique. (FR ISSN 0007-4330) **4167**

Bulletin de l'Oeuvre d'Orient. (FR ISSN 0007-4349) **3635**
Bulletin de l'U D T. see U D T Newsletter **2788**
Bulletin de l'U G I. see I G U Bulletin **2252**
Bulletin de la Murithienne. (SZ) **1541**, 498, 579
Bulletin de la Protection Civile de la Prefecture de Police see France. Service Interdepartemental de la Protection Civile. Bulletin **1273**
Bulletin de la Surete Nucleaire. (FR) **4098**
Bulletin de la Vulgarisation Forestiere see Foret - Entreprise **2100**
Bulletin de Liaison a l'Intention des Bibliothecaires, Archivistes et Documentalistes Africains see B L I B A D **2746**
Bulletin de Liaison de la Recherche en Informatique et en Automatique. (FR ISSN 0303-1276) **1412**
Bulletin de Litterature Ecclesiastique. (FR ISSN 0007-4322) **4257**
Bulletin de Mineralogie see European Journal of Mineralogy **3483**
Bulletin de Philosophie Medievale. (BE ISSN 0068-4023) **3763**
Bulletin de Theologie Ancienne et Medievale. (BE ISSN 0007-442X) **4167**
Bulletin Demographique des Nations Unies see Population Bulletin of the United Nations **3986**
Bulletin des Agriculteurs. (CN ISSN 0007-4446) **80**
Bulletin des Anysetiers. (FR) **1296**
Bulletin des Bibliotheques de France. (FR ISSN 0006-2006) **2750**
Bulletin des Droits de l'Homme see Human Rights Bulletin **3943**
Bulletin des Etudes Africaines de l'I N A L C O see Institut National des Langues et Civilisations Orientales. Bulletin des Etudes Africaines **2818**
Bulletin des Etudes Karaites. (BE ISSN 1148-6716) **4222**, 2428
Bulletin des Etudes Valeryennes. (FR ISSN 0335-508X) **2901**
Bulletin des Medecins Suisses. see Schweizerische Aerztezeitung **3151**
Bulletin des Recherches Agronomiques de Gembloux. (BE ISSN 0435-2033) **171**
Bulletin des Recherches Appliquees a la Protection de l'Homme au Travail see Bulletin on Applied Research for the Protection of Man at Work **5154**
Bulletin des Reglements Salariaux. see Wage Settlements Bulletin **997**
Bulletin des Sante et Production Animales en Afrique. see Bulletin of Animal Health and Production in Africa **213**
Bulletin des Sciences Agricoles. see Buletini i Shkencave Bujqesore **80**
Bulletin des Sciences Mathematiques. (FR ISSN 0007-4497) **3031**
Bulletin des Sciences Medicales. see Buletini i Shkencave Mjekesore **3084**
Bulletin des Sciences Naturelles. see Buletini i Shkencave Natyres **1541**
Bulletin des Sciences Techniques. see Buletini i Shkencave Teknike **4302**
Bulletin des Societes Chimiques Belges. (BE ISSN 0037-9646) **1171**
Bulletin des Stupefiants see Bulletin on Narcotics **1535**
Bulletin des Transports. (FR ISSN 0007-4519) **2606**, 4708
Bulletin des Transports Maritimes et Terrestres. (LE) **4647**
Bulletin du Bibliophile. (FR) **4124**
Bulletin du C I E T A see Centre International d'Etude des Textiles Anciens. Bulletin **4617**
Bulletin du Cancer. (FR ISSN 0007-4551) **3193**
▼Bulletin du Cancer - Radiotherapie. (FR ISSN 0924-4212) **3194**, 3357
†Bulletin du Cange. (NE) **5154**
Bulletin du F M I see I M F Survey **720**
Bulletin du Livre et Connaissance et Formation see Livres Hebdo **4141**

Bulletin du Musee Hongrois des Beaux-Arts. (HU ISSN 0133-5545) **320**, 267
Bulletin du Scoutisme Mondial. see World Scouting News **1246**
Bulletin Economique du Cambresis see Atout Cambresis **807**
Bulletin Economique et Fiscal du Burkina Faso. (UV) **809**
Bulletin Economique et Social du Maroc see Signes du Present **691**
Bulletin Ekonomi Indonesia. (IO ISSN 0216-0412) **833**, 4755
Bulletin Entomologique de Pologne. see Polskie Pismo Entomologiczne **537**
▼Bulletin Europeen du Moniteur. (FR) **607**
Bulletin Evangelique d'Information et de Presse. (GO) **4167**
†Bulletin Exterieur. (US ISSN 0163-7789) **5154**
Bulletin Faschismus - Zweite Weltkrieg. (GW) **2354**
Bulletin Fiduciaire. (BE) **768**, 2606
Bulletin Fiscal. (FR ISSN 0242-5912) **1088**
Bulletin for International Fiscal Documentation. (NE ISSN 0007-4624) **1089**
Bulletin for Psychologists see Psychological Test Bulletin **4041**
Bulletin Francais de la Peche et de la Pisciculture. (FR) **1484**
Bulletin Francais de Pisciculture see Bulletin Francais de la Peche et de la Pisciculture **1484**
Bulletin from Johnny Cake Hill. (US) **2401**, 4725
Bulletin G C I D. (Greek National Committee) (GR) **4822**, 1484
Bulletin - Genealogical Society of Old Tryon County see Genealogical Society of Old Tryon County. Bulletin **2152**
Bulletin Geodesique. (GW ISSN 0007-4632) **1587**
Bulletin Hebdomadaire see Weekly Bulletin **2198**
Bulletin Hispanique. (FR ISSN 0007-4640) **2354**, 2807, 2901
Bulletin Historique et Scientifique de l'Auvergne. (FR ISSN 0007-4659) **2354**, 4303
Bulletin I R P. (CN ISSN 0832-7475) **4015**
Bulletin Immobilier. (SZ ISSN 0007-4675) **4146**
Bulletin in Defense of Marxism. (US) **3876**
Bulletin International des Douanes. see International Customs Journal **1098**
Bulletin Jean Ray. (BE) **2901**
Bulletin Joly Mensuel d'Information des Societes. (FR) **902**
Bulletin Jugend und Literatur. (GW ISSN 0045-351X) **2750**, 1233, 4124
Bulletin KNOB see Koninklijke Nederlandse Oudheidkundige Bond. Bulletin **277**
Bulletin Koperasi see Edisi Chusus Bulletin Koperasi **863**
Bulletin L A R F. (CK) **769**, 648, 848
Bulletin Legislatif Belge. (BE) **2606**
Bulletin Linguistique et Ethnologique. (LU ISSN 0068-4066) **2807**
Bulletin Mathematique. (RM ISSN 0007-4691) **3031**
Bulletin Medical Franco-Japonais/Nichi-Futsu Igaku. (JA ISSN 0007-4705) **3084**
Bulletin Medicale de l'I P P F see I P P F Medical Bulletin **597**
Bulletin Mensuel d'Activite see South Pacific Commission. Monthly News of Activities **5280**
Bulletin Mensuel de la Normalisation Francaise see Enjeux **3446**
Bulletin Mensuel du Commerce Exterieur de l'Union Economique Belgo-Luxembourgeoise. (BE) **707**
Bulletin Monumental. (FR ISSN 0007-473X) **267**, 296, 320
Bulletin Motoristique. see Notiziario Motoristico **704**
Bulletin - National Science Foundation see N S F Bulletin **4325**

BULLETIN

Bulletin - New York State Archaeological Association (1987) see New York State Archaeological Association. Bulletin 280

Bulletin - News for the Human Science Researcher/Navorsingsnuus vir die Geesteswetenskaplike. (SA ISSN 1017-6136) 4367, 2504

Bulletin - Norges Geologiske Undersokelse see N G U Bulletin 1574

Bulletin O E P P see E P P O Bulletin 176

Bulletin of Abstracts: Measurement of Mechanical Quantities. see Referateorgan: Messen Mechanischer Groessen 1846

Bulletin of Abstracts: Welding and Allied Processes. see Referate: Schweissen und Verwandte Verfahren 3428

Bulletin of African Studies in Canada see Canadian Journal of African Studies 4368

Bulletin of Agri-Horticulture. (SI) 2123, 80

Bulletin of Agricultural Research in Botswana. (BS ISSN 0256-7512) 80

Bulletin of Agricultural Statistics of the Sudan see Sudan Yearbook of Agricultural Statistics 158

Bulletin of Agriculture Prices. (II) 81

Bulletin of Alloy Phase Diagrams see Journal of Phase Equilibria 3411

Bulletin of Animal Health and Production in Africa/Bulletin des Sante et Production Animales en Afrique. (KE ISSN 0378-9721) 213, 4807

Bulletin of Archaeology for Schools see Education Bulletin 271

Bulletin of Art Therapy see American Journal of Art Therapy 1733

Bulletin of Beef Cattle Science. (JA ISSN 0386-8419) 213

Bulletin of Biblical Studies. (GR) 4167

Bulletin of Bibliography. (US ISSN 0190-745X) 395, 2750

Bulletin of Bibliography and Magazine Notes see Bulletin of Bibliography 395

Bulletin of Biological Control. see Shengwu Fangzhi Tongbao 455

Bulletin of Biology see Biological Bulletin 431

Bulletin of Bird Ringing Activity. see Bollettino dell'Attivita di Inanellamento 562

Bulletin of Canadian Studies see British Journal of Canadian Studies 4430

†Bulletin of Chemical Thermodynamics (1977). (US ISSN 0149-2268) 5154

Bulletin of Chinese Language Teaching. see Yuwen Jiaoxue Tongxun 2853

Bulletin of Comparative Labour Relations. (NE) 974

Bulletin of Computer Aided Architectural Design see B O C A A D 5145

Bulletin of Concerned Asian Scholars. (US ISSN 0007-4810) 3952, 3635

Bulletin of Current Awareness Information on the Journal "Laboratory Technique". see Byulleten' Signal'noi Informatsii o Zhurnale "Laboratornoe Delo 5155

Bulletin of Czechoslovak Law. (CS ISSN 0323-2719) 2606

Bulletin of Dental Education. (US ISSN 0007-4837) 3229, 1745

Bulletin of Documentation. Agricultural-Plant Production. see Bilten Dokumentacije. Poljoprivreda. Biljna Proizvodnja 134

Bulletin of Documentation. Agricultural-Stockbreeding. see Bilten Dokumentacije. Poljoprivreda-Stocna Proizvodnja 134

Bulletin of Documentation. Civil Engineering - Superstructures and Final Work. see Bilten Dokumentacije. Gradjevinarstvo - Visokogradnja i Zavrsni Radovi u Gradjevinarstvu 1841

Bulletin of Documentation. Electrical Energy. see Bilten Dokumentacije. Elektroprivreda 1797

Bulletin of Documentation. Electrotechnics and Electronics. Manufacture of Electrical Machinery and Apparatus. Postal Services. see Bilten Dokumentacije. Elektrotehnika i Elektronika. Proizvodnja Elektricnih Masina i Aparata. Ptt Usluge 1883

Bulletin of Documentation. Environmental Protection and Waste Utilization. see Bilten Dokumentacije. Zastita Covekove Okoline i Iskoriscenje Otpadaka 1501

Bulletin of Documentation. Manufacture of Fabricated Metal Products. Manufacture of Miscellaneous Products. see Bilten Dokumentacije. Metalopreradjivacka Delatnost. Proizvodnja Raznovrsnih Proizvoda 1927

Bulletin of Documentation. Manufacture of Food Products. Manufacture of Beverages. see Bilten Dokumentacije. Proizvodnja Prehrambenih Proizvoda. Proizvodnja Pica 2084

Bulletin of Documentation. Manufacture of Non-Metalic Mineral Products-Manufacture of Construction Materials. see Bilten Dokumentacije. Prerada Nemetalnih Minerala-Proizvodnja Gradjevinskog Materijala 1167

Bulletin of Documentation. Metallurgy. see Bilten Dokumentacije. Metalurgija 3424

Bulletin of Documentation. Mining and Geology. see Bilten Dokumentacije. Rudarstvo i Geologija 3499

Bulletin of Documentation. Safety Precautions. see Bilten Dokumentacije. Zastita na Radu 4117

Bulletin of Documentation. Series D1. Chemistry and Chemical Industry. see Bilten Dokumentacije. Serija D1. Hemija i Hemijska Industrija 1191

Bulletin of Documentation. Series D6. Analytical Chemistry. see Bilten Dokumentacije. Serija D6. Analiticka Hemija 1191

Bulletin of Documentation. Series I1. Informatics. see Bilten Dokumentacije. Serija I1. Informatika 2748

Bulletin of Documentation. Series S1. Traffic. see Bilten Dokumentacije. Serija S1. Saobracaj 4662

Bulletin of Documentation. Town Planning and Architecture. see Bilten Dokumentacije. Urbanizam i Arhitektura 295

Bulletin of Earth Sciences. (II) 1541

Bulletin of Economic Research. (UK ISSN 0307-3378) 649

Bulletin of Electrochemistry. (II ISSN 0256-1654) 1212

Bulletin of Endemic Diseases. (IQ ISSN 0007-4845) 3218

Bulletin of Entomological Research. (UK ISSN 0007-4853) 529

Bulletin of Environmental Contamination and Toxicology. (US ISSN 0007-4861) 1980

Bulletin of Ethiopian Manuscripts. (ET) 4124

Bulletin of Experimental Archaeology. (UK) 267

Bulletin of Experimental Biology and Medicine. (English translation of: Byulleten Eksperimental'noi Biologii i Meditsiny) (US ISSN 0007-4888) 433, 3084

Bulletin of Forthcoming Anglo-Hellenic Events. (UK ISSN 0267-3517) 1995

Bulletin of Graduate Studies. Science and Engineering Research Edition. see Daigakuin Kenkyu Nenpo. 3: Rikogaku Kenkyuka Hen 1843

Bulletin of Grain Technology. (II ISSN 0007-4896) 81, 205

Bulletin of High Polymers. see Gaofenzi Tongxun 1226

Bulletin of Hispanic Studies. (UK ISSN 0007-490X) 2901, 2807

Bulletin of Historical Research in Musical Education. (US ISSN 0739-5639) 3543

Bulletin of Hungarian Scout Leaders and Parents. see Vezetok Lapja 1302

Bulletin of Indonesian Economic Studies.(AT ISSN 0007-4918) 848

Bulletin of Informatics and Cybernetics. (JA ISSN 0286-522X) 3031, 1440

Bulletin of Inventions and Summary of Patent Specifications. (UK ISSN 0261-023X) 3673

Bulletin of Iranian Studies see University of Teheran. Faculty of Letters and Humanities. Bulletin of Iranian Studies 2432

Bulletin of Iraq Publications Depository see Iraqi National Bibliography 403

†Bulletin of Islamic Studies. (UK ISSN 0267-2669) 5154

Bulletin of Judaeo-Greek Studies. (UK ISSN 0954-1179) 4222

Bulletin of Labour Statistics. (UN ISSN 0007-4950) 707

Bulletin of Latin American Research. (UK ISSN 0261-3050) 4367, 2401

Bulletin of Law, Science & Technology. (US ISSN 0362-3769) 2607, 4303, 4594

Bulletin of Legal Developments. (UK ISSN 0007-4969) 2607

Bulletin of Library Science. see Tushuguanxue Tongxun 2787

Bulletin of Marine Science. (US ISSN 0007-4977) 1602, 433

Bulletin of Materials Science. (II ISSN 0250-6327) 1916

Bulletin of Mathematical Biology. (US ISSN 0092-8240) 433, 3031

Bulletin of Mathematical Statistics see Bulletin of Informatics and Cybernetics 3031

Bulletin of Medico-Ethno-Botanical Research. (II) 3084, 498

Bulletin of Medieval Canon Law. New Series. (US ISSN 0146-2989) 2607, 2307

Bulletin of Microbiology. see Weishengwuxue Tongbao 558

Bulletin of Mines. see Rudarski Glasnik 3495

Bulletin of Molecular Biology and Medicine. (IT) 433

Bulletin of New Zealand Art History. (NZ ISSN 0110-4888) 320

Bulletin of Northern Ireland Law. (UK ISSN 0260-6550) 2607

Bulletin of Number Theory and Related Topics/Boletin de Teoria de Numeros y Temas Conexos. (AG) 3031

Bulletin of Peace Proposals. (UK ISSN 0007-5035) 3876

Bulletin of Physical Education. (UK ISSN 0007-5043) 1745

Bulletin of Polonia. see Biuletyn 1993

Bulletin of Pure & Applied Sciences. Section A: Zoology. (II ISSN 0970-0765) 580

Bulletin of Pure & Applied Sciences. Section B: Botany. (II ISSN 0970-4612) 498

Bulletin of Pure & Applied Sciences. Section C: Chemistry. (II ISSN 0970-4620) 1171

Bulletin of Pure & Applied Sciences. Section D: Physics. (II ISSN 0970-6569) 3815

Bulletin of Pure & Applied Sciences. Section E: Mathematics. (II ISSN 0970-6577) 3031

Bulletin of Pure & Applied Sciences. Section F: Geology. (II ISSN 0970-4639) 1556

†Bulletin of Research in Music Education. (US) 5154

†Bulletin of Research in the Humanities.(US ISSN 0160-0168) 5154

Bulletin of Research Management. see Kutatasszervezesi Tajekoztato 4322

Bulletin of Science Technology and Society. (US ISSN 0270-4676) 4303, 4367, 4594

Bulletin of Scientific and Technological Achievements. see Kexue Jishu Yanjiu Chengguo Gongbao 4320

Bulletin of Sugar Beet Research. Supplement/Tensai Kenkyu Hokoku Hokan. (JA ISSN 0068-4090) 171

Bulletin of Sung-Yuan Studies see Journal of Sung-Yuan Studies 3640

Bulletin of Teaching Material. see Jiaocai Tongxun 1709

Bulletin of the Academy of Sciences. see Kwahakwon Tongbo 4322

Bulletin of the American Academy of Psychiatry and the Law see American Academy of Psychiatry and the Law. Bulletin 3329

Bulletin of the American Dahlia Society, Inc. see American Dahlia Society. Bulletin 2121

Bulletin of the Astronomical Institutes of Czechoslovakia. (UK ISSN 0004-6248) 363, 49

Bulletin of the Atomic Scientists. (US ISSN 0096-3402) 3952

Bulletin of the Comediantes. (US ISSN 0007-5108) 2901

Bulletin of the Computational Statistics of Japan. see Keisanki Tokeigaku 4576

Bulletin of the Council for Research in Music Education see Council for Research in Music Education. Bulletin 3547

Bulletin of the European Communities. (EI ISSN 0007-5116) 848

Bulletin of the European Communities and Supplements. (EI ISSN 0068-4120) 848

Bulletin of the History of Dentistry. (US ISSN 0007-5132) 3229

Bulletin of the History of Medicine. (US ISSN 0007-5140) 3084

Bulletin of the Medical Society of the County of Queens and the Academy of Medicine of Queens. (US) 3084

Bulletin of the National Braille Association, Inc. see National Braille Association. Bulletin 2294

Bulletin of the National Museums of Sri Lanka. see Spolia Zeylanica 4345

Bulletin of the Pan American Health Organization see Pan American Health Organization. Bulletin 4109

Bulletin of the Seismological Laboratory (Reno) see University of Nevada. Seismological Laboratory. Bulletin 1596

Bulletin of the Southeastern Archaeological Conference see Southeastern Archaeology 286

Bulletin of the Veterinary Institute in Pulawy see Veterinary Institute, Pulawy. Bulletin 4818

Bulletin of the Yamaguchi Medical School see Yamaguchi University. School of Medicine. Bulletin 3163

Bulletin of Tibetology. (II ISSN 0007-5159) 2337, 236, 4430

Bulletin of Volcanic Eruptions. (JA ISSN 0525-1524) 1587

Bulletin of Volcanology. (GW ISSN 0258-8900) 1587

Bulletin of Yale University see Yale University. Bulletin 1720

Bulletin of Zoo Management. (AT ISSN 0084-8182) 580

†Bulletin of Zoological Nomenclature. (UK ISSN 0007-5167) 5154

Bulletin Officiel de la Marine Marchande.(FR) 4725

Bulletin Officiel de la Propriete Industrielle Statistiques see B.O.P.I. Statistiques 3673

Bulletin Officiel du Ministere de l'Environnement et du Cadre de Vie et du Ministere des Transports. (FR ISSN 0154-0033) 4055

Bulletin Officiel du Travail et de l'Emploi.(FR) 1004

Bulletin on Ageing. (AU ISSN 0251-6802) 2271, 3980

†Bulletin on Applied Research for the Protection of Man at Work. (FR ISSN 0759-9161) 5154

Bulletin on Current Research in Soviet and East European Law. (CN) 2607

Bulletin on Narcotics. (UN ISSN 0007-523X) 1535

Bulletin on Scale Insects see Studies on the Morphology and Systematics of Scale Insects 538

▼Bulletin on Soviet and East European Law. (US) 2720, 902

Bulletin on the Rheumatic Diseases. (US ISSN 0007-5248) 3368

Bulletin on the T F P's see Bulletin on the 15 T F P S 5154

†Bulletin on the 15 T F P S. (American Society for the Defense of Tradition, Family and Property) (US ISSN 0897-5809) **5154**
Bulletin on Training. (US ISSN 0272-8486) **1063**
Bulletin Ornithologique. (CN ISSN 0007-5256) **563**
Bulletin - Peabody Museum of Natural History *see* Peabody Museum of Natural History. Bulletin **4333**
Bulletin Quotidien. (FR) **3876**
Bulletin Quotidien d'Afrique. (FR ISSN 0007-5264) **902**
Bulletin Rapide de Droit des Affaires. (FR ISSN 0395-451X) **1004, 2607**
Bulletin Reservoirs Souterrains Non Etanches. *see* Leaking Underground Storage Tank Newsletter **5226**
Bulletin - Royal Tropical Institute *see* Royal Tropical Institute. Bulletin **118**
Bulletin S E V - V S E. (Schweizerischer Elektrotechnischer Verein) (SZ) **1883, 1332**
Bulletin - S V P *see* Environnement **1954**
Bulletin Scientifique. Section A: Sciences Naturelles, Techniques et Medicales. (CI ISSN 0350-1558) **3167, 3084**
Bulletin Scientifique. Section B: Sciences Humaines. (CI ISSN 0350-1604) **2519, 2504**
Bulletin Scientifique de Bourgogne. (FR ISSN 0373-2061) **4303, 3656**
Bulletin Signaletique. Part 110: Informatique-Automatique-Recherche Operationnelle-Gestion-Economie *see* P A S C A L Explore. E 34: Robotique. Automatique et Automatisation des Processus Industriels **1405**
Bulletin Signaletique. Part 110: Informatique-Automatique-Recherche Operationnelle-Gestion Economie *see* P A S C A L Explore. E 33. Informatique **1405**
Bulletin Signaletique. Part 120: Astronomie - Physique Spatiale - Geophysique *see* P A S C A L Explore. E 49: Meteorologie **3444**
Bulletin Signaletique. Part 130: Physique Mathematique, Optique, Acoustique, Mecanique, Chaleur *see* P A S C A L Folio. F 10: Mecanique et Acoustique et Transfert de Chaleur **3025**
Bulletin Signaletique. Part 145: Electronique *see* P A S C A L Explore. E 20: Electronique et Telecommunications **1776**
Bulletin Signaletique. Part 166: G A P H Y O R. Base de Donnees *see* G A P H Y O R. Base de Donnees **3819**
Bulletin Signaletique. Part 320: Biochimie. Biologie Moleculaire et Cellulaire *see* P A S C A L Folio. F 52: Biochimie. Biophysique Moleculaire. Biologie Moleculaire et Cellulaire **466**
Bulletin Signaletique. Part 340: Microbiologie-Virologie-Immunologie *see* P A S C A L Explore. E 61: Microbiologie: Bacteriologie, Virologie, Mycologie, Protozoaires Pathogenes **466**
Bulletin Signaletique. Part 340: Microbiologie-Virologie-Immunologie *see* P A S C A L Explore. E 62: Immunologie **466**
Bulletin Signaletique. Part 361: Reproduction. Gynecologie. Obstetrique. Embryologie. Endocrinologie *see* P A S C A L Explore. E 64: Endocrinologie Humaine et Experimentale. Endocrinopathies **3179**
Bulletin Signaletique. Part 363: Genetique *see* P A S C A L Explore. E 58: Genetique **466**
Bulletin Signaletique. Part 364: Protozoaires et des Invertebres. Zoologie Generale et Appliquee *see* P A S C A L Thema. T 260: Zoologie Fondamentale et Appliquee des Invertebres (Milieu Terrestre, Eaux Douces) **467**

Bulletin Signaletique. Part 365: Zoologie des Vertebres. Ecologie Animale. Physiologie Appliquee Humaine *see* P A S C A L Folio. F 53: Anatomie et Physiologie des Vertebres **466**
Bulletin Signaletique. Part 370: Biologie et Physiologie Vegetales *see* P A S C A L Folio. F 56: Ecologie Animale et Vegetale **467**
Bulletin Signaletique. Part 370: Biologie et Physiologie Vegetales. Sylviculture *see* P A S C A L Folio. F 55: Biologie Vegetale **466**
Bulletin Signaletique. Part 519: Philosophie. (FR ISSN 0007-554X) **3787, 4, 4212**
Bulletin Signaletique. Part 520: Sciences de l'Education. (FR ISSN 0223-341X) **1675, 4**
Bulletin Signaletique. Part 522: Histoire des Sciences et des Techniques. (FR ISSN 0007-5574) **2328**
Bulletin Signaletique. Part 523: Histoire et Sciences de la Litterature. (FR ISSN 0007-5582) **2981, 4, 4643**
Bulletin Signaletique. Part 524: Sciences du Langage. (FR ISSN 0007-5590) **2855, 4**
Bulletin Signaletique. Part 525: Prehistoire *see* Bulletin Signaletique. Part 525: Prehistoire et Protohistoire **2328**
Bulletin Signaletique. Part 525: Prehistoire et Protohistoire. (FR ISSN 0181-1894) **2328, 4, 290**
Bulletin Signaletique. Part 526: Art et Archeologie. (FR ISSN 0007-5612) **352, 4, 290**
Bulletin Signaletique. Part 527: Histoire et Sciences des Religions. (FR ISSN 0180-9296) **4212, 4**
Bulletin Signaletique. Part 527: Sciences Religieuse *see* Bulletin Signaletique. Part 527: Histoire et Sciences des Religions **4212**
Bulletin Signaletique. Part 528: Bibliographie Internationale de Science Administrative. (FR ISSN 0150-8695) **707, 4**
Bulletin Signaletique. Part 528: Science Administrative *see* Bulletin Signaletique. Part 528: Bibliographie Internationale de Science Administrative **707**
Bulletin Signaletique. Part 529: Ethnologie. (FR) **254**
Bulletin Signaletique. Part 529: Sociologie. (FR) **4457, 4, 254, 290**
Bulletin Signaletique. Part 529: Sociologie - Ethnologie *see* Bulletin Signaletique. Part 529: Sociologie **4457**
Bulletin Signaletique. Part 530: R A A (Repertoire d'Art et d'Archeologie. Nouvelle Serie) *see* B H A **351**
Bulletin Signaletique. Part 740: Metaux. Metallurgie *see* P A S C A L Thema. T 240: Metaux. Metallurgie **3427**
Bulletin Signaletique. Part 761: Microscopie Electronique. Diffraction Electronique *see* P A S C A L Explore. E 30: Microscopie Electronique et Diffraction Electronique **466**
Bulletin Signaletique. Part 780: Polymeres. Peintures. Bois. Cuirs *see* P A S C A L Folio. F 24: Polymeres. Peintures. Bois **1202**
Bulletin Signaletique. Part 880: Genie Chimique. Industries Chimique et Parachimique *see* P A S C A L Folio. F 23: Genie Chimique. Industries Chimique et Parachimique **1202**
Bulletin Signaletique. Part 885: Nuisances *see* P A S C A L Explore. E 36: Pollution de l'Eau, de l'Air et du Sol, Dechets, Bruit **1974**
Bulletin Signaletique. Part 891: Industries Mecaniques *see* P A S C A L Folio. F 10: Mecanique et Acoustique et Transfert de Chaleur **3025**
Bulletin Signaletique. Part 892: Batiment. Travaux Publics. Transports *see* P A S C A L Folio. F 25: Transports Terrestres et Maritimes **4666**

Bulletin Signaletique: Bibliographie des Sciences de la Terre. Section 221. Gisements Metalliques et Non Metalliques. Economie Miniere *see* P A S C A L Folio. F 41: Gisements Metalliques et Non-Metalliques. Economie Miniere **3502**
Bulletin Signaletique: Bibliographie des Sciences de la Terre. Section 227: Paleontologie *see* P A S C A L Folio. F 47: Paleontologie **3661**
Bulletin Signaletique d'Information Administrative. (FR ISSN 0293-9614) **4079**
Bulletin Signaletique des Telecommunications. (FR ISSN 0007-5302) **1332**
Bulletin Social. (FR ISSN 0242-5874) **974**
Bulletin Statistique des Peches Maritimes. *see* I C E S Fisheries Statistics **2051**
Bulletin Suisse de Mineralogie et Petrographie. *see* Schweizerische Mineralogische und Petrographische Mitteilungen **3495**
Bulletin sur les Dechets Nucleaires. *see* Nuclear Waste Bulletin **1986**
Bulletin sur les Relations du Travail. (CN ISSN 0704-0873) **974**
Bulletin Technique. (SZ ISSN 0007-5736) **3998**
Bulletin Technique Apicole. (FR ISSN 0335-3710) **81**
Bulletin Technique de l'A.T.G. *see* Association des Anciens Eleves de l'Ecole d'Ingenieurs de Geneve. Bulletin Technique **1815**
Bulletin Technique du Machinisme et de l'Equipement Agricoles. (FR ISSN 0299-8661) **161**
The Bulletin; the Newsweekly of the Capital of Europe. (BE ISSN 0007-4047) **2174**
Bulletin to Management. (US ISSN 0525-2156) **1063**
Bulletin Trimestriel F A O de Statistiques. *see* F A O Quarterly Bulletin of Statistics **137**
Bulletin Usuel des Lois et Arretes. (BE) **2607**
Bulletin van die Munisipale Naslaanbiblioteek. *see* Municipal Reference Library Bulletin **4091**
Bulletin Voyages. (CN) **4755**
Bulletin with Newsweek. (AT) **2171**
Bulletin - Yale University Art Gallery *see* Yale University Art Gallery Bulletin **3535**
Bulletins of American Paleontology. (US ISSN 0007-5779) **3656**
†Bulletins on Science and Technology for the Handicapped. (US ISSN 0731-5775) **5154**
Bullettino Storico Empolese. (IT ISSN 0007-5795) **2354, 320**
Bullettino Storico Pistoiese. (IT ISSN 0007-5809) **2354**
Bullinger's Postal and Shippers Guide for the United States and Canada. (US ISSN 0068-4201) **1352, 4725**
Bullion Advisory. (US) **941**
Bullpen. (US) **4501**
Bullrush. (US) **2146**
▼Bulls and Bears: Winning in the Stock Market in Good Times and Bad. (CN) **941**
▼Bull's Eye. (CN ISSN 1041-3669) **213**
Bulwark. (US ISSN 0741-5788) **2701, 2712**
Bulwark. (UK ISSN 0045-3536) **4232**
Bumazhnaya Promyshlennost' (RU ISSN 0007-5817) **3662**
Bummi. (GW ISSN 0323-8954) **1250**
Bumper. (NE) **2901**
Bunadarrit. (IC ISSN 0251-2661) **81, 213**
Bunchgrass Historian. (US) **2307**
Der Bund. (AU) **1995, 3876**
Bund der Deutschen Katholischen Jugend. Informationsdienst. (GW ISSN 0007-5833) **1250, 4257, 4400**
Bund der Mitteldeutschen e.V. Beratungsdienst *see* B M D - Beratungsdienst **3940**

Bund Deutscher Eisenbahn-Freunde Jahrbuch *see* B D E F - Jahrbuch **4708**
Bund Deutscher Kriegsopfer. Jahrbuch. (GW) **1296**
Bund Deutscher Kunsterzieher Mitteilungen *see* B D K - Mitteilungen **1617**
Bunda College of Agriculture. Research Bulletin *see* Bunda Journal of Agricultural Research **81**
Bunda Journal of Agricultural Research.(MW) **81**
Bundes Arbeitsgemeinschaft der Mittel- und Grossbetriebe des Einzelhandels e.V. Nachrichten *see* B A G - Nachrichten **833**
Bundesanstalt fuer Alpenlaendische Landwirtschaft. Bericht. (AU) **81**
Bundesanstalt fuer Alpenlaendische Landwirtschaft. Veroeffentlichungen. (AU ISSN 1010-6146) **81**
Bundesanstalt fuer Alpenlaendische Landwirtschaft Gumpenstein. Versuchsergebnisse *see* Sortenversuchsergebnisse **120**
†Bundesanstalt fuer Materialforschung und -pruefung. Amts- und Mitteilungsblatt. (GW) **5154**
Bundesanstalt fuer Materialpruefung. Jahresbericht *see* Germany (Federal Republic, 1949-). Bundesanstalt fuer Materialforschung und -pruefung. Jahresbericht **1917**
Bundesanstalt fuer Pflanzenbau und Samenpruefung, Vienna. Jahrbuch *see* Bundesanstalt fuer Pflanzenbau, Vienna. Jahrbuch **498**
Bundesanstalt fuer Pflanzenbau, Vienna. Jahrbuch. (AU) **498, 171**
Bundesarbeitsblatt. (GW) **974**
Bundesarbeitsgemeinschaft Hilfe fuer Behinderte. Berichte. Jahresspiegel. (GW) **1734, 3084**
Bundesarbeitsgemeinschaft Hilfe fuer Behinderte. Jahresspiegel *see* Bundesarbeitsgemeinschaft Hilfe fuer Behinderte. Berichte. Jahresspiegel **1734**
Die Bundesbahn. (GW ISSN 0007-5876) **4708**
Bundesbaublatt. (GW ISSN 0007-5884) **2484**
Bundesbruder Saengerschaft Franco-Palatia Bayreuth. (GW) **3543, 1296**
Bundesforschungsanstalt fuer Forst- und Holzwirtschaft, Hamburg. Mitteilungen. (GW ISSN 0007-5892) **2113, 2096**
Bundesforschungsanstalt fuer Landeskunde und Raumordnung. Seminare - Symposien - Arbeitspapiere. (GW ISSN 0930-3839) **2484**
Bundesforschungsanstalt fuer Landwirtschaft. Mitteilungen und Informationen. (GW ISSN 0723-5321) **148, 171**
Bundesgesundheitsblatt. (GW ISSN 0007-5914) **4098**
Bundesgrenzschutz *see* B G S **3951**
Bundesinfo - Impulse. (GW) **1250**
Bundesinstitut fuer Bevoelkerungsforschung Mitteilungen *see* B I B Mitteilungen **3979**
Bundesinstitut fuer Ostwissenschaftliche und Internationale Studien. Berichte. (GW ISSN 0435-7183) **3952**
Bundesinstitut fuer Sportwissenschaft. Berichte und Aspekte (Year) *see* Germany. Bundesinstitut fuer Sportwissenschaft. Biennial Reports **4473**
Bundesministerium fuer Forschung und Technologie Journal *see* B M F T Journal **4594**
Bundesministerium fuer Forschung und Technologie Risiko- und Sicherheitsforschung *see* B M F T Risiko- und Sicherheitsforschung **4098**
Bundesministerium fuer Wirtschaftliche Zusammenarbeit Materialien *see* B M Z - Materialien **926**
Bundespolizei. (GW) **1511**
Bundesschulmusikwoche. (GW) **3543**
Bundestag Report. (GW ISSN 0933-2731) **3876**

6004 BUNDESVERBAENDE

Bundesverbaende des Deutschen Gueterkraftverkehrs Nachrichten see B D G Nachrichten **4743**
Bundesverband Buergerinitiativen Umweltschutz Info-Dienst see B B U Info-Dienst **1944**
Bundesverband der Deutschen Industrie Deutschland Liefert see B D I Deutschland Liefert **901**
Bundesverband der Deutschen Susswarenindustrie. Jahresbericht. (GW) **2087**
Bundesverband der Geschaeftsstellenleiter der Assekuranz Nachrichten see V G A Nachrichten **2544**
Bundesverband des Deutschen Textileinzelhandels e.V. Marketing-Berater see B T E Marketing-Berater **1034**
Bundesverband Deutscher Vermoegensberater. Infodienst. (GW) **941**
Bundesverband Deutscher Zeitungsverleger. Zeitung. (GW) **2567**
Bundesverband Montagebau und Fertighauser Rundschau see B M F Rundschau **601**
Bundesversorgungsblatt see Bundesarbeitsblatt **974**
Die Bundesverwaltung. (GW ISSN 0007-5930) **4055**
Die Bundeswehr. (GW ISSN 0007-5949) **3453**
†Bundeswehr und Wirtschaft. (GW) **5154**
Bundeswehrverwaltung. (GW) **2607, 3453**
Bungaku/Literature. (JA ISSN 0389-4029) **2901**
Bungakukai. (JA) **2901**
Bungei Shunju. (JA) **2207**
Bunka Kagaku Kiyo. see Journal of Cultural Sciences **2509**
Bunkazai no Chu-kin-gai/Insect & fungus Damage to Cultural Properties. (JA ISSN 0389-729X) **529, 498**
Bunken. (GW ISSN 0932-268X) **3635**
Bunko Kenkyu. see Spectroscopical Society of Japan. Journal **3857**
Bunseki Kagaku. (JA ISSN 0525-1931) **1204**
Bunsengesellschaft fuer Physikalische Chemie. Berichte. (GW ISSN 0005-9021) **1224**
Bunte. (GW) **2188**
†Das Bunte Blatt. (GW ISSN 0007-5965) **5154**
Bunte Blumenwelt. (GW ISSN 0007-5973) **2142**
Bunte Hund. (GW) **1250**
Bunte Illustrierte see Bunte **2188**
Bunte Oesterreich see Bunte **2188**
Bunte Tierwelt. (GW ISSN 0341-9770) **3709**
Bunte Wagen see In Sachen Spiel und Feier **4634**
Bunty. (UK) **1250**
Bunuk. see Bankers **765**
Bunyan Studies. (UK ISSN 0954-0970) **2901, 4167**
Buona Cucina. (IT) **2445**
Buona Tavola see Bella (Milan, 1947) **4838**
Buono. (IT) **2062**
Buoyant Flight. (US ISSN 0361-5065) **49**
Bur. (US ISSN 0007-6007) **3229**
Burajiru Nikkei Kigyo Nenkan. see Empresas Japonesas do Brasil. Annuario **1134**
Burbujas. (AG ISSN 0007-6015) **2291, 1250**
Burda. (SZ) **1289**
Burda Babymaschen. (GW) **3590**
Burda Blusen, Roecke, Hosen. (GW) **1289**
Burda Brautmode. (GW) **1289**
Burda Faschingsheft. (GW) **2434**
Burda Filethaekeln. (GW) **3590**
Burda Grosses Bastelheft. (GW) **2434**
Burda Grosses Weihnachtsheft. (GW) **2434**
Burda International. (GW) **1283, 372, 1289**
Burda Kindermaschen. (GW) **3590**
Burda Kleinkindermode. (GW) **1289**
Burda Kreuzstich. (GW) **3590**
Burda Maschenmuster. (GW) **3590**
Burda Meine Gute Kueche. (GW) **2445**
Burda Miss B Trends. (GW) **1289**
Burda Mode fuer Maedchen und Jungen. (GW) **1289**
Burda Moden. (GW ISSN 0007-6031) **1289, 2445**
Burda Moden (Arabic Edition). (SZ) **372, 1283, 3590**
Burda Moden (Austria). (GW) **1289**
Burda Moden (Greece). (GR) **1289**
Burda Trachtenmode. (GW) **1289**
Burda Trachtenstrickmode. (GW) **1289**
Burda Umstandsmode. (GW) **1289**
Burda Unser Baby. (GW) **1289**
Burda Weihnachtsbacken. (GW) **2445**
†Le Bureau. (CN ISSN 0007-604X) **5154**
†Bureau et Informatique. (FR ISSN 0766-5229) **5154**
Bureau International de l'Heure. Rapport Annuel see International Earth Rotation Service. Annual Report **365**
Bureau International des Containers Code see B I C - Code **3647**
Bureau International des Societes Gerant les Droits d'Enregistrement et de Reproduction Mecanique. Bulletin.(FR ISSN 0572-7529) **3998, 4124**
Bureau of Business Practice Management Letter. (US) **1004**
Bureau of Catholic Indian Missions. Newsletter. (US) **4257, 1995**
Bureau of Educational Research. Discussion Papers. (KE) **1619**
Bureau of Educational Research. Seminar Papers. (KE) **1619**
Bureau of Radiological Health Research Grants Program (Washington) see U.S. Bureau of Radiological Health. Research Grants Program **5294**
Bureau of Standards Review see Z B S Review **1086**
Bureau of Wholesale Sales Representatives News. (US) **1283**
Bureau Universitaire de Recherche Operationnelle. Cahiers. (FR ISSN 0078-950X) **1004**
Bureau Veritas. Bulletin Technique. (FR ISSN 0007-5752) **4725**
Bureaucrat see The Public Manager **4071**
Bureaux d'Etudes. (FR ISSN 1148-7305) **3016, 1883**
Bureaux d'Etudes Automatise see Bureaux d'Etudes **3016**
Bureaux de France see Espace Bureau **1058**
Bureaux et Systemes. (SZ) **1004, 1057**
Burein. see Brain **29**
Burgan Bank. Annual Report. (KU) **769**
Burgenbote. (AU) **1484, 320**
Burgenlaendische Forschungen. (AU ISSN 0007-621X) **2354**
Burgenlaendische Gemeinschaft. (AU ISSN 0007-6228) **2173**
Burgenlaendische Heimatblaetter. (AU ISSN 0007-6236) **2354**
Burgenlaendische Landwirtschaftskammer. Mitteilungsblatt. (AU ISSN 0007-6244) **81**
Burgenlaendischer Agrarkurier. (AU) **81**
Burgenlaendisches Leben. (AU ISSN 0007-6252) **2188, 2173**
Burgenlaendischer Wirtschaftsdienst. (AU) **809**
Burgense. (SP ISSN 0521-8195) **4167**
Burggeist. (GW) **1250**
Buried History. (AT ISSN 0007-6260) **268, 4167**
Buried Treasure. (US ISSN 1043-0806) **1250**
Burke Road Cityscope. (AT) **4160**
Burke's Family Index. (UK) **2146**
Burke's Guide to Country Houses. (UK) **4755**
†Burke's Royal Families of the World. Vol. 1: Europe and Latin America. (UK) **5154**
Burke's Royal Families of the World. Vol. 2: Africa and the Middle East. (UK) **2146**
Burkina Faso. Direction de l'Hydraulique et de l'Equipement Rural. Service I.R.H. Rapport d'Activites. (UV) **4822, 171**
Burkina Faso. Direction des Eaux et Forets et de la Conservation des Sols. Rapport Annuel. (UV) **2096, 2037**
Burkina Faso. Institut National de la Statistique et de la Demographie. Bulletin Annuaire d'Information Statistique et Economique. (UV) **707**
Burkina Faso. Ministere de l'Eau. Annuaire Hydrologique du Burkina. (UV) **4822**
Burkina Faso. Ministere de l'Eau. Bulletin Hydrologique du Burkina. (UV) **4822**
Burkina Faso. Service des Statistiques Agricoles. Annuaire. (UV) **81**
Burlington Magazine. (UK ISSN 0007-6287) **320**
Burlington Northern Railroad News see B N News **4708**
Burlington Story. (US) **2401**
Burma Medical Journal. (BR ISSN 0007-6295) **3084**
Burma Research Society. Journal/ Myanma Naing Ngan Thuteithana Athin. (BR) **4367**
Burmah Chinthe see Chinthe **3684**
Burn Resources in North America. (US) **3307**
Burnaby Centennial B O A R D. (CN) **1124**
Burnaby Magazine. (CN ISSN 1182-0683) **2176**
Burnett Family Newsletter. (US ISSN 0730-4978) **2146**
Burning Bush. (US ISSN 0007-6309) **4167**
Burns. (UK ISSN 0305-4179) **3307**
Burns Chronicle Club Directory. (UK) **2901**
Burns Mantle Best Play Annual. (US) **4630**
Burnt Sienna. (US) **2989**
Burocrazia. (IT) **4055**
Burrelle's Clipping Analyst. (US) **29**
Burrelle's New England Media Directory (Year). (US ISSN 0883-9999) **29**
Burrelle's New Jersey Media Directory (Year). (US ISSN 0883-9778) **29**
Burrelle's New York State Media Directory (Year). (US) **29**
Burrelle's Pennsylvania Media Directory (Year). (US ISSN 0276-7872) **29**
Burroughs Bulletin. (US ISSN 0007-6333) **2901**
Burroughsiana. (UK) **2901**
Burt Franklin Ethnic Bibliographical Guides. (US) **2030**
Burundi. Departement des Etudes et Statistiques. Bulletin Annuaire. (BD) **4565**
Burundi. Departement des Etudes et Statistiques. Bulletin Trimestriel. (BD) **4565**
Burundi. Departement des Etudes et Statistiques. Informations Statistiques Mensuelles. (BD) **4565**
Burundi. Institut de Statistiques et d'Etudes Economiques. Annuaire Statistique. (BD) **707**
Burundi. Institut de Statistiques et d'Etudes Economiques. Bulletin Mensuel des Prix. (BD) **707**
Burundi. Institut de Statistiques et d'Etudes Economiques. Bulletin Statistique Trimestriel. (BD) **707**
Burundi. Institut de Statistiques et d'Etudes Economiques. Comptes Economiques. (BD) **707**
†Burundi. Ministere de l'Economie et des Finances. Bulletin Economique et Financier. (BD) **5154**
Burundi. Ministere de la Justice. Bulletin Officiel. (BD) **2607**
Burwell Directory of Information Brokers. (US) **2750**
Bus. (UK) **1467, 1475**
†Bus & Coach Management. (UK) **5154**
Bus and Truck Transport see Truck Fleet **4749**
Bus-Fahrt. (GW ISSN 0341-5244) **4755, 4647**
Bus Fayre. (UK ISSN 0143-9162) **4647**
Bus Garage Index. (US) **4647**
Bus Industry Directory see Bus Ride: Bus Industry Directory **4647**
Bus Industry Magazine. (US ISSN 0739-7194) **4647**
Bus Operator. (US) **4647**
Bus Review see Bus Industry Magazine **4647**
Bus Ride. (US ISSN 0192-8902) **4647**
Bus Ride: Bus Industry Directory. (US ISSN 0363-3764) **4647**
Bus Tourist. (GW) **4755**
Bus Tours Magazine. (US ISSN 0199-6096) **4647, 4755**
Bus und Bahn. (GW) **4647**
Bus World. (US ISSN 0162-9689) **4685, 4755**
Busby Papers. (US ISSN 0738-5765) **1089**
La Busca. (US) **395, 4467**
Buses. (UK ISSN 0007-6392) **4647**
Buses Annual see Buses Yearbook **4647**
Buses Extra. (UK ISSN 0141-9927) **4647**
Buses International. (US) **4647**
Buses Yearbook. (UK) **4647**
Bush League see Sobek **4556**
Bushdriver. (AT) **4685**
Bushong Bulletin. (US) **2146**
Bushwhackers and Rock Thumpers see Sutler **2165**
Business. (KE) **649**
Business. (UK ISSN 0268-6384) **649**
Business. (XK ISSN 1010-5719) **649**
Business. see Mercado **873**
†Business (Atlanta). (US ISSN 0163-531X) **5154**
Business (Little Rock). (US) **809**
Business (Parma). (IT) **649**
Business (Turin). (IT) **649**
Business Accounting for Lawyers Newsletter. (US) **748, 2607**
Business Administration. (UK) **833**
Business Administration Bulletin. see Deltion Dieekiseos Epichiriseon **1007**
Business Advisory Client Newsletter. (US) **748, 649**
The Business Advocate. (CN) **649**
Business Advocate see Business Counsel **2707**
Business Age. (US ISSN 0886-8166) **1113**
Business Alabama Monthly. (US ISSN 1050-091X) **649**
Business America. (US ISSN 0190-6275) **833, 902**
Business Analysis of Main Enterprises in Japan see Financial Statements of Enterprises in Japan **716**
Business Analyst. (Il ISSN 0007-6430) **649**
Business & Acquisition Newsletter. (US ISSN 0738-7253) **769**
Business and Administration see Institute of Administration and Commerce of South Africa. Journal **1013**
Business and Commercial Aviation. (US ISSN 0007-6570) **49**
Business and Economic History. (US ISSN 0894-6825) **649**
Business & Economic Report & Kansas Economic Indicators. (US) **848**
Business & Economic Review. (US ISSN 0007-6465) **649**
Business and Economics Perspectives see Journal of Business and Economic Perspectives **673**
Business & Employment Law News. (CN) **2707, 1502**
Business and Environment. (US) **902**
Business and Finance. (IE ISSN 0007-6473) **769**
Business & Finance in Ontario. (CN) **649**
Business & Finance in Scotland. (UK) **649**
Business and Government: A Monthly Survey of Official Publications for Business and Government. (UK) **2750, 649**
Business and Health. (US ISSN 0739-9413) **2529**

Business and Incentive Strategies. (US) 29
Business & Incentives. (US) 1034
▼Business & Industrial Security. (CN) 1526, 649
Business & Industrial Trade Fairs Ltd. Exhibition Calendar see B & I Exhibition Calendar 28
Business and Industry. (US ISSN 0021-0463) 1034
†Business & Office Equipment Selector. (SA) 5154
Business & Professional Ethics Journal. (US ISSN 0277-2027) 3763, 1816
Business and Professional People for the Public Interest Newsletter see B P I Newsletter 1944
Business and Professional Woman (Canada). (CN ISSN 0045-3587) 3624, 4838
Business and Professional Woman (England). (UK ISSN 0045-3595) 3625, 4838
Business & Public Affairs see B & P A 647
Business and Society. (US ISSN 0007-6503) 649
Business and Society Review. (US ISSN 0045-3609) 649
Business and Tax Planning Quarterly see Cost Management Update 1091
Business & Technology Daily News. see Nikkan Kogyo Shinbun 682
▼Business and the Environment. (US ISSN 1052-7206) 1944, 848, 941
Business & the Law. (CN ISSN 0825-4982) 2707
Business Archives. (UK ISSN 0007-6538) 649
Business Archives and History see Australian Economic History Review 889
Business Archives Council. Principles and Practice. (UK) 649
Business Asia. (US ISSN 0572-7545) 649
†Business Assistance Monograph Series.(US ISSN 0146-4744) 5154
Business Atlanta. (US ISSN 0192-0855) 649
Business Aviation see Business Aviation Weekly 4671
Business Aviation & Regional Transport.(BE ISSN 0776-7595) 49
Business Aviation Digest. (US) 49
Business Aviation Weekly. (US) 4671
Business Banker International. (IE ISSN 0956-1498) 769
Business Barometer & Digest see I F M A World 2072
Business Blue Book of S.A. (SA) 649
Business Blue-Book of Southern Africa see Business Blue Book of S.A 649
Business Book Review. (US ISSN 0741-8132) 649, 4124
Business Brief. (SA) 848
Business Bulletin. (UK) 649
†Business Bulletin. (US) 5154
Business China. (US) 848
Business Chronicle. (UK) 809
Business Classified Rates and Data. (US) 40, 29, 395
Business Cleveland see Corporate Cleveland 657
Business Committee for the Arts, Inc. News see B C A News 647
Business Communications Review. (US ISSN 0162-3885) 1361
Business Computer Digest. (US ISSN 0737-0946) 825, 1389, 1458, 1467
Business Computer Index. (US ISSN 0741-2363) 1403, 4, 825
Business Computer Report see Executive Computer Report 1395
†Business Computer Reseller News. (CN) 5154
Business Computer Review see Southwest Computer and Business Equipment Review 1474
Business ComputerNews. (CN ISSN 0838-438X) 825
†Business Computing & Communications. (UK) 5154

▼Business Concepts. (US ISSN 1055-8217) 649
Business Conditions see Economic Perspectives 861
†Business Conditions Digest. (US ISSN 0146-7735) 5154
Business Conditions Malaysia. (MY ISSN 0127-0001) 848
Business Conditions Survey. (CN) 707
Business Contact see Belgo-Luxembourg Chamber of Commerce in Great Britain. Journal 808
Business Contact. (RU) 902
Business Contacts in Finland. (FI ISSN 0355-0346) 1124
Business Council for the U N Briefing. (US) 3952, 926
Business Council of Australia Bulletin. (AT ISSN 0814-4273) 649
Business Counsel. (US) 2707, 649
Business Credit. (US ISSN 0897-0181) 769, 1034
†Business Data Processing: a Wiley Series. (US) 5155
Business Detroit see Corporate Detroit Magazine 657
Business Digest. (UK) 649
Business Digest see Business Leader 651
Business Digest of Central Massachusetts. (US ISSN 0744-6012) 1113
Business Digest of Delaware Valley. (US) 1113
Business Digest of Greater Bangor. (US) 649
Business Digest of Greater Burlington. (US) 649
Business Digest of Greater Waterbury. (US ISSN 1046-168X) 649
Business Digest of Lehigh Valley. (US) 650
Business Digest of Southeastern Massachusetts. (US) 650
Business Directory. (US) 834
Business Directory of Hong Kong. (HK) 1124
Business Documents. (US) 3998
Business Driver. (US) 1034, 4685
Business Dynamics see B & P A 647
Business East Midlands. (UK ISSN 0958-7918) 650
Business Eastern Europe. (US) 848
Business Economics. (US ISSN 0007-666X) 650
Business Economist. (UK ISSN 0306-5049) 650
Business Education see Management Bibliographies and Reviews 728
Business Education Films Catalog. (US) 650, 1619, 3504
Business Education Forum. (US ISSN 0007-6678) 650, 1701
Business Education Guide. (US) 650
Business Education Index. (US ISSN 0068-4414) 1675, 707
▼Business - Education Insider. (US) 848, 1745
Business Education International. (UK) 834
†Business Education Journal. (US ISSN 0007-6686) 5155
Business Education Today. (UK ISSN 0951-1512) 1745, 1057
Business Education World. (US ISSN 0007-6694) 1745
†Business Electronics Dealer. (US) 5155
▼Business Entertainment Guide. (HK) 4755
†Business Environment. (II) 5155
Business Equipment Digest. (UK ISSN 0007-6708) 1057
Business Ethic Resource. (US) 2707, 650
Business Ethics. (US) 650
▼Business Ethics. (UK ISSN 0962-8770) 650
▼Business Ethics Quarterly. (US ISSN 1052-150X) 650
Business Europe. (US) 902, 1073
Business Examiner. (CN) 650
Business Examiner, South Island Edition.(CN) 650
Business Executive. (UK ISSN 0951-1792) 1004, 1682
†Business Executives' Expectations. (US ISSN 0889-6674) 5155

Business Expectations see U S Survey of Business Expectations 1086
Business Express. (UK) 650
Business Eye. (PH ISSN 0116-3590) 650
Business Facilities. (US ISSN 0746-0023) 4146
Business Failure Record. (US) 848
Business Farmer. (US) 81
Business Finance see Greece's Weekly for Business and Finance 910
Business First. (US ISSN 0749-9418) 650
Business First Magazine. (US) 848, 4146
Business Flyer. (US) 4671
Business for Central New Jersey. (US ISSN 1042-8704) 650
†Business Forecasts. (US) 5155
Business Formations and Failures. (CN) 707
Business Forms and Systems see Business Forms, Labels and Systems 3998
Business Forms, Labels and Systems. (US) 3998
Business Forum (Los Angeles). (US ISSN 0733-2408) 650
Business Franchise Guide. (US) 1113, 2607
Business Graduates Association Address Book see Association of M B A Address Book 1003
Business Guide. (CN) 650
Business Guide Book to Jakarta. (IO) 1124
Business Haiti. (HT) 809
Business Herald. (Il ISSN 0007-6783) 1004
Business History. (UK ISSN 0007-6791) 650
Business History Newsletter. (UK ISSN 0260-5171) 889
Business History Review. (US ISSN 0007-6805) 650
Business History Studies. (Il) 650
Business Horizons. (US ISSN 0007-6813) 650
Business Ideas. (US ISSN 0738-7024) 650
Business in Broward. (US) 1113
Business in Calgary. (CN) 650
Business in Gainesville. (US) 650
▼Business in Greece. (GR) 651, 848
Business in Kent. (UK) 651
Business in Nebraska. (US ISSN 0007-683X) 848
Business in Palm Beach County. (US) 1113
Business in Thailand. (TH ISSN 0125-0140) 848
Business in the U.S.S.R. (International Edition). (FR ISSN 1150-4382) 651
Business in Vancouver. (CN) 651
Business in Yorkshire. (UK ISSN 0263-1067) 651
Business Index. (US) 707, 4
Business India. (Il ISSN 0254-5268) 834
Business Indicator Report. (US) 3998, 1113
Business Indicators. (AT ISSN 0727-2979) 848
Business Industry Technology Service see B I T S 704
Business Information Alert. (US ISSN 1042-0746) 707, 651, 2750
Business Information Digest. (LE) 651
†Business Information for Dallas. (US) 5155
Business Information from Your Public Library. (US ISSN 0892-6034) 2750, 651
Business Information Review. (UK ISSN 0266-3821) 1124
Business Information Yearbook. (UK ISSN 0953-9263) 651
Business Insider. (US) 809
Business Insight (Kalamazoo). (US) 651
Business Insights. (CN) 651
Business Insurance. (US ISSN 0007-6864) 2529
Business Interiors see Today's Facility Manager 2555
Business International. (US ISSN 0007-6872) 902

Business International Corp. Turkey Monitor see B I - Turkey Monitor 901
Business International Executive Compensation Report see B I - P E R S Executive Compensation Report 1003
Business International Forecasting Services see Asia - Pacific Forecasting Service 646
Business International Money Report. (US ISSN 0161-0384) 769
Business Japan see Japan 21st 1079
Business Journal. (PH ISSN 0116-452X) 809
Business Journal (Phoenix). (US) 651, 848
Business Journal (Portland). (US ISSN 0742-6550) 848
Business Journal (Sacramento). (US) 651
Business Journal (San Jose). (US ISSN 0886-5922) 651
The Business Journal of Charlotte. (US) 651
Business Journal of New Jersey. (US ISSN 0889-3403) 651
Business Journal Serving Greater Milwaukee. (US ISSN 0740-2899) 651
Business Journal Serving Phoenix & The Valley of the Sun. (US) 651
Business Journal Serving Sonoma, Marin, & Napa Counties. (US) 651
Business Journal's Directory of Manufacturing. (US) 1124
Business Korea. (KO) 651
Business Korea Yearbook (Year). (KO) 651
Business Lanka. (CE) 651
Business Latin America. (US ISSN 0007-6880) 848, 902
Business Law Brief. (UK) 2707
Business Law Memo see Business Lawyer Update 2707
Business Law Monographs. (US) 2707, 651
Business Law News see Business & Employment Law News 2707
Business Law Reports (2nd Series). (CN ISSN 0703-5551) 2707, 651
Business Law Review. (UK ISSN 0143-6295) 2707, 651
Business Laws of Egypt. (UK) 2707, 834
Business Laws of Iraq. (UK) 2707, 834
Business Laws of Kuwait. (UK) 2707, 834
Business Laws of Saudi Arabia. (UK) 2707, 834
Business Laws of United Arab Emirates.(UK) 2707, 834
Business Lawyer. (US ISSN 0007-6899) 2707, 651
Business Lawyer Update. (US ISSN 0884-1977) 2707, 651
Business Leader. (US) 651
Business Leader see Scarborough Business Magazine 1117
†Business Library Management. (UK ISSN 0951-9971) 5155
Business Library Newsletter. (US ISSN 0191-4006) 2750, 651
Business Library Review. (US ISSN 1045-7798) 769
Business Life. (UK) 4671
Business Life Magazine. (US) 29
The Business Link. (US) 809
Business Machine Dealer. (US) 1057
Business Mailers Review. (US ISSN 0739-3873) 651
Business Management. see Kiyup Kyungyung 1017
Business Market News. (US) 651
Business Marketing. (US ISSN 0745-5933) 1034
Business Marketing Digest. (UK) 1034
Business Memo from Belgium. (US ISSN 0007-6945) 809
Business Mexico. (MX) 809
Business Micro see Computing Today 5170
Business Monitor: Miscellaneous Series. M2 Cinemas. (UK ISSN 0068-4449) 3504
Business Monitor: Miscellaneous Series. M3 Company Finance. (UK ISSN 0068-4457) 769

6006 BUSINESS MONITOR

Business Monitor: Miscellaneous Series. M4 Overseas Transactions. (UK ISSN 0068-4465) **902**
†Business Month. (US ISSN 0892-4090) **5155**
Business Monthly see Oakland Business Monthly **683**
Business New Hampshire Magazine. (US ISSN 1046-9575) **834**
Business New York. (US) **651**
Business News. (CN ISSN 0834-020X) **651**
Business News. (IO) **651**
Business News. see Xinwen Bao **700**
Business News. (AT) **902**
Business News. South Wales Edition. (UK) **848**
Business News. West of England Edition. (UK) **848**
Business News from Australia. (US) **848**
Business News Index see M I R A Automotive Business Index **727**
Business: North Carolina. (US) **1113**
Business North East. (UK) **651**
†Business of Fur. (US) **5155**
Business of Herbs. (US ISSN 0736-9050) **2123**, **1034**
Business of New Hampshire see Business New Hampshire Magazine **834**
Business of Sports. (US) **4467**, **651**
Business of Tourism. (GR) **2472**, **4755**
Business Officer. (US ISSN 0147-877X) **1725**
Business One Investor's Handbook. (US) **941**
Business One Irwin Business and Investment Almanac. (US) **651**
Business Opportunities. (SI ISSN 0129-4202) **834**, **902**, **1034**
Business Opportunities Digest. (US ISSN 0007-6953) **1113**
Business Opportunities Handbook. (US) **1113**
Business Opportunities in Spain. (SP) **848**
Business Opportunities Journal. (US ISSN 0193-3221) **941**, **4146**
Business Opportunity Appraiser. (US) **941**
Business Organizations, Agencies, and Publications Directory. (US ISSN 0888-1413) **1125**
Business Organizations and Agencies Directory see Business Organizations, Agencies, and Publications Directory **1125**
Business Organizations: Corporate Acquisitions and Mergers. (US) **2707**, **651**
Business Organizations: Franchising. (US) **1113**
Business Organizations: Pension and Profit-Sharing Plans. (US) **2707**, **974**
Business Organizations: Professional Corporations and Associations. (US) **651**, **2707**
Business Organizations with Tax Planning. (US) **1089**
Business Outlook see Business Outlook for West Michigan **848**
Business Outlook for West Michigan. (US ISSN 0748-4216) **848**
Business Owner. (US ISSN 0190-4914) **652**, **1004**
Business P R C. (HK) **834**, **926**
The Business Partner. (US) **652**
Business Partner Hungary/Geschaeftspartner Ungarn/Kereskedelmi Partenr Magyarorszag. (HU) **652**
Business People Magazine of Greater Fort Wayne. (US) **652**
Business Periodicals Index. (US ISSN 0007-6961) **707**, **4**
Business Perspectives. (US ISSN 0896-3703) **652**
▼Business Philadelphia. (US) **809**
The Business Press. (US) **652**
Business Product News. (US) **1057**
Business - Professional Advertising Association Communicator see B - P A A Communicator **28**

Business - Professional Advertising Association Membership Directory and Yellow Pages see B - P A A Membership Directory and Yellow Pages **28**
Business Properties. (US) **4146**
Business Proposals of Yamaguchi Prefecture. (JA) **902**
▼Business Publication Profiles. (US) **29**, **4124**
Business Publication Rates and Data see Standard Rate and Data Service. Business Publication Rates and Data **41**
Business Publications Audit of Circulations. Annual Report. (US) **29**
Business Publishing. (US ISSN 1060-2208) **1468**, **4124**
Business Puerto Rico. (PR) **652**
Business Pulse. (US) **834**
Business Quarterly. (CN ISSN 0007-6996) **652**, **1004**
Business Radio. (US ISSN 0746-8911) **1355**
Business Radio - Action see Business Radio **1355**
Business Record. (US) **652**
Business Report (Abridged Version). (GW ISSN 0343-1975) **652**
Business Report (Unabridged Version). (GW) **652**
Business Research Guides. (UK ISSN 0957-9869) **1004**, **1034**, **2750**
Business Review/Bijinesu Rebyu. (JA) **652**
Business Review. (TH ISSN 0125-0477) **848**
Business Review. (US ISSN 1042-6418) **941**
†Business Review. (CN) **5155**
Business Review (Philadelphia) see Federal Reserve Bank of Philadelphia. Business Review **865**
The Business Review of Northeast Ohio.(US) **652**
Business Review Weekly. (AT ISSN 0727-758X) **1004**
Business Round - Up. (BL) **809**
Business Scotland. (UK) **848**
Business Software Catalog. (US) **1476**, **1125**
Business Software Magazine see P C Accounting **5254**
▼Business Source. (CN) **652**
Business South East. (UK ISSN 0262-8597) **834**
Business South West. (UK) **652**
Business Southwest. (US) **809**
▼Business Speaker's Digest. (US ISSN 1055-3568) **2567**
Business Spectator. (ET) **809**
Business Spotlight - Namibia. (SX) **809**
†Business Starts Record. (US ISSN 0895-4615) **5155**
Business Strategies. (US) **652**
▼Business Strategy Review. (UK ISSN 0955-6419) **1004**
Business Studies on the U.S.S.R. (US ISSN 1044-498X) **902**
Business Studies Series. (IE) **652**
Business Systems & Equipment. (UK ISSN 0007-7097) **1057**
Business Systems Product Update see Macintosh Update **1461**
Business Taiwan. (CH) **652**
†Business Tax Report. (US ISSN 0897-9979) **5155**
Business Times. (NR ISSN 0331-2585) **652**
Business Times. (MY) **652**, **148**, **4291**
Business Times. (SI) **652**
Business Times. (TH) **652**
Business Times. (US) **848**
Business to Business. (CN) **652**
Business Today see Business America **833**
†Business Today. (UK) **5155**
Business Today (Princeton). (US ISSN 0007-7100) **1306**
Business Today (St. Paul). (US) **809**
Business Tokyo. (JA ISSN 0914-0026) **652**
Business Tort of Fraud & Misrepresentation. (US) **2708**
Business Torts. (US) **2708**, **652**
Business Travel. see Zakenreis **4798**

▼Business Travel International. (UK ISSN 0958-2010) **3391**, **652**, **4755**
Business Travel Management. (US ISSN 1046-5057) **1004**, **4755**
Business Travel News. (US) **4755**
Business Traveler International. (US) **4755**, **652**
Business Traveler Magazine. (US) **4755**, **652**
Business Traveler's Airport Hotel Directory. (US) **4755**
Business Traveler's America's Greatest Cities see Business Traveler's Airport Hotel Directory **4755**
Business Traveler's Greatest Hotels see Business Traveler's Hotel Guide **4755**
Business Traveler's Hotel Guide. (US) **4755**, **2472**
†Business Traveler's Newsletter. (US ISSN 1040-4635) **5155**
Business Traveller. (UK ISSN 0309-9334) **4755**, **652**
Business Traveller Asia-Pacific. (HK ISSN 0255-7312) **4755**
Business Traveller International. (US) **4755**, **652**
Business Trends see Economic Commentary **661**
Business Trends: Argentine Economic Legislation. see Tendencias Economicas: Legislacion Economicas Argentina **694**
Business Trends Asia Report: Indonesia.(MY) **848**
Business Trends in New York State. (US ISSN 0007-7127) **849**
Business Venezuela. (VE ISSN 0045-3641) **809**
Business Ventures. (US) **941**, **4146**
Business View see Florida Business - Southwest **866**
Business Week. (US ISSN 0007-7135) **652**
Business Week - China. (US) **652**, **902**
Business Weekly/Shang Yeh Chou K'an.(CH) **652**
Business Weekly. (GH) **849**
Business West see Business South West **652**
Business West. (US) **652**, **2243**
Business West Midlands. (UK ISSN 0958-7942) **653**
Business Who's Who Australian Buying Reference see The Business Who's Who Australian Products and Trade Names Guide **1034**
The Business Who's Who Australian Products and Trade Names Guide. (AT) **1034**
The Business Who's Who of Australia. (AT ISSN 0068-4503) **1125**
Business Who's Who of Australia and Australian Purchasing Yearbook see The Business Who's Who of Australia **1125**
Business World. (II) **653**
▼Business World. (CN ISSN 0847-2386) **769**, **941**, **1004**, **1034**
Business World. (MY) **809**
†Business World. (UK) **5155**
Business Writer see Bottom Line Communicator **1332**
Businesses & Assets. (UK) **1034**
Businessmac. (US) **1458**
Businessman's Directory, The Republic of China. (CH) **1125**
Businessman's Law. (SA ISSN 0045-3668) **2708**, **653**
Buskap og Avdraatt. (NO ISSN 0007-7194) **213**
Buskursbuch. (GW ISSN 0178-9988) **4685**
Busqueda. (UY) **849**, **3876**
†Buss. (US ISSN 0193-6832) **5155**
Buss - Svensk Omnibustidning/Swedish Bus & Coach Magazine. (SW ISSN 0282-7654) **4685**
Bussen. (NO) **4647**
Buster. (UK) **1250**
Busverkehr. (GW ISSN 0720-4507) **4647**
Busy East see Atlantic Advocate **5140**
Busy Solicitors' Digest. (UK ISSN 0263-4430) **2607**
Butane Propane. (FR ISSN 0007-7240) **3683**

Butane - Propane News. (US ISSN 0007-7259) **3683**
Butcher and Processor. (UK ISSN 0268-1781) **2062**
Buteo see Bladsmutten **562**
Butler Alumni Quarterly. (US) **1306**
Butler Aviation's Echelon. (US) **2222**, **1004**
Butler Parker. (GW) **2188**
Butlleti Informatiu de Circular Farmaceutica. (SP) **3720**
Butonia. (GW) **1284**
Al-Butrul wal-Sina'a fi Abu Dhabi/Petroleum and Industry in Abu Dhabi.(TS) **3705**
†Butson Family Newsletter. (US ISSN 0743-4235) **5155**
Butsuri. (JA ISSN 0029-0181) **3815**
Butt see Independent (Arlington) **4129**
Butter-Fat. (CN ISSN 0007-7275) **198**
Butterfield Bulletin. (US) **320**, **653**
Butterflies and Children's Crafts see Children's Album **1251**
Butterfly Net. (US) **353**
Butterick Home Catalog. (US ISSN 0007-7305) **1289**, **4617**
Butterworths Annotations to the New Zealand Statutes. (NZ) **2607**
Butterworths Australian Tax Handbook. (AT ISSN 1033-0313) **1089**
Butterworths Australian Tax Legislation. (AT) **1089**
Butterworths Budget Tax Tables. (UK ISSN 0525-3063) **1089**
Butterworths Commercial Service. (NZ) **2708**
Butterworths Company Law Cases. (UK ISSN 0267-145X) **2708**
Butterworths Company Law Service. (UK) **2708**
Butterworths Company Reports see Morison's Company Law Reports **2711**
Butterworths Consolidated Legislation Service of South Africa. Monthly Bulletin see Butterworths Legislation Service. Monthly Bulletin **2607**
Butterworths Conveyancing Bulletin. (NZ ISSN 0111-9656) **2607**
Butterworths Costs Service. (UK) **2607**
Butterworths County Court Precedents & Pleadings. (UK) **2607**
Butterworths Current Law. (NZ ISSN 0110-070X) **2607**
Butterworths District Court Reports. (NZ) **2607**
Butterworths District Courts Practice - Civil. (NZ) **2701**
Butterworths Family Law Bulletin. (NZ) **2716**
Butterworths Family Law Reports. (NZ) **2716**
Butterworths Family Law Service. (NZ) **2716**
Butterworths Family Law Service. (UK) **2717**
Butterworths International Law Directory. (UK) **2720**
†Butterworths International Medical Reviews: Clinical Endocrinology. (UK ISSN 0260-0072) **5155**
†Butterworths International Medical Reviews: Gastroenterology. (UK ISSN 0260-0110) **5155**
†Butterworths International Medical Reviews: Neurology. (UK ISSN 0260-0137) **5155**
†Butterworths International Medical Reviews: Obstetrics and Gynecology. (UK ISSN 0144-9478) **5155**
Butterworths International Medical Reviews: Ophthalmology. (UK ISSN 0260-0145) **3298**
†Butterworths International Medical Reviews: Orthopaedics. (UK ISSN 0260-0153) **5155**
Butterworths International Medical Reviews: Otolaryngology. (UK ISSN 0260-0102) **3314**
†Butterworths International Medical Reviews: Pediatrics. (UK ISSN 0260-0161) **5155**
Butterworths Journal of International Banking and Financial Law. (UK ISSN 0269-2694) **2607**, **769**
Butterworths Law Digest see Mallal's Monthly Digest **2652**

Butterworths Law Directory and Diary. (UK) **2607**, 1125
Butterworths Law of Food & Drugs. (UK) **2607**, 2062
Butterworths Legal Services Directory. (UK) **2607**, 3673
Butterworths Legislation Service. (UK) **2607**
Butterworths Legislation Service. Monthly Bulletin. (SA) **2607**
Butterworths Orange Tax Handbook. (UK ISSN 0141-1500) **1089**
Butterworths Property Law Handbook. (UK) **2607**, 4146
Butterworths Road Traffic Service. (UK) **2607**, 4717
Butterworths Tax Alert. (SA) **1089**
Butterworths Tax Guide. (AT) **1089**
Butterworths Taxation Library. (NZ) **1089**
†Butterworths Trading Law Cases. (UK ISSN 0269-2805) **5155**
Butterworths U K Tax Guide. (UK) **2607**
Butterworth's Wrongful Dismissal Practice Manual. (CN) **2607**, 974
Butterworths Yellow Tax Handbook. (UK ISSN 0141-3856) **1089**
Buttons. (UK ISSN 0262-5326) **1251**
†Buut. (NE ISSN 0167-5303) **5155**
Buvar. (HU ISSN 0007-7356) **433**
Buxom. (US) **3396**
Buxom Belle Courier. (US ISSN 0007-7364) **3604**
Buy Books Where, Sell Books Where. (US ISSN 0732-6599) **4124**, 2750
Buy from India. (II ISSN 0304-968X) **1125**
Buy or Sell Your Business. (UK) **1113**, 2607
Buyer. (UK ISSN 0142-6796) **902**, 2720
Buyer. (SA ISSN 0007-7372) **1284**, 4617
Buyer *see* Baking Buyer **2087**
Buyers' Guide. (IT ISSN 0007-7380) **902**
Buyers' Guide. (KO) **1125**
Buyers Guide: Footnotes *see* Performing Arts Buyers Guide: Footnotes **1531**
Buyers Guide for Fresh Produce *see* Food Service Guide to Fresh Produce **2091**
Buyers Guide for the Health Care Industry. (US) **2459**, 1125
Buyers Guide for the Health Care Institutions *see* Buyers Guide for the Health Care Industry **2459**
Buyers' Guide: Nuclear Industry in Japan. (JA) **1804**
Buyer's Guide of Cardio-Respiratory Equipment and Supplies. (US) **3364**
Buyer's Guide of Tokyo (Year). (JA) **1502**
Buyer's Guide Timber Frame Homes. (US ISSN 1054-1136) **607**
Buyers' Guide to Outdoor Advertising. (US) **29**
Buyers' Guide to the Automotive Industry of Great Britain for International Buyers *see* S M M T Buyers Guide **4701**
Buyer's Guide to the New York Market. (US) **1125**
Buyers' Guide: Watch Industry, Jewellery and Allied Trades. *see* Guide des Acheteurs: Horlogerie, Bijouterie et Branches Annexes **5202**
Buyers Laboratory Test Reports. Series 1: Test Reports on Office Products. (US) **1057**
▼Buying and Selling Businesses - Personal Property. (AT) **769**, 1113
▼Buying Group News. (US) **1034**
▼Buying Habits of Golf Course Superintendents. (US) **4501**, 1034
†Buying Office Products. (US) **5155**
Buying or Selling Your Business *see* Buy or Sell Your Business **1113**
Buying Strategy Forecast. (US ISSN 0733-0103) **1035**
Buyouts. (US) **941**
Buyouts and Acquisitions Magazine *see* Corporate Growth Magazine **2709**
Buzetski Zbornik. (CI) **268**, 2354
▼Buzz. (US ISSN 1053-3605) **2222**
Buzzworm. (US ISSN 0898-2996) **1484**

Bwino: Health Care News. (ZA) **3800**, 3604
Bwletin Diwinyddol *see* Ysgrifau Diwinyddol **4210**
By og Bygd. (NO ISSN 0084-8212) **2354**, 236
Byarozka. (BW ISSN 0007-7429) **1251**
Bydgoskie Towarzystwo Naukowe. Wydzial Nauk Humanistycznych. Prace. Seria B (Jezyk i Literatura). (PL ISSN 0068-4570) **2807**, 2901
Bydgoskie Towarzystwo Naukowe. Wydzial Nauk Humanistycznych. Prace. Seria C (Historia i Archeologia). (PL ISSN 0068-4589) **2354**
Bydgoskie Towarzystwo Naukowe. Wydzial Nauk Humanistycznych. Prace. Seria D (Sztuka). (PL ISSN 0067-947X) **320**
Bydgoskie Towarzystwo Naukowe. Wydzial Nauk Technicznych. Prace. Seria Z: (Prace Zbiorowe). (PL ISSN 0068-4597) **4594**
†Bye Cadmos. (US ISSN 0363-5236) **5155**
Byelorussian Books. *see* Knigi Belorusskoi S.S.R **404**
Byelorussian Institute of Arts and Sciences. Annals. *see* Belaruski Instytut Navukii Mastatstva. Zapisy **2352**
Byelorussian Publications. *see* Pechat Belorusskoi S.S.R **409**
Byelorussian Times. (US ISSN 0276-1416) **1995**
Byelorussian Voice. *see* Bielaruski Holas **1993**
Byelorussian Youth. (US) **1995**
Byers Election Law. (US) **2607**, 3876
Byg & Trae. (DK) **607**
Bygd. (DK ISSN 0007-7445) **2243**
Bygd och Natur. (SW ISSN 0345-7982) **1484**, 1944
Bygdeserien. (FI) **296**
Bygdeungdommen. (NO) **1251**
Bygg & Traevaruhandeln. (SW) **607**
Bygge Forum. (DK) **607**
†Bygge Nyt. (DK ISSN 0007-7488) **5155**
†Bygge Nyts Leverandoerregister. (DK ISSN 0007-7488) **5155**
Bygge og Bo. (NO) **2484**
Bygge- og Bolipolitiske Oversigt. (DK ISSN 0107-119X) **607**
Byggeindustrien/Danish Building Industry. (DK ISSN 0007-750X) **607**
Byggeindustrien. (NO) **607**
Byggekunst. (NO ISSN 0007-7518) **296**
Byggenytt. (NO) **608**
Byggeri. (DK ISSN 0107-1866) **608**
Byggforskning *see* Tidskriften Byggforskning **634**
Byggherren. (NO ISSN 0332-6152) **608**
Byggindustrin. (SW ISSN 0349-3733) **608**
Byggmesteren. (NO) **608**
Byggnadsarbetaren. (SW ISSN 0007-7569) **639**
Byggnadskostnadsindex. *see* Finland. Tilastokeskus. Indeksitiedotus RK. Rakennuskustannusindeksi **637**
Byggnadstidningen/Building News. (SW ISSN 0007-7607) **608**
Byggreferat. (SW ISSN 0345-1941) **637**, 4
†Bygningsarbeideren. (NO) **5155**
Bygningskonstruktoerernes Fagblad. (DK) **608**
Bygningskonstruktoerernes Medlemsorientering *see* Bygningskonstruktoerernes Fagblad **608**
Bygningsstatiske Meddelelser. (DK ISSN 0106-3715) **608**
Bygone Kent. (UK ISSN 0262-5342) **2354**
Byhornet. (DK ISSN 0105-6433) **2354**, 268
Byline. (US ISSN 0744-4249) **2567**
Byminner. (NO ISSN 0007-7631) **2354**
Byoin/Hospital. (JA ISSN 0385-2377) **2459**

Byoin Kanri/Hospital Administration. (JA ISSN 0386-9571) **2459**
Byoin Setsubi. *see* Hospital Engineering Association of Japan. Journal **2464**
Byoin Yoran/Japanese Hospital Directory. (JA ISSN 0408-0904) **2459**
Byplan. (DK ISSN 0007-7658) **2484**
Byron Journal. (UK ISSN 0301-7257) **2989**
Byron Society Newsletter. (US ISSN 0196-8998) **2901**
Byte. (US ISSN 0360-5280) **1436**, 1458, 1468
†Byte Engineers. (US) **5155**
Byulleten' Eksperimental'noi Biologii i Meditsiny. (RU ISSN 0365-9615) **434**, 3084
Byulleten' Inostrannoi Kommercheskoi Informatsii. (RU ISSN 0007-7674) **902**
Byulleten' po Narkoticheskim Sredstvam *see* Bulletin on Narcotics **1535**
†Byulleten' Signal'noi Informatsii o Zhurnale "Laboratornoe Delo/Bulletin of Current Awareness Information on the Journal "Laboratory Technique". (UR) **5155**
Byulleten' Stroitel'noi Tekhniki. (RU ISSN 0007-7690) **608**
Byways (Fairfax). (US) **4755**, 4671
Byzantina. (GR) **1275**
Byzantina Australiensia. (AT) **2354**, 2901
Byzantina Kai Metabyzantina. (US ISSN 0742-1141) **2428**
Byzantina Neerlandica. (NE ISSN 0525-4507) **2354**
Byzantine and Modern Greek Studies. (UK ISSN 0307-0131) **2807**, 2901
Byzantine Studies/Etudes Byzantines. (US ISSN 0095-4608) **2504**
Byzantinische Zeitschrift. (GW ISSN 0007-7704) **3635**, 2307
Byzantinobulgarica. (BU ISSN 0068-4686) **2354**
Byzantinoslavica. (NE ISSN 0007-7712) **3635**
Byzantion. (BE) **3635**, 320
Byzantion Nea Hellas. (CL ISSN 0716-2138) **2504**, 2807
C A A C Inflight Magazine. (Civil Aviation and Administration of China) (JA) **4671**
C A A C Inflight Magazine. *see* Zhongguo Minhang **4678**
†C A A Magazine. (Chicago Athletic Association) (US) **5155**
▼C A A News and Views. (Canadian Automobile Association) (CN) **4685**
C A A Newsletter (New York). (College Art Association) (US) **320**
C A A Newsletter (San Francisco). (Chinese for Affirmative Action) (US) **1995**, 3940
C A A Research Series *see* K A C Research Series **276**
C A A S Monograph Series *see* Afro-American Culture and Society Monograph Series **4364**
C A A S News. (Computer-Assisted Appraisal Section) (US ISSN 8755-3732) **4146**, 805
C A A S Newsletter *see* C A A S Report **4367**
C A A S Report. (Center for Afro-American Studies) (US ISSN 1051-4589) **4367**
C A A S Special Publication Series. (Center for Afro-American Studies) (US ISSN 0882-5300) **4367**, 1995
C A A T Newsletter. (Campaign Against Arms Trade) (UK ISSN 0142-7113) **3876**, 3940
C A A T Tracks. (Ontario Colleges of Applied Arts and Technology) (CN ISSN 0829-254X) **2750**
C A B A News Bulletin. (Canadian Amateur Boxing Association) (CN) **4467**
C A B Air Carrier Traffic Statistics. (Civil Aeronautics Board) (US ISSN 0731-3411) **49**
C A B E Journal. (Connecticut Association of Boards of Education, Inc.) (US) **1725**

C.A.B. International Bureau of Agricultural Economics. Annotated Bibliographies Series A. (UK) **134**
C.A.B. International Bureau of Agricultural Economics. Annotated Bibliographies. Series B: Agricultural Policy and Rural Development in Africa. (UK) **134**
†C.A.B. International. Bureau of Animal Breeding and Genetics. Technical Communications. (UK) **5155**
C.A.B. International. Bureau of Nutrition. Annotated Bibliographies. (UK) **3613**
†C.A.B. International. Bureau of Nutrition. Technical Communications.(UK) **5155**
†C.A.B. International. Bureau of Pastures and Field Crops. Bulletin. (UK) **5155**
C.A.B. International. Bureau of Soils. Annotated Bibliographies. (UK) **134**
†C.A.B. International. Bureau of Soils. Technical Communications. (UK) **5155**
C A B International Database News. (US) **1443**
C.A.B. International. Forestry Bureau. Annotated Bibliographies. (Commonwealth Agricultural Bureaux) (UK) **2111**, 395
†C.A.B. International. Forestry Bureau. Technical Communications. (UK) **5155**
†C.A.B. International. Institute of Biological Control. Technical Communications. (UK) **5155**
C.A.B. International. Mycological Institute. Phytopathological Papers. (Commonwealth Agricultural Bureaux) (UK) **498**
†C A B L I S. (Current Awareness Bulletin for Library and Information Staff) (UK ISSN 0954-9196) **5155**
C A B News. (National Association of Citizens Advice Bureaux) (UK) **2607**, 3940
C.A.B. Prompts Series: Chickpea and Pigeon Peas Prompts. (Commonwealth Agricultural Bureaux) (UK ISSN 0953-2307) **134**
C.A.B. Prompts Series: Groundnut Prompts. (Commonwealth Agricultural Bureaux) (UK ISSN 0953-2293) **135**
C A B S *see* Chemical Abstracts - Biochemistry Sections **1199**
†C A B's Annual Report. (UK) **5155**
C.A.C.C. Newsletter *see* Christian Anti-Communism Crusade. Newsletter **3879**
C A C D Journal. (California Association for Counseling and Development) (US) **4015**
C A C Journal. (US) **1296**
C A C News *see* Chicago Artists' News **321**
C A C Newsletter. (American Philatelic Society, Chapter Activities Committee) (US) **3750**
C A C Report. (Computer Aids Corporation) (US) **1389**, 1416
C A C S W News. (Canadian Advisory Council on the Status of Women) (CN ISSN 1188-2654) **4838**, 2607
C A - C T F *see* Clinical Abstracts - Current Therapeutic Findings **3168**
C A D - C A M Abstracts. (Computer Aided Design - Computer Aided Machinery) (UK ISSN 0958-1499) **1420**, 1877
C A D - C A M Abstracts. (Computer Aided Design - Computer Aided Manufacturing) (US ISSN 0882-1437) **1403**
C A D - C A M Alert *see* C A D - C I M Alert **1412**
C A D - C A M & Robotics. (CN ISSN 0822-0603) **1420**
C A D - C A M Digest. (UK ISSN 0263-6190) **1420**
†C A D - C A M Digest. (US) **5156**
C A D - C A M in Bedrijf *see* C A Techniek **1412**

C A D - C A M Index see C A D - C A M Abstracts Annual **5156**

C A D - C A M International. (UK ISSN 0261-6920) **4594**

†C A D - C A M: Management Strategies. (Computer Aided Design - Computer Aided Manufacturing) (US ISSN 0741-0042) **5156**

C A D - C A M Profiles see C A D - C A M Abstracts **1420**

C A D - C A M Report. (Computer Aided Design - Computer Aided Manufacturing) (GW) **1420**

C A D - C A M Systems. (Computer Aided Design - Computer Aided Machinery) (CN) **1420**

C A D - C A M Technology see C I M Technology **5157**

C A D - C A M Update. (US) **1420**

C A D - C I M Alert. (Computer-Aided Design, Computer-Integrated Manufacturing) (US ISSN 8756-842X) **1412**, 1420

C A - D E News. (Council for Alcohol - Drug Education of N.J.) (US) **1535**

C A D U Publications see A R D U Publication **67**

C A Dalyst. (US ISSN 0820-5450) **1420**

C A E D Report see C A R D Report (Ames, 1971) **5156**

C A E L L Journal. (Computer Assisted English Language Learning) (US) **1416**

C A E L News. (Council for Adult and Experiential Learning) (US) **1682**

C A E News. (CN ISSN 0007-7739) **49**, 1883

C A F C Dialogue/A C C P Dialogue. (Canadian Association of Fire Chiefs) (CN ISSN 0706-1382) **2031**

C A F Dispatch. (Confederate Air Force) (US) **3453**, 2401

C.A.F.I.P. Bulletin. (Canadian Association for Israel Philately) (CN) **3750**

C A F M System & Strategies (Year). (US) **1443**, 1476

C A F O D Journal. (Catholic Fund for Overseas Development) (UK) **926**, 4257

C A F Revue. (Caisse Nationale des Allocations Familiales) (FR) **4400**

C A H P E R Journal see Canadian Association for Health, Physical Education and Recreation. Journal **3800**

C A H P E R Keeps In Touch see In Touch (Glouchester) **3804**

C A H S Journal. (Canadian Aviation Historical Society) (CN ISSN 0007-7771) **49**

C A Highlights. (Communicating for Agriculture) (US) **81**

C A I Informa. (Centro Argentino de Ingenieros) (AG) **1883**

†C A I News. (Community Association Institute) (US ISSN 0276-0428) **5156**

†C A I News Briefs. (Confederation of Australian Industry) (AT) **5156**

C A - Insight. (Computer Associates International Inc.) (US) **1458**

C A J Bulletin. (Canadian Association of Journalists) (CN ISSN 1184-0641) **2567**

C A J Christliche Arbeiter-Jugend see Aktion **4162**

C A J E X. (Cardiff Association of Jewish Ex-Servicemen and Women) (UK) **1995**

†C A K. (Computer Anwendungen - Computer Applications - Universitaet Karlsruhe) (GW ISSN 0179-7379) **5156**

C A L Anthology. (Conservatory of American Letters) (US) **2989**

C A L C Report. (National Clergy and Laity Concerned) (US ISSN 0739-9189) **3952**, 4167

C A L F News see C A L F News Cattle Feeder **213**

C A L F News Cattle Feeder. (Concerning America's Livestock Feeders) (US) **213**

C A L I C O. Monograph Series. (Computer Assisted Language & Instruction Consortium) (US) **1416**, 1701, 1745

C A L I C O Journal. (Computer Assisted Language & Instruction Consortium) (US ISSN 0742-7778) **1688**, 1458, 1468

C A L L. (Current Awareness - Library Literature) (US ISSN 0091-5270) **2750**

C A L L Digest see C A E L L Journal **1416**

C A L L S see California Academic Libraries List of Serials **5158**

C A L Newsletter see Conservatory of American Letters Newsletter **2908**

C A L U S Research Reports. (Centre for Advanced Land Use Studies) (UK) **4146**, 608

C A L Underwriter. (California Association of Life Underwriters) (US ISSN 0199-2414) **2529**

C A M A C O L. Asamblea Nacional. Documento. (Camara Colombiana de la Construccion (CAMACOL)) (CK) **608**

C A M A C O L. Revista. (Camara Colombiana de la Construccion (CAMACOL)) (CK ISSN 0120-5102) **608**

C A M A Parade. (Children's Apparel Manufacturers Association) (CN) **1284**

C A M - I Cameos. (Computer Aided Manufacturing - International Inc.) (US) **1412**

C A M L Newsletter/A C B M Nouvelles. (Canadian Association of Music Libraries) (CN ISSN 0383-1299) **3543**, 2750

C A M R A S O News see B C T C - C A M R A S O - In-Site **1281**

C A M S Manual of Motor Sport. (Confederation of Australian Motor Sport) (AT ISSN 1033-0526) **4467**

C A M S Report. (Confederation of Australian Motor Sport) (AT) **4467**, 4685

C A Magazine. (Chartered Accountant) (CN ISSN 0317-6878) **748**

C A N Directory: Wholesalers of Organic Produce and Products see Organic Wholesalers Directory & Yearbook: Organic Food & Farm Supplies **112**

C A N H C - Gram (California Association for Neurologically Handicapped Children) see The Gram **1736**

C A N M E T Reports. (Canada Centre for Mineral and Energy Technology) (CN ISSN 0705-5196) **3479**

C A O. (Contemporary Astrological Observations) (US) **358**

C A O Times see C A O **358**

C A P A M I see Workshop on Computer Architecture for Pattern Analysis and Machine Intelligence **5306**

C A P F see Chemical Age Project File **1172**

†C A P International Outlook. (Charles A. Pesko) (US) **5156**

C A P Legislation. (Common Agricultural Policy) (UK) **81**

C A P Monitor. (Common Agricultural Policy) (UK ISSN 0142-5633) **81**

C A P Sule (Levittown). (Children of Aging Parents) (US) **2271**, 4430

C A P Today. (College of American Pathologists) (US ISSN 0891-1525) **3085**

C A Quarterly. (Creditanstalt-Bankverein) (AU) **849**

C A R see Canadian Auto Review **4686**

C A R A Seminary Directory. (Center for Applied Research in the Apostolate) (US) **4257**

C A R D A T S Technical Report. (Caribbean Agricultural Rural Development, Advisory and Training Service) (GD) **81**

†C A R D Report (Ames, 1971). (Center for Agricultural and Rural Development) (US ISSN 0271-7190) **5156**

C A R D Report (Ames, 1986). (Center for Agricultural and Rural Development) (US ISSN 0886-3970) **81**

C A R E. (Citizens Association for Racial Equality) (NZ) **4430**

C A R E Newsletter. (Campaign Against Racial Exploitation (Australia) Inc.) (AT) **1995**, 3940

C A R N E S see Computer Aided Research in Near Eastern Studies **2330**

C A R P News. (Canadian Association of Retired Persons) (CN) **2271**

C.A.R. Scope see Arthritis News **3368**

C A R T see Truck Australia **1875**

C A S A see Llais **1316**

C A S BioTech Updates. Agriculture. (Chemical Abstracts Service) (US ISSN 0890-7528) **135**, 4, 462, 1191

C A S BioTech Updates. Antibody Conjugates. (US ISSN 0895-6499) **1191**, 4, 3167

C A S BioTech Updates. Biochemical Immobilization & Biocatalytic Reactors. (US ISSN 0895-6626) **1191**, 4, 462, 489

C A S BioTech Updates. Biosensors. (US ISSN 0884-7479) **462**, 4, 489, 1191

C A S BioTech Updates. Cell & Tissue Culture. (US ISSN 1040-709X) **462**, 4, 489, 1191

C A S BioTech Updates. Commercial Fermentation. (US ISSN 1045-8565) **1191**, 4, 462

C A S BioTech Updates. D N A & R N A Probes. (US ISSN 1045-8581) **462**, 4, 469, 1191

C A S BioTech Updates. D N A Formation & Repair. (US ISSN 0895-6618) **462**, 4, 469

C A S BioTech Updates. Environmental Biotechnology. (US ISSN 0884-7452) **1972**, 4, 489, 1191

C A S BioTech Updates. Enzymes in Biotechnology. (US ISSN 1040-7081) **463**, 4, 489, 1191

C A S BioTech Updates. Genetic Engineering. (US ISSN 0884-7460) **463**, 4, 469, 540

C A S BioTech Updates. Nucleic Acid & Protein Sequences. (US ISSN 1045-859X) **463**, 4, 469

C A S BioTech Updates. Pharmaceutical Applications. (US ISSN 0884-7487) **1191**, 4, 463

C A S BioTech Updates. Product Purification & Separation. (US ISSN 1040-7103) **1191**, 4

▼C A S BioTech Updates. Slow-Release Pharmaceuticals. (Chemical Abstracts Service) (US) **3720**

C A S E A - A C E A S Newsletter. (Canadian Association for Studies in Educational Administration) (CN) **1725**

C A S E Outlook. (US ISSN 0895-2108) **1476**

C A S E Strategies. (Computer-Aided Systems Engineering) (US ISSN 1045-1986) **1877**

C A S E Trends. (US ISSN 1046-5944) **1443**

C A S Journal. (Catgut Acoustical Society) (US ISSN 1053-7694) **3543**

C A S L I S, Calgary Chapter. Newsletter. (Canadian Association of Special Libraries and Information Services) (CN ISSN 0821-3127) **2750**

C A S Newsletter. (Catholic Archives Society) (UK ISSN 0262-6896) **4257**

C A S Nyt. (Centrale Afdeling for Sygehushygiejne) (DK ISSN 0901-067X) **3085**

C A S S I see Chemical Abstracts Service Source Index **1199**

C A Selects. (Chemical Abstracts Service) (US) **1191**, 4

C A Selects. A I D S and Related Immunodeficiencies. (US ISSN 1040-7111) **3167**, 4, 3218

C A Selects. Acid Rain & Acid Air. (US ISSN 0885-0097) **1972**, 4, 1976

C A Selects. Activated Carbon. (US ISSN 1045-8514) **1192**, 4

C A Selects. Adhesives. (US ISSN 0162-7686) **1192**, 4

C A Selects. Adsorption. (US ISSN 1045-8506) **1192**, 4

C A Selects. Air Pollution (Books & Reviews). (US ISSN 0895-5980) **1972**, 395, 1192, 1976

▼C A Selects. Alkoxylated Oleochemicals. (US ISSN 1051-3884) **1192**, 4, 463

C A Selects. Alkylation & Catalysts. (US ISSN 0895-5964) **1192**, 4

C A Selects. Allergy and Antiallergic Agents. (US ISSN 1047-8191) **3167**, 4, 3184

C A Selects. Alzheimer's Disease & Related Memory Dysfunctions. (US ISSN 1047-8183) **3167**

C A Selects. Amino Acids, Peptides and Proteins. (US ISSN 0275-701X) **463**, 4

C A Selects. Analytical Electrochemistry.(US ISSN 0160-8959) **1192**, 4

C A Selects. Animal Longevity and Aging. (US ISSN 0162-7694) **463**, 4

C A Selects. Anti-Inflammatory Agents and Arthritis. (US ISSN 0148-2394) **3167**, 4

▼C A Selects. Antiarrhythmics. (US ISSN 1051-3892) **3167**, 4, 3205, 3747

C A Selects. Antibacterial Agents. (US ISSN 0890-1848) **1192**, 4

C A Selects. Anticonvulsants & Antiepileptics. (US ISSN 1047-8175) **3167**

C A Selects. Antifungal & Antimycotic Agents. (US ISSN 1047-8167) **463**, 4, 550

C A Selects. Antioxidants. (US ISSN 0275-7028) **1192**, 4

C A Selects. Antitumor Agents. (US ISSN 0148-2386) **3167**, 4, 3194

C A Selects. Artificial Sweeteners. (US ISSN 0890-1813) **2084**, 4

C A Selects. Asymmetric Synthesis & Induction. (US ISSN 0890-183X) **1192**, 4

C A Selects. Atherosclerosis & Heart Disease. (US ISSN 0148-2378) **3167**, 4

C A Selects. Atomic Spectroscopy. (US ISSN 0195-4911) **3836**, 4

C A Selects. Automated Chemical Analysis. (US ISSN 0740-0683) **1192**, 4

C A Selects. Bactericides, Disinfectants and Antiseptics see C A Selects. Antibacterial Agents **1192**

C A Selects. Batteries & Fuel Cells. (US ISSN 0162-7708) **1192**, 4

C A Selects. Beta-Lactam Antibiotics. (US ISSN 0148-2459) **3747**, 5

C A Selects. Biogenic Amines & the Nervous System. (US ISSN 0162-7716) **3167**, 5

C A Selects. Biological Information Transfer. (US ISSN 0162-7724) **463**, 5, 1192

C A Selects. Block & Graft Polymers. (US ISSN 0734-8851) **1192**, 5

C A Selects. Blood Coagulation. (US ISSN 0162-7732) **3167**, 5

▼C A Selects. Calcium Channel Blockers. (US ISSN 1051-3906) **1192**, 5, 474, 3747

C A Selects. Carbohydrates (Chemical Aspects). (US ISSN 0740-0756) **1192**, 5

C A Selects. Carbon & Graphite Fibers. (US ISSN 0890-1856) **1192**, 5

C A Selects. Carbon & Heteroatom N M R. (US ISSN 0190-9401) **1192**, 5

C A Selects. Carbon Fiber Composites. (US ISSN 0895-5956) **1192**, 5

C A Selects. Carcinogens, Mutagens & Teratogens. (US ISSN 0148-2408) **3167**, 5

C A Selects. Catalysis (Applied & Physical Aspects). (US ISSN 0146-440X) **1192**, 5

C A Selects. Catalysis (Organic Reactions). (US ISSN 0146-4396) **1192**, 5

C A Selects. Catalyst Regeneration. (US ISSN 0734-8800) **1192**, 5

C A Selects. Catalytic & Kinetic Analysis. (US ISSN 0890-1864) **1192, 5**
C A Selects. Ceramic Materials (Journals). (US ISSN 0895-5948) **1167, 5, 1192**
C A Selects. Ceramic Materials (Patents). (US ISSN 0885-0100) **1167, 5, 3679**
C A Selects. Chelating Agents. (US ISSN 0734-8797) **1193, 5**
C A Selects. Chemical Engineering Operations. (US ISSN 1040-712X) **1193, 5**
C A Selects. Chemical Hazards, Health & Safety. (US ISSN 0190-9398) **3623, 5**
C A Selects. Chemical Instrumentation. (US ISSN 0195-4938) **2525, 5, 1193**
C A Selects. Chemical Processing Apparatus. (US ISSN 0195-4946) **1848,** 1842
C A Selects. Chemical Vapor Deposition.(US ISSN 0885-0119) **1193, 5**
C A Selects. Chemiluminescence. (US ISSN 1040-7138) **1193, 5**
C A Selects. Chemistry of Ir, Os, Rh, & Ru. (US ISSN 1040-7146) **1193, 5**
C A Selects. Coal Science and Process Chemistry. (US ISSN 0146-4426) **1193, 5,** 3499
C A Selects. Coatings, Inks, & Related Products. (US ISSN 0275-7036) **3656, 5**
C A Selects. Colloids (Applied Aspects). (US ISSN 0160-8967) **1193, 5**
C A Selects. Colloids (Macromolecular Aspects). (US ISSN 0190-9444) **1193, 5**
C A Selects. Colloids (Physicochemical Aspects). (US ISSN 0160-8975) **1193, 5**
C A Selects. Color Science. (US ISSN 0885-0127) **1193, 5**
C A Selects. Colorants and Dyes. (US ISSN 0734-8789) **1282, 5**
C A Selects. Composite Materials (Polymeric). (US ISSN 1040-7154) **1193, 5**
C A Selects. Computers in Chemistry. (US ISSN 0160-9025) **1193, 5, 4359**
C A Selects. Conductive Polymers. (US ISSN 0885-0135) **1193, 5**
C A Selects. Controlled Release Technology. (US ISSN 0740-0748) **1193, 5**
C A Selects. Corrosion. (US ISSN 0146-4434) **1193, 5**
C A Selects. Corrosion-Inhibiting Coatings. (US ISSN 0749-7296) **3656, 5**
C A Selects. Cosmetic Chemicals. (US ISSN 0275-7044) **375, 5**
C A Selects. Crosslinking Reactions. (US ISSN 0740-0721) **1193, 5**
C A Selects. Crystal Growth. (US ISSN 0162-7740) **1193, 5**
C A Selects. Detergents, Soaps, & Surfactants. (US ISSN 0162-7767) **1193, 5**
C A Selects. Distillation Technology. (US ISSN 0275-7052) **1193, 5**
C A Selects. Drilling Muds. (US ISSN 0749-730X) **3705, 5**
C A Selects. Drug Analysis Biological Fluids & Tissues. (US ISSN 1045-8530) **1193, 5,** 463
C A Selects. Drug & Cosmetic Toxicity. (US ISSN 0162-7775) **3747, 5**
C A Selects. Drug Delivery Systems & Dosage Forms. (US ISSN 1040-7162) **3747, 5**
C A Selects. Drug Interactions. (US ISSN 1047-8205) **3167, 5,** 3747
C A Selects. Elastomers. (US ISSN 1045-8557) **1193, 5**
C A Selects. Electrically Conductive Organics. (US ISSN 0885-0143) **1193, 5**
C A Selects. Electrochemical Organic Synthesis. (US ISSN 0734-8770) **1193, 5**
C A Selects. Electrochemical Reactions. (US ISSN 0146-4442) **1194, 5**
C A Selects. Electrodeposition. (US ISSN 0162-7783) **1194, 5**
C A Selects. Electron & Auger Spectroscopy. (US ISSN 0146-4450) **3836, 5**
C A Selects. Electron Spin Resonance (Chemical Aspects). (US ISSN 0146-4469) **1194, 5**
C A Selects. Electronic Chemicals & Materials. (US ISSN 0885-0151) **1194, 5**
C A Selects. Electrophoresis. (US ISSN 0195-4962) **1194, 5**
C A Selects. Emulsifiers and Demulsifiers. (US ISSN 0734-8754) **1194, 5**
C A Selects. Emulsion Polymerization. (US ISSN 0195-4970) **1194, 5**
C A Selects. Energy Reviews & Books. (US ISSN 0162-7791) **1798, 5**
C A Selects. Enhanced Petroleum Recovery. (US ISSN 0734-8746) **3705, 5**
C A Selects. Environmental Pollution. (US ISSN 0160-9041) **1972, 5,** 1976
C A Selects. Enzyme Applications. (US ISSN 0895-593X) **1194, 5**
C A Selects. Enzyme Assays. (US ISSN 0895-5808) **1194, 5**
C A Selects. Epoxy Resins. (US ISSN 0275-7060) **1194, 5**
C A Selects. Fats & Oils. (US ISSN 0275-7079) **1194, 5**
C A Selects. Fermentation Chemicals. (US ISSN 0740-0713) **1194, 5**
C A Selects. Fiber Optics and Optical Communication. (US ISSN 0890-1872) **3836, 5**
C A Selects. Fiber-Reinforced Plastics. (US ISSN 0734-869X) **3868, 5**
C A Selects. Flammability. (US ISSN 0162-7805) **1194, 5,** 2035
C A Selects. Flavors & Fragrances. (US ISSN 0148-2327) **1194, 5,** 375
C A Selects. Fluidized Solids Technology. (US ISSN 0195-4989) **1194, 5**
C A Selects. Fluoropolymers. (US ISSN 0895-5921) **1194, 5**
C A Selects. Food & Feed Analysis. (US ISSN 0895-5913) **2084, 5,** 1194
▼C A Selects. Food, Drugs, & Cosmetics - Legislative & Regulatory Aspects. (US ISSN 1051-3914) **2084,** 2698, 3747
C A Selects. Food Toxicity. (US ISSN 0162-7813) **1194, 5,** 2084
C A Selects. Forensic Chemistry. (US ISSN 0362-9880) **1194, 5,** 3167
C A Selects. Formulation Chemistry. (US ISSN 0890-1880) **1194, 5**
C A Selects. Free Radicals (Biochemical Aspects). (US ISSN 0895-5905) **1194, 5,** 463
C A Selects. Free Radicals (Organic Aspects). (US ISSN 0895-5972) **1194, 5**
C A Selects. Fuel & Lubricant Additives. (US ISSN 0195-4997) **1194, 5,** 3705
C A Selects. Fungicides. (US ISSN 0160-9068) **1194, 5,** 135
C A Selects. Gas Chromatography. (US ISSN 0146-4477) **1195, 5**
C A Selects. Gaseous Waste Treatment.(US ISSN 0160-9076) **1195, 5**
C A Selects. Gel Permeation Chromatography. (US ISSN 0146-4485) **1195, 5**
C A Selects. Heat-Resistant and Ablative Polymers. (US ISSN 0162-7821) **1195, 5**
C A Selects. Herbicides. (US ISSN 0160-9084) **1195, 5,** 463
C A Selects. High Performance Liquid Chromatography. (US ISSN 0195-5217) **1195, 5**
C A Selects. Hot-Melt Adhesives. (US ISSN 0895-5891) **1195, 6**
▼C A Selects. Hypertension & Antihypertensives. (US ISSN 1051-3922) **3167, 6,** 474
C A Selects. Immunochemical Methods. (US ISSN 1048-874X) **3167, 6,** 3184
C A Selects. Indoor Air Pollution. (US ISSN 1047-8213) **4117, 6,** 1972
C A Selects. Infrared Spectroscopy (Organic Aspects). (US ISSN 0190-9428) **3836, 6**
C A Selects. Infrared Spectroscopy (Physicochemical Aspects). (US ISSN 0190-9436) **3836, 6**
C A Selects. Initiation of Polymerization.(US ISSN 0734-8843) **1195, 6**
C A Selects. Inorganic Analytical Chemistry. (US ISSN 0275-7087) **1195, 6**
C A Selects. Inorganic & Organometallic Reaction Systems. (US ISSN 0195-5012) **1195, 6,** 3424
C A Selects. Inorganic Chemicals & Reactions. (US ISSN 0275-7095) **1195, 6**
C A Selects. Insecticides. (US ISSN 0160-9092) **463, 6,** 1195
C A Selects. Ion Chromatography. (US ISSN 0890-1899) **1195, 6**
C A Selects. Ion-Containing Polymers. (US ISSN 0195-5020) **1195, 6**
C A Selects. Ion Exchange. (US ISSN 0146-4493) **1195, 6**
C A Selects. Isomerization & Catalysts. (US ISSN 0895-5883) **1195, 6**
C A Selects. Laser Applications. (US ISSN 0195-5039) **1195,** 1224
C A Selects. Laser-Induced Chemical Reactions. (US ISSN 0885-0178) **1195, 6**
C A Selects. Leukotrienes. (US ISSN 1047-8086) **1195, 6,** 463, 474
C A Selects. Liquid Crystals. (US ISSN 0148-2351) **1195, 6**
C A Selects. Liquid Waste Treatment. (US ISSN 0160-9106) **1195, 6**
C A Selects. Lubricants, Greases, & Lubrication. (US ISSN 0734-8738) **1195, 6**
C A Selects. Mass Spectrometry. (US ISSN 0362-9872) **1195, 6,** 3836
C A Selects. Membrane Separation. (US ISSN 1040-7197) **1195, 6**
C A Selects. Memory & Recording Devices & Materials. (US ISSN 0890-1821) **1196, 6,** 1842
C A Selects. Metallo Enzymes & Metallo Coenzymes. (US ISSN 0160-9114) **1196, 6,** 3424
C A Selects. Monoclonal Antibodies. (US ISSN 1047-8094) **3167, 6,** 463, 550
C A Selects. Natural Product Synthesis. (US ISSN 0740-0691) **1196, 6**
C A Selects. New Antibiotics. (US ISSN 0895-5875) **3747, 6**
C A Selects. New Books in Chemistry. (US ISSN 0148-2416) **1196, 6,** 395
C A Selects. New Plastics. (US ISSN 0734-8673) **3868, 6**
C A Selects. Nitrogen Fixation. (US ISSN 1047-8108) **1196, 6**
C A Selects. Nonlinear Optical Materials.(US ISSN 0895-5867) **3836, 6**
C A Selects. Novel Natural Products. (US ISSN 0734-872X) **1196, 6**
C A Selects. Novel Pesticides & Herbicides. (US ISSN 0749-7318) **1196, 6,** 463
C A Selects. Novel Polymers from Patents. (US ISSN 0734-8819) **3679, 6,** 1196
C A Selects. Nutritional Aspects of Cancer. (US ISSN 1047-8116) **3167, 6,** 3194
C A Selects. Occupational Exposure & Hazards. (US ISSN 1047-8124) **3623, 6**
▼C A Selects. Oleochemicals Containing Nitrogen. (US ISSN 1052-1976) **1196, 6,** 463, 474
▼C A Selects. Omega-3 Fatty Acids & Fish Oil. (US ISSN 1052-1984) **1196, 6,** 463, 474
C A Selects. Optical and Photosensitive Materials. (US ISSN 0195-5063) **3836, 6,** 1196
C A Selects. Optimization of Organic Reactions. (US ISSN 0195-5071) **1196, 6**
C A Selects. Organic Analytical Chemistry. (US ISSN 0275-7117) **1196, 6**
C A Selects. Organic Optical Materials. (US ISSN 0885-0186) **1196, 6**
C A Selects. Organic Reaction Mechanisms. (US ISSN 0162-7848) **1196, 6**
C A Selects. Organic Stereochemistry. (US ISSN 0195-508X) **1196, 6**
C A Selects. Organo-Transition Metal Complexes. (US ISSN 0160-9130) **1196, 6**
C A Selects. Organofluorine Chemistry. (US ISSN 0160-905X) **1196, 6**
C A Selects. Organometallics in Organic Synthesis. (US ISSN 0895-5859) **1196, 6**
C A Selects. Organophosphorous Chemistry. (US ISSN 0162-783X) **1196, 6**
C A Selects. Organosilicon Chemistry. (US ISSN 0362-9899) **1196, 6**
C A Selects. Organosulfur Chemistry (Journals). (US ISSN 1040-7189) **1196, 6**
C A Selects. Organotin Chemistry. (US ISSN 0195-5101) **1196, 6**
C A Selects. Osteoporosis & Related Bone Loss. (US ISSN 1047-8132) **3167, 6**
C A Selects. Oxidation Catalysts. (US ISSN 1040-7170) **1197, 6**
C A Selects. Oxide Superconductors. (US ISSN 1040-7219) **1197, 6**
C A Selects. Paint Additives. (US ISSN 0734-8762) **3656, 6**
C A Selects. Paper Additives. (US ISSN 0734-8711) **3667, 6**
C A Selects. Paper & Thin-Layer Chromatography. (US ISSN 0146-4515) **1197, 6**
C A Selects. Paper Chemistry. (US ISSN 1040-7200) **1197, 6**
C A Selects. Pesticide Analysis. (US ISSN 1047-8140) **463, 6,** 165, 529
C A Selects. Pharmaceutical Analysis. (US ISSN 0890-1902) **3747, 6**
C A Selects. Pharmaceutical Chemistry (Journals). (US ISSN 0890-1910) **3747, 6**
C A Selects. Pharmaceutical Chemistry (Patents). (US ISSN 0890-1929) **3747, 6,** 3679
C A Selects. Phase Transfer Catalysis. (US ISSN 0885-0194) **1197, 6**
▼C A Selects. Phospholipids (Chemical Aspects). (US ISSN 1051-3930) **463, 6,** 474, 1197
C A Selects. Photobiochemistry. (US ISSN 0148-2335) **1197, 6**
▼C A Selects. Photocatalysts. (US ISSN 1051-3949) **1197, 6**
C A Selects. Photochemical Organic Synthesis. (US ISSN 0885-0208) **1197, 6**
C A Selects. Photochemistry. (US ISSN 0362-9856) **1197, 6**
C A Selects. Photoresists. (US ISSN 0885-0216) **1197, 6**
C A Selects. Photosensitive Polymers. (US ISSN 0749-7326) **1197, 6**
C A Selects. Plasma & Reactive Ion Etching. (US ISSN 0749-7334) **1197, 6**
C A Selects. Plastic Films. (US ISSN 0195-511X) **3868, 6**
C A Selects. Plastics Additives. (US ISSN 0734-8681) **3868, 6**
C A Selects. Plastics Fabrication & Uses. (US ISSN 0275-7125) **3868, 6**
C A Selects. Plastics Manufacture & Processing. (US ISSN 0275-7133) **3868, 6**
C A Selects. Platinum and Palladium Chemistry. (US ISSN 0890-1937) **1197, 6**
C A Selects. Pollution Monitoring. (US ISSN 0160-9149) **1973, 6,** 1976
C A Selects. Polyacrylates (Journals). (US ISSN 0890-1945) **1197, 6**
C A Selects. Polyacrylates (Patents). (US ISSN 1045-8549) **1197, 6**
C A Selects. Polyesters. (US ISSN 0734-8703) **1197, 6**
C A Selects. Polyimides. (US ISSN 0895-5840) **1197, 6**
C A Selects. Polymer Blends. (US ISSN 0734-8827) **1197, 6**

C A Selects. Polymer Degradation. (US ISSN 0734-8835) **1197**, 6
C A Selects. Polymer Morphology. (US ISSN 0195-5128) **1197**, 6
C A Selects. Polymerization Catalysts. (US ISSN 1045-8573) **1197**, 6
C A Selects. Polymerization Kinetics & Process Control. (US ISSN 0885-0224) **1197**, 7
C A Selects. Polyurethanes. (US ISSN 0740-0705) **1197**, 7
C A Selects. Porphyrins. (US ISSN 0195-5136) **1197**, 7
C A Selects. Prostaglandins. (US ISSN 0148-2343) **1197**, 7
C A Selects. Proton Magnetic Resonance. (US ISSN 0190-941X) **1198**, 7
C A Selects. Psychobiochemistry. (US ISSN 0362-9848) **463**, 7, 1198, 3747
C A Selects. Quaternary Ammonium Compounds. (US ISSN 0890-1953) **1198**, 7
C A Selects. Radiation Chemistry. (US ISSN 0146-4523) **1198**, 7
C A Selects. Radiation Curing. (US ISSN 0749-7342) **1198**, 7
C A Selects. Raman Spectroscopy. (US ISSN 0148-2432) **1198**, 7
C A Selects. Recovery & Recycling of Wastes. (US ISSN 0160-9157) **1198**, 7
C A Selects. Selenium & Tellurium Chemistry. (US ISSN 0749-7350) **3424**, 7
C A Selects. Silicas & Silicates. (US ISSN 0890-1961) **1198**, 7
C A Selects. Siloxanes & Silicones. (US ISSN 0895-5832) **1198**, 7
C A Selects. Silver Chemistry. (US ISSN 0148-2440) **3424**, 7
C A Selects. Solar Energy. (US ISSN 0148-236X) **1798**, 1810
C A Selects. Solid & Radioactive Waste Treatment. (US ISSN 0160-9165) **1198**, 7
C A Selects. Solid State N M R. (US ISSN 0895-5824) **1198**, 7
C A Selects. Solvent Extraction. (US ISSN 0146-4531) **1198**, 7
C A Selects. Spectrochemical Analysis. (US ISSN 0885-0232) **1198**, 7
C A Selects. Steroids (Biochemical Aspects). (US ISSN 0160-9173) **3747**, 7, 1803
C A Selects. Steroids (Chemical Aspects). (US ISSN 0160-9181) **1198**, 7, 3747
C A Selects. Structure-Activity Relationships. (US ISSN 0895-5816) **1198**, 7
C A Selects. Surface Analysis. (US ISSN 0195-5152) **1198**, 7
C A Selects. Surface Chemistry (Physicochemical Aspects). (US ISSN 0146-454X) **1198**, 7
C A Selects. Synfuels. (US ISSN 0195-5160) **1198**, 7
C A Selects. Synthetic High Polymers. (US ISSN 0275-7168) **1198**, 7
C A Selects. Synthetic Macrocyclic Compounds. (US ISSN 0195-5179) **1198**, 7
C A Selects. Thermal Analysis. (US ISSN 0195-5187) **1198**, 7, 3836
C A Selects. Thermochemistry. (US ISSN 0162-7864) **1198**, 7
C A Selects. Trace Element Analysis. (US ISSN 0160-919X) **1198**, 7
C A Selects. Ulcer Inhibitors. (US ISSN 1047-8159) **3167**
C A Selects. Ultrafiltration. (US ISSN 0195-5195) **1198**, 7
C A Selects. Ultraviolet & Visible Spectroscopy. (US ISSN 0195-5209) **1199**, 7, 3836
C A Selects. Virucides & Virustats. (US ISSN 1047-8078) **463**
C A Selects. Water-Based Coatings. (US ISSN 0749-7369) **3656**, 7
C A Selects. Water Treatment. (US ISSN 0740-073X) **1199**, 7
C A Selects. X-Ray Analysis & Spectroscopy. (US ISSN 0162-7872) **3837**, 7, 1199
C A Selects. Zeolites. (US ISSN 0190-4949) **1199**, 7

C A Services Today. (US ISSN 1056-2850) **1199**, 4594
C A T see Civil Aviation Training **4672**
C A T see Car & Accessory Trader **4686**
†C A T. (Canadian Automotive Training) (CN) **5156**
C A T A C. (AG) **4647**
C A T M O G. (Concepts and Techniques in Modern Geography) (UK ISSN 0306-6142) **2243**
C A T N I see Catchword and Trade Name Index **4614**
†C.A.T.S. Reports. (Centre for Advanced T V Studies) (UK) **5156**
†C A T S Tales. (Childrens Activities Time Society, Inc.) (AT) **5156**
C A Techniek. (NE) **1412**, 1877
†C A U. (Construccion Arquitectura Urbanismo) (SP) **5156**
C A U C E Bulletin. (Canadian Association for University Continuing Education) (CN) **1701**
C A U S Newsletter. (Color Association of the United States) (US) **1284**, 1251, 4838
C A U T Bulletin/A C P U Bulletin. (Canadian Association of University Teachers) (CN ISSN 0007-7887) **1701**
C A V E Newsletter. (Catholic Audio-Visual Educators) (US) **1745**, 4257
C & I. (Controle & Instrumentacao - Automatizacao) (BL ISSN 0101-0794) **2521**
C & L Applications. (UK ISSN 0957-4085) **2796**, 2750
▼C B A A Magazine. (CN) **4671**
C B A A News. (Christian Bookselling Association of Australia Inc.) (AT) **4124**
C B A Annual Report. (Council for British Archaeology) (UK ISSN 0589-9028) **268**
C B A Media Guide Yearbook. (Continental Basketball Association) (US) **4501**
C B A Newsletter. (Continental Basketball Association) (US) **4501**
C B A Record. (Chicago Bar Association) (US ISSN 0892-1822) **2607**
C B A S S E Newsletter. (Commission on Behavioral and Social Sciences and Education) (US ISSN 0734-5119) **4367**
C B A Update see C B A Newsletter **4501**
C B C Classical Record Reference Book. (Canadian Broadcasting Corporation) (CN) **3543**
C B C Engineering Review/Revue Technique de Radio-Canada. (Canadian Broadcasting Corporation) (CN ISSN 0068-8401) **1355**
C B C Features. (US) **4124**, 1233
C B C for the People see For the People **5195**
†C B C Quarterly. (Citizens Budget Commission) (US ISSN 0731-8758) **5156**
C B D Weekly Release. (US) **653**, 4055
C B E Environmental Review. (Citizens for a Better Environment) (US) **1484**
C B E Report. (Association for Community Based Education) (US) **1619**
C B E Views. (Council of Biology Editors Inc.) (US) **4124**, 434
C.B.F. News. (Children's Book Foundation) (UK ISSN 0266-4216) **4124**
C B Funk. (GW ISSN 0938-4022) **1355**
†C B Funk Magazin. (SP) **5156**
▼C B G Price Guide. (Comics Buyers Guide) (US) **2434**
C B H S Newsletter. (Children's Books History Society) (UK) **4124**
C B I A News. (Connecticut Business and Industry Association) (US ISSN 0199-686X) **849**, 974
C B I Annual Report. (Confederation of British Industry) (UK ISSN 0268-2273) **653**

▼C B I - Coopers & Lybrand Deloitte Survey of Financial Services. (Confederation of British Industry) (UK) **653**
C B I Economic Situation Report. (Confederation of British Industry) (UK) **849**
C B I Financial Times Distributive Trades Survey. (UK) **1035**
C B I Forskning - Research. (Cement-och Betonginstitutet) (SW ISSN 0346-6906) **608**
C B I Industrial Survey. (Confederation of British Industry) (UK) **653**
C B I Industrial Trends Survey see C B I Quarterly Industrial Trends Survey **653**
C B I Informerar. (Cement- och Betonginstitutet) (SW ISSN 0282-6283) **608**
C B I Members Bulletin see C B I News **653**
C B I Monthly Trends Enquiry see C B I Industrial Survey **653**
C B I News. (Confederation of British Industry) (UK ISSN 0140-2188) **653**
C B I News. (US) **3403**
C B I Quarterly Industrial Trends Survey. (Confederation of British Industry) (UK) **653**
C B I Rapporter - Reports. (Cement-och Betonginstitutet) (SW ISSN 0346-8240) **608**
C B I Rekommendationer-Recommendations see C B I Informerar **608**
C B M C Contact. (Christian Business Men's Committee of USA) (US ISSN 0890-0442) **653**
C B M Freundesbrief. (Christian Blind Mission International Inc.) (US) **4167**, 2291
▼C B M I Family Magazine. (Christian Blind Mission International Inc.) (US) **2291**, 4400
C B M News. (Certified Ballast Manufacturers) (US ISSN 0007-7941) **1883**
C B M R Monographs. (Center for Black Music Research) (US ISSN 1042-8836) **3543**, 1995
C B M S. N S F. Regional Conference Series in Applied Mathematics. (Society for Industrial and Applied Mathematics, Conference Board of the Mathematical Sciences) (US ISSN 0163-9439) **3062**
†C B Magazine. (US ISSN 0007-795X) **5156**
C B N/Danish Gazette for C O M A L Language. (DK ISSN 0108-4925) **1429**
C B News. (UK) **1355**
†C.B.R.I. Abstracts. (Central Building Research Institute) (II ISSN 0007-7968) **5156**
C B Radio - S 9. (US ISSN 0145-4560) **1355**
C B Report. (US ISSN 0146-5813) **1701**
C B Review. (Central Bank of the Philippines) (PH ISSN 0115-1401) **769**, 849
C B S see Cardinal Bea Studies **4258**
C B S A Capsules. (Copper & Brass Servicenter Association) (US) **3403**
†C B S News Index. (US ISSN 0362-3238) **5156**
C B S Newsletter. (NE ISSN 0169-6289) **498**
C B T Directions. (Computer Based Training) (US ISSN 0898-8498) **1389**
C. Brewer Today. (US) **1073**
C C A Advocate. (Community College Association) (US) **1701**
C C: A & H see Current Contents: Arts & Humanities **2519**
C C: A B & E S see Current Contents: Agriculture, Biology & Environmental Sciences **136**
C C A B Circulate. (Canadian Circulations Audit Board, Inc.) (CN) **29**
C C A C Review. (California College of Arts and Crafts) (US ISSN 0045-3919) **1306**

C C A F V (Current Contents, Agricultural, Food and Veterinary Sciences) see Current Contents: Agriculture, Biology & Environmental Sciences **136**
C C A I. (BE ISSN 0773-4182) **1332**, 2807
C C A I Monthly News Letter. (Coal Consumers Association of India) (II ISSN 0376-7787) **3479**
C C A N see Construction Computer Applications Newsletter **612**
C C A News. (Consumer Credit Association) (UK) **769**, 1004, 1113, 2608
C C A R Journal. (Central Conference of American Rabbis) (US) **4222**
C C B C Newsletter. (Council of Community Blood Centers) (US) **3271**, 3800
C C B D Newsletter. (Council for Children with Behavioral Disorders) (US) **1734**, 1233
C C B News see C.B.F. News **4124**
†C C B Outlook (Braille Edition). (Canadian Council of the Blind) (CN) **5156**
†C C B Outlook (Large Print Edition). (Canadian Council of the Blind) (CN ISSN 0007-7984) **5156**
C C B S E (Current Contents, Behavioral, Social and Educational Sciences) see Current Contents: Social & Behavioral Sciences **4457**
▼C C C F's Newsletter. (Chaos Computer Club France) (FR) **1423**, 1332
C C: C M see Current Contents: Clinical Medicine **3169**
C C C N. (California Community Care News) (US) **2459**
C C C O News Notes. (Central Committee for Conscientious Objectors) (US ISSN 0008-5952) **3940**
C C D M Minority Student Recruitment Guide. (Council on Career Development for Minorities, Inc.) (US) **1701**
C C E A Newsletter. (Commonwealth Council for Educational Administration) (AT ISSN 0310-1878) **1725**
C C: E T & A S see Current Contents: Engineering, Technology & Applied Sciences **1842**
C C E T S W Reporting see Central Council for Education and Training in Social Work. Report of Council Meeting **4401**
C C F A Communique. (Crohn's and Colitis Foundation of America, Inc.) (US) **3266**
C C F A Foundation Focus. (Crohn's & Colitis Foundation of America, Inc.) (US ISSN 0897-6759) **3266**
C C H Accounting Articles see Accounting Articles **702**
C C H Australian Companies and Securities Legislation. (AT) **2708**
C C H Compliance Guide for Plan Administrators see Compliance Guide for Plan Administrators **1006**
C C H Journal of Asian Pacific Taxation.(AT ISSN 1031-8364) **902**, 1089, 2608
C C H Journal of Australian Taxation. (AT ISSN 1032-1810) **1089**
C C H - O S H A Compliance Guide see Human Resources Management - O S H A Compliance **3617**
C C H R A - C H R A Progress Notes see C H R A Progress Notes **3085**
C C H R Newsletter. (Citizens Committee on Human Rights) (AT) **3940**
C C - H S A see Current Contents - Health Services Administration **5175**
C C H Tax Action Digest. (AT ISSN 0814-6489) **1089**
C C H Tax Planning Review. (Commerce Clearing House, Inc.) (US ISSN 0363-4396) **1089**
C C I see Clima Commerce International **2298**

C C I A Background Information. (World Council of Churches, Commission of the Churches on International Affairs) (SZ) **4167**, 3952

†C C I Action. (New York Chamber of Commerce and Industry, Inc.) (US) **5156**

C C I Annual Report. (Cape Chamber of Industries) (SA) **809**

C C I C A Annual. (Catholic Commission on Intellectual and Cultural Affairs) (US) **4257**

C C I R Green Books see C C I R Plenary Assembly (17th Dussledorf Germany, 1990) **1355**

C C I R Plenary Assembly (17th Dussledorf Germany, 1990). (US) **1355**

C C I T T Red Books. (International Telegraph and Telephone Consultative Committee) (US) **1361**

C C I Technical Bulletins. (Canadian Conservation Institute) (CN ISSN 0706-4152) **1484**

C C I V S News see News from C C I V S **4415**

C C L/Literature Canadienne Pour la Jeunesse. (Canadian Children's Literature) (CN ISSN 0319-0080) **4124**, 1251

C C L A Bulletin - A C L C Newsletter see Comparative Literature in Canada **2907**

C C L A Record see Australian Correspondence Chess Quarterly **4465**

C C L M News see C L M P Newsletter **4124**

C C: L S see Current Contents: Life Sciences **464**

C C M see Contemporary Christian Music **3547**

C C M I Reports see Impact (Rockville) **1363**

C C M Update. (Contemporary Christian Music) (US) **3543**

C C N Information. (Council of Churches in Namibia) (SX) **4232**, 4257

C C N M A News see El Sol **2024**

C - C O R E News. (Centre for Cold Ocean Resources Engineering) (CN ISSN 0381-6486) **1816**, 1602

C C Orienrering. (Coordination Committee for Polish-Jewish Youth in Denmark) (DK ISSN 0109-2979) **1233**

C C - P A L S Communications Network. (California Coalition of People for Alternative Learning Situations) (US) **1745**

C C P A Newsletter. (Canadian Center for Policy Alternatives) (CN) **4055**

C C: P C & E S see Current Contents: Physical, Chemical & Earth Sciences **1200**

C C P Party School Magazine. see Dangxiao Luntan **3890**

C C R see Current Chemical Reactions **1200**

C C R Business Review. (CN ISSN 0840-7061) **1171**

C C R Inhouse Database see Current Chemical Reactions Inhouse Database for R E A C C S **1200**

C C: S & B S see Current Contents: Social & Behavioral Sciences **4457**

C C S Bulletin see Vision (Stamford) **1971**

C C S Focus. (Computing & Communications Services) (CN ISSN 0831-4926) **1390**

C C S S see C C S S. Federazione delle Societa Medico-Scientifiche. Italiane Bollettino Congressi (Year) **3085**

C C S S. Federazione delle Societa Medico-Scientifiche. Italiane Bollettino Congressi (Year). (Comitato per la Collaborazione tra Societa Medico-Scientifiche Italiane) (IT) **3085**, 3271, 3391

C C T A Cable Communique. (Canadian Cable Television Association) (CN ISSN 0710-2240) **1370**

C C T A Communique see C C T A Cable Communique **1370**

C C T A News see C C T A Cable Communique **1370**

C C T Newsletter. (Choreographers Theatre) (US) **1529**, 3543

C C T V Applications & Technology. (Close Caption Television) (US) **1526**, 1073

C C U M C Leader. (Consortium of College and University Media Centers) (US) **1745**, 3504

C C W H P - C G W H Newsletter. (Coordinating Committee on Women in the Historical Profession - Conference Group on Women's History) (US) **4858**, 2401

C D A Actueel. (NE) **3876**

C D A Journal see California Dental Association. Journal **3229**

C D A News see Chemical Design Automation News **1412**

C D Actueel see C D A Actueel **3876**

C D B News. (Caribbean Development Bank) (BB) **769**

C D C - A I D S Weekly. (Centers for Disease Control - Acquired Immune Deficiency Syndrome) (US ISSN 0884-903X) **3218**, 434, 653, 4098

C D C Monographs. Studies in African and Asian Demography. (Cairo Demographic Centre) (UA) **3991**

C D C Occasional Papers. (Cairo Demographic Centre) (UA) **3991**

C D C Working Papers. (Cairo Demographic Centre) (UA) **3991**

C D Computing News. (Compact Disc) (US ISSN 0893-4843) **1423**

C D Data Report. (US ISSN 8755-5727) **2750**

C D F Reports. (Children's Defense Fund) (US ISSN 0276-6531) **1233**

C D Guide. (Compact Disc) (US) **4460**, 3543

†C D H A Journal. (California Dental Hygienists Association) (US) **5156**

C D H Bayern. (GW) **653**

†C D H Kontakter. (GW) **5156**

C D - Housing Register. (Community Development Services, Inc.) (US ISSN 1050-3811) **2484**

C.D. Howe Institute Commentary. (CN ISSN 0824-8001) **653**

C.D. Howe Institute. Policy Review and Outlook. (CN ISSN 0826-9939) **653**

C.D. Howe Research Institute. Policy Review and Outlook see C.D. Howe Institute. Policy Review and Outlook **653**

†C D - I News. (Compact Disc Interactive) (US) **5156**

C D I U P A. Bulletin Bibliographique see Bibliographie Internationale des Industries Agro-Alimentaires **134**

C D - Info. (Christian Democrat International) (BE) **3877**

C D L Reporter see Decency Reporter **4433**

C D M S Notes. (Cryospheric Data Management System) (US) **1556**

C D N L A O Newsletter. (Conference of Directors of National Libraries on Resource Sharing in Asia and Oceania) (JA ISSN 0914-6601) **2750**

C D Publisher News. (Compact Disc) (US) **4143**

C D - R O M. (FR) **1448**

C D - R O M Databases. (Compact Disc - Read Only Memory) (US ISSN 0897-3296) **2796**

C D - R O M Directory. (UK) **1412**, 1453

C D - R O M EndUser. (US ISSN 1042-8623) **2796**

C D - R O M International. (FR ISSN 0987-8238) **1448**, 1443

C D - R O M Librarian. (US ISSN 0893-9934) **2750**, 1370, 1476

C D - R O M Newsletter. (UK) **1476**

C D - R O M Professional. (US ISSN 1049-0833) **2796**

▼C D - R O M Professional Inside News. (US) **2796**

†C D - R O M Review. (Compact Disc - Read Only Memory) (US ISSN 0891-3188) **5156**

▼C D - R O M Shoppers Guide. (US ISSN 1048-406X) **2796**

C D - R O M Sourcebook. (US) **2796**

C D - R O Ms in Print. (US ISSN 0891-8198) **1403**, 396

C D R Project Paper. (Centre for Development Research) (DK ISSN 0106-0805) **926**, 4367

C D R Reports. (Council for Disability Rights) (US) **3940**, 1734

C D R Research Reports. (Centre for Development Research) (DK ISSN 0108-6596) **926**, 4367

C D Review. (Compact Disc) (US ISSN 1044-1700) **4460**

C D Review Digest see C D Review Digest - Classical **3588**

C D Review Digest see C D Review Digest - Jazz, Popular, etc **3588**

C D Review Digest - Classical. (US ISSN 1045-0114) **3588**, 7

C D Review Digest - Jazz, Popular, etc. (US ISSN 1045-0122) **3588**, 7

†C D Review's Compact Disc Yearbook. (US) **5156**

C D S Connection. (Cataloging Distribution Service) (US ISSN 0895-2485) **2750**

C D U Gerlingen Inform. (Christlich Demokratische Union) (GW) **3877**

C E A Advisor. (Connecticut Education Association) (US ISSN 0007-8050) **1619**

C E A Critic. (College English Association) (US ISSN 0007-8069) **2901**, 1745

C E A Forum. (College English Association) (US ISSN 0007-8034) **1745**

C E A Handbook/Ki-es-Ki. (Canadian Education Association) (CN ISSN 0068-8657) **1619**

C E A L Directory. (Committee on East Asian Libraries) (US) **2750**, 2337

C E A M. (Centro de Estudios y Asesoramiento Metalurgico) (SP) **653**

C E A News. (California Escrow Association) (US) **4146**

C E A S E News. (Concerned Educators Allied for a Safe Environment) (US) **1485**, 1804

C E A S H see Cahiers d'Economie Appliquee aux Sciences Humaines **2504**

C E A Spotlight see C E A Voice **1619**

C E A Voice. (Columbus Education Association) (US ISSN 0882-5017) **1619**

C E B E D E A U. Tribune see Tribune d'Eau **4829**

C E B V. (Communaute Economique du Betail et de la Viande) (UV) **213**

C E C - Chemical Engineering Catalog. (US ISSN 0276-8429) **1848**

C E C M Bulletin d'Information. (Commission des Ecoles Catholiques de Montreal) (CN ISSN 0714-9670) **1619**

C E C M Information Bulletin see C E C M Bulletin d'Information **1619**

C E C - M R Newsletter. (Council for Exceptional Children, Division on Mental Retardation) (US) **1734**, 1233

C E C - M Report see C E C - M R Newsletter **1734**

C E C Newsletter see Last Word **1829**

C E C Revista. (Centro de Estudos Cientificos) (BL ISSN 0034-7361) **4303**

C E C T A L Conference Papers Series. (Centre for English Cultural Tradition and Language) (UK ISSN 0261-314X) **2807**, 2901

C E Computing Review. (Civil Engineers) (US ISSN 1044-8179) **1877**

C E D A Cortex Cassettes. (Committee for Economic Development of Australia) (AT) **1073**

C E D A Current Annual. (Canadian Electrical Distributors Association) (CN) **1883**

C E D A Information Papers (I P Series). (Committee for Economic Development of Australia) (AT) **849**

C E D A M Notiziario Bibliografico. (Casa Editrice Dott. Antonio Milani) (IT ISSN 0007-8158) **396**

C E D A "M" Series see C E D A Monograph Series **1073**

C E D A Monograph Series. (Committee for Economic Development of Australia) (AT) **1073**

C E D A "P" Series. (Committee for Economic Development of Australia) (AT) **1073**

†C.E.D.E. Coleccion-Debates. (Centro de Estudios sobre Desarrollo Economico) (CK) **5156**

†C E D E Documentos de Trabajo. (Centro de Estudios sobre Desarrollo Economico) (CK) **5156**

†C E D E F O P News. (European Centre for the Development of Vocational Training (CEDEFOP)) (EI ISSN 0252-855X) **5156**

C E D E J Departement des Sciences Sociales. Bulletin see C E D E J Egypte - Monde Arabe **2608**

▼C E D E J Egypte - Monde Arabe. (Centre d'Etudes et de Documentation Economique, Juridique et Sociale) (UA ISSN 0752-4412) **2608**, 653, 4367

C E D E M Notizie. (Centro di Documentazione Economica e di Marketing) (IT) **1035**

C E D H U. (Centro de Estudios Humanitarios) (PY ISSN 1017-2785) **2608**, 4838

C E D P A World Wide. (Centre for Development and Population Activities) (US) **4838**, 927, 3980

C E D R E S. Revue Economique et Sociale. (Centre d'Etudes, de Recherche Economique et Social) (UV) **148**, 889

C E E see Electrical Construction Technology **1887**

†C E E. (Canadian Electronics Engineering) (CN ISSN 0008-3461) **5156**

C E E International. Droit et Affaires. (Communaute Economique Europeenne) (FR) **2720**

C E E Report see Marine Conservation News **1491**

C E F P Journal see Educational Facility Planner **1630**

C E F Trailblazer. (Clinton - Essex - Franklin Library System) (US) **2750**

†C E G B Abstracts. (Central Electricity Generating Board) (UK ISSN 0267-0372) **5156**

†C E G B Research. (Central Electricity Generating Board) (UK ISSN 0305-7194) **5156**

C E G E P Plus. (College d'Enseignement Generale et Professionnel de Valleyfield) (CN) **1306**

C E I - Communications Engineering International. (UK) **1332**

C E I M A Adquisiciones Reciente. (Centro de Estudios e Investigaciones Sobre Mercados Agropecuario) (CK) **135**

C E I P Fund. Connections. (US) **1944**, 3625

C E I R (Cooperative Economic Insect Report) see C P P R **171**

C E I Update. (Competitive Enterprise Institute) (US) **653**, 2608

C E M A Bulletin. (Conveyor Equipment Manufacturers Association) (US) **3016**

†C E M A G R E F Nouvelles. (Centre National du Machinisme Agricole du Genie Rural, des Eaux et des Forets) (FR ISSN 0249-5686) **5156**

C E M A M Reports. (Center for the Study of the Modern Arab World) (LE) **3635**

C E M L A Boletin Bimensual see Centro de Estudios Monetarios Latinoamericanos. Boletin Bimensual **771**

C E N (Construction Equipment News) see Thomson's Construction Australia **634**

C E N C U S: Central Excise and Customs Journal. (II ISSN 0376-7809) **902**

C E N D E S Boletin Industrial. (Centro de Desarrollo Industrial) (EC ISSN 0523-9141) **1073**

†C E N P A F A L Buletin. (Centro de Pastoral Familiar para America Latina) (CK) **5156**

C E N S I S Note e Commenti. (Centro Studi Investimenti Sociali) (IT) 4430, 4400

C E N S I S Quindicinale di Note e Commenti see C E N S I S Note e Commenti 4430

▼C E O - International Strategies. (US) 902

C E O Interviews. (US) 653

†C E O Newsletter. (Chief Executive Officer) (US) 5156

C E P A D. Informe Anual. (Comite Evangelico Pro-Ayuda al Desarrollo) (NQ) 4400

C E P A L Review. (Comision Economica para America Latina y el Caribe) (UN ISSN 0251-2920) 849

C E P A L Studies and Reports. see Estudios e Informes de la C E P A L 929

C.E.P.I.I. Lettre. (Centre d'Etudes Prospectives et d'Informations Internationales) (FR ISSN 0243-1947) 849

C E P News. (Caribbean Environment Programme) (UN) 1944

C E P Newsletter see C E P Research Report 1502

C E P Reports and C E P Books. (Council on Economic Priorities) (US) 1502

C E P Reports and C E P Studies see C E P Reports and C E P Books 1502

C E P Research Report. (Council on Economic Priorities) (US) 1502

C E P S Papers. (Centre for European Policy Studies) (BE) 3952, 889

C E P S Working Documents. (Centre for European Policy Studies) (BE) 3952, 889

C E P S Working Documents (Economic) see C E P S Working Documents 3952

C E P S Working Documents (Political) see C E P S Working Documents 3952

C E R. (IT) 1161

The C E R Cular. (U.S. Coastal Engineering Research Center) (US) 1602, 1816

C E R E S Cahiers. Serie Linguistique. (Centre d'Etudes et de Recherches Economiques et Sociales) (TI ISSN 0564-7975) 2807

C E R F Net News. (US) 1426

C E R L A L C: El Libro en America Latina y el Caribe. (CK ISSN 0121-1242) 4124, 2750

C E R N Courier. (SZ ISSN 0304-288X) 3846

C E R N - H E R A Reports. (SZ ISSN 0366-5690) 3846

C E R N Reports. (SZ ISSN 0007-8328) 3846

C E R N School of Computing. Proceedings. (SZ ISSN 0304-2898) 4359

C E R N School of Physics. Proceedings. (SZ ISSN 0531-4283) 3846

C E S I C Studies in International Conflict. (SW ISSN 1100-4177) 3952

†C E T A Bulletin. (Chinese-English Translation Assistance Group) (US) 5156

C E T E S B Jornal. (Companhia de Tecnologia de Sanemento Ambiental) (BL) 1944

C F A Digest. (Chartered Financial Analyst) (US ISSN 0046-9777) 769

C F A News (Miami). (Center for Fine Arts) (US) 3522

C F A News (Washington). (Consumer Federation of America) (US ISSN 0732-8281) 1502

C F A Newsletter see A I M R Newsletter 758

C - F A R see C - F A R Newsletter 927

C - F A R Newsletter. (Citizens for Foreign Aid Reform Inc.) (CN ISSN 0826-4228) 927

C F B Cold Lake Courier. (Canadian Forces Base) (CN ISSN 0045-8872) 3453

C F B Gagetown Gazette. (Canadian Forces Base Gagetown) (CN ISSN 0713-391X) 3453

C F D C Annual Report see Telefilm Canada Annual Report 3518

C F D T Aujourd'hui. (Confederation Francaise Democratique du Travail) (FR ISSN 0294-8397) 2581

C F D T Magazine. (Confederation Francaise Democratique du Travail) (FR ISSN 0395-5621) 4367

C F L Facts, Figures and Records. (Canadian Football League) (CN) 4498

C F M A see Classiques Francais du Moyen Age 2906

C F O. (Chief Financial Officer) (US) 653

C F O Alert. (Chief Financial Officer) (US) 748

C F O Journal. (Colorado Field Ornithologists) (US ISSN 0362-9902) 563

C F O - Magazine. (NE) 3276, 4098

C.F.P. Chaud - Froid - Plomberie. (FR ISSN 0750-1552) 2298

C F P Today. (Institute of Certified Financial Planners) (US ISSN 1058-4455) 1004

C F S Notebook see C S F Notebook 3877

C G. (Computer und Grafik) (GW ISSN 0934-6082) 1420

C G A Magazine. (Certified General Accountants' Association of Canada) (CN ISSN 0318-742X) 748

C G, Car Graphic see Car Graphic 4686

C G Information see C G Kurier 5156

†C G Kurier. (GW) 5156

C G O U Technical Report. (U.S. Coast Guard, Oceanographic Unit) (US) 1602

C G Professional. (Computer Graphics) (US) 1420

C G R B Bulletin (Citizen's Governmental Research Bureau) see P P F Bulletin 4093

C G R O Newsletter see C L G R O Newsletter 2451

†C Gazette. (US) 5156

C H A C Directory see Catholic Health Association of Canada. Directory 3086

C H A C Info/Info A C C S. (Catholic Health Association of Canada) (CN ISSN 0822-8426) 2459, 3085, 4257

C H A C Review. (CN ISSN 0226-5923) 2459, 3085, 4257

C H A I Lights. (Concern for Helping Animals in Israel) (US) 230

C H C G Pulse. (Canadian Health Care Guild) (CN ISSN 0706-2192) 3276, 2581

C H E C Journal. (Commonwealth Human Ecology Council) (UK) 4099, 1944

C H E C News see C H E C Journal 4099

C H E C Points. (Commonwealth Human Ecology Council) (UK ISSN 0142-1972) 4099, 1944

C H F Newsbriefs. (Cooperative Housing Foundation) (US ISSN 0895-5735) 2484, 927

C H I Dispatch. (Confederate Historical Institute) (US) 2401, 3453

C H I L D Newsletter. (Children's Healthcare is a Legal Duty) (US) 1233, 2608, 4280

†C H O M I - Das. (Clearing House on Migration Issues) (AT ISSN 0312-200X) 5156

C H R A Progress Notes. (Canadian College of Health Record Administrators, Canadian Health Record Association.) (CN) 3085, 2750

C H R I C A News. (Committee for Health Rights in Central America) (US) 927, 4099

C H W Letter. (CN ISSN 0834-1508) 941

C I A C. (W P C Information Center for the Americas and the Caribbean) (CU) 3877

†C I A O. (Cuisine International America & Overseas) (US ISSN 1040-5585) 5156

C I A O Magazine. (CN) 1995

C I A Revue. (Confederation Internationale des Accordeonistes) (AU ISSN 0574-9468) 3543

C I A T Internacional. (Centro Internacional de Agricultura Tropical) (CK ISSN 0120-4092) 81

C I A T International. (Centro Internacional de Agricultura Tropical) (CK ISSN 0120-4084) 81

C I A T Report/Informe CIAT. (Centro Internacional de Agricultura Tropical) (CK ISSN 0120-3169) 81

†C I B & T Analyst. (Center for International Business and Trade) (US) 5156

C I B Daily Maritime News Bulletin. (Congressional Information Bureau, Inc.) (US) 4725

C I B E D O - Beitraege zum Gespraech Zwischen Christen und Muslimen. (GW ISSN 0721-0035) 4167, 4218

C I B Edifici Intelligenti. (Computer Integrated Building) (IT ISSN 0394-8706) 296, 608

C I C. Boletin Informativo. (CU) 1619

C I C A Dialogue. (Canadian Institute of Chartered Accountants) (CN ISSN 0045-4982) 748

C.I.C.A.E. Bulletin d'Information. (Confederation Internationale des Cinemas d'Art et d'Essai) (FR ISSN 0526-6513) 3504

C I C A Handbook. (Canadian Institute of Chartered Accountants) (CN ISSN 0068-8983) 748

C I C F R I Newsletter. (Central Inland Capture Fisheries Research Institute) (II ISSN 0970-6143) 2037

C I C I A M S News - Nouvelles - Nachrichten. (International Catholic Committee of Nurses and Medico Social Assistants) (BE ISSN 0007-8417) 3276

C I C I B A Lettre d'Information. (GO) 1995

C I C I M: Revue pour le Cinema Francais. (Centro d'Information Cinematographique) (GW) 3504

C I C Informacion. (Centro Informativo de la Construccion) (SP) 608

C I C M Informations. see I C M C Newsletter 5208

C I C Net: The Circuit. (Committee on Institutional Cooperation) (US) 1426

†C I C R I S Directory. (Cooperative Industrial and Commercial Reference and Information Service) (UK) 5156

C I C's State School Directories. (Curriculum Information Center) (US ISSN 0162-9646) 1692

C I D see Computing Information Directory 1404

C I D. (Cuba Independiente y Democratica) (US) 3877

C I D A Annual Report/A C D I Rapport Annuel. (CN ISSN 0828-0584) 927

C I D A E. (Centro de Investigacion y Difusion Aeronautico Espacial) (UY ISSN 0797-0072) 49

C I D: Electronica y Procesamiento de Datos. (CU) 1764

C I D X Messenger. (Canadian International DX Radio Club) (CN ISSN 0045-3706) 1355

C I Directory. (Cosmetics International) (UK) 375

†C I E - Journal. (Commission Internationale de l'Eclairage) (AU ISSN 0252-9246) 5157

C I E - News. (Commission Internationale de l'Eclairage) (AU) 1883, 1862

C.I.E. Newsletter. (Central Institute of Education) (II ISSN 0007-8425) 1619

C I E P L A N Coleccion Estudios. (Corporacion de Investigaciones Economicas para Latinoamerica) (CL ISSN 0716-0631) 849

C I E S Communication. (International Center for Companies of the Food Trade and Industry) (FR) 2062, 902

C.I.E.S. Quarterly Review see C I E S Communication 2062

C I E Travel Express. (Covas Iompair Eireann) (IE) 4755

C I F A Technical Papers. (Food and Agriculture Organization of the United Nations, Committee for Inland Fisheries of Africa) (UN) 2037

C-I-G World. (Colorado Interstate Gas Co.) (US) 3683

C I H S M News see Congress News 2403

†C.I.I.A. Symposia. (Commission Internationale des Industries Agricole et Alimentaires) (GW ISSN 0340-2002) 5157

C I I D Informa see I D R C Reports 930

C II - E S R I Business Forecast. (Confederation of Irish Industry) (IE) 1073

C I I Journal. (Chartered Insurance Institute) (UK ISSN 0957-4883) 2529

C I I L. Adult Literacy Series. (II) 1682, 1745

C I I L. Bilingual Hindi Series. (II) 2807, 1745

C I I L. Folklore Series. (Central Institute of Indian Languages) (II) 2053, 2337

C I I L. Grammar Series. (II) 2807, 1745

C I I L. Occasional Monograph Series. (II) 2807, 1745

C I I L Bilingual Education Series. (Central Institute of Indian Languages) (II) 2807, 1745

C I I L Border and Tribal Languages. Adult Literacy Series. (Central Institute of Indian Languages) (II) 1682, 1745

C I I L Common Vocabulary Series. (Central Institute of Indian Languages) (II) 2807, 1745

C I I L Documentation Series. (II) 2807, 1745

C I I L Intensive Course Series. (II) 2807, 1745

C I I L - K V S. Mother Tongue Series - Apni Boli. (II) 2807, 1745

C I I L Occasional Bulletin Series. (II) 2807, 1745

C I I L Phonetic Reader Series. (II) 2807, 1745

C I I L Pictorial Glossary Series. (II) 2807, 1745

C I I L Reading Series. (II) 2807, 1745

C I I L Second Language Textbook Series. (II) 2807, 1745

C I I L Sociolinguistics Series. (II) 2807, 1745

C.I.I. Newsletter. (Confederation of Irish Industry) (IE) 1073

C I J Bulletin see C A J Bulletin 2567

C I L see Computers in Libraries 1459

C I L E C T News see C I L E C T Newsletter 1370

C I L E C T Newsletter. (Centre International de Liaison des Ecoles de Cinema et de Television) (AT) 1370, 3504

C I L L see Institut de Linguistique de Louvain. Cahiers 2818

C I L T see Amsterdam Studies in the Theory and History of Linguistic Science. Series 4: Current Issues in Linguistic Theory 2802

†C I M. (Computer Integrated Manufacturing) (SP ISSN 0214-0446) 5157

C I M Bulletin. (Canadian Institute of Mining, Metallurgy & Petroleum) (CN ISSN 0317-0926) 3479

▼C I M - C A D Fuehrer. (GW) 1429, 1468

C I M Construction Journal. (Construction Industries of Massachusetts, Inc.) (US) 1862

C I M Directory. (Canadian Institute of Mining, Metallurgy & Petroleum) (CN ISSN 0068-9009) 3480, 3403

†C I M E. (Computers in Mechanical Engineering) (US ISSN 0745-9726) 5157

†C I M M Y T Review. (Centro Internacional de Mejoramiento de Maiz y Trigo) (MX ISSN 0304-5463) **5157**
C I M Management. (GW ISSN 0179-2679) **1390**
C I M Notes *see* Cleveland Institute of Music (Newsletter) **3546**
C I M - Praxis. (GW ISSN 0931-3125) **1412**
C I M Reporter. (Canadian Institute of Mining, Metallurgy & Petroleum) (CN ISSN 0701-0710) **3480**
C I M Strategies. (Computer-Integrated Manufacturing) (US ISSN 0748-9250) **1412**
†C I M Technology. (Computer Integrated Manufacturing) (US) **5157**
C I N *see* Computers in Nursing **3225**
C I N A. (Canadian Intravenous Nurses Association) (CN) **3276**
C I N A H L *see* Cumulative Index to Nursing & Allied Health Literature **3169**
C I N A - Nytt *see* N I A S - Nytt **3641**
C I N C O M: Courses in Communications. (Communications Institute) (US ISSN 0742-3632) **1692**, 1370
C I N D A. (UN) **3837**, 7
C I N T E R F O R - Documentacion. (Centro Interamericano de Investigacion y Documentacion sobre Formacion Profesional) (UY ISSN 0577-2915) **1619**
C I N T E R F O R Estudios y Monografias. (Centro Interamericano de Investigacion y Documentacion sobre Formacion Profesional) (UY ISSN 0577-2931) **1619**
C I N T E R F O R Noticias *see* Centro Interamericano de Investigacion y Documentacion sobre Formacion Profesional. Boletin **1620**
C I New Products Review. (Cosmetics International) (UK) **375**
C I O. (Chief Information Officer) (US ISSN 0894-9301) **825**
†C I O Letter. (Chief Information Officer) (US ISSN 0891-4044) **5157**
†C I O Monthly. (Chief Information Officer) (US) **5157**
C I P *see* Cardiology in Practice **3206**
C I P A. (Chartered Institute of Patent Agents) (UK ISSN 0306-0314) **3673**
C I P Descriptions of Plant-Parasitic Nematodes. (Institute of Parasitology) (UK ISSN 0305-0351) **580**
†C I P Keys to the Nematode Parasites of Vertebrates. (Institute of Parasitology) (UK ISSN 0305-2729) **5157**
C I P L *see* Amsterdam Studies in the Theory and History of Linguistic Science. Series 2: Classics in Psycholinguistics **2802**
†C.I.P. Newsletter. (Capital Improvement Project) (US) **5157**
C I P S Review. (Canadian Information Processing Society) (CN ISSN 0701-8681) **1390**, 1458, 1468
C I R A Bulletin. (Centre International de Recherches sur l'Anarchisme) (SZ) **3877**
C I R A S News. (Center for Industrial Research and Service) (US) **4594**, 1816, 4303
C I R A Scope (Chicago and Illinois Restaurant Association) *see* Illinois Food Service News **2476**
C I R C A Art Magazine. (UK ISSN 0263-9475) **320**
C I R E S Cahiers. (Centre Ivoirien de Recherches Economiques et Sociales) (IV) **653**, 4430
C I R I A. Bulletin *see* C I R I A Annual Report **1862**
C I R I A Annual Report. (Construction Industry Research and Information Association) (UK ISSN 0305-4047) **1862**, 608
C I R I A News. (UK ISSN 0141-2817) **1862**, 608
C I R I A Report. (UK ISSN 0305-408X) **1862**, 608

C I R I A Technical Note. (UK ISSN 0305-1781) **1862**, 608
C.I.R.M. (Centro Internazionale Radio-Medico) (IT) **3085**, 1370
C I R News. (Committee of Interns and Residents) (US) **3085**, 974
C I R P A Newsletter. (Canadian Independent Record Production Association) (CN ISSN 0840-6154) **4460**
C.I.R.P. Annals. (SZ ISSN 0007-8506) **1927**
C I R V I Bollettino. (Centro Interuniversitario di Ricerche sul Viaggio in Italia) (IT ISSN 0394-1434) **4755**
C I S. (Chromosome Information Service) (JA ISSN 0574-9549) **540**
C I S Abstracts *see* Safety and Health at Work **3623**
C I S E Newsletter. (Centro Informazioni Studi Esperienze) (IT) **4594**
C I S Federal Register Index. (Congressional Information Service) (US ISSN 0741-2878) **4079**, 7, 4055
C I S Index. (Congressional Information Service) (US ISSN 0007-8514) **4079**, 7
C I S M Journal A C S G. (Canadian Institute of Surveying and Mapping) (CN ISSN 0841-8233) **2244**, 1877
C I S Newsletter *see* Policy **685**
C I S Policy Report *see* Policy **685**
C I S Soviet Travel Newsletter. (Commonwealth Independent States) (US ISSN 1059-4957) **4755**, 1035
C I S T I News/Actualites I C I S T. (Canada Institute for Scientific and Technical Information) (CN ISSN 0715-8661) **4359**, 4594
C I T A Exam Reviews *see* For Formulation Chemists Only **375**
C I T E Reports. (UK) **4595**
C I V I S: International Foundation Report. (Centro Informazione Vivisezionista Internazionale Scientifica) (SZ) **20**
C I W Newsletter *see* Spectra: C I W Newsletter **4345**
C J A and H S A Annual Report and Accounts. (Council of Justice to Animals and Humane Slaughter Association) (UK ISSN 0264-8741) **230**
C J A and H S A Newsletter. (Council of Justice to Animals and Humane Slaughter Association) (UK ISSN 0263-1407) **230**
C J A News. (Christians for Justice Action) (US) **4232**
C: J E T *see* Communication: Journalism Education Today **1622**
C J F Annual Report. (Council of Jewish Federations, Inc.) (US) **4400**
C J F Annual Review *see* C J F Annual Report **4400**
C J F Endowment Review. (Council of Jewish Federations, Inc.) (US) **4400**, 1995
C J S A Forum. (Criminal Justice Statistics Association, Inc.) (US) **1511**
C JSS - RCSS *see* Canadian Journal of Sport Sciences **4468**
C K of A Journal. (Catholic Knights of America) (US ISSN 0007-8530) **1296**
C L. (CartoLibraio) (IT) **3662**, 2281
C L A C S O Boletin *see* David y Goliath **4370**
C L A Directory. (Canadian Library Association) (CN) **2750**
C.L.A. Feliciter *see* Feliciter **2757**
C L A G Yearbook *see* Conference of Latin Americanist Geographers Yearbook **2245**
C L A Guidelines. (Coin Laundry Association) (US) **4617**
C L A Journal. (College Language Association) (US ISSN 0007-8549) **2807**, 2901
C L A News *see* Journal of the Coin Laundry and Drycleaning Industry **1281**

C L A News. (Coin Laundry Association) (US) **4617**
C L A Newsletter *see* California Libraries **2751**
C L A O Journal. (US ISSN 0733-8902) **3299**
C L A Organization Handbook and Membership List *see* C L A Directory **2750**
C L A S E. (Citas Latinoamericanas en Ciencias Sociales y Humanidades) (MX) **2519**, 7, 396, 707
†C L A S S Forum. (Cooperative Library Agency for Systems and Services) (US ISSN 0162-492X) **5157**
C L C Today/C T C Aujourd'hui. (CN) **974**
C L E A R Exam Review. (Council on Licensure, Enforcement & Regulation) (US) **4099**, 2608
C L E C *see* Carib-Latin Energy Consultant **1784**
C L E I R P P A. Bulletin Documentaire Mensuel. (Centre de Liaison, d'Etude, d'Information et de Recherche sur les Porblemes des Personnes Agees) (FR) **2271**
C L E I R P P A Annees - Documents. (FR ISSN 0184-6531) **2271**
C L E Journal and Register. (US) **2608**, 1701
C L E N Exchange Newsletter. (Continuing Library Education Network and Exchange Round Table) (US) **2750**
C L E Register *see* C L E Journal and Register **2608**
C L E T V. (Continuing Legal Education) (US) **2608**
C L G - Information. (GW ISSN 0323-7117) **1171**
C L G R O Newsletter. (Coalition for Lesbian and Gay Rights in Ontario) (CN) **2451**, 3940
C L I S Observer. (Centre for Library and Information Study) (II ISSN 0970-0943) **2750**
C L L *see* Creole Language Library **2810**
C L M P Newsletter. (Council of Literary Magazines and Presses) (US) **4124**
C L O Bulletin. (Centrale Landsdienaren Organisatie) (SR) **2581**
C L R. (Clinical Laboratory Reference) (US ISSN 0093-8076) **3258**, 2521
C L R Reports. (Council on Library Resources, Inc.) (US ISSN 0892-0605) **2750**
C.L.S. Bulletin *see* Charles Lamb Bulletin **2904**
C L S I Newsletter *see* C L S I Newsletter of Library Automation **2750**
C L S I Newsletter of Library Automation. (US) **2750**
C L S Quarterly. (US ISSN 0736-0142) **2608**, 4167
C L S U Scientific Journal. (Central Luzon State University) (PH) **81**, 1816, 4595
C L U Comment (English Edition). (Canadian Institute Chartered Life Underwriters) (CN ISSN 0382-7038) **2529**
C L U Journal *see* American Society of C L U. Journal **5135**
†C L W Contents Monthly. (College of Librarianship Wales) (UK ISSN 0269-056X) **5157**
†C L W Library Catalogue. (College of Librarianship Wales) (UK) **5157**
C - Lehti. (FI ISSN 0783-8921) **1468**
C M A. (CN ISSN 0831-3881) **748**, 1004
C M A Close Up *see* Close Up Magazine **3546**
C M A Newsletter. (College Media Advisers) (US) **1306**
C M: A Reviewing Journal of Canadian Materials for Young People. (CN) **2750**
C M A S Bulletin d'Information/C M A S Newsletter. (Confederation Mondiale des Activites) (FR ISSN 0007-8603) **1602**, 434
C M A S Newsletter. *see* C M A S Bulletin d'Information **1602**

C M B Newsletter. (Ghana Cocoa Marketing Board) (GH ISSN 0007-8611) **1035**, 171
C M C I *see* Compumath Citation Index **3062**
C M C News. (Computers and the Media Center) (US ISSN 0738-8845) **1350**
C M: Canadian Materials for Schools and Libraries *see* C M: A Reviewing Journal of Canadian Materials for Young People **2750**
†C M D. (Current Medical Dialog) (US ISSN 0007-862X) **5157**
C M D S. (Christian Medical & Dental Society) (US) **3085**, 4167
C M E. (SA) **3085**
C M E A News. (California Music Educators Association) (US ISSN 0007-8638) **3543**, 1688
†C M E Annual Report. (Center for Music Experiment) (US) **5157**
C M E - Continuing Medical Education. (CN) **3085**, 1701
C M E News *see* Saskatchewan Medical Journal **3151**
C M G Conference Proceedings. (US) **1390**
C M G Transactions. (US) **1390**
C M I Descriptions of Fungi and Bacteria. (Mycological Institute) (UK) **434**
C M I Descriptions of Pathogenic Fungi and Bacteria *see* C M I Descriptions of Fungi and Bacteria **434**
C M I Distribution Maps of Plant Diseases. (Mycological Institute) (UK ISSN 0012-396X) **498**
C M I News Letter. (International Maritime Committee) (SW) **4725**
C M I T *see* Current Medical Information and Terminology **5175**
C M I Year Book. (SW) **4725**
C M J New Music Report. (College Media Journal) (US) **3543**, 1370
C.M.J. Quarterly *see* Shalom **4226**
C M J S Centerpieces. (Cohen Center for Modern Jewish Studies) (US ISSN 0887-1639) **1995**, 3980, 4222, 4430
C M L E A Journal. (California Media and Library Educators Association) (US ISSN 0196-3309) **2751**, 1619
C M L R Antitrust Reports. (UK) **2708**
C M M. (Confectionery Manufacture & Marketing) (UK ISSN 0007-8654) **2087**
†C M M A Industry Update. (Clock Manufacturers and Marketing Association) (US) **5157**
C - M News. (Concrete - Masonry) (US) **608**
C - M Newsletter *see* C - M News **608**
C M P A Newsletter. (Canadian Magazine Publishers Association) (CN ISSN 0315-6621) **4124**
†C M P Bulletin. (California Museum of Photography) (US ISSN 0731-2377) **5157**
C M P in Construction (Computers, Productivity and Management) *see* Construction Computer Applications Newsletter **612**
C M R E Monetary Tracts *see* C M R E Monographs **769**
C M R E Monographs. (Committee for Monetary Research and Education, Inc.) (US ISSN 0734-0486) **769**
C M R S Annual Report. (Central Mining Research Station) (II) **3480**
C M R S Bulletin. (II) **3480**
C M S News. (Center for Maritime Studies) (IS ISSN 0792-6073) **1602**, 268, 434
C M S Notes. (Canadian Mathematical Society) (CN) **3031**
C M T C Newsletter *see* Conscience **3941**
C M T Newsletter. (CN ISSN 0831-6279) **3229**
C M U Journal of Agriculture, Food and Nutrition *see* C M U Journal of Science **81**
C M U Journal of Science. (Central Mindanao University) (PH ISSN 0116-7847) **81**, 3604
C-Magazin. (GW ISSN 0935-0373) **4167**

C Magazine. (CN ISSN 0829-2906) 320, 3522, 3789
C N see Rivista di Coniglicoltura 225
C N see Commercial News U S A 904
C N A Bulletin see California Nurse 3276
†C N A: The Nutrition Connection. (Consumers for Nutrition Action, Inc.) (US) 5157
C N C Statistiques. (Centre National de la Cinematographie) (FR) 3519
C N I D A Informa. (Centro Nacional de Informacion - Direccion General del Derecho de Autor) (MX ISSN 0185-2493) 396, 4124
C N I Weekly Report see Nutrition Week 3611
C N L. (Colonial Newsletter) (US ISSN 0010-1443) 3598, 1619
C N L - Quarterly World Report see C N L - World Report 2901
C N L R see Canadian Native Law Reporter 2611
C N L - World Report. (Council on National Literatures) (US) 2901
C N P R Revue des Entreprises. (FR ISSN 0399-8975) 1073
†C N R Voice. (Center for Nursing Research) (US) 5157
C N S Bulletin. (Canadian Nuclear Society) (CN ISSN 0714-7074) 1804
C N S Focus. (Cargo Network Services) (US) 4671
C N S Malignancies--Diagnosis, Treatment see I C R D B Cancergram: C N S Malignancies - Diagnosis, Treatment 3175
C N U C E D Bulletin see U N C T A D Bulletin 923
C N V - Opinie. (Christelijk Nationaal Vakverbond in Nederland) (NE) 4167, 2581
†C O A D Words. (Churches Council on Alcohol and Drugs) (UK ISSN 0260-6429) 5157
C O A G - Informa. (Coordinadora de Organizaciones de Agricultores y Ganaderos) (SP) 213
C O A Review see Perrin & Treggett's Review 1538
C O D A Newsletter. (Children of Deaf Adults) (US ISSN 0885-7962) 2286
C O D A T A Bulletin. (Committee on Data for Science and Technology) (US ISSN 0366-757X) 4303, 4595
C O D A T A Newsletter. (Committee on Data for Science and Technology) (FR ISSN 0538-6918) 4303
C O D E S R I A Bulletin. (SG) 2332, 927
C O D I A. (Colegio Dominicano de Ingenieros, Arquitectos y Agrimensores) (DR ISSN 0045-7310) 1862, 296
†C O E Events. (College of Education) (US) 5157
C O F I E C. Informe Anual. (Compania Financiera Ecuatoriana de Desarrollo) (EC) 769
C O F O Memo. (Coalition of Family Organizations) (US) 2445
C O G E L Guardian. (Council on Governmental Ethics Laws) (US) 2608, 3877, 4055
C O G E L Newsletter see C O G E L Guardian 2608
C O G Newsletter. (Covenant of the Goddess) (US) 4280
C O G Nition. (Canadian Organic Growers) (CN) 2123
C O H S E Journal. (Confederation of Health Service Employees) (UK) 4099, 2459, 3276, 4835
C O I. Feuille d'Information see C O I. Hoja de Informacion 171
C O I. Hoja de Informacion. (Consejo Oleicola Internacional) (SP) 171
†C O I N T Reports. (Communication and Information Technology) (US ISSN 0198-8840) 5157
C O L T see Camping & Outdoor Leisure Trader 4543
C O M see C O M - Nuovi Tempi 4167
C O M A R see Code of Maryland Regulations 4057
C O M Documents. (EI) 3952

C O M E C O N Data. (Council for Mutual Economic Assistance) (US ISSN 0263-3701) 902
C O M E C O N Foreign Trade Data. (Council for Mutual Economic Assistance) (US) 902
C O M L A Newsletter. (Commonwealth Library Association) (JM ISSN 0378-1070) 2751
C O M - Nuovi Tempi. (IT) 4167
C O M P M E D see I E E E Engineering in Medicine and Biology Society. International Conference 3225
C O M P S A C / I E E E Computer Society's International Computer Software & Applications Conference. Proceedings. (US ISSN 0730-3157) 1476
C O M S A T Technical Review. (Communications Satellite Corporation) (US ISSN 0095-9669) 1332
C O N A Journal. (Canadian Orthopaedic Nurses Association) (CN ISSN 0708-6474) 3307, 3276, 3319
C O N C I L I U M. (GW ISSN 0588-9804) 4167
C O N S E R Microfiche. (Cooperative Online Serials) (CN ISSN 0707-3747) 396
C O P A Conversation. (Canadian Office Products Association) (CN) 1057
C O P F News. (Canadian Ornamental Plant Foundation) (CN) 2123
C O P H Bulletin. (National Congress of Organizations of the Physically Handicapped, Inc.) (US ISSN 0007-8808) 3085
C O P I Press. (Communicator of the Electronic Printing Industry) (US) 1390
C O R D Bulletin. (Congress on Research in Dance) (US) 1529
C O R D Newsletter. (Congress on Research in Dance) (US ISSN 0734-4856) 1529
C O R E. (Collected Original Resources in Education) (UK ISSN 0308-6909) 1619
C O R E J see Contents of Recent Economics Journals 711
C O R E Magazine. (Congress of Racial Equality) (US ISSN 0300-743X) 3940, 1995
C O R E S T A. (Centre de Cooperation pour les Recherches Scientifiques Relatives au Tabac (Coresta)) (FR ISSN 0010-8723) 4646, 7
C O R Letter. (US) 4232
C O R O S Chronicle. (Collectors of Religion on Stamps) (US) 3750
C O R S. see I N F O R Journal 1451
C O S M E P Newsletter. (Committee of Small Magazine Editors & Publishers) (US) 4124
†C O S - M O S Digital Integrated Circuits. (US ISSN 0093-8270) 5157
C O S P A R Information Bulletin. (Committee on Space Research) (US ISSN 0045-8732) 49
C O S P E N News. (Committee on Special Educational Needs) (UK ISSN 0262-2793) 1734
C O S T E D Newsletter. (Committee on Science and Technology in Developing Countries) (II) 4303, 4595
C O T A L. (Confederacion de Organizaciones Turisticas de la America Latina) (AG ISSN 0007-8859) 4755
C P see Colture Protette 2124
C P A see National Directory of Corporate Public Affairs 681
C P A (Year) see Today's C P A 757
C P A Administrative Report. (US) 1063, 748, 1035
C P A Associates. Update. (Certified Public Accountant) (US) 748
C P A Client Bulletin. (American Institute of Certified Public Accountants) (US) 748, 1004, 1035, 1113
C P A Digest. (US ISSN 0741-3610) 748, 1089
The C P A Journal. (US ISSN 0732-8435) 748

C P A Letter. (US ISSN 0094-792X) 748
C P A Managing Partner Report. (US ISSN 0894-1815) 748, 1004
C P A Marketing Report. (US ISSN 0279-1021) 1035, 748
C P A Micro Report. (Certified Public Accountant) (US) 805
C P A Personnel Report. (US ISSN 0745-0877) 1063, 748
C P A Profit Report. (US) 941
C P A Proposal Alert see C P A Marketing Report 1035
C P A Seminar Report see C P A Digest 748
▼C P A Software News. (US) 825, 748
C P & T. (Casting Plant and Technology) (GW ISSN 0177-1469) 3403
C P & T International. (Casting Plant & Technology) (GW ISSN 0935-7262) 3403
C P B Report. (Corporation for Public Broadcasting) (US) 1370
C P C see Current Papers on Computers & Control 1404
C P C see Current Problems in Cardiology 3207
C P C Annual. (College Placement Council, Inc.) (US ISSN 0749-7474) 3625
C P C Career & Job Fair Finder. (College Placement Council, Inc.) (US ISSN 1046-1183) 3625
C P C National Directory. (US ISSN 8755-8378) 3625
C P C Salary Survey. (College Placement Council, Inc.) (US ISSN 0196-1004) 3625, 1701
C P C U Journal see Society of Chartered Property and Casualty Underwriters. Journal 2543
C P C U News. (Society of Chartered Property & Casualty Underwriters) (US ISSN 0007-8883) 2529
C P C U Public Affairs Forum. (Society of Chartered Property & Casualty Underwriters) (US) 2529
C P C U Update. (Society of Chartered Property & Casualty Underwriters) (US) 2529
C P Ca see Current Problems in Cancer 3196
C P D A News. (Council for Periodical Distributors Associations) (US ISSN 0590-711X) 4124
C P D R see Current Problems in Diagnostic Radiology 3358
C P Digest. (Cardiovascular Pulmonary) (US) 3205
C P E M Digest see Conference on Precision Electromagnetic Measurements. Digest 1884
C P E R. (California Public Employee Relations) (US ISSN 0194-3073) 974, 4055
C P F I Newsletter. (Christian Pharmacists Fellowship International) (US) 3720, 4232, 4257
C P H A Health Digest. (Canadian Public Health Association) (CN ISSN 0703-5624) 3800
C P I Digest. (Chemical Process Industries) (US ISSN 0891-1886) 3868, 7, 1199
†C P I Equipment Reporter. (US) 5157
C P I Product Profiles. (CN) 1171, 1125
C P I Purchasing. (Chemical Process Industries) (US ISSN 0746-9012) 1035, 1171
C P I Purchasing Chemicals Directory. (US ISSN 0746-9012) 1848, 1125
C P I Purchasing's Equipment Buyers Guide. (Chemical Process Industries) (US) 1848, 1035
C P J - R P C see Canadian Pharmaceutical Journal 3720
C P L Bibliographies. (Council of Planning Librarians) (US) 2499, 2792
C P L Newsletter. (Council of Planning Librarians) (US ISSN 0045-8791) 2484, 2751
C P M. (GW) 1251
C P M C Nafles. (IT) 809

C.P. Newsletter Monthly. (NZ ISSN 0112-8388) 3750
C P P see Current Problems in Pediatrics 3320
C P P A X Newsletter. (Citizens for Participation in Political Action) (US ISSN 0194-0856) 3877
C P P R. (Cooperative Plant Pest Report) (US ISSN 0363-0889) 171, 529
C P R - J. (Contingency Planning & Recovery Journal) (US ISSN 0899-4595) 1433
C P R - R see C P R - J 1433
C P S see Current Problems in Surgery 3378
C P S A see Copenhagen Political Studies Abstracts 3936
C.P.S. Bulletin see Peacemaker 3914
†C P S Reporter. (Cultural - Political - Scientific) (GW ISSN 0007-8921) 5157
C P T. (Physicians' Current Procedural Terminology) (US ISSN 0276-8283) 3085
C P U News. (Commonwealth Press Union) (UK) 2568
C P U Quarterly see C P U News 2568
▼C Plus Plus Journal. (US) 1476, 1429
C Plus Plus Report. (US ISSN 1040-6042) 1429
C Q. (US ISSN 0007-893X) 1355
C Q see Connecticut Quarterly 2908
C Q Almanac. (Congressional Quarterly Inc.) 3877
C Q Chess News. (AT) 4467
C Q - D L. (GW ISSN 0178-269X) 1355
C Q Ham Radio. (JA ISSN 0007-8964) 1355
C Q Radio Amateur. (SP ISSN 0212-4696) 1883, 1125
C Q Researcher. (US ISSN 1056-2036) 3877, 4367
C Q Researcher Bound Volume. (US) 3877
C Q's Washington Alert. (US) 4085
C R A. (FR) 4685
C R A - H M D A Update. (US) 769
C R A Newsletter. (Colorado River Association) (US) 4822
C R A Petroleum Economics Monthly. (Charles River Associates Incorporated) (US) 3683, 849
C R A Reporter. (US) 2484
C R A Review. (Charles River Associates Incorporated) (US) 1073
C R B Commodity Index Report. (US) 941
C R B Futures Chart Service. (Commodity Research Bureau) (US) 941
†C R B Outlook. (Commodity Research Bureau) (US) 5157
C R C Critical Reviews in Analytical Chemistry see Critical Reviews in Analytical Chemistry 1205
C R C Critical Reviews in Biochemistry see Critical Reviews in Biochemistry and Molecular Biology 475
C R C Critical Reviews in Biomedical Engineering see Critical Reviews in Biomedical Engineering 469
C R C Critical Reviews in Biotechnology see Critical Reviews in Biotechnology 489
C R C Critical Reviews in Clinical Laboratory Sciences see Critical Reviews in Clinical Laboratory Sciences 3091
C R C Critical Reviews in Diagnostic Imaging see Critical Reviews in Diagnostic Imaging 3357
C R C Critical Reviews in Environmental Control see Critical Reviews in Environmental Control 1946
C R C Critical Reviews in Food Science and Nutrition see Critical Reviews in Food Science and Nutrition 2065
C R C Critical Reviews in Immunology see Critical Reviews in Immunology 3184
C R C Critical Reviews in Microbiology see Critical Reviews in Microbiology 550

C R C Critical Reviews in Oncology - Hematology see Critical Reviews in Oncology - Hematology 3196
C R C Critical Reviews in Plant Sciences see Critical Reviews in Plant Sciences 174
C R C Critical Reviews in Solid State and Materials Sciences see Critical Reviews in Solid State & Materials Sciences 3816
C R C Critical Reviews in Toxicology see Critical Reviews in Toxicology 1981
C R: Centennial Review. (US ISSN 0162-0177) 2504, 2901, 4367
C R D I Explore see I D R C Reports 930
C R E - Action. (Standing Conference of Rectors, Presidents and Vice-Chancellors of the European Universities) (SZ ISSN 1011-9019) 1701
C R E D I F Bulletin Bibliographique. (Centre de Recherche et d'Etude pour la Diffusion du Francais) (FR ISSN 0765-1937) 2807
C R E E D News. (Christian Rescue Effort for the Emancipation of Dissidents) (US) 4167
C R E Information see C R E - Action 1701
C R E S S Notes see E R I C - C R E S S Bulletin 1626
C R I A R L Newsletter. (Consortium of Rhode Island Academic and Research Libraries) (US ISSN 0882-6846) 2751
C R I A W Papers. (Canadian Research Institute for the Advancement of Women) (CN) 4838
C R I Abstracts. (Cement Research Institute of India) (II ISSN 0576-9922) 637, 7
C R I C Rapport de Recherche. (BE ISSN 0770-0725) 4303, 4595
C R I Communications Update Service. (Communications Research Institute) (US ISSN 0271-4795) 1332
C R I Current Contents. (II ISSN 0970-7891) 637
C R I D E Cahiers. (Centre de Recherches Interdisciplinaires pour le Developpement de l'Education (CRIDE)) (ZR) 1619
C R I F Bulletin. (Centre de Recherches, de Reflexion et d'Information Feministes) (FR) 4838
†C R I News. (Cranfield Rural Institute) (UK) 5157
C R I S E S Alternative Press Exhibition Catalog. (Critical Research Institute for Social and Environmental Sciences) (US) 396
C R I S E S Catalog see C R I S E S Alternative Press Exhibition Catalog 396
C R I Technology Digest. (II) 608
C R L see College & Research Libraries 2752
C R L A Newsletter. (College Reading and Learning Association) (US) 1682, 1701, 1734, 1745
▼C R N A: the Clinical Forum for Nurse Anesthetists. (US) 3190, 3276
C R N L E Reviews Journal. (Centre for Research in the New Literatures in English) (AT ISSN 0157-3705) 2860, 2901
C R O M T E C Working Paper Series. (Centre for Research on Organisations, Management and Technical Change) (UK) 1004
C R O P see Computing Resources for the Professional 5170
C R P C Info. (Capital Region Planning Commission) (US) 2484, 4085
C.R. Quarterly Review. (UK) 4167
C R R I Road Abstracts. (Central Road Research Institute) (II ISSN 0045-6055) 1842, 7
C R Report see College Republican 3880
C R S Networking Newsletter see L A Co-ops and the Shared Housing Networker 4411
C R S Perspectives. (Centre for Resource Studies) (CN ISSN 0228-1821) 3480, 653

C R U S News see Information Research News 2762
C S A and the Consumer. (Canadian Standards Association) (CN ISSN 0011-2313) 3445, 1502
C S A Fraternal Life. (Czechoslovak Society of America) (US) 1995
C S A Information Update see Canadian Standards Association. Info Update 3445
C S A Neurosciences Abstracts. (Cambridge Scientific Abstracts) (US ISSN 0141-7711) 3168, 7
C S A News. (Costume Society of America) (US) 1289, 2401
C S A News. (Council of Supervisors and Administrators of the City of New York) (US) 1725
C S A Newsletter see C S A News 1725
C S A S Occasional Papers. (Centre for Southern African Studies) (UK) 2332
C S A Update. (Cambridge Scientific Abstracts) (US) 4355, 7
C S C China Steel Technical Report - Zhonggang Jibao see China Steel Technical Report 3404
C S C Newsletter. (Community of the Sisters of the Church) (AT ISSN 0007-9073) 4232
C S C Reports. (Cooking for Survival Consciousness) (US ISSN 0741-739X) 3604, 3800
C.S.D. Advance Locator see Advance Locator for Capitol Hill 3870
C S D Newsletter. (Coalition on Sexuality and Disability, Inc.) (US) 2283
†C S E C Newsletter. (Cesareans, Support, Education and Concern) (US) 5157
C S E L T Infotel. (IT ISSN 0391-5379) 1346, 1361, 1883
C S E L T Technical Reports. (IT ISSN 0393-2648) 1332, 1361
C S E Monograph Series in Evaluation. (Center for the Study of Evaluation) (US) 1745
C S E News. (Camping & Sports Equipment Ltd.) (UK ISSN 0008-2406) 4542
C S F M Journal. (California State Fire Marshal) (US) 2031
C S F Notebook. (Center for the Study of Federalism) (US) 3877
†C S G Backgrounder. (Council of State Governments) (US) 5157
C S I Communications. (Computer Society of India) (II) 1390
C S I Congressional Record Abstracts: Energy Edition. (Capitol Services, Inc.) (US) 4080, 1798
C S I Congressional Record Abstracts: Foreign Affairs Edition. (US) 4080, 7, 3952
C S I Congressional Record Abstracts: Master Edition. (US) 4080, 7
C S I Congressional Record Abstracts: National Defense Edition. (US) 4080, 7
C S I Congressional Record Report. (US) 2608, 4055
C S I Federal Index. (US) 4080, 7
C S I Federal Register. (US) 2608, 4055
C S I Federal Register Abstracts: Master Edition. (US) 4080, 7
C S I Newsdigest. (US ISSN 0163-5018) 608
C S I O Communications. (Central Scientific Instruments Organization) (II ISSN 0304-9841) 2521
C S I R Annual Report see C S I R Annual Report - Technology Impact 4303
C S I R Annual Report - Technology Impact. (SA) 4303, 4595
C S I R Handbook. (Council for Scientific and Industrial Research) (GH) 4303
C S I R O Abstracts see C S I R O Index 4355
C S I R O Directory. (Commonwealth Scientific and Industrial Research Organization) (AT ISSN 0157-7204) 4303, 4595

C.S.I.R.O. Division of Coal Technology and Division of Fuel Technology. Annual Reports see Commonwealth Scientific and Industrial Research Organization. Division of Coal and Energy Technology. Annual Report 1946
C.S.I.R.O. Division of Fisheries. Research Report. (Commonwealth Scientific and Industrial Research Organization) (AT ISSN 1031-9956) 2038, 1602
C S I R O Division of Materials Science. Research Report see C S I R O Division of Materials Science & Technology Report 1213
C S I R O Division of Materials Science & Technology Report. (AT ISSN 1035-7599) 1213, 3815
C.S.I.R.O. Division of Oceanography. Research Report. (Commonwealth Scientific and Industrial Research Organization) (AT ISSN 1031-9964) 1602
†C S I R O Film Catalogue. (Commonwealth Scientific and Industrial Research Organization) (AT ISSN 0069-7192) 5157
C S I R O Food Research Quarterly. (AT ISSN 0310-9070) 2063
C S I R O Index. (AT ISSN 0311-5836) 4355, 7
C S I R O Net News. (AT ISSN 0726-657X) 1390
C S I R O Rural Research. (AT ISSN 0036-0090) 81
C S I R O Rural Sector Report. (Commonwealth Scientific and Industrial Research Organization) (AT) 81
C S I R O Wool Textile News. (Commonwealth Scientific and Industrial Research Organization.) (AT ISSN 0312-5211) 4617
†C S I R Publications/W N N R Publikasies. (Council for Scientific and Industrial Research) (SA ISSN 0301-6145) 5157
C S I R Research Reports see South Africa. Division of Roads and Transport Technology. Bulletins 4721
C S I R Research Review see C S I R Publications 5157
C S I R Special Reports see South Africa. Division of Roads and Transport Technology. P A D Series 4721
C S Journal see Cued Speech Journal 2286
C S L Bulletin. (New York C.S. Lewis Society) (US ISSN 0883-9980) 2901
C S M. (US) 1035
C S M A. Executive Newswatch. (Chemical Specialties Manufacturers Association) (US) 1171
C S M C R I Newsletter. (Central Salt and Marine Chemicals Research Institute) (II) 1602, 1171
C S M Informatie. (NE ISSN 0165-9375) 171
C S M News see Christian Socialist 3879
C.S.O. Statistical Bulletins. (Central Statistical Office) (TR) 4565
C S O Update. (US) 1390
C S P A Stateside. (Council of State Planning Agencies) (US ISSN 0743-8494) 4055
C S P: Critical Social Policy. (UK ISSN 0261-0183) 4400, 3877
C S P Directory. (Board of Certified Safety Professionals) (US) 3615, 1816, 4099
C.S.P. World News. (CN ISSN 0702-7958) 2989
C S Q - Computational Statistics Quarterly see Computational Statistics 4569
C S R Connection. (Customer Service Representative) (US) 2529
C S R Construction News. (AT ISSN 1034-9596) 1862
C S R Hotline. (Customer Service Representative) (US ISSN 0894-6418) 1035

C U   6015

C S S A Newsletter. (Cactus & Succulent Society of America (Lawndale)) (US) 2123
C S S E Contact. (Canadian Society of Safety Engineering) (CN ISSN 0713-3421) 3615
C S S E D C Quarterly see English Leadership Quarterly 1749
C S S Papers. (Center for Strategic Studies) (YU ISSN 0353-0353) 3952
†C S S R. Kronika Vnitropolitickych Udalosti. (CS ISSN 0303-2221) 5157
C S S R Bulletin. (Council of Societies for the Study of Religion) (US) 4167
C S S S Digest. (Center for the Study of Sport in Society) (US) 4467, 4430
C-Store Week see U S Oil Week 3703
C T. (GW) 1390
C T see Critical Theory 2810
C T see Revista Brasileira de Clinica e Terapeutica 3147
C T A A. Boletim de Pesquisa. (Centro Nacional de Pesquisa de Tecnologia Agroindustrial de Alimentos) (BL ISSN 0101-630X) 2063
C T A Action. (California Teachers Association) (US ISSN 0742-2121) 1701
C.T.A. Journal. (II) 3504
C T A - N E A Action see C T A Action 1701
C T B Info. (Centre Technique du Bois et de l'Ameublement) (FR ISSN 0296-8541) 2113
C T C Aujourd'hui. see C L C Today 974
C T C Reporter see Transnational Corporations 923
C.T. Directory of Southern Africa see Braby's Commercial Directory of Southern Africa 1123
C T G Gazette. (Commercial Travellers' Guild) (AT) 1035
C T I C Reports see Cable Update 1371
C T I Journal. (Cooling Tower Institute) (US ISSN 0273-3250) 3683, 1816
C T K Dokumentacni Prehled. (Ceskoslovenska Tiskova Kancelar) (CS ISSN 0590-501X) 2568
C T L A Forum. (California Trial Lawyers Association) (US ISSN 0889-7751) 2608
C T N. (Confectioner, Tobacconist, Newsagent) (UK) 2087, 4643
C T O. (Call to Order) (UK ISSN 0260-5821) 320
C T P A News. (California Travel Parks Association, Inc.) (US) 4755, 4542
C T T News and Reports see Capital Taxes News & Reports 1090
C.T.T.S. Annual. (College of Textile Technology, Serampore) (II ISSN 0084-8859) 4617
C T V D: Cinema - T V - Digest. (US ISSN 0007-9219) 3504, 1370
C U see Cirugia del Uruguay 3377
C U A Magazine. (Catholic University of America) (US) 1306
C U B Communicator. (Concerned United Birthparents, Inc.) (US) 4430
C U E Newsletter. (US) 1688, 1417
C U F C Leader see C C U M C Leader 1745
C U I S. (Credit Union Information Service) (US) 769, 829
†C U I S Resources. (Credit Union Information Service) (US) 5157
C U L P see California Union List of Periodicals 396
C U N Y Forum. (City University of New York) (US) 2807
C U P A Journal. (US ISSN 1046-9508) 1063, 1701
C U P A News. (College & University Personnel Association) (US ISSN 0892-7855) 1725
C U P E Journal see Canadian Union of Public Employees. The Public Employee 2581
C U P News Exchange. (Canadian University Press) (CN) 1306
C U S A N. (Catholics United for Spiritual Action) (US) 4257, 4400

6016 C U

C U S Bulletin. (Centre for Urban Studies) (BG) **2484**

C U S I P Corporate Directory. (Committee on Uniform Security Identification Procedures) (US) **941**

C U S I P Master Directory. (American Bankers Association, Committee on Uniform Security Identification Procedures) (US) **941**

C U S O Advocate. (CN) **927**

C U S O Forum. (CN ISSN 0823-5740) **927**

†C U S O Journal. (CN ISSN 0821-1272) **5157**

C U T A - A C T U Forum. (Canadian Urban Transit Association) (CN) **4717**

C Users Journal. (US ISSN 0898-9788) **1429**

C V. (Cardiovascular) (GW ISSN 0940-8770) **3205**

C V-C F N News Bulletin see Ecuador. Corporacion Financiera Nacional. News Bulletin **1093**

C V C Report. (Creative Video Consulting) (US) **1384**

C V G I P: Graphical Models and Image Processing. (US ISSN 1049-9652) **1420**

C V G I P: Image Understanding. (US ISSN 1049-9660) **1420**

C V P R see I E E E Computer Society Conference on Computer Vision and Pattern Recognition. Proceedings **1421**

C V R Hotel Guide to Southern Africa. (SA) **4755**, 2472

C V R Travel and Hotel Guide to Southern Africa see C V R Hotel Guide to Southern Africa **4755**

C V Tech see Journal of Cardiovascular and Pulmonary Technology **3209**

†C V: The College Magazine. (CareerVision, Inc.) (US ISSN 1042-3672) **5157**

C V World Report see C V **3205**

C W A News. (Communications Workers of America) (US ISSN 0007-9227) **2581**, 1332

C W A O News. (Coalition of Women's Art Organizations) (US) **320**, 4838

C W C Connections. (Communications Electronic, Electrical, Technical and Salaried Workers of Canada) (CN) **1883**

C W F see T W F **1282**

C W G E A Newsletter. (Cooperative Whole Grain Education Association) (US) **2087**

C W I. Monographs. (Centrum voor Wiskunde en Informatica) (NE) **3064**

C W I. Publications. (Centrum voor Wiskunde en Informatica) (NE) **3064**

C W I. Syllabi. (Centrum voor Wiskunde en Informatica) (NE) **3064**

C W I. Tracts. (Centrum voor Wiskunde en Informatica) (NE) **3031**, 1390

C W I Credit Professional see Credit Professional **5174**

C W I Herald. (Christian Witness to Israel) (UK ISSN 0308-5252) **4167**

C W I Quarterly. (Centrum voor Wiskunde en Informatica) (NE ISSN 0922-5366) **1455**

C W L News. (Catholic Women's League) (UK) **4838**, 4257

C W M. (US) **2901**

C W M Report. (Council for World Mission) (UK) **4232**

C W R U: The Magazine of Case Western Reserve University. (US ISSN 1042-9220) **1306**

C W R U Today see C W R U: The Magazine of Case Western Reserve University **1306**

†C W S Connections. (Church World Service) (US) **5157**

†C Y A Newsletter. (Canadian Yachting Association) (CN) **5157**

C y L Moda Intima. (Corseteria y Lenceria) (SP) **1284**

C Y P News Service see In Common **1238**

C Z B Report. (Christliches Zentrum Berlin e.V.) (GW) **4281**

C Z-Chemie-Technik see Chemie-Technik **1851**

C Z I Export Directory. (RH) **1125**

C Z I Industrial Review. (RH) **653**

C 3 I Handbook. (Command, Control, Communications and Intelligence) (US) **3453**, 1332

C 3 I News. (US) **3453**

C 4 I Report see Defense & Aerospace Electronics **3456**

Ca see Ceramica per l'Architettura **1162**

Ca - A Cancer Journal for Clinicians. (US ISSN 0007-9235) **3194**

Ca Cinema. (FR) **3504**

Ca m'Interesse. (FR ISSN 0243-1335) **4303**, 4595

Ca Va. (UK ISSN 0007-9243) **2807**, 1745

Cab Driver. (UK) **4685**

Cab Trade News. (UK) **4647**

†Cabaret 246. (UK) **5157**

†Cabbage Patch Kids. (US) **5157**

Cabbages and Kings. (AT ISSN 0310-1584) **2344**

Cabin Crew Safety. (US ISSN 0898-5758) **49**

Cabin Crew Safety Bulletin see Cabin Crew Safety **49**

Cabinet Maker. (UK) **2557**

Cabinet Maker and Retail Furnisher see Cabinet Maker **2557**

†Cabinet Manufacturing & Fabricating. (US) **5157**

Cabinet Manufacturing and Fabricating Today see Cabinet Manufacturing & Fabricating **5157**

Cabinetmaker. (US) **2557**

CABIOS see Computer Applications in the Biosciences **4359**

Cabirion: Gay Books Bulletin. (US) **2451**, 4124

The Cable. (US) **1306**

Cable. (UK ISSN 0045-3714) **1883**

Cable Age. (US ISSN 0279-4004) **1370**

Cable and Station Coverage Atlas. (US) **1370**

Cable and Station Coverage Atlas and 35-Mile Zone Maps see Cable and Station Coverage Atlas **1370**

Cable Communications Magazine. (CN ISSN 0318-0069) **1370**

Cable Contacts (Year). (US) **1370**

Cable Guide. (US) **1370**

Cable Hour T V Magazine see T V Magazine **1381**

†Cable Marketing. (US ISSN 0279-8891) **5157**

Cable Optics. (US ISSN 1051-1938) **1332**

Cable Plus. (US) **1370**

Cable Rep - Interconnect Directory see Cable Spot Advertising Directory **29**

†Cable Reports. (US) **5157**

Cable Spot Advertising Directory. (US) **29**, 1370

Cable Strategies see M S O **5230**

Cable T V Advertising. (US ISSN 0270-885X) **1370**, 29

Cable T V and New Media Law & Finance. (US) **2608**, 1370

Cable T V Banker - Broker. (US ISSN 0893-2131) **1370**, 769

†Cable T V Business. (US ISSN 0745-2802) **5157**

Cable T V - D B S Services. (UK) **1370**

Cable T V Facts. (US) **29**, 1370

Cable T V Finance see Cable T V Banker - Broker **1370**

Cable T V Financial Databook. (US ISSN 0736-8143) **1370**

Cable T V Franchising. (US ISSN 0731-0269) **1370**

Cable T V Investor. (US ISSN 0731-0250) **1370**, 941

Cable T V Investor Charts. (US ISSN 0732-7757) **1370**, 941

Cable T V Law and Finance see Cable T V and New Media Law & Finance **2608**

Cable T V Law Reporter. (US ISSN 0749-7652) **1370**, 2608

Cable T V Magazine Network. (US) **1370**

Cable T V Programming. (US ISSN 0278-503X) **1370**, 2608

Cable T V Publicity Outlets - Nationwide see T V & Cable Publicity Outlets - Nationwide **1380**

Cable T V Tax Letter. (US ISSN 0730-6202) **1370**, 1089

Cable T V Technology. (US ISSN 0276-5713) **1370**

Cable Television Engineering see International Cable **1375**

Cable - Television Sports Newsletter see Cablesports Newsletter **4467**

Cable Theft Newsletter. (US) **1370**, 1035

Cable TV Regulation see Cable T V Franchising **1370**

Cable TV Station Authorization Report. (US) **1346**, 1371

Cable TV Station Distribution File. (US) **1346**, 1371

Cable Update. (US) **1371**

Cable Video Briefs. (US) **1371**, 1384

Cable World. (US ISSN 1042-7228) **1371**

Cablecast see Cable T V Investor **1370**

Cablecaster. (CN ISSN 0840-9153) **1371**

▼Cablefax. (US) **1371**

†CableFile. (US ISSN 0363-1915) **5157**

Cablesports Newsletter. (US) **4467**, 1371

CableVision. (US ISSN 0361-8374) **1371**

Cabore. (BL ISSN 0007-9316) **2901**

Cabot Market Letter. (US) **941**

†Cabrio. (SP) **5157**

Cacanadadada Review. (US) **2989**

Cacaos, Cafes, Sucres. (FR ISSN 0007-9332) **2063**

Caccia e Pesca. (IT) **4542**

Cacciatore Italiano. (IT) **4542**

Cacciattore Svizzero. see Schweizer Jaeger **4555**

La Cacerola. (UY) **4838**

Cache Citizen. (US) **2222**

†Cache Review. (US ISSN 0734-8428) **5157**

Cactaceas y Suculentas Mexicanas. (MX ISSN 0526-717X) **498**, 570

Cactus and Succulent Journal. (US ISSN 0007-9367) **498**

Cactus and Succulent Journal of Great Britain see Bradleya **497**

Cactus & Succulent Society of America (Lawndale) Newsletter see C S S A Newsletter **2123**

Cadastro Delta. (BL) **653**

Cadastro Industrial do Para. (BL) **1073**

Cadastro Industrial do Rio Grande do Sul see Anuario das Industrias do Estado do Rio Grande do Sul **1072**

CadCam International see C A D - C A M International **4594**

Cadeau et l'Entreprise. (FR) **29**, 1035

Cadence (Austin). (US ISSN 0887-9141) **1458**

Cadence (Redwood). (US ISSN 0162-6973) **3543**

Cadence Investment Advisors Performance Survey. (US) **941**

Cadence Universe Performance Report.(US) **941**

Cadencies to Mozart's Concerts. (RU) **3543**

Cadenza. (US ISSN 0007-9405) **3543**

Cadenza. (CN ISSN 0703-8380) **3543**, 1746

Caderno de Direito Economico. (BL) **2608**

Caderno de Direito Natural. (BL) **2608**

Caderno de Pesquisas Tributarias. (BL) **2608**

Cadernos B A D see Cadernos de Biblioteconomia, Arquivistica e Documentacao **2751**

Cadernos Brasileiros de Arquitetura. (BL) **296**

†Cadernos Condicao Feminina. (PO) **5157**

Cadernos de Biblioteconomia, Arquivistica e Documentacao. (PO ISSN 0007-9421) **2751**

Cadernos de Ciencias Sociais. (PO) **4367**

†Cadernos de Estudos Brasileiros. (BL) **5158**

Cadernos de Estudos Linguisticos. (BL ISSN 0102-5767) **2807**

†Cadernos de Estudos Rurais e Urbanos. (BL ISSN 0304-2669) **5158**

Cadernos de Estudos Sociais. (BL) **4367**

Cadernos de Folclore. (BL ISSN 0575-0075) **2053**

Cadernos de Pesquisa. (BL ISSN 0100-1574) **1619**, 4838

Cadernos de Psicologia Aplicada. (BL) **4015**

Cadernos do C.E.A.S. (BL) **4430**, 3877

Cadernos Pedagogicos. (BL) **1619**

Cadernos Rioarte. (BL) **4430**

Cadet. (JA) **1502**, 3396

Cadillac Golf Classic. (CN) **4502**

Cadmium Abstracts see Cadscan **3424**

Cadmos. (SZ) **2354**, 2901

Cadre Pharmaceutique see Industrie Sante **3729**

Cadres and Profession see Cadres C F D T **2581**

Cadres C F D T. (FR ISSN 0398-3145) **2581**

Cadres et Maitrise. (FR) **974**

Cadscan. (UK) **3424**

Caducee. (FR ISSN 0007-9480) **3085**

Caduceus: A Museum Journal for the Health Sciences. (US) **3522**, 3085

Caduceus: A Museum Quarterly for the Health Sciences see Caduceus: A Museum Journal for the Health Sciences **3522**

Caert-Thresoor. (NE ISSN 0167-4994) **2244**

Caesaraugusta. (SP ISSN 0007-9502) **268**, 236

Caesarian see Curio **1309**

Caesura Magazine. (US) **2901**, 2989

Cafard Libere. (SG) **2860**

Cafe, Cacao, The. (FR ISSN 0007-9510) **81**, 2063

Cafe D'Afrique/African Coffee. (IV) **2063**

Cafe Review. (US) **2901**

Cafe Solo. (US ISSN 0007-9537) **2989**

Cafeteria. (US) **2989**

Cafeteria Bladet. (DK) **2472**

Cafeteria Motel Bladet see Cafeteria Bladet **2472**

Cafetier. (SZ) **2472**

Cafetier, Restaurateur Parisien. (FR) **2472**

Cage & Aviary Birds. (UK ISSN 0007-9561) **563**, 3709

Cagliaritano. (IT) **2204**

Cagrindex: Abstracts of the Agricultural Literature of the Caribbean. (TR ISSN 0255-8319) **135**, 7

Cahier Jean Ray see Bulletin Jean Ray **2901**

Cahier S B S see S B C Booklet **798**

Cahier Technique du Biologiste. (FR ISSN 0753-3918) **434**

Cahiers Africains d'Administration Publique. (MR) **4055**

Cahiers Alsaciens d'Archeologie d'Art et d'Histoire. (FR ISSN 0575-0385) **268**, 320

Cahiers Archeologiques. (FR ISSN 0068-4945) **268**

Cahiers Astrologiques. (FR ISSN 0007-9596) **358**

Cahiers Balkaniques. (FR) **2807**

Cahiers Binchois. (BE) **268**

Cahiers Bleus. (FR ISSN 0338-7208) **4124**

Cahiers Bourbonnais. (FR ISSN 0007-9618) **2901**, 320

Cahiers Bretons/Ar Gwyr. (FR ISSN 0068-4953) **4367**, 2053

Cahiers Bruxellois. (BE ISSN 0007-9626) **2354**

Cahiers Canadiens de Sociologie. see Canadian Journal of Sociology **4430**

Cahiers Charles du Bos. (FR ISSN 0575-0415) **2901**

Cahiers Confrontation. (FR ISSN 0222-5956) **2860**

Cahiers Critiques de Therapie Familiale et de Pratiques de Reseaux. (FR ISSN 0241-5453) **4015**, 4430

Cahiers D'Action Francaise see Aspects de la France **3874**
Cahiers d'Action Litteraire. (FR ISSN 0007-9650) **2901**, 4124
Cahiers d'Agriculture Pratique des Pays Chauds see Actuel Developpement **925**
Cahiers d'Anesthesiologie. (FR ISSN 0007-9685) **3190**
Cahiers d'Anthropologie et Biometrie Humaine. (FR ISSN 0758-2714) **434**, 236
Cahiers d'Archeologie et d'Histoire du Berry. (FR ISSN 0007-9693) **268**, 2307
Cahiers d'Economie Appliquee aux Sciences Humaines. (FR) **2504**, 653
Cahiers d'Economie et Sociologie Rurales. (FR ISSN 0755-9208) **148**, 4367
Cahiers d'Economie Politique. (FR) **889**
Cahiers d'Etude et de Recherche. (FR ISSN 0298-7899) **889**, 2581, 3877
Cahiers d'Etudes Africaines. (FR ISSN 0008-0055) **236**
Cahiers d'Etudes Arabes. (FR) **3635**, 2807
Cahiers d'Etudes Cathares. (FR ISSN 0008-0063) **4167**
Cahiers d'Etudes Chinoise. (FR) **3635**, 2807
Cahiers d'Etudes et de Recherches Francophones Sante. (FR) **3085**
Cahiers d'Etudes Mongoles et Siberiennes see Etudes Mongoles et Siberiennes **239**
Cahiers d'Histoire see Universite Laval. Les Cahiers d'Histoire **2325**
Cahiers d'Histoire (Lyon). (FR ISSN 0008-008X) **2307**
Cahiers d'Histoire (Paris). (FR) **3877**
Cahiers d'Histoire de Deux-Montagnes. (CN ISSN 0226-7063) **2401**, 2053
Cahiers d'Histoire de Seconde Guerre Mondiale. see Bijdragen tot de Geschiedenis van de Tweede Wereldoorlog **2353**
Cahiers d'Histoire Juridique et Politique.(MG) **2608**
Cahiers d'O R L et de Chirurgie Cervico-Faciale. (FR) **3314**
Cahiers d'Oto-Rhinolaryngologie see Cahiers d'O R L et de Chirurgie Cervico-Faciale **3314**
Cahiers d'Outre-Mer. (FR ISSN 0045-3765) **2244**
†Cahiers de Bibliographie Therapeutique Francaise. Edition Medicale. (FR ISSN 0007-9715) **5158**
Cahiers de Biologie Marine. (FR ISSN 0007-9723) **434**
Cahiers de Biotherapie. (FR ISSN 0575-0563) **3085**
†Cahiers de Bruges/Bruges Quarterly. (BE ISSN 0575-0571) **5158**
Cahiers de Civilisation Medievale. (FR ISSN 0007-9731) **2307**, 320, 2901
Cahiers de Civilisation Medievale. Supplement. (FR ISSN 0068-5011) **2307**, 320, 2901
Cahiers de Droit. (CN ISSN 0007-974X) **2608**
Cahiers de Droit Europeen. (BE ISSN 0007-9758) **2608**
Cahiers de Droit Fiscal International. (NE) **2720**
Cahiers de Feminisme. (FR ISSN 0154-7763) **4838**, 3940
Cahiers de Geographie de la Sante/Journal of Geography of Health. (FR) **3085**
Cahiers de Geographie du Quebec. (CN ISSN 0007-9766) **2244**
Cahiers de Josephologie. (CN ISSN 0007-9774) **4257**
Cahiers de Jules Romains. (FR) **2902**
Cahiers de Kinesitherapie. (FR ISSN 0007-9782) **3371**, 3213
Cahiers de l'A C F A S see Association Canadienne-Francaise pour l'Avancement des Sciences. Cahiers Scientifiques **4300**

Cahiers de l'Actualite Religieuse et Sociale see Cahiers pour Croire Aujourd'hui **4167**
Cahiers de l'Adapt. (FR) **1734**
Cahiers de l'Afrique Occidentale et de l'Afrique Equatoriale see A.F.P. Cahiers de l'Afrique Occidentale et de l'Afrique Equatoriale **3869**
Cahiers de l'Afrique Occidentale Francaise see A.F.P. Cahiers de l'Afrique Occidentale et de l'Afrique Equatoriale **3869**
Cahiers de l'Analyse des Donnees. (FR ISSN 0339-3097) **2751**
Cahiers de l'Asie du Sud-Est. (FR) **3635**, 2807
Cahiers de l'Audition. (FR ISSN 0980-3483) **2286**
Cahiers de l'Avenir de la Bretagne. (FR ISSN 0182-2705) **2308**, 3940
Cahiers de l'Energumene. (FR) **2902**
Cahiers de l'Est. (FR) **2902**, 3877
Cahiers de l'Homme. (FR ISSN 0068-5046) **236**
Cahiers de l'I L S E R. (FR ISSN 0759-8661) **2807**
Cahiers de l'Institut d'Etudes Germaniques. (FR ISSN 0767-7529) **2902**, 2807
Cahiers de l'Institut de Linguistique de Louvain see Institut de Linguistique de Louvain. Cahiers **2818**
Cahiers de l'Iroise. (FR ISSN 0007-9898) **2354**, 320, 2902, 2989
Cahiers de l'Orient. (FR ISSN 0767-6468) **3635**
Cahiers de l'Oronte. (LE ISSN 0007-991X) **2902**
Cahiers de l'U E R Froissart see Valenciennes **2973**
Cahiers de l'Universite de Perpignan. (FR ISSN 0769-0770) **2902**, 2308, 2608
Cahiers de la Ceramique Egyptienne. (UA ISSN 0259-7381) **268**
Cahiers de la Cinematheque. (FR) **3504**
Cahiers de la Communication. (FR) **1332**
Cahiers de la Femme. see Canadian Woman Studies **4859**
Cahiers de la Fonderie. (FR) **3429**
Cahiers de la Formation. (FR) **4167**
Cahiers de la Mediterranee. (FR ISSN 0395-9317) **2354**
Cahiers de la Photographie. (FR ISSN 0294-4081) **3789**
Cahiers de la Puericultrice. (FR ISSN 0007-9820) **1233**, 3800
Cahiers de la Recherche - Developpement. (FR ISSN 0760-579X) **81**
Cahiers de la Reconciliation. (FR ISSN 0007-9839) **3877**
Cahiers de la Renaissance Vaudoise. (SZ ISSN 0007-9847) **2902**
Cahiers de Lexicologie. (FR ISSN 0007-9871) **2807**
Cahiers de Linguistique Asie Orientale. (FR ISSN 0153-3320) **2808**
Cahiers de Linguistique Hispanique Medievale. (FR) **2808**
Cahiers de Linguistique Theorique et Appliquee. (RM) **2808**
†Cahiers de Litterature et de Poesie: Poetes et Leurs Amis. (FR ISSN 0032-1974) **5158**
Cahiers de Litterature Orale. (FR) **2808**
Cahiers de Mariemont. (BE) **3522**
Cahiers de Medecine Interprofessionnelle. (FR ISSN 0007-9936) **3085**
Cahiers de Micropaleontologie. (FR ISSN 0068-5054) **3656**
Cahiers de Nutrition et de Dietetique. (FR ISSN 0007-9960) **3604**
Cahiers de Paleoanthropologie. (FR ISSN 0293-1176) **3656**, 236
Cahiers de Paleontologie. (FR ISSN 0766-0502) **3656**
Cahiers de Paleontologie Est-Africaine. (FR ISSN 0298-248X) **3656**
Cahiers de Philologie. (FR ISSN 0153-5048) **2808**
Cahiers de Poetique Comparee. (FR) **3635**, 2989
Cahiers de Praxematique. (FR ISSN 0765-4944) **2808**, 4430

Cahiers de Psychologie Cognitive/European Bulletin of Cognitive Psychology. (FR ISSN 0249-9185) **4015**
Cahiers de Psychomecanique de Langage. (CN ISSN 0068-5070) **2808**
Cahiers de Recherche en Gestion des Entreprises. (FR ISSN 0249-5570) **1035**
Cahiers de Recherche Ethique. (CN) **4167**
Cahiers de Saint-Michel de Cuxa. (FR ISSN 0068-5089) **2902**
Cahiers de Sante Publique see Public Health Papers **4110**
Cahiers de Semiotique Textuelle. (FR ISSN 0766-4214) **2902**
Cahiers de Sexologie Clinique. (FR) **3085**
Cahiers de Sociologie Economique see Cahiers de Sociologie Economique et Culturelle **849**
Cahiers de Sociologie Economique et Culturelle. (FR ISSN 0761-9871) **849**
Cahiers de Sociologie et de Demographie Medicales. (FR ISSN 0007-9995) **3980**, 4099
Cahiers de Traductologie. (CN) **2808**
Cahiers de Tunisie. (TI ISSN 0008-0012) **2504**
Cahiers Debussy. (FR ISSN 0395-1200) **3543**
Cahiers des Ameriques Latines. (FR ISSN 1141-7161) **4367**
Cahiers des Amis du Lexique Francais see Dico - Plus **2811**
Cahiers des Arts Visuels au Quebec. (CN ISSN 0711-4818) **320**
Cahiers des Etudes Anciennes. (CN ISSN 0317-5065) **268**
Cahiers des Explorateurs. (FR ISSN 0526-8133) **2244**, 236
Cahiers des Ingenieurs Agronomes see Ingenieurs de la Vie **180**
Cahiers des Naturalistes. (FR ISSN 0008-0039) **4303**
Cahiers des Religions Africaines. (ZR ISSN 0008-0047) **4281**, 4430
Cahiers des Sciences Humaines. (FR ISSN 0768-9829) **4367**
Cahiers du Bilinguisme/Land un Sproch.(FR ISSN 0045-3773) **2808**
Cahiers du Cinema. (FR ISSN 0008-011X) **3504**
Cahiers du Communisme. (FR ISSN 0008-0136) **3877**
Cahiers du Credit Mutuel. (FR ISSN 0395-8175) **769**
Cahiers du DLSL see University of Lausanne. Departement des Langues et des Sciences du Langage. Cahiers **2850**
Cahiers du G I T A. (FR ISSN 0295-9909) **4631**
Cahiers du L A C I T O - Revue d'Ethnolinguistique. (BE ISSN 0994-7736) **2808**, 236
Cahiers du Memontois. (FR ISSN 0180-9261) **268**
Cahiers du Monde Russe et Sovietique. (FR ISSN 0008-0160) **2354**, 3635, 3877
†Cahiers du Sart Tilman. (BE ISSN 0575-0970) **5158**
Cahiers du Scenario. (BE) **3504**
Cahiers du Tourisme. Serie A: France. (FR ISSN 0068-5151) **4755**
Cahiers du Tourisme. Serie B: Etranger. (FR ISSN 0768-3162) **4755**
Cahiers du Tourisme. Serie C: Recherche Fondamentale et Appliquee - Methodologie. (FR ISSN 0768-0279) **4755**
Cahiers du Tourisme. Serie D: Statistiques. (FR ISSN 0294-6831) **4799**
Cahiers du Tourisme. Serie E: Legislation. (FR ISSN 0767-2667) **4755**, 2608
▼Cahiers du Tourisme. Serie F: Banque de Donnees Statistiques. (FR) **4799**
Cahiers Economiques de Bruxelles. (BE ISSN 0008-0195) **653**
Cahiers Economiques et Monetaires. (FR) **769**, 653

Cahiers Economiques et Sociaux. (ZR ISSN 0008-0209) **653**
Cahiers Elisabethains. (FR ISSN 0184-7678) **2354**, 2902
Cahiers Europeens. see Notes from Europe **5249**
Cahiers Evangile. (FR ISSN 0222-9714) **4167**
Cahiers Ferdinand de Saussure. (SZ ISSN 0068-516X) **2808**
Cahiers Francais. (FR ISSN 0008-0217) **2186**
Cahiers Geographiques de Rouen. (FR ISSN 0181-0839) **2244**
Cahiers Geologiques. (FR ISSN 0008-0241) **1556**
Cahiers Haut-Marnais. (FR ISSN 0008-025X) **2308**, 2902
Cahiers Henri Bosco. (FR ISSN 0753-4590) **2902**
Cahiers Internationaux d'Histoire Economique et Sociale. see Quaderni Internazionali di Storia Economica e Sociale **2382**
Cahiers Internationaux de Psychologie Sociale. (BE) **4015**
Cahiers Internationaux de Sociologie. (FR ISSN 0008-0276) **4430**
Cahiers Internationaux de Symbolisme. (BE ISSN 0008-0284) **3763**
Cahiers Leopold Delisle. (FR ISSN 0399-1415) **2308**, 268
Cahiers Ligures de Prehistoire et d'Archeologie see Cahiers Ligures de Prehistoire et de Protohistoire **268**
Cahiers Ligures de Prehistoire et de Protohistoire. (IT) **268**
Cahiers Linguistiques d'Ottawa. (CN ISSN 0315-3967) **2808**
Cahiers Lorrains. (FR ISSN 0758-6760) **2354**, 268
Cahiers Marxistes. (BE ISSN 0591-0633) **3877**
Cahiers Medico-Sociaux. (SZ ISSN 0409-8757) **3085**
Cahiers Naturalistes. (FR ISSN 0008-0365) **2902**
Cahiers Nepalais. (FR ISSN 0068-5194) **3877**
†Les Cahiers Nicoletains. (CN ISSN 0708-6431) **5158**
Cahiers Nivellois. (BE) **2990**
Cahiers Numismatiques. (FR ISSN 0008-0373) **3598**
†Cahiers O R S T O M Serie Entomologie Medicale et Parasitologie. (FR ISSN 0029-7224) **5158**
Cahiers O R S T O M Serie Hydrobiologie see Revue d'Hydrobiologie Tropicale **453**
Cahiers O R S T O M Serie Hydrologie see Hydrologie Continentale **4825**
Cahiers O R S T O M Serie Pedologie. (FR ISSN 0029-7259) **1556**
Cahiers O R S T O M Serie Sciences Humaines see Cahiers des Sciences Humaines **4367**
Cahiers Paul-Louis Courier. (FR ISSN 0084-8239) **2902**
Cahiers Pedagogiques. (FR ISSN 0008-042X) **1619**
Cahiers Philosophiques. (FR ISSN 0241-2799) **3763**
Cahiers Philosophiques Africains/African Philosophical Journal. (ZR) **3763**
Cahiers pour Croire Aujourd'hui. (FR ISSN 0987-2213) **4167**, 4430
Cahiers Psychiatriques Genevois. (SZ ISSN 1016-9229) **3085**
Cahiers Quebecois de Demographie. (CN ISSN 0380-1721) **3980**
Cahiers Raciniens. (FR ISSN 0008-0454) **2902**
Cahiers Rationalistes. (FR ISSN 0008-0462) **4303**, 3274
Cahiers Raymond Abellio. (FR ISSN 0763-1529) **3763**
Cahiers Regionaux. (FR) **849**
Cahiers Roumains d'Etudes Litteraires. (RM) **2902**
Cahiers Saint-Exupery. (FR) **2902**
†Cahiers Saint-John Perse. (FR) **5158**
Cahiers Sociale Geschiedenis. (NE) **2354**
†Cahiers Suisses Romain Rolland. (SZ) **5158**
Cahiers Tarnais. (FR) **268**

CAHIERS TECHNIQUES

Cahiers Techniques A F R O see A F R O Technical Papers **4096**
Cahiers Techniques du Batiment. (FR ISSN 0241-6794) **608**
Cahiers Territoires. (FR ISSN 0981-1761) **2608**
Cahiers-Theatre see Cahiers Theatre Louvain **4631**
Cahiers Theatre Louvain. (BE ISSN 0771-4653) **4631**
Cahiers Tristan l'Hermit. (FR) **2990**
Cahiers Victoriens et Edouardiens. (FR ISSN 0220-5610) **2902**
Cahiers Vilfredo Pareto. (SZ ISSN 0008-0497) **4368**
Cahiers Wallons. (BE) **2860**, 2174
Cahiers Zairois d'Etudes Politiques et Sociales. (ZR) **3877**, 4368
Cahiers Zairois de la Recherche et du Developpement. (ZR) **2169**
Caijing Kexue/Finance and Economics. (CC ISSN 1000-8306) **769**, 849
Caijing Wenti Yanjiu/Financial and Economic Studies. (CC ISSN 1000-176X) **769**
Caijing Yanjiu/Study of Finance & Economics. (US) **769**
Caijun see Disarmament **3457**
Cailiao Gongcheng/Material Engineering. (CC ISSN 1001-4381) **49**
Cailiao Kexue see Chinese Journal of Materials Science **3404**
Cailiao Kexue Jinzhan/Advances in Material Science. (CC ISSN 1000-8500) **3403**
Caiman Barbudo. (CU) **2860**
Caimao Jingji/Finance and Trade Economics. (CC) **769**, 902
Cain Connections. (US ISSN 0899-1375) **2146**
The Cairn. (CN ISSN 0701-0281) **3523**, 320
Cairngorm Club Journal. (UK ISSN 0068-5267) **4467**
Cairo Bulletin see Egypt News **3956**
Cairo Chamber of Commerce. Journal/ Ghurfat al-Tigara al-Qahira. Magalla. (UA) **809**
Cairo Demographic Centre Monographs. Studies in African and Asian Demography see C D C Monographs. Studies in African and Asian Demography **3991**
Cairo Demographic Centre Occasional Papers see C D C Occasional Papers **3991**
Cairo Demographic Centre Working Papers see C D C Working Papers **3991**
Cairo Papers in Social Sciences. (UA) **4368**
Caissa's Chess News. (US) **4468**
Caisse Centrale de Cooperation Economique. Rapport Annuel. (FR) **829**
Caisse d'Epargne de l'Etat du Grand-Duche de Luxembourg. Rapports et Bilans see Banque et Caisse d'Epargne de l'Etat, Luxembourg. Rapports et Bilans **768**
Caisse Nationale des Allocations Familiales Revue see C A F Revue **4400**
Caisse Nationale des Autoroutes. Rapport Annuel. (FR) **4717**
Caisses Centrales de Mutualite Sociale Agricole. Statistiques. (FR) **707**, 2608
Caiwu yu Kuaiji. (CC) **748**
Caizheng/Finance. (CC) **769**
Caizheng Yanjiu/Financial Research. (CC ISSN 0494-075X) **770**
Caja de Ahorros y Monte de Piedad de las Baleares. Memoria. (SP ISSN 0409-9192) **770**
Caja de Credito Agrario, Industrial y Minero. Financiamiento de la Pequena y Mediana Industria. (CK) **1113**
Cajanus. (JM ISSN 0376-7655) **3604**
Cake and Cockhorse. (UK ISSN 0008-0535) **2355**
Cal - O S H A Reporter. (Occupational Safety and Health Association) (US ISSN 1054-1209) **3615**
Cal - Tax News. (US ISSN 0008-0543) **1089**

Cal - Vet Insurance Plans. Annual Report. (US) **2529**, 3453
Cal-Western Appaloosa. (US) **4532**
Calabria - Domani. (IT) **2204**
Calabria Letteraria. (IT) **2902**, 2053, 2990
Calabria Nobilissima. (IT ISSN 0008-056X) **320**, 2355, 2902
Calamana. (BG) **2581**, 974
Calao. (FR ISSN 0335-6469) **1251**
Calapooya Collage. (US ISSN 1040-8339) **2902**
Las Calaveras. (US) **2401**
Calavo Newsletter. (US) **172**
Calcified Tissue Abstracts. (US ISSN 0008-0586) **463**, 7
Calcified Tissue International. (US ISSN 0171-967X) **522**
Calcoin News. (US ISSN 0008-0616) **3598**
Calcolo. (IT ISSN 0008-0624) **3031**
†Calculators - Computers Magazine. (US ISSN 0164-7830) **5158**
Calcutta Gazette. (II ISSN 0045-3838) **4055**
Calcutta Historical Journal. (II ISSN 0254-9794) **2337**
Calcutta Journal of Political Studies. (II) **3877**, 4055
Calcutta Management Association. Annual Report. (II ISSN 0068-5356) **1004**
Calcutta Management Association. Newsletter. (II) **1004**
Calcutta Market see Thapar's Indian Industrial Directory and Import and Export Directory of the World **1155**
Calcutta Mathematical Society. Bulletin. (II ISSN 0008-0659) **3031**
Calcutta Medical Journal. (II ISSN 0008-0667) **3085**
Calcutta Municipal Gazette. (II ISSN 0008-0675) **4085**
Calcutta Review. (II ISSN 0045-3846) **2199**
Calcutta Statistical Association. Bulletin. (II ISSN 0008-0683) **4565**
Calcutta Weekly Notes. (II ISSN 0045-3854) **2608**
Calcuttan. (II ISSN 0045-3862) **3877**, 320
Caldasia. (CK ISSN 0366-5232) **4303**
Calder Voice. (UK ISSN 0262-723X) **3877**
Caledonia Diocesan Times. (CN ISSN 0383-6509) **4232**
Caledonian. (CN ISSN 0381-856X) **2860**
Calendar see C B C Features **4124**
Calendar and Buyers and Services Guide for Local Governments (Year). (US) **4085**
Calendar for New Music. (US) **3543**
Calendar of Conferences, Meetings and Exhibitions to be Held in South Africa. (SA) **3391**, 2751, 4303
Calendar of Congresses of Medical Sciences. (SZ ISSN 0301-2891) **3391**, 3085
Calendar of Expiring Collective Agreements (Year). (CN ISSN 0381-4130) **2581**
Calendar of History Events. (US) **2401**, 2355
▼Calendar of Literary Facts. (US) **2860**, 2902
Calendar of Scientific and Technological Meetings in Israel. (IS ISSN 0333-6131) **3391**, 4303, 4595
Calendario Agricola. (VE) **148**
Calendario Cultural do Brasil. (BL) **4755**
Calendario de Eventos Tecnico-Cientificos Realizados no Brazil see Eventos em Politica Cientifica e Tecnologica **4597**
Calendario del Popolo. (IT) **4368**
Calendario Escolar. (AG) **1619**
Calendars of the United States House of Representatives and History of Legislation. (US) **3391**, 2608
†Calendher. (CN) **5158**
Calendrier Scolaire. see School Calendar **1661**
Calf News see C A L F News Cattle Feeder **213**
†Calgacus. (UK ISSN 0307-2029) **5158**

Calgary Airport Business Directory. (CN) **4671**
Calgary Business see Calgary Commerce **809**
Calgary City. (CN) **4755**
Calgary Commerce. (CN ISSN 0707-8064) **809**
Calgary in Fact. (CN) **849**
†Calgary Magazine. (CN ISSN 0707-4409) **5158**
Calgary STAMPede. (CN ISSN 0828-8755) **3750**
Calgary Visitors Guide see Calgary City **4755**
†Calgon Air - Water Report. (US) **5158**
Caliban. (FR ISSN 0575-2124) **2902**
Caliban. (US ISSN 0890-7269) **2902**
▼Calidad, Gestion y Tecnica. (GW ISSN 1131-6047) **3445**
California. Administrative Office of the Courts. Annual Report see Judicial Council Report to the Governor and Legislature **2640**
California. Agricultural Statistics Service. Agricultural Statistics Review. Summary. (US) **135**
California. Agricultural Statistics Service. Crop Weather Report. (US) **135**, 172, 3434
California. Agricultural Statistics Service. Dairy Industry Statistics. (US) **135**
California. Agricultural Statistics Service. Dairy Information Bulletin. (US) **135**, 198
California. Agricultural Statistics Service. Export of Agricultural Products. Statistical Appendix. (US) **135**
California. Agricultural Statistics Service. Exports of Agricultural Products. (US) **135**, 4565
California. Agricultural Statistics Service. Field Crop Review. (US) **135**, 172
California. Agricultural Statistics Service. Field Crop Statistics. (US) **135**
California. Agricultural Statistics Service. Fruit and Nut Acreage. (US ISSN 0527-2181) **135**
California. Agricultural Statistics Service. Fruit and Nut Review. (US) **135**, 172
California. Agricultural Statistics Service. Fruit and Nut Statistics. (US) **135**
California. Agricultural Statistics Service. Grape Acreage. (US) **135**, 172
California. Agricultural Statistics Service. Grape Crush Report. (US) **135**, 172
California. Agricultural Statistics Service. Livestock Review. (US) **135**, 213
California. Agricultural Statistics Service. Livestock Statistics. (US ISSN 0361-9095) **135**
California. Agricultural Statistics Service. Poultry Report. (US) **135**, 213
California. Agricultural Statistics Service. Vegetable Crops. (US) **135**, 172
California. Agricultural Statistics Service. Vegetable Review. (US) **135**, 172
California. Air Resources Board. Annual Report. (US ISSN 0068-5496) **1976**
California. Air Resources Board. Bulletin.(US) **1976**
California. Air Resources Board. Fact Sheets. (US) **1976**
California. Bureau of Criminal Statistics and Special Services. Criminal Justice Profile; Statewide. (US) **1524**
California. Bureau of Criminal Statistics. Crime and Delinquency see Crime and Delinquency in California **1524**
California. Bureau of Criminal Statistics. Criminal Justice Profile; Statewide see California. Bureau of Criminal Statistics and Special Services. Criminal Justice Profile; Statewide **1524**
California. Bureau of Entomology. Occasional Papers see Occasional Papers in Entomology **536**
†California. Council on Criminal Justice. Comprehensive Plan for Criminal Justice. (US ISSN 0093-8912) **5158**
California. Department of Consumer Affairs. Annual Report. (US) **1502**, 1035

California. Department of Industrial Relations. Annual Report see California. Department of Industrial Relations. Biennial Report **974**
California. Department of Industrial Relations. Biennial Report. (US) **974**, 3615
California. Department of Parks and Recreation. Archaeological Report see California Archeological Reports **268**
California. Department of the Youth Authority. Affirmative Action Statistics. (US ISSN 0362-4110) **974**
California. Department of Water Resources. Bulletin. (US ISSN 0084-8263) **4822**
California. Department of Water Resources. California State Water Project see Management of the California State Water Project **4826**
California. Division of Mines and Geology. Bulletin. (US ISSN 0008-1000) **1556**, 3480
California. Division of Mines and Geology. Special Report. (US ISSN 0527-0014) **1556**, 3480
California. Division of Oil and Gas. Annual Report of the State Oil and Gas Supervisor. (US ISSN 0362-1243) **3683**
California. Energy Commission. Biennial Fuels Report. (US) **1784**
California. Energy Commission. Biennial Report. (US) **1784**
California. Law Revision Commission. Reports, Recommendations and Studies. (US) **2608**
†California (Los Angeles). (US ISSN 0279-3768) **5158**
California. Office of Criminal Justice Planning. Research Update. (US) **1511**, 2712
California. Secretary of State. Roster see Roster - California State, County, City and Township Officials State Officials of the United States **4073**
California. State Board of Cosmetology. Rules and Regulations. (US ISSN 0094-4327) **372**, 2608
California. State Board of Equalization. Annual Report. (US ISSN 0068-5801) **1089**
California. Teachers Retirement Board. State Teacher's Retirement System; Annual Report to the Governor and the Legislature. (US ISSN 0090-5593) **1725**
California. Water Resources Center. Annual Report. (US ISSN 0575-4968) **1597**
California A F L - C I O News. (US ISSN 0008-0802) **2581**
†California Academic Libraries List of Serials. (US ISSN 0198-8433) **5158**
California Academy of Sciences. Academy Newsletter. (US ISSN 0008-0829) **4303**, 3523
California Academy of Sciences. Memoirs. (US) **4303**
California Academy of Sciences. Occasional Papers. (US ISSN 0068-5461) **4303**
California Academy of Sciences. Proceedings. (US ISSN 0068-547X) **4303**
California Accountancy Act with Rules and Regulations. (US) **748**
▼California Administrative and Antitrust Law. (US) **2608**
California Adnews. (US) **29**
California Advocate Newspaper. (US) **1995**
California Aggie. (US) **1306**
California Agrarian Action Project. Newsletter see Agrarian Advocate **68**
California Agricultural Directory (Year). (US ISSN 0575-5298) **81**
California Agricultural Export Directory. (US ISSN 0891-9097) **148**
California Agricultural Exporter see American Food and Ag Exporter Magazine **147**
California Agriculture. (US ISSN 0008-0845) **82**
California Air Basins. (US) **1976**

California Air Quality Data. (US) **1976**
California Alcohol Program Plan *see* California Alcohol Program: Report to the Legislature (Year) **1535**
California Alcohol Program: Report to the Legislature (Year). (US) **1535**
California and Nevada Legal Services Programs Directory. (US) **2608**
California and Western States Grape Grower *see* Grape Grower **178**
California Angler. (US ISSN 8750-8907) **4542**
California Apparel News. (US ISSN 0008-0896) **1284**
California Archeological Reports. (US) **268**
California Architecture and Architects. (US) **296**
California - Arizona Cotton. (US ISSN 0008-090X) **172**
California - Arizona Farm Press. (US ISSN 0164-5331) **82**
California Art Review. (US) **320**
California Association for Counseling and Development Journal *see* C A C D Journal **4015**
California Association of Life Underwriters Underwriter *see* C A L Underwriter **2529**
California Attorney Practice: Requirements, Ethics, and Responsibilities. (US) **2608**
California Basketball. (US) **4502**
California Beverage Hotline. (US) **380**
California Bicyclist. (US) **4516**
California Bowling News *see* Bowling News **4501**
California Broker. (US ISSN 0883-6159) **1113**
California Builder. (US) **608**
California Builder and Engineer. (US ISSN 0045-3900) **608**
California Builders and Contractors Directory. (US) **1125, 608**
California Business. (US ISSN 0008-0926) **849**
California Business Conditions. (US) **849**
California Business Law Practitioner. (US ISSN 0892-2349) **2708**
California Business Law Reporter. (US ISSN 0199-669X) **2708**
California Business Times *see* San Francisco Business Times **839**
California Cable Letter. (US ISSN 0740-0527) **1332, 1619, 2608, 4085**
California Cattleman. (US ISSN 0008-0942) **213**
California Chamber of Commerce Alert. (US ISSN 0882-0929) **809**
California Chess Journal. (US) **4468**
California Chiropractic Association Journal. (US ISSN 0899-0204) **3213**
California CitySports Magazine. (US) **4468**
California Civil Actions: Pleading and Practice. (US) **2701**
California Closely Held Corporations: Tax Planning and Practice Guide. (US) **1089, 2608**
California Coalition of People for Alternative Learning Situations Communications Network *see* C C - P A L S Communications Network **1745**
California College of Arts and Crafts Review *see* C C A C Review **1306**
California Communities. (US ISSN 0194-2913) **2484**
California Community Care News *see* C C N **2459**
California Community Colleges. Master Plan and Inventory of Programs. (US) **1701**
California Community Property with Tax Analysis. (US) **1089**
California Compensation Cases. (US) **2609, 974, 2529**
California Computer News. (US) **1390**
California Condor *see* The Raptor Report **566**
California Connections. (US ISSN 0893-0694) **1125, 3625, 4085**
▼California Construction Law Manual, 3-E. (US) **2609, 608**

California Cooperative Oceanic Fisheries Investigations Reports. (US ISSN 0575-3317) **580**
California Corporations Code and Corporate Securites Rules. (US) **2708, 834**
California Correctional News. (US ISSN 0194-1682) **1511**
California County. (US) **4055**
California County Fact Book. (US) **4565**
California County Law Library Basic List.(US ISSN 0068-5879) **2609**
California Courier. (US ISSN 0008-0950) **1995, 2222**
California Criminal Defense Practice. (US) **2712, 1511**
California Criminal Defense Reporter. (US) **2712, 1511**
California Dental Association. Journal. (US ISSN 0008-0977) **3229**
California Dental Hygienists Association Journal *see* C D H A Journal **5156**
California Deposition and Discovery Practice. (US) **2701**
California Directory of Water Resources Expertise. (US) **4822**
California Economic Indicators. (US ISSN 0575-2426) **849**
California Eligible Securities List. (US) **941**
California Employer. (US ISSN 0098-1435) **974**
California Employers' Guide to Employee Handbooks and Personnel Policy Manuals. (US) **974**
California Employment Law. (US) **974**
▼California Employment Law Letter. (US ISSN 1049-9334) **2609, 974**
California Engineer. (US ISSN 0008-1027) **1816**
California English. (US) **1746, 2808**
California Environmental Directory. (US ISSN 0148-0324) **1944**
California Environmental Yearbook and Directory *see* California Environmental Directory **1944**
California Escrow Association News *see* C E A News **4146**
California Events Annual. (US) **4685, 4755**
California F P. (US ISSN 0410-2894) **3085**
California Facts. (US ISSN 0883-6264) **1780**
California Family Law Monthly. (US) **2717, 4400, 4838**
California Family Law: Practice and Procedure. (US) **2717, 4430**
California Family Tax Planning. (US) **1089**
California Farmer. (US ISSN 0008-1051) **82**
California Fire Service. (US) **2031, 4099**
California Fish and Game. (US ISSN 0008-1078) **1485, 580, 4542**
California Food. (US) **2063**
California Football. (US) **4502**
California Forestry and Forest Products.(US ISSN 0008-1094) **2113**
California Forestry Note. (US) **2096**
California Forms of Jury Instruction. (US) **2609**
California Fresh Fruit and Vegetable Shipments by Rail, Truck, and Air. (US ISSN 0270-384X) **4648, 2063**
California Fruit Grower. (US) **2063**
California G P *see* California F P **3085**
California Garden. (US ISSN 0008-1116) **2123**
California Genealogical Society Newsletter. (US ISSN 1058-5133) **2146**
California Geology. (US ISSN 0026-4555) **1556**
California Government & Politics Annual. (US ISSN 0084-8271) **3877**
California Grange News. (US ISSN 0008-1124) **82**
California Grocer. (US) **2090**
California Grower. (US ISSN 0888-1715) **172**
California Handbook. (US ISSN 0068-5615) **4055, 1780**

California Highway Patrolman. (US ISSN 0008-1140) **1511**
California Highways. (US) **4755**
California History (San Francisco). (US ISSN 0162-2897) **2401**
California Homes *see* California Homes and Lifestyles **4146**
California Homes and Lifestyles. (US ISSN 0734-5453) **4146**
California Horse Review. (US) **4532**
California Horticultural Society. Newsletter. (US) **2123**
California Hotline. (US) **770**
California Hungarians Weekly. *see* Californiai Magyarsag **1995**
California in Print. (US ISSN 0738-694X) **4055**
California Income Tax Laws (Year). (US) **1089**
California Industrial Relations Reports. (US ISSN 0008-1191) **974**
California Inntouch. (US) **2472, 4755**
California Insect Survey. Bulletin. (US ISSN 0068-5631) **529**
†California Institute of Technology. Division of Engineering and Applied Science. Research Report. (US) **5158**
California Institute of Technology. Division of Geological and Planetary Sciences. Report on Geological and Planetary Sciences for the Year. (US ISSN 0045-3943) **1556, 363**
California Insurance Law and Practice. (US) **2609, 2529**
California Insurance Law and Regulation Reporter. (US) **2529**
California International Trade Register. (US ISSN 0270-4862) **1125, 902**
California Inventor. (US) **3673, 1113**
California Journal. (US ISSN 0008-1205) **3877, 4055**
California Journal Almanac of State Government and Politics *see* Almanac of California Government and Politics **5133**
California Journal Newsfile. (US) **3877, 4055**
California Kitchens & Baths. (US) **608**
California Labor Market Bulletin. (US) **849, 974**
California Landscaping. (US) **2123**
California Law of Employee Injuries and Workmen's Compensation. (US) **2609, 974, 2529**
California Law Review. (US ISSN 0008-1221) **2609**
California Lawyer. (US ISSN 0279-4063) **2609**
California League of Savings Institutions. Legislation and Regulation Update. (US) **770, 2609**
California Legionnaire. (US) **3453**
California Libraries. (US ISSN 1056-1528) **2751**
†California Lodging Industry. (US) **5158**
California Macadamia Society. Yearbook. (US ISSN 0068-5720) **172**
California Management Review. (US ISSN 0008-1256) **1005**
California Manufacturers Register. (US ISSN 0068-5739) **1125**
California Media and Library Educators Association Journal *see* C M L E A Journal **2751**
California Men's Stylist. (US) **1289**
California Mining Journal. (US ISSN 0008-1299) **3480**
California Monitor of Education *see* National Monitor of Education **1756**
California Monthly. (US ISSN 0008-1302) **1306**
California Morbidity. (US) **3218**
California Municipal Bond Advisor. (US ISSN 0749-2375) **941**
California Museum Directory. (US) **3523**
California Music Educators Association News *see* C M E A News **3543**
California Native Plant Society. Bulletin. (US) **498**
California Natural History Guides. (US ISSN 0068-5755) **434**
California - Nevada Campbook. (US) **4756, 4542**

CALIFORNIA SCHOOL   6019

California, Nevada TourBook *see* Tourbook: California, Nevada **4790**
California Newspaper Publishers Association. Directory and Rate Book.(US) **2568, 2577**
California Newspaper Publishers' Association. Newspaper Directory *see* California Newspaper Publishers Association. Directory and Rate Book **2568**
California Notary Law Primer. (US) **2609**
California Nurse. (US ISSN 0008-1310) **3276**
California Nursing Review *see* Nurseweek **3283**
California - O S H A Reporter *see* Cal - O S H A Reporter **3615**
California Odd Fellow and Rebekah. (US) **1296**
California Official Reports. (US) **2609**
California Optometry. (US ISSN 0273-804X) **3299**
California Ornamental Crops Report. (US) **82**
California Paralegal Magazine. (US ISSN 1040-2640) **2609**
California Parks & Recreation. (US) **1485**
California Peace Officer. (US) **1511**
California Pelican. (US ISSN 0008-1361) **2860**
California Periodicals Index. (US ISSN 0730-1367) **7**
California Periodicals on Microfilm. (US) **396**
California Personnel & Guidance Association. Monographs. (US) **3625**
California Pharmacist. (US) **3720**
California Physician. (US ISSN 8750-1813) **3085**
California Planning and Development Report. (US ISSN 0891-382X) **4055, 2484, 4146**
California Plant Pathology. (US ISSN 0094-3800) **498**
California Points and Authorities. (US) **2609, 3504**
California Political Week. (US ISSN 0195-6175) **3877, 4055**
California Pride. (US) **2581, 4055**
The California Prisoner. (US ISSN 0884-0075) **1511**
California Private School Directory. (US ISSN 0098-5147) **1692**
California Products Liability Actions. (US) **2609, 1502**
California Professional Photographer. (US) **3789**
California Public Agency Practice. (US) **2609, 4055**
California Public Employee Relations *see* C P E R **974**
California Public School Directory. (US ISSN 0068-5771) **1692**
California Publisher. (US ISSN 0008-1434) **2568**
California Quarterly. (US ISSN 0045-3978) **2902**
California R V & Camping Guide. (US) **4756**
†California Rare Fruit Growers. Annual Journal. (US) **5158**
†California Rare Fruit Growers. Annual Yearbook. (US) **5158**
California Reader. (US) **1746**
California Real Estate Journal. (US) **4146**
California Real Estate Magazine. (US ISSN 0008-1450) **4146**
California Real Estate Reporter. (US) **4146, 653**
California Regulatory Law Reporter. (US ISSN 0739-7860) **2609**
California Report. (US) **1944**
†California Restaurant Operations. (US) **5158**
California Riviera Magazine. (US) **2222**
California Roster *see* Roster - California State, County, City and Township Officials State Officials of the United States **4073**
California Savings and Loan Hotline *see* California Hotline **770**
California School Boards *see* California School Boards Journal **1619**

6020 CALIFORNIA SCHOOL

California School Boards Journal. (US) **1619**
California School Employee. (US ISSN 0008-1515) **1725**
California School Law Digest. (US ISSN 0094-2057) **1725**, 2609
California School Nurse. (US) **3276**
California Senior Citizen. (US) **2271**
California Services Register. (US ISSN 0271-6615) **653**
California Sociologist. (US ISSN 0162-8712) **4430**
California Southern Baptist. (US ISSN 0008-1558) **4232**
California Sports Car. (US) **4686**
California Staats - Zeitung. (US) **1995**
California State Board of Equalization. Reports. (US) **1089**, 4055
California State Contracts Register. (US) **653**, 608
California State Employee see California Pride **2581**
California State Fire Marshal Journal see C S F M Journal **2031**
California State Health Plan. (US) **2460**
California State Library Foundation Bulletin. (US ISSN 0741-0344) **2751**, 2401
California State Plan for Rehabilitation Facilities. (US) **4400**
California State Poetry Quarterly. (US ISSN 0896-6338) **2990**
California State Publications. (US ISSN 0008-1574) **396**
California State University, Los Angeles. Center for the Study of Armament and Disarmament. Occasional Papers Series. (US) **3952**
California Statesman. (US) **3877**
California Statesman's Foreign Policy Review. (US) **3877**
California Statesman's Legislative Survey. (US) **3877**
California Strawberry Report. (US) **82**
California Studies in Classical Antiquity see Classical Antiquity **1275**
California Studies in the History of Art. (US ISSN 0068-5909) **320**
California Surveyor. (US) **2244**
California Tax Handbook (Year). (US) **1089**
California Taxation. (US) **1089**, 4055
California Teacher. (US ISSN 0410-3556) **1619**, 2581
California Teachers Association Action see C T A Action **1701**
California Tech. (Associated Students of the California Institute of Technology) (US ISSN 0008-1582) **1306**
California Technology Stock Letter. (US ISSN 8756-2154) **941**
California Today. (US ISSN 0739-8042) **1944**, 1485
California Tomato Grower. (US ISSN 0527-3277) **172**
California Tort Reporter. (US) **2609**
California Torts. (US) **2701**
California Travel Parks Association, Inc. News see C T P A News **4755**
California Trial Guide. (US) **2701**
California Trial Lawyers Association Forum see C T L A Forum **2608**
California Trial Lawyers Forum see C T L A Forum **2608**
California Trucker. (US) **4743**
California Trucking Association. Newsletter see Caltrux **4743**
California Union List of Periodicals. (US ISSN 0095-8034) **396**
California Veckoblad. (US) **1995**
California Veteran. (US) **3453**
California Veterinarian. (US ISSN 0008-1612) **4807**
California Voice. (US) **1995**
California Water Pollution Control Association. Bulletin. (US ISSN 0008-1620) **4822**, 1976
California Water Resources Center. Contribution. (US ISSN 0575-4941) **4822**
California Water Resources Directory. (US) **4822**
California Weekly Explorer. (US ISSN 0197-7547) **1251**, 2244, 2401
California Western International Law Journal. (US ISSN 0886-3210) **2720**

California Western Law Review. (US ISSN 0008-1639) **2609**
California Wine Report. (US) **82**, 380
California Wineletter. (US ISSN 0008-1655) **380**
California Woman. (US ISSN 0008-1663) **4838**
California Women. (US ISSN 0193-7618) **4838**
California Wool Growers Association. Bi-Weekly Newsletter see California Wool Growers Newsletter **213**
California Wool Growers Newsletter. (US) **213**
California Work Injuries and Illnesses. (US ISSN 0164-1530) **3623**, 974, 4565
California Workers' Compensation Reporter. (US ISSN 0363-129X) **2609**, 974
California Youth Authority's Status of Female Employees. Report. (US) **974**, 4838
Californiai Magyarsag/California Hungarians Weekly. (US ISSN 0744-8600) **1995**
Californians in Congress. (US ISSN 0068-6530) **4055**, 417
Caliper. (CN ISSN 0045-4001) **4400**
Call. (CE ISSN 0045-401X) **2860**
Call. (II ISSN 0008-1728) **3877**
Call - A.P.P.L.E. (US ISSN 8755-4909) **1468**, 1458
Call and Post. (US ISSN 0045-4036) **1995**
Call Number. (US ISSN 0008-1744) **2751**
Call of St. John/Stern van St. John. (SA ISSN 0379-458X) **4099**
Call to Action. (US) **1619**
Call to Order see C T O **320**
Call to Prayer. (US) **4167**
Callahan's Credit Union Directory. (US ISSN 0888-8671) **653**
Callahan's Fund Advisor. (US) **941**
Callaloo. (US ISSN 0161-2492) **2902**, 1995
Callboard. (CN ISSN 0045-4044) **4631**
Callboard (San Francisco). (US) **4631**
Calle. (EC) **2185**
Called Bond Record see Standard & Poor's Called Bond Record **964**
Called Bond Service. (US) **941**
†Called Out. (US) **5158**
Calligrapher. (UK) **2434**, 1296, 1352
Calligraphy. see Shufa **344**
Calligraphy and Painting. see Shu yu Hua **343**
Calligraphy Appreciation and Review. see Shufa Shangping **344**
Calligraphy Idea Exchange see Calligraphy Review **320**
Calligraphy Review. (US ISSN 0895-7819) **320**
Calligraphy Weekly. see Shufa Bao **344**
Calling All Scots. (US) **1995**
Calliope (Baltimore). (US) **4631**
Calliope (Bristol). (US) **2990**, 2902
Calliope (Peterborough). (US ISSN 1050-7086) **2308**, 1251, 1275, 2902
Calli's Tales. (US ISSN 0733-9097) **1485**
Callsign Index to Non-Government Master Frequency Data Base. (US) **1346**
Calore. (IT ISSN 0008-1760) **2298**
Calorie Control Commentary. (US ISSN 1049-1791) **3604**, 2063
CALPHAD. (Computer Coupling of Phase Diagrams and Thermochemistry) (US ISSN 0364-5916) **4359**
Calquarium. (CN ISSN 0045-4052) **3709**
Caltrux. (US) **4743**
Calumet. (US) **1995**, 2401
Calunderwriter. (US) **2529**
Calvary Review. (US ISSN 0008-1779) **4232**
Calvert County Genealogy Newsletter. (US ISSN 0895-8939) **2146**
Calvijn. (NE ISSN 0008-1787) **4232**
Calvin Coolidge Memorial Foundation Newsletter. (US) **2401**

Calvin Theological Journal. (US ISSN 0008-1795) **4232**
Calvinist Contact. (CN ISSN 0410-3882) **4232**, 1296
Calwer Theologische Monographien. Reihe A: Bibelwissenschaft. (GW) **4167**
Calwer Theologische Monographien. Reihe B: Systematische Theologie und Kirchengeschichte. (GW) **4167**
Calwer Theologische Monographien. Reihe C: Praktische Theologie und Missionswissenschaft. (GW) **4167**
Calypso. (GW) **1619**
Calypso. (US ISSN 1051-1857) **2990**
†Calypso. (TR) **5158**
Calypso Log. (US ISSN 8756-6354) **1944**, 1485, 1602
Calyx. (US ISSN 0147-1627) **320**, 2990
Camacol News. (US) **809**
Camagueyano. (US) **1995**
La Camara. (SP) **809**
Camara Argentina de Productos Quimicos. Boletin Informativo. (AG ISSN 0008-1841) **1171**
Camara Brasileira do Livro. Centro de Catalogacao na Fonte. Oficina de Livros: Novidades Cataloqadas na Fonte. (BL ISSN 0101-6903) **2751**
Camara Chileno - Alemana de Comercio e Industria. Annual Report. (CL) **810**
Camara Chileno - Suiza de Comercio. Boletin Nuevo. (CL) **810**
Camara Colombiana de la Construccion. Boletin Mensual de Estadistica. (CK) **608**
Camara Colombiana de la Construccion. Boletin Trimestrial. (CK) **608**
Camara Colombiana de la Construccion (CAMACOL) Asamblea Nacional. Documento see C A M A C O L. Asamblea Nacional. Documento **608**
Camara Colombiana de la Construccion (CAMACOL) Revista see C A M A C O L. Revista **608**
Camara de Comerciantes en Artefactos para el Hogar. Revista. (AG) **2557**, 834
Camara de Comercio. Boletin Informativo see Comercio **813**
Camara de Comercio Americana. Boletim. (PO) **810**
Camara de Comercio de Bogota. Boletin. (CK ISSN 0008-185X) **810**
Camara de Comercio de Bogota. Revista. (CK ISSN 0120-4289) **810**
Camara de Comercio de Bogota. Servicio Informativo. (CK) **810**
Camara de Comercio de Bogota. Servicio Informativo Mensual see Camara de Comercio de Bogota. Servicio Informativo **810**
Camara de Comercio de Costa Rica. Magazine. (CR) **810**
Camara de Comercio de Guayaquil. Revista see Comerciante **813**
†Camara de Comercio de La Guaira. Boletin Estadistico. (VE ISSN 0008-1876) **5158**
Camara de Comercio de Lima. Boletin Semanal see Camara de Comercio de Lima. Boletin Semanal - Informativo Legal **810**
Camara de Comercio de Lima. Boletin Semanal - Informativo Legal. (PE) **810**
Camara de Comercio de Lima. Informativo Legal see Camara de Comercio de Lima. Boletin Semanal - Informativo Legal **810**
Camara de Comercio de Lima Revista Mensual see Comercio y Produccion **813**
Camara de Comercio de Nicaragua. Boletin Comercial. (NQ) **810**
Camara de Comercio de Quito. Boletin de Informacion Comercial. (EC) **810**
Camara de Comercio e Industria Boliviano - Alemana. Bulletin Bolivia - Germany. (BO) **810**
Camara de Comercio e Industria Boliviano - Alemana. Carta de Informacion. (BO) **810**

Camara de Comercio e Industria Luso - Alema. Informationen. (PO) **810**
Camara de Comercio Hispano-Sueca de Madrid. Info. (SP) **810**
Camara de Comercio, Industria y Agricultura Venezolano-Italiano. (VE) **810**
Camara de Comercio Luso-Britanica. Bi-monthly Magazine. (PO) **810**
Camara de Comercio Paraguayo - Alemana. (PY) **810**
Camara de Comercio Suiza-Argentina. Bulletin. (AG) **810**
Camara de Comercio Uruguay - U S A. Revista. (UY) **810**
Camara de Comercio Uruguayo-Britanica. Revista. (UY ISSN 0008-1914) **653**
Camara de Estudos e Debates Economicos e Sociais Colecao C E D E S. Grandes Temas see Colecao C E D E S. Grandes Temas **84**
Camara de Industria y Comercio Argentino-Alemana. Boletin/Deutsch-Argentinische Industrie- und Handelskammer. Mitteilungen. (AG ISSN 0008-2112) **810**
Camara de Industriales de Caracas. Noti. (VE) **653**, 1073
Camara de Industrias del Uruguay. Guia de Socios y de Productos see Products of Uruguay **1083**
Camara Informa. (FR) **810**
Camara Nacional de Comercio. Informe Anual. (UY) **810**
Camara Nacional de Comercio. Publicaciones. (UY) **810**
Camara Nacional de Comercio. Revista.(UY) **810**
Camara Nacional de Comercio de Chile. Boletin de Informes Comerciales. (CL) **810**
Camara Nacional de Comercio de Chile. Informativo. (CL) **810**
Camara Nacional de Comercio de Managua. Boletin see Camara de Comercio de Nicaragua. Boletin Comercial **810**
Camara Nacional de Comercio e Industrias de Managua. Boletin see Camara de Comercio de Nicaragua. Boletin Comercial **810**
Camara Nacional de la Industria de Transformacion. Boletin Informativo. (MX) **1073**
Camara Nacional de la Industria del Hierro y del Acero. Informe del Presidente. (MX) **3403**
Camara Oficial de Comercio e Industria de Alava. Boletin Informativo. (SP) **810**
Camara Oficial de Comercio, Industria y Navegacion de Barcelona. Boletin. (SP ISSN 0008-1930) **810**
†Camara Oficial de Comercio Informacion. (SP) **5158**
Camara Oficial de la Propiedad Urbana de la Provincia de Avila. Boletin Informativo. (SP) **608**
Camara Oficial de la Propiedad Urbana de la Provincia de Malaga. Hoja Informativa. (SP) **4146**
Camara Panamena de la Construccion. Lista de Precios de Materiales de Construccion. (PN) **608**
Camara Panamena de la Construccion. Prestaciones Laborales en la Construccion. (PN) **608**, 974
Camara Venezolano Britanica de Comercio e Industria. Anuario. (VE) **810**
Camaraderie. (FR) **1296**, 1233
Camaras Oficiales de Comercio, Industria y Navegacion de la Region Vasconavarra. Coyuntura Industrial Regional see Boletin de Coyuntura y Estadistica del Pais Vasco **808**
Camaro America Newsletter. (US) **4686**
Camaro Corral. (US) **4686**
Camaro Trans-Am. (US) **4686**
Camas. (CN) **1306**
Cambio! (US) **1995**
Cambio Empresarial. (HO) **2180**
Cambio 16. (SP) **2860**
Cambrensis. (UK) **2902**
Cambria: A Welsh Geographical Review.(UK ISSN 0306-9796) **2244**

Cambrian Law Review. (UK ISSN 0084-8328) **2609**
Cambridge Air Surveys. (UK ISSN 0068-659X) **268**
Cambridge Antiquarian Society. Proceedings. (UK) **2355**, 268
▼Cambridge Archaeological Journal. (UK ISSN 0959-7743) **268**
Cambridge Authors' and Printers' Guides *see* Cambridge Authors' and Publishers' Guides **4124**
Cambridge Authors' and Publishers' Guides. (UK) **4124**, 3998
Cambridge Bibliographical Society. Transactions. (UK ISSN 0068-6611) **396**
Cambridge Bibliographical Society. Transactions. Monograph Supplements. (UK ISSN 0068-662X) **396**
Cambridge Classical Studies. (UK) **1275**
Cambridge Classical Texts and Commentaries. (UK ISSN 0068-6638) **1275**
Cambridge Computer Science Texts. (UK) **1390**
Cambridge Earth Science Series. (UK) **1541**
Cambridge Economic Handbooks. New Series. (UK) **653**
Cambridge Financial Manager. (US) **849**, 941
Cambridge Geographical Studies. (UK ISSN 0068-6654) **2244**
Cambridge Greek and Latin Classics. (UK) **2902**
Cambridge Journal of Economics. (UK ISSN 0309-166X) **653**
Cambridge Journal of Education. (UK ISSN 0305-764X) **1701**
Cambridge Latin American Studies. (UK ISSN 0068-6689) **2401**
Cambridge Latin Texts. (UK) **2808**, 2902
Cambridge Law Journal. (UK ISSN 0008-1973) **2609**
Cambridge Medicine. (UK) **3085**
Cambridge Medieval Celtic Studies. (UK ISSN 0260-5600) **2355**, 2808, 2902
Cambridge Monographs in Experimental Biology. (UK ISSN 0068-6697) **434**
Cambridge Monographs on Mathematical Physics. (UK) **3815**, 3031
Cambridge Monographs on Mechanics and Applied Mathematics. (UK) **3842**, 3031
Cambridge Monographs on Physics. (UK) **3815**
Cambridge Opera Journal. (UK ISSN 0954-5867) **3543**
Cambridge Papers in Social Anthropology. (UK ISSN 0068-6719) **236**
Cambridge Papers in Sociology. (UK ISSN 0068-6727) **4430**
Cambridge Philological Society. Proceedings. (UK ISSN 0068-6735) **1275**, 2808
Cambridge Philological Society. Proceedings. Supplement. (UK ISSN 0068-6743) **1275**, 2808
Cambridge Philosophical Society. Biological Reviews. (UK ISSN 0006-3231) **434**
Cambridge Philosophical Society. Mathematical Proceedings. (UK ISSN 0305-0041) **3031**, 3815
Cambridge Philosophical Society. Proceedings. Mathematical and Physical Sciences *see* Cambridge Philosophical Society. Mathematical Proceedings **3031**
Cambridge Planetary Science Series. (UK) **1556**
Cambridge Poetry Magazine *see* Poetry Now **3002**
Cambridge Quarterly. (UK ISSN 0008-199X) **2902**
Cambridge Review. (UK ISSN 0008-2007) **2860**
Cambridge Scientific Abstracts Neurosciences Abstracts *see* C S A Neurosciences Abstracts **3168**
Cambridge Scientific Abstracts Update *see* C S A Update **4355**

Cambridge Scientific Biochemistry Abstracts: Part 1. Biological Membranes. (US ISSN 8756-7504) **463**, 7
Cambridge Scientific Biochemistry Abstracts: Part 2. Nucleic Acids. (US ISSN 8756-7512) **463**, 7
Cambridge Scientific Biochemistry Abstracts: Part 3. Amino-Acids, Peptides & Proteins. (US ISSN 8756-7520) **464**, 7, 1199
Cambridge Solid State Science Series. (UK) **3815**
Cambridge South Asian Studies. (UK ISSN 0575-6863) **2337**
Cambridge Studies in Chinese History, Literature and Institutions. (UK) **2337**
Cambridge Studies in Cultural Systems.(UK) **236**
Cambridge Studies in Early Modern History. (UK ISSN 0084-8336) **2308**
Cambridge Studies in Economic History *see* Studies in Economic History and Policy **898**
Cambridge Studies in English Legal History. (UK) **2731**
Cambridge Studies in Historical Geography. (UK) **2244**
Cambridge Studies in International and Comparative Law: New Series. (UK) **2609**
Cambridge Studies in Linguistics. (UK ISSN 0068-676X) **2808**
Cambridge Studies in Mathematical Biology. (UK) **434**
Cambridge Studies in Medieval Life and Thought. Fourth Series. (UK) **2355**
Cambridge Studies in Medieval Life and Thought. Third Series *see* Cambridge Studies in Medieval Life and Thought. Fourth Series **2355**
Cambridge Studies in Oral and Literate Culture. (UK) **236**
Cambridge Studies in Social Anthropology. (UK ISSN 0068-6794) **236**
Cambridge Studies in Sociology. (UK ISSN 0068-6808) **4430**
Cambridge Studies in the History and Theory of Politics. (UK ISSN 0575-6871) **3877**
Cambridge Texts in the Physiological Sciences. (UK) **570**
Cambridge Town, Gown & County Series. (UK) **2193**
Cambridge Tracts in Mathematics. (UK) **3031**
Cambridge Tracts in Mathematics and Mathematical Physics *see* Cambridge Tracts in Mathematics **3031**
Cambridge University. Department of Applied Economics. Monographs. (UK ISSN 0068-6832) **653**
Cambridge University. Department of Applied Economics. Occasional Papers. (UK ISSN 0068-6840) **654**
Cambridge University. Department of Applied Economics. Papers in Industrial Relations and Labour. (UK) **974**
Cambridge University. Institute of Criminology. Bibliographical Series. (UK ISSN 0068-6883) **1524**
Cambridge University. Institute of Criminology. Occasional Papers. (UK) **1511**
Cambridge University. Oriental Publications. (UK ISSN 0068-6891) **2337**
Cambridge University Library. Genizah Series. (UK) **396**
Cambridge University Library. Historical Bibliography Series. (UK) **396**, 2308
Cambridge University Library Librarianship Series. (UK) **2751**
Cambridge University Medical Library Bulletin. (UK) **2751**, 3085
Cambridge University Reporter. (UK) **1701**
Cambridge Urban and Architectural Studies. (UK) **2484**, 296
Cambridgeshire Business. (UK) **810**
Cambridgeshire Farmers. (UK) **82**, 2123

Cambridgeshire Farmers' Journal *see* Cambridgeshire Farmers **82**
Cambridgeshire Life Magazine. (UK) **2193**
Cambridgeshire Pride. (UK) **2193**
Cambus. (SP ISSN 0211-2930) **4686**
Camcorder Report. (US) **1384**
▼Camcorder Review. (US) **1384**
Camden County Record. (US ISSN 0008-2031) **2222**
Camden Fourth Series. (UK ISSN 0068-6905) **2355**
Camden History Review. (UK ISSN 0305-4756) **2355**
Camel Bells. *see* Tuo Ling **2970**
Camellia. *see* Shan Cha **2959**
Camellia Journal. (US ISSN 0008-204X) **2123**
Cameo. (US) **372**
Cameo Newsletter *see* Aging News **2270**
Camera *see* Camera New Zealand **3789**
Camera *see* Photo Answers **3794**
†Camera. (GW ISSN 0008-2066) **5158**
Camera & Darkroom Photography. (US ISSN 1056-8484) **3789**
Camera Buyer's Guide. (AT) **3789**
Camera Canada. (CN ISSN 0008-2090) **3789**, 1251
Camera dei Deputati. Bollettino di Informazioni Costituzionali e Parlamentari. (IT) **2705**, 4055
Camera di Commercio della Spezia. Rassegna Commerciale *see* Spezia Oggi **822**
Camera di Commercio di Milano *see* Realta Economica **821**
Camera di Commercio, Industria, Artigianato e Agricoltura. Bollettino Mensile *see* Camera di Commercio, Industria, Artigianato e Agricoltura di Forli. Rassegna Economica **811**
Camera di Commercio, Industria, Artigianato e Agricoltura di Belluno. Rassegna Economica. (IT ISSN 0008-2147) **810**
Camera di Commercio, Industria, Artigianato e Agricoltura di Cuneo. Notiziario Economico. (IT) **810**
Camera di Commercio, Industria, Artigianato e Agricoltura di Ferrara. Listino dei Prezzi all'Ingrosso. (IT ISSN 1120-3900) **810**
Camera di Commercio, Industria, Artigianato e Agricoltura di Ferrara. Notiziario Mensile. (IT ISSN 1120-3943) **810**
Camera di Commercio, Industria, Artigianato e Agricoltura di Forli. Rassegna Economica. (IT) **811**
†Camera di Commercio, Industria, Artigianato e Agricoltura di Padova. Notiziario Estero. (IT) **5158**
Camera di Commercio, Industria, Artiginato e Agricoltura di Padova. Rapporti. (IT) **811**
Camera di Commercio Italiana di Rio de Janeiro. Quarterly Review. (BL) **811**
Camera di Commercio Italiana per la Gran Bretagna e il Commonwealth. Segnalazioni. (IT ISSN 0037-0940) **811**
†Camera International. (GR ISSN 0259-8280) **5158**
Camera New Zealand. (NZ ISSN 0114-264X) **3789**
Camera Obscura. (US ISSN 0270-5346) **3504**, 4858
Camera - Stylo. (FR) **3504**
Cameras. *see* Zhaoxiangji **3798**
Cameron: Supreme and District Courts Practice N.S.W. (AT ISSN 0729-2570) **2609**
Cameron's Foodservice Promotions Reporter. (US) **2063**, 2472
Cameroon. Direction de la Statistique et de la Comptabilite Nationale. Bulletin Mensuel de Statistique. (CM) **4565**
Cameroon. Direction de la Statistique et de la Comptabilite Nationale. Note Annuelle de Statistique. (CM) **707**, 4565
Cameroon. Provincial Statistical Service of the South West. Annual Statistical Report, South West Province. (CM) **4566**

Cameroon. Regie Nationale des Chemins de Fer. Compte Rendu de Gestion. (CM) **4708**
Cameroon. Regie Nationale des Chemins de Fer. Statistiques. (CM) **4708**
Cameroon Development Corporation. Annual Report and Accounts/Rapport Annuel et Compte-Rendu Financier. (CM) **1073**
Cameroon Panorama. (CM) **4257**
Cameroon Times. (CM) **2169**
Cameroon Tribune. (CM) **2169**
Cameroon Year Book. (CM ISSN 0301-7753) **2244**
Cameroun. Direction de la Statistique et de la Comptabilite Nationale. Comptes Nationaux du Cameroun *see* Comptes Nationaux du Cameroun **1091**
Cameroun Agricole, Pastorale et Forestier. (CM) **82**
Cameroun Selection. (FR) **902**
Camford Chemical Report. (CN) **1171**
Camillian *see* Vision (Milwaukee) **4278**
Camillusbode. (NE ISSN 0008-221X) **4258**
Caminho. (PO) **1251**, 4167
Camino. (IT) **296**, 2549
Caminos *see* Mas Caminos **4652**
Camion. (IT ISSN 0008-2252) **4743**
Cammello. (IT) **4756**
Cammino. (IT ISSN 0008-2260) **4258**
Cammino Economico. (IT ISSN 0008-2279) **2860**
Camouflage Air Journal. (FR ISSN 0300-452X) **49**
Camp. (GW) **4542**
Camp Chase Gazette. (US) **3453**
Camp Directors Purchasing Guide. (US) **4542**, 1125
†Camp Fire Leadership. (US ISSN 0092-1289) **5158**
Camp Valencia. (SP) **82**
Campagnes Oceanographiques Francaises. (FR) **1603**
Campaign. (UK ISSN 0008-2309) **29**
Campaign. (US) **2434**, 3453
Campaign Against Arms Trade Newsletter *see* C A A T Newsletter **3876**
Campaign Against Racial Exploitation (Australia) Inc. Newsletter *see* C A R E Newsletter **1995**
Campaign Australia. (AT) **2451**, 2860
Campaign California Report. (US ISSN 0890-3956) **4055**
Campaign Guide for Congressional Candidate and Committees. (US) **3877**
Campaign Guide for Corporations and Labor Organizations. (US) **3878**
Campaign Guide for Nonconnected Committees. (US) **3878**
Campaign Guide for Party Committees *see* Campaign Guide for Political Party Committees **3878**
Campaign Guide for Political Party Committees. (US) **3878**
Campaign Magazine. (US) **3878**
†Campaign Practices Reports. (US ISSN 0361-056X) **5158**
Campaign Report - Jobs With Peace Campaign. (US) **3878**
Campaigner *see* Campaigner & Animal's Defender **230**
Campaigner. (UK) **3878**
Campaigner & Animal's Defender. (UK) **230**
Campaigns and Elections. (US ISSN 0197-0771) **3878**
Campana. (US ISSN 0022-8206) **1995**
Campania Documenti. (IT) **2355**
Campania Sacra. (IT ISSN 0392-1352) **2355**, 4167
Campbell Contacts in America. (US ISSN 1055-1018) **2146**
Campbell Law Review. (US ISSN 0198-8174) **2609**
Campbell Paterson's Loose-Leaf Colour Catalogue of New Zealand Stamps (Specialised). (NZ) **3750**
Campbell's List. (US ISSN 0742-8987) **2609**

CampBook. Western Canada and Alaska. see Western Canada Alaska Campbook **4797**
Campeggio Italiano. (IT ISSN 0008-2325) **4542**
Camper see Outdoor Action **4552**
Camper Coachman see MotorHome **4550**
Camper Sites Guide see Family Sites Guide **4545**
Camperways. (US ISSN 0744-8120) **4756**, **4542**
Campesino. (CL ISSN 0008-2341) **82**
Campesino. (CK ISSN 0008-235X) **2183**
Campground Management. (US ISSN 0162-3796) **4542**
Camping. (DK ISSN 0045-4125) **4542**
Camping. (GW) **4543**
Camping and Caravan Site Selector. (UK ISSN 0266-4437) **4756**
Camping & Caravanning. (UK) **4543**
Camping and Caravanning Club Handbook and Sites List see Your Big Sites List: Camping and Caravanning Club Sites List **4560**
Camping and Caravanning Club Handbook and Sites List see Your Place in the Country: A Guide to Camping and Caravanning Club Sites **4560**
Camping and Caravanning in Britain. (UK) **4543**
Camping and Caravanning U.K. see Camping and Caravanning in Britain **4543**
Camping & Outdoor Leisure Trader. (UK) **4543**, **2738**
Camping and Outdoor Life see Camping & Caravanning **4543**
Camping and R V Magazine. (US ISSN 0896-5706) **4543**
Camping & Sports Equipment Ltd. News see C S E News **4542**
Camping and Trailer see Camping & Walking **4543**
Camping & Walking. (UK ISSN 0952-5106) **4543**, **4756**
Camping Benelux see Holland Camping **4548**
Camping Canada. (CN ISSN 0384-9856) **4543**
Camping-Car. (FR) **4648**, **4468**
Camping, Caravaning in France see Michelin Red Guide Series: Camping, France **4777**
Camping Caravanning and Sports Equipment Trades Directory. (UK ISSN 0068-6948) **1125**, **4543**
Camping-Caravanning-Revue. (SZ ISSN 0008-2414) **4543**
Camping Club Handbook and Sites List see Your Big Sites List: Camping and Caravanning Club Sites List **4560**
Camping Club Handbook and Sites List see Your Place in the Country: A Guide to Camping and Caravanning Club Sites **4560**
Camping in Italy. (IT) **4756**
Camping in Ontario. (CN) **4543**
Camping Journal see Caravan Camping-Journal **4543**
Camping Magazine. (US ISSN 0008-2376) **4543**
Camping Revue. (AU) **4468**, **4756**
Campitur: Camping, Caravaning, Villaggi Turistici. (IT) **4543**, **4756**
El Campo. (MX ISSN 0008-2473) **82**
Campo. (SP ISSN 0212-2146) **82**, **770**
Campo. (BL ISSN 0008-2465) **213**
Campo Abierto. (SP ISSN 0213-9529) **1746**
Campo Grande. (PO) **2860**
Campo Moderno y Chacra. (AG) **82**
Campo y Mecanica. (US ISSN 0211-4704) **82**
†Campos. (FR ISSN 0220-2425) **5158**
Campus. (US) **3453**
Campus (Lennoxville). (CN ISSN 0008-2481) **1306**
Campus Activities Programming. (US) **1701**, **4631**
Campus Canada. (CN ISSN 0829-3309) **1306**
Campus Carrier. (US) **1306**

Campus Digest. (US) **1306**
Campus Law Enforcement Journal. (US) **1511**, **1725**
Campus Leader. (PH ISSN 0008-252X) **1620**, **1306**
Campus Life. (US ISSN 0008-2538) **1306**
Campus News (Manchester). (US) **1306**
Campus Safety see Campus Safety Newsletter **4099**
Campus Safety Newsletter. (US) **4099**, **1725**
Campus Security Report. (US ISSN 1055-4319) **1526**, **1701**
Campus Times. (US) **1306**
†Campus U S A. (US) **5158**
Campus Voice. (US) **1306**
Campus Watch. (US ISSN 1050-5644) **1701**, **3940**
Can Makers Report. (UK) **2063**, **3647**
Can Manufacturers Institute. Annual Metal Can Shipments Report see Annual Can Shipments Report **3647**
Can Shipments see Annual Can Shipments Report **3647**
Can Shipments Report. (US) **3647**
Can - U.K. Link. (Canada-United Kingdom Chamber of Commerce) (UK) **811**
▼Can - U K Newsletter. (UK) **296**
†Canada. Agriculture Canada. Animal Research Centre. Research Report. (CN) **5158**
Canada. Agriculture Canada. Annual Report of Prairie Farm Rehabilitation Administration. (CN) **172**, **1944**, **4822**
Canada. Agriculture Canada. Annual Report on Prairie Farm Rehabilitation and Related Activities see Canada. Agriculture Canada. Annual Report of Prairie Farm Rehabilitation Administration **172**
Canada. Agriculture Canada. Engineering & Statistical Research Institute, Ottawa. Research Report. (CN) **172**
Canada. Agriculture Canada. Food Research Institute, Ottawa. Research Report. (CN ISSN 0068-7308) **2063**
Canada. Agriculture Canada. Forage Notes. (CN) **205**
Canada. Agriculture Canada. Hatchery Outlook see Canada. Agriculture Canada. Hatchery Review **213**
Canada. Agriculture Canada. Hatchery Review. (CN) **213**
Canada. Agriculture Canada. Livestock Market Review. (CN ISSN 0068-7324) **213**
Canada. Agriculture Canada. Market Commentary see Canada. Agriculture Canada. Market Outlook and Analysis Division. Policy Branch. Market Commentary **82**
Canada. Agriculture Canada. Market Outlook and Analysis Division. Policy Branch. Market Commentary. (CN) **82**
Canada. Agriculture Canada. Marketing and Trade Division. Animal and Animal Products: Outlook see Canada. Agriculture Canada. Market Outlook and Analysis Division. Policy Branch. Market Commentary **82**
Canada. Agriculture Canada. Policy Branch. Trade in Agricultural Products see Canada's Trade in Agricultural Products **148**
Canada. Agriculture Canada. Research Station, Melfort, Saskatchewan. Highlights. (CN) **82**
Canada. Agriculture Canada. Research Station, Melfort, Saskatchewan. Research Station Report see Canada. Agriculture Canada. Research Station, Melfort, Saskatchewan. Highlights **82**
Canada. Bureau de la Main-d'Oeuvre Feminine. Les Femmes dans la Population Active see Canada. Women's Bureau. Women in the Labour Force **975**

Canada. Canadian Forestry Service. Insect and Disease Conditions in Canada see Canada. Forestry Canada. Insect and Disease Conditions in Canada **2096**
Canada. Canadian Forestry Service - Maritimes, Fredericton, New Brunswick. Information Report M-X see Canada. Forestry Canada - Maritimes Region, Fredericton, New Brunswick. Information Report M-X **2097**
Canada. Canadian Import Tribunal. Annual Report see Canada. Canadian International Trade Tribunal. Annual Report **902**
Canada. Canadian International Trade Tribunal. Annual Report. (CN ISSN 0846-6629) **902**
Canada. Canadian International Trade Tribunal Bulletin/Canada. Tribunal Canadien du Commerce Exterieur. Bulletin. (CN ISSN 0843-6509) **902**
Canada. Canadian Radio - Television and Telecommunications Commission. Annual Report. (CN) **1371**, **1355**
Canada. Canadian Wildlife Federation. Publication List. (CN) **1485**
Canada. Centre des Statistiques de l'Aviation. Bulletin de Service. see Canada. Statistics Canada. Aviation Statistics Centre. Service Bulletin **4662**
Canada. Commissioner of Official Languages. Annual Report. (CN ISSN 0382-1161) **4055**
Canada. Conseil du Tresor. Budget des Depenses. Partie I: Plan de Depenses du Gouvernement. see Canada. Treasury Board Secretariat. Estimates. Part I: Government Expenditures Plan **4056**
Canada. Conseil du Tresor. Partie II: Budget des Depenses Principal. see Canada. Treasury Board Secretariat. Estimates. Part II: Estimates **4056**
Canada. Conseil National de Recherches. Publications. see Canada. National Research Council of Canada. Publications **5159**
Canada. Correctional Investigator. Annual Report. (CN ISSN 0383-4379) **1511**
Canada. Department of Agriculture. Engineering Research Service, Ottawa. Research Report see Canada. Agriculture Canada. Engineering & Statistical Research Institute, Ottawa. Research Report **172**
Canada. Department of Agriculture. Forage Notes see Canada. Agriculture Canada. Forage Notes **205**
Canada. Department of Consumer & Corporate Affairs. Annual Report. (CN) **4056**
Canada. Department of Consumer and Corporate Affairs. Director of Investigation and Research. Annual Report. (CN) **849**
†Canada. Department of Energy, Mines and Resources. Canada Oil and Gas Lands Administration Annual Report (Year). (CN) **5158**
Canada. Department of External Affairs. Reference Papers. (CN) **3952**
Canada. Department of External Affairs. Statements and Speeches. (CN) **3952**
Canada. Department of Finance. Economic Review see Canada. Department of Finance. Quarterly Economic Review **1089**
Canada. Department of Finance. Quarterly Economic Review. (CN) **1089**
Canada. Department of Fisheries and Oceans. Annual Report. (CN ISSN 0711-0782) **2038**
†Canada. Department of Fisheries and Oceans. Communications Directorate. Statistics on Sales of Sport Fishing Licences in Canada. (CN) **5158**
Canada. Department of Fisheries and Oceans. Pacific Region. Annual Summary of British Columbia Catch Statistics. (CN) **2051**

Canada. Department of Indian Affairs and Northern Development Canada. Schedule of Wells. (CN) **1556**
†Canada. Department of Indian Affairs and Northern Development. Mines and Minerals Statistics: Claims Activities. (CN) **5158**
Canada. Department of Indian Affairs and Northern Development. Mines and Minerals Statistics: North of 60 see Canada. Department of Indian Affairs and Northern Development. Mines and Minerals Statistics: Claims Activities **5158**
Canada. Department of Indian and Northern Affairs. Schedule of Wells, Oil and Gas North of 60. see Canada. Department of Indian Affairs and Northern Development Canada. Schedule of Wells **1556**
Canada. Department of Industry, Trade and Commerce. Small Business Loans Act. Annual Report see Canada. Department of Regional Industrial Expansion. Small Businesses Loans Act. Annual Report **1113**
Canada. Department of Insurance. Report. Co-Operative Credit Associations. (CN ISSN 0068-7383) **2529**, **770**
Canada. Department of Insurance. Report of the Superintendent of Insurance. (CN ISSN 0068-7405) **2529**
Canada. Department of Insurance. Report. Small Loans Companies and Money-Lenders. (CN ISSN 0068-7413) **2529**, **770**
Canada. Department of Insurance. Report. Trust and Loan Companies. (CN ISSN 0068-7391) **2529**, **770**
Canada. Department of National Defence. Defence (Year). (CN ISSN 0383-4638) **3453**
Canada. Department of National Defence. Directorate of History. Monograph Series. (CN) **3453**
Canada. Department of National Health and Welfare. Annual Report. (CN ISSN 0068-7456) **4099**, **4400**
†Canada. Department of National Health and Welfare. Library. Acquisitions. (CN) **5158**
Canada. Department of National Revenue. Excise News. (CN ISSN 0708-9031) **1089**
Canada. Department of National Revenue. Report: Customs, Excise and Taxation. (CN) **1089**
Canada. Department of Regional Industrial Expansion. Small Businesses Loans Act. Annual Report.(CN) **1113**
Canada. Earth Physics Branch. Geodynamic Series. (CN) **1587**
Canada. Energy, Mines and Resources Canada. Indian and Northern Affairs. Canada Oil and Gas Lands Administration Frontier Lands Released Information. (CN) **3683**
Canada. Energy, Mines and Resources Canada. Indian and Northern Affairs. Canada Oil and Gas Lands Administration Released Geophysical-Geological Data see Canada. Energy, Mines and Resources Canada. Indian and Northern Affairs. Canada Oil and Gas Lands Administration Frontier Lands Released Information **3683**
Canada. Environment Canada. Annual Report. (CN ISSN 0711-1320) **1944**
Canada. Environment Canada. Conservation and Protection Service. Annual Summary: National Air Pollution Surveillance. (CN) **1976**, **1944**
Canada. Environment Canada. Conservation and Protection Service. Monthly Summary: National Air Pollution Surveillance. (CN) **1976**, **1944**

CANADA. STATISTICS

Canada. Environment Canada. Environment Protection Service. Annual Summary: National Air Pollution Surveillance *see* Canada. Environment Canada. Conservation and Protection Service. Annual Summary: National Air Pollution Surveillance **1976**

Canada. Environment Canada. Environmental Protection Series Reports. (CN) **1945, 172, 3684**

†Canada. Environment Canada. Forestry Service Research Notes. (CN ISSN 0228-9989) **5158**

Canada. Environment Canada. Information Reports Digest - Digest des Rapports d'Information *see* Canada. Forestry Canada. Publications Digest - Abrege des Publications **2111**

Canada. Environment Canada. Land *see* Canada. Environment Canada. Sustainable Development **5158**

†Canada. Environment Canada. Sustainable Development. (CN ISSN 0840-4666) **5158**

Canada. Environmental Canada. Environmental Protection Service. Monthly Summary: National Air Pollution Surveillance *see* Canada. Environment Canada. Conservation and Protection Service. Monthly Summary: National Air Pollution Surveillance **1976**

Canada. Fisheries and Environment Canada. Annual Report *see* Canada. Department of Fisheries and Oceans. Annual Report **2038**

†Canada. Fisheries and Environment Canada. Occasional Paper. (CN) **5159**

Canada. Fisheries and Environment Canada. Report of Operations Under the Canada Water Act. (CN) **1485**

Canada. Fisheries Research Board. Journal *see* Canadian Journal of Fisheries and Aquatic Sciences **2038**

Canada. Forestry Canada. Insect and Disease Conditions in Canada. (CN) **2096**

Canada. Forestry Canada - Maritimes Region, Fredericton, New Brunswick. Information Report M-X. (CN) **2097**

Canada. Forestry Canada. Ontario Region. Forestry Newsletter. (CN) **2097**

Canada. Forestry Canada. Ontario Region. Survey Bulletin. (CN) **2097**

Canada. Forestry Canada. Publications Digest - Abrege des Publications. (CN ISSN 1183-7918) **2111**

Canada. Geological Survey. Bulletin. (CN ISSN 0068-7626) **1556**

Canada. Geological Survey. Economic Geology Report. (CN) **1556**

Canada. Geological Survey. Index of Publications of the Geological Survey of Canada. (CN ISSN 0707-2996) **1550, 7**

Canada. Geological Survey. Memoir. (CN ISSN 0068-7634) **1556**

Canada. Geological Survey. Miscellaneous Report. (CN ISSN 0068-7642) **1556**

Canada. Geological Survey. Monthly Information Circular. (CN) **1550**

Canada. Geological Survey. Paper. (CN ISSN 0068-7650) **1556**

Canada. Grain Commission. Economics and Statistics Division. Canadian Grain Exports. (CN ISSN 0317-4980) **205, 903**

Canada. Grain Commission. Economics and Statistics Division. Exports of Canadian Grain and Wheat Flour. (CN ISSN 0832-6215) **205**

Canada. Grain Commission. Economics and Statistics Division. Visible Grain Supplies and Disposition. (CN ISSN 0380-8718) **205, 148**

Canada. Great Lakes Forestry Centre. Forestry Newsletter *see* Canada. Forestry Canada. Ontario Region. Forestry Newsletter **2097**

Canada. Great Lakes Forestry Centre. Survey *see* Canada. Forestry Canada. Ontario Region. Survey Bulletin **2097**

Canada. Hydrographic Service. Activity Report/Canada. Service Hydrographique. Rapport des Activites. (CN ISSN 0701-6786) **4822**

Canada. Hydrographic Service. Annual Report *see* Canada. Hydrographic Service. Activity Report **4822**

†Canada. Hydrographic Service. Water Levels. Vol. 1: Daily Means. (CN ISSN 0706-2354) **5159**

†Canada. Hydrographic Service. Water Levels. Vol. 2: Tidal Highs and Lows. (CN ISSN 0706-2346) **5159**

Canada. Immigration and Demographic Policy Group. Immigration Statistics. (CN) **3991, 3980**

Canada. Immigration Division. Immigration Statistics *see* Canada. Immigration and Demographic Policy Group. Immigration Statistics **3991**

Canada. Indian and Northern Affairs Canada. Mines and Mineral Activities (Year). (CN) **3480**

†Canada. Information Canada. Municipal Report. (CN ISSN 0381-0976) **5159**

Canada. Information Commissioner. Annual Report. (CN) **2720, 3940**

Canada. Institut Forestier National de Petawawa. Rapports d'Information. *see* Canada. Petawawa National Forestry Institute. Information Reports **2097**

Canada. Investment Canada. Annual Report. (CN ISSN 0839-9506) **941**

Canada. Labour Canada. Annual Report on Proceedings under the Canada Labour Code, Part III (Labour Standards)/Canada. Labour Canada. Rapport Annuel sur les Mesures Prises en Vertu du Code Canadien du Travail, Partie III (les Normes du Travail). (CN) **974**

†Canada. Labour Canada. Annual Review - Revue Annuelle. (CN) **5159**

Canada. Labour Canada. Federal Mediation and Conciliation Service. Annual Report on Proceedings Under the Canada Labour Code. Part 1/ Canada. Labour Canada. Service Federal de Mediation et de Conciliation. Rapport des Activites Entreprises en Vertu du Code Canadien du Travail. Partie 1. (CN) **975**

Canada. Labour Canada. Major Wage Settlements - Grands Reglements Salariaux. (CN) **975**

Canada. Labour Canada. Rapport Annuel sur les Mesures Prises en Vertu du Code Canadien du Travail, Partie III (les Normes du Travail). *see* Canada. Labour Canada. Annual Report on Proceedings under the Canada Labour Code, Part III (Labour Standards) **974**

Canada. Labour Canada. Service Federal de Mediation et de Conciliation. Rapport des Activites Entreprises en Vertu du Code Canadien du Travail. Partie 1. *see* Canada. Labour Canada. Federal Mediation and Conciliation Service. Annual Report on Proceedings Under the Canada Labour Code. Part 1 **975**

Canada. Law Reform Commission. Administrative Law Series. Study Papers. (CN) **2610**

Canada. Law Reform Commission. Annual Report. (CN ISSN 0382-1463) **2610, 4056**

Canada. Law Reform Commission. Criminal Law Series. Study Papers. (CN) **2712**

Canada. Law Reform Commission. Modernization of Statutes. Study Papers. (CN) **2610**

Canada. Law Reform Commission. Protection of Life Series. Study Papers. (CN) **2610**

Canada. Law Reform Commission. Report to Parliament. (CN) **2610**

Canada. Law Reform Commission. Working Paper. (CN) **2610**

Canada. Marine Environmental Data Service. Manuscript Report Series *see* Canadian Manuscript Report of Fisheries and Aquatic Sciences **1945**

Canada. Marine Environmental Data Service. Monthly and Ten Yearly Means Water Levels - Moyennes Mensuelles et Annuelles des Niveaux d'Eau. (CN) **1597**

Canada. Maritimes Forest Research Centre, Fredericton, New Brunswick. Information Report M-X *see* Canada. Forestry Canada - Maritimes Region, Fredericton, New Brunswick. Information Report M-X **2097**

Canada. Mineral Policy Sector. Mineral Bulletins. (CN) **3480**

Canada. Mineral Policy Sector. Mineral Information Bulletin *see* Canada. Mineral Policy Sector. Mineral Bulletins **3480**

Canada. Ministere de l'Agriculture, des Pecheries et de l'Alimentation. Catalogue des Engins de Peche du Quebec. (CN) **2038**

Canada. Ministry of State for Science and Technology. Annual Report. (CN) **4303, 4595**

Canada. Musees Nationaux. Publications d'Oceanographie Biologique *see* Canada. National Museums, Ottawa. Publications in Biological Oceanography **5159**

Canada. National Energy Board. Annual Report. (CN ISSN 0068-7901) **1784**

Canada. National Energy Board. Information Bulletins. (CN ISSN 0825-0170) **4056**

Canada. National Energy Board. Reasons for Decision. (CN) **1784**

Canada. National Energy Board. Regulatory Agenda. (CN) **4056**

Canada. National Farm Products Marketing Council. Annual Report. (CN ISSN 0383-414X) **148**

†Canada. National Museums, Ottawa. Publications in Biological Oceanography. (CN ISSN 0068-7995) **5159**

†Canada. National Research Council of Canada. Publications/Canada. Conseil National de Recherches. Publications. (CN) **5159**

Canada. National Transportation Agency. Annual Report. (CN) **4648**

Canada. Northern Forestry Centre. Forest Management Note. (CN ISSN 0714-1181) **2097**

†Canada. Northern Forestry Centre. Forestry Report. (CN ISSN 0709-9959) **5159**

Canada. Northern Forestry Centre. Information Report. (CN ISSN 0704-7673) **2097**

Canada. Northern Natural Resources and Environment Branch. Mining Section. North of 60: Mines and Mineral Activities *see* Canada. Indian and Northern Affairs Canada. Mines and Mineral Activities (Year) **3480**

†Canada. Office of the Superintendent of Financial Institutions. List of Securities. (CN) **5159**

Canada. Pacific Forest Research Centre. Information Report. (CN) **2097**

Canada. Petawawa National Forestry Institute. Information Reports/ Canada. Institut Forestier National de Petawawa. Rapports d'Information. (CN ISSN 0228-0736) **2097**

Canada. Petawawa National Forestry Institute. Program Review. (CN ISSN 0710-4251) **2097**

Canada. Privacy Commissioner. Annual Report. (CN ISSN 1433, 2720, 3878

Canada. Register of Post Graduate Dissertations in Progress in History and Related Subjects. (CN) **2308**

Canada. Service Hydrographique. Rapport Annuel *see* Canada. Hydrographic Service. Activity Report **4822**

Canada. Service Hydrographique. Rapport des Activites. *see* Canada. Hydrographic Service. Activity Report **4822**

Canada. Statistics Canada. Aggregate Productivity Measures. (CN ISSN 0317-7882) **707, 4566**

Canada. Statistics Canada. Aggregate Productivity Trends - Tendances de la Productivite des Agregats *see* Canada. Statistics Canada. Aggregate Productivity Measures **707**

Canada. Statistics Canada. Air Charter Statistics. (CN ISSN 0828-8208) **4662, 4566**

Canada. Statistics Canada. Air Passenger Origin and Destination. Canada - United States Report. (CN ISSN 0705-4343) **4662, 4566**

Canada. Statistics Canada. Air Passenger Origin and Destination. Domestic Report. (CN ISSN 0703-2692) **4662, 7**

Canada. Statistics Canada. Annual Report. (CN ISSN 0703-2633) **4566**

Canada. Statistics Canada. Aviation Statistics Centre. Service Bulletin/ Canada. Centre des Statistiques de l'Aviation. Bulletin de Service. (CN ISSN 0068-7057) **4662, 4566**

Canada. Statistics Canada. Beverage and Tobacco Products Industries. (CN ISSN 0835-0019) **4646, 4566**

†Canada. Statistics Canada. Boatbuilding and Repair/Construction et Reparation d'Embarcations. (CN ISSN 0527-4834) **5159**

†Canada. Statistics Canada. Breweries/ Brasseries. (CN ISSN 0527-4869) **5159**

Canada. Statistics Canada. Building Permits. (CN ISSN 0318-8809) **637, 4566**

Canada. Statistics Canada. Building Permits. Annual Summary. (CN ISSN 0575-7975) **637, 4566**

Canada. Statistics Canada. Cable Television. (CN) **1346, 1371, 4566**

Canada. Statistics Canada. Cable Television - Teledistribution *see* Canada. Statistics Canada. Cable Television **1346**

Canada. Statistics Canada. Canada's Mineral Production: Preliminary Estimates. (CN ISSN 0380-7797) **3499, 4566**

Canada. Statistics Canada. Canadian Economic Observer. (CN ISSN 0835-9148) **708, 4566**

Canada. Statistics Canada. Canadian Statistical Review *see* Canada. Statistics Canada. Canadian Economic Observer **708**

Canada. Statistics Canada. Cane and Beet Sugar Processors *see* Canada. Statistics Canada. Food Industries **2084**

Canada. Statistics Canada. Carpet, Mat and Rug Industry *see* Canada. Statistics Canada. Textile Products Industries **4628**

†Canada. Statistics Canada. Causes of Death, Provinces by Sex and Canada by Sex and Age. (CN ISSN 0380-7533) **5159**

Canada. Statistics Canada. Clothing Industries. (CN ISSN 0835-006X) **1288, 4566**

Canada. Statistics Canada. Coal and Coke Statistics. (CN ISSN 0380-6847) **3499, 4566**

Canada. Statistics Canada. Coal Mines. (CN ISSN 0705-436X) **3499, 4566**

†Canada. Statistics Canada. Coffin and Casket Industry/Industrie des Cercueils. (CN ISSN 0527-4915) **5159**

†Canada. Statistics Canada. Communications and Energy Wire and Cable Industry. (CN ISSN 0833-2002) **5159**

†Canada. Statistics Canada. Communications and Other Electronic Industries. (CN ISSN 0828-9824) **5159**

6024 CANADA. STATISTICS

Canada. Statistics Canada. Communications Equipment Manufacturers - Fabricants d'Equipement de Telecommunication see Canada. Statistics Canada. Communications and Other Electronic Industries **5159**

Canada. Statistics Canada. Communications Service Bulletin. (CN ISSN 0380-0334) **1347, 4566**

Canada. Statistics Canada. Community Antenna Television - Services de Television a Antenne Collective see Canada. Statistics Canada. Cable Television **1346**

Canada. Statistics Canada. Community Colleges and Related Institutions, Postsecondary Enrollment and Graduates. (CN ISSN 0832-6657) **1675, 4566**

†Canada. Statistics Canada. Consolidated Government Finance: Fiscal Year Ended Nearest to December 31. (CN ISSN 0575-8254) **5159**

Canada. Statistics Canada. Construction in Canada. (CN ISSN 0527-4974) **637, 4566**

Canada. Statistics Canada. Consumer Prices and Price Indexes. (CN ISSN 0380-691X) **708, 4566**

†Canada. Statistics Canada. Control and Sale of Alcoholic Beverages in Canada. (CN ISSN 0705-4319) **5159**

†Canada. Statistics Canada. Cordage and Twine Industry/Corderie et Ficellerie (Fabrication). (CN ISSN 0527-4990) **5159**

Canada. Statistics Canada. Corporation Financial Statistics. (CN ISSN 0575-8262) **708, 4566**

Canada. Statistics Canada. Corporation Taxation Statistics. (CN ISSN 0576-0119) **708, 4566**

†Canada. Statistics Canada. Cotton Yarn and Cloth Mills/Filature et Tissage du Coton. (CN ISSN 0527-5016) **5159**

Canada. Statistics Canada. Credit Unions. (CN ISSN 0576-0100) **708, 4566**

Canada. Statistics Canada. Crude Petroleum and Natural Gas Industry. (CN ISSN 0068-7103) **3705, 4566**

Canada. Statistics Canada. Crude Petroleum and Natural Gas Production. (CN ISSN 0702-6846) **3705**

Canada. Statistics Canada. Direct Selling in Canada. (CN ISSN 0590-5702) **708, 4566**

Canada. Statistics Canada. Education in Canada. (CN ISSN 0706-3679) **1675, 4566**

†Canada. Statistics Canada. Educational Staff in Community Colleges/Personnel d'Enseignement des Colleges Communautaires. (CN ISSN 0382-411X) **5159**

†Canada. Statistics Canada. Electric Lamp and Shade Manufacturers/Industrie des Lampes Electriques et des Abat-Jour. (CN ISSN 0384-4161) **5159**

Canada. Statistics Canada. Electric Power Statistics Volume 1: Annual Electric Power Survey of Capability and Load. (CN ISSN 0380-951X) **1798,** 1801

Canada. Statistics Canada. Electrical Contracting Industry see Canada. Statistics Canada. Electrical Trade Contractors **1798**

Canada. Statistics Canada. Electrical Trade Contractors. (CN ISSN 0835-104X) **1798,** 1801

Canada. Statistics Canada. Elementary - Secondary School Enrolment. (CN ISSN 0704-6596) **1675, 4566**

Canada. Statistics Canada. Employment, Earnings and Hours. (CN ISSN 0380-6936) **708, 4566**

Canada. Statistics Canada. Enrolment in Community Colleges see Canada. Statistics Canada. Community Colleges and Related Institutions, Postsecondary Enrollment and Graduates **1675**

Canada. Statistics Canada. Estimates of Labour Income. (CN ISSN 0318-9007) **708, 4566**

†Canada. Statistics Canada. Estimates of Population for Canada and the Provinces - Estimations de la Population du Canada et des Provinces. (CN ISSN 0708-7012) **5159**

Canada. Statistics Canada. Exports by Commodity. (CN ISSN 1181-6732) **708**

Canada. Statistics Canada. Exports - Merchandise Trade see Canada. Statistics Canada. Exports, Merchandise Trade H S Based **708**

Canada. Statistics Canada. Exports, Merchandise Trade H S Based. (CN ISSN 0844-8361) **708, 4566**

Canada. Statistics Canada. Fabricated Metal Products Industries. (CN ISSN 0835-0124) **3424, 4566**

Canada. Statistics Canada. Family Incomes, Census Families. (CN ISSN 0703-7368) **708,** 3991, **4566**

†Canada. Statistics Canada. Farm Net Income. (CN ISSN 0068-712X) **5159**

Canada. Statistics Canada. Farm Products Price Index. (CN ISSN 0835-0906) **135, 4566**

†Canada. Statistics Canada. Federal Government Employment. (CN ISSN 0575-8491) **5159**

†Canada. Statistics Canada. Federal Government Employment in Metropolitan Areas. (CN ISSN 0527-5148) **5159**

†Canada. Statistics Canada. Federal Government Finance: Revenue and Expenditure, Assets and Liabilities. (CN ISSN 0575-8521) **5159**

Canada. Statistics Canada. Field Crop Reporting Series. (CN ISSN 0575-8548) **135, 4566**

Canada. Statistics Canada. Financial Statistics of Education. (CN ISSN 0703-9328) **1675, 4566**

Canada. Statistics Canada. Food Industries. (CN ISSN 0835-0000) **2084, 4566**

†Canada. Statistics Canada. Foundation Garment Industry/Industrie des Corsets et Soutiens-Gorge. (CN ISSN 0384-2967) **5159**

Canada. Statistics Canada. Fruit and Vegetable Production. (CN ISSN 0383-008X) **136, 4566**

Canada. Statistics Canada. Gas Utilities, Transport and Distribution Systems. (CN ISSN 0527-5318) **3705, 4566**

Canada. Statistics Canada. General Review of the Mineral Industries, Mines, Quarries and Oil Wells. (CN ISSN 0575-8645) **3499, 4566**

Canada. Statistics Canada. Glass and Glass Products Industries see Canada. Statistics Canada. Non-Metallic Mineral Products Industries **1167**

Canada. Statistics Canada. Glass and Glass Products Manufacturers-Fabricants de Verre et d'Articles en Verre see Canada. Statistics Canada. Non-Metallic Mineral Products Industries **1167**

Canada. Statistics Canada. Gypsum Products. (CN ISSN 0380-7223) **637, 4566**

Canada. Statistics Canada. Highway, Road, Street and Bridge Contracting Industry see Canada. Statistics Canada. Highway, Road, Street and Bridge Contractors **1842**

Canada. Statistics Canada. Highway, Road, Street and Bridge Contractors. (CN ISSN 0835-1058) **1842, 4566**

Canada. Statistics Canada. Historical Labour Force Statistics, Actual Data, Seasonal Factors, Seasonally Adjusted Data. (CN ISSN 0703-2684) **708, 4566**

†Canada. Statistics Canada. Homicide in Canada: a Statistical Perspective. (CN ISSN 0825-432X) **5159**

Canada. Statistics Canada. Homicide Statistics see Canada. Statistics Canada. Homicide in Canada: a Statistical Perspective **5159**

Canada. Statistics Canada. Household Facilities and Equipment. (CN ISSN 0318-5273) **2450, 4566**

†Canada. Statistics Canada. Housing Starts and Completions. (CN ISSN 0319-8278) **5159**

Canada. Statistics Canada. Imports - Merchandise Trade see Canada. Statistics Canada. Imports, Merchandise Trade H S Based **708**

Canada. Statistics Canada. Imports, Merchandise Trade H S Based. (CN ISSN 0844-8353) **708, 4566**

Canada. Statistics Canada. Index Numbers of Farm Prices of Agricultural Products see Canada. Statistics Canada. Farm Products Price Index **135**

Canada. Statistics Canada. Industrial Corporations, Financial Statistics. (CN ISSN 0380-7525) **708, 4566**

Canada. Statistics Canada. Infomat. (CN ISSN 0380-0547) **4566**

Canada. Statistics Canada. International Travel. (CN ISSN 0838-3952) **4799, 4566**

†Canada. Statistics Canada. Knitting Mills - Bonneterie. (CN ISSN 0384-3343) **5159**

†Canada. Statistics Canada. Leather Glove Factories/Fabriques de Gants en Cuir. (CN ISSN 0384-3300) **5159**

†Canada. Statistics Canada. List of Canadian Hospitals. (CN ISSN 0831-7313) **5159**

Canada. Statistics Canada. List of Canadian Hospitals and Special Care Facilities see Canada. Statistics Canada. List of Canadian Hospitals **5159**

Canada. Statistics Canada. Listing of Supplementary Documents. (CN ISSN 0228-5134) **4566**

Canada. Statistics Canada. Livestock and Animal Products Statistics. (CN ISSN 0068-7154) **136, 4566**

†Canada. Statistics Canada. Local Government Finance: Revenue and Expenditure, Assets and Liabilities, Actual. (CN ISSN 0703-2749) **5160**

Canada. Statistics Canada. Manufacturers of Electric Wire and Cable - Fabricants de Fils et de Cables Electriques see Canada. Statistics Canada. Communications and Energy Wire and Cable Industry **5159**

†Canada. Statistics Canada. Manufacturers of Industrial Chemicals/Fabricants de Produits Chimiques Industriels. (CN ISSN 0527-5539) **5160**

†Canada. Statistics Canada. Manufacturers of Soap and Cleaning Compounds/Fabricants de Savon et de Produits de Nettoyage. (CN ISSN 0384-3912) **5160**

†Canada. Statistics Canada. Manufacturing Industries Division. Potash Mines/Mines de Potasse. (CN ISSN 0382-4020) **5160**

Canada. Statistics Canada. Manufacturing Industries of Canada: Sub-Provincial Areas. (CN ISSN 0382-4012) **708, 4566**

Canada. Statistics Canada. Market Research Handbook. (CN ISSN 0590-9325) **708, 4566**

Canada. Statistics Canada. Mechanical Contracting Industry see Canada. Statistics Canada. Mechanical Trade Contractors **1842**

Canada. Statistics Canada. Mechanical Trade Contractors. (CN ISSN 0835-1031) **1842,** 637, **4566**

Canada. Statistics Canada. Men's Clothing Industries see Canada. Statistics Canada. Clothing Industries **1288**

Canada. Statistics Canada. Merchandising Inventories. (CN ISSN 0380-7177) **708, 4566**

Canada. Statistics Canada. Mineral Wool Including Fibrous Glass Insulation. (CN ISSN 0229-6098) **637, 4566**

†Canada. Statistics Canada. Miscellaneous Leather Products Manufacturers/Fabricants d'Articles Divers en Cuir. (CN ISSN 0384-4811) **5160**

Canada. Statistics Canada. Miscellaneous Manufacturing Industries see Canada. Statistics Canada. Other Manufacturing Industries **709**

Canada. Statistics Canada. Motion Picture Theatres and Film Distributors. (CN ISSN 0380-6294) **3519, 4566**

†Canada. Statistics Canada. Motor Vehicle, Part 1, Rates and Regulations/Vehicules a Moteur, Partie 1, Charges Fiscales et Reglementation. (CN ISSN 0527-5822) **5160**

Canada. Statistics Canada. Motor Vehicle. Part 2. Motive Fuel Sales see Canada. Statistics Canada. Road Motor Vehicles, Fuel Sales **4662**

†Canada. Statistics Canada. Motor Vehicle, Part 4, Revenues/Vehicules a Moteur, Partie 4, Recettes. (CN ISSN 0527-5849) **5160**

†Canada. Statistics Canada. Motor Vehicle Traffic Accidents/Accidents de la Circulation Routiere. (CN ISSN 0527-5865) **5160**

Canada. Statistics Canada. National Income and Expenditure Accounts. (CN) **708, 4566**

Canada. Statistics Canada. Non-Metallic Mineral Products Industries. (CN ISSN 0835-0167) **1167, 4566**

Canada. Statistics Canada. Non-Metallic Products Industries see Canada. Statistics Canada. Non-Metallic Mineral Products Industries **1167**

Canada. Statistics Canada. Non-Residential General Building Contracting Industry see Canada. Statistics Canada. Non-Residential General Contractors and Developers **637**

Canada. Statistics Canada. Non-Residential General Contractors and Developers. (CN ISSN 0835-1066) **637, 4566**

†Canada. Statistics Canada. Office Furniture Manufacturers/Industrie des Meubles de Bureau. (CN ISSN 0384-4080) **5160**

Canada. Statistics Canada. Oil Pipe Line Transport. (CN ISSN 0380-4615) **3705**

Canada. Statistics Canada. Oils and Fats. (CN ISSN 0527-5911) **2084, 4566**

Canada. Statistics Canada. Other Manufacturing Industries. (CN ISSN 0835-0191) **709, 4566**

Canada. Statistics Canada. Paper and Allied Products Industries. (CN ISSN 0835-0094) **3667,** 2111

Canada. Statistics Canada. Passenger Bus and Urban Transit Statistics. (CN ISSN 0383-5766) **4662, 4567**

Canada. Statistics Canada. Passenger Bus and Urban Transit Statistics. (CN ISSN 0829-1756) **4662, 4567**

Canada. Statistics Canada. Pension Plans in Canada. (CN ISSN 0701-5488) **2546, 4567**

Canada. Statistics Canada. Primary Iron and Steel. (CN ISSN 0380-7851) **3424, 4567**

Canada. Statistics Canada. Primary Metal Industries. (CN ISSN 0835-0116) **3403**

Canada. Statistics Canada. Printing, Publishing and Allied Industries. (CN ISSN 0575-9412) **4007, 4140, 4567**

Canada. Statistics Canada. Private and Public Investment in Canada. Outlook see Canada. Statistics Canada. Private and Public Investment in Canada, Intentions **709**

Canada. Statistics Canada. Private and Public Investment in Canada, Intentions. (CN ISSN 0823-065X) **709, 4567**

Canada. Statistics Canada. Private and Public Investment in Canada, Mid-Year Review see Canada. Statistics Canada. Private and Public Investment in Canada. Revised Intentions **709**

Canada. Statistics Canada. Private and Public Investment in Canada. Revised Intentions. (CN ISSN 0823-0668) **709, 4567**

Canada. Statistics Canada. Production of Poultry and Eggs. (CN ISSN 0068-7189) **136, 4567**

Canada. Statistics Canada. Products Shipped by Canadian Manufacturers. (CN ISSN 0575-9455) **709, 4567**

†Canada. Statistics Canada. Provincial and Territorial Government Employment/Emploi dans les Administrations Provinciales et Territoriales. (CN ISSN 0825-9224) **5160**

Canada. Statistics Canada. Provincial Government Employment see Canada. Statistics Canada. Provincial and Territorial Government Employment **5160**

Canada. Statistics Canada. Provincial Government Enterprise Finance: Income and Expenditure, Assets, Liabilities and Net Worth. (CN ISSN 0575-9463) **709, 4567**

†Canada. Statistics Canada. Provincial Government Finance: Assets, Liabilities, Source and Application of Funds. (CN ISSN 0710-1023) **5160**

Canada. Statistics Canada. Provincial Government Finance: Assets, Liabilities, Sources and Uses of Funds see Canada. Statistics Canada. Provincial Government Finance: Assets, Liabilities, Source and Application of Funds **5160**

Canada. Statistics Canada. Quarterly Estimates of Trusteed Pension Funds.(CN ISSN 0700-205X) **709, 4567**

Canada. Statistics Canada. Quarterly Report on Energy Supply. Demand in Canada. (CN ISSN 0702-0465) **1798, 4567**

Canada. Statistics Canada. Radio and Television Broadcasting. (CN ISSN 0575-9560) **1347, 4567**

Canada. Statistics Canada. Railway Carloadings. (CN ISSN 0380-6308) **4662, 4567**

Canada. Statistics Canada. Railway Operating Statistics. (CN ISSN 0380-5964) **4662, 4567**

Canada. Statistics Canada. Report on Fur Farms. (CN ISSN 0318-7888) **2738, 4567**

Canada. Statistics Canada. Restaurant, Caterer and Tavern Statistics. (CN ISSN 0226-2320) **2482, 4567**

Canada. Statistics Canada. Retail Chain and Department Stores. (CN ISSN 0227-017X) **709, 4567**

Canada. Statistics Canada. Retail Trade.(CN ISSN 0380-6146) **709**

†Canada. Statistics Canada. Road and Street Length and Financing/Voies Publiques, Longueur et Financement. (CN ISSN 0706-3105) **5160**

Canada. Statistics Canada. Road Motor Vehicles, Fuel Sales. (CN ISSN 0703-654X) **4662, 4567**

Canada. Statistics Canada. Road Motor Vehicles, Registrations. (CN ISSN 0706-067X) **4662, 4567**

Canada. Statistics Canada. Rubber and Plastic Products Industries. (CN ISSN 0835-0027) **4294, 4567**

Canada. Statistics Canada. Rubber Products Industries see Canada. Statistics Canada. Rubber and Plastic Products Industries **4294**

Canada. Statistics Canada. Sawmills and Planing Mill and Shingle Mill Products Industries see Canada. Statistics Canada. Wood Industries **2112**

Canada. Statistics Canada. Security Transactions with Non-Residents. (CN ISSN 0702-6587) **709, 4567**

†Canada. Statistics Canada. Shipbuilding and Repair/Construction et Reparation de Navires. (CN ISSN 0527-6144) **5160**

Canada. Statistics Canada. Shipping in Canada. (CN ISSN 0835-5533) **4663, 4567**

†Canada. Statistics Canada. Shipping Statistics/Statistiques Maritime. (CN ISSN 0527-6160) **5160**

†Canada. Statistics Canada. Slaughtering and Meat Processors/ Abattage et Conditionnement de la Viande. (CN ISSN 0384-4951) **5160**

Canada. Statistics Canada. Smelting and Refining see Canada. Statistics Canada. Primary Metal Industries **3403**

†Canada. Statistics Canada. Stocks of Frozen Meat Products/Stocks de Viandes Congelees. (CN ISSN 0703-7333) **5160**

Canada. Statistics Canada. Surface and Marine Transport. (CN ISSN 0828-2897) **4663, 4567**

†Canada. Statistics Canada. Surgical Procedures and Treatments/ Interventions Chirurgicales et Traitements. (CN ISSN 0317-3720) **5160**

Canada. Statistics Canada. Survey of Canadian Nursery Trades Industry. (CN ISSN 0318-5184) **2141, 4567**

Canada. Statistics Canada. System of National Accounts, Canada's International Investment Position. (CN) **709, 4567**

Canada. Statistics Canada. System of National Accounts, National Income and Expenditure Accounts see Canada. Statistics Canada. National Income and Expenditure Accounts **708**

Canada. Statistics Canada. Telecommunications Statistics. (CN ISSN 0703-7252) **1347, 4567**

Canada. Statistics Canada. Telephone Statistics. (CN ISSN 0707-9753) **1347, 1361, 4567**

Canada. Statistics Canada. Textile Products Industries. (CN ISSN 0319-891X) **4628, 4567**

Canada. Statistics Canada. The Labour Force. (CN ISSN 0380-6804) **709, 4567**

Canada. Statistics Canada. Tobacco Products Industries see Canada. Statistics Canada. Beverage and Tobacco Products Industries **4646**

Canada. Statistics Canada. Travel Between Canada and Other Countries see Canada. Statistics Canada. International Travel **4799**

Canada. Statistics Canada. Trusteed Pension Funds - Financial Statistics. (CN ISSN 0835-4634) **709, 4567**

Canada. Statistics Canada. Urban Transit see Canada. Statistics Canada. Passenger Bus and Urban Transit Statistics **4662**

Canada. Statistics Canada. Vending Machine Operators. (CN ISSN 0527-6411) **709, 4567**

Canada. Statistics Canada. Water Transportation see Canada. Statistics Canada. Shipping in Canada **4663**

Canada. Statistics Canada. Wholesale Trade. (CN ISSN 0380-7894) **709, 4567**

Canada. Statistics Canada. Wood Industries. (CN ISSN 0835-0078) **2112, 4567**

†Canada. Statistics Canada. Wool Production and Supply. (CN ISSN 0300-0265) **5160**

Canada. Treasury Board. Access Register. (CN) **770**

Canada. Treasury Board. Index of Federal Information Banks see Canada. Treasury Board. Index to Personal Information **770**

Canada. Treasury Board. Index of Federal Information Banks see Canada. Treasury Board. Access Register **770**

Canada. Treasury Board. Index to Personal Information. (CN) **770**

Canada. Treasury Board Secretariat. Estimates. Part I: Government Expenditures Plan/Canada. Conseil du Tresor. Budget des Depenses. Partie I: Plan de Depenses du Gouvernement. (CN) **4056**

Canada. Treasury Board Secretariat. Estimates. Part II: Estimates/Canada. Conseil du Tresor. Partie II: Budget des Depenses Principal. (CN) **4056**

Canada. Tribunal Canadien du Commerce Exterieur. Bulletin. see Canada. Canadian International Trade Tribunal Bulletin **902**

Canada. Women's Bureau. Women in the Labour Force. (CN) **975, 2610, 4838**

Canada (Year). (US ISSN 0749-2561) **4756**

Canada, A Portrait. (CN ISSN 0840-6014) **4567**

Canada A-Z. (CN ISSN 0824-4766) **1125, 3480, 3684**

Canada Addictions Foundation. Directory/Fondation Canadienne des Toxicomanies. Repertoire. (CN ISSN 0705-5587) **1535**

Canada Air Mail Notes. (US) **3750**

Canada - Alberta. Forest Resource Development Agreement. Reports. (CN) **2097**

Canada & Arab World. (CN ISSN 0706-7909) **1995**

Canada and International Relations. (CN ISSN 0847-0510) **903**

Canada & the World. (CN ISSN 0043-8170) **4368, 1620, 2308**

Canada Armenian Press see Canada Armenian Press. Newsletter **4281**

Canada Armenian Press. Newsletter. (CN) **4281**

Canada Business Corporations Act with Regulations. (CN ISSN 0317-6649) **2708**

Canada Centre for Mineral and Energy Technology Reports see C A N M E T Reports **3479**

Canada Century Home see Century Home **2549**

Canada Corporations Law Reporter. (CN) **2708**

Canada Council Annual Report and Supplement/Rapport Annuel du Conseil des Arts du Canada et son Supplement. (CN ISSN 0576-4300) **320, 3504, 4631**

Canada d'Aujourd'hui. see Canada Today **2176**

Canada d'Aujourd'hui. see Canada Today **3878**

Canada Darpan. (CN) **1995**

Canada Diseases Weekly Report/ Rapport Hebdomadaire des Maladies au Canada. (CN ISSN 0382-232X) **4099**

Canada Gazette: Part 1: Government, Divorce, Bankruptcy Notices, Etc. (CN ISSN 0045-4192) **2610**

Canada Gazette: Part 2: Statutory Instruments. (CN) **2610**

Canada Gazette: Part 2: Statutory Orders and Regulations see Canada Gazette: Part 2: Statutory Instruments **2610**

Canada Grains Council. Annual Report. (CN ISSN 0700-2866) **205**

Canada Grains Council. Statistical Handbook. (CN) **205**

Canada Health Manpower Inventory see Health Personnel in Canada **3103**

†Canada in World Affairs. (CN ISSN 0068-7685) **5160**

Canada Income Tax Guide. (CN ISSN 0008-2694) **1089**

Canada Income Tax Guide with Canadian Income Tax Act. Regulations & Rulings. (CN) **1089**

Canada Institute for Scientific and Technical Information. Annual Report/Institut Canadien de l'Information Scientifique et Technique. Rapport Annuel. (CN ISSN 0703-0320) **4303**

Canada Institute for Scientific and Technical Information News see C I S T I News **4359**

▼Canada Japan Business Journal. (CN) **903**

Canada - Japan, the Export - Import Picture. (CN ISSN 0702-0333) **903**

Canada Japan Trade Council. Newsletter. (CN ISSN 0045-4214) **811**

Canada Journal. (CN) **2176**

Canada Labour Service. (CN ISSN 0008-2708) **2610, 975**

†Canada Land Inventory. Report. (CN ISSN 0068-7693) **5160**

Canada Legal Directory. (CN) **2610**

Canada Livestock Meat Trade Report. (CN) **213**

Canada Lumberman see Canadian Forest Industries **2113**

Canada Lutheran see Eastern Synod Lutheran **4236**

Canada Mortgage and Housing Corporation. Annual Report. (CN ISSN 0226-0336) **2484**

Canada Mortgage and Housing Corporation Recent Research Funded by C M H C see Recent Research Funded by C M H C **2495**

Canada Music Book see Musicanada **5241**

Canada Nucleaire. see Nuclear Canada **1807**

Canada on Stage: The National Theatre Yearbook. (CN) **4631**

Canada Pension and Old Age Security Legislation see Canada Pension Plan, Old Age Security Act and Pension Benifits Standards Act **2610**

Canada Pension Plan, Old Age Security Act and Pension Benifits Standards Act. (CN) **2610**

Canada Petroleum Industry. (US) **3684, 1125**

Canada Postal Guide Part 1: Postal Law and Regulations. (CN) **1352**

Canada Postal Guide Part 2: International Mails, Rates and Conditions. (CN) **1352**

Canada Poultryman. (CN ISSN 0008-2732) **213**

Canada Quilts see Canada Quilts Magazine **3590**

Canada Quilts Magazine. (CN) **3590, 353**

†Canada Report. (CN ISSN 0384-9252) **5160**

Canada Reports. (CN) **2176**

Canada Statute Citator. (CN) **2610**

Canada-Svensken/Swedish Canadian. (CN ISSN 0045-4249) **1995**

Canada Tax Cases. (CN ISSN 0008-2740) **1089**

†Canada Tax Letter. (CN ISSN 0712-6662) **5160**

Canada Tax Service. (CN ISSN 0008-2759) **1089**

Canada Times. (CN) **1995**

Canada Today/Canada d'Aujourd'hui. (UK ISSN 0306-8145) **2176**

Canada Today/Canada d'Aujourd'hui. (US ISSN 0045-4257) **3878**

†Canada: Travel Information. (CN ISSN 0709-9762) **5160**

Canada - U.K. Link see Can - U.K. Link **811**

Canada - U.K. Year Book. (UK ISSN 0309-0329) **811**

Canada - U S Business Law Review. (CN) **2708, 654**

Canada-United Kingdom Chamber of Commerce Can - U.K. Link see Can - U.K. Link **811**

Canada - United States Law Journal. (US ISSN 0163-6391) **2720**

Canada Who's Who of the Poultry Industry. (CN ISSN 0068-8134) **213**

Canada Works! (CN) **2581**

†Canada Yearbook. (CN ISSN 0068-8142) **5160**

Canadan Uutiset. (CN ISSN 0008-2775) **1995,** 2176
Canada's Atlantic Folklore and Folklife Series. (CN ISSN 0708-4226) **2053,** 3543
Canada's Business Climate. (CN ISSN 0045-4303) **849**
Canada's Contract Magazine *see* Contract Magazine **2549**
Canada's Furniture Magazine. (CN ISSN 0711-0030) **2557**
Canada's International Investment Position *see* Canada. Statistics Canada. System of National Accounts, Canada's International Investment Position **709**
Canada's Mental Health. (CN ISSN 0008-2791) **3085,** 4015
Canada's Navy Annual. (CN) **3453**
Canada's Office Automation Magazine *see* Office Systems & Technology **1060**
Canada's Original Bridal Buyers' Guide. (CN) **3066,** 1289
Canada's Tax Treaties. (CN) **2610,** 1089
Canada's Trade in Agricultural Products.(CN ISSN 0317-7483) **148**
Canada's West. (CN) **4756**
Canada's Wings *see* High Flight **54**
Canadian (Belleville). (CN ISSN 0008-2805) **2286**
Canadian (Totonto). (CN) **4648**
Canadian (Vernon). (CN) **4802**
▼Canadian A I D S News/S I D A: Realites. (US ISSN 1188-0325) **3218**
Canadian Aberdeen-Angus News *see* Angus Times **210**
Canadian Academy of Sport Medicine Review *see* Clinical Journal of Sport Medicine **3371**
Canadian Acoustics/Acoustique Canadienne. (CN ISSN 0711-6659) **3859**
Canadian Administrator. (CN ISSN 0008-2813) **1726**
Canadian Advertising Rates and Data. (CN) **40,** 396
Canadian Advisory Council on the Status of Women. Annual Report - Rapport Annuel. (CN ISSN 0705-6028) **4838**
Canadian Advisory Council on the Status of Women News *see* C A C S W News **4838**
Canadian Aerial Applicators Association Newsletter. (US) **49,** 82
Canadian Aeronautics and Space Journal. (CN ISSN 0008-2821) **49**
Canadian Aggregates Magazines. (CN) **608**
Canadian Agricultural Economics and Farm Management Society. Proceedings of the Workshop *see* Canadian Agricultural Economics and Farm Management Society. Workshop and Annual Meeting Proceedings **148**
Canadian Agricultural Economics and Farm Management Society. Workshop and Annual Meeting Proceedings. (CN) **148**
Canadian Agricultural Engineering. (CN ISSN 0045-432X) **82**
Canadian Agricultural Insect Pest Review. (CN ISSN 0068-8185) **172**
Canadian Air Comments *see* Atlas Copco Comments **5140**
Canadian Aircraft Operator. (CN ISSN 0008-2848) **4671**
Canadian Almanac and Directory. (CN ISSN 0068-8193) **396,** 2176
Canadian Alpine Journal. (CN ISSN 0068-8207) **4543,** 3066
The Canadian Amateur. (CN ISSN 0318-0867) **1355**
Canadian Amateur Advanced Study Guide. (CN) **1355**
Canadian Amateur Boxing Association News Bulletin *see* C A B A News Bulletin **4467**
Canadian Amateur Certificate Study Guide *see* Canadian Amateur Study Guide for the Basic Qualification **1355**

Canadian Amateur Study Guide for the Basic Qualification. (CN) **1355**
▼Canadian - America Public Policy. (US ISSN 1047-1073) **3952**
Canadian and International Education/Education Canadienne et Internationale. (CN ISSN 0315-1409) **1620**
Canadian and Provincial Golf Records. (CN ISSN 0316-8131) **4502**
Canadian Annual Review of Politics and Public Affairs. (CN ISSN 0315-1433) **2401**
Canadian Apparel Manufacture. (CN ISSN 0705-3010) **1284**
▼Canadian Applied Mathematics Quarterly. (US) **3031**
Canadian Appraiser/Evaluateur Canadien. (CN ISSN 0383-6649) **4146**
Canadian Aquaculture *see* Northern Aquaculture **2047**
Canadian Arab World Review/Revue du Monde Arabe. (CN) **1995**
Canadian Arabian News. (CN ISSN 0008-2864) **4532**
Canadian Archer. (Federation of Canadian Archers) (CN) **4468**
Canadian Architect. (CN ISSN 0008-2872) **296**
Canadian Architect's Yardsticks for Costing *see* Yardsticks for Costing **309**
Canadian Area Development. (CN ISSN 0843-6673) **4303,** 4595
Canadian Art. (CN ISSN 0825-3854) **320**
Canadian Art Sales Index. (CN ISSN 0229-8961) **320,** 352
Canadian Artists Series. (CN ISSN 0383-5405) **320**
Canadian Asian Studies Association. Revue *see* Asia Horizon Azie **5139**
Canadian Association for American Studies. Newsletter. (CN) **2504**
Canadian Association for Health, Physical Education and Recreation. Journal. (CN ISSN 0834-1915) **3800,** 1746
Canadian Association for Israel Philately Bulletin *see* C.A.F.I.P. Bulletin **3750**
Canadian Association for Laboratory Animal Science Newsletter. (CN ISSN 0045-4354) **3258**
Canadian Association for Studies in Educational Administration Newsletter *see* C A S E A - A C E A S Newsletter **1725**
Canadian Association for University Continuing Education Bulletin *see* C A U C E Bulletin **1701**
Canadian Association of African Studies. Newsletter/Association Canadienne des Etudes Africaines. Bulletin. (CN ISSN 0228-8397) **1702,** 1995
Canadian Association of Anatomists. Bulletin. (CN) **434,** 3085
Canadian Association of College and University Student Services. Bulletin. (CN) **1702**
Canadian Association of Fire Chiefs Dialogue *see* C A F C Dialogue **2031**
Canadian Association of Geographers. Directory. (CN ISSN 0707-3844) **2244**
Canadian Association of Geographers. Newsletter *see* Canadian Association of Geographers. Directory **2244**
Canadian Association of Journalists Bulletin *see* C A J Bulletin **2567**
Canadian Association of Law Libraries. Newsletter *see* Canadian Law Libraries **2751**
Canadian Association of Music Libraries Newsletter *see* C A M L Newsletter **3543**
Canadian Association of Pathologists. Newsletter. (CN ISSN 0703-8372) **3085**
Canadian Association of Radiologists. Journal/Association Canadienne des Radiologistes. Journal. (CN ISSN 0008-2902) **3357**
Canadian Association of Retired Persons News *see* C A R P News **2271**

Canadian Association of Slavists Newsletter. (CN ISSN 0381-6133) **2504,** 2808, 4368
Canadian Association of University Business Officers. Bulletin. (CN ISSN 0316-4543) **1702,** 1005
Canadian Association of University Research Administrators. Bulletin. (CN ISSN 0707-7955) **1702,** 1005
Canadian Association of University Research Administrators. Research Bulletin *see* Canadian Association of University Research Administrators. Bulletin **1702**
Canadian Association of University Teachers Bulletin *see* C A U T Bulletin **1701**
Canadian Athletic Director and Coach. (CN ISSN 0045-4427) **4468,** 1620
Canadian Author & Bookman. (CN ISSN 0008-2937) **4124,** 2902
Canadian Authors Association Newsline.(CN) **2902,** 4124
Canadian Auto Review. (CN) **4686**
Canadian Automobile Association. Annual Report. (CN ISSN 0707-624X) **4686**
Canadian Automobile Association. C A A Public Policy. (CN) **4686**
Canadian Automobile Association. Policies and Resolutions *see* Canadian Automobile Association. Statement of Policy **4686**
Canadian Automobile Association. Public Policy Newsletter *see* Canadian Automobile Association. C A A Public Policy **4686**
Canadian Automobile Association. Statement of Policy. (CN ISSN 0702-2441) **4686**
Canadian Automobile Association News and Views *see* C A A News and Views **4685**
†Canadian Automotive Aftermarket Directory - Marketing Guide. (CN) **5160**
Canadian Automotive Fleet. (CN) **4686**
Canadian Automotive Technician. (CN ISSN 1180-2065) **4686**
Canadian Automotive Trade. (CN ISSN 0008-2945) **4686**
Canadian Automotive Training *see* C A T **5156**
Canadian Autoparts Marketing. (CN) **4686,** 1035
Canadian Aviation *see* Aviation & Aerospace **47**
Canadian Aviation Historical Society Journal *see* C A H S Journal **49**
Canadian Aviation News. (CN ISSN 0829-2132) **4671**
Canadian Ayrshire Review. (CN ISSN 0008-2961) **213**
Canadian Band Association (Ontario). Newsletter. (CN) **3544**
Canadian Band Directors Association. Newsletter *see* Canadian Band Association (Ontario). Newsletter **3544**
Canadian Band Journal. (CN ISSN 0703-9077) **3544**
Canadian Banker. (CN ISSN 0822-6830) **770**
Canadian Banking Law Newsletter *see* Canadian Financial Services Alert **2610**
Canadian Bankruptcy Reports. (3rd Series). (CN ISSN 0068-8347) **770**
Canadian Baptist. (CN ISSN 0008-2988) **4232**
Canadian Bar Association. Annual Report of Proceedings. (CN ISSN 0318-4935) **2610**
Canadian Bar Association. British Columbia Branch. Program Report. (CN ISSN 0384-5753) **2610**
Canadian Bar National. (CN ISSN 0315-2286) **2610**
Canadian Bar Review. (CN ISSN 0008-3003) **2610**
Canadian Beekeeping. (CN) **82**
Canadian Beverage Review. (CN ISSN 0008-3011) **380**
Canadian Bible Society Quarterly Newsletter. (CN ISSN 0832-1590) **4167**

Canadian Biker Magazine. (CN ISSN 0820-8344) **4516**
Canadian Biochemical Society. Bulletin. (CN ISSN 0008-302X) **474**
Canadian Boating. (CN ISSN 0045-4494) **4523**
Canadian Book Prices Current. (CN ISSN 0576-470X) **4124**
Canadian Book Review Annual. (CN ISSN 0383-770X) **4124**
Canadian Books for Young People/Livres Canadiens pour la Jeunesse. (CN) **1247,** 396
Canadian Books in Print. (CN ISSN 0068-8398) **396**
Canadian Botanical Association. Bulletin.(CN ISSN 0008-3046) **498**
Canadian Broadcasting Corporation Classical Record Reference Book *see* C B C Classical Record Reference Book **3543**
Canadian Broadcasting Corporation Engineering Review *see* C B C Engineering Review **1355**
Canadian Building. (CN ISSN 0008-3070) **608**
†Canadian Building Abstracts. (CN ISSN 0008-3089) **5160**
Canadian Building Digest. (CN ISSN 0008-3097) **609**
†Canadian Building News. (CN ISSN 0045-4508) **5160**
Canadian Building Supply Dealer. (CN) **609,** 1125
Canadian Bulletin of Cardiovascular Nursing *see* Canadian Journal of Cardiovascular Nursing **3276**
Canadian Bulletin of Fisheries and Aquatic Sciences. (CN ISSN 0706-6503) **2038,** 434
Canadian Bulletin of Medical History/Bulletin Canadien d'Histoire de la Medecine. (CN ISSN 0823-2105) **3085**
Canadian Bureau for International Education. Annual Report. (CN) **1721**
Canadian Business. (CN ISSN 0008-3100) **654,** 1251
Canadian Business Aircraft Association. Communique. (CN) **4672**
Canadian Business Aircraft Association. Membership Bulletin. (CN) **4672**
Canadian Business Aircraft Association. News Brief. (CN) **4672**
Canadian Business Aircraft Association. Newsletter *see* Canadian Business Aircraft Association. News Brief **4672**
Canadian Business Aircraft Association. Newsletter *see* Canadian Business Aircraft Association. Operations Bulletin **4672**
Canadian Business Aircraft Association. Newsletter *see* Canadian Business Aircraft Association. Membership Bulletin **4672**
Canadian Business Aircraft Association. Newsletter *see* Canadian Business Aircraft Association. Communique **4672**
Canadian Business Aircraft Association. Operations Bulletin. (CN) **4672**
Canadian Business Index. (CN ISSN 0227-8669) **709,** 7
Canadian Business Journal *see* Halton Business Journal **667**
Canadian Business Law Journal. (CN ISSN 0319-3322) **2708**
†Canadian Business Law Newsletter. (CN) **5160**
Canadian Business Life. (CN) **654,** 1502
Canadian Business Review. (CN ISSN 0317-4026) **654**
Canadian C.S. Lewis Journal. (UK) **2902**
Canadian C D - R O M News. (CN) **1476**
Canadian Cable Television Association Cable Communique *see* C C T A Cable Communique **1370**
Canadian Camper. (CN ISSN 0316-280X) **4543**
†Canadian Camping. (CN ISSN 0834-325X) **5160**
Canadian Camping and R V Dealer *see* Canadian R V Dealer **4543**

Canadian Canon Law Society. (CN ISSN 0703-1963) **4258**
Canadian Cases on Employment Law. (CN) **2610**, 1063
Canadian Cases on Employment Law Reports see Canadian Cases on Employment Law **2610**
Canadian Cases on the Law of Insurance (2nd Series). (CN ISSN 0824-2585) **2610**, 2529
Canadian Cases on the Law of Torts (2nd Series). (CN ISSN 0701-1733) **2610**
Canadian Catholic Historical Studies. (CN ISSN 0827-1704) **4258**, 2308
Canadian Catholic Review. (CN ISSN 0714-7724) **4258**
Canadian Cattle Buyer. (CN ISSN 0843-9613) **213**
Canadian Center for Policy Alternatives Newsletter see C C P A Newsletter **4055**
Canadian Ceramic Society. Journal. (CN ISSN 0068-8444) **1161**
Canadian Ceramics Quarterly see Canadian Ceramic Society. Journal **1161**
Canadian Certified General Accountants' Research Foundation. Study Papers. (CN) **748**, 903
Canadian Charolais Banner see Charolais Banner **214**
Canadian Charter of Rights Annotated. (CN) **2610**
Canadian Charter of Rights Decisions. (CN ISSN 0821-719X) **2610**
Canadian Chartered Accountant see C A Magazine **748**
†Canadian Chemical Industry: A Corpus Survey. (CN) **5160**
Canadian Chemical News/Actualite Chimique Canadienne. (CN ISSN 0823-5228) **1171**, 1848
Canadian Chemical, Pharmaceutical and Product Directory. (CN ISSN 0068-8452) **1125**
Canadian Chemical Processing see Process Industries Canada **1859**
Canadian Chess Chat. (CN ISSN 0045-4540) **4468**
Canadian Childbirth Educator. (CN) **3276**
Canadian Children's Annual. (CN ISSN 0316-8484) **1251**
Canadian Children's Literature see C C L **4124**
Canadian Chiropractic Association. Journal. (CN ISSN 0008-3194) **3213**
Canadian Chronicle see International Wildlife (Canadian Edition) **1490**
Canadian Church Historical Society Journal. (CN ISSN 0008-3208) **4167**, 2308
Canadian Churchman see Anglican Journal **4229**
Canadian Circulation of U S Magazines. (US) **40**
Canadian Circulations Audit Board, Inc. Circulate see C C A B Circulate **29**
Canadian Circumpolar Library. Bulletin. (CN) **2267**, 396, 4368
†Canadian Circumpolar Library. Miscellaneous Publications. (CN) **5160**
Canadian Circumpolar Library. Occasional Publications Series. (CN) **2401**
Canadian Circumpolar Library. Report of Activities. (CN) **2401**
Canadian Citations. (CN ISSN 0835-9776) **2610**
Canadian Civil Aircraft Register. (CN ISSN 0527-6497) **49**, 4672
Canadian Civil Aviation. (CN ISSN 0826-6026) **4663**, 4672
Canadian Clinical Laboratory. (CN ISSN 0712-6875) **3258**
Canadian Co-Operative Association. News Service. (CN) **829**
†Canadian Co-Operative Association. Working Papers. (CN) **5160**
Canadian Co-operative Wool Growers Magazine. (CN ISSN 0829-075X) **213**
Canadian Coin Box. (CN ISSN 0045-4575) **3544**

Canadian Coin News. (CN ISSN 0702-3162) **3598**
Canadian College of Health Record Administrators Progress Notes see C H R A Progress Notes **3085**
Canadian Commercial Law Guide. (CN) **2708**, 1035
Canadian Commission for Unesco. Annual Report. (CN ISSN 0317-5693) **3952**
Canadian Commission for UNESCO. Bulletin/Commission Canadienne pour UNESCO. Bulletin. (CN ISSN 0008-4557) **1620**, 3952
Canadian Communications Network Letter. (CN ISSN 0825-3021) **1371**
Canadian Communications Reports see Canadian Communications Network Letter **1371**
†Canadian Communications Reports. (CN) **5160**
Canadian Community Publisher see Publisher **4135**
Canadian Competition Policy Record. (CN ISSN 0228-1961) **2610**, 834
Canadian Composer/Compositeur Canadien. (CN ISSN 0008-3259) **3544**
†Canadian Composers Series. (CN) **5160**
Canadian Computer Dealer News. (CN) **1466**
Canadian Computer Law Reporter. (CN ISSN 0822-6709) **1390**, 2610
Canadian Computer Reseller. (CN) **1432**
Canadian Conference of Catholic Bishops. National Bulletin on Liturgy. (CN) **4258**
Canadian Conference of the Arts. Arts News. (CN ISSN 0843-9583) **320**
Canadian Conference of the Arts. Miscellaneous Reports see Canadian Conference of the Arts. Arts News **320**
Canadian Conservation Institute Technical Bulletins see C C I Technical Bulletins **1484**
Canadian Consulting Engineer. (CN ISSN 0008-3267) **1816**
Canadian Consumer. (CN ISSN 0008-3275) **1502**, 1251
Canadian Copper/Cuivre Canadien. (CN ISSN 0008-3291) **3403**
†Canadian Corporate Law Reporter. (CN ISSN 0835-9245) **5160**
Canadian Corporate Secretary's Guide. (CN) **1005**, 2610
Canadian Council of Churches. Council Communicator see Entre - Nous **4176**
Canadian Council of Churches. Record of Proceedings. (CN ISSN 0701-4309) **4167**
†Canadian Council of Professional Engineers. News Brief - Communique.(CN ISSN 0008-3313) **5160**
Canadian Council of Teachers of English. Newsletter. (CN ISSN 0705-386X) **1746**, 2808
Canadian Council of the Blind Outlook (Braille Edition) see C C B Outlook (Braille Edition) **5156**
Canadian Council of the Blind Outlook (Large Print Edition) see C C B Outlook (Large Print Edition) **5156**
Canadian Council on Animal Care. Resource see Conseil Canadien de Protection des Animaux. Ressource **230**
Canadian Council on Social Development. Annual Report - Rapport Annuel. (CN ISSN 0068-8584) **4400**
Canadian County Historical Society Bulletin. (US) **2401**
Canadian Courier. see Corriere Canadese **1998**
Canadian Courses and Seminars see Short Courses and Seminars **1027**
Canadian Criminal Cases. (CN ISSN 0008-3348) **2712**
Canadian Criminal Justice Association. Bulletin/Association Canadienne de Justice Penale. Bulletin. (CN ISSN 0843-8439) **1511**

Canadian Critical Care Nursing Journal. (CN ISSN 0826-6778) **3085**
Canadian Curling News. (CN ISSN 0045-4648) **4543**
Canadian Current Law. (CN ISSN 0835-9768) **2610**
Canadian Current Law and Canada Citations see Canadian Current Law **2610**
Canadian Current Tax. (CN ISSN 0317-6495) **1090**
Canadian Customs and Excise Reports see National Trade and Tariff Service **1101**
▼Canadian Cyclist. (CN ISSN 1180-1352) **4516**
Canadian Daily Stock Charts see Dailies **944**
Canadian Dancers News. (CN ISSN 0315-3959) **1529**
Canadian Datasystems. (CN ISSN 0008-3364) **1436**, 1390, 1448
Canadian Defence Quarterly/Revue Canadienne de Defense. (CN ISSN 0315-3495) **3453**
Canadian Dental Assistants Association. Journal. (CN ISSN 0833-8264) **3229**
Canadian Dental Association. Journal/Association Dentaire Canadienne. Journal. (CN ISSN 0008-3372) **3229**
Canadian Dental Hygienist see Canadian Dental Hygienists Association. Probe **3229**
Canadian Dental Hygienists Association. Probe. (CN ISSN 0834-1494) **3229**
Canadian Dental Management. (CN) **3229**
Canadian Dietetic Association. Journal/Association Canadienne des Dietetistes. Revue. (CN ISSN 0008-3399) **3604**
Canadian Dimension. (CN ISSN 0008-3402) **3878**
Canadian Direct Marketing News. (CN) **1035**
†Canadian Directory of Awards for Graduate Study (Year)/Repertoire Canadien des Bourses d'Etudes Superieures (Year). (CN ISSN 0711-8635) **5161**
Canadian Directory of Professional Photography. (CN) **3789**
Canadian Directory of Shopping Centres. (CN) **1035**
▼Canadian Directory of Top Computer Executives. (US) **1424**
Canadian Do-It-Yourself Magazine see Select Homes **306**
Canadian Doctor. (CN ISSN 0008-3429) **3085**
†Canadian Drama/Art Dramatique Canadien. (CN ISSN 0317-9044) **5161**
Canadian Driver - Owner see Driver - Owner **4744**
Canadian Ecumenical News. (CN ISSN 0227-8243) **4167**
Canadian Education and Research Digest see Education Canada **1628**
Canadian Education Association. Newsletter. (CN ISSN 0008-3445) **1620**
Canadian Education Association Handbook see C E A Handbook **1619**
Canadian Education Index/Repertoire Canadien sur l'Education. (CN ISSN 0008-3453) **1675**, 7
Canadian Electrical Association. Bulletin see Canadian Electrical Association. Connections **1801**
Canadian Electrical Association. Connections. (CN) **1801**
Canadian Electrical Association. Engineering and Operating Division. Transactions. (CN ISSN 0576-5161) **1883**
Canadian Electrical Distributors Association Current Annual see C E D A Current Annual **1883**
Canadian Electrical Engineering Journal see Canadian Journal of Electrical and Computer Engineering **1883**
Canadian Electronics. (CN) **1764**
Canadian Electronics Engineering see C E E **5156**

Canadian Electronics Engineering Annual Buyer's Guide. (CN ISSN 0008-3461) **1883**
Canadian Electronics Engineering Components and Equipment Directory see Canadian Electronics Engineering Annual Buyer's Guide **1883**
Canadian Emergency News. (CN ISSN 0847-947X) **2460**, 2031
Canadian Emergency Services News see Canadian Emergency News **2460**
Canadian Employment and Equality Rights. (CN ISSN 0831-4535) **1063**, 975
Canadian Employment Benefits & Pension Guide. (CN) **2529**, 2581
Canadian Employment Benefits and Pension Guide Reports see Canadian Employment Benefits & Pension Guide **2529**
Canadian Employment Law Guide. (CN) **2610**
Canadian Employment Law Today. (CN) **2610**
Canadian Employment Safety and Health Guide. (CN) **3615**, 2610
Canadian Energy News. (CN ISSN 0319-3403) **1784**, 3684
Canadian Energy Program Reporter. (CN) **1784**
Canadian Engineering & Industrial Year Book. (CN ISSN 0068-8665) **1816**, 1073
Canadian Entomologist. (CN ISSN 0008-347X) **529**
Canadian Environmental Advisory Council. Annual Review. (CN) **1945**
Canadian Environmental Advisory Council. Reports. (CN) **1945**
Canadian Environmental Control Newsletter. (CN ISSN 0318-0794) **1945**
Canadian Environmental Law. (CN) **2610**, 1945
Canadian Environmental Law News see Canadian Environmental Law Report. New Series **1945**
Canadian Environmental Law Report. New Series. (CN ISSN 0707-7874) **1945**, 2610
Canadian Environmental Mediation Newsletter. (CN ISSN 0831-4020) **1945**
Canadian Environmental Protection. (CN) **1945**, 2610
Canadian Estate Planning and Administration Reporter. (CN) **1090**
Canadian Ethnic Studies. (CN ISSN 0008-3496) **1995**
Canadian Ethnic Studies Association. Bulletin/Societe Canadienne d'Etudes Ethniques. Bulletin. (CN ISSN 0315-8705) **1996**
Canadian Facility Management. (CN) **4146**
Canadian Fact Book on Poverty/Donnees de Base sur la Pauvrete au Canada. (CN) **4400**
Canadian Family Law Guide. (CN) **2717**
Canadian Family Law Quarterly. (CN ISSN 0832-6983) **2717**
Canadian Family Physician/Medecin de Famille Canadien. (CN ISSN 0008-350X) **3086**
Canadian Far Eastern Newsletter. (CN ISSN 0045-4737) **2337**
Canadian Farm Economics. (CN ISSN 0008-3518) **148**
Canadian Federal Government Handbook. (CN) **417**, 4056
†Canadian Federation for the Humanities. Annual Report. (CN ISSN 0225-6932) **5161**
Canadian Federation for the Humanities. Bulletin. (CN ISSN 0707-8048) **2504**
Canadian Federation of Biological Societies. Newsletter. (CN ISSN 0068-8681) **434**
Canadian Federation of Biological Societies. Programme and Proceedings of the Annual Meeting. (CN) **434**
†Canadian Federation of Film Societies. Newsletter. (CN ISSN 0705-2162) **5161**

6028 CANADIAN FEDERATION

Canadian Federation of Music Teachers' Associations. News Bulletin see Canadian Music Teacher **3544**
Canadian Federation of Music Teachers' Associations. Newsletter. (CN) **3544**, 1746
Canadian Fiction. (CN ISSN 0045-477X) **2902**
Canadian Field-Naturalist. (CN ISSN 0008-3550) **4303**
Canadian Film Series. (CN ISSN 0705-548X) **3504**
Canadian Financial Institutions see Financial Observer **780**
Canadian Financial Services Alert. (CN) **2610**, 770
Canadian Firefighter. (CN ISSN 0704-6391) **2031**
Canadian Fisheries. Statistical Highlights. (CN) **2051**
†Canadian Fisherman. (CN) **5161**
Canadian Fishing Annual. (CN) **4543**
Canadian Flight. (CN ISSN 0008-3577) **49**
Canadian Florist, Greenhouse and Nursery. (CN ISSN 0008-3585) **2142**
Canadian Folk Music Bulletin. (CN ISSN 0829-5344) **3544**
Canadian Folk Music Journal. (CN ISSN 0068-8746) **3544**
Canadian Food and Packaging Directory. (CN ISSN 0068-8754) **1125**, 2063
Canadian Food Trade Directory & Buyers Guide. (CN ISSN 0833-174X) **2063**
Canadian Football League Facts, Figures and Records see C F L Facts, Figures and Records **4498**
Canadian Footwear & Leather Directory.(CN ISSN 0068-8762) **1125**, 2736, 4360
Canadian Footwear Journal. (CN ISSN 0705-1433) **4360**, 2736
Canadian Forces Base Cold Lake Courier see C F B Cold Lake Courier **3453**
Canadian Forces Base Gagetown Gagetown Gazette see C F B Gagetown Gazette **3453**
Canadian Forces Base Kingston Official Directory. (CN) **1125**
Canadian Foreign Relations. (CN) **3952**
Canadian Forest Fire Weather Index. (CN) **2097**
Canadian Forest Industries. (CN ISSN 0318-4277) **2113**
Canadian Forester. (CN) **2529**
Canadian Free Press. (CN) **1996**
Canadian Free Trader. (CN ISSN 0831-4527) **903**
Canadian Free Trader International Supplement. (CN ISSN 1183-2088) **903**
Canadian Freemason. (CN) **1296**
Canadian Friend. (CN ISSN 0382-7658) **4232**
Canadian Fruitgrower. (CN ISSN 0045-4885) **2123**
Canadian Funeral Director. (CN ISSN 0319-3225) **2119**
Canadian Funeral News. (CN ISSN 0382-5876) **2119**
Canadian Funeral Service see Canadian Funeral Director **2119**
Canadian Furniture & Furnishings Directory. (CN ISSN 0068-8789) **1125**, 2557
Canadian Furniture, Cabinetry & Woodworking Supply Directory. (CN) **1125**, 2557
Canadian Furniture, Furnishings & Woodworking Supply Directory see Canadian Furniture, Cabinetry & Woodworking Supply Directory **1125**
Canadian Garden News. (CN) **2123**
Canadian Gardening. (CN ISSN 0847-3463) **2123**
†Canadian Gas Association. Membership Directory. (CN ISSN 0315-8233) **5161**
Canadian Gas Association Directory see Directory of Natural Gas Company Operations **3684**
Canadian Gas Facts. (CN ISSN 0316-3547) **3684**, 1784

Canadian Gemmologist. (CN ISSN 0226-7446) **2563**, 1556
†Canadian Genealogist. (CN ISSN 0707-3232) **5161**
Canadian General Aviation News. (CN ISSN 0821-6673) **49**, 4672
Canadian Geographer/Geographe Canadien. (CN ISSN 0008-3658) **2244**
Canadian Geographic. (CN ISSN 0706-2168) **2176**
Canadian Geotechnical Journal/Revue Canadienne de Geotechnique. (CN ISSN 0008-3674) **1542**, 1862
Canadian German Trade. (CN) **849**, 834
Canadian Gideon. (CN ISSN 0316-2907) **4167**
Canadian Gladiolus Society. Annual. (CN ISSN 0319-1915) **2124**
Canadian Goods and Services Tax Reporter. (CN) **1090**
Canadian Government Buyer see Government Business **1040**
Canadian Government Programs and Services. (CN ISSN 0045-4893) **4056**
†Canadian Government Series. (CN ISSN 0068-8835) **5161**
Canadian Grain Commission Grain Research Laboratory. Annual Report.(CN ISSN 0317-1892) **205**
Canadian Grain Exports see Canada. Grain Commission. Economics and Statistics Division. Canadian Grain Exports **205**
Canadian Grocer. (CN ISSN 0008-3704) **2090**
Canadian Guernsey Journal. (CN) **214**
Canadian Guider. (CN ISSN 0300-435X) **1251**
Canadian Gunner. (CN ISSN 0068-8843) **3453**
Canadian H R Reporter. (CN ISSN 0838-228X) **1063**
Canadian Hackney Stud Book. (CN ISSN 0382-5795) **4532**
Canadian Hairdresser. (CN ISSN 0008-3720) **372**
Canadian Hardware, Electrical & Building Supply Directory. (CN ISSN 0456-3867) **1125**, 1883
Canadian Health Care Guild Pulse see C H C G Pulse **3276**
Canadian Health Care Management. (CN) **2529**, 3086
▼Canadian Health Case Law Digest. (CN) **3086**, 2610
Canadian Health Facilities Law Guide. (CN) **2610**, 4099
Canadian Health Insurance Facts see Canadian Life and Health Insurance Facts **2529**
Canadian Heart Foundation. Annual Report see Heart and Stroke Foundation of Canada. Annual Report **3208**
Canadian Heavy Equipment Guide. (CN) **609**
Canadian Hereford Digest. (CN ISSN 0008-3739) **214**
†Canadian Heritage. (CN ISSN 0225-1485) **5161**
Canadian High Growth Investment Letter. (CN) **941**
†Canadian Highway Carriers Guide. (CN ISSN 0702-8733) **5161**
Canadian Historical Association. Historical Booklets - Brochures Historiques. (CN ISSN 0068-886X) **2401**
Canadian Historical Association. Historical Papers. (CN ISSN 0068-8878) **2308**
Canadian Historical Association. Newsletter. (CN ISSN 0382-4764) **2308**
Canadian Historical Review. (CN ISSN 0008-3755) **2308**
Canadian Home Economics Journal. (CN ISSN 0008-3763) **2445**
Canadian Home Style Magazine. (CN) **2549**
Canadian Homebuilt Aircraft News. (CN) **49**
Canadian Horseman. (CN ISSN 0840-6200) **4533**, 4807

Canadian Horticultural Council. Annual Meeting Reports. (CN ISSN 0068-8908) **2124**
Canadian Horticultural Council. Committee on Horticultural Research. Annual Reports. (CN ISSN 0068-8916) **2124**
Canadian Horticultural History/Histoire de l'Horticulture au Canada. (CN ISSN 0828-8259) **2124**
Canadian Hospital see Leadership in Health Services **2467**
Canadian Hospital Directory/Annuaire des Hopitaux du Canada. (CN ISSN 0068-8932) **2460**
Canadian Hotel & Restaurant. (CN ISSN 0008-3801) **2472**
†Canadian Hotel & Restaurant (Annual). (CN) **5161**
Canadian Hotel and Restaurant's Product Hot Lines - Produits Vedettes see Canadian Hotel & Restaurant (Annual) **5161**
Canadian Hotel, Restaurant, Institution & Store Equipment Directory. (CN ISSN 0381-5765) **1125**, 2472
Canadian House & Home. (CN) **2445**
Canadian Housing Statistics. (CN ISSN 0068-8940) **2499**
†Canadian Human Rights Advocate. (CN ISSN 0828-7252) **5161**
Canadian Human Rights Yearbook/ Annuaire Canadien des Droits de la Personne. (CN ISSN 3940, 3878
Canadian Hungarians. see Kanadai Magyarsag **2010**
Canadian Immigration Hotline. (CN) **3980**
Canadian Importers Association. Importers' Bulletin see Importweek **911**
Canadian Income Tax Act, Regulations & Rulings. (CN) **1090**
Canadian Income Tax Research Index. (CN) **709**, 7, 2698
Canadian Independent Adjuster. (CN ISSN 0008-3828) **2529**
Canadian Independent Record Production Association Newsletter see C I R P A Newsletter **4460**
Canadian Industrial Equipment News. (CN ISSN 0008-3836) **3016**
Canadian Industrial Health and Safety News see Canadian Occupational Health & Safety News **3615**
Canadian Industrial Incentives Legislation. (CN) **2611**, 1090
Canadian Industrial Relations and Personnel Developments. (CN ISSN 0045-4966) **975**
Canadian Industrial Transportation League. Transport Info. (CN ISSN 0826-8770) **4718**
Canadian Industry Report of Fisheries and Aquatic Sciences. (CN ISSN 0704-3694) **2038**, 1603
Canadian Industry Shows and Exhibitions. (CN ISSN 0068-8967) **3391**
Canadian Information and Image Management Society. Micro Notes see Canadian Information & Image Management Society. Newsletters **2522**
Canadian Information & Image Management Society. Newsletters. (CN) **2522**
Canadian Information Processing/ Informatique Canadienne. (CN) **1448**
Canadian Information Processing Society. Computer Census. (CN ISSN 0316-8956) **1448**
Canadian Information Processing Society Review see C I P S Review **1390**
Canadian Institute Chartered Life Underwriters Comment (English Edition) see C L U Comment (English Edition) **2529**
Canadian Institute for Advanced Research in Artificial Intelligence and Robotics. (US) **1407**
Canadian Institute of Chartered Accountants. Uniform Final Examination Report. (CN ISSN 0713-357X) **749**

Canadian Institute of Chartered Accountants Dialogue see C I C A Dialogue **748**
Canadian Institute of Chartered Accountants Handbook see C I C A Handbook **748**
Canadian Institute of Food Science and Technology. Journal - Institut Canadien de Science et Technologie Alimentaires. Journal see Food Research International **2070**
Canadian Institute of Forestry. Annual Report. (CN ISSN 0068-8991) **2097**
Canadian Institute of Mining, Metallurgy & Petroleum Bulletin see C I M Bulletin **3479**
Canadian Institute of Mining, Metallurgy & Petroleum Directory see C I M Directory **3480**
Canadian Institute of Mining, Metallurgy & Petroleum Reporter see C I M Reporter **3480**
Canadian Institute of Surveying and Mapping Journal A C S G see C I S M Journal A C S G **2244**
Canadian Insurance. (CN ISSN 0008-3879) **2529**
Canadian Insurance. Annual Statistical Issue. (CN ISSN 0068-9025) **2546**
Canadian Insurance Claims Directory. (CN) **2529**
Canadian Insurance Law Bulletin Service. (CN ISSN 0068-9033) **2529**
Canadian Insurance Law Reporter. (CN ISSN 0045-4990) **2611**, 2529
Canadian Insurance Law Review. (CN) **2611**, 2529
†Canadian Intellectual Property Reports.(CN ISSN 0824-2623) **5161**
Canadian Intellectual Property Review. (CN ISSN 0825-7256) **3673**, 2611
Canadian Intelligence Service. (CN) **849**
Canadian Interiors. (CN ISSN 0008-3887) **2549**, 296
Canadian International DX Radio Club Messenger see C I D X Messenger **1355**
▼Canadian International Trade Directory. (CN ISSN 1180-0828) **903**
Canadian Intravenous Nurses Association see C I N A **3276**
Canadian Ionospheric Data. (CN ISSN 0045-5024) **1587**
Canadian Iris Society. Newsletter. (CN) **2124**
Canadian Issues/Themes Canadiens. (CN ISSN 0318-8442) **2504**, 4368
Canadian Jersey Breeder. (CN ISSN 0008-3909) **214**
Canadian Jersey Herd Record. (CN ISSN 0382-6406) **214**
Canadian Jeweller. (CN ISSN 0008-3917) **2563**
Canadian Jewellery & Giftware Directory. (CN ISSN 0068-9041) **1125**, 2281, 2563
Canadian Jewish Archives (New Series). (CN ISSN 0576-5528) **1996**, 4222
Canadian Jewish Congress. National Archives Newsletter. (CN ISSN 0824-8907) **1996**, 7
Canadian Jewish Herald. (CN ISSN 0706-280X) **1996**, 3952
Canadian Jewish Historical Society Journal. (CN ISSN 0706-3547) **1996**, 2401
Canadian Jewish News. (CN ISSN 0008-3941) **1996**, 4222
Canadian Journal of Administrative Law & Practice. (CN ISSN 0835-6742) **2611**
Canadian Journal of Administrative Sciences. (CN ISSN 0825-0383) **654**
Canadian Journal of African Studies/ Revue Canadienne des Etudes Africaines. (CN ISSN 0008-3968) **4368**

Canadian Journal of Agricultural Economics. (CN ISSN 0008-3976) 148
Canadian Journal of Anaesthesia/Journal Canadien d'Anesthesie. (CN ISSN 0832-610X) 3191
Canadian Journal of Animal Science. (CN ISSN 0008-3984) 214
Canadian Journal of Applied Spectroscopy. (CN) 3852, 1204
Canadian Journal of Applied Sport Science see Canadian Journal of Sport Sciences 4468
Canadian Journal of Archaeology. (CN ISSN 0705-2006) 268
Canadian Journal of Arms Collecting see Arms Collecting 256
Canadian Journal of Behavioural Science/Revue Canadienne des Sciences du Comportement. (CN ISSN 0008-400X) 4015, 4430
Canadian Journal of Biochemistry and Cell Biology - Revue Canadien de Biochimie et Biologie Cellulaire see Biochemistry and Cell Biology 473
Canadian Journal of Botany/Journal Canadien de Botanique. (CN ISSN 0008-4026) 499
Canadian Journal of Cardiology. (CN ISSN 0828-282X) 3205, 3258, 3376
Canadian Journal of Cardiovascular Nursing. (CN ISSN 0843-6096) 3276, 3205
Canadian Journal of Chemical Engineering. (CN ISSN 0008-4034) 1848
Canadian Journal of Chemistry/Journal Canadien de Chimie. (CN ISSN 0008-4042) 1171
Canadian Journal of Civil Engineering/Revue Canadienne de Genie Civil. (CN ISSN 0315-1468) 1863
Canadian Journal of Communication. (CN ISSN 0705-3657) 1371
Canadian Journal of Community Mental Health/Revue Canadienne de Sante Mentale Communautaire. (CN ISSN 0713-3936) 4015, 4099
Canadian Journal of Continuing Medical Education. (CN) 1702
Canadian Journal of Criminology/Revue Canadienne de Criminologie. (CN ISSN 0704-9722) 1511
Canadian Journal of Dermatology. (CN ISSN 0843-4247) 3246
Canadian Journal of Development Studies/Revue Canadienne d'Etudes du Developpement. (CN ISSN 0225-5189) 4368
Canadian Journal of Diagnosis. (CN) 3086
▼Canadian Journal of Drama and Theatre. (CN ISSN 1183-1243) 4631
Canadian Journal of Earth Sciences/Journal Canadien des Sciences de la Terre. (CN ISSN 0008-4077) 1542
Canadian Journal of Economics/Revue Canadienne d'Economie. (CN ISSN 0008-4085) 654
Canadian Journal of Education/Revue Canadienne de l'Education. (CN ISSN 0380-2361) 1620
Canadian Journal of Educational Communication. (CN ISSN 0710-4340) 1746
Canadian Journal of Electrical and Computer Engineering. (CN ISSN 0840-8688) 1883, 1417
†Canadian Journal of English Language Arts. (CN ISSN 0045-4613) 5161
Canadian Journal of Exploration Geophysics. (CN) 1587
Canadian Journal of Fisheries and Aquatic Sciences. (CN ISSN 0706-652X) 2038
Canadian Journal of Forest Research. (CN ISSN 0045-5067) 2097
Canadian Journal of Gastroenterology. (CN ISSN 0835-7900) 3266
Canadian Journal of Genetics and Cytology - Journal Canadien de Genetique et de Cytologie see Genome 543
Canadian Journal of Herbalism. (CN) 3720

Canadian Journal of Higher Education/Revue Canadienne d'Enseignement Superieur. (CN ISSN 0316-1218) 1702
Canadian Journal of History/Annales Canadiennes d'Histoire. (CN ISSN 0008-4107) 2308
Canadian Journal of History of Sport/Revue Canadienne de l'Histoire des Sports. (CN) 4468, 1620
Canadian Journal of Hospital Pharmacy.(CN ISSN 0008-4123) 3720, 2460
Canadian Journal of Infection Control see Canadian Journal of Infectious Diseases 3218
▼Canadian Journal of Infectious Diseases. (CN) 3218
▼Canadian Journal of Infectious Diseases. (CN) 3218
Canadian Journal of Insurance Law. (CN ISSN 0822-109X) 2529, 2611
Canadian Journal of Irish Studies. (CN ISSN 0703-1459) 2504, 1996, 2902
Canadian Journal of Italian Studies. (CN ISSN 0705-3002) 2903, 2355, 3763
Canadian Journal of Law & Jurisprudence. (CN ISSN 0703-900X) 2611
Canadian Journal of Law and Society/Revue Canadienne de Droit et Societe. (CN ISSN 0829-3201) 2611, 4430
Canadian Journal of Life Insurance. (CN ISSN 0706-5582) 2529
Canadian Journal of Linguistics/Revue Canadienne de Linguistique. (CN ISSN 0008-4131) 2808
Canadian Journal of Marketing Research. (CN ISSN 0829-4836) 1035
Canadian Journal of Mathematics/Journal Canadien de Mathematiques.(CN ISSN 0008-414X) 3031
Canadian Journal of Medical Radiation Technology/Journal Canadien des Techniques en Radiation Medicale. (CN ISSN 0820-5930) 3357
Canadian Journal of Medical Technology. (CN ISSN 0008-4158) 3258
Canadian Journal of Microbiology/Journal Canadien de Microbiologie. (CN ISSN 0008-4166) 550
Canadian Journal of Native Education. (CN ISSN 0710-1481) 1620, 1996
Canadian Journal of Netherlandic Studies/Revue Canadienne d'Etudes Neerlandaises. (CN ISSN 0225-0500) 2903, 320, 2355
Canadian Journal of Neurological Sciences. (CN ISSN 0317-1671) 3333
Canadian Journal of Nursing Administration. (CN ISSN 0838-2948) 3276
Canadian Journal of Nursing Research/Revue Canadienne de Recherche en Sciences Infirmieres. (CN ISSN 3276
Canadian Journal of Ob-Gyn see Canadian Journal of Ob-Gyn & Women's Health Care 3290
Canadian Journal of Ob-Gyn & Women's Health Care. (CN ISSN 1183-2517) 3290
Canadian Journal of Occupational Therapy/Revue Canadienne d'Ergotherapie. (CN ISSN 0008-4174) 3086
Canadian Journal of Operational Research and Information Processing see I N F O R Journal 1451
Canadian Journal of Ophthalmology/Journal Canadien d'Ophtalmologie. (CN ISSN 0008-4182) 3299
Canadian Journal of Optometry/Revue Canadienne d'Optometrie. (CN ISSN 0045-5075) 3299
Canadian Journal of Otolaryngology see Journal of Otolaryngology 3315
Canadian Journal of Pediatrics. (CN ISSN 0843-4263) 3319
Canadian Journal of Philosophy. (CN ISSN 0045-5091) 3763

Canadian Journal of Physics/Journal Canadien de Physique. (CN ISSN 0008-4204) 3815
Canadian Journal of Physiology and Pharmacology/Journal Canadien de Physiologie et Pharmacologie. (CN ISSN 0008-4212) 570, 3720
Canadian Journal of Plant Pathology. (CN ISSN 0706-0661) 499, 522
Canadian Journal of Plant Science. (CN ISSN 0008-4220) 499
Canadian Journal of Political & Social Theory/Revue Canadienne de Theorie Politique et Sociale. (CN ISSN 0380-9420) 3878, 4430
Canadian Journal of Political Science/Revue Canadienne de Science Politique. (CN ISSN 0008-4239) 3878
Canadian Journal of Program Evaluation/Revue Canadienne d'Evaluation de Programme. (CN ISSN 0834-1516) 1005
†Canadian Journal of Psychiatric Nursing. (CN ISSN 0008-4247) 5161
Canadian Journal of Psychiatry/Revue Canadienne de Psychiatrie. (CN ISSN 0706-7437) 3333
Canadian Journal of Psychology/Revue Canadienne de Psychologie. (CN ISSN 0008-4255) 4015
Canadian Journal of Public Health. (CN ISSN 0008-4263) 4099
Canadian Journal of Radiography, Radiation Therapy, Nuclear Medicine see Canadian Journal of Medical Radiation Technology 3357
Canadian Journal of Regional Science/Revue Canadienne des Sciences Regionales. (CN ISSN 0705-4580) 889, 927
Canadian Journal of Remote Sensing. (CN) 49, 1332
Canadian Journal of Social Work Education see Canadian Social Work Review 4400
Canadian Journal of Sociology/Cahiers Canadiens de Sociologie. (CN ISSN 0318-6431) 4430
Canadian Journal of Soil Science. (CN ISSN 0008-4271) 172
Canadian Journal of Special Education. (CN) 1734
Canadian Journal of Spectroscopy see Canadian Journal of Applied Spectroscopy 3852
Canadian Journal of Sport Sciences/Revue Canadienne des Sciences du Sport. (US ISSN 0833-1235) 4468, 3371
Canadian Journal of Statistics/Revue Canadienne de Statistique. (CN ISSN 0319-5724) 4567
Canadian Journal of Surgery/Journal Canadien de Chirurgie. (CN ISSN 0008-428X) 3376
Canadian Journal of University Continuing Education. (CN ISSN 0318-9090) 1702, 1682
Canadian Journal of Veterinary Research/Revue Canadienne de Recherche Veterinaire. (CN ISSN 0830-9000) 4807, 3086
Canadian Journal of Women and the Law/Revue Femmes et Droit. (CN ISSN 0832-8781) 2611, 4858
Canadian Journal of Zoology/Journal Canadien de Zoologie. (CN ISSN 0008-4301) 580
Canadian Journal on Aging/Revue Canadienne du Vieillissement. (CN ISSN 0714-9808) 2271
Canadian Key Business Directory. (CN ISSN 0315-0879) 1126
Canadian Laboratory see Canadian Clinical Laboratory 3258
Canadian Labour Law Reporter. (CN ISSN 0008-4328) 975, 2611
Canadian Labour - Monde Syndical see C L C Today 974
Canadian Labour Relations Board Reports. (CN ISSN 0317-0535) 975, 2611
Canadian Labour Terms. (CN ISSN 0068-905X) 975
Canadian Lacombe Breeders Association. Newsletter. (CN ISSN 0008-4344) 214

CANADIAN MEDICAL 6029

Canadian Ladies' Golf Association. Year Book. (CN ISSN 0084-8565) 4502
Canadian Law Libraries/Bibliotheques de Droit Canadiennes. (CN ISSN 1180-176X) 2751, 2611
Canadian Law List. (CN ISSN 0084-8573) 2611
Canadian Lawyer. (CN ISSN 0703-2129) 2611
Canadian Leader. (CN ISSN 0711-5377) 1233
Canadian Leathercraft. (CN ISSN 0045-5121) 353, 2736
Canadian Library Association Directory see C L A Directory 2750
Canadian Library Association Feliciter see Feliciter 2757
Canadian Library Journal. (CN ISSN 0008-4352) 2751
Canadian Library Yearbook see Directory of Libraries in Canada 2755
†Canadian Life and Health Insurance Association. Quarterly Review. (CN) 5161
Canadian Life and Health Insurance Facts. (CN ISSN 0068-9157) 2529
Canadian Life Insurance Facts see Canadian Life and Health Insurance Facts 2529
Canadian Literature/Litterature Canadienne. (CN ISSN 0008-4360) 2903
Canadian Literature Index. (CN) 2981, 7
Canadian Living. (CN ISSN 0382-4624) 2176
Canadian Living's Food Magazine. (CN) 2063
Canadian Locations of Journals Indexed for MEDLINE/Depots Canadiens des Revues Indexees pour MEDLINE. (CN ISSN 0707-7629) 3168, 7
Canadian Locksmith Magazine. (CN) 641
Canadian Machinery & Metalworking. (CN ISSN 0008-4379) 3016, 3403
Canadian Magazine Index. (CN ISSN 0829-8777) 396
Canadian Magazine Publishers Association Newsletter see C M P A Newsletter 4124
Canadian Manager. (CN ISSN 0045-5156) 1005
†Canadian Manufacturer. (CN) 5161
Canadian Manufacturers Association. President's Letter. (CN) 1073, 849
Canadian Manuscript Report of Fisheries and Aquatic Sciences. (CN ISSN 0706-6473) 1945, 1603
Canadian Maritime Bibliography. (CN ISSN 0835-6963) 4663, 2401
Canadian Market Outlook. (CN) 998, 849
Canadian Masonry Contractor. (CN) 609
Canadian Master Tax Guide. (CN) 1090
Canadian Mathematical Bulletin/Bulletin Canadien de Mathematiques. (CN ISSN 0008-4395) 3031
Canadian Mathematical Congress. Notes, News and Comments see C M S Notes 3031
Canadian Mathematical Society. Conference Proceedings. (US ISSN 0731-1036) 3031
Canadian Mathematical Society Notes see C M S Notes 3031
†Canadian Meat Council. Facts, Figures, Comment. (CN) 5161
Canadian Medical and Biological Engineering Society. Newsletter/Societe Canadienne de Genie Biomedical. Bulletin. (CN ISSN 0384-1820) 3086, 3258
Canadian Medical Association Journal/Association des Medicins du Canada. Journal. (CN ISSN 0008-4409) 3086
Canadian Medical Directory. (CN ISSN 0068-9203) 3086

Canadian Mental Health Association. Annual Report/Association Canadienne pour la Sante Mentale. Rapport Annuel. (CN ISSN 0068-9211) **4015, 4099**
Canadian Messenger. (CN) **4258**
Canadian Messenger of the Sacred Heart. (CN ISSN 0820-554X) **4281**
Canadian Metallurgical Quarterly. (US ISSN 0008-4433) **3403**
Canadian Meteorological and Oceanographic Society. Annual Congress. (CN) **3434**
Canadian Meteorological and Oceanographic Society. Climatological Bulletin. (CN ISSN 0541-6256) **3434**
Canadian Mineralogist. (CN ISSN 0008-4476) **1556, 3480**
Canadian Minerals Yearbook/Annuaire des Mineraux du Canada. (CN ISSN 0068-9270) **3480**
Canadian Mines Handbook. (CN ISSN 0068-9289) **3480**
†Canadian Mines Register of Dormant and Defunct Companies. (CN ISSN 0068-9297) **5161**
†Canadian Mines Register of Dormant and Defunct Companies. Supplement.(CN ISSN 0068-9300) **5161**
Canadian Mining Journal. (CN ISSN 0008-4492) **3480, 1556, 3615**
Canadian Mining Journal's Mining Sourcebook see Southam Mining Group's Mining Sourcebook **3496**
Canadian Mining Journal's Reference Manual & Buyers' Guide. (CN ISSN 0315-9140) **3480**
†Canadian Mining Law. (CN) **5161**
Canadian Modern Language Review. (CN ISSN 0008-4506) **2808, 1620**
Canadian Monarchist see Monarchy Canada **3908**
Canadian MoneySaver. (CN ISSN 0713-3286) **942, 1090, 1502**
Canadian Museum of Flight & Transportation. Museum Newsletter. (CN ISSN 0820-8336) **3523, 49**
Canadian Museum of Nature. Syllogeus.(CN) **4303**
Canadian Music Directory. (CN ISSN 0381-5730) **1126, 3544**
Canadian Music Educator. (CN) **3544, 1620**
Canadian Music Educators Association. Newsletter. (CN ISSN 0045-5172) **3544**
Canadian Music Teacher. (CN ISSN 0319-6356) **3544**
Canadian Music Trade. (CN ISSN 0225-9435) **3544**
Canadian Musician. (CN ISSN 0708-9635) **3544**
Canadian Muslim. (CN ISSN 0707-2945) **4218, 1996**
Canadian National Annual Report. (CN) **4648, 1361**
Canadian National Energy Forum Proceedings. (CN) **1784, 1883, 3684**
Canadian National Institute for the Blind. National Annual Report. (CN ISSN 0068-9378) **2291, 4400**
Canadian Native Law Reporter. (CN ISSN 0225-2279) **2611, 1996**
Canadian News Facts. (CN ISSN 0008-4565) **2176**
Canadian News Index. (CN ISSN 0225-7459) **2577, 7**
Canadian Notes & Queries/Questions & Reponses Canadiennes. (CN ISSN 0576-5803) **2504, 4368**
Canadian Nuclear Association. Annual International Conference Proceedings.(CN) **1804**
Canadian Nuclear Society. Annual Conference Proceedings. (CN ISSN 0227-1907) **1804**
Canadian Nuclear Society. Annual Conference Summaries. (CN ISSN 0227-0129) **1804**
Canadian Nuclear Society. Transactions see Canadian Nuclear Society. Annual Conference Summaries **1804**
Canadian Nuclear Society Bulletin see C N S Bulletin **1804**

Canadian Numismatic Journal. (CN ISSN 0008-4573) **3598**
Canadian Numismatic Research Society. Transactions. (CN ISSN 0045-5202) **3598**
Canadian Nurse see Canadian Nurse - L'Infirmiere Canadienne **3276**
Canadian Nurse - L'Infirmiere Canadienne. (CN) **3276, 4099**
Canadian Nurses Association. Entrance Requirements for Diploma Schools of Nursing and Schools of Practical Nursing see Canadian Nurses Association. Nursing Programs and Entrance Requirements at Canadian Universities **3276**
Canadian Nurses Association. Nursing Programs and Entrance Requirements at Canadian Universities. (CN ISSN 1180-4920) **3276, 1620**
Canadian Nurses Association. Nursing Programs and Entrance Requirements at Canadian Universities see Canadian Nurses Association. Nursing Programs and Entrance Requirements at Canadian Universities **3276**
Canadian Nursing Home Journal. (CN ISSN 0847-5520) **2460**
Canadian Nursing Management. (CN) **3276**
Canadian Occupational Health & Safety News. (CN ISSN 0709-5252) **3615**
Canadian Occupational Safety. (CN ISSN 0008-4611) **3615**
Canadian Occupational Safety & Health Law. (CN ISSN 0704-3724) **3615, 2611**
Canadian Office Products and Stationery. (CN ISSN 0008-462X) **1057**
Canadian Office Products Association Conversation see C O P A Conversation **1057**
Canadian Oil & Gas. (CN) **3684, 2611**
†Canadian Oil & Gas Handbook. (CN ISSN 0710-622X) **5161**
▼Canadian Oncology Nursing Journal/ Revue Canadienne de Nursing Oncologique. (CN) **3276, 3194**
Canadian Opera Company Magazine. (CN) **3544**
Canadian Opera Company News. (CN) **3544**
Canadian Opera Guild. Guild News see Overtures (Toronto) **5254**
Canadian Operating Room Nursing Journal. (CN ISSN 0712-6778) **3276, 3376**
Canadian Oral History Association. Journal. (CN ISSN 0383-6894) **2401**
Canadian Organic Growers Nition see C O G Nition **2123**
Canadian Ornamental Plant Foundation News see C O P F News **2123**
Canadian Orthopaedic Nurses Association Journal see C O N A Journal **3307**
Canadian Outlook. (CN ISSN 0829-8416) **849**
Canadian Packaging. (CN ISSN 0008-4654) **3647**
Canadian Paediatric Society. News Bulletin. (CN ISSN 0831-7682) **3319**
Canadian Pages. see Kanadske Listy **2010**
Canadian Paper Analyst. (CN ISSN 0705-6710) **3662**
Canadian Papers in Rural History. (CN) **2401, 82, 2355**
Canadian Paraplegic Association. Annual Report. (CN ISSN 0068-9424) **4400**
Canadian Parliamentary Guide (Year)/ Guide Parlementaire Canadien. (CN ISSN 0315-6168) **3878**
Canadian Parliamentary Review. (CN ISSN 0229-2548) **4056**
Canadian Patent Reporter. (CN ISSN 0008-4689) **2611, 3673**
▼Canadian Pay Equity Compliance Guide. (CN) **1063**
Canadian Payments Directories. (CN) **770**

Canadian Payroll Management Guide. (CN) **1063**
Canadian PennyMines Analyst see Canadian Resources and PennyMines Analyst **942**
Canadian Percheron Broadcaster. (CN) **214**
Canadian Periodical Index. (CN ISSN 0008-4719) **7**
†Canadian Perspective. (CN ISSN 0705-6680) **5161**
Canadian Pest Management Society Proceedings. (CN ISSN 0227-7980) **172**
†Canadian Petroleum. (CN ISSN 0008-4735) **5161**
Canadian Pharmaceutical Journal/ Revue Pharmaceutique Canadienne. (CN ISSN 0828-6914) **3720**
Canadian Philatelist. (CN ISSN 0045-5253) **3750**
Canadian Philosophical Reviews/Revue Canadienne de Comptes Rendus en Philosophie. (CN ISSN 0228-491X) **3763**
Canadian Photographer. (CN) **3789**
Canadian Physiotherapy Association. Sports Physiotherapy Division. Newsletter. (CN) **3086**
Canadian Pit and Quarry see Construction Record **1864**
Canadian Plains Bulletin. (CN ISSN 0316-0343) **4303**
Canadian Plant Biotech News. (CN) **489, 82, 2097**
Canadian Plant Disease Survey. (CN ISSN 0008-476X) **499, 82**
Canadian Plastics. (CN ISSN 0008-4778) **3861**
Canadian Plastics Directory and Buyer's Guide. (CN ISSN 0068-9459) **3861**
Canadian Poetry (London, Ont.). (CN ISSN 0704-5646) **2990**
Canadian Police Chief see Canadian Police Chief Newsletter **1511**
Canadian Police Chief Newsletter. (CN ISSN 0713-4517) **1511**
Canadian Police College. Journal. (CN ISSN 0705-8810) **1511, 1306**
Canadian Political News & Life. (CN) **3878**
†Canadian Political Science Association. Updating Theses in Canadian Political Science, Completed and in Progress. (CN) **5161**
Canadian Pool & Spa Marketing. (CN ISSN 0227-3330) **4468**
†Canadian Ports and Seaways Directory. (CN ISSN 0068-9467) **5161**
Canadian Postmaster/Maitre de Poste Canadien. (CN ISSN 0008-4794) **2581, 1352**
Canadian Power and Sail see Canadian Boating **4523**
Canadian Power Illustrated. (CN) **4523**
Canadian Practitioner and Review. (CN ISSN 0382-7453) **3086**
Canadian Prairie Lily Society. Newsletter. (CN) **2124**
Canadian Premiums and Incentives. (CN) **1035**
Canadian Printer. (CN ISSN 0849-0767) **3998**
Canadian Printer and Publisher see Canadian Printer **3998**
Canadian Prison Law. (CN) **2712, 1511**
†Canadian Pro Football. (CN) **5161**
†Canadian Process Equipment & Control News. (CN ISSN 0318-0859) **654**
†Canadian Product Law Guide. (CN) **5161**
Canadian Product Safety Guide see Canadian Product Law Guide **5161**
Canadian Programmable Control Conference and Exhibition. Conference Proceedings. (US ISSN 0829-4887) **1429**
Canadian Property Management. (CN ISSN 0834-3357) **609**
Canadian Psychological Review see Canadian Psychology **4015**
Canadian Psychology. (CN ISSN 0708-5591) **4015**
Canadian Public Administration/ Administration Publique du Canada. (CN ISSN 0008-4840) **4056**

Canadian Public Health Association Health Digest see C P H A Health Digest **3800**
Canadian Public Policy/Analyse de Politiques. (CN ISSN 0317-0861) **849**
Canadian Publishers Directory. (CN ISSN 0008-4859) **4125**
Canadian Pulp and Paper Association. Annual Newsprint Supplement. (CN ISSN 0316-4241) **3667**
Canadian Pulp and Paper Association. Annual Report. (CN) **3662**
Canadian Pulp and Paper Association. Monthly Newsprint Statistics. (CN) **3662**
Canadian Pulp and Paper Association. Pulp and Paper Report see Canadian Pulp and Paper Association. Annual Report **3662**
Canadian Pulp and Paper Association. Technical Section. Proceedings. (CN) **3662**
Canadian Pulp and Paper Association. Technical Section. Transactions see Journal of Pulp & Paper Science **3663**
†Canadian Pulp and Paper Association. Woodlands Section. Publications. (CN) **5161**
Canadian Pulp and Paper Industry see Logging & Sawmilling Journal **2116**
Canadian Quaker Historic Newsletter see Canadian Quaker History Journal **4281**
Canadian Quaker History Journal. (CN ISSN 1180-968X) **4281, 2401**
▼Canadian R & D Directory. (CN ISSN 1183-1677) **903, 2720, 4595**
Canadian R V Dealer. (CN ISSN 0710-9326) **4543**
†Canadian R V Trade. (CN ISSN 0847-9283) **5161**
Canadian Rail/Rail Canadien. (CN ISSN 0008-4875) **4708, 4648**
Canadian Railway Club. Newsletter. (CN ISSN 0226-157X) **4708**
▼Canadian Railway Modeller. (CN ISSN 1181-7909) **2434**
Canadian Real Estate. (CN) **4146**
▼Canadian Real Estate Adviser. (CN) **4146**
Canadian Real Estate Income Tax Guide. (CN) **1090, 4146**
Canadian Red Book. (CN ISSN 0045-527X) **4686**
Canadian Red Cross Blood Transfusion Service. Annual Report. (CN) **3271**
Canadian Red Cross Society. Annual Report. (CN ISSN 0068-9572) **4400**
Canadian Red Cross Society. Manitoba Division. News and Views. (CN ISSN 0700-9828) **4400**
Canadian Rehabilitation Council. Annual Report/Conseil Canadien de Readaptation. Rapport Annuel. (CN) **1734, 2283**
Canadian Rehabilitation Council for the Disabled. Annual Report see Canadian Rehabilitation Council. Annual Report **1734**
Canadian Religious Conference. Bulletin.(CN ISSN 0316-8743) **4168**
Canadian Rental Service. (CN ISSN 0383-7920) **654**
†Canadian Research. (CN ISSN 0319-1974) **5161**
Canadian Research and Development see Canadian Research **5161**
Canadian Research Institute for the Advancement of Women. Newsletter/ Institut Canadien de Recherches sur les Femmes. Bulletin. (CN ISSN 0229-7256) **4838**
Canadian Research Institute for the Advancement of Women Papers see C R I A W Papers **4838**
Canadian Resources and PennyMines Analyst. (CN) **942**
Canadian Retailer (Toronto). (CN) **1035**
Canadian Review see Canadian Market Outlook **998**
Canadian Review of American Studies. (CN ISSN 0007-7720) **2401, 2903**

CANADIAN YEARBOOK

Canadian Review of Art Education Research see Canadian Review of Art Education Research and Issues **1620**

Canadian Review of Art Education Research and Issues. (CN) **1620, 320**

Canadian Review of Comparative Literature/Revue Canadienne de Litterature Comparee. (CN ISSN 0319-051X) **2903**

Canadian Review of Sociology and Anthropology/Revue Canadienne de Sociologie et d'Anthropologie. (CN ISSN 0008-4948) **4430, 236**

Canadian Review of Studies in Nationalism. (CN ISSN 0317-7904) **2308, 2504, 4368**

Canadian Rider see Western Rider **4539**

Canadian Rights Reporter. (CN ISSN 0715-4860) **2611**

Canadian Rodeo News. (CN ISSN 0317-7785) **4533**

Canadian Roofing Contractor. (CN) **609**

Canadian Rose Annual. (CN ISSN 0068-9602) **2124**

Canadian Sailing Review/Revue Canadienne de Voile. (CN) **4523**

Canadian Sailor. (CN ISSN 0008-4972) **3453**

Canadian Sales Meetings and Conventions see Meetings & Incentive Travel **3393**

Canadian Sales Tax Reporter. (CN) **1090**

Canadian Sales Tax Reports see Canadian Sales Tax Reporter **1090**

Canadian Scene. (CN ISSN 0045-5334) **2176**

Canadian School Executive. (CN ISSN 0228-0914) **1726**

Canadian Scout Executive see Scout Executive **1244**

†Canadian Secretary. (CN ISSN 0709-5236) **5161**

Canadian Securities Law Reporter. (CN ISSN 0045-5342) **2611, 942**

Canadian Security. (CN ISSN 0709-3403) **1526**

Canadian Seed Growers Association. Annual Report. (CN ISSN 0068-9610) **172**

Canadian Self-Medication see Self-Medication **3743**

Canadian Serbian. see Kanaski Srbobran **2010**

Canadian Serials Directory/Repertoire des Publications Seriees Canadiennes. (CN ISSN 0000-0345) **2792**

Canadian Service Employee see Canada Works **2581**

Canadian Shareowner. (CN ISSN 0836-0960) **942**

Canadian Shipper. (CN ISSN **4743, 4725**

Canadian Shipping and Marine Engineering. (CN ISSN 0008-4980) **4725, 1923**

Canadian Short Story Library. (CN) **2903**

Canadian Ski Pro Canadien. (CN) **4543**

Canadian Slavonic Papers/Revue Canadienne des Slavistes. (CN ISSN 0008-5006) **2504, 2808, 4368**

Canadian Slovak. see Kanadsky Slovak **2010**

Canadian Small Business Financing and Tax Planning Guide. (CN) **1113, 1090**

Canadian Small Business Guide. (CN) **1113**

Canadian Social Studies: History and Social Science Teacher. (CN) **1746, 2308, 4368**

Canadian Social Trends. (CN ISSN 0831-5698) **4567, 2176**

Canadian Social Work Review/Revue Canadienne de Service Social. (CN ISSN 0820-909X) **4400**

Canadian Society for Cell and Molecular Biology Bulletin/Societe Canadienne de la Biologie Cellulaire et Moleculaire Bulletin. (CN ISSN 0319-1729) **523**

Canadian Society for Cell Biology Bulletin see Canadian Society for Cell and Molecular Biology Bulletin **523**

Canadian Society for Education Through Art. Annual Journal see Canadian Society for Education Through Art. Journal **1620**

Canadian Society for Education Through Art. Journal. (CN) **1620, 320**

Canadian Society for Education Through Art. Newsletter. (CN ISSN 0045-5369) **1620, 320**

Canadian Society for Horticultural Science. Journal see Canadian Society for Horticultural Science. Newsletter **2124**

Canadian Society for Horticultural Science. Newsletter. (CN) **2124**

Canadian Society for Immunology. Bulletin. (CN ISSN 0068-9653) **3184**

Canadian Society for Mechanical Engineering. Transactions. (CN ISSN 0315-8977) **1927**

Canadian Society of Biblical Studies. Bulletin/Societe Canadienne des Etudes Bibliques. Bulletin. (CN ISSN 0068-970X) **4168**

Canadian Society of Environmental Biologists Newsletter. (CN ISSN 0318-5133) **1485, 1945, 2038**

Canadian Society of Exploration Geophysicists. Journal see Canadian Journal of Exploration Geophysics **1587**

Canadian Society of Forensic Science Journal/Societe Canadienne des Sciences Judiciaires Journal. (CN ISSN 0008-5030) **2611, 1511**

Canadian Society of Laboratory Technologists. Bulletin/Association Canadienne des Technologistes de Laboratoire. Bulletin. (CN ISSN 0381-5838) **3258**

Canadian Society of Military Medals and Insignia. Journal. (CN ISSN 0701-0427) **3453**

Canadian Society of Plant Physiologists. Bulletin/Societe Canadienne de Physiologie Vegetale. Bulletin. (CN ISSN 1183-9597) **499, 82, 570, 2097**

Canadian Society of Safety Engineering Contact see C S S E Contact **3615**

Canadian Special Publication of Fisheries and Aquatic Sciences. (CN ISSN 0706-6481) **2038, 434**

†Canadian Specialty Foods Retailer. (CN) **5161**

Canadian Sport Parachuting Association CanPara see CanPara **4543**

Canadian Sportfishing. (CN) **4543**

Canadian Sporting Goods & Playthings. Directory. (CN ISSN 0316-7771) **1126, 4468**

▼Canadian Sportscard Collector. (CN) **2434, 4468**

Canadian Sportsman. (CN ISSN 0008-5073) **4533**

Canadian Stamp News. (CN) **3750**

Canadian Standards Association. Annual Report. (CN) **3445**

Canadian Standards Association. Catalogue. (CN) **3445**

Canadian Standards Association. Info Update. (CN) **3445**

Canadian Standards Association Consumer see C S A and the Consumer **3445**

Canadian Statistics Index. (CN ISSN 0832-655X) **4567**

Canadian Steam. (CN ISSN 0045-5393) **4648, 1816**

Canadian Studies. (US) **1996**

Canadian Studies in Population. (CN ISSN 0380-1489) **3980**

Canadian Studies Update. (US) **1702**

Canadian Surveyor - Geometre Canadien see C I S M Journal A C S G **2244**

Canadian Swine. (CN ISSN 0045-5423) **214**

Canadian Tax Foundation. Provincial and Municipal Finances. (CN ISSN 0317-946X) **1090**

Canadian Tax Foundation. Tax Conference. Report of Proceedings. (CN ISSN 0316-3571) **1090**

Canadian Tax Journal. (CN ISSN 0008-5111) **1090**

Canadian Tax News. (CN ISSN 0319-2431) **1090**

▼Canadian Tax Objections and Appeal Procedures. (CN) **1090, 2611**

Canadian Tax Papers. (CN ISSN 0008-512X) **1090**

Canadian Tax Reporter. (CN ISSN 0008-5138) **1090**

Canadian Taxpayer. (CN ISSN 0225-0608) **1090**

†Canadian Teachers' Federation. Bibliographies in Education. (CN) **5161**

Canadian Technical Asphalt Association. Proceedings of the Annual Conference. (CN ISSN 0068-984X) **609**

Canadian Technical Report of Fisheries and Aquatic Sciences. (CN ISSN 0706-6457) **2038, 434**

Canadian Technology Investment Letter see Canadian High Growth Investment Letter **941**

Canadian Telecom. (CN ISSN 0836-0782) **1333**

Canadian Telephone and Cable Television Journal see Cable Communications Magazine **1370**

Canadian Textile Directory. (CN ISSN 0068-9858) **1126, 4617**

Canadian Theatre Review. (CN ISSN 0315-0836) **4631**

Canadian Theosophist. (CN ISSN 0045-544X) **3763**

Canadian Theses/Theses Canadiennes. (CN ISSN 0068-9874) **396**

Canadian Thoroughbred. (CN ISSN 0830-0593) **4533**

Canadian Tide and Current Tables. (CN ISSN 0068-9882) **1603**

Canadian Tobacco Grower. (CN ISSN 0008-5189) **4643**

Canadian Token. (CN ISSN 0703-895X) **3598**

Canadian Tourist Travel Guide of Canada. (CN) **4756**

Canadian Trade & Commodity Tax Cases. (CN) **1090**

Canadian Trade and Commodity Tax Combinations see Canadian Trade & Commodity Tax Cases **1090**

Canadian Trade Index. (CN ISSN 0068-9904) **1126**

Canadian Trade Law Reporter. (CN) **2708, 903**

Canadian Training Magazine see T & D Canada: The Human Resources Development Journal **1070**

Canadian Transport. (CN ISSN 0045-5466) **4648, 2581**

Canadian Transportation see Canadian Transportation and Distribution Management **4648**

Canadian Transportation and Distribution Management. (CN ISSN 0008-5200) **4648, 1035**

▼Canadian Transportation Law Reporter. (CN) **2611, 4648**

Canadian Trapper. (CN ISSN 0317-0756) **2736**

Canadian Travel News. (CN ISSN 0319-7107) **4756**

†Canadian Travel News Weekly. (CN ISSN 0319-7093) **5161**

Canadian Travel Press see Canadian Travel Press Weekly **4756**

Canadian Travel Press Weekly. (CN ISSN 0831-9138) **4756**

Canadian Treasurer. (CN) **770**

Canadian Treasury Management Review. (CN ISSN 0829-4003) **770, 942**

†Canadian Truckers' Guide. (CN) **5161**

Canadian Underwriter. (CN ISSN 0008-5251) **2529**

†Canadian Unemployment Insurance Legislation. (CN) **5161**

Canadian Union of Public Employees. Journal see Canadian Union of Public Employees. The Public Employee **2581**

Canadian Union of Public Employees. The Public Employee. (CN) **2581, 4056**

Canadian University Distance Education Directory. (CN) **1682**

Canadian University Music Review/Revue de Musique des Universites Canadiennes. (CN ISSN 0710-0353) **3544, 1746**

Canadian University Press News Exchange see C U P News Exchange **1306**

†Canadian Urban Transit Association. Proceedings. (CN ISSN 0316-7933) **5161**

Canadian Urban Transit Association Forum see C U T A - A C T U Forum **4717**

Canadian Variety Merchandise Directory. (CN ISSN 0068-9955) **1126**

Canadian Vending. (CN ISSN 0068-5278) **1035**

Canadian Vet Supplies. (CN ISSN 0825-754X) **4807**

Canadian Veterinary Journal/Revue Veterinaire Canadienne. (CN ISSN 0008-5286) **4807**

Canadian Vocational Journal. (CN ISSN 0045-5520) **1746**

Canadian Volleyball Annual and Rule Book. (CN) **4502**

Canadian War Museum. Historical Publications. (CN) **2308**

Canadian Water and Wastewater Association. Bulletin/Association Canadienne des Eaux Potables et Usees. Bulletin. (CN) **4822**

Canadian Water and Wastewater Association. Newsletter see Canadian Water and Wastewater Association. Bulletin **4822**

Canadian Water Resources Journal/Revue Canadienne des Resources en Eau. (CN ISSN 0701-1784) **4823**

Canadian Water Well. (CN ISSN 1180-050X) **4823, 172**

Canadian Weekly Law Sheet. (CN ISSN 0008-5308) **2611**

Canadian Weekly Publisher see Publisher **4135**

Canadian Weekly Stock Charts: Mines and Oils see Weekly Stock Charts - Canadian Resource Companies **969**

Canadian Weightlifting Journal - Journal Canadien d'Halterophilie see Performance **5256**

Canadian Welder and Fabricator see Welding & Fabricating Canada **3430**

Canadian West. (CN ISSN 0829-5026) **2401**

Canadian Western Aviation News see Canadian Aviation News **4671**

Canadian Who's Who. (CN ISSN 0068-9963) **418**

Canadian Wildlife Service. Occasional Papers. (CN ISSN 0576-6370) **1485**

Canadian Wildlife Service. Progress Notes/Service Canadien de la Faune. Cahiers de Biologie. (CN ISSN 0069-0023) **1485**

Canadian Wildlife Service. Report Series. (CN ISSN 0069-0031) **1485, 434**

Canadian Woman Studies/Cahiers de la Femme. (CN ISSN 0713-3235) **4859**

Canadian Women's Periodicals Index. (CN) **4858, 7, 4861, 4861**

Canadian Women's Periodicals: Title Word Index see Canadian Women's Periodicals Index **4858**

Canadian Wood Processing. (CN) **2557**

▼Canadian Woodprocessing News. (CN) **3662**

Canadian Wool Grower see Canadian Co-operative Wool Growers Magazine **213**

Canadian Workshop. (CN ISSN 0704-0717) **2501, 639**

Canadian World Federalist/Federaliste Mondial du Canada. (CN ISSN 0382-8662) **2720, 3952**

Canadian Wrestler/Lutteur Canadien. (CN ISSN 0705-176X) **4468**

Canadian Yachting. (CN ISSN 0384-0999) **4523**

Canadian Yachting Association Newsletter see C Y A Newsletter **5157**

Canadian Yearbook of International Law.(CN ISSN 0069-0058) **2720**

CANADIANA

Canadiana. (CN ISSN 0008-5391) 396
Canadiana Authorities. (CN ISSN 0225-1574) 2751
Canadiana Germanica. (CN ISSN 0703-1599) 1996, 2401
Canadiana on Microfiche. (CN ISSN 0225-3216) 396
Canadiana Pre-1901. (CN) 396
Canadiana 1867-1900: Monographs (Microfiche Edition) see Canadiana Pre-1901 396
Canadians in the Third World see C I D A Annual Report 927
Canado-Americain. (US ISSN 0576-6478) 1996, 3952
Canal & Riverboat Monthly. (UK) 4523
Canal Society of Ohio. Newsletter. (US ISSN 0890-7137) 2401, 4725
Canal Times. (US) 4725, 2401
Canal - Verein. Mitteilungen. (GW) 2355
Canal Zone Philatelist. (US ISSN 0746-004X) 3750
Canales. (US ISSN 1042-3281) 1996
Canard Enchaine. (FR ISSN 0008-5405) 2860
Canarias Motor. (SP) 4686
Canary Islands Shipping Handbook 1983. (UK ISSN 0263-7073) 4725, 1126
Canberra and District Historical Society. Journal see Canberra Historical Journal 2344
Canberra Anthropology. (AT ISSN 0314-9099) 236
▼Canberra Cityscope. (AT) 4160
Canberra Consumer. (AT ISSN 0008-5413) 1503
Canberra Cyclist. (AT) 4516
Canberra Historical Journal. (AT ISSN 0313-5977) 2344
Canberra Linguist. (AT ISSN 0311-4627) 2808, 1996
Canberra Papers in Continuing Education. (AT ISSN 0310-1649) 1682
Canberra Survey. (AT ISSN 0045-5628) 849
Cancer. see Aizheng 3192
Cancer. (US ISSN 0008-543X) 3194
Cancer. see Syopa 3202
Cancer and Metastasis Reviews. (US) 3194
Cancer Biochemistry Biophysics. (US ISSN 0305-7232) 3194, 474, 485
†Cancer Biology Reviews. (US ISSN 0198-6473) 5161
†Cancer Calendar. (US) 5161
†Cancer Campaign. (GW ISSN 0342-8893) 5161
▼Cancer Care. (UK ISSN 0960-9768) 3194
▼Cancer Causes & Control. (UK ISSN 0957-5243) 3194
Cancer Cells. (US ISSN 1042-2196) 3194
Cancer Chemotherapy and Biological Response Modifiers. (NE) 3194
Cancer Chemotherapy and Pharmacology. (GW ISSN 0344-5704) 3194
Cancer Chemotherapy Annual see Cancer Chemotherapy and Biological Response Modifiers 3194
Cancer Communications see Oncology Research 3201
Cancer Control Journal. (US ISSN 0191-3794) 3194
Cancer Detection and Management-- Biological Markers see I C R D B Cancergram: Cancer Detection and Management - Biological Markers 3175
Cancer Detection and Management-- Diagnostic Radiology see I C R D B Cancergram: Cancer Detection and Management - Diagnostic Radiology 3175
Cancer Detection and Management-- Nuclear Medicine see I C R D B Cancergram: Cancer Detection and Management - Nuclear Medicine 3175
†Cancer Detection and Prevention. (US ISSN 0361-090X) 5161

Cancer Drug Delivery see Selective Cancer Therapeutics 3202
▼Cancer Epidemiology, Biomarkers & Prevention. (US) 3194
Cancer Facts and Figures. (US ISSN 0069-0147) 3194
Cancer Forum. (AT ISSN 0311-306X) 3194
Cancer Genetics & Cytogenetics. (US ISSN 0165-4608) 3194
Cancer Immunology, Immunotherapy. (GW ISSN 0340-7004) 3194
Cancer in Ontario. (CN ISSN 0315-9884) 3194
Cancer in Puerto Rico. (PR ISSN 0896-9035) 3194
Cancer Incidence in Slovenia. see Incidenca Raka v Sloveniji 3198
Cancer Incidence in Sweden. (SW ISSN 0069-0155) 3194
Cancer Institute Scientific Report. (JA) 3194
Cancer Investigation. (US ISSN 0735-7907) 3195
Cancer Letter. (US ISSN 0096-3917) 3195
Cancer Letters. (IE ISSN 0304-3835) 3195
Cancer Metastasis Reviews see Cancer and Metastasis Reviews 3194
Cancer News. (US ISSN 0008-5464) 3195
Cancer News Journal see Cancer Victors Journal 3195
Cancer Nursing. (US ISSN 0162-220X) 3277, 3195
Cancer Nursing News. (US) 3277, 3195
▼Cancer Prevention. (US ISSN 1043-8491) 3195
Cancer Research. (US ISSN 0008-5472) 3195
Cancer Research Campaign. Annual Report. (UK ISSN 0365-9623) 3195
Cancer Research Techniques and Applications see I C R D B Cancergram: Cancer Research Techniques and Applications 5208
Cancer Review. (US) 3195
†Cancer Reviews. (DK ISSN 0109-5668) 5161
Cancer Surveys. (US ISSN 0261-2429) 3195
Cancer Therapy and Control. (US ISSN 0896-5080) 3195
▼Cancer Therapy Reports. (US) 3195
Cancer Therapy Update. (NE ISSN 0924-6533) 3195
Cancer Treatment and Research see Breast Cancer Research and Treatment 3193
†Cancer Treatment Reports. (US ISSN 0361-5960) 5162
Cancer Treatment Reviews. (UK ISSN 0305-7372) 3195
Cancer Victors Journal. (US ISSN 0891-0766) 3195
Cancer Weekly see N C I Cancer Weekly 3200
Cancergram. (US) 3168, 7
Cancha. (VE) 4502
Canciones Cifradas - J L A. (SP) 3544
Cancro. (IT ISSN 0008-5480) 3195
Cancun, Cozumel, and Isla Mujeres. (US) 4756
Cancun Scene see Cancun Tips 4756
Cancun Tips. (MX) 4756
Candelabrum Poetry Magazine. (UK) 2990
Candian Theses on Microfiche (Supplement) see Canadian Theses 396
Candid Facts/A Propos. (CN) 3086
Candle see Good News (New Berlin) 4265
Candle (Macomb). (US ISSN 0008-5510) 2445
Candlelighters Childhood Cancer Foundation Annotated Bibliography and Resource Guide see Candlelighters Childhood Cancer Foundation Bibliography and Resource Guide 3168
Candlelighters Childhood Cancer Foundation Bibliography and Resource Guide. (US) 3168, 396, 1247

Candlelighters Childhood Cancer Foundation Progress Reports. (US) 1251, 3195
Candlelighters Childhood Cancer Foundation Quarterly Newsletter. (US) 3195, 3319
Candlelighters Childhood Cancer Foundation Youth Newsletter. (US) 3195, 1233
Candlelighters Foundation Progress Reports see Candlelighters Childhood Cancer Foundation Progress Reports 1251
Candlelighters Foundation Quarterly Newsletter see Candlelighters Childhood Cancer Foundation Quarterly Newsletter 3195
Candlelighters Foundation Youth Newsletter see Candlelighters Childhood Cancer Foundation Youth Newsletter 3195
Candour. (UK) 2861
Candy Buyers Directory. (US) 1126, 2087
Candy Dish. (US) 2087
Candy Industry. (US ISSN 0745-1032) 2087
Candy Industry Buying Guide. (US) 2087
Candy Marketer (Cleveland). (US ISSN 0886-3741) 2087
Candy Wholesaler. (US ISSN 0162-5136) 2087
Candy World Illustrated. (US) 2087, 4643
The Cane Collector's Chronicle. (US) 2434
Cane Toad Times. (AT ISSN 0155-7157) 2861
Canelobre. (SP ISSN 0213-0467) 2861
Canfield Family Association. Publication.(US) 2146
Cani, Gatti e Compagnia. (IT) 4808
Canine Chronicle. (US) 3709
†Canine Collectors Companion. (US ISSN 0748-9188) 5162
Canine Courier. (US) 3709, 1511
Canine Listener. (US) 2286, 3709
Canine Practice. (US ISSN 1057-6622) 4808
Canning and Packing see Tin International 3422
Canning Trade see Food Production - Management 2069
Cannocchiale. (IT ISSN 0008-5618) 2504
Cannon. (US) 1306, 4168
†Cannon. (CN ISSN 0711-4370) 5162
Cannons of Construction. (CN) 2611
Canoa Fluviale. (IT) 4523
Canoe. (US ISSN 0360-7496) 4523
Canoe and Kayak Racing News. (US) 4523
Canoe - Camper. (UK ISSN 0008-5626) 4524
Canoe Focus. (UK) 4524
Canoe Kayak Magazine. (FR) 4524
Canoeist. (UK ISSN 0269-9982) 4524
Canoeist Booklist. (US) 4498, 1073
Canola Digest. (CN) 172
Canola Guide. (CN ISSN 0841-209X) 82
Canoma. (CN ISSN 0319-5228) 2244
Canon Jahrbuch fuer Videofilmer. (GW ISSN 0931-1920) 3504, 1384
Canon Law Abstracts. (IE ISSN 0008-5650) 4212, 7
Canopy see Canopy International 2097
Canopy International. (PH) 2097
CanPara. (Canadian Sport Parachuting Association) (CN ISSN 0319-3896) 4543
Cansang Tongbao/Sericulture Bulletin. (CC ISSN 0258-4069) 82
Cantaclaro. (MX) 214
Canteras y Explotaciones. (SP ISSN 0008-5677) 3480, 3016
Canterbury Botanical Society. Journal. (NZ ISSN 0110-5892) 499
Canterbury Cathedral Chronicle. (UK) 4232
Canterbury Diocesan News Service. (UK ISSN 0260-9924) 4232

Canterbury Diocesan Notes see Canterbury Diocesan News Service 4232
Cantieri Strade Costruzioni. (IT) 609
Cantrills Filmnotes. (AT ISSN 0158-4154) 3504, 320
Canu Gwerin/Folk Song. (UK) 3544, 2053
Canvas. (US) 2903, 321
Canvas Products Review see Industrial Fabric Products Review 4620
†Canvass. (US) 5162
†Caorlespiaggia. (IT) 5162
Caotang - Dufu Yanjiu Xuekan see Dufu Yanjiu Xuekan 2864
Caoutchoucs et Plastiques. (FR ISSN 0035-3175) 4291, 3861
Caoyuan/Prairie. (CC ISSN 0496-3326) 2903
Cap-aux-Diamants. (CN ISSN 0829-7983) 2401
Cap Levant. (FR ISSN 0750-4160) 1296, 1251
Capa. (JA) 3789
Capacity Management Review. (US ISSN 1049-2194) 1448
Capacity Utilization Rates in Canadian Manufacturing. (CN ISSN 0700-1517) 709
Capacity Utilization Tape. (US) 770
Capaha Arrow. (US ISSN 0008-5774) 1306
Cape Breton's Magazine. (CN ISSN 0319-4639) 2401, 1996, 2053
Cape Business Enquirer. (SA) 3016
Cape Chamber of Industries Annual Report see C C I Annual Report 809
Cape Cod and Islands Atlas and Guide Book. (US) 4756
Cape Cod Business Journal. (US) 654
Cape Cod Guide. (US) 4756
Cape Cod Home & Garden. (US ISSN 1045-7771) 4756
Cape Cod Life. (US ISSN 0199-7238) 2222
Cape Cod Resort Directory. (US) 4756
Cape Herald see Community Newspapers 2216
Cape Horner Journal. (AT) 4725
Cape Horners - Australia. Newsletter see Cape Horner Journal 4725
Cape Librarian/Kaapse Bibliotekaris. (SA ISSN 0008-5790) 2751
Cape of Good Hope Imvo - News. (US) 1702, 1306
Cape Rock. (US ISSN 0146-2199) 2990, 3789
Cape Show Programme and Catalogue. (SA) 82
Cape Times Peninsula Directory. (SA) 1126
Cape Town Photographic Society Syllabus. (SA ISSN 0008-5820) 3789
Cape Verde. Ministry of Foreign Affairs. Boletim Informativo. (CV) 2169
Capell's Circulation Report. (US ISSN 0736-9077) 4125, 29
Caper Times. (CN) 1306
Capetonian. (SA) 2216
Capexil Monthly Export Bulletin see Chemicals & Allied Products Export News 903
Capilano Courier. (CN) 1306
Capilano Review. (CN ISSN 0315-3754) 2903, 321
Capital. (GW ISSN 0008-5847) 654
Capital. (II ISSN 0008-5839) 654
Capital. (IT) 654
†Capital (Denver, 1989). (US) 5162
The Capital. (US ISSN 0885-4718) 2146
Capital Adjustments. (US) 1090
Capital and Class. (UK ISSN 0309-8168) 654, 3878
Capital Changes Reports. (US ISSN 0008-5855) 1090, 942
Capital Chinese News. (CN) 1996
Capital Comments. (US) 2114
Capital Costs: Projected Power Plants (Year) see Projected Capital Costs: U S Electric Utility Plants 1802
Capital de la Poesia. (AG) 2990
Capital District Business Review. (US ISSN 0192-527X) 849
Capital Gains Tax. (AT) 1090
Capital Gay. (UK) 2451

†Capital Goods Review. (US ISSN 0008-588X) **5162**
Capital Ideas see Governors' Weekly Bulletin **3896**
Capital Improvement Project Newsletter see C.I.P. Newsletter **5157**
Capital Institute of Medical Sciences. Journal. see Shoudu Yixueyuan Xuebao **3153**
Capital Investments of the World Petroleum Industry. (US ISSN 0577-571X) **942**
Capital Journal. (US) **3878**
Capital Letter. (US) **942**
Capital Magazine. (US) **4756**
▼Capital Markets. (GR) **770**, **654**
Capital News. (AT) **3544**
Capital of Yan. see Yan Du **4393**
Capital Outlook: Tallahassee - Jacksonville. (US) **1996**
Capital P C Monitor. (US ISSN 0884-0830) **1426, 1458, 1468**
▼Capital Preservation Strategist. (US) **942**
Capital Press. (US) **82, 2097**
Capital Punishment. (US) **1511**
Capital Region Planning Commission Info see C R P C Info **2484**
Capital Source. (US) **3878**
Capital Sports Focus. (US ISSN 1041-5742) **4468, 3371**
Capital Taxes and Estate Planning Quarterly. (UK) **1090**
Capital Taxes News & Reports. (UK ISSN 0264-7834) **1090**
Capital University Law Review. (US) **1511**
▼Capitale Oggi. (IT) **2204**
Capitale Sud. (IT) **654**
Capitalism, Nature, Socialism. (US ISSN 1045-5752) **3878, 1485**
Capitalist. (II) **654**
Capitol Comedy. (US) **2861**
Capitol Government Reports Weekly. (US) **4056**
Capitol Line-Up. (US) **214, 2611**
Capitol Services, Inc. Congressional Record Abstracts: Energy Edition see C S I Congressional Record Abstracts: Energy Edition **4080**
Capitol Update. (US) **4056, 654**
Capitulo Criminologico. (VE) **1511, 2611**
Capletra. (SP) **2808**
Caponier. (US) **2401**
Capper's. (US ISSN 0892-1148) **2222**
Cappuccitti Consultants New Markets Newsletter see Italian Voice **2007**
Capricho. (BL ISSN 0008-5944) **2983**
Capricho. (MX) **2983**
Caps and Flints. (AT ISSN 0045-5695) **2434**
†Capstone Journal of Education. (US ISSN 0272-8931) **5162**
Capsule (Levittown) see C A P Sule (Levittown) **2271**
Capsule (Wyandotte). (US) **2460**
Capsule Comments see Capsule (Wyandotte) **2460**
Captain George's Penny Dreadful. (CN ISSN 0317-6193) **2861**
Captain Lillie's Coast Guide and Radiotelephone Directory. (CN ISSN 0318-3742) **4725, 1126**
Caption. (US) **1371, 1734, 2286, 3314**
Captive Insurance Company Review. (UK ISSN 0262-7701) **2529**
Car. (SA ISSN 0008-5995) **4686**
Car. (UK ISSN 0008-5987) **4686**
Car & Accessory Trader. (UK) **4686**
Car and Driver. (US ISSN 0008-6002) **4686**
Car and Driver Buyers Guide. (US) **4686**
Car and Driver Road Test Annual. (US) **4686**
Car and Driver Yearbook see Car and Driver Buyers Guide **4686**
▼Car & HiFi. (GW) **4686**
Car and Locomotive Cyclopedia. (US) **4708**
Car & Parts Annual. (US ISSN 0008-6975) **4686, 256**
Car Audio & Electronics. (US ISSN 0898-3720) **4460, 1883, 4686**
Car Audio & FM. (IT) **3544, 4686**

Car Audio Annuario. (IT) **1884, 4686**
Car Book (Year). (US ISSN 0893-1208) **1503, 4686**
Car Buyer. (UK) **4686**
Car Care Center News see Car Care Mall News **5162**
Car Care Corner Commentary. (US) **1113**
†Car Care Mall News. (US) **5162**
Car Care News. (US) **4686**
†Car Choice. (UK) **5162**
Car Collector and Car Classics. (US ISSN 0164-5552) **4686, 256**
†Car Corral. (US ISSN 1045-7216) **5162**
Car Costs. (CN ISSN 0705-1298) **4686**
Car Craft. (US ISSN 0008-6010) **4686, 4468**
Car Dealer Insider Newsletter. (US ISSN 0148-6721) **4686**
Car Exchange see Car Collector and Car Classics **4686**
Car Facts. (US) **4686**
Car Fleet Management see Company Car (Redhill) **4688**
Car Graphic. (JA ISSN 0915-1702) **4686**
Car Guraffiku see Car Graphic **4686**
Car Hi Fi. (UK) **4686**
Car Mechanics. (UK ISSN 0008-6037) **4687**
Car Numbers Magazine. (UK) **4687**
Car Owners see Motor World **4697**
Car Pages. (US) **4687**
Car Prices. (US) **4687**
Car Rental & Leasing Insider Newsletter. (US ISSN 0008-6053) **4687**
Car Road. (JA) **4687**
†Car Shows and Auctions. (US) **5162**
Car Stereo Review. (US ISSN 0894-3443) **1884, 1371**
Car Styling. (JA) **4687**
Car Top. (JA) **4687**
Car Trader. (US ISSN 1047-4404) **4687, 1035**
Car Wash Review see American Carwash Review **4679**
Cara. (IE ISSN 0008-6088) **4802**
Cara Caravan Camper. (IT) **4543**
†Carabinier de Lausanne. (SZ ISSN 0008-6096) **5162**
Carabiniere. (IT ISSN 0008-610X) **4056**
Caracas. (VE) **4756**
Caracas Stock Exchange. Annual Report. see Bolsa De Valores de Caracas. Anuario Bursatil **940**
Caracas Stock Exchange. Quarterly Bulletin. see Bolsa de Valores de Caracas. Revista Trimestral **940**
Caractere. (FR ISSN 0008-6126) **3998**
Caracteres. (FR ISSN 0008-6134) **2990**
Caravan. see Al-Qafilah **2058**
Caravan see Alive **2857**
Caravan see Coe Review **2906**
Caravan. see Al-Qafilah **3700**
Caravan. (CN ISSN 0835-2003) **4258, 1682**
Caravan see Caravan and Outdoor Life **4543**
Caravan see Caravan Magazine **4756**
Caravan & Chalet Parks Guide. (UK ISSN 0269-8730) **4756, 4687**
Caravan and Chalet Sites Guide see Caravan & Chalet Parks Guide **4756**
Caravan and Outdoor Life. (SA ISSN 0379-4636) **4543**
Caravan Bladet. (SW ISSN 0008-6169) **4543**
Caravan Business Plus Caravan Industry. (UK ISSN 0268-5558) **4756**
Caravan Buyers Manual. (AT) **4756**
Caravan Camping Directory. (AT) **1126, 4543**
Caravan Camping-Journal. (GW) **4543**
Caravan Holidays. (UK) **4756, 2484**
Caravan Industry Supplies & Services Directory. (UK) **1126, 4543**
Caravan Magazine. (UK ISSN 0268-0440) **4756**
Caravan Motorcaravan & Camping. (UK) **4543**

Caravan Notizie see Auto Caravan Notizie **4753**
Caravan Park, Camping & Backpacking Guide to Southern Africa/ Woonwapark, Kamper and Voetslaangids vir Suider-Afrika. (SA) **4543**
Caravan Sites. (UK) **4756**
Caravan Test. (AT) **4756**
Caravanier. (FR ISSN 0399-7715) **4543**
Caravaning. (GW ISSN 0008-6185) **4648**
Caravaning. (IT) **4756, 4543**
Caravanner. (US ISSN 0008-6193) **4756**
Caravanning Monthly see Caravan Magazine **4756**
†Caravel America. (IT) **5162**
Caravelle. (FR ISSN 0008-6152) **2355**
†Carbide and Tool Journal. (US ISSN 0192-8333) **5162**
†Carbohydrate Antigens. (UK ISSN 0952-0309) **5162**
Carbohydrate Chemistry see Carbohydrate Chemistry. Part 1: Mono-Di-Tri-saccharides & Their Derivatives **1216**
Carbohydrate Chemistry see Carbohydrate Chemistry. Part 2: Macromolecules **1216**
Carbohydrate Chemistry. Part 1: Mono-Di-Tri-saccharides & Their Derivatives.(UK) **1216**
Carbohydrate Chemistry. Part 2: Macromolecules. (UK) **1216**
†Carbohydrate Metabolism. (UK ISSN 0142-8470) **5162**
Carbohydrate Polymers. (UK ISSN 0144-8617) **1216**
Carbohydrate Research. (NE ISSN 0008-6215) **1217**
Carbon. (US ISSN 0008-6223) **1217, 1213**
Carbon & High Performance Fibres Directory. (UK ISSN 0268-0491) **3861, 4617**
Carbonates and Evaporites. (US ISSN 0891-2556) **1556**
Carcinogenesis. (UK ISSN 0143-3334) **3195**
Carcinogenesis. (US ISSN 0147-4006) **3195**
Carcinogenesis Abstracts see Cancergram **3168**
▼Card Collector's Price Guide. (US) **2434, 4502**
▼Card Fax. (US) **770**
Card Industry Directory. (US) **770**
Card News. (US ISSN 0894-0797) **770**
Card Player. (US) **4468**
Card Talk. (CN) **1296**
Cardamom see Spice India **122**
Cardamom Statistics. (II) **136**
Cardarelli. (IT) **3086**
Cardiac Alert. (US ISSN 0194-2557) **3800, 3205**
Cardiac Imaging Video Journal. (NE ISSN 0921-5166) **3205**
†Cardiac Impulse. (US) **5162**
Cardiac Surgery. (US ISSN 0887-9850) **3205, 3376**
Cardiff Association of Jewish Ex-Servicemen and Women see C A J E X **1995**
Cardiff Working Papers in Welsh Linguistics/Papurau Gwaith Ieithyddol Cymraeg Caerdydd. (UK ISSN 0263-0362) **2808**
Cardinal. (US) **563**
Cardinal Bea Studies. (PH) **4258**
Cardio. (US ISSN 0742-9622) **3205**
▼Cardio Intervention. (US) **3205**
Cardiologia. (IT) **3205**
Cardiologia nel Mondo. (IT ISSN 0008-6320) **3168, 8**
Cardiologie. (FR ISSN 0983-4532) **3205**
†Cardiologisch-Angiologisches Bulletin. (GW ISSN 0179-7166) **5162**
Cardiologist's Compendium of Drug Therapy. (US) **3720, 3205**
Cardiology. (SZ ISSN 0008-6312) **3205**
Cardiology. see Kardiologiya **3210**
Cardiology (Bethesda). (US) **3205**

Cardiology (Year). (US ISSN 0275-0066) **3206**
Cardiology Board Review. (US ISSN 0888-8418) **3206**
Cardiology Clinics. (US ISSN 0733-8651) **3206**
Cardiology in Practice. (UK ISSN 0262-5547) **3206**
Cardiology in Practice. (CN) **3206**
†Cardiology Product News. (US) **5162**
Cardiology Update. (US ISSN 0163-1675) **3206**
†Cardiomyology. (IT ISSN 0394-073X) **5162**
†Cardiopulmonary News and Interviews.(US) **5162**
▼Cardioscience. (IT ISSN 1015-5007) **3206**
Cardiostimolazione. (IT ISSN 0390-5403) **3206**
Cardiothoracic Surgery Series. (US) **3206, 3376**
Cardiovascular see C V **3205**
Cardiovascular and Interventional Radiology. (US ISSN 0174-1551) **3206**
Cardiovascular Clinics. (US ISSN 0069-0384) **3206**
Cardiovascular Diseases see Texas Heart Institute Journal **3212**
Cardiovascular Diseases; Current Status and Advances see Clinical Cardiology Monographs **5166**
Cardiovascular Drugs and Therapy. (US ISSN 0920-3206) **3206, 3720**
▼Cardiovascular Guidelines. (AT) **3206**
Cardiovascular News see Newspaper of Cardiology **3210**
Cardiovascular Nursing. (US ISSN 0008-6355) **3277**
▼Cardiovascular Pathology. (US ISSN 1054-8807) **3206**
Cardiovascular Pharmacology. (UK ISSN 0263-7243) **3206, 3720**
Cardiovascular Physiology. (UK ISSN 0142-8012) **570, 3206, 3371**
Cardiovascular Pulmonary Digest see C P Digest **3205**
Cardiovascular Research. (UK ISSN 0008-6363) **3206**
Cardiovascular Reviews & Reports. (US ISSN 0197-3118) **3206**
Cardiovascular Reviews & Reports (Edicion Espanola). (SP) **3206**
▼Cardiovascular Risk Factors. (SP ISSN 1130-7501) **3206**
Cardiovascular Surgery. (US ISSN 0069-0406) **3206, 3376**
Cardozo Arts & Entertainment Law Journal. (US ISSN 0736-7694) **2611, 321, 1333, 4125**
Cardozo Law Review. (US) **2611**
Cardozo Studies in Law and Literature. (US) **2611**
Cards International. (IE ISSN 0956-5558) **805**
Care and Repair. (UK) **609, 2557**
Care Connection. (CN ISSN 0843-9966) **3277**
†Care Magazine. (UK) **5162**
Care of the Elderly. (UK ISSN 0955-4262) **2271**
Care Weekly. (UK ISSN 0952-8636) **4400**
Care World Report. (US) **4400**
Career & Competition Times. (II) **3625**
Career Center Bulletin. (US ISSN 0738-7075) **3625**
Career Development Bulletin see Career Center Bulletin **3625**
Career Development for Exceptional Individuals. (US ISSN 0885-7288) **1734**
Career Development Quarterly. (US ISSN 0889-4019) **3625**
Career Directions. (US) **3625**
Career Education. (US) **1682, 3625**
†Career Education News. (US) **5162**
Career Education That Works for America. (US) **1692, 1682**
Career Focus. (US) **3625, 1996**
Career Futures Magazine. (US) **3625**
Career Guidance and Counselling see Institute of Guidance Counsellors. Journal **3628**
The Career Guide. (US ISSN 0891-0596) **3625**

6034 CAREER LETTER

Career Letter for Managers see Executive Strategies **1010**
Career Opportunities News. (US ISSN 0739-5043) **3625**
Career Options. (CN ISSN 0835-3913) **1702**
Career Pilot. (US ISSN 1048-8898) **49**
Career Planning & Adult Development Journal. (US ISSN 0736-1920) **1682**, 3625, 4015, 4400
Career Planning and Adult Development Network Newsletter. (US ISSN 0898-1353) **1682**, 3625, 4015, 4400
Career Success. (US) **3625**
Career Training see Career Education **1682**
Career Vision. (US) **1306**, 3625
Career Woman Magazine. (US ISSN 8755-9218) **4838**, 3625
Career World. (US ISSN 0361-8994) **3625**, 1682
Careers. (AT) **3625**
Careers. (US) **3625**
Careers Adviser. (UK) **3625**
Careers and Guidance Teacher see National Association of Career & Guidance Teachers. Journal **1730**
Careers & Majors. (US ISSN 1059-5856) **3625**, 1692
Careers and the College Grad. (US) **3625**
Careers & the Disabled. (US) **2283**, 1734, 3625
Careers and the Engineer. (US) **3625**, 1816
Careers and the Handicapped see Careers & the Disabled **2283**
Careers and the M B A. (US) **3625**, 654
Careers Cop: I S C O Careers Bulletin. (Independent Schools Careers Organisation) (UK) **1620**, 3625
Careers Digest. (II) **3625**
Careers Encyclopedia. (UK) **3626**
Careers Guide. (AT) **3626**
Careers in Botany. (US) **499**
Careers in Depth. (US ISSN 0069-0449) **3626**
Careers in Hospitals and Health Services in Victoria. (AT) **3626**
Careers in the Communication Arts & Sciences. (US) **3626**, 1333
Careers Journal see Careers Officer **3626**
Careers Officer. (UK) **3626**
Careers Quarterly see Careers Officer **3626**
Careers Weekly. (AT) **3626**
Careerscope. (UK) **3626**
CareerVision, Inc. The College Magazine see C V: The College Magazine **5157**
Carefree Enterprise Magazine. (US ISSN 0738-9604) **2222**
Caregiver. (US) **2271**
▼CareGiving. (US) **2271**, 4400
Caretas. (PE) **654**
Carga Util. (SP) **1073**
Cargill Bulletin. (US) **172**
Cargill Crop Bulletin see Cargill Bulletin **172**
Cargo Clan. (HK) **4725**
Cargo Express. (CN ISSN 0834-9797) **4648**
Cargo Facts. (US ISSN 0278-0801) **4672**
Cargo Handling Abstracts see I C H C A Quarterly Bulletin **4664**
Cargo Network Services Focus see C N S Focus **4671**
Cargo Systems see Cargo Systems International **4648**
Cargo Systems International. (UK ISSN 0306-0985) **4648**
Cargo Tank Hazardous Material Regulations. (US) **4743**
Cargonews Asia. (HK ISSN 0252-9610) **4725**
†Cargonews Yearbook. (HK) **5162**
Cargovision. (NE) **4672**, 903, 4648
Cargoware International. (UK) **4725**
Cargoworld. (GW ISSN 0172-9314) **4725**
Carguide. (CN) **4687**
Carib-Basin Trade Update see Caribbean Trend Watch **903**
Carib Hebdo. (MQ) **2239**

Carib-Latin Energy Consultant. (TR ISSN 0253-0538) **1784**
Caribe. (US) **1996**
Caribbean (Year). (US) **4756**
Caribbean Action. (US ISSN 0890-684X) **927**
Caribbean Affairs. (TR ISSN 1011-5765) **2861**, 2239
Caribbean Agricultural Rural Development, Advisory and Training Service Technical Report see C A R D A T S Technical Report **81**
Caribbean - American Directory. (US ISSN 0275-2883) **1126**
Caribbean Archives/Archives Antillaises/Archivos del Caribe. (GP ISSN 0396-2679) **2401**, 2751
Caribbean Aviation and Tourism News/Noticiero Aeronautico y Turismo Caribense. (NA) **49**, 4756
Caribbean Aviation News see Caribbean Aviation and Tourism News **49**
Caribbean, Bermuda, and the Bahamas (Year) see Bahamas (Year) Including Turks & Caicos **4753**
Caribbean, Bermuda, and the Bahamas (Year) see Bermuda (Year) **4754**
Caribbean, Bermuda, and the Bahamas (Year) see Caribbean (Year) **4756**
Caribbean Business. (PR ISSN 0194-8326) **654**
Caribbean Business Directory. (US) **1126**
Caribbean Challenge. (JM ISSN 0008-6436) **4168**
Caribbean Chronicle see Caribbean Insight **903**
Caribbean Chronicle. (UK) **903**
Caribbean Chronicle. (VI) **3277**
Caribbean Community Secretariat CariCom Bibliography see CariCom Bibliography **5162**
Caribbean Community Secretariat Caricom Perspective see Caricom Perspective **850**
Caribbean Congress of Labour. Labour Viewpoint. (BB) **2581**
Caribbean Congress of Labour. Perspectives on Caribbean Labour see Caribbean Congress of Labour. Labour Viewpoint **2581**
Caribbean Congress of Labour. Report. (BB ISSN 0576-7547) **2581**
Caribbean Conservation Association. Newsletter see Caribbean Conservation News **1485**
Caribbean Conservation News. (BB) **1485**
Caribbean Contact. (BB) **2239**
Caribbean Dateline. (US) **942**, 849, 4756
Caribbean Development Bank. Annual Report. (BB) **770**
Caribbean Development Bank. Board of Governors. Annual Meeting of the Board of Governors: Summary of Proceedings. (BB) **770**
Caribbean Development Bank News see C D B News **769**
Caribbean Diet Digest. (VI) **3604**
Caribbean Documentation Centre. Current Awareness Bulletin. (UN ISSN 0251-9089) **396**
†Caribbean Economic Almanac. (TR ISSN 0069-0481) **5162**
Caribbean Environment Programme News see C E P News **1944**
▼Caribbean Ethnology. (VI) **236**
Caribbean Family Planning Affiliation. Annual Report. (AQ) **596**
Caribbean Geography. (JM ISSN 0252-9939) **2244**
Caribbean Handbook. (AQ) **654**
Caribbean Insight. (UK ISSN 0142-4742) **903**
Caribbean Journal of Education. (JM ISSN 0376-7701) **1620**
Caribbean Journal of Religious Studies. (JM ISSN 0253-066X) **4168**
Caribbean Journal of Science. (PR ISSN 0008-6452) **434**, 2520, 2520, 2520
▼Caribbean Life. (US) **1996**
Caribbean Monograph Series. (PR ISSN 0069-0511) **2402**
Caribbean Monthly Bulletin. (PR ISSN 0576-7598) **2861**
Caribbean Newsletter. (BB) **1503**

Caribbean Newsletter. (US ISSN 0894-0223) **3952**, 849
Caribbean Nurses Organization. Newsletter. (US) **3277**
Caribbean Occasional Series. (PR) **2402**
Caribbean Ports Handbook. (JM) **4725**
Caribbean Quarterly. (JM ISSN 0008-6495) **2861**, 2239
Caribbean Reporter. (PR) **2472**
Caribbean Research Institute. Report. (VI) **2402**, 434, 1485
Caribbean Review. (US ISSN 0008-6525) **2861**
▼Caribbean Review of Books. (JM ISSN 1018-2926) **2903**, 4125
Caribbean Sports & Travel. (US) **4468**
Caribbean Stamp Exchange and Penpal Bulletin. (JM) **3750**
Caribbean Studies. (PR ISSN 0008-6533) **4368**, 321, 2504
Caribbean Studies (Lewiston). (US) **2239**
Caribbean Studies (New York). (US ISSN 0275-5793) **2402**
Caribbean Studies Newsletter. (US ISSN 0271-6577) **3952**, 903
Caribbean Times. (UK ISSN 0951-6379) **1996**
Caribbean Tourism. (BB) **4756**
Caribbean Tourism Statistical Report. (BB) **4756**
Caribbean Trade. (US) **903**
Caribbean Travel and Life. (US ISSN 0891-9496) **4756**
Caribbean Treasures. (US ISSN 0890-796X) **4757**
Caribbean Trend Watch. (US ISSN 0888-1065) **903**
Caribbean Update. (US ISSN 8756-324X) **903**, 850, 927
The Caribbean Writer. (VI ISSN 0893-1550) **2903**
Caribe. (CU ISSN 0864-1331) **2184**
Caribe Contemporaneo. (MX ISSN 0185-2426) **2239**
Caribe Magazine. (US) **321**
CaribeCom News. (US) **1350**
Cariboo Chilcotin Travel Guide. (CN) **4757**, 2472
Caricia. (BL) **2983**
†CariCom Bibliography. (Caribbean Community Secretariat) (GY) **5162**
Caricom Perspective. (Caribbean Community Secretariat) (GY ISSN 0254-962X) **850**
Caries Research. (SZ ISSN 0008-6568) **3229**
Carillon. (CN ISSN 0008-6576) **1306**, 2861
Carillon News. (US ISSN 0730-5001) **3544**
Carina. (GW) **1289**
Carina Burda see Carina **1289**
Carindex: Science & Technology. (TR ISSN 1011-4866) **4355**, 8, 4614
Carindex: Social Sciences and Humanities. (TR ISSN 0250-7617) **4394**, 8, 2504
Caring. (CN) **3277**
Caring see Practical Caring **4416**
†Caring (Rochester). (US) **5162**
Caring (Washington). (US ISSN 0738-467X) **3277**, 4400
Caring Community. (US) **4258**
Carinho. (BL) **4838**
Carinthia 1. (AU ISSN 0008-6606) **2355**, 2053
Caritas. (LI) **4258**
Caritas see Caritas-Zeitschrift **4400**
Caritas. (GW ISSN 0008-6614) **4400**
Caritas-Gemeinschaft. Publication. (GW) **3277**
Caritas India Bulletin. (II) **2337**
Caritas; Jahrbuch des Deutschen Caritasverbandes. (GW ISSN 0069-0570) **4400**
Caritas-Kalender. (GW) **4168**, 1780
Caritas-Korrespondenz. (GW ISSN 0008-6622) **4400**
Caritas-Zeitschrift. (AU) **4400**
Caritasschwester see Caritas-Gemeinschaft. Publication **3277**
Carl Newell Jackson Lectures. (US ISSN 0528-1458) **2053**, 4168
Carleton Germanic Papers. (CN ISSN 0317-7254) **2903**
Carleton Mathematical Series see Mathematical Preprints **3046**

Carleton-Ottawa Mathematical Lecture Note Series see Lecture Notes in Mathematics **3043**
Carleton Papers in Applied Language Studies. (CN ISSN 0824-7714) **2808**, 1746
Carleton University, Ottawa. Norman Paterson School of International Affairs. Bibliography Series. (CN ISSN 0383-2848) **3952**
†Carlsberg Research Communications. (DK ISSN 0105-1938) **5162**
Carlsbergfondet Aarsskrift. (DK) **3523**
Carlsonreport for Shopping Center Management. (US ISSN 0889-2288) **1005**, 4146
Carlyle Annual. (US) **418**, 2903
Carlyle Newsletter see Carlyle Annual **418**
Carmarthen Museum. Publication. (UK) **3523**
Carmel see Speling **4202**
Carmel. (IE ISSN 0008-6665) **4258**
Carmel in the World. (IT ISSN 0394-7742) **4258**
Carmel in the World Paperbacks. (IT ISSN 0394-7750) **4258**
Carmelite. (AT ISSN 1035-0993) **4258**
Carmelus. (IT ISSN 0008-6673) **4258**, 1620, 2308, 2328
Carn. (UK) **3952**
Carnahan Conference on Security Technology. Proceedings. (US) **1526**
Carnation Nutrition Education Series. (US) **3604**
Carne. (SP) **214**
The Carnegie. Annual Report. (US) **3523**
Carnegie Corporation of New York. Grants and Appropriations. (US) **2504**
Carnegie Council Newsletter. (US) **3952**, 3763
Carnegie Endowment for International Peace. Financial Report. (US ISSN 0094-3029) **3952**
†Carnegie Endowment for International Peace in the 1970's. (US) **5162**
Carnegie Foundation for the Advancement of Teaching. Annual Report. (US ISSN 0069-0651) **1620**
Carnegie Institute. Annual Report see The Carnegie. Annual Report **3523**
Carnegie Institution of Washington. Year Book. (US ISSN 0069-066X) **4303**
Carnegie Institution of Washington Spectra: C I W Newsletter see Spectra: C I W Newsletter **4345**
Carnegie International. (US) **3523**
Carnegie Magazine. (US ISSN 0008-6681) **321**, 2903, 3544
Carnegie-Mellon Symposia on Cognition Series. (US) **4015**, 1233
Carnegie Museum of Natural History. Annals of Carnegie Museum. (US ISSN 0097-4463) **4304**, 236, 434, 3656
Carnegie Museum of Natural History. Bulletin. (US ISSN 0145-9058) **4304**, 236, 434, 3656
Carnegie Museum of Natural History. Special Publications. (US ISSN 0145-9031) **4304**
Carnegie Quarterly. (US ISSN 0576-7954) **1620**
†Carnegie Research Papers. (UK) **5162**
Carnegie-Rochester Conference Series on Public Policy. (NE ISSN 0167-2231) **654**
Carnegie Symposium on Cognition see Carnegie-Mellon Symposia on Cognition Series **4015**
Carnet de Mode. (IT) **1289**
Carnets de l'Enfance see Assignment Children **1232**
Carnets de Zoologie see Ecozoo **582**
Carnica 2000. (SP) **214**
Carnival Currents. (US) **4757**
Carnival Pump. (US) **1162**
Carnivore. (US ISSN 0190-5724) **434**, 236, 1945
Carnivorous Plant Newsletter. (US ISSN 0190-9215) **499**
†Carnuntum Jahrbuch. (AU ISSN 0411-129X) **5162**

Carol Mull's Market Forecast see The Astro-Investor 938
Carola. (CL) 4838
Carolina Agent. (Carolinas Association of Professional Insurance Agents) (US) 654
Carolina Alumni Review. (US) 1306
Carolina Business. (US) 654
Carolina ChemTips. (US ISSN 0748-0466) 1171
Carolina Christian. (US ISSN 0008-672X) 4168
Carolina Comments. (US ISSN 0576-808X) 2402
Carolina Country. (US ISSN 0008-6746) 1884
Carolina Cruising see Coastal Cruising 4524
Carolina Farmer. (US) 82
Carolina Fish Finder Magazine. (US) 4543
Carolina Food Dealer. (US) 2063, 2090
Carolina Gardener. (US) 2124
Carolina Golfer. (US ISSN 0008-6770) 4502
Carolina Herald. (US) 2146
Carolina Highways. (US ISSN 0008-6789) 4718
Carolina Journal of Pharmacy. (US ISSN 0528-1725) 3720
Carolina Literary Companion. (US ISSN 1047-2789) 2903
Carolina Planning. (US ISSN 0164-0070) 2484
Carolina Quarterly. (US ISSN 0008-6797) 2903
Carolina Real Estate Journal. (US) 4146
Carolina Report. (US) 4056
Carolina Sportsman. (US ISSN 0008-6800) 4543
Carolina Tips. (US ISSN 0045-5865) 434, 1746
Carolina Women Today. (US) 2222
Carolinas Association of Professional Insurance Agents Carolina Agent see Carolina Agent 654
Carolinas Genealogical Society. Bulletin. (US ISSN 0363-440X) 2146
Carolinea. (GW ISSN 0176-3997) 1542, 499, 580
Carolinian. (US ISSN 0045-5873) 2222
Carolo-Wilhelmina Mitteilungen. (GW ISSN 0176-0629) 4595, 2504
Carologue. (US) 2402
Carol's Singles. (US) 4362
Carotenoids Other Than Vitamin A. (UK ISSN 0069-0732) 474
Carotte Moderne. (FR) 4643
Carousel. (US) 2903
Carpatho - Rusyn American. (US ISSN 0749-9213) 1996, 418, 2053, 2355
Carpenter. (US ISSN 0008-6843) 639, 2581
Carpenter and Joiner. (AT) 609
Carpenter and Related Family Historical Journal. (US) 2146
Carpet & Floorcoverings Review. (UK ISSN 0263-4236) 2557
Carpet & Rug Industry. (US ISSN 0192-4486) 4617, 2557
Carpet and Rug Industry Review. (US) 2556
Carpet and Rug Institute. Directory. (US) 4617
Carpet and Rug Institute. Directory and Report see Carpet and Rug Institute. Directory 4617
Carpet and Rug Institute. Review-State of the Industry see Carpet and Rug Industry Review 2556
Carpet Annual. (UK ISSN 0069-0767) 4617
†Carpet Manufacturer International. (UK) 5162
Carpet Specifier's Handbook. (US ISSN 0095-6457) 4617
Carpets. (NP) 654
Carpi Citta. (IT) 4085
Carrefour Africain. (UV) 2169
Carrefour des Metiers. (FR) 3626
Carrell. (US ISSN 0008-6894) 2751
Carriage Driving. (UK ISSN 0958-1820) 4533
Carriage Journal. (US ISSN 0008-6916) 2434

Carribean Directory see Caribbean Business Directory 1126
Carrier. (US) 1468, 1361, 1458
Carrier Pidgin. (US ISSN 0739-3474) 2808
Carrier Reports. (US ISSN 0008-6924) 4663, 770
Carrionflower Writ. (AT ISSN 0815-452X) 2903, 2990
Carroll Alumni Journal. (US) 1306
Carroll Business Bulletin. (US ISSN 0008-6932) 654
Carroll Cables. (US ISSN 0892-2152) 2146
Carroll County History Journal. (US) 2402
Carroll Studies see Lewis Carroll Society of North America. Chapbook 2982
Carrosserie. (NE ISSN 0008-6940) 4687
Carrosserie. (FR) 4687
†Carrousel. (FR ISSN 0220-6137) 5162
Carrousel Art. (US ISSN 0740-0780) 321
Carrozziere Italiano. (IT ISSN 0008-6959) 4648
Carry. (AU) 609
Cars & Car Conversions. (UK ISSN 0008-6967) 4687
Cars & Parts. (US ISSN 0008-6975) 4687, 256
Cars and Trucks see Automotive Executive 4683
Carson - Newman College, Jefferson City, Tennessee. Faculty Studies. (US ISSN 0069-0783) 1702
Carsport Magazine. (UK) 4687
Carsus Jugoslaviae. see K R S Jugoslavije 1570
Carswell's Practice Cases. (3rd Series). (CN ISSN 0706-5388) 2611
La Carta. (US) 2063, 1996
Carta Abierta. (US ISSN 0198-1021) 1996
Carta da Amazonia. (BL) 850
Carta de Arawak. (DR) 321
Carta de Archivo. (CK) 2402, 2751
Carta de Colciencias. (CK ISSN 0120-5986) 4304
Carta de Espana Emigracion. (SP) 2217
Carta de Gerencia. (CK) 1005, 2611
Carta Dominicana. (DR) 654
Carta Economica del Ecuador. (EC ISSN 0528-1865) 850
Carta Geologica de Chile. (CL ISSN 0716-0194) 1556
Carta Geologica do Brasil ao Milionesimo. (BL) 1556
▼Carta Hidrogeologica de Chile. (CL ISSN 0716-7555) 1556
Carta Informativa. (BL) 903
Carta Metalurgica. (CK) 1916
Carta Minera. (PE) 3480, 3684
Carta Semanal de Cafe. (GT) 148
Cartactual. (HU ISSN 0008-7009) 2244
Cartaz. (PO) 4757
Carte d'Identite du Senegal. (SG) 4056
Carte Scoperte. (IT) 2903
Carte Segrete. (IT ISSN 0008-7025) 2903, 321
Carteggi Umanistici. (IT) 2355
†CarTel. (US) 5162
Cartellina. (IT ISSN 1120-4621) 3544
Carter Engineers News. (US) 1816
†Carteria de Comercion Exterior. Informacao Semanal. (BL ISSN 0019-9737) 5162
Carter's Criminal Law of Queensland. (AT) 2712
Carter's Price Guide to Antiques in Australia. (AT) 256, 2549
†Cartes de Peches de Chalutiers Quebecois. Cahier Special d'Information. (CN) 5162
Cartes Postales et Collections. (FR ISSN 0183-8490) 2434
Cartes Synoptiques de la Chromosphere Solaire et Catalogues des Filaments et des Centres d'Activite. (FR) 363
Cartha. (DK) 3523
Carthage. (TI) 2332, 3878
Carthusian. (UK ISSN 0008-7033) 1306
Carti in Curs de Aparitie. (RM) 396

Carto-Philatelist. (US ISSN 0891-0758) 3750
Cartographic Information see Cartographic Perspectives 2244
Cartographic Journal. (UK ISSN 0008-7041) 2244
Cartographic Perspectives. (US) 2244
Cartographica. (CN ISSN 0317-7173) 2244
Cartographie Mondiale see World Cartography 2266
Cartography. (AT ISSN 0069-0805) 2244
Cartography and Geographic Information Systems. (US) 2244
Cartolaio. see Papeterist 3664
CartoLibraio see C L 3662
La Cartolina. (IT) 2434
Cartologica. (CN ISSN 0045-5881) 2267
Cartonnages & Emballages Modernes. (FR ISSN 0247-8390) 3648
Cartoon Art Museum Newsletter. (US) 3523, 321
Cartoon World. (US) 321, 2861
Cartoonist Profiles. (US ISSN 0008-7068) 321
†Cartoons. (US) 5162
Cartophilic Notes & News. (UK ISSN 0008-7076) 2434
†Cartwheel. (UK) 5162
Carwash Journal. (US ISSN 0008-7092) 4687
Cary Arboretum Newsletter see I E S Newsletter 1957
Caryologia. (IT ISSN 0008-7114) 523
Casa. (IT ISSN 0008-7122) 4400
†Casa. (SZ ISSN 1010-5786) 5162
Casa & Giardino. (IT) 2445
Casa Antiques. (IT) 256
Casa Claudia. (BL) 2549, 296
Casa de las Americas. (CU ISSN 0008-7157) 2861
Casa de Velasquez, Madrid. Melanges/ Casa de Velasquez, Madrid. Miscellanies. (FR ISSN 0076-230X) 321, 268, 2308
Casa de Velasquez, Madrid. Miscellanies. see Casa de Velasquez, Madrid. Melanges 321
Casa & Decoracao. (BL) 2549
Casa e Decoracao. (PO) 2557
Casa e Jardim. (BL) 2549
Casa e Jardim. (PO) 2557, 2124
Casa Editrice Dott. Antonio Milani Notiziario Bibliografico see C E D A M Notiziario Bibliografico 396
Casa Nostra. (IT) 2204
Casa Oggi. (IT) 2204
Casa Stile. (IT) 2549
Casa Vogue. (IT ISSN 0008-7173) 2549
Casabella. (IT ISSN 0008-7181) 296
Casalecchio Notizie. (IT) 4056
Casalinghi Stile see Casa Stile 2549
Casana. (IT ISSN 0008-719X) 2204
Casarredo & Contract. (IT) 2549
Casarredo International see Casarredo & Contract 2549
†Casarredo Middle East. (IT ISSN 0393-5140) 5162
Casas y Jardines. (AG ISSN 0008-7203) 2557
Casaviva. (IT) 2557
Cascade Beer News. (US) 380
Cascade Caver. (US ISSN 0008-7211) 1557
Cascade Horseman. (US) 4533
Cascade Trucker. (US) 4743
Case al Mare. (IT) 296, 2549
Case Alumnus. (US) 1306
Case Analysis. (US ISSN 0149-6948) 4368, 4015, 4430
Case and Comment (Bismarck) see Case & Counsel 4400
Case and Comment Magazine (Rochester). (US ISSN 0008-7238) 2612
Case & Counsel. (US ISSN 0008-7246) 4400
Case di Campagna. (IT) 296, 2549
Case di Montagna. (IT) 296, 2549
Case Management Advisor. (US ISSN 1053-5500) 3086
▼Case Manager. (US) 3086, 2529
Case Search Monthly. (UK) 2698
Case Studies in Cultural Anthropology. (US) 236

Case Studies in Education and Culture. (US) 1620
†Case Studies in Emergency Medicine. (US) 5162
†Case Western Reserve Journal of International Law. (US ISSN 0008-7254) 5162
Case Western Reserve Law Review. (US ISSN 0008-7262) 2612
Case Western Reserve University. Warner Swasey Observatory. Publications. (US ISSN 0160-2500) 363
Case Western Reserve University School of Dentistry: Alumni Magazine. (US) 3229
Case Western Reserve University School of Dentistry: Dental Alumni News see Case Western Reserve University School of Dentistry: Alumni Magazine 3229
†Casebook Series on European Politics and Society. (UK) 5162
Casebooks in Earth Sciences. (US) 1557
Cases and Materials on Constitutional Law. (US) 2705
Cases and Materials on the Law of the European Communities. (US) 2720
Cases and Materials on Trade Regulation. (US) 2612
†Cases to be Heard by the Supreme Court of Canada. (CN ISSN 0709-6968) 5162
†Casesamling. (DK ISSN 0107-5586) 5162
Y Casglwr. (UK) 4140, 396
Cash. (AU) 903
Cash and Carry see Checkout 1035
Cash & Carry Management. (UK) 2090
Cash & Carry Wholesaler. (UK ISSN 0262-4648) 2090
Cash Box. (US ISSN 0008-7289) 3544
Cash Flow Enhancement Report. (US ISSN 1053-0347) 749
Cash Management Digest and Analysis see Cash Management Performance Report 749
Cash Management News. (UK ISSN 0268-6635) 770, 903
Cash Management Performance Report. (US) 749, 1005
Cash Manager see Treasury Manager 801
Cash Newsletter. (US) 1113
▼Cash Rich Companies. (US ISSN 1054-9994) 942
Cash Rich Cos see Cash Rich Companies 942
The Cashew. (II ISSN 0970-2423) 172
Cashew Bulletin. (II ISSN 0008-7300) 2063
Cashew Causerie see The Cashew 172
Cashflow see Corporate Cashflow 773
Casino Chronicle. (US ISSN 0889-9797) 4468, 2472
Casino Digest. (US ISSN 8755-6103) 4468, 4757
Casino Gaming International. (US) 4468
Casino World. (US) 2472, 4757
Casopis Lekaru Ceskych. (CS ISSN 0008-7335) 3086
Casopis Matice Moravske. (CS ISSN 0323-052X) 2355, 3878
Casopis pro Mineralogii a Geologii/ Journal of Mineralogy and Geology. (CS ISSN 0008-7378) 1557
Casopis Pro Moderni Filologii. (NE ISSN 0862-8459) 2808, 2903
Casopis pro Pestovani Matematiky/ Journal for the Cultivation of Mathematics. (CS ISSN 0528-2195) 3032
Casopis za Suvremenu Povijest/ Magazine of Contemporary History. (YU ISSN 0590-9597) 2308, 2355
Casopis za Zgodovino in Narodopisje. (XV ISSN 0590-5966) 2355
Cass Library of African Studies. Africana Modern Library. (UK ISSN 0069-0880) 236
Cass Library of African Studies. General Studies. (UK ISSN 0069-0899) 2332

Cass Library of African Studies. Researches and Travels. (UK ISSN 0069-0902) **2332**
Cass Library of African Studies. South African Studies. (UK ISSN 0069-0910) **2332**
Cass Library of African Studies. Travels and Narratives. (UK ISSN 0069-0929) **2332**
Cass Library of Industrial Classics. (UK ISSN 0069-0937) **654**
Cass Library of Science Classics. (UK ISSN 0069-0945) **4304**
Cassa di Risparmio delle Provincie Lombarde Quarterly. (IT ISSN 0008-7408) **850**
Cassa di Soccorso e Malattia per i Dipendenti dell'Azienda Trasporti Municipali di Milano. Bollettino d'Informazione. (IT ISSN 0008-7416) **4401**
Cassal Bequest Lectures. (UK ISSN 0069-0961) **2903**
Cassandra. (US) **4839**, 3277
Cassava Newsletter see Yuca Boletin Informativo **130**
Cassazione Penale. (IT ISSN 0008-7424) **2612**
Casse-Tete Magazine. (FR ISSN 0224-7232) **2434**
Cassell and Publishers Association Directory of Publishing in Great Britain, the Commonwealth, Ireland, South Africa and Pakistan see Cassell and Publishers Association Directory of Publishing in the United Kingdom, Commonwealth and Overseas **4125**
Cassell and Publishers Association Directory of Publishing in the United Kingdom, Commonwealth and Overseas. (UK) **4125**
▼Cassell, Publishers Association and the Federation of European Publishers Associations. Directory of Publishing in Continental Europe. (UK) **4125**
Cassella-Riedel Archiv. (GW ISSN 0008-7440) **2188**
Cassette. (US) **3709**
Cassette Books. (US ISSN 0363-9029) **2291**, 2751
Cassette Gazette. (FR) **2903**, 3544
Cassiopeia. (CN ISSN 0715-4747) **363**
Cast Metals. (UK) **3403**
Castanea. (US ISSN 0008-7475) **499**
Castelli Romani. (IT ISSN 0391-7096) **2053**
Il Castello. (IT ISSN 0008-7491) **2204**
Il Castello di Elsinore. (IT) **4631**
Castellum. (IT) **296**
Casting Design & Application. (US) **3404**
Casting Digest/Imono Daijesuto. (JA ISSN 0019-2813) **3404**
Casting Digest. (US) **3404**
Casting Engineering see Casting World **3404**
Casting Engineering and Foundry World see Casting World **3404**
Casting, Forging & Heat Treatments. see Chutanzo, Netsushori **3404**
Casting Plant and Technology see C P & T **3403**
Casting Plant & Technology International see C P & T International **3403**
▼Casting Source Directory. (US) **1126**, 3404
Casting World. (US ISSN 0887-9060) **3404**
Castings Buyer. (UK) **3404**
Castle Dracula. (US) **3010**, 3504
Castle Lite. (US) **2402**
†Castle Lodge News and Views. (UK ISSN 0260-0544) **5162**
Castle Street Circular see Liverpool Link **4412**
Castoro Cinema. (IT ISSN 0392-4440) **3504**
Castries Catholic Chronicle see Catholic Chronicle **4258**
Castrum Peregrini. (NE ISSN 0008-7556) **2861**
Casual Living. (US) **2557**

Casualty Actuarial Society. Discussion Paper Program. (US) **2546**, 4567
Casualty Actuarial Society. Forum. (US) **2546**, 4567
Casualty Actuarial Society. Proceedings.(US ISSN 0893-2980) **2546**, 4567
Casualty Actuarial Society. Yearbook. (US ISSN 0895-6022) **2546**, 4567
Casualty Return. (UK ISSN 0268-0815) **4725**
Casualty Return Statistical Summary of Merchant Ships Totally Lost, Broken Up, Etc see Casualty Return **4725**
Casualty Simulation. (UK ISSN 0008-7580) **4099**
Casus Belli. (FR ISSN 0243-1327) **2434**, 4468
Cat. (UK ISSN 0008-7599) **3709**
Cat-a-Log. (AT) **4516**
Cat Call. (AT) **3709**
Cat Collectors. (US) **2434**, 3709
Cat Companion from Friskies. (US) **3709**
Cat Fanciers' Association. Annual Yearbook. (US) **3709**
Cat Fanciers' Magazine. (AT) **3709**
Cat Fancy. (US ISSN 0892-6514) **3709**
Cat Feet. (US) **2990**
▼Cat Lover. (US) **3709**
Cat Talk see Cat Collectors **2434**
Cat World. (US ISSN 0163-1926) **3709**
Cat World. (UK ISSN 0952-2875) **3709**
Cat World Annual. (UK) **3709**
Catacombes. (FR) **4168**, 3940
Catalan Review. (SP) **2903**
Catalan Writing. (SP ISSN 0214-3089) **2903**
Catalog Age. (US ISSN 0740-3119) **29**, 4125
†Catalog Business. (US) **5162**
▼Catalog Connection. (US) **2281**, 1284, 2557, 2563
Catalog for Government Inventions Available for Licensing. (US) **3674**
Catalog for Government Inventions for Licensing see Catalog for Government Inventions Available for Licensing **3674**
Catalog Handbook. (US ISSN 1042-6167) **1126**
Catalog Marketer. (US ISSN 0730-9937) **1035**
Catalog of Captioned Films for the Deaf.(US ISSN 0093-7215) **3504**, 2286
Catalog of Charts and Other Hydrographic Publications. see Catalogus van Nederlandse Zeekaarten en Andere Hydrografische Publikaties **4823**
Catalog of Current Law Titles. (US ISSN 1049-796X) **2792**, 2612, 2751
Catalog of Dealers' Prices for Marine Shells. (US ISSN 0084-862X) **580**
Catalog of Federal Domestic Assistance see U.S. General Services Administration. Catalog of Federal Domestic Assistance **4076**
†Catalog of Fossil Spores and Pollen. (US ISSN 0148-642X) **5163**
Catalog of Museum Publications and Media. (US ISSN 3536, 8
Catalog of Publisher Information. (US) **4125**
Catalog of U.S. Valves. (US) **1126**, 3016
†Catalog Product News. (US) **5163**
Catalog Showroom Business see C S M **1035**
Catalog Showroom Merchandiser see C S M **1035**
Catalogazione de Cimeli Geocartografici.(IT) **2244**
Cataloging & Classification Quarterly. (US ISSN 0163-9374) **2751**
Cataloging Bulletin (Edina) see Hennepin County Library Cataloging Bulletin **2760**
Cataloging Service Bulletin see U.S. Library of Congress. Cataloging Service Bulletin **2788**

Catalogo (Year) Productos del I N E G I. (Instituto Nacional de Estadistica, Geografia e Informatica) (MX ISSN 0186-0437) **8**
Catalogo Automoviles Turismos. (SP) **4757**, 4687
Catalogo Bisuteria y Bisuteros see Bisuteria y Bisuteros **2563**
Catalogo Bolaffi dei Vini Rossi d'Italia see Catalogo dei Vini d'Italia **380**
Catalogo Brasileiro de Engenharia Sanitaria e Ambiental. (BL) **1863**
Catalogo Colectivo de Libros y Monografias Economicas. (CK ISSN 0120-4564) **709**
Catalogo Colectivo de Publicaciones Periodicas Existentes en Bibliotecas Cientificas y Tecnicas Argentina. (AG) **4140**
Catalogo Colectivo de Publicaciones Periodicas Existentes en las Bibliotecas de la Universidad. (MX) **396**
Catalogo Coletivo de Publicacoes Periodicas (in Microfiches) see Catalogo Coletivo Nacional de Publicacoes Periodicas (in Microfiches) **396**
Catalogo Coletivo Nacional de Publicacoes Periodicas (in Microfiches). (BL) **396**
Catalogo Dante. (IT) **2903**, 321, 2053, 2308
Catalogo de Equipatalleres. (SP) **4687**
Catalogo de Exportadores see Repertorio de Exportadores **821**
Catalogo de Importadores see Repertorio de Importadores **821**
Catalogo de Instalaciones, Equipos y Utensilios para Ganaderia. (SP) **214**
Catalogo de Libros Antiguos y Modernos. (SP) **4140**, 8
Catalogo de Pesquisas Concluidas e Em Desenvolvimento. (BL) **1702**
Catalogo de Publicaciones Didacticas Latinoamericanas de Formacion Profesional. (UY) **1682**
Catalogo de Publicaciones Latinoamericanas Sobre Formacion Profesional. (UY ISSN 0069-1046) **1620**, 396
Catalogo degli Editori Italiani. (IT) **4125**
Catalogo dei Libri in Commercio/Italian Books in Print. (IT) **397**
Catalogo dei Periodici Italiani. (IT) **397**
Catalogo dei Vini d'Italia. (IT) **380**
Catalogo dell'Arte Italiana dell'Ottocento.(IT) **321**
Catalogo dell'Arte Moderna Italiana. (IT) **321**
Catalogo della Grafica Italiana. (IT) **321**, 3998
Catalogo della Pittura Italiana dell' Ottocento see Catalogo dell'Arte Italiana dell'Ottocento **321**
Catalogo della Scultura Italiana. (IT) **321**
Catalogo Espanol del Envase, Embalaje y Artes Graficas Aplicadas. (SP) **3648**
Catalogo Expoferro. (SP) **3404**
Catalogo Guida dell'Imballaggio (Year). (IT) **3648**
†Catalogo Ilustrado de las Plantas de Cundinamarca. (CK) **5163**
Catalogo Legale. (IT) **2612**, 654
Catalogo Motoristico. (IT) **4687**, 1126, 4743
Catalogo Nacional del Envase, Embalaje y Artes Graficas Aplicadas see Catalogo Espanol del Envase, Embalaje y Artes Graficas Aplicadas **3648**
Catalogo Nazionale Bolaffi d'Arte Moderna see Catalogo dell'Arte Moderna Italiana **321**
Catalogo Nazionale Bolaffi della Grafica see Catalogo della Grafica Italiana **321**
Catalogo Productos y Servicios del Estado de Mexico. (MX) **1126**
Catalogo Recambios y Accesorios. (SP) **4687**
Catalogo Relojes y Relojeros. (SP) **2563**
Catalogo Repertorio Macchine e Motori.(IT) **161**
Catalogo Siderurgico. (SP) **3404**

Catalogo Unificato. (IT) **903**
Catalogue Afnor (Normes Francaises). (FR ISSN 0750-7046) **3445**
Catalogue & Index. (UK ISSN 0008-7629) **2792**, 8
Catalogue Biennale Internationale de Lausanne. (SZ) **321**, 4617
Catalogue Collectif des Publications Scientifiques dans les Bibliotheques Canadiennes. see Union List of Scientific Serials in Canadian Libraries **4358**
Catalogue des Normes Francaises see Catalogue Afnor (Normes Francaises) **3445**
Catalogue des Produits Agrees Par Qualite-France. (FR ISSN 0069-1100) **834**
Catalogue: English Translations of German Standards (Year). (GW ISSN 0174-3805) **3445**
Catalogue General Classique. (FR) **3544**
Catalogue General de l'Industrie et du Commerce Automobile de Belgique. (BE) **4687**
Catalogue National du Genie Climatique-Chauffage et Conditionnement d'Air/National Catalogue of Heating and Air Conditioning/Nazionaler Katalog der Heizung und Klimatisierung. (FR ISSN 0153-999X) **2298**
Catalogue National du Traitement des Surfaces de l'Anticorrosion et des Traitements Thermiques. (FR ISSN 0396-1214) **3653**
Catalogue of American Amphibians and Reptiles. (US) **580**
Catalogue of Arabic Manuscripts in Salar Jung Museum see Concise Descriptive Catalogue of Arabic Manuscripts in the Salar Jung Museum and Library **3536**
Catalogue of Australian Brass and Concert Band Music see Catalogue of Australian Brass Music **3544**
Catalogue of Australian Brass Music. (AT) **3544**
Catalogue of Australian Choral Music. (AT) **3544**
Catalogue of Australian Keyboard Music. (AT) **3544**
Catalogue of Books Recommended for Libraries/Sentei Tosho Somokuroku. (JA) **397**
Catalogue of British Official Publications Not Published by H.M.S.O. (UK ISSN 0260-5619) **397**
Catalogue of Canadian Recreation and Leisure Research. (CN) **2738**, 4543, 4757
Catalogue of Conferences, Seminars, Workshop. (US) **1682**, 4168
Catalogue of Contemporary Welsh Music. (UK) **3544**
†Catalogue of N A L Technical Translations. (National Aeronautical Laboratory) (II ISSN 0077-2968) **5163**
Catalogue of Palaearctic Diptera. (NE) **529**
Catalogue of Persian Manuscripts in Salar Jung Museum see Concise Descriptive Catalogue of the Persian Manuscripts in the Salar Jung Museum and Library **3536**
†Catalogue of Polish Feature Films. (PL) **5163**
Catalogue of Reproductions of Paintings, 1860-1979. (UN ISSN 0069-1143) **321**
Catalogue of Solar Radiation Data. see Katalog Radiatsionnykh Dannykh **3438**
Catalogue of Statistical Materials of Developing Countries. (JA) **4567**
Cataloguing Australia. (AT ISSN 0312-4371) **2751**
Catalogus Faunae Austria. (AU) **434**
Catalogus Films en Video. (NE) **3504**, 1384
Catalogus Florae Austria. (AU) **499**, 2124
Catalogus Fossilium Austria. (AU) **434**
Catalogus Musicus. (GW ISSN 0069-116X) **3544**

Catalogus Translationem et Commentatorium. (US ISSN 0528-2594) **2981**
Catalogus van Academische Geschriften in Nederland Verschenen see Bibliografie van Nederlandse Proefschriften **391**
Catalogus van Nederlandse Zeekaarten en Andere Hydrografische Publikaties/Catalog of Charts and Other Hydrographic Publications. (NE ISSN 0920-9786) **4823**
Catalonia see Catalonia Culture **2217**
Catalonia Culture. (SP ISSN 0213-7534) **2217**
Cataluna Exporta. (SP ISSN 0069-1178) **811**
Catalunya Ayer y Hoy. (CR) **2355**
Catalysis by Metal Complexes. (NE) **1217**
Catalysis Letters. (SZ ISSN 1011-372X) **1171**
Catalysis Reviews: Science and Engineering. (US ISSN 0161-4940) **1225**, 1849
Catalysis: Science and Technology. (US) **1171**
Catalysis Today. (NE ISSN 0920-5861) **1849**, 1171
Catalyst (Amherst). (US ISSN 0008-7661) **4368**
Catalyst (Atlanta). (US ISSN 0896-7423) **2903**
▼Catalyst (Chicago). (US) **1726**
Catalyst (Des Moines). (US ISSN 0730-711X) **2751**
The Catalyst. (CN) **2176**
Catalyst (London). (UK ISSN 0144-9931) **2751**
Catalyst (Long Beach). (US) **2563**
Catalyst (Marietta). (US) **3594**, 3668, 3800
Catalyst (Melbourne). (AT) **1306**
Catalyst (Menlo Park). (US ISSN 0897-3318) **1417**, 1458, 1468, 1734
Catalyst (Montpelier). (US ISSN 0742-6534) **942**
Catalyst (New York, 1978) see Journal of Progressive Human Services **4410**
Catalyst (Philadelphia). (US ISSN 0008-767X) **1171**
Catalyst (St. Davids). (US) **4401**, 4258
Catalyst (Seattle). (US ISSN 0739-8506) **321**, 2990
Catalyst (Toronto). (CN ISSN 0824-2062) **3940**, 4430
Catalyst (Vancouver). (CN ISSN 0834-2466) **1746**, 4304
Catalyst Directory Newsletter. (US) **3594**, 1005, 1063
Catalyst for Change. (US ISSN 0739-2532) **1746**, 1726
Catalyst for Environment - Energy. (US ISSN 0194-1445) **1945**, 1784
Catalyst for Environmental Quality see Catalyst for Environment - Energy **1945**
Catalyst G C S E Science Review. (UK ISSN 0958-3629) **4304**
Catalyst Perspective see Catalyst Directory Newsletter **3594**
Catalyst: Research at the University of Calgary. (CN) **4304**
Catalysts in Chemistry. (UK ISSN 0309-5770) **1225**
†Cataract; International Journal of Cataract Surgery. (US ISSN 0740-6967) **5163**
Catastrophism and Ancient History. (US ISSN 0733-8058) **268**
Catastrophism and Ancient History. Proceedings. (US ISSN 0890-5592) **268**
Catch. (UK ISSN 0008-7696) **1746**
Catch. (NZ) **2038**
Catchword and Trade Name Index. (UK ISSN 0261-0191) **4614**, 8
Catechesi. (IT ISSN 0391-5433) **4258**
Catechist. (US ISSN 0008-7726) **4168**
Catechistes d'Aujourd'hui see Points de Repere **4195**
Catechist's Connection. (US) **4258**

Catecholamines and Adrenergic Receptors see Adrenergic Receptors **3715**
Catechumenate. (US ISSN 1040-659X) **4258**
Category Reports. (US) **2063**, 380
Catena. (GW ISSN 0341-8162) **1557**
Catena Supplement. (GW ISSN 0722-0723) **1557**
Catequetica. (SP ISSN 0528-2772) **4168**
Catering. (UK) **2472**
Catering. (SP ISSN 0214-9028) **2472**
Catering (London, 1984) see Britain's Catering Industry **2472**
Catering & Accommodation Management. (NZ) **2472**
Catering and Health. (UK ISSN 0267-3851) **3604**
Catering and Hotel News see Catering and Hotel News International **2472**
Catering and Hotel News International. (BA) **2472**
Catering & Licensing Review. (UK) **2472**
Catering Buyer. (UK ISSN 0956-9146) **2063**
Catering Industry Employee. (US ISSN 0008-7815) **2581**
Catering Management see Catering & Accommodation Management **2472**
Catering Manager's Buyer's Guide (Year) see Catering Buyer **2063**
Catering Today. (US ISSN 0884-4984) **2063**, 2472
Catering Update. (UK ISSN 0269-7696) **2472**
▼Catering World. (UK) **2472**
Catgut Acoustical Society. Journal see C A S Journal **3543**
Catgut Acoustical Society Journal see C A S Journal **3543**
Cathair na Mart. (IE ISSN 0332-4117) **2355**
Catharsis. (US ISSN 1058-6326) **2990**
Cathartic. (US ISSN 0145-8310) **2903**
Cathcart Chronicle. (SA ISSN 0008-7866) **2216**
Cathedra. (IS ISSN 0334-4657) **2428**, 2244
Cathedral. (US) **2568**, 4232
Cathedral Age. (US ISSN 0008-7874) **4232**
Cathedral College of the Laity Newsletter. (US) **4168**
Cathedrals & Monastic Buildings in the British Isles see Courtauld Institute Illustration Archives. Archive 1 **323**
▼Cather Studies. (US ISSN 1045-9871) **2903**
Cather Yearbook. (US ISSN 1048-8618) **2903**
Catheterization and Cardiovascular Diagnosis. (US ISSN 0098-6569) **3206**
The Catholic. (UK) **4258**, 4125
Catholic Activist. (US) **4258**, 3878
Catholic Advance. (US ISSN 0008-7904) **4258**
Catholic Agitator. (US ISSN 0045-5970) **4258**
Catholic Aid News. (US) **2529**, 4258
Catholic Almanac. (US ISSN 0069-1208) **4258**
Catholic Answer. (US) **4258**
Catholic Archives. (UK ISSN 0261-4316) **4258**
Catholic Archives Society Newsletter see C A S Newsletter **4257**
Catholic Audio-Visual Educators Newsletter see C A V E Newsletter **1745**
Catholic Bible Quarterly Monograph Series. (US) **4168**
Catholic Biblical Quarterly. (US ISSN 0008-7912) **4258**
Catholic Broadcasters Association. Newsletter see Unda - U S A Newsletter **1383**
Catholic Cemetery. (US) **2119**, 4258
Catholic Challenge. (US ISSN 8756-7482) **4258**
Catholic Chinese Weekly. see Kung Kao Po **4267**
Catholic Chronicle. (US ISSN 0008-7971) **4258**

Catholic Chronicle. (XK) **4258**
Catholic Commentator. (US) **4259**
Catholic Commission on Intellectual and Cultural Affairs Annual see C C I C A Annual **4257**
Catholic Counter-Reformation in the XXth Century. (FR) **4259**
Catholic Courier. (US) **4259**
Catholic Digest. (US ISSN 0008-7998) **4259**, 2222
Catholic Directory (San Diego). (US) **4259**
Catholic Directory (San Francisco). (US) **1126**, 4259
Catholic Directory for Scotland. (UK ISSN 0306-5677) **4259**
Catholic Directory for the Clergy and Laity in Scotland see Catholic Directory for Scotland **4259**
Catholic Directory of England and Wales. (UK) **4259**
Catholic Directory of Southern Africa. (SA) **4259**
Catholic Directory of the Archdiocese of Baltimore. (US) **4259**
Catholic Directory of the Diocese of Albany. (US) **4259**
Catholic Education. (UK) **4259**, 1620
Catholic Forester. (US ISSN 0008-8048) **2223**, 2530
Catholic Free Press. (US ISSN 0008-8056) **4259**
Catholic Fund for Overseas Development Journal see C A F O D Journal **926**
Catholic Gazette. (UK ISSN 0008-8064) **4259**
Catholic Health Association of Canada. Directory. (CN ISSN 0828-5748) **3086**, 4259
Catholic Health Association of Canada Info see C H A C Info **2459**
Catholic Health Association of the United States. Guidebook. (US) **2460**, 4168
Catholic Health World. (US ISSN 8756-4068) **2460**, 4168
Catholic Herald. (UK ISSN 0008-8072) **4259**
Catholic Herald. (US) **4259**
†Catholic Heritage. (US) **5163**
Catholic Historical Review. (US ISSN 0008-8080) **4259**, 2308
Catholic Housing Aid Society. Annual Report. (UK) **2484**
Catholic Hungarians' Sunday/Katolikus Magyarok Vasarnapja. (US) **2197**
Catholic Hungarians' Sunday. see Katolikus Magyarok Vasarnapja **4267**
Catholic India. (II) **4259**
Catholic International Education Office. Bulletin Nouvelle Serie see O I E C Bulletin **4193**
Catholic Journalist. (US ISSN 0008-8129) **2568**, 4259
Catholic Key. (US) **4259**
Catholic Knight Magazine. (US) **2530**
Catholic Knights of America Journal see C K of A Journal **1296**
Catholic Lawyer. (US ISSN 0008-8137) **2612**, 4259
Catholic Library Association. Northern Illinois Chapter. Newsletter. (US ISSN 0008-8161) **2751**, 4259
Catholic Library Association. Parish and Community Libraries News see Parish and Community Libraries News **2778**
Catholic Library World. (US ISSN 0008-820X) **2751**
Catholic Life see P I M E World **4272**
Catholic Media Council. Information Bulletin. (GW ISSN 0930-8679) **4259**, 1333
Catholic Medical Quarterly. (UK ISSN 0008-8226) **3086**, 4259
Catholic Messenger. (US ISSN 0008-8234) **4259**
Catholic Near East Magazine. (US ISSN 0164-0674) **3940**, 3952, 4168
Catholic New Times. (CN ISSN 0701-0788) **4259**
Catholic New York. (US ISSN 0278-1174) **4259**
Catholic News Service Origins, C N S Documentary Service see Origins, C N S Documentary Service **4272**
Catholic Nurse Journal. (UK) **3277**

Catholic Peace Fellowship Bulletin. (US ISSN 0008-8277) **4259**
Catholic Periodical and Literature Index. (US ISSN 0008-8285) **4212**, 8
The Catholic Pharmacist. (US) **3720**, 4259
Catholic Pictorial. (UK ISSN 0008-8293) **4259**
Catholic Press Directory. (US ISSN 0008-8307) **397**
Catholic Quote. (US) **4259**
Catholic Register. (CN ISSN 0383-1620) **4259**
Catholic Relief Services. Annual Report. (US) **4401**
Catholic Review (Baltimore). (US ISSN 0008-8315) **4259**
Catholic Review (New York). (US ISSN 0008-8323) **2291**, 4259
†Catholic Rural Life. (US ISSN 0008-8331) **5163**
Catholic School Bulletin see Momentum (Washington) **1648**
Catholic School Studies. (AT) **4259**
Catholic Sentinel (Archdiocese of Portland, Oregon). (US ISSN 0162-2102) **4259**
Catholic Sentinel (Diocese of Baker). (US ISSN 0162-0363) **4259**
Catholic Spirit (Austin). (US) **4259**
Catholic Spirit (Wheeling). (US) **4260**
Catholic Standard. (UK ISSN 0008-8366) **4260**
Catholic Standard. (GY) **4260**
Catholic Study Council Bulletin. (US) **4260**
Catholic Sun. (US ISSN 0744-267X) **4260**
Catholic Telegraph. (US) **4260**
Catholic Telephone Guide. (US) **4260**
Catholic Theological Society of America. Proceedings. (US ISSN 0069-1267) **4260**
Catholic Thought from Lublin. (US) **4260**, 3763
Catholic Times. (US ISSN 0745-6050) **4260**, 2223
Catholic Times see Universe **4277**
Catholic Traveler. (US) **4757**, 4260
Catholic Truth see The Catholic **4258**
Catholic Twin Circle. (US) **4260**
Catholic Twin Circle Weekly Magazine see Catholic Twin Circle **4260**
Catholic University Law Review. (US ISSN 0008-8390) **2612**, 4260
Catholic University Medical College Journal. (KO) **3086**
Catholic University of America Magazine see C U A Magazine **1306**
Catholic Update. (US) **4260**
Catholic Virginian. (US ISSN 0008-8404) **4260**
Catholic Voice. (GH ISSN 0008-8412) **4260**
Catholic Voice. (US ISSN 0744-9585) **4260**
Catholic War Veteran. (US ISSN 0886-1811) **4401**
Catholic Week. (US) **4260**
Catholic Weekly. (AT ISSN 0008-8420) **4260**
Catholic Weekly. (US ISSN 0008-8439) **4260**
Catholic Witness. (US ISSN 0008-8447) **4260**
Catholic Women's League News see C W L News **4838**
Catholic Worker. (US ISSN 0008-8463) **3878**
Catholic Workman. (US ISSN 0008-8471) **4260**
The Catholic World. (US ISSN 1042-3494) **4260**
Catholic Youth Ministry see Youth Ministry Quarterly (New Hampton) **4210**
Catholica. (GW ISSN 0008-8501) **4260**
Catholicisme Hier, Aujourd'hui, Demain. (FR) **4260**
Catholics United for Spirtual Action see C U S A N **4257**
Catlogo Repertorio Macchine e Motori see Catalogo Repertorio Macchine e Motori **161**
Cato Journal. (US ISSN 0273-3072) **3878**

Cato Policy Report. (US ISSN 0743-605X) **829**
Catplan Report. (US) **1090**, 825
Cats. (UK ISSN 0260-3837) **3709**
Cats Magazine. (US ISSN 0008-8544) **3709**
Cats' Protection League. Derby and District Branch. Newsletter see Waifarers **232**
†Catsnips. (IE) **5163**
Cattle. see Nautakarja **202**
Cattle Business. (US) **214**, 654
Cattle Guard. (US) **214**
Cattleman. (US ISSN 0008-8552) **214**
Cattleman. (AT) **214**
Cattlemen. (CN ISSN 0008-3143) **214**
Cauce. (CL) **2180**
Cauda Pavonis. (US) **2903**
Cauldron. (US) **1306**
†Cauldron. (AT) **5163**
Causa - U S A Report. (US) **2861**, 4168
†Causa y Efecto. (CK) **5163**
Cause. Proceedings of National Conference. (US ISSN 1043-7290) **1688**
Cause - Effect Magazine. (US ISSN 0164-534X) **1688**
Causes of Action. (US) **2612**
Causes of Death in Denmark. see Doedsaarsagerne **3991**
Caustic. (II ISSN 0008-8579) **1171**
Caution Magazine. (UK) **4099**
Caux Information. (SZ) **3952**
Cavalcade and Directory of Acts and Attractions see Cavalcade of Acts & Attractions **4631**
Cavalcade of Acts & Attractions. (US) **4631**
Cavalcade of Auto Racing. (US) **4468**
Cavalier. (US) **3396**
Cavalier Daily. (US ISSN 0008-8609) **1306**
Cavalier King Charles Spaniel Club of America. Bulletin see Cavalier King Charles Spaniel Club, U S A. Bulletin **3709**
Cavalier King Charles Spaniel Club, U S A. Bulletin. (US) **3709**
Cavalletto e Tavolozza. (IT ISSN 0045-5997) **321**
Cavallino Magazine. (US ISSN 0889-2504) **4687**
Cavallo Magazine. (IT) **230**, 4533
Cave Exploration Group. South Australia. Newsletter. (AT) **1557**
Cave Geology. (US) **1557**
Cave Research Group of Great Britain Newsletter see Caves & Caving **1557**
Cave Science: Transactions of the British Cave Research Association. (UK ISSN 0263-760X) **1557**
Caveat. (US) **1307**
Caveat Emptor Consumers Bulletin. (US) **1503**
Caves and Caverns. (US) **4757**, 1557
Caves & Caving. (UK ISSN 0142-1832) **1557**
Cayman Gazette. (CJ) **2612**, 4085
Cayman Islands. Currency Board. Report. (CJ) **1090**
Cayman Islands. Education Department. Report of the Chief Education Officer.(CJ) **1620**
Cayman Islands. Government Information Services. Annual Report. (CJ) **4056**
Cayman Islands. Legislative Assembly. Minutes. (CJ ISSN 0300-4740) **4056**
Cayman Islands Chamber of Commerce Directory. (CJ) **811**
Cayman Islands Chamber of Commerce Newsletter. (CJ) **811**
†Cayman Islands Handbook and Businessman's Guide. (CJ) **5163**
†Cayman Islands Holiday Guide. (CJ) **5163**
†Cayman Islands Nor'wester. (CJ) **5163**
†Cayman Islands Real Estate Review. (CJ) **5163**
Cayman Islands Yearbook and Business Directory. (CJ) **1126**
Caza Fotografica. (SP) **4304**

Caza y Pesca. (SP ISSN 0212-5625) **4543**
Caza y Pesca Nautica. (VE) **4543**
CD Data Report see C D Data Report **2750**
CD-I News see C D - I News **5156**
CD-ROM EndUser see C D - R O M EndUser **2796**
CD-ROM International see C D - R O M International **1448**
CD-ROM Newsletter see C D - R O M Newsletter **1476**
CD-ROM Review see C D - R O M Review **5156**
CD-ROM Sourcebook see C D - R O M Sourcebook **2796**
Ce D R E S Documenti. (Centro Documentazione e Ricerche Economico-Sociali) (IT) **4056**
Ce Fastu? (IT) **2808**
Ce Mois-Ci a l'Alliance. (AT) **1620**, 1296, 2903
Ce Qu'il Faut Savoir des Nations Unies see Everyone's United Nations **3957**
Cebal. (DK) **2808**
Cebu. (VE) **214**
Cebu. (MX) **214**
Cecidologia Indica see Cecidologia Internationale **529**
Cecidologia Internationale. (II ISSN 0008-8676) **529**
Cedar Post. (US) **2223**
Cedars-Sinai Compass see Cedars - Sinai Medical Center Compass **2460**
Cedars - Sinai Medical Center Compass.(US ISSN 0008-8684) **2460**
Cehui Tongbao/Journal of Surveying. (CC ISSN 0494-0911) **2244**
Cehui Yicong. (CC ISSN 1000-8586) **2244**
Ceiba. (HO ISSN 0008-8692) **82**, 434
Ceiba. (PR) **2903**, 4368
Ceilidh. (US ISSN 0741-0794) **2904**
Ceinar. (AG) **3952**
Cekong Jishu/Measurement & Control Technology. (CC ISSN 1000-8829) **49**
The Celator. (US ISSN 1048-0986) **3598**, 321
Celebrasian. (CN) **1996**, 2451
Celebrate. (CN ISSN 0381-7466) **4260**
Celebrate Life! (US) **3594**
Celebration. (US ISSN 0883-9174) **2990**
Celebration (Kansas City) see Celebration: a Creative Worship Service **4260**
Celebration: a Creative Worship Service.(US ISSN 0094-2421) **4260**
Celebrations. (US) **1746**, 1251
Celebrer. (FR ISSN 0240-4656) **4260**
Celebriamo. (IT ISSN 0008-8706) **3544**, 4260
▼Celebrity Birthday Directory. (US) **3519**, 397, 3588
Celebrity Bulletin. (UK ISSN 0045-6020) **418**
Celebrity Confidential. (US) **3396**
Celebrity Directory. (US) **3505**, 3544
Celebrity Focus see Celebrity Plus **5163**
†Celebrity Plus. (US ISSN 0897-4381) **5163**
Celebrity Service International Contact Book. (US ISSN 0069-1372) **4631**, 3505
Celebrity Skin. (US) **3396**
Celebrity Sleuth. (US) **3396**
Celestial Mechanics see Celestial Mechanics and Dynamical Astronomy **363**
Celestial Mechanics and Dynamical Astronomy. (NE ISSN 0923-2958) **363**
Celestinesca. (US ISSN 0147-3085) **2904**, 268, 3635
Celiang Yuan/Surveyor. (CC) **2244**
†Celibate Woman. (US ISSN 0735-4398) **5163**
Celik. (YU ISSN 0008-8722) **1073**
Cell. (US ISSN 0092-8674) **523**
Cell and Chromosome Research Journal. (II ISSN 0254-2935) **523**

Cell and Developmental Biology of the Eye. (US) **3299**
Cell and Tissue Kinetics see Cell Proliferation **523**
Cell and Tissue Research. (GW ISSN 0302-766X) **523**
Cell Biochemistry and Function. (UK ISSN 0263-6484) **474**, 3086
Cell Biology and Toxicology. (US ISSN 0742-2091) **1980**, 523
Cell Biology - Cytogenetics see I C R D B Cancergram: Cell Biology - Cytogenetics **5208**
Cell Biology - Growth Regulation, Differentiation see I C R D B Cancergram: Cell Biology - Growth Regulation and Differentiation **5208**
Cell Biology International Reports. (UK ISSN 0309-1651) **523**, 474
Cell Biology--Kinetics see I C R D B Cancergram: Cell Biology - Cell Kinetics **5208**
Cell Biology Monographs. (US ISSN 0172-4665) **523**
Cell Biophysics. (US ISSN 0163-4992) **474**
Cell Calcium (Edinburgh). (UK ISSN 0143-4160) **523**, 3086
Cell Calcium (Sheffield). (UK ISSN 0142-8020) **474**, 3086
Cell Contact Phenomena. (UK ISSN 0142-8039) **523**, 485, 3195
Cell Cycle. (UK ISSN 0263-7251) **523**, 3720
Cell Differentiation. (UK ISSN 0263-726X) **523**, 540, 3720
Cell Differentiation and Development see Mechanisms of Development **525**
Cell Membranes. (UK ISSN 0142-8047) **523**, 485, 3086
Cell Membranes, Methods and Reviews.(US) **434**
Cell Motility see Cell Motility and the Cytoskeleton **523**
Cell Motility and the Cytoskeleton. (US ISSN 0886-1544) **523**
Cell Nucleus. (UK ISSN 0141-299X) **523**, 3086
Cell Proliferation. (UK ISSN 0960-7722) **523**
†Cell Research/Xibao Yanjiu. (CC ISSN 1001-0602) **5163**
Cell Structure and Function. (JA ISSN 0386-7196) **523**
†Cell Surface Reviews. (NE) **5163**
▼Cell Transplantation. (UK ISSN 0963-6897) **474**
Cellar Notes. (US) **380**, 2472
▼Cells and Materials. (US ISSN 1051-6794) **3086**
▼Cellular and Mobile International. (US) **1361**
Cellular & Molecular Biology. (US ISSN 0145-5680) **523**
▼Cellular and Molecular Mechanisms of Inflammation. (US ISSN 1052-5882) **434**, 3720
Cellular & Molecular Neurobiology. (US ISSN 0272-4340) **3333**
Cellular Business. (US) **1361**
Cellular Buyers' Guide. (US) **1362**
Cellular Handbook see R C R Cellular Handbook **1358**
Cellular Immunology. (US ISSN 0008-8749) **3184**, 523
Cellular Investor. (US ISSN 0898-0403) **1362**, 942
Cellular Marketing. (US ISSN 0890-2402) **1362**, 1035
Cellular Neurobiology. (US) **434**, 3333
▼Cellular Physiology and Biochemistry.(SZ ISSN 1015-8987) **474**
Cellular Polymers. (UK ISSN 0262-4893) **3862**, 1217
Cellular Sales & Marketing. (US ISSN 0892-2683) **1362**, 1113
Cellular Signalling. (UK ISSN 0898-6568) **524**, 550, 3086, 3720
†Cellule. (BE ISSN 0008-8757) **5163**
Cellulosa e Carta. (IT ISSN 0008-8765) **2114**, 3662
Cellulose Chemistry and Technology. (RM ISSN 0576-9787) **1217**
Celsius. (AT) **2298**
Celtic League Annual see Carn **3952**
Celtic News see Carn **3952**

Celtic Studies. (US) **1996**
Celtic Studies Bibliography for (Year). (US) **397**
Celtic View. (UK) **4502**
Celtica. (IE ISSN 0069-1399) **1702**
Celuloza si Hirtie. (RM ISSN 0008-879X) **3662**
Cement. (NE ISSN 0008-8811) **609**
Cement. (CI ISSN 0008-882X) **609**
Cement and Concrete Composites. (UK) **609**
Cement and Concrete Research. (US ISSN 0008-8846) **609**
Cement Association of Japan. Review of the General Meeting. (JA) **609**
Cement Association of Japan. Review of the General Meeting. Technical Session. (JA) **609**
Cement, Concrete, and Aggregates. (US ISSN 0149-6123) **1863**
Cement Industry Technical Conference. Record see I E E E Cement Industry Technical Conference. Record **620**
Cement: Latin American Industrial Report. (US) **609**
Cement - Lime - Gypsum. Edition B. see Z K G: Ausgabe B **1876**
Cement Market and Outlook see European Cement Association. European Annual Review **637**
Cement- och Betonginstitutet Forskning - Research see C B I Forskning - Research **608**
Cement- och Betonginstitutet Informerar see C B I Informerar **608**
Cement- och Betonginstitutet Rapporter - Reports see C B I Rapporter - Reports **608**
Cement, Quarry and Mineral Aggregates Newsletter. (US) **3615**
Cement Research Institute of India. Annual Report see National Council for Cement and Building Materials. Annual Report **626**
Cement Research Institute of India Abstracts see C R I Abstracts **637**
Cement Special. (UK ISSN 0008-8889) **609**
Cement Standards of the World. (BE) **609**
Cement Technology. see Shuini Jishu **632**
Cement, Wapno, Gips. (PL ISSN 0008-8897) **609**
Cemento. (IT) **609**
Cemento-Hormigon. (SP ISSN 0008-8919) **609**
Cemento Portland. (AG ISSN 0008-8927) **609**
Cements Research Progress. (US ISSN 0363-8642) **1162**
Cemetery Dance. (US) **3010**
Cemetery Management. (US ISSN 0270-5281) **2119**
Cencrastus. (UK ISSN 0264-0856) **2904**
Cenicafe. (CK ISSN 0008-8951) **2063**, 82
Cenit/Zenith. (CR ISSN 0034-9828) **2861**
Cenobio. (SZ ISSN 0008-896X) **2861**
Censo de Poblacion y Viviendas. (CU) **3991**, 4567
Censored see Spectrum (Olathe) **2785**
Censorship News. (US ISSN 0749-6001) **2568**, 3940
▼Census Highlights. (US) **3980**
Census of Agriculture (Year). (CY) **136**, 4567
Census of Distribution see Census of Wholesale and Retail Trade **709**
Census of Industrial Production in Zambia. (ZA ISSN 0069-1429) **709**
Census of Inland Shipping in the Netherlands at Locks and Bridges. see Statistiek van de Scheepvaartbeweging in Nederland **4667**
Census of Maine Manufactures. (US ISSN 0090-7111) **1073**
Census of Manufacturing Industries of Puerto Rico. (PR ISSN 0552-5276) **1073**
Census of Motor Traffic on Main International Traffic Arteries. (UN) **4718**

Census of Private Non-Profit Making Institutions in Fiji. A Report. (FJ) **709**, **4567**
Census of Traffic on Main International Traffic Arteries see Census of Motor Traffic on Main International Traffic Arteries **4718**
Census of U.S. Civil Aircraft. (US ISSN 0069-1437) **4672**
Census of Wholesale and Retail Trade. (CY) **709**
Cent Blagues. (FR ISSN 0045-6047) **2861**
Centaur. (UY) **4757**
†Centauro. (IT ISSN 0393-5442) **5163**
Centauros. (AG ISSN 0008-8986) **4533**
Centaurus. (DK ISSN 0008-8994) **4304**, **3032**, **4595**
Centenary College Conglomerate. (US ISSN 0008-9001) **1307**
Centennial Psychology Series. (US) **4015**
Centennial Review see C R: Centennial Review **2504**
Centennial State Libraries. (US) **2751**, **1682**
Center. (Il) **2199**
Center (New York). (US ISSN 8755-2019) **296**
Center City Report. (US ISSN 0891-1029) **2484**, **1113**
Center Focus. (US) **4430**
Center for Adult Diseases, Osaka. Annual Report. (JA ISSN 0078-6632) **3086**
Center for Agricultural Economic Research, Rehovot. Working Papers. (IS) **148**
Center for Anthropological Studies. Contributions to Anthropological Studies. (US) **236**
Center for Anthropological Studies. Ethnohistorical Report Series. (US) **236**, **268**
Center for Anthropological Studies. Spanish Borderlands Research. (US) **236**, **268**
Center for Applied Research in the Apostolate Seminary Directory see C A R A Seminary Directory **4257**
Center for Applied Research in the Apostolate Seminary Forum. (US ISSN 0890-0426) **4260**
Center for Black Music Research Monographs see C B M R Monographs **3543**
Center for Children's Books. Bulletin. (US ISSN 0008-9036) **397**, **1233**, **4125**
Center for Chinese Research Materials. Bibliographical Series. (US ISSN 0084-6902) **2792**
Center for Chinese Research Materials. Newsletter. (US ISSN 0008-9044) **3646**
Center for Creative Leadership. Technical Report. (US) **1005**
Center for European Studies Working Paper Series. (US) **2355**
Center for Fine Arts News (Miami) see C F A News (Miami) **3522**
Center for Hermeneutical Studies in Hellenistic and Modern Culture. Protocol Series of the Colloquies. (US ISSN 0098-0900) **2505**
Center for Holocaust Studies Newsletter. (US ISSN 0737-8092) **2355**, **1996**
▼Center for Intelligence Studies. Reprint Series. (US) **3952**
Center for International Business and Trade Analyst see C I B & T Analyst **5156**
Center for Law and Education. Newsnotes. (US ISSN 0276-203X) **1620**, **2612**
Center for Migration Studies Newsletter.(US ISSN 8756-4467) **3980**
Center for Music Experiment Annual Report see C M E Annual Report **5157**
Center for Nursing Research Voice see C N R Voice **5157**
Center for Parent Education Newsletter.(US) **1620**, **1233**

Center for Peace and Conflict Studies. Occasional Papers. (US ISSN 0732-0078) **3952**
Center for Peace and Conflict Studies - Detroit Council for World Affairs. Newsletter. (US) **3953**, **1620**
Center for Philosophic Exchange. Annual Proceedings. (US) **3763**
Center for Pre-Columbian Studies. Conference Proceedings see Dumbarton Oaks Conference Proceedings **271**
Center for Process Studies. Newsletter. (US ISSN 0360-618X) **3763**, **4281**
Center for Reformation Research. Newsletter. (US) **2308**
Center for Research in Water Resources Newsletter see Watermarks **4833**
Center for Research Libraries. Handbook. (US) **2751**
Center for Self-Sufficiency Update. (US ISSN 0736-3044) **1682**, **2445**, **4839**
Center for Social Policy and Practice in the Workplace Newsletter. (US) **4430**, **975**
Center for Soviet and East-European Studies in the Performing Arts. Bulletin. (US ISSN 0008-9095) **2505**, **2904**, **4631**
Center for Sports Sponsorship's Sponsor Quest. (US ISSN 0747-6817) **4468**
Center for Strategic and International Studies. Significant Issues Series. (US) **3878**
Center for Strategic Studies Papers see C S S Papers **3952**
Center for Teaching About Peace and War. Newsletter see Center for Peace and Conflict Studies - Detroit Council for World Affairs. Newsletter **3953**
Center for the Study of Democratic Institutions. Center Magazine see New Perspectives Quarterly **3910**
Center for the Study of Early Man. Current Research see Current Research in the Pleistocene **270**
Center for the Study of Sport in Society Digest see C S S S Digest **4467**
Center for the Study of the Presidency. Annual Report. (US) **3878**
Center for the Study of the Presidency. Center House Bulletin see Presidential Studies Quarterly **3919**
Center for the Study of the Presidency. Proceedings. (US) **3878**
Center Magazine. (US ISSN 0748-6464) **321**, **1529**, **3544**, **4631**
†Center Management. (US) **5163**
Center News. (US) **3196**
Center of Attention. (US) **321**
Center of Educational Research. Copenhagen Business School. Report.(DK ISSN 0109-6257) **655**, **1702**
†Center Point. (US) **5163**
Center Quarterly. (US ISSN 0890-4634) **3789**
Center Stage (Maitland). (US) **2990**
Center Stage (New York). (US) **4631**, **2451**
Center View. (US) **1945**
Center Voice. (US ISSN 0894-8984) **2452**
Centering. (US) **2990**
Centers. (US) **4146**
Centers for Disease Control - Acquired Immune Deficiency Syndrome Weekly see C D C - A I D S Weekly **3218**
Centers of Civilization Series. (US ISSN 0069-1461) **2308**
Centerscope. (US) **3086**
Centerviews. (US ISSN 0746-1402) **903**, **3953**
El Centinela. (US) **4232**
Cento. (US ISSN 0008-9141) **1307**
Centra Bulteno see Semajna Bulteno **2840**
Centraal Bureau voor Genealogie. Jaarboek. (NE) **2146**
Centraal Bureau voor Genealogie. Mededelingen. (NE ISSN 0165-6473) **2146**
†Centraal Orgaan voor de Economische Betrekkingen met het Buitenland. Report of Activities. (NE) **5163**

Central. (UK) **1307**
Central Accessioning List about Library and Information Science. see Konyvtari es Informatikai Kozponti Gyarapodasi Jegyzek **5224**
Central Africa Historical Association. Local Series Pamphlets see Historical Association of Zimbabwe. Local Series Pamphlets **2333**
Central African Journal of Medicine. (RH ISSN 0008-9176) **3086**
Central African Power Corporation. Annual Report and Accounts. (RH ISSN 0069-147X) **1884**
Central African Zionist Digest. (RH ISSN 0008-9184) **3878**
Central Alberta Adviser. (CN) **83**
†Central America Bulletin. (US ISSN 0893-7699) **5163**
Central America NewsPak. (US ISSN 0887-0594) **2568**
Central America Report. (GT ISSN 0254-2471) **3878**, **655**
Central America Report. (US) **4168**, **3878**
Central America Stamp Catalogue. (UK ISSN 0142-9876) **3750**
Central America Update. (US ISSN 1054-8882) **3878**
Central America Update. (CN ISSN 0823-7689) **3953**, **927**
Central American Historical Institute. Update see Envio **2405**
Central and Inner Asian Studies. (US ISSN 0893-2301) **2337**, **3953**
Central Archives for the History of the Jewish People Newsletter/Arkhiyon ha-Merkazi le-Toldot ha-Am ha-Yehudi. Yediot. (IS) **2429**
Central Asia. (PK) **3635**
Central Asia Book Series. (US) **2337**
Central Asia Stamp Catalogue. (UK ISSN 0142-9884) **3750**
Central Asian Survey. (UK ISSN 0263-4937) **3879**, **2337**
Central Asiatic Journal. (GW ISSN 0008-9192) **3635**, **2808**
Central Bank of Barbados. Annual Report. (BB ISSN 0304-6796) **850**
Central Bank of Barbados. Annual Statistical Digest. (BB ISSN 0255-8440) **770**
Central Bank of Barbados. Balance of Payments. (BB ISSN 0255-8432) **710**
Central Bank of Barbados. Economic and Financial Statistics. (BB ISSN 0378-178X) **770**, **710**
Central Bank of Barbados. Economic Review. (BB ISSN 0255-7460) **770**
Central Bank of Barbados. Quarterly Report see Central Bank of Barbados. Economic Review **770**
Central Bank of Ceylon see Central Bank of Sri Lanka. Bulletin **850**
Central Bank of Ceylon. Annual Report see Central Bank of Sri Lanka. Annual Report **771**
Central Bank of Ceylon. Report and Accounts see Bank of Ceylon. Annual Report and Accounts **763**
Central Bank of Ceylon. Staff Studies see Central Bank of Sri Lanka. Staff Studies **850**
Central Bank of China. Annual Report. (CH ISSN 0069-150X) **770**
Central Bank of China. Quarterly. (CH) **770**
Central Bank of Cyprus. Annual Report.(CY ISSN 0069-1518) **770**
Central Bank of Cyprus. Bulletin. (CY ISSN 0008-9230) **770**
Central Bank of Egypt. Annual Report. (UA) **770**
Central Bank of Egypt. Board of Directors. Report see Central Bank of Egypt. Annual Report **770**
Central Bank of Egypt. Economic Review. (UA ISSN 0008-9249) **850**
Central Bank of Gambia. Quarterly Bulletin. (GM) **850**
Central Bank of Iceland. Economic Statistics. (IC ISSN 0256-193X) **710**, **4567**
Central Bank of Iraq. Quarterly Bulletin. (IQ ISSN 0008-9257) **770**, **850**

CENTRAL BANK 6039

Central Bank of Iraq, Baghdad. Report. (IQ ISSN 0069-1534) **771**
Central Bank of Ireland. Annual Report. (IE ISSN 0069-1542) **771**
Central Bank of Ireland. Irish Economic Statistics. (IE ISSN 0332-2696) **710**, **771**
Central Bank of Ireland. Monthly Statistics. (IE ISSN 0791-1785) **771**
Central Bank of Ireland. Quarterly Bulletin. (IE ISSN 0069-1542) **771**
Central Bank of Ireland. Statistical Supplement see Central Bank of Ireland. Monthly Statistics **771**
Central Bank of Jordan. Annual Report/Bank al-Markazi al-Urduni. Annual Report. (JO ISSN 0069-1550) **771**
Central Bank of Jordan. Monthly Statistical Bulletin. (JO) **850**
Central Bank of Jordan. Quarterly Bulletin see Central Bank of Jordan. Monthly Statistical Bulletin **850**
Central Bank of Kenya. Annual Economic Report. (KE) **771**
Central Bank of Kenya. Annual Report see Central Bank of Kenya. Annual Economic Report **771**
Central Bank of Kenya. Economic and Financial Review see Central Bank of Kenya. Quarterly Economic Review **850**
Central Bank of Kenya. Quarterly Economic Review. (KE) **850**
Central Bank of Kuwait. Annual Report. (KU) **771**
Central Bank of Kuwait. Economic Report. (KU) **850**
Central Bank of Kuwait. Monthly Monetary Review. (KU) **771**, **850**
Central Bank of Kuwait. Monthly Monetary Tables see Central Bank of Kuwait. Monthly Monetary Review **771**
Central Bank of Kuwait. Quarterly Statistical Bulletin. (KU) **771**, **850**
Central Bank of Malta. Annual Report. (MM ISSN 0577-0653) **771**
Central Bank of Malta. Quarterly Review. (MM ISSN 0008-9273) **771**
Central Bank of Nigeria. Annual Report and Statement of Accounts. (NR ISSN 0069-1577) **771**
Central Bank of Nigeria. Economic and Financial Review. (NR ISSN 0008-9281) **850**
Central Bank of Nigeria. Monthly Report. (NR ISSN 0008-929X) **771**
Central Bank of Somalia. Annual Report and Statement of Accounts. (SO) **771**
Central Bank of Somalia. Bulletin/Bankiga Dhexe ee Soomaaliya. Faafin. (SO) **710**, **4567**
Central Bank of Somalia. Monthly Report. (SO) **771**
Central Bank of Sri Lanka. Annual Report. (CE) **771**
Central Bank of Sri Lanka. Bulletin. (CE) **850**
Central Bank of Sri Lanka. Staff Studies.(CE) **850**
†Central Bank of Sri Lanka, Review of the Economy/Arthika Vivaranaya. (CE) **5163**
Central Bank of Swaziland. Annual Report. (SQ) **771**
Central Bank of Swaziland. Quarterly Review. (SQ ISSN 0378-1593) **771**
Central Bank of Syria. Quarterly Bulletin.(SY) **850**, **771**
Central Bank of the Bahamas. Annual Report and Statement of Accounts. (BF) **771**
Central Bank of the Bahamas. Quarterly Review. (BF) **771**
Central Bank of the Gambia. Annual Report. (GM) **771**
Central Bank of the Philippines Review see C B Review **769**
Central Bank of the Republic of Turkey. Annual Report. (TU) **771**
Central Bank of the Republic of Turkey. Monthly Statistical and Evaluation Bulletin. (TU) **771**

6040 CENTRAL BANK

Central Bank of the Republic of Turkey. Quarterly Bulletin. *see* Turkiye Cumhuriyet Merkez Bankasi. Aylik Bulten **802**
Central Bank of the Republic of Turkey. Quarterly Economic Information Report. (TU) **850**
Central Bank of Trinidad and Tobago. Annual Economic Survey. (TR ISSN 1011-6311) **771**
Central Bank of Trinidad and Tobago. Annual Report. (TR ISSN 0069-1593) **771**
Central Bank of Trinidad and Tobago. Monthly Statistical Digest. (TR ISSN 1011-6338) **710, 4567**
Central Bank of Trinidad and Tobago. Quarterly Economic Bulletin. (TR ISSN 1011-6346) **850**
Central Bank of Trinidad and Tobago. Quarterly Statistical Digest. (TR ISSN 1011-6362) **710, 4567**
Central Bank of Trinidad and Tobago. Statistical Digest *see* Central Bank of Trinidad and Tobago. Monthly Statistical Digest **710**
Central Bank of Trinidad and Tobago. Statistical Digest *see* Central Bank of Trinidad and Tobago. Quarterly Statistical Digest **710**
Central Bank of Yemen. Annual Report. (YE ISSN 0301-6625) **771**
Central Building Research Institute. Building Research Note. (II) **609**
Central Building Research Institute. List of Publications. (II ISSN 0557-322X) **637**
Central Building Research Institute Abstracts *see* C.B.R.I. Abstracts **5156**
Central Business Review. (US ISSN 1053-9263) **655**
Central California Jewish Heritage. (US) **1996, 4222**
Central California Register. (US) **4260**
Central-China Normal University. Journal (Natural Science Edition). *see* Huazhong Shifan Daxue Xuebao (Ziran Kexue Ban) **4313**
Central-China Normal University. Journal (Social Science Edition). *see* Huazhong Shifan Daxue Xuebao (Shehui Kexue Ban) **4374**
Central-China University of Science and Engineering. Journal. *see* Huazhong Ligong Daxue Xuebao **4313**
Central Coast. (US) **2223**
Central Committee for Conscientious Objectors News Notes *see* C C C O News Notes **3940**
Central Committee of the Bulgarian Communist Party. Information Bulletin. (BU ISSN 0861-038X) **3879**
Central Conference of American Rabbis. Yearbook. (US ISSN 0069-1607) **4212, 4222**
Central Conference of American Rabbis Journal *see* C C A R Journal **4222**
Central Conference of Teamsters. Chairman's Report *see* Central Conference of Teamsters. Officers' Report **2581**
Central Conference of Teamsters. Officers' Report. (US ISSN 0069-1615) **2581**
Central Conservatory of Music. Journal. *see* Zhongyang Yinyue Xueyuan Xuebao **3587**
Central Council for Education and Training in Social Work. Report of Council Meeting. (UK) **4401, 1682**
Central - East Europe Business Analyst. (UK) **903**
Central Electric Railfans' Association. Bulletin. (US ISSN 0069-1623) **4708**
Central Electricity Generating Board. Report and Accounts. Annual. (UK) **1884**
Central Electricity Generating Board Abstracts *see* C E G B Abstracts **5156**
Central Electricity Generating Board Research *see* C E G B Research **5156**
Central European History. (US ISSN 0008-9389) **2355**

Central Florida Magazine *see* Orlando Magazine **4781**
Central Georgia Genealogical Society. Quarterly. (US) **2146**
Central Glass and Ceramic Research Institute. Bulletin. (II ISSN 0008-9397) **1162**
Central Hall Artists Newsletter. (US) **321**
Central Illinois Economic-Business Review *see* Economic-Business Review **5184**
Central Illinois Historical Messenger *see* Historical Messenger **4240**
Central Inland Capture Fisheries Research Institute. Annual Report. (II ISSN 0970-6267) **2038**
Central Inland Capture Fisheries Research Institute. Bulletin. (II ISSN 0970-616X) **2038**
Central Inland Capture Fisheries Research Institute Newsletter *see* C I C F R I Newsletter **2037**
Central Inland Fisheries Research Institute. Annual Report *see* Central Inland Capture Fisheries Research Institute. Annual Report **2038**
Central Inland Fisheries Research Institute Newsletter *see* C I C F R I Newsletter **2037**
Central Institute of Education Newsletter *see* C.I.E. Newsletter **1619**
Central Institute of Medicinal and Aromatic Plants Current Research on Medicinal and Aromatic Plants *see* Current Research on Medicinal and Aromatic Plants **500**
Central Institute of Nationalities. Journal. *see* Zhongyang Minzu Xueyuan Xuebao **2030**
Central Intelligence Agency. Monographs. (US) **3879, 850, 3453**
Central Intelligence Agency. Monographs. All Communist Countries Reports. (US) **3879, 850, 3453**
Central Intelligence Agency. Monographs. All Countries Reports. (US) **3879, 850, 3453**
Central Intelligence Agency. Monographs. All Non-Communist Country Reports. (US) **3879, 850, 3453**
Central Intelligence Agency. Monographs. China Reports. (US) **3879, 850, 3453**
Central Intelligence Agency. Monographs. Maps Only. (US) **3879, 850, 3453**
Central Intelligence Agency. Monographs. U.S.S.R. Reports. (US) **3879, 850, 3453**
Central Issues in Anthropology. (US) **236**
†Central Issues in Philosophy Series. (US) **5163**
Central Japan Journal of Orthopaedic & Traumatic Surgery/Chubu Nippon Seikei Geka Saigai Geka Gakkai Zasshi. (JA ISSN 0008-9443) **3307**
Central Kentucky Researcher. (US ISSN 0095-1439) **2146**
Central Literary Magazine. (UK ISSN 0069-164X) **2904**
Central Luzon State University Scientific Journal *see* C L S U Scientific Journal **81**
Central Marine Fisheries Research Institute. Bulletin. (II ISSN 0577-084X) **2038, 1603**
Central Michigan Life. (US ISSN 0008-9451) **1307**
Central Midland Enterprise. (UK) **811**
Central Mindanao University Journal of Science *see* C M U Journal of Science **81**
Central Mine Planning & Design Institute. Current Awareness Service. (II) **3499**
Central Mine Planning & Design Institute. Manuals. (II) **3480**
Central Mining Research Station Annual Report *see* C M R S Annual Report **3480**
Central Mining Research Station, Dhanbad. Progress Research *see* C M R S Annual Report **3480**

Central Mississippi Planning and Development District. Annual Report. (US) **2484**
Central Nacional de Pesquisa de Mandioca e Fruticultura. Relatorio Tecnico Anual. (BL ISSN 0101-2711) **83**
†Central Naugatuck Valley Regional Planning Agency. Annual Report. (US ISSN 0069-1674) **5163**
Central Nervous System Trauma *see* Journal of Neurotrauma **3309**
Central New Jersey Office Buildings *see* New Jersey Office Buildings **4154**
Central New York Academy of Medicine. Bulletin. (US ISSN 0008-946X) **3086**
Central New York Business Journal. (US) **850**
Central New York Business Review *see* Central New York Business Journal **850**
Central Nova Business News. (CN) **655**
Central Nova Business News. (CN) **811**
Central Ohio Digest *see* Milk Marketer **201**
Central Oklahoma Home Builder. (US) **609**
†Central Opera Service Bulletin. (US ISSN 0008-9508) **5163**
Central Park. (US ISSN 0273-3323) **2861**
Central Penn Business Journal. (US) **655**
Central Plantation Crops Research Institute. Annual Report. (II ISSN 0374-7115) **83, 148, 499**
Central Plantation Crops Research Institute. Newsletter. (II) **83, 499**
Central Plantation Crops Research Institute. Research Highlights. (II) **83, 499**
Central Public Opinion/Chuokoran. (JA) **2207**
Central Public Opinion's Management Affairs *see* Will **1031**
Central Queensland News. (AT) **83, 214, 3480**
Central Review *see* Central Public Opinion **2207**
Central Road Research Institute, New Delhi. Road Research Paper. (II ISSN 0069-1690) **4718**
Central Road Research Institute Road Abstracts *see* C R R I Road Abstracts **1842**
Central Salt and Marine Chemicals Research Institute Newsletter *see* C S M C R I Newsletter **1602**
Central Scientific Instruments Organization Communications *see* C S I O Communications **2521**
Central Scotland Chamber of Commerce Quarterly Bulletin. (UK) **811**
Central Sericultural Research and Training Institute. Annual Report. (II ISSN 0304-6818) **83**
Central-South Institute of Mining and Metallurgy. Journal. *see* Zhongnan Kuangye Xueyuan Xuebao **3498**
Central-South University of Finance and Economics. Journal. *see* Zhongnan Caijing Daxue Xuebao **899**
Central Southern Farmer. (UK) **83**
Central State Business Review *see* Central Business Review **655**
Central State Speech Journal *see* Communication Studies **1333**
Central States Anthropological Society. Proceedings *see* Central Issues in Anthropology **236**
Central States Archaeological Journal. (US ISSN 0008-9559) **268**
Central States Conference on the Teaching of Foreign Languages. Education Series. (US) **2808, 1746**
Central States Trucker. (US) **4743**
Central Statistical Office Statistical Bulletins *see* C.S.O. Statistical Bulletins **4565**
Central Texas Archeologist. (US ISSN 0882-3693) **268, 3657**
Central Times *see* New Times **4245**
Central Tobacco Research Institute and its Regional Research Stations. Annual Report. (II) **4643**

Central Wisconsin Resorter. (US) **4757**
Centralblatt fuer das Gesamte Forstwesen. (AU ISSN 0008-9583) **2097**
Centrale de l'Enseignement du Quebec Nouvelles C E Q *see* Nouvelles C E Q **1652**
Centrale Landsdienaren Organisatie Bulletin *see* C L O Bulletin **2581**
Centralian Advocate. (AT) **2171**
Centralight. (US) **1307**
Centralite. (PH) **1307**
Centralny Instytut Ochrony Pracy. Prace. (PL ISSN 0509-6510) **3615**
Centralny Katalog Zagranicznych Wydawnictw Ciaglych w Bibliotekach Polskich. (PL ISSN 0239-8931) **397**
Centralny Osrodek Badan i Rozwoju Techniki Drogowej. Prace *see* Instytut Badawczy Drog i Mostow. Prace **1826**
†Centralny Osrodek Badan i Rozwoju Techniki Kolejnictwa. Prace. (PL) **5163**
Centre. (BE) **2520, 4168**
Centre Aixois de Recherches Anglaises. Actes du Colloque. (FR ISSN 0240-8864) **2904**
Centre Belge d'Histoire Rurale. Publications/Belgisch Centrum voor Landelijke Geschiedenis. Publikaties. (BE ISSN 0076-1192) **2355**
Centre Calling. (II) **596**
Centre Catholique des Intellectuels Francais. Recherches et Debats. (FR ISSN 0008-9605) **2505, 4260**
Centre County Heritage. (US) **2402**
Centre Culturel Francais, Alger. Rencontres Culturelles. (AE ISSN 0069-1720) **2904**
Centre Culturel Francais de Yaounde. Programme Saison. (CM) **321, 3544, 4631**
Centre Culturel Portugais. Actes des Colloques. (FR) **2505**
Centre Culturel Portugais. Archives. (FR) **2981**
Centre d'Ecologie Forestiere. Notes Techniques *see* Centre de Recherches sur l'Elevage et les Productions Fourrageres en Haute Belgique. Notes Techniques. B: Herbageres **2097**
†Centre d'Ecologie Forestiere et Rurale. Communications. (BE) **5163**
Centre d'Ecologie Forestiere et Rurale. Notes Techniques. A: Forestieres *see* Centre de Recherche et de Promotion Forestieres. Documents **2097**
Centre d'Ecologie Forestrie et Rurale. Notes Techniques. B: Herbageres *see* Centre de Recherches sur l'Elevage et les Productions Fourrageres en Haute Belgique. Notes Techniques. B: Herbageres **2097**
Centre d'Enquetes Statistiques de Caen. Enquete Annuelle d'Entreprise: Industries Diverses. (FR) **710, 4567**
Centre d'Enseignement Superieur de Brazzaville. Annales. (CF) **1702**
Centre d'Entraide Genealogique de Franche-Comte. Bulletin *see* Genealogie Franc - Comtoise **2152**
Centre d'Etude de la Population et Centre d'Etude de la Population et de la Famille. Annual Report. *see* Population and Family Study Centre. Progress Report **3986**
†Centre d'Etude des Matieres Plastiques. Bulletin de Documentation. (FR ISSN 0008-9702) **5163**
Centre d'Etude des Revenus et des Couts. Documents. (FR ISSN 0336-1470) **1090**
Centre d'Etudes de l'Asie de l'Est. Cahiers. (CN ISSN 0839-4555) **3635**
Centre d'Etudes, de Recherche Economique et Social Revue Economique et Sociale *see* C E D R E S. Revue Economique et Sociale **148**

CENTRE REGIONAL 6041

Centre d'Etudes et de Documentation Africaines. Cahiers. (BE ISSN 0250-1619) **2332**, 850, 3879

Centre d'Etudes et de Documentation Economique, Juridique et Sociale Egypte - Monde Arabe see C E D E J Egypte - Monde Arabe **2608**

Centre d'Etudes et de Recherches Scientifiques de Biarritz. Bulletin. (FR ISSN 0528-4465) **1603**

Centre d'Etudes Ethnologiques. Publications see Centre d'Etudes Ethnologiques Bandundu. Publications **236**

Centre d'Etudes Ethnologiques. Publications. Serie 2: Memoires et Monographies. (ZR) **236**, 2332, 4430

Centre d'Etudes Ethnologiques. Publications. Serie 3: Travaux Linguistiques. (ZR) **2808**

Centre d'Etudes Ethnologiques Bandundu. Publications. (ZR) **236**, 2332, 4430

Centre d'Etudes Prospectives et d'Informations Internationales Lettre see C.E.P.I.I. Lettre **849**

Centre d'Histoire Contemporaine du Languedoc-Roussillon. Bulletin. (FR ISSN 0244-9404) **2355**, 3879

Centre d'Histoire Economique et Sociale de la Region Lyonnaise. Bulletin. (FR ISSN 0249-5902) **2355**, 4368

Centre d'Histoire et d'Art de la Thudinie. Publications. (BE) **2355**, 321

Centre d'Information des Banques de Donnees see B D **1443**

Centre d'Information des Utilisateurs de Progiciel. Catalogue. (FR ISSN 0985-0791) **825**

Centre d'Information et de Documentation Scientifique et Technique. Archives du Centre National de Recherches Oceanographiques. (MG) **1603**

Centre d'Information et de Documentation Scientifique et Technique. Recherches Pour le Developpement. (MG) **435**

Centre de Cartographie Phytosociologique. Communications see Centre d'Ecologie Forestiere et Rurale. Communications **5163**

Centre de Cooperation pour les Recherches Scientifiques Relatives au Tabac (Coresta) see C O R E S T A **4646**

Centre de Documentation Siderurgique. Bulletin Analytique. (FR ISSN 0007-4063) **3425**, 8

†Centre de Formation des Journalistes. Feuillets. (FR ISSN 0008-9648) **5163**

Centre de Genealogie et d'Histoire des Iles d'Amerique. (FR) **2146**, 2402

Centre de Geomorphologie, Caen. Bulletin. (FR ISSN 0068-4791) **1557**

Centre de l'Astronomie et des Sciences Spatiales. Observations Solaires. (RM) **363**

Centre de Liaison, d'Etude, d'Information et de Recherche sur les Porblemes des Personnes Agees Bulletin Documentaire Mensuel see C L E I R P P A. Bulletin Documentaire Mensuel **2271**

Centre de Recherche d'Histoire et Civilisation de Byzance. Travaux et Memoires. (FR) **2355**, 2308, 2429

Centre de Recherche en Civilisation Canadienne - Francaise. Cahiers. see French - Canadian Civilization Research Center. Cahiers **2406**

Centre de Recherche en Litterature Canadienne - Francaise. Cahiers see French - Canadian Civilization Research Center. Cahiers **2406**

Centre de Recherche et de Promotion Forestieres. Documents. (BE ISSN 0775-3446) **2097**

Centre de Recherche Industrielles en Afrique Centrale. Bulletin d'Information see Sciences, Techniques, Informations C R I A C **1084**

Centre de Recherches, de Reflexion et d'Information Feministes Bulletin see C R I F Bulletin **4838**

Centre de Recherches en Mathematiques Pures. P 1. (SZ) **3032**

Centre de Recherches en Mathematiques Pures. Publications. Serie 2. Monographies. (SZ) **3032**

Centre de Recherches en Mathematiques Pures. Publications. Serie 3. Oeuvres. (SZ) **3032**

Centre de Recherches en Mathematiques Pures. Publications. Serie 4. Conferences Communications. (SZ) **3032**

Centre de Recherches et d'Etudes des Situations Interculturelles. Cahiers. (FR) **4368**

Centre de Recherches et d'Etudes Historiques de la Seconde Guerre Mondiale. Bulletin. (BE ISSN 0772-120X) **2355**

Centre de Recherches Historiques. Cahiers. (FR ISSN 0990-9141) **2355**

Centre de Recherches Oceanographiques d'Abidjan. Documents Scientifiques. (IV) **1603**, 2038

Centre de Recherches pour le Developpement International. Rapport Annuel. see International Development Research Centre. Annual Report **671**

Centre de Recherches Science et Vie. Cahiers. (FR) **4304**, 4595

Centre de Recherches sur l'Elevage et les Productions Fourrageres en Haute Belgique. Notes Techniques. B: Herbageres. (BE) **2097**

Centre Europeen d'Etudes Bourguignonnes (XIVe-XVIe S.). Publication. (BE ISSN 0069-1895) **2355**, 2245

Centre Europeen de la Culture. Bulletin see Cadmos **2354**

Centre for Advanced Land Use Studies Research Reports see C A L U S Research Reports **4146**

Centre for Advanced T V Studies Reports see C.A.T.S. Reports **5156**

Centre for Cold Ocean Resources Engineering News see C - C O R E News **1816**

Centre for Development and Population Activities World Wide see C E D P A World Wide **4838**

Centre for Development Research. Publications. (SW ISSN 0348-5676) **83**, 3879

Centre for Development Research Project Paper see C D R Project Paper **926**

Centre for Development Research Research Reports see C D R Research Reports **926**

Centre for European Policy Studies. Newsletter. (BE) **3953**

Centre for European Policy Studies Papers see C E P S Papers **3952**

Centre for European Policy Studies Working Documents see C E P S Working Documents **3952**

Centre for Housing Research. Discussion Paper. (UK ISSN 0952-2603) **2484**

Centre for Intergroup Studies. Annual Report. (SA) **4431**

Centre for Library and Information Study Observer see C L I S Observer **2750**

Centre for Plant Breeding and Reproduction Research. Annual Report. (NE) **83**, 2063

Centre for Research in Algebra and Number Theory. (CN) **3032**

Centre for Research in Algebra and Related Fields see Centre for Research in Algebra and Number Theory **3032**

Centre for Research on Organisations, Management and Technical Change Working Paper Series see C R O M T E C Working Paper Series **1004**

Centre for Resource Studies. Annual Report. (CN) **3480**

Centre for Resource Studies. Proceedings. (CN) **3480**

Centre for Resource Studies. Technical Papers. (CN) **3480**

Centre for Resource Studies Perspectives see C R S Perspectives **3480**

Centre for Resources Studies. Working Papers. (CN ISSN 0226-7616) **3480**

Centre for South-East Asian Studies. Bibliography and Literature Series. (UK ISSN 0269-1760) **2337**

Centre for South-East Asian Studies. Occasional Papers. (UK ISSN 0269-1779) **2337**, 3635

Centre for the History of European Expansion. Newsletter see Itinerario **2315**

Centre for the Study of Communication and Culture. Newsletter see Communication Research Trends **1333**

Centre for Urban and Community Studies. Bibliographic Series. (CN ISSN 0316-4691) **2484**, 2245, 4431

Centre for Urban and Community Studies. Major Report Series. (CN ISSN 0319-4620) **2485**, 3980, 4431

Centre for Urban and Community Studies. Research Papers. (CN ISSN 0316-0068) **2485**, 3980, 4431

Centre for Urban Studies Bulletin see C U S Bulletin **2484**

Centre Genealogique de l'Essonne. Bulletin. (FR) **2146**

Centre Genealogique de l'Ouest. Revue Trimestrielle. (FR ISSN 0183-6242) **2146**

Centre Genevois d'Anthropologie. Bulletin. (BE ISSN 0777-5466) **237**

Centre I N F F O. Bulletin de Liason see Bulletin Officiel du Travail et de l'Emploi **1004**

Centre International d'Etude des Textiles Anciens. Bulletin. (FR) **4617**, 321

Centre International d'Etudes Poetiques. Courrier. (BE ISSN 0771-6443) **2990**

Centre International de Documentation Arachnologique. Bulletin d'Information et de Liaison. see Arachnologia - Bulletin d'Information et de Liaison du C I D A **528**

Centre International de Documentation Arachnologique. Liste des Travaux Arachnologiques. (FR ISSN 0295-060X) **464**, 8

Centre International de Documentation Occitane. Bibliotheque. Catalogue. (FR) **2808**

Centre International de Documentation Occitane. Serie Bibliographique. (FR) **397**, 2355

Centre International de Documentation Occitane. Serie Etudes. (FR ISSN 0398-3765) **2356**

Centre International de l'Enfance. Programme of Activities. (FR) **1233**, 4839

Centre International de Liaison des Ecoles de Cinema et de Television Newsletter see C I L E C T Newsletter **1370**

Centre International de Recherches sur l'Anarchisme Bulletin see C I R A Bulletin **3877**

Centre Interuniversitaire d'Histoire Contemporaine. Cahiers/ Interuniversitair Centrum voor Hedendaagse Geschiedenis. Medelingen. (BE ISSN 0577-179X) **2356**

Centre Jean Berard. Cahier. (IT) **268**

Centre Lyonnais d'Acupuncture de Saint-Luc. Bulletin de Liaison. (FR ISSN 0338-7070) **3086**

Centre Magazine. (CN) **641**

Centre Midi Magazine see Mineurs de France: Edition Centre-Midi **3489**

†Centre National d'Art et de Culture Georges Pompidou. Annuaire des Concepteurs. (FR) **5163**

Centre National d'Etudes Spatiales. Rapport d'Activite. (FR ISSN 0069-2034) **49**

Centre National de Documentation Scientifique et Technique. Rapport d'Activite. (BE ISSN 0069-1968) **4595**, 4304

Centre National de Documentation sur les Toxicomanies. Bulletin de Liaison. (FR ISSN 0995-3671) **3720**

Centre National de la Cinematographie. Bulletin d'Information. (FR ISSN 0397-8435) **3505**

Centre National de la Cinematographie Statistiques see C N C Statistiques **3519**

Centre National de la Recherche Scientifique. Annuaire Europeen d'Administration Publique. (FR ISSN 0221-5918) **4056**

Centre National de la Recherche Scientifique. Colloques Internationaux.(FR) **2505**

Centre National de la Recherche Scientifique. Colloques Internationaux. Sciences Humaines see Centre National de la Recherche Scientifique. Colloques Internationaux **2505**

Centre National de la Recherche Scientifique. Monographies d'Econometrie. (FR) **655**

Centre National de la Recherche Scientifique. Seminaire d'Econometrie. Monographies see Centre National de la Recherche Scientifique. Monographies d'Econometrie **655**

Centre National de Recherches Appliques au Developpement Rural. Departement de Recherches Agronomiques. Rapport Annuel. (MG) **83**

Centre National de Recherches Appliques au Developpement Rural. Departement de Recherches Agronomiques. Rapport d'Activite. (MG) **83**

†Centre National de Recherches Archeologiques en Belgique. Repertoires Archeologiques. Serie A: Repertoires Bibliographiques/ Nationaal Centrum voor Oudheidkundige Navorsingen in Belgie. Oudheidkundige Repertoria. Reeks A: Bibliografische Repertoria. (BE ISSN 0069-1992) **5163**

†Centre National de Recherches Archeologiques en Belgique. Repertoires Archeologiques. Serie B: Repertoires des Collections. (BE ISSN 0069-200X) **5163**

†Centre National de Recherches Archeologiques en Belgique. Repertoires Archeologiques. Serie C: Repertoires Divers. (BE ISSN 0069-2018) **5163**

Centre National de Recherches Pharmaceutiques. Archives. (MG) **3720**

Centre National du Machinisme Agricole du Genie Rural, des Eaux et des Forets Nouvelles see C E M A G R E F Nouvelles **5156**

Centre of Fine Arts Quarterly. see Meiyuan **335**

Centre Protestant d'Etudes de Geneve. Bulletin. (SZ) **4232**, 3763

Centre Protestant d'Etudes et de Documentation. Bulletin. (FR ISSN 0181-7671) **4212**

Centre Quebecois de Relations Internationales. Collection Dossiers. (CN) **3953**

▼Centre Rankings. (UK ISSN 0958-7322) 710, 1126

Centre Regional de Documentation Pedagogique. Studi. (FR) **1620**

Centre Regional de Documentation Pedagogique de Toulouse. Annales. (FR ISSN 0069-2069) **1620**

Centre Regional de Promotion du Livre en Afrique. Bulletin d'Information. see Regional Centre for Book Promotion in Africa. Bulletin of Information **4136**

Centre Regional de Recherche et de Documentation Pedagogiques de Lyon. Annales. (FR ISSN 0069-2050) **1746**

6042 CENTRE REGIONAL

Centre Regional de Recherche et de Documentation Pedagogiques de Rennes. Studi *see* Centre Regional de Documentation Pedagogique. Studi **1620**

Centre Suisse de Documentation en Matiere d'Enseignement et d'Education. Bulletin. (SZ) **1620**

Centre Technique des Eaux Usees. Bulletin. *see* Wastewater Technology Centre Newsletter **4831**

Centre Technique du Bois et de l'Ameublement. Cahiers. (FR ISSN 0008-9885) **2114**

Centre Technique du Bois et de l'Ameublement. Profils. (FR) **2112**

Centre Technique du Bois et de l'Ameublement. Revue Documentaire *see* Centre Technique du Bois et de l'Ameublement. Profils **2112**

Centre Technique du Bois et de l'Ameublement Info *see* C T B Info **2113**

Centre Technique du Papier. Feuillets Bibliographiques. (FR) **3662**

Centrepiece. (US) **1307**

Centrepoint. (UK ISSN 0577-1935) **3879**

†Centrepoint. (NZ ISSN 0111-5308) **5163**

Centres de Recherches Exploration - Production ELF Aquitaine. Bulletin. (FR ISSN 0396-2687) **3684**, 1557

Centric. (US) **3669**

†Centrifugal Pump Spec Book. (US) **5163**

†Centrifugal Pump Specifications. (US) **5163**

Centro America Odontologica. (ES ISSN 0008-9907) **3230**

Centro Argentino de Ingenieros Informa *see* C A I Informa **1883**

Centro Brasileiro de Analise e Planejamento Novos Estudos C E B R A P *see* Novos Estudos C E B R A P **3911**

Centro Camuno di Studi Preistorici. Archivi. (IT) **268**, 321

Centro Camuno di Studi Preistorici. Bollettino. (IT ISSN 0577-2168) **268**, 321, 4168

Centro Camuno di Studi Preistorici. Studi Camuni. (IT) **268**, 321

Centro Camuno di Studi Preistorici. Symposia. (IT) **321**, 268, 4168

Centro Cultural Portugues. Arquivos *see* Centre Culturel Portugais. Archives **2981**

Centro de Bibliotecologia, Archivologia e Informacion. Anuario. (MX) **2752**

Centro de Desarrollo Industrial Boletin Industrial *see* C E N D E S Boletin Industrial **1073**

Centro de Desarrollo Industrial del Ecuador. Boletin de Noticias Tecnicas.(EC) **1073**

Centro de Desarrollo Industrial del Ecuador. Noticias Tecnicas *see* Centro de Desarrollo Industrial del Ecuador. Boletin de Noticias Tecnicas **1073**

Centro de Documentacion y Estudios. Informativo Campesino. (PY ISSN 1017-6047) **3980**

Centro de Documentacion y Estudios. Informativo Laboral. (PY ISSN 1017-6055) **975**

Centro de Documentacion y Estudios. Informativo Mujer. (PY ISSN 1017-6063) **4839**

†Centro de Edafologia y Biologia Aplicada. Anuario. (SP ISSN 0210-8623) **5163**

Centro de Estudios Avanzados de Puerto Rico y el Caribe. Revista. (PR) **2402**, 268

Centro de Estudios de la Realidad Economica y Social. Serie Cochabamba. (BO) **4431**, 850

Centro de Estudios de la Realidad Economica y Social. Serie Estudios Regionales. (BO) **850**, 4431

Centro de Estudios de la Realidad Economica y Social. Serie Estudios Urbanos. (BO) **4431**, 850

Centro de Estudios de la Realidad Economica y Social. Serie Movimientos Sociales. (BO) **4431**, 850

Centro de Estudios de la Realidad Puertorriquena. Cuadernos. (PR) **3879**

Centro de Estudios e Investigaciones Sobre Mercados Agropecuario Adquisiciones Reciente *see* C E I M A Adquisiciones Reciente **135**

Centro de Estudios Genealogicos de Cordoba. Boletin. (AG) **2146**

Centro de Estudios Humanitarios *see* C E D H U **2608**

Centro de Estudios Indigenas. Anuario. (MX) **237**, 1996

Centro de Estudios Martianos. Anuario. (CU) **2402**

Centro de Estudios Monetarios Latinoamericanos. Boletin Bimensual. (MX ISSN 0186-7229) **771**

Centro de Estudios Monetarios Latinoamericanos. Ensayos. (MX ISSN 0577-2451) **771**

Centro de Estudios Orientales. Anuario. (MX ISSN 0066-8249) **2337**

Centro de Estudios Publicos. Documento de Trabajo. (CL ISSN 0716-1123) **850**, 2612, 3879

†Centro de Estudios Sobre Desarrollo Economico. Cuadernos. (CK) **5163**

Centro de Estudios Urbanos y Regionales. Boletin (AG ISSN 0326-8470) **4431**

Centro de Estudios Urbanos y Regionales. Cuadernos. (AG ISSN 0326-1417) **4431**

Centro de Estudios Urbanos y Regionales. Informes de Investigacion. (AG) **4431**

Centro de Estudios y Asesoramiento Metalurgico *see* C E A M **653**

Centro de Estudios y Promocion del Desarrollo (DESCO) Resumen Semanal *see* Resumen Semanal **3922**

Centro de Estudios y Promocion del Desarrollo. Serie Publicaciones Previas. (PE) **655**

Centro de Estudios Cientificos Revista *see* C E C Revista **4303**

Centro de Estudios de Cabo Verde. Revista: Serie de Ciencias Humanas. (CV) **4368**

Centro de Estudios Regionais. Boletim Cultural. (PO) **237**, 268

Centro de Fisica da Atmosfera de Lisboa. Boletim. (PO ISSN 0870-4716) **1587**

Centro de Historia del Estado Falcon. Boletin. (VE ISSN 0008-9990) **2402**

Centro de Historia del Tachira. Boletin. (VE ISSN 0411-5023) **2402**

Centro de Informacion Documental de Archivos. Boletin de Informacion. (SP ISSN 0210-9492) **2752**

Centro de Informaciones y Estudios del Uruguay. Cuadernos. (UY) **4368**

Centro de Investigacion y Accion Social. Boletin Mensual *see* Centro de Investigacion y Accion Social. Revista **4368**

Centro de Investigacion y Accion Social. Revista. (AG ISSN 0325-1306) **4368**

Centro de Investigacion y Promocion del Campesinado. Cuadernos de Investigacion. (BO) **850**

Centro de Investigaciones Agricolas de Tamaulipas. Informe Anual de Labores. (MX ISSN 0084-8697) **83**

Centro de Investigaciones Regionales de Mesoamerica. Serie Monografica. (US ISSN 0252-9971) **4368**

Centro de Navegacion Transatlantica. C.N.T. Handbook. River Plate Handbook for Shipowners and Agents. (AG) **4725**

Centro de Navegacion Transatlantica. C.N.T. Year Book; Ship Owners' and Agents' Handbook, River Plate Ports *see* Centro de Navegacion Transatlantica. C.N.T. Handbook. River Plate Handbook for Shipowners and Agents **4725**

Centro de Pastoral Familiar para America Latina Buletin *see* C E N P A F A L Buletin **5156**

Centro de Pesquisa Agropecuaria do Tropico Umido. Boletim de Pesquisa. (BL ISSN 0100-8102) **83**

Centro de Pesquisas do Cacau. Boletim Tecnico. (BL ISSN 0100-0845) **83**

Centro de Pesquisas do Cacau. Informe de Pesquisas. (BL) **83**, 2038

Centro de Pesquisas do Cacau. Informe Tecnico *see* Centro de Pesquisas do Cacau. Informe de Pesquisas **83**

▼Centro de Ricerche Storiche, Rovigno. La Ricerca. (CI) **2356**

Centro de Salud "Max Arias Schreiber", Lima. Congreso Nacional de Tuberculosis y Enfermedades Respiratorias. (PE ISSN 0069-2166) **3364**

Centro di Documentazione Economica e di Marketing Notizie *see* C E D E M Notizie **1035**

Centro di Documentazione Sul Movimento dei Disciplinati. Quaderni *see* Centro di Ricerca e di Studio Sul Movimento dei Disciplinati. Quaderni **2308**

Centro di Ricerca e di Studio Sul Movimento dei Disciplinati. Quaderni. (IT) **2308**

Centro di Ricerche Storiche, Rovigno. Atti. (CI ISSN 0352-1427) **2356**

Centro di Ricerche Storiche, Rovigno. Collana degli Atti. (CI ISSN 0353-3301) **2356**

Centro di Ricerche Storiche, Rovigno. Documenti. (CI) **2356**

▼Centro di Ricerche Storiche, Rovigno. Etnia. (CI ISSN 0353-3271) **2356**

Centro di Ricerche Storiche, Rovigno. Fonti. (CI) **2356**

Centro di Ricerche Storiche, Rovigno. Monografie. (CI ISSN 0353-328X) **2356**

Centro di Ricerche Storiche, Rovigno. Quaderni. (CI ISSN 0350-6746) **2356**

Centro di Ricerche Storiche, Rovigno. Ricerche Sociali. (CI ISSN 0353-474X) **2356**

Centro di Riferimento Italiano Diane. Notiziario. (IT ISSN 0392-0143) **1390**

Centro di Studi di Letteratura Italiana in Piemonte Guido Gozzano. Saggi e Testi. (IT) **2904**

Centro di Studi Vichiani. Bollettino. (IT ISSN 0392-7334) **3763**

Centro Documentazione e Ricerche Economico-Sociali Ce D R E S Documenti *see* Ce D R E S Documenti **4056**

Centro Informativo de la Construccion Informacion *see* C I C Informacion **608**

Centro Informazione Vivisezionista Internazionale Scientifica International Foundation Report *see* C I V I S: International Foundation Report **230**

Centro Informazioni Studi Esperienze Newsletter *see* C I S E Newsletter **4594**

Centro Interamericano de Artesanias y Artes Populares. Boletin de Informacion *see* Artesanias de America **316**

Centro Interamericano de Fotointerpretacion. Revista. (CK ISSN 0120-2499) **2245**

Centro Interamericano de Investigacion y Documentacion sobre Formacion Profesional. Boletin. (UY ISSN 0577-2907) **1620**

Centro Interamericano de Investigacion y Documentacion sobre Formacion Profesional. Informes. (UY) **1620**

Centro Interamericano de Investigacion y Documentacion sobre Formacion Profesional. Serie Bibliografica. (UY) **1620**

Centro Interamericano de Investigacion y Documentacion sobre Formacion Profesional Documentacion *see* C I N T E R F O R - Documentacion **1619**

Centro Interamericano de Investigacion y Documentacion sobre Formacion Profesional Estudios y Monografias *see* C I N T E R F O R Estudios y Monografias **1619**

Centro Internacional de Agricultura Tropical. Annual Report *see* C I A T Report **81**

Centro Internacional de Agricultura Tropical Internacional *see* C I A T Internacional **81**

Centro Internacional de Agricultura Tropical International *see* C I A T International **81**

Centro Internacional de Agricultura Tropical Report *see* C I A T Report **81**

Centro Internacional de Mejoramiento de Maiz y Trigo Review *see* C I M M Y T Review **5157**

Centro Internazionale di Studi di Architettura "Andrea Palladio" di Vicenza. Annali di Architettura. (IT) **296**

Centro Internazionale Radio-Medico *see* C.I.R.M **3085**

Centro Interuniversitario di Ricerche sul Viaggio in Italia Bollettino *see* C I R V I Bollettino **4755**

Centro Latinoamericano de Demografia. Boletin Demografico. (UN ISSN 0378-5386) **3980**

Centro Latinoamericano de Demografia. Notas de Poblacion. (UN ISSN 0303-1829) **3980**

Centro Latinoamericano de Demografia. Serie A. *see* United Nations. Regional Centre for Demographic Training and Research in Latin America. Serie A **3988**

Centro Latinoamericano de Demografia. Serie C. *see* United Nations. Regional Centre for Demographic Training and Research in Latin America. Serie C **3988**

Centro Latinoamericano de Demografia. Serie D. *see* United Nations. Regional Centre for Demographic Training and Research in Latin America. Serie D **3988**

Centro Latinoamericano de Demografia. Serie E. *see* United Nations. Regional Centre for Demographic Training and Research in Latin America. Serie E **3988**

Centro Latinoamericano de Demografia. Serie OI: Publicaciones Conjuntas con Instituciones Nacionales de Paises de America Latina. (UN) **3980**

Centro Latinoamericano de Economia Humana. Publicaciones. (UY) **4431**

Centro Micologico Friulano. Bollettino. (IT) **499**

Centro Nacional de Investigaciones Cientificas. Revista: Ciencias Fisicas *see* Revista de Ciencias Quimicas **1187**

Centro Naval. Boletin. (AG ISSN 0009-0123) **3453**

Centro Pan-Americano de Febre Aftosa. Boletin. (UN ISSN 0009-0131) **4099**

Centro Pan-Americano de Febre Aftosa. Cuadernos *see* Centro Pan-Americano de Febre Aftosa. Boletin **4099**

Centro Panamericano de Zoonosis. Monografias Cientificas y Tecnicas. (UN) **4304**

Centro Panamericano de Zoonosis. Notas Tecnicas. (UN) **4808**

Centro Panamericano de Zoonosis. Publicaciones Especiales. (UN) **4808**

Centro Panamericano de Zoonosis. Serie de Bibliografias. (UN) **4820**

Centro para las Culturas Populares y Tradicionales. Boletin. (VE) **3544**, 2053

Centro Ricerche Biopsichiche. (IT ISSN 0392-3398) **4015**

Centro Ricerche e Documentazione sull'Antichita Classica. Monografie. (IT) **1275**

Centro Studi Investimenti Sociali Note e Commenti *see* C E N S I S Note e Commenti **4430**

CESKOSLOVENSKA SPOLECNOST 6043

Centro Studi Parapsicologici. Bollettino see Quaderni di Parapsicologia **3671**
Centro Studi per la Magna Grecia, Naples. Pubblicazioni Proprie. (IT ISSN 0069-2204) **268**
Centro Studi Russia Cristiana. Rivista see L'Altra Europa **311**
Centro Superiore di Logica e Scienze Comparate. Quaderni. (IT) **3763**
Centrul de Astronomie si Stiinte Spatiale. Anuarul Astronomic. (RM) **363**
Centrum Jana Pawla II Biuletyn. (US) **418, 4260**
Centrum voor Onderzoek en Voorlichting voor de Pluimveehouderij "Het Spelderholt". Jaarsverlag. (NE ISSN 0927-0353) **214**
Centrum voor Rassenonderzoek en Zaadtechnologie. Jaarsverslag. (NE) **172**
Centrum voor Rassenonderzoek en Zaadtechnologie. Mededelingen. (NE) **172**
Centrum voor Wiskunde en Informatica Newsletter see C W I Quarterly **1455**
Centrum voor Wiskunde en Informatica Quarterly see C W I Quarterly **1455**
Centur. (UY) **4687, 4757**
Centuries. see Szazadok **2324**
Century Graphics. (US) **2223**
Century Home. (CN ISSN 0838-9330) **2549**
Century 21. (US) **4146**
†Ceol. (IE ISSN 0009-0174) **5163**
Cephalagia. (NO ISSN 0333-1024) **3333**
Cephalopod Newsletter. (UK ISSN 0260-681X) **580, 1557, 3657**
Ceram Research News. (UK) **1162**
Ceramic Abstracts. (US ISSN 0095-9960) **1167, 8**
Ceramic Arts & Crafts. (US ISSN 0009-0190) **353**
Ceramic Bulletin see American Ceramic Society. Bulletin **1161**
Ceramic Engineering and Science Proceedings. (US ISSN 0196-6219) **1162**
Ceramic Forum International. (GW ISSN 0173-9913) **1162**
Ceramic Hobbyist see Canadian Ceramic Society. Journal **1161**
Ceramic Industries International. (UK) **1162**
Ceramic Industry. (US ISSN 0009-0220) **1162**
Ceramic Industry Data Book Buyers Guide. (US ISSN 0009-0220) **1162**
Ceramic Projects see Ceramics (Livonia) **1162**
Ceramic Review. (UK ISSN 0144-1825) **1162**
†Ceramic Scope. (US ISSN 0009-0247) **5163**
Ceramic Scope Buyer's Guide. (US) **1162**
Ceramic Society of Japan. Journal. see Seramikkusu Kyokai Shi **1166**
Ceramic Source. (US ISSN 8756-8187) **1162**
Ceramic Study Group. Newsletter. (AT) **1162**
Ceramic Teaching Projects and Trade News see Ceramics (Livonia) **1162**
Ceramic Tile Fashion see Fashion Ceramic Tiles **1163**
†Ceramic World. (US) **5163**
Ceramica. (BL ISSN 0366-6913) **1162**
Ceramica. (IT) **1162**
Ceramica Acta. (IT) **1162**
†Ceramica de Cultura Maya. (US ISSN 0577-3334) **5164**
Ceramica Informacion. (SP) **1162**
Ceramica Informazione. (IT ISSN 0009-0271) **1162**
La Ceramica Moderna. (IT ISSN 0392-8225) **4595**
Ceramica per l'Architettura. (IT) **1162**
Ceramica per l'Edilizia Internationale. (IT ISSN 0392-4890) **609**
Ceramica y Cristal. (AG ISSN 0325-0229) **1162**
Ceramics see Ceramic Industries International **1162**
Ceramics (Fresno). (US) **353, 2434**
Ceramics (Livonia). (US) **1162**
Ceramics Industries Journal see Ceramic Industries International **1162**
Ceramics International. (UK ISSN 0272-8842) **1162**
Ceramics Japan. see Seramikkusu **1166**
Ceramics: Latin American Industrial Report. (US) **1162**
Ceramics Monthly. (US ISSN 0009-0328) **1162**
Ceramics Studies Journal. see Taoci Yanjiu **1166**
Ceramics, the Magazine of Techniques see Ceramics (Livonia) **1162**
Ceramique Moderne. (FR ISSN 0009-0336) **1162**
Ceramurgia. (IT ISSN 0045-6152) **1163**
CERannuario. (IT ISSN 0392-6834) **1163**
Cerberus Alarm see Alarm **2031**
Cerberus Security. (SZ) **1526**
Cercetari de Lingvistica. (RM) **2809**
Cercle Belge de la Librairie. Annuaire. (BE) **4125, 2752**
Cercle d'Etudes Numismatiques. Bulletin. (BE ISSN 0009-0344) **3598, 2308**
Cercle d'Etudes Numismatiques. Travaux. (BE ISSN 0069-2247) **3598**
Cercle d'Histoire et d'Archeologie de Saint-Ghislain et de la Region. Anales. (BE) **2356, 268**
Cercle d'Histoire et d'Archeologie de Saint-Ghislain et de la Region. Miettes d'Histoire see Cercle d'Histoire et d'Archeologie de Saint-Ghislain et de la Region. Anales **2356**
Cercle de Beckett. see Beckett Circle **2898**
Cercle Ernest Renan. Bulletin see Cercle Ernest Renan. Cahiers **4168**
Cercle Ernest Renan. Cahiers. (FR ISSN 0411-5562) **4168, 2308**
Cercle Fustec de Coulanges. Documents. (FR) **2356, 3879**
Cercle Genealogique de Lorraine. Revue see Genealogie Lorraine **2152**
Cercle Historique et Archeologique de Renaix et du Tenement d'Inde. Annales. see Geschied- en Oudheidkundige Kring van Ronse en het Tenement van Inde. Annalen **2363**
Cercle Historique et Folklorique de Braine-le-Chateau de Tubize et des Regions Voisines. Annales. (BE) **2356, 268**
Cercle Hutois des Sciences et Beaux-Arts. Annales. (BE) **2356, 268**
Cercle Royal d'Histoire et d'Archeologie d'Ath et de la Region. Bulletin. (BE) **269**
Cercle Royal d'Histoire et d'Archeologie d'Ath et de la Region et Musees Athois. Annales. (BE) **269**
Cercle Royal d'Histoire et d'Archeologie d'Ath et de la Region et Musees Athois. Etudes et Documents. (BE ISSN 0771-5692) **269**
Cercle Royal Historique et Archeologique de Courtrai. Memoires. see Koninklijke Geschied- en Oudheidkundige Kring van Kortrijk. Handelingen **2372**
Cerddoriaeth Cymru. see Welsh Music **3586**
Cereal Chemistry. (US ISSN 0009-0352) **2063**
Cereal Foods World. (US ISSN 0146-6283) **205, 2063**
Cereal Research Communications. (HU ISSN 0133-3720) **205**
Cereal Rust Bulletin. (US) **172**
Cereal Science Today see Cereal Foods World **205**
Cereals and Oilseeds Review. (CN ISSN 0820-9030) **136**
Cerebral Circulation and Metabolism/Circulation et Metabolisme du Cerveau. (FR ISSN 0264-6900) **3333**
▼Cerebral Cortex. (US ISSN 1047-3211) **3086**
†Cerebral Function Symposium. Proceedings. (US) **5164**
Cerebro. (GW) **3206, 3333**
Cerebrovascular and Brain Metabolism Reviews. (US ISSN 1040-8827) **3333**
Cerebrovascular Diseases see Princeton Research Conferences on Cerebrovascular Diseases **3211**
▼Cerebrovascular Diseases. (SZ ISSN 1015-9770) **3333, 3271**
Ceredigion. (UK ISSN 0069-2263) **2308**
Ceres. (UN ISSN 0009-0379) **83, 148**
Cerevisia see Cerevisia and Biotechnology **489**
Cerevisia and Biotechnology. (BE) **489, 380, 2063**
CERfornitori. (IT ISSN 0392-6850) **1163**
Cerkev v Sedanjem Svetu. (XV ISSN 0009-0387) **4260**
Cerkovnyj Vistnik. see Church Messenger **4171**
Cerkveni Glasbenik. (XV ISSN 0351-496X) **3545**
Cermin Masyarakat. (MY) **2209**
Cernakov Odkaz see Slobodne Slovensko **2884**
Cerrahpasa Medical Faculty. Journal/Cerrahpasa Tip Fakultesi Dergisi. (TU ISSN 0376-7833) **3087**
Cerrahpasa Medical Review. (TU) **3087**
Cerrahpasa Tip Fakultesi Dergisi. see Cerrahpasa Medical Faculty. Journal **3087**
Cerro Gordo News see Cerro Gordo Town Forum **2485**
Cerro Gordo Town Forum. (US) **2485**
Certezze. (IT) **4168**
Certificated Engineer/Gediplomeerde Ingenieur. (SA ISSN 0009-0409) **1927, 1884**
Certified Accountant. (UK ISSN 0306-2406) **749**
Certified Accountants Journal see Certified Accountant **749**
Certified Ballast Manufacturers News see C B M News **1883**
Certified Coin Dealer Newsletter. (US) **3598**
Certified Copy. (US ISSN 0749-5684) **2147**
Certified Engineering Technician. (US ISSN 0746-6641) **1816**
Certified General Accountant see C G A Magazine **748**
Certified General Accountants' Association of Canada Magazine see C G A Magazine **748**
Certified Irrigation Specialists and Technicians Directory. (US) **1126**
Certified Public Accountant Associates. Update see C P A Associates. Update **748**
Certified Public Accountant Micro Report see C P A Micro Report **805**
Cervantes. (US ISSN 0277-6995) **2904**
Cervantes and His Times. (US ISSN 1054-1403) **2904**
Cerveza y Malta. (SP ISSN 0300-4481) **380**
Cervo Volante. (IT) **2990**
Cesareans, Support, Education and Concern Newsletter see C S E C Newsletter **5157**
Ceska Archeologicka Spolecnost. Zpravy/Czech Archaeological Society. News. (CS) **269**
Ceska Bibliografie. (CS ISSN 0577-3490) **397**
Ceska Literatura/Czech Literature. (NE ISSN 0009-0468) **2904**
Ceska Mykologie/Czech Mycology. (CS ISSN 0009-0476) **499**
Ceskoslovenska Acedemie Ved. Ustav v Brne. Prirodovedne Prace/Acta Scientiarum Naturalium Academiae Scientiarum Bohemoslovacae Brno. (CS) **4304**
Ceskoslovenska Akademie Ved. Acta Technica. (CS ISSN 0001-7043) **1816, 1884, 3842**
Ceskoslovenska Akademie Ved. Archeologicky Ustav. Zachranne Oddeleni. Bulletin see Vyzkumy v Cechach **289**
Ceskoslovenska Akademie Ved. Archivni Zpravy. (CS ISSN 0323-1313) **2356**
Ceskoslovenska Akademie Ved. Brnenska Zakladna. Prace see Ceskoslovenska Acedemie Ved. Ustav v Brne. Prirodovedne Prace **4304**
Ceskoslovenska Akademie Ved. Geograficky Ustav, Brno. Zpravy. (CS ISSN 0375-6122) **2245**
Ceskoslovenska Akademie Ved. Rozpravy. M P V: Rada Matematickych a Prirodnich Ved. (CS ISSN 0069-228X) **4304**
Ceskoslovenska Akademie Ved. Rozpravy. S V: Rada Spolecenskych Ved. (CS ISSN 0069-2298) **4368**
Ceskoslovenska Akademie Ved. Rozpravy. T V: Rada Technickych Ved. (CS ISSN 0069-2301) **4595**
Ceskoslovenska Akademie Ved. Ustav pro Jazyk Cesky. Onomasticky Zpravodaj. (CS ISSN 0232-0266) **2356, 2809**
Ceskoslovenska Akademie Ved. Ustredni Archiv. Archivni Zpravy. (CS) **2752**
Ceskoslovenska Akademie Ved. Vestnik/Czechoslovak Academy of Sciences. Bulletin. (CS ISSN 0009-0492) **4304**
Ceskoslovenska Akademie Zemedelska. Vestnik. (CS) **83**
Ceskoslovenska Armada. (CS ISSN 0009-0506) **3454**
Ceskoslovenska Dermatologie. (CS ISSN 0009-0514) **3246**
Ceskoslovenska Epidemiologie, Mikrobiologie, Imunologie. (CS ISSN 0009-0522) **550**
Ceskoslovenska Farmacie. (CS ISSN 0009-0530) **3720**
Ceskoslovenska Fysiologie/Czechoslovak Physiology. (CS ISSN 0009-0557) **570, 3087**
Ceskoslovenska Gastroenterologie a Vyziva. (CS ISSN 0009-0565) **3266**
Ceskoslovenska Gynekologie. (CS ISSN 0374-6852) **3290**
Ceskoslovenska Hygiena. (CS ISSN 0009-0573) **3800**
Ceskoslovenska Informatika see I'91 **2765**
Ceskoslovenska Neurologie see Ceskoslovenska Neurologie a Neurochirurgie **3333**
Ceskoslovenska Neurologie a Neurochirurgie. (CS ISSN 0301-0597) **3333, 3376**
Ceskoslovenska Oftalmologie. (CS ISSN 0009-059X) **3299**
Ceskoslovenska Otolaryngologie. (CS ISSN 0009-0603) **3314**
Ceskoslovenska Patologie. (CS ISSN 0009-0611) **3087, 435**
Ceskoslovenska Pediatrie. (CS ISSN 0069-2328) **3319**
Ceskoslovenska Psychiatrie. (CS ISSN 0069-2336) **3333**
Ceskoslovenska Psychologie/Czechoslovak Psychology. (CS ISSN 0009-062X) **4015**
Ceskoslovenska Radiologie. (CS ISSN 0069-2344) **3357**
Ceskoslovenska Roentgenologie see Ceskoslovenska Radiologie **3357**
Ceskoslovenska Rusistika see Casopis Pro Moderni Filologii **2808**
Ceskoslovenska Rusistika see Svet Literatury **2967**
Ceskoslovenska Spolecnost Archeologicka. Zpravy see Ceska Archeologicka Spolecnost. Zpravy **269**
Ceskoslovenska Spolecnost Mikrobiologicka. Bulletin. (CS ISSN 0009-0646) **550**
Ceskoslovenska Spolecnost Zemepisna. Sbornik see Ceskoslovenske Geograficke Spolecnosti. Sbornik **2245**
Ceskoslovenska Spolecnost Zoologicka. Vestnik/Czechoslovak Zoological Society. Bulletin. (CS ISSN 0042-4595) **580**

Ceskoslovenska Standardizace see Magazin C S N **3447**
Ceskoslovenske Stomatologie. (CS ISSN 0009-0654) **3230**
Ceskoslovenska Tiskova Kancelar Dokumentacni Prehled see C T K Dokumentacni Prehled **2568**
Ceskoslovenska Zemedelska Bilbiografie/Czechoslovak Agricultural Bibliography. (CS ISSN 0232-0851) **136, 397**
Ceskoslovenske Geograficke Spolecnosti. Sbornik/Czechoslovak Geographical Society. Journal. (CS ISSN 0231-5300) **2245**
Ceskoslovenske Rybarstvi see Rybarstvi **2048**
Ceskoslovenske Spoje see P T T Revue **1341**
Ceskoslovenske Zdravotnictvi. (CS ISSN 0009-0689) **4099**
Ceskoslovenski Vybor pro Spolupraci s F A O. Bulletin. (CS) **83**
Ceskoslovensko. (CS) **3750**
Ceskoslovensko-Sovetske Vztahy. (CS) **2356**
Ceskoslovensky Casopis Historicky/ Czechoslovak Historical Journal. (CS ISSN 0045-6187) **2356**
Ceskoslovensky Casopis pro Fyziku. (CS ISSN 0009-0700) **3815**
Ceskoslovensky Hornik a Energetik. (CS ISSN 0009-0719) **3480, 2581**
Ceskoslovensky Kolorista. (CS ISSN 0009-0727) **1281**
Ceskoslovensky Kras. (CS ISSN 0373-7179) **2245**
†Ceskoslovensky Rozhlas a Televize. (CS ISSN 0009-0735) **5164**
†Ceskoslovensky Sach. (CS ISSN 0009-0743) **5164**
Ceskoslovensky Vojak. (CS ISSN 0009-0751) **3454, 3879**
Ceskoslovesky Architekt see Architekt **293**
Cesky Bratr. (CS ISSN 0009-0778) **4232**
Cesky Jazyk a Literatura. (CS ISSN 0009-0786) **1621, 2809, 2904**
Cesky Lid/Czech People. (CS ISSN 0009-0794) **237, 2053**
Cessna Owner. (US) **49**
C'est Pour Quand. (CN ISSN 0705-3215) **1233**
Ceste i Mostovi/Roads and Bridges. (CI ISSN 0411-6380) **1863, 1005, 4672, 4718**
Ceylon Chamber of Commerce. Annual Review of Business and Trade (Year). (CE) **811**
Ceylon Chamber of Commerce. Register of Members. (CE) **811**
Ceylon Churchman. (CE) **4232**
Ceylon College of Obstetricians and Gynaecologists. Journal. (CE) **3290**
Ceylon Commerce. (CE) **834**
Ceylon Geographer. (CE) **2245, 1542**
Ceylon Historical Journal. (CE ISSN 0577-4691) **2337**
Ceylon Institute of Scientific & Industrial Research. Annual Report. (CE) **4304, 4595**
Ceylon Journal of Medical Science. (CE ISSN 0011-2232) **3087, 3604, 4099**
Ceylon Journal of Science. Biological Sciences. (CE ISSN 0069-2379) **435**
Ceylon Journal of the Humanities see Sri Lanka Journal of the Humanities **2515**
Ceylon Medical Journal. (CE ISSN 0009-0875) **3087**
Ceylon National Bibliography see Sri Lanka National Bibliography **4142**
Ceylon Rationalist Ambassador. (CE ISSN 0577-4772) **3763**
Ceylon Shipping Corporation. Annual Report & Statement of Accounts. (CE) **4725**
Ceylon Tourist Board. Annual Statistical Report. (CE) **4799**
Ceylon Tourist Board. Monthly Bulletin on the Performance of the Tourism Sector. (CE) **4799**
Ceylon Veterinary Journal see Sri Lanka Veterinary Journal **4816**
ChaCom. (UK) **811**

Chad. Bulletin Mensuel de Statistiques. (CD) **710**
†Chadashot ha-Chaklaut. (IS) **5164**
Chadashot Pensia. (IS) **655**
Chadashot Tikshoret Nitunim. (IS) **1390**
Chadburn. (US) **2402**
†Chagyo Gijutsu Kenkyu/Study of Tea. (JA ISSN 0366-6123) **5164**
Chai Magazine. (KE) **2063**
Chai Today. (US) **1996**
Chain Drug Review. (US ISSN 0164-9914) **1005**
Chain Merchandiser. (US ISSN 0009-0921) **2063**
Chain Reaction. (AT ISSN 0312-1372) **1945, 3879**
Chain Saw Age. (US ISSN 0009-093X) **2114**
†Chain Shoe Stores and Leased Shoe Department Operators. (US ISSN 0069-2387) **5164**
Chain Store Age Drug Magazine see Drug Store News **1038**
Chain Store Age General Merchandise Edition see Chain Store Age General Merchandise Trends **5164**
†Chain Store Age General Merchandise Trends. (US) **5164**
Chainsaw & Small Engine. (US) **641**
Chaiyou Ji/Diesel Engine. (CC ISSN 1001-4357) **1927**
Ha-Chaklaim. (IS) **83**
Chakra. (US) **2904,** 321
Chakra. (BG) **4401**
Chalcedon Report. (US) **4168, 3763, 3879**
Chaleur et Climats. (BE) **2298,** 1884
Chalice. (US) **2147**
Chalk Circle. (US) **2904**
Challenge. (AT ISSN 0311-0486) **1621**
The Challenge. (PK) **3364**
Challenge (Armonk). (US ISSN 0577-5132) **655**
Challenge (Carthage). (US ISSN 0745-6298) **1746,** 1233
Challenge (Convent Station). (US ISSN 0277-1675) **2452, 3396**
Challenge (London, 1960). (UK ISSN 0009-1006) **1251**
Challenge (London, 1961). (UK ISSN 0009-0999) **4232, 3953**
Challenge (New York). (US ISSN 0009-1049) **3879**
Challenge (Sandbach). (UK ISSN 0009-1014) **4168**
Challenge (Wheaton). (US) **4232**
Challenge (Worthing). (UK) **2193**
Challenge Advocate. (AT) **4401, 4015**
†Challenge of Excellence Annual Report.(US) **5164**
Challenge of the 80's see Nebraska Highway Program **4720**
†Challenge of the '80s Update. (US) **5164**
Challenged American see Moving Forward **2294**
Challenger see Volunteer (New York, 1961) **5302**
Challenger (Buffalo). (US ISSN 1040-8886) **1996**
Challenger (Petaluma). (US) **4232**
Challenger Society. Newsletter see Ocean Challenge **1609**
†Chalmers Tekniska Hoegskola. Institutionen foer Skeppshydromekanik. Rapport/ Chalmers University of Technology. Department of Ship Hydromechanics. Report. (SW ISSN 0009-112X) **5164**
Chalmers University of Technology. Department of Sanitary Engineering. Publications. (SW ISSN 0280-4026) **4823,** 1945
Chalmers University of Technology. Department of Ship Hydromechanics. Report. see Chalmers Tekniska Hoegskola. Institutionen foer Skeppshydromekanik. Rapport **5164**
Chamber Bulletin see Going Concerns **816**
Chamber Business News. (US) **811**
Chamber Comment see Chamber Comment and the Chamber Newsbulletin **811**

Chamber Comment and the Chamber Newsbulletin. (CN) **811**
Chamber de Commerce et d'Industrie de Meurthe et Moselle. Dossiers. (FR) **811**
Chamber Executive. (US ISSN 0884-8114) **811**
Chamber Insider. (US) **811**
Chamber Link. (IE) **811**
†Chamber Message. (US) **5164**
Chamber Music see Chamber Music Magazine **3545**
Chamber Music Magazine. (US ISSN 8755-0725) **3545**
Chamber News. (US) **811**
Chamber News see Thai - Chinese Chamber of Commerce. News **823**
Chamber News see Zululand Chamber of Commerce and Industry. News **825**
Chamber of Commerce. Greater Lubbock. (US) **811**
Chamber of Commerce and Industries of South West Africa. Newsletter see Business Spotlight - Namibia **809**
Chamber of Commerce and Industry. Trade Journal. (PK) **811**
Chamber of Commerce and Industry in West Java. Member List/Kamar Dagang dan Industri di Jawa Barat. Daftar Anggota. (IO) **811**
Chamber of Commerce Journal see London Chamber **819**
Chamber of Commerce Newspaper. (NE) **811**
Chamber of Commerce of Sierra Leone. Journal. (SL ISSN 0080-9527) **811**
Chamber of Commerce of the U S A in Uruguay. Newsletter. (UY) **811**
Chamber of Commerce of Vanuatu. Monthly Bulletin. (NN) **811**
Chamber of Economy of Vojvodina. Business Information. (YU) **811**
Chamber of Mines' Newsletter. (SA) **3480**
Chamber of Mines of South Africa. Mining Survey. (SA ISSN 0026-5268) **3480**
Chamber Patrika. (NP) **811**
The Chamber Today. (US ISSN 0279-0785) **811**
Chamber Update. (US) **811**
Chamberlain Association News. (US ISSN 0882-987X) **2147**
Chamberlain Chain. (US ISSN 1041-6579) **2147**
Chamber's Trade Directory. (PK) **1126**
Chamberview see Business Today (St. Paul) **809**
Chambre d'Agriculture New Caledonia. Bulletin see Agri Infos **69**
Chambre d'Industrie, Antwerp. Bulletin see Chambre de Commerce et d'Industrie d'Anvers. Bulletin **812**
Chambre de Commerce, Antwerp. Bulletin see Chambre de Commerce et d'Industrie d'Anvers. Bulletin **812**
Chambre de Commerce Belgo - Italienne Annuaire. (BE) **811**
Chambre de Commerce Belgo - Italienne Echanges see Chambre de Commerce Belgo - Italienne Exchange **811**
Chambre de Commerce Belgo - Italienne Exchange. (BE) **811**
Chambre de Commerce, d'Agriculture, d'Elevage, d'Industrie et des Mines de la Republique Islamique de Mauritanie. Bulletin. (MU) **811**
Chambre de Commerce, d'Agriculture, d'Industrie et d'Artisanat du Niger. Weekly Bulletin. (NG) **812**
Chambre de Commerce, d'Agriculture, d'Industrie et des Mines du Gabon. Bulletin. (GO ISSN 0045-6276) **812**
Chambre de Commerce, d'Agriculture et d'Industrie. Informations Economiques. (CD) **812**
Chambre de Commerce, d'Agriculture et d'Industrie du Togo. Bulletin Mensuel.(TG) **812**
Chambre de Commerce, d'Artisanat et d'Industrie de Haute-Volta. Annuaire see Chambre de Commerce, d'Industrie et d'Artisanat du Burkina Faso. Annuaire **812**

Chambre de Commerce, d'Industrie et d'Agriculture de Litturi. Bulletin. (ZR) **812**
Chambre de Commerce, d'Industrie et d'Agriculture du Kisai. Bulletin. (ZR) **812**
Chambre de Commerce, d'Industrie et d'Artisanat du Burkina Faso. Annuaire. (UV) **812**
Chambre de Commerce, d'Industrie et des Mines du Cameroun. Bulletin d'Information. (CM ISSN 0008-2198) **812**
Chambre de Commerce, d'Industrie et des Mines du Cameroun. Compte-Rendu d'Activites. (CM) **812**
Chambre de Commerce, d'Industrie et des Mines du Cameroun. Import Export. (CM) **812**
Chambre de Commerce, d'Industrie et des Mines du Cameroun. Rapport Annuel. (CM ISSN 0069-2530) **3480**
Chambre de Commerce de Brazzaville. Bulletin Mensuel. (CF) **812**
Chambre de Commerce de Bruxelles. Bulletin Officiel see Entreprendre **815**
Chambre de Commerce de la Republique de Cote d'Ivoire. Bulletin. (IV) **812**
Chambre de Commerce de Tunis. Bulletin. (TI) **812**
Chambre de Commerce du Sud de la Tunisie. Bulletin Economique see Chambre de Commerce et d'Industrie du Sud. Bulletin **812**
Chambre de Commerce Espagnole en Belgique. Bulletin. (BE) **812**
Chambre de Commerce Espagnole en Belgique. Revue. (BE) **812**
Chambre de Commerce et d'Industrie d'Anvers. Bulletin. (BE) **812**
Chambre de Commerce et d'Industrie d'Auxerre. Documentation Economique. (FR ISSN 0183-4037) **812**
Chambre de Commerce et d'Industrie de Casablanca. Revue Mensuelle. (MR) **812, 850**
Chambre de Commerce et d'Industrie de Djibouti. Bulletin Periodique see Chambre Internationale de Commerce et d'Industrie de Djibouti. Bulletin Periodique **812**
Chambre de Commerce et d'Industrie de la Provence - Cote d'Azur - Corse. Conjoncture. (FR ISSN 0220-9241) **812**
Chambre de Commerce et d'Industrie de la Republique Populaire de Benin. Note Hebdomadaire. (DM) **812**
†Chambre de Commerce et d'Industrie de Nouvelle Caledonie. Bulletin. (NL) **5164**
†Chambre de Commerce et d'Industrie de Paris. Bulletin Mensuel. (FR ISSN 0009-1219) **5164**
Chambre de Commerce et d'Industrie de Rouen. Bulletin Economique. (FR ISSN 0009-1227) **812**
Chambre de Commerce et d'Industrie du Centre. Bulletin. (BE) **812**
Chambre de Commerce et d'Industrie du Dahomey. Note Hebdomadaire see Chambre de Commerce et d'Industrie de la Republique Populaire de Benin. Note Hebdomadaire **812**
Chambre de Commerce et d'Industrie du Sud. Bulletin. (TI) **812**
Chambre de Commerce et d'Industrie Francaise pour la Belgique et le Grand-Duche Luxembourg Commerce Exterieur. (BE) **812**
Chambre de Commerce Franco-Asiatique. Annuaire des Membres. (FR ISSN 0069-2557) **812**
Chambre de Commerce Franco-Danoise. Bulletin. see Dansk-Fransk Handelsunion. Bulletin **905**
Chambre de Commerce Franco-Sovietique. Lettre d'Information. (FR) **812**
Chambre de Commerce Israel - France. Bulletin. (IS) **812**
Chambre de Commerce Japonaise en France. Annuaire. (FR ISSN 0069-2565) **812**

Chambre de Commerce Neerlandaise pour la Belgique et le Luxembourg, S.C. Revue Commerciale/Nederlandse Kamer van Koophandel voor Belgie en Luxemburg, C.V. Handelsoverzicht. (BE ISSN 0017-7334) **812**

Chambre Francaise de Commerce et d'Industrie du Maroc. Revue Conjoncture. (MR ISSN 0528-8231) **812**

Chambre Francaise de Commerce et d'Industrie en Algerie. Economic News Bulletin. (AE) **812**

Chambre Franco Allemande de Commerce et d'Industrie. Liste des Membres. (FR) **812**

Chambre Internationale de Commerce et d'Industrie de Djibouti. Bulletin Periodique. (FT) **812**

Chambre Officielle Franco Allemande de Commerce et d'Industrie. Liste des Membres *see* Chambre Franco Allemande de Commerce et d'Industrie. Liste des Membres **812**

Chambre Regionale de Commerce et d'Industrie d'Alsace. Rapport sur les Activites. (FR) **812**

Chambre Syndicale de la Construction. Bulletin. (BE) **609**

Chambre Syndicale de la Siderurgie Francaise. Bulletin Statistique. Serie Bleue. Commerce Exterieur *see* Comptoir Francais des Produits Siderurgiques. Bulletin Statistique. Serie Bleue. Commerce Exterieur **3404**

Chambre Syndicale de la Siderurgie Francaise. Bulletin Statistique. Serie Rouge. Production *see* Comptoir Francais des Produits Siderurgiques. Bulletin Statistique. Serie Rouge. Production **3404**

Chambre Syndicale des Aciers Pour Emballage. Rapport Statistiques Annuel. (FR) **3425**

†Chambre Syndicale des Mines de Fer de France. Bulletin Technique. (FR ISSN 0009-126X) **5164**

†Chambre Syndicale des Mines de Fer de France. Rapport d'Activite. (FR ISSN 0069-259X) **5164**

Chambre Syndicale des Producteurs de Fer-blanc. Rapport Statistiques Annuel *see* Chambre Syndicale des Aciers Pour Emballage. Rapport Statistiques Annuel **3425**

Chambre Syndicale du Commerce Automobile de Belgique. Bulletin Mensuel *see* Autotechnica **4684**

Chambre Syndicale Nationale des Electriciens et Specialistes de l'Automobile. Annuaire. (FR) **1884, 4687**

Chambre Syndicale Nationale des Entreprises et Industries de l'Hygiene Publique. Annuaire. (FR ISSN 0069-2603) **4099**

Chambre Tuniso-Francaise de Commerce et d'Industrie. Bulletin d'Information. (TI) **813**

Chambres a Coucher. (CN) **2557**
Chambres d'Agriculture. (FR) **83**
Chaminade Literary Review. (US) **2904**
Chaminade Newsletter. (US) **1307**
Chaminade University Newsletter *see* Chaminade Newsletter **1307**
Champ Channels. (US ISSN 0747-9840) **580, 3669**
Champ Social. (FR ISSN 0339-686X) **4401**
Champagne de Cognac. (FR) **172**
La Champagne Economique. (FR ISSN 1146-8599) **655**
Champagne News. (US ISSN 0009-1294) **214**
Champaign County Genealogical Society Newsletter. (US) **2147**
Champaign County Genealogical Society Quarterly. (US ISSN 0277-2086) **2147**
Champaign County Historical Archives Historical Publications Series. (US) **2402, 3789**
Champak. (II ISSN 0009-1332) **1251**
Champignon. (GW ISSN 0009-1308) **172**

Champignoncultuur. (NE ISSN 0009-1316) **172**
Champion. (US ISSN 0744-9488) **2712, 1511**
†Champion. (CN ISSN 0229-3455) **5164**
Champion d'Afrique. (FR ISSN 0181-9224) **4468**
Champion d'Afrique *see* Champion d'Afrique **4468**
Champion du Zaire. (ZR) **4468**
Champlain Bugle. (CN) **1307**
Champlain Society, Toronto. Report. (CN ISSN 0069-2646) **2308**
▼Champs du Signe. (FR) **2809**
Champs-Elysees. (US ISSN 0886-005X) **2186**
Chanakya Defence Annual. (II ISSN 0069-2654) **3454**
Chanar Standart/Quality and Standards.(MP) **1005**
Chance. (US ISSN 0933-2480) **4567, 1390**
Chancellor College. Department of Religious Studies. Staff Seminar Paper. (MW) **4168**
Chancellor College. Journal of Social Science *see* Malawi Journal of Social Science **4379**
†Chancen. (GW) **5164**
Chandamama. (II) **1251**
Chandigarh Post. (II) **3879**
Chandoba. (II) **2199**
Chandrabhaga (West Bengal). (II ISSN 0009-1359) **2904**
Chaney Chronical. (US) **2904**
Chang Cheng/Great Wall. (CC) **2904**
Chang Feng Yue Xun. *see* Music from China. News **3564**
Chang Shou/Longevity. (CC) **2271**
Changchun Institute of Posts and Telecommunications. Journal. *see* Changchun Youdian Xueyuan Xuebao **1333**
Changchun Youdian Xueyuan Xuebao/Changchun Institute of Posts and Telecommunications. Journal. (CC ISSN 1000-1794) **1333**
Change *see* Numismatique & Change **3601**
Change (Washington). (US ISSN 0009-1383) **1702**
Change Exchange. (US ISSN 0886-2435) **2612**
Changer. (SZ ISSN 1017-2874) **3953**
Changer le Cinema. (FR ISSN 0339-8978) **3505**
Changer - Tribune de Caux *see* Changer **3953**
Changes. (UK ISSN 0263-8371) **4401, 4015**
Changes (De Peve) *see* Coming Changes **2452**
Changes (Deerfield Beach). (US) **1535**
▼Changes (London, 1990). (UK ISSN 0960-748X) **3879**
Changes Newsletter *see* Coming Changes Newsletter **3594**
Changing Economy in Indonesia. (NE) **850**
Changing Issues in the Family. (US) **4431**
†Changing Japan. (JA) **5164**
Changing Medical Markets. (US) **3087, 1005**
Changing Men. (US ISSN 0889-7174) **3400**
Changing Public Attitudes on Governments and Taxes. (US ISSN 0272-6017) **1090**
Changing Times *see* Kiplinger's Personal Finance **1506**
Changing Work *see* G E O: Grassroots Economic Organizing Newsletter **3627**
Changjiang (Duozhong Wenxue) Congkan/Yangtze Literature. (US) **2904**
Changjiang Kexueyuan Yuanbao/Yangtze River Scientific Research Institute. Journal. (CC ISSN 1001-5485) **1923**
Changjiang Wenyi/Yangtz Literature and Art. (CC ISSN 0528-838X) **2904, 321**
†Channel (Los Angeles). (US ISSN 0195-3508) **5164**

Channel D L S. (Division for Library Services) (US ISSN 0146-1095) **2752**
Channel Islands Catering News. (UI) **2472**
Channel Islands Specialised Catalogue. (UK ISSN 0142-5625) **3750**
†Channel T V Times. (UI) **5164**
Channel Tunnel Bulletin. (UK) **4708**
Channels *see* N A W Report **4092**
Channels. (FR) **4232**
Channels (Exeter). (US ISSN 0009-1510) **29, 4401**
Channels of Blessing. (UK ISSN 0009-1529) **2291, 4168**
Channels of Communications *see* Channels: the Business of Communications **5164**
†Channels: the Business of Communications. (US) **5164**
Chanoyu Quarterly. (JA ISSN 0009-1537) **3635, 321**
Chansons d'Aujourd'hui. (CN ISSN 0227-5023) **3545**
Chant Choral Magazine. (FR) **3545**
Chante et Ris. (FR) **3545, 1251**
Chantecler *see* Ce Mois-Ci a l'Alliance **1620**
The Chanticleer. (US ISSN 0009-1561) **1307**
Chantiers Cooperatifs. (FR ISSN 0009-1596) **609**
Chantiers de France. (FR ISSN 0397-4650) **609**
Chantiers de Pedagogie Mathematique. (FR ISSN 0395-7837) **1746, 3032**
Les Chantiers du Cardinal. (FR ISSN 0009-160X) **4168**
†Chantiers Magazine. (FR) **5164**
†Chantiers Pedagogiques. (CN ISSN 0009-1618) **5164**
Chants des Peuples. (FR ISSN 0395-7845) **2904**
Chao Krung. (TH) **2220**
Chao Sheng. (CC) **2904**
▼Chaos. (US ISSN 1054-1500) **3815**
Chaos. (DK ISSN 0108-4453) **4168**
Chaos. (CN ISSN 0706-5337) **4304**
Chaos Computer Club France Newsletter *see* C C C F's Newsletter **1423**
▼Chaos, Solitons and Fractals. (UK ISSN 0960-0779) **3032, 3064**
Chap-Lett. (US) **4260**
Chapa y Pintura. (SP) **3653**
Chaplair. (US) **4232**
Chaplin. (SW ISSN 0045-6349) **3505**
Chapman. (UK ISSN 0308-2695) **2904**
†Chapman Chatter. (US ISSN 0883-1181) **5164**
Chapter I Handbook: Understanding and Implementing the New Regulations *see* Chapter I Handbook: Understanding and Implementing the Program **1726**
Chapter I Handbook: Understanding and Implementing the Program. (US ISSN 0737-2094) **1726**
Chapter One (New York, 1987). (US ISSN 0895-3384) **1849, 1307**
Chapter 11: Reorganizations. (US) **2708, 1090**
▼Chapter 11 Update. (US ISSN 1055-9477) **2708**
Chapter 12: Farm Reorganizations. (US) **2612, 83**
Chapter 13: Practice and Procedure. (US) **2612**
Chapter 290. (CN) **4056, 975, 1005**
Char-Koosta News. (US ISSN 0528-8592) **1996, 2053**
†Character II (Chicago). (US ISSN 0883-1718) **5164**
Characters in 20th-Century Literature. (US) **2904**
Characters - Singapore and Malaysia Editions. (SI ISSN 0129-3389) **1333**
Charadista. (PO ISSN 0300-4368) **2214**
Charadrius. (GW ISSN 0174-1004) **563**

†Charbonnages de France. Publications Techniques. (FR ISSN 0009-1685) **5164**
Charbonneau Connection. (US ISSN 1046-5901) **2147**
Charcuterie et Gastronomie. (FR ISSN 0222-0377) **2090**
Chardon *see* Minute **3907**
Charge Fiscale en Suisse - Chefs-lieux Cantonaux, Chiffres Cantonaux. *see* Steuerbelastung in der Schweiz - Kantonshauptorte, Kantonsziffern **1107**
Charge Fiscale en Suisse - Personnes Physiques par Communes. *see* Steuerbelastung in der Schweiz - Natuerliche Personen nach Gemeinden **740**
Charger. (CN) **4533**
Charhdi Kala. (CN) **1996**
Charioteer. (US ISSN 0577-5574) **2196, 1996, 2904**
Charisma. (US ISSN 0279-0424) **4168**
Charisma. (GW) **4232**
Charitable Giving and Solicitation. (US) **1090**
▼Charitable Organizations of the U S. (US) **4401**
Charite Annalen. Neue Folge. (GW ISSN 0232-7090) **3087**
Charities Digest (Year). (UK ISSN 0590-9783) **4401**
Charities U S A. (US ISSN 0364-0760) **4401**
Chariton Review. (US ISSN 0098-9452) **2904**
Charity. (UK ISSN 0265-5209) **4401**
Charity and Children. (US ISSN 0009-1723) **1233, 4232**
Charity Statistics *see* Charity Trends **4425**
Charity Trends. (UK) **4425, 4567**
The Charlatan. (CN ISSN 0315-1859) **1307**
Charles A. Pesko International Outlook *see* C A P International Outlook **5156**
Charles C. Adams Center for Ecological Studies. Occasional Papers. (US ISSN 0009-1766) **435**
Charles C. Moskowitz Lectures *see* Joseph I. Lubin Memorial Lectures **673**
Charles Eliot Norton Lectures. (US) **2505**
Charles H. MacNider Museum Newsletter. (US) **3523**
Charles Lamb Bulletin. (UK ISSN 0308-0951) **2904**
Charles Lamb Society. Journal *see* Charles Lamb Bulletin **2904**
Charles Redd Monographs in Western History. (US ISSN 0162-217X) **2308**
Charles Rennie Mackintosh Society Newsletter. (UK ISSN 0141-559X) **296**
Charles River Associates Incorporated Petroleum Economics Monthly *see* C R A Petroleum Economics Monthly **3683**
Charles River Associates Incorporated Review *see* C R A Review **1073**
Charles S. Peirce Society. Transactions. (US ISSN 0009-1774) **3763**
Charleston Magazine. (US) **2223**
Charlotte County Florida Land Owner. (US ISSN 1047-1413) **4146**
Charlottenborg Foraarsudstillingen. (DK ISSN 0109-3479) **321**
Charlottes. (CN ISSN 0316-6724) **2402**
Charm *see* Glamour **1291**
Charm. (JA) **3590**
Charme. (IT) **2983**
Charolais. (FR ISSN 0395-8183) **214**
Charolais Banner. (CN ISSN 0824-1767) **214**
Charolais Connection. (CN ISSN 0828-7600) **214**
Charolais Journal. (US) **214**
Charona. (UY) **1251**
Charoshet. (IS) **655**
Charpente-Menuiserie-Parquets *see* Nouveau Journal de Charpente-Menuiserie-Parquets **640**
Chart. (US ISSN 0069-2778) **3277**

CHART

Chart and Compass International. (UK) 4401, 4168
Chart Watch. (UK ISSN 0262-9577) 3545
Chartac Accountancy News. (AT) 749
Chartac Accounting Report see Chartac Accountancy News 749
Chartac Tax Planning News. (AT) 749
Chartac Taxation Report see Chartac Tax Planning News 749
Chartcraft Weekly Commodity Service. (US) 942
Chartcraft Weekly Options Service. (US) 942
Charter. (AT ISSN 1035-0748) 749
Charter. (US ISSN 0069-2786) 2505
Charter Connections. (US ISSN 0887-1132) 2147
Chartered Accountant see Charter 749
Chartered Accountant. (II ISSN 0009-188X) 749
Chartered Accountant Magazine see C A Magazine 748
Chartered Builder. (UK) 610
Chartered Building Societies Institute. Journal. (UK ISSN 0954-7207) 771
Chartered Financial Analyst Digest see C F A Digest 769
Chartered Institute of Building. Handbook. (UK) 610
Chartered Institute of Building. Year Book see Chartered Institute of Building. Handbook 610
Chartered Institute of Management Accountants. Framework Series In Accounting. (UK) 749
Chartered Institute of Management Accountants. Occasional Papers Series. (UK) 749
†Chartered Institute of Marketing. Marketer. (UK) 5164
Chartered Institute of Patent Agents see C I P A 3673
Chartered Institute of Public Finance and Accountancy. Administration of Justice. Estimates. (UK ISSN 0264-6552) 1524, 1511
Chartered Institute of Public Finance and Accountancy. Capital Expenditure and Debt Financing Statistics. Actuals. (UK ISSN 0263-2985) 710, 4567
Chartered Institute of Public Finance and Accountancy. Cemeteries & Crematoria Statistics. Actuals. (UK ISSN 0263-2969) 4117, 4567
Chartered Institute of Public Finance and Accountancy. Cemeteries Statistics. Actuals see Chartered Institute of Public Finance and Accountancy. Cemeteries & Crematoria Statistics. Actuals 4117
Chartered Institute of Public Finance and Accountancy. Charges for Leisure Services. Actuals. (UK ISSN 0142-1484) 4498, 2738, 4567
Chartered Institute of Public Finance and Accountancy. Charges for Water Services. (UK) 4835, 4568
Chartered Institute of Public Finance and Accountancy. Conference Handbook. (UK) 749
Chartered Institute of Public Finance and Accountancy. Costs of Water Services. (UK) 4835, 4568
Chartered Institute of Public Finance and Accountancy. Crematoria Statistics. Actuals see Chartered Institute of Public Finance and Accountancy. Cemeteries & Crematoria Statistics. Actuals 4117
Chartered Institute of Public Finance and Accountancy. Direct Labour Organisation Statistics. Actuals. (UK) 637, 610
Chartered Institute of Public Finance and Accountancy. Direct Labour Statistics. Actuals see Chartered Institute of Public Finance and Accountancy. Direct Labour Organisation Statistics. Actuals 637
Chartered Institute of Public Finance and Accountancy. Education Statistics. Actuals. (UK ISSN 0309-5614) 1675, 4568
Chartered Institute of Public Finance and Accountancy. Education Statistics. Estimates. (UK ISSN 0307-0514) 1675, 710
†Chartered Institute of Public Finance and Accountancy. Education Statistics. Unit Costs. (UK ISSN 0264-7125) 5164
Chartered Institute of Public Finance and Accountancy. Environmental Health Statistics. Actuals. (UK ISSN 0266-9552) 4117, 4099
Chartered Institute of Public Finance and Accountancy. Finance and General Statistics. Estimates. (UK) 710, 4568
Chartered Institute of Public Finance and Accountancy. Financial General and Rating Statistics see Chartered Institute of Public Finance and Accountancy. Finance and General Statistics. Estimates 710
Chartered Institute of Public Finance and Accountancy. Fire Service Statistics. Actuals. (UK ISSN 0309-622X) 2035, 4568
Chartered Institute of Public Finance and Accountancy. Fire Service Statistics. Estimates. (UK ISSN 0307-0573) 2035, 4568
†Chartered Institute of Public Finance and Accountancy. Highways and Transportation. Actuals. (UK ISSN 0260-9886) 5164
Chartered Institute of Public Finance and Accountancy. Highways and Transportation Statistics. Estimates. (UK ISSN 0260-9894) 4663, 4568
Chartered Institute of Public Finance and Accountancy. Homelessness Statistics. (UK ISSN 0144-4514) 2499, 4568
Chartered Institute of Public Finance and Accountancy. Housing Part 1: Rents. Actuals Statistics see Chartered Institute of Public Finance and Accountancy. Housing Rents Statistics. Actuals 2499
†Chartered Institute of Public Finance and Accountancy. Housing Revenue Accounts Statistics. Actuals. (UK ISSN 0260-4078) 5164
Chartered Institute of Public Finance and Accountancy. Housing Revenue Account Statistics. Estimates. (UK) 2499, 4568
Chartered Institute of Public Finance and Accountancy. Housing Rents Statistics. Actuals. (UK ISSN 0260-406X) 2499, 4568
Chartered Institute of Public Finance and Accountancy. Housing Statistics. Estimates see Chartered Institute of Public Finance and Accountancy. Housing Revenue Account Statistics. Estimates 2499
Chartered Institute of Public Finance and Accountancy. Leisure and Recreation Statistics. Estimates. (UK ISSN 0141-187X) 4498, 2738, 4568
Chartered Institute of Public Finance and Accountancy. Leisure Estimate Statistics see Chartered Institute of Public Finance and Accountancy. Leisure and Recreation Statistics. Estimates 4498
Chartered Institute of Public Finance and Accountancy. Leisure Usage. Actuals. (UK ISSN 0266-9560) 4498, 2738, 4568
Chartered Institute of Public Finance and Accountancy. Local Authority Airports. Accounts and Statistics see Chartered Institute of Public Finance and Accountancy. Local Authority Airports. Accounts and Statistics. Actuals 4663
Chartered Institute of Public Finance and Accountancy. Local Authority Airports. Accounts and Statistics. Actuals. (UK) 4663, 4568
Chartered Institute of Public Finance and Accountancy. Local Government Comparative Statistics. Estimates. (UK ISSN 0260-9762) 4080, 4568
Chartered Institute of Public Finance and Accountancy. Local Health and Social Services Statistics see Chartered Institute of Public Finance and Accountancy. Personal Social Services Statistics. Actuals 4425
Chartered Institute of Public Finance and Accountancy. Personal Social Services Statistics. Actuals. (UK ISSN 0309-653X) 4425, 4568
Chartered Institute of Public Finance and Accountancy. Personal Social Services Statistics. Estimates. (UK ISSN 0144-610X) 4425, 4568
Chartered Institute of Public Finance and Accountancy. Planning and Development Statistics. Estimates. (UK ISSN 0144-901X) 2499, 4568
Chartered Institute of Public Finance and Accountancy. Planning Estimates Statistics. Actuals see Chartered Institute of Public Finance and Accountancy. Planning and Development Statistics. Estimates 2499
†Chartered Institute of Public Finance and Accountancy. Police Statistics. Actuals. (UK ISSN 0144-9915) 5164
Chartered Institute of Public Finance and Accountancy. Police Statistics. Estimates. (UK ISSN 0144-9885) 1524, 4568
Chartered Institute of Public Finance and Accountancy. Probation. Estimates. (UK ISSN 0264-6544) 4425, 4401
Chartered Institute of Public Finance and Accountancy. Probation Statistics. Actuals. (UK ISSN 0140-8291) 4425, 4568
Chartered Institute of Public Finance and Accountancy. Public Library Statistics. Actuals. (UK ISSN 0309-6629) 2793, 4568
Chartered Institute of Public Finance and Accountancy. Public Library Statistics. Estimates. (UK ISSN 0307-0522) 2793, 4568
Chartered Institute of Public Finance and Accountancy. Revenue Collection Statistics. Actuals. (UK ISSN 0260-5546) 710, 4568
†Chartered Institute of Public Finance and Accountancy. School Meals Statistics. (UK ISSN 0266-2949) 5164
Chartered Institute of Public Finance and Accountancy. Trading Standards and Consumer Protection Statistics. Actuals see Chartered Institute of Public Finance and Accountancy. Trading Standards Statistics. Actuals 710
Chartered Institute of Public Finance and Accountancy. Trading Standards Statistics. Actuals. (UK ISSN 0260-6372) 710, 4568
Chartered Institute of Public Finance and Accountancy. United Kingdom Water Industry (Books 1 & 2) see Chartered Institute of Public Finance and Accountancy. Charges for Water Services 4835
Chartered Institute of Public Finance and Accountancy. United Kingdom Water Industry (Books 1 & 2) see Chartered Institute of Public Finance and Accountancy. Costs of Water Services 4835
Chartered Institute of Public Finance and Accountancy. Waste Collection Statistics. Actuals. (UK ISSN 0260-7603) 4080, 4568
Chartered Institute of Public Finance and Accountancy. Waste Disposal Statistics. Actuals. (UK ISSN 0140-0150) 4080, 4117, 4568
Chartered Institute of Public Finance and Accountancy. Waste Disposal Statistics. Estimates. (UK ISSN 0140-0142) 4080, 4117, 4568
Chartered Institute of Transport. Annual.(NR) 4648
†Chartered Institute of Transport. Handbook. (UK ISSN 0306-9559) 5164
Chartered Institute of Transport. Journal see Transport (London) 4657
Chartered Insurance Institute Journal see C I I Journal 2529
Chartered Insurance Institute, London. Journal see C I I Journal 2529
Chartered Land and Minerals Surveyor see Land and Minerals Surveying 1871
Chartered Mechanical Engineer see Professional Engineering 1938
Chartered Quantity Surveyor. (UK ISSN 0142-5196) 1863
Chartered Secretary see Boardroom 1057
Chartered Surveyor Weekly. (UK) 4146
Charterhouse. Board Earnings (Year). (UK) 771
Chartering Annual. (US) 4725
Charting Housing Trends. (US) 771, 4146
Chase. (US ISSN 0009-1952) 4543
Chase Pacesetter. (US) 2223
Chase World Guide for Exporters. (US) 903
Chaseform Jumping Annual. (UK) 4468
Chaseform Note-Book. (UK) 4533
Chasers and Hurdlers. (UK) 4533
Chase's Annual Events. (US ISSN 0740-5286) 1780
Chaski see Tarea 1666
Chasqui. (US ISSN 0145-8973) 2904, 2809
Chasseur d'Images. (FR ISSN 0396-8235) 3789
Chasseur Suisse. see Schweizer Jaeger 4555
Chastity and Holiness Magazine. (CN ISSN 0843-1736) 4168
Chat. (US ISSN 0009-1987) 563
Chat. (UK) 4839
Chatar. (CS) 296, 2124, 4543
Chateau. (CN) 2176
Chateauguay Valley Historical Society Annual Journal/Journal Annuel de la Societe Historique de la Vallee de la Chateauguay. (CN ISSN 0319-1249) 2402
Chatelaine (English edition). (CN ISSN 0009-1995) 4839, 2176
Chatelaine (French edition). (CN ISSN 0317-2635) 4839, 2176
Chatelaine Mere Nouvelle see Chatelaine's New Mother 1233
Chatelaine's New Mother. (CN) 1233, 3290
†Chatham House Papers. (UK ISSN 0143-5795) 5164
Chatswood Cityscope. (AT) 4160
Chattahoochee Review. (US ISSN 0741-9155) 2904
Chatter. (CN) 2124
Chaucer Library. (US) 2904
Chaucer Research Report see Chaucer Review 2904
Chaucer Review. (US ISSN 0009-2002) 2904
Chaud - Froid - Plomberie see C.F.P. Chaud - Froid - Plomberie 2298
Chaudronnerie Tolerie. (FR) 2581, 2298
Chauffage et Ventilation. see Heizung und Lueftung 2300
Chauffage Urbain. see Fernwaerme International 2299
Chauffage - Ventilation - Conditionnement. (FR ISSN 0009-2029) 2298
Chauffoer Nyt. (DK) 4687
Chauffoeren. (DK ISSN 0901-3946) 4687
Chaukhambha Oriental Research Studies. (II) 3635
Chausser. (FR ISSN 0247-7181) 2736, 4360
Chautauqua - Cattaraugus Library System Newsletter. (US) 2752
Chautauqua County Agricultural News. (US) 83
Chautauqua Genealogist. (US) 2147
Chaye/Tea. (CC) 2063
Chaye Kexue/Science of Tea. (CC) 2063
Chaye Kexue Jianbao/Scientific Bulletin of Tea. (CC) 172
Chaye Wenzhai/Tea Abstracts. (CC) 2084

Chayim Yafim. (IS) **4468**, 3800
Cheap Eats in Sydney. (AT) **2472**
Cheap Investor. (US ISSN 0747-7236) **942**
Check! (CN) **4468**
Check Club Newsletter. (US) **772**, 1503
Check Collector. (US) **3598**
Check-in. (GW ISSN 0934-5140) **4757**, 655
Check it Out! (CN) **2752**, 1251
Check Mate. (JA) **1289**
Check Sample. (US) **3087**
"Check the Oil!" Magazine. (US ISSN 1042-7341) **2434**, 256, 3684
Check Your Tax see Check Your Tax and Money Facts **1090**
Check Your Tax and Money Facts. (UK) **1090**
Check List see Check Collector **3598**
Checklist of Basic American Legal Publications see Pimsleur's Checklist of Basic American Legal Publications **2700**
Checklist of British Official Serial Publications. (UK ISSN 0084-8085) **2793**
Checklist of Official New Jersey Publications. (US ISSN 0146-0838) **4080**
Checklist of Official Publications of the State of New York. (US ISSN 0077-9296) **4056**
Checklist of Publications of the State of Arizona. (US) **397**
Checkmate. (JA) **3396**
Checkout. (GW) **1035**
Checkout. (IE) **1035**
Checkpoint. (AT ISSN 0311-0737) **4232**
Checkpoint (Washington). (US) **4304**, 4595
Cheekwood. Botanical Gardens and Fine Arts Center (Calendar). (US) **321**, 499
Cheekwood Mirror see Cheekwood. Botanical Gardens and Fine Arts Center (Calendar) **321**
Cheer News Today. (US ISSN 0893-8091) **4468**
Cheering Words. (UK ISSN 0009-2126) **4168**, 1251
Cheese Market News. (US) **198**
Cheese Reporter. (US ISSN 0009-2142) **198**
Chef. (UK) **2063**, 2472
Chef see Das Recht der Wirtschaft **2670**
Chef du Service Alimentaire. (CN ISSN 0830-0895) **2063**
Chef Institutional. (US ISSN 0192-7116) **2472**
Chef International. (GW ISSN 0170-1800) **2473**, 2063
Chef-Magazin fuer Klein- und Mittelbetriebe. (SZ) **1073**
Chef-Nyt. (DK ISSN 0108-2108) **1058**
Chef-Nyt - Kontor-Nyt see Chef-Nyt **1058**
Chef of the Foodservice Industry see Chef du Service Alimentaire **2063**
Chefs-d'Oeuvre de la Galerie Nationale du Canada. see Masterpieces in the National Gallery of Canada **335**
Hacheinuch ve Sivevo. (IS) **1621**
Cheiron. (Il ISSN 0379-542X) **4808**
Cheiron Newsletter. (US) **4368**, 4015
†Chekhoslovatskogo Prava Biuleten. (CS) **5164**
Chekhoslovatskoye Kino see Czechoslovak Film **3507**
Chekhoslovatskoye Motor-Reviu see Czechoslovak Motor Review **5176**
Chela see Cuadernos para la Historia de la Evangelizacion en America Latina **2404**
Chelmer Working Papers in Environmental Planning. (UK ISSN 0144-9877) **4368**, 1945
▼Chelovek. (RU ISSN 0236-2007) **2505**
Chelsea. (US ISSN 0009-2185) **2904**
Chelsea Spelaeological Society. Newsletter. (UK ISSN 0045-6381) **1557**
Chelsea Spelaeological Society. Records. (UK ISSN 0309-409X) **1557**

Cheltenham Ladies College Magazine. (UK) **1307**
Chem-Facts: Ammonia. (UK) **1171**
▼Chem-Facts: Belgium. (UK) **1171**
▼Chem-Facts: Ethylene & Propylene. (UK) **1171**
Chem-Facts: Federal Republic of Germany. (UK) **1171**
Chem-Facts: Methanol. (UK) **1171**
▼Chem-Facts: Netherlands. (UK) **1171**
Chem-Facts: Polyethylene. (UK) **1217**
Chem-Facts: Polypropylene. (UK) **1217**
Chem-Facts: United Kingdom. (UK) **1171**
Chem Matters. (US) **1171**, 1251
†Chem News. (SA) **5164**
Chem Sources International. (US) **1126**, 1172
Chem Sources U S A. (US) **1126**, 1172
Chem Thirteen News. (CN ISSN 0703-1157) **1172**
Chemcyclopedia. (US) **1172**
Chemdata. (SA) **1172**
Chemeca - Australasian Conference on Chemical Engineering. Proceedings. (AT) **1849**, 3684
ChemEcology. (US ISSN 0738-7776) **1945**, 1172, 1976, 3800
Chemexcil Export Bulletin. (Il ISSN 0009-2207) **903**, 375, 1849
Chemexcil Monthly Bulletin. (Il) **3720**, 375
†Chemfacts: Scandinavia. (UK) **5164**
Chemia. (PL ISSN 0554-8241) **1172**
Chemia Analityczna. (PL ISSN 0009-2223) **1204**
Chemia Stosowana see Polish Journal of Applied Chemistry **1185**
Chemia Stosowana. Seria B. Zagadnienia Inzynierii i Apartury Chemicznej see Inzynieria Chemiczna i Procesowa **1855**
Chemia w Szkole. (PL ISSN 0411-8634) **1172**
†Chemica Scripta. (SW ISSN 0004-2056) **5164**
Chemical Abstracts. (US) **1199**, 8
Chemical Abstracts. see Kagaku Shoho **1202**
Chemical Abstracts - Applied Chemistry and Chemical Engineering Sections. (US ISSN 0090-8363) **1199**, 8
Chemical Abstracts - Biochemistry Sections. (US ISSN 0009-2304) **1199**, 8, 464
Chemical Abstracts - Macromolecular Sections. (US ISSN 0009-2274) **1199**, 8
Chemical Abstracts - Organic Chemistry Sections. (US ISSN 0009-2282) **1199**, 8
Chemical Abstracts - Physical and Analytical Chemistry Sections see Chemical Abstracts - Physical, Inorganic and Analytical Chemistry Sections **1199**
Chemical Abstracts - Physical, Inorganic and Analytical Chemistry Sections. (US ISSN 0278-1832) **1199**, 8
Chemical Abstracts - Section Groupings.(US ISSN 0009-2258) **1199**, 8
Chemical Abstracts Service BioTech Updates. Agriculture see C A S BioTech Updates. Agriculture **135**
Chemical Abstracts Service BioTech Updates. Slow-Release Pharmaceuticals see C A S BioTech Updates. Slow-Release Pharmaceuticals **3720**
Chemical Abstracts Service Selects see C A Selects **1191**
Chemical Abstracts Service Source Index. (US ISSN 0001-0634) **1199**, 8
Chemical Age see Manufacturing Chemist **1856**
Chemical Age of India. (Il ISSN 0009-2320) **1172**
Chemical Age Project File. (UK) **1172**
Chemical Analysis. (US ISSN 0069-2883) **1205**
Chemical and Biochemical Engineering Quarterly. (CI ISSN 0352-9568) **469**, 1849
Chemical and Engineering News. (US ISSN 0009-2347) **1849**

Chemical and Oil Industry. see Khimicheskoe i Neftyanoe Mashinostroenie **1856**
Chemical and Petroleum Engineering. (English translation of: Khimicheskoe i Neftyanoe Mashinostroenie) (US ISSN 0009-2355) **1849**, 3684
Chemical & Pharmaceutical Bulletin. (JA ISSN 0009-2363) **1172**, 3720
Chemical and Process Engineering see Process Engineering **1858**
Chemical and Process Engineering Abstracts. see Verfahrenstechnische Berichte **1847**
Chemical Bond. (US ISSN 0009-2398) **1172**
Chemical Bulletin. (US ISSN 0009-2401) **1172**
Chemical Business. (US ISSN 0731-8774) **1172**
Chemical Business. (Il) **1849**, 1877
Chemical Business Bulletins (Series): Adhesives and Latexes. (UK) **710**, 1199
Chemical Business Bulletins (Series): Agrochemicals. (UK) **710**, 1199
Chemical Business Bulletins (Series): Chemical and the Environment. (UK) **710**, 1199
Chemical Business Bulletins (Series): Chemical and the Food Industry see Chemical Business Bulletins (Series): Chemical and the Environment **710**
Chemical Business Bulletins (Series): Chemicals and the Electronics Industry. (UK) **710**, 1199
Chemical Business Bulletins (Series): Company Acquisition and Formation. (UK) **710**, 1199
Chemical Business Bulletins (Series): Cosmetics and Toiletries. (UK) **710**, 1199
Chemical Business Bulletins (Series): Fertilizers. (UK) **710**, 1199
Chemical Business Bulletins (Series): Health Care Products. (UK) **710**, 1199
Chemical Business Bulletins (Series): Novelty and Trends. (UK) **710**, 1199
Chemical Business Bulletins (Series): Paints and Coatings. (UK) **710**, 1199
Chemical Business Bulletins (Series): Plastics and Rubber Applications. (UK) **710**, 1199
Chemical Business Bulletins (Series): Speciality Chemicals. (UK) **710**, 1199
Chemical Business of India see Chemical Business **1849**
Chemical Business Update. (UK ISSN 0950-6144) **710**, 1199
Chemical Buyers Directory see O P D Chemical Buyers Directory **1148**
Chemical Buyers Guide. (CN ISSN 0069-2891) **1126**
Chemical Carcinogenesis - Aromatic Hydromatic Hydrocarbons and Heterocyclic Analogs see I C R D B Cancergram: Chemical Carcinogenesis - Aromatic Hydrocarbons and Heterocyclic Analogs **5208**
Chemical Carcinogenesis - Azo Dyes, Aryl Amines, and Related Compounds see I C R D B Cancergram: Chemical Carcinogenesis - Azo Dyes, Aryl Amines, and Related Compounds **5208**
Chemical Carcinogenesis - Miscellaneous Agents see I C R D B Cancergram: Chemical Carcinogenesis - Miscellaneous Agents **5208**
Chemical Carcinogenesis - Nitroso Compounds see I C R D B Cancergram: Chemical Carcinogenesis - Nitroso Compounds **5208**
Chemical Daily. see Kagaku Kogyo Nippo **1182**
Chemical Dependency. (US ISSN 1042-315X) **1535**, 4099
Chemical Design Automation News. (US ISSN 0886-6716) **1412**, 1172
Chemical Digest. (Il) **1172**
Chemical Distillations. (US) **1172**

Chemical Education. (KO) **1172**, 1849
Chemical Engineer. (UK ISSN 0302-0797) **1849**
Chemical Engineering. (US ISSN 0009-2460) **1849**
Chemical Engineering. see Kagaku Kogaku **1856**
Chemical Engineering Abstracts. see Vegyipari Szakirodalmi Tajekoztato **1203**
Chemical Engineering Abstracts. (UK ISSN 0262-6438) **1842**
Chemical Engineering and Machinery. see Huagong Jixie **1854**
Chemical Engineering and Processing. (SZ ISSN 0255-2701) **1849**
Chemical Engineering and Technology. (GW ISSN 0930-7516) **1849**
Chemical Engineering Communications. (US ISSN 0098-6445) **1849**
Chemical Engineering: Concepts and Reviews. (UK ISSN 0734-1644) **1850**
Chemical Engineering Education. (US ISSN 0009-2479) **1850**, 1702
Chemical Engineering Equipment Buyer's Guide. (US ISSN 0272-4057) **1850**
Chemical Engineering Faculties. (US) **1850**, 1702
Chemical Engineering Faculties of Canada and the United States see Chemical Engineering Faculties **1850**
Chemical Engineering in Australia. (AT ISSN 0157-9762) **1850**
Chemical Engineering Index see Process Engineering Index **1846**
Chemical Engineering Journal see Chemical Engineering Journal and Biochemical Engineering Journal **1850**
Chemical Engineering Journal and Biochemical Engineering Journal. (SZ) **1850**, 469
Chemical Engineering Monographs. (NE) **1850**
Chemical Engineering Progress. (US ISSN 0360-7275) **1850**
Chemical Engineering Progress. Safety in Air and Ammonia Plants see Ammonia Plant Safety and Related Facilities **1848**
Chemical Engineering Research & Design. (UK ISSN 0263-8762) **1850**
Chemical Engineering Science. (US ISSN 0009-2509) **1850**
Chemical Engineering World. (Il ISSN 0009-2517) **1850**, 4595
Chemical Engineers. see Huaxue Gongchengchi **1854**
Chemical Equipment. (US ISSN 0009-2525) **1850**
Chemical Equipment Literature Review. (US) **1850**
Chemical Equipment News. (SA) **1850**, 1172
Chemical Era. (Il ISSN 0009-2533) **1172**
Chemical Factory. see Kagaku Kojo **5223**
Chemical Geology. (NE ISSN 0009-2541) **1542**
Chemical Geology. Isotope Geoscience Section. (NE ISSN 0168-9622) **1557**, 1597
Chemical Guide to the United States. (US ISSN 0069-2972) **1850**
Chemical Hazards in Industry. (UK ISSN 0265-5721) **3615**, 1172
Chemical Highlights. (US ISSN 0009-255X) **1217**
Chemical Immunology. (SZ ISSN 1015-0145) **3184**
Chemical India Annual. (Il ISSN 0304-1166) **1850**
Chemical Industries Centers Newsletter see Chemical Industries Newsletter **1172**
Chemical Industries Newsletter. (US) **1172**, 1035
Chemical Industries Series. (US) **1850**
Chemical Industry. see Chemicky Prumysl **1173**
Chemical Industry. see Hemijska Industrija **1854**

CHEMICAL INDUSTRY

Chemical Industry Developments see Chemical Business **1849**
Chemical Industry Directory see Chemical Industry Europe **1851**
Chemical Industry Europe. (UK) **1851**
Chemical Industry Monitor. (US) **1172**
Chemical Industry News. (Il ISSN 0009-2576) **1851**
Chemical Industry Notes. (US ISSN 0045-639X) **1199, 8, 1842**
Chemical Industry Update (North American Report). (US ISSN 0732-5568) **1199, 8**
Chemical Industry Update (Overseas Report). (US ISSN 0732-5576) **1199, 8**
Chemical Insight. (UK ISSN 0045-6403) **1172**
Chemical Journal of Chinese Universities. (CC ISSN 1000-9213) **1172, 1702**
Chemical Magazine. see Chemisch Magazine **1174**
Chemical Manufacturers Association. Federal Legislation. (US) **1851**
Chemical Marketing Reporter. (US ISSN 0090-0907) **1172**
Chemical Monitor. (US ISSN 1049-1015) **1205, 2522**
Chemical Monographs Review. (US) **1172**
Chemical Monthly. see Monatshefte fuer Chemie **1184**
Chemical Newsletter. (US) **3615, 1172, 1851**
▼The Chemical Packaging Review. (US ISSN 1054-5131) **3648, 1172, 1945**
Chemical Papers. see Slovenska Chemicka Spolocnost. Chemicke Zvesti **1187**
Chemical Peddler. (US ISSN 0069-2999) **1126, 1035, 1172**
Chemical Physics. (NE ISSN 0301-0104) **1225, 3815**
Chemical Physics Letters. (NE ISSN 0009-2614) **1225**
Chemical Plants and Processing see Chemie-Anlagen und Verfahren **1851**
Chemical Process Industries Digest see C P I Digest **3868**
Chemical Process Industries Purchasing see C P I Purchasing **1035**
Chemical Process Industries Purchasing's Equipment Buyers Guide see C P I Purchasing's Equipment Buyers Guide **1848**
Chemical Processing. (US ISSN 0009-2630) **1851**
Chemical Processing see Processing **1859**
Chemical Processing Ad-Lits. (US) **1851**
Chemical Processing Guide and Directory see Chemical Processing's Problem Solver's Resource for the C P I **1172**
Chemical Processing Technology for Tomorrow. (US) **1851**
Chemical Processing's Problem Solver's Resource for the C P I. (US) **1172**
Chemical Regulation Reporter. (US ISSN 0148-7973) **1945, 1172**
Chemical Research in Toxicology. (US ISSN 0893-228X) **1980, 3720**
Chemical Review. see Hemijski Pregled **1178**
Chemical Reviews. (US ISSN 0009-2665) **1173**
▼Chemical Safety. (US) **1851**
▼Chemical Safety Sheets. (NE) **1173, 3615**
Chemical Senses. (UK ISSN 0379-864X) **570**
Chemical Society. Annual Reports on the Progress of Chemistry. Section A: Physical and Inorganic Chemistry see Royal Society of Chemistry. Annual Reports on the Progress of Chemistry. Section A: Inorganic Chemistry **1214**

Chemical Society, London. Annual Reports on the Progress of Chemistry. Section A: General, Physical and Inorganic Chemistry see Royal Society of Chemistry. Annual Reports on the Progress of Chemistry. Section A: Inorganic Chemistry **1214**
Chemical Society, London. Journal. Section A: Inorganic, Physical and Theoretical Chemistry see Royal Society of Chemistry. Journal: Dalton Transactions **1214**
Chemical Society, London. Quarterly Reviews see Royal Society of Chemistry. Reviews **1187**
Chemical Society of Ethiopia. Bulletin. (ET ISSN 1011-3924) **1173**
Chemical Society of Japan. Bulletin. (JA ISSN 0009-2673) **1173**
Chemical Society of Japan. Chemistry and Industrial Chemistry. Journal. see Nippon Kagaku Kaishi **1184**
Chemical Society of Pakistan. Journal. (PK ISSN 0253-5106) **1173**
Chemical Society Reviews see Royal Society of Chemistry. Reviews **1187**
Chemical Specialties Manufacturers Association Executive Newswatch see C S M A. Executive Newswatch **1171**
Chemical Speciation and Bioavailability. (UK ISSN 0954-2299) **1945**
Chemical Spotlight. (US ISSN 0411-8871) **1173**
Chemical Substances Control. (US ISSN 0271-1478) **1173, 2612**
Chemical Take-Off. (Il ISSN 0045-6497) **1173**
Chemical Times see Chemical Business **1849**
Chemical Times & Trends. (US ISSN 0149-2381) **1173**
Chemical Titles. (US ISSN 0009-2711) **1200, 8**
Chemical-Toxicological Series. Bulletins. (US ISSN 0073-7488) **3616**
Chemical Waste Litigation Reporter. (US ISSN 0889-0633) **1945, 2612**
Chemical Week. (US ISSN 0009-272X) **1851**
Chemical Weekly. (Il ISSN 0045-6500) **1173**
Chemical Weekly. see Chemisch Weekblad **1174**
Chemical Worker. (US ISSN 0162-637X) **2581**
Chemically Modified Surfaces. (US ISSN 0884-948X) **1225**
Chemicals. (UK) **1173**
Chemicals, Adhesives and Pharmaceuticals (Year). (SA ISSN 1015-230X) **1851**
Chemicals & Allied Products Export News. (Il ISSN 0009-2738) **903, 1173**
Chemicals and Allied Products Export Promotion Council. Exporters Directory. (Il ISSN 0531-5980) **903, 1173**
Chemicals & Polymers News. (UK) **3684, 3862**
Chemicals - International. (Il ISSN 0009-2746) **1173**
Chemicals: Latin American Industrial Report. (US) **1173**
Chemicals Today. (US) **1851, 1173**
Chemicke Listy/Journal of Chemistry. (CS ISSN 0009-2770) **1173**
Chemicke Vlakna. (CS ISSN 0528-9432) **4617**
Chemicky Prumysl/Chemical Industry. (CS ISSN 0009-2789) **1173, 1851**
Chemico-Biological Interactions. (IE ISSN 0009-2797) **1980, 435, 474**
Chemie-Anlagen und Verfahren. (GW ISSN 0009-2800) **1851**
Chemie der Erde/Geochemistry. (GW ISSN 0009-2819) **1557**
Chemie der Pflanzenschutz- und Schaedlingsbekaempfungsmittel. (US) **499**
Chemie fuer Labor und Betrieb see Chemie in Labor und Biotechnik **1205**
Chemie in der Schule. (GW ISSN 0009-2843) **1173, 1621**

Chemie in Labor und Biotechnik. (GW) **1205**
Chemie in Unserer Zeit. (GW ISSN 0009-2851) **1173**
Chemie-Ingenieur-Technik. (GW ISSN 0009-286X) **1851, 3258**
Chemie Magazine. (BE ISSN 0379-7651) **1173**
Chemie, Physik und Technologie der Kunststoffe in Einzeldarstellungen see Polymers - Properties and Applications **3867**
Chemie-Technik. (GW ISSN 0340-9961) **1851**
†Chemie und Technik in der Landwirtschaft und Genossenschaftliche Ratschlaege. (GW) **5164**
Chemiearbeiter. (AU) **975, 1173**
Chemiefasern - Textil-Industrie. (GW ISSN 0340-3343) **4617**
Chemiekaarten. (NE) **3616**
Chemik. (PL ISSN 0009-2886) **1173**
Chemiker-Zeitung see Journal fuer Praktische Chemie **1180**
Chemindex: Chemical Buyers Guide for Japan (Year). (JA) **1126, 1173**
ChemInform. (GW ISSN 0931-7597) **1200, 8**
Cheminot. (SZ ISSN 0009-2916) **2581, 4708**
Cheminot de France. (FR ISSN 0245-7318) **2581, 4708**
Cheminot Retraite. (FR) **2581, 4708**
Chemins de Fer. (FR ISSN 0009-2924) **4708**
Chemisch Magazine/Chemical Magazine. (NE ISSN 0167-2746) **1174**
Chemisch Weekblad/Chemical Weekly. (NE) **1174**
Chemisch Weekblad - Chemische Courant see Chemisch Weekblad **1174**
Chemische Berichte. (GW ISSN 0009-2940) **1174**
†Chemische Gesellschaft der DDR. Mitteilungsblatt. (GW ISSN 0411-8987) **5164**
Chemische Industrie. (GW ISSN 0009-2959) **1851**
†Chemische Industrie International. (GW ISSN 0009-2967) **5164**
Die Chemische Produktion. (GW ISSN 0170-0456) **1851**
Chemische Rundschau. (SZ ISSN 0009-2983) **1174, 3720**
Chemische Technik. (GW ISSN 0045-6519) **1174**
Chemisches Informationsdienst see ChemInform **1200**
Chemist. (US ISSN 0009-3025) **1174**
Chemist & Druggist. (UK ISSN 0009-3033) **3720**
Chemist & Druggist Directory. (UK ISSN 0262-5881) **3720**
Chemist & Druggist Price List. (UK) **3720**
Chemist & Drugstore News. (Il ISSN 0009-3041) **3720**
Chemist Catalogue. (AT) **1174**
Chemistry and Binding. see Huaxue yu Nianhe **1854**
Chemistry and Biochemistry of Amino Acids, Peptides, and Proteins. (US ISSN 0069-3111) **474**
Chemistry and Chemical Industry. see Kagaku to Kogyo (Tokyo) **1182**
Chemistry and Ecology. (US ISSN 0275-7540) **1174, 474, 1945**
Chemistry and Industry. (UK ISSN 0009-3068) **1174, 1851**
Chemistry and Industry and Laboratory Management see Chemistry in Industry **1851**
†Chemistry and Pharmacology of Drugs. (US) **5164**
Chemistry and Physics of Carbon: A Series of Advances. (US ISSN 0069-3138) **1217**
Chemistry and Physics of Lipids. (IE ISSN 0009-3084) **475**
Chemistry and Soil Research Institute. Annual Report. (RH) **172**
Chemistry and Technology of Fuels and Oils. (English translation of: Khimiya i Tekhnologiya Topliv i Masel) (US ISSN 0009-3092) **3684**

Chemistry Bulletin. see Huaxue Tongbao **1178**
†Chemistry in Australia. (AT ISSN 0314-4240) **5165**
Chemistry in Britain. (UK ISSN 0009-3106) **1174**
Chemistry in Industry. (NZ) **1851**
Chemistry in New Zealand. (NZ) **1174**
Chemistry International. (UK ISSN 0193-6484) **1174, 1851**
Chemistry Letters. (JA ISSN 0366-7022) **1174**
Chemistry of Functional Groups. (US ISSN 0069-3146) **1174**
Chemistry of Heterocyclic Compounds (New York, 1951). (US ISSN 0069-3154) **1217**
Chemistry of Heterocyclic Compounds (New York, 1965). (English translation of: Khimiya Geterotsiklicheskikh Soedinenii) (US ISSN 0009-3122) **1217**
Chemistry of Materials. (US ISSN 0897-4756) **1851**
Chemistry of Natural Compounds. (English translation of: Khimiya Prirodnykh Soedinenii) (US ISSN 0009-3130) **1217**
Chemistry of Natural Products. (UK ISSN 0069-3162) **1217**
Chemistry of Plant Protection. (US ISSN 0937-2148) **1174, 499**
▼Chemistry Review. (UK ISSN 0959-8464) **1174**
Chemistry Teaching. see Huaxue Jiaoxue **1178**
Chemists and Chemistry. (NE) **1174, 418**
Chemists' Quarterly see Kimika **1182**
Chemists Review. (PK ISSN 0009-3149) **3720**
▼Chemoecology. (GW ISSN 0936-5214) **1217, 435**
Chemometrics and Intelligent Laboratory Systems. (NE ISSN 0169-7439) **1205, 1390**
Chemoreception Abstracts. (US ISSN 0300-1261) **1200, 8**
Chemosphere. (US ISSN 0045-6535) **1981, 1174**
Chemotherapy. (SZ ISSN 0009-3157) **3720**
Chemotherapy. see Nihon Kagaku Ryoho Gakkai Zasshi **3736**
Chempress. (NE ISSN 0009-3173) **1851, 3404**
▼Chemputer Guide. (US) **1424, 1174**
Chemsa. (SA) **1851**
Chemtech. (US) **1852**
Chemtracts: Analytical, Physical and Inorganic Chemistry see Chemtracts: Inorganic Chemistry **1200**
▼Chemtracts: Biochemistry and Molecular Biology. (US ISSN 1045-2680) **1200, 8, 464**
Chemtracts: Inorganic Chemistry. (US ISSN 1051-7227) **1200, 8**
▼Chemtracts: Macromolecular Chemistry. (US ISSN 0899-7829) **1200, 8**
Chemtracts: Organic Chemistry. (US ISSN 0895-4445) **1200, 8, 1217**
Chemtronics see Advanced Materials for Optics and Electronics **1211**
Chemung Historical Journal. (US) **2402**
Cheng Ming Monthly. (HK) **2197**
Chengdu Daxue Xuebao (Shehui Kexue Ban)/Chengdu University. Journal (Social Science Edition). (CC) **4368**
Chengdu Daxue Xuebao (Ziran Kexue Ban)/Chengdu University. Journal (Natural Science Edition). (CC) **4304**
Chengdu Keji Daxue Xuebao/Chengdu University of Science and Technology. Journal. (CC ISSN 0253-2263) **4304**
Chengdu University. Journal (Natural Science Edition). see Chengdu Daxue Xuebao (Ziran Kexue Ban) **4304**
Chengdu University. Journal (Social Science Edition). see Chengdu Daxue Xuebao (Shehui Kexue Ban) **4368**
Chengdu University of Science and Technology. Journal. see Chengdu Keji Daxue Xuebao **4304**

Chengshi Gaige yu Fazhan/Urban Reform and Development. (CC) **2485**, **850**
Chengshi Gongyong Shiye/Public Utilities. (CC ISSN 1001-599X) **4056**
Chengshi Guihua. (CC ISSN 1002-1329) **2485**
Chengshi Guihua Huikan. (CC ISSN 1000-3363) **1863**, **2485**
Chengshi Jinrong/Urban Finance. (CC) **772**
Chengshi Wenti/Urban Issues. (CC) **4368**
Chengshi Yanjiu/Urban Studies. (CC) **4368**
Chengxiang Jianshe/Urban and Rural Construction. (CC) **2485**, **4146**
Chenji Xuebao/Acta Sedimentologica Sinica. (CC) **1557**
Chequered Flag. (SA) **4687**
Cherbourg Port Handbook. (UK ISSN 0268-649X) **1126**, **4725**
Cheri. (US) **3396**
Cheri Book of Lingerie. (US) **3396**
Cheri Letters. (US) **3396**
Cheri Pillow Talk. (US) **3396**
Cherie Magazine. (SI) **4839**
Cherie Moda/Cherie Mode. (IT ISSN 0009-3203) **1289**
Cherie Mode. see Cherie Moda **1289**
Cherith. (US) **4839**, **2445**
Cherokee Advocate. (US) **1996**
Cherokee Ancestor Directory for Research. (US) **2147**
Cherokee Boys Club Newsletter. (US) **1996**, **1234**
Cherokee One Feather. (US ISSN 0890-4448) **1996**
Cherokee Voice. (US) **4401**, **1996**
Cherry. (US) **3396**, **2861**
Cherry Diamond. (US) **1296**
Cherwell. (UK ISSN 0308-731X) **1307**
Cherwell Guide to Oxford. (UK) **4757**
Chesapeake and Ohio Historical Magazine. (US ISSN 0886-6287) **4708**, **2402**
Chesapeake and Ohio Historical Newsletter see Chesapeake and Ohio Historical Magazine **4708**
Chesapeake Bay Foundation. Annual Report. (US) **1945**
Chesapeake Bay Foundation News. (US) **1945**
Chesapeake Bay Magazine. (US ISSN 0045-656X) **4524**, **4757**
Cheshire Archaeological Bulletin. (UK ISSN 0307-6628) **269**
Cheshire Farmer. (UK) **83**
Cheshire History. (UK ISSN 0141-8696) **269**, **2356**
Cheshire Life. (UK ISSN 0009-3289) **2193**
Cheshire Ornithological Association. Bird Report. (UK ISSN 0262-7655) **563**
Cheshire Smile. (UK ISSN 0009-3297) **2290**, **2460**
Chesopiean. (US ISSN 0009-3300) **269**, **237**
Chess. (UK) **4468**
Chess. see Guoji Xiangqi **4473**
Chess Asia. (PH) **4469**
Chess Chow. (US) **4469**
Chess Collector. (UK) **4469**
Chess Computer World. (UK) **4469**, **1419**
Chess Correspondent. (US ISSN 0009-3327) **4469**
†Chess Gazette. (US) **5165**
Chess Horizons. (US ISSN 0147-2569) **4469**
Chess in Australia. (AT ISSN 0009-3343) **4469**
Chess in Indiana. (US ISSN 1044-8888) **4469**
Chess in the R S A. (SA) **4469**
Chess in U S S R. (IT) **4469**
Chess Informant. see Sahovski Informator **4486**
†Chess International. (US ISSN 0897-7305) **5165**
Chess Journalist. (US) **2568**, **4469**
Chess Life. (US ISSN 0197-260X) **4469**
Chess Life and Review see Chess Life **4469**

Chess Mate. (II ISSN 0970-9142) **4469**
†Chess Notes. (SZ) **5165**
Chess Post. (UK ISSN 0960-1422) **4469**
Chess Review see Chess Life **4469**
ChessBase Magazin. (GW) **4469**
Chesstamp Review. (US) **3750**, **4469**
Chest. (US ISSN 0012-3692) **3364**, **3206**
Chest Surgery. see Grudnaya Khirurgiya **3379**
Chester County Biz. (US) **655**
Chester County Genealogical Society. Bulletin see Chester District Genealogical Society. Bulletin **2147**
Chester District Genealogical Society. Bulletin. (US) **2147**
Chester White Journal. (US ISSN 0009-3386) **214**
Chester Zoo News. (UK) **580**
Chesterton Review. (CN ISSN 0317-0500) **2905**
Chestnut Grower. (US) **172**, **2124**
Chestnut Hill Local. (US ISSN 0009-3394) **2223**
Chestnutworks see Chestnut Grower **172**
Chetham Society Publications - Remains, Historical and Literary, Connected with the Palatine Countries of Lancaster and Chester. (UK ISSN 0080-0880) **2356**
Chetwynd Echo. (CN) **2176**
Chetwynd Reporter see Chetwynd Echo **2176**
Cheval Infos see Cheval Star **4533**
Cheval Magazine. (FR ISSN 0245-3614) **4533**
Cheval Star. (FR) **4533**
Cheveaux de Penny see Cheval Star **4533**
Chevre. (FR ISSN 0045-6608) **214**
Chevrolet High Performance see Chevy High Performance **4687**
Chevron U S A Odyssey. (US ISSN 0886-5418) **4757**
Chevron World. (US ISSN 0148-3102) **3684**
Chevy Action. (US) **4687**
Chevy Camper see Chevy Outdoors **4543**
Chevy - Corvette Buyer's Guide. (US) **4687**
Chevy High Performance. (US) **4687**
Chevy Outdoors. (US ISSN 0893-2778) **4543**
Chevy Power. (US) **4687**
Chewonki Chronicle. (US) **1485**, **1945**
Chez Nous see Chester Zoo News **580**
Chez Nous. (UK ISSN 0009-3424) **2809**, **1746**
Chhandita. (II ISSN 0009-3432) **2905**
Chi e' Chi del Giornalismo dell'Auto. (IT) **2568**
Chi e Chi in Svizzera? see Swiss Biographical Index of Prominent Persons **421**
Chi e Dove. (IT) **3545**
Chi Sono. (IT) **418**, **3545**, **4469**
Chia Ho Tien Ying. see Golden Movie News **3511**
Chiang Mai Medical Bulletin. (TH ISSN 0125-5983) **3087**
Chiasma see Australian Rural Science Annual **78**
Chiazze. (IT) **2204**
Chiba Daigaku Engeigakubu Gakujutsu Hokoku. see Chiba University. Faculty of Horticulture. Technical Bulletin **2124**
Chiba Daigaku Kogakubu Kenkyu Hokoku. see Chiba University. Faculty of Engineering. Journal **1816**
Chiba Igaku Zasshi/Chiba Medical Journal. (JA ISSN 0303-5476) **3087**
Chiba Medical Journal. see Chiba Igaku Zasshi **3087**
Chiba University. Faculty of Engineering. Journal/Chiba Daigaku Kogakubu Kenkyu Hokoku. (JA ISSN 0577-6848) **1816**
Chiba University. Faculty of Horticulture. Technical Bulletin/Chiba Daigaku Engeigakubu Gakujutsu Hokoku. (JA ISSN 0069-3227) **2124**

Chic Letters. (US) **3396**
Chic Magazine. (US ISSN 0194-648X) **3396**
Chicago. (US ISSN 0362-4595) **4757**, **3545**
Chicago. Municipal Reference Library. Checklist of Publications Issued by the City of Chicago. (US ISSN 0300-712X) **4085**
Chicago. Municipal Reference Library. Recent Additions. (US ISSN 0300-7081) **4085**
Chicago (Year). (US) **4757**
Chicago Academy of Sciences. Bulletin. (US ISSN 0009-3491) **4304**
Chicago Advertising & Media. (US) **29**
▼Chicago & Cook County Marketing Directory. (US) **1126**
†Chicago Anthropology Exchange. (US) **5165**
Chicago Apparel News. (US ISSN 0195-0819) **1284**
Chicago Architectural Journal. (US ISSN 0731-8545) **296**
Chicago Architecture Foundation News. (US) **296**, **321**, **3523**, **4757**
Chicago Area Transportation Study. Annual Report. (US) **4648**
Chicago Art Review. (US) **321**
Chicago Artists' News. (US) **321**, **1005**, **1035**, **3523**
Chicago Athletic Association Magazine see C A A Magazine **5155**
Chicago Bar Association Record see C B A Record **2607**
Chicago Bar Record see C B A Record **2607**
Chicago Board Options Exchange. (US) **942**
Chicago Bowler. (US ISSN 0009-3513) **4502**
Chicago Catholic see The New World **4271**
Chicago Chronicle. (US) **1702**, **1307**
Chicago Clinical Chemist. (US) **1174**
Chicago Computer Guide. (US) **1458**
Chicago Construction News see Dodge Construction News. Chicago Edition **616**
Chicago Daily Hide and Tallow Bulletin. (US ISSN 0009-3521) **2736**, **214**
Chicago Daily Law Bulletin. (US ISSN 0362-6148) **2612**
Chicago Dental Society Fortnightly Review see Chicago Dental Society Review **3230**
Chicago Dental Society Review. (US ISSN 0091-1666) **3230**
▼Chicago District Golfer. (US) **4502**
Chicago Enterprise. (US) **655**
Chicago Film & Video News. (US) **3505**, **1384**
Chicago Genealogical Society. Newsletter. (US ISSN 0193-8770) **2147**
Chicago Genealogist. (US ISSN 0009-3556) **2147**
Chicago Guide see Chicago **4757**
Chicago Guides to Writing, Editing, and Publishing. (US) **4125**
Chicago Healthcare. (US) **3800**, **3604**
Chicago Herpetological Society. Bulletin.(US ISSN 0009-3564) **580**
Chicago History. (US ISSN 0272-8540) **2402**
Chicago History of American Civilization.(US ISSN 0069-3278) **2402**
Chicago History of American Religion. (US) **4168**
Chicago History of Science and Medicine. (US ISSN 0073-2745) **2308**, **3087**
†Chicago Illini. (US ISSN 0009-3572) **5165**
Chicago - Kent Law Review. (US) **2612**
Chicago Lawyer. (US ISSN 0199-8374) **2612**
Chicago Lectures in Mathematics. (US ISSN 0069-3286) **3032**
Chicago Lectures in Physics. (US ISSN 0069-3294) **3816**
Chicago Life. (US) **2223**
Chicago Linguistic Society. Papers from the Regional Meetings. (US ISSN 0577-7240) **2809**

Chicago Magazine. (US) **2223**
Chicago Market. (US) **2281**
Chicago Maroon. (US ISSN 0009-3610) **1307**
Chicago Media Directory. (US) **2568**
Chicago Medicine. (US ISSN 0009-3637) **3087**
†Chicago Mercantile Exchange Yearbook. (US ISSN 0577-7259) **5165**
Chicago Metro Golfer. (US) **4502**
Chicago Motor Club Home & Away. (US) **4757**
Chicago Mountaineer. (US) **4544**
Chicago Nurse. (US ISSN 0199-2066) **3277**
Chicago Parent News. (US) **1234**
†Chicago Psychoanalytic Literature Index. (US ISSN 0009-3661) **5165**
Chicago Purchasor. (US ISSN 0009-367X) **1035**
Chicago Renaissance. (US) **2905**, **3789**
Chicago Reporter. (US ISSN 0300-6921) **4431**
Chicago Review. (US ISSN 0009-3696) **2905**
Chicago Schools and Careers. (US) **1692**, **3626**
Chicago Schools Journal see Illinois Schools Journal **1638**
Chicago Sports Profiles. (US) **4469**
Chicago Studies. (US ISSN 0009-3718) **4260**
Chicago Studies in the History of Judaism. (US) **4222**
Chicago Symphony Orchestra. (US) **3545**
Chicago Talent Sourcebook (No.). (US) **3998**, **321**
Chicago Theological Seminary Register. (US) **4168**
†Chicago Times. (US ISSN 0894-5640) **5165**
Chicago Union Teacher. (US) **1621**
Chicagoland Dining and Nightlife Guide see Chicagoland Dining Guide **4757**
Chicagoland Dining Guide. (US) **4757**
Chicagoland Golf. (US) **4502**
Chicagoland Senior American see Senior American **2278**
Chicagoland Wedding Guide. (US) **3066**
El Chicano. (US) **1996**
Chicano de San Bernardino see El Chicano **1996**
Chicano Index. (US) **2030**, **397**
Chicano - Latino Law Review. (US) **2612**, **1997**
Chicano Law Review see Chicano - Latino Law Review **2612**
Chicano Periodical Index see Chicano Index **2030**
Chicano Studies Library Newsletter. (US) **1997**
The Chichester Leaflet. (UK) **4232**
Chichester Magazine. (UK) **4232**
Chichester News see The Chichester Leaflet **4232**
Chickadee. (CN ISSN 0707-4611) **1251**, **4304**
Chickasaw Times Past. (US) **2147**, **2402**
Chicora Foundation Research. (US ISSN 1055-2855) **269**, **3523**
Chicora Foundation Research Series. (US ISSN 0882-2042) **269**
Chicorel Index Series. (US) **397**
†Chicory (Baltimore). (US ISSN 0009-3793) **5165**
Chicory (Baton Rouge). (US) **2752**
Chidori. see Plover **5259**
Chief see Chief - Civil Service Leader **3626**
Chief - Civil Service Leader. (US ISSN 0746-7761) **3626**
†Chief Economist Commentary. (US) **5165**
▼Chief Economist's Letter. (US) **850**
Chief Engineer. (US) **1816**
Chief Executive see Chief Executives Think Tank. Economic Research Reports **850**
Chief Executive Magazine. (US ISSN 0160-4724) **1005**
Chief Executive Officer Newsletter see C E O Newsletter **5156**
Chief Executive Opinion. (US) **655**

CHIEF EXECUTIVES

Chief Executives Think Tank. Economic Research Reports. (PK) **850**
Chief Financial Officer see C F O **653**
Chief Financial Officer Alert see C F O Alert **748**
Chief Financial Officer NewsBrief. (US) **772**
Chief Fire Executive. (US) **4099, 1005**
Chief Information Officer see C I O **825**
Chief Information Officer Journal. (US ISSN 0899-0182) **1455**
Chief Information Officer Letter see C I O Letter **5157**
Chief Information Officer Monthly see C I O Monthly **5157**
Chief of Police. (US) **1511**
Chiefs of State and Cabinet Members of Foreign Governments. (US) **3953, 1526**
Chiefs of State and Cabinet Ministers of the American Republics. (US ISSN 0250-6114) **4056**
Chieftain. (US) **1307**
Chien see Le Chien Magazine **3709**
Chien d'Or/Golden Dog. (CN ISSN 0315-467X) **2905**
Le Chien Magazine. (SZ) **3709**
Chiens 2000. (FR) **3709**
La Chiesa nel Tempo. (IT) **4168**
Chiffres d'Affaires du Commerce de Detail. see Detailhandelsumsaetze **713**
Chigaku Kyoiku. see Education of Earth Science **1543**
Chigaku Zasshi/Journal of Geography. (JA ISSN 0022-135X) **1542, 2245**
Chigiana. (IT ISSN 0069-3391) **3545**
Chigwell Local History Society. Transactions. (UK ISSN 0306-5197) **2356**
Chihuahua News. (US) **3709**
Chihuahuan Desert Discovery. (US) **1542, 435**
Chihuahuan Desert Newsbriefs. (US) **1542, 435**
Los Chihuahuas. (US ISSN 0273-2335) **3709**
Chijo. see Earth **87**
Chika Shigen Chosajo Hokoku/ Geological Survey of Hokkaido. Report. (JA ISSN 0441-0785) **1542, 1557**
Chikasui Gakkaishi. see Journal of Groundwater Hydrology **1599**
Chikitsak Barta. (II) **3087**
Chikitsak Samaj. (II ISSN 0009-3858) **3087**
Chikudenchi/Storage Battery. (JA ISSN 0009-3866) **1884**
Chikuho Hakubutsu/Naturhistorica Chikuhoana. (JA) **4304**
Chikusan no Kenkyu/Animal Husbandry.(JA ISSN 0009-3874) **214**
Child. (US ISSN 0894-7988) **1234, 1746**
Child. (SU) **1251**
Child Abuse & Neglect. (US ISSN 0145-2134) **1234, 4431**
▼Child Abuse Review. (UK ISSN 0952-9136) **4401, 4015**
Child Accident Prevention Foundation of Australia. Quarterly Journal see Safeguard **1243**
Child Adoption see Adoption and Fostering **4397**
Child Advocacy and Protection Newsletter see Children and the Law **1234**
Child and Adolescent Social Work Journal. (US ISSN 0738-0151) **4431, 1234**
Child and Family. (US ISSN 0009-3882) **1234, 1621**
Child & Family Behavior Therapy. (US ISSN 0731-7107) **4015**
Child and Family Magazine. (CN) **1503, 1251**
Child and Family Policy. (US) **1621**
Child and Man. (UK ISSN 0009-3890) **1621**
Child and Youth Care Forum. (US ISSN 1053-1890) **1234, 4015**
Child and Youth Care Quarterly see Child and Youth Care Forum **1234**
Child & Youth Services. (US ISSN 0145-935X) **4401, 1234**

▼Child Assessment News. (US ISSN 1055-0518) **1234, 4015**
Child Behavior and Development. (US ISSN 0193-7421) **3319, 3333, 4015**
Child Care Action News. (US) **1234, 3396, 4839**
Child Care Focus. (CN ISSN 0847-3234) **1234, 1746, 4401**
Child: Care, Health and Development. (UK ISSN 0305-1862) **3319**
Child Care Information Exchange. (US ISSN 0164-8527) **1726**
Child Care: Whose Priority see State Child Care Fact Book (Year) **5283**
Child Development. (US ISSN 0009-3920) **1234, 4016**
Child Development Abstracts and Bibliography. (US ISSN 0009-3939) **1247, 8**
Child Education. (UK ISSN 0009-3947) **1621**
Child Education Special see Infant Projects **1638**
Child Find News. (US) **1511, 1234**
†Child Health and Development. (SZ ISSN 0251-2467) **5165**
Child Health Talk. (US) **1234, 1997, 4401**
Child in His Family see International Association of Child and Adolescent Psychiatry and Allied Professions. Yearbook **5215**
Child Language Teaching and Therapy. (UK ISSN 0265-6590) **1734, 1746**
Child Life. (US ISSN 0009-3971) **1251**
▼Child Magazine's Guide to Having a Baby. (US) **1234, 3800**
Child Nephrology and Urology. (SZ ISSN 1012-6694) **3387, 3319**
Child Nurturance. (US) **1234**
Child Protection Report. (US ISSN 0147-1260) **1234**
Child Psychiatry and Human Development. (US ISSN 0009-398X) **3333, 3319**
†Child Psychiatry Quarterly. (II ISSN 0009-3998) **5165**
Child Safety Review. (UK ISSN 0957-4107) **1234, 1503, 4099**
Child Study Center Bulletin see Child Study Journal **1621**
Child Study Journal. (US ISSN 0009-4005) **1621, 1234, 4016**
†Child Study Journal Monograph. (US ISSN 0099-0116) **5165**
Child Welfare. (US ISSN 0009-4021) **4401, 1234**
Child Welfare League of America. Directory of Member And Associate Agencies Listing see Child Welfare League of America. Directory of Member And Associate Agencies **4401**
Child Welfare League of America. Directory of Member And Associate Agencies. (US) **4401**
†Child Welfare League of America. From the Desk of the Executive Director. (US) **5165**
Child Welfare Quarterly. (JA) **4401**
Child Welfare Research Quarterly see Megamot **4442**
Child, Youth, and Family Futures Clearinghouse. (US ISSN 1055-9221) **4401, 3396, 4839**
Childbirth (Year). (US) **3290**
†Childbirth Alternatives Quarterly. (US ISSN 0272-6319) **5165**
†Childbirth Educator. (US ISSN 0279-490X) **5165**
▼Childbirth Instructor. (US) **3290, 1746**
Childbirth Without Pain Education Association. Memo. (US) **3290**
Childbirth Without Pain Education Association. Newsletter see Childbirth Without Pain Education Association. Memo **3290**
▼ChildCare. (US) **1234**
Childhood Education. (US ISSN 0009-4056) **1621, 1234**
†Childhood in Poetry. (US) **5165**
†Children. (US) **5165**
†Children and Animals. (US) **5165**
Children and Culture. see Barn och Kultur **2746**

Children & Society. (UK ISSN 0951-0605) **1234, 3319**
Children & Teens Today. (US ISSN 0732-7420) **1234**
Children and the Law. (US) **1234, 2612**
Children and War Newsletter. (UK ISSN 0956-3113) **1234, 3953**
Children and Youth Services Review. (US ISSN 0190-7409) **1234, 4401**
Children Before the Court. (US) **2612, 1234**
Children in Custody. (US ISSN 0147-9881) **1234**
Children in Finland. (FI ISSN 0783-6244) **4401, 1234**
Children in Hospitals (Newsletter). (US) **4401**
Children in the Tropics. (FR ISSN 0379-2269) **1235, 3800**
Children - Musicians. (RU) **3545, 1235**
Children of Aging Parents Sule (Levittown) see C A P Sule (Levittown) **2271**
Children of China. see Zhonghua Ernu **1247**
Children of Deaf Adults Newsletter see C O D A Newsletter **2286**
Children of the Earth. (US) **4281**
Children Today. (US ISSN 0361-4336) **1235, 1621, 4401**
Children Welcome see Children Welcome! Family Holiday Guide **4757**
Children Welcome! Family Holiday Guide. (UK) **4757**
Childrens Activities Time Society, Inc. Tales see C A T S Tales **5156**
Children's Aid Society News. (US) **4401, 1235**
Children's Aid Society Newsletter see Children's Aid Society News **4401**
Children's Aid Society of Ottawa. Information Bulletin see Echo (Ottawa) **5183**
Children's Album. (US ISSN 0749-8659) **1251, 1235, 2434, 2905**
Children's Apparel Manufacturers Association Parade see C A M A Parade **1284**
Children's Apparel Merchandising Aids see C A M A Parade **1284**
Children's Art Exchange Newsletter see Brushstrokes **320**
Children's Authors and Illustrators. (US) **424, 2981**
Children's Bible Study Older Pupil. (US ISSN 0273-3161) **4232**
Children's Bible Study Teacher. (US ISSN 0273-3153) **4232**
Children's Bible Study Younger Pupil. (US ISSN 0273-317X) **4233**
Children's Big World. see Ertong Dashijie **1254**
Children's Book Foundation News see C.B.F. News **4124**
Childrens Book News. (CN ISSN 0705-0038) **4125, 1251**
Children's Book Review. (US ISSN 0890-5746) **1251, 2905**
Children's Book Review Index. (US ISSN 0147-5681) **1247, 8**
Children's Book Review Service. (US ISSN 0090-7987) **4125, 2752**
Children's Books and Recordings: Suggested as Holiday Gifts see Children's Books: One Hundred Titles for Reading and Sharing **4125**
Children's Books: Awards and Prizes. (US ISSN 0069-3472) **4125**
Children's Books History Society Newsletter see C B H S Newsletter **4124**
Children's Books in Print. (US ISSN 0069-3480) **397, 2981**
Children's Books in Print. (UK ISSN 0577-781X) **397**
Children's Books International. Proceedings. (US ISSN 0163-1756) **1251**
Children's Books of the Year. (US) **1251, 1621, 4125**
Children's Books of the Year. (UK ISSN 0266-4232) **4125, 1251**
Children's Books: One Hundred Titles for Reading and Sharing. (US) **4125**

▼Children's Bookwatch. (US) **1247, 1235**
Children's Business. (US ISSN 0884-2280) **1289, 1235**
Children's Cartoon. see Ertong Manhua **325**
Children's Catalog. (US) **1247**
†Children's Choices of Canadian Books. (CN) **5165**
Children's Choir. (US ISSN 0895-7428) **4233**
Children's Choir Newsletter see Americas Boychoir - International Children's Choir Federation. Newsletter **3538**
Childrens Clothing International. (UK ISSN 0261-6025) **1284, 1235**
Children's Creation. see Ertong Chuangzhao **1632**
Children's Defense Fund Reports see C D F Reports **1233**
Children's Digest. (II ISSN 0009-4080) **1251**
Children's Digest (1980). (US ISSN 0272-7145) **1251**
†Children's Environments Quarterly. (US ISSN 0886-0505) **5165**
Children's Epoch. see Ertong Shidai **1254**
Children's Folklore Review. (US ISSN 0739-5558) **1235, 2053**
Children's Health Care see Children's Health Care Journal **4402**
Children's Health Care Journal. (US ISSN 0273-9615) **4402**
Children's Healthcare is a Legal Duty Newsletter see C H I L D Newsletter **1233**
Children's Hospice International Newsletter. (US) **3319, 2460**
Children's Hospital Medical Center, Boston. News see Children's World **2460**
Children's Hospital Quarterly. (US ISSN 0899-5869) **3319**
Children's House - Children's World. (US) **1235, 1621**
Children's House Magazine see Children's House - Children's World **1235**
Children's Joy. see Paethiki Hara **1653**
Children's Language. (US ISSN 0163-2809) **2809**
Children's Leader see Leader in the Church School Today **4241**
Children's Leadership. (US ISSN 0162-461X) **4233**
Children's Legal Rights Journal. (US ISSN 0278-7210) **2612, 1235**
Children's Libraries Newsletter see Orana **2778**
Children's Literary Almanac see International Directory of Children's Literature **4141**
Children's Literature. see Ertong Wenxue **1254**
Children's Literature (New Haven). (US ISSN 0092-8208) **2905**
Children's Literature Abstracts. (US ISSN 0306-2015) **1247, 8, 4140**
Children's Literature Association Quarterly. (US ISSN 0885-0429) **2752, 1235**
Children's Literature in Education. (US ISSN 0045-6713) **1235, 1621**
Children's Literature Review. (US ISSN 0362-4145) **1251**
Children's Literature Series. (II) **2905, 1251**
Children's Magazine Guide. (US ISSN 0743-9873) **1247, 8**
Children's Media Market Place. (US ISSN 0734-8169) **1035**
▼Children's Ministry. (US ISSN 1054-1144) **1235, 4168**
Children's Music. see Ertong Yinyue **3550**
Children's News. (US) **1235**
Children's Own. (JM ISSN 0009-4153) **1251**
Children's Pictorial. see Ertong Huabao **1254**
Children's Playmate. (US ISSN 0009-4161) **1251**
Children's Story Pictorial. see Ertong Gushi Huabao **1254**
Children's Styles. (JA ISSN 0009-417X) **1289**

Children's Video Report. (US ISSN 0883-6922) **1384**, 1251
Children's Voice. (US ISSN 1057-736X) **4402**
Children's Welfare Association of Victoria. Newsletter. (AT) **1235**, 4402
Children's World. *see* Haizi Tiandi **1238**
Children's World. (II ISSN 0009-420X) **1251**
Children's World. *see* Kayhan-e Bacheha **1258**
Children's World. (US) **2460**
Children's Writer's and Illustrator's Market. (US ISSN 0897-9790) **4125**, 321, 1251
Childrenswear Manufacturers Association. Newsletter. (US) **1284**
Childright. (UK ISSN 0265-1459) **1235**
Child's Guardian. (UK ISSN 0009-4218) **4402**
Child's Nervous System. (GW ISSN 0256-7040) **3333**, 3319
Child's Play. (US) **1235**, 3319
Child's World. *see* Lapsen Mailma **4412**
Childworld. (US) **1235**, 4168
Chile. Direccion de Presupuestos. Calculo de Entradas de la Nacion. (CL) **1090**
Chile. Direccion de Presupuestos. Departamento de Estudios Financieros. Finanzas Publicas. (CL) **1090**
Chile. Direccion de Presupuestos. Exposicion sobre el Estado de la Hacienda Publica. (CL) **1090**
Chile. Direccion de Presupuestos. Instrucciones para la Ejecucion de la Ley de Presupuestos. (CL) **1091**
Chile. Direccion de Presupuestos. Ley de Presupuestos. (CL) **1091**
Chile. Instituto de Investigaciones Agropecuarias. Agricultura Tecnica. (CL ISSN 0365-2807) **83**
Chile. Instituto de Investigaciones Agropecuarias. Memoria Anual. (CL) **83**
Chile. Instituto Nacional de Estadisticas. Anuario Estadistico *see* Chile. Instituto Nacional de Estadisticas. Series Estadisticas **4568**
Chile. Instituto Nacional de Estadisticas. Boletin de Edificacion. (CL) **4568**
Chile. Instituto Nacional de Estadisticas. Boletin Estadistico Mensual. (CL) **3980**
Chile. Instituto Nacional de Estadisticas. Comercio Exterior. (CL) **710**, 903
Chile. Instituto Nacional de Estadisticas. Compendio Estadistico. (CL) **4568**
Chile. Instituto Nacional de Estadisticas. Estadisticas Agropecuarias. (CL) **136**
Chile. Instituto Nacional de Estadisticas. Estadisticas de Salud. (CL) **4117**
Chile. Instituto Nacional de Estadisticas. Indice de Precios al Consumidor. (CL) **711**
Chile. Instituto Nacional de Estadisticas. Indice de Remuneraciones. (CL) **711**
Chile. Instituto Nacional de Estadisticas. Indice de Salarios *see* Chile. Instituto Nacional de Estadisticas. Indice de Remuneraciones **711**
Chile. Instituto Nacional de Estadisticas. Informativo Estadistico. (CL) **4568**
Chile. Instituto Nacional de Estadisticas. Series Estadisticas. (CL) **4568**
Chile. Instituto Nacional de Estadisticas. Sintesis Estadistica *see* Chile. Instituto Nacional de Estadisticas. Informativo Estadistico **4568**
Chile. Servicio de Impuestos Internos. Boletin. (CL ISSN 0716-145X) **1091**
Chile. Servicio Nacional de Geologia y Mineria. Boletin. (CL ISSN 0020-3939) **1557**
Chile. Servicio Nacional de Pesca. Anuario Estadistico de Pesca. (CL ISSN 0716-0976) **2038**, 4568

Chile. Superintendencia de Bancos. Boletin Estadistico *see* Chile. Superintendencia de Bancos e Instituciones Financieras. Informacion Financiera **772**
Chile. Superintendencia de Bancos e Instituciones Financieras. Informacion Financiera. (CL ISSN 0716-2820) **772**
Chile. Superintendencia de Seguridad Social. Boletin de Estadisticas de Seguridad *see* Chile. Superintendencia de Seguridad Social. Seguridad Social: Estadisticas **2546**
Chile. Superintendencia de Seguridad Social. Seguridad Social: Estadisticas.(CL) **2546**
Chile Agricola. (CL ISSN 0379-5845) **83**
Chile Democratico Bulletin. (US) **2180**
Chile Economic Report. (US) **903**
†Chile Fights. (UK) **5165**
Chile Filatelico. (CL) **3751**
Chile Forestal. (CL ISSN 0716-1190) **2097**
Chile Pepper. (US) **2445**, 3604
Chile: Summary of Recent Events *see* Chilean Review **3879**
Chilean Chemical Society. Bulletin. *see* Sociedad Chilena de Quimica. Boletin **1188**
Chilean Forestry News. (CL ISSN 0716-1344) **2097**
Chilean News. (UK) **3953**
Chilean Newsbrief *see* Chilean Review **3879**
Chilean Review. (US) **3879**
Chileans. (UK) **2124**, 1485
†Chilenet. (US) **5165**
Chilled Foods *see* Frozen and Chilled Foods **2071**
Chiltern Enterprise. (UK) **813**
Chilton's Auto Repair Manual. (US ISSN 0069-3634) **4687**
Chilton's Automotive Industries *see* Automotive Industries **4683**
Chilton's Automotive Marketing. (US ISSN 0193-3264) **4687**, 1035
Chilton's Commercial Carrier Journal. (US ISSN 0734-1423) **4743**
Chilton's Distribution *see* Chilton's Distribution Magazine **4648**
Chilton's Distribution Magazine. (US ISSN 0273-6721) **4648**
Chilton's E C N - Electronic Component News. (US ISSN 0193-614X) **1764**
Chilton's Food Engineering. (US ISSN 0193-323X) **2064**
Chilton's Food Engineering International.(US ISSN 0148-4478) **2064**
Chilton's Hardware Age. (US ISSN 8755-254X) **641**, 2501
Chilton's I A N *see* Instrumentation & Automation News **2522**
Chilton's I and C S *see* Instrumentation and Control Systems **2523**
Chilton's Import Automotive Repair Manual *see* Chilton's Import Car Repair Manual **4687**
Chilton's Import Car Repair Manual. (US) **4687**
Chilton's Industrial Maintenance & Plant Operation. (US ISSN 8755-2523) **1005**
Chilton's Industrial Safety & Hygiene News. (US ISSN 8755-2566) **3616**
Chilton's Iron Age *see* Iron Age **3409**
Chilton's Iron Age: Manufacturing Management *see* Metalworking News **5235**
Chilton's Jewelers' Circular-Keystone. (US ISSN 0194-2905) **2563**
Chilton's Labor Guide and Parts Manual. Motor Age Professional Mechanics Edition. (US ISSN 0749-5579) **4687**
Chilton's Motor Age. (US ISSN 0193-7022) **4688**
Chilton's Motor-Age Professional Automotive Service Manual. (US ISSN 0363-2393) **4688**
Chilton's Motorcycle and A T V Repair Manual. (US) **4516**

Chilton's Motorcycle Repair Manual *see* Chilton's Motorcycle and A T V Repair Manual **4516**
Chilton's Product Design and Development. (US) **1816**
Chilton's Review of Optometry. (US ISSN 0147-7633) **3299**
Chilton's Truck and Off-Highway Industries *see* Truck & Off-Highway Industries **4748**
Chilton's Truck and Van Repair Manual.(US) **4688**
Chilton's Truck Repair Manual *see* Chilton's Truck and Van Repair Manual **4688**
Chilun/Gear. (CC ISSN 1001-2281) **3016**
Chimes. (HK ISSN 0069-3642) **2905**
The Chimes (La Mirada). (US) **1307**
Chimes (Notre Dame). (US ISSN 0009-4285) **2905**, 1307
Chimica Didactica. (GW ISSN 0172-7567) **1175**, 1746
Chimica e Petrolchimica. (IT) **1852**
Chimici Igienisti. Bollettino. (IT) **1175**
Chimie *see* Chemie Magazine **1173**
Chimie Actualites. (FR ISSN 0009-4323) **1852**
Chimie Analytique *see* Analusis **1203**
Chimie Magazine. (FR ISSN 0245-940X) **1852**
Chimika Chronika. General Edition. (GR ISSN 0366-5526) **1175**
Chimika Chronika. New Series. (GR ISSN 0366-693X) **1175**
Chin Ch'u K'ou Mao I T'ung Chi Yueh Pao. *see* China, Republic. Ministry of Finance. Department of Statistics. Monthly Statistics of Exports and Imports **711**
Chin Jih Ching Chi. *see* Economy Today **662**
Chin Jih Yu Cheng. *see* Postal Service Today **1354**
Chin - Nitayasarnpap. (CC) **2181**
Chin Tai Chung-kuo. *see* Modern China **2874**
China. (CC ISSN 1000-9299) **2181**
China *see* China Trader Newsletter **3751**
China Advertising. *see* Zhongguo Guanggao **40**
China Aero Information/Zhongguo Hangkong Xinxi. (CC ISSN 1003-6008) **49**
China Aerospace Abstracts. (CC ISSN 1002-6592) **50**
China Agribusiness Report. (HK) **148**
China Agriculture and Trade Report. (US) **148**
China Aktuell. (GW ISSN 0341-6631) **3879**
China and Africa/Zhongguo yu Feizhou. (CC) **3953**
China and Pacific Rim Letter. (US ISSN 1044-890X) **3953**
China Automotive Journal/Xiandai Qiche. (HK) **4688**, 4743
†China Aviation Journal. (HK) **5165**
China Books. (CC) **4125**
China - Britain Trade Review. (UK) **903**
China Bulletin *see* China Notes **4233**
China Business and Trade. (US ISSN 0731-7700) **903**
▼China Business Law Guide. (AT) **2708**, 655
China Business Review. (US ISSN 0163-7169) **903**
China Cartoons. *see* Zhongguo Manhua **351**
China Center of Advanced Science and Technology Series. (UK ISSN 0894-2536) **4304**, 4595
China City Planning Review. (CC ISSN 1002-8447) **2485**
China Civil Engineering Journal. *see* Tu-Mu Gongcheng Xuebao **1875**
China Clipper. (US ISSN 0885-9779) **3751**
China Coal Industry Yearbook. (HK ISSN 0258-3062) **3480**
China Coal Society. Journal. *see* Meitan Xuebao **3488**
China Communications and Transportation Yearbook. *see* Zhongguo Jiaotong Nianjian **1346**
China Computerworld. (CC) **1448**, 1390

CHINA MARKET 6051

China Culture Newspaper. *see* Zhongguo Wenhua Bao **2183**
China Current Laws. (HK ISSN 1011-2359) **2612**
China Customs. *see* Zhongguo Haiguan **925**
†China Daily News. (US ISSN 0889-9002) **5165**
China Dairy Industry. *see* Zhongguo Rupin Gongye **204**
China de Hoy *see* China Today **2181**
China Development Corporation. Annual Report. (CH) **1073**
China Directory (Year)/Zhongguo Zuzhibie Renmingbu/Chugoku Soshikibetsu Jinmeibo. (JA) **3953**, 418, 4056
China Drug Purchase Audit. (US) **3720**
China Earth Sciences. (NE ISSN 0923-6805) **1542**, 1557, 1587
China Economic Express (Japanese Edition). (HK ISSN 1011-2898) **850**
China Economic Express (Korean Edition). (HK ISSN 1013-5375) **850**
China Economic News. *see* Zhongguo Jingji Xinwen **888**
China Economic Review. (US ISSN 1043-951X) **850**
China Exchange News. (US ISSN 0272-0086) **4304**
China Exchange Newsletter *see* China Exchange News **4304**
China Facts and Figures Annual. (US ISSN 0190-602X) **3879**, 2337, 4568
China Film Yearbook. *see* Zhongguo Dianying Nianjian **3520**
China Finance. *see* Zhongguo Jinrong **804**
China Finance Year Book. *see* Zhongguo Jinrong Nianjian **804**
China Forestry Education. *see* Zhongguo Linye Jiaoyu **2111**
China Forum. (CH) **2337**
China Gazeta la Picha. (CC ISSN 1000-9302) **2181**
China Glass & Tableware. (US ISSN 0009-4382) **1163**
China Glass and Tableware Red Book Directory. (US ISSN 0069-3677) **1163**
China Guidebook. (US ISSN 0734-6549) **2181**, 4757
China Hand. (US) **655**
†China-Handel. (GW ISSN 0178-7438) **5165**
China Health Pictorial. *see* Zhongguo Weisheng Huakan **4116**
China Heute *see* China Today **2181**
China Heute. (GW) **4168**
China Historical Materials of Science and Technology. *see* Zhongguo Ke-Ji Shiliao **4353**
China Hoje *see* China Today **2181**
China im Bild. (CC ISSN 1000-9264) **2181**
China Industrial Economics Research. *see* Zhongguo Gongye Jingji Yanjiu **1000**
China Informatics. (HK) **1423**, 1350, 1362
China Information. (NE ISSN 0920-203X) **3646**
China Institute in America. Bulletin. (US) **3635**, 321, 1621
China Institute of Atomic Energy. Annual Report. (CC) **1804**
China Law Reporter. (US) **2720**
China Law Yearbook. *see* Zhongguo Falu Nianjian **2697**
China Laws for Foreign Business. (AT) **2708**, 903
China Letter. (HK ISSN 0379-2862) **850**
China Letter *see* China and Pacific Rim Letter **3953**
China - Liaodong Peninsula International Exchange. *see* Zhongguo - Liaodong Bandao Guoji Jiaoliu **3978**
China Light Industry Yearbook. *see* Zhongguo Qinggongye Nianjian **701**
China Market. (HK ISSN 0258-3054) **851**
China Market. (US) **903**
China Market Atlas *see* New Asian Market Atlas **918**

CHINA MEDIA

China Media Book. (UK ISSN 0953-7457) **29**
China Medical Abstracts (Birth Control and Gynecology). see Zhongguo Yixue Wenzhai (Jihua Shengyu, Fuchan Kexue) **3182**
China Medical Abstracts (Internal Medicine) see Zhongguo Yixue Wenzhai (Neike Xue) **3182**
China Medical Abstracts (Pediatrics). see Zhongguo Yixue Wenzhai (Erkexue) **3182**
China Medical Abstracts (Stomatology). see Zhongguo Yixue Wenzhai (Kouqiang Yixue) **3182**
China Medical Board of New York. Annual Report. (US ISSN 0069-3685) **3087**
China News Analysis. (HK ISSN 0009-4404) **2181, 2568, 3879**
China News Update. (US) **4233**
China Newsletter. (JA ISSN 0285-7529) **903**
China Newsletter. (HK) **2181**
China Notes. (US ISSN 0009-4412) **4233**
China Now. (UK ISSN 0045-6764) **3879**
China Numismatics. see Zhongguo Qianbi **3602**
China Ocean Engineering. (US ISSN 0890-5487) **1816, 1603**
China Oil Painting. see Zhongguo Youhua **351**
China Oil Pictorial. see Zhongguo Shiyou Huabao **3704**
China Packaging. see Zhongguo Baozhuang **3652**
China Painter. (US ISSN 0889-8189) **321**
China, People's Republic. National People's Congress. Standing Committee. Bulletin. see Zhonghua Renmin Gongheguo. Quanguo Renda Changweihui Gongbao **4078**
China, People's Republic. People's Supreme Court. Bulletin. see Zhonghua Renmin Gongheguo Zuigao Renmin Fayuan Gongbao **2697**
China, People's Republic. State Council. Bulletin. see Zhonghua Renmin Gongheguo Guowuyuan Gongbao **4078**
China, People's Republic. Supreme People's Procurate Post. see Zhonghua Renmin Gongheguo. Zuigao Renmin Jianchayuan Gongbao **4078**
China People's University. Journal. see Zhongguo Renmin Daxue Xuebao **4393**
China Philately. (CC) **3751**
China Pictorial. (CC ISSN 0009-4420) **2181**
China Plastic and Rubber Journal/Zhongguo Cuoliao Xiangjiao. (HK) **3862, 4291**
China Postal Affairs. see Zhongguo Youzheng **1354**
China Publishing Yearbook. see Zhongguo Chuban Nianjian **4139**
China Quarterly. (UK ISSN 0009-4439) **3635**
China Railroad. see Zhongguo Tielu **4717**
China Railway Science. see Zhongguo Tiedao Kexue **4717**
China Railway Society. Journal. see Tiedao Xuebao **4715**
China Real Estate News. see Zhongguo Fangdi Xinxi **4159**
China Reconstructs see China Today **2181**
China Report. (US ISSN 0009-4455) **3953, 4368**
China Report: Economic Affairs. (US) **655**
China Report: Political, Sociological, and Military Affairs. (US) **3879, 3454, 4431**
China Report: Science and Technology. (US) **4304, 4595**
China, Republic. Central Geological Survey. Bulletin. (CH ISSN 1012-6821) **1557**
China, Republic. Executive Yuan. Directorate-General of Budget, Accounting & Statistics. Monthly Bulletin of Statistics. (CH) **4568**
China, Republic. Executive Yuan. Directorate-General of Budget, Accounting & Statistics. National Income in Taiwan Area, R.O.C. (CH ISSN 0257-5671) **711, 851**
China, Republic. Executive Yuan. Directorate-General of Budget, Accounting & Statistics. Quarterly National Economic Trends, Taiwan Area. (CH ISSN 0257-5663) **851**
China, Republic. Executive Yuan. Directorate-General of Budget, Accounting & Statistics. Report on the Survey of Personal Income Distribution in Taiwan Area. (CH ISSN 0257-5752) **998**
China, Republic. Executive Yuan. Directorate-General of Budget, Accounting & Statistics. Social Indicators (Year). (CH ISSN 0257-5736) **4568**
China, Republic. Export Processing Zone Administration. Exports of E P Z see Export Processing Zone Concentrates **907**
China, Republic. Machinery and Electrical Apparatus Industry Yearbook/Chung Hua Min Kuo Chi Ch'i yu Tien Kung Ch'i Ts'ai Nien Chien. (CH) **1765, 3016**
†China, Republic. Mining Research and Service Organisation. M R S O Special Report. (CH) **5165**
China, Republic. Ministry of Finance. Department of Statistics. Monthly Statistics of Exports and Imports/Chin Ch'u K'ou Mao I T'ung Chi Yueh Pao. (CH) **711, 903, 4568**
China, Republic. Ministry of Finance. Department of Statistics. Yearbook of Tax Statistics. (CH) **711**
China, Republic. National Central Library. Newsletter. (CH ISSN 0034-5016) **2752**
China, Republic. Telecommunication Laboratories. T L Technical Journal. (CH ISSN 1015-0730) **1884**
China, Republic. Telecommunication Laboratories. Technical Reports see China, Republic. Telecommunication Laboratories. T L Technical Journal **1884**
China, Republic of. Report on Tourism. Statistics (Year). (CH) **4799, 4568**
†China Review. (HK) **5165**
China Revista Ilustrada. (CC ISSN 1000-9280) **2181**
China Rice Science. see Zhongguo Shuidao Kexue **208**
China Road Journal. see Zhongguo Gonglu Xuebao **4723**
China Rubber Industry. see Xiangjiao Gongye **4294**
China Rural Finance. see Zhongguo Nongcun Jinrong **804**
China Screen/Zhongguo Yinmu. (CC) **3505**
China Shiprepair. see Zhongguo Xiuchuan **4742**
†China Sources. (US ISSN 0258-977X) **5165**
China Sports/Zhongguo Tiyu. (CC ISSN 0577-8948) **4469**
China Spring. (US ISSN 0735-8237) **3940, 3953**
China Stamp Catalogue. (UK ISSN 0142-9892) **3751**
China Statistical Yearbook. (HK ISSN 1052-9225) **4568**
China Statistics. see Zhongguo Tongji **4592**
China Statistics Series. (US) **4568**
China Steel Technical Report/Chung Kang Chi Pao. (CH ISSN 1015-6070) **3404**
China Telecommunication Construction/Zhongguo Dianxin Jianshe. (HK ISSN 1017-5199) **1362**
China Textile/Zhongguo Fazhi. (HK) **4617, 1284**
China Textile Engineering Association. Journal. see Fangzhi Xuebao **4618**
China Textile University. Journal see Zhongguo Fangzhi Daxue Xuebao **4628**
China Today. (CC ISSN 1003-0905) **2181**
China Tourism. (HK) **4757**
China Trade Report. (HK ISSN 0009-448X) **903**
China Trader Newsletter. (US) **3751**
China Transport. (HK ISSN 0258-3259) **4648, 2245**
China Travel Press. (HK) **4757**
China Tribune/Chung-kuo Lun T'an. (CH) **2219, 2181**
China University of Science and Technology. Journal. see Zhongguo Kexue Jishu Daxue Xuebao **4354**
China Update. (US) **1721**
China Water & Wastewater. see Zhongguo Geshui Paishui **1877**
China Women's Health. see Zhongguo Funu Jiankang **3297**
Chinafrica. (CC) **2181**
Chinamac Journal/Jixie Zhizao. (HK) **3016**
China's Advertising Journal. see Zhongguo Guanggao Bao **40**
China's Cultural Relics News. see Zhongguo Wenwu Bao **290**
China's Customs Statistics. (HK ISSN 0258-3046) **711, 834**
China's Economic Structure Reform. see Zhongguo Jingji Tizhi Gaige **1000**
China's Elderly Daily. see Zhongguo Laonian Bao **2280**
China's Exports. (HK) **903**
China's Famous People. see Huaxia Mingren **419**
China's Food News. see Zhongguo Shipin Bao **2084**
China's Foreign Trade. (CC ISSN 0009-4498) **904**
China's Fruit Trees. see Zhongguo Guoshu **131**
China's Industry News. see Zhonghua Gongshang Shibao **888**
China's Latest Economic Statistics: Confidential Monthly Report. (HK) **711**
China's Latest Statistics: Confidential Monthly Report see China's Latest Economic Statistics: Confidential Monthly Report **711**
China's Military: P L A in (Year). (Sun Yat-sen Center for Policy Studies) (US) **2337, 3454**
China's Public Health. see Zhongguo Gonggong Weisheng **4116**
China's Scholars Abroad. see Shenzhou Xueren **1716**
China's Science. see Zhongguo Kexue Bao **4353**
China's Sports News. see Zhongguo Tiyu Bao **4497**
China's Taxation. see Zhongguo Shuiwu **1112**
China's Textiles. see Zhongguo Fangzhi Bao **4628**
China's Theater. see Zhongguo Xiju **4642**
China's Tibet see Zhongguo Xizang **2183**
China's Township Enterprises. see Zhongguo Xiangzhen Qiye **1119**
China's Volleyball. see Zhongguo Paiqiu **4515**
Chinatown News. (CN ISSN 0009-4501) **1997**
Chinchilla-Post. (GW) **580**
Chincoteague Beachcomber. (US) **4757**
La Chine. (CC ISSN 1000-9272) **2181**
Chine au Present see China Today **2181**
Chinese Academy of Medical Sciences and Peking Union Medical College. Proceedings - Zhongguo Yixue Kexueyuan, Zhongguo Xiehe Yike Daxue Xuebao see Chinese Medical Sciences Journal **3087**
Chinese Academy of Sciences. Bulletin. (CC) **4304**
Chinese Academy of Sciences. Institute of Atmospheric Physics. Annual Report see Zhongguo Kexueyuan Daqi Wulisuo Nianbao **5309**
Chinese Academy of Social Sciences. Graduate School. Journal. see Zhongguo Shehui Kexueyuan Yanjiushengyuan Xuebao **4393**
Chinese Acupuncture and Moxibustion. see Zhongguo Zhenjiu **3165**
Chinese Administration Management. see Zhongguo Xingzheng Guanli **4078**
Chinese Agricultural Chemical Society. Journal. (CH ISSN 0578-1736) **173, 1175**
Chinese Agricultural Meteorology. see Zhongguo Nongye Qixiang **3444**
Chinese Agricultural Sciences. see Zhongguo Nongye Kexue **131**
Chinese Agriculture Abstracts - Agricultural Engineering. see Zhongguo Nongye Wenzhai - Nongye Gongcheng **145**
Chinese Agriculture Abstracts - Aquatic Products. see Zhongguo Nongye Wenzhai - Shuichan **2052**
Chinese America. (US) **3635**
Chinese American Forum. (US ISSN 0895-4690) **4431**
Chinese and Foreign Fairy Tales Pictorial. see Zhongwai Tonghua Huakan **1272**
Chinese & Foreign Garments. see Zhongwai Fuzhuang **1295**
Chinese and Foreign Literature. see Zhongwai Wenxue **2980**
Chinese and Foreign Stories. see Zhongwai Gushi **2980**
Chinese and Foreign Technology Information. see Zhongwai Jishu Qingbao **4354**
Chinese & World T V. see Zhongwai Dianshi **1384**
▼Chinese Andrology. (CC) **3087**
Chinese Annals of Mathematics. Series A. (US) **3032**
Chinese Annals of Mathematics. Series B. (SZ ISSN 0252-9599) **3032**
Chinese Apiculture. see Zhongguo Yangfeng **131**
Chinese Aquatic Products. see Zhongguo Shuichan **2050**
Chinese Architecture/Zhongguo Jianzhu.(CC) **296**
Chinese Art. see Zhongguo Yishu **351**
Chinese Art Society of America. Archives see Archives of Asian Art **312**
Chinese Astronomy and Astrophysics. (US ISSN 0275-1062) **363**
Chinese Beets. see Zhongguo Tiancai **131**
Chinese Bicycles. see Zhongguo Zixingche **4521**
Chinese Biochemical Journal. see Shengwu Huaxue Zazhi **483**
Chinese Biochemical Society. Journal. (CH ISSN 0379-7368) **475, 485**
Chinese Biological Abstracts. see Zhongguo Shengwuxue Wenzhai **468**
Chinese Book Reviews. see Zhongguo Tushu Pinglun **4139**
Chinese Broadcasting University Education. see Zhongguo Dianda Jiaoyu **1688**
Chinese Bulletin of Pharmacology. see Zhongguo Yaolixue Tongbao **3746**
Chinese Calligraphy. see Zhongguo Shufa **351**
Chinese Calligraphy and Painting. see Zhongguo Shuhua **351**
Chinese - Canadian Magazine. (CN) **1997**
Chinese Ceramics. see Zhongguo Taoci **1167**
▼Chinese Chemical Letters. (UK ISSN 1001-8417) **1175**
Chinese Chemical Society. Journal (Taipei). (CH ISSN 0009-4536) **1175**
Chinese Chess. see Xiang Qi **4497**
Chinese Child Development. see Zhongguo Ertong Fazhan **1247**
Chinese Children. see Zhongguo Ertong **1272**
Chinese Christians Today see Chinese Today **4233**
Chinese Commodity Economics. see Zhongguo Wuzi Jingji **701**
Chinese Contemporary History. see Zhongguo Xiandai Shi **2343**
Chinese Cookery. see Zhongguo Pengren **2450**
Chinese Culture. see Hanzi Wenhua **2507**

Chinese Culture. (CH ISSN 0009-4544) 3636
Chinese Culture Association, Magazine. (US) 1997
Chinese Culture Quarterly/Chiu Chou Hsueh K'an. (HK) 3636
Chinese Desert. see Zhongguo Shamo 1549
Chinese Economic History Research. see Zhongguo Jingjishi Yanjiu 899
Chinese Economic Monthly. (HK) 655
Chinese Economic Review/Chung-kuo Ching Chi P'ing Lun. (CH) 655
Chinese Economic Studies. (US ISSN 0009-4552) 655
Chinese Education. (US ISSN 0009-4560) 1621
Chinese Elevator. see Zhongguo Dianti 636
Chinese Engineers. see Zhongguo Gongchengshi 1841
Chinese-English Translation Assistance Group Bulletin see C E T A Bulletin 5156
Chinese Entrepreneurs. see Zhongguo Qiyejia 1119
Chinese Equipment Management. see Zhongguo Shebei Guanli 1032
Chinese Fashions. see Zhongguo Fuzhuang 1295
Chinese First Aid Medical Science. see Zhongguo Jijiu Yixue 3164
Chinese Flowers - Potted Landscape. see Zhongguo Huahui Penjing 2141
Chinese Folk Culture. (CC) 2905
Chinese Food. see Zhongguo Shipin 2450
Chinese for Affirmative Action Newsletter (San Francisco) see C A A Newsletter (San Francisco) 1995
Chinese Four Treasures of the Study. see Zhongguo Wenfang Sibao 1062
▼Chinese Geographical Science/Zhongguo Dili Kexue. (CC ISSN 1002-0063) 1557
†Chinese Geography and Environment. (US ISSN 0896-2979) 5165
Chinese Geology. see Zhongguo Dizhi 1586
Chinese Geology Abstracts see Zhongguo Dizhi Wenzhai 1552
Chinese Handicapped. see Zhongguo Canjiren 2285
Chinese Harbor. see Zhongguo Gangkou 4742
Chinese Herbal Medicine. see Zhong Cao Yao 3746
Chinese Historian. (US) 3636, 2402
Chinese Historical Society of America. Bulletin. (US ISSN 0577-9065) 1997, 2337, 2402
Chinese Hospital Management. see Zhongguo Yiyuan Guanli 2470
Chinese Human Affairs. see Zhongguo Renshi 1071
Chinese Industry & Commerce. see Zhongguo Gongshang 841
Chinese Information Processing. see Zhongwen Xinxi 2791
Chinese Inorganic Analytical Chemistry Abstracts. see Zhongguo Wuji Fenxi Huaxue Wenzhai 1203
Chinese Institute of Chemical Engineers. Journal. (CH ISSN 0368-1653) 1852
Chinese Institute of Engineers. Journal. (CH ISSN 0253-3839) 1816
Chinese Institute of Labor Movement. Journal. see Zhongguo Gongyun Xueyuan Xuebao 2592
Chinese Internal Combustion Engine Engineering. see Neiranji Gongcheng 1921
Chinese Journal of Acoustics. (CC ISSN 0217-9776) 3859
Chinese Journal of Administration. (CH ISSN 0009-4579) 1005
Chinese Journal of Aeronautics. (CC ISSN 1000-9361) 50
Chinese Journal of Anaesthesiology. see Zhonghua Mazuixue Zazhi 3192
Chinese Journal of Animal Science. see Zhongguo Xumu Zazhi 4820
Chinese Journal of Antibiotics. see Zhongguo Kangshengsu Zazhi 3746
Chinese Journal of Applied Mathematics. see Acta Mathematicae Applicatae Sinica 3026
Chinese Journal of Applied Physiology. see Zhongguo Yingyong Shenglixue Zazhi 575
Chinese Journal of Arid Land Research. (US ISSN 0898-5146) 1542
Chinese Journal of Atmospheric Sciences. (English translation of: Daqi Kexue) (US) 3434
Chinese Journal of Automation. (English translation of: Zidonghua Xuebao) (US) 1412
Chinese Journal of Biochemistry and Biophysics. (US ISSN 0898-512X) 475, 485
Chinese Journal of Biotechnology. (English translation of: Shengwu Gongcheng Xuebao) (US ISSN 1042-749X) 489
Chinese Journal of Botany. (CC ISSN 1001-0718) 499
Chinese Journal of Burns and Wounds. see Zhongguo Shaoshang Chuangshang Zazhi 3250
Chinese Journal of Cancer Research/Zhongguo Aizheng Yanjiu. (CC ISSN 1000-9604) 3196
Chinese Journal of Cardiology. see Zhonghua Xin-Xueguanbing Zazhi 3213
Chinese Journal of Chemistry. (CC ISSN 1001-604X) 1175
Chinese Journal of Chemistry see Zhongguo Huaxue 1191
Chinese Journal of Clinical Oncology. see Zhongguo Zhongliu Linchuang 3203
Chinese Journal of Computer Science and Technology. (CC ISSN 1000-9000) 1482, 1416, 1426
Chinese Journal of Contemporary Mathematics. (US ISSN 0898-5111) 3032
Chinese Journal of Disinfection. see Zhongguo Xiaoduxue Zazhi 3164
Chinese Journal of Education. see Zhongguo Jiaoyu Bao 1673
Chinese Journal of Electrotechnics. see Diangong Jishu Xuebao 1885
Chinese Journal of Endemic Disease Prevention and Treatment. see Zhongguo Difangbing Fangzhi Zazhi 3164
Chinese Journal of Endocrinology and Metabolism. see Zhonghua Neifenmi Daixie Zazhi 3256
Chinese Journal of Engineering Thermophysics. (English translation of: Gongcheng Re-Wuli Xuebao) (US ISSN 1043-8033) 1927
Chinese Journal of Epidemiology. see Zhonghua Liuxingbingxue Zazhi 3165
Chinese Journal of Flowers. see Zhongguo Huahui Bao 2141
Chinese Journal of Forensic Sciences. see Zhongguo Fayixue Zazhi 3266
Chinese Journal of Gastroenterology. see Zhonghua Xiaohua Zazhi 3270
Chinese Journal of Genetics. (English translation of: Yichuan Xuebao) (US ISSN 0898-5138) 540
Chinese Journal of Geochemistry. (CC ISSN 1000-9426) 1557, 1175
Chinese Journal of Geophysics. (English translation of: Diqiu Wuli Xuebao) (US ISSN 0898-9591) 1587, 2245
Chinese Journal of Geriatrics. see Zhonghua Laonian Yixue Zazhi 2280
Chinese Journal of Hematology. see Zhonghua Xueyexue Zazhi 3274
Chinese Journal of Immunology. see Zhongguo Mianyixue Zazhi 3189
Chinese Journal of Infectious Diseases. see Zhonghua Chuanranbing Zazhi 3165
Chinese Journal of Infrared and Millimeter Waves. (English translation of: Hongwai Yanjiu, Ser. A) (US ISSN 0890-9903) 3852
Chinese Journal of Integrated Traditional and Western Medicine. see Zhong-Xiyi Jiehe Zazhi 3164
Chinese Journal of Internal Medicine. see Zhonghua Neike Zazhi 3165
Chinese Journal of Lasers see Zhongguo Jiguang 3858
Chinese Journal of Leprosy. see Zhongguo Mafeng Zazhi 3164
†Chinese Journal of Low Temperature Physics. (English translation of: Diwen Wuli Xuebao) (US ISSN 1044-1085) 5165
Chinese Journal of Materials Science. (CH ISSN 0379-6906) 3404, 1852, 1916
Chinese Journal of Mechanical Engineering. (CC ISSN 1000-9345) 1927
Chinese Journal of Medical History. see Zhonghua Yishi Zazhi 3165
Chinese Journal of Metal Science & Technology. (CC ISSN 1000-3029) 3404, 3425
Chinese Journal of Metallurgy/Zhongguo Jinshu Kexue Jishu Zazhi. (CC) 3404
Chinese Journal of Microbiology see Chinese Journal of Microbiology and Immunology 550
Chinese Journal of Microbiology and Immunology. (CH) 550, 3184
Chinese Journal of Microbiology and Immunology. see Zhonghua Weishengwuxue he Mianyixue Zazhi 3189
Chinese Journal of Neurology and Psychology. see Zhonghua Shenjing-Jingshenke Zazhi 3356
Chinese Journal of Neurosurgery. see Zhonghua Shenjing Waike Zazhi 3356
Chinese Journal of Nonferrous Metal. see Youse Jinshu 3424
Chinese Journal of Nuclear Physics. (CC ISSN 1001-6031) 3847
Chinese Journal of Nuclear Science and Engineering. see He Kexue yu Gongcheng 1805
Chinese Journal of Numerical Mathematics and Applications. (US ISSN 0899-4358) 3032
Chinese Journal of Obstetrics and Gynecology. see Zhonghua Fu-Chanke Zazhi 3297
Chinese Journal of Oceanology and Limnology. (CC ISSN 0254-4059) 1603, 1597
Chinese Journal of Oncology. see Zhonghua Zhongliu Zazhi 3203
Chinese Journal of Orthopedics. see Zhonghua Guke Zazhi 3312
Chinese Journal of Paper Manufacturing. see Zhongguo Zaozhi 3667
Chinese Journal of Parasitology and Parasitosis. see Zhongguo Jishengchongxue yu Jishengchongbing Zazhi 559
Chinese Journal of Pathology and Physiology. see Zhongguo Bingli Shengli Zazhi 3164
Chinese Journal of Pediatrics. see Zhonghua Erke Zazhi 3327
Chinese Journal of Pharmaceutical Industry. see Zhongguo Yiyao Gongye Zazhi 3746
Chinese Journal of Physical Medicine. see Zhonghua Wuli Yixue Zazhi 3165
Chinese Journal of Physical Therapy. see Zhonghua Liliao Zazhi 3165
Chinese Journal of Physiological Sciences. (CC ISSN 0258-6428) 570
Chinese Journal of Physiology/Chung-kuo Sheng Li Hsueh Tsa Chih. (CH ISSN 0304-4920) 570, 3087
Chinese Journal of Planned Management. see Zhongguo Jihua Guanli 701
Chinese Journal of Plastic Surgery and Burns. see Zhonghua Zhengxing Shaoshang Waike Zazhi 3386
Chinese Journal of Polymer Science. (CC ISSN 0256-7679) 1217, 1852
Chinese Journal of Population Science. (US ISSN 1044-8403) 3980
Chinese Journal of Power Sources. see Dianyuan Jishu 1885
Chinese Journal of Preventive Medicine. see Zhonghua Yufang Yixue Zazhi 3165
Chinese Journal of Psychology. (CH ISSN 1013-9656) 4016
Chinese Journal of Public Health. see Zhongguo Gonggong Weisheng Xuebao 4116
Chinese Journal of Recovery. see Zhongguo Kangfu Yixue Zazhi 3164
Chinese Journal of Russian Teaching. see Zhongguo E Yu Jiaoxue 2854
†Chinese Journal of Semiconductors. (English translation of: Bandaoti Xuebao) (US ISSN 0899-9988) 5165
Chinese Journal of Space Science. see Kongjian Kexue Xuebao 58
Chinese Journal of Space Science and Technology. see Zhongguo Kongjian Kexue Jishu 66
Chinese Journal of Sports Medical Science. see Zhongguo Yundong Yixue Zazhi 3373
Chinese Journal of Surgery. see Zhonghua Waike Zazhi 3386
Chinese Journal of Veterinary Medicine. see Zhongguo Shouyi Zazhi 4820
Chinese Journal of Zoology. see Dongwuxue Zazhi 581
Chinese Journalist. see Zhongguo Jizhe 2577
Chinese Language Construction. see Yuwen Jianshe 2853
Chinese Language Learning. see Yuwen Xuexi 2853
Chinese Language Research. see Yuwen Yanjiu 2853
Chinese Language Teachers Association. Journal. (US ISSN 0009-4595) 2809, 1621
Chinese Law and Government. (US ISSN 0009-4609) 2612, 3879
Chinese Lawyers. see Zhongguo Lushi 2697
Chinese Light Industry Economics. see Zhongguo Qinggongye Jingji 841
Chinese Literature. (CC ISSN 0009-4617) 2905, 3636
Chinese Literature: Essays, Articles, Reviews. (US ISSN 0161-9705) 2905
Chinese Lumber. see Zhongguo Mucai 2119
Chinese Martial Arts. see Zhonghua Wushu 4497
Chinese Mathematics Abstracts. see Zhongguo Shuxue Wenzhai 3063
†Chinese Mechanical Engineering Abstracts. (US ISSN 1040-6174) 5165
Chinese Medical Journal/Zhonghua Yixue Zazhi Yingwen Ban. (CC ISSN 0366-6999) 3087
Chinese Medical Photography Technology. see Zhongguo Yixue Yingxiang Jishu 3363
Chinese Medical Sciences Journal. (CC ISSN 1001-9294) 3087, 435, 3720
Chinese Medicine Bulletin. see Zhongyao Tongbao 3746
Chinese Mental Health Journal. see Zhongguo Xinli Weisheng Zazhi 4051
Chinese Museums. see Zhongguo Bowuguan 3535
Chinese Music. (US ISSN 0192-3749) 3545
Chinese Music. see Zhongguo Yinyue 3587
Chinese National Bibliography. (CH ISSN 0301-5165) 2793
Chinese Navigation. see Zhongguo Hanghai 4742
Chinese Optics and Applied Optics Abstracts. see Zhongguo Guangxue yu Yingyong Guangxue Wenzhai 3839
Chinese Painting. see Zhongguo Hua 351
Chinese Peasants' Gazette. see Nongmin Ribao 110
The Chinese Pen. (CH) 2905
Chinese Personnel Management. see Zhongguo Renshi Guanli 1071
Chinese Pharmaceutical Abstracts. see Zhongguo Yaoxue Wenzhai 3748
Chinese Pharmaceutical Bulletin. see Yaoxue Tongbao 3746
Chinese Pharmaceutical Journal. see Zhongguo Yaoxue Zazhi 3746
Chinese Philatelic Magazine. see Ji You 3753

CHINESE PHOTOGRAPHY

Chinese Photography. see Zhongguo Sheying **3798**
Chinese Physics. (US ISSN 0273-429X) **3816**, 363
Chinese Physics Abstracts. see Zhongguo Wuli Wenzhai **3839**
†Chinese Physics - Lasers. (US ISSN 0887-3518) **5165**
Chinese Physics Letters/Zhongguo Wuli Kuaibao. (US ISSN 0256-307X) **3816**
Chinese Picture Stories. see Zhongguo Lianhuanhua **351**
Chinese Pioneers. see Zhongguo Shaonian Bao **1272**
Chinese Policy and Administration of Science and Technology. see Zhongguo Keji Zhengce yu Guanli **4078**
Chinese Primary Health Care. see Zhongguo Chuji Weisheng Baojian **3164**
Chinese Privately-Owned Science and Technology Enterprises. see Zhongguo Minban Keji Shiye **841**
Chinese Radio, Film and Television. see Zhongguo Guangbo Yingshi **1361**
Chinese Rare Earth Society. Journal see Journal of Rare Earths **3411**
Chinese Real Estate. see Zhongguo Fangdichan **4159**
Chinese Republican Studies Newsletter see Republican China **2341**
Chinese Rural Doctors. see Zhongguo Xiangcun Yisheng **3164**
Chinese Rural Economics. see Zhongguo Nongcun Jingji **160**
Chinese Scholarly Works in English. (US) **3636**, 2505, 4368
Chinese Science. (US ISSN 0361-9001) **4304**, 2337, 3636
Chinese Science Abstracts. Part A. (CC ISSN 0254-5179) **4355**, 8
Chinese Science Abstracts. Part B. (CC ISSN 0254-4903) **4355**, 8
Chinese Science and Technology Periodicals Research. see Zhongguo Keji Qikan Yanjiu **4139**
Chinese Science Bulletin. (CC ISSN 1001-6538) **4305**
Chinese Scientific and Technological Industry. see Zhongguo Keji Chanye **1031**
Chinese Seamen. see Zhongguo Haiyuan **4742**
Chinese Seamen's News. (CH) **4725**
Chinese Seismology. see Zhongguo Dizhen **1596**
Chinese Self-Study. see Zhongwen Zixiu **2854**
Chinese Silicate Society. Bulletin. see Guisuanyan Tongbao **1213**
Chinese Silicate Society. Journal. see Guisuanyan Xuebao **1213**
Chinese Social Science Documentations Index. see Zhongguo Shehui Kexue Wenxian Tilu **4396**
Chinese Society for Internal Combustion Engines. Transactions. see Neiranji Xuebao **1936**
Chinese Society for Scientific and Technical Information. Journal. see Qingbao Xuebao **2780**
Chinese Society of Agricultural Machinery. Transactions. see Nongye Jixie Xuebao **163**
Chinese Sociology and Anthropology. (US ISSN 0009-4625) **4431**, 237
Chinese Spices. see Zhongguo Tiaoweipin **2084**
Chinese Stories. see Zhongguo Gushi **2979**
Chinese Studies for Pupils. see Xiaoxuesheng Yuwen Xuexi **2852**
Chinese Studies in History. (US ISSN 0009-4633) **2308**, 3636
Chinese Studies in History and Philosophy see Chinese Studies in History **2308**
Chinese Studies in Philosophy. (US ISSN 0023-8627) **3745**
Chinese Talent. see Zhongguo Rencai **1071**
Chinese Taoism. see Zhongguo Daojiao **4216**
Chinese Tea. see Zhongguo Chaye **2084**

Chinese Teaching in the World. see Shijie Hanyu Jiaoxue **2841**
Chinese Textile. see Zhongguo Fangzhi **4627**
Chinese Times. (CN) **1997**
Chinese Today. (US) **4233**
Chinese Traditional Patent Medicine. see Zhong Cheng Yao **3746**
Chinese Translators Journal. see Zhongguo Fanyi **2854**
Chinese United Journal. (US ISSN 0891-1436) **1997**
Chinese University of Hong Kong. Chung Chi College. Music Department. Holdings of the Chinese Music Archives. (HK) **3545**
Chinese University of Hong Kong. Institute of Chinese Studies. Journal. (HK) **3636**
Chinese Vegetables. see Zhongguo Shucai **197**
Chinese Women and Children's Health. see Zhongguo Fuyou Baojian **3297**
Chinese Youth. see Zhongguo Qingnian **1272**
Chinese Youth Daily. see Zhongguo Qingnian Bao **1272**
Chinese Youth Movement. see Zhongguo Qingyun **3936**
Chinese Youth Study. see Zhongguo Qingnian Yanjiu **1247**
Chinesische Medizin. (GW ISSN 0930-2786) **3087**, 3636
†Ch'ing Documents/Ku Kung Wen Hsien. (CH ISSN 0009-465X) **5165**
Ching Feng. (HK ISSN 0009-4668) **4168**, 3636
Ching Pao. see The Mirror **2197**
▼Chingisiyn Tug/Genghis Khan's Banner. (MP) **1997**
Chinmaya Mission West News. (US ISSN 0199-6487) **4168**
The Chinook. (US) **1307**
Chinoperl Papers. (US ISSN 0193-7774) **3636**, 2905
Chinthe. (UK) **3684**
Chip. (SP) **1390**
Chip. (GW ISSN 0170-6632) **1458**
†Chip. (IT ISSN 0392-9353) **5165**
Chip Chats. (US ISSN 0577-9294) **353**, 639
Chip Sonderhefte. (GW) **1390**
Chipper - Snacker see Snack World **2081**
Chips Off the Writer's Block. (US ISSN 1045-2958) **2568**, 4125
Chirality. (US ISSN 0899-0042) **550**, 3720
Chiribotan. (JA) **580**, 2038
Chiricu. (US ISSN 0277-7223) **2905**, 2861, 4631
Chirigaku Hyoron A. see Geographical Review of Japan. Series A **2250**
Chirigaku Hyoron B. see Geographical Review of Japan. Series B **2250**
Chiron. (GW ISSN 0069-3715) **269**
Chiron Review. (US ISSN 1046-8897) **2990**
Chiropodist see Journal of British Podiatric Medicine **3379**
Chiropody Review. (UK ISSN 0009-4714) **3376**
Chiropractic. (US ISSN 0897-6058) **3213**
Chiropractic History. (US ISSN 0736-4377) **3213**, 418, 2308
Chiropractic Journal. (US) **3213**
Chiropractic Journal of Australia. (AT ISSN 1036-0913) **3213**
Chiropractic Products. (US ISSN 1041-2360) **3213**
Chiropractic Sports Medicine. (US ISSN 0889-6976) **3213**, 3371
Chiropractic Technique. (US ISSN 0899-3467) **3213**
Chiropractors' Association of Australia. Membership Directory. (AT ISSN 1037-8839) **3214**
Chirugia Gastroenterologica see Surgical Gastroenterology **5285**
Der Chirurg. (GW ISSN 0009-4722) **3168**
Chirurgia. (BU ISSN 0450-2167) **3377**
Chirurgia. (IT) **3377**
Chirurgia degli Organi di Movimento. (IT ISSN 0009-4749) **3377**

Chirurgia del Piede/Foot Surgery. (IT) **3377**
Chirurgia della Testa e del Collo. (IT ISSN 0394-9079) **3377**
Chirurgia e Patologia Sperimentale. (IT ISSN 0009-4757) **3377**
Chirurgia Epatobiliare. (IT ISSN 0393-1471) **3377**
Chirurgia Gastroenterologica (Italian Edition). (IT ISSN 0009-4765) **3267**, 3377
Chirurgia Italiana. (IT ISSN 0009-4773) **3377**
Chirurgia Maxillofacialis et Plastica/Maxillofacial and Plastic Surgery. (CI ISSN 0009-4781) **3377**
†Chirurgia Narzadow Ruchu i Ortopedia Polska. (PL ISSN 0009-479X) **5165**
Chirurgia Plastica see European Journal of Plastic Surgery **3378**
Chirurgia Triveneta. (IT ISSN 0009-4811) **3377**
Chirurgie. (FR ISSN 0001-4001) **3377**
Chirurgie Pediatrique see European Journal of Pediatric Surgery **3378**
Chirurgien-Dentiste de France. (FR ISSN 0009-4838) **3230**
Chirurgische Praxis. (GW ISSN 0009-4846) **3377**
†Chirurgischen Arbeitsgemeinschaft. Verhandlung. (GW ISSN 0720-3462) **5165**
Chiryo. see Journal of Therapy **3118**
Chiryo Oyobi Shono see Journal of Therapy **3118**
Chishitsugaku Ronshu/Geological Society of Japan. Memoirs. (JA ISSN 0385-8545) **1557**
Chishitsugaku Zasshi. see Geological Society of Japan. Journal **1563**
†Chisholm Gazette. (AT) **5165**
Chisholm Trail. (US) **2147**
Chislennye Metody v Dinamike Razrezhennykh Gazov. (RU) **3842**
Chit Chat. (GH) **2192**
Chitalishte. (BU ISSN 0009-4862) **1621**
Chitarre. (IT) **3545**
Chitra Bangla. (BG) **2174**
Chitra-Bikshan. see Citrabikshana **3506**
Chitra Desh. (BG) **2174**
Chitralekha. (II) **2199**
Chitrali. (BG ISSN 0009-4870) **2174**
Chitralok. (II) **3505**
Chittagong Port Authority. Monthly Bulletin see Chittagong Port Authority. Port Folio, Port of Chittagong **4725**
Chittagong Port Authority. Port Folio, Port of Chittagong. (BG) **4725**
Chittagong Port Authority. Yearbook. (BG) **4726**
Chittagong Port Trust. Yearbook of Information see Chittagong Port Authority. Yearbook **4726**
†Chitty's Law Journal. (CN ISSN 0009-4889) **5165**
Chitukuko Cha Amayi M'Malawi. (MW) **927**
Chiu Chou Hsueh K'an. see Chinese Culture Quarterly **3636**
Chizu no Tomo/Map and Landscape. (JA) **2245**
Chizu Senta Nyusu. see Japan Map Center News **2254**
Chlodnictwo. (PL ISSN 0009-4919) **2298**
Chloroplasts. (UK ISSN 0264-9640) **499**, 475, 550
Chmelarstvi. (CS ISSN 0373-403X) **173**
Chobisco. (BE) **2087**
Chocolate and Nut World. (US) **2087**
Chocolate News. (US) **2064**
Chocolate Singles. (US) **4362**, 1997
Chocolatier. (US) **2064**
Choctaw Community News. (US) **1997**
Choi Nenpo/Yearbook of Tidal Records.(JA) **1603**
Choice. (AT ISSN 0009-496X) **1503**
Choice. (HK) **1503**
Choice. see Ekloyi **2184**
Choice. (UK ISSN 0262-2270) **2271**
Choice (Binghamton). (US) **2990**, 321
Choice (Chula Vista). (US) **3196**

Choice (Middletown). (US ISSN 0009-4978) **4140**
Choice: economic review. see Epilogi **777**
Choice in Dying. (US) **4431**
Choice in Education. (US) **1621**
†Choices. (UK ISSN 0953-1475) **5165**
†Choices (Birmingham). (US) **5165**
Choices (New York). (US ISSN 0883-475X) **2445**, 1746
Choices: A Core Collection for Young Reluctant Readers. (US ISSN 0735-6358) **1251**
Choices in American Public Affairs see Choices (Birmingham) **5165**
Choices in Cardiology. (US) **3206**
▼Choices Satellite T V. (US) **1371**
Choifung. (HK) **2197**
†Choir Director's Library. (UR) **5165**
Choir Herald. (US) **3545**
Choirs Ontario. (CN ISSN 0822-4749) **3545**
Choisir. (SZ ISSN 0009-4994) **4168**
Choisir. (FR) **4839**
Choix Artistique et Litteraire. (FR ISSN 0009-5001) **2861**
Choix Jeunesse: Jeux et Jouets see Jeux et Jouets **2281**
Chokolade Konfekture og Sukkervare Industrien see Konfekturehandleren **2088**
▼Cholesterol & Lipoproteins. (UK ISSN 0964-7597) **475**
Chonggi Kanhaengmul Kisa Saegin/Korean Periodicals Index. (KO) **8**
Chongqing Daxue Xuebao/Chongqing University. Journal. (CC ISSN 1000-582X) **4305**
Chongqing Environmental Sciences. see Chongqing Huanjing Kexue **1945**
Chongqing Huanjing Kexue/Chongqing Environmental Sciences. (CC ISSN 1001-2141) **1945**
Chongqing Keji/Chongqing Science and Technology. (CC) **4305**, 4595
Chongqing Medicine. see Chongqing Yiyao **3087**
Chongqing Science and Technology. see Chongqing Keji **4305**
Chongqing University. Journal. see Chongqing Daxue Xuebao **4305**
Chongqing Yiyao/Chongqing Medicine. (CC ISSN 1000-7911) **3087**
Chonguk Kiopche Chongnam/Directory of Korean Business. (KO) **1126**
Chongyongnyon. (KO) **851**
Chopper Noise see Alternate Energy Transportation Newsletter **5133**
Chor. (GW) **3545**
Choral Journal. (US ISSN 0009-5028) **3545**
Choral Praise. (US ISSN 0362-0409) **4233**
Chord and Discord. (US ISSN 0069-3758) **3545**
Der Chordirigent. (GW ISSN 0009-5036) **3545**
Choreographers Theatre Newsletter see C C T Newsletter **1529**
Choreography and Dance. (US ISSN 0891-6381) **4631**
†Chorherrenstift Klosterneuburg. Jahrbuch. (AU) **5165**
Choristers Guild Letters. (US) **3545**, 1251
Chorleywood Digest. (UK ISSN 0263-2632) **2064**
Chormagazin. (AU) **3545**, 1296
Chorography. (PO) **2245**
Der Chorsaenger. (GW ISSN 0172-2255) **3545**
Chorszene. (GW) **3545**
Chorten. (AT ISSN 0813-3573) **4214**
Chorus. (CN ISSN 0821-1108) **3545**
Chorus! (US ISSN 1044-7857) **3545**
Chosen Gakujutsu Tsuho/Korean Scientific Information. (JA ISSN 0577-9774) **4614**
Chosen People. (US ISSN 0164-5323) **1997**, 4222
Chosen Shogakkai Gakujutsu Ronbunshu/Korean Scholarship Association in Japan. Science Report.(JA ISSN 0287-802X) **3032**
Choson Munhak/Korean Literature. (KN) **2905**
Choson Yesul/Korean Arts. (KN) **321**

Chovatel. (CS) 214
Chrism. (UK) 4168
Christ au Monde. see Christ to the World 4261
Christ for the Nations. (US) 4168
Christ in der Gegenwart. (GW ISSN 0170-5148) 4261
Christ in Our Home. (US ISSN 0412-2968) 4233
Christ to the World/Christ au Monde. (IT ISSN 0011-1465) 4261
Christ und Buch. (GW ISSN 0009-5087) 4169
Christadelphian. (UK ISSN 0009-5117) 4281
Christelijk Nationaal Vakverbond in Nederland Opinie see C N V - Opinie 4167
Christelijk Oosten. (NE ISSN 0009-5141) 4169, 3636
Christelijke Muziekbode see Muziekbode 3569
Christen Democratische Verkenningen. (NE) 3879
Christen Heute. (GW ISSN 0930-5718) 4261, 4233
Die Christengemeinschaft. (GW ISSN 0009-5184) 4169, 321
Christenlehre. (GW ISSN 0009-5192) 4233
Christiaan de Wet Annale. (SA ISSN 0379-4695) 2332, 321
Christian Action Journal. (UK) 4169
Christian Advertising Forum. (US) 29, 4169
Christian Aid News. (UK) 4233
Christian Alert. (US) 4169
Christian Anti-Communism Crusade. Newsletter. (US ISSN 0195-9387) 3879
Christian Arena. (UK ISSN 0264-598X) 4169
Christian Attitudes on Jews and Judaism see Christian Jewish Relations 4169
Christian Beacon. (US ISSN 0009-5265) 4233, 3879
Christian Blind Mission International Inc. Family Magazine see C B M I Family Magazine 2291
Christian Blind Mission International Inc. Freundesbrief see C B M Freundesbrief 4167
Christian Bookseller see Christian Retailing 4125
Christian Bookselling Association of Australia Inc. News see C B A A News 4124
Christian Brethren Review see Partnership Christian Brethren Review 4246
Christian Business Men's Committee of USA Contact see C B M C Contact 653
Christian Businessman. (US) 655
Christian Century. (US ISSN 0009-5281) 4169
Christian Challenge. (US ISSN 0890-6793) 4233
Christian Chiropractor. (US) 3214, 4169
Christian Chiropractors Association Journal. (US) 3214, 4169
The Christian Chronicle. (US) 4169
Christian Comment see Audenshaw Papers 4164
Christian Community see Threshing Floor 4206
Christian Conquest. (US ISSN 0892-9300) 4169
Christian Contender. (US ISSN 0893-8571) 4281
Christian Democrat International. Information Bulletin see C D - Info 3877
Christian Democrat International Info see C D - Info 3877
Christian Education Journal. (US) 4169
Christian Education Today. (US ISSN 0884-5506) 4233, 1702
Christian Educators Journal. (US) 4169
Christian Endeavor World. (US ISSN 0009-5338) 4169
Christian Endeavour Programme Book. (UK) 4281

Christian Endeavour Topic Book see Christian Endeavour Programme Book 4281
Christian Example. (US ISSN 1080-8000) 4281
Christian Family. (UK ISSN 0269-4689) 4169
Christian Family Catalog. (US) 2281, 4169
†Christian Film & Video. (US ISSN 0890-3387) 5166
Christian Forum. (MW) 4169
Christian Graduate see Christian Arena 4169
Christian Herald. (UK ISSN 0953-4385) 4169
Christian Herald (Chappaqua). (US ISSN 0009-5354) 4169
Christian History Magazine. (US ISSN 0891-9666) 4169, 2308
Christian Home & School. (US ISSN 0009-5389) 4169
Christian Index (Atlanta). (US ISSN 0362-0832) 4212, 4233
Christian Index (Memphis). (US ISSN 0744-4060) 4233
Christian Info. (CN) 4169
Christian Institute for Ethnic Studies in Asia. Bulletin. (PH ISSN 0045-6810) 4169, 3636
Christian Ireland Today. (US ISSN 1040-8622) 4431, 1997, 4169
Christian Irishman. (UK) 4169
Christian Jewish Relations. (UK ISSN 0144-2902) 4169, 3879, 4431
Christian Leader. (US ISSN 0009-5419) 4281
Christian Leadership see Leader (Anderson) 4187
Christian Librarian. (US ISSN 0412-3131) 2752, 4233
Christian Librarian. (UK ISSN 0309-4170) 2752, 4125, 4233
Christian Life Communicator see Christian Life Communities Harvest 4261
Christian Life Communities Harvest. (US ISSN 0739-6422) 4261
Christian Literature. (GR) 4281
Christian Living. (US ISSN 0009-5435) 4169, 2223
Christian Magnifier. (US) 2292, 4233
Christian Management Report. (US) 1063, 749, 825, 4169
†Christian Management Review. (US ISSN 0892-4708) 5166
Christian Marks Society Newsletter. (US) 2147
Christian Medical & Dental Society see C M D S 3085
Christian Medical & Dental Society Journal. (US) 3087, 4169
Christian Medical and Dental Society News and Report see C M D S 3085
Christian Medical College Vellore Alumni Journal. (II ISSN 0009-5451) 3087, 1307
Christian Medical Society Journal see Christian Medical & Dental Society Journal 3087
Christian Messenger. (GH ISSN 0009-5478) 4233
The Christian Ministry. (US ISSN 0033-4138) 4169
Christian Mission. (US ISSN 8750-7765) 4233
Christian Missions in Many Lands. (US ISSN 0744-4052) 4169
Christian Monthly. (US ISSN 0009-5494) 4233
Christian Mother (Pittsburgh). (US) 4169, 4839
Christian Music. (UK ISSN 0958-2630) 4233
Christian Music Directories: Printed Music. (US) 3545
Christian Music Directories: Recorded Music. (US ISSN 1048-6844) 3545, 4169, 4460
Christian New Age Quarterly. (US ISSN 0899-7292) 4169, 3594
Christian News. (US ISSN 0009-5516) 4233
Christian News from Israel. (IS ISSN 0009-5532) 4170
†Christian News World. (UK) 5166
Christian Nurse. (II ISSN 0009-5540) 3277

†Christian Outlook. (US ISSN 0897-5590) 5166
Christian Parenting Today. (US ISSN 1040-8088) 4170
Christian Pathway. (US) 1251, 4170
†Christian Peace Conference. (CS ISSN 0009-5567) 5166
Christian Periodical Index. (US ISSN 0069-3871) 4212, 8
Christian Pharmacists Fellowship International Newsletter see C P F I Newsletter 3720
Christian Poet. (US) 2990
Christian Prisoners in the U.S.S.R. (US) 4170, 3879
Christian Puzzler. (UK ISSN 0958-3858) 4233
Christian Ranchman. (US) 4170
Christian Reader. (US) 4170
Christian Record. (US ISSN 0009-5575) 2292
Christian Record Talking Magazine. (US ISSN 0009-5583) 2292, 4170
Christian Rescue Effort for the Emancipation of Dissidents News see C R E E D News 4167
Christian Research Journal. (US) 4170
Christian Retailing. (US ISSN 0749-2510) 4125, 4170
Christian Scholar's Review. (US ISSN 0017-2251) 4170
Christian School Builder. (US) 1746, 4170
Christian Science Bible Lessons (Braille Edition). (US ISSN 0146-7166) 2292, 4281
Christian Science Journal. (US ISSN 0009-5613) 4281
Christian Science Monitor Index. (US ISSN 0893-245X) 2577, 8
Christian Science Open Forum. (US) 4281
Christian Science Quarterly (Inkprint Edition). (US ISSN 0145-7365) 4281
Christian Science Sentinel. (US ISSN 0009-563X) 4281
Christian Service Committee of the Churches in Malawi. Annual Report. (MW) 4170
Christian Single. (US ISSN 0191-4294) 2738, 4233
Christian Singles News. (US) 4362, 4170
Christian Social Action. (US ISSN 0164-5528) 4233, 4431
Christian Socialist. (UK ISSN 0009-5648) 3879, 4170
Christian Standard. (US ISSN 0009-5656) 4170
Christian Statesman. (US ISSN 0009-5664) 4170, 3879, 4368
Christian Statesman see Christian Today 4233
Christian Talking Magazine. (US) 2292, 4233
Christian Today. (UK) 4233
†Christian Unity Magazine. (US) 5166
Christian Vision. (CN ISSN 0843-7602) 4170, 2905
Christian Voice. (PK ISSN 0009-5699) 4261
Christian Week. (CN ISSN 0835-412X) 4233
Christian Week see Church of England Newspaper 4234
Christian Witness to Israel Herald see C W I Herald 4167
Christian Woman. (US ISSN 0009-5702) 4170
Christian Woman. (AT) 4170, 4839
Christian Woman see Woman Alive 4210
Christian Words. (UK) 4233
Christian Writers Newsletter see Cross and Quill 4235
Christiana Albertina. (GW ISSN 0578-0160) 1542, 655
Christianity and Crisis. (US ISSN 0009-5745) 4170
Christianity and Judaism in Antiquity. (US) 4170, 4222
Christianity and Literature. (US ISSN 0148-3331) 2861, 4170
Christianity Today. (US ISSN 0009-5753) 4170
Christianity under Stress. (US) 4170
Christians for Justice Action News see C J A News 4232

Christians in Crisis. (US ISSN 1044-5846) 4170, 3940
Christians in Education see Education Newsline 1629
Christians Writing see Studio 2966
Christianskaya Democratia. (BE) 3879
Christlich Demokratische Union Gerlingen Inform see C D U Gerlingen Inform 3877
Christlich-Paedagogische Blaetter. (AU ISSN 0009-5761) 4170, 1251
Christliche Demokratie. (AU ISSN 0254-4334) 2356, 851, 3879, 4431
Die Christliche Familie. (GW) 4233
Die Christliche Frau. (GW ISSN 0009-5788) 4839, 4261
Christliche Friedenskonferenz see Christian Peace Conference 5166
Christliche Innerlichkeit. (AU ISSN 0009-5796) 4170
Christliches Zentrum Berlin e.V. Report see C Z B Report 4281
Christmas (Minneapolis). (US) 4170, 2223
Christmas: An American Annual of Christmas Literature and Art see Christmas: The Annual of Christmas Literature and Art 2905
Christmas: The Annual of Christmas Literature and Art. (US) 2905
Christmas Tree Lookout. (US) 2097
Christmas Trees Magazine. (US ISSN 0199-0217) 83, 2097
Christmas: Year Round Needlework & Craft Ideas. (US) 3590, 353
Christoffel-Blindenmission. Bericht. (US ISSN 0009-580X) 4170, 2292
Christophany. (AT ISSN 0728-0351) 4233, 1702
Christopher News Notes. (US ISSN 8755-6901) 4170
Christopher Street. (US ISSN 0146-7921) 2861, 2452
Christophorus. (GW ISSN 0009-5818) 4261, 1621
Christ's College Magazine. (UK) 1702
Christus. (FR ISSN 0009-5834) 4261
Christus ist Sieger. (GW) 4233
Christus Rex see Social Studies 4450
Christusstaat. (GW) 4233
Chromatogram. (US) 1205
Chromatogram. see Se Pu 3857
Chromatographia. (GW ISSN 0009-5893) 1205
Chromatographic Science Series. (US ISSN 0069-3936) 1205
Chromatography Abstracts. (UK ISSN 0268-6287) 1200, 8
Chromatography and Analysis. (US) 1852
Chrome Yellow see School Bus Briefs 4656
Chromosoma. (GW ISSN 0009-5915) 540
Chromosome Information Service see C I S 540
Chronica. (US ISSN 0009-5931) 2356, 321
Chronica Dermatologica. (IT ISSN 0011-1759) 3246
Chronica Horticulturae. (NE) 2124
Chronica Nova. (SP) 2356
Chronicle. (UK) 1307
Chronicle. (CN ISSN 0227-1192) 2176
Chronicle (Ann Arbor). (US ISSN 0440-9426) 2402
Chronicle (Austin) see H P Chronicle 1460
Chronicle (Grayslake). (US) 1307
Chronicle (Hamden). (US) 1307
Chronicle (Hempstead). (US) 1307
The Chronicle (Westfield). (US) 1307
Chronicle Career Index. (US ISSN 0276-0355) 3631
Chronicle Career Index Annual see Chronicle Career Index 3631
Chronicle College Charts see Chronicle Four-Year College Databook 1692
Chronicle Financial Aid Guide. (US) 1702
Chronicle Four-Year College Databook. (US ISSN 0191-3670) 1692
Chronicle of Higher Education. (US ISSN 0009-5982) 1702, 1307

CHRONICLE

Chronicle of Latin American Economic Affairs. (US ISSN 1054-8874) **851, 3879**
Chronicle of Parliamentary Elections and Developments. (SZ) **3879, 2612**
Chronicle of Philanthropy. (US ISSN 1040-676X) **4402**
Chronicle of the Catholic Church in Lithuania. (US ISSN 0197-0348) **4261, 1997**
Chronicle of the Horse. (US ISSN 0009-5990) **4533**
Chronicle of U S Classic Postal Issues. (US ISSN 0009-6008) **3751**
Chronicle Student Aid Annual see Chronicle Financial Aid Guide **1702**
Chronicle Two-Year College Databook. (US ISSN 0191-3662) **1692**
Chronicle Vocational School Manual. (US ISSN 0276-0371) **1692**
Chronicles. (US ISSN 0887-5731) **2905**
Chronicles of Culture see Chronicles **2905**
Chronicles of Oklahoma. (US ISSN 0009-6024) **2402**
Chronicles of St. Mary's. (US) **2402**
Chronico. (GR) **2861**
Chronika. (IS) **1997**
Chronika Aisthetikis. see Annales d'Esthetique **312**
Chronika tes Chalkidikes. (GR) **2356, 269**
Chronique. (BE) **610**
Chronique d'Egypte. (BE ISSN 0009-6067) **3636, 269, 2429**
Chronique de l'I R S A C. (Institut pour la Recherche Scientifique en Afrique Centrale) (ZR ISSN 0009-6040) **4305**
Chronique de la Recherche Miniere. (FR ISSN 0182-564X) **3480**
Chronique de Politique Etrangere see Studia Diplomatica **3973**
Chronique des Anysetiers. (FR) **1296**
Chronique des Grains see Grain Facts **206**
Chronique du Transporteur. (FR ISSN 0755-1088) **4648**
Chronique Judiciaire D'Haiti. (HT) **2612, 3879**
Chroniques d'Actualite de la S.E.D.E.I.S. (Societe d'Etudes et de Documentation Economiques, Industrielles et Sociales) (FR ISSN 0396-437X) **851, 4368**
Chroniques d'Histoire Maconnique. (FR ISSN 0240-7418) **1297**
Chronist see Tiroler Chronist **2392**
Chronmy Przyrode Ojczysta. (PL ISSN 0009-6172) **1485, 1945**
Chronobiologia. (IT ISSN 0390-0037) **435, 3251**
Chronobiology International. (US ISSN 0742-0528) **435, 3088**
Chronology & Catastrophism Review. (UK) **1557, 363, 3657**
Chronology of Trees and Shrubs in South-West Asia and Adjacent Regions. (PL) **2097**
Chrysalis. (US ISSN 0888-9384) **3763, 322**
Chrysanthemum. (US ISSN 0090-5771) **2124**
Chrysler Power. (US) **4688**
Chrysler 300 Club News. (US) **256**
Chrysostom. (UK) **4170**
Chrzescijanskie Stowarzyszenie Spoleczne. Information Bulletin. (PL ISSN 0578-0594) **4261**
Chrzescijanskie Stowarzyszenie Spoleczne. Materialy Problemowe. (PL) **4261**
Chu Feng. (CC) **2053, 2905**
Chuanbo Gongcheng/Ship Engineering. (CC ISSN 1000-6982) **4726, 1816**
Chuanbo Sheji Tongxun. (CC ISSN 1001-4624) **4726**
Chuanbo Shijie/Ship World. (US) **4726**
Chuangye Zhe/Entrepreneurs. (CC) **655**
Chuanqi Wenxue Xuankan/Selected Legendary Literature. (CC ISSN 1003-2738) **2905**
Chuanxi Lu see Philosophical Research **3776**

Chuban Faxing Yanjiu/Publishing and Distributing Research. (CC) **4125**
Chuban Gongzuo/Publishing Affairs. (CC ISSN 1001-2680) **4125**
Chuban Shiliao/Historical Material on Publishing. (CC) **4125**
Chubu Daigaku Kogakubu Kiyo. see Chubu University. College of Engineering. Memoirs **1817**
Chubu Institute of Technology. Memoirs. Series A see Chubu University. College of Engineering. Memoirs **1817**
Chubu Nippon Seikei Geka Saigai Geka Gakkai Zasshi. see Central Japan Journal of Orthopaedic & Traumatic Surgery **3307**
Chubu University. College of Business Administration and Information Science. Journal. (JA ISSN 0910-8874) **655**
Chubu University. College of Engineering. Memoirs/Chubu Daigaku Kogakubu Kiyo. (JA ISSN 0910-8629) **1817, 4595**
Chubu University. College of International Studies. Journal. (JA ISSN 0910-8882) **927**
Chugoku Denryoku K.K. Gikken Jiho. see Chugoku Electric Power Co. Technical Laboratory Report **1884**
Chugoku Denryoku K.K. Shao see Chugoku Electric Power Co. Technical Laboratory Report **1884**
Chugoku Electric Power Co. Technical Laboratory Report/Chugoku Denryoku K.K. Gikken Jiho. (JA ISSN 0009-6237) **1884**
Chugoku Gaho. (CC ISSN 1000-9337) **2181**
Chugoku Soshikibetsu Jinmeibo. see China Directory (Year) **3953**
Chuki Keizai Yosoku/Five-Year Economic Forecast. (JA) **851**
Chukung. (CH ISSN 1011-6761) **3404**
Ch'ulpan Moonwha/Korean Book Journal. (KO ISSN 0009-6245) **4125, 397**
Ch'un Ch'iu. see The Observation Post **338**
Chun Feng/Spring Breeze. (CC ISSN 1001-621X) **2905**
Chung-Ang Herald. (KO ISSN 0009-6253) **1307**
Chung Chi Bulletin. (HK ISSN 0009-6261) **1307**
Chung Hua Min Kuo Chi Ch'i yu Tien Kung Ch'i Ts'ai Nien Chien. see China, Republic. Machinery and Electrical Apparatus Industry Yearbook **1765**
Chung Hua Min Kuo T'ai-wan Sheng She Hui Shih Yeh T'ung Chi. see Social Affairs Statistics of Taiwan **4426**
Chung Hua Nung Yeh Hui Hsueh Pao. see Agricultural Association of China. Journal **71**
Chung Kang Chi Pao. see China Steel Technical Report **3404**
Chung Kung Yen Chiu/Studies on Chinese Communism. (CH ISSN 1015-9355) **3879**
Chung-kuo Ching Chi P'ing Lun. see Chinese Economic Review **655**
Chung-kuo Fo Chiao. (CH) **4214, 3763**
Chung-kuo Kung Ch'eng Je Wu Li. see Engineering Thermophysics in China **5186**
Chung-kuo Lun T'an. see China Tribune **2219**
Chung-kuo Sheng Li Hsueh Tsa Chih. see Chinese Journal of Physiology **570**
Chung-Kuo Ta-Lu Yen-Chiu/Mainland China Studies. (CH ISSN 1013-2716) **3880**
Chung-Mei Yueh-K'an. see West & East **3977**
Chung Shan Hsueh Shu Wen Hua Ch'i K'an. see Sun Yat-sen Cultural Foundation Bulletin **4389**
Chung-Wai Literary Monthly. (CH ISSN 0303-0849) **2905, 2990**

Chung Yang Yen Chiu Yuan. Chin Tai Shih Yen Chiu So Ch'i K'an. see Academia Sinica. Institute of Modern History. Bulletin **2305**
Chung Yang Yen Chiu Yuan Shu Hsueh Yen Chiu So T'ung Pao. see Academia Sinica. Institute of Mathematics. Bulletin **3026**
Chung Yang Yen Chiu Yuan Wu Li Hsueh Yen Chiu So Nien Pao. see Academia Sinica. Institute of Physics. Annual Report **3812**
Chuo Daigaku Rikogakubu Kiyo/Chuo University. Faculty of Science and Engineering. Bulletin. (JA ISSN 0578-2228) **4305, 4595**
Chuo Law Review/Hogaku Shinpo. (JA ISSN 0009-6296) **2612**
Chuo Suisan Kenkyujo Kenkyu Hokoku/National Research Institute of Fisheries Science. Report. (JA) **2038**
Chuo University. Faculty of Science and Engineering. Bulletin. see Chuo Daigaku Rikogakubu Kiyo **4305**
Chuokoran. see Central Public Opinion **2207**
Chuokoron. (JA) **2207**
Chuokoron Keiemondai see Will **1031**
Chuokoron Management Affairs. see Will **1031**
Church. (US ISSN 0883-5667) **4261**
Church. see Crkva **4282**
Church Administration. (US ISSN 0412-4553) **4233, 1005**
Church Advocate. (US ISSN 0009-630X) **4170**
Church & Nation. (AT ISSN 0314-6200) **4233**
Church and Society. (US ISSN 0037-7805) **4233, 4431**
Church and Society Newsletter. (SZ) **4170, 4595**
Church & State. (US ISSN 0009-6334) **4170, 3880**
Church and Synagogue Libraries. (US ISSN 0009-6342) **2752, 4170**
Church and Synagogue Library Association. News Bulletin see Church and Synagogue Libraries **2752**
Church and the Jewish People see Current Dialogue **4173**
Church Army. Front Line see Church Army. Front Line Annual Report **4234**
Church Army. Front Line Annual Report.(UK) **4234**
Church Army. Frontline News. (UK) **4171**
Church Army. Review see Church Army. Frontline News **4171**
▼Church Business. (CN) **4171, 610, 1005, 1476**
Church Computing News. (US) **1458, 4171**
Church Gazette see Anglican Gazette **4229**
Church Growth Digest. (UK) **4171**
Church Herald. (US ISSN 0009-6393) **4234**
Church Heritage. (AT) **4234**
Church History. (US ISSN 0009-6407) **4171**
Church Lads' and Church Girls' Brigade. Annual Report. (UK ISSN 0045-2831) **1235, 4171**
Church Law & Tax Report. (US) **2612, 4171**
Church Life. (US ISSN 8750-8613) **4171**
Church Management: The Clergy Journal see Clergy Journal **4171**
Church Media Library Magazine. (US ISSN 0884-6197) **2752, 4234**
Church Messenger/Cerkovnyj Vistnik. (US) **4171**
†Church Ministries Workers. (US) **5166**
Church Monuments. (UK ISSN 0268-7518) **296**
Church Monuments Society Newsletter see Church Monuments **296**
Church Music see Music and Liturgy **3564**
Church Music Quarterly. (UK ISSN 0307-6334) **3545**
The Church Music Report. (US) **3545, 4171**

Church Musician. (US ISSN 0009-6466) **3545**
Church News. (AT ISSN 1031-5837) **4234**
†Church News. (UK ISSN 0009-6474) **5166**
Church News (Salt Lake City). (US) **4281**
Church Observer. (UK ISSN 0009-6682) **4171**
Church of England. General Synod. Report of Proceedings. (UK ISSN 0307-7225) **4234**
Church of England Historical Society (Diocese of Sydney). Journal. (AT ISSN 0009-6490) **4234, 2308**
Church of England Newspaper. (UK ISSN 0007-8255) **4234**
Church of England Yearbook. (UK ISSN 0069-3987) **4234**
Church of God Evangel. (US) **4234**
Church of God Missions. (US ISSN 0009-6504) **4234**
Church of Ireland Gazette. (UK ISSN 0009-6512) **4234**
Church of Light Quarterly. (US ISSN 0009-6520) **3594, 358, 3669**
Church of Scotland. Yearbook. (UK ISSN 0069-3995) **4234**
Church of Scotland Braille Magazine. (UK) **2292, 4171**
Church Pianist. (US) **3545**
Church Pocket Book and Diary. (UK) **4171**
Church Pulpit Year Book. (UK ISSN 0069-4002) **4171**
Church Recreation see Church Recreation Magazine **4234**
Church Recreation Magazine. (US ISSN 0162-4652) **4234**
Church Scene. (AT ISSN 0009-6563) **4234**
Church Teachers. (US ISSN 0164-6451) **4171, 1621**
Church Times. (UK ISSN 0009-658X) **4234**
Church Training see Discipleship Training **4236**
Church World. (US ISSN 0009-6601) **4171**
Church World Service Connections see C W S Connections **5157**
Churches Council on Alcohol and Drugs Words see C O A D Words **5157**
Churches Speak. (US) **4171**
Churchman. (UK ISSN 0009-661X) **4234**
Churchman's Human Quest see Human Quest **4181**
Churchman's Magazine. (UK ISSN 0009-6636) **4234**
Churchman's Pocket Book and Diary see Church Pocket Book and Diary **4171**
Churchscape. (UK ISSN 0262-4966) **296, 322**
Churchwoman. (US ISSN 0009-6598) **4171**
†Churchyard. (US) **5166**
Churinga. (US) **2171**
Chutanzo, Netsushori/Casting, Forging & Heat Treatments. (JA) **3404**
Chutti. (BG) **2174**
Chuzhongsheng Shuxue Fudao/Mathematics Tutoring for Junior High School Students. (CC) **3032, 1252**
Ci Kan/Verses. (US) **3545, 2990**
Ciao. (CN ISSN 0382-8557) **1997**
Ciao Girl. (IT) **1252, 1235**
Ciao Si Gira. (IT) **3505**
Ciao 2001. (IT) **1252, 3546**
Ciba Collection of Medical Illustrations. (US ISSN 0084-8786) **3088, 322**
Ciba-Geigy Journal. (SZ) **1217, 3720**
Cibedo - Dokumentation und Texte see C I B E D O - Beitraege zum Gespraech Zwischen Christen und Muslimen **4167**
Cibles. (FR ISSN 0009-6679) **2434, 4469**
Cicada. (US ISSN 0891-2386) **2990**
Ciceroniana. (IT ISSN 0009-6687) **2905**
Cicindela. (US ISSN 0590-6334) **529**
Ciclo Vida y Obra. (SP) **3546**
Ciel et Espace. (FR ISSN 0373-9139) **363**

Ciel et Terre. (BE ISSN 0009-6709) **363**, 1587, 3434
Ciencia. (DR) **4305**
Ciencia. (BL ISSN 0084-8794) **4305**
Ciencia. (MX ISSN 0185-075X) **4305**, **4368**
Ciencia. (CU) **4305**
Ciencia Agronomica. (BL ISSN 0045-6888) **83**
Ciencia Agropecuaria. (PN) **83**
Ciencia & Tropico. (BL ISSN 0304-2685) **4369**
Ciencia Biologica: Biologia Molecular e Celular. (PO ISSN 0378-875X) **580**
Ciencia da Informacao. (BL ISSN 0100-1965) **2752**
Ciencia del Suelo/Argentine Society of Soil Science. Journal. (AG ISSN 0326-3169) **173**
Ciencia e Cultura. (BL ISSN 0009-6725) **4305**
Ciencia e Industria Farmaceutica. (SP ISSN 0210-0819) **3720**
Ciencia e Investigacion. (AG ISSN 0009-6733) **4305**
Ciencia e Investigacion Agraria. (CL ISSN 0304-5609) **84**
Ciencia e Tecnica Fiscal. (PO) **1091**
Ciencia en la U.R.S.S. *see* Nauka v S.S.S.R **4329**
Ciencia Interamericana. (US ISSN 0009-675X) **4305**, **4595**
Ciencia Medica. (SP ISSN 0212-6052) **3088**
Ciencia para Todos. (MX) **4305**, **4595**
Ciencia Pediatrika. (SP ISSN 0211-3465) **3319**
Ciencia Pharmaceutica. (SP ISSN 1131-5253) **3721**
Ciencia Tecnologia y Desarrollo. (CK ISSN 0120-1573) **4305**, **4595**
Ciencia Tomista. (SP ISSN 0210-0398) **4261**
Ciencia y Desarrollo. (MX ISSN 0185-0008) **4305**, **4595**
Ciencia y Naturaleza. (EC ISSN 0009-6768) **4305**
Ciencia y Sociedad. (DR ISSN 0378-7680) **4305**
Ciencia y Tecnica. (SP) **4355**, **4614**
Ciencia y Tecnica en la Agricultura. Serie: Apicultura. (CU) **84**
Ciencia y Tecnica en la Agricultura. Serie: Arroz. (CU ISSN 0138-8789) **84**
Ciencia y Tecnica en la Agricultura. Serie: Cafe y Cacao. (CU ISSN 0138-6093) **173**
Ciencia y Tecnica en la Agricultura. Serie: Canera. (CU ISSN 0138-7014) **173**
Ciencia y Tecnica en la Agricultura. Serie: Citricos *see* Ciencia y Tecnica en la Agricultura. Serie: Citricos y Otros Frutales **173**
Ciencia y Tecnica en la Agricultura. Serie: Citricos y Otros Frutales. (CU ISSN 0138-8835) **173**
Ciencia y Tecnica en la Agricultura. Serie: Economia Agropecuaria. (CU ISSN 0138-8584) **148**
Ciencia y Tecnica en la Agricultura. Serie: Ganado Porcino. (CU ISSN 0138-8738) **214**
Ciencia y Tecnica en la Agricultura. Serie: Hortalizas, Papas, Granos y Fibras. (CU ISSN 0138-8630) **173**
Ciencia y Tecnica en la Agricultura. Serie: Mecanizacion de la Agricultura.(CU ISSN 0138-8681) **161**
Ciencia y Tecnica en la Agricultura. Serie: Pastos y Forrajes. (CU ISSN 0138-8533) **205**
Ciencia y Tecnica en la Agricultura. Serie: Proteccion de Plantas. (CU ISSN 0138-8932) **173**
Ciencia y Tecnica en la Agricultura. Serie: Riego y Drenaje. (CU ISSN 0138-8487) **173**
Ciencia y Tecnica en la Agricultura. Serie: Suelos y Agroquimica. (CU ISSN 0138-8983) **173**
Ciencia y Tecnica en la Agricultura. Serie: Tabaco. (CU ISSN 0138-8185) **4643**

Ciencia y Tecnica en la Agricultura. Serie: Veterinaria. (CU) **4808**
Ciencia y Tecnica en la Agricultura. Serie: Viandas, Hortalizas y Cranos *see* Ciencia y Tecnica en la Agricultura. Serie: Hortalizas, Papas, Granos y Fibras **173**
Ciencia y Tecnica en la Agricultura. Serie: Viandas, Hortalizas y Granos *see* Ciencia y Tecnica en la Agricultura. Serie: Viandas Tropicales **173**
Ciencia y Tecnica en la Agricultura. Serie: Viandas Tropicales. (CU ISSN 0138-8886) **173**, **205**, **2124**
Ciencia y Tecnologia. (CR ISSN 0378-052X) **4305**
Ciencia y Tecnologia *see* Colombia: Ciencia y Tecnologia **4305**
Ciencia y Tecnologia del Mar. (CL) **1603**
Ciencia y Tecnologia Pesquera. (CU ISSN 0864-3873) **2038**
Ciencias. (SP ISSN 0009-6776) **4305**
Ciencias Biologicas. (CU ISSN 0138-7154) **435**
Ciencias de la Agricultura. (CU ISSN 0138-7251) **84**
Ciencias de la Tierra y el Espacio. (CU) **1542**
Ciencias Economicas. (BL) **655**
Ciencias Economicas. (CR ISSN 0252-9521) **889**
Ciencias Economicas. Revista. (AG) **749**, **772**
Ciencias em Museus. (BL ISSN 0103-2909) **3523**
Ciencias Humanas. (BL) **2861**
Ciencias Juridicas y Sociales. (ES) **2612**
▼Ciencias Matematicas. (CR) **3032**
Ciencias Pedagogicas. (CU) **1621**
Ciencias Sociales. (CK) **4369**
Ciencias Socias Hoje (Year). (BL) **4369**
Ciencias Tecnicas Fisicas y Matematicas. (CU ISSN 0253-7397) **4595**, **4305**
Cientifica. (BL ISSN 0100-0039) **173**
Cieplownictwo, Ogrzewnictwo, Wentylacja. (PL) **1817**
Ciervo. (SP ISSN 0045-6896) **2217**
Cieslik's Puppenmagazin. (GW ISSN 0931-1556) **2434**
Cifras de Cuentas Nacionales. (CR) **4568**
Cifras sobre Produccion Agropecuaria. (CR) **148**
Cifras sobre Produccion Industrial. (CR) **1073**
Cigarette Card News and Trade Card Chronicle. (UK ISSN 0009-6822) **2435**
Cill Dara and Liffey Valley News. (IE) **2202**
Cill Dara News *see* Cill Dara and Liffey Valley News **2202**
Cimaise. (FR ISSN 0009-6830) **322**, **296**
Cimarron Review. (US ISSN 0009-6849) **2905**, **2505**, **4369**
Cimbebasia. (SX ISSN 1012-4926) **2505**, **237**, **269**
Cimbebasia. Series A: Natural History. (SX ISSN 0590-6342) **435**
Cimbebasia. Series B: Cultural History. (SX) **4369**
Cimbebasia Memoirs. (SX) **4369**
Cimbora. (RM) **1252**
Cimbra. (SP ISSN 0210-0479) **1863**
Ciments, Betons, Platres, Chaux. (FR ISSN 0397-006X) **610**
†Ciments et Chaux. (FR) **5166**
La Cina. (CC ISSN 1000-9310) **2181**
Cina. (IT ISSN 0529-7451) **2337**
Cina Notizie. (IT ISSN 1120-4249) **655**, **904**
Cinch. Australian Criminology Database.(AT) **1511**
Cinch in Print *see* Cinch. Australian Criminology Database **1511**
Cincinnati. Division of Police. Annual Report. (US ISSN 0091-8806) **1512**
Cincinnati Art Museum. Annual Report. (US) **3523**
†Cincinnati Bible Seminary. Seminary Review. (US) **5166**

Cincinnati Business Courier. (US) **655**
Cincinnati Classical Studies. New Series.(NE ISSN 0169-7692) **1275**
Cincinnati Gazette *see* Milk Marketer **201**
Cincinnati Herald. (US) **1997**
Cincinnati Historical Society Bulletin *see* Queen City Heritage **2420**
Cincinnati Journal of Magic. (US) **3669**, **3763**
Cincinnati Law Review. (US ISSN 0009-6881) **2612**
Cincinnati Magazine. (US) **2223**
Cincinnati Medicine. (US ISSN 0163-0075) **3088**
Cincinnati Poetry Review. (US) **2990**
Cincinnati Purchasor. (US ISSN 0009-6903) **1035**
Cinco Dias. (SP) **655**
Cinderella Philatelist. (UK ISSN 0009-6911) **3751**
Cine Advance. (II) **3505**
Cine & Media. (BE ISSN 0771-0518) **3505**, **1333**
Cine Blitz. (II) **3505**
Cine-Bulles. (CN) **3505**
Cine Checoslovaco *see* Czechoslovak Film **3507**
Cine Cubano. (CU ISSN 0009-6946) **3505**
Cine-Fiches de Grand Angle. (BE ISSN 0773-2279) **3505**
Cine-Guia. (CU) **3505**
Cine News. (SI ISSN 0009-6954) **3789**, **3505**
Cine-Oja. (VE) **3505**
Cine-Revue. (BE ISSN 0045-6918) **3505**
Cine Technicians' Association of South India. Journal *see* C.T.A. Journal **3504**
Cine Weekly. *see* Amruta **2198**
Cineaction! (CN) **3505**
Cineaste. (US ISSN 0009-7004) **3505**
Cinebulletin. (SZ ISSN 1018-2098) **3505**
Cinecorriere. (IT) **3505**
Cinecronache. (IT ISSN 0009-7020) **3505**
Cinedossier. (AT ISSN 0813-1600) **3505**
†CineFan. (US ISSN 0277-5891) **5166**
Cinefantastique. (US ISSN 0145-6032) **3505**, **3010**
Cinefex. (US ISSN 0198-1056) **3505**
Cineforum. (IT ISSN 0009-7039) **3505**
Cineguia. (SP ISSN 0069-4134) **3505**, **1371**, **4631**
Cinema. (BG) **3505**
Cinema. (SZ) **3505**
Cinema. (IT) **3505**
Cinema. (TS) **3505**
Cinema (Year). (FR ISSN 0045-6926) **3505**
Cinema Blue. (US) **3396**, **1371**
Cinema Blue Presents Erotic Stars. (US) **3396**, **1371**
Cinema Blue Presents Red-Hot Couples.(US) **3396**, **1371**
Cinema - Canada. (CN ISSN 0009-7071) **3505**, **1252**
Cinema d'Oggi. (IT) **3506**
Cinema de Amadores. (PO ISSN 0009-708X) **3506**
Cinema Domani. (IT) **3506**
Cinema e Societa. (IT ISSN 0009-7152) **3506**
Cinema Francais Production. (FR ISSN 0292-7292) **3506**
Cinema in India. (II) **3506**
†Cinema India - International. (II) **5166**
Cinema Journal. (US ISSN 0009-7101) **3506**
Cinema Lombardia. (IT) **3506**, **1371**
Cinema News. (US) **3506**
Cinema Nuovo. (IT ISSN 0009-711X) **3506**
Cinema Organ. (UK) **3546**
Cinema Papers. (AT) **3506**
†Cinema Papers Yearbook. (AT ISSN 0158-698X) **5166**
Cinema Politique. (FR ISSN 0335-6280) **3506**, **3880**
Cinema the World over. (PK) **3506**
Cinema 9. (FR) **3506**

Cinemacabre. (US ISSN 0198-1064) **3506**
Cinemaction. (FR) **3506**
Cinemaranjani. (II) **3506**
Cinemascope Magazine. (CN) **3506**
CinemaScore *see* Soundtrack! Incorporating CinemaScore **3581**
†Cinemasessanta. (IT) **5166**
Cinemasud. (IT ISSN 0009-7160) **3506**
Cinemateca Revista. (UY) **3506**
Cinematic Creation. *see* Dianying Chuangzuo **3507**
Cinematograf. (SP ISSN 0213-1773) **3506**, **2356**
Cinematograph. (US ISSN 0886-6570) **3506**
Cinematographe. (FR) **3506**
Cinematographers, Production Designers, Costume Designers & Film Editors Guide. (US ISSN 0894-8674) **1126**, **3506**
Cinematography. *see* Nghe Thuat Dien Anh **3515**
Cinemonkey. (US ISSN 0162-0126) **3506**
†Cineromanzo. (IT ISSN 0412-5568) **5166**
Cineschedario - Letture Drammatiche. (IT ISSN 0024-1458) **3506**, **4631**
Cinescopio. (IT) **3506**
Cineset. (AG) **3506**
Cinesiologia. (IT) **570**
Cinesiologie. (FR ISSN 0009-7209) **3371**
Cinethique. (FR) **3506**
CineVue. (US) **3506**
Cinmay Smrti Pathagara. (II) **2905**, **322**
Cinquante Millions de Consommateurs *see* 50 Millions de Consommateurs **1509**
Cintana Dhara. (CE) **4369**
Cintarea Romaniei *see* Timp Liber **347**
Cintrafor. (US) **2114**
Ciociaria. (IT) **4757**
Cioe. (IT) **1252**
Cip. (UK) **1252**
Circa *see* C I R C A Art Magazine **320**
Circadian Rhythms *see* Biological Rhythms **570**
Circe. (FR ISSN 0069-4177) **2905**
Circle. (UK) **1252**
Circle. (CN ISSN 0227-2091) **4469**
Circle *see* Thrower **4558**
Circle (Jamaica Plain). (US) **1997**, **2612**, **3880**
Circle (Portland). (US) **2990**
Circle in the Square Broadsheet. (UK) **2990**
Circle K. (US ISSN 0745-1962) **1307**
Circle Network News. (US ISSN 1047-4196) **4281**
Circle of State Librarians. Bulletin *see* State Librarian **2786**
Circle Track. (US ISSN 0734-5437) **4469**
Circlets. (US) **2990**
Circolo Culturale B.G. Duns Scoto di Roccarainola. Atti. (IT ISSN 0392-9884) **269**, **4369**
Circolo Matematico di Palermo. Rendiconti. (IT ISSN 0009-725X) **3032**
Circolo Rosselli. Quaderni. (IT) **1297**, **3880**
Circolo Speleologico Romano. Notiziario.(IT ISSN 0009-7268) **1557**
Circuit *see* Circuit - Foton **1371**
Circuit Cellar Ink. (US ISSN 0896-8985) **1458**
Circuit Design *see* Printed Circuit Design **1777**
Circuit Ferme. (CN) **1063**, **1355**
Circuit - Foton. (VE) **1371**
▼Circuit Industriel. (CN) **610**, **1916**
†Circuit Industriel. (CN) **5166**
Circuit News *see* Electricity U K **1889**
Circuit News (Webb City). (US ISSN 1058-9317) **1448**
Circuit News Assembly. (US ISSN 1058-9325) **1448**
Circuit Rider (Nashville). (US ISSN 0146-9924) **4234**
Circuit Rider (Springfield). (US ISSN 0741-8264) **2147**

6058 CIRCUIT WORLD

Circuit World. (UK) **4595**
Circuitree International see Circuitree Magazine **1765**
Circuitree Magazine. (US) **1765**
Circuits Assembly. (US ISSN 1054-0407) **1765**
Circuits Manufacturing see Circuits Assembly **1765**
Circuits, Systems, and Signal Processing. (US ISSN 0278-081X) **1352, 1333, 1390**
Circulaire d'Information see South Pacific Commission. Information Circular **885**
Circular C I A T. (MX ISSN 0084-8689) **84**
Circular of Meteoric Dust. see Ryuseijin Kaiho **371**
Circulation see American Newspaper Markets Circulation **2567**
Circulation. (US ISSN 0009-7322) **3207**
Circulation Auditing Around the World. (FR) **40**
Circulation Data and Marketing Data. see Oplagstal og Markedstal **36**
Circulation et Metabolisme du Cerveau. see Cerebral Circulation and Metabolism **3333**
Circulation Hotline see Competitive Publishing Hotline **4125**
Circulation Management. (US ISSN 0888-8191) **4125**
Circulation Research. (US ISSN 0009-7330) **3207**
Circulation 91. (US) **29**
Circulatory Shock. (US ISSN 0092-6213) **3207**
Circulo. (US ISSN 0009-7349) **2505**
Circulo Argentino de Odontologia. Revista. (AG ISSN 0325-7479) **3230**
Circulo Colombo Suizo. Boletin Informativo see Bitacora Colombo Suizo **808**
Circulo Odontologico de Cordoba. Revista. (AG ISSN 0045-6942) **3230**
Circulo Odontologico de Rosario. Revista. (AG ISSN 0009-7357) **3230**
Circulo Poetico. (US) **2990**
Circum-Spice. (US ISSN 0069-4215) **2752**
Circumference. (US) **1297**
Circus. (US) **3546**
Circus-Gids Nederland. (NE) **4631**
Circus-Parade. (GW) **4631**
Circus Report. (US ISSN 0889-5996) **4631**
Cirencester Excavations. (UK) **269, 2356**
Ciret Studien. (GW ISSN 0170-5679) **655**
Cirplan. (UK ISSN 0950-8732) **4234, 2356**
Cirque dans l'Univers. (FR ISSN 0009-7373) **4631**
Cirugia del Uruguay. (UY ISSN 0009-7381) **3377**
Cirugia Espanola. (SP ISSN 0009-739X) **3377**
Cirugia Pediatrica. (SP ISSN 0214-1221) **3377, 3319**
Cirugia Plastica del Uruguay see Cirugia Plastica Uruguaya **3377**
Cirugia Plastica Uruguaya. (UY ISSN 0009-7403) **3377**
Cirugia y Cirujanos. (MX ISSN 0009-7411) **3377**
Cishu Yanjiu/Journal of Lexicographical Studies. (CC ISSN 1000-6125) **2809**
Cistercian Studies Quarterly. (US ISSN 0578-3224) **4171**
Cistercienser Chronik. (AU ISSN 0379-8291) **297, 4261**
Citadel Film Series. (US) **3506**
Citas Latinoamericanas en Ciencias Sociales y Humanidades see C L A S E **2519**
†Citatel. (CS ISSN 0009-7438) **5166**
Citation. (US ISSN 0009-7446) **3264**
Cite. (FR ISSN 0756-3205) **3880**
Cite Newsletter see Teaching English **1761**
Cite Nouvelle. (FR) **3880, 4234**
Citeaux. (BE ISSN 0774-4919) **4261**

Cites Unies. (FR ISSN 0529-8016) **3953**
Cithara. (US ISSN 0009-7527) **4171, 2505**
†Citicorp Report to Investors. (US) **5166**
Cities see 976 Cities Plus **1057**
Cities. (UK ISSN 0264-2751) **4085**
Cities and Villages. (US ISSN 0009-7535) **2485**
†Citilife. (US) **5166**
The Citizen. (SI) **2216**
Citizen (Denver). (US ISSN 0009-7543) **4056**
†Citizen (Jackson). (US ISSN 0578-3283) **5166**
Citizen Action. (II) **4431, 2612**
Citizen Advocacy News. (AT) **4402**
Citizen Airman. (US) **50**
Citizen Alert Newsletter. (US) **1945**
Citizen News. (US) **4402**
Citizen Participation. (US) **1503**
Citizens Advice Notes Service. (UK) **2612**
Citizens Association for Racial Equality see C A R E **4430**
Citizens' Band. (UK ISSN 0261-0361) **1355**
Citizens Band What C B see What C B **5304**
Citizens Budget Commission Quarterly see C B C Quarterly **5156**
Citizens' Business. (US ISSN 0009-756X) **4085**
Citizens Committee on Human Rights Newsletter see C C H R Newsletter **3940**
Citizens' Council see Citizen (Jackson) **5166**
Citizens for a Better Environment Environmental Review see C B E Environmental Review **1484**
Citizens for Foreign Aid Reform Inc. Newsletter see C - F A R Newsletter **927**
Citizens for Participation in Political Action Newsletter see C P P A X Newsletter **3877**
Citizen's Guide to Local Government. (US) **4056**
Citizen's Guide to School District Budgeting see Citizen's Guide to School Districts **1726**
Citizen's Guide to School Districts. (US) **1726**
Citizens Union Foundation. Occasional Paper Series. (US) **4085**
Citizens Union Reports. (US) **4085**
Citizens Union Research Foundation. Occasional Paper Studies see Citizens Union Foundation. Occasional Paper Series **4085**
Citoyen. (CN) **3880**
Citrabikshana/Chitra-Bikshan. (II) **3506**
Citrograph. (US ISSN 0009-7578) **173, 2064**
Citrus and Vegetable Magazine. (US ISSN 0009-7586) **173**
Citrus Engineering Conference. Transactions. (US ISSN 0412-6300) **173**
Citrus Industry Magazine. (US ISSN 0009-7594) **2064**
Citta. (IT) **2204**
Citta (Milan). (IT) **4146**
†Citta Calabria. (IT) **5166**
Citta di Riga. (IT) **322**
Citta di Saronno. (IT) **4056**
Citta di Vita. (IT ISSN 0009-7632) **4171, 322**
Citta e Campagna. (IT) **297**
Citta e Societa. (IT ISSN 0009-7640) **2485**
Citta Futura. (IT ISSN 0045-6977) **2861**
Citta Nuova (Rome). (IT) **2204**
▼Citta Oggi. (IT) **2204**
Cittadino Canadese. (CN ISSN 0009-7667) **1997**
Cittanova. (IT ISSN 0393-4977) **269, 2356**
The City (San Francisco). (US) **2223**
†City Almanac. (US ISSN 0009-7683) **5166**
City & Country Club Life. (US ISSN 0897-4926) **2223**
City & Country Home. (CN ISSN 0715-5689) **2549**

City and County. (UK) **813**
City and Guilds Handbook. (UK) **1682**
City & Society (Washington). (US ISSN 0893-0465) **237**
City & State. (US ISSN 0885-940X) **4056, 1091**
▼City & State's (Year) Resource Guide.(US) **4056, 1005, 1126**
City and Suburban Travel. (US ISSN 0045-6985) **4648**
City & Town (North Little Rock). (US ISSN 0193-8371) **4085**
City Art Museum of Saint Louis. Bulletin see St. Louis Art Museum. Bulletin **3532**
City Beautiful. (NZ ISSN 0009-7705) **2124**
†City Business Courier. (UK ISSN 0009-7713) **5166**
City Changes see International Investment Banking Report **671**
City Club Gadfly. (US) **4085**
City College Alumnus. (US ISSN 0045-6993) **1307**
City - County Magazine. (US) **2223**
City Cyclist. (US) **4516, 4648**
City Directory (Year). (UK ISSN 0308-9088) **942**
City Dweller. (CN) **2176**
City Employment see Current Governments Reports: City Employment **712**
City Fiscal Conditions in (Year). (US) **4085**
▼City Fitness. (US) **3800, 4469**
City Guide. (US) **4757**
City Guide - Broadway Magazine. (US) **4757, 4631**
City Hall Digest. (US ISSN 0190-0005) **4085**
City Lights Review. (US) **2990, 2861**
City Limits. (US ISSN 0199-0330) **2485**
City Living see Chicago Magazine **2223**
City Magazine. (HK) **2197**
City News. (US) **1252**
City News (Newcastle upon Tyne). (UK ISSN 0261-3964) **2193**
City of Birmingham Directory of Industry & Commerce. (UK ISSN 0266-9064) **1126**
City of Birmingham Symphony Orchestra. Annual Prospectus. (UK) **3546**
City of Birmingham Symphony Orchestra. Prom Prospectus see City of Birmingham Symphony Orchestra. Summer Season Brochure **3546**
City of Birmingham Symphony Orchestra. Summer Season Brochure.(UK) **3546**
City of Chicago Building Code. (US) **610, 1884, 2612**
City of London Directory & Livery Companies Guide. (UK ISSN 0142-5072) **1126**
City of London Recorder. (UK) **2193**
City of London School Chronicle. (UK) **1621**
▼City of New York Council Digest. (US) **2613**
City of New York Parks & Recreation. Annual Report. (US) **1485**
City of Ottawa. Corporate Financial and Statistical Information. (CN ISSN 0831-7496) **1091**
City of Ottawa. Financial and Other Statistics see City of Ottawa. Corporate Financial and Statistical Information **1091**
City of Ottawa Coin Club. Monthly Bulletin. (CN ISSN 0045-7019) **3598**
City of Perth. Annual Report see City of Perth. Lord Mayor's Report **4085**
City of Perth. Lord Mayor's Report. (AT) **4085**
City of Stockholm. Annual Financial Report (Year). (SW) **4085**
†City of Toronto Planning and Development Department. City Planning. (CN) **5166**
City of Toronto Planning Board. City Planning see City of Toronto Planning and Development Department. City Planning **5166**

City of Westminster Chamber of Commerce Directory see Westminster Chamber of Commerce Directory **824**
City Products and Services Guide. (US) **1073**
City Rant. (US) **2905**
City Record. (US) **4085**
City Recorder see City of London Recorder **2193**
City Reflections. (UK) **1307**
†City Rhythm. (AT) **5166**
City Runner. (JA) **4544**
City Sierran. (US) **1945, 2245**
City Terrace Comet. (US) **1997**
City Today. (HK) **2197**
†City University Business School. Economic Review. (UK ISSN 0266-7339) **5166**
City University of New York Forum see C U N Y Forum **2807**
City-Zeitung (Hannover). (GW) **2188**
CityBusiness (Metairie) see New Orleans CityBusiness **1116**
CityBusiness - Twin Cities see Minneapolis - St. Paul CityBusiness **680**
Cityguide see Panorama (Boston) **4782**
Cityguide - The San Francisco Bay Area and Northern California. (US ISSN 0277-0342) **4757**
Cityscape. (UK) **1307**
Cityscope see Godwins Cityscope **867**
Cityside. (CN) **1307**
CitySports Magazine see California CitySports Magazine **4468**
CitySports Magazine see MetroSports Magazine **4479**
Ciudad de Dios. (SP ISSN 0009-7756) **4261**
Ciudad Nueva Internacional. (SP) **2217**
Ciudad y Territorio. (SP ISSN 0210-0487) **4085**
Ciudadano. (SP) **1503**
La Civetta. (IT) **322**
Civic Affairs. (II ISSN 0009-7772) **4085**
Civic Public Works. (CN ISSN 0829-772X) **4086**
Civic Public Works Reference Manual and Buyer's Guide. (CN) **4057**
Civic Trust Awards. (UK) **297, 610, 1945**
Civica Scuola di Musica. Quaderni. (IT) **3546**
Civica Stazione Idrobiologica di Milano. Quaderni. (IT) **435**
The Civil Abolitionist. (US) **3088, 230**
Civil Actions Against State Government: Its Divisions, Agencies, and Offices. (US) **2701**
Civil Actions Against the United States: Its Agencies, Offices, and Employees. (US) **2613**
Civil Aeronautics Board Air Carrier Traffic Statistics see C A B Air Carrier Traffic Statistics **49**
Civil Affairs Journal & Newsletter. (US ISSN 0045-7035) **3880**
Civil Aircraft Accident Reports. (HK) **4672, 4057**
Civil Aircraft Markings. (UK) **4672**
Civil & Military Law Journal. (II ISSN 0045-7043) **2735, 2701**
Civil and Military Review. (II) **3454, 4125, 4402**
Civil Aviation. see Al-Tairan al-Madani **63**
Civil Aviation Administration of China. Journal. see Zhongguo Minhang Bao **4798**
Civil Aviation and Administration of China Inflight Magazine see C A A C Inflight Magazine **4671**
Civil Aviation Economics and Technology. see Minhang Jingji yu Jishu **59**
Civil Aviation in Pakistan: Half-Yearly Newsletter. (PK) **50**
Civil Aviation Institute of China. Journal. see Zhongguo Minhang Xueyuan Xuebao **66**
Civil Aviation News. (UK) **4672, 2581**
Civil Aviation Review. (UK) **50**
▼Civil Aviation Training. (UK) **4672**
Civil Censorship Study Group Bulletin. (US) **3751**

Civil Commitment in Minnesota. (US) 2701
Civil Document Processing Manual. (CN) 2701
Civil Engineer. (II) 1863
Civil Engineer in South Africa/Siviele Ingenieur in Suid-Afrika. (SA ISSN 0009-7845) 1863
Civil Engineering see Construction Weekly 1864
Civil Engineering. see Ingenieria Civil 1867
Civil Engineering. see Inzinierske Stavby 1868
Civil Engineering. see P T - Civiele Techniek 1872
Civil Engineering A S C E. (US ISSN 0360-0556) 1863
Civil Engineering Advisory Council. Annual Report/Siviele Ingenieurswese-Adviesraad. Jaarverslag. (SA) 1863
Civil Engineering & Hydraulic Engineering Abstracts. see Melyepitesi es Vizepitesi Szakirodalmi Tajekoztato 1845
Civil Engineering and Public Works Review see Construction Weekly 1864
Civil Engineering Contractor. (SA ISSN 0009-7888) 1863
†Civil Engineering for Practicing & Design Engineers. (US ISSN 0277-3775) 5166
Civil Engineering Hydraulics Abstracts. (UK ISSN 0305-9456) 1842, 8
Civil Engineering in Japan. (JA ISSN 0578-3747) 1863
Civil Engineering News. (US) 1863
Civil Engineering Report Series see Water Resources Report Series 4833
Civil Engineering Series. (US) 1863
Civil Engineering Surveyor. (UK ISSN 0266-139X) 1863
†Civil Engineering Systems. (UK ISSN 0263-0257) 5166
Civil Engineering Technician see Civil Engineering Technology 1863
Civil Engineering Technology. (UK) 1863
Civil Engineering Working Papers. (AT ISSN 0156-2126) 1863
Civil Engineers Computing Review see C E Computing Review 1877
Civil Judicial Statistics. see Norway. Statistisk Sentralbyraa. Sivilrettsstatistikk 5249
Civil Justice Quarterly. (UK) 2701
Civil Law Cases. (PK) 2701
Civil Libertarian. (US) 3940, 4402
Civil Liberties (New York). (US ISSN 0009-790X) 3940
Civil Liberties (Seattle) see Civil Liberties of Washington 3941
Civil Liberties Alert. (US) 3391, 3940
Civil Liberties in New York see N.Y. Civil Liberties 3945
Civil Liberties of Washington. (US) 3941
Civil Liberties Reporter. (US ISSN 0009-7934) 2701, 3941
Civil Liberties Review. (US ISSN 0888-0417) 3941
Civil Liberty see Civil Liberty Agenda 3941
Civil Liberty. (AT) 3941
Civil Liberty Agenda. (UK) 3941
Civil Litigation Reporter. (US ISSN 0199-0802) 2701
Civil Procedure see B A R - B R I Bar Review. Civil Procedure 2701
Civil Procedure Victoria. (AT) 2701
Civil Protection. (UK) 1273
Civil R I C O Litigation Reporter. (US) 2701, 1512
Civil R I C O Report. (US ISSN 0884-0032) 2701
Civil Rights and Civil Liberties Litigation: The Law of Section 1983, 3-E. (US) 2701, 3941
Civil Rights Litigation and Attorney Fees Annual Handbook. (US ISSN 0887-1191) 2701
Civil Rights Newsletter. (SA ISSN 0045-706X) 3941
Civil Servant. (NR) 4057
Civil Servant. see Dimosios Ypallilos 4058

Civil Servant in the Defence Forces. see Foersvarstjaenstemannen 979
Civil Service Journal see Management (Washington) 1019
Civil Service News. (MF) 2581, 4057
Civil Service News. (US) 4057
Civil Service News Releases see Civil Service News 4057
Civil Service Pensioner. (GW) 2271, 4402
Civil Service Reporter. (PH ISSN 0300-3620) 4057
Civil Service Year Book. (UK ISSN 0302-329X) 4057
Civil Transport Data Sheets. (UK ISSN 0009-806X) 50, 4672
Civil War. (US ISSN 0897-6015) 3454, 2402
Civil War Collectors' Dealer Directory. (US ISSN 0094-1182) 256, 3454
Civil War History. (US ISSN 0009-8078) 2402
▼The Civil War Lady. (US) 3454, 4839
Civil War News. (US) 2402
Civil War Round Table Digest. (US ISSN 0009-8086) 2402
Civil War Times Illustrated. (US ISSN 0009-8094) 2402
Civilforsvar. (DK ISSN 0107-0665) 1273
Civilian - Based Defense: News and Opinion. (US ISSN 0886-6015) 3953, 2308, 3454
Civilian Congress. (US) 2613, 3454, 3880, 4431
Civilingenjoeren. (SW ISSN 0348-6087) 1863
†Civilisation Libertaire. (FR ISSN 0007-957X) 5166
Civilisation Malgache. (FR ISSN 0578-3917) 237
Civilisations. (BE ISSN 0009-8140) 4431
Civilisations de l'Europe Centrale et du Sud-Est. (FR) 4431
Civilisations et Societes. (FR ISSN 0069-4290) 2356, 4369
Civilised Transport see National Council on Inland Transportation. Newsletter 4720
Civilization and Society: Studies in Social, Economic and Cultural History. (US) 2308, 4369
Civilization of the American Indian. (US ISSN 0069-4304) 2402
Civiloekonomen. (DK) 655
Civilta Asiatica. (IT ISSN 0069-4312) 2337
Civilta Cattolica. (IT ISSN 0009-8167) 4261, 2861
Civilta Cibernetica. (SM) 4305
Civilta del Bere. (IT) 380
Civilta Veneziana. Dizionari Dialettali e Studi Linguistici. (IT ISSN 0069-4339) 2809
Civilta Veneziana. Fonti e Testi. Serie Prima: Fonti e Testi per la Storia dell'Arte Veneta. (IT ISSN 0069-4355) 322, 2356
Civilta Veneziana. Fonti e Testi. Serie Terza. (IT ISSN 0069-4347) 2356
Civilta Veneziana. Saggi. (IT ISSN 0069-4371) 2356
Civilta Veneziana. Studi. (IT ISSN 0069-438X) 2356
Civis Mundi. (NE ISSN 0030-3283) 3880, 3953
Civitan Magazine. (US ISSN 0194-5785) 1297
Civitas. (SZ) 2861, 2169
Civitas. (IT ISSN 0009-8191) 3880
Civitas Abolitionist see The Civil Abolitionist 3088
Cizi Jazyky. (CS) 1621, 2809
Cladistics: The International Journal of the Willi Hennig Society. (US ISSN 0748-3007) 499, 529, 580
Claims. (US) 2530
The Claims Forum. (US) 975, 2530, 2613
Clair Foyer see Famille Magazine 2187
Clairlieu: Tijdschrift gewijd aan de Geschiedenis der Kruisheren. (BE) 4171, 2308
Clamavi. (NE ISSN 0166-3488) 4402
Clan Guthrie News. (US) 2147

Clan Hunter News. (UK) 1297, 2147
Clan MacDonald Annual. (CN) 1307
Clan MacLeod Society U S A. Newsletter. (US) 2147
Clan MacNeil Association of America. Galley. (US ISSN 0163-9951) 2147
Clan MacTavish Association Newsletter. (US) 2147
Clan McLaren Society, U S A. Quarterly. (US ISSN 0009-8213) 2147
Clan Ross Newsletter. (US ISSN 0731-2032) 1997, 2147, 2356
Clandestine Confidential. (US) 1371
Clansman (Halifax). (CN ISSN 0832-5189) 1997, 2053, 2147
Clara. (SP) 3590
Claremont Reading Conference. Yearbook. (US ISSN 0886-6880) 1746
Claretianum. (IT ISSN 0578-4182) 4261
Claridad. (UY ISSN 0009-823X) 2238
Clarin Economico. (AG ISSN 0009-8256) 851
Clarin Internacional. (AG) 2170
Clarinet. (US ISSN 0361-5553) 3546
Clarinet and Saxophone. (UK ISSN 0260-390X) 3546
Clarinette Magazine. (FR ISSN 0761-9553) 3546
Clarion. (US) 322, 3523
Clarion Call. (US ISSN 0896-8071) 3594, 3953
Clarion Herald. (US) 4261
Clarion Magazine. (US) 1307
Clarion University Alumni Magazine see Clarion Magazine 1307
Claris Technical Solutions. (US) 1476
Clarity. (II) 3880
Clarity. (UK ISSN 0263-6743) 4281
†Clarity Magazine. (US) 5166
Clark Clarion. (US) 2147
Clark County Historical Society. Newsletter. (US) 2402
Clark County History. (US ISSN 0090-449X) 2403
†Clark Now. (US ISSN 0009-8272) 5166
Clark University News. (US) 1307
Clarke Burton News Analysis. (US) 1390
Clarke Burton Report. (US) 1390
Clarke College Courier. (US) 1307
Clarke Hall & Morrison on Children. (UK) 1235, 2613
Clarks' Directory of Southern Hospitals see Hospital Blue Book (Official Southern Edition) 2464
Clark's Directory of Southern Textile Mills see American Textile Directory 4616
Clarkson, Tetrault Regulatory Reporter - Broadcasting. (CN) 1333
Clarkson, Tetrault Regulatory Reporter - Telecom. (CN) 1333
Clasicos Colombianos. (CK ISSN 0069-4444) 2905
▼Clasificacion Mexicana de Ocupaciones. (MX) 3632, 4568
Class. (IT) 1063
Class Act. (CN) 1252, 1235
Class Magazine. (US ISSN 0747-3826) 2223
Class Struggle. (NO) 3880
Classic. (SA) 2861, 2905
Classic America see Nineteenth Century (Westfield) 2416
Classic & Sportscar. (UK ISSN 0263-3183) 4688, 256
Classic Auto Restorer. (US ISSN 1042-5683) 256
Classic Bike. (UK) 4517
Classic Boating. (US) 4524
Classic Car. (US ISSN 0009-8310) 256
Classic Car Mechanics see Your Classic 4706
Classic Cars see Thoroughbred and Classic Cars 4703
▼Classic Cars National Buyer's Guide. (US) 4688
Classic Cross-Stitch. (US) 3590
▼Classic Homestyles. (CN ISSN 1181-7925) 610
Classic Images. (US ISSN 0275-8423) 3506

Classic Literature Knowledge. see Gudian Wenxue Zhishi 2921
†Classic Motor Cycle. (UK) 5166
†Classic Old Car Value Guide. (US) 5166
Classic Old Car Value Guide Annual see Classic Old Car Value Guide 5166
†Classic T V. (US) 5166
Classic Toy Trains. (US ISSN 0895-0997) 2435
Classic Trucks. (US) 4743
†Classic Yoga International. (II) 5166
Classica. (PO ISSN 0870-0141) 1275
Classica et Mediaevalia. (DK ISSN 0106-5815) 1275
Classical. (US ISSN 1048-4507) 3546
Classical and Medieval Literature Criticism. (US ISSN 0896-0011) 2905
Classical and Modern Literature: A Quarterly. (US ISSN 0197-2227) 2905
Classical and Quantum Gravity. (UK ISSN 0264-9381) 3816, 3032
Classical Antiquity. (US ISSN 0278-6656) 1275
Classical Association. Proceedings. (UK ISSN 0069-4460) 2906, 2308
Classical Association of New England. Annual Bulletin. (US) 1275
Classical Association of the Pacific Northwest. Bulletin. (US) 1275
Classical Bulletin. (US ISSN 0009-8337) 1275, 2403
Classical Calliope see Calliope (Peterborough) 2308
The Classical Catalogue. (UK) 3546
Classical Discourse. (US) 2906
Classical Guitar. (UK ISSN 0950-429X) 3546
Classical Homoeopathy Quarterly. (GW ISSN 0934-1854) 3214
Classical Journal. (US ISSN 0009-8353) 1276, 1621, 2403, 2906
Classical Music. (UK ISSN 0961-2696) 3546
Classical Music and Album Reviews see Classical Music 3546
Classical Music Magazine. (CN) 3546
Classical Numismatic Review. (UK) 3598
Classical Outlook. (US ISSN 0009-8361) 1276, 1621
Classical Philology. (US ISSN 0009-837X) 1276, 2809
Classical Quarterly. (UK ISSN 0009-8388) 1276
Classical Review. (UK ISSN 0009-840X) 1276
Classical Views. see Echos du Monde Classique 1276
Classical World. (US ISSN 0009-8418) 1276
Classici del Giallo. (IT ISSN 0009-8426) 2983
Classici Italiani Minori. (IT) 2906
Classici Urania. (IT) 2983
Classics and Today's World. (US) 2906, 2809
†Classics in Psychoanalysis. (US) 5166
Classics in the History and Philosophy of Science. (US ISSN 1042-4628) 4305, 3763
Classics of British Historical Literature. (US ISSN 0069-4509) 2906, 2356
Classics of Soviet Mathematics. (US ISSN 0743-9199) 3032
Classics of World Music Culture. (RU) 3546
Classicum. (AT ISSN 0155-0659) 1276, 2809
Classification Management. (US ISSN 0009-8434) 1005
Classified Advertising Report. (US) 29, 4125
Classified Directory of Dahlias and Guide to Judging. (UK) 2124
Classified Directory of Wisconsin Manufacturers. (US ISSN 0069-4525) 1127
Classified Exchange. (US) 639
Classified Index of N.L.R.B. and Related Court Decisions. (US) 711, 975

CLASSIFIED INDEX

Classified Index of National Labor Relations Board Decisions and Related Court Decisions *see* Classified Index of N.L.R.B. and Related Court Decisions **711**
Classified International Business Directory for China. (HK) **1127**
Classiques de la Pensee Politique. (SZ ISSN 0069-4533) **3880**
Classiques Francais du Moyen Age. (FR ISSN 0755-1959) **2906**
Classmate. (CN ISSN 0315-906X) **1746**
†Classmate. (US ISSN 0888-9376) **5166**
Classroom. (AT ISSN 0727-1255) **1746**
†Classroom. (CN ISSN 0825-4729) **5166**
Classroom Clips. (US) **1621**
Classroom Computer Learning *see* Technology and Learning **1691**
Classroom Computing *see* Classroom **1746**
Classroom Interaction Newsletter *see* Journal of Classroom Interaction **1642**
Claudel Studies. (US ISSN 0090-1237) **2861**
Claudia. (AG ISSN 0009-8493) **4839**
Claudia. (BL ISSN 0009-8507) **4839**
Claudia. (MX ISSN 0009-8515) **4839**
Claudia Moda. (BL) **1289**
Clausthaler Geologische Abhandlungen. (GW ISSN 0009-8523) **1557**, **3480**
Claustrophobia. (US) **3088**, **4016**
Clave. (SP ISSN 0045-7116) **1058**
Clave. (CU) **3880**
Claves para Interpretar los Hechos. (AG) **3880**
Clavier. (US ISSN 0009-854X) **3546**
Clavier's Piano Explorer. (US ISSN 0279-0858) **3546**
Clavis Kleine Kunsthistorische Monografieen. (NE) **322**
Clavis Kunsthistorische Monografieen. (NE) **322**
Clay Minerals. (UK ISSN 0009-8558) **1542**
Clay Research. (II ISSN 0255-7193) **1542**
Claymore *see* Scottish Legion News **3471**
Clays and Clay Minerals. (US ISSN 0009-8604) **3481**
The Clayton-Fillmore Report. (US ISSN 1047-6083) **851**, **4146**
Clean Air. (AT ISSN 0009-8647) **1976**
Clean Air. (UK ISSN 0300-5143) **1976**
Clean Air Clarion. (AT ISSN 0155-2899) **3941**, **4099**
Clean Air Conference (Gt. Brit.). (UK ISSN 0301-9039) **1976**
Clean Air Journal. *see* Tydskrif vir Skoonlug **1979**
Clean Air Report. (US) **1976**
Clean Coal - Synfuels Letter. (US) **1784**
Clean Coal Technologies. (US) **1798**
Clean Water Action News. (US) **4823**
Clean Water Report. (US ISSN 0009-8620) **1976**
Clean Yield. (US ISSN 0882-3820) **942**
Cleanfax Magazine. (US ISSN 1042-6442) **1281**
Cleaning and Restoration. (US ISSN 0886-9901) **1281**
Cleaning Business. (US) **1114**, **1005**
Cleaning Business News. (UK) **1281**
Cleaning-Finishing-Coating Digest. (US) **3404**
Cleaning Maintenance. (UK) **610**
Cleaning Maintenance and Big Buildings Management *see* Cleaning Maintenance **610**
Cleaning Management. (US ISSN 1051-5720) **610**
Cleaning Materials Equipment & Services. (UK) **1281**
Cleaning Technology News. (UK) **1225**
Cleanrooms. (US) **1073**
▼CleanRooms International. (US) **3616**
Clear Beginnings. (US) **2906**, **4839**

Clear Track. (US ISSN 0193-3477) **4708**
Clearing House. (US ISSN 0009-8655) **1621**
Clearing House for Local Authority Social Services Research *see* Social Services Research **4420**
Clearing House Newsletter. (US) **1485**
Clearing House on Migration Issues Das *see* C H O M I - Das **5156**
▼Clearinghouse Directory. (US ISSN 1053-0460) **397**
Clearinghouse Review. (US ISSN 0009-868X) **2613**
Clearwater Navigator. (US) **1945**, **1485**, **2038**
Clearwaters. (US) **1976**, **4823**
Clearway. (UK ISSN 0009-8698) **4718**, **1512**
Clefs d'Or. (FR) **2581**, **2473**
Cleft Palate - Craniofacial Journal. (CN ISSN 1055-6656) **3377**, **3230**
Cleft Palate Journal *see* Cleft Palate - Craniofacial Journal **3377**
Clematis. (AT) **1945**
Clements' Encyclopedia of World Governments. (US ISSN 0145-9678) **3953**
Clements' International Report. (US ISSN 0145-9678) **3953**
Clemson University. College of Architecture. Journal. (US) **297**, **322**
Clemson University. College of Architecture. Semester Review *see* Clemson University. College of Architecture. Journal **297**
Clemson University. Department of Forest Resources. Forest Research Series. (US) **2097**
Clemson University. Department of Forest Resources. Forestry Bulletin. (US) **2097**
Clemson University. Department of Forest Resources. Technical Paper. (US) **2098**
Clemson University. Division of Computing and Information Technology. Newsletter *see* D C I T Update **1394**
Clemson University. Water Resources Research Institute. Report. (US ISSN 0069-4657) **4823**
Clemson World. (US) **1307**
Cleo. (IT) **1252**
Cleo. (AT ISSN 0310-1797) **4839**
Cleo en la Moda. (AG ISSN 0009-8728) **2736**, **1284**, **4360**, **4617**
Cleo Internacional *see* Cleo en la Moda **2736**
Clepsidra. (AG) **2983**
Clergy Journal. (US ISSN 0009-6431) **4171**
Clergy Review *see* Priests and People **4273**
Clerical Salary Review. (AT) **1063**, **1005**, **3626**
Clerical Salary Survey & Employment Practices (Year). (CN) **3632**
Clerk *see* A P E X **2579**
Clerk of Works. (UK ISSN 0020-2789) **610**, **297**
Clessidra. (IT ISSN 0009-8752) **2563**
Cleveland Chess Bulletin. (US) **4469**
Cleveland Clinic Journal of Medicine. (US ISSN 0891-1150) **3088**
Cleveland Clinic Quarterly *see* Cleveland Clinic Journal of Medicine **3088**
Cleveland Engineering. (US ISSN 0009-8809) **1817**
▼Cleveland Enterprise. (US ISSN 1059-3055) **655**
Cleveland Food Dealer. (US ISSN 0009-8817) **2090**
Cleveland Foundation. Annual Report. (US) **4402**, **4099**
Cleveland Foundation Perspective *see* Perspective (Cleveland) **4416**
Cleveland Institute of Music (Newsletter). (US) **3546**
Cleveland Jewish News. (US ISSN 0009-8825) **1997**
Cleveland Magazine. (US ISSN 0160-8533) **2223**
Cleveland-Marshall Law Review *see* Cleveland State Law Review **2613**

Cleveland Museum of Art. Bulletin. (US ISSN 0009-8841) **322**
Cleveland Physician. (US) **3088**
Cleveland Public Library Staff Association. News and Views. (US ISSN 0009-885X) **2752**
Cleveland State Law Review. (US ISSN 0009-8876) **2613**
Clevelander. (US ISSN 0009-8892) **851**
Clic. (SW) **1290**
Click. (UK ISSN 0142-1042) **2809**, **1746**
†Clic's Legal Materials Letter. (CN ISSN 0704-0393) **5166**
Client Counseling Update *see* Competitions (Chicago) **2614**
Client Tax Newsletter. (US) **749**
Client Update. (US) **2613**
Client's Monthly Alert. (US) **749**, **1091**
Cliff News. (US) **1308**
Clifton Magazine. (US) **2906**
Clik. (CN ISSN 0835-3565) **1252**, **1235**
Clima Commerce International. (GW ISSN 0009-8914) **2298**
†Climate Control. (II ISSN 0009-8930) **5166**
Climate Dynamics. (GW ISSN 0930-7575) **3434**
Climate Monitor. (UK ISSN 0140-458X) **3434**
▼Climate Research. (GW ISSN 0936-577X) **3445**
Climatic Change. (NE ISSN 0165-0009) **3434**
Climatic Table of Japan. (JA) **3434**
Climatological Data. (US) **3434**
Climatological Data for Jakarta Observatory. (IO ISSN 0009-8957) **3434**
Climatology and Hydrology *see* Geographical Abstracts: Physical Geography **2268**
Climber *see* Climber and Hillwalker **4544**
Climber and Hillwalker. (UK ISSN 0955-3045) **4544**
Climbing. (US ISSN 0045-7159) **4544**
Climbing Art. (US) **4544**
Clin-Alert. (US ISSN 0069-4770) **3747**, **8**
Clin d'Oeil. (CN) **1290**, **372**, **4839**
Clinch River Breeder Reactor Plant. Technical Review. (US) **1804**, **1784**
Clinica. (UK ISSN 0144-7777) **3088**, **1005**
†La Clinica. (IT ISSN 0366-6778) **5166**
Clinica & Terapia Cardiovascolare. (IT ISSN 0392-1344) **3207**
†Clinica Anestesiologica. (SP ISSN 0210-4660) **5166**
Clinica Cardiovascular. (SP ISSN 0212-1808) **3207**
Clinica Chimica Acta. (NE ISSN 0009-8981) **3088**, **1175**
Clinica Chirurgica del Nord America. (IT ISSN 0393-7577) **3377**
Clinica Dietologica. (IT) **3604**
Clinica e Investigacion en Arteriosclerosis. (SP ISSN 0214-9168) **3207**
Clinica e Investigacion en Ginecologia y Obstetricia. (SP ISSN 0210-573X) **3290**
Clinica e Laboratorio. (IT ISSN 0391-2035) **3258**
▼Clinica e Terapia. (IT) **3088**
Clinica Europea. (IT ISSN 0009-9007) **3088**
†Clinica Ginecologica. (SP ISSN 0210-4938) **5166**
Clinica Medica del Nord America. (IT ISSN 0393-7585) **3088**
Clinica Neuropsichiatrica. (IT) **3333**
Clinica Oculistica e Patologia Oculare. (IT ISSN 0391-8998) **3299**
Clinica Odontoiatrica del Nord America. (IT ISSN 0393-7593) **3230**
Clinica Ostetrica e Ginecologica. (IT ISSN 0393-7607) **3290**
Clinica Otorinolaringoiatrica *see* Nuova, Clinica Otorinolaringoiatrica **3315**
Clinica Pediatrica. (IT ISSN 0009-9058) **3319**

Clinica Pediatrica del Nord America. (IT) **3319**
Clinica; Portavoz del Internado. (SP) **3088**
Clinica Terapeutica. (IT ISSN 0009-9074) **3088**
Clinica Termale. (IT) **3088**
Clinica Veterinaria. (IT ISSN 0009-9082) **4808**
Clinica y Analisis Grupal. (SP ISSN 0210-0657) **4016**
Clinical Abstracts - Current Therapeutic Findings. (US ISSN 1043-3031) **3168**, **8**
Clinical Allergy *see* Clinical and Experimental Allergy **3184**
Clinical Anatomy. (US ISSN 0897-3806) **435**
Clinical and Biochemical Analysis. (US ISSN 0095-4861) **475**, **1205**, **3088**
Clinical and Experimental Allergy. (UK ISSN 0954-7894) **3184**
Clinical and Experimental Dermatology. (UK ISSN 0307-6938) **3246**
Clinical and Experimental Hypertension. Part A: Theory and Practice. (US ISSN 0730-0077) **3088**
Clinical and Experimental Hypertension. Part B: Hypertension in Pregnancy. (US ISSN 0730-0085) **3088**, **3290**
Clinical and Experimental Hypnosis *see* International Journal of Clinical and Experimental Hypnosis **3274**
Clinical and Experimental Immunology. (UK ISSN 0009-9104) **3184**
Clinical and Experimental Metastasis. (UK ISSN 0262-0898) **3196**
Clinical and Experimental Neurology. (AT ISSN 0158-1597) **3333**
Clinical and Experimental Obstetrics and Gynecology. (IT ISSN 0390-6663) **3290**
Clinical and Experimental Optometry. (AT ISSN 0816-4622) **3299**
Clinical and Experimental Pharmacology and Physiology. (AT ISSN 0305-1870) **570**, **3721**
Clinical and Investigative Medicine/Medecine Clinique et Experimentale. (CN ISSN 0147-958X) **3088**
Clinical and Laboratory Haematology. (UK ISSN 0141-9854) **3271**
▼Clinical Autonomic Research. (UK ISSN 0959-9851) **3088**
Clinical Biochemist Reviews. (AT ISSN 0159-8090) **475**
†Clinical Biochemistry (San Diego). (US) **5166**
Clinical Biochemistry (Tarrytown). (US ISSN 0009-9120) **475**, **3088**
†Clinical Biochemistry Reviews (Melbourne). (US) **5166**
†Clinical Biochemistry Reviews (Tarrytown). (US ISSN 0272-9881) **5166**
Clinical Biomechanics. (US ISSN 0191-7870) **3088**
Clinical Biomechanics. (UK ISSN 0268-0033) **3214**
Clinical Cancer Immunology and Biological Therapy *see* I C R D B Cancergram: Clinical Cancer Immunology and Biological Therapy **5208**
Clinical Cancer Letter. (US ISSN 0164-985X) **3196**
Clinical Cancer Monographs. (UK ISSN 0954-7495) **3196**
Clinical Cardiology. (US ISSN 0160-9289) **3207**
Clinical Cardiology Alert. (US ISSN 0741-4218) **3207**
†Clinical Cardiology Monographs. (US) **5166**
Clinical Chemistry. (US ISSN 0009-9147) **3088**, **1175**
Clinical Chemistry and Enzymology Communications. (US ISSN 0892-2187) **475**, **1175**
Clinical Chemistry Lookout. (NE ISSN 0345-200X) **3168**, **8**
Clinical Chemistry News. (US ISSN 0161-9640) **3089**
▼Clinical Chiropractic Report. (US) **3214**
Clinical Connection. (US ISSN 0890-409X) **1734**

Clinical Consult. (US) **3721**
Clinical Consultations in Obstetrics and Gynecology. (US ISSN 1043-0660) **3290**
Clinical Cytogenetics. (UK ISSN 0260-5872) **540, 524, 3290**
Clinical Dental Briefings. (US) **3230**
Clinical Dermatology/Hifuka No Rinsho.(JA ISSN 0018-1404) **3246**
Clinical Diabetes. (US) **3251**
▼Clinical Diagnostics Today. (CN) **3089**
▼Clinical Dysmorphology. (UK ISSN 0962-8827) **3290**
Clinical Ecology. (US ISSN 0735-9306) **435**
Clinical Electroencephalography. (US ISSN 0009-9155) **3333**
Clinical Endocrinology. (UK ISSN 0300-0664) **3251**
Clinical Engineering Information Service.(US ISSN 0277-0393) **3258,** 214
Clinical Engineering Section Newsletter. (US) **2522,** 1916, 2460
Clinical Engineering Series. (US) **3089**
Clinical Evaluation and Treatment of Multiple Myeloma and other Gammopathies *see* I C R D B Cancergram: Leukemia and Multiple Myeloma - Diagnosis, Treatment **3175**
Clinical Experience *see* Hospital Practice **3106**
Clinical Eye and Vision Care. (US ISSN 0953-4431) **3299**
Clinical Focus. *see* Linchuang Huicui **3122**
Clinical Genetics. (DK ISSN 0009-9163) **540**
Clinical Gerontologist. (US ISSN 0731-7115) **2271, 4402**
Clinical Hemorheology. (US ISSN 0271-5198) **3271**
Clinical Imaging. (US ISSN 0899-7071) **3357**
†Clinical Immunobiology. (US) **5167**
Clinical Immunology and Immunopathology. (US ISSN 0090-1229) **3184**
Clinical Immunology Newsletter. (US ISSN 0197-1859) **3184**
Clinical Infant Reports. Monograph. (US) **3319**

Clinical Infectious Diseases. (US) **3218**
Clinical Investigation. (GW) **3089**
Clinical Journal of Pain. (US ISSN 0749-8047) **3334,** 3191

Clinical Journal of Sport Medicine. (US ISSN 1050-642X) **3371,** 3307
Clinical Kinesiology. (US) **3371,** 1734
Clinical Lab Letter. (US ISSN 0197-8454) **3258**
Clinical Laboratory International. (BE) **3258**
Clinical Laboratory Management Newsletter *see* Management Briefs **2467**

Clinical Laboratory Management Review. (US ISSN 0888-7950) **1005,** 3089
Clinical Laboratory Product Comparison System. (US) **3258,** 2460
Clinical Laboratory Reference *see* C L R **3258**
Clinical Laboratory Science. (US ISSN 0894-959X) **3089**
Clinical Laser Monthly. (US ISSN 0746-469X) **3377**
Clinical Linguistics & Phonetics. (UK ISSN 0269-9206) **3334,** 1734, 2809
Clinical Management. (US) **3089**
Clinical Management in Physical Therapy *see* Clinical Management **3089**
Clinical Materials. (UK ISSN 0267-6605) **3089**
Clinical Medicine. *see* Klinicheskaya Meditsina **3120**
Clinical Microbiology Newsletter. (US ISSN 0196-4399) **3089**
Clinical Microbiology Reviews. (US ISSN 0893-8512) **550**

†Clinical Monographs in Obstetrics and Gynecology. (US) **5167**
Clinical Nephrology. (GW ISSN 0301-0430) **3387**
Clinical Neurology. *see* Rinsho Shinkeigaku **3353**
Clinical Neurology and Neurosurgery. (NE ISSN 0303-8467) **3334,** 3377
Clinical Neuropathology. (GW ISSN 0722-5091) **3334**
Clinical Neuropharmacology. (US ISSN 0362-5664) **3721,** 3334
Clinical Neurophysiology. *see* Neurophysiologie Clinique **3347**
Clinical Neuropsychologist. (NE ISSN 0920-1637) **3334**
Clinical Neurosurgery: Proceedings. (US ISSN 0069-4827) **3334,** 3377
Clinical Nuclear Medicine. (US ISSN 0363-9762) **3357**
Clinical Nurse Specialist. (US ISSN 0887-6274) **3277**
▼Clinical Nursing Research. (US ISSN 1054-7738) **3277**
Clinical Nutrition. (UK ISSN 0261-5614) **3604,** 3089
Clinical Obstetrics and Gynecology. (US ISSN 0009-9201) **3290**
Clinical Obstetrics and Gynecology. *see* Rinsho Fujinka Sanka **3296**
Clinical Oncology *see* European Journal of Surgical Oncology **3197**
Clinical Oncology Alert. (US ISSN 0886-7186) **3196**
Clinical Orthopaedic Surgery. *see* Rinsho Seikei Geka **3311**
Clinical Orthopaedics and Related Research. (US ISSN 0009-921X) **3307**
Clinical Otolaryngology and Allied Sciences. (UK ISSN 0307-7772) **3314**
Clinical Pediatrics. (US ISSN 0009-9228) **3319**
Clinical Pediatrics. *see* Shonika **3326**
Clinical Pediatrics Series. (US) **3319**
Clinical Perspectives in Obstetrics and Gynecology. (US) **3290**
Clinical Pharmacokinetic Newsletter. (US) **3721**
Clinical Pharmacokinetics. (NZ ISSN 0312-5963) **3721**
Clinical Pharmacokinetics Drug Data Handbook (Year). (NZ ISSN 0114-0892) **3721**
Clinical Pharmacology. (US ISSN 0898-6398) **3721,** 1692
Clinical Pharmacology & Therapeutics. (US ISSN 0009-9236) **3721**
Clinical Pharmacology Research *see* International Journal of Clinical Pharmacology Research **3729**
Clinical Pharmacology Series. (US) **3721**
Clinical Pharmacy. (US ISSN 0278-2677) **3721**
Clinical Physics and Physiological Measurement. (UK ISSN 0143-0815) **3089,** 3816
Clinical Physiology. (UK ISSN 0144-5979) **3089,** 570
†Clinical Physiology and Biochemistry. (SZ ISSN 0252-1164) **5167**
Clinical Physiology Series. (US) **570**
Clinical Practice in Urology. (US) **3387**
▼Clinical Practice of Gynecology. (US ISSN 1043-3198) **3290**
Clinical Practice Recommendations. (US ISSN 0149-5992) **3251**
Clinical Preventive Dentistry. (US ISSN 0163-9633) **3230**
Clinical Prosthetics and Orthotics *see* Journal of Prosthetics and Orthotics **3118**
Clinical Psychiatry. *see* Seishin Igaku **3354**
Clinical Psychiatry News. (US ISSN 0270-6644) **3334**
Clinical Psychologist. (US ISSN 0009-9244) **4016**
Clinical Psychology Forum. (UK ISSN 0269-0144) **4016**
Clinical Psychology Review. (US ISSN 0272-7358) **4016**
Clinical Radiology. (UK ISSN 0009-9260) **3357,** 3196
Clinical Rehabilitation. (UK ISSN 0269-2155) **3089**

†Clinical Report on Aging. (US ISSN 0890-2267) **5167**
Clinical Reproduction and Fertility. (AT ISSN 0725-556X) **3290**
Clinical Research. (US ISSN 0009-9279) **3168**
Clinical Research and Regulatory Affairs. (US) **3721**
Clinical Research Practices and Drug Regulatory Affairs *see* Clinical Research and Regulatory Affairs **3721**
Clinical Respiratory Physiology *see* European Respiratory Journal **3365**
Clinical Reviews in Allergy. (US ISSN 0731-8235) **3184**
Clinical Rheumatology. (BE) **3369**
Clinical Science. (UK ISSN 0143-5221) **3089,** 435
Clinical Social Work Journal. (US ISSN 0091-1674) **4402**
Clinical Sociology Review. (US ISSN 0730-840X) **4431**
Clinical Sports Medicine. (UK ISSN 0953-9875) **3371**
Clinical Study. *see* Kurinikaru Sutadi **3281**
Clinical Supervisor. (US ISSN 0732-5223) **4402**
Clinical Symposia. (US ISSN 0009-9295) **3089**
Clinical Therapeutics. (US ISSN 0149-2918) **3089**
Clinical Topics in Infectious Disease. (US) **3089,** 3218
Clinical Transplantation. (DK ISSN 0902-0063) **3377**
Clinical Treatment of Cancer--Radiation Therapy *see* I C R D B Cancergram: Clinical Treatment of Cancer - Radiation Therapy **3175**
Clinical Trials and Meta-Analysis. (NE) **3089,** 3258
Clinical Trials Journal *see* Clinical Trials and Meta-Analysis **3089**
Clinical Vision Sciences. (UK ISSN 0887-6169) **3299**
Clinically Important Adverse Drug Interactions. (NE) **3721,** 3258
Clinicas Cardiologicas de Norteamerica. (Spanish translation of: Cardiology Clinics of North America) (SP) **3207**
▼Clinicas de Anestesiologia de Norteamerica. (SP) **3191**
Clinicas de Atencion Primaria de Norteamerica. (Spanish translation of: Primary Care - Clinics in Office Practice) (SP) **3320**
Clinicas de Medicina de Urgencias de Norteamerica. (SP) **3089**
Clinicas de Medicina Deportiva de Norteamerica. (SP) **3089,** 4469
Clinicas de Perinatologia de Norteamerica. (Spanish translation of: Clinics in Perinatology) (SP) **3089**
Clinicas Medicas de Norteamerica. (Spanish translation of: Medical Clinics of North America) (SP) **3089**
Clinicas Obstetricas y Ginecologicas de Norteamerica. (Spanish translation of: Clinical Obstetrics and Gynecology) (SP ISSN 0009-9333) **3290**
Clinicas Odontologicas de Norteamerica. (Spanish translation of: Dental Clinics of North America) (SP) **3230**
Clinicas Otorrinolaringologicas de Norteamerica. (Spanish translation of: Otolaryngologic Clinics of North America) (SP) **3314**
Clinicas Pediatricas de Norteamerica. (Spanish translation of: Pediatrics Clinics of North America) (SP) **3320**
Clinicas Quirurgicas de Norteamerica. (Spanish translation of: Surgical Clinics of North America) (SP) **3377**
Clinician. (Il ISSN 0009-9341) **3089**
▼Clinician's Manual on Hyperlipidemia (Year). (US ISSN 0958-1650) **3168,** 3207
▼Clinician's Manual on Hypertension (Year). (US ISSN 0952-6307) **3168,** 3207

Clinician's Research Digest. (US ISSN 8756-3207) **4016**
Clinicien. (CN) **3089**
▼Clinics in Applied Nutrition. (US ISSN 1053-0452) **3604**
Clinics in Chest Medicine. (US ISSN 0272-5231) **3364**
▼Clinics in Communication Disorders. (US ISSN 1054-8505) **1734,** 1746
Clinics in Dermatology. (US ISSN 0738-081X) **3246**
Clinics in Developmental Medicine. (UK ISSN 0069-4835) **3320,** 3334
Clinics in Endocrinology and Metabolism *see* Endocrinology and Metabolism Clinics **3253**
Clinics in Gastroenterology *see* Gastroenterology Clinics **3268**
Clinics in Geriatric Medicine. (US ISSN 0749-0690) **2271**
Clinics in Immunology and Allergy *see* Immunology and Allergy Clinics of North America **3186**
Clinics in Laboratory Medicine. (US ISSN 0272-2712) **3258**
Clinics in Obstetrics and Gynaecology *see* Obstetrics and Gynecology Clinics **3295**
Clinics in Perinatology. (US ISSN 0095-5108) **3291**
Clinics in Plastic Surgery. (US ISSN 0094-1298) **3377**
Clinics in Podiatric Medicine & Surgery. (US ISSN 0891-8422) **3090**
Clinics in Sports Medicine. (US ISSN 0278-5919) **3371**
Clinique. (FR ISSN 0009-935X) **3090**
La Clinique, Ophtalmologique. (FR ISSN 0009-9368) **3299**
ClinMed - C D. (US) **3168**
Clinton County, Indiana Roots *see* Historic Genealogical Magazine **2408**
Clinton - Essex - Franklin Library System Trailblazer *see* C E F Trailblazer **2750**
Clinton Historical Society. Newsletter. (US) **2403**
Clinton St. (US) **2906**
Clinton St. Quarterly *see* Clinton St. **2906**
Clio. (IT) **2308**
Clio. (GW ISSN 0933-0747) **4835,** 3291, 4839
Clio (Fort Wayne). (US) **2309,** 2906
Clio (Lisbon). (PO ISSN 0870-4104) **2356**
Clio (Providence). (US) **2309**
Clio Bibliography Series. (US) **2328,** 2519
Clio Medica. (NE ISSN 0045-7183) **3090**
Clio Notizie. (IT) **4839,** 975
▼Clip. (US) **3546,** 1371
Clipboard. (US) **1621**
The Clipper. (SZ) **2064**
Clipper Studies in the Theater. (US ISSN 0748-237X) **4631,** 2906
Clips. (GW) **372,** 1290
Clips. (US) **4648**
Clips From Bear's Home Movies. (US) **2906**
Clique. (JA) **4839**
†Clique. (UK ISSN 0009-9422) **5167**
Clivages. (FR) **2990**
Cloche. *see* Bell **198**
Clock Manufacturers and Marketing Association Industry Update *see* C M M A Industry Update **5157**
ClockDial. (US) **380**
Clocks *see* Antique Clocks **2563**
Clocktower. (US ISSN 0009-9430) **1308**
Clockwatch Review. (US ISSN 0740-9311) **2906,** 322, 3546
Clockwork. (UK ISSN 0306-1604) **1621,** 2809
Clogher Record. (IE) **2356,** 2147
Close Caption Television Applications & Technology *see* C C T V Applications & Technology **1526**
Close Examination Report: Jozankei Valley Region/Seimitsu Chosa Hokokusho: Jozankei Chiiki. (JA) **3481**
Close Shave. (US) **3396**

6062 CLOSE UP

Close Up Magazine. (US ISSN 0896-372X) **3546**
Closed-End Fund Digest. (US) **942**
Closed Loop. (US ISSN 0739-036X) **1916**, 1927, 3842
†Closely Held Business. (US) **5167**
Closely Held Corporation: Tax, Financial and Estate Planning. (US) **1091**
Closer Contact. (AT ISSN 1036-4013) **4234**
Closer Walk. (US) **4171**
CloseUp. (US) **1308**
Closing Officer's Guide. (US) **2613**, 4146
Closing the Gap. (US ISSN 0886-1935) **1688**, 1458, 1734
Clot see Clot and Hematologic Malignancies **3271**
Clot and Hematologic Malignancies. (IT ISSN 0393-487X) **3271**
The Cloth Doll. (US ISSN 8755-2655) **3590**
Clothed with the Sun see N: Nude and Natural **3806**
Clothes Line. (SA) **2581**, 1284
Clothing and Footwear Institute Year Book and Membership Register. (UK) **1284**, 4360
Clothing and Footwear Journal see Apparel International **1283**
Clothing and Textile Arts Index. (US ISSN 0887-2937) **1288**, 357
Clothing & Textiles Research Journal. (US ISSN 0887-302X) **1284**, 4617
▼Clothing for Less Newsletter. (US ISSN 1053-6507) **1503**
Clothing Institute Journal see Apparel International **1283**
Clothing Institute Year Book and Membership Register see Clothing and Footwear Institute Year Book and Membership Register **1284**
Clothing Machinery, Plant see Clothing Machinery Times **3016**
Clothing Machinery Times. (UK ISSN 0305-7046) **3016**, 1284
Clothing Manufacturers Association of the U S A. Members News Bulletin. (US) **1284**
Clothing, Textiles, and Footwear (Year). (SA) **1284**, 1127, 4360
Clothing World. (UK ISSN 0267-3622) **1284**
Cloud Family Journal. (US ISSN 0883-0940) **2147**
Cloudline. (US) **2990**
Clover Information Index. (UK ISSN 0140-1939) **4140**
Clover Newspaper Index. (UK) **2577**
Cloverview. (US) **4595**
Club. (UK ISSN 0009-9503) **1621**, 2809
Club and Food Service see Military Club & Hospitality **2077**
Club and Institute Journal. (UK ISSN 0009-952X) **1297**
Club Business International. (US ISSN 1043-9692) **1114**, 3800
Club Committee & Northern Free Trade News. (UK ISSN 0009-9538) **1297**
Club Cricket Conference Official Handbook. (UK) **4502**
Club de Gourmets. (SP) **2473**, 4757
Club de la Grammaire. Cahiers. (SZ ISSN 0008-0128) **2809**
Club des Hebraisants. (FR ISSN 0763-062X) **4222**
Club Director. (US) **1297**
Club Filatelico de Caracas. Gaceta Mensual. (VE) **3751**
Club Goldenrod. (US) **2452**
Club, Hotel, Motel Journal. (AT) **2473**
Club-Illustrierte. (GW) **1297**
Club Industry Magazine. (US) **3800**
Club International. (US) **3396**
Club Knorr a la Carte Journal. (CN) **2445**
Club Living. (US ISSN 0160-6166) **4469**, 1297
Club Magazin. (GW ISSN 0933-7075) **4688**
Club Magazine. (US ISSN 0747-0827) **3396**
Club Maison. (FR) **2549**
Club Management. (US ISSN 0009-9589) **1297**

Club Managers Journal see Secretaries and Managers Journal of Australia **1027**
Club Marine. (AT ISSN 0817-8585) **4524**
Club Mirror. (UK ISSN 0045-7213) **1297**
Club Motorsport News. (US) **4469**
Club Secretary. (UK ISSN 0009-9635) **1297**
Clubdate Magazine. (US) **1503**, 4839
Clube de Engenharia/Engineering Club. (BL) **1817**
Clube Filatelico de Portugal. Boletim. (PO ISSN 0009-9651) **3751**
Clube Militar. Revista. (BL ISSN 0101-6547) **3454**
Clube Naval Revista. (BL ISSN 0102-0382) **3454**
Clubhouse. (US) **1252**, 4234, 4261
Clues (Bowling Green). (US) **2906**
Clues (Lincoln). (US) **2147**, 1997
Clumber Spaniel Correspondence. (AT ISSN 0819-5862) **3709**, 230
Clwyd Historian. (UK ISSN 0260-0250) **2356**
Clydebank Post. (UK) **2193**
Clydesdale Bank Scottish Football League Review see B & Q Scottish Football League Review **4500**
Clydesdale News. (US) **214**
Clydesdale Stud Book. (UK) **4533**
†Co. (US) **5167**
Co Action Magazine see Authorware **1475**
Co-Ed see Choices (New York) **2445**
Co-Laborer. (US ISSN 0896-0038) **4171**, 4839
Coach and Bus Week. (UK) **4648**
Coaches & Parties Welcome. (UK) **4757**
Coaching Clinic. (US ISSN 0009-9880) **4502**
▼Coaching Connection. (US) **4469**
Coaching Digest see Physical Education Digest **4483**
Coaching Director. (AT ISSN 0814-7752) **4469**
Coaching Journal and Bus Review. (UK ISSN 0009-9899) **4648**
†Coaching Volleyball. (US ISSN 0894-4237) **5167**
†Coaching Women's Basketball. (US ISSN 0894-4245) **5167**
Coachmart see Coach and Bus Week **4648**
Coachmart. (UK) **4757**
Coal. (US ISSN 1040-7820) **3481**
Coal. see Uhli **3497**
Coal Abstracts. (UK ISSN 0309-4979) **3499**
Coal Age see Coal **3481**
Coal & Synfuels Technology. (US ISSN 0883-9735) **1784**
†Coal-Based Synfuels. (US ISSN 0741-7713) **5167**
Coal Calendar. (UK ISSN 0143-6287) **3481**, 1175
Coal Consumers Association of India Monthly News Letter see C C A I Monthly News Letter **3479**
Coal Data. (US ISSN 0145-417X) **3481**
Coal Distribution. (US) **1784**, 3481
Coal Economics Study. see Meitan Jingji Yanjiu **679**
Coal-Energy News. (US) **1784**
Coal Facts. (US) **3481**
Coal Industry Management. see Meitan Qiye Guanli **1021**
The Coal Journal. (US) **3481**
Coal Local. (US ISSN 1049-0574) **3481**
Coal Mine Directory. (US) **1127**
Coal Mining see Coal **3481**
Coal Mining Newsletter. (US) **3616**, 3481
Coal News. (UK ISSN 0009-997X) **3481**
Coal News. (US) **3481**
Coal Outlook. (US ISSN 0162-2714) **3481**, 1784
Coal People. (US) **3481**
Coal Preparation. (US ISSN 0734-9343) **3481**
†Coal Preparation and Pollution Control. (US ISSN 0741-5257) **5167**
Coal Production (Year). (US) **3481**

Coal Production Annual see Coal Production (Year) **3481**
Coal Prospects and Policies in I E A Countries. (FR) **3481**
Coal Research Projects. (UK) **3481**
Coal Science and Technology. (NE) **3481**, 1784
Coal Selecting Techniques. see Xuanmei Jishu **3498**
†Coal Situation. (US) **5167**
Coal Statistics International. (US) **3499**, 4568
▼Coal Trades Review. (UK) **3481**
Coal Traffic Annual. (US ISSN 0069-4916) **3481**
Coal Transportation Report. (US ISSN 0732-8397) **4708**, 1784
Coal Unit Performance Data Base. (US) **1884**, 1784
Coal Voice. (US) **3481**
Coal Week. (US ISSN 0149-578X) **3481**
Coal Week International. (US) **3481**
Coaldat Marketing Report (Monthly) see Coaldat Monthly (Suppliers Format) **1035**
Coaldat Marketing Report (Quarterly) see Coaldat Quarterly **1036**
Coaldat Monthly (Producing District Format). (US ISSN 1041-0988) **1035**, 1784
Coaldat Monthly (Suppliers Format). (US ISSN 1041-097X) **1035**, 1784
Coaldat Monthly (Utility Format). (US ISSN 1041-0996) **1035**, 1784
Coaldat Productivity Report. (US ISSN 0893-973X) **3499**
Coaldat Quarterly. (US) **1036**, 1785
Coaldust. (AU) **2053**
Coalition for Lesbian and Gay Rights in Ontario Newsletter see C L G R O Newsletter **2451**
Coalition of Family Organizations Memo see C O F O Memo **2445**
Coalition of Women's Art Organizations News see C W A O News **320**
Coalition on Sexuality and Disability, Inc. Newsletter see C S D Newsletter **2283**
Coalition: The Torah Action Journal. (US) **4222**
CoalTrans. (UK ISSN 0269-381X) **4726**
Coarse Angler. (UK) **4544**
Coas: New Mexico Archaeology and History. (US) **269**, 2403
†Coast. (US ISSN 0010-0005) **5167**
Coast (Bay Head). (US) **2223**
Coast and Country. (US) **2223**
Coast Business. (US) **655**
Coast Guard Engineer's Digest. (US ISSN 0013-8177) **1817**
Coast Marine and Transportation Directory. (US) **4726**
Coast to Coast. (CN) **4469**
Coast to Coast Magazine. (US) **4648**
Coastal Bend Council of Governments. Monthly Update. (US) **2485**
Coastal Cruising. (US) **4524**, 4757
Coastal Engineering. (NE ISSN 0378-3839) **1863**
Coastal Engineering in Japan. (JA ISSN 0578-5634) **1863**
Coastal Engineering Research Council. Proceedings. (US) **1863**, 1603
Coastal Farmer see Natal Farmer **108**
†Coastal Law Memo. (US) **5167**
Coastal Management. (US ISSN 0892-0753) **1603**, 1945, 2734
Coastal Research. (US ISSN 0271-5376) **1603**
Coastal Research Notes see Coastal Research **1603**
Coastal Zone Management. (US ISSN 0045-723X) **1485**, 1603
Coastal Zone Management Journal see Coastal Management **1603**
Coasters see Beermat Magazine **2434**
Coastguard. (UK) **4726**
Coastlines. (US) **942**
Coastwatch. (US) **1603**, 1945
Coat of Arms. (UK ISSN 0010-003X) **2147**
Coates's Herd Book (Beef). (UK ISSN 0069-4924) **215**
Coates's Herd Book (Dairy). (UK ISSN 0069-4932) **198**

Coatings. (CN ISSN 0225-6363) **3653**
Coatings Adlibra see C P I Digest **3868**
Coatings and Plastics Preprints see Polymeric Materials Science and Engineering **1222**
†Coatney-Courtney Exchange. (US) **5167**
Cobble Hill News. (US) **851**
Cobblestone. (US ISSN 0199-5197) **1252**, 2403
▼COBOL Journal. (GW ISSN 0938-9377) **1476**
Cobouw. (NE ISSN 0010-0064) **610**
Coburger Landesstiftung. Jahrbuch. (GW ISSN 0084-8808) **2356**
Coca-Cola Bottler. (US) **1036**
Coca-Cola Journal. (GW) **380**
Coche Actual. (SP) **4688**
Cochise. (GW) **3880**
Cocina y Hogar. (SP ISSN 0045-7248) **2445**
Cockpit. (SZ ISSN 0010-0110) **50**
Cockpit see Vliegtuigparade **65**
Cockpit Forum. (NO ISSN 0332-9798) **50**
Cockpit Report. (GW) **4672**
Cockshaw's Construction Capsules see Cockshaw's Construction Labor News & Opinion **975**
Cockshaw's Construction Labor News & Opinion. (US ISSN 0094-0372) **975**, 610
Cockshaw's Open Shop News and Trends see Cockshaw's Construction Labor News & Opinion **975**
Cocktail. (GW) **1252**
†COCLICO. (Consommateurs, Clients, Consommateurs) (FR) **5167**
Cocoa Growers Bulletin. (UK ISSN 0045-7256) **173**
Cocoa Research Institute. Annual Report. (GH ISSN 0300-1385) **2064**
Cococassette. (US) **1468**, 1458
Cocommunity. (IO ISSN 0215-1510) **173**
Coconut Bulletin. (CE ISSN 0255-4119) **84**
Coconut Statistical Yearbook. (IO) **173**
Coconut Telegraph. (FJ) **84**
Cocos. (CE ISSN 0255-4100) **84**
Cocos Clarion see Kabar Cocos **2171**
Cocuk Sagligi ve Hastaliklari Dergisi. (TU ISSN 0010-0161) **3320**
Coda see Coda Magazine **3546**
Coda Magazine. (CN ISSN 0820-926X) **3546**
Code. (GW ISSN 0932-3473) **3880**, 655
Code and Regulations. (US) **2613**
Code de la Formation Professionelle. see Schluessel fuer Berufsausbildung **1686**
Code des Societes. (FR) **1005**
Code Names Dictionary. (US) **2752**
Code News (Cleveland). (US ISSN 0735-9330) **610**, 2613
Code of Federal Regulations. (US) **2613**
Code of Federal Regulations Index. (US ISSN 0000-1058) **2698**
Code of Maryland Regulations. (US) **4057**, 2613
Code One. (US) **50**
Code Permanent Construction et Urbanisme. (FR) **610**
Code Permanent Environnement et Nuisances. (FR) **1945**
Codes and Abbreviations for the Use of the International Telecommunications Services. (UN) **1362**
Codes Larcier. (BE ISSN 0010-0188) **2613**
†CodeWorks. (US) **5167**
Codex Committee on Pesticide Residues. Report on the Meeting see Pesticide Residues in Food **4110**
Codex Filatelica. (US ISSN 0896-3533) **3751**, 237, 269
Codex: Journal of the Centre for the Study of Christianity in Islamic Lands.(UK ISSN 0267-1557) **4171**, 3636
Codice del Vaticano II. (IT) **4261**
Codices Arabici Antiqui. (GW ISSN 0340-6393) **3636**

Codices Manuscripti. (AU ISSN 0379-3621) **2752**, 1276
Codices Manuscripti Bibliothecae Universitatis Leidensis. (NE ISSN 0169-8672) **2906**
Codicillus. (SA ISSN 0010-020X) **2613**
Coding Clinic for ICD-9-CM. (US ISSN 0742-9800) **2460**
Coe Review. (US) **2906**
CoED Journal see Computers in Education Journal **1689**
Coelacanth. (SA) **2332**
†Coeur. (FR ISSN 0010-0226) **5167**
Coeur et Medecine Interne see Revue de Medecine Interne **3149**
Coeur et Sante. (FR) **3800**, 3207
Coeur 2000. (FR) **3207**
Coexistence. (NE ISSN 0587-5994) **4369**, 3880
Coffee & Cocoa International. (UK ISSN 0262-5938) **2064**
Coffee Annual. (US) **2064**, 173
Coffee Board of Kenya. Annual Report, Balance Sheet and Accounts. (KE) **2064**
Coffee County Historical Society Quarterly. (US) **2403**
Coffee House: Contemporary Greek Arts and Letters see Aegean Review: Greek Arts and Letters **2892**
Coffee Intelligence. (US) **2064**, 173
Coffee International see Coffee & Cocoa International **2064**
Coffee International Directory. (UK ISSN 0264-5378) **2064**
Coffee Mazdoor Sahakari. (II ISSN 0010-0250) **2064**
Coffee Research Institute. Annual Report. Coffee Research Station. (RH) **173**
Coffee Review. see Revista Cafetalera **2080**
▼Coffeehouse Poets' Quarterly. (US) **2990**
Y Cofiadur. (UK) **4234**
Cogeneration. (US) **1785**, 1817
Cogeneration Journal. (US ISSN 0883-5985) **1785**, 1817, 1884
Cogeneration Report see Independent Power Report **1791**
Cogent Comments. (US) **942**
Coggeshall Historical Association Bulletin. (US) **2147**
Cogitations on Law and Government. (US ISSN 0741-9333) **2613**, 3880
Cogito. (GW ISSN 0178-8728) **1390**, 1333
Cogito. (FR) **2435**
Cogito. (UK ISSN 0950-8864) **3763**, 1702
Cognition. (NE ISSN 0010-0277) **4016**
Cognition and Computing. (US) **1417**
Cognition and Emotion. (UK ISSN 0269-9931) **4016**
Cognition and Instruction. (US ISSN 0737-0008) **4016**, 1621
Cognition and Language. (US) **2809**, 4016
Cognition and Literacy. (US) **1621**, 4016
▼Cognitive Brain Research. (NE ISSN 0926-6410) **3334**, 3225
Cognitive Development. (US ISSN 0885-2014) **4016**
▼Cognitive Linguistics. (GW ISSN 0936-5907) **2809**
Cognitive Neuropsychology. (UK ISSN 0264-3294) **4016**
Cognitive Psychology. (US ISSN 0010-0285) **4016**
Cognitive Rehabilitation see Journal of Cognitive Rehabilitation **1737**
Cognitive Science. (US ISSN 0364-0213) **4016**, 2809
Cognitive Science Series (Cambridge). (US ISSN 0732-1295) **4016**
Cognitive Science Series: Technical Monographs and Edited Collections. (US) **4016**
Cognitive Systems. (NE ISSN 0256-663X) **4016**, 485, 2809
Cognitive Therapy and Research. (US ISSN 0147-5916) **4016**
Cognizer Almanac. (US ISSN 1060-3557) **1877**

Cognizer Report. (US ISSN 1057-8374) **1350**
Cohen Center for Modern Jewish Studies Centerpieces see C M J S Centerpieces **1995**
Cohen 15-40 Report. (US) **749**
Coiffeur de France. (FR) **372**
Coiffeur et Coiffures see Kapper en Kapsels **373**
Coiffure. (NE) **372**
Coiffure de Paris. (FR ISSN 0010-034X) **372**
Coiffure Gallery. (NE) **372**
Coin see Coin Monthly (1980) **3598**
Coin and Medal News see Coin News **3598**
Coin Dealer Newsletter. (US) **3598**
†Coin Digest. (SI ISSN 0129-0967) **5167**
Coin Hoards. (UK ISSN 0140-1149) **3598**
Coin Laundry Association Guidelines see C L A Guidelines **4617**
Coin Laundry Association News see C L A News **4617**
Coin Monthly (1980). (UK) **3598**
Coin News. (UK ISSN 0955-4386) **3598**
Coin-Op see American Coin-Op **1281**
Coin Previewer. (US) **3599**, 942
Coin Prices. (US ISSN 0010-0412) **3599**
Coin Slot see World's Fair **1057**
Coin Slot (Wheat Ridge). (US) **2435**
Coin, Stamp, Antique News see Canadian Coin News **3598**
Coin Wholesaler. (US ISSN 0045-7280) **3599**
Coin World. (US ISSN 0010-0447) **3599**
Coin World Almanac. (US ISSN 0361-0845) **3599**
Coin World Annual Price Guide. (US) **3599**, 942
Coin Yearbook. (UK ISSN 0307-6571) **3599**
Coinage. (US ISSN 0010-0455) **3599**
Coinage of the Americas Conference. Proceedings. (US ISSN 8756-6265) **3599**
COINfidential Report. (US) **3599**
Coins. (US ISSN 0010-0471) **3599**
Coins Market Values. (UK ISSN 0069-4983) **3599**
Coir. (II ISSN 0530-0495) **4617**
Coke and Chemistry U.S.S.R. (English translation of: Koks i Khimiya) (US ISSN 0010-0501) **1852**
Coke Oven Managers' Association. Year Book. (UK ISSN 0069-4991) **3481**, 3404
Coke Plant Report see Quarterly Coal Report **1794**
▼Cokefish. (US) **2990**
▼Cokemaking International. (GW ISSN 0937-9258) **3481**
Colaboracion Internacional. (CU) **904**, 851
Colada. (SP ISSN 0010-0544) **3404**
Colby Library Quarterly see Colby Quarterly **2906**
Colby Magazine. (US) **1308**
Colby Quarterly. (US ISSN 1050-5873) **2906**
Cold-Drill. (US ISSN 0084-8816) **2906**
Cold Facts. (US) **3840**
Cold Regions Science and Technology. (NE ISSN 0165-232X) **4595**
Cold Spring Harbor Laboratory. Abstracts of Papers Presented at Meetings. (US ISSN 0084-8824) **435**
Cold Spring Harbor Laboratory. Annual Report. (US ISSN 0069-5009) **435**
Cold Spring Harbor Laboratory. Symposia on Quantitative Biology. (US ISSN 0091-7451) **435**
Cold Spring Harbor Monograph Series. (US ISSN 0270-1847) **435**
Cold Storage & Distribution Federation. Directory. (US) **2298**
Cold Storage Report Monthly see Monthly Summary **108**
Cold Storage Report Monthly Summary see Monthly Summary **108**

Cole Chronicle. (US ISSN 0887-1264) **2147**, 2403
Colecao Arquivos de Folclore. (BL) **2053**
Colecao C E D E S. Grandes Temas. (Camara de Estudos e Debates Economicos e Sociais) (BL) **84**
Colecao Caminhos Brasileiros. (BL) **3880**
Colecao Cinema. (BL) **3506**
Colecao de Estudos Bibliograficos. (BL) **397**
Colecao de Estudos Filologicos. (BL ISSN 0587-6435) **2809**
Colecao de Estudos Historicos. (BL) **2403**
Colecao de Estudos Juridicos. (BL ISSN 0530-0657) **2731**
Colecao dos Autores Celebres da Literatura Brasileira. (BL) **2906**
Colecao Economia. (BL) **851**
Colecao Ecumenismo e Humanismo. (BL) **3763**
Colecao Encanto Radical. (BL) **2861**
Colecao Escritores Brasileiros. (BL) **2906**
Colecao Jornalismo Catarinense. (BL) **2568**
Colecao Pesquisa. (BL) **2053**
Colecao Polemicas do Nosso Tiempo. (BL) **2861**
Colecao Primeiros Passos. (BL) **2861**
Colecao Rodolfo Garcia. (BL) **397**
Colecao Teatro. (BL) **4631**
Colecao Temas Brasileiros. (BL) **2403**
Colecao Tendencias. (BL) **3880**
Colecao Tirando de Letra. (BL) **2906**
Coleccao Arquivos. (PO) **2356**
Coleccao Ensaio. (PO) **2906**
Coleccao Forma. (PO) **2990**
Coleccao Horizonte Universitario. (PO) **3880**, 655
Coleccao Literatura. (PO) **2906**
Coleccao N'gola. (PO) **2332**, 2861
Coleccao: Poesia (Lisbon). (PO) **2990**
Coleccao Poesia (Porto). (PO) **2990**
Coleccion Amanece. (AG) **4171**
Coleccion "Aniversarios Culturales". (VE ISSN 0069-5033) **418**
Coleccion Antropologia e Historia. (ES) **237**
Coleccion Aragon. (SP) **2357**
Coleccion Arquitectura - Perspectivas. (SP) **297**
Coleccion Arquitectura y Critica. (SP) **297**
Coleccion "Bahia". (SP) **2990**
Coleccion Biblioteca de Castilla y Leon. Serie Arte. (SP) **322**
Coleccion Biblioteca de Castilla y Leon. Serie Geografia. (SP) **2245**
Coleccion Biblioteca de Castilla y Leon. Serie Historia. (SP) **2357**
Coleccion Biblioteca de Castilla y Leon. Serie Literatura. (SP) **2906**
Coleccion Canonica. (SP ISSN 0069-505X) **4171**
Coleccion Cien Temas Basicos. (UY) **3880**
Coleccion Ciencia Urbanistica. (SP ISSN 0069-5068) **2485**, 297
Coleccion Ciencias Biologicas. (SP) **435**
Coleccion Ciencias, Humanidades e Ingenieria. (SP) **4305**
Coleccion Ciencias Medicas de Bolsillo. (SP) **3090**
Coleccion Comunicacion Visual. (SP) **1333**
Coleccion Correspondencia Diplomatica de los Nuncios en Espana. (SP) **2357**
Coleccion Cuadernos C E D A L. (CR) **3880**
Coleccion Cuadernos de Trabajo Social. (SP) **4402**
Coleccion de Economia. (SP) **889**
Coleccion Debate. (ES) **3880**
Coleccion Direccion de Empresas y Organizaciones. (SP) **1005**
Coleccion Directores de Cine. (SP) **3506**
Coleccion: Documentos e Historia de la Ciencia en Colombia. (CK) **4305**
Coleccion Editorial Universitaria. (GT) **1542**
Coleccion Ensayos. (AG) **2861**
Coleccion Estructuras y Formas. (SP ISSN 0071-1632) **297**

COLEGIO 6063

Coleccion Estudios Latinoamericanos. (AG) **2906**, 2403
Coleccion Estudios Politicos. (DR) **3880**
Coleccion Ethos - Arte. (SP) **3546**, 322
Coleccion Fe e Historia. (CL) **4369**
Coleccion Filosofica. (SP ISSN 0069-5076) **3763**
Coleccion "Foros y Seminarios." Serie Foros. (VE ISSN 0069-5084) **2403**
Coleccion "Foros y Seminarios." Serie Seminarios. (VE ISSN 0069-5092) **2403**
Coleccion Fundacion F O E S S A. Serie Estudios. (Fundacion Fomento de Estudios Sociales y Sociologia Aplicada) (SP) **4431**
Coleccion Historia. (PY) **2403**
Coleccion Historia de la Iglesia. (SP) **4261**
Coleccion Historica. (SP ISSN 0069-5106) **2357**
Coleccion "Humanism y Ciencia". (VE ISSN 0069-5114) **2505**
Coleccion Iberica. (SP) **3880**
Coleccion Ingenieria. (SP) **1817**
Coleccion Juridica. (SP ISSN 0069-5122) **2731**
Coleccion Jurisprudencia y Textos Legales. (SP) **2731**
†Coleccion la Alquitrana. (VE) **5167**
Coleccion la Empresa y Su Entorno. Serie A C. (SP) **1005**
Coleccion la Empresa y Su Entorno. Serie L. (SP) **1005**
Coleccion Libros de Enfermeria. (SP) **3277**
Coleccion Libros de Medicina. (SP) **3090**
Coleccion Linguistica Indigena see La Evolucion Fonologica del Protovaltuat **2813**
Coleccion Literatura. (PY) **2906**
Coleccion Manuales de Finanzas Publicas. (DR) **1091**
Coleccion Medicina see Coleccion Libros de Medicina **3090**
Coleccion Miguel Salguero. (CR) **1997**, 2906
Coleccion Monografias Politicas. (VE) **3880**
Coleccion Mundo Antiguo. (SP ISSN 0077-2054) **2309**
Coleccion Oriente-Occidente. (AG) **3636**
Coleccion Pentesilea. (SP) **2990**
Coleccion Poesia del Nuevo Tiempo. (AG) **2990**
Coleccion Poliedro. (SP) **2906**
Coleccion Popular de Literatura Nicaraguense. Documentos. (NQ) **2906**
Coleccion Punto y Linea. (SP) **2861**
Coleccion Senda Abierta. Serie 2 (Azul): Judaismo. (SP) **4222**
Coleccion Signo y Sociedad. (MX) **2990**
Coleccion Tablero. (SP) **655**
Coleccion Tecnologia y Sociedad. (SP) **4595**
Coleccion Temas Basicos de Ingenieria. (SP) **1817**
Coleccion Temas de Arquitectura Actual.(SP ISSN 0082-2701) **297**
Coleccion Teologica. (SP) **4261**
Coleccion Textos Legislativos. (VE) **2613**
Coleccion Viera y Clavijo. (SP) **3880**
Coleccion Vortex see Asociacion de Hispanistas de las Americas. Coleccion Monografias **2988**
Colecciones Basicas C I N T E R F O R. (UY) **1621**
Colega Agropecuario. (CK) **84**
Colegio Brasileiro de Cirurgioes. Revista. (BL) **3377**
Colegio Colombiano de Quimicos Farmaceuticos. Boletin see Sociedad Colombiana de Quimicos Farmaceuticos. Boletin **3743**
Colegio de Abogados. Revista. (CR ISSN 0010-0587) **2613**
Colegio de Abogados de Buenos Aires. Revista. (AG ISSN 0325-8955) **2613**

COLEGIO

Colegio de Abogados de la Ciudad de Buenos Aires. Boletin Informativo see Colegio de Abogados de Buenos Aires. Revista **2613**
Colegio de Abogados de la Ciudad de Buenos Aires. Revista see Colegio de Abogados de Buenos Aires. Revista **2613**
Colegio de Abogados de Puerto Rico. Revista. (PR ISSN 0010-0579) **2613**
†Colegio de Agentes de Cambio y Bolsa de Barcelona. Servicio de Estudios e Informacion. Boletin Financiero. (SP ISSN 0522-3822) **5167**
Colegio de Arquitectos de Chile. Revista Oficial. (US) **297**
Colegio de Ingenieros Arquitectos y Agrimensores de Puerto Rico. Revista. (PR ISSN 0010-0609) **1863**
Colegio de Ingenieros de Caminos, Canales y Puertos. Boletin de Informacion. (SP ISSN 0010-0617) **1863**
Colegio de Ingenieros de Venezuela. Boletin Informativo. (VE ISSN 0010-0625) **1817**
Colegio de Ingenieros de Venezuela. Directorio. (VE) **1817**
Colegio de Ingenieros de Venezuela. Noticero. (VE) **1817**
Colegio de Ingenieros de Venezuela. Revista. (VE) **1817**
Colegio de Mexico. Biblioteca. Lista de Obras en Canje. Publicaciones Periodicas. (MX) **2577**
Colegio de Mexico. Estudios Economicos. (MX) **889, 1091**
Colegio de Profesores de Venezuela. Seccional No. 1. Boletin Informativo. (VE ISSN 0010-0633) **1622**
Colegio Dominicano de Ingenieros, Arquitectos y Agrimensores see C O D I A **1862**
Colegio Mayor de Nuestra Senora del Rosario. Biblioteca. Boletin Informacion. (CK) **2752**
Colegio Mayor P. Felipe Scio. Publicaciones. (SP) **4261**
Colegio Medico de El Salvador. Archivas. (ES ISSN 0010-0641) **3090**
Colegio Militar do Rio de Janeiro. Revista Didactica. (BL ISSN 0080-3103) **1622**
Colegio Nacional de Enfermeras. Revista. (MX ISSN 0045-7329) **3277**
Colegio Oficial de Farmaceutico. Circular Farmaceutica. (SP ISSN 0009-7314) **3721**
Colegio Universitario de Almeria. Anales.(SP) **1308**
Colegios Medicos de Espana. Consejo General. Boletin Informativo see Informativo Medico **3108**
Coleman Camping Annual see Coleman Outdoor Annual **5167**
†Coleman Outdoor Annual. (US) **5167**
Coleopterists Bulletin. (US ISSN 0010-065X) **530**
Cole's Register of British Antiquarian & Secondhand Bookdealers. (UK) **4125, 1127**
Colfeian. (UK ISSN 0010-0676) **1308**
Colgate Scene. (US) **1308**
Colimpex Agricultural Execupad. (SA) **84**
Colimpex Architect's Execupad. (SA) **297**
Colimpex Electrical Execupad. (SA) **1884**
Colimpex Insurance Brokers Execupad. (SA) **2530**
Colimpex Medical Execupad. (SA) **3090**
Colimpex Mining Execupad. (SA) **3481**
Colimpex Paediatric Execuped. (SA) **3277**
▼Colin's Magazine. (US) **2906, 1390**
Collaboration. (US ISSN 0164-1522) **3763, 1997, 4171**
†Collage. (CN) **5167**
Collage (Claremont). (US) **1308**
Collage (New Cumberland). (US ISSN 0883-2781) **942, 1884**
Collage (Wheeling). (US ISSN 0745-2810) **2223**
Collagen and Related Research see Matrix **3124**
Collana Corpus Antiquitatum Americanensium Italia. (IT) **269**
Collana Corpus Vasorum Antiquorum Italia. (IT) **269**
Collana di Cultura. (IT ISSN 0069-5165) **2906**
Collana di Monografie delle Biblioteche d'Italia. (IT) **2752**
Collana di Musiche Veneziane Inedite o Rare. (IT) **3546**
Collana di Poesia. (IT) **2990**
Collana di Storia Moderna e Contemporanea. (IT ISSN 0391-3279) **2357**
Collana di Studi e Saggi. (IT ISSN 0069-5203) **2906**
Collana di Studi Paleontologici. (IT) **237, 269, 3657**
†Collana di Studi Su Problemi Urbanistici Fiorentino. (IT) **5167**
Collana di Testi e di Critica. (IT) **2906**
Collana Ricciana. Fonti. (IT ISSN 0069-5254) **4261**
Collaps. (PL) **3010**
Collationes Mariales Instituti Carmelitani. (IT ISSN 0394-7769) **4261**
†Colleccio de Materials. (SP) **5167**
Collect Birds on Stamps. (UK) **3751**
Collect British Stamps. (UK ISSN 0069-5262) **3751**
Collect Channel Islands and Isle of Man Stamps. (UK) **3751**
Collect Mammals on Stamps. (UK) **3751**
Collect Railways on Stamps. (UK) **3751**
Collect Ships on Stamps. (UK) **3751**
Collectanea Bibliographica Carmelitana. (IT ISSN 0394-7777) **397, 2309, 4261**
Collectanea Botanica. (SP ISSN 0010-0730) **499**
Collectanea Cisterciensia. (BE ISSN 0378-4916) **4261**
Collectanea Franciscana. (IT ISSN 0010-0749) **4261**
†Collectanea Historiae Musicae. (IT ISSN 0069-5270) **5167**
Collectanea Instituti Anthropos. (GW) **237**
Collectanea Mathematica. (SP ISSN 0010-0757) **3032**
Collected Original Resources in Education see C O R E **1619**
Collected Papers from the Journal of the Royal Society of New Zealand. (NZ ISSN 0112-2479) **4305**
Collected Papers of the Annual Meeting, Southeast Regional Group, American Accounting Association see American Accounting Association. Southeast Regional Group. Collected Papers of the Annual Meeting **746**
Collected Papers on Sciences of Atmosphere and Hydrosphere. (JA ISSN 0547-1435) **1542**
Collected Papers on South Asia. (UK ISSN 0141-0156) **3636**
Collectible Automobile. (US ISSN 0742-812X) **4688, 256**
Collectif (Montreal). (CN) **1308**
Collectif (Sherbrooke). (CN) **1308**
Collecting and Breeding/Saishu to Shiku. (JA ISSN 0036-3286) **540**
Collection: Artistes Canadiens see Canadian Artists Series **320**
Collection Building. (US ISSN 0160-4953) **2752**
Collection Ca-Cinema. (FR) **3506**
Collection Choix. (CN ISSN 0709-874X) **3953**
Collection d'Etudes Musicologiques. see Sammlung Musikwissenschaftlicher Abhandlungen **3579**
Collection de la Revue des Etudes Juives. (BE ISSN 0777-785X) **1997, 4222**
Collection des Travaux de l'Academie Internationale d'Histoire des Sciences see Academie Internationale d'Histoire des Sciences. Collection des Travaux **4296**
Collection Documents Systemes Agraires. (FR) **84**
Collection Formation des Enseignants et Formation Continue. (FR) **3032**
Collection l'Etat et le Citoyen see Repertoire Administratif **5268**
Collection Management. (US ISSN 0146-2679) **2752**
Collection Monographique Rodopi en Litterature Francaise Contemporaine. (NE) **2906, 418**
Collection of Australian Stamps. (AT ISSN 0727-4211) **3751, 2344**
Collection of Bibliographic and Research Resources. (US ISSN 0886-6724) **2698, 397, 2720**
Collection of Czechoslovak Chemical Communications. (UK ISSN 0010-0765) **1175**
Collection of Documents for the Study of International Non-Governmental Relations. (BE ISSN 0503-2407) **2720**
Collection of Historical Materials. see Shixue Jikan **2322**
Collection of Works and Documents Illustrating the History of Paper. see Monumenta Chartae Papyraceae Historiam Illustrantia **3663**
Collection Oralites-Documents. (FR ISSN 0220-746X) **2809**
Collection Orientations. (FR) **4016, 1622**
Collection Philosophica. (CN) **3763**
Collection Psychologie. (FR) **4016**
Collection Psychologie et Pedagogie de la Musique. (FR) **3546, 4016**
Collection Psychologie et Pedagogie du Sport. (FR) **4017, 4469**
Collection Psychologie et Pedagogie du Travail. (FR) **4017**
Collection Radiographie du Capital - Les Liaisons Financieres see Les Liaisons Financieres **789**
Collection Sciences de l'Education. (FR) **1622**
Collection Stendhalienne. (SZ) **2906**
Collection Tests Psychologiques. (FR) **4017**
Collection Vietnamienne. (BE) **2906**
Collectionneur Francais. (FR ISSN 0588-2583) **2435**
Collectionneur, Philateliste et Marcophile. (FR) **3751**
Collections (Buffalo). (US ISSN 0160-0664) **4305**
Collections (Columbia). (US ISSN 1046-2252) **3523, 322, 353**
Collections Baur. Bulletin. (SZ ISSN 0010-0781) **3523, 3636**
Collections Education - Pedagogie. (FR) **1622**
Collections et Monnaies see Cartes Postales et Collections **2434**
Collective Bargaining in Higher Education and the Professions. Annual Bibliography. (US ISSN 0738-1913) **1702, 2581**
Collective Bargaining Information Monthly. (CN ISSN 0826-8800) **2581**
Collective Bargaining Negotiations & Contracts. (US ISSN 0010-079X) **975**
Collective Bargaining Review. (CN ISSN 0010-0803) **975**
Collective Bargaining Settlements in New York State. (US ISSN 0045-7345) **975**
†Collective Networker Newsletter. (US) **5167**
▼Collective Voice. (US) **3880, 4431**
Collectivites-Express. (FR ISSN 0010-0811) **829**
▼Collector. (FR) **29, 322, 1290**
Collector. (US ISSN 0010-082X) **772**
Collector and Investor. (SA) **2435, 256, 942**
Collector Car News. (US ISSN 0888-1944) **256**
Collector Editions. (US ISSN 0733-2130) **2435, 322**
Collectors' Auction (Baltimore) see Harris Auction Galleries. Collectors' Auction **3524**
Collectors Cars Price Guide and Auction Review. (UK) **256**
Collectors Club Philatelist. (US ISSN 0010-0838) **3751, 2403**
▼Collectors Directory. (AT ISSN 1036-6997) **2435**
Collectors Items. (UK ISSN 0261-2550) **3546**
Collector's Marketplace Monthly. (US) **3751**
Collectors Mart. (US ISSN 0744-9879) **256**
Collectors Mart. (UK) **2435**
Collectors News see Collectors News & the Antique Reporter **256**
Collectors News & the Antique Reporter. (US ISSN 0162-1033) **256**
Collectors of Religion on Stamps Chronicle see C O R O S Chronicle **3750**
Collectors' Showcase. (US ISSN 0744-5989) **257, 3599**
†Collectors World. (UK) **5167**
Collectrix. (US ISSN 0738-9981) **257**
Collegamento. (IT) **3721**
College Administrator and the Courts. (US ISSN 0192-1371) **2613, 1702**
College Admissions Data see College Admissions Data Handbook **1692**
College Admissions Data Handbook. (US) **1692**
College Admissions Data Service see College Admissions Data Handbook **1692**
College Admissions Index of Majors & Sports. (US) **1692**
College Alumni and Military Publications. (US) **1308, 3454**
College Alumni Publications see College Alumni and Military Publications **1308**
College and Junior Tennis. (US ISSN 0279-1153) **4502**
College & Pro Basketball Action. (US) **4502**
College & Research Libraries. (US ISSN 0010-0870) **2752**
College & Research Libraries News. (US ISSN 0099-0086) **2752**
College and University. (US ISSN 0010-0889) **1702**
College and University Administrators Directory. (US ISSN 0195-3990) **1726**
College and University Admissions and Enrollment, New York State. (US ISSN 0147-5894) **1702**
College and University Business Officer see Business Officer **1725**
College and University Computer Directory: Facilities and Personnel (Year). (US) **1688**
College and University Degrees Conferred, New York State. (US ISSN 0077-9172) **1702**
College and University Employees, New York State. (US ISSN 0093-3414) **1703**
College and University Enrollment in New York State see College and University Admissions and Enrollment, New York State **1702**
College and University Newsletter see Campus Safety Newsletter **4099**
College and University Personnel Association. Journal see C U P A Journal **1063**
College & University Personnel Association News see C U P A News **1725**
College Art Association Monographs see Monographs on the Fine Arts **336**
College Art Association Newsletter (New York) see C A A Newsletter (New York) **320**
College Band Directors National Association Journal. (US ISSN 0742-8480) **3546**
College Blue Book. (US ISSN 0069-5572) **1693**
College Board News. (US) **1703**
College Board Review. (US ISSN 0010-0951) **1703**
College Boulevard News. (US) **655**
College Bound. (US) **1703, 1693**
College Broadcaster. (US) **1371**
▼College by Mail - Etc. Newsletter. (US) **1703**
College Catalog Collection. (US ISSN 0733-1355) **1703**
College Catalog Collection on Microfiche. (US) **1622, 2752**

College Composition and Communication. (US ISSN 0010-096X) **1746**
College d'Enseignement Generale et Professionnel de Valleyfield Plus *see* C E G E P Plus **1306**
College de France. Annuaire. (FR ISSN 0069-5580) **1703**
College de France. Institut des Hautes Etudes Chinoises. Memoirs. (FR) **3636**
College des Medecins et Chirurgiens de la Province de Quebec. Bulletin *see* Corporation Professionnelle des Medecins du Quebec. Bulletin **3091**
College English. (US ISSN 0010-0994) **1746**
College English Association Critic *see* C E A Critic **2901**
College English Association Forum *see* C E A Forum **1745**
College Facts Chart. (US ISSN 0069-5688) **1693**
College Football *see* Petersen's College Football **4509**
College for Financial Planning. Digest. (US) **772**
College Grants from Uncle Sam. (US) **1703**
College-Industry Education Conference. Proceedings. (US) **1817**, **1703**
College Information Booklet. (US) **1703**, **3214**
College Jean-de-Brebeuf. Bulletin du College, des Parents et des Anciens. (CN) **1308**
College Language Association Journal *see* C L A Journal **2807**
College Law Digest. (US ISSN 0045-737X) **2613**, **1726**
College Literature. (US ISSN 0093-3139) **2906**
College Loans from Uncle Sam. (US) **1703**
College Marketing Alert. (US ISSN 0882-9268) **1622**, **655**
College Mathematics Journal. (US ISSN 0746-8342) **3032**
College Media Advisers Newsletter *see* C M A Newsletter **1306**
College Media Directory. (US ISSN 1046-4255) **397**
College Media Journal New Music Report *see* C M J New Music Report **3543**
College Media Review. (US ISSN 0739-1056) **2568**, **1308**, **1622**
College Music Symposium. (US ISSN 0069-5696) **3546**
†College Musician. (US) **5167**
College of American Pathologists Today *see* C A P Today **3085**
College of Anaesthetists. Newsletter. (UK) **3191**
College of Dairy Agriculture, Hokkaido. Journal *see* Rakuno Gakuen Daigaku Kiyo. Jinbun Shakai Kagaku Hen **115**
College of Dairy Agriculture, Hokkaido. Journal *see* Rakuno Gakuen Daigaku Kiyo. Shizen Kagaku Hen **203**
College of Dairying. Journal: Cultural and Social Sciences. *see* Rakuno Gakuen Daigaku Kiyo. Jinbun Shakai Kagaku Hen **115**
College of Dairying. Journal: Natural Science. *see* Rakuno Gakuen Daigaku Kiyo. Shizen Kagaku Hen **203**
College of Engineering, Trivandrum. Magazine. (II) **1817**
College of Insurance. Academic Bulletin.(US) **2530**
College of Librarianship Wales Contents Monthly *see* C L W Contents Monthly **5157**
College of Librarianship Wales Library Catalogue *see* C L W Library Catalogue **5157**
College of Librarianship Wales Serials in C L W Library *see* Serials in C L W Library **5276**
College of Medicine of South Africa. Transactions. (SA ISSN 0375-3220) **3090**
College of Physicians and Surgeons of British Columbia. Annual Report. (CN) **3090**

College of Physicians and Surgeons of British Columbia. Medical Directory. (CN ISSN 0069-5726) **3090**
†College of Physicians and Surgeons of Ontario. Interim Report. (CN ISSN 0045-7388) **5167**
College of Physicians of Philadelphia. Transactions & Studies. (US ISSN 0010-1087) **3090**
College of St. Scholastica Times Magazine. (US) **1308**
College of St. Thomas. Magazine *see* University of St. Thomas Magazine **1328**
College of Speech and Language Therapists. Bulletin. (UK ISSN 0953-6086) **1735**
College of Speech Therapists. Bulletin *see* College of Speech and Language Therapists. Bulletin **1735**
College of Textile Technology, Serampore Annual *see* C.T.T.S. Annual **4617**
College Outlook and Career Opportunities. (US) **1693**
College Placement Annual *see* C P C Annual **3625**
College Placement Council, Inc. Annual *see* C P C Annual **3625**
College Placement Council, Inc. Career & Job Fair Finder *see* C P C Career & Job Fair Finder **3625**
College Placement Council, Inc. Salary Survey *see* C P C Salary Survey **3625**
College Planning - Search Book. (US) **3626**
College Press Service. (US ISSN 0010-1125) **1703**, **2568**
College Preview. (US ISSN 1050-7159) **1703**
College Reading and Learning Association Newsletter *see* C R L A Newsletter **1682**
College Reading Association. Monographs. (US) **2793**
College Recruiting Report. (US ISSN 0361-5057) **1703**
College Republican. (US) **3880**, **1308**
College Royal des Medecins et Chirurgiens du Canada. Annales. *see* Royal College of Physicians and Surgeons of Canada. Annals **3150**
College Services Administration. Journal.(US) **1726**
College Store Executive. (US ISSN 0010-1141) **1036**, **1703**
College Store Journal. (US ISSN 0010-115X) **1036**
College Student Affairs Journal. (US) **1308**
College Student and the Courts. (US ISSN 0145-1472) **2613**, **1703**
College Student Journal. (US ISSN 0146-3934) **1703**
College Swimming Coaches Association of America Newsletter. (US) **4469**
College Teaching. (US ISSN 8756-7555) **1703**
College Times *see* College Voice (Staten Island) **1308**
College Transfer Guide. (US) **1693**
College Union *see* College Union & On-Campus Hospitality **1308**
College Union & On-Campus Hospitality.(US) **1308**
College - University Foodservice Who's Who. (US) **1127**, **2064**, **3604**
College Voice (Staten Island). (US) **1308**
College Voice (Trenton). (US ISSN 0010-1192) **1308**
†College Woman. (US) **5167**
Colleges and Universities with Accredited Social Work Degree Programs. (US) **1693**, **4402**
Colleges and Universities with Accredited Undergraduate Social Work Programs *see* Colleges and Universities with Accredited Social Work Degree Programs **1693**
Collegian *see* The Chanticleer **1307**
Collegian (Brookings). (US) **1308**
Collegian (Elyria). (US ISSN 0010-1206) **1308**
Collegian (Tulsa). (US) **1308**
Collegiate Baseball. (US ISSN 0530-9751) **4502**

Collegiate Career Woman Magazine *see* Career Woman Magazine **4838**
Collegiate Insider. (US) **1703**
Collegiate Microcomputer. (US ISSN 0731-4213) **1688**, **1703**
Collegiate Press Service *see* College Press Service **1703**
Collegio. (US ISSN 0010-1249) **1308**
Collegium Antropologicum. (CI ISSN 0350-6134) **237**
Collegium Carolinum. Bohemia-Jahrbuch *see* Bohemia: Zeitschrift fuer Geschichte und Kultur der Bohemischen Laender **2353**
Collegium Carolinum. Veroeffentlichungen. (GW ISSN 0530-9794) **2357**
Collegium Musicum: Yale University. (US ISSN 0147-0108) **3546**
†Collegium Philosophicum Jenense. (GW) **5167**
Collezioni Donna. (IT) **1290**
Collezioni e Musei Archeologici del Veneto. (IT ISSN 0392-0879) **269**
Collie Club of America. Bulletin. (US) **3709**
†Collie Cues. (US) **5167**
Collie Review. (US) **3709**
Collie-Shetland Sheepdog Review *see* Collie Review **3709**
Collie Variety. (US) **3709**
Collier Bankruptcy Cases. (US ISSN 0099-1848) **772**
Collier Bankruptcy Compensation Guide.(US) **772**, **2613**
Collier Bankruptcy Manual. (US) **772**, **2613**
Collier Farm Bankruptcy Guide. (US) **772**, **84**
Collier Handbook for Creditors' Committees. (US) **772**, **2613**
Collier Lending Institutions and the Bankruptcy Code. (US) **772**, **2613**
Collier on Bankruptcy. (US) **772**, **2613**
Collier Quarterly. (US) **2147**
Collier Real Estate Transactions and the Bankruptcy Code. (US) **772**, **4146**
Colliery Guardian. (UK ISSN 0010-1281) **3481**
Collin Chronicles. (US) **2147**
Collision. (US ISSN 0739-7437) **4688**
Collision Parts Journal. (US) **4688**
Collision Repair Digest *see* Collision Repair Specialist **4688**
Collision Repair Specialist. (US) **4688**
Collision-Tow-Age *see* Collision **4688**
Colloid and Polymer Science. (GW ISSN 0303-402X) **1217**, **1225**
Colloid Journal of the U S S R. (English translation of: Kolloidnyi Zhurnal) (US ISSN 0010-1303) **1225**, **3816**
Colloids and Surfaces. (NE ISSN 0166-6622) **1225**
Colloques Economiques. (SZ) **655**
Colloques Internationaux d'Histoire Maritime. Travaux. (FR ISSN 0069-5815) **4726**
Colloques Langues'O. (FR) **3636**
Colloques Phytosociologiques. (GW) **500**
Colloqui Cremonese. (IT ISSN 0010-132X) **322**, **2906**
Colloquia Germanica. (SZ ISSN 0010-1338) **2809**, **2907**
Colloquia in Anthropology. (US ISSN 0146-4167) **237**
Colloquia Mathematica Societatis Janos Bolyai. (NE) **3032**
Colloquio: Letras. (PO ISSN 0010-1451) **2907**
Colloquium. (CN) **1927**
Colloquium Geographicum. (GW ISSN 0588-3253) **2245**
Colloquium Helveticum. (SZ ISSN 0179-3780) **2907**
Colloquium Mathematicum. (PL ISSN 0010-1354) **3032**
Colloquium Mosbach. (US ISSN 0366-5887) **475**
Colloquium on the History of Landscape Architecture. Papers. (US) **297**
Colloquium on the Law of Outer Space. Proceedings. (US ISSN 0069-5831) **50**, **2721**
Colloquy. (US) **1036**

Colo-Proctology. (GW ISSN 0174-2450) **3090**
Cologne. Travel-Report. (GW) **4757**
Cologne Convention *see* Koelner Kongress Report **3393**
Colombia. Corporacion Nacional de Turismo. Boletin de Estadistica Turistica. (Year). (CK) **4799**
Colombia. Corporacion Nacional de Turismo. Boletin Informativo C E N T U R. (Centro de Informacion Turistico) (CK) **4757**
Colombia. Corporacion Nacional de Turismo. Catalogo Nacional de Tesis de Turismo y Hoteleria. (CK ISSN 0121-1870) **4757**
Colombia. Corporacion Nacional de Turismo. Catalogo Turistico. (CK ISSN 0121-1889) **4757**
Colombia. Corporacion Nacional de Turismo. Cronica Turistica. (CK) **4758**
Colombia. Departamento Administrativo Nacional de Estadistica. Anuario Demografico. (CK) **3991**, **3980**
Colombia. Departamento Administrativo Nacional de Estadistica. Anuario de Comercio Exterior. (CK) **904**, **711**
Colombia. Departamento Administrativo Nacional de Estadistica. Anuario de Estadisticas Fiscales y Financieras. (CK) **711**
Colombia. Departamento Administrativo Nacional de Estadistica. Anuario de Estadisticas Industriales. (CK) **711**, **1073**, **4568**
Colombia. Departamento Administrativo Nacional de Estadistica. Anuario de Justicia. (CK) **4568**
Colombia. Departamento Administrativo Nacional de Estadistica. Anuario General de Estadistica - Justicia *see* Colombia. Departamento Administrativo Nacional de Estadistica. Anuario de Justicia **4568**
Colombia. Departamento Administrativo Nacional de Estadistica. Anuario General de Estadistica - Transportes y Comunicaciones. (CK) **4663**, **1347**, **4568**
Colombia. Departamento Administrativo Nacional de Estadistica. Boletin de Estadistica. (CK ISSN 0120-6281) **4568**
Colombia. Departamento Administrativo Nacional de Estadistica. Choco Estadistico. (CK ISSN 0120-6745) **4568**
Colombia. Departamento Administrativo Nacional de Estadistica. Division Politico-Administrativa. (CK) **4057**
Colombia. Departamento Administrativo Nacional de Estadistica. Estadisticas Historicas. (CK) **4569**
Colombia. Departamento Administrativo Nacional de Estadistica. Industria Manufacturera Nacional *see* Colombia. Departamento Administrativo Nacional de Estadistica. Anuario de Estadisticas Industriales **711**
Colombia. Direccion General del Presupuesto. Proyecto de Presupuesto. (CK) **1091**
Colombia. Ministerio de Defensa. Boletin. (CK ISSN 0010-1389) **3454**
†Colombia. Ministerio de Educacion Nacional. Educacion para Desarrollo. (CK) **5167**
Colombia. Ministerio de Minas y Energia. Memoria al Congreso de la Republica. (CK) **1558**
Colombia. Ministerio de Trabajo, Higiene y Prevision Social. Memoria *see* Colombia. Ministerio de Trabajo y Seguridad Social. Memoria al Congreso Nacional **975**
Colombia. Ministerio de Trabajo y Seguridad Social. Memoria al Congreso Nacional. (CK) **975**, **2530**
Colombia. Observatorio Astronomico Nacional. Anuario. (CK ISSN 0120-2758) **363**
Colombia. Observatorio Astronomico Nacional. Publicaciones. (CK ISSN 0067-9518) **363**

COLOMBIA. SUPERINTENDENCIA

Colombia. Superintendencia Bancaria. Informe de Labores. (CK) **772**
Colombia. Superintendencia Bancaria. Revista. (CK ISSN 0120-4017) **772**
Colombia. Superintendencia Bancaria. Seguros y Capitalizacion. (CK) **656, 2530**
Colombia: Ciencia y Tecnologia. (CK ISSN 0120-5595) **4305**
Colombia Economica see Exclusivedades de Economia **864**
Colombia Exporta. (CK ISSN 0120-727X) **904**
Colombia Geografica. (CK) **2245**
Colombia Medica. (CK) **3090**
Colombia Report see International Report (Irvine) **3962**
Colombia: sus Gentes y Regiones. (CK ISSN 0120-6907) **2245**
Colombia Today. (US ISSN 0010-1397) **2183**
Colombian American Business. see Comercio Colombo Americano **813**
Colombian Business Guide. (CK) **1127**
Colombian Economy. (CK) **998**
Le Colombien. (CN ISSN 0384-0298) **1297**
Colombo Law Review. (CE ISSN 0069-5939) **2613**
Colombo Observatory. Report. (CE) **363**
Colombo Plan Bureau. The Colombo Plan Council Report. (CE) **927**
Colombo Plan for Co-operative Economic and Social Development in Asia and the Pacific. Consultative Committee. Proceedings and Conclusions. (CE) **927**
Colombo Plan for Co-operative Economic and Social Development in Asia and the Pacific. Consultative Committee. Report see Colombo Plan for Co-operative Economic and Social Development in Asia and the Pacific. Consultative Committee. Proceedings and Conclusions **927**
Colombo Plan for Co-operative Economic and Social Development in Asia and the Pacific. Development Perspectives. Country Issues Papers by Member Governments to the Consultative Committee. (CE) **927**
Colombo Plan Newsletter. (CE ISSN 0010-1419) **927**
Colombophilie. (FR) **3709**
Colonial American Studies. (US) **2403**
Colonial Courier. (US ISSN 0010-1435) **2147**
Colonial Homes. (US ISSN 0195-1416) **610, 2549**
Colonial Newsletter see C N L **3598**
Colonial Rottweiler Club Newsletter. (US) **3709**
Colonial Society of Massachusetts. Publications. (US) **2403**
Colonial Waterbirds. (US) **563**
Colonial Williamsburg Archaeological Series. (US ISSN 0069-5971) **269, 2403**
Colonial Williamsburg Historic Trades. (US ISSN 0897-7216) **353**
†Colonial Williamsburg Occasional Papers in Archaeology. (US) **5167**
†Colonial Williamsburg Studies in Colonial Chesapeake History and Culture. (US) **5167**
Colonie Quarterly. (US) **3880**
Colonnades. (US) **2861**
Colony see Question Mark **1521**
Coloquio: Artes. (PO ISSN 0870-3841) **322, 3546, 4631**
Coloquio de Estudos Luso Brasileiros. Anais. (JA ISSN 0069-598X) **2809, 4369**
Color Association of the United States Newsletter see C A U S Newsletter **1284**
Color Micro Journal see 68 Micro Journal **1466**
Color News. (US) **372, 29**
▼Color Publishing. (US ISSN 1055-9701) **4125, 3998**
Color Research and Application. (US ISSN 0361-2317) **1852, 3653, 3789**
▼Color Wheel. (US) **2990**
Color y Decoracion en el Hogar. (SP) **2549**

Colorado. Department of Administration. Division of Accounts & Control. Comprehensive Annual Financial Report. (US) **4057**
Colorado. Division of Wildlife. Division Report. (US ISSN 0276-0231) **1945**
Colorado. Division of Wildlife. Special Report. (US ISSN 0084-8875) **1485**
Colorado. Division of Wildlife. Technical Publication. (US ISSN 0084-8883) **1485**
Colorado Agribusiness Roundup. (US) **148, 215, 851**
Colorado Archaeological Society Memoir Series. (US) **269**
Colorado Beverage Analyst. (US ISSN 0010-1516) **380**
Colorado Business. (US ISSN 0092-5071) **851**
Colorado City Retail Sales by Standard Industrial Classification. (US ISSN 0732-071X) **834**
Colorado Collections. (US ISSN 0892-077X) **2147**
Colorado College Bulletin. (US) **1308**
Colorado Council of Genealogical Societies. Newsletter. (US) **2147**
Colorado Dental Association. Journal. (US ISSN 0010-1559) **3230**
Colorado Directory of Camping, Lodges, Cabins, Fun Things to Do. (US) **4758**
Colorado Directory of Camping, R Vs, Cabins, Fun Things to Do see Colorado Directory of Camping, Lodges, Cabins, Fun Things to Do **4758**
Colorado Editor. (US ISSN 0010-1567) **2568**
Colorado Education & Library Directory.(US) **2752**
Colorado Education Directory see Colorado Education & Library Directory **2752**
Colorado Engineer. (US ISSN 0010-1583) **1817**
Colorado Episcopalian. (US ISSN 0883-6728) **4234**
Colorado Express. (US ISSN 0146-9991) **4758, 2403**
▼Colorado Expression. (US ISSN 0010-) **2223**
Colorado Field Ornithologists Journal see C F O Journal **563**
Colorado Genealogical Chronicles. (US ISSN 0892-0788) **2147**
Colorado Genealogist. (US ISSN 0010-1613) **2147**
Colorado Heritage. (US ISSN 0272-9377) **2403**
Colorado Heritage News see Colorado History News **2403**
Colorado History News. (US ISSN 0895-0083) **2403**
Colorado Homes & Lifestyles. (US ISSN 0272-6904) **2549, 2124, 4431**
Colorado Hunting, Fishing & Outdoor Guide. (US) **4544**
Colorado Interstate Gas Co. World see C-I-G World **3683**
Colorado Job Finder. (US) **4086, 3626**
▼Colorado Journal of International Environmental Law and Policy. (US ISSN 1050-0391) **2721, 1945**
Colorado Journal of Pharmacy. (US ISSN 0010-163X) **3721**
Colorado Kairos. (US) **4171, 4431**
Colorado Labor Force Review. (US) **975**
Colorado Laws Enacted Affecting Municipal Governments. (US) **4086, 2613**
Colorado Lawyer. (US ISSN 0363-7867) **2613**
Colorado Legionnaire. (US) **3454**
Colorado Libraries. (US ISSN 0147-9733) **2753**
Colorado M A C News. (Media Agencies Clients) (US) **29, 1333**
Colorado Manpower Review see Colorado Labor Force Review **975**
Colorado Medicine. (US ISSN 0199-7343) **3090**
Colorado Municipalities. (US ISSN 0010-1664) **4086**
Colorado Music Educator. (US ISSN 0010-1672) **3546, 1622**

Colorado Native Plant Society. Newsletter see Aquilegia **2122**
Colorado North Review. (US ISSN 0194-0589) **2907**
Colorado Nurse. (US ISSN 0010-1680) **3277**
Colorado Official State Vacation Guide. (US) **4758**
Colorado Outdoors. (US ISSN 0010-1699) **4544, 1485**
Colorado Prospector. (US ISSN 0010-1702) **2403**
Colorado Rail Annual. (US ISSN 0069-6048) **4708**
Colorado Rancher and Farmer. (US ISSN 0010-1729) **84**
Colorado Review. (US ISSN 1046-3348) **2862**
Colorado River Association Newsletter see C R A Newsletter **4822**
Colorado School of Mines. Professional Contributions. (US ISSN 0069-6056) **3482, 1542, 3657**
Colorado School of Mines Quarterly. (US ISSN 0163-9153) **3482, 1542**
Colorado Shakespeare Festival Annual see On - Stage Studies **4636**
Colorado Ski and Winter Recreation Statistics. (US ISSN 0084-8891) **4498**
Colorado Springs Business Journal. (US) **656**
Colorado State and Country Retail Sales by Standard Industrial Classification. (US) **656**
Colorado State Library Newsletter see Centennial State Libraries **2751**
Colorado State University. Atmospheric Science Paper. (US ISSN 0067-0340) **3434**
Colorado State University Libraries. Publication. (US ISSN 0084-8905) **2753**
Colorado Statesman. (US) **3880, 4057**
Colorado, Utah TourBook see Tourbook: Colorado, Utah **4790**
Colorado-Wyoming Academy of Sciences. Journal. (US ISSN 0096-2279) **4305**
Colorectal Cancers--Diagnosis, Treatment see I C R D B Cancergram: Colorectal Cancer - Diagnosis, Treatment **3175**
Colored Stone. (US ISSN 1046-462X) **2563, 3482**
Colorgram. (US) **3789**
Colorin Colorado. (UY) **1252**
Coloristical Review. see Kolorisztikai Ertesito **1856**
▼Colour. (US) **4125, 3998**
Colour Circle see Colourama **322**
Colour in Fashion. see Liuxing Se **1292**
Colour Index: Additions & Amendments.(UK) **4628, 8**
Colour Society. Journal. (Il ISSN 0588-5094) **3653**
Colourage. (Il ISSN 0010-1826) **1281, 4617**
Colourama. (UK) **322, 3852**
Colours/Alwan. (JO) **1308**
Colposcopy and Gynecologic Laser Surgery see Journal of Gynecologic Surgery **3294**
Cols Bleus. (FR ISSN 0010-1834) **3454**
Colstonian. (UK ISSN 0010-1842) **1622**
†Colt American Handgunning Annual. (US ISSN 0364-071X) **5167**
Colt Studio Publications. (US) **3396**
Il Coltivatore. (IT) **84**
Coltivatore Diretto. (IT) **84, 2613**
Coltivatore Ennese. (IT) **84**
Il Coltivatore Italiano. (IT) **84**
Coltivatore Marchigiano. (IT) **84**
Coltivatore Reggiano. (IT) **84**
Coltivatori Cuneese. (IT) **84**
Colton Clarion. (US ISSN 0896-9590) **2147**
Coltsfoot. (US ISSN 0279-4969) **500, 2053**
Colture Protette. (IT ISSN 0390-0444) **2124**
Columban Mission. (US ISSN 0095-4438) **4261**
The Columbia. (US ISSN 8755-2914) **2147**

Columbia (New Haven). (US ISSN 0010-1869) **4261**
Columbia (New York). (US ISSN 0162-3893) **1308**
Columbia: A Magazine of Poetry and Prose. (US ISSN 0161-486X) **2907, 2990**
Columbia Basin Farmer. (US ISSN 0010-1877) **84**
Columbia Biological Series. (US ISSN 0069-6285) **435**
Columbia Business Law Review. (US ISSN 0898-0721) **2613, 656**
Columbia College Today. (US ISSN 0572-7820) **1308**
Columbia Daily Spectator. (US ISSN 0010-1893) **1308**
Columbia Disc Golf News see Disc Golf World News **4545**
Columbia Duck & Goose Shooting. (US) **4544**
Columbia Engineering Research. (US) **1817**
†Columbia Essays on the Great Economists. (US ISSN 0069-6323) **5167**
Columbia Film Review see Columbia Film View **3506**
Columbia Film View. (US) **3506**
▼Columbia Gorge Magazine. (US) **4758**
Columbia Historical Society. Record see Washington History **2426**
Columbia Human Rights Law Review. (US ISSN 0090-7944) **2613**
Columbia Jester. (US ISSN 0010-1915) **1308**
Columbia Journal of Environmental Law.(US ISSN 0098-4582) **2613, 1945**
Columbia Journal of Law and Social Problems. (US ISSN 0010-1923) **2614, 4431**
Columbia Journal of Transnational Law. (US ISSN 0010-1931) **2721**
Columbia Journal of World Business. (US ISSN 0022-5428) **904**
Columbia Journalism Review. (US ISSN 0010-194X) **2568**
Columbia Law Alumni Observer. (US ISSN 0093-304X) **2614**
Columbia Law Observer see Columbia Law Alumni Observer **2614**
Columbia Law Review. (US ISSN 0010-1958) **2614**
Columbia Law School News. (US) **1308, 4431**
Columbia Library Columns. (US ISSN 0010-1966) **2753**
Columbia - Luzerne - Wyoming - Lycoming Farm and Home News see Seven County Farm and Home News **119**
Columbia Magazine. (US) **656**
▼Columbia Metropolitan. (US) **2223**
Columbia Review (New York). (US ISSN 0010-1982) **2907, 2862**
Columbia River Water Management Report. (US ISSN 0360-6864) **4823**
Columbia Series in Molecular Biology. (US) **524**
Columbia Studies in Economics. (US ISSN 0069-6331) **656**
Columbia Studies in the Classical Tradition. (NE ISSN 0166-1302) **1276**
Columbia Today see Columbia (New York) **1308**
Columbia Union Visitor. (US) **4281**
Columbia University. American Language Program. Bulletin. (US) **2809**
Columbia University. East Asian Institute. Studies. (US) **3636, 2337**
†Columbia University. Harriman Institute. Studies. (US) **5167**
Columbia University. Institute on East Central Europe. East Central European Studies. (US) **2357**
Columbia University Graduate School of Business. Dissertations Series. (US) **656**
Columbia University - Presbyterian Hospital School of Nursing. Alumnae Association. Magazine. (US ISSN 0069-634X) **3277**

Columbia University Record. (US ISSN 0747-4504) **1308**
Columbia - V L A Journal of Law & the Arts. (US ISSN 0888-4226) **322, 2614**
Columbian (Chicago). (US ISSN 0010-2024) **1297**
Columbian (Columbus). (US) **3751**
Columbiana. (US ISSN 0893-276X) **1485,** 4431
Columbus Bride and Groom. (US) **3066,** 1290
Columbus Business Journal. (US) **656**
Columbus Computer Xchange. (US) **1458, 825, 1443, 1468**
Columbus Education Association Voice see C E A Voice **1619**
Columbus Free Press. (US) **2862**
Columbus Logbook. (NE) **50**
▼Columbus Market. (US) **2281**
Columbus Monthly. (US) **2223**
Columbus Times. (US) **1997**
Columbus 92. (IT) **2357**
The Columns (Fairmont). (US ISSN 0010-2091) **1308**
Columns (Madison). (US ISSN 0196-1306) **2403**
▼Columns (Minneapolis). (US) **2530**
Columns (Seattle). (US ISSN 1047-8604) **1308**
Com. (AU) **1390**
COM - A N D. (US ISSN 0738-4270) **825**
Com Ge Bulletin. (NE) **1390**
Com-O-Lib see C A A T Tracks **2750**
Com - S A C. (Computer Security, Auditing and Controls) (US ISSN 0738-4262) **1433**
Comarca de Suzano. (BL ISSN 0010-2105) **2175**
Combat. (PK ISSN 0010-2121) **3880**
Combat Craft see Navy International **3467**
Combat Crew. (US ISSN 0010-213X) **3454,** 50
Combat Culturel. (FR) **3880**
Combat Fleets of the World see Naval Institute Guide to Combat Fleets of the World **3466**
Combat Handguns. (US) **4469,** 257
†Combat Mission. (US) **5167**
Combat Nature. (FR ISSN 0184-7473) **1946,** 2186
Combat Ouvrier. (MQ) **2581**
Combat pour la Diaspora. (FR) **3880**
Combatiente. (CU) **3454**
Combattant 1940-1945. (BE) **3454**
Combinations. (US ISSN 0145-899X) **3789**
Combinatorica. (HU ISSN 0209-9683) **3032**
▼Combinatorics, Probability & Computing. (US ISSN 0963-5483) **3064**
Combined Cumulative Index to Obstetrics and Gynecology. (US ISSN 0884-8092) **3168,** 8, 3291
Combined Cumulative Index to Pediatrics. (US ISSN 0190-4981) **3168,** 8, 3320
Combined Jersey Herd Book, Directory and Elite Register of the U.K. see Jersey Herd Book and Members Directory **219**
Combined Simulation. (DK ISSN 0106-357X) **1435**
Comboni Missions. (US ISSN 0279-3652) **4261**
Combroad. (UK) **1371**
Combustibles. (BE) **3684**
Combustion and Flame. (US ISSN 0010-2180) **1817,** 2031
Combustion, Explosion, and Shock Waves. (English translation of: Fizika Goreniya i Vzryva) (US ISSN 0010-5082) **1852**
Combustion Institute. Western States Section. Papers. (US ISSN 0010-2199) **1852,** 1225
Combustion Science and Technology. (US ISSN 0010-2202) **1225,** 4099
Comda Key. (CN) **1058**
Come - All - Ye. (US ISSN 0736-6132) **2053,** 2403
Come and See. (CN ISSN 0316-3040) **4171**
Come Back Safely. (US) **4743**

Come Board Sailing see Windsurf **4531**
Come Gardening. (UK) **2292**
Come Learn Beginners. (UK ISSN 0950-7191) **4171,** 1746
Come Learn Juniors. (UK ISSN 0950-7213) **4171,** 1746
Come Learn Primaries. (UK ISSN 0950-7205) **4171,** 1746
Come Out! (SZ) **2452**
Comeback. (UK ISSN 0264-858X) **1721**
Comecon Data (Year). (UK) **927**
Comecon Merchant Ships. (UK) **4726**
Comecon Reports. (UK) **851**
†Comedia. (UK) **5167**
Comedie Francaise. (FR ISSN 0759-125X) **4631**
Comedy Buyers Bulletin. (US) **2862**
Comedy U S A Newswire. (US) **4469**
Comedy Writers Bulletin. (US) **1371**
Comenius. (NE ISSN 0167-9163) **1622,** 4402
Comentarios Bibliograficos Americanos. (US ISSN 0010-2237) **4140**
Comentarios Economicos de Actualidad.(BO) **656**
†Comentarios Sobre el Desarrollo Internacional. (US ISSN 0146-8537) **5167**
Comentarios sobre la Situacion Economica. (CL) **851**
Comercial and Industrial Directory of Panama. see Directorio Comercial e Industrial de Panama **1128**
Comerciante. (EC ISSN 0008-1868) **813**
Comercio. (CR) **813**
Comercio. (HO ISSN 0010-2245) **813**
Comercio. (PE ISSN 0010-2253) **834**
Comercio. (MX) **904**
Comercio & Mercados. (BL ISSN 0010-227X) **834**
Comercio Colombo Americano/Colombian American Business. (CK ISSN 0010-2288) **813**
Comercio e Industria. Suplemento Quicenal see Comercio Industria **813**
Comercio Ecuatoriano Americano/Ecuadorian American Business. (EC) **813**
Comercio Ecuatoriano. (EC ISSN 0010-2296) **813**
Comercio Exterior. (BL) **904**
Comercio Exterior. (MX ISSN 0185-0601) **904**
Comercio Exterior see Revista Comercio Exterior de Colombia **920**
Comercio Exterior de la Comunidad Valenciana. (SP) **813**
Comercio Hispano Britanico. (UK ISSN 0010-2326) **813**
Comercio Industria. (SP ISSN 0213-0637) **813**
Comercio, Industria, Servicos. (PO) **813**
Comercio Industria y Navegacion see La Camara **809**
Comercio Portugues see Comercio, Industria, Servicos **813**
Comercio y Produccion. (DR ISSN 0010-2342) **813**
Comercio y Produccion. (PE ISSN 0008-1892) **813**
Comercio y Produccion. (PR ISSN 0010-2350) **813**
Comestible. (SP) **2064**
Comet. (AT ISSN 0158-4243) **1622**
ComeUnity. (US) **2862**
Comex Weekly Market Report. (US) **942**
Comfort Engineering. (UK) **2298**
Comhar. (IE ISSN 0010-2369) **2862,** 2202
Comic Art Collection. (US ISSN 0192-5881) **2753,** 322, 4125
Comic Paper Magazin see C P M **1251**
Comic Reader. (US) **2862**
Comicos. (US) **2184**
Comics Buyers Guide. (US ISSN 0745-4570) **2435**
Comics Buyers Guide Price Guide see C B G Price Guide **2434**
Comics Interview. (US) **322,** 2983

Comics Journal. (US ISSN 0194-7869) **322,** 4125
▼Comics Retailer. (US) **1114,** 322
Comics Scene. (US) **1252**
▼CoMiMex. (US) **610,** 3482
Coming Attractions. (US) **1384**
Coming Changes. (US) **2452,** 4839
Coming Changes Newsletter. (US) **3594**
Coming Up! see San Francisco Bay Times **2457**
Comision Catolica Internacional de Migration. Informe Anual. see International Catholic Migration Commission. Annual Report **5216**
Comision de Integracion Electrica Regional. Directorio del Sector Electrico. (UY) **1884**
Comision de Integracion Electrica Regional. Recursos Energeticos de los Paises de la C I E R. (UY) **3684,** 4823
Comision Economica para America Latina y el Caribe Review see C E P A L Review **849**
Comision Interamericana de Mujeres. Asamblea Extraordinaria. Acta Final. see Inter-American Commission of Women. Special Assembly. Final Act **3943**
Comision Interamericana del Atun Tropical. Boletin. see Inter-American Tropical Tuna Commission. Bulletin **2043**
Comision InterAmericana del Atun Tropical. Informe Anual. see Inter-American Tropical Tuna Commission. Annual Report **2043**
Comision Nacional de Promocion y Proteccion de los Derechos Humanos. Boletin. (NQ) **3941**
Comissao Goiana de Folclore. Boletim. (BL) **2053**
Comitato dei Geografi Italiani. (IT) **2245**
Comitato per la Collaborazione tra Societa Medico-Scientifiche Italiane Federazione delle Societa Medico-Scientifiche. Italiane Bollettino Congressi (Year) see C C S S. Federazione delle Societa Medico-Scientifiche. Italiane Bollettino Congressi (Year) **3085**
Comitatus. (US ISSN 0069-6412) **2907,** 322, 2309
Comite Belge de la Distribution. Editions Speciales/Belgisch Comite voor de Distributie. Speciale Uitgaven. (BE) **1036**
Comite Belge de la Distribution. Information Specialisee see Comite Belge de la Distribution. Editions Speciales **1036**
Comite Central de la Bonneterie Belge. Report see Belgian Knitwear Association. Report **2087**
Comite Consultatif pour la Masse et les Grandeurs Apparentes. (FR ISSN 1016-3778) **3445**
Comite Consultif de la Normalisation et de la Qualite du Francais a l'Universite Laval. Bulletin see Terminologie **2847**
Comite de Accion Interamericana de Colombia. Boletin. (CK) **3880**
Comite de Controle de l'Electricite et du Gaz. Rapport Annuel. (BE) **1884,** 3684
Comite de Iglesias para Ayudas de Emergencia. Cuadernos. (PY) **3941**
Comite de Iglesias para Ayudas de Emergencia. Estudios. (PY) **3941**
Comite de Iglesias para Ayudas de Emergencia. Notas Trimestrales. (PY) **3941**
Comite des Associations d'Armateurs des Communautes Europeens. Annual Report. (BE) **4726**
Comite des Travaux Historiques et Scientifiques. Section de Geographie. Actes du Congres National des Societes Savantes. (FR ISSN 0071-8424) **2245**
Comite des Travaux Historiques et Scientifiques. Section de Philologie et Histoire. Actes du Congres National des Societes Savantes. (FR) **2357**

COMMENT 6067

Comite des Travaux Historiques et Scientifiques. Section des Sciences. Actes du Congres National des Societes Savantes. (FR) **4305**
Comite des Travaux Historiques et Scientifiques. Section des Sciences. Comptes Rendus du Congres National des Societes Savantes see Comite des Travaux Historiques et Scientifiques. Section des Sciences. Actes du Congres National des Societes Savantes **4305**
Comite du Folklore Champenois. Bulletin. (FR ISSN 0413-9593) **2053**
Comite Evangelico Pro-Ayuda al Desarrollo Informe Anual see C E P A D. Informe Anual **4400**
Comite Hispano-Sueco. Camara de Comercio de Suecia en Espana. Circular Informativa see Camara de Comercio Hispano-Sueca de Madrid. Info **810**
Comite Interafricain d'Etudes Hydrauliques. Bulletin de Liaison see Interafrican Committee for Hydraulic Studies. Liaison Bulletin **4826**
Comite International de Cooperation dans les Recherches Nationales en Demographie. Actes des Seminaires. (FR) **3980**
Comite International des Poids et Mesures. Comite Consultatif d'Electricite. (Rapport et Annexes). (FR ISSN 0069-6455) **3445,** 1884
Comite International des Poids et Mesures. Comite Consultatif de Photometrie et Radiometrie. (Rapport et Annexes). (FR) **3445,** 3852
Comite International des Poids et Mesures. Comite Consultatif de Thermometrie. Rapports et Annexes. (FR ISSN 0069-6463) **3445,** 3840
Comite International des Poids et Mesures. Comite Consultatif des Unites (Rapport et Annexes). (FR ISSN 0373-3181) **3445**
Comite International des Poids et Mesures. Comite Consultatif pour la Definition de la Seconde. (Rapport et Annexes). (FR ISSN 0588-6228) **3445**
Comite International des Poids et Mesures. Comite Consultatif pour la Definition du Metre (Rapport et Annexes). (FR ISSN 0253-2182) **3445**
Comite International des Poids et Mesures. Comite Consultatif pour les Etalons des Mesure des Rayonnements Ionisants (Rapport et Annexes). (FR ISSN 0255-3147) **3445**
Comite International des Poids et Mesures. Proces-Verbaux des Seances. (FR ISSN 0370-2596) **3445**
Comite International des Poids et Mesures. Systeme International d'Unites. (FR) **3445**
Comite Solidarite Philippines. Bulletin. (FR) **3941,** 2213
Comites de Prevention du Batiment et des Travaux Publics. Cahiers. (FR ISSN 0010-244X) **610**
Comm-Ent: Hastings Journal of Communications and Entertainment Law see Hastings Communications and Entertainment Law Journal (Comm - Ent) **2631**
Comma. (IT) **2090**
Command, Control, Communications and Intelligence Handbook see C 3 I Handbook **3453**
Command, Control, Communications & Intelligence Jane's C 3 I Systems see Jane's C 3 I Systems **3461**
Commando see Paratus **3468**
Comme les Autres. (FR ISSN 0010-2520) **922**
Comment. see Commentaire (Don Mills) **2530**
Comment see Governing Georgia **4061**

6068 COMMENT

Comment and Opinion: A Weekly Survey of the South African Press and Radio *see* South African Digest **5279**

Comment Evaluer la Part du Trafic Maritime de Notre Commerce Exterieur qui Echappe aux Ports Francais. (FR) **4663**

†Comment on Education. (CN ISSN 0315-4351) **5167**

Commentaire. (FR ISSN 0180-8214) **2907**

Commentary (Don Mills)/Comment. (CN ISSN 0382-7046) **2530**

Commentaires des Principales Decisions du Tribunal Administratif de la Reunion. (RE) **4057**

Commentarii Mathematici Helvetici. (SZ ISSN 0010-2571) **3032**

Commentarii Mathematici Universitatis Sancti Pauli/Rikkyo Daigaku Sugaku Zasshi. (JA ISSN 0010-258X) **3033**

Commentarium pro Religiosis et Missionariis. (IT ISSN 0010-2598) **4261**

Commentary *see* Market Research Society. Journal **1045**

Commentary. (US ISSN 0010-2601) **2862**

Commentary. (SI ISSN 0084-8956) **2862**

Commentationes Humanarum Litterarum. (FI ISSN 0069-6587) **2505**

Commentationes Mathematicae Universitatis Carolinae. (CS ISSN 0010-2628) **3033**

Commentationes Physico-Mathematicae *see* Commentationes Physico-Mathematicae et Chemico-Medicae **3816**

Commentationes Physico-Mathematicae et Chemico-Medicae. (FI ISSN 0788-5717) **3816**, 475, 1175, 3033, 3090

Commentationes Scientiarum Socialium.(FI ISSN 0355-256X) **4369**

Commentator. (US ISSN 0010-2652) **1308**, 1997

†Comments. (US) **5167**

Comments and Corrections. (US) **4057**

Comments & Criticisms. (US ISSN 0267-9469) **4017**, 3763

Comments from C A S T. (US ISSN 0194-4096) **84**, 2064, 2124, 3604

Comments on Agricultural and Food Chemistry. (US ISSN 0892-2101) **84**, 2064

Comments on Argentine Trade. (AG ISSN 0010-2660) **813**

Comments on Astrophysics. (US ISSN 0146-2970) **363**, 3816

Comments on Atomic and Molecular Physics. (US ISSN 0010-2687) **3847**

Comments on Condensed Matter Physics. (US ISSN 0885-4483) **3816**

▼Comments on Developmental Neurobiology. (US ISSN 0896-5099) **3334**, 435

Comments on Inorganic Chemistry. (US ISSN 0260-3594) **1213**

Comments on Molecular and Cellular Biophysics. (US ISSN 0143-8123) **485**

Comments on Money and Credit. (US) **772**

Comments on Nuclear and Particle Physics. (US ISSN 0010-2709) **3847**

Comments on Plasma Physics and Controlled Fusion. (US ISSN 0374-2806) **3847**, 3816

Comments on Solid State Physics *see* Comments on Condensed Matter Physics **3816**

Comments on Theoretical Biology. (US ISSN 0894-8550) **435**

Comments on Toxicology. (US ISSN 0886-5140) **1981**, 3090, 3721

Commercant. (FR) **1114**

Commerce *see* Associated Chambers of Commerce of Zimbabwe. Commerce **807**

Commerce. (NP) **834**, 904

Commerce *see* Revue Commerce **839**
Commerce. *see* Thuong Mai **839**
Commerce. (II ISSN 0010-275X) **851**
†Commerce. (US ISSN 0010-2741) **5167**
Commerce. Le Point. (CN ISSN 0380-9811) **834**
Commerce Africain. *see* African Trade **899**
Commerce B.C. *see* Chamber Comment and the Chamber Newsbulletin **811**
Commerce Business Daily. (US ISSN 0095-3423) **1036**, 1073
Commerce Clearing House, Inc. Tax Planning Review *see* C C H Tax Planning Review **1089**
Commerce du Levant. (LE ISSN 0010-2814) **834**, 904
Commerce et Cooperation. (FR ISSN 0222-6618) **813**
Commerce et Perspectives. (FR) **656**
†Commerce Exterieur de l'U.E.B.L. Avec les Pays d'Afrique. (BE) **5167**
†Commerce Exterieur de l'U.E.B.L. Avec les Pays d'Amerique Latine/Buitenlandse Handel van de B.L.E.U. Met de Landen van Latijns Amerika. (BE) **5167**
†Commerce Exterieur de l'U.E.B.L. Avec les Pays d'Asie/Buitenlandse Handel van de B.L.E.U. Met de Landen van Azie. (BE) **5167**
†Commerce Exterieur de l'U.E.B.L. Avec les Pays de l'Est/Buitenlandse Handel van de B.L.E.U. Met de Oostlanden. (BE) **5167**
†Commerce Exterieur de l'U.E.B.L. Avec les Pays de la C.E.E/Buitlandse Handel van de B.L.E.U. Met de E.E.G.-Lidstaten. (BE) **5168**
†Commerce Exterieur de l'U.E.B.L. Avec les Pays Industrialises (Autre Que les Pays de la C.E.E. et l'A.E.L.E.)/Buitenlandse Handel van de B.L.E.U. met de Industrielanden (Niet E.E.G.- en E.V.A.- Lidstaten). (BE) **5168**
Commerce Exterieur de la Cote d'Ivorie: Resultats et Evolution. (IV) **904**
Commerce Exterieur de la Grece. (GR) **711**
Commerce Exterieur des Regions Provence, Cote d'Azur et Corse. (FR) **813**
Commerce Exterieur: Nomenclature des Pays. *see* External Trade: Nomenclature of Goods **908**
Commerce Francais de la Pomme de Terre. (FR) **173**
Commerce Franco-Suisse. (SZ ISSN 0010-2830) **813**
Commerce Hotline *see* Milwaukee Commerce Hot-line **838**
Commerce in Belgium *see* AmCham **806**
Commerce in France. (FR ISSN 0010-2849) **813**
Commerce in Nigeria *see* Nigerian Business Journal **820**
Commerce International *see* London Commerce **819**
Commerce Magazine. (UK) **834**
Commerce Magazine (Bucks, Beds, Northants) *see* Commerce Magazine **834**
Commerce Montreal. (CN ISSN 0318-4560) **813**
Commerce News *see* Edmonton Chamber of Commerce. Commerce News **815**
Commerce-Reparation Automobile. (FR) **4688**, 4517
Commerce: The Journal of Minority Business *see* Minority Business Today **1116**
Commerce Yearbook of Ports, Shipping and Shipbuilding. (II) **4726**
Commerce Yearbook of Public Sector. (II ISSN 0591-1710) **834**
Commerce Yearbook of Road Transport. (II) **4718**
Commerce Yearbook of Shipping and Shipbuilding *see* Commerce Yearbook of Ports, Shipping and Shipbuilding **4726**
Commerces. (FR) **851**
The Commercial. (MK) **656**
Commercial Agriculture in Zimbabwe. (RH ISSN 0259-3238) **84**

†Commercial Air Transport Industry. (UK) **5168**
Commercial and Financial Chronicle. (US ISSN 0163-2876) **942**
†Commercial and Industrial Floorspace Statistics. (UK ISSN 0262-5334) **5168**
Commercial Architecture. (JA) **297**
Commercial Bank of Ethiopia. Annual Report. (ET ISSN 0588-6694) **772**
Commercial Bank of Ethiopia. Market Report. (ET ISSN 0045-7574) **772**
Commercial Bank of Ethiopia. Trade Directory. (ET) **1127**
Commercial Bank of Greece. Economic Bulletin. (GR ISSN 0013-0028) **851**
Commercial Bank of Greece. Report. (GR) **772**
Commercial Bank of Greece. Report of the Chairman of the Board of Directors. (GR ISSN 0424-9402) **772**
Commercial Bank of Kuwait. Annual Report of the Board of Directors and Accounts. (KU) **772**
†Commercial Construction Report. (US) **5168**
Commercial Courier. (MM ISSN 0010-2938) **813**
Commercial Crime International. (UK ISSN 1012-2710) **1512**, 656
Commercial Economics and Management. *see* Shangye Jingji yu Guanli **1027**
Commercial Expansion Reporter *see* Sales Prospector **1084**
Commercial Fish Farmer and Aquaculture News *see* Aquaculture Magazine **2036**
Commercial Fisheries News. (US) **2038**
Commercial Fisheries Product News *see* Fisheries Product News **2040**
Commercial Fishing. (UK ISSN 0143-652X) **2038**
Commercial Fishing. (NZ) **2038**
†Commercial Fishing Newsletter. (US) **5168**
Commercial Herald. (II ISSN 0010-3012) **834**
Commercial Horticulture. (AT) **173**
Commercial Inc. (US ISSN 1061-138X) **4146**
Commercial Insolvency Reporter. (CN ISSN 0832-7688) **2614**
Commercial Interiors International. (UK) **2549**
Commercial Investment Real Estate Journal. (US ISSN 0887-4778) **4146**, 942
Commercial Journal. (II ISSN 0010-3039) **834**
Commercial Law Bulletin. (US) **2614**
†Commercial Law Digest. (CN ISSN 0832-235X) **5168**
Commercial Law Gazette. (II) **2721**
Commercial Law Journal. (US ISSN 0010-3055) **2614**
Commercial Law Report. (US) **2614**, 656
Commercial Laws of Europe. (UK ISSN 0141-7258) **2614**
Commercial Lease Law Insider. (US ISSN 0736-0517) **4146**, 2614
Commercial Leases. (UK) **942**
Commercial Leasing Law and Strategy. (US) **4146**
†Commercial Lender's Alert. (US) **5168**
Commercial Lending Newsletter. (US) **772**
Commercial Lending Review. (US ISSN 0886-8204) **772**
Commercial Loan Documentation Guide.(US) **772**, 2614
Commercial Master File: Restricted. (US) **1347**
Commercial Master File Supplement: Restricted. (US) **1347**
Commercial Motor. (UK ISSN 0010-3063) **4743**
Commercial News. (CN) **656**
Commercial News U S A. (US) **904**
†Commercial News U S A. New Products Annual Directory. (US ISSN 0270-2460) **5168**
▼Commercial Paper and Payment Systems. (US) **2614**

Commercial Paper Ratings Guide *see* Standard & Poor's Commercial Paper Ratings Guide **964**
Commercial Photo. (JA) **3789**
Commercial Photography. (AT) **3789**
Commercial Photography Journal. (JA) **3789**
Commercial Printing. (SA) **3998**
Commercial Profile. (US) **4146**
▼Commercial Property News. (US) **4147**
Commercial Property Register *see* Property Register **4155**
†Commercial Record. (US ISSN 0010-3098) **5168**
Commercial Remodeling *see* Commercial Renovation **610**
Commercial Renovation. (US) **610**
Commercial Review. (US) **205**
†Commercial Shipper. (UK) **5168**
†Commercial Space. (US) **5168**
†Commercial Space Report. (US ISSN 0735-9314) **5168**
Commercial Transport. (SA) **4743**
Commercial Transport *see* Commercial Transport and Transport Managers Journal **4743**
Commercial Transport and Transport Managers Journal. (IE) **4743**, 4726
Commercial Travellers' Guild Gazette *see* C T G Gazette **1035**
Commercial Vehicle Data Digest. (SA) **4743**
Commercial Vehicle Dealers' Digest *see* Commercial Vehicle Dealers' Guide **4743**
Commercial Vehicle Dealers' Guide. (SA) **4743**
Commercial Vessel Yearbook. (AT ISSN 1030-0759) **2039**
Commercial West *see* Northwestern Financial Review **793**
Commercial West Bank Directory *see* Northwestern Bank Directory: Upper Midwest **1148**
Commercial West Bank Directory of Upper Midwest *see* Northwestern Bank Directory: Upper Midwest **1148**
Commerciale Bollettino della Laniera. Supplemento. (IT) **4617**
Commerciante. (IT) **834**
Commercio. (IT) **834**
Commercio del Colore e Hobby. (IT) **1281**
Commercio del Popolo. (IT) **834**
Commercio Edile. (IT) **610**
Commercio Elettrico. (IT ISSN 0392-3479) **1884**
Commercio Turismo. (IT ISSN 0017-0151) **834**, 4758
Commercio Veronese. (IT) **656**
Commercium. (II ISSN 0010-3160) **834**
Commerzbank, Frankfurt. Business Notes. (GW) **851**
Commission. (US ISSN 0010-3179) **4234**
Commission Bancaire. Rapport Annuel. (FR) **772**
Commission Belge de Bibliographie. Bulletin *see* Commission Belge de Bibliographie et de Bibliologie. Bulletin **397**
Commission Belge de Bibliographie et de Bibliologie. Bulletin. (BE) **397**
Commission Canadienne pour UNESCO. Bulletin. *see* Canadian Commission for UNESCO. Bulletin **1620**
Commission de la Bourse de Bruxelles. Indices et Statistiques. Bulletin Mensuel. (BE) **942**
Commission de Pacifique Sud. Fiche Technique *see* Pest Advisory Leaflet **187**
Commission Departementale d'Histoire et d'Archeologie. Bulletin. (FR ISSN 0758-2722) **269**, 297
Commission des Anciennes Lois et Ordonnances de Belgique. Proces-Verbaux *see* Commission Royale des Anciennes Lois et Ordonnances de Belgique. Bulletin **2309**

Commission des Communautes Europeennes. Rapports Annuels sur l'Etat des Travaux de Recherches Encouragees par la CECA see Commission of the European Communities. Annual Reports on the Progress of Research Work Promoted by the ECSC 4099

Commission des Ecoles Catholiques de Montreal Bulletin d'Information see C E C M Bulletin d'Information 1619

Commission for Scientific Research in Greenland. Newsletter see Danish Polar Center. Newsletter 4306

Commission for the Geological Map of the World. Bulletin. (FR ISSN 0074-9427) 1558

Commission Internationale Catholique pour les Migrations. Rapport Annuel. see International Catholic Migration Commission. Annual Report 5216

Commission Internationale de l'Eclairage Journal see C I E - Journal 5157

Commission Internationale de l'Eclairage News see C I E - News 1883

Commission Internationale des Industries Agricole et Alimentaires Symposia see C.I.I.A. Symposia 5157

Commission of the European Communities. Annual Reports on the Progress of Research Work Promoted by the ECSC. (EI) 4099

Commission of the European Communities. Collection of Agreements. (EI) 904, 2721

Commission of the European Communities. Community Law. (BE ISSN 0590-6563) 2721

Commission of the European Communities. Directorate of Taxation. Inventory of Taxes. (EI) 1091

Commission of the European Communities. Documentation Bulletin. (EI) 3936, 8

Commission of the European Communities. Europa Transport. Annual Report. (EI) 4648

Commission of the European Communities. European Regional Development Fund. Annual Report. (EI) 927

Commission of the European Communities. Expose sur l'Evolution Sociale dans la Communaute see Commission of the European Communities. Report on the Social Developments 4369

Commission of the European Communities. Financial Report. (EI ISSN 0590-6571) 1091

†Commission of the European Communities. Index to (Year) C O M Documents. (EI) 5168

Commission of the European Communities. Marches Agricoles: Serie "Prix". Notes Explicatif. (EI) 148

Commission of the European Communities. Marches Agricoles: Serie "Prix". Produits Animaux. (EI) 149, 215

Commission of the European Communities. Marches Agricoles: Serie "Prix". Produits Vegetaux. (EI) 149, 173

†Commission of the European Communities. Monthly Catalogue. Part A: Publications. (EI ISSN 0256-7121) 5168

Commission of the European Communities. Operation of Nuclear Power Stations. (EI) 1804

Commission of the European Communities. Report on Competition Policy. (EI) 1073, 904

Commission of the European Communities. Report on the Social Developments. (EI) 4369

Commission of the European Communities. Report on the Social Situation see Commission of the European Communities. Report on the Social Developments 4369

†Commission of the European Communities. Studies: Social Policy Series. (EI) 5168

Commission of the European Communities. Terminology and Computer Applications. Translation and Terminology Bulletin see Terminologie et Traduction 2847

Commission of the European Communities. Trade Union Information Bulletin. (EI) 2581

Commission of the European Communities, Directory. (EI ISSN 0591-1745) 2721

Commission Royale d'Histoire. Bulletin. (BE ISSN 0001-415X) 2309

Commission Royale de Toponymie et de Dialectologie. Bulletin/Koninklijke Commissie voor Toponymie en Dialectologie. Handelingen. (BE ISSN 0774-8396) 2809

Commission Royale des Anciennes Lois et Ordonnances de Belgique. Bulletin/Koninklijke Commissie voor de Uitgave der Oude Wetten en Verordeningen van Belgie. Handelingen. (BE) 2309, 2614

Commissione Archeologica Comunale di Roma. Bollettino/Archaeological Commission of Rome. Bulletin. (IT) 269

Commissione Tributaria Centrale. (IT) 1091, 2614

Commissions Royales d'Art et d'Archeologie. Bulletin see Belgium. Commission Royale des Monuments et des Sites. Bulletin 295

Committee for Aerospace Structures. Research Report. (JA) 50

Committee for Economic Development of Australia Cortex Cassettes see C E D A Cortex Cassettes 1073

Committee for Economic Development of Australia Information Papers (I P Series) see C E D A Information Papers (I P Series) 849

Committee for Economic Development of Australia Monograph Series see C E D A Monograph Series 1073

Committee for Economic Development of Australia Series see C E D A "P" Series 1073

Committee for Health Rights in Central America News see C H R I C A News 927

†Committee for Human Rights in Grenada. Bulletin. (US) 5168

Committee for Monetary Research and Education, Inc. Monographs see C M R E Monographs 769

Committee for the Educational Rights of Students Newsletter. (US) 1622

Committee of Interns and Residents News see C I R News 3085

Committee of Small Magazine Editors & Publishers Newsletter see C O S M E P Newsletter 4124

Committee on Institutional Cooperation. Annual Report. (US ISSN 0069-6854) 1703

Committee on Institutional Cooperation Net: The Circuit see C I C Net: The Circuit 1426

Committee on Invisible Exports. Annual Report see British Invisible Exports Council. Annual Report 902

Committee on Science and Technology in Developing Countries Newsletter see C O S T E D Newsletter 4303

Committee on Space Research Information Bulletin see C O S P A R Information Bulletin 49

Committee on Special Educational Needs News see C O S P E N News 1734

Committee to Combat Huntington's Disease Newsletter see Marker 3344

Committee to Restore the Constitution. Bulletin. (US) 3880, 1503

Commline. (US ISSN 0744-2386) 1446

Commodex System. (US) 942

Commodities see Futures (Cedar Falls) 947

Commodities Law Letter. (US ISSN 0277-2930) 2614

Commodities Litigation Reporter. (US ISSN 0887-784X) 2614

Commodities Magazine Reference Guide to Futures Markets see Futures Magazine Reference Guide to Futures Markets 947

Commodity Analyst Financial Charts. (AT) 942, 772

Commodity Analyst International Charts.(AT) 942, 772

Commodity Analyst Share Charts. (AT) 942, 772

Commodity Classification for Foreign Trade Statistics: Japan see Export Statistical Schedule of Japan (Year) 907

Commodity Classification for Foreign Trade Statistics: Japan see Import Statistical Schedule of Japan (Year) 911

Commodity Closeup see Trends in Futures 967

Commodity Drain Report of Florida's Primary Forest Industries see Florida Wood-Using Industry Directory 2099

Commodity Futures Forecast Service. (US) 942, 84

Commodity Futures Law Reports. (US) 2614, 942

Commodity Information Systems. (US) 942, 149

Commodity Perspective. (US) 942

Commodity Price Charts. (US) 942

Commodity Price Monthly. (CH ISSN 0257-5698) 851, 904

Commodity Price Statistics Monthly. (CH ISSN 0257-5728) 711, 4569

Commodity Prices. (US) 943

Commodity Research Bureau Futures Chart Service see C R B Futures Chart Service 941

Commodity Research Bureau Outlook see C R B Outlook 5157

Commodity Spread Trader see Spread Trader 964

Commodity Trade and Price Trends. (UN ISSN 0251-401X) 927

Commodity Trade Statistics. (UN ISSN 0010-3233) 711, 4569

Commodity World News see Futures World News 947

Commodity Year Book. (US ISSN 0069-6862) 943

Commodity Yearbook Statistical Abstract Service see Commodity Yearbook Statistical Update 136

Commodity Yearbook Statistical Update.(US) 136, 8

Commodore Computer Club. (IT) 1468, 1429, 1466

†Commodore Disk User. (UK ISSN 0953-0614) 5168

†Commodore Magazine. (US ISSN 0744-8724) 5168

Commodore User. (UK) 1468, 1458

Commodore World. (US) 1468, 1458

Commodore World (Italy). (US) 1468, 1458

Common Agricultural Policy Legislation see C A P Legislation 81

Common Agricultural Policy Monitor see C A P Monitor 81

Common Boundary. (US ISSN 0885-8500) 4017, 4171

Common, Carrier Conference-Irregular Route. Newsletter. (US) 4708

Common Carrier Individual Land Mobile Data Base Name Sequence. (US) 1347

Common Carrier Land Mobile Base Station Cumulative Staff Study. (US) 1347

Common Carrier Land Mobile Base Station Cumulative Staff Study Listing. (US) 1347

Common Carrier Land Mobile Base Stations Data Base (Suppliers). (US) 1347

Common Carrier Microwave Antenna, Licensee, and Transmitter File. (US) 1347

Common Carrier Microwave Authorization File (Licensees). (US) 1347

Common Carrier Microwave Construction Permit File. (US) 1347, 637

Common Carrier Microwave Data Base. (US) 1347

Common Carrier Microwave Pending Application Dump. (US) 1347

Common Carrier Week. (US ISSN 0743-4812) 1362

Common Cause Magazine. (US ISSN 0271-9592) 3880

†Common Focus. (US) 5168

Common Good see Pro Ecclesia Magazine 4273

Common Ground see Union Matters 2591

Common Ground. (UK ISSN 0010-325X) 4171, 4431

Common Ground (Alexandria). (US ISSN 0885-6133) 4147

Common Ground (Des Moines). (US) 4261

Common Ground (San Anselmo). (US) 4017

Common Ground Hawaii. (US) 4017

▼Common Knowledge. (US ISSN 0961-754X) 3764, 2907

Common Life. (UK ISSN 0010-3276) 3880

Common Lives - Lesbian Lives. (US ISSN 0891-6969) 2452, 4839

Common Market Law Reports. (UK ISSN 0588-7445) 2614

Common Market Law Review. (NE ISSN 0165-0750) 2721

Common Market News. (UK ISSN 0300-4406) 851

Common Market News Letter see Common Market News 851

Common Market Reports. (US ISSN 0572-9750) 904

†Common Name - Kartei Pflanzenschutz- und Schaedlingsbekaempfungsmittel. (GW ISSN 0138-4074) 5168

Common Sense. 3880

Common Sense. (AT) 3880, 656

†Common Sense Economics. (CN ISSN 0319-7549) 5168

Common Sense in Jefferson County. (US) 3881

Common Sense Pest Control Quarterly. (US ISSN 8756-7881) 530, 3709, 4099

Common Wealth see Common Wealth Journal 3881

Common Wealth Journal. (UK) 3881

†Commonplace Book. (US ISSN 0010-3314) 5168

Commons, Open Spaces and Footpaths Preservation Society. Journal see Open Spaces 4552

Commonweal. (US ISSN 0010-3330) 2862, 4261

Commonwealth. (CN ISSN 0010-3357) 2862, 3881

Commonwealth. (FR ISSN 0395-6989) 2862

†Commonwealth. (UK ISSN 0010-3411) 5168

Commonwealth Agricultural Bureaux International. Forestry Bureau. Annotated Bibliographies see C.A.B. International. Forestry Bureau. Annotated Bibliographies 2111

Commonwealth Agricultural Bureaux International. Mycological Institute. Phytopathological Papers see C.A.B. International. Mycological Institute. Phytopathological Papers 498

Commonwealth Agricultural Bureaux Prompts Series: Chickpea and Pigeon Peas Prompts see C.A.B. Prompts Series: Chickpea and Pigeon Peas Prompts 134

Commonwealth Agricultural Bureaux Prompts Series: Groundnut Prompts see C.A.B. Prompts Series: Groundnut Prompts 135

Commonwealth and Colonial History Newsletter. (NZ ISSN 0045-7620) 2309

Commonwealth Bibliographies. (UK ISSN 0306-1124) 397

Commonwealth Broadcasting Association. Handbook. (UK) 1371

Commonwealth Bureau of Agricultural Economics. Annotated Bibliographies Series A see C.A.B. International Bureau of Agricultural Economics. Annotated Bibliographies Series A 134

6070 COMMONWEALTH BUREAU

Commonwealth Bureau of Agricultural Economics. Annotated Bibliographies. Series B: Agricultural Policy and Rural Development in Africa *see* C.A.B. International Bureau of Agricultural Economics. Annotated Bibliographies. Series B: Agricultural Policy and Rural Development in Africa **134**

†Commonwealth Bureau of Animal Health. Review Series. (UK ISSN 0069-6927) **5168**

†Commonwealth Bureau of Horticulture and Plantation Crops. Horticultural Review. (UK ISSN 0069-6986) **5168**

†Commonwealth Bureau of Horticulture and Plantation Crops. Research Reviews. (UK ISSN 0069-6994) **5168**

†Commonwealth Bureau of Horticulture and Plantation Crops. Technical Communications. (UK ISSN 0069-7001) **5168**

Commonwealth Bureau of Nutrition. Annotated Bibliographies *see* C.A.B. International. Bureau of Nutrition. Annotated Bibliographies **3613**

Commonwealth Bureau of Soils. Annotated Bibliographies *see* C.A.B. International. Bureau of Soils. Annotated Bibliographies **134**

Commonwealth Council for Educational Administration Newsletter *see* C C E A Newsletter **1725**

Commonwealth Currents. (UK ISSN 0141-8513) **3953**

Commonwealth Forestry Bureau Annotated Bibliographies *see* C.A.B. International. Forestry Bureau. Annotated Bibliographies **2111**

Commonwealth Forestry Review. (UK ISSN 0010-3381) **2098**

Commonwealth Foundation Occasional Paper (No.). (AT ISSN 0069-7087) **1726**

Commonwealth Geological Liaison Office. Newsletter *see* Earth Sciences Programme Newsletter **1559**

Commonwealth Government Directory. (AT) **4057**

Commonwealth Human Ecology Council Journal *see* C H E C Journal **4099**

Commonwealth Human Ecology Council Points *see* C H E C Points **4099**

Commonwealth Income Tax Statistics *see* Australia. Department of the Treasury. Income Tax Statistics **703**

Commonwealth Independent States Soviet Travel Newsletter *see* C I S Soviet Travel Newsletter **4755**

Commonwealth Institute, London. Annual Report. (UK ISSN 0069-7109) **2245**, 3953

Commonwealth International Law Cases. (US) **2721**

Commonwealth Law Bulletin. (UK ISSN 0305-0718) **2614**

Commonwealth Law Reports. (AT ISSN 0069-7133) **2734**

CommonWealth Letters. (US ISSN 0893-9136) **4147**, 851, 943

Commonwealth Library Association Newsletter *see* C O M L A Newsletter **2751**

Commonwealth Magazine. (US ISSN 0010-3365) **2223**

Commonwealth Magistrates' Conference. Report. (UK ISSN 0307-6539) **2734**

Commonwealth Mycological Institute. Phytopathological Papers *see* C.A.B. International. Mycological Institute. Phytopathological Papers **498**

Commonwealth Novel in English. (US ISSN 0732-6734) **2907**, 2505, 2862, 3636

Commonwealth of Australia Gazette *see* Commonwealth of Australia Gazette: Public Service **4057**

Commonwealth of Australia Gazette: General. (AT) **4057**

Commonwealth of Australia Gazette: Periodic. (AT) **4057**

Commonwealth of Australia Gazette: Public Service. (AT) **4057**

Commonwealth of Australia Gazette: Special. (AT) **4057**

Commonwealth of Kentucky. Annual Economic Report (Year). (US) **656**

Commonwealth of Pennsylvania. Airport Directory. (US) **50**

Commonwealth of Pennsylvania Aeronautical Chart. (US) **50**

Commonwealth Parliamentary Association. Malawi Branch. Conference. Report of Proceedings. (MW) **4057**

Commonwealth Parliamentary Association. Malawi Branch. Executive Committee. Annual Report. (MW) **4057**

Commonwealth Philately. (US) **3751**

Commonwealth Press Union News *see* C P U News **2568**

Commonwealth Professional. (AT ISSN 0045-7639) **4057**

Commonwealth Record. (AT ISSN 0313-5136) **4057**

†Commonwealth Report. (US) **5168**

Commonwealth Scientific and Industrial Research Organization. Annual Report. (AT ISSN 0069-7184) **4595**

Commonwealth Scientific and Industrial Research Organization. Division of Animal Health. Report. (AT ISSN 1031-1580) **4808**

Commonwealth Scientific and Industrial Research Organization. Division of Animal Health. Research Report *see* Commonwealth Scientific and Industrial Research Organization. Division of Animal Health. Report **4808**

Commonwealth Scientific and Industrial Research Organization. Division of Atmospheric Physics. Annual Report *see* Commonwealth Scientific and Industrial Research Organization. Division of Atmospheric Research. Research Report **3434**

Commonwealth Scientific and Industrial Research Organization. Division of Animal Production. Report. (AT ISSN 0155-7742) **571**, 580

Commonwealth Scientific and Industrial Research Organization. Division of Atmospheric Physics. Technical Paper *see* Commonwealth Scientific and Industrial Research Organization. Division of Atmospheric Research. Technical Paper **3434**

Commonwealth Scientific and Industrial Research Organization. Division of Animal Production. Technical Report.(AT) **571**, 215

Commonwealth Scientific and Industrial Research Organization. Division of Atmospheric Research. Research Report. (AT ISSN 0159-0219) **3434**

Commonwealth Scientific and Industrial Research Organization. Division of Atmospheric Research. Technical Paper. (AT) **3434**

Commonwealth Scientific and Industrial Research Organization. Division of Biomolecular Engineering. Annual Report. (AT) **475**

†Commonwealth Scientific and Industrial Research Organization. Division of Building Research. Technical Paper. (AT) **5168**

Commonwealth Scientific and Industrial Research Organization. Division of Coal and Energy Technology. Annual Report. (AT) **1946**, 1785

Commonwealth Scientific and Industrial Research Organization. Division of Exploration Geoscience. Annual Report. (AT) **3482**

Commonwealth Scientific and Industrial Research Organization. Division of Entomology. Report. (AT ISSN 0069-732X) **530**

†Commonwealth Scientific and Industrial Research Organization. Division of Entomology. Technical Paper. (AT ISSN 0069-7338) **5168**

Commonwealth Scientific and Industrial Research Organization. Division of Fisheries and Oceanography. Report *see* Commonwealth Scientific and Industrial Research Organization. Marine Laboratories. Report **2039**

Commonwealth Scientific and Industrial Research Organization. Division of Food Processing. Report of Research. (AT) **2064**

†Commonwealth Scientific and Industrial Research Organization. Division of Food Processing. Technical Paper. (AT) **5168**

Commonwealth Scientific and Industrial Research Organization. Division of Food Research. Report of Research *see* Commonwealth Scientific and Industrial Research Organization. Division of Food Processing. Report of Research **2064**

Commonwealth Scientific and Industrial Research Organization. Division of Geomechanics. Abstracts of Published Papers. (AT ISSN 0310-1894) **1842**

Commonwealth Scientific and Industrial Research Organization. Division of Geomechanics. Geomechanics Computer Programs. (AT ISSN 0816-6013) **4359**

Commonwealth Scientific and Industrial Research Organization. Division of Geomechanics. Geomechanics of Coal Mining Report. (AT ISSN 0726-6510) **3482**

Commonwealth Scientific and Industrial Research Organization. Division of Geomechanics. Technical Report. (AT ISSN 0069-7249) **3482**, 1542, 1863

Commonwealth Scientific and Industrial Research Organization. Division of Horticulture. Report. (AT) **2124**

Commonwealth Scientific and Industrial Research Organization. Division of Horticultural Research. Report *see* Commonwealth Scientific and Industrial Research Organization. Division of Horticulture. Report **2124**

Commonwealth Scientific and Industrial Research Organization. Division of Plant Industry. Plant Introduction Review *see* Australian Plant Introduction Review **170**

Commonwealth Scientific and Industrial Research Organization. Division of Soils. Annual Report. (AT ISSN 1032-5441) **173**

Commonwealth Scientific and Industrial Research Organization. Division of Soils. Divisional Report. (AT ISSN 0725-8526) **174**

Commonwealth Scientific and Industrial Research Organization. Division of Soil Mechanics. Technical Report *see* Commonwealth Scientific and Industrial Research Organization. Division of Geomechanics. Technical Report **3482**

Commonwealth Scientific and Industrial Research Organization. Division of Soils. Research Report *see* Commonwealth Scientific and Industrial Research Organization. Division of Soils. Annual Report **173**

Commonwealth Scientific and Industrial Research Organization. Division of Tropical Crops and Pastures. Annual Report. (AT ISSN 0816-8474) **174**, 500

Commonwealth Scientific and Industrial Research Organization. Division of Tropical Crops and Pastures. Biennial Research Report. (AT ISSN 1036-0220) **174**, 500

Commonwealth Scientific and Industrial Research Organization. Division of Tropical Crops and Pastures. Genetic Resources Communication. (AT ISSN 0159-6071) **174**, 215

Commonwealth Scientific and Industrial Research Organization. Division of Tropical Crops and Pastures. Research Report. (AT ISSN 0156-2444) **84**

Commonwealth Scientific and Industrial Research Organization. Division of Tropical Crops and Pastures. Tropical Agronomy Technical Memorandum. (AT ISSN 0157-9711) **84**

Commonwealth Scientific and Industrial Research Organization. Division of Tropical Crops and Pastures. Technical Paper. (AT) **174**, 500

†Commonwealth Scientific and Industrial Research Organization. Division of Textile Physics. Annual Report. (AT) **5168**

Commonwealth Scientific and Industrial Research Organization. Division of Tropical Pastures. Technical Paper *see* Commonwealth Scientific and Industrial Research Organization. Division of Tropical Crops and Pastures. Technical Paper **174**

Commonwealth Scientific and Industrial Research Organization. Division of Wildlife and Ecology. Project Report. (AT) **1485**

Commonwealth Scientific and Industrial Research Organization. Division of Wildlife and Ecology. Technical Memorandum. (AT) **1485**

†Commonwealth Scientific and Industrial Research Organization. Division of Wildlife and Ecology. Technical Paper.(AT) **5168**

Commonwealth Scientific and Industrial Research Organization. Division of Wildlife and Rangelands Research. Project Report *see* Commonwealth Scientific and Industrial Research Organization. Division of Wildlife and Ecology. Project Report **1485**

Commonwealth Scientific and Industrial Research Organization. Division of Wildlife and Rangelands Research. Technical Memorandum *see* Commonwealth Scientific and Industrial Research Organization. Division of Wildlife and Ecology. Technical Memorandum **1485**

Commonwealth Scientific and Industrial Research Organization. Division of Wildlife and Rangelands Research. Technical Paper *see* Commonwealth Scientific and Industrial Research Organization. Division of Wildlife and Ecology. Technical Paper **5168**

Commonwealth Scientific and Industrial Research Organization. Herbarium Australiense. Brunonia *see* Australian Systematic Botany **495**

†Commonwealth Scientific and Industrial Research Organization. Industrial Research News. (AT ISSN 0045-7647) **5168**

Commonwealth Scientific and Industrial Research Organization. Institute of Animal and Food Sciences. Annual Report *see* C S I R O Rural Sector Report **81**

Commonwealth Scientific and Industrial Research Organization. Institute of Animal Production and Processing. Report *see* C S I R O Rural Sector Report **81**

Commonwealth Scientific and Industrial Research Organization. Institute of Energy and Earth Resources. Annual Report. (AT ISSN 0729-056X) **3482**

Commonwealth Scientific and Industrial Research Organization. Institute of Energy and Earth Resources. Division of Mineral Physics and Mineralogy. Biennial Report *see* Commonwealth Scientific and Industrial Research Organization. Division of Exploration Geoscience. Annual Report **3482**

Commonwealth Scientific and Industrial Research Organization. Institute of Energy and Earth Resources. Investigation Report. (AT ISSN 0726-1780) **3482**

Commonwealth Scientific and Industrial Research Organization. Institute of Energy and Earth Resources. Minerals & Energy Bulletin. (AT ISSN 0159-9178) **3482**

Commonwealth Scientific and Industrial Research Organization. Institute of Energy and Earth Resources. Technical Communication. (AT ISSN 0726-1772) **3482**

Title

Commonwealth Scientific and Industrial Research Organization. Institute of Earth Resources. Annual Report. see Commonwealth Scientific and Industrial Research Organization. Institute of Energy and Earth Resources. Annual Report **3482**

Commonwealth Scientific and Industrial Research Organization. Institute of Earth Resources. Investigation Report. see Commonwealth Scientific and Industrial Research Organization. Institute of Energy and Earth Resources. Investigation Report **3482**

Commonwealth Scientific and Industrial Research Organization. Institute of Earth Resources. Technical Communication see Commonwealth Scientific and Industrial Research Organization. Institute of Energy and Earth Resources. Technical Communication **3482**

†Commonwealth Scientific and Industrial Research Organization. Marine Laboratories. Fishery Situation Report. (AT ISSN 0157-8081) **5168**

†Commonwealth Scientific and Industrial Research Organization. Marine Laboratories. Microfiche Report. (AT ISSN 0726-4283) **5168**

Commonwealth Scientific and Industrial Research Organization. Marine Laboratories. Report. (AT ISSN 0725-4598) **2039**, 1603

†Commonwealth Scientific and Industrial Research Organization. Wheat Research Unit. Report. (AT ISSN 0069-7680) **5168**

Commonwealth Scientific and Industrial Research Organization. Wool Textile News see C S I R O Wool Textile News **4617**

Commonwealth Scientific and Industrial Research Organization Directory see C S I R O Directory **4303**

Commonwealth Scientific and Industrial Research Organization Division of Fisheries. Research Report see C.S.I.R.O. Division of Fisheries. Research Report **2038**

Commonwealth Scientific and Industrial Research Organization Division of Oceanography. Research Report see C.S.I.R.O. Division of Oceanography. Research Report **1602**

Commonwealth Scientific and Industrial Research Organization Film Catalogue see C S I R O Film Catalogue **5157**

Commonwealth Scientific and Industrial Research Organization Rural Sector Report see C S I R O Rural Sector Report **81**

Commonwealth Statutes Annotations. (AT) **2731**

Commonwealth Statutes Cumulative Supplement see Commonwealth Statutes Annotations **2731**

Commonwealth Teaching Service. Annual Report. (AT) **1622**

†Commonwealth Today. (UK ISSN 0950-7043) **5168**

Commonwealth Universities Yearbook. (UK ISSN 0069-7745) **1703**

Commpost. (US) **1984**, 1485

Communal Computing News. (US) **1459**, 4171

Communaute Economique du Betail et de la Viande see C E B V **213**

Communaute Economique Europeenne International. Droit et Affaires see C E E International. Droit et Affaires **2720**

Communaute Europeenne du Charbon et de l'Acier. Commission des Communautes Europeenes. Comite Consultatif. Annuaire see European Coal and Steel Community. Consultative Committee. Yearbook **929**

Communaute Europeenne du Charbon et de l'Acier. Commission des Communautes Européennes. Comite Consultatif. Manuel see European Coal and Steel Community. Consultative Committee. Handbook **929**

Communautes Educatives. (FR ISSN 0245-2030) **1693**

†Communautes et Liturgies. (BE) **5168**

Commune di Genova. Notiziario Statistico Mensile. (IT) **4569**

Communes d'Europe. (FR ISSN 0414-1105) **4086**

Communes de France. (FR ISSN 0573-0910) **4086**

Communes Forestieres de France. (FR) **4086**, 2098

Communicable Diseases Intelligence. (AT ISSN 0725-3141) **3218**

Communicare. (SA ISSN 0259-0069) **1333**, 29, 2568

†Communicare. (US ISSN 0279-1196) **5168**

Communicate. (UK) **1362**

Communicate (Yellowknife). (CN) **1622**

Communicating for Agriculture Highlights see C A Highlights **81**

Communicating Together. (CN ISSN 0822-0638) **1688**, 1350, 1735

Communicatio. (SA ISSN 0250-0167) **1333**

Communicatio Publica. (SZ) **1333**

Communicatio Socialis. (GW ISSN 0010-3497) **4171**, 29

Communication. (CN) **749**

Communication. (CN) **1333**, 1371, 2568

Communication see World Communication **1345**

Communication (London, 1967). (UK ISSN 0045-7663) **1735**, 4402

Communication (London, 1975). (US ISSN 0305-4233) **1333**

Communication Abstracts. (US ISSN 0162-2811) **1347**, 8

†Communication & Broadcasting. (UK ISSN 0305-3601) **5169**

Communication and Cognition. (BE ISSN 0378-0880) **1333**, 2809

Communication and Cybernetics. (US ISSN 0340-0034) **1440**

Communication and Information Technology Reports see C O I N T Reports **5157**

Communication and the Human Condition. (US ISSN 0275-2069) **2907**

Communication Arts. (US ISSN 0010-3519) **29**, 3998

Communication Arts International. (US ISSN 0010-3500) **1371**, 3506

Communication Booknotes. (US ISSN 0748-657X) **1347**, 8

Communication Briefings. (US ISSN 0730-7799) **30**, 1333

Communication Education. (US ISSN 0363-4523) **1622**

Communication Industries/Tsushin Kogyo. (JA ISSN 0041-381X) **1362**

Communication Information see Communication **1333**

Communication: Journalism Education Today. (US ISSN 0010-3535) **1622**, 1333, 2568

Communication Media in Higher Education: A Directory. (US) **1371**, 1693

Communication Monographs. (US ISSN 0363-7751) **1622**, 2809

Communication News. (US) **1005**, 1333

Communication Newsletter see Educational Innovation and Information **1721**

Communication Outlook. (US ISSN 0161-4126) **1350**, 1688

Communication Quarterly. (US ISSN 0146-3373) **1622**, 1333, 4631

Communication Research. (US ISSN 0093-6502) **1333**

Communication Research and Broadcasting. (GW) **1371**

Communication Research Reports. (US ISSN 0882-4096) **1333**

Communication Research Trends. (UK ISSN 0144-4646) **1333**

▼Communication Serials. (US ISSN 1041-7893) **1347**

Communication Statistics. (IO) **4569**

Communication Studies. (US) **1333**

Communication Technology and Development. see Tongxin Jishu yu Fazhan **1360**

†Communication: The Human Context. (US) **5169**

▼Communication Theory. (US ISSN 1050-3293) **2809**

Communication World. (US ISSN 0744-7612) **1005**

Communicationes. (BE) **1622**

Communicationes. (VC) **4262**

†Communicationes Instituti Forestalis Fenniae. (FI ISSN 0358-9609) **5169**

Communications. (FR ISSN 0588-8018) **1333**

Communications. (US ISSN 0010-356X) **1355**, 1362

Communications. (UK ISSN 0266-8009) **1362**, 1446

†Communications. (SZ ISSN 0340-0158) **5169**

Communications Africa. (UK ISSN 0962-3841) **1333**

▼Communications & Computer News. (US ISSN 1057-0071) **1446**, 1426

Communications and Control Engineering Series. (US) **1817**

Communications and the Law. (US ISSN 0162-9093) **1333**, 2614

Communications Concepts. (US ISSN 0741-0069) **30**, 1333, 2568, 3998

†Communications Consultant. (US) **5169**

Communications Daily. (US ISSN 0277-0679) **1371**

Communications de Demographie Historique. see Historisch-Demographische Mitteilungen **3982**

Communications de Historia Artis Medicinae. see Orvostorteneti Kozlemenyek **3138**

Communications Electronic, Electrical, Technical and Salaried Workers of Canada Connections see C W C Connections **1883**

Communications - Engineering and Design. (US ISSN 0191-5428) **1371**

Communications - Engineering Digest see Communications - Engineering and Design **1371**

Communications Engineering International see C E I - Communications Engineering International **1332**

Communications for Symbolic and Algebraic Manipulation. see Sushiki Shori Tsushin **3057**

Communications from the International Brecht Society. (US ISSN 0740-8943) **2907**, 4631

Communications Ideas, Plans & Strategies Report see Williams Report **1071**

Communications in Algebra. (US ISSN 0092-7872) **3033**

Communications in Applied Numerical Methods. (UK ISSN 0748-8025) **3033**, 1863, 1916

▼Communications in Finance. (US) **1362**, 772, 943

†Communications in Japan. (JA) **5169**

Communications in Mathematical Physics. (GW ISSN 0010-3616) **3816**, 3033

Communications in Partial Differential Equations. (US ISSN 0360-5302) **3033**

Communications in Soil Science and Plant Analysis. (US ISSN 0010-3624) **174**

Communications in Statistics. Part A: Theory and Methods. (US ISSN 0361-0926) **4569**

Communications in Statistics. Part B: Simulation and Computation. (US ISSN 0361-0918) **4569**, 1435

Communications in Statistics. Part C: Stochastic Models. (US ISSN 0882-0287) **4569**

Communications in Theoretical Physics/Lilun Wuli. (CC ISSN 0253-6102) **3816**

Communications Industries Report. (US) **1333**

Communications Institute. Transcript. (US ISSN 1040-4848) **1622**, 1333

Communications Institute Courses in Communications see C I N C O M: Courses in Communications **1692**

Communications International. (UK ISSN 0305-2109) **1333**

Communications: Latin American Industrial Report. (US) **1334**

Communications Law & Policy in Australia. (AT) **2614**, 1334

Communications Lawyer. (US ISSN 0737-7622) **2614**, 1334

Communications Link see Link (Ashland) **2033**

Communications Management. (UK) **1005**

Communications Networking Services. (US) **1426**

Communications News. (US ISSN 0010-3632) **1334**

Communications of the Operations Research Society of Japan. see Opereshonzu Risachi **1023**

Communications on Pure and Applied Mathematics. (US ISSN 0010-3640) **3033**

Communications Product Report. (US ISSN 0743-0671) **1350**, 1468

†Communications Products & Systems. (US) **5169**

Communications Research Institute Communications Update Service see C R I Communications Update Service **1332**

Communications Research Laboratory. Journal/Tsushinsogo Kenkyujo Eibun Ronbunshu. (JA ISSN 0914-9260) **1371**

Communications Research Laboratory. Review. see Tsushin Sogo Kenkyujo Kiho **1383**

Communications Satellite Corporation Technical Review see C O M S A T Technical Review **1332**

†Communications Standards Management. (US) **5169**

†Communications Systems Engineering: Postal Applications. (US ISSN 1051-2691) **5169**

†Communications Systems Worldwide. (UK ISSN 0267-1395) **5169**

Communications Technology. (US ISSN 0884-2272) **1372**

Communications Today. see Xiandai Tongxin **1354**

Communications, Transport, Posts and Telegraphs. see Giao thong-Van tai and Buu Dien **1336**

Communications Update. (AT ISSN 0815-1210) **1334**, 2614

Communications Week see Canadian Communications Network Letter **1371**

Communications Week International. (US ISSN 0746-8121) **1334**

Communications Worker. (IE) **2581**

Communications Workers of America News see C W A News **2581**

Communications World. (AT ISSN 0817-1904) **1390**, 1334

CommunicationsWeek. (US) **1334**

Communicator. (UK ISSN 0953-3699) **1334**

Communicator (Des Moines). (US) **3941**

Communicator (Fort Worth). (US) **1884**

†Communicator (Indianapolis). (US) **5169**

Communicator (Johnstown). (US) **3230**

Communicator (New Delhi). (II) **1355**, 1334

Communicator (Reno) see Communicator Community News **2223**

Communicator (St. John's). (CN) **4057**

Communicator (Washington). (US) **237**

Communicator (Washington, 1953). (US) **772**

Communicator Community News. (US) **2223**

Communicator of Scientific and Technical Information see Communicator **1334**

6072 COMMUNICATOR

Communicator of the Electronic Printing Industry Press see C O P I Press **1390**
Communicator Showcase. (US) **30**, **1785**
Communidad. (SW ISSN 0283-2925) **3881**
Communio. (SP ISSN 0010-3705) **4172**
Communio. (US ISSN 0094-2065) **4262**
Communio Viatorum. (CS ISSN 0010-3713) **4172**
Communion. (AT ISSN 0004-9662) **4281**
Communique see Mutual Piper **2538**
Communique (Chicago). (US ISSN 0199-9028) **4147**
Communique (Columbus). (US) **4234**
Communique (Columbus, 1967). (US ISSN 1043-0695) **1058**, **1746**
Communique (Dallas). (US) **1334**
†Communique (Indianapolis). (US) **5169**
Communique (Iowa City). (US) **3230**
Communique (Ithaca). (US) **1308**, **3090**
Communique (Ottawa). (CN ISSN 0319-7468) **4402**, **1235**
The Communique (Pittsburgh, 1984). (US) **1308**
Communique (Silver Spring). (US ISSN 0164-775X) **4017**
Communique (Vancouver). (CN) **3334**
Communique (Washington, 1971). (US) **656**, **927**
Communique (Washington, 1972) see A P T Communique **1482**
†Communiqu'elles. (CN ISSN 0710-5118) **5169**
Communisme. (FR ISSN 2209-7007) **3881**
Communisme ou Civilisation see Revue Internationale du Mouvement Communiste **3923**
†Communist and Workers Parties. Information Bulletin. (CN) **5169**
Communist Economies see Communist Economies and Economic Transformation **890**
Communist Economies and Economic Transformation. (UK) **890**, **3881**
Communist Law Journal see Review of Socialist Law **2672**
Communist Review. see Tap Chi Cong San **3929**
†Communist Viewpoint. (CN ISSN 0010-3756) **5169**
†Le Communiste. (CN ISSN 0709-3845) **5169**
Communistes Francais et l'Europe. (FR) **3881**
Communities. (US ISSN 0199-9346) **829**, **3594**
Communities see California Communities **2484**
Community. (UK) **4402**
Community (Alexandria). (US) **4402**
Community (Chicago). (US ISSN 0010-3772) **4431**, **1997**, **4402**
Community Action. (CN ISSN 0833-0816) **4402**
Community Action Magazine. (UK) **2485**
Community Affairs. (US) **4057**, **2485**
Community and Junior College Journal see Community, Technical, and Junior College Journal **1703**
Community & Junior College Libraries. (US ISSN 0276-3915) **2753**
Community and Real Estate News. (AT ISSN 0157-5783) **4147**
Community Arts News see At the Centre **5140**
Community Association Institute News see C A I News **5156**
Community Association Law Reporter. (US ISSN 0190-1192) **2485**, **829**, **2614**
Community Bank Marketing News. (US) **773**
Community Bank Marketing Newsletter see Community Bank Marketing News **773**
The Community Bank President. (US ISSN 0276-0908) **773**
Community Care. (UK ISSN 0307-5508) **4402**

Community Care - Social Work in Action see Community Care **4402**
Community College Journalist. (US) **2568**
Community College Review. (US ISSN 0091-5521) **1703**
Community College Social Science Journal see Community College Social Science Newsletter **4369**
Community College Social Science Newsletter. (US) **4369**
Community College Week. (US ISSN 1041-5726) **1703**
Community Comments see Community Service Newsletter **4432**
Community Crime Prevention Digest. (US ISSN 0889-5767) **1512**
Community Currents. (UK ISSN 0264-4088) **4425**, **8**
Community Dental Health. (UK ISSN 0265-539X) **3230**
Community Dentistry and Oral Epidemiology. (DK ISSN 0301-5661) **3230**, **4099**
Community Development Digest. (US ISSN 1050-3250) **2485**
Community Development Executive. (US ISSN 0747-7503) **813**
Community Development Journal. (UK ISSN 0010-3802) **4402**, **4057**
Community Development Services, Inc. Housing Register see C D - Housing Register **2484**
Community Development Society. Journal. (US ISSN 0010-3829) **2485**
Community Digest. (CN) **2176**
Community Economics. (US ISSN 1045-4322) **829**, **943**, **2485**
Community Education International. (UK ISSN 0256-0925) **1683**, **1946**
Community Education Network. (UK ISSN 0262-706X) **1622**
†Community Education Newsletter. (AT ISSN 0156-2878) **5169**
Community Enterprise. (US) **773**, **4147**
Community Eye Health. (UK ISSN 0953-6833) **3299**
▼Community Health Funding Report. (US ISSN 1050-3250) **4057**, **3090**
Community Health Studies see Australian Journal of Public Health **4098**
Community History. (AT) **2344**, **2053**, **2147**, **3523**
Community Improvement Corporation. Annual Report see Regional Development Corporation. Annual Report **882**
▼Community Investment and Affordable Housing. (US) **943**, **773**, **2485**
Community Jobs (Washington). (US ISSN 0195-1157) **3626**
Community Junior College: Quarterly of Research and Practice. (US ISSN 0277-6774) **1683**, **1703**
Community Law Week Newsletter. (US) **2614**
Community Leader Briefings. (US ISSN 1044-6222) **4086**
Community Leaders and Noteworthy Americans see Community Leaders of America **418**
Community Leaders of America. (US) **418**
Community Living of Florida. (US) **2223**
Community Medicine see Journal of Public Health Medicine **4410**
†Community Memory News. (US) **5169**
Community Mental Health Journal. (US ISSN 0010-3853) **4402**, **3334**, **4017**
†Community Network. (UK) **5169**
†Community News (Boulder). (US) **5169**
Community News (Salem). (US) **2452**
Community Newspapers. (SA) **2216**
Community of the Sisters of the Church Newsletter see C S C Newsletter **4232**
Community Outlook. (UK ISSN 0262-8759) **3090**, **3277**
Community Pharmacy. (UK) **3721**, **1036**

Community Pharmacy in Australia see Guild Digest (Year) **3747**
Community Property see B A R - B R I Bar Review. Community Property **2602**
Community Psychiatric Nursing Journal.(UK ISSN 0265-7007) **3334**, **3277**
Community Psychiatry Journal. (II) **3334**, **4017**
Community Publication Rates and Data see Standard Rate and Data Service. Community Publication Rates and Data **41**
Community Quarterly. (AT ISSN 0814-401X) **4431**, **2485**
Community Radio News. (US) **1372**
▼Community Reinvestment Quarterly. (US) **773**
Community Relations Report. (US) **1334**, **4057**
Community Report. (EI) **851**
Community Resources Directory see Volunteerism **4423**
Community Review. (US ISSN 0163-8475) **1703**
†Community Service Business. (US ISSN 0747-6086) **5169**
Community Service Newsletter. (US ISSN 0277-6189) **4432**
Community Service Statistics: Scotland. (UK ISSN 0144-5081) **4425**, **4569**
Community Services Catalyst. (US ISSN 0739-9227) **1683**
Community Spirit Magazine (Carmel). (US) **1946**, **2505**, **4057**
Community Sports News. (US) **4469**
Community Stress Prevention. (IS) **4017**
Community Studies Series. (UK ISSN 0143-7704) **4369**, **2809**
Community, Technical, and Junior College Journal. (US) **1703**
Community, Technical, and Junior College Times. (US) **1693**
Community Television Review. (US) **1372**
Community Transport Magazine. (UK ISSN 0263-9378) **4648**, **4402**
Community Transportation Reporter. (US ISSN 0895-4437) **4648**, **84**
Community Unit Cable: Full Record. (US) **1347**
†Community View. (UK ISSN 0260-5244) **5169**
Community Yellow Pages. (US) **2452**
Communixations see Uniforum Monthly **1401**
Commutation et Transmission. (FR ISSN 0242-1283) **1334**
Commuter Air see Commuter Air International **4672**
Commuter Air Carrier Traffic Statistics see Air Carrier Industry Schedule Service Traffic Statistics. Medium Regional Carriers **4669**
Commuter Air International. (US ISSN 1054-7436) **4672**
Commuter - Regional Airline News. (US ISSN 1040-5402) **4672**
Commuter Regional Airline News International. (US) **4672**
Commuter World. (UK ISSN 0265-4504) **4672**
Como. (IT) **4369**
▼Como. (JA) **4839**
Compact. (US) **3482**, **1946**
†Compact Disc. (US) **5169**
Compact Disc Computing News see C D Computing News **1423**
Compact Disc Guide see C D Guide **4460**
Compact Disc Interactive News see C D - I News **5156**
Compact Disc Publisher News see C D Publisher News **4143**
Compact Disc - Read Only Memory Databases see C D - R O M Databases **2796**
Compact Disc - Read Only Memory Review see C D - R O M Review **5156**
Compact Disc Review see C D Review **4460**
Compagnie Europeenne et d'Outre-Mer. Rapports see Compagnie Financiere Europeenne et d'Outre-Mer. Finoutremer. Rapport Annuel **904**

Compagnie Financiere Europeenne et d'Outre-Mer. Finoutremer. Rapport Annuel. (BE) **904**
Compagnie Nationale des Commissaires aux Comptes. Conseil National. Bulletin. (FR) **2614**
Companheiros. (PO ISSN 0010-3969) **4544**
Companhia de Tecnologia de Sanemento Ambiental Jornal see C E T E S B Jornal **1944**
Companhia Estadual de Tecnologia de Saneamento Basico e de Defesa do Meio Ambiente. Directoria Relatoria Anual. (BL) **4099**, **1946**
Companhia Paranaense de Energia. Boletim Estatistico Mensal. (BL) **1798**, **1801**
Companhia Paranaense de Energia. Informe Estadistica Anual. (BL) **1798**
Companhia Paranaense de Energia. Informe Estatistico Anual. (BL) **1798**, **4569**
Companhia Paulista de Forca e Luz. Assessoria de Planejamento e Controle. Boletim Estatistico see Companhia Paulista de Forca e Luz. Mercado de Energia Eletrica. Relatorio Estadistico Anual **1884**
†Companhia Paulista de Forca e Luz. Boletim Estatistico. (BL) **5169**
Companhia Paulista de Forca e Luz. Mercado de Energia Eletrica. Relatorio Estadistico Anual. (BL) **1884**
Compania Argentina de Seguros. Memoria y Balance General see Brujula **2528**
Compania Financiera Ecuatoriana de Desarrollo Informe Anual see C O F I E C. Informe Anual **769**
Companies and Securities Law Journal. (AT ISSN 0729-2775) **2708**
Companies and Their Brands. (US ISSN 1047-6393) **1127**
Companion Animal News. (US) **3709**
Companion Animal Practice see Feline Practice **4809**
Companion in Zeor. (US) **3010**
Companion of St. Francis and St. Anthony. (CN ISSN 0010-3985) **4262**
Companion to Animal Pratice see Canine Practice **4808**
Company. (US ISSN 0886-1293) **4262**, **1308**, **1622**
Company. (UK ISSN 0141-1144) **4839**
Company Accountant. (UK) **749**
Company Car (Redhill). (UK ISSN 0267-8519) **4688**
Company Director. (AT) **1005**, **2614**
Company Law Digest. (UK ISSN 0260-4620) **2708**
Company Law Institute of India. Reports of Company Cases Including Banking & Insurance. (II ISSN 0045-7787) **2708**, **773**, **2530**
Company Lawyer see Company Lawyer and Company Lawyer Digest **2708**
Company Lawyer and Company Lawyer Digest. (UK) **2708**
Company News and Notes. (II ISSN 0010-4027) **1073**
Company Secretary's Review. (UK ISSN 0309-703X) **1058**
Company-Stats Semiconductor Profile Service. (US) **1765**
Compaq Magazin. (GW ISSN 0932-7177) **1390**
Comparability Update. (US) **4125**
The Comparatist. (US ISSN 0195-7678) **2907**
Comparatistica. (IT ISSN 1120-7094) **2862**
Comparativa. (SZ) **2614**, **3941**
Comparative and International Education Society. Newsletter. (US ISSN 0010-4043) **1622**
Comparative and International Law Journal of Southern Africa. (SA ISSN 0010-4051) **2721**
Comparative Animal Nutrition. (SZ ISSN 0304-5374) **580**, **4808**
Comparative Biochemistry and Physiology. Part A: Comparative Physiology. (US ISSN 0300-9629) **571**, **475**

Comparative Biochemistry and Physiology. Part B: Comparative Biochemistry. (US ISSN 0305-0491) **475**
Comparative Biochemistry and Physiology. Part C: Comparative Pharmacology & Toxicology. (US ISSN 0742-8413) **475**, **1981**, **3721**
Comparative Civilizations Review. (US ISSN 0733-4540) **4432**, **237**, **2505**
Comparative Criticism. (UK ISSN 0144-7564) **2907**
Comparative Drama. (US ISSN 0010-4078) **2907**
Comparative Economic and Financial Statistics Japan and Other Major Countries. (JA) **711**
Comparative Economic Studies. (US ISSN 0888-7233) **890**
Comparative Education. (UK ISSN 0305-0068) **1622**
Comparative Education. *see* Vergleichende Paedagogik **1670**
Comparative Education Review. (US ISSN 0010-4086) **1622**
Comparative Education Society in Europe. Proceedings of the General Meeting *see* Aims of Education and Development of Personality. Comparative Aspects. Proceedings of the CESE Conference **1614**
Comparative Ephemeris (Year). (US ISSN 0889-9630) **363**
Comparative Guide to American Colleges. (US ISSN 0893-1216) **1693**
Comparative History of India and Indonesia. (NE) **3636**
Comparative Immunology, Microbiology and Infectious Diseases. (US ISSN 0147-9571) **550**, **4808**
Comparative Juridical Review. (US ISSN 0069-7893) **2614**
Comparative Labor Law Journal. (US ISSN 0147-9202) **2614**
Comparative Law Journal. *see* Hikaku Ho Kenkyu **2632**
Comparative Law Review/Hikakuho Zasshi. (JA ISSN 0010-4116) **2614**
Comparative Literary and Film Studies: Europe, Japan, and the Third World. (US ISSN 0899-9902) **2907**, **3506**
Comparative Literature. (US ISSN 0010-4124) **2907**, **2809**
Comparative Literature in Canada/ Litterature Comparee au Canada. (CN) **2907**
Comparative Literature Studies. (US ISSN 0010-4132) **2907**, **2809**
Comparative Management. (UK) **1006**
▼Comparative Medicine. (US ISSN 1058-2401) **3258**
Comparative Physiology. (SZ ISSN 1015-1702) **571**
Comparative Physiology and Ecology. (II ISSN 0379-0436) **435**, **571**
Comparative Political Studies. (US ISSN 0010-4140) **3881**
Comparative Romance Linguistics Newsletter. (US ISSN 0010-4167) **2809**
Comparative Social Research. (US ISSN 0195-6310) **4432**
Comparative State Politics. (US ISSN 1047-1006) **3881**, **2614**
Comparative State Politics Newsletter *see* Comparative State Politics **3881**
Comparative Statistics of Industrial Office Real Estate Markets. (US) **4147**
Comparative Strategy. (US ISSN 0149-5933) **3881**
Comparative Studies in Overseas History. (NE ISSN 0922-9744) **2357**
Comparative Studies in Society and History. (UK ISSN 0010-4175) **4432**, **2309**
Comparative Studies in Sociology *see* Comparative Social Research **4432**
Comparative Urban and Community Research. (US ISSN 0892-5569) **4432**

Compare. (UK ISSN 0305-7925) **1622**
Compare Notes Series. (CN) **1997**, **3953**
Comparison *see* New Comparison **2941**
Comparison of State Unemployment Insurance Laws. (US) **2530**, **975**
Comparison Report on Engineering Scanning Systems *see* Engineering Document Management System Comparison Report **1444**
Compas d'Or. *see* Gulden Passer **4128**
Compass. (CN) **2581**
Compass. (UK ISSN 0045-7809) **4172**
Compass (Jacksonville). (US) **1308**
Compass (Norman). (US ISSN 0010-4213) **1542**
Compass: Computer Assurance (Conference). (US) **1884**, **1433**
Compass Magazine. (US) **1073**
Compass Magazine. (AT) **4262**
Compass Quarterly *see* Compass Magazine **1073**
Compass Readings. (US ISSN 1051-7383) **4802**
Compass Sport - Orienteer. (UK ISSN 0263-6697) **4469**
Compassion. *see* Sharapat **4220**
†Compassion Magazine. (US ISSN 0895-1721) **5169**
Compassion Magazine (Colorado Springs). (US) **4234**, **927**, **1721**
Compassion Update *see* Compassion Magazine (Colorado Springs) **4234**
CompCon: I E E E Computer Society International Conference. (US) **1390**
Compel. (UK ISSN 0332-1649) **3064**, **1877**
Compendia. (UK) **2856**
Compendia Rerum Iudaicarum Ad Novum Testamentum. (NE) **4222**
Compendio Dati. (IT) **4086**
†Compendio Estadistico Centroamericano. (GT ISSN 0588-912X) **5169**
Compendio Estadistico de America *see* Statistical Compendium of the Americas **5283**
Compendio Statistico *see* Compendio Statistico Italiano (Year) **4569**
Compendio Statistico Italiano (Year). (IT ISSN 0069-7958) **4569**
Compendium des Produits et Specialites Pharmaceutiques *see* Compendium of Pharmaceuticals and Specialties **3721**
Compendium Gezondheidsstatistiek Nederland/Compendium Health Statistics of the Netherlands. (NE) **4117**
Compendium Health Statistics of the Netherlands. *see* Compendium Gezondheidsstatistiek Nederland **4117**
Compendium Musicum. (PL) **3546**
Compendium Newsletter. (US ISSN 0198-9103) **1485**, **1946**
Compendium of Advanced Courses in Colleges of Further & Higher Education. (UK) **1703**, **1693**
Compendium of Analytical Methods. (CN) **2064**
Compendium of Continuing Education in Dentistry. (US ISSN 0196-1756) **3230**
Compendium of Drug Therapy *see* Cardiologist's Compendium of Drug Therapy **3720**
Compendium of Drug Therapy *see* Family Physician's Compendium of Drug Therapy **3725**
Compendium of Drug Therapy *see* Internist's Compendium of Drug Therapy **3730**
Compendium of Government Issues Affecting Direct Marketing. (US) **1036**, **30**
Compendium of New Zealand Farm Production Statistics. (NZ) **136**
Compendium of Pharmaceuticals and Specialties. (CN ISSN 0069-7966) **3721**
Compendium of Plant Disease Series. (US) **174**
Compendium of Research. (CN) **2485**

Compendium on Continuing Education for the Practicing Veterinarian. (US ISSN 0193-1903) **4808**
Compensation (Washington, 1982). (US ISSN 0732-5282) **1064**, **975**, **4086**
Compensation & Benefits Management.(US ISSN 0748-061X) **1064**, **2530**
Compensation and Benefits Review. (US) **1006**
Compensation and Benefits Survey of College and University Chief Executive Officers *see* Compensation, Benefits and Conditions of Employment for College and University Chief Executive Officers **975**
Compensation, Benefits and Conditions of Employment for College and University Chief Executive Officers. (US) **975**, **1703**
Compensation in Human Resources Development *see* Compensation in Training & Development **975**
Compensation in Manufacturing - Engineers and Managers. (US ISSN 0278-0992) **975**
Compensation in the Accounting - Financial Field. (US) **975**
Compensation in the M I S - D P Field. (US) **975**
Compensation in the Security - Loss Prevention Field. (US) **975**, **1526**
Compensation in Training & Development. (US) **975**
Compensation of Attorneys (Non-Law Firms). (US) **975**, **2614**
Compensation of Industrial Engineers. (US) **975**, **1925**
Compensation Planning Journal *see* Tax Management Compensation Planning Journal **1029**
Compensation Review *see* Compensation and Benefits Review **1006**
Compensation Strategy and Management. (US) **1064**, **2614**
Compere di San Giorgio. (IT) **813**
Competition. (US) **2435**
Competition Angler. (US ISSN 1047-1669) **4544**, **3396**
Competition Law *see* Competition Law in Western Europe and the U S A **2721**
Competition Law in the European Communities. (UK ISSN 0141-769X) **2721**
Competition Law in Western Europe and the U S A. (NE) **2721**
Competition Leader. (II) **656**
Competition Master. (II) **1746**
Competition Policy in O E C D Countries. (FR) **927**, **1073**
Competition Refresher. (II) **656**
Competition Rider *see* Amateur Rider **4531**
Competition Success Review. (II) **656**
Competitions (Chicago). (US) **2614**
▼Competitions (Louisville). (US) **322**, **297**
The Competitive Advantage. (US ISSN 0886-1994) **1036**
Competitive Enterprise Institute Update *see* C E I Update **653**
Competitive Publishing Hotline. (US) **4125**
Competitivedge *see* Furniture Retailer (Greensboro) **2559**
Compeuro. Proceedings. (US) **1390**
CompFlash. (US ISSN 0147-1570) **1064**
Compilaciones Tematicas. (CU) **2184**
Compilation of Nationally Averaged Rental Rates. (US) **2485**, **4147**
Compilation of State and Federal Privacy Laws. (US ISSN 0882-9136) **2615**
Compiler. (US) **1512**
Compilers' Friend. *see* Bianji zhi You **4121**
Complan Handbook. (AT ISSN 0314-0164) **149**
Compleat Anbar. (UK) **1006**
Compleat Lawyer. (US ISSN 0741-9066) **2615**
Compleat Mother. (US ISSN 0829-8564) **3291**, **1235**
Compleat Smoker. (US) **4643**

Complement *see* Complement and Inflammation **5169**
†Complement (Sheffield). (UK ISSN 0263-7286) **5169**
†Complement and Inflammation. (SZ ISSN 1012-8204) **5169**
Complementary Medical Research. (UK ISSN 0268-4055) **3214**, **3271**
Complementary Medicine Index. (UK ISSN 0950-6667) **3168**, **8**, **3613**
Complete Baseball Record Book. (US) **4502**
Complete Catalogue of Plays (Year). (US) **4631**
Complete Coffee Coverage. (US) **2064**
Complete Commodity Futures Directory.(US) **1127**, **943**
Complete Communication Coordination Monitor. (US) **1334**, **1006**
Complete Directory of Large Print Books and Serials. (US ISSN 0000-1120) **2285**, **397**, **2292**
▼Complete Guide to Closed-End Funds.(US) **943**
Complete Guide to Mechanic's and Materialman's Lien Laws of Texas. (US) **2615**
Complete Internal Revenue Code *see* Internal Revenue Code **1098**
Complete Sportsman: Guns & Hunting. (US) **4544**
Complete Woman. (US) **4839**
Completing the Internal Market of the European Community: 1992 Legislation - Business. (UK) **2721**, **656**
Completing the Internal Market of the European Community: 1992 Legislation - Financial Services and Capital Movements. (UK) **2721**, **773**
Completing the Internal Market of the European Community: 1992 Legislation. (UK) **2721**
Completing the Internal Market of the European Community: 1992 Legislation - Transport, Customs & Travel. (UK) **2721**
Completing the Internal Market of the European Community: 1992 Legislation - Technical Standards. (UK) **2721**
Completing the Internal Market of the European Community: 1992 Legislation - Veterinary & Phytosanitary Controls. (UK) **2721**, **4808**
Complex Variables: Theory and Application. (US ISSN 0278-1077) **3033**
▼Complexity. (UK ISSN 0964-1815) **1877**, **3064**
Compliance Examination Update. (US) **2615**, **773**
Compliance Guide for Plan Administrators. (US ISSN 0274-8304) **1006**
Compliance Program Guidance Manuals. (US) **4099**, **2615**
Complications in Surgery. (US ISSN 1053-749X) **3377**, **3218**
Complice. (SP) **4839**
Component. (US) **610**
Components in Electronics. (UK) **1765**
Comportamiento Humano. (AG ISSN 0010-4329) **3764**, **3941**
†Composer and His Songs. (UR) **5169**
Composer - U S A. (US) **3546**
Composers of the Americas/ Compositores de America. (US ISSN 0069-8016) **3547**, **418**
†Composers of Wales Series. (UK) **5169**
Composers' Voice. (NE) **3547**
Composicion Arquitectonica. (SP ISSN 0214-4832) **297**
Composite Catalog of Oil Field Equipment & Services. (US) **3684**, **1127**
Composite Materials Science *see* Science and Engineering of Composite Materials **1187**
Composite Polymers. (UK ISSN 0952-6919) **3862**, **4291**
Composite Structures. (UK ISSN 0263-8223) **1864**, **1927**
Composites. (UK ISSN 0010-4361) **1916**

6074 COMPOSITES

Composites & Adhesives Newsletter. (US ISSN 0888-1227) **3862**
▼Composites Engineering. (UK ISSN 0961-9526) **1817, 1916**
Composites et Nouveaux Materiaux (Paris, 1980). (FR ISSN 0763-0018) **1163**
Composites in Manufacturing. (US) **1916**
Composites Industry Monthly. (US) **656**
▼Composites Manufacturing. (UK ISSN 0956-7143) **1928**
Composites Quarterly. (US) **1817**
Composites Science and Technology. (UK ISSN 0266-3538) **4595, 4617**
Compositeur Canadien. *see* Canadian Composer **3544**
Compositio Mathematica. (NE ISSN 0010-437X) **3033**
Composition. *see* Synthesis **1288**
Composition of the W M O. (UN) **3434**
Composition Studies - Freshman English News. (US) **1747**
Compositores de America. *see* Composers of the Americas **3547**
Compost Journal *see* Soil & Health Journal **2139**
Compoundings. (US ISSN 1042-508X) **3684, 1852**
Comprehensive Analytical Chemistry. (NE) **1205**
Comprehensive Biochemistry *see* New Comprehensive Biochemistry **480**
Comprehensive Chemical Kinetics. (NE ISSN 0069-8040) **1225**
Comprehensive Directory of Sports Addresses *see* Sports Address Bible **4491**
Comprehensive Education. (UK ISSN 0588-9278) **1726**
Comprehensive Endocrinology. (US ISSN 0160-242X) **3251**
Comprehensive Environmental Response, Compensation and Liability Information. (US) **1946**
†Comprehensive Gerontology. Section A: Clinical and Laboratory Sciences. (DK) **5169**
†Comprehensive Gerontology. Section B: Behavioural, Social and Applied Sciences. (DK) **5169**
†Comprehensive Gerontology. Section C: Interdisciplinary Topics. (DK) **5169**
Comprehensive Immunology. (US ISSN 0149-1148) **3184**
▼Comprehensive Index to Oregon Statutes (Year). (US) **2698, 8**
Comprehensive Manuals in Pediatrics. (US) **3168, 3320**
Comprehensive Manuals in Radiology. (US ISSN 0172-4843) **3357**
Comprehensive Manuals of Surgical Specialities. (US ISSN 0172-4827) **3378**
▼Comprehensive Mental Health Care. (US ISSN 1051-7782) **4017**
Comprehensive Plan for Criminal Justice (Sacramento) *see* California. Council on Criminal Justice. Comprehensive Plan for Criminal Justice **5158**
Comprehensive Psychiatry. (US ISSN 0010-440X) **3334, 3274, 4017**
Comprehensive Psychotherapy. (UK ISSN 0275-7222) **4017**
Comprehensive Therapy. (US ISSN 0098-8243) **3090**
Comprendre. (IT ISSN 0010-4418) **2862**
Compressed Air. (US ISSN 0010-4426) **1928**
Compressed Air Magazine *see* Compressed Air **1928**
Compressor News *see* Compressor News and Patents **3016**
Compressor News and Patents. (US) **3016, 1852, 2298, 3674**
Compromiso Politico y Social. (AG) **3881**
Compstan *see* Computer Standards Conference. Proceedings **5170**
CompStat Symposium. Proceedings. (Computational Statistics) (NE) **4569**
Comptabilite et Mecanographie. (FR) **749**

Compte de la Nation. (CF) **711**
Compte-Rendu de Recherches Pedagogiques. *see* Reporting Classroom Research **1658**
†Comptel Magazine. (US) **5169**
Comptes Economiques de la Guadeloupe. (GP) **711**
Comptes Economiques de la Martinique.(MQ) **711**
Comptes Economiques de la Nation. (NG) **711**
Comptes Economiques Nationaux du Rwanda. (RW) **711**
Comptes Nationaux de la Suisse. *see* Nationale Buchhaltung der Schweiz **754**
Comptes Nationaux du Cameroun. (CM) **1091**
Comptes Rendus de Therapeutique et de Pharmacologie Clinique. (FR ISSN 0293-9908) **3090**
Comptoir Francais des Produits Siderurgiques. Bulletin Statistique. Serie Bleue. Commerce Exterieur. (FR) **3404, 3482**
Comptoir Francais des Produits Siderurgiques. Bulletin Statistique. Serie Rouge. Production. (FR) **3404, 3482**
Compton's Yearbook. (US) **1780**
Comptroller General's Procurement Decisions. (US ISSN 0095-2117) **851, 2615**
Compu-Data. (GR) **1424**
CompuBibs. (US) **2328**
Compulife's MicroMarket Blue Disc. (US) **1432, 1424, 1453, 1459**
Compumath Citation Index. (US ISSN 0730-6199) **3062, 8, 1403**
CompuServe. (US) **1468, 1426**
Computable. (NE ISSN 0010-4450) **1448**
Computacion Personal. (US) **1468**
Computacion Personal. (CL ISSN 0716-4858) **2796**
Computational and Applied Mathematics. *see* Matematica Aplicada e Computacional **3065**
Computational and Linguistic Approaches to Literature. (US) **2856, 2907**
▼Computational Complexity. (SZ ISSN 1016-3328) **3064**
▼Computational Geometry. (NE ISSN 0925-7721) **1390, 3033**
Computational Intelligence/Intelligence Informatique. (US ISSN 0824-7935) **1390, 1435, 1482**
Computational Linguistics. (US ISSN 0891-2017) **2856**
▼Computational Materials Science. (NE ISSN 0927-0256) **1916, 3033**
Computational Mathematics and Applications. (US) **1440**
▼Computational Mathematics and Modeling. (US ISSN 1046-283X) **3064, 3033**
Computational Mechanics. (GW ISSN 0178-7675) **1928**
†Computational Mechanics Communications. (US ISSN 0957-2899) **5169**
Computational Microelectronics. (US) **3816**
Computational Seismology. (US ISSN 0733-5792) **1587, 4359**
Computational Statistics. (GW) **4569**
Computational Statistics and Data Analysis. (NE ISSN 0167-9473) **1403**
Computational Statistics CompStat Symposium. Proceedings *see* CompStat Symposium. Proceedings **4569**
Compute. (US ISSN 0194-357X) **1459, 1468**
Computech. (SA) **4595**
Computek. (CN ISSN 0827-262X) **1390**
Computer. (US) **1391, 1459**
Computer. (IT) **1391**
Computer Abstracts. (UI ISSN 0010-4469) **1403, 8**
▼Computer Abstracts on Microfiche. (US) **1403, 825, 2796**
Computer Access for the Blind in Education and Employment. (US) **2292, 1689**

Computer Accounting Letter. (CN) **825, 749**
Computer Address. (GW) **1391**
Computer Advertising News *see* Adweek's Marketing Computers **1423**
Computer Age. (GR) **1391**
Computer Age. *see* Jisuanji Shidai **1397**
Computer Age - Software Digest *see* Software Industry Report **1480**
Computer-Aided Chemical Engineering. (NE) **1877, 1852**
Computer-Aided Design. (UK ISSN 0010-4485) **1420**
Computer-Aided Design. *see* Szamitogepes Muszaki Tervezes **1846**
Computer Aided Design - Computer Aided Machinery Abstracts *see* C A D - C A M Abstracts **1420**
Computer Aided Design - Computer Aided Machinery Systems *see* C A D - C A M Systems **1420**
Computer Aided Design - Computer Aided Manufacturing Abstracts *see* C A D - C A M Abstracts **5156**
Computer Aided Design - Computer Aided Manufacturing Management Strategies *see* C A D - C A M: Management Strategies **5156**
Computer Aided Design - Computer Aided Manufacturing Report *see* C A D - C A M Report **1420**
Computer-Aided Design, Computer-Integrated Manufacturing Alert *see* C A D - C I M Alert **1412**
†Computer Aided Design i Danmark. (DK ISSN 0573-9985) **5169**
Computer-Aided Design of Electronic Circuits. (NE) **1877**
Computer Aided Design Report. (US ISSN 0276-749X) **1420**
Computer-Aided Engineering. (US ISSN 0733-3536) **1877, 1420**
Computer-Aided Engineering Journal. (UK ISSN 0263-9327) **1877, 1412**
Computer-Aided Geometric Design. (NE ISSN 0167-8396) **1420**
Computer Aided Manufacturing - International Inc. Cameos *see* C A M - I Cameos **1412**
Computer-Aided Process Control Abstracts. (UK ISSN 0955-4319) **1403, 1407**
Computer Aided Research in Near Eastern Studies. (US ISSN 0742-2334) **2330, 2429, 3636**
Computer-Aided Systems Engineering Strategies *see* C A S E Strategies **1877**
Computer Aids Corporation Report *see* C A C Report **1389**
Computer and Communications. (US) **1448, 825**
Computer and Communications Buyer. (US ISSN 0272-4553) **1432**
Computer and Communications Documents Microfile *see* Computer and Communications Technology Documents Microfile **1350**
Computer and Communications Technology Documents Microfile. (UK) **1350**
Computer & Control Abstracts. (UK ISSN 0036-8113) **1403, 8**
Al Computer and Electronics. (LE) **1391**
Computer and Information Systems *see* Computer and Information Systems Abstracts Journal **1403**
Computer and Information Systems Abstracts Journal. (US ISSN 0191-9776) **1403, 8**
†Computer & Software News. (US) **5169**
Computer and Technology Law Journal *see* Santa Clara Computer and High-Technology Law Journal **2677**
Computer & Video Games. (UK ISSN 0261-3697) **1419, 1384**
†Computer Answers. (UK ISSN 0264-4479) **5169**
Computer Anwendungen - Computer Applications - Universitaet Karlsruhe *see* C A K **5156**
†Computer Applications. (UK ISSN 0308-4221) **5169**

Computer Applications and Software. *see* Jisuanji Yingyong yu Ruanjian **1397**
Computer Applications in Archaeology. (UK) **290**
†Computer Applications in Shipping and Shipbuilding. (NE) **5169**
Computer Applications in Social Work and Allied Professions *see* New Technology in the Human Services **4459**
Computer Applications in the Biosciences. (UK ISSN 0266-7061) **4359**
▼Computer Artist. (US) **352**
Computer-Assisted Composition Journal.(US ISSN 1047-2452) **1417, 1476, 1689**
Computer Assisted English Language Learning Journal *see* C A E L L Journal **1416**
Computer Assisted Language & Instruction Consortium Journal *see* C A L I C O Journal **1688**
Computer Assisted Language & Instruction Consortium Monograph Series *see* C A L I C O. Monograph Series **1416**
▼Computer Assisted Language Learning. (US) **2856, 1689**
Computer Associates International Inc. Insight *see* C A - Insight **1458**
Computer Audit Update. (UK ISSN 0960-2593) **1433, 749**
Computer-Based Information Systems in Information Management. (US) **1443**
Computer Based Training Directions *see* C B T Directions **1389**
Computer Book Review. (US ISSN 0737-0334) **1391, 1403, 4125**
Computer Bulletin. (UK ISSN 0010-4531) **1391**
Computer Business. (US ISSN 0732-8346) **1391, 1334, 1884**
Computer Buyer's Guide and Handbook.(US ISSN 0738-9213) **1459, 1432, 1468**
▼Computer Buying World. (US) **1459**
Computer Chess News Sheet. (UK) **1419, 4469**
Computer Chess Reports. (US) **4469, 1391**
Computer Commentary. (AT) **1391**
Computer Communications. (UK ISSN 0140-3664) **1446**
Computer Communications Review. (US ISSN 0146-4833) **1446**
†Computer Contents. (US) **5169**
Computer Control Quarterly. (AT) **1433**
Computer Counsel. (US) **1391, 2615**
Computer Coupling of Phase Diagrams and Thermochemistry CALPHAD *see* CALPHAD **4359**
Computer Crime Law Reporter. (US) **1512, 1391**
Computer Currents (Dallas). (US) **1423**
Computer Currents (Framingham). (US) **1423**
Computer Curriculum Resources *see* Educational Computing Chronicle **5184**
†Computer Daily. (US) **5169**
Computer Data Storage Newsletter. (FR ISSN 0988-3452) **1453**
Computer Database. (US) **1403, 8**
Computer Dealer *see* Reseller Management **1433**
Computer Dealer News. (CN ISSN 0834-4612) **1432**
†Computer Decisions. (US ISSN 0010-4558) **5169**
Computer Design. (US ISSN 0010-4566) **1420**
Computer Design and Architecture Series. (US) **1416**
Computer Design News. (US) **1420**
Computer Directory and Buyer's Guide. (US) **1424**
Computer - Disability News. (US) **2285, 1689, 1735**
†Computer Display Review. (US ISSN 0010-4582) **5170**
▼Computer e Videogiochi. (IT) **1419, 1384**
Computer Economics Report. (US ISSN 0739-0874) **1448**

Computer Economics Sourcebook. (US) **1448**, 1036
▼Computer Education. (IL) **1417**
Computer Education. (UK ISSN 0010-4590) **1689**, 1417
Computer-Electronic Service News see Service News (Yarmouth) **1400**
Computer Engineering. see Jisuanji Gongcheng **1418**
▼Computer Engineering and Computer Science. (US) **1418**
Computer Entertainer. (US ISSN 0890-2143) **1419**, 1423
Computer Entrepreneur. (US) **1423**
Computer Equipment Review see Library Computer Systems & Equipment Review **2798**
Computer Exploration and Application. see Diannao Kaifa yu Yingyong **1394**
Computer Expo (Year): Exhibition Guide.(HK) **3391**, 1391
Computer for Beginners. see Al-Computer lil-Mubtaddi'in **1392**
Computer Forum. (SZ) **1391**
Computer Fraud and Security Bulletin. (UK ISSN 0142-0496) **1434**, 1526
Computer Fun and Games. (US) **1419**
Computer Game Review. (US) **1419**
Computer Gaming World. (US ISSN 0744-6667) **1419**, 1468
Computer gia Olous. (GR) **1391**
†Computer Grafica e Applicazioni. (IT) **5170**
Computer Graphics (Eugene) see Computer Graphics World **1421**
Computer Graphics (New York). (US ISSN 0097-8930) **1421**
Computer Graphics (New York, 1987). (US) **1421**
Computer Graphics (San Diego). (US) **1421**
Computer Graphics Directory see Computer Graphics World Buyers Guide **1421**
Computer Graphics Forum. (UK ISSN 0167-7055) **1421**
Computer Graphics Professional see C G Professional **1420**
†Computer Graphics Review. (US ISSN 1041-2263) **5170**
†Computer Graphics Systems. (US) **5170**
†Computer Graphics Technology. (AT) **5170**
†Computer Graphics Today. (US ISSN 0747-9670) **5170**
Computer Graphics World. (US ISSN 0271-4159) **1421**
Computer Graphics World Buyers Guide.(US ISSN 0895-2760) **1421**
†Computer Hot Line. (US) **5170**
†Computer Hot Line Weekly (Newsstand Edition). (US) **5170**
Computer in Teaching and Learning. see Jisuanji Jiao yu Xue **1690**
Computer Industry Abstracts see Computer Industry Forecasts **1403**
Computer Industry Forecasts. (US ISSN 0894-6213) **1403**
Computer Industry Litigation Reporter. (US ISSN 0740-1469) **2615**, 1423
Computer Industry Report. (US ISSN 0889-082X) **1449**, 825
Computer Industry Update. (US ISSN 0744-0081) **1403**, 8
Computer Industry Week. (US) **1423**
Computer Information Review. (US) **825**
Computer Insider. (US) **1391**
Computer Integrated Building Edifici Intelligenti see C I B Edifici Intelligenti **296**
Computer Integrated Manufacturing see C I M **5157**
†Computer-Integrated Manufacturing Review. (US ISSN 0748-0474) **5170**
Computer-Integrated Manufacturing Strategies see C I M Strategies **1412**
Computer-Integrated Manufacturing Systems. (UK ISSN 0951-5240) **1877**
Computer Integrated Manufacturing Technology see C I M Technology **5157**

Computer Issues. (PH ISSN 0115-8686) **1391**, 1455
Computer Journal. (UK ISSN 0010-4620) **1391**
The Computer Journal. (US ISSN 0748-9331) **1391**
Computer Journal. (US) **1459**
Computer Katalog. (GW ISSN 0177-4603) **1468**
Computer Language. (US ISSN 0749-2839) **1413**
Computer Languages. (US ISSN 0096-0551) **1429**
Computer Law & Practice. (UK ISSN 0266-4801) **1391**, 1434
Computer Law and Security Report. (UK ISSN 0267-3649) **1434**, 1006
Computer Law & Tax Report. (US ISSN 0361-7203) **1391**, 1091, 2615
Computer-Law Journal. (US ISSN 0164-8756) **1391**, 1334, 2615
Computer Law Monitor. (US ISSN 0741-8809) **1391**, 1334, 2615
Computer Law Reporter. (US ISSN 0739-7771) **1391**, 2615
Computer Law Series. (NE) **1391**, 2615
Computer Law Strategist. (US ISSN 0747-8933) **1391**, 1434, 2615
Computer Lawyer. (US) **1391**, 2615
Computer Letter. (US) **1459**
Computer Library see Computer Library's Computer Periodicals Database **2793**
Computer Library's Computer Periodicals Database. (US) **2793**, 8, 2796
Al-Computer lil-Mubtaddi'in/Computer for Beginners. (TS) **1392**
Computer Listing Service's Machinery & Equipment Guide. (US) **3016**
Computer Literature Index. (US ISSN 0270-4846) **1403**, 8
Computer Living - New York. (US) **1392**, 1459, 1468
Computer Magazin. (GW) **1392**
Computer Marketing Newsletter. (US ISSN 0886-7194) **1432**, 1036
†Computer Marketplace Magazine. (US) **5170**
Computer Media Directory. (US) **1425**, 4143
Computer Merchandising see Computer Reseller Monthly **5170**
Computer Methods & Programs in Biomedicine. (NE ISSN 0169-2607) **3225**
Computer Methods in Applied Mechanics and Engineering. (SZ ISSN 0045-7825) **1877**
Computer Monthly. (UK) **1468**
Computer Music Journal. (US ISSN 0148-9267) **3589**, 4460
Computer N C C Daily. (US) **1392**
†Computer Networking Symposium. Proceedings. (US) **5170**
Computer Networks and I S D N Systems. (NE ISSN 0169-7552) **1426**
Computer News for Physicians see Physicians Financial News **795**
Computer News International. (US) **1459**
†Computer Newsletter (Bracknell). (UK) **5170**
Computer Newsletter (Cambridge) see Computer Bulletin **1391**
†Computer Optics. (US ISSN 0955-355X) **5170**
†Computer P R Update. (US ISSN 0893-5947) **5170**
Computer Paper. (CN ISSN 0840-3929) **1392**, 3662
Computer Peripherals. (UK) **1453**
Computer Peripherals Review see Computer Review **1453**
Computer Persoenlich. (GW ISSN 0722-0987) **1468**
Computer Physics Communications. (NE ISSN 0010-4655) **4359**
†Computer Physics Reports. (NE ISSN 0167-7977) **5170**
Computer Pictures. (US ISSN 0883-5683) **1421**
Computer-Praxis A B C. (GW) **1392**
Computer Price Guide. (US ISSN 0045-7841) **1432**, 1425
Computer Product News. (BE) **1453**

†Computer Product Selling. (US) **5170**
†Computer Products. (US ISSN 0161-6862) **5170**
Computer Produkte Software. (GW ISSN 0939-1142) **1058**, 1476
†Computer Programming Management.(US ISSN 0736-3621) **5170**
Computer Progress. (US) **1392**
Computer Protocols. (US ISSN 0899-126X) **1392**
Computer Publicity News. (US ISSN 0276-9972) **1432**, 1036, 1392
Computer Publishers & Publications. (US ISSN 0740-4085) **4143**
†Computer Publishing. (US) **5170**
Computer Publishing and Advertising Report. (US ISSN 0740-6231) **4143**
Computer Readable Bibliographic Data Bases see Computer - Readable Databases **1403**
Computer - Readable Databases. (US ISSN 0271-4477) **1403**, 1425
Computer Report/Konpyuta Repoto. (JA ISSN 0385-6658) **1392**
Computer Report. (UK ISSN 0306-6886) **1446**
Computer Research and Development. see Jisuanji Yanjiu yu Fazhan **1418**
†Computer Reseller Monthly. (US ISSN 0890-3980) **5170**
Computer Reseller News. (US ISSN 0893-8377) **1432**
▼Computer Reseller Sources. (US) **1433**
Computer Retail News see Computer Reseller News **1432**
Computer Retailers' Guide. (US) **1468**, 1459
Computer Review. (US ISSN 0093-416X) **1453**
Computer-Schach und -Spiele. (GW ISSN 0176-2400) **1419**
Computer Science/Olum-e Kampiuter. (IR) **1392**
Computer Science and Applied Mathematics see Computer Science and Scientific Computing **1392**
Computer Science and Scientific Computing. (US) **1392**, 3064
Computer Science Education. (US ISSN 0899-3408) **1392**, 1689, 1747
Computer Science in Economics and Management. (NE ISSN 0921-2736) **825**, 851, 1006
Computer Science Technical Report Anthology. (US) **1392**
Computer Security Alert. (US) **1434**
Computer Security and Privacy Abstracts. (UK ISSN 0958-1413) **1403**
Computer Security and Privacy Profiles see Computer Security and Privacy Abstracts **1403**
Computer Security Applications Conference. (US) **66**
Computer Security, Auditing and Controls Com - S A C see Com - S A C **1433**
Computer Security Buyers Guide. (US) **1434**, 1127
Computer Security Digest. (US) **1434**
Computer Security Journal. (US ISSN 0277-0865) **1434**, 1526
Computer Security Newsletter see Computer Security Alert **1434**
†Computer Security Products Report. (US) **5170**
Computer Services Software see Britain's P.C. Manufacturers **5153**
Computer Shopper. (US ISSN 0886-0556) **1433**, 1392, 1459, 1468
Computer Society of India. Journal. (II ISSN 0045-7892) **1392**
Computer Society of India Communications see C S I Communications **1390**
Computer Software. (JA ISSN 0289-6540) **1476**
Computer Software & Applications Conference (Proceedings) see C O M P S A C **1476**
Computer Software Engineering Series. (US ISSN 0888-2088) **1877**, 1476
Computer Software Protection Law. (US) **1476**, 2615

▼Computer Software Protection Law. Supplement. (US) **1476**, 2615
Computer Sources. (US) **5170**
Computer Spectrum. (SZ ISSN 1017-3803) **1392**
Computer Speech & Language. (UK ISSN 0885-2308) **1429**
Computer-Spiele Per Post. (GW) **1419**
Computer Standards and Interfaces. (NE ISSN 0920-5489) **1392**
†Computer Standards Conference. Proceedings. (US) **5170**
Computer Street Journal see Texas Desktop News **5289**
Computer Student. (US) **1468**, 1459
Computer Studies: Computers in Business. (US) **825**
Computer Studies: Computers in Education. (US) **1689**
Computer Studies: Computers in Society. (US) **4458**
Computer Survey. (UK ISSN 0010-4760) **1425**, 1453
Computer Sweden. (SW) **1392**
Computer Systems News see Systems and Networks Integration **1439**
Computer Systems Science and Engineering. (UK ISSN 0267-6192) **1436**
Computer Systems Series. (US) **1436**
Computer Talk. (UK) **1392**
Computer Technology and the Law. (US) **2615**, 1392
Computer Technology Review. (US ISSN 0278-9647) **1392**
Computer Terminals Review see Computer Review **1453**
Computer und Grafik see C G **1420**
Computer und Recht. (GW ISSN 0179-1990) **1392**, 1334, 2615
Computer Update see B C S Update **1458**
Computer Use in Social Services Network. Newsletter see Computers in Human Services **4458**
Computer User (Minneapolis). (US ISSN 0742-5902) **1392**, 1459, 1468
Computer Users Handbook. (SA) **1453**, 1058, 1476
Computer User's Survival Magazine. (US ISSN 1053-3834) **1468**
Computer Users' Year Book. (UK) **1436**
Computer-Using Educators Newsletter see C U E Newsletter **1688**
Computer Viruses. (US) **1476**, 1434
Computer Vision, Graphics, and Image Processing see C V G I P: Graphical Models and Image Processing **1420**
Computer Vision, Graphics, and Image Processing see C V G I P: Image Understanding **1420**
Computer Weekly. (UK ISSN 0010-4787) **1392**
Computer Weekly. see Automatisering Gids **1448**
Computer White Paper see Informatization White Paper **1396**
Computer Words. (CN ISSN 0840-8173) **1392**
Die Computer-Zeitung. (GW ISSN 0341-5406) **1392**
Computerbildung. (GW ISSN 0930-3227) **1689**
ComputerCraft. (US) **353**, 352
ComputerData see Info Canada **1451**
Computereport. (IT) **1392**
Computergram International. (US) **1392**
Computeriter. (US ISSN 8756-7911) **1468**, 2568, 4125
Computerized Medical Imaging and Graphics. (US ISSN 0895-6111) **3225**, 3357
Computerized Radiology see Computerized Medical Imaging and Graphics **3225**
ComputerLand Magazine. (US) **825**, 1468
Computermarkt. (SZ ISSN 0254-5012) **1392**, 656
Computernews. (CN ISSN 0315-4661) **1393**
Computerreport der Neue Juristischen Wochenschrift. (GW ISSN 0934-8778) **2705**, 2615
Computers/Machshavim. (IS ISSN 0333-7413) **1393**

COMPUTERS

†Computers. (CN ISSN 0382-1005) 5170
Computers and Applied Chemistry. see Jisuanji yu Yingyong Huaxue 4359
Computers and Artificial Intelligence/Pocitace a Umela Inteligencia. (CS) 1407, 1440
Computers and Biomedical Research. (US ISSN 0010-4809) 3225
Computers & Chemical Engineering. (US ISSN 0098-1354) 1878, 1175, 1852
Computers & Chemistry. (US ISSN 0097-8485) 4359, 475, 1175
Computers and Composition. (US ISSN 8755-4615) 1417, 1689
Computers and Computing Information Resources Directory. (US ISSN 0894-8941) 1449
Computers & Education. (US ISSN 0360-1315) 1689
Computers & Electrical Engineering. (US ISSN 0045-7906) 1878, 1884
Computers and Electronics in Agriculture. (NE ISSN 0168-1699) 165
Computers & Fluids. (US ISSN 0045-7930) 1878
Computers & Geosciences. (US ISSN 0098-3004) 1878, 1542
Computers and Geotechnics. (UK ISSN 0266-352X) 1878, 1421
Computers & Graphics. (US ISSN 0097-8493) 1421
Computers & Industrial Engineering. (US ISSN 0360-8352) 1878, 1925
†Computers & Industrial Engineering Annual Conference. Proceedings. (US) 5170
Computers and Libraries see C & L Applications 2796
†Computers and Math Series. (US ISSN 0888-2193) 5170
Computers & Mathematics with Applications. (US ISSN 0898-1221) 3064
Computers and Medicine (Glencoe). (US ISSN 0163-0547) 3225
†Computers and Medieval Data Processing/Informatique et Etudes Medievales. (CN ISSN 0384-5060) 5170
Computers & Mining. (US) 3482, 1558, 4359
Computers & Office Equipment: Latin American Industrial Report. (US) 1393, 1058
Computers & Operations Research. (US ISSN 0305-0548) 1393
Computers and People. (US ISSN 0361-1442) 1393, 1413
Computers and People Series. (US) 1393, 2520
†Computers & Philosophy. (US) 5170
Computers and Philosophy Newsletter see Computers & Philosophy 5170
Computers & Programs. (US) 1459, 1468
Computers & Security. (UK ISSN 0167-4048) 1434, 1526
Computers & Society. (US ISSN 0095-2737) 4458
Computers & Structures. (US ISSN 0045-7949) 1878
▼Computers and the History of Art. (US ISSN 1048-6798) 352
Computers and the Humanities. (NE ISSN 0010-4817) 2520, 1459
Computers and the Media Center News see C M C News 1350
Computers and the Social Sciences see Social Science Computer Review 1691
Computers and Translation see Machine Translation 2856
Computers, Environment and Urban Systems. (US ISSN 0198-9715) 1975, 4083
†Computers for Design & Construction. (US ISSN 0734-5402) 5170
Computers in Accounting. (US ISSN 0740-7270) 825, 1459, 1468
Computers in Banking. (US ISSN 0742-6496) 805
Computers in Biology and Medicine. (US ISSN 0010-4825) 3225
Computers in Cardiology. (US ISSN 0276-6574) 3225
▼Computers in Civil & Consulting Engineering. (US) 1878, 1864
Computers in Education. (CN ISSN 0823-9940) 1689
Computers in Education Journal. (US) 1689, 1417
†Computers in Education Series. (US ISSN 0888-2177) 5170
Computers in Genealogy. (UK ISSN 0263-3248) 2168
▼Computers in H R Management. (Human Resource) (US ISSN 1047-6458) 825, 1006
Computers in Healthcare. (US ISSN 0745-1075) 3225, 2460
Computers in Human Behavior. (US ISSN 0747-5632) 4458, 4017
Computers in Human Services. (US ISSN 0740-445X) 4458
Computers in Industry. (NE ISSN 0166-3615) 826
Computers in Libraries. (US ISSN 1041-7915) 1459, 2796
Computers in Libraries: Buyers Guide & Consultant Directory. (US) 1468, 2796
Computers in Mechanical Engineering see C I M E 5157
Computers in Music Research. (US ISSN 1046-1744) 3589
Computers in Nursing. (US ISSN 0736-8593) 3225
†Computers in Personnel. (US ISSN 0887-980X) 5170
Computers in Physics. (US ISSN 0894-1866) 3840
Computers in Schools see Information Technology & Learning 1690
†Computers in Science. (US ISSN 0893-1909) 5170
Computers in the Classroom see Computers in Education 1689
Computers in the Schools. (US ISSN 0738-0569) 1689, 1459, 1468
†Computers - R - Digital. (US) 5170
†Computers, Reading and Language Arts. (US ISSN 0737-500X) 5170
Computers Today. (II) 1393
Computerschaak. (NE) 1419, 4469
ComputerScope. (IE) 826
†Computerstunde. (GW) 5170
ComputerTalk Directory of Medical Computer Systems. (US ISSN 0739-6201) 3225, 1459
ComputerTalk Directory of Medical Systems see ComputerTalk Directory of Medical Computer Systems 3225
ComputerTalk Directory of Pharmacy Systems see ComputerTalk Pharmacy Systems Buyers Guide 3721
ComputerTalk for the Pharmacist. (US ISSN 0736-3893) 3721, 1459, 3225
ComputerTalk Pharmacy Systems Buyers Guide. (US) 3721, 1459, 3225
Computerweek. (SA) 1393
Computerwelt. (AU) 1446
Computerwhat? (US) 1468
Computerwoche. (GW) 1393
Computerworld. (US ISSN 0010-4841) 1393, 1423, 1459, 1468
Computerworld. (DK ISSN 0107-5217) 1393
Computerworld. see Szamitastechnika 1401
Computerworld Argentina. (AG) 1393
Computerworld Australia. (AT ISSN 0813-295X) 1449
Computerworld Benelux see Computerworld Netherlands 1393
Computerworld de Mexico, S.A. de C.V. (US) 1393
Computerworld - Espana. (SP) 1393
†Computerworld Focus. (US) 5170
Computerworld Focus on Integration. (US) 1426
Computerworld Hong Kong. (HK) 1423
Computerworld Italia. (IT) 1393
Computerworld Japan. (GW) 1393
Computerworld Netherlands. (NE) 1393, 1413
Computerworld Norway. (NO) 1393
Computerworld Venezuela. (US) 1393

†Compute's Amiga Resource. (US ISSN 1043-0792) 5170
†Compute's Apple Applications. (US ISSN 0895-9595) 5170
Compute's Apple: Special Applications Issue see Compute's Apple Applications 5170
†Compute's Gazette. (US ISSN 0737-3716) 5170
†Compute's Gazette Disk & Magazine. (US) 5170
†Compute's P C Magazine. (US ISSN 0893-8261) 5170
Computing. (US ISSN 0010-485X) 1393
Computing. (UK) 1393
Computing and Communications Decisions. (UK) 1393
Computing & Communications Protection. (US) 1434, 1526
Computing & Control Engineering Journal. (UK ISSN 0956-3385) 1878, 826, 1817
Computing & Management. (US ISSN 0743-6262) 805, 1006
Computing Canada. (CN ISSN 0319-0161) 1476
Computing Decisions see Computing and Communications Decisions 1393
Computing Decisions. (HK) 1393
Computing Equipment. (UK ISSN 0266-4283) 1453
Computing Information Directory. (US ISSN 0887-1175) 1404, 8
Computing Journal Abstracts. (UK ISSN 0309-8885) 1404, 8
Computing News. (US) 1393, 1689
Computing Now! (CN ISSN 0823-6437) 1468
†Computing Resources for the Professional. (US ISSN 0276-5756) 5170
Computing Reviews. (US ISSN 0010-4884) 1404
Computing S.A. (SA) 1393
Computing Services Bulletin see University Computing Systems Dispatch 1401
Computing Supplementa. (US ISSN 0344-8029) 1393
Computing Systems. (US ISSN 0895-6340) 1429, 1436
▼Computing Systems in Engineering. (US ISSN 0956-0521) 1878
Computing Teacher. (US ISSN 0278-9175) 1393, 1689, 1747
Computing Times. (US) 1459
†Computing Today. (UK ISSN 0142-7210) 5170
Computist. (US) 1468, 1459
Computopia. (JA ISSN 0010-4906) 1393
Computor Edge. (US) 1459
Compuviews. (CN) 1394
Compuwest see Computek 1390
COMSAT Technical Review see C O M S A T Technical Review 1332
Comsearch: Broad Topics see Grant Guides 4426
Comsearch: Geographics see Grant Guides 4426
Comsearch: Subjects see Grant Guides 4426
ComSec Letter see Surveillance 1528
†Comstock Quarterly. (US ISSN 1042-9948) 5170
Comstock's. (US) 656
Comte de Jette Bulletin/Graafschap Jette Bulletin. (BE ISSN 0010-4914) 269, 2053, 2309
Comune Democratico. (IT ISSN 0010-4930) 4086
Comune di Bologna. Notiziario Mensile see Bologna 4085
Comune di Carpi see Carpi Citta 4085
Comune di Cervia. (IT) 2204
†Comune di Roma. Ufficio di Statistica e Censimento. Bollettino Statistico. (IT ISSN 0010-4957) 5170
Comune di Roma. Ufficio di Statistica e Censimento. Notiziario Statistico Mensile. (IT ISSN 0010-4965) 3991
Comuni d'Europa. (IT ISSN 0010-4973) 4086, 3881
Comuni d'Italia. (IT) 4057
Comunicacion. (AG) 30
Comunicacion. (VE) 1334

Comunicacion Integral. (CK) 30
Comunicaciones. (US) 1350, 1334
Comunicaciones Biologicas. (AG ISSN 0326-1956) 435, 3090
Comunicazioni Scientifiche di Psicologia Generale. (IT) 4017
Comunicazioni Sociali. (IT ISSN 0392-8667) 1334
Comunidad. (SP) 4262
Comunidad Escolar. (SP) 1622
Comunidad Europea. (SP) 2615
Comunidad Informatica. (MX ISSN 0185-8114) 4057
Comunidades y Culturas Peruanas. (PE) 237, 2053
Comunione e Liberazione see Litterae Communionis 4188
Comunismo. (IT ISSN 0393-6740) 3881
Comunismo ou Civilizacao see Revue Internationale du Mouvement Communiste 3923
Comunita e Storia. (IT) 4262
Comunita Ebraica di Milano. Bollettino. (IT) 1997
Comunita Europee see Dossier Europa 3891
Comunita Internazionale. (IT ISSN 0010-5066) 3953, 2721
Comunita Islamica. (IT) 4218
Comunita Israelitica di Milano. Bollettino see Comunita Ebraica di Milano. Bollettino 1997
Comunita Mediterranea. (IT ISSN 0045-7981) 3953, 2615
Comunita Sportiva. (IT ISSN 0393-7984) 1252, 1235, 4469
Comunita Viva. (CN) 2176
Comuniunea Romaneasca/Rumanian Communion. (US ISSN 0197-1441) 2215
Con Aero see Conservation Aeronautics Magazine 50
†Con Brio. (CN ISSN 0707-5103) 5171
Con Edison Library Bulletin. (US ISSN 0010-5090) 1798
Con la Guardia en Alto. (CU) 3454
Con - Science. (PH) 4595
Conacex Noreste Boletin Informativo see Conacex Noreste Magazine 904
Conacex Noreste Magazine. (MX) 904
Conad. (Consorzio Nazionale Dettaglianti) (IT) 834
ConCamIn see Industria 836
Concatenation. (AT) 2796
†Conceive Magazine. (US ISSN 1042-1297) 5171
Concentus Musicus. (GW) 3547
Conceptions Southwest. (US) 322, 2907
Conceptos Boletin. (AG) 4432, 4369
Conceptos de Matematica. (AG ISSN 0010-5147) 3033
Concepts and Techniques in Modern Geography see C A T M O G 2243
Concepts in Action. (US) 656
Concepts in Chemistry. (US) 1175
Concepts in Communication Informatics and Librarianship. (II) 2753, 2796, 4126
Concepts in Immunopathology. (SZ ISSN 0255-7983) 3251
▼Concepts in Neuroscience. (SI ISSN 0129-0568) 485, 475, 571, 4017
Concepts in Pediatric Neurosurgery. (SZ ISSN 0251-2068) 3334, 3320
†Concepts in Toxicology. (SZ ISSN 0254-8739) 5171
Conceptus. (AU ISSN 0010-5155) 3764
Conceptus-Studien. (AU ISSN 0259-0670) 3764
Concern. (UK ISSN 0591-017X) 1235, 4402
Concern. (SW ISSN 1101-1939) 2114
Concern. (CN) 3277
Concern (Anaheim). (US) 3090
†Concern Bulletin. (US) 5171
Concern for Dying - Society for the Right to Die Newsletter see Choice in Dying 4431
Concern for Helping Animals in Israel Lights see C H A I Lights 230
Concern News. (US) 4402

Concerned Educators Allied for a Safe Environment News see C E A S E News 1485
Concerned United Birthparents, Inc. Communicator see C U B Communicator 4430
Concerning America's Livestock Feeders News Cattle Feeder see C A L F News Cattle Feeder 213
Concerns. (CN ISSN 0045-799X) 1535
Concerns (Washington). (US) 1623, 2615
Concert see Live in Concert 3561
†Concert Repertoire of Bayan Player. (UR) 5171
Concert Shots. (US) 3547
Concertacion. (DR) 3881
Concertina and Free Reed see Concertina & Squeezebox 3547
Concertina & Squeezebox. (US) 3547
Concessionaire. (US) 2064
Concetto. (UK ISSN 0140-315X) 1308
La Conchiglia/Shell. (IT ISSN 0394-0152) 580
Concho River Review. (US) 2907, 2403
Conchological Society Special Publication. (UK ISSN 0144-9826) 580
Conchologists' Newsletter. (UK) 580
Conciencia. (PN) 596
Conciliation Courts Review see Family and Conciliation Courts Review 2717
Conciliation Quarterly. (US) 4234
Conciliatore. (IT ISSN 0010-5228) 4369
Concilium. (FR) 4172
Concilium. (UK ISSN 0010-5236) 4172
Concilium. (NE ISSN 0167-1200) 4172
Concise Descriptive Catalogue of Arabic Manuscripts in the Salar Jung Museum and Library. (II) 3536
Concise Descriptive Catalogue of the Persian Manuscripts in the Salar Jung Museum and Library. (II) 3536
Concise Statistical Yearbook of Greece. (GR ISSN 0069-8245) 4569
Concord. (UK ISSN 0300-4384) 2193
Concord. (US ISSN 0741-9872) 2452, 4281
▼Concord and the North. (US) 2223
Concord Business. (US) 656
Concord Inflight Entertainment Guide. (UK) 4672
Concord Review. (US) 2403, 1252
Concord Saunterer. (US) 2907
Concordia Alumni News. (US) 1309
Concordia Historical Institute Quarterly. (US ISSN 0010-5260) 4234, 2309
Concordia Journal. (US ISSN 0145-7233) 4172
Concordia Letter. (US) 943, 851
Concordia Theological Quarterly. (US) 4172
Concordia Torch. (US ISSN 0010-5287) 2530
Concours Medical. (FR ISSN 0010-5309) 3090
Concourse. (UK) 1309
Concrete. (UK ISSN 0010-5317) 610
Concrete see Concrete Producers News 611
Concrete Abstracts. (US ISSN 0045-8007) 637, 8
Concrete and Masonry Cost Data see Means Concrete Cost Data (Year) 624
Concrete Construction. (US ISSN 0010-5333) 610
Concrete Construction and Architecture.(II ISSN 0010-5341) 610
Concrete Industry Bulletin. (US ISSN 0010-535X) 610
Concrete International: Design & Construction. (US ISSN 0162-4075) 610
Concrete Journal. see Konkuriito Kogaku 622
Concrete - Masonry News see C - M News 608

Concrete Pipe Industry Statistics. (US ISSN 0360-2877) 1842, 1916, 4569
Concrete Pipe News. (US ISSN 0045-8015) 610
Concrete Plant and Production. (UK ISSN 0264-0236) 610
Concrete Producers News. (US ISSN 0899-8671) 611
Concrete Products. (US ISSN 0010-5368) 611
Concrete Repair Digest. (US) 611
Concrete Society. Technical Report. (UK) 611
Concrete Trader. (US) 611
Concrete Works International see Concrete 610
The Concrete Yearbook. (UK ISSN 0069-8288) 611
Concurrency: Practice and Experience. (UK ISSN 1040-3108) 1430
▼Concurrent Engineering. (US) 1878
Conde Nast Traveler. (US) 4758
Condensed Matter News. (US ISSN 1056-7046) 1884
Condensed Matter Theories. (US ISSN 0893-861X) 3816, 1210
Condenser. (SA) 656
Condiciones de Trabajo. (MX) 3616
Condition. (GW ISSN 0340-2991) 4469, 2271, 3800
Condition Monitor. (UK ISSN 0268-8050) 1817, 1413
Condition Monitoring Journal. (UK ISSN 0950-9178) 3016, 1923, 1928
Condition of Education. (US ISSN 0098-4752) 1675
Condition of Farmworkers and Small Farmers. (US) 84, 975
Conditioned Response. (US ISSN 0887-1612) 2990
Conditions. (US ISSN 0147-8311) 4839, 2452, 2907
Conditions of Work: A Cumulative Digest see Conditions of Work Digest 975
Conditions of Work Digest. (UN ISSN 0257-3512) 975, 2615
Condizionamento dell'Aria, Riscaldamento, Refrigerazione. (IT) 2298
Condo Sales Report. (US) 4147
Condominio e Inquilinato. (IT) 4147
Condominium. (CN ISSN 0849-6714) 2485
†Condominium Development Guide. (US) 5171
Condominium Magazine see Condominium 2485
Condor (Tempe). (US ISSN 0010-5422) 563
Condor Call. (US) 1485, 1946
Conduct of Civil Litigation in British Columbia. (CN) 2615
The Conductor. (UK) 3547
Conductors' Guild. Journal. (US ISSN 0734-1032) 3547
Conduit. (UK ISSN 0144-8439) 2357, 269
Conector. (AG) 3230
Confeccion Industrial. (SP) 1284, 4617
Confectie. (BE) 1284, 4617
†Confectioner. (US ISSN 0010-5457) 5171
Confectioner, Tobacconist, Newsagent see C T N 2087
Confectionery and Tobacco News see C T N 2087
Confectionery Buyer's Guide see C M M 2087
Confectionery Manufacture & Marketing see C M M 2087
Confectionery Production. (UK ISSN 0010-5473) 2087
Confederacao Brasileira de Desportos. Relatorio see Confederacao Brasileira de Futebol. Relatorio 4469
Confederacao Brasileira de Futebol. Relatorio. (BL) 4469
Confederacao Nacional do Comercio. Assessoria Juridica. Boletim Informativo. (BL) 834
Confederacao Nacional do Comercio. Conselho Tecnico Consultivo. Carta Mensal. (BL ISSN 0101-4315) 834

Confederacao Nacional do Comercio. Divisao de Divulgacao. Carta Mensal see Confederacao Nacional do Comercio. Conselho Tecnico Consultivo. Carta Mensal 834
Confederacao Nacional do Comercio. Divisao Juridico-Legislativa. Boletim see Confederacao Nacional do Comercio. Assessoria Juridica. Boletim Informativo 834
Confederacion Colombiana de Camaras de Comercio. Asamblea General. Informe Final. (CK) 813
Confederacion Colombiana de Camaras de Comercio. Sintesis Mensual. (CK) 813
Confederacion de Camaras Industriales de los Estados Unidos Mexicanos Industria see Industria 836
Confederacion de Organizaciones Turisticas de la America Latina see C O T A L 4755
Confederacion Espanola de Cajas de Ahorros. Fondo para la Investigacion Economica y Social. Coyuntura Economica see Confederacion Espanola de Cajas de Ahorros. Fundacion Fondo para la Investigacion Economica y Social. Coyuntura Economica 851
Confederacion Espanola de Cajas de Ahorros. Fundacion Fondo para la Investigacion Economica y Social. Coyuntura Economica. (SP ISSN 0210-0738) 851
Confederacion Latinoamericana de Asociaciones Cristianas de Jovenes. Confederacion. (UY) 4172
Confederacion Latinoamericana de Asociaciones Cristianas de Jovenes. Contacto. (UY) 4172
Confederacion Latinoamericana de Asociaciones Cristianas de Jovenes. Carta. (UY) 4172
Confederacion Sudamericana de Asociaciones Cristianas de Jovenes. Noticias see Asociacion 1232
Confederate Air Force Dispatch see C A F Dispatch 3453
Confederate Historical Institute Dispatch see C H I Dispatch 2401
†Confederate Historical Institute Journal.(US ISSN 0734-3671) 5171
Confederation des Industries Ceramiques de France. Annuaire. (FR ISSN 0069-830X) 1163
Confederation Francaise Democratique du Travail Aujourd'hui see C F D T Aujourd'hui 2581
Confederation Francaise Democratique du Travail Magazine see C F D T Magazine 4367
Confederation Internationale des Accordeonistes Revue see C I A Revue 3543
Confederation Internationale des Cinemas d'Art et d'Essai Bulletin d'Information see C.I.C.A.E. Bulletin d'Information 3504
Confederation Mondiale des Activites Bulletin d'Information see C M A S Bulletin d'Information 1602
Confederation Musicale de France. Journal. (FR) 3547
†Confederation Nationale de la Construction. Annuaire. (BE ISSN 0045-8023) 5171
Confederation of Australian Industry News Briefs see C A I News Briefs 5156
Confederation of Australian Motor Sport Manual of Motor Sport see C A M S Manual of Motor Sport 4467
Confederation of Australian Motor Sport Report see C A M S Report 4467
Confederation of British Industry Annual Report see C B I Annual Report 653
Confederation of British Industry Coopers & Lybrand Deloitte Survey of Financial Services see C B I - Coopers & Lybrand Deloitte Survey of Financial Services 653
Confederation of British Industry Economic Situation Report see C B I Economic Situation Report 849

Confederation of British Industry Industrial Survey see C B I Industrial Survey 653
Confederation of British Industry News see C B I News 653
Confederation of British Industry Quarterly Industrial Trends Survey see C B I Quarterly Industrial Trends Survey 653
Confederation of Chambers of Commerce Central Southern England Directory. (UK) 813
Confederation of Engineering Industry. Handbook of Statistics see Confederation of Indian Industry. Handbook of Statistics 1842
Confederation of Finnish Industries. List of Members. see Teollisuuden Keskusliitto. Jasenluettelo 1155
Confederation of Health Service Employees Journal see C O H S E Journal 4099
Confederation of Indian Industry. Handbook of Statistics. (II) 1842, 1817
Confederation of Industry News see Enterprise (Brisbane) 663
Confederation of Irish Industry Business Forecast see C I I - E S R I Business Forecast 1073
Confederation of Irish Industry Newsletter see C.I.I. Newsletter 1073
Confederation of Western Australian Industry. Confederation Report. (AT ISSN 0810-1442) 976
Confederazione Italiana dei Servizi Pubblici degli Enti Locali. Annuario. (IT) 4086
Conference see Conference & Common Room 1623
Conference & Common Room. (UK ISSN 0265-4458) 1623
Conference & Incentive Travel. (UK) 4758, 656
The Conference Blue Book. (UK ISSN 0260-2431) 3391
Conference Board. Report on Company Contributions see Conference Board. Survey of Corporate Contributions 656
Conference Board. Survey of Corporate Contributions. (US ISSN 0146-0986) 656
†Conference Board. Utility Investment Report. (US ISSN 0896-2510) 5171
Conference Board. Utility Investment Statistics. Utility Appropriations see Conference Board. Utility Investment Report 5171
Conference Board Briefing. (US ISSN 0899-6741) 1006
Conference Board Cumulative Index. (US ISSN 0069-8350) 656
Conference Board of Canada. Business Attitudes and Investment Spending Intentions see Conference Board of Canada. Index of Business Confidence 943
Conference Board of Canada. Consumer Attitudes and Buying Intentions see Conference Board of Canada. Index of Consumer Attitudes 1036
Conference Board of Canada. Index of Business Confidence. (CN) 943, 711
Conference Board of Canada. Index of Consumer Attitudes. (CN) 1036, 711
Conference Board of Canada. Quarterly Provincial Forecast see Provincial Outlook 882
Conference Board of the Mathematical Sciences. Regional Conference Series in Applied Mathematics see C B M S. N S F. Regional Conference Series in Applied Mathematics 3062
†Conference Board Statistical Bulletin. (US ISSN 0010-5554) 5171
Conference Board's Human Resources Briefing. (US) 1064
†Conference Board's Management Briefing: Business Finance. (US ISSN 0896-2553) 5171
Conference Board's Management Briefing: Human Resources see Conference Board's Human Resources Briefing 1064

6078 CONFERENCE BOARD'S

Conference Board's Management Briefings: Marketing see Conference Board's Marketing Briefing **1036**
Conference Board's Marketing Briefing. (US) **1036**
Conference Catholique Canadienne. Bulletin National de Liturgie see Liturgie, Foi et Culture **4268**
Conference Chronicles. (US) **3391**
Conference des Eveques Catholiques du Canada. Bulletin National de Liturgie see Liturgie, Foi et Culture **4268**
Conference Generale des Poids et Mesures. Comptes Rendus des Seances. (FR ISSN 1016-5983) **3445**
The Conference Green Book. (UK ISSN 0260-2199) **3391**
Conference Group for Social and Administrative History. Transactions. (US) **4369**
Conference International de l'Education. Rapport Final. see International Conference on Education. Final Report **1639**
Conference Internationale sur les Phenomenes d'Ionisation dans les Gaz. Comptes Rendus. (BW ISSN 0573-3022) **1225**
Conference of Directors of National Libraries on Resource Sharing in Asia and Oceania Newsletter see C D N L A O Newsletter **2750**
Conference of Electrical Engineering Problems in the Rubber and Plastics Industries. I E E E Conference Record. (US ISSN 0272-4685) **4291**, **3862**
Conference of Latin Americanist Geographers Yearbook. (US) **2245**
Conference of Presidents of Major American Jewish Organizations. Annual Report. (US ISSN 0160-7057) **1997**, **4222**
Conference of Presidents of Major American Jewish Organizations. Report see Conference of Presidents of Major American Jewish Organizations. Annual Report **1997**
Conference of South African Surveyors. Proceedings/Konferensie van Suid-Afrikaanse Opmeters. Verrigtinge. (SA) **1864**, **2245**
Conference of Southeast Asian Librarians. Proceedings. (SI) **2753**
Conference of State Sanitary Engineers. Report of Proceedings. (US ISSN 0069-8474) **4099**
Conference of Vice-Chancellors. Proceedings. (II) **1703**
Conference of Vice-Chancellors. Report. (II) **1703**
Conference on Alternative State and Local Public Policies. Newsletter see Ways & Means **4077**
†Conference on American Economic Enterprise. Papers. (US) **5171**
Conference on Artificial Intelligence Applications. Proceedings. (US ISSN 1043-0989) **1407**, **826**, **1878**
Conference on Bank Structure and Competition. Proceedings. (US ISSN 0084-9154) **773**
Conference on Commercial Biotechnology (Year). (US) **489**
Conference on Contingency Planning for Plastics. Proceedings see Plastics Conference Proceedings (Year) **3865**
Conference on Coordination Chemistry Proceedings. (CS) **1175**
Conference on Crime Countermeasures and Security. Proceedings see Carnahan Conference on Security Technology. Proceedings **1526**
Conference on Data Systems Languages. Data Base Task Group. Report. (US ISSN 0090-7383) **1430**
Conference on Editorial Problems: University of Toronto. (US ISSN 0891-1908) **2907**, **322**, **2357**, **3764**
Conference on Electrical Insulation and Dielectric Phenomena. Annual Report. (US ISSN 0084-9162) **1884**
Conference on Engineering in Medicine and Biology. Record. (US) **3090**

Conference on Frontiers in Education. Digest see Frontiers in Education Conference. Proceedings **1892**
Conference on Ground Water. Proceedings. (US ISSN 0094-9671) **1597**
†Conference on Human Relations in Industry. Proceedings. (II ISSN 0069-8555) **5171**
Conference on Labor, New York University. Proceedings see Annual National Conference on Labor at New York University. Proceedings **971**
Conference on Latin American History Newsletter. (US ISSN 0010-5570) **2403**
Conference on Local Computer Networks (Proceedings). (US) **1426**
Conference on Modern Jewish Studies Annual see Modern Jewish Studies Annual **2939**
Conference on Precision Electromagnetic Measurements. Digest. (US) **1884**, **2522**
Conference on Remote Systems Technology. Proceedings. (US ISSN 0069-8644) **1804**, **1817**
Conference on Research in Income and Wealth see Studies in Income and Wealth **1000**
Conference on Software Maintenance. Proceedings. (US) **1476**
Conference on Space Simulation. Proceedings. (US) **50**, **1946**, **4595**
Conference on Teacher Education in the Eastern Caribbean. Report see Eastern Caribbean Standing Conference on Teacher Education. Report **1748**
Conference on U S Technology Policy. Proceedings. (US) **4595**
Conference on United Nations Procedures. Report see United Nations Issues Conference. Report **3975**
Conference Papers Annual Index. (US ISSN 0194-0546) **3395**, **8**, **3391**, **4355**
Conference Papers Index. (US ISSN 0162-704X) **3395**, **8**, **3391**, **4355**
Conference Record, Industry Applications Society, I E E E - I A S Annual Meeting see Industry Applications Society. I E E E - I A S Annual Meeting. Conference Record **1899**
Conference Religieuse Canadienne. Bulletin see Canadian Religious Conference. Bulletin **4168**
Conference Reports Series see United Nations Children's Fund. Programme Division. Conference Reports Series **4422**
Conference Universitaire Suisse. Rapport Annuel. (SZ) **1704**
Conference World. (UK ISSN 0143-7895) **3391**
†Conferences and Exhibitions International. (UK ISSN 0260-8316) **5171**
Conferences du Cenacle. (LE ISSN 0010-5589) **2862**
†Conferences Meetings & Exhibitions Welcome. (UK ISSN 0260-776X) **5171**
Conferencia de Facultades Latinoamericanas de Derecho. (Documentos Oficiales). (PE ISSN 0573-4347) **2615**
Conferencias. (PE ISSN 0010-5600) **2862**
Conferencias de Bioquimica. (CL ISSN 0069-8784) **435**, **475**
Conferenza Italiana Superiori Maggiori. Notiziario. (IT) **4262**
Conferenze - Accademia Polacca delle Scienze (1978) see Accademia Polacca delle Scienze. Conferenze **2502**
†Confetti. (US) **5171**
Confetti (Elk Grove Village). (US ISSN 0897-5973) **30**, **322**, **1334**
Confettiere. see Confiseur **2088**
Confezione. (IT) **1284**, **1290**
†Confidences Magazine. (FR) **5171**
Confident Christian. (NP) **4172**

Confident Consumer Magazine. (US) **1503**
Confident Living. (US ISSN 0017-2154) **4234**
†Confidential Report from Zurich. (US) **5171**
Confidenze. (IT) **4839**
Confins see Lucre-Hatif **2935**
Confiserie. (FR) **2087**
Confiseur/Confettiere. (SZ) **2088**
Confiteria Espanola. (SP ISSN 0210-1920) **2088**
Conflict see Studies in Conflict and Terrorism **3973**
Conflict and Consciousness: Studies in War, Peace and Social Thought. (US ISSN 0899-9910) **4432**
Conflict Bulletin. (UK) **3953**
Conflict Management and Peace Science. (US ISSN 0738-8942) **3881**
Conflict Quarterly. (CN ISSN 0227-1311) **2862**
Conflict Resolution see Journal of Conflict Resolution **4377**
Conflict Resolution Notes. (US) **2615**, **237**, **4402**
Conflict Studies. (UK ISSN 0069-8792) **3953**
Confluence. (US) **3523**, **418**
Confluence. (UN) **4823**
▼Confluence (Wichita). (US) **1309**
Confluent. (BE) **2174**
Confluents. (FR) **2309**
Confluents Psychanalytiques. (FR) **4017**
Confrontacion. (AG) **3881**
Confrontation. (US ISSN 0010-5716) **2907**, **1309**, **2990**
Confrontation - Change Literary Review see Confrontation - Change Review **656**
Confrontation - Change Review. (US ISSN 0363-9460) **656**, **4432**
Confructa. (GW ISSN 0342-5800) **2064**
Confucius & Mencius Society of the Republic of China. Journal. (CH) **4214**, **4369**
Congenital Anomalies. (JA ISSN 0914-3505) **3090**
Congenital Malformations Surveillance see U.S. Centers for Disease Control. Congenital Malformations Surveillance **468**
Congiuntura Economica Lombarda. (IT ISSN 0045-8082) **851**
Congiuntura Estera. (IT ISSN 0010-5740) **1073**
Congiuntura Industriale in Emilia-Romagna. (IT) **851**
Congiuntura Italiana. (IT ISSN 0010-5759) **1073**
Conglio. (IT) **3709**
Congo. Centre National de la Statistique et des Etudes Economiques. Annuaire Statistique. (CF) **4080**
Congo. Centre National de la Statistique et des Etudes Economiques. Bulletin de Statistique. (CF) **4080**
Congo. Centre National de la Statistique et des Etudes Economiques. Bulletin Mensuel de la Statistique. (CF ISSN 0010-5805) **4569**
Congo. Centre National de la Statistique et des Etudes Economiques. Bulletin Trimestriel de la Conjoncture. (CF) **4080**, **711**
Congo. Centre National de la Statistique et des Etudes Economiques. Cadre Comptable National. (CF) **711**
Congo. Centre National de la Statistique et des Etudes Economiques. Cadre Macro-economique. (CF) **711**
Congo-Afrique see Zaire - Afrique **3935**
Congo Disque. (ZR ISSN 0010-5775) **3547**
Congo Sports. (ZR) **4469**
Congregation News. (US) **2286**, **1997**
Congregational Church in England and Wales. Congregational Year book see United Reformed Church in the United Kingdom. United Reformed Church Year Book **4251**
Congregational Council for World Mission. Annual Report see C W M Report **4232**

Congregational Historical Society. Transactions see United Reformed Church History Society. Journal **4251**
Congregational Journal. (US ISSN 0361-2376) **4234**
Congregational Library. Bulletin. (US ISSN 0010-5821) **2753**, **4234**
Congregational Monthly see Reform **4247**
Congregational Year Book. (UK ISSN 0266-7088) **4212**
Congregationalist. (US ISSN 0010-5856) **4234**
Congres Archeologique de France (Publication). (FR ISSN 0069-8881) **269**, **297**
Congres International d'Histoire des Sciences. Actes. (SW ISSN 0074-9540) **4305**, **2568**
Congres International de la Population. Proceedings see International Population Conference. Proceedings **3983**
Congres International des Etudes Byzantines. Actes. see International Congress for Byzantine Studies. Acts **2368**
Congres Mensuel. (CN) **3391**
†Congreso Internacional de Americanistas. Actas. (PE) **5171**
Congreso Internacional de Vivienda Popular. (CK) **4369**
Congreso Judio Latinoamericano. Boletin Informativo O J I. (AG) **1997**
†Congreso Judio Latinoamericano. Coloquio. (AG) **5171**
Congreso Latinamericano de Siderurgia. Memoria Tecnica. (CL ISSN 0589-2813) **3404**
Congreso Mexicano de Control de Calidad. Annual Proceedings. (MX) **3445**
Congreso Nacional de Arqueologia. Actas see Folletos de Divulgacion **272**
Congreso Nacional de Bibliotecas. Ponencias, Comunicaciones y Cronica. (SP) **2753**
Congresos de Estudios Vascos. (SP) **237**
Congresos Indigenistas Interamericanos. Actas. (MX ISSN 0074-0810) **237**
Congress. (US) **4057**, **3881**
Congress and the Nation. (US) **3881**, **4057**
Congress and the Presidency. (US ISSN 0734-3469) **3881**, **2403**, **4057**
†Congress Calendar G D R. (GW ISSN 0233-2213) **5171**
Congress F A T I P E C. (FR ISSN 0430-2222) **1852**
Congress for Recreation and Parks. Proceedings see Congress for Recreation and Parks. Symposium for Leisure Research. Abstracts **4498**
Congress for Recreation and Parks. Symposium for Leisure Research. Abstracts. (US) **4498**, **2738**
Congress in Park and Recreation Administration. Programme. (UK) **3391**
Congress in Park and Recreation Administration. Reports. (UK) **4544**
Congress in Print. (US) **3881**
Congress Marches Ahead. (II ISSN 0376-5776) **3881**
Congress Monthly see American Jewish Congress. Congress Monthly **1990**
Congress News. (US) **2403**
Congress News. (CE ISSN 0045-6217) **2582**
Congress of International Congress Organizers and Technicians. Proceedings. (BE ISSN 0573-5661) **3391**
Congress of Micronesia. House of Representatives. Journal. (TT) **2615**, **4057**
Congress of Micronesia. Senate. Journal. (TT) **2615**, **4057**
Congress of Racial Equality Magazine see C O R E Magazine **3940**
Congress on Research in Dance Bulletin see C O R D Bulletin **1529**

Congress on Research in Dance Newsletter see C O R D Newsletter 1529
Congress Resister. (SA) 3881, 3941
Congress und Seminar see Management & Seminar 1398
Congress Watcher see Public Citizen 1507
Congressional Action. (US) 2615, 813
Congressional Activities. (US ISSN 0733-0200) 4057
Congressional Daily Monitor see Congressional Monitor 3881
Congressional Digest. (US ISSN 0010-5899) 3881
Congressional Directory see U.S. Congress. Congressional Directory 5295
Congressional Index. (US) 2698
Congressional Information Bureau, Inc. Daily Maritime News Bulletin see C I B Daily Maritime News Bulletin 4725
Congressional Information Service Federal Register Index see C I S Federal Register Index 4079
Congressional Information Service Index see C I S Index 4079
Congressional Insight. (US ISSN 0196-0784) 3881
Congressional Legislative Reporting. (US) 2615, 4086
Congressional Monitor. (US ISSN 0010-5902) 3881
Congressional Presentation, Fiscal Year see U.S. International Development Cooperation Agency. Congressional Presentation, Fiscal Year 936
Congressional Quarterly Inc. Almanac see C Q Almanac 3877
Congressional Quarterly Service. Weekly Report. (US ISSN 0010-5910) 3881, 4057
Congressional Quarterly's Editorial Research Reports see C Q Researcher 3877
Congressional Record Digest and Tally of Roll Call Votes. (US ISSN 0069-892X) 4057
Congressional Record Scanner. (US) 3936
Congressional Research Service Review.(US ISSN 0193-8029) 4057
Congressional Roll Call (Year). (US) 3881
Congressional Staff Directory. (US ISSN 0069-8938) 3881, 4057
Congressional Summary see Summary of Congress 3929
Congressional Yellow Book. (US ISSN 0191-1422) 4057, 418
Congresso. (CN) 1997
Congresso Brasileiro de Economia e Sociologia Rural. Anais. (BL ISSN 0102-2253) 149
▼Congresso Brasileiro de Ornitologia. Resumos. (BL) 563
Congresso Europeo di Storia Ospitaliera. Atti. (IT ISSN 0589-3267) 2460
Congresso Latinoamericano de Hidraulica (Papers). (BL ISSN 0589-3305) 4823
Congresso Nacional de Botanica. Anais. (BL ISSN 0102-3306) 500
Congressus Numerantium. (CN ISSN 0384-9864) 3033
Coniectanea Biblica. New Testament Series. (SW ISSN 0069-8946) 4172
Coniectanea Biblica. Old Testament Series. (SW ISSN 0069-8954) 4172
Coniectanea Neotestamentica see Coniectanea Biblica. New Testament Series 4172
Conimbriga. (PO ISSN 0084-9189) 269
Conjonction. (HT ISSN 0304-5757) 2197
Conjoncture/Al-Alam al-Iqtisadiy. (TI) 851
Conjoncture Economique see Etudes de Conjoncture: Evolutions et Tendances 4571
▼Conjoncture in France. (FR ISSN 1152-9776) 711, 851

Conjoncture Suisse et Perspectives see Schweizerische Konjunktur und Vorausschau 884
Conjunctions. (US ISSN 0278-2324) 2908
Conjunto. (CU ISSN 0010-5937) 4631
Conjuntura Economica. (BL ISSN 0010-5945) 851
Conmilit. (HK ISSN 1013-9214) 3454
Conn P I R G Channel. (Connecticut Public Interest Research Group) (US) 1503
Connaissance de l'Eure. (FR) 2309, 322
Connaissance de l'Orient. Collection Unesco d'Oeuvres Representatives. (FR ISSN 0589-3496) 2908
Connaissance de l'Ouest. (FR ISSN 0396-2024) 2245, 1073
Connaissance de la Chasse. (FR) 4544
Connaissance de la Region. (FR ISSN 0223-4270) 813
Connaissance de la Vigne et du Vin see Journal International des Sciences de la Vigne et du Vin 182
Connaissance des Arts. (FR ISSN 0293-9274) 322
Connaissance des Arts-Plaisir see Connaissance des Arts 322
Connaissance des Temps. (FR ISSN 0181-3048) 363
Connaissance du Pays d'Oc. (FR ISSN 0336-9455) 4758, 1997
Connaissance du Rail. (FR ISSN 0222-4844) 4708
Connaissons Nos Voisins. (CN) 4758
Connaitre la Wallonie/To Know Wallony.(BE ISSN 0010-602X) 2357
Connect see Teen Power (1979) 1267
Connect see Network World 1351
Connect. (UN) 1946
Connect (Boston). (US) 1747, 1372
Connect (Brattleboro). (US ISSN 1041-682X) 1747, 3033, 4305
Connect Times see Consumer Information Appliance 1362
Connecticut. (US ISSN 0163-1136) 2223
Connecticut. Advisory Council on Vocational and Career Education. Vocational Education Evaluation Report see Connecticut. State Council on Vocational-Technical Education. Vocational Education Evaluation Report 1623
Connecticut. Agricultural Experiment Station, New Haven. Bulletin. (US ISSN 0097-0905) 530
Connecticut. Commission on the Deaf and Hearing-Impaired. Annual Report.(US) 2286
Connecticut. Commission to Study and Investigate the Problems of Deaf and Hearing-Impaired Persons. Annual Report see Connecticut. Commission on the Deaf and Hearing-Impaired. Annual Report 2286
Connecticut. Council on Environmental Quality. Annual Report. (US ISSN 0095-4624) 1946
Connecticut. Department of Community Affairs Division of Research and Program Evaluation. Construction Activity Authorized by Building Permits. Summary see Connecticut Housing Production and Permit Authorized Construction 611
Connecticut. Department of Correction. Publications. (US ISSN 0090-2756) 1512
Connecticut. Department of Environmental Protection. Citizens' Bulletin see Connecticut Environment 5171
Connecticut. Department on Aging. Report to the Governor and General Assembly. (US ISSN 0090-6077) 2271
Connecticut. Judicial Department. Report. (US ISSN 0098-8138) 2615
†Connecticut. Labor Department. Bulletin. (US ISSN 0010-6143) 5171

Connecticut. Law Revision Commission. Annual Report. (US) 2615
Connecticut. State Council on Vocational-Technical Education. Vocational Education Evaluation Report. (US) 1623
Connecticut Academy of Arts and Sciences. Memoirs. (US ISSN 0069-8970) 4306, 2505
Connecticut Academy of Arts and Sciences. Transactions. (US ISSN 0069-8989) 2505, 4306
Connecticut Ancestry. (US ISSN 0197-2103) 2148
Connecticut Antiquarian see The Landmark (Hartford) 258
Connecticut Appellate Practice & Procedure. (US) 2615
Connecticut Association of Boards of Education, Inc. Journal see C A B E Journal 1725
Connecticut Backgammon Magazine see Waterbury Chess Club Bulletin 4496
Connecticut Bar Journal. (US ISSN 0010-6070) 2615
Connecticut Beverage Journal. (US ISSN 0191-8818) 380
Connecticut Business and Industry see C B I A News 849
Connecticut Business and Industry Association News see C B I A News 849
Connecticut Business Journal see Fairfield County Business Journal 865
Connecticut C P A Quarterly. (US) 749
Connecticut Corporation Statutes and Forms. (US) 2708
Connecticut Education Association. Legislative Bulletin. (US) 1623, 2615
Connecticut Education Association Advisor see C E A Advisor 1619
Connecticut English Journal. (US) 1623, 2809, 2908
†Connecticut Environment. (US) 5171
▼Connecticut Facts - Rhode Island Facts. (US ISSN 1050-4613) 1780
▼Connecticut Family. (US) 1235, 2445
Connecticut Family Law Citations. (US) 2717
Connecticut Family Law Journal. (US) 2615
Connecticut Fireside. (US ISSN 0300-8258) 2223
Connecticut Fireside and Review of Books see Connecticut Fireside 2223
Connecticut Florists' Newsletter see Greenhouse Newsletter 2128
Connecticut Government. (US ISSN 0010-6119) 4057
Connecticut Health Bulletin. (US ISSN 0010-6127) 4099
Connecticut Historical Society. Bulletin. (US ISSN 0885-4831) 2403, 322, 4172
Connecticut Historical Society. Notes & News. (US) 2403
Connecticut Hospice Newsletter. (US) 3800, 4017
Connecticut Housing Market. Annual Report. (US) 2485
Connecticut Housing Production and Permit Authorized Construction. (US) 611
Connecticut Insurance Law Review. (US) 2530, 2615
Connecticut Law Journal. (US) 2615
The Connecticut Law Reporter. (US) 2731
The Connecticut Law Reporter, Bound Series. (US) 2731
Connecticut Law Review. (US ISSN 0010-6151) 2615
Connecticut Law Tribune. (US ISSN 0198-0289) 2615
Connecticut Libraries. (US ISSN 0010-616X) 2753
Connecticut Market Data. (US ISSN 0573-665X) 1036
Connecticut, Massachusetts, Rhode Island TourBook see Tourbook: Connecticut, Massachusetts, Rhode Island 4790
Connecticut Master Transportation Plan.(US ISSN 0069-9039) 4648

Connecticut Medicine. (US ISSN 0010-6178) 3090
Connecticut Motor Transport News. (US) 4743
Connecticut News Handbook. (US ISSN 0277-5956) 2577, 2568
Connecticut Notary Law Primer. (US) 2615
Connecticut Nursing News. (US ISSN 0278-4092) 3277
Connecticut Nutmegger. (US ISSN 0045-8120) 2148
Connecticut Office Buildings see Westchester - Connecticut Office Buildings 4159
Connecticut Parent. (US) 4839, 1235, 3396
†Connecticut Periodical Index. (US) 5171
Connecticut Pharmacist. (US) 3721
Connecticut Poetry Review. (US ISSN 0277-7770) 2991, 4631
Connecticut Public Interest Research Group Conn P I R G Channel see Conn P I R G Channel 1503
Connecticut Quarterly. (US) 2908
Connecticut Real Estate Journal. (US) 4147
Connecticut Real Estate Law Journal. (US) 4147, 2615
Connecticut Real Property Statutes. (US) 2615, 4147
Connecticut Realtor. (US) 4147
Connecticut - Rhode Island Directory of Manufacturers. (US) 1127
Connecticut River Review. (US ISSN 0897-0998) 2991
†Connecticut River Valley Covered Bridge Society. Bulletin. (US ISSN 0090-8517) 5171
Connecticut Service Directory see George D. Hall's Connecticut Service Directory 1136
Connecticut State Dental Association. Journal. (US ISSN 0010-6232) 3230
Connecticut State Library Update C S L see Update C S L 2790
Connecticut Time Limitations. (US) 2616
Connecticut Traveler. (US) 4758
†Connecticut Travels. (US) 5171
Connecticut Vacation Guide. (US) 4758
Connecticut Walk Book. (US ISSN 0092-5764) 4544
Connecticut Water Resources Bulletin. (US ISSN 0589-400X) 1597
Connecticut West. (US) 4758
Connecticut Woodlands. (US ISSN 0010-6259) 2098
Connecticut Workers' Compensation Review Opinions. (US) 976, 2616
Connecticut Writer. (US) 2908
Connection. see Qesher 2575
Connection. (GW ISSN 0932-5565) 3594
Connection (Alexandria). (US) 2862
Connection (Boston). (US) 1704
Connection Science. (UK ISSN 0954-0091) 1407
Connection Technology. (US ISSN 8756-4076) 1765
Connections/Connexions. (CN ISSN 0828-301X) 3090
Connections (Boston, 1989). (US) 4758, 2271
Connections (Dayton). (US) 3881, 1623, 4402
†Connections (Fullerton, 1987). (US ISSN 0894-170X) 5171
Connections (Knoxville). (US) 1252
Connections (London) see Duty Free Magazine 4802
Connections (Pointe Claire). (CN ISSN 0707-7130) 2148
Connections (Springfield). (US) 3626, 4839
Connections (Toledo, 1956). (US) 4726
Connections Journal. (US) 1459
Connections: Kimball Family Association Newsletter. (US ISSN 0890-0639) 2148
Connective Issues. (US ISSN 8756-9086) 3207, 2292
Connective Tissue Diseases/Malattie del Tessuto Connettivo. (IT) 3369

CONNECTIVE TISSUE

Connective Tissue Research. (US ISSN 0300-8207) **524**
Connector *see* International Connector for Jewish Singles **4362**
Connector. (US) **4402**, 1735
Connexion. (UK) **1446**, 1426
Connexion *see* U M E Connexion **5293**
Connexions. *see* Connections **3090**
ConneXions (Mountain View). (US ISSN 0894-5926) **1426**
Connexions (Oakland). (US ISSN 0886-7062) **4839**
Connexions Digest. (CN ISSN 0708-9422) **3882**, 3936, 4369
Connexus. (US) **2223**
Connoisseur *see* Town and Country **2236**
Connoisseurs Bird Journal. (UK) **563**
Connoisseurs Guide to California Wine. (US ISSN 0161-6668) **380**, 3998
ConnStruction Magazine. (US) **611**
Conny. (GW) **1252**
Conocer la Vida y el Universo. (SP) **4306**
Conocimiento de la Nueva Era. (AG ISSN 0010-6291) **3669**
Conoscenza. (IT ISSN 0010-6305) **3764**, 4172
Conquiste dei Pensionati. (IT) **4403**
Conquiste del Lavoro. (IT ISSN 0010-6348) **2582**
Conradiana. (US ISSN 0010-6356) **2908**
Consacrazione e Servizio. (IT ISSN 0035-600X) **4172**
Conscience. (US) **3941**
Conscience and Military Tax Campaign *see* Conscience **3941**
Conscience Canada Newsletter. (CN ISSN 0823-8669) **3941**, 1485
Conscience et Liberte. (SZ ISSN 0259-0360) **3941**, 4172
Conscientia. (GW ISSN 0589-4069) **3764**
▼Conscious Consumer. (US) **1946**, 2616
▼Consciousness and Cognition. (US ISSN 1053-8100) **4017**
Consciousness and Self-Regulation: Advances in Research *see* Consciousness and Self-Regulation: Advances in Research and Theory **4017**
Consciousness and Self-Regulation: Advances in Research and Theory. (US) **4017**
Consecrated Life. (US ISSN 0884-7010) **4262**
Conseil Canadien de Protection des Animaux. Ressource. (CN ISSN 0700-5245) **230**
Conseil Canadien de Readaptation. Rapport Annuel. *see* Canadian Rehabilitation Council. Annual Report **1734**
Conseil de Presse du Quebec. Rapport Annuel. (CN ISSN 0708-0131) **1372**
Conseil de Recherches en Sciences Naturelles et en Genie du Canada. Liste des Bourses et Subventions de Recherche. *see* Natural Sciences and Engineering Research Council of Canada. List of Scholarships and Grants in Aid of Research **1712**
Conseil de Recherches en Sciences Naturelles et en Genie du Canada. Rapport du President. *see* Natural Sciences and Engineering Research Council of Canada. Report of the President **1712**
Conseil de Recherches Medicales. Actualites. *see* Medical Research Council Newsletter **3127**
Conseil General des Peches pour la Mediterranee. Depats et Documents Techniques. *see* General Fisheries Council for the Mediterranean. Proceedings and Technical Papers **5199**
Conseil Mondial des Societes d'Education Comparee. Bulletin d'Information. *see* World Council of Comparative Education Societies. Newsletter **1672**
Conseil National de la Consommation. Annual Report. (FR) **1503**
Conseil National de la Recherche Scientifique. Rapport Annuel *see* National Council for Scientific Research. Annual Report **1712**
Conseil National de Recherches du Canada. Division de Genie Electrique. Bulletin. *see* National Research Council, Canada. Division of Electrical Engineering. Bulletin **5243**
Conseil National de Recherches du Canada. Institut de Technologie de l'Information. Rapport Annuel *see* National Research Council of Canada. Institute for Information Technology. Annual Report **4604**
Conseil National du Patronat Francais. Annuaire. (FR) **1006**
Conseil Suisse de la Science. Rapport Annuel. *see* Schweizerischer Wissenschaftsrat. Jahresbericht **4338**
Conseiller Alcovit-Protector *see* Alcovit **75**
Conseiller Comptable. (ZR) **1091**
Conseiller des Assurances et de la Finance. (FR) **2530**, 773
Conseiller du Commerce Exterieur. (FR) **927**
Conseiller Immobilier *see* Canadian Real Estate Adviser **4146**
Conseillers aux Etudiants Etrangers. Bulletin. *see* I S A Bulletin **1722**
Conseils Sols et Murs. (FR ISSN 0395-2673) **2549**
Consejo Central Ejecutivo del Partido Liberal de Honduras. Memoria. (HO) **3882**
Consejo de Arqueologia. Boletin. (MX) **269**
†Consejo Latinoamericano de Ciencias Sociales. Serie Poblacion. Informe de Investigacion. (AG) **5171**
†Consejo Nacional de Investigaciones Cientificas y Tecnicas. Informe sobre un Ano de Labor. (AG) **5171**
Consejo Nacional de Investigaciones Cientificas y Tecnologicas. Departamento de Educacion. Directorio Nacional de Cursos de Postgrado. (VE) **1704**
Consejo Nacional para Investigaciones Cientificas y Tecnologicas, Costa Rica. Informe Anual. (CR ISSN 0253-2492) **4595**
Consejo Oleicola Internacional Hoja de Informacion *see* C O I. Hoja de Informacion **171**
Consejo Superior de Investigaciones Cientificas. Cuadernos de Economia. (SP ISSN 0210-0266) **656**
Consejo Superior de Investigaciones Cientificas. Grupos de Montana de Accion Cultural. Boletin Informativo. (SP) **4544**
Consejo Superior Universitario Centroamericano. Actas de la Reunion Ordinaria. (CR ISSN 0589-4301) **1704**
Consensus (Kansas City). (US) **943**
Consensus (Ottawa). (CN ISSN 0380-1314) **3445**
Consequences. (FR ISSN 0760-629X) **2908**, 322
†Conser Tables. (US ISSN 0190-3608) **5171**
Conserva. (SA ISSN 0258-3313) **1485**, 2216
Conservation Administration News. (US ISSN 0192-2912) **2753**
Conservation Aeronautics Magazine. (US) **50**, 1485
Conservation and Renewable Energy Technologies for Building Technologies. (US) **1810**
Conservation and Renewable Energy Technologies for Industrial Technologies. (US) **1785**, 1811
Conservation and Renewable Energy Technologies for Transportation Technologies. (US) **1785**, 1811
Conservation and Renewable Energy Technologies for Utility Technologies. (US) **1785**, 1811
Conservation Biology. (US ISSN 0888-8892) **1486**, 435
Conservation Commission News. (US ISSN 0027-6537) **1486**
Conservation Council of Ontario. Conference Proceedings. (CN) **1486**
Conservation Council of Ontario. Reports. (CN) **1486**
Conservation Council of South Australia. Newsletter *see* Environment Conservation News **1487**
Conservation Directory. (US ISSN 0069-911X) **1486**
Conservation Education. (UK ISSN 0262-2203) **1486**
Conservation Foundation Letter *see* W W F & C F Letter **5302**
Conservation in Kansas. (US ISSN 0094-1670) **1486**
Conservation News. (AT) **1486**
Conservation News. (UK ISSN 0309-2224) **1486**
Conservation News Digest. (US) **2098**, 1486
Conservation North Queensland. (AT ISSN 0816-875X) **1486**, 1946
Conservation of Cultural Property in India. (II ISSN 0376-7965) **269**
Conservation of Library Materials. (US ISSN 0069-9136) **2753**
Conservation of Nature. *see* Shizen Hogo **1497**
Conservation Volunteer *see* The Minnesota Volunteer **1492**
Conservation Voter. (US) **1946**, 1486, 3882, 4823
Conservationist. (US ISSN 0010-650X) **1486**, 580, 4544
Conservative and Unionist Central Office. Monthly News *see* Conservative News Line **3882**
Conservative Baptist Association of America. Update *see* Challenge of the '80s Update **5164**
Conservative Baptist Impact *see* Impact (Wheaton) **4240**
†Conservative Digest. (US ISSN 0146-0978) **5171**
Conservative Judaism. (US ISSN 0010-6542) **4222**
Conservative News Line. (UK) **3882**
▼Conservative Review. (US ISSN 1047-5990) **3882**, 4432
Conservative Speculator. (US) **943**
Conservatoire de Musique de Geneve. Bulletin. (SZ ISSN 0010-6550) **3547**
The Conservator. (UK ISSN 0140-0096) **1486**
Conservatory of American Letters Anthology *see* C A L Anthology **2989**
Conservatory of American Letters Newsletter. (US) **2908**
Conservazione delle Carte Antiche. (IT) **257**
Conserve. (US) **1486**
†Conserve Neighborhoods. (US) **5171**
Conserver. (UK ISSN 0143-4144) **1486**
Consigli Pratici. (IT) **4839**
Consiglio di Stato. (IT ISSN 0010-6569) **2616**
Consiglio Nazionale dell' Ordine dei Giornalisti Informazione *see* O G Informazione **1341**
Consol News. (US ISSN 0010-6577) **3482**
Consolidated Federal Funds Report. (US) **4058**
†Consolidated Report on Elementary and Secondary Education in Colorado. (US ISSN 0095-5329) **5171**
▼Consolidated Returns Tax Report. (US) **1091**
Consolidated Tax Return (Supplement). (US) **1091**
▼Consolidated Treaties & International Agreements: European Community Document Service. (US ISSN 1059-8561) **2721**
▼Consolidated Treaties & International Agreements: United States Current Document Service. (US ISSN 1053-9905) **2722**
Le Consommateur Canadien. (CN ISSN 0315-1867) **1503**
Consommateurs Actualites *see* I N C Hebdo Consommateurs Actualites **1505**
Consommateurs, Clients, Consommateurs COCLICO *see* COCLICO **5167**
Consort. (UK) **3547**
Consort. (CN) **3547**
Consortium for Drama & Media in Higher Education. Newsletter. (UK) **4631**, 1372, 1529, 3506
Consortium of College and University Media Centers Leader *see* C C U M C Leader **1745**
Consortium of Rhode Island Academic and Research Libraries Newsletter *see* C R I A R L Newsletter **2751**
Consortium on Revolutionary Europe Proceedings. (US ISSN 0093-2574) **2357**, 397, 418, 4369
Consorzio Nazionale Dettaglianti Conad *see* Conad **834**
Consorzio Provinciale per la Pubblica Lettura. Informazione Bibliografica. (IT ISSN 0391-6812) **397**
Consorzio Universitario. Pubblicazioni. Sezione Miscellanea. (IT) **1704**
Conspectus Florae Orientalis. (IS) **500**
Conspiracy Digest. (US) **2309**
Conspiracy of Silence. (CN) **2991**
Constabulary Gazette. (UK ISSN 0010-6607) **1512**
Constantian. (US ISSN 0270-532X) **3882**, 2148
Constatto Elettrico. (IT ISSN 1120-2351) **1884**
Constitution (New York). (US ISSN 1046-0896) **3882**
†Constitution (Washington). (US ISSN 0882-5955) **5171**
Constitution Chronicle. (US) **3454**, 4726
Constitutional and Parliamentary Information. (FR ISSN 0010-6623) **3882**
Constitutional Commentaries. (US) **2705**
Constitutional Commentary. (US ISSN 0742-7115) **3941**
Constitutional Law *see* B A R - B R I Bar Review. Constitutional Law **2705**
Constitutional Law Journal. (II ISSN 1049-4987) **2616**
†Constitutional Limitations on Criminal Procedures. (US) **5171**
▼Constitutional Political Economy. (US ISSN 1043-4062) **2706**, 3882
Constitutional Reform. (UK ISSN 0269-2511) **2706**
Constru-Noticias. (MX) **611**
▼Construcao Hoje. (US) **611**
Construcao Minas Centro Oeste. (BL ISSN 0102-0501) **611**
Construcao Norte Nordeste. (BL ISSN 0102-051X) **611**
Construcao Regiao Sul. (BL ISSN 0102-0528) **611**, 1864
Construcao Rio de Janeiro. (BL ISSN 0100-1671) **611**, 1864
Construcao Sao Paulo. (BL ISSN 0010-6631) **611**
Construccion Arquitectura Urbanismo *see* C A U **5156**
Construccion Pan-Americana. (US ISSN 0192-4230) **611**
Construccion Pan-Americana International Buyer's Guide. (US) **1127**, 611
Construccion y Tecnologia. (MX ISSN 0187-7895) **611**
Construct in Steel. (AT ISSN 1030-2581) **611**, 3404
Constructeur. *see* Ndertuesi **626**
De Constructeur. (NE ISSN 0010-6658) **1864**
Constructia de Masini. (RM) **1928**
Construction. (US ISSN 0010-6704) **611**
Construction. (IE) **611**
Construction. (BE) **611**
Construction. *see* Izgradnja **1868**
Construction *see* Journal of Construction Engineering and Management **1869**
Construction Afrique *see* Afrique Expansion **599**
Construction Alberta News. (CN) **611**, 1817
Construction Alert. (SA ISSN 1014-8329) **611**
Construction and Architectural Specifiers Guide. Annual Review. (UK) **297**

Construction and Building Materials. (UK ISSN 0950-0618) **611**, 1864
Construction and Contract News. (HK) **611**, 1864
Construction and Design Law Digest. (US) **611**, 2616
▼Construction & Engineering Materials.(US) **1817**, 611
Construction and Finance Guide *see* Log Homes Design, Construction & Finance Issue **5228**
†Construction & Mining Equipment Selector. (SA) **5171**
Construction and Mining Machinery en Espanol. (US) **611**, 3482
Construction and Property News. (IE ISSN 0376-7213) **611**
†Construction Annual. (GW) **5171**
Construction Association of Korea. Construction News Service. (KO) **611**
Construction Association of Montreal and the Province of Quebec. Bulletin *see* Association de la Construction de Montreal et du Quebec. Bulletin **600**
Construction Atlantic (Year). (CN) **611**
Construction Bargaineer. (US ISSN 0740-0187) **611**
Construction Briefings. (US ISSN 0162-3176) **611**
Construction Bulletin. (US) **611**
Construction Canada. (CN ISSN 0228-8788) **297**
Construction Claims Citator. (US) **612**, 2616
Construction Claims Monthly. (US ISSN 0272-4561) **612**, 2616
Construction Claims Training Guide. (US ISSN 0899-5982) **612**, 2616
Construction Client Newsletter. (US) **749**, 612
Construction Comment. (CN) **612**
Construction Computer Applications Directory. (US) **612**, 1476
Construction Computer Applications Newsletter. (US) **612**
Construction Computing. (UK ISSN 0264-6854) **1878**
†Construction Consultant. (US ISSN 0892-4619) **5171**
Construction Contractor. (US ISSN 0162-3168) **612**
Construction Costs: U S Steam Electric Plants. (US) **1884**, 1785
Construction de Logements en Suisse. *see* Wohnbautaetigkeit in der Schweiz **639**
Construction Digest. (US ISSN 0010-6739) **612**
Construction Dimensions Magazine. (US ISSN 0194-8903) **612**
Construction Directory *see* Construction Industries of Massachusetts Directory **1127**
Construction Employers Federation. Bulletin. (UK) **612**
Construction Employment Guide in the National and International Field. (US) **3626**
Construction Engineering. *see* Pozemni Stavby **5260**
Construction Engineering Research Institute Foundation Report. *see* Kensetsu Kogaku Kenkyujo Hokoku **1919**
Construction Equipment. (US ISSN 0192-3978) **612**, 1864
Construction Equipment Buyers' Guide. (US) **612**, 2098, 3482
Construction Equipment Distribution. (US ISSN 0010-6755) **612**
Construction Equipment Guide (Fort Dodge) *see* Hot Line Construction Equipment Monthly Update **619**
Construction Equipment Guide (Glenside). (US) **612**
Construction Equipment Guide Southeast Circulation. (US) **612**
Construction Equipment Innovations. (US) **612**, 1864
Construction Equipment Operation and Maintenance. (US ISSN 0010-6771) **612**
Construction Equipment Specifications Guide. (US) **612**, 1864

Construction et Reparation d'Embarcations. *see* Canada. Statistics Canada. Boatbuilding and Repair **5159**
Construction et Reparation de Navires. *see* Canada. Statistics Canada. Shipbuilding and Repair **5160**
Construction Exchange. (US) **612**
Construction Foreman's and Supervisor's Letter *see* Construction Supervision & Safety Letter **613**
Construction Francaise *see* Construction Neuve et Ancienne **613**
Construction History. (UK) **612**, 297
Construction in Hawaii. (US ISSN 0069-9187) **612**
Construction Industries and Trade Annual. (Il) **612**
Construction Industries and Trade Journal *see* Construction Industries and Trade Annual **612**
Construction Industries of Massachusetts Directory. (US) **1127**, 612, 4718
Construction Industries of Massachusetts, Inc. Construction Journal *see* C I M Construction Journal **1862**
Construction Industry in Toowoomba. (AT) **612**
Construction Industry International. (UK) **612**
Construction Industry Research and Information Association Annual Report *see* C I R I A Annual Report **1862**
Construction Labor News. (US ISSN 0161-990X) **976**, 612
Construction Labor Report. (US ISSN 0010-6836) **976**, 612
Construction: Latin American Industrial Report. (US) **612**
Construction Law Adviser. (US) **612**, 2616
Construction Law Journal. (UK) **612**, 2616
Construction Law Letter. (CN ISSN 0827-3480) **612**, 2616
Construction Law Reports. (CN ISSN 0824-2593) **613**, 2616
Construction Lawyer. (US ISSN 0272-0116) **613**, 2616
Construction Litigation Reporter. (US ISSN 0279-1102) **613**, 2616
Construction Machinery and Building Supplies. (GW ISSN 0179-1028) **613**
Construction Management. (UK) **613**, 1006
Construction Management and Economics. (UK) **613**
Construction Management Modernization. *see* Jianzhu Guanli Xiandaihua **622**
Construction Management: Register of Members. (UK ISSN 0268-2478) **613**
Construction Manitoba. (CN) **613**
▼Construction Marketing Today. (US) **613**, 1036
Construction Material Prices/Wolgan Konsol Mulka. (KO) **613**
Construction Metallique. *see* Steel Design **307**
Construction Navale. (FR) **4726**
Construction Neuve et Ancienne. (FR ISSN 0335-2021) **613**
Construction News. (UK ISSN 0010-6860) **613**
Construction News. (US ISSN 0160-5607) **613**
Construction Newsletter. (US) **3616**, 613
Construction Plant and Equipment *see* Construction Weekly **1864**
Construction Products. (UK) **613**
Construction Products Postcard Service.(UK) **613**
Construction Record. (CN) **1864**, 613
Construction Repair *see* International Journal of Construction Maintenance & Repair **621**
Construction Report. (US) **2460**
Construction Review. (US ISSN 0010-6917) **613**, 2485
Construction Risk Management. (US) **613**, 2530

Construction Science *see* Construction History **612**
Construction Sightlines. (CN ISSN 0708-1073) **613**
Construction Specifications Canada. Magazine. (CN) **613**
Construction Specifier. (US ISSN 0010-6925) **613**
Construction Supervision & Safety Letter. (US ISSN 0744-7167) **613**
Construction Supervisor. (AT) **613**
Construction Survey. (US) **613**, 656
Construction Times. (US ISSN 0744-2149) **613**
Construction Today. (UK ISSN 0141-5999) **1864**
Construction Weekly. (UK ISSN 0956-9189) **1864**
Construction Workers. *see* Jianzhu Gongren **622**
Construction Writers Association. Newsletter. (US ISSN 0069-9217) **613**
Constructional Review. (AT ISSN 0010-695X) **613**, 297
Constructioneer. (US ISSN 0010-6968) **1817**, 613
Constructions Equipements pour les Loisirs. (FR ISSN 0010-6976) **613**, 4469
Constructions Executees et Constructions Projetees. *see* Bautaetigkeit und Bauvorhaben in der Schweiz **637**
†Constructive Action Newsletter. (US) **5171**
Constructive Approximation. (US ISSN 0176-4276) **3033**
Constructor. (AG ISSN 0010-7018) **613**, 1864
Constructor. (US ISSN 0162-6191) **613**
Constructura. (BL) **2809**, 2908
Construire. (SZ ISSN 0010-7034) **614**, 2298
Construire. (MR) **614**
Construire en Acier. *see* Bauen in Stahl **295**
Construire Ensemble. (UV) **85**
Constuire l'Afrique. (SG) **656**
Consudel. (NE ISSN 0010-7042) **2088**
Consulente Immobiliare. (IT ISSN 0010-7050) **4147**
Consulenza. (IT) **656**
†Consulta. (SP ISSN 0210-5632) **5171**
Consultant. (UK) **3800**
Consultant (Columbia). (US ISSN 0010-7085) **2098**
Consultant (Greenwich). (US ISSN 0010-7069) **3090**
Consultant (Seattle). (US) **2064**, 2473
†Consultant Exchange. (US) **5171**
The Consultant Pharmacist. (US ISSN 0888-5109) **3721**
Consultant Radiologist and Radiotherapist *see* Rad for Radiographers, Radiologists and Radiotherapists **3361**
Consultants and Consulting Organizations *see* Consultants and Consulting Organizations Directory **1006**
Consultants and Consulting Organizations Directory. (US ISSN 0196-1292) **1006**, 1127
Consultants' and Contractors' Newsletter. (US) **1449**
Consultant's Certified Coin Report. (US) **943**
Consultant's Coin Report *see* Consultant's Certified Coin Report **943**
Consultant's Digest *see* Consulting Opportunities Journal **1006**
Consultants Directory for Business and Industry. (US ISSN 1042-153X) **1127**
Consultants News. (US ISSN 0045-8201) **1006**
Consultation. (FR ISSN 0751-7718) **3091**
†Consultation. (US ISSN 8756-6508) **5171**
Consultation on Church Union. Digest. (US) **4172**

Consulting Engineer *see* Construction Weekly **1864**
Consulting Engineers - Canada - Ingenieurs Conseils *see* Association of Consulting Engineers of Canada. Directory of Member Firms and Their Services **1815**
Consulting Medical Laboratories. Bulletin. (JO ISSN 0254-7147) **3091**
Consulting Opportunities Journal. (US ISSN 0273-4613) **1006**, 3626
Consulting Rates and Business Practices. Annual Survey. (US) **3626**, 656
Consulting Services. (US) **1175**, 1852
Consulting - Specifying Engineer. (US ISSN 0892-5046) **1817**
Consumatori. (IT) **1503**
Consumenten Reisgids. (NE) **4758**, 1036
Consumer. (NZ ISSN 0110-5949) **1503**
Consumer. *see* Katanalotis **1506**
Consumer Action. (NZ) **1503**
Consumer Affairs Bureau. Annual Report. (AT) **1503**
Consumer Affairs Council. Annual Report. (AT) **1503**
Consumer Affairs Council of the Australian Capital Territory. Annual Report *see* Consumer Affairs Bureau. Annual Report **1503**
Consumer Affairs Letter. (US ISSN 0270-0999) **1503**
†Consumer Affairs Newsletter. (US) **5171**
Consumer Bulletin. (SI) **1503**
Consumer Choice. (IE ISSN 0790-486X) **1503**
Consumer Comment. (AT ISSN 0045-8236) **1503**
Consumer Confidence Survey. (US) **1036**
Consumer Credit. (UK) **773**
Consumer Credit and Truth-In-Lending Compliance Report. (US ISSN 0300-6034) **2616**, 773
Consumer Credit Association News *see* C C A News **769**
Consumer Credit Association of the United Kingdom. Membership Directory. (UK) **773**, 1036
Consumer Credit Control. (UK) **2616**, 656
Consumer Credit Delinquency Bulletin. (US) **773**, 1503
Consumer Credit Delinquency Rates *see* Consumer Credit Delinquency Bulletin **773**
Consumer Credit Guide Reports. (US) **2616**, 1503
†Consumer Credit Law Review. (US) **5171**
Consumer Credit Legislation. (UK) **2616**, 1503
†Consumer Credit Letter. (US) **5171**
Consumer Currents. (MY) **1503**
Consumer - Economist. (BG) **656**, 927
†Consumer Electronics. (US ISSN 0362-4722) **5172**
Consumer Europe (Year). (UK ISSN 0308-4353) **1036**
Consumer - Farmer Cooperator. (US) **2485**, 2445
Consumer Federation of America News (Washington) *see* C F A News (Washington) **1502**
Consumer Finance Newsletter. (US) **1091**
†Consumer Food and Health. (NZ ISSN 0114-5436) **5172**
Consumer Guide Elite Cars *see* Collectible Automobile **4688**
Consumer Guide Magazine. (US ISSN 0097-8337) **4688**
Consumer Health and Nutrition Index. (US ISSN 0883-1963) **3614**, 8
Consumer Home and Garden. (NZ ISSN 0113-6739) **2124**, 614
Consumer Information *see* Consumer Information Catalog **397**
▼Consumer Information Appliance. (US) **1362**, 4595
Consumer Information Catalog. (US) **397**, 1503

CONSUMER LAW

Consumer Law and Economics. see Konsumentraett och Ekonomi **1506**
Consumer Law Today. (UK) **2616, 1503**
Consumer Lending Report. (US) **773**
Consumer Magazine and Agri-Media Rates and Data see Standard Rate and Data Service. Consumer Magazine and Agri-Media Rates and Data **41**
Consumer Magazine Profiles. (US) **30**
†Consumer Markets Abroad. (US ISSN 0893-3561) **5172**
†Consumer Markets in Central and East Africa. (UK) **5172**
†Consumer Markets in the Far East. (UK) **5172**
Consumer Pharmacist. (US) **3721**
Consumer Price Index see U.S. Bureau of Labor Statistics. C P I Detailed Report **1000**
Consumer Price Index. (EI) **1509**
Consumer Price Index (Ottawa). (CN ISSN 0703-9352) **1509**
Consumer Price Index (Victoria). (CN) **1509**
Consumer Price Index in Urban Areas of Iran. (IR) **998**
Consumer Price Index: Pacific Cities and U.S. City Average. (US) **852**
Consumer Price Indexes for Thailand see Journal of Commerce **870**
Consumer Price Indices see Consumer Price Index **1509**
▼Consumer Product Litigation Reporter. (US ISSN 1052-9632) **2616**
Consumer Product Safety Guide. (US) **1503**
Consumer Reports. (US ISSN 0010-7174) **1503**
Consumer Reports Health Letter see Consumer Reports on Health **3800**
Consumer Reports News Digest. (US) **1503**
Consumer Reports on Health. (US) **3800**, **1503**
Consumer Reports Travel Letter. (US ISSN 0887-8439) **4758**, 1503
Consumer Selection Guide for Refrigerators and Freezers (Year). (US) **2557**, 1036, 1884, 2298
Consumer Selection Guide for Room Air Conditioners (Year). (US) **2557**, 1036, 1884, 2298
Consumer Sourcebook. (US ISSN 0738-0518) **1503**
Consumer Transpotopics see Transportation Consumer **4658**
Consumer Trends. (US) **773**
Consumer U S A (Year). (UK ISSN 0952-9543) **1036**, 1127
Consumer Views. (AT ISSN 0812-5074) **1503, 4058**
Consumer Voice. (UK) **1503**
†Consumer Voice. (NZ ISSN 0114-541X) **5172**
Consumers Affairs Council of Tasmania. Annual Report. (AT) **1504**, 4403
Consumers Digest. (US ISSN 0010-7182) **1504**
Consumer's Digest. (KE) **1504**
Consumers Directory see International Consumer Directory **1505**
Consumers Federated Groups of the Philippines. Newsletter. (PH) **1504**
▼Consumers for Health Care Reform Newsletter. (US) **1504**, 2530
Consumers for Nutrition Action, Inc. The Nutrition Connection see C N A: The Nutrition Connection **5157**
▼Consumers Guide. (CN) **4147**
Consumers Index. (US ISSN 0094-0534) **1509**, 8
Consumers Protection Council of Tasmania. Annual Report see Consumers Affairs Council of Tasmania. Annual Report **1504**
Consumers' Research see Consumer's Research Magazine **1504**
Consumer's Research Magazine. (US) **1504**
Consumer's Resource Handbook. (US) **1504**
Consumers Voice. (US ISSN 0010-7190) **1504**
Consumers' Watch. (SA) **1504**
Consumer's Watchdog see Consumers' Watch **1504**

Consuming Interest. (AT ISSN 0728-3008) **1504**, 1946, 3882
Consuming Passions. (US ISSN 0741-7748) **4839**, 3604
Consumo Industrial de Energia Electrica do Estado da Bahia. (BL) **1884**
Consumption Guide. see Xiaofei Zhinan **1509**
Contabilidad Administracion see Contaduria. Administracion **749**
Contabilidad Nacional de Espana. (SP ISSN 0069-9292) **1091**
Contabilidad, Teoria y Practica. (CL) **749**
Contact. (FR) **813, 834**
Contact see Prairie Wind **1966**
Contact. (IE ISSN 0332-2491) **2286**, 4403
Contact. (CN ISSN 0714-3192) **2809**, 1747
Contact. (GW) **3299**
Contact. (SZ) **4172**, 3091
Contact. (BE) **4617**
†Contact. (AU ISSN 0010-7239) **5172**
Contact (Aldershot). (UK) **4172**
Contact (Amherst) see Massachusetts Magazine **1711**
Contact (Blackburn South). (AT ISSN 1030-7052) **4234**
Contact (Bromley). (UK ISSN 0010-7255) **1884**
Contact (Columbia). (US) **1726**
Contact (Crawley, 1947). (UK) **2193**
†Contact (Goodna, Qld.). (AT ISSN 0728-7569) **5172**
†Contact (Grawn). (US) **5172**
Contact (High Point). (US) **2557**
Contact (London, 1961). (UK ISSN 0308-0633) **1623**, 1235
Contact (Montreal). (CN ISSN 0838-018X) **4147**
Contact (Ottawa). (CN) **3882**
Contact (Parkville). (AT) **1747**
Contact (Quebec). (CN ISSN 0832-7556) **2176**
Contact (South Yorra). (AT) **4672**
Contact (Sutton Coldfields). (UK ISSN 0262-107X) **4262**
▼Contact! (Tucson). (US) **50**
Contact and Intraocular Lens Medical Journal see C L A O Journal **3299**
Contact avec le Danemark see Contact with Denmark **2357**
Contact: Bulletin Pedagogique. (ML) **1623**
Contact Dermatitis. (DK ISSN 0105-1873) **3246**
Contact Food News. (AT) **2064**
Contact Lens see Contact Lens Journal **3299**
Contact Lens Forum see Contact Lens Spectrum **3299**
Contact Lens Journal. (UK ISSN 0306-9575) **3299**
Contact Lens Spectrum. (US) **3299**
Contact Lens Update. (US ISSN 0885-9264) **3168**, 3299
Contact Monthly see Contact Food News **2064**
Contact Point. (US ISSN 0010-7301) **3230**
Contact Quarterly. (US ISSN 0198-9634) **1529**, 3800
Contact Rungis le Trait d'Union. (FR) **2064**
Contact: The UK News Contact Directory see Hollis Press & Public Relations Annual **1040**
Contact with Denmark. (DK ISSN 0105-7669) **2357**
Contact 2. (US ISSN 0197-6796) **2991**, 2862
Contactblad. (NE ISSN 0010-731X) **4234**
Contacto. (AG ISSN 0589-5081) **2582**
Contacto. (US) **3168**, 3299
Contacto: Mini-Abstracts see Contacto **3168**
Contactologia. (GW ISSN 0171-9599) **3299**
Contactologia-Bucherei. (GW ISSN 0724-6226) **3299**
Contactos Extraterrestres. (MX) **50**
Contacts. (US) **30**, 1372
Contacts. (GW) **927**
Contacts. (SA ISSN 0250-2003) **4126**, 4631

Contacts. (FR ISSN 0045-8325) **4172**
Contacts see Music Business Contacts **5241**
Contacts & Facilities in the Australian Entertainment Industry. (AT ISSN 1032-6456) **4631**, 1529, 3547
Contacts and Facilities in the Entertainment Industry see Contacts & Facilities in the Australian Entertainment Industry **4631**
Contacts Franco Italiens. (IT) **813**, 904
Contacts in Agriculture. (NZ ISSN 0110-6902) **85**, 1127
Contaduria. Administracion. (MX) **749**
Container Age. (JA ISSN 0289-8322) **4648**
Container Contacts. (GW) **4648**, 1127
Container in Italia e nel Mondo see Eurotransports **4649**
Container Management. (UK ISSN 0269-7726) **4726**
Container News. (US ISSN 0010-7360) **4648**
Containering News see Freight & Container Weekly **666**
Containerisation International. (UK ISSN 0010-7379) **4649**
Containerisation International Yearbook.(UK ISSN 0305-7402) **4649**
Containerization and Material Handling Annual. (CN) **3648**, 4649
Containers. (FR) **3648**, 4649
Contamination Control Abstracts. (UK) **1842**, 3747
Contatti con la Danimarca see Contact with Denmark **2357**
†Contax. (UK) **5172**
Contemplative Review see Living Prayer **4188**
Contempo. (US ISSN 0162-1971) **4235**
Contemporanea. (US ISSN 0897-8271) **322**
Contemporanea. (IT) **2309**, 2908
Contemporanul Ideea Europeana. (RM) **2197**
Contemporary/Tang Tai. (HK) **2197**
Contemporary Accounting Research. (CN ISSN 0823-9150) **749**
Contemporary African Monographs. (TZ ISSN 0069-9330) **2332**
Contemporary Agriculture. see Savremena Poljoprivreda **118**
†Contemporary American Art Critics. (US) **5172**
Contemporary American History Series. (US ISSN 0069-9357) **2403**
Contemporary Analyses in Education. (UK) **1623**
Contemporary Approaches to Ibsen. (NO) **2908**, 2357
Contemporary Architects. (US) **297**
Contemporary Art Centre of South Australia. Broadsheet. (AT ISSN 0819-677X) **322**, 297, 3506
Contemporary Art Society of Australia. Broadsheet see Contemporary Art Centre of South Australia. Broadsheet **322**
Contemporary Astrological Observations see C A O **358**
Contemporary Authors. (US ISSN 0010-7468) **418**
Contemporary Authors Autobiography Series. (US ISSN 0748-0636) **418**
Contemporary China Institute Publications. (UK ISSN 0085-2856) **3636**
Contemporary China Papers. (AT) **2337**, 3882
Contemporary Christian Music. (US) **3547**, 4172
Contemporary Christian Music Update see C C M Update **3543**
Contemporary Cinema. see Dangdai Dianying **3507**
†Contemporary Community Health Series. (US) **5172**
Contemporary Concepts in Physics. (US ISSN 0272-2488) **3816**
Contemporary Crises see Crime, Law and Social Policy **1512**
Contemporary Dermatology see Canadian Journal of Dermatology **3246**

Contemporary Dialysis see Contemporary Dialysis & Nephrology **3387**
Contemporary Dialysis & Nephrology. (US ISSN 0899-837X) **3387**
▼Contemporary Doll. (US ISSN 1052-486X) **2435**
Contemporary Drama. see Dangdai Xiju **4632**
Contemporary Drama Series. (US ISSN 0069-9381) **2908**
Contemporary Drug Problems. (US ISSN 0091-4509) **1535**, 2616
Contemporary Education. (US ISSN 0010-7476) **1623**
Contemporary Educational Psychology. (US ISSN 0361-476X) **1623**, 4017
Contemporary Endocrinology. (US) **3251**
Contemporary Era. see Dangdai **2910**
Contemporary European Affairs. (US ISSN 0955-3843) **3882**
▼Contemporary European History. (UK ISSN 0960-7773) **2357**
Contemporary Existentialism. (US ISSN 0895-0520) **3764**
Contemporary Family Therapy. (US ISSN 0892-2764) **4017**, 4432
Contemporary Folk Art. (US) **353**
Contemporary Foreign Literature. see Dangdai Waiguo Wenxue **2910**
Contemporary France. (UK ISSN 0951-9297) **2357**, 2505
Contemporary French Civilization. (US ISSN 0147-9156) **2357**
Contemporary Gastroenterology. (US) **3267**
Contemporary Geriatric Medicine. (US) **2271**
Contemporary German Studies: Occasional Papers. (UK ISSN 0268-1331) **2908**, 2357, 4432
Contemporary Government Series. (US) **4058**
Contemporary Graphic Artists. (US ISSN 0885-8462) **418**, 3998
†Contemporary Health Issues. (NZ) **5172**
Contemporary Hematology - Oncology. (US ISSN 0197-3649) **3271**
Contemporary Hypnosis. (UK ISSN 0960-5290) **4017**
Contemporary Internal Medicine. (US ISSN 1042-9646) **3091**
Contemporary Issues Criticism. (US ISSN 0732-7455) **2862**
Contemporary Issues Series. (UK ISSN 0069-942X) **4432**
Contemporary Japanese Books. (JA) **398**, 4126
Contemporary Japanese Economics. see Xiandai Riben Jingji **700**
Contemporary Literary Criticism Series. (US ISSN 0091-3421) **2908**
Contemporary Literature. (US ISSN 0010-7484) **2908**
Contemporary Long-Term Care. (US) **2460**
Contemporary Long-Term Care Reimbursement Bulletin. (US) **2460**
▼Contemporary Management in Critical Care. (US ISSN 1050-9623) **3091**
†Contemporary Management in Internal Medicine. (US ISSN 1050-9607) **5172**
▼Contemporary Management in Obstetrics and Gynecology. (US ISSN 1050-9615) **3291**
Contemporary Management Series. (US) **3091**
Contemporary Marxism see Social Justice **1523**
Contemporary Mathematics. (US ISSN 0271-4132) **3033**
Contemporary Metabolism. (US ISSN 0193-340X) **3251**
Contemporary Monthly. (HK) **2197**
Contemporary Music. see Nutida Musik **3571**
Contemporary Music Review. (US ISSN 0749-4467) **3547**
Contemporary Music Studies. (US ISSN 0891-5415) **3547**
Contemporary Musicians. (US ISSN 1044-2197) **3547**, 418
Contemporary Nephrology. (US) **3387**
Contemporary Neuroimaging. (US) **3357**

Contemporary Neurology Series. (US ISSN 0069-9446) **3334**
Contemporary News Weekly see Contemporary Monthly **2197**
Contemporary Novels. see Dangdai Xiaoshuo **2910**
Contemporary Ob-Gyn see Canadian Journal of Ob-Gyn & Women's Health Care **3290**
Contemporary Ob-Gyn. (US ISSN 0090-3159) **3291**
▼Contemporary Oncology. (US) **3196**
Contemporary Optometry. (US) **3299**
Contemporary Orthopaedics. (US) **3307**
Contemporary Pacific. (US ISSN 1043-898X) **2171**
Contemporary Pediatrics see Canadian Journal of Pediatrics **3319**
Contemporary Pediatrics. (US ISSN 8750-0507) **3320**
Contemporary Perspectives in Rehabilitation. (US) **1735**
Contemporary Philosophy. (US ISSN 0732-4944) **3764**
†Contemporary Philosophy Series. (US ISSN 0414-7790) **5172**
Contemporary Photographers. (US) **3789**
Contemporary Physics. (UK ISSN 0010-7514) **3816**
Contemporary Physics. (US) **3816**
Contemporary Poetry Series. (US) **2991**
Contemporary Poland. (PL ISSN 0010-7522) **3882**
Contemporary Policy Issues. (US ISSN 0735-0007) **656**
Contemporary Problems of Childhood. (US ISSN 0147-1082) **1235**
†Contemporary Psychiatry. (US ISSN 0277-8041) **5172**
Contemporary Psychoanalysis. (US ISSN 0010-7530) **4017**
Contemporary Psychology. (US ISSN 0010-7549) **4017**
†Contemporary Radiology. (CN ISSN 0835-4545) **5172**
Contemporary Record. (UK ISSN 0950-9224) **2357, 3882**
Contemporary Record Society. Society News. (US) **3547**
†Contemporary Religious Movements: A Wiley-Interscience Series. (US) **5172**
Contemporary Review. (UK ISSN 0010-7565) **2862**
Contemporary Reviews in Obstetrics and Gynaecology. (UK ISSN 0953-9182) **3291**
†Contemporary Scripts. (US) **5172**
Contemporary Social Issues: A Bibliographic Series. (US ISSN 0887-3569) **4457, 398**
Contemporary Sociology. (US ISSN 0094-3061) **4457**
▼Contemporary South Asia. (UK ISSN 0958-4935) **3882**
Contemporary Southeast Asia. (SI ISSN 0129-797X) **3882, 2337**
Contemporary Sports. see Dangdai Tiyu **4470**
Contemporary Studies in Applied Behavioral Science. (US) **4432**
Contemporary Studies in Economic and Financial Analysis. (US) **656, 773**
Contemporary Studies in Sociology. (US) **4432**
Contemporary Surgery. (US) **3378**
Contemporary Theatre, Film & Television. (US ISSN 0749-064X) **418, 4631**
▼Contemporary Theatre Review. (US ISSN 1048-6801) **4631**
Contemporary Theatre Studies. (US ISSN 1049-6513) **4631**
Contemporary Thought. (UA) **2862**
Contemporary Times. (US) **3626**
Contemporary Topics in Immunobiology.(US ISSN 0093-4054) **3184, 435**
Contemporary Topics in Information Transfer. (NE) **1455, 1446**
Contemporary Topics in Laboratory Animal Science. (US ISSN 1056-1471) **3258**
Contemporary Topics in Molecular Immunology. (US ISSN 0090-8800) **3184**

Contemporary Topics in Pure and Applied Condensed Matter Science. (US ISSN 1043-3996) **3816**
Contemporary Urology. (US) **3387**
Contemporary Verse Two. (CN ISSN 0831-9502) **2991, 2862**
Contemporary Wales. (UK ISSN 0951-4937) **4369, 852, 1623, 4058**
Contemporary Women Writers of Spain.(US) **2908, 4839**
Contemporary Writers Review. see Dangdai Zuojia Pinglun **2910**
†Contempt. (US) **5172**
Contenido. (MX ISSN 0010-7581) **2210**
▼Contention. (US ISSN 1056-1072) **4432**
†Contentions (New York). (US ISSN 1041-1771) **5172**
Contents. (JA ISSN 0385-6747) **3747, 8**
Contents List of Soviet Scientific Periodicals. (Il ISSN 0304-5358) **4355, 8**
Contents of Periodicals on Latin America. (US ISSN 0882-2743) **3936, 3953**
Contents of Recent Economics Journals.(UK ISSN 0045-8368) **711, 8**
Contents Pages in Education. (UK ISSN 0265-9220) **1675**
Contents Pages in Management. (UK ISSN 0306-3224) **711**
Contenuti. (IT ISSN 0010-762X) **2908, 322**
Contest Hotline. (US ISSN 0195-9735) **2435**
Contest Magazine see Jaybee **2437**
Contest News-Letter. (US) **2435**
Contesto. (IT) **2908**
▼Contests for Students. (US) **1252**
Context. (US ISSN 0361-8854) **4172**
Context South. (US ISSN 1045-2265) **2991, 322**
Conti degli Italiani. (IT ISSN 0390-6574) **4080**
Contigo see T V Contigo **1381**
Continent Cendrars. (SZ) **2908**
Continent Magazine. (CH) **269**
Continental (Dallas). (US) **2223, 4672, 4758**
Continental Basketball Association Media Guide Yearbook see C B A Media Guide Yearbook **4501**
Continental Basketball Association Newsletter see C B A Newsletter **4501**
Continental Bulletin. (US ISSN 0010-7697) **2530**
Continental Cablevision Program Guide.(US) **1372**
Continental Comments. (US) **4688**
Continental Franchise Review. (US ISSN 0045-8376) **656, 1036**
Continental Motoring Holidays. (UK) **4758, 4688**
Continental Motoring News. (UK) **4758**
Continental Newstime. (US) **852, 3882**
Continental Paint and Resin News see European Paint and Resin News **3653**
Continental Profiles. (US) **4802**
Continental Research Series. (HK ISSN 0069-9535) **2337**
Continental Shelf Research. (US ISSN 0278-4343) **1603, 1946**
Continental Spectator. (US) **4362, 3396**
Contingencies. (US) **2530**
Contingency Journal see Enterprise Systems Journal **1450**
Contingency Planning & Recovery Journal see C P R - J **1433**
Contintentaler Stahlmarkt see Stahlmarkt **3420**
Continuation Education. (US ISSN 0361-6908) **1683**
Continuing Care. (US ISSN 2460, 4403
Continuing Care Coordinator see Continuing Care **2460**
Continuing Education see Continuing Educator **4172**
Continuing Education Alternatives Update. (US ISSN 0736-1696) **1683**
Continuing Education and Media. see W & M **1688**

†Continuing Education Directory for Metropolitan Toronto. (CN ISSN 0045-8384) **5172**
Continuing Educator. (US) **4172**
Continuing Higher Education see Journal of Continuing Higher Education **1685**
Continuing Higher Education Review. (US) **1704**
Continuing Inquiry. (US) **3882**
Continuing Legal Education see C L E T V **2608**
Continuing Library Education Network and Exchange Round Table Exchange Newsletter see C L E N Exchange Newsletter **2750**
Continuing the Conversation. (US ISSN 0889-468X) **3764, 1440, 4017**
Continuite. (CN ISSN 0714-9476) **2403**
Continuity. (US ISSN 0277-1446) **2309**
Continuity and Change. (UK ISSN 0268-4160) **3980, 269, 4432**
Continuo. (US) **3547**
Continuo. (AT ISSN 0310-6802) **3547, 2753**
▼Continuum. (US) **2505, 4369**
Continuum. (CN ISSN 0381-0925) **2616**
Continuum (Washington) see Continuing Higher Education Review **1704**
Continuum Mechanics and Thermodynamics. (US ISSN 0935-1175) **3840, 3842**
Continuum of Care. (CN) **2460, 4099**
Continuum: Problems in French Literature from the Renaissance to the Early Enlightenment. (US ISSN 0899-4307) **2908**
Contour. (NE ISSN 0166-7831) **1683**
Contours. (US) **1284**
Contra Costa County Office of Education Newsletter see Contra Costa Schools **1726**
Contra Costa Schools. (US) **1726**
Contra Costa Woman. (US) **4839**
Contraband. (NZ ISSN 0113-3292) **904**
Contraband (Lake Charles). (US ISSN 0888-7586) **1309**
†Contraband (Sumas). (US) **5172**
Contraception. (US ISSN 0010-7824) **596, 3291**
Contraception - Fertilite - Sexualite. (FR ISSN 0301-861X) **596**
Contraceptive Delivery Systems see Advances in Contraceptive Delivery Systems **595**
Contraceptive Technology Update. (US ISSN 0274-726X) **596**
Contract. (US ISSN 0010-7832) **2549**
Contract Appeals Decisions. (US) **2616**
Contract Bridge Bulletin. (US ISSN 0010-7840) **4470**
Contract Cleaning see Building Services Contractor **607**
Contract Employment Weekly. (US) **1127, 3626**
Contract Engineer Weekly see Contract Employment Weekly **1127**
Contract Journal (1979). (UK) **614**
Contract Magazine. (CN ISSN 0833-9406) **2549, 297, 1058**
Contract Management. (US) **1006, 4058**
Contracting Business. (US ISSN 0279-4071) **2298**
†Contracting Intelligence. (US) **5172**
Contractor. (US ISSN 0897-7135) **614**
Contractor and Builder. see Kablan Veboneh **622**
Contractor Profit News. (US ISSN 0741-4617) **614, 1006**
▼Contractor's Business Management Report. (US ISSN 1058-9260) **749, 639**
Contractors Equipment Guide. (US) **614**
Contractor's Guide. (US ISSN 0273-5954) **614, 297**
Contractors Hot Line. (US ISSN 0192-6330) **614, 1036**
Contractor's Market Center. (US) **1036, 614**

Contracts see B A R - B R I Bar Review. Contracts **2602**
†Contracts Reference Directory. (US) **5172**
Contractspeler. (NE ISSN 0045-8406) **4470, 4517, 4533**
La Contraddizione. (IT) **3882**
Contrapunkt. (GW ISSN 0343-3935) **1252, 4235**
Contrapunto. (CR) **1355, 1372**
Contrarian's View. (US) **943**
Contrary Investor. (US ISSN 0010-793X) **943**
Contrary Investor Follow-up Service. (US ISSN 0015-6019) **943**
Contrary Opinion Library. (US) **943**
Contrast see New Contrast **2942**
†Contrast. (US ISSN 0164-5587) **5172**
Contrastes. (FR ISSN 0247-915X) **2809**
Contrastes: Revista de Historia Moderna. (SP ISSN 0213-5477) **2357**
Contrastive Linguistics. see S'postavitelno Ezikoznanie **2843**
Contrattazione. (IT) **976**
Contre-Poison. (FR) **1623**
Contrebis. (UK ISSN 0307-5087) **269**
Contree. (SA ISSN 0379-9867) **2332**
Contremaitre. see Werkmeister **4613**
Contrepoint. (FR ISSN 0010-7964) **2862, 3882**
Contribuciones. (AG ISSN 0326-4068) **927**
Contribuicoes em Ciencias Sociais. (BL) **4369**
Contribuicoes em Desenvolvimento Urbano. (BL) **2485**
Contribuicoes em Economia. (BL) **657**
Contribuicoes em Psicologia, Psiquiatria e Psicanalise. (BL) **4017, 3334**
Contributii Botanice. (RM ISSN 0069-9616) **500**
Contribution in Marine Science see Contributions in Marine Science - Monographic Series **435**
Contribution to Precambrian Geology. (US) **1558**
Contributions. see Prilozi **282**
Contributions a la Connaissance des Elites Africaines. (FR) **418, 2332**
Contributions from the Department of Astronomy, University of Kyoto see Kyoto University. Department of Astronomy. Contributions **366**
Contributions from the Department of Astronomy, University of Tokyo see University of Tokyo. Department of Astronomy. Contributions **370**
Contributions from the Indian Institute of Tropical Meteorology see Indian Institute of Tropical Meteorology. Contributions **3436**
Contributions from the Kwasan and Hida Observatories, University of Kyoto see Kyoto University. Kwasan and Hida Observatories. Contributions **366**
Contributions from the New York Botanical Garden. (US ISSN 0736-0509) **500**
Contributions in Afro-American and African Studies. (US ISSN 0069-9624) **2332, 2403**
Contributions in American History. (US ISSN 0084-9219) **2403**
Contributions in American Studies. (US ISSN 0084-9227) **2403**
▼Contributions in Asian Studies. (US ISSN 1053-1866) **3636**
Contributions in Biology and Geology. (US) **435, 1558, 3657**
Contributions in Comparative Colonial Studies. (US ISSN 0163-3813) **2403**
Contributions in Criminology and Penology. (US ISSN 0732-4464) **1512**
Contributions in Drama and Theatre Studies. (US ISSN 0163-3821) **4632**
Contributions in Economics and Economic History. (US ISSN 0084-9235) **890**
Contributions in Ethnic Studies. (US ISSN 0196-7088) **1997**

CONTRIBUTIONS

Contributions in Family Studies. (US ISSN 0147-1023) **4432**
Contributions in Intercultural and Comparative Studies. (US ISSN 0147-1031) **4432**
Contributions in Labor History *see* Contributions in Labor Studies **976**
Contributions in Labor Studies. (US ISSN 0886-8239) **976**
▼Contributions in Latin American Studies. (US ISSN 1054-6790) **2403, 4369**
Contributions in Legal Studies. (US ISSN 0147-1074) **2616**
Contributions in Librarianship and Information Science. (US ISSN 0084-9243) **2753**
Contributions in Marine Science - Monographic Series. (US) **435**
Contributions in Medical History *see* Contributions in Medical Studies **3091**
Contributions in Medical Studies. (US ISSN 0886-8220) **3091**
Contributions in Military History *see* Contributions in Military Studies **3454**
Contributions in Military Studies. (US ISSN 0883-6884) **3454**
Contributions in Oceanography *see* Texas A & M University. College of Geosciences. Contributions in Oceanography **1611**
Contributions in Philosophy. (US ISSN 0084-926X) **3764**
Contributions in Political Science. (US ISSN 0147-1066) **3882**
Contributions in Psychology. (US ISSN 0736-2714) **4017**
Contributions in Science. (US ISSN 0459-8113) **4306**
Contributions in Sociology. (US ISSN 0084-9278) **4432**
Contributions in Women's Studies. (US ISSN 0147-104X) **4839**
Contributions of the Astronomical Observatory on Skalnate Pleso. *see* Prace Astronomickeho Observatoria na Skalnatom Plese **368**
Contributions to Atmospheric Physics/Beitraege zur Physik der Atmosphaere. (GW ISSN 0005-8173) **3434**
Contributions to Current Research in Geophysics. (SZ) **1587**
Contributions to Economic Analysis. (NE ISSN 0573-8555) **890**
Contributions to Entomology. *see* Beitraege zur Entomologie **529**
Contributions to Epidemiology and Biostatistics. (SZ ISSN 0377-3574) **4099**
Contributions to Gynecology and Obstetrics. (SZ ISSN 0304-4246) **3291**
Contributions to Himalayan Geology. (II) **1558**
Contributions to Human Development. (SZ ISSN 0301-4193) **3091, 571**
Contributions to Human History. (CN ISSN 0832-8609) **2403**
Contributions to Indian Sociology. (US ISSN 0069-9667) **4432**
Contributions to Library Science. *see* Bijdragen tot de Bibliotheekwetenschap **2748**
Contributions to Marine Scientific Research. *see* Beitraege zur Meereskunde **1602**
Contributions to Microbiology and Immunology. (SZ ISSN 0301-3081) **3184, 550**
Contributions to Mineralogy and Petrology. (GW ISSN 0010-7999) **1558, 3482**
†Contributions to Museum Studies. (CN) **5172**
Contributions to Music Education. (US ISSN 0190-4922) **3547**
Contributions to Natural Science. (CN ISSN 0829-609X) **1542**
Contributions to Nepalese Studies. (NP) **2337, 3636**
Contributions to Nephrology. (SZ ISSN 0302-5144) **3387**
Contributions to Oncology/Beitraege zur Onkologie. (SZ ISSN 0250-3220) **3091**

Contributions to Plasma Physics. (GW ISSN 0863-1042) **3816**
Contributions to Political Economy. (UK ISSN 0277-5921) **852, 3882**
Contributions to Primatology. (SZ ISSN 0301-4231) **580**
Contributions to Residential Treatment. (US) **4017, 1235, 1735**
Contributions to Sedimentology. (GW ISSN 0343-4125) **1558**
Contributions to Southeast Asian Ethnography. (US ISSN 0217-2992) **237**
†Contributions to Tertiary and Quaternary Geology. (NE ISSN 0165-280X) **5172**
Contributions to the History of Labor and Society. (NE ISSN 0921-500X) **2582**
Contributions to the History of Natural Sciences and Technology in the Baltic/Iz Istorii Estestvoznaniya i Tekhniki Pribaltiki. (LV ISSN 0130-3252) **4306, 4595**
Contributions to the Sociology of Jewish Languages. (NE ISSN 0169-7846) **2810, 4222**
Contributions to the Study of Aging. (US ISSN 0732-085X) **2271**
Contributions to the Study of Anthropology. (US ISSN 0890-9377) **237**
Contributions to the Study of Art and Architecture. (US) **352, 309**
Contributions to the Study of Childhood and Youth. (US ISSN 0273-124X) **1235**
Contributions to the Study of Computer Science. (US ISSN 0734-757X) **1394**
Contributions to the Study of Education. (US ISSN 0196-707X) **1623**
Contributions to the Study of Mass Media and Communications. (US ISSN 0732-4456) **1347**
Contributions to the Study of Music and Dance. (US ISSN 0193-9041) **3547, 1529**
Contributions to the Study of Popular Culture. (US ISSN 0198-9871) **237, 4432**
Contributions to the Study of Religion. (US ISSN 0196-7053) **4172**
Contributions to the Study of Science Fiction and Fantasy. (US ISSN 0193-6875) **3010, 2908**
Contributions to the Study of World History. (US ISSN 0885-9159) **2309, 1997**
Contributions to the Study of World Literature. (US ISSN 0738-9345) **2908**
†Contributions to Vertebrate Evolution. (SZ ISSN 0376-4230) **5172**
Contributions to Zoology - Amsterdam. *see* Bijdragen tot de Dierkunde **579**
Il Contributo. (IT) **3764**
Control. (SP) **30**
Control. (UK) **1006**
Control. (JA ISSN 0911-0704) **3033, 1817**
Control. (FR ISSN 1141-4804) **4672**
Control (Chicago). (US) **2522**
Control Ad - Lits. (US) **2522**
Control and Computers. (CN ISSN 0730-9538) **1413**
Control and Cybernetics. (PL ISSN 0324-8569) **1440**
Control and Dynamic Systems *see* Control and Dynamic Systems: Advances in Theory and Applications **50**
Control and Dynamic Systems: Advances in Theory and Applications. (US ISSN 0090-5267) **50**
Control and Instrumentation. (UK ISSN 0010-8022) **1413**
Control and Measurement *see* Control and Instrumentation **1413**
Control, Cibernetica y Automatizacion. (CU) **1440, 1407**
Control Column. (UK) **50**
†Control Data World. (US ISSN 0892-4295) **5172**
Control de Calidad Asistencial. (SP ISSN 0213-8328) **3091**

Control de Publicidad y Ventas *see* Control **30**
Control Engineering. (US ISSN 0010-8049) **1413**
Control Engineering Conference. Proceedings. (US) **1413**
Control Industry Inside Report. (US) **1413**
Control Magazine. (UK ISSN 0069-973X) **322**
Control of Pollution Encyclopedia. (UK) **1976, 2616**
Control Software Directory for Process Control. (US) **1413**
Control Systems. (UK ISSN 0266-2493) **826**
Controle & Instrumentacao - Automatizacao *see* C & I **2521**
Controlled Clinical Trials. (US ISSN 0197-2456) **3258**
Controlled Release Newsletter. (US) **1217, 3391**
Controlled Release Society. International Symposium on Controlled Release of Bioactive Materials. Proceedings. (US) **1217, 3721**
Controlled Substances Handbook. (US) **1535, 1512**
The Controller. (SZ ISSN 0010-8073) **50, 4718**
Controller. (US) **4672**
Controller Magazin. (GW ISSN 0343-267X) **1006**
†Controllers Quarterly. (US ISSN 8756-5684) **5172**
The Controller's Report. (US ISSN 0895-2787) **749**
Controllers Update. (US ISSN 8756-5676) **749**
Controlli Numerici Macchine a C N Robot Industriali *see* Automazione Integrata **2521**
Controlling. (GW ISSN 0935-0381) **1413**
Controlling Benefits & Deferred Compensation. (US ISSN 1053-5349) **1064**
Controls and Systems. (US) **1818**
Controluce. (IT) **2204**
Controversia. (CK ISSN 0120-4165) **3882**
Convencion Bancaria y de Instituciones Financieras. (CK) **773**
Convene. (US) **1006, 3391**
†Convenience Care Update. (US ISSN 0887-0144) **5172**
Convenience Store. (UK ISSN 0267-9361) **2090, 2088**
Convenience Store Decisions. (US) **2090**
†Convenience Store Management. (US) **5172**
Convenience Store Merchandiser *see* Convenience Store Management **5172**
Convenience Store News. (US ISSN 0045-8422) **2091**
Convenience Store News Industry Report. (US) **2091**
Convenience Store People. (US) **2091**
Convenient Automotive Services Retailer. (US) **4688**
Convenios Centroamericanos de Integration Economica. (GT ISSN 0553-6863) **927**
Convention. (AT) **2473**
Convention Herald. (US) **4172**
Convention Industry. *see* T W **3394**
Convention of Electrical and Electronics Engineers in Israel. Proceedings. (US) **1885**
Convention Rostrum. (AT ISSN 0156-0166) **3391**
Convention World *see* Association Meetings **3391**
†Conventional and Nuclear Submarines of the World. (UK) **5172**
Conventions and Expositions. (US) **1006, 3391**
Conventions & Meetings Canada. (CN ISSN 0226-8922) **3391**
Conventionsouth. (US) **3392**
Convergence. (CN ISSN 0010-8146) **1683**
†Convergence. (SZ ISSN 0010-8154) **5172**

Convergence: International Colloquium on Automotive Electronic Technology. Proceedings *see* Convergence: International Congress on Transportation Electronics. Proceedings **4688**
Convergence: International Congress on Transportation Electronics. Proceedings. (US) **4688, 1885**
Convergencia. (BL) **2908**
Convergent World *see* Network Computing News **1463**
Conversaciones Internacionales de Historia. (SP) **2357**
Conversation et Traduction. (SZ ISSN 0010-8170) **2810**
Conversations with Writers. (US) **2568, 2223**
Converter. *see* Bianyaqi **1883**
Converter. (UK ISSN 0010-8189) **3662**
Converter Directory. (UK ISSN 0309-2143) **1127**
Converting Magazine. (US ISSN 0746-7141) **3662**
Converting Today. (UK ISSN 0264-715X) **3662, 3648**
Conveyancer and Property Lawyer. (UK ISSN 0010-8200) **4147, 2616**
Conveyancing Bulletin. (SA) **2616**
Conveyancing Service New South Wales. (AT) **2616**
Conveyor Equipment Manufacturers Association Bulletin *see* C E M A Bulletin **3016**
Conviction Magazine *see* Fellowship Today **4238**
Convictions. (US) **1512**
Convivium. (BL ISSN 0102-2636) **3882**
Convocation News *see* Encounter **1311**
Convorbiri Literare. (RM ISSN 0010-8243) **2908**
Convulsive Therapy. (US ISSN 0749-8055) **3334**
Cook Knowledge. *see* Pengtiao Zhishi **2449**
Cook Political Report. (US) **3882, 4058**
Cookbook Digest. (US ISSN 0010-826X) **2445**
Cookbook Review. (US) **2445**
Cookbook Series *see* Specialty Cooking **3612**
Cookeia. (RH ISSN 0250-2992) **2332**
Cooking Edge. (US ISSN 1040-1903) **2445**
Cooking for Four Seasons. *see* Shiki no Aji **2449**
Cooking for Profit. (US ISSN 0091-861X) **2064, 2473**
Cooking for Survival Consciousness Reports *see* C S C Reports **3604**
Cooking Light. (US ISSN 0886-4446) **2445, 3604**
†Cook's. (US ISSN 0886-943X) **5172**
Cook's Crier. (US) **2148**
Cook's Index. (US ISSN 0731-8634) **2450, 8**
Cookson Ceramics and Antimony Limited Monthly Bulletin for the Ceramic Industry *see* Cookson Monthly Bulletin for the Ceramic Industry **1163**
Cookson Monthly Bulletin for the Ceramic Industry. (UK) **1163**
†Cookstove News. (US) **5172**
Cool Traveler. (US ISSN 1044-3495) **2908, 4758**
Coolibri. (GW) **3523, 2862**
Cooling Tower Institute Journal *see* C T I Journal **3683**
Coombe Lodge Report. (UK ISSN 0305-8441) **1704**
Coon-Hound Corner. (US) **4544**
Coonhound Bloodlines. (US) **3709**
Co-op America Quarterly. (US) **852**
Co-Op Communicator. (CN) **829**
Co-Op Cornerstone. (CN) **829**
Co-Op Country News *see* Harvest States Journal **95**
†Coop Fachblatt fuer Unternehmungsfuehrung/Revue d'Economie d'Enterprise. (SZ) **5172**
Coop Italia. (IT) **829**
Co-op Japan Information. (JA) **829**
Co-Op Networker. (US) **4432**

Coop News. (NR) **829**
Co-op News. (US) **2064**
Co-Op News (Hanover). (US) **1504**
Co-op Power. (US) **1885**
Co-op Source Directory. (US ISSN 0736-0878) **30**
Co-op Trade. *see* Szovet Kereti Kereskedelem **832**
Coop - Zeitung. (SZ) **829**
▼Cooper Collection (Grawn). (US ISSN 1058-4021) **2148**
Cooper Heller Research. Newsletter. (US) **8, 657**
†Cooper Monographs on English and American Language and Literature. (GW ISSN 0069-9780) **5172**
Cooperacion. (MX) **927**
Cooperacion Libre. (AG ISSN 0010-8316) **829**
Cooperador Dental. (AG ISSN 0069-9799) **3230**
Cooperateur Agricole. (CN ISSN 0315-1204) **85**
Cooperatie. (NE ISSN 0009-9783) **829**
Cooperatieve Vereniging Verenigde Bloemenveilingen Aalsmeer Bode *see* V B A Bode **832**
Cooperation: (BE ISSN 0770-7223) **829**
Cooperation. *see* Shituf **832**
Cooperation Agricole. (FR ISSN 0010-8359) **85**
Cooperation and Conflict. (UK ISSN 0010-8367) **3953**
Cooperation et Developpement *see* Actuel Developpement **925**
Cooperation for Development. (SJ) **927**
Cooperation in Turkey. (TU) **829**
Cooperation Technique *see* Actuel Developpement **925**
Cooperation Technique. Bulletin. (UN ISSN 1010-8947) **1352**
Cooperativa (Macerata). (IT) **85**
Cooperativa Antigruppo Siciliano. (IT) **2991**
Cooperativa Centro di Documentazione. Notiziario. (IT ISSN 0392-4270) **398**
Cooperative Accountant. (US ISSN 0010-8391) **749, 829**
Cooperative America *see* America Cooperativa **829**
Cooperative and Rural Development Bank. Annual Report and Accounts. (TZ) **773**
Co-operative Bank of Kenya. Annual Report & Accounts. (KE) **773**
Cooperative Bank of Taiwan. Annual Report/Tai-wan Sheng Ho-tso Chin-k'u. Annual Report. (CH) **773**
Cooperative Banker *see* N A F S C O B Bulletin **791**
Cooperative Business Journal. (US ISSN 0893-3391) **829**
Co-Operative Communications. (UK) **149, 829, 1036**
Cooperative Education Association Membership Directory. (US ISSN 0069-9810) **1623**
Cooperative Education Association Newsletter. (US ISSN 0010-843X) **1623**
Cooperative Educational Abstracting Service *see* International Bureau of Education. Bulletin **1677**
Cooperative Farmer. (US ISSN 0010-8448) **85**
Co-Operative Game Catalog. (CN) **4470**
Cooperative Housing Bulletin. (US ISSN 0097-9759) **2485**
Cooperative Housing Foundation Newsbriefs *see* C H F Newsbriefs **2484**
Cooperative Housing Journal. (US ISSN 0589-6355) **2485**
Cooperative Industrial and Commercial Reference and Information Service Directory *see* C I C R I S Directory **5156**
Cooperative Law Journal. (II) **2616**
Cooperative Library Agency for Systems and Services Forum *see* C L A S S Forum **5157**
Cooperative Life/Gekkan Kyodotai. (JA) **4432**
Co-Operative News. (UK ISSN 0009-9821) **830**

Co-operative News (Scottish Edition) *see* Co-Operative News **830**
Cooperative News International. (US) **927, 85, 830**
Cooperative Online Serials Microfiche *see* C O N S E R Microfiche **396**
Cooperative Partners. (US ISSN 0896-9426) **830**
Cooperative Perspective. (II) **85**
Cooperative Plant Pest Report *see* C P P R **171**
Cooperative Press in South-East Asia. (II) **2568**
Co-operative Rostrum. *see* Synergatiko Vima **2184**
Co-operative Statistics. (UK) **830**
Cooperative Sugar Press News. (II) **830**
Cooperative Trade Directory for Southeast Asia. (II ISSN 0069-9837) **830, 1127**
Cooperative Trafipro Umunyamalyango. (RW) **976**
Co-operative Union. Annual Report and Financial Statements (Year). (UK) **830**
Co-Operative Union of Canada. News Service *see* Canadian Co-Operative Association. News Service **829**
Cooperative Vennootschappen. (BE) **657, 749**
Cooperative Village *see* Zemia **2592**
Cooperative Whole Grain Education Association Newsletter *see* C W G E A Newsletter **2087**
Co-operatively Speaking. (US) **1623**
Co-operatives. *see* Szovetkezet **832**
Cooperatives et Developpement. (CN ISSN 0712-2748) **830**
Co-Operatives Quarterly. (CH ISSN 0009-9856) **830**
Cooperativismo y Desarrollo *see* Universidad y Cooperativismo **887**
Cooperator. (II ISSN 0010-8464) **830**
Cooperatore Agricolo. (IT) **85**
†Cooperator's Bulletin. (II ISSN 0045-8503) **5172**
Cooperazione. (IT ISSN 0391-674X) **927**
Cooperazione di Credito. (IT ISSN 0010-8480) **830**
Cooperazione e Societa. (IT ISSN 0010-8499) **830**
Cooperazione e Trasporti. (IT) **4649**
Cooperazione Educativa. (IT ISSN 0010-8502) **1623**
Cooperazione in Agricoltura. (IT) **85**
Cooperazione Italiana. (IT ISSN 0010-8510) **830**
Coordinadora de Organizaciones de Agricultores y Ganaderos Informa *see* C O A G - Informa **213**
Coordinating Committee on Women in the Historical Profession - Conference Group on Women's History Newsletter *see* C C W H P - C G W H Newsletter **4858**
Coordination Chemistry. (UK ISSN 0069-9845) **1175**
Coordination Chemistry Reviews. (NE ISSN 0010-8545) **1175**
Coordination Committee for Polish-Jewish Youth in Denmark Orientering *see* C C Orientering **1233**
Coordination Council on Deafness of Nova Scotia. News *see* Atlantic Silent News **2286**
Coordinator (Los Angeles) *see* Continuing Care **2460**
Coordinator (Memphis). (US ISSN 0279-6163) **750**
Coordinator (St. Paul). (US) **3800**
Coosa Valley View. (US) **657, 2223**
†Cope. (US) **5172**
Copeia. (US ISSN 0045-8511) **580**
Copenhagen HandelsBank. Report and Accounts *see* Den Danske Bank Aktieselskab. Report and Accounts **775**
Copenhagen Political Studies Abstracts. (DK ISSN 0107-0452) **3936**
Copenhagen School of Economics and Business Administration. Marketing Institute. Working Papers. (DK ISSN 0109-3401) **1036**
Copenhagen Stock Exchange. Annual Report. *see* Koebenhavns Fondsboers. Aarsrapport **953**

Copenhagen - This Week. (DK) **4758**
Copie Zero *see* Revue de la Cinematheque **3516**
†Copier Duplicator News. (US) **5172**
Copier Faxts. (US) **1058**
Copier Review. (US) **1058**
Coping. (US ISSN 1043-8637) **3196**
Coping Catalog. (US) **1535**
Coping with Medical Issues. (NE) **3091**
Copper Abstracts *see* International Copper Information Bulletin **3425**
Copper & Brass Servicenter Association Capsules *see* C B S A Capsules **3403**
Copper State Bulletin. (US ISSN 0098-4841) **2148**
Copper Survey *see* World Copper Databook **3498**
Copper Topics. (US) **3404, 1928**
Copperbelt Education. (ZA) **1623**
Copperbelt of Zambia Mining Industry Year Book *see* Zambia Mining Yearbook **3498**
Coppia Moderna. (IT) **2204**
Coptic Gnostic Library *see* Nag Hammadi Studies **4191**
Coptic Studies. (NE ISSN 0167-5818) **4172**
Coptologia. (CN ISSN 0229-1134) **4172, 4281**
Copts. (US ISSN 0360-649X) **4172**
Copula. (US) **2908**
†Copy. (GW) **5172**
Copy Editor. (US) **2568**
Copy Magazine. (US) **3998**
Copycat Magazine. (US ISSN 0886-5612) **1747**
Copyright. (UN ISSN 0010-8626) **3674**
Copyright Bulletin. (UN ISSN 0010-8634) **2616, 3674**
Copyright Clearance Center. Report. (US ISSN 1044-2332) **4126, 3674**
Copyright Directory: Attorneys, Professors, Government Agencies, Congressional Committees, Searchers, Clearinghouses, Hotlines & Associations, (Year). (US ISSN 1050-5156) **3679, 398**
Copyright Law in Business and Practice.(US) **2616, 3674**
Copyright Law Reports. (US) **3674**
Copyright Law Symposium. (US ISSN 0069-9950) **3674**
Copyright Laws and Treaties of the World. (UN) **3674**
Copyright Laws and Treaties of the World. Supplement. (UN ISSN 0069-9969) **3674**
Copyright Reporter. (AT ISSN 0725-0509) **3674**
Copyright Society of the U.S.A. Journal. (US ISSN 0886-3520) **2616, 2568**
Coquitlam Magazine. (CN ISSN 0845-9738) **2176**
†Cor & Coronarien. (GW ISSN 0721-393X) **5172**
Cor et Vasa. (CS ISSN 0010-8650) **3207**
Coraddi. (US) **322, 1529, 2908**
Coral Reef Newsletter. (GU) **500**
Coral Reefs. (GW) **1603**
Coral Springs Monthly. (US) **2223**
Coranto. (US ISSN 0010-8669) **2908**
Corax. (GW ISSN 0589-686X) **563**
Cord. (IO) **174**
Cord. (US ISSN 0010-8685) **4262**
†Cord Sportfacts Guns Guide. (US ISSN 0590-6776) **5172**
†Cord Sportfacts: Hunting. (US ISSN 0092-8216) **5172**
Cord Weekly. (CN) **1309**
Cordell Construction Reports. (AT) **614**
Cordell's Building Cost Guide. Commercial and Industrial. (AT) **614**
Cordell's Building Cost Guide. Housing. (AT) **614**
Cordell's Building Cost Guide. New Construction *see* Cordell's Building Cost Guide. Commercial and Industrial **614**
Cordell's Cost Guide. Housing Alterations and Additions *see* Cordell's Building Cost Guide. Housing **614**

CORNELL BIENNIAL 6085

Cordell's Price Index of Building Materials. (AT ISSN 0311-7472) **614**
Cordell's Who's Who in Building: Architects. (AT) **614**
Cordell's Who's Who in Building: Builders. (AT) **614**
Cordell's Who's Who in Building: Developers. (AT) **614, 297**
Cordell's Who's Who in Building: Housing *see* Cordell's Who's Who in Building: Builders **614**
Cordell's Who's Who in Building: Non-Housing *see* Cordell's Who's Who in Building: Architects **614**
Cordell's Who's Who in Design Specifying *see* Cordell's Who's Who in Building: Developers **614**
Corderie et Ficellerie (Fabrication). *see* Canada. Statistics Canada. Cordage and Twine Industry **5159**
Corderie Francaise. (FR) **3648**
Cordiality. (US) **2223, 2445**
Cordulia. (CN) **530**
CORE *see* C O R E **1619**
Core Journals in Cardiology. (NE ISSN 0165-9405) **3168, 9, 3207**
Core Journals in Clinical Neurology. (NE ISSN 0165-1056) **3168, 9**
Core Journals in Dermatology. (NE ISSN 0167-5796) **3168, 3246**
Core Journals in Gastroenterology. (NE ISSN 0165-8719) **3168, 3267**
Core Journals in Obstetrics - Gynecology. (NE ISSN 0376-5059) **3169, 9**
Core Journals in Ophthalmology. (NE ISSN 0165-1005) **3169, 9**
Core Journals in Pediatrics. (NE ISSN 0376-5040) **3169, 9**
†Core Series in Primary Care: Allergy - Immunology Guide. (US) **5172**
†Core Series in Primary Care: Arthritis - Rheumatology Guide. (US) **5173**
†Core Series in Primary Care: Cardiology Guide. (US) **5173**
†Core Series in Primary Care: Diabetes Management Guide. (US) **5173**
†Core Series in Primary Care: Gastroenterology Guide. (US) **5173**
†Core Series in Primary Care: Geriatric Medicine Guide. (US) **5173**
†Core Series in Primary Care: Infectious Disease Guide. (US) **5173**
†Core Series in Primary Care: Psychiatry in Primary Care Guide. (US) **5173**
†Core Series in Primary Care: Sexual Medicine Guide. (US) **5173**
Core Teacher. (US ISSN 0045-8538) **1747**
▼Corel Magazine. (US) **1421**
Corella. (AT ISSN 0155-0438) **563**
Corgi Quarterly. (US) **3710**
Corhealth. (US) **3091, 1512**
Corinthian Horse Sport. (CN ISSN 0829-2930) **4533**
Corinthian Horse Sport in Canada *see* Corinthian Horse Sport **4533**
Cork Historical and Archaeological Society. Journal. (IE ISSN 0010-8731) **269, 2357**
Cork Weekly Examiner and Weekly Herald *see* Irish Weekly Examiner **2203**
Corkscrew. (US) **380, 1036**
Corletter *see* C O R Letter **4232**
Cormoran y Delfin. (AG ISSN 0010-8766) **2991**
Cormorant *see* Marine Ornithology **565**
Cormorant News Bulletin. (US ISSN 0045-8554) **257, 4688**
Cormosea Bulletin. (US ISSN 0734-449X) **3636**
Cormosea Newsletter *see* Cormosea Bulletin **3636**
Corn Annual. (US ISSN 0069-9993) **174**
Corn Belt Library System. Sum and Substance. (US ISSN 1041-343X) **2753**
▼Corn Farmer. (US) **85**
Corn - Soy Guide. (CN) **174**
Cornea. (US ISSN 0277-3740) **3299**
Cornell Alumni News. (US) **1309**
Cornell Biennial Electrical Engineering Conference. (US ISSN 0070-0002) **1885**

Cornell Countryman. (US ISSN 0010-8782) 85
Cornell Daily Sun. (US) 1309
Cornell East Asia Papers see Cornell East Asia Series 3636
Cornell East Asia Series. (US ISSN 1050-2955) 3636
Cornell Engineer. (US ISSN 0010-8790) 1818
Cornell Field Crops and Soils Handbook.(US) 174
Cornell Focus. (US) 85, 435
Cornell Hotel & Restaurant Administration Quarterly. (US ISSN 0010-8804) 2473
†Cornell International Agriculture Mimeographs. (US) 5173
Cornell International Industrial and Labor Relations Reports. (US ISSN 0070-0029) 976
Cornell International Law Journal. (US ISSN 0010-8812) 2722
Cornell Journal of Architecture. (US ISSN 0731-5384) 297
Cornell Law Forum. (US ISSN 0010-8839) 2616
Cornell Law Review. (US ISSN 0010-8847) 2616
Cornell Linguistic Contributions. (NE ISSN 0169-779X) 2810
Cornell Lunatic. (US) 2862
Cornell Plantations. (US ISSN 0010-8863) 2124, 500, 2309
Cornell Recommendations for Commercial Florist Crops. (US) 2142
Cornell Recommendations for Commercial Potato Production see Pest Management Recommendations for Commercial Vegetable and Potato Production 187
Cornell Recommendations for Commercial Tree-Fruit Production see Pest Management Recommendations for Commercial Tree-Fruit Production 187
Cornell Recommendations for Commercial Turfgrass Management. (US) 174
Cornell Recommendations for Commercial Vegetable Production see Pest Management Recommendations for Commercial Vegetable and Potato Production 187
Cornell Recommendations for Field Crops. (US) 174
Cornell Recommendations for Pest Control for Commercial Production and Maintenance of Trees & Shrubs. (US) 174
†Cornell Recommendations to Homeowners for Chemical Control of Biting Flies in New York State. (US) 5173
†Cornell Recommendations to Municipalities for Chemical Control of Biting Flies in New York State. (US) 5173
Cornell Studies in Industrial and Labor Relations. (US ISSN 0070-0053) 976
Cornell University. Cooperative Research Newsletter see Birdscope 562
Cornell University. Department of City and Regional Planning. Regional Science Dissertation and Monograph Series. (US) 2485
Cornell University. Department of City and Regional Planning. Research Reports. (US) 2485
Cornell University. Department of City and Regional Planning. Working Papers in Planning. (US) 2485
Cornell University. Library. John M. Echols Collection on Southeast Asia. Accessions List. (US) 3646
Cornell University. Modern Indonesia Project Publications. Monographs, Translations, Bibliographies see Cornell University. Modern Indonesia Project Publications. Monographs, Translations, Bibliographies, Interim Reports 3636

Cornell University. Modern Indonesia Project Publications. Monographs, Translations, Bibliographies, Interim Reports. (US ISSN 0589-7300) 3636, 398
Cornell University. New York State College of Agriculture and Life Sciences. Biometrics Unit. Annual Report. (US) 464
Cornell University. Program in Urban and Regional Studies. Research Reports see Cornell University. Department of City and Regional Planning. Research Reports 2485
▼Cornell University. Southeast Asia Program. Translation Series. (US) 3636
Cornell University Medical College Alumni Quarterly. (US ISSN 0010-8898) 3091, 1309
Cornell Veterinarian. (US ISSN 0010-8901) 4808
Corner. (DK ISSN 0107-9794) 322
Cornerstone (Ann Arbor). (US) 1704, 4839
Cornerstone (Chicago). (US ISSN 0275-2743) 4172
Cornerstone (Lincoln). (US ISSN 0270-5699) 2403
▼The Cornerstone (New Providence). (US) 4126
Cornerstone Clues. (US) 2148
Cornfield Review. (US ISSN 0363-4574) 2908, 322
Cornhusker Family Physician. (US) 3091
Cornish Archaeology. (UK ISSN 0070-024X) 269
Cornish Banner/Baner Kernewek. (UK ISSN 0306-9079) 1997
Cornish Biological Records. (UK) 435, 1997
Cornish Farmer and Grower. (UK) 85
Cornish Methodist Historical Association Journal. (UK) 4235
Cornish Nation. (UK ISSN 0045-8570) 2357
Cornsilk from DeKalb County, II. (US ISSN 0731-8375) 2148
†Cornucopia Magazine. (NZ ISSN 0113-2644) 5173
Cornucopia Project Newsletter see Regeneration Newsletter 5268
Cornwall Blue Book Guide and County Handbook. (UK) 4758
Corona. (US ISSN 0270-6687) 2908, 3764
▼Coronary Artery Disease. (US ISSN 0954-6928) 3169, 3207
Coronica. (US ISSN 0193-3892) 2810
Coros Chronicle see C O R O S Chronicle 3750
Corpo Clip. (CN ISSN 0843-140X) 2753
Corpoandes see Corporacion de los Andes. Revista 1074
Corporacion Costarricense de Financiamiento Industrial. Memoria Anual. (CR) 1074
Corporacion de Investigaciones Economicas para Latinoamerica Coleccion Estudios see C I E P L A N Coleccion Estudios 849
Corporacion de los Andes. Revista. (VE) 1074
Corporacion Financiera Colombiana. Ejercicio. (CK) 657
Corporacion Hotelera de Colombia. Boletin Informativo. (CK) 2473
Corporate A V (Year). (GW) 1334, 1372
†Corporate Accounting. (US ISSN 0745-5119) 5173
Corporate Accounting International. (IE) 750
Corporate Acquisitions, Mergers and Divestitures. (US) 2708
Corporate Action. (US) 1127
Corporate and Business Law Journal. (AT ISSN 1033-2405) 2708
Corporate & Commercial Aviation see Aviation Today 48
Corporate & Incentive Travel. (US ISSN 0739-1587) 4758
Corporate Annual Report Newsletter. (US) 1334, 2568
Corporate Artnews. (US ISSN 8755-2582) 322

Corporate Aviation Safety Seminar. Proceedings. (US ISSN 0736-4709) 50, 4672
†Corporate Barter & Countertrade. (US) 5173
†Corporate Benefit Plans (Year). (US) 5173
Corporate Board. (US ISSN 0746-8652) 1006
Corporate Brief. (AT) 852, 773
Corporate Capital Transactions Alert see Corporate Capital Transactions Coordinator 750
Corporate Capital Transactions Coordinator. (US) 750, 1091
Corporate Cashflow. (US ISSN 1040-0311) 773, 852
▼Corporate Cashflow Directory. (US ISSN 1040-0311) 773, 852
Corporate Cleveland. (US) 657
†Corporate Commentary. (US) 5173
†Corporate Communications Report. (US ISSN 0010-8952) 5173
Corporate Community Relations Newsletter. (US) 4432, 852
▼Corporate Computing. (US) 826
Corporate Control Alert. (US ISSN 0743-0272) 2708
Corporate Controller. (US) 750
†Corporate Controllers Report. (US ISSN 0274-6107) 5173
Corporate Counsellor. (US) 2708
Corporate Cruise News. (US) 4758
Corporate Design see Today's Facility Manager 2555
Corporate Detroit Magazine. (US) 657
†Corporate Diagrams and Administrative Personnel of the Chemical Industry. (US ISSN 0574-1181) 5173
Corporate Directory see Corporate Directory of US Public Companies 943
Corporate Directory of US Public Companies. (US) 943
Corporate E F T Report. (US ISSN 0272-0299) 773, 805
▼Corporate Elite. (CN) 657
▼Corporate Environmental Data Clearinghouse Reports. (US) 2709, 1984
†Corporate Ethics Monitor. (CN ISSN 0841-1956) 5173
Corporate Examiner. (US ISSN 0361-2309) 657, 773
Corporate Finance. (US ISSN 0894-6817) 773
Corporate Finance. (UK) 773
Corporate Finance Bluebook. (US ISSN 0740-2546) 1127, 773
Corporate Finance Letter. (US) 773
Corporate Finance Sourcebook. (US ISSN 0163-3031) 657
Corporate Financial Letter see The Finance Director 5192
Corporate Financing see Institutional Investor 950
Corporate Financing Week. (US) 773, 943
†Corporate Fitness. (CN ISSN 0892-9319) 5173
Corporate Fitness Buyer's Guide see Corporate Fitness Directory 3800
Corporate Fitness Directory. (US) 3800
▼Corporate Fleet Management. (CN) 1006, 4688
Corporate Foundation Profiles. (US) 4425
†Corporate Fund Raising Directory (Year). (US) 5173
Corporate Giving Directory. (US ISSN 1055-0623) 4403
Corporate Giving Watch. (US ISSN 0747-8003) 4403
Corporate Giving Yellow Pages. (US ISSN 1058-689X) 657
Corporate Governance Bulletin. (US) 2709
Corporate Growth. (US) 657
Corporate Growth Magazine. (US ISSN 0898-8390) 2709, 943
Corporate Headquarters. (US) 1998, 1006
†Corporate Health. (US) 5173
Corporate Jobs Outlook! (US ISSN 0892-5232) 3626, 834
†Corporate Law Locator. (US) 5173

Corporate Legal Letter. (UK ISSN 0141-4852) 2709
Corporate Legal Times. (US) 2709
Corporate Management. (AT ISSN 1034-0408) 1006
Corporate Management Tax Conference.(CN ISSN 0070-0282) 1091
Corporate Meetings & Incentives. (US ISSN 0745-1636) 1006
Corporate Observer. (II) 657
Corporate Officers and Directors Liability Litigation Reporter. (US ISSN 0887-7793) 2709
†Corporate Philanthropy. (US) 5173
▼Corporate Plan Reserve Bank of New Zealand. (NZ ISSN 1170-344X) 1006
Corporate Planning Journal see Local Government Policy Making 4090
Corporate Practice Commentator. (US ISSN 0010-8995) 2709
Corporate Practice Series. (US ISSN 0162-5691) 2709
Corporate Publishing see MicroPublishing Report 4143
Corporate Real Estate Executive. (US ISSN 1042-9115) 4147
Corporate Real Estate Journal see Corporate Real Estate Executive 4147
Corporate Report see Ingram's Magazine 671
Corporate Report Fact Book. (US ISSN 0589-7920) 1127
†Corporate Report Fact Book Wisconsin.(US) 5173
Corporate Report Minnesota. (US) 1006, 773
Corporate Report Who's Who in Upper Midwest Business see Corporate Report Fact Book 1127
Corporate Report Wisconsin. (US) 657
Corporate Responsibility. (US) 657
Corporate Responsibility Monitor. (US ISSN 0742-5406) 1006, 976
†Corporate Restructuring. (US ISSN 0896-775X) 5173
Corporate Restructuring Special Report.(US) 904, 657, 943
Corporate Risk Management. (US ISSN 1046-5626) 943, 1006
Corporate Secretary. (US) 1058
Corporate Secretary's Guide. (US) 1058
Corporate Security. (US ISSN 1040-4201) 1526
Corporate Security Digest. (US ISSN 0894-3826) 1526
Corporate Shareholder. (US) 943
Corporate Software & Solutions (International). (US) 826
†Corporate Sports. (US) 5173
▼Corporate Tax Burden Rises As Profits Fall. (US) 1091
Corporate Taxation. (US) 1091, 750
Corporate Taxation in Latin America see Taxation in Latin America 1110
Corporate Technology Directory. (US ISSN 0887-1930) 4595
†Corporate Television. (US ISSN 0889-4523) 5173
Corporate Travel. (US ISSN 0882-8709) 4758
†Corporate TrendTract. (US) 5173
Corporate Venturing News. (US) 943
†Corporate Video Decisions. (US) 5173
Corporate Yellow Book. (US ISSN 1058-2908) 1006, 657
Corporate 1000 see Corporate Yellow Book 1006
Corporate 1000 Yellow Book see Corporate Yellow Book 1006
Corporate 500: the Directory of Corporate Philanthropy. (US ISSN 0197-937X) 4403, 1127
Corporation des Ingenieurs Forestiers du Quebec. Congres Annuel. Texte des Conferences see Ordre des Ingenieurs Forestiers du Quebec. Congres Annuel. Texte des Conferences 2106
Corporation for Public Broadcasting Report see C P B Report 1370
†Corporation Law Guide. (US) 5173

Corporation Professionnelle des Medecins du Quebec. Annuaire Medical. (CN ISSN 0315-226X) **3091**

Corporation Professionnelle des Medecins du Quebec. Bulletin. (CN ISSN 0315-2979) **3091**

Corporation Records *see* Standard & Poor's Corporation Records **964**

Corporations *see* B A R - B R I Bar Review. Corporations **2706**

Corps Diplomatique et Representants Consulaires et Autres au Canada. *see* Diplomatic Corps and Consular and Other Representatives in Canada **3955**

Corps Ecrit. (FR) **2505**

Corpus Administrative Index. (CN ISSN 0703-7384) **4058**

Corpus Almanac & Canadian Sourcebook. (CN ISSN 0823-1133) **1780**

Corpus Catholicorum. (GW ISSN 0070-0320) **4262**

Corpus Chemical Report *see* Camford Chemical Report **1171**

Corpus Christianorum. Continuatio Mediaevalis. (BE) **4262**

Corpus Christianorum. Series Apocryphorum. (BE) **4262**

Corpus Christianorum. Series Graeca. (BE) **4172**

Corpus Christianorum. Series Latina. (BE) **4262**

Corpus de Mosaicos Romanos de Espana. (SP) **269**

Corpus dei Papiri Filosofici Greci e Latini. Studi e Testi. (IT) **1276**, **3764**

Corpus der Byzantinischen Miniaturenhandschriften (C B M). (GW) **1276**

Corpus des Luthistes Francais. (FR) **2357**

Corpus Hispanorum de Pace. (SP ISSN 0589-8056) **2403**

Corpus Medicorum Graecorum. (GW ISSN 0070-0347) **3091**

Corpus Mensurabilis Musicae. (GW ISSN 0070-0363) **3547**

Corpus Musicae Popularis Hungaricae. *see* Regi Magyar Dallamok Tara **3577**

Corpus Occupational Health and Safety Management Handbook. (CN) **3616**, 1007

Corpus of Early Keyboard Music. (GW) **3547**

Corpus Philosophorum Medii Aevi. Serie I. Subsidia. (IT) **3764**

Corpus Philosophorum Medii Aevi. Serie II. Testi e Studi. (IT) **3764**

Corpus Sacrae Scripturae Neerlandicae Medii Aevii. (NE) **2908**

Corpus Scriptorum Christianorum Orientalium: Aethiopica. (BE ISSN 0070-0398) **4281**, 3636

Corpus Scriptorum Christianorum Orientalium: Arabica. (BE ISSN 0070-0401) **4281**, 3636

Corpus Scriptorum Christianorum Orientalium: Armeniaca. (BE ISSN 0070-041X) **4281**, 3636

Corpus Scriptorum Christianorum Orientalium: Coptica. (BE ISSN 0070-0428) **4281**, 3636

Corpus Scriptorum Christianorum Orientalium: Iberica. (BE ISSN 0070-0436) **4281**, 3636

Corpus Scriptorum Christianorum Orientalium: Subsidia. (BE ISSN 0070-0444) **4281**, 3636

Corpus Scriptorum Christianorum Orientalium: Syriaca. (BE ISSN 0070-0452) **4281**, 3636

Corpus Scriptorum de Musica. (GW ISSN 0070-0460) **3547**

Corpus Vasorum Antiquorum. Italia. (IT ISSN 0070-0479) **3523**

Corpus Vasorum Antiquorum (Netherlands). (NE) **3523**, 1276

†Corpus Vexillorum Mundi. (US) **5173**

Corpus Vitrearum. (FR) **2357**

Corpus Vitrearum Medii Aevi. (GW ISSN 0232-1459) **322**, 2309, 2357

Corral Dust. (US) **2309**, 3523

Correct Craft Tribune *see* Nautique News **4527**

▼Correctional Foodservice Magazine. (US) **2064**, 1512

Correctional Industries Association Newsletter. (US) **4058**, 1007, 4403

Corrections Compendium. (US ISSN 0738-8144) **1512**

Corrections Digest. (US ISSN 0010-9045) **1512**

Corrections Today. (US ISSN 0190-2563) **1512**

Corrective and Social Psychiatry and Journal of Behavioral Technology Methods and Therapy. (US ISSN 0093-1551) **4017**, 3334

Correio Agricola (Brazil). (BL) **174**

Correio Agricola (Portugal). (Portuguese translation of: Pflanzenschutz Kurier) (PO) **174**

Correio da Unesco. (BL) **1623**

Correio de Varsovia *see* Warsaw Newsletter **5302**

Correio Portugues. (CN ISSN 0045-8643) **1998**

Correio Portugues. (AT) **1998**

Correios e Telecomunicacoes de Portugal. Anuario Estatistico. (PO) **1334**, 1352

Correios e Telecomunicacoes de Portugal. Boletim Oficial. (PO) **1362**

Correlation. (UK ISSN 0260-8790) **358**

Correo de Arte Hispano. (SP) **322**

Correo de la O I P *see* I O J Newsletter **2570**

Correo de Varsovia *see* Warsaw Newsletter **5302**

Correo del Arte. (SP) **322**

Correo del Sur. (MX ISSN 0010-910X) **2210**

Correo Economico. (MX ISSN 0010-9118) **852**

Correo Editorial. (CK ISSN 0121-1390) **4126**, 4140

El Correo Fronterizo. (MX ISSN 0186-5757) **2245**, 2403

Correo Latinoamericano. (CN) **1998**

Correre. (IT) **3800**

Correre dell'Autoriparatore. (IT) **4688**

Correspondance de la Presse. (FR) **2568**

Correspondance de la Publicite. (FR) **30**

Correspondance Economique. (FR) **657**

Correspondance Municipale *see* Territoires - Correspondance Municipale **4095**

Correspondence Chess. (UK) **4470**

Correspondence Educational Directory. (US) **1623**

Correspondence Society of Surgeons. Collected Letters. (US ISSN 0162-6477) **3378**

Correspondent (Appleton). (US ISSN 0364-1066) **2530**, 1297

▼Correspondent (Topeka). (US) **773**

Corresponsal Internacional Agricola *see* International Fertilizer Correspondant **181**

Correze Magazine. (FR) **2186**, 4758

Corridor Real Estate Journal. (US ISSN 1048-7948) **4147**

Corridors. (IT) **2991**

Corriere A V I S. (Associazione Volontari Italiani del Sangue (Turin)) (IT) **4099**

Corriere Africano. (IT ISSN 0589-8366) **2862**

Corriere Canadese/Canadian Courier. (CN ISSN 0045-866X) **1998**

Corriere d'Italia. (GW ISSN 0010-924X) **1998**, 2188

Corriere dei Ciechi. (IT ISSN 0010-9169) **2292**

Corriere dei Costruttori. (IT) **614**

Corriere dei Laringectomizzati. (IT) **4403**, 3314

Corriere dei Piccoli. (IT ISSN 0010-9185) **1252**

Corriere dei Trasporti. (IT ISSN 0010-9193) **4726**

Corriere del Commercio. (IT) **813**

Corriere del Farmacista. (IT ISSN 0010-9207) **3721**

Corriere del Mezzogiorno. (IT) **3882**, 323, 4306, 4758

Corriere dell'Adda. (IT) **3882**

Corriere della Pesca e dell'Aquacoltura. (IT) **2039**

Corriere della Sibaritide. (IT) **2205**

Corriere di Caracas. (VE ISSN 0010-9231) **1998**

Corriere di Roma. (IT) **85**

Corriere di Trecate. (IT) **2205**

Corriere Fitopatologico. (IT ISSN 0010-9258) **530**, 500

Corriere Stenografico. (IT ISSN 0010-9290) **1058**

Corriere Tributario. (IT) **657**

Corriere Unesco. (UN) **237**, 2309

Corriere Vinicolo. (IT) **380**

Corrispondenza Meridionale. (IT) **2862**

Corrispondenza Socialista. (IT ISSN 0010-9304) **3882**

Corrispondenze Letterarie, Scientifiche ed Erudite dal Rinascimento all'Eta Moderna. (IT) **2505**

Corrosion. (US ISSN 0010-9312) **1928**, 3404

Corrosion Abstracts. (US ISSN 0010-9339) **1842**, 9, 3425

Corrosion and Coatings. (SA ISSN 0377-8711) **3653**, 3404

Corrosion and Coatings Buyer's Guide. (SA) **3653**

Corrosion Australasia. (AT) **1212**

Corrosion Control Abstracts. (English translation of: Referativnyi Zhurnal. Korroziya i Zashchita ot Korrozii) (UK ISSN 0010-9347) **3425**, 9

Corrosion Engineering. (English translation of: Zairyo to Kankyo) (US ISSN 0892-4228) **3404**, 1212

†Corrosion Engineer's Source Book. (US) **5173**

†Corrosion Monograph Series. (US) **5173**

Corrosion Prevention and Control. (UK ISSN 0010-9371) **3404**, 4596

Corrosion Prevention - Inhibition Digest. (US ISSN 0364-3301) **3404**

Corrosion Reviews. (UK) **3404**

Corrosion Science. (US ISSN 0010-938X) **3405**

Corrosion Technology *see* Anti-Corrosion Methods and Materials **3402**

Corrosion y Proteccion *see* Revista Iberoamericana de Corrosion y Proteccion **3418**

Corrugated Containers Conference (Year). (US ISSN 1058-0883) **3648**, 3662

Corruption and Reform. (NE ISSN 0169-7528) **2616**

Corsa. (AG) **4688**

Corset de France *see* Dessous Mode International **1284**

Corseteria y Lenceria Moda Intima *see* C y L Moda Intima **1284**

Corsi Internazionali di Cultura sull'Arte Ravennate e Bizantina. Atti. (IT) **323**, 269

Corso di Sociologia. (IT) **4432**

Corsonat. (II) **1486**, 1542

Corstorphine Journal. (US) **2148**

Cort. (SP) **2217**

Cortex. (IT ISSN 0010-9452) **3334**

Cortina. (IT) **2205**

Cortison Spiegel. (GW ISSN 0933-002X) **3251**

Cortlandt Forum. (US ISSN 1048-5791) **3091**

Corvallis Streets Poetry Magazine. (US) **2991**

Corvette - Chevy Buyer's Guide *see* Chevy - Corvette Buyer's Guide **4687**

Corvette Fever. (US ISSN 0195-1661) **4688**

Corvette Illustrated. (US) **4688**

Corvette Quarterly. (US ISSN 0897-4179) **4688**

An Cosantoir. (IE) **3454**

Cosas. (CL) **3953**

Coscienza. (IT) **4262**

Coscienza del Cittadino. (IT) **3882**

Coscienza del Tempo. (IT) **2505**

Cosmatom. (UK ISSN 0143-926X) **3816**

Cosmesi. (IT) **375**

Cosmetech *see* For Formulation Chemists Only **375**

Cosmetic Dentistry for G Ps *see* G P **3233**

Cosmetic Dermatology. (US) **3246**

Cosmetic Insider's Report. (US ISSN 0275-4681) **375**

Cosmetic Science and Technology Series. (US) **3091**, 375

Cosmetic World. (US ISSN 0589-8447) **372**

Cosmetic World News. (UK ISSN 0305-0319) **375**

Cosmetics and Toiletries. (US ISSN 0361-4387) **375**

Cosmetics & Toiletries & Household Products Marketing News in Japan. (UK) **1036**

Cosmetics International. (UK) **375**

Cosmetics International Directory *see* C I Directory **375**

Cosmetics International New Products Review *see* C I New Products Review **375**

Cosmetics: Latin American Industrial Report. (US) **372**

Cosmic-Ray Intensity. (JA) **371**

Cosmic Research. (English translation of: Kosmicheskie Issledovaniya) (US ISSN 0010-9525) **1818**, 363

†Cosmic Science Research Center. Newsletter. (US) **5173**

Cosmic Voice. (US) **3594**, 3669

Cosmo Man. (UK) **2193**

Cosmopolitan. (US ISSN 0010-9541) **4839**

Cosmopolitan. (NE) **4839**

Cosmopolitan. (GR) **4839**

Cosmopolitan (Australia). (AT ISSN 0310-2076) **2171**

Cosmopolitan (British Edition). (UK ISSN 0141-0555) **2193**

Cosmopolitan (France). (FR) **4839**

Cosmopolitan (Germany). (GW) **4840**, 1290

Cosmopolitan (Italy). (IT) **4840**

Cosmopolitan (Japan). (JA) **4840**, 1290

Cosmopolitan (South Africa). (SA) **4840**, 1290

Cosmopolitan Contact. (US ISSN 0010-955X) **3953**

Cosmopolitan en Espanol. (US) **4840**

Cosmopolitan Nova. (BL) **4840**

†Cosmopolitan's Beauty Guide. (US) **5173**

†Cosmopolitan's Super Diet & Exercise Guide. (US) **5173**

Cosmorama. (IT ISSN 0045-8716) **4758**

Cosmorama Pictorial. (HK ISSN 0010-9568) **2197**

Cosmos. (UK ISSN 0010-9576) **3010**

Cosmos tou Tennis/World of Tennis. (GR) **4502**, 4470

Cosmos Weekly. (HK) **1372**

Cossor News. (UK) **1765**

Cost Accounting Standards Guide. (US) **750**

Cost and Production Survey Report. (US ISSN 0196-2434) **3091**, 4569

Cost and Quality of Fuels for Electric Utilities (F E R C 423). (US) **1798**, 1801

Cost Control News. (US) **773**

Cost Data for Landscape Construction. (US ISSN 0271-2067) **1864**

Cost Engineer. (UK ISSN 0010-9606) **1007**

Cost Engineering (Morgantown, 1980). (US ISSN 0274-9696) **1818**

Cost Engineering Series. (US) **1852**

Cost Engineers' Notebook. (US) **1818**, 750

Cost Management Update. (US) **1091**

Cost of Doing Business - Corporations. (US) **852**

Cost of Doing Business for Retail Sporting Goods Stores. (US ISSN 0736-0703) **834**, 4470

Cost of Doing Business - Partnerships & Proprietorships. (US) **852**

Cost of Health Care in the Netherlands. *see* Kosten en Financiering van de Gezondheidzorg in Nederland **4107**

Cost of Personal Borrowing in the United States. (US ISSN 0091-3855) **773**

Cost of Picking and Hauling Florida Citrus Fruits. (US ISSN 0093-6553) **149**, 2064

Cost of Social Security. (UN ISSN 0538-8295) **4403**
Cost Reduction Digest *see* Value Engineering and Management Digest - Defense Contract Guide **1030**
Costa Rica. Archivo Nacional. Revista. (CR ISSN 0034-9003) **2309, 2245**
†Costa Rica. Centro de Informacion Estadistica. Anuario Estatistico. (CR) **5173**
Costa Rica. Direccion General de Estadistica y Censos. Encuesta de Hogares, Empleo y Desempleo: Area Metropolitana de San Jose. (CR) **711**
Costa Rica. Direccion General de Estadistica y Censos. Inventario de las Estadisticas Nacionales. (CR ISSN 0589-8544) **4569**
Costa Rica. Direccion General de la Tributacion Directa. Estadistica Demografia Fiscal del Impuesto Sobre la Renta. Periodos. (CR) **1091**
†Costa Rica. Instituto Geografico Nacional. Informe Semestral. (CR ISSN 0045-8740) **5173**
Costa Rica. Ministerio de Hacienda Oficina del Presupuesto. Informe. (CR ISSN 0070-0576) **1091**
Costa Rica. Ministerio de Obras Publicas y Transportes. Memorias. (CR) **4718**
Costa Rican Beacon. (CR) **943**
Costa Smeralda Magazine. (IT) **4758**
CostaGolf. (SP) **4502**
Costal Bend Council of Governments. State of the Region *see* Coastal Bend Council of Governments. Monthly Update **2485**
Costantinian. (CH) **4262**
Costarossa. (IT) **3882**
Costerus. (US ISSN 0165-9618) **2810, 2908**
Costruire. (IT) **614**
Costruire in Acciaio. *see* Bauen in Stahl **295**
Costruire in Laterizio. (IT ISSN 0394-1590) **614**
Costruire per Abitare *see* Costruire **614**
Costruttori Italiani nel Mondo. (IT ISSN 0589-8765) **614**
Costruttori Romani. (IT ISSN 0010-9657) **614**
Costruzioni. (IT ISSN 0010-9665) **1864, 614, 4726**
Costruzioni Metalliche. (IT ISSN 0010-9673) **1864, 614**
Costume. (UK ISSN 0590-8876) **1290, 2357**
Costume Jewelry Review. (US) **2563**
Costume Society of America Bibliography. (US) **1288, 398**
Costume Society of America News *see* C S A News **1289**
Costume Society of America Newsletter *see* C S A News **1289**
Costume Society of Ontario. Newsletter. (CN ISSN 0834-2520) **1290, 2053**
Cote d'Azur Agricole et Horticole *see* Cultiver en Provence Cote d'Azur **5175**
Cote d'Ivoire en Chiffres. (SG) **2332**
Cote-d'Ivoire Selection. (FR ISSN 0221-5780) **904**
Cote des Arts. (FR ISSN 0152-3791) **323**
Cote Inter-Europe du Bateau d'Occasion.(FR) **4524**
Coteau Heritage. (US) **2403**
Cotistics Bi-annual Cotton Statistical Bulletin. (PK) **4617**
Cotistics Quarterly Cotton Statistical Bulletin *see* Cotistics Bi-annual Cotton Statistical Bulletin **4617**
Coton et Fibres Tropicales. (FR ISSN 0010-9711) **85, 174**
Coton et Fibres Tropicales. Bulletin Bibliografique *see* Coton et Fibres Tropicales **85**
Cotswold Life. (UK ISSN 0010-9746) **2193**
Cottage Cheese *see* Cherith **4839**
Cottage Connection. (US) **1114**
Cottage Connections. (US) **4840**
Cottage Garden Society. Newsletter. (UK) **2124**

Cottage Life. (CN ISSN 0838-2395) **2176**
Cotton. Part 1: Bi-monthly Review of the World Situation. (US) **4617, 85**
Cotton. Part 1: Monthly Review of the World Situation *see* Cotton. Part 1: Bi-monthly Review of the World Situation **4617**
Cotton. Part 2: World Statistics. (US) **4628, 136, 4617**
Cotton and Allied Textile Industries *see* International Textile Manufacturing **4620**
Cotton and Tropical Fibres. (UK ISSN 0961-3528) **136, 9**
Cotton and Tropical Fibres Abstracts *see* Cotton and Tropical Fibres **136**
Cotton Corporation of India. Annual Report. (II ISSN 0304-6907) **149**
†Cotton Development. (II ISSN 0045-8759) **5173**
Cotton Digest *see* Cotton Digest International **4617**
Cotton Digest International. (US) **4617, 85**
Cotton Farming. (US ISSN 0574-2323) **174**
Cotton Gin and Oil Mill Press. (US ISSN 0010-9800) **4617**
†Cotton Ginnings by States. (US) **5173**
Cotton Grower. (US ISSN 0194-9772) **174**
Cotton International. (US ISSN 0070-0673) **4617**
Cotton Lint and Seed Marketing Board. Annual Report and Accounts. (KE) **174**
Cotton Outlook. (UK) **4617**
†Cotton Statistics Monthly/Menka Tokei Geppo. (JA ISSN 0574-2374) **5173**
Cottonboll. (US ISSN 0196-8238) **2753**
Cottonwood. (US) **2908**
Cottonwood Monthly. (US) **1747**
Cottonwood Review *see* Cottonwood **2908**
Coulee Continue. (CN ISSN 0712-4724) **3616, 1064, 3405, 4596**
Coulicou. (CN ISSN 0822-7098) **1252**
Coulicou. (FR) **1252**
Coulisse Diplomatique *see* Flash Actualite **3894**
Council and Community. (AT ISSN 0728-5582) **4086**
Council Columns. (US) **4403**
†Council Connection. (US) **5173**
Council for a Livable World. Newsletter. (US) **3454, 1785, 1804, 1946**
Council for Adult and Experiential Learning News *see* C A E L News **1682**
Council for Agricultural Science and Technology. Special Publications. (US ISSN 0194-407X) **85, 2064**
Council for Agricultural Science and Technology. Task Force Reports. (US ISSN 0194-4088) **85, 2064**
Council for Alcohol - Drug Education of N.J. News *see* C A - D E News **1535**
Council for Basic Education. Occasional Papers. (US ISSN 0070-069X) **1623**
Council for British Archaeology. Churches Committee. Bulletin. (UK) **269, 297**
Council for British Archaeology. Newsletter and Calendar of Excavations *see* British Archaeological News **267**
Council for British Archaeology Annual Report *see* C B A Annual Report **268**
Council for Children with Behavioral Disorders Newsletter *see* C C B D Newsletter **1734**
Council for Court Excellence Annual Report. (US) **2616**
Council for Disability Rights Reports *see* C D R Reports **3940**
Council for Exceptional Children Newsletter *see* C E C - M R Newsletter **1734**

Council for Higher Education. Planning and Budgeting Committee. Annual Report. (IS) **1704**
Council for Higher Education. Planning and Grants Committee. Annual Report *see* Council for Higher Education. Planning and Budgeting Committee. Annual Report **1704**
Council for Mineral Technology (MINTEK). Special Publication *see* Mintek. Special Publications **3491**
Council for Mutual Economic Assistance Data *see* C O M E C O N Data **902**
Council for Mutual Economic Assistance Foreign Trade Data *see* C O M E C O N Foreign Trade Data **902**
Council for Periodical Distributors Associations News *see* C P D A News **4124**
Council for Research in Music Education. Bulletin. (US ISSN 0010-9894) **3547, 1623**
Council for Scientific and Industrial Research Handbook *see* C S I R Handbook **4303**
Council for Scientific and Industrial Research Publications *see* C S I R Publications **5157**
Council for the Defence of Government Schools Newsletter *see* D O G S Newsletter **1726**
Council for the Protection of Rural England. Quarterly Bulletin *see* Countryside Campaigner **1486**
Council for the Social Sciences in East Africa. Social Science Conference. Proceedings. (TZ) **4369**
Council for Tobacco Research, U.S.A. Report. (US ISSN 0361-1612) **3091, 1535, 4643**
Council for World Mission Report *see* C W M Report **4232**
†Council Notes. (US ISSN 0146-1117) **5173**
Council of American Building Officials. One and Two Family Dwelling Code. (US) **614**
Council of Better Business Bureaus. Annual Report *see* Council of Better Business Bureaus. Business Advisory Series **1504**
Council of Better Business Bureaus. Business Advisory Series. (US) **1504**
Council of Biology Editors Inc. Views *see* C B E Views **4124**
Council of Churches in Namibia Information *see* C C N Information **4232**
Council of Community Blood Centers Newsletter *see* C C B C Newsletter **3271**
Council of Europe. Central Library. Biblio Bulletin. Series: Legal Affaires *see* Council of Europe. Documentation Section. Biblio Bulletin. Series: Legal Affairs **2698**
Council of Europe. Central Library. Biblio Bulletin. Series: Political and Social Affairs *see* Council of Europe. Documentation Section. Biblio Bulletin. Series: Political, Economic and Social Affairs **3937**
†Council of Europe. Centre Naturopa. Documentation Series. (FR) **5174**
Council of Europe. Centre Naturopa. Newsletter. (FR) **1486**
Council of Europe. Committee of Independent Experts on the European Social Charter. Conclusions. (FR) **4403, 3953**
Council of Europe. Consultative Assembly. Texts Adopted by the Assembly *see* Council of Europe. Parliamentary Assembly. Texts Adopted by the Assembly **2722**
Council of Europe. Directorate of Legal Affairs. Information Bulletin on Legislative Activities. (FR ISSN 0252-0877) **2616**
Council of Europe. Directorate of Legal Affairs. Newsletter on Legislative Activities *see* Council of Europe. Directorate of Legal Affairs. Information Bulletin on Legislative Activities **2616**

Council of Europe. Documentation and Information Centre for the Environment and Nature. Documentation Series *see* Council of Europe. Centre Naturopa. Documentation Series **5174**
Council of Europe. Documentation and Information Centre for the Environment and Nature. Newsletter *see* Council of Europe. Centre Naturopa. Newsletter **1486**
Council of Europe. Documentation Centre for Education in Europe. Newsletter. (FR ISSN 0252-0591) **1623**
Council of Europe. Documentation Section. Biblio Bulletin. Series: East - West Relations. (FR) **3937**
Council of Europe. Documentation Section. Biblio Bulletin. Series: Legal Affairs. (FR) **2698**
Council of Europe. Documentation Section. Biblio Bulletin. Series: Political, Economic and Social Affairs.(FR) **3937, 711**
Council of Europe. European Treaty Series. (FR ISSN 0070-105X) **2722**
Council of Europe. Parliamentary Assembly. Documents: Working Papers. (FR ISSN 0252-0656) **2722**
Council of Europe. Parliamentary Assembly. Official Report of Debates.(FR ISSN 0252-0664) **2722**
Council of Europe. Parliamentary Assembly. Orders of the Day, Minutes of Proceedings. (FR ISSN 0377-1962) **2722**
Council of Europe. Parliamentary Assembly. Texts Adopted by the Assembly. (FR ISSN 0377-6093) **2722**
Council of Europe. Standing Committee on the European Convention on Establishment (Individuals). Periodical Report. (FR) **3941**
Council of Europe. Steering Committee on Regional and Municipal Matters. Study Series: Local and Regional Authorities in Europe *see* Council of Europe. Study Series: Local and Regional Authorities in Europe **4086**
Council of Europe. Study Series: Local and Regional Authorities in Europe. (FR) **4086**
Council of Europe. Symposium on Legal Processing. Proceedings. (FR) **2705**
Council of Europe Forum. (FR ISSN 0252-0958) **3882**
Council of Exceptional Children. Division for Early Childhood. Journal *see* Journal of Early Intervention **1737**
Council of Forest Industries of British Columbia. Newsletter. (CN) **2098**
Council of Graduate Schools in the United States. Proceedings of the Annual Meeting. (US ISSN 0070-1076) **1704**
Council of Jewish Federations, Inc. Annual Report *see* C J F Annual Report **4400**
Council of Jewish Federations, Inc. Endowment Review *see* C J F Endowment Review **4400**
Council of Justice to Animals and Humane Slaughter Association Annual Report and Accounts *see* C J A and H S A Annual Report and Accounts **230**
Council of Justice to Animals and Humane Slaughter Association Newsletter *see* C J A and H S A Newsletter **230**
Council of Literary Magazines and Presses Newsletter *see* C L M P Newsletter **4124**
Council of Logistics Management Annual Conference Proceedings. (US) **1036**
Council of Ontario Universities. Research Division. Application Statistics. (CN ISSN 0382-912X) **1675**
†Council of Ontario Universities Quadrennial Review. (CN) **5174**

Council of Ontario Universities Triennial Review *see* Council of Ontario Universities Quadrennial Review **5174**
Council of Planning Librarians Bibliographies *see* C P L Bibliographies **2499**
Council of Planning Librarians Newsletter *see* C P L Newsletter **2484**
Council of Polytechnic Librarians. Annual Statistics. (UK) **2793**
Council of Societies for the Study of Religion Bulletin *see* C S S R Bulletin **4167**
Council of State Governments. Suggested State Legislation *see* Suggested State Legislation **4075**
Council of State Governments Backgrounder *see* C S G Backgrounder **5157**
Council of Supervisors and Administrators of the City of New York News *see* C S A News **1725**
Council of the European Communities. Review of the Council's Work. (EI) **852**
Council of the Mystic Arts. Newsletter. (US) **4281**
Council on Abandoned Military Posts. Periodical *see* Council on America's Military Past. Periodical **2404**
Council on America's Military Past. Periodical. (US ISSN 0010-9967) **2404**, **3454**
Council on Career Development for Minorities, Inc. Minority Student Recruitment Guide *see* C C D M Minority Student Recruitment Guide **1701**
Council on Consumer Information. Proceedings of Annual Conference *see* American Council on Consumer Interests. Proceedings of the Annual Conference **1502**
Council on Economic Priorities Reports and C E P Books *see* C E P Reports and C E P Books **1502**
Council on Economic Priorities Research Report *see* C E P Research Report **1502**
Council on Foreign Relations. Annual Report. (US ISSN 0192-236X) **3953**
Council on Foundations. Annual Report. (US) **4403**
Council on Governmental Ethics Laws Guardian *see* C O G E L Guardian **2608**
Council on Hemispheric Affairs News and Analysis. (US) **927**, **3954**
Council on International Nontheatrical Events. Yearbook. (US) **3506**
Council on Library - Media Technical Assistants. Newsletter. (US) **2753**
Council on Library Resources Annual Report. (US) **2753**
Council on Library Resources, Inc. Reports *see* C L R Reports **2750**
Council on Licensure, Enforcement & Regulation Exam Review *see* C L E A R Exam Review **4099**
Council on National Literatures World Report *see* C N L - World Report **2901**
†Council on Outdoor Education. Newsletter. (US) **5174**
Council on Tall Buildings and Urban Habitat. Collected Papers. (US) **2486**, 614
Council on Tall Buildings and Urban Habitat. Proceedings. (US) **2486**, 614
Council on Technology Teacher Education. Yearbook. (US) **1623**
Council on Undergraduate Research Newsletter. (US ISSN 0890-8273) **1704**
Council Review *see* American Council of Life Insurance. Council Review **2526**
Council Spotlight Booknotes. (US) **398**, **3954**
Councilor. (US ISSN 0010-9991) **3941**
Councils, Committees and Boards. (UK ISSN 0070-1211) **4058**
Counsel. (US) **30**, 1036

Counseling and Human Development. (US ISSN 0193-7375) **1623**, 1235
Counseling and Values. (US ISSN 0160-7960) **4262**, 1735, 4403
The Counseling Psychologist. (US ISSN 0011-0000) **4017**
Counselling Psychology Quarterly. (UK ISSN 0951-5070) **4018**, 3334
Counsellor. (AT) **2582**
Counsellor of Basotho. *see* Moeletsi Oa Basotho **4269**
Counselor. *see* Al-Mushir **4191**
Counselor *see* Delaware Valley Counselor **5178**
Counselor (Arlington). (US) **1535**
Counselor (Langhorne). (US ISSN 0011-0027) **30**
Counselor (Wheaton). (US) **1252**, **4172**
Counselor Education and Supervision. (US ISSN 0011-0035) **1623**, **4018**
Counselor Education Directory: Personnel and Programs *see* Counselor Preparation (Year) **1623**
Counselor Preparation (Year). (US ISSN 0271-5368) **1623**
Countdown. (US ISSN 0746-8830) **50**
Countdown. (CN ISSN 0383-6436) **2862**
Countdown Magazine. (UK) **2193**
Countdown Today *see* Countdown Magazine **2193**
Counter-Terrorism and Security Intelligence *see* Security Intelligence Report **3924**
Counterman. (US) **4688**
Counterplay. (CN ISSN 0832-0136) **4470**
Counterpoint. (AT) **1885**
Counterterrorism and Security *see* International Counterterrorism & Security **1526**
†Countertrade & Barter. (US ISSN 0951-7588) **5174**
Countertrade Outlook. (US) **943**, 904
Countertrends Update - Eastern Europe *see* Eastern European Finance Update **777**
Countries in Crisis. (US) **3954**, 852
Countries of the World and Their Leaders Yearbook. (US ISSN 0196-2809) **3882**
Country. (GW) **2549**
Country (Greendale). (US ISSN 0895-0377) **2223**
Country Accents. (US) **2557**, 2445
Country Almanac. (US) **2445**, 2549, 2557
Country America. (US) **3547**, 2224
▼Country and Distance Rider. (UK) **4533**
Country and Western Roundabout. (UK ISSN 0011-0094) **3547**
Country Canada. (CN) **2281**
Country Chronicle. (US) **85**
†Country Churchman. (UK ISSN 0011-0124) **5174**
Country Club. (US) **4502**
Country Crazy. (US) **3547**
Country Crier. (US) **2271**
Country Dance and Song. (US ISSN 0070-1262) **1529**, 2053, 3547
Country Dance & Song Society News. (US) **1529**
Country Dance Lines. (US) **1529**
Country Dancer *see* Country Dance and Song **1529**
Country Database *see* Country Forecasts **3883**
Country Decorating Ideas. (US) **2549**, 2445, 2557
The Country Decorator. (US) **2549**
Country Folk Art Magazine. (US) **354**
Country Folks. (US) **85**
Country Forecasts. (US ISSN 1041-3553) **3883**, 773, 904, 943
Country Gardens. (US) **2124**
Country Gentleman. (US ISSN 0147-4928) **2224**
Country Guide. (CN ISSN 0383-7114) **85**
Country Handcrafts. (US ISSN 0745-3116) **354**
Country Heritage. (US ISSN 0733-8759) **3547**

Country Home. (US ISSN 0737-3740) **2549**, 2445, 2557
Country Homes & Interiors. (UK ISSN 0951-3019) **2549**, 257, 2445, 4758
Country Inns, Bed & Breakfast. (US ISSN 0898-560X) **4758**
Country Journal. (US) **2224**
Country Kitchens. (US) **2550**
Country Lady's Daybook *see* Country Lady's Daybook - Country Classified **4432**
Country Lady's Daybook - Country Classified. (US) **4432**
Country Landowner. (UK ISSN 0011-0159) **4147**
Country Life *see* National Country Life **108**
Country Life. (UK ISSN 0045-8856) **2193**
Country Life in British Columbia. (CN ISSN 0011-0183) **85**
Country Living (Columbus). (US ISSN 0747-0592) **830**, 1885
Country Living (Covington). (US ISSN 0011-0205) **85**
Country Living (New York). (US ISSN 0732-2569) **2550**
Country Living (Owego). (US ISSN 0011-0191) **1486**, 2124
†Country Living Dream Homes. (US) **5174**
Country Living Remodeling. (US) **2550**
Country Music News. (CN ISSN 0714-8356) **3548**
Country Music Newsletter. (AT) **3548**
Country Music People. (UK ISSN 0591-2237) **3548**
Country Music Round up. (UK ISSN 0140-5721) **3548**
Country Music Sourcebook. (US ISSN 0273-1428) **3548**
Country Profile. Algeria. (UK ISSN 0269-6053) **3883**, 852
Country Profile. Angola, Sao Tome & Principe. (UK ISSN 0269-7092) **3883**, 852, 890
Country Profile. Argentina. (UK ISSN 0269-4468) **3883**, 852, 890
Country Profile. Australia. (UK ISSN 0269-4476) **3883**, 852, 890
Country Profile. Austria. (UK ISSN 0269-4484) **3883**, 852, 890
Country Profile. Bahrain, Qatar. (UK ISSN 0269-7335) **3883**, 852, 890
Country Profile. Bangladesh. (UK ISSN 0269-8145) **3883**, 852, 890
Country Profile. Belgium, Luxembourg. (UK ISSN 0269-4352) **3883**, 852, 890
Country Profile. Belize, Bahamas, Bermuda. (UK ISSN 0269-4514) **3883**, 852, 890
Country Profile. Bolivia. (UK ISSN 0269-5952) **3883**, 852, 890
Country Profile. Botswana, Lesotho, Swaziland. (UK ISSN 0269-7394) **3883**, 852, 890
Country Profile. Brazil. (UK ISSN 0269-4492) **3883**, 852, 890
Country Profile. Bulgaria, Albania. (UK ISSN 0269-6398) **3883**, 852, 890
Country Profile. Cameroon, Central African Republic, Chad. (UK ISSN 0269-7963) **3883**, 852, 890
Country Profile. Canada. (UK ISSN 0269-4379) **3883**, 852, 890
Country Profile. Chile. (UK ISSN 0269-5081) **3883**, 852, 890
Country Profile. China, North Korea. (UK ISSN 0269-509X) **3883**, 852, 890
Country Profile. Colombia. (UK ISSN 0269-5103) **3883**, 852, 890
Country Profile. Commonwealth of Independent States. (UK) **3883**, 852, 890
Country Profile. Congo. (UK ISSN 0269-6363) **3883**, 852, 890
Country Profile. Cote d'Ivoire. (UK ISSN 0269-7068) **3883**, 852, 890
Country Profile. Cuba. (UK ISSN 0269-5111) **3883**, 852, 890
Country Profile. Czechoslovakia. (UK ISSN 0269-8048) **3883**, 852, 890

COUNTRY PROFILE 6089

Country Profile. Denmark, Iceland. (UK ISSN 0269-5138) **3883**, 852, 890
Country Profile. Dominican Republic, Haiti, Puerto Rico. (UK ISSN 0269-512X) **3884**, 852, 890
Country Profile. Ecuador. (UK ISSN 0269-7971) **3884**, 852, 890
Country Profile. Egypt. (UK ISSN 0269-5227) **3884**, 852, 890
Country Profile. Ethiopia, Somalia, Djibouti. (UK ISSN 0269-7084) **3884**, 852, 890
Country Profile. Finland. (UK ISSN 0269-5332) **3884**, 852, 890
Country Profile. France. (UK ISSN 0269-5340) **3884**, 852, 890
Country Profile. Gabon, Equatorial Guinea. (UK ISSN 0269-6371) **3884**, 852, 890
Country Profile. Germany. (UK ISSN 0264-4495) **3884**, 852, 890
Country Profile. Ghana. (UK ISSN 0269-4549) **3884**, 852, 890
Country Profile. Greece. (UK ISSN 0269-5367) **3884**, 852, 890
Country Profile. Guatemala, El Salvador, Honduras. (UK ISSN 0269-4387) **3884**, 852, 890
Country Profile. Guinea, Mali, Mauritania. (UK ISSN 0269-4417) **3884**, 852, 890
Country Profile. Guyana, Barbados, Windward & Leeward Islands. (UK ISSN 0269-8110) **3884**, 852, 890
Country Profile. Hong Kong, Macau. (UK ISSN 0269-7319) **3884**, 852, 890
Country Profile. Hungary. (UK) **3884**, 852, 890
Country Profile. India, Nepal. (UK ISSN 0269-5359) **3884**, 852, 890
Country Profile. Indochina: Vietnam, Laos, Cambodia. (UK ISSN 0269-6622) **3884**, 852, 890
Country Profile. Indonesia. (UK ISSN 0269-5375) **3884**, 852, 890
Country Profile. Iran. (UK ISSN 0269-5960) **3884**, 852, 890
Country Profile. Iraq. (UK ISSN 0269-4395) **3884**, 852, 890
Country Profile. Ireland. (UK ISSN 0269-5324) **3884**, 852, 890
Country Profile. Israel. (UK ISSN 0269-5383) **3884**, 852, 890
Country Profile. Italy. (UK ISSN 0269-5391) **3884**, 852, 890
Country Profile. Jamaica. (UK ISSN 0269-4506) **3884**, 852, 890
Country Profile. Japan. (UK ISSN 0269-5405) **3884**, 852, 890
Country Profile. Jordan. (UK ISSN 0269-8072) **3885**, 852, 890
Country Profile. Kenya. (UK ISSN 0269-4530) **3885**, 852, 890
Country Profile. Kuwait. (UK ISSN 0269-7327) **3885**, 852, 890
Country Profile. Lebanon, Cyprus. (UK ISSN 0269-7351) **3885**, 853, 890
Country Profile. Libya. (UK ISSN 0269-6347) **3885**, 853, 890
Country Profile. Madagascar, Comoros. (UK ISSN 0269-736X) **3885**, 853, 890
Country Profile. Malawi. (UK ISSN 0269-4522) **3885**, 853, 890
Country Profile. Malaysia, Brunei. (UK ISSN 0269-5588) **3885**, 853, 890
Country Profile. Malta. (UK ISSN 0269-8137) **3885**, 853, 890
Country Profile. Mauritius, Seychelles. (UK ISSN 0269-7378) **3885**, 853, 890
Country Profile. Mexico. (UK ISSN 0269-5596) **3885**, 853, 890
Country Profile. Morocco. (UK ISSN 0269-6614) **3885**, 853, 890
Country Profile. Mozambique. (UK ISSN 0269-7017) **3885**, 853, 890
Country Profile. Namibia. (UK ISSN 0269-7386) **3885**, 853, 890
Country Profile. Netherlands. (UK ISSN 0264-4886) **3885**, 853, 890

COUNTRY PROFILE

Country Profile. New Zealand. (UK ISSN 0269-5618) **3885**, 853, 890

Country Profile. Nicaragua, Costa Rica, Panama. (UK ISSN 0269-4409) **3885**, 853, 890

Country Profile. Niger, Burkina Faso. (UK ISSN 0269-8064) **3885**, 853, 890

Country Profile. Nigeria. (UK ISSN 0269-6339) **3885**, 853, 891

Country Profile. Norway. (UK ISSN 0269-5626) **3885**, 853, 891

Country Profile. Oman, Yemen. (UK ISSN 0269-7343) **3885**, 853, 891

Country Profile. Pacific Islands: Fiji, Solomon Islands, Western Samoa, Vanuatu, Tonga. (UK ISSN 0269-8080) **3885**, 853, 891

Country Profile. Pakistan, Afghanistan. (UK ISSN 0269-5634) **3885**, 853, 891

Country Profile. Papua New Guinea. (UK ISSN 0269-8099) **3885**, 853, 891

Country Profile. Peru. (UK ISSN 0269-5944) **3885**, 853, 891

Country Profile. Philippines. (UK ISSN 0269-5979) **3886**, 853, 891

Country Profile. Poland. (UK ISSN 0269-5219) **3886**, 853, 891

Country Profile. Portugal. (UK ISSN 0269-5987) **3886**, 853, 891

Country Profile. Romania. (UK ISSN 0269-638X) **3886**, 853, 891

Country Profile. Saudi Arabia. (UK ISSN 0269-6355) **3886**, 853, 891

Country Profile. Senegal. (UK ISSN 0269-6037) **3886**, 853, 891

Country Profile. Sierra Leone, Liberia. (UK ISSN 0269-5057) **3886**, 853, 891

Country Profile. Singapore. (UK ISSN 0269-7041) **3886**, 853, 891

Country Profile. South Africa. (UK ISSN 0269-8153) **3886**, 853, 891

Country Profile. South Korea. (UK ISSN 0269-7955) **3886**, 853, 891

Country Profile. Spain. (UK ISSN 0269-5995) **3886**, 853, 891

Country Profile. Sri Lanka. (UK ISSN 0269-5073) **3886**, 853, 891

Country Profile. Sudan. (UK ISSN 0269-705X) **3886**, 853, 891

Country Profile. Sweden. (UK ISSN 0269-6002) **3886**, 853, 891

Country Profile. Switzerland. (UK ISSN 0269-6010) **3886**, 853, 891

Country Profile. Syria. (UK ISSN 0269-6045) **3886**, 853, 891

Country Profile. Taiwan. (UK ISSN 0269-7025) **3886**, 853, 891

Country Profile. Tanzania. (UK ISSN 0269-6630) **3886**, 853, 891

Country Profile. Thailand, Burma. (UK ISSN 0269-5065) **3886**, 853, 891

Country Profile. The Gambia, Guinea-Bissau, Cape Verde. (UK) **3886**, 853, 891

Country Profile. Togo, Benin. (UK ISSN 0269-8056) **3886**, 853, 891

Country Profile. Trinidad & Tobago. (UK ISSN 0269-8102) **3886**, 853, 891

Country Profile. Tunisia. (UK ISSN 0269-8129) **3886**, 853, 891

Country Profile. Turkey. (UK) **3886**, 853, 891

Country Profile. U S S R see Country Profile. Commonwealth of Independent States **3883**

Country Profile. Uganda. (UK ISSN 0269-7076) **3886**, 853, 891

Country Profile. United Arab Emirates. (UK ISSN 0269-6606) **3886**, 853, 891

Country Profile. United Kingdom. (UK ISSN 0269-798X) **3887**, 853, 891

Country Profile. United States of America. (UK ISSN 0269-8005) **3887**, 853, 891

Country Profile. Uruguay, Paraguay. (UK ISSN 0269-7998) **3887**, 853, 891

Country Profile. Venezuela, Suriname, Netherlands Antilles. (UK ISSN 0269-607X) **3887**, 853, 891

Country Profile. Yugoslavia. (UK ISSN 0269-803X) **3887**, 853, 891

Country Profile. Zaire, Rwanda, Burundi.(UK ISSN 0269-6320) **3887**, 853, 891

Country Profile. Zambia. (UK ISSN 0269-7300) **3887**, 853, 891

Country Profile. Zimbabwe. (UK ISSN 0269-4360) **3887**, 853, 891

Country Profiles. (UK ISSN 0161-5475) **3887**, 853, 891

Country Quest. (UK ISSN 0011-0213) **2193**

Country Quick 'n Easy Cookin' (US) **2445**

Country Report. Algeria. (UK ISSN 0269-5723) **853**, 891, 3887

Country Report. Angola, Sao Tome & Principe. (UK) **853**, 891, 3887

Country Report. Argentina. (UK ISSN 0269-4468) **853**, 891, 3887

Country Report. Australia. (UK ISSN 0269-7106) **853**, 891, 3887

Country Report. Austria. (UK ISSN 0269-5170) **853**, 891, 3887

Country Report. Bahrain, Qatar. (UK ISSN 0269-7335) **853**, 891, 3887

Country Report. Bangladesh. (UK ISSN 0269-431X) **854**, 891, 3887

Country Report. Belgium, Luxembourg. (UK ISSN 0269-4158) **854**, 891, 3887

Country Report. Brazil. (UK ISSN 0269-5731) **854**, 891, 3887

Country Report. Cameroon, Central African Republic, Chad. (UK ISSN 0269-4336) **854**, 891, 3887

Country Report. Canada. (UK ISSN 0269-4166) **854**, 891, 3887

Country Report. Chile. (UK ISSN 0269-5197) **854**, 891, 3887

Country Report. China, North Korea. (UK ISSN 0269-6231) **854**, 891, 3887

Country Report. Colombia. (UK ISSN 0269-7157) **854**, 891, 3887

Country Report. Commonwealth of Independent States. (UK) **854**, 891, 3887

Country Report. Congo, Gabon, Equatorial Guinea. (UK ISSN 0269-7246) **854**, 891, 3887

Country Report. Cote d'Ivoire. (UK ISSN 0269-7254) **854**, 891, 3887

Country Report. Cuba, Dominican Republic, Haiti, Puerto Rico. (UK ISSN 0269-5251) **854**, 891, 3887

Country Report. Czechoslovakia. (UK ISSN 0269-4298) **854**, 891, 3887

Country Report. Denmark, Iceland. (UK ISSN 0269-574X) **854**, 891, 3887

Country Report. East Germany see Country Report. Germany **854**

Country Report. Ecuador. (UK ISSN 0269-7165) **854**, 891, 3887

Country Report. Egypt. (UK ISSN 0269-526X) **854**, 891, 3887

Country Report. Finland. (UK ISSN 0269-5901) **854**, 891, 3887

Country Report. France. (UK ISSN 0269-5286) **854**, 891, 3887

Country Report. Germany. (UK) **854**, 891, 3887

Country Report. Ghana, Sierra Leone, Liberia. (UK ISSN 0269-7181) **855**, 891, 3887

Country Report. Greece. (UK ISSN 0269-591X) **855**, 891, 3887

Country Report. Guatemala, El Salvador, Honduras. (UK ISSN 0269-4220) **855**, 891, 3887

Country Report. Guinea, Mali, Mauritania. (UK ISSN 0269-7203) **855**, 891, 3887

Country Report. Hong Kong, Macau. (UK ISSN 0269-6762) **855**, 891, 3887

Country Report. Hungary. (UK ISSN 0269-4301) **855**, 892, 3887

Country Report. India, Nepal. (UK ISSN 0269-5294) **855**, 892, 3887

Country Report. Indochina: Vietnam, Laos, Cambodia. (UK ISSN 0269-5677) **855**, 892, 3887

Country Report. Indonesia. (UK ISSN 0269-5413) **855**, 892, 3887

Country Report. Iran. (UK ISSN 0269-5448) **855**, 892, 3887

Country Report. Iraq. (UK ISSN 0269-4395) **855**, 892, 3887

Country Report. Ireland. (UK ISSN 0269-5278) **855**, 892, 3887

Country Report. Israel. (UK ISSN 0269-5928) **855**, 892, 3887

Country Report. Italy. (UK ISSN 0269-5421) **855**, 892, 3887

Country Report. Jamaica, Belize, Bahamas, Bermuda. (UK ISSN 0269-7130) **855**, 892, 3887

Country Report. Japan. (UK ISSN 0269-5405) **855**, 892, 3888

Country Report. Jordan. (UK ISSN 0269-722X) **855**, 892, 3888

Country Report. Kenya. (UK ISSN 0269-4239) **855**, 892, 3888

Country Report. Kuwait. (UK ISSN 0269-5715) **855**, 892, 3888

Country Report. Lebanon, Cyprus. (UK ISSN 0269-5693) **855**, 892, 3888

Country Report. Libya. (UK ISSN 0269-4328) **856**, 892, 3888

Country Report. Madagascar, Mauritius, Seychelles, Comoros. (UK ISSN 0269-5154) **856**, 892, 3888

Country Report. Malaysia, Brunei. (UK ISSN 0269-6703) **856**, 892, 3888

Country Report. Mexico. (UK ISSN 0269-5596) **856**, 892, 3888

Country Report. Morocco. (UK ISSN 0269-6126) **856**, 892, 3888

Country Report. Namibia, Botswana, Lesotho, Swaziland. (UK ISSN 0269-6746) **856**, 892, 3888

Country Report. Netherlands. (UK ISSN 0269-6134) **856**, 892, 3888

Country Report. New Zealand. (UK ISSN 0269-7114) **856**, 892, 3888

Country Report. Nicaragua, Costa Rica, Panama. (UK ISSN 0269-4247) **856**, 892, 3888

Country Report. Nigeria. (UK ISSN 0269-4204) **856**, 892, 3888

Country Report. Norway. (UK ISSN 0269-4182) **856**, 892, 3888

Country Report. Oman, Yemen. (UK) **856**, 892, 3888

Country Report. Pacific Islands: Papua New Guinea, Fiji, Solomon Islands, Western Samoa, Vanuatu, Tonga. (UK ISSN 0269-7122) **856**, 892, 3888

Country Report. Pakistan, Afghanistan. (UK ISSN 0269-7173) **856**, 892, 3888

Country Report. Peru, Bolivia. (UK ISSN 0269-543X) **856**, 892, 3888

Country Report. Philippines. (UK ISSN 0269-428X) **856**, 892, 3888

Country Report. Poland. (UK ISSN 0269-6193) **856**, 892, 3888

Country Report. Portugal. (UK ISSN 0269-5456) **856**, 892, 3888

Country Report. Romania, Bulgaria, Albania. (UK ISSN 0269-5669) **857**, 892, 3888

Country Report. Saudi Arabia. (UK ISSN 0269-6215) **857**, 892, 3888

Country Report. Senegal, The Gambia, Guinea-Bassau, Cape Verde. (UK ISSN 0269-719X) **857**, 892, 3888

Country Report. Singapore. (UK ISSN 0269-6711) **857**, 892, 3888

Country Report. South Africa. (UK ISSN 0269-6738) **857**, 892, 3888

Country Report. South Korea. (UK ISSN 0269-669X) **857**, 892, 3888

Country Report. Spain. (UK ISSN 0269-4263) **857**, 892, 3888

Country Report. Sri Lanka. (UK ISSN 0269-4174) **857**, 892, 3888

Country Report. Sudan. (UK ISSN 0269-6150) **857**, 892, 3888

Country Report. Sweden. (UK ISSN 0269-6142) **857**, 892, 3888

Country Report. Switzerland. (UK ISSN 0269-6169) **857**, 892, 3888

Country Report. Syria. (UK ISSN 0269-7211) **857**, 892, 3888

Country Report. Taiwan. (UK ISSN 0269-672X) **857**, 892, 3888

Country Report. Tanzania, Mozambique.(UK ISSN 0269-6223) **857**, 892, 3888

Country Report. Thailand, Burma. (UK ISSN 0269-5189) **857**, 892, 3888

Country Report. Togo, Niger, Benin, Burkina Faso. (UK ISSN 0269-7262) **857**, 892, 3888

Country Report. Trinidad & Tobago, Guyana, Barbados, Windward & Leeward Islands. (UK ISSN 0269-7149) **857**, 892, 3888

Country Report. Tunisia, Malta. (UK ISSN 0269-7238) **857**, 892, 3888

Country Report. Turkey. (UK ISSN 0269-5464) **857**, 892, 3888

Country Report. U S A. (UK ISSN 0269-6185) **858**, 892, 3888

Country Report. U S S R see Country Report. Commonwealth of Independent States **854**

Country Report. Uganda, Ethiopia, Somalia, Djibouti. (UK ISSN 0269-5685) **858**, 892, 3888

Country Report. United Arab Emirates. (UK ISSN 0269-5162) **858**, 892, 3888

Country Report. United Kingdom. (UK ISSN 0269-5472) **858**, 892, 3888

Country Report. Uruguay, Paraguay. (UK ISSN 0269-6177) **858**, 892, 3888

Country Report. Venezuela, Suriname, Netherlands Antilles. (UK ISSN 0269-6754) **858**, 892, 3888

Country Report. West Germany see Country Report. Germany **854**

Country Report. Yugoslavia. (UK ISSN 0269-4190) **858**, 892, 3888

Country Report. Zaire, Rwanda, Burundi. (UK ISSN 0269-5510) **858**, 892, 3888

Country Report. Zambia. (UK ISSN 0269-4271) **858**, 892, 3888

Country Report. Zimbabwe, Malawi. (UK ISSN 0269-4255) **858**, 892, 3888

Country Reports. (UK) **858**, 893, 3888

Country Risk Update. (US) **904**, 1526

Country Sampler. (US) **2224**

Country-Side. (UK ISSN 0011-023X) **4306**

Country Song Roundup. (US ISSN 0011-0248) **3548**

Country Sports Directory. (UK) **1127**, 4544

Country Standard. (UK ISSN 0011-0256) **85**

Country Stitch. (US) **3590**

▼Country Style Homes, Plans and Designs. (US) **297**

†Country Sun. (CN) **5174**

Country Teacher. (US) **1624**

Country Today. (US) **85**

Country Vacations U.S.A. see Farm, Ranch and Country Vacations **4762**

Country Victorian Accents. (US) **2550**

Country Victorian Decorating. (US) **2550**

Country - Wide. (NZ) **85**

Country Woman. (US ISSN 0892-8525) **4840**, 85

Country Yossi Family Magazine. (US) **1998**

Country Youth. see Nongcun Qingnian **1261**

Countryman. see Agrotis **74**

Countryman. (AT ISSN 0011-0264) **85**

Countryman. (UK ISSN 0011-0272) **2193**

Countryside. (CN ISSN 1057-3372) **2176**

▼Countryside. (US) **2224**

Countryside and Small Stock Journal. (US ISSN 8750-7595) **215,** 3710
Countryside Campaigner. (UK ISSN 0268-5795) **1486**
Countryside Commission News. (UK ISSN 0264-8822) **1486,** 4544
Countryside Monthly see Dog & Country 5181
Countrywoman. (UK ISSN 0011-0302) **4840**
County (Des Moines) see Iowa County 4089
County Agents Directory. (US ISSN 0739-4330) **85**
County and Municipal Year Book for Scotland see Scotland's Regions 4073
County Bar Update. (US ISSN 0279-9626) **2616**
County Border Times. (UK ISSN 0263-015X) **2193**
County Care. (US ISSN 1041-7877) **3626,** 1726
County Councils Gazette see County News 4086
County Court Practice. (UK ISSN 0269-3291) **2617**
County Economic Indicators. (US) **858**
County Executive Directory. (US ISSN 0742-1702) **4086**
County Fare - Pointsett Register. (US) **2224**
County Kildare Archaeological Society. Journal. (IE) **269**
County Lines. (US ISSN 0195-4121) **2224**
County Louth Archaeological and Historical Journal. (IE ISSN 0070-1327) **270**
County Louth Archaeological Journal see County Louth Archaeological and Historical Journal 270
County Magazine. (CN ISSN 0826-3035) **2176**
County News. (UK) **4086**
County News. (US ISSN 0744-9798) **4086**
County Penetration Reports. (US) **40,** 4569
County Planning Department. Surrey County Council. Technical Report. (UK) **2486**
County Progress. (US ISSN 0011-0353) **4058**
County Wide. (US) **2224**
Coup. (US) **657**
Coup d'Oeil sur le Saguenay-Lac-Saint-Jean. (CN ISSN 0709-2679) **4758**
†Coup de Peigne. (CN) **5174**
Coup de Pouce. (CN ISSN 0822-3033) **2064**
Coup de Pouce Extra. (CN) **2065**
Coupe. (GW) **3396**
Coupler. (CN) **4708**
Couples Only. (US) **3396**
▼Coupon Treasure Hunt Newsletter. (US ISSN 1053-6523) **1504,** 2091
Couponer Newsletter. (US) **30**
Cour Europeenne des Droits de l'Homme. Publications. Serie A: Arrets et Decisions. see European Court of Human Rights. Publications. Series A: Judgments and Decisions 3941
Cour Europeenne des Droits de l'Homme. Publications. Serie B: Memoires, Plaidoiries et Documents. see European Court of Human Rights. Publications. Series B: Pleadings, Oral Arguments and Documents 3942
Cour Internationale de Justice. Annuaire see International Court of Justice. Yearbook 2724
Courage. see Himmat **3897**
Courage see Zivilcourage **3978**
Courage in the Struggle for Justice and Peace. (US) **4432,** 4172
Courageous Contrarian. (US) **943,** 1007
▼Courants. (FR ISSN 1146-5786) **4823**
Courier (Beaufort West). (SA ISSN 0011-0426) **2216**
Courier (Farmers Branch). (US) **1309**
Courier (Lexington). (US) **4758**

Courier (London). (UK ISSN 0011-0396) **1352,** 1362
Courier (Mequon). (US) **1309**
Courier (New York, 1954). (US) **3764,** 4403
Courier (Newark). (US) **3523**
Courier (Paris). (UN) **3954,** 2505, 4306
Courier-Journal see Catholic Courier 4259
Courrier Australien. (AT ISSN 0011-0442) **2186,** 2171
Courrier C E R N see C E R N Courier 3846
Courrier Consulaire du Burkina Faso. (UV ISSN 0574-3370) **813**
Courrier de Gand. (BE ISSN 0770-9021) **2174**
Courrier de l'Antigaspillage/Bollettino sul Risparmio d'Energia/Energie-Spar-Nachrichten. (SZ) **1486**
Courrier de l'Industrie. (TI) **657**
Courrier de la Microcopie. (FR ISSN 0396-5791) **3789**
Le Courrier de la Nature. (FR) **563**
Courrier de la Nature, l'Homme et l'Oiseau see Le Courrier de la Nature 563
Courrier de la Nouvelle-Ecosse. (CN) **1998**
Courrier de la Planete. (FR ISSN 1161-8043) **149,** 2065
Courrier de Varsovie see Warsaw Newsletter 5302
Courrier des Droits de l'Homme see Human Rights Newsletter 3943
Courrier des Echecs. (FR ISSN 0011-0507) **4470**
Courrier des Pays de l'Est. (FR ISSN 0590-0239) **657,** 3888
Courrier du Bois. (BE) **2114**
†Courrier du C N R S Supplement. (FR) **5174**
Courrier du Littoral see Courrier du Littoral et de Bruges 2174
Courrier du Littoral et de Bruges. (BE) **2174**
Courrier du Meuble. (FR ISSN 0751-6320) **2557**
Courrier du Vietnam. (VN ISSN 0045-8902) **3888**
Courrier Economique. (MR) **858**
Courrier Europeen. (FR ISSN 0011-0574) **3888**
Courrier-Expression. (FR ISSN 0998-6316) **2908**
Courrier Grec. (CN) **1998**
Courrier Hebdomadaire. (BE) **3888**
Courrier Hippique. (CN) **4533**
Courrier Sportif du Benin. (CM) **4470**
†Courrier Technique Arts Graphiques. (FR) **5174**
Cours de Perfectionnement du Notariat.(CN ISSN 0316-1234) **2617**
Course Trends. (US) **1683**
Course Trends in Adult Learning see Course Trends 1683
Courses et Elevage. (FR ISSN 0300-5607) **4533**
Court Case Digest. (US) **2734**
†Court Cases of Interest to the Ombudsman Institution. (CN ISSN 0227-6178) **5174**
Court Crier see Court Manager **2731**
Court Excellence. (US) **2731**
Court Forms, Precedents & Pleadings - N S W. (AT) **2731**
Court Forms, Precedents & Pleadings - Queensland. (AT) **2731**
†Court Improvement Bulletin. (US) **5174**
▼Court Management & Administrative Report. (US) **2731**
†Court Management Journal. (US ISSN 0276-1661) **5174**
Court Manager. (US) **2731**
Court News. (US) **2731**
†Court of Appeals for the Federal Circuit Newsletter. (US) **5174**
Court of Justice of the European Communities. Recueil de la Jurisprudence see Court of Justice of the European Communities. Report of Cases of the Court 2722
Court of Justice of the European Communities. Report of Cases of the Court. (EI) **2722**

Court Review. (US ISSN 0011-0647) **2731**
Courtauld Institute Illustration Archives. Archive 1. (UK ISSN 0307-8051) **323,** 297
Courtauld Institute Illustration Archives. Archive 2. (UK ISSN 0307-806X) **323**
Courtauld Institute Illustration Archives. Archive 3. (UK ISSN 0307-8078) **323**
Courtauld Institute Illustration Archives. Archive 4. (UK ISSN 0307-8086) **323**
Courtenay Facsimiles see Courtenay Reformation Facsimiles 2357
Courtenay Library of Reformation Classics. (UK ISSN 0070-1394) **2357,** 4172
Courtenay Reformation Facsimiles. (UK) **2357,** 4172
Courtenay Studies in Reformation Theology. (UK ISSN 0070-1408) **2357,** 4172
Courtier Nautique. (BE) **4726**
Courtroom Currents. (US) **2731**
Court's Charge Reporter. (US) **2731**
▼Courts, Health Science & the Law. (US ISSN 1043-8483) **2617,** 4099, 4306
Cousin Huntin' see Tree Talks **2166**
Cousins et Cousines. (US) **2148**
Covas Iompair Eireann Travel Express see C I E Travel Express 4755
Coven. (CN) **1624**
Covenant. (CN) **1998**
Covenant Companion. (US ISSN 0011-0671) **4281**
Covenant of the Goddess Newsletter see C O G Newsletter 4280
Covenant Voice. (UK) **4281**
Covenanters - The Leader. (UK) **4173,** 1235
†Coventry Evening Telegraph Year Book & Who's Who. (UK) **5174**
Cover. (US ISSN 0277-6723) **2505,** 30
Cover. (UK ISSN 0084-9405) **2530**
Cover Note. (AT) **2530**
Covered Bridge Topics. (US ISSN 0011-071X) **2404,** 1486
Covered Employment Trends in New Jersey see Trends in Employment and Wages 886
Covered Wagon. (US ISSN 0574-3680) **2404**
Covert Action Information Bulletin. (US ISSN 0275-309X) **3888**
Covert Intelligence Letter. (US) **3454,** 3954
Covicrier. (VI) **1946,** 4823
Covjek i Promet. (CI ISSN 0350-8765) **4100,** 4718
Covjek i Prostor. (CI ISSN 0011-0728) **323,** 297
Cow Country. (US ISSN 0279-8204) **215**
Cow Neck Peninsula Historical Journal. (US) **2404,** 2053
Cow News & Bull Views. (US) **215,** 904, 927
Cowan Clan United. Newsletter. (US ISSN 0090-6093) **2148**
Cowan Investment Survey. Midas. (AT) **943**
Cowan Investment Survey. Weekly Market Digest see Cowan Investment Survey. Midas 943
Coward Family Newsletter. (US) **2148**
Cowboy Artists of America Newsletter. (US) **3523,** 323, 2404
Coweta County Genealogical Society Magazine. (US) **2148**
The Cowl. (US) **1309**
†Cowles Foundation Monographs. (US) **5174**
Coydog Review. (US) **2991**
†Coyuntura Comercial. Alava. (SP ISSN 0211-5379) **5174**
Coyuntura Economica. (CK ISSN 0120-3576) **858**
†Coyuntura Industrial. (SP) **5174**
Coyuntura Industrial. Boletin. (SP) **813**
†Coyuntura Industrial y Utilizacion de la Capacidad Productiva de Alava. (SP ISSN 0211-1284) **5174**
Coyuntura Latinoamericana see Coyuntura Economica 858
C'oz. (AT ISSN 0819-5218) **657**

Crab. (US ISSN 0300-7561) **2753**
Crab Creek Review. (US ISSN 0738-7008) **2908**
Crab Gab see Malus **2134**
Cracked. (US) **2862**
Cracked Collectors Edition. (US) **2862**
Cracked Digest. (US) **2862**
Cracker see The Clipper **2064**
Cracker Crumbs. (US) **2148**
▼Cracker - Snack World. (US) **2065**
Craft A.C.T. (AT ISSN 0813-6734) **354**
Craft and Needlework Age. (US) **354,** 2435
Craft & Needlework Age Annual Trade Directory. (US ISSN 0887-9818) **3590**
Craft and Needlework Age - World of Miniatures see Craft and Needlework Age 354
†Craft - Art - Needlework Digest. (US) **5174**
Craft Arts International Magazine. (AT ISSN 0814-6586) **354,** 323
Craft Arts Magazine see Craft Arts International Magazine 354
†Craft Australia. (AT ISSN 0311-046X) **5174**
Craft Buyer's Guide see E.I.D.C.T. - C.D.T. Year Book 5183
Craft Connection. (US) **354**
Craft Horizons with Craft World see American Craft 353
Craft Marketing News. (US ISSN 1046-9699) **354,** 1114
Craft New South Wales see Crafts N.S.W. 354
▼Craft Related Newsletters, Periodicals & Publications. (US ISSN 1053-2013) **354**
Craft Supply Directory see Craft Supply Magazine 354
Craft Supply Magazine. (US) **354**
Craft Supply Report see Craft Supply Magazine 354
Craft Victoria. (AT ISSN 0158-7048) **354**
CraftNews. (CN ISSN 0319-7832) **354**
CrafTrends. (US) **354**
Crafts. (UK ISSN 0306-610X) **354**
Crafts. (US ISSN 0148-9127) **354**
†Crafts Competitions and Prizes. (AT ISSN 0816-360X) **5174**
†Crafts Council News. (AT) **5174**
Crafts Fair Guide. (US ISSN 0273-7957) **354**
Crafts Industry Guide N.S.W.: Printout. (AT ISSN 0814-5490) **354**
Crafts N.S.W. (AT ISSN 0726-6758) **354**
Crafts 'n Things. (US ISSN 0146-6607) **354**
Crafts Plus Magazine. (CN) **354**
Crafts Report. (US) **354**
Craftsman see Ontario Craft **356**
Craftsman's Directory (Year) Part 1. (UK ISSN 0261-2135) **354**
Craftsmen Review. (US) **3998**
Craftworks for the Home. (US) **354**
Craig - Links. (US) **2148**
Crain's Chicago Business. (US ISSN 0149-6956) **657**
Crain's Cleveland Business. (US ISSN 0197-2375) **858,** 834
Crain's Detroit Business. (US) **657**
†Crain's International Business. (US) **5174**
Crain's New York Business. (US) **657**
Cramb Insight see Industry Review **912**
Cramped and Wet. (US) **2991**
Cranberries. (US ISSN 0011-0787) **2065**
Cranbrook Institute of Science, Bloomfield Hills, Michigan. Bulletin. (US ISSN 0070-1416) **4306**
Cranes Today. (UK ISSN 0307-0018) **3016**
Cranes Today Handbook. (UK ISSN 0260-745X) **614**
Cranfield Rural Institute News see C R I News 5157
Cranial Letter. (US) **3214**
Cranio see Cranio: Journal of Craniomandibular Practice 3091
Cranio: Journal of Craniomandibular Practice. (US) **3091**

Cranwells Building Supplies. (NZ) 1127, 614
Crapouillot. (FR) 2862
Crappie. (US) 4544
Cras. (DK ISSN 0105-0583) 323, 270, 297, 3523
Crawford Chronicle. (UK ISSN 0265-5705) 2148
Crawford Exchange. (US ISSN 1043-7401) 2148
Crawford Families Exchange see Crawford Exchange 2148
Crawford Perspectives. (US) 943
Crawford's Directory of City Connections. (UK) 1127, 773
†Crawl Out Your Window. (US) 5174
Crawlspace. (US) 2991
Crazyhorse. (US ISSN 0011-0841) 2909
CrazyQuilt. (US ISSN 0887-5308) 2909
Crea. (JA) 2909
Cream City Review. (US ISSN 0884-3457) 2909
Creating Excellence. (US ISSN 1045-7011) 2224
Creation. (UK) 4173, 4306
Creation - Evolution. (US ISSN 0738-6001) 4173
Creation Ex Nihilo. (AT ISSN 0819-1530) 4173, 4306
Creation Ex Nihilo Technical Journal. (AT ISSN 1036-2916) 4173, 4306
Creation Research Society Quarterly. (US ISSN 0092-9166) 4173, 4306
Creations. (FR) 323, 1235
Creations. (US) 3594
Creations Lingerie. (FR) 1284
Creative. (US ISSN 0737-5883) 30
†Creative Arts & Crafts Handbook. (UK) 5174
Creative Black Book. (US ISSN 0738-9000) 30
Creative Black Book. Portfolio Edition. (US ISSN 0740-283X) 30, 3789
Creative Book Selection Index. (II ISSN 0378-7494) 4140, 9
Creative Camera. (UK ISSN 0011-0876) 3789
Creative Child and Adult Quarterly. (US ISSN 0098-7565) 1235, 4018
Creative Classroom. (US ISSN 0887-042X) 1747
Creative Crafters Journal see Handmade Accents 355
Creative Delaware Valley. (US) 323, 1036
Creative Forum. (II) 2909
Creative Handbook. (UK) 354, 323
†Creative Ideas for Living. (US) 5174
†Creative Ideas Needle and Craft. (US) 5174
Creative Intelligence Enhancement. (US) 4432, 1007, 1624, 4018
Creative Kids. (US) 1252
Creative Leap International Newsletter. (CN ISSN 0833-1146) 1007
Creative Loafing. (US ISSN 0889-8685) 2224
▼Creative Machine. (US) 3590
Creative Management see Management Policies & Personnel Law 1019
Creative Marketing. (US) 1036, 30
†Creative Meetings. (US) 5174
Creative Mind. (UK ISSN 0260-8278) 2862
Creative Moment World Poetry and Criticism. (US) 2991
Creative Needlecraft see Fashion and Craft 1290
Creative Products News. (US ISSN 0273-9240) 354, 3590
Creative Quilting. (US ISSN 0887-3690) 3590
Creative Review. (UK ISSN 0262-1037) 1036, 30
Creative Selling see Peak Performance Selling 1049
Creative Signs and Displays see Creative 30
Creative Source. (CN ISSN 0709-7727) 30, 3789
Creative Source Australia. (AT ISSN 0726-3589) 354, 323, 3789
Creative Trade Finance - Eastern Europe see Eastern Europe Finance 777
Creative Training Techniques. (US) 1624, 1007
Creative Video Consulting Report see C V C Report 1384
Creative Woman. (US ISSN 0736-4733) 4840, 323, 2909
Creative Woodwork and Crafts. (US) 639
Creative Writing. (US ISSN 0011-0930) 2991
Creativity. (US ISSN 0097-6075) 30, 323
Creativity. (CN) 30, 1036
Creativity. see Sang Tao 690
▼Creativity and Innovation Management. (UK ISSN 0963-1690) 657
Creativity and Innovation Network see Creativity and Innovation Yearbook 657
Creativity and Innovation Yearbook. (UK ISSN 0953-4199) 657
Creativity in Action. (US ISSN 0093-5263) 1007, 1624, 3764
Creativity Network see Creativity and Innovation Yearbook 657
Creativity Research Journal. (US) 4018
Creator. (US ISSN 1045-0815) 3548, 4173
†Creator. (JA) 5174
Creces. (CL ISSN 0716-0313) 4306
Credereoggi. (IT) 4262
Credit (Washington). (US ISSN 0097-8345) 774, 2617
Credit Agricole Annual Report see France. Caisse Nationale de Credit Agricole. Rapport sur le Credit Agricole Mutuel 782
Credit and Collection Management Bulletin see Credit & Collection Manager's Letter 774
Credit & Collection Manager's Letter. (US) 774, 1007
▼Credit & Finance. (US ISSN 1055-8225) 657
Credit and Financial Management see Business Credit 769
Credit Card Management. (US) 774
Credit Card Merchant. (US) 774, 1526
Credit Card News. (US) 774
Credit Communal de Belgique. Actes des Colloques Internationaux. Collection Histoire. Series in 8. (BE) 2357
Credit Communal de Belgique. Bulletin Trimestriel. (BE ISSN 0011-099X) 4086
Credit Control. (UK ISSN 0143-5329) 774
Credit-Curier. (GW) 858, 1007
Credit Executive. (US ISSN 0011-1007) 774, 1036
Credit Management. (UK ISSN 0265-2099) 1036, 1007
Credit Manager. (SA) 774
Credit Manual of Commercial Laws. (US ISSN 0070-1467) 774, 1036
Credit Market Statistics. see Norway. Statistisk Sentralbyraa. Kredittmarked Statistikk 731
Credit Markets see MuniWeek 957
†Credit Professional. (US) 5174
Credit Reporter see D & B Creditnews 775
▼Credit Risk Management. (US ISSN 1054-5069) 774
Credit Suisse. Bulletin. (SZ ISSN 0011-1023) 774, 858
Credit Union Board C E O Newsletter see Credit Union Newsletter for Directors 774
Credit Union Director. (US) 774
Credit Union Executive. (US ISSN 0011-1058) 774, 830
Credit Union Financial Profiles. (US) 774
Credit Union Information Service see C U I S 769
Credit Union Information Service Resources see C U I S Resources 5157
Credit Union Law Service. (US) 2617, 774
Credit Union Leadership Letter see Credit Union Newswatch 774
Credit Union Magazine. (US ISSN 0011-1066) 774, 830
Credit Union Management. (US ISSN 0273-9267) 774
Credit Union Manager Newsletter. (US) 774
Credit Union Marketing see Credit Union Management 774
Credit Union News. (US ISSN 0199-9311) 774
Credit Union Newsletter for Directors. (US ISSN 1058-1561) 774
Credit Union Newswatch. (US ISSN 0889-5597) 774
Credit Union Regulator. (US) 774
Credit Union Report. (US) 774, 830
Credit Union Review. (IE ISSN 0790-505X) 774, 830
Credit Union Times. (US) 774
Credit Union Way. (CN) 774, 830
Credit Union Week. (US) 774, 2617
Credit Union World Reporter. (US ISSN 0043-8952) 774
†Credit Union Yearbook. (US ISSN 0074-4468) 5174
Credit World. (US ISSN 0011-1074) 774
†Creditalk. (US ISSN 0045-9011) 5174
Creditanstalt-Bankverein. Annual Report. (AU) 774
Creditanstalt-Bankverein. Report see Creditanstalt-Bankverein. Annual Report 774
Creditanstalt-Bankverein Quarterly see C A Quarterly 849
Creditinform. (NO) 775
Credito Popolare. (IT ISSN 0011-1090) 775
Creditreform see Creditinform 775
Creditweek. (US ISSN 0731-1974) 943
Creem. (US ISSN 0011-1147) 3548
†Creem Close-Up Metal Rock 'N' Roll. (US) 5174
†Creem Rock Shots. (US) 5174
Creeping Bent. (US ISSN 8756-0291) 2909
Crefal Circular Informativa. (MX) 1683
Creighton Law Review. (US ISSN 0011-1155) 2617
Cremationist of North America. (US) 2119
Cremona Produce see Cremona Produce - Cultura e Tradizione 1998
Cremona Produce - Cultura e Tradizione. (IT ISSN 1120-0103) 1998
Creole Language Library. (US ISSN 0920-9026) 2810
Crescendo. (CN) 3548
†Crescendo (Garrett Park). (US) 5174
Crescendo (Interlochen). (US ISSN 0011-1171) 323
Crescent Chatter. (AT) 4758
Crescent International. (CN ISSN 0705-3754) 4218
Crescent Review. (US ISSN 0749-2871) 2909
Cresset. (US ISSN 0011-1198) 2862
Crest. (US) 1309
Crest. (CN ISSN 0843-5634) 4808
Crested Circle. (UK ISSN 0262-7140) 354
†Cresterea Patrimoniului Muzeal. (RM) 5174
Cretaceous Research. (UK ISSN 0195-6671) 1542
Creuset, la Voix des Cadres see Cadres et Maitrise 974
Crez. (UK) 2193
Cri. (BE) 4147
Criativa. (BL) 4840
Cricket. (US ISSN 0090-6034) 1252
Cricket. (NE ISSN 0011-1236) 4502
Cricket Letter. (US) 904
Cricket Quadrant. (AT ISSN 0310-9356) 4502
Cricket Samrat. (II) 4502
Cricket Statistician. (UK) 4498
Cricketer. (PK) 4502
Cricketer. (AT) 4502
Cricketer International. (UK ISSN 0266-7398) 4502
Cricketer Quarterly Facts and Figures. (UK ISSN 0266-7401) 4502
Crime & Delinquency. (US ISSN 0011-1287) 1512
Crime and Delinquency in California. (US) 1524, 4569
Crime and Fire Prevention see Security Gazette 1527
Crime and Justice. (US) 1512
Crime and Justice Network Newsletter. (US) 1512, 4281
Crime and Social Deviance. see Avareyanut Vestiya Cheurati 4399
Crime and Social Justice see Social Justice 1523
Crime & Society. (II) 2712
▼Crime Beat. (US) 1512
Crime Control Digest. (US ISSN 0011-1295) 1512
Crime in Nebraska see State of Nebraska Uniform Crime Report 1523
Crime in the United States see Uniform Crime Reports for the United States 1523
Crime in Virginia. (US ISSN 0146-5759) 1512
Crime Laboratory Digest. (US ISSN 0743-1872) 3264
Crime, Law, and Deviance Series. (US) 1512, 4369
Crime, Law and Social Policy. (NE) 1512, 4403
Crime Prevention News. (UK) 1512
Crime Victims Digest. (US ISSN 0884-5107) 1512
Criminal Appeal Reports. (UK ISSN 0070-1521) 1512
Criminal Appeal Reports (Sentencing). (UK) 2712
▼Criminal Behaviour and Mental Health. (UK ISSN 0957-9664) 4018, 1512
†Criminal Injuries Compensation. (CN) 5174
Criminal Justice. (UK) 1512
Criminal Justice (Chicago). (US ISSN 0887-7785) 2712
Criminal Justice (San Diego). (US ISSN 0748-2868) 1512, 4432
Criminal Justice Abstracts. (US ISSN 0146-9177) 1524, 9
Criminal Justice & Behavior. (US ISSN 0093-8548) 1513, 4018
Criminal Justice Digest. (US ISSN 0889-5724) 1513
Criminal Justice Ethics. (US ISSN 0731-129X) 2712
Criminal Justice History. (US ISSN 0194-0953) 1513
Criminal Justice Information Exchange Directory. (US) 1513
Criminal Justice Journal (San Diego). (US) 2712
Criminal Justice Newsletter. (US ISSN 0045-9038) 1513
Criminal Justice Periodical Index. (US ISSN 0145-5818) 1525, 9
†Criminal Justice Plan (Richmond). (US ISSN 0362-8353) 5174
Criminal Justice Plan for New Jersey see New Jersey. State Law Enforcement Planning Agency. Applicants Guide 5245
Criminal Justice Review. (US ISSN 0734-0168) 2712
Criminal Justice Statistics Association, Inc. Forum see C J S A Forum 1511
Criminal Law see B A R - B R I Bar Review. Criminal Law 1510
Criminal Law Advocacy Reporter. (US) 2712
Criminal Law Bulletin. (US ISSN 0011-1317) 2712
†Criminal Law Digest. (US) 5174
▼Criminal Law Forum. (US ISSN 1046-8374) 1513, 2722
Criminal Law in New South Wales. Volume 1: Indictable Offences. (AT ISSN 0705-7377) 2712
Criminal Law in New South Wales. Volume 2: Summary Offences. (AT ISSN 0705-7385) 2712
Criminal Law Journal. (II ISSN 0011-1325) 2713
Criminal Law Journal. (AT ISSN 0314-1160) 2713
Criminal Law Journal of Ohio. (US ISSN 1042-5942) 1513
Criminal Law Outline. (US ISSN 0145-7322) 2713
Criminal Law Quarterly. (CN ISSN 0011-1333) 2713
Criminal Law Reporter. (US ISSN 0011-1341) 2713

Criminal Law Review. (US ISSN 0192-3323) **1513**
Criminal Law Review. (UK ISSN 0011-135X) **2713**
Criminal Law Victoria. (AT) **2713**
Criminal Lawyers Commonplace Book. (CN) **2713**
Criminal Organizations. (US) **1513**
Criminal Politics. (US) **943**
Criminal Practice & Procedure N S W. (AT) **2713**
Criminal Procedure. (CN) **2713**
Criminal Reports (4th Series). (CN ISSN 0383-9494) **2713**
Criminal Statistics. *see* Netherlands. Centraal Bureau voor de Statistiek. Criminaliteit en Strafrechtspleging **1525**
Criminal Statistics. *see* Norway. Statistisk Sentralbyraa. Kriminalstatistikk **1525**
Criminal Statistics, Scotland. (UK ISSN 0307-6717) **1525**
Criminal Victimization in the United States. (US ISSN 0095-5833) **1513**
Criminalist's Source Book. (US) **1525, 3264**
Criminaliteit en Strafrechtspleging *see* Netherlands. Centraal Bureau voor de Statistiek. Criminaliteit en Strafrechtspleging **1525**
Criminologie. (CN ISSN 0316-0041) **1513**
Criminology. (US ISSN 0011-1384) **1513**
▼Criminology and Crime Control Policy. (US) **1513**
Criminology and Penology Abstracts *see* Criminology, Penology & Police Science Abstracts **1525**
Criminology Australia. (AT ISSN 1033-4777) **1513**
Criminology, Penology & Police Science Abstracts. (NE) **1525, 9**
Crimson Arrow *see* Arrow (Kenosha) **1304**
Crimson Circle Magazine. (UK) **2909**
†Crimson Dawn. (US) **5174**
†Crimson Fullmoon. (US) **5174**
Crimson News. (US) **1309**
Cripple Care News *see* Towards Independence **2290**
Crippled Children. *see* Teashi no Fujiyuuna Kodomotachi **3156**
La Crise. (CN) **1309**
Crisi e Letteratura. (IT ISSN 0011-1406) **2909, 2505, 2991**
Crisis. (CN ISSN 0227-5910) **4018**
Crisis (New York, 1910). (US ISSN 0011-1422) **1998, 3941**
Crisis (Notre Dame). (US) **4262**
Crisp Newsletter. (US) **2148**
Criss Cross. (GW) **1235, 1252, 1309**
Cristallo. (IT ISSN 0011-1449) **2505**
Cristianesimo nella Storia. (IT ISSN 0393-3598) **4173**
Cristianesimo Oggi. (IT) **4262**
Il Cristiano. (IT ISSN 0394-0284) **4235**
Cristion. (UK) **4173**
Crit. (US ISSN 0277-6863) **297**
Criteria *see* Art and Poetry Today **313**
Criterio. (AG ISSN 0011-1473) **2862**
Criterio Economico. (CK) **658**
Criterio Universitario. (MX) **2505**
Criterion. (US) **1309, 2568**
Criterios. (CU) **3888**
Critic. (UK ISSN 0015-1203) **3507, 2568**
Critic (Chicago). (US ISSN 0011-149X) **2505, 4262**
Critica. (PE) **893**
Critica. (US) **1998**
Critica. (UY) **2238**
Critica. (MX ISSN 0011-1503) **3764**
Critica Andina. (PE) **4369**
Critica d'Arte. (IT ISSN 0011-1511) **323**
Critica del Diritto. (IT) **3889**
Critica Giudiziaria. (IT) **2617**
Critica Hispanica. (US ISSN 0278-7261) **2909**
Critica Letteraria. (IT) **2810, 2909**
Critica Marxista/Marxist Criticism. (IT ISSN 0011-152X) **3889**
Critica Penale. (IT) **2617, 2357**
Critica Social. (BL) **4403**

Critica Sociologica. (IT ISSN 0011-1546) **4432**
Critica Storica. (IT ISSN 0011-1554) **2309**
Critica Umbra. (IT) **3889**
Critical Arts. (SA) **1334**
Critical Bibliography of French Literature. (US) **2909**
Critical Care Clinics. (US ISSN 0749-0704) **3091**
Critical Care Medicine. (US ISSN 0090-3493) **3091**
Critical Care Nurse. (US ISSN 0279-5442) **3277**
Critical Care Nursing Quarterly. (US) **3277**
Critical Care Quarterly *see* Critical Care Nursing Quarterly **3277**
Critical Care Report. (US) **3091**
†Critical Communications Review. (US) **5174**
†Critical Essays in Modern Literature. (US ISSN 0070-153X) **5174**
Critical Inquiry. (US ISSN 0093-1896) **2863**
Critical Issues. (US ISSN 0194-1909) **3889, 1946, 2617**
Critical Issues in Developmental & Behavioral Pediatrics. (US) **4018, 3320**
Critical Issues in Facilities Management.(US) **1726, 1007, 1818**
▼Critical Issues in Teacher Education. (US) **1747**
Critical Pedagogy Networker. (AT ISSN 1033-808X) **1624**
Critical Perspectives in Social Theory. (US) **4369**
▼Critical Perspectives on Accounting. (UK ISSN 1045-2354) **750**
Critical Quarterly. (UK ISSN 0011-1562) **2909, 2863**
Critical Reports on Applied Chemistry. (UK ISSN 0263-5917) **1175, 85, 3722**
Critical Research Institute for Social and Environmental Sciences Alternative Press Exhibition Catalog *see* C R I S E S Alternative Press Exhibition Catalog **396**
Critical Review. (US ISSN 0891-3811) **2863, 2909, 4126**
Critical Review. (AT) **2909, 2309, 3764**
Critical Review Melbourne *see* Critical Review **2909**
Critical Reviews in Analytical Chemistry.(US ISSN 1040-8347) **1205**
Critical Reviews in Biochemistry and Molecular Biology. (US ISSN 1040-9238) **475**
Critical Reviews in Biocompatibility. (US ISSN 0748-5204) **3091**
Critical Reviews in Biomedical Engineering. (US) **469, 3091**
Critical Reviews in Biotechnology. (US) **489**
Critical Reviews in Clinical Laboratory Sciences. (US ISSN 1040-8363) **3091**
Critical Reviews in Clinical Neurobiology *see* Critical Reviews in Neurobiology **3334**
Critical Reviews in Diagnostic Imaging. (US ISSN 1040-8371) **3357**
Critical Reviews in Environmental Control. (US ISSN 1040-838X) **1946**
▼Critical Reviews in Eukaryotic Gene Expression. (US ISSN 1045-4403) **540**
Critical Reviews in Food Science and Nutrition. (US ISSN 1040-8398) **2065**
Critical Reviews in Immunology. (US ISSN 1040-8401) **3184**
Critical Reviews in Microbiology. (US ISSN 1040-841X) **550**
Critical Reviews in Neurobiology. (US ISSN 0892-0915) **3334, 435**
Critical Reviews in Oncogenesis. (US ISSN 0893-9675) **3196**
Critical Reviews in Oncology - Hematology. (NE ISSN 1040-8428) **3196, 3271**

Critical Reviews in Oral Biology and Medicine. (US ISSN 1045-4411) **3230**
Critical Reviews in Physical & Rehabilitation Medicine. (US ISSN 0896-2960) **3091, 1735**
Critical Reviews in Plant Sciences. (US) **174**
Critical Reviews in Poultry Biology *see* Poultry Science Reviews **224**
Critical Reviews in Solid State & Materials Sciences. (US ISSN 1040-8436) **3816**
▼Critical Reviews in Surface Chemistry.(US ISSN 1049-9407) **1225**
Critical Reviews in Therapeutic Drug Carrier Systems. (US ISSN 0743-4863) **3722**
Critical Reviews in Toxicology. (US ISSN 1040-8444) **1981, 3722**
Critical Sociology. (US ISSN 0896-9205) **2863, 4432**
Critical Studies. (US) **2909**
†Critical Studies in Film and Television. (US) **5174**
Critical Studies in Mass Communication.(US ISSN 0739-3180) **1372**
Critical Studies on Black Life and Culture. (US) **1998, 2053**
Critical Survey. (UK ISSN 0011-1570) **2863**
Critical Texts: A Newsletter in Critical Theory and the History of Criticism *see* Critical Texts: A Review of Theory and Criticism **2863**
Critical Texts: A Review of Theory and Criticism. (US ISSN 0730-2304) **2863, 2909**
Critical Theory. (US ISSN 0920-3060) **2810, 4840**
Critical Wave. (UK) **3010**
Criticism. (US ISSN 0011-1589) **2909, 2505**
Criticism and Interpretation. *see* Bikoret Veparshanut **2504**
Criticism Monthly. *see* Wenlun Yuekan **2889**
Criticon. (GW ISSN 0011-1597) **2863**
Criticon. (FR ISSN 0247-381X) **2991, 2909**
Critique. (UK ISSN 0301-7605) **3889**
Critique. (FR ISSN 0011-1600) **4126**
Critique (West Vancouver). (CN ISSN 0735-6501) **3594, 2863, 3764**
Critique of Anthropology. (UK ISSN 0308-275X) **237, 4432**
Critique of Trade Union Rights in Countries Affiliated with the League of Arab States. (US ISSN 1062-7863) **2582**
Critique of Trade Union Rights in Countries Affiliated with the League of Arab States. Documentation Supplement. (US) **2592, 2582**
Critique Regionale. (BE ISSN 0770-0075) **4432, 858, 976**
Critique Socialiste. (FR ISSN 0045-9089) **3889**
†Critique: Southern California Public Policy and Administration. (US) **5174**
Critique: Studies in Modern Fiction. (US ISSN 0011-1619) **2909**
Critiques de l'Economie Politique. (FR ISSN 0045-9097) **893**
Critiques de Notre Temps Et... (FR ISSN 0070-1556) **2909**
Crittenden Excess & Surplus Insider. (US) **2530**
Crittenden Insurance Markets Newsletter. (US) **2530**
Crittenden Report. (US) **4147**
Crkva/Church. (YU) **4282**
Crkva u Svijetu. (CI ISSN 0352-4000) **4282**
Croatian Mountaineer. *see* Hrvatski Planinar **4474**
Croatian Way. *see* Hrvatski Put **3897**
Croatica Chemica Acta. (CI ISSN 0011-1643) **1175**
Croc. (CN) **2177**
Croce. (IT ISSN 0011-1651) **4262**
Crocevia. (IT) **4086**
Crochet. (US) **3590**
Crochet d'Art. (FR) **3590**

Crochet Fantasy. (US ISSN 8750-8877) **3590**
Crochet Fun *see* Crochet Home **3590**
Crochet Home. (US ISSN 1046-719X) **3590, 354**
Crochet Patterns. (US) **3590**
Crochet Today Fashions *see* Crochet World Special **3590**
Crochet World. (US) **3590**
Crochet World Special. (US ISSN 1041-0759) **3590**
Crocker Communication Resources Newsletter *see* Resources (Lake Oswego) **1342**
The Crofter. (US) **85**
Crohn's & Colitis Foundation of America, Greater New Jersey Chapter. Newsletter. (US) **3267**
Crohn's & Colitis Foundation of America. Greater New York Chapter. Update. (US) **3267**
Crohn's and Colitis Foundation of America, Inc. Communique *see* C C F A Communique **3266**
Crohn's & Colitis Foundation of America, Inc. Foundation Focus *see* C C F A Foundation Focus **3266**
Croire et Servir. (FR ISSN 0755-7205) **4235**
Croissance des Jeunes Nations *see* Croissance - Le Monde en Developpement **3954**
Croissance - Le Monde en Developpement. (FR) **3954**
Croissance Urbaine et Progres des Nations. (FR ISSN 0070-1572) **893**
Croissant. (JA) **2445**
Croix. (FR) **4262**
Croix de Benin. (DM) **4262**
†Crol. (SP ISSN 0011-1694) **5174**
Cromos. (CK ISSN 0011-1708) **2183**
Cromwelliana. (UK ISSN 0307-5583) **2357**
Cronac Viva *see* Due Alfieri **4471**
Cronaca Filatelica. (IT) **3751**
Cronaca Vera. (IT) **2205**
Cronache. (IT) **1885, 1372**
Cronache Agricole. (IT) **85**
Cronache Castellane. (IT ISSN 0392-5803) **297**
Cronache dal Gruppo Stet. (IT) **1362, 1394, 1885**
Cronache del Teatro. (IT) **4632**
Cronache dell'Agricoltura. (IT) **85**
Cronache di Archeologia. (IT) **270, 323**
Cronache di Archeologia e di Storia dell'Arte *see* Cronache di Archeologia **270**
Cronache e Opinioni. (IT ISSN 0574-475X) **4840**
Cronache Farmaceutiche. (IT ISSN 0011-1783) **3722**
Croner's Buying and Selling Law. (UK) **2617, 1036**
Croner's Care Home Management. (UK) **4403**
Croner's Catering. (UK) **2473**
Croner's Coach and Bus Operations. (UK) **4649**
Croner's Dangerous Substances. (UK) **3616**
Croner's Employment Law. (UK) **2617, 1064**
Croner's Executive Companion. (UK) **1007**
Croner's Guide to Corporation Tax. (UK) **1091**
Croner's Health and Safety at Work. (UK) **3616, 2617**
Croner's Premises Management. (UK) **1007, 614, 2486**
Croner's Reference Book for Employers.(UK ISSN 0070-1580) **1064**
Croner's Reference Book for Exporters. (UK ISSN 0070-1599) **904**
Croner's Reference Book for Importers. (UK ISSN 0070-1602) **904**
Croner's Reference Book for the Self-Employed *see* Croner's Reference Book for the Self-Employed and Smaller Business **1091**
Croner's Reference Book for the Self-Employed and Smaller Business. (UK) **1091**

Croner's Reference Book for V A T. (UK) **1091**
Croner's Reference Book for Value Added Tax see Croner's Reference Book for V A T **1091**
Croner's Road Transport Operation. (UK ISSN 0070-1610) **4744**
Croner's World Directory of Freight Conferences. (UK ISSN 0070-1629) **4726**
Cronica. (RM ISSN 1220-4560) **2215**
Cronica de Albacete see Cronica de Albacete y de Castilla la Mancha **2217**
Cronica de Albacete y de Castilla la Mancha. (SP) **2217**
Cronica Documental de las Malvinas. (AG) **3889**
Cronica Tributaria. (SP ISSN 0210-2919) **1091**
Cronicas Economicas. (UY) **658**
Cronicl Powys/Powys Chronicle. (UK ISSN 0261-1104) **2148**
Cronorama. (IT ISSN 0390-1807) **2863**
Crooked Roads. (US) **2991**
Crop Breeding Institute. Annual Report. (RH) **174**
†Crop Dust. (US) **5175**
Crop Physiology Abstracts. (UK ISSN 0306-7556) **136, 9**
Crop Production see U.S. Crop Reporting Board. Crop Production **195**
Crop Protection. (UK ISSN 0261-2194) **174**
Crop Protection Courier (International). (GW ISSN 0590-1243) **174**
Crop Protection Monographs. (US) **435**
Crop Research. (UK) **174, 500, 2124**
Crop Science. (US ISSN 0011-183X) **174**
Crops. (UK ISSN 0266-5174) **175**
†Crops and Soils Magazine. (US ISSN 0162-5098) **5175**
†Crops Guide. (CN) **5175**
Crops in India. (II ISSN 0011-1872) **85, 2039**
Cropwood Round-Table Conference Papers. (UK) **1513**
Croquet Gazette. (UK ISSN 0011-1880) **4502**
El Croquis de Arquitectura y de Diseno. (SP ISSN 0212-5633) **297**
Cross. (PH) **4262, 1297**
Cross & Cockade International. (UK) **3454, 50**
Cross and Quill. (US) **4235, 2568, 4262**
Cross and Talk. (JA ISSN 0911-5625) **1334, 30, 1036**
Cross-Bias. (UK ISSN 0896-4610) **2991, 2863**
Cross-Canada Writers' Magazine see Paragraph **2947**
Cross-Canada Writers' Quarterly see Paragraph **2947**
Cross Channel Trade. (FR) **813**
Cross Country. (US ISSN 0318-6075) **2991**
Cross Country Ski Area Operations Survey. (US) **4544**
Cross Country Ski Areas of America Newsletter see Nordic Network **4551**
Cross Country Skier. (US ISSN 0278-9213) **4544**
Cross-Cultural Psychology Bulletin. (US ISSN 0710-068X) **4018**
Cross Cultural Research and Methodology Series see Sage Series in Cross Cultural Research and Methodology **4045**
Cross Currents. (JA ISSN 0289-1239) **1747, 2810**
Cross Currents see Cross Currents: Religion and Intellectual Life **4173**
†Cross Currents. (US ISSN 0748-0164) **5175**
Cross Currents: Religion and Intellectual Life. (US) **4173, 1704**
Cross Magazin. (GW ISSN 0933-7792) **4517**
Cross of Languedoc. (US ISSN 0011-1961) **4235, 1998**
†Cross Quick. (US) **5175**

Cross Quick - Cross Stitch. (US) **3590, 354**
Cross-Rates Currency Advisory Service see International Risk Management Advisor **786**
Cross-Reference see Touchstone (Nashville) **2516**
Cross River State. Ministry of Economic Development and Reconstruction. State Development Plan. (NR) **1091**
Cross Section. (AT) **3033, 1747**
Cross Sections. (US ISSN 0747-5543) **858**
Cross Stitch & Country Crafts. (US) **3590, 354**
▼Cross Stitch! Magazine. (US ISSN 1056-7542) **3590, 354**
Cross-Stitch Plus. (US ISSN 1054-3430) **3590**
Cross Stitch Plus. (US) **3591, 354**
▼Cross Stitch Sampler. (US) **354**
Cross-Stitcher. (US) **3591, 354**
Cross Tie Bulletin see Crossties **4708**
Cross Timbers Review. (US ISSN 0890-8885) **2909, 435**
Cross Trail News. (CN ISSN 0319-8561) **1529**
Crosscurrent. (UK ISSN 0260-6313) **1624**
Crosscurrent. (AT) **4823**
†Crosscurrent. (NZ) **5175**
Crosscurrents. (US ISSN 0739-2354) **2909, 323**
Crosscurrents. (CN ISSN 0704-6588) **4433, 2863, 3889**
Crossed Sabers Newsletter. (US) **2404**
Crossener Heimatgruesse. (GW) **2357**
Crossline see Cross **4262**
Crosslink. (NZ ISSN 0113-2024) **4235**
Crossosoma. (US ISSN 0891-9100) **500, 2124**
CrossRoad Trails. (US) **2148**
Crossroads. (CN) **175**
Crossroads. (AT ISSN 0334-4649) **3889, 3954**
Crossroads. (US) **4222, 4596**
Crossroads (DeKalb). (US ISSN 0741-2037) **2337, 2505**
Crossroads (Le Mars). (US ISSN 0045-9119) **4282**
Crossroads (Pittsburgh). (US ISSN 0011-2054) **3954**
Crossroads Communique. (US) **3954**
†Crossroads Montrose. (US) **5175**
Crosstalk see Crosstalk and Anglican Journal Episcopal **4235**
Crosstalk and Anglican Journal Episcopal. (CN ISSN 0845-4795) **4235**
Crossties. (US ISSN 0097-4536) **4708**
Crossways see Word and Deed **3224**
Crosswords. (US) **500, 2124**
▼Croton Bug. (US) **2991**
†Croton Review. (US ISSN 0741-6210) **5175**
Crotonese. (IT) **2205**
Crow. (US) **2863, 1334**
†Crowdancing Quarterly. (US) **5175**
Crowley Review. (US) **2065**
Crown. (UK ISSN 0045-9127) **1624, 2810**
Crown/Huang Kuan. (CH) **2219**
Crown Agents Quarterly Review see Crown Agents Review **3954**
Crown Agents Review. (UK) **3954**
Crown Journal. (UK) **614**
Crown Office Digest. (UK) **2617**
Crow's Weekly Letter. (US) **2114**
Croyants en Liberte. (FR) **4173**
Croydon Advertiser. (UK ISSN 0011-2089) **2193**
Croydon Bibliographies for Regional Survey. (UK ISSN 0309-8591) **4355**
Croydon Chamber of Commerce Directory. (UK) **814**
Croydon Natural History & Scientific Society. Bulletin. (UK ISSN 0309-6149) **4306**
Croydon Natural History & Scientific Society. Proceedings and Transactions. (UK ISSN 0309-8656) **4306**
Croydon Times see Croydon Advertiser **2193**
Crucible. (US ISSN 0011-2119) **1175**

Crucible. (CN ISSN 0381-8047) **1624, 4306**
Crucible see New Crucible **1964**
Crucible. (UK ISSN 0011-2100) **4235**
Cruciferae Newsletter. (UK ISSN 0263-9459) **86, 2124**
Cruel Sports see Wildlife Guardian **232**
Cruise and Vacation Views. (US) **4758**
Cruise Digest Reports. (US ISSN 0886-5604) **4758, 4726**
Cruise Entertainment Magazine. (US) **2452**
Cruise Industry Annual (Year) see Cruise Industry News Annual **4758**
Cruise Industry News. (US ISSN 0893-1240) **4758, 4726**
Cruise Industry News (Newsletter) see Cruise Industry News **4758**
Cruise Industry News Annual. (US ISSN 1047-3378) **4758, 4726**
Cruise Industry News Quarterly. (US) **4758, 4726**
Cruise Trade. (US) **4758**
Cruise Travel. (US ISSN 0199-5111) **4759**
Cruise Vacations see Cruises and Tours **4759**
Cruiser. (US) **2098, 1486, 1946, 2404**
▼Cruises and Tours. (US) **4759**
Cruising Association. Bulletin see Cruising Association. Magazine **4524**
Cruising Association. Magazine. (UK) **4524**
Cruising Association Yearbook. (UK) **4524**
Cruising Helmsman. (AT) **4524**
Cruising World. (US ISSN 0098-3519) **4524**
Crump Family Newsletter. (US) **2148**
Crusade Messenger see Crusader **1252**
Crusader. (UK) **1252, 4173**
Crusader (Memphis). (US ISSN 0011-2151) **4235, 1235, 1252**
Crusader (Toronto). (CN ISSN 0382-4314) **4235**
Crusader Magazine (Grand Rapids). (US) **1252, 4235**
Crusselle-Freeman Church and Center of the Deaf Golden C F News see Golden C F News **2287**
Crustaceana. (NE ISSN 0011-216X) **580**
Crustaceana. Supplements. (NE ISSN 0167-6563) **581**
Crustal and Upper Mantle Structure in Europe. Monographs. (US) **1587**
Crutchfield's Car Stereo Magazine. (US) **4460, 4688**
Crux. (SA) **2909**
Crux. (CN ISSN 0011-2186) **4173**
Crux. (UK) **4235**
Crux Mathematicorum. (CN ISSN 0705-0348) **3033**
Crux of the News. (US ISSN 0591-2296) **4173**
Cruz Ansata. (PR) **2505**
†Cruz Vermelha Portugesa. Boletim de Informacao. (PO ISSN 0870-3701) **5175**
Cruzada Eucaristica. (PO ISSN 0011-2194) **1252, 4173**
Cruzado. (MX ISSN 0011-2208) **3889**
Cruzeiro. (BL ISSN 0011-2216) **2175**
Cryo-Letters. (UK ISSN 0143-2044) **571, 475, 500, 1225**
Cryobiology. (US ISSN 0011-2240) **485**
CryoGas International. (US ISSN 1052-0139) **3840**
Cryogenic Engineering Conference Proceedings see Advances in Cryogenic Engineering **3840**
Cryogenic Information Report see CryoGas International **3840**
Cryogenics. (UK ISSN 0011-2275) **3840**
Cryophysics Newsletter. (SZ) **3840**
Cryospheric Data Management System Notes see C D M S Notes **1556**
Crypt of Cthulhu. (US) **3010, 2909**
Cryptanthus Society. Journal. (US ISSN 1060-1236) **2124**
▼Cryptic Scholar. (US) **2309**

Cryptogamic Botany. (GW ISSN 0935-2147) **500**
Cryptogamica Helvetica. (SZ) **500**
Cryptogamie: Algologie. (FR ISSN 0181-1568) **500**
Cryptogamie: Bryologie et Lichenologie. (FR ISSN 0181-1576) **500**
Cryptogamie: Mycologie. (FR ISSN 0181-1584) **500**
Cryptogram Detective. (US) **2985**
Cryptologia. (US ISSN 0161-1194) **3033, 1434, 4306**
Cryptosystems Journal. (US ISSN 0899-8159) **1468**
Cryptozoology. (US ISSN 0736-7023) **581**
Crystal Lattice Defects see Crystal Lattice Defects and Amorphous Materials **1210**
Crystal Lattice Defects and Amorphous Materials. (UK ISSN 0732-8699) **1210, 3816**
Crystal Mirror. (US ISSN 0097-7209) **4214**
Crystal Palace Matters. (UK ISSN 0144-6401) **297, 2357, 3523**
Crystal Properties and Preparation. (SZ) **3816**
Crystal Rainbow. (US ISSN 0891-2971) **4173, 3594**
Crystal Research and Technology. (GW ISSN 0232-1300) **1210**
Crystal Structure Communications see Acta Crystallographica. Section C: Crystal Structure Communications **1210**
Crystallography Reviews. (US ISSN 0889-311X) **1210**
Crystals: Growth, Properties and Applications. (US ISSN 0172-5076) **1210**
Csaladi Haz. (HU ISSN 0865-0047) **2445**
Ctenar. (CS ISSN 0011-2321) **2753, 2909**
Cuaderno. see Notebook (Barstow) **2944**
▼Cuaderno de Historia Obrera. (PY ISSN 1017-6071) **976**
Cuaderno de Informacion Oportuna. (MX ISSN 0186-0445) **858**
Cuaderno de Informacion Oportuna Regional. (MX ISSN 0186-047X) **858**
Cuaderno Literario Azor. (SP ISSN 0572-2969) **2863, 2909**
Cuadernos Americanos. (MX ISSN 0185-156X) **2863**
†Cuadernos Bibliograficos. (SP ISSN 0590-1545) **5175**
Cuadernos C I P C A (Serie Popular). (BO) **1683, 4433**
Cuadernos Cinematograficos. (SP ISSN 0214-462X) **3507**
Cuadernos de Algebra. (SP) **3033**
Cuadernos de Alternativa. (UY) **3889**
Cuadernos de Antropologia. (GT) **237**
Cuadernos de Arquitectura see Quaderns d'Arquitectura i Urbanisme **305**
Cuadernos de Arquitectura Docencia. (MX) **297**
Cuadernos de Arquitectura Mesoamericana. (MX) **297**
Cuadernos de Arquitectura Virreinal. (MX) **297**
Cuadernos de Bibliografia Educacional see Cuadernos de Informacion Educacional **1675**
Cuadernos de Bibliografia Nicaraguense.(NQ) **2981**
Cuadernos de Capacitacion Campesina. (PE) **4369**
Cuadernos de Capacitacion Popular see Cuadernos de Capacitacion Campesina **4369**
Cuadernos de Capacitation. (PE) **4173**
Cuadernos de Ciencias Biologicas. (SP) **436**
Cuadernos de Ciencias Humanas. (CK) **2505**
Cuadernos de Comunicacion Alternativa.(BO) **1334**
Cuadernos de Critica. (AG ISSN 0011-2380) **2863**
Cuadernos de Critica (Mexico). (MX ISSN 0185-2604) **3764, 2863**
Cuadernos de Derecho Internacional Privado. (UY) **2722**

Cuadernos de Economia *see* Consejo Superior de Investigaciones Cientificas. Cuadernos de Economia **656**
Cuadernos de Economia. (CL ISSN 0716-0046) **658**
Cuadernos de Educacion. (CL ISSN 0716-0496) **1624**
Cuadernos de Estudio. (PE) **4262**
Cuadernos de Estudios Cooperativos. (SP) **830**
Cuadernos de Estudios Gallegos. (SP) **4369**
Cuadernos de Estudios Judios. (AG) **1998**
Cuadernos de Estudios Latinoamericanos. (AG) **3889**
Cuadernos de Estudios Medievales. (SP) **2357**
Cuadernos de Etnologia y Etnografia de Navarra. (SP ISSN 0590-1871) **237**
Cuadernos de Filologia. (SP) **2810**
Cuadernos de Filologia Clasica. (SP ISSN 0210-0746) **2810**
Cuadernos de Fitopatologia. (SP ISSN 0213-4128) **2098, 500**
Cuadernos de Geografia. (SP ISSN 0210-086X) **2245**
Cuadernos de Geologia. (SP ISSN 0366-600X) **1558**
Cuadernos de Historia. (CL ISSN 0716-1832) **2404**
Cuadernos de Historia de la Farmacia. (SP ISSN 0210-6566) **3722**
Cuadernos de Historia de la Salud Publica. (CU ISSN 0045-9178) **4100**
Cuadernos de Historia del Arte. (AG ISSN 0070-1688) **323**
Cuadernos de Historia del Arte. (MX ISSN 0185-1691) **323**
Cuadernos de Historia del Islam. (SP) **2429**
Cuadernos de Historia del Islam. Serie Monografica Islamica Occidentalia *see* Cuadernos de Historia del Islam **2429**
Cuadernos de Historia Regional. (AG) **4369**
Cuadernos de Informacion Economica. (VE ISSN 0590-1979) **658**
Cuadernos de Informacion Educacional. (PE) **1675, 398**
Cuadernos de Investigacion Filologica. (SP ISSN 0211-0547) **2810, 2909**
Cuadernos de Investigacion Geografica. (SP ISSN 0211-6820) **2245**
Cuadernos de Investigacion Historia *see* Cuadernos de Investigacion Historica. Brocar **2358**
Cuadernos de Investigacion Historica. Brocar. (SP ISSN 0214-4670) **2358**
Cuadernos de la C E P A L. (UN ISSN 0252-2195) **830**
Cuadernos de Linguistica. (MX) **2810**
Cuadernos de los Institutos. (AG) **2617**
Cuadernos de Maipu. (AG) **2170**
Cuadernos de Marcha. (UY ISSN 0185-061X) **2505**
Cuadernos de Musica. (MX ISSN 0185-1896) **3548**
Cuadernos de Nuestra America. (CU) **2863, 3889**
Cuadernos de Orientacion Familiar *see* Delta (Barcelona) **4174**
Cuadernos de Pedagogia. (SP ISSN 0210-0630) **1624**
Cuadernos de Planeamiento. (AG) **858**
Cuadernos de Poetica. (DR ISSN 0257-6457) **2991**
Cuadernos de Prehistoria. (SP) **270**
Cuadernos de Psicologia. (CL) **4018**
Cuadernos de Psicologia. (CK) **4018**
Cuadernos de Realidades Sociales. (SP ISSN 0302-7724) **4433**
Cuadernos de Salud Publica *see* Public Health Papers **4110**
†Cuadernos de Semiotica. (UY) **5175**
Cuadernos de Sociologia. (NQ ISSN 1010-528X) **4433**
Cuadernos de Trabajo de Historia. (SP) **2358**
Cuadernos de Traduccion e Interpretacion. (SP ISSN 0212-0550) **2810**

†Cuadernos del C R E F A L. (MX) **5175**
Cuadernos del Camino. (AG) **2863**
Cuadernos del Cendes *see* Universidad Central de Venezuela. Centro de Estudios del Desarrollo. Cuadernos del C E N D E S **4455**
Cuadernos del Taller de Folklore. (PE) **2053**
Cuadernos del 26. (UY) **3889**
Cuadernos Economicos Trimestrales. (CU) **893**
Cuadernos Geograficos. (SP ISSN 0210-5462) **2245**
Cuadernos Hispanoamericanos. (SP ISSN 0011-250X) **2863**
Cuadernos Historicos. (PY) **2404, 4058**
†Cuadernos Internacionales de Historia Psicosocial del Arte. (SP) **5175**
Cuadernos Latinoamericanos de Economia Humana *see* Centro Latinoamericano de Economia Humana. Publicaciones **4431**
Cuadernos N T. (SP) **2505**
Cuadernos para el Debate Regional. (PE ISSN 4001-4029) **2486**
Cuadernos para el Estudio de la Estetica y la Literatura. (AG) **2909**
Cuadernos para la Historia de la Evangelizacion en America Latina. (PE ISSN 1012-2737) **2404, 4173**
Cuadernos Politecnicas. (MX) **3889**
†Cuadernos Politicos. (MX ISSN 0185-027X) **5175**
Cuadernos Populares. (PE) **4173**
Cuadernos Salmantinos de Filosofia. (SP ISSN 0210-4857) **3764**
Cuadernos Simancas de Investigaciones Historicas: Monografias. (SP) **2358**
Cuadernos Trimestrales de Poesia. (PE ISSN 0011-2550) **2991**
Cuadernos Universitarios. (NQ ISSN 0011-2569) **2909**
Cuadernos Valencianos de Historia de la Medicina y de la Ciencia. (SP ISSN 0011-2577) **3092, 4306**
Cuatro Titulos. (MX) **1683**
Cub. (UK ISSN 0964-8070) **1309**
Cuba. Centro de Informacion y Divulgacion Agropecuario. Boletin de Resenas. Serie: Arroz *see* Cuba. Centro de Informacion y Documentacion Agropecuario. Boletin de Resenas. Serie: Arroz **86**
Cuba. Centro de Informacion y Divulgacion Agropecuario. Boletin de Resenas. Serie: Avicultura. (CU) **215**
Cuba. Centro de Informacion y Divulgacion Agropecuario. Boletin de Resenas. Serie: Cafe y Cacao *see* Cuba. Centro de Informacion y Documentacion Agropecuario. Boletin de Resenas. Serie: Cafe y Cacao **175**
Cuba. Centro de Informacion y Divulgacion Agropecuario. Boletin de Resenas. Serie: Citricos y Otras Frutales *see* Cuba. Centro de Informacion y Documentation Agropecuario. Boletin de Resenas. Serie: Citricos **175**
Cuba. Centro de Informacion y Divulgacion Agropecuario. Boletin de Resenas. Serie: Forestales *see* Cuba. Centro de Informacion y Documentacion Agropecuario. Boletin de Resenas. Serie: Forestales **2098**
Cuba. Centro de Informacion y Divulgacion Agropecuario. Boletin de Resenas. Serie: Ganado Porcino *see* Cuba. Centro de Informacion y Documentacion Agropecuario. Boletin de Resenas. Serie: Ganado Porcino **215**
Cuba. Centro de Informacion y Divulgacion Agropecuario. Boletin de Resenas. Serie: Genetica y Reproduccion *see* Cuba. Centro de Informacion y Documentacion Agropecuario. Boletin de Resenas. Serie: Mejoramiento Animal **581**

Cuba. Centro de Informacion y Divulgacion Agropecuario. Boletin de Resenas. Serie: Mecanizacion *see* Cuba. Centro de Informacion y Documentacion Agropecuario. Boletin de Resenas. Serie: Mecanizacion de la Agricultura **161**
Cuba. Centro de Informacion y Divulgacion Agropecuario. Boletin de Resenas. Serie: Pastos *see* Cuba. Centro de Informacion y Documentacion Agropecuario. Boletin de Resenas. Serie: Pastos y Forrajes **205**
Cuba. Centro de Informacion y Divulgacion Agropecuario. Boletin de Resenas. Serie: Proteccion de Plantas *see* Cuba. Centro de Informacion y Documentacion Agropecuario. Boletin de Resenas. Serie: Proteccion de Plantas **175**
Cuba. Centro de Informacion y Divulgacion Agropecuario. Boletin de Resenas. Serie: Plantas Medicinales *see* Cuba. Centro de Informacion y Documentacion Agropecuario. Boletin de Resenas. Serie: Plantas Medicinales **500**
Cuba. Centro de Informacion y Divulgacion Agropecuario. Boletin de Resenas. Serie: Riego y Drenaje *see* Cuba. Centro de Informacion y Documentacion Agropecuario. Boletin de Resenas. Serie: Riego y Drenaje **175**
Cuba. Centro de Informacion y Divulgacion Agropecuario. Boletin de Resenas. Serie: Suelos y Agroquimica *see* Cuba. Centro de Informacion y Documentacion Agropecuario. Boletin de Resenas. Serie: Suelos y Agroquimica **175**
Cuba. Centro de Informacion y Divulgacion Agropecuario. Boletin de Resenas. Serie: Veterinaria *see* Cuba. Centro de Informacion y Documentacion Agropecuario. Boletin de Resenas. Serie: Veterinaria **4808**
Cuba. Centro de Informacion y Divulgacion Agropecuario. Boletin de Resenas. Serie: Viandas, Hortalizas y Granos *see* Cuba. Centro de Informacion y Documentacion Agropecuario. Boletin de Resenas. Serie: Hortalizas, Papas, Granos y Fibras **175**
Cuba. Centro de Informacion y Divulgacion Agropecuario. Boletin de Resenas. Serie: Viandas, Hortalizas y Granos *see* Viandas Tropicales. Boletin de Resenas **195**
Cuba. Centro de Informacion y Documentacion Agropecuario. Boletin de Resenas. Serie: Arroz. (CU ISSN 0138-838X) **86**
Cuba. Centro de Informacion y Documentacion Agropecuario. Boletin de Resenas. Serie: Avicultura *see* Cuba. Centro de Informacion y Divulgacion Agropecuario. Boletin de Resenas. Serie: Avicultura **215**
Cuba. Centro de Informacion y Documentacion Agropecuario. Boletin de Resenas. Serie: Cafe y Cacao. (CU ISSN 0138-8436) **175**
Cuba. Centro de Informacion y Documentacion Agropecuario. Boletin de Resenas. Serie: Economia Agropecuaria. (CU) **149**
Cuba. Centro de Informacion y Documentacion Agropecuario. Boletin de Resenas. Serie: Forestales. (CU ISSN 0138-7782) **2098**
Cuba. Centro de Informacion y Documentacion Agropecuario. Boletin de Resenas. Serie: Ganado Porcino. (CU) **215**
Cuba. Centro de Informacion y Documentacion Agropecuario. Boletin de Resenas. Serie: Hortalizas, Papas, Granos y Fibras. (CU ISSN 0138-8231) **175**
Cuba. Centro de Informacion y Documentacion Agropecuario. Boletin de Resenas. Serie: Mejoramiento Animal. (CU) **581, 86**

Cuba. Centro de Informacion y Documentacion Agropecuario. Boletin de Resenas. Serie: Mecanizacion de la Agricultura. (CU) **161**
Cuba. Centro de Informacion y Documentacion Agropecuario. Boletin de Resenas. Serie: Proteccion de Plantas. (CU ISSN 0138-8088) **175**
Cuba. Centro de Informacion y Documentacion Agropecuario. Boletin de Resenas. Serie: Plantas Medicinales. (CU ISSN 0138-8037) **500**, 3722
Cuba. Centro de Informacion y Documentacion Agropecuario. Boletin de Resenas. Serie: Pastos y Forrajes.(CU ISSN 0138-7839) **205**
Cuba. Centro de Informacion y Documentacion Agropecuario. Boletin de Resenas. Serie: Riego y Drenaje. (CU ISSN 0138-788X) **175**
Cuba. Centro de Informacion y Documentacion Agropecuario. Boletin de Resenas. Serie: Suelos y Agroquimica. (CU ISSN 0138-7936) **175**
Cuba. Centro de Informacion y Documentacion Agropecuario. Boletin de Resenas. Serie: Veterinaria. (CU ISSN 0138-8134) **4808**
Cuba. Centro de Informacion y Documentation Agropecuario. Boletin de Resenas. Serie: Citricos. (CU ISSN 0138-8339) **175**
Cuba. Comite Estatal de Estadisticas. Revista Estadistica. (CU) **4569**
Cuba. Mining and Geology. (CU) **3482, 1558**
Cuba. Ministerio de Cultura. Cartelera. (CU) **3889**
Cuba. Ministerio de Educacion Superior. Centro Agricola. (CU) **86**
Cuba. Ministerio de Educacion Superior. Centro Azucar. (CU) **175**
Cuba. Ministerio de la Agricultura. Centro de Informacion y Divulgacion Agropecuario. Noticiero Agropecuario. Suplemento. (CU) **86**
Cuba. Ministerio de la Agricultura. Centro de Informacion y Documentacion Agropecuario. Extranjeras. (CU ISSN 0138-614X) **86**
Cuba. Ministerio de la Agricultura. Centro de Informacion y Documentacion Agropecuario. Noticiero Agropecuario. (CU ISSN 0138-614X) **86**
Cuba. Ministerio de la Agricultura. Centro de Informacion y Documentacion Agropecuario. Noticiero Agropecuario. Suplemento Agrometeorologico. (CU ISSN 0138-6190) **3434, 86**
Cuba. Ministerio de la Industria Ligera. Revista Ciencia y Tecnica. (CU ISSN 0138-7049) **4306**
Cuba. Ministerio del Azucar. Instituto de Investigaciones de la Cana de Azucar. Boletin. (CU) **175**
Cuba. Ministerio del Comercio Exterior. Boletin de Informacion Comercial. (CU) **904**
Cuba. Ministerio del Comercio Exterior. Boletin Semanal de Precios. Petroleo y Metales. (CU) **904, 3684**
Cuba. Ministerio del Comercio Exterior. Reporte Mensual del Azucar. (CU) **711, 9, 904**
Cuba. Ministerio del Comercio Exterior. Reporte Semanal del Azucar. (CU) **904**
Cuba. Ministerio del Comercio Exterior. Semanal de Precios de los Alimentos. Boletin. (CU) **904**
Cuba. Oficina Nacional de Invenciones, Informacion Tecnica y Marcas. Boletin Oficial. (CU ISSN 0011-2615) **3674**
Cuba Azucar. (CU ISSN 0590-2916) **175, 2065**
Cuba: Economia Planificada. (CU ISSN 0864-1420) **998, 893**
Cuba Economic News *see* Cuba Noticias Economicas **5175**
Cuba en Cifras. (CU) **711, 4569**

CUBA

Cuba en el Ballet. (CU ISSN 0864-1307) **1529**
Cuba Foreign Trade. (CU) **904**
Cuba Independienta y Democratica see C I D **3877**
Cuba Internacional. (CU ISSN 0011-2593) **3889**, 323, 2909
†Cuba Noticias Economicas. (CU ISSN 0011-2607) **5175**
Cuba Noticias Turisticas. (CU) **4759**
†Cuba Papel. (CU) **5175**
Cuba: Political Executions and Human Rights. (US) **3941**
Cuba Quarterly Economic Report. (CU ISSN 0138-7766) **711**, 4569
Cuba Review see Cubatimes **3889**
Cuba Socialista. (CU) **2863**
Cuba Update. (US ISSN 0196-0830) **3954**
Cuban American National Foundation. Publication. (US) **3941**
Cuban Economy see Economia Cubana **860**
Cuban Journal of Agricultural Science see Revista Cubana de Ciencia Agricola **116**
Cuban Studies/Estudios Cubanos. (US ISSN 0361-4441) **3889**
Cuban Studies Newsletter - Boletin de Estudios Cubanos see Cuban Studies **3889**
Cuban Topics. (US) **3751**
Cuban Update. (US) **3941**
Cubatabaco. (CU) **4643**
Cubatabaco Internacional. (CU) **4643**
Cubatimes. (US) **3889**
Cube. (US) **3010**, 1297
†Cubit. (UK ISSN 0260-2202) **5175**
Cubs Vine Line. (US ISSN 1047-3084) **4502**
Cucina Bella. (IT) **2557**
La Cucina Italiana. (IT) **2445**
Cue International see Theatre Crafts International **4640**
Cue of Theta Alpha Phi. (US ISSN 0011-2666) **4632**
Cue Sheet. (US ISSN 0888-9015) **3548**, 3507
Cued Speech Annual see Cued Speech Journal **2286**
Cued Speech Center Lines. (US ISSN 1041-6196) **2286**, 1735
Cued Speech Journal. (US ISSN 1059-8243) **2286**, 1735
La Cuenta. (US) **750**, 1998
Cuento. (MX ISSN 0185-2477) **2210**
Cuestion. (MX) **2210**
Cuestiones Actuales del Socialismo see Aktuelna Pitanja Socijalizma **3871**
Cuestiones de la Economia Planificado. (CU) **893**
Cuestiones Economicas. (EC) **775**, 858
Cuestiones Pedagogicas. (SP ISSN 0213-1269) **1747**
Cuicuilco. (MX ISSN 0185-1659) **237**, 2404
Cuihua Xuebao/Journal of Catalysis. (CC ISSN 0253-9837) **1213**
Le Cuir Paris. (FR ISSN 0011-2690) **2736**
Cuisinart Cook see Cooking Edge **2445**
Cuisine et Vins de France. (FR ISSN 0011-2704) **2065**, 380
Cuisine International America & Overseas see C I A O **5156**
Cuisines et Salles de Bains. (CN) **2550**
Cuivre Canadien. see Canadian Copper **3403**
Cukoripar. (HU ISSN 0011-2720) **2065**
Culfordian. (UK) **1309**
Culinarian. (US) **2473**
†Culinary Arts News. (US ISSN 0734-7073) **5175**
Culinary Trends. (US) **2473**
Culpepper Letter. (US ISSN 8750-3697) **1476**, 1433
Cult Awareness Network News. (US) **4018**, 4282
Cult Movie. (IT) **3507**
Cult Observer. (US) **4433**
Cultic Studies Journal. (US ISSN 0748-6499) **4433**
Cultivador Moderno. (SP ISSN 0011-2747) **86**
Cultivar. (FR) **86**, 175
Cultivar. (US) **86**, 2124

†Cultiver en Provence Cote d'Azur. (FR) **5175**
Cultivos Tropicales. (CU ISSN 0258-5936) **175**
Cultura. (BL) **2505**
Cultura. (ES ISSN 0011-2755) **2863**
Cultura (Bologna). (IT) **2505**
Cultura (Quito). (EC) **775**
Cultura (Rome). (IT ISSN 0391-8505) **2505**
Cultura Boliviana. (BO ISSN 0011-2763) **2863**
Cultura e Fe. (BL) **4173**
†Cultura e Mass Media. (IT ISSN 0392-2111) **5175**
Cultura e Scuola. (IT ISSN 0011-2771) **1624**
Cultura, Historia y Filosofia. (PO ISSN 0870-4546) **2358**, 3764
Cultura Ludens. (IT ISSN 0882-3049) **2863**
Cultura Nacional. (AG) **3889**, 4369
Cultura nel Mondo. (IT ISSN 0011-2798) **2909**, 323
Cultura Neolatina. (IT) **2909**
Cultura Peruana. (PE) **237**
Cultura Sarda. (IT) **2358**
Cultura Universitaria. (VE) **2505**
Cultural and Creative News see Art Times **353**
Cultural Anthropology. (US ISSN 0886-7356) **237**
†Cultural Climate. (US) **5175**
Cultural Comercial. (HO ISSN 0011-2836) **834**
Cultural Context of Infancy. (US) **4018**
Cultural Correspondence. (US) **2863**, 2909
Cultural Critique. (US ISSN 0882-4371) **323**
Cultural Cyprus. see Pneumatiki Kypros **2879**
Cultural Democracy. (US ISSN 0730-9503) **2863**
Cultural Dynamics. (NE ISSN 0921-3740) **3764**
Cultural Exchange. see Wenhua Jiaoliu **1724**
Cultural Hermeneutics see Philosophy and Social Criticism **2513**
Cultural Information Service. (US ISSN 0097-952X) **1624**, 1334
Cultural Life. see Kulturen Zivot **2871**
Cultural Life in Sweden see Viewpoint Sweden **2218**
Cultural Policy. (FR ISSN 0252-0869) **3954**, 3889
Cultural - Political - Scientific Reporter see C P S Reporter **5157**
Cultural Post see Arts Review **5139**
Cultural Preview. see Kultur Vorschau Europa **3903**
Cultural Relics. see Wenwu **289**
Cultural Research Institute. Bulletin. (II ISSN 0011-2895) **4369**, 4403
Cultural Studies. (UK ISSN 0950-2386) **4433**, 2863
Cultural Survival. Occasional Papers. (US) **237**, 4433
Cultural Survival Quarterly. (US ISSN 0740-3291) **237**, 4433
Cultural Survival Report. (US) **237**, 4433
Cultural Trends. (UK ISSN 0954-8963) **352**
Cultural Watchdog Newsletter. (US) **2863**
Culture and Art. see Thaqafa wa Fann **346**
Culture and Arts. see Van Hoa Nghe Thuat **348**
Culture and Education see Kultur un Lebn **2011**
Culture & History. (DK ISSN 0902-7521) **237**
Culture and Life. see Kultuur ja Elu **2011**
Culture & Life. see Wenhua yu Shenghuo **2183**
Culture and Life. see Kul'tura i Zhizn **3964**
Culture & Recreation. see Wenhua Yule **2739**
Culture & Tradition. (CN ISSN 0701-0184) **2053**
Culture, Arts and Crafts see China Tourism **4757**
Culture Communique. (CN ISSN 0822-6016) **2177**

▼Culture Concrete. (US) **2991**
Culture de la Ville Europeene. see Culture of European Cities **297**
Culture et Societe. (BD) **2863**
Culture, Illness and Healing. (NE) **237**
Culture, Medicine and Psychiatry. (NE ISSN 0165-005X) **238**, 3092, 3334
Culture Musicale. (IT) **3548**
Culture of European Cities/Culture de la Ville Europeene/Europaeische Stadtkultur. (US ISSN 0893-6862) **297**, 323
Culture of Southeast China. see Dongnan Wenhua **270**
Culture of the Word. see Kultura Slova **2822**
Culture Populaire Albanaise. (AA ISSN 0257-6074) **2053**
Cultured Dairy Products Journal. (US ISSN 0045-9259) **198**
Cultured Marble News. (US) **1114**, 2435
Culturen. (NE) **238**
Cultures see Cultures au Zaire et en Afrique **4369**
Cultures au Zaire et en Afrique. (ZR ISSN 0302-5640) **4369**, 238, 2332
Cultures du Canada Francais. (CN ISSN 0825-2777) **2404**, 1998, 2909, 4369
Cultures et Societe de l'Est. (FR ISSN 0765-0213) **4433**, 2358
▼Cultuur Historisch Jaarboek voor Flevoland. (NE) **2358**
Cultuurtechnisch Tijdschrift see Tijdschrift Landinrichting **194**
†Cum Notis Variorum. (US ISSN 0161-1186) **5175**
Cumberland and Westmorland Antiquarian and Archaeological Society. Research Series. (UK) **270**
Cumberland and Westmorland Antiquarian and Archaeological Society. Transactions. (UK ISSN 0309-7986) **270**
Cumberland Flag. (US) **4235**
Cumberland Law Review. (US ISSN 0360-8298) **2617**
Cumberland Poetry Review. (US ISSN 0731-7980) **2991**
Cumberland Presbyterian. (US ISSN 0011-2976) **4235**
Cumberland-Samford Law Review see Cumberland Law Review **2617**
Cumbria. (UK ISSN 0011-2984) **2193**
Cumbria Farmer. (UK) **86**
Cumitechs. (Cumulative Techniques and Procedures in Clinical Microbiology) (US) **3092**
▼Cumpa. (AG) **3889**
Cumulated Abridged Index Medicus. (US ISSN 0090-1377) **3169**, 9
Cumulated Index Medicus. (US ISSN 0090-1423) **3169**, 9
†Cumulative Bibliography of Literature Examined by the Radiation Shielding Information Center. (US) **5175**
Cumulative Book Index. (US ISSN 0011-300X) **398**, 4126
Cumulative Changes 1986 Code and Regulations. (US) **1091**
Cumulative Index to Biological Abstracts R R M see Biological Abstracts - R R M Cumulative Index **462**
Cumulative Index to Nursing & Allied Health Literature. (US ISSN 0146-5554) **3169**, 9
Cumulative Stock Profits. (US ISSN 0011-3026) **943**
Cumulative Techniques and Procedures in Clinical Microbiology Cumitechs see Cumitechs **3092**
Cunicultura. (SP ISSN 0210-1912) **215**
Cuniculture. (FR ISSN 0152-3058) **215**
Cunninghamia. (AT ISSN 0727-9620) **500**
CUNYForum see C U N Y Forum **2807**
Cunzhen Jianshe/Village and Town Construction. (CC) **297**, 614
Cuoco. (IT) **2473**, 2445
Cuoio Pelli Materie Concianti. (IT ISSN 0011-3034) **2736**, 4360
Cuore e Circolazione see Giornale Italiano di Cardiologia **3208**

Cuore e Vasi. (IT ISSN 0391-8904) **3092**
Cupid's Destiny. (US) **2909**, 30
†Cuprum. (PL) **5175**
Curacao Trade and Industry Association. Newsletter. (NA) **858**
Curacao Trade and Industry Directory. (NA) **1127**
Curandero Newsletter. (US) **3092**
Curare. (GW ISSN 0344-8622) **238**
Curationis see Nursing R S A Verpleging **3284**
Curator. (US ISSN 0011-3069) **3523**
Curierul Romanesc. (RM) **2863**
Curio. (AT) **1309**
Curiospress International. (FR) **398**
Curlew. (CN ISSN 0011-3093) **563**
▼Curley. (US) **2991**
Curly Cues. (US ISSN 0887-2406) **4533**
Currencies and Interest Rates: The Outlook for 1991 and Beyond. (UK ISSN 0957-6584) **775**
Currencies of the World see Die Waehrungen der Welt **743**
Currency and Interest Rate Outlook. (UK ISSN 0955-6656) **775**
Currency Bulletin. (UK) **775**, 943
Currency Confidential. (UK ISSN 0955-5323) **775**
Currency Forecasters' Digest. (US) **859**
Currency Forecasting Service see Currency Confidential **775**
Currency Management see Currency Confidential **775**
Currency Profiles. (UK ISSN 0143-0769) **775**
Currency Quarterly. (UK) **775**
Current. (UK ISSN 0142-1050) **1747**, 2810
▼Current. (NZ ISSN 1170-6244) **1885**
Current. (PK) **3889**
†Current. (SA) **5175**
Current (Great Neck) see N P T A Management News **3663**
Current (Newark). (US) **436**, 1624
Current (Washington, 1960). (US ISSN 0011-3131) **1624**, 3889
Current (Washington, 1982). (US) **1372**, 1624
Current A I D S Literature. (UK ISSN 0952-8075) **3169**, 9, 3218
Current Advances in Applied Microbiology & Biotechnology. (US ISSN 0964-8712) **464**, 398, 489, 550
Current Advances in Biochemistry see Current Advances in Protein Biochemistry **464**
Current Advances in Cancer Research. (US ISSN 0895-9803) **3169**, 398, 3196
Current Advances in Cell and Developmental Biology. (US ISSN 0741-1626) **464**, 398
Current Advances in Clinical Chemistry. (US ISSN 0885-1980) **1200**, 3092
Current Advances in Ecological and Environmental Sciences. (US ISSN 0955-6648) **1973**, 9, 1501
Current Advances in Ecological Sciences see Current Advances in Ecological and Environmental Sciences **1973**
Current Advances in Endocrinology & Metabolism. (US ISSN 0964-8720) **3169**, 398, 571, 3251
Current Advances in Genetics and Molecular Biology. (US ISSN 0741-1642) **464**, 398
Current Advances in Immunology see Current Advances in Immunology & Infectious Diseases **3169**
Current Advances in Immunology & Infectious Diseases. (US ISSN 0964-8747) **3169**, 398, 3184, 3218
Current Advances in Microbiology see Current Advances in Applied Microbiology & Biotechnology **464**
Current Advances in Neuroscience. (US ISSN 0741-1677) **3169**, 398, 3334
Current Advances in Pharmacology and Toxicology see Current Advances in Toxicology **3747**
Current Advances in Physiology see Current Advances in Endocrinology & Metabolism **3169**

Current Advances in Plant Science. (US ISSN 0306-4484) **464**, 398
Current Advances in Protein Biochemistry. (US ISSN 0965-0504) **464**, 398
Current Advances in Toxicology. (US ISSN 0965-0512) **3747**, 398, 1981, 3092
Current Affairs. *see* Epikeri **2184**
Current Affairs Bulletin. (AT ISSN 0011-3182) **2171**
Current African Issues. (SW ISSN 0280-2171) **2332**
Current Agro-Technology for Potato Production. (PK) **86**, 175
†Current Aircraft Prices. (UK) **5175**
Current American Government. (US ISSN 0196-612X) **3889**
Current Anaesthesia and Critical Care. (UK ISSN 0953-7112) **3191**
Current Antarctic Literature. (US) **4306**
Current Anthropology. (US ISSN 0011-3204) **238**
Current Archaeology. (UK ISSN 0011-3212) **270**
†Current Asian & Australasian Directories. (UK) **5175**
Current Australian and New Zealand Legal Literature Index. (AT ISSN 0310-5415) **2698**, 9
Current Award Trends. (US) **2617**
Current Awareness. S D I Service. (Scientific Documentation Centre Ltd.) (UK) **3092**, 436, 4596
Current Awareness Abstracts. (US) **1842**, 9
Current Awareness Abstracts. (UK) **2753**
Current Awareness Bulletin *see* Current Awareness Abstracts **2753**
Current Awareness Bulletin for Library and Information Staff *see* C A B L I S **5155**
Current Awareness in Biological Sciences. (US ISSN 0733-4443) **464**, 9
Current Awareness in Health Education.(US) **3800**
Current Awareness in Particle Technology. (UK ISSN 0376-4842) **1842**, 9
Current Awareness - Library Literature *see* C A L L **2750**
Current Awareness Profile on Quantum Chemistry. (US) **1175**
Current Bibliographies on Science and Technology: Biology, Pharmacy and Food Science. (KO) **464**, 9, 136, 3747
Current Bibliographies on Science and Technology: Chemistry and Chemical Industry. (KO) **1200**, 9
Current Bibliographies on Science & Technology: Electrical Engineering and Electronics. (KO) **1765**, 1842, 1885
Current Bibliographies on Science and Technology: Mechanical Engineering & Construction Engineering. (KO) **3425**, 9, 4614
Current Bibliographies on Science and Technology: Metallurgy, Natural Resources & Energy. (KO) **3425**, 1798, 3405
Current Bibliography of Plastic & Reconstructive Surgery. (US ISSN 0149-5348) **3169**
Current Bibliography on African Affairs. (US ISSN 0011-3255) **3937**, 398, 3954
Current Bibliography on Science and Technology *see* Current Bibliographies on Science and Technology: Mechanical Engineering & Construction Engineering **3425**
Current Bibliography on Science and Technology: Chemistry and Chemical Engineering (Foreign)/Kagaku Gijutsu Bunken Sokuho. Kagaku, Kagaku Kogyo-hen (Gaikoku-hen). (JA ISSN 0011-3271) **1200**, 9, 1842
Current Bibliography on Science and Technology: Chemistry and Chemical Engineering (Japanese)/Kagaku Gijutsu Bunken Sokuho Kagaku. Kagaku Kogyo-hen (Kokunai-hen). (JA ISSN 0385-6003) **1200**, 9, 1842

Current Bibliography on Science and Technology: Civil Engineering and Architecture. *see* Kagaku Gijutsu Bunken Sokuho. Doboku, Kenchiku Kogaku Hen **1845**
Current Bibliography on Science and Technology: Earth Science, Mining and Metallurgy/Kagaku Gijutsu Bunken Sokuho. Kinzoku Kogaku, Kozan Kogaku, Chikyu no Kagaku-hen. (JA ISSN 0011-3301) **1550**, 9, 3425, 3499
Current Bibliography on Science and Technology: Electronics and Electrical Engineering/Kagaku Gijutsu Bunken Sokuho. Denki Kogaku-hen. (JA ISSN 0011-3298) **1842**, 1765, 1885
Current Bibliography on Science and Technology: Energy/Kagaku Gijutsu Bunken Sokuho. Enerugi-hen. (JA ISSN 0387-4001) **1798**
Current Bibliography on Science and Technology: Environmental Pollution/Kagaku Gijutsu Bunken Sokuho. Kankyo Kogai-hen. (JA ISSN 0385-6011) **1973**, 1976
Current Bibliography on Science and Technology: Life Sciences/Kagaku Gijutsu Bunken Sokuho. Raifusaiensu Hen. (JA ISSN 0285-5100) **464**
Current Bibliography on Science and Technology: Management Science and Systems Engineering/Kagaku Gijutsu Bunken Sokuho. Kanri Shisutemu Gijutsu-hen. (JA ISSN 0011-3328) **712**
Current Bibliography on Science and Technology: Mechanical Engineering/Kagaku Gijutsu Bunken Sokuho. Kikai Kogaku-hen. (JA ISSN 0011-331X) **1842**, 9
Current Bibliography on Science and Technology: Nuclear Engineering/Kagaku Gijutsu Bunken Sokuho. Genshiryoku Kogaku-hen. (JA ISSN 0011-3263) **1842**, 9
Current Bibliography on Science and Technology: Pure and Applied Physics/Kagaku Gijutsu Bunken Sokuho. Butsuri, Oyobutsuri-hen. (JA ISSN 0011-3336) **3837**, 9
Current Biographies of Leading Archaeologists. (US ISSN 0361-4735) **418**
Current Biography. (US ISSN 0011-3344) **418**
Current Biography Yearbook. (US ISSN 0084-9499) **418**
▼Current Biology. (US ISSN 0960-9822) **464**
Current Biotechnology Abstracts. (UK ISSN 0264-3391) **464**, 9, 489, 4355
Current Books for Academic Libraries *see* Directions (Bridgewater) **4126**
Current British Directories. (UK ISSN 0070-1858) **712**
Current British Journals. (UK ISSN 0269-0012) **398**
Current Business in Sweden. (SW ISSN 0346-9468) **859**
Current Business Reports. (US) **859**
Current Business Reports: Monthly Retail Trade, Sales and Inventories. (US) **712**
Current Business Reports: Monthly Wholesale Trade: Sales and Inventories. (US ISSN 0363-8553) **835**
Current Canadian Books/Livres Canadiens Courants. (CN ISSN 0316-9448) **4126**
Current Canadian Imprints Catalogued *see* Current Canadian Books **4126**
Current Canadian Ophthalmic Practice *see* Ophthalmic Practice **3303**
Current Career and Occupational Literature (Year). (US ISSN 0161-0562) **3632**, 9
Current Central Legislation. (II ISSN 0253-6579) **2617**
Current Chemical Concepts. (US) **1175**
Current Chemical Reactions. (US ISSN 0163-6278) **1200**, 9
Current Chemical Reactions Inhouse Database for R E A C C S. (US) **1200**

Current Christian Books. (US ISSN 0270-2347) **4212**, 398
Current Christian Books. Authors and Titles *see* Current Christian Books **4212**
Current Christian Books. Titles, Authors, and Publishers *see* Current Christian Books **4212**
Current Citations on Strabismus, Amblyopia, and Other Diseases of Ocular Motility. (US ISSN 0090-1164) **3299**
Current Clinical Chemistry *see* Current Advances in Clinical Chemistry **1200**
Current Clinical Practice. (NE) **3092**
Current Clinical Topics in Infectious Diseases. (UK ISSN 0195-3842) **3218**
Current Comedy for Speakers. (US) **1334**
Current Comments. (US ISSN 0892-5798) **3258**, 436
Current Communications in Cell and Molecular Biology Series. (US) **551**
Current Communications in Molecular Biology *see* Current Communications in Cell and Molecular Biology Series **551**
†Current Compensation References. (US ISSN 0011-3360) **5175**
†Current Concepts in Nutrition. (US ISSN 0090-0443) **5175**
†Current Concepts of Cerebrovascular Disease: Stroke. (US ISSN 0884-4194) **5175**
Current Construction Costs. (US ISSN 0161-7257) **614**
Current Construction Reports. (US) **614**
Current Construction Reports: Housing Starts. (US ISSN 0498-8442) **2486**, 614
Current Construction Reports: Housing Units Authorized by Building Permits.(US) **2486**, 614
Current Construction Reports: New One Family Homes Sold and for Sale *see* Current Construction Reports: New One-Family Houses Sold and for Sale **2486**
Current Construction Reports: New One-Family Houses Sold and for Sale. (US) **2486**
Current Construction Reports: Value of New Construction Put in Place. (US ISSN 0363-8294) **615**
Current Consumer *see* Current Consumer & Lifestudies **2445**
Current Consumer & Lifestudies. (US ISSN 0745-0265) **2445**, 1504
Current Contents Africa. (GW ISSN 0340-7632) **9**, 2332
Current Contents: Agriculture, Biology & Environmental Sciences. (US ISSN 0090-0508) **136**, 9, 1973
Current Contents: Arts & Humanities. (US ISSN 0163-3155) **2519**, 398
Current Contents: Clinical Medicine. (US) **3169**, 9
Current Contents: Clinical Pratice *see* Current Contents: Clinical Medicine **3169**
Current Contents: Engineering, Technology & Applied Sciences. (US ISSN 0095-7917) **1842**, 9
†Current Contents - Health Services Administration. (US ISSN 0893-5165) **5175**
Current Contents in Management *see* Contents Pages in Management **711**
Current Contents: Life Sciences. (US ISSN 0011-3409) **464**, 9, 3169
Current Contents of Academic Journals in Japan. (JA ISSN 0386-7293) **398**
Current Contents of Foreign Journals: Management & Economics. (KO) **712**, 9
Current Contents of Journals in Managerial Sciences *see* Current Contents of Foreign Journals: Management & Economics **712**
Current Contents of Periodicals on the Middle East. (IS ISSN 0333-9858) **9**

Current Contents: Physical, Chemical & Earth Sciences. (US ISSN 0163-2574) **1200**, 9, 1550, 3837
Current Contents: Social & Behavioral Sciences. (US ISSN 0092-6361) **4457**, 9, 1675
Current Developments. (US) **943**
Current Developments *see* Dixson Library Report **2755**
Current Diagnostic Pediatrics. (US ISSN 0172-1232) **3320**
Current Dialogue. (SZ) **4173**
Current Digest of the Post-Soviet Press.(US) **3937**, 9, 2578, 4394
Current Digest of the Post-Soviet Press. Annual Index. (US) **3937**, 9
Current Digest of the Soviet Press *see* Current Digest of the Post-Soviet Press **3937**
Current Digest of the Soviet Press. Annual Index *see* Current Digest of the Post-Soviet Press. Annual Index **3937**
▼Current Directions in Psychological Science. (UK ISSN 0963-7214) **4018**
Current Dynamics. (II) **1074**
†Current Economic and Industrial Relations Indicators. (CN ISSN 0707-5766) **5175**
▼Current Employment. (US ISSN 1055-8292) **3626**
Current Endocrinology. (NE) **3251**
†Current Energy Patents. (US ISSN 0273-298X) **5175**
Current Engineering Practice. (II ISSN 0045-9291) **1818**
Current Esperanto Book List. (US) **2855**
†Current European Directories. (UK ISSN 0070-1955) **5175**
Current Events. (US ISSN 0011-3492) **1252**, 1624
Current Events (Fredericton) *see* N.B. Power News **1904**
Current Events in Namibia. (SX) **3889**
Current Eye Research. (UK ISSN 0271-3683) **3299**
Current Forestry. *see* Gendai Ringyo **2101**
Current Gastroenterology. (US ISSN 0198-8085) **3267**
Current Genealogical Publications. (US) **2148**
Current Genetics. (GW ISSN 0172-8083) **540**
Current Geographical Publications. (US ISSN 0011-3514) **2267**
Current Geological and Geophysical Studies in Montana. (US ISSN 0092-9565) **1558**, 1587
Current Governments Reports. (US) **4058**
Current Governments Reports: City Employment. (US ISSN 0091-9209) **712**
Current Governments Reports: City Government Finances. (US ISSN 0082-9439) **1092**
Current Governments Reports: County Government Employment. (US) **4058**, 976
Current Governments Reports: County Government Finances. (US ISSN 0098-678X) **1092**
Current Governments Reports: Finances of Employee Retirement Systems of State and Local Governments. (US ISSN 0096-3224) **1092**, 976, 4058
Current Governments Reports: Finances of Selected Public Employee Retirement Systems. (US) **1092**, 976, 4058
Current Governments Reports: Government Finances. (US ISSN 0095-3741) **1092**
†Current Governments Reports: Local Government Finances in Major County Areas. (US) **5175**
Current Governments Reports: Public Employment. (US) **976**
Current Governments Reports: Quarterly Summary of Federal, State, and Local Tax Revenue. (US) **1092**
Current Governments Reports: State and Local Government Special Studies. (US) **1092**

Current Governments Reports: State Government Finances. (US ISSN 0090-5895) **712**
Current Governments Reports: State Government Tax Collections. (US) **1092**
Current Governments Reports: State Government Tax Collections see Current Governments Reports: State Government Tax Collections **1092**
Current Guide to Federal Taxes. (US) **1092**
Current Hawaiiana see Hawaiian Acquisition List **402**
Current Health 1. (US ISSN 0199-820X) **3800**, 1747
Current Health 2. (US) **3800**, 1747
†Current Hematology and Oncology. (US ISSN 0739-4810) **5175**
Current Hepatology. (US ISSN 0198-8093) **3092**, 3251
Current History. (US ISSN 0011-3530) **3889**, 2309
Current Housing Reports. (US) **2486**
Current Housing Reports: American Housing Survey for Metropolitan Areas. (US) **2486**
Current Housing Reports: American Housing Survey for the United States and Regions see Current Housing Reports: American Housing Survey for the United States **2486**
Current Housing Reports: American Housing Survey for the United States.(US) **2486**
Current Housing Reports: Annual Housing Survey: Metropolitan Areas see Current Housing Reports: American Housing Survey for Metropolitan Areas **2486**
Current Housing Reports: Housing Characteristics. (US ISSN 0498-8450) **2486**
Current Housing Reports: Housing Vacancies. (US ISSN 0498-8469) **2486**
Current Housing Reports: Market Absorption of Apartments. (US ISSN 0363-8286) **2486**
Current Housing Situation see Housing Market Statistics **720**
Current Income Tax Law. (II) **1092**, 2617
Current Index to Journals in Education. (US ISSN 0011-3565) **1675**, 9
Current Index to Journals in Science and Technology: Biology, Agriculture, Pharmacy see Current Bibliographies on Science and Technology: Biology, Pharmacy and Food Science **464**
Current Index to Journals in Science and Technology: Chemistry and Chemical Industry see Current Bibliographies on Science and Technology: Chemistry and Chemical Industry **1200**
Current Index to Journals in Science and Technology: Electrical Engineering and Electronics see Current Bibliographies on Science & Technology: Electrical Engineering and Electronics **1765**
Current Index to Journals in Science and Technology: Mechanical, Metallurgical, Natural Resources and Construction Engineering see Current Bibliographies on Science and Technology: Mechanical Engineering & Construction Engineering **3425**
Current Index to Statistics. (US ISSN 0364-1228) **3062**, 9, 4569
Current Indian Statutes. (II ISSN 0011-3573) **2617**
†Current Industrial Relations Scene in Canada. (CN ISSN 0318-952X) **5175**
Current Industrial Reports. (US ISSN 0498-8477) **1074**
Current Industrial Reports: Broadwoven Fabrics (Gray). (US) **4628**, 4569
Current Industrial Reports: Fats and Oils. Oilseed Crushings. (US ISSN 0145-5168) **2084**, 4569
Current Industrial Reports: Fats and Oils. Production, Consumption, and Factory and Warehouse Stocks see Current Industrial Reports: Fats and Oils. Production, Consumption, and Stocks **2085**

Current Industrial Reports: Fats and Oils. Production, Consumption, and Stocks. (US) **2085**, 4569
Current Industrial Reports: Finished Fabrics. Production, Inventories, and Unfilled Orders see Current Industrial Reports: Broadwoven Fabrics (Gray) **4628**
Current Information in the Construction Industry. (UK ISSN 0306-1914) **615**
Current Issues (Alexandria). (US ISSN 0161-6641) **3954**
Current Issues in Catholic Higher Education. (US) **1624**, 4262
Current Issues in Criminal Justice. (AT ISSN 1034-5329) **1513**
Current Issues in Higher Education. (US ISSN 0070-1971) **1704**
Current Issues in Music Education. (US ISSN 0070-198X) **1747**, 3548
Current Issues in Psychoanalytic Practice. Journal see Current Issues in Psychoanalytic Practice. Monographs **4018**
Current Issues in Psychoanalytic Practice. Monographs. (US) **4018**
Current Issues in the Financial Securities Industry see Current Issues in the Financial Services Industries **750**
Current Issues in the Financial Services Industries. (US) **750**, 775
Current Issues in Toxicology. (US) **1981**, 3722
Current Japanese Periodicals for (Year). (JA) **4140**, 398
Current Law. (UK ISSN 0011-362X) **2617**
Current Law Index. (US ISSN 0196-1780) **2698**, 9
Current Law Service. (SA) **2617**
Current Leather Literature see Leather Science Abstracts **2738**
Current Lifestudies see Current Consumer & Lifestudies **2445**
Current List on Foreign Patents see Foreign Patents Information Bulletin **3679**
Current Literature in Family Planning. (US ISSN 0092-6000) **598**
Current Literature in Nephrology see Current Literature in Nephrology, Hypertension and Transplantation **3169**
Current Literature in Nephrology, Hypertension and Transplantation. (US) **3169**, 9
Current Literature in Plant Science see Applied Botany Abstracts **461**
Current Literature in Traffic and Transportation. (US ISSN 0011-3654) **4663**, 9
Current Literature on Aging see Abstracts in Social Gerontology: Current Literature on Aging **2280**
Current Literature on Occupational Pensions see Current Literature on Pensions **976**
Current Literature on Pensions. (UK) **976**
Current Literature on Science of Science. (UK ISSN 0379-4504) **4355**, 9, 4614
Current Literature on Social Security see Social Security Library Bulletin **2542**
Current Malaysian Serials (Non-Government)/Terbitan Bersiri Kini Malaysia (Bukan Kerajaan). (MY ISSN 0127-1555) **398**
Current Malaysian Serials - Terbitan Bersiri Kini Malaysia see Current Malaysian Serials (Non-Government) **398**
Current Mammalogy. (US ISSN 0899-577X) **581**
Current Management Literature. (II ISSN 0376-7604) **712**, 9
Current Mathematical Publications. (US ISSN 0361-4794) **3062**
Current Media see Writing (Northbrook) **2977**
Current Medical Diagnosis and Treatment. (US ISSN 0092-8682) **3092**
Current Medical Dialog see C M D **5157**

†Current Medical Information and Terminology. (US ISSN 0070-2005) **5175**
Current Medical Practice. (II ISSN 0011-3700) **3092**
Current Medical Research and Opinion. (UK ISSN 0300-7995) **3092**
Current Microbiology. (US ISSN 0343-8651) **551**
Current Military and Political Literature. (UK ISSN 0954-3589) **3954**, 9, 3454, 3476, 3937
Current Military Literature see Current Military and Political Literature **3954**
Current Minnesota Labor Conditions. (US) **976**
Current Municipal Problems. (US ISSN 0011-3727) **4086**, 2617
Current Musicology. (US ISSN 0011-3735) **3548**
Current Nephrology. (US ISSN 0148-4265) **3387**
Current Neuro-Ophthalmology. (US ISSN 0893-0147) **3299**
Current Neurology. (US ISSN 0161-780X) **3334**
Current Notes on International Affairs see Australian Foreign Affairs and Trade: The Monthly Record **3951**
▼Current Obstetric Medicine. (US ISSN 1051-077X) **3291**
▼Current Obstetrics and Gynaecology. (UK ISSN 0957-5847) **3291**
Current Oceanography. see Kaiyo Jiho **1546**
The Current of Kappa Delta Epsilon. (US) **1309**
†Current Oncology Series. (NE) **5175**
Current Opinion in Anaesthesiology. (US ISSN 0952-7907) **3170**, 9, 3191
▼Current Opinion in Biotechnology. (US ISSN 0958-1669) **489**, 464, 4614
Current Opinion in Cardiology. (US ISSN 0268-4705) **3170**, 9, 3207
Current Opinion in Cell Biology. (US ISSN 0955-0674) **464**, 9, 524
▼Current Opinion in Dentistry. (US ISSN 1046-0764) **3170**, 3230
Current Opinion in Gastroenterology. (US ISSN 0267-1379) **3170**, 9, 3267
▼Current Opinion in Genetics & Development. (US ISSN 0959-437X) **464**, 540
Current Opinion in Immunology. (US ISSN 0952-7915) **3170**, 9, 3184
Current Opinion in Infectious Diseases. (US ISSN 0951-7375) **3170**, 9, 3218
▼Current Opinion in Lipidology. (US ISSN 0957-9672) **3170**, 3207
▼Current Opinion in Neurobiology. (US ISSN 0959-4388) **465**, 3334
Current Opinion in Neurology & Neurosurgery. (US ISSN 0951-7383) **3170**, 9, 3334
Current Opinion in Obstetrics & Gynecology. (US ISSN 1040-872X) **3170**, 9, 3291
Current Opinion in Oncology. (US ISSN 1040-8746) **3170**, 9, 3196
▼Current Opinion in Ophthalmology. (US ISSN 1040-8738) **3170**, 9, 3299
▼Current Opinion in Orthopaedics. (US ISSN 1041-9918) **3170**, 9, 3307
Current Opinion in Pediatrics. (US ISSN 1040-8703) **3170**, 9, 3320
Current Opinion in Psychiatry. (US ISSN 0951-7367) **3170**, 9, 3334
Current Opinion in Radiology. (US ISSN 1040-869X) **3170**, 9, 3357
Current Opinion in Rheumatology. (US ISSN 1040-8711) **3170**, 9, 3369
▼Current Opinion in Structural Biology. (US ISSN 0959-440X) **465**, 475
Current Ornithology. (US ISSN 0742-390X) **563**
Current Orthopaedics. (UK ISSN 0268-0890) **3307**
Current Packaging Abstracts. (US ISSN 0890-4227) **3652**, 9
▼Current Paediatrics. (UK ISSN 0957-5839) **3320**
Current Papers in Physics. (UK ISSN 0011-3786) **3837**, 10, 363

Current Papers on Computers & Control. (UK ISSN 0011-3794) **1404**
Current Perspectives in Social Theory. (US ISSN 0278-1204) **4433**
Current Perspectives on Implantable Devices. (UK) **3230**, 469
Current Physics Index. (US ISSN 0098-9819) **3837**, 10
Current Physics Microform. (US ISSN 0045-9348) **3816**
Current Podiatry see Journal of Current Podiatric Medicine **3380**
▼Current Politics and Economics of Europe. (US ISSN 1057-2309) **3889**, 859
Current Politics and Economics of Japan. (US ISSN 1056-7593) **3889**, 859
▼Current Politics of Russia. (US) **3954**
Current Politics of the Soviet Union see Current Politics of Russia **3954**
Current Population Reports. (US ISSN 0082-9471) **3980**
Current Population Reports: Consumer Income see Current Population Reports: Population Characteristics, Special Studies, Consumer Income **998**
Current Population Reports: Consumer Income. Money Income of Households, Families and Persons in the United States (Year). (US) **998**
Current Population Reports: Local Population Estimates. (US) **3980**
Current Population Reports: Population Characteristics. (US ISSN 0363-6836) **3980**
Current Population Reports: Population Characteristics. Geographical Mobility. (US) **3980**
Current Population Reports: Population Characteristics. Household and Family Characteristics. (US) **3980**
Current Population Reports: Population Characteristics. Marital Status and Living Arrangements. (US) **3980**
Current Population Reports: Population Characteristics. Residents of Farms and Rural Areas. (US) **3981**
Current Population Reports: Population Characteristics. Rural and Rural Farm Population see Current Population Reports: Population Characteristics. Residents of Farms and Rural Areas **3981**
Current Population Reports: Population Characteristics. School Enrollment: Social and Economic Characteristics of Students. (US) **3981**
†Current Population Reports: Population Characteristics. Social and Economic Characteristics of the Black Population. (US) **5175**
Current Population Reports: Population Characteristics, Special Studies, Consumer Income. (US) **998**, 3981
Current Population Reports: Population Estimates and Projections. (US) **3981**
Current Population Reports: Population Estimates and Projections. Estimates of the Population of the United States and Components of Population Change see Current Population Reports: Population Estimates and Projections. United States Population Estimates and Components of Change **3981**
Current Population Reports: Population Estimates and Projections. United States Population Estimates and Components of Change. (US) **3981**
Current Population Reports: Population Estimates and Projections. United States Population Estimates by Age, Sex and Race see Current Population Reports: Population Estimates and Projections. United States Population Estimates by Age, Sex, Race and Hispanic Origin **3981**
Current Population Reports: Population Estimates and Projections. United States Population Estimates by Age, Sex, Race and Hispanic Origin. (US) **3981**

Current Population Reports: Special Censuses. (US) 3981
Current Population Reports: Special Studies. (US ISSN 0498-8485) 3981
Current Practice in Surgery. (UK ISSN 0952-0627) 3378
Current Practices in Dryland Resources and Technology see Dryland Resources and Technology Annual (Year) 4824
Current Practices in Environmental Science and Engineering see Progress in Environmental Science & Technology 1966
Current Practices in Geotechnical Engineering see Progress in Geotechnical Engineering 1578
Current Primate References. (US ISSN 0590-4102) 465, 581
Current Problems in Cancer. (US ISSN 0147-0272) 3196
Current Problems in Cardiology. (US ISSN 0146-2806) 3207
Current Problems in Dermatology. (SZ ISSN 0070-2064) 3246
Current Problems in Dermatology. (US ISSN 1040-0486) 3246
Current Problems in Diagnostic Radiology. (US ISSN 0363-0188) 3358
†Current Problems in Geriatrics. (US ISSN 1052-4002) 5175
Current Problems in Obstetrics and Gynecology see Current Problems in Obstetrics and Gynecology and Fertility 3291
Current Problems in Obstetrics and Gynecology and Fertility. (US ISSN 8756-0410) 3291
Current Problems in Pediatrics. (US ISSN 0045-9380) 3320
†Current Problems in Pulmonology. (US) 5175
Current Problems in Surgery. (US ISSN 0011-3840) 3378
▼Current Problems in Urology. (US ISSN 1052-4010) 3387
Current Procedural Terminology see C P T 3085
Current Programs see Conference Papers Index 3395
Current Programs Annual Index see Conference Papers Annual Index 3395
Current Psychological Research see Current Psychology (New Brunswick) 4018
Current Psychological Research and Reviews see Current Psychology (New Brunswick) 4018
Current Psychology (Hendersonville). (US) 4018
Current Psychology (New Brunswick). (US ISSN 1046-1310) 4018
Current Publications in Legal and Related Fields. (US ISSN 0011-3859) 2698
Current Pulmonology. (US ISSN 0163-7800) 3364
Current References in Fish Research. (US ISSN 0739-540X) 2039
Current Research in Behavioral Sciences in Israel see Current Research in the Social Sciences in Israel 4457
Current Research in Britain. Biological Sciences. (UK ISSN 0267-1956) 465, 10, 2793
Current Research in Britain. Humanities.(UK ISSN 0267-1972) 2519, 10
Current Research in Britain. Physical Sciences. (UK ISSN 0267-1948) 4355, 10, 2793
Current Research in Britain. Social Sciences. (UK ISSN 0267-1964) 4394, 10, 2793
Current Research in British Studies by American and Canadian Scholars. (US ISSN 0590-417X) 2519, 2505, 4369
Current Research in Film. (US ISSN 0748-8580) 3507

Current Research in French Studies at Universities and Polytechnics in the United Kindom see Current Research in French Studies at Universities and Polytechnics in the United Kingdom and Ireland 2855
Current Research in French Studies at Universities and Polytechnics in the United Kingdom and Ireland. (UK) 2855, 398, 2981
Current Research in French Studies at Universities and University Colleges in the United Kingdom see Current Research in French Studies at Universities and Polytechnics in the United Kingdom and Ireland 2855
Current Research in Library & Information Science. (UK ISSN 0263-9254) 2753
Current Research in Social Security/ Recherches en Securite Sociale/ Forschung in der Sozialen Sicherheit/ Investigaciones en la Seguridad Social. (SZ ISSN 0379-0290) 2530
Current Research in the Pleistocene. (US ISSN 8755-898X) 270, 3657
Current Research in the Social Sciences in Israel. (IS ISSN 0334-7303) 4457
Current Research on Medicinal and Aromatic Plants. (Central Institute of Medicinal and Aromatic Plants) (II) 500
†Current Research on Peace and Violence. (FI ISSN 0356-7893) 5176
Current Science. (US ISSN 0011-3905) 1252, 1624, 4306
Current Science. (II ISSN 0011-3891) 4306
Current Science and Technology Research in Japan. (JA ISSN 0288-6022) 4355
Current Sociology/Sociologie Contemporaine. (UK ISSN 0011-3921) 4433
Current Soviet Policies. (US) 3889
Current Studies in Hematology and Blood Transfusion. (SZ ISSN 0258-0330) 3271
Current Studies in Librarianship. (US) 2753
Current Surgery. (US ISSN 0149-7944) 3378
Current Surgical Diagnosis & Treatment. (US ISSN 0894-2277) 3378
Current Sweden. (SW ISSN 1101-6345) 2218
Current Swedish Periodicals. see Svensk Tidskriftsfoerteckning 413
Current Tax Reporter. (II ISSN 0971-0043) 1092
Current Tax Reporter (Supreme Court) see Current Tax Reporter 1092
Current Technical Literature. (CE) 4614, 10
Current Technology Index. (UK ISSN 0260-6593) 4614, 10
Current Therapeutic Research. (US ISSN 0011-393X) 3092
Current Therapeutics. (AT ISSN 0311-905X) 3722
†Current Therapy. (CN) 5176
Current Thoughts & Trends. (US ISSN 1054-8688) 4212
†Current Titles and Abstracts in Immunology, Transplantation and Allergy. (NE ISSN 0169-1244) 5176
Current Titles in Dentistry. (DK ISSN 0903-3483) 3170, 10, 3230
Current Titles in Electrochemistry. (II ISSN 0037-9689) 1200, 10
†Current Titles in Ocean, Coastal, Lake & Waterway Sciences. (US ISSN 0883-4725) 5176
Current Titles in Speleology. (UK) 1550
Current Topics in Bioenergetics. (US ISSN 0070-2129) 485, 3800
Current Topics in Cellular Regulation. (US ISSN 0070-2137) 436
Current Topics in Chinese Science. Section A: Physics. (UK ISSN 0732-4383) 3816

Current Topics in Chinese Science. Section B: Chemistry. (UK ISSN 0732-4391) 1175
Current Topics in Chinese Science. Section C: Mathematics. (UK ISSN 0732-4405) 3033
Current Topics in Chinese Science. Section D: Biology. (UK ISSN 0732-4413) 436
Current Topics in Chinese Science. Section E: Astronomy. (UK ISSN 0732-4421) 363
Current Topics in Chinese Science. Section F: Earth Science. (UK ISSN 0732-443X) 1542
Current Topics in Chinese Science. Section G: Medical Science. (UK ISSN 0732-4448) 3092
Current Topics in Developmental Biology. (US ISSN 0070-2153) 436
Current Topics in Early Childhood Education. (US ISSN 0363-8332) 1624
Current Topics in Environmental and Toxicological Chemistry. (UK ISSN 0275-2581) 1981, 1175, 1946, 3722
Current Topics in Experimental Endocrinology. (US ISSN 0091-7397) 3251
Current Topics in Human Intelligence. (US ISSN 8755-0040) 4018
Current Topics in Learning Disabilities. (US) 4018
Current Topics in Materials Science. (NE ISSN 0165-1854) 3817
Current Topics in Membranes and Transport. (US ISSN 0070-2161) 524, 436, 581
Current Topics in Microbiology and Immunology. (US ISSN 0070-217X) 551
Current Topics in Neuroendocrinology. (US) 3335, 3251
Current Topics in Nutrition and Disease.(US ISSN 0191-2453) 3604
Current Topics in Pathology. (US ISSN 0070-2188) 3092, 436
Current Topics in Remote Sensing. (US ISSN 1045-7208) 2245
Current Topics of Contemporary Thought. (US ISSN 0275-9098) 4306
Current Treatment of Cancer. (US) 3196
Current Treaty Index. (US ISSN 0731-8189) 2698, 2722
Current Trends in Geology. (II) 1558
Current Trends in Life Sciences. (II ISSN 0378-7540) 436
†Current Trends in Programming Methodology. (US) 5176
Current U.S. Government Periodicals on Microfiche see Index to U.S. Government Periodicals 15
Current Vacancies for Graduates. (UK) 3626
Current Weekly. (II ISSN 0011-3123) 2199
Current Work in the History of Medicine. (UK ISSN 0011-3999) 3170
Current World Affairs. (US ISSN 1050-4850) 1274, 398
Current World Leaders. (US ISSN 0192-6802) 3889, 3954
Current World Leaders - Biography and News see Current World Leaders 3889
Current World Leaders - Speeches, Reports and Position Papers see Current World Leaders 3889
Currently: Ontario Museum News. (CN) 3523
Currents. (CN ISSN 0715-7045) 1998
Currents (Des Moines). (US ISSN 0739-7828) 1785, 1946
Currents (Stamford). (US) 4759
Currents (Washington). (US ISSN 0748-478X) 1704
Currents in Comparative Romance Languages and Literatures. (US ISSN 0893-5963) 2909, 2810
Currents in Theology and Mission. (US ISSN 0098-2113) 4173
Currents of Encounter. (NE) 4173

Curricula in the Atmospheric, Oceanic and Related Sciences. (US) 3434, 1704
Curriculum. (UK ISSN 0143-8689) 1747
Curriculum and Teaching. (AT ISSN 0726-416X) 1747, 1721, 1726
†Curriculum Australia. (AT ISSN 0815-4678) 5176
Curriculum Information Center State School Directories see C I C's State School Directories 1692
Curriculum Inquiry. (US ISSN 0362-6784) 1747
▼Curriculum Journal. (UK ISSN 0960-8567) 1747
Curriculum, Materials, Methods. see Kecheng - Jiaocai - Jiaofa 1753
Curriculum Plans see United Methodist Church. Curriculum Plans 5294
Curriculum Product News. (US) 1726, 1747
Curriculum Product Review see Curriculum Product News 1726
Curriculum Review. (US ISSN 0147-2453) 1747
Curriculum Theory Network see Curriculum Inquiry 1747
Curry County Echoes. (US) 2404
Cursillo. (AU ISSN 0011-4057) 4173
Curtains. (UK) 2909
Curtin University. School of Biology. Bulletin. (AT) 436
Curtin University of Technology. Library. Annual Report. (AT) 2753
Curtin University of Technology. Library. Monograph Fiche Catalogue. (AT) 2753
Curtin University of Technology. Library. Western Library Studies. (AT) 2753
Curtin University of Technology. Mulga Research Centre Journal. (AT ISSN 0818-8238) 436, 1946, 2098, 3482
Curtis's Botanical Magazine see Kew Magazine 2133
Cusan see C U S A N 4257
Cusanus-Gesellschaft. Buchreihe. (GW ISSN 0070-2234) 4173
Cushitic Language Studies. see Kuschitische Sprachstudien 2822
Cushman Foundation for Foraminiferal Research. Special Publication. (US ISSN 0070-2242) 3657
Custer-Washita Newsletter see Western Plains Library System Newsletter 2790
Custom Applicator. (US ISSN 0011-4111) 175
Custom Builder. (US ISSN 0895-2493) 615, 1785, 1818
Custom Car. (UK ISSN 0591-2334) 4688
Custom Chemical Synthesis Services in France. (UK) 1127, 1175
Custom Chemical Synthesis Services in Other European Countries. (UK) 1127, 905, 1176
Custom Chemical Synthesis Services in the U.K. (UK) 1127, 1176
Custom Chemical Synthesis Services in West Germany. (UK) 1127, 1176
Custom Home. (US) 615
Custom Integrated Circuits Conference. Proceedings. see I E E E Custom Integrated Circuits Conference. Proceedings 1894
Custom Rodder. (AT ISSN 0817-6795) 4688
Custom Rodder see Popular Cars 4699
Custom Tailor. (US ISSN 0011-412X) 1284
Custom Tailors and Designers Association of America. News Letter. (US) 1290, 1284
Custom Truck & Trail Canada. (CN) 4688
†Custom Vans & Trucks. (AT ISSN 0313-5276) 5176
▼Custom Woodworking Business. (US) 639
Customer Assurance Report see Customer Profit Report 1036
Customer Communicator. (US) 1064
Customer Profit Report. (US) 1036

6100 CUSTOMER SERVICE

Customer Service Management Bulletin *see* Customer Service Manager's Letter **1007**
Customer Service Manager's Letter. (US) **1007**, **1504**
Customer Service Newsletter. (US ISSN 0145-8442) **1007**
Customer Service Representative Connection *see* C S R Connection **2529**
Customer Service Representative Hotline *see* C S R Hotline **1035**
Customs and Practices of Notaries Public and Digest of Notary Laws in the U.S. *see* Journal of Notarial Acts and Recordkeeping Practices **2640**
Customs and Practices of Notaries Public and Digest of Notary Laws in the U.S. *see* Notary Public Practices & Glossary **2662**
Customs Brief *see* Industry Review **912**
Customs Bulletin. (US ISSN 0011-4146) **1092**, **2617**
Customs Imports and Exports Journal. (PK ISSN 0011-4154) **905**, **1092**
Customs Officer's Association of Australia. Fourth Division. Fourth Division Customs Officer. (AT) **905**
Customs Statistics. *see* Haiguan Tongji **719**
Custos. (SA ISSN 0379-9921) **1486**
†Cut. (UK ISSN 0951-5127) **5176**
Cut Your Own Taxes and Save (Year). (US) **1092**
Cutbank. (US ISSN 0734-9963) **2991**
Cutis. (US ISSN 0011-4162) **3247**
Cultivar 2000 *see* Cultivar **86**
Cuttin' Hoss Chatter. (US ISSN 0090-8711) **4533**
†Cutting Edge Quarterly (Ann Arbor). (US ISSN 0882-6951) **5176**
Cutting Through. (US) **1372**
Cutting Tool Business *see* Modern Woodworking **3021**
Cutting Tool Engineering. (US ISSN 0011-4189) **3016**
Cutting Tool - Machining Digest. (US) **3016**
Cuvantul Romanesc. (CN ISSN 0705-8365) **1998**
Cuvar Jadrana. (CI ISSN 0011-4200) **3454**
Cuyahoga Review. (US ISSN 0737-139X) **2909**, **2309**
Cwy Ye: Cherokee Blood Newsletter. (US) **2148**, **1998**
Cyberlog. (US) **3225**, **1459**, **1468**, **1476**
Cybernetic. (US ISSN 0883-4202) **1440**
Cybernetica. (BE ISSN 0011-4227) **1440**
Cybernetics *see* Cybernetics and Systems Analysis **1441**
Cybernetics. *see* Kybernetika **1442**
Cybernetics Abstracts. (English translation of: Referativnyi Zhurnal. Tekhnicheskaya Kibernetika) (UK ISSN 0011-4243) **1404**, 10
Cybernetics and Computing Technology. (English translation of: Kibernetika i Vychislitel'naya Tekhnika) (US ISSN 0739-8417) **1440**, **1413**
Cybernetics and Systems (Bristol). (US ISSN 0196-9722) **1440**, **1436**
Cybernetics and Systems (New York). (US) **1441**, **1436**
Cybernetics and Systems Analysis. (English translation of: Kibernetika) (US) **1441**
Cybernetics: Documents de Travail. *see* Cybernetics: Works in Progress **1441**
Cybernetics: Works in Progress/Cybernetics: Documents de Travail. (BE) **1441**
Cybium. (FR ISSN 0399-0974) **2039**
Cycad Society Newsletter. (US) **500**, **2124**
Cyclamen Journal. (UK ISSN 0143-3571) **2124**
Le Cycle. (FR) **4517**
Cycle (New York, 1952) *see* Cycle World **4517**
Cycle (New York, 1970). (US) **1984**, **1486**

Cycle Australia *see* Australasian Dirt Bike **4515**
Cycle Buyers Guide. (US ISSN 0070-2277) **4688**
Cycle Canada. (CN ISSN 0319-2822) **4517**
†Cycle Guide. (US ISSN 0011-4278) **5176**
Cycle News. (US) **4517**
Cycle Ontario. (CN) **4517**
Cycle Street and Touring Guide. (US ISSN 0272-8923) **4517**
Cycle Touring & Campaigning. (UK) **4517**, **4544**
Cycle Trader. (UK) **4517**
Cycle World. (US ISSN 0011-4286) **4517**
Cycle World Buyer's Guide. (US) **4517**
Cycle World Road Test Annual *see* Cycle World Test Annual and Buyers Guide **4517**
Cycle World Test Annual and Buyers Guide. (US ISSN 0270-2746) **4517**
Cycle 1. (CN) **4517**
Cyclerace Magazine. (JA) **4517**
Cycles (Irvine). (US ISSN 0011-4294) **893**, **4369**
†Cycles (Sharon). (US ISSN 0896-7636) **5176**
Cycletouring *see* Cycle Touring & Campaigning **4517**
Cyclic Amp *see* Signal Transduction & Cyclic Nucleotides **483**
Cycling: B.C. (CN) **4517**
Cycling U.S.A. (US) **4517**
Cycling Weekly. (UK ISSN 0011-4316) **4517**
Cycling World. (UK ISSN 0143-0238) **4517**
Cycling World. (AT) **4517**, **4718**
Cyclisme *see* Velo Magazine **4521**
Cyclist. (US) **4517**
Cyclists' Yellow Pages. (US) **4517**, **1127**
Cyclo 2000. (FR) **4517**
Cyclone. (IS) **3454**
Cyclopedia. (CN) **1624**
Cyclotourisme. (FR) **4517**
Cyclotouriste. (FR) **4517**
Cycnos. (FR ISSN 0992-1893) **2863**
Cycon Communications' Computer P R Update *see* Computer P R Update **5170**
Cyfres Barddoniaeth Pwyllgor Cyfieithiadau Yr Academi. (UK) **2991**
Cyfres Clasuron Yr Academi. (UK) **2910**
†Cyfres Llygad y Ffynnon. (UK) **5176**
Cygnus. (II) **2910**
Cykel- och Sporthandlaren *see* Fritidshandlaren Cykel och Sport **4518**
Cykelbranchen. (DK) **4517**
Cykle-Jul. (DK ISSN 0107-7805) **4517**
Cyklen. (DK ISSN 0109-4211) **4517**
Cykling. (SW ISSN 0280-3038) **4517**
†Cyklistika. (CS ISSN 0011-4413) **5176**
Y Cylchgrawn Efengylaidd. (UK ISSN 0143-0076) **4235**
Cylchgrawn Llyfrgell Genedlaethol Cymru/National Library of Wales Journal. (UK ISSN 0011-4421) **2754**
Cylinder Head & Block Identification Guide. (US) **4688**
Cylinder Theory Reports. (US ISSN 0011-443X) **893**, **943**
Cymbiosis. (US ISSN 0895-6936) **3548**
Cymrir Plant *see* Cip **1252**
Cymro Lluandain/London Welshman. (UK ISSN 0024-6204) **2863**
†Cynegeticus. (US ISSN 0160-2543) **5176**
Cypher. (UK) **3010**
Cypress Basin Genealogical and Historical Society Quarterly *see* Cypress Basin Genealogical and Historical Society Reporter **2148**
Cypress Basin Genealogical and Historical Society Reporter. (US) **2148**, **2404**
Cypriot Woman. *see* Kypria **4846**
Cypris. (US ISSN 0886-3806) **3657**, **581**

Cyprus. Agricultural Research Institute. Agricultural Economics Report. (CY ISSN 0379-0827) **149**
Cyprus. Agricultural Research Institute. Annual Report *see* Cyprus. Agricultural Research Institute. Annual Review **86**
Cyprus. Agricultural Research Institute. Annual Review. (CY) **86**
Cyprus. Agricultural Research Institute. Miscellaneous Reports. (CY ISSN 0253-6749) **86**
Cyprus. Agricultural Research Institute. Technical Bulletin. (CY ISSN 0070-2315) **86**
Cyprus. Budget: Estimates of Revenue and Expenditure. (CY ISSN 0070-2323) **1092**
†Cyprus. Chief Veterinary Officer. Annual Report. (CY) **5176**
Cyprus. Department of Agriculture. Annual Report (Year). *see* Cyprus. Tmimatos Georgias. Etisia Ekthesi (Year) **86**
Cyprus. Department of Agriculture. Land Use Section. Annual Report. (CY) **175**
Cyprus. Department of Agriculture. Land Use Section. Soils and Plant Nutrition Sub-section. Annual Report *see* Cyprus. Department of Agriculture. Land Use Section. Annual Report **175**
Cyprus. Department of Antiquities. Annual Report. (CY ISSN 0070-2374) **270**
Cyprus. Department of Antiquities. Monographs. (CY ISSN 0070-2366) **270**
▼Cyprus. Department of Customs and Excise. Activities and Annual Statistical Data. (CY) **712**, **905**
Cyprus. Department of Customs and Excise. Annual Report. (CY) **905**
Cyprus. Department of Fisheries. Annual Report on the Department of Fisheries and the Cyprus Fisheries. (CY ISSN 0379-086X) **2039**, **1486**
†Cyprus. Department of Social Welfare Services. Annual Report. (CY ISSN 0070-2404) **5176**
Cyprus. Department of Statistics and Research. Agricultural Statistics. (CY ISSN 0379-0924) **136**, **4569**
Cyprus. Department of Statistics and Research. Agricultural Survey. *see* Cyprus. Department of Statistics and Research. Agricultural Statistics **136**
Cyprus. Department of Statistics and Research. Census of Cottage Industry. (CY) **4569**
Cyprus. Department of Statistics and Research. Census of Industrial Production. (CY) **712**, **4569**
Cyprus. Department of Statistics and Research. Census of Poultry. (CY) **136**, **215**, **4569**
Cyprus. Department of Statistics and Research. Construction and Housing Report *see* Cyprus. Department of Statistics and Research. Construction and Housing Statistics **637**
Cyprus. Department of Statistics and Research. Construction and Housing Statistics. (CY) **637**
Cyprus. Department of Statistics and Research. Criminal Statistics. (CY ISSN 0253-8695) **1525**, **4569**
Cyprus. Department of Statistics and Research. Demographic Report. (CY ISSN 0590-4846) **3991**
Cyprus. Department of Statistics and Research. Demographic Survey. (Year). (CY) **3991**, **4569**
Cyprus. Department of Statistics and Research. Economic Indicators. (CY ISSN 0253-8555) **859**, **1074**
Cyprus. Department of Statistics and Research. Economic Report. (CY ISSN 0070-2412) **712**
Cyprus. Department of Statistics and Research. Education Statistics. (CY) **1675**
Cyprus. Department of Statistics and Research. Functions and Services. (CY) **4569**

Cyprus. Department of Statistics and Research. Household Expenditure Survey *see* Cyprus. Department of Statistics and Research. Household Income and Expenditure Survey **712**
Cyprus. Department of Statistics and Research. Household Income and Expenditure Survey. (CY) **712**
Cyprus. Department of Statistics and Research. Imports and Exports Statistics. (CY ISSN 0253-858X) **712**
Cyprus. Department of Statistics and Research. Industrial Statistics. (CY ISSN 1010-1160) **712**
Cyprus. Department of Statistics and Research. Multi-Round Demographic Survey. Migration in Cyprus. (CY) **3991**, **4569**
Cyprus. Department of Statistics and Research. Multi-Round Demographic Survey. Main Report *see* Cyprus. Department of Statistics and Research. Demographic Survey. (Year) **3991**
Cyprus. Department of Statistics and Research. Questionnaires for Censuses and Surveys. (CY) **4569**
Cyprus. Department of Statistics and Research. Short-Term Industrial Indicators *see* Cyprus. Department of Statistics and Research. Economic Indicators **859**
Cyprus. Department of Statistics and Research. Statistical Abstract. (CY ISSN 0253-875X) **4394**, **4569**
†Cyprus. Department of Statistics and Research. Statistical Pocket Book. (CY) **5176**
Cyprus. Department of Statistics and Research. Statistics of Imports and Exports. (CY ISSN 0070-2420) **712**, **905**
Cyprus. Department of Statistics and Research. Tourism, Migration and Travel Statistics. (CY ISSN 0253-8709) **4799**, **3991**
Cyprus. Development Estimates. (CY ISSN 0084-9510) **1092**
Cyprus. Five Year Plans. (CY) **859**
Cyprus. Geological Survey Department. Annual Report. (CY ISSN 0574-8267) **1542**
Cyprus. Geological Survey Department. Bulletin. (CY) **1543**
Cyprus. Geological Survey Department. Memoirs. (CY ISSN 0574-8259) **1543**
Cyprus. Loan Commissioners. Accounts and Statistics for the Year. (CY ISSN 0574-8305) **1092**
†Cyprus. Meteorological Service. Summary of the Weather in Cyprus. (CY ISSN 0379-0916) **5176**
†Cyprus. Mines Service. Annual Report. (CY) **5176**
Cyprus. Ministry of Health. Department of Medical & Public Health Services. Annual Report. (CY) **4117**
Cyprus. Ministry of Labour and Social Insurance. Annual Report. (CY ISSN 0070-2390) **976**, **2530**
†Cyprus. Ministry of Labour and Social Insurance. Department of Social Welfare Services. Social Welfare Report. (CY) **5176**
†Cyprus. Ministry of Labour and Social Insurance. Labour Review. (CY ISSN 0256-8314) **5176**
Cyprus. Official Gazette. (CY) **2184**
Cyprus. Tmimatos Georgias. Etisia Ekthesi (Year)/Cyprus. Department of Agriculture. Annual Report (Year). (CY ISSN 0379-0851) **86**
Cyprus. Tourism Organisation. Annual Report. (CY) **4759**, **905**
Cyprus Bulletin. (CY ISSN 0011-4456) **4058**
Cyprus Chamber of Commerce and Industry Directory. (CY ISSN 0070-2331) **1127**
Cyprus Development Bank. Annual Report. (CY) **775**
Cyprus Diplomatist. (CY) **3954**
Cyprus Economics. *see* Ekonomiki Kypros **663**
Cyprus Life. (CY) **2184**

Cyprus Research Centre. Annual. *see* Kentron Epistemonikon Ereunon. Epeteris **1278**
The Cyprus Review. (CY ISSN 1015-2881) **4370**
Cyprus Time Out. (CY ISSN 0256-1069) **4759**, 1074
Cyprus To-day. (CY ISSN 0045-9429) **1624**
Cyprus Weekly. (CY) **2184**
Cyrano's Journal. (US ISSN 0740-5405) **1334**, 1372
Cyrus J. Lawrence Portfolio Strategy Service. Weekly Economic Data. (US) **943**
†Cystic Fibrosis G A P Conference Reports. (US ISSN 0196-2418) **5176**
Cystic Fibrosis News. (IE) **3092**
Cystisk Fibrose. (DK ISSN 0901-4500) **3092**
Cytobiological Review. *see* Cytobiologische Revue **5176**
Cytobiologie *see* European Journal of Cell Biology **560**
†Cytobiologische Revue/Cytobiological Review/Revue Cytobiologique/Revista Citobiologica. (SZ) **5176**
Cytobios. (UK ISSN 0011-4529) **524**, 3092
Cytogenetics and Cell Genetics. (SZ ISSN 0301-0171) **541**, 3092
Cytokine. (UK ISSN 1043-4666) **541**
Cytokines. (SZ ISSN 1013-9982) **551**, 524, 3092
Cytokines *see* Growth Factors & Cytokines **3185**
Cytologia/Kitorogia. (JA ISSN 0011-4545) **524**
Cytology. *see* Tsitologiya **527**
Cytology and Genetics. (English translation of: Tsitologiya i Genetika) (US ISSN 0095-4527) **541**
Cytometry (New York). (US ISSN 0196-4763) **524**
▼Cytopathology. (UK ISSN 0956-5507) **524**
Cytoskeleton. (UK ISSN 0268-1625) **524**
Cytotechnology. (NE ISSN 0920-9069) **524**, 4596
Czas/Polish Times. (CN ISSN 0045-9445) **1998**
Czasopismo Geograficzne/Geographical Journal. (PL ISSN 0045-9453) **2245**
Czasopismo Stomatologiczne. (PL ISSN 0011-4553) **3230**
Czasopismo Techniczne *see* Czasopismo Techniczne. Series B: Budownictwo **615**
Czasopismo Techniczne *see* Czasopismo Techniczne. Series M: Mechanika **3843**
Czasopismo Techniczne. Series B: Budownictwo. (PL ISSN 0137-5911) **615**
Czasopismo Techniczne. Series M: Mechanika. (PL ISSN 0137-592X) **3843**
Czech Archaeological Society. News. *see* Ceska Archeologicka Spolecnost. Zpravy **269**
Czech Architecture. (CS) **297**
Czech Books for You. (CS) **398**
Czech Books in Print *see* Czech Books for You **398**
Czech Literature. *see* Ceska Literatura **2904**
Czech Mycology. *see* Ceska Mykologie **499**
Czech People. *see* Cesky Lid **237**
Czechoslovak Academy of Sciences. Bulletin. *see* Ceskoslovenska Akademie Ved. Vestnik **4304**
Czechoslovak Academy of Sciences. Hydrobiological Institute. Annual Report. (CS ISSN 0232-0533) **436**
Czechoslovak Academy of Sciences. Institute of Landscape Ecology. Section of Hydrobiology. Annual Report *see* Czechoslovak Academy of Sciences. Hydrobiological Institute. Annual Report **436**
Czechoslovak Agricultural Bibliography. *see* Ceskoslovenska Zemedelska Bilbiografie **136**
†Czechoslovak Cooperator. (CS) **5176**

Czechoslovak Digest *see* Information from Czechoslovakia **2184**
†Czechoslovak Economic Digest. (CS ISSN 0045-9461) **5176**
Czechoslovak Economic Papers. (CS ISSN 0590-5001) **658**
†Czechoslovak Ecumenical News/Tschechoslowakische Oekumenische Nachrichten. (CS) **5176**
Czechoslovak Film. (CS ISSN 0011-4588) **3507**
Czechoslovak Foreign Trade. (CS ISSN 0011-460X) **905**
Czechoslovak Geographical Society. Journal. *see* Ceskoslovenske Geograficke Spolecnosti. Sbornik **2245**
Czechoslovak Glass Review *see* Glass Review **1164**
Czechoslovak Historical Journal. *see* Ceskoslovensky Casopis Historicky **2356**
Czechoslovak History Newsletter. (US) **1998**, 2358, 3954
Czechoslovak Information Bulletin *see* Information from Czechoslovakia **2184**
Czechoslovak Journal of Physics. (US) **3817**
Czechoslovak Life. (CS ISSN 0011-4634) **2184**
Czechoslovak Mathematical Journal. (US ISSN 0011-4642) **3033**
Czechoslovak Medicine. (CS) **3092**
†Czechoslovak Motor Review. (CS ISSN 0011-4650) **5176**
Czechoslovak National Workshop on Seismic Data Acquisition and Computer Processing. Proceedings. (CS) **1588**, 4359
Czechoslovak Newsletter. (US) **3954**, 1998
Czechoslovak Physiology. *see* Ceskoslovenska Fysiologie **570**
Czechoslovak Psychology. *see* Ceskoslovenska Psychologie **4015**
†Czechoslovak Scientific and Technical Periodicals Contents. (CS ISSN 0045-9488) **5176**
Czechoslovak Society of America Fraternal Life *see* C S A Fraternal Life **1995**
Czechoslovak Specialist. (US) **3751**
Czechoslovak Zoological Society. Bulletin. *see* Ceskoslovenska Spolecnost Zoologicka. Vestnik **580**
Czechoslovakia. Federalni Statisticky Urad. Statisticka Rocenka. (CS ISSN 0070-248X) **4569**
Czechoslovakia. Federalni Statisticky Urad. Statisticke Prehledy. (CS) **4569**
Czechoslovakia. Federalni Urad pro Normalizaci a Mereni. Vestnik. (CS ISSN 0042-4714) **3446**
Czechoslovakia & Poland Stamp Catalogue. (UK ISSN 0142-9795) **3751**
Czechout. (UK ISSN 0142-3525) **3751**
▼Czerwony Karzel/Red Dwarf. (PL) **3010**
Czeschin's Mutual Fund Outlook and Recommendations. (US) **943**
Czlowiek i Spoleczenstwo. (PL ISSN 0239-3271) **4018**, 1624, 4433
C1 Molecule Chemistry. (US ISSN 0275-7567) **1176**
▼C2C Abstracts: Japan - Analytical Chemistry. (US ISSN 1049-1260) **1200**, 10
▼C2C Abstracts: Japan - Ceramics. (US ISSN 1049-1252) **1167**, 10, 1200
▼C2C Abstracts: Japan - Chemical Engineering. (US ISSN 1049-1279) **1843**, 10, 1200
▼C2C Abstracts: Japan - Crystallography. (US ISSN 1049-1287) **1201**, 10
▼C2C Abstracts: Japan - Hydrocarbons. (US ISSN 1049-1295) **1201**, 10
▼C2C Abstracts: Japan - Inorganic Chemistry. (US ISSN 1049-1309) **1201**, 10
▼C2C Abstracts: Japan - Materials Science. (US ISSN 1049-1317) **1843**, 10, 1201

▼C2C Abstracts: Japan - Metals. (US ISSN 1049-1384) **3425**, 10, 1201, 1843
▼C2C Abstracts: Japan - Organic Chemistry. (US ISSN 1049-1325) **1201**, 10
▼C2C Abstracts: Japan - Physical Chemistry. (US ISSN 1049-1333) **1201**, 10
▼C2C Abstracts: Japan - Plastics. (US ISSN 1049-1341) **3868**, 10, 1201
▼C2C Abstracts: Japan - Polymer Chemistry. (US ISSN 1049-135X) **1201**, 10
▼C2C Abstracts: Japan - Surface Chemistry. (US ISSN 1049-1368) **1201**, 10, 1843
▼C2C Abstracts: Japan - Textiles. (US ISSN 1049-1376) **4628**, 10, 1201
C2C Currents: Japan - Chemistry. (US ISSN 1049-1228) **1201**, 10
▼C2C Currents: Japan - Computers. (US ISSN 1049-1244) **1404**, 10
▼C2C Currents: Japan - Electronics. (US ISSN 1049-1236) **1765**, 10
C2C Currents: Japan - Materials. (US ISSN 1049-121X) **1843**, 10, 1201
D A A I *see* Design and Applied Arts Index **352**
D A B Information. (Dansk Almennyttigt Boligselskab af 1942 s.m.b.a.) (DK ISSN 0108-4585) **2486**
D A C - Digital Audio Club. (IT) **1885**, 4688
D A C News. (Detroit Athletic Club) (US ISSN 0011-4707) **1297**
D A F i Tal. (Dansk Atletik Forbund) (DK ISSN 0107-4547) **4498**
D A F Magazine. (NE) **4744**
D A F Trucks Magazine *see* D A F Magazine **4744**
D A G - Journal. (Deutsche Angestellten-Gewerkschaft) (GW ISSN 0935-6592) **2582**
D A G - Schiffahrt. (Deutsche Angestellten-Gewerkschaft) (GW) **4726**
D A J V - Newsletter. (Deutsch-Amerikanische Juristen-Vereinigung) (GW) **2722**
D A R. (Deutsches Autorecht) (GW ISSN 0012-1231) **2617**, 4688
D A R - Geluiden. (Vereniging Dierenambulance Rotterdam) (NE) **231**
D A S C News *see* Diamond and Structural Carbon News **1225**
D A S U P. (Deutsch-Africanischen Studentenbundes, Universitaet Pretoria) (SA ISSN 0011-4731) **1309**
D A T Z. (GW ISSN 0723-4066) **2039**
D A U Bladet *see* Brydning **4467**
D A V Magazine. (Disabled American Veterans) (US ISSN 0011-474X) **3454**
D & B Creditnews. (Dun & Bradstreet Ltd.) (UK ISSN 0261-8982) **775**
D & B Reports. (US ISSN 0746-6110) **1037**
D'Ars. (IT ISSN 0011-6726) **323**
D'Art. (SP ISSN 0211-0768) **323**
D B. (Diablo Business) (US) **835**, 826
D B. (Deine Bahn) (GW) **4708**
D B A - Deli Bake Advocate. (US) **2091**
D B B Magazin. (Deutscher Beamtenbund) (GW) **2582**
D B B Nachrichten fuer den Oeffentlichen Dienst. (Deutscher Beamtenbund, Landesbund Bremen e.V.) (GW ISSN 0721-8206) **4058**
D B C C Photographic Society. Newsletter. (Photo Society of Dayton Beach Community College) (US) **3789**, 323
D B - Deutsche Bauzeitung. (GW ISSN 0721-1902) **297**, 615
†D B E D Newsletter. (Department of Business and Economic Development) (US) **5176**
D B I - Pressespiegel. (Deutsches Bibliotheksinstitut) (GW ISSN 0175-6893) **2754**

D B - Kundenbrief. (Deutsche Bundesbahn) (GW ISSN 0011-4758) **4708**
D B M S. (Database Management Systems) (US ISSN 1041-5173) **1476**, 1007
D B P Bulletin. (Development Bank of the Philippines) (PH) **944**, 1114
D B P H News *see* U.S. Library of Congress. National Library Service for the Blind and Physically Handicapped. News **2296**
D B Report. (Deutsche Bundesbahn) (GW ISSN 0072-1549) **4708**
D B S News *see* Satellite News **1342**
D B Z. (Deutsche Bauzeitschrift) (GW ISSN 0011-4782) **298**
D B Z *see* Deutsche Behindertenzeitschrift **3093**
D B Z. (Deutsche Zeitung fuer Briefmarkenkunde) (GW ISSN 0011-4790) **3751**
D B 2 and S Q L - D S Users Bulletin. (US) **1468**, 1459
D C. (CN ISSN 1180-4971) **372**
D C A M M Report. (Danish Center for Applied Mathematics and Mechanics) (DK ISSN 0106-6366) **3033**, 3843
D C A News. (Distribution Contractors Association) (US) **3684**, 615
D C A R A News. (Deaf Counseling Advocacy and Referral Agency) (US) **2286**
D C A Reports *see* Community Affairs **4057**
D C A T Bulletin *see* D C A T Digest **3722**
D C A T Digest. (Drug, Chemical and Allied Trades Association) (US) **3722**, 375, 2065
D C & *see* Dewey Decimal Classification Additions, Notes and Decisions **2754**
D C B A Brief. (DuPage County Bar Association) (US) **2617**
D C C - Camping Fuehrer Europa. (Deutscher Camping Club e.V.) (GW ISSN 0078-3943) **4759**
D C C - Caravan Modellfuehrer *see* D C C - Caravan und Motorcaravan Modellfuehrer **4689**
D C C - Caravan und Motorcaravan Modellfuehrer. (Deutscher Camping Club e.V.) (GW) **4689**, 4544
D C C N *see* Dimensions of Critical Care Nursing **3277**
D C C - Touristik Service. (Deutscher Camping Club e.V.) (GW) **4759**, 4544
D C C Trade Directory. (Delhi Chamber of Commerce) (II) **814**, 1127
D.C. Code Updater. (US) **4086**, 2617
D C Dateline *see* School Administrator **1731**
†D.C. Directory. (US ISSN 0740-3984) **5176**
D C G Informationen. (Deutsche Cichliden-Gesellschaft e.V.) (GW ISSN 0724-7435) **581**
D C I T Update. (Division of Computing & Information Technology) (US) **1394**
D.C. Libraries *see* Intercom (Washington, 1971) **2763**
D C - Magazine/D C - Newsbrief. (NE) **2211**
D C N *see* Daily Commercial News and Shipping Guide **5177**
D C - Newsbrief. *see* D C - Magazine **2211**
D.C. Real Estate Reporter. (US ISSN 0738-6931) **4147**, 2617
D C S Manila Teachers of Secondary English English Quarterly *see* M S T English Quarterly **1754**
D.C. Tracts. (US ISSN 1041-469X) **3214**, 3307
†D C Update. (US) **5176**
D D B *see* Der Deutsche Badebetrieb **3801**
D D F - Das Drogisten Fachblatt *see* D D F - Journal **3722**
D D F - Journal. (GW) **3722**
D D H *see* Das Dachdecker-Handwerk **615**
D D P *see* Doctors for Disaster Preparedness Newsletter **3094**
D D R Film Information. (GW) **3507**

DD 6101

†D D R - Medizin-Report. (GW ISSN 0323-4614) **5176**
†D D R Report. (GW ISSN 0341-5457) **5176**
D D R - Revue. *see* G D R Review **2189**
D D R Studien/East German Studies. (US ISSN 0882-7095) **2309, 3889**
D D S - Der Deutscher Schreiner und Tischler. (GW ISSN 0341-8839) **2558,** 639
†D D V - Analysen. (Danske Vedligeholdelsesforening) (DK ISSN 0107-5403) **5176**
D D W *see* Dianshi Dianying Wenxue **3507**
D D Z *see* Deutsche Drogisten Zeitung **3722**
D E. (CS) **1624, 3889**
D E A B - Rundbrief. (Dachverband der Entwicklungspolitischen Aktionsgruppen in Baden-Wuerttemberg) (GW) **928**
D E A Registration File - Active *see* Drug Enforcement Administration Registration File - Active **3095**
D E C A Dimensions. (Distributive Education Clubs of America) (US) **1037,** 1007
D E C Communicator. (Division for Early Childhood) (US) **1735,** 1235
D E C Computing. (UK) **1466**
D E C Professional. (Digital Equipment Corporation) (US ISSN 0744-9216) **1394**
D E C Today. (UK ISSN 0269-0489) **1394**
D E C U S Israel News. (Digital Equipment Computer Users Society) (IS) **1394**
D E C User. (Digital Equipment Corp.) (UK ISSN 0263-6530) **1394,** 1459
D E C World. (Digital Equipment Corporation) (US) **1453, 1394, 1476**
D E D Brief. (Deutscher Entwicklungsdienst) (GW) **928**
D E - der Elektromeister und Deutsches Elektrohandwerk. (GW) **1885**
D E - Domestic Engineering *see* Plumbing, Heating, Piping **2302**
D E G *see* Organisationen og Tal i Gartneriet **2136**
D E H O G A Jahresbericht. (Deutscher Hotel- und Gaststaettenverband e.V.) (GW) **2473**
D E I *see* Die Ernaehrungsindustrie **2066**
†D E I Cuadernos. (Departamento Ecumenico de Investigaciones) (CR) **5176**
D E K Haandbog. (Dansk Elektroteknisk Komite) (DK ISSN 0107-4466) **1885**
D.E.L.T.A. *see* Documentacao de Estudos em Linguistica Teorica e Aplicada **2811**
D E M A *see* Data Entry Management Association. Newsletter **1449**
D E M A Newsletter *see* Selling Scuba **4555**
D E M M Monthly. (NZ) **1818,** 615, 1785
D E M M Product News *see* D E M M Monthly **1818**
D E R: Disc-Edv-Report. (GW) **1476**
D E S Action Voice. (US) **4100**
D E S Activities Report. (Department of Economic Security) (US) **4058**
D E S C O Resumen Semanal *see* Resumen Semanal **3922**
D E S E D. (Departamento Geral de Selecao e Desenvolvimento do Pessoal) (BL) **859**
D E S Litigation Reporter. (US ISSN 0276-5675) **2617**
D E S Magazine. (US) **4744**
D E S W O S - Brief. (Deutsche Entwicklungshilfe fuer Soziales Wohnungs- und Siedlungswesen e.V.) (GW ISSN 0935-1809) **928,** 2486
†D E T. (GW ISSN 0323-3553) **5176**
D E Technology *see* E S D Technology **1819**
D F Actualites *see* A Propos (Paris) **388**

D F H - Rapport. (Danmarks Fiskeri og Havundersoegelser) (DK ISSN 0109-4432) **2039**
D F N Mitteilungen. (Verein zur Foerderung eines Deutschen Forschungsnetzes) (GW ISSN 0177-6894) **1446**
D F V L R - Forschungsberichte und D F V L R - Mitteilungen *see* D L R - Forschungsberichte **50**
D F V L R Jahresbericht *see* D L R - Jahresbericht **50**
D F V L R - Nachrichten *see* D L R - Nachrichten **51**
▼D F W Empowerment Report. (Dallas - Fort Worth) (US) **1114,** 1998
D F W People - The Airport Newspaper. (US) **4672**
D F Z Wirtschaftsmagazin. (Deutsches Fachzeitschriften-Magazin) (GW ISSN 0341-549X) **1074**
D G A A E Nachrichten. (Deutsche Gesellschaft fuer Allgemeine und Angewandte Entomologie) (GW ISSN 0931-4873) **530**
D G Bank Deutsche Genossenschaftsbank. Bericht ueber das Geschaeftsjahr. (GW) **775**
D G D Schriftenreihe. (Deutsche Gesellschaft fuer Dokumentation e.V.) (GW ISSN 0344-5372) **2754**
D G das Hessische Gastgewerbe. (GW) **2473**
D G Deutsche Gaststaette - Deutsche Hotel-Zeitung Gastwirt und Hotelier. (GW) **2473**
D G E G-Nachrichten. (GW ISSN 0722-0170) **4708**
D G F Mitteilungsblatt. (Deutsche Gesellschaft fuer Fachkrankenpflege e.V.) (GW) **3092**
D G I P - Intern. (GW ISSN 0935-2066) **4018**
D G L R Jahrbuecher. (Deutsche Gesellschaft fuer Luft und Raumfahrt e.V.) (GW ISSN 0070-4083) **50**
D G Review. (US) **1459,** 1468
D G S. (Deutsche Gefluegelwirtschaft und Schweineproduktion) (GW ISSN 0340-3858) **215**
D G S Digest. (Department of General Services) (US) **4086**
D G S Energy Manager *see* D G S Powerlines **4086**
D G S Greenthumb. (Department of General Services) (US) **4086**
D G S P Rundbrief. (Deutsche Gesellschaft fuer Soziale Psychiatrie e.V.) (GW) **3335**
D G S Powerlines. (Department of General Services) (US) **4086**
D G S Reporter *see* D G S Digest **4086**
D G U Information. (Danmark Geologiske Undersoegelse) (DK ISSN 0109-2367) **1558**
D G World. (Data General Australia) (AT) **1453,** 1394
D H Driftsoekonomi *see* Driftsoekonomi **659**
†D.H.E. Data Briefs. (Department of Higher Education) (US) **5176**
†D.H.E. Research Note. (Department of Higher Education) (US) **5176**
D H F - Deutsche Hebe- und Foerdertechnik. (GW ISSN 0723-7901) **3016**
D.H. Hill Library Focus *see* N C S U Libraries Focus **2774**
†D.H. Hill Library Serials Catalog. (US) **5176**
D H Lawrence Review. (US ISSN 0011-4936) **2910**
D H Lawrence Society of North America. Newsletter. (US) **2910**
D H Z Markt. (NE) **1037**
D H Z - Vakhandel *see* De Vakhandel **643**
D I *see* Diario Israelita **1999**
D I A. (Decisions, Issues and Alternatives) (IS) **3889**
D I A. (Daten, Informationen, Argumente) (GW) **4173**
D I A Yearbook. (UK) **1946**
D I A Yearbook - Design Action *see* D I A Yearbook **1946**
D I C Boletin *see* Universidad Autonoma de Santo Domingo. Direccion de Investigaciones. D I C Boletin **4349**

D I C P - The Annals of Pharmacotherapy. (US ISSN 1042-9611) **3722**
D I D S Doings. (Decision Information Display System) (US) **1449**
D I D S - T I R: Master Requirements *see* Defense Integrated System Total Item Record: Master Requirements **3476**
D I D S - T I R: Segments A, B, C *see* Defense Integrated Data System Total Item Record: Segments A, B, C **3476**
D I Dagbladpers. (NE) **2568**
D I F Flyaarbog. (Dansk Ingenioerforening) (DK ISSN 0107-0886) **50**
D I M A *see* Die Maschine **3020**
D I M S Bulletin. (Dansk Idraetsmedicinsk Selskab) (DK ISSN 0108-7320) **3092**
D I N. Catalogue of Technical Rules. (Deutsches Institut fuer Normung e.V. (D I N)) (GW) **4596,** 2617
D I N - Handbooks. (Deutsches Institut fuer Normung e.V. (D I N)) (GW ISSN 0722-7337) **3446**
D I N - Katalog fuer Technische Regeln *see* D I N. Catalogue of Technical Rules **4596**
D I N Mitteilungen & Elektronorm. (Deutsches Institut fuer Normung e.V.) (GW ISSN 0722-2912) **3446**
D I N Newservice *see* Preview (Tempe) **1538**
D I N - Taschenbuecher. (GW ISSN 0342-801X) **3446**
D I S A Information. Measurement and Analysis *see* Dantec Information **3446**
D I S A M Journal. (Defense Institute of Security Assistance Management) (US) **3954,** 1526
D I S C Instruments International. (FR) **3548**
D I S P. (Dokumente und Informationen zur Schweizerischen Orts-, Regional- und Landesplanung) (SZ ISSN 0251-3625) **2486,** 1074
D I T. (Drustvo Inzenjera i Tehnicara "Nafta - Gas") (YU ISSN 0352-0870) **3684**
D I T. (Documentatie en Informatie over Toerisme) (NE ISSN 0012-4109) **4759**
D I T N: Diabetes in the News *see* Diabetes in the News **3251**
D I Y Retailing *see* Do-it-Yourself Retailing **641**
D I Y Week. (Do-It-Yourself) (UK ISSN 0954-8823) **641,** 2501
D I Z Schriften. (Dokumentations und Informations Zentrum Emslandlager) (GW) **3454,** 2358
D J H *see* Danmarks Journalistshoejskoles Aarskrift **1704**
D J H. (Deutsches Jugend - Herbergswerk) (GW) **4759**
D J I - Bulletin. (Deutsches Jugendinstitut) (GW ISSN 0930-7842) **1236**
D J I F Fritid. (Danske Jernbaner Idraets og Fritidsforbund) (DK ISSN 0901-3741) **2435,** 4470
D J K - Aktiv. (Deutsche Jugendkraft e.V.) (GW) **4470**
D J M Enzyme Report *see* BioEngineering News **468**
D J O E F - Haandbogen. (Danmarks Jurist- og Oekonomforbund) (DK ISSN 0108-3627) **2617,** 658
D J Times. (US) **3548**
D K. (DK ISSN 0109-3371) **3751**
D K B Economic Report. (Dai-Ichi Kangyo Bank) (JA ISSN 0385-2350) **859**
D K I Literatur-Schnelldienst Kunststoffe Kautschuk Fasern. (Deutsches Kunststoff-Institut) (GW ISSN 0932-7754) **3868**
D K K F - Nyt. (Dansk Katolsk Kvinde-Forbund) (DK ISSN 0109-1476) **4840,** 4262
†D K - Mitteilungen. (GW ISSN 0011-4987) **5176**
D K Newsletter. (II) **398,** 4126
D L A Bulletin. (Division of Library Automation) (US ISSN 0272-037X) **2796,** 1413

D L D Times. (Division of Learning Disabilities) (US) **1735**
D L G - Mitteilungen. (GW ISSN 0341-0412) **86**
D L R - Forschungsberichte. (Deutsche Forschungsanstalt fuer Luft- und Raumfahrt e.V.) (GW) **50**
D L R G - Aktuell. (GW) **4470**
D L R - Jahresbericht. (Deutsche Forschungsanstalt fuer Luft- und Raumfahrt e.V.) (GW ISSN 0938-2194) **50**
D L R - Mitteilungen. (Deutsche Forschungsanstalt fuer Luft- und Raumfahrt e.V.) (GW ISSN 0176-7739) **50**
D L R - Nachrichten. (Deutsche Forschungsanstalt fuer Luft- und Raumfahrt e.V.) (GW ISSN 0937-0420) **51**
D L S U Business & Economics Review. (De La Salle University) (PH ISSN 0116-7111) **658**
D L S U Dialogue. (De La Salle University) (PH ISSN 0115-6594) **2505,** 4370
D L S U Engineering Journal. (De La Salle University) (PH ISSN 0116-7103) **1818**
D L S U Graduate Journal. (De La Salle University) (PH ISSN 0115-6640) **4370,** 1624, 4306
D L T Flugzeit. (GW) **4759**
D L V - Volkssport-Kalender. (Deutsch Leichtathletik-Verband) (GW) **4470**
D L W Informationen zur Bau- und Einrichtungspraxis *see* D L W Nachrichten **2550**
D L W Nachrichten. (GW ISSN 0172-2867) **2550,** 298
D L Z. (Die Landwirtschaftliche Zeitschrift) (GW ISSN 0011-5010) **86**
D M. (GW ISSN 0416-5551) **1037**
D M. (Disease-a-Month) (US ISSN 0011-5029) **3092**
†D M A Matters. (Direct Marketing Association) (US) **5176**
D M A Statistical Fact Book. (Direct Marketing Association) (US ISSN 1049-6092) **1037,** 30
D M A Washington Report *see* Marketing Advents **1046**
D M C - Bladet. (Danske Motorcyklisters Raad) (DK ISSN 0109-3649) **4517**
D.M.C. Informatiom *see* Netvaerkstedet **1022**
D M I News. (Danish Maritime Institute) (DK ISSN 0905-3549) **4726,** 3434
D M I Update *see* D M I News **4726**
D M M P *see* Direct Marketing Market Place **1037**
D M News. (US ISSN 0194-3588) **1037**
D M S Market Intelligence Reports: Aerospace Companies. (US) **3454,** 51
D M S Market Intelligence Reports: "AN" Equipment. (US) **3454**
D M S Market Intelligence Reports: Anti-Submarine Warfare. (US) **3454,** 51
D M S Market Intelligence Reports: C 3 I. (US) **3455,** 51
D M S Market Intelligence Reports: Civil Aircraft. (US) **51, 3455**
D M S Market Intelligence Reports: Defense Market. (US) **3455,** 51
D M S Market Intelligence Reports: Electronic Systems. (US) **3455,** 51
D M S Market Intelligence Reports: Electronic Warfare. (US) **3455,** 51
†D M S Market Intelligence Reports: Gas Turbine Engines. Gas Turbine Markets. (US) **5176**
D M S Market Intelligence Reports: Latin America & Australasia. (US) **3455**
D M S Market Intelligence Reports: Middle East - Africa. (US) **3455**
D M S Market Intelligence Reports: Military Aircraft. (US) **3455,** 51
D M S Market Intelligence Reports: Military Vehicles. (US) **3455**
D M S Market Intelligence Reports: Missiles. (US) **3455,** 51
D M S Market Intelligence Reports: NATO & Europe. (US) **3455,** 51

D M S Market Intelligence Reports: Ordnance. (US) **3455**
D M S Market Intelligence Reports: Radar. (US) **3455**, 51
D M S Market Intelligence Reports: Space Systems. (US) **3455**, 51
D M S Market Intelligence Reports: Warships. (US) **3455**
D M T Journal. (Deutsche Montan Technologie fuer Rohstoff, Energie, Umwelt) (GW) **3482**
†D M U Luft. A. (DK) **5176**
D M U - Nyt. (Dansk Modelbaads Union) (DK ISSN 0108-8718) **2435**
D M W B E Action Newsletter. (Disadvantaged Minority and Women Business Enterprises) (US) **4649**, 4840
D M Z - Lebensmittelindustrie und Milchwirtschaft. (GW) **198**
D Magazine. (Dallas) (US ISSN 0161-7826) **2224**
D N A see D N A and Cell Biology **476**
D N A. (Deoxyribonucleic Acid) (UK ISSN 0142-8640) **541**, 475
D N A and Cell Biology. (US ISSN 1044-5498) **476**
D N A and Protein Engineering Techniques. (US ISSN 0894-7937) **469**
D N A in Action see D N A Newsletter **2617**
D N A Newsletter. (US) **2617**
D N A Probes. (UK ISSN 0266-6308) **541**, 3258
D N A Tumor Viruses in Non-Primate Systems see I C R D B Cancergram: D N A Tumor Viruses in Non-Primate Systems **5208**
D N O C S - Fins e Atividades. (Departamento Nacional de Obras Contra as Secas) (BL) **175**, 1923
D N P A. (Departamento Nacional de Producao Animal) (BL) **215**
D N R - Kurier. (Deutscher Naturschutzring) (GW ISSN 0179-017X) **1946**
D N R Monday. (Daily News Record) (US) **1290**, 3396
D N V. (Der Neue Vertrieb) (GW ISSN 0343-5598) **4126**
D N Z. Deutsche Naehmaschinen-Zeitung see D N Z International **3016**
D N Z International. (Die Naehmaschinen-Zeitung) (GW ISSN 0011-507X) **3016**
D.O. (Doctor of Osteopath) (US ISSN 0011-5088) **3214**, 2617
D O B I see Dokumentationsdienst Bibliothekswesen **2756**
D O C P A L Latin American Population Abstracts. see D O C P A L Resumenes Sobre Poblacion en America Latina **3991**
D O C P A L Resumenes Sobre Poblacion en America Latina/D O C P A L Latin American Population Abstracts. (UN ISSN 0378-5378) **3991**
D O E. (NE ISSN 0038-7258) **4632**, 1747
D O E This Month. (U.S. Department of Energy) (US) **1785**
D O G Career Guides Series. (Directory of Opportunities for Graduates) (UK) **3626**
D O G S Newsletter. (Council for the Defence of Government Schools) (AT ISSN 0816-7656) **1726**
D O K: Politik - Praxis Recht. (GW ISSN 0936-6156) **2617**, 2530
D O P S Nyt. (Dansk Optisk Selskab) (DK ISSN 0901-4632) **3852**
The D O S Authority. (US ISSN 1055-0569) **1436**
D O S International. (Disk Operating System) (GW ISSN 0933-1557) **1468**
D O S S U Journal. (Dogs on Stamps Study Unit) (US ISSN 0882-0236) **3751**
D O S T Annual Report see Philippines. Department of Science and Technology. Annual Report **4333**
D O S T Technology Journal see Philippine Technology Journal **4606**

D O X A Bollettino. (IT ISSN 0006-6656) **30**
D P A. (Foreningen Danske Praktiserende Arkitekter) (DK ISSN 0105-6603) **298**
D P Budget. (Data Processing) (US ISSN 0890-4316) **1449**
D P F Newsletter. (Diaper Pail Fraternity) (US) **2452**, 1236
D P H Journal. (Division for Physically Handicapped) (US) **2290**, 1735
D P H Newsletter. (Division for Physically Handicapped) (US) **2290**, 1735
D P I Dispatch see Dispatch (Des Moines) **1625**
D P I Yellow Pages see Directory of Nebraska Services **4058**
D P Index and Software Register see Information Technology Index **1452**
D P Market Facts. (Data Processing) (CN ISSN 0711-7884) **1394**, 1037, 1449
D.P.T. Today see Desktop Publishing Today **4143**
D P W see Deutsche Papierwirtschaft **3662**
D P W & C Bulletin see M P W Bulletin **4081**
D P W V - Nachrichten see Nachrichten - Paritaet **4413**
D Pol Bl see Deutsches Polizeiblatt **1513**
D Q R. (Dutch Quarterly Review) (NE) **2910**
D R C Africa News see D R C News **4235**
D R C Book & Monograph Series. (US ISSN 0164-1875) **4100**, 1273, 1946
D R C Historical and Comparative Disasters Series. (US ISSN 0164-1867) **4433**
D R C News. (Dutch Reformed Church) (SA) **4235**
†D R G Monitor. (Diagnosis Related Group) (US ISSN 0741-6512) **5176**
D R I - McGraw-Hill Asian Review. (Data Resources) (US) **859**, 998
D R I - McGraw-Hill Automotive Review.(US) **4689**
D R I - McGraw-Hill Chemical Industry Review. (US) **1176**
D R I - McGraw-Hill Commercial Truck Monitor. (US) **4744**
D R I - McGraw-Hill Cost and Price Review: International Focus. (US) **859**
D R I - McGraw-Hill Cost and Price Review: U S Long-Range Focus. (US) **859**
D R I - McGraw-Hill Cost and Price Review: U S Short-Range Focus. (US) **859**
D R I - McGraw-Hill Cost and Price Review: Utility Focus. (US) **859**
D R I - McGraw-Hill Energy Review. (US) **1785**, 859
D R I - McGraw-Hill Energy Review: Canadian Industry Focus. (US) **1785**
D R I - McGraw-Hill Energy Review: Coal Industry Focus. (US) **3684**, 1785
D R I - McGraw-Hill Energy Review: Electricity Industry Focus. (US) **1801**
D R I - McGraw-Hill Energy Review: Natural Gas Review. (US) **3684**, 1785
D R I - McGraw-Hill European Review. (US) **859**, 998
D R I - McGraw-Hill Industry Review. (US) **859**
D R I - McGraw-Hill Japanese Review. (US) **859**, 998
D R I - McGraw-Hill Latin American Review. (US) **859**, 998
D R I - McGraw-Hill Middle East and African Review. (US) **859**, 998
D R I - McGraw-Hill Monthly Traffic Monitor. (US) **4718**
D R I - McGraw-Hill Review of the U.S. Economy. (US) **859**, 998
D R I - McGraw-Hill Review of the U S Economy: Long Range Focus. (US) **859**, 998
D R I - McGraw-Hill Steel Industry Review. (US) **3405**

D R I - McGraw-Hill Transportation Review. (US) **4649**
D R I - McGraw-Hill U S Executive Report. (US) **658**
D R I - McGraw-Hill U S Forecast Summary. (US) **859**, 998
D R I - McGraw-Hill U S Long-Term Review see D R I - McGraw-Hill Review of the U S Economy: Long Range Focus **859**
D R I - McGraw-Hill U S Markets Review: Industry Focus. (US) **1074**, 859
D R N see Development Research News **928**
D R: The Fashion Business. (UK) **1290**, 1284
D R U Nytt see Henry - D R U Nytt **2868**
D S A M Orientering see Practicus **3143**
D S B. (Die Schweizer Baustoff-Industrie) (GW ISSN 0174-5336) **615**
D S B Bladet. (Danske Statsbaner) (DK ISSN 0900-3665) **4649**
D S F - Journal. (Gesellschaft fuer Deutsch-Sowjetische Freundschaft Berlin West) (GW ISSN 0011-5142) **3954**
D S I Notat. (Dansk Sygehus Institut) (DK ISSN 0106-6706) **2460**
†D S I R Discussion Paper. (Department of Scientific and Industrial Research) (NZ ISSN 0110-5221) **5176**
†D S I R Industrial Information Series. (NZ ISSN 0111-8587) **5176**
D S I R Plant Protection Report. (Department of Scientific and Industrial Research) (NZ ISSN 0114-8818) **530**
D S - Kontakt. (Danmarks Skolelederforening) (DK ISSN 0107-301X) **1624**
D S L's Praesentationshaefte. (Danske Sprog- og Litteraturselskab) (DK ISSN 0105-208X) **2910**, 2810
D S M Letter. (US) **1885**
D S N A Newsletter. (Dictionary Society of North America) (US) **2754**, 2810
D S S Newsletter. (Department of Social Services) (US) **4403**
D S T Z - Deutsche Stenografenzeitung. (GW ISSN 0011-5169) **1058**
D S U -Nyt see D S U'eren **3889**
D S U'eren. (DK ISSN 0905-5525) **3889**
D S W R. (Datenverarbeitung - Steuer - Wirtschaft - Recht) (GW ISSN 0341-5449) **1449**
D S W '12 Nachrichten. (Darmstaedter Schwimm- und Wassersportclub 1912 e.V.) (GW) **4470**
D T E - N E A Newsletter see Down to Earth North East Australia Newsletter **3594**
D T Forum see Dansk Turisme **4759**
D T L - Nyt. (Dansk Teknisk Laererforening) (DK) **1624**
D t t P see Documents to the People **2756**
D T V - Intern. (Deutscher Textilreinigungs-Verband e.V.) (GW) **1281**, 4617
D T W - Deutsche Tieraerztliche Wochenschrift. (GW ISSN 0341-6593) **4808**
D, the Magazine of Dallas see D Magazine **2224**
D u D see Datenschutz und Datensicherung **1434**
D U K H E. (UK) **1693**
D U L J see Dar es Salaam University Law Journal **2618**
D U M A C. (Ducks Unlimited de Mexico, A.C.) (MX) **1946**
D.V.B.A. Publicaciones Tecnicas. (Direccion de Vialidad) (AG ISSN 0011-5177) **4718**
D V Bogen. (Danske Vognmaend Hovedorganisationen) (DK) **4649**
D V Dialog. (UN) **1436**
D V H Quarterly. (Division for the Visually Handicapped) (US) **1236**, 1735
D V I - Infos. (Deutsches Video Institut e.V.) (GW) **1334**, 1394

D V M Management. (Doctor of Veterinary Medicine) (US) **4808**, 1007
D V M Newsmagazine. (US ISSN 0012-7337) **4808**
D V R News. (Division of Vocational Rehabilitation) (US) **4403**
D V R Newsletter see D V R News **4403**
D.V.R.P.C. Annual Report see Delaware Valley Regional Planning Commission. Annual Report **1074**
D V R Report. (Deutscher Verkehrssicherheitsrat e.V.) (GW) **4718**
D V V - Kurier. (Deutscher Volkssportverband) (GW) **4544**
D V W Hessen Mitteilungen. (Deutschen Verein fuer Vermessungswesen e.V.) (GW ISSN 0173-6280) **1864**
D V Z. (Deutsche Verkehrs - Zeitung) (GW ISSN 0012-0901) **4718**
D V Z Brief. (Deutsche Verkehrs - Zeitung) (GW) **4649**
D W see Dialectes de Wallonie **2811**
D. W. (NE) **3722**, 375
D W D Newsletter. (Death with Dignity) (CN ISSN 0847-1797) **2617**, 3092, 3764, 4433
D W I Journal: Law & Science. (US ISSN 0889-0234) **4689**, 2617
D W J - Info. (Deutsche Waldjugend) (GW) **2098**, 3392, 4544
D W V - Kontakt see D T V - Intern **1281**
D W V - Mitteilungen. (Deutscher Wissenschaftler Verband) (GW ISSN 0011-5193) **1297**
D X see Diffusion Express **1843**
D Xers Magazine. (US) **1459**, 1468
Da Cultura. (PO) **323**
Da Huilang Huabao. (CC) **1252**
Daa och Nu. (SW ISSN 0345-2212) **2358**
Da'at. (IS ISSN 0334-2336) **3764**, 3594
Dacca University Studies. Part A: Humanities see Dhaka University Studies. Part A: Arts, Humanities, and Social Science **2506**
Dacca University Studies. Part B: Science see Dhaka University Studies. Part B: Science **4307**
Dacca Visva Vidyalaya Patrika see Dhaka Bisvabidyalaya Patrika **2174**
Dach und Wand. (SZ) **615**
Dach und Wand Abdichtung. (AU) **615**
Dachau Review. (GW ISSN 0934-361X) **2358**
Dachauer Hefte. (GW ISSN 0257-9472) **2358**
Das Dachdecker-Handwerk. (GW) **615**
Der Dachdeckermeister. (GW ISSN 0343-382X) **615**
Dachshund. (GW ISSN 0011-5231) **3710**
†Dachshund Reporter. (US) **5177**
Dachverband der Entwicklungspolitischen Aktionsgruppen in Baden-Wuerttemberg Rundbrief see D E A B - Rundbrief **928**
Dacia; Revue d'Archeologie et d'Histoire Ancienne. (RM ISSN 0070-251X) **270**
Dacoromania. (GW) **2810**, 2910
Dacs Money-Maker Newsletter see Dax Money-Maker Newsletter **658**
▼Dad. (US) **3396**, 1236
Dada - Surrealism. (US ISSN 0084-9537) **2910**, 323
Dade County Teacher see U T D Today **1668**
Dadi Gouzao yu Chengkuangxue/ Geotectonica et Metallogenia. (CC) **1558**, 1588
Dados e Ideias. (BL) **1394**
Dados Estatisticos da Movimentacao de Carga e Passageiros. (BL) **4726**
Dados Estatisticos da Navegacao see Dados Estatisticos da Movimentacao de Carga e Passageiros **4726**
Dados Sobre a Situacao da Agropecuaria Municipal no Estado do Parana. (BL) **149**
Dads Only. (US) **4433**, 1236, 2445
Dae Woo Securities Monthly. (KO) **944**
Daedalus. (SW ISSN 0070-2528) **3523**, 4306, 4596

6104 DAEDALUS

Daedalus (Cambridge). (US ISSN 0011-5266) **2506**, 4306
Daehan Hwahak Hoe Jee. *see* Korean Chemical Society. Journal **1182**
Daemm Journal. (GW) **615**
Daenische Revue *see* Denmark Review **859**
Daenische Rundschau *see* Danish Journal **2185**
Daenische Themen *see* Factsheet Denmark **2001**
Daenischer Handelskalender. *see* Udenrigs Handelskalenderen for Danmark **1156**
Daf Litarbut Yehudit. (IS) **4222**
Daffodil Journal. (US ISSN 0011-5290) **2124**
Daffodils. (UK ISSN 0070-2544) **2124**
Daftar Pengadaan Bahan Indonesia. *see* Indonesian Acquisitions List **403**
Dafuer. (IT) **1252**
†Dagdryp. (DK ISSN 0900-1581) **5177**
Dagelijks Beleid. (NE) **1007**
Dagens Danmark. (DK ISSN 0109-7644) **775**
Dagens Industri. (SW ISSN 0346-640X) **658**
Dagestanskii Etnograficheskii Sbornik. (RU) **4433**, 238
Daginstitutionen. (DK ISSN 0107-6345) **1236**
Dagspressen. (NO ISSN 0011-5304) **2568**
Daguerreotypes. (US) **4498**
Daheim bei der W A G. (Wohnungsaktiengesellschaft Linz) (AU ISSN 0011-5320) **2486**
Daheim und Draussen *see* Gruss aus der Weltweiten Brueder-Unitaet - Daheim und Draussen **4239**
Dahlem Workshop Reports. Life Sciences Research Report. (US) **436**
Dahlem Workshop Reports. Physical and Chemical Sciences Research Report. (US) **3817**, 1176
Dahlias of Today. (US) **2124**
Dai Doan Ket/Great Unity. (VN) **3890**
Dai-Ichi Kangyo Bank Economic Report *see* D K B Economic Report **859**
Daidalos. (GW ISSN 0721-4235) **298**
Daigakuin Kenkyu Nenpo. 3: Rikogaku Kenkyuka Hen/Bulletin of Graduate Studies. Science and Engineering Research Edition. (JA ISSN 0288-8750) **1843**
Daihan Yangrihag Jabji *see* Korean Journal of Pharmacology **3733**
Daiichi Kogyo Seiyaku Shaho. (JA ISSN 0011-5355) **1217**
Daikikyo Shinpojumu. (JA) **363**, 3434
Dailies. (CN) **944**
The Daily. (CN ISSN 0827-0465) **4570**
Daily Action Stock Charts *see* Trendline Daily Action Stock Charts (Monthly) **966**
Daily Athenaeum. (US ISSN 0011-5371) **1309**
Daily Bible Study. (US) **4235**
Daily Blessing. (US ISSN 0011-538X) **4282**
Daily Bread. (UK) **4235**
Daily Bread. (US ISSN 0092-7147) **4282**
Daily Breeze Economic Review. (US) **859**
Daily Bulletin. (HU) **2198**
Daily Bulletin (Brooklyn). (US) **2617**, 859
Daily Californian. (US ISSN 1050-2300) **1309**
Daily Cardinal. (US ISSN 0011-5398) **2224**
Daily Collegian (Fresno). (US) **1309**
Daily Collegian (University Park). (US) **1309**
Daily Commerce. (US ISSN 0279-4195) **4147**
Daily Commercial News and Construction Record. (CN) **615**
†Daily Commercial News and Shipping Guide. (US) **5177**
Daily Congressional Monitor *see* Congressional Monitor **3881**
Daily Construction Service. (US ISSN 0011-5401) **615**
Daily Development. (US) **4018**
Daily Devotions for the Deaf. (US ISSN 0744-9100) **2286**, 4235
Daily Eastern News. (US) **1309**
▼Daily Environment Report. (US ISSN 1060-2976) **1946**, 2617
Daily Express Guide to World Cars. (UK) **4689**
Daily Food & Drink Report. (US ISSN 1044-1433) **2065**
Daily Forty-niner. (US) **1309**
Daily Free Press. (US) **1309**
Daily Gleaner-Farmers Weekly. (JM ISSN 0011-541X) **86**
Daily Gleaner-Food Supplement. (JM ISSN 0011-5428) **2065**
Daily Graphs. American Stock Exchange - O.T.C. (US ISSN 1055-0658) **944**
Daily Graphs. Long Term Values. (US) **944**
Daily Graphs. N.Y.S.E. (US) **944**
Daily Graphs. N.Y.S.E.-O.T.C. *see* Daily Graphs. N.Y.S.E **944**
Daily Graphs. Stock Option Guide. (US) **944**
Daily Hadady Charts. (US) **944**
Daily Jang London. (UK) **1998**, 4218
Daily Journal of Commerce. (US) **835**, 1114
Daily Kent Stater. (US ISSN 0011-5444) **1309**
Daily Labor Report. (US ISSN 0418-2693) **976**
Daily Law Journal Record *see* Journal Record **675**
Daily List of Well Authorizations. (CN) **3705**
Daily Listener. (LB) **2169**
Daily Mail. Money Mail Savers Guide. (UK) **775**, 944
Daily Mail Book of Home Plans. (UK) **298**
Daily Mail Income Tax Guide. (UK) **1092**
Daily Mail Motor Review. (UK) **4689**
Daily Mail Skier's Holiday Guide *see* Audi - Daily Mail Skier's Holiday Guide **5141**
Daily Market Report. (US) **944**
Daily Munger Oilogram. (US) **3684**
Daily Nation. (KE) **2169**
Daily Nebraskan. (US) **1309**
Daily News Digest. (US) **2224**
Daily News Record. (US ISSN 0011-5460) **4618**
Daily News Record Monday *see* D N R Monday **1290**
Daily Newspaper Circulation Rate Book.(US) **41**
Daily Notes. (UK) **4235**
Daily Observer. (LB) **2169**
Daily Orange. (US) **1309**
Daily Other. (US) **1309**
Daily Pacific Builder. (US) **615**
Daily Pennsylvanian. (US) **2224**, 1309
Daily Planetary Guide. (US ISSN 0743-6408) **358**
The Daily Record. (US) **658**, 2617
Daily Report for Executives. (US ISSN 0148-8155) **1007**
Daily Reporter. (US ISSN 0360-9510) **2617**, 775
Daily Shipping News. (US) **4726**
Daily Stock Price Record. American Stock Exchange *see* Standard & Poor's Daily Stock Price Record. American Exchange **964**
Daily Stock Price Record. New York Stock Exchange *see* Standard & Poor's Daily Stock Price Record. New York Stock Exchange **964**
Daily Stock Price Record. Over-the-Counter *see* Standard & Poor's Daily Stock Price Record. Over the Counter Exchange **964**
Daily Summary of the Japanese Press. (JA) **2578**, 2207
Daily Tar Heel. (US) **1309**
Daily Targum. (US) **1309**
Daily Tax Report. (US ISSN 0092-6884) **1092**
Daily Territorial. (US) **658**, 2617
Daily Texan. (US) **1309**
Daily Titan. (US) **1309**
Daily Transcript. (US) **4147**
Daily University Star *see* University Star **1329**
Daily Variety. (US ISSN 0011-5509) **1372**, 3507, 3548, 4632
Daily Walk. (US) **4235**
Daily Washington Law Reporter. (US) **2617**
Daily Watchwords. (UK) **4235**
Daily Weather Maps. (JA) **3434**
Daily Word. (US ISSN 0011-5525) **2292**, 4173
Dainichi-Nippon Densen Jiho - Dainichi-Nippon Cables Review *see* Mitsubishi Densen Kogyo Jiho **1903**
†Dairy. (US) **5177**
Dairy and Field Crop Digest. (US) **198**, 175
Dairy and Food Industries Supply Association. Progress Report. (US) **2065**
Dairy and Food Industries Supply Association. Regulatory Update. (US) **2065**
Dairy and Food Industries Supply Association. Reporter. (US) **2065**
Dairy and Food Industries Supply Association. Technical Bulletin. (US) **2065**
Dairy and Food Sanitation *see* Dairy, Food and Environmental Sanitation **4100**
▼Dairy & Frozen Foods. (US) **2065**
Dairy and Ice Cream Field *see* Dairy Field **2088**
Dairy Contact. (CN ISSN 0383-6207) **198**
Dairy Council Digest. (US ISSN 0011-5568) **3604**
Dairy-Deli Wrap-Up. (US) **2065**
Dairy Economics Research Report *see* University of New England. Department of Agricultural Economics and Business Management. Dairy Economics Research Report (No.) **204**
Dairy Engineering *see* Dairy Industries International **2065**
Dairy Executive. (IE ISSN 0790-732X) **198**
Dairy Executive. Directory and Diary. (IE) **198**
Dairy Extra *see* Dairy Today **199**
Dairy Facts and Figures at a Glance. (CN ISSN 0317-6207) **136**
Dairy Farmer. (UK ISSN 0011-5576) **198**
Dairy Farmer Quarterly Magazine. (CN) **198**
Dairy Field. (US ISSN 0198-9995) **2088**
Dairy, Food and Environmental Sanitation. (US ISSN 1043-3546) **4100**, 198, 2065
Dairy Foods. (US ISSN 0888-0050) **2065**, 198
Dairy Foods Market Directory. (US ISSN 0888-0050) **2065**, 1127
Dairy Foods Newsletter. (US) **198**
Dairy Goat Journal. (US ISSN 0011-5592) **215**
Dairy Goat Society of Australia. Victorian Branch Newsletter. (AT ISSN 0815-9769) **215**
Dairy Guide. (CN ISSN 0011-5606) **198**
Dairy Guide. (II ISSN 0970-3438) **198**
Dairy Herd Management. (US ISSN 0011-5614) **198**
Dairy Herd Workshop. (US) **198**
Dairy India Yearbook. (II ISSN 0970-9932) **198**, 215, 4808
Dairy Industries *see* Dairy Industries International **2065**
Dairy Industries International. (UK ISSN 0308-8197) **2065**
Dairy Industry Leader. (AT ISSN 0810-4115) **199**
Dairy Industry Newsletter *see* Dairy Foods Newsletter **198**
Dairy Industry Research Report *see* Guelph Dairy Research Report **200**
Dairy: Latin American Industrial Report. (US) **199**
Dairy Market News. (US) **199**
Dairy Market Report *see* Dairy Market Review **199**
Dairy Market Review. (CN) **199**
Dairy Markets Weekly. (UK ISSN 0957-8625) **199**
Dairy Policy. (CN ISSN 0318-2967) **199**
▼Dairy Producer. (US) **199**
Dairy Producer Highlights. (US) **199**
Dairy Research Review. (US) **199**
Dairy Review. (CN ISSN 0300-0753) **136**
Dairy Roundup. (US) **199**
Dairy Science Abstracts. (UK ISSN 0011-5681) **136**, 10
Dairy Shorthorn Journal *see* Shorthorn Journal **226**
Dairy Today. (US) **199**
Dairy World. (US ISSN 0736-4962) **199**
Dairyfarming Annual. (NZ) **199**
Dairyman. (US ISSN 0011-572X) **199**
†Dairyman Buyers Guide and Directory. (US) **5177**
†Dairyman's Digest and Primary Producer. (AT) **5177**
Dairymen's Digest. (US ISSN 0745-5399) **199**
Dairymen's Digest: North Central Region Edition. (US ISSN 0745-9033) **199**
Dairymen's Digest: Southern Region Edition. (US ISSN 0164-6486) **199**
Dairynews. (US ISSN 0011-5738) **199**
Dais *see* Monopoly **1318**
Daito Bunka Daigaku Kiyo. Shizen Kagaku/Daito Bunka University. Bulletin. Natural Sciences. (JA ISSN 0912-2346) **4306**
Daito Bunka University. Bulletin. Natural Sciences. *see* Daito Bunka Daigaku Kiyo. Shizen Kagaku **4306**
Daito Hogaku/Journal of Law and Politics. (JA) **2617**
†Daiwa Fishing Annual. (US ISSN 0145-613X) **5177**
Daiyamondo Kabushiki-Toshi-Ban. *see* Diamond, Stock Investment Edition **944**
Dajiang Nanbei/South & North of the Yangtse River. (CC) **2337**
Dak Tar. (II ISSN 0011-5762) **1352**, 1362
Dakar Medical. (SG) **3092**
Dakota Counsel. (US) **1785**, 86, 1946, 3482
Dakota Country. (US ISSN 0194-5769) **4544**
Dakota Homestead Newsletter. (US) **2148**
Dakota Outdoors. (US ISSN 0891-902X) **4544**
Dakota Wallaces Farmer. (US) **86**
†Dakshinesia. (II) **5177**
Dal Comune-Notizie. (IT) **1946**, 1486
DaLee Newsletter. (US) **2148**
Dalennau Testun *see* Choices **5165**
Dalesman. (UK ISSN 0011-5800) **2193**
Dalhousie Dental Journal. (CN) **3230**
Dalhousie Gazette. (CN ISSN 0011-5819) **1309**
Dalhousie Law Journal. (CN ISSN 0317-1663) **2618**
Dalhousie Magazine. (CN) **1309**
Dalhousie Review. (CN ISSN 0011-5827) **2863**, 2910, 3764
Dalhousie University. Computer Centre. Newsletter *see* University Computing and Information Services Newsletter **1401**
Dalhousie University. School of Library and Information Studies. Newsletter. (CN) **2754**
Dalhousie University. School of Library and Information Studies. Occasional Papers. (CN) **2797**, 2754
Dalhousie University. School of Library and Information Studies. Y-A Hotline. (CN) **2754**
Dalhousie University. School of Library Service. Y-A Hotline *see* Dalhousie University. School of Library and Information Studies. Y-A Hotline **2754**
Dalhousie University. University Libraries and School of Library Service. Occasional Papers *see* Dalhousie University. School of Library and Information Studies. Occasional Papers **2797**

Dalian Institute of Aquatic Products. Journal. *see* Dalian Shuichan Xueyuan Xuebao **2039**
Dalian Ligong Daxue Xuebao/Dalian University of Technology. Journal. (CC ISSN 1000-8608) **4306**
Dalian Medical Institute. Journal. *see* Dalian Yixueyuan Xuebao **3092**
Dalian Shuichan Xueyuan Xuebao/ Dalian Institute of Aquatic Products. Journal. (CC ISSN 1000-9957) **2039**
Dalian University of Technology. Journal. *see* Dalian Ligong Daxue Xuebao **4306**
Dalian Yixueyuan Xuebao/Dalian Medical Institute. Journal. (CC ISSN 1000-5676) **3092**
▼Dalil ad-Dawriat li-Dawlat al-Imarat al-Arabiyyah al-Muttahidah/Directory of the Periodicals in the United Arab Emirates. (TS) **398**
Dalil al-Ahram al-Tibbi/Al-Ahram Medical Guide. (UA) **3092**
Dalil al-Dara'ib/Tax Guide. (UA) **1092**
Dalil Al-Kuwait al-Yawm. (KU) **2698**
Dalil el Arab. *see* Arab Directory **1991**
Dalka. (SO ISSN 0045-9542) **2332**
Dallas. (US ISSN 0011-5835) **814**
Dallas Apparel News. (US ISSN 0279-4888) **1284**
Dallas Business Journal. (US) **658**
Dallas Child. (US) **1236**
Dallas Cowboys Outlook. (US) **4502**
Dallas Craftsman. (US) **2582**
Dallas - Fort Worth Business Journal. (US) **658**
Dallas - Fort Worth Empowerment Report *see* D F W Empowerment Report **1114**
Dallas - Fort Worth Home Buyer's Guide. (US) **4147, 2486**
Dallas - Fort Worth Living *see* Dallas - Fort Worth Home Buyer's Guide **4147**
Dallas Genealogical Society. Quarterly *see* Dallas Quarterly **2148**
Dallas Greensheet. (US) **1504**
Dallas Institute of Humanities and Culture. Institute Newsletter. (US) **2506**
Dallas Magazine *see* D Magazine **2224**
Dallas Medical Journal. (US ISSN 0011-586X) **3092**
†Dallas Museum of Art. Annual Report. (US) **5177**
†Dallas Opera Magazine. (US ISSN 0731-8529) **5177**
Dallas Quarterly. (US) **2148, 2404**
Dallas Recovery. (US) **3800**
Dallo Scoglio di Santa Rita. (IT) **4173**
Dalmatian Quarterly. (US) **3710**
Dalton Carpet Journal. (US) **2558**
Dalton Transactions *see* Royal Society of Chemistry. Journal: Dalton Transactions **1214**
▼Dalton's Allentown, Bethlehem, Lancaster Metropolitan Directory: Business - Industry. (US) **1127**
Dalton's Baltimore - Washington Metropolitan Directory: Business - Industry. (US) **1127**
Dalton's New York Metropolitan Directory: Business - Industry. (US) **1128**
Dalton's Philadelphia Metropolitan Directory: Business - Industry. (US) **1128**
Daltons Weekly. (UK ISSN 0011-5894) **4147, 30**
Dalyaglyady Litaraturny Zbornik. (BW) **2910**
Damals. (GW ISSN 0011-5908) **2309**
Damascus Road. (US) **2910**
Damernas Vaerld. (SW ISSN 0011-5916) **2218, 1290**
Damon Runyon Memorial Fund for Cancer Research. Report *see* Damon Runyon - Walter Winchell Cancer Research Fund. Annual Report **3196**
Damon Runyon - Walter Winchell Cancer Research Fund. Annual Report. (US ISSN 0095-6775) **3196**
Dampf und Reise. (GW ISSN 0933-7598) **4708, 4759**

Damron Road Atlas. (US) **4759, 2245, 2452**
Het Damspel. (NE ISSN 0011-5959) **4470**
▼Dan Haul. (UK ISSN 0965-7746) **1486, 581**
Dan River Anthology (Year). (US) **2910**
Dan Sha News *see* Dannzha **1998**
Dana. (DK ISSN 0106-553X) **2039**
Dana-Report. (DK ISSN 0070-2668) **1603, 436**
Dana Review. (US) **1309**
Danas/Today. (CI) **2863**
Dance & Dancers. (UK ISSN 0011-5983) **1529**
Dance and Music Series. (US) **1529, 3548**
Dance Art. *see* Tantsovo Izkustvo **1532**
Dance Australia. (AT ISSN 0159-6330) **1529, 323, 1624, 3092**
Dance Book Forum. (US ISSN 0271-9940) **1529**
Dance Chronicle. (US ISSN 0147-2526) **1529**
Dance Connection. (CN ISSN 0838-1313) **1529**
Dance: Current Selected Research. (US ISSN 0894-4849) **1529, 2309**
Dance Directory (Year). (US ISSN 0070-2676) **1529**
Dance Exercise Today *see* I D E A Today **3804**
Dance Films Association. Bulletin *see* Dance on Camera News **1530**
Dance Gazette. (UK ISSN 0306-0128) **1529**
Dance Magazine. (US ISSN 0011-6009) **1529**
Dance Magazine Annual Performing Arts Directory *see* Stern's Performing Arts Directory **1532**
Dance Magazine College Guide. (US ISSN 0193-1202) **1529, 1693**
Dance Magazine Directory of College and University Dance *see* Dance Magazine College Guide **1529**
Dance Medicine-Health Newsletter. (US) **3307, 1530, 3371**
Dance News. (NZ ISSN 0112-4951) **1530**
Dance Notation Bureau Newsletter. (US) **1530, 2810**
†Dance Notation Journal. (US ISSN 0737-0997) **5177**
Dance on Camera News. (US) **1530, 3507**
Dance Pages. (US) **1530**
Dance Research. (UK ISSN 0264-2875) **1530**
Dance Research Journal. (US ISSN 0149-7677) **1530**
Dance Teacher. (UK) **1530, 1747**
Dance Teacher Now. (US ISSN 0199-1795) **1530, 1624**
Dance Theatre Journal. (UK) **1530**
Dancers for Disarmament Newsletter. (US) **1530, 3890**
Dancing. *see* Wudao **1532**
Dancing Times. (UK ISSN 0011-605X) **1530**
Dancing U S A. (US ISSN 1053-5454) **1530, 3548**
Dancing Year Book. (UK) **1530**
Dancscene. (US ISSN 0745-3949) **1530**
Dandelion. (CN) **2991, 323, 2910**
Dandelion. (US ISSN 3764, 3890**
Dandoknotater. (DK ISSN 0108-7606) **4306**
Dandy. (SP ISSN 0011-6068) **1290**
Daneshgah-e Esfahan. Daneshkade-Ye Pezeshki. Nashriye-Ye Ketabkhaneh. *see* University of Esfahan. Faculty of Medicine. Library Bulletin **5297**
Daneshgah-e Ferdowsi. Daneshkade-Ye Elahiyat Va Ma'aref-e Eslami. Nashriyeh. *see* University of Ferdowsi. Faculty of Theology and Islamic Studies. Publication **4221**
Daneshgah-e Ferdowsi. Daneshkade-Ye Pazeshki. Nameh. *see* University of Ferdowsi. Faculty of Medicine. Letters **3160**
Daneshgah-e Jondishapur. Daneshkade-Ye Pezesaki. Bultan-e Ketabkhaneh. *see* Jundi Shapur University. Faculty of Medicine. Library Bulletin **2766**

Daneshgah-e Tabriz. Daneshkade-ye Ulume Ensani va Ijtima'i. Nashriyeh. *see* University of Tabriz. Faculty of Human and Social Sciences. Publication **2518**
Daneshgah-e Teheran. Daneshkade-Ye Darusazi. Majalleh. *see* University of Teheran. School of Pharmacy. Journal **3745**
Daneshgah-e Teheran. Daneshkade-Ye Adabiyat va 'olum-e Ensani. Majalle-Ye Iranshenasi. *see* University of Teheran. Faculty of Letters and Humanities. Bulletin of Iranian Studies **2432**
Daneshgah-e Teheran. Daneshkade-Ye Dam'ezeshki. Nashriye-Ye Ketabkhaneh. *see* University of Teheran. Faculty of Veterinary Medicine. Library Bulletin **5298**
Daneshgah-e Teheran. Daneshkade-Ye Pezeshki. Nashriye-Ye Ketabkhaneh. *see* University of Teheran. Faculty of Medicine. Library Bulletin **2789**
Daneshgah-e Teheran. Ketabkhane-Ye Markazi. Nashriye-Ye Ketabkhaneh. *see* University of Teheran. Central Library. Library Bulletin **2789**
Daneshkade Pezeshki. (IR) **3092**
Daneshmand. (IR ISSN 1011-3495) **4306, 4596**
Danfoss Journal. (DK ISSN 0011-6076) **1818**
Dang Jian/Party Construction. (CC) **3890**
Dang'an Xue Yanjiu. (CC) **2754**
Dang'an yu Lishi/Archives and History. (US ISSN 1000-4165) **2754, 2309**
Dang'anxue Tongxun/Archives Science Bulletin. (CC ISSN 1001-201X) **2754, 2337**
Dangdai/Contemporary Era. (CC ISSN 0257-0165) **2910**
Dangdai Dianying/Contemporary Cinema. (CC ISSN 1002-4646) **3507**
Dangdai Meisujia/Modern Artist. (CC) **323**
Dangdai Sulian Wenxue *see* Sulian Wenxue (Liankan) **2967**
Dangdai Tiyu/Contemporary Sports. (CC) **4470**
Dangdai Waiguo Wenxue/Contemporary Foreign Literature. (US ISSN 1001-1757) **2910**
Dangdai Wentan/Modern Literary World.(CC) **2910**
Dangdai Wentan Bao. (CC) **2863**
Dangdai Xiaoshuo/Contemporary Novels. (CC ISSN 1000-7946) **2910**
Dangdai Xiju/Contemporary Drama. (CC) **4632, 1372**
Dangdai Xumu/Modern Animal Husbandry. (CC) **215**
Dangdai Zuojia/Modern Writers. (CC) **2910**
Dangdai Zuojia Pinglun/Contemporary Writers Review. (CC) **2910**
Dangerous Properties of Industrial Materials Report. (US ISSN 0270-3777) **3616**
Dangxiao Luntan/C C P Party School Magazine. (US) **3890, 1310**
Dania Polyglotta. (DK ISSN 0070-2714) **2981, 398**
Danica. (US) **4282, 1998**
Danish Bibliography of Computer Science. *see* Dansk E D B Bibliografi **1404**
Danish Building Industry. *see* Byggeindustrien **607**
Danish Contract *see* Nordic Contract **2554**
Danish Dental Journal. *see* Tandlaegebladet **3243**
Danish Engineer's Weekly. *see* Ingenioeren **1825**
Danish Films. (DK ISSN 0418-3304) **3507**
Danish Folk High School Today *see* Danish Folkehoejskole Today **1683**
Danish Folkehoejskole Today. (DK) **1683**
Danish Foreign Office Journal *see* Danish Journal **2185**
Danish Forest and Landscape Research.(DK) **2098**

Danish Gazette for C O M A L Language. *see* C B N **1429**
Danish Gazette for Plant Varieties. *see* Meddelelser fra Sortsafproevningen **509**
Danish Handcraft Guild. *see* Haandarbejdets Fremme **3591**
Danish Hydraulics. (DK ISSN 0109-5110) **1923**
Danish Illustration (Year). (DK ISSN 0903-6962) **323**
Danish Index of Articles: Newspapers and Periodicals. *see* Dansk Artikelindeks: Aviser og Tidsskrifter **2578**
Danish Index of Reviews. *see* Dansk Anmeldelsesindeks **4140**
Danish Journal. (DK ISSN 0011-6084) **2185**
Danish Journal of Education. *see* Dansk Paedagogisk Tidsskrift **1624**
Danish Journal of Plant and Soil Science. *see* Tidsskrift for Planteavl **519**
▼Danish Literary Magazine. (DK ISSN 0906-5369) **2910**
Danish Maritime Institute News *see* D M I News **4726**
Danish Medical Bulletin. (DK ISSN 0011-6092) **3092**
Danish National Bibliography. Articles in Books. *see* Artikler i Boeger **389**
Danish National Bibliography: Music. *see* Dansk Musikfortegnelse **3548**
Danish Offshore Guide *see* Danish Offshore Guide and Yearbook **3684**
Danish Offshore Guide and Yearbook. (DK) **3684**
Danish Ophthalmological Society. Transactions. (DK) **3300**
Danish Photography (Year). (DK) **3790**
Danish Pioneer. *see* Danske Pioneer **1998**
Danish Plant Protection Service. Annual Report *see* Denmark. Plant Directorate. Annual Report **2098**
Danish Polar Center. Newsletter. (DK) **4306**
Danish Review of Game Biology. (DK ISSN 0374-7344) **581**
Danish Ships and Shipping. *see* Danmarks Skibe og Skibsfart **4663**
Danish Technical Magazine. *see* Dansk Teknisk Tidsskrift **3446**
Danish Veterinary Journal. *see* Dansk Veterinaertidsskrift **4808**
Danish Wood Industry. *see* Trae og Industri **2118**
Danish Yearbook of Philosophy. (DK ISSN 0070-2749) **3576**
Dankbrief *see* Aktuell Josefs - Gesellschaft **4397**
Danke fuer ihre Hilfe. (GW) **2119, 3455**
Danmark Export: Food & Beverages/ Produits Alimentaires & Boissons/ Lebensmittel & Getraenke. (DK ISSN 0108-3910) **905**
Danmark Geologiske Undersoegelse Information *see* D G U Information **1558**
Danmark i Tal. (DK ISSN 0107-7139) **4570**
Danmarks Amtsraad. (DK ISSN 0011-6106) **4086**
Danmarks Biblioteksskole. Skrifter. (DK ISSN 0069-9861) **2754**
†Danmarks Biblioteksskole. Studier. (DK) **5177**
Danmarks Deltagelse i det Internationale Udviklingssamarbejde. Aarsrapport. (DK ISSN 0106-0090) **928**
Danmarks Fiskeri- og Havundersoegelser. Ferskvandsfiskerilaboratoriet. Meddelelser. *see* Meddelelser fra Ferskvandsfiskerilaboratoriet **2045**
Danmarks Fiskeri og Havundersoegelser. Intern Rapport *see* D F H - Rapport **2039**
Danmarks Fiskeri og Havundersoegelser Rapport *see* D F H - Rapport **2039**
Danmarks Folkehoejskoler. (DK ISSN 0108-3082) **1693**
Danmarks Geologiske Undersoegelse/ Geological Survey of Denmark. (DK ISSN 0011-6114) **1558**

DANMARKS GEOLOGISKE

†Danmarks Geologiske Undersoegelse. Aarbog/Geological Survey of Denmark. Yearbook. (DK ISSN 0105-063X) **5177**
Danmarks Geologiske Undersoegelse. Serie A/Geological Survey of Denmark. Series A. (DK ISSN 0901-0270) **1558**
Danmarks Geologiske Undersoegelse. Serie B/Geological Survey of Denmark. Series B. (DK ISSN 0901-0289) **1558**
Danmarks Geologiske Undersoegelse. Serie C/Geological Survey of Denmark. Series C. (DK ISSN 0900-6362) **1558**
Danmarks Geologiske Undersoegelse. Serie D/Geological Survey of Denmark. Series D. (DK ISSN 0900-6257) **1558**
†Danmarks Handels Tidende. (DK ISSN 0045-9585) **5177**
Danmarks Hoejskoler *see* Danmarks Folkehoejskoler **1693**
Danmarks Journalisthoejskoles Aarskrift. (DK ISSN 0108-285X) **1704, 2568**
Danmarks Jurist- og Oekonomforbund OE F - Haandbogen *see* D J OE F - Haandbogen **2617**
Danmarks Laererhoejskole. Geografisk Institut. Skrifter. (DK ISSN 0105-4856) **2245**
Danmarks Laererhoejskole. Institut for Informatik. Arbejdspapir. (DK ISSN 0900-5781) **1624**
Danmarks Laererhoeskole. Institut for Paedagogik og Psykologi. Testsamling. (DK ISSN 0107-1637) **1624, 4018**
Danmarks Nationalbank. Beretning og Regnskab (Dansk Udgave). (DK ISSN 0108-6979) **775**
Danmarks Nationalbank. Monetary Review. (DK ISSN 0011-6149) **775**
Danmarks Nationalbank. Report and Accounts for the Year (Year). (DK ISSN 0108-6995) **775**
Danmarks Restauranter *see* Nyt Danmarks Restauranter **2478**
Danmarks Retsforbunds Ungdom Henry - D R U Nytt *see* Henry - D R U Nytt **2868**
Danmarks Riges Breve *see* Diplomatarium Danicum **5180**
Danmarks Skibe og Skibsfart/Danish Ships and Shipping. (DK ISSN 0070-3486) **4663**
Danmarks Skolelederforening Kontakt *see* D S - Kontakt **1624**
†Danmarks Skotidende. (DK) **5177**
Danmarks Statistics. Statistical News. *see* Denmark. Danmarks Statistik. Statistike Efterrenninger **5178**
Danmarks Tekniske Bibliotek. Katalog. (DK ISSN 0900-4645) **2754**
Danmarks Tekniske Hoejskole. Afdelingen for Baerende Konstruktioner. Serie F. (DK ISSN 0108-0571) **615**
Danmarks Tekniske Hoejskole. Afdelingen for Baerende Konstruktioner. Serie I. (DK ISSN 0108-058X) **615**
Danmarks Tekniske Hoejskole. Afdelingen for Baerende Konstruktioner. Serie R. (DK ISSN 0108-0768) **1916**
Danmarks Tekniske Hoejskole. Fysisk Laboratorium 1. Report. (DK ISSN 0105-0907) **3817**
Danmarks Tekniske Hoejskole. Institutet for Veje, Trafik og Byplan. Notat/Technical University of Denmark. Institute of Roads, Transport and Town Planning. Paper. (DK ISSN 0107-0134) **4718, 2486**
Danmarks Tekniske Hoejskole. Instituttet for Landmaaling og Fotogrammetri. Meddelelse. (DK ISSN 0105-5194) **2245**
Danmarks Tekniske Hoejskole. Instituttet for Teleteknik. Rapport I T.(DK ISSN 0105-8541) **1334**
Danmarks Tekniske Hoejskole. Laboratoriet for Akustik. Publikation. (DK ISSN 0105-2853) **3859**
Danmarks Tekniske Hoejskole. Matematisk Institut. Mat - P R. (DK ISSN 0106-9306) **3034**
Danmarks Transport-Tidende. (DK ISSN 0106-0724) **4649**
Danmarks Turist Vejviser. (DK ISSN 0109-6125) **4759**
Danmarks Unge Katolikker Nyt fra D U K *see* Nyt fra D U K **4271**
Danmarks Vareindfoersel og- Udfoersel/External Trade of Denmark. (DK ISSN 0070-2781) **712**
Danmarks 15000 Stoerste Virksomheder/Denmark's 15000 Largest Companies. (DK) **1128, 1074**
Danmarks 200 Stoerste Virksomheder. (DK ISSN 0106-9977) **1074**
Danmarksposten. (DK ISSN 0011-6157) **2185**
Dannzha. (CN ISSN 0833-3831) **1998**
Dans le Vent. (FR) **2292,** 1253
Dans les Media, Demain. (MG) **2568**
Dansalan Quarterly. (PH) **4433,** 4218
Danses. (BE ISSN 0011-6173) **1530**
Dansk Almennyttigt Boligselskab af 1942 s.m.b.a. Information *see* D A B Information **2486**
Dansk Anmeldelsesindeks/Danish Index of Reviews. (DK ISSN 0106-1488) **4140,** 10
Dansk Arbejde. (DK ISSN 0011-6181) **1074**
Dansk Arbejdsgiverforening. Statistikken. (DK ISSN 0107-0851) **712**
Dansk Artikelindeks: Aviser og Tidsskrifter/Danish Index of Articles: Newspapers and Periodicals. (DK ISSN 0106-147X) **2578,** 10
Dansk Artilleri-Tidsskrift. (DK ISSN 0011-6203) **3455**
Dansk Artist Forbund. Show Guide. (DK ISSN 0109-8411) **323**
Dansk Atlet Union Brydning *see* Brydning **4467**
Dansk Atletik Forbund. Statistik *see* D A F i Tal **4498**
Dansk Atletik Forbund Tal *see* D A F i Tal **4498**
Dansk Beton. (DK) **615**
Dansk Botanisk Arkiv *see* Opera Botanica **512**
Dansk Brandvaern *see* Brandvaern **2031**
Dansk Bridge. (DK ISSN 0011-6238) **4470**
Dansk Dendrologisk Aarsskrift. (DK ISSN 0416-6906) **500**
Dansk Digtregister. (DK ISSN 0107-4431) **2991**
Dansk Dragesport *see* Dragesport **4471**
Dansk E D B Bibliografi/Danish Bibliography of Computer Science. (DK ISSN 0108-7517) **1404,** 398
Dansk Elektroteknisk Komite Haandbog *see* D E K Haandbog **1885**
Dansk Elforsyning. (DK ISSN 0106-4711) **1885**
Dansk Energi Tidsskrift. (DK ISSN 0108-8068) **1785,** 658
Dansk Erhvervsfjerkrae. (DK ISSN 0045-9607) **215**
Dansk Faellesrejse Forening. Medlemsblad. (DK ISSN 0109-6486) **4759**
Dansk Fagpresse. (DK ISSN 0106-0120) **2568**
Dansk Fagpresseforenings Medlemsliste *see* Fagpressenoeglen **2569**
Dansk Fagpressekatalog. (DK ISSN 0109-0968) **2578**
Dansk Filatelistisk Tidsskrift. (DK ISSN 0903-2444) **3751**
Dansk Fiskeritidende. (DK ISSN 0011-6270) **2039**
Dansk Forsikrings Aarbog. (DK ISSN 0106-2735) **2530**
Dansk Forsikrings Tidende - Assuranceoeren *see* Forsikring **2532**
Dansk Fotografi. (DK) **3790**
Dansk Fotografisk Tidsskrift. (DK) **3790**
Dansk-Fransk Handelsunion. Bulletin/Chambre de Commerce Franco-Danoise. Bulletin. (DK ISSN 0109-2669) **905**
Dansk Froeavl. (DK) **175**
Dansk Geologisk Forening. Aarsskrift. (DK ISSN 0420-1132) **1558**
Dansk Geologisk Forening. Bulletin/Geological Society of Denmark. Bulletin. (DK ISSN 0011-6297) **1558**
Dansk Grafia. (DK ISSN 0107-7112) **3998**
Dansk Handelsblad. (DK ISSN 0045-9615) **2091**
Dansk Historisk Aarsbibliografi. (DK ISSN 0107-0436) **2328**
Dansk Idraet. (DK ISSN 0109-5536) **4470**
Dansk Idraetsmedicinsk Selskab Bulletin *see* D I M S Bulletin **3092**
Dansk Illustreret Skibsliste. (DK ISSN 0107-8011) **4726**
Dansk Industri. (DK ISSN 0045-9623) **1074**
Dansk Industri Efter 1870. (DK) **2358,** 658
Dansk Ingenioerforening. Flyveteknisk Sektion. Aarbog *see* D I F Flyaarbog **50**
Dansk Ingenioerforening Flyaarbog *see* D I F Flyaarbog **50**
Dansk Institut for Personaleraadgivning Information *see* I P Information **1066**
Dansk Jagt *see* Jaeger **4549**
Dansk Japansk Venskabsforenings Blad.(DK ISSN 0107-6396) **3954**
Dansk Karate Forbund *see* Dansk Karate Forbund. Medlemsblad **4470**
Dansk Karate Forbund. Medlemsblad. (DK ISSN 0109-8705) **4470**
Dansk Katolsk Kvinde-Forbund Nyt *see* D K K F - Nyt **4840**
Dansk-Kemi. (DK ISSN 0011-6335) **1176**
Dansk Kirkehilsen. (DK) **4173**
Dansk Kirurgisk Selskab. Nyhedsbrev. (DK ISSN 0900-4041) **3378**
†Dansk Kulturhistorie og Bevidsthedsdannelse 1880-1920. (DK) **5177**
Dansk Landbrug. (DK ISSN 0904-9363) **86**
Dansk Lydfortegnelse. (DK ISSN 0107-9816) **3588**
Dansk Maskinhandlerforening. Handbog.(DK ISSN 0302-5349) **161**
Dansk Media Index. (DK) **1347,** 1334
Dansk Medicinhistorisk Aarbog/Yearbook of Danish Medical History. (DK ISSN 0084-9588) **3093**
Dansk Missionsblad. (DK ISSN 0011-6378) **4173**
Dansk Modelbaads Union Nyt *see* D M U - Nyt **2435**
Dansk Moenstertidende. (DK ISSN 0903-8825) **3674,** 323
▼Dansk Musik Aarbog (Year). (DK ISSN 0905-6300) **3548**
Dansk Musiker Tidende *see* Musikeren **3568**
Dansk Musikfortegnelse/Danish National Bibliography: Music. (DK ISSN 0105-8045) **3548**
Dansk Natur - Dansk Skole. (DK ISSN 0106-5726) **2185**
Dansk Optisk Selskab Nyt *see* D O P S Nyt **3852**
Dansk Ornitologisk Forenings Tidsskrift. (DK ISSN 0011-6394) **563**
Dansk Paedagogisk Tidsskrift/Danish Journal of Education. (DK ISSN 0011-6408) **1624**
Dansk Patenttidende. (DK ISSN 0011-6416) **3674**
Dansk Pelsdyravl. (DK ISSN 0011-6424) **2736**
Dansk Presse. (DK ISSN 0106-5343) **2568,** 30, 1037
Dansk Psykolognyt *see* Psykolog Nyt **4043**
Dansk Radio Industri *see* Radiobranchen **1359**
Dansk Reklame *see* Markedsfoering **34**

Dansk Rumforskninginstitut. Publikationer. (DK ISSN 0109-6605) **51**
Dansk Sangindeks. (DK ISSN 0108-2272) **3588**
Dansk Skovbrugs Tidsskrift. (DK ISSN 0905-295X) **2098**
Dansk Skovforenings Tidsskrift *see* Dansk Skovbrugs Tidsskrift **2098**
▼Dansk Sociologi. (DK ISSN 0905-5908) **4433**
Dansk Sportsheste Avlsforbunds Stambog *see* Stambog **4538**
Dansk Squash. (DK ISSN 0107-2242) **4502**
Dansk Sygehus Institut Notat *see* D S I Notat **2460**
Dansk Taxi Tidende. (DK) **4689**
Dansk Teknisk Laererforening Nyt *see* D T L - Nyt **1624**
Dansk Teknisk Litteraturselskab. Skriftserie. (DK ISSN 0416-6981) **4596**
Dansk Teknisk Tidsskrift/Danish Technical Magazine. (DK ISSN 0011-6505) **3446**
Dansk Teologisk Tidsskrift. (DK ISSN 0105-3191) **4173**
Dansk Textil Exportguide - Danish Textile Export Guide *see* Export Guide - Dansk Textil og Beklaedning **4618**
Dansk Turisme. (DK ISSN 0904-1796) **4759**
Dansk Udsyn. (DK ISSN 0106-4622) **2358**
Dansk Ungdom og Idraet *see* Ungdom og Idraet **4496**
Dansk V V S. (DK ISSN 0902-5456) **2298**
Dansk Varemaerketidende. (DK) **3674**
Dansk Vejtidsskrift. (DK ISSN 0011-6548) **1864**
Dansk Veterinaertidsskrift/Danish Veterinary Journal. (DK ISSN 0106-6854) **4808**
Danske Assurandoerer *see* Assurandoeren **2527**
De Danske Aviser. (DK) **2185**
Den Danske Bank. Orientering. (DK ISSN 0107-8224) **658**
Danske Bank af 1871. Orientering *see* Den Danske Bank. Orientering **658**
Den Danske Bank Aktieselskab. Report and Accounts. (DK) **775**
Danske Bibelselskab. Medlemsbrev *see* Nyt fra Bibelselskabet **4193**
Danske Bibelselskabs Aarbog. (DK ISSN 0109-5846) **4173**
Danske Bibelselskabs Aarsberetning *see* Danske Bibelselskabs Aarbog **4173**
Danske Bogmarked *see* Bogmarkedet **4121**
Danske Forlaeggerforening. Faelleslagerkatalog. (DK ISSN 0070-282X) **398**
Danske Fysioterapeuter. (DK ISSN 0105-0648) **3093**
Det Danske Hedeselskab. Forsoegsvirksomheden. Beretning. (DK ISSN 0903-5664) **86,** 436
Danske Illustratorer *see* Danish Illustration (year) **323**
Danske Jernbaner Idraets og Fritidsforbund Fritid *see* D J I F Fritid **2435**
Danske Kommuner. (DK ISSN 0011-6572) **4086**
†Danske Kulturinstitut. Nyt. (DK) **5177**
Danske Laegemiddelstandarder. (DK ISSN 0105-7480) **3722**
Danske Magazin. (DK ISSN 0070-2846) **2358**
Danske Malermestre. (DK ISSN 0905-6440) **3653**
Danske Motorcyklisters Raad Bladet *see* D M C - Bladet **4517**
Danske Pioneer/Danish Pioneer. (US ISSN 0747-3869) **1998**
Danske Plantevaernskonference. (DK ISSN 0109-3142) **500**
Danske Sprog- og Litteraturselskab Praesentationshaefte *see* D S L's Praesentationshaefte **2910**
Danske Statsbaner Bladet *see* D S B Bladet **4649**
Danske Statslaan *see* Statens Laantagning og Gaeld **4075**

Danske Statsskoves Udbytte af Ved og Penge see Skov og Natur **2108**
Danske Studier. (DK) **2358**
Danske Vedligeholdelsesforening Analysen see D D V - Analysen **5176**
Danske Vinblad. (DK ISSN 0109-5684) **380**
Danske Vognmaend. (DK ISSN 0011-6629) **4744**
Danske Vognmaend Hovedorganisationen Bogen see D V Bogen **4649**
Danskerne. (DK ISSN 0107-4393) **2185**
Dante Studies. (US ISSN 0070-2862) **2910**
Dantec Information. (US ISSN 0900-5579) **3446**, 1885
▼Dantologia. (IT) **2910**
Danubian Historical Studies. (HU ISSN 0238-132X) **2358**
Danyag. (PH) **2506**, 1624, 4306
Danzare. (IT ISSN 0394-8137) **1530**
Daode yu Wenming/Morality and Civilization. (CC) **3890**
Dapai Tamar. (IS) **2203**
Dapai Tochen Vetaktzerim. (IS) **2085**
Daphnis. (NE ISSN 0300-693X) **2910**
Dapim Licheker Tikufat Hashoah. (IS ISSN 0333-5151) **2309**
Dappim - Research in Literature. (IS ISSN 0334-0686) **2910**
Daqi Kexue/Scientia Atmospherica Sinica. (CC ISSN 0254-0002) **3434**
Daqi Kexue Jinzhan see Advances in Atmospheric Sciences **3432**
Dar es Salaam Medical Journal. (TZ) **3093**
Dar es Salaam University Law Journal. (TZ ISSN 0418-3770) **2618**
Darbininkas. (US ISSN 0011-6637) **4262**
†Du Darfst. (GW ISSN 0177-1531) **5177**
Daring. (US) **2983**
Dark Horizons. (UK) **3011**
Dark Horse see Good Day Sunshine **3553**
▼The Dark Man: The Journal of Robert E. Howard Studies. (US) **2910**, 2983, 3011
†Dark Visions. (US) **5177**
Dark Winds. (US) **2910**, 2991
Darkroom & Creative Camera Techniques. (US ISSN 0195-3850) **3790**
Darkroom Photography see Camera & Darkroom Photography **3789**
Darling. (IT) **2983**
Darling see Femina **4842**
Darlington Astronomical Society. Newsletter. (UK ISSN 0260-7794) **363**
Darmstaedter Archivschriften. (GW) **2358**
Darmstaedter Blaetter fuer Kulturelle Evolution. (GW ISSN 0340-6296) **3954**
Darmstaedter Schwimm- und Wassersportclub 1912 e.V. 12 Nachrichten see D S W '12 Nachrichten **4470**
Darnall, Darnell - Dawn to Dusk. (US ISSN 0883-7724) **2148**
Darpon. (UK ISSN 0011-6718) **2864**
Darshak. (II ISSN 0045-9658) **323**
Darshan. (US ISSN 0892-130X) **3764**
Darshana International. (II ISSN 0011-6734) **3764**, 4018, 4214
Dart. (SA) **238**
Dartmoor Sheep Breeders' Association. Annual Flock Book. (UK) **215**
Dartmouth Alumni Magazine. (US) **1310**
Dartmouth Business News. (CN ISSN 0824-2682) **814**
Dartmouth College Library Bulletin. (US ISSN 0011-6750) **2754**
Dartmouth Medical School Alumni Magazine see Dartmouth Medicine **3093**
Dartmouth Medicine. (US) **3093**, 1310
Dartmouth Review. (US) **1310**

†Dartnell Office Administration Service. (US ISSN 0011-6769) **5177**
Darts Player. (UK ISSN 0267-2286) **4470**
Darts World. (UK ISSN 0140-6000) **4470**
Darum. (GW) **4235**
Daruvarski List. (CI) **2864**
Darwin Gay and Lesbian Newsletter. (AT) **2452**
Darwin Gay Informer see Darwin Gay and Lesbian Newsletter **2452**
Darwiniana. (AG ISSN 0011-6793) **500**
Darzs un Drava/Gardening and Beekeeping. (LV ISSN 0132-6457) **2125**
Das aktuelle Monatsmagazin see Monatsmagazin **4778**
Das Beste aus Reader's Digest (German Braille Edition) see Reader's Digest - Das Beste (German Braille Edition) **2295**
Das Beste aus Reader's Digest (German Edition) see Reader's Digest - Das Beste (German Edition) **2191**
Das Deutsche Schuhmacherhandwerk see Der Schuhmacher **4361**
Das Schaufenster (Stuttgart) see Apotheke Heute **3717**
Dasein see Context South **2991**
Daseinsanalyse. (SZ ISSN 0254-6221) **3335**
Dat Was de Toestand in de Wereld. (NE) **2309**
Data. (DK) **1449**
Data (Athens) see Compu-Data **1424**
Data & Knowledge Engineering. (NE ISSN 0169-023X) **1394**
Data Bank. (US) **775**
Data Base (Cincinnati). (US) **1689**, 1459, 1468
Data Base Alert see DataBase Alert **1425**
Data Base Directory see DataBase Directory **1425**
Data Base Management. (US ISSN 0735-9977) **1443**
▼Data Base Management. (US) **1444**
Data Base Monthly see D G Review **1459**
Data Base Newsletter. (US ISSN 0735-3677) **1444**
Data Base Plus see Data Base Reports **2530**
Data Base Product Reports. (US ISSN 0740-6800) **1444**, 1459
Data Base Reports. (US) **2530**
Data Based Advisor. (US ISSN 0740-5200) **1476**, 1430
†Data Book of Social Studies Materials and Resources. (US ISSN 0747-4857) **5177**
Data Book on Illinois Higher Education. (US ISSN 0098-5279) **1704**
Data-Boy Magazine see Data-Boy - Nightlife **2452**
Data-Boy - Nightlife. (US) **2452**
Data Broadcasting Report. (US ISSN 0882-5726) **1334**
Data Bus. (US) **1449**
†Data Business. (UK) **5177**
Data Center - Nyt see A U D - Nyt **1388**
Data Center Operations Management. (US ISSN 0736-3648) **1446**
Data Centrum. (US) **3093**
Data Channels. (US ISSN 0093-7290) **1449**, 1689
Data Communications. (US ISSN 0363-6399) **1446**, 826, 1426
Data Communications and Processing/Data Tsushin. (JA ISSN 0285-9394) **1449**
Data Communications Buyers' Guide. (US ISSN 0194-195X) **1446**, 1425, 1426
Data Communications Management. (US ISSN 0736-0002) **1446**
Data Communications Product Directory. (US) **1350**, 1453, 1476
Data Communications Reports. (US) **1446**
†Data Communications Source Book. (US) **5177**
Data Communications Systems see Data Communications **1446**

Data Conversion Newsletter see Imaging Service Bureau News **1451**
Data-Data Iklim di Indonesia. (IO ISSN 0303-1969) **3435**
Data Dictionary from the Call and Income Report. (US) **712**
Data Entry Awareness Report. (US ISSN 0747-9549) **1449**
Data Entry Management Association. Newsletter. (US) **1449**, 826
Data Entry Services Directory. (US ISSN 0899-4579) **1449**, 1128
Data Extract. (AT ISSN 0729-7920) **1372**, 1297, 2435
Data General Australia World see D G World **1453**
Data General News see D G World **1453**
Data Handling in Science and Technology. (NE) **1444**, 4359
Data India. (II ISSN 0377-6832) **2199**
Data Informer see Lesko's Info - Power Newsletter **1427**
▼Data Interchange. (US) **1446**
†Data Management. (US) **5177**
Data Management Update. (US ISSN 0735-3677) **1444**
Data Manager. (IT) **1444**
Data Networking. (US) **1446**
Data News. (BE) **1350**, 1453, 1476
Data News. (BL ISSN 0100-6142) **1394**
Data of Glaciological Studies. see Materialy Glyatsiologicheskikh Issledovanii **1592**
Data on Denmark see Danmark i Tal **4570**
Data on the Medicaid Program: Eligibility - Service - Expenditures see Medicare and Medicaid Data Book **2537**
Data Processing see Information and Software Technology **1451**
Data Processing and Communications Security see Computing & Communications Protection **1434**
Data Processing Budget see D P Budget **1449**
Data Processing Digest. (US ISSN 0011-6858) **1449**
Data Processing Management see Information Management: Strategies, Systems, and Technologies **1451**
Data Processing Management Association Inside D P M A see Inside D P M A **1452**
Data Processing Manager's Letter. (US) **1007**
Data Processing Market Facts see D P Market Facts **1394**
Data Procession Salary Survey & Employment Practices (Year). (CN) **3632**
Data Product News. (CN) **1449**, 1459, 1469
Data Report see Siemens-Magazin COM **5277**
Data Report of Hydrographic Observations. Series of Astronomy and Geodesy. see Kaijo Hoan-cho. Suiro-bu Kansoku Hokoku. Tenmon Sokuchi Hen **1592**
Data Report of Hydrographic Observations. Series of Satellite Geodesy. see Kaijo Hoan-cho. Suiro-bu Kansoku Hokoku. Eisei Sokuchi Hen **1592**
Data Resource Management. (US ISSN 1053-5594) **820**, 1007
Data Resources Asian Review see D R I - McGraw-Hill Asian Review **859**
Data Resources European Review see D R I - McGraw-Hill European Review **859**
Data Resources Japanese Review see D R I - McGraw-Hill Japanese Review **859**
Data Resources Latin American Review see D R I - McGraw-Hill Latin American Review **859**
Data Resources McGraw-Hill Asian Review see D R I - McGraw-Hill Asian Review **859**
Data Resources Middle East and African Review see D R I - McGraw-Hill Middle East and African Review **859**

Data Resources Steel Industry Review see D R I - McGraw-Hill Steel Industry Review **3405**
Data Security Management. (US ISSN 0746-7281) **1434**, 1526
Data Security Manual. (NE) **1434**, 1526
Data Sets: Cuneiform Texts. (US ISSN 0742-1427) **2330**, 2429
Data Sources. (US ISSN 0744-1673) **1425**, 1426, 1444, 1449
Data Sources' Guide to V A Rs and Distributors. (US ISSN 8755-7339) **1425**
†Data Storage Report. (UK ISSN 0267-5447) **5177**
Data Training. (US ISSN 0884-2604) **1449**, 1064, 1683
Data Transmission Network. (US) **86**
Data Trends News Digest. (US) **1449**
Data Trends Report on D E C and I B M. (US) **1459**
Data Tsushin. see Data Communications and Processing **1449**
Data Welt see P C Praxis **1472**
Database (New York). (US ISSN 0095-0033) **1444**
Database (Weston). (US ISSN 0162-4105) **1444**
DataBase Alert. (US ISSN 0737-951X) **1425**
Database and Network Journal. (UK ISSN 0265-4490) **1444**, 1426
DataBase Directory. (US ISSN 0749-6680) **1425**
Database End-User see Database Searcher **1459**
Database Management Systems see D B M S **1476**
Database Programming & Design. (US ISSN 0895-4518) **1430**, 1436
Database Review. (US ISSN 1042-2595) **2797**
Database Searcher. (US ISSN 0891-6713) **1459**, 1444
Database Technology. (US ISSN 0951-9327) **1444**
Database Update see Business Computer Digest **825**
†Databus. (NE ISSN 0167-1340) **5177**
†Databusiness. (UK) **5177**
Datacenter Manager. (US) **1430**, 1007
Datacom. (GW ISSN 0176-3288) **1446**
Datacom Reader. (US ISSN 0886-2400) **1404**
DataComms Book (Year). (UK) **1446**
Datacoms. (US) **1449**
Datalignum. (IT ISSN 0393-330X) **2558**
†Datalink. (UK) **5177**
†Datalink. (US) **5177**
Datalogi O. (DK ISSN 0108-3708) **1689**, 1394
Datalogiske Skrifter. (DK ISSN 0109-9779) **1394**
Datamation. (US ISSN 0011-6963) **1449**
▼Datamation P C Products. (US) **1469**, 1449
DataNet. (US ISSN 0912-5833) **1423**
DataPac Caribbean see DataPac Caribbean Business Trends **859**
DataPac Caribbean Business Trends. (JM) **859**
Datapro Communications Perspectives. (US) **1350**
Datapro Directory of Microcomputer Hardware. (US) **1425**, 1433, 1459, 1469
Datapro Directory of Microcomputer Software. (US ISSN 0730-8795) **1425**, 1459, 1476
†Datapro Directory of On-Line Services. (US ISSN 0730-7071) **5177**
Datapro Directory of Software. (US ISSN 0730-8779) **1476**
Datapro Management of Applications Software. (US) **1476**
Datapro Management of Data Communications see Managing Data Networks **1452**
Datapro Management of E D P Systems see Managing Information Technology **1452**
Datapro Management of International Telecommunications. (US) **1446**

6108 DATAPRO MANAGEMENT

Datapro Management of Microcomputer Systems see Managing L A Ns 1461
Datapro Management of Office Automation. (US) 1449
Datapro Management of Telecommunications see Managing Voice Networks 1364
Datapro Manufacturing Automation Series. (US) 826, 1413
Datapro Network Management Information Service. (US) 1426
†Datapro Newscom. (US) 5177
Datapro Office Products Evaluation Service. (US ISSN 0730-8825) 1058
Datapro Reports on Banking Automation. (US ISSN 0730-8809) 805, 1449
Datapro Reports on Communications Alternatives see Broadband Networking 1349
Datapro Reports on Communications Software. (US) 1350
Datapro Reports on Copiers and Duplicators see Datapro Office Products Evaluation Service 1058
Datapro Reports on Data Communications see Data Networking 1446
Datapro Reports on Data Communications International. (US) 1446
Datapro Reports on Document Imaging Systems. (US) 1446
Datapro Reports on Electronic Publishing Systems. (US) 4143
Datapro Reports on Information Security. (US) 1450, 1526
Datapro Reports on Information Security International. (US) 1434
Datapro Reports on International Communications Equipment. (US) 1334
Datapro Reports on International Communications Software. (US) 1350
Datapro Reports on International Networks & Services. (US) 1426
Datapro Reports on International Networks Management. (US) 1426
Datapro Reports on International Telecommunications. (US) 1334
Datapro Reports on International UNIX & Open Systems. (US) 1426
Datapro Reports on Marketing Information Systems. (US) 826, 1037
Datapro Reports on Microcomputers. (US) 1459
†Datapro Reports on Minicomputers. (US ISSN 0275-0813) 5177
Datapro Reports on Office Automation. (US) 1450, 826
Datapro Reports on Office Automation International. (US) 1413
Datapro Reports on P C and L A N Communications. (US) 1469, 1350
Datapro Reports on P C Communications see Datapro Reports on P C and L A N Communications 1469
Datapro Reports on Retail Automation. (US ISSN 0730-8817) 826, 1450
Datapro Reports on Service & Support. (US) 1350
†Datapro Reports on Software. (US) 5177
†Datapro Reports on Telecommunications. (US ISSN 0735-8458) 5177
Datapro Reports on UNIX Systems & Software. (US) 1436, 1476
†Datapro Reports on Word Processing. (US ISSN 0272-3336) 5177
†Datapro 70. (US ISSN 0045-9704) 5177
Dataquest. (II ISSN 0970-034X) 1394, 1444
Dataseguros. (CK) 2546
Datatextile. (US) 4618
Datatid. (NO ISSN 0332-8171) 1394
Dataweek. (SA) 4596
DataWorld. (US ISSN 0190-6585) 1450
Datazine. (US) 1347, 1372

Datch Information. (DK ISSN 0905-0221) 2283, 1735
Date Book. (US) 4362
Date Palm Journal. (UN ISSN 0252-3353) 175
Datek Imaging Supplies Annual see Imaging Supplies Annual 4007
Datek Imaging Supplies Monthly. (US ISSN 1050-6993) 4007
Dateline Delhi. (II ISSN 0011-698X) 2199
Dateline Hong Kong. (UK) 2197
Dateline Magazine. (UK) 4362
Daten, Informationen, Argumente see D I A 4173
Daten und Information. (GW) 4080, 3991
Datenjournal. (LH ISSN 0011-7005) 3093
Die Datenschleuder. (GW) 1430
Datenschutz-Berater. (GW ISSN 0170-7256) 1434
Datenschutz und Datensicherung. (GW) 1434, 1450
Datenschutz und Datensicherung - Informationsrecht - Kommunikationssysteme see Datenschutz und Datensicherung 1434
Datenverarbeitung - Steuer - Wirtschaft - Recht see D S W R 1449
Dati e Tariffe Pubblicitarie. (IT ISSN 0038-9501) 30
Datornytt, med Maskin- och Programvara. (SW ISSN 0348-4998) 1430
†Datos Etno-Linguisticos. (PE) 5177
Datos Socio-Economicos de Costa Rica. (CR) 859
Datos y Cifras de la Ensenanza en Espana. (SP ISSN 0070-2897) 1624
Daugava. (LV) 2910
Daugavas Vanagu Menesraksts. (CN ISSN 0418-4297) 1998
†Daugherty Family Newsletter. (US ISSN 0883-8550) 5177
Daughters of Sarah. (US ISSN 0739-1749) 4840, 4173
Daughters of the American Revolution Magazine. (US ISSN 0011-7013) 2404
Dauphin. (BE ISSN 0773-0292) 1253
Davar. (AG ISSN 0011-703X) 2864
Davenport Newsletter. (US) 2148
David and Alfred Smart Gallery Bulletin see David & Alfred Smart Museum of Art. Bulletin 3523
David & Alfred Smart Museum of Art. Bulletin. (US) 3523
David Davies Memorial Institute of International Studies, London. Annual Memorial Lecture. (UK ISSN 0070-2900) 3954
David Hall's Inside View. (US) 3599, 944
†David McCalden Revisionist Newsletter.(US ISSN 0733-5946) 5177
David y Goliath. (AG) 4370
†Davidson Update. (US) 5177
Davis Medieval Texts and Studies. (NE ISSN 0169-7994) 2358
Davison's Salesman's Book. (US ISSN 0363-5252) 1128, 4618
Davison's Textile Blue Book. (US ISSN 0070-2951) 1128, 4618
▼Davison's Textile Blue Book Europe. (US) 4628, 398
Davison's Textile Buyer's Guide. (US) 4628, 398
†Davka. (US ISSN 0011-7048) 5177
Davke. (AG) 1998, 4222
Davy's Devon Herd Book. (UK ISSN 0070-2986) 215
Al-Da'wah al-Islamiyyah. (LY) 4218
Dawes Family Newsletter see J.W. Dawes Family Newsletter 2155
Dawhat al-Mutanabbi' (TS) 1253
Dawn see Zarja 2029
Dawn. (ZA) 3941
Dawn (Honesdale) see Yoga International 3597
Dawn (Weekend Edition). (PK) 2213
Dawn for the Orange County Woman. (US) 4840

Dawn Magazine (Baltimore). (US) 1998
†Dawn Overseas Weekly. (PK) 5177
Dawn Song see Dawn Song and All Day 1486
Dawn Song and All Day. (UK ISSN 0070-3001) 1486
Dawn Train. (IE ISSN 0332-4281) 2864, 3890
Al-Dawri. (QA) 4470
†Dawson and Hind. (CN ISSN 0703-6507) 5177
Dawsons Guide - Australian & Worldwide Hotels. (AT) 4759
Dawsons Venue Directory. (AT ISSN 0815-6794) 4759, 2473, 3392
Dawutai. (CC) 4632
Dax Dynamic Showcase. (US ISSN 0161-3464) 658
Dax Money-Maker Newsletter. (US ISSN 0147-1112) 658
Daxue Huaxue/University Chemistry. (CC ISSN 1000-8438) 1176
Daxue Keji/University Science and Technology. (CC) 4306, 4596
Daxue Tushuguan Xuebao/Journal of University Libraries. (CC) 2754
Daxuesheng/University Student. (CC) 1704
Day by Day. (UK ISSN 0011-7080) 2864
Day Care and Early Education. (US ISSN 0092-4199) 4403, 1236, 4018
Day Care U S A. (US) 4403
Day One Diary. (UK) 4173
†Day Researcher. (US ISSN 0743-216X) 5177
Day to Remember. (US) 2148
Day Trips and Short Breaks see Coachmart 4757
Dayanisma. (GW) 1998
Dayanisma/Solidaritet. (DK ISSN 0108-8580) 3954
Daybreak. (US) 1998
Daybreak Star see Daybreak Star Indian Reader 1998
Daybreak Star Indian Reader. (US) 1998, 1253
Daylily Journal. (US ISSN 0744-0219) 2125
Daytime Digest. (US) 1372
Daytime T V. (US) 1372
Daytime T V Presents. (US) 1372
Daytime T V's Greatest Stories. (US) 1372
Dayton Art Institute. Annual Report. (US) 3523
Dayton Art Institute. Annual Report and Bulletin see Dayton Art Institute. Annual Report 3523
Dayton Business Reporter. (US) 658, 4147
Dayton Jewish Chronicle. (US) 1998
Dayton Stamp Club. Newsletter. (US) 3751
Dazhong Dianshi/T V for the Masses. (CC) 1372
Dazhong Dianying/Popular Cinema. (CC ISSN 0492-0929) 3507
Dazhong Jiankang/Ordinary People's Health. (CC) 3800
Dazhong Sheying/Popular Photography.(CC ISSN 0494-4372) 3790
Dazhong Wenyi. (CC) 323, 2910
Dazhong Xiaoshuo/Popular Short Stories. (CC) 2910
Dazhong Xinlixue/Popular Psychology. (CC) 4018
Dazhong Yixue/Popular Medicine. (CC ISSN 1000-8470) 3093
Daziran/Nature. (CC ISSN 0255-7800) 4306
Daziran Tansuo/Exploration of Nature. (CC ISSN 1000-4041) 1946
Db, The Sound Engineering Magazine. (US ISSN 0011-7145) 4460
Dbembe. (UG) 2220
DDR Verkehr see Internationales Verkehrswesen 4719
Ddraig Goch. (UK) 3890
De Boekarbeider see Travailleur du Livre 4138
De Bond. (BE) 2174
De Economia. (SP) 658
De Facto see Uni-Press 1669
De Goeje Fund. Publications. see De Goeje Stichting. Uitgaven 3636

De Goeje Stichting. Uitgaven/De Goeje Fund. Publications. (NE ISSN 0169-8257) 3636
De Jure. (SA) 2618
De Juventud: Revista de Estudios e Investigaciones see Revista de Estudios de Juventud 4417
De l'Automobile et de l'Aeronautique. (FR) 4689, 51
De La Salle University. Department of History and Area Studies. Anuaryo - Annales. (PH ISSN 0115-6276) 2337
De La Salle University Business & Economics Review see D L S U Business & Economics Review 658
De La Salle University Dialogue see D L S U Dialogue 2505
De La Salle University Engineering Journal see D L S U Engineering Journal 1818
De La Salle University Graduate Journal see D L S U Graduate Journal 4370
De los Cuatro Vientos. (MX) 2210
De Luxe & Red Cab News. (AT) 4689
De Natura Rerum. (GW ISSN 0931-8305) 3093
De Paul Law Review. (US ISSN 0011-7188) 2618
De Schouw see Gawalo - V K L Journaal 2299
De Textos. (BO) 4433, 3722, 4840
De Veiligheid - Safety see Arbeidsomstandigheden 3614
▼De Vere Hotels Magazine. (UK) 2473
De Windsurfer see Surf and Fun 4493
De Witt Digest & Review. (US) 2224
Deacon. (US ISSN 0045-9771) 4235
▼Dead Beat Poet Production. (US) 2991
Dead of Night. (US ISSN 1049-0892) 3011
Dead Relix see Relix 3577
Deadline. (US) 2568, 3954
Deaf American. (US ISSN 0011-720X) 2286
Deaf Artists of America News see Uncharted 347
Deaf - Blind News Summary. (US) 2292, 2286
Deaf Center News. (US) 2287
Deaf Coloradan. (US) 2287, 1504
Deaf Community News see NorCal Community Forum 2288
Deaf Community Services Magazine of San Diego. (US) 2287, 4403
Deaf Counseling Advocacy and Referral Agency News see D C A R A News 2286
Deaf Newsletter. (UK ISSN 0265-7074) 2287, 2754
Deakin University. Guide to Off-Campus Studies see Deakin University, Off-Campus Guide 1310
Deakin University, Off-Campus Guide. (AT) 1310
The Deal Makers. (US) 4147
Dealer Communicator. (US) 3998
Dealer Progress. (US) 175
Dealerama see Photo and Electronics Marketing 3794
DealerNews. (US ISSN 0888-4234) 4517
Dealers (Washington). (US) 2114
Dealers' Choice. (US) 4689
Dealerscope Merchandising. (US ISSN 0888-4501) 1765, 2558
▼Dealerscope Merchandising First of the Month. (US) 1037, 1885
Dealing with Technology. (US ISSN 0955-2138) 805
Deals on Wheels. (AT) 4744
Dean and Director see Program Trends for Business & Industry 1730
Dean Archaeology. (UK ISSN 0954-8874) 270
Deanotations. (US) 2991
Dear Doctor. (US) 3093
Dear Penelope. (US) 2224
Dearquitectura. (PR) 298
Death. (US ISSN 0161-4835) 4018, 3800
Death and Dying. (US ISSN 0748-285X) 4370, 2119, 4173
†Death and Dying A to Z. (US) 5177
Death Education Series see Series in Death Education, Aging, and Health Care 4046

†Death Rattle. (US) **5177**
Death Studies. (US ISSN 0748-1187) **4018, 2271, 4433**
Death with Dignity Newsletter *see* D W D Newsletter **2617**
Deathrealm. (US) **3011, 2910**
Debat. (FR ISSN 0246-2346) **2506**
Debate. (PE) **2864**
Debate/Hiwar. (JO) **3890, 1310, 4058**
Debate Agrario. (PE) **86**
Debate Socialista. (PE) **3890**
Debates Andinos. (PE) **4370**
Debates en Antropologia *see* Anthropologica (Lima) **234**
Debates en Sociologia. (PE) **4433**
†Debates in Clinical Surgery. (US ISSN 1040-1733) **5177**
†Debates in Medicine. (US) **5177**
Debates of the European Parliament. (EI ISSN 0071-3015) **2722**
Debates Sociais. (BL) **4403**
Debates Urbano Regionales. (PE) **2486**
Debby. (IT) **1253**
Debitant de Tabac. (FR) **4643**
Debonair. (II) **2864**
†Debreceni Orvostudomanyi Egyetem Evkonyve. (HU ISSN 0133-9060) **5178**
Debrett's Distinguished People of Today *see* Debrett's People of Today **2148**
Debrett's Handbook *see* Debrett's People of Today **2148**
Debrett's Peerage & Baronetage. (UK) **2148**
Debrett's People of Today. (UK) **2148, 418**
Les Debrouillards. (CN) **1253, 4306**
Debt-Equity Swap Handbook. (US) **905, 944**
Debts and Career Plans of Osteopathic Medical Students. (US) **1704, 3214**
Decalogue Journal. (US ISSN 0011-7250) **2618**
Decanter. (UK ISSN 0141-6014) **380, 2065**
Deccan College. Postgraduate & Research Institute. Bulletin. (II ISSN 0045-9801) **4370, 2337, 2810**
Deccan Geographer. (II ISSN 0011-7269) **2246, 4759**
December. (US ISSN 0070-3141) **2910**
†December Rose. (US ISSN 0748-1195) **5178**
Decency Reporter. (US) **4433, 2618**
Decentralize! (US) **3890**
Dechema Monographien. (GW ISSN 0070-315X) **1205, 3258**
Decheniana-Beihefte (Bonn). (GW ISSN 0416-833X) **436, 1543**
Le Decideur. (CN) **658**
Deciduous Fruit Grower/ Sagtevrugteboer. (SA ISSN 0011-7285) **2125**
Decision. (UK) **658**
Decision. (MX ISSN 0185-1985) **814**
Decision. (II ISSN 0304-0941) **1007**
Decision. *see* Odlocanje **4093**
Decision (Minneapolis). (US ISSN 0011-7307) **4235**
Decision Information Display System Doings *see* D I D S Doings **1449**
Decision Line. (US) **1007**
Decision Research. (US) **1007**
Decision Sciences. (US ISSN 0011-7315) **1007**
Decision Sciences Institute. Annual Meeting Proceedings. (US ISSN 0360-375X) **1007**
Decision Support Systems. (NE ISSN 0167-9236) **1007, 826**
Decisions & Developments. (US) **2618**
Decisions and Reports on Rulings of the Assistant Secretary of Labor for Labor - Management Relations *see* U.S. Labor - Management Services Administration. Decisions and Reports on Rulings of the Assistant Secretary of Labor for Labor - Management Relations **5295**
Decisions in Imaging Economics. (US) **3225**
Decisions, Issues and Alternatives *see* D I A **3889**

Decisions of the Comptroller General of the United States. (US ISSN 0011-7323) **4058**
Decisions of the Department of the Interior *see* U.S. Department of the Interior. Decisions of the Department of the Interior **4076**
Decisions of the United States Courts Involving Copyrights. (US ISSN 0070-3176) **3674**
Deck Plan Guide *see* Ford's Deck Plan Guide **4767**
Decker Communication Report *see* Executive Communications **5189**
Decks Awash. (CN ISSN 0317-7076) **2177**
Declassified Documents Catalog. (US ISSN 1046-4239) **3937, 10, 3954**
Declassified Documents Quarterly Catalog *see* Declassified Documents Catalog **3937**
Le Declin. (CN) **1310**
Deco. (GW) **2550**
Decor. (US ISSN 0011-7358) **2558, 2281**
Decor Elegante. (US) **2550, 298**
Decor Guide *see* Home & Decor **2559**
†Decorating Ambiance. (US) **5178**
Decorating & Design Sourcebook. (CN) **2550**
Decorating Contractor Annual Directory.(UK ISSN 0070-3192) **2550**
Decorating Digest. (US ISSN 0889-2210) **2550**
Decorating Made Easy *see* Decorating Remodeling **2550**
Decorating Products Retail Sales Report. (US) **2550**
Decorating Products Sales Report *see* Decorating Products Retail Sales Report **2550**
Decorating Products Trends Advisory. (US) **2550, 3653**
Decorating Remodeling. (US) **2550**
▼Decorating Remodeling Best Kitchen Plan Designs. (US) **2550**
Decorating Retailer. (US ISSN 0011-7404) **2550**
▼Decorating Retailer's Decorating Registry. (US) **2550**
Decorating Retailer's Directory of the Wallcovering Industry. (US) **2550**
Decoration. *see* Zhuangshi **351**
Decoration. (FR) **2550**
Decoration Chez-Soi. (CN ISSN 0705-1093) **2550**
Decorative Artist's Workbook. (US) **354**
Decorative Arts Digest. (US ISSN 0888-076X) **354**
Decorative Design. (JA) **2435**
†Decorative Products World. (US ISSN 1045-5914) **5178**
Decorative Rug. (US ISSN 1045-8816) **2558**
Decorative Rug Review *see* Decorative Rug **2558**
Decormag. (CN ISSN 0315-047X) **2550**
Decors *see* Decors New Editions **2558**
Decors New Editions. (BE ISSN 0773-4034) **2558**
Decouverte Freudienne. (FR) **4018**
Decoy Magazine. (US ISSN 1055-0364) **2435**
Decubitus. (US ISSN 0898-1655) **3247**
DECUScope. (Digital Equipment Computer Users Society) (US ISSN 0011-7447) **1394, 1459**
Deep Ecologist. (AT) **1946**
Deep Foundations News. (US) **1864**
Deep Sea Fisheries Development Project Reports. (NL ISSN 1017-9259) **2039**
Deep-Sea Research. Part A: Oceanographic Research Papers. (US ISSN 0198-0149) **1603, 10, 465, 1550**
Deep-Sea Research. Part B: Oceanographic Literature Review. (US ISSN 0198-0254) **1550, 10, 465**
†Deep Sky. (US ISSN 0735-3073) **5178**
Deep South Genealogical Quarterly. (US) **2148**
Deer and Big Game. (US) **4544**

Deer & Deer Hunting. (US ISSN 0164-7318) **4544**
Deer Farmer. (NZ ISSN 0110-7992) **215**
†Deer Farmers Journal of N.S.W. (AT) **5178**
Deer Hunting *see* Field & Stream Deer Hunter's Guide Annual **4545**
Deer Hunting (Los Angeles) *see* Big Game Hunting **4542**
Deer Talk *see* Deer Farmers Journal of N.S.W **5178**
Deer Trail. (US) **4544**
Deer Unlimited Magazine. (US) **4544**
Defaulted Bonds Newsletter. (US) **944**
Defazet. (GW ISSN 0012-009X) **3653**
DEFDOCS Microfile *see* Defence Documents Microfile **3455**
Defects in Crystalline Solids *see* Defects in Solids **1210**
Defects in Solids. (NE) **1210, 3817**
Defence. (UK ISSN 0142-6184) **3455**
Defence Africa and Middle East *see* Defence **3455**
▼Defence and the Economy. (GR) **3455, 658**
Defence Documents Microfile. (UK) **3455**
▼Defence Economics. (US ISSN 1043-0717) **3455**
Defence Force Journal *see* Australian Defence Force Journal **3452**
Defence Helicopter. (UK ISSN 0963-116X) **51, 3455**
Defence Helicopter World *see* Defence Helicopter **51**
Defence Industry Digest. (UK) **658, 3455**
Defence Journal. (PK ISSN 0257-2141) **3455**
Defence Lawyers Trial Book. (CN) **2713**
Defence Management. (II) **3455**
Defence Manager *see* Defence Management **3455**
†Defence Minister and Chief of Staff. (UK ISSN 0952-908X) **5178**
Defence Review. (PK) **3455**
Defence Science Journal. (II ISSN 0011-748X) **3455, 4306, 4596**
†Defence Today. (IT ISSN 1120-1665) **5178**
Defender. (AT ISSN 0811-6407) **1273**
Defender. (US ISSN 0011-7501) **1310**
Defender (Wilmington). (US ISSN 0011-7498) **1998**
Defenders. (US ISSN 0162-6337) **1486, 581, 1946**
Defenders of Wildlife Magazine *see* Defenders **1486**
Defending D W Is in Washington. (US) **2713**
Defensa. (SP ISSN 0211-3732) **3456**
†Defensa Electronica. (SP) **5178**
Defensa Latino Americana *see* Defence **3455**
Defense (Year). (US ISSN 0737-1217) **3456**
Defense - Aerospace Business Digest *see* Aerospace Financial News **3449**
Defense - Aerospace Directory. (US) **3456, 51**
Defense Analysis. (UK ISSN 0743-0175) **3456**
Defense & Aerospace Electronics. (US ISSN 1056-747X) **3456, 1407**
▼Defense & Aerospace Electronics. (US) **3456, 51**
Defense and Aerospace Markets. (US) **3456, 51**
Defense and Aerospace Notes. (AT ISSN 1032-4674) **658, 3456**
†Defense & Diplomacy. (US ISSN 1044-3177) **5178**
Defense & Disarmament Alternatives. (US) **3890**
Defense and Disarmament News *see* Defense & Disarmament Alternatives **3890**
Defense & Economy World Report. (US) **3456, 51**
Defense & Foreign Affairs. (US ISSN 0277-4933) **3890, 3456**

Defense and Foreign Affairs Strategic Policy. (US) **3456, 3954**
Defense and Foreign Affairs Weekly. (US) **3456, 3954**
†Defense Budget Intelligence. (US) **5178**
†Defense Budget Service. (US) **5178**
▼Defense Cleanup. (US ISSN 1052-0635) **1984**
Defense Computing *see* Defense Electronics **1765**
Defense Contract Litigation Reporter. (US ISSN 1047-1758) **2713**
Defense Counsel Journal. (US ISSN 0895-0016) **2701**
Defense Daily. (US ISSN 0889-0404) **51, 3456**
Defense des Grades de la Police Nationale. (FR) **2582, 3456**
Defense des Vegetaux *see* Phytoma **188**
Defense Electronics. (US ISSN 0278-3479) **1765**
Defense et Armement - Heracles International. (FR) **3456**
Defense Foreign Affairs Handbook. (US ISSN 0160-5836) **3456, 3954**
Defense Housing. (US ISSN 1047-6504) **3456, 2486**
Defense Industry. (AT) **3456**
Defense Industry Service. (US) **3456, 1128**
Defense Institute of Security Assistance Management Journal *see* D I S A M Journal **3954**
Defense Integrated Data System Total Item Record: Segment V. (US) **3476**
Defense Integrated Data System Total Item Record: Segments A, B, C. (US) **3476**
Defense Integrated System Total Item Record: Master Requirements. (US) **3476**
Defense Law Journal. (US ISSN 0011-7587) **2702**
Defense Manual. (US ISSN 0191-877X) **2702**
▼Defense Manufacturers & Suppliers Association of America Newsletter. (US) **3456**
Defense Marketing International. (US ISSN 1044-3975) **3456, 1037**
Defense Media Review. (US ISSN 0893-0619) **3456**
Defense Monitor. (US ISSN 0195-6450) **3456**
Defense Nationale. (FR ISSN 0336-1489) **3456**
Defense News. (US ISSN 0884-139X) **3456**
Defense of Equal Employment Claims. (US) **976**
Defense of Japan. (JA) **3456**
Defense Organization Service. (US) **3456, 4058**
Defense Organization Service - Industry *see* Defense Industry Service **3456**
†Defense Organization Service - Procurement. (US) **5178**
†Defense Organization Service - R D T & E. (US) **5178**
Defense Program Service - Procurement *see* Defense Programs Service **3457**
Defense Programs Service. (US) **3457**
Defense Programs Service - R D T and E (Research, Development, Test and Evaluation) *see* Defense Programs Service **3457**
Defense Reference Reports. (US ISSN 0099-166X) **3457**
Defense Science *see* Aerospace & Defense Science **3449**
Defense Science and Electronics *see* Aerospace & Defense Science **3449**
Defense Spending in the 1990s: Impact on California. (US) **859, 1092**
Defense Technology Business. (US ISSN 1047-353X) **3457, 658, 4596**
†Defense Technology International. (US) **5178**
Defense Transportation Journal. (US ISSN 0011-7625) **4649, 1273**
Defense Update. (IS ISSN 0931-7317) **3457**
Defense Week. (US ISSN 0273-3188) **3457**
†Defense World. (US) **5178**

6110 DEFENSER

Defenser see Vaern om Danmark 3474
Defensor-Chieftain. (US ISSN 0011-7633) 2224
Defi see Challenge (New York) 3879
Defi-Sciences. (CN) 1310
Defiscience. (CN) 1310
Deformacion Metalica. (SP ISSN 0210-685X) 3405
DeGarmo Lectures see Annual DeGarmo Lectures 1699
Degre Second see Faux Titre 2866
Degre Second: Studies in French Literature. (US ISSN 0148-561X) 2910
Degre Second: Studies in French Literature from the Renaissance to the Present see Degre Second: Studies in French Literature 2910
Degree Course Offers. (UK) 1704
Degree Studies and the Accountancy Profession see Approved Courses for Accountancy Education 747
Degres. (BE ISSN 0770-8378) 2810, 3764
Deguo Yixue/Deutsche Medizin. (CC ISSN 0178-3351) 3170, 10
Degussa International. (GW) 1852
Degussa Report. (GW) 1852
Dehi Razakar. (PK) 86
Dehio: Handbuch der deutschen Kunstdenkmaeler. (GW) 323, 298
Dei Delitti e delle Pene. (IT) 1513
Deike Gedenktage. (GW ISSN 0341-6771) 418
Deike-Press. (GW ISSN 0342-1732) 323
Dein Reich Komme. (GW ISSN 0011-7692) 4174
Deine Bahn see D B 4708
Deine Gesundheit. (GW ISSN 0415-1798) 3801
†Deine Stadt. (GW) 5178
Z Dejin Hutnictvi. (CS) 3405, 2358
Z Dejin Vied a Techniky na Slovensku. (CS) 2358
Dejiny Socialistickeho Ceskoslovenska. (CS ISSN 0232-0150) 2358
Dejiny Ved a Techniky/History of Sciences and Technology. (CS ISSN 0300-4414) 4306, 4596
†Dekalb Literary Arts Journal. (US ISSN 0011-7714) 5178
Deke Quarterly. (US ISSN 0164-8314) 1297
Dekk Aktuelt. (NO) 4291
Del-Chem Bulletin. (US ISSN 0095-8387) 1176
Del Condominium Life. (CN) 2550
Del - Mar Biz. (US) 658
Del-Mar-Va Heartland. (US) 86, 4544
▼Delaney Report. (US) 30, 1037
Delavska Enotnost. (XV ISSN 0011-7722) 2582
Delaware. Court of Chancery. Delaware Chancery Reports see Delaware Reporter 2618
Delaware. Department of Highways and Transportation. Traffic Summary. (US ISSN 0070-329X) 4718
Delaware. Department of Natural Resources and Environmental Control. Annual Report. (US ISSN 0084-9642) 1946, 1486
Delaware. Department of Public Instruction. Educational Personnel Directory. (US ISSN 0091-6188) 1624
Delaware. Department of Public Instruction. Teacher Supply and Demand see Supply and Demand: Educational Personnel in Delaware 1666
Delaware. State Board of Education. Report of Educational Statistics. (US ISSN 0362-8787) 1624
Delaware. State Highway Department. Traffic Summary see Delaware. Department of Highways and Transportation. Traffic Summary 4718
Delaware. State Treasurer. Annual Report. (US ISSN 0084-9685) 1092
Delaware Agenda. (US) 86
†Delaware Art Museum. Annual Report. (US) 5178

Delaware Art Museum Bulletin see Delaware Art Museum Quarterly 3523
Delaware Art Museum Quarterly. (US) 3523
Delaware Beverage Monthly. (US) 380
Delaware Conservationist. (US ISSN 0045-9852) 1486
Delaware Corporate Law Reporter. (US) 2709
Delaware Corporate Litigation Reporter.(US ISSN 1042-5756) 2709
Delaware Corporation Law Update. (US ISSN 0888-434X) 2709
Delaware Court Reporter. (US) 2731
Delaware Directory of Commerce and Industry. (US ISSN 0272-8117) 1128
Delaware Documentation. (US) 2404
Delaware Genealogical Society. Journal. (US ISSN 0731-3896) 2148
Delaware Geological Survey Bulletins. (US ISSN 0070-3273) 1558
Delaware Geological Survey Reports of Investigations. (US ISSN 0011-7749) 1558
Delaware History. (US ISSN 0011-7765) 2404
Delaware Journal of Corporate Law. (US ISSN 0364-9490) 2709
Delaware Law Monthly. (US) 2618
Delaware Library Association Bulletin. (US ISSN 0011-7773) 2754
Delaware Medical Journal. (US ISSN 0011-7781) 3093
Delaware Museum of Natural History. Monograph Series. (US ISSN 0084-9650) 4307
Delaware Museum of Natural History. Reproduction Series. (US ISSN 0084-9669) 4307
Delaware Nurses' Association Reporter. (US) 3277
Delaware Reporter. (US ISSN 0091-5564) 2618
Delaware River Basin Biennial Water Resources Conference. Proceedings. (US) 4823
Delaware River Basin Water Resources Conference. Proceedings see Delaware River Basin Biennial Water Resources Conference. Proceedings 4823
Delaware Sea Grant Reporter. (US) 2039, 1603
Delaware Symposia Series see Delaware Symposium on Language Studies Series 2810
Delaware Symposium on Language Studies Series. (US) 2810
Delaware Today. (US ISSN 0011-779X) 2224
Delaware Valley. (US ISSN 1052-4592) 4759
†Delaware Valley Counselor. (US) 5178
Delaware Valley Planning News. (US) 4649
Delaware Valley Regional Planning Commission. Annual Report. (US) 1074
Delegates. (UK) 3392
Delegates World Bulletin see Diplomatic World Bulletin and Delegates World Bulletin 3955
Delegation Archeologique Francaise en Iran. Cahiers. (FR ISSN 0765-104X) 270
Delegation Archeologique Francaise en Iran. Memoires. (NE ISSN 0169-880X) 270, 323
Delegation Generale pour l'Armement Info D G A see Info D G A 3460
Delek. Annual Report. (IS) 3684
Delfin. (GW ISSN 0724-2689) 323, 1624, 4307, 4370
Delfino. (IT) 1535
Delft Progress Report. (NE ISSN 0304-985X) 1176, 1852, 3817
Delfts Bouwkundig Studenten Gezelschap Styles. Mededelingen. (NE ISSN 0011-782X) 1310
Delhi. Chamber of Commerce. Bulletin. (II) 814
Delhi Chamber of Commerce Trade Directory see D C C Trade Directory 814
Delhi Law Review. (II) 2618

Delhi Law Times. (II ISSN 0011-7846) 2618
Delhi Medical Journal. (II ISSN 0011-7854) 3093
†Deli-Dairy. (US) 5178
Deli-Dairy Management see Deli-Dairy 5178
Deli-Dairy World see Chain Merchandiser 2063
Deli News. (US ISSN 0011-7862) 2091
Delibros. (SP ISSN 0214-2694) 4126
Delicious! (US) 3604, 3801
Delikt en Delinkwent. (NE ISSN 0045-9879) 1513
Delineavit et Sculpsit. (NE ISSN 0923-9790) 3998
Le Delire. (CN) 1310
Delius. (UK ISSN 0306-0373) 3548
Deliverer. (UK ISSN 0011-7897) 4235, 4403
Delivery Trasporti Commerciali. (IT) 4744
Dell Horoscope. (US ISSN 0018-5116) 358
Dell Horoscope Purse Books. (US) 358
Dellcrest Children's Centre Newsletter see Dellcrest News 5178
†Dellcrest News. (CN) 5178
†Dellplain Latin American Studies. (US) 5178
Delmarva Country. (US) 86
Delmarva Farmer. (US) 87
Delmenhorster Kegler Zeitung. (GW) 4502
Delmon see Dilmun 270
Delo. (YU ISSN 0011-7935) 2864
Delo in Varnost. (XV ISSN 0011-7943) 976, 3616
Deloitte & Touche Review. (US) 750
Deloraine Times & Star. (CN) 87
Delos. (US ISSN 0011-7951) 2910
Delovye Lyudi see Business in the U.S.S.R. (International Edition) 651
Delovye Svyazi see Business Contact 902
Delphin. (GW ISSN 0011-796X) 4470
Delphinium Society Yearbook. (UK) 2125
Delpinoa. (IT ISSN 0416-928X) 436
†Delta. (FR ISSN 0396-7549) 5178
Delta (Barcelona). (SP) 4174
Delta (Budapest). (HU ISSN 0011-7994) 4307, 1818
Delta (Paris). (FR) 1253, 1624
Delta (Tigre). (AG ISSN 0011-7978) 87, 2098
Delta (Warsaw). (PL) 3034, 3817
Delta (Washington) see Mathematics Magazine 3047
Delta del Parana. (AG ISSN 0045-9895) 2098
Delta Digest. (US) 87
Delta Epsilon Sigma Journal. (US ISSN 0745-0958) 1310
Delta Farm Press. (US ISSN 0011-8036) 87
Delta Kappa Gamma Bulletin. (US ISSN 0011-8044) 1704
Delta Pi Epsilon. Research Bulletin. (US ISSN 0416-9336) 1747
Delta Pi Epsilon Journal. (US ISSN 0011-8052) 1704, 658
Delta Research Monograph. (NZ ISSN 0110-4748) 1624, 1253
Delta's New Product News. (US) 2065
Deltawerken. (NE ISSN 0011-8079) 4823
Deltio N A T O see N A T O Review 3908
Deltio tis Ellinikis Ktiniatrikis Eterias. see Hellenic Veterinary Medical Society. Bulletin 4810
Deltion Dieekiseos Epichiriseon/Business Administration Bulletin. (GR ISSN 0011-8087) 1007
Deltion Pneumatikes kai Kallitechnikes Drasteriotetos see Anagnostika Hetaireia Kerkyras. Deltion 2348
Deluxe. (US) 775, 944
Demag Kurier. (GW ISSN 0011-815X) 1928
Demain. (FR ISSN 0751-5812) 1236
Demain d'Avantage qu'Hier. (FR) 4174
Demama Shelanv see Our Review 2288

Demb Ak Tey/Yesterday and Today. (SG) 2910, 1999
▼Dementia. (SZ ISSN 1013-7424) 3335, 2271, 3722
Dementia 13. (UK) 3011
Demeter-Blaetter. (GW) 2065, 3801
Demeter Kongress Kalender Medizin. (GW ISSN 0933-9760) 3392, 3093
Demeure Historique. (FR) 298
Demeures et Chateaux. (FR ISSN 0291-1191) 4147, 30, 298
Demo Memo. (US) 615
Democracia. (UY) 3890
Democracy. see Minzhu 3907
Democracy and Law. see Democrazia e Diritto 2618
Democracy & Legal Systems. see Minzhu yu Fazhi 3907
Democracy and Science. see Minzhu yu Kexue 3907
Democracy in the World. (US) 3890
Democrat. (UK) 30, 1114, 3941
Democrat. (SA) 3890
Democrat. (CN ISSN 0070-3346) 3890
†Democrat (Washington). (US ISSN 0011-8192) 5178
Democrate. see Al Dimuqrati 2169
Le Democrate. (SG) 3890
Democratic Forum. (II ISSN 0301-9055) 2199
Democratic Journalist. (CS ISSN 0011-8214) 2568
Democratic Left. (US ISSN 0164-3207) 3890
Democratic Republic of the Sudan Gazette/Jaridah al-Rasmiyah li-Jumhuriyat al-Sudan al-Dimuqratiyah.(SJ) 4058, 2618
Democratic Republic of the Sudan Gazette. Legislative Supplement. (SJ) 4058, 2618
Democratic Republic of the Sudan Gazette. Special Legislative Supplement see Democratic Republic of the Sudan Gazette. Legislative Supplement 4058
Democratic World. (II ISSN 0301-9047) 3890
Democratie Moderne. (FR ISSN 0011-8222) 3890
Democrazia e Diritto/Democracy and Law. (IT ISSN 0416-9565) 2618, 2864
Demografia. (HU ISSN 0011-8249) 3981
Demograficheskie Issledovaniya. (KR ISSN 0207-0383) 3981
Demografie. (CS ISSN 0011-8265) 3991
Demographic Guide to Arizona (Year). (US) 3981
Demographic Handbook for Africa/Guide Demographie de l'Afrique. (UN) 3981
Demographic Monographs. (US ISSN 0275-9594) 3981
Demographic Yearbook. (UN ISSN 0082-8041) 3981
Demographie Africaine: Bulletin de Liaison. (CM ISSN 0151-1408) 3981
Demographie et Sciences Humaines see Population 3985
Demographie et Societes. (FR ISSN 0070-3362) 3981
Demography. (US ISSN 0070-3370) 3981
Demography India. (II ISSN 0970-454X) 3981
Demokraat. (SA ISSN 0011-829X) 3890
▼Demokraticheskaya Gazeta. (RU) 3890
Demokraticheskii Zhurnalist see Democratic Journalist 2568
Demokratische Gemeinde. (GW ISSN 0011-8303) 4086
Die Demokratische Schule. (GW ISSN 0011-8311) 1726
Demolition Age. (US ISSN 0362-7772) 615
Demos. (GW ISSN 0011-832X) 254, 10
Demos. (NE ISSN 0169-1473) 3981
Demosiografiki/Journalism. (GR) 2569
Dempa Digest. (JA ISSN 0288-6103) 1765

Dempa Shinbun/Electronics Daily. (JA) 1765
Dempsey Canadian Letter. (US) 658
Dempsey Canadian Newsletter see Dempsey Canadian Letter 658
†Demyelinating Diseases. (UK ISSN 0142-8373) 5178
▼Den' (RU) 2864
Den Rigtige Slagter see Koedbranchen 2076
†Denaro Capital. (IT) 5178
Denbigh Gazette. (US) 2224, 2404
▼Deneuve. (US) 2452, 4840
Den'gi i Kredit. (RU ISSN 0011-8362) 775
▼Denise. (HU ISSN 0864-9227) 2983
Denken en Doen. (NE ISSN 0011-8370) 2445
†Denken, Schauen, Sinnen. (GW ISSN 0070-3419) 5178
Denki Kagaku Newsletter see Electrochemistry and Industrial Physical Chemistry 1212
Denki Kagaku Oyobi Kogyo Butsuri Kagaku. see Electrochemistry and Industrial Physical Chemistry 1212
Denki Seiko. see Electric Furnace Steel 3405
Denki Seirigaku. see Electrophysiology 5185
Denki Tsushin Daigaku Denki Tsushin Kenkyu Shisetsu Nenpo. see University of Electro-Communications. Research Institute for Communication Sciences. Annual Report 5297
Denkmaeler der Buchkunst. (GW ISSN 0341-2474) 324
Denkmalpflege in Baden-Wuerttemberg. (GW ISSN 0340-2495) 324
Denkmalpflege in Niedersachsen. Berichte. (GW ISSN 0720-9835) 270
Denkmalpflege Informationen. (GW) 4058
Denmark. Arbejdstilsynet. Rapport. (DK ISSN 0106-6838) 976
Denmark. Betaenkning fra Miljoestyrelsen. (DK ISSN 0900-3738) 1946
†Denmark. Bibliotekstilsynet Informerer.(DK ISSN 0106-3626) 5178
Denmark. Danmarks Fiskeri- og Havundersoegelser. Skrifter fra see Fisk og Hav 2041
†Denmark. Danmarks Statistik. Arbejdsloesheden. (DK ISSN 0070-346X) 5178
†Denmark. Danmarks Statistik. Arbejdsmarkedsstatistik: Kvartalsvis Regionalstatistik. (DK ISSN 0105-0788) 5178
Denmark. Danmarks Statistik. Befolkningens Bevaegelser. (DK ISSN 0070-3478) 3991, 3981
†Denmark. Danmarks Statistik. Bygningsopgoerelsen. (DK ISSN 0108-7568) 5178
Denmark. Danmarks Statistik. Detailpriser. (DK ISSN 0417-0164) 4570
Denmark. Danmarks Statistik. Driftsregnskabsstatistik for Industrien see Denmark. Danmarks Statistik. Regnskabsstatistik for Industrien 712
Denmark. Danmarks Statistik. Faerdselsuheld. (DK ISSN 0070-3516) 3991, 4100
Denmark. Danmarks Statistik. Handelsstatistiske Meddelelser. Maanedsstatistik over Udenrigshandelen see Denmark. Danmarks Statistik. Udenrigshandel 713
Denmark. Danmarks Statistik. Indkomster og Formuer. (DK ISSN 0107-105X) 712
Denmark. Danmarks Statistik. Indkomster og Formuer Ved Slutligningen see Denmark. Danmarks Statistik. Indkomster og Formuer 712
Denmark. Danmarks Statistik. Industristatistik. (DK ISSN 0070-3532) 712

Denmark. Danmarks Statistik. Kommunale Finanser. (DK ISSN 0106-9802) 4080
Denmark. Danmarks Statistik. Kommunale Finanser for Regnskabsaaret see Denmark. Danmarks Statistik. Kommunale Finanser 4080
Denmark. Danmarks Statistik. Konjunkturtendenser i Udvalgte Lande. (DK ISSN 0109-1271) 712
Denmark. Danmarks Statistik. Kreditmarkedsstatistik. see Denmark. Danmarks Statistik. Penge og Kapitalmarked 712
Denmark. Danmarks Statistik. Kriminalstatistik. (DK ISSN 0070-3540) 1525
Denmark. Danmarks Statistik. Kvartalsstatistik for Industrien see Denmark. Danmarks Statistik. Varestatistik for Industri. Series A 713
Denmark. Danmarks Statistik. Kvartalsstatistik for Industrien see Denmark. Danmarks Statistik. Varestatistik for Industri. Series B 713
Denmark. Danmarks Statistik. Kvartalsstatistik for Industrien see Denmark. Danmarks Statistik. Varestatistik for Industri. Series C 713
Denmark. Danmarks Statistik. Kvartalsstatistik for Industrien see Denmark. Danmarks Statistik. Varestatistik for Industri. Series D 713
Denmark. Danmarks Statistik. Kvartalsstatistik for Industrien. Varestatistik, 4. Kvartal og Aaret see Denmark. Danmarks Statistik. Varestatistik for Industri 713
Denmark. Danmarks Statistik. Kvartalsstatistik over Udenrigshandelen see Udenrigshandelen Fordelt paa Varer og Lande 741
Denmark. Danmarks Statistik. Landbrugsstatistik. (DK) 136
Denmark. Danmarks Statistik. Landbrugsstatistik. Herunder Gartneri og Skovbrug see Denmark. Danmarks Statistik. Landbrugsstatistik 136
Denmark. Danmarks Statistik. Loen- og Indkomststatistik. (DK ISSN 0107-8771) 712
Denmark. Danmarks Statistik. Maanedlig Beskaeftigelses- og Loenstatistik for Industri/Monthly Statistics of Industrial Employment and Labour Costs. (DK ISSN 0105-1083) 712
Denmark. Danmarks Statistik. Maanedlig Ordre- og Omsaetningsstatistik for Industri. (DK ISSN 0105-0877) 712
Denmark. Danmarks Statistik. Nationalregnskabsstatistik. (DK ISSN 0108-8173) 4080
Denmark. Danmarks Statistik. Penge og Kapitalmarked/Money and Credit Market. (DK ISSN 0108-5476) 712
Denmark. Danmarks Statistik. Prisstatistik. (DK) 712
Denmark. Danmarks Statistik. Regnskabsstatistik for Industrien. (DK ISSN 0108-738X) 712
Denmark. Danmarks Statistik. Skatter og Afgifter. (DK ISSN 0105-1164) 712
†Denmark. Danmarks Statistik. Statistike Efterreninger/Danmarks Statistics. Statistical News. (DK ISSN 0105-9750) 5178
Denmark. Danmarks Statistik. Statistisk Aarbog. (DK ISSN 0070-3567) 4570
Denmark. Danmarks Statistik. Statistisk Tiars-Oversigt/Denmarks Statistics. Statistical Ten-Year Review. (DK ISSN 0070-3583) 4570
Denmark. Danmarks Statistik. Statistiske Meddelelser. (DK ISSN 0106-6439) 4570

Denmark. Danmarks Statistik. Statistiske Undersogelser. (DK ISSN 0039-0682) 4570
Denmark. Danmarks Statistik. Udenrigshandel/External Trade. (DK ISSN 0108-5506) 713
†Denmark. Danmarks Statistik. Valgene til de Kommunale og Amtskommunale Raad. (DK ISSN 0107-0371) 5178
Denmark. Danmarks Statistik. Varestatistik for Industri/ Manufacturers' Sales of Commodities.(DK ISSN 0107-7031) 713
Denmark. Danmarks Statistik. Varestatistik for Industri. Series A. (DK ISSN 0107-0967) 713
Denmark. Danmarks Statistik. Varestatistik for Industri. Series B. (DK ISSN 0107-0975) 713
Denmark. Danmarks Statistik. Varestatistik for Industri. Series C. (DK ISSN 0107-0983) 713
Denmark. Danmarks Statistik. Varestatistik for Industri. Series D. (DK ISSN 0107-0991) 713
Denmark. Danmarks Statistik. Vejviser i Statistiken. (DK ISSN 0109-8314) 4570
Denmark. Dantest-Nyt. Aarsberetning. (DK) 3446
Denmark. Direktoratet for Arbejdstilsynet. Arbejdstilsynets Aarsberetning. (DK ISSN 0900-6885) 976
Denmark. Direktoratet for Kriminalforsorgen. Kriminalforsorgen see Kriminalforsorgens Aarsberetning 1517
Denmark. Direktoratet for Kriminalforsorgen. Kriminalpolitisk Forskningsgruppe. Forskningsrapport.(DK) 1513
Denmark. Direktoratet for Patent- og Varemaerkevaesenet. Aarsberetning see Denmark. Patentdirektoratet. Aarsberetning 3674
Denmark. Direktoratet for Toldvaesenet. Toldvaesnet Aktiviteter see Denmark. Direktoratet for Toldvaesenet. Toldvaesnets Aarsberetning 5178
†Denmark. Direktoratet for Toldvaesenet. Toldvaesnets Aarsberetning. (DK ISSN 0109-6672) 5178
Denmark. Egnsudviklingsraadet. Beretning see National Agency of Industry and Trade. Annual Reports (Year) 1081
Denmark. Energiministeriet. Energiforskningsprogram. (DK ISSN 0108-4011) 1785
Denmark. Energistyrelsen. Nyt fra Energistyrelsen. (DK ISSN 0108-7495) 1785
Denmark. Finansministeriet. Budgetdepartementet. Budgetredegoerelse see Denmark. Finansministeriet. Redegoerelse om den Offentlige Sektor 1092
Denmark. Finansministeriet. Redegoerelse om den Offentlige Sektor. (DK) 1092
Denmark. Finanstilsynet. Banker of Sparekasser see Denmark. Finanstilsynet. Beretning 775
Denmark. Finanstilsynet. Beretning. (DK ISSN 0905-0965) 775
Denmark. Finanstilsynet. Beretning. Bilag 1: Pengeinstitutterm.v. (DK) 2530
Denmark. Finanstilsynet. Beretning. Bilag 2: Livsforsikringsselskaber m.v. (DK) 944
Denmark. Finanstilsynet. Beretning. Bilag 3: Skadesforsikringsselskaber. (DK) 775
Denmark. Finanstilsynet. Beretning. Bilag 4: Boersomraadet. (DK) 775
Denmark. Finanstilsynet. Beretning. Bilag 5: Investeringsforeninger. (DK ISSN 0905-0965) 944
Denmark. Finanstilsynet. Fondsboersen of Boersmaeglerselskaber see Denmark. Finanstilsynet. Beretning 775

Denmark. Finanstilsynet. Forsikringsselskaber og Pensionskasser m.v. see Denmark. Finanstilsynet. Beretning 775
Denmark. Finanstilsynet. Investeringsforeninger see Denmark. Finanstilsynet. Beretning 775
Denmark. Fiskeriministeriet. Forsoegslaboratorium. Aarsberetning.(DK ISSN 0070-3605) 2039, 436
Denmark. Forbrugerstyrelsen. Pjecer. (DK) 1504
Denmark. Forbrugerstyrelsen. Raad og Resultater. (DK) 1504
Denmark. Forbrugerstyrelsen. Tekniske Meddelelser. (DK) 1504
Denmark. Forskningsafdelingen. Forskning. (DK ISSN 0906-5822) 4596
Denmark. Forskningsafdelingen. Forskning og Samfund see Denmark. Forskningsafdelingen. Forskning 4596
Denmark. Forskningscenter Risoe. Risoe-R. (DK) 1804, 1785, 1818
Denmark. Forskningsdirektoratet. Forskning og Samfund see Denmark. Forskningsafdelingen. Forskning 4596
Denmark. Forsoeganslaeg Risoe. Fysikafdelingen. Annual Progress Report see Denmark. Risoe National Laboratory. Physics Department. Annual Progress Report 3817
Denmark. Forsoegsanslaeg Risoe. Risoe-R see Denmark. Forskningscenter Risoe. Risoe-R 1804
Denmark. Forsoegslaboratoriet. Beretning see Denmark. Statens Husdyrbrugsforsoeg. Beretning 215
Denmark. Forsvarsministeriet. Aarlige Redegoerelse. (DK ISSN 0109-5757) 3457, 1273
Denmark. Forsvarsministeriet. Forsvarsministerens Aarlige Redegoerelse see Denmark. Forsvarsministeriet. Aarlige Redegoerelse 3457
Denmark. Indenrigsministeriet. Indenrigsministeriets Afgoerelser og Udtalelser om Kommunale Forhold. (DK ISSN 0108-979X) 4058
Denmark. Jordbrugsoekonomisk Institut. Aarsberetning see Denmark. Statens Jordbrugsoekonomiske Institut. Aarsberetning 658
Denmark. Jordbrugsoekonomisk Institut. Serie D: Gartneri-Regnskabsstatistik/ Economic Results in Danish Horticulture. (DK ISSN 0107-5705) 149, 136
Denmark. Jordbrugsoekonomiske Institut. Landbrugets Oekonomi/ Economy of the Agricultural Sector. (DK ISSN 0106-1291) 658
Denmark. Jordbrugsoekonomiske Institut. Rapport/Reports. (DK ISSN 0107-5357) 149
Denmark. Jordbrugsoekonomiske Institut. Serie C: Landbrugets Prisforhold. (DK ISSN 0107-5691) 149
Denmark. Kg. Veterinaer- og Landbohoejskole. Meddelelser see Denmark. Kgl. Veterinaer- og Landbohoejskole. Forskningsrapport 175
Denmark. Kgl. Veterinaer- og Landbohoejskole. Forskningsrapport/ Reseach Report. (DK ISSN 0905-8478) 175
Denmark. Kongelige Bibliotek. Fund og Forskning. (DK ISSN 0069-9896) 2754
Denmark. Landbrugsministeriet, Forskningssekretariatet. Kortlaegning.(DK ISSN 0906-1770) 87
Denmark. Landbrugsministeriet, Forskningssekretariatet. Rammeplaner. (DK ISSN 0906-1894) 87
Denmark. Levnedsmiddelstyrelsen. Publikation. (DK ISSN 0107-0517) 2065

DENMARK. LOVINFORMATION

Denmark. Lovinformation fra Miljoestyrelsen. (DK ISSN 0900-2758) **1946, 2618**

Denmark. Miljoe Danmark. (DK ISSN 0903-5907) **1946**

†Denmark. Miljoekreditraadet. Beretning. (DK ISSN 0108-7487) **5178**

Denmark. Miljoeministeriet. Miljoeministerens Redegoerelse om Landsplanlaegning. (DK ISSN 0108-6901) **2486**

Denmark. Miljoeministeriet. Miljoeministeriets Lovregister. (DK ISSN 0109-1913) **2618, 1946**

Denmark. Miljoestyrelsen Analytisk-Kemiske Laboratorium. Aarsberetning see Denmark. Miljoministeriet. Danmarks Miljoundersogelser. Afdeling for Miljokemi **1946**

Denmark. Miljoestyrelsen. Havforureningslaboratorium. Report of the Marine Pollution Laboratory. (DK ISSN 0107-7430) **1946, 4726**

Denmark. Miljoestyrelsen Kemikaliekontrol. Aarsberetning see Denmark. Miljoministeriet. Danmarks Miljoundersogelser. Afdeling for Miljokemi **1946**

Denmark. Miljoestyrelsen. Oversigt over Godkendte Bekaempelsesmidler see Denmark. Orientering fra Miljoestyrelsen **1946**

Denmark. Miljoministeriet. Danmarks Miljoundersogelser. Afdeling for Miljokemi. (DK) **1946**

Denmark. Ministeriet for Groenland. Statistike Meddelelser see Groenlandsdepartementet. Statistike Meddelelser **5201**

Denmark. Nationalmuseet. Arbejdsmark.(DK ISSN 0084-9308) **3523**

Denmark. Nationalmuseet. Publications: Archaeological Historical Series. (DK) **270**

Denmark. Nationalmuseet. Publications: Ethnographical Series. (DK) **238**

Denmark. Nationalmuseet. Working Papers. (DK) **3523**

Denmark. Orientering fra Miljoestyrelsen. (DK ISSN 0107-2722) **1946**

Denmark. Patentdirektoratet. Aarsberetning. (DK) **3674**

Denmark. Patentdirektoratet. Direktorat under Forandring see Denmark. Patentdirektoratet. Aarsberetning **3674**

†Denmark. Planlaegningsraadet for Forskningen - Dandok - Statens 6 Forskningsraad. Beretning. (DK ISSN 0105-452X) **5178**

†Denmark. Planstyrelsen. Regionplanorientering. (DK ISSN 0105-9602) **5178**

Denmark. Plant Directorate. Annual Report. (DK) **2098**

Denmark. Redegoerelse fra Miljoestyrelsen. (DK ISSN 0900-6788) **1946**

Denmark. Rigsbibliotekarembedet. Accessionkatalog see Denmark. Statens Bibliotekstjeneste. ALBA - Accessionskatalogen **398**

Denmark. Rigsbibliotekarembedet. ALBA - Accessionskatalogen see Denmark. Statens Bibliotekstjeneste. ALBA - Accessionskatalogen **398**

Denmark. Risoe National Laboratory. Physics Department. Annual Progress Report. (DK) **3817**

Denmark. Socialforskningsinstituttet. Arbejdsnotater. (DK ISSN 0904-9398) **4403**

Denmark. Socialforskningsinstituttet. Beretning om Socialforskningsinstituttets Virksomhed. (DK ISSN 0107-4377) **4403**

Denmark. Socialforskningsinstituttet. Pjecer. (DK ISSN 0905-0957) **4403, 4433**

Denmark. Socialforskningsinstituttet. Socialforskningsinstituttets Virksomhed see Denmark. Socialforskningsinstituttet. Beretning om Socialforskningsinstituttets Virksomhed **4403**

Denmark. Socialforskningsinstuttet. Rapporter. (DK ISSN 0903-6814) **4403**

Denmark. Statens Bibliotekstjeneste. ALBA - Accessionskatalogen. (DK) **398**

Denmark. Statens Bibliotekstjeneste. Retningslinier. (DK ISSN 0905-555X) **2754**

Denmark. Byggeforskningsinstitut. Aarsberetning see S B I Aarsberetning **631**

†Denmark. Statens Byggeforskningsinstitut. Landbrugsbyggeri. (DK ISSN 0589-6665) **5178**

†Denmark. Statens Byggeforskningsinstitut. Projektresumeer. (DK ISSN 0904-2253) **5178**

Denmark. Statens Filmcentral. Information og Beretning. (DK ISSN 0109-4076) **3507**

Denmark. Statens Filmcentral. Katalog over 16mm Film see Denmark. Statens Filmcentral. S F C, 16mm Film **5178**

Denmark. Statens Filmcentral. S F C Catalogue see Denmark. Statens Filmcentral. S F C Film og Video Catalogue **3507**

Denmark. Statens Filmcentral. S F C Film og Video Catalogue. (DK) **3507, 1384**

▼Denmark. Statens Filmcentral. S F C Video. (DK) **3507, 1384**

†Denmark. Statens Filmcentral. S F C, 16mm Film. (DK ISSN 0105-5526) **5178**

Denmark. Statens Filmcentral. Statistik over Udlejning af 16 MM Film i Finansaaret see Denmark. Statens Filmcentral. Statistik over Udlejning og Deponering af 16 MM Film og Video i Finansaaret **3519**

Denmark. Statens Filmcentral. Statistik over Udlejning og Deponering af 16 MM Film og Video i Finansaaret. (DK) **3519, 1347, 1385**

Denmark. Statens Husdyrbrugsforsoeg. Aarsrapport. (DK) **3710**

Denmark. Statens Husdyrbrugsforsoeg. Beretning. (DK ISSN 0105-6883) **215, 551, 571**

Denmark. Statens Husdyrbrugsforsoeg. Indeks. (DK ISSN 0105-9807) **215**

Denmark. Statens Husholdningsraad. Pjecer see Denmark. Forbrugerstyrelsen. Pjecer **1504**

Denmark. Statens Husholdningsraad. Raad og Resultater see Denmark. Forbrugerstyrelsen. Raad og Resultater **1504**

Denmark. Statens Husholdningsraad. Tekniske Meddelelser see Denmark. Forbrugerstyrelsen. Tekniske Meddelelser **1504**

Denmark. Statens Jordbrugsoekonomiske Institut. Aarsberetning. (DK ISSN 0108-7479) **658**

Denmark. Statens Jordbrugsoekonomiske Institut. Serie A: Landbrugets Regnskabsstatistik. (DK ISSN 0107-5675) **149, 136**

†Denmark. Statens Jordbrugsoekonomiske Institut. Serie B: Oekonomien i Landbrugets Driftsgrene/Economics of Agricultural Enterprises. (DK ISSN 0107-5683) **5178**

Denmark. Statens Kunstfond. Beretning.(DK ISSN 0107-2951) **324**

Denmark. Statens Ligningsdirektorat og Ligningsraadet. Indkomst- og Formueskat see Denmark. Statsskattedirektoratet og Ligningsraadet. Meddelelser 1. Haefte: Indkomst- og Formueansaettelser **5178**

†Denmark. Statens Mejeriforsoeg. Beretning. (DK ISSN 0366-3221) **5178**

Denmark. Statens Paedagogiske Forsoegscenter. Arbejdsbeskrivelse. (DK ISSN 0107-4652) **1624**

Denmark. Statens Paedagogiske Forsoegscenter. Projektbeskrivelser see Denmark. Statens Paedagogiske Forsoegscenter. Arbejdsbeskrivelse **1624**

Denmark. Statens Uddannelsesstoette. Haandbog. (DK) **1625**

Denmark. Statens Uddannelsesstoette. Regelsamling for Stoetteaaret see Denmark. Statens Uddannelsesstoette. Haandbog **1625**

Denmark. Statens Vejlaboratorium. Laboratorierapport. (DK ISSN 0106-312X) **4718**

Denmark. Statens Vejlaboratorium. Notat. (DK ISSN 0109-5315) **4718**

Denmark. Statsskatedirektoratet og Ligningsraadet. Vurdering af Fast Ejendom see Denmark. Statsskattedirektoratet og Ligningsraadet. Meddelelser 2. Haefte: Vurdering af Fast Ejendom **5179**

†Denmark. Statsskattedirektoratet og Ligningsraadet. Meddelelser 1. Haefte: Indkomst- og Formueansaettelser. (DK ISSN 0106-4908) **5178**

†Denmark. Statsskattedirektoratet og Ligningsraadet. Meddelelser 2. Haefte: Vurdering af Fast Ejendom. (DK) **5179**

Denmark. Teknologistyrelsen. Nyhedsbrev. (DK ISSN 0109-0070) **4596**

Denmark. Undervisningsministeriet. Datakontoret. Statistik for de Videregaaende Uddannelser. (DK ISSN 0108-4267) **1675**

Denmark. Undervisningsministeriet. Oekonomisk-Statistiske Konsulent. Statistik for de Videregaaende Uddannelser see Denmark. Undervisningsministeriet. Datakontoret. Statistik for de Videregaaende Uddannelser **1675**

Denmark. Vejdirektoratet. Aarsberetning. (DK ISSN 0109-2405) **4718**

Denmark. Vejdirektoratet. Aarsrapport see Denmark. Vejdirektoratet. Aarsberetning **4718**

Denmark. Vejdirektoratet. Black-Spotundersoegelse paa Hovedlandeveje see Sikkerhedsmaessig Vurdering og Prioritering af Mindre Anlaegsarbejder paa Hovedlandeveje **4721**

Denmark. Vejdirektoratet. Oekonomisk-Statistisk Afdeling. Trafikrapport. (DK) **4718**

Denmark. Vejdirektoratet. Trafikrapport see Denmark. Vejdirektoratet. Oekonomisk-Statistisk Afdeling. Trafikrapport **4718**

Denmark. Vejledning fra Miljoestyrelsen.(DK) **1947**

†Denmark Bibliotekstilsynet. Beretning. (DK ISSN 0107-8003) **5179**

Denmark Quarterly Review. (DK ISSN 0011-8427) **859**

Denmark Review. (DK ISSN 0418-6745) **859**

Denmark's Development Assistance. Annual Report. (DK) **928**

Denmarks Statistics. Statistical Ten-Year Review. see Denmark. Danmarks Statistik. Statistisk Tiars-Oversigt **4570**

Denmark's 15000 Largest Companies. see Danmarks 15000 Stoerste Virksomheder **1128**

Denni Hlasatel. (US) **1999**

Denning Law Journal. (UK ISSN 0269-1922) **2618**

Denning Law Society. Journal see Dar es Salaam University Law Journal **2618**

Dennitsa. (RU) **1310, 3405**

Denominations in America. (US ISSN 0193-6883) **4174**

Denpa Kenkyujo Kiho - Radio Research Laboratory. Review see Tsushin Sogo Kenkyujo Kiho **1383**

Denpa Koho/Electronic Navigation Review. (JA) **4726, 1355**

Denpun Kagaku. see Japanese Society of Starch Science. Journal **2074**

Denriso Geppo. see Ionospheric Data in Japan **3437**

Denryoku Shinpo see Energy Forum **1788**

Dens. (DK) **3230**

Densal. (US ISSN 0894-2056) **4214**

Densanki Riyo Ni Kansuru Shinpojumu Koengaiyo/Proceedings of the Symposium of Computer Research. (JA) **1864, 1394**

Densenbyo Tokei see Japan. Ministry of Health and Welfare. Statistics and Information Department. Statistical Report on Communicable Diseases **3176**

Denshi Gijutsu. see Electronic Engineering **1767**

Denshi Joho Tsushin Gakkai Ronbunshi (A). see Institute of Electronics, Information and Communication Engineers. Transactions (Section A) **1773**

Denshi Joho Tsushin Gakkai Ronbunshi (B-I). see Institute of Electronics, Information and Communication Engineers. Transactions (Section B-I) **1773**

Denshi Joho Tsushin Gakkai Ronbunshi (B-II). see Institute of Electronics, Information and Communication Engineers. Transactions (Section B-II) **1773**

Denshi Joho Tsushin Gakkai Ronbunshi (C-I). see Institute of Electronics, Information and Communication Engineers. Transactions (Section C-I) **1773**

Denshi Joho Tsushin Gakkai Ronbunshi (C-II). see Institute of Electronics, Information and Communication Engineers. Transactions (Section C-II) **1774**

Denshi Joho Tsushin Gakkai Ronbunshi (D-I). see Institute of Electronics, Information and Communication Engineers. Transactions (Section D-I) **1437**

Denshi Joho Tsushin Gakkai Ronbunshi (D-II). see Institute of Electronics, Information and Communication Engineers. Transactions (Section D-II) **1437**

Denshi Joho Tsushin Gakkaishi. see Institute of Electronics, Information and Communications Engineers. Journal **1774**

Denshi Shashingakkaishi. see Electrophotography **3790**

Dent - Tax. (GW ISSN 0177-7483) **3230**

Dental Abstracts. (US ISSN 0011-8486) **3171, 10**

Dental Admission Testing Program. (US) **3230**

Dental Annual. (UK ISSN 0266-6073) **3230**

Dental Asepsis Review. (US ISSN 0733-9836) **3230**

Dental Assistant Journal. (US ISSN 0011-8508) **3231**

Dental Assisting see Dental Office **3231**

Dental Association of South Africa. Journal/Tandheelkundige Vereniging van Suid Afrika. Tydskrif. (SA ISSN 0011-8516) **3231**

Dental Association of Thailand. Journal. (TH ISSN 0045-9917) **3231**

Dental Cadmos. (IT ISSN 0011-8524) **3231**

Dental Clinics of North America. (US ISSN 0011-8532) **3231**

Dental Computer Newsletter. (US ISSN 0738-9744) **3225, 1459, 3231**

Dental Corps International. (GW) **3231, 3457**

Dental Dialogue. (II) **3231**

†Dental-Dienst. (GW ISSN 0011-8559) **5179**

Dental Digest see Quintessence International **3241**
Dental Echo. (GW ISSN 0011-8575) **3231**
Dental Economics. (US ISSN 0011-8583) **3231**
Dental Equip. (SP) **2522, 3231**
Dental Equipment and Supply Guide. (GW ISSN 0935-8447) **3231**
Dental Guide. (CN ISSN 0070-3656) **3231**
Dental Health Adviser. (US) **3231**
Dental Hygiene see Journal of Dental Hygiene **3236**
Dental Images. (US ISSN 0070-3664) **3231**
▼Dental Implantology Update. (US) **3231**
Dental Lab Management Today. (US ISSN 8750-9539) **3231**
Dental Lab Products. (US ISSN 0146-9738) **3231**
Das Dental-Labor. (GW ISSN 0011-8656) **3231**
Dental Laboratorie Bladet. (DK ISSN 0070-3672) **3231**
Dental Laboratory. (UK ISSN 0957-5138) **3231**
Dental Laboratory Buyer's Guide see Dental Laboratory Review Buyer's Guide **3258**
Dental Laboratory Conference. News & Views. (US) **3231**
Dental Laboratory News. (US ISSN 0011-8664) **3231, 3258**
†Dental Laboratory Review. (US ISSN 0011-8672) **5179**
Dental Laboratory Review Buyer's Guide. (US) **3258, 3231**
†Dental Management. (US ISSN 0011-8680) **5179**
Dental Materials. (US ISSN 0109-5641) **3231**
Dental Office. (US) **3231**
Dental Outlook/Shikai Tenbo. (JA ISSN 0011-8702) **3231**
†Dental Outlook. (AT ISSN 0418-694X) **5179**
Dental Practice. (UK ISSN 0011-8710) **3231**
Dental Practice Directory. (UK) **3231, 1128**
Dental Practice Management. (CN) **3231, 1007**
Dental Practice Success see G P **3233**
Dental Products Annual Report see Dental Products Report **3232**
Dental Products Report. (US ISSN 0011-8737) **3232**
Dental Products Report International. (US) **4596**
Dental Reporter. (AT) **3232, 1007, 1037**
Dental Service Quarterly. (PH) **3232**
Dental Society of Western Pennsylvania. Bulletin. (US) **3232**
Dental Statistics Handbook. (US) **3171**
Dental Student - Dentalpractice see Dentist (Waco) **3232**
Dental Study Club. (CN) **3232**
Dental Team see Today's F D A **3243**
Dental Teamwork. (US) **3232**
Dental Technician. (UK ISSN 0011-8796) **3232**
Dental Technician Yearbook & Directory.(UK) **3232**
Dental Update. (UK ISSN 0305-5000) **3232**
Dental Update. (SA ISSN 1011-5986) **3232**
Dental Watch see Clinical Dental Briefings **3230**
Dentaletter. (CN) **3232**
Denteksa. (SA ISSN 0259-563X) **3232**
Dentist. (UK ISSN 0266-3414) **3232**
Dentist (Waco). (US) **3232, 1625**
Dentistry (Year). (US ISSN 0277-3635) **3232**
Dentistry in Japan. (JA ISSN 0070-3737) **3232**
Dentistry Today. (US) **3232**
Dentists' Computer News. (US) **3225, 3232**
†Dentist's Desk Reference. (US) **5179**
†Dentists Medical Digest. (US ISSN 0196-2701) **5179**
Dento Maxillo Facial Radiology. (UK ISSN 0250-832X) **3358, 3378**

†Denton Dispatch. (US) **5179**
Dentsu Japan Marketing - Advertising Yearbook. (JA ISSN 0386-6076) **30, 1037**
Denver Arts Center Programs. (US) **4632, 1530, 3548**
Denver Business. (US ISSN 0746-2964) **658**
The Denver Business Journal. (US) **658**
Denver Daily Journal. (US) **615**
Denver Housing Guide. (US) **4147, 2486**
Denver Journal of International Law and Policy. (US ISSN 0196-2035) **2722**
Denver Law Journal see Denver University Law Review **2618**
Denver Living see Denver Housing Guide **4147**
Denver Magazine. (US ISSN 0161-4886) **2224**
Denver Post Index. (US ISSN 0893-2441) **2578**
Denver Quarterly. (US ISSN 0011-8869) **2506**
Denver Register see National Catholic Register **4270**
Denver University Law Review. (US) **2618**
Denver Weekly News. (US) **1999**
Deoxyribonucleic acid see D N A **541**
Departamento Ecumenico de Investigaciones Cuadernos see D E I Cuadernos **5176**
Departamento Nacional de Obras Contra as Secas Fins e Atividades see D N O C S - Fins e Atividades **175**
Departement des Statistiques des Transports. Bulletin Mensuel de Statistiques see France. Observatoire Economique et Statistique des Transports. Note de Conjoncture **4663**
Departements et Communes. (FR ISSN 0045-9984) **4086**
The Department Chair. (US ISSN 1049-3255) **1726, 1704**
Department of Animal Breeding and Genetics. Report. (SW ISSN 0347-9706) **215, 199**
Department of Business and Economic Development Newsletter see D B E D Newsletter **5176**
Department of Economic Security Activities Report see D E S Activities Report **4058**
Department of Fisheries. Research Division. Annual Report. (ZA) **2039**
Department of General Services Digest see D G S Digest **4086**
Department of General Services Greenthumb see D G S Greenthumb **4086**
Department of General Services Powerlines see D G S Powerlines **4086**
Department of Higher Education Data Briefs see D.H.E. Data Briefs **5176**
Department of Higher Education Research Note see D.H.E. Research Note **5176**
Department of Libraries Archives see O D L Archives **2777**
Department of Libraries Record see O D L Record **2777**
Department of Libraries Source see O D L Source **2777**
Department of Scientific and Industrial Research Discussion Paper see D S I R Discussion Paper **5176**
Department of Scientific and Industrial Research Plant Protection Report see D S I R Plant Protection Report **530**
Department of Social Services Newsletter see D S S Newsletter **4403**
Department of State Bulletin see U.S. Department of State. Bulletin **5295**
Department of Town and Country Planning. Working Paper Series. (UK ISSN 0951-385X) **4058, 2486**
†Department Store Economist. (US) **5179**
Department Store Sales & Stocks. (CN ISSN 0380-7045) **713**

Department Store Workers' Union. Local 1-S News. (US ISSN 0011-8915) **2582**
Departures. (US) **4759**
DePauw. (US) **1310**
Depeche. see Dispatch **5181**
Depeche Commerciale et Agricole. (FR ISSN 0011-8931) **149**
Depeche Mode see Profession Textile **1294**
Depeche Veterinaire. (FR ISSN 0180-3573) **4808**
Dependable's List Marketing Newsletter see SpeciaLists' MarketPlus Newsletter **1054**
Deporte, Derecho del Publico. (CU) **4470**
Deporte-Derecho del Pueblo. (CU ISSN 0138-6611) **4470**
Deporte Total. (CL) **4470**
Deporte 2000. (SP) **4470**
Deportes. (VE) **4470**
Deportes. (DR) **4470**
Deposit Insurance Corporation. Annual Report: Directors' Report, Balance Sheet and Accounts. (II ISSN 0304-6966) **2530**
Depots Canadiens des Revues Indexees pour MEDLINE. see Canadian Locations of Journals Indexed for MEDLINE **3168**
Depreciation & Capital Planning. (US) **1092**
Deprem Arastirma Bulteni. (TU) **1588**
Depression Briefing. (UK ISSN 0957-4573) **4018**
Depthnews. (PH) **2569**
Depthnews Indonesia. (IO) **2202**
▼Deputatskii Vestnik. (RU) **2215**
Deputazione di Storia Patria per l'Umbria. Bollettino. (IT ISSN 0300-4422) **2358**
Der Beamten-Bund see D B B Magazin **2582**
Der Biologieunterricht see Unterricht Biologie **459**
Der Neue Vertrieb see D N V **4126**
Der Stenopraktiker see Der Bueropraktiker **1619**
Der Zahnarzt see Z W R **3244**
Derby Diocesan News. (UK ISSN 0953-9301) **4235**
Derby Trader. (UK) **905**
Derbyshire Archaeological Journal. (UK ISSN 0070-3788) **270**
Derbyshire Farmer. (UK) **87**
Derbyshire Life and Countryside. (UK ISSN 0011-8990) **2193**
Derecho. (PE) **2618**
Derecho Civil. Anuario. (SP ISSN 0210-301X) **3941**
Derecho del Trabajo. (AG) **976, 2618**
Derecho Penal Contemporaneo. (MX ISSN 0045-9992) **1513**
Derecho Penal y Ciencias Penales. Anuario. (SP ISSN 0210-3001) **2618, 3890, 4307**
Derecho Penal y Criminologia. (CK) **1513**
Derecho y Ciencias Sociales. (MX) **2618, 4370**
Derevoobrabatyvayushchaya Promyshlennost' (RU ISSN 0011-9008) **639**
Derivatives Week. (US) **944**
†Derives. (CN ISSN 0383-7521) **5179**
Dermascope. (US) **372**
Dermato-Venerologie see Revista de Medicina Interna, Neurologie, Psihiatrie, Neuro-Chirurgie, Dermato-Venerologie **3353**
Dermatologia. (MX ISSN 0185-4038) **3247**
Dermatologia Clinica. (IT ISSN 0392-1395) **3247**
Dermatologia i Venerologia. (BU ISSN 0417-0792) **3247**
Dermatologia Internationalis see International Journal of Dermatology **3248**
Dermatologia Oggi. (IT ISSN 0394-2503) **3247**
Dermatologic Clinics. (US ISSN 0733-8635) **3247**
Dermatologica. (SZ ISSN 0011-9075) **3247**
Dermatologische Monatsschrift. (GW ISSN 0011-9083) **3247**

Il Dermatologo. (IT) **3247**
Dermatologo Ospedaliero see Il Dermatologo **3247**
Dermatology and Urology - Hifu to Hitsunyo see Nishi Nihon Journal of Dermatology **3249**
Dermatology Clinical Digest Series. (US) **3247**
†Dermatology in Practice. (UK ISSN 0262-5504) **5179**
Dermatology Nursing. (US) **3247**
Dermatology Series. (US) **3247**
Dermatology Times. (US ISSN 0196-6197) **3247**
Dermatology, Venerology, Andrology. see Zentralblatt Haut- und Geschlechtskrankheiten **3182**
Dermatosen in Beruf und Umwelt. (GW ISSN 0343-2432) **3247**
Derniere Guerre ou L'Histoire Controversee de la Deuxieme Guerre Mondiale. (SZ) **2358**
La Derniere Heure. (BE) **2174**
Dernieres Nouvelles d'Alsace. (FR) **2186**
Dernieres Nouvelles du Lundi. (FR) **2186**
Deryn see Cip **1252**
Des Moines. Public Library. Monthly Memo. (US ISSN 0011-9156) **2754**
Des Moines Skywalker. (US) **2224**
Desalination. (NE ISSN 0011-9164) **4823**
Desalination Directory. (IS) **4823**
Desarme see Disarmament **3457**
Desarmement see Disarmament **3457**
Desarrollo see Development **928**
Desarrollo de Base. (US ISSN 0733-6594) **928, 4433**
Desarrollo de Base see Grassroots Development **930**
Desarrollo Economico. (AG ISSN 0046-001X) **1074**
Desarrollo Economico - Revista de Ciencias Sociales. (AG) **928, 4370**
Desarrollo Indoamericano. (CK) **1074**
Desarrollo Nacional. (US ISSN 0099-1694) **4058, 615, 1864**
†Desarrollo Rural en las Americas. (CR ISSN 0046-0028) **5179**
Desarrollo y Cooperacion. (GW ISSN 0723-7006) **928**
†Desarrollo y Humanismo. (BO) **5179**
Desarrollo y Sociedad. (CK ISSN 0120-3584) **859**
Descant. (US ISSN 0011-9210) **2911**
Descant. (CN ISSN 0382-909X) **2911**
Descendants of Daniel Cole Society. (US) **2148**
Descendants of James Bingham of County Down, Northern Ireland. Newsletter. (US) **2148**
Descendants of Richard Risley in America. (US ISSN 1048-8901) **2148**
Descendants of Richard Risley Senior. (US ISSN 1046-4220) **2148**
Descendants of the Emperors. see Yanhuang Zisun **2183**
Descent. (UK ISSN 0046-0036) **1558**
Descent. (AT ISSN 0084-9731) **2148**
†Descriptions of Plant Viruses. (UK ISSN 0305-2680) **5179**
Descriptive and Applied Linguistics. Annual Reports see International Christian University. Language Research Bulletin **2819**
Desde Este Lado/From This Side. (US) **2991**
†Desempenho Recente da Industria da Construcao Civil do RS. (BL) **5179**
Desenvolvimento Brasileiro see Brazil Development Series **1073**
Desenvolvimento de Base see Grassroots Development **930**
Deseret News. (US) **4282**
Deseret News Church Almanac. (US ISSN 0093-786X) **4282**
Desert Airman. (US) **3457, 51**
Desert Bighorn Council. Transactions. (US ISSN 0418-7598) **1486**
Desert Institute. Bulletin. (UA) **87**
Desert Locust Control Organization for Eastern Africa. Annual Report. (ET ISSN 0418-761X) **175**

Desert Mobile Home News. (US) 2224
Desert Plants. (US ISSN 0734-3434) 175
Desert Rancher. (US ISSN 0046-0044) 87
Desert Research Institute Publications in the Social Sciences. (US ISSN 0271-1001) 238
Desert Tortoise Council. Proceedings of Symposium. (US ISSN 0191-3875) 1543, 436
Desert Voice. (US) 4282
Desfile. (BL ISSN 0021-7301) 2445
Desh. (II) 2911
Design. (US) 298, 4544
Design. (II ISSN 0011-9261) 324, 298, 2550
Design. (UK ISSN 0011-9245) 1916
Design and Applied Arts Index. (UK ISSN 0953-0681) 352, 2444, 4007
Design and Art Direction Annual see British Design & Art Direction Annual 3998
Design & Art in Greece/Themata Chorou & Technon. (GR) 298, 324
Design & Drafting News. (US) 1818, 4596
Design and Technology Association Primary D A T A see Primary D A T A 1757
Design & Technology Teaching. (UK ISSN 0958-3017) 1747, 324
Design Automation see A S I C & E D A 1411
Design Book Review. (US ISSN 0737-5344) 298, 615, 2550
Design Brief. (SA) 1128, 1007
▼Design, Codes and Cryptography. (US ISSN 0925-1022) 3034
Design Compudata (Year) see C A F M System & Strategies (Year) 1443
Design Cost & Data. (US) 298, 615
Design Cost and Data for Management of Building Design see Design Cost & Data 298
Design Denmark. (DK ISSN 0900-3517) 324
Design Directory see Design Firm Directory 1128
Design Engineering. (CN ISSN 0011-9342) 1818
Design Engineering Services Index see Vendor Product Comparison (Design Engineering) 1056
Design Firm Directory. (US ISSN 0889-7611) 1128, 2550
Design Firm Management & Administration Report. (US ISSN 1057-2864) 1007
Design Firm Management and Administration Report see Design Firm Management & Administration Report 1007
Design for Arts in Education. (US ISSN 0732-0973) 324, 354, 1747
Design for Living. see Bonytt 2549
Design for Manufacture Alergy. (US) 1074
Design from Denmark see Design from Scandinavia 2550
Design from Scandinavia. (DK ISSN 0108-0695) 2550
Design Graphics World see Design Management 4596
†Design Horizons. (US ISSN 0882-1526) 5179
Design in Finland. (FI ISSN 0782-4327) 2550
Design in Greece see Design & Art in Greece 298
†Design International. (UK ISSN 0265-1092) 5179
†Design International. Issue A. (GW) 5179
†Design International. Issue B. (GW) 5179
Design Issues. (US ISSN 0747-9360) 324
Design Line. (US) 298, 615, 2550
Design Management. (US ISSN 1042-8534) 4596
▼Design Management Journal. (US ISSN 1045-7194) 1007
Design Manual. (US) 615
Design Methods and Theories. (US ISSN 0147-1147) 298
Design Net. (US) 1459

Design News. (US ISSN 0011-9407) 4596, 3017
Design News Electrical - Electronic Directory see Design News O E M - Suppliers Special Issue 3017
Design News O E M - Suppliers Special Issue. (US) 3017
Design Perspectives. (US) 1818
Design Product News. (CN ISSN 0319-8413) 1818
Design Products and Application. (UK) 1818, 4596
Design Quarterly. (US ISSN 0011-9415) 298, 2550, 3523, 3790
Design-Report. (GW ISSN 0932-3724) 4596
Design Research News. (US) 298, 2486
Design Review. (UK) 4596
Design Solutions. (US ISSN 0277-3538) 2550, 298
Design Spirit. (US) 298, 3594
Design Studies. (UK ISSN 0142-694X) 298, 4596
Design Systems Strategies. (US ISSN 0895-6790) 309, 1864, 1878
Design Times. (US ISSN 1041-0422) 2550, 2810
†Design Today. (US) 5179
Design und Elektronik. (GW ISSN 0933-8667) 1453, 1476
Design v Teorii a Praxi see Prumyslovy Design 1834
Design World. (AT ISSN 0810-6029) 2550, 298
Designed in Finland see Design in Finland 2550
Designer. (US) 1421
Designer. (II) 1818
†Designer. (UK ISSN 0011-9423) 5179
Designer Home Plans. (US) 2550, 298
†Designer Specifier. (US) 5179
Designer's Best Home Plans. (CN ISSN 1181-7933) 615
Designer's Choice see D C 372
Designers' Collection Home Plans. (US ISSN 0897-6228) 615, 2550
Designers Digest. (GW) 324, 3790
Designers Illustrated. (US) 2550
Designers' Journal. (UK ISSN 0264-8148) 2550, 298
†Designers' Kitchens & Baths. (US) 5179
Designers West. (US ISSN 0192-1487) 2550, 298
Designers West Resource Directory. (US ISSN 0192-1487) 2551, 298
▼Designers World. (US ISSN 1057-8277) 2551
Designfax see Designfax Magazine 1818
Designfax Magazine. (US) 1818
Designing and Making see 3-D Education 5309
Designment. (US) 2551, 298
Designs. (CN ISSN 0835-2526) 2551
Desktop Communications. (US ISSN 1042-3923) 1459, 4143
Desktop Dialog. (GW ISSN 0936-8833) 1459
Desktop Products Guide. (US) 1128, 380
Desktop Publisher (Elkview) see The Yellowstone Desktop Publishing Letter 4144
Desktop Publisher (Maple Glen). (US) 4143
Desktop Publishing Journal. (US) 4143
Desktop Publishing - Office Automation Buyer's Guide and Handbook see P C Upgrade 4144
Desktop Publishing Today. (UK) 4143, 4126
Desktop Publishing Users' Report. (US ISSN 0743-2933) 4143
Desktop Software & Solutions (International). (US) 1459
Despatch. (AT ISSN 0046-0079) 3457, 2344
Despatch see Service 4419
Despencer. (US) 2148
Desserts! (US) 2445
Dessinateurs, Peintres et Sculpteurs de Belgique see Jaarboek der Schone Kunsten 331

Dessins et Modeles Internationaux see International Designs Bulletin 3675
Dessous Mode International. (FR) 1284
Destabanda. (UY) 2864
†Destin International. (FR) 5179
Destination Calgary. (CN) 4759
†Destination Canada Meetings and Conventions. (CN ISSN 0834-017X) 5179
Destination Discovery. (US) 1372
Destination London see Meeting in London 4776
Destination of Shipments of Western Wood Species by State. (US ISSN 0195-9336) 2112, 2114
Destination Washington. (US) 4759
Destinations. (CN) 4759
▼Destinations (Alexandria). (US) 4759
Destinations (Washington). (US ISSN 0279-8468) 4759
Destinations Spa. see Spa Destinations 4787
†Destinos. (MX) 5179
▼Destiny. (US) 1999, 3954
†Destiny. (UK ISSN 0266-3120) 5179
Detail. (GW ISSN 0011-9571) 298, 615
Detail/Diteru. (JA ISSN 0012-4133) 298
Detail-Bladet. (DK ISSN 0109-1751) 1037
Detail-Fiskehandler-Bladet. (DK) 2039
Detailed Annual Report of the Registrar General for Ireland see Ireland (Eire) Central Statistics Office. Tuarascail Ar Staidreamh Beatha - Report on Vital Statistics 4575
Detailed Regulations for Vehicles. see Detailforskrifter for Koeretoejer 4718
Detailforskrifter for Koeretoejer/Detailed Regulations for Vehicles. (DK ISSN 0108-1306) 4718
Detailhandelsumsaetze/Chiffres d'Affaires du Commerce de Detail. (SZ) 713
†Detaillant en Alimentation. (CN) 5179
Details. (US ISSN 0740-4921) 2224, 3396
Detective. (BG) 1513
Detective (Falls Church). (US ISSN 0744-2955) 3457, 1513
Detective Cases. (US) 2985
Detective Dragnet. (US) 2985
Detective Files. (US) 2985
Detective Story Magazine see Hardboiled Detective 2985
Detention Reporter. (US ISSN 0742-552X) 1513, 2618
Detergo. (IT ISSN 1120-6942) 1281
Detergo L P T see Detergo 1281
Detroit and Suburban Lutheran see Tri-County Lutheran 4251
Detroit Athletic Club News see D A C News 1297
Detroit College of Law Review. (US ISSN 0099-135X) 2618
Detroit Dental Bulletin. (US ISSN 0011-9601) 3232
Detroit Edison Today. (US) 1785
▼Detroit Film and Video News. (US) 3507, 1385
Detroit Focus Quarterly. (US) 324
Detroit Institute of Arts. Bulletin. (US ISSN 0011-9636) 324
Detroit Jewish News see Detroit Jewish News Ltd. Partnership 1999
Detroit Jewish News Ltd. Partnership. (US) 1999, 4222
Detroit Labor Market Review. (US) 976
Detroit Labor News. (US) 2582
The Detroit Lawyer. (US ISSN 0011-9652) 2618
Detroit Marketplace. (US) 2224
Detroit Medical News. (US) 3093
Detroit Monographs in Musicology. Studies in Music. (US) 3548
Detroit Monography in Musicology see Detroit Monographs in Musicology. Studies in Music 3548
Detroit Monthly. (US ISSN 0149-5976) 2224
Detroit News Index. (US ISSN 0893-2433) 2578

Detroit News Travel Directory see Detroit Newspaper Agency. Travel Directory 4672
Detroit Newspaper Agency. Travel Directory. (US) 4672, 4726, 4759
†Detroit Public Library. M R L Bulletin. (US) 5179
Detroit Society for Genealogical Research. Magazine. (US ISSN 0011-9687) 2149
Detroit Studies in Music Bibliography. (US ISSN 0070-3885) 3588
Detroit Teacher. (US ISSN 0011-9695) 1625, 2582
Detroiter. (US ISSN 0011-9709) 814
Detroiter Business News see Detroiter 814
Detskaya Literatura. (RU ISSN 0130-3104) 1236, 2911
Deuda Externa de Chile. (CL ISSN 0716-2219) 658, 775
Deurbraak see Democrat 3890
Deutsch-Africanischen Studentenbundes, Universitaet Pretoria see D A S U P 1309
Deutsch als Fremdsprache. (GW ISSN 0011-9741) 2810
Deutsch-Amerikanische Geschaeftsbeziehungen/German American Business Contacts. (GW ISSN 0932-2973) 658
Deutsch-Amerikanische Juristen-Vereinigung Newsletter see D A J V - Newsletter 2722
Deutsch-Amerikanische Studien. see American-German Studies 3949
Deutsch - Amerikanisches Wirtschaftsjahrbuch (Year) see United States - German Economic Yearbook (Year) 923
Deutsch-Argentinische Industrie- und Handelskammer. Mitteilungen. see Camara de Industria y Comercio Argentino-Alemana. Boletin 810
†Deutsch-Auslaendische Beziehungen. Schriftenreihe. (GW ISSN 0080-7125) 5179
Deutsch - Betrifft Uns. (GW ISSN 0178-0417) 2810, 1747
Deutsch-Brasilianische Hefte. (GW ISSN 0341-7239) 4370
Deutsch-Chinesisches Forum. (GW) 1999
Der Deutsch Eisenbahner. (GW ISSN 0343-7108) 976
Deutsch - Finnische Rundschau. (GW ISSN 0176-8751) 2186
Deutsch Leichtathletik-Verband Volkssport-Kalender see D L V - Volkssport-Kalender 4470
Deutsch Lernen. (GW ISSN 0341-3675) 1683, 2810
Deutsch-Slawische Forschungen zur Namenkunde und Siedlungsgeschichte. (GW ISSN 0070-3893) 2358, 2810
Deutsche Akademie fuer Sprache und Dichtung. Jahrbuch. (GW ISSN 0070-3923) 2810, 2911
Deutsche Akademie fuer Sprache und Dichtung. Schriftenreihe. (GW) 2911
Deutsche Akademie fuer Staedtebau und Landesplanung. Mitteilungen. (GW ISSN 0011-9822) 2486
Deutsche Angestellten-Gewerkschaft Journal see D A G - Journal 2582
Deutsche Angestellten-Gewerkschaft Schiffahrt see D A G - Schiffahrt 4726
Deutsche Annalen. (GW) 2358
Der Deutsche Apotheker. (GW ISSN 0011-9849) 3722
Deutsche Apotheker Zeitung. (GW ISSN 0011-9857) 3722
Der Deutsche Arzt. (GW ISSN 0011-9873) 3093
Der Deutsche Badebetrieb. (GW ISSN 0343-3838) 3801
Deutsche Baecker Zeitung. (GW ISSN 0046-0117) 2088
Deutsche Bank Bulletin. (GW ISSN 0722-3250) 775, 859
Deutsche Bauern-Korrespondenz. (GW ISSN 0343-3846) 87
Deutsche Bauindustrie - Jahresbericht. (GW) 615
Deutsche Baumschule. (GW ISSN 0011-992X) 2125, 500

Deutsche Bauzeitschrift see D B Z 298
Deutsche Beamte see Beamte Heute 2580
Deutsche Behindertenzeitschrift. (GW ISSN 0939-4702) 3093, 1735, 3320
Deutsche Berufs- und Fachschule see Zeitschrift fuer Berufs- und Wirtschaftspaedagogik 1764
Deutsche Berufsverband der Hals-, Nasen-, Ohrenaerzte e.V. Cologne) see H N O (Cologne) 3314
Deutsche Bibliographie. C D - R O M Edition see Deutsche Nationalbibliographie. C D - R O M edition 4141
Deutsche Bibliographie. Fuenfjahres-Verzeichnis see Deutsche Nationalbibliographie. Fuenfjahres-Verzeichnis 4141
Deutsche Bibliographie. Halbjahres-Verzeichnis see Deutsche Nationalbibliographie. Halbjahres-Verzeichnis 398
Deutsche Bibliographie. Hochschulschriften-Verzeichnis see Deutsche Nationalbibliographie. Hochschulschriften-Verzeichnis 4141
Deutsche Bibliographie. Musiktontraeger-Verzeichnis see Deutsche Nationalbibliographie. Musiktontraeger-Verzeichnis 4462
Deutsche Bibliographie. Schallplatten-Verzeichnis see Deutsche Nationalbibliographie. Musiktontraeger-Verzeichnis 4462
†Deutsche Bibliographie. Verzeichnis Amtlicher Druckschriften. (GW) 5179
Deutsche Bibliographie. Woechentliches Verzeichnis. Ausgabe 1 Amtsblatt der Deutschen Bibliothek see Deutsche Nationalbibliographie. Woechentliches Verzeichnis. Ausgabe A Amtsblatt der Deutschen Bibliothek 4141
Deutsche Bibliographie: Musikalien-Verzeichnis see Deutsche Nationalbibliographie: Verzeichnis der Musikalien und Musikschriften 3588
Deutsche Bibliographie: Neuerscheinungen-Sofortdienst see Deutsche Nationalbibliographie: Vorankuendigungen, Monographien und Periodika 398
Deutsche Bibliothek. (GW ISSN 0420-0152) 2911, 2991
Deutsche Bibliotheksstatistik Teil A: Oeffentliche Bibliotheken. (GW) 2793
Deutsche Bibliotheksstatistik Teil B: Wissenschaftliche Bibliotheken. (GW ISSN 0720-969X) 2793
Deutsche Botanische Gesellschaft. Berichte see Botanica Acta 497
Deutsche Branchen-Fernsprechbuch Liefern und Leisten 1143
Deutsche Briefmarken - Revue. (GW ISSN 0930-858X) 3751, 3599
Deutsche Buecher. (NE ISSN 0167-2185) 2981, 3937
†Deutsche Buecherei. Jahrbuch. (GW ISSN 0459-004X) 5179
Die Deutsche Buehne. (GW ISSN 0011-975X) 4632
Deutsche Bundesbahn Kundenbrief see D B - Kundenbrief 4708
Deutsche Bundesbahn Report see D B Report 4708
Deutsche Bundesbank. Geschaeftsbericht. (GW ISSN 0070-394X) 776
Deutsche Bundesbank. Mitteilungen. (GW ISSN 0011-9997) 776
Deutsche Bundesbank. Monatsberichte. (GW ISSN 0012-0006) 776
Deutsche Bundesbank. Monatsberichte. Statistische Beihefte. Reihe 1: Bankenstatistik nach Bankengruppen.(GW ISSN 0419-9014) 713, 776
Deutsche Bundesbank. Monatsberichte. Statistische Beihefte. Reihe 4: Saisonbereinigte Wirtschaftszahlen. (GW ISSN 0418-8330) 713, 776
Deutsche Bundesbank. Monatsberichte. Statistische Beihefte. Reihe 2: Wertpapierstatistik. (GW ISSN 0418-8314) 713, 776
Deutsche Bundesbank. Monatsberichte. Statistische Beihefte. Reihe 5: Waehrungen der Welt. (GW) 713, 776
Deutsche Bundesbank. Monatsberichte. Statistische Beihefte. Reihe 3: Zahlungsbilanzstatistik. (GW ISSN 0418-8322) 713, 776
Deutsche Bundesbank. Monthly Report. see Deutsche Bundesbank. Monatsberichte 776
Deutsche Bundesbank. Report see Deutsche Bundesbank. Geschaeftsbericht 776
Deutsche Cichliden-Gesellschaft e.V. Informationen see D C G Informationen 581
Deutsche Demokratische Republik. Gesetzblatt. (GW ISSN 0138-1644) 2618
†Deutsche Demokratische Republik. Komitee fuer Menschenrechte. Schriften und Informationen. (GW) 5179
Deutsche Dendrologische Gesellschaft. Mitteilungen. (GW ISSN 0070-3958) 500, 2098
Deutsche Dialektgeographie. (GW ISSN 0179-3233) 2810
Deutsche Dogge Periodical. see Great Dane Periodical 583
Deutsche Drogisten Zeitung. (GW ISSN 0174-0164) 3722
Deutsche Eisenbahntechnik see D E T 5176
Deutsche Entomologische Zeitschrift. (GW ISSN 0012-0073) 530
Deutsche Entwicklungshilfe fuer Soziales Wohnungs- und Siedlungswesen e.V. Brief see D E S W O S - Brief 928
Deutsche Farben-Zeitschrift see Defazet 3653
Das Deutsche Firmen-Alphabet. (GW ISSN 0418-8381) 1128
Deutsche Fischerei-Zeitung. Zeitschrift fuer die Binnenfischerei der DDR 5308
Deutsche Forschungsanstalt fuer Luft- und Raumfahrt e.V. Forschungsberichte see D L R - Forschungsberichte 50
Deutsche Forschungsanstalt fuer Luft- und Raumfahrt e.V. Jahresbericht see D L R - Jahresbericht 50
Deutsche Forschungsanstalt fuer Luft- und Raumfahrt e.V. Mitteilungen see D L R - Mitteilungen 50
Deutsche Forschungsanstalt fuer Luft- und Raumfahrt e.V. Nachrichten see D L R - Nachrichten 51
Deutsche Forschungsgemeinschaft. Denkschriften zur Lage der Deutschen Wissenschaft. (GW ISSN 0070-3974) 4307
Deutsche Forschungsgemeinschaft. Forschungsberichte. (GW ISSN 0070-3982) 4307
Deutsche Forschungsgemeinschaft. Kommissionenmitteilungen. (GW ISSN 0070-3990) 4307
Deutsche Forschungsgemeinschaft. Mexiko-Projekt. (GW ISSN 0418-842X) 4307
Der Deutsche Forstmann. (GW ISSN 0012-012X) 2098
Deutsche Gaertnerboerse see Gaertnerboerse und Gartenwelt 2126
Deutsche Gaue. (GW ISSN 0070-4016) 2358
Deutsche Gefluegelwirtschaft see D G S 215
Deutsche Gefluegelwirtschaft und Schweineproduktion see D G S 215
Deutsche Gehoerlosen-Zeitschrift see Gemeinsam 5199
Deutsche Gehoerlosen-Zeitung. (GW) 2287, 4470
Deutsche Geld- und Kreditinstitute. Banken-Ortslexikon. (GW) 776
Deutsche Gemmologische Gesellschaft. Zeitschrift. (GW ISSN 0343-7892) 2563
Deutsche Genossenschaftsbank. Bericht see D G Bank Deutsche Genossenschaftsbank. Bericht ueber das Geschaeftsjahr 775
Deutsche Geodaetische Kommission. Jahresbericht. (GW ISSN 0938-846X) 2246
Deutsche Geodaetische Kommission. Veroeffentlichungen: Reihe A. Theoretische Geodaesie. (GW ISSN 0938-2836) 2246
Deutsche Geodaetische Kommission. Veroeffentlichungen: Reihe B. Angewandte Geodaesie. (GW ISSN 0065-5317) 2246
Deutsche Geodaetische Kommission. Veroeffentlichungen: Reihe C. Dissertationen. (GW ISSN 0065-5325) 2246
Deutsche Geodaetische Kommission. Veroeffentlichungen: Reihe D. Tafelwerke. (GW ISSN 0065-5333) 2246
Deutsche Geodaetische Kommission. Veroeffentlichungen: Reihe E. Geschichte und Entwicklung der Geodaesie. (GW ISSN 0065-5341) 2246
Deutsche Geographische Blaetter see Uebersee-Museum, Bremen. Veroeffentlichungen. Reihe C: Geographie 2264
Deutsche Geologische Gesellschaft. (GW) 1558
Deutsche Geologische Gesellschaft. Zeitschrift. (GW ISSN 0012-0189) 1558
Deutsche Geschichte. Jahresberichte. (GW ISSN 0075-286X) 2358
Deutsche Gesellschaft fuer Allgemeine und Angewandte Entomologie. Mitteilungen. (GW ISSN 0344-9084) 530
Deutsche Gesellschaft fuer Allgemeine und Angewandte Entomologie Nachrichten see D G A A E Nachrichten 530
Deutsche Gesellschaft fuer Angiologie. Mitteilungen. (GW ISSN 0931-5551) 3271
Deutsche Gesellschaft fuer Chronometrie. Jahrbuch. (GW ISSN 0070-4040) 2563
Deutsche Gesellschaft fuer Dokumentation e.V. Schriftenreihe see D G D Schriftenreihe 2754
Deutsche Gesellschaft fuer Fachkrankenpflege e.V. Mitteilungsblatt see D G F Mitteilungsblatt 3092
Deutsche Gesellschaft fuer Geschichte der Medizin, Naturwissenschaft und Technik. Nachrichtenblatt. (GW ISSN 0027-7460) 3093
Deutsche Gesellschaft fuer Gynaekologie und Geburtshilfe. Mitteilungen. (GW ISSN 0723-8029) 3291
Deutsche Gesellschaft fuer Innere Medizin. Verhandlungen. (US ISSN 0070-4067) 3093
Deutsche Gesellschaft fuer Luft und Raumfahrt e.V. Jahrbuecher see D G L R Jahrbuecher 50
Deutsche Gesellschaft fuer Musik des Orients. Mitteilungen. (GW ISSN 0417-2051) 3548
Deutsche Gesellschaft fuer Orthopaedie und ihre Grenzgebiete. Verhandlungen see Zeitschrift fuer Orthopaedie und Ihre Grenzgebiete 3312
Deutsche Gesellschaft fuer Orthopaedie und Traumatologie. Mitteilungsblatt. (GW ISSN 0723-8002) 3307
Deutsche Gesellschaft fuer Pathologie. Verhandlungen. (GW ISSN 0070-4113) 3093, 436
Deutsche Gesellschaft fuer Pharmakologie und Toxikologie. Mitteilungen. (GW ISSN 0934-4640) 3722
Deutsche Gesellschaft fuer Soziale Psychiatrie e.V. Rundbrief see D G S P Rundbrief 3335
Deutsche Gesellschaft fuer Unfallheilkunde. Mitteilungen und Nachrichten. (GW ISSN 0177-3747) 3093
Deutsche Gesellschaft fuer Urologie. Mitteilungen. (GW ISSN 0178-4625) 3387
Deutsche Gesellschaft fuer Urologie. Verhandlungen. (US) 3387
Deutsche Gesellschaft fuer Urologie. Verhandlungsbericht see Deutsche Gesellschaft fuer Urologie. Verhandlungen 3387
Deutsche Gesellschaft fuer Versicherungsmathematik. Blaetter. (GW ISSN 0012-0200) 2530
Deutsche Gesellschaft fuer Volkskunde. D G V Informationen. (GW) 2053
Deutsche Getraenke Wirtschaft. (GW ISSN 0724-4266) 380
Deutsche Gewaesserkundliche Mitteilungen. (GW ISSN 0012-0235) 4823, 1597
Deutsche Handelsakten des Mittelalters und der Neuzeit. (GW ISSN 0170-3080) 2358
Deutsche Handelskammer in Oesterreich (Bulletin). (AU ISSN 0012-0251) 814
Deutsche Handwerks Zeitung. (GW ISSN 0343-4346) 976
Deutsche Hebammen-Zeitschrift. (GW ISSN 0012-026X) 3291
Deutsche Hochschule fuer Koerperkultur. Wissenschaftliche Zeitschrift see Leipziger Sportwissenschaftliche Beitraege 4478
Deutsche Hockey Zeitung. (GW) 4470
Deutsche Hotel Zeitung see D G Deutsche Gaststaette - Deutsche Hotel-Zeitung Gastwirt und Hotelier 2473
Der Deutsche Hugenott. (GW ISSN 0012-0294) 4235, 2358
Deutsche Hydrographische Zeitschrift. (GW ISSN 0012-0308) 1603
Deutsche Hydrographische Zeitschrift. Ergaenzungsheft. Reihe A. (GW ISSN 0070-4164) 1603
Deutsche Hydrographische Zeitschrift. Ergaenzungsheft. Reihe B. (GW ISSN 0070-4172) 1603
Deutsche Industriebank. Geschaeftsbereich Volkswirtschaft. I K B - Mitteilungen. (GW ISSN 0940-0001) 658
Deutsche Industriebank. Volkswirtschaftliche Abteilung. V W - Mitteilungen see Deutsche Industriebank. Geschaeftsbereich Volkswirtschaft. I K B - Mitteilungen 658
Deutsche Ingenieurschule see Die Neue Hochschule 1831
Deutsche Jagd-Zeitung. (GW ISSN 0724-2654) 4544
Deutsche Jugend. (GW ISSN 0012-0332) 1236, 4433
Deutsche Jugendkraft e.V. Aktiv see D J K - Aktiv 4470
Deutsche Katholik in Kanada. (CN ISSN 0381-8950) 1999, 4262
Deutsche Keramik. (GW) 1163
Deutsche Keramische Gesellschaft. Berichte see Ceramic Forum International 1162
Deutsche Keramische Gesellschaft. Fachausschussberichte. (GW) 1163
Deutsche Krankenhausgesellschaft. Jahresbericht. (GW) 2460
Deutsche Krankenpflege-Zeitschrift. (GW ISSN 0012-074X) 3277
Deutsche Krebsgesellschaft. Mitteilungen. (GW ISSN 0932-7479) 3196
Deutsche Kuestenschiffahrt. (GW) 4726
Deutsche Kunst und Denkmalpflege. (GW ISSN 0012-0375) 324, 298
Deutsche Landjugend see Die Neue D. L 109
▼Deutsche Landwirt. (GW ISSN 0938-8818) 87
Der Deutsche Lebensmittel-Einzelhandel im Spiegel der Statistik (Year). (GW ISSN 0720-1206) 2085
Deutsche Lebensmittel-Rundschau. (GW ISSN 0012-0413) 2065
Die Deutsche Lebensversicherung. Jahrbuch. (GW ISSN 0070-4237) 2530
Der Deutsche Lehrer im Ausland. (GW ISSN 0418-8802) 2810, 1747
Deutsche Lehrerzeitung. (GW ISSN 0012-0421) 1747

Deutsche Lesegesellschaft. Buchempfehlungen see Stiftung Lesen. Lese-Empfehlungen 1266
Deutsche Literaturzeitung. (GW ISSN 0012-043X) 2911, 4307
Deutsche Maler- und Lackiererzeitschrift die Mappe. (GW) 3653
Das Deutsche Malerblatt. (GW ISSN 0012-0448) 3653
Deutsche Mathematiker Vereinigung. Jahresbericht. (GW ISSN 0012-0456) 3034
Deutsche Mathematiker Vereinigung. Mitteilungen. (GW) 3034
Deutsche Medizin. see Deguo Yixue 3170
Deutsche Medizinische Wochenschrift/German Medical Weekly. (GW ISSN 0012-0472) 3093
Deutsche Milchwirtschaft. (GW ISSN 0012-0480) 199
Deutsche Molkerei-Zeitung see D M Z - Lebensmittelindustrie und Milchwirtschaft 198
Deutsche Montan Technologie fuer Rohstoff, Energie, Umwelt Journal see D M T Journal 3482
Deutsche Morgenlaendische Gesellschaft. Zeitschrift. (GW ISSN 0341-0137) 3636
Deutsche Morgenlaendische Gesellschaft. Zeitschrift. Supplementa. (GW ISSN 0341-0803) 3636
†Deutsche Musikbibliographie. (GW ISSN 0012-0502) 5179
Deutsche Nation in Geschichte und Gegenwart see Deutschland in Geschichte und Gegenwart 2358
Deutsche National-Zeitung. (GW ISSN 0012-0510) 3890
Deutsche Nationalbibliographie. C D - R O M edition. (GW) 4141
Deutsche Nationalbibliographie. Fuenfjahres-Verzeichnis. (GW) 4141
Deutsche Nationalbibliographie. Halbjahres-Verzeichnis. (GW) 398
Deutsche Nationalbibliographie. Hochschulschriften-Verzeichnis. (GW) 4141, 1675
Deutsche Nationalbibliographie. Musiktontraeger-Verzeichnis. (GW) 4462
Deutsche Nationalbibliographie. Reihe A: Neuerscheinungen des Buchhandels. (GW ISSN 0323-3596) 4141
Deutsche Nationalbibliographie. Reihe B: Neuerscheinungen Ausserhalb des Buchhandels. (GW ISSN 0323-3642) 4141
Deutsche Nationalbibliographie. Reihe C: Dissertationen und Habilitationsschriften. (GW ISSN 0012-0545) 398, 1625
Deutsche Nationalbibliographie. Woechentliches Verzeichnis. Ausgabe 1 Amtsblatt der Deutschen Bibliothek. (GW) 4141
Deutsche Nationalbibliographie: Verzeichnis der Musikalien und Musikschriften. (GW) 3588, 398
Deutsche Nationalbibliographie: Vorankuendigungen, Monographien und Periodika. (GW) 398
Deutsche Notar-Zeitschrift. (GW ISSN 0340-8604) 4058, 2618
Deutsche Oper Berlin Aktuell. (GW) 3548
Deutsche Optikerzeitung. (GW ISSN 0344-7103) 3300
Deutsche Orient-Gesellschaft. Abhandlung. (GW) 270
Deutsche Orient-Gesellschaft. Mitteilungen. (GW ISSN 0342-118X) 2429, 270
Deutsche Ostkunde. (GW ISSN 0415-6102) 2358, 1625, 2246, 2911
Deutsche Papierwirtschaft. (GW ISSN 0070-4296) 3662
Der Deutsche Pelztierzuechter. (GW ISSN 0012-0553) 2736
Deutsche Physikalische Gesellschaft. Verhandlungen. (GW ISSN 0420-0195) 3817
Deutsche Polizei. (GW ISSN 0012-057X) 1513

†Deutsche Post (Berlin). (GW ISSN 0012-0588) 5179
Deutsche Post (Frankfurt). (GW ISSN 0012-0596) 2582, 1352
Deutsche Presse. (CN) 1999
Deutsche Presseforschung. (GW) 2569
Deutsche Rechtsprechung. (GW ISSN 0012-060X) 2618
†Deutsche Reisebuero-Zeitung. (GW ISSN 0034-3668) 5179
Deutsche Reiterliche Vereinigung. Report. (GW) 4533
Deutsche Rentenversicherung. (GW ISSN 0012-0618) 2530
Deutsche Richterzeitung. (GW ISSN 0340-8612) 2618
Deutsche Schachblaetter. (GW ISSN 0012-0650) 4470
Deutsche Schafzucht. (GW ISSN 0720-0862) 215
Deutsche Schiller-Gesellschaft. Jahrbuch. (GW ISSN 0070-4318) 2911
Die Deutsche Schrift. (GW ISSN 0012-0693) 324, 3998
Deutsche Schuetzenzeitung. (GW ISSN 0012-0707) 4470
Die Deutsche Schule. (GW ISSN 0012-0731) 1625
Deutsche Schwarzbunte. (GW) 215
Deutsche Schwesternzeitung see Deutsche Krankenpflege-Zeitschrift 3277
Deutsche Seiler-Zeitung. (GW ISSN 0012-0758) 4618
Deutsche Shakespeare-Gesellschaft West. Jahrbuch. (GW ISSN 0070-4326) 2911
Deutsche Sparkassenzeitung. (GW ISSN 0012-0766) 776
Deutsche Sportfischer-Zeitung. (GW) 4544
Deutsche Sprache. (GW ISSN 0340-9341) 2810
Deutsche Sprache in Europa und Uebersee. (GW ISSN 0170-3153) 2810
Deutsche Steuer-Zeitung. (GW ISSN 0724-5637) 1092
Deutsche Steuer-Zeitung. Eildienst see Steuer-Eildienst 1106
Der Deutsche Strassenverkehr. (GW ISSN 0012-0804) 4718
Der Deutsche Tabakbau. (GW ISSN 0012-0820) 4643
Der Deutsche Techniker. (GW) 4596
Deutsche Tennis Zeitung. (GW ISSN 0176-0599) 4502
Deutsche Texte des Mittelalters. (GW ISSN 0070-4334) 2911
Deutsche Tieraerztliche Wochenschrift see D T W - Deutsche Tieraerztliche Wochenschrift 4808
Deutsche Trachtenzeitung. (GW) 2053, 2358
Deutsche Umschau. (GW ISSN 0723-4295) 3890
Deutsche Universitaets-Zeitung. (GW) 1704, 1310
Deutsche Urmacher-Zeitschrift see Goldschmiede und Uhrmacher Zeitung - European Jeweler 2564
Deutsche Vereinigung von Winnipeg. Mitteilungen. (CN ISSN 0046-0141) 1999
Deutsche Verkehrs - Zeitung see D V Z 4718
Deutsche Verkehrs - Zeitung Brief see D V Z Brief 4649
Deutsche Verkehrsteuer-Rundschau see Umsatzsteuer- und Verkehrsteuer-Recht 1111
Deutsche Verkehrswissenschaftliche Gesellschaft. Schriftenreihe. Reihe A. Dokumentation. (GW) 4649
Deutsche Verwaltungspraxis. (GW ISSN 0343-9496) 1007
Deutsche Vierteljahrsschrift fuer Literaturwissenschaft und Geistesgeschichte. (GW ISSN 0012-0936) 2506
Die Deutsche Volkshochschule. (GW) 3764, 4307
Deutsche Volleyball Zeitschrift. (GW ISSN 0170-1509) 4502
Deutsche Waldensee (GW ISSN 0174-786X) 4174
Deutsche Waldjugend Info see D W J - Info 2098

Der Deutsche Weinbau. (GW ISSN 0012-0979) 175
Deutsche Wissenschaftliche Kommission fuer Meeresforschung. Berichte see Meeresforschung 1608
Deutsche Wochen-Zeitung. (GW ISSN 0302-7503) 2188
Deutsche Wohnungswirtschaft. (GW ISSN 0012-0995) 4147
Deutsche Zahn- Mund- und Kieferheilkunde see Zahn- Mund- und Kieferheilkunde 3244
Deutsche Zahnaerztliche Zeitschrift. (GW ISSN 0012-1029) 3232
Deutsche Zeitschrift fuer Akupunktur. (GW ISSN 0415-6412) 3093
Deutsche Zeitschrift fuer Biologische Veterinaermedizin see Zeitschrift fuer Ganzheitliche Tiermedizin 4820
Deutsche Zeitschrift fuer Biologische Zahnmedizin. (GW ISSN 0178-7276) 3232
Deutsche Zeitschrift fuer Mund, Kiefer- und Gesichtschirurgie. (GW ISSN 0343-3137) 3232
Deutsche Zeitschrift fuer Onkologie/Journal of Oncology. (GW ISSN 0931-0037) 3196
Deutsche Zeitschrift fuer Philosophie. (GW ISSN 0012-1045) 3764
Deutsche Zeitschrift fuer Sportmedizin. (GW ISSN 0344-5925) 3371
Deutsche Zeitschrift fuer Verdauungs- und Stoffwechselkrankheiten see Gastroenterologisches Journal 3174
Deutsche Zeitung fuer Briefmarkenkunde see D B Z 3751
Deutsche Zoologische Gesellschaft. Verhandlungen. (GW ISSN 0070-4342) 581
Deutsche Zuckerruebenzeitung. (GW) 175
Deutschen Braumeister- und Malzmeister-Bundes. Mitteilungsblatt.(GW) 380
Deutschen Kunststoff-Institut. Mitteilungen. (GW ISSN 0936-0352) 3862, 1176
Deutschen Verein fuer Vermessungswesen e.V. Hessen Mitteilungen see D V W Hessen Mitteilungen 1864
Deutscher Aerokurier see Aerokurier 43
Deutscher Alpenverein. (GW ISSN 0012-1088) 4544
Deutscher Altphilologen-Verband. Mitteilungsblatt. (GW ISSN 0011-9830) 1276, 2810
Deutscher Angelsport see Rute und Rolle 4554
Deutscher Beamtenbund, Landesbund Bremen e.V. Nachrichten fuer den Oeffentlichen Dienst see D B B Nachrichten fuer den Oeffentlichen Dienst 4058
Deutscher Beamtenbund Magazin see D B B Magazin 2582
Deutscher Camping Club e.V. Camping Fuehrer Europa see D C C - Camping Fuehrer Europa 4759
Deutscher Camping Club e.V. Caravan und Motorcaravan Modellfuehrer see D C C - Caravan und Motorcaravan Modellfuehrer 4689
Deutscher Camping Club e.V. Touristik Service see D C C - Touristik Service 4759
Deutscher Drucker. (GW ISSN 0012-1096) 3998
Deutscher Entwicklungsdienst Brief see D E D Brief 928
Deutscher Forschungsdienst. Applied Science. (GW ISSN 0722-0847) 4307
Deutscher Forschungsdienst. Berichte aus der Wissenschaft. (GW ISSN 0722-5318) 4307
Deutscher Forschungsdienst. Berichte aus der Wissenschaft (Auslandausgabe). (GW ISSN 0722-0812) 4307
Deutscher Forschungsdienst. Berichte aus der Wissenschaft - Auswahl Medizin. (GW ISSN 0940-4783) 3093

Deutscher Forschungsdienst. Sonderdienst Angewandte Wissenschaft. (GW ISSN 0722-5229) 4307
Deutscher Forschungsdienst. Sonderdienst Angewandte Wissenschaft (Auslandausgabe). (GW ISSN 0722-0820) 4307
Deutscher Forschungsdienst. Special Science Reports. (GW ISSN 0933-7814) 4307
Deutscher Forschungsdienst Magazin. (GW ISSN 0178-8965) 4307
Deutscher Forstverein. Jahresbericht. (GW) 2098
Deutscher Fussball-Bund. Amtliche Mitteilungen. (GW) 4502
Deutscher Gartenbau. (GW ISSN 0341-2091) 2125
Deutscher Germanisten-Verband. Mitteilungen. (GW ISSN 0418-9426) 2810
Deutscher Glaserkalender. (GW) 1163
Deutscher Hauskalender. (GW) 2188
Deutscher Hochschulfuehrer. (GW) 1693
Deutscher Hochschulverband. Mitteilungen. (GW ISSN 0437-6315) 1704
Deutscher Hotel- und Gaststaettenverband e.V. Jahresbericht see D E H O G A Jahresbericht 2473
Deutscher Hugenotten-Verein E.V. Geschichtsblaetter. (GW ISSN 0344-2934) 2358, 4235
Deutscher Jagdterrierclub. Nachrichtenblatt. (GW) 3710, 231
Deutscher Kaninchenzuechter. (GW) 3710
Deutscher Kleintier Zuchter: Ausgabe Gefluegel. (GW) 2435
Deutscher Kleintier Zuchter: Ausgabe Gemischte. (GW) 2435
Deutscher Kleintier Zuchter: Ausgabe Kaninchen. (GW) 2435
Deutscher Kongress Kalender Zahnmediziner. (GW) 3392, 3232
Deutscher Kurier. (GW) 2188
Deutscher Lebensmittelgrosshandel. (GW ISSN 0012-1134) 2065, 2091
Deutscher Lebensmittelhandel. (GW ISSN 0012-1142) 2066
Deutscher Naturschutzring Kurier see N R - Kurier 1946
Deutscher Palaestina-Verein. Zeitschrift. (GW ISSN 0012-1169) 3636, 270, 2246
Deutscher Radio- und Fernseh-Fachverband e.V. Magazin see R F - Magazin 1358
Deutscher Raiffeisenverband. Raiffeisen-Informationen. (GW) 830
Deutscher Shiffbau see Verband fuer Schiffbau und Meerestechnik. Jahresbericht 4741
Deutscher Studenten-Anzeiger. (GW ISSN 0012-1177) 1310
Deutscher Studienkreis. (GW ISSN 0174-2809) 1683
Deutscher Textilreinigungs-Verband e.V. Intern see D T V - Intern 1281
Deutscher Tischtennis Sport. (GW ISSN 0930-0791) 4503
Deutscher Turner-Bund. Jahrbuch der Turnkunst. (GW ISSN 0075-2401) 4470
Deutscher Verein fuer Kunstwissenschaft. Zeitschrift. (GW ISSN 0044-2135) 324
Deutscher Verein fuer Oeffentliche und Private Fuersorge. Nachrichtendienst.(GW ISSN 0012-1185) 4403
Deutscher Verkehrssicherheitsrat e.V. Report see D V R Report 4718
Deutscher Versand-Einkaufsfuehrer. (GW) 1128
Deutscher Volkskalender Nordschleswig.(DK ISSN 0107-8720) 4759
Deutscher Volkssportverband Kurier see D V V - Kurier 4544
Deutscher Warenhandel. (GW) 859
Deutscher Werbekalender. (GW) 30
Deutscher Wetterdienst. Berichte. (GW ISSN 0072-4130) 3435

Deutscher Wetterdienst. Bibliographien. (GW ISSN 0072-4149) **3444,** 398

Deutscher Wetterdienst. Jahresbericht. (GW ISSN 0433-8251) **3435**

Deutscher Wetterdienst. Monatlicher Witterungsbericht. (GW ISSN 0435-7965) **3435**

Deutscher Wetterdienst. Seewetteramt. Einzelveroeffentlichungen. (GW ISSN 0072-1603) **3435**

Deutscher Wissenschaftler Verband Mitteilungen *see* D W V - Mitteilungen **1297**

Deutscher Zahnaerztekalender. (GW) **3232**

Deutsches Adelsblatt. (GW ISSN 0012-1193) **2149**

Deutsches Aerzteblatt. (GW ISSN 0012-1207) **3093**

Deutsches Archaeologisches Institut. Athenische Abteilung. Mitteilungen · Athenische Mitteilungen. (GW ISSN 0342-1295) **270**

Deutsches Architektenblatt. (GW ISSN 0012-1215) **298**

Deutsches Archiv fuer Erforschung des Mittelalters. (GW ISSN 0012-1223) **2309**

Deutsches Autorecht *see* D A R **2617**

Deutsches Baublatt. (GW) **615**

Deutsches Bibliotheksinstitut Pressespiegel *see* D B I - Pressespiegel **2754**

Deutsches Bridge-Verbandsblatt. (GW) **4470**

Deutsches Buecherverzeichnis. (GW ISSN 0323-374X) **4141**

Deutsches Buehnen-Jahrbuch. (GW ISSN 0070-4431) **4632**

Deutsches Bundes-Adressbuch der Firmen aus Industrie, Handel und Verkehr *see* Deutsches Bundes-Adressbuch: Industrie, Gross- und Aussenhandel, Dienstleistungen, Organisationen **1128**

Deutsches Bundes-Adressbuch: Industrie, Gross- und Aussenhandel, Dienstleistungen, Organisationen. (GW ISSN 0343-589X) **1128**

Deutsches Dante-Jahrbuch. (GW ISSN 0070-444X) **2911**

Deutsches Elektrohandwerk *see* D E - der Elektromeister und Deutsches Elektrohandwerk **1885**

Deutsches Fachzeitschriften-Magazin Wirtschaftsmagazin *see* D F Z Wirtschaftsmagazin **1074**

Deutsches Geschlechterbuch. (GW) **2149**

Deutsches Gewaesserkundliches Jahrbuch. Donaugebiet. (GW ISSN 0340-5176) **4823,** 1597

Deutsches Gewaesserkundliches Jahrbuch. Kuestengebiet der Nord- und Ostsee. (GW ISSN 0340-5184) **4823,** 1597

Deutsches Gewaesserkundliches Jahrbuch. Rheingebiet Teil 2: Main. (GW ISSN 0173-7260) **4823,** 1597

Deutsches Handwerksblatt. (GW ISSN 0012-1274) **324**

Deutsches Hydrographisches Institut. Jahresbericht. (GW ISSN 0070-4458) **1603**

Deutsches Industrieinstitut. Berichte zu Gewerkschaftsfragen *see* Institut der Deutschen Wirtschaft. Gewerkschaftsreport **2584**

Deutsches Institut fuer Normung e.V. (D I N) Catalogue of Technical Rules *see* D I N. Catalogue of Technical Rules **4596**

Deutsches Institut fuer Normung e.V. (D I N) Handbooks *see* D I N - Handbooks **3446**

Deutsches Institut fuer Normung e.V. Mitteilungen und Elektronorm *see* D I N Mitteilungen & Elektronorm **3446**

Deutsches Institut fuer Wirtschaftsforschung. Vierteljahrshefte zur Wirtschaftsforschung. (GW ISSN 0340-1707) **659**

Deutsches Institut fuer Wirtschaftsforschung. Wochenbericht.(GW ISSN 0012-1304) **859**

Deutsches Jugend - Herbergswerk *see* D J H **4759**

Deutsches Jugendinstitut Bulletin *see* D J I - Bulletin **1236**

Deutsches Krankenhaus Adressbuch. (GW) **2460**

Deutsches Krebsforschungszentrum. Veroeffentlichungen. (GW ISSN 0070-4229) **3196**

Deutsches Kunststoff-Institut Literatur-Schnelldienst Kunststoffe Kautschuk Fasern *see* D K I Literatur-Schnelldienst Kunststoffe Kautschuk Fasern **3868**

Deutsches Meteorologisches Jahrbuch, Bundesrepublik Deutschland. (GW ISSN 0724-7125) **3435**

†Deutsches Mittelalter, Kritische Studientexte der Monumenta Germaniae Historica. (GW ISSN 0340-8396) **5179**

Deutsches Mozartfest. (GW) **3548**

Deutsches Muenzen Magazin. (GW) **3599**

Deutsches Museum. Abhandlungen und Berichte. (GW ISSN 0012-1339) **3523**

Deutsches Musikleben (Year). (GW ISSN 0415-7435) **3548,** 1530

†Deutsches Patentamt. Bekanntmachungen. (GW) **5179**

▼Deutsches Patentamt. Bekanntmachungen 1. Grund- und Rohstoffindustrie, Chemie und Huettenwesen, Bauwesen und Bergbau. (GW ISSN 0232-7643) **3674**

▼Deutsches Patentamt. Bekanntmachungen 2. Elektrotechnik, Physik, Feinmechanik und Optik, Akustik. (GW ISSN 0232-7694) **3674**

▼Deutsches Patentamt. Bekanntmachungen 3. Uebrige Verarbeitungsindustrie und Arbeitsverfahren, Maschinen- und Fahrzeugbau, Ernaehrung, Landwirtschaft. (GW ISSN 0232-7740) **3674**

Deutsches Polizeiblatt. (GW ISSN 0175-4815) **1513**

Deutsches Rotes Kreuz der Deutschen Demokratischen Republik. (GW) **4403**

Deutsches Schiffahrtsarchiv. (GW ISSN 0343-3668) **4726,** 2358

Deutsches Soldatenjahrbuch. (GW ISSN 0417-3635) **3457**

†Deutsches Sportecho: Reihe A. (GW ISSN 0323-8628) **5179**

†Deutsches Sportecho: Reihe B. (GW ISSN 0232-4814) **5179**

Deutsches Steuerrecht. (GW ISSN 0012-1347) **1092,** 2618

Deutsches Taschenbuch fuer Maler und Lackierer (Year). (GW) **3653**

Deutsches Textilforum *see* Textilforum **4626**

Deutsches Tieraerzteblatt. (GW ISSN 0340-1898) **4808**

Deutsches Turnen. (GW ISSN 0343-5318) **4470**

Deutsches Verlagsregister. (GW) **4126**

Deutsches Verwaltungsblatt. (GW ISSN 0012-1363) **2618,** 4058

Deutsches Video Institut e.V. Infos *see* D V I - Infos **1334**

Deutsches Volksheimstaettenwerk. Informationsdienst. (GW ISSN 0012-1371) **4148**

Deutsches Waffen-Journal. (GW ISSN 0012-138X) **2435**

Deutsches Wollforschungsinstitut. Vortraege. (GW) **4618**

Deutschkanadisches Jahrbuch. *see* German-Canadian Yearbook **2003**

Deutschkurse/German Language Courses. (AU ISSN 0012-1398) **1747**

Deutschland Archiv. (GW ISSN 0012-1428) **3890**

Deutschland-Berichte. (GW ISSN 0012-1436) **3890**

Deutschland in Geschichte und Gegenwart. (GW ISSN 0340-5710) **2358**

Deutschland-Journal. (GW) **2188**

Deutschland-Magazin. (GW ISSN 0012-141X) **3890,** 2864, 3457

Deutschlandfunk. Geschaeftsbericht. (GW) **1372**

Deutschlandfunk. Jahrbuch *see* Deutschlandfunk. Geschaeftsbericht **1372**

Deutschsprachige Verlage. (GW) **4126**

Deutschsprachige Zeitschriften. (GW) **398**

Deutschsprachige Zeitschriften Deutschland - Oesterreich - Schweiz *see* Deutschsprachige Zeitschriften **398**

Deutschunterricht (Berlin). (GW ISSN 0012-1460) **1625**

Der Deutschunterricht. (GW ISSN 0340-2258) **1625**

Deutschunterricht im Suedlichen Afrika. (SA ISSN 1016-4367) **2810,** 1625

Deutschunterricht in Suedafrika *see* Deutschunterricht im Suedlichen Afrika **2810**

Developer. (SA) **776**

Developer. (AT ISSN 0012-1525) **4148**

Developers and Chains. (CN) **1114**

Developing Economies. (JA ISSN 0012-1533) **928**

Developing Horizons in Special Education Series. (UK) **1747**

Developing Hydropower in Washington State. (US) **1923,** 4823

†Developing Nations Monograph Series One. (US) **5179**

Developing Railways. (UK ISSN 0309-1465) **4709**

▼Developing World Communications. (UK) **1362**

Developing World Health. (UK) **928**

Developing World Transport. (UK) **4649,** 928

Developing World Water. (UK) **4823**

Development. (UK ISSN 0950-1991) **436,** 3093

Development. (IT ISSN 1011-6370) **928,** 3954

Development/Developpement. (CN) **928**

Development. *see* Razvoj **934**

Development/Tanmiyah. (JO) **1074**

†Development. (RH) **5179**

Development (Arlington). (US ISSN 0888-6067) **615,** 4148

Development Academy of the Philippines. Annual Report *see* Development Academy of the Philippines. President's Report to the Board of Trustees **1074**

Development Academy of the Philippines. President's Report to the Board of Trustees. (PH) **1074**

Development Administration Journal. (PH ISSN 0115-7000) **4058**

Development and Change. (UK ISSN 0012-155X) **4370,** 928, 3954

Development and Cooperation. (GW ISSN 0723-6980) **928**

Development and International Cooperation. (XV) **928,** 859

Development and Psychopathology. (UK ISSN 0954-5794) **4018,** 3335

Development & Socio-Economic Progress. (UA) **860**

Development and South-South Cooperation *see* Development and International Cooperation **928**

Development Anthropology Network. (US ISSN 8756-0488) **238**

Development Assistance to the Democratic Republic of the Sudan *see* Report on Development Cooperation to the Democratic Republic of the Sudan **934**

Development Bank of Mauritius. Report and Accounts. (MF) **776**

Development Bank of Solomon Islands. Annual Report. (BP) **776,** 928

Development Bank of the Philippines Bulletin *see* D B P Bulletin **944**

Development Bank of Zambia. Annual Report. (ZA) **776**

Development Business. (UN) **928,** 3954

†Development Co-operation: Review of N.Z. Official Development Assistance. (NZ) **5179**

Development Communication Report. (US ISSN 0192-1312) **4596,** 1625

Development Dialogue. (SW ISSN 0345-2328) **3954,** 928

Development Disability Bulletin. (CN ISSN 1184-0412) **3335,** 1735

Development Dossier. (AT ISSN 0815-9424) **928**

Development Education. (UK) **1747**

Development Finance Company of Kenya. Annual Report and Statement of Accounts. (KE) **776**

Development Forum. (UN ISSN 0251-6632) **928**

Development Forum. (MY ISSN 0126-5105) **1074**

†Development Forum. (US) **5180**

Development Forum. Business Edition *see* Development Business **928**

Development, Growth and Differentiation/Hassei, Seicho, Bunka.(JA ISSN 0012-1592) **436**

▼Development Hotline. (IT ISSN 1014-9635) **928,** 3954

Development in Mammals. (NE) **581**

Development Information Abstracts/Bulletin Analytique sur le Developpement/Resumenes de Informacion sobre el Desarrollo. (UN ISSN 0254-2412) **713**

▼Development Journal. (UK ISSN 0957-4115) **928**

Development News. *see* Kaifa Bao **871**

Development News Digest *see* Development Dossier **928**

Development of Education in Pakistan. (PK ISSN 0080-1321) **1625**

Development Oriented Research in Agriculture. (NE) **87,** 928

Development Policy and Administrative Review. (II ISSN 0251-317X) **4058**

Development Policy Review. (UK ISSN 0950-6764) **928**

Development Research. *see* Fazhan Yanjiu **665**

Development Research Digest. (US) **4403**

Development Research News. (PH ISSN 0115-9097) **928**

Development: Seeds of Change *see* Development **928**

Development Studies Journal. *see* Estudios del Desarrollo **4434**

Development Trends (Year). (US) **2486**

Developmental and Behavioral Pediatrics: Selected Topics *see* Critical Issues in Developmental & Behavioral Pediatrics **4018**

Developmental and Cell Biology Monographs *see* Developmental and Cell Biology Series **436**

Developmental and Cell Biology Series. (UK) **436**

Developmental and Comparative Immunology. (US ISSN 0145-305X) **3184,** 551, 3093

Developmental Biology. (US ISSN 0012-1606) **436**

Developmental Brain Research. (NE ISSN 0165-3806) **3335**

Developmental Disabilities. (US) **4019**

Developmental Dynamics. (US ISSN 1058-8388) **436,** 3093

Developmental Genetics. (US ISSN 0192-253X) **541**

▼Developmental Immunology. (US ISSN 1044-6672) **3184**

Developmental Medicine and Child Neurology. (UK ISSN 0012-1622) **3320,** 3335

Developmental Neuropsychology. (US ISSN 8756-5641) **4019**

Developmental Neuroscience. (SZ ISSN 0378-5866) **3335**

Developmental Pharmacology and Therapeutics. (SZ ISSN 0379-8305) **3722,** 3320

Developmental Psychobiology. (US ISSN 0012-1630) **436,** 4019

Developmental Psychology. (US ISSN 0012-1649) **4019**

Developmental Review. (US ISSN 0273-2297) **4019**

Developments. (US) **2486,** 4148

Developments in Agricultural and Managed Forest Ecology. (NE ISSN 0166-2287) **2098,** 87

Developments in Agricultural Economics. (NE) **149**

DEVELOPMENTS

Developments in Agricultural Engineering. (NE) **175**
Developments in Animal and Veterinary Sciences. (NE) **4808**
Developments in Aquaculture and Fisheries Science. (NE) **581**, 2039
Developments in Atmospheric Science. (NE) **3435**
Developments in Biochemistry. (NE) **476**
Developments in Bioenergetics and Biomembranes. (NE) **469**
Developments in Biological Standardization. (SZ ISSN 0301-5149) **3446**, 437, 489
Developments in Cancer Research. (NE) **3196**
Developments in Civil Engineering. (NE) **1864**
Developments in Clinical Psychology. (US) **4019**
Developments in Crop Science. (NE) **175**
Developments in Earth and Planetary Sciences. (NE) **1558**
Developments in Economic Geology. (NE) **1558**
Developments in Endocrinology. (NE) **3251**
Developments in Environmental Modelling. (NE) **1947**
Developments in Food Preservation. (UK) **2066**
Developments in Food Proteins. (UK) **2066**
Developments in Food Science. (NE) **1218**
Developments in Geochemistry. (NE) **1558**
Developments in Geomathematics. (NE) **1588**, 3034
Developments in Geotechnical Engineering. (NE) **1864**
Developments in Geotectonics. (NE ISSN 0419-0254) **1559**
Developments in Hydrobiology. (NE) **437**, 1597
Developments in Immunology. (NE) **437**
Developments in Industrial Microbiology.(NE ISSN 0070-4563) **551**
Developments in International Law. (NE) **2722**
Developments in Manufacturing Industry see Journal of Industry and Commerce **1079**
Developments in Marine Biology. (NE) **1604**, 437
Developments in Marketing Science. (US ISSN 0149-7421) **1037**
Developments in Mineral Processing. (NE) **1559**
Developments in Nanotechnology. (US) **3817**, 1885
Developments in Neuroscience. (NE) **3335**
Developments in Oncology. (NE) **3196**
Developments in Ophthalmology. (SZ ISSN 0250-3751) **3300**
Developments in Palaeontology and Stratigraphy. (NE) **3657**
Developments in Petroleum Science. (NE) **3684**
Developments in Petrology. (NE) **1559**
Developments in Plant and Soil Sciences. (NE) **175**
Developments in Plant Biology. (NE) **500**
Developments in Precambrian Geology. (NE) **1559**
Developments in Psychiatry. (NE ISSN 0166-2481) **3335**
Developments in Rubber Technology. (UK ISSN 0262-1584) **4291**
Developments in Sedimentology. (NE ISSN 0070-4571) **1559**
Developments in Soil Science. (NE) **176**
†Developments in Solar System and Space Science. (NE) **5180**
Developments in Solid Earth Geophysics. (NE ISSN 0070-458X) **1588**
Developments in the European Communities. Report. (IE) **860**
Developments in Toxicology and Environmental Science. (NE) **1981**
Developments in Transport Studies see Transportation **4658**
Developments in Water Science. (NE) **1597**
DevelopNet News. (US) **4596**
Developpement. see Development **928**
Developpement Social en Perspectives. (CN) **4403**
Devenir. (SZ ISSN 1015-8154) **3093**
Devenir Historico. (AG ISSN 0012-1665) **2309**
Devi. (II) **2199**
Devi-Bhagavat Presentation. (US) **3764**, 1704
Deviance. (US) **2911**
Deviance et Societe. (SZ ISSN 0378-7931) **4433**, 4019
Deviant Behavior. (US ISSN 0163-9625) **4433**, 1513, 4019
Devices & Diagnostics Letter. (US ISSN 0098-7573) **3093**, 3258
Devilirium. (US) **1310**
Devil's Box. (US) **3548**
Devil's Millhopper. (US) **2991**
†Le Devoir Economique. (CN) **5180**
Devon and Cornwall Notes and Queries. (UK ISSN 0012-1681) **2358**
Devon Archaeological Society. Newsletter. (UK) **270**
Devon Archaeological Society. Proceedings. (UK ISSN 0305-5795) **270**
Devon Archaeology. (UK ISSN 0264-7540) **270**
Devon Farmer. (UK) **87**
Devon Historian. (UK ISSN 0305-8549) **2358**
Devon Tourism Review. (UK ISSN 0269-0551) **4759**
Devonport News. (UK ISSN 0046-0184) **3457**, 4726
Devonshire Association for the Advancement of Science, Literature and Art. Report and Transactions. (UK ISSN 0309-7994) **324**, 2911, 4307
Devotee. (US) **3548**
Devotions (Cincinnati). (US) **4235**
Dew Claw. (US) **3710**
Dewan Masyarakat. (MY) **2209**
Dewan Pelajar. (MY) **1253**
Dewan Perintis. (MY) **1253**
Dewey Decimal Classification Additions, Notes and Decisions. (US ISSN 0083-1573) **2754**
Dewitt County Genealogical Society. Quarterly. (US ISSN 0890-4456) **2149**
Deyu Xuexi/Learning German. (CC) **2810**, 1747
Al-Dhafra. (TS) **2220**
Al-Dhaid. (TS) **4470**
Dhaka Bisvabidyalaya Patrika. (BG) **2174**
Dhaka Courier. (BG) **2174**
Dhaka Digest. (BG) **2174**
Dhaka Law Reports: Civil Digest. (BG) **2618**
Dhaka University Studies. Part A: Arts, Humanities, and Social Science. (BG) **2506**, 4370
Dhaka University Studies. Part B: Science. (BG) **4307**
Dhandha. (II ISSN 0300-4309) **3034**, 4470
Dhaniram Bhalla Granthamala. (II) **3637**, 2337
Dharma. (MY ISSN 0012-1746) **4174**, 3764
Dharma Combat. (US) **4174**, 2569, 3764
Dharma-vision. see The Dharmachaksu **4214**
Dharma Voice. (US) **4214**
Dharma World. (JA ISSN 0387-5970) **4214**
The Dharmachaksu/Dharma-vision. (TH) **4214**
Dharmaduta. (MP) **4214**
Dharmagoso Bimonthly. see Fa Yin **4214**
Dharmayug. (II ISSN 0417-3937) **2199**
Dhivara. (CE) **2039**
Di C T A Journal. (District Council Technical Association) (UK ISSN 0952-4894) **615**, 2486, 4086
Di Cyan Bulletin. (US) **3335**, 3722, 4019
Dia. (AG) **2170**
Al Dia. (UK ISSN 0950-8473) **3954**, 976
Dia a Dia see Forward Day By Day **4238**
Dia Cuatro Que Fuera... (SP) **4470**
Dia Medico. (AG ISSN 0012-1762) **3093**
Dia Regno/Divine Kingdom: Christian Esperanto Magazine. (US ISSN 0167-9554) **4174**, 2810
Diabete. (IT ISSN 0394-901X) **3251**
Diabete & Metabolisme. (FR ISSN 0338-1684) **3251**
Diabetes. (FI ISSN 0046-0192) **3251**
Diabetes. (US ISSN 0012-1797) **3251**
Diabetes. (DK ISSN 0901-3652) **3251**
Diabetes Annual. (NE) **3251**
Diabetes Care. (US ISSN 0149-5992) **3251**
Diabetes Countdown. (US) **3251**
Diabetes Dialogue. (CN ISSN 0703-5764) **3251**, 3801
Diabetes Dialogue see Diabetes Update **3252**
Diabetes Educator. (US ISSN 0145-7217) **3093**
Diabetes Forecast. (US ISSN 0095-8301) **3251**
Diabetes in the News. (US ISSN 0893-5939) **3251**
Diabetes-Journal. (GW ISSN 0341-8812) **3252**
Diabetes Mellitus. (UK ISSN 0263-7294) **3093**, 476, 571, 3252
Diabetes - Metabolism Reviews. (UK ISSN 0742-4221) **3252**
Diabetes, Nutrition & Metabolism, Clinical and Experimental. (IT ISSN 0394-3402) **3252**, 3605
Diabetes Research and Clinical Practice.(NE ISSN 0168-8227) **3252**
Diabetes Self-Management. (US ISSN 0741-6253) **3252**, 1735, 3093, 3801
Diabetes Spectrum. (US ISSN 1040-9165) **3252**
Diabetes Update. (US) **3252**
Diabetic Association of India. Journal. (II ISSN 0970-4035) **3252**
Diabetic Medicine. (UK ISSN 0742-3071) **3252**, 3267, 3277
The Diabetic Traveler. (US ISSN 0899-2398) **3801**, 4759
Diabetikeren. (NO ISSN 0419-0505) **3252**
Diabetologia. (GW ISSN 0012-186X) **3252**
Diabetologia Croatica. (CI ISSN 0350-1892) **3252**, 3258
Diablo. (US ISSN 1051-3434) **2224**
Diablo Business see D B **835**
Diablo Descendents Newsletter. (US) **2149**
Diabolo. (GW) **2864**
Diachronica. (NE ISSN 0176-4225) **2811**
Diaconalogue. (US) **4235**
†Diaconate Magazine. (US) **5180**
Diaconia Christi. (GW ISSN 0933-0771) **4262**
Diacritica. (PO ISSN 0870-8967) **2911**, 3764
Diacritics. (US ISSN 0300-7162) **2911**
†Diaet - Therapie. (GW ISSN 0722-0448) **5180**
†Diaframma International Photographers. (IT) **5180**
Diagnosis see Canadian Journal of Diagnosis **3086**
Diagnosis. (IT) **3093**
†Diagnosis. (US ISSN 0163-3228) **5180**
Diagnosis Related Group Length of Stay by D R G and Payment Source see Length of Stay by D R G and Payment Source **2470**
Diagnosis Related Group Monitor see D R G Monitor **5176**
†Diagnostic and Clinical Immunology. (US) **5180**
Diagnostic & Interventional Radiology. (GW ISSN 0998-433X) **3358**
Diagnostic Cardiology. (CN ISSN 0847-2157) **3207**
Diagnostic Cytopathology. (US ISSN 8755-1039) **524**
Diagnostic Engineering. (UK ISSN 0269-0225) **1928**, 750, 3616
Diagnostic Imaging. (US ISSN 0194-2514) **3358**
Diagnostic Imaging & Radiology Product Comparison System. (US) **3358**
Diagnostic Imaging International. (US) **3358**
Diagnostic Imaging Scan. (US) **3094**
Diagnostic Microbiology and Infectious Disease. (US ISSN 0732-8893) **551**, 3218
▼Diagnostic Molecular Pathology. (US) **3094**
▼Diagnostic Oncology. (SZ ISSN 1013-8129) **3196**
Diagnostic Radiology Series. (US) **3358**
Diagnostic Testing Alert see Internal Medicine Alert **3109**
Diagnostica. (GW ISSN 0012-1924) **4019**
†Diagnosticos A P E C. (BL) **5180**
Diagnostics. (FR) **3094**
†Diagnostics & Clinical Testing. (US) **5180**
▼Diagnostics Intelligence. (US ISSN 1054-9609) **3722**, 3094
Diagnostique. (US ISSN 0737-2477) **1735**, 1748
Diagnostyka Laboratoryjna. (PL ISSN 0012-1932) **3094**, 3258
Diagonal. (FR ISSN 0338-0610) **2486**
Diagrama Economico. (BO) **659**
Diagrammin. (AU ISSN 0419-9081) **1444**
Diakon. (GW) **4235**
Diakonia. (GW ISSN 0012-1967) **4174**
Diakonia. (NQ) **4262**
Diakonie. (AU) **4174**
Diakonie. (GW ISSN 0341-826X) **4174**
Diakonie im Rheinland. (GW ISSN 0012-1975) **4235**
Diakonie Report. (GW ISSN 0342-1643) **4174**, 4403
Diakonieschwester. (GW) **4174**
Diakonische Werk see Diakonie Report **4174**
Diakrisis. (GW) **4235**
Dial-a-Poem Poets. (US) **2991**
Dial Computing. (UK ISSN 0955-5099) **1128**
Dial Electrical - Electronics. (UK ISSN 0953-6949) **1765**
Dial Electrical Electronics Sales Contacts. (UK) **1128**
Dial Engineering. (UK ISSN 0955-4335) **1916**, 1928
Dial Engineering Sales Contacts. (UK) **1128**
†Dial Safety, Security, Health & Hygiene. (UK) **5180**
Dialect. see Fangyan **2813**
Dialect. (CN ISSN 0383-8528) **4403**, 3335
Dialectes de Wallonie. (BE ISSN 0773-7688) **2811**
Dialectic. (AT ISSN 0084-9804) **3764**
Dialectica. (SZ ISSN 0012-2017) **3764**
Dialectica. (MX) **4370**
Dialectical Anthropology. (NE ISSN 0304-4092) **238**, 3890
Dialectics. see Dijalektika **4307**
Dialectics and Humanism. (PL) **3764**
Dialectics and Revolution. (NE) **3765**
Dialectiques see Que Faire de l'Economie **3778**
Dialetti d'Italia. (IT ISSN 0012-2025) **2911**, 2811
Dialettica. (IT) **3765**
Dialog. (GW) **1885**
Dialog. (PL ISSN 0012-2041) **4632**
Dialog. Beitraege zur Friedensforschung.(AU) **4370**
Dialog (Norman). (US) **1310**
Dialog (St. Paul). (US ISSN 0012-2033) **4174**
Dialog der Gesellschaft. (GW ISSN 0419-0637) **30**
Dialoghi di Archeologia. (IT ISSN 0392-8535) **270**

Dialogi. (XV ISSN 0012-2068) **2864**
Dialogo. (IT ISSN 0012-2084) **3765**, **4307**, **4433**
Dialogo. (AU) **3954**
Dialogo. (CR) **4433**, 1748, 3981
Dialogo (Jesi). (IT) **3890**
Dialogo Ecumenico. (SP ISSN 0210-2870) **4174**
Dialogo Social. (PN ISSN 0046-0206) **4433**, 659, 3890
Dialogos. (IT ISSN 0012-2106) **1625**
Dialogos. (PR ISSN 0012-2122) **3765**
Dialogos Hispanicos de Amsterdam. (NE) **2811**, 2911
Dialogue. (TI) **2169**
Dialogue. (RW ISSN 0257-0017) **2169**, **4235**
Dialogue see D L S U Dialogue **2505**
Dialogue. (FR) **2911**, **4370**
Dialogue. (GO) **3890**
Dialogue. see Sihot **4046**
Dialogue. (CE ISSN 0012-2181) **4282**
Dialogue (Columbus). (US ISSN 0279-568X) **324**
Dialogue (Kingston). (CN ISSN 1184-6283) **4236**
Dialogue (Milwaukee). (US ISSN 0012-2246) **3765**
†Dialogue (Ottawa). (CN ISSN 0700-3048) **5180**
Dialogue (Salem). (US) **2292**
Dialogue (Washington)/Facetas. (US ISSN 0012-2262) **3954**
Dialogue: A Journal of Mormon Thought. (US ISSN 0012-2157) **4282**
Dialogue & Alliance. (US ISSN 0891-5881) **4174**
Dialogue: Canadian Philosophical Review/Revue Canadienne de Philosophie. (CN ISSN 0012-2173) **3765**
Dialogue in Instrumental Music Education. (US ISSN 0147-7544) **1748**, **3548**
Dialogue India. (II) **2991**
Dialogue on Campus. (US ISSN 0012-2289) **4174**
Dialogue on Liberty. (US) **3890**, **2864**
Dialogue pour le Progres see Dialogue **2169**
Dialoguer. (FR ISSN 0012-2297) **4433**, **4058**
Dialogues d'Histoire Ancienne. (FR) **2309**
Dialogues et Cultures. (FR ISSN 0226-6881) **2811**, 1748
Dialogues in Contemporary Psychology Series. (US) **4019**
Dialogues in Dermatology. (US) **3247**
Dialogues in Pediatric Urology. (US ISSN 0164-9507) **3320**, **3387**
Dialogues in Public Policy. (US) **4058**
Dialyse og Transplantation see Nyrenyt **3389**
Der Dialysepatient. (GW ISSN 0724-0252) **3387**
Dialysis & Transplantation. (US ISSN 0090-2934) **3387**
Diamantes Oro see Joyas & Joyeros **2565**
Diamond/Bessatsu Daiyamondo. (JA) **1007**
Diamond. (US) **1310**
▼Diamond and Related Materials. (NE ISSN 0925-9635) **1210**, 1916
Diamond and Structural Carbon News. (US) **1225**
Diamond Box (Year). (JA) **2207**
Diamond Harvard Business. (JA) **1007**
Diamond Hitchhiker Cobwebs. (US) **2991**
Diamond Industria. (JA ISSN 0385-7360) **835**
Diamond Insight. (US ISSN 0954-5581) **2563**, 905, 944, 1504
Diamond Registry. Bulletin. (US ISSN 0199-9753) **2563**
Diamond Report. (JA) **944**
Diamond, Stock Investment Edition/Daiyamondo Kabushiki-Toshi-Ban. (JA) **944**
Diamond Walnut News see Sun-Diamond Grower **2082**
Diamond World. (II ISSN 0970-7727) **2563**

Diamond World Review. (IS ISSN 0333-5380) **2563**
Diamonds in the Rough see Distressed Property Investor's Monthly **4148**
Diamond's Industria see Diamond Industria **835**
Diamond's Japan Business Directory (Year). (JA ISSN 0910-1780) **1128**
Dian Shijie/Electrical World. (CC ISSN 1000-1344) **1885**
Diana. (AG ISSN 0012-2327) **4544**
Diana (Florence). (IT ISSN 0012-2343) **4544**
Diana (Marcianise). (IT ISSN 0012-2335) **2864**, 3890
Diana Armi. (IT ISSN 0012-2351) **2435**
Diana's Almanac. (US) **2911**
Diana's Bimonthly. (US ISSN 0046-0222) **2991**
Diana's Bimonthly Almanac see Diana's Bimonthly **2991**
Diance yu Yibiao/Electronic Measuring and Meters. (CC ISSN 1001-1390) **2522**
Diandu yu Huanbao/Electroplating and Environmental Protection. (CC ISSN 1000-4742) **1885**, 1947
Diandu yu Jingshi/Plating and Finishing.(CC ISSN 1001-3849) **1212**
Diane. (UK ISSN 0012-236X) **2292**
Diangong Jishu Xuebao/Chinese Journal of Electrotechnics. (CC ISSN 1000-6753) **1885**
Dianhua Jiaoyu/Audio-Visual Education Programs. (CC) **1625**
Dianli Jishu/Electric Power. (CC ISSN 1000-145X) **1885**
Dianli Xitong Zidonghua. (CC) **1413**
Dianli Xitong Zidonghua/Automation of Electric Power Systems. (CC) **1885**, 1413
Diannao Kaifa yu Yingyong/Computer Exploration and Application. (CC) **1394**
Dianoia. (MX ISSN 0419-0890) **3765**
Dianqi Chuandong/Electric Drive. (CC ISSN 1001-2095) **1885**
Dianqi Zidonghua. (CC ISSN 1000-3886) **1413**
Dianshi Dianying Wenxue/TV and Film Literature. (CC ISSN 1000-0151) **3507**, 1372, 2911
Dianshi Yuekan/Television Monthly. (CC) **1372**
Dianwang Jishu/Power System Technology. (CC ISSN 1000-3673) **1885**
Dianxin Jishu/Telecommunication Technology. (CC ISSN 1000-1247) **1362**
Dianxin Jishu Jikan see Telecoms Technical Quarterly **1366**
Dianxin Kexue/Telecommunications Science. (CC ISSN 0493-2218) **1334**
Dianying Chuangzuo/Cinematic Creation. (CC ISSN 0257-0173) **3507**
Dianying Gushi/Film Stories. (CC ISSN 0493-2374) **3507**
Dianying Huakan/Film Pictorial. (CC) **3507**
Dianying Jieshao. (CC) **3507**
Dianying Shijie/Film World. (CC) **3507**
Dianying Wenxue/Film Literature. (CC ISSN 0495-5692) **3507**
Dianying Xinzuo/New Films. (CC) **3507**
Dianying Yishu/Film Art. (CC ISSN 0257-0181) **3507**, 4460
Dianying Yuebao/Movie Monthly. (CC) **3507**
Dianying zhi You/Film Fans. (CC) **3507**
Dianying Zuopin/Film Scripts. (CC ISSN 1001-5582) **3507**
Dianyuan Jishu/Chinese Journal of Power Sources. (CC ISSN 1002-087X) **1885**
Dianzi Jishu/Electronic Technology. (CC ISSN 1000-0755) **1765**, 1885
Dianzi Jishu Yingyong/Applications of Electronic Technique. (CC) **1765**, 1885

Dianzi Kexue Jishu/Electronic Science and Technology. (CC) **1765**, 1885
Dianzi Kexue Xuekan. (CC ISSN 0258-798X) **1765**, 1885
Dianzi Shijie/Electronic World. (CC) **1765**, 1885
Dianzi Xuebao/Acta Electronica Sinica. (CC ISSN 0372-2112) **1765**, 1885
Dianzi yu Zidonghua/Electronics and Automation. (CC) **1413**
Diapason. (RW) **1310**
Diapason. (RU) **2911**
Diapason. (US ISSN 0012-2378) **3548**
Diapason. (FR) **3548**
Diaper Pail Fraternity Newsletter see D P F Newsletter **2452**
Diario de Centro America. (GT) **4058**
Diario de Congresos Medicos. (SP ISSN 0210-5578) **3392**, 3094
Diario Extra. (CR) **2180**
Diario Israelita. (BL) **1999**
Diario Oficial de la Comunidades Europeas see European Communities. Diario Oficial **4059**
Diarist's Journal. (US) **2911**
Diarrhoeal Diseases/Maladies Diarrheiques. (FR ISSN 1011-8594) **3171**, 3267
Diary. (UK) **1290**, 375, 4840
Diary of Social Legislation and Policy. (AT ISSN 0725-2455) **4058**, 4403
▼Diaspora: A Journal of Transnational Studies. (US ISSN 1044-2057) **4370**, 3981
Diaspora - M I V A. (GW) **4262**, 4689
Il Dibattito Federalista. (IT) **3890**
Dibevo see Dibevo Vakblad **3710**
Dibevo Vakblad. (NE) **3710**
Al-Diblomasi/Diplomat. (TS) **3955**
Dibrugarh University. Centre for Sociological Study of the Frontier Region. North Eastern Research Bulletin. (II) **4433**
Dic-Agri see Dictionnaire - Annuaire de l'Agriculture et de l'Agro-Alimentaire **87**
Dicarta. (IT) **3662**
Diccionario Agroquimico see Diccionario de Especialidades Agroquimicas **87**
Diccionario de Especialidades Agroquimicas. (MX) **87**, 1176
Diccionario de Especialidades Bioquimicas. (MX) **476**
Diccionario de Especialidades en Analisis Clinicos. (MX) **1205**
Diccionario de Especialidades Farmaceuticas. (MX) **3722**
Diccionario de Especialidades Odontologicas. (MX) **3232**
▼Diccionario de Especialidades Oftamologicas. (MX) **3300**
▼Diccionario de Especialidades para la Industria Alimentaria. (MX) **2066**
▼Diccionario de Tecnologia e Insumos Medicos. (MX) **2460**
Dicengxue Zazhi/Journal of Stratigraphy. (CC ISSN 0253-4959) **1559**, 1588
Dichan. (TH) **2220**
Dichter und Zeichner. (GW ISSN 0070-4695) **324**, 2991
Dicine. (MX) **3507**
Dicionario de Especialidades Farmaceuticas. (BL) **3722**
Dick Davis Digest. (US) **944**
Dick Documents. (US) **2149**
Dick Vitale's Basketball. (US ISSN 1054-2213) **4503**
Dickens Quarterly. (US ISSN 0742-5473) **2911**
Dickens Studies Annual see Dickens Studies Annual: Essays on Victorian Fiction **2911**
Dickens Studies Annual: Essays on Victorian Fiction. (US) **2911**
Dicken's Universe. (US) **2911**
Dickensian. (UK ISSN 0012-2440) **2911**
Dickinson County Heritage Center. Gazette. (US) **2404**
Dickinson County Historical Society. Gazette see Dickinson County Heritage Center. Gazette **2404**
Dickinson International Law Annual see Dickinson Journal of International Law **2722**

Dickinson Journal of International Law. (US ISSN 0887-283X) **2722**, **3955**
Dickinson Law Review. (US ISSN 0012-2459) **2618**
Dickinson Studies. (US ISSN 0164-1492) **2992**
Dico - Plus. (FR ISSN 0399-7081) **2811**
Dictionaries. (US ISSN 0197-6745) **2754**, 2811
Dictionaries, Encyclopedias, and Other Word-Related Books. (US) **2855**
†Dictionary Catalog of Official Publications of the State of New York. (US) **5180**
Dictionary of Canadian Biography. (CN ISSN 0070-4717) **418**
Dictionary of Contemporary American Artists. (US) **324**, 418
Dictionary of Contemporary Artists see International Directory of Exhibiting Artists **352**
Dictionary of Contemporary Quotations. (US ISSN 0360-215X) **2911**, 2811
Dictionary of Criminal Justice. (US) **1513**
Dictionary of International Biography. (UK ISSN 0419-1137) **418**
†Dictionary of Latin American and Caribbean Biography. (UK ISSN 0070-4733) **5180**
Dictionary of Literary Biography. (US) **424**, 2911
Dictionary of Literary Biography Yearbook. (US ISSN 0731-7867) **2911**, 418
Dictionary of Mauritian Biography. see Dictionnaire de Biographie Mauricienne **418**
A Dictionary of Modern Politics. (UK) **3890**
Dictionary of Old English. Publications. (CN ISSN 0826-8134) **2811**
Dictionary of Scandinavian Biography. (UK) **418**
Dictionary Society of North America Newsletter see D S N A Newsletter **2754**
Dictionnaire - Annuaire de l'Agriculture see Dictionnaire - Annuaire de l'Agriculture et de l'Agro-Alimentaire **87**
Dictionnaire - Annuaire de l'Agriculture et de l'Agro-Alimentaire. (FR) **87**
Dictionnaire de Biographie Mauricienne/Dictionary of Mauritian Biography. (MF) **418**, 2332
Dictionnaire de l'Industrie Francaise. (FR) **1128**, 1074
Dictionnaire des Communes (Lavauzelle et Cie). (FR) **4058**, 1780
Dictionnaire des Valeurs des Meubles et Objets d'Art. (FR ISSN 0070-4776) **324**
Dictionnaire du Marche Commun. (FR) **905**, 2618
Dictionnaire Joly Bourse et Produits Financiers. (FR) **944**
Dictionnaire Joly Concurrence. (FR) **659**, 2618
Dictionnaire Joly Pratique des Contrats Internationaux. (FR) **905**, 2722
Dictionnaire Joly Societes a Responsibilite Limitee. (FR) **1008**
Dictionnaire Joly Societes Anonymes. (FR) **1008**
Dictionnaire Permanent de la Construction. (FR ISSN 0012-2467) **615**
Dictionnaire Permanent Difficultes des Entreprises. (FR) **1008**
Dictionnaire Permanent Droit des Affaires. (FR ISSN 0012-2475) **2618**
Dictionnaire Permanent Droit Europeen des Affaires. (FR) **2722**
Dictionnaire Permanent Entreprise Agricole. (FR ISSN 0012-2483) **87**
Dictionnaire Permanent Epargne et Produits Financiers. (FR) **776**
Dictionnaire Permanent Fiscal. (FR ISSN 0012-2491) **1092**
Dictionnaire Permanent Gestion Immobiliere. (FR) **1008**, 4148
Dictionnaire Permanent Rural see Dictionnaire Permanent Rural (Droit, Social, Agricole) **87**

Dictionnaire Permanent Rural (Droit, Social, Agricole). (FR) **87**
Dictionnaire Permanent Securite et Conditions de Travail. (FR) **976, 3616**
Dictionnaire Permanent Social. (FR ISSN 0012-2513) **4433**
Dictionnaire Vidal. (FR ISSN 0419-1153) **3722**
Dictionnaires du Savoir Moderne. (FR ISSN 0073-4640) **1780**
Didactica Classica Gandensia. (BE ISSN 0070-4792) **1276**
Didakometry and Sociometry. (SW ISSN 0346-5020) **4019,** 1625
Didaktik der Berufs- und Arbeitswelt. (GW ISSN 0721-5932) **1683**
Didaktik der Mathematik. (GW ISSN 0343-5334) **1748, 3034**
Didaskalia. (PO ISSN 0253-1674) **4262**
Didatica. (BL ISSN 0101-059X) **1625**
Didattica delle Scienze e Informatica nella Scuola. (IT ISSN 0419-1218) **1748, 3034, 4307**
Didattica Nuova. (IT) **1748**
†Didattica Scientifica. (IT) **5180**
Diderot Studies. (SZ ISSN 0070-4806) **3765**
▼Die & Mould Technology International.(SI ISSN 0218-2610) **3017**
Die Apothekenhelferin *see* Apothekenhelferin Heute **3717**
▼Die Casting Buyers Guide. (US ISSN 1056-6090) **3017, 3405**
Die Casting Engineer. (US ISSN 0012-253X) **1916, 3405**
Die Casting Industry Blue Book *see* Die Casting Buyers Guide **3017**
Die Casting Management. (US ISSN 0745-449X) **3405**
Die Kommenden *see* Novalis **2877**
Die Landwirtschaftliche Zeitschrift *see* D L Z **86**
Die Meinung *see* Journal fuer Sozialforschung **4439**
Die Naehmaschinen-Zeitung International *see* D N Z International **3016**
Die Schweizer Baustoff-Industrie *see* D S B **615**
Die Welt von A bis Z *see* Gymnase **1255**
Die Wirtschaft *see* Die Neue Wirtschaft **681**
Diebeners Goldschmiede- und Uhrmacher-Jahrbuch *see* Goldschmiede- und Uhrmacher-Jahrbuch **2564**
Diebold Management Report. (GW ISSN 0341-3683) **826**
Dieciocho. (US ISSN 0163-0415) **2911,** 1999
Dieet- en Huishoudkunde. *see* Dietetics & Home Economics **3605**
Diehard. (US ISSN 0896-7970) **4503**
Dielheimer Blaetter zum Alten Testament *see* Dielheimer Blaetter zum Alten Testament und seiner Rezeption in der Alten Kirche **4174**
Dielheimer Blaetter zum Alten Testament und seiner Rezeption in der Alten Kirche. (GW) **4174**
Diemaking Diecutting Intelligence Newsletter. (US **4618,** 1281
Diemaking, Stamping & EDMing. (US) **3017**
Dienender Glaube. (GW ISSN 0012-2572) **4174**
Diensgids vir Gesigsgestremde Suid-Afrikaners. (SA) **2292**
Dienst am Kinde *see* Sonntagschulmitarbeiter **1664**
†Dienst am Wort - Gedanken zur Sonntagspredigt. (GW ISSN 0720-9916) **5180**
Dienst Landbouwkundig Onderzoek. Staring Centrum, Instituut voor Onderzoek van het Landelijke Gebied. Jaarverslag. (NE ISSN 0924-0160) **176,** 1947, 4823
Dienst Landbouwkundig Onderzoek. Staring Centrum, Instituut voor Onderzoek van het Landelijk Gebied. Rapporten. (NE ISSN 0924-3070) **176,** 1947, 4823

Dienstleistungen. Ausgabe A: Fachzeitschrift fuer Theorie und Praxis der Haus- und Stadtwirtschaftlichen Dienstleistungen. (GW ISSN 0232-7546) **1064**
Dienstleistungen. Ausgabe B: Fuer Testilreinigung und Hauswirtschaftliche Dienstleistungen. (GW ISSN 0232-8399) **1064**
Die Dienststellen des Freistaates Bayern in den Kreisfreien Staedten und Landkreisen. (GW) **4058**
Diepzee. (NE ISSN 0166-5618) **2911**
Dier - En - Arts/Veterinarian. (NE ISSN 0920-2412) **4809**
Dies und Das *see* Pazifische Rundschau **2019**
Diesel. (IT) **1928,** 4470, 4649
Diesel and Gas Turbine Catalog. (US) **1928**
Diesel and Gas Turbine Progress Worldwide *see* Diesel & Gas Turbine Worldwide **1928**
Diesel and Gas Turbine World Wide Catalog *see* Diesel and Gas Turbine Catalog **1928**
Diesel & Gas Turbine Worldwide. (US ISSN 0278-5994) **1928**
Diesel Car Digest. (US ISSN 0160-7065) **4689**
Diesel Engine. *see* Chaiyou Ji **1927**
Diesel Engineers and Users Association. Transactions *see* Institution of Diesel and Gas Turbine Engineers. Transactions **1930**
Diesel Equipment Superintendent. (US ISSN 0012-2610) **4744,** 1928
Diesel - Lehti. (FI ISSN 0012-2629) **1928,** 4689
Diesel Locomotive Question & Answer Manual. (US ISSN 0070-4830) **4709**
Diesel Progress Engines & Drives. (US ISSN 1040-8878) **1928**
Diesel Progress North American *see* Diesel Progress Engines & Drives **1928**
Diesseits. (GW ISSN 0932-6162) **3890**
†Diet. (UK ISSN 0142-8624) **5180**
Diet & Health Magazine. (US) **3801,** 3605
Diet and Health Series *see* Diet & Health Magazine **3801**
Dietary Aspects of Carcinogenesis *see* I C R D B Cancergram: Dietary Aspects of Carcinogenesis **5208**
Dietetica Clinica e Malattie della Nutrizione. (IT) **3605**
Dietetics & Home Economics/Dieet- en Huishoudkunde. (SA ISSN 0378-5254) **3605,** 2445
Dietetique en Action. (CN ISSN 0834-3160) **3605**
Dietisten. (SW) **3605**
Dietsche Warande en Belfort. (BE ISSN 0012-2645) **2864,** 324
Diez Minutos. (SP) **2217**
La Difesa delle Piante. (IT) **176**
Difesa Oggi. (IT ISSN 1120-1657) **3457**
La Difesa Penale. (IT ISSN 0394-9036) **2618**
Difesa Sociale. (IT ISSN 0012-2653) **4100**
Differences. (FR ISSN 0247-9095) **3890**
Differences. (US ISSN 1040-7391) **4859,** 4433
A Different Light Review. (US) **2452,** 398, 2864, 4840
Different Worlds. (US) **2983,** 4470
Differentia. US ISSN 0890-4294) **1999**
Differential and Integral Equations. (US ISSN 0893-4983) **3034**
Differential Equations. (US English translation of: Differentsial'nye Uravneniya) (US ISSN 0012-2661) **3034**
▼Differential Geometry and Its Applications. (NE ISSN 0926-2245) **3034**
Differentiation. (GW ISSN 0301-4681) **437**
Difficulties. (US) **2864**

Diffusion and Defect Data. (LH ISSN 0377-6883) **3405,** 1804
Diffusion Data *see* Diffusion and Defect Data **3405**
Diffusion Express. (FR ISSN 1142-3153) **1843,** 1885
Difofu *see* Sedibeng **2295**
Difusion Economica. (EC ISSN 0012-2696) **659**
Dig Around. (UK) **4403**
Digest. *see* Intisari **950**
Digest. (UK) **2698**
Digest de Securite Generale. *see* General Safety Digest **3459**
Digest Documentation Organique. (FR ISSN 0292-935X) **2618**
Digest for Home Furnishers. (US) **2558**
Digest fuer Jugend und Bildungeinrichtungen. (GW ISSN 0722-0014) **4403**
Digest of Activities of Congress. (US ISSN 0733-0227) **4058**
Digest of Building Contract Awards. (US) **616**
Digest of Changes in C U S I P. (US) **776**
Digest of Chiropractic Economics. (US ISSN 0415-8407) **3214**
Digest of Commercial Laws of the World. (US ISSN 0419-1285) **2722,** 905
Digest of Current Industrial and Labour Law. (II ISSN 0419-1293) **2618,** 976
Digest of Health Statistics for England and Wales *see* Health and Personal Social Services Statistics **4102**
Digest of Labour Cases. (II ISSN 0012-2750) **2619**
Digest of Legal Activities of International Organizations and Other Institutions. (US ISSN 0070-4857) **2619**
Digest of Motor Laws *see* American Automobile Association. Digest of Motor Laws **4679**
Digest of Neurology & Psychiatry. (US ISSN 0012-2769) **3171,** 10
Digest of Opinions of the Attorney General. (US ISSN 0012-2777) **2619**
Digest of Science of Labour. *see* Rodo no Kagaku (Kawasaki, 1946) **3621**
Digest of Software Reviews: Education. (US) **1689,** 1476
Digest of Technical Papers *see* S I D International Symposium. Digest of Technical Papers **1836**
†Digest of the Arab Press. (US ISSN 0896-2138) **5180**
Digest of the U F V A. (University Film Video Association) (US) **3507,** 1385
Digest of United Kingdom Energy Statistics. (UK ISSN 0307-0603) **1798**
Digest of Welsh Statistics. (UK ISSN 0262-8295) **4570**
Digest of World Events. (PK ISSN 0070-4873) **2309,** 3955
Digest on Gay Rights. (CN) **2619,** 2452
Digestion. (SZ ISSN 0012-2823) **3267**
Digestive Diseases. (SZ ISSN 0257-2753) **3267**
Digestive Diseases and Sciences. (US ISSN 0163-2116) **3267**
Digestive Surgery. (SZ ISSN 0253-4886) **3378**
Digesto Economico. (BL) **860**
Digging Stick. (SA ISSN 1013-7521) **270,** 238
Diggings. (AT) **270**
Diggin's. (US) **2404**
Digital Audio and Compact Disc Review *see* C D Review **4460**
Digital Audio and Compact Disc Review Yearbook *see* C D Review's Compact Disc Yearbook **5156**
Digital Design *see* E S D: The Electronic System Design Magazine **5183**
▼Digital Desktop. (US) **1469**
Digital Directions Report. (US) **1450**
Digital Equipment Computer Users Society DECUScope *see* DECUScope **1394**

Digital Equipment Computer Users Society Israel News *see* D E C U S Israel News **1394**
Digital Equipment Corp. User *see* D E C User **1394**
Digital Equipment Corporation Professional *see* D E C Professional **1394**
Digital Equipment Corporation World *see* D E C World **1453**
Digital I Cs D.A.T.A. Digest. (US) **1765**
Digital Media. (US) **1459**
Digital News. (US) **1459,** 1453, 1476
Digital Retailing *see* P C Retailing **1433**
Digital Review. (US ISSN 0739-4314) **1460**
†Digital Review Buyers Guide. (US) **5180**
▼Digital Signal Processing. (US ISSN 1051-2004) **1765,** 1885
Digital System Design Series. (US ISSN 0888-2118) **1878,** 1421
Digitale Bilddiagnostik *see* Aktuelle Radiologie **3357**
Digitalvaerlden. (SW) **1460**
Dignity - U S A. (US ISSN 0147-1139) **2452,** 4262
Dijalektika/Dialectics. (YU ISSN 0350-1272) **4307,** 3765
Dikobraz. (CS ISSN 0012-284X) **2864**
Dikta. (US ISSN 0363-5414) **2754,** 2292
Dili/Geography. (CC) **2246**
Dili Jiaoxue/Geography Teaching. (CC ISSN 1000-078X) **1748,** 2246
Dili Jiaoyu/Geographical Education. (CC) **2246**
Dili Kexue/Scientia Geographica Sinica. (CC ISSN 1000-0690) **2246**
Dili Xuebao/Acta Geographica Sinica. (CC ISSN 0375-5444) **2246**
Dili Yanjiu/Geographical Research. (CC ISSN 1000-0585) **2246**
Dili Zhishi/Geographical Knowledge. (CC ISSN 0257-019X) **2246**
Diliman Review. (PH ISSN 0012-2858) **2864**
Dilixue yu Guotu Yanjiu. (CC ISSN 1001-8107) **1559**
Dillingham Family Genealogy Exchange Bulletin. (US) **2149**
Dilmun. (BA) **270**
Dilthey-Jahrbuch. (GW ISSN 0175-0135) **3765**
Dimanche. (BE ISSN 0012-2866) **4262**
Dime Novel Round-Up. (US ISSN 0012-2874) **4126,** 2435
Dimensio. (FI ISSN 0782-6648) **3034,** 1176, 1625, 3817
Dimension. (SA ISSN 0046-0265) **4236**
Dimension (Austin). (US ISSN 0012-2882) **2912**
Dimension (Birmingham). (US ISSN 0162-6825) **4236**
Dimension Historica de Chile. (CL ISSN 0716-1484) **2404**
Dimension: Languages (Year). (US ISSN 0070-4881) **1748,** 2811
Dimensional Stone Magazine. (US ISSN 0883-0258) **616**
Dimensione. (IT) **776**
Dimensione Energia. (IT) **1785**
Dimensione Lavoro. (IT) **2582**
Dimensione Psi. (IT) **3669**
Dimensione Salute. (IT) **3801,** 3094
Dimensioni. (IT ISSN 0012-2904) **2864**
Dimensioni e Problemi della Ricerca Storica. (IT) **2358**
Dimensioni Nuove. (IT ISSN 0391-5468) **2205**
Dimensions (Little Rock). (US ISSN 0160-6425) **1236**
Dimensions (Montreal). (CN ISSN 0709-2334) **1625**
Dimensions (Rimrock). (US) **3669,** 3626, 4019
Dimensions (Waterbury). (US) **2912**
Dimensions: A Journal of Holocaust Studies. (US ISSN 0882-1240) **1999,** 2309
Dimensions in Health Service *see* Leadership in Health Services **2467**

Dimensions of Critical Care Nursing. (US ISSN 0730-4625) **3277**
†Dimensions of Philippine Exports. (PH) **5180**
Dimensions Science et Technologie *see* Science and Technology Dimensions **5274**
Diming Congkan/Journal of Place Names. (CC) **2246**
Diming Zhishi/Place Names. (US) **2246**
Dimosios Ypallilos/Civil Servant. (CY) **4058**
Dimossiotis *see* Nea Dimossiotis **35**
Al Dimuqrati/Democrate. (SJ) **2169**
Din Fastighet. (SW ISSN 0280-6347) **616**
Dinah. (US) **2452**, **4840**
Dinaman. (II ISSN 0012-3005) **2199**
Dinamica Economica. (BO ISSN 0012-2939) **659**
Dinamica Social. (AG) **659**
Dinamika. (IO) **1074**
Dinamika i Prochnost' Mashin. (KR ISSN 0419-1544) **3843**, **1928**
Dinamika Izluchayuschego Gaza. (RU) **3684**
Dinamis. (AG) **2404**
Dine Israel. (IS ISSN 0070-4903) **2619**
Dine Out. (UK ISSN 0144-655X) **2473**
Dinero. (SP) **659**
Diners. (AG) **4759**
Diners Club *see* Guida ai Punti di Credito **2474**
Diners Club. (AG) **4759**
Diners Club Magazine. (GW) **4759**
Diners Club Magazine *see* Globo **4768**
Dines Letter. (US ISSN 0012-2971) **944**
Dinnington & Maltby Trader. (UK) **2193**
Dinshah Health Society Newsletter. (US) **3214**, **3801**
Dinteria. (SX ISSN 0012-3013) **500**
Diocesan Magazine. (GY) **4262**
Diocesan Times. (CN ISSN 0382-9391) **4236**
Diode D.A.T.A. Digest. (US ISSN 1040-0249) **1765**, **1885**
Diogene *see* Diogenes (English Edition) **4433**
†Diogenes. (BL) **5180**
Diogenes (English Edition). (UN ISSN 0392-1921) **4433**, **3765**
Dionysos. (US ISSN 1044-4149) **2912**
Diorama Letterario. (IT ISSN 0394-2473) **2864**
Diotima. (GR) **3765**
Diozese Gurk. Jahrbuch/Krske Skofije. Zbornik. (AU) **4262**, **1999**
Diozese Hildesheim in Vergangenheit und Gegenwart. (GW) **4262**
Dipanvita *see* Meira **2997**
▼Dipartimento di Discipline Storiche. Pubblicazione. (IT) **2309**
Dipavali. (II) **2992**
Diplomacy. (KO) **3890**
▼Diplomacy & Statecraft. (UK ISSN 0959-2296) **3955**, **2358**
Diplomacy World. (US) **4470**
Diplomat. (PK) **3955**
Diplomat. (UK ISSN 0951-032X) **3955**
Diplomat. *see* Al-Diblomasi **3955**
†Diplomatarium Danicum. (DK ISSN 0070-4938) **5180**
Diplomate *see* Environmental Engineering **1951**
▼Diplomaten Spiegel. (GW) **3955**
Diplomatic & Consular Year Book. (UK) **3955**
Diplomatic Bookshelf *see* Diplomatic Bookshelf & Review **4126**
Diplomatic Bookshelf & Review. (UK) **4126**
Diplomatic Corps and Consular and Other Representatives in Canada/Corps Diplomatique et Representants Consulaires et Autres au Canada. (CN ISSN 0486-4514) **3955**
Diplomatic History. (US ISSN 0145-2096) **2309**, **3955**
Diplomatic List and List of Representatives of United Nations and Its Specialized Agencies and Other Missions. (NP) **3955**

Diplomatic List - Diplomatic and Consular Representatives in New Zealand. (NZ) **3955**
Diplomatic Observer/Observateur Diplomatique/Internationales Diplomatisches Magazin. (GW ISSN 0172-3227) **3955**
Diplomatic Service List. (UK) **3955**
Diplomatic World Bulletin and Delegates World Bulletin. (US ISSN 0363-8200) **3955**
Diplomatist. (UK ISSN 0012-3110) **3955**, **3457**
Diplomees. (FR) **4840**
Les Diplomes. (CN ISSN 0228-9636) **1310**
Diplomlandwirt *see* V D L - Journal **128**
Diqiu Huaxue. (CC ISSN 0379-1726) **1559**, **1176**
Diqiu Wuli Xuebao/Acta Geophysica Sinica. (CC ISSN 0001-5733) **1588**, **2246**
Dirasat. Series A: Humanities. (JO ISSN 0255-8033) **2506**, **4307**
Dirasat. Series B: Pure and Applied Sciences. (JO ISSN 0253-424X) **4307**, **437**
Al-Dirasat al-Islamiyyah. (PK ISSN 0002-399X) **4218**
Dirasat Arabiyat/Arab Studies. (LE ISSN 0417-5190) **3891**
Dirasat Handasiyyah/Engineering Studies. (TS) **1818**
Dirasat Tarbawiyyah/Educational Studies. (TS) **1625**
Dirassat. (LY) **659**
Direccion de Bibliotecas Archivos y Museos. Bibliografia Chilena. (CL ISSN 0716-176X) **399**
Direccion de Vialidad Publicaciones Tecnicas *see* D.V.B.A. Publicaciones Tecnicas **4178**
Direccion General de los Registros y del Notariado. Anuario. (SP) **2619**
Direct. (GW) **1253**, **4262**
Direct (Stamford). (US) **1037**, **1008**
Direct Access. (CN ISSN 0827-5033) **1433**
Direct Confrontation. (US) **2619**
Direct Effect. (BE) **1037**
†Direct Energy Conversion (Oak Ridge, 1982). (US ISSN 0735-2484) **5180**
Direct from Cuba. (CU ISSN 0046-0338) **3891**
Direct from Midrex. (US) **3405**
Direct Line. (US ISSN 0743-7625) **1037**, **30**
Direct Line. (BE ISSN 0417-5271) **2569**
Direct Link. (US) **1735**
Direct Mail Databook. (UK) **1037**, **30**
Direct Mail List Rates and Data *see* Standard Rate and Data Service. Direct Mail List Rates and Data **41**
Direct Marketing Association. Annual Report. (US) **1037**, **31**
Direct Marketing Association Matters *see* D M A Matters **5176**
Direct Marketing Association Statistical Fact Book *see* D M A Statistical Fact Book **1037**
Direct Marketing Communicator. (CN) **1037**, **31**
Direct Marketing Directory. Who's Who in Direct Marketing. (AT) **1037**, **31**
Direct Marketing in Japan. (JA) **1037**
Direct Marketing Journal *see* Directions (New York) **1037**
Direct Marketing Magazine. (US) **1037**, **31**
Direct Marketing Market Place. (US ISSN 0192-3137) **1037**, **31**
Direct Response. (US) **1037**
Direct Response Marketing to Schools Newsletter *see* School Marketing Newsletter **1731**
Direct Response Specialist. (US) **31**, **1037**
Direct Selling Association. International Bulletin. (US) **1037**
Direct Selling: Association Membership Roster Listing Major Companies and Commodities *see* Who's Who in Direct Selling **1056**
▼Direct Source. (US) **4148**
Direct Taxes Bulletin. (II) **1092**
Direct Textile Bulletin. (II) **4618**

Directed Energy - Avionics Data Sheets. (UK) **51**
Direction. (UK) **4236**
Direction (Alexandria). (US ISSN 0092-7449) **4744**
Direction et Gestion des Entreprises. (FR ISSN 0012-320X) **1008**
Direction Informatique. (CN ISSN 0842-1951) **1450**
Direction of Trade *see* Direction of Trade Statistics **713**
Direction of Trade Statistics. (UN ISSN 0252-306X) **713**, **905**
Directional Antenna Data Base. (US) **1348**
Directions. (NZ) **2212**
Directions (Austin). (US) **1394**
Directions (Bridgewater). (US ISSN 0360-473X) **4126**, **1625**, **2754**
Directions (Chicago). (US) **4545**
Directions (Columbus). (US) **2460**
Directions (Edgerton). (US) **1310**
Directions (Lawrenceville) *see* Rider College Magazine **1323**
Directions (New York). (US ISSN 0883-9727) **1037**, **31**
Directions for Utah Libraries. (US ISSN 0899-5877) **2754**
▼Directions in Chaos. (SI) **3817**
Directoire Enterprises Textiles de Processus Cotonnier. *see* Directory of the Spanish Cotton-System Textile Enterprises **4618**
Director. (UK ISSN 0012-3242) **1008**
Director. (II ISSN 0012-3250) **1008**
Director. (US ISSN 0199-3186) **2119**
Director of Nursing Labor Alert *see* Health Labor Relations Alert **3103**
Directori Empreses Textils de Proces Cotoner. *see* Directory of the Spanish Cotton-System Textile Enterprises **4618**
Directories in Print. (US ISSN 0275-5580) **399**
†Directories of Hawaii. (US ISSN 0094-209X) **5180**
Directorio Agropecuario de Colombia. (CK) **87**
Directorio Colombiano de Unidades de Informacion. (CK) **2754**
Directorio Comercial e Industrial. (ES) **814**
Directorio Comercial e Industrial de Panama/Comercial and Industrial Directory of Panama. (PN) **1128**
Directorio de Especialistas IberoAmericanos em Informacao e Documentacao. *see* Directorio de Especialistas IberoAmericanos en Informacion y Documentacion **2754**
Directorio de Especialistas IberoAmericanos en Informacion y Documentacion/Directorio de Especialistas IberoAmericanos em Informacao e Documentacao. (SP) **2754**
Directorio de Instituciones Financieras. (CK) **776**
Directorio de la Educacion Superior en Colombia. (CK ISSN 0120-5056) **1693**
Directorio de la Exportacion. *see* Export Directory Chile **1135**
Directorio de Medios *see* Directorio M P M - Medios Impresos **41**
Directorio de Servicios para Familias Migrantes. *see* Directory of Services for Migrant Families **5181**
Directorio Empresas Textiles de Proceso Algodonero. *see* Directory of the Spanish Cotton-System Textile Enterprises **4618**
Directorio Hispano. (US) **1128**
Directorio Industrial Azucarero. (VE) **176**
Directorio Industrial de Colombia. (CK) **1128**
Directorio M P M - Agencias y Anunciantes/M P M - Mexican Advertising Agencies Directory. (Medios Publicitarios Mexicanos, S.A.) (MX) **31**
Directorio M P M - Medios Audiovisuales/M P M - Mexican Audiovisual Media Rates & Data. (Medios Publicitarios Mexicanos, S.A.) (MX) **41**, **31**, **399**

Directorio M P M - Medios Impresos/M P M - Mexican Print Media Rates & Data. (Medios Publicitarios Mexicanos, S.A.) (MX) **41**, **31**, **399**
Directorio Nacional de Entidades Cooperativos. (CK) **830**, **1128**
Directorio Nacional de la Industria de los Plasticos y Proveedores (Year) *see* Anuario Latinoamericano de los Plasticos **3861**
Directorio Nacional de Profesionales. (CK) **3626**
Directorium fuer das Bistum Trier. Liturgischer Kalender. (GW) **4263**
Directors & Boards. (US ISSN 0364-9156) **1008**
Directors Early Warner *see* Company Director **1005**
Directors Economic Review *see* Company Director **1005**
Directors Guild of America. Directory of Members. (US ISSN 0419-2052) **2582**
Director's Law Reporter *see* Company Director **1005**
Director's Monthly. (US) **1008**
Directors Newsletter *see* Funeral Service Insider **2119**
Directorship. (US ISSN 0193-4279) **1008**
Directory. Diocesan Agencies of Catholic Charities and Catholic Charities U S A Member Institutions. United States, Puerto Rico and Canada *see* Directory of Catholic Charities, Diocesan Agencies and Organizations. United States, Puerto Rico and Canada (Year) **4404**
Directory: A Guide to Colleges, Vocational-Technical Schools and Special Purpose Institutions *see* Georgia Post-Secondary School Directory: A Guide to Colleges, Vocational-Technical Schools & Special Purpose Institutions **1694**
Directory - American Bell Association *see* American Bell Association. Directory **3537**
Directory and Handbook - Baptist Missionary Association of America *see* Baptist Missionary Association of America. Directory and Handbook **4230**
Directory and Statistics of Oregon Libraries. (US ISSN 0162-0290) **2793**
Directory and Who's Who in Liberia. (LB) **1128**
Directory for Disabled People. (UK ISSN 0309-4413) **4403**
Directory for Exceptional Children. (US ISSN 0070-5012) **1735**, **4019**
Directory for Older People. (UK) **2271**
Directory for the Nonwoven Fabrics and Disposable Soft Goods Industries *see* International Directory of the Nonwoven Fabrics Industry **4620**
Directory: Graduate Programs in Public Affairs and Administration *see* Graduate Programs in Public Affairs and Public Administration **4062**
Directory Industry Buyers Guide *see* Directory Publishers Buyers Guide **5181**
†Directory Information Service. (US ISSN 0146-7085) **5180**
Directory Iron and Steel Plants. (US ISSN 0070-5039) **3405**
Directory Marketplace. (US ISSN 0894-346X) **4126**, **399**, **1128**
Directory: North Dakota City Officials. (US ISSN 0090-1989) **4086**
Directory of A S U Latin Americanists. (Arizona State University) (US) **2404**
Directory of Accredited Camps. (CN ISSN 0316-1226) **4545**
Directory of Accredited Home Study Schools. (US) **1693**
Directory of Advertising and Marketing Services *see* Handbook of Advertising and Marketing Services **32**
Directory of African Universities. (GH) **1704**
Directory of Afrikanamerican Research Centers. (US) **1999**

6122 DIRECTORY

Directory of Agricultural Co-Operatives in the United Kingdom. (UK) **149**, 1128
Directory of Agricultural, Horticultural and Fishery Co-Operatives in the United Kingdom *see* Directory of Agricultural Co-Operatives in the United Kingdom **149**
Directory of Aids for Disabled and Elderly People. (UK) **4403**
Directory of Alberta's Agricultural Processing Industry. (CN ISSN 0708-3017) **149**, 1128
Directory of Alcohol and Drug Treatment Resources in Ontario. (CN ISSN 0228-863X) **1535**
Directory of American Business in Argentina *see* American Business in Argentina **1120**
Directory of American Firms Operating in Foreign Countries. (US ISSN 0070-5071) **905**, 1128
Directory of American Fulbright Scholars. (US) **1721**
Directory of American Horticulture *see* North American Horticulture: A Reference Guide **2135**
Directory of American Medical Education *see* A A M C Directory of American Medical Education **1724**
Directory of American Philosophers. (US ISSN 0070-508X) **3765**
Directory of American Poets and Fiction Writers. (US ISSN 0734-0605) **2992**, 4126
Directory of American Research and Technology. (US ISSN 0886-0076) **4596**
Directory of American Sailing Schools and Charter Operators. (US) **4524**
Directory of American Savings and Loan Associations. (US ISSN 0070-5098) **776**
Directory of American Scholars. (US ISSN 0070-5101) **418**
Directory of American Youth Organizations (Year). (US) **1253**, 1236, 1297
Directory of Arizona Exporters. (US) **1128**, 905
Directory of Associations in Canada. (CN ISSN 0316-0734) **1128**
Directory of Audio-Visual Programs for the Health Sciences and Related Fields. (US ISSN 0891-947X) **3094**
Directory of Australian Academic and Research Libraries. (AT) **2754**
Directory of Australian Academic Libraries *see* Directory of Australian Academic and Research Libraries **2754**
Directory of Australian Associations. (AT ISSN 0110-666X) **1128**, 10, 399
Directory of Australian Composers. (AT ISSN 0815-5232) **3548**
Directory of Australian Music Organisations. (AT ISSN 0157-6402) **3549**
Directory of Australian Public Libraries. (AT ISSN 0729-4271) **2754**
Directory of Automotive Aftermarket Suppliers (Year). (US ISSN 0736-0452) **1128**, 641
Directory of Bay Area Public Interest Organizations. (US) **2619**
Directory of Behavioral Graduate Study *see* Directory of Graduate Training in Behavior Therapy **1693**
Directory of Biomedical and Health Care Grants. (US ISSN 0883-5330) **1675**, 3171
Directory of Bond Agents *see* Standard and Poor's Directory of Bond Agents **964**
Directory of Book, Catalog, and Magazine Printers *see* Directory of Book Printers **4126**
Directory of Book Printers. (US) **4126**, 1128
Directory of Book Publishers and Wholesalers *see* Directory of Book Publishers, Distributors and Wholesalers **4126**
Directory of Book Publishers, Distributors and Wholesalers. (UK) **4126**
Directory of British Associations. (UK ISSN 0070-5152) **1128**
Directory of British Biotechnology. (UK ISSN 0265-8275) **1129**, 489
Directory of British Caving Clubs (Year). (UK) **4545**, 1559
Directory of Brush and Allied Trades *see* Brush and Allied Trades Directory **1124**
Directory of Builders and Contractors. (II) **616**
Directory of Buying Offices and Accounts. (US ISSN 0070-5195) **1284**
Directory of C S I R O Research Programs. (AT ISSN 0727-6753) **4307**
Directory of Canadian Chartered Accountants. (CN ISSN 0527-9275) **750**
Directory of Canadian Community Funds and Councils *see* United Way of Canada. Directory of Members **4423**
Directory of Canadian Consultants, Copywriters & Contract Publishers. (CN) **4126**, 3674
Directory of Canadian Map Collections. (CN ISSN 0070-5217) **2246**, 2754
Directory of Canadian Orchestras and Youth Orchestras/Annuaire Canadien des Orchestres et Orchestres des Jeunes. (CN ISSN 0705-6249) **3549**
Directory of Canadian Universities (Year)/Repertoire des Universites Canadiennes (year). (CN ISSN 0706-2338) **1693**
Directory of Canadian Universities and Colleges *see* Directory of Canadian Universities (Year) **1693**
Directory of Candy Brokers *see* Candy Buyers Directory **1126**
Directory of Cardamom Planters. (II) **176**, 1129
Directory of Career Resources for Minorities. (US) **976**
Directory of Cartoonists - Gagwriters - Short Humor Markets. (US) **1129**, 2912
Directory of Catholic Charities, Diocesan Agencies and Organizations. United States, Puerto Rico and Canada (Year). (US) **4404**
Directory of Central America Organizations. (US) **1129**, 3941
Directory of Central Atlantic States Manufacturers *see* George D. Hall's Directory of Central Atlantic States Manufacturers **1136**
Directory of Certified Appliances and Accessories. (CN ISSN 0847-527X) **3684**, 1785
Directory of Certified Dehumidifiers. (US) **2298**
Directory of Certified Humidifiers. (US) **2298**
Directory of Certified Ophthalmic Medical Assistants. (US) **3300**
Directory of Certified Products & Companies & Accredited Laboratories in Singapore. (SI) **1074**
Directory of Certified Products in Singapore *see* Directory of Certified Products & Companies & Accredited Laboratories in Singapore **1074**
Directory of Certified Refrigerators and Freezers. (US) **2298**
Directory of Certified Room Air Conditioners. (US) **2298**
Directory of Chain Restaurant Operators (Year). (US ISSN 0411-7085) **1129**, 2473
Directory of Chemical Engineering Consultants. (US) **1852**
Directory of Chemical Engineering Research in Canada. (CN ISSN 0070-525X) **1852**
Directory of Chemical Engineering Research in Canadian Universities. *see* Directory of Chemical Engineering Research in Canada **1852**
Directory of Chemical Producers - Canada. (US) **1176**, 1129
Directory of Chemical Producers - East Asia. (US) **1176**, 1129
Directory of Chemical Producers - U S A. (US ISSN 0012-3277) **1176**, 1129
Directory of Chemical Producers - Western Europe. (US) **1176**, 1129
Directory of Chinese American Librarians. (US) **2754**
Directory of Chinese External Economic Organizations & Industrial/ Commercial Enterprises. (HK ISSN 0259-1146) **1129**
Directory of Church of England Social Services *see* Social Responsibility **4419**
†Directory of Churches and Synagogues. (US) **5180**
Directory of City Policy Officials. (US) **4087**
Directory of Co-Operative Naturalists' Projects in Ontario. (CN ISSN 0707-0942) **563**, 1486
Directory of Coconut Processing Machinery, Equipment, Manufacturers & Suppliers. (IO) **136**, 399
Directory of Coconut Products Exporters. (IO) **136**, 399
Directory of Coconut Products Importers. (IO) **136**, 399
Directory of Coin Collectors. (US) **3599**, 1129
Directory of College and University Libraries in New York State. (US ISSN 0070-5276) **2754**
Directory of College Facilities and Services for People with Disabilities. (US) **1693**, 1735
Directory of College Facilities and Services for the Disabled *see* Directory of College Facilities and Services for People with Disabilities **1693**
Directory of College Stores. (US ISSN 0084-988X) **1037**
Directory of Colorado Libraries *see* Colorado Education & Library Directory **2752**
Directory of Colorado Manufacturers. (US ISSN 0084-9898) **1129**
Directory of Commerce & Industry. (SY) **1129**
Directory of Common Motor Carrier Agency Tariffs. (US) **4649**
Directory of Community Legislation in Force. (EI) **2619**
Directory of Community Newspapers. (US) **399**
Directory of Community Resources and Services. (US) **4404**
Directory of Community Services for Drug Abuse in California *see* Drug Abuse: Directory of Community Services in California **1535**
Directory of Community Services in Metropolitan Toronto. (CN ISSN 0315-0631) **4404**
Directory of Community Services of Greater Montreal/Repertoire des Services Communautaires du Grand Montreal. (CN ISSN 0319-258X) **4404**
Directory of Company Histories of the Book Industries/Verzeichnis von Jubilaeumsschriften der Graphischen Industrie. (AT ISSN 0729-6568) **4007**, 4141
Directory of Company Secretaries. (II ISSN 0070-5322) **1008**
Directory of Computer & Software Storefront Dealers (Year). (US) **1425**, 1129, 1433, 1476
Directory of Computer Installations: Mid-Atlantic State. (US) **1425**, 1436, 1453, 1466, 1476
Directory of Computer Installations: New York Metropolitan Area - New York, New Jersey & Connecticut. (US) **1425**, 1436, 1453, 1466, 1476
Directory of Computer Software. (US ISSN 0748-1543) **1129**, 1477
Directory of Computer Software and Related Technical Reports *see* Directory of Computer Software **1129**
Directory of Computer Training *see* Directory of Training **1394**
Directory of Computerized Data Files *see* Directory of U.S. Government Software for Mainframes and Microcomputers **1133**
Directory of Connecticut Libraries and Media Centers. (US) **1129**, 2754
Directory of Connecticut Libraries and Media Centers Including Finding *see* Directory of Connecticut Libraries and Media Centers **1129**
Directory of Connecticut Manufacturers *see* George D. Hall's Directory of Connecticut Manufacturers **1136**
Directory of Consulting Engineering Services in North Carolina. (US) **1818**, 1129
Directory of Consumer Electronics (Year). (US) **1129**, 3790
Directory of Consumer Electronics, Photography and Major Appliance Retailers and Distributors (Year) *see* Directory of Consumer Electronics (Year) **1129**
Directory of Contract Wallcoverings and Specifications. (US) **1129**, 2551
Directory of Contractors and Public Works Annual and Construction Industries Buyers Guide *see* European Directory of Contractors **617**
Directory of Convenience Stores *see* Progressive Grocer's Directory of Convenience Stores **2080**
Directory of Conventions. (US ISSN 0417-5751) **3392**
Directory of Cooperatives, Voluntaries & Wholesale Grocers (Year). (US ISSN 0277-1969) **1129**
Directory of Corporate Affiliations. (US ISSN 0070-5365) **1129**
Directory of Corporate Counsel *see* Law & Business Directory of Corporate Counsel **2711**
Directory of Corporate Financing *see* Handbook of Corporate Finance **783**
Directory of Correctional Services in Canada - Repertoire des Services de Correction du Canada *see* Justice - Directory of Services **1517**
†Directory of Courses: Tourism, Hospitality, Recreation. (CN ISSN 0705-8160) **5180**
Directory of Craft Info *see* Crafts Industry Guide N.S.W.: Printout **354**
Directory of Crematoria. (UK ISSN 0143-3164) **1129**, 2119
Directory of Criminal Justice Information Sources. (US) **1513**, 1434
Directory of Criminal Justice Issues in the States. (US) **1513**, 2619
Directory of Dance Companies. (US ISSN 0363-972X) **1530**
Directory of Day Schools in the United States and Canada. (US) **1693**, 1999
Directory of Day Schools in the United States, Canada and Latin America *see* Directory of Day Schools in the United States and Canada **1693**
Directory of Dealers in Secondhand and Antiquarian Books in the British Isles *see* Sheppard's Book Dealers in British Isles **4137**
Directory of Demographic Research Centers. *see* Annuaire des Centres de Recherche Demographique **3979**
Directory of Dental and Allied Dental Educators *see* Directory of Dental Educators **3232**
Directory of Dental Educators. (US) **3232**
Directory of Department Stores (Year). (US ISSN 0419-2508) **1129**
Directory of Departments and Programs of Religious Studies in North America. (US) **4174**
Directory of Development and Training Institutes in Africa. (SG) **928**, 1129, 1625
Directory of Directories *see* Directories in Print **399**
†Directory of Directories: Publishers Volume. (US ISSN 0890-5525) **5180**
Directory of Directors. (II ISSN 0070-542X) **418**, 1008
Directory of Directors. (UK ISSN 0070-5438) **1008**
Directory of Discount Department Stores (Year). (US ISSN 0897-5442) **1129**
Directory of Discount Department Stores, Catalog Showrooms (Year) *see* Directory of Discount Department Stores (Year) **1129**

Title

†Directory of Distinguished Americans. (US) **5180**
Directory of Drug Store and H B A Chains (Year). (US ISSN 0730-2703) **1129**
Directory of E D P Management. (CN) **1450**
Directory of East Asian Collections in North American Libraries *see* C E A L Directory **2750**
Directory of Economic Research Centres in India. (II) **1130**
Directory of Editorial Resources *see* Directory of Publications Resources **4126**
Directory of Editors & Publishers. (US) **4126, 2569**
Directory of Educational Facilities for the Learning Disabled *see* Directory of Services and Facilities for the Learning Disabled **1735**
Directory of Educational Institutions. (US) **1693**
Directory of Educational Institutions in New Mexico. (US ISSN 0084-991X) **1625**
Directory of Electric Generating and Distributing Companies *see* Directory of Electric Utility Industry **1885**
Directory of Electric Light and Power Companies *see* Directory of Electric Utility Industry **1885**
Directory of Electric Utility Industry. (US) **1885, 1130, 3684**
Directory of Electrical Wholesale Distributors. (US) **1130**
Directory of Electronic Services and Communications Networks in Australia and New Zealand. (AT) **1362**
Directory of Electronics and Instrumentation *see* Directory of Technology **1885**
Directory of Electronics, Instruments and Computers *see* Electronics & Instruments Directory **5185**
Directory of Emergency and Special Care Units (Year). (UK) **3094**
Directory of Employers Associations, Trade Unions, Joint Organizations Etc. (UK) **976**
Directory of Employers Offering Employment to New University Graduates *see* Employers of New University Graduates: Directory **1134**
Directory of Engineering - Architectural Minority and Women Owned Firms. (US) **1818, 1130**
Directory of Engineering Capacity. (UK) **1130**
Directory of Engineering Societies and Related Organizations. (US ISSN 0070-5470) **1818, 1130**
Directory of Engineers *see* Institution of Engineers of Ireland. Register of Chartered Engineers and Members **1826**
Directory of Engineers and Land Surveyors Registered in South Carolina. (US ISSN 0420-2155) **1818, 1130**
Directory of English-Speaking Churches Abroad. (UK) **4174**
Directory of Environmental Information Sources. (US) **1947, 1130**
Directory of Environmental Organizations. (US ISSN 0270-1111) **1486, 1947**
Directory of European Associations. Part 1: National Industrial Trade and Professional Associations *see* Directory of European Industrial & Trade Associations **1130**
Directory of European Associations. Part 2: National Learned, Scientific and Technical Societies *see* Directory of Professional & Learned Societies **4307**
▼Directory of European Business. (UK) **1130**
Directory of European Community Trade and Professional Associations. (BE ISSN 0771-7865) **1130**
Directory of European Industrial & Trade Associations. (UK) **1130**
Directory of European Retailers & International Buying Agents. (UK) **1037, 1130**

Directory of Executive Recruiters. (US ISSN 1059-163X) **1008**
Directory of Exhibit Opportunities *see* Association of American Publishers. Exhibits Directory **4121**
Directory of Exhibitors Taipei International Trade Fairs *see* (Year) Directory of Taiwan's Leading Exporters **1132**
Directory of Experts, Authorities and Spokespersons *see* Yearbook of Experts, Authorities & Spokespersons **1384**
Directory of Export Buyers in the U.K. (UK ISSN 0142-4769) **1130, 905**
Directory of Exporters. (CE) **814**
Directory of Exporters. (US) **1130**
Directory of Exporters (Year). (PK) **905**
Directory of Faculty Contracts and Bargaining Agents in Institutions of Higher Education. (US ISSN 0276-7805) **1704, 2582**
Directory of Faculty of Departments and Programs of Religious Studies in North America. (US) **4174**
Directory of Family Day Care Associations & Support Groups. (US) **1236, 1253**
Directory of Family 'One-Name' Periodicals. (US) **2168**
Directory of Federal Aid for Health and Allied Fields. (US) **4404**
Directory of Federal Aid for the Aging. (US) **4404, 2271**
Directory of Federal Aid for the Handicapped. (US) **4404, 1735, 2287, 2292**
Directory of Federal and State Business Assistance. (US) **1130**
Directory of Federal Laboratories. (US) **1130, 4596**
Directory of Federal Laboratory Resources and Technologies. (US) **3258**
†Directory of Federally Supported Research in Universities/Repertoire de la Recherche dans les Universites Subventionnee Par le Gouvernement Federal. (CN ISSN 0316-0297) **5180**
Directory of Fee-Based Information Services *see* Burwell Directory of Information Brokers **2750**
Directory of Fellowship Programs in Geriatric Medicine. (US) **2272, 1704**
†Directory of Financial Aids for Women. (US ISSN 0732-5215) **5180**
Directory of First Degree and Diploma of Higher Education Courses *see* Directory of First Degree and Undergraduate Courses **1704**
Directory of First Degree and Undergraduate Courses. (UK) **1704**
Directory of Florida Industries. (US) **1130**
Directory of Florida Writers *see* Guide to Florida Writers **1137**
Directory of Food Service Distributors (Year). (US ISSN 0271-7662) **1130, 2091**
Directory of Foreign Firms Operating in the United States. (US ISSN 0070-5543) **1130**
Directory of Foreign Manufacturers in the U S. (US) **1130**
Directory of Foreign Trade Organizations in Eastern Europe. (US) **905, 1130**
Directory of Franchising Organizations. (US ISSN 0070-556X) **1037**
Directory of Free Programs, Performing Talent and Attractions. (US ISSN 0736-7759) **1372**
Directory of Free Vacation & Travel Information. (US) **4759**
Directory of Fulbright Alumni. (II ISSN 0084-9936) **1704**
Directory of Funparks & Attractions. (US) **4759**
Directory of Further Education. (UK) **1705**
Directory of Garment Manufacturers. (CE) **1130, 1284**
Directory of Gas Distribution, Transmission and Production Companies *see* Directory of Natural Gas Company Operations **3684**

Directory of Gas Utility Companies *see* Gas Utility Industry **3687**
Directory of Genealogical Societies in the U S A and Canada *see* Meyer's Directory of Genealogical Societies in the U S A & Canada **2158**
Directory of General Merchandise, Variety & Specialty Stores (Year). (US) **1130**
Directory of General Merchandise, Variety Chains and Specialty Stores (Year) *see* Directory of General Merchandise, Variety & Specialty Stores (Year) **1130**
Directory of Geoscience Departments, North America. (US) **1543, 1693**
Directory of Geoscience Departments, United States and Canada *see* Directory of Geoscience Departments, North America **1543**
Directory of Geriatrics Program for Residencies and Fellowships *see* Directory of Fellowship Programs in Geriatric Medicine **2272**
Directory of Government Document Collections and Librarians. (US ISSN 0276-959X) **2754**
Directory of Government Production Prime Contractors *see* Government Production Prime Contractors Directory **1137**
Directory of Graduate Medical Education. (US) **1705, 3094**
†Directory of Graduate Programs in the Communication Arts and Sciences. (US ISSN 0732-2755) **5180**
Directory of Graduate Programs in the Speech Communication Arts and Sciences *see* Directory of Graduate Programs in the Communication Arts and Sciences **5180**
Directory of Graduate Training in Behavior Therapy. (US) **1693, 3335, 4019**
Directory of Grant-Making Trusts. (UK ISSN 0070-5624) **4404**
Directory of Grants in the Humanities. (US ISSN 0887-0551) **1675, 399, 1705**
†Directory of Grants in the Physical Sciences. (US ISSN 0890-541X) **5180**
Directory of Hardlines Distributors (Year). (US) **1130, 835**
Directory of Hazardous Waste Services. (CN) **1984, 1130**
Directory of Health Facilities *see* Health Facilities Directory (Sacramento) **4407**
Directory of High-Volume Independent Restaurants (Year). (US) **1130, 2473**
Directory of Higher Education *see* Illinois. Board of Higher Education. Directory of Higher Education **1708**
Directory of Higher Education in Alabama. (US) **1705**
Directory of Historical Organizations in the United States and Canada. (US) **2404**
Directory of Historical Societies and Agencies in the United States and Canada *see* Directory of Historical Organizations in the United States and Canada **2404**
Directory of History Departments and Organizations (Year). (US) **1693, 2404**
Directory of Holocaust Institutions. (US) **1999**
Directory of Holocaust Resource Centers, Institutions, and Organizations in North America *see* Directory of Holocaust Institutions **1999**
Directory of Home Care Services in New York *see* Home Care Services in New York State **5205**
Directory of Home Center Operators & Hardware Chains (Year). (US ISSN 0272-0167) **1130, 2558**
Directory of Home Furnishings Retailers (Year). (US ISSN 0888-0166) **1131, 2558**
Directory of Homosexual Organizations and Publications. (US) **2452**
Directory of Hong Kong Industries. (HK) **1131**

▼Directory of Hospital Telephone Numbers (Year). (UK) **2460**
Directory of Hotel and Motel Companies. (US) **2473**
Directory of Hotel and Motel Systems *see* Directory of Hotel and Motel Companies **2473**
Directory of Humor Magazines & Humor Organizations in America (and Canada). (US) **399, 2864**
Directory of In-Bond Plants (Maquiladoras) in Mexico. (US) **1131**
Directory of Incentive Travel International. (US ISSN 0732-6572) **4760**
Directory of Independent Hospitals and Health Services. (UK) **2460, 3094**
Directory of Independent IBM Personal Computer Hardware and Software *see* Infopro: The Directory **1460**
Directory of Indian Engineering Exporters. (II ISSN 0417-5964) **1131, 1818**
Directory of Indian Exporters. (II) **905**
Directory of Industrial Establishments in Punjab. (PK) **1131**
Directory of Industrial Laboratories in Israel. (IS) **1818, 1131**
†Directory of Industry Data Sources, U.S. and Canada. (US ISSN 0278-0119) **5180**
Directory of Information and Referral Agencies in the United States and Canada. (US) **4404, 1504**
†Directory of Information on Medical Practitioners in Malaysia. (MY) **5180**
Directory of Information Resources for the Handicapped. (US) **2283**
Directory of Information Sources in Japan. (JA) **2755**
Directory of Insurance Companies Licensed in New York State. (US ISSN 0070-5691) **2530**
Directory of Intellectual Property Attorneys. (US) **2619, 4148**
Directory of Interior Designers. (II ISSN 0256-4025) **2551**
Directory of International Coconut Research Workers. (IO) **136, 399**
Directory of International Corporate Giving in America. (US) **1131, 4404**
Directory of International Mail *see* International Mail Manual **1353**
Directory of International Music Education Dissertations in Progress. (US) **3549, 1625**
Directory of International Personnel in Tanzania *see* Directory: Organizations of the United Nations System in the United Republic of Tanzania **929**
Directory of International Sources of Business Information. (UK) **1131**
†Directory of International Trade. (US) **5180**
Directory of Internships, Residencies and Registrarships Available in Victorian Hospitals. (AT ISSN 0157-2784) **2460, 3626**
Directory of Investor-Owned Hospitals, Hospital Management Companies and Health Systems *see* Directory of Investor-Owned Hospitals, Residential Treatment Facilities and Centers, Hospital Management Companies and Health Systems **2460**
Directory of Investor-Owned Hospitals, Residential Treatment Facilities and Centers, Hospital Management Companies and Health Systems. (US) **2460**
Directory of Iranian Newspapers. (IR) **399**
Directory of Iranian Periodicals/ Rahnamay-i Majallah-ha-y Iran. (IR ISSN 0378-7443) **399**
†Directory of Iron and Steel Works of the United States and Canada. (US) **5180**
Directory of Israel. (IS) **1131**
Directory of Israeli Merchants and Manufacturers *see* Directory of Israel **1131**
Directory of Japanese Addresses in Europe. (GW) **1131**

DIRECTORY

Directory of Japanese Affiliated Companies in U S A and Canada. (JA) 1131

Directory of Japanese Firms, Offices and Other Organizations in the United States see Directory of Japanese Affiliated Companies in U S A and Canada 1131

▼Directory of Japanese Jewelers (Year). (JA) 713, 399

Directory of Japanese Scientific Periodicals. see Nihon Kagaku Gijutsu Kankei Chikuji Kankobutsu Soran 4357

Directory of Japanese Technical Resources see Directory of Japanese Technical Resources in the United States 1131

Directory of Japanese Technical Resources in the United States. (US) 1131, 4596

Directory of Jewish Community Centers.(US) 1999

Directory of Jewish Federations, Welfare Funds and Community Councils. (US ISSN 0161-2638) 4404

†Directory of Jewish Health and Welfare Agencies. (US ISSN 0419-2818) 5180

Directory of Jewish Resident Summer Camps. (US) 4545, 1999

Directory of Kansas Manufacturers and Products. (US ISSN 0070-5721) 1131

Directory of Key Bulgarian Government and Party Officials. (BU) 3891

Directory of Korean Business. see Chonguk Kiopche Chongnam 1126

Directory of Labor Organizations. (US) 2582

Directory of Labor Unions and Employee Organizations in New York State. (US) 2582

Directory of Labour Organizations in Canada/Repertoire des Organisations de Travailleurs et Travailleuses au Canada. (CN ISSN 0075-7578) 2582

†Directory of Land and Hydrographic Survey Services in the United Kingdom. (UK ISSN 0260-5007) 5180

Directory of Law Libraries. (US) 2619, 2755

Directory of Law Teachers. (US ISSN 0070-573X) 2619

Directory of Law Teachers/Annuaire des Professeurs de Droit. (CN ISSN 0383-8358) 2619

Directory of Lawyer Referral Services. (US) 2619

Directory of Leading Chain Stores (Year). (US ISSN 0415-9594) 1131

Directory of Leading Private Companies see Directory of Leading Private Companies, Including Corporate Affiliations 1131

Directory of Leading Private Companies, Including Corporate Affiliations. (US) 1131

Directory of Legal Aid and Defender Offices in the United States see Directory of Legal Aid and Defender Offices in the United States and Territories 2619

Directory of Legal Aid and Defender Offices in the United States and Territories. (US) 2619

Directory of Libraries and Library Resources in the South Central Research Library Council Region see Directory of Libraries and Library Systems in the South Central Research Library Council Region 2755

Directory of Libraries and Library Systems in the South Central Research Library Council Region. (US) 2755

Directory of Libraries in Canada. (CN) 2755

Directory of Libraries in Manitoba. (CN ISSN 0317-8536) 2755

Directory of Libraries in Southeast Saskatchewan see Southeast Regional Library (Saskatchewan) Library Directory 5280

Directory of Library & Information Professionals. (US) 2755

†Directory of Library Reprographic Services. (US ISSN 0160-6077) 5180

Directory of Library Resources for the Blind and Physically Handicapped see Library Resources for the Blind and Physically Handicapped (Large Print Edition) 2771

Directory of Library Systems in New York State. (US) 2755

Directory of Licensed Products. (US) 616

Directory of Literary Magazines. (US) 2992

Directory of Little Magazines, Small Presses and Underground Newspapers see International Directory of Little Magazines and Small Presses 4141

Directory of Long Island Libraries and Media Centers. (US) 1131, 2755

Directory of Long Island Libraries and Media Centers Including Finding see Directory of Long Island Libraries and Media Centers 1131

Directory of Long-Term Care Centres in Canada/Repertoire des Centres de Soins de Longue Duree au Canada. (CN ISSN 0226-5419) 2272, 3277

Directory of Louisiana Cities, Towns and Villages. (US ISSN 0092-0614) 4087

Directory of Louisiana Manufacturers. (US ISSN 0275-1089) 1131

Directory of Low Cost Vacations with a Difference. (US) 4760

Directory of Machine Tools and Related Products see U S Machine Tool Directory 1940

Directory of Mail Drops in the United States and Canada see Directory of U.S. Mail Drops 1352

Directory of Mailing List Companies. (US ISSN 0419-2923) 1131, 31

Directory of Mailing List Houses see Directory of Mailing List Companies 1131

Directory of Maine Labor Organizations. (US) 2582

▼Directory of Major Mailers & What They Mail (Year). (US ISSN 1045-6201) 1131, 31

Directory of Major Malls. (US ISSN 0732-5983) 4148, 1037

Directory of Management Consultants. (US) 1008

Directory of Management Consultants in the UK. (UK) 1008

Directory of Management Training see Directory of Training 1394

†Directory of Manufacturers, State of Hawaii. (US ISSN 0190-3047) 5180

Directory of Marine Scientists in the United States see U S Directory of Marine Scientists 5293

Directory of Market Comparability Programs & Membership. (US) 4126

Directory of Massachusetts Libraries and Media Centers and Buyers' Guide see Directory of Massachusetts Libraries and Media Centers Including Buyer's Guide 5180

†Directory of Massachusetts Libraries and Media Centers Including Buyer's Guide. (US) 5180

Directory of Massachusetts Manufacturers see George D. Hall's Directory of Massachusetts Manufacturers 1136

Directory of Materials Suppliers. (US) 2031, 2558

Directory of Medical Institutions Conducting Clinical Research and Services for Persons with the Marfan Syndrome and Related Connective Tissue Disorders. (US) 3094

Directory of Medical Libraries in New York State. (US ISSN 0070-5810) 2755

Directory of Medical Practitioners Malaysia see Directory of Information on Medical Practitioners in Malaysia 5180

Directory of Medical Schools Worldwide.(US) 3094, 1693

Directory of Medical Specialists. (US ISSN 0070-5829) 3094, 418

Directory of Membership & Precast Concrete Products. (US) 616, 1131

Directory of Membrane & High Tech Separations (Year). (US) 4596

Directory of Men's and Boys' Wear Specialty Stores (Year). (US ISSN 0277-9625) 1131, 1284

Directory of Merger and Acquisition Firms and Professionals. (US ISSN 1048-6097) 1131

Directory of Metallurgical Consultants & Translators. (US) 1131, 3405

Directory of Michigan Institutions of Higher Education. (US) 1693

Directory of Michigan Literary Publishers. (US) 4126

Directory of Michigan Manufacturers see Michigan Manufacturers Directory 1047

Directory of Michigan Municipal Officials.(US ISSN 0148-7442) 4087

Directory of Middle East Importers. (US) 905

Directory of Middle East Imports see Directory of Middle East Importers 905

Directory of Mining Programs. (US) 3482, 4359

Directory of Ministries in Higher Education. (US) 1705, 4236

Directory of Minnesota City Officials. (US) 4087

Directory of Minnesota Municipal Officials see Directory of Minnesota City Officials 4087

Directory of Missouri Libraries. (US ISSN 0092-4067) 2755

Directory of Model - Talent Agencies and Schools USA and International. (US) 1131, 1693, 3626

Directory of Montana Schools. (US) 1726

Directory of Movers. (US) 4744

†Directory of Multihospital Systems. (US ISSN 0731-8510) 5180

Directory of Municipal and County Officials in Colorado (Year). (US) 4087

Directory of Municipal Bond Dealers of the United States. (US ISSN 0094-100X) 944

Directory of Municipal Natural Gas Systems. (US) 3684

Directory of Municipal Officials of New Mexico see Directory of New Mexico Municipal Officials 4058

†Directory of Museums & Living Displays. (UK ISSN 0267-9698) 5181

Directory of Museums, Art Galleries and Archives of British Columbia. (CN ISSN 0714-7023) 3524

Directory of Music Faculties in Colleges & Universities U S and Canada. (US ISSN 0098-664X) 3549, 1625

Directory of National Environmental Organizations. (US ISSN 1040-1555) 1947, 1486

Directory of Natural Gas Company Operations. (CN) 3684, 1785

Directory of Nebraska Manufacturers. (US ISSN 0070-5926) 1131

Directory of Nebraska Services. (US) 4058, 4404

Directory of New England Manufacturers. (US ISSN 0889-0382) 1132

Directory of New Mexico Municipal Officials. (US) 4058

Directory of New York State Public Schools and Administrators see Directory of Public Schools and Administrators, New York State 1726

Directory of Nonprofit Immigration Counseling Agencies. (US ISSN 0277-724X) 3981

Directory of Nonpublic Schools and Administrators, New York State. (US) 1726

Directory of North American Fairs, Festivals and Expositions. (US ISSN 0361-4255) 4545, 4632

Directory of North Carolina Municipal Officials. (US) 4087

Directory of North Dakota Manufacturers see Directory of North Dakota Manufacturers and Food Processors 1132

Directory of North Dakota Manufacturers and Food Processors. (US) 1132

†Directory of Nurses with Doctoral Degrees. (US) 5181

Directory of Nursing Home Facilities. (US ISSN 0888-7624) 4404

Directory of Obsolete Securities. (US) 944

Directory of Official Architects and Planners see Directory of Official Architecture and Planning 298

Directory of Official Architecture and Planning. (UK) 298, 1947

Directory of Oil Marketing and Wholesale Distributors see Oil Marketing Industry 3696

Directory of Oil Well Drilling Contractors see Drilling & Well Servicing Contractors 3684

Directory of Oil Well Supply Companies see Oil Well Supply Industry 3696

Directory of Oklahoma. (US) 4058

Directory of On-Going Research in Cancer Epidemiology. (FR) 3196

Directory of Online Databases. (US ISSN 0193-6840) 1444, 1425, 1426

Directory of Ontario Lumber & Building Materials Retailers. Buyer's Guide & Product Directory. (CN) 1132, 2114

Directory of Operating Theatres and Departments of Surgery (Year). (UK) 3378

†Directory of Opportunities for Graduates. (UK ISSN 0070-6019) 5181

Directory of Opportunities for Graduates. Vol.6: Administration, Management, Marketing and Sales see Directory of Opportunities for Graduates. Vol.6: Buying, Marketing, Selling 1132

Directory of Opportunities for Graduates. Vol.6: Buying, Marketing, Selling. (UK) 1132, 1037, 3626

Directory of Opportunities for Graduates Career Guides Series see D O G Career Guides Series 3626

Directory of Oregon Manufacturers. (US ISSN 0070-6027) 1132

Directory of Organizations and Researchers in Educational Management see Directory of Organizations in Educational Management 1726

Directory of Organizations Concerned with Scientific Research and Technical Services in Zimbabwe. (RH) 4307

Directory of Organizations in Educational Management. (US) 1726

Directory of Osteopathic Postdoctoral Education. (US) 2460, 1705

Directory of Outplacement Firms. (US ISSN 0735-3707) 976

Directory of Overseas Summer Jobs. (UK ISSN 0070-6051) 1132, 3626

Directory of Pakistan Exporters see Directory of Exporters (Year) 905

Directory of Pakistani Scholars Abroad. (PK ISSN 0070-606X) 1721

Directory of Pathology Training Programs (Year). (US ISSN 0070-6086) 3094, 437

†Directory of Periodicals Online: News, Law & Business. (US ISSN 0884-089X) 5181

†Directory of Periodicals Online: Science & Technology. (US ISSN 0884-0911) 5181

Directory of Periodicals Published in India. (II ISSN 0970-9266) 4126, 399

Directory of Periodicals Publishing Articles on English and American Literature and Language. (US ISSN 0070-6094) 2912, 2811

Directory of Personal Image Consultants. (US ISSN 0163-6537) **1132**, 372
Directory of Philippine Garment & Textile Exporters. (PH) **1284**
Directory of Physics & Astronomy Staff (Year). (US ISSN 0361-2228) **1705**, 363, 3817
Directory of Plumbing Research Recommendations. (US) **2298**
Directory of Poetry Publishers. (US) **2992**, 4126
Directory of Polish Officials. (US ISSN 0090-9955) **418**
Directory of Political Newsletters *see* Directory of Political Periodicals **1132**
▼Directory of Political Periodicals. (US ISSN 1057-0578) **1132**, 3937, 4080
▼Directory of Portable Databases. (US ISSN 1045-8352) **1444**, 1477
Directory of Post-Graduate and Post-Experience Courses. (UK ISSN 0266-8459) **1705**
Directory of Postgraduate and Post-Graduate Experience Courses *see* Directory of Post-Graduate and Post-Experience Courses **1705**
▼Directory of Postgraduate Study. (AT ISSN 1035-5405) **1132**, 1693, 3626
Directory of Postsecondary Institutions. (US) **1693**
†Directory of Power Plant Managers. (US) **5181**
▼Directory of Power Plants in Japan. (US) **1801**, 1785
Directory of Power Plants in the European Community. (US) **1801**
Directory of Primes. (US ISSN 0887-4042) **1132**
Directory of Private Hospitals and Health Services *see* Directory of Independent Hospitals and Health Services **2460**
Directory of Private Schools *see* Directory of Private Vocational Schools **1693**
Directory of Private Vocational Schools. (US) **1693**, 1683
Directory of Producers and Drilling Contractors: California *see* Western Petroleum Industry **3703**
Directory of Producers and Drilling Contractors: Kansas *see* Midcontinent Petroleum Industry **3692**
Directory of Producers and Drilling Contractors Northeast: Michigan, Indiana, Illinois, Kentucky *see* Northeast Petroleum Industry **3694**
Directory of Producers and Drilling Contractors: Rocky Mountain Region, Williston Basin, Four Corners New Mexico *see* Rocky Mountain Petroleum Industry **3700**
Directory of Producers and Drilling Contractors Southeast: Louisiana, Arkansas, Florida, Georgia *see* Southeast Petroleum Industry **3701**
Directory of Producers and Drilling Contractors: Texas *see* Texas Petroleum Industry **3702**
Directory of Professional & Learned Societies. (UK) **4307**
Directory of Professional Genealogists. (US) **2149**
Directory of Professional Personnel: State Higher Education Agencies and Boards. (US) **1705**
Directory of Professional Puppeteers. (UK) **4632**
Directory of Programs in Linguistics. (US) **2811**
Directory of Property Investors and Developers. (AT) **944**, 4148
Directory of Psychology Internships: Programs Offering Behavioral Training. (US) **1693**, 4019
Directory of Public Elementary and Secondary Education Agencies. (US) **1625**
Directory of Public Refrigerated Warehouses. *see* International Directory of Public Refrigerated Warehouses **2300**
Directory of Public Schools and Administrators, New York State. (US) **1726**

Directory of Public Schools in the U S. (US) **1693**
Directory of Public Vocational Technical Schools and Institutes. (US) **1132**, 1693, 3626
Directory of Publications Resources. (US) **4126**
Directory of Published Proceedings. Series P C E : Pollution Control & Ecology. (US ISSN 0093-5816) **3395**, 1973
Directory of Published Proceedings. Series S E M T - Science, Engineering, Medicine and Technology. (US ISSN 0012-3293) **3395**, 4355, 4614
Directory of Published Proceedings. Series S S H - Social Sciences - Humanities. (US ISSN 0012-3307) **3395**, 2519, 4394
Directory of Recognized Accrediting Bodies. (US) **1705**
Directory of Regional Councils. (US) **4059**
Directory of Religious Broadcasting. (US ISSN 0731-0331) **1372**, 1693
Directory of Research and Developmental Projects. (AT ISSN 0157-3608) **1625**, 1236, 1735, 1748
Directory of Research and Special Libraries in Ghana. (GH) **2755**
†Directory of Research, Development and Demonstration Projects. (US ISSN 0270-8264) **5181**
Directory of Research, Development, and Demonstrations *see* Directory of Research, Development and Demonstration Projects **5181**
Directory of Research Grants. (US ISSN 0146-7336) **1705**
Directory of Research Institutes in Israel. (IS) **4307**, 2755
Directory of Research Organisations and Facilities in South Africa. (SA) **4307**, 4596
Directory of Research Recommendations for Manufactured Housing - Recreation Vehicles *see* Directory of Research Recommendations for Mobile Homes and Recreational Vehicles **2298**
Directory of Research Recommendations for Mobile Homes and Recreational Vehicles. (US) **2298**
Directory of Resources for Alcoholics *see* Coping Catalog **1535**
Directory of Restaurant & Fast Food Chains in Canada (Year). (CN) **2066**, 1132
Directory of Retail Chains in Canada. (CN) **1132**
Directory of Retailer Owned Cooperatives, Wholesaler Sponsored Voluntaries & Wholesale Grocers *see* Directory of Cooperatives, Voluntaries & Wholesale Grocers (Year) **1129**
Directory of San Francisco Attorneys. (US ISSN 0092-9174) **2619**
Directory of Science Resources for Maryland *see* Maryland High-Tech Directory (Year) **4323**
Directory of Scientific and Technical Associations and Institutes in Israel *see* Directory of Scientific and Technical Associations in Israel **4307**
Directory of Scientific and Technical Associations in Israel. (IS ISSN 0334-2824) **4307**, 4596
Directory of Scientific and Technical Libraries in Thailand. (TH ISSN 0858-1630) **2755**
Directory of Scientific and Technical Societies in South Africa *see* Directory of South African Associations **4307**
Directory of Scientific Directories *see* Directory of Technical and Scientific Directories **4307**
Directory of Scientific Libraries in Thailand *see* Directory of Scientific and Technical Libraries in Thailand **2755**
Directory of Scientific Periodicals of Pakistan. (PK) **4355**, 10

Directory of Scientific Research in Indian Universities. (II ISSN 0376-8554) **4355**
Directory of Scientific Research in Nigeria. (NR ISSN 0070-6280) **4307**
Directory of Scientific Research Organisations in South Africa *see* Directory of Research Organisations and Facilities in South Africa **4307**
Directory of Selected U S Cogeneration, Small Power and Industrial Power Plants. (US) **1801**
Directory of Services and Facilities for the Learning Disabled. (US) **1735**, 1693
†Directory of Services for Migrant Families/Directorio de Servicios para Familias Migrantes. (US ISSN 0362-7179) **5181**
Directory of Services for Victims of Crime/Repertoire des Services aux Victimes d'Actes Criminels. (CN ISSN 0847-3668) **1514**
Directory of Services for Visually Handicapped South Africans *see* Diensgids vir Gesigsgestremde Suid-Afrikaners **2292**
Directory of Shipowners and Shipbuilding. (UK) **4726**
†Directory of Shop-by-Mail Bargain Sources. (US) **5181**
Directory of Single Unit Supermarket Operators (Year). (US ISSN 0896-2162) **1132**, 2091
Directory of Small Area Statistics, Queensland. (AT ISSN 1032-8408) **4570**
Directory of Small Magazine - Press Editors and Publishers. (US ISSN 0095-6414) **4141**, 399
Directory of Social Action Programmes *see* Action Stations: The Directory of Social Action Programmes **5130**
Directory of South African Associations/ Gids van Suid-Afrikaanse Verenigings.(SA) **4307**, 4596
▼Directory of South African Publishers.(SA ISSN 1018-7626) **4126**, 2755
Directory of Southern African Libraries. (SA) **2755**
Directory of Special Databases in Israel. (IS) **1425**, 1446
†Directory of Special Education and Guidance Services in New Zealand. (NZ) **5181**
Directory of Special Libraries and Information Centers. (US) **2755**
Directory of Special Libraries and Information Centers in the U S and Canada *see* Directory of Special Libraries and Information Centers **2755**
Directory of Special Libraries and Information Sources (Year). (IO) **2755**
Directory of Special Libraries in Ghana *see* Directory of Research and Special Libraries in Ghana **2755**
Directory of Special Libraries in Israel. (IS ISSN 0070-637X) **2755**
Directory of Special Libraries in the Montreal Area/Repertoire des Bibliotheques Specialisees de la Region de Montreal. (CN ISSN 0319-2563) **2755**
†Directory of Special Opportunities for Women. (US ISSN 0273-2157) **5181**
Directory of Special Programs for Minority Group Members; Career Information Services, Employment Skills, Banks, Financial Aid Sources. (US ISSN 0093-9501) **1132**, 1693, 1999
Directory of Specialist Bookdealers in the UK Handling Mainly New Books. (UK) **4126**
†Directory of State and Federal Funds Available for Business Development. (US ISSN 0070-640X) **5181**
†Directory of State and Local Child Support Advocacy Groups. (US) **5181**
Directory of State Corporations. (CE) **1132**

Directory of State, County, and Federal Officials. (US ISSN 0440-4947) **4059**
Directory of State Court Clerks & County Courthouses (Year). (US ISSN 1042-4172) **4059**, 2619
Directory of State Education Agencies. (US) **1625**
Directory of Statisticians. (US ISSN 0278-405X) **4570**
Directory of Steel Foundries in the United States, Canada and Mexico. (US ISSN 0070-6426) **1132**, 3405
†Directory of Sudden Infant Death Syndrome Programs and Resources. (US) **5181**
Directory of Suicide Prevention and Crisis Intervention Centers. (US) **4019**, 3335
Directory of Summer Jobs Abroad. (UK ISSN 0308-7123) **1132**, 3626
Directory of Summer Jobs in Britain. (UK ISSN 0143-3490) **1132**, 3626
Directory of Summer Law Programs *see* Student Guide to Summer Law Study Programs **2683**
Directory of Supermarket, Grocery & Convenience Store Chains (Year). (US ISSN 0196-1845) **1132**, 2091
Directory of Taiwan. (CH) **399**
(Year) Directory of Taiwan's Leading Exporters. (CH) **1132**
Directory of Technical and Further Education. (UK ISSN 0309-5290) **1132**, 3626
Directory of Technical and Scientific Directories. (UK) **4307**
Directory of Technology. (NZ ISSN 0112-9058) **1885**
Directory of Tennessee Municipal Officials. (US) **4059**
Directory of Testing Laboratories. (US ISSN 0895-7886) **3843**
Directory of Texas Manufacturers. (US ISSN 0070-6450) **1132**
Directory of Texas Wholesalers. (US) **1132**
Directory of the Arts. (CN ISSN 0832-865X) **324**, 4632
Directory of the Australian Gas Industry *see* The Australian Gas Industry Directory (Year) **3682**
Directory of the Canadian Horse Industry. (CN ISSN 0831-5183) **4533**
Directory of the Canning, Freezing, Preserving Industries. (US) **1132**, 2066
Directory of the College Student Press in America *see* College Media Directory **397**
Directory of the Cultural Organizations of the Republic of China. (CH ISSN 0419-3733) **1676**, 10
Directory of the Forest Products Industry. (US ISSN 0070-6477) **1132**, 2114
Directory of the French Nuclear Industry. (FR ISSN 0066-2593) **1804**, 1818
Directory of the Japanese Publishing Industry. (JA) **4126**, 31
Directory of the Mutual Savings Banks of the United States *see* National Council of Savings Institutions Directory **792**
Directory of the National Productivity Organizations in A P O Member Countries. (JA) **1074**, 928
Directory of the Periodicals in the United Arab Emirates. *see* Dalil ad-Dawriat li-Dawlat al-Imarat al-Arabiyyah al-Muttahidah **398**
Directory of the Refractories Industry (Year). (US) **1132**
Directory of the Scientists, Technologists, and Engineers of the P C S I R. (Pakistan Council of Scientific and Industrial Research) (PK) **4307**, 1133, 1818, 4596
†Directory of the Solar Industry. (US) **5181**

DIRECTORY

Directory of the Spanish Cotton-System Textile Enterprises/Directorio Empresas Textiles de Proceso Algodonero/Directori Empreses Textils de Proces Cotoner/Directoire Enterprises Textiles de Processus Cotonnier. (SP) **4618**, 1133
Directory of the Stainless Steel Industry *see* Stainless Steel Directory **3420**
Directory of the Turf *see* The Turf Directory **4538**
Directory of the World's Largest Service Companies. (US ISSN 1014-8507) **944**
Directory of Theme & Amusement Parks. (US) **4760**
Directory of Top Computer Executives. (US ISSN 0193-9920) **1425**
Directory of Trade and Professional Associations in Metropolitan Toronto *see* Directory of Trade and Professional Associations in the Toronto Region **1133**
Directory of Trade and Professional Associations in the Toronto Region. (CN) **1133**
Directory of Training. (UK) **1394**, 1008
▼The Directory of Training Programmes. (AT ISSN 1036-5125) **1008**
†Directory of Travel Information Sources for the Pacific Islands. (US) **5181**
Directory of Trust Institutions. (US) **776**
Directory of Trust Institutions of United States and Canada *see* Directory of Trust Institutions **776**
Directory of U.K. Subsidiaries and Affiliates in Australia *see* Australian British Business Directory **5143**
Directory of U.S. Based Agencies Involved in International Health Assistance. (US) **3094**, 3801
Directory of U.S. Government Software for Mainframes and Microcomputers. (US) **1133**, 1425
Directory of U.S. Labor Organizations (Year). (US ISSN 0734-6786) **2582**
Directory of U.S. Mail Drops. (US) **1352**
Directory of U.S. Subsidiaries of British Companies. (US) **814**, 1133
Directory of U K Fluid Power Distributors. (UK) **1133**, 1597
Directory of U S and Canadian Scrap Plastics Processors and Buyers. (US) **3862**, 1947, 3648
Directory of U S Utility Gas Turbine and Combined Cycle Power Plants. (US) **1801**
Directory of Undergraduate Political Science Faculty (Year). (US) **3891**, 1625
Directory of Unit Trusts *see* Unit Trust Yearbook **802**
Directory of United States Exporters. (US) **905**, 1133
Directory of United States Importers. (US ISSN 0070-6531) **905**, 1133
Directory of United States Standardization Activities *see* Standards Activities of Organizations in the U S **3449**
Directory of Unpublished Experimental Mental Measures. (US ISSN 0731-8081) **4019**, 4433
Directory of V A Rs *see* Directory of Value Added Resellers (Year) **1133**
Directory of Value Added Resellers (Year). (US ISSN 0884-8300) **1133**
Directory of Veterans Organizations. (US) **3457**
▼Directory of Video Retailers. (US) **1133**, 1385
Directory of Visiting Fulbright Scholars and Occasional Lecturers. (US) **1721**
Directory of Water Resources Expertise *see* California Directory of Water Resources Expertise **4822**
†Directory of Westchester Libraries and Media Centers Including Buyers' Guide. (US) **5181**
Directory of Wire Companies of North America. (US) **1133**

Directory of Women in Business, Professions & Management. (AT ISSN 0817-587X) **1133**, 3626, 4840
Directory of Women's & Children's Wear Specialty Stores (Year). (US ISSN 0277-9617) **1133**, 1284
Directory of Wool, Hosiery and Fabrics. (II) **4618**, 1133
Directory of World Chemical Producers (Year). (US ISSN 0196-0555) **1176**, 1133
Directory of World Jewish Press and Publications. (IS) **4126**, 1999
Directory of World Leaders & Factbook (Year). (US ISSN 1043-2043) **905**, 3955
Directory: Organizations of the United Nations System in the United Republic of Tanzania. (UN) **929**
†Directory Publishers Buyers Guide. (US) **5181**
Directory - Technical Association of the Pulp and Paper Industry *see* Technical Association of the Pulp and Paper Industry. Directory **3666**
Directory to the Furnishing Trade. (UK ISSN 0070-6604) **2558**
Directory World. (US) **1133**
Direito Administrativo. (PO) **2619**
Direito & Justica. (BL) **2619**
Direkt Effekt *see* Adjo Direct **1032**
Direkt-Kontakt Betriebsbedarf. (GW) **1037**, 31
Direkt Marketing *see* Adjo Direct **1032**
Direkte Aktion. (GW) **860**, 2582
Direkte Bundessteuer - Statistik der Veranlagungsperiode (Year)/Impot Federal Direct - Statistique de la Periode de Taxation (Year). (SZ) **713**
Direkte Bundessteuer, Steuerertraege und Kopfquoten der Veranlagungsperiode/Impot Federal Direct, Rendement et Cotes par Tete de la Periode de Taxation. (SZ) **713**
Direktor. (YU ISSN 0419-3903) **1008**
Direktorium fuer das Bistum Muenster. (GW) **4174**
Dires. (FR ISSN 0766-5350) **4019**
Diretorio Brasileiro da Industria Farmaceutica. (BL ISSN 0070-6612) **3722**
Direttore Commerciale. (IT ISSN 0012-3323) **1037**
Direzione e Scuola *see* Dirigenti Scuola **1726**
Dirigeant. (FR ISSN 0294-8281) **3891**
Dirigente Construtor. (BL ISSN 0012-3358) **616**
Dirigente d'Azienda. (IT) **1008**
Dirigente E.N.E.L. (Ente Nazionale per l'Energia Elettrica (ENEL)) (IT) **1785**
Dirigente Industrial. (BL ISSN 0012-3366) **1008**
Dirigente Municipal. (BL ISSN 0419-3911) **4087**
Dirigente Rural. (BL ISSN 0012-3374) **161**
Dirigenti Aziende Industriali. (IT) **1008**
Dirigenti Industria. (IT) **1008**
Dirigenti Scuola. (IT ISSN 0392-2812) **1726**
Dirigo Me *see* Me **335**
Diritto Aereo. (IT ISSN 0012-3390) **2619**, 51
Diritto del Commercio Internazionale. (IT) **905**, 2619
Diritto del Lavoro. (IT ISSN 0012-3404) **2619**
▼Diritto dell'Agricoltura. (IT) **87**, 2619
†Diritto dell'Impresa (Naples, 1987). (IT) **5181**
Diritto dell'Informazione e dell'Informatica. (IT) **2755**, 2619
Diritto della Banca e del Mercato Finanziario. (IT) **776**
Diritto delle Radiodiffusioni e delle Telecomunicazioni. (IT ISSN 0012-3412) **2619**, 1355, 1372
▼Diritto delle Relazioni Industriali. (IT) **976**, 2619
Diritto di Autore. (IT ISSN 0012-3420) **3674**, 2619
Diritto di Famiglia e delle Persone. (IT) **2619**

Diritto e Giurisprudenza. (IT ISSN 0012-3439) **2619**
Diritto e Practica dell'Aviazione Civile. (IT) **4672**, 2619
Diritto e Pratica nell'Assicurazione. (IT ISSN 0417-6766) **2619**, 2530
Diritto e Pratica Tributaria. (IT ISSN 0012-3447) **2619**
Diritto e Societa (Naples). (IT ISSN 0390-8542) **2619**
Diritto e Societa (Padua). (IT) **2619**
Diritto Ecclesiastico e Rassegna di Diritto Matrimoniale. (IT) **4174**
Diritto ed Economia. (IT) **2619**, 659
Diritto Europeo dei Trasporti. *see* European Transport Law **4649**
Diritto Fallimentare e delle Societa Commerciali. (IT) **2619**
Diritto Marittimo. (IT ISSN 0012-348X) **2619**, 4726
Diritto Processuale Amministrativo. (IT) **2619**
Dirksen Congressional Center. Report *see* Congress **4057**
†Dirsmith Group. Publication. (US) **5181**
▼Dirt. (US) **1253**
Dirt Bike. (US ISSN 0364-1546) **4517**
Dirt Bike Crash and Burn. (US) **4517**
Dirt Rider Magazine. (US ISSN 0735-4355) **4518**
Dirt Wheels. (US) **4518**
†Dirty Bum: A Magazine. (US ISSN 0894-9573) **5181**
Dir'u al-Islam. (TS) **4218**, 3457
Dir'u al-Watan. (TS) **3457**
Dirva. (US) **1999**
†Dis - Ability Law Briefs. (US ISSN 1042-2099) **5181**
Di's Meet People. (US) **4362**
Disabilities Regulation News. (US) **3094**, 2620
Disability Aids Directory. (AT ISSN 0812-4663) **4404**
Disability and Rehabilitation. (UK ISSN 0963-8288) **3094**
Disability, Handicap & Society. (UK ISSN 0267-4645) **4434**
Disability Income and Health Insurance. (US ISSN 0742-5619) **2530**
Disability Issues. (US) **2292**, 2287, 4404
Disability Now. (UK) **2290**
Disability Rag. (US ISSN 0749-8586) **2283**, 976, 3941
Disabled American Veterans Magazine *see* D A V Magazine **3454**
Disabled Driver. (UK) **4689**
Disabled Outdoors Magazine. (US) **4545**, 2283
Disarmament. (UN ISSN 0251-9518) **3457**
Disarmament Forum. (FI) **3457**
Disarmament Newsletter. (UN ISSN 0257-1897) **3891**
Disarmament Times. (UN ISSN 0259-3629) **3891**
Disaster Management. (II ISSN 0255-5018) **1273**, 4100
Disaster Management. (UK) **4100**
Disaster Prevention/Bosai. (JA ISSN 0006-7873) **4100**
Disasters. (UK ISSN 0361-3666) **1588**, 3435
Disc Collector. (US ISSN 0731-843X) **3549**, 4460
▼Disc Golf Journal. (US ISSN 1055-4785) **4503**
Disc Golf World News. (US ISSN 0892-2357) **4545**
▼Disc Magazine. (US ISSN 1052-4053) **2797**
†Disc Sports. (US) **5181**
Discerning Traveler. (US) **4760**
Discharge Planning Update. (US ISSN 0276-4652) **2461**
Discharges and Electrical Insulation in Vacuum *see* International Symposium on Discharges and Electrical Insulation in Vacuum. Proceedings **1900**
Discinform. (DK ISSN 0107-9042) **4470**
Disciple (St. Louis). (US ISSN 0092-8372) **4174**
Discipleship Journal. (US ISSN 0273-5865) **4236**
Discipleship Training. (US) **4236**

Discipliana. (US ISSN 0732-9881) **4236**
Disciplina del Commercio. (IT) **835**
Discipline. (US) **1625**
Discipline and Grievances. (US ISSN 0012-351X) **976**
Discipline and Grievances for Supervisors in Local, State and Federal Government. (US) **976**, 2620, 4087
Disclosure. (US ISSN 0196-8203) **1504**
Disclosure Database Review. (US) **826**
Disclosure Online News *see* Disclosure Database Review **826**
Disclosure Record. (US ISSN 0094-2561) **944**
Disclosure - Worldscope Company Profiles. (US) **944**
Disclosures. (US) **750**
Disco & Dancing. (IT) **1530**, 3549
Discographical Forum. (UK ISSN 0012-3544) **3549**
Discographies. (US ISSN 0192-334X) **4460**
Discography Series. (US ISSN 0095-8115) **3549**
Discoteca Alta Fedelta *see* Discoteca Hi Fi **3549**
Discoteca Hi Fi. (IT) **3549**
Discount Merchandiser. (US ISSN 0012-3579) **1038**
Discount Store News. (US ISSN 0012-3587) **1038**
Discountbutikker *see* Supermarkeder og Andre Store Dagligvarebutikker (Year) **1118**
▼Discounting Practice in the Computer Industry. (US) **1450**, 1038
Discourse. (US ISSN 0730-1081) **1335**, 2506
Discourse. (AT ISSN 0159-6306) **1705**
Discourse. (II ISSN 0253-519X) **4282**
Discourse Analysis Monographs. (UK ISSN 0307-1006) **2811**
▼Discourse & Society. (UK ISSN 0957-9265) **4019**, 4434
Discourse Processes. (US ISSN 0163-853X) **2811**
Discourse Units in Human Communication for Librarians. (US ISSN 0070-6663) **2755**
Discover (Burbank). (US ISSN 0274-7529) **4308**, 4596
Discover (Palo Alto). (US) **4760**
Discover Bulgaria. (BU ISSN 0204-8418) **4760**
Discover Costa Rica. (US) **4760**
▼Discover Ecuador. (US) **4760**
Discover Guatemala. (US) **4760**
Discover Hawaii *see* Discover Hawaii Sales Planner **4760**
Discover Hawaii Sales Planner. (US) **4760**, 835
▼Discover Honduras. (US) **4760**
Discover K C *see* Discover Mid-America **2404**
Discover Mid-America. (US) **2404**
Discover North America. (UK ISSN 0951-8126) **4760**
Discover North America Travel Industry Directory. (UK ISSN 0951-8134) **1133**, 4760
Discover the Bible. (CN ISSN 0018-912X) **4263**
†Discover the Far East. (UK) **5181**
Discover the Platinum Coast. (US) **4760**
†Discoveries (Kansas City). (US) **5181**
Discoveries (Port Townsend). (US ISSN 0896-8322) **3549**, 257
Discoveries in Pharmacology. (NE) **3722**
Discoveries in the Judaean Desert of Jordan. (US ISSN 0070-668X) **270**
Discovery *see* Checkpoint **4232**
Discovery. (CN ISSN 0319-8480) **4308**, 437, 1487
Discovery. (HK) **4760**
Discovery (Birmingham). (US ISSN 0162-198X) **4236**
Discovery (Chicago). (US ISSN 0012-3641) **4760**, 4689
Discovery (New Haven). (US ISSN 0012-3625) **4308**, 238
Discovery (New York). (US) **1253**, 4174

Discovery (Richmond). (US ISSN 0300-7316) **2309**, 298, 1487
Discovery Crew Science Club News. (US) **1253**, 4308
†Discovery Five Hundred. (US ISSN 0899-8329) **5181**
Discovery Guide to Cairo. (UK) **4760**
Discovery Guide to Egypt. (UK) **4760**
Discovery in Illinois. (US) **2620**
▼Discovery Proceedings in Federal Practice, 2-E. (US) **2620**
Discovery Through Art *see* Art Education **1616**
Discovery Y M C A. (US ISSN 8755-965X) **4404**, 1236, 4503
Discrepancias. (AG) **2620**
Discret. (GW ISSN 0724-6978) **3549**
Discrete and Computational Geometry. (US ISSN 0179-5376) **3034**, 1394
Discrete Applied Mathematics. (NE ISSN 0166-218X) **3034**
▼Discrete Ephemera. (US) **324**, 2992
▼Discrete Event Dynamic Systems: Theory & Applications. (NE ISSN 0924-6703) **1435**
Discrete Mathematics. (NE ISSN 0012-365X) **3034**
▼Discrete Mathematics and Applications. (English translation of: Diskretnaya Matematika) (NE ISSN 0924-9265) **3034**
Discrete Semiconductors Direct Alternate Sources & Replacements. (US ISSN 1043-6367) **1765**
Discrete-Stats: Forecasts, Analysis & Trends. (US) **713**, 860
Discretio. (IT ISSN 0012-3668) **2864**, 2506
Disc'ribe. (US) **3549**
Discurso. (PY) **2912**
Discurso Literario *see* Discurso **2912**
Discurso y Realidad. (AG ISSN 0327-2214) **3765**
Discussion Papers in the African Humanities. (US) **2506**, 2332
Discussione. (IT ISSN 0416-0371) **3891**
Discussions in Environmental Health Planning. (US) **1947**, 2486
Discussions in Neuroscience. (NE ISSN 0254-8852) **3335**
Discussions on Teaching. (US ISSN 0277-2736) **1625**
Disease-a-Month *see* D M **3092**
Disease Information. (FR ISSN 1012-5329) **4809**
Disease Markers. (UK ISSN 0278-0240) **3196**
Diseases of Aquatic Organisms. (GW ISSN 0177-5103) **581**, 530, 551
Diseases of the Colon and Rectum. (US ISSN 0012-3706) **3378**
Diseases of the Esophagus. (IT) **3094**, 3378
Diseases of the Skin. (SA) **3247**
Disegnare e Dipingere. (Italian translation of: Artist's Magazine) (IT) **324**
Disiji Yanjiu/Quaternaria Sinica. (CC ISSN 1001-7410) **1559**
Disinfection and Sterilization *see* Zhongguo Xiaoduxue Zazhi **3164**
Disinfestazione. (IT) **4100**
Disk Operating System International *see* D O S International **1468**
Disk - Trend Report. (US) **1433**
Diskette Gazette. (US) **1460**
Diskretnaya Matematika. (RU ISSN 0234-0860) **3034**
Diskurs. (GW) **4404**
Diskus. (GW ISSN 0012-3730) **1253**
Diskus Brief. (GW) **2039**
Diskussion Deutsch. (GW ISSN 0342-1589) **2811**, 1748
Dislocations in Solids. (NE) **3817**, 1210
Dismantler. (CN ISSN 0711-3765) **3457**, 3955
Dismantlers Digest *see* Automotive Recycling **4683**
Dismoda. (SP) **4718**
▼Disney Adventures. (US) **1253**
Disney Channel Magazine. (US) **1372**
▼Disney Fan. (JA) **4760**
Disney News. (US) **2738**
Disneyland (Year). (US) **4760**
†Disneyland Annual. (UK) **5181**

†Disney's Duck Tales. (US) **5181**
Disorders of Human Communication. (US ISSN 0173-170X) **1335**
†Dispatch/Depeche. (CN) **5181**
Dispatch (Des Moines). (US) **1625**
Dispatch (Springfield). (US ISSN 0419-4187) **2404**
▼Dispatch (Washington). (US) **3955**
Dispatcher (Columbus). (US) **1885**
Dispatcher (San Francisco, 1942). (US ISSN 0012-3765) **2582**
Dispatcher (San Francisco, 1953). (US) **3751**
Display. (DK ISSN 0107-7481) **1426**
Display & Design Ideas. (US ISSN 1049-9172) **2551**
Display and Imaging *see* Molecular Crystals and Liquid Crystals Science and Technology. Section D: Display and Imaging **3855**
Display and Imaging Technology *see* Molecular Crystals and Liquid Crystals Science and Technology. Section D: Display and Imaging **3855**
Display Producers and Screen Printers Association. Monthly *see* S P A News **4005**
Displays. (UK ISSN 0141-9382) **1421**, 1453
Disposables and Nonwovens. (UK ISSN 0012-3811) **4618**
Disposiciones Generales. (SP ISSN 0214-4131) **4059**
Disposito - Teoria, Discursu, Produccion *see* Revista Americana de Estudios Semioticos y Culturales **2837**
Dispute Resolution. (US ISSN 0271-2709) **2620**
Dispute Resolution Program Directory (Year). (US ISSN 0731-4833) **2620**
Disquisitiones Mathematicae Hungaricae. (HU ISSN 0070-671X) **3034**
Dissent (New York). (US ISSN 0012-3846) **3891**
Dissertation Abstracts. (US) **2519**, 4355
Dissertation Abstracts International. Section A: Humanities and Social Sciences. (US ISSN 0419-4209) **2520**, 4394
Dissertation Abstracts International. Section B: Physical Sciences and Engineering. (US ISSN 0419-4217) **4355**, 10, 4614
Dissertation Abstracts International. Section C: European Abstracts *see* Dissertation Abstracts International. Section C: Worldwide **399**
Dissertation Abstracts International. Section C: Worldwide. (US ISSN 1042-7279) **399**, 2520, 2520, 2520, 4355
†Dissertationes Archaeologicae Gandenses. (BE ISSN 0419-4241) **5181**
Dissertationes Botanicae. (GW ISSN 0070-6728) **501**
Dissertationes Mathematicae/Rozprawy Matematyczne. (PL ISSN 0012-3862) **3034**
Dissertationes Orientales. (CS) **3637**
Dissertationes Pharmaceuticae et Pharmacologicae *see* Polish Journal of Pharmacology and Pharmacy **3740**
Dissolution of Marriage. (US) **2717**
Distance (Paris). (FR) **2186**
Distance Education. (AT ISSN 0158-7919) **1625**
Distillers Feed Conference. Proceedings.(US) **380**, 176
▼Distinctions. (US) **776**, 1504, 2272
Distinguished Home Plans. (US ISSN 0897-6236) **616**
Distinguished Home Plans and Products *see* Distinguished Home Plans & Products - Custom Home Plans Guide **616**
Distinguished Home Plans & Products - Custom Home Plans Guide. (US) **616**, 298
Distressed Property Investor's Monthly. (US ISSN 1048-2938) **4148**, 944

Distressed Real Estate Law Alert. (US ISSN 0892-4198) **2620**, 4148
Distribucion Actualidad. (SP) **1038**
Distributed Computing. (GW ISSN 0178-2770) **1394**
Distributed Language Translation. (US) **2856**, 2811
†Distributed Processing Product Reports. (US) **5181**
Distributed Processing Report *see* Distributed Processing Product Reports **5181**
Distributie Vandaag *see* Distribution d'Aujourd'Hui **1038**
Distribution. (GW) **1038**
Distribution. *see* Al-Tawzi **3702**
Distribution. (UK ISSN 0954-2094) **4649**
Distribution Center Management. (US ISSN 0894-7651) **1038**, 1008
Distribution Contractors Association News *see* D C A News **3684**
Distribution d'Aujourd'Hui. (BE ISSN 0012-3935) **1038**
Distribution Maps of Pests. (UK ISSN 0952-634X) **87**, 530
Distribution of Dentists in the U S. (US) **3232**
Distribution of High School Graduates and College Going Rate, New York State. (US ISSN 0077-9210) **1625**
Distribution of Personal Wealth. Regional Data. *see* Netherlands. Centraal Bureau voor de Statistiek. Vermogensverdeling. Regionale Gegevens **731**
Distributique. (FR) **1394**
Distributique Europe. (FR ISSN 1146-6456) **1460**, 1477
Distributive Education Clubs of America Dimensions *see* D E C A Dimensions **1037**
Distributive Trades Survey *see* C B I Financial Times Distributive Trades Survey **1035**
Distributive Worker. (US ISSN 0012-3986) **977**
Distributor. (US ISSN 0898-1213) **2298**
Distributor Manufacturer News B B S I Convention Preview. (US) **1074**
Distributor's & Wholesaler's Advisor. (US) **1038**, 1008
Distributor's Link. (US) **659**
Distribuzione Organizzata. (IT) **835**
District Bank Review *see* National Westminster Bank Quarterly Review **792**
District Council Journal. (US ISSN 0748-1179) **4059**
District Council Technical Association Di C T A Journal *see* Di C T A Journal **615**
District Court Act and Rules: New South Wales *see* District Court Procedure (N.S.W.) **2620**
District Court Practice. (AT) **2620**
District Court Procedure (N.S.W.). (AT) **2620**
District Heating *see* District Heating and Cooling **2298**
District Heating. *see* Fernwaerme International **2299**
District Heating and Cooling. (US) **2298**
District Mail/Distrikspos. (SA ISSN 0012-4028) **2216**
District Memoir. (MY ISSN 0126-9046) **1559**, 1176, 3657
District News. (CN) **2177**
District of Columbia. Air Monitoring Division. Annual Report on the Quality of the Air in Washington, D.C. *see* District of Columbia. Air Monitoring Section. Annual Report on the Quality of the Air in Washington, D.C **5181**
†District of Columbia. Air Monitoring Section. Annual Report on the Quality of the Air in Washington, D.C. (US) **5181**
District of Columbia Bar. Bar Report. (US) **2620**
District of Columbia Dental Society. Newsletter. (US) **3232**
Distrikspos. *see* District Mail **2216**
Distrofia Muscolare. (IT ISSN 0012-4087) **3094**

Disturbios de Comunicacao. (BL) **1335**
Dit Laegemagasin. (DK) **3801**
Ditchley Conference Reports. (UK ISSN 0263-3221) **4370**, 2620
Ditchley Journal *see* Ditchley Newsletter **4370**
Ditchley Newsletter. (UK ISSN 0262-8015) **4370**, 2620
Diteru. *see* Detail **298**
Dithmarschen. (GW ISSN 0012-4125) **2309**, 2053
Ditmas Park West Newsletter. (US) **2224**
Dits et Vecus Populaires. (FR) **1625**
Divadelni a Filmove Noviny *see* Divadelni Noviny **4632**
Divadelni Noviny. (CS ISSN 0012-4141) **4632**
Dive. (CN) **4470**
Dive Boat Calendar & Travel Guide: International Edition. (US) **4524**, 4470
Dive Boat Calendar and Travel Guide: Pacific Coast Edition *see* Dive Boat Calendar & Travel Guide: International Edition **4524**
Dive Rescue Specialist *see* Searchlines **4112**
▼Dive Training. (US) **4471**
Diver. (NE) **2912**
Diver. (UK) **4471**
Diver. (US ISSN 0273-8589) **4471**
Diver Magazine. (CN ISSN 0706-5132) **4471**, 2435, 4760
Diversion (New York). (US) **4471**, 3094
Diversion (Tappan). (US) **4760**
Diversions. (US) **3396**
Diversity. (US ISSN 0744-8163) **501**, 541
Dividend Record (Daily) *see* Standard & Poor's Dividend Record (Daily) **964**
Dividend Record (Quarterly) *see* Standard & Poor's Dividend Record (Quarterly) **964**
Dividend Record (Weekly) *see* Standard & Poor's Dividend Record (Weekly) **964**
Dividends from Wood Research. (US) **2112**, 399
Divine Kingdom: Christian Esperanto Magazine. *see* Dia Regno **4174**
Divine Life. (II ISSN 0012-4206) **4217**
Divine Slave Gita. (US ISSN 0733-5369) **4282**
Divine Voice. *see* Divya Vani **4217**
Diving Down Under. (AT) **4471**
†Diving World (Van Nuys). (US) **5181**
Divinitas. (VC ISSN 0012-4222) **4263**
Divisie vir Pad- en Vertoertegnologie. *see* South Africa. Division of Roads and Transport Technology. Annual Report **5279**
Divisie vir Pad- en Vervoertegnologie. *see* South Africa. Division of Roads and Transport Technology. Transport Statistics **4667**
Divisie vir Pad- en Vervoertegnologie. Gebruikershandboeke en Rekenaarprogramme. *see* South Africa. Division of Roads and Transport Technology. User Manuals and Computer Programs **4707**
Division d'Aide et de Cooperation Francaise. Bulletin Trimestriel de Statistique. (CX) **713**
Division Interdisciplinar para la Familia *see* Instituto de Ciencias para la Familia **2635**
Divitiae Musicae Artis. Series A. (NE) **3549**
Divorce Chats. (US ISSN 0012-4230) **4434**, 2620
†Divorce Ministry Newsletter. (US) **5181**
Divorce Tax Planning Strategies. (US) **1092**
Divorce Taxation. (US) **1092**
Divrei ha-Akademia ha-Leumit ha-Yisraelit Lemadaim. (IS ISSN 0334-2816) **2506**, 2912, 3765
Divrei ha-Akademia ha-Leumit ha-Yisraelit Lemadaim-ha-Hativa le-Madaei ha-Teva. (IS) **4308**, 581, 1559, 3034
Divulga. (VE) **4308**
Divulgacao. (AO) **1074**

DIVULGACION

Divulgacion. (MX ISSN 0188-3984) **324**
Divulgacion Juridica. (CU) **2620**
Divulgacion Legislativa. (CU) **2620**
Divulgaciones Etnologicas. (CK) **238**
Divus Thomas. (IT ISSN 0012-4257) **4174**, 3765
Divya Vani/Divine Voice. (II ISSN 0012-4265) **4217**
Diwan al-Tadween al-Qanouni. Nashrat. *see* Adala **5130**
Diwen Wuli Xuebao. (CC ISSN 1000-3258) **3840**
Dix-Huitieme Siecle. (FR ISSN 0070-6760) **2506**
Dix-Septieme Siecle. (FR ISSN 0012-4273) **2912**
Dixie Contractor. (US ISSN 0012-4281) **616**
Dixie Gun Works Blackpowder Annual. (US) **4545**
†Dixie Gun Works Muzzleloaders' Annual. (US ISSN 0146-6143) **5181**
Dixie Logger and Lumberman *see* Logger and Lumberman **2116**
Dixie Trucker *see* Fastline for Dixie Truckers **4744**
Dixon & McVeagh's Road Traffic Law. (NZ) **2620**, 4718
Dixson Library Report. (AT ISSN 0728-6481) **2755**
Al-Diya' (TS) **4218**
Diya Dianqi. (CC ISSN 1001-5531) **1886**
Dizhen/Journal of Seismology. (CC ISSN 1000-3274) **1588**
Dizhen Dici Guance yu Yanjiu/Observation and Study of Earthquakes and Geomagnetism. (CC) **1588**
Dizhen Dizhi/Seismology and Geology. (CC ISSN 0253-4967) **1588**, 1559
Dizhen Dizhi Yicong/Translated Literature on Seismology and Geology. (CC) **1588**
Dizhen Gongcheng yu Gongcheng Zhendong/Earthquake Engineering and Engineering Vibration. (CC ISSN 1000-1301) **1588**, 1818
Dizhen Wenzhai/Seismology Abstracts. (CC) **1550**, 10, 1559
Dizhen Xuebao. (CC ISSN 0253-3782) **1588**
Dizhi Keji Dongtai/Geology Science and Technology Development. (CC) **1559**
Dizhi Keji Guanli/Scientific and Technological Management in Geological Exploration. (CC) **1008**, 1559
Dizhi Kexue/Scientia Geologica Sinica. (CC ISSN 0563-5020) **1559**
Dizhi Lun-Ping/Geological Review. (CC) **1559**
Dizhi Xuebao. (CC ISSN 0001-5717) **1559**
Dizhi Zhaokuang Luncong. (CC ISSN 1001-1412) **1559**
Dizionario Bibliografico delle Riviste Giuridiche Italiane. (IT ISSN 0419-4632) **2698**
Dizionario Enciclopedico d'Informazioni. (IT) **1780**
Al-Djeich. (AE) **3457**, 3891
Djeliba. (IV) **4174**
Djezair. (AE ISSN 0012-4311) **4760**
Al-Djeza'iriyyah. (AE) **4840**
Djibouti. Direction Nationale de la Statistique. Bulletin de Statistique et de Documentation. (FT) **4080**, 4570
Djibouti. Service de Statistique et de Documentation. Bulletin de Statistique et de Documentation *see* Djibouti. Direction Nationale de la Statistique. Bulletin de Statistique et de Documentation **4080**
Djurens Raett. (SW ISSN 0345-2409) **231**
Djurfront *see* Djurens Raett **231**
Djurskyddet *see* Djurtidningen Djurskyddet **231**
Djurtidningen Djurskyddet. (SW) **231**
Dnipro. (KR ISSN 0012-4354) **2864**
Do It Yourself (Croydon). (UK ISSN 0012-4370) **2501**

Do-It-Yourself (Hampton). (UK) **2501**, 3396
Do-It-Yourself Report. (UK ISSN 0263-5437) **2501**, 1038
Do-it-Yourself Retailing. (US) **641**, 2501
Do-It-Yourself Week *see* D I Y Week **641**
Do Kyaung Tha. (BR) **2220**
Do Re Mi *see* Doremi **1253**
▼Do Vostrebovaniya. (LV) **2209**
Doane's Agricultural Report. (US ISSN 0093-5271) **87**
DobEdition. (US ISSN 1046-1043) **3710**
Doberman World. (US) **3710**
The Dobie Connection. (US) **418**
Doboku Gakkai Nenji Koenkai Koen Gaiyoshu/Japan Society of Civil Engineers. Proceedings of the Annual Conference. (JA) **1864**
Doboku Gakkai Ronbunshu/Japan Society of Civil Engineers. Proceedings. (JA ISSN 0289-7806) **1864**
Doboku Gakkaishi. *see* Japan Society of Civil Engineers. Journal **1868**
Doboku Keikakugaku Shinpojumu/Symposium on Civil Engineering Planning. Proceedings. (JA) **1864**
Dobro Pozhalovat v Chekhoslovakiyu *see* Welcome to Czechoslovakia **4796**
Dobrudschabote. (GW) **238**
Doc; Documentazione *see* Doc Italia **1705**
Doc Italia. (IT) **1705**
Docencia Postsecundaria. (MX ISSN 0185-3597) **1705**
Docete. (IT) **1625**
Doch! *see* Unterwegs (Leverkusen) **1269**
Dock and Harbour Authority. (UK ISSN 0012-4419) **4726**
Docket Call (Richmond). (US) **2620**
Ad-Doctor. (UA ISSN 0012-4435) **3094**
Doctor. (UK ISSN 0046-0451) **3094**
Doctor. (JA) **3094**
Doctor Jazz Magazine. (NE ISSN 0166-2309) **3549**
Doctor of Osteopath *see* D.O **3214**
Doctor of Veterinary Medicine Management *see* D V M Management **4808**
Doctor Who Magazine. (UK ISSN 0957-9818) **1372**, 4632
Doctoral Dissertations on Asia. (US ISSN 0098-4485) **3646**
†Doctoral Programs in Nursing. (US) **5181**
Doctors for Disaster Preparedness Newsletter. (US) **3094**, 1273
Doctor's Office. (US ISSN 0733-2262) **3094**
▼Doctors' Orders. (US) **3247**
Doctor's People. (US) **3214**
Doctor's Review. (CN ISSN 0821-5758) **4760**, 3094
Doctor's Shopper. (US) **3094**
Doctrine and Life. (IE ISSN 0012-446X) **4263**
Doctrine Juridique Belge. (BE) **2620**
Document Assembly User Group News. (US) **2705**, 1477
Document Concernant le Releve Statistique Scolaire. *see* Dokumentation zu Schulstatistischen Erhebungen **1726**
Document Image Automation. (US ISSN 1054-9692) **2755**, 1372
Document Image Automation Update. (US ISSN 1054-9706) **1372**, 2755
Document Image Processing *see* O M N I **1385**
†Document Management. (US) **5181**
Document Survie *see* Planete Survie **2187**
Documenta. (BL) **1625**
Documenta. (SW ISSN 0347-5719) **4308**
Documenta Chopiniana. (PL) **3549**
Documenta et Monumenta Orientis Antiqui. (NE ISSN 0169-7943) **2429**
Documenta Musicae Novae. (BE) **3549**
Documenta Ophthalmologica. (NE ISSN 0012-4486) **3300**

Documenta Ophthalmologica Proceedings Series. (NE) **3300**
Documenta Romaniae Historica. Serie A: La Moldavie. (RM ISSN 0070-6825) **2358**
Documenta Romaniae Historica. Serie B: La Valachie. (RM ISSN 0070-6833) **2359**
Documentacao Amazonica. (BL ISSN 0101-4854) **399**
Documentacao de Estudos em Linguistica Teorica e Aplicada. (BL ISSN 0102-4450) **2811**
Documentacion Administrativa. (SP ISSN 0012-4494) **4059**
†Documentacion Bibliotecologica. (AG ISSN 0070-6841) **5181**
Documentacion Cervantina. (US) **2912**
Documentacion de la Seguridad Social Americana. (SZ ISSN 0250-6041) **2530**
Documentacion Iberoamericana. (SP ISSN 0584-7109) **3955**
Documentacion Internacional. (UY) **2722**
Documentacion Latinoamericana. *see* Dokumentationsdienst Lateinamerika **399**
Documentacion Social. (SP) **4370**
Documentaco e Direito Comparado. (PO) **3891**, 3941
Documentaliste - Sciences de l'Information. (FR ISSN 0012-4508) **2755**
Documentary Editing. (US ISSN 0196-7134) **2506**, 2404
Documentary Reference Collections. (US) **2309**
Documentatie en Informatie over Toerisme *see* D I T **4759**
Documentatie Revue. (NE) **1038**
Documentatieblad: The Abstracts Journal of the African Studies Centre Leiden. (NE ISSN 0166-2694) **4394**, 2981, 3937
Documentatieblad Werkgroep 18e Eeuw. (NE) **2359**
Documentatiegroep 40-45. Maandorgaan *see* Terugblik 40-45 **2392**
Documentation *see* Nationale Maatschappij van Belgische Spoorwegen. Documentatiebulletin **4712**
Documentation Bulletin for South-East Asia. (II) **399**, 830
Documentation Cards. *see* Karty Dokumentacyjne **2794**
Documentation Catholique. (FR ISSN 0012-4613) **4263**
Documentation Commerciale et Comptable. (BE ISSN 0012-4621) **750**
Documentation Danoise *see* Factsheet Denmark **2001**
Documentation et Bibliotheques. (CN ISSN 0315-2340) **2755**
Documentation Europeenne - Serie Agricole. (EI ISSN 0537-6297) **87**
Documentation Europeenne - Serie Syndicale et Ouvriere. (EI) **977**
Documentation in Public Administration.(II) **4080**
Documentation, Information-R A T P *see* Regie Autonome des Transports Parisiens. Bulletin de Documentation et d'Information **4655**
Documentation, Libraries and Archives: Bibliographies and Reference Works. (UN) **2793**
Documentation, Libraries and Archives: Studies and Research. (UN) **2755**
Documentation List: Africa. (II ISSN 0418-582X) **2328**, 10
Documentation Newsletter. (US ISSN 0738-8128) **2755**
Documentation on Asia. (II ISSN 0419-5345) **3937**
Documentation par l'Image. (FR ISSN 0046-0478) **4308**, 1625
Documentation Photographique. (FR ISSN 0419-5361) **3790**
Documentation Politique Internationale. *see* International Political Science Abstracts **3938**
Documentation Rapide du Chef d'Enterprise *see* Bulletin Rapide de Droit des Affaires **1004**

Documentation Services Index. (US) **1133**, 1058
Documentation sur la Recherche Feministe. *see* Resources for Feminist Research **4860**
Documentation - Technique, Scientifique et Commerciale. (FR ISSN 0012-4583) **4355**, 4614
†Documentation Theatrale. (FR) **5181**
†Documentation Touristique: Bibliographie Analytique Internationale. (FR ISSN 0767-2640) **5181**
Documentation Tribology. *see* Dokumentation Tribologie **5182**
Documentazione Europea - Serie Agricola *see* Documentation Europeenne - Serie Agricole **87**
†Documented Survey on Metallurgical Developments. (II) **5181**
Documenti. (IT) **2205**
Documenti dell'Arciere. (IT) **2359**
Documenti della Scuola. (IT) **1236**, 1625
Documenti di Storica Italiana. (IT) **2359**
Documenti di Vita Comunale. (IT ISSN 0012-4737) **4087**
Documenti e Richerche d'Arte Alessandrina. (IT) **270**, 324
Documenti Sulle Arti del Libro. (IT ISSN 0070-6906) **399**
†Documentos. (VE ISSN 0012-4753) **5181**
Documentos de Educacion Cooperativa *see* Tribuna Cooperativa **832**
Documentos de Geohistoria Regional. (AG ISSN 0325-9404) **2404**, 2246
Documentos de Reinado de Fernando VII. (SP) **2359**
Documentos Institucionales Oficiales. (BO) **4434**
Documentos Oficiales de la Organizacion de los Estados Americanos: Lista General Indice Analitico *see* Organization of American States. Official Records. Indice y Lista General **2418**
Documentos Regionales. (PE) **2486**
Documentos Taller Multidisciplinario del Medio Ambiente. (CL) **1947**
Documents. *see* Wenxian **416**
Documents. (FR ISSN 0151-0827) **2328**, 10
Documents d'Actualite Internationale. (FR) **2722**, 3955
Documents d'Esglesia. (SP) **4174**
Documents d'Etudes. (FR) **2620**
Documents d'Histoire de l'Art Canadien. *see* Documents in the History of Canadian Art **5181**
Documents d'Histoire Maghrebine. (FR) **3637**
Documents de Cartographie Ecologique *see* Revue d'Ecologie Alpine **516**
Documents de Linguistique Quantitative.(FR ISSN 0085-4786) **2856**
Documents et Debats. (FR ISSN 0012-477X) **4019**
Documents et Informations Parlementaires. (FR) **3891**
Documents et Recherches sur l'Economie des Pays Byzantins, Islamiques et Slaves et Leurs Relations Commerciales au Moyen Age *see* Documents et Recherches sur le Monde Byzantins, Neohellenique et Balkanique **893**
Documents et Recherches sur le Monde Byzantins, Neohellenique et Balkanique. (FR ISSN 0070-6957) **893**
Documents Historiques des Sciences. (BE) **2359**, 4308
Documents in American Industrial History. (US) **659**, 2404
Documents in Film Studies. (US) **3507**
Documents in Imperial History. (US ISSN 0749-4831) **2309**
†Documents in Socialist History. (UK) **5181**
†Documents in the History of Canadian Art/Documents d'Histoire de l'Art Canadien. (CN ISSN 0383-4514) **5181**
Documents of Modern History. (US) **2309**

†Documents of Revolution. (US) **5181**
Documents Pedozoologiques. (FR ISSN 0180-9555) **176**
Documents Philateliques. (FR) **3751**
Documents pour l'Enseignement Economique et Social. (FR ISSN 0396-8898) **893**
Documents Pour le Medecin du Travail. (FR ISSN 0339-6517) **3616**
Documents sur l'Esperanto. Nouvelle Serie *see* Esperanto-Dokumentoj. Nova Serio **2812**
Documents Tarifaires Transport. (FR) **4649**, 659
Documents to the People. (US ISSN 0091-2085) **2756**
Documents to the People of New York State. (US ISSN 0749-0356) **2756**, 4059
Dodd Diggings. (US ISSN 0736-2854) **2149**
Dodge Assemblies Cost Data. (US) **616**
Dodge Construction News. Chicago Edition. (US ISSN 0012-480X) **616**
Dodge Construction News. Los Angeles Edition. (US) **616**
Dodge Construction Systems Costs *see* Dodge Assemblies Cost Data **616**
Dodge Digest of Building Cost Data *see* Digest of Building Contract Awards **616**
Dodge Digest of Building Costs and Specifications *see* Dodge Square Foot Cost Data **616**
Dodge Heavy Construction Cost Data *see* McMahon Heavy Construction Cost Guide **623**
Dodge Manual for Building Construction Pricing and Scheduling *see* Dodge Unit Cost Data **616**
Dodge Remodelling and Retrofit Cost Data *see* Repair & Remodelling Quarterly **630**
Dodge Square Foot Cost Data. (US) **616**
Dodge Unit Cost Data. (US) **616**
Dod's Parliamentary Companion. (UK ISSN 0070-7007) **3891**
Doeblinger Heimatmuseum *see* Doeblinger Museumsblaetter **2359**
Doeblinger Museumsblaetter. (AU) **2359**
Doedsaarsagerne/Causes of Death in Denmark. (DK ISSN 0108-5646) **3991**, 4117
Doedsaarsagerne i Kongeriget Danmark *see* Doedsaarsagerne **3991**
Doehetzelf. (NE) **2445**, 2125
Der Doemensianer. (GW ISSN 0344-6816) **380**
Doen en Laten - Working Safely *see* Uoorkomen **3622**
Doeveforsorgens Historiske Selskab *see* Doevehistorisk Tidsskrift **2359**
Doevehistorisk Tidsskrift. (DK) **2359**
Doeves Jul. (DK ISSN 0105-7723) **2287**
Doeves Tidsskrift. (NO ISSN 0332-6942) **2287**, 1735
Dofasco Illustrated News. (CN) **3405**
Dog (Marshall). (US ISSN 0194-9756) **3710**
†Dog & Country. (UK ISSN 0268-9502) **5181**
Dog Breeding. (US) **3710**
Dog Fancy. (US ISSN 0892-6522) **3710**
Dog News *see* Dog News and Family Pets **3710**
Dog News and Family Pets. (UK ISSN 0309-1031) **3710**
Dog River Review. (US ISSN 0749-260X) **2992**
Dog Sports. (US ISSN 0194-6706) **3710**, 4471
Dog Watch. (US) **3710**
Dog Watch. (AT) **4726**
†Dog Week. (US) **5182**
Dog World. (UK ISSN 0012-4885) **3710**
Dog World. (US ISSN 0012-4893) **3710**
Dog World Annual. (UK ISSN 0070-7015) **3710**

Doga Bilim Dergisi. Series B: Engineering - Environmental Science *see* Doga Turkish Journal of Engineering and Environmental Science **1819**
Doga Bilim Dergisi. Series D: Veterinary and Animal Sciences *see* Doga Turkish Journal of Veterinary and Animal Sciences **4809**
Doga Turk Biyoloji Dergisi. *see* Doga Turkish Journal of Biology **437**
Doga Turk Botanik Dergisi. *see* Doga Turkish Journal of Botany **501**
Doga Turk Eczacilik Dergisi. *see* Doga Turkish Journal of Pharmacy **3722**
Doga Turk Fizik Dergisi. *see* Doga Turkish Journal of Physics **3817**
Doga Turk Kimya Dergisi. *see* Doga Turkish Journal of Chemistry **1176**
Doga Turk Matematik Dergisi. *see* Doga Turkish Journal of Mathematics **3034**
Doga Turk Muhendislik ve Cevre Bilimleri Dergisi. *see* Doga Turkish Journal of Engineering and Environmental Science **1819**
Doga Turk Saglik Bilimleri Dergisi. *see* Doga Turkish Journal of Medical Sciences **3094**
Doga Turk Tarim ve Ormancilik Dergisi. *see* Doga Turkish Journal of Agriculture and Forestry **87**
Doga Turk Veterinerlik ve Hayvancilik Dergisi. *see* Doga Turkish Journal of Veterinary and Animal Sciences **4809**
Doga Turk Zooloji Dergisi. *see* Doga Turkish Journal of Zoology **581**
Doga Turkish Journal of Agriculture and Forestry/Doga Turk Tarim ve Ormancilik Dergisi. (TU ISSN 1010-7649) **87**, 2098
Doga Turkish Journal of Biology/Doga Turk Biyoloji Dergisi. (TU ISSN 1010-7576) **437**
Doga Turkish Journal of Botany/Doga Turk Botanik Dergisi. (TU ISSN 1011-0887) **501**
Doga Turkish Journal of Chemistry/Doga Turk Kimya Dergisi. (TU ISSN 1010-7614) **1176**
Doga Turkish Journal of Engineering and Environmental Science/Doga Turk Muhendislik ve Cevre Bilimleri Dergisi. (TU ISSN 1010-7606) **1819**, 1947
Doga Turkish Journal of Mathematics/Doga Turk Matematik Dergisi. (TU ISSN 1010-7622) **3034**
Doga Turkish Journal of Medical Sciences/Doga Turk Saglik Bilimleri Dergisi. (TU ISSN 1010-7584) **3094**
Doga Turkish Journal of Medicine and Pharmacy *see* Doga Turkish Journal of Medical Sciences **3094**
▼Doga Turkish Journal of Pharmacy/Doga Turk Eczacilik Dergisi. (TU) **3722**
Doga Turkish Journal of Physics/Doga Turk Fizik Dergisi. (TU ISSN 1010-7630) **3817**
Doga Turkish Journal of Physics and Astrophysics *see* Doga Turkish Journal of Physics **3817**
Doga Turkish Journal of Veterinary and Animal Sciences/Doga Turk Veterinerlik ve Hayvancilik Dergisi. (TU ISSN 1010-7592) **4809**, 215
Doga Turkish Journal of Zoology/Doga Turk Zooloji Dergisi. (TU ISSN 1011-0895) **581**
Dogar's General Knowledge Digest. (PK ISSN 0012-4907) **3891**, 4308
Dogs in Canada. (CN ISSN 0317-1485) **3710**
Dogs in Canada Annual. (CN) **3710**
Dogs U S A. (US ISSN 0895-5581) **3710**
Dohanyipar. (HU ISSN 0012-4931) **4643**
Dohner Family Newsletter. (US) **2149**
Doing Business with Eastern Europe. (US) **905**
Doitsu Bungaku. (JA ISSN 0387-2831) **2912**, 2811
Dojin News. *see* Dojin Nyusu **1205**

Dojin Nyusu/Dojin News. (JA ISSN 0385-1516) **1205**, 476, 3722
Dok *see* Arbejdsmiljoet - Netop Nu **3623**
Dokhtaran va Pesaran. (IR) **1253**
Dokita. (NR ISSN 0046-0508) **3094**
Dokkyo Journal of Medical Sciences. (JA ISSN 0385-5023) **3094**
Doklady Biochemistry. (English translation of: Doklady Akademii Nauk S.S.S.R.) (US ISSN 0012-4958) **476**
Doklady Biological Sciences. (English translation of: Doklady Akademii Nauk S.S.S.R.) (US ISSN 0012-4966) **437**
Doklady Biophysics. (English translation of: Doklady Akademii Nauk S.S.S.R.) (US ISSN 0012-4974) **485**
Doklady Botanical Sciences. (English translation of: Doklady Akademii Nauk S.S.S.R.) (US ISSN 0012-4982) **501**, 437
Doklady Chemical Technology. (English translation of: Doklady Akademii Nauk S.S.S.R.) (US ISSN 0012-4990) **1852**
Doklady Chemistry. (English translation of: Doklady Akademii Nauk S.S.S.R.) (US ISSN 0012-5008) **1176**
Doklady Physical Chemistry. (English translation of: Doklady Akademii Nauk S.S.S.R.) (US ISSN 0012-5016) **1225**
Dokument und Analyse. (GW) **2188**
Dokumentacja Geograficzna. (PL ISSN 0012-5032) **2246**
Dokumentacni Prehled C T K *see* C T K Dokumentacni Prehled **2568**
Dokumentation Arbeitsschutz Unfallverhuetung Arbeitsmedizin. (GW) **3616**, 3722
Dokumentation der Gesetze und Verordnungen Osteuropas. (AU ISSN 0012-5075) **2620**
Dokumentation Deutsche Finanzrechtsprechung. (GW ISSN 0175-5293) **2620**
Dokumentation fuer Umweltschutz und Landespflege *see* Dokumentation Naturschutz und Landschaft **1501**
†Dokumentation Gefaehrdung durch Alkohol, Rauchen, Drogen, Arzneimittel. (GW ISSN 0341-8022) **5182**
Dokumentation Medizin im Umweltschutz. (GW ISSN 0342-0795) **3171**, 10, 4117
Dokumentation Naturschutz und Landschaft. (GW) **1501**, 10, 1973
†Dokumentation Neusprachlicher Unterricht. (GW ISSN 0343-3420) **5182**
Dokumentation Ostmitteleuropa. (GW ISSN 0340-3297) **4370**, 2506
Dokumentation Regelungstechnik *see* V D I. Informationsdienst Regelungstechnik **1847**
Dokumentation Sozialmedizin, Oeffentlicher Gesundheitsdienst, Gesundheitserziehung. (GW ISSN 0932-5387) **3171**, 10, 4117
Dokumentation Sprachwissenschaftliche Forschungsvorhaben. (GW ISSN 0724-4320) **2811**, 1705, 2756
Dokumentation Strasse. (GW ISSN 0012-5148) **1843**, 10
†Dokumentation Tribologie/Documentation Tribology. (GW ISSN 0340-3475) **5182**
Dokumentation Wasser. (GW ISSN 0012-5156) **4823**
Dokumentation zu Schulstatistischen Erhebungen/Document Concernant le Releve Statistique Scolaire. (SZ) **1726**
Dokumentations und Informations Zentrum Emslandlager Schriften *see* D I Z Schriften **3454**
Dokumentationsarchiv des Oesterreichischen Widerstandes. Mitteilungen. (AU) **2359**
Dokumentationsdienst Afrika. Ausgewaehlte Neuere Literatur. (GW ISSN 0342-040X) **399**, 2169
Dokumentationsdienst Afrika. Kurzbibliographie. (GW ISSN 0720-2032) **2169**

Dokumentationsdienst Afrika. Reihe A. (GW ISSN 0342-0442) **399**, 2169
Dokumentationsdienst Asien und Suedpazifik. Ausgewaehlte Neuer Literatur. (GW ISSN 0936-9171) **4394**
Dokumentationsdienst Asien und Suedpazifik. Kurzbibliographie. (GW ISSN 0938-3638) **4394**
Dokumentationsdienst Asien und Suedpazifik. Reihe A. (GW ISSN 0937-5929) **4394**
Dokumentationsdienst Bibliothekswesen.(GW ISSN 0176-781X) **2756**
Dokumentationsdienst Bildung und Kultur. (GW ISSN 0724-4401) **1676**
Dokumentationsdienst Lateinamerika/Documentacion Latinoamericana. (GW ISSN 0342-037X) **399**
Dokumentationsdienst Vorderer Orient. Ausgewaehlte Neuere Literatur. (GW ISSN 0937-5937) **4394**
Dokumentationsdienst Vorderer Orient. Kurzbibliographie. (GW ISSN 0938-2666) **4394**
Dokumentationsdienst Vorderer Orient. Reihe A. (GW ISSN 0937-5945) **399**, 4370
Dokumente. (GW ISSN 0012-5172) **2188**, 3955
Dokumente und Informationen zur Schweizerischen Orts-, Regional- und Landesplanung *see* D I S P **2486**
Dokumente zum Hochschulsport. (GW ISSN 0173-0843) **4471**, 1705
†Dokumente zur Aussenpolitik der Deutschen Demokratischen Republik.(GW ISSN 0418-9906) **5182**
Dokumente zur Deutschlandpolitik. (GW ISSN 0070-7031) **3891**, 2359
Dokumente zur Deutschlandpolitik. Beihefte. (GW ISSN 0341-3276) **3891**, 2359
Dokumenti - Informacije. (YU ISSN 0351-5494) **4632**
Dolce Vita. (IT) **2205**
Dolenjski Gozdar. (XV) **2114**
Dolgozo No. (RM) **4840**
▼Doll Artistry. (US) **2435**, 354
Doll Castle News. (US ISSN 0363-7972) **2435**
Doll Collector's Price Guide. (US) **2435**
Doll Crafter. (US) **355**
Doll Designs. (US ISSN 1050-4796) **2435**, 355
▼Doll Life. (US) **2435**
Doll Reader. (US ISSN 0744-0901) **2435**, 2281
Dollars & Cents. (US) **1008**, 776, 2620
Dollars and Cents of Shopping Centers. (US ISSN 0070-704X) **4148**
Dollars & Sense. (US ISSN 0012-5245) **860**, 1999
DollarSense. (US ISSN 0194-8490) **776**, 944
Dollmaking. (US ISSN 0885-2707) **2435**, 355
Dolls. (US ISSN 0733-2238) **2435**
†Dolls & Dolls' House. (UK ISSN 0955-1646) **5182**
Dollstar. (US) **1253**
Dolly. (AT) **1253**
Dolly. (IT) **1253**
Dolphin. (US) **1310**
Dolphin. (DK ISSN 0106-4487) **2912**
Dolphin Book Club News. (US ISSN 0012-5261) **4126**
Dolphin Digest. (US) **4471**
Dolphin Dreams Newsletter. (US) **581**
Dolphin Log. (US ISSN 8756-6362) **1253**, 1487, 1947
Dolphin-Moon Press "Signatures" Series.(US) **2992**
Dom. (GW) **4263**
Domani di Noi Ragazzi. (IT) **2205**
Dombi *see* Cultures au Zaire et en Afrique **4369**
Dome. (US ISSN 1041-1607) **298**
Domenica. (IT ISSN 0012-5288) **4263**
Domenica del Corriere. (IT ISSN 0012-5296) **2205**
Domenica Quiz. (IT) **4471**

6130 DOMESTIC AFFAIRS

▼Domestic Affairs. (US ISSN 1060-0655) **3891**
Domestic Animal Endocrinology. (US ISSN 0739-7240) **3252**, 4809
Domestic Cars Service & Repair. (US) **4689**
Domestic Human Needs Networker. (US) **4404**
Domestic Light Trucks & Vans Service & Repair. (US) **4689**
Domestic Mail Manual. (US) **1352**
Domestic Oceanborne and Great Lakes Commerce of the United States see Domestic Waterborne Trade of the United States **4726**
Domestic Relations Journal of Ohio. (US ISSN 1042-5934) **2717**
Domestic Relations: The Substantive Law. (US) **2717**
Domestic Textiles & Wallcoverings Trade Journal. (AT) **4618**
Domestic Waterborne Trade of the United States. (US) **4726**, 835
Dominant Newsletter. (US) **4019**, 1297
Dominatrix Cross Roads. (US) **3396**, 4840
Domingo. (BL) **4263**
Dominica. Ministry of Finance and Development. Annual Overseas Trade Report. (DQ ISSN 0417-9382) **905**
Dominica. Ministry of Finance and Development. Statistical Digest see Dominica. Ministry of Finance and Development. Statistical Division. Digest **860**
Dominica. Ministry of Finance and Development. Statistical Division. Digest. (DQ) **860**
Dominica. Ministry of Finance and Development. Vital Statistics Report. (DQ) **860**
Dominica. Quarterly Bulletin of Tourism Statistics. (DQ) **4799**
Dominica. Registrar of Co-Operative Societies. Report. (DQ) **87**
Dominica Agricultural and Industrial Development Bank. Annual Report and Financial Statements see National Commercial & Development Bank. Annual Report and Financial Statements **792**
Dominica Nurses Association. Newsletter. (DQ) **3277**
Dominica Official Gazette. (DQ) **3891**
Dominical. (VE) **2238**
Dominican Republic. Centro Dominicano de Promocion de Exportaciones. Boletin Estadistico. (DR) **905**, 713
Dominican Republic. Centro Dominicano de Promocion de Exportaciones. Informes see Exportador Dominicano **907**
Dominican Republic. Centro Nacional de Investigaciones Agropecuarias. Laboratorio de Sanidad Vegetal. Sanidad Vegetal. (DR) **437**
Dominican Republic. Direccion General de Bellas Artes. Catalogo de la Bienal de Artes Plasticas. (DR) **324**
Dominican Republic. Oficina Nacional de Presupuesto. Ejecucion del Presupuesto see Dominican Republic. Oficina Nacional de Presupuesto. Ejecucion Presupuestaria. Informe **4059**
Dominican Republic. Oficina Nacional de Presupuesto. Ejecucion Presupuestaria. Informe. (DR) **4059**
Dominican Republic. Secretaria de Estado de Industria y Comercio. Revista. (DR) **835**, 1074
Dominican Republic. Secretaria de Obras Publicas y Comunicaciones. Estadistica see Dominican Republic Secretaria de Estado de Obras Publicas y Comunicaciones. OPC **4059**
Dominican Republic. Secretaria de Sanidad y Asistencia Publica. Cuadros Estadisticos. (DR) **4425**
Dominican Republic. Secretariado Tecnico de la Presidencia. Boletin. (DR) **3891**
Dominican Republic. Superintendencia de Bancos. Anuario Estadistico. (DR) **776**
Dominican Republic. Superintendencia de Bancos. Informe Estadistico Trimestral. (DR) **776**
Dominican Republic Secretaria de Estado de Obras Publicas y Comunicaciones. OPC. (DR) **4059**
Dominion Astrophysical Observatory, Victoria. Publications. (CN ISSN 0078-6950) **363**, 3817
Dominion Law Reports. (CN ISSN 0012-5350) **2620**
Dominion Museum Records see National Museum of New Zealand Records **3530**
†Dominion Report Service. (CN) **5182**
Dominion Sunday Times. (NZ) **2212**
Dominion Tax Cases. (CN ISSN 0046-0567) **1092**
Domino. (CS) **1253**
†Domino. (CN) **5182**
▼Domostroi. (RU) **616**
Domov. (CS ISSN 0012-5369) **2551**, 2558
Domova Pokladnica. (CS) **2912**, 3392, 3891, 4760
Domspatz. (GW) **4632**, 3524, 3549
Domus. (IT ISSN 0012-5377) **299**, 2551
Domus Magazin. (GW) **944**, 4148
Don see Don & Adonis **2452**
Don. (RU ISSN 0012-5393) **2864**
Don Balon. (SP) **4503**
Don Bell Reports. (US) **4263**
Don Don. (JA) **2207**
Don Heinrich's College Football. (US ISSN 1054-2191) **4503**
Don Heinrich's Pro Preview. (US ISSN 1054-2221) **4503**
Don & Adonis. (GW) **2452**
Donald Duck & Co. (NO) **1253**
Donaldson's Port Elizabeth Directory see Donaldson's Port Elizabeth, Uitenhage and Despatch Directory **1133**
Donaldson's Port Elizabeth, Uitenhage and Despatch Directory. (SA ISSN 0416-2706) **1133**
Donan Igakukai. (JA ISSN 0288-1829) **3094**
Donau Bote see Nemzetor **2875**
Der Donauschwabe. (GW ISSN 0012-5423) **1999**
†Donauschwaebisches Schrifttum. (GW ISSN 0070-7074) **5182**
Doncaster Ancestor. (UK ISSN 0144-459X) **2149**
Dong-A Munhua/East Asia Culture. (KO) **3637**, 2912
Dong-A Nyonkam. (KO) **2209**
Dong Hai/East China Sea. (CC) **2912**
Dong Xi Nan Bei/East - West - South - North. (CC ISSN 1000-7296) **2181**
Dongbei Difangshi Yanjiu/Studies - Local History of Northeast China. (CC) **2337**
Dongbei Gongxueyuan Xuebao/Northeast Institute of Technology. Journal. (CC ISSN 0253-4258) **4596**, 4308
Dongbei Linye Daxue Xuebao/Northeast Forestry University. Journal. (CC ISSN 1000-5382) **2098**
Dongbei Nongxueyuan Xuebao/Northeast Institute of Agriculture. (CC ISSN 0253-228X) **87**
Dongbei Shida Xuebao (Zhexue Shehui Kexue Ban)/Northeast Normal University. Journal (Philosophy, Social Science Edition). (CC) **4370**, 3765
Dongbei Shida Xuebao (Ziran Kexue Ban)/Northeast Normal University. Journal (Natural Science Edition). (CC ISSN 1000-1832) **4308**
Dongfang Qigong/Oriental Qigong. (CC) **3801**
Dongfang Qiyejia/Oriental Entrepreneurs. (CC) **659**
Dongfang Shijie/Oriental World. (US) **2337**, 3637
Dongfang Xuebao. see Toho Gakuho **3644**
Donghua Dawang. (CC) **324**
Dongjing Wenxue. (CC) **2912**
Dongli Gongcheng/Dynamic Engineering. (CC ISSN 1000-6761) **1928**
Dongli Jixue Wenzhai/Power Machinery Abstracts. (CC ISSN 1001-6937) **1843**, 1928
Dongnan Daxue Xuebao/Southeast University. Journal. (CC ISSN 1001-0505) **4370**
Dongnan Wenhua/Culture of Southeast China. (CC ISSN 1001-179X) **270**, 238
Dongnan Ya Yanjiu/Southeast Asian Studies. (CC) **3637**
Dongnan Ya Zongheng. (CC) **4370**
Dong'ou/Eastern Europe. (CC) **4370**
Dongwu Daxue Zhongguo Yishu Shi Jikan see Soochow University Journal of Chinese Art History **5279**
Dongwu Falu Xuebao see Soochow Law Review **2680**
Dongwu Fenlei Xuebao/Acta Zootaxonomica Sinica. (CC ISSN 1000-0739) **581**
Dongwu Jingji Shangxue Xuebao see Soochow Journal of Economics and Business **691**
Dongwu Shuli Xuebao see Soochow Journal of Mathematics **3056**
Dongwu Waiyu Xuebao see Soochow Journal of Foreign Languages and Literatures **2842**
Dongwu Wenshi Xuebao see Soochow Journal of Humanities **2515**
Dongwu Xuebao/Acta Zoologica Sinica. (CC ISSN 0001-7302) **581**
Dongwu Zhengzhi Shehui Xuebao see Soochow Journal of Political Science & Sociology **4388**
Dongwuxue Yanjiu/Zoological Study. (CC) **581**
Dongwuxue Zazhi/Chinese Journal of Zoology. (CC ISSN 0250-3263) **581**
Dongyue Luncong/Dongyue Tribune. (CC) **4370**
Dongyue Tribune. see Dongyue Luncong **4370**
Donizetti Society. Journal. (UK ISSN 0307-1448) **3549**
Donizetti Society Newsletter. (UK) **3549**
Donkey Digest. (AT ISSN 1031-6280) **231**, 4533
Donna. (IT) **1290**, 4840
Donna. (CN) **1999**
Donna & Mamma. (IT) **4840**
Donna di Casa. (IT ISSN 0046-0591) **4840**
Donna e Societa. (IT) **4840**
Donna Moderna. (IT) **4840**, 4835
Donnapiu see Marie Claire - Donnapiu **4847**
Donne e Politica - Women and Politics see Reti - Pratiche e Saperi di Donne **3922**
Donnees de Base sur la Pauvrete au Canada. see Canadian Fact Book on Poverty **4400**
Donnees Sociales. (FR ISSN 0758-6531) **4404**
†Donnelley Directory Record. (US) **5182**
Dono. (IT ISSN 0012-544X) **3207**
Donoghue's Money Fund Report see I B C - Donoghue's Money Fund Report **949**
Donoghue's Moneyletter. (US ISSN 0197-7083) **944**, 776
Donor Briefing. (US) **4404**
Donor Update see Exchange (New York) **4405**
Don't Miss Out: The Ambitious Student's Guide to Financial Aid. (US ISSN 0277-6987) **1705**
Donum Dei. (CN ISSN 0318-0123) **4174**
Donyaye Varzesh. (IR) **4471**
Dookola Swiata. (PL ISSN 0012-5458) **1253**
Doopsgezinde Bijdragen. (NE ISSN 0167-0441) **2359**, 4236
The Door. (US ISSN 1044-7512) **4236**
The Door. (UK) **4236**
Door & Operator Industry. (US) **616**
Door & Window Retailing. (US) **616**, 1038
Door County Almanak. (US) **2224**
Door of Hope. (US) **4174**
Doorkijk. (NE ISSN 0012-5482) **1819**
Doors and Hardware. (US ISSN 0361-5294) **642**, 616
Doors Quarterly Magazine. (GW) **3549**
Doortocht. (NE ISSN 0012-5504) **4263**
Doppelpunkt. (GW) **31**
Doprava/Transport. (CS ISSN 0012-5520) **4649**
Dor le-Dor see Jewish Bible Quarterly **4184**
El Dorado. (US ISSN 0095-165X) **238**, 270
Dorchester County Genealogical Magazine. (US ISSN 8755-2353) **2149**
Dorchester Magazine. (UK) **2473**
Dorem Afrike. (SA) **1999**
Doremi. (BE ISSN 0773-0179) **1253**
Dorf Aktuell see Land Aktuell **3904**
Doriana. (IT ISSN 0417-9927) **4308**
Doris Lessing Newsletter. (US ISSN 0882-486X) **2912**
Dorland's Medical Directory. Delaware Valley Edition see Dorland's Medical Directory. Eastern Pennsylvania and Southern New Jersey Edition **3095**
Dorland's Medical Directory. Eastern Pennsylvania and Southern New Jersey Edition. (US) **3095**
Dorm Magazine see Student Life **5284**
Dormant Brain Self-Release Research Reports. (US) **3335**
Dornier Post. (GW ISSN 0012-5563) **51**
Dornodahiny Sudlal/Oriental Studies. (MP) **3637**
Doro to Konkurito/Road and Concrete. (JA ISSN 0285-6018) **616**
Dorot. (US ISSN 0886-2796) **2149**, 1999
Dorset. (UK ISSN 0046-0621) **2359**
Dorset Down Flock Book. (UK) **215**
Dorset Farmer. (UK ISSN 0012-5598) **87**
Dorset Horn and Poll Dorset Sheep Breeders' Association. Flock Book. (UK) **215**
Dorset Life. (UK ISSN 0959-1079) **2193**
Dorset Natural History & Archaeological Society. Monograph Series. (UK) **270**
Dorset Natural History and Archaeological Society. Proceedings. (UK ISSN 0070-7112) **4308**, 270
Dorset Plus. (UK) **2193**
Dorset Worthies. (UK ISSN 0070-7120) **418**
Dortmund. (GW) **4087**
Dortmunder Beitraege zur Landeskunde.(GW) **437**, 1543, 3657
Dortmunder Beitraege zur Zeitungsforschung. (GW ISSN 0417-9994) **2569**
Dortmunder Bekanntmachungen. (GW) **4087**
Dortmunder Messebrief. (GW) **3392**
Doshisha American Studies. (JA ISSN 0420-0918) **2404**
Doshisha Bungaku see Doshisha Literature **2912**
Doshisha Daigaku Keizaigaku Ronso. see Doshisha University Economic Review **659**
Doshisha Daigaku Rikogaku Kenkyu Hokoku/Doshisha University. Science and Engineering Review. (JA ISSN 0036-8172) **1819**
Doshisha Literature. (JA ISSN 0046-063X) **2912**, 2811
Doshisha Studies in Foreign Literature. (JA ISSN 0286-2832) **2912**
Doshisha University. Science and Engineering Review. see Doshisha Daigaku Rikogaku Kenkyu Hokoku **1819**
Doshisha University Economic Review/Doshisha Daigaku Keizaigaku Ronso. (JA ISSN 0387-3021) **659**
Doshitsu Kogakkai Ronbun Hokokushu. see Japanese Society of Soil Mechanics and Foundation Engineering. Journal **1868**
Doshkol'noe Vospitanie. (RU ISSN 0012-561X) **1625**
†Dossier (Oneonta). (US) **5182**

†Dossier (Washington, D.C.). (US ISSN 0891-5741) **5182**
Dossier Benelux. *see* Benelux Dossier **847**
†Dossier - Catalogo Equipo Electrico. (SP) **5182**
Dossier - Catalogo Frenos. (SP) **4689**
Dossier Componenti. (IT) **1886, 2551**
Dossier de l'Art. (FR) **324**
Dossier di Urbanistica e Cultura del Territorio. (IT) **2486**
Dossier Europa. (EI) **3891**
Dossier Europa - Emigrazione. (IT ISSN 0391-3457) **3981**
Dossier Oleo. (SP) **2066**
Dossiers Antilles Guyane. Etudes Diverses. (GP ISSN 0291-8706) **860**
Dossiers d'Archeologie. (FR) **270**
Dossiers de Demographie de la Belgique. (BE) **3981**
Les Dossiers de l'Art Public. (FR ISSN 0756-5860) **324**
Dossiers de l'Economie Reunionnaise. (RE ISSN 0292-6792) **860**
Dossiers de l'Education. (FR ISSN 0294-0809) **1625**
†Dossiers de l'Outre-Mer. (FR ISSN 0769-3478) **5182**
Dossiers de la Bible. (FR ISSN 0761-7267) **4175**
Dossiers et Documents. (FR) **2186**
Dossiers Radiovision. (FR) **1355, 1625**
Dost aur Dosti. (II) **1253**
Dostoevsky Studies. (US) **2912, 2864**
†Dotaito Nyusu Reta/Dotite News Letter. (JA ISSN 0012-5660) **5182**
Dotite News Letter. *see* Dotaito Nyusu Reta **5182**
Dots and Dashes. (US) **1362**
Dots and Taps. (CN ISSN 0012-5679) **2292, 2287**
Dottore in Scienze Agrarie. (IT ISSN 0012-5687) **87**
Douai Magazine. (UK ISSN 0012-5695) **1310, 4175**
Double Glazing - Domestic, Industrial and Commercial *see* Window Industries **1167**
Double Liaison. (FR ISSN 0012-5709) **3653**
Double Reed. (US ISSN 0741-7659) **3549**
Double Take. (UK) **1310**
Double Talk (Amelia). (US ISSN 0889-8804) **1236, 4434**
Doughty Tree. (US ISSN 0897-3350) **2149**
Douglas Properties International. (US) **4148**
Douglasia. (US) **501**
Douglass Alumnae Bulletin. (US) **1310**
†Douglass Series on Women's Lives and the Meaning of Gender. (US) **5182**
Douleur et Analgesie. (SZ ISSN 1011-288X) **3095**
Douthit Family Tree. (US) **2149**
Dove. *see* Ha-Yonah **2029**
Dover Port Handbook. (UK ISSN 0265-1165) **4727, 1133**
Dovetail. (US) **4175, 2864**
Dovetail - Peaces *see* Dovetail **4175**
Dow in Italia *see* Notizie Dow **1185**
Dow Jones Investor's Handbook *see* Business One Investor's Handbook **941**
Dow Jones-Irwin Business and Investment Almanac *see* Business One Irwin Business and Investment Almanac **651**
Dow Jones Newspaper Fund. Advisor Update. (US) **2569**
Dow Theory Forecasts. (US ISSN 0300-7324) **944**
Dow Theory Letters. (US) **944**
Dowbeaters. (US) **944**
Dowline. (US ISSN 1052-3545) **1426, 1460, 1469**
Down Beat. (US ISSN 0012-5768) **3549**
Down East Magazine. (US ISSN 0012-5776) **2224**
Down Home Music Newsletter. (US) **3549, 4460**
Down to Earth. (US) **1176, 87**

Down to Earth North East Australia Newsletter. (AT) **3594, 1487**
Downeast Ancestry. (US ISSN 0891-0960) **2149**
Downeast Libraries *see* Maine Entry **2772**
Downhill Only Journal. (UK ISSN 0070-718X) **4545**
Download *see* Telecom - Eye - Bee - Em **1343**
Downside Review. (UK ISSN 0012-5806) **4263**
▼Downtime. (US) **3017**
Downtown Athletic Club Journal. (US ISSN 0046-0656) **1297**
Downtown Idea Exchange. (US ISSN 0012-5822) **2486**
Downtown Promotion Reporter. (US ISSN 0363-2830) **31**
†Dowse Market Letter. (US) **5182**
▼Doyles Dispute Resolution Practice - Asia Pacific. (AT) **2620, 2722**
▼Doyles Dispute Resolution Practice - North America. (AT) **2620, 2722**
Dozenal Journal. (UK ISSN 0260-4884) **3034**
Dr. Alexander Grant's Health Gazette. (US) **3095**
Dr. Carter's Caribbean Diet Digest *see* Caribbean Diet Digest **3604**
Dr. Dobb's Journal. (US ISSN 1044-789X) **1460, 1469**
Dr. Dobb's Journal of Software Tools *see* Dr. Dobb's Journal **1460**
Dr. Dobb's Journal: Software Tools for Advanced Programmers *see* Dr. Dobb's Journal **1460**
Dr. Med. Mabuse. (GW ISSN 0173-430X) **3095, 3722**
▼Dr. Samuel Mudd Newsletter. (US) **2404, 2620**
Drachenflieger *see* Drachenflieger Magazin **51**
Drachenflieger Magazin. (GW) **51, 4545**
Dracula News Journal. (US) **3011, 2053**
Draeger Review. *see* Draegerheft **3482**
Draegerheft/Draeger Review. (GW ISSN 0012-5857) **3482**
Draft Horse Journal. (US ISSN 0012-5865) **215, 4533**
Drafting Wills and Trust Agreements. (US) **2715**
Drafts & Designs. (US) **4618**
†Drag Racing. (US ISSN 0894-5187) **5182**
Dragesport. (DK ISSN 0109-5595) **4471**
Dragoco Report. (GW ISSN 0012-5881) **375**
Dragoco Report: Flavoring Information Service. (GW ISSN 0720-1249) **2066**
Dragon. (UK ISSN 0012-589X) **2912, 324, 3507, 3549**
Dragon Magazine. (US ISSN 0279-6848) **1253**
▼Dragonfang. (US) **2992**
Dragonfly. (US ISSN 0364-359X) **2992**
Dragon's Teeth. (US ISSN 0142-6494) **1236, 1625**
Draht. (GW ISSN 0012-5911) **3405, 1819, 1886, 3017**
Draht und Kabel Panorama. (GW ISSN 0940-2691) **3405**
Drahtwelt. (GW ISSN 0012-592X) **3405**
Drake Law Review. (US ISSN 0012-5938) **2620**
Drake Update. (US) **1310**
Drama. (UK ISSN 0012-5946) **4632**
Drama. *see* Xiju **4642**
Drama & Film Monthly. *see* Juying Yuebao **4634**
▼Drama Criticism. (US) **4632, 2912**
Drama Literature. *see* Xiju Wenxue **2978**
Drama-Logue. (US) **3507, 1372, 4632**
The Drama Magazine. (UK) **4632**
Drama - Theatre Teacher. (US ISSN 1046-5022) **4632, 1748**
†Dramapaedagogik i Nordisk Perspektiv. (DK ISSN 0900-7350) **5182**
Dramascripts Series. (UK ISSN 0070-7198) **2912**

Dramatics. (US ISSN 0012-5989) **4632, 1625, 1748**
†Dramatist's Bible. (US) **5182**
Dramatists Guild Newsletter. (US) **4632**
Dramatists Guild Quarterly. (US ISSN 0012-6004) **4632**
Dramatists Sourcebook. (US ISSN 0733-1606) **4632**
Dramau'r Byd. (UK ISSN 0141-1179) **4632**
Draperies & Window Coverings. (US ISSN 0279-4918) **2551**
Drapers Records *see* D R: The Fashion Business **1290**
Drapery and Fashion Weekly *see* Fashion Weekly **1291**
Draudzes Vestis. (CN ISSN 0701-0214) **4236**
Draugas. (US) **4263, 1999**
Draughting & Design. (UK ISSN 0951-5704) **1819**
Drawing. (US ISSN 0191-6963) **324**
Drawing Paper. (UK ISSN 0143-8425) **324**
▼Dream Cell. (UK) **3011**
Dream Guys. (US) **1253, 1372, 3549**
Dream Home Magazine. (US) **616, 2558**
Dream Journal. (US) **2992**
Dream Network. (US ISSN 1054-6707) **3594, 4019**
Dream Network Bulletin *see* Dream Network **3594**
Dream Science Fiction *see* New Moon **3013**
Dream Switchboard. (US) **4019**
Dreamin' (US) **2224**
▼Dreaming. (US ISSN 1053-0797) **571, 3335, 4019**
Dreams and Nightmares. (US ISSN 0897-0238) **2992, 3011**
Dreams & Visions. (CN ISSN 0843-445X) **2912, 4175**
†Dreamshore. (US) **5182**
Drechseln. (GW ISSN 0720-0528) **355**
Dredging & Port Construction. (UK) **4727**
Dredging Seminar. Proceedings. (US) **4823**
Drehpunkt. (SZ ISSN 0012-6055) **2912**
Die Drei. (GW ISSN 0012-6063) **4370**
Dreihammer. (AU ISSN 0012-6071) **4618**
Dreikoenigsbote. (GW ISSN 0012-608X) **4236**
Dreiser Newsletter *see* Dreiser Studies **2912**
Dreiser Studies. (US ISSN 0896-6362) **2912**
▼Dreissena Polymorpha Information Review. (US) **581**
Drejtesia Popullore/Justice Populaire. (AA ISSN 0304-2731) **2620**
Dreloma. (II) **4214**
Drenthe. (NE ISSN 0024-8592) **2211**
Drents Landbouwblad *see* Landbode (Groningen) **104**
Dresden Enterprise. (US) **2224**
Dresdener Bank - Economic Quarterly *see* Trends **886**
▼Dresdener Behoerden Spiegel. (GW) **4087**
Dresdener Kunstblaetter. (GW) **3524**
†Dresdner Monats-Blaetter. (GW ISSN 0012-6101) **5182**
Dress. (US ISSN 0361-2112) **1290, 2310**
Dressage & C T. (US ISSN 0147-796X) **4533**
Dressage and Combined Training *see* Dressage & C T **4533**
Dressage Magazine. (UK ISSN 0958-1804) **4533**
Dressage Review *see* Dressage Magazine **4533**
Dressmaking. (JA ISSN 0012-611X) **1290**
Dressmaking & Madam's Style Book. (JA) **1290**
Drevarska Dokumentacia *see* Drevarske Informacie **2112**

Drevarske Informacie/Wood Information.(CS ISSN 0862-9358) **2112, 10**
Drevarsky Vyskum/Wood Research. (CS ISSN 0012-6136) **2114**
Drevneishie Gosudarstva na Territorii S.S.S.R/Ancient States in the Territory of the U.S.S.R. (RU) **271, 2359**
Drevo/Wood. (CS ISSN 0012-6144) **639**
Drew. (US ISSN 0889-0153) **1310**
Drew Gateway. (US ISSN 0012-6152) **4236**
Drexel Faculty Publication. (US) **4308**
Drie Talen. (NE ISSN 0012-6187) **2811**
†Drift. (UK) **5182**
Driftsoekonomi. (DK ISSN 0106-9535) **659**
Driftsteknikerbogen. (DK ISSN 0108-6707) **4596**
†Drilling. (UK) **5182**
Drilling Activity Report. (CN ISSN 0228-5630) **3684**
Drilling and Land Report. (CN) **3482**
Drilling and Pumping Journal *see* Oilfield Review **3696**
Drilling & Well Servicing Contractors. (US) **3684, 1133**
Drilling Contractor. (US ISSN 0046-0702) **3685**
Drilling-D C W *see* Drilling **5182**
Drilling News. (UK ISSN 0955-7369) **1928, 1559**
Drilling News *see* Mining Mirror **3490**
Drilling Permits. (US) **3685**
Drilling - the Wellsite Magazine. (US) **3685, 1785**
†Drillsite. (CN ISSN 0228-7587) **5182**
Drinking Driver in Minnesota. (US) **2620**
Drinking Driving Law Letter. (US ISSN 0730-2568) **4689, 2620**
Drinking Water & Backflow Prevention. (US ISSN 8755-3457) **1864, 4100**
Drinking Water News *see* Clean Water Report **1976**
▼Drinking Water Research. (US ISSN 1055-9140) **4823**
Drinks/Slijtersvakblad. (NE ISSN 0037-6841) **380**
Drinks. (GW) **380**
Drinks International. (UK ISSN 0012-625X) **380**
Drinnen und Draussen. (GW) **149, 161**
Driscoll Insider. (US) **944**
†Drishti. (US) **5182**
Drita. (AA) **2864**
Der Dritte Weg. (GW ISSN 0012-6268) **2864**
Dritte Welt Materialien. (GW) **2310, 3955**
Drive *see* Ulster Motorist **4704**
†Drive! (Chatsworth). (US) **5182**
Drive! (Pleasant Hill). (US) **4689**
Drive On *see* Taxi Talk **4703**
Drive Safely. (US) **4718**
Driver Letter. (US) **4649**
Driver - Owner. (CN) **4744**
Drivers Club Magazine *see* D C - Magazine **2211**
Drivers License Guide *see* I D Checking Guide (Year) **1515**
Drives and Controls. (UK ISSN 0950-5490) **1923, 1886, 1928**
Driving. (US) **4689**
Driving Digest Magazine. (US ISSN 0276-7074) **4533**
Driving Magazine. (UK) **4689**
Drobiarstwo/Poultry Industry. (PL ISSN 0416-3540) **215, 4809**
Drobne Hospodarske Zvieratco *see* Chovatel **214**
Drochaid/Bridge. (CN ISSN 0703-1491) **1999**
Drogfritt Liv. (SW) **1535, 3723**
Droghiere *see* Distribuzione Organizzata **835**
†Drogi Kolejowe. (PL ISSN 0137-284X) **5182**
Drogist. (NE ISSN 0012-6330) **3723, 375**
Drogisten Weekblad *see* D W **3722**
Drogownictwo. (PL ISSN 0012-6357) **1864, 616**

6132 DROGUERIA

Drogueria & Perfumeria see Tiendas de Drogueria & Perfumeria **377**
†Droguerie Couleurs. (FR) **5182**
Droguerie Francaise la Couleur. (FR) **1038**
Droit/Al-Haqq. (UA) **2620, 3891**
Droit d'Auteur. (UN ISSN 0012-6365) **3674**
Droit de la Construction. see Baurecht **2604**
Droit de la Securite Sociale. (BE) **2620**
Droit de Vivre. (FR ISSN 0012-6373) **3955**
Droit et Economie. (FR ISSN 0012-639X) **2620, 659**
Droit et Economie Politique. see Qanoun Wal Iqtisad **2669**
†Droit et Liberte. (FR ISSN 0012-6411) **5182**
Droit et Pratique du Commerce International/International Trade Law and Practice. (FR ISSN 0335-5047) **2722**
Droit et Societe. (FR) **2620, 4434**
Droit Europeen des Transports. see European Transport Law **4649**
Droit International Prive. (FR) **2722**
Droit Maritime Francais. (FR ISSN 0012-642X) **2734**
Droit Nucleaire. (FR ISSN 1016-4995) **1804, 2620**
Droit Polonais Contemporain. (PL ISSN 0070-7325) **2620**
Droit Social. (FR ISSN 0012-6438) **2620, 4370**
Droit Yougoslave. see Yugoslav Law **2696**
Droits. (FR) **2620**
Drood Review of Mystery. (US ISSN 0893-0252) **2985, 2912**
Drop Shipping News. (US) **1038**
Drop Shipping Source Directory of Major Consumer Product Lines. (US) **1133, 1038**
Drosera. (GW ISSN 0341-406X) **501, 581**
Drosophila Information Service. (US ISSN 0070-7333) **541**
Drought Network News. (US) **4824, 176, 1487**
Droughtmaster Digest. (AT ISSN 0310-0081) **215**
Drovers Journal. (US ISSN 0012-6454) **216**
Druck. (GW ISSN 0179-5988) **1726**
Druck - A B C. (GW) **3998**
Druck Intern. (GW) **3998**
Druck-Print. (GW ISSN 0012-6462) **3998**
Druck-Sachen. (GW) **3998**
Druckindustrie. (SZ ISSN 0046-0737) **3998**
Druckluft-Praxis see Drucklufttechnik **1928**
Drucklufttechnik. (GW) **1928**
Der Druckspiegel. (GW ISSN 0012-6500) **3998**
Druckwelt. (GW ISSN 0012-6519) **3998**
Drug Abstracts Monthly. (UK) **1540, 3747**
Drug Abuse and Alcoholism Newsletter. (US ISSN 0160-0028) **1535**
Drug Abuse Bibliography. (US ISSN 0093-2515) **1540, 399**
Drug Abuse Current Awareness Bulletin see I S D D Current Awareness Bulletin **1540**
Drug Abuse: Directory of Community Services in California. (US) **1535**
Drug Abuse Update. (US ISSN 0739-6562) **1535, 10, 4643**
†Drug Addiction. (UK ISSN 0142-8381) **5182**
Drug and Alcohol Dependence. (IE ISSN 0376-8716) **1535**
Drug and Alcohol Review. (UK ISSN 0959-5236) **1535**
▼Drug and Alcohol Testing. (US) **2620, 1205**
Drug and Chemical Toxicology. (US ISSN 0148-0545) **3723, 1981**
Drug and Chemical Toxicology Series. (US) **3723, 1981**
Drug and Cosmetic Catalog. (US ISSN 0732-0760) **3723, 375**
Drug and Cosmetic Industry. (US ISSN 0012-6527) **3723, 375**

Drug and Device Product Approval List. (US) **3258, 2522**
Drug and Therapeutics Bulletin. (UK ISSN 0012-6543) **3723**
†Drug and Therapeutics Letter. (US) **5182**
Drug Approval and Licensing Procedures in Japan. (JA ISSN 0289-9922) **3723**
Drug, Chemical and Allied Trades Association Digest see D C A T Digest **3722**
Drug Data Report. (SP) **3723**
Drug Design and Delivery see Drug Design and Discovery **3723**
Drug Design and Discovery. (US ISSN 1055-9612) **3723**
Drug Development and Evolution. (GW ISSN 0343-4842) **3723**
Drug Development and Industrial Pharmacy. (US ISSN 0363-9045) **3723**
Drug Development Communications see Drug Development and Industrial Pharmacy **3723**
Drug Development Research. (US ISSN 0272-4391) **3723**
The Drug Educator. (US ISSN 0897-7321) **1535**
Drug Enforcement Administration Registration File - Active. (US) **3095, 1514**
Drug Enforcement Report. (US ISSN 0894-1300) **1514**
Drug Facts and Comparisons. (US ISSN 0277-9714) **3723**
Drug-free Dwellings. (US) **1535**
Drug Induced Disorders. (NE) **1535**
Drug Information Journal. (US ISSN 0092-8615) **3723**
Drug Intelligence and Clinical Pharmacy see D I C P - The Annals of Pharmacotherapy **3722**
Drug Interaction Facts. (US) **3723**
Drug Interactions (Philadelphia) see Drug Interactions and Updates **3723**
Drug Interactions (Vancouver) see Drug Interactions and Updates **3723**
Drug Interactions and Updates. (US) **3723**
Drug Interactions Newsletter see Drug Interactions and Updates **3723**
Drug Law Report. (US ISSN 0734-6166) **1535, 2620**
Drug License Opportunities. (UK) **3723**
Drug Merchandising. (CN ISSN 0012-6586) **3723**
Drug Metabolism and Disposition. (US ISSN 0090-9556) **3723**
Drug Metabolism and Drug Interactions.(UK) **3723**
Drug Metabolism Newsletter. (US ISSN 0199-7912) **3724**
Drug Metabolism Reviews. (US ISSN 0360-2532) **3095, 3724**
Drug News. (II ISSN 0026-8194) **3724**
Drug News & Perspectives. (SP ISSN 0214-0934) **3724**
Drug Newsletter. (US ISSN 0731-5163) **3724, 4100**
†Drug-Nutrient Interactions. (US ISSN 0272-3530) **5182**
Drug Product Index - International. (US) **3747**
Drug Product Index - U S A. (US) **3747**
Drug Research. see Arzneimittel-Forschung **3718**
Drug Research Reports: The Blue Sheet see Health Policy & Biomedical Research: The Blue Sheet **3104**
Drug Store Market Guide. (US ISSN 0277-3716) **1133, 1038, 3724**
Drug Store News. (US ISSN 0191-7587) **1038**
Drug Store News Reference for Pharmacy Practice. (US) **3724**
Drug Targeting. (UK ISSN 0952-0317) **3724, 476, 3258**
▼Drug Targeting and Delivery. (US ISSN 1058-241X) **3724**
Drug Therapy. (US ISSN 0001-7094) **3724**
Drug Topics. (US ISSN 0012-6616) **3724**
Drug Topics Marketing Guide see Marketing Guide **5232**

Drug Topics Red Book. (US ISSN 0070-7376) **3724**
Drug Topics Red Book Update. (US) **3724**
†Drug Trade Name Cross Reference List. (US) **5182**
Drug Utilization Review. (US ISSN 0884-8998) **3724**
Drugarce. (XN ISSN 0012-6632) **1253**
Druglink. (UK ISSN 0305-4349) **1535**
Drugs. (NZ ISSN 0012-6667) **3724**
Drugs and Biology Guidance Manual. (US) **4100, 2620, 3724**
Drugs and Device Recall Bulletin. (US ISSN 8756-5935) **3724, 3277, 4100**
Drugs & Drug Abuse Education. Newsletter. (US ISSN 0744-2823) **1536**
Drugs & Society. (US ISSN 8756-8233) **1536**
Drugs and the Pharmaceutical Sciences.(US) **3724**
†Drugs: Australia. (AT ISSN 0817-3052) **5182**
▼Drugs Available Abroad. (US ISSN 1051-7723) **3724**
Drugs in Current Use and New Drugs see Modell's Drugs in Current Use and New Drugs **3735**
Drugs in Prospect. (US) **3724**
Drugs in Research. (US) **3724, 3095**
Drugs in the Workplace. (US ISSN 1040-4228) **1536, 977**
Drugs in Use. (US) **3724, 3095**
Drugs Made in Germany. (GW ISSN 0012-6683) **3724**
Drugs of the Future. (SP ISSN 0377-8282) **3724**
Drugs Under Experimental and Clinical Research. (SZ ISSN 0378-6501) **3724**
Drugs Under Research see Drugs Under Experimental and Clinical Research **3724**
Druid Henge. (US) **3669, 4282**
Drukwerk see F N V Magazine (Amsterdam) **3999**
Drum. (CN ISSN 0012-6721) **2177**
Drum. (GH) **2192**
Drum. (SA ISSN 0419-7674) **2216, 1999**
Drum. (US ISSN 0899-5443) **2912, 324, 3891**
▼Drum! (US) **3549**
†Drum. (PP) **5182**
Drum Corps News. (US ISSN 0012-6748) **3549**
Drum Corps World. (US ISSN 0164-3223) **3549**
Drumbeat. (AT) **3648**
Drumlin. (US) **2246**
†Drumm Bibliographies. (US) **5182**
Drummer. (US) **2452**
Drums & Percussion. (GW) **3549**
Drury Mirror. (US) **1310**
Drustveni Proizvod i Narodni Dohodak. (YU ISSN 0300-2527) **713**
Drustvo Inzenjera i Tehnicara "Nafta - Gas" see D I T **3684**
Drustvo Konzervatora Srbije. Glasnik. (YU) **1487, 271, 299, 324**
Drustvo Ekologa Bosne i Hercegovine. Bilten. Serija A - Ekoloske Monografije. (BN ISSN 0352-0781) **501, 1947**
Druzba. (CS) **2811**
Druzhba. (RU ISSN 0320-1031) **1253**
Druzhba Narodov. (RU ISSN 0012-6756) **2864**
Druzina/Family. (XV) **4263**
Druzina in Dom. (AU ISSN 0012-6764) **4175**
Drvna Industrija. (CI ISSN 0012-6772) **2114, 3017**
▼Dry Crik Review. (US) **2992**
Dryade. (BE ISSN 0012-6799) **324, 2912**
Drycleaners News. (US ISSN 0012-6802) **1281**
Drydock. (UK ISSN 0143-5000) **4727**
Drying Technology. (US ISSN 0737-3937) **1225**
Dryland Resources and Technology Annual (Year). (II) **4824**

Du. (SZ ISSN 0012-6837) **325**
Du-Bladet see Under Paraplyen **1245**
Du Pont Magazine. (US ISSN 0046-0834) **659, 1176**
Du Shu/Reading. (CC ISSN 0257-0270) **2912**
Du Sol a la Table. (FR ISSN 1143-3833) **1947, 87**
Du und das Tier. (GW ISSN 0341-5759) **3710**
La Dua Jarcento. Informilo. (AU) **2811**
Duanpian Xiaoshuo/Short Stories. (CC) **2912**
Dubai. Government of Dubai. Official Gazette. see Dubai. Hukumat Dubai. Al-Jaridah al-Rasmiyyah **4059**
Dubai. Hukumat Dubai. Al-Jaridah al-Rasmiyyah/Dubai. Government of Dubai. Official Gazette. (TS) **4059**
Dubai External Trade Statistics/ Ihsa'iyyat Dubai lil-Tijarah al-Kharijiyyah. (TS) **713**
Dubai International Airport. see Matar Dubai al-Dawli **4775**
Dubbon. (IS) **1253**
Dublin. National Library of Ireland. Council of Trustees Report. (IE ISSN 0332-0006) **2756**
Dublin Chamber of Commerce Journal see Trade-Links Journal **922**
Dublin Historical Record. (IE ISSN 0012-6861) **2359**
Dublin Institute for Advanced Studies. Communications. Series A. (IE ISSN 0070-7414) **3817**
Dublin Institute for Advanced Studies. Communications. Series D see Dublin Institute for Advanced Studies. School of Cosmic Physics. Geophysical Bulletin **1588**
Dublin Institute for Advanced Studies. School of Cosmic Physics. Geophysical Bulletin. (IE ISSN 0070-7422) **1588**
†Dublin Magazine. (IE ISSN 0012-687X) **5182**
Dublin Seminar for New England Folklife. Annual Proceedings. (US) **4434**
Dublin University Law Journal. (IE) **2621**
Dubrovacki Horizonti. (CI ISSN 0419-7925) **2359**
Dubrovacki Vjesnik. (CI ISSN 0012-690X) **2864**
Dubuque Leader. (US ISSN 0012-6918) **977**
Duca Post. (CN ISSN 0012-6934) **776, 830**
Ducas. (CS) **2359**
Duck Soup. (US) **2864**
Duck Stamp Data. (US) **3751, 4545**
Duckburg Times. (US ISSN 0887-2155) **2435, 3507**
Ducks Unlimited. (US ISSN 0012-6950) **1487**
Ducks Unlimited de Mexico, A.C. see D U M A C **1946**
Ductile Iron News. (US) **3405**
Ductile Iron Pipe News. (US) **2298**
Duda. (MX) **4370**
Dude Rancher see Dude Rancher Magazine - Directory **4760**
Dude Rancher Directory see Dude Rancher Magazine - Directory **4760**
Dude Rancher Magazine - Directory. (US) **4760**
Dudley Chamber of Industry & Commerce Directory. (UK) **1133**
Dudu. (KE ISSN 0258-8498) **530**
Due Alfieri. (IT) **4471**
†Due Ruote. (IT) **5182**
Due South. (UK) **355, 1530, 2912, 3549**
Duesseldorf. Statistisches Jahrbuch see Nordrhein-Westfalen. Statistisches Jahrbuch **4581**
Duesseldorf in Zahlen. (GW ISSN 0418-1263) **4570**
Duesseldorf Magazin. (GW ISSN 0046-0796) **4087**
Duesseldorfer Amtsblatt. (GW ISSN 0012-7019) **4087**
Duesseldorfer Drachen-Post. (GW) **2181**
Duesseldorfer Hefte. (GW ISSN 0012-7027) **4760**
Duesseldorfer Jahrbuch. (GW ISSN 0342-0019) **2359**

Duesseldorfer Museen. (GW) 3524
Duesseldorfer Uni-Zeitung. (GW) 1310
Dufu Yanjiu Xuekan/Journal of Dufu Studies. (CC ISSN 1003-5702) 2864, 2992
Dugnad. (NO) 2359, 1999
Duiksport see Onderwaterwereld 4482
Duilian - Minjian Duilian Gushi/Antithetical Couplet - Folk Stories about Antithetical Couplet. (CC) 2912
Duisburg. Amt fuer Statistik und Stadtforschung. Daten und Information see Daten und Information 4080
Duisburg. Amt fuer Statistik und Stadtforschung. Statistischer Monatsbericht see Statistischer Monatsbericht 4082
Duisburger Journal. (GW ISSN 0343-3277) 2359
Duisburger Studien. (GW) 3765, 4434
Duitse Boek see Deutsche Buecher 2981
Duitse Kroniek. (NE ISSN 0012-7051) 3955, 325, 2912
Duiwai Jingji Maoyi/Journal of Foreign Economics and Trade. (CC) 905
Duiwai Jingji Maoyi Daxue Xuebao/Foreign Economics and Trade University. Journal. (CC) 905
Duiwai Jingmao/International Economics and Trade. (CC) 905
Duiwai Jingmao Shiwu. (CC) 905
Duke Endowment. Annual Report. (US ISSN 0419-8050) 2506
Duke Endowment. Issues. (US) 2506
Duke Law Journal. (US ISSN 0012-7086) 2621
Duke Mathematical Journal. (US ISSN 0012-7094) 3034
Duke Monographs in Medieval and Renaissance Studies. (US) 2359
Duke Press Global Issues Series. (US) 3891, 1947
Duke Press Policy Studies. (US) 3891
Duke University. Center for International Studies. Publications. (US) 3955
†Duke University. Center for the Study of Aging and Human Development. Reports on Advances in Research. (US) 5182
Duke University Center for International Studies Publications. (US) 3955
Duke University Libraries. (US ISSN 0895-4909) 2756, 1626
DukEngineer. (US ISSN 0046-0818) 1819
Dukes County Intelligencer. (US ISSN 0418-1379) 2404
Dukhovna Akademiya SV. Kliment Okhridski. Godishnik. (BU ISSN 0323-9578) 4175, 2359
Dulcelandia. (MX) 2088
Dulcimer Players News. (US ISSN 0098-3527) 3549
Duluthian. (US ISSN 0012-7116) 814
▼Duma. (RU) 3891
Dumars Reviews. (US) 2992
Dumbarton and Vale of Leven Reporter.(UK) 2193
Dumbarton Oaks Conference Proceedings. (US) 271, 325
Dumbarton Oaks Papers. (US ISSN 0070-7546) 271
Dumbarton Oaks Studies. (US ISSN 0070-7554) 271
Dumbarton Oaks Texts. (US ISSN 0070-7562) 2310
Dumjahn's Jahrbuch fuer Eisenbahnliteratur. (GW) 4709
Dumki z Dunaju. (CI) 1999
Dumortiera. (BE) 501
Dun & Bradstreet Looks at Business. (US) 860
Dun & Bradstreet Ltd. Creditnews see D & B Creditnews 775
Dun and Bradstreet Metalworking Directory see Dun's Industrial Guide - The Metalworking Directory 3405
Dun and Bradstreet Middle Market Directory see Million Dollar Directory Series 1048
Dun and Bradstreet Million Dollar Directory see Million Dollar Directory Series 1048

Dun and Bradstreet/Seyd's Register see Dun & Bradstreet Standard Register 1133
Dun & Bradstreet Standard Register. (US) 1133
Dun & Bradstreet's Guide to Your Investments. (US ISSN 0098-2466) 944
Dun's Business Rankings. (US ISSN 0734-2845) 1133
Dun's Dataline. (US) 826, 1469
Dun's Gazette. (AT ISSN 0818-5093) 1008
Dun's Industrial Guide - The Metalworking Directory. (US ISSN 0278-8799) 3405, 1133
Dun's 5,000 Survey. (US) 659
Dunantuli Szemle see Vasi Szemle 2394
Duncan's Radio Market Guide. (US) 1133, 1356
Dundee and Tayside Chamber of Commerce and Industry. Buyer's Guide and Trade Directory. (UK) 814, 1133
Dundee Chamber of Commerce. Buyer's Guide and Trade Directory see Dundee and Tayside Chamber of Commerce and Industry. Buyer's Guide and Trade Directory 814
Dundee Chamber of Commerce Journal see Dundee Tayside 814
Dundee Tayside. (UK ISSN 0306-0241) 814
Dune Buggies & Hot VWs. (US ISSN 0012-7132) 4689, 4471
Dungeon Adventures. (US) 1253
DungeonMaster. (US) 2452, 1683
Dunhill Liability Loss Report. (CN ISSN 0706-8964) 2530
Dunhill Personal Injury & Death Reports. (CN) 2530, 2621
Dunhill Personal Injury Awards Annotator see Dunhill Personal Injury & Death Reports 2530
Dunhuang Studies. see Dunhuang Yanjiu 271
Dunhuang Yanjiu/Dunhuang Studies. (CC ISSN 1000-4106) 271, 325
Dunia. (SP) 4840, 1290
Dunia Maritim. (IO) 4727
Dunia Usaha. (IO) 1074
Dunia Wanita. (IO) 4840
Dunlop Estates News. (MY) 4291
Dunmow Broadcast & District Advertiser. (UK) 2193
Dunn & Hargitt's Commodity Service. (US ISSN 0012-7167) 944
Dunn Report. (US) 4126, 4007
Dunnell Minnesota Digest. (US) 2621
Dunoon Observer & Argyllshire Standard. (UK) 3999, 4127
Dunrobin Piper. (US ISSN 0741-5273) 1999
DunsEuropa. (UK) 1038
Dunsink Observatory. Publications. (IE ISSN 0070-7643) 364
Dunstaffnage Marine Laboratory and Scottish Marine Biological Association. Annual Reports. (UK) 437
Dunya al-Maktabat. (BA) 2756
Duo Yun. (CC ISSN 1000-6028) 325
Duodecim. (FI ISSN 0012-7183) 3095
Duodecimal Bulletin. (US ISSN 0046-0826) 3035
DuPage County Bar Association Brief see D C B A Brief 2617
▼DuPage County Marketing Directory. (US) 1133
Duplex Planet. (US ISSN 0882-2549) 2053, 2912
DuPont Registry. (US) 4689
Duquesne Law Review. (US ISSN 0093-3058) 2621
Duquesne Studies. Language and Literature Series. (US) 2811, 2912
Duquesne Studies. Philological Series see Duquesne Studies. Language and Literature Series 2811
Duran-Duran. (AT) 4434
Durban Corporation Directory. (SA ISSN 0378-9195) 1133
Durban High School Old Boys' Club. Bulletin. (SA ISSN 0012-7221) 1297
†Durban Metropolitan Economy Project.(SA) 5182

Durban Municipal Library. Annual Report. (SA) 2756
Durban Museum Novitates. (SA ISSN 0012-723X) 581
Durch. (AU ISSN 1010-8378) 325
Durch die Fensterscheibe. (US ISSN 0882-5874) 2149
Durch Stipendien Studieren. (GW ISSN 0070-7767) 1626
Durchblick und Dienst. (GW) 4236
Durchbruch. (GW) 1626
Durez Molder Newsbriefs see OxyChem Newsbriefs 3864
Durham Archaeological Journal. (UK) 271, 2359
Durham Business Directory & Consumers' Guide. (CN) 1133
Durham Classified Business Directory & Consumers' Guide see Durham Business Directory & Consumers' Guide 1133
Durham Community Sports News. (US) 4471
Durham University Geological Society. Journal see Arthur Holmes Society. Journal 1541
Durham University Journal. (UK ISSN 0012-7280) 2912, 1276, 2310
Durkee Family Newsletter. (US ISSN 0892-208X) 2149
Durlach am Wochenende. (GW) 2188
Duroc News. (US ISSN 0012-7299) 216
Dursleh Urlag/Fine Arts. (MP) 325
Durum Kernels. (US) 205
Duster. (US) 1310
▼Dusty Dog. (US) 2992
Dusty Trails. (US) 2149
Dutch American Genealogist see Dutch Church Transcripts 2149
Dutch Archaeological and Historical Society. Studies. (NE ISSN 0169-8060) 271, 2359
Dutch Art and Architecture Today - D A and A T see Kunst en Museumjournaal 333
Dutch-Australian Weekly. (AT ISSN 0012-7310) 1999
Dutch Birding. (NE ISSN 0167-2878) 563
Dutch Central Bank. Quarterly Bulletin. see De Nederlandsche Bank N.V. Quarterly Bulletin 792
Dutch Chemical Industry Handbook. (NE) 1134, 1176
Dutch Church Transcripts. (US) 2149, 4236
Dutch Company Yearbook. (NE) 659
Dutch Ed. see Promosafe 3620
Dutch Film. (NE) 3508
Dutch Quarterly Review see D Q R 2910
Dutch Quarterly Review of Anglo American Letters see D Q R 2910
Dutch Reformed Church News see D R C News 4235
Dutch Theses. see Bibliografie van Nederlandse Proefschriften 391
Dutch Vacuum Society. Journal. see N E V A C Blad 3825
Dutchess County Historical Society. Yearbook. (US ISSN 0739-8565) 2404
Duty and Tax-Free Shop World Guide Series see Best 'N' Most in D F S 901
Duty Free Magazine. (UK) 4802
Duzhe Wenzhai/Reader's Digest. (CC ISSN 1000-0453) 2181
Dvigateli Vnutrennego Sgoraniya. (KR ISSN 0419-8719) 3843, 1928
†Dvorak Developments. (US ISSN 0743-4200) 5182
Dvorak International. Quarterly. (US) 1058, 1482
Dvorak International. Typing Manual for Computer and Typewriter. (US) 1058, 1482
Dwarf Conifer Notes. (US) 2125
Dwarf Iris Society Portfolio. (US ISSN 0418-2057) 2125
Dwelling. see Vivienda 308
Dwon Lwak/People's Voice. (UG ISSN 0419-8735) 2220
DX Magazine. (GW ISSN 0175-6877) 2149
DX Monitor. (US ISSN 0899-9732) 1356, 2435

DX Ontario. (CN ISSN 1183-0344) 1356
DX Reporter. (US) 1356, 2435
Dyason House Papers see Asian Pacific Review 5139
Dychova Hudba. (CS) 3549
Dydaktyka Szkoly Wyzszej. (PL ISSN 0420-2384) 1705
Dyers Dyegest see Textile Industries Dyegest Southern Africa 4625
Dyes and Pigments. (UK ISSN 0143-7208) 1176, 3817
Dyke Diannic Wicca Separatist Amazon Magick. (US) 2452, 4840
Dyn. (UK) 238
Dyna. (CK ISSN 0012-7353) 1819, 3482
Dyna. (SP ISSN 0012-7361) 1819
Dynamath. (US ISSN 0732-7773) 1253, 3035
Dynamic. (US) 3891, 1253
Dynamic Business. (US ISSN 0279-4039) 1114
Dynamic Chiropractic. (US) 3214
Dynamic Economics Series see Dynamic Economics: Theory and Applications (Series) 659
Dynamic Economics: Theory and Applications (Series). (NE) 659
Dynamic Engineering. see Dongli Gongcheng 1928
Dynamic Psychotherapy see Psychoanalysis and Psychotherapy 3352
Dynamic Supervision. (US ISSN 0012-7396) 1008
Dynamica. (SA ISSN 0250-0027) 659
Dynamical Properties of Solids. (NE) 3843
▼Dynamics and Control. (NE ISSN 0925-4668) 1437
Dynamics and Stability of Systems. (UK ISSN 0268-1110) 1394, 4308
Dynamics of Atmospheres and Oceans. (NE ISSN 0377-0265) 3435, 1604
Dynamik im Handel. (GW ISSN 0722-6950) 2091, 1008
Dynamis. (SP ISSN 0211-9536) 3095
Dynamisch Oost-Nederland. (NE ISSN 0921-3619) 659
Dynamisch Overijssel see Dynamisch Oost-Nederland 659
Dynamite. (US ISSN 0163-3562) 1253
Dynamite International. (NE ISSN 0012-7418) 3549, 1297
Dynamite Write Children News. (CN) 1253, 1236
Dynamo Newsletter. (US) 1460
Dynasty. (CH) 4802
Dynix Dataline. (US ISSN 8756-2294) 2797
Dyo. (GR) 1253
Dyr i Natur og Museum. (DK ISSN 0109-1190) 581
Dyrenes Ret. (DK) 4809
Dyskusja. (PL) 1999, 2912
Dysmorphology and Clinical Genetics. (US ISSN 0893-6633) 541
Dysphagia. (US ISSN 0179-051X) 3095
Dystonia Dialogue. (US) 3095
▼Dzah Dzeel/Market. (MP) 1038
Dzaluu Dzohion Buteegch/Young Inventor. (MP) 4308, 4596
▼Dzar Bichig/Publicity Herald. (MP) 1372, 3508
Dzieje Lublina. (PL ISSN 0419-8816) 2359
Dzieje Najnowsze. (PL ISSN 0419-8824) 2310
Dzieje Polskiej Granicy Zachodniej. (PL ISSN 0070-7791) 2359
Dziennik Polski i Dziennik Zolnierza/Polish Daily and the Soldiers Daily. (UK) 1999, 3941
Dziennik Zwiazkowy/Polish Daily. (US) 1999
Dziko. (MW ISSN 0420-2392) 2246
Dzimtenes Balss see Tevzemes Avize 2886
Dzvin. (KR) 2864
▼E. (US ISSN 1046-8021) 1947
†E. (GW) 5182

E A

E A A. Technical Counselor Newsletter. (Experimental Aircraft Association) (US) **51**, 2435

E A A Experimenter. (Experimental Aircraft Association) (US ISSN 0894-1289) **51**, 4672

E A A Review. (Edinburgh Architectural Association) (UK ISSN 0307-1634) **299**

E A A S Newsletter. (European Association for American Studies) (FR ISSN 0423-6645) **3955**

E A C R O T A N A L Information. (Eastern African Centre for Research on Oral Traditions and African National Languages) (TZ) **2811**, 2912

E A C R O T A N A L Studies & Documents. (Eastern African Centre for Research on Oral Traditions and African National Languages) (TZ) **2811**, 2912

E A F; Ethnographisch-Archaeologische Forschungen Bereich Ur- und Fruehgeschichte und dem Bereich Ethnographie der Sektion Geschichte der Humboldt-Universitaet *see* E A Z **238**

E A G Publicaciones. (Secretaria de Estado de Agricultura y Ganaderia) (AG) **87**

E A N H S Bulletin. (East Africa Natural History Society) (KE) **437**, 1487, 1559, 1947

E A O. (Enseignement Assiste par Ordinateur) (FR) **4597**

E A P Digest. (Employee Assistance Programs) (US ISSN 0273-8910) **1536**

E A P R Abstracts of Conference Papers. (European Association for Potato Research) (NE) **176**

E A R. (Edinburgh Architecture Research) (UK ISSN 0140-5039) **299**

E A R C O S Quarterly. (East Asia Regional Council of Overseas Schools) (US) **1721**

†E A R for Children. (Evaluation of Audio Recordings) (US ISSN 0734-5542) **5182**

▼E A R S L Advances in Remote Sensing. (European Association of Remote Sensing Laboratories) (FR ISSN 1017-4613) **1543**

E A R S L Directory. (FR ISSN 0257-053X) **1134**, 1543

E A R S L News *see* E A R S L Newsletter **1543**

E A R S L Newsletter. (European Association of Remote Sensing Laboratories) (FR ISSN 0257-0521) **1543**

E A S C O N. Electronics and Aerospace System Conference and Exposition. (Record) *see* I E E E - A E S C O N. Aerospace and Electronics System Conference. Record **1894**

E A Supplement. (Encyclopedia of Associations) (US ISSN 0028-4238) **1780**

E A T C Monographs in Theoretical Computer Science. (US) **1394**

E A: the Journal of the National Association of Enrolled Agents. (US) **659**

E A Z. (Ethnographisch-Archaeologische Zeitschrift) (GW ISSN 0012-7477) **238**, 271

E Alert. (US) **659**

E & B Guide. (Estimators & Buyers') (CN) **3999**

E & M J *see* Engineering & Mining Journal **3483**

E & M J International Directory of Mining. (Engineering & Mining Journal) (US) **3482**

E & M J International Directory of Mining and Mineral Processing Operations *see* E & M J International Directory of Mining **3482**

E & M J Mining Activity Digest. (Engineering & Mining Journal) (US) **3405**, 3482

†E & M Newsletter. (CN ISSN 0703-6892) **5182**

▼E & P Environment. (Exploration & Production) (US ISSN 1054-6464) **3685**, 1947

E B. (GW ISSN 0938-8702) **659**, 1008, 1114

E B A E - I C A E Newsletter *see* E B A E Newsletter **1683**

E B A E Newsletter. (European Bureau of Adult Education) (NE) **1683**

E B B *see* Economic Bulletin Board **861**

E B G *see* Japan Electronics Buyers' Guide **1141**

E B - Metronom. (GW) **3549**

E B P R Research Reports *see* Spencer's Research Reports on Employee Benefits **994**

E B Quarterly. (US) **776**, 1064, 1092

E B R I Issue Brief. (Employee Benefit Research Institute) (US ISSN 0887-137X) **1064**, 2530

E B U Monographs, Legal and Administrative Series. (European Broadcasting Union) (SZ) **1372**

E B U Review. Geneva Edition. (Programmes, Administration, Law) *see* E B U Review. (Programmes, Administration, Law Edition) **5182**

†E B U Review. (Programmes, Administration, Law Edition). (European Broadcasting Union) (SZ) **5182**

E B U Review, Technical *see* E B U Technical Review **1335**

E B U Seminars for Producers and Directors of Educational Television for Schools and Adults. (European Broadcasting Union) (SZ) **1373**

E B U Technical Review. (European Broadcasting Union) (SZ ISSN 0251-0936) **1335**, 1373

E B U Workshops for Producers and Directors of Television Programmes for Children and Young People. (European Broadcasting Union) (SZ) **1373**

E C A Magazine. (Engineering Contractors' Association) (US ISSN 0896-3169) **616**, 1864

E C A Publication. (Engineering Contractors' Association) (US) **1864**

†E C A Year Book Desk Diary. (Electrical Contractors' Association) (UK) **5182**

E C Agricultural Price Indices *see* Agricultural Statistics Series No.3: European Communities Index of Agricultural Prices **132**

E C & M *see* Electrical Construction & Maintenance **1887**

E C & M's Electrical Products Yearbook. (Electrical Construction and Maintenance) (US ISSN 0093-3236) **1886**

E C B Newsletter *see* G A T F World **3999**

E C D *see* Energy Conservation Digest **1787**

E C Dairy Facts and Figures. (European Community) (UK) **199**

E.C. Doors and Windows. (Evangelical Congregational Church) (US) **4236**

E C E Teacher *see* Early Childhood Teacher **1626**

E C Energy Monthly. (UK) **1785**

The E C Grants and Loans Databases. (UK) **776**, 2621

†E C J R: European Court of Justice Reporter. (UK ISSN 0262-5156) **5183**

E C L R: European Competition Law Review. (UK ISSN 0144-3054) **2621**

E.C.M. News. (European Christian Mission (Australian Section) Inc.) (AT) **4175**

E C M T Statistical Report on Road Accidents. (European Council of Ministers of Transport) (FR) **4663**, 10, 4117

E C N Literature News. (Electronic Component News) (US) **1766**

E C O D O C. (FR ISSN 0292-1782) **713**, 10

E C O L News. (Environmental Conservation Library) (US) **1947**, 1487, 1785

†E C O - L O G Information Services. (CN ISSN 0704-4062) **5183**

▼E C Public Contract Law. (European Community) (GW ISSN 0939-4508) **4087**

E C S G News *see* I I C I T News **1773**

E C S L News. (European Centre for Space) (NE) **51**

E C S S I D Bulletin. (HU ISSN 0139-3669) **4370**

E C S School Libraries Bulletin *see* School Libraries Bulletin **2783**

E C U Newsletter. (IT) **3891**

E D A. (Electronic Design Automation Ltd.) (UK ISSN 0951-5690) **1766**, 4597

E D A C *see* European Conference on Design Automation **1413**

E D A M Newsletter *see* Early Drama, Art, and Music Review **4632**

E D A P *see* European Directory of Agrochemical Products **88**

E D A V. (Educazione Audiovisiva) (IT ISSN 0393-098X) **1748**

E D B *see* Energy Data Base **1787**

†E D B - Kursuskatalog. (DK ISSN 0108-9900) **5183**

E D C Newsletter. (European Documentation Centre) (UK ISSN 0262-9216) **2756**, 399

E D F Letter. (Environmental Defense Fund) (US ISSN 0163-2566) **1947**, 2621

E D F Newsletter *see* E D F Letter **1947**

E D F Notebook. (PH) **659**

▼E D I. (Electrical Design and Installation) (US) **1886**

▼E D I in Finance Newsletter. (Electronic Data Interchange) (UK ISSN 0960-4634) **805**

E D I Monthly Report. (Electronic Data Interchange) (US) **1450**

E D I News. (Electronic Data Interchange) (US ISSN 0894-9212) **1446**

▼E D I T. (European Dimension in Teaching) (UK ISSN 0962-4244) **1626**

†E D I World. (UK ISSN 0955-1255) **5183**

E D M A - Gram. (European Direct Marketing Association) (BE) **31**, 1038

E D M Digest *see* Diemaking, Stamping & EDMing **3017**

▼E D M S Journal. (Electronic Document Management Systems) (US ISSN 1058-0379) **1444**

E D M Today. (US) **3017**

▼E D N Asia. (Electronics Design News) (US) **1766**

E D N Career News *see* E D N News **1766**

E D N Magazine. (Electronics Design News) (UK) **1766**

E D N News. (US) **1766**

E D N Product News *see* E D N News **1766**

E D P A C S. (US ISSN 0736-6981) **1434**

E D P Auditing. (Electronic Data Processing) (US ISSN 0746-7265) **1450**

E D P Auditor *see* E D P Auditor Journal **1450**

E D P Auditor Journal. (Electronic Data Processing) (US) **1450**, 1434, 1526

E D P Auditors Association. Control Objectives. (Electronic Data Processing) (US) **1450**, 826, 1058

E D P Auditors Association. Update. (Electronic Data Processing) (US) **1450**, 826, 1058

†E D P Buyer's Guide. (Electronic Data Processing) (CN) **5183**

E D P China Report *see* China Informatics **1423**

E D P Guide. (CN) **1450**

E D P In-Depth Reports. (Electronic Data Processing) (CN ISSN 0315-3819) **1450**

E D P Japan Report *see* I D C Japan Report **1424**

E D P Notizie *see* Information e Technology **1058**

E D P Performance Management Handbook *see* I S Capacity Management Handbook Series **1451**

E D P Performance Review *see* Capacity Management Review **1448**

E D P Telematica Notizie *see* Information e Technology **1058**

E D P Weekly. (Electronic Data Processing) (US ISSN 0012-7558) **1450**

E D R A. Annual Conference Proceedings *see* Environmental Design Research Association. Annual Conference Proceedings **299**

E D U C O M Bulletin *see* E D U C O M Review **1689**

E D U C O M Review. (US) **1689**

E D U Q. (CN ISSN 0712-4635) **1676**

E D V & Recht. (AU) **1394**, 2621

E D V - Aspekte. (GW ISSN 0232-6833) **1450**

E D V in Medizin und Biologie - E D V in Medicine and Biology *see* Biometrie and Informatik **3083**

E E (Epargne Europe) *see* E U F I - Journal **776**

E E A. Association of the Electronics, Telecommunications & Business Equipment Industries. Annual Report. (Electronic Engineering Association) (UK) **1886**

E E C - Asia Report. (BE) **905**

E E C Dairy Facts and Figures *see* E C Dairy Facts and Figures **199**

†E E C Information Services. (European Economic Community) (UK ISSN 0262-9380) **5183**

†E E C Information Services. Bulletin. (European Economic Community) (UK) **5183**

▼E E C Newsletter. (NE) **2722**

E E C S - E R L News. (Electrical Engineering & Computer Sciences, Electronics Research Laboratory) (US) **1886**, 1394

E E C - Tin in Tinplate. (European Economic Community) (UK) **3405**, 3648

E E E - Magazine of Circuit Design Engineering *see* E D N Magazine **1766**

E E-Electrical Equipment *see* E E Product News **1766**

E E: Evaluation Engineering. (US ISSN 0149-0370) **1766**

E E G-E M G. (GW ISSN 0012-7590) **3335**

E E G Journal *see* Electroencephalography and Clinical Neurophysiology Including Evoked Potentials and Electromyography and Motor Control **3335**

E E G Labor. (GW ISSN 0170-8287) **3207**

†E E G Vademecum/Selected Agri-Figures of the E.E.C. (NE) **5183**

E E H *see* Explorations in Economic History **894**

†E E I Environmental Journal. (Edison Electric Institute) (US) **5183**

E E I Power Directory *see* Environmental Directory of U.S. Power Plants **1891**

E E I Statistical Releases. Electric Output. (Edison Electric Institute) (US ISSN 0012-7612) **1843**, 1798, 1886

E E I Superdirectory of Power Plant Environmental Data. (US) **1801**, 1947

E E I Washington Letter. (Edison Electric Institute) (US) **1886**, 4059

E E M. (Electronic Engineers Master) (US ISSN 0732-9016) **1766**

E E M A C Report *see* Scanner **1907**

E E O C Compliance Manual. (Equal Employment Opportunity Commission) (US) **977**

†E E O C Compliance Manual (Weekly). (U.S. Equal Employment Opportunity Commission) (US) **5183**

E E O Compliance Manual. (Equal Employment Opportunity) (US) **977**, 2621

†E E O Report. (Equal Employment Opportunity) (US ISSN 0276-5853) **5183**

E E O Review. (US ISSN 0148-6934) 1064, 977

E E O Spotlight see Federal Staffing Digest 4060

E E P S see East European Politics & Societies 3891

E E Product News. (Electronics - Electrical) (US) 1766

E E R. (Environmental Events Record) (UN) 1947

E E R C News. (Earthquake Engineering Research Center) (US ISSN 0739-7704) 1865

E E R C Reports. (Earthquake Engineering Research Center) (US ISSN 0271-0323) 1865

E E R I Newsletter. (Earthquake Engineering Research Institute) (US ISSN 0270-8337) 1543, 1819

E E S I Weekly Bulletin see U.S. Congress. Environmental and Energy Study Institute. Weekly Bulletin 1970

E E's Electronic Distributor see Electronics Distribution Today 5185

†E F B. (Eisenhaendler Fachblatt) (GW ISSN 0046-0877) 5183

E F D S S News see English Dance and Song 3550

E F G Highlights. (US) 3396

E F I L Documentation. (European Federation for Intercultural Learning) (BE) 1721

E F I L Newsletter. (European Federation for Intercultural Learning) (BE) 1721

E F I News. see E F I Nytt 713

E F I Nytt/E F I News. (Ekonomiska Forskningsinstitutet) (SW) 713, 10

E F L Gazette. (UK ISSN 0732-5819) 4370

E F O Collector. (US) 3751

E F S Paa Vaeg see Till Tjaenst 1668

E F S Start see Till Tjaenst 1668

E F T A Bulletin. (European Free Trade Association) (SZ ISSN 0012-7655) 906

E F T A Trade. (European Free Trade Association) (SZ ISSN 0531-4119) 906

†E F T Press Alert. (Electronic Fund Transfer) (US) 5183

E F T Report. (Electronic Funds Transfer) (US ISSN 0195-7287) 805

E G. (End Game) (BE ISSN 0012-7671) 4471

†E G & G Monitor. (US) 5183

E G G Ink. (US) 659

E G Informationen. (GW) 3955

E G Informationen fuer die Schule. (Kommission der Europaeischen Gemeinschaft) (GW) 1626

†E G Magazin. (Europaeische Gemeinschaft) (GW ISSN 0343-6667) 5183

†E G U Bulletin. (CS ISSN 0007-4594) 5183

E G V Information. (Ensomme Gamles Vaern Fonden) (DK ISSN 0107-8275) 4404

E H - Elektro Handel. (GW ISSN 0013-5542) 1766

E H P. (Environmental Health Perspectives) (US ISSN 0091-6765) 1947, 4100

E.H.P. Environmental Health Perspectives see E H P 1947

E I. (Excerpta Indonesica) (NE ISSN 0046-0885) 254, 2328, 2855, 2981

E I. (Elektronik Industrie) (GW ISSN 0174-5522) 1766

E I A Guide see Hi-Tech Buyers Guide 1040

E I A J Newsletter. (Electronics Industries Association Japan) (JA) 1766

▼E I A News. (European Information Association) (UK) 3955

E I A Publications Directory: A User's Guide. (Energy Information Administration) (US) 1785

E I A Review see Environmental Impact Assessment Review 1951

E I B - Information. (European Investment Bank) (EI ISSN 0250-3891) 945

E I C. (Electronique Industrielle & Commerciale) (CN) 1766

E I C see Electrical - Electronics Insulation Conference. Proceedings 1888

†E.I.D.C.T. - C.D.T. Year Book. (Educational Institute of Design Craft & Technology) (UK ISSN 0266-9544) 5183

E I Digest. (US ISSN 1042-251X) 1984

E I - Elettroradio Informazioni. (IT) 1766

E I - Elettroradio Informazioni International. (IT) 1766

E I K see Journal of Information Processing and Cybernetics 1441

E I M Mededelingen. (Economisch Instituut voor het Midden- en Kleinbedrijf) (NE ISSN 0012-768X) 1114

E I P Economic Forecasting Service. (Economic and Industrial Publications) (PK) 860

E I P Industrial Research Service. (Economic and Industrial Publications) (PK) 1074

E I P Investors Service. (Economic and Industrial Publications) (PK) 945

E I P R: European Intellectual Property Review. (UK ISSN 0142-0461) 2621

E I R see Executive Intelligence Review 3893

E I S Cumulative. (Environmental Impact Statement) (US ISSN 0190-0250) 1973

E I S: Digests of Environmental Impact Statements. (US) 1973, 10

E I U Business Update see E I U Europe - Pacific Update 659

E I U Europe - Pacific Update. (Economist Intelligence Unit) (UK) 659

E I U World Outlook. (Economist Intelligence Unit) (UK ISSN 0424-3331) 860

E K-Bladet. (Erhvervskvinders Klub) (DK ISSN 0108-9773) 659, 4840

E L C A Yearbook see Evangelical Lutheran Church in America (Year) 4237

E L C O M P Magazine. (GW ISSN 0171-0958) 1469

▼E L F. (Eclectic Literary Forum) (US ISSN 1054-3376) 2913

E L F see E L F Aquitaine 3685

E L F. (European Labour Forum) (EI ISSN 0960-5398) 3955, 977

E L F Aquitaine. (FR ISSN 0012-7701) 3685, 1785

E L F - Aquitaine News. (FR ISSN 0249-1729) 3685, 1785

E L G News. (Education Librarians Group) (UK) 2756

E L H. (English Literary History) (US ISSN 0013-8304) 2913, 2310

E L N A Buleteno see Esperanto - U S A 2812

E L N A Newsletter see Esperanto - U S A 2812

†E L O. (GW ISSN 0341-4175) 5183

E L T Documents. (UK ISSN 0736-2048) 4370

E L T S A Newsletter. (End Loans to South Africa) (UK) 3955

E - Lehti see Meidan Liike 5235

E M A - Elektrische Maschinen. (GW ISSN 0013-5445) 1886

E M A Journal. (Employment Management Association) (US) 1064, 977, 1008, 3626

E M A Reporter. (Employment Management Association) (US) 977, 1064

E M B O Journal. (European Molecular Biology Organization) (UK ISSN 0261-4189) 476

†E M C. (US) 5183

E M C Technology & Interference Control News. (Electro-Magnetic Compatibility) (US ISSN 0278-4270) 4597

▼E M C Test and Design. (Electromagnetic Compatability) (US) 1886

E M: Ebony Man. (US) 1999, 355

E M I E Bulletin. (Ethnic Materials Information Exchange Round Table) (US ISSN 0737-9021) 1999

E M J: Engineering Management Journal. (US ISSN 1042-9247) 1819

E M K Aktuell. (Evangelisch-methodische Kirche) (GW) 4236

E M M S. (Electronic Mail & Micro Systems) (US ISSN 8756-2537) 1335, 1008, 1350

E M N I D - Informationen see Umfrage und Analyse 39

E M O National Digest see Emergency Preparedness Digest 1273

E M S A Bulletin. (Electron Microscopy Society of America, Inc.) (US ISSN 0146-6119) 559, 3405

†E M S Access (Year). (Emergency Medical Service) (US ISSN 1040-4929) 5183

E M S - Jahrbuch. (Evangelisches Missionswerk in Suedwestdeutschland e.V.) (GW) 4236

The E M S Leader. (US ISSN 0897-0297) 3095, 2461

E M W - Informationen. (Evangelisches Missionswerk) (GW ISSN 0175-7695) 4175

E M World (Electronic Mail) see Postal World 1354

E N A - Economic News from Austria. (US) 860

▼E N A Nursing Scan in Emergency Care. (Emergency Nurses Association) (US) 3171, 10, 3277

E N E A Notiziario-Energia e Innovazione. (IT ISSN 0393-716X) 1785, 4597

E N F O Newsletter. (TH ISSN 0125-1783) 1947

E N I Annual Report. (Ente Nazionale Idrocarburi) (IT) 1785, 1819, 3482, 4618

E N I L Revue. (Ecoles Nationales d'Industrie Laitiere des Organismes Associes) (FR) 199

E N L B see Emergency Nurse Legal Bulletin 3278

E N N. (Electronic News Network) (US ISSN 1060-7870) 1450

E N R. (US ISSN 0891-9526) 1865, 616

E N R Directory of Contractors. (US ISSN 0098-6453) 616

E N R Directory of Design Firms. (US ISSN 0098-6305) 1819, 616, 1134

E N S B A N A Cahiers see Ecole Nationale Superieure de Biologie Appliquee a la Nutrition et a l'Alimentation. Cahiers 3605

E O News Settimanale. (IT) 1766

E O R T C Monograph Series see European Organization for Research on Treatment of Cancer. Monograph Series 3197

E O S - E S D Technology. (Electrical Overstress - Electrostatic Discharge) (US) 4597

E O S - E S D Technology see E O S - E S D Technology Europe 4597

E O S - E S D Technology Europe. (Electrical Overstress - Electrostatic Discharge) (US) 4597

E P see Eisenbahn-technische Praxis 5184

E P A Bulletin see Journal of Educational Planning and Administration 1729

E P A Journal. (U.S. Environmental Protection Agency) (US) 1947

E P A Newsletter. (European Photochemistry Association) (GW ISSN 1011-4246) 1225

E P A Pesticide Label File. (Environmental Protection Agency) (US) 1852

E P A Policy Alert. (Environmental Protection Agency) (US) 1947, 1487, 2621

E P A Publications Bibliography Quarterly Abstracts Bulletin. (US ISSN 0196-0091) 1973

E P & P see Electronic Publishing & Printing 4127

E P & T. (Electronic Products and Technology) (CN ISSN 0708-4366) 1766

E P & T's Electrosource Product Reference Guide & Telephone Directory. (CN) 1766

E P B: Electronic Publishing and Bookselling see Electronic Publishing Business 5185

E P D Film. (GW ISSN 0176-2044) 3508

E P E. (UK) 1886, 1819, 4727

E P E. (European Production Engineer) (GW) 1928, 3017, 3862

E P F Newsletter. (Episcopal Peace Fellowship) (US) 4236

E P F P R. (Egyptian Population and Family Planning Review) (UA) 596

E P I A see Electric Power Industry Abstracts 5185

E P I E Gram: Equipment and Materials see E P I E Gram: The Newsletter of Systemic Change 1626

E P I E Gram: The Newsletter of Systemic Change. (Educational Products Information Exchange Institute) (US) 1626

E P I: Environmental Product Index. (US) 1973, 10, 1984

E P L B see Emergency Physician Legal Bulletin 3096

E P M Entertainment Marketing Sourcebook. (US) 1038, 3674

E P Magazine. (NZ) 4471

E P News. (EI ISSN 0250-5754) 2722

E P O: Catalogo de Equipos para Oficina. (VE) 1058

E P P O Bulletin. (UK ISSN 0250-8052) 176

E P R see Electronic Product Review 1768

E P R I Guide. (Electric Power Research Institute) (US) 1886

E P S see Education Physique et Sport 1748

E P S see Ecumenical Press Service 4175

E P S I G News. (Electronic Publishing Special Interest Group) (US ISSN 1042-3737) 4127

E P S 1 see Education Physique et Sportive au 1er Degre 4471

E P Z A News. (Export Processing Zone Authority) (PH) 906

E Q see Education Quarterly 1629

E Q. (JA) 2985

E Q. (US ISSN 1050-7868) 4460, 1886

E Q A M see Electronic Quality Assurance Microfile 1768

E R A. (Svenska Elverksfoereningen) (SW ISSN 0013-9939) 1886

E R A Technology News. (Electrical Research Association) (UK) 1038, 1819, 3405

E R B Measures. (Educational Records Bureau) (US) 1626

E R B Newsletter see E R B Measures 1626

E R B Occasional Paper Series see University of Dar es Salaam. Economic Research Bureau. Occasional Paper 697

E R B Papers see University of Dar es Salaam. Economic Research Bureau. Papers 697

E-R-C Directory. (Employee Relocation Council) (US ISSN 0160-9629) 4148

E R C O Lichtbericht. (GW) 2558

E R G A. Bibliografico. (SP ISSN 0213-943X) 3623, 10, 3616

E R I C - C R E S S Bulletin. (E R I C Clearinghouse on Rural Education and Small Schools) (US) 1626

E R I C - C U E Trends and Issues. (US ISSN 0889-8022) 1626, 1236, 1999

E R I C - C U E Urban Diversity Series. (US ISSN 0889-8030) 1626

E R I C Clearinghouse for Junior College see E R I C Information Bulletin 1705

†E R I C Clearinghouse for Junior Colleges. Horizons Issues. Monograph Series. (US) 5183

E R I C Clearinghouse for Junior Colleges Digest. (Educational Resources Information Center) (US) **1705**

E R I C Clearinghouse on Rural Education and Small Schools Bulletin see E R I C - C R E S S Bulletin **1626**

E R I C Clearinghouse on Teacher Education. Current Issues Publications. (Educational Resources Information Center) (US) **1626**

E R I C Clearinghouse on Tests, Measurement, and Evaluation. T M E Report Series. (Educational Resources Informational Center) (US) **1626, 4019**

E R I C Clearinghouse on Urban Education. Digest. (US ISSN 0889-8049) **1626, 1236, 1999**

E R I C - I R Update. (Educational Resources Information Center - Information Resources) (US) **2797, 1626, 4597**

E R I C Information Bulletin. (Educational Resources Information Center) (US) **1705**

†E R I C - R C S Newsletter. (US) **5183**

E R I C Two-Year College Information Bulletin see E R I C Information Bulletin **1705**

E R I Perspective. (Energy Research Institute) (SA) **1785**

E R I S A Newsletter. (Employee Retirement Income Security Act) (US ISSN 8755-5379) **977**

E R I S A: The Law and the Code. (Employee Retirement Income Security Act) (US) **977, 2621**

E R M see E R M Journaal **1886**

E R M Installatiejournaal see Installatie Journaal **1899**

E R M Journaal. (NE) **1886, 1038**

E R R Bound Volume see C Q Researcher Bound Volume **3877**

E R S Bulletin. (Educational Research Service) (US) **1726**

E - S A see Christian Social Action **4233**

E S A Bulletin. (European Space Agency) (NE ISSN 0316-4265) **51**

E S A Bulletin see Epiphyllum Bulletin **501**

E S A Foelgeforskning. (DK ISSN 0109-1115) **51**

E S A - I R S News & Views. (European Space Agency) (US) **2797, 67**

E S A Journal. (European Space Agency) (NE ISSN 0379-2285) **51**

E S A Newsletter. (Entomological Society of America) (US ISSN 0273-7353) **530**

E S A - P S S Series see E S A Procedures, Standards and Specifications Series **51**

E S A Procedures, Standards and Specifications Series. (European Space Agency) (NE) **51**

†E.S.A. Quarterly News Bulletin. (Executive Secretaries' Association) (UK) **5183**

E S A R B I C A Journal. (International Council on Archives, Eastern and Southern Africa Regional Branch) (RH ISSN 0376-4753) **2756**

E S A Scientific - Technical Reports, Notes and Memoranda. (European Space Agency) (NE) **51**

E S C A P Energy News. (United Nations Economic and Social Commission for Asia and the Pacific) (UN) **1785**

E S C O L Proceedings. (Eastern States Conference on Linguistics) (US) **2811**

E S C W A Population Bulletin. (Economic and Social Commission for Western Asia) (UN ISSN 0258-1914) **3981**

E S D Technology. (Engineering Society of Detroit) (US ISSN 8750-7811) **1819**

†E S D: The Electronic System Design Magazine. (US ISSN 0893-2565) **5183**

E S E Notes. (Environmental Sciences and Engineering) (US ISSN 0546-4552) **1947**

E S F (Year). (Environmental Science and Forestry) (US) **2098, 1947**

E S G - Nachrichten see Ansaetze **4163**

E S I G see Expert Systems in Government Conference **5189**

E S J see Al-Majallah al-Ihsa'iyyah al-Misriyyah **4578**

E S O A A Newsletter see Eight-Sheet Outdoor Report **31**

E S O Foelgeforskning. (European Southern Observatory) (GW ISSN 0108-9358) **364**

E S O P see Epigraphic Society. Occasional Papers **271**

E S O P E. (Etudes Sociales-Politiques, Economiques) (FR ISSN 0421-4226) **3891**

E S O P Report. (Employee Stock Ownership Plan) (US) **1008, 945**

E S P Journal see English for Specific Purposes **1749**

E S P News. (US) **3662**

E S Q. (US ISSN 0093-8297) **2913**

E S R. Newsletter. (Eastern Ski Representatives Association) (US) **4545**

E S R Buyers' Guide. (Eastern Ski Representatives Association) (US) **4545**

E S R C Data Archive Bulletin. (Economic and Social Research Council Data Archive) (UK) **4370**

E S R C Studentship Handbook. (Economic and Social Research Council) (UK ISSN 0269-2554) **1693, 4371**

E S S Employment Newsletter see Executive Search Service News **4405**

†E S V Programmbereiche Philologie-Volkskunde- Geschichte. (Erich Schmidt Verlag) (GW) **5183**

E S V Programmbereiche Recht - Wirtschaft - Technik - Umwelt see E S V Sortimenter Informationen Recht - Wirtschaft - Technik - Umwelt - Philologie **4127**

E S V Sortimenter Informationen Recht - Wirtschaft - Technik - Umwelt - Philologie. (Erich /Schmidt Verlag GmbH & Co. (Bielefeld)) (GW) **4127**

E.S. Woodward Lectures in Economics. (CN) **659**

E - Sheet Weekly Update. (CN) **1947**

E T A see Elektrowaerme International. Part A: Elektrowaerme im Technischen Ausbau **2298**

E T A Association Newsletter see E T A Technician Association News **1766**

E.T.A. Hoffmann-Gesellschaft. Mitteilungen. (GW ISSN 0073-2885) **2913**

E T A Technician Association News. (Electronics Technicians Association) (US) **1766**

E T B A Investment Guide see Hellenic Industrial Development Bank. Investment Guide **948**

E T B - T U G see Chaleur et Climats **2298**

E T C H. (Ethical Tablet and Capsule Handbook) (AT ISSN 0157-9509) **3724**

E T Cetera. (Early Typewriter Collectors Association) (US) **1058, 257**

E T E P. (European Transactions on Electrical Power Engineering) (GW ISSN 0939-3072) **1886**

E T I. (Electronique Techniques et Industries) (FR ISSN 0760-0909) **1766**

E T I: Electronics Today International. (UK ISSN 0957-0438) **1766**

E T Ideas. (US) **1626**

E T Journal see Journal of Enterostomal Therapy **3380**

E T R and D see Educational Technology Research & Development **1748**

E T S Developments. (Educational Testing Service) (US ISSN 0046-1547) **1626**

E T S News. (Electric Thermal Storage) (US) **1886**

E T T I see Educational and Training Technology International **1748**

E T V. (Educazione e Televisione) (IT) **1626, 1373**

E T V Newsletter. (Educational Television) (US ISSN 0012-8023) **1748**

E T Z. (GW) **1886**

E T Z Archiv see E T E P **1886**

E Tipografia see Tipografia **4006**

E U D I S E D - R & D Bulletin. (European Documentation and Information System for Education) (GW ISSN 0378-7192) **1676**, 10

E U F I - Journal. (European Financial Services) (EI) **776**

E U L A R Bulletin. (European League Against Rheumatism) (SZ ISSN 0379-1041) **3369**

E U T Reports see Eindhoven University of Technology. Research Reports **1886**

E und W. (Elektro und Wirtschaft Verlagsgesellschaft mbH) (AU) **1886, 659**

E V News see Electric Vehicle News **4689**

E W see Economic Week **777**

E W Design Engineers' Handbook see E W Design Engineers' Handbook and Manufacturers Directory **1819**

E W Design Engineers' Handbook and Manufacturers Directory. (Electronic Warfare) (US) **1819**

E W G-Warenhandel. (GW ISSN 0014-3871) **906**

E W R. (GW) **380**

E W Special. (NE) **4649**

E W W see English World Wide **2812**

E Z - Eisenwaren und Hausrat. (GW) **642**

E Z Search - Mining. (US) **3482, 4359**

E Z W - Texte. (Evangelische Zentralstelle fuer Weltanschauungsfragen) (GW ISSN 0344-9106) **4175, 3765**

Eads Bridge. (US) **2913**

Eagle. (UK) **1253**

Eagle (Colorado Springs). (US) **4503**

Eagle (Corpus Christi) see Eagle Investigators' News **1514**

Eagle (Galena). (US) **1947, 1487**

Eagle (Naugatuck). (US) **1999, 2054, 2404**

Eagle (New York). (US) **3457**

The Eagle (Phoenix). (US) **776**

Eagle (Price). (US) **1626**

Eagle (Washington). (US ISSN 0012-8082) **1310**

Eagle Investigators' News. (US) **1514, 1526**

Eagle Leader. (US) **1297**

Eagle Magazine. (US) **1297**

Eagle Wing Press see Eagle (Naugatuck) **1999**

Eagle's Eye. (US ISSN 0046-0915) **2000**

Eagle's Voice. see Wanbli Ho **2028**

Eaglet. (US ISSN 0732-1007) **2149**

Ealing Gazette Series. (UK) **2193**

†Ealing Miscellany. (UK) **5183**

Ear and Hearing. (US ISSN 0196-0202) **3314**

Ear: Magazine of New Music. (US ISSN 0893-9500) **3549, 3594**

Ear, Nose and Throat Journal. (US ISSN 0145-5613) **3314**

Early American Industries Association. Chronicle. (US ISSN 0012-8147) **1074**

Early American Life. (US ISSN 0012-8155) **2558**, 355, 2551

Early American Literature. (US ISSN 0012-8163) **2913**

Early Child Development and Care. (US ISSN 0300-4430) **1236**, 3320

Early Childhood Music see Ultimate Early Childhood Music Resource **3585**

Early Childhood Music Quarterly see Ultimate Early Childhood Music Resource **3585**

Early Childhood News. (US) **1236**

Early Childhood Research Quarterly. (US ISSN 0885-2006) **1626**

Early Childhood Teacher. (US) **1626**, 1460, 1477, 1689

Early China. (US ISSN 0362-5028) **2337**

Early Days. (AT ISSN 0080-4738) **2344**

▼Early Development and Parenting. (UK ISSN 1057-3593) **4019**

Early Drama, Art, and Music Review. (US ISSN 1048-9401) **4632**, 325, 2913, 3549

Early Education and Development. (US ISSN 1040-9289) **1626**, 4019

Early Human Development. (IE ISSN 0378-3782) **3291**, 3320

Early Intervention. (US ISSN 1058-8396) **1735**, 1236, 3320

Early Irish Law Series. (IE ISSN 0790-4657) **2359**, 2621

Early Keyboard Journal. (US ISSN 0899-8132) **3549**

Early Keyboard Studies Newsletter. (US ISSN 0882-0201) **3550**, 1748

Early Latin Church. (US) **4175**, 2000

Early Man News. (GW ISSN 0174-4224) **271**, 238

▼Early Modern History Review. (UK ISSN 0962-0648) **2310**

Early Morn African Violet Group Newsletter. (AT ISSN 1033-0003) **2125**

Early Music. (UK ISSN 0306-1078) **3550**

Early Music History. (UK ISSN 0261-1279) **3550**

Early Music Newsletter. (US) **3550**

Early Music Record Services. Monthly Review. (UK ISSN 0144-8072) **3550**

†Early Records of Upper East Tennessee. (US) **5183**

Early Typewriter Collectors Association Cetera see E T Cetera **1058**

Early Warning Forecast. (US ISSN 0733-0138) **860**

Early Warning Report. (US ISSN 0193-3655) **1373**

Early Years. (UK ISSN 0957-5146) **1748**

Early Years - K-8 see Teaching K-8 **1761**

Early 18th & 19th Century Sculpture in the British Isles see Courtauld Institute Illustration Archives. Archive 4 **323**

Earn & Learn: Cooperative Education Opportunities Offered by the Federal Government. (US ISSN 0277-7002) **1705**

Earnings and Employment Trends. (CN) **713**

Earnings - Industry and Services. (EI ISSN 0259-0492) **713**, 4570

Earnshaw's Infants' and Children's Review see Earnshaw's Infants, Girls and Boys Wear Review **1284**

Earnshaw's Infants, Girls and Boys Wear Review. (US ISSN 0161-2786) **1284**, 1236

Earnshaw's Plus Sizes. (US) **1290**

EARSeL Advances in Remote Sensing see E A R S L Advances in Remote Sensing **1543**

EARSeL Newsletter see E A R S L Newsletter **1543**

Earth/Chijo. (JA) **87**

Earth. (US) **616**

▼Earth (Waukesha). (US ISSN 1056-148X) **1543**

Earth and Cosmos - D J O. see Aarde en Kosmos - D J O **4295**

Earth and Mineral Sciences. (US ISSN 0026-4539) **1543**, 3482

Earth and Planetary Science Letters. (NE ISSN 0012-821X) **1543**

Earth Construction and Transport. see Maarakennus ja Kuljetus **4745**

Earth Corps: The Daily Planet. (US) **4308**

Earth First! (US ISSN 1047-7195) **1487**, 1947

Earth Garden. (AT ISSN 0310-222X) **4434**

Earth Guild - Grateful Union Mail Order Catalog see Earth Guild Mail Order Catalog **4141**

Earth Guild Mail Order Catalog. (US) **4141**

Earth in Space. (US) **364**

Earth Island Journal. (US ISSN 1041-0406) **1947**, 1487

Earth Matters see Common Ground (Des Moines) **4261**

Earth, Moon and Planets. (NE ISSN 0167-9295) **364**

Earth Observation Quarterly. (NE) 51
Earth-Oriented Applications of Space Technology see Space Technology 4609
†Earth Resources: A Continuing Bibliography with Indexes. (US ISSN 0145-5605) 5183
Earth Resources Mapping in Africa. (KE) 2246
†Earth Science. (US ISSN 0012-8228) 5183
Earth Science and Related Information. (AT ISSN 0311-3531) 1550
†Earth Science Bulletin. (US ISSN 0012-8236) 5183
Earth Science Conservation. (UK ISSN 0142-2324) 1543, 1487
Earth Science Reviews. (NE ISSN 0012-8252) 1543
Earth Sciences History. (US) 1543
Earth Sciences Programme Newsletter. (UK) 1559
Earth Sciences Series. (UN ISSN 0070-7910) 1543
Earth Surface Processes and Landforms. (UK ISSN 0197-9337) 1559
Earth System Monitor. (US) 1604
Earthkeeper. (CN) 1947
Earthkeeping see Earthkeeping Ontario 88
Earthkeeping Ontario. (CN ISSN 1183-630X) 88, 4175
▼EarthLight. (US ISSN 1050-0413) 4175, 1487
Earthmind Newsletter. (US) 1785
Earthmover and Civil Contractor. (AT ISSN 0314-4224) 1865, 616
Earthmovers see Earthmover and Civil Contractor 1865
Earthmoving. see Maansiirto 1871
Earthquake Engineering and Engineering Vibration. see Dizhen Gongcheng yu Gongcheng Zhendong 1588
Earthquake Engineering and Structural Dynamics. (UK ISSN 0098-8847) 1865
Earthquake Engineering Research Institute Newsletter see E E R I Newsletter 1543
Earthquake History of the United States. (US) 1588
Earthquake Prediction Research. (NE ISSN 0286-0619) 1588
Earthquake Research in China. (US ISSN 0891-4176) 1559, 1588
Earthquake Research in Shanxi. see Shanxi Dizhen 1594
Earthquake Spectra. (US ISSN 8755-2930) 1588
EarthQuest. (US) 1947
Earth's Daughters. (US ISSN 0163-0989) 4840, 2913
Earthtreks Digest see Earthtreks Magazine 5183
†Earthtreks Magazine. (US) 5183
Earthwatch. (US ISSN 8750-0183) 4308, 4371
Earthwatch Oregon. (US) 1947
Earthwise see Earthwise Review 2992
Earthwise Consumer. (US) 1504
Earthwise Literary Calendar. (US ISSN 0190-1761) 2992, 325
Earthwise Review. (US) 2992, 1487
Earwig. (NZ) 2864
East. (JA ISSN 0012-8295) 2207, 2337, 3637
East Africa High Commissions Desert Locust Survey. Report see Desert Locust Control Organization for Eastern Africa. Annual Report 175
East Africa Journal. (TZ ISSN 0012-8309) 2332
East Africa Journal of Rural Development see Eastern Africa Journal of Rural Development 149
East Africa Natural History Society Bulletin see E A N H S Bulletin 437
East Africa Report on Trade and Industry. (KE) 860
East African Academy. Foundation Lectures see Kenya National Academy for Advancement of Arts and Sciences. Foundation Lectures 2510

East African Academy. Proceedings see Kenya National Academy for Advancement of Arts and Sciences. Proceedings 2510
East African Agricultural and Forestry Journal. (KE ISSN 0012-8325) 88, 2098
East African Community. East African Meteorological Department. Annual Report see Kenya Meteorological Department. Annual Report 3438
East African Community. Economic and Statistical Review. (KE ISSN 0012-9992) 713
East African Development Bank. Annual Report. (UG ISSN 1015-0676) 776
East African Economic Review. (KE) 659
East African Freshwater Fisheries Research Organization. Annual Report see Uganda Freshwater Fisheries Research Organization. Annual Report 2050
East African Geographical Review. (UG ISSN 0070-7961) 2246
East African Institute of Malaria and Vectorborne Diseases. Annual Report.(TZ) 3218
East African Law Journal. (KE) 2621
East African Management Journal. (KE ISSN 0012-8341) 1008
East African Medical Journal. (KE ISSN 0012-835X) 3095
East African Pharmaceutical Journal. (KE) 3724
East African Quarterly Economic and Statistical Bulletin see East African Community. Economic and Statistical Review 713
East African Research Information Centre. E A R I C Information Circular see Kenya National Academy for Advancement of Arts and Sciences. Research Information Circulars 2333
East African Studies. (TZ ISSN 0424-0928) 4371
East Africana Accessions Bulletin. (TZ ISSN 0856-0455) 2328
East and Maghreb. (IS) 2000, 2506
East and West. (IT ISSN 0012-8376) 3637
East and West Series. (II ISSN 0012-8384) 4175, 3765
East Anglia Guide. (UK) 4760
East Anglian Archaeology. Report. (UK ISSN 0307-2460) 271
East Anglian Bibliography. (UK ISSN 0046-0958) 399
East Anglian Farmers Guide. (UK) 88
East Anglican Ship and Boat Builders Employers Association. Quarterly Newsletter. (UK) 4727
East Asia. (GW ISSN 0723-8398) 860, 3959
East Asia Bibliography. (UK) 714, 399
East Asia Culture. see Dong-A Munhua 3637
East Asia High Tech Review. (US) 4597
†East Asia Library Series. (US) 5183
East Asia Millions see East Asia's Millions 4175
East Asia Regional Council of Overseas Schools Quarterly see E A R C O S Quarterly 1721
East Asian Cultural Studies see Asian Research Trends: a Humanities and Social Science Review 3634
East Asian Historical Monographs. (US) 3637, 2338
East Asian Pastoral Review. (PH) 4263
East Asian Research Aids and Translations. (US) 3637
East Asian Social Science Monographs. (US) 2338, 4371
East Asia's Millions. (US) 4175
East Carolina University Publications in History. (US ISSN 0070-8089) 2405
East China Institute of Engineering. Journal. see Huadong Gongxueyuan Xuebao 1823

East China Normal University. Journal (Education Edition). see Huadong Shifan Daxue Xuebao (Jiaoyu Ban) 1637
East China Normal University. Journal (Natural Science Edition). see Huadong Shifan Daxue Xuebao (Ziran Kexue Ban) 4313
East China Normal University. Journal. (Social Science Edition). see Huadong Shifan Daxue Xuebao (Zhexue Shehui Kexue Ban) 4374
East China Sea. see Dong Hai 2912
East Coast Angler. (US) 4545
East Coast Iron Biker News. (US) 4518
East Coast Rocker. (US) 3550
East Cork News. (IE) 2864
East Europe Agriculture see East Europe & USSR Agriculture & Food 1134
East Europe & China Agriculture & Food see East Europe & USSR Agriculture & Food 1134
▼East Europe & The Republics. (US ISSN 1060-6157) 776, 906
East Europe & USSR Agriculture & Food. (UK) 1134, 88
East Europe in German Books. (US ISSN 0070-8097) 4799, 2328
East Europe Monographs. (US ISSN 0070-8100) 3955
East Europe Report. (US) 3891, 4434
East European Banker. (IE) 776
East European Industrial Monitor. (US) 906, 1074
East European Insurance Report. (UK) 2531
East European Markets. (UK ISSN 0262-0456) 659, 776
East European News. (US) 977, 3891
East European Politics & Societies. (US ISSN 0888-3254) 3891, 2359
East European Quarterly. (US ISSN 0012-8449) 4371
East European Statistics Service. (BE) 714
East European Trade. (II ISSN 0012-8457) 906
East - Florida Gazette. (US) 2405
East German Studies. see D D R Studien 2309
East Kentuckian. (US ISSN 0424-107X) 2149
East Lakes Geographer. (US ISSN 0070-8127) 2246
East Libraries Bulletin see Northern Librarian 2777
East Midland Geographer. (UK ISSN 0012-8481) 2246
East Midlands Bibliography. (UK ISSN 0029-2885) 2328
East Midlands Business Directory. (UK) 814
East Midlands Chamber of Commerce Regional Directory see East Midlands Business Directory 814
East of England Show Catalogue. (UK) 88
East Riding Archaeologist. (UK ISSN 0012-852X) 271
East Riding Farmer. (UK) 88
East St. Louis Monitor. (US ISSN 0046-0966) 2000
East Side Chamber of Commerce Newsletter. (US ISSN 0012-8538) 814
East Side Monthly. (US) 2225
East Sussex Farmer. (UK ISSN 0012-8546) 88
East Tennessean. (US) 1310
East Tennessee Development District Economic Statistics. (US) 4570, 860
East Tennessee Historical Society's Publications. (US ISSN 0361-6193) 2405
East Tennessee Roots. (US) 2149
East Texan. (US) 1310
East Texas Historical Journal. (US) 2405
East Texas Medicine. (US) 3095
†East Timor Update. (US) 5183
East - West Business Analyst see Central - East Europe Business Analyst 903

EASTERN EUROPE 6137

East-West Center. Papers see East-West Population Institute. Papers 3981
▼East-West Center. Views. (US ISSN 1055-9795) 3955
East-West Digest. (UK ISSN 0012-8627) 3955
East-West Education. (US) 1626
East West European Economic Interaction. (US) 659
East - West Film Journal. (US ISSN 0891-6780) 3508
East West Journal see East West: The Journal of Natural Health and Living 3801
East-West Population Institute. Papers. (US) 3981
East-West Population Institute. Working Papers. (US) 3981
East - West - South - North. see Dong Xi Nan Bei 2181
†East-West Statistics Service. (BE) 5183
East-West Technology Digest. (US ISSN 0145-1421) 4597
East West: The Journal of Natural Health and Living. (US ISSN 0888-1375) 3801
East - West Ties. (US) 2000
†East Wind. (US) 5183
East Yorkshire Local History Series. (UK ISSN 0070-8208) 2359
East Yorkshire Local History Society. Bulletin. (UK) 2359
Eastbournian. (UK ISSN 0012-8643) 1310
Easter Seal Communicator see National Easter Seal Communicator 4414
Eastern Africa Journal of Rural Development. (UG) 149
Eastern Africa Law Review. (TZ ISSN 0012-8678) 2621
Eastern African Centre for Research on Oral Traditions and African National Languages Information see E A C R O T A N A L Information 2811
Eastern African Centre for Research on Oral Traditions and African National Languages Studies & Documents see E A C R O T A N A L Studies & Documents 2811
Eastern Aftermarket Journal. (US ISSN 0192-3595) 4689
Eastern Anthropologist. (II ISSN 0012-8686) 238
†Eastern Archives of Ophthalmology. (II ISSN 0301-469X) 5183
Eastern Art Report. (UK) 325, 2429
Eastern Automotive Journal see Eastern Aftermarket Journal 4689
Eastern Basketball Magazine. (US ISSN 0195-0223) 4503
Eastern Boating see Eastern, Southeast Boating Newspaper (Eastern Edition) 4524
Eastern Boating see Eastern, Southeast Boating Newspaper (Southeast Edition) 4524
Eastern Bowhunting. (US) 4545, 2621
Eastern Buddhist. (JA ISSN 0012-8708) 4214, 3765
Eastern Canada Campbook. (US ISSN 0363-2091) 4760, 4545
Eastern Canada Tour Book see Tourbook: Atlantic Provinces and Quebec 4790
Eastern Caribbean Central Bank. Quarterly Commercial Banking Statistics. (XI) 777
Eastern Caribbean Standing Conference on Teacher Education. Report. (BB) 1748
Eastern Catholic Life. (US) 4263
Eastern Churches News Letter. (UK ISSN 0012-8732) 4282
Eastern Dental Society Bulletin. (US ISSN 0012-8759) 3232
Eastern Economic Journal. (US ISSN 0094-5056) 659
Eastern Economist. (II ISSN 0012-8767) 860
Eastern Europe. see Dong'ou 4370
Eastern Europe (Year). (US) 4760
▼Eastern Europe and the Commonwealth of Independent States (Year). (UK) 3891, 860

EASTERN EUROPE

Eastern Europe and the U S S R (Year) see Eastern Europe and the Commonwealth of Independent States (Year) **3891**
▼Eastern Europe Finance. (US) **777**
Eastern Europe Times see Eastern Europe Finance **777**
▼Eastern European and Soviet Telecom Report. (US) **1335**
Eastern European Economics. (US ISSN 0012-8775) **659**
Eastern European Finance Update. (US) **777**
Eastern European Studies in Sociology and Anthropology see International Journal of Sociology **4438**
Eastern Evening News. (UK ISSN 0012-8791) **2194**
Eastern Finance Association. Proceedings of the Annual Meeting see Financial Review (Champaign) **781**
▼Eastern Floors. (US) **2558**
Eastern Football News. (UK) **4503**
Eastern Grape Grower and Winery News see Vineyard and Winery Management **195**
Eastern Hemisphere Petroleum Directory see European Petroleum Directory **3685**
Eastern Kansas Register. (US ISSN 0012-883X) **4263**
Eastern Librarian. (BG ISSN 0012-8848) **2756**
Eastern Massachusetts Regional Library System. Eastern Region News. (US ISSN 0012-8899) **2756**
Eastern Metals Review see Engineering & Metals Review **3405**
Eastern Milk Producer. (US) **199**
Eastern Mineral Law Foundation. Annual Institute. (US ISSN 0733-6098) **2621**
Eastern Mineral Law Foundation. Case Update. (US ISSN 0749-7709) **2621**, 3482
Eastern Mineral Law Foundation Newsletter. (US) **2621**, 3482
Eastern New Mexico University. Contributions in Anthropology. (US ISSN 0070-8232) **238**, 271
Eastern News see Daily Eastern News **1309**
Eastern News. (CN) **2000**
Eastern Packing News see National Packing News **3650**
Eastern Pharmacist. (II ISSN 0012-8872) **3724**
Eastern Puma Network News. (US) **581**
Eastern Purchasing Journal see Materials Management Journal of India **1047**
Eastern Quarter Horse Journal see Eastern-Western Quarter Horse Journal **4533**
Eastern Railway Magazine. (II ISSN 0012-8880) **4709**
Eastern Review (Brooklyn). (US ISSN 0012-8902) **3550**
†Eastern Review (New York). (US) **5183**
Eastern Ski Representatives Association Buyers' Guide see E S R Buyers' Guide **4545**
Eastern Ski Representatives Association Newsletter see E S R. Newsletter **4545**
Eastern, Southeast Boating Newspaper (Eastern Edition). (US ISSN 1045-8131) **4524**
Eastern, Southeast Boating Newspaper (Southeast Edition). (US ISSN 1045-814X) **4524**
Eastern States Archeological Federation. Bulletin. (US) **271**
Eastern States Conference on Linguistics Proceedings see E S C O L Proceedings **2811**
Eastern Studies. see Tohogaku **3644**
Eastern Suburbs Reporter. (AT) **31**, 2171
Eastern Synod Lutheran. (CN ISSN 0831-4446) **4236**
Eastern Today. (US) **1310**
Eastern Transportation Law Seminar Papers and Proceedings see Transportation Law Institute Papers and Proceedings **2687**

Eastern Trucker see Truck News **4749**
Eastern-Western Quarter Horse Journal. (US ISSN 0191-7714) **4533**
Eastern Woods & Waters. (CN ISSN 0827-8911) **4545**
Eastern Worker. (PK ISSN 0012-8953) **977**
Easterner. (US) **2756**
Eastman Fine Chemicals News. (US) **1218**, 1852
Eastman Notes. (US ISSN 0147-345X) **3550**
Eastside Parent. (US) **1236**
Eastside Sun. (US) **2000**
▼Eastsideweek. (US) **2225**
EastWest. (US) **2213**
Easy Data Computer Comparisons. (US) **1433**
Easy Living. (CN) **2177**
†Easy Living. (US) **5183**
Easy Reeding. (US) **3550**
†Easy Rider. (GW) **5183**
Easy Speakeasy. (FR) **2864**
Easyriders. (US ISSN 0046-0990) **4518**
▼Eating Disorders Review. (US ISSN 1048-6984) **3605**, 4019
Eating Well. (US) **3801**
Eats & Treats. see Gut Essen **2474**
Eau, Energie, Air. see Wasser, Energie, Luft **4831**
L'Eau, l'Industrie, les Nuisances. (FR) **4824**, 1074
Eau Pure. (FR ISSN 0424-2033) **4824**
L'Eau Vive. (CN) **2000**
Eaux - Vives. (FR) **4263**
†Ebb and Flow. (AT ISSN 0729-0403) **5183**
Ebbes. (GW) **2054**
Eberbacher Geschichtsblatt. (GW) **2359**
Eberly's Michigan Journal. (US ISSN 0163-6650) **2225**
Ebony. (US ISSN 0012-9011) **2000**, 372, 2225
Ebony Man see E M: Ebony Man **1999**
Ebsco Bulletin of Serials Changes. (US ISSN 0360-0637) **2756**, 399
Eburnea. (IV ISSN 0046-1024) **2169**
Ecclaire. (UV ISSN 0046-1032) **3891**
Ecclesia. (SP ISSN 0012-9038) **4263**
Ecclesia see Kiongozi **4267**
Ecclesia Mater. (IT) **4263**
Ecco tua Madre. (IT) **4263**
Echad. (US ISSN 0743-7757) **2000**
L'Echange. (CN ISSN 0706-5205) **2756**
Echange d'Informations sur les Recherches en Droit Europeen. see Exchange of Information on Research in European Law **2698**
Echange-Sante. (FR ISSN 0760-8675) **4404**
Echange - Travail. (FR ISSN 0240-396X) **977**
Echanges. (FR ISSN 0397-0736) **4175**
Echanges Internationaux et Developpement. (FR) **929**
Echec Plus. (CN ISSN 0825-0049) **4471**
Echiquier Belge. (BE) **4471**
Echiquier Issen. (FR) **4471**
Echo. (SZ ISSN 0012-9143) **1626**, 2582
Echo/Han Sheng. (CH ISSN 0012-9135) **2219**
Echo. (AT) **2445**, 1284, 1626, 4618
Echo. (NE ISSN 0012-9119) **4282**
L'Echo (Brussels). (BE) **659**
Echo (De Aar). (SA ISSN 0011-7161) **2216**
Echo (Huntsville). (US ISSN 0046-1059) **1514**
†Echo (Ottawa). (CN ISSN 0705-1123) **5183**
The Echo. (US) **2000**
Echo (Skokie). (US ISSN 0046-1067) **1297**
Echo (Vinderhoute). (BE) **777**
Echo aus Afrika und Anderen Erdteilen. (GW) **4175**
Echo aus Deutschland. (GW ISSN 0343-0405) **2188**

Echo de l'Imprimerie et des Arts Graphiques see Echo de la Presse et de la Publicite **2569**
Echo de l'Industrie. (LU) **1008**
Echo de l'O N A P. see N A P O News **4413**
Echo de l'Union. (FR ISSN 0243-0738) **2272**, 4404
Echo de la Bourse see L'Echo (Brussels) **659**
Echo de la Liberte de l'Ouest. (FR ISSN 0012-9224) **3941**, 1626
Echo de la Mode. (FR) **1290**
Echo de la Presse et de la Publicite. (FR ISSN 0012-9232) **2569**
Echo de la Timbrologie. (FR ISSN 0012-9240) **3752**
Echo de Saint see Unir: Echo de Saint Louis **2971**
L'Echo de Sanyo. (FR) **1469**, 1460
Echo der Frau. (GW) **4840**
Echo der Liebe. (GW ISSN 0252-2527) **4263**
Echo der Liefde see Echo der Liebe **4263**
Echo des Bois. (BE) **2114**
Echo des Concierges. (FR) **616**
Echo des Recherches. (FR ISSN 0012-9283) **1335**
Echo des Tirages. (BE) **777**
Echo du Meuble. (BE ISSN 0772-6287) **2558**
L'Echo du Transport. (CN ISSN 0705-7040) **4744**
Echo-Handelsjournal. (GW) **659**
Echo Missionaire/Mission News. (CN ISSN 0318-9872) **4175**
Echo News. (AT) **2445**
Echo of Iran. (IR) **860**
Echo of Islam. (IR) **4218**
L'Echo Sportif. (UA) **4471**
Echo Touristique. (FR) **4760**
Echo uit Afrika see Echo uit Afrika en Andere Werelddelen **4175**
Echo uit Afrika en Andere Werelddelen. (NE) **4175**
Echo z Afryki i Innych Kontynentow. (US) **4263**
Echocardiography. (US ISSN 0742-2822) **3207**
Echoes. (US ISSN 0012-933X) **2405**
Echoes. (UK) **4175**
Echoes. (CN ISSN 0012-9321) **4404**
Les Echos. (FR) **860**
Echos see Echos-Flash **1819**
Les Echos Africains. (MR) **777**
Echos des Charites de St. Vincent de Paul see Equipes St Vincent **4404**
Echos du Monde Classique/Classical Views. (CN ISSN 0012-9356) **1276**
Echos-Flash. (BE) **1819**
Echos Vedettes. (CN) **2000**
Echte Waarheid see Plain Truth **4287**
Eck Family Newsletter. (US) **2149**
Eck Mata Journal see Eckankar Journal **4282**
Eckankar Journal. (US) **4282**
Eckenbrueller. (GW) **1626**
Eclair. (MG) **2209**
Eclairage Plus Magazine. (CN) **1886**
Eclaireur des Coiffeurs. (FR) **372**
Eclats de Rire. (FR ISSN 0337-8659) **2864**
Eclectic. (US) **2913**
Eclectic Literary Forum see E L F **2913**
Eclectic Muse. (CN) **2992**
Eclectic Theosophist. (US ISSN 0046-1105) **3765**, 3669
Ecletica Quimica. (BL ISSN 0100-4670) **1176**, 3817
Eclosion. (CN) **1310**
Eco. (US) **1487**, 1947
Eco. (MX ISSN 0422-2555) **2405**
Eco. (CK ISSN 0012-9410) **2913**
Eco Catolico. (CR) **4263**
†L'Eco Cuoio. (IT ISSN 0012-9437) **5183**
Eco d'Italia. (CN) **2000**
Eco d'Italia. (UY ISSN 0012-9534) **2205**
Eco de Nayarit. (MX ISSN 0012-9445) **2210**
Eco de Sitges. (SP) **2569**
Eco degli Oratori e dei Circoli Giovanili. (IT ISSN 0012-9453) **1236**
Eco del Santuario di N.S. di Lourdes. (IT) **4263**

Eco dell'Industria Tessile. (IT ISSN 0012-9526) **4618**
Eco della Riviera. (IT ISSN 0012-9488) **4760**, 4471
Eco della Scuola Nuova. (IT ISSN 0012-9496) **1626**
L'Eco Delle Valli Valdesi. (IT) **4175**
L'Eco di Gibilmanna. (IT) **4263**
L'Eco di San Gabriele. (IT) **4263**
L'Eco di San Germano. (IT) **4263**
Eco-Humane Letter. (US) **1487**
Eco Info see Queensland Conservation Council Newsletter **1496**
Eco-Letter see Eco-Humane Letter **1487**
Eco-Log Canadian Pollution Legislation. (CN ISSN 0824-7528) **1973**, 10, 1976
Eco-Log Week. (CN ISSN 0315-0380) **1973**, 10, 1984
Eco Motori. (IT ISSN 0422-2628) **4689**
Eco-News see Econews **1949**
†Eco-News. (US) **5183**
EcoAlert. (CN ISSN 0833-448X) **1948**, 1785, 4824
Ecodecision. (CN) **1948**
†Ecofile. (AT ISSN 0812-843X) **5183**
Ecoflash. (FR ISSN 0296-4449) **660**
Ecoforum. (KE ISSN 0250-9989) **1948**
Ecography. (DK ISSN 0906-7590) **1948**, 437
Ecol News. (US) **1948**
Ecole des Parents. (FR ISSN 0424-2238) **1683**, 1236
Ecole du Grand Paris. (FR ISSN 0982-5339) **2582**, 1705
Ecole et la Famille. (FR) **1626**
Ecole et la Nation-Actualites. (FR) **1626**, 3891
Ecole et Vie. (LU) **1626**
Ecole Francaise d'Extreme-Orient. Bulletin. (FR ISSN 0336-1519) **3637**
Ecole Francaise de Rome. Collection. (FR) **271**, 2310
Ecole Francaise de Rome. Melanges: Antiquite. (FR) **271**
Ecole Francaise de Rome. Melanges: Moyen Ages, Temps Moderne. (FR) **2359**
Ecole Francaise des Attaches de Presse. Association des Anciens Eleves. Annuaire. (FR ISSN 0070-8321) **2569**
Ecole Maternelle Francaise. (FR ISSN 0012-9585) **1694**
†Ecole Nationale Superieure d'Agronomie et des Industries Alimentaires. Bulletin. (FR ISSN 0374-6003) **5183**
Ecole Nationale Superieure de Biologie Appliquee a la Nutrition et a l'Alimentation. Cahiers. (FR) **3605**
Ecole Nationale Superieure de Techniques Avancees . Rapport d'Activite sur les Recherches. (FR) **4597**
Ecole Normale Superieure. Annales Scientifiques. (FR ISSN 0012-9593) **3035**
Ecole Normale Superieure a Cracovie. Etudes Monographiques. see Wyzsza Szkola Pedagogiczna im. Komisji Edukacji Narodowej w Krakowie. Prace Monograficzne **2518**
Ecole Nouvelle. (GV) **1626**
†Ecole Polytechnique Federale de Lausanne. Publication. (SZ) **5183**
Ecole Pratique des Hautes Etudes. Centre de Recherches sur le Portugal de la Renaissance. Series Textes. (FR) **2359**, 2913
Ecole Pratique des Hautes Etudes. Quatrieme Section. Historiques et Philologiques. Annuaire see Livret de la Quatrieme Section, Ecole Pratique Hautes Etudes **2317**
Ecoles des Lettres. (FR) **1626**
Ecoles Nationales d'Industrie Laitiere des Organismes Associes Revue see E N I L Revue **199**
Ecologae Geologicae Helvetiae. (SZ ISSN 0012-9402) **1559**
Ecologia. (SP ISSN 0210-2536) **437**, 1487
Ecologia Agraria. (IT ISSN 0012-9607) **88**, 1948

Ecologia en Bolivia. (BO) **437**, 1543
Ecologia y Desarrollo. (PE) **437**, 1948
Ecological Abstracts. (UK ISSN 0305-196X) **1973**, 10
▼Ecological Applications. (US ISSN 1051-0761) **1948**, 437
Ecological Economics. (NE ISSN 0921-8009) **1948**, 1487
▼Ecological Engineering. (NE ISSN 0925-8574) **1948**, 489, 1819
Ecological Entomology. (UK ISSN 0307-6946) **530**
Ecological Health Law Report see Ecological Illness Law Report **5184**
†Ecological Illness Law Report. (US ISSN 8755-9013) **5184**
Ecological Life Style. News Letter see Practical Alternatives **1966**
Ecological Modelling. (NE ISSN 0304-3800) **1975**, 1948
Ecological Monographs. (US ISSN 0012-9615) **1948**, 51
Ecological Psychology. (US ISSN 1040-7413) **4019**, 1487
Ecological Research. (JA ISSN 0912-3814) **437**
Ecological Research Committee. Ecological Bulletins. (DK) **1948**
Ecological Society of America. Bulletin. (US ISSN 0012-9623) **1948**, 437
Ecological Society of Australia. Proceedings. (AT ISSN 0070-8348) **437**
Ecological Studies; Analysis and Synthesis. (US ISSN 0070-8356) **437**
Ecologist (1979). (UK ISSN 0261-3131) **1948**
Ecology. (US ISSN 0012-9658) **1948**, 437
Ecology see Soviet Journal of Ecology **1969**
Ecology see University of Georgia. Institute of Ecology. Annual Report **1970**
Ecology Abstracts. (US ISSN 0143-3296) **1973**, 10, 4835
Ecology & Conservation Studies. (UK ISSN 0144-6258) **1487**, 1948
Ecology Center Newsletter see Ecology Center Terrain **1948**
Ecology Center Terrain. (US) **1948**
Ecology Digest. (US) **1948**
Ecology Law Quarterly. (US ISSN 0046-1121) **2621**, 1948
Ecology of Food and Nutrition. (US ISSN 0367-0244) **3605**
Ecology Reports. (US) **1948**
Ecology U S A. (US ISSN 0098-6615) **1948**
Ecomedia Bulletin. (CN) **3891**
Ecomese. (IT) **88**
Econ: Environmental Contractor see Econ: The Environmental Magazine for Real Property Trends **1949**
Econ: The Environmental Magazine for Real Property Trends. (US) **1949**
Econews. (HU) **835**
Econews. (US ISSN 0885-7237) **1949**
Econews. (UK ISSN 0955-6176) **1949**, 3891
Economap. (MR) **660**
Econometric Reviews. (US ISSN 0747-4938) **860**
Econometric Theory. (UK ISSN 0266-4666) **893**
Econometrica. (UK ISSN 0012-9682) **660**
Econometrics and Operations Research. see Oekonometrie und Unternehmensforschung **683**
Economia. (EC ISSN 0012-9704) **660**
Economia. (GT ISSN 0046-113X) **660**
Economia. (JA ISSN 0012-9712) **660**
Economia. (AG ISSN 0325-0830) **660**
Economia. (PO ISSN 0870-3531) **660**
Economia. (PE) **660**
Economia. (IT) **660**
Economia see Revista Economia **688**
Economia. (GW) **814**

Economia Alavesa. (SP ISSN 0568-8876) **814**
Economia & Management. (IT) **1009**
Economia Andina. (PE) **998**
Economia Aretina. (IT ISSN 0012-9747) **814**
Economia Aziendale. (IT) **660**
Economia Brasileira e suas Perspectivas - A P E C A O. (BL) **860**
Economia Brindisina. (IT) **814**
Economia Cafetera. (CK ISSN 0046-1148) **149**, 176
Economia Colombiana. (CK ISSN 0422-2733) **860**
Economia Cubana. (CU) **860**
Economia D'Azienda e Bilanci. (IT) **750**
Economia de America Latina. (MX) **860**
Economia de Cordoba. (AG ISSN 0013-0435) **860**
Economia de Mocambique. (MZ) **860**
†Economia del Lavoro (Rome). (IT ISSN 0392-1212) **5184**
Economia del Trabajo see Hombre y Trabajo **981**
Economia della Marca Trevigiana. (IT) **814**
Economia delle Fonti di Energia. (IT) **1785**
Economia delle Scelte Pubbliche/Journal of Public Finance and Public Choice. (IT) **1093**
Economia e Banca. (IT ISSN 0393-9243) **777**
Economia e Diritto del Terziario. (IT) **660**, 2621
Economia e Lavoro. (IT ISSN 0012-978X) **977**
Economia e Politica Industriale. (IT) **660**
Economia e Sociologia. (PO ISSN 0870-6026) **860**, 4434
Economia e Storia (Rome). (IT ISSN 0070-8402) **893**
Economia ed Ambiente. (IT) **660**
Economia Guipuzcoana. (SP) **814**
Economia Industrial. (SP ISSN 0422-2784) **1074**
Economia Informa. (MX) **660**
Economia Internacional. (SP ISSN 0012-9801) **660**
Economia Internazionale. (IT ISSN 0012-981X) **660**
Economia Isontina. (IT) **814**
Economia Lariana. (IT) **814**
Economia Marche. (IT ISSN 1120-9593) **860**
Economia Mexicana. (MX) **660**
Economia Montana - Linea Ecologica. (IT ISSN 0012-9836) **2098**, 88, 1949, 1973
Economia Pesarese. (IT) **814**
Economia Politica. (MX ISSN 0531-8203) **660**
Economia Politica. (HO ISSN 0424-2483) **660**
Economia Politica. (IT ISSN 1120-2890) **660**
Economia Politica see Historia Economica **868**
Economia Pubblica. (IT) **1074**
†Economia Salvadorena (San Salvador, 1946). (ES ISSN 0012-9860) **5184**
Economia Salvodorena (San Salvador, 1975) see El Salvador, Informe Economico y Social **863**
Economia, Societa e Istituzioni. (IT) **4434**, 660
Economia Trentina. (IT ISSN 0012-9879) **814**
Economia Vascongada. (SP) **860**
Economia y Administracion. (CL ISSN 0012-9887) **1009**, 660
Economia y Ciencias Sociales. (VE ISSN 0012-9895) **660**
Economia y Desarrollo. (CU ISSN 0252-8584) **660**
Economic Abstracts see Key to Economic Science **726**
Economic Accounts. (CN ISSN 0229-1665) **714**
Economic Affairs. (II ISSN 0424-2513) **660**
Economic Affairs. (UK ISSN 0265-0665) **660**, 3891
Economic Age. (II) **860**
Economic Al-Ahram. see Al-Ahram al-Iqtisadi **2185**

Economic Analysis and Policy. (AT ISSN 0046-1199) **660**
Economic Analysis and Workers Management. (YU ISSN 0351-286X) **660**
Economic Analysis of North American Ski Areas. (US ISSN 0147-4243) **4545**, 660
Economic and Business Bulletin see Journal of Economics and Business **674**
Economic & Business Review. (II ISSN 0012-995X) **660**
Economic and Commercial News. (II ISSN 0970-0560) **660**
Economic and Energy Indicators. (US) **3955**, 860
▼Economic & Financial Computing. (UK ISSN 0962-2780) **826**
Economic and Financial Prospects. (SZ ISSN 0256-3525) **861**
Economic and Financial Report. (CL ISSN 0716-2421) **777**
Economic and Fiscal Policy. (CN) **861**
Economic and Industrial Democracy. (UK ISSN 0143-831X) **3892**, 660
Economic and Industrial Publications Economic Forecasting Service see E I P Economic Forecasting Service **860**
Economic and Industrial Publications Industrial Research Service see E I P Industrial Research Service **1074**
Economic and Industrial Publications Investors Service see E I P Investors Service **945**
Economic & Investment Consensus. (US) **945**
Economic and Political Weekly. (II ISSN 0012-9976) **661**, 3892
Economic and Scientific Research Foundation. Annual Report. (II ISSN 0070-8437) **661**
Economic & Shipping Review. (IO) **4727**, 861
Economic and Social Commission for Western Asia Population Bulletin see E S C W A Population Bulletin **3981**
Economic and Social History in the Netherlands. (NE ISSN 0925-1669) **2359**
Economic and Social History Surveys. (UK ISSN 0140-0061) **661**
Economic and Social Progress in Latin America see Economic and Social Progress in Latin America; Annual Report **861**
Economic and Social Progress in Latin America; Annual Report. (US ISSN 0095-2850) **861**
Economic and Social Research Council Studentship Handbook see E S R C Studentship Handbook **1693**
Economic and Social Research Institute. General Research Series. (IE) **661**
Economic and Social Research Institute. Policy Series. (IE) **661**
Economic and Social Research Institute. Publications Series. Paper see Economic and Social Research Institute. General Research Series **661**
Economic and Social Review. (IE ISSN 0012-9984) **661**, 4371
Economic and Social Statistics of Sri Lanka. (CE) **714**, 4457, 4570
Economic and Social Survey of Asia and the Pacific. (UN ISSN 0252-5704) **861**
Economic and Tax Report. (US ISSN 1043-6820) **4744**, 1093
Economic and Trade World. see Jing Mao Shijie **672**
Economic Anthropology. (US) **238**
†Economic Books: Current Selections. (US ISSN 0093-2485) **5184**
Economic Botany. (US ISSN 0013-0001) **501**
Economic Bulletin. (LY) **661**
†Economic Bulletin. (AT) **5184**
Economic Bulletin (Aldershot). (UK ISSN 0343-754X) **661**
Economic Bulletin (London). (UK ISSN 0309-7854) **3892**
Economic Bulletin (San Diego). (US) **861**
Economic Bulletin Board. (US) **861**

ECONOMIC HISTORY 6139

Economic Bulletin for Asia and the Far East see Economic Bulletin for Asia and the Pacific **861**
Economic Bulletin for Asia and the Pacific. (UN ISSN 0378-455X) **861**
Economic Bulletin for Europe (Annual). (UN) **861**
Economic Bulletin for Europe (Quarterly) see Economic Bulletin for Europe (Annual) **861**
Economic Bulletin for Europe (Quarterly) see Economic Studies **862**
Economic Bulletin for Europe (Quarterly) see United Nations Economic Commission for Europe. Occasional Studies **887**
Economic Bulletin for Latin America see C E P A L Review **849**
Economic Bulletin of Ghana. (GH ISSN 0013-0044) **661**
†Economic-Business Review. (US) **5184**
Economic Commentary. (US ISSN 0428-1276) **661**, 777, 861
Economic Council of Canada. Annual Report. (CN ISSN 0070-847X) **861**
Economic Council of Canada. Annual Review. (CN ISSN 0070-8488) **861**
Economic Council of Canada. Au Courant. (CN ISSN 0226-224X) **661**
Economic Council of Canada. Bulletin see Economic Council of Canada. Au Courant **661**
†Economic Council of Canada. Discussion Papers. (CN ISSN 0225-8013) **5184**
Economic Democrat see Campaign California Report **4055**
Economic Development and Cultural Change. (US ISSN 0013-0079) **929**, 4434
Economic Development and Law Center Report. (US ISSN 0731-6941) **861**, 2486, 2621
Economic Development Briefing. (UK ISSN 0268-2184) **945**
Economic Development Digest. (UK ISSN 0266-4194) **714**, 861
†Economic Development Programme for the Republic of South Africa. (SA ISSN 0070-8518) **5184**
Economic Development Quarterly. (US ISSN 0891-2424) **893**, 4059
Economic Development Review. (US ISSN 0742-3713) **1075**
Economic Digest. (CS) **661**
Economic Echo from Yugoslavia see Yugoslavia Echo **925**
Economic Education. see Ediyn Dzasgiyn Bolovsrol **662**
Economic Education Bulletin. (US ISSN 0424-2769) **661**
Economic Eye. (JA ISSN 0389-0503) **998**
Economic Fact Book on Metropolitan Milwaukee see Metropolitan Milwaukee Economic Fact Book **873**
Economic Forecast. (NZ) **661**
Economic Forecast and Information. see Jingji Yuce yu Xinxi **673**
Economic Forecasts. (UK ISSN 0169-1767) **861**
Economic Geography. (US ISSN 0013-0095) **2247**
Economic Geography. see Jingji Dili **2254**
Economic Geology see Geological Abstracts **1551**
Economic Geology and the Bulletin of the Society of Economic Geologists. (US ISSN 0361-0128) **1560**
Economic Growth in Tennessee, Annual Report. (US) **1075**
Economic Growth Report see Community Development Digest **2485**
Economic Handbook of the Machine Tool Industry. (US ISSN 0070-8550) **3017**
Economic Herald. see Privredni Vjesnik **686**
Economic History. see Hospodarske Dejiny **2368**
Economic History Review. (UK ISSN 0013-0117) **893**

6140 ECONOMIC HOME

▼Economic Home Owner. (US ISSN 1055-8284) 616, 2501
Economic Horizons. see Afaq Iqtisadiyyah 644
Economic Impact of the Negro Traveler.(US) 4760, 2000
†Economic Index Market. (US) 5184
Economic Indicators. (PH) 714, 998
Economic Indicators (Charleston). (US ISSN 0278-8381) 4059
Economic Indicators (Washington). (US ISSN 0013-0125) 861
Economic Indicators of Turkey. (TU) 998
Economic Information. see Jingji Cankao 672
Economic Information on Argentina. (AG ISSN 0325-2388) 861
Economic Inquiry. (US ISSN 0095-2583) 661
▼Economic Insight. (US) 777, 861
Economic Issues. see Jingji Wenti 672
Economic Journal. (UK ISSN 0013-0133) 661
Economic Journal. see Keizaigaku Ronsan 676
Economic Journal of Nepal. (NP) 929, 893
Economic Justice Report. (CN) 3955, 661
Economic Leaflets. (US ISSN 0013-0141) 661
Economic Legislation Review. see Przeglad Ustawodawstwa Gospodarczego 882
Economic Logic. (US) 945, 861
Economic Management. see Jingji Guanli 1015
Economic Message. see Mensagem Economica 790
Economic Microbiology. (US) 551
Economic Modelling. (UK ISSN 0264-9993) 661
Economic Monthly see Economic Journal of Nepal 929
Economic News Daily Bulletin. (CH) 777
Economic News of Bulgaria. (BU ISSN 0013-0176) 814
Economic News Overseas Weekly see Business Taiwan 652
Economic Notes. (IT ISSN 0391-5026) 661, 893
Economic Notes see L R A's Economic Notes 985
Economic Opportunity Report. (US ISSN 0013-0206) 4404, 4059
Economic Outlook. (AT) 661
Economic Outlook. (PK) 861
Economic Outlook. (UK ISSN 0140-489X) 861, 777
Economic Outlook see Perspectives 879
†Economic Outlook for New Jersey. (US) 5184
Economic Outlook for the Bohai Bay. see Huan Bohai Jingji Liaowang 669
†Economic Outlook U.S.A. (US ISSN 0095-3830) 5184
Economic Panorama see Panorama Economico 878
Economic Perspectives. (US ISSN 0164-0682) 861
Economic Perspectives: An Annual Survey of Economics. (US ISSN 0142-5900) 893
Economic Poisons see Pesticides (Sacramento) 188
Economic Policy. (UK ISSN 0266-4658) 661
Economic Policymaking. see Jingji Juece Bao 895
Economic Presentation see Economic Trends (Cleveland) 862
Economic Prospects - Consumer Survey Results see European Economy. Series B: Business and Consumer Survey Results 864
Economic Record. (AT ISSN 0013-0249) 661
Economic Reflections see Journal of Economic Reflections 674
Economic Reform. see Jingji Gaige 895
Economic Reform News. see Tigai Xinxi 1000
Economic Report of the President. (US) 861

Economic Report on Scottish Agriculture. (UK) 149
Economic Reporter. (HK ISSN 0013-0265) 861
Economic Research. see Jingji Yanjiu 896
Economic Research Institute. Paper see Economic and Social Research Institute. General Research Series 661
Economic Research Journal. (PH) 661
Economic Results in Danish Horticulture. see Denmark. Jordbrugsoekonomisk Institut. Serie D: Gartneri-Regnskabsstatistik 149
Economic Review/Keizai Ronso. (JA ISSN 0013-0273) 661
Economic Review. (PK ISSN 0531-8955) 661
Economic Review. (BG ISSN 0070-8631) 662
Economic Review. (CE) 662
Economic Review. (IO) 662
Economic Review. (UK ISSN 0265-0290) 662
Economic Review. see Kozgazdasagi Szemle 676
Economic Review. see Keizai Kenkyu 676
Economic Review. see Keizai Ohrai 676
Economic Review. see Stopanski Pregled 693
Economic Review. (US ISSN 0013-0281) 777
Economic Review. (CH ISSN 0013-029X) 861
Economic Review. (YU ISSN 0013-0303) 861
Economic Review. (RH ISSN 0256-1603) 862
Economic Review (Tokyo, 1925). see Keizai Shirin 676
Economic Review (Year). (JM ISSN 0259-9171) 862
†Economic Review and Outlook. (CN) 5184
Economic Review and Report see International Understanding 3962
Economic Review of Agriculture. (KE) 149
Economic Review of the Arab World. (LE ISSN 0013-032X) 862
Economic Review of the Year - The Greek Economy. (GR ISSN 1105-252X) 862, 662
Economic Review of Travel in America. (US ISSN 0733-642X) 4760
†Economic Road Maps. (US ISSN 0884-4887) 5184
†Economic Scene. (II) 5184
Economic Science. see Jingji Kexue 672
Economic Science. see Keizai Kagaku 676
Economic Situation in the Community see European Economy 864
Economic Situation in the Federal Republic of Germany. (GW ISSN 0431-6045) 862
†Economic Situation in the Year. (PO) 5184
Economic Situation of Air Transport. Review and Outlook (Years). (UN) 4672
Economic Society of Australia and New Zealand. New South Wales and Victorian Branches. Economic Papers see Economic Society of Australia Economic Papers 662
Economic Society of Australia Economic Papers. (AT ISSN 0812-0439) 662
Economic Society of Finland. Journal. see Ekonomiska Samfundets Tidskrift 663
Economic Studies. (II ISSN 0013-0362) 662
Economic Studies. (UN) 862
Economic Studies. (AF) 893
Economic Survey. see Norway. Statistisk Sentralbyraa. Oekonomisk Utsyn 5249
Economic Survey of Asia and the Far East see Economic and Social Survey of Asia and the Pacific 861
Economic Survey of Europe. (UN ISSN 0070-8712) 862

Economic Survey of India see Economic Survey of Maharashtra 862
Economic Survey of Indian Agriculture see India. Ministry of Agriculture. Bulletin on Commercial Crops Statistics 138
†Economic Survey of Japan. (JA ISSN 0021-4833) 5184
Economic Survey of Latin America see Economic Survey of Latin America and the Caribbean 862
Economic Survey of Latin America and the Caribbean. (UN ISSN 0257-2184) 862
Economic Survey of Liberia. (LB ISSN 0303-853X) 862
Economic Survey of Maharashtra. (II) 862
Economic Survey of Singapore. (SI ISSN 0376-8791) 862
Economic Systems. (GW ISSN 0939-3625) 893
Economic Systems Research. (UK ISSN 0953-5314) 893
▼Economic Theory. (US ISSN 0938-2259) 893
Economic Theory & Business Management. see Jingji Lilun yu Jingji Guanli 1015
Economic Times. (BG) 662
Economic Times. (II ISSN 0013-0389) 777, 862
Economic Times. (CE) 777, 862
▼Economic Times. (US ISSN 1050-0200) 862
Economic Titles see Economic Titles - Abstracts 714
Economic Titles - Abstracts. (NE ISSN 0166-5057) 714, 10
Economic Topics. (US) 777
Economic Topics for Savings and Loan Management see Economic Topics 777
Economic Trends. (II) 814
Economic Trends. (UK ISSN 0013-0400) 862
Economic Trends. (BG) 862
Economic Trends (Chicago). (US ISSN 0882-5807) 2461
Economic Trends (Cleveland). (US ISSN 0748-2922) 862
Economic Trends: Japan. (JA) 862
Economic Tribune. see Jingji Luntan 672
Economic Week. (US) 777, 862
Economic World see Keizaikai 676
Economic World. (US ISSN 0164-3525) 862
Economic World - South. see Jingji Shijie - Nanfang 672
Economic World's Directory of Japanese Companies in the U S A. (US) 1134
Economic Yearbook of Member States of the Organization of African Unity. see Annuaire Economique des Pays Membres de l'Organisation de l'Unite Africaine 843
Economic Yearbook of Tunisia. (TI ISSN 0070-8747) 862
Economica. (UK ISSN 0013-0427) 662
Economical Journal. see Ekonomicky Casopis 663
Economicos Tachydromos. (GR ISSN 0013-0443) 862
Economics. (UK ISSN 0300-4287) 662
Economics. (AT) 662, 1748
Economics Abstracts. see Jingjixue Wenzhai 725
Economics & Business. (UK ISSN 0884-8335) 714
Economics and Business see Business Library Review 769
†Economics and Business Letter. (US) 5184
Economics and Finance in Indonesia. (IO) 662
Economics and Management. see Jingji yu Guanli 1015
Economics and Philosophy. (UK ISSN 0266-2671) 862
Economics & Politics. (UK ISSN 0954-1985) 893, 3892
Economics and Social Development. see Jingji yu Shehui Fazhan 673
Economics Classics - Old and Rare Books on Economics. (US) 893, 2405

Economics for Agricultural Technology. see Nongye Jishu Jingji 155
Economics in Hong Kong and Macao. see Gang Ao Jingji 666
Economics Letters. (SZ ISSN 0165-1765) 893
Economics of Agricultural Enterprises. see Denmark. Statens Jordbrugsoekonomiske Institut. Serie B: Oekonomien i Landbrugets Driftsgrene 5178
Economics of Education Review. (US ISSN 0272-7757) 1726
▼Economics of Innovation and New Technology. (US ISSN 1043-8599) 4597
Economics of Planning. (NE ISSN 0013-0451) 862
Economics Selections see Economics & Business 714
Economics Working Papers. (US ISSN 0094-6451) 714
Economics Working Papers: Bibliography. (US) 714
Economicus. (BG) 893
Economie. (AE) 862
Economie Agricole au Canada see Canadian Farm Economics 148
†Economie Algerienne. (FR) 5184
Economie Appliquee. (FR ISSN 0013-0494) 662
L'Economie Belge en (Year). (BE ISSN 0771-5641) 862
Economie Camerounaise. (FR) 862
Economie Champenoise. (FR ISSN 0151-1793) 862
L'Economie de la Reunion. (RE ISSN 0750-0769) 862
Economie de la Tunisie en Chiffres. (TI ISSN 0070-878X) 862
Economie et Commerce see Laval Administration 1017
Economie et Developpement see Unite de Programmation du Ministere. Bulletin de Conjoncture 887
Economie et Finances Agricoles/ Agricultural Economics and Finance. (FR ISSN 0070-8798) 149
Economie et Humanisme. (FR ISSN 0245-9132) 4371
Economie et Politique. (FR) 3892
Economie et Prevision. (FR ISSN 0249-4744) 893
Economie et Socialisme. (MR ISSN 0851-0458) 863, 893
Economie et Societe. (FR ISSN 0070-8801) 662
Economie et Statistique see France. Institut National de la Statistique et des Etudes Economiques. Economie et Statistique 717
Economie Familiale/Home Economics. (FR ISSN 0397-8389) 2446
Economie Francaise en Perspectives Sectorielles (Vols.1-5) see Previsions Glissantes Detaillees en Perspectives Sectorielles (Vol.35): Sante 879
Economie Francaise en Perspectives Sectorielles (Vols.1-5) see Previsions Glissantes Detaillees en Perspectives a Moyen Terme 879
Economie Francaise en Perspectives Sectorielles (Vols.1-5) see Previsions Glissantes Detaillees en Perspectives Macroeconomiques a Court et Moyen Terme (Year) 879
Economie Francaise en Perspectives Sectorielles (Vols.1-5) see Previsions Glissantes Detaillees en Perspectives Sectorielles (Vol.4): Industries du Bois et de l'Ameublement 880
Economie Francaise en Perspectives Sectorielles (Vols.1-5) see Previsions Glissantes Detaillees en Perspectives Sectorielles (Vol.1): Agriculture 880
Economie Francaise en Perspectives Sectorielles (Vols.1-5) see Previsions Glissantes Detaillees en Perspectives Sectorielles (Vol.5): Construction de Machines 880
Economie Francaise en Perspectives Sectorielles (Vols.1-5) see Previsions Glissantes Detaillees en Perspectives Sectorielles (Vol.2): Industries Agro-Alimentaires 880

Economie Francaise en Perspectives Sectorielles (Vols.1-5) see Previsions Glissantes Detaillees en Perspectives Sectorielles (Vol.3): Textile - Habillement - Cuir **880**
Economie Francaise en Perspectives Sectorielles (Vols.1-5) see Previsions Glissantes Detaillees en Perspectives Sectorielles (Vol.6): Equipement Industriel **880**
Economie Francaise en Perspectives Sectorielles (Vols.1-5) see Previsions Glissantes Detaillees en Perspectives Sectorielles (Vol.7): Mecanique de Precision **880**
Economie Francaise en Perspectives Sectorielles (Vols.1-5) see Previsions Glissantes Detaillees en Perspectives Sectorielles (Vol.8): Fonderie et Transformation des Metaux **880**
Economie Francaise en Perspectives Sectorielles (Vols.1-5) see Previsions Glissantes Detaillees en Perspectives Sectorielles (Vol.9): Construction Electrique et Electronique Grand-Public **880**
Economie Francaise en Perspectives Sectorielles (Vols.1-5) see Previsions Glissantes Detaillees en Perspectives Sectorielles (Vol.10): Construction Electrique Professionnelle **880**
Economie Francaise en Perspectives Sectorielles (Vols.1-5) see Previsions Glissantes Detaillees en Perspectives Sectorielles (Vol.11): Construction Electronique Professionnelle **880**
Economie Francaise en Perspectives Sectorielles (Vols.1-5) see Previsions Glissantes Detaillees en Perspectives Sectorielles (Vol.12): Construction Automobile **880**
Economie Francaise en Perspectives Sectorielles (Vols.1-5) see Previsions Glissantes Detaillees en Perspectives Sectorielles (Vol.13): Construction Aerospatiale **880**
Economie Francaise en Perspectives Sectorielles (Vols.1-5) see Previsions Glissantes Detaillees en Perspectives Sectorielles (Vol.14): Energie **880**
Economie Francaise en Perspectives Sectorielles (Vols.1-5) see Previsions Glissantes Detaillees en Perspectives Sectorielles (Vol.15): Siderugie et Premiere Transformation de l'Acier **880**
Economie Francaise en Perspectives Sectorielles (Vols.1-5) see Previsions Glissantes Detaillees en Perspectives Sectorielles (Vol.16): Industrie des Non-Ferreux **880**
Economie Francaise en Perspectives Sectorielles (Vols.1-5) see Previsions Glissantes Detaillees en Perspectives Sectorielles (Vol.17): Chimie Minerale **880**
Economie Francaise en Perspectives Sectorielles (Vols.1-5) see Previsions Glissantes Detaillees en Perspectives Sectorielles (Vol.18): Chimie Organique **880**
Economie Francaise en Perspectives Sectorielles (Vols.1-5) see Previsions Glissantes Detaillees en Perspectives Sectorielles (Vol.19): Parachimie et Pharmacie **881**
Economie Francaise en Perspectives Sectorielles (Vols.1-5) see Previsions Glissantes Detaillees en Perspectives Sectorielles (Vol.20): Transformation du Caoutchouc et des Matieres Plastiques **881**
Economie Francaise en Perspectives Sectorielles (Vols.1-5) see Previsions Glissantes Detaillees en Perspectives Sectorielles (Vol.21): Industrie du Verre **881**
Economie Francaise en Perspectives Sectorielles (Vols.1-5) see Previsions Glissantes Detaillees en Perspectives Sectorielles (Vol.22): Industrie des Pates, Papiers et Cartons **881**
Economie Francaise en Perspectives Sectorielles (Vols.1-5) see Previsions Glissantes Detaillees en Perspectives Sectorielles (Vol.23): Emballages **881**
Economie Francaise en Perspectives Sectorielles (Vols.1-5) see Previsions Glissantes Detaillees en Perspectives Sectorielles (Vol.24): Logement **881**
Economie Francaise en Perspectives Sectorielles (Vols.1-5) see Previsions Glissantes Detaillees en Perspectives Sectorielles (Vol.25): Batiments d'Activite **881**
Economie Francaise en Perspectives Sectorielles (Vols.1-5) see Previsions Glissantes Detaillees en Perspectives Sectorielles (Vol.26): Travaux Publics **881**
Economie Francaise en Perspectives Sectorielles (Vols.1-5) see Previsions Glissantes Detaillees en Perspectives Sectorielles (Vol.27): Materiaux de Construction I **881**
Economie Francaise en Perspectives Sectorielles (Vols.1-5) see Previsions Glissantes Detaillees en Perspectives Sectorielles (Vol.28): Materiaux et Composants de Construction II **881**
Economie Francaise en Perspectives Sectorielles (Vols.1-5) see Previsions Glissantes Detaillees en Perspectives Sectorielles (Vol.29): Industries de la Communication **881**
Economie Francaise en Perspectives Sectorielles (Vols.1-5) see Previsions Glissantes Detaillees en Perspectives Sectorielles (Vol.30): Banques **881**
Economie Francaise en Perspectives Sectorielles (Vols.1-5) see Previsions Glissantes Detaillees en Perspectives Sectorielles (Vol.31): Assurances **881**
Economie Francaise en Perspectives Sectorielles (Vols.1-5) see Previsions Glissantes Detaillees en Perspectives Sectorielles (Vol.32): Commerce **881**
Economie Francaise en Perspectives Sectorielles (Vols.1-5) see Previsions Glissantes Detaillees en Perspectives Sectorielles (Vol.33): Transports **881**
Economie Francaise en Perspectives Sectorielles (Vols.1-5) see Previsions Glissantes Detaillees en Perspectives Sectorielles (Vol.34): Tourisme, Hotellerie, Restauration, Loisirs **881**
Economie Francaise en Perspectives Sectorielles (Vols.1-5) see Previsions Glissantes Detaillees en Perspectives Sectorielles (Vol.36): Services Publics **881**
Economie Francaise en Perspectives Sectorielles (Vols.1-5) see Previsions Glissantes Detaillees en Perspectives Sectorielles (Vol.37): Services aux Entreprises **881**
†Economie Gabonaise. (FR) **5184**
▼Economie Guineenne. (FR) **863**
Economie Ivoirienne. (FR) **863**
Economie Libanaise et Arabe. (LE ISSN 0013-0540) **814**
Economie Prospective Internationale. (FR ISSN 0242-7818) **906**
Economie Rurale. (FR ISSN 0013-0559) **150, 863**
Economie Sucriere. see Zuckerwirtschaft **2084**
Economies et Societes. (FR) **662**
Economies et Societes. Serie AB. Economie du Travail. (FR ISSN 0068-4821) **662, 977**
Economies et Societes. Serie AF. Histoire Quantitative de l'Economie Francaise. (FR ISSN 0068-4864) **893**
Economies et Societes. Serie AG. Progres et Agriculture. (FR ISSN 0068-4899) **150**
Economies et Societes. Serie EM. Economie Mathematique et Econometrie. (FR ISSN 0013-0567) **894**
Economies et Societes. Serie F. Developpement, Croissance, Progres des Pays en Voie de Developpement. (FR ISSN 0068-4813) **929**
Economies et Societes. Serie G. Economie Planifiee. (FR ISSN 0068-483X) **894**
Economies et Societes. Serie M. Philosophie - Sciences Sociales Economie. (FR ISSN 0068-4880) **894, 3765**
Economies et Societes. Serie MO. Economie Monetaire. (FR) **777**
Economies et Societes. Serie P. Relations Economiques Internationales. (FR ISSN 0068-4902) **894, 929**
Economies et Societes. Serie S. Etudes de Marxologie. (FR ISSN 0068-4856) **894**
Economies et Societes. Serie SG. Science de Gestion. (FR) **1009**
Economies et Societies. Serie T. Information - Recherche Innovation. (FR ISSN 0068-4872) **662**
Economisch- en Sociaal-Historisch Jaarboek. (NE) **894, 2359**
Economisch en Sociaal Tijdschrift. (BE ISSN 0013-0575) **662**
Economisch-Historisch Jaarboek see Economisch- en Sociaal-Historisch Jaarboek **894**
Economisch Instituut voor Het Midden-en Kleinbedrijf. Year Report. (NE ISSN 0070-8836) **1114**
Economisch Instituut voor het Midden-en Kleinbedrijf Mededelingen see E I M Mededelingen **1114**
Economisch Profiel Nederlandse Antillen. (NA) **714**
Economisch-Statistische Berichten. (NE ISSN 0013-0583) **863**
De Economist. (NE ISSN 0013-063X) **662**
Economist. see Jingji Shi **672**
Economist. see Jingjixue Jia **673**
Economist. (JA ISSN 0013-0621) **863**
Economist. (UK ISSN 0013-0613) **863, 894**
Economist. (US) **863**
Economist Intelligence Unit Europe - Pacific Update see E I U Europe - Pacific Update **659**
Economist Intelligence Unit World Outlook see E I U World Outlook **860**
Economista. (AG ISSN 0013-0648) **777**
Economista. (SP ISSN 0013-0656) **777**
L'Economiste Egyptien. (UA ISSN 0013-0672) **863**
Economiste Gabonais. (GO) **906**
Economy. see Gazdasag **667**
Economy. (UG) **863**
Economy. (AU ISSN 1013-9095) **906**
Economy and Commerce. see Al-Iqtisad wal-Tijarah **914**
Economy and Law. (HK ISSN 1011-9108) **894, 2621**
Economy and Society. (UK ISSN 0308-5147) **4371, 662, 3892**
▼Economy and the Foreign Policy. (GR) **894, 662**
Economy Bulletins. (UK) **465**
Economy in Figures. (MF) **814**
Economy of Asia and Pacific Rim. see Yatai Jingji **700**
Economy of the Agricultural Sector. see Denmark. Jordbrugsoekonomiske Institut. Landbrugets Oekonomi **658**
†Economy of the Principality of Liechtenstein. (LH) **5184**
Economy Today/Chin Jih Ching Chi. (CH) **662**
Ecorissa. (II) **662, 4434**
Ecos. (UK ISSN 0143-9073) **1487**
Ecos. (AT ISSN 0311-4546) **1949**
▼Ecos. (RU) **1949**
Ecos. (PE) **2864**
Ecos. (US) **2992**
Ecos. (VE ISSN 0013-0680) **4404**
Ecos de A L A D I. (Asociacion Latinoamericana de Integracion) (AG) **3892, 662**
▼Ecoservice. (CS) **662**
▼EcoSource. (CN) **1973, 10**
Ecosphere. (US) **4760, 1949**
Ecosystems of the World. (NE) **1949**
Ecotass (English Edition). (UK ISSN 0733-5989) **863**
▼Ecotoxicology. (UK ISSN 0963-9292) **1981**
Ecotoxicology and Environmental Safety.(US ISSN 0147-6513) **1981, 4100**
Ecotropica. Ecosistemas Tropicales. Boletin. (CK ISSN 0120-8993) **1604, 437**
Ecozoo. (CN) **582**
Ecphorizer. (US ISSN 0744-057X) **2225**
Ecquid Novi. (SA ISSN 0256-0054) **2569**
Ecran Fantastique. (FR) **3508**
†Ecrit du Temps. (FR ISSN 0293-9320) **5184**
L'Ecrit-Voir. (FR ISSN 0752-5222) **325**
Ecrits de Paris. (FR ISSN 0013-0710) **2186**
Ecrits du Canada Francais. (CN ISSN 0013-0729) **2913, 2864**
Ecrits Libres. (FR ISSN 0070-8860) **4175**
Ecstasy. (II) **4217**
▼Ecu. (FR) **714**
Ecu - Link. (US) **4236**
Ecuador. (EC) **863**
Ecuador. Centro de Desarrollo Industrial. Boletin Estadisticas. see Ecuador. Centro de Desarrollo Industrial. Boletin Estadisticas. Economicas **1075**
Ecuador. Centro de Desarrollo Industrial. Boletin Estadisticas. Economicas. (EC) **1075**
Ecuador. Centro de Desarrollo Industrial. Informe de Labores. (EC ISSN 0070-8887) **1075**
Ecuador. Comision de Valores. Corporacion Financiera Nacional. Memoria see Ecuador. Corporacion Financiera Nacional. Memoria **1093**
Ecuador. Corporacion Financiera Nacional. Boletin Estadistico. (EC) **863**
Ecuador. Corporacion Financiera Nacional. Memoria. (EC) **1093**
Ecuador. Corporacion Financiera Nacional. News Bulletin. (EC) **1093**
Ecuador. Departamento de Estadisticas Fiscales. Estadisticas Fiscales. (EC) **714**
Ecuador. Direccion de Aviacion Civil. Estadisticas de Trafico Aereo see Boletin Estadistico de Trafico Aereo Internacional **4662**
Ecuador. Direccion de Aviacion Civil. Mathematics. (EC) **4672, 3035**
Ecuador. Direccion General de Recaudaciones. Boletin. (EC) **1093**
†Ecuador. Instituto Nacional de Estadistica y Censos. Encuesta Anual de Recursos y Actividades de Salud. (EC) **5184**
Ecuador. Instituto Nacional de Estadistica y Censos. Estadistica del Trabajo. (EC ISSN 0070-8917) **714**
Ecuador. Instituto Nacional de Investigaciones Agropecuarias. Informe Tecnico. (EC) **176**
Ecuador. Instituto Nacional de Meteorologia e Hidrologia. Anuario Hidrologico. (EC) **1597**
Ecuador. Instituto Nacional de Meteorologia e Hidrologia. Anuario Meteorologico. (EC) **3435**
Ecuador. Instituto Nacional de Meteorologia e Hidrologia. Boletin Climatologico. (EC) **3435**
Ecuador. Ministerio de Energia y Minas. Informe de Labores. (EC) **1785, 3482**
Ecuador. Ministerio de Industrias, Comercio e Integracion. Boletin de Informacion de las Empresas Acogidas a la Ley de Fomento Industrial. (EC) **1075**
Ecuador. Ministerio de Industrias, Comercio e Integracion. Documento. (EC) **835**
Ecuador. Ministerio de Industrias, Comercio e Integracion. Empresas Acogidas a la Ley de Fomento Industrial. Directorio Industrial. (EC) **1134**
Ecuador. Ministerio de Industrias, Comercio e Integracion. Informe a la Nacion. (EC) **835**

Ecuador. Ministerio de Recursos Naturales y Energeticos. Informe de Labores see Ecuador. Ministerio de Energia y Minas. Informe de Labores **1785**
Ecuador. Servicio Nacional de Meteorologia e Hidrologia. Anuario Hidrologico see Ecuador. Instituto Nacional de Meteorologia e Hidrologia. Anuario Hidrologico **1597**
Ecuador. Servicio Nacional de Meteorologia e Hidrologia. Anuario Meteorologico see Ecuador. Instituto Nacional de Meteorologia e Hidrologia. Anuario Meteorologico **3435**
Ecuador. Superintendencia de Bancos. Boletin see Ecuador. Superintendencia de Bancos. Boletin Bancario y Financiero **777**
Ecuador. Superintendencia de Bancos. Boletin Bancario y Financiero. (EC) **777**
Ecuador. Superintendencia de Bancos. Documentos. (EC) **777**
Ecuador. Superintendencia de Bancos. Inversiones Extranjeras en el Ecuador. (EC) **777**
Ecuador. Superintendencia de Bancos. Memoria. (EC) **777**
Ecuador Economico. (EC ISSN 0070-8925) **662**
Ecuador Guia Turistica. (EC) **4761**
Ecuadorian American Business. see Comercio Ecuadoriano Americano **813**
Ecuadorian - American Chamber of Commerce. Annual Directory. (EC) **814**
Ecuatorial. (UK ISSN 0260-2113) **2992**
Ecumenical Courier. (US ISSN 0013-0761) **4175**
Ecumenical News. (IO) **4175**
Ecumenical Notes see One in Christ **4271**
Ecumenical Press Service. (SZ) **4175**
Ecumenical Review. (SZ ISSN 0013-0796) **4175**
Ecumenical Trends. (US ISSN 0360-9073) **4175**
Ecumenism. (CN ISSN 0383-4301) **4175**
†Ecumenist. (US ISSN 0013-080X) **5184**
Ecunews. (SA) **4175**
Eczacilik Bulteni see Acta Pharmaceutica Turcica **3715**
Ed.Tech.News. see A E T T Journal - E T T I **1743**
Ed: One Club, One Horse, One World. (US) **1373**, 1297
†Edb Nyt. (DK ISSN 0109-6109) **5184**
Edda. (NO ISSN 0013-0818) **2913**
Edebiyat. (US ISSN 0364-6505) **2913**
Edeka Handels-Rundschau. (GW) **662**
Die Edelkatze. (GW ISSN 0013-0826) **3710**
Edelmetaal. (NE) **2563**, 3405
Edelmetaal Uurwerken Edelstenen. (NE) **2563**
Edelweiss Berg-Roman. (GW) **2983**
Edesipar. (HU ISSN 0013-0842) **2088**
Edessaika Chronika. (GR) **2359**
Edgar Brookes Academic and Human Freedom Lecture. (SA ISSN 0070-8976) **1705**, 2142
Edgar Wallace Society Newsletter see Crimson Circle Magazine **2909**
The Edge. (CN ISSN 0840-4445) **1236**, 1253
Edge. (JA) **1290**
†Edge. (US) **5184**
▼Edge Detector. (CN) **3011**
Edges. (US) **2435**
Edgewood College Today. (US) **1310**
Ediafric. Plans de Developpement see Plans de Developpement des Pays d'Afrique Noire **879**
Ediciones del Pueblo. (PE) **2913**, 2054
Ediciones Peninsula. Serie Universitaria. Historia, Ciencia, Sociedad. (SP) **4371**
Edicoes Cadernos Culturais. (BL) **2864**

Edilizia Popolare. (IT) **616**
Edinburgh Academy Chronicle. (UK ISSN 0013-0893) **1626**
Edinburgh Architectural Association Review see E A A Review **299**
Edinburgh Architecture Research see E A R **299**
Edinburgh Bibliographical Society. Publications see Edinburgh Bibliographical Society Transactions **399**
Edinburgh Bibliographical Society Transactions. (UK ISSN 0140-7082) **399**
Edinburgh Chamber of Commerce and Manufactures Directory. (UK) **814**
Edinburgh Chamber of Commerce and Manufactures Journal. (UK) **814**
Edinburgh Gazette. (UK) **2194**
Edinburgh Medicine. (UK ISSN 0260-3934) **3095**
Edinburgh Review. (UK ISSN 0267-6672) **2864**
Edinburgh Studies in Culture and Society. (UK) **4434**
Edinburgh Studies in Sociology see Edinburgh Studies in Culture and Society **4434**
Edinenie. see Unification **2027**
Edisi Chusus Bulletin Koperasi. (IO ISSN 0852-0747) **863**
Edison Electric Institute. Statistical Yearbook of the Electric Utility Industry. (US) **1886**
Edison Electric Institute Environmental Journal see E E I Environmental Journal **5183**
Edison Electric Institute Statistical Releases. Electric Output see E E I Statistical Releases. Electric Output **1843**
Edison Electric Institute Washington Letter see E E I Washington Letter **1886**
Les Editeurs Belges de Langue Francaise. (BE) **399**
Editeurs Belges de Langue Francaise et Leurs Livres see Les Editeurs Belges de Langue Francaise **399**
Edith Wharton Newsletter see Edith Wharton Review **2913**
Edith Wharton Review. (US) **2913**, 4840
Editie Collection d'Art. (NE) **325**
Editio. (GW ISSN 0931-3079) **2913**, 3765, 4127
Edition Weiss-Blau. (GW) **4689**, 257
Editiones Arnamagnaeanae. Series A. (DK ISSN 0070-9069) **2913**, 2811
Editiones Arnamagnaeanae. Series B. (DK ISSN 0070-9077) **2913**, 2811
Editiones Arnamagnaeanae. Supplementum. (DK ISSN 0070-9085) **2913**
Editions Organisation. Fiches E O-Formation Permanente see Fiches E O - Formation Permanente **1010**
Editor (Rio de Janeiro). (BL) **4127**
Editor & Publisher International Year Book. (US ISSN 0424-4923) **1335**, 2569
Editor & Publisher Market Guide. (US) **1038**
Editor & Publisher Syndicate Directory. (US) **2569**, 2913
Editor & Publisher - the Fourth Estate. (US ISSN 0013-094X) **2569**, 31
Editor Newspapers - Lubbock - Odessa, Texas. (US) **31**, 2000
Editora /Meio e Mensagem Ltda. Agencias see M e M Agencias **1044**
Editora /Meio e Mensagem Ltda. Documento see M e M Documento **1044**
Editora /Revista dos Tribunais Incola see R T - Incola **2670**
†Editore. (IT) **5184**
Editorial Eye. (US ISSN 0193-7383) **4127**, 2569
Editorial Pace. (US) **2569**
Editorial Research Reports see C Q Researcher **3877**
Editorials on File. (US ISSN 0013-0966) **2328**, 10, 3937
Editor's Choice. (US ISSN 1060-2658) **2913**, 325

Editor's Clip Sheets. (AT ISSN 0726-4143) **4236**
Editor's Desk. (US) **2992**
Editor's Digest. (US) **4127**
Editors' Forum. (US ISSN 0746-3014) **2569**
Editors' Forum. (NR ISSN 0794-5655) **4127**
Editors' Notes. (US ISSN 0888-3173) **4127**, 1705, 2569
Editors of Astronomy Look at Earth see Earth (Waukesha) **1543**
Editors Only. (US ISSN 0735-8490) **2569**
Editor's Revenge. (US) **2569**, 1626, 2811
Editor's Workshop Newsletter. (US) **2569**
†EditSpeak. (US) **5184**
Edittech International. (US) **1350**, 1886
Editur. (SP ISSN 0422-6186) **4761**
Ediyn Dzasgiyn Bolovsrol/Economic Education. (MP) **662**
Edmagram see E D M A - Gram **31**
Edmondson Family Association Bulletin. (US) **2149**
Edmonton. (CN ISSN 0711-589X) **2177**
Edmonton Airport Business Directory. (CN) **4672**
Edmonton Antique Car Club. Bulletin see Running Board **4701**
Edmonton Area Series Report see Alberta - Edmonton Series Report **3979**
Edmonton Bullet. (CN) **2177**
Edmonton Chamber of Commerce. Commerce News. (CN ISSN 0704-8017) **815**
Edmonton Commerce and Industry. (CN) **835**
Edmonton Hundred Historical Society. Chronicle. (UK ISSN 0260-9355) **2359**
Edmonton Native News. (CN ISSN 0046-1296) **2177**, 2000
Edmonton Senior. (CN) **2272**
Edmonton Stamp Club Bulletin. (CN ISSN 0046-1318) **3752**
Edmund's Auto-Pedia see Edmund's Car Savvy **4689**
Edmund's Van, Pickup, Off Road Vehicles see Edmund's Van, Pickup, Sport Utility Buyer's Guide **4689**
Edmundite. (US ISSN 0013-1016) **4263**
Edmund's Car Savvy. (US) **4689**
Edmund's Economy Car Buying Guide. (US) **4689**
Edmund's Foreign Car Prices. (US ISSN 0531-7886) **4689**
Edmund's New Car Prices. (US) **4689**
Edmunds Prescription Drug Prices. (US) **3725**
Edmunds United States Coin Prices. (US) **3599**
Edmund's Used Car Prices. (US ISSN 0424-5059) **4689**
Edmund's Van, Pickup, Sport Utility Buyer's Guide. (US) **4689**
Edna Hibel Society Newsletter. (US) **325**
EdNews. (US) **1626**
EdPress News. (US) **1627**
EdPress Newsletter see EdPress News **1627**
Edseletter. (US ISSN 0046-1326) **4689**, 1297
Edubba. (AT ISSN 0085-0187) **2310**
Educacao e Realidade. (BL ISSN 0100-3143) **1627**
Educacao e Selecao. (BL) **1627**
Educacion. (PR ISSN 0013-1067) **1627**
Educacion. (VE ISSN 0013-1075) **1627**
Educacion. (MX ISSN 0185-0547) **1627**
Educacion. (PE) **1627**
Educacion. (US ISSN 0250-6130) **1627**
†Educacion. (SP) **5184**
Educacion (Havana). (CU) **1627**
Educacion en Iberoamerica: Sistema de Indicadores Socio-Economicos y Educativos see Sistema de Indicadores Socio-Economicos y Educativos de la O E I **4386**

Educacion Especial. (VE ISSN 0252-998X) **1735**
Educacion Fisica y Deporte. (CK ISSN 0120-677X) **4471**
Educacion Medica y Salud. (UN ISSN 0013-1091) **1694**, 3095, 3801
Educacion para el Desarrollo. (UY) **1627**
Educacion Sanitaria. (SP) **4100**
Educacion Superior. Revista see Educacion Superior y Sociedad **1705**
Educacion Superior Contemporanea. (CU) **1627**
†Educacion Superior y Desarrollo. (CK ISSN 0120-3819) **5184**
Educacion Superior y Sociedad. (VE ISSN 0798-1228) **1705**, 1683
Educacion y Pueblo. (BO) **1627**
Educadores. (SP ISSN 0013-1113) **1627**
Educadores del Mundo. (GW) **1627**
Educamus. (SA ISSN 0250-152X) **1627**
Educar. (CK ISSN 0120-162X) **1627**
Educare. (SA) **1627**
Educare. (UK ISSN 0141-7282) **1735**, 1705
Educated Traveler. (US) **4761**
Educateur. (FR ISSN 0013-113X) **1627**
Educateur et Bulletin Corporatif see Educateur: Revue de Pedagogie et d'Education **1627**
Educateur et Bulletin Corporatif see Educateur: Journal Corporatif et Syndical **1627**
Educateur: Journal Corporatif et Syndical. (SZ) **1627**
Educateur: Revue de Pedagogie et d'Education. (SZ) **1627**
Educating Exceptional Children see Annual Editions: Educating Exceptional Children **1733**
Educating in Faith. (US ISSN 0030-6819) **4263**, 1627, 3941
Educating the Disadvantaged see Readings on Equal Education **1740**
Education. see Bolovsrol **1618**
Education. (II ISSN 0013-1180) **1627**
Education. (UK ISSN 0013-1164) **1627**
Education. (US ISSN 0013-1172) **1627**
Education see Education News **1629**
Education see Education Journal **1629**
Education. see Olum-e Tarbiati **1652**
Education. see Al-Tarbiyyah **1666**
Education (Sydney). (AT ISSN 0013-1156) **1627**
Education Advisory. (CN) **1627**
Education & Careers in South Africa. (SA) **1627**, 3626
Education & Computing. (NE ISSN 0167-9287) **1689**, 1627
Education & Culture/Onderwys en Kultuur. (SA ISSN 0259-2029) **1627**
Education and Culture. Section 1: Cultural Development. (FR) **1627**
Education and Culture. Section 2: Higher Education and Research. (FR) **1627**
Education and Health. (UK ISSN 0265-1602) **1726**, 3095
Education and Law Journal. (CN ISSN 0838-2875) **2621**, 1627
Education and Occupation. see Jiaoyu yu Zhiye **1684**
Education and Psychological Research. (US ISSN 0279-0688) **1627**
Education and Psychology Review. (II ISSN 0046-1385) **1627**, 4019
Education and Science see Great Britain. Department of Education and Science. Annual Report **1635**
†Education and Self Management of the Psychiatric Patient. (US ISSN 0889-9657) **5184**
Education and Society in the Middle Ages and the Renaissance. (NE ISSN 0926-6070) **2359**, 1628
Education and Society Journal. (AT ISSN 0726-2655) **1628**, 4434
Education and the Law. (UK ISSN 0953-9964) **2621**, 1628

Education and Training. (UK ISSN 0040-0912) **1628**, 4597
Education and Training in Indexing and Abstracting. (US) **2756**, 1628
Education and Training in Mental Retardation. (US) **1735**
Education and Treatment of Children. (US ISSN 0748-8491) **1748**
Education and Urban Society. (US ISSN 0013-1245) **1628**, 3892, 4434
Education and Welfare. see Undervisning og Velferd **3473**
†Education Around the World. (US) **5184**
Education Authorities' Directory and Annual. (UK ISSN 0070-9131) **1628**
▼Education Beat. (US ISSN 1058-4226) **1628**
Education Bulletin. (UK ISSN 0952-9748) **271**, 1628
Education Canada. (CN ISSN 0013-1253) **1628**
Education Canadienne et Internationale. see Canadian and International Education **1620**
Education Commission of the States. National Assessment of Educational Progress. Assessment Reports see National Assessment of Educational Progress. Assessment Reports **1755**
Education Committees Year Book see Education Year Book **1629**
Education Computer News see Education Technology News **1417**
Education Daily. (US ISSN 0013-1261) **1628**
Education des Adultes see I.C.E.A. Cahiers **5208**
Education des Femmes. see Women's Education **4857**
Education Development Center. Annual Report. (US ISSN 0424-5407) **1628**
Education Digest. (US ISSN 0013-127X) **1628**
Education Director see Association Education Director **1003**
Education Directory. Local Education Agencies see Directory of Public Elementary and Secondary Education Agencies **1625**
Education Directory (School Year) - Colleges and Universities see Directory of Postsecondary Institutions **1693**
Education Economie. (FR ISSN 0990-5413) **662**
Education Enfantine. (FR ISSN 0013-1288) **1628**
Education Equipment. (UK ISSN 0013-1296) **1748**
Education Equipment Selector. (UK ISSN 0046-1415) **1726**
Education et Francophonie. (CN ISSN 0849-1089) **1628**
Education Express. (CN ISSN 0821-0705) **1628**, 1335
Education for Business and Management in the Region. (UK) **1705**, 1694
Education for Information. (NE ISSN 0167-8329) **2756**
Education for Librarianship: Australia. (AT ISSN 0813-4235) **2756**
Education for Migrant Children; Arizona State Plan see Arizona State Plan for the Education of Migratory Children **1616**
Education for Nursing: The Diploma Way. (US ISSN 0070-9166) **3278**, 1705
Education for Teaching see Journal of Further and Higher Education **1710**
Education for the Construction Industry in the Region. (UK) **1705**, 616
Education for the Elderly. see Laonian Jiaoyu **1685**
Education for the Handicapped see Practical Education for the Handicapped **1739**
Education for the Handicapped Law Report. (US ISSN 0744-4117) **1735**, 2283, 2621
Education for the People. (US) **1705**
Education for Tomorrow. (UK ISSN 0266-9145) **1628**

Education Forum. (CN ISSN 0840-9269) **1628**
Education Forward. (US) **1727**
Education Funding News. (US ISSN 0273-4443) **1727**
Education Gazette. (AT ISSN 0013-1334) **1628**
Education Gazette (Victoria). (AT ISSN 0013-1342) **1628**
Education Gazette and Teachers' Aid see Education Gazette (Victoria) **1628**
▼Education Grants Alert. (US) **1628**
Education Guidelines. (AT ISSN 0729-8528) **1676**
Education in Asia and Oceania: Reviews, Reports and Notes see Education in Asia and the Pacific: Reviews, Reports and Notes **1628**
Education in Asia and the Pacific: Reviews, Reports and Notes. (UN) **1628**
Education in Chemistry. (UK ISSN 0013-1350) **1176**, 1748
Education in Europe. Cultural Development. (FR) **1628**
Education in Europe. Section 1: Higher Education and Research. (FR ISSN 0070-9182) **1705**
▼Education In Focus. (US ISSN 1049-7250) **1628**
Education in Germany see Bildung und Wissenschaft **1618**
Education in India. (II) **1628**
Education in Japan; A Graphic Presentation. (JA ISSN 0070-9220) **1628**
Education in Kenya. (KE) **1676**, 1705
Education in Korea. (KO) **1721**
Education in O E C D Countries: Compendium of Statistical Information. (FR) **1629**
Education in Science. (UK ISSN 0013-1377) **1629**, 4308
Education in the North. (UK ISSN 0424-5512) **1629**
▼Education in the Public Eye. (US ISSN 1055-0860) **1629**
Education in the Royal County of Berkshire. (UK ISSN 0261-8966) **1629**
Education Index. (US ISSN 0013-1385) **1676**, 10
Education Journal. (SA ISSN 0259-207X) **1629**
†Education Law Bulletin. (US ISSN 0276-718X) **5184**
Education Leader. (CN) **1727**
Education Libraries. (CN ISSN 0148-1061) **2756**, 1629
Education Libraries Bulletin see Education Libraries Journal **2756**
Education Libraries Bulletin Supplements. (UK ISSN 0076-079X) **2756**
Education Libraries Journal. (UK ISSN 0957-9575) **2756**, 1629
Education Links. (AT ISSN 0814-6802) **1629**, 3892
Education Management Technology. (KO) **1748**
Education Manitoba. (CN ISSN 0704-2671) **1629**
Education Monitor. (US ISSN 1041-9462) **1629**
Education Musicale. (FR ISSN 0013-1415) **3550**
Education Network News. (US) **1629**, 2000
Education News. (AT ISSN 0013-1431) **1629**
Education News. (SA) **1629**
Education News. (US) **1629**
Education News from Metrologic see Laser Quest **2523**
Education Newsletter see Education San Diego County **1629**
Education Newsline. (US) **1629**, 4236
Education of Earth Science/Chigaku Kyoiku. (JA ISSN 0009-3831) **1543**
Education of the Handicapped. (US ISSN 0194-2255) **1735**, 2283
Education of the Visually Handicapped see Review (Washington) **2295**
Education par le Jeu et l'Environnement.(FR ISSN 0246-4438) **1629**

Education Permanente. (FR ISSN 0339-7513) **1629**, 4404
Education Physique et Sport. (FR ISSN 0245-8969) **1748**, 4471
Education Physique et Sportive au 1er Degre. (FR ISSN 0245-8977) **4471**
Education Quarterly. (II ISSN 0013-1482) **1629**
Education Quarterly. (PH) **1629**
▼Education Quarterly. (AT ISSN 1036-5427) **1629**
Education Reporter. (US ISSN 0013-1512) **1629**
Education Research and Perspectives. (AT ISSN 0311-2543) **1705**
Education Review. see Jiaoyu Pinglun **1641**
Education Rurale. (FR ISSN 0395-7691) **1629**
Education San Diego County. (US) **1629**
Education Sanitaire et Nutritionnelle d'Afrique Centrale. (BE ISSN 0004-5144) **3605**, 4100
Education, Science et Culture/Uburezi, Ubuhanga n'Umuco. (RW) **1629**, 2506
Education, Sociedad y Politica. Anuario see Anuario: Muensteraner Beitraege zur Latein Amerika Forschung **5137**
Education Statistics for the United Kingdom. (UK) **1629**
Education Statistics, New York State. (US) **1676**, 4570
Education Technology News. (US ISSN 1061-5008) **1417**, 1460, 1469
Education Three-Thirteen. (UK ISSN 0300-4279) **1629**
†Education Times. (US ISSN 0197-5374) **5184**
Education Today. (UK ISSN 0013-1547) **1629**
Education Today. (CN) **1727**
Education Today and Tomorrow see Education for Tomorrow **1628**
Education U S A. (US ISSN 0013-1571) **1629**
Education Update (St. Paul). (US) **1629**
†Education Update (Washington). (US) **5184**
†Education Victoria. (AT ISSN 0817-0975) **5184**
Education Week. (US ISSN 0277-4232) **1629**
Education Year Book. (UK ISSN 0143-5469) **1629**
Education 2000. (FR) **1748**
Educational Abstracts for Tanzania. (TZ ISSN 0856-0005) **1676**
Educational Activities Magazine. see Majallat al-Anshittah al-Tarbawiyyah **1646**
Educational Administration see Educational Management & Administration **1727**
Educational Administration Abstracts. (US ISSN 0013-1601) **1676**, 10
Educational Administration and History Monographs. (UK ISSN 0140-0428) **1727**, 2310
Educational Administration Quarterly. (US ISSN 0013-161X) **1727**
Educational Analysis see Contemporary Analyses in Education **1623**
Educational & Child Psychology. (UK) **4019**
Educational and Psychological Interactions. (SW ISSN 0070-9263) **4019**, 1629
Educational and Psychological Measurement. (US ISSN 0013-1644) **4020**, 1629
Educational and Training Technology International. (US ISSN 0954-7304) **1748**
Educational and Vocational Guidance - Bulletin A I O S P, I A E V G, I V S B B. (Association Internationale d'Orientation Scolaire et Professionelle) (GW) **3626**, 1683
Educational Bibliography. see Bibliographie Paedagogik **393**
Educational Book Review. (II) **2506**, 4371
Educational Broadcasting International see Media in Education & Development **1647**

Educational Building Digest. (UN) **616**, 1727
Educational Commission for Foreign Medical Graduates. Annual Report. (US ISSN 0145-2037) **3095**
Educational Communications and Technology Journal see Educational Technology Research & Development **1748**
†Educational Computing Chronicle. (US) **5184**
Educational Considerations. (US ISSN 0146-9282) **1630**
Educational Courses in Great Britain and America. (UK) **1630**
Educational Dealer. (US) **1748**
†Educational Development in Korea. (KO) **5184**
Educational Digest. (CN ISSN 0046-1482) **1630**
Educational Directory of Mississippi Schools see Mississippi Educational Directory **1695**
Educational Documentation and Information - Documentation et Information Pedagogiques see International Bureau of Education. Bulletin **1677**
Educational Evaluation & Policy Analysis. (US ISSN 0162-3737) **1630**
Educational Facility Planner. (US) **1630**, 299
Educational Film and Video (Year) see Educational Video and Film **5184**
Educational Film & Video Locator. (US ISSN 0000-0973) **3520**, 1348, 1676, 1748
Educational Forum. (US ISSN 0013-1725) **1706**
Educational Foundations. (US) **1748**
Educational Freedom. (US ISSN 0013-1741) **1630**
Educational Front see Zambia Educational Journal **1673**
Educational Gerontology. (US ISSN 0360-1277) **1683**, 2272
Educational Horizons. (US ISSN 0013-175X) **1630**
▼Educational I R M Quarterly. (US) **1748**, 1689, 2797
Educational Index of Arabic Periodicals. (BA) **1676**, 10
Educational Index of Foreign Periodicals.(BA) **1676**, 10
Educational India. (II ISSN 0013-1768) **1630**
Educational Indicative Abstracts. (BA) **1676**, 10
Educational Information Abstracts. (BA) **1676**, 10
Educational Innovation and Information. (UN) **1721**
Educational Institute of Design Craft & Technology Year Book see E.I.D.C.T. - C.D.T. Year Book **5183**
Educational Journal. (SA) **1630**
Educational Journal. see Hawliyah Kulliyah al-Tarbiyyah **1636**
Educational Law Review see Nihon Kyoikuho Gakkai Nenpo **2661**
Educational Leadership. (US ISSN 0013-1784) **1748**
Educational Leaflet see New York State Museum. Leaflet **4330**
Educational Legislation Index. (BA) **1676**, 10, 4080
Educational Management & Administration. (UK ISSN 0263-211X) **1727**
Educational Marketer. (US ISSN 0013-1806) **4127**, 1630
Educational Materials. see Kyoyuk Tarjo **1753**
Educational Measurement: Issues and Practice. (US ISSN 0731-1745) **1630**
Educational Media and Technology Yearbook. (US ISSN 8755-2094) **1748**
Educational Media Catalogs on Microfiche. (US) **1748**
Educational Media International. (UK ISSN 0952-3987) **1630**
†Educational Microcomputing Annual. (US) **5184**
Educational Miscellany. (II) **1630**

Educational Music, Elementary School. see Kyoiku Ongaku, Shogaku-ban **3560**

Educational Music, Junior High and High School. see Kyoiku Ongaku, Chugaku Koko-ban **3560**

Educational Music, Secondary School see Kyoiku Ongaku, Chugaku Koko-ban **3560**

Educational Oasis. (US ISSN 0892-2853) **1748**

Educational Opportunities of Greater Boston. (US) **1694**

Educational Personnel in Delaware see Supply and Demand: Educational Personnel in Delaware **1666**

Educational Perspectives. (US ISSN 0013-1849) **1630**

Educational Philosophy and Theory. (AT ISSN 0013-1857) **1630**

Educational Policy. (US ISSN 0895-9048) **1630**

Educational Products Information Exchange Institute Gram: The Newsletter of Systemic Change see E P I E Gram: The Newsletter of Systemic Change **1626**

Educational Prospects. see Jiaoyu Zhanwang **1641**

Educational Psychologist. (US ISSN 0046-1520) **4020**, 1630

Educational Psychology. see Psychologia Wychowawcza **1656**

Educational Psychology. (UK ISSN 0144-3410) **4020**, 1630

Educational Psychology in Practice. (UK ISSN 0266-7363) **4020**, 1630

Educational Psychology Review. (US ISSN 1040-726X) **1630**, 4020

†Educational R & D Report. (US) **5184**

Educational Record. (US ISSN 0013-1873) **1630**

Educational Records Bureau Measures see E R B Measures **1626**

Educational Reporter. (Il ISSN 0046-1539) **1630**

Educational Reports. see Pedagogiska Rapporter **1654**

Educational Research. (UK ISSN 0013-1881) **1630**

Educational Research. see Jiaoyu Yanjiu **1641**

Educational Research Quarterly. (US ISSN 0196-5042) **1630**

Educational Research Service Bulletin see E R S Bulletin **1726**

Educational Research Working Papers. (KE) **1630**

Educational Researcher. (US ISSN 0013-189X) **1630**

Educational Resources Information Center Clearinghouse for Junior Colleges Digest see E R I C Clearinghouse for Junior Colleges Digest **1705**

Educational Resources Information Center Clearinghouse on Teacher Education. Current Issues Publications see E R I C Clearinghouse on Teacher Education. Current Issues Publications **1626**

Educational Resources Information Center Information Bulletin see E R I C Information Bulletin **1705**

Educational Resources Information Center - Information Resources Update see E R I C - I R Update **2797**

Educational Resources Information Center Thesaurus of E R I C Descriptors see Thesaurus of E R I C Descriptors **1667**

Educational Review. (Il ISSN 0013-192X) **1631**

Educational Review. (UK ISSN 0013-1911) **1631**

Educational Review. see Kyoiku Hyoron **1645**

Educational Selective Abstracts. (BA) **1676**, 10

Educational Series - North Dakota Geological Survey see North Dakota. Geological Survey. Educational Series **1576**

▼Educational Software Review. (US) **1689**, 1477

Educational Software Selector see The Latest and Best of T E S S **1478**

Educational Standards in Japan. (JA) **1631**

Educational Statistics of Punjab. (PK) **1631**

Educational Studies. see Dirasat Tarbawiyyah **1625**

Educational Studies. (US ISSN 0013-1946) **1631**

Educational Studies. (UK ISSN 0305-5698) **1631**

Educational Studies. see Kyoiku Kenkyu **1645**

Educational Studies and Documents. (UN ISSN 0070-9344) **1631**

Educational Studies in Mathematics. (NE ISSN 0013-1954) **3035**, 1631

Educational T V Channel Newsletter. (US) **1297**, 2452

Educational Technology. (US ISSN 0013-1962) **1631**, 1689, 4597

Educational Technology Abstracts. (UK ISSN 0266-3368) **1676**, 10

Educational Technology Research. (JA ISSN 0387-7434) **4597**

Educational Technology Research & Development. (US ISSN 1042-1629) **1748**, 3508

Educational Television Newsletter see E T V Newsletter **1748**

Educational Testing Service Annual Report. (US ISSN 0091-8989) **1631**

Educational Testing Service Developments see E T S Developments **1626**

Educational Theatre News. (US ISSN 0013-1997) **4632**, 1631

Educational Theory. (US ISSN 0013-2004) **1631**

Educational Travel Planner. (CN ISSN 1183-1308) **4761**, 1631

Educational Trends. (Il) **1631**

†Educational User's Group Newsletter. (US) **5184**

†Educational Video and Film. (US) **5184**

EducatioNews. (US) **1727**, 1631

Educator see Guru Malaysia **1636**

Educator see National Educator **2229**

Educator. (PK ISSN 0013-2020) **2864**, 2213

Educatore. (IT) **1631**

Educators' Advocate. (US ISSN 0013-2047) **1631**

Educators Grade Guide to Free Teaching Aids. (US ISSN 0070-9387) **1749**

Educators' Guide to Corporate and Voluntary Support. (US) **662**, 1631

Educators' Guide to Corporate Support see Educators' Guide to Corporate and Voluntary Support **662**

Educators Guide to Free Audio and Video Materials. (US ISSN 0160-1296) **1749**, 1385

Educators Guide to Free Films. (US ISSN 0070-9395) **1749**

Educators Guide to Free Filmstrips and Slides. (US) **1749**

Educators Guide to Free Guidance Materials. (US ISSN 0070-9417) **1749**

Educators Guide to Free Health, Physical Education & Recreation Materials. (US ISSN 0424-6241) **1749**

Educators Guide to Free Home Economics Materials. (US ISSN 0883-2811) **2446**

Educators Guide to Free Science Materials. (US ISSN 0070-9425) **1749**

Educators Guide to Free Social Studies Materials. (US ISSN 0070-9433) **1749**

Educators Index of Free Materials. (US) **1749**

Educators Negotiating Service see Employers Negotiating Service **1727**

Educazione alla Sicurezza. (IT ISSN 0013-2071) **4100**

Educazione Audiovisiva see E D A V **1748**

Educazione dei Sordomuti. (IT) **2287**, 1735

Educazione e Televisione see E T V **1626**

Educazione Sanitaria e Medicina Preventiva see Educazione Sanitaria e Promozione della Salute **3801**

Educazione Sanitaria e Promozione della Salute. (IT) **3801**

Edukacja. (PL) **1631**

Edward H. Tarr Series. (US ISSN 0363-4558) **3550**

Edward Howell Family Association. Newsletter. (US ISSN 1045-2605) **2149**

Edward Sapir Monograph Series in Language, Culture, and Cognition. (US ISSN 0163-3848) **2811**

The Edwardean. (US ISSN 1048-8596) **2913**

Edwardian. (US) **1310**

Edwards County Historical Society. Quarterly. (US) **2405**

Edwards Journal. (US ISSN 0743-8591) **2149**

Eest Teaduste Akadeemia. Toimetised. Fuusika. Matemaatika/Estonian Academy of Sciences. Proceedings. Physics. Mathematics. (ER) **3817**, 3035

Eesti Elu/Estonian Life. (ER) **2186**

Eesti Filatelist/Estonian Philatelist. (US) **3752**

Eesti Haal/Estonian News. (UK) **2000**

Eesti Loodus/Estonian Nature. (ER ISSN 0131-5862) **4308**

Eesti Naine. (ER ISSN 0235-7488) **4840**, 355, 2088, 4835

Eesti Teaduste Akadeemia. Toimetised. Bioloogia/Estonian Academy of Sciences. Proceedings. Biology. (ER) **437**

Eesti Teaduste Akadeemia. Toimetised. Geoloogia/Estonian Academy of Sciences. Proceedings. Geology. (ER) **1560**

Eesti Teaduste Akadeemia. Toimetised. Keemia/Estonian Academy of Sciences. Proceedings. Chemistry. (ER) **1176**

▼Eesti Teaduste Akadeemia. Toimetised. Okoloogia/Estonian Academy of Sciences. Proceedings. Ecology. (ER ISSN 0868-5894) **437**

Eesti Teaduste Akadeemia. Toimetised. Uhiskonnateadused/Estonian Academy of Sciences. Proceedings. Social Sciences. (ER) **4371**

Eeva. (Fl ISSN 0355-2985) **4840**

Ef. (JA) **4840**

Effectif des Vehicules a Moteur en Suisse au 30 Septembre (Year). see Motorfahrzeugbestand in der Schweiz am 30. September (Year) **4665**

Effective Advertising. (US) **31**

Effektivt Landbrug/Productive Farming. (DK ISSN 0013-2187) **88**

Effeta. (IT ISSN 0013-2195) **2287**

Effluent and Water Treatment Journal. (UK ISSN 0013-2217) **1976**, 4824

Efrydiau Athronyddol. (UK ISSN 0142-3371) **3765**

Efterskoler. Fortegnelse. (DK ISSN 0108-8262) **1631**

Eftersyn. (DK ISSN 0109-3304) **325**

†Egad! (US) **5184**

Egan. (SP) **2913**

Egerer Zeitung. (GW ISSN 0013-2241) **2189**

Egeszsegneueles. (HU ISSN 0073-4004) **3801**

Egeszsegneveles Szakkonyvtara. (HU ISSN 0073-4012) **4100**

Egeszsegtudomany. (HU ISSN 0013-2268) **3095**

Egeszsegugyi Gazdasagi Szemle. (HU ISSN 0013-2276) **3095**

The Egg. (US) **4371**

†Egg (New York). (US) **5184**

Egg Industry. (US) **216**

Egg Market News Report. (US) **216**, 1038

Egg Producer. (CN ISSN 0821-4689) **216**

Egg Production Tests: United States and Canada. (US) **216**

Eglise a Lyon. (FR) **4263**

Eglise a Lyon et a Saint-Etienne see Eglise a Lyon **4263**

Eglise Aujourd'hui see Seve Eglise Aujourd'hui **4201**

L'Eglise Canadienne. (CN ISSN 0013-2322) **4175**

Eglise Catholique a Madagascar. (MG) **4263**

Eglise de Montreal. (CN ISSN 0381-0380) **4263**

Eglise en Alsace. (FR ISSN 0013-2330) **4263**

Eglise et Theologie. (CN ISSN 0013-2349) **4175**

Eglise Qui Chante. (FR ISSN 0013-2357) **3550**, 4175

Egnshistorisk Forening i Grundsoe. Aarsskrift. (DK ISSN 0109-0194) **2359**

Ego. (CN ISSN 0315-3037) **1290**

Ego see The Egoist **3892**

Ego Kids Magazine see F.L.Y.E.R.S. Kids **1290**

▼Ego Sport. (CN) **1290**

The Egoist. (UK) **3892**

Egon Ronay's Bulmer Pub Guide to Food and Accommodation see Egon Ronay's Guinness Pub Guide to Food and Accommodation **2473**

Egon Ronay's Dunlop Guide to Hotels and Restaurants in the British Isles see Egon Ronay's Lucas Guide to Hotels, Restaurants and Inns in Great Britain and Ireland **2473**

Egon Ronay's Guide to 500 Good Restaurants in Major Cities of Europe. (UK) **2473**, 4761

Egon Ronay's Guinness Pub Guide to Food and Accommodation. (UK) **2473**

Egon Ronay's Lucas Guide to Hotels, Restaurants and Inns in Great Britain and Ireland. (UK) **2473**

Egon Ronay's TWA Guide: 500 Good Restaurants in Major Cities, Europe and United States see Egon Ronay's Guide to 500 Good Restaurants in Major Cities of Europe **2473**

Egorag. (CN) **2992**

Egretta. (AU ISSN 0013-2373) **563**

Egyhazi Kronika. (HU ISSN 0133-0047) **4282**

Egypt. Central Agency for Public Mobilisation and Statistics. Monthly Bulletin of Foreign Trade. (UA ISSN 0027-0237) **714**

Egypt. Central Agency for Public Mobilisation and Statistics. Statistical Yearbook. (UA) **4570**

Egypt. Meteorological Authority. Annual Meteorological Report. (UA) **3435**

Egypt. Meteorological Authority. Meteorological Research Bulletin. (UA) **3435**

Egypt. Meteorological Authority. Monthly Weather Report. (UA) **3435**

Egypt. Ministry of Tourism. Statistical Bulletin. (UA ISSN 0041-4948) **4799**

Egypt. Population and Family Planning Board. Population Studies Quarterly Review see Egypt. Population Studies. Quarterly Review **3982**

Egypt. Population Studies. Quarterly Review. (UA) **3982**

Egypt. Service des Antiquites. Annales. (UA ISSN 0082-7835) **271**

Egypt. Specialised National Councils. Magazine. (UA) **863**

Egypt. Suez Canal Authority. Monthly Report. (UA) **4727**, 906

Egypt News. (Il) **3956**

Egypt Travel Magazine. (UA ISSN 0013-2381) **4761**

L'Egypte Contemporaine. (UA ISSN 0013-239X) **714**

Egypte - Sports - Cinema. (UA) **4471**, 3508

Egyptian Chamber of Commerce. Bulletin. (UA) **815**

Egyptian Computer Journal. (UA ISSN 0377-7154) **1394**

Egyptian Cotton Gazette. (UA ISSN 0013-2403) **4618**

Egyptian Cotton Statistics. (UA) **714**, 137

Egyptian Dental Journal. (UA ISSN 0070-9484) **3232**

Egyptian Gazette. (UA) **2185**

Egyptian Journal of Agronomy. (UA ISSN 0379-3575) **88**

Egyptian Journal of Animal Production. (UA ISSN 0302-4520) **216**

Egyptian Journal of Bilharziasis. (UA ISSN 0301-8849) **3218**
Egyptian Journal of Biomedical Engineering. (UA ISSN 1012-5558) **3258**
Egyptian Journal of Botany/Majallah al-Misriyah lil-Nabat. (UA ISSN 1011-3835) **501**
Egyptian Journal of Chemistry. (UA ISSN 0449-2285) **1176**
Egyptian Journal of Dairy Science. (UA ISSN 0378-2700) **199**
Egyptian Journal of Food Science/Majallah al-Misriyah li-Ulum al-Aghdhiya. (UA ISSN 1110-0192) **3605**
Egyptian Journal of Genetics and Cytology. (UA ISSN 0046-161X) **541, 524**
Egyptian Journal of Geology see United Arab Republic Journal of Geology **1583**
Egyptian Journal of Horticulture. (UA ISSN 1110-0206) **2125**
Egyptian Journal of Microbiology. (UA ISSN 0301-8172) **551**
Egyptian Journal of Pharmaceutical Sciences. (UA ISSN 0301-5068) **3725**
Egyptian Journal of Physics. (UA ISSN 1110-0214) **3817**
Egyptian Journal of Physiological Science. (UA ISSN 0301-8660) **571**
Egyptian Journal of Phytopathology. (UA ISSN 1110-0230) **501**
Egyptian Journal of Soil Science. (UA ISSN 0302-6701) **176**
Egyptian Journal of Veterinary Science. (UA ISSN 1110-0222) **4809**
Egyptian Library Journal/Sahifat al Makta-Bah. (UA ISSN 0531-6723) **2756**
Egyptian Mail. (UA) **2185**
Egyptian Medical Association. Journal. (UA ISSN 0013-2411) **3095**
Egyptian Museum. Library. Catalogue. (UA) **290, 399**
Egyptian Orthopaedic Journal/Al-Majallah Al-Misriyyah li-Jirahat al-'Itham. (UA ISSN 1110-1148) **3307**
Egyptian Population and Family Planning Review see E P F P R **596**
Egyptian Post. see Tachydromos - Egyptos **2886**
Egyptian Public Health Association Journal. (UA ISSN 0013-2446) **4100**
Egyptian Review of International Law/Revue Egyptienne de Droit International. (UA ISSN 0080-259X) **2722**
Egyptian Society of Endocrinology and Metabolism. Journal. (UA ISSN 0070-9506) **3252**
Egyptian Society of Parasitology. Journal. (UA ISSN 0253-5890) **3218**
Egyptian Statistical Journal. see Al-Majallah al-Ihsa'iyyah al-Misriyyah **4578**
Egyptian Surgical Society Quarterly Review. (UA ISSN 0013-2454) **3378**
Egyptological Editions. see Egyptologische Uitgaven **2429**
Egyptologische Uitgaven/Egyptological Editions. (NE) **2429**
Egyutt. (HU ISSN 0230-1806) **2756, 1236, 2811**
Ehe und Familie. (AU ISSN 0013-2470) **2173**
Ehe- und Familienrechtliche Entscheidungen. (AU) **2621**
Ehime Daigaku Kyoikugakubu Kiyo. Dai-3-bu. Shizen Kagaku/Ehime University. Faculty of Education. Memoirs. Series 3: Natural Sciences. (JA ISSN 0422-7727) **1560, 3657**
Ehime University. Faculty of Education. Memoirs. Series 3: Natural Sciences. see Ehime Daigaku Kyoikugakubu Kiyo. Dai-3-bu. Shizen Kagaku **1560**
Ehrenpreis Deutsche Keramik. (GW) **1163**

Ei-Beibungaku. see Studies in British & American Literature **2965**
Eibe. (GW) **1631**
Eibungaku Kenkyu. see Studies in English Literature **2965**
Eichenblatt. (GW) **3457**
Eichholzbrief. (GW ISSN 0013-2497) **3892**
Eicosanoids. (GW ISSN 0934-9820) **3095**
Eidgenoessenschaft Forschungsanstalt fuer Wald, Schnee und Landschaft. Mitteilungen. (SZ ISSN 1016-3158) **1487**
Eidgenoessische Anstalt fuer das Forstliche Versuchswesen. Berichte. (SZ ISSN 0259-3092) **2098**
Eidgenoessische Anstalt fuer das Forstliche Versuchswesen. Jahresbericht. (SZ ISSN 1011-9124) **2098**
Eidgenoessische Technische Hochschule. Institut fuer Orts-, Regional- und Landesplanung. Lehrmittel. (SZ) **2486**
Eidgenoessische Technische Hochschule Zuerich. Bibliothek. Schriftenreihe. (SZ ISSN 0514-0668) **2756**
Eidgenoessische Technische Hochschule Zuerich. Institut fuer Baustatik und Konstruktion. Allgemeine Berichte. (SZ) **1916**
Eidgenoessische Technische Hochschule Zuerich. Institut fuer Baustatik und Konstruktion. Versuchsberichte. (SZ) **1916**
Eidgenoessische Technische Hochschule Zuerich. Mitteilungen. Aerodynamik. (SZ ISSN 0084-5744) **3843**
Eidgenoessische Technische Hochschule Zuerich. Mitteilungen. Photoelastizitaet. (SZ ISSN 0084-5752) **3852**
Eidgenoessische Technische Hochschule Zuerich. Versuchsanstalt fuer Wasserbau, Hydrologie und Glaziologie. Jahresbericht. (SZ) **1597, 1923**
Eidgenoessische Technische Hochschule Zuerich. Versuchsanstalt fuer Wasserbau, Hydrologie und Glaziologie. Mitteilungen. (SZ) **1597, 1923**
Eidkunai Misim. (IS) **1093**
Eidos. (CN ISSN 0707-2287) **3765**
Eidos. (US ISSN 0740-8307) **4840, 2452**
Eidos, Erotica for Women see Eidos **4840**
Eiendomsmegleren. (NO) **4148**
Eier-Wild-Gefluegel-Markt. (GW ISSN 0013-2500) **2066, 199**
Eigen Aard. (BE) **4840**
Eigen Huis see Eigen Huis en Interieur **2551**
Eigen Huis en Interieur. (NE) **2551, 2558**
Die Eigentumswohnung. (GW) **2487, 2621**
Eigenwohner see Wohnungseigentum **636**
Eigeret Lechinuch. (IS) **1631**
Eight Ball. (US) **2569**
Eight O'Clock see Sunday Star **2212**
Eight Peak Index of Mass Spectra. (UK) **1201, 10**
Eight-Sheet Outdoor Rates and Allotments. (US) **31**
Eight-Sheet Outdoor Report. (US) **31**
Eight-Sheet Outdoor Sources. (US) **31**
Eighteen-Eleven. (US) **1514**
Eighteen Nineties Society. Journal. (UK) **2913**
Eighteenth Century: A Current Bibliography. (US ISSN 0161-0996) **399, 325, 2310, 3765**
Eighteenth-Century Fiction. (CN ISSN 0840-6286) **2913**
Eighteenth Century Life. (US ISSN 0098-2601) **2359, 325, 2913**
Eighteenth-Century Studies. (US ISSN 0013-2586) **2310, 325, 2913, 3550**
Eighteenth Century: Theory and Interpretation. (US ISSN 0193-5380) **2359, 2913**
Eighties. (US) **2865, 2992**
Eigo Kyoiku Jaanaru. see Modern English Journal **5238**

Eigse. (IE ISSN 0013-2608) **2811**
Eikones. (GR) **2196**
Eikonos. (SP ISSN 0210-4261) **3508, 4460**
Eilbote. (GW) **161**
Eildienst: Bundesgerichtliche Entscheidungen. (GW ISSN 0341-2261) **2621**
Ein- und Verkaufsfuehrer der Oesterreichischen Uhren- und Schmuckwirtschaft see Uhren Juwelen **2566**
Eina. (SP) **2098**
Einblicke. (GW ISSN 0930-8253) **1310**
Eindhoven University of Technology. Research Reports. (NE ISSN 0167-9708) **1886**
Eingefuehrte Motorfahrzeuge/Vehicules a Moteur Importes. (SZ) **4663**
Einhard Intern. (GW) **1236, 1631, 1727**
†Einheit. (GW ISSN 0013-2659) **5184**
Einhorn-Jahrbuch. (GW ISSN 0723-0877) **2359**
Einhorn Newsletter. (US) **662**
Einkaeufer im Markt. (GW ISSN 0930-8458) **1038, 1009**
Einkaufs 1x1 der Deutschen Industrie. (GW ISSN 0343-5881) **1134**
Einstein Quarterly Journal of Biology and Medicine. (US ISSN 0724-6706) **437, 3095**
Der Einzelhaendler. (GW) **662**
Einzelhandels Berater. (GW) **1009**
Eire - Ireland. (US ISSN 0013-2683) **2506, 2310, 2913**
Eirene. (NE ISSN 0046-1628) **2360, 271**
Eisbericht. (GW ISSN 0013-2705) **1560**
Eisei Dobutsu. see Japanese Journal of Sanitary Zoology **585**
Eisei Gyosei Gyomu Hokoku. see Japan. Ministry of Health and Welfare. Statistics and Information Department. Statistical Report on Public Health Administration and Services **4117**
Eisei Kagaku/Japanese Journal of Toxicology and Environmental Health.(JA ISSN 0013-273X) **1981, 3725, 4100**
Eisei Shikenjo Hokoku. see National Institute of Hygienic Sciences. Bulletin **4108**
Eisei Tokei Kara Mita Aichi-ken no Sugata. (JA) **4117**
Eisen und Stahl. (GW) **3425**
Eisenbahn. (AU ISSN 0013-2756) **4709**
Eisenbahn-Amateur. (SZ ISSN 0013-2764) **2436, 4709**
Eisenbahn Ingenieur Kalender (Year). (GW ISSN 0934-5930) **4709**
Eisenbahn-Journal. (GW ISSN 0720-051X) **4709**
Eisenbahn-Kurier. (GW ISSN 0170-5288) **2436**
Eisenbahn-Landwirt. (GW ISSN 0013-2772) **2125**
Eisenbahn Modellbahn Magazin. (GW ISSN 0342-1902) **4709, 2436**
†Eisenbahn-technische Praxis. (GW ISSN 0013-2837) **5184**
†Eisenbahn Zeitschrift. (GW) **5184**
Eisenbahner. (AU ISSN 0013-2799) **4709**
Eisenbahner. (SZ) **4709**
Eisenbahner. Ausgabe A & B see D B **4708**
Eisenbahnfachmann see D B **4708**
Der Eisenbahningenieur. (GW ISSN 0013-2810) **4709**
Eisenbahnpraxis see Der Eisenbahningenieur **4709**
Eisenbahntechnik see Neue Bahn **4712**
Eisenbahntechnische Rundschau. (GW ISSN 0013-2845) **4709**
Eisenhaendler Fachblatt see E F B **5183**
Eisenwaren-Zeitung see E Z - Eisenwaren und Hausrat **642**
Eisenwarenboerse. (GW ISSN 0013-2853) **642**
Eisenwarenhandel see Perspective **642**
Eiserne Lerche. (GW) **3550**

Eisma's Schildersblad see Eisma's Vakpers **3653**
Eisma's Vakpers. (NE) **3653**
Der Eisstockschuetze. (GW) **4471**
Eiszeitalter und Gegenwart. (GW ISSN 0424-7116) **3657**
Eitanim. (IS ISSN 0334-3928) **3095**
Eitione 77 Lesifrut Veletarbut. (IS) **2992**
Eiunim Bicheinuch. (IS ISSN 0334-2565) **1631**
Eiyogaku Zasshi. see Japanese Journal of Nutrition **3607**
Ejecutivos de Finanzas. (MX) **1009**
Ejendomsmaegleren. (DK ISSN 0013-2896) **4148**
Ejercito. (SP ISSN 0013-2918) **3457**
Ejercito. (CU) **3457**
Ek Bacharer Srestha Kabita. (II) **2992**
Ekaina. (FR ISSN 0751-8447) **1276, 2360**
Ekalabya. (II ISSN 0013-2926) **1254**
Ekarai Israel. (IS) **88**
Ekare. (VE) **777**
†Ekell Archives. (US) **5184**
Ekirei. see Postal Bell **5260**
Ekistic Index. (GR ISSN 0013-2934) **4457, 10, 2499**
Ekistics. (GR ISSN 0013-2942) **2487, 299**
Ekloyi/Choice. (CY) **2184**
Eko-Index. (CS ISSN 0042-1340) **714**
Eko Magazine. (US) **2000**
Ekoland. (NE) **88**
Ekologia C S R. (CS) **437, 501**
Ekologia Polska/Polish Journal of Ecology. (PL ISSN 0070-9557) **437**
Ekologia Polska. Seria B see Wiadomosci Ekologiczne **460**
Ekologiia. (BU ISSN 0204-7675) **438**
Ekologija see Acta Biologica Iugoslavica. Serija D: Ekologija **425**
Ekologiya Morya. (KR ISSN 0203-4646) **438**
Ekologiya Ptits Litovskoi S.S.R. (LI ISSN 0202-4195) **438**
Ekonomi dan Pembangunan. (IO) **662**
Ekonomi Indonesia. (IO) **662**
Ekonomicheskaya Gazeta. (RU ISSN 0013-3132) **662**
Ekonomicheskie Nauki. (RU ISSN 0013-3019) **662**
Ekonomicheskii Byulleten Niderlandov/Exporttijdschrift voor de Sovjetunie. (NE ISSN 0013-3000) **906**
Ekonomicko-Matematicky Obzor/Review of Econometrics. (CS ISSN 0013-3027) **663**
Ekonomicky Casopis/Economical Journal. (CS ISSN 0013-3035) **663**
Ekonomika i Organizatsiya Promyshlennogo Proizvodstva. (BW ISSN 0235-2427) **1075**
Ekonomika i Zhizn' (RU ISSN 0013-3051) **663**
Ekonomika Poljoprivreda. (YU ISSN 0013-306X) **150**
Ekonomika Polnohospodarstva. (CS) **150**
Ekonomika Prace. (CS) **4371**
Ekonomika Preduzeca. (YU) **663**
Ekonomika Proizvodnje Hrane see Ekonomika Poljoprivreda **150**
Ekonomika Radyanskoi Ukrainy. (KR ISSN 0131-775X) **894, 863**
Ekonomika Sel'skogo Khozyaistva. (RU ISSN 0013-3094) **150**
Ekonomika Sel'skokhozyaistvennykh i Pererabatyvayushchikh Predpriyatii. (RU) **663**
Ekonomika Sovetskoi Ukrainy. (KR ISSN 0131-7741) **894, 863**
Ekonomika Stroitel'stva. (RU ISSN 0013-3116) **616**
Ekonomika Udruzenog Rada see Ekonomika Preduzeca **663**
Ekonomika Ugol'noi Promyshlennosti. (RU) **3499**
Ekonomiki Kypros/Cyprus Economics. (CY) **663**
†Ekonomiko-Matematicheskie Metody Planirovaniya i Upravleniya. (UR) **5185**
Ekonomiko-Matematicheskie Metody v Planirovanii Narodnogo Khozyaistva. (TA) **894**

EKONOMISK DOKUMENTATION

Ekonomisk Dokumentation. (SW ISSN 0280-185X) **663**
Ekonomisk-Historiska Studier see Uppsala Studies in Economic History **898**
Ekonomiska Meddelanden see Svenska Bankfoereningen. Ekonomiska Meddelanden **885**
Ekonomiska Samfundets Tidskrift/Economic Society of Finland. Journal. (FI ISSN 0013-3183) **663**
Ekonomist. (YU ISSN 0013-3191) **663**
Ekonomista. (PL ISSN 0013-3205) **663**
Ekonomska Analiza - Economic Analysis see Economic Analysis and Workers Management **660**
Ekonomska Misao. (YU ISSN 0013-323X) **663**
Ekonomska Revija. (XV ISSN 0013-3256) **663**
Ekonomski Anali. (YU ISSN 0013-3264) **663**
Ekonomski Glasnik. (BN ISSN 0013-3272) **663**
Ekonomski Pregled. (CI ISSN 0424-7558) **663**
Ekota. (BG) **2174**
Ekran. (XV ISSN 0013-3302) **3508, 1373**
Ekran see Media Reporter **3513**
Ekran. (RU) **4632**
Eksperimentalna Medicina i Morfologija.(BU ISSN 0367-0643) **3259**
Eksperimental'naya i Prikladnaya Psikhologiya. (RU) **4020**
Eksperimental'naya Onkologiya/Experimental Oncology. (KR ISSN 0204-3564) **3196**
Eksperimental'noe Issledovanie Lichnosti i Temperamenta. (RU) **4020**
†Eksploatacja Kolei. (PL ISSN 0137-219X) **5185**
Eksport. (DK) **906**
Eksport Aktuelt. (NO ISSN 0800-6733) **906**
Eksportfremmeraadet. Beretning see Eksportkredit, Eksportfremme: Aarsberetninger **906**
Eksportkredit, Eksportfremme: Aarsberetninger. (DK ISSN 0108-7509) **906**
Eksportkreditraadet. Beretning see Eksportkredit, Eksportfremme: Aarsberetninger **906**
Ekspress-Informatsiya. Astronavtika i Raketodinamika. (RU ISSN 0132-1668) **66, 10**
Ekspress-Informatsiya. Aviastroenie. (RU ISSN 0207-5008) **66, 10**
Ekspress-Informatsiya. Detali Mashin. (RU ISSN 0131-7970) **3025, 11**
Ekspress-Informatsiya. Elektronika. (RU ISSN 0131-0747) **1766, 11**
Ekspress-Informatsiya. Gorodskoi Transport. (RU ISSN 0131-7962) **4663, 11**
Ekspress-Informatsiya. Informatika. (RU ISSN 0203-8889) **1819**
Ekspress-Informatsiya. Ispytatel'nye Pribory i Stendy. (RU ISSN 0131-7997) **2525, 11**
Ekspress-Informatsiya. Kontrol'no-Izmeritel'naya Tekhnika. (RU ISSN 0131-0224) **2525, 11**
Ekspress-Informatsiya. Korroziya i Zashchita Metallov. (RU ISSN 0131-0232) **3425, 11**
Ekspress-Informatsiya. Kvantovaya Radiotekhnika. (RU ISSN 0131-0208) **1348, 11, 1356**
Ekspress-Informatsiya. Nadezhnost' i Kontrol' Kachestva. (RU ISSN 0131-0275) **1843, 11**
Ekspress-Informatsiya. Organizatsiya Perevozok, Avtomatizirovanie, Telemekhanika i Svyaz' na Zheleznykh Dorogakh see Ekspress-Informatsiya. Organizatsiya Perevozok. Avtomatizirovannie Sistemy Upravlenia Transportom **4663**
Ekspress-Informatsiya. Organizatsiya Perevozok. Avtomatizirovannie Sistemy Upravlenia Transportom. (RU) **4663, 11**

Ekspress-Informatsiya. Peredacha Informatsii. (RU ISSN 0320-1058) **1348, 11**
Ekspress-Informatsiya. Podvodno-Tekhnicheskie, Vodolaznye i Sudopod'emnye Raboty. see Ekspress-Informatsiya. Podvodno-Tekhnicheskie, Vodolaznye i Sudopod'emnye Raboty. Gidrotekhnicheskie Sooruzheniya **3025**
Ekspress-Informatsiya. Podvodno-Tekhnicheskie, Vodolaznye i Sudopod'emnye Raboty. Gidrotekhnicheskie Sooruzheniya. (RU) **3025, 11**
Ekspress-Informatsiya. Porshnevye i Gazoturbinnye Dvigateli. (RU ISSN 0131-0356) **1843, 11**
Ekspress-Informatsiya. Pribory i Elementy Avtomatiki i Vychislitel'noi Tekhniki. (RU ISSN 0131-0380) **1404, 11**
Ekspress-Informatsiya. Promyshlennyi Organicheskii Sintez. (RU ISSN 0321-3668) **714, 11**
Ekspress-Informatsiya. Promyshlennyi Transport. (RU ISSN 0131-0402) **4663, 11**
Ekspress-Informatsiya. Protsessy i Apparaty Khimicheskikh Proizvodstv see Ekspress-Informatsiya. Protsessy i Apparaty Khimicheskikh Proizvodstv i Khimicheskaya Kibernetika **1843**
Ekspress-Informatsiya. Protsessy i Apparaty Khimicheskikh Proizvodstv i Khimicheskaya Kibernetika. (RU ISSN 0207-5024) **1843, 11**
Ekspress-Informatsiya. Pryamoe Preobrazovanie Teplovoi i Khimicheskoi Energii v Elektricheskuyu. (RU ISSN 0207-5032) **1785**
Ekspress-Informatsiya. Radiotekhnika Sverkhvysokikh Chastot. (RU ISSN 0131-0437) **1348, 11, 1356**
Ekspress-Informatsiya. Radiotekhnika Sverkhvysokikh Chastot i Kvantovaya Radiotekhnika see Ekspress-Informatsiya. Radiotekhnika Sverkhvysokikh Chastot **1348**
Ekspress-Informatsiya. Radiotekhnika Sverkhvysokikh Chastot i Kvantovaya Radiotekhnika see Ekspress-Informatsiya. Kvantovaya Radiotekhnika **1348**
Ekspress-Informatsiya. Sinteticheskie Vysokopolimernye Materialy. (RU ISSN 0131-047X) **1201, 11**
Ekspress-Informatsiya. Sistemy Avtomaticheskogo Upravleniya. (RU ISSN 0131-0488) **1404, 11**
Ekspress-Informatsiya. Tara i Upakovka see Ekspress-Informatsiya. Tara i Upakovka. Konteinery **3652**
Ekspress-Informatsiya. Tara i Upakovka. Konteinery. (RU ISSN 0131-0526) **3652, 11**
Ekspress-Informatsiya. Tekhnicheskaya Kibernetika. (RU ISSN 0131-0577) **1404, 11**
Ekubo. (JA) **1254**
Ekumenismo. (IT) **4175**
El. (SW ISSN 0013-399X) **1886**
El. (MX) **3397**
El Bodeguero see Florida Grocer **2091**
El Branschen. (SW ISSN 0013-4007) **1886**
El Entrepenoeren. (NO ISSN 0802-3212) **1886**
El Foro Mexicano. see Mexican Forum **5236**
El Ha'ayin see Sources of Contemporary Jewish Thought **2884**
El Installasjon og Handel see El Entrepenoeren **1886**
El & Energi. (DK ISSN 0107-3931) **1886, 1362**
El Paso Archaeological Society. Special Reports. (US ISSN 0070-9573) **271**
El Paso Archaeology. (US ISSN 0013-4023) **271, 1297**
El Paso Economic Review. (US ISSN 8750-6033) **663**
El Periodista Democrata see Democratic Journalist **2568**
El Popola Cinio/Zhongguo Baodao. (CC ISSN 0032-4361) **2181**

El Salvador. Direccion General de Estadistica y Censos. Anuario Estadistico. (ES ISSN 0080-5661) **4570**
El Salvador. Direccion General de Estadistica y Censos. Boletin Estadistico. (ES ISSN 0013-404X) **4570**
El Salvador. Ministerio de Agricultura y Ganaderia. Direccion General de Recursos Naturales Renovables. Plan Anual Operativo. (ES) **1487**
El Salvador. Ministerio de Comercio Exterior. Directorio de Offerta Exportable (Year). (Exportable Offer Directory) (ES) **906**
El Salvador. Ministerio de Comercio Exterior. Estadisticas. (ES) **714, 906**
El Salvador. Ministerio de Planificacion y Coordinacion del Desarrollo Economico y Social. Indicadores Economicos y Sociales. (ES ISSN 0581-4111) **4570**
El Salvador. Ministerio de Planificacion y Coordinacion del Desarrollo Economico y Social. Memoria de Labores. (ES) **863**
El Salvador. Superintendencia de Bancos y Otras Instituticiones Financieras. Estadisticas: Seguros, Finanzas, Bancos see El Salvador. Superintendencia del Sistema Financiero. Junta Monetaria. Anuario Estadistico: Seguros, Fianzas, Bancos **2546**
El Salvador. Superintendencia del Sistema Financiero. Junta Monetaria. Anuario Estadistico: Seguros, Fianzas, Bancos. (ES) **2546, 714, 777**
El Salvador: Coyuntura Economica. (ES) **663**
†El Salvador en Cifras. (ES) **5185**
El Salvador Filatelico. (ES) **3752**
El Salvador, Informe Economico y Social. (ES) **863**
Elainmaailma. (FI ISSN 0357-8747) **3710, 582**
Elan. (CN) **1290**
Elan. (FR ISSN 0013-4066) **2913**
Elan Image see Elan **2913**
Elan Poetique et Litteraire. (FR) **2992**
Elan Poetique Litteraire et Pacifiste. (FR ISSN 0397-0051) **2913, 2992**
Elanto. (FI) **830**
El-Arabi. (UA) **2185**
Elastomerics. (US ISSN 0146-0706) **4291**
Elastomerics Rubber Red Book. (US ISSN 0361-0640) **4291**
†Elastomeros. (BL) **5185**
Elbe Wochenblatt. (GW) **2189**
Elbe Wochenblatt fuer Sued Hamburg see Elbe Wochenblatt **2189**
Elbinger Nachrichten. (GW ISSN 0933-7334) **2360**
Elder Statesman see Today's Times **2279**
†Elder Viewpoint on Futures. (US) **5185**
Elder Voices. (US) **2272, 2000**
Elderhostel Catalog. (US) **1683, 1721**
Elderly Chinese. see Zhongguo Laonian **2280**
Elderly Health Services Letter. (US ISSN 0891-9275) **2272, 2461**
Elderly in the Literatures of the German-Speaking Countries. (US) **2913**
Elderly World. see Lauren Tiandi **2275**
Elders. (NE ISSN 0013-4082) **3982, 3956, 4371**
Elders Weekly. (AT) **216**
Eldridge Reeves Johnson Foundation for Medical Physics. Colloquium. Proceedings. (US ISSN 0070-959X) **3095**
Eldritch Science. (US) **3011**
Ele e Ela. (BL ISSN 0531-9153) **4840, 3397**
Elected and Appointed Black Judges in the United States. (US) **2731**
Election Administration Reports. (US ISSN 0145-8124) **4059**
Election Archives and International Politics. (II) **3892, 2722**

Election Archives Updating International Encyclopedia of Politics and Laws see Election Archives and International Politics **3892**
Election Laws of Hawaii see Election Laws of Hawaii Handbook **2621**
Election Laws of Hawaii Handbook. (US) **2621**
†Election Politics. (US ISSN 0742-5279) **5185**
Election Statistics. Municipal Councils. see Netherlands. Centraal Bureau voor de Statistiek. Statistiek der Verkiezingen. Gemeenteraden **3938**
Election Statistics. Second Chamber of the States-General. see Netherlands. Centraal Bureau voor de Statistiek. Statistiek der Verkiezingen. Tweede Kamer der Staten-Generaal **3938**
Elections au Conseil National (Year). see Nationalratswahlen (Year) **4081**
Electoral Studies. (UK ISSN 0261-3794) **3892**
Electra. (FR ISSN 0424-7701) **1886**
Electra. (DK) **1886**
Electra see Installatie Journaal **1899**
Electri-Onics see Electronic Manufacturing **5185**
Electri-Onics Desk Manual see Electronic Manufacturing Desk Manual **5185**
Electri-Onics - Electrical Manufacturing Edition see Electrical Manufacturing **1888**
Electric Company Magazine see Kid City **1258**
Electric Consumer. (US ISSN 0745-4651) **1801**
Electric Drive. see Dianqi Chuandong **1885**
Electric Energy Systems. (US) **1798, 1801**
Electric Furnace Conference Proceedings. (US) **3405**
Electric Furnace Steel/Denki Seiko. (JA ISSN 0011-8389) **3405**
Electric Letter see D S M Letter **1885**
Electric Light and Power. (US) **1887**
Electric Light and Power: Energy - Generation see Electric Light and Power **1887**
Electric Machines and Power Systems. (US ISSN 0731-356X) **1887, 3017**
Electric Pages. (US) **4007**
Electric Perspectives. (US ISSN 0364-474X) **1887**
Electric Plant Costs & Power Production Expenses. (US) **616**
▼Electric Plant Datapak. (US) **1801**
Electric Plant Ownerpak see Electric Plant Datapak **1801**
Electric Power. see Dianli Jishu **1885**
Electric Power Annual Report. (US) **1887**
Electric Power in Asia and the Pacific. (UN ISSN 0252-4406) **1887**
Electric Power in Canada. (CN ISSN 0070-962X) **1801**
†Electric Power Industry Abstracts. (US) **5185**
▼Electric Power International. (US) **1887**
Electric Power Monthly. (US ISSN 0732-2305) **1801**
†Electric Power Quarterly. (US) **5185**
Electric Power Research Institute Guide see E P R I Guide **1886**
Electric Power Systems Research. (SZ ISSN 0378-7796) **1887**
Electric Power Use by Industries. (US) **1798, 1801**
Electric Quarterly. (US) **2756, 1887, 3524**
Electric Railway Society. Journal. (UK ISSN 0013-4147) **4709**
Electric Rate Book. (US) **1798, 1801**
Electric Technology U.S.S.R. (English translation of: Elektrichestvo) (US ISSN 0013-4155) **1887**
Electric Thermal Storage News see E T S News **1886**
Electric Truck and Vehicle World see Batteries International **1883**
Electric Utility Fleet Management see Utility Fleet Management **4749**
†Electric Utility Generation Planbook. (US) **5185**
Electric Utility Power Purchase Contract Profiles. (US) **1801**

Electric Utility Week. (US) **1887**
Electric Vehicle Developments. (UK ISSN 0141-9811) **1887**
Electric Vehicle News. (AT ISSN 0818-8491) **4689**
Electric Vehicle Progress. (US ISSN 0190-4175) **4649**
Electric Vehicles. (UK) **4649**, **1887**
Electric Vehicles for Industry see Electric Vehicles **4649**
Electric Word. (NE ISSN 0921-2787) **1430**, **1446**
Electrical and Electronic Trader see Electrical Trader **5185**
Electrical & Electronics Abstracts. (UK ISSN 0036-8105) **1843**, **1766**, **1887**
Electrical and Electronics Incorporated Engineer see Electronics and Electrical Engineering **1769**
Electrical and Electronics Technician Engineers see Electrotechnology **1769**
Electrical and Radio Trading. (UK ISSN 0013-4228) **1356**, **1766**
Electrical Apparatus. (US ISSN 0190-1370) **1887**
Electrical Apparatus with Electric Heat see Electrical Apparatus **1887**
Electrical Blue Book. (CN) **1887**
Electrical Business. (CN ISSN 0013-4244) **1887**
Electrical Component Locator - Domestic Cars, Light Trucks & Vans. (US) **4690**, **4744**
Electrical Component Locator - Imported Cars, Light Trucks & Vans. (US) **4690**, **4744**
Electrical Construction & Maintenance. (US) **1887**
Electrical Construction and Maintenance Electrical Products Yearbook see E C & M's Electrical Products Yearbook **1886**
Electrical Construction Technology. (US) **1887**, **616**
Electrical Consultant see Electrical Systems Design **5185**
Electrical Contacts: I E E E Holm Conference on Electrical Contacts (Proceedings). (US) **1887**
Electrical Contracting News. (UK) **1887**
Electrical Contractor. (US ISSN 0033-5118) **1887**
Electrical Contractor (London). (UK ISSN 0308-7174) **1888**
Electrical Contractor and Retailer see Electrical Contractor (London) **1888**
Electrical Contractors' Association Year Book Desk Diary see E C A Year Book Desk Diary **5182**
Electrical Design. (UK) **1888**, **1335**
Electrical Design and Installation see E D I **1886**
Electrical Distributor. (US ISSN 0422-8707) **1888**
Electrical - Electronics Insulation Conference. Proceedings. (US) **1888**
Electrical - Electronics Insulation Conference. Record. (US ISSN 0070-9697) **1766**, **1888**
Electrical Engineer. (AT ISSN 0013-4309) **1888**
Electrical Engineer Magazine. (PH) **1888**
Electrical Engineering. see Elektrotechnika **1891**
Electrical Engineering Abstracts. see Elektrotechnikai Szakirodalmi Tajekoztato **1843**
Electrical Engineering & Computer Sciences News see E E C S - E R L News **1886**
Electrical Engineering and Electronics Series. (US) **1888**
Electrical Engineering Communications and Signal Processing see Electrical Engineering, Telecommunications and Signal Processing **1878**
Electrical Engineering in Japan. (US ISSN 0424-7760) **1888**

Electrical Engineering Problems in the Rubber and Plastics Industry Technical Conference. Record see Conference of Electrical Engineering Problems in the Rubber and Plastics Industries. I E E E Conference Record **4291**
Electrical Engineering, Telecommunications and Signal Processing. (US) **1878**, **1350**
Electrical Equipment. (UK ISSN 0013-4317) **1888**
Electrical Equipment News. (CN ISSN 0013-4333) **1888**
Electrical Equipment Representatives Association. Directory. (US ISSN 0070-9689) **1888**
Electrical Equipment Selector see Electrical Equipment **1888**
Electrical India. (II ISSN 0013-435X) **1888**
Electrical Industry. (NZ ISSN 0027-7185) **1888**
Electrical Insulation Conference. Proceedings see Electrical - Electronics Insulation Conference. Proceedings **1888**
Electrical Insulation Technical Conference. Record see Electrical - Electronics Insulation Conference. Record **1766**
Electrical Machinery: Latin American Industrial Report. (US) **1888**, **835**
Electrical Mail. (IE ISSN 0790-7508) **1038**
Electrical Manufacturing. (US ISSN 0895-3716) **1888**, **1075**
Electrical Marketing Newsletter. (US ISSN 0149-5771) **1038**, **1888**
Electrical News. (US) **1888**
Electrical Overstress - Electrostatic Discharge Technology see E O S - E S D Technology **4597**
Electrical Overstress - Electrostatic Discharge Technology Europe see E O S - E S D Technology Europe **4597**
†Electrical Power and Energy Systems. (UK ISSN 0142-0615) **5185**
Electrical Power Engineer see E P E **1886**
Electrical Products. (UK ISSN 0260-1656) **1888**
Electrical Products Yearbook see E C & M's Electrical Products Yearbook **1886**
Electrical Research Association Technology News see E R A Technology News **1038**
†Electrical Retailing. (UK) **5185**
Electrical Review. (UK ISSN 0013-4384) **1888**
Electrical Safety Bulletin. (CN) **1888**
†Electrical Systems Design. (US) **5185**
▼Electrical Systems Engineering. (CN) **1888**
Electrical Times. (UK ISSN 0013-4414) **1888**
†Electrical Trader. (UK) **5185**
Electrical Union World. (US ISSN 0041-686X) **2582**, **1888**
Electrical Week see Electric Utility Week **1887**
Electrical Wholesaler. (UK ISSN 0013-4422) **1888**
Electrical Wholesaling. (US ISSN 0013-4430) **1038**, **1888**
Electrical World see Australian, Asian & Pacific Electrical World **1882**
Electrical World. see Dian Shijie **1885**
Electrical World. (US ISSN 0013-4457) **1888**
Electrical World Directory of Electric Utilities. (US) **1888**, **1134**
Electrical Yearbook/Junki Yonkam. (KO) **1889**
Electricidade. (PO ISSN 0870-5364) **1889**
Electricidade, Energia, Electronica see Electricidade **1889**
Electricite/Elektriciteit. (BE ISSN 0013-4481) **1889**
Electricite see Strom **1908**
Electricite Automobile. (FR ISSN 0291-8234) **1889**, **4690**
Electricite de France. Bulletin de Documentation see Diffusion Express **1843**

Electricite de France. Direction des Etudes et Recherches. Bulletin. Collection des Notes Internes. Production d'Energie (Hydraulique, Thermique et Nucleaire). (FR) **1928**, **1819**
Electricite de France. Direction des Etudes et Recherches. Bulletin. Serie A: Nucleaire, Hydraulique, Thermique see Electricite de France. Direction des Etudes et Recherches. Bulletin. Collection des Notes Internes. Production d'Energie (Hydraulique, Thermique et Nucleaire) **1928**
Electricite de France. Direction des Etudes et Recherches. Bulletin. Serie B: Reseaux Electriques, Materiels Electriques see Electricite de France. Direction des Etudes et Recherches. Collection de Notes Internes. Materiel Electrique Transport et Distribution d'Energie **1889**
Electricite de France. Direction des Etudes et Recherches. Bulletin. Serie C: Mathematiques-Informatique see Electricite de France. Direction des Etudes et Recherches. Collection de Notes Internes. Mathematiques, Informatique, Telecommunications **3035**
▼Electricite de France. Direction des Etudes et Recherches. Collection de Notes Internes. Biologie, Sciences de la Terre et Environnement. (FR) **438**, **1543**, **1949**
Electricite de France. Direction des Etudes et Recherches. Collection de Notes Internes. Materiel Electrique Transport et Distribution d'Energie. (FR ISSN 1161-0581) **1889**
Electricite de France. Direction des Etudes et Recherches. Collection de Notes Internes. Mathematiques, Informatique, Telecommunications. (FR ISSN 1161-059X) **3035**
▼Electricite de France. Direction des Etudes et Recherches. Collection de Notes Internes. Organisation, Information, Environnement Social et Economique. (FR) **663**
▼Electricite de France. Direction des Etudes et Recherches. Collection de Notes Internes. Utilisations de l'Electricite. (FR) **1889**
Electricite de France. Documentation Technique see Diffusion Express **1843**
Electricite de France. Rapport d'Activite.(FR ISSN 0070-9735) **1889**
Electricite de France. Statistiques de la Production et de la Consommation. (FR ISSN 0070-9751) **1843**, **1889**
Electricite pour Tous see Strom **1908**
Electricite pour Vous see Pour Vous **1906**
Electricity and Electronics. (II ISSN 0013-4538) **1766**, **1889**
Electricity and Industry in Hokuriku. see Hokuriku no Denki to Kogyo **1799**
Electricity Conservation Quarterly. (II ISSN 0970-2318) **1889**, **1487**
Electricity Consumers Council. Annual Report. (UK ISSN 0261-2127) **1889**
†Electricity for China. (UK ISSN 0268-5949) **5185**
Electricity International. (US ISSN 0955-5439) **1889**
Electricity Journal. (US ISSN 1040-6190) **1889**
Electricity Statistics. see Norway. Statistisk Sentralbyraa. Elektrisitesstatistikk **1800**
Electricity Supply & Demand (Year). (US) **1889**
Electricity Supply Board. Marketing News see Electrical Mail **1038**
Electricity Supply Handbook. (UK ISSN 0070-976X) **1889**, **1916**
Electricity Today. (CN ISSN 0843-7343) **1889**
Electricity U K. (UK) **1889**
Electrics & Computers. see Elektronika Umachshavim **1394**
†Electro. (SI) **5185**
Electro. Annuaire. (FR) **1766**

Electro-Magnetic Compatibility Technology & Interference Control News see E M C Technology & Interference Control News **4597**
Electro Manufacturing. (US) **1878**
Electro Medical Trade Association. Products Directory. (UK) **3095**
Electro-Negoce. (FR ISSN 0153-9396) **1766**
Electro-Ocio. (SP ISSN 0212-6818) **1889**
Electro Optics. (UK ISSN 0013-4589) **3852**
Electro Optics Newsletter. (UK ISSN 0261-5657) **3852**
Electro-Radiologiste Qualifie de France. Annuaire see Medecin Electro-Radiologiste Qualifie de France **3360**
Electro-Revue. (SZ ISSN 0374-3101) **1889**
Electro-Revue. (BE) **1889**
Electro-Technology. (II ISSN 0013-4643) **1889**
Electroanalysis. (GW ISSN 1040-0397) **1205**
Electroanalytical Chemistry: A Series of Advances. (US ISSN 0070-9778) **1205**
Electrochemical Society. Extended Abstracts. (US) **1212**
Electrochemical Society. Journal. (US ISSN 0013-4651) **1212**
Electrochemical Society of India. Journal. (II ISSN 0013-466X) **1212**, **1225**
Electrochemical Society of Japan. Journal - Denki Kagaku see Electrochemistry and Industrial Physical Chemistry **1212**
Electrochemical Society Series. (US) **1212**
†Electrochemistry. (UK ISSN 0305-9979) **5185**
Electrochemistry and Industrial Physical Chemistry/Denki Kagaku Oyobi Kogyo Butsuri Kagaku. (JA ISSN 0366-9297) **1212**, **1852**
Electrochimica Acta. (US ISSN 0013-4686) **1212**
Electrocomponent Science Monographs.(US ISSN 0275-7230) **1889**
Electroencephalography and Clinical Neurophysiology see Electroencephalography and Clinical Neurophysiology Including Evoked Potentials and Electromyography and Motor Control **3335**
Electroencephalography and Clinical Neurophysiology Including Evoked Potentials and Electromyography and Motor Control. (IE ISSN 0921-884X) **3335**
Electrolux. Annual Report. (SW) **2558**
Electrolysis World. (US) **3247**, **372**
Electromagnetic Compatability Test and Design see E M C Test and Design **1886**
Electromagnetic News Report. (US ISSN 0270-4935) **1889**
Electromagnetics. (US ISSN 0272-6343) **1889**, **1588**
Electromechanical Bench Reference. (US) **1889**
Electromedica. (GW ISSN 0340-5389) **3095**
†Electromedical & Electrosurgical Equipment Spec Book. (US) **5185**
Electrometallurgy Bulletin see Bulletin of Electrochemistry **1212**
Electromyography and Clinical Neurophysiology. (BE ISSN 0301-150X) **3095**, **571**
Electromyography and Motor Control. (IE ISSN 0924-980X) **3335**
Electron. (NE ISSN 0013-4767) **1356**
The Electron. (US ISSN 0740-1922) **1766**
Electron - Engineering Review. see Eletron: Revista de Engenharia **1891**
Electron Microscopy Abstracts. (UK ISSN 0306-9869) **465**, **11**
†Electron Microscopy of Proteins. (UK) **5185**
Electron Microscopy Reviews. (US ISSN 0892-0354) **559**

ELECTRON MICROSCOPY

Electron Microscopy Society of America. Proceedings. (US ISSN 0424-8201) **559**
Electron Microscopy Society of America, Inc. Bulletin see E M S A Bulletin **559**
Electron Microscopy Society of Southern Africa. Proceedings/ Elektronmikroskopievereniging van Suidelike Afrika. Verrigtings. (SA ISSN 0250-0418) **559, 3852**
Electron Optics Reporter. (US) **1767**
Electron Spin Resonance see Electron Spin Resonance. Part B **1213**
Electron Spin Resonance see Electron Spin Resonance. Part A **1218**
Electron Spin Resonance. Part A. (UK) **1218**
Electron Spin Resonance. Part B. (UK) **1213**
Electron Spin Resonance Spectroscopy Abstracts. (UK ISSN 0301-7575) **3837, 11**
Electron Technology. (PL ISSN 0070-9816) **1767**
Electronaut. (NE ISSN 0013-5615) **1335, 4727**
Electronic and Atomic Collisions see International Conference on the Physics of Electronic and Atomic Collisions. Abstracts of Contributed Papers and Invited Papers **3847**
Electronic and Electrical Equipment Newsletter. (US) **1767, 1889**
Electronic Application News. (II ISSN 0013-4813) **1767**
Electronic Banking and Finance see Financial Technology Insight **826**
Electronic Bookstore for Executives. (US) **4127**
Electronic Business. (US ISSN 0163-6197) **1767**
▼Electronic Business Asia. (US) **1767**
Electronic Business Forecast. (US ISSN 0736-5705) **1767**
Electronic Buyers' News. (US) **1767, 1134**
Electronic Chemicals News. (US ISSN 0886-5671) **1767, 1176**
Electronic Claim Standard. (CN) **3725, 1450**
Electronic Combat Report see Inside Defense Electronics **3460**
Electronic Component News Literature News see E C N Literature News **1766**
Electronic Components Conference. Proceedings. (US ISSN 0569-5503) **1767**
Electronic Components of Assessed Quality Microfile see Electronic Quality Assurance Microfile **1768**
Electronic Components Symposium. Proceedings see Electronic Components Conference. Proceedings **1767**
Electronic Composition & Imaging. (CN ISSN 0838-9535) **4143**
Electronic Connector Study Group. Annual Connector Symposium. Proceedings see International Institute of Connector and Interconnection Technology. Annual Connector Symposium. Proceedings **1900**
Electronic Data Interchange Finance Newsletter see E D I in Finance Newsletter **805**
Electronic Data Interchange Monthly Report see E D I Monthly Report **1450**
Electronic Data Interchange News see E D I News **1446**
Electronic Data Processing Auditing see E D P Auditing **1450**
Electronic Data Processing Auditor Journal see E D P Auditor Journal **1450**
Electronic Data Processing Auditors Association. Control Objectives see E D P Auditors Association. Control Objectives **1450**
Electronic Data Processing Auditors Association. Update see E D P Auditors Association. Update **1450**
Electronic Data Processing Buyer's Guide see E D P Buyer's Guide **5183**

Electronic Data Processing In-Depth Reports see E D P In-Depth Reports **1450**
Electronic Data Processing Weekly see E D P Weekly **1450**
Electronic Design. (US ISSN 0013-4872) **1767**
Electronic Design Automation Ltd. see E D A **1766**
†Electronic Design's Gold Book. (US) **5185**
Electronic Display World. (US ISSN 0742-1532) **1767**
▼Electronic Distribution Today. (US) **1767**
Electronic Document Management Systems Journal see E D M S Journal **1444**
Electronic Education. (US ISSN 0278-5293) **1689, 1417**
Electronic Engineering. (UK ISSN 0013-4902) **1767, 1889**
Electronic Engineering/Denshi Gijutsu. (JA ISSN 0366-8819) **1767**
Electronic Engineering Association. Annual Report see E E A. Association of the Electronics, Telecommunications & Business Equipment Industries. Annual Report **1886**
Electronic Engineering Association Association of the Electronics, Telecommunications & Business Equipment Industries. Annual Report see E E A. Association of the Electronics, Telecommunications & Business Equipment Industries. Annual Report **1886**
Electronic Engineering Index. (UK ISSN 0308-8375) **1767, 11, 1889**
Electronic Engineering Times. (US ISSN 0192-1541) **1767**
Electronic Engineers Master see E E M **1766**
Electronic Equipment Monitor. (UK ISSN 0046-1717) **1767**
Electronic Equipment Monthly. (KO) **1767**
Electronic Equipment News. (UK ISSN 0013-4910) **1767**
Electronic Fund Transfer Press Alert see E F T Press Alert **5183**
Electronic Funds Transfer Report see E F T Report **805**
†Electronic Games Hotline. (US ISSN 0733-6039) **5185**
†Electronic Games Software Encyclopedia. (US) **5185**
Electronic Games Today. (US) **1419, 1038**
Electronic Gaming Monthly. (US) **1419**
Electronic House. (US ISSN 0886-6643) **299, 1413**
▼Electronic Imaging Report. (US ISSN 1057-0942) **1446, 1889**
Electronic Industries Association. Trade Directory and Membership List. (US ISSN 0091-9519) **1134, 1767**
Electronic Industries Association Electronics Foreign Trade see Electronics Foreign Trade **1769**
Electronic Industries Association's Executive Report. (US) **1767**
Electronic Industry Telephone Directory (Year). (US ISSN 0422-9053) **1134, 1767**
†Electronic Information Report. (US) **5185**
Electronic Learning. (US ISSN 0278-3258) **1689, 1417, 1749**
Electronic Library. (US ISSN 0264-0473) **2797**
Electronic Mail & Micro Systems see E M M S **1335**
†Electronic Manufacturing. (US ISSN 0895-3708) **5185**
†Electronic Manufacturing Desk Manual.(US) **5185**
†Electronic Manufacturing News. (US) **5185**
Electronic Market Data Book. (US ISSN 0070-9867) **1767**
Electronic Market Trends. (US) **1768**
Electronic Marketing Directory. (US ISSN 0070-7589) **1134, 1768**
Electronic Mass Media Age. (IT) **31**
▼Electronic Materials and Processing. (UK ISSN 0957-9737) **1768, 3852**

Electronic Materials Technology News. (US ISSN 1045-0955) **1768**
Electronic Measuring and Meters. see Diance yu Yibiao **2522**
Electronic Media. (US ISSN 0745-0311) **1373, 1356**
▼Electronic Media Daily Fax. (US) **1373**
Electronic Messaging News. (US ISSN 1044-9892) **1350**
Electronic Microscopy and Cellular Biology. see Microscopia Electronica y Biologia Celular **560**
Electronic Modeling. (US ISSN 0275-9136) **1768**
†Electronic Music Educator. (US ISSN 1044-3150) **5185**
Electronic Musician. (US ISSN 0884-4720) **3550**
Electronic Navigation Review. see Denpa Koho **4726**
▼Electronic Networking. (US ISSN 1051-4805) **1426**
Electronic News. (US ISSN 0013-4937) **1768**
Electronic News Financial Fact Book and Directory. (US ISSN 0070-9875) **1768**
Electronic News for China. (US ISSN 0259-1235) **1768**
Electronic News Network see E N N **1450**
Electronic Office. (US ISSN 0735-8423) **826, 1058**
Electronic Office. (UK) **1768**
Electronic Packaging & Production. (US ISSN 0013-4945) **1768**
Electronic Payments International. (IE ISSN 0954-0393) **805**
Electronic Photography News. (US ISSN 0896-0976) **3790**
Electronic Printing Systems: Directions in Digital Imaging. Conference Proceedings see Electronic Printing Systems: Professional Electronic Publishing Conference Proceedings **3999**
Electronic Printing Systems: Professional Electronic Publishing Conference Proceedings. (US) **3999, 4127**
Electronic Product Design. (UK ISSN 0263-1474) **1889**
Electronic Product News. (BE) **1768**
▼Electronic Product Review. (US) **1768**
Electronic Production. (UK ISSN 0306-333X) **1768**
Electronic Products. (US ISSN 0013-4953) **1768**
Electronic Products and Technology see E P & T **1766**
Electronic Progress. (US ISSN 0013-4961) **1768, 51**
▼Electronic Public Information Newsletter. (US ISSN 1057-834X) **2797, 4059**
Electronic Publishing. (UK ISSN 0894-3982) **4143**
Electronic Publishing Abstracts see World Publishing Monitor **1406**
Electronic Publishing & Printing. (US ISSN 0887-1876) **4127, 4143**
Electronic Publishing and Printing see Computer Publishing **5170**
†Electronic Publishing Business. (US ISSN 0888-0948) **5185**
Electronic Publishing Special Interest Group News see E P S I G News **4127**
Electronic Quality Assurance Microfile. (UK) **1768**
Electronic Representatives Directory (Year). (US ISSN 0887-4336) **1134, 1768**
Electronic Science and Technology. see Dianzi Kexue Jishu **1765**
Electronic Servicing see Electronic Servicing & Technology **1768**
Electronic Servicing & Technology. (US ISSN 0279-9922) **1768, 2501**
Electronic Shopping News see Information & Interactive Services Report **4143**
†Electronic Structure & Magnetism of Inorganic Compounds. (UK ISSN 0305-9766) **5185**
Electronic Systems News see Electronics Education **1689**

Electronic Technology. see Dianzi Jishu **1765**
Electronic Technology. (HK) **1768, 1450**
†Electronic Technology. (UK ISSN 0141-061X) **5185**
Electronic Times see Canadian Electronics **1764**
▼Electronic Trade & Transport News. (US ISSN 1050-9577) **1447**
Electronic Warfare see Jane's Radar and Electronic Warfare **3461**
Electronic Warfare Design Engineers' Handbook and Manufacturers Directory see E W Design Engineers' Handbook and Manufacturers Directory **1819**
Electronic Warfare Digest. (US ISSN 0884-4828) **3457**
Electronic World. see Dianzi Shijie **1765**
Electronic World News. (US) **1768, 1009**
Electronics. (US ISSN 0883-4989) **1768**
Electronics. see Eletronica **5185**
Electronics and Automation. see Dianzi yu Zidonghua **1413**
Electronics & Communication Engineering Journal. (UK ISSN 0954-0695) **1768, 1373**
Electronics and Communications Abstracts. (UK ISSN 0013-5119) **1348, 1768**
Electronics & Communications Abstracts. see Elektronikai es Hiradastechnikai Szakirodalmi **1348**
Electronics and Communications Abstracts Journal. (US ISSN 0361-3313) **1348, 1768**
Electronics and Communications in Japan. (US ISSN 0424-8368) **1769, 1335**
Electronics and Electrical Engineering. (UK) **1769, 1889**
†Electronics & Instruments Directory. (UK) **5185**
Electronics and Power see I E E Review **1898**
Electronics & Technology Today. (CN) **1769**
Electronics and Telecommunications Review. see Slaboproudy Obzor **1342**
Electronics Australia. (AT ISSN 0013-5135) **1769**
†Electronics Buyers' Guide. (US ISSN 0090-5291) **5185**
Electronics Communicator. (CN ISSN 0046-1733) **1769**
Electronics Daily. see Dempa Shinbun **1765**
Electronics Design News Asia see E D N Asia **1766**
Electronics Design News Magazine see E D N Magazine **1766**
†Electronics Distribution Today. (US) **5185**
Electronics Education. (UK) **1689**
Electronics - Electrical Engineering. see P T - Elektrotechniek - Elektronica **1904**
Electronics - Electrical Product News see E E Product News **1766**
Electronics for Kids of All Ages. (US) **1769, 1038**
Electronics for You. (II ISSN 0013-516X) **1769**
Electronics Foreign Trade. (Electronic Industries Association) (US) **1769**
Electronics Illustrated see Home Mechanix **2501**
Electronics Industries Association Japan Newsletter see E I A J Newsletter **1766**
Electronics Industry Outlook. (US) **1769, 945**
Electronics International - China Report.(CC) **1769**
Electronics: Latin American Industrial Report. (US) **1769**
Electronics Letters. (UK ISSN 0013-5194) **1769, 1362**
Electronics Manufacture and Test. (UK ISSN 0265-301X) **1769**
Electronics Manufacturing. (US) **1769**
Electronics Monthly see Everyday Electronics **1771**

Electronics News. (AT ISSN 0311-0230) **1769**
Electronics Packaging Forum. (US) **1769**
Electronics Purchasing. (US ISSN 0889-0196) **1769**
Electronics Report *see* Advanced Manufacturing Technology **1881**
Electronics Report *see* Inside Defense Electronics **3460**
Electronics Science. (CC) **1769**
Electronics Showcase. (UK ISSN 0269-2309) **1769**
Electronics Technicians Association Technician Association News *see* E T A Technician Association News **1766**
Electronics Test *see* Test & Measurement World **1909**
Electronics Times. (UK) **1769**
Electronics Today *see* Electronics & Technology Today **1769**
Electronics Today *see* New Electronics **1904**
Electronics Today International *see* E T I: Electronics Today International **1766**
†Electronics Trends (Cleveland). (US) **5185**
Electronics Weekly. (UK ISSN 0013-5224) **1769**
Electronics World & Wireless World. (UK ISSN 0266-3244) **1769**
Electronique. (SZ) **1769**
Electronique Applications. (FR) **1769**
Electronique Francaise *see* Groupement des Industries Electroniques. Rapport d'Activites **1771**
Electronique Industrielle & Commerciale *see* E I C **1766**
Electronique Pratique. (FR) **1769**
Electronique Techniques et Industries *see* E T I **1766**
Electronotes. (US ISSN 0160-1148) **3550**, 1889
Electrons in Semiconductors. *see* Elektrony v Poluprovodnikakh **3817**
Electrophoresis. (GW ISSN 0173-0835) **1177**
Electrophotography/Denshi Shashingakkaishi. (JA ISSN 0011-8478) **3790**
Electrophysiological Technologists' Association. Proceedings and Journal *see* Journal of Electrophysiological Technology **486**
†Electrophysiology/Denki Seirigaku. (JA) **5185**
Electroplating and Environmental Protection. *see* Diandu yu Huanbao **1885**
Electroplating and Metal Finishing *see* Finishing **3653**
Electrosoft. (UK ISSN 0269-9184) **3064**, 1878
Electrosonic World. (UK ISSN 0261-2666) **1335**
Electrotechnical Journal. *see* Elektrotechnicky Casopis **1890**
Electrotechnical Laboratory. Bulletin. (JA ISSN 0366-9092) **1394**, 1889
Electrotechnical News. (UK ISSN 0266-2450) **1916**, 1889
Electrotechnician. *see* Elektrotechnik **1891**
Electrotechnische Zeitschrift E T Z *see* E T Z **1886**
Electrotechnology. (UK ISSN 0306-8552) **1769**
Electrotecnia Popular. (SP ISSN 0013-5313) **1889**, 1769
Electrotehnica, Electronica si Automatica. Electrotehnica. (RM) **1769**
Eleftherotypia tis Defteras/Monday's Free Press. (CY) **2865**
Elegance. (HK) **372**
Elegance. (NE) **4840**, 1290
Elegant Bride. (US) **3066**
L'Elegante Uomo Sud. (IT) **1290**, 3397
Elegantissima. (IT) **1290**, 372
Elektor. (SP) **1889**
Elektor Electronics. (UK ISSN 0013-5895) **1770**
▼Elektor Electronics U S A. (US ISSN 1051-5690) **1770**
Elektor - Electronique. (FR ISSN 0181-7450) **1770**, 2501

Elektricheskie Stantsii. (RU ISSN 0013-5372) **1890**, 3446
Elektrichestvo. (RU ISSN 0013-5380) **1890**
Elektriciteit. *see* Electricite **1889**
Elektrie. (GW ISSN 0013-5399) **1890**
Elektrik Muhendisligi. (TU ISSN 0013-5402) **1890**
Der Elektriker. (GW ISSN 0936-3602) **1890**
Elektrikeren. (NO ISSN 0013-5410) **1890**
Elektrikeren. (DK) **1890**
Elektrische Bahnen. (GW ISSN 0013-5437) **4709**, 1890
Elektrische Energie Technik. (GW ISSN 0170-2033) **1890**
Elektrisches Nachrichten *see* Elektrisches Nachrichtenwesen **1890**
Elektrisches Nachrichtenwesen. (GW) **1890**, 1350
Elektrisitesstatistikk *see* Norway. Statistisk Sentralbyraa. Elektrisitesstatistikk **1800**
Elektrizitaet *see* Strom **1908**
Elektrizitaetswirtschaft. (GW ISSN 0013-5496) **1890**
Elektro. (NO ISSN 0013-550X) **1890**
Elektro and Radio *see* Elektro Journal **1890**
Elektro-Anzeiger. (GW ISSN 0013-5518) **1890**
Elektro Boerse. (GW ISSN 0343-3463) **1890**
Elektro-Data. (NE) **1890**
Elektro Forum. (SZ) **1890**
Elektro-Handel. (NO ISSN 0046-1776) **1890**
Elektro-Industrie. (GW) **1770**
Elektro-Jahr *see* Super Electronics. Jahrbuch **1779**
Elektro Journal. (AU) **1890**, 1373
Elektro med Elektronik. (NO) **1890**
Elektro Radio Handel. (AU) **1356**
Elektro und Wirtschaft Verlagsgesellschaft mbH *see* E und W **1886**
†Elektrodienst. (GW ISSN 0037-4687) **5185**
Elektroenergetika i Avtomatizatsiya Energoustanovok. (KR ISSN 0453-7998) **1819**
Das Elektrofach. (GW ISSN 0424-8562) **1890**
Der Elektrofachmann. (GW ISSN 0420-9885) **1890**
Elektromarkt. (GW ISSN 0013-5577) **1770**
Elektromedizin *see* Biomedizinische Technik **3082**
Elektron *see* Elektron-International **1335**
Elektron. (SA) **1890**
Elektron. (CS) **4308**
Elektron-International. (AU ISSN 0374-3098) **1335**, 1373
Elektronenmikroskopie. (GW ISSN 0936-6911) **559**, 3817
Elektronica. (NE ISSN 0168-7840) **1770**, 1356
Elektronica en Telecommunicatie *see* Nederlands Elektronica- en Radiogenootschap. Tijdschrift **1340**
Elektronica Revue. (NE) **1770**
Elektronik. (GW ISSN 0013-5658) **1770**
Elektronik Entwicklung. (GW ISSN 0172-6153) **1770**
Elektronik Indkoebsbogen. (DK ISSN 0108-8149) **1770**
Elektronik Industrie *see* E I **1766**
Elektronik Informationen. (GW ISSN 0343-6675) **1770**
Elektronik Journal. (GW ISSN 0013-5674) **1770**
Elektronik Nyt. (DK ISSN 0106-164X) **1770**
Elektronik Nyts Leverandoerregister. (DK) **1770**
Elektronik Packaging und Produktion *see* Elektronik Produktion und Prueftechnik **1770**
Elektronik Produktion und Prueftechnik.(GW) **1770**
Elektronik Report. (AU) **1928**
Elektronik-Technologie *see* E **5182**
Elektronik-Zeitung *see* E **5182**

Elektronika. (PL ISSN 0033-2089) **1770**
Elektronika Umachshavim/Electrics & Computers. (IS ISSN 0334-7680) **1394**
Elektronikai es Hiradastechnikai Szakirodalmi/Electronics & Communications Abstracts. (HU ISSN 0231-066X) **1348**, 11, 1770
Der Elektroniker. (GW ISSN 0531-9218) **1770**
Elektronikk. (NO ISSN 0013-5690) **1770**
Elektronikk Bransjen. (NO ISSN 0802-8559) **1770**, 1356
Elektronikpraxis. (GW ISSN 0341-5589) **1770**
Elektronikschau. (AU ISSN 0254-4318) **1373**
Elektronikvarlden. (SW ISSN 0281-1189) **1504**
Elektronische Informationsverarbeitung und Kybernetik *see* Journal of Information Processing and Cybernetics **1441**
Elektronmikroskopievereniging van Suidelike Afrika. Verrigtings. *see* Electron Microscopy Society of Southern Africa. Proceedings **559**
Elektronnaya Obrabotka Materialov. (MV ISSN 0013-5739) **1770**
Elektronnoe Modelirovanie. (RU ISSN 0204-3572) **1770**
Elektrony v Poluprovodnikakh/Electrons in Semiconductors. (LI) **3817**
Elektropraktiker. (GW ISSN 0013-5569) **1890**
Elektroprenos. (YU ISSN 0013-3248) **863**
Elektroprivreda Jugoslavije. (YU) **1890**
Elektrosvyaz'. (RU ISSN 0013-5771) **1335**, 1890
Elektrotechnical Review. *see* Elektrotechnicky Obzor **1890**
Elektrotechnical Review. *see* Elektrotehniski Vestnik **1891**
Elektrotechnicky Casopis/ Electrotechnical Journal. (CS ISSN 0013-578X) **1890**, 1819
Elektrotechnicky Obzor/Elektrotechnical Review. (CS ISSN 0013-5798) **1890**
Elektrotechniek *see* Energietechniek **1891**
Elektrotechnik. (GW ISSN 0013-581X) **1890**
Elektrotechnik. (SZ) **1890**
Elektrotechnik/Electrotechnician. (CS) **1891**
Elektrotechnika/Electrical Engineering. (HU ISSN 0367-0708) **1891**
†Elektrotechnika ir Mechanika. (UR) **5185**
Elektrotechnikai Szakirodalmi Tajekoztato/Electrical Engineering Abstracts. (HU ISSN 0231-0783) **1843**, 1891
Elektrotechnische Zeitschrift *see* E T Z **1886**
Elektrotehnicar. (CI ISSN 0013-5828) **1770**
Elektrotehnika. (CI ISSN 0013-5844) **1891**
Elektrotehniski Vestnik/Elektrotechnical Review. (XV ISSN 0013-5852) **1891**
Elektrotekhnika. (RU ISSN 0013-5860) **1891**
Elektroteknisk Tidsskrift *see* Elektro **1890**
Elektrovymiriuvalna Tekhnika *see* Informatsionno-Izmeritel'naya Tekhnika **1899**
Elektrowaerme im Technischen Ausbau *see* Elektrowaerme International. Part A: Elektrowaerme im Technischen Ausbau **2298**
Elektrowaerme International *see* Elektrowaerme International. Part A: Elektrowaerme im Technischen Ausbau **2298**
Elektrowaerme International *see* Elektrowaerme International. Part B: Industrielle Elektrowaerme **2299**
Elektrowaerme International. Part A: Elektrowaerme im Technischen Ausbau. (GW ISSN 0340-3513) **2298**

Elektrowaerme International. Part B: Industrielle Elektrowaerme. (GW ISSN 0340-3521) **2299**, 3405
Elektrowirtschaft. (GW ISSN 0013-5887) **1891**
Elektuur. (NE) **1891**
Elelmezesi Ipar/Food Industry. (HU ISSN 0013-5909) **2066**
Elelmiszertudomanyi es Elelmiszeripari Szakirodalmi Tajekoztato. (HU ISSN 0236-705X) **2066**
Elelmiszervizsgalati Kozlemenyek. (HU ISSN 0422-9576) **2066**, 4100
Element und Bau. (GW ISSN 0934-5914) **617**, 299
Element und Fertigbau *see* Element und Bau **617**
Elementa. (SW ISSN 0013-5933) **4308**, 1631
Elementa Ad Fontium Editiones. (IT ISSN 0070-9972) **2360**
Elementary School Chinese Teaching. *see* Xiaoxue Yuwen Jiaoxue **1763**
Elementary School Guidance & Counseling. (US ISSN 0013-5976) **1631**, 4020
Elementary School Journal. (US ISSN 0013-5984) **1631**
Elementary School Library Collection. (US) **2756**, 1631
Elementary School Pupils. *see* Xiao Xuesheng **1246**
Elementary School Science and Technology. *see* Xiaoxue Keji **4352**
Elementary School Years. *see* Xiaoxue Shidai **1271**
Elementary Teachers Guide to Free Curriculum Materials. (US ISSN 0070-9980) **1749**
Elementary Teacher's Ideas and Materials Workshop *see* E T Ideas **1626**
Elemente. (GW ISSN 0178-7659) **3765**, 3594
Elemente der Mathematik/Revue de Mathematiques Elementaries/Rivista di Matematica Elementare. (SZ ISSN 0013-6018) **3035**
Elements. (FR) **325**, 2865, 2913
†Elements. (CN ISSN 0046-1792) **5185**
Elenchos. (IT ISSN 0392-7342) **3765**
Elenchus Bibliographicus Biblicus *see* Elenchus of Biblica **4212**
Elenchus of Biblica. (VC) **4212**
Elenco dei Protesti Cambiari *see* Elenco dei Ufficiale Protesti Cambiari **815**
Elenco dei Ufficiale Protesti Cambiari. (IT) **815**
Elenco Ufficiale dei Protesti Cambiari Levati Nella Provincia di Torino. (IT ISSN 0013-6050) **815**
Elepaio. (US ISSN 0013-6069) **563**, 1949
Elephant-Ear. (US) **2913**
Eles & Elas. (PO) **4840**, 355, 1290
Eles e Elas - a Revista *see* A Revista **2857**
Eles e Elas - a Revista *see* Eles & Elas **4840**
Elet es Irodalom. (HU ISSN 0424-8848) **2865**
Elet es Tudomany. (HU ISSN 0013-6077) **4308**
Eletricidade Moderna. (BL) **1891**
Eletron: Revista de Engenharia/Electron - Engineering Review. (BL) **1891**
†Eletronica/Electronics. (BL) **5185**
Eletronica em Foco. (BL ISSN 0046-1814) **1891**
Eletronica para Todos. (BL) **1891**
Eletronica Popular *see* Antenna - Eletronica Popular **1368**
Elettrauto *see* Nuova Elettrauto **1904**
Elettricita *see* Strom **1908**
Elettrificazione. (IT ISSN 0013-6093) **1891**
Elettrodomestica. (IT ISSN 0013-6107) **1891**
Elettrodomestici - Gas - Casalinghi - la Tecnica nella Casa Moderna *see* Elettrodomestica **1891**
†Elettronica. (IT) **5185**
Elettronica e Telecomunicazioni. (IT ISSN 0013-6123) **1770**, 1335
Elettronica Oggi. (IT ISSN 0391-6391) **1770**
Elettronica 2000 Mister Kit. (IT) **1770**, 2436

6150 ELETTROTECNICA

Elettrotecnica. (IT ISSN 0013-6131) 1770
Eletunk. (HU ISSN 0133-4751) 2865
Eleuthere Kythrea. (CY) 2360
Elevations see Architect 292
Elevator World. (US ISSN 0013-6158) 617
Elevatori. (IT ISSN 1120-2289) 4649
Eleven. (US) 1373
Eleven/Irebun. (JA) 4503
Eleventh District Dental Society. Bulletin see Queens County Dental Society. Bulletin 3241
Eleventh Muse. (US) 2992
Eleveur de Lapins. (FR) 216
Eleveur Maine Anjou. (FR ISSN 0046-1822) 216
Eleveurs de Porcs see Porc Magazine 223
Elex. (NE ISSN 0167-7349) 1771
Elex. (FR ISSN 0990-736X) 1771
Elgar. (FR) 2000
Elgar Society. Journal. (UK ISSN 0143-1269) 3550
El-Hi Textbooks and Serials in Print. (US ISSN 0000-0825) 1676
Elim Evangel see Direction 4236
Elimu. (ZR) 4371
Elinstallatoeren. (SW ISSN 0013-6190) 1891
†Eliot Janeway Lectures on Historical Economics. (US) 5185
Eliot Sharp. (US) 945
Eliot Sharp's Municipal Newsletter see Eliot Sharp 945
Elisabeth Elliot Newsletter. (US ISSN 8756-1336) 4175
Elisabeth Kubler Ross Center Newsletter. (US) 4020
Elisabethbode. (NE ISSN 0013-6212) 4175
Elisha Mitchell Scientific Society. Journal. (US ISSN 0013-6220) 4308
Elite. (VE) 2238
Elites. (SP) 1009
Elixir. (CN) 2913
Elizabeth Zimmermann's Wool Gathering. (US) 3591
Elizabethan and Renaissance Studies. (AU) 2914
Elizabethan Club Series. (US ISSN 0085-0225) 2360
Elk Eye. (US) 2405
Elk Horn. (US) 2405
Elkab. (BE) 271
Elkhound Quarterly. (US) 3710
Elkins Eagle. (US ISSN 0887-1299) 2149, 2405
Elks Magazine. (US ISSN 0013-6263) 1297
†Ellamatta. (AT) 5185
Ellas. (VE) 4841
Elle. (US ISSN 0888-0808) 4841, 1290, 2225
Elle. (PO) 4841
Elle. (SP) 4841
Elle. (GW) 4841
Elle. (JA) 4841
Elle. (UK) 4841
Elle (Brazil). (BL) 4841
Elle (China). (HK) 372, 3801
Elle (France). (FR ISSN 0013-6298) 4841, 1290
Elle Decor. (US ISSN 1046-1957) 2558
Elle Italia. (IT) 4841, 4835
Ellen Glasgow Newsletter. (US ISSN 0160-7545) 2914
Ellenikos Typos. see Greek Press 2003
†Ellery Queen's Anthology. (US ISSN 0013-6301) 5185
Ellery Queen's Mystery Magazine. (US ISSN 0013-6328) 2985
Ellinika. (GR ISSN 0013-6336) 1276, 2054, 2360
Elliniki Odontiatriki Omospondia. Enemerotiko Deltio/Hellenic Dental Association. Journal. (GR) 3232
Ellinis. (AT) 2000
Ellinoamerikanikon Emborikon Epimelitirion. Business Directory. see American-Hellenic Chamber of Greece. Business Directory 807
Elliott Wave Commodity Forecast see Elliott Wave Currency & Commodity Forecast 945

Elliott Wave Commodity Letter see Elliott Wave Currency & Commodity Forecast 945
Elliott Wave Currency & Commodity Forecast. (US) 945
Elliott Wave Theorist. (US) 945
Ellipse. (CN ISSN 0046-1830) 2914
Ellipsis... (US ISSN 1040-1644) 2914
Ellis Cousins Newsletter. (US ISSN 0740-1477) 2149
Ellis Island Series: Immigration and the Pluralist Society. (US ISSN 0892-922X) 2405, 863, 4434
El-Elm/Sciences Monthly Magazine. (UA) 4308
Elm Fork Echoes. (US) 2405
Elmhurst College Magazine. (US) 1310
Elnyt. (DK ISSN 0107-962X) 1891
Elovilag see Buvar 433
Elrad. (GW) 1891
Elsevier. (NE) 2211
Elsevier Oceanography Series. (NE ISSN 0078-3226) 1604
†Elsevier Select. (NE ISSN 0013-6409) 5186
Elsevier Series in Forensic and Police Science. (NE) 3264, 1514
Elsevier Series in Practical Aspects of Criminal & Forensic Investigation. (NE) 3264, 1514
Elseviers Magazine see Elsevier 2211
Elsner: Handbuch fuer Strassenbau und Strassenverkehrstechnik see Elsners Handbuch fuer Strassenwesen 1865
Elsners Handbuch fuer Staedtischen Ingenieurbau see Elsners Handbuch fuer Staedtisches Ingenieurwesen 1819
Elsners Handbuch fuer Staedtisches Ingenieurwesen. (GW) 1819
Elsners Handbuch fuer Strassenwesen. (GW) 1865
Elsners Taschenbuch der Eisenbahntechnik see Eisenbahn Ingenieur Kalender (Year) 4709
†Elta. (US ISSN 0013-6417) 5186
Elteknik. (DK ISSN 0109-2359) 1891
Elteknik Aktuell Elektronik. (SW ISSN 0346-6310) 1771, 1335
Eltern. (GW ISSN 0046-1849) 1236, 1631
Eltern das Gesunde Kind. (GW) 1236
Eltern Sonderheft Mein Baby. (GW) 1236
Elternblatt. (AU ISSN 0013-6441) 1236, 1631, 4020
Der Elternbrief. (SZ ISSN 0013-645X) 1631
Elternforum. (GW ISSN 0934-8662) 1631, 1236
Elternhaus und Schule. (GW ISSN 0421-0670) 1631
Elu d'Aujourd'hui. (FR) 4087
Elu Local. (FR ISSN 0422-9932) 4059
Elverksjefen. (NO) 1891
Elvis Monthly. (UK ISSN 0013-6484) 3550, 3508
Elvis Now Fan Club. (US) 1297, 3550
Elvis World. (US) 3550, 1297
Ely Heritage. (US) 2149
Elysium: Journal of the Senses. (US) 3594, 3801
Em Aberto. (BL) 1632
Em Veyeled. (IS) 1236
Emajl-Keramika-Staklo. (CI ISSN 0013-6506) 1163
Emantalehti. (FI ISSN 0013-6522) 2446
Emarushon Kenkyu Kenkyu Hokoku. (JA) 364, 1177
Embalagem. (BL ISSN 0013-6530) 3648
Embalajes see Embalajes y Plasticos y Manufacturas 3648
Embalajes y Plasticos y Manufacturas. (SP ISSN 0210-1084) 3648
Emballage Digest. (FR ISSN 0013-6557) 3648
Emballageinstituttets Leverandoerhaandbog see Leverandoerhaandbogen (Skovlunde) 3649
Emballages. (FR ISSN 0013-6573) 3648

Emballering. (NO ISSN 0013-6581) 3648, 3017
Embalmer. (UK) 2119
▼Embarazo/Pregnancy. (US) 3291
EMBASE List of Journals Abstracted see List of Journals Abstracted (Year) 3177
Embassy of Switzerland Bulletin. (US ISSN 0046-1865) 4308, 3892, 4597
▼Embassy's Complete Boating Guide to Florida's East Coast. (US) 4524
Embassy's Complete Boating Guide to Long Island Sound. (US) 4524
Embassy's Complete Boating Guide to Rhode Island and Massachusetts. (US) 4524
Embedded Systems Programming. (US ISSN 1040-3272) 1418
Ember. (CN) 4841
Embers. (US ISSN 0731-0382) 2992
Emblematica. (US ISSN 0885-968X) 2360, 325, 2149
Embotellador see Beverage World En Espanol 379
†Embouteillage Conditionnement. (FR) 5186
Embroidery. (UK ISSN 0013-6611) 3591
Embroidery Directory. (US ISSN 0080-6811) 4618, 1134
Embroidery News. (US) 4618
Embros/Forward. (GR) 2196
Embros (Cyprus)/Forward. (CY) 2865
Embryo Transfer Newsletter. (US) 582, 4809
Emek. (AT) 2000
Ementario da Legislacao do Petroleo. (BL ISSN 0013-662X) 2698, 11, 3705
Ementario Forense. (BL ISSN 0013-6638) 2621
Emerald City Comix & Stories. (US) 2865, 2992
Emerald Hill, Sandridge & St. Kilda Times. (AT) 2171
Emerge! (US ISSN 0892-1490) 2452, 4175, 4841
Emerge (New York). (US ISSN 0899-1154) 2000, 2225
Emerge Playcouple. (US) 3397, 4841
Emergence see Emerge 2452
†Emergence: Journal for Evolving Consciousness. (US) 5186
Emergency. (US ISSN 0162-5942) 3307
†Emergency Care Quarterly. (US) 5186
Emergency Department Law. (US ISSN 1042-2978) 2621, 3095
Emergency Department Management. (US) 3096
Emergency Department News see Emergency Medicine News 3096
Emergency Economic Action Plans see Cyprus. Five Year Plans 859
Emergency Health Services Review see Journal of Ambulatory Care Marketing 3308
Emergency Librarian. (CN ISSN 0315-8888) 2757
Emergency Medical Service Access (Year) see E M S Access (Year) 5183
Emergency Medical Services. (US ISSN 0094-6575) 3307
Emergency Medical Technician Legal Bulletin. (US) 3096, 2621
Emergency Medicine. (US ISSN 0013-6654) 3307
Emergency Medicine and Ambulatory Care News see Emergency Medicine News 3096
Emergency Medicine Clinics of North America. (US ISSN 0733-8627) 3308
Emergency Medicine News. (US ISSN 1054-0725) 3096
Emergency Medicine Reports. (US ISSN 0746-2506) 3096
Emergency Medicine Reports Legal Briefings. (US) 3096, 2621
Emergency Nurse Legal Bulletin. (US ISSN 0098-1516) 3278, 2621
Emergency Nurses Association Nursing Scan in Emergency Care see E N A Nursing Scan in Emergency Care 3171

Emergency Pediatrics. (US ISSN 1044-3797) 3320
Emergency Physician Legal Bulletin. (US ISSN 0098-1524) 3096, 2621
Emergency Planning Digest see Emergency Preparedness Digest 1273
Emergency Post see Good News (Exeter) 4179
Emergency Prehospital Medicine. (CN ISSN 0836-7272) 3378
Emergency Preparedness Digest/Revue Protection Civile. (CN ISSN 0837-5771) 1273, 1804
Emergency Preparedness News. (US ISSN 0275-3782) 1273, 4059
Emergency Products Update. (US) 2031
Emergency Response Guidebook. (US) 4100, 4690
Emerging. (US ISSN 0890-538X) 3594, 3765
Emerging & Special Situations. (US) 945
†Emerging Automotive Industries Review. (US ISSN 0894-4156) 5186
Emerging Patterns of Work and Communications in an Information Age. (US ISSN 0882-3316) 1335, 3626
Emerick Family Newsletter. (US ISSN 0887-5693) 2149
Emerita. (SP ISSN 0013-6662) 2811, 1276
Emerson Studies in Theatre and Film. (US) 4632, 3508
▼Emerson's Auditor Change Report. (US) 750
Emerson's Professional Service Review. (US ISSN 0748-4763) 750
Emert's Stamp Quarterly. (US) 3752
Emet. (AT) 4222
†Emigranten. (DK ISSN 0900-7679) 5186
Emigrato Italiano. (IT ISSN 0013-6697) 4176
†Emigrazione. (IT ISSN 0013-6700) 5186
Emigre. (US ISSN 1045-3717) 325, 2865, 4434
Emily Dickinson Bulletin see Dickinson Studies 2992
Emirates Boy Scouts. see Kashshafat al-Imarat 1299
Emirates Documents. see Watha'iq Dawlat al-Imarat 2432
Emirates Events. see Waqa'i Dawlat al-Imarat 2432
Emirates Home. see Bait al-Imarat 2557
Emirates in Flight. see Al-Imarat fil-Ajwa 4803
Emirates Journal for Agricultural Sciences. see Majallat al-Imarat lil-'Ulum al-Zira'iyyah 106
Emirates Natural History Group Bulletin. see Jama'at al-Ta'rikh al-Tabi'i. Nashrat 4316
Emirates News. (TS) 2220
Emirates Woman. (TS) 4841
Emma. (GW ISSN 0721-9741) 4841
Emmanuel. (US ISSN 0013-6719) 4263
Emmaus. (NE) 4434
Emmenager a Montreal. see Moving to Montreal 4153
Emmy. (US ISSN 0164-3495) 1373
Emory Law Journal. (US ISSN 0094-4076) 2621
Emory Magazine. (US ISSN 0013-6727) 1310
Emory Studies in Early Christianity. (US ISSN 1043-5816) 4176
†Emory Today. (US) 5186
Emory University Journal of Medicine. (US ISSN 0891-7043) 3096
Emory Vico Studies. (US ISSN 0883-6000) 3765
Emory Wheel. (US) 1311
Emotion. (GW) 1785, 3196, 4020
Emotion. (US) 4020
Emotional First Aid. (US ISSN 0739-828X) 4020, 4404
Emotions and Behavior. Monograph. (US ISSN 0734-9890) 3335
Empathic Parenting. (CN ISSN 0825-7531) 1236

Emphasis on Faith and Living. (US ISSN 0194-5246) **4176**
Empire! (US) **2914**
Empire for the S F Writer *see* Waystation for the S F Writer **4138**
Empire State Agency Forum *see* Forum (Syracuse) **2532**
Empire State Farmer. (US ISSN 0886-9693) **88**, 199
Empire State Food Service News. (US) **2473**, 2066
Empire State Geogram. (US ISSN 0013-676X) **1560**
Empire State Iris Society Newsletter. (US ISSN 0013-6786) **2125**
Empire State Mason. (US ISSN 0013-6794) **1297**
Empire State Realtor. (US) **4148**
Empire State Report. (US ISSN 0747-0711) **3892**, 4059
Empire State Report Weekly *see* Empire State Report **3892**
Empirica. (GW ISSN 0340-8744) **863**
Empirical Economics. (GW ISSN 0377-7332) **663**
Empirical Study of the Arts. (US ISSN 0276-2374) **325**
Empirische Paedagogik. (GW ISSN 0931-5020) **1749**
Empleo y Desempleo en Puerto Rico/Employment and Unemployment in Puerto Rico: Calendar Years. (PR ISSN 0555-6635) **977**
Emplo Review/Tydskrif. (SA) **2582**, 4649
L'Emploi/Stelle/Posto. (SZ) **3627**
Emploi dans les Administrations Provinciales et Territoriales. *see* Canada. Statistics Canada. Provincial and Territorial Government Employment **5160**
Emploi et Immigration Canada. Rapport Annuel. *see* Employment and Immigration Canada. Annual Report **2531**
Employ. (US) **3627**, 1487, 4545
Employee Assistance Program Management Letter. (US ISSN 0896-0941) **977**, 1009
Employee Assistance Programs Digest *see* E A P Digest **1536**
Employee Assistance Quarterly. (US ISSN 0749-0003) **1064**, 1536
Employee Benefit Cases. (US ISSN 0273-236X) **977**
Employee Benefit Costs in Canada. (CN ISSN 0701-1539) **977**
Employee Benefit News. (US) **977**, 1009
Employee Benefit Notes. (US ISSN 0887-1388) **977**
Employee Benefit Plan Review. (US ISSN 0013-6808) **977**
Employee Benefit Research Institute Issue Brief *see* E B R I Issue Brief **1064**
Employee Benefits Alert. (US) **1064**, 750
Employee Benefits Annual (Year) *see* Employee Benefits Issues: The Multiemployer Perspective **977**
Employee Benefits Basics. (US) **977**
Employee Benefits Compliance Coordinator. (US ISSN 0273-768X) **1064**, 750
Employee Benefits Issues: The Multiemployer Perspective. (US) **977**, 1064
Employee Benefits Journal. (US ISSN 0361-4050) **977**
▼Employee Benefits Management. (US) **1009**
Employee Benefits Practices. (US) **977**
Employee Benefits Report. (US) **1064**, 977, 1009
Employee Communication (New York). (US ISSN 0885-7202) **1064**
Employee Communications Guide. (US) **1064**
Employee Health and Fitness. (US ISSN 0199-6304) **3801**
Employee Ownership *see* Employee Ownership Report **663**
Employee Ownership Report. (US ISSN 0899-8833) **663**
Employee Relations. (UK ISSN 0142-5455) **977**

Employee Relations and Human Resources Bulletin. (US ISSN 0744-7779) **978**
†Employee Relations Bulletin (New York). (US) **5186**
Employee Relations in Action. (US ISSN 0013-6824) **978**
Employee Relations Law Journal. (US ISSN 0098-8898) **2622**, 978
Employee Relations Report. (US ISSN 0735-4738) **978**, 1009, 1064
Employee Relocation Council Directory *see* E-R-C Directory **4148**
Employee Responsibilities and Rights Journal. (US ISSN 0892-7545) **978**
Employee Retirement Income Security Act. Report to Congress *see* U.S. Department of Labor. Employee Retirement Income Security Act. Report to Congress **996**
Employee Retirement Income Security Act Newsletter *see* E R I S A Newsletter **977**
Employee Retirement Income Security Act The Law and the Code *see* E R I S A: The Law and the Code **977**
Employee Services Management. (US ISSN 0744-3676) **1009**, 4471, 4761
Employee Stock Ownership Plan Report *see* E S O P Report **1008**
Employee Testing & the Law. (US ISSN 0889-5422) **1064**, 1514, 4020
Employees of Diplomatic Missions. (US ISSN 0501-9664) **3956**
Employer. (NZ ISSN 0046-1903) **1009**, 978
Employer Resources Newsletter. (US) **3999**, 978
Employer's Guide Purchasing Managed Health Care Services. (US) **3096**
Employers Guide to A B A Approved N A L P Member Law Schools *see* Employers Guide to Law Schools **2622**
Employers Guide to Law Schools. (US) **2622**
Employers Guide to Recruiting in Australian Universities and Colleges of Advanced Education *see* Guide to Campus Recruiting **1694**
Employers' Health Costs Savings Letter. (US ISSN 0740-9087) **2531**, 1009
Employers Negotiating Service. (US) **1727**, 2582
Employers of New Community College Graduates: Directory. (CN ISSN 0381-3711) **1134**, 3627
Employers of New University Graduates: Directory. (CN ISSN 0381-372X) **1134**, 3627
Employers' Review. (AT ISSN 0013-6832) **3616**
Employment Affairs Report. (UK ISSN 0267-5374) **978**
Employment Alert. (US ISSN 0882-6250) **1064**
Employment and Earnings and Monthly Report on the Labor Force *see* U.S. Bureau of Labor Statistics. Employment and Earnings **742**
Employment and Earnings: United States. (US ISSN 0271-4787) **714**
Employment and Immigration Canada. Annual Report/Emploi et Immigration Canada. Rapport Annuel. (CN) **2531**
Employment and Immigration Commission. Annual Report *see* Employment and Immigration Canada. Annual Report **2531**
Employment and Labour Law Reporter. (CN) **978**, 2622
Employment and the Economy. Atlantic Coastal Region. (US) **863**, 978
Employment and the Economy. Northern New Jersey Region. (US) **863**
Employment and the Economy. Southern New Jersey Region. (US) **863**
Employment and Training Reporter. (US ISSN 0146-9673) **1064**
Employment and Unemployment in Puerto Rico: Calendar Years. *see* Empleo y Desempleo en Puerto Rico **977**

Employment and Vacancies Statistics in: Wholesale, Retail and Import - Export Trades, Restaurants and Hotels. (HK) **3632**, 714
Employment and Vacancy Statistics in: Transport, Storage and Communication Financing, Insurance, Real Estate and Business Services, Community, Social and Personal Services. (HK) **3632**
Employment and Vacancy Statistics: Manufacturing, Mining and Quarrying, Electricity and Gas. (HK) **714**, 863
Employment Coordinator. (US) **978**
Employment Digest. (UK ISSN 0309-4995) **1065**
Employment Discrimination. (US) **1065**, 2622
Employment Discrimination Coordinator. (US) **1065**, 750
Employment Discrimination Coordinator: Primary Source Materials. (US) **1065**, 750
Employment Guide. (US) **1065**, 978
Employment in Alberta. (CN) **2622**, 978, 3627
Employment in British Columbia. (CN) **2622**, 978, 3627
Employment in Connecticut. (US) **978**
Employment in Illinois. (US) **978**
Employment in Iowa. (US) **978**
Employment in Minnesota. (US) **978**
Employment in Missouri. (US) **978**, 2622
Employment in Ohio. (US) **978**
Employment in Ontario. (CN) **2622**, 978, 3627
Employment in Oregon. (US) **978**
Employment in Texas. (US) **978**
Employment in Washington State. (US) **978**
Employment in Wisconsin. (US) **978**
Employment Information in the Mathematical Sciences. (US ISSN 0163-3287) **3035**
Employment Initiatives. (UK ISSN 0952-0430) **978**
Employment Institute's Economic Report. (UK) **978**, 863
Employment Law Desk Book for Tennessee Employers. (US) **2622**, 978
Employment Law Guide (Year). (US) **2622**, 978
▼Employment Law Reports. (IE ISSN 0791-2560) **2622**
Employment Leader. (CN) **1065**, 3627
Employment Litigation Reporter. (US) **2622**, 978
Employment Management Association Journal *see* E M A Journal **1064**
Employment Management Association Reporter *see* E M A Reporter **977**
Employment News. (UK ISSN 0963-5548) **2582**, 2757
Employment News. (II) **3627**
Employment Opportunities (Cleveland). (US) **3627**, 863
Employment Opportunities (Englewood). (US) **3627**, 325
Employment Outlook for New England College Graduates. (US) **3627**, 978
Employment Outlook Survey. (US) **978**, 863
Employment, Output and Capital Formation in the Industrial Sector *see* Cyprus. Department of Statistics and Research. Industrial Statistics **712**
†Employment Output and Trade of U.S. Manufacturing Industries. (US) **5186**
Employment Practice Guide. (US) **3627**
Employment Relations Abstracts *see* Work Related Abstracts **743**
Employment Relations Bulletin. (US ISSN 0746-9683) **978**
Employment Relations Today. (US ISSN 0745-7790) **978**, 2622
†Employment Report. (UK ISSN 0142-2197) **5186**
Employment Report for Maryland and Metropolitan Baltimore *see* Maryland Labor Market Dimensions **988**
Employment Review. (US ISSN 0013-6883) **978**

Employment Safety and Health Guide. (US ISSN 0093-1535) **3616**, 2622
Employment Service and Unemployment Insurance Operations. (US) **3627**, 2531
Employment Standards Legislation in Canada. (CN) **978**
▼Employment Tax Forms. (US) **1093**
Employment Testing. (US) **2622**, 978
Employment Training News. (UK) **1065**
Employment, Wages and Material Prices in the Construction Industry. (HK) **3632**, 637
Empoli. (IT ISSN 0013-6891) **4087**
Emporia State Research Studies. (US) **2405**, 582, 2914, 4020
Empreiteiro. (BL) **617**
Empresa Brasileira de Telecommunicacoes. Relatorio Anual. (BL) **1335**
Empresa Brasileira de Turismo. Anuario Estatistico. (BL) **4761**
Empresa Brasileira de Turismo. Calendario de Congresos Nacionales y Internacionais/International and National Meeting Events. (BL) **3392**
Empresa Brasileira de Turismo. Calendario Turistico. (BL) **4761**
Empresa Brasileira de Turismo. Tourist Calendar *see* Empresa Brasileira de Turismo. Calendario Turistico **4761**
Empresa de Navegacao da Amazonia. Estatistica da Navegacao. (BL) **4727**
Empresa Nacional de Electricidad. Memoria. (CL) **1891**
Empresa Nacional de Energia Electrica. Datos Estadisticos. (HO) **1798**, 1801
Empresa Nacional de Telecomunicaciones del Peru. Memoria Anual. (PE) **1373**
Empresa Publica. (MX ISSN 0186-6486) **1038**
Empresas Japonesas do Brasil. Annuario/Burajiru Nikkei Kigyo Nenkan. (BL) **1134**
Empress Chinchilla Breeder. (US ISSN 0013-6905) **2736**
Empty Closet. (US) **2452**
Emschergenossenschaft. Jahresberichte. (GW) **830**
Emser Hefte. (GW) **3482**
Emshock Letter. (US) **3594**, 3765
Emu. (AT ISSN 0158-4197) **563**
En Avant. (FR ISSN 0013-6921) **4176**
En Concreto. (MX) **2487**
En Eglise. (CN ISSN 0317-851X) **4263**
En Equipe A C G F au Service de l'Evangile. (Action Catholique Generale Feminine) (FR) **4263**
En Equipe au Service de l'Evangile *see* En Equipe A C G F au Service de l'Evangile **4263**
En Guardia. (CU) **3457**
En la Calle Recta. *see* In de Rechte Straat **4182**
En Marcha. (NQ) **3892**
En Marche. (BE ISSN 0013-6964) **3801**, 2531
En Passant. (CN ISSN 0822-5672) **4471**
En Passant. (US) **4471**
En Passant Poetry. (US ISSN 0271-5023) **2992**
En Passant Poetry Quarterly *see* En Passant Poetry **2992**
En Route. (UK) **4545**
▼En Route Technology. (US ISSN 1057-5618) **4707**
En Tern. Informations og Debatblad *see* D S U'eren **3889**
En Tete. (CN ISSN 0822-8531) **1311**
En Ville. (CN ISSN 0826-7731) **4761**
Ena. (GR) **4841**, 2196
Enact. (II ISSN 0013-6980) **4632**
Enbi to Porima/Vinyls and Polymers. (JA ISSN 0013-8460) **1218**, 1852
Encanto Radical *see* Coleccao Encanto Radical **2861**
Encapsulator. (AT ISSN 1034-8719) **3725**

ENCEPHALE

Encephale. (FR ISSN 0013-7006) **3335**
Encephalitis Surveillance for the Americas see Vigilancia Epidemiologica de las Encefalitis en las Americas **5301**
Enchantment. (US ISSN 0046-1946) **2225**
Enchoria. (GW ISSN 0340-627X) **2811**
Enciclopedia Nacional del Petroleo Petrolquimica y Gas. (SP) **3685**
Encinitas. (US) **2225**
Enclitic. (US ISSN 0193-5798) **2865**, 3508
Encomia. (US ISSN 0363-4841) **2914**
Encore. (AT) **1373**
Encore (Blacksburg). (US ISSN 0071-0164) **2914**, 4632
Encore Directory. (AT) **1134**
Encounter. (AT) **1311**
Encounter! (US ISSN 0162-4547) **4236**
Encounter see Liberation **4241**
Encounter (Indianapolis, 1956). (US ISSN 0013-7081) **4176**
Encounter (Indianapolis, 1971) see In Touch (Indianapolis) **5211**
Encounter (Joliet). (US) **1311**
Encounter (London, 1953). (UK ISSN 0013-7073) **2865**
Encounter (London, 1990). (UK ISSN 0958-2797) **4176**, 4236
Encounter Indianapolis. (US) **4761**
Encounter Monthly. see Wenhui Yuekan **2889**
Encounterer. (US) **4020**, 3335
Encounters. (US) **2405**, 4371
Encouragement. see Hagemi **3102**
Encres Vives. (FR ISSN 0013-7103) **2992**
Encuentro. (BO) **325**, 2405
Encuentro see Encounters **2405**
Encuentro. (NQ ISSN 0424-9674) **2506**
Encuentro Nacional de Investigadores en Administracion. Memorias. (CK) **4059**
Encuesta Agropecuaria. (VE) **150**
†Encuesta de Expectativas Agropecurias. (AG ISSN 0325-9153) **5186**
Encuesta de Hogares: Ocupacion y Desocupacion. (UY) **998**
Encuesta Industrial see Guatemala. Direccion General de Estadistica. Encuesta de la Industria Manufacturera Fabril **4573**
Encuesta Industrial: Resultados Nacionales. (VE) **714**
Encuesta Nacional de Ingresos y Gastos de los Hogares. (MX) **4570**
†Encuesta Nacional del Empleo Total Pais. (CL) **5186**
Encyclia. (US ISSN 0196-9110) **4308**, 325
Encyclopaedia Africana. Information Report. (GH ISSN 0013-712X) **2332**, 4371
Encyclopaedia Judaica Year Book. (IS ISSN 0303-7819) **4222**
▼Encyclopaedia of Economic Development. (II) **1780**
Encyclopedia AZ. (FR) **1780**
▼Encyclopedia Bananica. (CN ISSN 1180-5331) **2914**
Encyclopedia of American Religions. (US) **4176**
Encyclopedia of American Religions: Religious Creeds. (US) **4176**
Encyclopedia of Associations. (US ISSN 0071-0202) **1780**
Encyclopedia of Associations Supplement see E A Supplement **1780**
Encyclopedia of Banking Law. (UK) **2622**, 777
Encyclopedia of Business Information Sources. (US ISSN 0071-0210) **1009**
Encyclopedia of Geographic Information Sources. (US) **2247**
Encyclopedia of Governmental Advisory Organizations. (US ISSN 0092-8380) **4059**
Encyclopedia of Information Systems and Services see Information Industry Directory **1425**
Encyclopedia of Insider Trading see Summary of Insider Transactions **965**
Encyclopedia of Occultism and Parapsychology. (US ISSN 0731-7840) **3669**
Encyclopedia of Physical Science & Technology Yearbook. (US ISSN 0898-9842) **4308**, 1780, 3817, 4597
Encyclopedia of Plant Physiology. New Series. (US) **501**
Encyclopedia of Social Work. (US ISSN 0071-0237) **4404**
Encyclopedia of World Problems and Human Potential. (GW) **3956**, 4434
Encyclopedia Year Book. (US ISSN 0196-0172) **1780**
Encyclopedic Dictionary of American Government. (US) **3892**, 4059
Encyclopedic Dictionary of American History. (US) **2405**
Encyclopedic Dictionary of Economics. (US) **1009**, 1780
Encyclopedic Dictionary of Psychology. (US) **4020**
Encyclopedic Dictionary of Sociology. (US) **4434**
Encyclopedic Knowledge. see Baike Zhishi **4301**
†Encyclopedic Yearbook of Jazz. (US) **5186**
Encyclopedie d'Utovie. (FR ISSN 0396-4957) **4308**
Encyclopedie Politique Arabe. Documents et Notes. (UA ISSN 0013-7146) **3892**
End see The Issue (St. Laurent) **1315**
End Game see E G **4471**
†End Journal. (UK ISSN 0267-0224) **5186**
End Loans to South Africa Newsletter see E L T S A Newsletter **3955**
End of Season National Business Survey. (US) **4545**, 663
End Papers. (UK ISSN 0262-7922) **3941**, 3956
End Point Express. (US) **777**
End-Time News. (CN ISSN 0702-844X) **4236**
End Times Messenger see A C O P Messenger **4227**
End-Use Markets for Plastics. (US ISSN 0013-7154) **3868**, 11
End-User Computing Management see Auerbach Information Management Series **1455**
Endangered Species Update. (US) **1487**, 438, 1949
Endangered Wildlife. (SA ISSN 1016-1902) **1487**
Endas Piemonte. (IT) **2205**
Endeavour (Silver Spring). (US) **2287**
Endeavour (Tarrytown). (US ISSN 0160-9327) **4308**
Endless Vacation. (US ISSN 0279-4853) **4761**
Endocrine Pathology. (US ISSN 1046-3976) **3252**
Endocrine Regulations. (CS) **3252**
Endocrine Research. (US ISSN 0743-5800) **3252**
Endocrine Reviews. (US ISSN 0163-769X) **3252**
Endocrine Society of Australia. Proceedings. (AT ISSN 0312-4738) **3252**
Endocrine Tumors - Diagnosis, Treatment, Pathophysiology see I C R D B Cancergram: Endocrine Tumors - Diagnosis, Treatment, Pathophysiology **3175**
Endocrinologia. (SP ISSN 0211-2299) **3252**
Endocrinologia Experimentalis see Endocrine Regulations **3252**
Endocrinologia Iugoslavica. (XV ISSN 0351-1677) **3253**, 3291, 3320, 3358
Endocrinologia Japonica/Nihon Naibunpi Gakkai. (JA ISSN 0013-7219) **3253**
▼The Endocrinologist. (US ISSN 1051-2144) **3253**
Endocrinology. (US ISSN 0013-7227) **3253**
Endocrinology Abstracts see C S A Neurosciences Abstracts **3168**
Endocrinology and Metabolism Clinics. (US ISSN 0889-8529) **3253**
Endocytobiosis and Cell Research. (GW ISSN 0256-1514) **541**, 476
Endodontics & Dental Traumatology. (DK ISSN 0109-2502) **3232**
Endokrinologie see Experimental and Clinical Endocrinology **3253**
Endokrinologie - Informationen. (GW ISSN 0721-667X) **3253**
Endokrynologia Polska. (PL ISSN 0423-104X) **3253**
Endometriosis Association International Newsletter see Endometriosis Association Newsletter **3291**
Endometriosis Association Newsletter. (US ISSN 0897-1870) **3291**, 4841
Endoscopy. (GW ISSN 0013-726X) **3267**
Endoscopy Review. (US) **3096**
Endoskopie Heute. (GW ISSN 0933-811X) **3267**
Endoskopisi. (CY) **2184**
▼Endothelium. (UK ISSN 0957-3518) **571**
ENDS Report see Environmental Data Services. Report **1951**
Endustri Muhendisligi. (TU) **1928**
Enercom. (US) **1786**
Energetic Life/Kassei. (JA) **1683**
Energetica. (RM ISSN 0421-1715) **1786**
Energeticar. (CI ISSN 0350-3771) **1786**
Energeticheskoe Mashinostroenie. (KR ISSN 0424-9844) **3843**, 1928
Energeticos. (MX) **1786**
Energetik. (RU ISSN 0013-7278) **1786**, 1891
Energetika/Power Engineering. (CS ISSN 0013-7286) **1801**
Energetyka. (PL ISSN 0013-7294) **1786**, 1891
Energi Information. (DK ISSN 0108-4577) **1786**
Energi og Planlaegning. (DK ISSN 0900-8063) **1786**
Energia. (SP ISSN 0210-2056) **1786**, 1891
Energia. (CU) **1786**
Energia. (IS) **1786**
Energia. (IT ISSN 0392-7911) **1786**
Energia: Bibliografia Seletiva. (BL ISSN 0102-3519) **1798**, 1804
Energia e Innovazione see E N E A Notiziario-Energia e Innovazione **1786**
†Energia ed Idrocarburi/Energy and Hydrocarbons. (IT) **5186**
Energia Elettrica. (IT ISSN 0013-7308) **1891**, 1786, 1865, 1923
Energia es Atomtechnika. (HU ISSN 0013-7316) **1804**
Energia Industrial. (AG) **1075**
Energia Nuclear. (AG) **1804**
Energia Nuclear e Agricultura. (BL ISSN 0100-3593) **88**, 1804
Energiagazdalkodas. (HU) **1786**
Energiaipari es Energiagazdalkodasi Tajekoztato/Power Engineering Abstracts. (HU ISSN 0231-0678) **1798**, 11, 3837
Energibeheer see Energie & Milieutechnologie **1786**
Energie. (GW ISSN 0013-7359) **1786**, 1949, 4597
Energie Alternative: Habitat, Territorio, Energia. (IT ISSN 0391-5360) **1786**, 1487, 1949
Energie Electrique au Canada see Electric Power in Canada **1801**
Energie en Algerie. (FR) **1786**
Energie & Milieutechnologie/Energy & Environment Technology. (NE ISSN 0925-2924) **1786**, 1973
Energie et Creation. (FR ISSN 0982-6238) **4020**
Energie et Creativite see Energie et Creation **4020**
Energie Fluide - L'Air Industriel. (FR) **3017**
Energie-Spar-Nachrichten. see Courrier de l'Antigaspillage **1486**
Energie Spektrum. (GW ISSN 0179-9932) **1811**
Energie Spektrum International. (GW) **1786**
Energie und Umwelt. (GW) **1891**
Energieanwendung. (GW ISSN 0013-7405) **1786**, 1804
Energiedepesche. (GW ISSN 0933-8055) **1786**, 1504
Energieonderzoek Centrum Nederland. Jaarverslag/Netherlands Energy Research Foundation. Activities Report. (NE) **1786**, 1949
Energiespectrum. (NE ISSN 0165-2117) **1804**
Energietechniek. (NE) **1891**, 1819
Energietechnik. (GW ISSN 0013-7421) **1786**, 1798, 1819
Energieversorgung Oesterreichs. (AU) **1798**, 4570
Energiewirtschaft. (AU ISSN 0423-1163) **1786**
Energiewirtschaftliche Tagesfragen. (GW ISSN 0720-6240) **1786**, 1891, 3685
Energija. (CI ISSN 0013-7448) **1786**, 1891
Energomashinostroenie/Power Machinery Construction. (RU ISSN 0013-7456) **1786**, 1928
Energumene see Cahiers de l'Energumene **2902**
Energy. (US ISSN 0360-5442) **1786**, 1949
Energy. (FI ISSN 0782-2952) **1786**, 1891
Energy see Journal of Energy Engineering **1869**
Energy Abstracts. (US ISSN 0093-8408) **1798**, 11, 1843
†Energy Abstracts for Policy Analysis. (US ISSN 0098-5104) **5186**
Energy Action. (UK) **1787**
Energy Action Bulletin see Energy Action **1787**
Energy Analects. (CN ISSN 0315-1654) **1787**, 3685
Energy and Buildings. (SZ ISSN 0378-7788) **1787**, 617
†Energy and Education. (US) **5186**
Energy and Engineering Science. (US ISSN 1042-1939) **1787**, 1819
Energy and Environment Alert. (US) **1787**, 1487, 1949
Energy & Environment Technology. see Energie & Milieutechnologie **1786**
Energy & Fuels. (US ISSN 0887-0624) **1787**, 1177
Energy and Housing Report. (US) **1787**, 1487
Energy and Hydrocarbons. see Energia ed Idrocarburi **5186**
Energy and Nuclear Sciences International Who's Who. (UK) **1787**, 1804
Energy and Resources. see Enerugi Shigen **1789**
†Energy & the Environment. (SA) **5186**
†Energy and the Environment. (US ISSN 0275-5289) **5186**
Energy Asia. (SI) **3685**, 1787
†Energy Balance. (UK ISSN 0268-1528) **5186**
Energy Balances of O E C D Countries. (FR) **1787**
Energy Books Quarterly. (US ISSN 0892-5461) **1798**
▼Energy Business Review. (CY) **1787**, 663
†Energy: Canada Health & Fitness. (CN) **5186**
†Energy Clearinghouse. (US ISSN 0273-3102) **5186**
Energy Conservation. see Sho Enerugi **1836**
Energy Conservation and Utilization Technologies. (US) **1487**, 4597
Energy Conservation Digest. (US ISSN 0195-4474) **1787**, 1798
Energy Conservation News. (US ISSN 0161-6595) **1787**
Energy Conversion and Management. (US ISSN 0196-8904) **1787**, 1804, 1891
Energy Daily. (US ISSN 0364-5274) **1787**
Energy Data Base. (US) **1787**
Energy Data Book and Diary. (UK) **1798**, 1787
Energy Design Update. (US ISSN 0741-3629) **617**, 299

ENGINEERING GEOLOGY 6153

Energy Developments see Energie Spektrum International **1786**
†Energy Developments in Japan. (US ISSN 0161-8091) **5186**
Energy Digest. (UK ISSN 0367-1119) **1787**, 1949, 3685
Energy Digest see T I D E **1796**
Energy Economics. (UK ISSN 0140-9883) **1787**, 894
▼Energy, Economics and Climate Change. (US) **1949**
Energy Economist. (UK ISSN 0262-7108) **1787**, 663, 863
Energy Engineering. (US ISSN 0199-8595) **1787**
†Energy, Environment and Development in Africa. (SW ISSN 0281-8515) **5186**
Energy Environment Monitor. (II ISSN 0970-3446) **1788**, 1949
▼Energy Environment Report. (CN) **1788**, 1949
Energy Exploration and Exploitation. (UK ISSN 0144-5987) **1788**, 1560
▼Energy Focus. (US) **1788**
Energy Forum. (JA ISSN 0388-5267) **1788**, 1891
Energy from Biomass see Energy from Biomass and Municipal Waste **5186**
†Energy from Biomass and Municipal Waste. (US) **5186**
Energy in Agriculture see Bioresource Technology **487**
Energy in Denmark. (DK ISSN 0901-3768) **1788**
Energy in Europe. (EI ISSN 0256-6141) **1788**
Energy in Japan. (JA) **1788**, 1891, 1949, 3685
Energy in Japan Quarterly Report see Energy in Japan **1788**
Energy in the News. (US) **835**
Energy in Venezuela. Quarterly Bulletin. (VE) **1788**, 3482
Energy Index see Energy Information Abstracts Annual **1799**
Energy Industries Council Catalogue (Year). (UK) **1788**
†Energy Information. (US) **5186**
Energy Information Abstracts. (US ISSN 0147-6521) **1799**, 11
Energy Information Abstracts Annual. (US ISSN 0739-3679) **1799**, 11
Energy Information Directory. (US) **1788**, 399, 3674
Energy Insider see D O E This Month **1785**
Energy Journal. (US ISSN 0195-6574) **1788**
Energy: Latin American Industrial Report. (US) **1788**
Energy Law Journal. (US ISSN 0270-9163) **2622**, 1788
Energy Magazine. (US ISSN 0149-9386) **1788**, 1949
Energy Management see Energy Management and Federal Energy Guidelines **1788**
Energy Management. (II) **1788**
Energy Management and Federal Energy Guidelines. (US) **1788**, 1949, 2622
Energy News Brief. (US ISSN 1059-289X) **1788**, 1949
Energy News Digest. (US ISSN 0270-5540) **1949**, 1804
Energy News Exchange. (US) **1788**
Energy Newsletter see Energy Studies Review **1789**
Energy Policies and Programs of I E A Countries see Energy Policies of I E A Countries **1788**
Energy Policies of I E A Countries. (FR) **1788**
Energy Policy. (UK ISSN 0301-4215) **1788**, 1804, 1949, 3685
Energy Policy Studies. (US ISSN 0882-3537) **1788**
Energy Pricing News. (CN ISSN 0711-5784) **1788**
Energy Processing - Canada. (CN ISSN 0319-5759) **1788**, 3685
†Energy Progress. (US ISSN 0278-4521) **5186**
Energy R & D Summary and Sources. (UK ISSN 0144-4247) **1788**

Energy Report. (US ISSN 0888-8183) **1788**, 3685
Energy Report. (UK ISSN 0093-7657) **1789**, 3483, 3685
Energy Report from Chase see Petroleum Situation **5257**
Energy Research. (NE ISSN 0167-692X) **1789**
Energy Research Abstracts. (US ISSN 0160-3604) **1799**, 11
Energy Research Institute Perspective see E R I Perspective **1785**
†Energy Research Reports. (US ISSN 0190-4876) **5186**
Energy Resources Tax Reporter. (US) **1093**
Energy Review (Santa Barbara). (US ISSN 0094-8063) **1799**, 11, 1973, 3705
†Energy Saving and Alternative Energy Sources Newsletter. (EI) **5186**
†Energy Sense. (US) **5186**
Energy Shipping. (UK ISSN 0267-629X) **1789**
Energy Sources. (US ISSN 0090-8312) **1789**, 1891, 3685, 3817
Energy Sources. see Neng Yuan **1793**
Energy Statistics. (US ISSN 0739-3075) **3705**
Energy Statistics Yearbook. (UN ISSN 0256-6400) **1799**
Energy Storage and Distribution Program Summary see Conservation and Renewable Energy Technologies for Utility Technologies **1785**
Energy Storage and Distribution Program Summary see Conservation and Renewable Energy Technologies for Industrial Technologies **1785**
Energy Storage and Distribution Program Summary see Conservation and Renewable Energy Technologies for Transportation Technologies **1785**
Energy Storage Systems. (US) **1799**
Energy Studies Review. (CN ISSN 0843-4379) **1789**, 1949
Energy Systems and Policy. (US ISSN 0090-8347) **1789**, 1819, 3817
†Energy Systems Product News. (US) **5186**
Energy Technology see Energy Technology Conference. Proceedings **1789**
†Energy Technology. (SW ISSN 0348-7369) **5186**
Energy Technology Conference. Proceedings. (US ISSN 0161-6048) **1789**
†Energy - Teknik & Miljoe. (DK) **5186**
Energy Today. (US ISSN 0093-500X) **1789**, 1804, 3685, 3817
Energy Trends. (UK ISSN 0308-1222) **1789**, 1891, 3685
Energy User News. (US ISSN 0162-9131) **1789**, 663, 1504
Energy World. (UK ISSN 0307-7942) **1789**, 3685
Energy World Yearbook. (UK) **1789**
Energyfiche. (US) **1799**, 11, 1973
†Energygrams. (US ISSN 0731-6291) **5186**
†Energylab Newsletter. (DK ISSN 0900-419X) **5186**
†Energywide. (NZ) **5186**
Enerpresse. (FR ISSN 0153-9442) **1789**
Enerugi Foramu see Energy Forum **1788**
Enerugi Shigen/Energy and Resources. (JA ISSN 0285-0494) **1789**, 1487
Enfance. (FR ISSN 0013-7545) **1236**, 3320, 4020
Enfance et la Mode. (FR ISSN 0046-1962) **1290**
L'Enfant. (BE ISSN 0013-7553) **1236**, 3801
Enfant en Milieu Tropical. (FR ISSN 0013-7561) **1236**, 3801
Enfants. (CN) **4841**, 1236
Enfants du Monde. (UN ISSN 0013-757X) **4404**, 1236, 3956
Enfants S'amusent. (FR ISSN 0750-8158) **1254**, 2436
Enfermagem. (BL) **3278**

Enfermedades Infecciosas see Enfermedades Infecciosas y Microbiologia Clinica **3219**
Enfermedades Infecciosas y Microbiologia Clinica. (SP ISSN 0213-005X) **3219**
Enfermera al Dia. (MX ISSN 0185-0970) **3278**
Enfermeras. (MX) **3278**
▼Enfermeria Clinica. (SP) **3278**
▼Enfermeria Intensiva. (SP ISSN 1130-2399) **3278**
Enfo. (US ISSN 0276-9956) **1949**
Enfoprensa. (MX) **3892**, 2405
†Enfoque. (US) **5186**
Enforcement Journal. (US ISSN 0042-2347) **1514**
Enfys. (UK ISSN 0013-7596) **2000**
Engagement. (GW) **1749**, 1727
Engei Gaido/Guide to Gardening. (JA) **2125**
Engei Gakkai Zasshi. see Japanese Society for Horticultural Science. Journal **2132**
Engei Shin Chishiki: Hana no Go. see New Information on Horticulture: Flowers **2135**
Engei Shin Chishiki: Yasai no Go. see New Information on Horticulture: Vegetables **2135**
Engel-Poh Family History Newsletter. (US ISSN 0737-688X) **2149**
Engelsk Fodbold. (DK ISSN 0109-1417) **4503**
Engenharia (Revista) see Engenharia Civil **1865**
Engenharia Agricola. (BL ISSN 0100-6916) **88**, 1789, 3017
Engenharia Civil. (BL) **1865**
Engenharia Industrial. (BL) **1819**
Engenharia Sanitaria. (BL) **1865**
Engine Data Sheets. (UK ISSN 0013-774X) **51**
Engineer. (CN) **1819**
Engineer. (UK ISSN 0013-7758) **1819**
Engineer. (CE) **1819**
Engineer. (US) **1819**
Engineer. see Al-Muhandis **1831**
Engineer and M.E.A. News see Engineer - I.M.E. News **1929**
Engineer Buyers Guide. (UK ISSN 0071-0288) **1819**, 1134
Engineer - I.M.E. News. (Institution of Mechanical Engineers (India)) (II) **1929**
Engineer of California. (US ISSN 0277-1233) **1819**
Engineer of Southern California see Engineer of California **1819**
Engineered Materials Abstracts. (US ISSN 0951-9998) **1843**, 11
Engineered Materials Directory of Consultants & Translators. (US) **1134**, 3405
Engineered Systems. (US ISSN 0891-9976) **2299**, 1929, 3017
Engineering. (UK ISSN 0013-7782) **1819**
Engineering. see Technicka Praca **1837**
Engineering-Actualites see Genie Industriel: Revue **1822**
Engineering Analysis see Engineering Analysis with Boundary Elements **1929**
Engineering Analysis with Boundary Elements. (UK ISSN 0955-7997) **1929**
Engineering and Contract Record see Construction Record **1864**
Engineering and Inspection Annual Report. (CN) **3483**
Engineering & Metals Review. (II) **3405**
Engineering & Mining Journal. (US ISSN 0095-8948) **3483**, 1819
Engineering & Mining Journal International Directory of Mining see E & M J International Directory of Mining **3482**
Engineering & Mining Journal Mining Activity Digest see E & M J Mining Activity Digest **3405**
Engineering & Science. (US ISSN 0013-7812) **1819**, 4309
Engineering and Science Review. (US) **1819**

Engineering Applications of Artificial Intelligence. (UK ISSN 0952-1976) **1407**, 1820, 1878
Engineering Associate see Engineers Australia **1821**
Engineering Capacity. (UK ISSN 0306-0179) **1820**
Engineering Capacity Register see Engineering Capacity **1820**
Engineering Club. see Clube de Engenharia **1817**
Engineering College Research and Graduate Study. (US) **1820**, 1706
Engineering Committee on Oceanic Resources. Proceedings of the General Assembly. (US) **4824**, 1820
Engineering Components and Materials Index see Engineering Design and Manufacturing Index **1929**
Engineering Computers. (UK ISSN 0263-4759) **1418**, 1453, 1477
Engineering Contacts. (US) **1820**
Engineering Contractors' Association Magazine see E C A Magazine **616**
Engineering Contractors' Association Publication see E C A Publication **1864**
Engineering: Cornell Quarterly. (US ISSN 0013-7871) **1820**
Engineering Costs and Production Economics see International Journal of Production Economics **1827**
Engineering Cybernetics see Soviet Journal of Computer & Systems Sciences **1443**
Engineering Data Management. (US) **1450**
Engineering Department Management & Administration Report. (US ISSN 1056-1773) **1820**
Engineering Design. (II) **1820**
Engineering Design and Manufacturing Index. (UK) **1929**
Engineering Design Graphics Journal. (US ISSN 0046-2012) **4597**
Engineering Design Optimization. Newsletter see V M A Engineering Newsletter **1880**
Engineering Digest. (CN ISSN 0013-7901) **1820**
Engineering Dimensions. (CN ISSN 0227-5147) **1820**, 1949
Engineering Distributor. (UK ISSN 0260-4922) **1820**
Engineering Document Management System Comparison Report. (US ISSN 1061-9550) **1444**, 1878
Engineering Economist. (US ISSN 0013-791X) **1820**, 663
Engineering Education see A S E E Prism **1813**
Engineering Education in the Region. (UK) **1706**, 1820
Engineering Education News see A S E E Prism **1813**
Engineering Employers' Federation Directory. (UK ISSN 0141-7592) **1820**
Engineering Enrollment Data see American Association of Engineering Societies. Engineering Manpower Commission. Engineering and Technology Enrollments (Year) **1814**
Engineering Evidence, 2-E. (US) **2622**, 1820
Engineering Forum. (PK ISSN 0013-7936) **1820**
Engineering Foundation Annual Report. (US) **1820**
Engineering Fracture Mechanics. (US ISSN 0013-7944) **1916**
Engineering Gazette. (UK) **1820**
Engineering Geology. (NE ISSN 0013-7952) **1865**
†Engineering Geology Abstracts. (US ISSN 0742-3101) **5186**
Engineering Geology & Geotechnical Engineering Symposium. Proceedings. (US) **1865**
Engineering Geology and Soils Engineering Symposium. Proceedings see Engineering Geology & Geotechnical Engineering Symposium. Proceedings **1865**
†Engineering Geology Case Histories. (US ISSN 0071-0326) **5186**

ENGINEERING

Engineering in Medicine and Biology Conference. Record see Conference on Engineering in Medicine and Biology. Record **3090**
Engineering in Miniature. (UK) **2436**
Engineering Index Annual. (US ISSN 0360-8557) **1843**, 11
Engineering Index Cumulative Index. (US) **1843**, 11
Engineering Index Monthly. (US ISSN 0742-1974) **1843**, 11
Engineering Index Monthly and Author Index see Engineering Index Monthly **1843**
Engineering Industries & Trade Journal. (II ISSN 0013-7987) **1820**
Engineering Industries Association. Classified Directory and Buyers Guide. (UK ISSN 0071-0342) **1820**, 1134
Engineering Industries Association. Diary. (UK) **1820**
Engineering Industries Gazette see Engineering Gazette **1820**
Engineering Information. Notes and Comment see Notes & Comment **1845**
Engineering Institution of Zambia. Journal see Zambian Engineer **1841**
Engineering Journal. (US ISSN 0013-8029) **1865**
Engineering Journal of Singapore. (SI ISSN 0129-6531) **1820**
Engineering Lasers. (UK) **1891**
Engineering Management & Equipment Digest. (NZ ISSN 0110-3563) **1009**, 1820
Engineering Management International see Journal of Engineering and Technology Management **1015**
Engineering Manpower Bulletin. (US ISSN 0013-8037) **1820**
Engineering Materials. see Kogyo Zairyo **1919**
Engineering Mechanics. see Gongcheng Lixue **1917**
Engineering News. (PK ISSN 0013-8061) **1820**
Engineering News. (BG) **1820**
Engineering News. (SA ISSN 0257-8646) **1820**
Engineering News. see Ingenioer - Nytt **1825**
Engineering News. (UK ISSN 0267-5145) **1929**
Engineering News-Record see E N R **1865**
Engineering Now. (US) **1820**
Engineering Now see Certificated Engineer **1927**
Engineering Optimization. (US ISSN 0305-215X) **1820**
Engineering Outlook. (US) **1820**
Engineering Outlook at the University of Illinois at Urbana-Champaign see Engineering Outlook **1820**
Engineering Plastics. (UK ISSN 0952-6900) **3862**
Engineering Polonais see Polish Engineering **1833**
Engineering Production. see Strojirenska Vyroba **3023**
Engineering Research Centres. (UK) **1820**
Engineering Review. see Revista de Ingenieria **1835**
Engineering Science Library. see Ingenieurwissenschaftliche Bibliothek **1825**
Engineering Sciences Data Index see Validated Engineering Data Index **1847**
Engineering Sciences Data Unit Index see Validated Engineering Data Index **1847**
Engineering Services Management. (UK ISSN 0951-7871) **617**
Engineering Societies of New England. Journal see New England Engineering Journal **1831**
Engineering Society of Detroit Technology see E S D Technology **1819**
Engineering Software Exchange. (US ISSN 0743-2984) **1878**, 1477
Engineering Structures. (UK ISSN 0141-0296) **1865**
Engineering Studies. see Dirasat Handasiyyah **1818**

†Engineering Thermophysics in China/Chung-kuo Kung Ch'eng Je Wu Li. (US ISSN 0196-5964) **5186**
Engineering Times. (II ISSN 0013-8134) **1820**
Engineering Times. (US ISSN 0195-6876) **1821**
Engineering Times Annual Directory. (II) **1821**
†Engineering Tools. (US) **5186**
Engineering und Automation. (GW ISSN 0939-205X) **1789**
Engineering Week. (SA) **1821**
Engineering with Computers. (US ISSN 0177-0667) **1879**
Engineering World. (UK) **1821**
Engineering World. (II) **1821**
▼Engineering World. (AT ISSN 1036-1677) **1821**
Engineerogram. (US) **1821**
Engineers. see Enjiniasu **1821**
Engineers and Engines Magazine. (US ISSN 0013-8142) **4709**, 2310
Engineers Australia. (AT) **1821**
Engineers' Digest. (UK ISSN 0013-8169) **1821**
Engineer's Digest (Overland Park). (US ISSN 0192-1290) **1821**
Engineer's Digest (Washington) see Coast Guard Engineer's Digest **1817**
Engineers Journal. (IE ISSN 0332-1711) **1821**
Engineer's Magazine. see Magallat Al-Mohandeseen **1830**
†England and Wales National Health Service. Health Services Costing Returns. (UK) **5186**
England on Fifty Dollars a Day. (US ISSN 1042-8399) **4761**
England on Forty Dollars a Day see England on Fifty Dollars a Day **4761**
†England's Best Holidays. (UK ISSN 0267-3398) **5186**
Englera. (GW ISSN 0170-4818) **501**
Englisch. (GW ISSN 0013-8185) **2811**, 1632
Englisch Amerikanische Studien. (GW) **2310**
Englisch an Volkshochschulen see Zielsprache Englisch **2854**
English. (UK ISSN 0013-8215) **2914**, 2992
English Academy Review. (SA) **2914**, 1632
English Amateur Golf. (UK) **4503**
English and American Studies in German. (GW ISSN 0071-0490) **2811**
English and Media Magazine. (UK) **2914**, 1749
English Benedictine Congregation. Ordo.(UK) **4263**
English Ceramic Circle. Transactions. (UK ISSN 0071-0547) **1163**
English Churchman see English Churchman & St. James's Chronicle **4236**
English Churchman & St. James's Chronicle. (UK) **4236**
English Cocker Quarterly. (US) **3710**
English Dance and Song. (UK ISSN 0013-8231) **3550**, 1530, 2054
English Education. (US ISSN 0007-8204) **1632**, 2812
†English Enquiries. (US ISSN 0898-5464) **5186**
English Farmer. (UK) **88**
English Folk Dance and Song Society. Journal see Folk Music Journal **3551**
English for Specific Purposes. (US ISSN 0889-4906) **1749**, 2812
English Goethe Society. Publications. (UK) **2914**, 2992
English Guernsey Herd Book. (UK ISSN 0071-0571) **216**
English Historical Documents. (US ISSN 0071-058X) **2360**
English Historical Review. (UK ISSN 0013-8266) **2360**
†English Hops. (UK ISSN 0261-2674) **5186**
English in Africa. (SA ISSN 0376-8902) **2865**
English in Australia. (AT ISSN 0046-208X) **2812**
English in Education. (UK ISSN 0425-0494) **1749**, 2812

English in Texas. (US ISSN 0425-0508) **1632**
English Journal. (US ISSN 0013-8274) **1632**
English Language and Orientation Programs in the United States. (US ISSN 0071-0601) **1749**
English Language Journal/Revista de la Lengua Inglesa. (AG) **2812**, 1749
English Language Learning. see Yingyu Xuexi **2853**
English Language Notes. (US ISSN 0013-8282) **2914**
English Language Research Journal. (UK) **2812**
English Language Teaching see English Language Teaching Journal **2812**
English Language Teaching Journal. (UK ISSN 0307-8337) **2812**, 1749
English Leadership Quarterly. (US ISSN 0738-1409) **1749**, 2812
English Leaflet see Leaflet (Lexington) **2824**
English Legal Manuscripts. (NE) **2622**
English Lineages and Queries see English Enquiries **5186**
English Literary History see E L H **2913**
English Literary Renaissance. (US ISSN 0013-8312) **2914**
English Literature in Transition (1880-1920). (US ISSN 0364-3549) **2914**
English Little Magazines. (UK ISSN 0071-061X) **2914**
English Magazine see English and Media Magazine **2914**
English Monarch Series. (US ISSN 0071-0628) **2360**
English National Opera Programme. (UK) **4632**
English Place-Name Society. (UK ISSN 0071-0636) **2812**
English Place - Name Society Journal. (UK) **2247**
English Quarterly. (CN ISSN 0013-8355) **1749**, 1632, 2914
▼English Review. (UK ISSN 0955-8950) **2812**, 1749
▼English Rider. (CN) **4533**
English Schools Swimming Association Handbook. (UK) **4471**
English Self-Study. see Yingyu Zixue **2853**
English Setter Association of America. Newsletter. (US) **3710**
English Speaking: The E-S U News see English Speaking Union Today **3956**
English Speaking Union Today. (US) **3956**
English Studies. (NE ISSN 0013-838X) **2812**, 2914
English Studies in Africa. (SA ISSN 0013-8398) **2506**, 2914
English Studies in Canada. (CN ISSN 0317-0802) **2914**
English Teachers' Journal (Israel). (IS ISSN 0333-533X) **1749**
English Teaching and Research for Elementary and Secondary Schools. see Zhongxiaoxue Yingyu Jiaoxue yu Yanjiu **2854**
English Teaching Forum see Forum (Washington, 1980) **2814**
English Teaching Guidance see English Teachers' Journal (Israel) **1749**
English Today. (UK ISSN 0266-0784) **2812**
English Tourist Board. Annual Report. (UK) **4761**
English Usage in Southern Africa. (SA ISSN 0046-2098) **2812**
English Westerners' Brand Book. (UK ISSN 0013-8401) **3457**
English Westerners' Tally Sheet. (UK ISSN 0013-841X) **3457**
English World Wide. (NE ISSN 0172-8865) **2812**
Engrais see Negoce et Agriculture **185**
Engrami. (YU ISSN 0351-2665) **3335**, 4020
Engravers Journal. (US ISSN 0099-0043) **663**
Engrenage. (FR) **1821**
Enhanced Energy Recovery News. (US ISSN 0271-7085) **1789**
Enhanced Oil-Recovery Field Reports. (US ISSN 0160-337X) **3685**, 1821

Enhanced Recovery Week see Advanced Recovery Week **1783**
Enhanced Services Outlook. (US ISSN 0897-2915) **1362**
Enigma. (CU) **2865**, 3892
Enigma. (YU ISSN 0013-8436) **4471**
Enimerossi/Briefing. (CY) **2184**
Enjeux. (FR ISSN 0223-4866) **3446**
Enjine!-Enjine! (US ISSN 0362-2487) **2031**, 257
Enjiniasu/Engineers. (JA ISSN 0013-8444) **1821**, 1009
Enjoy. (US) **1504**
Enjoy. (CN) **2473**
†Enjoying the Arts. (US) **5186**
Enlightenment/Keihatsu. (JA) **1683**
Enlightenment and Dissent. (UK ISSN 0262-7612) **2310**, 3892
The Enlightenment: German and Interdisciplinary Studies. (US ISSN 1043-576X) **2360**
L'Ennemi. (FR) **325**, 2914
Ennepi. (IT) **777**
Enoch Pratt Free Library. Staff Reporter. (US ISSN 0013-8495) **2757**
Enohobby. (IT) **380**
Enotecnico. (IT) **380**
Enotria. (IT) **380**
Enquete Annuelle sur l'Activite des Organismes de Securite Sociale. (GR ISSN 0256-3630) **4425**
Enquete Permanente sur l'Utilisation des Vehicules de Transport en Commun de Personnes en (year). (FR) **4663**
Enquete sur les Entreprises Industrielles et Commerciales du Togo. (TG) **835**, 1075
Enquetes et Documents d'Histoire Africaine. (BE ISSN 0772-6112) **2332**
Enquirer Newsletter. (US) **2405**
Enquires. (SI) **815**
Enquiry. (UK ISSN 0013-8509) **2000**
Enquiry. (II ISSN 0013-8517) **3892**, 4434
Enrich! (US) **815**, 1114
Enrico Fermi International Summer School of Physics. (NE) **3817**
Enrolled Actuaries Report. (US) **2531**, 750, 3035
EnRoute. (CN ISSN 0703-0312) **4761**, 663, 4672
Ensaios de Opiniao. (BL) **2865**
Ensaios F E E. (Fundacao de Economia e Estatistica) (BL) **894**, 3892
Ensaios Linguisticos. (BL) **2812**
Ensanian Physicochemical Institute. Journal. (US ISSN 0013-8533) **3817**, 1225
†Ensayistas. (US ISSN 0148-8627) **5187**
Ensayo y Testimonio. (UY ISSN 0071-0679) **2914**
Ensayos: Coleccion Economia. (MX) **863**
Ensayos E C I E L. (Programa de Estudios Conjuntos para la Integracion Economica Latinoamericano) (BL ISSN 0102-0617) **863**
Ensayos Sobre Politica Economica. (CK ISSN 0120-4483) **663**
Enseignants. (CN ISSN 0046-2101) **1632**
Enseignement Assiste par Ordinateur see E A O **4597**
Enseignement du Francais aux Etrangers. (FR) **1721**
Enseignement du Russe. (FR ISSN 0300-2608) **2914**, 2812
L'Enseignement et la Pedagogie en Roumanie. (RM) **1632**
Enseignement Mathematique. (SZ ISSN 0013-8584) **3035**
L'Enseignement Philosophique. (FR ISSN 0986-1653) **1632**
Enseignement Public. (FR ISSN 0223-5986) **1632**
Enseignement Superieur en Cote-d'Ivoire. (IV) **1632**
Ensemble. (US) **4633**, 1530, 3508
Ensenanza de la Religion. (SP) **4176**
Ensenanza e Investigacion en Psicologia. (MX ISSN 0185-1594) **4020**
Enshu no Shizen/Nature of Enshu. (JA ISSN 0386-5037) **4309**

Ensign. (CN) **3457**
Ensign. (US ISSN 0884-1136) **4282**
Ensign Talking Book. (US) **2292,
4282**
Ensomme Gamles Vaern Fonden
Information *see* E G V Information
4404
Ensovoort. (SA ISSN 0257-2036)
2992
Ente Nazionale Idrocarburi. Report and
Statement of Accounts. (IT ISSN
0071-0687) **3685**
Ente Nazionale Idrocarburi Annual
Report *see* E N I Annual Report
1785
Ente Nazionale per l'Energia Elettrica
(ENEL) Dirigente E.N.E.L. *see*
Dirigente E.N.E.L **1785**
†Ente Provinciale per Il Turismo di
Nuoro. Notiziario. (IT ISSN 0013-
8622) **5187**
Entente Africaine. (IV ISSN 0013-
8630) **2000**
Enterprise. *see* Ha-Mifal **1081**
Enterprise. (Il ISSN 0013-8673)
1114
Enterprise. (CN ISSN 0013-8657)
2177
Enterprise (Brisbane). (AT ISSN 0816-
1631) **663, 978**
Enterprise (Deakin) *see* Australian
Jaycee **1296**
Enterprise (Hobart). (AT) **815**
Enterprise (Kensington). (AT ISSN
0085-0268) **835**
Enterprise (New York). (US) **2531**
Enterprise (Salt Lake City). (US) **663**
†Enterprise (Washington). (US ISSN
0191-5215) **5187**
Enterprise and Development *see*
European Community Affairs **815**
Enterprise Culture. *see* Qiye Wenhua
2951
†Enterprise Farming. (UK) **5187**
Enterprise Management. *see* Qiye
Guanli **1025**
Enterprise Medical Journal. *see* Gongqi
Yikan **3101**
▼Enterprise Networking. (US) **1350**
Enterprise Organization. *see* Podnikova
Organizace **1024**
Enterprise Studies. *see* Qiye Yanjiu
1117
Enterprise Systems Journal. (US ISSN
1053-6566) **1450, 1477**
Enterpriser. *see* Foeretagaren **1076**
†Enterprises Agricoles. (FR ISSN
0046-2152) **5187**
Entertainment and Sports Lawyer. (US
ISSN 0732-1880) **2622, 3508,
3550, 4471**
†Entertainment at Large. (US) **5187**
Entertainment Bits. (US ISSN 0192-
8430) **1530, 3550**
Entertainment Eyes. (US) **3550**
†Entertainment Facilities Buyers Guide.
(US) **5187**
Entertainment Guide. (CN) **1373**
Entertainment Industry Series. (US
ISSN 0071-0695) **1038**
▼Entertainment Law. (US) **2622**
Entertainment Law & Business. (US)
2622
Entertainment Law & Finance. (US)
2622, 1009, 1373, 4633
Entertainment Law Reporter. (US ISSN
0270-3831) **2622, 1373, 3508,
4127**
▼Entertainment Law Review. (UK ISSN
0959-3799) **2622**
Entertainment Litigation Reporter. (US
ISSN 1047-4137) **2622**
Entertainment Magazine. (US ISSN
0742-9568) **3550, 3508, 4633**
Entertainment Magazine. (CN) **3550,
4633**
Entertainment Marketing Letter. (US
ISSN 1048-5112) **1038, 3674**
Entertainment Plus. (US) **3550,
3508**
Entertainment, Publishing and the Arts
Handbook. (US ISSN 0739-1897)
1373, 4127, 4633
Entertainment Research Report. (US)
2225
Entertainment Today. (US) **2225**
▼Entertainment Weekly. (US) **2225**
Entertainment Worker. (AT ISSN 0818-
9846) **2582**

Enthousiaste *see* Automobiles
Classiques **4682**
Enthusiast. (US ISSN 0027-2167)
4518
†Enthusiast. (CN) **5187**
Entomography. (US ISSN 0734-9874)
530
Entomologia Experimentalis et
Applicata. (NE ISSN 0013-8703)
530
Entomologia Generalis. (GW ISSN
0171-8177) **530**
Entomologica Fennica. (FI ISSN 0785-
8760) **530**
Entomologica Germanica *see*
Entomologia Generalis **530**
Entomologica Scandinavica. (DK ISSN
0013-8711) **530**
Entomological Knowledge. *see*
Kunchong Zhishi **536**
Entomological News. (US ISSN 0013-
872X) **530**
Entomological Review. (English
translation of: Entomologicheskoye
Obozreniye) (US ISSN 0013-8738)
530
Entomological Review of Japan. (JA
ISSN 0286-9810) **531, 438**
Entomological Society of Alberta.
Proceedings. (CN ISSN 0071-0709)
531
Entomological Society of America.
Annals. (US ISSN 0013-8746)
531
Entomological Society of America.
Bulletin *see* American Entomologist
528
Entomological Society of America.
Miscellaneous Publications. (US
ISSN 0071-0717) **531**
Entomological Society of America
Newsletter *see* E S A Newsletter
530
Entomological Society of Australia
(N.S.W.) Journal *see* General and
Applied Entomology **533**
Entomological Society of British
Columbia. Journal. (CN ISSN 0071-
0733) **531**
Entomological Society of Canada.
Bulletin. (CN ISSN 0071-0741)
531
Entomological Society of Canada.
Memoirs. (CN ISSN 0071-075X)
531
Entomological Society of Egypt. Bulletin.
see Societe Entomologique d'Egypte.
Bulletin **537**
Entomological Society of India. Bulletin
of Entomology. (Il ISSN 0013-
8762) **531**
Entomological Society of Manitoba.
Proceedings. (CN ISSN 0315-2146)
531
Entomological Society of New Zealand.
Bulletin. (NZ ISSN 0110-4527)
531
Entomological Society of Nigeria.
Bulletin *see* Nigerian Journal of
Entomology **589**
Entomological Society of Ontario.
Proceedings. (CN ISSN 0071-0768)
531
Entomological Society of Pennsylvania.
Newsletter. (US ISSN 0071-0776)
531
Entomological Society of Southern
Africa. Journal. (SA ISSN 0013-
8789) **531**
Entomological Society of Southern
Africa. Memoirs. (SA ISSN 0373-
4242) **531**
Entomological Society of Southern
Africa. Proceedings of the Congress.
(SA) **531**
Entomological Society of Washington.
Memoirs. (US) **531**
Entomological Society of Washington.
Proceedings. (US ISSN 0013-8797)
531
Entomologicke Problemy. (CS ISSN
0071-0792) **531**
Entomologie et Phytopathologie
Appliquees. (IR ISSN 0013-8800)
531
Entomologische Berichten. (NE ISSN
0013-8827) **531**

Entomologische Blaetter fuer Biologie
und Systematik der Kaefer. (GW
ISSN 0013-8835) **531**
Entomologisk Tidskrift. (SW ISSN
0013-886X) **531**
Entomologiske Meddelelser. (DK ISSN
0013-8851) **531**
Entomologiste. (FR ISSN 0013-8886)
532
Entomologist's Gazette. (UK ISSN
0013-8894) **532**
Entomologist's Monthly Magazine. (UK
ISSN 0013-8908) **532**
Entomologist's Record. (UK ISSN
0013-8916) **532**
Entomology Abstracts. (US ISSN 0013-
8924) **465, 11**
Entomology Memoirs *see* South Africa.
Department of Agriculture.
Entomology Memoirs **538**
Entomology Newsletter. (BL) **532**
Entomon. (Il ISSN 0377-9335) **532**
Entomonograph. (NE ISSN 0106-
2808) **532**
Entomophaga. (FR ISSN 0013-8959)
532
Entourage. (CN ISSN 0829-8815)
3336, 1735, 4371
Entr'Acte. (FR ISSN 0013-8975)
3550
Entr'acte. (NE ISSN 0924-560X)
3550, 1530
Entraide Genealogique. (CN ISSN
0226-6245) **2149,** 2405
Entrainements. (FR) **1929**
Entrance *see* Exit **2916**
Entre. (SW ISSN 0345-2581) **4633**
Entre - Nous. (CN) **4176**
Entredichos. (AG) **4020**
Entree. (US) **4761,** 2066
Entremetteur. (CN) **1311**
Entrepenadmeddelanden *see*
Leveranstidningen Entreprenad **622**
Entreprendre. (BE) **815**
L'Entrepreneur. (ZR) **663**
Entrepreneur. (US ISSN 0163-3341)
1114
Entrepreneur W E M Review *see* Warta
Ekonomi Maritim Review for
Entrepreneurs **4741**
Entrepreneurial Economy *see*
Entrepreneurial Economy Review
663
Entrepreneurial Economy Review. (US
ISSN 0899-7721) **663**
Entrepreneurial Manager's Newsletter.
(US ISSN 0272-0396) **1009,
1114**
Entrepreneurial Woman. (US) **1114,
3627, 4841**
Entrepreneurs. *see* Chuangye Zhe **655**
Entrepreneurs & Investors Annual. (US)
1114, 945, 4597
Entrepreneur's Digest. (US) **1114**
Entrepreneur's Franchise Yearbook *see*
Entrepreneur's Guide to Franchise &
Business Opportunities **1114**
Entrepreneur's Guide to Franchise &
Business Opportunities. (US) **1114,**
945
†Entrepreneur's Guide to Homebase
Business. (US) **5187**
Entrepreneurship & Regional
Development. (UK ISSN 0898-
5626) **664**
▼Entrepreneurship, Innovation and
Change. (US) **1114**
Entrepreneurship: Theory and Practice.
(US ISSN 1042-2587) **1114**
Entreprenoeren. (DK) **617**
Entrepresse. (FR) **2569,** 664
Entreprise *see* L'Entreprise - A pour
Affaires **1009**
Entreprise/Onderneming. (BE ISSN
0777-6349) **2299**
L'Entreprise - A pour Affaires. (FR)
1009
Entreprise et Carrieres. (FR) **664,
3627**
L'Entreprise et l'Homme. (BE ISSN
0046-2160) **1009**
Entreprise Europeenne. (FR ISSN
0014-9373) **617,** 1865
L'Entreprise Ivoirienne. (IV) **815**
Entreprises Formation. (FR ISSN 0765-
5762) **1065**
Entreprises Rhone Alpes. (FR ISSN
0751-588X) **1075**

Entretien des Textiles. (FR ISSN 0181-
8120) **4618**
Entretiens sur l'Antiquite Classique. (SZ
ISSN 0071-0822) **1276**
Entropie. (FR ISSN 0013-9084)
1789, 1929
Entry. (US ISSN 0886-845X) **3790,**
325
Entscheidung. (GW ISSN 0013-9092)
4236
Entscheidungen der Finanzgerichte. (GW
ISSN 0421-2991) **777**
Entscheidungen der Oberlandesgerichte
in Zivilsachen. (GW ISSN 0425-
1288) **2622**
Entscheidungen der
Oberverwaltungsgerichte fuer das
Land Nordrhein-Westfalen in
Muenster sowie fuer die Laender
Niedersachsen und Schleswig-
Holstein in Lueneburg. (GW) **2622**
Entscheidungen der Spruchstellen fuer
Fuersorgestreitigkeiten. (GW ISSN
0343-656X) **4404**
Entscheidungen des
Bundesgerichtshofes in Zivilsachen.
(GW ISSN 0435-7124) **2622**
†Entscheidungen des
Bundesoberseeamtes und der
Seeamter der Bundesrepublik
Deutschland. (GW) **5187**
Entscheidungen des
Bundesverfassungsgerichts. (GW
ISSN 0433-7646) **2622**
Entscheidungen des
Bundesverwaltungsgerichts. (GW
ISSN 0013-9106) **2623**
Entscheidungen zum Wirtschaftsrecht -
E W I R. (GW ISSN 0177-9303)
863, 2623
Entschluss. (AU ISSN 0017-4602)
4176
Entsorga-Magazin -
Entsorgungswirtschaft. (GW) **1821,**
1949
Entsorgungs-Technik. (GW ISSN 0935-
7688) **1949**
EntsorgungsPraxis. (GW ISSN 0724-
6870) **1949**
Entwicklung des
Motorfahrzeugbestandes in der
Schweiz/Evolution de l'Effectif des
Vehicules a Moteur en Suisse. (SZ)
4663
Entwicklung und Laendlicher Raum.
(GW ISSN 0343-6462) **88**
Entwicklung und Zusammenarbeit. (GW
ISSN 0721-2178) **4434**
Entwicklungen in Nordrhein-Westfalen
im Jahre (Year). (GW) **4570**
Entwicklungsgeschichte und Systematik
der Pflanzen. *see* Plant Systematics
and Evolution **515**
Entwicklungslaender-Studien. (GW ISSN
0722-0111) **714,** 929, 1560,
3096
Entwicklungspolitische Korrespondenz.
(GW) **3956**
Entwicklungszusammenarbeit im Sport.
(GW ISSN 0932-7797) **4471**
Entwurf. (GW ISSN 0343-6519)
4236, 1749
Envasamiento. (AG ISSN 0325-0415)
3648
Envase y Embalaje *see* Guia del Envase
y Embalaje **3648**
Envaspres. (SP) **3648**
Envers du Decor. (CN ISSN 0319-
8650) **4633**
Envest. (US) **945,** 1789
Envio. (NQ ISSN 0259-4374) **2405,**
3892
Enviraction *see* Energy and Environment
Alert **1787**
Enviro. (SW ISSN 1101-7341) **1976,**
1949
Envirofiche. (US) **1973,** 11, 465
Environ. (TR) **1949**
Environ. (US ISSN 0883-9719) **1949**
Environment. (AT) **1949,** 438,
1789, 2171
Environment. (CN) **2299**
▼Environment (San Diego). (US)
1949
Environment (Washington). (US ISSN
0013-9157) **1949**
Environment Abstracts. (US ISSN
0093-3287) **1973,** 11, 465,
1976

Environment Abstracts Annual. (US ISSN 0000-1198) **1973**, 11, 1976
Environment Advisor. (US) **1984**, 4100
Environment and Art Letter. (US ISSN 1040-6611) **299**, 325, 4263
Environment and Behavior. (US ISSN 0013-9165) **4434**, 4020
▼Environment & Development. (US) **1949**, 2487
Environment and Ecology. (II ISSN 0970-0420) **1949**
▼Environment & Industry Digest. (UK ISSN 0958-2126) **1929**, 1949
Environment and Planning A. (UK ISSN 0308-518X) **2487**, 1949, 2247
Environment and Planning B: Planning & Design. (UK ISSN 0265-8135) **2487**, 299
Environment and Planning C: Government & Policy. (UK ISSN 0263-774X) **4059**, 1093
Environment and Planning D: Society & Space. (UK ISSN 0263-7758) **2487**, 4434
Environment and Urbanization. (UK ISSN 0956-2478) **1949**
▼Environment Business. (UK ISSN 0959-7042) **1950**
Environment Conservation News. (AT) **1487**
Environment Features. (FR) **1950**
Environment Herald. see Huanjing Daobao **1957**
Environment Information Access see Environment Abstracts **1973**
Environment International. (US ISSN 0160-4120) **1950**
Environment News Digest. (US) **1950**
Environment Newsletter. (WS) **1950**, 1487
Environment Protection Engineering. (PL ISSN 0324-8828) **1950**
Environment R S A see Conserva **1485**
Environment Report. (US ISSN 0013-9203) **1950**
Environment Reporter. (US ISSN 0013-9211) **1950**
▼Environment Risk. (UK ISSN 0965-3813) **1950**
▼Environment Today. (US) **1950**, 438
Environment Victoria. (AT ISSN 0727-5366) **1487**, 1950
Environment Views. (CN ISSN 0701-9637) **1950**
Environment W.A. see Environment **1949**
Environment Week. (US ISSN 1041-8105) **1950**
Environmental Action. (US ISSN 0013-922X) **1950**
Environmental and Experimental Botany. (US ISSN 0098-8472) **501**, 1950
Environmental and Molecular Mutagenesis. (US ISSN 0893-6692) **438**
Environmental and Occupational Carcinogenesis see I C R D B Cancergram: Environmental and Occupational Carcinogenesis **5208**
Environmental and Planning Law Journal. (AT ISSN 0813-300X) **2623**, 1950
Environmental and Siting. (US) **3837**
Environmental and Urban Issues. (US ISSN 1044-033X) **1950**, 2487, 4087
Environmental Approvals in Canada. (CN) **1950**, 2623
†Environmental Assessment of the Alaskan Continental Shelf. Annual Reports Summary. (US) **5187**
Environmental Audits. (US) **1950**, 2623
Environmental Awareness. (II ISSN 0254-8798) **1950**, 1487
Environmental Biology. (US) **1950**, 438, 1789
Environmental Biology of Fishes. (NE ISSN 0378-1909) **582**
Environmental Building Developments Ltd. News see Practical Alternatives **1966**
Environmental Bulletin (Morristown). (US) **1487**

Environmental Business Journal. (US ISSN 1045-8611) **1950**, 664
▼Environmental Businesses in Japan: Industrial & Company News (Year). (JA) **835**
▼Environmental Careers. (US) **3627**, 1950
†Environmental Chemistry. (UK ISSN 0305-7712) **5187**
▼Environmental Citizen Suits. (US) **2623**, 1950
Environmental Claims Journal. (US ISSN 1040-6026) **1950**, 2623
Environmental Coalition on Nuclear Power News from E C N P see News from E C N P **1964**
Environmental Coalition on Nuclear Power Newsletter. (US) **1789**, 1804, 1951
Environmental Communicator. (US) **1951**, 1632
Environmental Compliance Update. (US) **1951**, 2623
Environmental Conservation. (SZ ISSN 0376-8929) **1951**, 1487
Environmental Conservation and Management in Agriculture and Forestry. see Ochrana a Tvorba Zivotniho Prostredi v Zemedelstvi a Lesnictvi **112**
Environmental Conservation Engineering. see Kankyo Gijutsu **1961**
Environmental Conservation Library News see E C O L News **1947**
The Environmental Contract Opportunity Report. (US) **4059**, 1951
Environmental Control Abstracts. see Kornyezetvedelmi Szakirodalmi Tajekoztato **1974**
Environmental Control News for Southern Industry. (US ISSN 0013-9238) **1951**
Environmental Data Services. Report. (UK ISSN 0260-1249) **1951**
Environmental Defense Fund. Annual Report. (US ISSN 0091-9837) **1951**
Environmental Defense Fund Letter see E D F Letter **1947**
Environmental Design Research Association. Annual Conference Proceedings. (US) **299**, 2487
Environmental Directory. (UK) **1951**
Environmental Directory of U.S. Power Plants. (US) **1891**
Environmental Education and Information. (UK ISSN 0144-9281) **1951**
Environmental Engineering. (UK ISSN 0954-5824) **1821**, 1951
Environmental Engineering. (US) **1951**, 1821
Environmental Engineering Newsletter. (US) **1951**
Environmental Engineering Selection Guide. (US ISSN 0896-3827) **1951**, 1821
Environmental Entomology. (US ISSN 0046-225X) **532**
Environmental Ethics. (US ISSN 0163-4275) **3765**, 1951
Environmental Events Record see E E R **1947**
Environmental Eye. (CN ISSN 0847-1541) **1951**
▼Environmental Finance. (US ISSN 1054-8017) **750**
Environmental Fluid Mechanics. (NE) **1543**
Environmental Forum. (US ISSN 0731-5732) **1951**
Environmental Geochemistry and Health. (UK) **1951**, 3483
Environmental Geology see Vermont Division of Geology and Mineral Resources. Environmental Geology **1584**
Environmental Geology and Water Sciences. (US) **1560**
Environmental Health. (UK ISSN 0013-9270) **4100**
Environmental Health and Safety News. (US) **3616**
Environmental Health and Safety News see Environmental Health and Safety News **3616**
Environmental Health Criteria. (UN ISSN 0250-863X) **1951**, 4100

Environmental Health Letter. (US ISSN 0196-0598) **3096**, 1951
Environmental Health Monthly. (US) **1951**, 3801
Environmental Health News. (US) **1951**
Environmental Health Perspectives see E H P **1947**
Environmental Health Report. (US ISSN 0897-862X) **1973**, 4117
Environmental Health Review. (CN ISSN 0319-6771) **4100**, 1951
†Environmental Health Review, Australia. (AT ISSN 0818-5670) **5187**
Environmental History Review. (US) **1951**, 2405
Environmental Hong Kong (Year). (HK) **4059**, 1951
Environmental Hotline (Albuquerque). (US ISSN 1040-1725) **1951**, 1487, 1560, 1597
Environmental Hotline (Columbus) see Ohio Environmental Report **1965**
Environmental Impact Assessment Review. (US ISSN 0195-9255) **1951**
†Environmental Impact Assessment Worldletter. (US) **5187**
Environmental Impact Statement Cumulative see E I S Cumulative **1973**
▼Environmental Insurance Coverage. (US) **2531**, 1952, 2623
Environmental Lab. (US) **1952**
Environmental Law (Portland). (US ISSN 0046-2276) **1952**, 2623
Environmental Law (Washington). (US ISSN 0748-8769) **2623**, 1952
▼Environmental Law Anthology. (US) **2623**, 1952
Environmental Law Handbook. (US) **1952**, 2623
Environmental Law in New York. (US) **1952**, 2623
Environmental Law Journal. (JA) **1952**
Environmental Law Journal of Ohio. (US ISSN 1045-599X) **1952**, 2623
Environmental Law Newsletter. (US ISSN 0163-545X) **2623**, 1952
Environmental Law Reform Group. Publication. (AT) **1952**
Environmental Law Reporter. (US ISSN 0046-2284) **1952**, 2623
▼Environmental Liability. (US) **2623**, 1952
Environmental Management. (US) **4100**
Environmental Management (Denver). (US ISSN 1051-2837) **1952**
Environmental Management (New York). (US ISSN 0364-152X) **1952**
▼Environmental Management & Health.(UK ISSN 0956-6163) **1952**, 3096
Environmental Management Report see Environmental Management Review **1952**
Environmental Management Review. (US) **1952**, 1009, 1487, 2623
Environmental Manager. (US ISSN 1043-786X) **1952**, 1009
Environmental Manager's Compliance Advisor. (US ISSN 0887-9753) **1952**
Environmental Medicine. (JA ISSN 0287-0517) **3096**, 1952
Environmental Monitor see Coastal Zone Management **1485**
Environmental Monitoring and Assessment. (NE ISSN 0167-6369) **1952**
Environmental Mutagenesis see Environmental and Molecular Mutagenesis **438**
Environmental News Digest. (MY ISSN 0127-7162) **1952**, 1487, 1543
Environmental Newsline. (US) **1952**
Environmental Nutrition. (US ISSN 0893-4452) **3605**, 2066, 2446
Environmental Nutrition Newsletter see Environmental Nutrition **3605**
Environmental Opportunities. (US ISSN 0736-9603) **1952**, 1487, 3605
Environmental Outlook. (US) **1952**
Environmental Periodicals Bibliography. (US) **1974**
†Environmental Physiology. (UK ISSN 0142-8659) **5187**

Environmental Planning. (IS) **1952**, 2487
Environmental Policy Alert. (US) **1952**
Environmental Policy and Law. (NE ISSN 0378-777X) **1952**, 2623
Environmental Policy Review: The Soviet Union and East Europe. (IS ISSN 0792-0032) **1953**
▼Environmental Politics. (UK ISSN 0964-4016) **3956**
Environmental Pollution. (UK ISSN 0269-7491) **1977**
Environmental Pollution. Series A. Ecological and Biological see Environmental Pollution **1977**
Environmental Pollution. Series B. Chemical and Physical see Environmental Pollution **1977**
Environmental Pollution and Prevention. see Huanjing Wuran yu Fangzhi **1957**
Environmental Pollution in Meguro Ward. see Meguro-ku no Kogai **1962**
Environmental Pollution in Niigata City. see Niigata-shi ni Okeru Kogai **1964**
Environmental Professional. (US ISSN 0191-5398) **1953**
Environmental Progress (New York). (US ISSN 0278-4491) **1953**, 1852
Environmental Progress (Springfield). (US) **1953**, 1487
▼Environmental Protection. (US) **1953**
Environmental Protection Agency Pesticide Label File see E P A Pesticide Label File **1852**
Environmental Protection Agency Policy Alert see E P A Policy Alert **1947**
Environmental Protection in Transportation (Water Transport Edition). see Jiaotong Huanbao (Shuiyun Ban) **1959**
Environmental Protection Report see National Environmental Enforcement Journal **1963**
†Environmental Protection: The Legal Framework. (US) **5187**
Environmental Quality Abstracts see Biology Digest **462**
Environmental Radiation Surveillance in Washington State. Annual Report. (US ISSN 0509-769X) **1953**, 4100
Environmental Radioactivity Annual Report see New Zealand. Department of Health. National Radiation Laboratory. Environmental Radioactivity Annual Report **1964**
Environmental Radioactivity at Risoe see Environmental Radioactivity in Denmark **3817**
Environmental Radioactivity in Denmark. (DK ISSN 0106-407X) **3817**
Environmental Radioactivity in Greenland. (DK ISSN 0108-0962) **3817**
Environmental Radioactivity in the Faroes. (DK ISSN 0107-9069) **3817**
Environmental Regulations from the State Capitols. (US) **1953**
Environmental Research. (US ISSN 0013-9351) **1953**
Environmental Research in Japan. (JA) **1953**
▼Environmental Resource Economics. (NE ISSN 0924-6460) **1953**, 664, 1487
Environmental Review see Environmental History Review **1951**
▼Environmental Safety Alert. (US) **1953**
Environmental Safety Digest. (US) **1953**
Environmental Sanitation Abstracts - Low Cost Options. (TH ISSN 0125-2186) **1953**, 1974
Environmental Sanitation Reviews. (TH ISSN 0125-5088) **1953**
Environmental Science & Engineering. (CN) **1953**
Environmental Science and Forestry Year) see E S F (Year) **2098**
Environmental Science & Technology. (US ISSN 0013-936X) **1953**

Environmental Science and Technology: A Wiley-Interscience Series of Texts and Monographs. (US ISSN 0194-0287) **1953**, 4597
Environmental Sciences and Engineering Notes see E S E Notes **1947**
Environmental Software. (UK ISSN 0266-9838) **1975**, 1477, 1879
Environmental Spectrum. (US ISSN 0013-9386) **1953**
Environmental Statutes. (US ISSN 0736-573X) **1953**, 2623
Environmental Technology. (UK) **1954**
Environmental Technology Letters see Environmental Technology **1954**
Environmental Telephone Directory. (US) **1954**, 1134
▼Environmental Testing and Analysis. (US) **1954**
Environmental Topics. (US ISSN 1046-5294) **1954**
Environmental Toxicology and Chemistry. (US ISSN 0730-7268) **1981**, 476, 4100
Environmental Toxicology and Water Quality. (US ISSN 1053-4725) **1981**, 4824
Environmental Waste Management. (US) **1984**
Environmental Watch. (US) **1954**
Environmentalist. (UK ISSN 0251-1088) **1954**
Environmentarian. (US) **2125**
Environments. (CN ISSN 0711-6780) **1954**, 2487
Environments. see Svivot **1969**
▼Environmetrics. (UK ISSN 1180-4009) **1954**
Environnement. (CN) **1954**
Environs. (US) **1954**
Envoi. (US ISSN 0897-4888) **2914**, 2360
Envoi. (UK ISSN 0013-9394) **2992**
Envol/Flight. (CN ISSN 0707-7165) **563**
Envoy (New York). (US) **2992**
Envoy (Pittsburgh). (US ISSN 0013-9408) **4176**, 4020
Envoy (San Diego). (US) **1311**
Envoy (Washington) see C U A Magazine **1306**
Enzyme. (SZ ISSN 0013-9432) **476**, 3253
Enzyme and Microbial Technology. (US ISSN 0141-0229) **551**
Enzyme Engineering. (US ISSN 0094-8500) **476**
†Enzyme Isolation and Purification. (UK ISSN 0261-4626) **5187**
Enzyme Regulation. (UK ISSN 0142-8071) **476**
Enzymologia see Molecular and Cellular Biochemistry **480**
Eolika Grammata. see Lettres Eoliennes **2932**
Eos. (SP ISSN 0013-9440) **532**
Eos. (US ISSN 0096-3941) **1588**
Eos. (PL ISSN 0012-7825) **2812**
Eos. (IT ISSN 0392-6699) **3185**, 3725
Eotu. (US) **2914**
Eotvos Lorand Geophysical Institute of Hungary. Annual Report/Magyar Allami Eotvos Lorand Geofizikai Intezet evi Jelentese. (HU ISSN 0524-8655) **1588**
Epanouir. (FR) **1735**, 4404
Epatologia. (IT ISSN 0013-9475) **3096**
Ephemera News. (US) **4127**
Ephemerides Iuris Canonici. (IT ISSN 0013-9491) **4264**
Ephemerides Liturgicae. (IT ISSN 0013-9505) **4176**
Ephemerides Liturgicae. Collectio Subsidia. (IT) **4176**
Ephemerides Mariologicae. (SP ISSN 0425-1466) **4264**
Ephemerides of the Faint Satellites of Jupiter and Saturn. (FR ISSN 0769-1041) **364**
Ephemerides of the Satellites of Jupiter, Saturn and Uranus. (FR) **364**
Ephemerides Theologicae Lovanienses. (BE ISSN 0013-9513) **4264**, 2310
Ephemeris. (AT) **364**

†Ephemeris of the Sun, Polaris and Other Selected Stars with Companion Data and Tables. (US ISSN 0071-0962) **5187**
Epi-Gram. (US) **4100**
Epicerie Francaise. (FR) **2091**
L'Epicier. (CN ISSN 0013-9521) **2091**
Epicier. see Kruidenier **2093**
Epicurean. (AT ISSN 0013-9548) **2066**, 380
Epicurean Revue. (US ISSN 0895-738X) **2473**, 4761
Epidecides Lunaires/Lunar Epidecis. (FR ISSN 0240-8376) **364**
Epidemiologia Cientifica: Teoria y Practica. (EC) **3096**, 3320
Epidemiologic Reviews. (US ISSN 0193-936X) **3096**
Epidemiological Bulletin. (CE) **3096**, 4100
Epidemiological Surveillance of Rabies for the Americas. (UN) **4809**, 4100
Epidemiologija, Mikrobiologija i Infekciozni Bolesti. (BU ISSN 0425-1482) **3219**
Epidemiology. (US ISSN 1044-3983) **3096**
Epidemiology and Infection. (UK ISSN 0950-2688) **3219**
Epidemiology Monitor. (US ISSN 0744-0898) **3096**
Epigraphia Indica. (II ISSN 0013-9564) **271**
Epigraphic Society. Occasional Papers. (US) **271**, 2812
Epigraphic Society. Occasional Publications see Epigraphic Society. Occasional Papers **271**
Epigraphica. (IT ISSN 0013-9572) **271**
Epigraphica Anatolica. (GW ISSN 0174-6545) **2360**
Epigraphische Studien. (GW ISSN 0071-0989) **2310**
Epikaira. (GR) **2196**
Epikeri/Current Affairs. (CY) **2184**
Epilepsi. (DK ISSN 0107-2668) **3336**
Epilepsia. (US ISSN 0013-9580) **3336**
Epilepsie. (SZ) **3336**
Epilepsie. (FR) **3336**
†Epilepsy. (UK ISSN 0261-4634) **5187**
Epilepsy Research. (NE ISSN 0920-1211) **3336**, 3725
Epilepsy Today. (UK) **3336**
Epiletter. (AT ISSN 0729-7823) **4404**, 1683, 3336
Epilogi/Choice: economic review. (GR ISSN 1105-2503) **777**
Epimenides/Epimenis. (FR ISSN 0240-8368) **364**, 1604
Epimenis. see Epimenides **364**
Epiphany Journal. (US ISSN 0273-6969) **4176**
Epiphyllum Bulletin. (US) **501**
Epirotiki Estia. (GR ISSN 0021-0765) **2360**
Episcopal Clerical Directory. (US) **4236**
Episcopal Diocese of Connecticut. Historiographer see Historiographer **5205**
Episcopal Peace Fellowship Newsletter see E P F Newsletter **4236**
Episcopal Recorder. (US ISSN 0013-9610) **4236**
†Episcopalian. (US ISSN 0013-9629) **5187**
Episimos Ephemeris tis Kyriakes Demokratias/Official Gazette for the Sunday Democrats. (CY) **2184**
Episkopet see Kirkens Undervisning **4187**
Episodes (Herndon). (US ISSN 0705-3797) **1560**
▼Episodes (New York). (US) **1373**
Episteme. (NE) **4309**
Epistemologia. (IT) **3765**
Epistimoniki Epetirida tis Filosofikis Scholis Tmima Filologias see Aristotle University of Thessaloniki. School of Philosophy. Philology Department. Scientific Yearbook **2804**
Epistimoniki Epiteris Kteniatrikis Scholis.(GR) **4809**

Epites- Epiteszettudomany/Building and Architectural Science. (HU ISSN 0013-9661) **617**, 299
Epites es Kozlekedestudomanyi Kozlemenyek see Epites-Epiteszettudomany **617**
Epitesugyi Ertesito. (HU ISSN 0133-6436) **617**, 2623
Epitesugyi Szemle. (HU ISSN 0013-967X) **617**
†Epithelia. (UK ISSN 0269-4565) **5187**
▼Epithelial Cell Biology. (US) **524**
Epitheoresis Synkoinoniakou Dikaiou. (GR) **4649**
Epitheorisis Ethnikis Amynis/National Defense Revue. (GR) **3457**
Epitheorisis Koinonikon Erevnon. see Greek Review of Social Research **4373**
Epitoanyag. (HU ISSN 0013-970X) **617**
La Epoca. (CL) **2180**
Epoca. (IT ISSN 0013-9718) **2205**
Epoca. (PY ISSN 0013-9726) **2914**, 4633
Epoch (Adairsville). (US) **3765**
Epoch (Ithaca). (US ISSN 0145-1391) **2914**, 2992
Epoche. (US ISSN 4176, 2310
Epokha. (RU) **3892**
Eprouvette see Defisicence **1310**
†Epsilon Letter. (US) **5187**
†Epsilon Marketing Letter. (US) **5187**
†Epsilon Non-Profit Letter. (US) **5187**
Epson LifeBoat. (US) **1469**
†Epson Today. (US ISSN 0830-9434) **5187**
Epuletgepeszet. (HU ISSN 0013-9742) **617**
Epworth Review. (UK) **4236**
Eqtesad-e-Melli. (IR) **978**
Equal Credit Opportunity Manual (Supplement). (US) **777**
Equal Employment Opportunity. Annual Program. (US) **3941**
Equal Employment Opportunity Commission Compliance Manual see E E O C Compliance Manual **977**
Equal Employment Opportunity Compliance Manual see E E O Compliance Manual **977**
Equal Employment Opportunity Report see U.S. Equal Employment Opportunity Commission. Annual Report **996**
Equal Employment Opportunity Report see E E O Report **5183**
Equal Opportunities International. (UK ISSN 0261-0159) **4859**, 3941
Equal Opportunities Review. (UK ISSN 0268-7143) **979**
Equal Opportunity. (US) **2000**, 3627
Equal Opportunity in Higher Education see School Law News **1731**
Equal Opportunity: The Minority Student Magazine see Equal Opportunity **2000**
Equal Rights. (US) **4841**, 3941
Equal Time Newspaper. (US) **2452**
Equality N O W! (National Organization for Women) (US) **4841**
Equality News. (CN) **2000**
Equals One. (II ISSN 0013-9815) **2199**
Equestrian Trade News. (UK) **4533**
Equestrian Trails. (US ISSN 0013-9831) **4533**
†Equestrian Year. (UK ISSN 0260-8111) **5187**
Equilife. (CN) **4533**
†Equine Abstracts. (GW ISSN 0176-8018) **5187**
Equine Athlete. (US ISSN 1047-8620) **4809**, 4533
Equine Behaviour. (UK) **4534**
Equine Business Journal. (US) **4534**, 664
Equine Employment and Education Guide. (CN ISSN 0836-1355) **4534**
Equine Images. (US) **325**
Equine Medicine. (US) **4809**, 231
Equine Practice. (US ISSN 0162-8941) **4809**
Equine Research Centre Newsletter. (CN ISSN 0835-5509) **4809**, 4534

Equine Sportsmedicine News see Journal of Equine Veterinary Science **4811**
Equine Times. (US) **4534**
Equine Veterinary Data. (US ISSN 0739-9065) **4809**
Equine Veterinary Education. (UK ISSN 0957-7734) **4809**, 1749
Equine Veterinary Journal. (UK ISSN 0425-1644) **4809**
▼Equine Welfare. (UK) **4534**
Equinews see Enterprise (New York) **2531**
Equinews. (CN ISSN 0828-864X) **4534**, 4809
Equinox. (US) **2452**
Equinox. (CN ISSN 0710-9911) **4761**
Equinoxe. (FR ISSN 0765-5320) **2039**
Equip H see Guia del Equipamiento Hospitalario **2522**
Equip' Hotel. (FR) **2473**
Equipack. (SP ISSN 0212-5226) **3648**
L'Equipe. (FR) **4471**
†Equipe. (BL ISSN 0046-239X) **5187**
Equipe de Odontologia Sanitaria. Boletim. (BL) **3233**
Equipement Industriel-Achats et Entretien see Achats et Entretien - Equipement Industriel **1032**
Equipement Mecanique, Carrieres et Materiaux see Le Moniteur - Materiels et Chantiers **625**
Equipes St Vincent. (FR ISSN 0763-5184) **4404**, 4264
†Equipment Connection. (CN) **5187**
Equipment Construction. (BE) **617**
Equipment Data Base. (US) **1891**, 1789
Equipment des Jardins see Market **2560**
Equipment Directory of Audio-Visual, Computer and Video Products. (US ISSN 0884-2124) **1134**, 1335, 1385, 1395
Equipment Echoes. (US ISSN 0897-5159) **617**, 2405, 3483
Equipment Guide News see Equipment Today **617**
Equipment Journal. (CN) **617**
Equipment Leasing & Asset-Based Borrowing Report. (US ISSN 1051-6573) **750**
Equipment Leasing Newsletter. (US) **2623**, 1038, 1075
Equipment Maintenance and Qualification Newsletter see Nuclear Plant Maintenance Newsletter **1808**
Equipment Management. (US ISSN 0733-3056) **3017**
Equipment Manufacturers Institute. First of the Week Newsletter. (US) **161**, 1075, 3017
Equipment Manufacturers Institute. Retail Sales Reports. (US) **161**, 1075, 3017
Equipment Manufacturers Institute. State of the Industry. (US) **161**, 1075, 3017
Equipment Review see Clothing Machinery Times **3016**
Equipment Today. (US ISSN 0891-141X) **617**
Equipment World. (US ISSN 1057-7262) **3017**, 1038
Equipo see Guia de la Industria: Equipo y Aparatos **3017**
Equipo Domestico - Electrodomesticos. (SP) **2558**
Equipos Productos Industriales. (US) **1134**
Equipos y Productos. Biomedicina. (CU) **3096**
Equipos y Productos. Tecnologia. (CU) **4597**
Equipotel. (PO) **2473**
Equipping Youth. (US ISSN 0196-0911) **4236**, 1236
Equitable Distribution Journal. (US ISSN 0743-247X) **2623**
Equitable Distribution of Property. (US) **2623**, 4148
Equities. (US) **945**
†Equities. (UK) **5187**
Equities International see Equities **5187**

EQUITY

Equity and Choice. (US ISSN 0882-3863) **1727**
Equity & Excellence. (US ISSN 0894-0681) **1632**
Equity International. (UK) **945**, 777
Equity Investment Strategy Report. (US) **945**
Equity Journal. (UK) **4633**
Equity News. (US ISSN 0013-9890) **4633**
Equivalences. (BE) **2812**
Equivalences. see Equivalencias **2992**
Equivalencias/Equivalences. (SP ISSN 0211-8181) **2992**
Equofinality. (UK) **2992**
Equus. (US ISSN 0149-0672) **4534**, 582, 4809
Era. (IT ISSN 0046-2403) **2865**
Era. (FI ISSN 0356-3464) **4545**
†Era of Arnold Bennett. (US) **5187**
Era Socialista. (RM) **3892**, 4434
Eramies. (FI) **4545**
Eranos. (SW ISSN 0013-9947) **2812**
Erasmus Directory. (EI) **1676**, 1706
Erasmus in English. (CN ISSN 0071-1063) **2506**
Erasmus of Rotterdam Society Yearbook. (US ISSN 0276-2854) **4176**, 2360, 3765
Erasmus Studies. (CN ISSN 0318-3319) **2506**
Erasmus Universiteit, Rotterdam. Centrum voor Maatschappijgeschiedenis. Mededelingen/Information Bulletin. (NE) **4434**
Erba d'Arno. (IT ISSN 0394-5618) **2914**, 2310
Erba d'Arno. Quaderni. (IT ISSN 1120-4923) **2914**, 2310
Erbe und Auftrag. (GW ISSN 0013-9963) **4264**
L'Erborista. (IT ISSN 0394-8196) **3725**, 2125
Erboristeria Domani. (IT) **3605**
Ercilla. (CL ISSN 0013-9971) **2180**
Ercole Marelli. (IT) **1891**
Die Erde. (GW ISSN 0013-9998) **2247**
Erdem. (TU) **2000**
Erdeyi Figyelo. (RM) **2215**
Erdinger Land. (GW) **2360**
Erdkreis. (GW ISSN 0014-0007) **2189**
Erdkunde. (GW ISSN 0014-0015) **2247**
Erdkundliches Wissen. (GW ISSN 0425-1741) **2247**
Az Erdo. (HU ISSN 0014-0031) **2098**
Erdoel. (AU) **3685**
Erdoel-Erdgas see Erdoel - Erdgas - Kohle **3685**
Erdoel - Erdgas - Kohle. (GW ISSN 0179-3187) **3685**
Erdoel-Informationsdienst. (GW ISSN 0343-6705) **1789**, 3685
Erdoel und Kohle, Erdgas, Petrochemie.(GW ISSN 0014-0058) **3685**, 1852, 3483
Erdogazdasag es Faipar. (HU ISSN 0014-0066) **2114**
Erdstall. (GW) **271**
Erdwissenschaftliche Forschung. (GW ISSN 0170-3188) **1543**
Erehwon. (US) **2992**
Eretz. (IS ISSN 0334-9578) **2203**
Eretz-Israel. Archaeological, Historical and Geographical Studies. (IS ISSN 0071-108X) **271**, 2247, 2338
Erfahrungsheilkunde/Acta Medica Empirica. (GW ISSN 0014-0082) **3096**
Erfinder und Neuheitendienst. (GW) **3674**
Erfolg. (GW ISSN 0343-6691) **1058**
Erfolgreich Heimwerken. (GW) **617**
Erfolgsberater see E B **659**
Das Erfrischungsgetraenk - Mineralwasser-Zeitung. (GW) **380**
Ergatiki Phoni/Worker's Voice. (CY) **979**
Ergatiko Vima/Worker's Herald. (CY) **979**
Ergebnisse der Inneren Medizin und Kinderheilkunde. New Series/ Advances in Internal Medicine and Pediatrics. (US ISSN 0071-111X) **3096**, 3320

Ergebnisse der Limnologie/Advances in Limnology. (GW ISSN 0071-1128) **1597**, 438
Ergebnisse der Mathematik und Ihrer Grenzgebiete. Neue Folge. (US ISSN 0071-1136) **3035**
†Ergebnisse der Plasmaphysik und der Gaselektronik. Schriftenreihe. (GW) **5187**
Ergebnisse und Fortschritte der Zoologie see Fortschritte der Zoologie **583**
Ergo! (US) **2865**
Ergodic Theory and Dynamical Systems.(UK ISSN 0143-3857) **3035**
Ergonomia. (PL ISSN 0137-4990) **4309**
Ergonomia. (HU ISSN 0014-0120) **4434**
Ergonomics. (UK ISSN 0014-0139) **1821**, 4020
Ergonomics Abstracts. (UK ISSN 0046-2446) **1843**, 11, 4051
Ergoterapeuten. (DK ISSN 0105-8282) **3096**
Erhverskvinders Klub Bladet see E K-Bladet **659**
Erhverssprog. (DK ISSN 0107-9166) **2812**, 664
†Erhvervfremmende og Forbrugerpolitiske Foranstaltninger. (DK ISSN 0105-5992) **5187**
Erhvervs-Bladet. (DK ISSN 0014-0155) **1075**
Erhvervs-Jordbruget. (DK) **88**
Erhvervs-Orientering Stat Amt, Kommune. (DK ISSN 0109-9310) **664**
Erhvervsfrugtavleren see Frugtavleren **178**
Erhvervshistorisk Aarbog (year). (DK) **2360**
Erhvervslederen (Frederiksberg, 1981). (DK ISSN 0108-3775) **664**
Erhvervslederen (Frederiksberg, 1984). (DK ISSN 0109-792X) **664**
Erhvervslivets A B C - Danmarks 20000 Stoerste Virksomheder - Company A B C - Denmark's 20000 Largest Companies see Danmarks 15000 Stoerste Virksomheder **1128**
Erhvervsnoeglen. (DK ISSN 0105-6662) **1683**
Eria. (SP) **2247**
†Eric - Crier Newsletter. (US ISSN 0014-0163) **5187**
Erich /Schmidt Verlag GmbH & Co. (Bielefeld) Sortimenter Informationen Recht - Wirtschaft - Technik - Umwelt - Philologie see E S V Sortimenter Informationen Recht - Wirtschaft - Technik - Umwelt - Philologie **4127**
Erich Schmidt Verlag Programmbereiche Philologie-Volkskunde- Geschichte see E S V Programmbereiche Philologie-Volkskunde- Geschichte **5183**
Ericsson Review. (SW ISSN 0014-0171) **1362**
Erie & Chautauqua Magazine. (US) **2225**
Erie County Farm News see Farm News of Erie and Wyoming Counties **90**
Erie Motorist. (US) **4761**
Erinnophilie International. (GW) **3752**
Erinnyen. (GW ISSN 0179-163X) **3765**
Eriu. (IE) **2914**
Erkenntnis. (NE ISSN 0165-0106) **3765**
Erkennungsblaetter. (GW ISSN 0421-3750) **3457**
Erkrankungen der Zootiere. (GW ISSN 0138-5003) **4809**
Erlanger Bausteine zur Fraenkischen Heimatforschung. (GW) **2310**, 399, 501
Erlanger Geologische Abhandlungen. (GW ISSN 0071-1160) **1560**
Ermlandbriefe. (GW ISSN 0014-0201) **4176**
Ernaehrungs Umschau. (GW ISSN 0340-2371) **3605**
Ernaehrungsdienst. (GW ISSN 0014-0228) **205**, 3605
Ernaehrungsforschung. (GW ISSN 0071-1179) **3605**

Die Ernaehrungsindustrie. (GW ISSN 0343-9704) **2066**
Ernaehrungsrundbrief. (GW ISSN 0721-5118) **3605**
Ernaehrungswirtschaft (Graelfing). (GW) **2091**
Ernaeringsnyt. (DK ISSN 0109-3290) **2066**
Ernest Bloch Lectures. (US ISSN 0071-1187) **1706**
Ernest Bloch Society. Bulletin. (US) **3550**
Ernest Bloch Society. Newsletter see Ernest Bloch Society. Bulletin **3550**
Erneuerung in Kirche und Gesellschaft. (GW ISSN 0171-6204) **4236**, 4264
Erneuerung und Abwehr. (GW) **4236**
Ernie Mills' Legislative Report. (US) **4059**
Ernst & Young Financial Planning Reporter. (US) **945**, 1093
Ernst-Mach-Institut, Freiburg. Bericht. (GW ISSN 0340-8833) **4309**
Ernst-Mach-Institut, Freiburg. Wissenschaftlicher Bericht see Ernst-Mach-Institut, Freiburg. Bericht **4309**
†Ernst-Moritz-Arndt-Universitaet Greifswald. Wissenschaftliche Zeitschrift. Gesellschaftswissenschaftliche Reihe.(GW ISSN 0138-1016) **5187**
†Ernst-Moritz-Arndt-Universitaet Greifswald. Wissenschaftliche Zeitschrift. Mathematisch-Naturwissenschaftliche Reihe. (GW ISSN 0138-2853) **5187**
†Ernst-Moritz-Arndt-Universitaet Greifswald. Wissenschaftliche Zeitschrift. Medizinische Reihe. (GW ISSN 0138-1067) **5187**
Ernstia. (VE ISSN 0252-8274) **501**
Eroeffnungen. (AU ISSN 0014-0252) **2914**
Erotic Fiction Quarterly. (US ISSN 0887-5057) **2914**
Erotic Writer's and Collector's Market. (US) **4127**, 3397, 4841
Erotic X-Film Guide. (US) **3397**
Errant News. (US ISSN 1049-4782) **325**, 271, 4176
Erre U. (IT ISSN 0014-0260) **3892**
Error Trends Coin Magazine. (US) **3599**
Errorgram see Errorscope **3599**
Errorscope. (US) **3599**
Die Ersatzkasse. (GW ISSN 0014-0279) **4404**, 3801
Ersatzkassen-Report. (GW ISSN 0170-2793) **979**
Ertekezesek a Torteneti Tudomanyok Korebol. (HU ISSN 0071-1233) **2310**
Ertong Chuangzhao/Children's Creation.(CC) **1632**, 1254
Ertong Dashijie/Children's Big World. (CC) **1254**
Ertong Gushi Huabao/Children's Story Pictorial. (CC) **1254**
Ertong Huabao/Children's Pictorial. (CC) **1254**
Ertong Manhua/Children's Cartoon. (CC) **325**
Ertong Shidai/Children's Epoch. (CC ISSN 0423-3174) **1254**
Ertong Wenxue/Children's Literature. (CC ISSN 0257-6562) **1254**
Ertong Wenxue Xuankan/Selected Writings - Children's Literature. (CC) **1254**
Ertong Xiaoshuo/Short Stories for Children. (CC) **1254**, 2914
Ertong Yinyue/Children's Music. (US) **3550**, 1254
Ertragsbilanz der Schweiz see Zahlungsbilanz der Schweiz **1112**
Eruul Mend/Health. (MP) **3801**, 4100
Erwachsenenbildung in Oesterreich. (AU) **1683**, 1727
Erweckliche Stimme. (GW) **4236**
Erwerbsgaertner see Deutscher Gartenbau **2125**
Erwerbsobstbau. (GW ISSN 0014-0309) **2125**
Erythrocytes. (UK) **3271**

Erzieherbrief. (GW ISSN 0939-7507) **3956**
Erziehung und Unterricht. (AU ISSN 0014-0325) **1632**
Erziehung und Unterricht. (SZ ISSN 0071-125X) **1632**
Erziehung und Wissenschaft. (GW ISSN 0342-0671) **1632**
Erziehung und Wissenschaft Niedersachsen. (GW ISSN 0170-0723) **1632**, 2582
Erziehungs- und Schulgeschichte Jahrbuch. (GW ISSN 0075-2622) **1632**
Erziehungskunst. (GW ISSN 0014-0333) **1632**
Erzmetall. (GW ISSN 0044-2658) **3405**, 3483
Esakia. (JA ISSN 0071-1268) **532**
Esalen Catalog. (US) **4020**
Esbou Al-Riadi. (SY) **4471**
Escala. (CK) **299**
Escale. (FR) **4727**
Escalpelo. (PR ISSN 0014-0341) **1311**, 3096
Escandalo. (MX) **2983**
Escaparate Farmaceutico. (SP) **3725**
Escape. (UK ISSN 0266-1667) **2915**, 325
Escape Committee see Escape: The Career Change Magazine **3627**
Escape Magazine. (US) **2225**
Escape: The Career Change Magazine. (UK ISSN 0951-1806) **3627**
Escapees. (US) **4690**, 4545, 4761
Escapees Club. Annual Directory. (US) **4690**, 4545
Escarabajo de Oro. (AG) **2865**
Escarbica Journal see E S A R B I C A Journal **2756**
▼Escenarios. (AG) **3550**
Eschew Obfuscation Review. (US) **2992**
Esclavage. (FR) **4404**
Escoba. (BO) **4841**
Escoge la Vida! (US) **3982**, 4264, 4404
Escola de Agronomia da Amazonia. Boletim see Faculdade de Ciencias Agrarias do Para. Boletim **89**
Escola Superior de Agricultura "Luiz de Queiroz". Anais. (BL ISSN 0071-1276) **88**
†Escola Superior de Agricultura "Luiz de Queiroz". Boletim de Divulgacao. (BL ISSN 0071-1292) **5187**
El Escribano. (US ISSN 0014-0376) **2405**
Escrime. see Fechten **4472**
Escritos. (CK ISSN 0120-1263) **2915**, 3765
Escritura: Teoria y Critica Literarias. (VE ISSN 1011-7989) **2915**
Escuela de Administracion y Finanzas y Tecnologias Revista Universidad E A F I T see Revista Universidad E A F I T **1026**
Escuela de Gerentes de Cooperativas. Cartillas de Cooperacion. (SP ISSN 0084-5132) **1075**
Escuela de Gerentes de Cooperativas. Coleccion Textos. (SP ISSN 0084-5159) **1075**
Escuela de Gerentes de Cooperativas. Cuadernos de Practicas. (SP ISSN 0084-5167) **1075**
Escuela de Gerentes de Cooperativas. Serie Especial. (SP ISSN 0084-5175) **1075**
Escuela Tecnica Superior de Ingenieros de Montes. Biblioteca. Boletin Bibliografico y Documental see Escuela Tecnica Superior de Ingenieros de Montes. Biblioteca. Boletin Bibliografico y Documental. Informacion Forestal. Serie B: Publicaciones Periodicas **2112**
Escuela Tecnica Superior de Ingenieros de Montes. Biblioteca. Boletin Bibliografico y Documental. Informacion Forestal. Serie A: Monografias. (SP ISSN 0212-226X) **2112**, 438, 1821
Escuela Tecnica Superior de Ingenieros de Montes. Biblioteca. Boletin Bibliografico y Documental. Informacion Forestal. Serie B: Publicaciones Periodicas. (SP ISSN 0212-2278) **2112**, 438, 1821

Escutcheon. (AT ISSN 0046-2489) **2149**
Eselsohr. (AU) **2915**
Eskimo. (CN ISSN 0318-7551) **4264**, 2000
Eso - Etimos/Ever - Ready. (CY) **2184**
Eso Monographs. (US) **3096**
Esopo. (IT) **4127**
Esotera. (GW ISSN 0003-2921) **3594**, 3669
Esoteric Review. (US ISSN 0741-8795) **3669**
†Esoteric Science Journal. (UK) **5187**
Esoterica. (IT) **358**
†Esoterik-Almanach. (GW ISSN 0931-3818) **5187**
Esoterik und Wissenschaft. (GW ISSN 0170-4249) **3669**
Espace Bureau. (FR ISSN 1148-5566) **1058**
Espace Geographique. (FR ISSN 0046-2497) **2247**
Espace Rural. (FR ISSN 0764-7557) **88**
Espace 90. (FR) **1954**
Espaces - Populations - Societes. (FR ISSN 0755-7809) **3982**, 2247
Espaces Tropicaux. (FR) **2247**
Espaces Verts. (CN ISSN 0846-5339) **2125**
Espacio de Critica e Investigacion Teatral. (AG) **4633**
Espacios de Critica y Produccion. (AG) **3765**
L'Espagne. (FR) **815**
Espana Agricola y Ganadera. (SP ISSN 0213-3792) **216**
Espana Hostelera y Turistica. (SP) **4761**, 2473
Espana - Sus Monumentos y Artes; Su Naturaleza e Historia. (SP) **2360**
Espanol Actual. (SP ISSN 0425-2772) **2812**
Espansione. (IT ISSN 0014-0554) **1075**
Esparavel. (CK ISSN 0014-0562) **2992**
Espasa Universitaria. Filosofia y Pensamiento. (SP) **3765**
Especial Labores. (SP) **3591**
Especialidades Odontologicas. (BL) **3233**, 3725
Especialist. (BL ISSN 0102-7077) **2812**
El Espectacular. (US) **1373**, 3508, 3550
Esperanta Ligilo. (FR ISSN 0014-0600) **2292**
†Der Esperantist. (GW ISSN 0014-0619) **5187**
Esperantist's Magazine. see Pola Esperantisto **2834**
Esperanto. (NE ISSN 0014-0635) **2812**, 2865, 3956
Esperanto-Actualites see Revue Francaise d'Esperanto **2838**
Esperanto Documents. (US ISSN 0165-2575) **2812**
Esperanto Documents. New Series see Esperanto-Dokumentoj. Nova Serio **2812**
Esperanto-Dokumentoj. Nova Serio. (NE ISSN 0165-2524) **2812**, 3956, 4434
Esperanto en Skotlando. (UK ISSN 0014-0643) **2812**
Esperanto - Interlangue Universelle. (FR ISSN 0046-2500) **2812**
Esperanto - Lingvo Internacia. (FR ISSN 0014-066X) **2812**
†Esperanto Lobby News. (UK) **5187**
Esperanto News see La Brita Esperantisto **2806**
Esperanto - Nytt. (NO ISSN 0802-0442) **2812**, 1749
Esperanto Teacher. (UK ISSN 0046-2527) **2812**
Esperanto - U S A. (US) **2812**, 1237
Esperienza. (IT ISSN 0014-0678) **4405**
Esperienze e Progetti. (IT) **1632**
Esperienze Letterarie. (IT) **2865**
Espero. (SW ISSN 0014-0694) **2813**
Espial Canadian Data Base Directory. (CN) **1404**, 11, 2797
Espiritu. (SP ISSN 0014-0716) **3766**, 4176
L'Espoir du Monde. (SZ ISSN 0014-0732) **3892**

†Esportare. (IT) **5187**
Esportazione. (IT ISSN 0014-0740) **906**
Espresso. (IT ISSN 0423-4243) **2205**
Espresso. (GW) **3892**
Esprit. (FR ISSN 0014-0759) **2865**
Esprit. (GW) **3892**
Esprit Createur. (US ISSN 0014-0767) **2915**
†Esprit de Corps. (SA) **5187**
Esprit et Liberte see Esquisse d'Une Philosophie de la Religion **4237**
Esprit et Vie. (FR ISSN 0014-0775) **4176**
Esprit Libre. (FR ISSN 0014-0783) **4020**, 1632, 3801
Esprit Saint. (FR ISSN 0396-969X) **4176**
Esqui Acuatico y Otros Deportes. (VE) **4545**
Esquimalt Lookout. (CN) **3457**
Esquire. (GW) **2551**, 1290
Esquire (1979). (US ISSN 0194-9535) **3397**
Esquire Fortnightly see Esquire (1979) **3397**
Esquisse d'Une Philosophie de la Religion. (FR) **4237**
Essais de Dialectologie Interlinguale. (NE) **2813**
Essais Philosophiques. (BE ISSN 0071-1349) **3766**
Essay and General Literature Index. (US ISSN 0014-083X) **2981**, 11
Essay Proof Journal. (US ISSN 0014-0848) **3752**
Essays and Monographs in Colorado History. (US ISSN 0899-0409) **2405**
Essays and Studies. (US ISSN 0071-1357) **2915**
Essays by Divers Hands. (US ISSN 0261-216X) **2915**
Essays for the Third Century. (US) **3892**, 2405
Essays in Arts and Sciences. (US ISSN 0361-5634) **4309**, 2506
Essays in Biochemistry. (US ISSN 0071-1365) **476**
Essays in Chemistry. (US ISSN 0071-1373) **1177**
Essays in Church History in Hungary. see Magyar Egyhaztorteneti Vazlatok **2374**
Essays in Criticism. (UK ISSN 0014-0856) **2915**
Essays in Economic and Business History. (US ISSN 0896-226X) **894**
Essays in Foreign Languages and Literature see Language and Culture **2823**
Essays in Graham Greene. (US ISSN 0738-0763) **2915**
Essays in History. (US ISSN 0071-1411) **2310**
Essays in International Finance. (US ISSN 0071-142X) **777**
Essays in Literature. (US ISSN 0094-5404) **2915**
†Essays in Physics. (US ISSN 0071-1438) **5188**
Essays in Poetics. (UK ISSN 0308-888X) **2915**, 4633
Essays in Public Works History. (US) **4059**, 2310
Essays in Theatre. (CN ISSN 0821-4425) **4633**
Essays on Asian Theater, Music and Dance. (US) **4633**, 1530, 3550
Essays on Canadian Writing. (CN ISSN 0316-0300) **2915**
Essays on Fantastic Literature. (US ISSN 0891-9593) **3011**, 2915
†Essays on Modern Music. (US) **5188**
Essays on the Economy and Society of the Sudan. (SJ) **864**, 2218, 4371
Essecome. (IT ISSN 0394-8625) **1526**
Essen und Trinken. (GW) **2066**, 380, 2446, 4841
Essence (New York). (US ISSN 0014-0880) **4841**, 2000
Essence (Wayne). (US) **2865**
Essences of Japan. see Kokka **332**
Essendon Gazette. (AT) **2171**
Essener Universitaetsberichte. (GW ISSN 0935-3658) **4309**

Essentia. (US) **3669**
Essential Articles. (US ISSN 0071-1470) **2915**
Essential News for Kids. (US) **1254**
Essentials. (UK ISSN 0953-6337) **4841**, 2446
Essentials of Adolescence. (US) **4020**
L'Essentiel. (CN) **4841**
Essenze-Derivati Agrumari. (IT ISSN 0014-0902) **1218**
Essere. (IT) **3766**, 3669
Essex Countryside. (UK ISSN 0014-0910) **2194**
Essex County Medical Society. Bulletin. (US ISSN 0014-0937) **3096**
†Essex Education. (UK) **5188**
Essex Family Historian. (UK ISSN 0140-7503) **2149**
Essex Farmer. (UK) **88**
Essex Farmers Journal see Essex Farmer **88**
Essex Genealogist. (US ISSN 0279-067X) **2149**
Essex Institute Historical Collections. (US ISSN 0014-0953) **2310**, 2149
Essex Journal. (UK ISSN 0014-0961) **271**, 2360
Essex Naturalist. (UK ISSN 0071-1489) **438**
Essex Naturalists' Trust Bulletin see Watch Over Essex **1499**
†Essex Recusant. (UK) **5188**
Essex Review see Essex Journal **271**
Essex Review of Children's Literature. (UK ISSN 0144-4816) **1237**
Essex Union List of Serials. (UK ISSN 0305-3679) **399**
Esso in Malaysia. (MY) **3685**
Esso Italiana. Informazioni Economiche see Argomenti Esso **3682**
Essobron. (NE ISSN 0014-1046) **3685**
Essor. (FR ISSN 1152-6963) **906**
Essor de l'Electricite et de l'Electronique.(FR) **1891**, 2582
Essor de la Quincaillerie. (FR) **642**
Essor des Jeunes. (CM) **4264**
Essor du Comminges. (FR ISSN 0014-1062) **3892**
Essor Economique et Commercial. (FR ISSN 0012-8015) **664**
Essor Francais du Commerce Exterieur/French Foreign Trade Directory. (FR) **906**
Essor Rural. (UV) **150**
Est et Ouest. (FR ISSN 0014-1267) **3956**
Est - Ovest. (IT ISSN 0046-256X) **864**, 3956
Est Sesia. (IT ISSN 0014-1100) **176**
Establecimientos Manufactureras en Puerto Rico. (PR) **714**, 4570
Estacion Experimental de Aula Dei. Anales. (SP ISSN 0365-1800) **176**, 501
Estacion Experimental Region Agropecuaria Pergamino. Informe Tecnico. (AG ISSN 0325-1799) **88**, 216
Estadio. (EC) **4471**
Estadistica. (US ISSN 0014-1135) **4570**
Estadistica Bancaria see Chile. Superintendencia de Bancos e Instituciones Financieras. Informacion Financiera **772**
Estadistica Basica del Sistema Educativo Nacional. (MX) **1676**
Estadistica de Criminalidad. (CK) **1525**
Estadistica de Energia Electrica. (SP) **1799**, 1801
Estadistica de Prospeccion y Produccion de Hidrocarburos. (SP) **3705**
Estadistica del Cemento. (SP) **637**
Estadistica del Comercio Exterior de Espana. (SP ISSN 0071-1527) **714**
Estadistica Educativa see Argentina. Ministerio de Cultura y Educacion. Estadisticas de la Educacion **1674**
Estadistica Panamena. Boletin. (PN) **4570**
Estadistica Panamena. Estadistica Electoral see Estadistica Panamena. Situacion Politica, Administrativa y Justicia. Seccion 611. Estadistica Electoral **3937**

Estadistica Panamena. Indicadores Economicos y Sociales. Seccion 011. Indicadores Economicos y Sociales. (PN ISSN 0378-4940) **864**
†Estadistica Panamena. Inversiones Directas Extranjeras en Panama. (PN) **5188**
Estadistica Panamena. Situacion Cultural. Seccion 511. Educacion. (PN ISSN 0378-4967) **1676**, 4570
Estadistica Panamena. Situacion Demografica. Seccion 221. Estadisticas Vitales. (PN ISSN 0379-4237) **3991**, 4570
†Estadistica Panamena. Situacion Demografica. Seccion 221. Estadisticas Vitales - Cifras Preliminares. (PN ISSN 0378-6749) **5188**
Estadistica Panamena. Situacion Demografica. Seccion 231. Migracion Internacional. (PN ISSN 0378-4975) **3991**
Estadistica Panamena. Situacion Economica. Seccion 312. Produccion Pecuaria. (PN ISSN 0378-2581) **137**, 4570
Estadistica Panamena. Situacion Economica. Seccion 312. Superficie Sembrada y Cosecha de Arroz, Maiz y Frijol de Bejuco. (PN ISSN 0378-2565) **137**, 4570
Estadistica Panamena. Situacion Economica. Seccion 312. Superficie Sembrada y Cosecha de Cafe, Tabaco y Cana de Azucar. (PN ISSN 0378-2573) **137**, 4570
Estadistica Panamena. Situacion Economica. Seccion 314, 321, 323, 324, 325. Industria. (PN ISSN 0378-2557) **714**
Estadistica Panamena. Situacion Economica. Seccion 321 y 325. Industria Encuesta. (PN ISSN 0379-4245) **714**
Estadistica Panamena. Situacion Economica. Seccion 323. Indice de Produccion Fisica de la Industria Manufacturera. (PN) **714**, 4570
Estadistica Panamena. Situacion Economica. Seccion 323. Indice de Volumen Fisico de la Produccion Industrial see Estadistica Panamena. Situacion Economica. Seccion 323. Indice de Produccion Fisica de la Industria Manufacturera **714**
Estadistica Panamena. Situacion Economica. Seccion 331-Comercio. Anuario de Comercio Exterior. (PN) **715**, 4570
Estadistica Panamena. Situacion Economica. Seccion 331-Comercio. Comercio Exterior (Annual) see Estadistica Panamena. Situacion Economica. Seccion 331-Comercio. Anuario de Comercio Exterior **715**
Estadistica Panamena. Situacion Economica. Seccion 331. Comercio Exterior (Preliminary Report). (PN ISSN 0378-4983) **715**, 4570
Estadistica Panamena. Situacion Economica. Seccion 333. Transporte.(PN ISSN 1012-3555) **4649**
Estadistica Panamena. Situacion Economica. Seccion 333-334. Transporte y Comunicaciones see Estadistica Panamena. Situacion Economica. Seccion 334. Comunicaciones **1335**
Estadistica Panamena. Situacion Economica. Seccion 333-334. Transporte y Comunicaciones see Estadistica Panamena. Situacion Economica. Seccion 333. Transporte **4649**
Estadistica Panamena. Situacion Economica. Seccion 334. Comunicaciones. (PN ISSN 1012-3547) **1335**
Estadistica Panamena. Situacion Economica. Seccion 341. Balanza de Pagos. (PN ISSN 0378-7397) **1093**, 906
Estadistica Panamena. Situacion Economica. Seccion 342. Cuentas Nacionales. (PN ISSN 0378-2603) **864**, 4059

Estadistica Panamena. Situacion Economica. Seccion 343. Hacienda Publica. (PN) **715**
Estadistica Panamena. Situacion Economica. Seccion 343-344. Hacienda Publica y Finanzas *see* Estadistica Panamena. Situacion Economica. Seccion 343. Hacienda Publica **715**
Estadistica Panamena. Situacion Economica. Seccion 343-344. Hacienda Publica y Finanzas *see* Estadistica Panamena. Situacion Economica. Seccion 344. Finanzas **777**
Estadistica Panamena. Situacion Economica. Seccion 344. Finanzas. (PN) **777**
Estadistica Panamena. Situacion Economica. Seccion 351. Indice de Precios al por Mayor y al Consumidor. (PN ISSN 0378-2522) **715**, **4570**
Estadistica Panamena. Situacion Economica. Seccion 351. Precios Pagados por el Productor Agropecuario. (PN ISSN 0378-2530) **137**, **4570**
Estadistica Panamena. Situacion Economica. Seccion 351. Precios Recibidos por el Productor Agropecuario. (PN ISSN 0378-2611) **137**
Estadistica Panamena. Situacion Economica. Seccion 352. Hoja de Balance de Alimentos. (PN ISSN 0378-4991) **715**, **4570**
Estadistica Panamena. Situacion Fisica. Seccion 121-Clima. Meteorologia *see* Estadistica Panamena. Situacion Fisica. Seccion 121. Meteorologia **3435**
Estadistica Panamena. Situacion Fisica. Seccion 121. Meteorologia. (PN) **3435**
Estadistica Panamena. Situacion Politica, Administrativa y Justicia. Seccion 611. Estadistica Electoral. (PN) **3937**
Estadistica Panamena. Situacion Politica, Administrativa y Justicia. Seccion 631. Justicia. (PN ISSN 0378-259X) **2698**, **4570**
Estadistica Panamena. Situacion Social. Seccion 431. Asistencia Social *see* Estadistica Panamena. Situacion Social. Seccion 431. Servicios de Salud **4425**
Estadistica Panamena. Situacion Social. Seccion 431. Servicios de Salud. (PN) **4425**, **4571**
Estadistica Panamena. Situacion Social. Seccion 441. Estadisticas del Trabajo. (PN ISSN 0379-072X) **715**
Estadistica Panamena. Situacion Social. Seccion 441 - Trabajo y Salarios. Estadisticas del Trabajo *see* Estadistica Panamena. Situacion Social. Seccion 441. Estadisticas del Trabajo **715**
Estadistica Panamena. Situacion Social. Seccion 451. Accidentes de Transito.(PN ISSN 0378-6765) **4457**, **4571**
Estadisticas de la Aviacion Civil en Espana. (SP ISSN 0421-4986) **4672**
Estadisticas del Comercio Exterior de Mexico. Informacion Preliminar. (MX ISSN 0186-0496) **715**, **4571**
Estadisticas del Comercio Exterior de Venezuela. Periodicidad Anual *see* Anuario del Comercio Exterior de Venezuela **702**
Estadisticas Macroeconomicas de Centroamerica. (GT) **715**, **998**
Estadisticas Minera de Espana. (SP) **3483**
Estadisticas Minera y Metalurgica de Espana *see* Estadisticas Minera de Espana **3483**
Estadisticas Relativas a la Ciencia y a la Tecnologia. *see* Unesco. Statistics on Science and Technology **4358**

Estadisticas, Seguros, Fianzas, Bancos *see* El Salvador. Superintendencia del Sistema Financiero. Junta Monetaria. Anuario Estadistico: Seguros, Fianzas, Bancos **2546**
Estadistico del Petroleo. Boletin. (SP) **3685**
Estado das Culturas e Previsao de Colheitas. (PO ISSN 0870-2594) **88**
Estados Unidos: Perspectiva Latinoamericana. Cuadernos Semestrales. (MX) **3956**
Estampille *see* L'Estampille - L'Objet d'Art **2865**
L'Estampille - L'Objet d'Art. (FR) **2865**
Estandarte Obrero. (US ISSN 0276-4954) **979**, **2582**
Estano. (BO ISSN 0014-1194) **3483**
Estanquero 11. (CL) **864**, **3892**
Estar Viva. (SP) **4841**
Estate Administration. (US) **2623**
Estate Agency News. (UK) **4148**
Estate Agent. (UK ISSN 0260-1001) **4148**
Estate and Financial Planners Alert. (US) **945**
Estate & Property News. (IE) **4148**, **617**
Estate Planners Quarterly *see* Financial Estate Planners Quarterly **2531**
Estate Planning. (US ISSN 0014-1216) **945**, **1093**
Estate Planning. (US ISSN 0094-1794) **945**
Estate Planning and California Probate Reporter. (US ISSN 0273-7027) **2623**
Estate Planning & Taxation Coordinator.(US) **945**, **1093**
Estate Planning Checklists and Forms. (US ISSN 0014-1224) **945**, **1093**
Estate Planning for Farmers and Ranchers, 2-E. (US) **1093**, **88**
†Estate Planning Law Locator. (US) **5188**
Estate Planning Review. (US ISSN 0098-2873) **2623**
Estate Planning: Wills and Trusts. (US) **2623**
Estate Planning: Wills, Trusts and Forms. (US) **2623**
Estate Powers & Trusts Law of New York. (US) **2715**
Estates and Trusts Journal. (CN) **2715**
Estates and Trusts Quarterly *see* Estates and Trusts Journal **2715**
Estates & Trusts Reports. (CN ISSN 0706-5655) **2715**
Estates Gazette. (UK ISSN 0014-1240) **4148**
Estates Gazette Digest of Land and Property Cases *see* Estates Gazette Law Reports **2715**
Estates Gazette Law Reports. (UK) **2715**
Estates, Gifts and Trusts Journal *see* Tax Management Estates, Gifts and Trusts Journal **966**
Estates Times. (UK ISSN 0014-1259) **4148**
Estates Times Deals Digest. (UK) **4148**
Estatistica Brasileira de Energia/ Brazilian Energy Statistics. (BL ISSN 0512-350X) **1799**
Estatisticas da Energia: Continente e Ilhas Adjacentes *see* Portugal. Estatisticas da Energia: Continente, Acores e Madeira **5260**
Estes Educator News. (US) **1749**, **2436**
Estes Trails. (US ISSN 0737-481X) **2149**
▼Estetica (Bologna). (IT ISSN 1121-0036) **3766**
Estetica Hairfashion. *see* Estetica Modacapelli **372**
Estetica Modacapelli/Estetica Hairfashion. (IT) **372**
Esteticka Vychova. (CS ISSN 0014-1283) **1632**, **325**, **3550**
Estetika/Aesthetics. (UK ISSN 0014-1291) **325**, **3766**
Estheticienne. (NE ISSN 0014-1321) **372**
Estimado de Produccion y Consumo de Azucar. (CU) **906**

Estimados Sobre Requerimientos de Importacion de Azucar. (CU) **906**
The Estimate. (US ISSN 1043-1667) **3457**, **3956**
Estimated Resident Populations by Age and Sex in Statistical Local Areas, Victoria. (AT) **3991**, **4571**
Estimated World Requirements of Narcotic Drugs *see* Narcotic Drugs: Estimated World Requirements for (Year) **3811**
†Estimated World Requirements of Narcotic Drugs. Supplement. (UN ISSN 0082-8327) **5188**
The Estimates. (US) **3956**
Estimates of Area and Production of Principal Crops in India. Summary Tables *see* Area and Production of Principal Crops in India. Summary Tables **168**
Estimates of Consolidated Fund Expenditure *see* Ghana **867**
Estimates of Revenue and Expenditure. (CN) **715**
Estimates of the Population of the United States and Components of Population Change *see* Current Population Reports: Population Estimates and Projections. United States Population Estimates and Components of Change **3981**
Estimates of the Population of the United States by Age, Sex and Race *see* Current Population Reports: Population Estimates and Projections. United States Population Estimates by Age, Sex, Race and Hispanic Origin **3981**
Estimates of the Revenue and Expenditure of the Kingdom of Lesotho. (LO) **1093**
Estimators & Buyers' Guide *see* E & B Guide **3999**
Estiquirin. (HO) **4371**
Esto America. (US ISSN 0748-3058) **2000**
Estomodeo/Stomatology. (SP ISSN 0212-4939) **3233**
Estonian Academy of Sciences. Proceedings. Biology. *see* Eesti Teaduste Akadeemia. Toimetised. Bioloogia **437**
Estonian Academy of Sciences. Proceedings. Chemistry. *see* Eesti Teaduste Akadeemia. Toimetised. Keemia **1176**
Estonian Academy of Sciences. Proceedings. Ecology. *see* Eesti Teaduste Akadeemia. Toimetised. Okoloogia **437**
Estonian Academy of Sciences. Proceedings. Geology. *see* Eesti Teaduste Akadeemia. Toimetised. Geoloogia **1560**
Estonian Academy of Sciences. Proceedings. Physics. Mathematics. *see* Eest Teaduste Akadeemia. Toimetised. Fuusika. Matemaatika **3817**
Estonian Academy of Sciences. Proceedings. Social Sciences. *see* Eesti Teaduste Akadeemia. Toimetised. Uhiskonnateadused **4371**
Estonian Independent *see* The Baltic Independent **3951**
Estonian Life. *see* Eesti Elu **2186**
Estonian Nature. *see* Eesti Loodus **4308**
Estonian News. *see* Eesti Haal **2000**
Estonian Philatelist. *see* Eesti Filatelist **3752**
Estos Tiempos. (US) **2000**, **2405**
Estrada. (AA) **4633**
Estrategia. (CK) **664**
Estrategia. (CL ISSN 0716-1255) **777**
Estrella de Esperanza. (US) **4282**
Estrellitas. (PR) **1373**
Estreno. (US ISSN 0097-8663) **4633**, **2813**, **2915**
Estructuras y Formas *see* Coleccion Estructuras y Formas **297**
L'Estuaire Genealogique. (CN ISSN 0824-4936) **2150**
Estuaries. (US ISSN 0160-8347) **438**, **1954**

Estuaries and Coastal Waters of the British Isles. (UK ISSN 0261-0663) **465**, **399**
Estuaries of the British Isles *see* Estuaries and Coastal Waters of the British Isles **465**
Estuarine and Coastal Marine Science *see* Estuarine, Coastal and Shelf Science **1604**
Estuarine, Coastal and Shelf Science. (UK ISSN 0272-7714) **1604**, **438**
Estudia y Ahorra. (SP) **778**
Estudio Agustiniano. (SP ISSN 0425-340X) **4264**
Estudio Economico Mundial *see* World Economic Survey **888**
Estudion sobre la Elaboracion, la Comercializacion y la Distribucion de los Productos Basicos *see* Studies in the Processing, Marketing and Distribution of Commodities **1054**
Estudios. (PY ISSN 1012-2478) **2506**
Estudios. (SP ISSN 0210-0525) **4176**, **2360**, **2915**, **3766**
Estudios Andinos. (BO ISSN 0014-1429) **3892**
▼Estudios Andinos. (PE) **4371**
Estudios Atacamenos. (CL ISSN 0716-0925) **271**
Estudios Biblicos. (SP ISSN 0014-1437) **4176**
Estudios Biblicos para Ninos: Alumnos. (US ISSN 0890-3115) **4237**, **1254**
Estudios Biblicos para Ninos: Maestros. (US ISSN 0890-3123) **4237**, **1254**
Estudios Centro Americanos. (ES ISSN 0014-1445) **4371**
Estudios Clasicos. (SP ISSN 0014-1453) **1276**
Estudios Cubanos. *see* Cuban Studies **3889**
Estudios de Arte y Estetica. (MX ISSN 0071-1659) **325**
Estudios de Asia y Africa. (MX ISSN 0185-0164) **3637**
Estudios de Ciencias y Letras. (UY ISSN 0256-3061) **325**
Estudios de Coyuntura. (VE) **664**
Estudios de Cultura Maya. (MX ISSN 0071-1667) **2405**
Estudios de Cultura Nahuatl. (MX) **2405**
Estudios de Derecho. (CK ISSN 0014-1461) **2623**
Estudios de Deusto. (SP ISSN 0423-4847) **4371**
Estudios de Economia. (CL ISSN 0304-2758) **664**
Estudios de Filologia Griega. (SP) **2813**
Estudios de Filologia Inglesa. (SP ISSN 0210-7953) **2813**
Estudios de Filologia Latina. (SP) **2813**
Estudios de Folklore. (MX ISSN 0071-1683) **2054**
Estudios de Historia Moderna y Contemporanea de Mexico. (MX ISSN 0014-147X) **2405**
Estudios de Historia Novohispana. (MX ISSN 0185-2523) **2405**
Estudios de Historia Social. (SP ISSN 0210-1416) **4371**, **2310**
Estudios de la Seguridad Social. (SZ ISSN 0379-0266) **2531**
Estudios de Literatura. (MX ISSN 0071-1691) **2915**
Estudios de Literatura Contemporanea. (SP ISSN 0071-1705) **2915**
Estudios de Planificacion Familiar. (CK) **596**
Estudios de Poblacion. (CK) **3982**
Estudios de Poblacion y Desarrollo. (BO) **4434**
Estudios de Promocion Femenina. (BO) **4841**
Estudios de Recursos Humanos. (BO) **4434**
Estudios de Sociologia Familiar. (BO) **4434**
▼Estudios del Desarrollo/Development Studies Journal. (VE ISSN 1013-4069) **4434**
Estudios Demograficos y Urbanos. (MX ISSN 0186-7210) **3982**

Estudios e Informes de la C E P A L/C E P A L Studies and Reports. (UN ISSN 0256-9795) **929**
Estudios Eclesiasticos. (SP ISSN 0210-1610) **4176**
Estudios Economicos. (AG) **664**
Estudios Empresariales. (SP ISSN 0425-3698) **1009**
Estudios en Educacion Matematica see Studies in Mathematics Education **1723**
Estudios en el Extranjero. see Study Abroad **1723**
Estudios Etnohistoricos del Ecuador. (EC) **2405**, 238
Estudios Filologicos. (CL ISSN 0071-1713) **2813**, 2915
Estudios Filosoficos. (SP ISSN 0210-6086) **3766**
Estudios Filosoficos. (VE) **3766**
Estudios Folkloricos Paraguayos. (PY) **2054**
†Estudios Fronterizos Mexico - Estados Unidos. (MX) **5188**
Estudios Geograficos. (SP ISSN 0014-1496) **2247**
Estudios Geologicos. (SP ISSN 0367-0449) **1543**
Estudios Historicos. (AG) **2405**, 3956
Estudios Historicos. (PE) **2405**
Estudios Historicos sobre San Sebastian. Boletin. (SP ISSN 0014-150X) **2360**
Estudios Historicos y Documentos de los Archivos de Protocolos. (SP) **2360**
Estudios Interdisciplinarios. (AG ISSN 0302-2420) **3892**
Estudios Internacionales see Estudios Politicos **3892**
Estudios Internacionales. (CL ISSN 0716-0240) **3956**
Estudios Internacionales. (SP) **3956**
Estudios Josefinos. (SP ISSN 0210-7074) **4264**
Estudios Latinoamericanos. (PL ISSN 0137-3080) **2405**
Estudios Lulianos see Studia Lulliana **2390**
Estudios Medicos y Biologicos. Boletin. (MX ISSN 0020-3858) **3096**, 438
Estudios Mexicanos. see Mexican Studies **2511**
Estudios Michoacanos. (MX) **2405**, 238, 4434
Estudios Migratorios Latinoamericanos. (AG ISSN 0326-7458) **3982**
Estudios Norteamericanos. (CL ISSN 0716-1468) **3892**
Estudios Oceanologicos. (CL ISSN 0071-173X) **1604**
Estudios Orientales see Estudios de Asia y Africa **3637**
Estudios Paraguayos. (PY ISSN 0251-2483) **2405**, 2506
Estudios Pedagogicos. (CL ISSN 0716-050X) **1706**
Estudios Politicos. (MX ISSN 0185-1616) **3892**
Estudios Politicos. (SP) **3892**
Estudios Publicos. (CL ISSN 0716-1115) **864**, 2310, 2623, 3892
Estudios sobre el Communismo. (CL ISSN 0014-1550) **3892**
Estudios Sociales. (CL ISSN 0716-0321) **4371**
Estudios Sociales. (DR) **4434**
Estudios Sociales Centroamericanos. (CR ISSN 0303-9676) **4371**
Estudios Sociologicos. (MX ISSN 0185-4186) **4434**
Estudios Trinitarios. (SP ISSN 0210-0363) **4176**
Estudios Turisticos. (SP ISSN 0423-5037) **4761**
Estudios Urbanos. (BO) **4434**
Estudios y Fuentes del Arte en Mexico. (MX ISSN 0071-1748) **325**
Estudos Afro-Asiaticos. (BL ISSN 0101-546X) **3893**
Estudos Baianos. (BL) **2915**
†Estudos Brasileiros. (BL ISSN 0100-2635) **5188**
Estudos de Antropologia Cultural see Estudos de Antropologia Cultural e Social **238**
Estudos de Antropologia Cultural e Social. (PO ISSN 0870-4457) **238**

Estudos de Geografia das Regioes Tropicais. (PO) **2247**
Estudos de Geografia do Mediterraneo e das Ilhas Atlantidas. (PO) **2247**
Estudos de Geografia Fisica. (PO) **2247**
Estudos de Geografia Humana e Regional. (PO) **2247**, 4761
Estudos Economicos see Revista Estudos Economicos **689**
Estudos Ensaios e Documentos. (PO ISSN 0870-001X) **4309**
Estudos Germanicos. (BL ISSN 0101-837X) **2915**
Estudos Historicos. (BL) **2405**
Estudos Ibero-Americanos see Revista de Estudos Ibero-Americanos **2021**
Estudos Italianos em Portugal. (PO) **325**, 2310, 2915
Estudos Juridicos. (BL ISSN 0100-2538) **2623**
Estudos Leopoldenses. (BL ISSN 0014-1607) **1954**
Estudos para o Planeamento Regional e Urbano. (PO) **2247**
Estudos Politicos e Sociais. (PO ISSN 0014-1623) **3893**, 4434
Estudos Portugueses e Africanos. (BL ISSN 0103-1821) **4371**, 2915
Estudos sobre o Nordeste. (BL) **864**
Estudos Tecnologicos. (BL ISSN 0101-5303) **4309**, 299, 1560, 1821
Estudos Universitarios. (BL ISSN 0425-4082) **1706**
Esu Wenxue see Sulian Wenxue (Liankan) **2967**
Eswau Huppeday. (US ISSN 0747-5810) **2150**
Et Cetera see ETC **2813**
Et la Lumiere Fut. (FR ISSN 0046-2586) **2292**
Et-Lehti. (FI ISSN 0355-7227) **2186**
Et-mol. (IS) **2000**
L'Eta dell'Acquario. (IT) **3669**
Eta Evolutiva. (IT ISSN 0392-0658) **4020**
Eta Verde. (IT) **1954**
Etablissements Medicaux pour Enfants. (FR) **2461**, 1237
Etage. (GW ISSN 0721-7072) **664**, 835, 906, 1058
L'Etain et ses Usages. (BE ISSN 0014-1631) **3405**, 1213
Etape. (CN ISSN 0708-1987) **3336**
Etat du Monde. (FR ISSN 0757-6714) **664**
Etc. (US) **2757**
ETC. (US ISSN 0014-164X) **2813**
Etc. Montreal. (CN ISSN 0835-7641) **325**
ETCetera see E T Cetera **1058**
Etchings & Odysseys. (US) **3011**
Etendard de la Bible et Heraut du Royaume de Christ. (FR) **4176**
Eter-Aktuellt. (SW ISSN 0014-1658) **1373**
Eternity. (US ISSN 0014-1682) **4282**
Etesia Statistike. Erevna tou Karkinou/ Annual Statistical Survey of Cancer. (GR ISSN 0302-9697) **3171**, 3196, 4571
Etgar (Rehovot). (IS) **1254**, 3035
Ethical Record. (UK ISSN 0014-1690) **3766**
Ethical Tablet and Capsule Handbook see E T C H **3724**
Ethics: An International Journal of Social, Political and Legal Philosophy.(US ISSN 0014-1704) **3766**
▼Ethics & Behavior. (US ISSN 1050-8422) **4020**
Ethics & International Affairs (Journal). (US) **3956**, 1749
Ethics and International Affairs (Newsletter). (US ISSN 0892-6794) **3956**, 1749, 3766
Ethics and Medicine. (UK) **3096**
Ethics and Medics. (US) **3766**, 3096
†Ethics & Perspectives! (US ISSN 1011-3878) **5188**
Ethics and Public Policy Center Newsletter. (US) **3893**, 4176
Ethics: Easier Said than Done. (US ISSN 0897-0106) **3766**
†Ethics in Education. (CN) **5188**
▼Ethics Journal. (US ISSN 1060-0698) **1009**, 1632

Ethik in der Medizin. (US ISSN 0935-7335) **3766**, 2623, 3096
▼Ethik und Sozialwissenschaften. (GW ISSN 0937-938X) **4371**
Ethiope Law Series. (NR) **2623**
Ethiopia. Customs Head Office. External Trade Statistics. (ET ISSN 0425-4309) **715**
Ethiopia. Department of Labour and Employment. Employment and Manpower Division. Employment Service Information. (ET) **979**
Ethiopian Business see Business Spectator **809**
Ethiopian Chamber of Commerce. Directory of Agriculture. (ET) **88**
Ethiopian Chamber of Commerce. Directory of Industry. (ET) **815**
Ethiopian Chamber of Commerce. Statistical Digest. (ET) **815**
Ethiopian Jewry Report. (CN) **4222**, 3941
Ethiopian Journal of African Studies. (ET) **2332**
Ethiopian Journal of Agricultural Sciences. (ET ISSN 0257-2605) **88**
Ethiopian Journal of Development Research. (ET) **1075**, 929
Ethiopian Journal of Education. (ET ISSN 0425-4414) **1632**
Ethiopian Library Association. Bulletin. (ET ISSN 0014-1747) **2757**
Ethiopian Manuscripts Microfilm Library. Bulletin. (ET) **2328**
Ethiopian Medical Journal. (ET ISSN 0014-1755) **3096**
Ethiopian Monograph Series see Northeast African Monograph Series **2017**
Ethiopian Publications: Books, Pamphlets, Annuals and Periodical Articles. (ET ISSN 0071-1772) **400**
†Ethiopian Red Cross Society Newsletter. (ET) **5188**
Ethiopian Trade Journal. (ET) **815**
Ethiopianist Notes see Northeast African Studies **2017**
Ethiopique. (SG) **3893**
Ethiopiques. (FR) **2332**, 3893
†Ethnic Affairs. (US ISSN 0894-0932) **5188**
Ethnic American Voluntary Organizations. (US ISSN 0737-1411) **4405**, 2000
Ethnic and Racial Studies. (UK ISSN 0141-9870) **2000**, 3941
Ethnic Chronology Series. (US ISSN 0071-1780) **2406**
†Ethnic Directory of Canada. (CN) **5188**
Ethnic Forum. (US ISSN 0278-9078) **2000**
Ethnic Groups. (US ISSN 0308-6860) **2001**, 3893, 4434
Ethnic Groups in California. (US) **2001**
Ethnic History of Chicago. (US) **2001**
Ethnic Information Sources of the U S. (US ISSN 0738-1719) **2001**
Ethnic Newsletter see Ethnic Reporter **2001**
Ethnic Reporter. (US) **2001**
Ethnic Review. (US) **2001**
Ethnic Studies Report. (CE ISSN 1010-5832) **2001**
▼Ethnicity & Disease. (US ISSN 1049-510X) **3097**, 2001
Ethnies. (FR ISSN 0295-9151) **2001**
Ethnike Trapeza tes Hellados. Apologismos. see National Bank of Greece. Annual Report **791**
EthnoArts Index. (US ISSN 0893-0120) **352**, 11, 238, 325
Ethnographia. (HU ISSN 0014-1798) **238**
Ethnographic Review. see Neprajzi Ertesito **246**
Ethnographical Museum of Sweden. Monograph Series see Folkens Museum - National Museum of Ethnography **240**
L'Ethnographie. (BE ISSN 0336-1438) **238**
Ethnographisch-Archaeologische Zeitschrift see E A Z **238**
Ethnohistory. (US ISSN 0014-1801) **238**, 2310

ETUDES CINEMATOGRAPHIQUES 6161

†Ethnologia. (NE ISSN 0071-1845) **5188**
Ethnologia Polona. (PL ISSN 0137-4079) **2001**
Ethnologia Scandinavica. (SW ISSN 0348-9698) **238**
Ethnologie Francaise/French Ethnology. (FR ISSN 0046-2616) **239**
Ethnology. (US ISSN 0014-1828) **239**
Ethnology, Ecology & Evolution. (IT ISSN 0394-9370) **582**
Ethnomusicology Newsletter. (US) **3550**, 239
Ethnopsychologie see Cahiers de Sociologie Economique et Culturelle **849**
Ethnos. (SW ISSN 0014-1844) **239**
Ethology. (GW ISSN 0179-1613) **582**, 216, 4020
Ethology and Sociobiology. (US ISSN 0162-3095) **4371**
Ethos. (IT) **3766**
Ethos. (AG ISSN 0325-5387) **3766**
Ethos see Ethos Papers **4371**
Ethos see Ethos Annual **4371**
Ethos (Ames). (US) **2506**
Ethos (Washington). (US ISSN 0091-2131) **239**, 4434
Ethos Annual. (AT) **4371**
Ethos - Die Zeitschrift fuer die Ganze Familie. (SZ) **4176**, 2001
Ethos Papers. (AT) **4371**
Etica & Ciencia. (AG ISSN 0326-9442) **4309**
L' Etichetta. (IT) **2205**
Etienne Gilson Series. (CN ISSN 0708-319X) **3766**
Etin. (US) **3508**, 1385
Etincelle. (GP) **3893**
Etnie. (IT) **2001**
Etnografia. (PL ISSN 0209-2077) **2054**, 239
Etnografia Polska. (PL ISSN 0071-1861) **239**
Etnografski Muzej na Cetinju. Glasnik. (YU) **239**
Etnografski Muzej u Beogradu. Glasnik. (YU ISSN 0350-0322) **239**
Etnologia see Studi Etno-Antropologici e Sociologici **250**
Etnologia - Antropologia Culturale. (IT) **239**
Etnologia y Folklore. (CU) **239**, 2054
Etnologie et Traditions Populaires de l'Iran/Mardon Sensai Va Farhange-e Amme-e Iran. (IR) **2001**, 2054
Etnologiska Studier. (SW ISSN 0374-7530) **239**
Etnoloski Pregled/Revue d'Ethnologie. (YU ISSN 0423-5509) **239**
Etnostoria. (IT) **2054**
Etobicoke Business. (CN) **864**
Etoiles. see Yllkat **1271**
Etologia. (SP ISSN 1130-3204) **582**, 4020
Ettela'at Banovan. (IR) **4841**
Ettela'at Haftegi. (IR) **2202**
Ettela'at Va Tazeha-Ye Fanni. see Informations et Nouveautes Techniques **4315**
Ettore Majorana International Science Series. Life Sciences. (US ISSN 0896-4343) **438**
Etude des Conditions Economiques et Sociales en Afrique see Survey of Economic and Social Conditions in Africa **935**
Etudes. (FR ISSN 0014-1941) **2865**, 4264
Etudes a l'Etranger. see Study Abroad **1723**
Etudes Aequatoria. (ZR) **239**, 2813
Etudes Anglaises. (FR ISSN 0014-195X) **2915**
Etudes Asiatiques. see Asiatische Studien **3634**
Etudes Balkaniques. (BU ISSN 0014-1976) **2360**, 2054, 2813, 2915
Etudes Baudelairiennes. (SZ ISSN 0531-9455) **2915**, 2992
Etudes Byzantines. see Byzantine Studies **2504**
Etudes Celtiques. (FR ISSN 0373-1928) **2813**
Etudes Cinematographiques. (FR ISSN 0014-1992) **3508**, 4633

6162 ETUDES CLASSIQUES

Etudes Classiques. (BE ISSN 0014-200X) **1276**
Etudes Creoles. (CN ISSN 0708-2398) **2813**
Etudes d'Histoire Africaine/Studies in African History. (ZR ISSN 0071-1993) **2332**
Etudes d'Histoire de l'Art. (BE ISSN 0071-1969) **325**
Etudes d'Histoire Economique et Sociale. (BE ISSN 0071-1977) **894**
Etudes d'Histoire et de Politique. *see* Studies in History and Politics **2323**
Etudes Dahomeennes. (DM ISSN 0014-2018) **2332, 4434**
Etudes de Conjoncture: Evolutions et Tendances. (MR ISSN 0851-9722) **4571**
Etudes de Droit Libanais *see* Proche-Orient Etudes Juridiques **2668**
Etudes de Lettres. (SZ ISSN 0014-2026) **2915**
Etudes de Linguistique Appliquee. (FR ISSN 0071-190X) **2813**
Etudes de Philologie, d'Archeologie et d'Histoire Ancienne. (BE ISSN 0071-1926) **2813**
Etudes de Philologie et d'Histoire. (SZ ISSN 0071-1934) **2915, 2360**
Etudes de Phonologie, Phonetique et Linguistique Descriptive du Francais/Studien zur Phonologie, Phonetik und Linguistik des Franzoesischen. (GW ISSN 0176-7879) **2813**
Etudes de Pollution Atmospherique a Paris et dans les Departments Peripheriques. (FR ISSN 0071-1942) **1977**
Etudes Eburneennes. (IV ISSN 0423-5673) **239**
†Etudes Ecologiques. (CN) **5188**
Etudes et Carrieres. (SZ) **1706**
Etudes et Documentation de la R T A. (FR ISSN 0153-906X) **4690**
Etudes et Documents d'Histoire Economique et Financiere. (FR ISSN 1151-9037) **894**
Etudes et Sports Sous-Marins *see* Subaqua **4557**
Etudes et Travaux d'Archeologie Marocaine. (MR ISSN 0071-2027) **271**
Etudes Ethno-Linguistiques Maghreb-Sahara. (FR ISSN 0757-7699) **2813, 239**
Etudes Finno-Ougriennes. (FR ISSN 0071-2051) **2813, 2915**
Etudes Francaises. (CN ISSN 0014-2085) **2915**
Etudes Francaises. *see* Faguo Yanjiu **4372**
Etudes Francaises dans le Monde *see* Universites **1719**
Etudes Freudiennes. (FR ISSN 0014-2107) **4020**
Etudes Germaniques. (FR ISSN 0014-2115) **2915**
Etudes Gregoriennes. (FR ISSN 0071-2086) **3550, 4176**
Etudes Historiques. (HU ISSN 0071-2108) **2310**
Etudes Historiques. *see* Studime Historike **2324**
Etudes Historiques. (BU ISSN 0525-0846) **2360**
Etudes Internationales. (CN ISSN 0014-2123) **3956, 2310**
Etudes Inuit Studies. (CN ISSN 0701-1008) **2001**
Etudes Irlandaises. (FR ISSN 0183-973X) **2360, 2915**
Etudes Jurif. (FR) **1093**
Etudes Linguistiques. (FR ISSN 0071-2124) **2813**
Etudes Litteraires. (CN ISSN 0014-214X) **2915**
Etudes Mesoamericaines. (MX ISSN 0378-5726) **239**
Etudes Migrations. *see* Studi Emigrazione **3988**
Etudes Mongoles *see* Etudes Mongoles et Siberiennes **239**
Etudes Mongoles et Siberiennes. (FR) **239, 2813**
Etudes Nervaliennes et Romantiques. (BE) **2915**
Etudes Nigeriennes. (NG) **239**

Etudes Normandes. (FR ISSN 0014-2158) **2360, 664, 2247**
Etudes Ocean Indien. (FR) **2813, 239, 271**
Etudes Orientales. (BE ISSN 0531-1926) **3637**
Etudes Philologiques. *see* Studime Filologjike **3783**
Etudes Philosophiques. (FR ISSN 0014-2166) **3766**
Etudes Philosophiques et Litteraires *see* Interdisciplinarite Etudes Philosophiques et Litteraires **3769**
Etudes Politiques. (SZ) **3893**
Etudes Prehistoriques. (FR) **271**
Etudes Preliminaires aux Religions Orientales dans l'Empire Romain. (NE ISSN 0531-1950) **4176, 3637**
Etudes Psychotherapiques. (FR) **4020**
Etudes Rabelaisiennes. (SZ) **2915**
Etudes Rimbaudiennes *see* Rimbaud Vivant **2882**
Etudes Romanes de Lund. (SW ISSN 0347-0822) **2813, 2915**
Etudes Rurales. (FR ISSN 0014-2182) **4434, 664, 2247, 2310**
Etudes Rwandaises. (RW) **2332, 239**
Etudes Rwandaises. Lettres et Sciences Humaines *see* Etudes Rwandaises. Sciences Naturelles et Appliquees **1632**
Etudes Rwandaises. Sciences Naturelles et Appliquees. (RW ISSN 1011-4874) **1632**
Etudes Savoisiennes. (FR) **2360**
Etudes Scientifiques. (FR) **4371, 4309**
Etudes Senegalaises. (SG) **4434, 2332**
Etudes Sociales. (FR ISSN 0014-2204) **4434**
Etudes Sociales et Syndicales. (FR ISSN 0014-2212) **4434**
Etudes Sociales-Politiques, Economiques *see* E S O P E **3891**
Etudes Sovietiques. (FR ISSN 0014-2220) **2215**
Etudes Strategiques et Militaires (Collection). (CN ISSN 0712-7561) **2855, 400**
Etudes sur l'Enseignement des Mathematiques *see* Studies in Mathematics Education **1723**
Etudes sur l'Herault. (FR ISSN 0249-1664) **2360**
Etudes sur la Transformation, la Commercialisation et la Distribution des Produits de Base *see* Studies in the Processing, Marketing and Distribution of Commodities **1054**
Etudes sur le Judaisme Medieval. (NE ISSN 0169-815X) **4222**
Etudes sur les Mondes Hispanophones. (FR) **2916, 2360**
Etudes Teilhardiennes/Teilhardian Studies. (FR ISSN 0082-2612) **4176**
Etudes Theologiques et Religieuses. (FR ISSN 0014-2239) **4237**
Etudes Togolaises. (TG ISSN 0531-2051) **239**
Etudes Tsiganes. (FR ISSN 0014-2247) **4435**
Etudes Universitaires sur l'Integration Europeenne/University Studies on European Integration. (EI ISSN 0071-2213) **3956**
Etudes Vietnamiennes. (VN ISSN 0531-206X) **3893**
Etudes Zairoises. (ZR) **3893**
Etudiant. (FR ISSN 0766-6330) **1254, 1632**
Etudiants du Monde *see* World Student News **1672**
Etyka. (PL ISSN 0014-2263) **3766**
Etzb'oni. (IS) **1254**
Eucarpia. (NE ISSN 0071-2221) **501**
Eucharistic Minister. (US ISSN 0743-524X) **4264**
Euclides. (NE) **3035, 1749**
Eudora Welty Newsletter. (US ISSN 0146-7220) **2916, 400**
Eugene O'Neill Newsletter *see* Eugene O'Neill Review **2916**
Eugene O'Neill Review. (US ISSN 1040-9483) **2916, 4633**
Eugenics Quarterly *see* Social Biology **547**

Eugenics Society Bulletin *see* Biology and Society **5149**
Eugenics Special Interest Group Bulletin.(US) **541, 3982**
Euhemer. (PL ISSN 0014-2298) **4176**
Die Eule. (GW ISSN 0174-3465) **4841**
Eulenhof Basterbrief *see* Der Eulenhof Beraterbrief **4127**
Der Eulenhof Beraterbrief. (GW) **4127**
Eulenspiegel. (GW ISSN 0423-5975) **2865**
Eulenspiegel-Jahrbuch. (GW ISSN 0531-2159) **2916, 2054**
Eumak Dong-A. (KO) **3551**
Euntes Docete. (VC ISSN 0394-9850) **4264, 4176**
Eupalino. (IT) **299**
Euphorbia Journal. (US ISSN 0737-8823) **2125**
Euphorion. (GW ISSN 0014-2328) **2916**
Euphytica. (NE ISSN 0014-2336) **176**
Eurail Guide. (US ISSN 0085-0330) **4761, 4709**
Eurasian Language Archives. (US ISSN 0898-0454) **2813**
Eureka. (IT) **1254**
Eureka. (UK) **1821, 1929**
Eureka. (FR ISSN 0046-2667) **2916**
Eureka: the Archimedean's Journal. (UK ISSN 0071-2248) **3035**
Euro Abstracts *see* Euro Abstracts Section I. Euratom and EEC Research **3837**
Euro Abstracts Section I. Euratom and EEC Research. (EI) **3837, 11**
Euro Abstracts Section II. Coal and Steel. (EI ISSN 0378-3472) **3499, 11, 3425**
Euro Bulletin. (BE) **2473**
Euro-City. (AU) **4761**
Euro Cooperation; Economic Studies on Europe. (FR ISSN 0302-0622) **664**
▼Euro-East Telecommunications. (US) **1335**
Euro-Focus. (GW ISSN 0936-1928) **3300**
Euro III - Vs *see* III - Vs Review **1773**
Euro Kompass Denmark. Chemicals *see* Kompass Select Export. Chemical Industry **915**
Euro Kompass Denmark. Construction *see* Kompass Select Export. Building Construction, Contractors **915**
Euro Kompass Denmark. Electrical and Electronic Equipment *see* Kompass Select Export. Electrical and Electronic Equipment **915**
Euro Kompass Denmark. Foods and Beverages *see* Kompass Select Export. Food Industry **915**
Euro Kompass Denmark. Furniture *see* Kompass Select Export. Furniture **915**
Euro Kompass Denmark. Machinery *see* Kompass Select Export. Machine Industry **915**
Euro Kompass Denmark. Metal *see* Kompass Select Export. Metal Products **915**
Euro Kompass Denmark. Paper and Graphic Arts *see* Kompass Select Export. Paper Industry, Graphic Arts **915**
Euro Kompass Denmark. Plastics and Rubber *see* Kompass Select Export. Rubber Industry, Plastics Industry **915**
Euro Kompass Denmark. Scientific and Industrial Instruments *see* Kompass Select Export. Scientific and Industrial Instruments, Watch Industry **915**
Euro Kompass Denmark. Services *see* Kompass Select Export. Business Services **915**
Euro Kompass Denmark. Textiles, Clothing and Footwear *see* Kompass Select Export. Textiles, Clothing and Footwear **915**
Euro Kompass Denmark. Transport Equipment *see* Kompass Select Export. Transport Equipment **916**
Euro Kompass Denmark. Wood Industry *see* Kompass Select Export. Wood Industry **916**

Euro Piano. (GW ISSN 0014-2387) **3551**
†Euro Reports and Studies. (UN ISSN 0250-8710) **5188**
†Euro Transport Journal. (GW) **5188**
Euro TV Investor. (US ISSN 1043-9420) **1335**
Euro - Who's Who. (BE) **418, 1134**
Euroa Gazette. (AT) **2171**
Euroasiatica. (IT) **2813**
Eurobids. (UK) **664**
Eurobiologiste. (FR ISSN 0999-5749) **476**
†EuroBrief. (UK ISSN 0954-4011) **5188**
▼Eurocarne. (SP) **2066**
Euroclay *see* World Ceramics & Refractories **1167**
Eurocon: European Conference on Electrotechnics. (US) **1892**
Eurodeco. (FR) **2558**
▼EuroDirectory. (US) **1134, 31**
†Eurodoc File. (UK) **5188**
Euroednews. (UK ISSN 0260-8979) **1632**
Eurofach Electronica. (SP) **1771**
EUROFIMA Annual Report *see* European Company for the Financing of Railway Rolling Stock. Annual Report **4709**
Eurofinas. Annual Report *see* European Federation of Finance House Associations. Annual Report **778**
Eurofinas. Newsletter *see* European Federation of Finance House Associations. Newsletter **778**
Eurofish Report. (UK ISSN 0140-8720) **2039**
Eurofood. (UK ISSN 0955-5404) **2066**
Eurofood Monitor. (UK ISSN 0960-7943) **2066, 2722**
Euroforum *see* Community Report **851**
Euroforum (Brussels) *see* Bulletin of the European Communities **848**
Eurofruit. (UK) **2091, 176**
Eurofrutta. (IT) **2125**
Eurographic Seminars. (US) **1395**
Euroil. (NO ISSN 0802-9474) **3685**
Eurokunst *see* Eurokunst: Besser Reisen & Mehr Erleben **4761**
Eurokunst: Besser Reisen & Mehr Erleben. (GW) **4761**
Eurolink Age. (EI) **2272**
†Euromarket Report. (UK) **5188**
Euromarketing. (UK ISSN 0952-3820) **31**
Euromecum. (GW) **1706**
Euromedia Investor. (US ISSN 1041-3014) **1373, 945**
Euromicro Journal *see* Microprocessing and Microprogramming **1462**
Euromoney. (UK ISSN 0014-2433) **778**
Euromoney Capital Markets Guide. (UK) **778**
Euromoney Corporate Finance *see* Corporate Finance **773**
Euromoney Syndication Guide *see* Euromoney Capital Markets Guide **778**
Euromoney Trade Finance Report *see* Trade Finance & Banker International **801**
The Euromonitor Book Report (Year). (UK) **4127, 4141**
Euromonitor Reports on D I Y and Home Improvement Markets *see* Do-It-Yourself Report **2501**
Euromueble. (SP ISSN 0210-5489) **2558**
Euronet Diane News *see* X I I I Magazine **1346**
Euronews Construction. (UK) **617**
Europ. (FR ISSN 0180-7897) **2865, 2569**
Europ-Oil Prices *see* Weekly Petroleum Argus **3703**
Europa. (GW ISSN 0932-0520) **2360**
Europa. Revue de Presse Europeenne. (FR ISSN 0071-2299) **2569**
Europa a Tavola. (IT) **2446, 2066**
Europa-Archiv. (GW ISSN 0014-2476) **3956**
Europa Camping und Caravaning. Internationaler Fuehrer. (GW ISSN 0071-2272) **4545, 4761**
Europa Chemie. (GW ISSN 0014-2484) **1852**

EUROPEAN COMMISSION 6163

L'Europa della C E E. (IT) **2723**
Europa Domani. (IT) **778**
Europa Ethnica. (AU ISSN 0014-2492) **2001, 3893**
Europa Handbuch der Werbegesellschaften. (GW ISSN 0085-0349) **31**
Europa-Korrespondenz. (AU ISSN 0014-2522) **3893**
Europa Medica see Panminerva Medica - Europa Medica **3139**
Europa Medica see Revista Clinica Espanola **3147**
Europa Medicophysica. (IT ISSN 0014-2573) **3097**
Europa Mediterranea. (IT) **2360**
Europa Report see International Computer Update **1445**
Europa-Rochade. (GW ISSN 0179-3934) **4471**
Europa Star Diamond Intelligence Briefs.(SZ) **3483**
Europa Star - International Jewellery Magazine. (SZ ISSN 0014-2603) **2563**
Europa Transport. (EI) **4649**
†Europa u. Jugend. (GW) **5188**
Europa World Year Book. (UK ISSN 0956-2273) **1780**
Europa Year Book: A World Survey see Europa World Year Book **1780**
Europa 1992. (US ISSN 1049-9040) **906, 945**
Europa 2000. (IT) **2205**
Europaeische Dokumentation - Schriftenreihe Landwirtschaft see Documentation Europeenne - Serie Agricole **87**
Europaeische Ex Libris. see Bibliografi over Europaeiske Kunstneres Ex Libris **352**
Europaeische Gegenwart. (GW ISSN 0931-5233) **864**
Europaeische Gemeinschaft fuer Kohle und Stahl. Beratender Ausschuss. Jahrbuch see European Coal and Steel Community. Consultative Committee. Yearbook **929**
Europaeische Gemeinschaft Magazin see E G Magazin **5183**
Europaeische Grundrechte Zeitschrift. (GW ISSN 0341-9800) **2623**
Europaeische Hefte. see Notes from Europe **5249**
Europaeische Integration. Mitteilungen. (EI) **3893**
Europaeische Integration - Auswahlbibliographie. (GW) **400**
†Europaeische Integration - Dokumentation. (GW ISSN 0723-4384) **5188**
Europaeische Intervention see Europaeische Integration. Mitteilungen **3893**
Europaeische Rundschau. (AU) **3956, 864**
Europaeische Schriften. (GW ISSN 0071-2329) **3956**
Europaeische Sicherheit. (GW) **3457**
Europaeische Sicherheit. Ausgabe "A". (GW) **3457**
Europaeische Stadtkultur. see Culture of European Cities **297**
†Europaeische Volksmusikinstrumente. Handbuch. (GW ISSN 0073-0025) **5188**
Europaeische Wehrkunde. (GW) **3457**
Europaeische Wehrkunde. Ausgabe "A" see Europaeische Sicherheit. Ausgabe "A **3457**
Europaeische Wehrkunde - Wehrwissenschaftliche Rundschau see Europaeische Sicherheit **3457**
Europaeische Zeitschrift fuer Forstpathologie. see European Journal of Forest Pathology **2099**
Europaeische Zeitschrift fuer Kombinatorik. see European Journal of Combinatorics **3035**
▼Europaeische Zeitschrift fuer Wirtschaftsrecht. (GW ISSN 0937-7204) **2623**
Europaeische Zeitung. (GW) **3956**
Europaeische Zeitung Europa-Union see Europaeische Zeitung **3956**
Europaeischer Molkerei und Kaeserei Adresskalender. (GW ISSN 0724-3219) **199**

Europaeischer Wetterbericht. (GW ISSN 0341-2970) **3435**
†Europaeischer Wirtschaftsdienst. Chemie-Dienst. (GW) **5188**
Europaeischer Wirtschaftsdienst. Eildienst Holz. (GW) **2114**
Europaeischer Wirtschaftsdienst. Einkaufsberater fuer die Moebelindustrie. (GW) **2558**
Europaeischer Wirtschaftsdienst. Informationsbrief Holz - Zellstoff - Papier. (GW) **3662**
Europaeischer Wirtschaftsdienst. Kunststoff-Dienst. (GW) **3862**
Europaeischer Wirtschaftsdienst. Laubholz-Dienst. (GW) **2114**
Europaeischer Wirtschaftsdienst. Moebel-Dienst. (GW) **2558**
Europaeischer Wirtschaftsdienst. Papier- und Zellstoff-Dienst. (GW) **3662**
Europaeischer Wirtschaftsdienst. Pulp and Paper Service. (GW) **3662**
†Europaeischer Wirtschaftsdienst. Textil- und Chemiefaser-Dienst. (GW) **5188**
Europaeischer Wirtschaftsdienst. Timber-Service. (GW) **2114**
Europaeisches Forum. (GW) **3956**
Europaeisches Patentblatt. (GW) **3674**
Europaeisches Transportrecht. see European Transport Law **4649**
Europaische Archiv fur Soziologie. see European Journal of Sociology **4435**
Europaische Bibliographie der Sowjet- und Oesteuropastudien. see European Bibliography of Soviet, East European and Slavonic Studies **2328**
Europaisches Patentamt. Amtsblatt/European Patent Office. Official Journal. (GW ISSN 0170-9291) **3674**
Europarecht. (GW ISSN 0531-2485) **2723**
Europastimme. (AU ISSN 0014-2727) **3956**
Europe. (EI ISSN 0191-4545) **864, 906, 3956**
Europe. (FR ISSN 0014-2751) **2865**
Europe (Year). (US) **4761**
Europe America Series. (US) **2406, 2310**
Europe by Eurail. (US) **4761, 4709**
Europe de Tradition Orale. (FR ISSN 0755-9313) **2813, 239**
Europe-Echecs. (FR ISSN 0014-2794) **4471, 1419**
Europe Energy. (BE) **1789**
Europe Entreprises. see European Intelligence **864**
Europe Environment. (BE) **1954**
Europe for Business Travelers. (US) **4761, 664**
Europe in the Middle Ages. (NE) **2360**
Europe - Latin America Report: Science and Technology. (US) **4309, 4597**
Europe Left. (UK ISSN 0046-2705) **3893, 3941**
Europe Magazine. (EI) **906, 864, 3956**
Europe-Magazine. (BE) **2865, 3893**
Europe Oil-Telegram. (GW ISSN 0014-2824) **3685**
Europe on Forty Dollars a Day. (US) **4761**
Europe on Thirty Dollars a Day see Europe on Forty Dollars a Day **4761**
Europe Outremer. (FR) **3956**
Europe Pulse see Pulse (Wheaton) **4196**
Europe Report. (US) **4177**
Europe Review. (UK) **864**
Europe Sans Frontieres. (UK) **664**
Europe Sud-Est. (GR) **3893**
Europe Today. see Evropa Danas **5189**
▼European Academy of Dermatology and Venereology. Journal. (NE ISSN 0926-9959) **3247**
European Access. (EI ISSN 0264-7362) **664**
European Accountant. (IE) **750**
European Accounting Association. Newsletter. (BE) **750**
European Action Report. (UK) **4237**
European Adhesives and Sealants. (UK) **3406**
European Advertising, Marketing, and Media Data (Year). (UK) **31, 1038**
European Affairs. (NE) **2865**

European and American Painting, Sculpture and Decorative Arts, Volume 1: 1300-1800. (CN) **325**
European and Mediterranean Plant Protection Organization. Publications. Series A: Reports of Technical Meetings see E P P O Bulletin **176**
†European and Mediterranean Plant Protection Organization. Publications. Series B: Plant Health Newsletter. (FR ISSN 0071-2396) **5188**
European and North American Scrap Directory see International Scrap Directory **3409**
†European Applied Research Reports: Environmental and Natural Resources Section. (US ISSN 0272-4626) **5188**
European Applied Research Reports: Nuclear Science and Technology Section. (US ISSN 0379-4229) **3847**
European Applied Research Reports Special Topics Series. (US ISSN 0273-2998) **3847**
European Aquaculture Society. Special Publications. (BE ISSN 0774-0689) **1604, 582, 2039**
European Aquaculture Society Quarterly Newsletter see Aquaculture Europe Magazine **1602**
European Archives of Biology. (BE ISSN 0003-9624) **438**
European Archives of Psychiatry and Neurological Sciences. (GW ISSN 0175-758X) **3336**
European Art Exhibitions. Catalog. (FR ISSN 0071-2426) **325**
European Aspects, Law Series. (FR ISSN 0531-2671) **2623**
European Aspects, Social Studies Series.(FR ISSN 0531-2663) **4435**
†European Association for American Studies. Biennial Report. (BE) **5188**
European Association for American Studies Newsletter see E A A S Newsletter **3955**
European Association for Animal Production. Publications. (IT ISSN 0071-2477) **216**
European Association for Personnel Management. Congress Reports. (FR ISSN 0071-2493) **1065**
European Association for Potato Research Abstracts of Conference Papers see E A P R Abstracts of Conference Papers **176**
European Association for Research on Plant Breeding. Report of the Congress see Eucarpia **501**
European Association of Remote Sensing Laboratories Advances in Remote Sensing see E A R S L Advances in Remote Sensing **1543**
European Association of Remote Sensing Laboratories Newsletter see E A R S L Newsletter **1543**
†European Atomic Energy Community. Contamination Radioactive des Denrees Alimentaires dans les Pays de la Communaute. (EI) **5188**
European Atomic Energy Community. Resultats des Mesures de la Radioactivite Ambiante dans les Pays de la Communaute: Air-Retombee-Eaux. (EI) **4100**
European Banker. (IE ISSN 0953-8399) **778**
European Bibliography of Soviet, East European and Slavonic Studies/Bibliographie Europeenne des Travaux sur l'URSS et l'Europe de l'Est/Europaische Bibliographie der Sowjet- und Oesteuropastudien. (FR ISSN 0140-492X) **2328, 400**
European Biophysical Journal see European Biophysics Journal **485**
European Biophysics Journal. (GW ISSN 0175-7571) **485**
European Biotechnology Newsletter. (FR ISSN 0765-2046) **489**
European Book Plates. see Bibliografi over Europaeiske Kunstneres Ex Libris **352**
European Bookdealers see Sheppard's Bookdealers in Europe **4137**

European Brewery Convention. Proceedings of the International Congress. (NE ISSN 0071-2531) **380**
European Broadcasting Union Monographs, Legal and Administrative Series see E B U Monographs, Legal and Administrative Series **1372**
European Broadcasting Union Review. (Programmes, Administration, Law Edition) see E B U Review. (Programmes, Administration, Law Edition) **5182**
European Broadcasting Union Seminars for Producers and Directors of Educational Television for Schools and Adults see E B U Seminars for Producers and Directors of Educational Television for Schools and Adults **1373**
European Broadcasting Union Technical Review see E B U Technical Review **1335**
European Broadcasting Union Workshops for Producers and Directors of Television Programmes for Children and Young People see E B U Workshops for Producers and Directors of Television Programmes for Children and Young People **1373**
European Bulletin and Press. (UK ISSN 0309-474X) **3893**
European Bulletin of Cognitive Psychology. see Cahiers de Psychologie Cognitive **4015**
European Bureau of Adult Education Newsletter see E B A E Newsletter **1683**
European Business. (BE) **664**
European Business Intelligence Briefing. (UK ISSN 0957-0039) **664**
The European Business Journal. (UK ISSN 0955-808X) **664**
▼European Business Law Review. (UK ISSN 0959-6941) **2623**
European Business Review. (UK ISSN 0955-534X) **664**
European Cancer News. (NE ISSN 0921-3732) **3197**
European Car. (US) **4690**
European Cement Association. European Annual Review. (BE) **637, 617**
European Cement Association. World Statistical Review. (BE) **637**
European Centre for Space News see E C S L News **51**
European Centre for the Development of Vocational Training (CEDEFOP) News see C E D E F O P News **5156**
European Ceramic Society. Journal. (UK ISSN 0955-2219) **1163**
†European Challenge. (SP) **5188**
European Chemical News. (UK ISSN 0014-2875) **1853**
European Christian Mission (Australian Section) Inc. News see E.C.M. News **4175**
European Civil Aviation Conference (Report of Session). (UN ISSN 0071-2558) **4672**
European Clinical Laboratory. (US ISSN 0888-7128) **3259**
European Co-Operation. (FR ISSN 0589-9575) **2723**
European Coal and Steel Community. Consultative Committee. Handbook. (EI) **929**
European Coal and Steel Community. Consultative Committee. Yearbook. (EI ISSN 0423-6831) **929**
European Coatings Journal. (GW ISSN 0930-3847) **3653**
European Coffee Report. (BE) **2066**
European Cognitive Psychology see European Journal of Cognitive Psychology **4020**
European Colloquium on Renal Physiology (Proceedings). (SW) **3388**
European Commercial Cases. (UK ISSN 0141-7266) **2624**
European Commission of Human Rights. Decisions and Reports. (FR ISSN 0379-8461) **3941**

EUROPEAN COMMUNITIES

European Communities. Diario Oficial. (EI) **4059**
European Communities. Economic and Social Committee. Annual Report (Year). (EI) **664, 3956**
European Communities. Economic and Social Committee. Bulletin. (EI ISSN 0010-2423) **664**
European Communities. Economic and Social Committee. Commission Documents. (EI) **664**
European Communities. Economic and Social Committee. Opinions and Reports *see* European Communities. Economic and Social Committee. Commission Documents **664**
†European Communities. Economic and Social Committee. Yearbook. (EI) **5188**
European Communities and Other European Organizations Who's Who *see* Euro - Who's Who **418**
▼The European Communities Encyclopedia and Directory (Year). (UK ISSN 0962-1032) **1780, 1134, 3956**
European Communities Legislation: Current Status. (UK) **2624**
European Community *see* Europe **864**
The European Community. (US ISSN 1045-3857) **906, 3893**
European Community Affairs. (US) **815**
European Community Dairy Facts and Figures *see* E C Dairy Facts and Figures **199**
European Community Law Series. (UK) **2723**
European Community Public Contract Law *see* E C Public Contract Law **4087**
†European Companies. (UK ISSN 0071-2582) **5188**
European Company for the Financing of Railway Rolling Stock. Annual Report. (SZ ISSN 0071-2264) **4709**
European Conference of Local and Regional Authorities. Official Reports of Debates *see* Standing Conference of Local and Regional Authorities of Europe. Official Reports of Debates **4074**
European Conference of Local and Regional Authorities. Texts Adopted *see* Standing Conference of Local and Regional Authorities of Europe. Texts Adopted **4074**
European Conference on Controlled Fusion and Plasma Physics. Proceedings. (SZ) **3847**
▼European Conference on Design Automation. (US) **1413**
European Conference on Mixing and Centrifugal Separation. Proceedings. (UK ISSN 0140-2129) **1853**
European Congress of Anaesthesiology. Proceedings. (SP ISSN 0071-2671) **3191**
European Congress of Cardiology. Abstracts of Papers. (UK ISSN 0421-7527) **3207**
European Congress of Cardiology. (Proceedings). (UK ISSN 0423-7242) **3207**
European Congress on Electron Microscopy. (IS ISSN 0071-2647) **559**
European Convention on Human Rights. Yearbook. (NE ISSN 0071-2701) **3941**
†European Cotton Industry Statistics. (IT ISSN 0423-7269) **5188**
European Council of Jewish Community Services. Exchange. (FR) **4405, 2001**
European Council of Jewish Community Services. Exchange Information Service *see* European Council of Jewish Community Services. Exchange **4405**
European Court of Human Rights. Publications. Series A: Judgments and Decisions/Cour Europeenne des Droits de l'Homme. Publications. Serie A: Arrets et Decisions. (GW ISSN 0073-3903) **3941**

European Court of Human Rights. Publications. Series B: Pleadings, Oral Arguments and Documents/Cour Europeenne des Droits de l'Homme. Publications. Serie B: Memoires, Plaidoiries et Documents. (GW ISSN 0073-3911) **3942**
European Cups. (UK) **4503**
European Cytokine Network. (FR ISSN 1148-5493) **541**
European Dairy Magazine. (GW ISSN 0936-6318) **199**
European Deal Review. (US) **664**
European Design Automation Conference Proceedings *see* European Conference on Design Automation **1413**
European Dimension in Teaching *see* E D I T **1626**
European Direct Marketing Association Gram *see* E D M A - Gram **31**
European Directory of Agrochemical Products. (UK) **88, 1177**
European Directory of Contractors. (UK) **617**
▼European Directory of Management Consultants. (UK) **1009**
European Directory of Marketing Information Sources. (UK ISSN 0950-656X) **1038**
European Documentation and Information System for Education Bulletin *see* E U D I S E D - R & D Bulletin **1676**
European Documentation Centre Newsletter *see* E D C Newsletter **2756**
European Earthquake Engineering. (IT ISSN 0394-5103) **1821, 1588**
European Economic Community Information Services *see* E E C Information Services **5183**
European Economic Community Information Services. Bulletin *see* E E C Information Services. Bulletin **5183**
European Economic Community Tin in Tinplate *see* E E C - Tin in Tinplate **3405**
European Economic Review. (NE ISSN 0014-2921) **664**
European Economics Editor. (GW) **1009, 2569**
European Economy. (EI ISSN 0379-217X) **864**
European Economy. Series A: Recent Economic Trends. (EI) **864**
European Economy. Series B: Business and Consumer Survey Results. (EI) **864**
European Economy. Supplement A: Recent Economic Trends *see* European Economy. Series A: Recent Economic Trends **864**
European Economy. Supplement B: Economic Prospects - Business Survey Results *see* European Economy. Series B: Business and Consumer Survey Results **864**
European Education. (US) **1632**
European Electrical & Electronic Engineering. (GW) **1892**
▼European Electro-Optics. (US) **1771**
European Electronic Component Distributor Directory. (UK ISSN 0143-2958) **1771, 1134**
European Electronics Companies File *see* World Electronics Companies File **1160**
European Electronics Directory (Year) - Components & Sub-Assemblies. (UK) **1134, 1771**
European Energy Report. (UK) **1789**
European Environmental Yearbook *see* Annuario Europeo dell'Ambiente **1943**
European Federation for Intercultural Learning Documentation *see* E F I L Documentation **1721**
European Federation for Intercultural Learning Newsletter *see* E F I L Newsletter **1721**
European Federation of Finance House Associations. Annual Report. (BE ISSN 0071-2787) **778**
European Federation of Finance House Associations. Newsletter. (BE ISSN 0300-4252) **778**

European File. (EI ISSN 0379-3133) **906**
European Financial Services Journal *see* E U F I - Journal **776**
European Food and Drink Review. (UK ISSN 0955-4416) **2066, 380**
European Food Trades Directory. (UK) **2066**
European Foundation for the Improvement of Living and Working Conditions. Annual Report. (EI) **4435**
European Free Trade Association. Annual Report. (SZ ISSN 0531-4127) **906**
European Free Trade Association Bulletin *see* E F T A Bulletin **906**
European Free Trade Association Trade *see* E F T A Trade **906**
European Freedom Review *see* Terra Nova **3973**
European Furniture Review. (GW) **2558, 1134**
European Gen - Set Directory. (UK) **1892**
European Generating Set Directory. (UK) **1892**
European Glass Directory and Buyer's Guide. (UK ISSN 0306-204X) **1134, 1163**
European Grassland Federation. Proceedings of the General Meeting. (BE ISSN 0071-2825) **176**
European Grocery Letter. (UK ISSN 0014-2948) **2091**
European Heart Journal. (UK ISSN 0195-668X) **3207**
European Helicopter Association Handbook. (UK) **4673**
European History Quarterly. (UK ISSN 0265-6914) **2360**
European Human Rights Reports. (UK ISSN 0260-4868) **2624, 3942**
European Illustration. (UK) **325**
European Industrial Relations Review. (UK ISSN 0309-7234) **979**
European Information Association News *see* E I A News **3955**
European Information Bulletin. (UK) **979, 2582**
European Information Service. (UK ISSN 0261-2747) **2757**
European Insight/Lettre Europeenne. (BE) **906**
European Intelligence/Europe Entreprises. (BE ISSN 0030-3593) **864, 1075**
European Investment Bank. Annual Report. (EI ISSN 0071-2868) **778**
European Investment Bank in (Year). (LU) **778**
European Investment Bank Information *see* E I B - Information **945**
European Investment Banking Report *see* International Investment Banking Report **671**
European Jeweler Special. (GW) **2563**
▼EuroPean Journal for Fluid Power. (GW ISSN 0937-8243) **1929**
▼European Journal of Agronomy. (FR) **176**
European Journal of Anaesthesiology. (UK ISSN 0265-0215) **3191**
▼European Journal of Applied Mathematics. (UK ISSN 0956-7925) **3035**
European Journal of Applied Physiology and Occupational Physiology. (GW ISSN 0301-5548) **571, 3097**
European Journal of Biochemistry. (GW ISSN 0014-2956) **476, 3097**
European Journal of Cancer and Clinical Oncology *see* European Journal of Cancer Part A **3197**
European Journal of Cancer Part A. (US ISSN 0964-1947) **3197**
▼European Journal of Cancer Part B: Oral Oncology. (UK ISSN 0964-1955) **3197**
▼European Journal of Cancer Prevention. (UK ISSN 0959-8278) **3197**
European Journal of Cardio-Thoracic Surgery. (GW ISSN 1010-7940) **3207**
European Journal of Cardiology *see* International Journal of Cardiology **3209**

European Journal of Cell Biology. (GW ISSN 0171-9335) **560, 524**
European Journal of Chiropractic. (UK ISSN 0263-9114) **3214**
European Journal of Clinical Chemistry and Clinical Biochemistry. (GW ISSN 0939-4974) **476**
European Journal of Clinical Investigation. (UK ISSN 0014-2972) **3097**
European Journal of Clinical Microbiology *see* European Journal of Clinical Microbiology & Infectious Diseases **551**
European Journal of Clinical Microbiology & Infectious Diseases. (GW ISSN 0934-9723) **551**
European Journal of Clinical Pharmacology. (GW ISSN 0031-6970) **3725**
▼European Journal of Clinical Research. (UK ISSN 0961-3692) **3097**
European Journal of Cognitive Psychology. (UK) **4020**
European Journal of Combinatorics/Journal Europeen de Combinatoire/Europaeische Zeitschrift fuer Kombinatorik. (UK ISSN 0195-6698) **3035**
European Journal of Communication. (UK ISSN 0267-3231) **1335**
European Journal of Dermatology. *see* Journal Europeen de Dermatologie **3248**
European Journal of Development Research. (UK ISSN 0957-8811) **929, 3893**
European Journal of Disorders of Communication. (UK ISSN 0963-7273) **1735**
European Journal of Drug Metabolism and Pharmacokinetics. (SZ ISSN 0378-7966) **3725**
European Journal of Education. (UK ISSN 0141-8211) **1632**
European Journal of Emergencies. *see* Journal Europeen des Urgences **3113**
European Journal of Engineering Education. (UK ISSN 0304-3797) **1821, 1632**
European Journal of Epidemiology. (GW) **3097, 3378**
European Journal of Forest Pathology/Journal Europeen de Pathologie Forestiere/Europaeische Zeitschrift fuer Forstpathologie. (GW ISSN 0300-1237) **2099**
European Journal of Gastroenterology and Hepatology. (US ISSN 0954-691X) **3171, 3267**
European Journal of Gynecological Oncology. (IT ISSN 0392-2936) **3197, 3291**
European Journal of Haematology. (DK ISSN 0902-4441) **3271**
European Journal of Haematology. Supplementum. (DK ISSN 0902-4506) **3272**
European Journal of Hospital Pharmacy.(GW ISSN 0939-9437) **3725**
European Journal of Immunogenetics. (UK ISSN 0960-7420) **541**
European Journal of Immunology. (GW ISSN 0014-2980) **3185**
European Journal of Implant and Refractive Surgery. (UK ISSN 0955-3681) **3300**
▼European Journal of Information Systems. (UK ISSN 0960-085X) **1456, 1009**
▼European Journal of Intercultural Studies. (UK ISSN 0952-391X) **4435**
European Journal of International Affairs. (IT ISSN 0394-6444) **3956, 906**
▼European Journal of International Law. (GW ISSN 0938-5428) **2723**
European Journal of Marketing. (UK ISSN 0309-0566) **1038**
European Journal of Mechanical Engineering. (NE ISSN 0777-2734) **1929, 1916, 3843**
European Journal of Mechanics A - Solids. (FR ISSN 0997-7538) **3843**

European Journal of Mechanics B - Fluids. (FR ISSN 0997-7546) **3843**
European Journal of Medicinal Chemistry. (FR ISSN 0009-4374) **476**, **1218**, **3725**
European Journal of Mineralogy. (GW ISSN 0935-1221) **3483**, **1560**
European Journal of Morphology. (NE ISSN 0924-3860) **3097**
European Journal of Neuroscience. (UK ISSN 0953-816X) **3336**, **476**
European Journal of Nuclear Medicine. (GW ISSN 0340-6997) **3358**
European Journal of Obstetrics, Gynecology and Reproductive Biology. (NE ISSN 0301-2115) **3291**
European Journal of Operational Research. (NE ISSN 0377-2217) **1009**
▼European Journal of Ophthalmology. (IT ISSN 1120-6721) **3300**
European Journal of Orthodontics. (UK ISSN 0141-5387) **3233**
European Journal of Pain. (GW ISSN 0939-6365) **3097**, **3191**
European Journal of Parapsychology. (NE) **3669**
European Journal of Pediatric Surgery. (FR ISSN 0939-7248) **3378**
European Journal of Pediatrics. (GW ISSN 0340-6199) **3320**
European Journal of Personality. (UK ISSN 0890-2070) **4020**
European Journal of Pharmaceutics and Biopharmaceutics. (GW ISSN 0939-6411) **3725**
European Journal of Pharmacology. (NE ISSN 0014-2999) **3725**
▼European Journal of Pharmacology. Environmental Toxicology and Pharmacology Section. (NE ISSN 0926-6917) **1981**, **3725**
European Journal of Pharmacology. Molecular Pharmacology Section. (NE ISSN 0922-4106) **3725**
European Journal of Physical Medicine and Rehabilitation. (AU ISSN 1017-6721) **3097**
European Journal of Physics. (UK ISSN 0143-0807) **3817**
European Journal of Plastic Surgery. (GW ISSN 0930-343X) **3378**
European Journal of Political Economy. (NE ISSN 0176-2680) **998**, **3893**
European Journal of Political Research. (NE ISSN 0304-4130) **3893**
European Journal of Population/Revue Europeenne de Demographie. (NE ISSN 0168-6577) **3992**
European Journal of Protistology. (GW ISSN 0932-4739) **3657**
European Journal of Psychology of Education. (PO ISSN 0256-2928) **1632**, **4020**
European Journal of Radiology. (NE ISSN 0720-048X) **3358**
European Journal of Respiratory Diseases see European Respiratory Journal **3365**
European Journal of Science Education see International Journal of Science Education **1640**
European Journal of Serials Librarianship. (US ISSN 1048-5287) **2757**
European Journal of Social Psychology. (UK ISSN 0046-2772) **4021**, **4435**
European Journal of Sociology/Archives Europeennes de Sociologie/ Europaische Archiv fur Soziologie. (UK ISSN 0003-9756) **4435**
European Journal of Soil Biology. (FR) **438**
European Journal of Solid State and Inorganic Chemistry. (FR ISSN 0992-4361) **1213**
European Journal of Special Needs Education. (UK ISSN 0885-6257) **1735**
European Journal of Surgical Oncology. (UK ISSN 0748-7983) **3197**
European Journal of Teacher Education.(UK ISSN 0261-9768) **1633**

▼European Journal of Theology. (UK ISSN 0960-2720) **4237**
European Journal of Vascular Surgery. (UK ISSN 0950-821X) **3208**, **3378**
European Joyce Studies. (NE) **2916**, **418**
European Judaism. (UK ISSN 0014-3006) **4222**
European Labor and Working Class History Newsletter see International Labor and Working Class History **983**
European Labour Forum see E L F **3955**
†European Law Digest. (UK ISSN 0305-8476) **5188**
European Law Letter see Business Law Brief **2707**
European Law Newsletter see Business Law Brief **2707**
European Law Review. (UK ISSN 0307-5400) **2624**
European League Against Rheumatism Bulletin see E U L A R Bulletin **3369**
European League for Economic Cooperation. Publications. (BE ISSN 0071-2884) **929**
European League for Economic Cooperation. Report of the Secretary General on the Activities of E.L.E.C. (BE ISSN 0531-7436) **929**
European League for Economic Cooperation. Reports of the International Congress. (BE ISSN 0071-2892) **929**
European Literary Market Place see International Literary Market Place **4130**
European Management Journal. (UK ISSN 0263-2373) **1009**
European Marketing Association. International Marketing and Research Conference. Journal. (UK) **1039**, **31**
European Marketing Association. Newsletter. (UK) **1039**, **31**
European Marketing Data and Statistics.(UK ISSN 0071-2930) **1039**
European Markets: a Guide to Company and Industry Information Sources. (US) **906**, **1134**
European Mediafacts. (UK) **1373**
European Microwave Conference Proceedings. (UK) **1892**
European Molecular Biology Organization Journal see E M B O Journal **476**
†European Monetary Agreement. Report of the Board of Management. (FR ISSN 0071-2957) **5188**
European Monographs in Social Psychology. (US) **4021**
European Motor Business. (UK ISSN 0267-8233) **4690**
European Neurology. (SZ ISSN 0014-3022) **3336**
▼European Neuropsychopharmacology.(NE ISSN 0924-977X) **3336**, **3725**
European Numismatics. (NE ISSN 0014-3030) **3599**
European Office Furniture. (GW) **2558**
European Offshore Petroleum Newsletter. (NO ISSN 0332-5210) **3685**
European Ophthalmological Society. Congress Acta. (FR ISSN 0301-326X) **3300**
European Organisation for Civil Aviation Equipment. General Assembly. Annual Report. (FR ISSN 0531-7444) **51**, **1892**
European Organization for Nuclear Research. Liste des Publications Scientifiques/List of Scientific Publications. (SZ ISSN 0304-2871) **3837**, **400**
European Organization for Nuclear Research. Repertoire des Communications Scientifiques. Index of Scientific Publications see European Organization for Nuclear Research. Liste des Publications Scientifiques/List of Scientific Publications **3837**

European Organization for Quality. Conference Proceedings. (SZ) **4597**, **1821**
European Organization for Quality Control. Conference Proceedings see European Organization for Quality. Conference Proceedings **4597**
European Organization for Research on Treatment of Cancer. Monograph Series. (US) **3197**
European Packaging Newsletter and World Report. (US ISSN 1052-2131) **3648**
European Paint and Resin News. (UK ISSN 0266-7800) **3653**
European Paper Institute. Annual Statistics. (FR) **3668**
European Parliament. Bulletin. (EI ISSN 0423-7846) **3956**
European Parliament. Christian-Democratic Group. Report on the Activities. (EI) **3893**
European Parliament. Committee Report. (EI) **3392**
European Parliament. Documents de Seance see European Parliament. Working Documents **2723**
European Parliament. Research and Documentation Papers. (EI) **1954**, **1504**, **4100**
European Parliament. Working Documents. (EI) **2723**
European Parliament News see E P News **2722**
European Patent Office. Annual Report. (GW ISSN 0724-7729) **3674**
European Patent Office. Official Journal. see Europaisches Patentamt. Amtsblatt **3674**
European Patent Office Reports. (UK ISSN 0269-0802) **3674**, **2723**
European Patents Handbook. (UK) **3674**
European Petroleum Directory. (US ISSN 0275-3871) **3685**
European Petroleum Yearbook/ Jahrbuch der Europaeischen Erdoelindustrie/Annuaire Europeen du Petrole. (GW ISSN 0342-6947) **3685**
European Photochemistry Association Newsletter see E P A Newsletter **1225**
European Photography. (UK) **3790**
European Photography. (GW ISSN 0172-7028) **3790**, **325**
European Plastics News. (UK ISSN 0306-3534) **3862**
European Political Cooperation Documentation Bulletin. (EI ISSN 0259-2290) **3893**
†European Political Data Newsletter. (NO ISSN 0333-273X) **5188**
European Polymer Journal. (US ISSN 0014-3057) **1218**
European Power News. (UK) **1892**, **1789**
European Production Engineer see E P E **1928**
European Psychiatry. (FR ISSN 0924-9338) **3336**
European Racehorse. (UK ISSN 0260-7468) **4534**
▼European Radiology. (GW ISSN 0938-7994) **3358**
European Regional Incentives. (UK) **864**
European Report/Europolitique. (BE) **778**
European Research see Marketing and Research Today **1046**
European Research Centres. (UK) **4309**, **1134**, **4597**
European Research in Regional Science.(UK ISSN 0960-6130) **2487**
European Research Library Cooperation. (GW) **2757**
European Respiratory Journal. (DK ISSN 0903-1936) **3365**
†European Review. (BE ISSN 0261-8249) **5188**
European Review of Agricultural Economics. (GW ISSN 0165-1587) **150**
European Review of Applied Psychology. see Revue Europeene de Psychologie Appliquee **4045**

European Review of Latin American and Caribbean Studies/Revista Europea de Estudios Latinoamericanos y del Caribe. (NE ISSN 0924-0608) **4371**
European Review of Native American Studies. (AU ISSN 0238-1486) **2001**
▼European Review of Social Psychology. (UK ISSN 1046-3283) **4021**
▼European Romantic Review. (US) **2916**
European Rubber Journal. (UK ISSN 0260-5317) **4291**
European Safety and Reliability Association. Bulletin. (EI ISSN 1010-8149) **4100**
European Savings Bank. Report. (EI) **778**
European Science Notes. (US) **4309**
European Scrap Directory see International Scrap Directory **3409**
European Sectoral Service see D R I - McGraw-Hill Industry Review **859**
European Sectoral Service Review see D R I - McGraw-Hill Industry Review **859**
European Security Industry Buyer's Guide (Year). (UK ISSN 0956-9170) **1526**, **2031**
European Semiconductor. (UK) **1771**
European Semiconductor Design and Production see European Semiconductor **1771**
†European Social Fund. Annual Report on the Activities of the New European Social Fund. (EI) **5188**
†European Socialist Thought Series. (UK) **5188**
European Sociological Review. (UK ISSN 0266-7215) **4435**
European Solid State Device Research Conference. Solid State Devices. (UK) **3859**
European Sources of Scientific and Technical Information. (UK) **4309**, **4597**
European Southern Observatory. Annual Report. (GW ISSN 0531-4496) **364**
European Southern Observatory Foelgeforskning see E S O Foelgeforskning **364**
European Space Agency Bulletin see E S A Bulletin **51**
European Space Agency Journal see E S A Journal **51**
European Space Agency News & Views see E S A - I R S News & Views **2797**
European Space Agency Procedures, Standards and Specifications Series see E S A Procedures, Standards and Specifications Series **51**
European Space Agency Scientific - Technical Reports, Notes and Memoranda see E S A Scientific - Technical Reports, Notes and Memoranda **51**
†European Spending Quarterly. (UK) **5188**
†European Sponsorship Newsletter. (FR ISSN 0995-2721) **5188**
▼European Studies. (DK ISSN 0906-0308) **2360**, **2916**, **4371**
European Studies see Exploring Europe **5189**
European Studies in Law. (NE) **2624**
European Studies Journal. (US ISSN 0820-6244) **2360**, **271**, **325**, **4177**
European Studies Newsletter. (US ISSN 0046-2802) **4371**, **2360**, **2506**
European Surgical Research. (SZ ISSN 0014-312X) **3378**
European Symposium on Chemical Reaction Engineering. Proceedings see International Symposium on Chemical Reaction Engineering. Proceedings **1855**
European Symposium on Concrete Pavements. Reports see International Symposium on Concrete Roads. Reports **1868**
European Tableware Buyers Guide. (UK) **355**
European Taxation. (NE ISSN 0014-3138) **1093**

EUROPEAN TELECOMMUNICATIONS

European Telecommunications. (US ISSN 8756-4459) **1362**
†European Tourism & Congress - Der Fremdenverkehr. (GW) **5188**
European Trade Union. Contacts. (CS) **2582**
European Transactions on Electrical Power Engineering see E T E P **1886**
European Transactions on Telecommunications and Related Technologies. (IT ISSN 1120-3862) **1335, 1362**
European Transport Law/Droit Europeen des Transports/Europaeisches Transportrecht/Diritto Europeo dei Trasporti/Europees Vervoerrecht. (BE ISSN 0014-3154) **4649, 2723**
European Travel and Entertainment Magazine. (US) **4761**
European Travel & Life. (US ISSN 0882-7737) **4761, 2361**
European Travel Guide for Jews. see Guide Touristique Europeen pour Israelites **2003**
European Trends. (UK ISSN 0014-3162) **864**
†European Truck & Trailer. (GW ISSN 0175-6281) **5188**
European Trucks Forecast Report. (US) **4744**
European University News. (EI ISSN 0014-3170) **1633, 3893**
European Update. (BE) **1093**
European Urology. (SZ ISSN 0302-2838) **3388**
European Water Pollution Control. (NE ISSN 0925-5060) **1977, 4824**
European Woodworking Machinery and Accessories. (GW) **2558**
▼European Work and Organizational Psychologist. (UK ISSN 0960-2003) **4021**
European Yearbook. (NE ISSN 0071-3139) **929**
Europees Vervoerrecht. see European Transport Law **4649**
Europeisk Nyhedsbrev. (DK ISSN 0900-5323) **906**
Europeo. (IT ISSN 0014-3189) **2205**
Europeo. (SP) **2217**
Europe's 15000 Largest Companies. (UK ISSN 0800-0638) **1075**
Europetroleum. (UK ISSN 0956-6333) **3685**
Europhysics Conference Abstracts. (SZ) **3837**
Europhysics Letters. (FR) **3817**
Europhysics News. (SZ ISSN 0531-7479) **3817**
Europiano. (SZ) **3551**
†Europick News. (UK) **5188**
Europolitique. see European Report **778**
Europro. Congress Summaries. (SZ) **3999**
EUROSIM - Simulation News Europe. (AU) **1435**
Euroski. (IT) **4471**
▼Euroslot. (UK) **1039**
Eurosocial Bulletin d'Information. see Eurosocial Newsletter **4405**
Eurosocial Nachrichten. see Eurosocial Newsletter **4405**
Eurosocial Newsletter/Eurosocial Bulletin d'Information/Eurosocial Nachrichten. (AU ISSN 0253-7427) **4405**
Eurosport and Freizeitmode see Sportshop **4492**
†Eurostat News. (EI ISSN 0378-4207) **5189**
Eurostatistics see Eurostatistics Data for Short Term Economic Analysis **715**
Eurostatistics Data for Short Term Economic Analysis. (EI) **715**
Eurosud. (IT ISSN 0014-3235) **3957**
Eurosurgery. (IT) **3378**
Eurotec. (SZ ISSN 0014-3243) **4597**
†Eurotechnologies. (FR) **5189**
†Eurotrade (Dutch Edition). (NE ISSN 0920-8437) **5189**
†Eurotrade (English Edition). (NE ISSN 0920-8453) **5189**
†Eurotrade (French Edition). (NE ISSN 0920-8445) **5189**
†Eurotrade (German Edition). (NE ISSN 0920-8461) **5189**
Eurotransports. (IT) **4649**

Eurotransports Illustrato see Eurotransports **4649**
Euroviande. (FR) **2066**
EuroVision Advance see Breakthrough (Wheaton) **4280**
Eurovolley Magazine. (GW) **4503**
Eurowatch. (US) **3957,** 929
†Euthanasia Review. (US ISSN 0884-2981) **5189**
Eva. (CS) **1290,** 372, 4841
Eva. (DR ISSN 0014-3286) **4841,** 2446
Eva see Eva Express **4841**
†Eva. (DK ISSN 0014-3278) **5189**
Eva Airways Verve. (CH) **4802**
Eva Express. (IT ISSN 0014-3308) **4841**
Evaluateur Canadien. see Canadian Appraiser **4146**
Evaluating and Buying a Franchise. (US) **864,** 945
Evaluation and Program Planning. (US ISSN 0149-7189) **4372**
Evaluation and Research in Education. (UK ISSN 0950-0790) **1633**
Evaluation and the Health Professions. (US ISSN 0163-2787) **3097**
Evaluation Comment. (US) **1633,** 4435
Evaluation Engineering see E E: Evaluation Engineering **1766**
Evaluation in Education see International Journal of Educational Research **1722**
Evaluation Methods Series see U.S. Civil Service Commission. Bureau of Personnel Management Evaluation. Evaluation Methods Series **5295**
Evaluation News see Evaluation Practice **4372**
Evaluation of Audio Recordings Children see E A R for Children **5182**
Evaluation of Drug Interactions. (US) **3725**
Evaluation Practice. (US ISSN 0886-1633) **4372**
Evaluation Review. (US ISSN 0193-841X) **4372**
Evaluator. (US ISSN 8756-775X) **257,** 325
Evangel. (UK) **4177**
Evangel. (US ISSN 0162-1890) **4237**
Evangelical & Reformed Historical Society Newsletter. (US) **4177,** 2406
Evangelical Baptist. (CN ISSN 0014-3324) **4237**
Evangelical Baptist Churches in Canada. Fellowship Yearbook. (CN ISSN 0317-266X) **4237**
Evangelical Beacon. (US ISSN 0014-3332) **4237**
Evangelical Catholic. (US) **4177**
Evangelical Congregational Church Doors and Windows see E.C. Doors and Windows **4236**
Evangelical Friend. (US ISSN 0014-3340) **4282**
Evangelical Lutheran Church in America (Year). (US) **4237**
†Evangelical Magazine. (UK ISSN 0046-2853) **5189**
Evangelical Magazine of Wales. (UK ISSN 0421-8094) **4237,** 2001, 2361
Evangelical Missions Quarterly. (US ISSN 0014-3359) **4177**
Evangelical Morning. see Yevanhelskyj Ranok **4253**
Evangelical Quarterly. (UK ISSN 0014-3367) **4177**
Evangelical Review Magazine. (US) **4177**
Evangelical Review of Theology. (UK ISSN 0144-8153) **4177**
Evangelical Theological Society. Journal.(US ISSN 0360-8808) **4237**
Evangelical Truth. (CN ISSN 0014-3375) **4282**
Evangelical Visitor. (US ISSN 0745-0486) **4177**
Evangelical Women's Caucus. Update. (US) **4177**
Evangelie en Maatschappij see C N V - Opinie **4167**
Evangelii Haerold. (SW ISSN 0345-2980) **4282**

Evangelikale Missiologie. (GW ISSN 0177-8706) **4237,** 2332, 2338, 2406
Evangelikus Elet. (HU) **4237**
Evangelio y Mision. (SP) **4177**
Evangelisch-Lutherische Landeskirche Sachsens. Amtsblatt. (GW ISSN 0423-8346) **4237**
Evangelisch-Lutherisches Missionswerk in Niedersachsen. Jahrbuch (Year). (GW) **4237**
Evangelisch-methodische Kirche Aktuell see E M K Aktuell **4236**
Der Evangelische Buchberater. (GW ISSN 0930-8873) **4282,** 2757
Der Evangelische Erzieher. (GW ISSN 0014-3413) **1633,** 4177
Evangelische Fachhochschulen Darmstadt, Freiburg, Ludwigshafen, Reutlingen. Hochschulbrief. (GW ISSN 0344-1466) **1633**
Evangelische Impulse. (GW) **2272,** 4177
Evangelische Jugend in Bayern. Nachrichten. (GW ISSN 0937-1729) **4237,** 1237
Evangelische Kinderpflege fuer Kindergarten, Hort, Heim und Familie see Theorie und Praxis der Sozialpaedagogik **1245**
Evangelische Kirche der Kirchenprovinz Sachsen. Amtsblatt. (GW ISSN 0232-6310) **4237,** 2624
Evangelische Kirche in Deutschland. Amtsblatt. (GW ISSN 0014-343X) **4237**
Evangelische Kirchenzeitung. (GW) **4237**
Evangelische Kommentare. (GW ISSN 0300-4236) **4177**
Evangelische Landeskirche in Wuerttemberg. Amtsblatt. (GW ISSN 0014-3529) **4237**
Evangelische Lutherische Kirche in Bayern. Pfarrer- und Pfarrerinnenverein. Korrespondenzblatt. (GW) **4237**
Evangelisch-Lutherische Kirche in Thueringen. Amtsblatt. (GW ISSN 0014-326X) **4237**
Evangelische Mission Jahrbuch see Jahrbuch Mission **4183**
Evangelische Pfarrgemeinde A.B. Wien-Favoriten-Christuskirche. Gemeindebrief. (AU ISSN 0016-6154) **4237**
Evangelische Sammlung. (GW) **4177**
Evangelische Theologie. (GW ISSN 0014-3502) **4177**
Evangelische Zentralstelle fuer Weltanschauungsfragen Texte see E Z W - Texte **4175**
Evangelischer Botschaft see Wort und Weg **4253**
Evangelischer Bund. (GW ISSN 0933-7857) **4237**
Evangelischer Bund. Materialdienst see Materialdienst des Konfessionskundlichen Instituts **4269**
Evangelischer Bund in Oesterreich. Schriftenreihe. (AU ISSN 0036-6943) **4237**
Evangelischer Digest. (GW ISSN 0177-185X) **4177,** 2189, 2272
Evangelischer Informationsdienst fuer Jugend- und Erwachsenbildung see Evangelischer Informationsdienst fuer Jugend- und Erwachsenbildung auf dem Lande **4237**
Evangelischer Informationsdienst fuer Jugend- und Erwachsenbildung auf dem Lande. (GW) **4237**
†Evangelischer Nachrichtendienst in der D D R. (GW ISSN 0014-3553) **5189**
Evangelisches Gemeindeblatt Berlin see Nathanael Evangelisches Gemeindeblatt **4244**
Evangelisches Gemeindeblatt fuer Wuerttemberg. (GW ISSN 0014-360X) **4237**
Evangelisches Missionswerk in Suedwestdeutschland e.V. Jahrbuch see E M S - Jahrbuch **4236**
Evangelisches Missionswerk Informationen see E M W - Informationen **4175**

Evangeliska Fosterlands-Stiftelsen Till Tjaenst see Till Tjaenst **1668**
Evangelism Today. (UK) **4177**
Evangelist see Pendulum **4195**
Evangelist see Wort und Weg **4253**
Evangelist (Albany). (US ISSN 0738-8489) **4264**
Evangelist (Pasadena). (US ISSN 0014-3626) **4282**
Evangelium-Gospel. (GW ISSN 0177-462X) **4237**
Evangelizing Today's Child. (US ISSN 0891-3846) **4238,** 1237, 1749
Evangelizzare. (IT) **4177**
Evangel's'kyj Golos see levanhel's'kyi Holos **4284**
Evangile et Liberte. (FR) **4238**
Evanjelicky Hlasnik. (YU ISSN 0014-3642) **4238**
Evans Ancestory. (US) **2150**
▼Evans & Novak Defense Letter. (US) **3458**
Evans-Novak Political Report. (US ISSN 0014-3650) **3893**
Evans Report. (CN) **1821**
Evansville - Vanderburgh County Public Libraries. Staff News Bulletin. (US) **2757**
Evansville - Vanderburgh County Public Library. Staff News Bulletin see Evansville - Vanderburgh County Public Libraries. Staff News Bulletin **2757**
Eve. (HK) **4841**
Eve. see Hawa'a **4844**
Eveil du Travailleur Togolais. (TG) **979**
Evelyn Booster. (DK) **3551**
Evelyn Waugh Newsletter see Evelyn Waugh Newsletter and Studies **2916**
Evelyn Waugh Newsletter and Studies. (US) **2916**
Even Uitblazen see Mixture **4644**
L'Evenement. (BE) **2174**
Evenement du Jeudi. (FR) **2186**
Evener see Rural Heritage **4537**
Evening. see Al-Missa **2185**
Evening Times Wee Red Book. (UK) **4503**
Evensongs/Yeh Ko. (CH) **2865**
Event. (CN ISSN 0315-3770) **2916**
Event. (US ISSN 0014-374X) **4238**
Event (Pequannock) see Naturally **3806**
Event South West. (UK) **2865**
Eventi e Interventi. (IT) **326,** 2916
Eventline. (NE) **1134**
Evento Teatrale. Sezione: Autori Italiani del Novecento. (IT) **4633**
Eventos em Politica Cientifica e Tecnologica. (BL) **4597, 4309**
▼Events - U S A. (US) **4761**
Ever - Ready. see Eso - Etimos **2184**
Evergreen. (II ISSN 0254-6426) **2099**
Evergreen Chronicles. (US ISSN 1043-3333) **2916,** 2452
Evergreen Monthly. (CH) **3801**
Everson Museum of Art Bulletin. (US) **3524**
Everwild. (CN) **1487**
Every Wednesday. (US) **2001**
Everybody's. (US ISSN 0164-9329) **2001**
Everybody's Money. (US ISSN 0423-8710) **778,** 830
Everyday Electronics. (UK ISSN 0262-3617) **1771**
Everyman's Science. (II ISSN 0531-495X) **4309,** 4597
Everyone's Backyard. (US ISSN 0749-3940) **1984,** 1954, 3616, 3942
Everyone's Income Tax Guide. (US) **1093**
Everyone's Songs. Series. (AT ISSN 0159-1991) **3551**
Everyone's United Nations. (UN ISSN 0251-690X) **3957**
Everything Book for Commodore. (US) **1469**
Everything Book for I B M. (US) **1469**
Everything You Ever Wanted to Know About the Toronto Stock Exchange see As a Matter of Fact **938**
Everywoman. (UK ISSN 0267-2294) **4841**
Eve's Weekly. (II ISSN 0014-3812) **4841,** 2199

EXECUTIVE COMPENSATION 6167

Evidence *see* B A R - B R I Bar Review. Evidence **2602**
Evidence Trial Manual for Texas Lawyers: Civil. (US) **2624**
Evidence Trial Manual for Texas Lawyers: Criminal. (US) **2624**
Evoked Potentials. (IE ISSN 0168-5597) **3336**
La Evolucion Fonologica del Protovaltuat. (MX) **2813**
Evolucion Socioeconomica de Espana. (SP) **4405**
Evolution. (US ISSN 0014-3820) **541**
▼Evolution and Cognition. (AU ISSN 0938-2623) **4021**
Evolution de l'Effectif des Vehicules a Moteur en Suisse. *see* Entwicklung des Motorfahrzeugbestandes in der Schweiz **4663**
Evolution de la Construction Navale *see* Construction Navale **4726**
Evolution Pharmaceutique. (FR) **3725**
Evolution Psychiatrique. (FR ISSN 0014-3855) **3336**
▼Evolutionary Anthropology. (US) **239**
Evolutionary Biology. (US ISSN 0071-3260) **541**
Evolutionary Ecology. (UK ISSN 0269-7653) **1954**
Evolutionary Monographs. (US ISSN 0272-0809) **438**, **239**
Evolutionary Theory *see* Evolutionary Theory and Review **438**
Evolutionary Theory and Review. (US) **438**, **239**
Evoluzione Agricola. (IT ISSN 0014-3863) **88**
Evphrosyne. (PO ISSN 0870-0133) **1276**
†Evropa Danas/Europe Today. (YU ISSN 0353-2976) **5189**
Evropa i Amerika. (RU) **2406**
Ewing Exchange. (US ISSN 0892-2144) **2150**
Ex - C B I Roundup. (US ISSN 0014-388X) **3458**
Ex-Imp Times. (II) **906**
Ex Libris. (GW ISSN 0014-391X) **4127**, **400**
Ex Libris (Portsmouth). (US ISSN 1042-6647) **4127**, **2310**
Ex Libris d'Europe. *see* Bibliografi over Europaeiske Kunstneres Ex Libris **352**
Ex Libris Francais. (FR ISSN 0395-269X) **4127**
Ex Nihilo Technical Journal *see* Creation Ex Nihilo Technical Journal **4173**
Ex - P O W Bulletin. (US ISSN 0161-7451) **3458**
Ex Tempore. (US ISSN 0276-6795) **3551**
Exact Change. (US ISSN 1051-1717) **299**, **2992**
Exact Science and Technology. Life Sciences. Lexicon. *see* Sciences Exactes et Technologie. Sciences de la Vie. Lexique **455**
Exame. (BL) **1075**
Examen. (MX) **3893**
Examen de la Situacion Economica de Mexico. (MX ISSN 0014-3960) **864**
Examiner (Raleigh). (US ISSN 0190-2733) **750**
Excalibur. (CN ISSN 0014-3987) **1311**
Excavaciones Arqueologicas en Espana. (SP ISSN 0071-3279) **271**
Excavating Contractor. (US ISSN 0014-3995) **617**, **1865**
Excavations and Surveys in Israel. (IS ISSN 0334-1607) **271**
Excavations at Dura-Europos. (US ISSN 0071-3287) **272**
Excel. (AT ISSN 0817-4792) **3371**
Excel Magazine. (US ISSN 0893-5017) **2001**
Excellence. (CN) **664**
Excellence (Louisville). (US ISSN 0886-9812) **1469**
Excellence (Ross). (US) **4690**
Excellence Education Journal. (US) **3893**, **2001**
Excellence in Teaching. (US ISSN 0740-9893) **1749**
Excelsa. (RH ISSN 0301-441X) **501**, **2125**
Excelsa Taxonomic Series. (RH) **501**

Excelsior. (US) **4059**
Exceptional Child *see* International Journal of Disability, Development and Education **1736**
Exceptional Child Education Resources. (US ISSN 0160-4309) **1676**, **11**, **1247**
Exceptional Children. (US ISSN 0014-4029) **1237**, **1633**, **4021**
Exceptional Human Experience. (US ISSN 1053-4768) **3672**
Exceptional News. (US) **1735**
Exceptional Parent. (US ISSN 0046-9157) **1237**
▼Exceptionality. (US ISSN 0936-2835) **1735**
▼Exceptionality Education Canada. (CN ISSN 1183-322X) **1736**
Exceritus. (UK) **1276**, **272**
Excerpta Botanica. Sectio A: Taxonomica et Chorologica. (GW ISSN 0014-4037) **501**
Excerpta Botanica. Sectio B: Sociologica.(GW ISSN 0014-4045) **502**
Excerpta e Dissertationibus in Iure Canonico. (SP) **4177**
Excerpta e Dissertationibus in Sacra Theologica. (SP) **4264**
Excerpta Indonesica *see* E I **254**
Excerpta Medica Abstract Journals. (NE ISSN 0921-822X) **3171**, **11**, **465**
Excerpta Medica. Section 1: Anatomy, Anthropology, Embryology & Histology. (NE ISSN 0014-4053) **3171**, **11**, **254**, **465**
Excerpta Medica. Section 2: Physiology.(NE ISSN 0014-4061) **3171**, **11**, **465**
Excerpta Medica. Section 3: Endocrinology. (NE ISSN 0014-407X) **3171**, **11**
Excerpta Medica. Section 4: Microbiology: Bacteriology, Mycology and Parasitology *see* Excerpta Medica. Section 4: Microbiology: Bacteriology, Mycology, Parasitology and Virology **3171**
Excerpta Medica. Section 4: Microbiology: Bacteriology, Mycology, Parasitology and Virology. (NE ISSN 0927-2771) **3171**, **11**, **465**
Excerpta Medica. Section 5: General Pathology and Pathological Anatomy.(NE ISSN 0014-4096) **3171**, **11**, **465**
Excerpta Medica. Section 6: Internal Medicine. (NE ISSN 0014-410X) **3171**, **11**
Excerpta Medica. Section 7: Pediatrics *see* Excerpta Medica. Section 7: Pediatrics and Pediatric Surgery **3172**
Excerpta Medica. Section 7: Pediatrics and Pediatric Surgery. (NE ISSN 0373-6512) **3172**, **11**
Excerpta Medica. Section 8: Neurology and Neurosurgery. (NE ISSN 0014-4126) **3172**, **11**
Excerpta Medica. Section 9: Surgery. (NE ISSN 0014-4134) **3172**, **11**
Excerpta Medica. Section 10: Obstetrics and Gynecology. (NE ISSN 0014-4142) **3172**, **11**
Excerpta Medica. Section 11: Otorhinolaryngology. (NE ISSN 0014-4150) **3172**, **11**
Excerpta Medica. Section 12: Ophthalmology. (NE ISSN 0014-4169) **3172**, **11**
Excerpta Medica. Section 13: Dermatology and Venereology. (NE ISSN 0014-4177) **3172**, **11**
†Excerpta Medica. Section 130: Clinical Pharmacology. (NE ISSN 0921-4496) **5189**
Excerpta Medica. Section 14: Radiology. (NE ISSN 0014-4185) **3172**, **11**
Excerpta Medica. Section 15: Chest Diseases, Thoracic Surgery and Tuberculosis. (NE ISSN 0014-4193) **3172**, **11**
Excerpta Medica. Section 16: Cancer. (NE ISSN 0014-4207) **3172**, **11**
Excerpta Medica. Section 17: Public Health, Social Medicine & Epidemiology. (NE ISSN 0924-5723) **4117**, **11**, **3172**

Excerpta Medica. Section 17: Public Health, Social Medicine and Hygiene *see* Excerpta Medica. Section 17: Public Health, Social Medicine & Epidemiology **4117**
Excerpta Medica. Section 18: Cardiovascular Diseases and Cardiovascular Surgery. (NE ISSN 0014-4223) **3172**, **11**
Excerpta Medica. Section 19: Rehabilitation and Physical Medicine.(NE ISSN 0014-4231) **3173**, **11**
Excerpta Medica. Section 20: Gerontology and Geriatrics. (NE ISSN 0014-424X) **2280**, **11**, **3173**
Excerpta Medica. Section 21: Developmental Biology and Teratology. (NE ISSN 0014-4258) **3173**, **11**, **465**
Excerpta Medica. Section 22: Human Genetics. (NE ISSN 0014-4266) **465**, **11**, **3173**
Excerpta Medica. Section 23: Nuclear Medicine. (NE ISSN 0014-4274) **3173**, **11**
Excerpta Medica. Section 24: Anesthesiology. (NE ISSN 0014-4282) **3173**, **12**
Excerpta Medica. Section 25: Hematology. (NE ISSN 0014-4290) **3173**, **12**
Excerpta Medica. Section 26: Immunology, Serology and Transplantation. (NE ISSN 0014-4304) **3173**, **12**
Excerpta Medica. Section 27: Biophysics, Bio-Engineering and Medical Instrumentation. (NE ISSN 0014-4312) **3173**, **12**, **465**
Excerpta Medica. Section 28: Urology and Nephrology. (NE ISSN 0014-4320) **3173**, **12**
Excerpta Medica. Section 29: Clinical and Experimental Biochemistry. (NE ISSN 0927-278X) **3173**, **12**, **465**
Excerpta Medica. Section 29: Clinical Biochemistry *see* Excerpta Medica. Section 29: Clinical and Experimental Biochemistry **3173**
Excerpta Medica. Section 30: Clinical and Experimental Pharmacology. (NE ISSN 0927-2798) **3747**, **12**, **1981**, **3173**
Excerpta Medica. Section 30: Pharmacology *see* Excerpta Medica. Section 30: Clinical and Experimental Pharmacology **3747**
Excerpta Medica. Section 31: Arthritis and Rheumatism. (NE ISSN 0014-4355) **3173**, **12**
Excerpta Medica. Section 32: Psychiatry. (NE ISSN 0014-4363) **3174**, **12**
Excerpta Medica. Section 33: Orthopedic Surgery. (NE ISSN 0014-4371) **3174**, **12**
†Excerpta Medica. Section 34: Plastic Surgery. (NE ISSN 0014-438X) **5189**
Excerpta Medica. Section 35: Occupational Health and Industrial Medicine. (NE ISSN 0014-4398) **3174**, **12**, **4117**
Excerpta Medica. Section 36: Health Economics and Hospital Management *see* Excerpta Medica. Section 36: Health Policy, Economics and Management **2470**
Excerpta Medica. Section 36: Health Policy, Economics and Management. (NE ISSN 0921-8068) **2470**, **12**, **3174**
†Excerpta Medica. Section 37: Drug Literature Index. (NE ISSN 0376-5091) **5189**
Excerpta Medica. Section 38: Adverse Reactions Titles. (NE ISSN 0001-8848) **3174**, **12**
Excerpta Medica. Section 40: Drug Dependence *see* Excerpta Medica. Section 40: Drug Dependence, Alcohol Abuse and Alcoholism **3174**
Excerpta Medica. Section 40: Drug Dependence, Alcohol Abuse and Alcoholism. (NE ISSN 0925-5958) **3174**, **12**, **1536**

Excerpta Medica. Section 46: Environmental Health and Pollution Control. (NE ISSN 0300-5194) **1974**, **12**, **1977**, **3174**, **4117**
Excerpta Medica. Section 47: Virology *see* Excerpta Medica. Section 4: Microbiology: Bacteriology, Mycology, Parasitology and Virology **3171**
Excerpta Medica. Section 48: Gastroenterology. (NE ISSN 0031-3580) **3174**, **12**
Excerpta Medica. Section 49: Forensic Science Abstracts. (NE ISSN 0303-8459) **3174**, **12**
Excerpta Medica. Section 50: Epilepsy Abstracts. (NE ISSN 0031-0743) **3174**, **12**
Excerpta Medica. Section 52: Toxicology. (NE ISSN 0167-8353) **3747**, **12**, **1981**, **3174**
†Excerpta Medica. Section 54: A I D S. (NE ISSN 0922-6532) **5189**
Excess Express. (US ISSN 0740-1388) **2531**
Exchange. (UK ISSN 0951-9785) **3247**, **3185**
Exchange (Fayetteville). (US) **1504**
Exchange (Kitchener). (CN ISSN 0824-457X) **664**
Exchange (New York). (US) **4405**
Exchange & Commissary News. (US ISSN 0014-4452) **3458**
Exchange and Mart. (UK ISSN 0014-4460) **4690**, **31**, **2194**
Exchange Book. (US ISSN 0890-9911) **4761**
Exchange of Information on Research in European Law/Echange d'Informations sur les Recherches en Droit Europeen. (FR ISSN 0252-0648) **2698**
Exchange Rate Outlook. (UK ISSN 0142-6044) **778**
Exchangite. (US ISSN 0014-4487) **1297**
Excise Tax Quarterly. (US) **4744**, **1093**
Excitement and Fascination of Science. (US) **4309**
Exclaimer. (US) **1706**, **88**, **1633**
Exclusive London. (UK) **4761**
Exclusividades de Economia. (CK) **864**
Exclusively Yours Magazine. (US) **2225**
Excursions en Autocar. (CN) **4762**
Exec-U-Letter. (US) **1075**
Exec-U-Tary. (US ISSN 0894-5748) **1058**, **4841**
Execs. (US) **665**
†Execu-Time. (US) **5189**
Executive. (KE ISSN 0251-0332) **864**
Executive. (PK) **1009**
Executive Accountant. (UK) **750**
Executive Action Report. (US) **2624**, **1093**
†Executive Administrator. (US) **5189**
†Executive and Ownership Report. (US) **5189**
Executive and Professional Employment Contracts. (US) **2624**
Executive Brief. (US) **1456**
Executive Brief: Philippine Business. (PH) **665**
Executive Briefing. (US) **2461**
Executive Business Magazine. (US) **665**
†Executive Communications. (US ISSN 0745-4783) **5189**
†Executive Compensation Alert. (US) **5189**
Executive Compensation & Taxation Coordinator. (US ISSN 0273-7612) **1093**
Executive Compensation Reports. (US ISSN 0738-6982) **979**
†Executive Compensation Service. Reports on International Compensation. Argentina. (US ISSN 0095-4144) **5189**
†Executive Compensation Service. Reports on International Compensation. Brazil. (US) **5189**
†Executive Compensation Service. Reports on International Compensation. Puerto Rico. (US ISSN 0090-9971) **5189**
Executive Compensation Survey (Year). (CN) **3632**

EXECUTIVE COMPENSATION

Executive Compensation Survey Report.(US) **2624**, 1065
Executive Computer Report. (UK) **1395**, 1444, 1460, 1469
Executive Computing. (US ISSN 0741-0050) **826**, 1469
Executive Cost of Living Survey. (MX) **815**
Executive Development. (UK ISSN 0953-3230) **1009**
†Executive Disclosure Guide. (US) **5189**
Executive Educator. (US ISSN 0161-9500) **1727**
Executive Excellence. (US) **1065**
Executive Female. (US ISSN 0199-2880) **4841**
Executive Female Digest see Executive Female **4841**
Executive Financial Women see Financial Woman Today **781**
Executive Fitness see Executive Fitness Newsletter **3801**
Executive Fitness Newsletter. (US ISSN 0014-4525) **3801**
Executive Fitness Newsletter. (HK) **3801**
Executive Forum. (US) **1075**
Executive Golfer. (US ISSN 0194-2387) **4503**
Executive Grapevine. (UK) **1009**
Executive Guide to Specialists in Industrial and Office Real Estate. (US) **4148**
Executive Health Club. (UK ISSN 0261-8230) **3801**
Executive Health Report see Executive Health's Good Health Report **3801**
Executive Health's Good Health Report. (US) **3801**
Executive Hong Kong. (HK) **1009**
Executive Housekeeping Today. (US ISSN 0738-6583) **3616**, 2461, 2473
Executive Intelligence Review. (US ISSN 0273-6314) **3893**, 929
†Executive Living. (US) **5189**
Executive Management see Retail Opportunity Letter **1026**
†Executive Mart. (US) **5189**
Executive Memorandum. (US) **3957**
Executive Men's Advertising Service. (US) **31**, 1284
Executive Men's Arts Series see Executive Men's Advertising Service **31**
Executive North East. (UK) **864**
†Executive on Sunday. (US) **5189**
Executive Pensions see Executives' and Directors' Pensions (Year) **2531**
Executive Planning Summary. (US) **665**
†Executive Productivity. (US) **5189**
Executive Recruiter News. (US) **1009**
Executive Report. (US) **1114**
Executive Report on Managed Care. (US ISSN 0898-9753) **2461**
Executive Search Service News. (US) **4405**, 3627
Executive Secretaries' Association Quarterly News Bulletin see E.S.A. Quarterly News Bulletin **5183**
Executive Speaker. (US ISSN 0271-3659) **31**
Executive Speeches. (US ISSN 0888-4110) **665**
Executive Strategies. (US) **1010**
▼Executive Suite. (US) **665**, 2001
Executive Suite Network News. (US) **1058**
†Executive Tax Return. (AT) **5189**
Executive Telecommunication Planning Guide see Planning Guide 1. Inter-L A T A Telecommunications Rates and Services **1365**
Executive Travel. (UK ISSN 0263-7685) **4762**
†Executive Trend Watch. (US) **5189**
Executive Update. (US ISSN 0733-5512) **1010**, 3392
Executive Wealth Advisory. (US) **945**
Executive Women International. Pulse. (US) **665**, 4841
Executive Women International. Times see Executive Women International. Pulse **665**
Executives' and Directors' Pensions (Year). (UK) **2531**
†Executives on the Move. (US) **5189**

Exegesis. (PR) **2916**
Exemplaria. (US ISSN 1041-2573) **2916**
Exempt Organizations Reports. (US) **1093**, 945
Exer-Safety News. (US) **3801**
Exercise and Sport Sciences Reviews. (US ISSN 0091-6331) **3371**
Exercise Exchange. (US ISSN 0531-531X) **1749**
Exercise for Men Only. (US) **3801**, 3395, 3397
Exercise Physiology: Current Selected Research. (US ISSN 0748-3155) **3801**, 3605
Exercise Standards and Malpractice Reporter. (US ISSN 0891-0278) **2624**, 3371, 3801
Exeter. (US ISSN 0195-0207) **1311**
Exeter Diocesan Directory. (UK) **4238**
Exeter Flying Post. (UK) **2865**
Exeter Museums Bulletin and View see Exeter Museums News **3524**
Exeter Museums News. (UK) **3524**
Exeter Studies in American & Commonwealth Arts. (UK) **2916**, 326, 3551
†Exeter University Gazette. (UK ISSN 0014-4622) **5189**
Exhaust News. (US ISSN 0192-7469) **4597**, 1954
Exhibit Builder. (US ISSN 0887-6878) **1039**
Exhibit Builder Source Book Directory (Year). (US) **1134**, 1039
Exhibit Marketing Magazine. (US) **1039**
Exhibit Review. (US) **906**, 1039, 1134
Exhibition Bulletin. (UK ISSN 0014-4649) **3392**, 4762
Exhibitions & Conferences. (UK ISSN 0307-6601) **3392**
Exhibitor Magazine. (US ISSN 0739-6821) **1039**, 31, 1114
▼Exhibits Asia. (PH ISSN 0116-9688) **3392**
Exil. (GW ISSN 0721-6742) **2865**
Exile. (CN) **2916**, 2865
Exile. (US ISSN 0421-9090) **2916**
Exilforschung. (GW) **4435**, 3942
Eximbank Letter. (US ISSN 0890-426X) **665**
Exit. (US ISSN 0195-3516) **2916**
Exit see V E S Newsletter **4456**
Exit 13 Magazine. (US ISSN 1054-3937) **2916**, 2865
Exkies. (NE) **3233**
Exlibris-Nyt. (DK ISSN 0014-4681) **4127**
Exlibriskunst und Graphik see Exlibriskunst und Graphik. Jahrbuch **326**
Exlibriskunst und Graphik. Jahrbuch. (GW ISSN 0172-2859) **326**
Exodus. (CN) **2001**
Exormisi/Starting Line. (CY) **2184**
Exotic Cars Quarterly. (US) **4690**
Expanded Shale, Clay and Slate Institute. Special Bulletins. (US) **1163**
Expanding Light Program Guide. (US) **3594**
Expansion. (FR ISSN 0014-4703) **1075**
Expansion. (MX) **1075**
Expansion Management. (US) **864**, 1010, 4148
Expansion Voyages. (FR) **4762**
Expatriate. (UK ISSN 0268-6910) **979**, 2531
†Expatriates Tax & Investment Intelligence. (UK ISSN 0269-4921) **5189**
Expatxtra! (UI) **778**, 945, 1093, 2531
Expectations. (US) **2292**, 1254
Expectations Monitor see Current Developments **943**
Expecting. (CN) **1237**
Expecting. (US ISSN 0014-472X) **3291**
Expedicionario. (BL) **3458**
Expediteur. (CN ISSN 0838-5416) **4649**
Expedition. (US ISSN 0014-4738) **239**, 272
Expedition see Traveller **4794**
Expedition World. (US) **4762**

Expense Analysis: Condominiums, Cooperatives and Planned Unit Developments. (US ISSN 0191-2208) **4148**
Experience. (US ISSN 1054-3473) **2624**, 2272
Experience Exchange Report. (US ISSN 0738-2170) **4148**
Experiences et Gestions Municipales. (FR) **4087**
Experientia. (SZ ISSN 0014-4754) **438**, 4309
Experientia. Supplementum. (SZ ISSN 0071-335X) **438**, 4309, 4597
†Experientiae. (BL ISSN 0014-4762) **5189**
Experiential Education. (US) **3627**
Experiment. (US ISSN 0014-4770) **2992**
Experiment in International Living. Annual Report. (US) **1721**
▼Experiment in Words. (US) **2992**
Experiment Theatre. (US) **4633**
Experimental Aging Research. (US ISSN 0361-073X) **4021**, 2272
Experimental Agriculture. (UK ISSN 0014-4797) **89**
Experimental Aircraft Association Experimenter see E A A Experimenter **51**
Experimental Aircraft Association Technical Counselor Newsletter. see E A A. Technical Counselor Newsletter **51**
Experimental & Applied Acarology. (NE ISSN 0168-8162) **438**, 89, 532
Experimental and Clinical Endocrinology.(GW ISSN 0232-7384) **3253**
▼Experimental and Clinical Gastroenterology. (UK ISSN 0353-9245) **3267**
Experimental and Clinical Immunogenetics. (SZ ISSN 0254-9670) **541**, 3259
Experimental and Clinical Psychiatry. (US) **3336**
Experimental and Molecular Pathology. (US ISSN 0014-4800) **3097**, 1205
Experimental and Toxicologic Pathology.(GW ISSN 0940-2993) **3259**, 1981, 3725
Experimental Animals/Jikken Dobutsu. (JA ISSN 0007-5124) **3259**
Experimental Astronomy. (NE ISSN 0922-6435) **364**, 2522
▼Experimental Basement. (US) **2993**
†Experimental Biology. (US) **5189**
Experimental Biology and Medicine see Issues in Biomedicine **442**
Experimental Botany; An International Series of Monographs. (US ISSN 0071-3392) **502**
Experimental Brain Research. (GW ISSN 0014-4819) **3336**
Experimental Brain Research. Supplementa. (US ISSN 0172-9039) **3336**
Experimental Cell Biology see Pathobiology **3139**
Experimental Cell Research. (US ISSN 0014-4827) **524**, 3097
Experimental Eye Research. (UK ISSN 0014-4835) **3300**
Experimental Gerontology. (US ISSN 0531-5565) **2272**
Experimental Heat Transfer. (US ISSN 0891-6152) **3840**
Experimental Hematology. (US ISSN 0301-472X) **3272**
Experimental Lung Research. (US ISSN 0190-2148) **3365**
Experimental Mechanics. (US ISSN 0014-4851) **1916**
Experimental Mechanics. see Shiyan Lixue **3845**
Experimental Musical Instruments. (US ISSN 0883-0754) **3551**
Experimental Mycology. (US ISSN 0147-5975) **502**
Experimental Neurology. (US ISSN 0014-4886) **3337**
Experimental Oncology. see Eksperimental'naya Onkologiya **3196**
Experimental Parasitology. (US ISSN 0014-4894) **3219**, 438

Experimental Pathology see Experimental and Toxicologic Pathology **3259**
Experimental Petroleum Geology. (CC) **1560**, 3685
Experimental Physiology. (UK ISSN 0958-0670) **571**, 3097
▼Experimental Rocket Flyer. (US) **51**
Experimental Study of Politics. (US ISSN 0046-2926) **3893**
Experimental Technique of Physics. see Experimentelle Technik der Physik **3818**
Experimental Techniques. (US ISSN 0732-8818) **1916**
Experimental Thermal and Fluid Science. (US ISSN 0894-1777) **1821**
Experimental Virology. (US) **551**
Experimentally Speaking see Experimental Techniques **1916**
Experimentelle Medizin. Mitteilungsblatt.(GW ISSN 0863-4645) **3259**
Experimentelle Technik der Physik/ Experimental Technique of Physics. (GW ISSN 0014-4924) **3818**
Experimentelle und Klinische Hypnose. (GW ISSN 0933-1093) **4021**, 3097
Experiments in Fluids. (GW ISSN 0723-4864) **1929**
Experiodica. (SZ ISSN 0014-4932) **2531**
The Expert. (US ISSN 0896-7725) **1407**
Expert and the Law. (US) **2624**
L'Expert Automobile. (FR ISSN 0755-110X) **4690**
Expert-Comptable Suisse. see Der Schweizer Treuhaender **756**
†Expert Evidence Reporter. (US) **5189**
Expert System Strategies see Intelligent Software **1408**
Expert Systems. (UK ISSN 0266-4720) **1407**, 1430
Expert Systems. (US) **1407**
Expert Systems. see Kennis Systemen **1447**
†Expert Systems. (US) **5189**
Expert Systems for Information Management. (UK) **1407**, 1430
†Expert Systems in Government Conference. (US) **5189**
Expert Systems in Government Symposium see Expert Systems in Government Conference **5189**
Expert Systems User see Expert Systems **1407**
▼Expert Systems with Applications. (US ISSN 0957-4174) **1437**
Experts. (CN ISSN 0839-1041) **2531**
Explicacion de Textos Literarios. (US ISSN 0361-9621) **2916**
Explicator. (US ISSN 0014-4940) **2916**
Exploitant Familial. (FR) **89**
Exploitation Problems of Machines. see Zagadnienia Eksploatacji Maszyn **1941**
†Explor. (US ISSN 0362-0867) **5189**
Exploradores. (US ISSN 0890-3093) **4238**, 1254
Exploration. (US) **2916**, 4762
Exploration and Import of Technology. see Jishu Kaifa yu Yinjin **4602**
▼Exploration & Mining Geology. (US ISSN 0964-1823) **1560**, 3483
Exploration & Production Environment see E & P Environment **3685**
Exploration Daily. (US) **3685**
Exploration Geophysics. (AT ISSN 0812-3985) **1588**
Exploration in British Columbia. (CN ISSN 0823-2059) **1560**, 3483
Exploration of Nature. see Daziran Tansuo **1946**
Exploration of the Deep Continental Crust. (US) **1560**
Exploration Technology, Geosynoptics and Geothermal Energy. see Technika Poszukiwan Geologicznych, Geosynoptyka i Goetermia **1582**
Explorations. (PK ISSN 0014-4975) **2813**, 2916
Explorations. (US) **2916**
Explorations in Economic History. (US ISSN 0014-4983) **894**

Explorations in Education. (US ISSN 0071-3481) 1633
Explorations in Ethnic Studies. (US ISSN 0730-904X) 2001
Explorations in Feminism. (UK) 4841
Explorations in Knowledge. (UK ISSN 0261-1376) 3766, 4309
Explorations in Music. see Yinyue Tansuo 3587
Explorations in Renaissance Culture. (US ISSN 0098-2474) 2507, 2361, 2916
Explorations in Sights and Sounds. (US ISSN 0733-3323) 2001
†Explorations in the World Economy. (US) 5189
Exploratorium Quarterly. (US ISSN 0889-8197) 4309, 326, 1254, 3818
Explore. (AT ISSN 0313-8747) 1633
Explore. (CN ISSN 0714-816X) 4545, 4471, 4762
Explore Minnesota see Minnesota Explorer 4778
Explore Minnesota Arts and Attractions see Explore Minnesota Traveler 5189
Explore Minnesota Bed and Breakfast - Historic Inns. (US) 4762
Explore Minnesota Biking. (US) 4518, 4762
Explore Minnesota Campground Guide. (US) 4762, 4545
Explore Minnesota Campgrounds see Explore Minnesota Campground Guide 4762
Explore Minnesota Canoeing, Backpacking and Hiking see Explore Minnesota Hiking 4762
Explore Minnesota Cross-country Skiing.(US) 4545, 4762
Explore Minnesota Downhill Skiing. (US) 4545, 4762
Explore Minnesota Hiking. (US) 4762, 4545
†Explore Minnesota Traveler. (US) 5189
Explorer (Cleveland). (US ISSN 0014-5009) 4309, 1487, 1954
Explorer (Falls Church). (US ISSN 0894-7929) 3233
Explorer (Lake Worth). (US) 3233
Explorer (Notre Dame). (US ISSN 0014-5017) 2916
Explorer (Washington). (US) 4762
Explorer News. (AT) 4762
Explorers Journal. (US ISSN 0014-5025) 364, 2247
Exploring. (US ISSN 0014-5033) 1254
Exploring A see Exploring 1 4238
Exploring A for Leaders see Exploring 1 for Leaders 4238
Exploring C see Exploring 2 4238
Exploring C for Leaders see Exploring 2 for Leaders 4238
†Exploring Europe. (UK) 5189
Exploring France. (UK) 4762
Exploring 1. (US ISSN 0745-032X) 4238, 1254
Exploring 1 for Leaders. (US ISSN 0745-0346) 4238, 1254
Exploring 2. (US) 4238, 1254
Exploring 2 for Leaders. (US ISSN 0745-0354) 4238, 1254
Explosives & Pyrotechnics. (US ISSN 0014-505X) 1853
Explosivstoffe. (GW ISSN 0014-5068) 1853
Expo (Kansas City). (US ISSN 1046-3925) 1010
Expo (Philadelphia) see Inside (Philadelphia) 2006
Expo Actualites. (FR) 906
†Expo Info. (US ISSN 0888-4722) 5189
Exponent. (US ISSN 0014-5076) 1311
Exponent II. (US) 4841, 3942
Exporama. (GW ISSN 0176-540X) 1134
Export see Export Today (London) 907
Export. (US ISSN 0014-519X) 907
Export-Adressbuch von Oesterreich see Austria Export Herold 1122
Export Alimentare e dei Prodotti Agricoli see Esportare 5187
Export Briefs see Trade Leads 922
Export Buyer's Guide. (US) 2091

†Export Canada. (CN ISSN 0708-1332) 5189
Export Channel (Consumer Edition) see Export Channel (Consumer Products Edition) 907
Export Channel (Consumer Products Edition). (NE) 907
Export Channel (Technical Edition) see Export Channel (Technical Products Edition) 907
Export Channel (Technical Products Edition). (NE) 907
Export Courier. (UK ISSN 0014-5122) 907
Export Credit Reports. (US) 907
Export Digest. (UK) 907
Export Directory Chile/Directorio de la Exportacion. (CL) 1135
Export Directory of Brazil/Guia Brasileiro de Exportacao. (BL) 1135
Export Directory of Denmark. (DK) 907
Export Directory - U.S. Buying Guide see Directory of United States Importers 905
Export Finance and Insurance Quarterly see Export Finance & Insurance Review 907
Export Finance & Insurance Review. (AT) 907
Export Finance Handbook. (SA) 907
Export Gazette. (Il ISSN 0970-6186) 907
Export Grafics U S A see Printing Product International 4004
Export Guide - Danish Textile and Clothing. see Export Guide - Dansk Textil og Beklaedning 4618
Export Guide - Dansk Textil og Beklaedning/Export Guide - Danish Textile and Clothing. (DK) 4618, 907
Export Guide to Europe (Year). (UK) 907
Export-Import Bank of Japan. Annual Report. (JA ISSN 0071-3503) 907, 778
Export-Import Bank of Korea. Annual Report. (KO) 907
Export-Import Bank of the United States. Annual Report. (US ISSN 0270-5109) 778
Export-Import Bank of the United States. Report to Congress on Export Credit Competition and the Export-Import Bank of the United States. (US) 778
Export-Import Bank of the United States. Semiannual Report to Congress on Export Credit Competition and the Export-Import Bank of the United States see Export-Import Bank of the United States. Report to Congress on Export Credit Competition and the Export-Import Bank of the United States 778
Export-Import Bank of the United States. Statement of Condition see Export-Import Bank of the United States. Annual Report 778
Export-Import Markets. (PR ISSN 0270-5184) 907
Export - Import News. (Il ISSN 0014-5149) 907
Export Information. (MW) 907
†Export Lines. (SI) 5189
Export Magazine. (NE ISSN 0168-7166) 907
Export Marketing Handbook. (SA) 1039, 907
†Export-Markt, Euro-Revue. (GW ISSN 0724-4509) 5189
Export News. (CN ISSN 0713-0341) 907
Export News. see Exportador Dominicano 907
Export News. (Il) 4127
Export Opportunities. (NE ISSN 0922-1808) 907
Export Opportunities Bulletin. (US) 907
Export Polygraph International (E P I) see Polygraph International 4003
Export Practice Handbook. (SA) 907
Export Processing Zone Authority News see E P Z A News 906
Export Processing Zone Concentrates. (CH) 907
Export Shipper see The Exporter 908

Export Shipping Manual see International Trade Reporter Export Reference Manual 913
Export Statistical Schedule of Japan (Year). (JA) 907, 715
Export Statistics of Afghanistan/Ihsa'iyah-i Amual-i Sadirati-i Afghanistan. (AF) 715, 4571
Export Times. (UK) 907
Export Today (London). (UK) 907
Export Today (Washington). (US ISSN 0882-4711) 907
Export Turkey. (TU) 907
Exportaciones Britanicas. see British Exports 1124
Exportador see Export 907
Exportador Dominicano/Export News. (DR) 907
Exportador Latinoamericano. (CK) 907
Exportadores de Sud Africa. see South African Exporters 921
Exportar es Crecer. (AG) 907
Exportateurs Sud-Africains. see South African Exporters 921
Exportation. (FR) 908
L'Exportation en Pratique/Exportpraxis. (SZ) 864
Exportation Monthly Review. see Revista Mensal de Exportacao 920
Exportations Britanniques. see British Exports 1124
The Exporter. (US ISSN 0736-9239) 908
Exporter Directory of African Coffee. see Annuaire des Exportateurs de Cafes Africains 900
Exporter Guide - Caribbean and Latin America see Export-Import Markets 907
Exporters' Encyclopaedia. (US ISSN 0732-0159) 908
†Exporters of Japanese Products. Directory. (JA) 5189
Exportoeren. (DK ISSN 0109-9043) 908
Exportpraxis. see L'Exportation en Pratique 864
†Exports by Pennsylvania Manufacturers. (US ISSN 0556-3585) 5190
Exports of the Republic of China. (CH ISSN 0301-9217) 908
Exporttijdschrift voor de Sovjetunie. see Ekonomicheskii Byulleten Niderlandov 906
†Les Expos. (CN ISSN 0835-3743) 5190
Expositiones Mathematicae. (GW ISSN 0723-0869) 3035
Expositor Bautista. (AG ISSN 0014-522X) 4238
†Expositor Biblico (Teacher Edition). (US ISSN 0014-5238) 5190
Expositor Dominical. (PO) 1633
Expository Times. (UK ISSN 0014-5246) 4177
Exposure (Boulder). (US ISSN 0098-8863) 3790
†Exposure (Los Angeles). (US) 5190
Exposure Draft (Accounting Standards). (AT ISSN 1030-5882) 750
Exposure Draft (Auditing Practice). (AT) 750
Expovisie. (NE ISSN 0014-5254) 3392
Expres. (CS) 2865
Express. (FR ISSN 0014-5270) 2865
Express. (GW ISSN 0343-5121) 3893
Express. (SP ISSN 1130-3751) 4762
Express. (US) 4802, 4709, 4762
Express Bulletins. (UK) 465
Express Documents. (FR ISSN 0014-5289) 778
Express-O see R I S D Voice 341
Express - Shakhmaty. (RU) 4471
Expressie. (NE) 3551
Expression/Maba. (IS ISSN 0046-2977) 1311
Expression. (AT ISSN 0085-039X) 2916
Expression see Oasis (London) 2944
Expression see Expression One 2993
Expression. (IT) 3893, 2205
Expression. (FR ISSN 0014-5327) 4842, 326
Expression One. (UK ISSN 0014-536X) 2993

Expressions: First State Journal. (US) 2993
▼Expressmale. (US) 3627, 3397
Expresso. (PO ISSN 0870-1970) 665
Expresso. (AG) 864
†Expresso Tilt. (US) 5190
Expressweek. (PH) 2213
Exquisite Corpse. (US ISSN 0740-7815) 2865
†Extebank Monthly Economic Report/Informacion Economica. Boletin. (SP ISSN 0014-5378) 5190
Extel Book of Prospectuses and New Issues Fiche Service see Extel Prospectuses and New Issues Fiche Service 5190
Extel Capital Gains Tax Service. (UK ISSN 0141-8335) 1093
Extel Dividend & Interest Record. (UK ISSN 0141-8327) 778, 750, 1093
Extel Handbook of Market Leaders. (UK ISSN 0308-9673) 945, 715
Extel Issuing House Year Book see Professional Advisers to New Issues 796
†Extel Prospectuses and New Issues Fiche Service. (UK) 5190
Extel Unlisted Securities Market Service see Secondary Markets Handbook 962
Extemporale. (GW ISSN 0014-5386) 1254
Extended Care Product News. (US) 3801, 3605
Extensao em Minas Gerais. (BL ISSN 0014-5394) 89
Extension see Intensive Agriculture 99
Extension. (US) 4264
Extension Bibliografica. (BO) 4394, 400
Extension Bulletin see New York State School of Industrial and Labor Relations. Bulletin 990
Extension Connection. (US) 89, 1297, 2446
Extension News - Albany - Rensselaer - Saratoga - Washington Counties. (US) 89
Extension Review. (US ISSN 0162-9875) 89, 1633
Extension Service Review see Extension Review 89
Extensions. (US) 3893
Extensions and Corrections to the U D C. (NE ISSN 0014-5424) 2757
†Exteriors. (US ISSN 0886-5949) 5190
Externado. (CK) 2624
External Affairs see International Perspectives 3961
External Affairs Review see New Zealand External Relations Review 3966
External Studies Gazette see Armidale News 1700
External Trade. see Denmark. Danmarks Statistik. Udenrigshandel 713
External Trade: Nomenclature of Goods/Commerce Exterieur: Nomenclature des Pays. (EI) 908
External Trade of Denmark. see Danmarks Vareindfoersel og-Udfoersel 712
External Trade of Liberia: Import and Export. (LB) 908
External Trade Statistics. see Verslunarskyrslur - External Trade 4591
External Trade Statistics of Gambia. (GM) 715, 908
External Trade Statistics of Ghana. (GH ISSN 0435-8805) 715, 908
Extra. (HO) 2180
Extra! (US ISSN 0145-3939) 2225
Extra. (CN) 3483
Extra Equity for Homebuyers. (US) 4148
Extra Income. (US ISSN 0888-367X) 1114
Extra - Spanish Language Newspaper. (US) 2001
Extra Special Cracked. (US) 2865
Extra 2200 South. (US ISSN 0014-1380) 4709
Extracellular Matrix. (UK ISSN 0268-1617) 524, 485

6170 EXTRACTS

Extracts see Melville Society Extracts 2937
Extrakte: Elektro und Unterhaltungs-Elektronik. (GW) 1771, 1892
Extrakte: Nahrung und Genuss. (GW) 2085, 388
Extrakte: Textilien und Bekleidung. (GW) 4628, 1288
Extraordinary Contractual Relief Reporter. (US) 864, 2624
Extrapolation. (US ISSN 0014-5483) 3011, 2916
Extraterrestres. (FR) 51
Extropy. (US ISSN 1057-1035) 3766
▼Exuberance. (UK ISSN 0959-4558) 3011
Exxon Air World. (US) 51
Exxon Aviation News Digest. (US) 52
Eyas. (US ISSN 0736-5470) 563
The Eye (Wilmington). (US ISSN 0743-2240) 1254
Eye Care. (II ISSN 0255-4062) 3300
Eye on L S S I. (Lutheran Social Services of Illinois) (US) 4405
Eye Opener. (US) 3337
Eye Science/Yanke Xuebao. (CC ISSN 1000-4432) 3300
Eye to Eye. (US) 3300
†Eyecare Australia. (AT ISSN 1032-4070) 5190
Eyecare Business. (US) 3300
Eyeopener. (CN ISSN 0014-5513) 1311
Eyepiece. (US ISSN 0146-7662) 364
Eyepiece. (UK) 3790, 3508
Eyes. (US) 3957
Eyespy. (AT ISSN 0811-9066) 1954, 502
Eyewitness Testimony: Strategies and Tactics. (US) 2624
L'Eylah. (UK ISSN 0142-2049) 2001, 4222
Eyu Xuexi/Learning Russian. (CC) 2813, 1749
Ez a Divat. (HU ISSN 0230-1202) 1290
Ezermester. (HU) 2501, 3397
F A A Aviation News. (Federal Aviation Administration, AFS-810) (US) 52
F A A General Aviation News see F A A Aviation News 52
F A C C C Bulletin. (Faculty Association of California Community Colleges) (US ISSN 0046-3159) 1706
F A C C C T S. (Faculty Association of California Community Colleges) (US) 1706
F A C E N A. (Facultad de Ciencias Exactas y Naturales y Agrimensura) (AG ISSN 0325-4216) 419, 1177, 3657
F A C E S. (Facultad de Ciencias Economicas y Sociales) (VE) 4372
F A C: Revista Practica de Medicina. (SP ISSN 0210-8852) 3097
F A C: Revista Practica del Estudiante de Medicina see F A C: Revista Practica de Medicina 3097
F A C S. (Funds Agent Custodians Suppliers) (US ISSN 0887-8161) 945
F A C S Newsletter. (Finnish American Club of Saima, Inc.) (US) 2225
F A C S of the Week: Mutual Fund News and Information. (Funds Agent Custodians Suppliers) (US) 778
F A C T. (Faith and Atheism in Communist Territories) (AT) 4177
F A E Update. (Foundation for Accounting Education) (US) 750, 1633
F A I. (Federazione Autotraportatori Italiani) (IT) 4744
F.A.I. Abstract Service. (Fertiliser Association of India) (II ISSN 0014-5564) 137, 12
F A K E Nyt see K C Nyt 4089
F A M - Fire and Materials. (UK ISSN 0308-0501) 1226, 1916, 2031
F A M L I. (Family Medicine Literature Index) (CN ISSN 0227-2393) 3174
†F A O Agricultural Development Paper. (Food and Agriculture Organization of the United Nations) (UN ISSN 0071-6960) 5190

F A O Agricultural Services Bulletin. (Food and Agriculture Organization of the United Nations) (UN ISSN 1010-1365) 150
F A O Agricultural Studies see F A O Animal Production and Health Series 216
F A O Animal Production and Health Series. (Food and Agriculture Organization of the United Nations) (UN ISSN 1010-9021) 216
F A O Commodity Review and Outlook. (UN ISSN 0071-7002) 150
F A O Documentation - Current Bibliography. (UN ISSN 0304-582X) 2051, 12, 137, 2112
F A O Economic and Social Development Paper. (UN ISSN 0259-2460) 665, 4435
F A O Fertilizer and Plant Nutrition Bulletin. (UN ISSN 0259-2495) 150
F A O Fertilizer Yearbook. (UN ISSN 0251-1525) 176
F A O Fisheries Circulars. (UN ISSN 0429-9329) 2039
F A O Fisheries Reports. (UN ISSN 0429-9337) 2039
F A O Fisheries Series. (UN ISSN 0259-2509) 2039
F A O Fisheries Studies see F A O Fisheries Series 2039
F A O Fisheries Synopsis. (UN ISSN 0014-5602) 2039
F A O Fisheries Technical Paper. (UN ISSN 0429-9345) 2039
F A O Food and Nutrition Series. (UN ISSN 1014-3181) 3605
†F A O Forestry Studies. (UN ISSN 0532-0283) 5190
F A O Irrigation and Drainage Papers. (UN ISSN 0254-5284) 4824
F A O Legislative Series see F A O Legislative Studies 89
F A O Legislative Studies. (UN) 89
†F A O Manuals in Fisheries Science. (UN ISSN 0071-7061) 5190
F A O Monthly Bulletin of Agricultural Economics and Statistics see F A O Quarterly Bulletin of Statistics 137
F A O Monthly Bulletin of Statistics see F A O Quarterly Bulletin of Statistics 137
F A O Nutritional Study see F A O Food and Nutrition Series 3605
F A O Plant Protection Bulletin (Miltilingual Edition). (UN ISSN 0254-9727) 502
F A O Quarterly Bulletin of Statistics/Bulletin Trimestriel F A O de Statistiques/Boletin Trimestral F A O de Estadisticas. (UN ISSN 1011-8780) 137
F A O Regional Conference for Africa. (UN ISSN 0429-9353) 89
F A O Regional Conference for Asia and the Far East. Report see F A O Regional Conference for Asia and the Pacific. Report 89
F A O Regional Conference for Asia and the Pacific. Report. (UN) 89
F A O Regional Conference for Europe. Report of the Conference. (UN) 89
F A O Regional Conference for Latin America and the Caribbean. Report. (UN) 89
F A O Regional Conference for the Near East. Report. (UN ISSN 0427-8089) 89
F A O Terminology Bulletin. (UN ISSN 0532-0313) 89
†F A O - W H O Expert Panel on Veterinary Education. Report of the Meeting. (UN ISSN 0429-9388) 5190
F A P E Review. (Fund for Assistance to Private Education) (PH) 1633
F A P I G. (First Atomic Power Industry Group) (JA ISSN 0014-5645) 1805
F A P Journal. (Fine Arts Philatelists) (US) 3752
F A P U Q Information see F A P U Q Nouvelles Universitaires 1706
F A P U Q Nouvelles Universitaires. (Federation des Associations de Professeurs des Universites du Quebec) (CN ISSN 0709-8006) 1706, 2582

F A R C E. (Fine Arts Research and Communications Enterprises) (US ISSN 0899-630X) 326, 2916, 2993
F A S A G A - Andalucia. (Federacion del Agricultores y Ganaderos de Andalucia) (SP) 216
F A S E B Journal. (Federation of American Societies for Experimental Biology) (US ISSN 0892-6638) 439
F A S - F A X: Canadian Newspapers. Daily Newspapers. (US ISSN 0098-2520) 41
F A S - F A X: United States and Canadian Newspapers. Weekly Newspapers. (US) 400
F A S - F A X: United States Newspapers. Daily Newspapers. (US) 41
F A S Handbook. (Federation of Astronomical Societies) (UK) 364
F A S Public Interest Report. (Federation of American Scientists) (US ISSN 0092-9824) 4309
F A S Report: Weekly Roundup of World Production and Trade. (Foreign Agricultural Service) (US) 864
F A T - Bladet. (Foreningen af Teleteknikere) (DK ISSN 0108-9048) 4597
F A T D see Federal Applied Technology Database 4598
F A U S A News. (Federated Australian University Staff Association) (AT) 1706, 979
F A V A Newsletter see Persistence of Vision 3515
F A W N S. (Fellowship of Australian Writers North Shore Regional) (AT ISSN 0155-4761) 2916, 2993
F & M Today. (Franklin & Marshall College) (US) 1311
F & O S Motor Carrier Annual Report. (Financial and Operating Statistics) (US ISSN 0160-4570) 4663
F & O S Motor Carrier Quarterly Report. (Financial and Operating Statistics) (US) 4663
F and S Index of Corporations and Industries see Predicasts F & S Index United States 735
F & S Reports. (Frost & Sullivan, Inc.) (US) 665
F & W - Fuehren und Wirtschaften im Krankenhaus. (GW ISSN 0175-4548) 2461, 1010, 1065
F.B.A. Quarterly see Art Magazine 5138
F B I see Fishing Business International 2041
F B I Law Enforcement Bulletin. (U.S. Federal Bureau of Investigation) (US ISSN 0014-5688) 1514
F B I News see Right to Know and the Freedom to Act 3946
F.B.L. see France, Belgique, Luxembourg 815
F B M - Fertigungstechnologie. (GW) 3406, 3017
F B O. (Fixed Base Operator) (US ISSN 0893-3081) 4673, 1010, 1039
F B U - Befael. (Frivilliga Befaelsutbildningsroerelsen) (SW ISSN 0005-7797) 3458
F C A Bulletin. (Farm Credit Administration) (US) 150
F C A Official Newsletter see Canadian Archer 4468
F C C Rulemaking Reports. (Federal Communications Commission) (US) 1335, 2624
F C C Telephone Equipment Registration List. (Federal Communications Commission) (US) 1362
F C C Week. (Federal Communications Commission) (US ISSN 0738-5714) 1335, 2624
F C D Packaging see Food, Cosmetics and Drugs Packaging 3648
F C I B Bulletin see F C I B International Bulletin 778
F C I B Country Credit Report. (Finance, Credit and International Business - National Association of Credit Management) (US) 778, 865, 3893

F C I B International Bulletin. (Finance, Credit and International Business - National Association of Credit Management) (US) 778
F C I B - N A C M. Minutes of Round Table Conference. (Finance, Credit and International Business - National Association of Credit Management) (US) 778, 865, 3893
F C L Action see F C L Action Alerts 3893
F C L Action Alerts. (Friends Committee on Legislation of California) (US ISSN 0071-9560) 3893, 1514, 4405
F C L Newsletter. (Friends Committee on Legislation of California) (US ISSN 0532-7091) 3893
F C N L Washington Newsletter. (Friends Committee on National Legislation) (US ISSN 0014-5734) 3893, 2624, 4059
F C T L. (Folia Chimica Theoretica Latina) (SP ISSN 0378-4843) 1177
F C Weekly see Freight & Container Weekly 666
†F C X Carolina Cooperator. (US ISSN 0195-3346) 5190
F D A Compliance Policy Guidance. Manual. (U.S. Food and Drug Administration) (US) 2066, 3725
F D A Compliance Policy Guide see F D A Compliance Policy Guidance. Manual 2066
F D A Consumer. (U.S. Food and Drug Administration) (US ISSN 0362-1332) 1504, 2066, 3725
F D A Drug Bulletin see F D A Medical Bulletin 3725
F D A Enforcement Report. (U.S. Food and Drug Administration) (US) 1514, 3725
F D A Inspection Operations Manual. (US) 2066, 3725
F D A Medical Bulletin. (U.S. Food and Drug Administration) (US) 3725
F D A Papers see F D A Consumer 1504
F D A Surveillance Index for Pesticides. (Food and Drug Administration) (US) 1853
F D C Control see F D C Control Newsletter 2066
F D C Control Newsletter. (Food, Drug, and Cosmetics) (US) 2066, 3446, 3725
F D C Newsletter (Federal Digital Cartography) see F G D Newsletter 2247
F-D-C Reports: The Pink Sheet see Prescription and O T C Pharmaceuticals: The Pink Sheet 3741
▼F D D I News. (US ISSN 1051-1903) 1335, 1427
F D F Feedback. (Food and Drink Federation) (UK) 2066, 2091
†F D G B. Rundschau. (GW ISSN 0323-5750) 5190
F D G B Review see F D G B. Rundschau 5190
F D I C Data Book - United States, States, Counties, Other Areas see Operating Banks and Branches. Data Book: United States, States, Counties, Other Areas 794
F D I C Data Book 1 - CT, ME, MA, NH, NJ, NY, PA, RI, VT, PR, VI see Operating Banks and Branches. Data Book 1: Connecticut, Maine, Massachusetts, New Hampshire, New Jersey, New York, Pennsylvania, Rhode Island, Vermont, Puerto Rico, Virgin Islands 794
F D I C Data Book 2 - DE, DC, FL, GA, MD, NC, SC, VA, WV see Operating Banks and Branches. Data Book 2: Delaware, District of Columbia, Florida, Georgia, Maryland, North Carolina, South Carolina, Virginia, West Virginia 794
F D I C Data Book 3 - IL, IN, KY, MI, OH, WI see Operating Banks and Branches. Data Book 3: Illinois, Indiana, Kentucky, Michigan, Ohio, Wisconsin 794

F D I C Data Book 4 - AL, AR, LA, MS, OK, TN, TX see Operating Banks and Branches. Data Book 4: Alabama, Arkansas, Louisiana, Mississippi, Oklahoma, Tennessee, Texas **794**

F D I C Data Book 5 - IA, KS, MN, MO, NE, ND, SD see Operating Banks and Branches. Data Book 5: Iowa, Kansas, Minnesota, Missouri, Nebraska, North Dakota, South Dakota **794**

F D I C Data Book 6 - AK, AZ, CA, CO, HI, ID, MT, NV, NM, OR, UT, WA, WY, PI see Operating Banks and Branches. Data Book 6: Alaska, Arizona, California, Colorado, Hawaii, Idaho, Montana, Nevada, New Mexico, Oregon, Utah, Washington, Wyoming, Pacific Islands **794**

F D I C Enforcement Decisions. (U.S. Federal Deposit Insurance Corporation) (US) **778**

F D I C Watch. (Federal Deposit Insurance Corporation) (US) **778**

F D I Dental World. (Federation Dentaire Internationale) (UK ISSN 0965-9986) **3233**

F D I News see F D I Dental World **3233**

F D M see Food Distributors Magazine **2068**

F D M - Furniture Design & Manufacturing. (US ISSN 0192-8058) **2558**

F D P A Power Planner see F P D A News **1929**

F E A A Newsletter. (Folk Education Association of America) (US) **1683**

†F E & Z N. (UK ISSN 0014-5785) **5190**

F E B Bulletin. (Federation des Entreprises de Belgique) (BE ISSN 0771-2987) **1075**, 1504

F E B E L G R A Tijdschrift. (Federatie van de Belgische Industrie) (BE) **3999**

F E B S Letters. (Federation of European Biochemical Societies) (NE ISSN 0014-5793) **476**, 485, 524

F E C Record see Federal Election Commission Record **3894**

F E D A News & Views. (Foodservice Equipment Distributors Association) (US) **2473**

F E D R I P Database see Federal Research in Progress Database **1822**

F E E Notes. (Foundation for Economic Education, Inc.) (US ISSN 0029-4012) **665**

F E L A Reporter & Railroad Liability Monitor. (Federal Employees Liability Act) (US) **2624**, 4709

F E L Actualites. (FR ISSN 0758-8526) **176**

F E M. (Finance Economy Management) (NE) **778**

F E M see Factory Equipment & Materials **3017**

F E M S. Microbiology. (Federation of European Microbiological Societies) (NE ISSN 0921-8254) **551**, 489

F E M S. Microbiology Ecology. (Federation of European Microbiological Societies) (NE ISSN 0168-6496) **551**, 489, 1954

F E M S. Microbiology Immunology. (Federation of European Microbiological Societies) (NE ISSN 0920-8534) **551**, 489, 3185

F E M S. Microbiology Letters. (Federation of European Microbiological Societies) (NE ISSN 0378-1097) **551**, 489

F E M S. Microbiology Reviews. (Federation of European Microbiological Societies) (NE ISSN 0168-6445) **465**, 489, 551

F E N: Australian Factory Equipment News see Factory Equipment News **4597**

F E N - Hebdo. (Federation de l'Education Nationale (FEN)) (FR ISSN 0751-8145) **1633**

F E N Informations see F E N - Hebdo **1633**

F E P Guidelines. (Fair Employment Practices) (US ISSN 0093-7630) **2624**

The F E R C Report. (US) **778**

F E R N Journal. (Further Education Research Network) (UK ISSN 0260-5058) **1706**

F E: The Magazine for Financial Executives see Financial Executive **1010**

F E U Quarterly see Far Eastern Law Review **2624**

F E W's News and Views. (Federally Employed Women Inc.) (US ISSN 0895-3619) **4842**, 3942, 4059

F F A New Horizons. (Future Farmers of America) (US) **89**, 1633

F F-Avisen. (Forsikringsfunksjonaerenes Landsforbund) (NO) **2531**

F F Communications. (Folklore Fellows) (FI ISSN 0014-5815) **2054**

F F Dabei. (GW ISSN 0532-9140) **1373**, 1356

F F P Bulletin. (Friends of the Filipino People) (US) **2001**

F F P Series in Food Products Marketing. (US) **1039**, 2066

F F S B see Handels-Magazin F S B und Fachblatt fuer Selbstbedienung **1040**

F F - Sudtiroler Illustrierte. (IT) **2205**

†F G C Quarterly. (Friends General Conference) (US ISSN 0361-0810) **5190**

F G D Newsletter. (Federal Geographic Data) (US ISSN 1055-8357) **2247**

F G G B Rundbriefe. (Forschungsgemeinschaft Grossbritannien) (GW) **3752**

F G W Vorschau. (Forschungsgesellschaft fuer Wohnen, Bauen und Planen) (AU) **617**

F.H.A. Homes see U.S. Federal Housing Administration. F H A Homes **2497**

F.H.I. Annual: Fresh and Industrialized Fruits and Vegetables. see Anuario F.H.I. Argentina: Frutas y Hortalizas Industriarizadas y Frescas **168**

F H Presse. (Fachhochschule Dortmund) (GW) **1633**

F I A B C I Press. (FR) **4148**

F I A B C I - U S A News. (US) **908**, 3392

F I A S-Report. (GW) **3752**

F I A Year Book of Automobile Sport. (FR) **4690**

F I C E Information. (Federation Internationale des Communautes d'Enfants-Denmark) (DK ISSN 0108-2418) **1237**

F I D - C R News. (Federation Internationale d'Information et de Documentation) (GW) **2757**

F I D - C R Newsletter see F I D - C R News **2757**

†F I D - C R Report Series. (International Federation for Documentation) (GW ISSN 0074-5804) **5190**

F I D Directory. (Federation Internationale d'Information et de Documentation) (NE ISSN 0379-3680) **2757**

F I D E. (Fundacion de Investigaciones para el Desarrollo) (US) **865**

F I D E Coyuntura y Desarrollo. (Fundacion de Investigaciones para el Desarrollo) (US) **929**

F I D I C International Directory of Consulting Engineers. (Federation Internationale des Ingenieurs Conseils) (UK) **1135**, 1821

F I D I Focus. (Federation Internationale des Demenageurs Internationaux) (UK) **4727**

F I D News Bulletin. (Federation Internationale d'Information et de Documentation) (NE ISSN 0014-5874) **2757**

†F I D - R I Meetings Reports. (Federation Internationale d'Information et de Documentation) (NE) **5190**

†F I D - R I Series on Problems of Information Science. (Federation Internationale d'Information et de Documentation) (NE ISSN 0203-6495) **5190**

F I D Yearbook see F I D Directory **2757**

F I E E Infos. (Federation des Industries Electriques et Electroniques) (FR ISSN 1145-2668) **1892**

F I F A. Handbook. (Federation Internationale de Football Association) (SZ) **4503**

F I F A. Olympic Football Tournament. (Federation Internationale de Football Association) (SZ) **4503**

F I F A. Technical Notes see F I F A. Technical Reports **4503**

F I F A. Technical Reports. (Federation Internationale de Football Association) (SZ) **4503**

F I F A. U-17 World Tournament. (SZ) **4503**

F I F A. World Cup. (SZ) **4503**

F I F A. World Youth Championship. (SZ) **4503**

F I F A Coca-Cola Cup see F I F A. World Youth Championship **4503**

F I F A Magazine. (SZ) **4503**

F I F A News. (SZ) **4503**

F I F A Official Bulletin see F I F A News **4503**

F I G A. (Fretted Instrument Guild of America) (US) **3551**

F I I R O Industrial Abstracts. (Federal Institute of Industrial Research, Oshodi) (NR) **715**, 12

F I I R O Technical Information Bulletin for Industry. (Federal Institute of Industrial Research, Oshodi) (NR) **1075**

†F.I.N.S. (Fishing Industry News Service) (AT ISSN 0726-0741) **5190**

F I O D S Revue. (Federation Internationale des Organisations de Donneurs de Sang Benevoles) (FR ISSN 0253-1321) **3208**

F I P E S O Newsletter. (Federation Internationale des Professeurs de l'Enseignement Secondaire Officiel) (FR) **1633**

F I P L V World News. (Federation Internationale des Professeurs de Langues Vivantes) (SZ) **1633**, 239, 2813

F I P S Publication see Federal Information Processing Standards Publication **3446**

F I R A Bulletin. (Furniture Industry Research Association (F I R A)) (UK ISSN 0014-5904) **2558**

F I R T - I F T R - Sibmas Bulletin. (Federation Internationale pour la Recherche Theatrale) (NE) **4633**

F I R und I A W Mitteilungen. (Forschungs Institut fuer Rationalisierung und dem Institut fuer Arbeits Wissenschaft) (GW ISSN 0934-6430) **665**

F I S Bulletin. (International Ski Federation) (SZ ISSN 0425-5291) **4545**

F I S Frettabref see Bref til Storkaupmanna **1123**

F I T Newsletter/Nouvelles de la F I T. (Federation Internationale des Traducteurs) (BE) **2813**

F I W - Schriftenreihe. (Forschunginstitut fuer Wirtschaftsverfassung und Wettbewerb e.V.) (GW ISSN 0071-769X) **665**

F L F. (Finanzierung, Leasing, Factoring) (GW ISSN 0174-3163) **1093**

F L G C Newsletter. (Friends for Lesbian and Gay Concerns) (US) **4177**, 2225, 2452

F L I C C Newsletter. (Federal Library and Information Center Committee) (US ISSN 0882-908X) **2757**

†F L I P Magazine. (Future Literature in Progress) (US) **5190**

F L's Medlevsavis see Medlemsavisen **3793**

▼F.L.Y.E.R.S. (CN) **1290**

F.L.Y.E.R.S. Kids. (CN) **1290**

F M see Foodmagazine **2092**

F M see Vox: Hebdomadaire Militaire **3475**

F M see Fracht Management **4650**

F M A Bulletin. (Fulfillment Management Association) (US) **1010**

F M A Today. (Fuel Merchants Association of New Jersey) (US) **3685**, 1039

F M A Today (Jacksonville). (Florida Medical Association) (US) **3097**, 2624

F - M Automation Newsletter (Facilities Management) see Harlow Report: Geographic Information Systems **826**

†F M Compilation of the Statutes of Canada. Revised Statutes. (CN) **5190**

F M Engineering Data Base. (US) **1348**, 1356

F M Engineering Data Base in Order by State. (US) **1348**, 1356

F M F Feedback see F D F Feedback **2066**

F M Guide. (US ISSN 0014-5971) **1356**, 3551

F M I Annual Financial Review. (Food Marketing Institute) (US) **2091**

F M I Issues Bulletin. (Food Marketing Institute) (US ISSN 0275-8059) **2091**

F M I Merchandising, Advertising and Promotion Newsletter see Food Marketing **2091**

F M I Monthly Index Service see Reference Point: Food Industry Abstracts **2085**

F M O News. (Federation of Mobile Home Owners of Florida) (US ISSN 0274-9882) **4148**

F M R. (Franco Maria Ricci International, Inc.) (US ISSN 0747-6388) **326**, 2205

F M S see Financial Managers' Statement **5192**

F M S Magazine see Integrated Manufacturing Systems **3025**

F M T. (Flug- und Modell-Technik) (GW ISSN 0015-458X) **2436**, 52

F M U Occasional Lectures. (Financial Management Unit) (II ISSN 0085-1795) **4059**

F Magazine. (FR) **4842**

F.N.I.B. see F.N.I.B. - Info **3278**

F.N.I.B. - Info/N.V.B.V. - Info. (Federation Nationale des Infirmieres Belges) (BE ISSN 0301-0813) **3278**

F N Magazine. (US) **1284**

F.N. Orientering. (DK ISSN 0014-5998) **3957**

F N V Magazine (Amsterdam). (NE) **3999**

F N V - Magazine (Woerden). (NE) **2582**

F N V News. (Federatie Nederlandse Vakbeweging) (NE) **2583**

F O A Orienterar Om. (Foersvarets Forskningsanstalt) (SW ISSN 0014-6013) **3458**

F O B Colon Free Zone. (PN) **835**

F O I A Update. (Freedom of Information Act) (US) **2569**, 3942

F O J I Newsletter see Friends of Julio International Newsletter **3552**

F O L K Newsletter see Nama Hatta Newsletter **4217**

F.O. Licht's International Coffee Report. (GW) **2066**

F.O. Licht's International Molasses Report. (GW ISSN 0014-6056) **2067**

F.O. Licht's International Sugar and Sweetener Report. (GW) **89**, 2067

F.O. Licht's International Sugar Report see F.O. Licht's International Sugar and Sweetener Report **89**

F O S see Foundations of Semiotics **2815**

F O S S see Fiber Optic Sensor and Systems **3852**

F O W U see Fiber Optics Weekly Update **1336**

F P A C Monthly Report. (Family Planning Association of China) (CH) **596**

F P A P Biennial Report. (Family Planning Association of Pakistan) (PK) **596**

F P D A News. (Fluid Power Distributors Association) (US) **1929**

F P G Weekly News Update see Federal Employees' News Digest **4060**

F P O P Bulletin. (Family Planning Organization of the Philippines) (PH) **596**

F P P see Free Paper Publisher, Inc **4128**

FP 6171

F P R D I Journal. (Forest Products Research and Industries Development Commission) (PH) **2114**
F P S Newsletter. (Fluid Power Society) (US) **1923**
F P Week. (Fairchild Publications, Inc.) (US) **945**
†F Q. (Foreskin Quarterly) (US) **5190**
F R A M. (Fra Ringkoebing Amts Museer) (DK ISSN 0108-3643) **3524**
F R A M E News. (Fund for the Replacement of Animals in Medical Experiments) (UK ISSN 0268-4306) **231**
F R A M E Technical News see F R A M E News **231**
F R C H. Newsletter. (Foundation for Research in Community Health) (II) **4101**
F R E S Newsletter (Federal Regulation of Employment Service) see Employment Coordinator **978**
F R I Monthly Portfolio. (Fund Raising Institute) (US ISSN 0014-6137) **4405**
F R M Weekly. (Fund Raising Management) (US) **778**
F R O E see Foersvarsforskningsreferat **1274**
F R V Kapala Cruise Report. (AT ISSN 0727-4335) **2039**
F S A Market Outlook. (US) **945**
F S A Quarterly Cycle Review. (US) **945**
F S B - Beboeren. (DK) **2487**
F S C Monthly Bulletin. (Federation of Southern Cooperatives) (US) **4405**
F S M B Handbook. (Federation of State Medical Boards) (US ISSN 0888-5656) **3097**
F S M B Newsletter see Federation of State Medical Boards of the United States. Federation Bulletin **3098**
†F S M Links. (Franciscan Sisters of Mary) (US) **5190**
F S R's Skattelove med Noter. (Foreningen af Statsautoriserede Revisorer) (DK ISSN 0905-4367) **1093**
F.S.S.C. Newsletter. (Foreign Student Service Council) (US) **1633**
F S U Faculty Publications see Florida State University. Publications of the Faculty **1706**
F T A Yearbook. (Freight Transport Association) (UK) **4649**
F T B-Handel. (Farben-Tapeten-Bodenbelaege) (GW ISSN 0175-6575) **665**, **4618**
F T C Freedom of Information Log. (Federal Trade Commission) (US ISSN 0161-7036) **908**, **2624**
F T C - Japan View: Information & Opinion From the Fair Trade Commission of Japan. (Fair Trade Commission) (JA) **908**
F T C S see International Symposium on Fault-Tolerant Computing. Digest of Papers **1397**
F T C: Watch. (Federal Trade Commission) (US ISSN 0196-0016) **908**
F T D Family. (Florists' Transworld Delivery Association) (US) **2142**
F T L. (Faster than Light) (IE) **3011**
F T London Policy Guide see World Policy Guide **2545**
F T M & A see F T Mergers & Acquisitions **665**
F T Mergers & Acquisitions. (Financial Times Business Information Ltd.) (UK) **665**
F T Q see Fashion Time Quarterly **5191**
F T S. (French Technology Survey) (FR ISSN 0985-2220) **4597**
F T Systems. (Fault Tolerant) (US ISSN 0740-4980) **1430**
F T T and Beta News. (UK ISSN 0015-1106) **2583**, **1373**, **3508**
F T T H Newsletter see Fiber to the Home **1336**
F und I-Bau. (GW ISSN 0340-2967) **299**, **617**
F und M, Feinwerktechnik und Messtechnik. (GW ISSN 0340-1952) **1822**, **1929**, **3446**, **3852**

F & S. (Filtrieren und Separien) (GW) **1177**, **3818**
F V W International. (GW) **4762**
F W N see Futures World News **947**
F W P Materials Engineering Journal. (SA) **3429**, **1822**
F W S Series. (US) **2099**
F W T A O Newsletter. (Federation of Women Teachers' Associations of Ontario) (CN) **1633**
F.W.Z. Review. (Federation of Women Zionists of Great Britain and Ireland) (UK) **2001**
F X C Newsletter. (US) **865**, **945**
F X O Report. (US) **1892**, **3458**
▼F X Week. (Foreign Exchange) (US ISSN 1050-0782) **908**
F.Y.E.O. see For Your Eyes Only **3458**
F Y I see For Your Information (New York) **326**
F Y I. (For Your Information) (CN) **4649**
F Y I - I M. (US ISSN 1055-1743) **2797**
F Y I Management Memo. (For Your Information) (US) **778**, **830**
F Y I to C E O's see Business Council for the U N Briefing **3952**
F 2 C O see For Formulation Chemists Only **375**
F-5 Service News see F-5 Technical Digest **52**
F-5 Technical Digest. (US) **52**, **3458**
Fa Yin/Dharmagoso Bimonthly. (CC) **4214**
Faaborg-Aarbogen. (DK ISSN 0106-8822) **2361**
Faaborg-Bogen see Faaborg-Aarbogen **2361**
Faaglar i Kvismaren. (SW ISSN 0283-2852) **563**
Faarskoetsel. (SW ISSN 0014-8598) **216**
Fab Guide. (UK) **3429**, **1822**
Faba Bean Abstracts. (UK ISSN 0260-8456) **137**, **12**
Fabbro see Limestone **2932**
Fabian News. (UK) **3893**
Fabian Newsletter. (AT) **3894**, **665**
Fabian Pamphlet. (UK) **3894**
Fabian Review see Fabian News **3893**
Fabian Society, Annual Report. (UK ISSN 0071-3570) **3894**
Fabian Tract see Fabian Pamphlet **3894**
The Fabric & Fiber Sourcebook. (US) **4618**
Fabricants d'Articles Divers en Cuir. see Canada. Statistics Canada. Miscellaneous Leather Products Manufacturers **5160**
Fabricants de Produits Chimiques Industriels. see Canada. Statistics Canada. Manufacturers of Industrial Chemicals **5160**
Fabricants de Savon et de Produits de Nettoyage. see Canada. Statistics Canada. Manufacturers of Soap and Cleaning Compounds **5160**
Fabricare News see I F I Fabricare News **1281**
Fabrication & Glazing Industries. (UK ISSN 0964-6779) **1163**
Fabricator. (US ISSN 0046-3035) **1075**
Fabricnews. (US) **4618**
Fabrics & Architecture. (US) **299**, **4618**
Fabrik og Bolig. (DK ISSN 0106-3324) **2361**
Fabrik 2000. (GW ISSN 0937-2733) **3406**
Fabrikkabeideren. (NO) **4618**
Fabriksarbetaren. (SW ISSN 0014-6234) **4597**
Fabriques de Gants en Cuir. see Canada. Statistics Canada. Leather Glove Factories **5159**
Fabula/Revue d'Etudes sur le Conte Populaire. (GW ISSN 0014-6242) **2054**
†Fabula. (FR ISSN 0755-0960) **5190**
†Fabula Press Award Reader. (GW) **5190**
Fabulous Mexico. (US ISSN 0429-9639) **4762**
Fabulous Mustangs and Exotic Fords. (US ISSN 0885-4750) **4690**
Face. see To Prossopo **2184**

The Face. (UK ISSN 0263-1210) **3551**, **1254**
Face au Risque. (FR ISSN 0014-6269) **2031**
†Face-to-Face (New York). (US ISSN 0361-6061) **5190**
Face to Face with Talent. (CN ISSN 0829-4747) **1373**, **1356**, **3508**, **4633**
Facena see F A C E N A **419**
Faces. (US ISSN 0749-1387) **1254**, **239**
Faces International. (US) **1373**
Faces Rocks. (US) **3551**
Facet. (DK ISSN 0108-9870) **2866**
†Facet. (US ISSN 0893-7974) **5190**
Facet Talk. (AT ISSN 1035-0977) **2436**
Facetas. see Dialogue (Washington) **3954**
Facets. see Fasette **1633**
Facets (Chicago). (US ISSN 0163-0512) **3097**, **4842**
Facets (Pearland). (US) **2563**, **4842**
Facets (San Diego). (US) **3233**
Facets Features. (US ISSN 0736-3745) **3508**, **1385**
Facets of Freshwater. (US ISSN 0046-306X) **4824**, **1954**
Facets of New York. (US) **2225**
Facetten. see Fasette **1633**
†Facetten. (AU) **5190**
Facettes. (FR ISSN 0014-6285) **2186**
Fachberater. (GW ISSN 0014-6293) **3999**
Fachberater fuer das Deutsche Kleingartenwesen. (GW ISSN 0014-6315) **2125**
Fachberichte fuer Metallbearbeitung see F B M - Fertigungstechnologie **3406**
Fachberichte International Steel and Metals Magazine see World Steel & Materials Fachberichte **3423**
Fachberichte Messen - Steuern - Regeln. (US ISSN 0172-5203) **4597**
Fachberichte Simulation. (US) **1435**
Fachblatt Music Magazin. (GW) **3551**
Fachbuchverzeichnis Bauwesen - Architecktur (Year). (GW ISSN 0343-6403) **309**, **617**
Fachbuchverzeichnis Chemie (Year). (GW ISSN 0343-6438) **1201**
Fachbuchverzeichnis Elektrotechnik - Elektronik (Year). (GW ISSN 0343-642X) **1771**, **1892**
Fachbuchverzeichnis Informatik - Datenverarbeitung (Year). (GW) **1404**
Fachbuchverzeichnis Maschinenbau (Year). (GW ISSN 0343-6411) **3025**
Fachbuchverzeichnis Mathematik - Physik (Year). (GW ISSN 0343-639X) **3062**, **3837**
Fachbuchverzeichnis Produktionstechnik (Year). (GW) **1844**
Fachdienst Germanistik. (GW ISSN 0175-2200) **2916**
Fachhefte Bulletin Technique. (SZ) **3999**
Fachhefte fuer Chemigraphie, Lithographie und Tiefdruck see Fachhefte Bulletin Technique **3999**
Fachhochschule Aalen. Bulletin. (GW) **1633**
Fachhochschule Bochum Fh-Bo-Journal see Fh-Bo-Journal **1311**
Fachhochschule Dortmund Presse see F H Presse **1633**
Fachhochschule fuer Bibliotheks- und Dokumentationswesen in Koeln. Amtliche Mitteilungen. (GW ISSN 0724-0775) **2757**
Fachliteratur zum Buch- und Bibliothekswesen/International Bibliography of the Book Trade and Librarianship. (GW ISSN 0071-3627) **2757**, **4127**
Fachpresse see Schweizer Fachpresse **2575**
Die Fachschule. (GW ISSN 0014-6390) **1749**
Fachschwester - Fachpfleger. (US ISSN 0172-5238) **3278**
Fachsprache. (AU) **2813**
Fachvereinigung Guterfernverkehr Hamburg. Mitteilungen. (GW) **4709**

Fachvereinigung Guterfernverkehr Schleswig-Holstein. Nachrichtendienst. (GW) **4709**
Fachzeitschrift fuer Alle Bereiche der Agrartechnik und Laendliches Bauen see Landtechnik **5226**
Fachzeitschrift fuer der Buerofachhandel see Fachzeitung fuer den Buerofachhandel **1058**
Fachzeitung fuer den Buerofachhandel. (GW) **1058**
Facial Plastic Surgery. (US ISSN 0736-6825) **3378**
Facies. (GW ISSN 0172-9179) **1543**, **1560**, **3657**
Facilities. (UK ISSN 0263-2772) **617**, **299**, **1010**
Facilities Design and Management. (US ISSN 0279-4438) **1010**, **299**
Facilities Directory/Repertoire des Salles de Spectacle. (CN) **1530**, **3551**, **4633**
Facilities Energy Report see Energy Conservation Digest **1787**
Facilities Forum. **1822**
Facilities Manager. (US ISSN 0882-7249) **1727**, **1010**
Facilities Planning News. (US ISSN 1045-7089) **299**, **617**, **1058**, **4148**
Facility Design and Management. (UK) **2551**, **1010**
Facility Management see Facility Design and Management **2551**
Facility Management Magazine. (NE) **665**
Facility Supplies Sourcebook see Entertainment Facilities Buyers Guide **5187**
Die Fackel. (GW ISSN 0014-6447) **4405**, **3458**
Fackfoereningsroerelsen see L O Tidningen **2585**
†Facklaeraren. (SW ISSN 0014-6463) **5190**
†Fackliga Vaerldsrorelsen. (Swedish translation of: World Trade Union Movement) (SW ISSN 0014-6471) **5190**
Facolta di Magistero di Firenze. Istituto di Storia. Annali. (IT ISSN 0391-9730) **2361**
Facolta di Scienze Nautiche. Annali see Istituto Universitario Navale. Facolta di Scienze Nautiche. Naples. Annali **4729**
▼Facsimile & Voice Services. (US) **1335**
†Facsimile Users' Directory. (US) **5190**
Fact & Figures Bouw (Year). (NE) **617**
Fact Book. (US) **1633**
Fact Book. Higher Education in Alabama see Directory of Higher Education in Alabama **1705**
Fact Book for Academic Administrators see Fact Book for Higher Education **1706**
Fact Book for Higher Education. (US) **1706**
Fact Book on Direct Marketing see D M A Statistical Fact Book **1037**
Fact Book on Higher Education in the South. (US ISSN 0191-1643) **1706**
Fact Book on Theological Education. (US) **4177**
Fact Finder. (US ISSN 0014-651X) **3894**
Fact Paper on Southern Africa. (SA) **3894**
Fact Sheet on the Netherlands. (NE) **4405**
Fact Sheet Series. (UK) **835**
Fact Sheets on Institutional Racism. (US) **3942**, **4435**
Fact Sheets on Institutional Sexism. (US) **3942**
Fact Sheets on the European Parliament. (EI) **3894**
Fact Technical Society. Journal. (II ISSN 0250-4782) **1853**
Facteurs Biologiques et Chimiques dans la Production des Animaux - Veterinaria. see Biologizace a Chemizace Zivocisne Vyroby - Veterinaria **4807**

FAMILIENDYNAMIK 6173

Factores Biologicos y Quimicos de la Production Animal - Veterinaria. see Biologizace a Chemizace Zivocisne Vyroby - Veterinaria **4807**
Factory see Purchasing **1051**
Factory Equipment & Materials. (SA) **3017**
Factory Equipment and Materials for Southern Africa see Factory Equipment & Materials **3017**
Factory Equipment News. (UK ISSN 0014-6579) **1039**
Factory Equipment News. (AT ISSN 0728-9413) **4597,** 1929
Factory Management. see Kojo Kanri **1017**
Factory Management. (AT) **1075**
Factory Mutual Record. (US ISSN 0014-6595) **2031**
Factory Outlet Shopping Guide for New England. (US) **1504**
Factotum. (UK ISSN 0141-3635) **2757,** 3999
Facts. (US ISSN 0427-8879) **2001**
Facts. (CN ISSN 0705-856X) **2583**
Facts. (UK ISSN 0306-0772) **3957**
Facts About Alaska: Alaska Almanac. (US ISSN 1051-5623) **4762**
Facts About Blacks. (US) **2001**
Facts About Haryana. (II) **4571**
Facts About Maryland Public Education see Fact Book **1633**
Facts About States for the Dentist Seeking a Location. (US ISSN 0517-1024) **3233**
Facts About Store Development. (US ISSN 0732-233X) **2091**
Facts and Advice for Airline Passengers.(US) **4673,** 4101, 4762
Facts and Figures see Economy in Figures **814**
Facts and Figures. (JA) **830**
Facts and Figures. (II ISSN 0301-7796) **865**
Facts and Figures. (FR) **1404**
Facts & Figures. (AU) **1789,** 929, 3685
Facts and Figures - Germany see B F G: Facts and Figures - Germany **844**
Facts and Figures on Footwear see Footwear Manual **4360**
Facts and Figures on Government Finance. (US ISSN 0071-3678) **1093**
Facts & Perspective. (US) **52**
Facts and Reports - Holland Committee on Southern Africa see Komitee Zuidelijk Afrika. Facts and Reports **2333**
Facts and Tendencies/Faits et Tendances. (YU ISSN 0014-7052) **4435**
Facts & Views see Yugoslav Facts and Views **3978**
†Facts for Action. (US) **5190**
Facts from the Foundation. (US) **2119**
Facts Investors Guide. (SA) **945**
Facts, Medicine and Health Care, Denmark. see Tal og Data, Medicin og Sundhedsvaesen **3744**
†Facts om Danmark. (DK ISSN 0108-996X) **5190**
Facts on File. Yearbook. (US ISSN 0196-0040) **2406,** 665, 4471
Facts on File World News Digest With Index. (US ISSN 0014-6641) **2310,** 665, 3894, 4471
Facts on Women at Work in Australia. (AT) **979,** 4842
Factsheet Denmark. (DK ISSN 0107-6183) **2001**
Factsheet Five. (US ISSN 0890-6823) **4127,** 2916
Factuelles. (FR) **4021**
Factum. (SZ) **2219**
Faculdade de Ciencias Agrarias do Para. Boletim. (BL ISSN 0100-2694) **89**
Faculdade de Ciencias Farmaceuticas de Araraquara. Revista see Revista de Ciencias Farmaceuticas **3742**
Faculdade de Filosofia, Ciencias e Letras de Araraquara. Cadeira de Politica. Boletim. (BL) **3894**
Faculdade de Odontologia de Pernambuco. Revista. (BL ISSN 0048-3419) **3233**

Faculdade de Odontologia de Porto Alegre. Revista. (BL) **3233**
Facultad de Ciencias Exactas y Naturales y Agrimensura see F A C E N A **419**
Facultad de Medicina de Barcelona. Departamento de Psiquiatria. Revista see Facultad de Medicina de Barcelona. Revista de Psiquiatria **3337**
Facultad de Medicina de Barcelona. Revista de Psiquiatria. (SP ISSN 0213-7429) **3337**
Facultad Nacional de Agronomia Medellin. Revista. (CK ISSN 0304-2847) **89,** 439, 2099, 3017
Faculte de Droit de Namur. Travaux. (BE) **2624**
Facultes de Droit dt de la Science Juridique. Annales d'Histoire see Facultes de Droit et de la Science Juridique. Revue d'Histoire **2624**
Facultes de Droit et de la Science Juridique. Revue d'Histoire. (FR ISSN 0765-4847) **2624,** 2310
Faculty Association of California Community Colleges see F A C C C T S **1706**
Faculty Association of California Community Colleges Bulletin see F A C C C Bulletin **1706**
Faculty Briefing. (US) **2624,** 1749
Faculty of Actuaries in Scotland. Transactions. (UK ISSN 0071-3686) **2531**
Faculty of Building. Register of Members see Construction Management: Register of Members **613**
Faculty of Science, Kragujevac. Collection of Scientific Papers. see Univerzitet Svetozar Markovic u Kragujevcu. Prirodno-Matematicki Fakultet. Zbornik Radova **4350**
Faculty White Pages. (US ISSN 1040-1288) **1706**
Fad. (US) **2225**
Faellesraadet Vedroerende Mineraliske Raastoffer i Groenland. Beretning see Joint Committee on Mineral Resources in Greenland. Annual Report **3486**
Faellesudvalget til Kaninavlens Fremme Beretning. (DK ISSN 0900-288X) **216**
Faena. (PE) **3894**
Faenza. (IT ISSN 0014-679X) **1163,** 326
†Faerdselsorientering. (DK ISSN 0106-4517) **5190**
Faerg och Fernissa. (SW ISSN 0427-9107) **3653**
Faerg och Lack Scandinavia. (DK ISSN 0037-6049) **3653**
Faeroesk Lovregister. (FA ISSN 0108-142X) **2624**
Al-Faez/Winner. (LE) **3397,** 4471
Fag Rag. (US ISSN 0046-3167) **2452**
Fagbladet Forbrugsgoder see Isenkram-Goer-det-Selv - Byggemarkedet **642**
Fagpressenoeglen. (DK ISSN 0108-2027) **2569**
Fagtidsskriftet Sykepleien. (NO) **3278**
Faguang Xuebao. (CC ISSN 1000-7032) **3852**
Faguo Yanjiu/Etudes Francaises. (CC) **4372,** 2361, 2813
Fahr mit Uns. (GW ISSN 0014-6803) **4718,** 4649
Fahren in Europa. (GW) **4762**
Fahren nach Skandinavien see Reisewege nach Skandinavien **4784**
Fahrerpost. (GW) **4744**
Fahrschule. (GW ISSN 0014-6838) **4690**
Fahrt Frei. (GW ISSN 0014-6846) **4709**
▼Fahrzeug. (GW) **4690**
Fahrzeug und Karosserie. (GW ISSN 0014-6862) **4690**
Der Fahrzeug- und Metall-Lackierer. (GW ISSN 0014-6854) **3406**
†Der Fahrzeughandel. (AU ISSN 0014-6870) **5190**
Fai da Te. (IT) **2436**
Fai da Te Motoverde. (IT) **2436**
Faiences Patriotiques. (FR ISSN 0985-9195) **1163**

Failed Bank and Thrift Litigation Reporter. (US ISSN 0887-7807) **2624,** 945
▼Failed L B O Litigation Reporter. (US) **2624**
Faims et Soifs des Hommes. (FR ISSN 0014-6889) **4405**
Fainansu. see Finance **779**
Faipar. (HU ISSN 0014-6897) **2114**
†Fair Credit Reporting Manual. (US) **5190**
Fair Employment Compliance. (US ISSN 0885-7172) **979,** 1065
Fair Employment Practices see B N A Labor Relations Reporter. Fair Employment Practices **972**
Fair Employment Practices see B N A Policy and Practice Series. Fair Employment Practices **973**
Fair Employment Practices Guidelines see F E P Guidelines **2624**
Fair Employment Practices Summary of Latest Developments. (US) **979**
Fair Employment Report. (US ISSN 0014-6919) **979**
Fair Housing: Discrimination in Real Estate, Community Development and Revitalization. (US) **2487,** 3942
Fair Lady. (SA ISSN 0014-6927) **4842**
▼Fair Lady Junior. (SA) **4842,** 1237
Fair News. (US ISSN 1043-3740) **3392**
Fair Play. (IE) **4471**
Fair Trade Commission Japan View: Information & Opinion From the Fair Trade Commission of Japan see F T C - Japan View: Information & Opinion From the Fair Trade Commission of Japan **908**
Fairchild Publications, Inc. Week see F P Week **945**
Fairchild Tropical Garden Bulletin. (US ISSN 0014-6943) **2125**
Fairchild's Financial Manual of Retail Stores. (US ISSN 0071-3716) **1039**
Fairchild's Textile & Apparel Financial Directory. (US) **4618,** 1284
Faire. (FR ISSN 0339-3070) **2866**
Faire Face. (FR ISSN 0014-6951) **3097,** 4405
Faire Part. (FR ISSN 0182-1717) **2916**
Fairey in Focus. (UK) **1929,** 1892, 1923
†Fairfax. (US ISSN 0885-1999) **5190**
Fairfax Connection. (US) **2225**
Fairfield County Business Journal. (US ISSN 0887-2252) **865**
Fairfield County Woman. (US) **4842**
Fairfield Experimental Horticulture Station. Summary Annual Review. (UK ISSN 0260-8081) **2125**
Fairplay International Shipping Weekly. (UK ISSN 0307-0220) **4727**
Fairplay Marine Computing Guide. (UK ISSN 0267-0879) **4727,** 1425
Fairplay Shipping Journal see Fairplay international Shipping Weekly **4727**
Fairplay World Ports Directory. (UK ISSN 0261-2356) **4727**
Fairplay World Shipping Directory. (UK ISSN 0140-5047) **4727**
Fairplay World Shipping Year Book see Fairplay World Shipping Directory **4727**
Fairs and Conventions Preview. see Messe- und Kongress-Vorschau **3393**
Fairs and Festivals (Year): Northeast and Southeast. (US ISSN 1059-5929) **355,** 4545, 4633
Fairs and Festivals in the Northeast see Fairs and Festivals (Year): Northeast and Southeast **355**
Fairs and Festivals in the Southeast see Fairs and Festivals (Year): Northeast and Southeast **355**
Fairs & Markets Diary: Central, South & South-West. (UK) **257**
Fairs & Markets Diary: London. (UK) **257**
Fairs & Markets Diary: North & Midlands. (UK) **257**
Fairshare. (US ISSN 0273-3560) **2624**
Fairuz. (LE) **1290**

Al-Faisal. (SU) **2216**
Faith. (UK) **4177**
Faith. (US) **4177**
Faith and Action. (SA) **4177**
Faith and Atheism in Communist Territories see F A C T **4177**
Faith and Fellowship. (US) **4238**
Faith and Form. (US ISSN 0014-7001) **299,** 2866
Faith and Freedom. (UK ISSN 0014-701X) **4177**
Faith and Heritage. (UK) **4177**
Faith and Mission. (US ISSN 0740-0659) **4238**
Faith and Order Papers. (SZ ISSN 0512-2589) **4177**
Faith and Philosophy. (US ISSN 0739-7046) **3766,** 4177
Faith & Reason (Front Royal). (US ISSN 0098-5449) **4177**
Faith and Reason (Wilmore) see Faith and Philosophy **3766**
Faith & Renewal. (US) **4177**
Faith & Worship. (UK ISSN 0309-1627) **4178**
Faith for Daily Living. (SA ISSN 0014-7044) **4282**
Faith 'n' Stuff. (US) **1254**
Faith Today. (CN ISSN 0832-1191) **4238,** 2866
▼Faith Works. (US) **4178**
Faithful and True. see Fidelis et Verus **4264**
Faithist Journal. (US) **3594**
Faits et Tendances. see Facts and Tendencies **4435**
Fajabefa Nyt see Evelyn Booster **3551**
Al-Fajr. (TS) **2220**
Fajr al-Jadid/New Dawn. (TS) **4842**
Al-Fajr Jerusalem Palestinian Weekly. (US) **3957**
Fakta. (FI ISSN 0358-626X) **665**
Fakten. (GW ISSN 0343-8449) **1789**
Fakty (Year). (PL) **2866**
Der Falke. (GW ISSN 0323-357X) **563**
Falken Nytt. (NO) **4690**
Falkland Islands Journal. (UK ISSN 0256-1824) **4762**
Falling Leaf. (UK ISSN 0956-2400) **3458,** 4021
Falmer. (UK ISSN 0141-4704) **1311**
Falmouth Port and Industry Handbook 1984. (UK ISSN 0260-9282) **4727,** 1135
False Creek News. (CN) **2177**
Falu yu Shenghuo/Law & Life. (CC) **2624**
Falvak Dolgozo Nepe. (RM) **89,** 2067
Fama. (NE) **2916**
Fama. (MX) **3508,** 1373
Famagusta Chamber of Commerce and Industry. Trade Information Bulletin. (CY) **815**
†Fame. (US) **5190**
Fament Stock Service Advisory. (US) **946**
Famiglia. (IT) **4372**
Famiglia Cristiana. (IT ISSN 0014-7095) **4178**
Famiglia T V. (IT) **1373**
Familia. (SA ISSN 0014-7117) **2150**
Familia. (RM) **2215**
†Familia. (DR) **5190**
Familia Crista. (BL ISSN 0014-7125) **4435,** 4178
Familia Cristiana. (MX) **4264**
La Familia de Hoy. (US) **2002,** 2446
†Familia Latina. (US ISSN 0741-7403) **5190**
Familia y Sociedad. (CK ISSN 0120-3215) **4435,** 4178, 4405
Familie Journalen. (GW ISSN 0014-7133) **2185**
Familie Statistikk see Norway. Statistisk Sentralbyraa. Familie Statistikk **5249**
Familien. (NO ISSN 0014-7141) **2212**
†Familien Danmarks Forbruger. Haandbog. (DK ISSN 0900-2049) **5190**
Familien-Kalender. (GW) **1536**
Familien und Jugend - Gottesdienste. (GW) **4178**
Familienblatt. (SZ ISSN 0014-715X) **1487**
Familiendynamik. (GW ISSN 0342-2747) **4021,** 4435

Familiengeschichtliche Blaetter see Familiengeschichtliche Blaetter und Mitteilungen 2150
Familiengeschichtliche Blaetter der Familie Schreiber-Scriba. (GW) 2150
Familiengeschichtliche Blaetter und Mitteilungen. (GW ISSN 0427-9522) 2150
Familienkundliches Jahrbuch Schleswig-Holstein. (GW ISSN 0430-0440) 2150
Familienpolitische Informationen. (GW ISSN 0176-9146) 2866
Familienverband Avenarius. Familienzeitschrift. (GW ISSN 0014-7176) 2150
Familieplanlaegning. (DK ISSN 0108-8793) 596
Families. (CN ISSN 0030-2945) 2150
Families in Israel. (IS ISSN 0333-9041) 3982
Families in Society. (US ISSN 1044-3894) 4405
Families Monthly. (CH) 3801
Families of the Aged see Senior Care Professional 2278
Families of Yancey Co. (US ISSN 0890-0361) 2150
Famille Avertie see Living Safety 4107
Famille Chretienne. (FR) 2187
Famille Magazine. (FR ISSN 0988-5757) 2187
Famille Nouvelle. (FR ISSN 0014-7184) 4178
Family. see Jiating 2447
Family see Christian Family 4169
Family. see Druzina 4263
Family. Australian Family Studies Database see Australian Family and Society Abstracts 4457
The Family (Boston). (US) 4264
Family (New York). (US) 3458
Family Advocate. (US ISSN 0163-710X) 2717
Family Affairs. (US) 3397, 4842
Family and Community Health. (US ISSN 0160-6379) 4101
Family and Conciliation Courts Review. (US ISSN 1047-5699) 2717
Family and Home Office Computing see Home Office Computing 1469
Family and School. see Oikogeneia kai Scholeio 1241
Family Associations, Societies & Reunions. (US) 2150
Family Backtracking. (US) 2150
Family Business. (US) 1114
Family Business Magazine see Frank Talk 1115
Family Business Review. (US ISSN 0894-4865) 1114
Family Care. (US) 3097
Family Circle. (US ISSN 0014-7206) 2446
Family Circle Great Ideas Christmas Helps & Holiday Baking. (US) 2446
Family Circle Great Ideas Microwave Cooking. (US) 2446
▼Family Circle's Best Home Plan Designs. (US) 299
Family Circle's Great Ideas. (US ISSN 0163-1306) 2446, 617
Family Court Reporter. (UK ISSN 0952-8199) 2717
Family Day Care Bulletin. (US) 1237
Family Digest see Real People 420
▼Family Dynamics of Addiction Quarterly. (US ISSN 1054-8726) 4021, 1536
Family Economics Review. (US ISSN 0425-676X) 1504, 2446
Family Expenditure in Canada. (CN ISSN 0838-3715) 715
Family Expenditure Survey. (IS) 4571
Family Farm Networker. (US) 89
Family Festivals see Festivals 5191
Family Findings. (US ISSN 0533-0939) 2150
Family Food Expenditure in Canada. (CN ISSN 0838-3898) 715
▼Family Fun. (US) 1254
Family Genealogies. (CN ISSN 0227-0994) 2150
Family Guide on Where to Go. (UK) 4762
Family Handyman. (US ISSN 0014-7230) 2501
Family Health Adviser. (US) 3097

Family Heat. (US) 3397
Family Historian. (US) 2150
Family History. (UK ISSN 0014-7265) 2150
Family History Capers. (US ISSN 0742-1419) 2150, 2406
Family History News and Digest. (UK ISSN 0309-8559) 2361, 3982
Family History World. Research News. (US ISSN 0884-3716) 2150
Family Holiday Guide see Children Welcome! Family Holiday Guide 4757
Family in America. (US ISSN 0892-2691) 4435
Family in Historical Perspective see Journal of Family History 4440
Family Law. (UK ISSN 0014-7281) 2717
†Family, Law and Democracy. (US) 5190
Family Law Guidebook. (US) 2717
Family Law Quarterly. (US ISSN 0014-729X) 2717
Family Law Reporter. (US ISSN 0148-7922) 2717
Family Law Reports. (UK ISSN 0261-4375) 2717
Family Law Reports. (AT ISSN 0706-7666) 2717
Family Law Service. (SA) 2717
Family Law Tax Guide. (US) 2717
Family Letter. (US ISSN 1041-9985) 4021, 1683
Family Letters. (US) 3397
Family Life. (UK ISSN 0143-7917) 4238
Family Life. (CN ISSN 0014-7303) 4282
Family Life Educator. (US ISSN 0732-9962) 4021, 1633
Family Life Guide. see Jiating Shenghuo Zhinan 2448
Family Living. (US) 2225
Family Local History Sources in Victoria.(AT ISSN 0812-3136) 2150
Family Magazine. (US) 2446, 2225
Family Matters. (US) 2717
Family Matters. (AT ISSN 1030-2646) 4435, 4405
Family Medicine. (US ISSN 0742-3225) 3097, 1633
Family Medicine. see Jiating Yixue 3113
Family Medicine Literature Index see F A M L I 3174
Family Medicine Programme. R.A.C.G.P. Victoria Newsletter. (Royal Australian College of General Practitioners) (AT) 3097
Family Medicine Teacher see Family Medicine 3097
Family Motor Coaching. (US ISSN 0360-3024) 4650, 4762
Family Notes see Family Notes: a Journal of the Hueck Families 2150
Family Notes: a Journal of the Hueck Families. (GW) 2150
Family Page Directory see Feature News Publicity Outlets 31
Family Perspective. (US ISSN 0014-7311) 4435, 2446, 4021
Family Pet. (US) 3710
Family Physician. (US ISSN 0014-732X) 3097
Family Physician. see Rofei ha-Mishpacha 3150
Family Physician's Compendium of Drug Therapy. (US ISSN 0276-4318) 3725
Family Planning see Family Planning Today 596
Family Planning Association of China Monthly Report see F P A C Monthly Report 596
Family Planning Association of Fiji. News. (FJ) 596, 3291
Family Planning Association of Gambia. Newsletter. (GM ISSN 0796-0174) 596
Family Planning Association of India. Report. (II ISSN 0377-7774) 596
Family Planning Association of Kenya. Annual Report. (KE) 596
Family Planning Association of Pakistan. Annual Report see F P A P Biennial Report 596

Family Planning Association of Pakistan Biennial Report see F P A P Biennial Report 596
†Family Planning in Five Continents. (UK ISSN 0538-9089) 5190
Family Planning Newsletter. (PH) 596
Family Planning Organization of the Philippines Bulletin see F P O P Bulletin 596
Family Planning Perspectives. (US ISSN 0014-7354) 596, 3291
†Family Planning - Population Reporter.(US ISSN 0090-0923) 5190
Family Planning Programs in Oklahoma.(US ISSN 0095-3121) 596
Family Planning Services; Annual Survey see U.S. Centers for Disease Control. Family Planning Services: Annual Summary 598
Family Planning Today. (UK ISSN 0309-1112) 596
▼Family Planning World. (US) 596
Family Practice. (UK ISSN 0263-2136) 3097
Family Practice. (CN) 3098
†Family Practice Alert. (US) 5190
Family Practice News. (US ISSN 0300-7073) 3098
Family Practice Recertification. (US ISSN 0163-6642) 3098
Family Practice Research Journal. (US ISSN 0270-2304) 3098
†Family Practitioner Services. (UK ISSN 0305-9669) 5190
Family Process. (US ISSN 0014-7370) 4021, 4435
Family Programmer. (US) 3801
Family Puzzlers. (US ISSN 0014-7389) 2150
Family Radio and T V see Personality 2216
Family Radio News. (US) 4178, 1356
Family Records Today. (US ISSN 0736-1858) 2150
Family Relations. (US ISSN 0197-6664) 4435, 1633
Family Safety & Health. (US ISSN 0749-310X) 4101, 2446
Family Saving Survey (Year). (JA ISSN 0448-7109) 715, 4571
Family Service Perspectives. (US) 4435, 1237
Family Sites Guide. (UK ISSN 0957-7327) 4545, 4690
Family Statistics. see Norway. Statistisk Sentralbyraa. Familie Statistikk 5249
Family Support Bulletin. (US) 2290, 3337
Family Systems Medicine. (US ISSN 0736-1718) 3098
Family Therapy. (US ISSN 0091-6544) 3337, 4405
Family Therapy Networker. (US ISSN 0739-0882) 4021, 1536, 4405
Family Therapy News. (US ISSN 0277-6464) 4021, 3066, 4405, 4435
†Family Therapy Today. (US ISSN 0887-9109) 5190
Family Ties. (US) 2150
▼Family Times (Eau Clair). (US) 2446
▼Family Times (Wilmington). (US) 1237
Family Travel Times. (US) 4762
Family Treasure. see Ikoyeneakos Thesavros 2447
Family Tree. (CN) 1237, 2150
Family Tree (Waco) see Heart of Texas Records 2150
Family Tree Digest. (US) 2150
Family Tree Exchange. (US) 2150
Family Tree Magazine. (UK ISSN 0267-1131) 2150
Family Tree Newsletter. (US) 2150
▼Family Tree Quarterly. (US ISSN 1059-0803) 2150
Family Treebune. (US) 2150
Family Walk. (US) 4238, 1254
Fan Club Monitor. (US) 1297
Fan Club Spotlight. (US) 1297
Fana de l'Aviation. (FR) 52
Fanatic. (UK) 2866
Fanatic Reader. (US) 2225, 12
Fancy Feathers. A P A News and Views.(US) 216

Fancy Food. (US) 2091
Fancy Food and Candy see Fancy Food 2091
Fancy Fowl. (UK) 216
Fandom Newsletter. (GW) 3011
Y Faner. (UK) 2866
Fanfare. (US ISSN 0148-9364) 3551
Fanfare. (UK) 3551
Fanfare. (AT) 4633
Fanfares. (CN ISSN 0046-3256) 4633
Fang. (GW) 2099, 4545
Fang Cao. (CC) 2917
Fang Cao Di. (CC) 2917
Fangdichan Dao Bao. see Real Estate Times 4157
Fangoria. (US) 3669
Fangyan/Dialect. (CC ISSN 0257-0203) 2813
Fangzhi Wenzhan/Textile Abstract. (CC ISSN 1000-3916) 4628
Fangzhi Xuebao/China Textile Engineering Association. Journal. (CC) 4618
Fanlight News. (US) 3098, 1633, 4435
Fannie Mae Investor Analyst Report. (US) 946
Fannin County Genealogical Quarterly. (US) 2150
▼Fans. (US) 4472, 1290
Fantasia. (GW) 3011, 326, 2917
Fantasiae (Los Angeles). (US ISSN 0094-2375) 3011
Fantastic Flyer Magazine. (US) 1254
Fantastic Worlds of Edgar Rice Burroughs. (US) 3011, 2917
Fantastica see Fangoria 3669
Fantastica Maglia. (IT) 3591
Fantastyka. (PL) 3011
▼Fantasy Baseball. (US ISSN 1046-9125) 2436, 4503
Fantasy Commentator. (US ISSN 1051-5011) 3011, 2993
Fantasy Football. (US) 4503
Fantasy Magazine see Marion Zimmer Bradley's Fantasy Magazine 3012
Fantasy Review see Science Fiction and Fantasy Book Review Annual 3014
Fantasy Tales. (UK) 3011
Fantasywelt. (GW ISSN 0935-0721) 4472, 3011
Fante di Quadri. (IT ISSN 0014-7524) 2507
Fantomet. (DK) 1254
Fanus. (PK) 2917
Far da Se. (IT) 2436
Far da Se Almanacco. (IT) 2436
Far East. (AT) 4264, 4405
Far East and Australasia (Year). (UK ISSN 0071-3791) 3894, 865
Far East Business. (HK) 865
Far East Businessman's Directory see A.A.'s Far East Businessman's Directory 1119
Far East Health. (UK ISSN 0143-0645) 4101, 2461
Far East Oil Laws and Concession Contracts see Basic Oil Laws & Concession Contracts: Asia & Australasia 2719
Far East Reporter (Houston). (US) 4282
Far East Scouting Bulletin see Asia - Pacific Scouting 1232
†Far East Shipping. (UK ISSN 0144-8781) 5191
Far East Traveler. (JA) 4762
Far Eastern Affairs. (RU) 2361, 3894
Far Eastern Agriculture. (UK ISSN 0266-8025) 89
Far Eastern Economic Review. (HK ISSN 0014-7591) 865
Far Eastern Law Review. (PH ISSN 0046-3272) 2624
Far Eastern Technical Review see Asian Review of Business and Technology 4594
▼Far Point. (UK ISSN 0964-1890) 3011
Far Seas Fisheries Research Laboratory. Bulletin see National Research Institute of Far Seas Fisheries. Bulletin 2046
Far Seas Fisheries Research Laboratory. S Series see National Research Institute of Far Seas Fisheries. S Series 2046
Fara. (US) 89

Faraday Discussions. (UK ISSN 0301-7249) 1226
Faraday Discussions of the Chemical Society see Faraday Discussions 1226
Faraday Transactions 2 see Royal Society of Chemistry. Journal: Faraday Transactions 1230
Faran. (US) 89
Faravid. (FI ISSN 0356-5629) 2361
Die Farbe. (GW ISSN 0014-7680) 3852, 3653
Farbe Aktuell. (AU) 3725, 1177
Farbe und Lack. (GW ISSN 0014-7699) 3653
Farbe und Raum. (GW ISSN 0014-7702) 617
Farben-Chemiker see Fett - Wissenschaft Technologie 1853
Farben-Tapeten-Bodenbelaege Handel see F T B-Handel 665
Farbenhaendler see Heim und Farbe 5204
Farbenkreis, Oesterreichische Malerzeitung. (AU ISSN 0014-7737) 3653
Farce. (US) 2917
Fardase see Far da Se 2436
Fardase Almanacco see Far da Se Almanacco 2436
Fare Box. (US ISSN 0014-7745) 3599
Fare Elettronica. (IT) 1771
Fare Musica. (IT) 3551
Farhang-e Iran Zamin. (IR ISSN 0014-7788) 3637, 2429
▼Farjad. (IR) 2202
Farm. (AT ISSN 0725-3338) 89, 150
Farm and Country. (CN ISSN 0046-3299) 89
Farm and Country see Farm Chronicle 90
Farm & Country Holidays. (UK) 4762
Farm and Dairy. (US ISSN 0014-7826) 199
Farm and Food. (IE) 89, 2067
Farm and Food Research see Farm and Food 89
Farm and Food Society Newsletter. (UK) 89, 1954
†Farm and Garden Index. (US ISSN 0193-8487) 5191
†Farm and Garden Periodicals on Microfilm. (US) 5191
Farm & Home News. (US ISSN 1040-8525) 89
Farm and Home Research. (US ISSN 0038-3295) 90
Farm and Home Science see Minnesota Science 4324
Farm and Industrial Equipment Institute. First of the Week Newsletter see Equipment Manufacturers Institute. First of the Week Newsletter 161
Farm and Industrial Equipment Institute. Retail Sales Reports see Equipment Manufacturers Institute. Retail Sales Reports 161
Farm and Industrial Equipment Institute. State of the Industry see Equipment Manufacturers Institute. State of the Industry 161
Farm and Land Realtor see Realtors Land Institute 4157
Farm & Power Equipment Dealer. (US ISSN 0892-6085) 161
Farm and Ranch. (US ISSN 0192-5237) 90
Farm and Ranch Guide. (US) 90
Farm & Ranch Living. (US ISSN 0276-170X) 90
Farm Animal Welfare Co-ordinating Executive. Newsletter. (UK ISSN 0144-6169) 216
Farm Broadcasters Letter. (US) 90
Farm Building News see Rural Builder 631
Farm Buildings and Engineering. (UK ISSN 0265-5373) 162
Farm Buildings and Equipment Directory. (UK) 162, 1135
Farm Bureau News. (US ISSN 0197-5617) 90
Farm Bureau Press. (US) 90
Farm Business Management see Farm Business Management Analysis Report 150

Farm Business Management Analysis Report. (US) 150
Farm Business Statistics for South East England. (UK) 137, 4571
Farm Cash Receipts. (CN ISSN 0703-7945) 137
Farm Chemicals. (US ISSN 0092-0053) 176, 1177
Farm Chemicals Handbook. (US ISSN 0430-0750) 177
Farm Chemicals International. (US ISSN 1043-8858) 177
Farm Chemicals Today. (AT ISSN 1031-3761) 177
Farm Chronicle. (US ISSN 0896-1883) 90
Farm Contractor. (UK ISSN 0144-0675) 90
Farm Credit Administration. Annual Report. (US) 150, 830
Farm Credit Administration Bulletin see F C A Bulletin 150
Farm Credit Corporation Canada. Annual Report. (CN ISSN 0071-3864) 778
Farm Credit Corporation Canada. Federal Farm Credit Statistics/ Statistiques du Credit Agricole Federal. (CN ISSN 0071-3872) 778
Farm Credit in the Canadian Financial System/Financement de l'Agriculture Canadienne. (CN) 778
Farm Economist see Oxford Agrarian Studies 156
Farm Equipment. (US ISSN 0014-7958) 162
Farm Equipment Catalog. (US) 162
Farm Equipment Guide see Hot Line Farm Equipment Guide 162
Farm Equipment International. (UK) 162
Farm Equipment Quarterly see Agri-Book Magazine. Farm Equipment Review 161
Farm Equipment Quarterly see Agri-Book Magazine. Farm Equipment Directory 161
Farm Equipment Wholesalers Association. Tips. (US) 162, 1075
Farm Facts see Kansas. State Board of Agriculture. Annual Report with Farm Facts 102
Farm Focus. (CN) 90
Farm Gate. (CN ISSN 0705-8748) 90
Farm Guide. (PK) 90
Farm Holiday Guide (England, Wales & Ireland). (UK) 4762
Farm Holiday Guide (Scotland Edition). (UK ISSN 0267-288X) 4762
Farm Holidays in Ireland. (IE) 4762
Farm Impact. (US) 90
Farm Income. (US) 150
Farm Incomes in England. (UK) 90
Farm Incomes in England and Wales see Farm Incomes in England 90
Farm Index see Farmline Magazine 91
Farm Industry News. (US ISSN 0199-6924) 90
Farm Journal. (US ISSN 0014-8008) 90
Farm Journal Extra see Top Producer 124
Farm Light & Power. (CN ISSN 0014-8032) 162
Farm Machinery Yearbook. see Nogyo Kikai Nenkan 163
Farm Management Notes see Farming in the East Midlands 177
Farm Management Notes for Asia and the Far East. (UN ISSN 0430-084X) 150
Farm Management Pocketbook. (UK) 150
Farm Mixer. (UK) 90
Farm News. (US) 90
Farm News and Views. (US) 90
Farm News of Erie and Wyoming Counties. (US) 90
Farm Production and Practice see AgLink Leaflets 68
Farm, Ranch and Country Vacations. (US ISSN 0195-8437) 4762
▼Farm Scientist. (PK) 4809, 216
Farm Show Magazine. (US ISSN 0163-4518) 162
Farm Smart. (US) 165

Farm Store. (US ISSN 0014-8121) 90
Farm Store Merchandising see Farm Store 90
†Farm Supplier. (US ISSN 0014-813X) 5191
Farm Talk. (US) 90
Farm Tax Saver. (US) 150
Farm Times. (US) 90
Farm Week (Bloomington). (US) 90
Farm Weekly. see Sevagram 119
Farm Woman see Country Woman 4840
Farmaceut. (YU) 3725
Farmaceuticky Obzor. (CS ISSN 0014-8172) 3725
Farmaceutisk Tidende. (DK ISSN 0014-8199) 3725
Farmaceutski Glasnik. (CI ISSN 0014-8202) 3725
Farmacevtisk Revy. (SW ISSN 0014-8210) 3726
Farmacevtski Vestnik. (XV ISSN 0014-8229) 3726, 485
Farmaci. (DK) 3726, 1177
Farmaci. Scientific Edition see Acta Pharmaceutica Nordica 3715
Farmacia/Pharmacy. (RM ISSN 0014-8237) 3726
Farmacia Naturale. (IT ISSN 0394-8196) 3726
Farmacia Notizie see Federfarma Notizie 3726
Farmacia Nuova. (IT ISSN 0014-8245) 3726
Farmacista Moderno. (IT) 3726
Farmacista Sociale. (IT ISSN 0014-8253) 3726
Farmacja Polska. (PL ISSN 0014-8261) 3726
Farmaco. (IT ISSN 0014-827X) 3726
Farmacoterapia/Journal of Pharmacology. (SP ISSN 0214-8935) 3726
Farmakologiya i Toksikologiya/ Pharmacology and Toxicology. (RU ISSN 0014-8318) 3726, 1981
Farmakoterapi. (NO ISSN 0014-8326) 3726
Farmatsevtychnyi Zhurnal. (KR ISSN 0014-8342) 3726
Farmatsia. (BU ISSN 0428-0296) 3726
Farmatsiya/Pharmacy. (RU ISSN 0367-3014) 3726
Farmer. (GY) 90
Farmer. (JM ISSN 0014-8350) 90
Farmer. (RH ISSN 1011-0488) 90
Farmer. (CN) 90
Farmer see Practical Farmer 115
Farmer and Grazier see Farmers & Stockowners 205
Farmer and Parliament. (II ISSN 0014-8369) 90
Farmer Business in Wales. (UK) 90
Farmer Cooperatives. (US ISSN 0364-0736) 91, 830
Farmer Stockman of the Midwest. (US) 91, 216
The Farmer - The Dakota Farmer. (US) 91
Farmers' Advance. (US) 91
Farmers and Consumers Market Bulletin. (US) 91, 2446
Farmers & Stockowners. (AT) 205, 216
Farmers Bulletin. (UK) 91
Farmers Club. Journal. (UK ISSN 0014-8393) 91
Farmer's Digest. (US ISSN 0046-3337) 91
Farmer's Exchange. (US) 91
Farmers' Exchange (Fayetteville). (US) 91
▼Farmers Fastline: Arkansas Edition. (US) 91
▼Farmers Fastline: Georgia Edition. (US) 162
Farmers Fastline: Illinois Edition. (US) 91
Farmers Fastline: Indiana Edition. (US) 91
Farmers Fastline: Iowa Edition. (US) 91
▼Farmers Fastline: Kansas Edition. (US) 162
Farmers Fastline: Kentucky Edition. (US) 91
Farmers Fastline: Missouri Edition. (US) 162

▼Farmers Fastline: Nebraska Edition. (US) 162
▼Farmers Fastline: North Carolina Edition. (US) 162
Farmers Fastline: Ohio Edition. (US) 91
▼Farmers Fastline: Tennessee Edition. (US) 162
▼Farmers Fastline: Virginia Edition. (US) 91
†Farmers Fastline: Wisconsin Edition. (US) 5191
†Farmers Federal Tax Alert. (US) 5191
Farmers' Friend. (CH ISSN 0014-8415) 91
Farmers Guardian. (UK ISSN 0014-8423) 91
Farmers Hot Line. (US) 91, 1039
Farmer's Journal see Farmweek 91
Farmer's Market. (US ISSN 0748-6022) 2917
Farmers Newsletter. (AT ISSN 0014-844X) 177
Farmer's Report. (US) 177
Farmer's Voice see Farmer's World 91
Farmers Weekly. (SA ISSN 0014-8482) 91
Farmers Weekly. (UK ISSN 0014-8474) 91
†Farmers Weekly. (AT ISSN 0014-8466) 5191
Farmers Weekly Review. (US) 91
Farmer's World. (KE) 91
Farmes Modernes see Tracteurs et Machines Agricoles 164
FarmFutures. (US ISSN 0091-1305) 91
Farming. (US) 150
Farming Business see Enterprise Farming 5187
Farming for Development. (FR) 91
Farming Forum see Australian Farm Manager 78
Farming in the East Midlands. (UK ISSN 0071-3961) 177
Farming in the East Midlands. Financial Results. (UK) 150
†Farming in Zambia. (ZA ISSN 0014-8504) 5191
Farming Mechanization. see Kikaika Nogyo 163
Farming News. (UK) 91
Farming Review. (UK) 91
Farming Today (Simcoe County Edition) .(CN) 91
Farming Today (Wellington-Waterloo-Perth Edition). (CN) 91
Farmis - Reptilen. (SW ISSN 0014-8520) 3726
Farmland Forum. (US) 1487
Farmland Market. (UK) 150
Farmland News. (US ISSN 0093-5832) 91
Farmline Magazine. (US ISSN 0270-5672) 91
Farmshine. (US ISSN 0745-7553) 199
Farmweek. (UK ISSN 0014-8547) 91
FarmWeek (Knightstown). (US) 92
Farnborough Air Show (Public Programme). (UK ISSN 0071-402X) 52
Il Faro. (GW ISSN 0014-8555) 2813
El Faro. (US) 3752
Faro del Silencio. (SP) 2287
†Faroerne og Groenland. (DK ISSN 0108-5557) 5191
Farogh-I-Urdu. (II ISSN 0014-8571) 2917
Farrago. (AT) 1311
Farrago Griffin see Farrago 1311
Farriers Journal see Forge (Year) 3406
Farumashia/Pharmacy. (JA ISSN 0014-8601) 3726
†Farvandvaesenets Trafikanalyse. (DK ISSN 0109-5811) 5191
Fasaden. (SW ISSN 0345-3251) 617
Fasciculi Historici. (PL ISSN 0071-4038) 2361
Fasciculi Mathematici. (PL ISSN 0044-4413) 3035
Fascinacion. (US) 3397
Fasciculi Archaeologiae Historicae. (PL ISSN 0860-0007) 272
Fasecolda see Revista Fasecolda 2541
Fasette/Facets/Facetten. (SX ISSN 0256-5994) 1633, 2332, 2917
Fashal. (BG) 92
Fashion. see Shizhuang 1294
Fashion. (IT) 4618

FASHION ACCESSORIES

Fashion Accessories. (US ISSN 0014-8644) **2564**, 2281
Fashion and Craft. (UK) **1290**, 3591
Fashion and Craft Courses Directory *see* Art, Craft, Design & Textile Technology Directory **1692**
Fashion Buyers Diary *see* Fashion Forecast **1290**
Fashion Calendar. (US ISSN 0014-8660) **1290**
Fashion Calendar *see* Fashion Monitor **1290**
Fashion Ceramic Tiles. (IT) **1163**
Fashion Color Forecast. (US) **1284**, 1290
Fashion Extras. (UK ISSN 0264-8555) **1290**, 2736
Fashion Forecast. (UK ISSN 0014-8679) **1290**
Fashion Forecast International. (UK) **1285**
Fashion Galleria. (US) **1290**
Fashion Garden *see* So-En **1294**
Fashion in China. *see* Zhongguo Shizhuang **1295**
†Fashion Index. (UK ISSN 0142-2081) **5191**
Fashion International. (US) **1290**
Fashion International *see* Fashion Record **1291**
Fashion Jewelry & Accessories. (CH) **2564**
Fashion Jewelry Plus. (US) **2564**
Fashion Knitting. (US) **3591**
Fashion Market Directory. (US) **1135**, 1285
Fashion Monitor. (UK) **1290**
Fashion Network Report. (US) **1291**
Fashion Newsletter. (US ISSN 0300-7111) **1291**
Fashion Poetry Patterns & Recitals News. (US) **4842**, 2446, 3591
Fashion Record. (UK) **1291**
†Fashion Time Quarterly. (US) **5191**
Fashion Update. (UK ISSN 0265-1084) **1291**
Fashion Weekly. (UK) **1291**
Fast Car. (UK) **4690**
Fast Ferry International. (UK ISSN 0954-3988) **4727**, 1822
Fast Folk Musical Magazine. (US ISSN 8755-9137) **3551**
Fast Food *see* Restaurant Business **2479**
Fast Foreword. (US) **3508**, 1749
Fast Forward. (UK) **1311**
†Fast Forward. (US ISSN 0896-2332) **5191**
Fast Grunn. (NO ISSN 0014-8733) **4178**
Fast Lane. (UK ISSN 0266-5182) **4690**
Fast Times. (US) **1254**
Fast Track News. (US) **4690**
Fastbacks *see* Phi Delta Kappa Fastbacks **1655**
†Fastener Age. (US ISSN 0895-4895) **5191**
Fastener Industry News. (US) **3406**
Fastener Standards. (US ISSN 0071-4046) **1916**
Fastener Technology *see* Fastener Technology International **642**
Fastener Technology International. (US ISSN 0746-2441) **642**
Faster than Light *see* F T L **3011**
†Fastest Growing Stocks. (US) **5191**
†Fastfacts European Hotel Locator. (US ISSN 0192-1347) **5191**
†Fastfacts U S A Hotel Motel Locator. (US ISSN 0197-9477) **5191**
Fastie Report. (US) **1460**
Fastighet (Year) *see* Din Fastighet **616**
Fastighetsfolket. (SW) **2446**
Fastighetstidningen. (SW ISSN 0348-5552) **4148**
†Fastline for Arkansas - Oklahoma Truckers. (US) **5191**
Fastline for Dixie Truckers. (US) **4744**, 31
Fastline for Florida Truckers. (US) **4744**
Fastline for Georgia Truckers. (US) **4744**
Fastline for Kentucky Truckers. (US) **4744**
Fastline for Tennessee Truckers. (US) **4744**, 31

Fastpitch Softball News Bulletin. (US) **4503**
Fat Apple Review. (US) **2452**
Fat Fendered Street Rods. (US) **4690**
Fat - Science Technology. *see* Fett - Wissenschaft Technologie **1853**
Fat Tuesday. (US ISSN 0276-2072) **2917**
Fataburen. (SW ISSN 0348-971X) **239**
Fatal Accident Reporting System. (US ISSN 0732-9792) **4718**
Fate. (US ISSN 0014-8776) **3669**
Fathers. (US) **3397**, 1237
Fathers' Journal. (US) **3397**, 3942
Fathers of the Church. (US ISSN 0014-8814) **4264**
Fathom. (US ISSN 0014-8822) **3458**, 4727
Fatigue & Fracture of Engineering Materials and Structures. (US ISSN 8756-758X) **1822**
Fatigue of Engineering Materials and Structures *see* Fatigue & Fracture of Engineering Materials and Structures **1822**
Fatima Findings. (US ISSN 0014-8830) **4282**
Fatos. (BL) **2175**
Fatos and Fotos *see* Fatos **2175**
Fatosi/Vaillant. (AA) **1254**
Fats and Oils. Oilseed Crushings *see* Current Industrial Reports: Fats and Oils. Oilseed Crushings **2084**
Fauji Akhbar *see* Sainik Samachar **3471**
Faulkner Facts and Fiddlings. (US ISSN 0430-1188) **2406**
Faulkner Journal. (US ISSN 0884-2949) **2917**
Faulkner Newsletter & Yoknapatawpha Review. (US ISSN 0733-6357) **419**, 2569
Faulkner Report on Microcomputers and Software. (US) **1460**
Fault Tolerant Systems *see* F T Systems **1430**
Fauna. (NO ISSN 0014-8881) **582**
Fauna & Flora. (SA ISSN 0046-3388) **1487**, 502, 582
Fauna & Flora (English Edition) *see* Fauna & Flora **1487**
Fauna d'Italia. (IT) **582**, 532, 563
Fauna Entomologica Scandinavica. (NE ISSN 0106-8377) **532**, 439
Fauna Hungariae. *see* Magyarorszag Allatvilaga **587**
†Fauna Norrlandica. (SW ISSN 0349-0823) **5191**
Fauna Norvegica Series A. Norwegian Fauna Except Entomology and Ornithology. (NO ISSN 0332-768X) **582**
Fauna Norvegica Series B. Norwegian Journal of Entomology. (NO ISSN 0332-7698) **532**
Fauna Norvegica Series C. Norwegian Journal of Ornithology. (NO ISSN 0332-7701) **563**
Fauna och Flora. (SW ISSN 0014-8903) **502**
Fauna of New Zealand. (NZ ISSN 0111-5383) **532**, 582
Fauna of Russia and Adjacent Countries. (IS) **582**
Fauna of the U.S.S.R. (IS) **582**
Fauna Palaestina. (IS) **582**
Fauna Slodkowodna Polski. (PL ISSN 0071-4089) **582**
Il Fauno. (IT) **326**
Faustball. (GW) **4503**
Faustchen. (AU) **2813**
Faux Titre. (NE ISSN 0167-9392) **2866**
▼Fava News. (US) **205**
Faversham Papers. (UK ISSN 0014-892X) **2361**
Faves. (US) **1254**, 3551
La Favilla. (IT ISSN 0393-4195) **3894**
Favonius. (US) **1276**
Favorably Positioned Stocks. (US ISSN 8756-4769) **946**
Favorite Brand Name Recipes. (US) **2446**, 2067
†Favorite Country Stars. (US) **5191**
Favorite Recipes *see* Favorite Brand Name Recipes **2446**

Favorite Westerns *see* Westerns & Serials **3519**
Fawazir. (LE) **4218**
Fawley Foundation Lectures. (UK ISSN 0071-4097) **4597**
▼Fax Directory of S A A R C. (II) **400**
Fax Facts. (US) **1350**
Fax Magazine. (US) **1058**
Fax Plus. (CN) **2461**
▼Fax 21. (UK) **3011**
Faxletter *see* Faxon Report **4143**
Faxon Guide to C D - R O M. (US) **2797**
Faxon Guide to Serials. (US) **400**
Faxon Librarians' Guide to Serials *see* Faxon Guide to Serials **400**
Faxon Report. (US ISSN 1048-3403) **4143**
FAXreporter. (US ISSN 1053-234X) **826**, 1362
Faxue/Science of Law. (CC) **2625**
Faxue Yanjiu/Studies in Law. (CC) **2625**
Faxue Yicong/Translated Law Literature.(CC) **2625**
Faxue yu Shijian/Law and Practice. (CC) **2625**
Faxue Zazhi/Journal of Jurisprudence. (CC ISSN 1001-618X) **2625**
†Fayette Connection. (US ISSN 0739-8093) **5191**
Fayette County (Ky.) Genealogical Society Quarterly. (US ISSN 0892-5194) **2150**
Fayixue Zazhi/Journal of Forensic Sciences. (CC) **3264**
Fayu Xuexi/Learning French. (CC) **2813**, 1749
Fazhan Yanjiu/Development Research. (CC) **665**
Fazhi. (CC) **2625**
Fazhi Jianshe/Law & Order. (CC ISSN 1000-3568) **2625**
Fazhi Liaowang/Legal Outlook. (CC) **1514**
Fazhi Ribao/Legal Daily. (US) **2625**
Fazhi Tiandi. (CC) **2625**
Fazhi yu Wenming/Legal System and Civilization. (CC) **2625**
La Fe Bautista. (US ISSN 0162-4504) **4238**
†Fear. (UK ISSN 0954-8017) **5191**
Fearnleys Mid-Week Report. (NO) **4727**
Fearnleys Monthly Report. (NO) **4727**
Fearnleys Review. (NO ISSN 0801-5589) **4727**
Feasta. (IE ISSN 0014-8946) **2202**
Feather Fancier. (CN ISSN 0380-352X) **216**
▼Feature. (CN) **1373**
Feature News Publicity Outlets. (US) **31**
Febox-Boxeo. (SP) **4472**
Fechten/Escrime/Scherma. (SZ) **4472**
Fechtsport. (GW) **4472**
Fed in Print. (US ISSN 0891-2769) **715**
Fed Tracker *see* Fed Tracker Special Report **665**
Fed Tracker - Reality Theory Newsletter.(US ISSN 0739-3563) **665**
Fed Tracker Special Report. (US) **665**
Feddes Repertorium. (GW ISSN 0014-8962) **502**
Fedelta. (IT) **4238**
Fedelta Apostolica *see* Fedelta **4238**
Feder *see* Publizistik und Kunst **2574**
Federacao dos Trabalhadores na Agricultura do Estado do Parana. Relatorio. (BL) **2583**
Federacio Esperantista Fervojista Austria Sekcio. Bulteno *see* I F E F, Austria Sekcio. Bulteno **4710**
Federacion Argentina de Periodistas. Gaceta. (AG) **4127**
Federacion del Agricultores y Ganaderos de Andalucia Andalucia *see* F A S A G A - Andalucia **215**
Federacion Espanola Galguera. Boletin Mensual Informativo *see* Galgos **4472**
Federacion Latinoamericana de Bancos. Revista *see* Revista FeLaBan **798**
Federacion Nacional de Cafeteros de Colombia. Boletin de Informacion Estadistica Sobre Cafe. (CK ISSN 0084-7941) **380**

Federacion Nacional de Cafeteros de Colombia. Informe de Labores de los Comites Departamentales de Cafeteros. (CK) **2067**, 177
Federacion Odontologica Colombiana. Revista. (CK ISSN 0046-354X) **3233**
Federacion Panamericana de Asociaciones de Facultades de Medicina. Boletin. (VE ISSN 0533-0327) **3098**
Federacion Sudamericana de Asociaciones Cristianas de Jovenes. Noticias *see* Confederacion Latinoamericana de Asociaciones Cristianas de Jovenes. Carta **4172**
Federal Administrative Law. (AT) **2625**, 4059
Federal & State Insurance Week. (US) **2531**
Federal and State Judicial Clerkship Directory. (US) **1135**, 2731
Federal Appeals: Jurisdiction and Practice. (US) **2625**
Federal Applied Technology Database. (US) **4598**
Federal Assistance Monitor. (US ISSN 1050-3242) **4059**
Federal Audit Guides. (US) **750**
Federal Aviation Administration: High Altitude Pollution Program. (US) **4673**
Federal Aviation Regulations for Pilots *see* Aim - Far (Year) **45**
Federal Banking Law Reports. (US) **779**, 2625
Federal Banking Laws (Supplement). (US) **779**, 2625
Federal Bar News & Journal. (US ISSN 0279-4691) **2625**
Federal Benefits for Veterans and Dependents, IS-1 Fact Sheet. (US) **3458**, 2531
Federal Budget Report. (US ISSN 0898-0071) **4059**
Federal Business Development Bank. Annual Report. (CN) **779**
Federal Buyers Guide. (US) **1135**
Federal Career Opportunities. (US ISSN 0279-2230) **3627**
Federal Carriers Cases. (US) **2625**
Federal Carriers Reports. (US) **4650**
Federal Civilian Work Force Statistics. Affirmative Employment Statistics. (US) **715**, 979
Federal Civilian Work Force Statistics. Equal Employment Opportunity Statistics *see* Federal Civilian Work Force Statistics. Affirmative Employment Statistics **715**
Federal Civilian Work Force Statistics. Pay Structure of the Federal Civil Service. (US) **715**, 979
Federal Civilian Work Force Statistics. Work Years and Personnel Costs. Executive Branch, United States Government. (US ISSN 0277-3325) **715**, 979
Federal Civilian Workforce Statistics. Employment and Trends. (US) **715**
Federal Civilian Workforce Statistics. Monthly Release *see* Federal Civilian Workforce Statistics. Employment and Trends **715**
Federal Civilian Workforce Statistics. Occupations of Federal White-Collar and Blue-Collar Workers. (US) **715**, 979
Federal Coal Management Report. (US) **3686**
Federal Communications Commission Reports. (US ISSN 0098-3942) **1335**
Federal Communications Commission Rulemaking Reports *see* F C C Rulemaking Reports **1335**
Federal Communications Commission Telephone Equipment Registration List *see* F C C Telephone Equipment Registration List **1362**
Federal Communications Commission Week *see* F C C Week **1335**
Federal Communications Law Journal. (US ISSN 0163-7606) **2625**, 1335
Federal Computer Market Report. (US) **1437**
Federal Computer Week. (US ISSN 0893-052X) **4083**, 1395

FEDERAL TAXATION   6177

Federal Contract Disputes. (US ISSN 0747-9700) **2625**
Federal Contracts Report. (US ISSN 0014-9063) **1075, 4059**
Federal Court of Appeal Decisions. (CN ISSN 0227-0390) **2731**
Federal Court of Canada Service. (CN) **2731**
Federal Court Practice. (AT) **2731**
Federal Court Procurement Decisions. (US ISSN 0734-9513) **2731**
Federal Court Reporter (Sydney). (AT) **2731**
Federal Court Reports (North Ryde). (AT ISSN 0813-7803) **2731**
Federal Credit Union. (US ISSN 1043-7789) **779**
Federal Criminal Investigator see Federal Investigator **1514**
Federal Data Base Finder. (US ISSN 0897-4810) **1425**
Federal Data Report. (US) **1450**
Federal Deposit Insurance Corporation Watch see F D I C Watch **778**
Federal Election Campaign Financing Guide. (US) **779, 4087**
Federal Election Commission Record. (US) **3894**
Federal Employee. (US ISSN 0014-9071) **4059**
Federal Employees' Almanac. (US ISSN 0071-4127) **4059**
Federal Employees Liability Act Reporter & Railroad Liability Monitor see F E L A Reporter & Railroad Liability Monitor **2624**
Federal Employees' News Digest. (US ISSN 0430-1692) **4060**
Federal Energy Guidelines. (US) **1789**
Federal Energy Regulatory Commission Reports. (US) **1789**
▼Federal Environmental Regulation. (US) **1954, 2625**
Federal Estate and Gift Tax Reports. (US) **4148, 1093**
Federal Estate and Gift Taxation (Supplement). (US) **1093**
Federal Estate and Gift Taxes. (US) **1093, 2625**
Federal Estate and Gift Taxes Explained see Federal Estate and Gift Taxes Explained, Including Estate Planning **1093**
Federal Estate and Gift Taxes Explained, Including Estate Planning. (US ISSN 0092-6531) **1093**
Federal Evidence Foundations. (US) **2625**
Federal Excise Tax. (US) **1093**
Federal Excise Tax Reports. (US) **1093**
Federal Executive Directory. (US ISSN 0270-563X) **4060, 1135**
Federal Executive Directory Annual. (US ISSN 1056-7275) **4060**
▼Federal Facilities Environmental Journal. (US ISSN 1048-4078) **1954**
Federal Funding Guide. (US ISSN 0273-4435) **4087, 2487, 4101, 4405**
Federal Funding Guide for Local Governments see Federal Funding Guide **4087**
Federal Funds Information for States Newsletter. (US) **4060**
Federal Geographic Data Newsletter see F G D Newsletter **2247**
Federal Government Legal Career Opportunities see Now Hiring **3630**
Federal Graduated Withholding Tax Tables. (US ISSN 0071-4135) **1093**
Federal Grants & Contracts Weekly. (US ISSN 0194-2247) **4060, 1706**
Federal Grants Management Handbook.(US ISSN 0195-2617) **665, 1010**
Federal Health Monitor. (US) **4101, 2625, 3098**
Federal Home Loan Bank of Atlanta. Annual Report. (US) **779, 4148**
Federal Home Loan Bank of Atlanta. Review. (US) **779, 4148**
Federal Home Loan Bank of Chicago. Annual Report. (US) **779**
†Federal Home Loan Bank of Cincinnati. Fifth District Review. (US) **5191**

Federal Home Loan Bank of Dallas. Annual Report. (US) **779**
†Federal Home Loan Bank of Dallas. Quarterly. (US) **5191**
Federal Home Loan Bank of Des Moines. Annual Report. (US) **779**
Federal Home Loan Bank of Des Moines. Statistical Reports. (US) **715**
Federal Home Loan Bank of Des Moines. Weekly Financial Bulletin. (US) **779**
Federal Home Loan Bank of Indianapolis. Annual Report. (US) **779**
Federal Home Loan Bank of Little Rock. Annual Report. (US) **779**
Federal Home Loan Bank of San Francisco. Annual Report. (US ISSN 0098-2830) **779**
†Federal Home Loan Bank of San Francisco. Proceedings of the Annual Conference. (US) **5191**
Federal Home Loan Bank of Seattle. Annual Report. (US) **779**
†Federal Home Loan Bank of Seattle. Bank Notes. (US) **5191**
Federal Home Loan Bank of Topeka. Annual Report. (US) **779**
Federal Home Loan Bank System. List of Member Institutions. (US) **2531**
Federal Home Loan Mortgage Corporation. Report. (US ISSN 0094-7156) **779**
Federal Income Tax Law. (US) **1093**
Federal Income Tax Regulations (New York). (US) **1093**
Federal Income Tax Regulations (Paramus) see Federal Tax Regulations **1094**
Federal Income Taxation of Banks and Financial Institutions (Supplement). (US) **1093, 779**
Federal Income Taxation of Corporate Liquidations. (US) **1093**
Federal Income Taxation of Real Estate.(US) **4149, 1093**
Federal Index Monthly see C S I Federal Index **4080**
Federal Industrial Law see Industrial Law: Federal **2710**
▼Federal Information Disclosure, 2-E. (US) **2625**
Federal Information Processing Standards Publication. (US) **3446**
Federal Institute of Industrial Research, Oshodi Industrial Abstracts see F I I R O Industrial Abstracts **715**
Federal Institute of Industrial Research, Oshodi Technical Information Bulletin for Industry see F I I R O Technical Information Bulletin for Industry **1075**
Federal Investigator. (US) **1514**
Federal Labor - Management and Employee Relations Consultant. (US) **979**
Federal Labor - Management Consultant see Federal Labor - Management and Employee Relations Consultant **979**
Federal Law Reports. (AT ISSN 0085-0462) **2625**
Federal Legislation Annotations. (AT ISSN 1036-3661) **4060, 2625**
Federal Legislative Bulletin see Chemical Manufacturers Association. Federal Legislation **1851**
Federal Librarian. (US ISSN 0273-1061) **2757**
Federal Library Resources. (US) **2757**
Federal Limitation Periods. (CN) **2625**
Federal Litigator. (US) **2625**
Federal Local Court Rules. (US) **2731**
Federal Managers Quarterly. (US ISSN 0893-8415) **1010**
Federal Maritime Commission Service. (US) **2734**
Federal Mine Safety and Health Review Commission Decisions. (US) **3483**
Federal Motor Vehicle Safety Standards and Regulations. (US) **4690**
†Federal News Clipsheet. (US) **5191**
Federal Organization Service. (US) **4060**
Federal Organization Service - Civil see Federal Organization Service **4060**
Federal Organization Service - Military see Defense Organization Service **3456**

Federal Outlays in Summary see U.S. Community Services Administration. Federal Outlays in Summary **1111**
Federal Parks & Recreation. (US) **1487, 1954, 2099**
Federal Personnel Guide. (US ISSN 0163-7665) **1065**
Federal Poet. (US ISSN 1041-4886) **2993**
Federal Probation. (US ISSN 0014-9128) **1514**
Federal Procurement Update. (US) **665, 4060**
Federal Programs Letter see Washington Environmental Protection Report **1971**
†Federal - Provincial Wildlife Conference. Transactions. (CN ISSN 0069-0007) **5191**
Federal Regional Executive Directory. (US ISSN 0742-1729) **4060, 1135**
▼Federal Regional Yellow Book. (US ISSN 1061-3153) **4060, 419**
Federal Register. (US ISSN 0097-6326) **2625**
Federal Register Highlights Newsletter. (US) **2625**
Federal Regulation of Energy. (US) **2625, 1805**
Federal Regulation of the Chemical Industry. (US) **2625, 1177**
Federal Regulatory Directory. (US ISSN 0195-749X) **3894, 4060**
Federal Republic of Germany - Partner of the World. (GW ISSN 0343-9062) **865, 908**
Federal Research in Progress Database.(US) **1822, 4060**
Federal Research Report. (US ISSN 0148-4109) **1633**
Federal Reserve Bank of Atlanta. Economic Review. (US ISSN 0732-1813) **865**
Federal Reserve Bank of Atlanta. Economics Update. (US ISSN 0899-6555) **865**
Federal Reserve Bank of Atlanta. Financial Update. (US ISSN 0899-6563) **779**
Federal Reserve Bank of Atlanta. Regional Update. (US ISSN 0899-6571) **865**
†Federal Reserve Bank of Atlanta. Research Paper Series. (US) **5191**
Federal Reserve Bank of Atlanta. Working Paper Series. (US) **779**
Federal Reserve Bank of Boston. Conference Series. (US ISSN 0361-8714) **865**
▼Federal Reserve Bank of Boston. Regional Review. (US) **865**
Federal Reserve Bank of Cleveland. Working Paper. (US) **779, 2531**
Federal Reserve Bank of Dallas. Business Review see Federal Reserve Bank of Dallas. Economic Review **865**
Federal Reserve Bank of Dallas. Economic Review. (US ISSN 0149-5364) **865**
Federal Reserve Bank of Dallas. Review see Federal Reserve Bank of Dallas. Economic Review **865**
Federal Reserve Bank of Kansas City. Banking Studies. (US ISSN 0743-6351) **779**
Federal Reserve Bank of Kansas City. Economic Review. (US ISSN 0161-2387) **865**
Federal Reserve Bank of Kansas City. Financial Letter see Regional Economic Digest **796**
Federal Reserve Bank of Minneapolis. Agricultural Credit Conditions Survey.(US ISSN 0737-948X) **779, 150**
Federal Reserve Bank of Minneapolis. Annual Report. (US ISSN 0361-8013) **779**
Federal Reserve Bank of Minneapolis. District Economic Conditions see Fedgazette: Federal Reserve Bank of Minneapolis Regional Business & Economics Newspaper **866**
Federal Reserve Bank of Minneapolis. Quarterly Review. (US ISSN 0271-5287) **779**

Federal Reserve Bank of New York. Annual Report. (US ISSN 0147-6580) **779**
Federal Reserve Bank of New York. Quarterly Review. (US ISSN 0147-6580) **865**
Federal Reserve Bank of Philadelphia. Business Review. (US ISSN 0007-7011) **865, 779**
Federal Reserve Bank of Richmond. Economic Review. (US ISSN 0094-6893) **865**
Federal Reserve Bank of Richmond. Monthly Review see Federal Reserve Bank of Richmond. Economic Review **865**
Federal Reserve Bank of St. Louis. Monthly Review see Federal Reserve Bank of St. Louis. Review **865**
Federal Reserve Bank of St. Louis. Review. (US ISSN 0014-9187) **865**
Federal Reserve Bank of San Francisco. Business Review see Federal Reserve Bank of San Francisco. Economic Review **865**
Federal Reserve Bank of San Francisco. Economic Review. (US ISSN 0363-0021) **865**
Federal Reserve Bank of San Francisco. Letter. (US) **865**
Federal Reserve Bank of San Francisco. Weekly Letter see Federal Reserve Bank of San Francisco. Letter **865**
Federal Reserve Basic Instructions. (US) **865**
Federal Reserve Bulletin. (US ISSN 0014-9209) **779**
Federal Reserve Forms. (US) **866**
Federal Reserve Instructions. (US) **866**
▼Federal Rules Citations. (US) **2625**
Federal Rules of Evidence News. (US) **2625**
Federal Rules Service. (US) **4060, 2626**
Federal Savings and Loan Insurance Corporation. List of Member Institutions see Federal Home Loan Bank System. List of Member Institutions **2531**
Federal Securities Law Report. (US) **2626, 946**
Federal Sentencing Reporter. (US ISSN 1053-9867) **1514, 2626**
Federal Staff Directory. (US) **4060, 3894**
Federal Staffing Digest. (US ISSN 1053-4652) **4060, 3942**
†Federal - State Executive Directory. (US ISSN 0734-4651) **5191**
Federal Supply Code for Manufacturers, United States and Canada. (US) **1075**
▼Federal Tax Advisor. (US) **1093**
▼Federal Tax Advisor - Control Edition. (US) **1093**
Federal Tax Articles. (US) **1094**
▼Federal Tax Aspects of Bankruptcy. (US) **1094**
Federal Tax Collections, Leins and Levies. (US) **1094, 2626**
Federal Tax Compliance Reports see Federal Tax Manual with Monthly Reports **1094**
Federal Tax Coordinator see Federal Tax Coordinator 2d **1094**
Federal Tax Coordinator 2d. (US ISSN 0738-8632) **1094**
Federal Tax Coordinator 2d. Weekly Alert. (US ISSN 0163-996X) **1094**
Federal Tax Expeditor see Federal Taxes Citator **1094**
Federal Tax Forms. (US) **1094**
Federal Tax Guide. (US) **1094**
Federal Tax Guide Reports. (US) **1094**
Federal Tax Litigation (Supplement). (US) **1094**
†Federal Tax Locator. (US) **5191**
Federal Tax Manual with Monthly Reports. (US) **1094**
▼Federal Tax Planning. (US) **1094**
Federal Tax Regulations. (US) **1094, 2626**
Federal Taxation of Insurance Companies. (US) **1094, 2531**
Federal Taxation of Oil and Gas Transactions. (US) **3686, 1094, 1790, 2626**

FEDERAL TAXES

Federal Taxes see Federal Taxes 2nd 1094
Federal Taxes Citator. (US) 1094
Federal Taxes 2nd. (US) 1094
Federal Technology Catalog. (US) 4598
Federal Technology Transfer. (US) 4598
Federal Times. (US ISSN 0014-9233) 4060
Federal Trade Commission. (US) 2626
Federal Trade Commission Freedom of Information Log see F T C Freedom of Information Log 908
Federal Trade Commission Watch see F T C: Watch 908
†Federal Trainer. (US) 5191
Federal Trial Evidence. (US) 2626
Federal Trial News. (US) 2626
Federal University of Ceara School of Medicine. Journal of Medicine. see Universidade Federal do Ceara. Centro de Ciencias da Saude. Revista de Medicina 3160
Federal Veterinarian. (US ISSN 0164-6257) 4809, 4101
Federal Yellow Book. (US ISSN 0145-6202) 4060
Federalismo Militante see Il Dibattito Federalista 3890
The Federalist. (US ISSN 0736-8151) 2406, 4060
Federalist. (IT ISSN 0393-1358) 3894
Federalist Paper. (US) 1311
Federalista see Federalist 3894
Federaliste see Federalist 3894
Federaliste Europeen. (LU ISSN 0014-9268) 3957
Federaliste Mondial du Canada. see Canadian World Federalist 2720
Federally Coordinated Program of Highway Research and Development see U.S. Federal Highway Administration. Federally Coordinated Program of Highway Research and Development 4722
Federally Employed Women Inc. News and Views see F E W's News and Views 4842
Federalni Ministerstvo Spoju. Vestnik. (CS) 1336
Federated Australian University Staff Association News see F A U S A News 1706
Federated Ironworkers' Association of Australia. Labor News see Federation of Industrial, Manufacturing and Engineering Employees. Labor News 2583
Federated Taxpayer's Association of Australia. Annual Taxation Summary see Australian Taxpayer's Association. Annual Taxation Summary 1088
Federatie Goud en Zilver. Vademecum. (NE) 2564, 3406
Federatie Nederlandse Vakbeweging News see F N V News 2583
Federatie van Bedrijfsverenigingen. Jaarverslag. (NE ISSN 0071-4151) 2531
Federatie van de Belgische Industrie Tijdschrift see F E B E L G R A Tijdschrift 3999
Federatie van Nederlandstalige Verenidenis voor Oudheidkunde en Geschiedenis van Belgische. Jaarboeken. see Federation Archeologique et Historique de Belgique. Annales 2361
Federation Aeronautique International. Annual Information Bulletin. (FR) 52
Federation Aeronautique International. General Conference Minutes (of the) Business Meetings see Federation Aeronautique International. Annual Information Bulletin 52
Federation Archeologique et Historique de Belgique. Annales/Federatie van Nederlandstalige Verenidenis voor Oudheidkunde en Geschiedenis van Belgische. Jaarboeken. (BE) 2361, 272, 2054
Federation Belge des Enterprises de Distribution. Courrier Hebdomadaire. (BE) 2067

Federation Belge des Entreprises de Distribution. Annual Report. (BE) 665
Federation Bulletin see Federation of State Medical Boards of the United States. Federation Bulletin 3098
Federation d'Associations de Techniciens des Industries des Peintures, Vernis, Emaux et Encres d'Imprimerie de l'Europe Continentale. Congress Proceedings see Congress F A T I P E C 1852
Federation d'Associations de Techniciens des Industries des Peintures, Vernis, Emaux et Encres d'Imprimerie de l'Europe Continentale. Annuaire Officiel. Official Yearbook. Amtliches Jahrbuch. (FR ISSN 0071-416X) 3653
Federation de l'Education Nationale (FEN) Hebdo see F E N - Hebdo 1633
Federation de l'Industrie Horlogere Suisse. Annual Report. (SZ) 2564
Federation de l'Industrie Horlogere Suisse. Revue. (SZ) 2564
Federation Dentaire Internationale Dental World see F D I Dental World 3233
Federation des Associations de Professeurs des Universites du Quebec Nouvelles Universitaires see F A P U Q Nouvelles Universitaires 1706
†Federation des Debitants de Tabac de l'Ile-de-France. Annuaire Officiel. (FR) 5191
Federation des Entrepreneurs de Nettoyage de France. Annuaire Officiel. (FR) 1281
Federation des Entreprises de Belgique. Rapport Annuel/Verbond van Belgische Ondernemingen. Jaarlyks Verslag. (BE) 1075, 1504
Federation des Entreprises de Belgique Bulletin see F E B Bulletin 1075
Federation des Entreprises de l'Industrie des Fabrications Metalliques, Mecaniques, Electriques et de la Transformation des Matieres Plastiques. Revue Mensuelle. (BE) 3406
Federation des Entreprises de l'Industrie des Fabrications Metalliques, Mecaniques, Electriques et de la Transformation des Matieres Plastiques. Bulletin d'Information Mensuel see Federation des Entreprises de l'Industrie des Fabrications Metalliques, Mecaniques, Electriques et de la Transformation des Matieres Plastiques. Revue Mensuelle 3406
Federation des Entreprises de l'Industrie des Fabrications Metalliques, Mecaniques, Electriques et de la Transformation des Matieres Plastiques. Centre de Recherches Scientifiques et Techniques. Section: Fonderie (FD). Research Reports. (BE) 3406
Federation des Industries Belges. Rapport Annuel see Federation des Entreprises de Belgique. Rapport Annuel 1075
Federation des Industries Chimiques de Belgique. Annuaire. (BE ISSN 0425-9076) 1135
Federation des Industries Chimiques de Belgique. Rapport Annuel. (BE ISSN 0085-0489) 866
Federation des Industries Electriques et Electroniques Infos see F I E E Infos 1892
Federation des Industries et Commerces Utilisateurs des Basses Temperatures. Rapport Statistique Annuel. (FR) 2067
Federation des Medecins Residents du Quebec. Bulletin. (CN) 3098
Federation des Medecins Residents et Internes du Quebec. Bulletin see Federation des Medecins Residents du Quebec. Bulletin 3098
Federation des Travaux Publics et des Transports. Revue see Infos Federales 4651
†Federation Equestre Francaise. Guide Officiel du Cavalier. (FR) 5191

Federation Exchange. (US ISSN 0888-5648) 3098
Federation Feminine Franco-Americaine. Bulletin. (US) 2002, 4842
Federation Forum see Planning and Action Newsletter 4416
Federation Francaise de Natation. Annuaire. (FR ISSN 0071-4194) 4524
Federation Francaise des Commissionnaires et Auxiliares de Transport Commissionnaires en Douane, Transitaires et Agents Aeriens Annuaire F F C A T see Annuaire F F C A T 1121
Federation Francaise des Societes de Sciences Naturelles. Revue see Societe Versaillaise des Sciences Naturelles. Bulletin 4344
Federation Francaise des Sports Equestres. Annuaire Officiel see Federation Equestre Francaise. Guide Officiel du Cavalier 5191
Federation Highlights. (US ISSN 0049-6987) 1954
Federation Horlogere Suisse. Bulletin see Federation de l'Industrie Horlogere Suisse. Revue 2564
Federation Internationale d'Information et de Documentation Directory see F I D Directory 2757
Federation Internationale d'Information et de Documentation Meetings Reports see F I D - R I Meetings Reports 5190
Federation Internationale d'Information et de Documentation News see F I D - C R News 2757
Federation Internationale d'Information et de Documentation News Bulletin see F I D News Bulletin 2757
Federation Internationale d'Information et de Documentation Series on Problems of Information Science see F I D - R I Series on Problems of Information Science 5190
Federation Internationale de Football Association Handbook see F I F A. Handbook 4503
Federation Internationale de Football Association Olympic Football Tournament see F I F A. Olympic Football Tournament 4503
Federation Internationale de Football Association Technical Reports see F I F A. Technical Reports 4503
Federation Internationale de Gymnastique. Bulletin. (SZ ISSN 0428-1659) 4472
Federation Internationale de Laiterie. Bulletin Annuel. see International Dairy Federation. Annual Bulletin 200
Federation Internationale de Laiterie. Memento Annuel. see International Dairy Federation. Annual Memento 200
Federation Internationale de Laiterie. Newsletter. see International Dairy Federation. Newsletter 200
Federation Internationale de Laiterie. Norme Internationale. see International Dairy Federation. International Standard 200
Federation Internationale de Rugby Amateur. Annuaire. (FR ISSN 0071-4267) 4503
Federation Internationale des Communautes d'Enfants-Denmark Information see F I C E Information 1237
Federation Internationale des Demenageurs Internationaux Focus see F I D I Focus 4727
Federation Internationale des Ingenieurs Conseils International Directory of Consulting Engineers see F I D I C International Directory of Consulting Engineers 1135
Federation Internationale des Organisations de Donneurs de Sang Benevoles Revue see F I O D S Revue 3208
Federation Internationale des Professeurs de l'Enseignement Secondaire Officiel Newsletter see F I P E S O Newsletter 1633

Federation Internationale des Professeurs de Langues Vivantes World News see F I P L V World News 1633
Federation Internationale des Traducteurs Newsletter see F I T Newsletter 2813
Federation Internationale du Batiment et des Trauvaux Publics. Revue see Entreprise Europeenne 617
Federation Internationale Laitiere. Catalogue des Publications. see International Dairy Federation. Catalogue of I D F Publications 139
Federation Internationale Motocycliste. Annuaire. (SZ ISSN 0071-4283) 4518
Federation Internationale pour la Recherche Theatrale Sibmas Bulletin see F I R T - I F T R - Sibmas Bulletin 4633
Federation Interprofessionnelle de la Congelation Ultra-Rapide. Rapport Statistique Annuel see Federation des Industries et Commerces Utilisateurs des Basses Temperatures. Rapport Statistique Annuel 2067
Federation Jazz. (US) 3551
Federation Nationale de l'Immobiliers. Informations F N A I M: Juridiques et Techniques. (FR) 4149, 2626
Federation Nationale de l'Industrie Laitiere. Bulletin d'Information. (FR ISSN 1150-5028) 199
Federation Nationale des Agents Immobiliers et Administrateurs de Biens-Syndics d'Immeubles Informations F.N.A.I.M. see Informations F.N.A.I.M 4151
Federation Nationale des Agents Immobiliers, Mandataires en Vente de Fonds de Commerce, Administrateurs de Bien, Syndics de Copropriete et Experts. Informations Juridiques see Federation Nationale de l'Immobiliers. Informations F N A I M: Juridiques et Techniques 4149
Federation Nationale des Agriculteurs Multiplicateurs de SEMENCES. Bulletin. (FR ISSN 0396-8936) 92
Federation Nationale des Anciens Combattants et Coalets des Transmissions. Liaison des Transmissions. (FR ISSN 0024-1709) 3458, 1336
Federation Nationale des Combattants Prisonniers de Guerre Combattants d'Algerie, Tunise et Maroc see P G - C A T M 3468
Federation Nationale des Hoteliers, Restaurateurs et Cafetiers du Grand-Duche de Luxembourg Informations see H O R E S C A - Informations 2474
Federation Nationale des Infirmieres Belges Info see F.N.I.B. - Info 3278
Federation Nationale des Photographes Professionnels Professionnelle. Report Magazine. (BE) 3790
Federation Nationale du Credit Agricole. Annuaire du Credit Agricole Mutuel. (FR ISSN 0071-4380) 779
Federation News. (UK ISSN 0014-9411) 2583
Federation News. (US ISSN 0014-942X) 2583
Federation News (Abbotsford). (AT ISSN 1036-3904) 1633
Federation News (Sydney). (AT ISSN 0158-5711) 979, 2583, 3616
Federation of American Health Systems. Review see American Health Systems Review 2458
Federation of American Hospitals. Review see American Health Systems Review 2458
Federation of American Scientists Public Interest Report see F A S Public Interest Report 4309
Federation of American Societies for Experimental Biology. Federation Proceedings see F A S E B Journal 439
Federation of American Societies for Experimental Biology Journal see F A S E B Journal 439
Federation of Astronomical Societies Handbook see F A S Handbook 364

Federation of Bangladesh Chambers of Commerce and Industry. Federation Journal. (BG) 815
Federation of British Tape Recordists. News and Views see Federation of British Tape Recordists. Recording News 4460
Federation of British Tape Recordists. Recording News. (UK) 4460
Federation of Building and Civil Engineering Contractors. Federation Bulletin see Construction Employers Federation. Bulletin 612
Federation of C.P.T.A. Associations of Ontario. Newsletter. (Federation of Catholic Parent-Teacher Associations of Ontario) (CN ISSN 0700-9070) 1633, 1237
Federation of Canadian Archers. Rules Book. (CN ISSN 0226-773X) 4472
Federation of Canadian Archers Canadian Archer see Canadian Archer 4468
Federation of Catholic Parent-Teacher Associations of Ontario Federation of C.P.T.A. Associations of Ontario. Newsletter see Federation of C.P.T.A. Associations of Ontario. Newsletter 1633
Federation of Egyptian Industries. Monthly Bulletin. (UA) 1076
Federation of Egyptian Industries. Year Book. see Ittihad al-Sinaat al-Misriyah. Year Book 1140
†Federation of European Biochemical Societies. (Proceedings of Meeting). (GW ISSN 0071-4402) 5191
Federation of European Biochemical Societies Letters see F E B S Letters 476
Federation of European Microbiological Societies Microbiology see F E M S. Microbiology 551
Federation of European Microbiological Societies Microbiology Ecology see F E M S. Microbiology Ecology 551
Federation of European Microbiological Societies Microbiology Immunology see F E M S. Microbiology Immunology 551
Federation of European Microbiological Societies Microbiology Letters see F E M S. Microbiology Letters 551
Federation of European Microbiological Societies Microbiology Reviews see F E M S. Microbiology Reviews 465
Federation of Genealogical Societies Forum. (US) 2150
Federation of Genealogical Societies Newsletter see Federation of Genealogical Societies Forum 2150
Federation of Industrial, Manufacturing and Engineering Employees. Labor News. (AT ISSN 0014-9276) 2583
Federation of Insurance and Corporate Counsel Quarterly. (US ISSN 0887-0942) 2626, 2531
Federation of Insurance Institutes Journal see Insurance Institute of India. Journal 2534
Federation of Jordanian Chambers of Commerce. Magazine. (JO) 815
Federation of Kenya Employers. Newsletter see Kenya Employer 985
Federation of Migros Cooperatives. Annual Report see Federation of Migros Cooperatives. Documentation and Information 830
Federation of Migros Cooperatives. Documentation and Information. (SZ) 830
Federation of Mobile Home Owners of Florida News see F M O News 4148
Federation of Oils, Seeds and Fats Associations. Newsletter. (UK) 177
Federation of Pakistan Chambers of Commerce and Industry. Annual Report. (PK) 815
Federation of Pakistan Chambers of Commerce and Industry. Brief Report of Activities. (PK ISSN 0071-4429) 815
Federation of Pakistan Chambers of Commerce and Industry. Directory of Exporters. (PK) 1135
Federation of Pakistan Chambers of Commerce and Industry. Trade Bulletin. (PK) 815

Federation of Private Residents Associations. Newsletter. (UK) 4149
Federation of Publishers and Booksellers Associations in India. Newsletter. (II) 4127
Federation of Southern Cooperatives Monthly Bulletin see F S C Monthly Bulletin 4405
Federation of State Medical Boards Handbook see F S M B Handbook 3097
Federation of State Medical Boards of the United States. Federation Bulletin.(US ISSN 0014-9306) 3098, 1749
Federation of Swedish Co-Operative Banks. Annual Report. (SW) 779, 830
Federation of Synagogues of South Africa. Federation Chronicle see Jewish Tradition 4224
Federation of Women Teachers' Associations of Ontario Newsletter see F W T A O Newsletter 1633
Federation of Women Zionists of Great Britain and Ireland Review see F.W.Z. Review 2001
Federation Professionnelle des Producteurs et Distributeurs d'Electricite de Belgique. Annuaire Statistique. (BE ISSN 0773-090X) 1799, 1801
Federation Professionnelle des Producteurs et Distributeurs d'Electricite de Belgique. Distribution de l'Energie. (BE ISSN 0778-6336) 1892
Federation Professionnelle des Producteurs et Distributeurs d'Electricite de Belgique. Repertoire des Centrales Electriques. (BE ISSN 0778-631X) 1892
Federation Professionnelle des Producteurs et Distributeurs d'Electricite de Belgique. Repertoire des Enterprises de Production d'Electricite see Federation Professionnelle des Producteurs et Distributeurs d'Electricite de Belgique. Repertoire des Centrales Electriques 1892
Federation Professionnelle des Producteurs et Distributeurs d'Electricite de Belgique. Secteurs de Distribution see Federation Professionnelle des Producteurs et Distributeurs d'Electricite de Belgique. Distribution de l'Energie 1892
Federation Protestante de France. Annuaire. (FR) 4238
Federation Quebecoise des Directeurs d'Ecole. Revue Information see Federation Quebecoise des Directeurs et Directices d'Ecole. Revue Information 1633
Federation Quebecoise des Directeurs et Directices d'Ecole. Revue Information.(CN) 1633
Federation Roundtable. (US) 2406
Federazione Associazione Imprese Distribuzione Notizie F A I D see Notizie F A I D 838
Federazione Autotraportatori Italiani see F A I 4744
Federazione dell'Industria. Newsletter. (IT) 2473
Federazione Italiana Pesca Sportiva ed Attivita Subacquee Notiziario F.I.P.S. see Notiziario F.I.P.S 5249
Federazione Medica. (IT ISSN 0014-9500) 3098
Federball. (GW ISSN 0323-3189) 4503
Federfarma Notizie. (IT) 3726
Federn - Ketten - Biegeteile. (GW ISSN 0940-2675) 3406
Fedgazette: Federal Reserve Bank of Minneapolis Regional Business & Economics Newspaper. (US ISSN 1045-3334) 866
Fedlink Technical Notes. (US ISSN 0737-4178) 2757
Fednews. (US) 2583, 4060
Fed's Fiscale Brochures. (NE) 1094
FedWatch. (US ISSN 1052-6471) 946
Fee Claudine. (FR) 2292, 1254
Fee Income Report. (US ISSN 0892-7383) 779

Feed Additive Compendium. (US ISSN 0071-450X) 205
†Feed and Farm Supply Dealer. (CN ISSN 0046-3604) 5191
Feed and Grain. (US) 205
Feed and Grain Times see Feed and Grain 205
Feed Bulletin. (US ISSN 0014-9543) 205
Feed Compounder. (UK ISSN 0950-771X) 205
Feed Control Comment. (US) 206, 216
Feed - Grain Equipment Times see Feed and Grain 205
Feed Industry Red Book. (US ISSN 0071-4518) 206, 1135
Feed International. (US) 206
Feed Management. (US ISSN 0014-956X) 206
Feed Production. see Siliao Bolan 208
Feed Trade. (JA ISSN 0014-9586) 206
Feedback. (US ISSN 0147-4871) 1373
Feedgram. (US) 206, 216
Feeds and Feeding. (UK ISSN 0961-978X) 206
Feedstuffs. (US ISSN 0014-9624) 206, 216
Feelin' Good. (US) 3801
▼Feeling. (BE) 4842
Feeling Great. (US) 3801
Feeling Sports Magazine. (US) 2292, 4472
Fegarbel Revue. (BE ISSN 0014-9640) 4690
Fegato. (IT ISSN 0014-9659) 3098
Feh! (US) 2993
Feherje see Feherje es Biotermek 2067
Feherje es Biotermek. (HU) 2067, 92
Fei Ch'ing Yen Chiu see Chung Kung Yen Chiu 3879
Fei Ch'ing Yueh Pao - Chinese Communist Affairs Monthly see Chung-Kuo Ta-Lu Yen-Chiu 3880
Fei Tian/Flying Apsaras. (CC ISSN 1002-803X) 2917
†Feingeraetetechnik. (GW ISSN 0014-9683) 5191
Der Feinschmecker. (GW) 2189
Feinschmecker fuer Aerzte. (GW ISSN 0933-6680) 3605
Fejer Megyei Konyvtaros. (HU ISSN 0139-2115) 2757
Felag Islenzkra Storkaupmanna Bref til Storkaupmanna see Bref til Storkaupmanna 1123
Feld und Wald see Agrar-Praxis 166
Feld Wald Wasser. (SZ ISSN 0014-9756) 1488, 4472
Feldscher and Midwife. see Fel'dsher i Akusherka 3291
Fel'dsher i Akusherka/Feldscher and Midwife. (RU ISSN 0014-9772) 3291
Feldversuchsfuehrer Pflanzenbau und Pflanzenzuchtung. (GW) 502
Feldwebel/Sergent-Major/Sergente Maggiore. (SZ ISSN 0014-9780) 3458
Feldwirtschaft see Neue Landwirtschaft 109
Feliciter. (Canadian Library Association) (CN ISSN 0014-9802) 2757
Felicity. (US) 2993
Feline Health Topics. (US) 4809
Feline Practice. (US ISSN 1057-6614) 4809
Felix. (UK ISSN 0140-0711) 1311
Felix Letter. (US ISSN 0895-0040) 3605
Felix Ravenna; Rivista di Antichita Ravennati, Cristiane e Bizantine. (IT ISSN 0085-0500) 326, 272
Fell Swoop. (US ISSN 1040-5607) 2917
Fellowship. (US ISSN 0014-9810) 3957
Fellowship Communique see Jubilee International 4186
Fellowship for Freedom in Medicine. Bulletin see Fellowship for Freedom in Medicine. Newsletter 3098
Fellowship for Freedom in Medicine. Newsletter. (UK ISSN 0305-9324) 3098

Fellowship in Prayer. (US ISSN 0014-9837) 4282, 2917
Fellowship Life & Lifestyles. (US) 4178
Fellowship of Australian Composers. Newsletter see Australian Composer 5143
Fellowship of Australian Writers North Shore Regional see F A W N S 2916
Fellowship of Reconciliation. Annual Report. (UK) 4178
Fellowship Today. (US ISSN 1045-3849) 4238
Fellowship Yearbook see Evangelical Baptist Churches in Canada. Fellowship Yearbook 4237
▼Fell's U S Coins Quarterly Investment Guide. (US) 3599, 946
Felsbau. (GW) 3483
Felt and Damaging Earthquakes. (UK ISSN 0144-2376) 1588
Feltornitologen see Fugle 564
†Feltundersoegelse. (DK ISSN 0109-856X) 5191
Fem. (MX) 4842
Fem Ego. (CN ISSN 0318-871X) 1291
Female Bodybuilding. (US) 3801, 4842
Female Patient. (US ISSN 0364-1198) 3291
Femeia. (RM ISSN 0046-3655) 4842
Femina. (SZ) 1291
Femina. (BL) 3292
Femina. (DK ISSN 0014-9853) 4842, 1291
Femina. (II ISSN 0430-2990) 4842
Femina. (SA) 4842
Femina. (IO) 4842
Femina Maanadens Magasin/Femina Monthly Magazine. (SW) 4842
Femina Monthly Magazine. see Femina Maanadens Magasin 4842
Feminaria. (AG) 4842, 2917
Feminine. (MY) 1291
▼Feminism & Psychology. (UK ISSN 0959-3535) 4021, 4842
Feminisms. (US ISSN 1041-1801) 4842
Der Feminist. (GW) 4842, 3397
Feminist Action/Action Feministe. (CN ISSN 0831-3377) 4842
Feminist Bookstore News. (US ISSN 0741-6555) 4127, 4842
Feminist Bookstores Newsletter see Feminist Bookstore News 4127
Feminist Collections. (US ISSN 0742-7441) 4859, 4127
Feminist Forum see Women's Studies International Forum 4861
Feminist Issues. (US ISSN 0270-6679) 4859
Feminist Periodicals. (US ISSN 0742-7433) 4859
Feminist Perspectives/Perspectives Feministes. (CN) 4842
Feminist Praxis. (UK) 4435, 4842
Feminist Renaissance. (US) 4842
Feminist Review. (UK ISSN 0141-7789) 4859
Feminist Studies. (US ISSN 0046-3663) 4859
Feminist Teacher. (US ISSN 0882-4843) 4859, 1749
†Feminist Writers' Guild National Newsletter. (US) 5191
Femme Chic. (FR ISSN 0010-0773) 1291
Femme d'Aujourd'hui et Patrie Suisse-Actualites see La Femme D'Aujourd'hui 1291
La Femme D'Aujourd'hui. (FR) 1291, 2219
Femme Elegante. (SP) 1291
Femme-Lines. (US ISSN 0014-9918) 1285
Femme Nouvelle. (FR) 4842
Femme Plus. (CN ISSN 0838-9446) 4842
Femme Pratique. (FR ISSN 0014-9926) 4842
Femmes au Village. (FR ISSN 0014-9934) 2446
Femmes d'Action. (CN ISSN 0226-9902) 4842
Femmes d'Aujourd'hui. (BE ISSN 0014-9950) 4842

Femmes d'Ici. (CN ISSN 0705-3851) **4842**, 3942
Femmes en Litterature. (FR) **2917**, 4842
Femminile. (IT) **4842**
▼Femnet. (SA) **4842**, 4650
Fen Shui see Shanxi Wenxue **2959**
Fen Tou/Struggle. (CH) **2866**
Fenarete-Letture d'Italia. (IT ISSN 0014-9969) **2866**
Fence Industry - Access Control Directory see Access Control Buyers' Guide **1120**
Fence Industry Directory see Access Control Buyers' Guide **1120**
Fence Post. (US) **92**
Fencer/Skermer. (SA) **4472**
Fencing Rules for Competitions see U S F A Rule Book: U S & International Rules **4495**
Fendexpress. (NE) **908**
Fendou/Struggle. (CC) **3894**
Fenestration. (US ISSN 0895-450X) **617**
Fengci yu Youmo/Satire & Humor. (US) **2866**
Fengjing Mingsheng/Scenic Spots and Historical Sites. (CC) **4762**
Fengnian see Harvest Semi-monthly **95**
La Fenice. (IT) **2310**, 272, 2813
Fenix. (PE ISSN 0015-0002) **2757**
Fennia. (FI ISSN 0015-0010) **2247**
Fenno-Ugrica. (GW ISSN 0341-311X) **2813**
Fenomeno. (NE ISSN 0921-2302) **2814**
Fenomenos Astronomicos. (SP ISSN 0210-8127) **364**
Das Fenster. (AU ISSN 0015-0029) **2917**, 326
Fenxi Huaxue/Analytical Chemistry. (CC) **1205**
Feon'ny Mama. (MG) **2531**
Feon'ny Mpiasa. (MG) **2583**
Fer-Blanc en France et dans le Monde. (FR ISSN 0085-0519) **3406**
Ferber's Freshwater Fisherman see Freshwater Fisherman **5197**
Ferguson Files. (US ISSN 1040-2276) **2150**
Ferguson-Florissant Schools. (US ISSN 0015-0037) **1633**
Ferguson's Ceylon Directory see Ferguson's Sri Lanka Directory (Year) **1135**
Ferguson's Sri Lanka Directory (Year). (CE) **1135**
FerieForum. (NO ISSN 0801-5880) **4762**
Ferien Magazin St. Peter - Ording. (GW) **4762**
Ferienbote. (SZ) **2473**
Ferienpost see Gaeste Journal **4768**
Fermate. (GW ISSN 0939-4664) **3551**
Ferment. (UK) **380**
Fermentation Industry. see Kvasny Prumysl **2076**
Fermentation Research Institute. Report. see Kogyo Gijutsuin. Biseibutsu Kogyo Gijutsu Kenkyujo. Kenkyu Hokoku **554**
▼Fermer. (RU) **92**
Fern Gazette. (UK ISSN 0308-0838) **502**
FERN Journal see F E R N Journal **1706**
Fernandes Bulletin see Revista Mensal de Exportacao **920**
Fernerkundung in Raumordung und Stadtebau. (GW ISSN 0176-1633) **2247**
Fernfahrer. (GW) **4744**
Der Fernmelde-Ingenieur. (GW ISSN 0015-010X) **1336**
Fernmelde Praxis see Telekom Praxis **1909**
FernReisen. (GW) **4762**
Fernschach der D D R. (GW) **4472**
Fernseh-Informationen. (GW ISSN 0015-0134) **1373**
Fernseh- und Kino-Technik. (GW ISSN 0015-0142) **3508**, 1373
Fernsehdienst. (GW ISSN 0233-030X) **1373**
Fernsehwoche. (GW) **2189**
Fernwaerme International/District Heating/Chauffage Urbain. (GW ISSN 0933-6540) **2299**

Feroelektro. (BN) **665**
Ferramenta e Casalinghi. (IT) **642**
Ferranti International News. (UK) **1450**
Ferrara. (IT) **2205**
Ferrara Economica. (IT ISSN 1120-396X) **815**
Ferrari Formula 1 Annual. (IT) **4690**
Ferrari Italian Style. (IT) **4690**, 3397, 4472
Ferrari World Magazine. (UK) **4690**
Ferrarissima. (IT ISSN 0393-3318) **4690**
Ferretaria. (VE) **3406**
Ferretecnic - F y T. (MX) **3406**
Ferritin see Immunohistochemistry **525**
Ferro Alloy Directory see Ferro Alloy Directory and Databook **3406**
Ferro Alloy Directory and Databook. (US ISSN 0953-721X) **3406**
Ferrocarriles Argentinos. (AG ISSN 0046-3698) **4709**
Ferroelectricity and Related Phenomena. (US ISSN 0275-9608) **1892**
Ferroelectrics. (US ISSN 0015-0193) **3818**, 1892
Ferroelectrics and Polar Materials. (US ISSN 0883-8283) **1892**
Ferroelectrics Bulletin see Condensed Matter News **1884**
Ferroelectrics Letters. (US ISSN 0731-5171) **1892**
Ferronales. (MX ISSN 0015-0207) **4709**
Ferroviere. (SZ ISSN 0015-0215) **2583**, 4709
Ferrum. (SZ) **3406**, 2310, 4598
Ferrum Bulletin. (US) **1311**
Ferry Travel Guide. (US) **4762**
Ferskvandsfiskeribladet. (DK ISSN 0015-0223) **2039**, 1954
Fertigteilbau und Industrialisiertes Bauen see F und I-Bau **299**
Fertigung. (GW) **3017**
Fertigung und Betrieb. (US ISSN 0171-5062) **1076**
Fertigungstechnik und Betrieb. (GW ISSN 0015-024X) **4598**
†Fertilisation. (UK ISSN 0268-1609) **5191**
Fertiliser Association of India. Fertiliser Statistics. (II ISSN 0430-327X) **137**, 4571
Fertiliser Association of India Abstract Service see F.A.I. Abstract Service **137**
Fertiliser Digest. (II) **177**
Fertiliser Marketing News. (II ISSN 0257-8034) **177**
Fertiliser News. (II ISSN 0015-0266) **177**
Fertiliser Technology. (II) **4598**, 4309
Fertilitaet, Sterilitaet, In-Vitro Fertilisation, Sexualitaet, Kontrazeption. (GW ISSN 0179-1796) **3292**, 3259
Fertility and Sterility. (US ISSN 0015-0282) **3292**
Fertilizacion. (SP ISSN 0532-9817) **92**
Fertilizer and Agricultural Chemical Newsletter. (US) **3616**
Fertilizer Financial Facts & Production Cost Survey. (US) **177**
Fertilizer Industry Round Table. Proceedings. (US) **92**
Fertilizer International. (UK ISSN 0015-0304) **177**
Fertilizer Record. (US) **150**, 177
Fertilizer Research. (NE ISSN 0167-1731) **177**
Fertilizer Science and Technology Series.(US ISSN 0071-4623) **177**
Fertilizer Trade Information Monthly Bulletin. (UN) **908**, 177
†Fertilizer Trends. (US ISSN 0071-4631) **5191**
†Fertilizers and Agriculture. (FR) **5191**
†Fessenden Review. (US ISSN 0883-9166) **5191**
Festa. (IT) **2866**
Der Feste Grund. (GW ISSN 0015-0320) **4238**
Festina Lente. (SA ISSN 0015-0347) **4087**
Festiniog Railway Magazine. (UK ISSN 0015-0355) **4709**
Festival. (BE ISSN 0015-0363) **4762**

Festival Quarterly. (US ISSN 8750-3530) **2866**
†Festivals. (US) **5191**
†Festivals Sourcebook. (US) **5191**
†Festivity! (US) **5191**
Festschrift Series. (US) **3551**
Fetal Diagnosis and Therapy. (SZ ISSN 1015-3837) **3292**
Fetal Medicine Review. (UK ISSN 0953-8267) **3292**, 3320
†Fetal Physiology. (UK ISSN 0261-4650) **5192**
Fetal Therapy see Fetal Diagnosis and Therapy **3292**
Fetes et Festivals. (CN) **1039**, 4762
Fetes et Saisons. (FR ISSN 0015-0371) **4178**
Fetish Letters. (US) **3397**
†Fetish Times. (US) **5192**
Fett - Wissenschaft Technologie/Fat - Science Technology. (GW ISSN 0931-5985) **1853**
Fette-Seifen-Anstrichmittel see Fett - Wissenschaft Technologie **1853**
Fettesian. (UK ISSN 0046-3701) **1311**
Feuermelder Rundbrief. (GW) **3752**
†Feuerungstechnik, Energie & Umwelt. (GW) **5192**
Feuerwehr-Jahrbuch. (GW ISSN 0071-4674) **2031**
Feuerwehr und Modell. (GW ISSN 0723-5437) **2031**, 2436
Der Feuerwehrmann. (GW ISSN 0178-5214) **2031**
Feuille Anarchiste. (FR ISSN 0015-041X) **3894**
Feuille de Route. (FR ISSN 0248-3165) **4405**
Feuille Officielle de la Protection Civile/ Mitteilungsblatt des Zivilschutzes/ Foglio d'Informazione della Protezione Civile. (SZ ISSN 0015-0428) **1273**
Feuille Suisse des Brevets, Dessins et Marques. see Schweizerisches Patent-, Muster- und Markenblatt **3678**
Feuillet Biblique. (CN ISSN 0225-2112) **4264**
†Feuillet Meteorologique. (CN) **5192**
Feuillet Rapide Fiscal Social. (FR ISSN 0150-5467) **1094**
Feuillets Analytiques. (FR) **2626**
Feuillets de Biologie. (FR ISSN 0428-2779) **439**
Feuillets de Radiologie. (FR ISSN 0181-9801) **3358**
Feuillets du Naturaliste. (CN ISSN 0827-1356) **1254**, 4309
Feux et Flammes. (FR) **2531**
Feux et Signaux de Brume. (FR ISSN 0223-5358) **4727**
Few-Body Systems. Acta Physica Austriaca. New Series. (AU ISSN 0177-7963) **3818**
Fh-Bo-Journal. (Fachhochschule Bochum) (GW ISSN 0179-6607) **1311**, 4598
Fiaccola. (IT) **4264**
Fiamma Nova. (IT) **2205**
Fiamme d'Argento. (IT) **1514**
Fiat Lux. (SA ISSN 0015-0495) **4060**, 2002
Fib-Aktuellt. (SW) **2218**
Fiber and Integrated Optics. (US ISSN 0146-8030) **3852**
Fiber Datacom. (US ISSN 1051-1954) **1350**
Fiber - Laser News see Fiber Optics News **1336**
Fiber Optic Sensor and Systems. (US ISSN 1051-1946) **3852**
Fiber Optics and Communications. (US ISSN 0275-0457) **1336**
Fiber Optics and Communications Weekly News Service see Fiber Optics Weekly Update **1336**
Fiber Optics Business. (US ISSN 1057-5375) **1362**
Fiber Optics Handbook and Buyers Guide. (US) **1336**
Fiber Optics Magazine. (US) **1336**
Fiber Optics News. (US ISSN 8756-2049) **1336**, 3852
Fiber Optics Weekly Update. (US ISSN 1051-189X) **1336**
Fiber Organon. (US) **4618**

Fiber Science Series. (US ISSN 0071-4682) **4618**
Fiber to the Home. (US ISSN 1051-192X) **1336**
Fiberarts. (US ISSN 0164-324X) **326**
Fiberoptic Product News. (US ISSN 0890-653X) **1362**, 4309, 4598
Fibonacci Quarterly. (US ISSN 0015-0517) **3035**
Fibre Chemistry. (English translation of: Khimicheskie Volokna) (US ISSN 0015-0541) **4618**
Fibre Forum see Textile-Fibre Forum **4625**
Fibre Market News. (US ISSN 0046-3728) **4618**
Fibre Optics Newsletter. (UK ISSN 0264-7249) **3852**
Fibreglass Composites News. (UK) **3862**
Fibreglass Insulation Review. (UK) **617**
Fibrinolysis. (UK ISSN 0268-9499) **3259**
Ficciones. (UY) **2866**
Ficelle see L'Eau Vive **2000**
Ficha de Informacion Laboral. (CL) **979**
Fichero Bibliografico Hispanoamericano. (PR ISSN 0015-0592) **4141**
Fiches d'Identification des Maladies et Parasites des Poissons, Crustaces et Mollusques. see I C E S Identification Leaflets for Diseases and Parasites of Fish and Shellfish **584**
Fiches d'Identification du Plancton. see I C E S Identification Leaflets for Plankton **584**
Fiches d'Identification du Zooplancton see I C E S Identification Leaflets for Plankton **584**
Fiches du Cinema. (FR ISSN 0336-9331) **3508**
Fiches E O - Formation Permanente. (FR) **1010**
Fiches Techniques R T A. (FR) **4690**
Fiches Techniques R T C. (FR) **4690**
Fiches Techniques R T D. (FR) **4690**
Fiches Techniques R T D Applications Agricoles. (FR) **162**
Fichier Afrique. (IV ISSN 1015-5376) **716**, 4394
Fichiers-Presse. (FR) **2578**, 12
▼Fichte-Studien. (NE ISSN 0925-0166) **3766**
Ficta-Difusora de Musica Antiqua. (AG) **3551**
Fiction. (US ISSN 0046-3736) **2917**
Fiction. (FR) **2917**
Fiction Catalog. (US ISSN 0160-4880) **2982**
Fiction Forum. (US ISSN 1046-1094) **2917**
Fiction International. (US ISSN 0092-1912) **2917**
†Fiction Network Magazine. (US ISSN 0741-6024) **5192**
Fiction Review. (II) **2917**
Fiction Writer's Market see Novel & Short Story Writer's Market **2944**
†Fiction Writer's Monthly. (US) **5192**
Fiddlehead. (CN ISSN 0015-0630) **2993**
Fiddlehead Forum. (US ISSN 0733-8015) **2125**
Fidelis et Verus/Faithful and True. (US ISSN 1041-7710) **4264**
Fidelity and Surety News. (US ISSN 0747-6582) **2626**, 2531
Fidelity Monitor. (US) **946**
Fides et Historia. (US) **2310**, 4178
Fidia Research Series. (US) **3098**
Fiduciaire Berichten see Bulletin Fiduciaire **768**
Fiduciary Standards in Pension and Trust Fund Management. (US) **2715**
▼Fiduciary Tax Guide. (US) **1094**
Field. see Hassadeh **95**
Field. (US ISSN 0015-0657) **2993**
Field. (UK ISSN 0015-0649) **4545**
Field Advisory News. (US) **3710**
Field & Production Report. (UK) **3686**
Field & Stream. (US ISSN 0015-0673) **4545**
Field & Stream Bass Fishing Annual. (US ISSN 0163-5468) **4545**
Field & Stream Deer Hunter's Guide Annual. (US) **4545**

Field & Stream Deer Hunting Annual *see* Field & Stream Deer Hunter's Guide Annual **4545**
Field & Stream Fishing Annual. (US ISSN 0362-6385) **4546**
Field & Stream Hunting Annual. (US ISSN 0361-3011) **4546**
Field Artillery. (US ISSN 0899-2525) **3458**
Field Artillery Journal *see* Field Artillery **3458**
Field Crop Abstracts. (UK ISSN 0015-069X) **137**, 12
Field Crops Research. (NE ISSN 0378-4290) **177**
Field Guide to Estate Planning, Business Planning & Employee Benefits. (US) **2531**
Field Hockey Rulebook. (US) **4472**
Field Museum of Natural History Bulletin *see* In the Field **4314**
Field Notes *see* Arkansas Archeological Society. Field Notes **265**
Field Notes of Rhode Island Birds. (US) **564**
Field of Vision. (US) **3508**, 3790
Field Studies. (UK ISSN 0428-304X) **1954**
Field Studies Council. Occasional Publications. (UK) **1954**
Fieldiana: Anthropology. (US ISSN 0071-4739) **239**
Fieldiana: Botany. (US ISSN 0015-0746) **502**
Fieldiana: Geology. (US ISSN 0096-2651) **1560**
Fieldiana: Zoology. (US ISSN 0015-0754) **582**
Fielding's Bermuda and the Bahamas. (US ISSN 0739-0769) **4762**
Fielding's Budget Europe. (US) **4763**
Fielding's Caribbean. (US) **4763**
Fielding's Economy Europe *see* Fielding's Budget Europe **4763**
Fielding's Europe. (US ISSN 0192-5326) **4763**
Fielding's Mexico. (US ISSN 0739-0793) **4763**
Fielding's Selective Shopping Guide to Europe. (US ISSN 0071-478X) **4763**
Fields *see* Christian Missions in Many Lands **4169**
In Fiera. (IT) **3392**
Fiera del Libro. (IT) **4127**, 3392
Fiera di Milano. (IT) **1039**
Fiere. (IT ISSN 0393-8050) **617**
Fiere nel Mondo. (IT) **1039**
†Fiery Foods Front. (US ISSN 0898-0039) **5192**
Fiery Synthesis. (US) **4282**
Fiesta. (US ISSN 0265-1270) **3397**
▼Fiesta en Video. (US) **1385**
Fiets. (NE) **4518**, 4650
Fifteen Days. *see* Petnaest Dana **340**
Fifth Column. (CN ISSN 0229-7094) **299**
Fifth Estate. (US ISSN 0015-0800) **2866**
†Fifth Sun. (US) **5192**
Fifth Wheel. (US ISSN 0015-0819) **4744**
Fifty Cell. (US) **2993**
Fifty-Five Plus. (CN ISSN 0840-4496) **2177**
Fifty Millesimal News Letter. (II ISSN 0015-0827) **3214**
Fifty Something Magazine. (US) **2272**
Fig Leaflet. (US) **2125**
Figaro. (MX ISSN 0015-0835) **2210**
Fight Racism! Fight Imperialism! (UK ISSN 0143-5426) **3894**
†Fight the Right. (US) **5192**
Fighter International. (US) **4472**
Fighters. (UK) **4472**
Fighters Monthly *see* Fighters **4472**
Fighting Back. (US) **3894**
Fighting Blindness News. (US ISSN 0899-7756) **3300**, 2292
Fighting Knives. (US) **4546**
Fighting Woman News. (US ISSN 0146-8812) **4472**, 4842
Figura. Nova Series. (SW ISSN 0071-481X) **326**, 2361
Figurentheater. (GW ISSN 0430-3873) **4633**
Figures de Wallonie. (BE ISSN 0069-5386) **2361**, 419

Figurino Moderno. (BL ISSN 0015-0851) **1291**
Figyelo. (HU ISSN 0015-086X) **665**
Fihrist. (LE) **400**, 12, 2429
Fiji. Bureau of Statistics. Aircraft Statistics. (FJ) **66**, 4571
Fiji. Bureau of Statistics. Census of Building and Construction. (FJ) **637**, 4571
Fiji. Bureau of Statistics. Census of Distribution and Services. (FJ) **716**, 4571
Fiji. Bureau of Statistics. Census of Industrial Production *see* Fiji. Bureau of Statistics. Census of Industries **716**
Fiji. Bureau of Statistics. Census of Industries. (FJ) **716**, 4571
Fiji. Bureau of Statistics. Consumer Price Index. (FJ) **716**, 4571
Fiji. Bureau of Statistics. Current Economic Statistics. (FJ ISSN 0015-0894) **716**, 4571
Fiji. Bureau of Statistics. Economic and Functional Classification of Government Accounts. (FJ) **716**, 1094, 4571
Fiji. Bureau of Statistics. Employment Survey of Fiji. (FJ) **716**, 979, 4571
Fiji. Bureau of Statistics. Fiji Fertility Survey. (FJ) **3992**, 4571
Fiji. Bureau of Statistics. Fiji Household Income and Expenditure Survey. (FJ) **716**, 4571
Fiji. Bureau of Statistics. Nationwide Unemployment Survey. (FJ) **716**, 979, 4571
Fiji. Bureau of Statistics. Population of Fiji. (FJ) **3992**, 4571
†Fiji. Bureau of Statistics. Quarterly Digest of Overseas Trade. (FJ) **5192**
Fiji. Bureau of Statistics. Quarterly Statistical Summary *see* Fiji. Bureau of Statistics. Current Economic Statistics **716**
Fiji. Bureau of Statistics. Quarterly Survey of Employment. (FJ) **716**, 979, 4571
Fiji. Bureau of Statistics. Shipping Statistics. (FJ) **4663**
Fiji. Bureau of Statistics. Statistical News. (FJ) **4571**
Fiji. Bureau of Statistics. Survey of Distributive Trade. (FJ) **716**, 4571
Fiji. Bureau of Statistics. Tourism and Migration Statistics. (FJ) **4799**, 3992, 4571
Fiji. Bureau of Statistics. Trade Report. (FJ) **716**, 4571
Fiji. Bureau of Statistics. Vital Statistics. (FJ) **716**, 4571
Fiji. Central Monetary Authority. Annual Report *see* Fiji. Reserve Bank of Fiji. Annual Report **1094**
Fiji. Central Monetary Authority. Quarterly Review *see* Fiji. Reserve Bank of Fiji. Quarterly Review **866**
Fiji. Department of Agriculture. Annual Report *see* Fiji. Ministry of Agriculture & Fisheries. Annual Report **92**
Fiji. Department of Agriculture. Annual Research Report. *see* Fiji. Ministry of Agriculture & Fisheries. Annual Research Report **92**
Fiji. Government Printing Department. Publications Bulletin. (FJ ISSN 0015-0916) **4080**
Fiji. Housing Authority. Report. (FJ) **2487**
Fiji. Mineral Resources Department. Annual Report. (FJ ISSN 0252-2462) **3483**
Fiji. Mineral Resources Department. Bulletin. (FJ) **1560**
Fiji. Mineral Resources Department. Economic Investigation. (FJ) **3483**
Fiji. Mineral Resources Department. Geothermal Report. (FJ ISSN 0250-7277) **1560**
Fiji. Mineral Resources Department. Hydrogeological Report. (FJ ISSN 1011-7512) **1560**
Fiji. Mineral Resources Department. Information Notes. (FJ ISSN 1016-2135) **1560**
Fiji. Mineral Resources Department. Memoir. (FJ) **1560**

Fiji. Mineral Resources Department. Report. (FJ) **1560**
Fiji. Mineral Resources Division. Annual Report *see* Fiji. Mineral Resources Department. Annual Report **3483**
Fiji. Mineral Resources Division. Bulletin *see* Fiji. Mineral Resources Department. Bulletin **1560**
Fiji. Mineral Resources Division. Economic Investigation *see* Fiji. Mineral Resources Department. Economic Investigation **3483**
Fiji. Ministry of Agriculture & Fisheries. Annual Report. (FJ ISSN 0071-4844) **92**
Fiji. Ministry of Agriculture & Fisheries. Annual Research Report. (FJ) **92**
Fiji. Ministry of Education. Report. (FJ) **1633**
Fiji. Ministry of Education, Youth and Sport. Report *see* Fiji. Ministry of Education. Report **1633**
Fiji. Office of the Ombudsman. Annual Report of the Ombudsman. (FJ) **2626**
Fiji. Printing Department Report. (FJ) **2569**
Fiji. Reserve Bank of Fiji. Annual Report.(FJ) **1094**
Fiji. Reserve Bank of Fiji. Quarterly Review. (FJ) **866**
Fiji Agricultural Journal. (FJ ISSN 0015-0886) **92**
Fiji Beach Press. (FJ) **4763**
Fiji Classification & Dictionary of Occupations. (FJ) **979**, 1135
Fiji Facts and Figures. (FJ) **716**, 4571
†Fiji Holiday. (FJ) **5192**
Fiji Information *see* Fiji Today **4060**
Fiji Library Association. Journal. (FJ) **2757**
Fiji Library Association. Newsletter. (FJ) **2757**
Fiji Library Directory. (FJ) **2757**
Fiji Magic. (FJ) **4763**
Fiji Medical Journal. (FJ) **3098**
Fiji Mineral Resources Division. Memoir *see* Fiji. Mineral Resources Department. Memoir **1560**
†Fiji National Bibliography. (FJ) **5192**
Fiji Register of Research and Investigations *see* South Pacific Research Register **412**
Fiji Royal Gazette. (FJ) **4060**
Fiji Sugar Year Book. (FJ) **2067**, 177
Fiji Today. (FJ) **4060**
Fiji Trade Review. (FJ) **665**
Fiji Women. (FJ) **4842**
Fikr-o-Nazar. (PK ISSN 0430-4055) **4218**
Fikrun Wa Fann. (GW ISSN 0015-0932) **2866**, 326
Filament. (US) **3508**
Filatelia. (RM ISSN 0428-3341) **3752**
Filatelia Cubana. (CU ISSN 0138-631X) **3752**
Filatelia Italiana. (IT ISSN 0015-0940) **3752**
Filateliai Szemle. (HU ISSN 0133-168X) **3752**
Filatelico. (IT) **3752**
Filatelie. (CS ISSN 0015-0959) **3752**
Filatelija. (CI ISSN 0015-0967) **3752**
Filatelisti. (FI) **3752**
Filatelistisk Katalog-Noegle/Philatelistic Catalogue Key/Philatelistischer Katalog-Schluessel. (DK ISSN 0108-0296) **3752**
Filatelia S.S.S.R. (RU ISSN 0015-0983) **3752**
Filature et Tissage du Coton. *see* Canada. Statistics Canada. Cotton Yarn and Cloth Mills **5159**
File *see* A C M Bulletin (Victorian Edition) **806**
File 770. (US) **3011**
Filia und Filius. (GW) **1254**
Filiere Farine. (FR ISSN 1140-5104) **2088**
Filiere Maille. (FR ISSN 0750-4764) **4619**
Filiere Viande *see* Filieres Viande et Peche **2067**
Filieres Viande et Peche. (FR ISSN 1143-7375) **2067**
†Filigrane. (FR ISSN 0298-7139) **5192**

Filing and Grants Bulletin *see* Telocator. Bulletin **1344**
Filipinka. (PL) **1254**
Filipino-American Herald. (US ISSN 0015-0991) **2002**
Filipino Journal. (CN) **2002**
Filipino Nurse *see* Philippine Journal of Nursing **3285**
Filipino Teacher. (PH ISSN 0015-1009) **1633**
Filippijnenbulletin. (NE) **3894**
Fillers for Publications. (US ISSN 0739-0033) **2569**, 4127
Filles d'Aujourd'hui. (CN ISSN 0227-0315) **1254**
Fillmore Bungle. (US) **2866**
Film. (PL ISSN 0015-1033) **3508**
Film. (UK ISSN 0015-1025) **3508**
Film. (IR) **3508**
Film. (IT) **3508**
Film a Divadlo. (CS) **1373**, 3508, 4633
Film a Doba. (CS ISSN 0015-1068) **3508**
Film Aarbogen. (DK ISSN 0109-2774) **3508**
Film & History. (US ISSN 0360-3695) **3508**, 2310
Film and Television Handbook (Year). (UK) **3508**, 1373
Film and Television Literature. *see* Yingshi Wenxue **2979**
Film and Television Technician *see* F T T and Beta News **2583**
Film & Video. (US ISSN 1041-1933) **3508**, 1385
Film and Video Acquisitions. (AT ISSN 0811-1235) **3520**, 400, 1348, 1385
Film & Video Finder. (US) **1676**, 12, 1385, 3520
†Film and Video Makers Directory. (US) **5192**
Film and Video Production *see* Film & Video **3508**
Film Art. *see* Dianying Yishu **3507**
Film Australia Business & Management Catalogue. (AT) **3508**, 1010
Film Australia Catalogue *see* Film Australia Education Catalogue **3508**
Film Australia Education Catalogue. (AT) **3508**, 239, 326, 1254, 1633
▼Film Australia Health & Welfare Catalogue. (AT) **3508**, 4101, 4405
Film Bill. (US) **3508**
Film Bulletin. (SZ) **3508**
Film Canada Yearbook. (CN ISSN 0831-5175) **3508**, 1373
Film Comment. (US ISSN 0015-119X) **3509**
▼Film Composers Guide. (US) **1135**, 3509
Film Criticism. (US ISSN 0163-5069) **3509**
Film Culture. (US ISSN 0015-1211) **3509**
Film Directions. (UK) **3509**
Film Directors: a Complete Guide. (US) **1135**, 3509
Film Dope. (UK ISSN 0305-1706) **3509**
Film-Echo - Filmwoche. (GW ISSN 0015-1149) **3509**
Film-Echo Filmwoche. Verleih-Katalog. (GW ISSN 0071-4879) **3509**
Film Edmonton *see* Freeze Frame **3511**
Film en Televisie *see* Film en Televisie - Video **3509**
Film en Televisie - Video. (BE) **3509**, 1373, 1385
Film Fans. *see* Dianying zhi You **3507**
Film Francais. (FR ISSN 0397-8702) **3509**
Film Francais-Cinematographie Francais *see* Film Francais **3509**
†Film History. (US ISSN 0892-2160) **5192**
Film Index. (AT ISSN 0015-1289) **3509**
Film Journal. (US ISSN 0199-7300) **3509**
Film-khane-ye Melli-e Iran. Name-ye/ National Film Archive of Iran. Quarterly. (IR) **3509**
Film Literature. *see* Dianying Wenxue **3507**

FILM LITERATURE

Film Literature Index. (US ISSN 0093-6758) **3520**, 12, 1373
Film Magasinet. (DK ISSN 0108-772X) **3509**
Film Maker. *see* Sineast **3517**
Film Mirror. (II) **3509**, 1291
Film Monthly. (UK) **3509**
Film Music Buyer's Guide. (US) **3509**, 3551
Film og Kino. (NO ISSN 0015-1351) **3509**
Film Pictorial. *see* Dianying Huakan **3507**
Film Preview Reports. (US) **3509**
Film Producers, Studios, Agents and Casting Directors Guide. (US ISSN 1058-2630) **1135**, 3509
Film Producers, Studios, Agents and Casting Directors Guide *see* Film Producers, Studios, Agents and Casting Directors Guide **1135**
†Film - Psychology Review. (US) **5192**
Film Quarterly. (US ISSN 0015-1386) **3509**
Film Reader. (US ISSN 0361-722X) **3509**
Film Review (London, 1951). (UK) **3509**
†Film Review (London, 1970). (UK ISSN 0071-4917) **5192**
Film Review Annual. (US ISSN 0737-9080) **3509**
Film Scripts. *see* Dianying Zuopin **3507**
Film Stories. *see* Dianying Gushi **3507**
Film, Szinhaz, Muzsika. (HU ISSN 0015-1416) **3509**, 3551, 4633
Film - Tape World. (US) **3509**
Film Tchecoslovaque *see* Czechoslovak Film **3507**
Film Threat. (US ISSN 0896-6389) **3509**
▼Film Threat Video Guide. (US) **1385**, 3509
Film U V *see* Klip **3513**
Film und Fakten. (GW ISSN 0934-0378) **3509**
Film und Fernsehen. (GW ISSN 0323-3227) **326**, 1336, 3509
Film und Fernsehen in Forschung und Lehre. (GW ISSN 0173-4970) **3509**, 1633, 3520
Film und Recht *see* Zeitschrift fuer Urheber- und Medienrecht **2697**
Film und TV Kameramann. (GW ISSN 0343-5571) **3509**
Film und Video. (GW) **3509**, 1385
Film - Video Canadiana. (CN ISSN 0836-1002) **3510**, 1385
Film World. *see* Dianying Shijie **3507**
Film World. (US) **3510**
Film World Directory of Adult Film & Video. (US) **1135**, 1385, 3510
Film World Guide. (US) **3510**
Film Writers Guide. (US) **1135**, 3510
Film Year Book (Year). *see* Filmarsboken **3510**
Filmarsboken/Film Year Book (Year). (SW ISSN 0071-4925) **3510**, 1373
Filmatiserede Boeger. (DK ISSN 0107-0940) **3510**, 400
Filmblaetter *see* Film-Echo - Filmwoche **3510**
Filmcritica. (IT ISSN 0015-1513) **3510**
Filme Cultura. (BL) **3510**
Filmechange. (FR ISSN 0181-4141) **2626**, 3510
Filmfare. (II ISSN 0015-1548) **3510**
Filmfaust. (GW ISSN 0176-1110) **3510**, 1373
Filmfax. (US) **3510**
Filmhaeftet: Tidskrift om Film och T V. (SW) **3510**
Filmi Duniya. (II) **3510**
Filmi Kaliyan. (II) **3510**
Filmihullu. (FI) **3510**
Filmjournalen. (NO ISSN 0015-1556) **3510**, 1254
Filmkritik. (GW ISSN 0015-1572) **3510**
Filmkultura. (HU ISSN 0015-1580) **3510**
Filmkunst. (AU ISSN 0015-1599) **3510**
Filmliste *see* Spielfilmliste **3518**
Filmlog. (UK) **3510**

Filmmakers and Film Production Services of Israel *see* Israel Film Industry Directory **3512**
Filmmaker's Review. (US) **3510**
Filmnews. (AT) **3510**
†Filmo. (FR ISSN 0294-0957) **5192**
Filmoteca Ultramarina Portuguesa. Boletim. (PO ISSN 0430-4497) **2310**, 3957
Filmovy Prehled. (CS ISSN 0015-1645) **3510**
Filmowy Serwis Prasowy. (PL) **3510**
Filmregistret. (DK ISSN 0106-8180) **3520**
Filmrutan. (SW ISSN 0015-1661) **3510**
Films a l'Ecran. (CN ISSN 0046-3825) **3510**
Films & Filming. (UK ISSN 0015-167X) **3510**, 1385
Films in Review. (US ISSN 0015-1688) **3510**
Films on Screen & Video *see* Films & Filming **3510**
†Films on Video. (UK) **5192**
Films: The Visualization of Anthropology.(US) **254**, 3520
Filmsaesonen: Dansk Filmfortegnelse. (DK ISSN 0107-1033) **3510**
Filmschau. (AU ISSN 0015-1696) **3510**
Filmspiegel. (GW ISSN 0015-1734) **3510**
Filmstatistisches Taschenbuch. (GW ISSN 0071-4941) **3520**
Filmstrip and Slide Set Finder. (US) **1676**, 12
Filmstudia. (IT) **3510**
Filmvidenskabeligt Arbog. (DK) **3510**
†Filmviews. (AT ISSN 0158-3778) **5192**
Filmviews Catalogue *see* Australian Catalogue of New Films and Videos **3503**
Filmvilag. (HU) **3510**
Filmwaerts. (GW) **3510**
Il Filo Metallico. (GW ISSN 0430-4578) **1892**, 1822, 3017
Filologia. (AG ISSN 0071-495X) **2814**, 2917
Filologia Angielska. (PL ISSN 0554-8144) **2814**
†Filologia Baltycka/Baltic Philology. (PL) **5192**
Filologia Klasyczna. (PL ISSN 0554-8160) **2814**, 1276
Filologia Moderna. (SP) **2814**, 2917
Filologia Moderna. (IT) **2814**
Filologia Polska. (PL ISSN 0554-8179) **2814**, 2917
Filologiai Kozlony/Philological Review. (HU ISSN 0015-1785) **2814**
Filologicheskie Nauki. (RU ISSN 0028-1212) **2814**
Filologos Colombianos. (CK ISSN 0071-4976) **2814**
Filoloski Fakultet. Katedra za Istocnoslovenski i Zapadnoslovenski Jazici i Knizeunosti. Slavisticki Studii. (XN ISSN 0352-3055) **2814**
Filomata. (PL ISSN 0015-1815) **2310**, 257
Filosofar Cristiano. (AG) **3766**
Filosofi og Videnskabsteori paa Roskilde Universitetscenter. (DK ISSN 0106-6668) **3766**, 4309
Filosofia. (IT ISSN 0015-1823) **3766**
Filosofia del Derecho. Anuario. (SP) **2626**
Filosofia della Religione. Testi e Studi. (IT) **4178**
Filosofia e Societa. (IT) **3766**
Filosofia e Teologia. (IT) **3766**
Filosofia Politica. (BL) **3894**
Filosofia Politica. (IT ISSN 0394-7297) **3894**, 2310, 3766
Filosofia Pubblica. (IT) **3766**
Filosoficky Casopis/Philosophical Journal. (CS ISSN 0015-1831) **3766**
Filosofiske Studier. (DK ISSN 0106-0449) **3766**
Filosofiya i Fizika. (RU) **3818**
Filosofska Dumka *see* Filosofskaya i Sotsiologicheskaya Mysl **3767**
Filosofska i Sotsiologichna Dumka *see* Filosofskaya i Sotsiologicheskaya Mysl **3767**

Filosofska Misul. (BU ISSN 0324-024X) **3766**
Filosofskaya i Sotsiologicheskaya Mysl' (KR) **3767**
Filosofskie Nauki (Alma-Ata). (KZ) **3767**
Filosofskie Nauki (Moscow). (RU ISSN 0015-1858) **3767**, 4309
Filotelico. (DR) **3752**
Filozofia. *see* Acta Universitatis Szegediensis de Attila Jozsef Nominatae. Sectio Philosophica **3760**
Filozofia/Philosophy. (CS ISSN 0046-385X) **3767**
Filozofia-Logika. (PL) **3767**
Filozofske Studije. (YU ISSN 0350-106X) **3767**
Filozofski Fakultet - Zadar. Razdio Filoloskih Znanosti. Radovi. (CI ISSN 0350-3623) **2814**, 2917
Filozofski Fakultet - Zadar. Razdio Filozofije, Psihologije, Sociologiji i Pedagogije. Radovi. (CI ISSN 0352-6798) **3767**, 1633, 4021, 4435
Filozofski Fakultet - Zadar. Razdio Povijesnih Znanosti. Radovi. (CI ISSN 0352-6712) **272**, 326
Fils, Tubes, Bandes et Profiles. (FR ISSN 0249-6704) **3406**
Filson Club History Quarterly. (US ISSN 0015-1874) **2406**
Filter: a Paper for Secondary Science Teachers. (AT ISSN 0310-6020) **1749**
Filtration & Separation. (UK ISSN 0015-1882) **1853**, 1954
Filtration et Techniques Separatives *see* Chimie Actualites **1852**
Filtration News. (US) **1954**, 3686
Filtrieren und Separien *see* F & S **1177**
Il Filugello. (IT) **815**
Fin de Siglo. (AG) **2170**, 3894
Fin de Siglo. (MX) **2210**
Fina Magazine. (PH) **4842**
Finafrica Bulletin *see* Savings and Development **798**
Final Frontier. (US ISSN 0899-4161) **52**
Final Quotes *see* Coastlines **942**
Final Skolidrott. (SW) **4546**
Financas Publicas. (BL ISSN 0301-7230) **1094**
Finance. (CN) **665**
Finance. *see* Caizheng **769**
Finance/Fainansu. (JA ISSN 0448-6072) **779**
Finance. (FR) **779**
Finance a Uver. (CS ISSN 0015-1920) **779**
Finance and Commerce. (US) **779**, 835, 2626
Finance and Development. (UN ISSN 0015-1947) **780**, 929
Finance and Economics. *see* Jinrong yu Jingji **673**
Finance and Economics. *see* Caijing Kexue **769**
Finance & Society. *see* Finans & Samfund **781**
Finance and Trade Economics. *see* Caimao Jingji **769**
Finance Bulletin. (LB) **866**
Finance Confidential. (UK ISSN 0262-5695) **780**
Finance, Credit and International Business - National Association of Credit Management Country Credit Report *see* F C I B Country Credit Report **778**
Finance, Credit and International Business - National Association of Credit Management International Bulletin *see* F C I B International Bulletin **778**
Finance, Credit and International Business - National Association of Credit Management Minutes of Round Table Conference *see* F C I B - N A C M. Minutes of Round Table Conference **778**
†The Finance Director. (UK) **5192**
Finance Economy Management *see* F E M **778**
†Finance for New Projects in UK. (UK) **5192**

Finance: Latin American Industrial Report. (US) **780**
Finance Over 50. (US) **946**, 866
Finance Week. (SA) **780**
Financement de l'Agriculture Canadienne. *see* Farm Credit in the Canadian Financial System **778**
Finances of Public School Systems. (US) **1676**, 4571
Finances Publiques. *see* Public Finance **4071**
Finances Publiques en Suisse. *see* Oeffentliche Finanzen der Schweiz **1103**
Financial Accountability & Management.(UK ISSN 0267-4424) **1094**
Financial Accounting Reporter *see* Journal of Corporate Accounting and Finance **753**
Financial Advertising Review. (US ISSN 0748-1845) **31**, 780
Financial Advisor. (US) **780**
Financial Aid for First Degree Study at Commonwealth Universities. (UK ISSN 0260-0749) **1706**
Financial Aids to Illinois Students. (US ISSN 0085-0543) **1706**
†Financial Analysis of a Group of Petroleum Companies. (US) **5192**
†Financial Analysis of the Motor Carrier Industry. (US ISSN 0099-2445) **5192**
Financial Analysts Journal. (US ISSN 0015-198X) **946**
Financial & Accounting Systems. (US) **1450**, 750
Financial and Economic Studies. *see* Caijing Wenti Yanjiu **769**
Financial and Estate Planning. (US) **780**
Financial & Investment Yearbook R O C.(CH) **946**, 780
Financial and Monetary Policy Studies. (NE) **780**
Financial and Monetary Studies *see* Financial and Monetary Policy Studies **780**
Financial and Operating Results of Department and Specialty Stores. (US ISSN 0547-8804) **835**
Financial and Operating Statistics Motor Carrier Annual Report *see* F & O S Motor Carrier Annual Report **4663**
Financial and Operating Statistics Motor Carrier Quarterly Report *see* F & O S Motor Carrier Quarterly Report **4663**
Financial Assistance for Library Education. (US ISSN 0569-6275) **1706**, 2757
Financial Characteristics of Member Savings and Loan Associations *see* Data Bank **775**
Financial Condition of Colorado Municipalities. (US) **4087**, 780
Financial Corporate - Municipal Bond Transfer Service. (US) **946**
Financial Economist Weekly. *see* Kin'yu Zaisei Jijo **788**
Financial Estate Planners Quarterly. (US ISSN 0423-4596) **2531**
Financial Exchange. (US) **908**
Financial Executive. (US ISSN 0895-4186) **1010**
Financial Executive's Country Risk Alert.(US) **908**
Financial Express. (II ISSN 0015-2005) **780**
Financial Fax. (US) **750**
Financial Forecast Letter *see* Money - Forecast Letter **955**
Financial Freedom Report. (US ISSN 0196-514X) **780**, 4149
Financial Gazette *see* South African Financial Gazette **799**
†Financial Gazette. (RH) **5192**
Financial Imaging News. (US) **780**
Financial Indicators and Corporate Financing Plans: A Semi-Annual Survey *see* Survey of Financial Indicators **5285**
▼Financial Industry Issues. (US) **780**
Financial Industry Number Standard Directory. (US ISSN 0362-1405) **780**
Financial Industry Studies. (US) **780**
Financial Industry Studies Working Papers. (US) **780**

FINLAND. CENTRAL 6183

Financial Institutions, Financial Statistics. (CN ISSN 0380-075X) **716**
Financial Institutions Forum see Birritu **847**
Financial Institutions Retirement Fund. Annual Report. (US) **1065, 1094**
▼Financial Leadership Speaks. (US ISSN 1055-8675) **780**
†Financial Litigation Review. (CN) **5192**
Financial Mail. (SA ISSN 0015-2013) **780**
Financial Management. (US ISSN 0046-3892) **1010**
Financial Management and Accounting for the Construction Industry. (US) **751, 617**
†Financial Manager. (US) **5192**
†Financial Managers' Statement. (US ISSN 0744-9062) **5192**
Financial Market Trends. (FR ISSN 0378-651X) **780**
Financial Marketing News see Financial Marketing Update **1039**
Financial Marketing Update. (UK) **1039, 31, 780**
▼Financial Markets, Institutions and Instruments. (US ISSN 0963-8008) **780**
Financial Monitor. (US) **780, 946**
Financial Observer. (CN) **780**
Financial Operations see Credit Union Management **774**
Financial Planners and Planning Organizations Directory. (US) **780**
Financial Planning (Atlanta). (US ISSN 0746-7915) **780, 946**
Financial Planning (New York). (US) **1010, 780**
Financial Planning News. (US ISSN 0893-7060) **780**
▼Financial Planning on Wall Street. (US) **946**
Financial Planning Series see Money Lines Magazine **791**
Financial Planning Today see Journal of Financial Planning Today **788**
Financial Position of Ontario Universities. (CN ISSN 0823-5872) **1727, 1706**
Financial Post. (CN ISSN 0015-2021) **780**
Financial Post Canadian Markets. (CN ISSN 0227-6038) **1039**
Financial Post Corporation Service. Eight Year Price Range see Financial Post Ten Year Price Range **780**
Financial Post Directory of Directors. (CN ISSN 0071-5042) **1010**
Financial Post Eight Year Price Range see Financial Post Ten Year Price Range **780**
Financial Post Magazine. (CN) **780, 946**
Financial Post Moneywise see Financial Post Magazine **780**
†Financial Post Report on the Nation. (CN) **5192**
Financial Post Survey of Industrials. (CN ISSN 0071-5050) **946**
Financial Post Survey of Mines see Financial Post Survey of Mines and Energy Resources **3483**
Financial Post Survey of Mines and Energy Resources. (CN ISSN 0227-1656) **3483, 1790**
†Financial Post Survey of Predecessor and Defunct Companies. (CN) **5192**
Financial Post Ten Year Price Range. (CN) **780, 946**
Financial Post 500. (CN) **946**
Financial Product News see Stanger's Investment Advisor **965**
†Financial Register. (US) **5192**
Financial Regulation Report. (UK) **781**
Financial Report - Carnegie Endowment for International Peace see Carnegie Endowment for International Peace. Financial Report **3952**
Financial Report of Ontario Universities. (CN) **1727, 1706**
Financial Reporting in Canada. (CN ISSN 0071-5115) **751**
Financial Research. see Caizheng Yanjiu **770**
Financial Results of Horticultural Holdings. (UK) **2125**
Financial Review. (NO) **781**

Financial Review (Champaign). (US ISSN 0732-8516) **781**
Financial Review (Kingston). (US ISSN 0066-5363) **781**
Financial Review of Alien Insurers. (US) **2531, 2626**
Financial Services, Law & Practice. (UK) **2626, 781**
The Financial Services Law Letter. (UK) **781, 2626**
Financial Services Report. (US ISSN 0894-7260) **781, 2626**
▼Financial Services Review. (US ISSN 1057-0810) **781**
Financial Services Week. (US) **781**
†Financial Services Yearbook. (US ISSN 0895-6359) **5192**
Financial Sourcebooks' Source. (US ISSN 0892-7812) **781, 866, 1010, 1039**
Financial Statement Preparation Manual. (US) **781**
Financial Statements and Operating Ratios for the Mortgage Banking Industry. (US ISSN 0278-6567) **781**
Financial Statements of Enterprises in Japan. (JA) **716**
Financial Statistics Monthly, Taiwan District, Republic of China. (CH) **716**
Financial Statistics of Japan. (JA ISSN 0289-1522) **716**
Financial Statistics of Selected Electric Utilities. (US) **1799, 1802**
Financial Stock Guide Service. Directory of Active Stocks. (US ISSN 0364-0752) **946**
Financial Stock Guide Service. Directory of Obsolete Securities see Directory of Obsolete Securities **944**
Financial Studies of the Small Business. (US ISSN 0363-8987) **781**
Financial Success Report see Ruff Times **962**
Financial Survey Company Directory. (UK) **4619**
Financial Technology Bulletin. (UK ISSN 0265-1661) **781, 4598**
Financial Technology Insight. (UK ISSN 0961-5342) **826, 805**
†Financial Technology News. (US) **5192**
Financial Times. see Jinrong Shibao **787**
Financial Times Business Information Ltd. Mergers & Acquisitions see F T Mergers & Acquisitions **665**
Financial Times Icelandic. see Fjarmalatidindi **782**
Financial Times International Year Books: Mining. (UK ISSN 0141-3244) **3483**
Financial Times International Year Books: Oil and Gas. (UK ISSN 0141-3228) **3686**
Financial Times International Year Books: Who's Who in World Oil and Gas. (UK ISSN 0141-3236) **3686**
Financial Times International Year Books: World Hotel Directory. (UK ISSN 0308-8464) **2473, 4763**
Financial Times International Year Books: World Insurance. (UK ISSN 0309-751X) **2531**
Financial Times of Canada. (CN ISSN 0839-2188) **781**
Financial Times of Canada. Guide to R R S Ps see Financial Times of Canada. R R S Ps (Year) **2531**
Financial Times of Canada. R R S Ps (Year). (CN) **2531**
Financial Times of Ceylon. (CE) **781**
Financial Times Tax Newsletter see Financial Times World Tax Report **1094**
†Financial Times World Business Weekly. (UK ISSN 0142-162X) **5192**
Financial Times World Shipping Yearbook. (UK) **4727**
Financial Times World Tax Report. (UK ISSN 0141-0741) **1094**
†Financial Trend. (US ISSN 0040-4195) **5192**
▼Financial Valuation: Businesses and Business Interests. (US) **2626**
Financial Woman Today. (US) **781, 4842**

Financial Women's Association of New York Newsletter. (US) **781, 4843**
Financial World. (US ISSN 0015-2064) **781**
Financial Yellow Book. (US ISSN 1058-2878) **1010**
Financial 1000 see Financial Yellow Book **1010**
Financial 1000 Yellow Book see Financial Yellow Book **1010**
Financieel Ekonomische Tijd. (BE) **665**
Financieel Overheidsbeheer see Financieel Overheidsmanagement **781**
Financieel Overheidsmanagement. (NE ISSN 0922-1026) **781, 751**
Financiele Koerier. (NE ISSN 0015-2099) **781**
Financiele Positie van de Landbouw. (NE ISSN 0921-4100) **92, 150**
Financier. (US ISSN 0745-242X) **781**
Financijska Praksa. (CI ISSN 0350-5669) **999**
Financing Agriculture. (II ISSN 0015-2110) **92, 781**
Financing and External Debt of Developing Countries. (FR) **929**
Financing and Insuring Exports: A User's Guide to Eximbank and F.C.I.A. Programs. (US) **781**
Financing Foreign Operations: Asia - Pacific. (US) **946, 908**
Financing Foreign Operations: Europe - Middle East - Africa. (US) **946, 908**
Financing Foreign Operations: Global Edition. (US ISSN 0015-2129) **946, 908**
Financing Foreign Operations: Latin America. (US) **946, 908**
†Financing Higher Education. (US) **5192**
Financing Local Government. (US) **1094**
Financni Zpravodaj. (CS ISSN 0322-9653) **781**
▼Finans & Samfund/Finance & Society. (DK ISSN 0905-9415) **781**
†Finanse. (PL) **5192**
Finansije. (YU ISSN 0015-2145) **781**
†Finanstidende. (DK ISSN 0015-2153) **5192**
Finansy S.S.S.R. (RU ISSN 0015-2161) **781**
Finanz-Compass. (AU) **781**
Finanz-Revue. (SZ ISSN 0015-2188) **781**
Finanz-Rundschau see Finanz-Rundschau Ausgabe A **1094**
Finanz-Rundschau Ausgabe A. (GW ISSN 0176-7771) **1094**
Finanz-Rundschau Ausgabe B. (GW ISSN 0176-778X) **1094**
Finanz und Wirtschaft. (SZ ISSN 0015-220X) **946**
Finanza Imprese e Mercati. (IT ISSN 1120-9461) **1094, 781**
Finanza Locale. (IT) **1094, 4060**
Finanza Marketing e Produzione. (IT) **1010**
Finanzarchiv. (GW ISSN 0015-2218) **1095**
Finanzas Publicas Estatales y Municipales de Mexico. (MX ISSN 0187-4853) **716, 1095, 4571**
Finanzas y Credito. (CU) **782**
Finanziere see Testata: il Finanziere **1110**
Finanzierung, Leasing, Factoring see F L F **1093**
▼Finanzierungs Berater. (GW ISSN 0939-7825) **782**
Finanzjournal mit Gebuehren- und Verkehrsteuerbeitragen. (AU ISSN 0015-2250) **782**
Finanznachrichten. (AU ISSN 0015-2269) **782**
Finanzrechtliche Erkenntnisse des Verwaltungsgerichtshofes. (AU ISSN 0015-2277) **1095, 2626**
Finanzwissenschaftliche Schriften. (GW) **894**
Finanzwoche Kapitalbrief fuer Anleger in Deutschland und der Schweiz. (GW) **946**
†Finders Keepers (Kinsman). (US) **5192**
Finders Keepers (Wellingborough) see Collectors Mart **2435**

Findex. (US ISSN 0273-4125) **716, 12**
Finding. (US ISSN 0892-7367) **2758, 31**
Finding the Source. (US ISSN 0891-1835) **239**
Fine Art & Auction Review. (CN ISSN 0833-0891) **257, 326**
Fine Art Trade Guild Journal. (UK ISSN 0308-0854) **326**
Fine Arts. see Dursleh Urlag **325**
Fine Arts Folio. (US) **2225**
Fine Arts Periodicals. (US) **352, 12**
Fine Arts Philatelists Journal see F A P Journal **3752**
Fine Arts Research and Communications Enterprises see F A R C E **326**
†Fine Arts Work Center in Provincetown. Visual Catalogue. (US) **5192**
Fine Balances - Juste Equilibre see C A C S W News **4838**
†Fine Chemicals Directory. (US ISSN 0740-3739) **5192**
▼Fine Foods. (US) **2067**
Fine Gael News. (IE) **3894, 2202**
Fine Gardening. (US ISSN 0896-6281) **2125**
Fine Homebuilding. (US ISSN 0273-1398) **618**
Fine Madness. (US ISSN 0737-4704) **2993, 2866**
Fine Mechanics and Optics. see Jemna Mechanika a Optika **3843**
Fine Print. (US ISSN 0361-3801) **3999, 4127**
†Fine Times. (US) **5192**
Fine Tuning. (US) **1373**
Fine Woodworking. (US ISSN 0361-3453) **639**
†FineLine. (US) **5192**
Finer Points Magazine. (US) **665**
Fine's Wisconsin Evidence. (US) **2626**
FineScale Modeler. (US ISSN 0277-979X) **2436**
Finest Hour. (US ISSN 0882-3715) **2310, 419, 2436**
Finger Lakes Library System. Newsletter. (US ISSN 0195-4016) **2758**
Finger Lakes Magazine. (US ISSN 0892-5658) **2225**
Finger Lakes Travel Guide see I Love New York: The Finger Lakes Travel Guide **4771**
Fingerprint News. (UK ISSN 0959-5937) **541**
Fingerprint World. (UK ISSN 0951-1288) **1514, 3264**
Fingerprints and Little Feats. (US) **1254, 3524**
Finishers' Management. (US ISSN 0015-2358) **3406**
Finishing. (UK ISSN 0264-2506) **3653**
Finishing Handbook and Directory. (UK ISSN 0071-5182) **3406**
Finishing Industries see Finishing **3653**
Finishing Line. (US) **3653**
Finishing Touches see Professional Builder **628**
Finistere. (IT) **2917**
Finisterra. (PO) **2247, 239**
Finite Element News. (UK ISSN 0309-6688) **1879, 1916**
Finite Elements in Analysis and Design. (NE ISSN 0168-874X) **1879, 1076, 1418**
Fink and Borstein Workers' Compensation Newsletter. (CN) **2531**
Fink-S see Finuc-S **400**
Finland. (FI ISSN 0356-827X) **2361, 3894**
Finland. Central Statistical Office. Building Construction Statistics. see Finland. Tilastokeskus. Talonrakennustilasto **637**
Finland. Central Statistical Office. Bulletin of Statistics. see Finland. Tilastokeskus. Tilastokatsauksia **4571**
Finland. Central Statistical Office. Causes of Death in Finland. see Finland. Tilastokeskus. Kuolemansyyt **716**

6184 FINLAND. CENTRAL

Finland. Central Statistical Office.
Construction of Dwellings. see
Finland. Tilastokeskus.
Asuntotuotanto 5192

Finland. Central Statistical Office.
Criminality. Criminal Cases Tried by
the Courts. see Finland.
Tilastokeskus. Rikollisuus.
Tuomioistuinten Tutkimat Rikokset
1525

Finland. Central Statistical Office.
Criminality. Criminality Known to the
Police. see Finland. Tilastokeskus.
Rikollisuus. Poliisin Tietoon Tullut
Rikollisuus 1525

Finland. Central Statistical Office. Farm
Economy. see Finland. Tilastokeskus.
Maatilatalous 137

Finland. Central Statistical Office.
Financing. see Finland. Tilastokeskus.
Rahoitus 716

Finland. Central Statistical Office.
Function of Courts. see Finland.
Tilastokeskus. Tuomioistuinten
Toiminta 1525

Finland. Central Statistical Office.
Government Statistics. see Finland.
Tilastokeskus. Valtion Tilastojulkaisut
4571

Finland. Central Statistical Office.
Handbooks. see Finland.
Tilastokeskus. Kaesikirjoja 4571

Finland. Central Statistical Office.
Income and Consumption. see
Finland. Tilastokeskus. Tulot ja
Kulutus 717

Finland. Central Statistical Office.
Industrial Statistics. see Finland.
Tilastokeskus. Teollisuustilasto 716

Finland. Central Statistical Office. Labour
Force Survey. see Finland.
Tilastokeskus. Tyovoimatutkimus
717

Finland. Central Statistical Office. Living
Conditions in Finland. see Finland.
Statistikcentralen. Statistiska
Meddelanden. Levnadsfoerhaallanden
i Finland 4457

Finland. Central Statistical Office.
Mortality. Life Tables. see Finland.
Tilastokeskus. Kuolleisuus.
Kuolleisuus- Ja Eloonjaamistauluja
3992

Finland. Central Statistical Office.
Municipal Elections. see Finland.
Tilastokeskus. Kunnallisvaalit 4080

Finland. Central Statistical Office.
Municipal Finances. see Finland.
Tilastokeskus. Kuntien Talous 716

Finland. Central Statistical Office.
National Elections. Parliamentary
Elections. see Finland. Tilastokeskus.
Valtiolliset Vaalit. Kansanedustajain
Vaalit 3937

Finland. Central Statistical Office.
Population. see Finland.
Tilastokeskus. Vaestoe 3992

Finland. Central Statistical Office.
Population and Housing Census. see
Finland. Tilastokeskus. Vaestoe- ja
Asuntolaskenta 3992

Finland. Central Statistical Office. Road
Traffic Accidents. see Finland.
Tilastokeskus.
Tieliikenneonnettomuudet 4663

Finland. Central Statistical Office.
Statistical Surveys. Cultural Statistics.
see Finland. Tilastokeskus.
Tilastollisia Tiedonantoja.
Kulttuuritilasto 4394

Finland. Central Statistical Office.
Statistical Surveys. Environmental
Statistics. see Finland. Tilastokeskus.
Tilastollisia Tiedonantoja.
Ympaeristoetilasto 1974

Finland. Central Statistical Office.
Statistical Surveys. Household Survey.
see Finland. Tilastokeskus.
Tilastollisia Tiedonantoja.
Kotitaloustiedustelu 716

Finland. Central Statistical Office.
Statistics of Income and Property.
see Finland. Tilastokeskus. Tulo- ja
Varallisuustilasto 717

Finland. Central Statistical Office.
Studies. see Finland. Tilastokeskus.
Tutkimuksia 717

Finland. Central Statistical Office.
Yearbook of Transport Statistics. see
Finland. Tilastokeskus.
Liikennetilastollinen Vuosikirja 4663

Finland. Folkpensionsanstalt. Statistisk
Aarsbok. see Finland.
Kansanelakelaitos. Tilastollinen
Vuosikirja 2546

Finland. Folkpensionsanstalten.
Beraettelse see Finland
Kansanelakelaitos. Toimintakertomus
2531

Finland. Handels och Industriministeriet.
Energistatistik. see Finland. Kauppa -
Jateollisuusministerioe. Energiatilastot
1799

Finland. Kansanelakelaitos. Julkaisuja.
Sarja A. (FI ISSN 0430-5205)
4372

Finland. Kansanelakelaitos. Julkaisuja.
Sarja AL. (FI ISSN 0355-4813)
2531, 3098

Finland. Kansanelakelaitos. Julkaisuja.
Sarja E. (FI ISSN 0355-4848)
4372

Finland. Kansanelakelaitos. Julkaisuja.
Sarja EL. (FI ISSN 0355-4856)
2531, 3098

Finland. Kansanelakelaitos. Julkaisuja.
Sarja M. (FI ISSN 0355-4821)
4372

Finland. Kansanelakelaitos. Julkaisuja.
Sarja ML. (FI ISSN 0355-483X)
2531, 3098

Finland. Kansanelakelaitos. Tilastollinen
Vuosikirja/Finland.
Folkpensionsanstalt. Statistisk
Aarsbok/Finland. Social Insurance
Institution. Statistical Yearbook. (FI
ISSN 0071-5247) 2546

Finland. Kansantalousosasto.
Kansantalouden Kehitysarvio.
Summary: National Budget for
Finland. (FI ISSN 0071-5255)
1095

Finland. Kansantalousosasto.
Taloudellinen Katsaus. Economic
Survey. (FI ISSN 0071-5271) 866

Finland. Kauppa -
Jateollisuusministerioe.
Energiatilastot/Finland. Handels och
Industriministeriet. Energistatistik. (FI
ISSN 0785-3165) 1799, 1790

Finland. Laakintohallitus. Laakarit,
Hammaslaakarit - Lakare,
Tandlaekare. (FI) 3098, 3233

Finland. Laakintohallitus. Laakarit,
Hammaslaakarit, Sairaalat see
Finland. Laakintohallitus. Laakarit,
Hammaslaakarit - Lakare,
Tandlaekare 3098

Finland. Merentutkimuslaitoksen.
Julkaisu see Finnish Marine Research
1604

Finland. Ministry of Labour. Labour
Reports. see Finland.
Tyovoimaministerio. Tyovoimakatsaus
5193

Finland. Ministry of Social Affairs and
Health. Planning Department.
Publications. (FI) 4405

Finland. Ministry of Social Affairs and
Health. Planning Department.
Reports. (FI) 4405

Finland. Ministry of Social Affairs and
Health. Research Department.
Special Social Studies. see Finland.
Sosiaali- ja Terveysministerio.
Tukimusosasto. Sosiaalisia
Erikoistutkimuksia 5192

Finland. National Board of Agriculture.
Statistics. Monthly Review of
Agricultural Statistics. (FI ISSN
0430-5329) 137

Finland. National Board of Social
Welfare. Homehelp. see Finland.
Sosiaalihallitus. Huoltoapu 4405

Finland. National Board of Social
Welfare. Social Assistance. see
Finland. Sosiaalihallitus.
Kodinhoitoapu 4405

Finland. National Board of Social
Welfare. Yearbook of Social Welfare
Statistics. see Finland.
Sosiaalihallitus. Sosiaalihuoltotilaston
Vuosikirja 4405

Finland. Patentti- ja Rekisterihallitus.
Mallioikeuslehti. (FI ISSN 0355-
4481) 3674

Finland. Patentti- ja Rekisterihallitus.
Patenttilehti. (FI ISSN 0031-2916)
3674

Finland. Patentti- ja Rekisterihallitus.
Tavaramerkkilehti. (FI ISSN 0039-
9922) 3675

Finland. Posti-ja Lennatinlaitos.
Kotimaisten Sanomalehtien Hinnasto.
Inhemsk Tidningstaxa. (FI ISSN
0071-5298) 400

Finland. Posti-ja Lennatinlaitos.
Ulkomaisten Sanomalehtien Hinnasto.
Utlandsk Tidningstaxa. (FI ISSN
0071-5301) 2569

Finland. Social Insurance Institution.
Annual Report see Finland
Kansanelakelaitos. Toimintakertomus
2531

Finland. Social Insurance Institution.
Statistical Yearbook. see Finland.
Kansanelakelaitos. Tilastollinen
Vuosikirja 2546

Finland. Socialstyrelsen.
Hemvaardshjaelp. see Finland.
Sosiaalihallitus. Kodinhoitoapu 4405

Finland. Socialstyrelsen. Socialhjaelp.
see Finland. Sosiaalihallitus.
Huoltoapu 4405

Finland. Socialstyrelsen.
Socialvaardsstatistisk Aarsbok. see
Finland. Sosiaalihallitus.
Sosiaalihuoltotilaston Vuosikirja
4405

†Finland. Sosiaali- ja Terveysministerio.
Tukimusosasto. Sosiaalisia
Erikoistutkimuksia/Finland. Ministry
of Social Affairs and Health.
Research Department. Special Social
Studies. (FI ISSN 0071-5336)
5192

Finland. Sosiaalihallitus. Huoltoapu/
Finland. National Board of Social
Welfare. Homehelp/Finland.
Socialstyrelsen. Socialhjaelp. (FI ISSN
0355-4759) 4405

Finland. Sosiaalihallitus. Kodinhoitoapu/
Finland. National Board of Social
Welfare. Social Assistance/Finland.
Socialstyrelsen. Hemvaardshjaelp. (FI
ISSN 0355-4767) 4405

Finland. Sosiaalihallitus.
Sosiaalihuoltotilaston Vuosikirja/
Finland. National Board of Social
Welfare. Yearbook of Social Welfare
Statistics/Finland. Socialstyrelsen.
Socialvaardsstatistisk Aarsbok. (FI
ISSN 0071-5328) 4405

Finland. Statistikcentralen.
Arbetskraftsundersoekningen. see
Finland. Tilastokeskus.
Tyovoimatutkimus 717

Finland. Statistikcentralen. Befolkning.
see Finland. Tilastokeskus. Vaestoe
3992

Finland. Statistikcentralen.
Bostadsproduktionen. see Finland.
Tilastokeskus. Asuntotuotanto 5192

Finland. Statistikcentralen. Brottslighet.
Brottslighet Som Kommit till Polisens
Kaennedom. see Finland.
Tilastokeskus. Rikollisuus. Poliisin
Tietoon Tullut Rikollisuus 1525

Finland. Statistikcentralen. Brottslighet.
Vid Domstolar Rannsakade Brott. see
Finland. Tilastokeskus. Rikollisuus.
Tuomioistuinten Tutkimat Rikokset
1525

Finland. Statistikcentralen. Doedlighet.
Doedlighets- och Livslaengdstabeller.
see Finland. Tilastokeskus.
Kuolleisuus. Kuolleisuus- Ja
Eloonjaamistauluja 3992

Finland. Statistikcentralen.
Doedsorsaker. see Finland.
Tilastokeskus. Kuolemansyyt 716

Finland. Statistikcentralen.
Domstolarnas Verksamhet. see
Finland. Tilastokeskus.
Tuomioistuinten Toiminta 1525

Finland. Statistikcentralen. Finansiering.
see Finland. Tilastokeskus. Rahoitus
716

Finland. Statistikcentralen. Folk- och
Bostadsraekningen. see Finland.
Tilastokeskus. Vaestoe- ja
Asuntolaskenta 3992

Finland. Statistikcentralen. Gaardsbruk.
see Finland. Tilastokeskus.
Maatilatalous 137

Finland. Statistikcentralen. Handboecker.
see Finland. Tilastokeskus.
Kaesikirjoja 4571

Finland. Statistikcentralen.
Husbyggnadsstatistik. see Finland.
Tilastokeskus. Talonrakennustilasto
637

Finland. Statistikcentralen. Imkomst och
Konsomtion. see Finland.
Tilastokeskus. Tulot ja Kulutus 717

Finland. Statistikcentralen, Indexrapport
AT. Loentagarnas
Foertjaenstnivaaindex. see Finland.
Tilastokeskus. Indeksitiedotus AT.
Palkansaajien Ansiotasoindeksi 716

Finland. Statistikcentralen. Indexrapport
KH. Konsumentprisindex. see Finland.
Tilastokeskus. Indeksitiedotus KH.
Kuluttajahintaindeksi 716

Finland. Statistikcentralen. Indexrapport
TH. Indexar Enligt Producentpris. see
Finland. Tilastokeskus.
Indeksitiedotus TH. Tuottajahintaiset
Indeksit 716

Finland. Statistikcentralen. Indexrapport
TR. Vaegbyggnadskostnadsindex. see
Finland. Tilastokeskus.
Indeksitiedotus TR.
Tienrakennuskustannusindeksi 1844

Finland. Statistikcentralen. Inkomst- och
Foermoegenhetstatistik. see Finland.
Tilastokeskus. Tulo- ja
Varallisuustilasto 717

Finland. Statistikcentralen.
Kommunalvalen. see Finland.
Tilastokeskus. Kunnallisvaalit 4080

Finland. Statistikcentralen.
Kommunernas Ekonomi. see Finland.
Tilastokeskus. Kuntien Talous 716

Finland. Statistikcentralen.
Samfaerdselstatistiskaarsbok. see
Finland. Tilastokeskus.
Liikennetilastollinen Vuosikirja 4663

Finland. Statistikcentralen. Statens
Statistiska Publikationer. see Finland.
Tilastokeskus. Valtion Tilastojulkaisut
4571

Finland. Statistikcentralen. Statistiska
Meddelanden.
Hushaallsbudgetundersoekningen.
see Finland. Tilastokeskus.
Tilastollisia Tiedonantoja.
Kotitaloustiedustelu 716

Finland. Statistikcentralen. Statistiska
Meddelanden Kulturstatistik. see
Finland. Tilastokeskus. Tilastollisia
Tiedonantoja. Kulttuuritilasto 4394

Finland. Statistikcentralen. Statistiska
Meddelanden. Levnadsfoerhaallanden
i Finland/Finland. Central Statistical
Office. Living Conditions in Finland.
(FI) 4457, 4571

Finland. Statistikcentralen. Statistiska
Meddelanden. Miljoestatistik. see
Finland. Tilastokeskus. Tilastollisia
Tiedonantoja. Ympaeristoetilasto
1974

Finland. Statistikcentralen. Statistiska
Oeversikter. see Finland.
Tilastokeskus. Tilastokatsauksia
4571

Finland. Statistikcentralen. Statliga Val.
Ridsdagsmannavalen. see Finland.
Tilastokeskus. Valtiolliset Vaalit.
Kansanedustajain Vaalit 3937

Finland. Statistikcentralen.
Undersoekningar. see Finland.
Tilastokeskus. Tutkimuksia 717

Finland. Statistikcentralen.
Vaegtrafikolyckor. see Finland.
Tilastokeskus.
Tieliikenneonnettomuudet 4663

†Finland. Tilastokeskus. Asuntotuotanto/
Finland. Statistikcentralen.
Bostadsproduktionen/Finland. Central
Statistical Office. Construction of
Dwellings. (FI ISSN 0355-2152)
5192

Finland. Tilastokeskus. Energiatilastot
see Finland. Kauppa -
Jateollisuusministerioe. Energiatilastot
1799

Finland. Tilastokeskus. Indeksitiedotus
AT. Palkansaajien Ansiotasoindeksi/
Finland. Statistikcentralen,
Indexrapport AT. Loentagarnas
Foertjaenstnivaaindex. (FI ISSN
0357-7201) 716

Finland. Tilastokeskus. Indeksitiedotus KH. Kuluttajahintaindeksi/Finland. Statistikcentralen. Indexrapport KH. Konsumentprisindex. (FI ISSN 0355-2381) **716**

Finland. Tilastokeskus. Indeksitiedotus RK. Rakennuskustannusindeksi/ Byggnadskostnadsindex/Building Cost Index. (FI ISSN 0355-239X) **637**

Finland. Tilastokeskus. Indeksitiedotus TH. Tuottajahintaiset Indeksit/Finland. Statistikcentralen. Indexrapport TH. Indexar Enligt Producentpris. (FI ISSN 0355-2403) **716**

Finland. Tilastokeskus. Indeksitiedotus TR. Tienrakennuskustannusindeksi/ Finland. Statistikcentralen. Indexrapport TR. Vaegbyggnadskostnadsindex. (FI ISSN 0355-2411) **1844**

Finland. Tilastokeskus. Kaesikirjoja/ Finland. Statistikcentralen. Handboecker/Finland. Central Statistical Office. Handbooks. (FI ISSN 0355-2063) **4571**

Finland. Tilastokeskus. Kansanedustajain Vaalit see Finland. Tilastokeskus. Valtiolliset Vaalit. Kansanedustajain Vaalit **3937**

Finland. Tilastokeskus. Kunnallisvaalit/ Finland. Statistikcentralen. Kommunalvalen/Finland. Central Statistical Office. Municipal Elections. (FI ISSN 0355-2217) **4080**

Finland. Tilastokeskus. Kuntien Finanssitilasto see Finland. Tilastokeskus. Kuntien Talous **716**

Finland. Tilastokeskus. Kuntien Talous/ Finland. Statistikcentralen. Kommunernas Ekonomi/Finland. Central Statistical Office. Municipal Finances. (FI ISSN 0359-081X) **716**

Finland. Tilastokeskus. Kuolemansyyt/ Finland. Statistikcentralen. Doedsorsaker/Finland. Central Statistical Office. Causes of Death in Finland. (FI ISSN 0355-2144) **716, 3098**

Finland. Tilastokeskus. Kuolleisuus- Ja Eloonjaamistauluja see Finland. Tilastokeskus. Kuolleisuus. Kuolleisuus- Ja Eloonjaamistauluja **3992**

Finland. Tilastokeskus. Kuolleisuus. Kuolleisuus- Ja Eloonjaamistauluja/ Finland. Statistikcentralen. Doedlighet. Doedlighets- och Livslaengdstabeller/Finland. Central Statistical Office. Mortality. Life Tables. (FI) **3992**

Finland. Tilastokeskus. Liikennetilastollinen Vuosikirja/ Finland. Statistikcentralen. Samfaerdselstatistiskaarsbok/Finland. Central Statistical Office. Yearbook of Transport Statistics. (FI ISSN 0430-5272) **4663**

Finland. Tilastokeskus. Liikepankit ja Kiinnitys Luottolaitokset see Finland. Tilastokeskus. Rahoitus **716**

Finland. Tilastokeskus. Maatilatalous/ Finland. Statistikcentralen. Gaardsbruk/Finland. Central Statistical Office. Farm Economy. (FI ISSN 0356-2913) **137**

Finland. Tilastokeskus. Osuuspankkitilasto see Finland. Tilastokeskus. Rahoitus **716**

Finland. Tilastokeskus. Rahoitus/ Finland. Statistikcentralen. Finansiering/Finland. Central Statistical Office. Financing. (FI ISSN 0784-8382) **716**

Finland. Tilastokeskus. Rikollisuus. Poliisin Tietoon Tullut Rikollisuus/ Finland. Statistikcentralen. Brottslighet. Brottslighet Som Kommit till Polisens Kaennedom/Finland. Central Statistical Office. Criminality. Criminality Known to the Police. (FI ISSN 0355-2160) **1525**

Finland. Tilastokeskus. Rikollisuus. Tuomioistuinten Tutkimat Rikokset/ Finland. Statistikcentralen. Brottslighet. Vid Domstolar Rannsakade Brott/Finland. Central Statistical Office. Criminality. Criminal Cases Tried by the Courts. (FI ISSN 0355-2179) **1525**

Finland. Tilastokeskus. Saastopankkitilasto see Finland. Tilastokeskus. Rahoitus **716**

Finland. Tilastokeskus. Talonrakennustilasto/Finland. Statistikcentralen. Husbyggnadsstatistik/Finland. Central Statistical Office. Building Construction Statistics. (FI ISSN 0430-5604) **637**

Finland. Tilastokeskus. Teollisuustilasto/ Finland. Central Statistical Office. Industrial Statistics. (FI ISSN 0071-5344) **716**

Finland. Tilastokeskus. Tieliikenneonnettomuudet/Finland. Statistiskcentralen. Vaegtrafikolyckor/ Finland. Central Statistical Office. Road Traffic Accidents. (FI ISSN 0355-2284) **4663**

Finland. Tilastokeskus. Tilastokatsauksia/Finland. Statistikcentralen. Statistiska Oeversikter/Finland. Central Statistical Office. Bulletin of Statistics.(FI ISSN 0015-2390) **4571**

Finland. Tilastokeskus. Tilastollisia Tiedonantoja see Finland. Tilastokeskus. Tilastollisia Tiedonantoja. Kotitaloustiedustelu **716**

Finland. Tilastokeskus. Tilastollisia Tiedonantoja. Kotitaloustiedustelu/ Finland. Statistikcentralen. Statistiska Meddelanden. Hushaallsbudgetundersoekningen/ Finland. Central Statistical Office. Statistical Surveys. Household Survey.(FI) **716**

Finland. Tilastokeskus. Tilastollisia Tiedonantoja. Kulttuuritilasto/Finland. Statistikcentralen. Statistiska Meddelanden Kulturstatistik/Finland. Central Statistical Office. Statistical Surveys. Cultural Statistics. (FI) **4394**

Finland. Tilastokeskus. Tilastollisia Tiedonantoja. Ympaeristoetilasto/ Finland. Statistikcentralen. Statistiska Meddelanden. Miljoestatistik/Finland. Central Statistical Office. Statistical Surveys. Environmental Statistics. (FI) **1974**

Finland. Tilastokeskus. Tilastotiedotus KT. Kansantalouden Tilinpito/National Raekenskaper/National Accounts. (FI ISSN 0355-2276) **716**

Finland. Tilastokeskus. Tilastotiedotus. Palkat Loner/Wages and Salaries. (FI ISSN 0784-8374) **716, 4571**

Finland. Tilastokeskus. Tilastotiedotus. Yritykset Foretag. (FI ISSN 0784-8463) **4571**

Finland. Tilastokeskus. Tulo- ja Omaisuustilasto see Finland. Tilastokeskus. Tulo- ja Varallisuustilasto **717**

Finland. Tilastokeskus. Tulo- ja Varallisuustilasto/Finland. Statistikcentralen. Inkomst- och Foermoegenhetstatistik/Finland. Central Statistical Office. Statistics of Income and Property. (FI ISSN 0780-9352) **717**

Finland. Tilastokeskus. Tulot ja Kulutus/ Finland. Statistikcentralen. Imkomst och Konsomtion/Finland. Central Statistical Office. Income and Consumption. (FI ISSN 0784-8420) **717**

Finland. Tilastokeskus. Tuomioistuinten Toiminta/Finland. Statistikcentralen. Domstolarnas Verksamhet/Finland. Central Statistical Office. Function of Courts. (FI ISSN 0355-2187) **1525**

Finland. Tilastokeskus. Tutkimuksia/ Finland. Statistikcentralen. Undersoekningar/Finland. Central Statistical Office. Studies. (FI ISSN 0355-2071) **717**

Finland. Tilastokeskus. Tyovoimatiedustelu see Finland. Tilastokeskus. Tyovoimatutkimus **717**

Finland. Tilastokeskus. Tyovoimatutkimus/Finland. Statistikcentralen. Arbetskraftsundersoekningen/Finland. Central Statistical Office. Labour Force Survey. (FI ISSN 0781-5611) **717**

Finland. Tilastokeskus. Vaestoe/Finland. Statistikcentralen. Befolkning/Finland. Central Statistical Office. Population. (FI) **3992**

Finland. Tilastokeskus. Vaestoe- ja Asuntolaskenta/Finland. Statistikcentralen. Folk- och Bostadsraekningen/Finland. Central Statistical Office. Population and Housing Census. (FI) **3992**

Finland. Tilastokeskus. Vaestolaskenta see Finland. Tilastokeskus. Vaestoe- ja Asuntolaskenta **3992**

Finland. Tilastokeskus. Vaestonmuutokset see Finland. Tilastokeskus. Vaestoe **3992**

Finland. Tilastokeskus. Valtiolliset Vaalit. Kansanedustajain Vaalit/Finland. Statistikcentralen. Statliga Val. Ridsdagsmannavalen/Finland. Central Statistical Office. National Elections. Parliamentary Elections. (FI) **3937**

Finland. Tilastokeskus. Valtiolliset Vaalit. Tasavallan Presidentin Vaalit Valisijamiesten. (FI ISSN 0355-2195) **3894, 3937**

Finland. Tilastokeskus. Valtion Tilastojulkaisut/Finland. Statistikcentralen. Statens Statistiska Publikationer/Finland. Central Statistical Office. Government Statistics. (FI ISSN 0357-0614) **4571**

Finland. Tullihallituksen Tilastotoimisto. Ulkomaankauppa-Kuukausijulkaisu/ Foreign Trade Monthly Bulletin see Finland. Tullihallitus. Ulkomaankauppa/Utrikeshandel/ Foreign Trade **717**

Finland. Tullihallitus. Ulkomaankauppa/ Utrikeshandel/Foreign Trade. (FI) **717**

†Finland. Tyovoimaministerio. Tyovoimakatsaus/Finland. Ministry of Labour. Labour Reports. (FI ISSN 0430-5280) **5193**

Finland. Ulkoasiainministerio. Ulkopoliittisia Lausuntoja ja Asiakirjoja. (FI ISSN 0071-528X) **3957**

Finland. Valtakunnansuunnittelutoimisto. Julkaisuja. Sarja A see Finland. Valtioneuvoston Kanslian. Julkaisuja **1076**

Finland. Valtioneuvoston Kanslian. Julkaisuja. (FI ISSN 0355-8878) **1076**

Finland. Vestientutkimuslaitos. Julkaisuja/Finland. Water Research Institute. Publications. (FI ISSN 0355-0982) **4824**

Finland. Water Research Institute. Publications. see Finland. Vestientutkimuslaitos. Julkaisuja **4824**

Finland Kansanelakelaitos. Toimintakertomus. (FI ISSN 0355-5003) **2531**

Finlande Industrielle. (FI ISSN 0359-7016) **979**

Finlandia Industrial. (FI) **908**

Finlands Ayrshireboskap see Nautakarja **202**

Finlands Bank. Aarsbok see Bank of Finland. Yearbook **764**

Finlands Bank. Publikationer. Serie A. see Suomen Pankki. Julkaisuja. Sarja A **693**

Finlands Bank. Publikationer. Serie B. see Suomen Pankki. Julkaisuja. Sarja B **693**

Finlands Bank. Publikationer. Serie C. see Suomen Pankki. Julkaisuja. Sarja C **693**

Finlands Bank. Publikationer. Serie D. see Suomen Pankki. Julkaisuja. Sarja D **693**

Finlands Industrifoerbund. Medlemsfoerteckning. see Teollisuuden Keskusliitto. Jasenluettelo **1155**

Finlands Kommunaltidskrift. (FI ISSN 0355-6093) **4087**

Finlands Laekartidning. see Suomen Laakarilehti **3155**

Finlands Litteratur. see Suomen Kirjallisuus **413**

Finlands Press. see Suomen Lehdisto **2575**

Finlandska Masskuldebrevslaan. see Suomen Joukkovelkakirjalainat **965**

Finnam Newsletter. (US) **2002**

†Finnfacts. (FI ISSN 0015-2412) **5193**

Finnisch-Ugrische Forschungen. (FI ISSN 0355-1253) **2814**

Finnisch-Ugrische Mitteilungen. (GW ISSN 0341-7816) **2814, 2917**

Finnische Geodaetische Institut. Veroeffentlichungen. see Suomen Geodeettisen Laitoksen. Julkaisuja **1595**

Finnische Handelsrundschau see Technik aus Finnland **922**

Finnish American Chamber of Commerce Newsletter. (US) **815, 2002**

Finnish American Chamber of Commerce Newsletter see Finnish American Chamber of Commerce Newsletter **815**

Finnish American Chamber of Commerce Newsletter Including Finnfacts Newsletter see Finnish American Chamber of Commerce Newsletter **815**

Finnish American Club of Saima, Inc. Newsletter see F A C S Newsletter **2225**

Finnish Anthropological Society. Journal. see Suomen Antropologi **250**

Finnish Architectural Review. see Arkkitehti **294**

Finnish Boatbuilding Industry. (FI ISSN 0356-7753) **4524**

Finnish Bond Issues. see Suomen Joukkovelkakirjalainat **965**

Finnish Broadcasting Company. Planning and Research Department. Research Reports. (FI) **1374**

Finnish Broadcasting Company. Section for Long-Range Planning. Research Reports see Finnish Broadcasting Company. Planning and Research Department. Research Reports **1374**

†Finnish Chemical Letters. (FI ISSN 0303-4100) **5193**

Finnish Chemistry. see Kemia - Kemi **1856**

Finnish Concrete. (FI) **618**

Finnish Dental Society. Proceedings. (FI ISSN 0039-551X) **3233**

Finnish Dental Society. Proceedings. Supplement. (FI ISSN 0355-4651) **3233**

Finnish Design Magazine Muoto. (FI) **299**

Finnish Economic Journal. see Kansantaloudellinen Aikakauskirja **675**

Finnish Fisheries Research. (FI ISSN 0301-908X) **2040**

Finnish Game Research. (FI ISSN 0783-4365) **582, 1488**

Finnish Geodetic Institute. Publications. see Suomen Geodeettisen Laitoksen. Julkaisuja **1595**

Finnish Geodetic Institute. Reports. see Suomen Geodeettisen Laitoksen. Tiedonantoja **1595**

Finnish Insurance Yearbook. see Suomen Vakuutusvuosikirja **2544**

Finnish Journal of Business Economics. see Liiketaloudellinen Aikakauskirja **677**

Finnish Journal of Dairy Science. (FI ISSN 0367-2387) **199**

Finnish Journal of Foreign Affairs. see Ulkopolitiikka **3975**

Finnish Marine Research. (FI ISSN 0357-1076) 1604
Finnish Medical Journal. see Suomen Laakarilehti 3155
Finnish Meteorological Institute. Contributions. (FI ISSN 0782-6117) 3435
Finnish Meteorological Institute. Geophysical Publications/Ilmatieteen Laitos. Geofysikaalisia Julkaisuja. (FI ISSN 0782-6087) 1589
Finnish Meteorological Institute. Publications. see Ilmatieteen Laitos. Meteorologisia Julkaisuja 3436
Finnish Meteorological Institute. Publications on Air Quality/Ilmatieteen Laitos. Ilmansuojelun Julkaisuja. (FI ISSN 0782-6095) 1977
Finnish National Bibliography. see Suomen Kirjallisuus 413
Finnish New York News. see New Yorkin Uutiset 2016
Finnish Photographic Yearbook. see Valokuvauksen Vuosikirja 3798
Finnish Society for Development Studies. Monograph Series. (SW) 4435
Finnish Trade Review. (FI ISSN 0015-2463) 908
Finommechanika see Finommechanika, Mikrotechnika 2522
Finommechanika, Mikrotechnika. (HU ISSN 0231-2662) 2522
Finsk Arkitekturtidskrift. see Arkkitehti 294
Finsk Fotografisk Arsbok. see Valokuvauksen Vuosikirja 3798
Finsk Palstidskrift. (FI ISSN 0430-5817) 2736
Finsk Veterinartidskrift. see Suomen Elainlaakarilehti 4816
Finska Fornminnesfoereningens Tidskrift. see Suomen Muinaismuistoyhdistyksen Aikakauskirja 287
Finska Kemistsamfundet. Meddelanden see Kemia - Kemi 1856
Finska Laekaresaellskapet. Handlingar. (FI ISSN 0015-2501) 3098
Finskij Torgovyj Zhurnal. (FI ISSN 0015-251X) 908
Finskt Museum. (FI ISSN 0355-1814) 272, 239, 3524
Finuc-S. (FI) 400
Finvestor Report - Stocks Around Five Dollars. (US) 946
Fiori dell'Organo see Celebriamo 3544
Fiori di S. Antonio. (IT ISSN 0015-2528) 4178
Fiorino. (IT) 782
Fiorisce Un Cenacolo. (IT ISSN 0015-2536) 2205
Fippu. (SG) 4843
Fire. (UK ISSN 0015-2544) 2031
Fire. see Gal 4768
Fire and Arson Investigator. (US) 1514, 2626
Fire & Flammability Bulletin. (UK ISSN 0952-2727) 2032, 3862, 4291
Fire and Police Personnel Reporter. (US ISSN 0164-6397) 1065, 1514, 2032
†Fire & Security Protection. (UK) 5193
Fire Australia. (AT ISSN 1032-6529) 2032
Fire, Casualty & Surety Bulletin. (US) 2531
Fire Chief. (US ISSN 0015-2552) 2032
Fire Command see N F P A Journal 2034
Fire Control Digest. (US ISSN 0889-5740) 2032
Fire Department Personnel Reporter see Fire and Police Personnel Reporter 1065
Fire Directory. (UK) 2032
Fire Engineering. (US ISSN 0015-2587) 2032
Fire Engineers Journal. (UK) 2032
Fire Fighting in Canada. (CN ISSN 0015-2595) 2032
Fire Fighting in China. see Zhongguo Xiaofang 2035
Fire International. (UK ISSN 0015-2609) 2032
Fire Journal see N F P A Journal 2034
†Fire Journal. (AT) 5193

Fire Lines. (US) 2583, 2032
Fire Losses in Canada. Annual Report/Pertes Causee par l'Incendie au Canada. Rapport Annuel. (CN) 2035
Fire Losses in Government of Canada Properties. Report/Pertes Dues a l'Incendie de Biens Immobiliers de l'Administration Federale. (CN) 2035
Fire Mark Circle of the Americas Journal. (US) 2531, 2032
Fire Mark Circle of the Americas Newsletter. (US) 2532, 2032
Fire Marshals Association of North America. Directory. (US ISSN 0090-5313) 2032
Fire News. (US ISSN 0015-2625) 2032
Fire News (London). (UK ISSN 0262-4451) 2032
Fire Photographers Journal. (US) 3790, 2032
Fire Prevention. (UK ISSN 0309-6866) 2032
Fire Prevention. see Kyoto Shobo 2033
Fire Prevention Canada. Information. (CN) 2032
Fire Prevention Canada. Public Report/Prevention des Incendies Canada. Rapport Public. (CN) 2032
Fire Prevention Canada Association. Information see Fire Prevention Canada. Information 2032
Fire Prevention Canada Association. Public Report see Fire Prevention Canada. Public Report 2032
Fire Prevention in Forests. see Senlin Fanghuo 2107
Fire Protection Contractor. (US ISSN 1043-2485) 2032
Fire Protection Directory. (UK ISSN 0071-5409) 2032
Fire Protection Handbook. (US ISSN 0071-5417) 2032
Fire Protection Reference Directory see N F P A Buyer's Guide 2034
Fire Protection Review see Fire & Security Protection 5193
Fire Research Institute of Japan. Report. see Shobo Kenkyujo Hokoku 2034
Fire Research News. (UK ISSN 0261-1589) 2032
Fire Research Publications. (US) 2035
Fire Safety Journal. (UK ISSN 0379-7112) 2032
†Fire Science Abstracts. (UK) 5193
Fire Science and Technology. (JA ISSN 0285-9521) 2032
Fire Service Bulletin see Gated Wye 2033
Fire Service Information. (US ISSN 0015-2668) 2032
Fire Statistics. see Netherlands. Centraal Bureau voor de Statistiek. Statistiek der Branden 2035
Fire Statistics United Kingdom. (UK ISSN 0260-3098) 2035, 3174
Fire Surveyor. (UK ISSN 0262-7981) 2032
Fire Systems. (US) 2033
Fire Technology. (US ISSN 0015-2684) 2033
Fire World. (UK ISSN 0262-3242) 2033, 2436
†Fire Yearbook. (US ISSN 0071-5468) 5193
Firearms, State Laws and Published Ordinances see State Laws and Published Ordinances, Firearms 2682
Firefighter News. (US) 2033
Firefighting Protection. see Zastita od Pozara 2035
FireHeart. (US ISSN 1046-6029) 3594, 3669
Firehouse. (US ISSN 0145-4064) 4101
Firehouse Magazine Buyers Guide. (US ISSN 0276-4881) 2033
Firelands Farmer. (US) 92
Fireman. (AT ISSN 0812-0056) 2033
†Firenze Chirurgica/Florence Journal of Surgery. (IT ISSN 0393-2214) 5193
Fireplug. (US) 2033

Fireside Companion see Good Old Days Specials 2920
Firewatch! (US) 2033
Fireweed. (CN ISSN 0706-3857) 4843, 326, 2917
Fireworks. (UK ISSN 0264-9780) 1177, 326, 2033
Fireworks Business. (US ISSN 8755-4372) 835, 2033
Firing Line. (US ISSN 0015-2722) 3894
Firma. (PL ISSN 0209-1607) 1076
Firma. (IT) 1297
▼Firmen der Neuen Bundeslaender. (GW) 1076
Firmenbuch Oesterreich. (AU) 1135
First Aider. (US) 3098
First Atomic Power Industry Group see F A P I G 1805
First Bass. (US) 3551
First Break. (UK ISSN 0263-5046) 1589
First Catholic Slovak Union of America. Minutes of Annual Meeting. (US ISSN 0275-6145) 4264
First Class. (GW) 2473
First Days. (US ISSN 0428-4836) 3752
First Down. (UK) 4503
First Edition see The Communique (Pittsburgh, 1984) 1308
First Empire State Corporation. Annual Report. (US) 782
First Empire State Corporation. Interim Report. (US) 782
First Facts On Foreign Exchange see First Facts On the Currency Market 782
▼First Facts On the Currency Market. (US) 782
First Fandom Magazine. (US) 3011
First for Women. (US ISSN 1040-9467) 2446
First Friday. (US ISSN 0094-0240) 830
First Hand. (US) 3397
First Hawaiian Bank. Economic Indicators. (US ISSN 0015-2757) 866
First Impressions. (US) 4127
First Jersey News see Newsbeam - NatWest N J 793
First Language. (UK ISSN 0142-7237) 2814, 1237
First Line/Yi Xing. (US) 2993, 2917
First Monday. (US ISSN 0145-1677) 3894
First National Bank of Boston. Economic Review. (US) 866
First National City Bank. Economic Week see Economic Week 777
First National City Bank. Economics Department. Weekly Executive Summary see Economic Week 777
First National City Bank, Liberia. Annual Report. (LB) 782
First Nighters' Curtaincall. (AT) 4633
First Opportunity. (US) 1706
First Principles. (US ISSN 0363-0447) 3942
First Priniciple see On Priniciple 3912
First Strike see The Numismatist 3601
First Teacher. (US ISSN 0744-7434) 1634, 1237
▼First Things. (US ISSN 1047-5141) 4178
First-Time Parents. (US) 1237, 3801
First Tuesday. (US) 4149
▼First Visit. (US) 1237
First Whole Rehab Catalog. (US) 2283, 1736
First Year of Life. (US) 1237, 3292, 3801
FirstHand Magazine. (US ISSN 0744-6349) 2452
Firsts: Collecting Modern First Editions. (US) 4127
Fiscal Letter. (US ISSN 0197-288X) 1095, 4060
Fiscal Press see Tolley's Practical Tax Newsletter 1111
Fiscal Reform in the Developing World. (US) 1095
Fiscal Studies. (UK ISSN 0143-5671) 1095
Fiscal Watchdog see Privatization Watch 3919

Fiscale en Administratieve Praktijkvragen. (NE ISSN 0165-2966) 1095
Fiscale Wenken. (BE) 1095
Fiscalite Europeenne. (FR) 1095
Fiscalite Europeenne: Droit International des Affaires. (FR) 1095
Fiscalite Europeenne Revue see Fiscalite Europeenne: Droit International des Affaires 1095
Fiscalite Quebecoise. (CN) 1095, 2626
Fiscaliteit. Monografieen. (BE) 782
Fisch. (GW) 1634
Fisch und Fang. (GW ISSN 0015-2838) 4546
Das Fischerblatt. (GW ISSN 0015-2854) 2040
Fischers Tarif Nachrichten fuer Eisenbahn und Kraftwagen. (GW ISSN 0015-2862) 4709
Fischmagazin. (GW) 2040
†Fischwirt. (GW ISSN 0428-5018) 5193
Fisco. (IT) 1095
Fiscologue see Fiskoloog 1095
Fiscologue International see Fiskoloog International 1095
Fiscoloog see Fiskoloog 1095
Fish and Eggs see Hokkaido Salmon Hatchery. Technical Report 2042
Fish and Game Finder. (US) 4546
▼Fish and Shellfish Immunology. (UK ISSN 1050-4648) 439
†Fish Boat - Sea Food Merchandising. (US ISSN 0015-2900) 5193
Fish Culture/Yoshoku. (JA ISSN 0044-0671) 2040
Fish Culturist. (US ISSN 0015-2919) 2040, 2436
Fish Disease Leaflets. (US ISSN 0071-5492) 2040
Fish Drum. (US ISSN 1051-1695) 2917, 4282
Fish Farmer. (UK ISSN 0262-9615) 2040
Fish Farming International. (UK ISSN 0262-0820) 2040
Fish Finder see Fish and Game Finder 4546
Fish Friers Review. (UK ISSN 0015-2927) 2473
†Fish Health News. (US) 5193
Fish Hoek Echo. (SA) 2216
Fish International. (GW) 2040
Fish Pathology. see Gyobyo Kenkyu 583
Fish Physiology & Biochemistry. (NE ISSN 0920-1742) 582, 2040
Fish Products see Frozen Food Management 2071
The Fish Sniffer. (US ISSN 0747-3397) 4546
Fish Trader. (UK) 2040
Fish Trader Yearbook. (UK) 2040
Fish Trades Gazette see Fish Trader 2040
Fish Trades Review. (AT ISSN 0046-3965) 2040
Fisher Families. (US ISSN 0890-9458) 2151
Fisheries. (US ISSN 0363-2415) 2040
Fisheries and Wildlife Research. (US) 2040, 4546
Fisheries Bulletin. (IE ISSN 0332-4338) 2040, 582
Fisheries Bulletin see Malawi. Fisheries Department. Fisheries Bulletin 2045
Fisheries Council of Canada. Bulletin. (CN ISSN 0046-3973) 2040
▼Fisheries Oceanography. (US ISSN 1054-6006) 2040, 582
Fisheries of Scotland Report. (UK ISSN 0080-1283) 2040
Fisheries of the United States. (US) 2040
Fisheries Product News. (US ISSN 1047-2525) 2040
Fisheries Research. (NE ISSN 0165-7836) 2040
Fisheries Research Data Report. (UK ISSN 0264-5130) 1954
†Fisheries Review. (US) 5193
Fisheries Statistics of Japan. (JA ISSN 0071-5581) 2040
Fisheries World. see Suisan Kai 2049
Fisherman. (CN ISSN 0015-2986) 2040

Fisherman. (US) **4546**
Fisherman & Leisure Life. (UK) **4546**
Fisherman Union of Indonesia. Central Governing Board. Annual Report/ Himpunan Nelayan Seluruh Indonesia. Dewan Pimpanan Pusat. Laporan Kegiatan. (IO) **2040**
†Fisherman's Journal. (AT ISSN 0155-4786) **5193**
Fishermen's Bulletin see Israel. Ministry of Agriculture. Department of Fisheries. Dayig u-Midgeh be-Yisrael - Fisheries and Fishbreeding in Israel **2044**
Fishermen's News. (US ISSN 0015-2994) **2040**
Fishery Bulletin. (US ISSN 0090-0656) **2040**
†Fishery Products Report - California. (US) **5193**
Fishery Research Bulletin see Alaska. Department of Fish and Game. Fishery Research Bulletin **1483**
Fishery Technology. (II ISSN 0015-3001) **2041**
Fisheye View Scuba Magazine. (US) **4472**
Fishing. see Halaszat **2042**
Fishing see Field & Stream Fishing Annual **4546**
†Fishing and Boating Illustrated. (US) **5193**
Fishing and Hunting News. (US ISSN 0015-301X) **4546**
Fishing Annual. (US) **4546**
Fishing Boat International see Fishing Business International **2041**
Fishing Boat World. (AT ISSN 1033-1247) **2041**
Fishing Business International. (FR) **2041**, 4524
Fishing Facts. (US) **4546**
†Fishing for Bass. (US) **5193**
Fishing in Maryland. (US ISSN 0164-0941) **4546**
Fishing Industry News Service see F.I.N.S **5190**
Fishing: Latin American Industrial Report. (US) **2041**
Fishing Magazine for Young Boy. (JA) **1255**, 4546
Fishing News. (UK ISSN 0015-3036) **2041**
Fishing News. (AT ISSN 0816-7885) **4546**
Fishing News International. (UK ISSN 0015-3044) **2041**
Fishing Smart. (US) **4546**
Fishing Tackle Dealer see Tackle & Guns **4557**
Fishing Tackle Retailer. (US) **4546**
Fishing Tackle Trade News. (US ISSN 0015-3060) **4546**
Fishing World. (US ISSN 0015-3079) **4546**
FishLines. (US) **2041**
Fish'n Canada News. (CN) **4546**
Fisica. (AG ISSN 0326-7512) **3818**
Fisica e Tecnologia see Il Nuovo Saggiatore **3826**
Fisica in Medicina see Physica Medica **3141**
Fisiopatologia della Riproduzione. (IT ISSN 0392-7733) **439**, 3098
Fisioterapia. (SP ISSN 0211-5638) **3278**
Fisk & Fri. (DK ISSN 0109-1581) **4546**
Fisk og Hav. (DK ISSN 0105-9211) **2041**
Fiskaren. (NO ISSN 0015-3095) **2041**
Fiskeindustrien see Norsk Fiskeindustri **2046**
Fiskejournalen. (SW) **4546**
Fisken og Havet. (NO ISSN 0071-5638) **2041**
Fiskeprodusenten see Norsk Fiskeindustri **2046**
Fisker Bladet. (DK) **2041**
Fiskeri- og Miljoeundersoegelser i Groenland. Serie 1. Aarsberetning see Fiskeriundersoegelser i Groenland. Aarsberetning **2041**
Fiskeriaarbogen. (DK ISSN 0900-9787) **2041**
Fiskeribladet. (NO) **2041**, 4546
Fiskeritidskrift foer Finland. (FI ISSN 0015-3125) **2041**

Fiskeriundersoegelser i Groenland. Aarsberetning. (DK ISSN 0905-5193) **2041**
Fiskets Gang. (NO ISSN 0015-3133) **2041**
Fiskifrettir. (IC ISSN 1017-3536) **2041**
Fiskoloog. (BE ISSN 0772-4837) **1095**
Fiskoloog International. (BE ISSN 0771-7520) **1095**
Fission Chips. (CN) **1790**, 1805, 1955, 3458
Fit see Ujena Girl **5294**
Fit durch Tip. (GW) **1255**, 4264
Fitech see Fitech International **2033**
Fitech International. (UK ISSN 0307-2118) **2033**
Fitness. (SZ) **3801**
Fitness see Health and Fitness (London) **3802**
†Fitness & Diet. (US) **5193**
Fitness Bulletin. (CN) **3802**
Fitness Equipment Dealer. (US) **4472**
Fitness in America. (US) **4498**, 717
†Fitness in Business. (US ISSN 0887-817X) **5193**
Fitness Industry Magazine see Multi - Sport Facility News **5240**
Fitness Management. (US ISSN 0882-0481) **3802**, 1010
▼Fitness Plus. (US) **3802**
▼Fitness Swimmer. (US) **4472**, 3802
Fitologija. (BU ISSN 0324-0975) **502**
Fitopatologia. (PE ISSN 0430-6155) **552**, 502
Fitopatologia Brasileira. (BL ISSN 0100-4158) **177**, 552
Fitosociologia. (IT) **502**
Fitossanidade. (BL ISSN 0100-4204) **502**
Fitoterapia. (IT ISSN 0367-326X) **502**, 1218, 3726
†Fitzgerald - Hemingway Annual. (US ISSN 0071-5654) **5193**
FitzHardinge's Nobiliary. (AT ISSN 0157-8804) **2151**
Fitzhugh Directory of Independent Hospitals and Provident Associations.(UK) **3098**, 1135, 2461, 4405
Fiuggi. (IT ISSN 0391-769X) **2205**
Five Counties Farming Review see Three Counties Farming Review **124**
Five Fingers Review. (US ISSN 0898-0233) **2917**, 4435
Five Foot Three. (UK) **4709**
Five Leaves Left. (UK) **2917**
Five Minutes with A C H E. (US) **1683**
Five Owls. (US ISSN 0892-6735) **1237**, 1749, 4127
Five Year Comparison of Production Expenses for Selected Steam Electric Plants see U S Steam Electric Plants: Five Year Production Costs **1910**
▼Five Year Comparison of Utility Power Production and Electric O & M Expenses. (US) **1892**, 1790
Five-Year Economic Forecast. see Chuki Keizai Yosoku **851**
Five Year Forecasts. (AT) **866**, 782
Five Years Work in Librarianship see British Librarianship & Information Work **2749**
Fixed Base Operator see F B O **4673**
Fixed Income Investor see Creditweek **943**
Fizicheskaya Mekhanika. (RU) **3843**
Fizik Muhendisligi Dergisi. see Journal of Physics Engineering **3823**
Fizika. (CI ISSN 0015-3206) **3818**
Fizika Aerodispersnykh Sistem. (KR ISSN 0367-1631) **3435**
Fizika i Khimiya Obrabotki Materialov. (RU ISSN 0015-3214) **1929**
Fizika i Tekhnika Poluprovodnikov. (RU ISSN 0015-3222) **1892**
Fizika i Tekhnika Vysokikh Davlenii. (KR ISSN 0203-4654) **1929**
Fizika Metallov i Metallovedenie. (RU ISSN 0015-3230) **3406**
Fizika Mnogochastichnykh Sistem. (KR ISSN 0206-3638) **3818**
Fizika Nizhnei Atmosfery. (RU) **3435**
Fizika Nizkikh Temperatur/Low Temperature Physics. (KR ISSN 0132-6414) **3840**

Fizika Plazmy. (RU ISSN 0367-2921) **3818**
Fizika Tverdogo Tela. (RU ISSN 0015-3249) **3818**
Fizikai Szemle. (HU ISSN 0015-3257) **3818**
Fiziko-Khimicheska Mekhanika/Physico-Chemical Mechanics. (BU ISSN 0204-5958) **1226**, 3843
Fiziko-Khimicheskaya Mekhanika i Liofilnost' Dispersnykh Sistem. (KR ISSN 0367-2409) **1226**
Fiziko-Khimicheskaya Mekhanika Materialov. (KR ISSN 0430-6252) **1226**
Fiziko-Matematichesko Spisanie. (BU ISSN 0015-3265) **3818**, 3035
Fiziko-Tekhnicheskie Problemy Razrabotki Poleznykh Iskopaemykh. (RU ISSN 0015-3273) **3483**
Fiziologicheski Aktivnye Veshchestva. (KR ISSN 0533-1153) **571**
Fiziologicheskii Zhurnal (Kiev). (KR ISSN 0201-8489) **571**, 3098
Fiziologicheskii Zhurnal (Moscow). (RU ISSN 0015-329X) **571**, 3098
Fiziologiia na Rasteniiata. (BU ISSN 0324-0290) **2125**
Fiziologiya Cheloveka. (RU) **571**
Fiziologiya i Biokhimiya Kul'turnykh Rastenii/Physiology and Biochemistry of Cultivated Plants. (KR ISSN 0256-1425) **571**, 476
Fiziologiya Rastenii. (RU ISSN 0015-3303) **502**
Fizkul'tura i Sport. (RU ISSN 0015-332X) **4472**
Fizyka. (PL ISSN 0554-825X) **3818**
Fizyka w Szkole. (PL ISSN 0426-3383) **3818**
Fizz. (UK) **2292**
Fjaederfae. (SW ISSN 0015-3338) **216**
Fjarmalatidindi/Financial Times Icelandic. (IC ISSN 0015-3346) **782**
Fjell og Vidde. (NO) **4546**
Fjernvarmen. (DK ISSN 0106-6234) **2299**
Fjoerfe. (NO ISSN 0015-3354) **216**
Fjordhesten. (DK ISSN 0108-7738) **4534**
†Flabbergast. (CN ISSN 0832-6002) **5193**
Flacara. (RM ISSN 0015-3362) **2215**
Flag. see Flamuri **5193**
Flag & Touch Football Rulebook and Official's Manual. (US) **4503**
Flag Bulletin. (US ISSN 0015-3370) **2310**
Flagstaff Institute. Journal. (US ISSN 0146-1958) **908**, 1076
Flair (Dutch Edition). (BE) **4843**
Flair (French Edition). (BE) **4843**
Flame. (AT) **3686**, 1790
Flame and Flavour. (II ISSN 0046-4031) **4643**
▼Flame Retardancy News. (US ISSN 1058-0948) **4598**, 2033
Flame Retardancy of Polymeric Materials Proceedings (Year). (US) **2033**, 1177
Flamenco. (SP) **2054**, 2247
Flamme see De Kaarsvlam **359**
Flammes Vives. (FR ISSN 0015-3486) **2866**, 2993
†Flamuri/Flag. (IT) **5193**
Flannery O'Connor Awards for Short Fiction. (US) **2917**
Flannery O'Connor Bulletin. (US ISSN 0091-4924) **2917**
Flap Internacional. (BL ISSN 0046-404X) **52**, 4673
Flare. (IT) **299**
Flare. (CN ISSN 0708-4927) **1291**
Flash. (SP) **815**
Flash. (CY) **2184**
Flash. (UK) **2292**, 4178
Flash. (BE) **2583**, 979
†Flash (Chicago). (US ISSN 0882-1925) **5193**
Flash (Landover). (US) **1352**, 1297
†Flash (Seattle). (US ISSN 0015-3508) **5193**
Flash Actualite. (FR ISSN 0015-3516) **3894**
Flash Alternative. (FR) **3894**

Flash Art International see Flash Art Italia **326**
Flash Art Italia. (IT ISSN 0394-1493) **326**
Flash Etats-Unis. (FR ISSN 0985-2662) **489**
Flash-Infor. (BD) **3894**
Flash Information. (SZ) **815**
Flash-Informations. (FR ISSN 0223-4696) **3308**, 3337
Flash Japon. (FR ISSN 0985-2654) **489**
Flash Market News. (US) **4127**, 2917
Flashback. (US ISSN 0428-5573) **2406**
Flashes from the Trade Unions. (CS) **2583**
Flashpoint see On Target **3912**
Flat Earth News. (US ISSN 8756-0313) **2507**, 4178
Flat Glass International see Fabrication & Glazing Industries **1163**
†Flatiron. (US) **5193**
Flautist. (AT ISSN 0311-0559) **3551**
Flauto Dolce see Recercare **3576**
Flavour & Fragrance Journal. (UK ISSN 0882-5734) **1218**, 375, 2067
Flea Market. (US) **532**
Flea Market Trader. (US ISSN 0364-023X) **257**
Flea News. (US) **532**
De Fleanende Krie. (NE ISSN 0015-3540) **4127**
Flecha. see Arrow (Brooklyn) **3950**
Fleece see Scrapie **1324**
Fleece and Flock. (AT ISSN 0314-7312) **216**
Fleet Association Directory. (US) **1039**, 4690
Fleet Distribution see Truck Parts & Service **4749**
Fleet Equipment. (US ISSN 0747-2544) **4744**
Fleet Financials. (US) **1039**, 4690
Fleet List. (UK) **3686**
Fleet News. (UK) **4650**
Fleet Operators Handbook. (UK ISSN 0953-9085) **4690**
Fleet Owner. (US) **4744**
Fleet Owner: Big Fleet Edition see Fleet Owner **4744**
†Fleet Owner: Small Fleet Edition. (US ISSN 0162-1025) **5193**
Fleet Safety Newsletter. (US ISSN 0547-888X) **4650**
Fleet Street Letter. (UK ISSN 0300-4228) **946**
Fleet Street Patent Law Reports see Fleet Street Reports **3675**
Fleet Street Reports. (UK) **3675**
Fleetline. (AT ISSN 0312-4681) **4650**, 257
Fleet's Guide: Commercial Real Estate Financing Sourcebook. (US ISSN 0899-9147) **4149**
Fleisch. (GW ISSN 0015-3575) **2067**
Fleisch-Lebensmittel-Markt. (GW ISSN 0170-0499) **2067**
Fleisch-Magazin. (GW) **2067**
Fleisch- und Lebensmittelhygiene. (GW) **4809**
Fleisch und Lebensmittelkontrolle see Fleisch- und Lebensmittelhygiene **4809**
Die Fleischerei. (GW ISSN 0015-3613) **2067**
Die Fleischerei. (GW) **2067**
Fleischerei-Technik. (GW ISSN 0176-9502) **2067**
Fleischereibedarf see Die Fleischerei **2067**
†Fleischleistungspruefung fuer Rinder, Legeleistungspruefung fuer Huehner, Fleischleistungspruefung fuer Schafe. (GW) **5193**
Die Fleischwirtschaft. (GW ISSN 0015-363X) **2067**
Fleischwirtschaft Espanol. (GW) **2067**
Fleischwirtschaft International. (GW ISSN 0179-2415) **2067**
Flemish American Heritage. (US) **2002**, 2151
Flemish Veterinary Journal. see Vlaams Diergeneeskundig Tijdschrift **4819**
†Flensburger Statistische Blaetter. (GW) **5193**
Flensburger Zahlenspiegel (Year). (GW) **4571**

Fletcher Forum *see* Fletcher Forum of World Affairs **3957**
Fletcher Forum of World Affairs. (US ISSN 1046-1868) **3957, 2723**
Fleur de Lys. (UK ISSN 0015-3648) **2292, 1255, 1297**
Fleur Design. (CN ISSN 0827-150X) **2142**
Fleurist. *see* Der Florist **2142**
Fleuriste de France *see* Fleurs de France **2142**
Fleurop Magazin. (GW) **2142**
Fleurs de France. (FR ISSN 0339-8390) **2142**
▼Fleurs, Plantes et Jardins. (CN) **2125**
Flex Magazine. (US ISSN 8750-8915) **3802**
Flexible Automation *see* Flexible Automation Flexible Fertigung **1413**
†Flexible Automation. (US ISSN 0732-7471) **5193**
Flexible Automation Flexible Fertigung. (GW) **1413, 1822**
FlexLines. (US) **1460**
†FlexNotes. (US) **5193**
Flexo. (US ISSN 1051-7324) **3999**
Flexo Espanol. (US ISSN 1051-6352) **3999**
Flexo-Europe. (FR ISSN 0765-3204) **3648**
Flexographic Technical Association. Report of the Proceedings: Annual Meeting and Technical Forum *see* Foundation of Flexographic Technical Association. Report of the Proceedings: Annual Meeting and Technical Forum **3999**
Flickers 'n' Frames. (UK) **3510, 3011**
Flickertale Newsletter. (US) **2758**
Flicks. (UK) **3510**
Fliegen *see* Check-in **4757**
Fliegen und Sparen. (GW) **4763**
Fliegende Blaetter. (GW) **4763**
Fliegenfischen. (GW ISSN 0178-0409) **4546**
Der Fliegenfischer. (GW) **4546**
Der Flieger. (GW ISSN 0015-3680) **52**
Flieger-Revue. (GW ISSN 0001-9445) **52, 4472**
Fliegerkalender. (GW) **52**
Fliegerkurier *see* Luftwaffe **58**
Fliegermagazin. (GW ISSN 0170-5504) **52**
Flies of the Nearctic Region. (GW) **532**
Fliesen und Platten. (GW) **1865**
Flight. *see* Envol **563**
Flight. *see* Ptisi **4676**
Flight Comment/Propos de Vol. (CN ISSN 0015-3702) **52**
Flight Deck. (AT ISSN 0819-419X) **665**
Flight International. (UK ISSN 0015-3710) **52**
Flight International Directory Part 1 - United Kingdom (Year). (UK) **4673**
Flight International Directory Part 2 - Mainland Europe and Ireland (Year). (UK) **4673**
Flight Log *see* New Jersey Aviation **59**
Flight Reports. (US ISSN 0194-9039) **4763**
Flight Safety *see* New Zealand Flight Safety **59**
Flight Safety Bulletin. (UK ISSN 0015-3737) **52**
Flight Safety Digest. (US ISSN 0898-5715) **52**
Flight Safety Foundation. Annual Index. (US) **4673, 4101**
Flight Safety Foundation News. (US ISSN 0428-5735) **52**
Flight Safety Foundation Newsletter *see* Flight Safety Foundation News **52**
Flight Test News. (US) **52**
Flight Training. (US ISSN 1047-6415) **52**
Flightline. (UK ISSN 0266-0504) **52**
Flightline. (US) **4673, 52**
Flinders Asian Studies Lecture. (AT ISSN 0085-0586) **3637**
Flinders Asian Studies Monograph. (AT) **3637**
Flinders Institute for Atmospheric and Marine Sciences. Computing Reports.(AT) **3435, 1604**

Flinders Institute for Atmospheric and Marine Sciences. Cruise Reports. (AT) **1604**
Flinders Institute for Atmospheric and Marine Sciences. Research Reports. (AT) **3435, 1604**
Flinders Institute for Atmospheric and Marine Sciences. Technical Reports. (AT) **3435, 1604**
Flinders Journal. (AT) **1311**
Flinders Journal of History and Politics. (AT ISSN 0726-7215) **2344, 3894**
Flindersweek *see* Flinders Journal **1311**
Flintlock & Powderhorn. (US) **2151, 2406**
Flintshire Historical Society. Publications, Journal and Record Series. (UK ISSN 0140-8429) **2361, 272**
▼Flip. (US) **1374, 1255**
Flipping Flippins. (US ISSN 0893-5041) **2151**
Floating. (US) **3259**
Floating Island. (US ISSN 0147-1686) **2917**
Flock Book of Devon Cornwall Longwool Sheep. (UK) **216**
Flock Book of Oxford Down Sheep. (UK) **216**
Floh. (GW) **1255**
Flohkiste. (GW) **1255**
Flood Control Journal *see* Water Resources Journal **4833**
Flood Report. (US) **1597, 1923, 2532**
Floodlight. (UK ISSN 0956-3709) **1694**
Floodtide. (US) **4178**
Floor and Flooring *see* Floors **2551**
†Floor Covering Business. (US ISSN 1041-2433) **5193**
Floor Covering News. (CN ISSN 0319-616X) **2551**
Floor Covering News. (US) **2551**
Floor Covering Weekly. (US ISSN 0015-3761) **2558**
Floor Covering Weekly Market Guide Series. (US) **2558**
Floor Coverings International. (US) **2558**
Flooring. (US ISSN 0162-881X) **2558**
Flooring Market Shopper. (US) **2551, 665**
Floors. (UK ISSN 0263-7693) **2551, 299**
Flor-Ala. (US) **1311**
Flora. (EC ISSN 0015-380X) **502**
Flora. (GW ISSN 0367-2530) **502**
Flora. (GW) **2125**
Flora *see* Flora International **2142**
Flora de Colombia. (CK ISSN 0120-4351) **502**
Flora Ecologica de Restingas do Sudeste do Brasil. (BL ISSN 0071-5751) **502**
Flora et Vegetatio Mundi. (GW ISSN 0071-576X) **502**
Flora International. (UK) **2142**
Flora-Line. (US ISSN 1062-855X) **2125, 2436**
Flora Malesiana. Series 1: Spermatophyta. (NE) **502**
Flora Malesiana. Series 2: Pteridophyta.(NE ISSN 0071-5786) **502**
Flora Malesiana Bulletin. (NE ISSN 0071-5778) **503**
Flora Neotropica. (US ISSN 0071-5794) **503**
Flora of Ecuador. (DK) **503**
Flora of Southern Africa. (SA) **503**
Flora of the U.S.S.R. (IS) **503**
Flora og Fauna. (DK ISSN 0015-3818) **4309**
Flora Polska: Rosliny Zarodnikowe Polski i Ziem Osciennych. (PL ISSN 0071-5824) **503**
Flora Slodkowodna Polski. (PL ISSN 0071-5840) **503**
▼FloraCulture International. (US ISSN 1051-9076) **2125**
Florae Poloniciae Teraruniqe Adiacentium Sconographia. *see* Atlas Flory Polskiej i Ziem Osciennych **495**

Florafacts. (US ISSN 0046-4082) **2142**
Floral and Nursery Times. (US) **2142**
Floral Marketing Association Directory and Buyer's Guide. (US) **2142**
Floral Marketing Directory and Buyer's Guide *see* Floral Marketing Association Directory and Buyer's Guide **2142**
Floral Mass Marketing. (US) **2142**
Floral Underawl & Gazette Times. (US ISSN 0149-7499) **2436, 4472**
Flore d'Afrique Centrale (Zaire - Rwanda - Burundi). (BE) **503**
Flore de la Nouvelle Caledonie et Dependances. (FR ISSN 0430-666X) **503**
Flore de Madagascar et des Comores. (FR) **503**
Flore du Cambodge, du Laos et du Vietnam. (FR ISSN 0071-5867) **503**
Flore du Cameroun. (CM ISSN 0071-5875) **503**
Flore du Congo, du Rwanda et du Burundi *see* Flore d'Afrique Centrale (Zaire - Rwanda - Burundi) **503**
Flore du Gabon. (FR ISSN 0071-5883) **503**
Florence (Year). (US) **4763**
Florence Journal of Surgery. *see* Firenze Chirurgica **5193**
Floresta. (BL ISSN 0015-3826) **2099**
Floricoltura Pesciatina. (IT ISSN 0015-3834) **2142**
Florida. Bureau of Geology. Geological Bulletins. (US ISSN 0085-0608) **1560**
Florida. Bureau of Geology. Information Circulars. (US ISSN 0085-0616) **1560**
Florida. Bureau of Geology. Map Series. (US ISSN 0085-0624) **1560**
Florida. Bureau of Geology. Report of Investigations. (US ISSN 0096-0489) **1560**
Florida. Bureau of Geology. Special Publications. (US ISSN 0085-0640) **1561**
Florida. Department of Agriculture and Consumer Services. Division of Plant Industry. Bulletin Series. (US ISSN 0428-6294) **503**
Florida. Department of Agriculture and Consumer Services. Entomology Circular. (US ISSN 0013-8932) **532**
Florida. Department of Agriculture and Consumer Services. Nematology Circular. (US ISSN 0360-7550) **439**
Florida. Department of Agriculture and Consumer Services. Plant Pathology Circular. (US ISSN 0032-0870) **503**
Florida. Department of Agriculture. Division of Plant Industry. News Bulletin *see* Plant Industry News **114**
Florida. Department of Banking & Finance. Annual Local Government Financial Report. (US ISSN 0094-8551) **1095**
Florida. Department of Corrections. Annual Report. (US) **4405**
Florida. Department of Education. Florida Statewide Assessment Program: State, District and Regional Report of Statewide Assessment Results. (US) **1676**
Florida. Department of Education. Professional Practices Council. Report. (US) **1634**
Florida. Department of Health and Rehabilitative Services. Annual Statistical Report. (US) **4425**
Florida. Department of Health and Rehabilitative Services. Quarterly Vital Statistics Report *see* Florida. Department of Health and Rehabilitative Services. Vital News and Quarterly Vital Statistics Report **3992**
Florida. Department of Health and Rehabilitative Services. Vital News and Quarterly Vital Statistics Report. (US) **3992**

Florida. Division of Family Services. Annual Statistical Report *see* Florida. Department of Health and Rehabilitative Services. Annual Statistical Report **4425**
Florida. Division of Motor Vehicles. Tags and Revenue. (US ISSN 0092-0177) **4650**
Florida. Division of Plant Industry. Biennial Report. (US ISSN 0071-5948) **92, 503**
Florida. Legislature. Joint Legislative Management Committee. Summary of General Legislation. (US ISSN 0090-1520) **2626**
†Florida. Mental Health Program Office. Statistical Report of Hospitals. (US ISSN 0094-2294) **5193**
Florida. State Board of Independent Colleges and Universities. Report. (US ISSN 0093-1071) **1706, 1694**
Florida Administrative Law Reports. (US ISSN 0194-4800) **2626**
Florida Administrative Practice. (US) **2626, 4060**
Florida Administrative Weekly. (US ISSN 0098-874X) **2626**
Florida Agricultural Research. (US) **92**
Florida and the Other Forty-Nine. (US) **717, 815**
Florida Anthropological Society Publications *see* Florida Anthropologist **239**
Florida Anthropologist. (US ISSN 0015-3893) **239, 272**
Florida Appellate Practice. (US) **2626**
Florida Avocado Administrative Committee. Annual Report. (US) **177**
Florida Avocado Administrative Committee. Meeting Minutes. (US) **177**
Florida Avocado Administrative Committee. Shipments Report. (US) **137**
Florida Banker. (US) **782**
Florida Banking. (US) **782**
†Florida Bar Case Summary Service. (US ISSN 0164-6427) **5193**
Florida Bar Journal. (US ISSN 0015-3915) **2626**
Florida Bar News. (US ISSN 0360-0114) **2626**
Florida Builder Magazine. (US ISSN 0015-3923) **618**
Florida Builders and Contractors Directory. (US ISSN 0276-8208) **1135, 618**
Florida Business - Southwest. (US) **866**
Florida Cancer News *see* LivingRight **3199**
Florida - Caribbean Edition *see* Dive Boat Calendar & Travel Guide: International Edition **4524**
Florida Cattleman and Livestock Journal. (US ISSN 0015-3958) **216**
Florida Civil Discovery Manual. (US) **2702**
▼Florida Civil Procedure. (US) **2702**
Florida Commercial Landlord - Tenant Law. (US) **2626, 4149**
Florida Communication Journal. (US) **1336, 1750**
Florida Community-County Comparison *see* Florida County Profiles **815**
Florida Comptroller. Condensed Comparative Statement of Assets and Liabilities of State-Chartered Commercial Banks and Trust Companies. (US) **782**
Florida Condominium Law Manual. (US) **2626, 4149**
Florida Construction Industry *see* Florida Constructor **618**
Florida Construction Law Manual, 2-E. (US) **2626, 618**
Florida Constructor. (US) **618**
Florida Consumer Law Manual. (US) **2626, 1504**
Florida Contractor. (US ISSN 0046-4112) **2299**
Florida Corporations Manual. (US) **2709**
Florida County Comparisons. (US) **717, 815**
Florida County Profiles. (US) **815**

Florida Creative Directory. (US) **3999**, 326
Florida Creditors' Rights Manual. (US) **2709**
Florida Criminal Defense Trial Manual. (US) **2713**
Florida Criminal Discovery & Pretrial Motions. (US) **2713**
Florida Criminal Procedure Service. (US) **2713**
Florida Criminal Sentencing Law. (US) **2713**
Florida Dental Association Today's F D A see Today's F D A **3243**
†Florida Economy. (US) **5193**
Florida Education Directory. (US) **1694**
Florida Educational Research and Development Council. Research Bulletin see Florida Educational Research Council. Research Bulletin **1634**
Florida Educational Research Council. Research Bulletin. (US) **1634**
Florida Electric Cooperative News see Florida Rural Electric News **1892**
Florida Employment Law Letter. (US ISSN 1041-3537) **2627**, 979
Florida Engineering Society. Journal. (US ISSN 0015-4032) **1822**
Florida Entomologist. (US ISSN 0015-4040) **532**
▼Florida Environmental & Land Use Letter. (US ISSN 1047-4641) **2627**, 1955
Florida Environmental and Urban Issues see Environmental and Urban Issues **1950**
Florida Evidence Manual. (US) **2627**
Florida Facts. (US ISSN 0895-8084) **1781**
Florida Family Law Practice. (US) **2717**
Florida Family Physician. (US ISSN 0015-4067) **3098**
Florida Festival Arts Directory see Florida Folklife Resource Directory **2054**
Florida Field Naturalist. (US ISSN 0738-999X) **564**
Florida Fireman. (US) **2033**
Florida Fish and Wildlife News. (US) **1488**
Florida Flambeau. (US) **2569**
Florida Foliage. (US) **2126**
Florida Folklife Resource Directory. (US) **2054**, 326, 3551
Florida Food & Beverage News. (US) **381**
Florida Food and Resource Economics. (US) **2067**
Florida Food Dealer. (US) **2091**, 2067
Florida Forecasts. (US) **665**
Florida Forum. (US ISSN 0191-4618) **618**, 2299
Florida Friends of Bluegrass Society. Newsletter. (US ISSN 0160-5119) **3551**
Florida Funeral Director. (US ISSN 0273-9747) **2119**
Florida Game & Fish. (US ISSN 0889-3322) **4546**
Florida Genealogical Society Journal. (US ISSN 0374-6240) **2151**
Florida Genealogist. (US ISSN 0161-4932) **2151**, 2406
Florida Geographer. (US ISSN 0739-0041) **2247**
Florida Golf. (US) **4503**
Florida Golf Reporter. (US) **4503**
Florida Golfer. (US) **4503**
Florida Grocer. (US ISSN 0191-586X) **2091**
Florida Grower and Rancher. (US ISSN 0015-4091) **92**
Florida Gulf Coast Homebuyer's Guide. (US) **4149**, 2487
Florida Historical Quarterly. (US ISSN 0015-4113) **2406**
Florida Home & Garden. (US ISSN 0898-9494) **2551**, 2126
†Florida Homefurnishings. (US ISSN 0274-8983) **5193**
Florida Hotel & Motel Journal. (US ISSN 8750-6807) **2474**
Florida Independent Accountant. (US) **751**
Florida Insight. (US) **4060**

Florida International Law Journal. (US ISSN 0882-6420) **2723**
Florida International University. Latin American and Caribbean Center. Occasional Papers Series. (US) **2406**
Florida Investor see Sound Money Investor **963**
Florida Journal of Anthropology. (US ISSN 0164-1662) **239**
†Florida Juvenile Procedure. (US) **2717**
†Florida Keys Magazine. (US ISSN 0271-6100) **5193**
Florida Land Use Restrictions. (US) **2627**, 1488
Florida Landscape Architecture. (US) **299**
Florida Law of Secured Transactions in Personal Property. (US) **2627**
Florida Law Review. (US) **2627**
Florida Law Weekly. (US ISSN 0274-8533) **2627**
Florida Leader. (US ISSN 0898-4387) **1311**, 1634
Florida Legal Research & Source Book. (US) **2627**
Florida Libertarian see Common Sense **3880**
Florida Lime Administrative Committee. Annual Report. (US) **177**
Florida Lime Administrative Committee. Meeting Minutes. (US) **177**
Florida Lime Administrative Committee. Shipments Report. (US) **137**
Florida Living. (US ISSN 0888-9600) **2225**
†Florida Lodging Industry. (US) **5193**
Florida Manufactured Home Living see Florida Retirement Living **2272**
Florida Manufacturers Register. (US ISSN 0882-9438) **1135**
Florida Marine Research Publications. (US ISSN 0095-0157) **439**
Florida Market Bulletin. (US) **92**
Florida Market Update. (US ISSN 0886-2729) **835**
Florida Mechanics Lein Manual. (US) **2627**
Florida Medical Association. Journal. (US ISSN 0015-4148) **3098**
Florida Medical Association Today (Jacksonville) see F M A Today (Jacksonville) **3097**
Florida Mortgage Broker. (US) **782**, 4149
Florida Motor Vehicle Liability Law. (US) **2627**, 4690
Florida Municipal Record see Quality Cities **4093**
Florida Museum Natural History. Bulletin. Biological Sciences. (US) **439**, 2310
Florida Music Director. (US ISSN 0046-4155) **3551**, 1634
Florida Naturalist. (US ISSN 0015-4172) **1488**, 582
Florida Negligence Law Manual. (US) **2627**
Florida Notary Law Primer. (US) **2627**
Florida Nurse. (US ISSN 0015-4199) **3278**
Florida Nurseryman. (US) **2126**
Florida Nursing News. (US) **3278**
Florida Outlook. (US) **866**
Florida P T A Bulletin. (US) **1727**
Florida Paralegal Series: Wills, Trusts, Estates. (US) **2627**
Florida Parishes Genealogical Newsletter. (US ISSN 8756-2316) **2151**
Florida Pharmacy Journal see Florida Pharmacy Today **3726**
Florida Pharmacy Today. (US) **3726**
Florida Photo News. (US) **3790**
Florida Planning and Development see Environmental and Urban Issues **1950**
Florida Plumbing and Heating Contractor see Florida Contractor **2299**
Florida Practice and Procedure. (US) **2627**
▼Florida Premises Liability. (US) **2627**, 4149
Florida Probate Code Manual. (US) **2627**
Florida Psychologist. (US) **4021**, 4435

Florida Public Documents. (US ISSN 0430-7801) **4060**
Florida Reading Quarterly. (US ISSN 0015-4261) **1634**
Florida Real Estate. (US) **4149**
Florida Real Estate and Development Update. (US ISSN 0887-3208) **4149**
▼Florida Real Estate Closings. (US) **2627**, 4149
Florida Real Estate Contracts. (US) **4149**, 2627
Florida Real Estate Transactions. (US) **4149**, 2627
Florida Realtor. (US ISSN 0199-5839) **4149**
Florida Reel. (US) **3511**, 1385
Florida Requirements for Teacher Certification. (US ISSN 0071-5999) **1706**
Florida Residential Landlord - Tenant Law Manual. (US) **2627**, 4149
Florida Restaurateur. (US) **2067**
Florida Retirement Living. (US ISSN 0160-5739) **2272**
Florida Review. (US ISSN 0742-2466) **2866**
Florida Rules of Court Service. (US) **2627**
Florida Rural Electric News. (US) **1892**
Florida School Herald. (US ISSN 0015-4288) **2287**, 1634, 2292
Florida Scientist. (US ISSN 0098-4590) **4309**
Florida Securities Law. (US) **2709**, 946
Florida Senate. (US ISSN 0093-4089) **2627**
Florida Senior News. (US) **2272**
Florida Shipper. (US ISSN 0884-8548) **4727**
Florida Singles Magazine and Date Book. (US) **4362**
Florida Specifier. (US ISSN 0740-1973) **1822**
Florida Speech Communication Journal see Florida Communication Journal **1336**
Florida Speleological Society. Special Papers. (US ISSN 0071-6006) **1561**
Florida Speleologist. (US) **1561**
Florida Sportsman. (US ISSN 0015-3885) **4546**
Florida State & Local Taxation. (US) **1095**
Florida State Collection of Arthropods. Occasional Papers. (US ISSN 0885-5943) **532**
Florida State Documents see Florida Public Documents **4060**
Florida State Museum. Bulletin. Biological Sciences see Florida Museum Natural History. Bulletin. Biological Sciences **439**
Florida State Poetry Society. Selected Poems. (US) **2993**
Florida State University. Center for Yugoslav-American Studies, Research, and Exchanges. Proceedings and Reports of Seminars and Research. (US) **2361**, 4372
Florida State University. Instructional Support Center. Film see Florida State University. Instructional Support Center. Film and Video **3520**
Florida State University. Instructional Support Center. Film and Video. (US) **3520**, 1348, 1385
Florida State University. Publications of the Faculty. (US ISSN 0428-6766) **1706**
Florida State University. Publications of the Faculty and Theses Directed see Florida State University. Publications of the Faculty **1706**
Florida State University. School of Library and Information Studies. Alumni Newsletter. (US) **2758**
Florida State University Bulletin: Research in Review see Florida State University Research in Review **4309**
Florida State University Law Review. (US ISSN 0096-3070) **2627**
Florida State University Research in Review. (US) **4309**
Florida Statistical Abstract. (US ISSN 0071-6022) **4571**

FLUESSIGES OBST 6189

Florida Statistical Abstracts Annual see Florida Statistical Abstract **4571**
Florida Summary Claims Handbook. (US) **2627**
Florida Sun Review. (US) **2225**
Florida Technology Review. (US ISSN 1043-6030) **4598**
Florida Thoroughbred. (US) **4534**
Florida TourBook see Tourbook: Florida **4790**
Florida Traffic & D U I Practice. (US) **4718**, 2627
Florida Trend. (US ISSN 0015-4326) **866**
Florida Triangle News. (US) **1311**
Florida Truck News. (US ISSN 0015-4334) **4744**
Florida Trucker see Fastline for Florida Truckers **4744**
Florida Underwriter. (US) **2532**
Florida Vital Statistics. (US) **3992**, 4571
Florida Vocational Journal. (US ISSN 0145-9376) **3627**, 1736
Florida Water Resources Journal. (US ISSN 0896-1794) **4824**
Florida Wildlife. (US ISSN 0015-4369) **1488**, 4546
Florida Wood-Using Industry Directory. (US) **2099**
Florida Woods & Waters Magazine. (US) **4546**
Florida Workers' Compensation Manual. (US) **979**, 2627
▼Florida World Magazine. (US) **4763**
Florida Zoning Law Manual. (US) **2627**
Floridagriculture. (US ISSN 0015-3869) **92**
Florida's Indian River Update. (US) **2225**
Florida's Visitors. (US) **4763**
Florilegium. (CN ISSN 0709-5201) **1276**, 2917
Florist. (GW ISSN 0015-4393) **2142**
Florist. (US ISSN 0015-4385) **2142**
Der Florist/Fleurist. (SZ) **2142**
Florist and Nursery Exchange see Seed World **192**
Florist Trade Magazine. (UK ISSN 0015-4415) **2142**
Floristische Rundbriefe. (GW) **503**
Florists' News. (UK) **2142**
Florists' Review. (US ISSN 0015-4423) **2142**
Florists' Transworld Delivery Association Family see F T D Family **2142**
Flotation Sleep Industry see Aqua: The Business Magazine for the Spa and Pool Industry **3799**
Flottans Maen. (SW ISSN 0015-4431) **3458**
Flour Milling and Baking Research Association. Annual Report and Accounts. (UK ISSN 0071-6243) **2067**
Flour Milling and Baking Research Association Abstracts. (UK ISSN 0430-7941) **2085**, 12, 137
†Flow Lines. (US) **5193**
Flow Measurement and Instrumentation.(UK ISSN 0955-5986) **2522**, 3446
Flow of Funds Account. (US) **866**
Flow of Funds in Taiwan District, Republic of China. (CH) **782**
▼Flower. (US) **2917**
Flower and Garden. (US ISSN 0162-3249) **2126**
Flower Arranger. (UK ISSN 0046-421X) **355**, 2126, 2436
Flower News. (US ISSN 0015-4490) **2142**
Flower of the Forest Black Genealogical Journal. (US) **2151**, 2002
Flower Shop. (CN) **2142**
Flower Trades Journal. (UK) **2142**
The Flowering Plants of Africa. (SA ISSN 0015-4504) **503**
Flowering Plants of South Africa see The Flowering Plants of Africa **503**
Flowers, Trees & Potted Landscapes. see Huamu Penjing **2131**
Flowers&. (US) **2142**
Flue Cured Tobacco Farmer. (US ISSN 0015-4512) **4643**
Fluechtlings Anzeiger see Mitteldeutscher Kurier **4443**
Fluechtlings Forum. (GW) **3982**
Fluessiges Obst. (GW) **381**

Fluessiggas. (GW ISSN 0721-5894) 1790, 3686
Flug-Informationen. (AU) 52
Flug Revue. (GW ISSN 0015-4547) 52
Flug- und Modell-Technik see F M T 2436
Flugasche. (GW ISSN 0724-1194) 2917
▼Flugbegleiter. (GW) 4673
Flugblatt. (GW) 4673
Flughafen Nachrichten Duesseldorf. (GW) 4673
Der Flugleiter. (GW ISSN 0015-4563) 4673, 4718
Flugplan Koeln-Bonn. (GW) 4673
Flugsicherheitsmitteilungen (FSM). (GW) 52
Flugsport-Informationen see Flug-Informationen 52
Flugurlaub see Aero Lloyd 4669
Flugzeug. (GW) 52, 2436
Fluid. (GW) 1923, 1929
▼Fluid Abstracts: Civil Engineering. (UK ISSN 0962-7170) 1844, 12
▼Fluid Abstracts: Process Engineering. (UK ISSN 0962-7162) 1844, 12
Fluid: Apparecchiature Idrauliche e Pneumatiche. (IT ISSN 0374-3225) 1923, 1929
Fluid Dynamics. (English translation of: Izvestiya Akademii Nauk SSSR. Mekhanika Zhidkosti i Gaza) (US ISSN 0015-4628) 3843
Fluid Dynamics Research. (NE ISSN 0169-5983) 1923, 1929
Fluid Dynamics Transactions. (PL ISSN 0137-6462) 3843
Fluid Flow Measurement Abstracts. (UK ISSN 0305-9235) 1844, 12
Fluid Mechanics of Astrophysics and Geophysics. (US ISSN 0260-4353) 3843
Fluid Mechanics - Soviet Research. (US ISSN 0096-0764) 1929
Fluid Phase Equilibria. (NE ISSN 0378-3812) 1226
Fluid Power Abstracts. (UK ISSN 0015-4644) 1844, 12
Fluid Power and Control Series. (US) 1923
Fluid Power Distributors Association News see F P D A News 1929
Fluid Power Handbook & Directory. (US ISSN 0428-7738) 1917, 1135
▼Fluid Power Service Center. (US) 3017
Fluid Power Society Newsletter see F P S Newsletter 1923
Fluid Power Standards. (US) 1929
Fluid Power Symposium. Proceedings. (UK ISSN 0140-2099) 1923
Fluid Sealing Abstracts. (UK ISSN 0015-4660) 1844, 12, 4614
Fluidics Quarterly see Journal of Fluid Control 1933
Fluidos. (SP ISSN 0211-1136) 1923, 1929
Fluids Handling see Fluids Handling Technology 3843
Fluids Handling Technology. (UK) 3843
Fluidtechnik see Fluid 1923
Fluoridation Census. (US) 3233
Fluoride. (US ISSN 0015-4725) 3174, 3233
Flur und Furche. (GW ISSN 0015-4733) 177
Flushing Whip. (US) 3710
Flute. (CN) 1514
Flute Talk. (US) 3551
Flutist Quarterly. (US ISSN 8756-8667) 3551
Fly Fisherman. (US ISSN 0015-4741) 4546
Fly Fishing Made Easy. (US) 4546
Fly-Nytt. (NO ISSN 0332-6934) 52
Fly Rod & Reel. (US) 4546
Flydoscope. (LU) 4802
Flyer International. (PK ISSN 0046-4236) 4673, 4763
Flyfisher. (US) 4546
Flyfishers Journal. (UK ISSN 0046-4228) 4546
Flyfishing. (US) 4546
Flyghorisont. (SW ISSN 0015-475X) 52
Flygposten. (SW ISSN 0015-4776) 4673

Flygrevyn. (SW ISSN 0015-4784) 52
Flygtekniska Foersoeksanstalten. Meddelande - Report. (SW ISSN 0081-5640) 52
Flygtningne Nyt. (DK ISSN 0900-2537) 4405
FlygvapenNytt. (SW ISSN 0015-4792) 52
Flying. (US ISSN 0015-4806) 53
Flying Angel. (UK ISSN 0015-4822) 4238
Flying Apsaras. see Fei Tian 2917
Flying Doctor Yearbook. (AT) 2461, 4673
Flying Dutchman Directions. (NE) 4802
Flying Dutchman International see Flying Dutchman Directions 4802
Flying Lady. (US ISSN 0015-4830) 4690
Flying M. (UK ISSN 0262-8201) 53, 3458
Flying Models. (US ISSN 0015-4849) 2436
Flying Needle. (US ISSN 0270-2959) 3591
Flying Physician. (US ISSN 0015-4857) 3098
Flying Review Magazine. (US) 53
Flying Safety. (US ISSN 0279-9308) 53, 3458, 4101
Flying Saucer Digest. (US) 53
Flying Saucer Review. (UK ISSN 0015-4881) 53
Flying Springbok/Vlieende Springbok. (SA) 4802
Flying Times. (US) 4673, 2225
Flypaper. (CN ISSN 0317-2481) 4547
Flypast. (UK ISSN 0262-6950) 53
†Flytninger. (DK) 5193
Flyv. (DK ISSN 0015-492X) 53
Foaia Noastra. (HU) 2198
Foc Nou. (SP) 4178, 2002
Focal Point. (US) 3292, 3320, 4843
†Focal Points. (US ISSN 0278-1808) 5193
†Foci. (HU ISSN 0238-4000) 5193
Focus. (AT ISSN 1032-9315) 618
Focus. (GH ISSN 0046-4260) 1311
Focus. (IS) 1706
Focus. (JA) 2207
Focus. (II) 2627
Focus. (SL) 2866
Focus see Left 2871
Focus. (GW ISSN 0721-1600) 3300
Focus. (CN) 3446
Focus. (CE) 4372
Focus (Alexandria). (US) 4021
Focus (Austin). (US) 2532
Focus (Columbus, 1967) see Focus Quarterly 5194
Focus (Dublin). (IE ISSN 0790-4940) 3790
Focus (Grantham). (UK ISSN 0143-7925) 4238
Focus (Indianapolis). (US) 4547
Focus (Kent). (UK) 3011, 2917
Focus (London) see Focus on Political Repression in Southern Africa 3942
Focus (London, 1982). (UK) 3894
Focus (Madison). (US ISSN 0195-5705) 4405
Focus (Moscow). (US) 1488, 2099
Focus (New York, 1950). (US ISSN 0015-5004) 2248
Focus (New York, 1978). (US) 3098
Focus (Overland Park). (US) 2091
Focus (Philadelphia). (US) 665
Focus (Princeton). (US) 1706
Focus (Regina). (CN) 2758
Focus (San Francisco). (US ISSN 1047-0719) 3219
Focus (Stoke-on-Trent). (UK) 815
Focus (Tallahassee). (US) 1634
Focus (Toronto). (CN) 2758
Focus (Warwickshire). (UK) 4178
Focus (Washington, 1970). (US ISSN 0740-0195) 3942, 2002
Focus (Washington, 1977). (US) 1488
Focus (Washington, 1978). (US) 4405, 2287, 2292
Focus (Washington, 1983). (US) 1039
Focus: An Economic Profile of the Apparel Industry. (US) 1285, 835
Focus: Biology see Annual Editions: Biology 428

†Focus - Education Professionals in Family Recovery. (US) 5193
Focus Japan. (JA ISSN 0388-0311) 908
Focus: Library Service to Older Adults, People with Disabilities. (US ISSN 0740-4956) 2758, 2272, 2287, 2292
Focus M U L. (Medizinischen Universitaet zu Luebeck) (GW) 3098
Focus Magazine (Detroit). (US) 1750
Focus Magazine (Hartford). (US ISSN 8750-5622) 2002
Focus - Metropolitan Philadelphia's Business Newsmagazine. (US ISSN 0193-502X) 665
Focus - Midwest see St. Louis Journalism Review 2575
†Focus On... (US) 5193
Focus on A I X see Auto C A D World 1426
†Focus on Asian Studies. (US ISSN 0046-4295) 5193
†Focus on Basics. (US ISSN 0899-188X) 5193
Focus on Business Education. (UK) 1750
Focus on Canadian Municipal Assessment and Taxation. (CN ISSN 0833-0123) 1095
Focus on Christian - Muslim Relations. (UK ISSN 0950-9720) 4178
†Focus on Critical Care. (US ISSN 0736-3605) 5193
Focus on Dance. (US ISSN 0071-6294) 1530
Focus on Exceptional Children. (US ISSN 0015-511X) 1736, 1237
Focus on Family and Chemical Dependence see Focus - Education Professionals in Family Recovery 5193
Focus on Festivals. (CN) 4763
Focus on Geriatrics and Rehabilitation. (US ISSN 0892-7103) 2272
Focus on Holland. (NE) 908
Focus on Indiana Libraries. (US ISSN 0015-5152) 2758
Focus on Industry and Commerce see Focus (Stoke-on-Trent) 815
Focus on International and Comparative Librarianship. (UK ISSN 0305-8468) 2758
Focus on International Joint Commission Activities. (CN ISSN 0832-6673) 4824, 1955
Focus on Law Studies. (US) 2627, 1706
Focus on Learning Problems in Mathematics. (US ISSN 0272-8893) 3035, 1736
Focus on Nature Conservation. (UK ISSN 0264-8474) 1488
Focus on Ohio Dentistry. (US) 3233
Focus on Pakistan. (PK) 4763
Focus on Panama. (PN) 4763
†Focus on Photography. (AT) 5193
Focus on Physical Distribution and Logistics Management. (UK ISSN 0952-2190) 4707
†Focus on Plants. (US) 5193
Focus on Political Repression in Southern Africa. (SA ISSN 0308-3586) 3942
Focus on Politics. (SA) 2310, 3894
Focus on Poverty Research see Focus (Madison) 4405
Focus on Rhodesia see Spotlight on Zimbabwe 2240
Focus on Robert Graves see Focus on Robert Graves and His Contemporaries 2917
Focus on Robert Graves and His Contemporaries. (US) 2917
Focus on Saskatchewan Libraries see Focus (Regina) 2758
†Focus on Sci-Tech. (US) 5194
Focus on Technology. (US) 4598, 1736, 2292
†Focus on the Americas. (US) 5194
Focus: on the Center for Research Libraries. (US ISSN 0275-4924) 2758
Focus on the Family. (US ISSN 0894-3346) 4178
Focus on the Garment Industry. (TR) 1285
Focus on Water. (US) 4824

Focus on Winnipeg Schools see Our Schools 1653
Focus on Women. (CN) 4843
†Focus paa Undervisning. (DK ISSN 0108-7746) 5194
†Focus Quarterly. (US ISSN 0744-1177) 5194
Focus: Social and Preventive Medicine. (CN ISSN 0015-5195) 4101
Focus Soviet Jewry. (IS) 3942, 4222
Focus: Teaching English Language Arts. (US ISSN 0163-5425) 1750, 2814
Focus: the Magazine of the North American Data General Users Group.(US) 1444
Focuses. (US ISSN 1040-3205) 1750, 2917
†Fodboldens Aarsrevy. (DK ISSN 0108-5077) 5194
Fodor's Acapulco, Ixtapa, Zihuatanijo. (US) 4763
Fodor's Affordable Europe. (US) 4763
Fodor's Affordable France. (US) 4763
Fodor's Affordable Germany. (US) 4763
Fodor's Affordable Great Britain. (US) 4763
Fodor's Affordable Italy. (US) 4763
Fodor's Alaska. (US ISSN 0271-2776) 4763
†Fodor's Amsterdam. (US) 5194
Fodor's Arizona. (US) 4763
Fodor's Atlantic City and the New Jersey Shore see Fodor's Vacations on the New Jersey Shore 4767
Fodor's Australia and New Zealand. (US) 4763
Fodor's Australia, New Zealand and the South Pacific see Fodor's Australia and New Zealand 4763
Fodor's Austria. (US ISSN 0071-6340) 4763
Fodor's Bahamas. (US) 4763
Fodor's Baja and Mexico's Pacific Coast Resorts. (US) 4763
Fodor's Barbados. (US) 4763
†Fodor's Bed & Breakfast Guide. (US) 5194
Fodor's Bed and Breakfasts and Country Inns and Other Weekend Pleasures: New England. (US) 4763
Fodor's Bed and Breakfasts and Country Inns and Other Weekend Pleasures: The Mid-Atlantic Region. (US) 4763
Fodor's Bed and Breakfasts and Country Inns and Other Weekend Pleasures: The South. (US) 4763
Fodor's Bed and Breakfasts and Country Inns and Other Weekend Pleasures: the West Coast. (US) 4764
Fodor's Beijing, Guangzhou and Shanghai see Fodor's China's Great Cities 4764
Fodor's Belgium and Luxembourg. (US ISSN 0071-6359) 4764
Fodor's Berlin. (US) 4764
Fodor's Bermuda. (US) 4764
Fodor's Boston. (US) 4764
Fodor's Brazil. (US ISSN 0163-0628) 4764
Fodor's Budapest. (US) 4764
Fodor's Budget Europe see Fodor's Affordable Europe 4763
Fodor's California. (US ISSN 0192-9925) 4764
Fodor's Canada. (US ISSN 0160-3906) 4764
Fodor's Canada's Great Country Inns by Anita Stewart. (US) 4764
Fodor's Canada's Maritime Provinces see Fodor's Nova Scotia, Prince Edward Island and New Brunswick 4766
Fodor's Cancun, Cozumel & the Yucatan Peninsula. (US) 4764
Fodor's Cancun, Cozumel, Merida and the Yucatan see Fodor's Cancun, Cozumel & the Yucatan Peninsula 4764
Fodor's Cape Cod. (US) 4764
Fodor's Caribbean. (US) 4764
Fodor's Carolinas & the Georgia Coast. (US) 4764
Fodor's Central America. (US ISSN 0270-8183) 4764
Fodor's Chesapeake see Fodor's Chesapeake Region 4766
Fodor's Chicago. (US) 4764

Fodor's China. (US) **4764**
Fodor's China's Great Cities. (US) **4764**
†Fodor's Colorado. (US ISSN 0276-9018) **5194**
Fodor's Commonwealth of Independent States and the Baltic Countries. (US) **4764**
Fodor's Cottages, Bed and Breakfasts and Country Inns of England and Wales by Elizabeth Gundry. (US) **4764**
Fodor's Cruises and Ports of Call. (US) **4764**
Fodor's Czechoslovakia. (US ISSN 0071-6367) **4764**
†Fodor's Dallas - Fort Worth. (US) **5194**
Fodor's Disney World & the Orlando Area. (US) **4764**
Fodor's Eastern Europe. (US) **4764**
Fodor's Egypt. (US ISSN 0147-8176) **4764**
Fodor's Euro Disney. (US) **4764**
Fodor's Europe. (US ISSN 0362-0204) **4764**
Fodor's Europe's Great Cities. (US) **4764**
†Fodor's Far West. (US ISSN 0192-3730) **5194**
Fodor's Florence and Venice see Fodor's Italy's Great Cities **4765**
Fodor's Florida. (US ISSN 0193-9556) **4764**
Fodor's France. (US ISSN 0071-6383) **4764**
Fodor's Fun in Acapulco see Fodor's Acapulco, Ixtapa, Zihuatanijo **4763**
Fodor's Fun in Barbados see Fodor's Barbados **4763**
Fodor's Fun in Disney World and the Orlando Area see Fodor's Disney World & the Orlando Area **4764**
Fodor's Fun in Jamaica see Fodor's Pocket Jamaica **4766**
Fodor's Fun in Las Vegas see Fodor's Las Vegas, Reno, Tahoe **4765**
Fodor's Fun in London see Fodor's Pocket London **4766**
Fodor's Fun in Maui see Fodor's Maui **4765**
Fodor's Fun in Montreal see Fodor's Montreal & Quebec City **4765**
†Fodor's Fun in New Orleans. (US) **5194**
Fodor's Fun in New York City see Fodor's Pocket New York City **4766**
Fodor's Fun in Paris see Fodor's Pocket Paris **4766**
†Fodor's Fun in Rio. (US) **5194**
†Fodor's Fun in Saint Martin. (US) **5194**
Fodor's Fun in San Francisco see Fodor's Pocket San Francisco **4766**
†Fodor's Fun in the Bahamas. (US) **5194**
†Fodor's Fun in the Riviera. (US) **5194**
Fodor's Fun in Waikiki see Fodor's Waikiki **4767**
Fodor's Germany. (US) **4764**
Fodor's Great American Vacations. (US) **4765**
Fodor's Great Britain. (US ISSN 0071-6405) **4765**
†Fodor's Great Travel Values: American Cities. (US) **5194**
Fodor's Great Travel Values: Britain see Fodor's Affordable Great Britain **4763**
†Fodor's Great Travel Values: Canada. (US) **5194**
†Fodor's Great Travel Values: Caribbean. (US) **5194**
Fodor's Great Travel Values: France see Fodor's Affordable France **4763**
Fodor's Great Travel Values: Germany see Fodor's Affordable Germany **4763**
†Fodor's Great Travel Values: Hawaii. (US) **5194**
Fodor's Great Travel Values: Italy see Fodor's Affordable Italy **4763**
†Fodor's Great Travel Values: Japan. (US) **5194**
†Fodor's Great Travel Values: London. (US) **5194**
†Fodor's Great Travel Values: Mexico. (US) **5194**

†Fodor's Great Travel Values: Spain. (US) **5194**
Fodor's Greater Miami and the Gold Coast see Fodor's Miami & the Keys **4765**
Fodor's Greece. (US ISSN 0071-6413) **4765**
Fodor's Hawaii. (US ISSN 0071-6421) **4765**
Fodor's Healthy Escapes. (US) **4765**, **3802**
Fodor's Holland. (US ISSN 0071-643X) **4765**
Fodor's Hong Kong. (US) **4765**
Fodor's Hong Kong and Macau see Fodor's Hong Kong **4765**
†Fodor's Houston & Galveston. (US) **5194**
Fodor's Hungary see Fodor's Budapest **4764**
Fodor's India. (US) **4765**
Fodor's India and Nepal see Fodor's India **4765**
†Fodor's Interstate - 10. (US) **5194**
†Fodor's Interstate - 55. (US) **5194**
†Fodor's Interstate - 75. (US) **5194**
†Fodor's Interstate - 80. (US) **5194**
†Fodor's Interstate - 95. (US) **5194**
Fodor's Ireland. (US ISSN 0071-6464) **4765**
Fodor's Israel. (US ISSN 0071-6588) **4765**
Fodor's Italy. (US ISSN 0071-6472) **4765**
Fodor's Italy's Great Cities. (US) **4765**
Fodor's Japan. (US) **4765**
Fodor's Japan and Korea see Fodor's Japan **4765**
†Fodor's Jordan & the Holy Land. (US) **5194**
Fodor's Kenya see Fodor's Kenya & Tanzania **4765**
Fodor's Kenya & Tanzania. (US) **4765**
Fodor's Korea. (US) **4765**
Fodor's Las Vegas, Reno, Tahoe. (US) **4765**
†Fodor's Lisbon. (US) **5194**
†Fodor's Loire Valley. (US) **5194**
Fodor's London. (US ISSN 0071-6596) **4765**
Fodor's Los Angeles. (US) **4765**
Fodor's Madrid see Fodor's Madrid and Barcelona **4765**
Fodor's Madrid and Barcelona. (US) **4765**
Fodor's Maine, Vermont, New Hampshire. (US) **4765**
Fodor's Maui. (US) **4765**
Fodor's Mexico. (US ISSN 0071-6499) **4765**
†Fodor's Mexico City & Acapulco. (US) **5194**
Fodor's Mexico's Baja see Fodor's Baja and Mexico's Pacific Coast Resorts **4763**
Fodor's Miami & the Keys. (US) **4765**
Fodor's Montreal & Quebec City. (US) **4765**
Fodor's Morocco. (US) **4765**
Fodor's Munich. (US) **4765**
Fodor's National Parks of the West. (US) **4765**
Fodor's New England. (US ISSN 0192-3412) **4765**
Fodor's New Mexico see Fodor's Santa Fe, Taos, Albuquerque **4766**
Fodor's New Orleans. (US) **4765**
Fodor's New York see Fodor's New York City **4765**
Fodor's New York City. (US) **4765**
Fodor's New York State see Fodor's Vacations in New York State **4767**
Fodor's New Zealand. (US) **4765**
†Fodor's Nineteen Thirty-Six on the Continent. (US) **5194**
Fodor's North Africa see Fodor's Morocco **4765**
Fodor's Norway. (US) **4765**
Fodor's Nova Scotia, Prince Edward Island and New Brunswick. (US) **4766**
Fodor's Pacific North Coast. (US) **4766**
Fodor's Paris. (US ISSN 0149-1288) **4766**
Fodor's People's Republic of China see Fodor's China **4764**

Fodor's Philadelphia see Fodor's Philadelphia & the Pennsylvania Dutch Country **4766**
Fodor's Philadelphia & the Pennsylvania Dutch Country. (US) **4766**
Fodor's Pocket Jamaica. (US) **4766**
Fodor's Pocket London. (US) **4766**
Fodor's Pocket New York City. (US) **4766**
Fodor's Pocket Paris. (US) **4766**
Fodor's Pocket Puerto Rico. (US) **4766**
Fodor's Pocket San Francisco. (US) **4766**
Fodor's Pocket Washington. (US) **4766**
Fodor's Portugal. (US ISSN 0071-6510) **4766**
†Fodor's Province of Quebec. (US) **5194**
†Fodor's Rockies. (US) **5194**
Fodor's Rome. (US ISSN 0276-2560) **4766**
†Fodor's Royalty Watching Guide. (US) **5194**
Fodor's San Diego. (US) **4766**
Fodor's San Francisco. (US) **4766**
Fodor's Santa Fe, Taos, Albuquerque. (US) **4766**
Fodor's Scandinavia. (US ISSN 0071-6529) **4766**
Fodor's Scandinavian Cities. (US) **4766**
Fodor's Scotland. (US) **4766**
Fodor's Seattle and Vancouver. (US) **4766**
†Fodor's Selected Hotels of Europe. (US) **5194**
†Fodor's Selected Resorts & Hotels of the U.S. (US) **5194**
Fodor's Singapore. (US) **4766**
Fodor's Ski Resorts of North America see Fodor's Skiing in the U S A & Canada **4766**
Fodor's Skiing in the U S A & Canada. (US) **4765**, **4547**
Fodor's South America. (US ISSN 0071-6537) **4766**
Fodor's South Pacific. (US) **4766**
Fodor's Southeast Asia. (US ISSN 0160-8991) **4766**
Fodor's Soviet Union see Fodor's Commonwealth of Independent States and the Baltic Countries **4764**
Fodor's Spain. (US ISSN 0071-6545) **4766**
Fodor's Sports: Cycling. (US) **4518**, **4766**
Fodor's Sports: Hiking. (US) **4547**, **4766**
Fodor's Sports: Running. (US) **4547**, **4766**
Fodor's Sports: Sailing. (US) **4524**, **4766**
Fodor's Stockholm, Copenhagen, Oslo, Helsinki and Reykjavik see Fodor's Scandinavian Cities **4766**
Fodor's Sunday in New York. (US) **4766**
Fodor's Sweden. (US) **4766**
Fodor's Switzerland. (US ISSN 0071-6553) **4766**
†Fodor's Sydney. (US) **5194**
†Fodor's Texas. (US) **5194**
Fodor's Thailand. (US) **4766**
Fodor's the Chesapeake Region. (US) **4767**
Fodor's the South. (US ISSN 0147-8680) **4767**
Fodor's Three-in-One: France. (US) **4767**, **2814**
Fodor's Three-in-One: Germany. (US) **4767**, **2814**
Fodor's Three-in-One: Italy. (US) **4767**, **2814**
Fodor's Three-in-One: Mexico. (US) **4767**, **2814**
Fodor's Three-in-One: Spain. (US) **4767**, **2814**
Fodor's Tokyo. (US) **4767**
Fodor's Toronto. (US) **4767**
Fodor's Touring Europe. (US) **4767**
Fodor's Touring U S A: Eastern Edition. (US) **4767**
Fodor's Touring U S A: Western Edition. (US) **4767**
Fodor's Turkey. (US ISSN 0071-6618) **4767**
Fodor's U S A. (US ISSN 0147-8745) **4767**

Fodor's U S & British Virgin Islands. (US) **4767**
Fodor's Vacations in New York State. (US) **4767**
Fodor's Vacations on the New Jersey Shore. (US) **4767**
Fodor's Vienna see Fodor's Vienna and the Danube Valley **4767**
Fodor's Vienna and the Danube Valley. (US) **4767**
†Fodor's Views to Dine by Around the World. (US) **5194**
Fodor's Virgin Islands see Fodor's U S & British Virgin Islands **4767**
Fodor's Virginia see Fodor's Virginia & Maryland **4767**
Fodor's Virginia & Maryland. (US) **4767**
Fodor's Waikiki. (US) **4767**
Fodor's Washington, D.C. (US) **4767**
†Fodor's Williamsburg, Jamestown & Yorktown. (US) **5194**
Fodor's Yugoslavia. (US ISSN 0071-657X) **4767**
Fodplejeren. (DK ISSN 0107-3362) **3098**
Fodspecialisten see Fodplejeren **3098**
Fodterapeuten. (DK) **3308**
†Foederalismus-Studien. (AU) **5194**
Foenstret. (SW ISSN 0015-6167) **1634**
Foerbundet Svenska Finlandsfrivilliga. Tidning. (SW ISSN 0015-5225) **3458**
Foerder Institute for Economic Research. Working Papers. (IS) **894**
Foerdermittel-Journal. (GW ISSN 0015-5233) **3017**, **4650**
Foerdermittelkatalog. (SZ) **3017**
Foerdern und Heben. (GW ISSN 0015-5241) **3017**
Foerdertechnik. (SZ) **4650**
Foerderungsdienst. (AU ISSN 0015-525X) **92**
Foeredrag vid Pyroteknikdagen. (SW ISSN 0348-6613) **1853**
Foeretagaren/Enterpriser. (SW ISSN 0015-5276) **1076**
Foerfattaren. (SW ISSN 0025-8547) **2569**
Foersaakringstidningen. (SW ISSN 0015-7880) **2532**
Foersaekrings Vaerlden. (SW ISSN 0345-3901) **2532**
Foersaekringsaarsbok foer Finland see Suomen Vakuutusvuosikirja **2544**
Foersaekringsanstaelld. (SW) **2532**
Foersaekringstidning. (FI ISSN 0355-7308) **2532**
Foersamlings- och Pastoratsfoervaltning see Svenska Kyrkans **4204**
Foerskolan. (SW ISSN 0015-5292) **1634**
Foersvar i Nutid. (SW ISSN 0046-4643) **3458**
Foersvarets Forskningsanstalt Orienterar Om see F O A Orienterar Om **3458**
Foersvarsforskningsreferat. (SW ISSN 0016-1543) **1274**, **12**
Foersvarstjaenstemannen/Civil Servant in the Defence Forces. (SW ISSN 0015-5306) **979**
Foerteckning Oever Advokater och Advokatbyraaer. (SW) **2627**
Foervaltningsraettslig Tidskrift. (SW ISSN 0015-8585) **2627**
Fog Light see Foghorn - Foglight **1395**
Foghorn see Foghorn - Foglight **1395**
Foghorn - Foglight. (US) **1395**
Fogli di Informazione. (IT ISSN 0393-5418) **4021**
Foglio d'Informazione della Protezione Civile. see Feuille Officielle de la Protection Civile **1273**
Foglio Svizzero dei Brevetti, Disegni e Marchi. see Schweizerisches Patent-, Muster- und Markenblatt **3678**
Fogorvosi Szemle. (HU ISSN 0015-5314) **3233**
Fogra-Literatur-Profil. (GW) **3999**
Fogra-Literaturdienst. (GW ISSN 0015-5322) **3999**
Fogra-Mitteilungen. (GW ISSN 0015-5330) **3999**
Fogra-Patentkurzberichte see Fogra-Patentschau **3999**
Fogra-Patentschau. (GW) **3999**, **3675**
Foi Aujourd'hui. (FR) **4178**

Foi et Developpement. (FR ISSN 0339-0462) **4372**, 929
Foi et Vie. (FR ISSN 0015-5357) **4178**, 2866
Foi et Vie de l'Eglise au Diocese de Toulouse. (FR ISSN 0015-5365) **4264**
Foil. (US ISSN 0015-5373) **1311**
Fokus. (SW) **3894**, 4843
Fokus paa Familien. (NO ISSN 0332-5415) **3337**, 4405
Folclore Svizzero. see Folklore Suisse **2055**
Fold es Eg. (HU ISSN 0015-539X) **1543**, 3767
†Folding Carton. (US ISSN 0738-761X) **5194**
Folding Carton Industry. (UK) **3648**
Foldrajzi Ertesito/Geographical Bulletin. (HU ISSN 0015-5403) **2248**
Foldrajzi Kozlemenyek. (HU ISSN 0015-5411) **2248**
Foldrajzi Monografiak. (HU ISSN 0428-819X) **2248**
Foldrajzi Tanulmanyok. (HU ISSN 0071-6650) **2248**
Foldtani Kozlony. (HU ISSN 0015-542X) **1561**
Folger News. (US) **2758**
Folha Bancaria. (BL ISSN 0015-5446) **782**
Folha Medica. (BL ISSN 0015-5454) **3098**
Folha Mensal do Estado das Culturas e Previsao de Colheitas see Estado das Culturas e Previsao de Colheitas **88**
Folia Allergologica see Folia Allergologica et Immunologica Clinica **5194**
†Folia Allergologica et Immunologica Clinica. (IT ISSN 0303-8432) **5194**
Folia Anatomica Iugoslavica. (BN ISSN 0352-9657) **3099**
Folia Anatomica Universitatis Conimbricensis. (PO) **3259**
Folia Biochimica et Biologica Graeca. (GR ISSN 0015-5489) **476**, 439
Folia Biologica. (UK ISSN 0015-5500) **439**
Folia Biologica. (PL ISSN 0015-5497) **439**
Folia Cardiologica see Giornale Italiano di Cardiologia **3208**
Folia Chimica Theoretica Latina see F C T L **1177**
Folia Dendrologica. (CS) **2099**, 439, 2126
Folia Entomologica Hungarica. (HU ISSN 0373-9465) **532**
Folia Entomologica Mexicana. (MX ISSN 0430-8603) **533**
Folia Facultatis Medicae Universitatis Comenianae Bratislaviensis. (CS) **3099**
Folia Facultatis Scientiarum Naturalium Universitatis Masarykianae Brunensis: Biologia. (CS) **439**
Folia Facultatis Scientiarum Naturalium Universitatis Masarykianae Brunensis: Chemia. (CS) **1177**
Folia Facultatis Scientiarum Naturalium Universitatis Masarykianae Brunensis: Geologia. (CS) **1561**
Folia Facultatis Scientiarum Naturalium Universitatis Masarykianae Brunensis: Geographia. (CS) **4309**
Folia Facultatis Scientiarum Naturalium Universitatis Masarykianae Brunensis: Physica. (CS) **3818**
Folia Facultatis Scientiarum Naturalium Universitatis Purkynianae Brunensis: Biologia see Folia Facultatis Scientiarum Naturalium Universitatis Masarykianae Brunensis: Biologia **439**
Folia Facultatis Scientiarum Naturalium Universitatis Purkynianae Brunensis: Chemia see Folia Facultatis Scientiarum Naturalium Universitatis Masarykianae Brunensis: Chemia **1177**
Folia Facultatis Scientiarum Naturalium Universitatis Purkynianae Brunensis: Geographia see Folia Facultatis Scientiarum Naturalium Universitatis Masarykianae Brunensis: Geographia **4309**

Folia Facultatis Scientiarum Naturalium Universitatis Purkynianae Brunensis: Physica see Folia Facultatis Scientiarum Naturalium Universitatis Masarykianae Brunensis: Physica **3818**
Folia Facultatis Scientriarum Naturalium Universitatis Purkynianae Brunensis: Geologia see Folia Facultatis Scientiarum Naturalium Universitatis Masarykianae Brunensis: Geologia **1561**
Folia Forestalia. (FI ISSN 0015-5543) **2099**
Folia Forestalia Polonica. Series A. Lesnictwo. (PL ISSN 0071-6677) **2099**
Folia Forestalia Polonica. Series B. Drzewnictwo. (PL ISSN 0071-6685) **2114**
Folia Geobotanica et Phytotaxonomica. (CS ISSN 0015-5551) **503**
Folia Geobotanica et Phytotaxonomica Bohemoslovaca see Folia Geobotanica et Phytotaxonomica **503**
Folia Geographica. Geographica-Oeconomica. (PL ISSN 0071-6707) **2248**
Folia Geographica. Geographica-Physica. (PL ISSN 0071-6715) **2248**, 1561
Folia Geographica Danica. (DK ISSN 0071-6693) **2248**
†Folia Haematologica. (GW ISSN 0323-4347) **5194**
Folia Histochemica et Cytobiologica. (PL) **524**, 439
Folia Historiae Artium. (PL ISSN 0071-6723) **326**
Folia Historica. (HU ISSN 0133-6622) **2361**
Folia Historica Bohemica. (CS ISSN 0231-7494) **2361**
Folia Historica del Nordeste. (AG ISSN 0325-8238) **2406**
Folia Humanistica. (SP ISSN 0015-5594) **4309**, 2507
Folia Linguistica. (GW ISSN 0165-4004) **2814**
Folia Medica Cracoviensia. (PL ISSN 0015-5616) **3099**
Folia Microbiologica. (UK ISSN 0015-5632) **552**
Folia Montana. see Banicke Listy **3479**
Folia Morphologica see Functional and Developmental Morphology **439**
Folia Neuropsiquiatrica del sur de Espana. (SP) **3337**
†Folia Neuropsychiatrica. (IT) **5194**
Folia Odontologica Practica. see Rinsho Shika **3242**
Folia Oeconomica Cracoviensia. (PL ISSN 0071-674X) **666**
Folia Oncologica. (IT ISSN 0392-047X) **3197**
Folia Ophthalmologica. (GW ISSN 0323-4932) **3300**
Folia Ophthalmologica Japonica/Nihon Ganka Kiyo. (JA ISSN 0015-5667) **3300**
Folia Orientalia. (PL ISSN 0015-5675) **3637**
Folia Parasitologica. (CS ISSN 0015-5683) **3219**, 552
Folia Pharmacologica Japonica/Nihon Yakurigaku Zasshi. (JA ISSN 0015-5691) **3726**
Folia Phoniatrica. (SZ ISSN 0015-5705) **3314**, 3337
Folia Praehistorica Posnaniensia. (PL ISSN 0239-8524) **272**, 2361
Folia Primatologica. (SZ ISSN 0015-5713) **582**
Folia Psychiatrica et Neurologica Japonica see Japanese Journal of Psychiatry and Neurology **3340**
Folia Quaternaria. (PL ISSN 0015-573X) **3657**
†Folia Slavica. (US ISSN 0160-9394) **5195**
Folia Venatoria. (CS) **4809**, 2099
Folia Veterinaria. (CS ISSN 0015-5748) **4809**
Folia Zoologica. (CS ISSN 0139-7893) **582**
Folio. (UK ISSN 0015-5772) **4127**, 2917
Folio (Berkeley). (US) **1356**

Folio (Birmingham). (US ISSN 0015-5756) **2917**
Folio (Brockport). (US ISSN 0882-3030) **2507**, 2917
Folio (North Hollywood). (US) **1356**, 3551
Folio (Stamford). (US ISSN 0046-4333) **4128**
Folio (Washington). (US) **2918**, 2993
Folio - K P F K see Folio (North Hollywood) **1356**
Folio Limnologica Scandinavica. (DK) **1597**
Folio: Source Book. (US) **4128**
Folio's Publishing News. (US ISSN 1043-8688) **4128**
Folium Diocesanum Bauzanense-Brixinense. (IT ISSN 0015-5802) **4178**
Folk Art Finder. (US ISSN 0738-8357) **326**
Folk Creativity. (RU) **2054**
Folk Custom Study. see Minsu Yanjiu **4380**
Folk Customs. see Min Su **2056**
Folk Dance Directory. (US ISSN 0163-528X) **1530**
Folk; Dansk Etnografisk Tidsskrift. (DK ISSN 0085-0756) **240**
Folk Directory. (UK) **1530**
Folk Education Association of America Newsletter see F E A A Newsletter **1683**
Folk Era Newsletter see Folk Era Today **3551**
Folk Era Today! (US) **3551**
Folk Fortaeller. (DK ISSN 0109-8365) **2361**
Folk Harp Journal. (US ISSN 0094-8934) **3551**
Folk in Kent. (UK) **1530**, 2054, 3551
Folk Life: Journal of Ethnological Studies. (UK ISSN 0430-8778) **240**
Folk Literature. see Literatura Ludowa **2056**
Folk Mass and Modern Liturgy see Modern Liturgy **4190**
Folk-Michel. (GW ISSN 0934-6449) **3551**
Folk Music Journal. (UK ISSN 0531-9684) **3551**, 1530
†Folk Music News. (UK) **5195**
Folk North-West. (UK) **3551**, 1530
Folk og Fritid. (DK ISSN 0015-5810) **1634**
Folk og Liv paa Roendeegnen-Dengang. (DK ISSN 0109-2766) **2361**
Folk og Minder fra Koebenhavn. (DK ISSN 0900-002X) **2361**
Folk Roots. (UK ISSN 0951-1326) **3551**
Folk School Association of America Newsletter see F E A A Newsletter **1683**
Folk Song. see Canu Gwerin **3544**
Folk Tales. see Minjian Gushi **2056**
Folk un Medine. (IS) **2002**
Folk Un Medine - Am u-Medinah see Folk, Velt un Medine **2002**
Folk, Velt un Medine/Am, Olam u-Medinah. (IS ISSN 0302-8186) **2002**
Folkblad Pibroch. (NE) **2054**, 3552
Folkbrief. (GW) **3552**
†Folkebiblioteksstatistik, Budgetter, Virksomhed. (DK ISSN 0105-6077) **5195**
Folkehoejskoler. (DK ISSN 0107-4504) **1694**
Folkeminder. (DK) **2054**
Folkens Museum - National Museum of Ethnography. (SW) **240**
†Folkesagn i Tekst og Billed fra Noerreherred. (DK ISSN 0900-3037) **5195**
Folkeskolen. (DK ISSN 0015-5837) **1634**
Folkeskolen i de Enkelte Kommuner see De Private Skoler i de Enkelte Kommuner **1697**
Folkestone and Dover Extra. (UK) **2054**
Folketingets Haandbog. (DK ISSN 0107-9670) **4060**
Folkets Framtid. (NO) **3894**
Folkets Historia. (SW ISSN 0349-6279) **2361**

Folkets Vael - DKSN see Drogfritt Liv **1535**
Folkevirke. (DK ISSN 0015-5845) **2866**
Folkhoegskolan. (SW ISSN 0348-4769) **1684**
Folkl-Liv see Ethnologia Scandinavica **238**
Folklife Annual. (US ISSN 0747-5322) **2054**
Folklife Center News. (US ISSN 0149-6840) **2054**
Folklivsskildringar och Bygdestudier. (SW ISSN 0071-6766) **2054**
Folklivsstudier. (FI ISSN 0085-0764) **240**
Fol'klor Urala. (RU) **2054**
Folklore. (FR ISSN 0015-5888) **2054**
Folklore. (II ISSN 0015-5896) **2054**, 240
Folklore. (UK ISSN 0015-587X) **2054**
Folklore. (CN ISSN 0824-3085) **2054**
Folklore. see Shan Hai Jing **2058**
Folklore Americano. (MX ISSN 0071-6774) **2054**
Folklore and Mythology Studies. (US ISSN 0162-6280) **2054**
Folklore & Society. (US) **2054**
Folklore Brabancon. (BE ISSN 0015-590X) **2054**
Folklore de France. (FR ISSN 0015-5918) **2054**
Folklore du Monde. (BE) **2054**
Folklore Fellows Communications see F F Communications **2054**
Folklore Fellows of India. News Bulletin. (II) **2054**
Folklore Forum. (US ISSN 0015-5926) **2055**, 240
Folklore News. (CE) **2055**
Folklore of American Holidays. (US) **2055**
▼Folklore of World Holidays. (US) **2055**
Folklore Society of Greater Washington Newsletter. (US ISSN 0015-5950) **2055**
Folklore Suisse/Folclore Svizzero. (SZ) **2055**
Folklorica Publications in Folksong and Balladry. (US) **3552**
Folksong in the Classroom. (US) **3552**, 1634, 2055
Folktales of the World. (US ISSN 0071-6804) **2055**
Folletos de Divulgacion. (UY) **272**, 240
Follow Up File. (US ISSN 0888-3955) **2569**, 1374
Fomento Agropecuario. (VE) **92**
Fomento de la Produccion. (SP ISSN 0015-6035) **1076**
Fomento Social see Revista de Fomento Social **4447**
Fomento y Produccion. (EC) **782**
Fonaiap Divulga. (Fondo Nacional de Investigaciones Agropecuarias) (VE) **92**
Fonction Publique. (SZ) **2583**, 4060
Fonctionnaire National see Service Economique Fonctionnaire **4073**
Fondamental. (FR) **4406**, 3197
Fondamenti. (IT) **2918**
Fondation Auschwitz. Bulletin. (BE ISSN 0772-652X) **2361**
Fondation Canadienne des Toxicomanies. Repertoire. see Canada Addictions Foundation. Directory **1535**
Fondation Louis de Broglie. Annales. (FR ISSN 0182-4295) **3818**, 3843
Fondation Maurice Careme. (BE) **2918**, 2993
Fondation pour la Recherche et le Developpement dans l'Ocean Indien. Documents et Recherches. (RE) **2333**
Fondazione A. Masieri. Giornale di Architettura. (IT) **299**
Fondazione Assi. Annali di Storia dell'Impresa. (IT ISSN 1120-9445) **666**
Fondazione Basso. Annali. (IT ISSN 0392-0003) **2310**
Fondazione Feltrinelli. Quaderni. (IT) **4128**

FOOD MARKETING 6193

Fondazione Giangiacomo Feltrinelli. Annali. (IT ISSN 0544-1374) **4372**
†Fondazione Giorgio Cini. Notizie. (IT) **5195**
Fondazione Giorgio Ronchi. Atti. (IT ISSN 0015-606X) **3852**
Fondazione Guarasci. Bollettino Mensile d'Informazione. (IT) **3894**, 2248
Fondazione Luigi Einaudi. Annali. (IT ISSN 0531-9870) **2205**
Fonderia. (IT ISSN 0015-6078) **3406**
Fonderie, Fondeur d'Aujourd'hui. (FR ISSN 0249-3136) **3406**
Fondi Risparmio & Investimento. (IT) **946**
Fondo de Cultura. Serie de Lecturas. (MX) **666**
Fondo de Inversiones para el Desarrollo Economico. Informe Trimestral. (DR) **782**
Fondo de Promocion de Exportaciones. Directorio de Exportadores/Export Directory. (CK) **908**
Fondo Nacional de Investigaciones Agropecuarias Fonaiap Divulga see Fonaiap Divulga **92**
Fonds Africain de Developpement. Rapport Annuel. see African Development Bank. Annual Report **925**
Fonds de Developpement Economique et Social. Conseil de Direction. Rapport. (FR ISSN 0071-6847) **1076**
Fono 2. (SP) **3552**
FonoForum. (GW ISSN 0015-6140) **3552**, 4460
Fontane-Blaetter. (GW ISSN 0015-6175) **2918**
Fontes see Towarzystwo Naukowe w Toruniu. Fontes **2392**
Fontes Archaeologici Posnanienses/Annales Musei Archaeologici Posnaniensis. (PL ISSN 0071-6863) **272**, 2361
Fontes Archaeologici Pragenses. (CS ISSN 0015-6183) **272**
Fontes Artis Musicae. (GW ISSN 0015-6191) **3588**
Fontes Iuris Gentium see Fontes Iuris Gentium. Section 2 **2723**
Fontes Iuris Gentium. Section 2. (US ISSN 0426-7230) **2723**
Fontes Linguae Vasconum. (SP ISSN 0046-435X) **2814**
Fontes Rerum Austriacarum. Reihe 1. Scriptores. (AU) **2361**
Fontes Rerum Austriacarum. Reihe 2. Diplomataria et Acta. (AU) **2361**
Fontes Rerum Austriacarum. Reihe 3. Fontes Juris. (AU ISSN 0071-6898) **2361**, 2627
Fonti di Storia Toscana. (IT) **2361**
Fonti e Studi per la Storia di Bologna e delle Province Emiliane e Romagnole.(IT) **326**, 2361
Fonti Orali. (IT) **2361**
Fonti Sui Comuni Rurali Toscani. (IT ISSN 0071-6901) **2361**
Food. see Die Naehrung **3609**
Food Additives and Contaminants. (UK ISSN 0265-203X) **3727**, 2067
†Food Additives - Descriptions, Functions and U.K. Legislations. (UK) **5195**
Food Agriculture and Plantation Journal.(II ISSN 0015-6213) **92**
Food Aid Convention see Food Aid Shipments **2067**
Food Aid Shipments. (UK) **2067**
Food Analyses see Foodmagazine - International **2092**
Food and Agricultural Immunology. (UK ISSN 0954-0105) **439**
Food and Agricultural Legislation. (UN ISSN 0015-6221) **2627**, 92, 2067
Food and Agricultural Organization of the United Nations. Plant Protection Committee for Southeast Asia and Pacific Region. Technical Document see Food and Agriculture Organization of the United Nations. Asia and Pacific Plant Protection Commission. Technical Document **178**

†Food and Agriculture Organization of the United Nations. Agricultural Planning Studies. (UN ISSN 0532-0194) **5195**
Food and Agriculture Organization of the United Nations. Asia and Pacific Plant Protection Commission. Quarterly Newsletter. (UN) **177**
Food and Agriculture Organization of the United Nations. Asia and Pacific Plant Protection Commission. Technical Document. (UN) **178**
Food and Agriculture Organization of the United Nations. Asia and the Pacific Commission on Agricultural Statistics. Periodic Report. (UN) **137**
Food and Agriculture Organization of the United Nations. Basic Texts. (UN ISSN 0532-0208) **92**
Food and Agriculture Organization of the United Nations. European Inland Fisheries Advisory Commission. Occasional Papers. (UN ISSN 0258-6096) **2041**
Food and Agriculture Organization of the United Nations. European Inland Fisheries Advisory Commission. Technical Papers. (UN ISSN 0532-940X) **2041**
Food and Agriculture Organization of the United Nations. Production Yearbook. (UN ISSN 0071-7118) **150**
Food and Agriculture Organization of the United Nations. Soils Bulletins. (UN ISSN 0532-0437) **178**
Food and Agriculture Organization of the United Nations. Trade Yearbook. (UN ISSN 0071-7126) **150**, 908
Food and Agriculture Organization of the United Nations. World Soil Resources Reports. (UN ISSN 0532-0488) **178**
Food and Agriculture Organization of the United Nations Agricultural Development Paper see F A O Agricultural Development Paper **5190**
Food and Agriculture Organization of the United Nations Agricultural Services Bulletin see F A O Agricultural Services Bulletin **150**
Food and Agriculture Organization of the United Nations Animal Production and Health Series see F A O Animal Production and Health Series **216**
Food and Agriculture Organization of the United Nations Conference. Report. (UN ISSN 0071-6944) **92**
Food and Agriculture Organization of the United Nations Technical Papers see C I F A Technical Papers **2037**
Food & Beverage. (SZ) **2474**
Food and Beverage Journal. (US) **2067**
Food & Beverage Marketing. (US ISSN 0731-3799) **2067**, 381
Food & Beverage Monitor. (US) **946**, 2067
Food & Beverage Newsletter. (US) **3616**, 4101
Food & Beverage Spotlight. (US) **946**, 2067
Food & Beverages. see Trofima & Pota **386**
Food and Beverages (Year). (SA ISSN 1012-7577) **2067**, 1135
▼Food and Bioproducts Processing. (UK ISSN 0960-3085) **477**, 1226
Food and Catering Education in the Region. (UK) **1706**
Food and Chemical Toxicology. (US ISSN 0278-6915) **1981**, 3099, 3727
Food and Cosmetics Guidance Manual. (US) **4101**, 2627
Food and Drink Federation Feedback see F D F Feedback **2066**
Food & Drink from Britain Buyers' Guide. (UK ISSN 0954-0431) **2067**
Food and Drink Trade Handbook. (UK) **2067**, 381
Food and Drug Administration. (US) **2627**, 2067, 3727
Food and Drug Letter. (US ISSN 0362-6466) **1076**, 3727

Food and Drug Packaging. (US ISSN 0015-6272) **3648**, 2067, 3727
†Food & Drug Packaging News. (CN) **5195**
Food and Drug Product News see Food & Drug Packaging News **5195**
The Food and Fiber Letter. (US ISSN 0739-6791) **92**, 2067
Food and Foodways. (US ISSN 0740-9710) **3605**, 240
Food and Hunger Notes. (US) **2067**
†Food & Justice. (US ISSN 0885-0704) **5195**
Food and Kitchen. see Mazone Umitbach **2077**
Food and Liquor Retailer. (AT ISSN 0156-0352) **2091**, 381
Food and Nonfood. (GW) **2091**
Food and Nutrition. (US ISSN 0046-4384) **3605**
†Food and Nutrition. (UN ISSN 0304-8942) **5195**
Food and Nutrition Bulletin. (UN ISSN 0379-5721) **3605**
Food and Nutrition - Eiyo to Shokuryo see Japanese Society of Nutrition and Food Science. Journal **3607**
Food and Nutrition in History and Anthropology. (US ISSN 0275-5769) **240**, 3605
Food & Nutrition News. (US ISSN 0015-6310) **3605**
Food and Nutrition Programs see U.S. Food and Nutrition Service. Food and Nutrition Programs **3614**
Food & Nutrition Update. (UK) **2068**
Food & Poverty Notes. (US) **4406**
Food & Service. (US ISSN 0891-0154) **2474**, 2068
Food & Wine. (US ISSN 0279-6740) **2068**, 381, 2446
Food Arts. (US ISSN 1042-9123) **2474**, 2068
Food Australia. (AT ISSN 1032-5298) **2068**
Food Biotechnology. (US ISSN 0890-5436) **489**, 178, 2068
Food Books Review. (UK ISSN 0142-2545) **4128**, 2068
Food Broker Quarterly. (US ISSN 0884-7185) **1039**, 2091
Food Broker: Sales and Marketing see Food Distributors Magazine **2068**
Food Business. (US ISSN 1049-5568) **2068**
Food Business Mergers & Acquisitions. (US) **2091**
Food Chemical News. (US ISSN 0015-6337) **2068**
Food Chemical News Guide. (US) **2068**
Food Chemistry. (UK ISSN 0308-8146) **1177**, 2068
Food Composition and Nutrition Tables/Zusammensetzung der Lebensmittel, Naehrwert Tabellen. (GW ISSN 0721-6912) **3605**
Food Consumption in the O E C D see O E C D. Food Consumption Statistics **2085**
▼Food Control. (UK ISSN 0956-7135) **2068**
Food, Cosmetics and Drugs Packaging. (UK ISSN 0951-4554) **3648**, 3862
Food Distribution Research Society. Newsletter. (US) **2068**, 1039
Food Distributors Magazine. (US) **2068**
Food, Drug, and Cosmetics Control Newsletter see F D C Control Newsletter **2068**
Food Drug Cosmetic Law Reports. (US) **2627**
Food Economics Yearbook. see Shokuryo Keizai Nenkan **1153**
Food Engineering see Chilton's Food Engineering **2064**
Food Engineering International see Chilton's Food Engineering International **2064**
Food Europe. (UK) **2068**, 908, 1010
Food Executive see Hotline Magazine **2072**
Food Farming and Agriculture. (II ISSN 0015-6396) **92**
†Food First Development Reports. (US ISSN 0895-3090) **5195**

Food First News. (US ISSN 0749-9825) **3894**, 3957
Food: Flavouring Ingredients Processing and Packaging see Food Ingredients & Processing International **2068**
†Food for Thought (Ann Arbor). (US) **5195**
Food for Thought (Los Angeles). (US ISSN 0198-0246) **2758**, 2068
▼Food Free or Cheap Newsletter. (US ISSN 1054-0768) **2446**, 1504
Food from Greece. (UK) **381**, 2068
†Food from Poland. (PL ISSN 0015-6418) **5195**
Food Front see Front Lines (Portland) **1505**
Food Herald. (US) **2068**, 2088, 2091
Food Hydrocolloids. (UK ISSN 0268-005X) **2068**
Food Hygienic Society of Japan. Journal/Shokuhin Eiseigaku Zasshi. (JA ISSN 0015-6426) **4101**, 3605
Food in Canada. (CN ISSN 0015-6442) **2068**
Food Industries Manual. (UK ISSN 0071-7177) **2068**
Food Industries of South Africa. (SA ISSN 0015-6450) **2068**
Food Industries Yearbook and Buyers' Directory see Food Industries Yearbook and Buyers' Guide **5195**
†Food Industries Yearbook and Buyers' Guide. (SA) **5195**
Food Industry. Elelmezesi Ipar **2066**
Food Industry. see Prumysl Potravin **2080**
Food Industry. see Shokuhin Kogyo **2081**
Food Industry Advisor. (US) **2091**
Food Industry Bulletin. (UK) **2068**
Food Industry Directory. (US) **1135**, 2068
Food Industry Directory see European Food Trades Directory **2066**
Food Industry Futures: a Strategy Service. (US ISSN 0046-4414) **2068**
Food Industry News. (NZ ISSN 0113-8901) **2068**
Food Industry News. (US) **2091**
Food Industry Newsletter. (US ISSN 0890-720X) **2068**
Food Industry Report. (US) **2068**
Food Industry Skirmisher. (US ISSN 0890-3263) **2068**
Food Industry Statistics Digest. (UK) **2085**, 2091, 4571
Food Industry Statistics Digest Up-Date see Food Industry Statistics Digest **2085**
Food Ingredients & Processing International. (UK) **2068**
Food Institute Report. (US ISSN 0745-4503) **2068**
Food Irradiation Newsletter. (UN) **2069**
Food, Its Science and Technology. (JA ISSN 0583-1164) **2069**, 92
Food: Latin American Industrial Report. (US) **2069**
Food Law Monthly. (UK ISSN 0262-0030) **2628**, 2069
Food Legislation Surveys. (UK ISSN 0144-2406) **2069**, 2628
▼Food Legislation Victoria. (AT) **2069**, 2628
Food Management. (US ISSN 0091-018X) **2069**
Food Manufacture. (UK ISSN 0015-6477) **2069**
Food Manufacture Ingredient and Machinery Survey. (UK) **2069**, 3017
Food Manufacture International. (UK ISSN 0267-1506) **2069**
Food Manufacturing News. (AT ISSN 0816-3634) **2069**
Food Market Abstracts. (UK ISSN 0268-0408) **2069**, 2085
Food Marketing see British Food Journal **2062**
Food Marketing. (US) **2091**, 1039
Food Marketing & Technology. (GW ISSN 0932-2744) **2069**, 1039
Food Marketing Industry Speaks. (US ISSN 0190-3349) **2091**

FOOD MARKETING

Food Marketing Institute Annual Financial Review see F M I Annual Financial Review **2091**
Food Marketing Institute Issues Bulletin see F M I Issues Bulletin **2091**
Food Mart News. (CN) **2069**
Food Merchandising for Non-Food Retailers. (US) **2091**
Food Merchants Advocate. (US ISSN 0015-6493) **2091**
Food Microbiology. (UK ISSN 0740-0020) **552, 2069**
Food Microstructure see Food Structure **3606**
Food Monitor see Why **4424**
Food News for Consumers. (US) **1504, 2069, 2446**
Food, Nutrition & Health Newsletter. (US ISSN 0160-8053) **2069, 3605**
Food Outlook see Retail Food Price Report **2080**
Food Packaging and Labeling Newsletter. (US ISSN 0194-2980) **2069**
Food Packer International. (UK) **2069**
Food People. (US) **2069**
Food Policy. (UK ISSN 0306-9192) **150**
Food Problems Research. see Liangshi Wenti Yanjiu **2076**
†Food Processing (Bristol). (UK) **5195**
Food Processing (Bromley). (UK) **2069**
Food Processing (Chicago). (US ISSN 0015-6523) **2069**
Food Processing Industry see Food Processing (Bromley) **2069**
Food Processing News. (NZ) **2069**
Food Processor. (AT) **2069**
▼Food Product Design. (US) **2069**
Food Production - Management. (US ISSN 0191-6181) **2069**
Food Production - Nutrition see Public Health Nutrition **4118**
Food Products & Equipment. (US) **2069**
Food Products and Equipment Literature Review. (US) **2069**
Food Protection Report. (US ISSN 0884-0806) **4101, 2069**
Food Quality and Preference. (UK ISSN 0950-3293) **2069**
Food Research Institute Bristol. Biennial Report see Institute of Food Research - Bristol Laboratory Biennial Report **5214**
Food Research Institute Studies. (US ISSN 0193-9025) **151, 2069**
Food Research International. (UK ISSN 0963-9969) **2070**
Food Retailing Review. (US) **2091**
Food Reviews International. (US ISSN 8755-9129) **2070**
▼Food Safety and Security. (UK ISSN 0964-4164) **2070, 3648**
Food Science/Ahara Vijnana. (II ISSN 0532-0968) **2070**
Food Science. (UK) **3606**
Food Science. see Shipin Ke-Ji **3612**
Food Science and Technology/Science et Technologie Alimentaire. (UK ISSN 0023-6438) **2070**
Food Science and Technology Abstracts.(UK ISSN 0015-6574) **2085, 12**
Food Science and Technology Today. (UK ISSN 0950-9623) **3606**
Food Science Series. (US ISSN 0071-7223) **2070**
Food Sciences. see Potravinarske Vedy **2079**
†Food Service Forum. (US ISSN 0892-757X) **5195**
Food Service Guide to Fresh Produce. (US) **2091**
Food Service Management/Gekkan Syokudo. (JA) **2474, 2070**
Food Service Research Abstracts. (US) **2070**
Food Shop. (AT) **2070, 979, 1010**
Food Structure. (US ISSN 1046-705X) **3606, 92, 2070**
▼Food Technologie Magazin. (GW ISSN 0937-700X) **2070**
Food Technologist. (NZ ISSN 0111-6606) **2070**
Food Technology. (US ISSN 0015-6639) **2070**

Food Technology and Biotechnology Review. see Prehrambeno-Tehnoloska i Biotehnoloska Revija **491**
Food Technology in Australia see Food Australia **2068**
Food Technology in New Zealand. (NZ ISSN 0015-6655) **2070**
Food Trade News. (US ISSN 0015-6663) **2070, 1039**
Food Trade Review. (UK ISSN 0015-6671) **2070**
Food Trades Directory and Food Buyer's Yearbook see European Food Trades Directory **2066**
Food World. (US) **2091**
Food World News. (UK ISSN 0260-1974) **2070**
Foodborne and Waterborne Disease in Canada. (CN) **2070**
Foodborne & Waterborne Disease Outbreaks. Annual Summary see U.S. Centers for Disease Control. Foodborne & Waterborne Disease Outbreaks. Annual Summary **4114**
Foodlines. (US ISSN 0736-0010) **4406, 866, 4060**
Foodmagazine. (NE ISSN 0165-1641) **2092**
Foodmagazine - International. (NE) **2092**
Foodnews. (UK) **199**
Foods Adlibra. (US ISSN 0146-9304) **2085, 12**
Foods Adlibra Foodservice Edition. (US) **2085, 12**
Foods Adlibra Seafood Edition. (US) **2085, 12**
Foods by Mail. (US) **2070**
Foodservice and Hospitality. (CN ISSN 0007-8972) **2474**
FoodService Director. (US) **2070**
The Foodservice Distributor. (US ISSN 0896-4505) **1135**
Foodservice East. (US ISSN 0885-6877) **2474, 2070**
Foodservice Equipment & Supplies Specialist. (US) **2474**
Foodservice Equipment Distributors Association News & Views see F E D A News & Views **2473**
Foodservice Equipment Specialist see Foodservice Equipment & Supplies Specialist **2474**
Foodservice Information Abstracts. (US) **2085, 12**
Foodservice Newsletter see Fresh Facts for Foodservice Newsletter **5197**
Foodservice Operators Guide. (US ISSN 1040-4546) **2070**
Foodservice Product News. (US ISSN 0199-7696) **2474, 2070**
Foodservice Report. (US) **2070**
Foodservice Today see I F M A World **2072**
▼Foodservice Yearbook International. (US) **1135, 2072**
Foodsman. (US ISSN 0015-6728) **2092**
Foodstuff Magazine - The Supermarket. see Levnedsmiddelbladet - Supermarkedet **2093**
Foodtalk. (US) **2070, 240**
Foodweek. (AT) **2092, 2070**
Foolscap. (UK ISSN 0952-3979) **2866, 2993**
▼The Foot. (UK ISSN 0958-2592) **3308**
Foot & Ankle. (US ISSN 0198-0211) **3308, 3371**
Foot Fraternity. (US) **2452**
Foot Prints. (US) **3894, 1955**
Foot Surgery. see Chirurgia del Piede **3377**
†Foot Worship. (US) **5195**
†Foot Worship News. (US) **5195**
Footbag World. (US) **4504**
Football Action. (US) **4504**
Football Association Year Book. (UK ISSN 0071-724X) **4504**
▼Football Basketball & Hockey Collector. (US) **2436, 4504**
Football Card Price Guide see The Sport Americana Football Card Price Guide **2442**
Football Case Book. (US ISSN 0163-6200) **4504**
Football Digest. (US ISSN 0015-6760) **4504**

Football Forecast (Year). (US ISSN 0364-8273) **4504**
Football Guide. (US ISSN 0069-5548) **4504**
Football Handbook. (US) **4504**
†Football Insight. (US) **5195**
Football News. (US) **4504**
Football Officials Handbook. (US) **4504**
Football Officials Manual. (US) **4504**
Football: Our Way. (US) **2918**
Football Preview (Year). (US ISSN 1054-0164) **4504**
Football Record. (AT ISSN 0015-6795) **4504**
Football Referee. (UK) **4504**
Football Register. (US ISSN 0071-7258) **4504**
Football Rulebook. (US) **4504**
Football Rules - Simplified and Illustrated. (US) **4504**
Football Statistician's Manual. (US) **4498**
Football Times. (AT) **4504**
Football Weekly News. (UK) **4504**
Football World. see Zuqiu Shijie **4515**
Foothill Quarterly. (US) **2918**
Foothills Inquirer. (US ISSN 0748-0970) **2151, 12, 2406**
†Footloose Librarian. (US ISSN 0733-3196) **5195**
Footnotes (Chicago). (US ISSN 0736-8879) **2758**
Footnotes (Willow Park). (US) **216**
▼Footnotes from the Arid Zone. (US ISSN 1053-7090) **2055**
Footplate/Voetplaat. (SA ISSN 0015-6809) **2583, 4709**
Footprint. (CN ISSN 0824-6017) **1311**
Footprints (Fort Worth). (US ISSN 0426-8261) **2151**
Footprints (Morristown). (US) **1488**
Footprints (Northampton). (UK ISSN 0143-3601) **2151**
Footprints (Plainview). (US) **1311**
Footprints in Time. (US) **2151**
Footwear Business International. (UK) **4360**
†Footwear Council. Bulletins. (US) **5195**
†Footwear Council. Newsletter. (US) **5195**
Footwear Digest International see Footwear Business International **4360**
Footwear Forum. (CN ISSN 0706-7534) **4360**
Footwear Industries of America. Executive Digest. (US) **4360, 2736**
Footwear Industries of America. Quarterly Report. (US) **4360**
Footwear Industry Statistical Review. (UK ISSN 0308-9398) **4362**
Footwear Manual. (US ISSN 0095-1048) **4360**
Footwear News. (US ISSN 0015-6833) **4360**
Footwear News Fact Book. (US ISSN 0429-0208) **4360**
▼Footwear Plus. (US) **4361**
†Footwear, Raw Hides and Skins, and Leatther Industry in O E C D Countries. (FR) **5195**
Footwork Magazine see Footwork: The Paterson Literary Review **2993**
Footwork: The Paterson Literary Review. (US) **2993, 2918**
For a Change. (US ISSN 0959-311X) **4372, 3767**
For a Lover of Vocal Music. (RU) **3552**
For Adults Only see Adult and Continuing Education Newsletter **1681**
For Canada's Children. (CN) **1237**
For Christ and Peace. (UK) **4178**
For Formulation Chemists Only. (US ISSN 0887-736X) **375, 372, 1205**
For Graduates Only. (US) **1706**
For Him. (UK ISSN 0958-0980) **3397**
For Kirke og Kultur see Kirke og Kultur **4187**
For Parents. (US ISSN 0277-612X) **1237**
For Patients Only. (US) **3388**
For Poets Only. (US ISSN 0887-0896) **2993**

For Reference. (US ISSN 0015-685X) **2758**
For Seniors Only. (US) **1634**
▼For the Bride by Demitrios. (US) **3066, 1291**
For the Children. see Weile Haizi **1246**
For the Defense. (US ISSN 0015-6884) **2628**
For the Love of Cross Stitch. (US) **3591**
†For the People. (US) **5195**
For the Record. (National Aeronautic Association) (US) **53**
For the Record (Columbus). (US) **2151**
For the Record (Lake Oswego). (US) **2628**
For the Record (Springfield). (US ISSN 0891-2653) **2406, 2758**
For the Record (Valley Forge). (US ISSN 1049-6742) **3099**
For Today's Children see Child **1234**
For Women. see Laisha **4846**
For You from Czechoslovakia. (CS ISSN 0015-6892) **815**
For Younger Readers, Braille and Talking Books (Large Print Edition). (US ISSN 0093-2825) **2285, 400, 1676, 2292**
For Your Eyes Only. (US ISSN 0738-4203) **3458**
For Your Information see F Y I **4649**
For Your Information (Buffalo). (US) **2758**
For Your Information (New York). (US ISSN 0890-2992) **326**
For Your Information Management Memo see F Y I Management Memo **778**
Forage. (AT) **92**
Forage Farmer. (US) **92**
Forage Network in Ethiopia Newsletter. (UN) **216**
Forages. (FR ISSN 0046-4481) **3686**
Foram Pembangunan. (MY ISSN 0126-5156) **866**
Forbes. (US ISSN 0015-6914) **1010, 666**
▼Forbes Japan. (JA) **666**
Forbidden Connections. (US) **3397, 4843**
Forbidden Letters. (US) **3397**
Forbruger. Haandbog see Familien Danmarks Forbruger. Haandbog **5190**
Forbrugerindeks. (DK ISSN 0105-9122) **1504**
Forbrugerklagenaevnet. Aarsberetning see Forbrugerstyrelsen. Juridisk Aarbog **1505**
Forbrugerklagenaevnet. Juridisk Aarbog see Forbrugerstyrelsen. Juridisk Aarbog **1505**
Forbrugerombudsmanden. Beretning see Forbrugerstyrelsen. Beretning **1505**
Forbrugerstyrelsen. Beretning. (DK) **1505**
Forbrugerstyrelsen. Juridisk Aarbog. (DK) **1505**
†Forbruget af Somatiske Sengepladser. (DK ISSN 0107-7627) **5195**
Forbruker-Rapporten. (NO ISSN 0046-449X) **1505**
Force. (IT ISSN 1120-1673) **1526**
Forced Exposure. (US ISSN 0893-5599) **2866, 3552**
Forceps, Snippets and A C O R N News see A C O R N Journal **2458**
Forces. (CN ISSN 0015-6957) **2177, 4824**
Forces Financial News. (UK) **782**
Forces Postal History Society. Newsletter. (UK) **3752**
Forces Weekly Echo. (UK) **3458**
Ford Almanac. (US) **1781, 92**
Ford Buyer's Guide. (US) **4691**
Ford Data Base Report. (US) **946**
Ford Enthusiast Magazine. (US) **4691, 2436**
Ford Estate. (US ISSN 0015-6981) **1311**
Ford Foundation Annual Report. (US ISSN 0071-7274) **4372, 1634, 2002, 2507, 4843**
Ford Foundation Letter see Ford Foundation Report **4372**
Ford Foundation Report. (US) **4372, 2002, 2507, 4843**

Ford Investment Management Report. (US) **946**
Ford, Mustang Buyer's Guide *see* Ford Buyer's Guide **4691**
Ford-Nachrichten. (GW ISSN 0015-7007) **4691**
Ford New Holland News. (US) **92**
Ford Times. (US ISSN 0015-7015) **4691**
Ford Value Report. (US) **946**
Ford World. (US ISSN 0046-4538) **979, 4691**
Fordham International Law Forum *see* Fordham International Law Journal **2628**
Fordham International Law Journal. (US ISSN 0747-9395) **2628**
Fordham Law Review. (US ISSN 0015-704X) **2628**
Fordham Urban Law Journal. (US) **2628**
Ford's Deck Plan Guide. (US ISSN 0096-1353) **4767, 4727**
Ford's Freighter Travel Guide and Waterways of the World. (US) **4767, 4727**
Ford's International Cruise Guide. (US ISSN 0015-7066) **4767, 4727**
Fordson and Old Tractor Magazine *see* Vintage Tractor **165**
Fordyce Letter. (US ISSN 0733-0324) **2709, 1065, 3627**
Fore. (US ISSN 0300-8509) **4504**
Forecast (Bridgewater). (US ISSN 0098-213X) **4128, 2758**
Forecast (Los Angeles). (US ISSN 0071-7282) **866**
Forecast (New York). (US ISSN 0890-9849) **2446, 1634**
Forecast Cumulative Sheets. (UK) **53**
Forecast Data Bank Cumulative Sheets *see* Forecast Cumulative Sheets **53**
Forecast for Home Economics *see* Forecast (New York) **2446**
Forecast of Housing Activity. (US ISSN 1056-5159) **866, 2487, 4149**
Forecaster. (US ISSN 0095-294X) **666**
Forecasts & Strategies. (US ISSN 0272-0868) **866**
Forecasts of Exchange Rate Movements *see* Currency Profiles **775**
Forecasts of Exchange Rate Movements (Dollar Edition) *see* Currency Profiles **775**
Forecourt Trader. (UK) **4691**
Forefront. (CN) **2532**
Forefront. (US ISSN 1040-8495) **3300**
Forehead. (US ISSN 0894-4008) **2993**
Foreign Activity Report. (US) **946**
†Foreign Aero-Space Literature/Gaikoku Koku Uchu Bunken Mokuroku. (JA ISSN 0454-191X) **5195**
Foreign Aeronautics Abstracts. *see* Guowai Hangkong Wenzhai **66**
Foreign Affairs. (US ISSN 0015-7120) **3957**
Foreign Affairs. *see* Kulpolitika **3964**
†Foreign Affairs Bulletin. (GW ISSN 0015-7139) **5195**
Foreign Affairs Journal. (NP) **3957**
Foreign Affairs Malaysia. (MY ISSN 0126-690X) **3957**
Foreign Affairs Record. (II) **3957**
Foreign Affairs Reports. (II ISSN 0015-7155) **3957**
Foreign-Affiliated Enterprises in Japan. (JA) **1076**
Foreign Agricultural Trade of the United States. (US ISSN 0046-4546) **151, 908**
Foreign Agriculture. (US ISSN 0015-7163) **151**
Foreign Agriculture - Agricultural Meteorology. *see* Guowai Nongxue - Nongye Qixiang **95**
Foreign Animal Husbandry Science and Technology. *see* Guowai Xumu Keji **217**
Foreign Callbook *see* International Callbook **1356**
Foreign Car Prices *see* New and Used Foreign and Japanese Car Prices **4698**
†Foreign Chemical Patent News/Gaikoku Tokkyo Sokuho, Kagaku-hen.(JA ISSN 0015-721X) **5195**
Foreign Composers. (RU) **3552**
Foreign Consular Offices in the United States. (US ISSN 0071-7320) **3957**
Foreign Direct Investment in the United States. (US) **908**
Foreign Economic Statistics Annual. (JA) **717**
†Foreign Economic Trends and Their Implications for the United States. (US ISSN 0090-9467) **5195**
Foreign Economics and Trade University. Journal. *see* Duiwai Jingji Maoyi Daxue Xuebao **905**
Foreign Education Development. *see* Waiguo Jiaoyu Dongtai **1671**
Foreign Education Material. *see* Waiguo Jiaoyu Ziliao **1671**
Foreign Exchange Bank of Korea *see* Korea Exchange Bank. Monthly Review **788**
Foreign Exchange Week *see* F X Week **908**
Foreign Geology Science and Technology. *see* Guowai Dizhi Keji **1567**
Foreign Government Offices in California. (US) **4060, 3957**
Foreign Intelligence Literary Scene. (US ISSN 0749-9132) **2918, 3458**
Foreign Investment in Canada. (US) **946, 2723**
▼Foreign Investment in Central and Eastern Europe. (US) **2723, 908**
Foreign Investment in the U S. (UK ISSN 0958-3076) **666**
Foreign Investment Opportunities in the Philippines *see* Investment Opportunities in the Philippines **951**
Foreign Investments in Brazil *see* Foreign Investments in Brazil. Legislation **908**
Foreign Investments in Brazil. Legislation. (BL) **908, 2709**
Foreign Language Annals. (US ISSN 0015-718X) **2814, 1750**
Foreign Language Teaching and Research. *see* Waiyu Jiaoxue yu Yanjiu **2851**
Foreign Language Teaching in Foreign Countries. *see* Guowai Waiyu Jiaoxue **2816**
Foreign Languages in Fujian. *see* Fujian Waiyu **2815**
Foreign Lasers. *see* Guowai Jiguang **3852**
Foreign Liabilities, Assets and Foreign Investments in Pakistan. (PK ISSN 0071-7339) **946**
Foreign Literature. (AA) **2918**
Foreign Literature. *see* Waiguo Wenxue **2974**
Foreign Literature Studies. *see* Waiguo Wenxue Yanjiu **2974**
Foreign Markets. *see* Rynki Zagraniczne **920**
Foreign Medical Science (Blood Transfusion and Blood). *see* Guowai Yixue (Shuxue yu Xueyexue Fence) **3272**
Foreign Medical Science (Clinical Biochemistry and Inspection). *see* Guowai Yixue (Linchuang Shengwu Huaxue yu Jianyan Fence) **3101**
Foreign Medical Science (Parasitosis). *see* Guowai Yixue (Jishengbing Fence) **552**
Foreign Medical Science - Internal Medicine. *see* Guowai Yixue - Neikexue Fence **3102**
Foreign Medical Sciences (Birth Control) . *see* Guowai Yixue (Jihua Shengyu Fence) **596**
Foreign Medical Sciences (Clinical Radiology). *see* Guowai Yixue (Linchuang Fangshexue Fence) **3358**
Foreign Medical Sciences (Gynecology & Obstetrics). *see* Guowai Yixue (Fuchan Kexue Fence) **3292**
Foreign Medical Sciences (Pediatrics). *see* Guowai Yixue (Erkexue Fence) **3320**
Foreign Medical Sciences (Pharmacology). *see* Guowai Yixue (Yaoxue Fence) **3727**
Foreign Medical Sciences (Respiratory Diseases). *see* Guowai Yixue (Huxi Xitong Fence) **3365**
Foreign Patents Information Bulletin. (KO) **3679, 12**
Foreign Policy (San Diego). (US ISSN 0748-2841) **3957, 929, 2406**
Foreign Policy (Washington). (US ISSN 0015-7228) **3957**
Foreign Policy Association. Headline Series. (US ISSN 0017-8780) **3957**
Foreign Policy News Clips. (US) **3957**
†Foreign Policy Preview. (US) **5195**
†Foreign Policy Research Institute Annual Report. (US) **5195**
Foreign Press Center Japan. Press Guide. (JA ISSN 0387-5040) **2569**
Foreign Production, Supply and Distribution of Agricultural Commodities. (US) **137**
Foreign Projects Newsletter. (US ISSN 0015-7244) **3957, 866, 929**
Foreign Relations of the United States. (US ISSN 0071-7355) **3957**
Foreign Report. (US) **3894, 666**
Foreign Science and Technology Catalogue - Geology. *see* Guowai Keji Ziliao Mulu - Dizhixue **1551**
Foreign Science and Technology Development. *see* Guowai Keji Dongtai **4311**
Foreign Science and Technology Literature Catalogue - Survey. *see* Guowai Keji Ziliao Mulu - Cehuixue **2268**
Foreign Service Journal. (US ISSN 0015-7279) **3957**
Foreign Silk. *see* Guowai Sichou **4619**
Foreign Social Science Bulletin. *see* Guowai Shehui Kexue Kuaibao **4373**
Foreign Social Science Dissertation Index. *see* Guowai Shehui Kexue Lunwen Suoyin **4394**
Foreign Stamps *see* Stamps and Foreign Stamps **5282**
▼Foreign State Immunity in Commercial Transactions. (US) **2723**
Foreign Student Service Council Newsletter *see* F.S.S.C. Newsletter **1633**
Foreign Tax Law Bi-Weekly Bulletin. (US ISSN 0095-7291) **2628, 1095**
Foreign Trade. (RU ISSN 0042-7721) **908**
▼Foreign Trade. (US) **909**
Foreign Trade. *see* Handel Zagraniczny **910**
Foreign Trade & Business Cycles Problems. *see* Problemi Spoljne Trgovine i Konjunkture **5262**
Foreign Trade and Investment. (US) **2723, 947**
Foreign Trade Bulletin. (II ISSN 0015-7317) **909**
Foreign Trade Fairs New Products Newsletter. (US ISSN 0883-4687) **909, 1039**
Foreign Trade Marketplace. (US) **909**
Foreign Trade of the Democratic People's Republic of Korea. (KN) **909**
†Foreign Trade Reports. Bunker Fuels. (US ISSN 0363-6798) **5195**
†Foreign Trade Reports. General Imports of Cotton, Wool and Manmade Fiber Manufacturers. (US) **5195**
Foreign Trade Reports. Summary of U.S. Export and Import Merchandise Trade *see* Foreign Trade Reports. U.S. Export and Import Merchandise Trade and Supplement **909**
†Foreign Trade Reports. U.S. Airborne Exports and General Imports. (US ISSN 0095-7771) **5195**
Foreign Trade Reports. U.S. Export and Import Merchandise Trade and Supplement. (US) **909**
Foreign Trade Reports. U.S. Exports - Schedule E - Commodity by Country *see* U.S. Merchandise Trade: Exports, General Imports, and Imports for Consumption - Standard International Trade Classification Revision 3 - Commodity by Country **923**
Foreign Trade Reports. U.S. General Imports and Imports for Consumption. Schedule A - Commodity by Country *see* U.S. Merchandise Trade: Exports, General Imports, and Imports for Consumption - Standard International Trade Classification Revision 3 - Commodity by Country **923**
†Foreign Trade Reports. U.S. Imports for Consumption and General Imports-TSUSA Commodity by Country of Origin: Annual (Year). (US) **5195**
Foreign Trade Reports. U.S. Trade with Puerto Rico and U.S. Possessions. (US ISSN 0565-1204) **909**
Foreign Trade Reports. U.S. Waterborne Exports and General Imports. (US ISSN 0095-0890) **909**
†Foreign Trade Reports. Vessel Entrances and Clearances. (US) **5195**
Foreign Trade Review. (II ISSN 0015-7325) **909**
Foreign Trade Statistics of Africa. Series A: Direction of Trade. (UN ISSN 0071-7398) **717**
†Foreign Trade Statistics of Africa. Series B: Trade by Commodity. (UN ISSN 0071-7401) **5195**
Foreign Trade Statistics of Africa. Series C: Summary Tables/Statistiques Africaines du Commerce Exterieur. Serie C: Tableaux Recapitulatifs. (UN) **717**
Foreign Trade Statistics of Asia and the Far East. Series A *see* Foreign Trade Statistics of Asia and the Pacific **717**
Foreign Trade Statistics of Asia and the Far East. Series B *see* Foreign Trade Statistics of Asia and the Pacific **717**
Foreign Trade Statistics of Asia and the Pacific. (UN ISSN 1011-4858) **717**
Foreign Trade Statistics of Asia and the Pacific. Series A *see* Foreign Trade Statistics of Asia and the Pacific **717**
Foreign Trade Statistics of Asia and the Pacific. Series B *see* Foreign Trade Statistics of Asia and the Pacific **717**
Foreign Trade Statistics of Bangladesh. (BG) **717**
Foreign Trade Statistics of Iran/Amar-e Bazargani-Ye Khareji-Ye Iran. (IR) **717**
Foreign Trade Statistics of Iran. Yearbook. (IR ISSN 0075-0492) **717**
Foreign Trade Statistics of the Philippines. (PH ISSN 0116-1822) **717**
Foreign Trade Statistics of Yemen Arab Republic. (YE) **717**
Foreldre og Barn. (NO) **1237**
Foreman *see* Supervision **994**
†Foreman's Letter. (US ISSN 0015-7333) **5195**
Foreman's Production Planner. (US) **1076, 1010**
Foreningen af Filmlaerer i Gymnasiet. Meddelelser *see* Medielaererforeningen for Gymnasiet og H F. Meddelelser **3513**
Foreningen af Katolske Skoler i Danmark Bulletin *see* K S Bulletin **1729**
Foreningen af Kommunale Chefer (KC) Nyt *see* K C Nyt **4089**
Foreningen af Statsautoriserede Revisorer Skattelove med Noter *see* F S R's Skattelove med Noter **1093**
Foreningen af Teleteknikere *see* F A T - Bladet **4597**
Foreningen af Teleteknikere Bladet *see* F A T - Bladet **4597**
Foreningen Danske Praktiserende Arkitekter *see* D P A **298**
Foreningen til Norske Fortidsminnesmerkers Bevaring. Aarbok. (NO ISSN 0071-7436) **2361**
Forensia. (US ISSN 0724-844X) **3264**

6196 FORENSIC

Forensic. (US ISSN 0015-735X) **1634**
†Forensic Engineering. (UK ISSN 0888-8817) **5195**
Forensic Quarterly. (US) **3264**
Forensic Register of Expert Consultants see San Francisco Bay Area Register of Experts and Consultants **2677**
Forensic Reports. (US ISSN 0888-692X) **3264**
†Forensic Science Gazette. (US ISSN 0046-4570) **5195**
Forensic Science International. (IE ISSN 0379-0738) **3264**
Forensic Science Progress. (US ISSN 0930-1461) **3264**
Forensic Science Society. Journal. (UK ISSN 0015-7368) **3264**
Forensic Science Society of India. Journal see Indian Journal of Forensic Sciences **3264**
Forensic Services Directory. (US ISSN 0192-3145) **2628**
Foresight. (CN ISSN 0711-3927) **2272**
Foresight. (CN ISSN 0384-5958) **2532**
Foresight (Birmingham). (UK) **3669**, 53, 3594
†Foresight (New York). (US) **5195**
Foresight (Washington, 1961). (US) **3300**, 2292
Foreskin Quarterly see F Q **5190**
Forest and Bird. (NZ ISSN 0015-7384) **1488**
Forest & Conservation History. (US ISSN 1046-7009) **2099**, 1488
Forest and Human Kind. see Senlin yu Renlei **2107**
Forest and Nature. see Skov og Natur **2108**
Forest and Timber. (AT ISSN 0015-7392) **2099**, 2114
Forest and Timber Industries Bulletin see Australasian Forest & Timber Bulletin **2096**
▼Forest Davis' Southern Football Recruiting. (US) **4504**
Forest Ecology and Management. (NE ISSN 0378-1127) **2099**, 439
Forest Farmer. (US ISSN 0015-7406) **2099**
Forest Farmer. Manual Edition. (US ISSN 0071-7452) **2099**
Forest Industries. (US ISSN 0015-7430) **2114**, 2099
Forest Industries Newsletter (Chicago). (US) **3616**, 2099
Forest Industries Newsletter (Washington) see In Focus (Washington) **2102**
Forest Industries Review see New Zealand Forest Industries **2116**
Forest Industry Affairs. (US) **2114**, 3662
Forest Industry Affairs Letter see Forest Industry Affairs **2114**
Forest Leaves see Pennsylvania Forests **2106**
Forest Notes. (US ISSN 0015-7457) **2099**, 1488
Forest of Education/Kyoiku-No-Mori. (JA) **1634**
▼Forest Perspectives. (US) **2099**
Forest Pest Management Institute. Information Report Series. (CN ISSN 0833-5540) **2099**, 533
†Forest Pest Management Institute. Technical Note Series. (CN ISSN 0826-0532) **5195**
Forest Pest Management Institute Newsletter. (CN ISSN 0714-1734) **2099**, 533
†Forest Pest Management Institute Program Review. (CN) **5195**
Forest Pests/Shinrin Boeki. (JA) **2099**
Forest Planning see Forest Watch **2100**
Forest Planning Canada. (CN ISSN 0832-1655) **2099**
Forest Products Abstracts. (UK ISSN 0140-4784) **2112**, 12
Forest Products Journal. (US ISSN 0015-7473) **2114**
Forest Products Research and Industries Development Commission Journal see F P R D I Journal **2114**
Forest Protection - Shinrin Boeki see Forest Pests **2099**

Forest Research Bulletin. (IO ISSN 0215-028X) **2099**
Forest Research Institute and Colleges, Dehra Dun. Quarterly News Letter. (II ISSN 0015-7481) **2100**
Forest Research Institute New Zealand. F R I Bulletin see New Zealand. F R I Bulletin **2105**
Forest Research Institute: Research Pamphlet. (MY ISSN 0126-8198) **2100**
Forest Resource Development Agreement Report. (CN ISSN 0835-0752) **2100**
Forest Science. (US ISSN 0015-749X) **2100**
Forest Science Monographs. (US ISSN 0071-7568) **2100**
Forest Service Cruising Procedures and Cruise Compilation Manual. (CN) **2114**
Forest Times. (CN ISSN 0706-7747) **2100**
Forest Tree Breeding. see Rinboku no Ikushu **2107**
Forest Tree Improvement. (DK ISSN 0105-4120) **2100**
Forest Watch. (US ISSN 1057-2724) **2100**, 1488
†Forest World. (US) **5195**
Foresta. (RM ISSN 0015-7503) **2114**, 815, 2558
Forestal. (CU ISSN 0426-9373) **2100**
Forestdale News see Bangladesh Journal of Forest Science **2096**
The Forester. (US) **1311**
Foresters Miscellany. (UK ISSN 0015-7511) **1297**
Forestry. (UK ISSN 0015-752X) **2100**
Forestry. see Lesnicka Prace **2103**
Forestry. see Lesnictvi **2104**
Forestry Abstracts. (UK ISSN 0015-7538) **2112**, 12
Forestry Abstracts. Leading Article Reprint Series. (UK ISSN 0071-7584) **2112**, 12
Forestry & British Timber. (UK ISSN 0308-7638) **2100**
Forestry Chronicle. (CN ISSN 0015-7546) **2100**
Forestry Facts see Yankee Woodlot **2111**
Forestry in China. see Zhongguo Linye **2111**
Forestry in Indonesia see Statistik Kehutanan Indonesia **2108**
Forestry Journal. see Lesnicky Casopis **2104**
Forestry: Latin American Industrial Report. (US) **2100**
Forestry Log. (AT) **2100**
Forestry Machinery. see Linye Jixie **2104**
Forestry Monthly. see Linye Yuekan **2104**
Forestry Newsletter of the Asia-Pacific Region. (UN ISSN 0532-0747) **2100**
Forestry on the Hill. (CN) **2100**
Forestry Research Institute of Malawi. Research Record. (MW) **2100**
Forestry Research West. (US) **2100**, 1955, 2114
Forestry Science. see Gorskostopanska Nauka **2101**
Forestry Update. (US) **2100**
Forests & People. (US ISSN 0015-7589) **2100**
Foret. (SZ ISSN 0015-7597) **2100**
Foret Conservation. (CN ISSN 0380-321X) **2100**
Foret - Entreprise. (FR ISSN 0150-6404) **2100**, 2114
Foret et Papier. (CN) **2100**
La Foret Privee. (FR ISSN 0153-0216) **2100**
Forets de France et Action Forestiere. (FR ISSN 0046-4619) **2100**
Forewarned. (US) **979**
Foreword see A S U National **2579**
†Forex Waves and Cycles. (US) **5196**
La Forge. (FR) **3895**, 2866
Forge (Year). (UK) **3406**
▼Forging. (US ISSN 1054-1756) **3406**
Forgotten Fantasy Library. (US ISSN 0163-6251) **3011**, 2918

Forintek Canada Corp., Western Laboratory. Special Publications. (CN ISSN 0824-2119) **2114**
†Forintek Review. (CN ISSN 0821-1841) **5196**
Forja. (SP) **1634**
†Forkel - Nachrichten aus Informatik und Wirtschaft. (GW) **5196**
Forlagsseriekatalog see Forlagsseriekatalog for Boerne- og Skolebiblioteker **1677**
Forlagsseriekatalog for Boerne- og Skolebiblioteker. (DK ISSN 0107-1491) **1677**
Forlagsvejviser. (DK ISSN 0109-405X) **4128**
Form. (GW ISSN 0015-7678) **2551**, 299
Form. (SW ISSN 0015-766X) **2551**, 299
Form. (US ISSN 0532-1700) **3999**
Form & Function. (US ISSN 0015-7686) **299**, 618
Form & Zweck. (GW ISSN 0429-1050) **618**, 299, 2551
Form Function Finland. (FI ISSN 0358-8904) **326**, 299
Form und Geist. (SZ ISSN 0015-7694) **4021**
Forma in Modo Naturale. (IT) **3802**, 372
Forma Italiae. Serie I. (IT) **272**
Forma Italiae. Serie II. Documenti. (IT) **272**
Forma y Funcion. (CK ISSN 0120-338X) **2814**
Formal Aspects of Computing. (UK ISSN 0934-5043) **1477**, 1395
▼The Formalist. (US ISSN 1046-7874) **2993**
Formally Inc. (UK) **2452**
Formaluce. (IT) **1892**
Formalwords. (US) **1291**, 3397
Formandsbladet. (DK) **618**, 1065
Format. (GW ISSN 0015-7759) **326**, 3999
Format. (UK ISSN 0015-7740) **2993**
Formation pour l'Agriculture et le Developpement Rural see Training for Agriculture and Rural Development **1687**
Formation Professionnelle (Year). see Berufsausbildung (Year) **1682**
Formations. (US ISSN 0741-5702) **2918**
Formator Symposium on Mathematical Methods for the Analysis of Large-Scale Systems. (CS) **3035**
Formazione e Lavoro. (IT ISSN 0015-7767) **3627**, 1634
Formazione e Societa. (IT) **4372**
Forme. (IT) **2446**
†Forme del Significato. (IT ISSN 0390-2153) **5196**
Le Forme e la Storia. (IT) **2814**
Forme Materiali ed Ideologie del Mondo Antico. (IT ISSN 0391-6030) **2311**
Forme Selezione see Forme **2446**
Formed by the merger of Police Science Abstracts see Criminology, Penology & Police Science Abstracts **1525**
Formes et Structures. (FR ISSN 1140-5597) **2487**
Formghi Quarterly. (UK) **3552**
Forming i Skolen. (NO ISSN 0333-2217) **326**, 1750
Formosan Medical Association. Journal/Taiwan I Hsueh Hui Tsa Chih. (CH ISSN 0371-7682) **3099**
Forms and Label Purchasing see Business Documents **3998**
Forms of Business Agreements. (US ISSN 0015-7805) **1010**
Forms Tech Reference Series. (US) **1058**
Formsmfg. (US) **3999**
Formula. (CN ISSN 0848-8630) **4691**
Formula 2000 see Formula **4691**
▼Formworks. (CN) **4691**
Fornvaennen. (SW ISSN 0015-7813) **272**
Foro Amministrativo. (IT) **2628**
Foro Cosentino. Rivista di Prassi Giuridica. (IT) **2628**
Foro del Desarrollo see Development Forum **928**
Foro Internacional. (MX ISSN 0185-013X) **3957**

Foro Italiano. (IT ISSN 0015-783X) **2628**
Foro Literario. (UY) **2918**
Foro Mexicano see Mexican Forum **5236**
Foro Napoletano. (IT ISSN 0015-7848) **2628**
Foro Penale. (IT ISSN 0015-7864) **2628**
Foro Universitario. (CK ISSN 0040-9502) **2628**
Forpride Digest see F P R D I Journal **2114**
Forras. (HU ISSN 0133-056X) **2361**
†Forretnings- og Bedriftsledaren. (NO ISSN 0071-7630) **5196**
Forschung. (GW ISSN 0172-1518) **4310**
Forschung Aktuell. (GW ISSN 0176-263X) **4310**
▼Forschung an der Universitaet Bielefeld. (GW ISSN 0937-2873) **4310**, 1311
†Forschung der Sozialistischen Berufsbildung. (GW ISSN 0323-4711) **5196**
Forschung Frankfurt. (GW ISSN 0175-0992) **4310**
Forschung im Ingenieurwesen. (GW ISSN 0015-7899) **1822**
Forschung im Strassenwesen. (GW ISSN 0340-3998) **1865**
Forschung in der Sozialen Sicherheit. see Current Research in Social Security **2530**
†Forschung, Lehre, Praxis. (GW ISSN 0323-326X) **5196**
Forschung mit V D I-Forschungsheft see V D I - Forschungshefte **5299**
Forschung und Praxis im Dialog. (GW) **3099**
Forschungen aus Staat und Recht. (US ISSN 0071-7657) **2628**
Forschungen und Beitraege zur Wiener Stadtgeschichte. (AU) **2311**
Forschungen zu Osteuropa. (GW) **3957**, 2361
Forschungen zur Aelteren Musikgeschichte. (AU) **3552**
Forschungen zur Antiken Sklaverei. (GW ISSN 0071-7665) **2311**
▼Forschungen zur Brandenburgischen und Preussischen Geschichte. (GW ISSN 0934-1234) **2361**
Forschungen zur Europaeischen und Vergleichenden Rechtsgeschichte. (AU) **2628**
Forschungen zur Geschichte Oberoesterreichs. (AU) **2361**
Forschungen zur Innsbrucker Universitaetsgeschichte. (AU ISSN 0429-1573) **1706**
Forschungen zur Kirchen- und Dogmengeschichte. (GW) **4178**
Forschungen zur Kunstgeschichte und Christlichen Archaeologie. (GW ISSN 0532-2189) **326**, 272
Forschungen zur Mittelalterlichen Geschichte. (GW ISSN 0071-7673) **2361**
Forschungen zur Osteuropaeischen Geschichte see Freie Universitaet Berlin. Osteuropa-Institut. Historische Veroeffentlichungen **2362**
Forschungen zur Raumentwicklung. (GW ISSN 0341-244X) **2487**
Forschungen zur Rechtsarchaeologie und Rechtlichen Volkskunde. (SZ) **2628**, 272, 2055
Forschungen zur Religion und Literatur des Alten und Neuen Testaments. (GW) **4178**
Forschungen zur Volks- und Landeskunde. (RM ISSN 0015-7902) **2055**
Forschungen zur Volkskunde. (GW) **240**
Forschungen zur Wirtschaftsgeschichte. (GW ISSN 0138-5100) **894**
Forschunginstitut fuer Wirtschaftsverfassung und Wettbewerb e.V. Schriftenreihe see F I W - Schriftenreihe **665**
Forschungs Institut fuer Rationalisierung und dem Institut fuer Arbeits Wissenschaft Mitteilungen see F I R und I A W Mitteilungen **665**

Forschungsarbeiten aus dem Strassenwesen. Schriftenreihe. (GW ISSN 0341-5872) **1865**
Forschungsbereichs Geo- und Kosmoswissenschaften. Veroeffentlichungen. (GW ISSN 0138-4600) **1589**
Forschungsbericht zur Ur- und Fruehgeschichte. (AU) **272**, 240, 2361
Forschungsberichte aus Technik und Naturwissenschaften/Reports in the Fields of Science and Technology. (GW ISSN 0343-5520) **4614**
Forschungsberichte des Landes Nordrhein-Westfalen. (GW) **2189**
Forschungsberichte zur D D R-Literatur.(NE ISSN 0168-9770) **2918**
Forschungsdokumentation zur Arbeitsmarkt- und Berufsforschung. (GW ISSN 0340-8973) **979**, 717, 1684
Forschungsgemeinschaft Berlin. Rundbrief. (GW) **3752**
Forschungsgemeinschaft Grossbritannien Rundbriefe see F G G B Rundbriefe **3752**
Forschungsgesellschaft fuer das Strassenwesen. Arbeitsgruppe Asphalt- und Teerstrassen. Schriftenreihe see Forschungsgesellschaft fuer Strassen- und Verkehrswesen. Arbeitsgruppe Asphalt- und Teerstrassen. Schriftenreihe **1865**
Forschungsgesellschaft fuer das Strassenwesen. Arbeitsgruppe Betonstrassen. Schriftenreihe see Forschungsgesellschaft fuer Strassen- und Verkehrswesen. Arbeitsgruppe Betonstrassen. Schriftenreihe **1865**
Forschungsgesellschaft fuer Strassen- und Verkehrswesen. Arbeitsgruppe Asphalt- und Teerstrassen. Schriftenreihe. (GW) **1865**
Forschungsgesellschaft fuer Strassen- und Verkehrswesen. Arbeitsgruppe Betonstrassen. Schriftenreihe. (GW) **1865**
Forschungsgesellschaft fuer Strassen- und Verkehrswesen. Arbeitsgruppe Mineralstoffe im Strassenbau. (GW) **4718**
Forschungsgesellschaft fuer Wohnen, Bauen und Planen Vorschau see F G W Vorschau **617**
Forschungsinstitut fuer Absatz und Handel. Schriftenreihe. (SZ) **835**
†Forschungsprobleme der Vergleichenden Literaturgeschichte. (GW ISSN 0071-7703) **5196**
Forschungsstelle fuer Jagdkunde und Wildschadenverhuetung. Schriftenreihe. (GW ISSN 0071-7711) **4547**, 2100
Forschungsstelle Ostmitteleuropa an der Universitaet Dortmund. Studien. (GW ISSN 0179-6356) **2362**
Forsikring. (DK ISSN 0105-4260) **2532**
Forsikringsfunksjonaerenes Landsforbund Avisen see F F-Avisen **2531**
Forsikringstidende. (NO ISSN 0015-7929) **2532**
Forskning i Groenland-Tusaat. (DK ISSN 0105-7502) **1543**, 3099
Forskning och Framsteg. (SW ISSN 0015-7937) **4310**, 4598
Forskningscenter Risoe. Aarsberetning/Risoe Annual Report. (DK) **1790**
Forskningscenter Risoe. Energi Systems Gruppen. Annual Progress Report. (DK) **1790**
†Forskningslaboratoriet for Frugt og Groentindustri. Aarsberetning. (DK ISSN 0106-2573) **5196**
Forsoegsanlaeg Risoe. see Forskningscenter Risoe. Energi Systems Gruppen. Annual Progress Report **1790**
Forsoegsanlaeg Risoe. Aarsberetning see Forskningscenter Risoe. Aarsberetning **1790**
Forst, Holz und Jagd Taschenbuch. (GW ISSN 0344-1296) **2101**, 53
Forst und Holz. (GW ISSN 0932-9315) **2101**, 2114

Forst- und Holzwirt see Forst und Holz **2101**
Forstarchiv. (GW ISSN 0300-4112) **2101**
Forstliche Mitteilungen. (GW ISSN 0015-797X) **2101**
Forstliche Umschau. (GW ISSN 0015-7988) **2112**, 12
Forstlige Forsoegsvaesen i Danmark see Danish Forest and Landscape Research **2098**
Forstpflanzen-Forstsamen. (GW ISSN 0015-7996) **2101**
Forstwissenschaftliche Forschungen. (GW ISSN 0071-772X) **2101**
Forstwissenschaftliches Centralblatt. (GW ISSN 0015-8003) **2101**
†Forsvar: Militaer Kritisk Magasin. (DK ISSN 0106-2093) **5196**
Forsvarets Forum. (NO ISSN 0332-9062) **3458**
Fort. (UK ISSN 0261-586X) **3458**, 299, 2362
Fort Apache Scout. (US) **2002**
Fort Belknap Genealogical Association. Bulletin. (US ISSN 0071-7738) **2151**
Fort Burgwin Research Center. Publications. (US ISSN 0071-7754) **2406**
Fort Concho and the South Plains Journal. (US) **2406**
Fort Concho Members Dispatch. (US) **3524**, 2406, 3458
Fort Concho Report see Fort Concho and the South Plains Journal **2406**
Fort Hare Papers. (SA ISSN 0015-8054) **4310**, 666, 2507
Fort Lauderdale Downtown. (US) **2225**
Fort Lauderdale Magazine. (US) **815**
Fort Point Salvo see Salvo **2421**
Fort Smith Historical Society. Journal. (US ISSN 0736-4261) **2406**
Fort Ticonderoga Museum. Bulletin. (US ISSN 0015-8070) **3458**, 2406, 3524
Fort Worth. (US ISSN 0015-8089) **815**
Fort Worth Commercial Recorder. (US ISSN 0015-8097) **835**
Fort Worth Como Monitor. (US ISSN 0046-466X) **2225**
Fort Worth Como Weekly see Fort Worth Como Monitor **2225**
Fortbildung und Praxis. (GW ISSN 0071-7835) **4406**
Fortbildungskurse fuer Rheumatologie. (SZ ISSN 0071-7851) **3369**
Forte. (UK) **2194**
Fortean Times. (UK ISSN 0308-5899) **3669**, 4310
Fortegnelse over Anerkendte Avlscentre, Aspirantbesaetninger, Opformeringsbesaetninger. (DK ISSN 0107-6922) **216**
Fortegnelse over Anerkendte Avlscentre, Fremavlssteder, Aspirantbesaetninger, Opformeringsbesaetninger see Fortegnelse over Anerkendte Avlscentre, Aspirantbesaetninger, Opformeringsbesaetninger **216**
Fortegnelse over Dansk Udviklingsforskning. (DK ISSN 0109-4955) **666**
Fortegnelse over Fabrikanter og Importoerer af Goedninger og Jordforbedringsmidler see Producenter og Importoerer af Goedninger og Jordforbedringsmidler **190**
Forth Dimensions. (US ISSN 0884-0822) **1430**, 1460, 1469
Forth Naturalist and Historian. (UK ISSN 0309-7560) **4310**, 1488, 1955
Forth Ports Handbook 1984. (UK ISSN 0262-8880) **4727**, 1135
Forth Valley Chamber of Commerce Quarterly Bulletin see Central Scotland Chamber of Commerce Quarterly Bulletin **811**
Forthcoming Books. (US ISSN 0015-8119) **400**
†Forthcoming Children's Books. (US ISSN 0000-0965) **5196**
Forthcoming International Scientific and Technical Conferences. (UK ISSN 0046-4686) **3392**, 4310

Fortid og Nutid. (DK ISSN 0106-4797) **2362**
Fortidsvern. (NO ISSN 0332-7205) **2362**
Fortitudine. (US ISSN 0362-9910) **3458**, 2311
Fortnight. (UK ISSN 0141-7762) **2866**
Fortnighter. (US) **1727**
Fortnightly see Contemporary Review **2862**
Fortnightly Al-Hilal. (CN) **2002**
Fortnightly Journal of Industry & Commerce. (II ISSN 0015-8127) **1076**
FORTRAN Forum. (US) **1430**
Fortress. (UK) **299**, 3458
Fortschritt-Berichte V D I. Reihe 13: Foerdertechnik. (GW ISSN 0178-9562) **1929**
Fortschritte der Arzneimittelforschung/Progress in Drug Research/Progres des Recherches Pharmaceutiques. (SZ ISSN 0071-786X) **3727**
Fortschritte der Botanik see Progress in Botany **515**
Fortschritte der Chemie Organischer Naturstoffe/Progress in the Chemistry of Organic Natural Products. (US ISSN 0071-7886) **1218**
▼Fortschritte der Diagnostik. (GW ISSN 0938-9407) **3099**
Fortschritte der Hochpolymeren-Forschung. see Advances in Polymer Science **1215**
Fortschritte der Kieferorthopaedie. (GW ISSN 0015-816X) **3308**
Fortschritte der Krebsforschung. see Recent Results in Cancer Research **3201**
Fortschritte der Medizin. (GW ISSN 0015-8178) **3099**
Fortschritte der Medizinischen Mikrobiologie/Progress in Medical Microbiology. (GW ISSN 0724-441X) **552**
Fortschritte der Mineralogie see European Journal of Mineralogy **3483**
Fortschritte der Neurologie, Psychiatrie. (GW) **3337**
Fortschritte der Onkologie. (GW ISSN 0323-5084) **3197**
Fortschritte der Ophthalmologie. (GW ISSN 0723-8045) **3300**
Fortschritte der Pflanzenzeuchtung. see Advances in Plant Breeding **166**
Fortschritte der Physik/Progress of Physics. (GW ISSN 0015-8208) **3818**
Fortschritte der Praktischen Dermatologie und Venerologie. (US ISSN 0071-7932) **3247**
Fortschritte der Tierzuechtung und Zuechtungsbiologie. see Advances in Animal Breeding and Genetics **539**
†Fortschritte der Urologie und Nephrologie. (GW) **5196**
Fortschritte der Verhaltensforschung. see Advances in Ethology **576**
Fortschritte der Veterinaermedizin. see Advances in Veterinary Medicine **4804**
Fortschritte der Zoologie/Progress in Zoology. (GW ISSN 0071-7991) **583**
Fortschritte im Acker- und Pflanzenbau. see Advances in Agronomy and Crop Science **166**
Fortschritte in der Arthroskopie. (GW ISSN 0930-925X) **3099**, 3369
Fortschritte in der Geologie von Rheinland und Westfalen. (GW ISSN 0071-8009) **1561**
Fortschritte in der Pharmakotherapie. see Advances in Pharmacotherapy **5131**
Fortschritte in der Tierphysiologie und Tierernaehrung. see Advances in Animal Physiology and Animal Nutrition **576**
Fortschrittliche Betriebsfuehrung und Industrial Engineering. (GW) **1010**, 1925
Der Fortschrittliche Landwirt. (AU ISSN 0015-8224) **92**
Fortune Directory. (US) **1135**, 1076

Fortune Double 500 see Fortune Directory **1135**
Fortune India. (II) **947**
Fortune Magazine. (US ISSN 0015-8259) **1010**
Fortune News. (US ISSN 0015-8275) **1514**, 4406
Fortune World Business Directory see Global 500 Directory **1136**
Forty-Niner Times see University Times (Charlotte) **1329**
Forum see Development Forum **928**
Forum. (UK ISSN 0963-8253) **1750**
Forum. (NE) **1790**
Forum. (SA ISSN 1016-7250) **2119**
Forum. see Zango **2240**
Forum. (PR) **2628**
Forum. (PL ISSN 0015-8402) **2866**
Forum. (CI ISSN 0015-8445) **2918**, 2866
Forum. (CN ISSN 0843-5995) **3458**
Forum. (DK ISSN 0108-3279) **3895**
†Forum. (IS ISSN 0334-2506) **5196**
†Forum (Aachen). (GW ISSN 0722-7647) **5196**
Forum. Berichte aus der Arbeit. (GW) **4178**, 4435
Forum (Cambridge). (US) **1750**, 4372
Forum (Essen). (GW ISSN 0937-8316) **4310**
Forum (Hamburg). (GW) **929**
Forum (London, 1967). (UK ISSN 0015-833X) **4021**, 4435
Forum (Lorenton). (US) **2866**, 4435
Das Forum (Munich). (GW ISSN 0176-3687) **1684**
Forum (Munich). (GW ISSN 0939-7256) **3099**
Forum (New York, 1974). (US) **3397**
Forum (New York, 1976). (US ISSN 0160-2195) **3397**
Forum (New York, 1978). (US) **666**, 947
The Forum (New York, 1978). (US ISSN 0194-8121) **1536**
Forum (New York, 1982). (US) **2002**
Forum (Philadelphia). (US) **299**
Forum (Scranton). (US ISSN 0015-8399) **2002**
The Forum. (US) **1311**
Forum (Syracuse). (US ISSN 0013-6743) **2532**
Forum (Tallahassee). (US ISSN 0744-6063) **1634**
Forum (Toronto) see Education Forum **1628**
Forum (Washington, 1963). (US ISSN 0015-8305) **2628**
Forum (Washington, 1970). (US) **2758**, 1311, 1684
Forum (Washington, 1978). (US) **1750**, 2814
Forum (Washington, 1980). (US) **2814**, 1750
Forum (Washington, 1984). (US) **1311**
†Forum (Wayland). (US) **5196**
†Forum Botanicum. (SA ISSN 0015-847X) **5196**
Forum Buero Wirtschaft. (GW ISSN 0176-232X) **1010**
Forum de la Force Terrestre. (BE ISSN 0015-8488) **3458**
Forum de Nutrition. see Nutrition Forum **3610**
Forum der Brauerei see Brauerei-Forum **379**
Forum der Letteren. (NE ISSN 0015-8496) **2918**, 2814
Forum der Psychiatrie. (GW ISSN 0071-8025) **3199**
Forum der Psychoanalyse. (GW ISSN 0178-7667) **4021**
Forum des Praktischen Arztes. (GW ISSN 0015-850X) **3099**
Forum des Transports Publics see Transports Urbains **4659**
Forum du Developpment see Development Forum **928**
†Forum Educacional. (BL ISSN 0100-9591) **5196**
†Forum Europa. (GW) **5196**
Forum Fabulatorum. (DK ISSN 0108-6715) **3011**
Forum foer Ekonomi och Teknik. (FI ISSN 0533-070X) **1076**

FORUM

Forum for Applied Research and Public Policy. (US ISSN 0887-8218) **1955**, 1790
Forum for Commerce and Industry *see* ChaCom **811**
Forum for Death Education & Counseling Newsletter. (US) **4021**
Forum for Development Studies. (NO) **3958**
Forum for Liberal Education *see* Liberal Education **1711**
Forum for Modern Language Studies. (UK ISSN 0015-8518) **2814**, 2918
Forum for Reading. (US ISSN 0738-9523) **1750**
Forum for Social Economics. (US) **894**
Forum for the Discussion of New Trends in Education *see* Forum **1750**
Forum for Utviklingsstudier *see* Forum for Development Studies **3958**
Forum Haus Ortlohn. Freundsbrief *see* Forum. Berichte aus der Arbeit **4178**
Forum International. (US) **2918**
Forum Jugendhilfe. (GW) **4406**, 1237
Forum Kritische Psychologie. (GW ISSN 0720-0447) **4021**
Forum Landmacht *see* Forum de la Force Terrestre **3458**
Forum Law Journal *see* The Law Forum **2645**
Forum Letter *see* Lutheran Forum. Forum Letter **4242**
Forum Liberal. (GW) **3895**, 2866
Forum Linguisticum. (US ISSN 0163-0768) **2814**
Forum Linguisticum. (GW) **2814**
Forum Loccum. (GW ISSN 0724-9780) **3895**, 666, 1634, 1955
Forum Mathematicum. (GW ISSN 0933-7741) **3035**
Forum Mikrobiologie *see* Bioforum **550**
Forum Modernes Theater. (GW ISSN 0930-5874) **4633**
Forum Musikbibliothek. (GW ISSN 0173-5187) **3552**
Forum Newsletter. (US) **4178**
Forum of Dancing. *see* Wudao Luncong **1532**
Forum of Education. (AT ISSN 0015-8542) **1706**
Forum of Osteopathy *see* D.O **3214**
Forum on Fundamental Surgical Problems. (US ISSN 0071-8041) **3378**
Forum Phoneticum. (GW ISSN 0341-3144) **2814**
Forum Politische Bildung. (GW ISSN 0934-0939) **1750**, 3895
Forum Religion. (GW ISSN 0343-7744) **4178**
Forum - Revista Invatamintului Superior.(RM ISSN 0015-8453) **1634**
Forum Sciences des Sports. *see* Sport Science Forum **4490**
Forum Specials. (US) **3397**
Forum Staedte-Hygiene. (GW ISSN 0342-202X) **1955**
Forum Today. (US) **3767**
†Forum U S A. (US) **5196**
Forum Universitaire. (ZR) **4372**, 2918
▼Forum Valutazione. (IT) **929**
Forum voor Architectuur. (NE) **299**
Forum Ware. (GW ISSN 0340-7705) **666**
Forum Wissenschaft. (GW ISSN 0178-6563) **4310**, 4598
Forumeer. (US ISSN 0015-8577) **2002**
Forvm. (AU) **2866**
Forward *see* Civil Aviation in Pakistan: Half-Yearly Newsletter **50**
Forward. (CN) **1536**
Forward. *see* Vorwaerts **2028**
Forward. *see* Embros **2196**
Forward. *see* Shetho **2220**
Forward. *see* Embros (Cyprus) **2865**
Forward *see* Mission Statement **4244**
Forward. (UK) **4406**, 4178
The Forward (Elkins). (US) **1311**
Forward (Kampala). (UG) **4372**, 3942
†Forward (Oakland). (US ISSN 0896-2707) **5196**
Forward and Back. (US) **1530**

Forward Day By Day. (US ISSN 1058-6784) **4238**
Forward Markets Bulletin. (II ISSN 0015-864X) **835**, 909
Forward Motion Magazine. (US) **3895**
Forward Times. (US) **2002**
†Forwood International. (IT ISSN 0393-5167) **5196**
Forza 7. (IT ISSN 0015-8666) **4524**
Foshan Wenyi. (CC) **2918**
Fossil. **3999**
†Fossil Energy Update. (US ISSN 0146-4299) **5196**
Fossilien. (GW ISSN 0175-5021) **3657**, 1561
Fossils/Kaseki. (JA ISSN 0022-9202) **3657**
Fossils. *see* Huashi **3657**
Fossils and Strata. (NO) **3657**
Foster Care. (UK ISSN 0262-8120) **1237**, 4406
Foster Natural Gas Report. (US ISSN 0095-1587) **3686**
Foster Parent Nourricier *see* Echo (Ottawa) **5183**
Fotec Fiber Optic Testing News. (US) **1336**, 3852
Foto. (HU ISSN 0427-0576) **3790**
Foto-Avisen. (DK ISSN 0046-4775) **3790**
Foto - Cine. (BL) **3790**, 3511
Foto Cine Guia. (AG) **3511**
Foto Creativ. (GW) **3790**
Foto, Film & Video. (DK) **3790**, 1385
Foto-Film-Ton *see* Foto-Film-Video-Tip **3790**
Foto-Film-Video-Tip. (SZ ISSN 0015-8690) **3790**, 4460
Foto Galaxis. (SP) **3790**
†Foto Indonesia. (IO ISSN 0126-057X) **5196**
Foto-Kino Revija. (YU ISSN 0015-8704) **3511**, 3790
Foto-Laboratorio. (IT) **3790**
▼Foto Media. (IO ISSN 0852-596X) **3790**
Foto Mundo *see* Fotomundo **3791**
Foto-Notiziario. (IT ISSN 0015-8720) **3790**
Foto-Notiziario Giornale. (IT) **3790**
Foto-Notiziario Professionale. (IT) **3790**
Foto och Filmteknik. (SW) **3790**
Foto og Smalfilm *see* Foto, Film & Video **3790**
†Foto-Revyen. (DK ISSN 0108-0016) **5196**
Foto Shoe *see* Foto Shoe 15 (English Edition) **4361**
Foto Shoe *see* Foto Shoe 30 **4361**
Foto Shoe America. (IT) **4361**
Foto Shoe 15. (IT) **4361**
Foto Shoe 15 (English Edition). (IT) **4361**
Foto Shoe 15-3 Nuovo Corriere della Calzatura *see* Foto Shoe 15 **4361**
Foto Shoe 30. (IT) **4361**
Foto-Visie. (NE) **3790**
Fotocamara con Popular Photography. (AG ISSN 0015-8771) **3790**, 3511
Fotocine 80. (IT) **3790**
Fotoflash. (CN ISSN 0318-7500) **3790**
Fotogeschichte. (GW ISSN 0720-5260) **3790**
Fotograf. (TU) **3790**, 326
Fotografare. (IT) **3790**, 1374
Fotografare Novita *see* Fotografare **3790**
Fotografia. (PL ISSN 0324-850X) **3791**
Fotografia Universal. (AG ISSN 0015-881X) **3791**
Fotografiamo. (IT) **3791**
Fotografie/Photography. (CS) **3791**
†Fotografie. (GW ISSN 0015-8836) **5196**
Fotografie Draussen. (GW ISSN 0935-414X) **3791**, 583
Fotografisk Tidskrift. (SW ISSN 0284-7035) **3791**
Fotogramas. (SP) **3511**
Fotogrammetriska Meddelanden/ Photogrammetric Reports. (SW ISSN 0071-8068) **2248**
▼Le Fotoguide. (IT) **1385**, 3511
Fotokino-Magazin. (GW ISSN 0015-8879) **3791**, 3511

FotoMagazin. (GW ISSN 0015-8712) **3791**
Fotomundo. (AG ISSN 0325-7150) **3791**, 3511, 4460
Fotomuveszet. (HU ISSN 0532-3010) **3791**
Foton. (VE ISSN 0015-8895) **3791**, 3511
Fotonyheterna. (SW ISSN 0015-8909) **3791**
Fotopratica. (IT) **3791**
Fotoromanza. (IT) **4843**, 2205
Fototecnica. (CU) **3791**
Fotowirtschaft. (GW) **3791**
Fouilles de Delphes: Collection. (FR) **272**
Foulees - le Nouveau Spiridon *see* Spiridon **5281**
Fouling Prevention Research Digest *see* Heat Transfer & Fluid Flow Service Digest **1853**
Fouling Shot. (US) **4472**
Foulsham's Original Old Moore's Almanack. (UK ISSN 0071-8084) **358**
Foundation. (UK ISSN 0306-4964) **3011**, 2918
Foundation Center. Annual Report. (US ISSN 0190-3357) **4425**
Foundation Center National Data Book *see* National Data Book of Foundations **4426**
Foundation Center Source Book Profiles.(US) **4425**
Foundation Directory. (US ISSN 0071-8092) **4425**
▼Foundation Directory Part 2: A Guide to Grant Programs Twenty Five Thousand Dollars to One Hundred Thousand Dollars. (US) **4406**
†Foundation Directory Supplement. (US) **5196**
Foundation Drilling. (US ISSN 0274-5186) **618**
Foundation for Accounting Education Update *see* F A E Update **750**
Foundation for Biomedical Research. Newsletter. (US) **439**
Foundation for Business Responsibilities. Dialogues. (UK) **666**
Foundation for Business Responsibilities. Discussion Paper. (UK ISSN 0073-7410) **666**
Foundation for Business Responsibilities. Occasional Papers. (UK ISSN 0073-7429) **666**
Foundation for Business Responsibilities. Research Paper. (UK ISSN 0073-7437) **666**
Foundation for Business Responsibilities. Seminar Papers. (UK) **666**
Foundation for Economic Education, Inc. Notes *see* F E E Notes **665**
Foundation for Reformation Research. Bulletin of the Library *see* Sixteenth Century Bibliography **2330**
Foundation for Reformation Research. Newsletter *see* Center for Reformation Research. Newsletter **2308**
Foundation for Research in Community Health Newsletter *see* F R C H. Newsletter **4101**
Foundation for Teaching Economics Newsletter *see* Teaching Economics **1761**
Foundation Giving (Year). (US) **4426**
Foundation Giving Watch. (US ISSN 0741-7004) **4406**
Foundation Grants Index. (US) **4426**
Foundation Grants Index Bibliography *see* Foundation Grants Index Bimonthly **5196**
†Foundation Grants Index Bimonthly. (US ISSN 0735-2522) **5196**
Foundation Grants to Individuals. (US) **4426**
Foundation Law Review. (PH ISSN 0015-8968) **2628**
Foundation News. (US ISSN 0015-8976) **31**
Foundation of Computing and Decision Sciences. (PL) **1879**
Foundation of Flexographic Technical Association. Report of the Proceedings: Annual Meeting and Technical Forum. (US) **3999**

Foundation of Thanatology. Archives. (US ISSN 0160-7081) **4022**
Foundation of Thanatology Series. (US) **4022**
Foundation Time. (PH ISSN 0015-8984) **2866**
†Foundation 500. (US) **5196**
Foundations. (UK ISSN 0144-378X) **4178**
Foundations in Library and Information Science. (US) **2758**
Foundations of America Series. (US) **2406**
Foundations of Control Engineering *see* Foundation of Computing and Decision Sciences **1879**
Foundations of Physics. (US ISSN 0015-9018) **3818**, 364, 477
Foundations of Physics Letters. (US ISSN 0894-9875) **3818**
Foundations of Semiotics. (US ISSN 0168-2555) **2815**
Foundations Today: Current Facts and Figures on Private Foundations *see* Foundation Giving (Year) **4426**
Founder Sounder. (US ISSN 0887-1892) **3552**, 2002, 4178
Founders Hall. (US ISSN 0279-3016) **1311**
Founding, Welding, Production Engineering Journal *see* F W P Materials Engineering Journal **3429**
Foundry *see* Foundry Management & Technology **3406**
Foundry Catalog File *see* Foundry Databook & Catalog File **3406**
Foundry Databook & Catalog File. (US) **3406**
Foundry Directory and Register of Forges. (US ISSN 0071-8130) **3406**
†Foundry Focus. (US ISSN 0269-7890) **5196**
Foundry Industry. *see* Slevarenstvi **3419**
Foundry Management & Technology. (US ISSN 0360-8999) **3406**
Foundry Trade Journal. (UK ISSN 0015-9042) **3406**
Foundry Trade Journal International. (UK) **3407**
†Foundry Worker. (UK ISSN 0015-9050) **5196**
Foundry World *see* Casting World **3404**
Foundry Yearbook. (UK ISSN 0306-4212) **3407**
Foundryman. (UK ISSN 0953-6035) **3407**
Fountain. *see* Al-Manhal **1259**
Fountain. *see* Mabua **2936**
Four and Five. (US ISSN 0015-9077) **1255**, 4178
Four Corners. (JA) **1634**, 1689
Four Corners. (AT) **2287**, 2171
Four County Agricultural News. (US) **151**, 199
Four Flags Tracer. (US) **2151**
Four Hundred. (US) **1460**
Four Quarters. (US ISSN 0015-9107) **2866**
Four Seasons (Berkeley). (US ISSN 0532-3215) **503**, 2126
Four Seasons Hotels and Resorts Magazine. (CN) **2177**
Four Wheeler Magazine. (US ISSN 0015-9123) **4691**
†Four Wheeler Specials. (US) **5196**
Four Worlds Journal. (US) **4222**
†Four Zoas. (US ISSN 0362-0247) **5196**
Fourah Bay Studies in Language and Literature. (SL) **2815**, 2918
Fourier. (SZ ISSN 0015-914X) **3458**
La Fournee. (CN ISSN 0015-9158) **2088**
Fournisseur de l'Agriculture *see* France Agriculture **93**
Foursquare World Advance. (US ISSN 0015-9182) **4282**
Fourteenth Century English Mystics Newsletter *see* Mystics Quarterly **2986**
Fourth Dimension *see* Samisdat **5273**
Fourth Estate. (CN ISSN 0015-9190) **2569**, 2866
Fourth Quadrant. (US) **358**
Fourth World Journal. (US ISSN 0882-3723) **3942**, 4406

Foward Vacancies see Future Vacancies for the Finalist **3627**
†Fox Chase. (US) **5196**
Fox Chase Cancer Center. Scientific Report. (US) **3197**, 541
Fox Magazine. (US) **3397**
Fox River Patriot. (US) **2225**
Fox Valley Living. (US) **2225**
†Fox 20. (US) **5196**
Foxfire. (US ISSN 0015-9220) **2055**
Foxfire Book Series. (US) **2055**
▼Foxhills Members Magazine. (UK) **2194**
Foxtalk. (US ISSN 1042-6302) **1430**, 1444
†Foxyriders. (US) **5196**
Foyers Mixtes. (FR ISSN 0015-9239) **4178**
Fra Als og Sundeved. (DK ISSN 0085-0845) **2362**, 2185
Fra Bjerringbro Kommune. (DK ISSN 0107-2757) **2362**
Fra Bornholms Museum. (DK ISSN 0107-4849) **3524**
Fra Bov Museum. (DK ISSN 0106-8229) **3524**, 2362
Fra Bov Sogns Museum see Fra Bov Museum **3524**
Fra Esbjerg Museums Virke see Mark og Montre **2374**
Fra Fysikkens Verden. (NO ISSN 0015-9247) **3818**
Fra Haug og Heidni. (NO ISSN 0015-9255) **272**, 1955
Fra Himmerland og Kjaer Herred. (DK) **2362**
Fra Holback Amt: Historiske Aarboeger. (DK ISSN 0107-878X) **2362**, 272
Fra Kvangaard til Humlekule. (DK ISSN 0107-895X) **2362**
Fra Nationalmuseets Arbejdsmark see Nationalmuseets Arbejdsmark **2377**
Fra Ribe Amt. (DK ISSN 0046-4864) **2362**
Fra Ringkoebing Amts Museer see F R A M **3524**
Fra Viborg Amt. Aarbog. (DK ISSN 0085-0853) **2362**
Fracastoro. (IT ISSN 0015-9271) **3099**
Fracht - Dienst. (GW ISSN 0939-7965) **4727**, 4650, 4709
Fracht Management. (GW ISSN 0342-3042) **4650**, 1010
Fracht-Schiffahrts-Konferenzen see Guetertransport in Seeverkehr **4728**
Fraenkische Geographische Gesellschaft. Mitteilungen. (GW ISSN 0071-8173) **2248**
Fraenkische Schule. (GW) **1634**
Fraenkische Studien see Wuerzburger Geographische Arbeiten **2266**
Fraenkischer Hauskalender und Caritaskalender. (GW ISSN 0173-5543) **419**, 2993, 4264, 4406
Fragechen see Fragezeichen **1255**
Fragen der Freiheit. (GW ISSN 0015-928X) **3895**, 894
†Fragen des Sozialistischen Weltsystems. (GW) **5196**
Fragezeichen. (GW) **1255**
Fragile. (GW) **2983**
Fragmenta Balcanica Musei Macedonici Scientiarum Naturalium. (XN ISSN 0015-9298) **560**
Fragmenta Coleopterologica. (JA ISSN 0429-2871) **533**
Fragmenta Entomologica. (IT ISSN 0429-288X) **533**
Fragmenta Faunistica. (PL ISSN 0015-9301) **583**
Fragmenta Floristica et Geobotanica. (PL ISSN 0015-931X) **2126**, 1955
Fragmenta Herbologica Jugoslavica. (CI ISSN 0350-3615) **92**, 503
Fragments see Banque Populaire Suisse. Journal **768**
▼Frais du Jour. (CN) **2070**
Fraktemann. (NO ISSN 0015-9352) **4727**
Fram: The Journal of Polar Studies. (US ISSN 0739-8158) **2406**
Frame-Work. (US ISSN 0895-6030) **3791**, 4435
Frames. (US) **3300**
Frames Architettura dei Serramenti. (IT) **618**, 2558

Frames Book (Year). (IT) **1135**, 618, 2558
Frames Porte e Finestre see Frames Architettura dei Serramenti **618**
Framework. (IE) **1255**, 3895
Framework. (UK ISSN 0306-7661) **3511**
Framework Forecast for the E E C Economies. (UK ISSN 0305-9936) **866**
Framework Forecast for the European Economic Community's Economies see Framework Forecast for the E E C Economies **866**
Framework Forecasts for the United Kingdom. (UK ISSN 0305-5620) **782**
Framing and Art. (UK ISSN 0957-929X) **326**, 2281, 2551
Framing & Art Buyer's World. (UK) **326**, 2436
Framing, Fine Art and Wall Decor see Framing and Art **326**
Franc - Nord see Franc - Vert **1488**
†Franc-Rire. (FR ISSN 0015-9379) **5196**
Franc - Vert. (CN ISSN 0822-7284) **1488**, 439, 1955
Francais au Nigeria. (NR ISSN 0015-9387) **2815**, 1750
Francais dans le Monde. (FR ISSN 0015-9395) **1634**
Francais Moderne. (FR ISSN 0015-9409) **2815**
Francaise Frisonne see La Prim Holstein **203**
France. (UK) **2187**
France. Activities Internationales. Rapport Annuel d'Activite-Electricite de France see France. Electricite de France International **1892**
†France. Bureau de Recherches Geologiques et Minieres. Agence Francaise pour la Maitrise de l'Energie. Geothermie-Actualites. (FR ISSN 0755-6365) **5196**
France. Bureau de Recherches Geologiques et Minieres. Bulletin. Section 1: Geologie de la France en France. Bureau de Recherches Geologiques et Minieres. Geologie de la France **1561**
France. Bureau de Recherches Geologiques et Minieres. Bulletin. Section 3: Hydrologie-Geologie de l'Ingenieur see France. Bureau de Recherches Geologiques et Minieres. Hydrogeologie **1597**
France. Bureau de Recherches Geologiques et Minieres. Bulletin Section 4: Geologie Generale see Geochronique **1561**
France. Bureau de Recherches Geologiques et Minieres. Documents. (FR ISSN 0221-2536) **1561**
France. Bureau de Recherches Geologiques et Minieres. Geologie de la France. (FR) **1561**
France. Bureau de Recherches Geologiques et Minieres. Hydrogeologie. (FR ISSN 0246-1641) **1597**
France. Bureau de Recherches Geologiques et Minieres. Manuels et Methodes. (FR ISSN 0245-9345) **1561**, 3483
France. Bureau de Recherches Geologiques et Minieres. Memoires. (FR ISSN 0071-8246) **1561**, 3483
France. Bureau de Recherches Geologiques et Minieres. Resume des Principaux Resultats Scientifiques et Techniques. (FR) **1561**
France. Bureau National d'Information Scientifique et Technique. Bulletin d'Information. (FR) **4310**
France. Caisse Nationale de Credit Agricole. Rapport sur le Credit Agricole Mutuel. (FR ISSN 0071-8254) **782**, 151
France. Caisse Nationale des Allocations Familiales. Statistiques Action Sociale.(FR ISSN 0181-0804) **4426**
France. Caisse Nationale des Allocations Familiales. Statistiques Prestations de Logement. (FR ISSN 0184-6469) **4406**

France. Caisse Nationale des Allocations Familiales. Statistiques Prestations Familiales. Resultats Generaux: Recettes, Depenses, Beneficiaires. (FR ISSN 0182-1598) **4426**
France. Centre d'Etudes de l'Emploi. Cahiers. (FR) **979**
France. Centre d'Etudes de l'Emploi. Dossiers de Recherche. (FR) **979**
France. Centre d'Etudes de l'Emploi. Lettre d'Information. (FR ISSN 0294-8400) **979**
France. Centre de Documentation et Informations. Information Fiscale et Sociale. (FR) **1095**
France. Centre de Recherche Zoologique. Departement de Genetique Animale. Bulletin Technique see France. Centre de Recherche Zootechnique. Departement de Genetique Animale. Bulletin Technique **5196**
†France. Centre de Recherche Zootechnique. Departement de Genetique Animale. Bulletin Technique. (FR ISSN 0249-5740) **5196**
France. Centre National de Documentation Pedagogique. Textes et Documents pour la Classe. (FR ISSN 0395-6601) **1634**
France. Centre National pour l'Exploitation des Oceans. Colloques. Actes see France. IFREMER. Centre de Brest. Colloques. Actes **1604**
France. Centre Regional Archeologique d'Alet. Dossiers. (FR ISSN 0399-6662) **272**
France. Comite des Travaux Historiques et Scientifiques. Bulletin Archeologique. (FR ISSN 0071-8394) **272**
France. Comite des Travaux Historiques et Scientifiques. Section d'Archeologie. Actes du Congres National des Societes Savantes. (FR ISSN 0071-8416) **272**
France. Comite des Travaux Historiques et Scientifiques. Section d'Histoire Moderne et Contemporaine. Actes du Congres National des Societes Savantes. (FR ISSN 0071-8440) **2362**
France. Commissariat a l'Energie Atomique. Annual Report. (FR ISSN 0071-8467) **1805**, 1790, 1822
France. Commissariat a l'Energie Atomique. Notes d'Information. (FR ISSN 0029-3997) **1805**, 1790, 1822
France. Commission Centrale des Marches. Guide du Fournisseur de l'Etat see France. Commission Centrale des Marches. Guide du Fournisseur de l'Etat et des Collectivites Locales **835**
France. Commission Centrale des Marches. Guide du Fournisseur de l'Etat et des Collectivites Locales. (FR ISSN 0071-8483) **835**
France. Commission Centrale pour la Navigation du Rhin. Rapport Annuel. (FR) **4727**
France. Commission Departementale d'Histoire et d'Archeologie. Memoires.(FR) **2362**
France. Commission Departementale des Monuments Historiques du Pas-de-Calais. Memoires. see France. Commission Departementale d'Histoire et d'Archeologie. Memoires **2362**
France. Commission des Operations de Bourse. Rapport au President de la Republique. (FR) **947**
France. Commission Industrie-Administration pour la Mesure. Recueil des Communications. (FR) **1822**
†France. Commission Nationale de l'Amenagement du Territoire. Rapport. (FR ISSN 0071-8491) **5196**
France. Conseil de Direction du Fonds de Developpement Economique et Social. Projet de Loi de Finances. (FR) **1076**

France. Conseil des Impots. Rapport au President de la Republique. (FR) **1095**
France. Conseil National de la Comptabilite. Bulletin Trimestriel. (FR) **4060**
France. Conseil National de la Comptabilite. Rapport d'Activite. (FR ISSN 0071-8513) **4060**
France. Conseil National du Credit. Rapport Annuel. (FR) **782**
France. Conseil National du Credit. Statistiques Mensuelles. (FR) **717**, 4571
France. Conseil National du Credit. Statistiques Trimestrielles. (FR) **717**, 4571
France. Delegation Generale a la Recherche Scientifique et Technique. Repertoire National des Laboratoires; la Recherche Universitaire; Sciences Exactes et Naturelles. Tome 4: Mathematiques, Sciences de l'Espace et de la Terre see France. Ministere de la Recherche et de l'Industrie. Repertoire National des Laboratoires; la Recherche Universitaire; Sciences Exactes et Naturelles. Tome 4: Mathematiques, Sciences de l'Espace et de la Terre **3036**
France. Delegation Generale a la Recherche Scientifique et Technique. Repertoire Permanent de l'Administration Publique see Repertoire Permanent de l'Administration Francaise **4072**
France. Departement des Statistiques de Transport. Memento de Statistiques des Transports see France. Observatoire Economique et Statistique des Transports. Memento de Statistiques des Transports **4663**
France. Direction de l'Espace Rural et de la Foret. Rapport sur le Fonds Forestier National. (FR) **2101**
France. Direction de la Documentation. Catalogue des Publications Editees ou Diffusees par la Documentation Francaise see A Propos (Paris) **388**
France. Direction des Affaires Economiques et Internationales. Informations Rapides. (FR ISSN 0291-8897) **866**, 909
France. Direction des Affaires Economiques et Internationales. Tableau de Bord Conjoncture. (FR ISSN 0243-8828) **2487**
France. Direction des Forets. Rapport sur le Fonds Forestier National see France. Direction de l'Espace Rural et de la Foret. Rapport sur le Fonds Forestier National **2101**
France. Direction du Batiment, des Travaux Publics et de la Conjoncture. Tableau de Bord Conjonctural du Logement see France. Direction des Affaires Economiques et Internationales. Tableau de Bord Conjoncture **2487**
France. Direction Generale de l'Aviation Civile. Bulletin Statistique. (FR) **66**
France. Direction Generale de la Concurrence et de la Consommation. Bulletin Officiel - Service des Prix. (FR) **1076**
France. Direction Generale de la Concurrence et des Prix. Bulletin Officiel des Services des Prix see France. Direction Generale de la Concurrence et de la Consommation. Bulletin Officiel - Service des Prix **1076**
France. Direction Generale des Douanes et Droits Indirects. Annuaire Abrege de Statistiques. (FR ISSN 0071-8637) **1095**
France. Direction Generale des Douanes et Droits Indirects. Commentaires Annuels des Statistiques du Commerce Exterieur. (FR ISSN 0071-8645) **909**
France. Direction Generale des Douanes et Droits Indirects. Statistiques du Commerce Exterieur: Importations - Exportations. Nomenclature: N.G.P. (Nomenclature Generale des Produits). (FR ISSN 0071-8688) **717**

6200 FRANCE. DIRECTION

France. Direction Generale des Impots. Precis de Fiscalite. (FR) **1095,** 2628
France. Direction Nationale des Douanes et Droits Indirects. Tableau General des Transports. (FR ISSN 0071-8726) **909**
France. Direction Nationale des Douanes et Droits Indirects. Transport du Commerce Exterieur. (FR ISSN 0071-8718) **909**
France. Dossiers de l'Audiovisuel. (FR) **1336**
France. Electricite de France International. (FR) **1892**
France. I.F.Re.Mer. Centre de Brest. Publications. Serie: Resultat des Campagnes a la Mer *see* Campagnes Oceanographiques Francaises **1603**
France. IFREMER. Centre de Brest. Colloques. Actes. (Institut Francais de Recherche pour l'Exploitation de la Mer (IFREMER)) (FR ISSN 0761-3962) **1604**
France. IFREMER. Centre de Brest. Publications. Serie: Rapports Economiques et Juridiques. (Institut Francais de Recherche pour l'Exploitation de la Mer (IFREMER)) (FR ISSN 0761-3938) **1604,** 2628
France. IFREMER. Centre de Brest. Publications. Serie: Rapports Scientifiques et Techniques. (FR ISSN 0761-3970) **1604**
France. Imprimerie Nationale. Annuaire. (FR ISSN 0078-9666) **4128**
France. Inspection Generale des Finances. Annuaire. (FR ISSN 0071-8742) **1095**
France. Institut International d'Administration Publique. Revue Francaise d'Administration Publique. (FR) **4060**
France. Institut National d'Etudes Demographiques. Cahiers de Travaux et Documents. (FR ISSN 0071-8823) **3982**
France. Institut National de la Sante et de la Recherche Medicale. Colloques.(FR ISSN 0763-7098) **3099,** 3392
France. Institut National de la Sante et de la Recherche Medicale. Bulletin d'Information *see* France. Institut National de la Sante et de la Recherche Medicale. INSERM Actualites **4101**
France. Institut National de la Sante et de la Recherche Medicale. INSERM Actualites. (FR ISSN 0755-4168) **4101,** 3099
France. Institut National de la Statistique et des Etudes Economiques. Annales *see* France. Institut National de la Statistique et des Etudes Economiques. Annales d'Economie et de Statistique **717**
France. Institut National de la Statistique et des Etudes Economiques. Annales d'Economie et de Statistique. (FR ISSN 0769-489X) **717**
France. Institut National de la Statistique et des Etudes Economiques. Bulletin Mensuel de Statistique. (FR ISSN 0007-4713) **4571**
France. Institut National de la Statistique et des Etudes Economiques. Courrier des Statistiques. (FR ISSN 0151-9514) **4571**
†France. Institut National de la Statistique et des Etudes Economiques. Collections. Serie C, Comptes et Planification. (FR ISSN 0533-0793) **5196**
†France. Institut National de la Statistique et des Etudes Economiques. Collections. Serie D, Demographie et Emploi. (FR ISSN 0533-0807) **5196**
†France. Institut National de la Statistique et des Etudes Economiques. Collections. Serie E, Enterprises. (FR ISSN 0533-0815) **5196**
†France. Institut National de la Statistique et des Etudes Economiques. Collections. Serie M, Menages. (FR ISSN 0533-0823) **5196**
†France. Institut National de la Statistique et des Etudes Economiques. Collections. Serie R, Regions. (FR ISSN 0533-0831) **5196**
France. Institut National de la Statistique et des Etudes Economiques. Documents Divers *see* Reunion. Institut National de la Statistique et des Etudes Economiques. Collection: Documents **736**
France. Institut National de la Statistique et des Etudes Economiques. Departements et Territoires d'Outre Mer. Bulletin Bibliographique. (FR ISSN 0020-2398) **400,** 666
France. Institut National de la Statistique et des Etudes Economiques. Economie et Statistique. (FR ISSN 0336-1454) **717**
France. Institut National de la Statistique et des Etudes Economiques. Economie et Statistique (Microfiche Edition). (FR ISSN 0336-1454) **717**
France. Institut National de la Statistique et des Etudes Economiques. Informations Rapides. (FR ISSN 0151-1475) **717**
France. Institut National de la Statistique et des Etudes Economiques. Tendances de la Conjoncture. (FR ISSN 0497-2007) **1076**
France. Institut National de Recherche et de Documentation Pedagogiques. Textes et Documents pour la Classe *see* France. Centre National de Documentation Pedagogique. Textes et Documents pour la Classe **1634**
France. Institut National de Recherche et de Securite pour la Prevention des Accidents du Travail et des Maladies Professionnelles. Cahiers de Notes Documentaires. (FR ISSN 0007-9952) **3616**
France. Laboratoire Central des Ponts et Chausees. Rapport de Recherche. (FR ISSN 0222-8394) **1865**
France. Laboratoire Central des Ponts et Chaussees. Rapport General d'Activite. (FR ISSN 0337-1573) **1865**
France. Laboratoire des Ponts et Chaussees. Rapport de Recherche *see* France. Laboratoire Central des Ponts et Chausees. Rapport de Recherche **1865**
France. Laboratoires des Ponts et Chaussees. Bulletin de Liaison. (FR ISSN 0458-5860) **1865**
France. Mediateur. Rapport Annuel du Mediateur. (FR) **3958**
France. Mininstere de l'Agriculture. Series "S". Structure et Environnement des Exploitations *see* France. Ministere de l'Agriculture et de la Foret. Analyses et Etudes. Etudes **137**
France. Ministere de l'Agriculture. Bulletin d'Information. (FR) **93**
France. Ministere de l'Agriculture. Bulletin Technique d'Information. (FR) **93**
France. Ministere de l'Agriculture. Cahiers de Statistiques Agricoles *see* France. Ministere de l'Agriculture et de la Foret. Analyses et Etudes. Cahiers **137**
France. Ministere de l'Agriculture. Collections de Statistique Agricole *see* France. Ministere de l'Agriculture et de la Foret. Analyses et Etudes. Etudes **137**
France. Ministere de l'Agriculture. Conjoncture Lait et Produits Laitiers *see* France. Ministere de l'Agriculture et de la Foret. Conjoncture Lait et Produits Laitiers **137**
France. Ministere de l'Agriculture et de la Foret. Analyses et Etudes. Cahiers.(FR ISSN 0998-4178) **137,** 4571
France. Ministere de l'Agriculture et de la Foret. Analyses et Etudes. Etudes. (FR ISSN 0998-4186) **137**
France. Ministere de l'Agriculture et de la Foret. Conjoncture Exterieur Agro-Alimentaire. (FR) **909,** 151
France. Ministere de l'Agriculture et de la Foret. Conjoncture Fruits. (FR) **151**
France. Ministere de l'Agriculture et de la Foret. Conjoncture Generale. (FR) **151**
France. Ministere de l'Agriculture et de la Foret. Conjoncture Grandes Cultures. (FR) **151**
France. Ministere de l'Agriculture et de la Foret. Conjoncture Lait et Produits Laitiers. (FR) **137,** 151
France. Ministere de l'Agriculture et de la Foret. Conjoncture Legumes. (FR) **151**
France. Ministere de l'Agriculture et de la Foret. Conjoncture Productions Animales. (FR) **151**
France. Ministere de l'Agriculture et de la Foret. Conjoncture Viticulture. (FR) **151**
France. Ministere de l'Agriculture et de la Foret. Donnees. (FR) **151**
France. Ministere de l'Agriculture et de la Foret. Donnees Chiffres Agriculture. (FR) **137,** 151
France. Ministere de l'Agriculture et de la Foret. Donnees Chiffrees. I A A. (FR) **138,** 151
France. Ministere de l'Agriculture et de la Foret. Productions de Bois et de Sciages. (FR) **2101**
France. Ministere de l'Agriculture et de la Foret. Serie Commerce Exterieur Bois et Derives. (FR) **151**
France. Ministere de l'Agriculture et de la Foret. Series Avicuture. (FR) **151**
France. Ministere de l'Agriculture et de la Foret. Series: Le Bulletin. (FR) **138**
France. Ministere de l'Agriculture et du Developpement Rural. Bulletin Technique d'Information *see* France. Ministere de l'Agriculture. Bulletin Technique d'Information **93**
France. Ministere de l'Agriculture. Informations Rapides Commerce Exterieur Agro-Alimentaire *see* France. Ministere de l'Agriculture et de la Foret. Conjoncture Exterieur Agro-Alimentaire **909**
France. Ministere de l'Agriculture. Informations Rapides. Fruits *see* France. Ministere de l'Agriculture et de la Foret. Conjoncture Fruits **151**
France. Ministere de l'Agriculture. Informations Rapides. Legumes *see* France. Ministere de l'Agriculture et de la Foret. Conjoncture Legumes **151**
France. Ministere de l'Agriculture. Informations Rapides. Production Animale *see* France. Ministere de l'Agriculture et de la Foret. Conjoncture Productions Animales **151**
France. Ministere de l'Agriculture. Informations Rapides. Secteur Avicole *see* France. Ministere de l'Agriculture et de la Foret. Series Avicuture **151**
France. Ministere de l'Agriculture. Informations Rapides. Statistiques des Entreprises *see* France. Ministere de l'Agriculture et de la Foret. Donnees Chiffrees. I A A **138**
France. Ministere de l'Agriculture. Informations Rapides. Viticulture *see* France. Ministere de l'Agriculture et de la Foret. Conjoncture Viticulture **151**
France. Ministere de l'Agriculture. Note de Conjoncture Production Vegetale *see* France. Ministere de l'Agriculture et de la Foret. Donnees **151**
France. Ministere de l'Agriculture. Production de Bois et de Sciages *see* France. Ministere de l'Agriculture et de la Foret. Productions de Bois et de Sciages **2101**
France. Ministere de l'Agriculture. Serie Commerce Exterieur Bois et Derives *see* France. Ministere de l'Agriculture et de la Foret. Serie Commerce Exterieur Bois et Derives **151**
France. Ministere de l'Agriculture. Series "S". Departements d'Outre-Mer *see* France. Ministere de l'Agriculture et de la Foret. Donnees Chiffres Agriculture **137**
France. Ministere de l'Agriculture. Series "S". Industries Agricoles et Alimentaires *see* France. Ministere de l'Agriculture et de la Foret. Donnees Chiffrees. I A A **138**
France. Ministere de l'Agriculture. Series "S". Industries Agricoles et Alimentaires *see* France. Ministere de l'Agriculture et de la Foret. Donnees **151**
France. Ministere de l'Agriculture. Series "S". Production Animales *see* France. Ministere de l'Agriculture et de la Foret. Donnees Chiffres Agriculture **137**
France. Ministere de l'Agriculture. Series "S". Production Vegetale et Forestieres *see* France. Ministere de l'Agriculture et de la Foret. Donnees Chiffrees. I A A **138**
France. Ministere de l'Agriculture. Series "S". Reseau d'Information Comptable Agricole *see* France. Ministere de l'Agriculture et de la Foret. Analyses et Etudes. Etudes **137**
France. Ministere de l'Agriculture. Series "S". Synthese Statistique Comptes et Revenus *see* France. Ministere de l'Agriculture et de la Foret. Analyses et Etudes. Etudes **137**
France. Ministere de l'Agriculture. Service Central des Enquetes et Etudes Statistiques. Bulletin de Statistique Agricole *see* France. Ministere de l'Agriculture et de la Foret. Series: Le Bulletin **138**
France. Ministere de l'Agriculture. Situation Agricole en France. Conjoncture Generale *see* France. Ministere de l'Agriculture et de la Foret. Conjoncture Generale **151**
France. Ministere de l'Agriculture. Situation Agricole en France. Note de Conjoncture Production Avicole. (FR ISSN 0243-6183) **151**
France. Ministere de l'Agriculture. Situation Agricole en France. Note de Conjoncture Production Bovine *see* Animaux Hebdo **147**
France. Ministere de l'Agriculture. Situation Agricole en France. Note de Conjoncture Production Porcine *see* Animaux Hebdo **147**
France. Ministere de l'Agriculture. Situation Agricole en France. Note de Conjoncture Production Vegetale *see* France. Ministere de l'Agriculture et de la Foret. Conjoncture Legumes **151**
France. Ministere de l'Agriculture. Situation Agricole en France. Note de Conjoncture Production Vegetale *see* France. Ministere de l'Agriculture et de la Foret. Conjoncture Fruits **151**
France. Ministere de l'Agriculture. Situation Agricole en France. Note de Conjoncture Productions Vegetale *see* France. Ministere de l'Agriculture et de la Foret. Conjoncture Grandes Cultures **151**
France. Ministere de l'Amenagement du Territoire, de l'Equipement, du Logement et des Transports. Bulletin Officiel. (FR ISSN 0399-0281) **4650**
France. Ministere de l'Economie, des Finances et du Budget. Balance des Paiements de la France. (FR) **1095,** 909
France. Ministere de l'Economie, des Finances et du Budget. Notes Bleues.(FR ISSN 0244-1179) **1095**

Title

FRANCE. SERVICE 6201

France. Ministere de l'Economie, des Finances et du Budget. Rapport du Conseil de Direction du Fond de Developpement Economique et Social *see* France. Conseil de Direction du Fonds de Developpement Economique et Social. Projet de Loi de Finances **1076**

France. Ministere de l'Economie et des Finances. Balance des Paiements Entre la France et l'Exterieur *see* France. Ministere de l'Economie, des Finances et du Budget. Balance des Paiements de la France **1095**

France. Ministere de l'Economie et des Finances. Bulletin Administratif des Assurances. (FR) **2532**

France. Ministere de l'Economie et des Finances. Caisses d'Epargne Ordinaire. (FR) **782**

France. Ministere de l'Economie et des Finances. Economie et Prevision. (FR) **666**

France. Ministere de l'Economie et des Finances. Statistiques et Etudes Financieres. Etudes Economiques. Serie Orange *see* France. Ministere de l'Economie et des Finances. Economie et Prevision **666**

France. Ministere de l'Economie et des Finances. Statistiques et Etudes Financieres. Finances Publiques. Serie Rouge. (FR) **666**

France. Ministere de l'Education Nationale. Bulletin Officiel. (FR ISSN 0291-5871) **1634**

France. Ministere de l'Environnement. Bilan d'Activite des Agences Financieres de Bassin. (FR) **1955**

France. Ministere de l'Environnement et du Cadre de Vie. Inspection Generale de l'Equipement. (FR) **4060**

France. Ministere de l'Industrie. Bulletin Mensuel de Statistique Industrielle *see* France. Service d'Etude des Strategies et des Statistiques Industrielles. Bulletin Mensuel de Statistique Industrielle **718**

France. Ministere de l'Industrie, des P & T et du Tourisme. Enquete Annuelle d'Entreprise *see* France. Service d'Etude des Strategies et des Statistiques Industrielles. La Situation de l'Industrie. Premiers Resultats **718**

France. Ministere de l'Industrie, des P & T et du Tourisme. Enquete Annuelle d'Entreprise *see* France. Service d'Etude des Strategies et des Statistiques Industrielles. La Situation de l'Industrie: Resultats Detailles **718**

France. Ministere de l'Industrie, des P & T et du Tourisme. Enquete Annuelle d'Entreprise *see* France. Service d'Etude des Strategies et des Statistiques Industrielles. La Situation de l'Industrie: Resultats Agreges **718**

France. Ministere de l'Industrie et de la Recherche. Repertoire National des Laboratoires; la Recherche Universitaire. Tome 1: Sciences de la Matiere. (FR) **3818**

France. Ministere de l'Industrie et de la Recherche. Repertoire National des Laboratoires; la Recherche Universitaire. Tome 2: Sciences de la Vie. (FR) **439**

France. Ministere de l'Industrie et de la Recherche. Repertoire National des Laboratoires; la Recherche Universitaire. Tome 3: Sciences Humaines et Sociales. (FR) **4372**

France. Ministere de l'Interieur. Repertoire *see* France. Ministere de l'Interieur. Repertoire Mensuel **1514**

France. Ministere de l'Interieur. Repertoire Mensuel. (FR) **1514**

France. Ministere de l'Urbanisme et du Logement. Conjoncture. (FR) **2487**

France. Ministere de l'Urbanisme et du Logement. Statistiques de la Construction. (FR) **638**

France. Ministere de l'Urbanisme et du Logement. Statistiques et Etudes Generales. (FR ISSN 0184-6892) **2499**, 4571

France. Ministere de l'Urbanisme et du Logement. Tableau de Bord du Batiment du Logement et des Travaux Publics. (FR) **2487**

France. Ministere de la Cooperation. Sous-Direction des Etudes de Developpement. Etudes et Documents *see* France. Ministere des Relations Exterieures. Sous-Directions des Etudes et Developpement. Etudes et Documents **3958**

France. Ministere de la Culture et de l'Environnement. Bilan d'Activite des Agences Financieres de Bassin *see* France. Ministere de l'Environnement. Bilan d'Activite des Agences Financieres de Bassin **1955**

France. Ministere de la Defense Nationale. Bulletin d'Information Technique et Scientifique. (FR ISSN 0015-9719) **3458**

France. Ministere de la Defense Nationale. Bulletin Officiel. (FR ISSN 0015-9727) **3458**

France. Ministere de la Recherche et de l'Industrie. Repertoire National des Laboratoires; la Recherche Universitaire; Sciences Exactes et Naturelles. Tome 4: Mathematiques, Sciences de l'Espace et de la Terre. (FR) **3036**

France. Ministere de la Sante et de la Famille. Bulletin Epidemiologique *see* France. Ministere des Affaires Sociales et de la Solidarite Nationale. Bulletin Epidemiologique **4101**

France. Ministere de la Sante et de la Securite Sociale. Annuaire des Statistiques Sanitaires et Sociales. (FR) **4101**

France. Ministere de la Sante et de la Securite Sociale. Bulletin Epidemiologique *see* France. Ministere des Affaires Sociales et de la Solidarite Nationale. Bulletin Epidemiologique **4101**

France. Ministere de la Sante et de la Securite Sociale. Bulletin Officiel. (FR) **4101**

France. Ministere de la Sante et de la Securite Sociale. Notes d'Information.(FR) **4101**

France. Ministere de la Sante. Note d'Information *see* France. Ministere de la Sante et de la Securite Sociale. Notes d'Information **4101**

France. Ministere de la Solidarite, de la Sante et de la Protection Sociale. Bulletin Officiel. (FR) **400**, 4101

France. Ministere des Affaires Sociales et de l'Integration. Bulletin Officiel. (FR) **4060**, 4101

France. Ministere des Affaires Sociales et de la Solidarite Nationale. Bulletin Epidemiologique. (FR) **4101**

France. Ministere des Affaires Sociales et de la Solidarite Nationale. Bulletin Mensuel des Statistiques du Travail. (FR ISSN 0338-4284) **717**

France. Ministere des Affaires Sociales et de la Solidarite Nationale. Ministere Charge de l'Emploi. Conventions Collectives. (FR ISSN 0759-0083) **4060**, 979

France. Ministere des Affaires Sociales et de la Solidarite Nationale. Secretariat d'Etat Charge de la Sante. Bulletin Officiel *see* France. Ministere des Affaires Sociales et de l'Integration. Bulletin Officiel **4060**

France. Ministere des Affaires Sociales et Solidarite National. Bulletin Officiel *see* France. Ministere de la Solidarite, de la Sante et de la Protection Sociale. Bulletin Officiel **400**

France. Ministere des Affaires Sociales. Information Actualites *see* France. Ministere de la Sante et de la Securite Sociale. Notes d'Information **4101**

France. Ministere des Armees. Bulletin Officiel des Armees. (FR) **3458**

France. Ministere des Relations Exterieures. Sous-Directions des Etudes et Developpement. Etudes et Documents. (FR) **3958**

France. Ministere du Budget. Budget *see* France. Ministere de l'Economie, des Finances et du Budget. Notes Bleues **1095**

France. Ministere du Budget. Notes Bleues *see* France. Ministere de l'Economie, des Finances et du Budget. Notes Bleues **1095**

France. Ministere du Travail. Dossiers Statistiques du Travail et de l'Emploi. (FR ISSN 0756-8630) **717**

France. Observatoire Economique et Statistique des Transports. Memento de Statistiques des Transports. (FR) **4663**

France. Observatoire Economique et Statistique des Transports. Note de Conjoncture. (FR ISSN 0244-7819) **4663**

France. Office des Migrations Internationales. OMISTATS. (FR) **3992**

France. Office National d'Etudes et de Recherches Aerospatiales. Activities. (FR ISSN 0078-3773) **53**

France. Office National d'Etudes et de Recherches Aerospatiales. Notes Techniques. (FR ISSN 0078-3781) **53**

France. Office National d'Etudes et de Recherches Aerospatiales. Publications. (FR ISSN 0078-379X) **53**

France. Office National d'Immigration. Statistiques de l'Immigration *see* France. Office des Migrations Internationales. OMISTATS **3992**

France. Office National d'Information sur les Enseignements. Bulletin d'Information. *see* France. Office National d'Information sur les Enseignements et les Professions. Bulletin d'Information **1634**

France. Office National d'Information sur les Enseignements et les Professions. Bulletin d'Information. (FR ISSN 0220-0562) **1634**

France. Parlement. Assemblee Nationale. Bulletin. (FR) **4061**

France. Parlement. Assemblee Nationale. Bulletin des Commissions. (FR) **4061**

France. Secretariat d'Etat aux Affaires Etrangeres Charge de la Cooperation. Direction de l'Aide au Developpement. Cote d'Ivoire. Dossier d'Information Economique. (FR) **929**

France. Secretariat d'Etat aux Affaires Etrangeres Charge de la Cooperation. Direction de l'Aide au Developpement. Mali. Dossier d'Information Economique. (FR) **929**

France. Secretariat d'Etat aux Affaires Etrangeres Charge de la Cooperation. Direction de l'Aide au Developpement. Niger. Dossier d'Information Economique. (FR) **929**

France. Secretariat d'Etat aux Affaires Etrangeres Charge de la Cooperation. Recueil des Traites et Accords de la France. (FR ISSN 0071-8971) **2723**

France. Secretariat d'Etat Charge de l'Environnement et de la Qualite de la Vie. Bulletin de Documentation de l'Environnement. (FR) **1974**, 400

France. Service d'Etude des Strategies et des Statistiques Industrielles. Annuaire de Statistique Industrielle. (FR) **718**

France. Service d'Etude des Strategies et des Statistiques Industrielles. Bulletin Mensuel de Statistique Industrielle. (FR) **718**

France. Service d'Etude des Strategies et des Statistiques Industrielles. Collections: Traits Fondamentaux du Systeme Industriel Francais. (FR ISSN 0244-7118) **718**

France. Service d'Etude des Strategies et des Statistiques Industrielles. Ingenierie, Etudes et Conseils *see* France. Service d'Etude des Strategies et des Statistiques Industrielles. Societes d'Etudes et de Conseils, Ingenieurs-Conseils **666**

France. Service d'Etude des Strategies et des Statistiques Industrielles. Les Chiffres Cles de l'Industrie. (FR) **718**

France. Service d'Etude des Strategies et des Statistiques Industrielles. Les Chiffres Cles de l'Industrie dans les Regions. (FR) **718**

France. Service d'Etude des Strategies et des Statistiques Industrielles. Les Consommations d'Energie dans l'Industrie. (FR) **1799**, 1802

France. Service d'Etude des Strategies et des Statistiques Industrielles. La Dispersion des Performances des Entreprises. (FR) **718**

France. Service d'Etude des Strategies et des Statistiques Industrielles. L'Implantation Etrangere dans l'Industrie. (FR) **718**, 835

France. Service d'Etude des Strategies et des Statistiques Industrielles. La Situation de l'Industrie. Premiers Resultats. (FR) **718**, 4571

France. Service d'Etude des Strategies et des Statistiques Industrielles. La Situation de l'Industrie: Resultats Agreges. (FR) **718**, 866

France. Service d'Etude des Strategies et des Statistiques Industrielles. La Situation de l'Industrie: Resultats Detailles. (FR) **718**, 866

France. Service d'Etude des Strategies et des Statistiques Industrielles. Resultats Mensuels des Enquetes de Branche. Ameublement. (FR) **2556**

France. Service d'Etude des Strategies et des Statistiques Industrielles. Resultats Mensuels des Enquetes de Branche. Industrie Chimique de Base.(FR) **1201**

France. Service d'Etude des Strategies et des Statistiques Industrielles. Resultats Mensuels des Enquetes de Branche. Industrie du Caoutchouc. (FR) **4294**

France. Service d'Etude des Strategies et des Statistiques Industrielles. Resultats Mensuels des Enquetes de Branche. Industrie du Verre. (FR) **1167**

France. Service d'Etude des Strategies et des Statistiques Industrielles. Resultats Mensuels des Enquetes de Branche. Industrie Pharmaceutique. (FR) **3747**

France. Service d'Etude des Strategies et des Statistiques Industrielles. Resultats Mensuels des Enquetes de Branche. Parachimie. (FR) **1201**

France. Service d'Etude des Strategies et des Statistiques Industrielles. Resultats Mensuels des Enquetes de Branche. Travail des Metaux. (FR) **3425**

France. Service d'Etude des Strategies et des Statistiques Industrielles. Resultats Mensuels des Enquetes de Branche. Travail Mecanique du Bois. (FR) **2112**

France. Service d'Etude des Strategies et des Statistiques Industrielles. Recueil Statistiques *see* France. Service d'Etude des Strategies et des Statistiques Industrielles. Collections: Traits Fondamentaux du Systeme Industriel Francais **718**

France. Service d'Etude des Strategies et des Statistiques Industrielles. Resultats Trimestriels des Enquetes de Branche. Fabrication d'Articles de Papeterie. (FR) **3668**

France. Service d'Etude des Strategies et des Statistiques Industrielles. Resultats Trimestriels des Enquetes de Branche. Fabrication de Materiel Medico-Chirurgical et des Protheses. (FR) **3174**

France. Service d'Etude des Strategies et des Statistiques Industrielles. Resultats Trimestriels des Enquetes de Branche. Industrie Chimique de Base. (FR) **1201**

France. Service d'Etude des Strategies et des Statistiques Industrielles. Resultats Trimestriels des Enquetes de Branche. Industrie de Caoutchouc.(FR) **4294**

Title

France. Service d'Etude des Strategies et des Statistiques Industrielles. Resultats Trimestriels des Enquetes de Branche. Industrie de l'Ameublement. (FR) **2556**
France. Service d'Etude des Strategies et des Statistiques Industrielles. Resultats Trimestriels des Enquetes de Branche. Industrie de l'Habillement. (FR) **1288**
France. Service d'Etude des Strategies et des Statistiques Industrielles. Resultats Trimestriels des Enquetes de Branche. Industrie du Verre. (FR) **1167**
France. Service d'Etude des Strategies et des Statistiques Industrielles. Resultats Trimestriels des Enquetes de Branche. Labos Photographiques et Cinematographiques. (FR) **3798**
France. Service d'Etude des Strategies et des Statistiques Industrielles. Resultats Trimestriels des Enquetes de Branche. Parachimie. (FR) **1201**
France. Service d'Etude des Strategies et des Statistiques Industrielles. Resultats Trimestriels des Enquetes de Branche. Travail des Metaux. (FR) **3425**
France. Service d'Etude des Strategies et des Statistiques Industrielles. Resultats Trimestriels des Enquetes de Branche. Transformation des Matieres Plastiques. (FR) **3868**
France. Service d'Etude des Strategies et des Statistiques Industrielles. Resultats Trimestriels des Enquetes de Branche. Travail Mecanique du Bois. (FR) **2112**
France. Service d'Etude des Strategies et des Statistiques Industrielles. Societes d'Etudes et de Conseils, Ingenieurs-Conseils. (FR) **666, 1822**
†France. Service de Relations Publiques et d'Information. Bibliotheque Centrale. Liste Mensuelle d'Acquisitions d'Ouvrages. Selection Hebdomadaire d'Articles Economiques. (FR) **5197**
France. Service du Traitement de l'Information et des Statistiques Industrielles. Annuaire de Statistique Industrielle see France. Service d'Etude des Strategies et des Statistiques Industrielles. Annuaire de Statistique Industrielle **718**
†France. Service du Traitement de l'Information et des Statistiques Industrielles. Bibliotheque Centrale. Bulletin Bibliographique. (FR) **5197**
†France. Service du Traitement de l'Information et des Statistiques Industrielles. Selection Hebdomadaire d'Articles Economiques. (FR) **5197**
France. Service du Traitement de l'Information et des Statistiques Industrielles. Societe d'Etudes et de Conseils, Ingenieurs-Conseils see France. Service d'Etude des Strategies et des Statistiques Industrielles. Societes d'Etudes et de Conseils, Ingenieurs-Conseils **666**
France. Service Interdepartemental de la Protection Civile. Bulletin. (FR) **1273**
France. Service Regional de Statistique Agricole. Bulletin de Statistique Agricole. (FR) **138**
France (Year). (US) **4767**
France Afrique. (FR) **866**
France Agricole. (FR ISSN 0046-4899) **93**
France Agriculture. (FR) **93**
France Alimentaire. (FR ISSN 0015-9484) **2070**
France - Allemagne. (FR ISSN 0071-8181) **3958**
France - Amerique. (US) **2002**
France and Colonies Philatelic Society. Journal see France & Colonies Philatelic Society of Great Britain. Journal **3752**
France & Colonies Philatelic Society of Great Britain. Journal. (UK ISSN 0269-5006) **3752**
France Aviation. (FR ISSN 0751-5596) **53**

France, Belgique, Luxembourg. (FR) **815**
France Catholique - Ecclesia. (FR) **4264**
France Composites. (FR ISSN 0985-0503) **3862**
France Cycliste. (FR) **4518**
France dans l'Europe de 1993. (FR) **666**
La France de l'Industrie et ses Services. (FR) **1135, 3675**
France des Points Chauds. (FR) **3895**
France Dimanche. (FR ISSN 0015-9549) **2187**
France, Direction de la Documentation. Tables de la Documentation Francaise see A Propos (Paris) **388**
France en Poche. Total Guide. (FR ISSN 0071-8734) **4767**
France Football. (FR) **4504**
France Forum. (FR ISSN 0046-4910) **3895, 4061**
France-Francis Family see Francis - King Bulletin **2151**
France Graphique. (FR ISSN 0015-9565) **3999, 4128**
France Horlogere. (FR ISSN 0015-9573) **2564**
France - Iberie Recherche. Etudes et Documents. (FR ISSN 0082-5409) **3895**
France - Iberie Recherche. Theses et Documents see France - Iberie Recherche. Theses et Recherches **2362**
France - Iberie Recherche. Theses et Recherches. (FR) **2362**
France Industrie. (FR) **1076**
France Informations. (FR ISSN 0015-959X) **3958**
†France - Islam. (FR) **5197**
France Japon Eco. (JA) **815**
†France - Loisirs. (UK ISSN 0015-9417) **5197**
France Magazine. (US ISSN 0886-2478) **2187**
France Mecanographique. (FR) **3999**
France Mutualite. (FR ISSN 0015-9670) **2187**
France - Pays Arabes. (FR ISSN 0533-0866) **2429, 3958**
France Pays-Bas Informations Rapides. (FR ISSN 0046-4945) **815**
France - Peinture. (FR ISSN 0071-9048) **3653**
France - Photographie. (FR) **3791**
France Plastiques. (FR ISSN 0071-9056) **3862**
France Protestante et les Eglises de Langue Francaise. (FR) **4238**
France Regions. (FR) **815**
France - Sports. (FR ISSN 0071-9102) **4472, 4547**
France Stamp Catalogue. (UK ISSN 0142-9809) **3752**
France Telecom. (FR) **1336, 1362**
France Tennis de Table. (FR) **4504**
France - Theatre. (FR ISSN 0015-9433) **4633**
France Today. (US ISSN 0888-8663) **2187**
France Travel News. (US) **4767**
France U.R.S.S. Magazine. (FR ISSN 0399-9505) **3958**
France - U.S.A. (FR ISSN 0015-9751) **3958**
Francexport. (FR ISSN 0244-710X) **1135, 12**
Franchise Actualites. (FR) **909**
Franchise Annual. (US ISSN 0318-8752) **1135**
The Franchise Handbook. (US ISSN 0882-5505) **1114**
Franchise Law Journal. (US ISSN 8756-7962) **2628, 666**
Franchise Legal Digest. (US) **2628**
Franchise Magazine. (UK ISSN 0268-8395) **1039, 909**
Franchise Update. (US) **666**
Franchise World. (UK ISSN 0144-0543) **1114**
Franchising Adviser. (US) **2628, 1010, 1039**
Franchising & Licensing of Public Services in Florida. (US) **1095**
†Franchising in the Economy. (US) **5197**
Franchising Investments Around the World. (US) **947**

Franchising Opportunities see Franchising World **1039**
†Franchising Opportunities Handbook. (US) **5197**
Franchising World. (US) **1039**
Francis Bacon Research Trust Journal. (UK ISSN 0262-8228) **3767, 4310**
Francis - King Bulletin. (US) **2151**
Francis Thompson Society. Journal see Eighteen Nineties Society. Journal **2913**
Franciscan. (UK ISSN 0532-579X) **4238**
Franciscan Notes see Inside San Francisco State University **1314**
Franciscan Sisters of Mary Links see F S M Links **5190**
Franciscan Studies. (US ISSN 0080-5459) **4264, 3767**
Franciscana. (BE ISSN 0015-9840) **4264**
Franciscanum. (CK ISSN 0120-1468) **3767, 4264**
Franciskaans Leven. (NE ISSN 0015-9794) **4264**
Francite. (US) **2815, 2918**
Franco - British Chamber of Commerce and Industry. Year Book. (FR) **816**
Franco-British Trade Directory. (UK ISSN 0071-917X) **1135, 816, 909**
Franco - British Trade Journal see Info **817**
Franco Maria Ricci International, Inc. see F M R **326**
Francobolli. (IT) **3752**
Francofonia. (IT) **2362, 2918**
Francofonia. Quaderni. (IT) **2362, 2918**
▼Francophonie. (UK ISSN 0957-1744) **2815**
Frank. (CN) **2177**
Frank. (FR ISSN 0738-9299) **2866, 326**
Frank Lloyd Wright Newsletter. (US ISSN 0160-7375) **299, 2551**
Frank Talk. (US) **1115**
Frankenland. (GW ISSN 0015-9905) **2362, 2918**
Frankenthal, Einst und Jetzt. (GW) **2189**
Frankfurt am Main. Amt fuer Statistik, Wahlen und Einwohnerwesen. Statistisches Jahrbuch. (GW) **4572**
Frankfurt am Main. Statistisches Amt und Wahlamt. Statistisches Jahrbuch see Frankfurt am Main. Amt fuer Statistik, Wahlen und Einwohnerwesen. Statistisches Jahrbuch **4572**
Frankfurt Magazin. (GW ISSN 0935-8994) **2189**
Frankfurt - Rhein Main Neckar Saar von Hinten. (GW) **2452, 4767**
Frankfurt von Hinten see Frankfurt - Rhein Main Neckar Saar von Hinten **2452**
Frankfurter. (GW) **2189**
†Frankfurter Abhandlungen zur Slavistik.(GW ISSN 0473-5277) **5197**
Frankfurter Althistorische Studien. (GW) **2362**
Frankfurter Beitraege zur Germanistik. (GW ISSN 0071-9226) **2918, 2815**
▼Frankfurter Finanzmarkt Bericht. (GW) **782**
Frankfurter Frauenblatt. (GW) **4843**
Frankfurter Gastronomie. (GW ISSN 0015-9964) **2474**
Frankfurter Hefte see Die Neue Gesellschaft - Frankfurter Hefte **3909**
Frankfurter Historische Abhandlungen. (GW ISSN 0170-3226) **2362**
Frankfurter Historische Vortraege. (GW ISSN 0170-3293) **2362**
Frankfurter Judaistische Beitraege. (GW ISSN 0342-0078) **2002, 2918, 4222**
Frankfurter Kirchliches Jahrbuch. (GW) **2362, 4178**
Frankfurter Lehrerzeitung. (GW) **1727, 2583**
Frankfurter Statistische Berichte. (GW ISSN 0177-7351) **4572**

Frankfurter Wissenschaftliche Beitrage. Rechts- und Wirtschaftswissenschaftlihe Reihe. (GW) **2628**
Frankfurter Woche. (GW) **4767**
Frankfurter Wochenschau see Frankfurter Woche **4767**
Franklin & Marshall College Today see F & M Today **1311**
Franklin County Historical Review. (US ISSN 0046-4961) **2406**
Franklin Flyer. (US) **2406**
Franklin Foundation Lecture Series. (US) **1065**
Franklin Institute. Journal. (US ISSN 0016-0032) **4310**
Franklin Mint Almanac. (US ISSN 0092-5039) **3599, 326**
Franklin Township Sentinel. (US ISSN 0016-0040) **2225**
Franklin's Insight. (US) **947**
Franklintonian. (US) **2151**
Frankrig Information. Nyhedsbrev. (DK ISSN 0900-2995) **2362**
De Franse Nederlanden/Pays-Bas Francais. (BE ISSN 0251-2408) **2175, 2002**
†Franz Delitzsch - Vorlesungen. Neue Folge. (GW) **5197**
Franziskanische Studien. (GW ISSN 0016-0067) **4264**
Franzius - Institut fuer Wasserbau und Kuesteningenieurwesen. Mitteilungen. (GW) **1923**
Franzoesisch Heute. (GW ISSN 0342-2895) **1750, 2815**
Frary Family Journal. (US ISSN 0887-6320) **2151**
Frary Family Newsletter. (US ISSN 0887-6312) **2151**
Fraser Forum. (CN ISSN 0827-7893) **866**
Fraser Opinion Letter. (US) **947**
Fraser Valley Magazine. (CN ISSN 0845-972X) **2177**
Fraser's Canadian Trade Directory. (CN ISSN 0071-9277) **1136, 1039**
Fraser's Potato Newsletter. (CN ISSN 0384-7322) **178**
Frat. (US ISSN 0739-9243) **2287, 2532**
Frater of Psi Omega. (US ISSN 0071-9285) **3233**
Fratergnos. (US ISSN 1041-2425) **1297**
Fraternal Herald. see Bratrsky Vestnik **2528**
Fraternal Monitor. (US ISSN 0016-0105) **2532**
Fraternite - Hebdo. (IV) **3895**
Fraternite - Matin. (IV) **3895**
Fraternity Monthly Magazine. (JA) **4619**
Frati Minori Cappuccini. Istituto Storico. Varia. (IT) **4264**
Frau see Frau Aktuell **4843**
Frau. (JA) **4843**
Frau Aktuell. (AU) **4843**
Frau Aktuell. (GW) **4843**
Frau im Leben. (GW ISSN 0016-0148) **4843**
Frau im Spiegel. (GW ISSN 0046-497X) **4843**
Frau in der Offenen Gesellschaft see Frau in Unserer Zeit **4843**
Frau in Unserer Zeit. (GW) **4843**
Frau mit Herz. (GW) **4843**
Frau Ohne Herz. (SZ) **4843, 2452, 2918**
Frau und Freizeit. (AU) **1291, 4843**
Frau und Kultur. (GW) **4843**
Frau und Mutter. (GW ISSN 0722-8120) **4178**
Frau und Politik. (GW ISSN 0016-0202) **3895**
Die Frau von Heute. (GW ISSN 0016-0210) **4843**
Fraud and Theft Newsletter see Credit Card Merchant **774**
▼Fraud, Window Dressing and Negligence in Financial Statements. (US) **2628**
†Frauen der Ganzen Welt. (GW ISSN 0016-0229) **5197**
Frauen und Film. (GW) **3511, 4843**
†Frauen und Schule. (GW ISSN 0177-4042) **5197**
▼Frauenaerztliches Seminar. (GW ISSN 0938-7463) **3099**

Der Frauenarzt. (GW ISSN 0016-0237) **3292**
Frauenbildungs- und Ferienhaus Osteresch. (GW) **4843**
Die Frauenfrage in Deutschland. Bibliographie. (GW ISSN 0344-1415) **4858**, 400
Frauenkulter see Frau und Kultur **4843**
Frauezitig. (SZ ISSN 1015-2431) **4843**
†Fraunhofer-Gesellschaft. Berichte. (GW ISSN 0342-1953) **5197**
Fraunhofer Gesellschaft. Mitteilungsblatt see Fraunhofer-Gesellschaft. Berichte **5197**
Fraunhofer-Institute fuer Produktionstechnik und Automatisierung Forschung und Praxis see I P A - Forschung und Praxis **1824**
Fravaer ved Anmeldte Arbejdsulykker. (DK ISSN 0109-5129) **3616**
FRAZ see Frauezitig **4843**
†Freddie Mac Reports. (US ISSN 0749-4645) **5197**
Il Freddo. (IT ISSN 0016-0296) **2299**
Frederick Findings. (US) **2151**
Frederick Forerunners. (US ISSN 0887-2139) **2151**
Frederiksberg Gennem Tiderne. (DK ISSN 0108-8777) **2362**
Frederiksborgmuseet. Aarsskrift see Carlsbergfondet Aarsskrift **3523**
†Frederiksvaerkegnens Museumsforening. Aarsskrift. (DK ISSN 0107-9476) **5197**
Fredningsstyrelsen Rapport. (DK ISSN 0900-9825) **1488**
Fredonia Statement see Statement (Fredonia) **1325**
Free. (IT) **2281**
Free Associations. (UK ISSN 0267-0887) **4022**, 3895, 4372
Free Azania. (SA) **3895**, 4843
Free China and Asia see Asian Outlook **3874**
Free China Journal. (CH ISSN 0255-9870) **2219**
Free China Review. (CH ISSN 0016-030X) **2219**
Free Church of Scotland. Monthly Record. (UK ISSN 0016-0334) **4282**
Free Estonia. see Vaba Eestlane **2027**
Free Fall Kiwi. (NZ) **4547**
Free Flight/Vol Libre. (CN ISSN 0827-2557) **53**, 4547
Free Focus. (US) **2918**, 4843
Free Grace Broadcaster. (US) **4178**
Free Inquiry. (US ISSN 0272-0701) **3767**
Free Inquiry in Creative Sociology. (US ISSN 0736-9182) **4435**
Free Labour World. (BE ISSN 0016-0350) **2583**
Free Lance. (US ISSN 0016-0369) **2918**, 2993
Free-Lance Writing & Photography. (UK ISSN 0016-0385) **2569**, 3791
Free Life. (UK ISSN 0260-5112) **3895**, 3767, 4436
Free Lunch. (US ISSN 1041-0945) **2993**
Free Magazines for Libraries. (US) **4128**, 2758
Free Man. see Adam Chofshe **3870**
Free Market Reader. (US) **894**
Free Materials for Schools and Libraries.(US ISSN 0836-0073) **1634**
Free Mind. (US) **3767**
Free Nation see Freedom Today **3942**
Free Palestine. (AT ISSN 0157-3845) **3942**, 3637
▼Free Paper Publisher, Inc. (US) **4128**, 31
Free Press. see Vapaa Sana **2027**
Free Press. (UK) **2461**
Free Press Network. (US) **2570**, 1374, 3942
Free Radical. (UK) **3895**, 2866
Free Radical Biology & Medicine. (US ISSN 0891-5849) **485**
Free Radical Research Communications. (US ISSN 8755-0199) **1177**
Free Slovakia. see Slobodne Slovensko **2884**

Free Sons Reporter. (US) **1297**, 2002
Free Speech see Free Speech Monitor **2918**
Free Speech see Free Speech Newsletter **3942**
Free Speech Monitor. (CN) **2918**
Free Speech Newsletter. (US) **3942**, 2702
Free Spirit (Brooklyn). (US) **3767**, 3594
Free Spirit (Minneapolis). (US ISSN 0895-2256) **1255**, 1634
Free State Educational News/Vrystaatse Onderwysnuus. (SA ISSN 0042-9228) **1634**
Free State Libraries/Vrystaatse Biblioteke. (SA ISSN 0016-0458) **2758**
Free State Warrior. (US) **1297**
Free! The Newsletter of Free Materials and Services see Free Materials for Schools and Libraries **1634**
Free Thinking School. see Svobodna Skola **2967**
Free Time. (US) **2225**
Free Trade Law Reporter. (CN) **2709**, 666
Free Trader see Licensee **383**
Free World/Jiyu Sekai. (JA ISSN 0021-6984) **3895**
Freebies. (US ISSN 0148-2092) **1505**
Freedom. (UK ISSN 0016-0504) **3895**
Freedom. (PK) **3895**
Freedom at Issue see Freedom Review **3958**
Freedom Digest. (KO) **3895**
Freedom First. (II ISSN 0016-0547) **3895**
Freedom from Hunger Campaign, Campaign Development Bulletin see Ideas and Action Bulletin **152**
Freedom in Education see Choice in Education **1621**
Freedom Magazine. (US) **2570**, 4282
Freedom Monitor. (US) **3942**
Freedom Network News. (US) **3767**, 3895
Freedom of Information Act Update see F O I A Update **2569**
Freedom of Information Review. (AT ISSN 0817-3532) **2628**
†Freedom of Information Service. (CN) **5197**
Freedom Review. (US) **3958**
Freedom Socialist. (US ISSN 0272-4367) **4843**, 3895
†Freedom to Express. (US) **5197**
Freedom to Read Foundation News. (US ISSN 0046-5038) **2758**, 4128
Freedom Today. (UK) **3942**
Freedom Writer. (US ISSN 1059-6372) **3942**
Freedomways. (US ISSN 0016-061X) **2002**, 2866, 3895
Freedonia Gazette. (US ISSN 0748-5247) **3511**
Freelance. (CN ISSN 0705-1379) **2918**, 4128
Freelance Editors' Association of Canada. Directory of Members. (CN ISSN 0226-9031) **1136**, 4128
▼Freelance Graphics Report. (US) **1421**, 1477
Freelance Writer's Report. (US ISSN 0731-549X) **2570**, 31, 3791, 4128
Freelancer's News. (US) **2570**
Freelancers of North America. (US) **4128**, 31, 1039, 3627
Freeland and Allied Families. (US) **2151**
Freeman. (US ISSN 0016-0652) **3895**
Freeman Footnotes. (US ISSN 0899-1626) **2151**
FreeMarket. (US) **894**
Freemarket Gold & Money Report. (US) **947**
Freer Gallery of Art, Washington, D.C. Occasional Papers. (US ISSN 0071-9382) **326**
Freestone Frontiers. (US) **2151**
Freethinker. (UK ISSN 0016-0687) **3767**, 4178
Freethought Today. (US ISSN 0882-8512) **4178**

Freeway. (US) **1255**, 4178
Freewheeler. (CN ISSN 0824-7226) **4406**, 1736, 3099
Freewheeling see Cycling World **4517**
Freeze Frame. (CN ISSN 0704-9536) **3511**
Freiberger Forschungshefte. Montanwissenschaften: Reihe A. Bergbau und Geotechnik, Arbeitsschutz und Sicherheitstechnik, Grundstoff-Verfahrenstechnik, Maschinen- und Energietechnik. (GW ISSN 0071-9390) **1790**
Freiberger Forschungshefte. Montanwissenschaften: Reihe B. Metallurgie und Werstofftechnik. (GW) **3407**
Freiberger Forschungshefte. Montanwissenschaften: Reihe C. Geowissenschaften. (GW ISSN 0071-9404) **1544**, 3657
†Freiberger Forschungshefte. Montanwissenschaften. Reihe D: Economic Sciences. (GW ISSN 0071-9412) **5197**
Freibeuter. (GW ISSN 0171-9289) **2189**
Freiburger Altorientalische Studien. (GW ISSN 0170-3307) **3637**
Freiburger Beitraege zur Indologie. (GW ISSN 0340-6261) **3637**
Freiburger Fernoestliche Forschungen. (GW ISSN 0724-4703) **3637**
Freiburger Geographische Hefte. (GW ISSN 0071-9447) **2248**
Freiburger Hausbesitzer Zeitung. (GW) **2487**
Freiburger Islamstudien. (GW ISSN 0170-3285) **3637**, 4218
Freiburger Kleinanzeiger. (GW) **31**, 1374
Freiburger Zeitschrift fuer Philosophie und Theologie. (SZ ISSN 0016-0725) **3767**, 4264
Freie Fahrt/Route Libre. (SZ) **4101**, 1536
Freie Lehrerstimme. (AU ISSN 0016-075X) **1634**, 3895
Freie Presse-Korrespondenz. (GW ISSN 0016-0768) **3895**
Freie Religion. (GW ISSN 0016-0776) **4178**
Freie Universitaet Berlin. John F. Kennedy-Institut fuer Nordamerika Studien. Materialien. (GW) **2406**
Freie Universitaet Berlin. Osteuropa-Institut. Balkanologische Veroeffentlichungen. (GW ISSN 0170-1533) **2815**
Freie Universitaet Berlin. Osteuropa-Institut. Berichte. (GW ISSN 0409-1477) **2507**, 2362, 3895
Freie Universitaet Berlin. Osteuropa-Institut. Bibliographische Mitteilungen.(GW ISSN 0067-5881) **2328**
Freie Universitaet Berlin. Osteuropa-Institut. Erziehungswissenschaftliche Veroeffentlichungen. (GW ISSN 0067-589X) **1634**, 3895
Freie Universitaet Berlin. Osteuropa-Institut. Historische Veroeffentlichungen. (GW ISSN 0067-5903) **2362**
Freie Universitaet Berlin. Osteuropa-Institut. Philosophische und Soziologische Veroeffentlichungen. (GW ISSN 0067-5911) **3767**, 3895, 4436
Freie Universitaet Berlin. Osteuropa-Institut. Rechtswissenschaftliche Veroeffentlichungen. (GW ISSN 0343-835X) **2628**
Freie Universitaet Berlin. Osteuropa-Institut. Slavistische Veroeffentlichungen. (GW ISSN 0067-592X) **2918**, 2815
Freie Universitaet Berlin. Osteuropa-Institut. Wirtschaftswissenschaftliche Veroeffentlichungen. (GW ISSN 0067-5938) **666**
Freie Universitaet Berlin. Studienhandbuch. (GW ISSN 0941-0155) **1311**
†Freie Welt. (GW ISSN 0427-5217) **5197**
Die Freie Wohnungswirtschaft. (GW ISSN 0016-0784) **4149**

Der Freie Zahnarzt. (GW ISSN 0340-1766) **3233**
Freien Deutschen Gewerschaftsbundes. Rundschau see F D G B. Rundschau **5190**
Freier Agrarhandel. (GW) **93**
Freies Asien. (GW) **3637**
Freies Deutsches Hochstift, Frankfurt am Main. Jahrbuch. (GW ISSN 0071-9463) **2918**
Freigeistige Aktion see Der Humanist **3768**
Freight. (UK ISSN 0016-0849) **4650**
Freight & Container Weekly. (SA) **666**
Freight Carriers. (AT) **4744**
Freight Cars Journal. (US ISSN 0742-9355) **4709**
Freight Forwarding see World Freight **4742**
†Freight Guide. (UK) **5197**
Freight Handler. (UK) **4650**
Freight Industry Yearbook. (UK ISSN 0071-9471) **4650**
Freight Management see Freight Management & Distribution Today **4650**
Freight Management & Distribution Today. (UK) **4650**
Freight Management Report. (US) **4650**
Freight Marketing Report see Freight Management Report **4650**
Freight Transport Association Yearbook see F T A Yearbook **4649**
Freighter Travel News. (US ISSN 0016-089X) **4767**
Freighting News see Freight & Container Weekly **666**
Freiheitliche Partei Oesterreichs Oberoesterreichische F P O - Nachrichten fuer Freiheit und Recht see Oberoesterreichische F P O - Nachrichten fuer Freiheit und Recht **3912**
Freiheitlicher Oberoesterreichischer Landeslehrer Verein. Zeitschrift see Freiheitlicher Oberoesterreichischer Lehrerverein. Zeitschrift **1634**
Freiheitlicher Oberoesterreichischer Lehrerverein. Zeitschrift. (AU) **1634**
Freiheitlicher Pressedienst. (AU) **3895**
Die Freiheitsglocke/Bell of Freedom. (GW ISSN 0016-0911) **3942**
Freinet Nyt. (DK ISSN 0109-9108) **1634**
Freitag. (GW) **3397**
Der Freiwillige. (GW ISSN 0016-092X) **3458**, 2311
Freizeit - Caravan - Camping Magazin. (GW) **4547**, 4767
Freizeit Im Sattel. (GW ISSN 0342-4758) **4534**
†Freizeit Pferde. (GW ISSN 0341-7182) **5197**
Freizeit Revue. (GW) **2436**
Freizeit und Kultur. (GW) **2189**
Der Freizeitgaertner. (GW ISSN 0016-0946) **2126**
Freizeitspiegel. (GW) **2189**
Fremantle Arts Review. (AT ISSN 0816-6919) **326**, 2918, 4633
Fremantle Gazette. (AT) **2171**
Fremantle Port News. (AT) **4727**
Fremdenverkehr in Oesterreich. (AU ISSN 0071-948X) **4767**
Fremdenverkehr - Tourismus and Kongress see European Tourism & Congress - Der Fremdenverkehr **5188**
Fremdenverkehrsbilanz der Schweiz/Balance Touristique de la Suisse. (SZ) **4799**
Fremdsprachen. (GW ISSN 0016-0970) **2815**, 1635
Fremdsprachen Lehren und Lerner. (GW) **2815**
Fremdsprachenunterricht. (GW) **2815**, 1635
Der Fremdsprachliche Unterricht. (GW ISSN 0340-2207) **2815**, 1635, 1750
Fremonitor. (US ISSN 0016-0997) **1635**
Fremont County Nostalgia News. (US ISSN 8756-8446) **2151**
Fremontia. (US ISSN 0092-1793) **503**
Fremsyn see Radikal Politik **3921**
Fremtiden see Udenrigs **3975**

Fremtider. (DK ISSN 0109-0917) **1336**
†French - American Commerce. (US ISSN 0016-1039) **5197**
French - American News. (US) **816**
French American Review. (US ISSN 1052-3952) **2918**, 2507
French Bulldog Club of America. Newsletter. (US) **3710**
French - Canadian Civilization Research Center. Cahiers/Centre de Recherche en Civilisation Canadienne - Francaise. Cahiers. (CN ISSN 0069-1771) **2406**, 2918
French Colonial Historical Society. Proceedings of the Meeting. (US ISSN 0362-7055) **2362**
French Company Handbook. (FR ISSN 0759-3694) **1136**
▼French Cultural Studies. (UK ISSN 0957-1558) **2362**
French Engineering Catalog. (FR ISSN 0245-0283) **1822**
French Ethnology. see Ethnologie Francaise **239**
French Farm and Village Holiday Guide. (UK) **4767**
French Foreign Trade Directory. see Essor Francais du Commerce Exterieur **906**
French Forum. (US ISSN 0098-9355) **2866**, 2815
French Historical Studies. (US ISSN 0016-1071) **2362**
French History. (UK ISSN 0269-1191) **2362**
French Institute, Pondicherry. Pondy Papers in Social Sciences. (II) **4372**
French Journal of Orthopaedic Surgery see Journal of Orthopaedic Surgery **3309**
French Literature Series. (US ISSN 0271-6607) **2982**
French Opera in the 17th and 18th Centuries. (US) **3552**
French Periodical Index/Repertoriex. (US ISSN 0362-5044) **400**
French Politics & Society. (US ISSN 0882-1267) **3895**, 2362
French Review. (US ISSN 0016-111X) **1635**, 2815
French Studies. (UK ISSN 0016-1128) **2918**, 2362
French Studies Bulletin. (UK ISSN 0262-2750) **2918**, 2362
French Technology Survey see F T S **4597**
French 7 Bibliography, Critical and Biographical References for the Study of Contemporary French Literature see French 20 Bibliography **2855**
French 17. (US ISSN 0191-9199) **2328**, 400, 2890
French 20 Bibliography. (US ISSN 0085-0888) **2855**, 400
Frenchline. (US) **2151**
Frendz. (UK ISSN 0046-5062) **2866**
Frente. (HO) **980**
Frente Nacional pro-Defensa del Petroleo Venezolano. Actuaciones. (VE) **3686**
Frequency Control Symposium. (US) **1771**, 3859
Frequency Symposium see Frequency Control Symposium **1771**
Frequent Buyer. (US) **1433**
Frequent Flyer see O A G Frequent Flyer **4676**
Frequenz. (GW ISSN 0016-1136) **1892**
Freres d'Armes. (FR ISSN 0016-1144) **3458**
▼Fresenius Environmental Bulletin. (SZ ISSN 1018-4619) **1955**, 439, 1177
Fresenius' Journal of Analytical Chemistry. (GW) **1205**
Fresenius' Zeitschrift fuer Analytische Chemie see Fresenius' Journal of Analytical Chemistry **1205**
Fresh Baked. (US) **2088**
†Fresh Facts for Foodservice Newsletter.(US) **5197**
Fresh Fruit and Vegetable Market News.(US) **178**
Fresh Fruit and Vegetable Market News: Weekly Summary, Shipments-Arrivals.(US) **151**, 178

Fresh Fruit and Vegetable Market News: Weekly Summary, Shipments, Unloads see Fresh Fruit and Vegetable Market News: Weekly Summary, Shipments-Arrivals **151**
Fresh Perspective. (CN) **1255**, 1635
†Fresh Produce Foodservice Directory. (US) **5197**
Fresh Produce Journal. (UK) **2071**, 178
Fresh Produce Workshop. (US) **2071**, 1039
Fresh Weekly. (HK) **1374**, 1291
Freshline. (US) **2071**, 1039
Freshman English News see Composition Studies - Freshman English News **1747**
Freshmen. (US) **3397**
Freshwater and Aquaculture Contents Tables. (UN) **2041**
Freshwater and Marine Aquarium. (US ISSN 0160-4317) **3710**
†Freshwater Biological Association. Annual Report. (UK ISSN 0374-7646) **5197**
Freshwater Biological Association. Occasional Publications. (UK ISSN 0308-6739) **439**
Freshwater Biological Association. Scientific Publications. (UK ISSN 0367-1887) **439**
Freshwater Biological Association Current Awareness Service. (UK) **465**, 439, 1955
Freshwater Biological Association Library List see Freshwater Biological Association Current Awareness Service **465**
Freshwater Biology. (UK ISSN 0046-5070) **439**
Freshwater Fish Protection. see Tansuigyo-Hogo **2049**
Freshwater Fisheries Laboratory Pitlochry. Annual Review. (UK ISSN 0951-3752) **2041**
Freshwater Fisheries Research Laboratory, Tokyo. Bulletin see National Research Institute of Aquaculture. Bulletin **2046**
†Freshwater Fisherman. (US) **5197**
▼Fresno Business and Industry News. (US) **666**
Fresno County Medical Society. Bulletin see Vital Signs (Fresno) **3161**
Fresno Daily Report. (US) **1514**, 1039
†Frets Magazine. (US ISSN 0162-0401) **5197**
Fretted Instrument Guild of America see F I G A **3551**
Freunde der Bayerischen Vor- und Fruehgeschichte. Mitteilungen. (GW) **2311**
Freundeskreis Blaetter. (GW ISSN 0177-011X) **3524**, 299
Freundin. (GW ISSN 0016-1187) **2446**, 4843
Freyr. (IC ISSN 0016-1209) **93**
Fri Koepenskap. (SW ISSN 0016-1217) **2092**
Friction. (US) **3397**, 1374
Friday. (JA) **2207**
Friday Flash. (US ISSN 0016-1233) **2532**
Friday Memo. (US) **1395**, 1336, 3675, 4128
Friday Report. (US ISSN 0046-5097) **1039**, 31
Fried Fish Caterer see Friers Catering Advertiser **2071**
Friede Ueber Israel. (GW ISSN 0938-6408) **4222**, 4238
Friede und Freiheit. (GW) **4238**
Frieden. (GW) **3895**
Frieden und Abruestung. (GW) **3895**
Die Friedens - Warte. (GW ISSN 0340-0255) **2723**, 3958
Friedensbote. (GW) **4238**
Friedensforschung Aktuell. (GW ISSN 0930-830X) **3895**, 1635, 3459
Friedensforum. (GW) **3895**
Friedensglocke. (GW) **4238**
Friedhof und Denkmal. (GW) **2119**
†Friedrich-Schiller-Universitaet Jena. Mathematisch-Naturwissenschaftliche Reihe. Wissenschaftliche Zeitschrift. (GW ISSN 0043-6836) **5197**

†Friedrich-Schiller-Universitaet Jena. Wissenschaftliche Zeitschrift. (GW ISSN 0138-1652) **5197**
Friend see Kultur un Lebn **2011**
Friend. (UK ISSN 0016-1268) **4283**
Friend. (US ISSN 0009-4102) **4283**, 1255
A Friend Indeed. (CN ISSN 0824-1961) **4843**, 3292, 3802, 4835
Friend International. (II ISSN 0046-5100) **2436**, 1255
Friend of Animals. (UK ISSN 0016-1276) **231**
Friend of Chemical Industry. see Huagong zhi You **1178**
Friend of Fine Arts. see Meishu zhi You **335**
Friend of Health. see Jiankang zhi You **3805**
Friend of Housewives. see Shufu no Tomo **4852**
Friend of Stars. see Hoshi no Tomo **365**
Friend of Tomorrow. see Asu no Tomo **2270**
Friend O'Wildlife. (US ISSN 0016-1284) **1488**
Friendly Companion. (UK ISSN 0016-1292) **4179**, 1255
Friendly Exchange. (US) **2225**, 2532
A Friendly Letter. (US ISSN 0739-5418) **4179**
Friendly Voice see You Sheng **3978**
Friendly Way. (UK) **4214**
Friendly Woman. (US ISSN 0740-5618) **4283**, 4843
†Friends (Surry). (US) **5197**
Friends (Warren). (US ISSN 0884-9889) **4691**
Friends Committee on Legislation of California Action Alerts see F C L Action Alerts **3893**
Friends Committee on Legislation of California Newsletter see F C L Newsletter **3893**
Friends Committee on National Legislation Washington Newsletter see F C N L Washington Newsletter **3893**
Friends Focus. (US) **1298**, 4633
Friends for Jamaica Newsletter see Caribbean Newsletter **3952**
Friends for Lesbian and Gay Concerns Newsletter see F L G C Newsletter **4177**
Friends General Conference Quarterly see F G C Quarterly **5190**
Friends Historical Society. Journal. (UK ISSN 0071-9587) **4283**
Friends Journal. (US ISSN 0016-1322) **4283**, 4436
Friends of Animals Act'ionLine. (US) **231**, 1488
Friends of Animals Reports see Friends of Animals Act'ionLine **231**
Friends of Automobile. see Qiche zhi You **4700**
Friends of China. see Zhongguo zhi You **3978**
Friends of Dog/Aiken No Tomo. (JA) **3710**
Friends of French Art. (US) **326**
Friends of George Sand Newsletter see George Sand Studies **2919**
Friends of Julio International Newsletter.(US) **3552**, 1298
Friends of Libraries U S A National Notebook. (US) **2758**
Friends of Music. see Ongaku no Tomo **3571**
▼Friends of Parks & Recreation. (US) **1488**, 4547
Friends of Peace Pilgrim. (US) **2918**
Friends of Photography. Newsletter see Re: View **3796**
Friends of the Amherst College Library. Newsletter. (US) **2758**
Friends of the Archives of Louisiana. Newsletter see Louisiana Archives and Manuscripts Association. Newsletter **2771**
Friends of the Australian Ballet. Bulletin.(AT) **1530**
Friends of the Court. (US) **2628**
Friends of the Dartmouth Library Newsletter. (US) **2758**
Friends of the Earth. Magazine. (US) **1955**

Friends of the Filipino People Bulletin see F F P Bulletin **2001**
Friends of the Library National Notebook see Friends of Libraries U S A National Notebook **2758**
Friends of the National Libraries. Annual Report. (UK) **2758**, 4128
Friends of the Trees Society Newsletter.(US) **2101**, 178
Friends of the Trees Society Yearbook. (US) **2126**, 2101
Friends of Wine. (US ISSN 0364-9474) **381**
Friends of Youth Newsletter. (US) **1237**, 4436
Friends' Quarterly. (UK ISSN 0016-1357) **4283**
Friends' Quarterly (Enfield). (US) **3524**, 4283
Friends Service Council. Annual Report see Quaker Peace & Service. Annual Report **4417**
Friends World News. (UK ISSN 0016-1365) **4283**
Friendscript. (US ISSN 0192-5539) **2758**
Friendship see World Friends **2443**
Friendship. see L'Amitie **2802**
Friendship Book of Francis Gay. (UK) **2866**
Friendship News. (UK) **1298**
Friers Catering Advertiser. (UK) **2071**
Fries Landbouwblad. (NE ISSN 0016-1373) **93**
Friese Veefokkerij see Veeteelt **228**
Friesia see Nordic Journal of Botany **511**
Frigoworld. (UK) **2071**
Frihet. (SW ISSN 0016-142X) **3895**
Friidrett. (NO ISSN 0332-9666) **4472**
Friidrott. (SW ISSN 0046-5135) **4472**
Friluftsliv. (SW) **4547**
Frimaerkens Verden. (DK ISSN 0108-4089) **3752**
Frimaerkesamleren. (DK ISSN 0016-1438) **3752**
Fringe Benefit Costs in Canada see Employee Benefit Costs in Canada **977**
Fringe Benefits Tax Guide. (US) **1095**
Fringe Benefits Tax Service see Australian Fringe Benefits Tax Service **1087**
Frio, Calor y Aire Acondicionado. (SP) **2299**
Fripounet. (FR ISSN 0016-1446) **1255**
Frisbe - Frisbee Family Association of America. Bulletin. (US) **2151**
†Frisbee Disc World. (US) **5197**
Frisbee World see Frisbee Disc World **5197**
▼Frisco Kids. (US) **1255**
Friseurhandwerk Friseurspiegel see Top Hair **374**
Friseurwelt. (GW ISSN 0016-1470) **373**
Frisk Bris. (FI) **2628**
Friskies Cat Companion see Cat Companion from Friskies **3709**
Frisko. (US) **2225**
†Friskoler og Private Grundsskoler. (DK ISSN 0108-4259) **5197**
Frisoerfagene see Frisoerfaget **373**
Frisoerfaget. (DK) **373**
Frisona Espanola. (SP ISSN 0211-3767) **216**
Frisur und Kosmetik. (GW ISSN 0323-410X) **373**
Frit Koebmandskab. (DK ISSN 0901-2745) **2092**
Fritidshandlaren Cykel och Sport. (SW ISSN 1100-052X) **4518**, 4472
Fritt Kjoepmannskap. (NO ISSN 0016-1519) **2092**
Fritts-Fritz Family Newsletter. (US) **2151**
Fritz-Hueser-Institut fuer Deutsche und Auslaendische Arbeiterliteratur. Informationen. (GW) **2982**, 718, 3174
Il Friuli Medico. (IT ISSN 0016-1535) **3099**
Frivakt. (NO ISSN 0046-5143) **4406**
Frivilliga Befaelsutbildningsroerelsen Befael see F B U - Befael **3458**

Frjals Verzlun. (IC ISSN 1017-3544) **1039**
Frobber. (US) **1460**
Frodskaparrit; Annales Societatis Scientiarum Faeroensis. (FA ISSN 0085-0896) **4310**
Frodskaparrit; Annales Societatis Scientiarum Faeronsis. Supplementa. (FA ISSN 0429-7539) **4310**
Der Froehliche Kreis. (AU ISSN 0016-156X) **2055**
†Froesi. (GW ISSN 0323-8806) **5197**
Frog Gone Review. (US) **2993**
Frogpond. (US) **2993**, 2918
Frohe Botschaft. (GW ISSN 0340-6091) **4179**
Frohlinger's Marketing Report. (US ISSN 1057-5316) **1039**, 31
Frohlinger's Marketing Strategist see Frohlinger's Marketing Report **1039**
Froid et la Climatisation. (FR ISSN 0046-5151) **2299**
From Duck Country. (CN) **1488**
From My Bookshelf. (CN ISSN 0829-4976) **2918**, 2002
From Nine to Five. (US ISSN 0016-1616) **1058**
From Portugal. (PO) **909**
From the Board Room. (US) **1635**
From the Centre. (CN) **909**
From the Clipboard. (US) **782**
From the Couch... (US) **3337**
From the Dragon's Den. (US ISSN 0732-5517) **3752**
From the Ground Up. (CN ISSN 0317-056X) **53**
From the Home & Housing Front. (US) **2272**
From the Shelves of the Root Cellar see Root Cellar Preserves **2163**
From the State Capitals. Alcoholic Beverage Control. (US ISSN 0734-0842) **381**
From the State Capitals. Banking see From the State Capitals. Banking Policies **5197**
†From the State Capitals. Banking Policies. (US ISSN 0749-2812) **5197**
From the State Capitals. Civil Rights. (US ISSN 0741-353X) **3942**, 4436
From the State Capitals. Construction Policies. (US) **4061**
From the State Capitals. Drug Abuse Control. (US ISSN 0734-0877) **1536**
From the State Capitals. Economic Development. (US ISSN 0734-1628) **1076**
From the State Capitals. Environmental Health see From the State Capitals. Waste Disposal and Pollution Control **1984**
From the State Capitals. Family Relations. (US ISSN 0741-3505) **1514**
From the State Capitals. Federal Action Affecting the States. (US ISSN 0734-1202) **4061**
From the State Capitals. General Trends. (US ISSN 0741-3475) **4061**
From the State Capitals. Industrial Development see From the State Capitals. Economic Development **1076**
From the State Capitals. Insurance Regulation. (US ISSN 0016-1748) **2532**
From the State Capitals. Justice Policies. (US ISSN 0749-2790) **2629**
From the State Capitals. Labor Relations. (US ISSN 0734-1105) **980**
From the State Capitals. Motor Vehicle Regulation. (US ISSN 0016-1810) **4691**
From the State Capitals. Parks and Recreation Trends. (US ISSN 0734-113X) **4061**
From the State Capitals. Public Assistance and Welfare Trends. (US ISSN 0734-1601) **4406**, 4101
From the State Capitals. Public Employee Policy. (US ISSN 0741-3521) **1065**, 4061
From the State Capitals. Public Health. (US ISSN 0734-1156) **4101**
From the State Capitals. Public Utilities.(US ISSN 0016-1888) **4061**
From the State Capitals. School Financing. (US ISSN 0734-0907) **1727**, 4087
From the State Capitals. Taxation and Revenue Policies. (US ISSN 0749-2820) **1095**
From the State Capitals. Taxes - Property. (US ISSN 0734-1121) **1095**
From the State Capitals. Tourist Business Promotion. (US ISSN 0734-1199) **4767**
From the State Capitals. Transportation Policies. (US ISSN 0749-2774) **4718**
From the State Capitals. Urban Development. (US ISSN 0741-3483) **2487**
From the State Capitals. Urban Transit see From the State Capitals. Transportation Policies **4718**
From the State Capitals. Waste Disposal and Pollution Control. (US) **1984**, 4101
From the State Capitals. Water Supply. (US ISSN 0734-1237) **4824**
From the State Capitals. Women and the Law. (US ISSN 0741-3572) **2629**, 4843
From the State Capitals. Workers Compensation see From the State Capitals. Labor Relations **980**
From the State Capitals: Public Safety. (US ISSN 0749-2782) **2033**, 4101
From This Side. see Desde Este Lado **2991**
From Within. see Mibifnim **154**
Frommer's Comprehensive Travel Guide. New England. (US ISSN 1056-5787) **4767**
Frommer's Dollarwise Guide to Egypt see Frommer's Egypt **4768**
Frommer's Dollarwise Guide to Germany see Frommer's Germany **4768**
Frommer's Dollarwise Guide to Italy see Frommer's Italy **4768**
Frommer's Egypt. (US ISSN 1044-226X) **4768**
Frommer's Germany. (US ISSN 1044-2405) **4768**
Frommer's Italy. (US ISSN 1044-2170) **4768**
Frommer's New England see Frommer's Comprehensive Travel Guide. New England **4767**
Fronimo. (IT) **3552**
Le Front. (CN) **1311**
Front. (YU ISSN 0016-2027) **2239**
Front and Finish: The Dog Trainer's News. (US) **3710**
Front Line Supervisor's Bulletin. (US) **1010**
Front Lines (Portland). (US ISSN 1058-0271) **1505**, 2092
Front Lines (Washington). (US) **929**
Front Page. (US) **1312**
Front Page. (US) **2452**
Front Page Detective. (US ISSN 0016-2043) **2985**
Front Page News see Performer **1531**
Front Room News see Craft Marketing News **354**
Front Royal Warren Sentinel. (US) **2225**
Front Striker Bulletin. (US ISSN 1041-1852) **2436**
Fronte Sanitario. (IT) **3099**
Frontera Norte. (MX ISSN 0187-7372) **2248**, 2406
Frontier. (UK ISSN 0266-5883) **666**
Frontier. (II ISSN 0016-2094) **3895**
Frontier Military Series. (US ISSN 0071-9641) **3459**, 2406
Frontier News. (AT ISSN 1033-2235) **4238**
Frontier Nursing Service Quarterly Bulletin. (US ISSN 0016-2116) **3278**
Frontiera. (IT ISSN 0016-2132) **2866**
Frontiera-Sardegna see Frontiera **2866**
Frontieres. (CN) **4022**, 240, 2119
▼Frontiers. (UK) **909**
Frontiers. (US) **2453**
Frontiers: a Journal of Women Studies. (US ISSN 0160-9009) **4859**
Frontiers in Aging Series. (US ISSN 0271-955X) **2272**
Frontiers in Applied Mathematics. (US) **3036**
Frontiers in Diabetes. (SZ ISSN 0251-5342) **3253**
Frontiers in Education Conference. Proceedings. (US ISSN 0190-5848) **1892**
Frontiers in European Radiology. (US) **3358**
Frontiers in Headache Research. (US) **3099**
Frontiers in Neuroendocrinology. (US ISSN 0532-7466) **3253**
Frontiers in Physics. (US ISSN 0429-7725) **3818**
▼Frontiers in Psychotherapy. (US) **4022**
Frontiers of Engineering and Computing in Health Care see I E E E Engineering in Medicine and Biology Society. International Conference **3225**
Frontiers of Gastrointestinal Research. (SZ) **3267**
Frontiers of Health Services Management. (US ISSN 0748-8157) **2461**, 3099, 3802
Frontiers of Hormone Research. (SZ ISSN 0301-3073) **3253**
†Frontiers of Matrix Biology. (SZ ISSN 0301-0155) **5197**
Frontiers of Medical and Biological Engineering. (NE ISSN 0921-3775) **3099**, 1822
Frontiers of Oral Physiology. (SZ ISSN 0301-536X) **3233**
Frontiers of Plant Science. (US ISSN 0016-2167) **503**
Frontiers of Power Conference. Proceedings. (US) **1790**, 4598
Frontiers of Power Technology Conference. Proceedings see Frontiers of Power Conference. Proceedings **1790**
Frontiers of Radiation Therapy and Oncology. (SZ ISSN 0071-9676) **3358**, 3197
Frontiersman (Philadelphia). (US) **1298**
Frontlijn. (NE ISSN 0016-2175) **4264**
Frontline. (UK) **2002**, 2866
Frontline. (II ISSN 0970-1710) **2199**
Frontline. (SA ISSN 0256-0240) **3895**
Frontline. (IS) **4223**
†Frontline (Oakland). (US) **5197**
Frontline (Washington) see Common Cause Magazine **3880**
Frontline News for Women see Women Today **4856**
Frontpage. (US ISSN 0016-2183) **2583**, 2570
Frost & Sullivan, Inc. Reports see F & S Reports **665**
Frost on the Vine. (US ISSN 0882-2514) **2151**
Frozen and Chilled Foods. (UK) **2071**
Frozen and Chilled Foods Year Book. (UK) **2071**
Frozen Fishery Products. Annual Summary. (US ISSN 0162-6108) **2051**, 4572
Frozen Food Age. (US ISSN 0016-2191) **2071**
Frozen Food Digest. (US ISSN 0889-5902) **2071**
Frozen Food Executive. (US) **2071**
Frozen Food Management. (UK) **2071**
Frozen Food Report. (US) **2071**
Frozen Foods see Frozen and Chilled Foods **2071**
Frozen Foods in Denmark. (DK) **2071**
Frozen Waffles. (US) **2866**
Fruchthandel. (GW ISSN 0429-7830) **178**, 1039, 2071
Fruchthandel Adressbuch. (GW ISSN 0344-0079) **1136**
Fruchtsaft-Industrie see Confructa **2064**
Fructidor International. (FR) **178**
Fructus. (DK ISSN 0109-0372) **4372**
Fruechte und Gemuese/Fruits et Legumes. (SZ ISSN 0016-2221) **178**
Fruehfoerderung Interdisziplinaer. (GW ISSN 0721-9121) **1736**, 3320
Fruehmittelalterliche Studien. (GW ISSN 0071-9706) **2362**
Frugt, Groent og Blomster. (DK ISSN 0046-5224) **2126**
Frugtavleren. (DK ISSN 0106-004X) **178**
Frugthandlerbladet see Frugt, Groent og Blomster **2126**
Fruit and Tree Nuts Situation and Outlook Report see U.S. Department of Agriculture. Fruit and Tree Nuts Situation and Outlook Report **195**
Fruit and Tropical Products. (UK ISSN 0142-1883) **2071**, 1040
Fruit and Vegetable Markets. (UK ISSN 0961-0464) **93**
Fruit and Vegetable Truck Rate see Fruit and Vegetable Truck Rate and Cost Summary **151**
Fruit and Vegetable Truck Rate and Cost Summary. (US) **151**, 178
Fruit and Vegetable Truck Rate Report. (US) **151**, 178
Fruit Belge. (BE ISSN 0016-2248) **178**
Fruit Country. (US) **178**
Fruit Gardener. (US) **2126**
Fruit Grower. (UK ISSN 0953-2188) **2126**
Fruit of the Vine. (US ISSN 0016-2264) **4283**
Fruit Research. see Instytut Sadownictwa i Kwiaciarstwa w Skierniewicach. Seria A: Prace Doswiadczalne z Zakresu Sadownictwa **2131**
Fruit Science Reports. (PL ISSN 0137-1479) **2126**, 503
Fruit Trades Journal see Fresh Produce Journal **2071**
Fruit Varieties Journal. (US ISSN 0091-3642) **2126**
Fruitbowl see One to One (Fresno) **1357**
Fruits. (FR ISSN 0248-1294) **2126**
Fruits A see Fruits **2126**
Fruits B see Fruits **2126**
Fruits et Abeilles. (FR ISSN 0429-7857) **93**
Fruits et Legumes. see Fruechte und Gemuese **178**
Fruits et Legumes Actualites see F E L Actualites **176**
Fruitteelt. (NE ISSN 0016-2302) **2071**
Frut. (SP ISSN 0214-0578) **178**
Fruticultura Profesional. (SP) **178**
Frutticoltura. (IT ISSN 0016-2310) **178**, 2126
Fryske Nammen. (NE) **2815**
Ft. Wayne Newsletter see Milk Marketer **201**
Ftiziatria see Pneumologia i Ftiziatria **3366**
Ftiziologia see Revista de Igiena, Bacteriologie, Virusologie, Parazitologie, Pneumoftiziologie **3367**
Fu Jen Studies. (CH ISSN 1015-0021) **2919**, 2815, 3637
Fuchsia Annual. (UK ISSN 0071-9730) **2126**
Fuchsia Fan. (US) **2126**
Fuchsia Fanfare. (SA) **2126**
Fuchsia Flash. (US) **2126**
Fuck. (IT) **2866**, 326
Fudan Journal (Natural Science Edition). see Fudan Xuebao (Ziran Kexue Ban) **4310**
Fudan Journal (Social Sciences Edition). see Fudan Xuebao (Shehui Kexue Ban) **4372**
Fudan Xuebao (Shehui Kexue Ban)/ Fudan Journal (Social Sciences Edition). (CC ISSN 0257-0289) **4372**
Fudan Xuebao (Ziran Kexue Ban)/Fudan Journal (Natural Science Edition). (CC ISSN 0427-7104) **4310**
Fudao Yuan. (CC ISSN 0427-7112) **3895**
Fudosan Kenkyu. see Real Estate Research **4156**

Fuehrer durch die technische Literatur. (GW ISSN 0071-9749) **4598**
Fuehrer zu Archaeologischen Denkmaelern in Deutschland. (GW ISSN 0071-9757) **272, 326**
Fuehrung und Organisation der Unternehmung. (SZ ISSN 0071-9765) **1011**
Fuel. (UK ISSN 0016-2361) **3686, 1790**
Fuel Abstracts and Current Titles see Fuel and Energy Abstracts **3705**
Fuel and Energy Abstracts. (UK ISSN 0140-6701) **3705, 12, 1844**
Fuel and Energy Management. see Gospodarka Paliwami i Energia **1790**
Fuel Merchants Association of New Jersey Today see F M A Today **3685**
Fuel Oil & Oil Heat. (US) **2299**
Fuel Oil News. (US ISSN 0016-2396) **2299**
Fuel Oil News and Road Tanker Transport. (UK) **3686**
Fuel Processing Technology. (NE ISSN 0378-3820) **3686**
▼Fuel Reformulation. (US) **3686**
Fuel Science and Technology International. (US ISSN 0884-3759) **1822**
Fueloil & Oil Heat. (US) **3686**
Fueloil and Oil Heat and Solar Systems see Fueloil & Oil Heat **3686**
Fuels and Lubricants. see Goriva i Maziva **3017**
Fuels and Materials Facilities. (US) **3837**
Fuentes Cartograficas Espanolas. (SP) **2248**
Fuentes e Investigaciones para la Historia del Peru. (PE) **2406**
Fuentes indigenas de la Cultura Nahuatl. (MX ISSN 0071-9773) **2406**
Fuentes para el Estudio de la Cultura Maya. (MX) **2406**
Fuentes Primarias. (BO) **240**
Fuer Arbeit und Besinnung. (GW ISSN 0016-2434) **4238**
†Fuer Dich. (GW ISSN 0323-5947) **5197**
Fuer die Sicherheit im Bergland see Sicherheit im Bergland **4555**
Fuer Heute. (GW ISSN 0016-2442) **4238**
Fuer Sie. (GW ISSN 0016-2450) **2189**
Fuer Sie aus der Tschechoslowakei see For You from Czechoslovakia **815**
Fuer Unsere Mitarbeiter. (GW) **3483**
Fuera de Coleccion. (SP) **2507**
Fuereinander. (GW) **1536**
Die Fuehrungskraft. (GW ISSN 0178-501X) **3483**
Fuersorger see Suchtprobleme und Sozialarbeit **1539**
Fuersorgerechtliche Entscheidungen. (GW) **4406**
Fuerstenfelder Grenzlandecho. (AU ISSN 0016-2469) **2173**
Fuerza Aerea. (CL ISSN 0716-4866) **3459, 53**
Fuerza Nueva. (SP ISSN 0016-2477) **3895**
Fugle. (DK ISSN 0107-3729) **564**
Fugle i Nordjylland see Fugle og Dyr i Nordjylland **564**
Fugle og Dyr i Nordjylland. (DK ISSN 0903-1731) **564**
Fugleiagttagelser i Ringkoebing Amt see Sandeviften **567**
Fuglevaern see Fugle **564**
Fugues. (CN) **2453**
Fuji Bank Bulletin see Fuji Economic Review **782**
Fuji Economic Review. (JA) **782, 866**
Fuji Electric Journal. (JA) **1892**
Fuji Electric Review. (JA ISSN 0429-8284) **1892**
Fujian Academy of Agricultural Science. Journal. see Fujian Sheng Nongkeyuan Xuebao **93**
Fujian Accounting. see Fujian Kuaiji **751**
Fujian Agricultural College. Journal. see Fujian Nongxueyuan Xuebao **93**

Fujian Agricultural Science and Technology. see Fujian Nongye Keji **93**
Fujian Agriculture. see Fujian Nongye **93**
Fujian Aquatic Products. see Fujian Shuichan **2041**
Fujian Architecture. see Fujian Jianzhu **299**
Fujian Chaye/Fujian Tea. (CC) **178**
Fujian Cifa see Fazhi Liaowang **1514**
Fujian Constructional Material. see Fujian Jiancai **618**
Fujian Cultural and Historical Records. see Fujian Wenshi Ziliao **2338**
Fujian Dili/Fujian Geography. (CC) **2248**
Fujian Dizhi/Fujian Geology. (CC ISSN 1001-3970) **1561**
Fujian Duiwai Jingmao/Fujian Foreign Trade. (CC) **909**
Fujian Education. see Fujian Jiaoyu **1635**
Fujian Environment. see Fujian Huanjing **1955**
Fujian Examination Guide to the Self-Taught. see Fujian Zixue Kaoshi **1684**
Fujian Finance. see Fujian Jinrong **782**
Fujian Foreign Trade. see Fujian Duiwai Jingmao **909**
Fujian Forestry. see Fujian Linye **2101**
Fujian Fruit Trees. see Fujian Guoshu **178**
Fujian Geography. see Fujian Dili **2248**
Fujian Geology. see Fujian Dizhi **1561**
Fujian Gong'an/Fujian Public Security. (CC) **1514**
Fujian Guoshu/Fujian Fruit Trees. (CC) **178**
Fujian Huabao/Fujian Pictorial. (CC ISSN 0429-8020) **2181, 3791**
Fujian Huanjing/Fujian Environment. (CC) **1955**
Fujian Institute of Forestry. Journal. see Fujian Linxueyuan Xuebao **2101**
Fujian Jiancai/Fujian Constructional Material. (CC) **618**
Fujian Jianzhu/Fujian Architecture. (CC) **299, 1865**
Fujian Jiaoyu/Fujian Education. (CC ISSN 0427-7058) **1635**
Fujian Jinrong/Fujian Finance. (CC) **782**
Fujian Journal of Traditional Chinese Medicine. see Fujian Zhongyi Yao **3099**
Fujian Journal of Veterinary and Animal Husbandry. see Fujian Xumu Shouyi **4810**
Fujian Kuaiji/Fujian Accounting. (CC) **751**
Fujian Linxueyuan Xuebao/Fujian Institute of Forestry. Journal. (CC ISSN 1001-389X) **2101**
Fujian Linye/Fujian Forestry. (CC) **2101**
Fujian Literature. see Fujian Wenxue **2919**
Fujian Luntan (Jingji Ban)/Fujian Tribune (Economics Edition). (CC ISSN 1000-8780) **866, 2507**
Fujian Luntan (Wen Shi Zhe Ban)/Fujian Tribune (Literature, History and Philosophy Edition). (CC ISSN 1000-8659) **2507**
Fujian Medical and Pharmacological Journal. see Fujian Yiyao Zazhi **3727**
Fujian Middle School Mathematics. see Fujian Zhongxue Shuxue **3036**
Fujian Middle School Teaching. see Fujian Zhongxue Jiaoxue **1635**
Fujian Nongxueyuan Xuebao/Fujian Agricultural College. Journal. (CC ISSN 0427-7082) **93, 178**
Fujian Nongye/Fujian Agriculture. (CC ISSN 0429-8047) **93**
Fujian Nongye Keji/Fujian Agricultural Science and Technology. (CC ISSN 0253-2301) **93**
Fujian Normal University. Journal (Natural Science Edition). see Fujian Shifan Daxue Xuebao. (Ziran Kexue Ban) **4310**
Fujian Normal University. Journal (Social Science Edition). see Fujian Shifan Daxue Xuebao (Shehui Kexue Ban) **4372**

Fujian Pictorial. see Fujian Huabao **2181**
Fujian Public Security. see Fujian Gong'an **1514**
Fujian Qiao Bao/Hometown - Overseas Chinese. (US) **2002**
Fujian Qingnian/Fujian Youth. (CC) **1255**
Fujian Relics and Museum. see Fujian Wenbo **272**
Fujian Sheng Nongkeyuan Xuebao/Fujian Academy of Agricultural Science. Journal. (CC ISSN 1000-7121) **93**
Fujian Shifan Daxue Xuebao (Shehui Kexue Ban)/Fujian Normal University. Journal (Social Science Edition). (CC ISSN 1000-5285) **4372**
Fujian Shifan Daxue Xuebao. (Ziran Kexue Ban)/Fujian Normal University. Journal (Natural Science Edition). (CC) **4310**
Fujian Shuichan/Fujian Aquatic Products. (CC) **2041**
Fujian Sports Science and Technology. see Fujian Tiyu Keji **4472**
Fujian Tea. see Fujian Chaye **178**
Fujian Theater. see Fujian Xiju **4633**
Fujian Tiyu Keji/Fujian Sports Science and Technology. (CC) **4472, 3371**
Fujian Tribune (Economics Edition). see Fujian Luntan (Jingji Ban) **866**
Fujian Tribune (Literature, History and Philosophy Edition). see Fujian Luntan (Wen Shi Zhe Ban) **2507**
Fujian Waiyu/Foreign Languages in Fujian. (CC) **2815**
Fujian Wenbo/Fujian Relics and Museum. (CC) **272, 3524**
Fujian Wenshi Ziliao/Fujian Cultural and Historical Records. (CC) **2338**
Fujian Wenxue/Fujian Literature. (CC ISSN 0257-0297) **2919**
Fujian Xiangtu. (CC) **2181**
Fujian Xiju/Fujian Theater. (CC ISSN 0257-0211) **4633**
Fujian Xuekan. (CC) **4372**
Fujian Xumu Shouyi/Fujian Journal of Veterinary and Animal Husbandry. (CC ISSN 1003-4331) **4810**
Fujian Yiyao Zazhi/Fujian Medical and Pharmacological Journal. (CC) **3727, 3099**
Fujian Youth. see Fujian Qingnian **1255**
Fujian Zhongxue Jiaoxue/Fujian Middle School Teaching. (CC) **1635**
Fujian Zhongxue Shuxue/Fujian Middle School Mathematics. (CC) **3036**
Fujian Zhongyi Yao/Fujian Journal of Traditional Chinese Medicine. (CC ISSN 0427-7074) **3099, 3259**
Fujian Zixue Kaoshi/Fujian Examination Guide to the Self-Taught. (CC) **1684**
Fujikura Technical Review. (JA ISSN 0429-8357) **1892**
Fujin Club see Mine **4848**
Fujin Gaho/Women's Graphic. (JA) **2446**
Fujin Koron. see Women's Public Opinion **4857**
Fujin no Tomo/Women's Friend. (JA) **1684, 2446, 4843**
Fujingaho Beauty. see Women's Graphic Beauty **374**
Fujinkoron. (JA) **2919, 4843**
Fujitsu. (JA ISSN 0016-2515) **1893**
Fujitsu Scientific & Technical Journal. (JA ISSN 0016-2523) **1893**
Fukui Daigaku Kyoikugakubu Kiyo. Dai 2-bu. Shizen Kagaku/Fukui University. Faculty of Education. Memoirs. Series 2: Natural Science. (JA ISSN 0071-9781) **4310**
Fukui-kenritsu Tanki Daigaku Kenkyu Kiyo/Fukui Prefectural College. Bulletin. (JA ISSN 0386-6262) **3036**
Fukui Prefectural College. Bulletin. see Fukui-kenritsu Tanki Daigaku Kenkyu Kiyo **3036**
Fukui Prefectural General Green Center. Forest Research Division. Annual Report. (JA ISSN 0288-8491) **2101**
Fukui University. Faculty of Education. Memoirs. Series 2: Natural Science. see Fukui Daigaku Kyoikugakubu Kiyo. Dai 2-bu. Shizen Kagaku **4310**

Fukui University. Faculty of Education. Memoirs. Series 3: Applied Science and Agricultural Science. (JA) **93**
Fukui University. Faculty of Education. Memoirs. Series 4: Applied Science and Home Economics. (JA) **2446**
Fukui University. Faculty of Education. Memoirs. Series 5: Applied Science and Technology. (JA) **4598**
Fukui University. Faculty of Education. Memoirs. Series 6: Physical Education. (JA) **1750**
Fukujuji. see Red Double-Barred Cross **3366**
Fukuoka Acta Medica/Fukuoka Igaku Zasshi. (JA ISSN 0016-254X) **3099**
Fukuoka Daigaku Rigaku Shuho/Fukuoka University. Central Research Institute. Science Reports. (JA ISSN 0386-118X) **3036**
Fukuoka Daigaku Sogo Kenkyujo. Shizen Kagaku Hen/Fukuoka University. Central Research Institute. Bulletin. (JA ISSN 0287-0002) **3036**
Fukuoka District Meteorological Observatory. Technical Times/Fukuoka Kanku Kishodai Gijutsu Tsushin. (JA ISSN 0016-2566) **3435**
Fukuoka District Meteorological Observatory. Unusual Meteorological Report/Fukuoka Kanku Kishodai Ijo Kisho Hokoku. (JA ISSN 0016-2558) **3435**
Fukuoka Environmental Research Center. Annual Report. see Fukuoka-Ken Eisei Kogai Senta Nenpo **4101**
Fukuoka Igaku Zasshi. see Fukuoka Acta Medica **3099**
Fukuoka Kanku Kishodai Gijutsu Tsushin. see Fukuoka District Meteorological Observatory. Technical Times **3435**
Fukuoka Kanku Kishodai Ijo Kisho Hokoku. see Fukuoka District Meteorological Observatory. Unusual Meteorological Report **3435**
Fukuoka-Ken Eisei Kogai Senta Nenpo/Fukuoka Environmental Research Center. Annual Report. (JA ISSN 0287-1254) **4101, 1955**
Fukuoka-ken Kisho Geppo. see Fukuoka Prefecture. Monthly Report of Meteorology **3435**
Fukuoka Kyoiku Daigaku Kiyo. Dai-3-Bunsatsu. Sugaku, Rika, Gijutsuka Hen/Fukuoka University of Education. Bulletin. Part 3: Mathematics, Natural Sciences and Technology. (JA ISSN 0532-811X) **4310, 3036, 4598**
Fukuoka Prefecture. Monthly Report of Meteorology/Fukuoka-ken Kisho Geppo. (JA ISSN 0016-2574) **3435**
Fukuoka University. Central Research Institute. Bulletin. see Fukuoka Daigaku Sogo Kenkyujo. Shizen Kagaku Hen **3036**
Fukuoka University. Central Research Institute. Science Reports. see Fukuoka Daigaku Rigaku Shuho **3036**
Fukuoka University of Education. Bulletin. Part 3: Mathematics, Natural Sciences and Technology. see Fukuoka Kyoiku Daigaku Kiyo. Dai-3-Bunsatsu. Sugaku, Rika, Gijutsuka Hen **4310**
Fukushima Daigaku Kyoikugakubu Ronshu. Rika Hokoku/Fukushima University. Faculty of Education. Science Reports. (JA ISSN 0387-0855) **4310**
Fukushima Igaku Zasshi. see Fukushima Medical Journal **3099**
Fukushima Journal of Medical Science. (JA ISSN 0016-2590) **3099**
Fukushima Medical Journal/Fukushima Igaku Zasshi. (JA ISSN 0016-2582) **3099**
Fukushima University. Faculty of Education. Science Reports. see Fukushima Daigaku Kyoikugakubu Ronshu. Rika Hokoku **4310**
Ful-, Orr-, Gegegyogyaszat. (HU ISSN 0016-237X) **3314**

Fulbright Association Newsletter. (US) 1721, 1706
Fulbright Newsletter. (II ISSN 0046-5259) 1312
Fulbright Scholar Program: Grants for Faculty and Professionals. (US) 1721
Fulbrighter's Newsletter see Fulbright Association Newsletter 1721
Fulcrum. (CN ISSN 0016-2604) 1312
Fulcrum. (SA ISSN 0071-979X) 1822
Fulda. Statistischer Bericht. (GW) 4572
Fuldaer Geschichtsblaetter. (GW ISSN 0016-2612) 2362
Fules. (HU ISSN 0016-240X) 2198
Fulfillment Management Association Bulletin see F M A Bulletin 1010
Full Circle. (US) 4843
Full Cry. (US ISSN 0016-2620) 4547
Full Disclosure. (US ISSN 1053-4962) 1526, 3942
▼Full Effect! (US) 3552, 1255
Full Gospel Business Men's Voice. (US ISSN 0042-8264) 4283
Full Tide. (CN ISSN 0046-5267) 2993
Fulls Informatius. (SP) 816
Fulltext Sources Online. (US) 400
†Fulness. (US ISSN 0276-4679) 5197
Fulton County (Illinois) Historical & Genealogical Society Newsletter. (US) 2406, 2151
Fulton County Daily Report. (US) 2629
Fulton County Folk Finder. (US) 2151
Fulton County Historical Society Quarterly see Fulton County Images 2151
Fulton County Images. (US) 2151, 2406
Fumu Bidu/Parents Monthly. (CC ISSN 1000-727X) 1237
Fun & Games. (BH) 2180
Fun Runner. (AT ISSN 0157-5295) 4472
Fun Times. (NR ISSN 0189-9228) 2212
Funboard. (GW) 4472
Function. (AT ISSN 0313-6825) 3036
Functional Analysis and Its Applications. (English translation of: Funktsional'nyi Analiz i ego Prilozheniya) (US ISSN 0016-2663) 3036
Functional and Developmental Morphology. (US) 439, 3099
Functional Ecology. (UK ISSN 0269-8463) 1488, 503, 583, 1955
Functional Grammar Series. (US) 2815
Functional Materials. (US) 1218
Functional Orthodontist. (US ISSN 8756-3150) 3233
Functional Photography (Woodbury). (US ISSN 0360-7216) 3791
Functiones et Approximatio Commentarii Mathematici. (PL ISSN 0208-6573) 3036
Functions of the Nervous System. (NE) 3337, 3099
Fund Action. (US) 782
Fund and Bank Review see Finance and Development 780
Fund Exchange. (US) 947
Fund Exchange Report see Fund Exchange 947
Fund for Animals Quarterly. (US) 1488, 3710
Fund for Assistance to Private Education Review see F A P E Review 1633
Fund for Free Expression. (US) 3942
Fund for the Replacement of Animals in Medical Experiments News see F R A M E News 231
Fund for U F O Research Quarterly Report. (US) 53
Fund Raising Institute Monthly Portfolio see F R I Monthly Portfolio 4405
Fund Raising Management. (US ISSN 0016-268X) 782
Fund Raising Management Weekly see F R M Weekly 778

Fundacao Centro de Pesquisas Economicas e Sociais do Piaui. Atividades C E P R O see Fundacao Centro de Pesquisas Economicas e Sociais do Piaui. Relatorio de Atividades 4436
Fundacao Centro de Pesquisas Economicas e Sociais do Piaui. Relatorio de Atividades. (BL) 4436, 666
Fundacao de Economia e Estatistica Ensaios F E E see Ensaios F E E 894
Fundacao Instituto Brasileiro de Geografia e Estatistica Indicadores I B G E see Indicadores I B G E 5212
Fundacao Instituto de Pesquisas Economicas Informacoes F I P E see Informacoes F I P E 671
Fundacao Joaquim Nabuco. Serie Cursos e Conferencias. (BL) 4436
Fundacao Joaquim Nabuco. Serie Documentos. (BL) 4436
Fundacao Joaquim Nabuco. Serie Estudos e Pesquisas. (BL) 4436
Fundacao Joaquim Nabuco. Serie Monografias. (BL) 4372
Fundacao Joaquim Nambuco. Serie Republica. (BL) 2406
Fundacao Nacional do Indio Jornal da F U N A I see Jornal da F U N A I 3944
Fundacao S E A D E. Revista see Revista Sao Paulo em Perspectiva 4384
Fundacao Servicos de Saude Publica. Revista. (BL ISSN 0304-2138) 4101, 1955, 3099
Fundacio Caixa de Pensiones. Informatiu see Fundacion la Caixa. Panorama 3524
†Fundacion Bariloche. Desarrollos Humano Social Publicaciones. (AG) 5197
Fundacion Bariloche. Grupo de Analisis de Sistemas Ecologicos. Publicaciones. (AG) 1955
Fundacion Bariloche. Instituto de Economia de la Energia. Publicaciones. (AG) 1790, 3483
Fundacion Bariloche. Memoria Anual. (AG) 4310
Fundacion de Investigaciones Economicas Latinoamericanas. Indicadores de Coyuntura. (AG ISSN 0537-3468) 866
Fundacion de Investigaciones para el Desarrollo see F I D E 865
Fundacion de Investigaciones para el Desarrollo Coyuntura y Desarrollo see F I D E Coyuntura y Desarrollo 929
Fundacion Dominicana de Desarrollo. Informe Anual. (DR) 866
Fundacion Ecumenica de Cuyo. Boletin de Documentacion. (AG) 3895
Fundacion Fomento de Estudios Sociales y Sociologia Aplicada Coleccion Fundacion F O E S S A. Serie Estudios see Coleccion Fundacion F O E S S A. Serie Estudios 4431
Fundacion Jimenez Diaz. Boletin. (SP ISSN 0016-2698) 3099
Fundacion Juan March. Anales. (SP) 2217
Fundacion Juan March. Boletin Informativo. (SP ISSN 0210-4148) 2217
Fundacion la Caixa. Panorama. (SP) 3524, 3552, 4310
Fundacion Los Andes de Estudios Sociales. Anuario. (EC) 4372
Fundacion Miguel Lillo. Miscelanea. (AG ISSN 0074-025X) 503, 533, 1561
Fundacion Miguel Lillo. Serie Conservacion de la Naturaleza. (AG) 503, 1488
Fundacion Puigvert. Anales. (SP) 3099
†Fundacion Rodriguez Demorizi. Boletin.(DR) 5197
Fundacion Servicio para el Agricultor. Noticias Agricolas. (VE ISSN 0029-4160) 93
Fundament. (AU ISSN 0016-2728) 2532
Fundamenta. (US) 2151
Fundamenta Informaticae. (NE ISSN 0169-2968) 1456, 1407

Fundamenta Informaticae see Annales Societatis Mathematicae Polonae. Seria 4: Fundamenta Informaticae 5136
Fundamenta Mathematicae. (PL ISSN 0016-2736) 3036
Fundamenta Psychiatrica. (GW ISSN 0931-0428) 3337
Fundamenta Scientiae. (FR ISSN 0160-7847) 4372
Fundamental and Applied Nematology. (FR) 583
Fundamental and Applied Toxicology. (US ISSN 0272-0590) 1982, 3099, 3727
Fundamental and Clinical Pharmacology. (FR ISSN 0767-3981) 3727
Fundamental Aspects of Pollution Control and Environmental Science. (NE) 1977
Fundamental News Service. (US ISSN 0896-5749) 4238
Fundamental Studies in Computer Science. (NE) 1395
Fundamental Studies in Engineering. (NE) 1822
Fundamental Theories of Physics. (NE) 3818
Fundamentalist. (US ISSN 0016-2744) 4238
†Fundamentalist Journal. (US) 5197
Fundamentals of Cosmic Physics. (US ISSN 0094-5846) 364, 3818
Fundamentals of Educational Planning. (UN ISSN 0071-9862) 1721
Fundamentals of Pure and Applied Economics Series. (US ISSN 0191-1708) 894
Fundamenty. (PL ISSN 0429-8918) 2214
Fundberichte aus Baden-Wuerttemberg. (GW) 272
Fundberichte aus Hessen. (GW ISSN 0071-9889) 272
Fundberichte aus Oesterreich. (AU) 300
Fundberichte aus Schwaben, Neue Folge see Fundberichte aus Baden-Wuerttemberg 272
Funde und Ausgrabungen im Bezirk Trier. (GW ISSN 0723-8630) 272, 327
Fundestelle fuer die Kommunalverwaltung in Baden-Wuerttemberg. (GW) 4087
Fundevogel. (GW ISSN 0176-2753) 1237
Fundgrube. (GW ISSN 0138-2004) 1561, 3657
Fundheft fuer Arbeits- und Sozialrecht. (GW ISSN 0173-1688) 2698, 400, 2592
Fundheft fuer Oeffentliches Recht. (GW ISSN 0071-9919) 2698
Fundheft fuer Steuerrecht. (GW ISSN 0532-8632) 2698, 1095
Fundheft fuer Zivilrecht. (GW ISSN 0071-9927) 2698
Fundicao. (PO) 3407
▼Fundicao e Servicos. (BL) 3407
Fundidor. (AG ISSN 0429-8950) 3407
Fundline. (US ISSN 1049-4332) 947
Funds Agent Custodians Suppliers see F A C S 945
Funds Agent Custodians Suppliers Week: Mutual Fund News and Information see F A C S of the Week: Mutual Fund News and Information 778
Funds Transfer Report. (US) 782
Die Fundstelle. (GW ISSN 0016-2779) 4087
Funeral Forum see Forum 2119
Funeral Service Abstracts see Thanatology Abstracts 4052
Funeral Service Insider. (US ISSN 0148-6705) 2119
Funeral Service Journal. (UK ISSN 0016-2800) 2119
Fungal Genetics Newsletter. (US ISSN 0895-1942) 439
Fungi Canadenses. (CN ISSN 0823-0552) 503, 178
Fungicide and Nematicide Tests. (US ISSN 0148-9038) 178
Funk. (GW) 1356

Funk Amateur. (GW ISSN 0016-2833) 1356
Funk Uhr. (GW) 2189
Funk und Elektronik. (GW) 2292
Funk und Fernsehen see F F Dabei 1373
Funkcialaj Ekvacioj, Serio Internacia. (JA ISSN 0532-8721) 3036
Funkschau. (GW ISSN 0016-2841) 1362, 1374, 4460
Funktionsanalyse Biologischer Systeme. (GW ISSN 0340-0840) 440, 571
Die Funktionskrankheiten des Bewegungsapparates. (GW ISSN 0258-2015) 3214, 3308, 3369
Funktsional'nyi Analiz i Ego Prilozheniya. (RU ISSN 0016-285X) 3036
Funny Times see We're Living in Funny Times 2889
Funparks Directory see Directory of Funparks & Attractions 4759
Funu/Women. (CC) 4843
Funu Gongzuo/Women's Affairs. (CC) 4843
Funu Shenghuo. (CC) 4843
Funu zhi You/Women's Friend. (CC) 4843
Al-Funun al-Sha'biyyah. (JO) 2055
Funworld. (US) 4768
Fuoco. (IT ISSN 0016-2876) 2867, 327
Fuoribordo. (IT) 4524
Fuorimargine. (IT) 4436
Fuoristrada. (IT) 1955, 4598
Fur Age Monthly see Fur Age Weekly 2736
Fur Age Weekly. (US ISSN 0016-2884) 2736
Fur and Leather Review see Fur Review 5197
Fur - Fish - Game. Harding's Magazine. (US ISSN 0016-2922) 4547
Fur Rancher. (US ISSN 0744-7701) 2736
†Fur Review. (UK ISSN 0260-2393) 5197
Fur Taker Journal. (US ISSN 0016-2965) 2736
Fur Weekly News. (UK ISSN 0016-2981) 2736
Die Furche. (AU ISSN 0016-299X) 2867
Furdek. (US) 2002
Fureai see Dansk Japansk Venskabsforenings Blad 3954
Furman Studies. (US ISSN 0190-4701) 2507
Furman University Bulletin. Furman Studies Issue see Furman Studies 2507
Furnished Holidays in Britain see Self-Catering and Furnished Holidays 4786
Furnishing & Appliance World. (NZ) 2558
Furnishing Floors. (AT) 2559
Furnishing Retailer & Contractor. (IE) 2559
Furnishing Textiles and Wallcoverings Trade Journal see Domestic Textiles & Wallcoverings Trade Journal 4618
Furnishings Record. (UK) 2559, 4619
Furniture. (PH) 2559
Furniture and Bedding Production see Furniture Manufacturer 2559
▼Furniture Components & Production International. (UK ISSN 0964-0940) 2559
The Furniture Executive. (US) 2559
Furniture History. (UK ISSN 0016-3058) 2559
Furniture Industry Research Association (F I R A) Bulletin see F I R A Bulletin 2558
Furniture: Latin American Industrial Report. (US) 2551
Furniture Manufacturer. (UK ISSN 0306-0519) 2559
Furniture Manufacturing Management. (US ISSN 0192-799X) 2559
Furniture News see Furniture - Today 2559
Furniture Production and Design see Canadian Wood Processing 2557
Furniture Record see Cabinet Maker 2557

Furniture Retailer (Greensboro). (US) **2559**, 1040
†Furniture Retailer (Nashville). (US) **5197**
Furniture - Today. (US ISSN 0194-360X) **2559**
†Furniture - Today's Manufacturing - Today. (US) **5197**
Furniture Transporter. (US) **4744**
Furniture Wood Digest see Wood Digest **2562**
Furniture Workers Press. (US ISSN 0016-3090) **2583**, 2559
Furniture World. (US) **2559**
Furniture World and Furniture Buyer and Decorator. (US ISSN 0016-3104) **2559**
Furong. (CC) **2919**
Al Furqan. (Il) **4218**
Furrow. (US ISSN 0016-3112) **93**
The Furrow. (IE ISSN 0016-3120) **4264**
Furrow (Australian Edition). (US) **93**
Furrow (United Kingdom Edition). (US) **93**
Further Education Research Network Journal see F E R N Journal **1706**
▼Further State(s) of the Art. (US) **2919**
Furukawa Review. (JA ISSN 0429-9159) **1893**
†Furusato Tenbo. (JA ISSN 0386-1465) **5197**
Fuse see Fuse Magazine **2177**
Fuse Magazine. (CN ISSN 0838-603X) **2177**
Fushe Yanjiu yu Fushe Gongyi Xuebao. (CC ISSN 1000-3436) **1805**
Fusion. (US ISSN 0016-3155) **1163**
Fusion. (GW ISSN 0173-9387) **1790**, 1805, 4310
†Fusion Energy Update. (US ISSN 0163-3856) **5198**
Fusion Engineering and Design. (NE ISSN 0920-3796) **1929**, 1917
Fusion Facilities Directory. (US) **1805**
Fusion Magazine. (CN ISSN 0832-9656) **1163**
Fusion Nucleaire. see Nuclear Fusion **3848**
Fusion Planning. (JA) **1291**
Fusion Power Associates Executive Newsletter. (US) **1805**
Fusion Power Report. (US ISSN 0276-2919) **1805**, 1790
Fusion Technology. (US ISSN 0748-1896) **1805**
Der Fuss. (GW ISSN 0427-7783) **3378**
Fussball Club Pforzheim. Club-Nachrichten. (GW ISSN 0009-9600) **4504**
Fussball-Weltzeitschrift. (GW) **4504**
Der Fussballtrainer. (GW ISSN 0016-3228) **4504**
Fussballtraining. (GW ISSN 0174-6227) **4504**, 4472
Fussboden Forum. (GW ISSN 0342-7269) **639**
Futari. (FI) **4504**
Futari no Heya/Plus One. (JA) **2207**
Futura. (GW) **3100**
Future. (UK) **816**
Future see Jaycees Magazine **1298**
Future. see Al Mostakbal **2015**
Future Choices. (US ISSN 1047-191X) **1237**, 4061
†Future Computing Systems. (UK ISSN 0266-7207) **5198**
Future Farmers of America. Between Issues. (US) **93**, 1635
Future Farmers of America. Newsletter. (US) **93**, 2126
Future Farmers of America New Horizons see F F A New Horizons **89**
Future Generation Computer Systems. (NE ISSN 0167-739X) **4359**
▼Future Home Technology News. (US ISSN 1051-9971) **1879**, 2559
Future Literature in Progress Magazine see F L I P Magazine **5190**
▼The Future of Children. (US ISSN 1054-8289) **1237**
Future Reflections. (US ISSN 0883-3419) **2292**
Future Survey. (US ISSN 0190-3241) **4355**, 12

Future Vacancies for the Finalist. (UK) **3627**
†Future Views (Dallas). (US) **5198**
Futurebook. (US) **4128**, 400
Futurebus plus Design. (US) **1421**
Futures. (UK ISSN 0016-3287) **4598**, 4061, 4436
Futures (Cedar Falls). (US ISSN 0746-2468) **947**
Futures (East Lansing). (US) **93**
Futures and Options. (CN ISSN 1183-4242) **947**, 782
Futures & Options World. (US) **1040**
Futures Factors - The Futures Portfolio Advisor see Options & Futures Factors - The Futures Portfolio Advisor **959**
Futures Industry see Managed Accounts Reports **954**
Futures Magazine Reference Guide to Futures Markets. (US) **947**
Futures Market Service. (US ISSN 0016-3295) **947**
Futures Research Quarterly. (US ISSN 8755-3317) **4310**, 400, 2311
Futures World see Futures & Options World **1040**
Futures World News. (US) **947**
FutureScan. (US) **866**, 4372
Futurescope. (US) **947**
Futuretech. (US) **4598**
FutureTech Strategic Markets. (US) **1040**, 4598
Futuribles. (FR ISSN 0337-307X) **4436**
Futurics. (US ISSN 0164-1220) **4436**, 4598
Futurific. (US ISSN 0738-9264) **4598**, 3895
The Futurist. (US ISSN 0016-3317) **4310**, 4598
Futuro. (AG ISSN 0016-3325) **2170**
Il Futuro dell'Uomo. (IT ISSN 0390-217X) **4310**
Futurology. (SZ) **4598**, 4310, 4373
Fuwo. (GW ISSN 0323-8407) **4504**
Fuzhou Daxue Xuebao (Shehui Kexue Ban)/Fuzhou University. Journal (Social Science Edition). (CC) **4373**
Fuzhou Daxue Xuebao (Ziran Kexue Ban)/Fuzhou University. Journal (Natural Science Edition). (CC ISSN 1000-2243) **4310**
Fuzhou University. Journal (Natural Science Edition). see Fuzhou Daxue Xuebao (Ziran Kexue Ban) **4310**
Fuzhou University. Journal (Social Science Edition). see Fuzhou Daxue Xuebao (Shehui Kexue Ban) **4373**
Fuzzy Sets and Systems. (NE ISSN 0165-0114) **3036**
Fyens Stiftsbog. (DK ISSN 0107-8399) **2362**
Fynboer og Arkaeologi. (DK ISSN 0109-1441) **272**
Fynske Aarboeger. (DK ISSN 0085-0918) **2362**
Fynske Laeger. (DK) **3100**
Fynske Minder. (DK ISSN 0427-7945) **2362**, 272, 327
Fysiatricky a Reumatologicky Vestnik. (CS ISSN 0072-0038) **3369**
Fysiatricky Vestnik see Fysiatricky a Reumatologicky Vestnik **3369**
Fysiktips. (DK ISSN 0109-6664) **3818**
Fysiokjemikeren see Bioingenioeren **1224**
Fysioterapeuten. (NO ISSN 0016-3384) **3100**
Fysioterapia. (FI) **3100**
Fysisk Tidsskrift. (DK ISSN 0016-3392) **3819**
G. (Grossmont College) (US) **1312**
G A. (Global Architecture) (JA) **300**
G A. (Gas und Architektur) (GW ISSN 0016-3406) **2299**, 300
G A A News Digest. (General Aviation Association (Australia)) (AT) **53**, 980
G A B see Genealogical Aids Bulletin **2152**
G A Document. (Global Architecture) (JA) **300**
†G A L A Realist. (Gay and Lesbian Atheists) (US) **5198**
G A L - Bulletin. (Gesellschaft fuer Angewandte Linguistik e.V.) (GW ISSN 0175-2103) **2815**

G A M A News Journal. (General Agents and Managers Association) (US) **2532**
G A N P A C Brief. (German-American National Political Action Committee) (US ISSN 1062-3868) **2002**, 3896
G A O Documents. (U.S. General Accounting Office) (US) **751**
G A O Review. (U.S. General Accounting Office) (US ISSN 0016-3414) **4061**, 751
G A P. (Groupe Avant-Premiere) (FR) **4619**
G A P E. (Guyana Association of Professional Engineers) (GY) **1822**
G A P H Y O R. Base de Donnees. (Gaz - Physique - Orsay) (FR ISSN 0761-3369) **3819**
G A S Lites. (Genealogical Association of Sacramento, Inc.) (US ISSN 0882-8377) **2151**
G A T F (Year) see G A T F World **3999**
†G A T F Education Report. (Graphic Arts Technical Foundation) (US) **5198**
G A T F Environmental Control Report see G A T F World **3999**
G A T F Second Sight. (Graphic Arts Technical Foundation) (US) **4598**
G A T F Technical Services Report see G A T F Second Sight **4598**
G A T F World. (Graphic Arts Technical Foundation) (US) **3999**, 4598
G A T T Focus. (General Agreement on Tariffs and Trade) (UN ISSN 0256-0119) **666**
G A T T Legal System and World Trade Diplomacy. (General Agreement on Tariffs and Trade) **2723**, 909
G A T T Studies in International Trade. (General Agreement on Tariffs and Trade) (UN) **909**
G and B. (IT) **3208**, 3185, 3365
G B Digest. (Girls Brigade) (AT) **4179**
G B E: Export Directory of Brazil see Export Directory of Brazil/Guia Brasileiro de Exportacao **1135**
G B H. (US) **1374**
G B Journal. (UK ISSN 0430-8913) **3752**
G B U Reporter. (Greater Beneficial Union of Pittsburgh) (US) **2532**, 2002
G B und G W - Gaertnerboerse und Gartenwelt see Gaertnerboerse und Gartenwelt **2126**
G C A Bar Code Reporter. (Graphic Communications Association) (US) **1450**
G C A Newsletter see Garden Center Newsletter **2126**
G C A Newsletter. (Golf Course Association) (US) **4504**
G C A Review. (Graphic Communications Association) (US) **4007**, 31, 4143
G C C A Newsletter. (Graduate Careers Council of Australia Ltd.) (AT) **1707**, 3627
G C Government Communications. (US) **2570**
G C N A Bulletin. (Guild of Carillonneurs in North America (San Antonio)) (US ISSN 0827-5955) **3552**
G C S A A Membership Directory see Golf Course Superintendents Association of America. Membership Directory **4505**
G C T (Gifted, Creative, Talented Children) see Gifted Child Today **1238**
G D G Report. (US ISSN 0883-3087) **1514**
G D R Monitor. (NE ISSN 0144-6355) **2867**
G D R - Monitor Special Series. (NE ISSN 0262-1789) **2363**
G D R Peace Council. Information. (GW ISSN 0016-3481) **3958**
G D R Review/D D R - Revue. (GW ISSN 0016-349X) **2189**, 485
G D S see Giornale del Serramento **618**
G D S - Zeitung. (Gewerkschaft Der Sozialversicherung) (GW ISSN 0173-2323) **2583**, 2532

G D W Informationen. (AU) **618**, 4149
G; Documentation Technique et Commerciale des Vendeurs de Gaz. (FR ISSN 0072-0046) **666**
G E A Educator. (Grossmont Education Association) (US) **1635**
G E C. (IT) **1336**
G E C Contact. (General Electric Co.) (AT) **1893**, 1040
G E C Engineering see G E C Review **1893**
G E C Journal of Research. (UK ISSN 0264-9187) **1893**, 1929
G E C Review. (General Electric Co., PLC) (UK ISSN 0267-9337) **1893**, 1929
G E E U - Gaz Eaux Eaux Usees. see G W A **3686**
G E I C O Direct. (Government Employees Insurance Company) (US) **2532**
G E I Lights. (Gesellschaft fuer Elektronische Informationsverarbeitung mbH) (GW) **1395**
G E I Newsletter. (Grief Education Institute) (US) **4022**
G E J - Gazeto. (GW) **2815**, 1721
G E M's Europe Report see Europe Report **4177**
G E N. (VE ISSN 0016-3503) **3267**
G E O: Grassroots Economic Organizing Newsletter. (US) **3627**, 830, 2583
G E O Report. (US) **1955**
▼G E P. (Geschichte Erziehung Politik) (GW) **4373**, 1750
G E S. Boletin de Informacion. (General Espanola de Seguros, S.A.) (SP) **2532**
G F A - Gallup National Gardening Survey (Year) see National Gardening Survey (Year) **2135**
G F F see Geologiska Foereningens i Stockholm. Foerhandlinger **1565**
†G F Magazine. (Gannett Foundation) (US) **5198**
G F O A Newsletter. (Government Finance Officers Association) (US ISSN 1051-6964) **4087**
†G F Spectrum. (Georg Fischer Aktiengesellschaft) (SZ) **5198**
G F W C Clubwoman. (General Federation of Women's Clubs) (US ISSN 0745-2209) **1298**, 4843
G G see Gaaf Goed **2559**
G - Geschichte mit Pfiff. (GW ISSN 0173-539X) **2311**
†G H A A Journal. (Group Health Association of America, Inc.) (US ISSN 0888-4250) **5198**
G H A A News see H M O Magazine **2532**
G H Gastrotel. (GW) **2474**
G H K Publik. (Gesamt Hochschule Kassel) (GW) **1694**
G H S Foot - Notes. (Georgia Historical Society) (US ISSN 0090-4368) **2406**
G I G Newsletter. (Gluten Intolerance Group of North America) (US ISSN 0890-507X) **3906**, 3267
G I P. (Germansk Instituts Publikationer) (DK ISSN 0106-0872) **2815**, 2363, 2919
G I P see Gastroenterology in Practice **3268**
G I P S. (Government Imprinted Penalty Stationery Society) (US) **3752**
G I Prisma. (Goethe Institut) (GW) **1722**
▼G I S Europe. (Geographic Information System) (US) **2268**
†G I S Forum. (Geographic Information Systems) (US ISSN 1041-2697) **5198**
G I S Newsletter. (Geoscience Information Society) (US) **1544**
†G I S R A. (Guyana Institute for Social Research and Action) (GY) **5198**
G I S World. (Geographic Information System) (US ISSN 0897-5507) **2268**
G I T. (GW ISSN 0016-3538) **3259**
G I T Spezial Chromotagraphie. (GW) **1205**
G K Round-up. (Il) **1058**

G L A D News. (Greater Los Angeles Council on Deafness, Inc.) (US ISSN 0739-7453) **2287**, 1736
G L A D Newsletter see London Disability News **4412**
G L A Newsletter see G L B Ames Newsletter **2453**
G L A S of (Year). (Gay and Lesbian Alliance at Stanford) (US) **2453**, 1312
G L B. (Gymnasiet Laerere i Billedkunst) (DK ISSN 0109-9442) **1635**, 327
G L B Ames Newsletter. (Gays, Lesbians and Bisexuals of Ames) (US ISSN 1059-065X) **2453**, 3942
G L C Voice. (US ISSN 0890-7951) **3942**, 2453
G L I B News. (Gaymen and Lesbians in Brookhaven) (US) **2453**
G L I B Notes see G L I B News **2453**
G L O W. (Gorgeous Ladies of Wrestling) (US) **4472**
G L V Mitteilungen. (Graphische Lehr- und Versuchsanstalt) (AU ISSN 0016-3562) **3999**, 1635
G M A P see Geographic Information, Mapping, and Positioning Newsletter **2249**
G M B Working Together. (UK) **2583**
G M D A Bulletin. (Greater Milwaukee Dental Association) (US ISSN 0884-6898) **3233**
G M D News and Information see G M D Newsline **1437**
G M D Newsletter see G M D Newsline **1437**
G M D Newsline. (US) **1437**, 1395
G M D-Spiegel. (Gesellschaft fuer Mathematik und Datenverarbeitung mbH) (GW ISSN 0724-4339) **1395**
G M I Alumni News. (US) **1312**
G M P Letter. (Good Manufacturing Practice) (US ISSN 0196-626X) **2522**
G M U Law Review. (George Mason University) (US ISSN 0741-8736) **2629**
G M V. (Government and Military Video) (US) **1385**, 3459, 4061
G M Z see A G M **3749**
G Magazine. (CN) **1421**
G N P see Guide National de Prescription des Medicaments **3727**
G O: Government Officers Magazine of Administration and Purchasing. (AT) **4061**
†G O M - Economie in Limburg. (Gewestelijke Ontwikkelingsmaatschappij Limburg) (BE) **5198**
G P. (US) **3233**
G P I see Gesundheitspolitische Informationen **4101**
G P Magazin. (GW) **3662**, 1163
G P N Educational Media. College - Adult see G P N Educational Video Catalog. College - Adult **1707**
G P N Educational Media. Elementary - Secondary see G P N Educational Video Catalog. Elementary - Secondary **1750**
G P N Educational Video Catalog. College - Adult. (Great Plains National Instructional Television Library) (US) **1707**, 1385
G P N Educational Video Catalog. Elementary - Secondary. (Great Plains National Instructional Television Library) (US) **1750**, 1385
G P N Newsletter. (Great Plains National Instructional Television Library) (US ISSN 0738-7555) **1374**, 1635
G P O. (Government Publications for Oklahoma) (US) **2758**
G P S A Engineering Data Book. (Gas Processors Suppliers Association) (US) **3686**, 1822
▼G P S Report. (Global Positioning Satellite) (US ISSN 1056-7127) **1363**, 53
▼G P S World. (Global Positioning System) (US ISSN 1048-5104) **2248**
G Q. (Gentlemen's Quarterly) (US ISSN 0016-6979) **1291**, 3397

G R see Genio Rurale **178**
G R. (Gift Reporter) (US ISSN 0894-4113) **2281**
G R A & I Annual Index see Government Reports Announcements and Index Annual Index **1844**
G R A Reporter. (Governmental Research Association, Inc.) (US ISSN 0016-3619) **4061**
G R C. Revue Trimestrielle. see R C M P Quarterly **1521**
G R C Information Bulletin see G R C News **2272**
G R C News. (Gerontology Research Center) (CN ISSN 1188-181X) **2272**
G R I (U.S. Government Reports Index) see Government Reports Announcements and Index Journal **4080**
G R I D. (Gas Research Institute Digest) (US) **3686**
†G R I F. (Groupe de Recherche et d'Information Feministes) (BE ISSN 0770-6138) **5198**
G R M U G Newsletter. (Great River Microcomputer Users Group) (US) **1469**, 1460
G S see Gay Scotland **2453**
G S A News and Information see G S A Today **1561**
G S A Today. (Geological Society of America) (US ISSN 1052-5173) **1561**
G S A Travel Marketing Magazine. (SA) **4768**
G S B U G see Bug Report **1467**
G S D News. (Harvard University Graduate School of Design) (US ISSN 0746-3677) **300**, 2487
G S F Mensch und Umwelt. (GW ISSN 0175-4521) **1955**, 4310
G S I S Monograph Series in World Affairs. (Graduate School of International Studies) (US ISSN 0077-0582) **3958**
G S M Chronicle. (Graduate School of Management) (US) **1312**
G S N see L G S N: Lesbian and Gay Studies Newsletter **2454**
G S N. Gesneriad Saintpaulia News. (US ISSN 0016-3627) **2126**
G S P C A "Shorthair". (German Shorthaired Pointer Club of America) (US) **1095**
G S R. (Gakki Shoho Review) (JA) **3552**, 909
G. Schirmer Highlights. (US) **3552**
G. Stanley Hall Lecture Series. (US ISSN 8756-7865) **4022**, 1750
G T see Giornale del Termoidraulico **1822**
†G T E Automatic Electric World-Wide Communications Journal. (General Telephone & Electronics) (US ISSN 0273-141X) **5198**
†G T E Journal of Research and Development. (General Telephone & Electronics) (US ISSN 0097-7721) **5198**
†G T E S Newsletter. (SA) **5198**
G T V Bulletin. (Groupements Techniques Veterinaires) (FR) **4810**
G U A Papers of Geology. (NE) **1561**
G V A Mitgliederverzeichnis. (Gesamtverband Autoteile-Handel e.V.) (GW ISSN 0171-5046) **4691**, 4518
G V Manager. (Gross Verbraucher) (GW ISSN 0940-8762) **1011**
G V - Praxis. (GW) **2071**
G V: Swiss. (GW) **2071**
G W A/G E E U - Gaz Eaux Eaux Usees.(SZ) **3686**, 4824
G W A - Gas Wasser Abwasser see G W A **3686**
G W A Yearbook. (Gesamtverband Werbeagenturen e.V.) (GW) **31**
G W F Gas- und Wasserfach see Wasser - Abwasser - G W F **4831**
G W G-Info see G W G - Zeitschrift **1736**
G W G - Zeitschrift. (Gesellschaft fuer Wissenschaftliche Gesprachspsychotherapie e.V.) (GW ISSN 0932-934X) **1736**
G W Hatchet. (George Washington University) (US) **1312**

G.W. Leibniz: Saemtliche Schriften und Briefe. (GW) **3767**, 2363
G W Magazine. (George Washington University) (US) **1312**
G W Review. (George Washington University) (US) **2919**
†G W T W Collectors Club Newsletter. (Gone With The Wind Collectors Club) (US) **5198**
G W Times see G W Magazine **1312**
G W U M C. Department of Biochemistry. Annual Spring Symposia Series. (George Washington University Medical Center) (US) **477**
G 5 Report. (CN) **1336**
Ga As I C Symposium. (US) **1771**
Gaaf Goed. (NE ISSN 0923-3660) **2559**, 4619
Gaardbrukeren. (NO ISSN 0801-2202) **93**
Gaba Reprints. (KE) **4179**
▼Gabbiani News. (IT) **1255**, 1955
Gabbitas, Truman & Thring Education after 16. (UK ISSN 0269-588X) **1694**, 1707
Gabbitas, Truman & Thring Guide to Boarding Schools & Colleges. (UK ISSN 0951-872X) **1694**
Gabbitas, Truman and Thring Guide to Independent Further Education see Gabbitas, Truman & Thring Education after 16 **1694**
Gabinetto Disegni e Stampe degli Uffizi. Cataloghi. (IT ISSN 0072-0070) **3524**
Gabinetto Disegni e Stampe degli Uffizi. Inventario. (IT) **3524**
Gabinetto Scientifico e Letterario G.P. Vieusseux. (IT) **2507**
Gabler Family Association Newsletter & Record. (US) **2151**
Gablers - Magazin. (GW ISSN 0932-3961) **1011**, 1095, 2709
Gabon. Direction de la Statistique et des Etudes Economique. Bulletin Mensuel de Statistique see Gabon. Direction Generale de l'Economie. Bulletin Mensuel de Statistique **4572**
Gabon. Direction Generale de l'Economie. Bulletin Mensuel de Statistique. (GO) **4572**
Gabon. Direction Generale des Finances et du Budget. Projet du Budget General. (GO) **1095**
Gabon. Ministere de l'Education Nationale. Annuaire Statistique de l'Enseignement. (GO) **1677**
Gabon d'Aujourd'hui. (GO) **1336**
Gabon Selection. (FR ISSN 0247-8315) **909**
Gabonaipar. (HU ISSN 0133-0918) **206**, 2071
Gabriel. (IT ISSN 0016-3694) **3752**, 4179
Gabriele see Sekretariat **1061**
Gabriel's Interiors Annual see Interiors Magazine **2553**
Gabriel's Interiors Magazine see Interiors Magazine **2553**
Gacela - Gazela. Revista de Estudios Latinoamericanos. (DK) **2407**
Gacela - Gazela. Tidsskrift for Latinamerikastudier see Gacela - Gazela. Revista de Estudios Latinoamericanos **2407**
La Gaceta. (US ISSN 0016-3724) **2225**
Gaceta. (MX ISSN 0016-3716) **2867**
Gaceta Aerea/Air Gazette. (VE) **53**
Gaceta Agricola. (MX) **93**
Gaceta Agronomica. (AG ISSN 0326-0992) **93**
Gaceta Arqueologica Andina. (PE) **272**
Gaceta Bibliotecaria del Peru. (PE ISSN 0433-0730) **2758**
Gaceta de la Universidad. (UY ISSN 0016-3759) **2867**
Gaceta Economica. (BO ISSN 0016-3767) **666**
Gaceta Filatelica. (AG) **3752**
Gaceta Genealogica. (AG) **2151**
Gaceta Hipica. (VE ISSN 0016-3775) **4534**
Gaceta Informativa see Gaceta Informativa I N E G I **866**
Gaceta Informativa de Legislacion. (MX) **2629**

GALACTICA 6209

Gaceta Informativa de Legislacion, Jurisprudencia y Bibliografia see Gaceta Informativa de Legislacion **2629**
Gaceta Informativa I N E G I. (Instituto Nacional de Estadistica, Geografia e Informatica) (MX) **866**, 1544
†Gaceta Matematica. (SP ISSN 0016-3805) **5198**
Gaceta Medica de Bilbao. (SP ISSN 0304-4858) **3100**
Gaceta Medica de Caracas. (VE) **3100**
Gaceta Medica de Mexico. (MX ISSN 0016-3813) **3100**
Gaceta Mensual see Club Filatelico de Caracas. Gaceta Mensual **3751**
Gaceta Numismatica. (SP ISSN 0210-2137) **3599**
Gaceta Rural. (SP ISSN 0016-3864) **93**
Gaceta Textil. (AG ISSN 0046-5364) **4619**
Gaden Raifu. see Garden Life **2127**
†Gadget. (US) **5198**
Gadney's Guides to International Contests, Festivals & Grants in Film & Video, Photography, TV-Radio Broadcasting, Writing & Journalism. (US) **1336**, 2570, 3511, 3791
Gadney's Guides to International Contests, Festivals and Grants in Film and Video, Photography, TV-Radio Broadcasting, Writing, Poetry, Playwriting and Journalism see Gadney's Guides to International Contests, Festivals & Grants in Film & Video, Photography, TV-Radio Broadcasting, Writing & Journalism **1336**
Gaea. (US) **1544**, 4843
An Gael. (US) **2002**
Gaelic Society of Inverness. Transactions. (UK) **2815**
Gaelic Sport. (IE) **4472**
Gaelic World. (IE ISSN 0332-1274) **4472**
Der Gaertner. (GW) **4238**
Gaertnerboerse und Gartenwelt. (GW ISSN 0936-3734) **2126**, 503
Gaertnerische Berufspraxis. (GW ISSN 0301-2719) **2126**
Gaertnerischer Fachhandel see Garten- und Freizeitmarkt **2127**
Gaesdoncker Blaetter. (GW) **1312**
Gaeste Journal. (GW) **4768**
GaFa - Garten - Fachhandel Saatgutwirtschaft. (GW ISSN 0724-7281) **2126**
Gaffa. (DK ISSN 0109-0097) **3552**
Gag Recap. (US) **327**, 2867
Gai Pied Hebdo. (FR ISSN 0755-0251) **2453**
Gai Saber see Lo Gai Saber **2827**
Gaia's Guide. (UK) **2453**, 4768, 4843
Gaiato. (PO ISSN 0016-3910) **4406**
Gaige/Reform. (CC) **4373**
Gaikoku Bungaku Kenkyu see Studies in British & American Literature **2919**
Gaikoku Koku Uchu Bunken Mokuroku. see Foreign Aero-Space Literature **5195**
Gaikoku Tokkyo Sokuho, Kagaku-hen. see Foreign Chemical Patent News **5195**
Gainsborough Journal see Gainsborough Trader **2194**
Gainsborough Trader. (UK) **2194**
Gairm. (UK ISSN 0016-3929) **2919**, 2194
Gaither Connection. (US) **2151**
Gakki Shoho/Music Trade in Japan. (JA) **3552**
Gakki Shoho Review see G S R **3552**
Gakujin/Alpinist. (JA) **4547**
Gakujutsu Geppo/Japanese Scientific Monthly. (JA ISSN 0387-2440) **4310**
Gakujutsu Zasshi/Kyoto College of Pharmacy. Scientific Journal. (JA ISSN 0288-349X) **3727**
▼Gal/Fire. (MP) **4768**
Gal-ed. (IS ISSN 0334-4258) **2002**
Gala see Gala International **3511**
Gala International. (IT) **3511**
▼Galactic Central Bibliographies. (US) **400**, 2919
†Galactic Discourse. (US) **5198**
Galactica. (PL) **3011**

6210 GALAKSIJA

Galaksija. (YU) **4311**
Galamukani! (SA ISSN 0016-3988) **4283**
Galaxea. (JA) **440**
Galaxia. (AG ISSN 0016-3996) **4619**, 1177
Galaxia 71. (VE) **2867**
Galaxie - Bis. (FR) **2983**
†Galaxy. (US ISSN 0016-4003) **5198**
Gale Directory of Publications see Gale Directory of Publications and Broadcast Media **400**
Gale Directory of Publications and Broadcast Media. (US ISSN 1048-7972) **400**
Gale Directory of Publications and Broadcast Media Update. (US ISSN 1048-7972) **400**
Gale International Directory of Publications. (US ISSN 1040-9351) **400**
Galeria Michele Malingue. Catalogo. (PY ISSN 1017-2823) **3524**
†Galerie - Informationen. (GW ISSN 0323-8865) **5198**
Galerie Nierendorf, Berlin. Kunstblaetter.(GW ISSN 0072-0089) **3524**
Galerie Sanct Lucas. Gemaelde Alter Meister. (AU) **3524**
Galgos. (SP) **4472**
Galicia y Rio de la Plata. Compania de Seguros. Memoria y Balance General.(AG) **2532**
▼Galilean Electrodynamics. (US ISSN 1047-4811) **3819**
†Galileo (Boston). (US ISSN 0162-8305) **5198**
Gallagher Presidents' Report see Gallagher Report **5198**
†Gallagher Report. (US ISSN 0016-4070) **5198**
Gallassia dell' Informazione. (IT) **1336**, 1395
Gallaudet Alumni Newsletter. (US) **1312**, 2287
Gallaudet Record see Gallaudet Today **2287**
Gallaudet Today. (US ISSN 0016-4089) **2287**
Gallaudet Today. Annual Legal Review. (US ISSN 0016-4089) **2629**
Galleria. (IT ISSN 0016-4097) **2919**
Galleria del Cavallino. Mostre. (IT) **3524**
Gallerie: Women Artists Monographs. (CN ISSN 0838-1658) **327**
Gallerie: Women's Art see Gallerie: Women Artists Monographs **327**
Gallery. see Hualang **328**
Gallery. (UK ISSN 0306-1256) **2993**
Gallery. (US ISSN 0195-072X) **3397**
Gallery. (AT ISSN 0814-7833) **3524**
†Gallery. (SA) **5198**
Gallery Specials. (US) **3397**
†Gallery Works. (US) **5198**
Galley see Clan MacNeil Association of America. Gallev **2147**
Galley Sail Review. (US ISSN 0016-4100) **2993**
Gallia. (FR ISSN 0016-4119) **272**
Gallia. Supplement. (FR ISSN 0072-0119) **272**
Gallia Prehistoire. (FR ISSN 0016-4127) **272**
Gallia Prehistoire. Supplement. (FR ISSN 0072-0100) **273**, 2248
Gallneukirchner Bote see Diakonie **4174**
Gallo see Quaderni de il Gallo **4196**
Galloway Gazette and Stranraer News. (UK) **1040**
Galloway Herd Book. (UK) **216**
Galloway Journal. (UK ISSN 0430-9928) **216**
Galloway News. (UK ISSN 0016-4178) **2194**
Gallup Poll Monthly. (US ISSN 1051-2616) **3896**
Gallup Report see Gallup Poll Monthly **3896**
Galpakabita. (Il ISSN 0016-4216) **2919**
Galpin Society Journal. (UK ISSN 0072-0127) **3552**
Galten Egnsarkiv. Annales. (DK ISSN 0108-0032) **2363**
Galvanize. (AT) **3407**

Galvano Teknisk Tidsskrift see Overflate Teknikk **1212**
Galvanotecnica e Nuove Finiture. (IT) **3407**
Galvanotecnica e Processi al Plasma and Galvanotecnica see Galvanotecnica e Nuove Finiture **3407**
Gam on Yachting. (CN ISSN 0016-4259) **4524**
Gambia. Central Statistics Department. Annual Report of External Trade Statistics see External Trade Statistics of Gambia **715**
Gambia. Central Statistics Department. Consumer Price Index. (GM) **4799**
Gambia. Central Statistics Department. Directory of Establishments. (GM) **1136**
Gambia. Central Statistics Department. Education Statistics. (GM) **1677**, 4572
Gambia. Central Statistics Department. Monthly Bulletin of Prices. (GM) **999**
Gambia. Central Statistics Department. Monthly Summary of External Trade Statistics. (GM) **718**, 909
Gambia. Central Statistics Department. Quarterly Survey of Employment and Earnings. (GM) **718**, 980
Gambia. Central Statistics Department. Summary of Tourist Statistics. (GM) **4799**, 4572
Gambia. Central Statistics Department. Tourist Statistics. (GM) **4799**, 4572
Gambia. Currency Board. Report see Central Bank of Gambia. Quarterly Bulletin **850**
Gambia. Education Department. Education Statistics see Gambia. Central Statistics Department. Education Statistics **1677**
Gambia. Oilseeds Marketing Board. Report see Gambia. Produce Marketing Board. Annual Report **151**
Gambia. Produce Marketing Board. Annual Report. (GM ISSN 0301-8423) **151**
Gambia News Bulletin. (GM ISSN 0046-5380) **2169**
Gambit. (US ISSN 0888-1928) **2436**
Gambit. (UK ISSN 0016-4283) **4633**
Gambit Revue. (GW ISSN 0937-5457) **4472**
Gambling Times see Win (Van Nuys) **4496**
Game & Fish. (US) **4547**
Game Bird Breeders, Aviculturists, Zoologists, & Conservationists Gazette. (US ISSN 0164-3711) **1488**, 440
Game Conservancy Annual Review. (UK) **1488**, 564
Game of Go. see Weiqi **4496**
†Game Player's. (US) **5198**
Game Player's Guide to Nintendo. (US ISSN 1059-2172) **1419**
Game Player's Nintendo Guide see Game Player's Guide to Nintendo **1419**
Game Player's P C Entertainment. (US ISSN 1059-2180) **1469**
Game Player's P C Strategy Guide see Game Player's P C Entertainment **1469**
Game Player's Sega Genesis Strategy Guide. (US ISSN 1052-763X) **1419**
Game Player's Strategy Guide to Game Boy Games see Game Player's Guide to Nintendo **1419**
Game Su. (TG) **1684**, 4843
Gamecock. (US ISSN 0016-4313) **4472**
GamePro. (US) **1419**, 1374, 4472
Games. (US ISSN 0199-9788) **4472**
Games and Economic Behavior. (US ISSN 0899-8256) **4022**, 3064
Games & Leisure Inc. (US) **4472**, 2738
Games Master see Games Master International **5198**
†Games Master International. (UK ISSN 0960-1325) **5198**
Gamete Research see Molecular Reproduction and Development **556**

†Gamete Research. (US ISSN 0148-7280) **5198**
Gaming & Wagering Business. (US) **4473**, 666
Gaming Business see Gaming & Wagering Business **4473**
Gaming Systems Source Directory. (US) **1136**, 4473
Gamle Loejt. (DK ISSN 0108-3791) **2363**
Gamma. (RM) **3036**
Gamma. (NE ISSN 0016-4380) **3358**
Gamma Field Symposia. (JA ISSN 0435-1096) **93**, 541
Gamut see Semper **1324**
Gamut. (US ISSN 0275-0589) **2225**
Gamut. (CN ISSN 0713-3545) **2867**, 2919
Gan Kenkyu, Jikken to Rinsho. see Tumor Research: Experimental and Clinical **3202**
Gan No Rinsho. see Japanese Journal of Cancer Clinics **3198**
Gan Sadeh Vemeshek. (IS) **178**
Gan v'Nof/Garden and Landscape. (IS ISSN 0016-4402) **2126**
Ganadero/Rancher. (MX) **216**
Ganado Porcino. (MX) **217**
Ganagrinco. (VE ISSN 0046-5399) **93**, 4810
Ganban Rikigaku Ni Kansuri Shinpojumu Ronbunshu/Proceedings of the Symposium on Rock Mechanics. (JA) **1865**, 1561
Gandhabba. (US) **2993**
Gandhi Marg. (Il ISSN 0016-4437) **2311**
Gandhi Peace Foundation Lectures. (Il) **3958**
Gandhian Perspectives. (Il) **4373**
Gang Ao Jingji/Economics in Hong Kong and Macao. (CC ISSN 1000-064X) **666**
Gangan. (NR ISSN 0016-4453) **2212**
Ganganatha Jha Kendriya Sanskrit Vidyapeetha. Journal. (Il) **3637**
Ganglia see Gronk **2867**
Gangtie/Iron and Steel. (CC ISSN 0449-749X) **3407**
Ganguang Cailiao/Sensitive Materials. (CC) **1177**
Ganguang Kexue yu Guanghuaxue/ Photographic Science and Photochemistry. (CC ISSN 1000-3231) **3791**
Ganita. (Il ISSN 0046-5402) **3036**
Ganita Bharati. (Il ISSN 0970-0307) **3036**, 2311
Ganka. see Ophthalmology **3303**
Ganmitram. (Il ISSN 0016-4496) **4436**, 2199
Gann see Japanese Journal of Cancer Research **3199**
Gann Monographs see Gann Monographs on Cancer Research **3197**
Gann Monographs on Cancer Research.(JA) **3197**
Gannett Center Journal see Media Studies Journal **1376**
Gannett Foundation Magazine see G F Magazine **5198**
Gansu Huabao/Gansu Pictorial. (CC ISSN 0451-3118) **2181**, 3791
Gansu Pictorial. see Gansu Huabao **2181**
Ganymede see The Way Fourth **4290**
Ganymedia. (US) **2453**
Ganztaegige Bildung und Erziehung. (GW ISSN 0323-3677) **1635**
Ganztagsschule. (GW ISSN 0344-2101) **1727**, 1750, 2758
Gaodeng Shifan Jiaoyu Yanjiu. (CC) **1635**
Gaodeng Xuexiao Huaxue Xuebao/Acta Chemica Scholarum Superiorum Sinensium. (CC) **1177**, 1707
Gaodeng Xuexiao Jisuan Shuxue Xuebao. (CC ISSN 1000-081X) **3036**
Gaofenzi Tongxun/Bulletin of High Polymers. (CC) **1226**, 1853
Gaofenzi Xuebao/Acta Polymerica Sinica. (CC ISSN 1000-3304) **1226**, 1853
Gaoneng Wuli - High Energy Physics see Xiandai Wuli Zhishi **3835**

Gaoneng Wuli yu He Wuli. (CC ISSN 0254-3052) **3847**, 1790
Gaoxiao Shehui Kexue/Social Sciences in Higher Education. (CC) **4373**
Gaoxiao Yingyong Shuxue Xuebao/ Journal of Applied Mathematics in Higher Education. (CC) **3036**
Gaoxiong Yixue Kexue Zazhi see Kaohsiung Journal of Medical Sciences **3119**
Gap Casa. (IT) **2559**
Gap Conference Reports. (US) **3100**
Gap Intimo e Mare. (IT) **1285**
Gap Italia. (IT) **1285**
Gap Italia Bambini. (IT) **1285**
Garabato. (PE ISSN 0254-797X) **2919**
Garage and Automotive Retailer. (UK ISSN 0264-0163) **4691**, 1136
Garage & Officina. (IT ISSN 0016-4542) **4691**
Garage & Service Station News. (CN) **4691**
Garage and Transport Group see Garage and Automotive Retailer **4691**
Garage & Transport Selector. (UK) **4650**
Garage, Tankstelle und Servicestation see Tankstelle und Garage **4703**
Garamut see World Missions Update **4290**
Garavi Gujarat. (UK) **2002**
Garbage. (US ISSN 1044-3061) **1955**
Garbo. (SP) **2217**
Garcia de Orta: Serie de Antropobiologia. (PO ISSN 0870-0168) **240**, 440
Garcia de Orta: Serie de Botanica. (PO ISSN 0379-9506) **503**
Garcia de Orta: Serie de Estudos Agronomicos. (PO ISSN 0378-8032) **93**
Garcia de Orta: Serie de Geografia. (PO ISSN 0379-9514) **2248**
Garcia de Orta: Serie de Geologia. (PO ISSN 0378-1240) **1561**
Garcia de Orta: Serie de Zoologia. (PO ISSN 0870-0001) **583**
Garda Review. (IE) **1514**
The Garden. (UK) **2126**
†Garden (Bronx). (US ISSN 0191-3999) **5198**
Garden and Landscape. see Gan v'Nof **2126**
Garden Answers. (UK) **2126**
Garden Center Bulletin. (US) **2126**
Garden Center Newsletter. (US) **2126**
Garden Club of America. Newsletter. (US) **2127**
Garden Design. (US ISSN 0733-4923) **2127**
†Garden Fax. (CN) **5198**
Garden Glories. (US) **2127**
Garden History. (UK ISSN 0307-1243) **2127**
Garden History Society. Newsletter. (UK) **2127**
Garden Journal see Garden (Bronx) **5198**
Garden Life/Gaden Raifu. (JA ISSN 0433-0919) **2127**
▼Garden Literature. (US) **2141**, 400
Garden News. (UK ISSN 0016-4593) **2127**
Garden Path. (US ISSN 0016-4607) **2127**
Garden Peskem. (AT ISSN 1030-0392) **2127**
Garden Railway. (US) **2436**
Garden Scene see Gardens & Backyards **2127**
Garden State Home and Garden see New Jersey Monthly **2230**
†Garden State Home & Garden. (US ISSN 1044-3576) **5198**
Garden State Parkway Quarterly Report see Garden State Parkway Traffic Report **4718**
Garden State Parkway Traffic Report. (US) **4718**
†Garden Supply Retailer. (US ISSN 0195-1386) **5198**
Garden Supply Retailer Green Book. (US ISSN 0195-1386) **2127**
Garden Trade News. (UK ISSN 0261-3816) **2127**

Garden Writers Bulletin see Garden Writers Newsletter 2127
Garden Writers Newsletter. (US) 2127
Gardener. (US ISSN 0016-464X) 2127
†Gardener/Tuinier. (SA) 5198
Gardener (Reigate) see Come Gardening 2292
†Gardener Magazine. (SA) 5198
Gardeners Chronicle - Horticulture Trade Journal see Horticulture Week 2130
Gardener's Guide to Pest Prevention and Control in the Home and Garden. (CN ISSN 0832-6509) 2127
Gardener's Index. (US ISSN 0897-5175) 2141, 12
Gardenia. (IT) 2127
Gardenia Society of America. (US) 2127
Gardening. (US ISSN 0270-3041) 2127
Gardening and Beekeeping. see Darzs un Drava 2125
Gardening & Outdoor Living. (US) 2127
Gardening and Viniculture. see Kerteszet es Szoleszet 2133
Gardening from Which? (UK) 2127
Gardening News. (AT) 2127, 503
Gardening News and Schedule. (AT) 2127
Gardens & Backyards. (AT ISSN 1035-655X) 2127
Gardens and Countrysides. (US) 4768
Gardens and More. (US) 2127
Gardens and More see Neil Sperry's Gardens 2135
Gardens' Bulletin, Singapore. (SI ISSN 0072-0178) 503
Gardens for All see National Gardening 2135
Gardens of England and Wales. (UK) 2127
†Gardens Southwest. (US) 5198
Gardens West. (CN ISSN 0863-4947) 2127
Gardez. (GW) 4473
Gargoyle. (CN ISSN 0318-0107) 1312
Garibaldi. (UY) 2867, 3896
Al-Garidah at-Tigariyyah al-Misriyyah. (UA) 667
Garland Folklore Casebooks. (US) 2055
Garlic Times. (US) 3606, 2127
Garlinghouse Home Plan Guide. (US) 300
Garment Journal. (PH) 1285
Garment Manufacturer's Index. (US) 1285, 4619
Garment Worker. (US ISSN 0016-4712) 2583, 1285
†Garment Worker. (UK) 5198
Garnet Letter. (US) 1312
Garri's Horse World U S A see America's Equestrian 4532
Garser Kulturbrief. (AU) 2363
Garside Forecast. (US) 947
Garston Docks Tide Table. (UK) 4727
Der Garten Drinnen und Draussen. (GW ISSN 0930-6749) 2127
Garten Organisch. (GW ISSN 0170-5385) 2127
Garten- und Freizeitmarkt. (GW ISSN 0342-4650) 2127
Garten und Landschaft. (GW ISSN 0016-4720) 2127, 300
Das Gartenamt. (GW ISSN 0016-4739) 2127
Gartenbau/Horticulture. (SZ ISSN 0016-4747) 2127
Gartenbau. (GW ISSN 0323-4835) 2127
Gartenbau in Baden. (GW) 2127
Der Gartenbauingenieur. (GW ISSN 0016-4763) 2128
Gartenbauwirtschaft. (AU) 2128
Gartenbauwirtschaft mit Gartenbau Nachrichten see Gartenbauwirtschaft 2128
Gartenbauwissenschaft. (GW ISSN 0016-478X) 2128
Gartenpraxis. (GW ISSN 0341-2105) 2128
Gartenwelt see Gaertnerboerse und Gartenwelt 2126
Garth Analysis. (US) 3896

Gartner Nyt. (DK) 2128
Gartner Tidende. (DK ISSN 0106-8393) 2128
Gartneren. (DK ISSN 0109-2324) 2128
Gartneryrket. (NO ISSN 0046-5437) 2128
†Gartneryrket - G-utgave. (NO) 5198
Garuda Magazine. (IO) 4802
Gary American. (US) 2226
†Gary Graphique. (US) 5198
Gary North's Remnant Review. (US) 667
Gas. (NE ISSN 0016-4828) 3686, 1790
Gas. (GW ISSN 0343-2092) 3686, 1790
Gas. see Plyn 3700
Gas Abstracts. (US ISSN 0016-4844) 3705, 12
Gas Aktuell. (GW ISSN 0340-6067) 1853
Gas and Fuel Corporation of Victoria. Annual Report. (AT ISSN 0072-0208) 3686
Gas and Heating Power. see Meiqi yu Reli 1903
Gas and Liquid Chromatography Abstracts see Chromatography Abstracts 1200
Gas Buyers Guide. (US ISSN 0897-8778) 3686
†Gas Calorimeter Workshop. Proceedings. (US) 5198
Gas Chromatography Abstracts Service see Gas Chromatography Literature - Abstracts & Index 1201
Gas Chromatography Literature - Abstracts & Index. (US ISSN 0016-4895) 1201, 12
Gas Chromatography - Mass Spectrometry Abstracts. (UK ISSN 0046-5461) 1201, 12, 3837
Gas Daily. (US ISSN 0885-5935) 3686
Gas Digest. (US ISSN 0161-4851) 3686
Gas Directory and Who's Who see Gas Industry Directory (Year) 3687
Gas Engineering & Management. (UK ISSN 0306-6444) 3687
Gas - Erdgas - G W F. (GW ISSN 0016-4909) 3687, 4824
Gas Facts. (US) 3687
Gas Industries E and A News see Gas Industries Magazine 3687
Gas Industries Magazine. (US) 3687
Gas Industry Directory (Year). (UK ISSN 0954-853X) 3687
Gas Industry Statistics (Year). (AT ISSN 0157-731X) 3705, 1799, 4572
Gas Liquefatti - le Apparecchiature. (IT ISSN 0016-495X) 3687
Gas Marketing. (UK ISSN 0308-7026) 3687
Gas Marketing and Domestic Gas see Gas Marketing 3687
Gas - Mazout - Electricite see C.F.P. Chaud - Froid - Plomberie 2298
Gas Price Index. (US) 3687
Gas Processing - Canada see Energy Processing - Canada 1788
Gas Processors Association. Annual Convention. Proceedings. (US ISSN 0096-8870) 3687
Gas Processors Association. Research Reports. (US) 3687
Gas Processors Association. Technical Publications. (US) 3687
Gas Processors Suppliers Association Engineering Data Book see G P S A Engineering Data Book 3686
Gas Research Institute Digest see G R I D 3686
Gas Safety Code. (CN) 3687
Gas Separation and Purification. (UK ISSN 0950-4214) 1853
▼Gas Storage Report. (US ISSN 1057-2279) 3687
Gas Supply and Demand Study. (AT) 3687, 1790, 3483
Gas-Teknik. (DK ISSN 0106-4355) 3687
Gas Turbine World. (US ISSN 0746-4134) 1917, 1790, 3687
Gas und Architektur see G A 2299
Gas Utility Industry. (US) 3687, 1136
Gas Waerme International. (GW ISSN 0020-9384) 2299

Gas, Wasser, Waerme. (AU ISSN 0016-5018) 3687, 2299
Gas World see Gas World International 3687
Gas World International. (UK) 3687
GaScope. (US ISSN 0016-4976) 3687
Gascor News. (AT) 3687
Gaseta Sanitaria. (SP ISSN 0213-9111) 4101, 3100
Gaseta Sanitaria de Barcelona see Gaseta Sanitaria 4101
Gasnytt. (SW ISSN 0039-6834) 3687
Gasoil. (IL) 3687
†Gasolin 23. (GW) 5198
Gaspesie. (CN ISSN 0227-1370) 2407, 2002
Gasser see C-I-G World 3683
Gastgewerbe. (GW) 2474
†Gastric and Duodenal Ulcer. (UK ISSN 0261-4669) 5198
Gastric Secretion. (UK ISSN 0142-8098) 571, 3267, 3727
Gastro-Entero-Hepatologie see Gastro-Verdauungs- und Stoffwechselerkrankungen 3267
Gastro-Enterologie Clinique et Biologique. (FR ISSN 0399-8320) 3267
Gastro-Enterologie Quotidienne. (FR ISSN 0016-5077) 3267
▼Gastro Show. (GW) 2474
Gastro-Verdauungs- und Stoffwechselerkrankungen. (GW) 3267
Gastroenterohepatoloski Arhiv/Archives of Gastroenterohepatology. (YU ISSN 0352-082X) 3267
Gastroenterologia Clinica. (Italian translation of: Clinics in Gastroenterology) (IT) 3267
Gastroenterologia Japonica. (JA ISSN 0435-1339) 3267
▼Gastroenterologia Oggi. (IT ISSN 1120-3641) 3267
Gastroenterologia y Hepatologia. (SP ISSN 0210-5705) 3268
Gastroenterological Endoscopy. (JA ISSN 0387-1207) 3268
Gastroenterological Surgery. (JA ISSN 0387-2645) 3268
Gastroenterologisches Journal. (GW ISSN 0863-1743) 3174, 12
Il Gastroenterologo. (IT ISSN 0391-8939) 3268
†Gastroenterology. (US ISSN 0016-5085) 5198
Gastroenterology and Endoscopy News. (US) 3268
Gastroenterology and Rheumatology in Practice see Gastroenterology in Practice 3268
Gastroenterology Clinics. (US ISSN 0889-8553) 3268
Gastroenterology in Practice. (UK) 3268, 3369
Gastroenterology International. (IT ISSN 0950-5911) 3268
Gastroenterology Journal. (US) 3268
Gastroenterology Nursing. (US ISSN 1042-895X) 3268
Gastroenterology Series. (US) 3268
Gastrointestinal Endoscopy. (US ISSN 0016-5107) 3268
Gastrointestinal Hormones. (UK ISSN 0142-8101) 3268, 3727
Gastrointestinal Radiology. (US ISSN 0364-2356) 3358, 3253
Gastronomie. (GW ISSN 0323-4762) 2474, 3606
Gastronomie see Plaisirs 2479
Gastronomie & Tourisme. (SZ) 4768, 2071, 2446
Gastronomie Magazine: l'Art Culinaire see Plaisirs 2479
Gastronomie-Rundschau. (GW ISSN 0016-5123) 2071
Gastronomie und Hotel Impulse. (GW ISSN 0720-3853) 2474, 2071
†Gastronomo. (IT ISSN 0016-514X) 5198
Gastwirt. (GW ISSN 0016-5158) 2474
The Gate. (UK ISSN 0955-0933) 3011
The Gate. (US ISSN 0886-6791) 3669
Gate. (GW) 4598

Gateaux/Gatou. (JA) 2088
Gateavisa. (NO) 2867
Gated Wye. (US) 2033
Gatelodge. (UK) 1514
Gateway. (CN ISSN 0016-5190) 1312
Gateway. (UK) 4406, 1237, 4238
Gateway (Ann Arbor) see Open Systems Report 1428
Gateway (Middlesboro). (US) 2407
Gateway Engineer. (US) 1822, 4598
Gateway Heritage. (US ISSN 0198-9375) 2407
Gateways see Pathways (Watsonville) 4215
Gathered View. (US) 3100, 3606
Gathering Gibsons. (US ISSN 0893-3162) 2151
El Gato Tuerto/One-Eyed Cat. (US ISSN 8755-3651) 2919, 327
Gatou. see Gateaux 2088
GATT-Fly Report see Economic Justice Report 3955
Gatwick News. (UK) 53
La Gauche. (CN ISSN 1183-2053) 3896, 2583, 4843
Gauche Socialiste see La Gauche 3896
Gaucher's Disease Newsletter. (US) 3100
Gaudeamus. (SW ISSN 0016-5247) 1312
Gaudeamus. (NE ISSN 0016-5239) 3552
Gaudeamus Information. English Edition. (NE ISSN 0533-9235) 3552
Gaudie. (UK) 1312
Gauke's Jahrbuch. (GW ISSN 0720-2520) 2919
Gauldalsminne. (NO) 2363
Gault Millau Guide Deutschland. (GW) 2474
Gault - Millau Magazine. (FR) 4768, 2474
Gauntlet. (CN) 1312
▼Gauntlet. (US ISSN 1047-4463) 2867, 2919, 3011
Gauss - Gesellschaft. Mitteilungen. (GW) 364, 3036, 3819
Gaussenia. (FR ISSN 0761-3067) 2101
Gavagai. (SP ISSN 0213-4403) 2815
Ga'vea - Brown. (US ISSN 0276-7910) 2919
The Gavel. (US ISSN 0363-5783) 2702
The Gavin Report. (US) 3552
Gawalo - V K L Journaal. (NE) 2299
Gay and Lesbian Alliance at Stanford Year) see G L A S of (Year) 2453
Gay and Lesbian Atheists Realist see G A L A Realist 5198
†Gay Association in Newfoundland. Newsletter. (CN) 5198
†Gay Bibliography. (US) 5199
Gay Book. (US) 2453
Gay Books Bulletin see Cabirion: Gay Books Bulletin 2451
Gay Chicago Magazine. (US) 2453
Gay Community News (Boston). (US ISSN 0147-0728) 2453
Gay Community News (Honolulu) see Hawaii's National Gay Community News 2453
Gay Counselling see Lesbian and Gay Counselling News 2455
Gay Express. (GW) 2453
Gay Infos. (FR) 2453
Gay Insurgent. (US ISSN 0163-9897) 2453
Gay International see Gay Infos 2453
Gay Left. (UK ISSN 0307-9813) 2453, 3896
Gay Life Magazine see Scene Out 2457
Gay News see Gay Times 2453
Gay News see Philadelphia Gay News 2456
Gay Peoples Chronicle. (US) 2453, 2226
Gay Scene. (US ISSN 0016-5298) 2453
Gay Scotland. (UK ISSN 0142-0313) 2453, 3942
Gay Star. (UK) 2453

GAY TEACHERS

Gay Teachers Association Newsletter see Lesbian & Gay Teacher's Association Newsletter **2455**
Gay Times. (UK) **2453**
Gay Vote. (US) **2453**, **3896**
Gay World see Formally Inc **2452**
†Gay Writes. (US) **5199**
Gay Youth Community News. (US) **2453**, 1237, 1255
Gaya. (PO) **2363**, 273
Gayana: Botanica. (CL ISSN 0016-5301) **504**
Gayana: Miscelanea. (CL ISSN 0374-7999) **440**
Gayana: Zoologica. (CL ISSN 0016-531X) **583**
Gayellow Pages. (US ISSN 0363-826X) **2453**, 1136
Gaymen and Lesbians in Brookhaven News see G L I B News **2453**
GayPaper. (US) **2453**
Gays, Lesbians and Bisexuals of Ames Ames Newsletter see G L B Ames Newsletter **2453**
Gays the Word Review. (UK) **2453**
Gayspring. (US ISSN 0896-5773) **2453**, 4238
Gayzette. (AT ISSN 0813-7196) **2453**
Gaz d'Aujourd'hui. (FR ISSN 0016-5328) **3687**
Gaz de France. Secretariat General. Schema d'Organisation Profor. (FR ISSN 0072-0321) **3687**
Gaz et L'Industrie see G; Documentation Technique et Commerciale des Vendeurs de Gaz **666**
Gaz Industry. see Gazovaya Promyshlennost **3687**
Gaz - Physique - Orsay Base de Donnees see G A P H Y O R. Base de Donnees **3819**
Gaz, Woda i Technika Sanitarna. (PL ISSN 0016-5352) **1924**, 2299
Gazdalkodas. (HU ISSN 0046-5518) **151**
Gazdasag/Economy. (HU ISSN 0016-5360) **667**
Gazdasag es Jogtudomany see Tarsadalomkutatas **2684**
Gazella. Annual Report and Scientific Articles. (CS) **583**
†Gazelle Review of Literature on the Middle East. (UK ISSN 0308-7999) **5199**
Gazer/Miron. (MX ISSN 0016-5379) **4768**
Gazeta Bankowa. (PL ISSN 0860-7613) **782**
Gazeta Cukrownicza. (PL ISSN 0016-5395) **2071**
Gazeta de Baixada. (UY ISSN 0037-8607) **583**
Gazeta do Agricultor. (MZ) **93**
Gazeta dos Desportos. (PO) **4473**
Gazeta Esportiva. (BL) **4473**
Gazeta Matematica. (RM) **3036**
Gazeta Niedzielna. (UK) **2214**, 4264
Gazeta Obserwatora I M G W/Journal of I M W M Observer. (Instytut Meteorologii i Gospodarki Wodnej) (PL ISSN 0208-4325) **3435**, 1544, 1955
Gazeta Obserwatora P I H M see Gazeta Obserwatora I M G W **3435**
Gazeta Polska. (US) **2002**
†Gazeta Turistica. (MX) **5199**
Gazeteer of India. (II ISSN 0072-0348) **2338**
Gazeti la Watoto see Kipepeo **1258**
Gazetim-panjakan'ny Repoblika Demokratika Malagasy/Journal Officiel de la Republique Democratique de Madagascar. (MG) **4061**
Gazetka Pioniera. (CS) **1255**
Gazetta Financiera. (PN) **782**
Gazette. (NE ISSN 0016-5492) **2570**, 1374
Gazette (Clayton). (US) **3524**
The Gazette (Cork). (IE) **1312**
Gazette (Melbourne) see Harness Racer **4534**
Gazette (New York). (US ISSN 0193-533X) **2985**
Gazette Apicole. (FR ISSN 0016-5506) **93**
Gazette de l'Hotel Drouot. (FR) **327**

Gazette de la Presse de Langue Francaise. (FR) **2570**
Gazette de la Region du Nord. (FR ISSN 0016-5514) **2629**
Gazette des Archives. (FR ISSN 0016-5522) **2363**
Gazette des Armes. (FR ISSN 0767-869X) **2436**
Gazette des Armes see Gazette des Armes **2436**
Gazette des Beaux Arts. (FR ISSN 0016-5530) **327**
Gazette des Communes, des Departements, des Regions. (FR) **1011**
Gazette des Communes et du Personnel Communal. (FR) **4087**
Gazette des Femmes. (CN ISSN 0704-4550) **4843**
Gazette du Bureau des Brevets. see Patent Office Record (Canada) **3677**
Gazette du Golfe. (DM) **2169**
Gazette du P C T see P C T Gazette **3680**
Gazette du Palais et du Notariat. (FR) **2629**
†Gazette Economique. (FR) **5199**
Gazette Hoteliere. (FR) **2474**
Gazette International Networking Institute. Proceedings. (US) **3100**
Gazette Medicale de France. (FR ISSN 0016-5557) **3100**
Gazette Monaco - Cote d'Azur. (MC) **2187**
Gazette Numismatique Suisse/Schweizer Muenzblaetter. (SZ ISSN 0016-5565) **3599**
Gazette of Law Journalism. (AT ISSN 0818-0148) **2629**, 2570
Gazette of the American Friends of Lafayette see American Friends of Lafayette. Gazette **2398**
Gazette of the United Republic of Tanzania. (TZ ISSN 0856-0323) **4061**
Gazette Officielle de la Chasse. (FR) **4547**
Gazette Officielle de la Peche. (FR ISSN 0046-5542) **4547**, 2041
Gazette Officielle de la Peche et Environnement see Gazette Officielle de la Peche **4547**
Gazette Officielle du Quebec: Avis Juridiques. (CN) **2629**
Gazette Officielle du Quebec: Lois et Reglements. (CN) **2629**
Gazette Officielle du Thermalisme. (FR) **3802**
Gazette Officielle du Tourisme. (FR ISSN 0016-5573) **4768**
Gazetteer of Canada/Repertoire Geographique du Canada. (CN ISSN 0576-1999) **2248**
Gazety Medikaly. (MG) **3100**
Gazi Husrevbegova Biblioteka. Anali. (BN ISSN 0350-1418) **3637**, 2338
▼Gazongids. (NE) **2128**
Gazovaya Promyshlennost/Gaz Industry. (RU ISSN 0016-5581) **3687**
Gazzetta. (CN) **2002**
Gazzetta Agricola. (IT) **93**
Gazzetta Chimica Italiana. (IT ISSN 0016-5603) **1177**
Gazzetta del Lunedi. (IT) **3896**
Gazzetta della Fotografia. (IT) **3791**
Gazzetta della Piccola Industria. (IT ISSN 0391-6138) **1115**
Gazzetta delle Arti. (IT ISSN 0016-5638) **327**, 2919, 3511, 3552
Gazzetta di Gaeta. (IT) **2507**
Gazzetta Filatelica. (IT ISSN 0016-5654) **3752**
Gazzetta Internazionale di Medicina e Chirurgia. (IT ISSN 0016-5662) **3378**
Gazzetta Medica Italiana - Aggiornamenti Clinicoterapeutici see Gazzetta Medica Italiana Archivio per le Scienze Mediche **3100**
Gazzetta Medica Italiana Archivio per le Scienze Mediche. (IT) **3100**
Gazzetta Sanitaria. (IT ISSN 0016-5697) **3100**
Gazzetta Valutaria e del Commercio Internazionale. (IT) **909**
Gazzettino Agricolo (Parma). (IT) **93**

Gazzettino dell' Economia. (IT) **867**
Gazzettino della Pesca. (IT) **2041**
Gazzettino della Scuola. (IT ISSN 0016-5719) **1635**
Gdanski Rocznik Kulturalny. (PL) **2363**
Gdanskie Studia Jezykoznawcze. (PL ISSN 0860-3456) **2815**
Gdanskie Towarzystwo Naukowe. Wydzial 1. Nauk Spolecznych i Humanistycznych. Komisja Archeologiczna. Prace. (PL ISSN 0072-0410) **2363**, 273
Gdanskie Towarzystwo Naukowe. Wydzial 1. Nauk Spolecznych i Humanistycznych. Seria Monografii. (PL ISSN 0433-230X) **2363**
Gdanskie Towarzystwo Naukowe. Wydzial 1. Nauk Spolecznych i Humanistycznych. Seria Popularnonaukowa "Pomorze Gdanskie". (PL ISSN 0072-0429) **2363**
Gdanskie Towarzystwo Naukowe. Wydzial 1. Nauk Spolecznych i Humanistycznych. Seria Zrodel. (PL ISSN 0072-0437) **2363**
Gdanskie Towarzystwo Naukowe. Wydzial 3. Nauk Matematyczno-Fizyczno-Chemicznych. Prace. (PL) **3036**, 4311
Gdanskie Towarzystwo Naukowe. Wydzial 3. Nauk Matematyczno-Przyrodniczych. Rozprawy see Gdanskie Towarzystwo Naukowe. Wydzial 3. Nauk Matematyczno-Fizyczno-Chemicznych. Prace **3036**
†Gdanskie Zeszyty Teatralne. (PL) **5199**
Ge Magazine. (FR ISSN 0754-9725) **2152**, 2187
Gea. (IT) **1955**
Gear. see Chilun **3016**
Gear Technology. (US ISSN 0743-6858) **1929**
Gebaeudigereiniger-Handwerk see Rationell Reinigen **629**
Gebbie Press All-in-One Directory. (US ISSN 0097-8175) **1136**, 1336
Gebetsapostolat und Seelsorge. (GW ISSN 0016-5735) **4179**
Geborener Deutscher. (US ISSN 1052-3189) **2152**, 2002
Gebouwmanagement see Facility Management Magazine **665**
Gebraucht Motorrad und Zubehoer Katalog. (GW) **4518**
Geburtshilfe und Frauenheilkunde. (GW ISSN 0016-5751) **3292**
GECAMINES Annual Report/GECAMINES Rapport Annuel. (Generale des Carrieres et des Mines) (ZR) **3483**
GECAMINES Rapport Annuel. see GECAMINES Annual Report **3483**
Gedenkstaetten Rundbrief. (GW) **2363**
Gedenktage des Mitteldeutschen Raumes. (GW ISSN 0341-0749) **419**, 2363
Gediplomeerde Ingenieur. see Certificated Engineer **1927**
Gedrag see Gedrag & Gezondheid **4022**
Gedrag & Gezondheid/Behaviour & Health. (NE) **4022**
Geelong News. (AT) **32**
Geelong Youth for Christ Newsrelease see Y F C Newsrelease **4253**
Geer Family Association Newsletter (Gear Geer Geere Gere). (US) **2152**
Geest en Leven. (NE) **4179**
Gefaehrdetenhilfe. (GW ISSN 0016-5794) **4406**
Gefaehrliche Fracht see Gefaehrliche Ladung **4650**
Gefaehrliche Ladung. (GW ISSN 0016-5808) **4650**
Gefiederte Welt. (GW ISSN 0016-5816) **564**
Gefluegel-Boerse. (GW ISSN 0016-5824) **3710**
Geflugel und Kleinvieh see Schweizerische Gefluegelzeitung **225**
Gegenbaurs Morphologisches Jahrbuch.(GW ISSN 0016-5840) **440**, 3100
Gegengift. (GW) **3616**

Gegenschein. (AT ISSN 0310-9968) **2867**
Gegenschein. (US) **2919**
Gegenschein Quarterly see Gegenschein **2919**
Gegenseitigkeit. see Mutualite **2538**
Gegenwart. (SZ ISSN 0016-5867) **2219**
Gegenwart. (GW ISSN 0016-5859) **2292**
Gegenwartskunde. (GW ISSN 0016-5875) **1635**
Geheim. (GW ISSN 0930-8571) **3958**
Gehoert Gelesen (Munich, 1954). (GW ISSN 0016-5883) **2919**
Geibun Mooks. (JA) **2207**
Geiger Report. (US) **32**
Geijutsu Shincho. (JA) **327**
Geiriadur Prifysgol Cymru. (UK ISSN 0072-0542) **2815**
Geist und Auftrag. (GW) **4264**
Geist und Leben. (GW ISSN 0016-5921) **4179**
Der Geistig Schaffende. (AU) **2867**
†Geistige Begegnung. (GW ISSN 0072-0550) **5199**
Geistige Behinderung. (GW ISSN 0173-9573) **1736**, 3337, 4022, 4406
Geka. see Surgery **3384**
Gekkan Asahi/Monthly Asahi. (JA) **2207**
Gekkan Bijutsu. see Monthly Art **336**
Gekkan Chusho-Kigyo. see Monthly Smaller Businesses **1116**
Gekkan Gasorin Sutando. see Monthly Gasoline Stand **3692**
Gekkan Gendai. (JA) **1011**
Gekkan Kendo Nippon. see Monthly Japanese Fencing **4479**
Gekkan Kibbutz see Cooperative Life **4432**
Gekkan Kyodotai. see Cooperative Life **4432**
Gekkan Kyoiku Journal. see Monthly Education Journal **1648**
Gekkan Kyusho Nihon. see Monthly Journal of Gasoline Service Stations **3692**
Gekkan Media Data/Media Data Japan. (JA ISSN 0387-7019) **32**
Gekkan Shakaito. (JA ISSN 0435-1754) **3896**
Gekkan Shonen-Champion. see Monthly Boy's Champion **1260**
Gekkan Syokudo. see Food Service Management **2474**
Gekkan Tenmon. (JA ISSN 0288-4216) **364**
Gekkan Tenmon Gaido see Tenmon Gaido **370**
Gekkan Yakuji. see Pharmaceuticals Monthly **3738**
Gelatiere Italiano. (IT ISSN 0016-5999) **2071**
Gelbe Liste Pharmindex. (GW) **3727**
Die Gelben Hefte. (GW ISSN 0016-6006) **3185**
Geld. (NE) **1505**, 782
Das Geld A B C. (GW) **782**
Geld en Onderneming. (BE) **782**, 751
Geld und Betrieb. (GW) **373**
▼Geldanlage Berater. (GW ISSN 0939-4966) **947**
Geldanlage und Steuern. (GW) **782**, 947
Gelders Erfgoed. (NE) **2363**, 273, 327
Gelders Oudheidkundig Contactbericht see Gelders Erfgoed **2363**
Gelderse Historische Reeks. (NE) **2363**
Geldinstitute. (GW ISSN 0343-8740) **783**
Gelditschia. (GW ISSN 0323-6862) **504**
Der Geldscheinsammler. (GW ISSN 0931-0681) **3599**
Geliotekhnika. (UZ ISSN 0016-6022) **4598**
Gelisme Dergisi. see Studies in Development **1028**
Gelosophist. (US ISSN 8756-2898) **2867**
Gelsenkirchen im Spiegel der Statistik. (GW) **4080**

GENERAL STUDIES 6213

Geltende Seekriegsrecht in Einzeldarstellungen see Das Geltende Seevoelkerrecht in Einzeldarstellungen **2723**
Das Geltende Seevoelkerrecht in Einzeldarstellungen. (GW) **2723, 3459**
Geluid en Omgeving. (BE) **1955**
Gem. (CN) **1312**
Gem & Jewellery Yearbook. (II) **2564**
Gem City News see Idaho Cities **4088**
Gem Craft see Popular Crafts **356**
Gem Politics One. (UK) **3958, 1955**
Gem State R.N. Newsletter see R.N. Idaho **3286**
Gema Jusan. (IO) **2202**
Gematologiya i Transfusiologiya/Hematology and Transfusiology. (RU ISSN 0234-5730) **3272**
Gemeenteblad van Amsterdam. (NE ISSN 0016-6049) **4087**
Gemeenteleven. (NE ISSN 0016-6065) **4179**
Gemeentewerken. (NE ISSN 0046-5577) **1866**
Die Gemeinde. (AU ISSN 0021-2334) **3896, 2002, 4223**
Gemeinde. (GW ISSN 0340-3653) **4087**
Die Gemeinde (Kassel). (GW ISSN 0016-6073) **4238**
Die Gemeinde (Stuttgart). (GW) **4061**
Gemeinde-Nachrichten. (GW) **2867**
Gemeinde Schoenaich - Rueckspiegel. (GW) **4087**
Gemeindebibelschule. (GW) **4179, 4238**
Gemeindebote. (AU ISSN 0016-609X) **4087**
Gemeindebote see Kirche in Marburg **4267**
Gemeindebrief. (AU ISSN 0016-6111) **4238**
Der Gemeindechor. (GW) **3552**
Der Gemeindehaushalt. (GW ISSN 0340-3645) **4087**
Die Gemeindekasse. (GW ISSN 0016-612X) **4087**
Gemeindekurier. (AU ISSN 0016-6146) **2173**
Gemeinden Nordrhein-Westfalens. (GW) **4572**
Gemeindeverwaltung in Rheinland - Pfalz. (GW ISSN 0016-6170) **4087**
†Gemeinsam. (GW ISSN 0138-2586) **5199**
Gemeinsame Koerperschaftsdatei. (GW ISSN 0724-6358) **2758**
Gemeinsames Amtsblatt des Landes Baden-Wuerttemberg. (GW ISSN 0016-6200) **4088**
Gemeinschaft der Wohnungseigentuemer-Informationen see G D W Informationen **618**
Gemeinschafts- und Sozialkunde. (GW) **1255**
Gemeinwirtschaft. (AU ISSN 0016-6227) **667**
Gemengde Branche (1978). (NE) **1163, 2281**
Gemischtwarenhandel. (GW ISSN 0016-6243) **2092**
Gems & Gemology. (US ISSN 0016-626X) **2564, 1210**
Gems and Minerals see Jewelry Making, Gems and Minerals **2437**
Gems of Geology. (US) **2152**
Gems of Russian and Soviet Music. (RU) **3552**
Gemuese. (GW ISSN 0016-6286) **2128**
Gemutlichkeit see Prosit **259**
Genadeklanken. (NE ISSN 0016-6324) **4179**
Genago Express. (CN) **1312**
Genau. (GW) **3862, 639**
Genava. (SZ ISSN 0072-0585) **273, 327**
▼Gend Info. (FR) **1514**
Gendai. (JA) **2207**
Gendai no Me. (JA ISSN 0435-219X) **3524**
Gendai no Toshokan. see Libraries Today **2768**
Gendai Ringyo/Current Forestry. (JA ISSN 0386-2321) **2101**
Gender and Education. (UK ISSN 0954-0253) **1635, 3400, 4859**

Gender and History. (UK ISSN 0953-5233) **2311, 3400, 4859**
Gender and Society. (US ISSN 0891-2432) **4436, 3400, 4859**
Genders. (US ISSN 0894-9832) **4859, 2507**
Gene. (NE ISSN 0378-1119) **541**
Gene Amplification and Analysis Series. (NE) **541, 3259**
▼Gene Expression. (UK ISSN 0957-3526) **541**
Gene Perret's Round Table. (US) **1374**
Geneagram. (US) **2152**
Genealogia. (US) **2152**
Genealogical Abstracts see Grassroots Catalog **2168**
Genealogical Aids Bulletin. (US ISSN 0738-5226) **2152**
†Genealogical and Historical Magazine of the South. (US) **5199**
Genealogical & Historical News. (US) **2152**
Genealogical Association of Sacramento. Quarterly see G A S Lites **2151**
Genealogical Association of Sacramento, Inc. Lites see G A S Lites **2151**
Genealogical Computer Pioneer. (US ISSN 0735-0287) **2168, 2152**
Genealogical Computing. (US ISSN 0277-5913) **2168**
Genealogical Forum of Oregon. Bulletin. (US) **2152**
Genealogical Forum of Portland, Oregon. Quarterly Bulletin see Genealogical Forum of Oregon. Bulletin **2152**
Genealogical Gems. (US) **2152**
Genealogical Helper. (US ISSN 0016-6359) **2152**
Genealogical Magazine of New Jersey. (US ISSN 0016-6367) **2152**
Genealogical Periodical Annual Index. (US) **2168**
Genealogical Research Directory. (AT) **2152**
Genealogical Societies and Historical Societies see Genealogical Societies & Historical Societies in the United States **2152**
Genealogical Societies & Historical Societies in the United States. (US) **2152, 2311**
Genealogical Society of Iredell County, NC Quarterly see Iredell County Tracks (NC) **2155**
Genealogical Society of Okaloosa County, Florida. Journal. (US ISSN 0148-6616) **2152**
Genealogical Society of Old Tryon County. Bulletin. (US ISSN 0092-7953) **2152**
Genealogical Society of Sarasota. Newsletter. (US) **2152**
Genealogical Society of Tidewater Virginia. Bulletin see Virginia Tidewater Genealogy **2167**
Genealogie. (GW ISSN 0016-6383) **2152**
Genealogie and Computer. (BE ISSN 0771-713X) **1395**
Genealogie Franc - Comtoise. (FR) **2152**
Genealogie Lorraine. (FR) **2152**
Genealogisches Handbuch des Bayerischen Adels. (GW ISSN 0085-0934) **2152**
Genealogisches Jahrbuch. (GW ISSN 0514-3292) **2152**
Genealogist (Salt Lake City). (US ISSN 0197-1468) **2152**
Genealogists' Magazine. (UK ISSN 0016-6391) **2152**
Genealogy America. (US) **2152**
Genealogy Bulletin. (US ISSN 1049-9571) **2152, 2407**
Genealogy Club Newsletter. (US) **2152**
Genealogy Club of America Magazine see Genealogy Digest **2152**
Genealogy Digest. (US ISSN 0098-7689) **2152**
Genealogysk Jierboekje. (NE) **2152**
Geneeskunde. (SA ISSN 0016-643X) **3100**
Geneeskunde - Biologie - Leefmilieu. see Medecine - Biologie - Environnement **3200**
Geneeskunde en Sport. (NE ISSN 0016-6448) **3371, 3100, 3802**

Geneeskundig Adresboek Nederland. (NE) **3100**
Geneeskundig Jaarboek Medicijnen. (NE) **3100**
Geneologicka a Heraldicka Spolecnost Prague. Zpravodaj. Acta Geneologica ac Heraldica. (CS ISSN 0139-8741) **2152**
Genera. (UK) **2993**
General. (US) **3837**
General Accounting Office Reports and Technology. (US) **751, 4061**
General Agents and Managers Association News Journal see G A M A News Journal **2532**
General Agreement on Tariffs and Trade. Basic Instruments and Selected Documents Series. Supplement. (UN ISSN 0072-0623) **909**
General Agreement on Tariffs and Trade. G A T T Activities in (Year). (UN ISSN 0072-615X) **909**
General Agreement on Tariffs and Trade. International Trade. (UN ISSN 0072-064X) **909**
General Agreement on Tariffs and Trade Focus see G A T T Focus **666**
General Agreement on Tariffs and Trade Legal System and World Trade Diplomacy see G A T T Legal System and World Trade Diplomacy **2723**
General Agreement on Tariffs and Trade Studies in International Trade see G A T T Studies in International Trade **909**
General and Applied Entomology. (AT ISSN 0158-0760) **533**
General and Comparative Endocrinology. (US ISSN 0016-6480) **3253**
General and Synthetic Methods. (UK ISSN 0141-2140) **1218**
General Aviation. (SA ISSN 0016-6502) **53**
General Aviation Accident Report. (US ISSN 0887-7823) **4673**
General Aviation Aircraft Shipment Report. (US) **4673**
General Aviation Airplane Shipment Report see General Aviation Aircraft Shipment Report **4673**
General Aviation Association (Australia) News Digest see G A A News Digest **53**
General Aviation Mechanics Journal. (US) **53**
General Aviation News & Flyer. (US ISSN 1052-9136) **53**
General Aviation News: The Green Sheet see General Aviation News & Flyer **53**
General Aviation Statistical Databook. (US) **4673**
General Clinical Research Centers. (US) **3175, 3259**
General Commission on Safety and Health in the Iron and Steel Industry. Report. (EI) **3617, 3407**
General Conference of the New Church. Yearbook. (UK ISSN 0072-0666) **4283**
General Convention of the New Jerusalem. Journal. (US) **4179**
General Council of the Assemblies of God. Memos. (US ISSN 0885-7776) **4283, 1237, 1750, 4843**
General Dental Council. Dentists Register. (UK ISSN 0072-0674) **3233**
General Dental Council. Minutes of the Proceedings. (UK ISSN 0072-0682) **3233**
▼General Dental Treatment. (UK) **3233**
General Dentistry. (US ISSN 0363-6771) **3234**
General Directory of the Perfume and Cosmetic Industry. see Guide de la Parfumerie **1137**
General Directory of the Press and Periodicals in Jordan and Kuwait. (SY ISSN 0072-0690) **4128, 2570**
General Directory of the Press and Periodicals in Syria. (SY ISSN 0072-0704) **4128, 2570**
General Education Reading Material Series. (II ISSN 0072-0720) **1635**

General Electric Co. Contact see G E C Contact **1893**
General Electric Co., PLC Review see G E C Review **1893**
General Engineer see Mechanical Incorporated Engineer **1935**
General Espanola de Seguros. Boletin de Informacion see G E S. Boletin de Informacion **2532**
General Espanola de Seguros, S.A. Boletin de Informacion see G E S. Boletin de Informacion **2532**
General Federation of Women's Clubs Clubwoman see G F W C Clubwoman **1298**
†General Fisheries Council for the Mediterranean. Proceedings and Technical Papers/Conseil General des Peches pour la Mediterranee. Depats et Documents Techniques. (UN ISSN 0072-0747) **5199**
General Fisheries Council for the Mediterranean. Reports of the Sessions. (UN ISSN 0072-0755) **2041**
General Fisheries Council for the Mediterranean. Studies and Reviews. (UN ISSN 0433-3519) **2041**
General Hospital Psychiatry. (US ISSN 0163-8343) **3337**
General Index to Iraqi Periodical Literature. Part A: Sciences and Engineering. (IQ ISSN 1012-3393) **1844, 4355**
General Index to Iraqi Periodical Literature. Part B: Humanities and Social Sciences. (IQ ISSN 1012-3415) **4394**
General Information Concerning Trademarks. (US ISSN 0083-3029) **3675**
General Insurance Guide. (US ISSN 0016-6545) **2532**
General Knowledge Digest see Dogar's General Knowledge Digest **3891**
General Linguistics. (US ISSN 0016-6553) **2815**
General Medical Council. Annual Report.(UK) **3100**
General Medical Council. Medical Register. (UK ISSN 0072-0763) **3100**
General Medical Council. Minutes. (UK) **3100**
†General Merchandise. Arabic Edition. (GW) **5199**
General Merchandise Distributors Council. Marketing Conference Transcripts. (US) **3392**
General Merchandise News. (US) **2092, 1040**
General Minutes of the Annual Conferences of the United Methodist Church see United Methodist Church. General Minutes of the Annual Conferences **4251**
General Motors Public Interest Report. (US) **1076, 4691**
General Motors Symposia Series. (US) **4691**
General, Municipal, Boilermakers and Allied Trades Union Journal see G M B Working Together **2583**
General Pharmacology. (US ISSN 0306-3623) **3727**
General Physics Advance Abstracts. (US ISSN 0749-4823) **3837**
General Physiology and Biophysics. (CS ISSN 0231-5882) **571, 485**
General Practitioner. (UK ISSN 0046-5607) **3100**
General Relativity and Gravitation. (US ISSN 0001-7701) **3819**
General Report on the Activities of the European Communities. (EI ISSN 0069-6749) **867**
General Safety Digest/Digest de Securite Generale. (CN ISSN 0707-0403) **3459**
General Science Index. (US ISSN 0162-1963) **4356, 12**
General Semantics Bulletin. (US ISSN 0072-0771) **2815**
General Social Surveys. (US ISSN 0161-3340) **4436**
General Stud Book. (UK ISSN 0072-078X) **4534**
General Studies Newsletter. (US) **1312**

GENERAL STUDIES

▼General Studies Review. (UK ISSN 0960-7609) **1635**
General Surgery News. (US) **3378**
General Systems Bulletin. (US) **4311**
General Systems Yearbook. (US ISSN 0072-0798) **4311**
General Teaching Council for Scotland. Bulletin. (UK ISSN 0142-2154) **1635**
General Technical Report P S W see U.S. Forest Service. Pacific Southwest Forest and Range Experiment Station. General Technical Report P S W **2109**
General Telephone & Electronics Automatic Electric World-Wide Communications Journal see G T E Automatic Electric World-Wide Communications Journal **5198**
General Telephone & Electronics Journal of Research and Development see G T E Journal of Research and Development **5198**
General Treaty for Central American Economic Integration. Permanent Secretariat. Carta Informativa. (GT ISSN 0553-6855) **929**
General Treaty for Central American Economic Integration. Permanent Secretariat. Newsletter. (GT ISSN 0553-6898) **929**
Generale Bank. Bulletin. (BE) **783**
Generale Bank. Report. (BE) **783**
Generale des Carrieres et des Mines. Monographie. (ZR) **3483**
Generale des Carrieres et des Mines GECAMINES Annual Report see GECAMINES Annual Report **3483**
Generale des Carrieres et Mines du Zaire. Monographie see Generale des Carrieres et des Mines. Monographie **3483**
▼Generalist Papers. (US ISSN 1048-0870) **2867**
Generaliste. (FR ISSN 0183-4568) **3100**
Generally Speaking. (CN) **2461**
Generals. (CN) **618**
Generating Availability Report (Year). (US) **1893**
Generating Unit Statistics (Year). (US) **1893**
Generation (Wayzata). (US) **4265**
Generation (Windsor). (CN ISSN 0533-7291) **2867**
Generation After. (US) **2311**, **2002**
Generations (Fredericton). (CN ISSN 0821-5359) **2152**
Generations (San Francisco). (US ISSN 0738-7806) **2272**
Generations (Wayzata). (US) **3337**
Generations (Winnipeg). (CN ISSN 0226-6105) **2152**
Generator. (US ISSN 0896-7431) **2993**, 327
Generator's Journal. (US) **1955**, 1790, 2629
†Generazione Zero. (IT ISSN 0046-5615) **5199**
Genes & Development. (US ISSN 0890-9369) **3100**
Genesee County Medical Society Bulletin. (US) **3100**
Genesee County Trends see AgImpact **68**
Genesee Valley Chemunications see Rochester Chemunications **1187**
Genesis see Historia Ilustrada **2210**
Genesis (Garden City). (US) **1312**
Genesis (New York). (US ISSN 1052-8555) **3397**
Genesis (Washington). (US) **3292**
Genesis of Behavior. (US) **3337**, 4022
Genesis 2. (US ISSN 0016-6669) **4223**
Genetic Analysis Techniques see Genetic Analysis: Techniques and Applications **542**
Genetic Analysis: Techniques and Applications. (US ISSN 1050-3862) **542**
Genetic Aspects of Carcinogenesis see I C R D B Cancergram: Genetic Aspects of Carcinogenesis **5208**
Genetic Counseling. (SZ) **542**
Genetic Engineer and Biotechnologist. (UK ISSN 0959-020X) **469**, 489

Genetic Engineering. (US ISSN 0196-3716) **542**, 552
Genetic Engineering and Biotechnology Yearbook. (NE) **542**, 489
Genetic Engineering Letter. (US ISSN 0276-1882) **542**
Genetic Engineering News. (US ISSN 0270-6377) **542**, 4598
Genetic Epidemiology. (US ISSN 0741-0395) **542**
Genetic Epistemologist. (US ISSN 0740-9583) **4022**, 542
Genetic Resource. (US) **542**, 4101
Genetic, Social, and General Psychology Monographs. (US ISSN 8756-7547) **4022**
Genetic Technology News. (US ISSN 0272-9032) **542**
Genetica. (NE ISSN 0016-6707) **542**
Genetica Agraria see Journal of Genetics & Breeding **102**
Genetica Iberica. (SP ISSN 0016-6693) **542**
Genetica Polonica. (PL ISSN 0016-6715) **542**, 504
Genetical Research. (UK ISSN 0016-6723) **542**
Genetics. (US ISSN 0016-6731) **542**
Genetics Abstracts. (US ISSN 0016-674X) **465**, 12
Genetics and Breeding. see Genetika a Slechteni **543**
Genetics and Plant Breeding. see Genetika i Selektsiia **543**
Genetics Newsletter/Genetika Nuusbrief. (SA) **542**
Genetics, Selection, Evolution. (FR ISSN 0999-193X) **543**, 217
Genetics Society of Canada Bulletin. (CN ISSN 0316-4357) **543**, 3392
Genetik. (GW ISSN 0435-284X) **543**
Genetika see Acta Biologica Iugoslavica. Serija F: Genetika **539**
Genetika. (RU ISSN 0016-6758) **543**
Genetika a Slechteni/Genetics and Breeding. (Ustav Vedeckotechnickych Informaci pro Zemedelstvi) (CS) **543**
Genetika i Selektsiia/Genetics and Plant Breeding. (BU ISSN 0016-6766) **543**
Genetika Nuusbrief. see Genetics Newsletter **542**
Genetique, Selection, Evolution see Genetics, Selection, Evolution **543**
Geneva - Africa/Geneve - Afrique. (SZ ISSN 0016-6774) **3958**, 2333, 4436
Geneva News and International Report. (SZ) **867**, 783, 3958
Geneva Papers on Risk and Insurance see Geneva Papers on Risk and Insurance Theory **2532**
Geneva Papers on Risk and Insurance Theory. (NE ISSN 0926-4957) **2532**
Geneve - Afrique. see Geneva - Africa **3958**
Genewatch. (US ISSN 0740-9737) **543**
Genghis Khan's Banner. see Chingisiyn Tug **1997**
Gengo Kenkyu. see Linguistic Society of Japan. Journal **2826**
Genie. (US) **2152**
Genie Construction. (CN ISSN 0016-6820) **618**
▼Genie Educatif. (FR) **1417**
Genie Industriel; Catalogue de l'Ingenierie. (FR ISSN 0072-0844) **1822**
Genie Industriel: Revue. (FR) **1822**
Genie Logiciel et Systemes Experts. (FR ISSN 0295-6322) **1430**, 1407
Genie Medical. (FR ISSN 0016-6839) **3100**
Genio Rurale. (IT ISSN 0016-6863) **178**
†Genitori e Scuola. (IT) **5199**
Genitourinary Cancers - Diagnosis, Treatment see I C R D B Cancergram: Genitourinary Cancers - Diagnosis, Treatment **3175**
Genitourinary Medicine see Genitourinary Medicine: The Journal of Sexual Health, STDs and HIV **3247**

Genitourinary Medicine: The Journal of Sexual Health, STDs and HIV. (UK) **3247**
Genken Kenkyu Seika Shorokusyu. see J A E R I Reports Abstracts **3837**
Genoa Port and Shipping Handbook. (UK) **1136**, 4727
Genome. (CN ISSN 0831-2796) **543**, 524
▼Genome Analysis. (US ISSN 1050-8430) **543**
Genomics. (US ISSN 0888-7543) **543**
Genootschap Amstelodamum. Jaarboek.(NE) **2363**
Genootschap Delfia Batavorum. Serie-Uitgave. (NE ISSN 0169-1023) **2363**
Genos. (FI ISSN 0016-6898) **2153**
Die Genossenschaften in der Bundesrepublik Deutschland. (GW) **830**
Die Genossenschaften in der Bundesrepublik Deutschland. Statistik. (GW) **830**, 4572
Genossenschaftsforum. (GW) **830**
Genossenschaftsverband Hannover. Mitteilungen. (GW) **830**
Genossenschaftsverband Niedersachsen. Mitteilungen see Genossenschaftsverband Hannover. Mitteilungen **830**
Genova Statistica see Commune di Genova. Notiziario Statistico Mensile **4569**
▼Genre (New York). (US) **3397**, 2453
Genre (Norman). (US ISSN 0016-6928) **2919**, 2815
Genre Human. (FR) **2507**, 3767
Gens Nostra, "Ons Geslacht". (NE ISSN 0016-6936) **2153**
Genshiryoku Chosa Jiho/Nuclear Industrial Survey. (JA) **1805**, 1790
Genshiryoku Hatsudensho. see Nuclear Power Plants in the World **1808**
Genshiryoku Kogyo. see Nuclear Engineering **1807**
Genshiryoku Nenkan/Nuclear Almanac. (JA) **1805**, 1790
Gent. (US) **3397**
La Gente. (US) **2002**
Gente. (IT ISSN 0016-6944) **2205**
Gente. (MX ISSN 0016-6952) **2210**
Gente. (PE) **2213**
Gente de Aztlan. (US) **2003**
Gente Mese. (IT) **2205**, 3896
Gente Motori. (IT) **4691**, 4518, 4524
Gente Viaggi. (IT) **4768**
Gente y la Actualidad. (AG) **2170**
GenteMoney. (IT) **2205**
Gentes. (IT ISSN 0016-6960) **4179**
Gentes Herbarum. (US ISSN 0072-0879) **504**
Gentle Places and Quiet Spaces see Stress Master **3597**
Gentleman. (II) **2199**
Gentleman Automobili. (IT) **4691**
Gentleman of Color. (US) **2003**
Gentlemen's Quarterly see G Q **1291**
†Gentofte-Bogen. (DK) **5199**
Gentse Bijdragen tot de Kunstgeschiedenis en Oudheidkunde. (BE ISSN 0772-7151) **327**, 300
Genuine Irish Old Moore's Almanac. (IE ISSN 0072-0887) **1781**
Genus. (IT ISSN 0016-6987) **3982**
Genys. (LI) **1255**
Geo. (GW) **1955**, 2248, 4768
Geo (Australia). (AT ISSN 0157-1338) **2248**
Geo (France). (FR ISSN 0220-8245) **2187**
Geo (Spain). (SP) **2217**
Geo - Archeologia. (IT) **273**
▼Geo Info Systems. (US) **2268**, 1975
Geo - Information - Systems. see Geo - Informations - Systeme **1544**
Geo - Informations - Systeme/Geo - Information - Systems. (GW ISSN 0935-1523) **1544**
Geo Katalog. Band 1. Touristische Veroeffentlichungen see Geo Katalog (Year). Volume 1. Touristische Veroeffentlichungen **2248**

Geo Katalog. Band 2. Geowissenschaften. (GW) **2248**, 1561
Geo Katalog. Band 2. International see Geo Katalog. Band 2. Geowissenschaften **2248**
Geo Katalog (Year). Volume 1. Touristische Veroeffentlichungen. (GW) **2248**, 4799
Geo-marine Letters. (US ISSN 0276-0460) **1561**, 1604
Geo Special. (GW) **2248**
Geoactive. (UK ISSN 0956-0629) **2248**, 1750, 2758
Geoarchaeology. (US ISSN 0883-6353) **273**
Geobios. (II ISSN 0251-1223) **440**, 1544
Geobios. (FR ISSN 0016-6995) **3657**
Geobios New Reports. (II ISSN 0253-3340) **440**, 1544
Geobotanisches Institut E T H, Stiftung Ruebel, Zurich. Berichte. (SZ ISSN 0373-7896) **504**
Geobotanisches Institut E T H, Stiftung Ruebel, Zurich. Veroeffentlichungen. (SZ ISSN 0254-9433) **504**
Geobyte. (US ISSN 0885-6362) **1395**, 1561, 3687
Geocarto International. (HK ISSN 1010-6049) **2248**, 1561
Geochemical Journal. (JA ISSN 0016-7002) **1544**
Geochemical Society of India. Journal. (II ISSN 0368-2323) **1561**
Geochemistry. see Chemie der Erde **1557**
Geochemistry International. (English translation of: Geokhimiya) (US ISSN 0016-7029) **1544**
GeoChile. (CL ISSN 0431-1930) **4768**
Geochimica et Cosmochimica Acta. (US ISSN 0016-7037) **1561**
Geochronique. (FR ISSN 0153-8446) **1561**
Geociencias. (BL ISSN 0101-9082) **1544**
Geocom Bulletin see Bibliography of Economic Geology **3479**
Geocosmic News. (US) **358**
GEODE. (US) **1312**
Geode. (NE) **1561**
Geoderma. (NE ISSN 0016-7061) **178**
Geodes. (IT) **4768**
Geodesia. (NE ISSN 0016-707X) **2248**
Geodesy and Cartography. see Geodezia es Kartografia **2249**
Geodesy, Mapping and Photogrammetry see Mapping Sciences & Remote Sensing **2256**
Geodetic Society of Japan. Journal. see Sokuchi Gakkaishi **2263**
Geodeticky a Kartograficky Obzor. (CS ISSN 0016-7096) **2249**, 1866
Geodetski List. (CI ISSN 0016-710X) **1544**
Geodetski Pregled. (XN) **1866**
Geodex Retrieval System for Geotechnical Abstracts. (US ISSN 0046-5658) **1844**, 12
Geodex Systems - Structural Information Service. (US) **1844**, 12
Geodezia es Kartografia/Geodesy and Cartography. (HU ISSN 0016-7118) **2249**
Geodeziya i Kartografiya. (RU ISSN 0016-7126) **1589**, 2249
Geodezja i Kartografia. (PL ISSN 0016-7134) **1589**, 2249
Geodrilling. (UK ISSN 0268-0165) **1866**
Geodynamique. (FR ISSN 0766-5105) **1589**
Geoecological Research. (GW ISSN 0170-3250) **1544**, 1955
Geoexploration see Journal of Applied Geophysics **1591**
Geofile. (UK ISSN 0267-7563) **2249**, 1955
Geofisica Internacional. (MX ISSN 0016-7169) **1589**
Geofizicheskii Byulleten' see Geophysical Transactions **1590**

Geofizicheskii Zhurnal/Journal of Geophysics. (KR ISSN 0203-3100) **1589**
Geofizika. (CI ISSN 0352-3659) **1589**
Geofizikai Kozlemenyek. *see* Geophysical Transactions **1590**
Geoforum. (US ISSN 0016-7185) **1544**
Geogaceta. (SP ISSN 0213-683X) **1561**
Geografia. (PL ISSN 0554-8128) **2249**
Geografia. (BL ISSN 0100-7912) **2249**
Geografia. (IT) **2249**, 1750
Geografia nelle Scuole. (IT ISSN 0431-1981) **2249**, 1750
Geografia Urbana. (BL ISSN 0533-9286) **2249**, 4436
Geografia w Szkole. (PL ISSN 0137-7566) **2249**
Geografica. (AG) **2249**
Geografica Universal. (BL) **2249**
Geograficke Prace *see* Zbornik Pedagogickej Fakulty v Presove U P J S v Kosiciach. Prirodne Vedy **2267**
Geograficky Casopis/Geographical Review. (CS ISSN 0016-7193) **2249**
Geografie *see* Universitatea "Al. I. Cuza" din Iasi. Analele Stiintifice. Geologie - Geografie **1583**
Geografija *see* Geografija ir Krastotvarka **2249**
Geografija ir Krastotvarka/Geography and Land Management. (LI) **2249**, 1561
Geografinis Metrastis/Geographical Year Book. (LI ISSN 0072-0917) **2249**
Geografisch Tijdschrift. (NE ISSN 0016-7215) **2249**
Geografisk Tidsskrift. (DK ISSN 0016-7223) **2249**
Geografiska Annaler. Series A. Physical Geography. (SW ISSN 0435-3676) **2249**
Geografiska Annaler. Series B. Human Geography. (SW ISSN 0435-3684) **240**
Geografiska Notiser. (SW ISSN 0016-724X) **2249**, 1750
Geografiya v Shkole. (RU ISSN 0016-7207) **2249**, 1635
Geografski Horizont. (CI ISSN 0016-7266) **2249**
Geografski List. (BN) **2249**
Geografski Obzornik/Geographic Horizon. (XV ISSN 0016-7274) **2249**
Geographe Canadien. *see* Canadian Geographer **2244**
Geographer. (II ISSN 0072-0909) **2249**
Geographers. (UK ISSN 0308-6992) **2249**
Geographia Medica. (HU ISSN 0300-807X) **2249**, 3100
Geographic Horizon. *see* Geografski Obzornik **2249**
Geographic Information, Mapping, and Positioning Newsletter. (US ISSN 1045-6732) **2249**, 1435
Geographic Information System Europe *see* G I S Europe **2268**
Geographic Information System World *see* G I S World **2268**
Geographic Information Systems Forum *see* G I S Forum **5198**
Geographica. (NR ISSN 0016-7290) **2249**
Geographica. (MY) **2250**
Geographica Helvetica. (SZ ISSN 0016-7312) **2250**, 240
Geographica Iugoslavica. (XV ISSN 0351-3238) **2250**
Geographical Abstracts: Economic Geography *see* Geographical Abstracts: Human Geography **2268**
Geographical Abstracts: Human Geography. (UK ISSN 0953-9611) **2268**
Geographical Abstracts: Landforms and the Quaternary *see* Geographical Abstracts: Physical Geography **2268**

Geographical Abstracts: Physical Geography. (UK ISSN 0954-0504) **2268**, 12, 1550
Geographical Analysis. (US ISSN 0016-7363) **2250**
Geographical Association of Nigeria. Journal *see* Nigerian Geographical Journal **2257**
Geographical Association of Tanzania Journal. (TZ ISSN 0016-738X) **2250**
Geographical Association of Western Australia. Bulletin. (AT) **2250**
Geographical Bulletin. *see* Foldrajzi Ertesito **2248**
Geographical Bulletin. (US ISSN 0731-3292) **2250**
Geographical Bulletin of India. (II) **2250**
Geographical Chronicles. *see* Geographika Chronika **2251**
Geographical Distribution of Financial Flows to Developing Countries. Disbursements - Commitments - Economic Indicators. (FR) **930**
Geographical Education. (AT ISSN 0085-0969) **1750**, 2250
Geographical Education. *see* Dili Jiaoyu **2246**
Geographical Field Group (Nottingham). Regional Studies. (UK ISSN 0078-2084) **2250**
Geographical Journal. *see* Czasopismo Geograficzne **2245**
Geographical Journal. (UK ISSN 0016-7398) **2250**
Geographical Journal of Nepal. (NP) **2250**
Geographical Knowledge. *see* Dili Zhishi **2246**
Geographical Magazine. (UK ISSN 0016-741X) **2250**
Geographical Observer. (II ISSN 0072-0925) **2250**
Geographical Outlook *see* Geographical View Point **2250**
Geographical Papers. (UK ISSN 0305-5914) **2250**
Geographical Perspectives. (US ISSN 0199-994X) **2250**
Geographical Research. *see* Dili Yanjiu **2246**
Geographical Research. (IR) **2250**
Geographical Research Forum *see* Geography Research Forum **2251**
Geographical Review. *see* Geograficky Casopis **2249**
Geographical Review. (US ISSN 0016-7428) **2250**
Geographical Review. *see* Przeglad Geograficzny **2260**
Geographical Review of Afghanistan. (AF ISSN 0016-7436) **2250**
Geographical Review of India. (II ISSN 0046-5690) **2250**
Geographical Review of Japan. Series A/Chirigaku Hyoron A. (JA ISSN 0016-7444) **2250**
Geographical Review of Japan. Series B/Chirigaku Hyoron B. (JA) **2250**
Geographical Review of Japan - Chirigaku Hyoron *see* Geographical Review of Japan. Series A **2250**
Geographical Review of Japan - Chirigaku Hyoron *see* Geographical Review of Japan. Series B **2250**
Geographical Society of China. Bulletin. (CH) **2250**, 1395
Geographical Society of New South Wales. Geography Bulletin *see* Geography Teachers Association of New South Wales. Geography Bulletin **2251**
Geographical Survey Institute, Tokyo. Bulletin/Kokudo Chiri-in Hokoku. (JA) **2250**
Geographical Thought *see* Uttar Bharat Bhoogol Patrika **2266**
Geographical View Point. (II ISSN 0046-5712) **2250**, 3982
Geographical Year Book. *see* Geografinis Metrastis **2249**
Geographie Aktuell. (GW ISSN 0178-7810) **2251**
Geographie Appliquee. *see* Operational Geographer **2258**
Geographie de la Sante. (FR) **2251**
Geographie - Ecologie - Environnement. (BE) **2251**, 1544

Geographie et Recherche. (FR ISSN 0184-7589) **2251**
Geographie Heute. (GW ISSN 0341-5279) **2251**, 1255
Geographie im Unterricht. (GW ISSN 0341-8057) **2251**
Geographie Physique et Quaternaire. (CN ISSN 0705-7199) **2251**
Geographie und ihre Didaktik. (GW ISSN 0343-7256) **2251**, 1750
Geographie und Schule. (GW ISSN 0171-8649) **2251**
Geographika Chronika/Geographical Chronicles. (CY) **2251**
Geographische Berichte. (GW ISSN 0016-7452) **2251**
Geographische Gesellschaft in Hamburg. Mitteilungen. (GW ISSN 0374-9061) **2251**
Geographische Gesellschaft in Wien. Mitteilungen *see* Oesterreichische Geographische Gesellschaft. Mitteilungen **2258**
Geographische Gesellschaft, Munich. Mitteilungen. (GW ISSN 0072-0941) **2251**
Geographische Gesellschaft von Bern. Jahrbuch. (SZ) **2251**
Geographische Gesellschaft zu Hannover. Jahrbuch *see* Hannoversche Geographische Arbeiten **2252**
Geographische Hochschulmanuskripte. (GW ISSN 0723-175X) **2251**
Geographische Hochschulmanuskripte. Diskussionspapiere. (GW ISSN 0723-1679) **2251**
Geographische Rundschau. (GW ISSN 0016-7460) **2251**
Geographische Rundschau. Beiheft *see* Praxis Geographie **2259**
Geographische Zeitschrift. (GW ISSN 0016-7479) **2251**
Geographisches Taschenbuch. (GW ISSN 0072-0968) **2251**
Geography. *see* Dili **2246**
Geography. (UK ISSN 0016-7487) **2251**
Geography and Land Management. *see* Geografija ir Krastotvarka **2249**
Geography of the British Isles Series. (UK) **2251**
Geography of World Agriculture. (HU ISSN 0303-6634) **2251**
Geography Research Forum. (US) **2251**
Geography Review. (UK ISSN 0950-7035) **2251**
Geography Teacher. (II ISSN 0016-7517) **2251**, 1635
Geography Teachers Association of New South Wales. Geography Bulletin. (AT ISSN 0156-9236) **2251**
Geography Teaching. *see* Dili Jiaoxue **1748**
GeoJournal. (NE ISSN 0343-2521) **1544**
Geokhimiia, Mineralogiia i Petrologiia. (BU ISSN 0324-1718) **1544**
Geokhimiya. (RU ISSN 0016-7525) **1562**, 1177
Geokhimiya i Rudoobrazovanie. (KR ISSN 0130-1128) **1562**
Geolgicky Prieskum. *see* Geologicky Pruzkum **1564**
Geolog. (CN) **1562**
Geologi. (FI ISSN 0046-5720) **1562**
Geologia. (PL) **1562**
Geologia Applicata e Idrogeologia. (IT ISSN 0435-3870) **1562**, 1597, 1866
Geologia Colombiana. (CK ISSN 0072-0992) **1562**
Geologia Sudetica. (PL ISSN 0072-100X) **1562**
Geologiai es Geofizikai Szakirodalmi Tajekoztato/Geology and Geophysics Abstracts. (HU ISSN 0230-7065) **1550**
Geologica Balcanica. (BU ISSN 0324-0894) **1562**
Geologica Bavarica. (GW ISSN 0016-755X) **1562**
Geologica de America Central. (CR) **1562**
Geologica et Palaeontologica. (GW ISSN 0072-1018) **1562**, 3657
Geologica Ultraiectina. (NE ISSN 0072-1026) **1562**

GEOLOGICAL SURVEY 6215

Geological Abstracts. (UK ISSN 0954-0512) **1551**, 12
Geological Abstracts: Geophysics and Tectonics *see* Geological Abstracts **1551**
Geological Association of Canada. Special Paper. (CN ISSN 0072-1042) **1562**
Geological Correlation. (UN ISSN 0302-069X) **1562**
Geological Fieldwork. (CN ISSN 0381-243X) **1562**
Geological Guidebooks *see* Virginia Polytechnic Institute and State University. Department of Geological Sciences. Geological Guidebooks **1585**
Geological Journal. (UK ISSN 0072-1050) **1562**
Geological Magazine. (UK ISSN 0016-7568) **1562**
Geological, Mining and Metallurgical Society of India. Bulletin. (II ISSN 0016-7576) **1562**, 3407, 3483
Geological, Mining and Metallurgical Society of India. Quarterly Journal *see* Indian Journal of Geology **1568**
Geological Quarterly. *see* Kwartalnik Geologiczny **1571**
Geological Reference Book. (CN) **1562**
Geological Review. *see* Dizhi Lun-Ping **1559**
Geological Review. *see* Przeglad Geologiczny **1578**
Geological Society. Journal. (UK ISSN 0016-7649) **1562**
Geological Society of America. Abstracts with Programs. (US ISSN 0016-7592) **1551**, 12
Geological Society of America. Bulletin. (US ISSN 0016-7606) **1563**
Geological Society of America. Memoirs.(US ISSN 0072-1069) **1563**
Geological Society of America. Memorials. (US ISSN 0091-5041) **1563**
Geological Society of America. Special Papers. (US ISSN 0072-1077) **1563**
Geological Society of America Today *see* G S A Today **1561**
Geological Society of Australia. Abstracts Series. (AT) **1551**, 1563
Geological Society of Australia. Journal *see* Australian Journal of Earth Sciences **1555**
Geological Society of Australia. Special Publication. (AT ISSN 0072-1085) **1563**
Geological Society of China. Memoirs. (CH) **1563**
Geological Society of China. Proceedings. (CH ISSN 0431-2155) **1563**, 1544, 1589
Geological Society of Denmark. Bulletin. *see* Dansk Geologisk Forening. Bulletin **1558**
Geological Society of Egypt. Annual Meeting. Abstracts of Papers. (UA ISSN 0446-4648) **1563**
Geological Society of India. Journal. (II ISSN 0016-7622) **1563**
Geological Society of Iraq. Journal. (IQ ISSN 0533-8301) **1563**
Geological Society of Jamaica. Journal. (JM ISSN 0435-401X) **1563**
Geological Society of Japan. Journal/ Chishitsugaku Zasshi. (JA ISSN 0016-7630) **1563**
Geological Society of Japan. Memoirs. *see* Chishitsugaku Ronshu **1557**
Geological Society of Malaysia. Bulletin. (MY ISSN 0126-6187) **1563**
Geological Society of South Africa. Geobulletin/Geologiese Vereniging van Suid-Africa. Geobulletin. (SA) **1563**
Geological Society of South Africa. Special Publication. (SA) **1563**
Geological Society of South Africa. Transactions *see* South African Journal of Geology **1581**
Geological Society of the Oregon Country. Geological Newsletter. (US ISSN 0270-5451) **1563**
Geological Survey. Bulletin. *see* Ustredni Ustav Geologicky. Vestnik **1584**

GEOLOGICAL SURVEY

Geological Survey of Denmark. see Danmarks Geologiske Undersoegelse **1558**
Geological Survey of Denmark. Series A. see Danmarks Geologiske Undersoegelse. Serie A **1558**
Geological Survey of Denmark. Series B. see Danmarks Geologiske Undersoegelse. Serie B **1558**
Geological Survey of Denmark. Series C. see Danmarks Geologiske Undersoegelse. Serie C **1558**
Geological Survey of Denmark. Series D. see Danmarks Geologiske Undersoegelse. Serie D **1558**
Geological Survey of Denmark. Yearbook. see Danmarks Geologiske Undersoegelse. Aarbog **5177**
Geological Survey of Greenland. Bulletin. see Groenlands Geologiske Undersoegelse. Bulletin **1567**
Geological Survey of Hokkaido. Report. see Chika Shigen Chosajo Hokoku **1542**
Geological Survey of India. News. (II ISSN 0378-4029) **1563**
Geological Survey of Ireland. Bulletin. (IE ISSN 0085-0985) **1563**
Geological Survey of Ireland. Guide Series. (IE ISSN 0790-0260) **1563**
Geological Survey of Ireland. Information Circulars. (IE ISSN 0085-0993) **1563**
Geological Survey of Ireland. Report Series. (IE ISSN 0790-0279) **1563**
Geological Survey of Ireland. Special Papers. (IE ISSN 0085-1019) **1563**
Geological Survey of N.S.W. Mineral Resources see New South Wales. Geological Survey. Mineral Resources Series **3492**
Geological Survey of Namibia. Communications. (SX) **1563**
Geological Survey of Namibia. Memoirs.(SX) **1563**
Geological Survey of Namibia. Reports on Open File. C D M Mineral Surveys.(SX) **1563**, **1589**
Geological Survey of Namibia. Reports on Open File. Economic Geology. (SX) **1563**
Geological Survey of Namibia. Reports on Open File. Engineering Geology. (SX) **1564**, **1822**
Geological Survey of Namibia. Reports on Open File. Geophysics. (SX) **1589**
Geological Survey of Namibia. Reports on Open File. Mineral Resource Series. (SX) **1564**
Geological Survey of Namibia. Reports on Open File. Regional Geology. (SX) **1564**
Geological Survey of South Australia. Bulletin. (AT ISSN 0016-7673) **1564**
Geological Survey of South Australia. Explanatory Notes. (AT ISSN 0572-0125) **1564**
Geological Survey of South Australia. Report of Investigations. (AT ISSN 0016-7681) **1564**
Geological Survey of South West Africa - Namibia. Communications see Geological Survey of Namibia. Communications **1563**
Geological Survey of South West Africa - Namibia. Memoirs see Geological Survey of Namibia. Memoirs **1563**
Geological Survey of Wyoming. Bulletin. (US) **1564**
Geological Survey of Wyoming. Educational Series. (US) **1564**
Geological Survey of Wyoming. Public Information Circulars. (US) **1564**
Geological Survey of Wyoming. Report of Investigations. (US) **1564**
Geological Surveying. see Geologicky Pruzkum **1564**
Geologicheskii Zhurnal. (KR ISSN 0367-4290) **1564**
Geologicheskii Zhurnal Armenii. (AI ISSN 0016-769X) **1564**
Geologicky Pruzkum/Geolgicky Prieskum/Geological Surveying. (CS ISSN 0016-772X) **1564**, **1589**

Geologicky Zbornik/Geology. Collection of Works. (CS ISSN 0016-7738) **1564**, **3483**
Geologie. (GW) **1564**
Geologie see Societe Belge de Geologie. Bulletin **1580**
Geologie Africaine/African Geology. (FR) **1564**
Geologie en Mijnbouw/Geology and Mining. (NE ISSN 0016-7746) **1564**, **3483**
Geologie Mediterraneenne. (FR ISSN 0397-2844) **1564**
Geologie und Palaeontologie in Westfalen. (GW ISSN 0176-148X) **1564**
Geologiese Vereniging van Suid-Africa. Geobulletin. see Geological Society of South Africa. Geobulletin **1563**
Geologija. (XV ISSN 0016-7789) **1564**
Geologische Abhandlungen Hessen. (GW ISSN 0341-4043) **1564**, **1589**, **3657**
Geologische Blaetter fuer Nordost-Bayern und Angrenzende Gebiete. (GW ISSN 0016-7797) **1564**
Geologische Bundesanstalt, Vienna. Abhandlungen. (AU ISSN 0378-0864) **1564**
Geologische Bundesanstalt, Vienna. Jahrbuch. (AU ISSN 0016-7800) **1564**, **3657**
Geologische Rundschau. (GW ISSN 0016-7835) **1565**
Geologisches Jahrbuch. Reihe A: Allgemeine und Regionale Geologie B.R. Deutschland und Nachbargebiete, Tektonik, Stratigraphie, Palaeontologie. (GW ISSN 0341-6399) **1565**, **3657**
Geologisches Jahrbuch. Reihe B: Regionale Geologie Ausland. (GW ISSN 0341-6402) **1565**
Geologisches Jahrbuch. Reihe C: Hydrogeologie. Ingenieurgeologie. (GW ISSN 0341-6410) **1565**, **1597**
Geologisches Jahrbuch. Reihe D: Mineralogie. Petrographie, Geochemie, Lagerstaettenkunde. (GW ISSN 0341-6429) **1565**, **3484**
Geologisches Jahrbuch. Reihe E: Geophysik. (GW ISSN 0341-6437) **1565**
Geologisches Jahrbuch. Reihe F: Bodenkunde. (GW ISSN 0341-6445) **1565**
Geologisches Jahrbuch Hessen. (GW ISSN 0341-4027) **1565**, **1589**, **3657**
▼Geologisches Landesamt Baden - Wuerttemberg. Informationen. (GW ISSN 0940-0834) **1565**
Geologisches Landesamt Baden-Wuerttemberg. Jahreshefte. (GW ISSN 0408-1560) **1544**, **3484**, **3657**
Geologisches Landesamt Baden-Wuettemberg. Abhandlungen. (GW ISSN 0408-1552) **1544**, **3484**, **3657**
Geologiska Foereningens i Stockholm. Foerhandlinger. (SW ISSN 0016-786X) **1565**
Geologist's Directory. (UK ISSN 0260-0463) **1565**
Geologiya i Geokhimiya Goryuchikh Iskopaemykh. (KR ISSN 0135-2164) **1565**
Geologiya Nefti i Gaza. (RU ISSN 0016-7894) **3688**
Geologiya Rudnykh Mestorozhdenii. (RU ISSN 0016-7908) **3484**
Geology (Boulder). (US ISSN 0091-7613) **1565**
Geology. Collection of Works. see Geologicky Zbornik **1564**
Geology Abroad. see Guowai Dizhi **1567**
Geology and Geophysics Abstracts. see Geologiai es Geofizikai Szakirodalmi Tajekoztato **1550**
Geology and Mining. see Geologie en Mijnbouw **1564**
Geology and World Deposits. (US) **1565**, **3407**

Geology, Exploration and Mining see Engineering and Inspection Annual Report **3483**
†Geology in British Columbia. (CN ISSN 0823-1257) **5199**
Geology of Nonmetallics see Geology and World Deposits **1565**
Geology of Petroleum. (GW ISSN 0720-8863) **1565**
Geology of the Pacific Ocean. (US ISSN 8755-075X) **1565**
Geology Science and Technology Development. see Dizhi Keji Dongtai **1559**
Geology Teaching see Teaching Earth Sciences **1582**
Geology Today. (UK ISSN 0266-6979) **1565**
Geoloski Vjesnik. (CI ISSN 0016-7924) **1565**
Geomagnetism and Aeronomy. (English translation of: Geomagnetizm i Aeronomiya) (US ISSN 0016-7932) **1589**, **1565**
Geomagnetizm i Aeronomiya. (RU ISSN 0016-7940) **1589**
Geomedical Monograph Series see Medizinische Laenderkunde. Geomedical Monograph Series **3130**
Geomethodica. (SZ ISSN 0171-1687) **1544**
Geometra. (IT ISSN 0016-7959) **1866**
Geometre. (FR ISSN 0016-7967) **1866**
Geometri Informazione. (IT) **618**
Geometriae Dedicata. (NE ISSN 0046-5755) **3036**
▼Geometric and Functional Analysis. (SZ ISSN 1016-443X) **3036**
Geomicrobiology Journal. (US ISSN 0149-0451) **552**, **477**
Geomimet. (MX) **3484**, **1565**
Geominas. (VE ISSN 0016-7975) **1544**, **3484**
Geomorphology. (NE ISSN 0169-555X) **1565**, **2251**
Geomundo. (US) **2251**
Geonews. (PK ISSN 0435-4311) **1566**
Geooekodynamik. (GW ISSN 0720-454X) **2251**, **1566**, **1597**
†Geophysica Norvegica. (NO ISSN 0072-1174) **5199**
Geophysical and Astrophysical Fluid Dynamics. (US ISSN 0309-1929) **1589**
Geophysical Directory. (US) **1589**, **3484**, **3688**
Geophysical Journal. (English translation of: Geofizicheskii Zhurnal) (US ISSN 0275-9128) **1589**
Geophysical Journal International. (UK ISSN 0952-4592) **1589**
Geophysical Journal of the R A S, D G G and E G S see Geophysical Journal International **1589**
Geophysical Magazine/Kisho-cho Obun Iho. (JA ISSN 0016-8017) **1589**
Geophysical Monograph Book Series see American Geophysical Union. Geophysical Monograph Book Series **1587**
Geophysical Prospecting. (UK ISSN 0016-8025) **1589**
†Geophysical Research Bulletin. (II ISSN 0378-6307) **5199**
Geophysical Research Letters. (US ISSN 0094-8276) **1589**
Geophysical Transactions/Geofizikai Kozlemenyek/Geofizicheskii Byulleten' (HU ISSN 0016-7177) **1590**
Geophysics. (US ISSN 0016-8033) **1590**
†Geophysics Abstracts. (US ISSN 0959-3071) **5199**
Geophysics and Astrophysics Monographs. (NE) **364**, **1590**
Geophysics: The Leading Edge of Exploration. (US ISSN 0732-989X) **1590**
Geophysik und Geologie. (GW ISSN 0138-2357) **1590**
Geophytology. (II ISSN 0376-5156) **3657**
Georg-August-Universitaet Goettingen. Informationen. (GW) **4311**

Georg Fischer Aktiengesellschaft Spectrum see G F Spectrum **5198**
Georg Forster: Saemtliche Schriften, Tagebuecher, Briefe. (GW) **2919**, **2993**
George C. Marshall Foundation. Topics. (US) **2407**, **3459**
George D. Hall's Connecticut Service Directory. (US) **1136**
George D. Hall's Directory of Central Atlantic States Manufacturers. (US ISSN 0889-0390) **1136**
George D. Hall's Directory of Connecticut Manufacturers. (US ISSN 0196-8270) **1136**
George D. Hall's Directory of Massachusetts Manufacturers. (US ISSN 0149-6913) **1136**
George D. Hall's Directory of North Carolina Manufacturers. (US) **1136**
George D. Hall's Massachusetts Service Directory. (US ISSN 0196-7185) **1136**
George D. Hall's New Jersey Manufacturers Directory. (US) **1136**
George D. Hall's New York Manufacturers Directory. (US ISSN 0272-1074) **1136**
George Eliot Fellowship Review. (UK) **2919**
George Eliot - George Henry Lewes Newsletter see George Eliot - George Henry Lewes Studies **2867**
George Eliot - George Henry Lewes Studies. (US) **2867**, **400**
George Ernest Morrison Lectures in Ethnology. (AT ISSN 0072-1190) **240**
George Herbert Journal. (US ISSN 0161-7435) **2993**
George Mason University Law Review see G M U Law Review **2629**
George Odiorne Letter. (US ISSN 0890-0914) **1011**
George Sand Newsletter see George Sand Studies **2919**
George Sand Studies. (US) **2919**, **4843**
†George Street Journal. (US ISSN 0746-9403) **5199**
George Washington Journal of International Law and Economics. (US) **2723**, **667**
George Washington Law Review. (US ISSN 0016-8076) **2629**
George Washington University Hatchet see G W Hatchet **1312**
George Washington University Magazine see G W Magazine **1312**
George Washington University Medical Center Department of Biochemistry. Annual Spring Symposia Series see G W U M C. Department of Biochemistry. Annual Spring Symposia Series **477**
George Washington University Review see G W Review **2919**
Georgeson Report. (US) **947**, **1011**
Georgetown Law Journal. (US ISSN 0016-8092) **2629**
Georgetown Magazine. (US ISSN 0745-9009) **1312**
Georgetown Medical Bulletin. (US ISSN 0016-8106) **3100**
Georgetown University Center for Strategic and International Studies. Significant Issues Series see Center for Strategic and International Studies. Significant Issues Series **3878**
Georgetown University Round Table on Languages and Linguistics. (US ISSN 0196-7207) **2815**
Georgetowner. (US ISSN 0730-9082) **2407**
†Georgia. Office of Planning and Budget. State Investment Plan. (US ISSN 0196-1098) **5199**
Georgia Advance Sheets. (US ISSN 8750-0515) **2629**
Georgia Advocate. (US ISSN 0435-5253) **1312**
Georgia Alert. (US ISSN 0435-5261) **1635**
Georgia Alumni Record. (US ISSN 0016-8130) **1312**
Georgia AnchorAge. (US ISSN 0016-8149) **4727**

Georgia Arrest, Search & Seizure. (US) 2629
Georgia Augusta. (GW ISSN 0016-8157) 1707
Georgia Automotive Business. (US) 4691
Georgia Bar Journal see Georgia State Bar Journal 2629
Georgia Beat. (US) 3896
Georgia Builder. (US) 618
Georgia Bulletin. (US) 4265
Georgia Business see Georgia Business and Economic Conditions 667
Georgia Business and Economic Conditions. (US ISSN 0279-3857) 667
Georgia Cattleman. (US) 217
Georgia College Alumni News Quarterly.(US) 1312
Georgia Condominium Law Manual. (US) 4149, 2629
Georgia Congress of Parents and Teachers. Annual Leadership Training Conference. Workshop for P T A Leaders. (US) 1727
Georgia Congress of Parents and Teachers. Annual Summer Institute. Handbook for P T A Leaders see Georgia Congress of Parents and Teachers. Annual Leadership Training Conference. Workshop for P T A Leaders 1727
Georgia Creditors' Rights. (US) 2629
Georgia Descriptions in Data. (US) 3992, 4572
Georgia Economic Outlook. (US ISSN 0884-1179) 667
Georgia Employment Law Letter. (US ISSN 1040-4813) 2629, 980
Georgia Engineer. (US ISSN 0016-822X) 1822
Georgia Environmental Law Letter. (US ISSN 1044-2324) 2629, 1955
†Georgia F O P News. (Georgia Fraternal Order of Police) (US) 5199
Georgia Facts. (US ISSN 1044-9086) 1781
Georgia Family Law Manual. (US) 2717
Georgia Farm Bureau News. (US) 93
Georgia Farmers Fastline see Farmers Fastline: Georgia Edition 162
Georgia Forestry. (US) 2101
Georgia Fraternal Order of Police Georgia F O P News see Georgia F O P News 5199
Georgia Future Farmer. (US ISSN 0016-8262) 93
Georgia Genealogical Magazine. (US ISSN 0435-5385) 2153
Georgia Genealogical Society Quarterly. (US) 2153
Georgia Geologic Survey. Bulletin. (US) 1566
Georgia Geologic Survey. Circular. (US) 1566
Georgia Geologic Survey. Circular 1. List of Publications. (US) 1551
Georgia Geologic Survey. Circular 2. Mining Directory of Georgia. (US) 3484
Georgia Geologic Survey. Circular 3. The Mineral Industry of Georgia. (US) 3484
Georgia Geologic Survey. Educational Series. (US) 1955
Georgia Geologic Survey. Geologic Guide. (US) 1566
Georgia Geologic Survey. Geologic Report. (US) 1566
Georgia Geologic Survey. Guidebook. (US) 1566
Georgia Geologic Survey. Miscellaneous Publication. (US) 1566
Georgia Geologic Survey. Open File Report. (US) 1566
Georgia Geologic Survey. Project Report. (US) 1566
Georgia Geological Survey. Information Circular. (US ISSN 0433-5473) 3484
Georgia Government Review see State and Local Government Review 4095
Georgia Grocer. (US) 2092
Georgia Historical Quarterly. (US ISSN 0016-8297) 2407

Georgia Historical Society Foot - Notes see G H S Foot - Notes 2406
†Georgia Housing Network. (US) 5199
Georgia Humanities. (US) 2507
Georgia Journal see Georgia Journal - Living 2226
Georgia Journal - Living. (US) 2226
†Georgia Journal of Accounting. (US ISSN 0275-8911) 5199
Georgia Journal of International and Comparative Law. (US ISSN 0046-578X) 2723
Georgia Journal of Science. (US ISSN 0016-8114) 4311
Georgia Labor Market Trends. (US) 980
Georgia Landlord - Tenant Law. (US) 4149, 2629
Georgia Law Letter. (US ISSN 0884-1217) 2629
Georgia Law Review. (US ISSN 0016-8300) 2629
Georgia Legislative Review. (US ISSN 0362-5931) 2629
Georgia Librarian. (US ISSN 0016-8319) 2758
Georgia Lineages and Queries see Georgia Queries 5199
Georgia Living see Georgia Journal - Living 2226
▼Georgia Magazin (Atlanta, 1990). (US) 2226
Georgia Magazine (Atlanta, 1945). (US) 2226
Georgia Manufacturers Register. (US ISSN 0896-4009) 1136
Georgia Manufacturing Directory. (US ISSN 0435-5482) 1136
Georgia Museum of Art. Bulletin. (US ISSN 0147-1902) 327
Georgia Museum of Art. News. (US) 3524
Georgia Music News. (US ISSN 0046-5798) 3552
Georgia, North Carolina, South Carolina TourBook see Tourbook: Georgia, North Carolina, South Carolina 4790
Georgia Nursing. (US ISSN 0016-8335) 3278
†Georgia Peace and Justice Report. (US) 5199
Georgia Post-Secondary School Directory: A Guide to Colleges, Vocational-Technical Schools & Special Purpose Institutions. (US) 1694
Georgia Probate Manual. (US) 2629
Georgia Professional Engineer. (US ISSN 0016-8351) 1822
†Georgia Queries. (US ISSN 0898-5413) 5199
Georgia Real Estate Law Letter. (US) 2629, 4149
Georgia Retailing News. (US ISSN 0191-9121) 1040
The Georgia Review. (US ISSN 0016-8386) 2919
Georgia Sportsman. (US ISSN 0199-6517) 4547
Georgia State Bar Journal. (US ISSN 0016-8416) 2629
Georgia State Literary Studies. (US ISSN 0884-8696) 2919
Georgia State Rules of Court. (US) 2731
Georgia State University Signal. (US ISSN 0016-8424) 1312
Georgia Statistical Abstract. (US ISSN 0085-1043) 718, 4572
Georgia Straight. (CN ISSN 0016-8432) 2177
Georgia Tech Alumni Magazine. (US) 1312
Georgia Trend. (US ISSN 0882-5971) 783
Georgia Trucker see Fastline for Georgia Truckers 4744
Georgia Vital Statistics Report. (US) 3992, 4117
Georgian see Link (Montreal) 2872
Georgian Annual. (US) 4283
Georgian Bay Regional Library System. Directory-Member Libraries. (CN ISSN 0380-8068) 2759
Georgian Bay Today. (CN ISSN 0849-5696) 2177
Georgian Monthly. (US) 4283

Georgian Newsletter see Georgian Monthly 4283
Georgia's Cities. (US) 4088
Georgist Journal. (US ISSN 0887-6290) 894
Geos. (CN ISSN 0374-3268) 1544, 3484
Geos. (VE ISSN 0435-5601) 1566
GEOS see Cahiers de Geographie de la Sante 3085
Geoscience Canada. (CN ISSN 0315-0941) 1545
Geoscience Documentation. (UK ISSN 0016-8483) 1551, 12
Geoscience Information Society. Proceedings. (US ISSN 0072-1409) 1545
Geoscience Information Society Newsletter see G I S Newsletter 1544
Geoscience Wisconsin. (US ISSN 0164-2049) 1566
Geosciences in Canada. (CN ISSN 0707-2422) 1566
▼Geoscientist. (UK ISSN 0961-5628) 1566
Geoscope. (CN ISSN 0046-581X) 2251
Geoserials see Geosources 1545
Geosources. (UK ISSN 0952-2700) 1545
Geostandards Newsletter. (FR ISSN 0150-5505) 1566
Geosur. (UY ISSN 0250-7609) 3958, 2251
Geotechnical Abstracts. (GW ISSN 0016-8491) 1844, 12
Geotechnical and Geological Engineering. (UK ISSN 0960-3182) 3484
Geotechnical Engineering. (TH ISSN 0046-5828) 1866, 1545
Geotechnical Fabrics Report. (US ISSN 0882-4983) 4619
Geotechnical News. (CN) 1566
Geotechnical Science Laboratories. Publications, Reports, and Theses. (CN ISSN 0831-5000) 1551, 1955
Geotechnical Testing Journal. (US ISSN 0149-6115) 1866
Geotechnik. (GW ISSN 0172-6145) 1822, 1566
Geotechnika. (NE ISSN 0926-5074) 1545
Geotechnique. (UK ISSN 0016-8505) 1866
Geotectonica et Metallogenia. see Dadi Gouzao yu Chengkuangxue 1558
Geotectonics. (English translation of: Geotektonika) (US ISSN 0016-8521) 1590
Geotehnika. (CI) 1566
Geoteknisk Institut, Copenhagen. Bulletin. (DK ISSN 0069-987X) 1590
Geotektonika. (RU ISSN 0016-853X) 1566
Geotektonika, Tektonofizika i Geodinamika. (BU ISSN 0324-1661) 1566
Geotektonische Forschungen. (GW ISSN 0016-8548) 1590
Geotermia. (VE ISSN 0253-1062) 1566
Geotextiles and Geomembranes. (UK ISSN 0266-1144) 485, 1866
Geothermal Energy. (US) 1799, 1802
Geothermal Energy Program Summary see Conservation and Renewable Energy Technologies for Utility Technologies 1785
Geothermal Energy Technology see Geothermal Energy 1799
Geothermal Energy Update see Geothermal Energy 1799
Geothermal Hotline. (US ISSN 0735-0503) 1802, 1566
†Geothermal Report. (US ISSN 0733-9100) 5199
Geothermal Resources Council. Bulletin.(US ISSN 0160-7782) 1802
Geothermal Resources Council. Special Report. (US ISSN 0149-8991) 1590

Geothermal Resources Council. Transactions. (US ISSN 0193-5933) 1590
Geothermal Science and Technology. (US ISSN 0890-5363) 1566
Geothermal World Journal. (US) 1802
Geothermics. (US ISSN 0375-6505) 1545
Geotimes. (US ISSN 0016-8556) 1545
Geotitles. (UK) 1551, 12
Geotitles Weekly see Geotitles 1551
Geowissen Kompakt. (GW ISSN 0341-7522) 1566
Die Geowissenschaften. (GW ISSN 0933-0704) 1545
Gep. (HU ISSN 0016-8572) 3017
Gepeszeti Szakirodalmi Tajekoztato/ Machinery Abstracts. (HU ISSN 0231-0686) 1844, 3025
Gepgyartastechnologia. (HU ISSN 0016-8580) 3017
Gepgyartastechnologiai es Szerszamgepipari Szakirodalmi Tajekoztato/Mechanical Engineering & Machine Tool Abstracts. (HU ISSN 0231-0694) 1844, 12, 3025
Gequ/Songs. (CC ISSN 0454-0816) 3552
Geraniums around the World. (US ISSN 0016-8599) 2128
Gereformeerd Kerkhistorisch Tijdschrift.(NE) 4239
Gereformeerd Theologisch Tijdschrift. (NE ISSN 0016-8610) 4239
Gereformeerde Vroueblad. (SA ISSN 0378-407X) 4239
Gerer et Comprendre/To Manage and To Understand. (FR) 3484, 1011
Gerfaut see Giervalk-Gerfaut 564
Geriaction. (AT) 2272
Geriatric and Residential Care News see Geriatric Care News 2272
Geriatric Care. (US) 2272, 1736, 2461
Geriatric Care News. (US) 2272, 3278, 4101
Geriatric Care Reference Book and Buyer's Guide see Nursing Home Yearbook 2277
Geriatric Consultant. (US) 2272
Geriatric Directory of Geriatric Publications. (US) 1136, 2272, 4406
Geriatric Guide to Pertinent Publications see Geriatric Directory of Geriatric Publications 1136
Geriatric Length of Stay by Diagnosis and Operation, United States. (US ISSN 0891-2173) 2470, 2280
Geriatric Medicine/Ronen Igaku. (JA) 2272
Geriatric Medicine. (UK) 2272
†Geriatric Medicine. (US) 5199
Geriatric Medicine Today. (US) 2272
▼Geriatric Nephrology and Urology. (NE ISSN 0924-8455) 3388, 2272, 3100
Geriatric Nursing. (US ISSN 0197-4572) 2272, 3278
Geriatric Nursing and Home Care see Nursing the Elderly 2277
Geriatrics. (US ISSN 0016-867X) 2273
Geriatrics. (IT ISSN 0392-9663) 2273
Geriatrics for GPs see Geriatric Medicine 2272
Geriatrics Survey. (US) 2273
Geriatrie fuer die Taegliche Praxis. (SZ ISSN 1011-2901) 2273
Geriatrie Moderne. see Moderne Geriatrie 2276
Geriatrie Praxis. (GW ISSN 0936-7152) 2273
Geriatrika. (SP ISSN 0212-9744) 2273
Gerichtsnotizen. (GW) 2629
Gerlands Beitraege zur Geophysik. (GW ISSN 0016-8696) 1590
German American Business Contacts. see Deutsch-Amerikanische Geschaeftsbeziehungen 658
German American Commerce see German American Trade 816
German-American National Political Action Committee Brief see G A N P A C Brief 2002

6218 GERMAN

German - American Studies see Yearbook of German - American Studies **2978**
German American Trade. (US) **816, 867**
▼German American Trade. (CN) **909**
German Arab Trade. (UA ISSN 0072-1433) **816**
German Blues Circle Info. (GW) **3552**
German Books in Print. see Verzeichnis Lieferbarer Buecher **415**
German Brief. (GW) **667, 4061**
German Business Weekly see German American Trade **816**
German-Canadian Yearbook/ Deutschkanadisches Jahrbuch. (CN ISSN 0316-8603) **2003, 2407**
German Chemical Engineering see Chemical Engineering and Technology **1849**
German Comments. (GW ISSN 0722-883X) **2189**
German Connection. (US ISSN 8755-1756) **2153**
†German Democratic Republic. Consumer Co-operative Societies. Magazine. (GW ISSN 0138-5410) **5199**
German History. (UK ISSN 0266-3554) **2363**
German Journal of Homeopathy. (GW ISSN 0931-5527) **3214**
German Journal of Psychology. (CN ISSN 0705-5870) **4051, 12**
German Language Courses. see Deutschkurse **1747**
German Life and Civilization. (US ISSN 0899-9899) **2363**
German Life and Letters. (UK ISSN 0016-8777) **2919, 1635**
German Maritime Industry Journal. (GW ISSN 0178-2495) **4727**
German Medical Weekly. see Deutsche Medizinische Wochenschrift **3093**
German Merchant Fleet. (GW ISSN 0070-4148) **4727**
German Mining see Mining & Energy **3490**
German Motor Tribune. (GW ISSN 0072-145X) **4691**
German News. (II ISSN 0016-8793) **2189**
German News Weekly see German News **2189**
▼German Politics. (UK ISSN 0964-4008) **3958**
German Politics & Society. (US ISSN 0882-7079) **3896, 2363**
German Postal Specialist. (US ISSN 0016-8823) **3752**
German Quarterly. (US ISSN 0016-8831) **2815, 1635**
German Queries. (US ISSN 0890-9490) **2003**
German Research. (GW ISSN 0172-1526) **4311**
German Research Service. (GW ISSN 0072-1476) **4311**
German Shepherd Dog Review. (US) **3710**
German Shepherd Quarterly. (US) **3710**
German Shorthaired Pointer Club of America Shorthair" see G S P C A "Shorthair **3710**
German Shorthaired Pointer News. (US) **3710**
German Standards (DIN) English Language. (UK) **1822, 4598**
German Studies. Section 1 see Philosophy and History **5258**
German Studies. Section 3 see Literature, Music, Fine Arts **5228**
German Studies Library Group Newsletter. (UK ISSN 0951-2616) **2759, 2815**
German Studies Review. (US ISSN 0149-7952) **2363, 2919, 3896**
German Teaching. (UK ISSN 0953-4822) **2816, 1750**
German-Thai Chamber of Commerce Handbook see German-Thai Chamber of Commerce Handbook and Directory **816**
German-Thai Chamber of Commerce Handbook and Directory. (TH) **816, 1136**
German Tribune. (GW ISSN 0016-8858) **2189**

German Vogue. (GW) **1291**
German Wine Review. (GW) **381**
German Yearbook of International Law. (GW ISSN 0344-3094) **2723**
German Yearbook on Business History. (US ISSN 0722-2416) **667**
Germana Esperanta Fervojista Asocio. Bulteno. (GW ISSN 0016-8866) **4709**
Germania. (GW ISSN 0016-8874) **273, 240**
Germanic Notes see Germanic Notes and Reviews **2816**
Germanic Notes and Reviews. (US) **2816, 2507**
Germanic Review. (US ISSN 0016-8890) **2816, 2919**
Germanica. (FR) **2919**
Germanisch-Romanische Monatsschrift. (GW ISSN 0016-8904) **2919**
Germanische Denkmaeler der Voelkerwanderungszeit. (GW ISSN 0418-9779) **273**
Germanistik. (GW ISSN 0016-8912) **2982, 2855**
Germanistische Linguistik. (GW ISSN 0072-1492) **2816**
Germanistische Mitteilungen. (BE ISSN 0344-5909) **2816**
Germano-Slavica. (CN ISSN 0317-4956) **2919**
Germansk Instituts Publikationer see G I P **2815**
Germany. Bundesinstitut fuer Sportwissenschaft. Biennial Reports. (GW) **4473, 3392, 4311**
Germany (Democratic Republic). Amt fuer Erfindungs- und Patentwesen. Bekanntmachungen see Deutsches Patentamt. Bekanntmachungen **5179**
Germany (Democratic Republic, 1949-). Meteorologischer Dienst. Abhandlungen. (GW ISSN 0138-5658) **3435**
Germany (Democratic Republic, 1949-). Ministerium fuer Hoch- und Fachschulwesen. Verfuegungen und Mitteilungen. (GW) **1707**
Germany. (Federal Republic). Bundesministerium fuer Verkehr. Strassenbaubericht. (GW) **4718**
Germany (Federal Republic, 1949-) Bundesanstalt fuer Arbeit. Amtliche Nachrichten. (GW ISSN 0007-585X) **980**
Germany (Federal Republic, 1949-). Bundesanstalt fuer Arbeit. Berufsberatung; Ergebnisse der Berufsberatungsstatistik. (GW) **718, 4572**
Germany (Federal Republic, 1949-). Bundesanstalt fuer Arbeit. Foerderung der Beruflichen Weiterbildung; Ergebnisse der Teilnehmerstatistik. (GW) **1750**
Germany (Federal Republic, 1949-). Bundesanstalt fuer Gewaesserkunde. Jahresbericht. (GW) **4824**
Germany (Federal Republic, 1949-). Bundesanstalt fuer Materialforschung und -pruefung. Jahresbericht. (GW ISSN 0934-9456) **1917**
Germany (Federal Republic, 1949-). Bundesanstalt fuer Strassenwesen, Erfahrungsaustausch ueber Erdarbeiten im Strassenbau. (GW) **1866**
Germany (Federal Republic, 1949-). Bundesaufsichtsamt fuer das Versicherungswesen. Geschaeftsbericht. (GW ISSN 0302-5608) **2532**
Germany (Federal Republic, 1949-) Bundesaufsichtsamt fuer das Versicherungswesen. Veroeffentlichungen. (GW ISSN 0170-236X) **2532**
Germany (Federal Republic, 1949-). Bundeskriminalamt. Polizeiliche Kriminalstatistik (Year). (GW ISSN 0431-5480) **1525**
Germany (Federal Republic, 1949-). Bundesminister fuer das Post- und Telekommunikation. Amtsblatt. (GW) **1352**

Germany (Federal Republic, 1949-). Bundesministerium Fuer Arbeit und Sozialordnung. Arbeits- und Sozialstatistik see Bundesarbeitsblatt **974**
Germany (Federal Republic, 1949-). Bundesministerium fuer Arbeit und Sozialordnung. Hauptergebnisse der Arbeits- und Sozialstatistik. (GW ISSN 0341-7840) **718**
Germany (Federal Republic, 1949-). Bundesministerium fuer Bildung und Wissenschaft. Forschungsbericht der Bundesregierung see Germany (Federal Republic, 1949-). Bundesministerium fuer Forschung und Technologie. Bundesbericht Forschung **4061**
Germany (Federal Republic, 1949-). Bundesministerium fuer das Post- und Fernmeldewesen. Amtsblatt see Germany (Federal Republic, 1949-). Bundesministerium fuer das Post- und Telekommunikation. Amtsblatt **1352**
†Germany (Federal Republic, 1949-). Bundesministerium fuer das Post- und Fernmeldewesen. Haushaltsrechnung, Nachweisung ueber die Einnahmen und Ausgaben der Deutschen Bundespost. (GW) **5199**
Germany (Federal Republic, 1949-). Bundesministerium fuer das Post- und Fernmeldewesen. Jahresrechnung, Nachweisung ueber die Einnahmen und Ausgaben der Deutschen Bundespost see Germany (Federal Republic, 1949-). Bundesministerium fuer das Post- und Fernmeldewesen. Haushaltsrechnung, Nachweisung ueber die Einnahmen und Ausgaben der Deutschen Bundespost **5199**
Germany (Federal Republic, 1949-). Bundesministerium fuer Ernaehrung, Landwirtschaft und Forsten. Agrarbericht der Bundesregierung. (GW) **94**
Germany (Federal Republic, 1949-). Bundesministerium Fuer Ernaehrung, Landwirtschaft und Forsten. Jahresbericht. Forschung im Bereich des Bundesministers. see Germany (Federal Republic, 1949-). Bundesministerium Fuer Ernaehrung, Landwirtschaft und Forsten. Jahresbericht. Forschung im Geschaeftsbereich des Bundesministers fuer Ernaerung, Land, Wirtschaft und Forsten **94**
Germany (Federal Republic, 1949-). Bundesministerium Fuer Ernaehrung, Landwirtschaft und Forsten. Jahresbericht. Forschung im Geschaeftsbereich des Bundesministers fuer Ernaerung, Land, Wirtschaft und Forsten. (GW ISSN 0343-7477) **94**
Germany (Federal Republic, 1949-). Bundesministerium fuer Ernaehrung, Landwirtschaft und Forsten. Statistischer Monatsbericht. (GW ISSN 0433-7344) **4572**
Germany (Federal Republic, 1949-). Bundesministerium fuer Forschung und Technologie. Bundesbericht Forschung. (GW) **4061**
Germany (Federal Republic, 1949-). Bundesministerium fuer Forschung und Technologie. B M F T Foerderungskatalog. (GW) **4311, 4598**
Germany (Federal Republic, 1949-). Deutscher Bundestag. Wissenschaftliche Dienste. Aufsaetze aus Zeitschriften und Sammelwerken see Germany (Federal Republic, 1949-). Deutscher Bundestag. Wissenschaftliche Dienste. Neue Aufsaetze in der Bibliothek **4356**
Germany (Federal Republic, 1949-). Deutscher Bundestag. Wissenschaftliche Dienste. Bibliographien. (GW) **400**
Germany (Federal Republic, 1949-). Deutscher Bundestag. Wissenschaftliche Dienste. Materialien. (GW ISSN 0344-9130) **400, 3958**

Germany (Federal Republic, 1949-). Deutscher Bundestag. Wissenschaftliche Dienste. Neuerwerbungen see Germany (Federal Republic, 1949-). Deutscher Bundestag. Wissenschaftliche Dienste. Neuerwerbungen der Bibliothek **401**
Germany (Federal Republic, 1949-). Deutscher Bundestag. Wissenschaftliche Dienste. Neue Aufsaetze in der Bibliothek. (GW ISSN 0931-8593) **4356, 12, 401**
Germany (Federal Republic, 1949-). Deutscher Bundestag. Wissenschaftliche Dienste. Neuerwerbungen der Bibliothek. (GW ISSN 0931-3397) **401**
Germany (Federal Republic, 1949-). Presse- und Informationsamt Bulletin Archive Supplement. (GW) **4061**
†Germany (Federal Republic, 1949-) Presse- und Informationsamt. Bulletin. (GW ISSN 0032-7794) **5199**
Germany (Federal Republic, 1949-) Statistisches Bundesamt. Fachserie 16, Loehne und Gehaelter, Reihe 2.2: Angestelltenverdienst in Industrie und Handel. (GW) **718**
Germany (Federal Rpublic, 1949-) Bundesanstalt fuer Arbeitsschutz. Amtliche Mitteilungen. (GW) **3617**
Germany, Federal Republic (1949-). Bundesinstitut fuer Sportwissenschaft. Sportwissenschaftliche Forschungsprojekte Erhebung (Year). (GW ISSN 0343-6565) **4473**
Germany Stamp Catalogue. (UK ISSN 0142-9817) **3752**
†Germany Stamp News. (CN ISSN 0016-8963) **5199**
Germination. (CN ISSN 0704-6286) **2993**
Germinations. (US) **2128, 178**
Germplasm Newsletter. (UN) **217**
†Gerodontics. (DK ISSN 0109-565X) **5199**
†Gerodontology. (US ISSN 0734-0664) **5199**
Geroldsecker Land. (GW) **2189**
Gerontologi og Samfund. (DK ISSN 0900-114X) **2273**
Gerontological Abstracts. (US) **2280, 12**
Gerontological Nursing see Journal of Gerontological Nursing **2275**
Gerontological Society. Monographs. (US) **2273**
Gerontologie see Tijdschrift voor Gerontologie en Geriatrie **2279**
Gerontologie (Year). (FR ISSN 0016-9005) **2273**
Gerontologisk Magasin see Aldring og Eldre. Gerontologisk Magasin **2270**
Gerontologist. (US ISSN 0016-9013) **2273**
Gerontology. (SZ ISSN 0304-324X) **2273**
Gerontology. (IS ISSN 0334-2360) **2273**
Gerontology. (US) **2273**
Gerontology & Geriatrics Education. (US ISSN 0270-1960) **2273**
Gerontology News. (US) **2273**
Gerontology News. Conference Calendar. (US) **2273**
Gerontology News. Grants - Fellowships - Jobs see Gerontology News **2273**
Gerontolosko Drustvo S R Srbije. (YU ISSN 0351-2886) **2273, 3982, 4101, 4406**
Gesamt Hochschule Kassel Publik see G H K Publik **1694**
Gesamthochschule Wuppertalerschriftenreihe Literaturwissenschaft see Wuppertaler Schriftenreihe Literatur **2977**
Gesamtregister mit den Rechtssaetzen und Fundstellen der Entscheidungen der Zeitschrift fuer Verkehrsrecht. (AU) **2698**
Gesamtstatistik der Kraftfahrtversicherung. (GW ISSN 0435-7442) **2546**

Gesamtverband Autoteile-Handel e.V. Mitgliederverzeichnis see G V A Mitgliederverzeichnis **4691**
Gesamtverband Werbeagenturen e.V. Yearbook see G W A Yearbook **31**
Gesamtverzeichnis der Zeitschriften und Serien in Bibliotheken der Bundesrepublik Deutschland Einschliesslich Berlin (West) see Zeitschriften - Datenbank (Z D B) **2791**
†Gesamtverzeichnis Oesterreichischer Dissertationen. (AU ISSN 0072-4165) **5199**
Gesar. (US ISSN 0738-2294) **4214**
Geschaeftsidee. (GW ISSN 0344-2292) **1115**, 32
Geschaeftsmann und Christ. (SZ ISSN 0016-9021) **4179**
Geschaeftspartner Ungarn. see Business Partner Hungary **652**
Ti Geschaeftsreise. (GW) **4768**
Geschichte. (GW) **2363**
Geschichte (Essen). (GW) **2311**
Geschichte Betrifft Uns. (GW ISSN 0176-943X) **1635**, 2311
Geschichte der Pharmazie. (GW ISSN 0939-334X) **3727**
Geschichte der Sozialistischen Laender Europas. Jahrbuch. (GW ISSN 0075-2665) **2363**
Geschichte des Arabischen Schrifttums. (NE) **2429**, 2919
Geschichte Erziehung Politik see G E P **4373**
Geschichte in Koeln. (GW ISSN 0720-3659) **2363**
Geschichte in Wissenschaft und Unterricht. (GW ISSN 0016-9056) **2311**
Geschichte Lernen. (GW ISSN 0933-3096) **1635**
Geschichte, Politik und ihre Didaktik. (GW ISSN 0343-4648) **2363**, 1635, 3896
Geschichte und Gesellschaft. (GW ISSN 0340-613X) **4373**, 2363
Geschichten aus dem Wienerwald see W Wintern **2481**
Geschichtliche Landeskunde. (GW ISSN 0072-4203) **2363**
Geschichtliches Eupen. (BE) **2363**
Geschichtsblaetter des Kreises Coesfeld.(GW ISSN 0723-2098) **2363**
Geschichtsblaetter fuer Waldeck. (GW ISSN 0342-0965) **2363**, 2055
†Geschichtsdidaktik. (GW) **5199**
Geschichtsunterricht und Staatsburgerkunde. (GW ISSN 0016-9072) **2487**
Geschichtswissenschaft. Zeitschrift see Zeitschrift fuer Geschichtswissenschaft **2327**
Geschiebe-Sammler. (GW ISSN 0340-4056) **2436**
Geschied- en Oudheidkundige Kring van Ronse en het Tenement van Inde. Annalen/Cercle Historique et Archeologique de Renaix et du Tenement d'Inde. Annales. (BE ISSN 0591-1133) **2363**
Geschied- en Oudheidkundige Kring voor Leuven en Omgeving. Jaarboek. (BE ISSN 0774-5435) **2364**
Geschiedenis van het Zuiden van Nederland. (NE) **2364**
Geschmacksmusterblatt. (GW ISSN 0934-7062) **3675**
Gesellschaft see Perspektiven **5257**
Gesellschaft der Geologie- und Bergbaustudenten. Mitteilungen. (AU) **1566**, 1597, 3657
Gesellschaft fuer Angewandte Linguistik e.V. Bulletin see G A L - Bulletin **2815**
Gesellschaft fuer Bibliothekswesen und Dokumentation des Landbaues. Mitteilungen. (GW ISSN 0433-860X) **138**, 12
Gesellschaft fuer Biologische Chemie, Mosbach. Colloquium see Colloquium Mosbach **475**
Gesellschaft fuer Deutsch-Sowjetische Freundschaft Berlin West Journal see D S F - Journal **3954**
Gesellschaft fuer die Geschichte des Protestantismus in Oesterreich. Jahrbuch. (AU) **2364**, 4239

Gesellschaft fuer die Geschichte und Bibliographie des Brauwesens. Jahrbuch. (GW ISSN 0072-422X) **381**
Gesellschaft fuer Elektronische Informationsverarbeitung mbH Lights see G E I Lights **1395**
†Gesellschaft fuer Griechische und Hellenistische Rechtsgeschichte. Akten. (AU) **5199**
†Gesellschaft fuer Kanada-Studien. Zeitschrift. (GW ISSN 0722-849X) **5199**
Gesellschaft fuer Kernforschung. Bericht ueber Forschungs- und Entwicklungsarbeiten see Kernforschungszentrum Karlsruhe. Ergebnisbericht ueber Forschung und Entwicklung **1806**
Gesellschaft fuer Mathematik und Datenverarbeitung mbH Spiegel see G M D-Spiegel **1395**
Gesellschaft fuer Natur und Heimatkunde. Heimatkundliche Mitteilungen. (AU) **2364**
Gesellschaft fuer Natur- und Voelkerkunde Ostasiens. Nachrichten.(GW ISSN 0016-9080) **3637**
Gesellschaft fuer Naturkunde in Wuerttemberg. Jahreshefte. (GW ISSN 0368-2307) **440**
Gesellschaft fuer Niedersaechsische Kirchengeschichte. Jahrbuch. (GW ISSN 0072-4238) **2364**, 4239
Gesellschaft fuer Reaktorsicherheit. Jahresbericht. (GW) **1822**
Gesellschaft fuer Salzburger Landeskunde. Mitteilungen. (AU) **2364**
Gesellschaft fuer Schleswig-Holsteinische Geschichte. Zeitschrift. (GW ISSN 0072-4254) **2364**
Gesellschaft fuer Verantwortung in der Wissenschaft. Schriften. (GW) **1955**, 1488
Gesellschaft fuer Vergleichende Kunstforschung in Wien. Mitteilungen.(AU) **3524**, 2364
Gesellschaft fuer Wissenschaftliche Gesprachspsychotherapie e.V. Zeitschrift see G W G - Zeitschrift **1736**
Gesellschaft Krankenwesen der D.D.R. Mitteilungen. (GW ISSN 0232-9476) **2461**
Gesellschaft Naturforschender Freunde zu Berlin. Sitzungsberichte. Neue Folge. (GW ISSN 0037-5942) **4311**
Gesellschaft pro Vindonissa. Jahresbericht. (SZ ISSN 0072-4270) **273**
Gesellschaft pro Vindonissa. Veroeffentlichungen. (SZ ISSN 0072-4289) **273**
Gesellschaft, Recht, Wirtschaft. (GW) **4373**
Gesellschaft und Politik. (AU ISSN 0016-9099) **3896**, 4436
Der Gesellschafter. (AU ISSN 0250-6440) **2709**
Gesellschaftspolitische Kommentare. (GW ISSN 0016-9102) **3896**
Gesetz- und Verordnungsblatt fuer Berlin. (GW) **2629**
Gesetz und Verordnungsblatt fuer das Land Hessen. (GW ISSN 0342-3557) **4088**
Gesetz- und Verordnungsblatt fuer Schleswig-Holstein. (GW ISSN 0016-9129) **4088**
Gesetzblatt fuer Baden-Wuerttemberg. (GW ISSN 0174-478X) **2629**
Gesher. (IS ISSN 0435-8406) **2003**, 4223
Gesicht. (US ISSN 0016-9145) **4223**, 2867, 3767
Gesichertes Leben. (GW ISSN 0016-9153) **4406**, 3802
Gesinsveiligheid. see S A Family Safety **4112**
Gesnerus. (SZ ISSN 0016-9161) **3100**, 4311
Gest-Guest Quarterly. (US) **2153**
Gest Home. (BE) **3278**
Gest Library Journal. (US ISSN 0891-0553) **2759**

Gesta. (US ISSN 0016-920X) **327**, 2364
Gestalt Journal. (US ISSN 0190-0412) **4022**, 3337
Gestalt Theory. (GW ISSN 0170-057X) **4022**
Gestalten und Verkaufen. (GW) **94**
Gestaltungs-Stunde. (GW) **1750**
Gestgjafinn. (IC ISSN 1017-3552) **2071**, 2446
Gestion. (CN ISSN 0701-0028) **667**
Gestion. (CL) **783**
Gestion et Technologie Agricoles. (CN) **94**
▼Gestion Hospitalaria. (SP ISSN 0214-8919) **2461**
Gestion Sociale. (FR) **1011**
Gestion 2000. (BE ISSN 0773-0543) **1076**
Gestione Informata. (IT) **1011**
Gestions Hospitalieres. (FR ISSN 0016-9218) **2461**
Gestos. (US) **4633**, 2003
Gestus. (US ISSN 0749-7644) **2919**, 4633
Gesund Leben. (GW ISSN 0016-9234) **3802**
Gesund und Sicher. (GW) **830**
Gesunde Pflanzen. (GW ISSN 0367-4223) **1955**
Gesundheit. (AU ISSN 0250-3689) **327**
Gesundheit. (GW ISSN 0016-9269) **3802**
Gesundheit in Betrieb und Familie see Gesundheit **3802**
†Gesundheitsblatt A O K Aktuell. (GW) **5199**
Gesundheitsfoerderung. (GW ISSN 0932-2884) **3811**, 3175
Gesundheitsnachrichten. (SZ ISSN 0016-9285) **3802**
Gesundheitspolitische Informationen/ Politique de la Sante: Informations. (SZ) **4101**
Gesundheitspolitische Umschau. (GW ISSN 0016-9307) **4102**
▼Get Ready for Baby. (US) **1237**
Get Ready Sheet. (US ISSN 0148-7566) **4128**, 1374
Get Rich News. (US) **1115**, 947
Get - Two - Gether. (US ISSN 0882-8598) **4362**
Getaway. (SA) **4547**
Getraenke see Getraenke Gastronomie **381**
Getraenke Gastronomie. (GW ISSN 0937-3926) **381**, 1040
Getraenke Handel. (GW) **381**
Getraenke Revue see Getraenke Handel **381**
Getraenkefachgrosshandel. (GW ISSN 0724-6153) **381**
Getraenkehandel. (GW ISSN 0016-9331) **381**
Getraenkeindustrie. (GW ISSN 0016-9323) **381**
Getraenkemarkt. (GW) **381**
▼GetraenkeReport. (GW) **381**
Getraenketechnik. (GW) **381**
Getreide, Mehl und Brot. (GW ISSN 0367-4177) **206**
Getroster Tag/Hopeful Day. (GW ISSN 0016-934X) **4239**
Getting About Britain. (UK ISSN 0954-0369) **4768**
Getting Around the Highlands and Islands. (UK) **4768**
†Getting Jobs. (US) **5199**
Getting There. (CN ISSN 0822-8450) **1255**, 1237
Getty Conservation Institute Newsletter. (US ISSN 0898-4808) **327**, 300, 1488
Gettysburg. (US) **2407**
Gettysburg Review. (US ISSN 0898-4557) **2993**
Gevangenisstatistiek see Netherlands. Centraal Bureau voor de Statistiek. Gevangenisstatistiek **1519**
Gewaltfreie Aktion. (GW ISSN 0016-9390) **3958**
Gewerbe Report. (GW) **1115**
Gewerbearchiv. (GW) **2709**, 1065
Gewerbliche Genossenschaft. (AU) **830**
Gewerbliche Rundschau see Chef-Magazin fuer Klein- und Mittelbetriebe **1073**

Gewerblicher Rechtsschutz und Urheberrecht. (GW ISSN 0016-9420) **3675**
Gewerblicher Rechtsschutz und Urheberrecht. Internationaler Teil. (GW ISSN 0435-8600) **3675**
Gewerkschaft Auguste Victoria Information see A V Information **3477**
Gewerkschaft Der Sozialversicherung Zeitung see G D S - Zeitung **2583**
Gewerkschaft Deutscher Lokomotivfuehrer und Anwaerter. Voraus. (GW) **4709**
Gewerkschaft Gartenbau, Land- und Forstwirtschaft. Forstliche Mitteilungen. (GW) **2101**
Gewerkschaftliche Bildungspolitik. (GW) **1635**, 1684
Gewerkschaftliche Monatshefte. (GW ISSN 0016-9447) **2583**
Gewerkschaftliche Praxis. (GW) **2583**, 1352
Gewerkschaftliche Rundschau. (SZ ISSN 0016-9455) **2583**
Gewerkschaftliche Umschau. (GW) **3663**, 1163
Gewerkschaftpost see G P Magazin **3662**
†Gewerkschaftsleben. (GW ISSN 0138-2691) **5199**
Gewestelijke Ontwikkelingsmaatschappij Limburg Economie in Limburg see G O M - Economie in Limburg **5198**
Gewina. (NE) **4311**
†Geyer's Office Dealer. (US) **5199**
Geyer's Who Makes It Directory. (US ISSN 0072-4327) **1058**
Gezeitentafeln. (GW ISSN 0084-9774) **1604**
Gezinsblad. (NE ISSN 0016-9498) **2211**
Gezinswetenschappelijke Documentatie. (BE) **3992**, 12
†Gezond Limburg. (NE ISSN 0016-9501) **5199**
Gezondheidszorg, Beleid en Organizatie.(BE) **2461**, 667, 3100
Al-Ghad al-Iqtisadi. (JO) **667**
Ghalib. (AT ISSN 0725-6590) **2003**
Ghana. (GH ISSN 0304-1190) **867**
Ghana. Central Bureau of Statistics. Consumer Price Index see Ghana. Statistical Service. Consumer Price Index **718**
Ghana. Central Bureau of Statistics. Economic Survey see Ghana. Statistical Service. Economic Survey **718**
Ghana. Central Bureau of Statistics. Motor Vehicle Registration see Ghana. Statistical Service. Motor Vehicle Registration **4691**
Ghana. Central Bureau of Statistics. Quarterly Digest of Statistics see Ghana. Statistical Service. Quarterly Digest of Statistics **4572**
Ghana. Meteorological Department. Agrometeorological Bulletin. (GH) **3435**, 94
Ghana. Meteorological Department. Climatological Notes. (GH) **3435**
Ghana. Meteorological Department. Monthly Summary of Evaporation. (GH) **3435**
Ghana. Meteorological Department. Monthly Summary of Rainfall. (GH ISSN 0431-8315) **3435**
Ghana. Meteorological Department. Monthly Weather Report. (GH ISSN 0431-8323) **3435**
Ghana. Meteorological Department. Professional Notes. (GH) **3435**
Ghana. Meteorological Department. Sun and Moon Tables for Ghana. (GH) **3435**
Ghana. Ministry of Education. Educational Statistics. (GH) **1677**
Ghana. National Council for Higher Education. Annual Report. (GH) **1707**
Ghana. National Council on Women and Development. Annual Report. (GH) **4843**
Ghana. Statistical Service. Consumer Price Index. (GH) **718**
Ghana. Statistical Service. Economic Survey. (GH) **718**, 4572

GHANA. STATISTICAL

Ghana. Statistical Service. Motor Vehicle Registration. (GH) **4691**
Ghana. Statistical Service. Quarterly Digest of Statistics. (GH) **4572**
Ghana. Supreme Military Council. Budget Proposals. (GH) **1095**
Ghana. Tourist Control Board. Bi-Annual Statistics on Tourism. (GH) **4799**, **4572**
Ghana: a Current Bibliography see Ghana National Bibliography **401**
Ghana Bee News. (GH) **94**
Ghana Builds see Ghana Review **2192**
Ghana Cocoa Marketing Board Newsletter see C M B Newsletter **1035**
Ghana Commercial Bank. Annual Report. (GH ISSN 0435-9348) **867**
Ghana Commercial Bank. Monthly Economic Bulletin see Ghana Commercial Bank. Quarterly Economic Review **867**
Ghana Commercial Bank. Quarterly Economic Review. (GH ISSN 0855-0417) **867**
Ghana Confidential. (GH) **867**
Ghana Digest. (GH) **2192**, **3896**
†Ghana Enterprise. (GH) **5199**
Ghana Farmer. (GH ISSN 0046-5917) **94**
Ghana Geographical Association. Bulletin. (GH ISSN 0016-9536) **2251**
Ghana Journal of Agricultural Science. (GH) **94**
Ghana Journal of Education. (GH) **1635**
Ghana Journal of Sociology. (GH ISSN 0435-9380) **4436**
Ghana Law Reports. (GH ISSN 0072-436X) **2629**
Ghana Library Journal. (GH ISSN 0016-9552) **2759**
Ghana Manufacturer. (GH) **1076**
Ghana Medical Journal. (GH ISSN 0855-0328) **3100**
Ghana National Bibliography. (GH ISSN 0072-4378) **401**
Ghana National Chamber of Commerce. Annual Report. (GH) **816**
Ghana National Chamber of Commerce. Newsletter see Ghana Enterprise **5199**
Ghana News. (US ISSN 0016-9579) **3896**
Ghana News Bulletin. (GH) **2192**
Ghana Population Studies. (GH) **3982**
Ghana Review. (GH ISSN 0016-9587) **2192**
Ghana Science Abstracts. (GH) **4356**, **13**
Ghana Studies Bulletin. (US ISSN 0266-2957) **2192**
Ghana Teacher's Journal see Ghana Journal of Education **1635**
Ghana's Foreign Trade. (GH) **909**
▼Ghanta. (IT) **1722**, **3637**
Ghaqda Bibljotekarji/Library Association Newsletter. (MM) **2759**
Ghetto Fighters House. (IS) **2203**
Ghost Dance. (US ISSN 0016-9633) **2993**
†Ghost Town Quarterly. (US) **5200**
Ghost Trackers Newsletter. (US) **3669**
Al-Ghurfa. (TS) **816**
Al-Ghurfat/Oman Commerce. (MK) **816**
Ghurfat al-Tigara al-Qahira. Magalla. see Cairo Chamber of Commerce. Journal **809**
Ghurfat Tijarah wa-Sina'ah Abu Dhabi. Al-Taqrir al-Sanawi. see Abu Dhabi Chamber of Commerce and Industry. Annual Report **806**
Giallo Mondadori. (IT) **2985**
Giannini Foundation of Agricultural Economics. Information Series. (US) **152**
Giannini Foundation of Agricultural Economics. Monograph. (US ISSN 0575-4208) **152**
Giannini Foundation of Agricultural Economics. Research Report. (US ISSN 0072-4459) **152**
Giant see Giant Farm Life **162**
Giant Cracked. (US) **2867**
Giant Farm Life. (CN) **162**
Giant Word Games. (UK) **4473**

GiantKilling see Advocate's Advocate **3870**
Giants Extra. (US) **4504**
The Giants Newsweekly. (US) **4504**
Giao thong-Van tai and Buu Dien/Communications, Transport, Posts and Telegraphs. (VN) **1336**
Giao Vien Nhan Dan/People's Theatre. (VN) **4633**
Giappone. (IT) **2338**
Giardini. (IT) **2128**
Giardino Fiorito. (IT ISSN 0016-965X) **2128**
Gib Acht. (GW ISSN 0016-9668) **1255**
Gibbons Stamp Monthly. (UK ISSN 0016-9676) **3752**
Gibraltar Point Observatory Report see Lincolnshire Bird Report **565**
Gibridnye Vychislitel'nye Mashiny i Kompleksy. (KR ISSN 0207-0111) **1441**
Gideon's Trumpet. (US) **2153**
Gidravlicheskie Mashiny. (KR ISSN 0130-1152) **3843**, **1929**
Gidrobiologicheskii Zhurnal. (KR ISSN 0375-8990) **440**, **1597**, **2041**
Gidroliznaya i Lesokhimicheskaya Promyshlennost' (RU ISSN 0016-9706) **1177**, **2114**
Gidromekhanika. (KR ISSN 0367-4088) **3843**
Gidrotekhnicheskoe Stroitel'stvo. (RU ISSN 0016-9714) **4824**, **1893**
Gidrotekhnika i Melioratsiya. (RU ISSN 0016-9722) **4824**
Gids. (NE ISSN 0016-9730) **2867**
Gids bij de Prijscourant. (NE ISSN 0922-7822) **947**
Gids Op Maatschappelijk Gebied. (BE) **2583**, **4265**
Gids van Suid-Afrikaanse Verenigings. see Directory of South African Associations **4307**
Giervalk-Gerfaut. (BE ISSN 0016-9757) **564**
Giessener Schriftenreihe Tierzucht und Haustiergenetik. (GW ISSN 0434-0035) **217**
Giesserei. (GW ISSN 0016-9765) **3407**
Giesserei-Erfahrungsaustausch. (GW ISSN 0016-9773) **3407**
Giesserei-Kalender. (GW ISSN 0340-8175) **3407**
Giesserei-Literaturschau. (GW ISSN 0721-9679) **3425**
Giesserei-Praxis. (GW ISSN 0016-9781) **3407**
Giesserei Rundschau. (AU ISSN 0016-979X) **3407**
Giessereiforschung. (GW ISSN 0046-5933) **3407**
Gietwerk Perspektief. (NE) **3407**
Gift see Gifts & Decorative Accessories **2281**
Gift and Decorative Accessories Buyers Directory. (US ISSN 0072-4505) **2281**, **1163**
Gift & Stationery Business. (US) **1136**, **2281**
Gift and Tableware Reporter see Gifts & Tableware(New York) **5200**
▼Gift Basket Review. (US ISSN 1050-0316) **355**, **1040**
Gift Buyer International. (UK ISSN 0016-9854) **1163**
†Gift Digest. (US) **5200**
Gift Reporter see G R **2281**
Gifted Child Quarterly. (US) **1237**, **4022**
Gifted Child Today. (US ISSN 0892-9580) **1238**
Gifted Children Monthly. (US) **1736**
Gifted Children Newsletter see Gifted Children Monthly **1736**
Gifted Education International. (UK ISSN 0261-4294) **1736**
Gifted Education Press Newsletter. (US) **1736**, **1238**
Gifted International. (US) **1736**, **4022**
Gifted Unlimited. (US) **1736**, **1238**
Gifts see Gifts International **2281**
Gifts & Decorative Accessories. (US ISSN 0016-9889) **2281**, **1163**
Gifts and Sundries see Fashion Jewelry & Accessories **2564**
†Gifts & Tableware(New York). (US ISSN 0163-2175) **5200**

Gifts & Tablewares. (CN) **2281**
Gifts International. (UK ISSN 0262-5946) **2281**
Giftware News. (US ISSN 0193-2551) **2281**
Gifu Daigaku Igakubu Kiyo. see Gifu University. School of Medicine. Archives **3100**
Gifu Daigaku Kyoikugakubu Kenkyu Hokoku. Shizen Kagaku/Gifu University. Faculty of Education. Science Report. Natural Science. (JA ISSN 0533-9529) **4311**
Gifu Daigaku Nogakubu Kenkyu Hokoku/Gifu University. Faculty of Agriculture. Research Bulletin. (JA ISSN 0072-4513) **94**
Gifu-ken Hakubutsukan Chosa Kenkyu Hokoku/Gifu Prefectural Museum. Bulletin. (JA ISSN 0388-550X) **4311**, **3524**
Gifu Pharmaceutical University. Annual Proceedings. (JA ISSN 0434-0094) **3727**
Gifu Prefectural Fisheries Experimental Station. Report. (JA ISSN 0389-6927) **2041**
Gifu Prefectural Museum. Bulletin. see Gifu-ken Hakubutsukan Chosa Kenkyu Hokoku **4311**
Gifu University. Faculty of Agriculture. Research Bulletin. see Gifu Daigaku Nogakubu Kenkyu Hokoku **94**
Gifu University. Faculty of Education. Science Report. Natural Science. see Gifu Daigaku Kyoikugakubu Kenkyu Hokoku. Shizen Kagaku **4311**
Gifu University. School of Medicine. Archives/Gifu Daigaku Igakubu Kiyo/Acta Scholae Medicinalis Universitatis in Gifu. (JA ISSN 0072-4521) **3100**
Gig. (GW) **2189**
Giganti del Basket. (IT) **4504**
Gigiena i Sanitariya/Hygiene and Sanitation. (RU ISSN 0016-9900) **3802**
Gigiena Truda i Professional'nye Zabolevaniya/Industrial Hygiene and Occupational Diseases. (RU ISSN 0016-9919) **3617**
Hagil Hechadash. (IS) **2273**
Gila Heritage. (US) **2153**
Gila Monster. (US) **1312**
▼Gilagamesh. (IQ) **327**
Gilbert Gallery. (US ISSN 0890-2372) **2153**
Gilbert Law Summaries. Administrative Law. (US) **2629**
Gilbert Law Summaries. Agency and Partnership. (US) **2709**
Gilbert Law Summaries. Antitrust. (US) **2709**
Gilbert Law Summaries. Bankruptcy. (US) **2709**
Gilbert Law Summaries. Basic Accounting for Lawyers. (US) **2709**, **751**
Gilbert Law Summaries. Business Law. (US) **2709**
Gilbert Law Summaries. California Bar Test Skills. (US) **2630**
Gilbert Law Summaries. Civil Procedure.(US) **2702**
Gilbert Law Summaries. Commercial Paper. (US) **2709**
Gilbert Law Summaries. Community Property. (US) **2630**
Gilbert Law Summaries. Conflict of Laws. (US) **2630**
Gilbert Law Summaries. Constitutional Law. (US) **2706**
Gilbert Law Summaries. Contracts. (US) **2709**
Gilbert Law Summaries. Corporations. (US) **2709**
Gilbert Law Summaries. Criminal Law. (US) **2713**
Gilbert Law Summaries. Criminal Procedure. (US ISSN 0193-8010) **2713**
Gilbert Law Summaries. Dictionary of Legal Terms. (US) **2630**
Gilbert Law Summaries. Estate and Gift.(US) **2630**
Gilbert Law Summaries. Evidence. (US) **2630**
Gilbert Law Summaries. Federal Courts.(US) **2731**

Gilbert Law Summaries. Future Interests. (US) **2630**
Gilbert Law Summaries. Income Tax 1 (Individual). (US) **2630**, **1095**
Gilbert Law Summaries. Income Tax 2 (Corporate). (US) **2709**, **1095**
Gilbert Law Summaries. Labor Law. (US) **2630**
Gilbert Law Summaries. Legal Ethics. (US) **2630**
Gilbert Law Summaries. Legal Research & Writing. (US) **2630**
Gilbert Law Summaries. Multistate. (US) **2630**
Gilbert Law Summaries. Personal Property. (US) **2630**
Gilbert Law Summaries. Property. (US) **2630**
Gilbert Law Summaries. Remedies. (US) **2630**
Gilbert Law Summaries. Sales. (US) **2630**
Gilbert Law Summaries. Secured Transactions. (US) **2630**
Gilbert Law Summaries. Securities Regulation. (US) **2630**, **947**
Gilbert Law Summaries. Torts. (US) **2630**
Gilbert Law Summaries. Trusts. (US) **2630**
Gilbert Law Summaries. Wills. (US) **2715**
Gilcrease Magazine of American History and Art. (US ISSN 0730-5036) **2407**, **327**
Gildea Review. (US) **1955**, **2128**, **4061**
Gildenweg. (AU ISSN 0016-9986) **1298**
Giles County Historical Society Bulletin. (US) **2407**
Gilleleje Museum. (DK ISSN 0109-6656) **2364**
Gillet Gillette Gillett Pride "n" Joy. (US ISSN 0890-4022) **2153**
Gilmore Genealogical Newsletter. (US) **2153**
Gil's Garden. (US) **2128**
Ginazim. (IS) **2919**
Gine Dips. (SP ISSN 0211-6901) **3292**
Ginecologia Clinica. (IT ISSN 0392-2944) **3292**
Ginecologia dell'Infanzia e dell'Adolescenza. (IT ISSN 0393-5337) **3292**
▼Ginecologia Oggi. (IT ISSN 1120-365X) **3292**
Ginecologia y Obstetricia Temas Actuales. (Spanish translation of: Clinics in Obstetrics and Gynecology) (SP) **3292**
Ginecorama. (IT ISSN 0391-8920) **3292**
†Ginekologia Polska. (PL ISSN 0017-0011) **5200**
Ginger. (UK ISSN 0956-3229) **4406**
Ginka. see Silver Flower **2441**
Ginnasta. (IT ISSN 0017-0046) **4473**
Ginseng Studies. see Renshen Yanjiu **116**
Gintong Butil/Golden Grain. (PH) **206**
Giocattoli. (IT ISSN 0017-0054) **2281**
Gioia. (IT ISSN 0017-0062) **4843**
Gioielli (Milan, 1974). (IT) **4843**
Gioielli (Milan, 1978) see Gioielli & Fascino **2564**
Gioielli & Fascino. (IT) **2564**
Gioielli di Rakam see Gioielli (Milan, 1974) **4843**
Giorgio Levi della Vida Conferences. Reports of the Conference. (US ISSN 0340-6369) **2429**
Giornale Botanico Italiano. (IT ISSN 0017-0070) **504**
Giornale Critico della Filosofia Italiana. (IT ISSN 0017-0089) **3767**
Giornale degli Alimentaristi see Panificazione e Pasticceria **2079**
Giornale degli Apparecchi Domestici. (IT ISSN 0392-3614) **1771**
Giornale degli Articoli Sportivi. (IT) **4473**
Giornale degli Economisti e Annali di Economia. (IT ISSN 0017-0097) **667**
Giornale dei Componenti Elettronici see Elettronica **5185**

Giornale dei Congressi Medici. (IT) **3392**, 3100
Giornale dei Distillatori (Nuovo). (IT ISSN 0017-0119) **381**
Giornale dei Gelatieri. (IT) **816**, 4768
Giornale dei Genitori. (IT ISSN 0017-0127) **1238**
Il Giornale dei Giocattoli. (IT) **2281**
Giornale dei Militari. (IT) **3459**
Giornale del Bieticoltore. (IT ISSN 0017-0143) **178**
Giornale del Cacciatore. (IT) **4547**
Giornale del Commercio Turismo. (IT) **835**, 4768
Giornale del Dirigente. (IT) **1011**
Giornale del Farmacista. (IT) **3727**
Giornale del Genio Civile. (IT ISSN 0017-016X) **1866**
Giornale del Maiscoltore. (IT ISSN 0391-7754) **206**
Giornale del Medico. (IT) **3100**
Giornale del Mezzogiorno. (IT ISSN 0017-0186) **3896**
Giornale del Serramento. (IT) **618**
Giornale del Termoidraulico. (IT) **1822**, 1924
Giornale dell'Arredamento. (IT ISSN 0393-4500) **2551**
Il Giornale dell'Arte. (IT ISSN 0394-0543) **327**
Giornale dell'Arteriosclerosi. (IT ISSN 0017-0224) **3208**
Giornale dell'Imballaggio *see* Imballaggio News **3649**
Giornale dell'Industria Minore. (IT) **1115**
Il Giornale dell'Ingegnere. (IT) **1822**
Giornale dell'Installatore Elettrico. (IT ISSN 0392-3630) **1893**
Giornale dell'Installatore Telefonico. (IT ISSN 1120-219X) **1363**
Giornale dell'Odontoiatra. (IT) **3234**
Il Giornale dell'Officina. (IT ISSN 0017-0240) **1011**
Giornale della Lamiera. (IT) **3407**
Giornale della Libreria. (IT ISSN 0017-0216) **4141**
Il Giornale della Musica. (IT ISSN 1120-6195) **3552**
Il Giornale della Subfornitura. (IT ISSN 0392-3622) **3407**
Giornale della Vela. (IT) **4524**
Giornale delle Assicurazioni - Espansion.(IT) **2532**
Giornale delle Latterie. (IT) **199**
Giornale dello Spettacolo. (IT ISSN 0017-0232) **1530**, 3552, 4633
Giornale di Agricoltura. (IT) **94**
Giornale di Anestesia Stomatologica. (IT ISSN 0391-5670) **3191**
Giornale di Astronomia. (IT ISSN 0390-1106) **364**
Giornale di Barga. (IT ISSN 0017-0259) **2205**
Giornale di Batteriologia, Virologia ed Immunologia. (IT ISSN 0390-5462) **552**
Giornale di Batteriologia, Virologia ed Immunologia ed Annali dell'Ospedale Maria Vittoria di Torino. Parte 1. Microbiologia *see* Giornale di Batteriologia, Virologia ed Immunologia **552**
Giornale di Batteriologia, Virologia ed Immunologia ed Annali dell'Ospedale Maria Vittoria di Torino. Parte 2. Sezione Clinica *see* Annali dell'Ospedale Maria Vittoria di Torino **549**
Il Giornale di Chirurgia. (IT) **3378**
Giornale di Chirurgia Plastica Ricostruttiva ed Estetica. (IT ISSN 1120-0405) **3378**
Giornale di Clinica Medica. (IT ISSN 0017-0275) **3101**
Giornale di Diritto del Lavoro e Relazioni Industriali. (IT) **980**
†Giornale di Emodinamica. (IT) **5200**
Giornale di Fisica. (IT ISSN 0017-0283) **3819**
Giornale di Gastroenterologia ed Endoscopia *see* Giornale Italiano di Endoscopia Digestiva **3268**
Giornale di Geologia. (IT ISSN 0017-0291) **1566**
Giornale di Gerontologia. (IT ISSN 0017-0305) **2273**

Giornale di Igiene e Medicina Preventiva. (IT ISSN 0017-0313) **3802**, 4102
Giornale di Malattie Infettive e Parassitarie. (IT ISSN 0017-0321) **3219**
Giornale di Medicina Militare. (IT ISSN 0017-0364) **3101**
Giornale di Metafisica. (IT) **3767**
Giornale di Microbiologia. (IT ISSN 0017-0380) **552**
Giornale di Neuropsichiatria dell'Eta Evolutiva. (IT ISSN 0392-4483) **3337**, 4022
Giornale di Neuropsicofarmacologia. (IT ISSN 0391-9048) **3337**, 3727
Giornale di Sicilia. (CN) **2003**
Giornale di Stomatologia e di Ortognatodonzia. (IT) **3234**
Giornale di Techniche Nefrologiche e Dialitiche. (IT ISSN 0394-9362) **3388**
†Giornale di Trasporti Industriali. (IT) **5200**
Giornale Economico. (IT ISSN 0017-0429) **816**
Giornale Internazionale di Dermatologia Pediatrica. (IT ISSN 1120-0499) **3247**, 3320
▼Giornale Italiano di Allergologia e Immunologia Clinica. (IT ISSN 1120-6373) **3185**
Giornale Italiano di Anestesia e di Analgesia *see* Minerva Anestesiologica **3191**
Giornale Italiano di Angiologia. (IT ISSN 0392-1387) **3208**
Giornale Italiano di Cardiologia. (IT ISSN 0046-5968) **3208**
Giornale Italiano di Chimica Clinica. (IT ISSN 0392-2227) **477**, 3101
Giornale Italiano di Chirurgia. (IT ISSN 0017-0453) **3379**
Giornale Italiano di Dermatologia e Venereologia. (IT ISSN 0533-7712) **3248**
Giornale Italiano di Diabetologia. (IT ISSN 0391-7525) **3253**
Giornale Italiano di Endoscopia Digestiva. (IT) **3268**
Giornale Italiano di Entomologia. (IT ISSN 0392-7296) **553**
Giornale Italiano di Farmacia Clinica. (IT ISSN 1120-3749) **3727**
Giornale Italiano di Filologia. (IT ISSN 0017-0461) **2816**, 3767
Giornale Italiano di Medicina del Lavoro.(IT ISSN 0391-9889) **3101**, 3617
Giornale Italiano di Nefrologia. (IT ISSN 0393-5590) **3388**
Giornale Italiano di Oncologia. (IT ISSN 0392-128X) **3197**
Giornale Italiano di Ortopedia e Traumatologia. (IT ISSN 0390-0134) **3308**
Giornale Italiano di Ostetricia e Ginecologia. (IT ISSN 0391-9013) **3292**
Giornale Italiano di Psicologia/Italian Journal of Psychology. (IT ISSN 0390-5349) **4022**
†Giornale Italiano di Psicologia. Quaderni. (IT) **5200**
Giornale Italiano di Ricerche Cliniche e Terapeutiche. (IT ISSN 0393-5957) **3101**
Giornale Italiano di Senologia. (IT ISSN 0391-9056) **3101**
Giornale Storico della Letteratura Italiana. (IT ISSN 0017-0496) **2920**
Giornale Storico della Lunigiana e del Territorio Lucense. (IT ISSN 0017-050X) **2364**, 273
Giornale Storico di Psicologia Dinamica.(IT ISSN 0391-2515) **4022**
Giornale Svizzero degli Impresari Costruttori. *see* Schweizer Bauwirtschaft **631**
Giornale Svizzero dei Macellai. *see* Schweizerische Metzger-Zeitung **2081**
Giornale Tecnico Professionale dell'Investigazione e dell'Informazione.(IT) **1514**
†Giornale Tributario - Espansione. (IT) **5200**

Giornalino. (IT) **1255**
†Giornalino. (US ISSN 0434-0299) **5200**
Giornalismo. (IT) **2570**
Giornalismo Europeo. (IT ISSN 0017-0518) **2570**
Giorno Poetry Systems L P's, C D's, Cassettes & Giorno Video Pak Series.(US) **2993**, 1385, 3552
Giovane Critica. (IT ISSN 0017-0526) **2867**
Giovane Odontoiatria. (IT) **3234**
Giovani Amici. (IT) **1255**
Giovani in Dialogo. (IT ISSN 0017-1336) **4265**
Giovanni's Room. (US) **2453**, 4843
Gioventu dei Campi. (IT) **94**
Gioventu Evangelica. (IT ISSN 0017-0542) **4179**
Gioventu Passionista/Passionist Youth. (IT ISSN 0072-4548) **4179**
Gippsland Anglican. (AT) **4239**
Gippsland Farmer. (AT) **94**
Girard Home News. (US ISSN 0017-0550) **2226**
Girl *see* My Guy **4849**
Girl About Town. (UK) **4844**
†Girl Annual. (UK ISSN 0262-9208) **5200**
Girl Scout Leader. (US ISSN 0017-0577) **1238**
Girls Brigade Digest *see* G B Digest **4179**
Girls - Girls. (US) **3397**
Girls Gymnastics Rules and Manual. (US) **4473**
Girls of Penthouse. (US ISSN 0031-4935) **3397**
Girls' Rodeo Association News. (US) **4534**
Giroscope. (UK) **2446**
Gissing Journal. (UK ISSN 0017-0615) **2920**
Gissing Newsletter *see* Gissing Journal **2920**
The Gist. (NE ISSN 0169-5959) **2071**, 1955, 3727
Gist *see* Dispatch (Washington) **3955**
Gist. (US ISSN 0732-7781) **4179**, 3767
Gister en Vandag/Yesterday and Today.(SA) **2311**, 1635
Gitarre *see* Zupfmusik Magazin **3587**
Gitarre & Laute. (GW ISSN 0172-9683) **3552**
Gite. (CN ISSN 0705-7520) **2474**
Gitit. (IS) **3552**, 1255
▼Gitlin on Divorce. (US) **2717**
Gitta. (NE) **1255**
Giurisprudenza Agraria Italiana. (IT ISSN 0434-040X) **94**, 2630
Giurisprudenza Annotata di Diritto Industriale. (IT) **2709**
Giurisprudenza Commerciale. (IT) **2709**, 783
Giurisprudenza Commerciale - Societa e Fallimento *see* Giurisprudenza Commerciale **2709**
Giurisprudenza Costituzionale. (IT) **2706**
Giurisprudenza delle Imposte. (IT) **2630**
Giurisprudenza di Merito. (IT) **2630**
Giurisprudenza Italiana. (IT ISSN 0017-0623) **2630**
Giussano. (IT) **4088**
Giustizia Civile. (IT ISSN 0017-0631) **2702**
Giustizia Civile. Massimario Annotato della Cassazione. (IT) **2630**
Giustizia Civile. Repertorio Generale Annuale. (IT) **2702**
Giustizia Nuova. (IT ISSN 0017-064X) **2630**, 327, 3896
Giustizia Penale. (IT ISSN 0017-0658) **2630**
Giving U S A. (US ISSN 0436-0257) **4406**
Giving U S A Update. (US ISSN 0899-3793) **4406**
Gizi Indonesia. (IO ISSN 0436-0265) **3606**
Gizmo. (US) **1893**, 1418, 1460
Gjuha Jone. (AA) **2816**
Gjuteriet. (SW ISSN 0017-0682) **3407**
Glacier Francais. (FR ISSN 0017-0704) **2088**

GLASNIK ARHIVA / 6221

Glaciological Data. (US ISSN 0149-1776) **1566**
Glaciology and Quaternary Geology. (NE) **1566**, 2252
Glad Rag. (UK ISSN 0265-8143) **3397**, 2453
Glad Tidings. (CN ISSN 0017-0720) **4239**
Glad Tidings of Good Things. (US ISSN 0017-0739) **4283**, 2292
Glades Star. (US ISSN 0431-915X) **2407**
Gladio Grams. (US ISSN 0431-9168) **2142**
Gladiolus Annual. (UK) **2142**
Gladius. (SP ISSN 0436-029X) **257**, 3459
Glamour. (US ISSN 0017-0747) **1291**, 373
Glamour. (IT) **4844**, 1291
Glamour. (FR) **4844**, 2187
Glanure des Noms. *see* Name Gleaner **2830**
Glareana. (SZ) **3552**
Glarmestertidende. (DK ISSN 0017-0755) **1163**
Glas Almaske Parohije. (YU) **4283**
Glas Istre. (CI ISSN 0017-0771) **2867**
Glas - Oesterreichische Glaserzeitung. (AU) **1163**
Glas Omladine. (YU ISSN 0017-0798) **1255**
Glas Podravine. (CI ISSN 0017-0801) **2867**
Glas-Porcelaen-Brugskunst - Koekkentoej. (DK ISSN 0903-3955) **1163**, 2446
Glas-Porcelaen-Gaver - Koekkentoej *see* Glas-Porcelaen-Brugskunst - Koekkentoej **1163**
Glas-Revue *see* Glass Review **1164**
Glas Svetih Ravnoapostola Cirila i Matodija. (CI) **4216**
Glas Trebinja. (BN ISSN 0017-0828) **2867**
Glas und Rahmen. (GW ISSN 0342-5142) **1163**
Glasenapp-Stiftung. (GW ISSN 0170-3455) **3637**
Glasforum. (GW ISSN 0017-0852) **300**
Glasgow & West of Scotland Family History Society. Newsletter. (UK ISSN 0141-8009) **2153**
Glasgow Archaeological Journal. (UK ISSN 0305-8980) **273**
Glasgow Chamber of Commerce. Annual Report. (UK) **816**
Glasgow Chamber of Commerce. Directory *see* Scotland Chambers of Commerce. National Directory **822**
Glasgow Chamber of Commerce. Information Newsletter. (UK) **816**
Glasgow Chamber of Commerce. Journal. (UK ISSN 0017-0860) **816**
Glasgow Chamber of Commerce. Regional Directory *see* Scotland Chambers of Commerce. National Directory **822**
Glasgow Chamber of Commerce and Manufactures Regional Directory *see* Scottish Chambers of Commerce National Directory **822**
Glasgow Directory of Voluntary Organizations. (UK ISSN 0143-7429) **4406**
Glasgow Mathematical Association Proceedings *see* Glasgow Mathematical Journal **3036**
Glasgow Mathematical Journal. (UK ISSN 0017-0895) **3036**
Glasgow Naturalist. (UK ISSN 0373-241X) **440**, 4311
Glasgow University Guardian. (UK ISSN 0017-0917) **1312**
Glasgow University Students' Handbook.(UK) **1635**
Glasilo D P M. (CI) **1255**
Glasilo M S. (YU ISSN 0353-5746) **3337**
Glasnik. (YU ISSN 0017-0925) **4216**
Glasnik Advokatske Komore Vojvodine *see* Advokatska Komora Vojvodine. Glasnik **2595**
Glasnik Arhiva i Drustva Arhivskih Radnika Bosne i Hercegovine. (BN ISSN 0436-046X) **2364**

GLASNIK DRUSTVA

Glasnik Drustva Konzervatora Srbije *see* Drustvo Konzervatora Srbije. Glasnik **1487**
Glasnik Etnografskog Instituta *see* Srpska Akademija Nauka i Umetnosti. Etnografski Institut. Glasnik **249**
Glasnik Hemicara i Tehnologa Bosne i Hercegovine. (CI ISSN 0367-4444) **1177**, 1853
Glasnik Hemijskog Drustva-Societe Chimique, Belgrade. Bulletin *see* Serbian Chemical Society. Journal **1187**
Glasnik Hrvatske Seljacke Stranke. (CN) **2003**
Glasnik Matematicki. (CI ISSN 0017-095X) **3037**
Glasnik Poljoprivredne Proizvodnje, Prerade i Plasmana. (YU ISSN 0017-0976) **94**
Glasnik Zemaljskog Muzeja u Sarajevu *see* Zemaljski Muzej Bosne i Hercegovine. Glasnik. Prirodne Nauke **4353**
Glasnost *see* Gateavisa **2867**
Glasnost *see* Glasnost News and Review **5200**
†Glasnost News and Review. (US ISSN 0895-1012) **5200**
Glasra. (IE ISSN 0332-0235) **504**
Glass (Leicester). (UK ISSN 0269-770X) **2920**, 4239
Glass (Redhill). (UK ISSN 0017-0984) **1163**
Glass Age. (UK ISSN 0017-0992) **300**
Glass Age Directory. (UK) **1136**, 1164
Glass and Ceramics. (English translation of: Steklo i Keramika) (US ISSN 0017-100X) **1164**
Glass and Ceramics Maker. *see* Sklar a Keramik **1166**
†Glass and Ceramics Newsletter. (US) **5200**
Glass and Glazing News. (UK ISSN 0260-6321) **1164**
Glass & Glazing Products. (UK) **1164**
Glass & Porselen. (NO ISSN 0802-5428) **1164**
Glass Art Society Journal. (US ISSN 0278-9426) **327**, 1164
Glass Audio. (US ISSN 1045-5027) **3552**, 4460
Glass Book. (IT) **1136**, 1164
Glass Canada. (CN) **1164**
Glass Collector's Digest. (US ISSN 0893-8660) **1164**, 257
Glass Craft News *see* Professional Stained Glass **356**
Glass Dealer *see* Glass Magazine **1164**
Glass Digest. (US ISSN 0017-1018) **1164**, 618
Glass Directory and Buyer's Guide *see* European Glass Directory and Buyer's Guide **1134**
Glass Factory Directory. (US) **1136**, 1164
Glass Industry. (US ISSN 0017-1026) **1164**
Glass International. (UK) **1164**
Glass: Latin American Industrial Report.(US) **1164**
Glass Magazine. (US ISSN 0747-4261) **1164**, 300
Glass News *see* Glass Factory Directory **1136**
Glass News Directory *see* Glass Factory Directory **1136**
Glass Packaging Institute. Annual Report. (US) **3648**
Glass, Potteries and Ceramic Annual. (II) **355**
Glass, Potteries and Ceramic Journal *see* Glass, Potteries and Ceramic Annual **355**
Glass Review. (CS) **1164**
Glass Science and Technology. (NE ISSN 0271-2938) **1164**
Glass Technology. (UK ISSN 0017-1050) **1167**, 13
Glass Will. (US) **2993**
Glass Workshop. (US ISSN 0017-1077) **355**, 1164
Glassboro Whit. (US) **1312**
Glassposten *see* Glass & Porselen **1164**

Glass's Car Check Book. (UK) **4691**
Glass's Commercial Vehicle Check Book.(UK) **4650**
Glass's Guide to Car Values. (UK) **4691**
Glass's Guide to Caravan Values. (UK) **2487**
Glass's Guide to Commercial Vehicle Values. (UK) **4691**
Glass's Guide to Motor Cycle Values. (UK) **4518**
Glass's Guide to Used Car Values *see* Glass's Guide to Car Values **4691**
Glass's Guide to Used Commercial Vehicle Values *see* Glass's Guide to Commercial Vehicle Values **4691**
Glass's Guide to Used Motor Cycle Values *see* Glass's Guide to Motor Cycle Values **4518**
Glass's Index of Registration Marks. (UK) **4691**
Glass's Motor Cycle Check Book. (UK) **4518**
Glastechnische Berichte. (GW ISSN 0017-1085) **1164**
Glasteknisk Tidskrift. (SW ISSN 0017-1093) **1164**
Glaswelt: Deutsche Glaserzeitung. (GW ISSN 0017-1107) **1164**
Glaube Hoffnung Liebe. (GW) **4179**
Glaube in der 2. Welt. (SZ ISSN 0254-4377) **4179**, 3942
Glaube und Heimat. (GW ISSN 0323-8202) **4239**
Glaube und Lernen. (GW ISSN 0179-3551) **4179**
Glaucoma. (US ISSN 0164-4645) **3300**
Glazed Expressions. (UK ISSN 0261-0329) **1164**
Gleams. (US) **2292**, 3300
Gleaner Index. (JM ISSN 0259-0336) **2578**
Gleanings. (CE) **4212**, 13
Gleanings (Keokuk). (US ISSN 1059-1664) **2153**
Gleanings in Bee Culture. (US ISSN 0017-114X) **94**
Gledista. (YU ISSN 0017-1166) **2507**, 4373
Gleitschirm. (SZ) **4473**, 4547
Glenbow. (CN ISSN 0710-3697) **2407**
Glenbow - Alberta Institute. Occasional Papers. (CN ISSN 0072-467X) **2407**, 2003
Glenbow Foundation. Archives Series *see* Glenbow Museum. Archives Series **5200**
†Glenbow Museum. Archives Series. (CN) **5200**
Glendale Law Review. (US ISSN 0363-2423) **2630**
Glenmary Challenge. (US) **4179**
Glenmary's Challenge *see* Glenmary Challenge **4179**
†Glens Falls Review. (US) **5200**
Glia. (US ISSN 0894-1491) **3337**
Glider Rider *see* Ultralight Flying **64**
†Glimpse of London with American Express. (UK) **5200**
Glimpses in Plant Research. (II ISSN 0971-1686) **504**
▼Global. (US) **909**
Global Affairs. (US ISSN 0886-6198) **3958**
Global and Planetary Change. (NE ISSN 0921-8181) **1566**
▼Global Appliance Report. (US) **2559**
Global Architecture *see* G A **300**
Global Architecture Document *see* G A Document **300**
Global Assessment *see* Global Assessment Annual Forecast **867**
Global Assessment Annual Forecast. (US) **867**, 909
Global Assessment Special Analyses. (US) **867**, 909
Global Biogeochemical Cycles. (US ISSN 0886-6236) **4311**, 4598
Global Business. (UK) **667**
†Global Business Issues. (CN) **5200**
Global Church Growth. (US ISSN 0731-1125) **4283**
Global Church Growth Bulletin *see* Global Church Growth **4283**
Global Climate Change *see* Ocean Science News **1609**

Global Climate Change Digest. (US ISSN 0897-4268) **1955**
Global Communications. (US ISSN 0195-2250) **1356**
Global Custodian. (US) **947**
▼Global Economics Prospects and the Developing Countries. (US ISSN 1014-8906) **930**, 783
Global Electronics. (US) **4598**
▼Global Environmental Change. (UK ISSN 0959-3780) **1956**
▼Global Environmental Change Report.(US ISSN 1049-9083) **1956**
Global Equity Analysis Report. (US) **783**
Global Finance. (US ISSN 0896-4181) **783**, 909
Global Finance Journal. (US) **909**
Global Investor. (UK) **783**, 867, 910, 947
Global Links. (US) **930**, 1722, 2003, 3958
▼Global Market Perspective. (US ISSN 1055-9671) **947**
Global Military Industralization *see* Atlantic Trade Report & Global Defense Industry **900**
▼Global Money Management. (US) **947**, 1011
†Global Networks. (US) **5200**
Global Opportunities Advertiser. (US) **32**, 910
Global Options Dataline. (US) **3896**, 867
†Global Perspectives. (US ISSN 0741-0204) **5200**
†Global Plastics Report. (CN ISSN 0835-1791) **5200**
Global Positioning Satellite Report *see* G P S Report **1363**
Global Positioning System World *see* G P S World **2248**
Global Report. (US ISSN 0730-9112) **3958**
Global Risk Assessments. (US ISSN 0739-4640) **910**, 3958
Global Science Journal. (NR ISSN 0795-6770) **4311**
Global Screen Pictorial. *see* Huanqiu Yinmu Huakan **3511**
▼Global Shareholder. (US) **947**, 910, 2630
▼Global Stamp News. (US) **3753**
Global Studies: Africa. (US) **3958**
Global Studies: China. (US) **3958**
▼Global Studies: Japan and the Pacific Rim. (US) **3958**
Global Studies: Latin America. (US) **3958**
Global Studies: Middle East. (US ISSN 1056-6848) **3958**
Global Studies: Soviet Union & Eastern Europe. (US) **3958**
Global Studies: Western Europe. (US) **3958**
Global Tapestry Journal. (UK ISSN 0141-1241) **2994**
Global Tectonics and Metallogeny. (GW ISSN 0163-3171) **1566**
▼Global Telcom Report. (US ISSN 1059-4485) **1363**, 1350
Global Trade. (US) **910**
Global Trade Executive *see* Global Trade **910**
▼Global Trade White Pages. (US ISSN 1054-8742) **1136**, 910
Global Trends. (US) **947**
Global 500 Directory. (US ISSN **1136**, 667
†Globalia Nyt. (DK ISSN 0900-078X) **5200**
The Globe. (UK) **1298**
Globe. (UK) **1298**, 4768
Globe. (AT ISSN 0311-3930) **2252**
Globe. *see* Huan Qiu **3959**
Globe (Boca Raton). (US) **2226**
Globe (Flushing). (US) **2003**
Globe (Miami). (US) **4633**
Globe and Laurel. (UK ISSN 0017-1204) **3459**
Globe and Mail Report on Business. (CN ISSN 0017-1212) **867**
Globe - Contact International. (FR) **910**
▼Globe Literary. (US) **2994**

Globecom. I E E E Global Telecommunications Conference. Conference Record. (US ISSN 0895-1195) **1336**
Globetrotter *see* Der Trotter **4794**
Globo. (SZ) **4768**
Globule Rouge. (CN) **1312**
Globus - Begleithefte. (GW ISSN 0931-539X) **1956**, 1488
Globusfreund. (AU ISSN 0436-0664) **2252**
Glocke *see* Zzap **1673**
Die Glocke vom Ettersberg. (GW) **2364**, 3942
Gloria Vanderbilt Designs for Your Home. (US ISSN 0362-5419) **2551**
Glorious Hope. *see* Slavna Nadeje **4249**
Glory. (II) **1255**, 2003
Glory. (CN) **2177**
Glory of India. (II ISSN 0970-1427) **3637**, 2338
Glory Songs. (US ISSN 0731-0781) **3552**, 4239
Glos. (US) **2003**, 783
Glos Nauczycielski. (PL ISSN 0017-1263) **1635**, 2583
Glos Polek/Polish Womens' Voice. (US ISSN 0199-0462) **2003**, 1298, 4844
▼Gloss. (CN ISSN 1180-4467) **373**
Gloss Magazine. (UK) **2446**
Glot. (NE ISSN 0166-5790) **2816**
Glotta. (GW ISSN 0017-1298) **1276**
Glottodidactica. (PL ISSN 0072-4769) **2816**
Gloucester Diocesan Gazette. (UK ISSN 0017-1301) **4179**
Gloucestershire and North Avon Farmer.(UK) **94**
Gloucestershire Farmer *see* Gloucestershire and North Avon Farmer **94**
Gloucestershire Local History Newsletter. (UK ISSN 0260-5139) **2364**
Gloucestershire Record Series. (UK) **2364**
Glow International. (US) **4179**
Glowna Biblioteka Lekarska. Biuletyn. (PL ISSN 0017-1344) **3101**
Gloxinian. (US ISSN 0017-1352) **504**, 2128
Glueckauf. (GW ISSN 0340-7896) **3484**
Glueckauf-Forschungshefte. (GW ISSN 0017-1387) **3484**
Gluecklich Leben. (GW) **2446**
Gluten Intolerance Group of North America Newsletter *see* G I G Newsletter **3606**
▼Glycobiology. (UK ISSN 0959-6658) **477**
Glycoconjugate Journal. (UK ISSN 0282-0080) **477**, 552
†Glycoproteins. (UK ISSN 0143-4314) **5200**
Glyndebourne Festival Programme Book. (UK ISSN 0434-1066) **3553**
†Gmac Quest. (US ISSN 0896-7121) **5200**
GmbH-Rundschau. (GW ISSN 0016-3570) **2630**
Gmuender Anzeiger. (GW) **1040**
†Gnadauer Mitteilungen. (GW ISSN 0232-489X) **5200**
Gnade und Herrlichkeit. (GW ISSN 0017-1409) **4179**
Gnanarthapradeepaya. (CE) **4265**
Gnome Baker. (US) **2920**, 327
Gnomon. (GW ISSN 0017-1417) **1277**, 4128
Gnosis. (US ISSN 0894-6159) **3594**, 3767
Gnosis. (CN ISSN 0316-618X) **3767**
Go. (CY ISSN 0256-4726) **4239**
Go/Igo. (JA) **4473**
Go! (SA) **4691**
Go. (SI ISSN 0217-765X) **4844**
Go (Burlingame) *see* GO West **4744**
Go (Charlotte). (US ISSN 0017-1441) **4768**, 4691
Go Ahead. *see* Au Large **1249**
†Go - Atlanta. (US) **5200**
†Go - Dallas. (US) **5200**
Go Devil. (US) **3688**, 4650
Go Magazine. (US) **2994**
†Go - New Orleans. (US) **5200**

Go Teach Beginners. (UK ISSN 0950-7221) **4179**, 1750
Go Teach Juniors. (UK ISSN 0950-7248) **4179**, 1750
Go Teach Primaries. (UK ISSN 0142-5935) **4179**, 1750
Go Teach Young Teens. (UK ISSN 0950-7256) **4179**, 1750
Go: The Authentic Guide to Atlanta *see* Go - Atlanta **5200**
Go: The Authentic Guide to Dallas *see* Go - Dallas **5200**
Go: The Authentic Guide to New Orleans *see* Go - New Orleans **5200**
Go: The Authentic Guide to the Nation's Capital *see* Go - Washington, DC **5200**
Go: The Rider's Manual. (US ISSN 1048-8758) **4518**
†Go - Washington, DC. (US) **5200**
GO West. (UK ISSN 0738-5935) **4744**
Go World. (JA ISSN 0286-0376) **4473**
Goa Chamber of Commerce and Industry. Bulletin. (II) **816**
Goa, Daman, and Diu. Directorate of Economics, Statistics, and Evaluation. Evaluation Report. (II) **867**
Goa Today. (II ISSN 0017-1484) **2199**
Goal. (US) **4473**
Goal Line. (US) **4473**
Gobbles. (US ISSN 0017-1506) **217**
Gocho/Okochi Memorial Foundation. Journal. (JA ISSN 0385-7433) **4311**
Gode Lydboeger. (DK ISSN 0107-5209) **401**
Godesberger Heimatblaetter. (GW ISSN 0436-1024) **2364**
Godhavn Geophysical Observatory. Magnetic Results *see* Godhavn Magnetic Results **1590**
Godhavn Magnetic Results. (DK ISSN 0109-4300) **1590**
Godishnik na Muzeite ot Severna Bulgariia. (BU ISSN 0204-4048) **2364**
Godisnjak Jugoslovenskih Pozorista/Yearbook of Yugoslav Theaters. (YU ISSN 0351-9120) **4633**
Godisnjak za Povijest Filozofije. (CI ISSN 0352-3306) **3767**
Godovoi Obzor Khimicheskoi Promyshlennosti *see* Annual Review of the Chemical Industry **1071**
Godowsky Society Newsletter. (UK) **3553**
God's Field. *see* Rola Boza **4274**
God's Special People. (US ISSN 0896-2413) **2283**, 4179
Godsdienst en Maatschappij. (NE) **4212**
Godwins Cityscope. (UK) **867**
Goedskingrapport. (DK ISSN 0901-1943) **178**
Goeie Nuus. *see* Good News **4179**
Goeldiana Zoologia. (BL ISSN 0103-6076) **583**
Goer det Selv. (DK ISSN 0901-4241) **2501**
Goer det Selv i Hjemmet *see* Goer det Selv **2501**
Goer det Selv Indeks. (DK ISSN 0105-8134) **2444**
Goetabanken *see* Gotabanken Economic Survey **867**
Goeteborg Psychological Reports. (SW ISSN 0301-0996) **4022**, 13
Goeteborg Studies in Conservation. (SW ISSN 0284-6578) **1488**
Goeteborg Studies in Educational Sciences. (SW ISSN 0436-1121) **1635**
Goeteborg Studies in Politics. (SW) **3896**
Goeteborg Women's Studies. (SW ISSN 0283-2399) **4844**
Goeteborger Germanistische Forschungen. (SW ISSN 0072-4793) **2816**, 2920
Goeteborgs Etnografiska Museum. Aarstryck - Annals. (SW ISSN 0280-3887) **240**
Goeteborgs - Koepmannen. (SW ISSN 0046-6050) **1040**
Goeteborgs Kungliga Vetenskaps- och Vitterhets-Samhaelle. Aarsbok. (SW ISSN 0436-113X) **2507**
Goeteborgs Kungliga Vetenskaps- och Vitterhets- Samhaelle. Handlingar *see* Acta Regiae Societatis Scientiarum et Litterarum Gothoburgensis. Botanica **493**
Goeteborgs Kungliga Vetenskaps- och Vitterhets-Samhaelle. Handlingar *see* Acta Regiae Societatis Scientiarum et Litterarum Gothoburgensis. Zoologica **576**
Goeteborgs Kungliga Vetenskaps- och Vitterhets-Samhaelle. Handlingar *see* Acta Regiae Societatis Scientiarum et Litterarum Gothoburgensis. Geophysica **1586**
Goeteborgs Kungliga Vetenskaps- och Vitterhets- Samhaelle. Handlingar *see* Acta Regiae Societatis Scientiarum et Litterarum Gothoburgensis. Humaniora **2502**
Goeteborgs Kungliga Vetenskaps- och Vitterhets-Samhaelle. Handlingar Bihang *see* Goeteborgs Kungliga Vetenskaps- och Vitterhets-Samhaelle. Aarsbok **2507**
Goeteborgs Universitet. Demographic Research Institute. Reports. (SW) **3982**
Goeteborgs Universitet. Ekonomisk-Historiska Institutionen. Meddelanden. (SW ISSN 0072-5080) **894**
Goeteborgs Universitet. Institutionen foer Praktisk Pedagogik. Rapport. (SW ISSN 0348-2219) **1750**
Goeteborgs Universitet. Nationalekonomiska Institutionen. Ekonomiska Studier. (SW ISSN 0434-2410) **894**
Goeteborgs Universitet. Oceanografiska Institutionen. Reports. (SW) **1604**
Goeteborgs Universitet. Statistiska Institutionen. Skriftserie. Publications.(SW ISSN 0072-5110) **4572**
†Goeteborgs Universitet. Universitetsbibliotek. Aarsberaettelse.(SW ISSN 0347-884X) **5200**
Goethe-Gesellschaft. Jahrbuch *see* Goethe-Jahrbuch **2920**
Goethe Institut Prisma *see* G I Prisma **1722**
Goethe-Institut zur Pflege der Deutschen Sprache im Ausland und zur Foerderung der Internationalen Kulturellen Zusammenarbeit. Jahrbuch. (GW) **2816**
Goethe-Institut zur Pflege Deutscher Sprache und Kultur im Ausland. Jahrbuch *see* Goethe-Institut zur Pflege der Deutschen Sprache im Ausland und zur Foerderung der Internationalen Kulturellen Zusammenarbeit. Jahrbuch **2816**
Goethe-Jahrbuch. (GW ISSN 0323-4207) **2920**
Goethe News and Notes. (US) **2920**
Goethe Woerterbuch. (GW) **2920**
Goethe Yearbook. (US ISSN 0734-3329) **2920**
Das Goetheanum. (SZ) **2920**
Goetikuss. (GW) **1635**, 1727, 4061, 4633
Goettinger Floristische Rundbriefe *see* Floristische Rundbriefe **503**
Goettinger Geographische Abhandlungen. (GW ISSN 0341-3780) **2252**
Goettinger Miszellen. (GW ISSN 0344-385X) **2311**
Goettinger Orientforschungen. Reihe I: Syriaca. (GW ISSN 0340-6326) **3637**, 2338
Goettinger Orientforschungen. Reihe II: Studien zur Spaetantiken und Fruehchristlichen Kunst. (GW ISSN 0173-2358) **3637**
Goettinger Orientforschungen. Reihe IV: Aegypten. (GW ISSN 0340-6342) **3637**, 2338
Goettinger Predigtmeditationen. (GW ISSN 0340-6083) **4179**
Goettinger Rechtswissenschaftliche Studien. (GW ISSN 2723, 2630
Goettinger Statistik. (GW) **4080**
Goettinger Studien zur Rechtsgeschichte. (GW) **2630**
Goettinger Universitaetsreden. (GW ISSN 0085-1108) **1707**
Goettingische Gelehrte Anzeigen. (GW ISSN 0017-1549) **2816**, 273
Goff's Guide to Cater Yourself Holidays.(UK) **4768**
Goff's Guide to Motels and Motorways in Great Britain and Ireland. (UK) **2474**
Goff's Guide to Motels in Great Britain and Europe *see* Goff's Guide to Motels and Motorways in Great Britain and Ireland **2474**
Goias, Brazil. Secretaria do Planejamento e Coordenacao. Boletim Estadistico. (BL) **4572**
Going and Growing. (US) **2128**
Going Concerns. (SA) **816**
Going Gaga. (US) **2920**
Going On *see* Checkpoint **4232**
Going Places *see* Going Places International **4768**
Going Places (Chicago). (US) **4768**
Going Places (Minot). (US) **4768**
Going Places (Schaumburg). (US) **4768**
†Going Places! (Washington). (US) **5200**
Going Places International. (UK) **4768**
Going Places Magazine. (CN) **4691**, 4768
Going Public *see* Going Public - The I P O Reporter **783**
Going Public - The I P O Reporter. (US ISSN 0278-0038) **783**
†Going Shopping Magazine. (UK) **5200**
Going-To-College Handbook. (US ISSN 0072-4904) **1707**
Goingsnake Messenger. (US) **2153**
Gokhale Institute Mimeograph Series. (II ISSN 0436-1326) **3896**, 667
Gokhale Institute of Politics and Economics. Studies. (II ISSN 0072-4912) **3896**, 667
Gokuldas Sanskrit Series. (II) **3767**
Gol. (CS) **4504**, 4473
▼Gold (Year). (US) **3484**
Gold and Blue. (US) **1312**
Gold & Silver Survey. (UK ISSN 0196-3546) **783**
Gold Book Classics & Antiques. (US) **4691**, 257
Gold Book Contemporary Vehicles. (US ISSN 1057-0535) **4691**
Gold Book of MultiHousing. (US ISSN 0195-847X) **618**, 2487
Gold Book Older Vehicles. (US ISSN 1057-0136) **4691**
Gold Book Special Interest Vehicles. (US) **4691**, 257
▼The Gold Book: The Complete Guide to Precious Metals. (CN) **947**
Gold Book Used Car Value Guide *see* Gold Book Older Vehicles **4691**
Gold Book Used Car Value Guide *see* Gold Book Contemporary Vehicles **4691**
Gold Bulletin. (SZ ISSN 0017-1557) **3425**
Gold Coast Cityscope. (AT) **4160**
Gold Dust *see* Air Pollution Management **1942**
†Gold in Catalysis. (US) **5200**
Gold Institute. International Conference on Gold & Silver in Medicine. Proceedings. (US) **3484**, 3101
Gold Life *see* Health Life **1684**
Gold Mining Stock Report. (US ISSN 0743-8508) **947**
Gold News/Nouvelles de l'Or. (US) **3484**, 3407
Gold Patent Digest *see* Gold Bulletin **3425**
Gold Prospector. (US) **3484**, 4547
Gold Standard News. (US) **948**, 867, 3484
Gold Torch. (US) **1312**
Gold und Silber *see* Gold und Silber - Uhren und Schmuck **2564**
Gold und Silber - Uhren und Schmuck. (GW ISSN 0017-1573) **2564**
Gold und Silber zum Sammeln. (GW) **3599**
Golda Meir Library Newsletter. (US) **2759**
Goldbecks' True Food. (US ISSN 0897-7275) **3606**
Golddust *see* Metalsmith **356**
Golden Age. (US) **2273**
Golden C F News. (Crusselle-Freeman Church and Center of the Deaf) (US) **2287**, 4179
Golden Dog. *see* Chien d'Or **2905**
†Golden Eye. (SA ISSN 0017-1581) **5200**
Golden Falcon. (UK) **4768**
Golden Fleece/Goue Vag. (SA ISSN 0257-2044) **217**
Golden Gate University Law Review. (US ISSN 0363-0307) **2630**
Golden Grain. *see* Gintong Butil **206**
Golden Hours. *see* Gouden Uren **4128**
Golden Isis. (US) **2994**
Golden Key. *see* Jin Yaoshi **2927**
Golden Keys Magazine. (UK) **4768**, 2474
Golden Legacy. (US ISSN 0046-6077) **2003**
The Golden Links. (CN) **1298**
Golden Links Bulletin *see* The Golden Links **1298**
Golden List of Beaches *see* Good Beach Guide **1956**
Golden List of British Beaches *see* Good Beach Guide **1956**
Golden Movie News/Chia Ho Tien Ying. (HK) **3511**
Golden Penthouse. (MX ISSN 0187-8999) **3397**
Golden Retriever World. (US) **3710**
Golden Roots of the Mother Lode. (US ISSN 8755-3023) **2153**
Golden Shield. *see* Jin Dun **2638**
Golden State. (US) **4768**
Golden State Report. (US ISSN 0884-9072) **4061**, 3896
Golden Times. *see* Huangjin Shidai **2182**
Golden Times. (US) **2273**
Golden Years Magazine. (US ISSN 0733-0529) **2273**
Golden Years Senior News *see* Golden Years Magazine **2273**
Das Goldene Blatt. (GW ISSN 0046-6093) **4844**
Goldene Gesundheit. (GW) **3101**, 4102
Di Goldene Keyt. (IS ISSN 0017-1638) **2994**
Der Goldene Pfennig. (GW ISSN 0017-1646) **1255**
Goldenseal. (US ISSN 0099-0159) **2407**
Goldfinch. (US ISSN 0278-0208) **2407**
Goldmann-Nachrichten. (GW ISSN 0176-1900) **2153**
Goldmanns Mitteilungen fuer den Buchhandel. (GW ISSN 0017-1670) **4128**
Goldmine. (US ISSN 8750-2577) **3553**
Goldschmiede- und Uhrmacher-Jahrbuch. (GW) **2564**
Goldschmiede und Uhrmacher Zeitung - European Jeweler. (GW ISSN 0932-464X) **2564**
Goldschmiede Zeitung - European Jeweler und Uhrmacherzeitschrift *see* Goldschmiede und Uhrmacher Zeitung - European Jeweler **2564**
†Goldsmith. (US ISSN 0274-7456) **5200**
Goldsmith's Journal *see* Metalsmith **356**
Goldthwait Polar Library Accessions List. (US ISSN 0743-7250) **2793**, 1545
Golem. (IT) **4598**
Golembe Reports. (US) **783**
Goleuad/Light. (UK ISSN 0017-1700) **4239**
Golf. (NE) **4504**
Golf. (UK ISSN 0017-1808) **4504**
Golf. (DK ISSN 0902-8927) **4504**
Golf and Sportsturf *see* Sportsturf **4512**
Golf Benelux *see* Golf **4504**
Golf Book of Records. (US) **4504**
Golf Club *see* Country Club **4502**
Golf Club Management & Equipment News. (UK ISSN 0267-1166) **4505**, 1011
Golf Clubmaker. (US) **4505**, 1076

GOLF

Golf - Contact *see* Golf Journal **4505**
Golf Course *see* English Amateur Golf **4503**
Golf Course Association Newsletter *see* G C A Newsletter **4504**
Golf Course Builders of America Directory. (US) **618**, 1136, 4505
Golf Course Management. (US ISSN 0192-3048) **4505**, 2128
Golf Course Management Letter. (US) **4505**
Golf Course News. (US) **4505**
Golf Course Superintendents Association of America. Membership Directory. (US ISSN 0436-1474) **4505**
Golf Course Superintendents Association of America. Proceedings of the International Golf Course Conference and Show. (US ISSN 0072-4947) **4505**
Golf Courses of Alberta *see* Golf Guide **4505**
▼Golf Development Magazine. (US) **4505**
Golf Digest. (US ISSN 0017-176X) **4505**
†Golf Digest Almanac (Year). (US ISSN 0742-4485) **5200**
Golf Digest Italia. (IT) **4505**
Golf en France. (FR) **4505**
Golf Europeen. (FR ISSN 0040-3458) **4505**
Golf for Women. (US) **4505**, 4844
Golf Georgia. (US) **4505**
Golf Guide. (US ISSN 0072-4955) **4473**
Golf Guide. (CN) **4505**
Golf Guide - Where to Play and Where to Stay. (UK ISSN 0263-4066) **4505**
Golf Illustrated. (US) **4505**
Golf in Victoria. (AT) **4505**
Golf Index. (US) **4505**
Golf Industry. (US ISSN 0160-6824) **4505**
▼Golf International Magazine. (US) **4505**
Golf Italiano. (IT) **4505**
Golf Journal. (US ISSN 0017-1794) **4505**
Golf Journal. (GW) **4505**, 4768
Golf Journal *see* S A Golf Journal **4510**
Golf Magazine. (JA) **4505**
Golf Magazine *see* Golf News **4505**
Golf Magazine (New York) *see* Golf **4504**
Golf News. (IT) **4505**
Golf News. (KE) **4505**
Golf News Magazine. (US) **4505**
Golf Pro Merchandiser. (US) **1040**, 4505
Golf Product News. (US) **4505**
▼Golf Property. (US) **4149**, 4505
Golf Reporter. (US) **4505**
Golf Scene Magazine. (US) **4505**
Golf Shop Operations. (US ISSN 0017-1824) **4505**
Golf Singapore Review. (SI ISSN 0017-1832) **4505**
Golf Tennis Polo. (GW) **4473**, 1291, 4534
Golf Tips. (US) **4506**
Golf Traveler. (US ISSN 0191-717X) **4506**
Golf Week. (IT) **4506**
Golf World. (UK ISSN 0017-1883) **4506**
Golf World. (US ISSN 0017-1891) **4506**
Golf Zeitung. (GW) **4506**
Golfclub Magazin. (GW ISSN 0931-573X) **4506**
Golfer. (SA ISSN 0017-1913) **4506**
Golfer's Companion. (IE) **4506**, 3101
Golfer's Handbook. (UK ISSN 0072-498X) **4506**
Golfer's Travel Guide. (US) **4506**, 4768
Golfexpert. (CN) **4506**
Golfing Year. (UK) **4506**
†GolfLifeStyle. (US) **5200**
Golfmagazin. (GW ISSN 0017-1735) **4506**
Il Golfo. (IT ISSN 0394-395X) **2867**
Golfweek. (US) **4506**
Golfwest *see* GolfLifeStyle **5200**
Golgotska Vest. (XV) **4239**

Golos Radzimy. (BW ISSN 0017-1948) **2174**
Goltdammer's Archiv fuer Strafrecht. (GW ISSN 0017-1956) **1515**
Golv till Tak. (SW ISSN 0345-3979) **2559**
Al-Gomhouria/Republic. (UA) **2185**
Gomitolo. (IT ISSN 0017-1964) **4619**
Gommista *see* Autoriparatore, il Gommista, Elettrauto **4684**
Gommone *see* Gommone e la Nautica per Tutti **4524**
Gommone e la Nautica per Tutti. (IT ISSN 1120-2262) **4524**
†Gonadotrophins. (UK ISSN 0143-425X) **5200**
Gondola. (SP) **152**
Gondwana Newsletter. (BL ISSN 0072-4998) **1545**
Gone Fishin'. (CN) **4547**
Gone With The Wind Collectors Club Collectors Club Newsletter *see* G W T W Collectors Club Newsletter **5198**
Gong. (IT) **1255**, 3553
Gong. (GW ISSN 0017-1999) **1374**
Gong. (CS) **2287**, 1736
Gong Lu/Roads. (CC ISSN 0451-0712) **4718**
Gong'an Yanjiu/Public Security Study. (CC) **1526**
Gongcheng Lixue/Engineering Mechanics. (CC) **1917**
Gongcheng Re-Wuli Xuebao. (CC ISSN 0253-231X) **3840**
Gongqi Yikan/Enterprise Medical Journal. (CC ISSN 1001-814X) **3101**
Gongren Zuzhi yu Huodong. (CC ISSN 1001-3237) **980**
Gongye Jianzhu/Industrial Construction.(CC ISSN 1000-8993) **618**
Gongye Kongzhi Jisuanji. (CC ISSN 1001-182X) **1413**
Gongye Lu/Journal of Industry Furnace.(CC ISSN 1001-6988) **1917**
Gongye Weishengwu/Industrial Microbiology. (CC ISSN 1001-6678) **552**
Gongye Zhanwang/Industrial Prospect. (CC) **4598**
Gonjun Bogen Jabji *see* Korean Journal of Public Health **4106**
Gonzaga Law Review. (US ISSN 0046-6115) **2630**
▼Goo Maral/Beautiful Doe. (MP) **373**
Good Apple Newspaper. (US) **1750**, 1238
Good Beach Guide. (UK) **1956**, 4547
Good Beer Guide. (UK ISSN 0265-0681) **381**
The Good Book Guide. (UK) **4128**
Good Camps Guide Britain (Year). (UK ISSN 0142-5978) **4768**, 4547
Good Camps Guide Europe (Year). (UK) **4768**, 4547
Good Camps Guide France (Year). (UK) **4768**, 4547
▼Good Cents. (US) **618**, 1790
Good Children. *see* Hao Ertong **1256**
Good Clean Fun. (US) **2920**
Good Company. (SA) **1255**
Good Cooking Series *see* Specialty Cooking **3612**
Good Day Sunshine. (US ISSN 1041-4118) **3553**, 1298
Good Dog! (US) **3710**
Good Earth *see* Green Drum **1488**
Good Earth Association. Newsletter. (US) **2128**
Good Food. (UK) **2071**
†Good Food. (US ISSN 0885-0690) **5200**
Good Food Guide. (UK ISSN 0072-5005) **2474**
Good Fruit Grower. (US ISSN 0046-6174) **2128**
Good Government. (AT ISSN 0818-2493) **895**, 3896, 4373
†Good Government. (US ISSN 0017-2065) **5200**
Good Health. (CN) **3802**, 3606
Good Health. (UK) **4102**, 3802
Good Holiday Magazine. (UK) **4768**
Good Hotel Guide *see* Which? Hotel Guide **2482**

Good Housekeeping. (UK ISSN 0017-2081) **2446**, 2194, 4844
Good Housekeeping. (US ISSN 0017-209X) **2446**, 4844
Good Housekeeping. (AT) **2446**
Good Housekeeping's Nine Months. (US) **1238**
Good Housekeeping's Victoria *see* Victoria **2237**
Good Impressions *see* Magnet Marketing **1045**
Good Life. (US) **2226**
Good Life Times. (US) **3594**, 3214, 3606
Good Manufacturing Practice Letter *see* G M P Letter **2522**
Good Money. (US ISSN 0742-4515) **948**
Good Money's Social Funds Guide. (US) **948**
Good Motoring. (UK ISSN 0017-2111) **4691**
Good Neighbor. (US) **4406**, 3802
Good Neighbours News. (UK) **4406**
Good News/Goeie Nuus. (SA ISSN 0017-2146) **4179**
Good News (Birmingham). (UK ISSN 0262-2874) **4179**
Good News (Exeter). (UK ISSN 0954-562X) **4179**
Good News (New Berlin). (US) **4265**, 4239
Good News (New York) *see* New York Good News **2230**
Good News (Wilmore). (US ISSN 0436-1563) **4239**
Good News Broadcaster *see* Confident Living **4234**
†Good News: Christian in Journalism. (US) **5200**
▼Good-News-Letter. (US) **3606**, 1255
The Good News Letter (Washington). (US) **4265**
Good News of Tomorrow's World *see* Plain Truth **4287**
Good Old Days. (US ISSN 0046-6158) **2920**
Good Old Days Specials. (US ISSN 1050-480X) **2920**
Good Packaging *see* Good Packaging Magazine **3648**
Good Packaging Magazine. (US ISSN 1049-3158) **3648**
Good Reading. (US) **4128**, 401
Good Reading for Everyone. (US) **4128**, 401
Good Sam Club's Recreational Vehicle Owners Directory *see* Trailer Life's Recreational Vehicle Campground and Services Directory **1156**
Good Sam's Hi-Way Herald *see* Highways **4548**
Good Ski Guide. (UK) **4547**
Good Ski Resorts Guide. (UK) **4547**
Good Stuff. (US ISSN 0882-4746) **2759**
Good Tidings. (CN) **4179**
Good Times. (CN) **2273**
Good Van Guide. (UK) **4744**
Good 5-Cent Cigar. (US) **1312**
Good 6500 *see* Good Food **2071**
Goodenough's Ghosts *see* Goodenows' Ghosts **2153**
Goodenows' Ghosts. (US) **2153**
Goodfellow Catalog of Wonderful Things. (US) **355**, 2436
Goodguys Goodtimes Gazette. (US) **4473**
Goodlife Magazine. (CN) **2177**
Goodlife's Home Renovation & Decor Catalogue. (CN) **618**
Goodlife's Tastes of Toronto. (CN) **1137**
Goodrich Gospel. (US) **2153**
Goods and Services Bulletin. (US) **1076**, 4061
Goods in Transit. (US) **2710**, 4650
Goods Vehicle Costing and Pricing Handbook. (UK) **4691**
Goods Vehicle Year Book *see* Freight Industry Yearbook **4650**
Goodwill Dimensions. (CN) **1736**
Goodwin Series. Occasional Papers. (SA ISSN 0304-3460) **273**
Goodwood Journal. (SI) **2474**
Goodwood Year Book. (UK) **4534**
Goofus Office Gazette. (US) **2867**
†Goofy. (GW) **5200**

Goole Port Handbook. (UK ISSN 0262-1622) **4727**, 1137
Gopher Music Notes. (US ISSN 0017-2235) **3553**, 1635
Gopher Oversea'r. (US) **3459**
▼Gopherwood Review. (US) **2994**
Gordian. (GW ISSN 0017-2243) **2071**
†Gordon Downtown Marketview. (US) **5200**
Gordon Office Market Report. (US) **4149**
Gordon Setter News. (US) **3711**
Gordon's Print Price Annual (Year). (US) **327**
Gore Zone. (US ISSN 0896-8802) **3511**
Gorge Guide. (US) **4524**
Gorgeous Ladies of Wrestling *see* G L O W **4472**
Gorilla. (US) **4022**, 583
Goriski Letnik. (XV ISSN 0350-2929) **3524**
Goriva i Maziva/Fuels and Lubricants. (CI ISSN 0350-350X) **3017**
Gorman's New Product News *see* Delta's New Product News **2065**
†Gornictwo Odkrywkowe. (PL ISSN 0043-2075) **5200**
Gornik. (PL ISSN 0017-226X) **2583**, 3484
Gornoslaskie Studia Socjologiczne. (PL ISSN 0072-5013) **4436**
Gornye Mashiny *see* Referativnyi Zhurnal. Gornoe i Neftepromyslovoe Mashinostroenie **3502**
Gornyi Zhurnal. (RU ISSN 0017-2278) **3484**
Goro *see* Serai **2208**
Gorskostopanska Nauka/Forestry Science. (BU ISSN 0017-2286) **2101**
Gortania. (IT ISSN 0391-5859) **1545**, 273, 440, 465
Gorteria. (NE ISSN 0017-2294) **504**
Goryo Daehakgyo Nonmunjip Science *see* Science and Technology **4339**
Gosford and Peninsula Times. (AT) **2171**
Goshen College Bulletin. (US ISSN 0017-2308) **1312**
Gospel Advocate. (US) **4179**
Gospel Choir. (US ISSN 0362-0417) **4239**, 3553
Gospel Herald. (CN ISSN 0829-4666) **4179**
Gospel Herald. (US ISSN 0017-2340) **4283**
Gospel Informatie-Handboek *see* Expressie **3551**
Gospel Magazine. (UK) **4239**
Gospel Messenger. (US ISSN 0017-2359) **2293**, 4179
Gospel Music Association. Resource Guide. (US) **3553**
Gospel Music Official Directory *see* Gospel Music Association. Resource Guide **3553**
Gospel of God. *see* Shree Hari Katha **3781**
Gospel Standard. (UK ISSN 0017-2367) **4180**, 1255
Gospel Time. (DK ISSN 0106-9586) **3553**
Gospel Truth. (US ISSN 0017-2383) **4283**, 3896
Gospel Witness *see* Indian Lutheran **4240**
Gospodarka i Administracja Terenowa *see* Rada Narodowa, Gospodarka, Administracja **882**
Gospodarka Materialowa. (PL ISSN 0017-2405) **1076**
Gospodarka Miesna. (PL ISSN 0367-4916) **217**, 2071
Gospodarka Paliwami i Energia/Fuel and Energy Management. (PL ISSN 0017-2413) **1790**, 3688
Gospodarka Planowa. (PL ISSN 0017-2421) **1076**
Gospodarka Rybna. (PL ISSN 0017-243X) **2041**
Gospodarka Wodna. (PL ISSN 0017-2448) **4824**
Gospodarstvo. (IT ISSN 0017-2456) **867**
▼Gospodin Narod. (RU) **3896**, 867
Gossage Regan Manager's Memo. (US ISSN 0890-3360) **2759**

GRADUATE FELLOWSHIP 6225

Gosse Bird Club Broadsheet. (JM) **564**
Gossner Mission. (GW) **4180**
Gosudarstvennaya Biblioteka S.S.S.R. im. V.I. Lenina. Informatsionnyi Byulleten' Novykh Inostrannykh Knig, Postupivshikh v Biblioteku. Seriya 1: Fiziko-Matematicheskie i Khimicheskie Nauki; Nauki o Zemle; Tekhnika i Tekhnicheskie Nauk. (RU ISSN 0041-8072) **4311**
Gosudarstvennaya Biblioteka S.S.S.R. im. V.I. Lenina. Informatsionnyi Byulleten' Novykh Inostrannykh Knig, Postupivshikh v Biblioteku. Seriya 3: Obshchestvennye Nauki; Khudozhestvennaya Literatura; Iskusstvo. (RU ISSN 0041-8080) **401**
Gosudarstvennyi Astronomicheskii Institut im. P.K. Shternberga. Soobshcheniya. (RU ISSN 0038-1489) **364**
Gosudarstvennyi Astronomicheskii Institut im. P.K. Shternberga. Trudy. (RU ISSN 0041-3453) **364**
Gosudarstvennyi Komitet Soveta Ministrov S.S.S.R. po Voprosam Truda i Zarabotnoi Platy. Byulleten' (RU ISSN 0007-7666) **980**
Gosudarstvennyi Muzei Izobrazitel'nykh Iskusstv im. Pushkina. Soobshcheniya. (RU ISSN 0077-1562) **3524**
Gotabanken Economic Survey. (SW) **867**
Gothenberg and Western Sweden Chamber of Commerce. Membership Directory see Western Sweden Chamber of Commerce. Membership Directory **824**
Gothenburg Studies in Art and Architecture. (SW ISSN 0348-4114) **327**, **300**
Gothenburg Studies in English. (SW ISSN 0072-503X) **2816**, **2920**
Gothenburg Studies in Social Anthropology. (SW ISSN 0348-4076) **240**
Gothenburg Studies in the History of Science and Ideas. (SW ISSN 0348-6788) **4311**
Gotherman's Ohio Municipal Service. (US ISSN 0739-6937) **4061**, **2630**
†Gothic. (US) **5200**
Gothic Chapbook Series see Gothic **5200**
Gothic Times. (US) **1312**
Gottes Wort. (GW ISSN 0017-2480) **4180**
Gottesdienst. (GW ISSN 0343-8732) **4180**
Gottesdienst und Kirchenmusik. (GW ISSN 0017-2499) **3553**
Gottesdienste mit Kindern und Jugendlichen see Familien und Jugend - Gottesdienste **4178**
Goucher see Goucher Quarterly **1313**
Goucher College Bulletin see Goucher College News **1312**
Goucher College News. (US) **1312**
Goucher Quarterly. (US) **1313**
Gouden Sleutels. (NE ISSN 0017-2529) **2474**
Gouden Uren/Golden Hours. (NE ISSN 0017-2537) **4128**
Goue Vag. see Golden Fleece **217**
Goulburn Valley Farmer see North Eastern Farmer **163**
Gould League Club Newsletter. (AT ISSN 1032-948X) **1956**, **1750**
Gould League of Victoria. Newsletter. (AT ISSN 1032-9218) **1956**, **1750**
Gourd. (US ISSN 0888-5672) **2128**
Gourgues Report. (US) **948**
Gourmed. (GW ISSN 0177-3941) **3101**, **3606**, **4769**
Gourmet. (US ISSN 0017-2553) **2071**, **4769**
Gourmet Club. (IT) **2446**
Gourmet News. (US ISSN 1052-4630) **2088**, **2092**
Gourmet Retailer. (US ISSN 0199-0357) **2071**
Gourmet Today (1986) see Gourmet News **2088**
Der GourmeTip. (GW ISSN 0935-8641) **2071**

GourmeTip International. (GW) **2446**
Gourmetour. (SP) **2474**, **4769**
Gourmet's Notebook. (US) **2474**, **2446**
Gouvernement et les Cabinets Ministeriels. (FR) **4061**, **419**
Governance. (US ISSN 0952-1895) **3896**
Governing. (US ISSN 0894-3842) **4088**
Governing Georgia. (US) **4061**
Government Accountants Journal. (US ISSN 0883-1483) **751**
Government Affairs. (US) **3999**
Government and Military Video see G M V 1 **1385**
Government and Municipal Contractors.(UK ISSN 0140-5764) **4061**
Government and Opposition. (UK ISSN 0017-257X) **3896**
Government and Politics Alert. (US ISSN 1054-5859) **4061**, **3896**
Government Assistance Almanac. (US ISSN 0883-8690) **4088**
Government Auctions Update see National Auctions & Sales **838**
Government Business. (CN) **1040**, **13**
Government Business Worldwide Report. (US) **910**, **3459**
†Government Buyer. (US) **5200**
Government College. Economic Journal. (PK ISSN 0424-2815) **667**
Government Computer News. (US ISSN 0738-4300) **4083**
▼Government Computing Digest. (CN) **1395**
Government Contract Costs, Pricing & Accounting Report. (US) **867**, **2630**
Government Contracting Review. (UK ISSN 0268-8948) **667**
Government Contractor. (US ISSN 0017-2596) **1076**, **2630**
Government Contracts Citator. (US ISSN 0434-2593) **867**, **2630**
Government Contracts Directory. (US ISSN 0072-5137) **1076**
Government Contracts Monographs. (US ISSN 0072-5153) **4061**
Government Contracts Reports. (US) **2630**, **4061**
Government Contracts Service. (US) **1011**, **2630**
Government Development Bank for Puerto Rico. Annual Report. (PR) **783**
Government Development Bank for Puerto Rico. Report of Activities see Government Development Bank for Puerto Rico. Annual Report **783**
†Government Documents and Information Conference. Proceedings.(US) **5200**
Government Employee Relations Report. (US ISSN 0017-260X) **980**, **4061**
Government Employees Insurance Company Direct see G E I C O Direct **2532**
Government Equipment News. (AT ISSN 0728-0874) **1137**, **3017**, **4061**
Government Executive. (US ISSN 0017-2626) **4061**
Government Finance Officers Association Newsletter see G F O A Newsletter **4087**
Government Finance Review. (US) **1096**
Government Funding for United Kingdom Business: A Complete Guide to Sources, Grants and Applicable Procedures. (UK) **867**
Government Gazette. (BH) **2180**
Government Gazette of Mauritius. (MF) **4061**
Government Gazette of Mauritius. Legal Supplement. Act. (MF) **4061**
Government Gazette of Mauritius. Legal Supplement. Government Notice. (MF) **4062**
Government Gazette of Mauritius. Legal Supplement. Proclamation. (MF) **4062**
Government Gazette of Mauritius. Special Legal Supplement. A Bill. (MF) **4062**

†Government Graphics Systems. (US) **5200**
▼Government Green Guide. (CN) **4062**, **1137**, **1866**, **1956**
Government Imprinted Penalty Stationery Society see G I P S **3752**
Government in Hawaii. (US ISSN 0072-517X) **4062**
Government Industrial Development Laboratory, Hokkaido. Annual Report. see Hokkaido Kogyo Kaihatsu Shikenjo Nenpo **1077**
Government Industrial Research Institute, Kyushu. Annual Report. see Kyushu Kogyo Gijutsu Shikenjo Nenpo **1080**
Government Information Quarterly. (US ISSN 0740-624X) **2759**, **4062**
Government Life Insurance Programs for Veterans and Members of the Services. Annual Report. (US) **2532**, **3459**
Government Manager. (US ISSN 0148-7949) **980**
Government Medical Officers' Association. Newsletter. (CE) **3101**
Government Microcomputer Letter. (US ISSN 0882-6587) **4088**
Government of Canada Publications Quarterly Catalogue. (CN ISSN 0709-0412) **401**
†Government Oriental Manuscripts Library. Bulletin. (II) **5200**
Government Primecontracts Monthly. (US ISSN 0887-4085) **1076**
Government Product News. (US ISSN 0017-2642) **4062**, **1040**
Government Product News and Purchasing Digest see Government Product News **4062**
Government Production Prime Contractors Directory. (US ISSN 0887-4107) **1137**
Government Productivity News. (US) **1076**
▼Government Programs. (US ISSN 1055-825X) **4406**, **1115**, **1635**
Government Programs and Projects Directory. (US ISSN 0737-5255) **4062**
Government Publications for Oklahoma see G P O **2758**
Government Publications Guide see Bibliographic Guide to Government Publications - U S **392**
Government Publications Review. (US ISSN 0277-9390) **4062**
Government Publisher. (US) **3999**, **4007**, **4128**, **4143**
Government Purchasing Guide. (CN ISSN 0046-6220) **4062**, **1040**
Government Reference Books. (US ISSN 0072-5188) **401**
Government Relations. (US) **1011**, **4062**
Government Relations Briefing. (US) **4506**
†Government Relations Watch. (US) **5200**
Government Report. (US) **32**, **2630**
Government Reports Announcements and Index Annual Index. (US) **1844**, **4080**
Government Reports Announcements and Index Journal. (US ISSN 0097-9007) **4080**, **13**
Government Research Centers Directory see Government Research Directory **4599**
Government Research Directory. (US ISSN 0882-3766) **4599**
Government-Sponsored Research on Foreign Affairs. (US ISSN 0194-8660) **3958**
Government Standard. (US ISSN 1041-5335) **2583**, **4062**
Government Support for British Business see Government Funding for United Kingdom Business: A Complete Guide to Sources, Grants and Applicable Procedures **867**
Government-Supported Research on Foreign Affairs see Government-Sponsored Research on Foreign Affairs **3958**
Government Surveyors' Association of Sri Lanka. News Sheet. (CE) **1823**
Government Technology. (US ISSN 1043-9668) **4083**

Government Tender Report. (US ISSN 0738-3096) **4744**
Government Traffic Bulletin. (US ISSN 0738-310X) **4745**
Government Training News. (US) **1684**
Government Union Critique. (US ISSN 0738-3312) **980**
Government Union Review. (US ISSN 0270-2487) **980**
Governmental Accounting Standards Board. Action Report. (US) **751**
Governmental Affairs Newsletter. (US) **4062**
Governmental Affairs Review. (US) **4088**
Governmental Finances (Washington) see Current Governments Reports: Government Finances **1092**
Governmental Research Association Directory. (US ISSN 0072-520X) **4062**
Governmental Research Association, Inc. Reporter see G R A Reporter **4061**
Governmental Risk Management Manual. (US) **2532**, **4062**
Governo. (IT) **3896**
Governors' Journal. (US) **2532**
Governors of American States, Commonwealths, and Territories. (US) **419**
Governors' Weekly Bulletin. (US ISSN 0888-8647) **3896**
Gower Federal Service - Mining. (US) **3484**
Gower Federal Service - Outer Continental Shelf. (US) **3484**, **2630**
Gown. (UK ISSN 0017-2693) **1313**
Goya. (SP ISSN 0017-2715) **327**
Gozdarski Vestnik/Slovenian Journal of Forestry. (XV ISSN 0017-2723) **2101**
G'phis see G'plus **2128**
G'plus. (SZ) **2128**
Graafikko see Kirjapainotaito - Graafikko **4002**
Graafschap Jette Bulletin. see Comte de Jette Bulletin **269**
Grab a Nickel. (US) **2920**
Gracas do Servo de Deus: Padre Cruz. (PO ISSN 0017-2758) **4180**
Gracas Padre Cruz, S.J. (PO) **4180**
Grace. (UK ISSN 0046-6239) **4180**
Grace and Truth. (SA ISSN 1012-5930) **4265**, **3942**
Grace Baptist Mission Herald. (UK) **4239**
Grace, Kennedy Foundation. Annual Report. (JM) **4406**
Grace Theological Journal. (US ISSN 0198-666X) **4180**
Grace Tidings. (US) **1313**, **4180**
Gracie's Index see South African Law Reports, Index & Noter-Up **2680**
Gracious Stays and Special Places. (US) **4769**
Gradbeni Vestnik. (XV ISSN 0017-2774) **618**, **1866**
Gradhiva. (FR ISSN 0764-8928) **240**
Gradina. (YU ISSN 0436-2616) **2239**
Gradinarska i Lozarska Nauka/Horticultural and Viticultural Science. (BU ISSN 0436-2624) **2128**
Gradinarstvo. (BU) **162**
Gradiva. (US ISSN 0363-8057) **2920**
Gradjevinski Fakultet. Institut za Materijale i Konstrukcije. Zbornik Istrazivackih Radova see Zbornik Istrazivackih Radova iz Oblasti Materijala u Gradjevinarstvu **1876**
Graduate Assistantship Directory in Computer Sciences. (US) **1425**
Graduate Careers. (UK ISSN 0017-2804) **3627**
Graduate Careers Council of Australia Ltd. Newsletter see G C C A Newsletter **1707**
Graduate Careers in Engineering. (AT ISSN 1032-2663) **1917**
Graduate Computerworld. (CN) **1395**, **1707**
Graduate Education in Nursing. (US) **3278**, **1694**, **1707**
Graduate Fellowship Awards Announced by National Science Foundation. (US ISSN 0072-5250) **1707**

6226 GRADUATE FORUM

Graduate Forum. (PH ISSN 0116-6417) **4311**
Graduate Library Education Programs. (US) **2759**
Graduate Library School Programs *see* Graduate Library Education Programs **2759**
Graduate Management Admission Test Official Guide for G M A T Review *see* Official Guide for G M A T Review **1022**
Graduate Management Research. (US ISSN 0264-6943) **1011**
Graduate Outlook. (AT ISSN 0314-0679) **3627**
Graduate Programs in Public Affairs and Public Administration. (US) **4062**
Graduate Programs: Physics, Astronomy, and Related Fields (Year). (US ISSN 0147-1821) **1707, 364, 3819**
Graduate Research in Education and Related Disciplines *see* Graduate Research in Urban Education and Related Disciplines **1707**
Graduate Research in Urban Education and Related Disciplines. (US) **1707**
Graduate School Guide. (US) **1694, 4265**
Graduate School Journal. (PH ISSN 0115-3110) **1727, 1707, 4062, 4436**
Graduate School Programs in Public Affairs and Public Administration *see* Graduate Programs in Public Affairs and Public Administration **4062**
Graduate Science Education Student Support and Postdoctorals *see* U.S. National Science Foundation. Selected Data on Students and Postdoctorals in Science & Engineering **1718**
Graduate Studies. (UK) **1707**
Graduate Study in Psychology and Associated Fields. (US) **4022, 1694**
Graduate Texts in Contemporary Physics. (US) **3819**
Graduate Texts in Mathematics. (US ISSN 0072-5285) **3037**
Graduate Training in Behavior Therapy and Experimental-Clinical Psychology.(US) **4022, 1694**
Graduate Woman *see* A A U W Outlook **1698**
Graduating Engineer. (US ISSN 0193-2276) **1823, 3627**
Graefe's Archive for Clinical and Experimental Ophthalmology/V. Graefes Archiv fuer Klinische und Experimentelle Ophthalmologie. (GW ISSN 0721-832X) **3301**
Graezer Beitraege. (AU) **2364**
Graffiti *see* City Reflections **1307**
Graffiti. (CN) **1313**
Graffiti. (IT) **2983**
†Graffiti. (US) **5201**
Grafia *see* Dansk Grafia **3998**
Grafia. (SW ISSN 0017-288X) **3999**
Grafiber News. (US) **3862**
Graficas Mundiales. (GW) **3999**
Grafico. (PO ISSN 0017-2928) **3999**
Grafico. (AG ISSN 0017-291X) **4473**
Graficus. (NE ISSN 0017-2936) **3999**
Graficus Magazine. (NE) **3999**
Grafiek. (BE ISSN 0017-2944) **3999**
Grafik Design und Technik *see* Designers Digest **324**
Grafisch Nederland. (NE ISSN 0922-1328) **4000, 1011**
Grafisch Nieuws. *see* Nouvelles Graphiques **4003**
Grafisk. (NO) **4000**
Grafisk Faktorstidning. (SW ISSN 0017-2979) **4000**
Grafisk Leverandoerhaandbog. (DK) **4000**
De Grafiske Fag. (DK ISSN 0017-2995) **4000, 4128**
Grafiskt Forum. (SW ISSN 0017-3002) **4000**
▼Graham Group. (US ISSN 1057-8218) **2153**
Graham House Review. (US ISSN 0145-7780) **2920**
Graham's Town Series. (SA) **419**
Grail. (CN ISSN 0828-4083) **4180**
Grain. (CN ISSN 0315-7423) **2920**

Grain Age. (US ISSN 0017-3029) **206**
Grain and Feed Market News. (US) **206, 217**
Grain & Feed Marketing. (US) **206, 1040**
Grain and Feedstuffs, California Market Summary and Average Prices. (US) **206**
Grain Directory - Buyers's Guide *see* Grain Guide - North American Grain Yearbook **1137**
Grain Facts. (CN ISSN 0381-2472) **206, 217**
Grain Guide - North American Grain Yearbook. (US) **1137, 206**
Grain Journal. (US ISSN 0274-7138) **206**
Grain Market News *see* Grain and Feed Market News **206**
Grain Matters. (CN ISSN 0383-4417) **206**
Grain Transportation Situation. (US) **4650, 206**
Grainews. (CN ISSN 0229-8090) **206**
Grainger Journal *see* Grainger Society Journal **3553**
Grainger Society Journal. (UK ISSN 0141-5085) **3553**
Grainlist (Year). (CN) **1137, 94**
Grains *see* Negoce et Agriculture **185**
The Gram. (US) **1736**
Gram Shilp. (II) **4311, 4599**
Grammateion. (CN) **2867, 327**
Gramophone. (UK ISSN 0017-310X) **4460**
Gramophone Classical Catalogue *see* The Classical Catalogue **3546**
Gramophone Classical Record Catalogue *see* The Classical Catalogue **3546**
Gramophone Spoken Word and Miscellaneous Catalogue *see* Gramophone Spoken Word Catalogue **4460**
Gramophone Spoken Word Catalogue. (UK) **4460**
Gran Musical. (SP) **3553**
Grana. (SW ISSN 0017-3134) **504**
Grana Palynologica *see* Grana **504**
Grand Angle *see* Cine-Fiches de Grand Angle **3505**
Le Grand Baton. (US ISSN 0434-3336) **3553**
Grand-Duche de Luxembourg en Chiffres (Year). (LU) **3992**
Grand Froid. (FR ISSN 0769-6833) **2071**
Grand Gourmet. (IT) **2474**
Grand Hotel. (IT) **2983**
Le Grand Huit. (FR ISSN 0982-9873) **4633, 1530, 3553**
Grand Invalide. (FR) **3459**
Grand Manan Historian. (CN ISSN 0316-2702) **2407**
Grand Nest Bulletin. (US). **1298**
Grand Prix. (TH) **2220**
Grand Rapids Business Journal. (US ISSN 1045-4055) **835**
Grand Rapids Magazine. (US ISSN 1055-5145) **2226**
Grand Rapids Parent. (US ISSN 1055-5153) **1238**
Grand River Valley Review. (US ISSN 0739-084X) **2407**
†Grand Slam. (CN ISSN 0701-0745) **5201**
Grand Street. (US ISSN 0734-5496) **2920**
Grand View Garden of Science. Journal. *see* Kexue Daguanyuan **4320**
▼Grandchild. (US) **1238**
Grande Gap. (IT) **1285**
Grande Hotel. (BL ISSN 0017-3142) **2983**
Grande Ilusao. (PO) **3511**
Grande Sinal. (BL ISSN 0046-6271) **4180**
Grandes Figures de la Charite. (FR ISSN 0072-5404) **2364**
Grandes Todos. (UY ISSN 0072-5439) **2920**
Grandes Vultos da Engenharia Brasileira. (BL) **1823**
Il Grandevetro. (IT) **2867**
Le Grandi Automobili/Great Cars. (IT ISSN 0392-6796) **4691**
GrandMasters. (US) **3802**

Grands Notables du Premier Empire. (FR) **419**
Grands Reportages. (FR ISSN 0182-0346) **2867**
Grange Advocate. (US) **94, 1298**
Grange Advocate for Rural Pennsylvania *see* Grange Advocate **94**
Grange News. (US) **94**
Grani. (GW ISSN 0017-3185) **2920**
Granite State Libraries. (US ISSN 0046-6301) **2759**
Granite State School Leader. (US) **1635**
Granja Avicola. (BL) **217**
Granma Internacional (Portuguese Edition). (CU ISSN 0864-4632) **3896**
Granma Internacional (Spanish Edition). (CU ISSN 0864-4616) **3896**
Granma International (English Edition). (CU ISSN 0864-4624) **3896**
Granma International (French Edition). (CU ISSN 0864-4640) **3896**
Grant Advisor. (US ISSN 0740-5383) **1707**
Grant Alert. (US) **1096, 2487, 4718**
Grant Guides. (US) **4426**
Granta. (UK ISSN 0017-3231) **2867**
Grantechs. (US ISSN 0145-8302) **401**
Granthagar. (II ISSN 0017-324X) **2759**
Granthalaya Vijnana. (II) **2759**
Grantham and Melton Trader. (UK) **2194**
Grants and Aid to Individuals in the Arts *see* National Directory of Grants and Aid to Individuals in the Arts, International **337**
Grants and Awards Available to American Writers. (US ISSN 0092-5268) **2920**
Grants for Graduate Students (Year) *see* Peterson's Grants for Graduate Students (Year) **1714**
Grants for Study Visits by University Administrators and Librarians *see* Awards for University Administrators and Librarians **1701**
†Grants Magazine. (US ISSN 0160-9734) **5201**
Grants Newsletter *see* Grantechs **401**
Grants Register. (UK) **1707**
Grants Register. (UK ISSN 0017-1722) **1722**
Grape Grower. (US ISSN 1049-670X) **178**
Grape Pest Control Guide. (US) **178**
Grapevine (Normal). (US) **1707, 1727**
Grapevine (Seaside). (US) **2453, 4844**
Grapevine Weekly. (US) **2226**
Graphic Arts Abstracts *see* G A T F World **3999**
Graphic Arts Blue Book. Delaware Valley-Ohio Edition. (US ISSN 1044-7970) **4000**
Graphic Arts Blue Book. Metro New York - New Jersey Edition. (US ISSN 1044-8527) **4000**
Graphic Arts Blue Book. Midwestern Edition. (US ISSN 1044-8535) **4000**
Graphic Arts Blue Book. Northeastern Edition. (US ISSN 1044-646X) **4000**
Graphic Arts Blue Book. Southeastern Edition. (US ISSN 1044-7989) **4000**
Graphic Arts Blue Book. West Coast Edition. (US) **4000**
Graphic Arts Japan. (JA) **327**
Graphic Arts Literature Abstracts *see* Institute of Paper Science and Technology. Graphic Arts Bulletin **4007**
Graphic Arts Monthly. (US ISSN 1047-9325) **4000**
Graphic Arts Monthly and the Printing Industry *see* Graphic Arts Monthly **4000**
Graphic Arts Product News (Chicago). (US ISSN 0274-5976) **4000**
Graphic Arts Research Center Newsletter *see* T & E News **4006**
†Graphic Arts Technical Foundation. Research Project Report. (US ISSN 0096-1159) **5201**

Graphic Arts Technical Foundation Education Report *see* G A T F Education Report **5198**
Graphic Arts Technical Foundation Second Sight *see* G A T F Second Sight **4598**
Graphic Arts Technical Foundation World *see* G A T F World **3999**
Graphic Communications Association Bar Code Reporter *see* G C A Bar Code Reporter **1450**
Graphic Communications Association Review *see* G C A Review **4007**
Graphic Communications World. (US) **4000, 4128**
Graphic Design: U S A. (US ISSN 0274-7499) **32, 4000**
Graphic Fund Forecaster. (US) **948**
Graphic Interface Conference. Proceedings *see* Graphics Interface. Proceedings - Comptes Rendus **1427**
Graphic Monthly. (CN ISSN 0227-2806) **4000**
Graphic Network. (US) **4000**
Graphic Work of Birger Sandzen. (US) **327**
Graphical Journal *see* Print **4003**
Graphical Survey of the Economy of Taiwan District, Republic of China. (CH) **867**
GraphiCommunicator. (US ISSN 0746-3626) **2583, 4000**
Graphics (Kissimmee) *see* Southern Graphics **4006**
Graphics Interface. Proceedings - Comptes Rendus. (CN ISSN 0713-5424) **1427**
Graphics Technology *see* Computer Graphics Technology **5170**
Graphics: U S A *see* Graphic Design: U S A **32**
Graphics Update. (US) **4000**
Graphics World. (UK ISSN 0142-8853) **327**
Graphicus. (IT ISSN 0017-3436) **4000**
Graphis. (SZ ISSN 0017-3452) **327, 32, 4000**
Graphis Annual *see* Graphis Design **327**
Graphis Design. (SZ) **327, 32, 4000**
Graphis Photo. (SZ) **3791**
Graphis Posters. (SZ) **327, 3791**
Graphisch Orgaan. (NE) **4000**
Graphische Kunst. (GW ISSN 0342-3158) **327**
Graphische Lehr- und Versuchsanstalt Mitteilungen *see* G L V Mitteilungen **3999**
Graphische Revue Oesterreichs. (AU ISSN 0017-3479) **4000**
Graphische Unternehmungen Oesterreichs. Jahrbuch. (AU ISSN 0075-2266) **4000**
Graphische Woche *see* Druckwelt **3998**
Graphiti *see* In Brief **330**
Graphix. (SA) **4000**
Graphix. (AT) **4000**
Graphoscope. (CN ISSN 0046-631X) **948**
Graphs and Combinatorics. (GW ISSN 0911-0119) **3064**
Graphs and Notes on the Economic Situation in the Community *see* European Economy **864**
Grasas y Aceites. (SP ISSN 0017-3495) **1218**
Grasduinen. (NE) **504, 583**
Grashuepfer. (IS) **1255**
Grasp. (UK) **4473**
Grass and Forage Science. (UK ISSN 0142-5242) **94**
Grass & Grain. (US) **206**
Grass Roots. (AT ISSN 0310-2890) **4436, 94, 240**
†Grass-Roots (Poole). (UK ISSN 0262-4753) **5201**
Grass Roots Campaigning. (US) **3896**
Grass Roots Perspectives on American History. (US ISSN 0148-771X) **2407**
Grassland Society of Southern Africa. Journal. (SA ISSN 0256-6702) **179**

Grassland Society of Southern Africa. Proceedings of the Annual Congresses *see* Grassland Society of Southern Africa. Journal 179
Grasslands Review. (US) 2994
Grasso Contact. (NE) 3017
Grassortiment *see* Grasso Contact 3017
Grassroots. (US) 1488
Grassroots. (PK) 2338
Grassroots. (Association of Development Agencies in Bangladesh) (BG) 4406
Grassroots Catalog. (US) 2168
Grassroots Development. (US ISSN 0733-6608) 930, 240, 4436
Grassroots Editor. (US ISSN 0017-3541) 2570
Grassroots Fundraising Journal. (US ISSN 0740-4832) 4406
Grassroots Motorsports. (US) 4692
Gratia. (GW ISSN 0343-1258) 2364
Graue Literatur zur Orts Regional- und Landesplanung. (GW ISSN 0340-112X) 2487
Grauer Panther. (GW ISSN 0178-5109) 2273, 3942
Graves Family Newsletter. (US ISSN 0146-0269) 2153
Graveur Flexograf. (GW ISSN 0015-7775) 4000
Gravida. (US ISSN 0191-0760) 2994
Gravida-Bridging *see* Gravida 2994
Gravure Bulletin *see* Gravure Magazine 4000
Gravure Environmental Newsletter. (US ISSN 0271-1699) 4000
Gravure Magazine. (US) 4000
▼Gray Areas. (US) 3553
Gray Panther Network. (US) 2273
Gray Sheet. (US) 3101
Graya. (UK) 2630
Graybar Outlook. (US ISSN 0017-3592) 1893
Gray's Sporting Journal. (US ISSN 0273-6691) 4547
†Grayson Gateway. (US) 5201
Grayson Gram. (US) 4810
Graywolf Annual. (US ISSN 0743-7471) 2920
Grazer Beitraege. (AU) 273, 1277
Grazer Linguistische Studien. (AU) 2816, 4436
Grazer Philosophische Studien. (NE ISSN 0165-9227) 3767
Grazhdanskaya Aviatsiya. (RU ISSN 0017-3606) 4673
Grazia. (IT) 4844
Great Activities Newspaper. (US ISSN 0743-5606) 1635, 3802
Great American Orators. (US ISSN 0898-8277) 401
▼Great American Video Business Newsletter. (US ISSN 1051-6050) 1385
Great Barrier Reef Marine Park Authority Bulletin *see* Great Barrier Reef Marine Park Authority Newsletter 5201
†Great Barrier Reef Marine Park Authority Newsletter. (AT) 5201
Great Barrier Reef Marine Park Authority Workshop Series. (AT ISSN 0156-5842) 1604
Great Basin Naturalist. (US ISSN 0017-3614) 504, 583
Great Basin Naturalist Memoirs. (US ISSN 0160-239X) 504, 583
Great Body. (US) 3802, 3606
Great Britain. Advisory Conciliation Arbitration Service. Work Research Unit. Information Service News and Abstracts *see* Great Britain. Advisory Conciliation Arbitration Service. Work Research Unit. News and Abstracts 718
Great Britain. Advisory Conciliation Arbitration Service. Work Research Unit. News and Abstracts. (UK ISSN 0960-2615) 718, 13
Great Britain. Air Transport Licensing Board. Report *see* Great Britain. Civil Aviation Authority. Annual Report and Accounts 4673
Great Britain. Air Transport Users Committee Annual Report. (UK) 4673

Great Britain. Atomic Energy Research Establishment. Harwell Information Bulletin *see* Great Britain. Harwell Laboratory. Harwell Information Bulletin 401
Great Britain. B A A Annual Report and Accounts. (UK) 4673
Great Britain. Board of Inland Revenue. The Survey of Personal Incomes. (UK) 1096, 999
Great Britain. British Airports Authority. Annual Report and Accounts *see* Great Britain. B A A Annual Report and Accounts 4673
Great Britain. British Geological Survey. Classical Areas of British Geology. (UK) 1567
Great Britain. British Geological Survey. Geomagnetic Bulletin. (UK) 1590
Great Britain. British Geological Survey. Memoirs. (UK) 1567
Great Britain. British Geological Survey. Overseas Geology and Mineral Resources. (UK ISSN 0030-7467) 1567, 3484
Great Britain. British Geological Survey. Overseas Memoirs. (UK ISSN 0951-6646) 1567
Great Britain. Building Research Establishment. Annual Report *see* Great Britain. Building Research Establishment. Annual Review 618
Great Britain. Building Research Establishment. Annual Review. (UK) 618
Great Britain. Building Research Establishment. B R E Digests. (UK) 618
Great Britain. Building Research Establishment. Reports. (UK) 2033, 618, 2114
Great Britain. Central Office of Information. Overseas Publications Division. Reference Pamphlets Series.(UK ISSN 0072-5722) 2364
Great Britain. Central Statistical Office. Annual Abstract of Statistics. (UK ISSN 0072-5730) 4572
Great Britain. Central Statistical Office. Annual Census of Production Reports. (UK) 718
Great Britain. Central Statistical Office. Business Monitor. (UK) 667
Great Britain. Central Statistical Office. Financial Statistics. (UK ISSN 0015-203X) 718, 4572
Great Britain. Central Statistical Office. Guide to Official Statistics. (UK ISSN 0261-1791) 4572
Great Britain. Central Statistical Office. Monthly Digest of Statistics. (UK ISSN 0308-6666) 4572
Great Britain. Central Statistical Office. Regional Statistics *see* Great Britain. Central Statistical Office. Regional Trends 4572
Great Britain. Central Statistical Office. Regional Trends. (UK ISSN 0261-1783) 4572
Great Britain. Central Statistical Office. Research Series. (UK ISSN 0072-5757) 4572
Great Britain. Central Statistical Office. Social Trends. (UK ISSN 0072-5765) 4436
Great Britain. Central Statistical Office. Statistical News. (UK ISSN 0017-3630) 4572
Great Britain. Central Statistical Office. Studies in Official Statistics. (UK ISSN 0081-8313) 4572
Great Britain. Civil Aviation Authority. Annual Report and Accounts. (UK ISSN 0306-3569) 4673
Great Britain. Civil Aviation Authority. Annual Statistics *see* Great Britain. Civil Aviation Authority. U.K. Airports Annual Statements of Movements, Passengers and Cargo 4673
Great Britain. Civil Aviation Authority. C A A Monthly Operating and Traffic Statistics *see* Great Britain. Civil Aviation Authority. U.K. Airlines Monthly Operating & Traffic Statistics 4663

Great Britain. Civil Aviation Authority. C A A Monthly Operating and Traffic Statistics *see* Great Britain. Civil Aviation Authority. U.K. Airports Monthly Statements of Movements, Passengers and Cargo 4663
Great Britain. Civil Aviation Authority. General Aviation Airmiss Bulletin. (UK) 4673
Great Britain. Civil Aviation Authority. General Aviation Airmisses *see* Great Britain. Civil Aviation Authority. General Aviation Airmiss Bulletin 4673
Great Britain. Civil Aviation Authority. General Aviation Safety Information Leaflets. (UK ISSN 0309-667X) 4673
Great Britain. Civil Aviation Authority. International Register of Civil Aircraft.(UK) 4673
Great Britain. Civil Aviation Authority. Library Bulletin. (UK ISSN 0141-9498) 4673
Great Britain. Civil Aviation Authority. U.K. Airlines Annual Operating, Traffic & Financial Statistics. (UK) 4673
Great Britain. Civil Aviation Authority. U.K. Airlines Monthly Operating & Traffic Statistics. (UK) 4663
Great Britain. Civil Aviation Authority. U.K. Airports Annual Statements of Movements, Passengers and Cargo. (UK) 4673
Great Britain. Civil Aviation Authority. U.K. Airports Monthly Statements of Movements, Passengers and Cargo. (UK) 4663
Great Britain. Civil Aviation Board. C A A Monthly Statistics *see* Great Britain. Civil Aviation Authority. U.K. Airlines Monthly Operating & Traffic Statistics 4663
Great Britain. Committee on Safety of Medicines. Report *see* Great Britain. Medicines Commission. Annual Report 4102
Great Britain. Commonwealth Association of Surveying and Land Economy. Survey Review. (UK) 1866, 1567
Great Britain. Department of Education and Science. Annual Report. (UK) 1635
Great Britain. Department of Education and Science. Architects and Building Branch. Broadsheets. (UK ISSN 0260-0471) 1727
Great Britain. Department of Education and Science. Building Bulletins. (UK ISSN 0072-5870) 1727
Great Britain. Department of Education and Science. Computer Board for Universities and Research Councils. Report. (UK ISSN 0072-582X) 1395
Great Britain. Department of Education and Science. Education Surveys. (UK ISSN 0072-5897) 1635
Great Britain. Department of Education and Science. Safety in Education. (UK ISSN 0262-5229) 4102, 1635, 3617
Great Britain. Department of Education and Science. Statistics of Education. (UK ISSN 0072-5900) 1677
Great Britain. Department of Employment. Changes in Rates of Wages and Hours of Work *see* Great Britain. Department of Employment. Statistics Division. Time Rates of Wages and Hours of Work 718
Great Britain. Department of Employment. Employment Gazette. (UK ISSN 0013-6859) 980
Great Britain. Department of Employment. Family Expenditure Survey. (UK ISSN 0072-5927) 999
Great Britain. Department of Employment. New Earnings Survey. (UK ISSN 0308-1419) 980
Great Britain. Department of Employment. Research. (UK) 980
Great Britain. Department of Employment. Statistics Division. Time Rates of Wages and Hours of Work. (UK) 718

Great Britain. Department of Employment. Work Research Unit. Information System Abstract *see* Great Britain. Advisory Conciliation Arbitration Service. Work Research Unit. News and Abstracts 718
Great Britain. Department of Energy. Development of the Oil and Gas Resources of the United Kingdom. (UK) 3688, 1790
Great Britain. Department of Energy. Publications. (UK ISSN 0951-855X) 1790, 1844
Great Britain. Department of Energy. Publications in Print *see* Great Britain. Department of Energy. Publications 1790
Great Britain. Department of Health and Social Security. Health Building Notes. (UK) 2461, 4406
Great Britain. Department of Health and Social Security. Health Equipment Notes. (UK ISSN 0141-1403) 2461, 4406
Great Britain. Department of Health and Social Security. Hospital Building Notes *see* Great Britain. Department of Health and Social Security. Health Building Notes 2461
Great Britain. Department of Health and Social Security. Hospital Equipment Notes *see* Great Britain. Department of Health and Social Security. Health Equipment Notes 2461
Great Britain. Department of Health and Social Security. Hospital In-Patient Inquiry. (UK ISSN 0072-6036) 4102, 4406
Great Britain. Department of Health and Social Security. On the State of the Public Health. (UK ISSN 0072-6087) 4102
Great Britain. Department of Health and Social Security. Social Security Statistics. (UK) 4406
†Great Britain. Department of the Environment and Department of Transport. Library. Library Bulletin. (UK ISSN 0140-170X) 5201
Great Britain. Department of the Environment and Department of Transport. Library Services. Annual List of Publications. (UK ISSN 0141-2604) 1974
Great Britain. Department of the Environment. Fire Research Station. Fire Notes *see* Great Britain. Building Research Establishment. Reports 2033
Great Britain. Department of the Environment. Fire Research Station. Technical Papers *see* Great Britain. Building Research Establishment. Reports 2033
Great Britain. Department of the Environment. Housing and Construction Statistics. (UK ISSN 0308-9819) 638
Great Britain. Department of the Environment. Library Services. D.O.E. Annual List of Publications *see* Great Britain. Department of the Environment and Department of Transport. Library Services. Annual List of Publications 1974
Great Britain. Department of the Environment. Local Government Financial Statistics: England and Wales. (UK ISSN 0308-1745) 4080, 718, 1096, 4088
Great Britain. Department of the Environment. Local Housing Statistics: England and Wales. (UK) 2500
Great Britain. Department of the Environment. Report on Research and Development. (UK) 1956, 4436
Great Britain. Department of Trade and Industry. Business Statistics Office Report on the Census of Production *see* Great Britain. Central Statistical Office. Annual Census of Production Reports 718
Great Britain. Department of Trade and Industry. Digest of Energy Statistics *see* Digest of United Kingdom Energy Statistics 1798

Great Britain. Department of Trade. Bankruptcy: General Annual Report *see* Great Britain. Department of Trade. Insolvency: General Annual Report **783**
Great Britain. Department of Trade. Companies: General Annual Report. (UK ISSN 0072-565X) **1076**
Great Britain. Department of Trade. Dealers in Securities and Authorised Unit Trust Schemes. (UK) **948**
Great Britain. Department of Trade. Insolvency: General Annual Report. (UK) **783**
Great Britain. Department of Trade. Insurance Business: Annual Report. (UK ISSN 0308-499X) **2532**
Great Britain. Department of Trade. Particulars of Dealers in Securities and of Trust Units *see* Great Britain. Department of Trade. Dealers in Securities and Authorised Unit Trust Schemes **948**
Great Britain. Department of Trade. Patents, Design and Trade Marks (Annual Report). (UK ISSN 0072-5706) **3675**
Great Britain. Departments of the Environment and Transport. Library. Library Bulletin *see* Great Britain. Department of the Environment and Department of Transport. Library. Library Bulletin **5201**
Great Britain. Directorate of Overseas Surveys. Survey Review *see* Great Britain. Commonwealth Association of Surveying and Land Economy. Survey Review **1866**
Great Britain. Economic and Social Research Council. Annual Report. (UK ISSN 0266-2043) **4373**
Great Britain. Economic & Social Research Council. Bursary Handbook.(UK) **4373,** 1707
Great Britain. Economic and Social Research Council. Report *see* Great Britain. Economic and Social Research Council. Annual Report **4373**
Great Britain. Economic & Social Research Council. Studentship Handbook. (UK) **4373,** 1707
†Great Britain. Electricity Council. Annual Report and Accounts. (UK ISSN 0307-1146) **5201**
Great Britain. Foreign and Commonwealth Office. Treaty Series. (UK ISSN 0072-6397) **3958**
Great Britain. General Register Office. Studies on Medical and Population Subjects. (UK ISSN 0072-6400) **3982,** 3101
Great Britain. H.M.S.O. Government Publications Sectional Lists. (UK) **618**
Great Britain. Harwell Laboratory. Harwell Information Bulletin. (UK ISSN 0144-6053) **401,** 4311
Great Britain. Health and Safety Executive. Health and Safety: Coal Mines. (UK) **3484**
Great Britain. Health and Safety Executive. Health and Safety: Mines. (UK) **3484**
Great Britain. Health and Safety Executive. Health and Safety: Quarries. (UK) **3484**
Great Britain. Home Office. Probation Statistics England & Wales (Year). (UK ISSN 0265-573X) **1515**
Great Britain. Home Office. Research Studies. (UK ISSN 0072-6435) **1515**
Great Britain. House of Commons. Parliamentary Debates. (UK) **4062**
Great Britain. Institute of Animal Physiology and Genetics Research. Report. (UK) **572,** 543
Great Britain. Institute of Animal Physiology. Report *see* Great Britain. Institute of Animal Physiology and Genetics Research. Report **572**
Great Britain. Institute of Geological Sciences. Classical Areas of British Geology *see* Great Britain. British Geological Survey. Classical Areas of British Geology **1567**
Great Britain. Institute of Geological Sciences. Geomagnetic Bulletin *see* Great Britain. British Geological Survey. Geomagnetic Bulletin **1590**
Great Britain. Institute of Geological Sciences. Memoirs of the Geological Survey of Great Britain *see* Great Britain. British Geological Survey. Memoirs **1567**
Great Britain. Institute of Geological Sciences. Overseas Geology and Mineral Resources *see* Great Britain. British Geological Survey. Overseas Geology and Mineral Resources **1567**
Great Britain. Institute of Geological Sciences. Overseas Memoirs *see* Great Britain. British Geological Survey. Overseas Memoirs **1567**
Great Britain. Institute of Terrestrial Ecology. Merlewood Research and Development Paper. (UK ISSN 0308-3675) **440**
Great Britain. Laboratory of the Government Chemist. Annual Report of the Government Chemist. (UK ISSN 0072-6524) **1177**
Great Britain. Land Resources Development Centre. Progress Report *see* Great Britain. Natural Resources Institute. Annual Report **930**
Great Britain. Medical Research Council. Annual Report (Year). (UK ISSN 0141-2256) **3101**
Great Britain. Medical Research Council. Handbook (Year). (UK ISSN 0309-0132) **3101**
Great Britain. Medical Research Council. Report *see* Great Britain. Medical Research Council. Annual Report (Year) **3101**
Great Britain. Medicines Commission. Annual Report. (UK) **4102**
Great Britain. Meteorological Office. Annual Report. (UK ISSN 0072-6605) **3435**
Great Britain. Meteorological Office. Monthly Weather Report. (UK ISSN 0027-0636) **3436**
Great Britain. Ministry of Agriculture, Fisheries and Food. Directorate of Fisheries Research. Aquatic Environment Monitoring Report. (UK ISSN 0142-2499) **1956,** 2042
Great Britain. Ministry of Agriculture, Fisheries and Food. Directorate of Fisheries Research. Fishing Prospects *see* Great Britain. Ministry of Agriculture, Fisheries and Food. Directorate of Fisheries Research. Fisheries Spotlight **2042**
Great Britain. Ministry of Agriculture, Fisheries and Food. Directorate of Fisheries Research. Fisheries Research Technical Report. (UK ISSN 0308-5589) **2042,** 1956
Great Britain. Ministry of Agriculture, Fisheries and Food. Directorate of Fisheries Research. Fisheries Spotlight. (UK ISSN 0955-2855) **2042**
Great Britain. Ministry of Agriculture, Fisheries and Food. Directorate of Fisheries Research. Laboratory Leaflet. (UK ISSN 0143-8018) **2042**
Great Britain. Ministry of Agriculture, Fisheries and Food. Directorate of Fisheries Research. Report of the Director of Fisheries Research. *see* Great Britain. Ministry of Agriculture, Fisheries and Food. Research into Fisheries and the Marine Environment. Report of the Director of Fisheries Research **2042**
Great Britain. Ministry of Agriculture, Fisheries and Food. Research into Fisheries and the Marine Environment. Report of the Director of Fisheries Research. (UK) **2042,** 1956
Great Britain. Ministry of Agriculture, Fisheries and Food. Technical Bulletin.(UK ISSN 0072-6729) **94**
Great Britain. National Film Finance Corporation. Annual Report. (UK ISSN 0072-6958) **3511**
Great Britain. National Health Service. Health Services Costing Returns *see* England and Wales National Health Service. Health Services Costing Returns **5186**
Great Britain. Natural Environment Research Council. Institute of Terrestrial Ecology. Annual Report. (UK) **1956**
Great Britain. Natural Environment Research Council. Report *see* Great Britain. Natural Environment Research Council. Institute of Terrestrial Ecology. Annual Report **1956**
Great Britain. Natural Environment Research Council. Report. (UK ISSN 0308-1125) **1956**
Great Britain. Natural Resources Institute. Annual Report. (UK) **930**
Great Britain. Natural Resources Institute. Bulletin. (UK) **1488,** 930
Great Britain. Office of Fair Trading. Report. (UK) **2630**
Great Britain. Office of Population Censuses and Surveys. Population Estimates: England and Wales. (UK) **3982**
Great Britain. Overseas Development Administration. Report on Research and Development. (UK ISSN 0950-9593) **930**
Great Britain. Overseas Development Natural Resources Institute *see* Great Britain. Natural Resources Institute. Annual Report **930**
Great Britain. Overseas Development Natural Resources Institute. Bulletin *see* Great Britain. Natural Resources Institute. Bulletin **1488**
†Great Britain. Property Services Agency. Construction References. (UK ISSN 0306-0152) **5201**
Great Britain. Public Works Loan Board. Report. (UK ISSN 0072-7032) **4062**
Great Britain. Royal Army Chaplains' Department. Journal. (UK) **3459,** 4180
Great Britain. Royal Commission on Ancient and Historical Monuments in Wales. Interim Report. (UK) **2364,** 273
Great Britain. Royal Commission on Historical Manuscripts. Secretary's Report to the Commissioners. (UK ISSN 0533-9685) **2311**
Great Britain. Royal Commission on the Ancient and Historical Monuments and Constructions in Wales and Monmouthshire. Interim Report *see* Great Britain. Royal Commission on Ancient and Historical Monuments in Wales. Interim Report **2364**
Great Britain. Royal Commission on the Ancient and Historical Monuments and Constructions of England. Interim Report *see* Great Britain. Royal Commission on the Historical Monuments of England. Interim Report **273**
Great Britain. Royal Commission on the Historical Monuments of England. Interim Report. (UK) **273,** 300
Great Britain. Royal Commission on the Historical Monuments of England. Newsletter. (UK ISSN 0957-0241) **273,** 2364
†Great Britain. Royal Greenwich Observatory. Annual Report. (UK ISSN 0308-3322) **5201**
Great Britain. Schools Council Publications. Curriculum Bulletins. (UK ISSN 0072-7113) **1750**
Great Britain. Schools Council Publications. Examinations Bulletins. (UK ISSN 0072-7121) **1636**
Great Britain. Schools Council Publications. Working Papers. (UK ISSN 0072-713X) **1636**
Great Britain. Science Research Council. Report *see* Science and Engineering Research Council. Report **4339**
†Great Britain. Scottish Health Services Planning Council. Annual Report. (UK ISSN 0080-7877) **5201**
Great Britain. Scottish Law Commission. Annual Report. (UK ISSN 0080-7915) **2631**
Great Britain. Sea Fish Industry Authority. Annual Report and Accounts. (UK) **2042**
Great Britain. Sea Fish Industry Authority. European Supplies Bulletin.(UK ISSN 0142-937X) **2042**
Great Britain. Sea Fish Industry Authority. Fisheries Economics Newsletter. (UK ISSN 0309-4294) **2042,** 867
Great Britain. Sea Fish Industry Authority. Household Fish Consumption in Great Britain. (UK ISSN 0262-3269) **2042**
Great Britain. Sea Fish Industry Authority. Key Indicators. (UK ISSN 0953-8348) **2051**
Great Britain. Sea Fish Industry Authority. Trade Bulletin. (UK) **2042,** 910
Great Britain. Social Science Research Council. Bursary Scheme *see* Great Britain. Economic & Social Research Council. Bursary Handbook **4373**
Great Britain. Social Science Research Council. Studentship Handbook *see* Great Britain. Economic & Social Research Council. Studentship Handbook **4373**
Great Britain. Soil Survey of England and Wales. Bulletin. (UK) **179**
Great Britain. Soil Survey of England and Wales. Records. (UK ISSN 0072-7180) **179**
†Great Britain. Soil Survey of England and Wales. Report. (UK ISSN 0072-7199) **5201**
Great Britain. Soil Survey of England and Wales. Special Surveys. (UK ISSN 0072-7202) **179**
Great Britain. Soil Survey of England and Wales. Technical Monographs. (UK ISSN 0072-7210) **179**
Great Britain. Treasury. Supply Estimates. (UK) **1096**
†Great Britain. University Grants Committee. Annual Survey. (UK ISSN 0072-7237) **5201**
Great Britain. Warren Spring Laboratory. Annual Review. (UK ISSN 0141-3279) **1956**
Great Britain. Warren Spring Laboratory. U K Smoke and Sulphur Dioxide Monitoring Networks. (UK) **1977,** 1956
Great Britain. Water Resources Board. Report. (UK ISSN 0072-7253) **4824**
Great Britain (Year). (US ISSN 0896-8683) **4769**
Great Britain and Ireland (Year) *see* Great Britain (Year) **4769**
Great Britain Collectors Club. Quarterly Newsletter. (US) **3753**
Great Britain Concise Stamp Catalogue.(UK) **3753**
Great Britain Correspondence Club. Quarterly Newsletter *see* Great Britain Collectors Club. Quarterly Newsletter **3753**
Great Britain Specialised Stamp Catalogue. (UK ISSN 0072-7229) **3753**
Great Britian. British Geological Survey. Technical Report. Fluid Processes Series. (UK) **1567**
Great Cars. *see* Le Grandi Automobili **4691**
The Great Circle. (AT ISSN 0156-8698) **2311,** 2344, 4727
Great Dane Club of America. Monthly Bulletin. (US) **3711**
Great Dane Periodical/Deutsche Dogge Periodical. (GW) **583**
Great Dane Reporter. (US) **3711**
†Great Dane Review. (US) **5201**
Great Decisions. (US ISSN 0072-727X) **3958**
Great Expectations. (CN ISSN 0823-9266) **3292,** 4844
Great Expeditions. (US ISSN 0706-7682) **4769**
†Great Foods Magazine. (US) **5201**
Great Ideas Newsletter. (US) **3802**
Great Ideas Today. (US ISSN 0072-7288) **2311**
Great Issues of the Day. (US ISSN 0270-7497) **3896,** 2920, 4436

Title

Great Lakes Advocate. (AT) 2920
Great Lakes and Connecting Channels Water Levels and Depths. (US) 1924
Great Lakes Boating Magazine. (US) 4524
Great Lakes Campbook. (US) 4769, 4547
Great Lakes Entertainer. (AT) 4769, 2042
Great Lakes Entomologist. (US ISSN 0090-0222) 533
Great Lakes Fisherman. (CN ISSN 0363-5171) 2042
Great Lakes Fishery Commission. Special Publication. (US) 2042
Great Lakes Fishery Commission (United States and Canada) Annual Report. (US ISSN 0072-7296) 2042
Great Lakes Fishery Commission (United States and Canada) Technical Report Series. (US ISSN 0072-730X) 2042
Great Lakes Fruit Growers News. (US) 179
Great Lakes Getaway. (US) 4769
Great Lakes Navigation. (CN) 4727
Great Lakes Red Book. (US ISSN 0072-7318) 4728
Great Lakes Research Checklist. (US ISSN 0072-7326) 4824
Great Lakes Sailing Scanner. (US ISSN 0194-4622) 4524
Great Lakes Sailor. (US) 4524
Great Lakes Science Advisory Board. Report. (CN ISSN 0710-8702) 4824
Great Lakes Travel & Living. (US ISSN 0887-6223) 4769
Great Lakes Vegetable Growers News. (US) 179
Great North Review. (UK ISSN 0307-3319) 4709
The Great Outdoors. (UK ISSN 0140-7570) 4547
Great Plains Journal. (US ISSN 0017-3673) 2226
†Great Plains Libraries. (US) 5201
Great Plains National Instructional Television Library. Recorded Visual Instruction see G P N Educational Video Catalog. College - Adult 1707
Great Plains National Instructional Television Library. Recorded Visual Instruction see G P N Educational Video Catalog. Elementary - Secondary 1750
Great Plains National Instructional Television Library Educational Video Catalog. College - Adult see G P N Educational Video Catalog. College - Adult 1707
Great Plains National Instructional Television Library Educational Video Catalog. Elementary - Secondary see G P N Educational Video Catalog. Elementary - Secondary 1750
Great Plains National Instructional Television Library Newsletter see G P N Newsletter 1374
Great Plains Quarterly. (US ISSN 0275-7664) 2407, 2252
The Great Race. (AT ISSN 0811-546X) 4473
Great River Microcomputer Users Group Newsletter see G R M U G Newsletter 1469
Great River Review. (US ISSN 0160-2144) 2920
Great Tao. (US) 4214, 2994
Great Unity. see Dai Doan Ket 3890
Great Valley Business News. (US) 835
Great Wall. see Chang Cheng 2904
Great West and Indian Series. (US ISSN 0072-7342) 2407
Great Western Echo. (UK) 4710, 2436
Great Western Real Estate Digest see Real Estate U S A 4157
Great Yarmouth Port and Industry Handbook. (UK ISSN 0260-9517) 4728, 1137
The Greater Baton Rouge Business Report. (US) 667
Greater Baton Rouge Manufacturers Directory. (US) 1137, 3663, 3862, 4291

Greater Beneficial Union of Pittsburgh Reporter see G B U Reporter 2532
Greater Boston Restaurant Guide. (US) 2474
Greater Buffalo Business Directory. (US) 1137
The Greater Cincinnati Business Record.(US) 667
Greater Cincinnati - Northern Kentucky Bride & Groom Magazine. (US) 3066, 3397
Greater Danbury Business Digest. (US) 667
Greater Hartford Family Magazine. (US) 2226
Greater Hartsville Chamber of Commerce Newsletter see Chamber News 811
Greater Kansas City Medical Bulletin. (US ISSN 0894-508X) 3101
Greater London Local History Directory and Bibliography. (UK) 2328
Greater London Papers. (UK ISSN 0072-7350) 4062
Greater Los Angeles Council on Deafness, Inc. News see G L A D News 2287
Greater Milwaukee Dental Association Bulletin see G M D A Bulletin 3233
Greater Milwaukee Dental Bulletin see G M D A Bulletin 3233
Greater Minneapolis see Guide to Leading Twin Cities Companies 836
Greater New Orleans Archivists Newsletter. (US) 2407, 2759
Greater Northeastern Regional Medical Library Program Newsletter see Middle Atlantic Perspective 3131
†Greater Ohio Valley Retailer. (US ISSN 0192-2467) 5201
Greater Philadelphia & Southern New Jersey Office Buildings. (US) 4149
Greater Philadelphia Desktop Publisher see Desktop Publisher (Maple Glen) 4143
Greater Phoenix Business Journal see Business Journal (Phoenix) 651
Greater Phoenix Jewish News. (US ISSN 0747-444X) 2003, 2226
Greater Portland Magazine. (US ISSN 0199-1728) 4088
Greater Seattle. (US) 2226
Greater Seattle Info-Guide. (US) 2226
Greater Vancouver Japanese Canadian Citizens Association Bulletin. (CN ISSN 0827-7230) 2003
Greater Washington Area Labor Summary see Metropolitan Washington D.C. Area Labor Summary 988
Greater Washington Board of Trade News. (US ISSN 0274-5496) 835
Greater Washington - Maryland Service Station and Automotive Repair Association. Membership Directory & Buyer's Guide. (US) 1137, 4692
Greater Waterbury Business Digest see Business Digest of Greater Waterbury 649
Greater Winnipeg Business Magazine. (CN ISSN 0830-8535) 667
Greater World see Greater World Newsletter 4180
Greater World Newsletter. (UK ISSN 0957-8935) 4180
Greca. (SP) 1291, 4844
Greece. (US) 3896, 867
Greece. (GR ISSN 0432-6105) 4769
Greece. National Statistical Service. Annual Industrial Survey. (GR ISSN 0072-7393) 719
Greece. National Statistical Service. Annual Statistical Survey on Mines, Quarries and Salterns. (GR ISSN 0072-7415) 3499, 4572
Greece. National Statistical Service. Building Activity Statistics. (GR ISSN 0256-7970) 638
†Greece. National Statistical Service. Bulletin de Statistique du Commerce Exterieur. (GR ISSN 0256-3614) 5201
Greece. National Statistical Service. Cultural Statistics. (GR ISSN 0256-3606) 352, 2982
Greece. National Statistical Service. Labour Force Survey. (GR ISSN 0256-3576) 719, 4572

Greece. National Statistical Service. Monthly Statistical Bulletin. (GR) 4572
Greece. National Statistical Service. Public Finance Statistics. (GR ISSN 0256-3568) 719
Greece. National Statistical Service. Results of Sea Fishery Survey by Motor Vessels. (GR ISSN 0256-3584) 2051, 4572
Greece. National Statistical Service. Revised Agricultural Price Indices. (GR) 138
Greece. National Statistical Service. Revised Consumer Price Index. (GR) 719
Greece. National Statistical Service. Shipping Statistics. (GR ISSN 0072-7423) 4664, 4572
Greece. National Statistical Service. Social Welfare and Health Statistics. (GR ISSN 0253-9454) 4426, 4117, 4572
Greece. National Statistical Service. Statistical Bulletin of Public Finance. (GR ISSN 0256-3592) 719
Greece. National Statistical Service. Statistics of the Declared Income of Legal Entities and Its Taxation. (GR ISSN 0302-1416) 719, 4572
Greece. National Statistical Service. Statistics on Civil, Criminal and Reformatory Justice. (GR ISSN 0256-3665) 1525, 4572
Greece. National Statistical Service. Statistics on the Declared Income of Physical Persons and Its Taxation. (GR ISSN 0302-1114) 719, 4572
Greece. National Statistical Service. Transport and Communication Statistics. (GR ISSN 0256-3657) 4664, 1348, 4572
Greece and Rome. (UK ISSN 0017-3835) 1277
Greece's Weekly for Business and Finance. (GR) 910, 2196
Greek Action Bulletin. (AT) 4406
Greek - American Trade. (GR ISSN 0046-6379) 816
Greek Annals of Ophthalmology. (GR) 3301
Greek Canadian Action - Drassis. (CN) 2003
Greek Canadian Reportage. (CN) 2003
Greek Coins in North American Collections see Ancient Coins in North American Collections 3598
Greek Economy in Figures (Year). (GR ISSN 0257-7240) 719, 667, 4572
Greek Export Directory. (GR) 816
Greek Gazette. (UK ISSN 0017-386X) 2003, 2194
Greek Herald. (AT) 2003
Greek Index Project Series. (CN ISSN 1183-1286) 2364, 2920
Greek Institute Review. (UK) 2867
Greek Mathematical Society. Bulletin/ Hellenike Mathematike Hetaireia. Deltion. (GR ISSN 0072-7466) 3037
Greek National Committee for Astronomy. Annual Reports of the Astronomical Institutes of Greece. (GR ISSN 0072-7385) 364
Greek Orthodox Calendar. (UK ISSN 0265-6922) 2003, 4283
Greek Orthodox Theological Review. (US ISSN 0017-3894) 4283, 2311, 3767
Greek Press/Ellenikos Typos. (US 0745-9645) 2003
Greek Review see Greek Institute Review 2867
Greek Review International. (UK ISSN 0262-8864) 2003
Greek Review of Social Research/ Epitheorisis Koinonikon Erevnon. (GR ISSN 0013-9696) 4373
Greek, Roman and Byzantine Monographs. (US ISSN 0072-7474) 1277
Greek, Roman and Byzantine Studies. (US ISSN 0017-3916) 1277
Greek, Roman, and Byzantine Studies. Scholarly Aids. (US ISSN 0072-7482) 1277

Greek Speleological Society. Deltion/ Societe Speleologique de Grece. Bulletin Trimestriel. (GR ISSN 0011-8117) 1567
Greek Sunday News/Kyriakatika Nea. (US) 4283, 2003
Greek Times. (AT) 2171
Greek Travel Pages. (GR) 4769
Green Anarchist. (UK ISSN 0957-5170) 3896, 1488, 1956
Green and White. (CN ISSN 0017-3924) 1313
Green Bay Catholic Compass. (US ISSN 8755-9323) 4265
Green Block. (US) 4710
Green Book. (UK ISSN 0017-3932) 162
Green Book (Cleveland). (US) 373
Green Book (New York). (US) 3791, 1488
▼The Green Book: Environmental Resource Directory. (US ISSN 1055-6893) 1956
Green Business Letter. (US ISSN 1056-490X) 667, 1956
Green Consumer Letter. (US ISSN 1049-2747) 1505, 1956
Green Drum. (UK ISSN 0263-0095) 1488
Green Engineering. (UK ISSN 0960-8796) 1956, 1823
Green Europe. (EI ISSN 0250-5886) 94
Green Europe. (UK ISSN 0141-2213) 94
Green Family Quarterly. (US) 2153
†Green Grapevine. (US) 5201
Green Guerilla Report. (US) 1956
Green Island. (UK ISSN 0017-3967) 2994
▼Green Library Journal. (US ISSN 1059-0838) 1956, 2759
Green Line. (UK) 1956
Green Magazine. (UK) 1956
Green Market Alert. (US) 1956
Green Markets. (US) 2128
Green Markets Dealer Report. (US) 2128, 948
Green Markets Newswires. (US) 2128
†Green Mountaineer. (US) 5201
Green Mountains Review. (US ISSN 0895-9307) 2920, 2994
Green Pages. (US) 1137, 1636
Green Pages. (IS) 2128
Green Pages: Directory of Non-Government Environmental Groups in Australia. (AT ISSN 0727-0119) 1488, 1956
Green Place Magazine. (AT) 2172
Green Power. see Gurin Pawa 2101
Green Revolution. (US ISSN 0017-3983) 4436
Green River Current. (US ISSN 0017-3991) 1313
Green River Review. (US ISSN 0017-4009) 2920, 2994
Green Scene. (US ISSN 0190-9789) 2128
Green Synthesis (San Pedro). (US) 2867, 1956
Green Thumb Gardening Newsletter. (US) 2128
Green World News. (US) 2128
Green Zero. (US) 2994
▼Green 2000. (US ISSN 1053-6418) 3648, 1956
GreenBook. (US ISSN 8756-534X) 1040
Greenbrier Historical Society. Journal. (US) 2407, 2153
Greene County Historical Journal. (US ISSN 0894-8135) 2407
†Greene Hills Echo. (US) 5201
Greene Hills of Home. (US) 2407
†Greener Gardening, Easier. (US) 5201
Greener Pastures Gazette. (US ISSN 0884-4089) 4149
Greengauge see Environment Business 1950
Greenhill Journal of Administration. (GH ISSN 0379-8658) 4062
Greenhouse see Garden Answers 2126
Greenhouse Canada. (CN ISSN 0712-4996) 2128
Greenhouse Effect Report. (US) 1956
Greenhouse Grower. (US ISSN 0745-7324) 2128

Greenhouse Manager. (US ISSN 0744-8988) **2128**
Greenhouse Newsletter. (US) **2128**
▼Greenhouse Product News. (US ISSN 1053-7104) **2142**
▼Greenkeeping. (US ISSN 1058-594X) **1505**, 1956
Greenland Biosciences see Meddelelser om Groenland, Bioscience **447**
Greenland Biosciences see Meddelelser om Groenland, Geoscience **1572**
†Greenland in Figures. (DK ISSN 0106-2875) **5201**
Greenland, Man and Society see Meddelelser om Groenland, Man & Society **244**
Greenline Guide to Residential Architects. (US) **300**
Greenmaster. (CN ISSN 0380-3333) **4506**, 2129
Greenpeace. (US ISSN 0899-0190) **1488**
Greenpeace Examiner see Greenpeace **1488**
Greenpeace Futurefile. (US) **1956**
Greenpeace Magazin. (GW ISSN 0939-3234) **1956**, 1273
Greenpeace Nachrichten see Greenpeace Magazin **1956**
Greenpeace Newsletter. (UK) **3896**
Greens. (DK) **1137**
Green's Commodity Market Comments see Powell Monetary Analyst **960**
Green's Magazine. (CN ISSN 0824-2992) **2920**
Greens Weekly Digest. (UK) **2631**
Greensboro Review. (US ISSN 0017-4084) **2920**
Greensward. (UK ISSN 0017-4092) **94**
Greentrees. (UK ISSN 0261-1139) **2153**
Greenville Woman see UPstate Magazine **2236**
Greenwich Magazine. (US) **2226**
▼Greenwood Educators' Reference Collection. (US ISSN 1056-2192) **1636**
Greenwood Encyclopedia of American Institutions. (US ISSN 0271-9509) **1636**
Greenwood Encyclopedia of Black Music. (US ISSN 0272-0264) **3553**, 2003
Greenwood Historical Encyclopedia of the World's Political Parties. (US) **3897**
Greenwood Library Management Collection. (US ISSN 0894-2986) **2759**
Greenwood's Guide to Great Lakes Shipping. (US ISSN 0072-7490) **4728**
Greetings. (US) **327**
La Greffe. (CN) **1313**
Gregorianum. (VC ISSN 0017-4114) **4265**, 3767
Gregorios o Palamas. (GR ISSN 1011-3010) **2364**, 4283
Grenada. Government Gazette. (GD) **2239**
Grenada Bulletin see Committee for Human Rights in Grenada. Bulletin **5168**
Grenada School Directory and Basic Educational Statistics. (GD) **1694**, 1677
Grenade. (US ISSN 0891-124X) **3459**
GrengeSpoun. (LU) **1956**
Grenzfragen. (GW) **4311**
Grenzfriedenshefte. (GW) **2867**
Grenzgebiete der Wissenschaft. (AU) **4311**
Grenzland. (DK ISSN 0107-9840) **2185**
Gressitt Center News. (US) **533**
Grey Bibliographies. (SA) **2793**
▼Grey Book. (CN ISSN 1183-3777) **138**, 910
Greyfriar-Siena Studies in Literature. (US ISSN 0533-2869) **2867**
Greyhound. (UK ISSN 0017-4157) **4473**
Greyhound Adviser. (AT) **3711**, 4473
Greyhound News. (IE) **4473**
Greyhound Owner & Breeder. (UK ISSN 0017-4165) **3711**

Greyhound Recorder. (AT) **3711**, 4473
Greyhound Review. (US) **4473**
Greyzone. (US) **3897**
Grial. (SP ISSN 0017-4181) **2920**
Gribble Annals see Plantagenet Productions **2948**
Gridiron. (UK ISSN 0269-0675) **4506**
Gridley Wave. (US ISSN 0017-419X) **3011**, 2920
Griechischen Christlichen Schriftsteller der ersten Jahrhunderte. (GW ISSN 0232-2900) **4180**, 2816
Grief Education Institute Newsletter see G E I Newsletter **4022**
Griekse en Latijnse Schrijvers. (NE ISSN 0169-8206) **1277**
Grier's Almanac. (US) **2226**
Grievance Bulletin. (CN) **980**, 2631, 3278
Grif see G R I F **5198**
La Griffe. (IT) **373**
Griffin. (US) **1313**
Griffin Report of Food Marketing. (US ISSN 0192-4400) **2071**
Griffith Observer. (US ISSN 0195-3982) **364**
Griffithiana. (IT) **3511**
Grih Shobha. (II) **4844**
Grihalakshmi. (II) **2199**
Grille. (IE ISSN 0017-4254) **3897**
Grimes Bulletin. (US) **2153**
La Grinta. (IT) **2205**
Le Griot. (CM) **2169**, 3511
Grist. (US ISSN 0031-2150) **1488**
Grist Mill. (US) **2407**
Griswold Family of England & America. (US) **2153**
Grit. (US ISSN 0017-4289) **2226**
Grit and Steel. (US ISSN 0017-4297) **4473**
Grit Best Recipes see Best Recipes **2444**
Grito del Sol Collection see T Q S News **2967**
Grizzly. (US) **1313**
Grlica/Turtledove. (XV ISSN 0017-4343) **3553**, 1636
Grob Angriff. (GW) **4473**
Grocer. (UK ISSN 0017-4351) **2092**
Grocer Directory see Grocer Marketing Directory **2092**
Grocer Marketing Directory. (UK) **2092**
Grocers' Journal see Grocers' Journal of California **2092**
Grocers' Journal of California. (US) **2092**
Grocers Report. (US ISSN 0160-8894) **2092**
Grocery Communications. (US ISSN 0017-4416) **2092**
Grocery Distribution. (US ISSN 0361-4034) **2072**
Grocery Market Bulletin. (UK) **2092**
Grocery Marketing. (US ISSN 0017-4394) **2092**
Grocery Update. (UK ISSN 0953-5268) **2092**
Grodur og Gardar. (IC ISSN 1017-3560) **2129**
Groen Viden. (DK ISSN 0903-0727) **179**
De Groene Amsterdammer. (NE ISSN 0017-4483) **2867**
Groene Krant. (BE) **94**
Groenland (Charlottenlund). (DK ISSN 0017-4556) **2196**
Groenland (Copenhagen)/Kalaallit Nunaat. (DK ISSN 0106-228X) **4572**
†Groenland i Tal. (DK ISSN 0106-0899) **5201**
Groenlands Befolkning/Kalatdlit Nunane Inuit. (DK ISSN 0105-0885) **3982**
Groenlands Fiskeritende. see Aulisarnermit Nutarsiagssat **2037**
Groenlands Geologiske Undersoegelse. Bulletin/Geological Survey of Greenland. Bulletin. (DK ISSN 0105-3507) **1567**
Groenlands Geologiske Undersoegelse. Rapport. (DK ISSN 0418-6559) **1567**
†Groenlandsdepartementet. Statistike Meddelelser. (DK) **5201**
Groenne Fag. (DK ISSN 0108-8920) **2129**

Groent Miljoe. (DK ISSN 0108-4755) **2129**
Groenten en Fruit. (NE ISSN 0017-4491) **2129**, 94
Groenten en Fruit - Vakdeel Fruit. (NE) **2129**, 94
Groenten en Fruit - Vakdeel Glasgroenten. (NE) **2129**, 94
Groenten en Fruit - Vakdeel Paddestoelen. (NE) **2129**, 94
Groenten en Fruit - Vakdeel Vollegrondsgroenten. (NE) **2129**, 94
Groepsvoeding Informatiekrant see Groepsvoedingsinformatie **5201**
†Groepsvoedingsinformatie. (NE) **5201**
Gromada - Rolnik Polski. (PL) **94**
Grondboor en Hamer. (NE ISSN 0017-4505) **1567**
Grondverzet & Bouwtransport. (NE) **618**
Groniek. (NE ISSN 0169-2801) **2364**
Groniek. Onafhankelijk Gronings Historisch Studentenblad see Groniek **2364**
Groningen - Amsterdam Studies in Semantics. (US) **2816**
Gronk. (CN ISSN 0017-453X) **2867**
Gronkopings Veckoblad. (SW ISSN 0017-4548) **2867**
Groom & Board. (US ISSN 0199-8366) **3711**
▼Groomers Europe. (NE) **3711**
Groomers Voice. (US) **3711**
Groote Schrijver-Genesiusblad see Pen en Toets **1488**
Gross Domestic Product by Industry. (CN ISSN 0711-852X) **4572**
Gross Island Product of Guam. (GU) **1076**
Gross Verbraucher Manager see G V Manager **1011**
Gross Wartenberger Heimatblatt. (GW ISSN 0017-4599) **401**
Der Grosse A D A C Ski Atlas (Year). (Allgemeiner Deutscher Automobil-Club e.V.) (GW) **4547**, 4769
Grosse Elektronik Atlas. (GW) **1771**
Grosse Entschluss see Entschluss **4176**
Grosse Heimatbuecher. (SZ ISSN 0072-7725) **2364**
▼Grosse Komponisten. (GW) **3553**
Das Grosse Leben. (GW ISSN 0932-2981) **3606**, 1488, 3594
Grosse Naturforscher. (GW ISSN 0072-7741) **419**
Grosse Pointer. (US) **4524**
Grosshandel-Aussenhandel. (GW) **910**
Grosshandelskaufmann see Handel **5203**
Grosshandelspreisindes/Indice des Prix de Gros. (SZ) **719**
Grossmont College see G **1312**
Grossmont Education Association Educator see G E A Educator **1635**
Grossmont Educator see G E A Educator **1635**
Grossunternehmen in Oesterreich. (GW) **1076**
▼Grossunternehmen in Ungarn. (GW) **1077**
Grosswetterlagen Europas. (GW ISSN 0017-4645) **3436**
Grosvenor Guide to London. (UK) **4769**
Grotiana. (NE ISSN 0167-3831) **2631**
Grotta della Vipera. (IT) **2920**
Grotte d'Italia. (IT) **1567**, 1598, 2252
Ground Engineering. (UK ISSN 0017-4653) **1866**
▼Ground Engineering Yearbook. (UK ISSN 0959-9959) **1137**, 618, 1823
Ground Floor. (US) **948**
Ground Saucer Watch Newsletter. (US) **53**
Ground Water. (US ISSN 0017-467X) **1598**
Ground Water Age. (US ISSN 0046-645X) **4824**
Ground Water Monitor. (US ISSN 0882-6188) **4824**, 1488, 1956
Ground Water Monitoring Review. (US ISSN 0277-1926) **1598**, 4824
Ground Water Review. (US) **2994**

Ground Waters Hydrological Yearbook. see Rocznik Hydrologiczny Wod Podziemnych **1600**
Grounds Maintenance. (US ISSN 0017-4688) **2129**
▼Grounds Maintenance (Japanese Edition). (US) **2129**
Grounds Management Forum. (US) **2129**
Groundsman. (UK ISSN 0017-4696) **4547**, 4473
†Groundswell (Albany). (US ISSN 8756-9094) **5201**
Groundswell (Washington). (US ISSN 0162-7899) **1805**, 1790
The Groundwater Newsletter. (US ISSN 0090-5070) **1598**
Groundwater Pollution News. (US ISSN 0899-3521) **1977**, 4824
Group (Loveland). (US ISSN 0163-8971) **1238**, 4180
Group (New York). (US ISSN 0362-4021) **4022**
Group Analysis. (UK) **4022**
Group Analysis: International Panel and Correspondence see Group Analysis **4022**
Group & Organization Management. (US ISSN 1059-6011) **4022**
Group and Organization Studies see Group & Organization Management **4022**
Group for the Advancement of Psychiatry. Publication. (US) **3337**
Group for the Use of Psychology in History. Newsletter see Psychohistory Review **4040**
Group Health Association of America, Inc. Journal see G H A A Journal **5198**
Group Health Journal see G H A A Journal **5198**
Group Members Only see Teenage **5288**
Group News see Trafalgar House News **635**
Group Practice Journal. (US ISSN 0199-5103) **3101**, 2461
Group Practice Managed Healthcare News. (US) **3101**
Group Practice News see Group Practice Managed Healthcare News **3101**
Group Research Report. (US ISSN 0017-4742) **3897**
Group Travel/Voyage en Groupe. (CN ISSN 0711-6136) **4769**
▼Group Travel Leader. (US) **4769**, 2273
Groupe Avant-Premiere see G A P **4619**
Groupe Bruxelles Lambert. Annual Reports. (BE) **948**
Groupe Bruxelles Lambert. Interim Reports. (BE) **948**
Groupe d'Etude des Rythmes Biologiques. Bulletin. (FR ISSN 0154-0238) **440**
Groupe de Recherche et d'Etudes Nord-Americaines. Actes du Colloque. (FR) **2920**
Groupe de Recherche et d'Information Feministes see G R I F **5198**
Groupe des Chambres Syndicales du Batiment et des Travaux Publics du Departement de l'Oise. Monthly Review. (FR) **619**
Groupe Familial. (FR) **4436**
Groupe Interdisciplinaire du Theatre Antique. Textes et Documents. (FR ISSN 0993-5835) **4633**
Groupe International d'Etude de la Ceramique Egyptienne. Bulletin de Liaison. (UA ISSN 0255-0903) **273**, 355
Groupe Linguistique d'Etudes Chamito-Semitiques. Comptes Rendus. (FR) **2816**
Groupement des Industries Electroniques. Rapport d'Activites. (FR) **1771**
Groupement des Industries Electroniques. Statistiques Annuelles. (FR) **1771**, 4572
Groupement des Societes Immobilieres d'Investissement. Annuaire. (FR ISSN 0066-2933) **783**

Groupement International pour la Recherche en Stomatologie et Odontologie. Bulletin. (BE ISSN 0303-7479) **3234**
Groupements Techniques Veterinaires Bulletin *see* G T V Bulletin **4810**
†Groups: a Journal of Group Dynamics and Psychotherapy. (US ISSN 0093-4763) **5201**
Group's Jr. High Ministry Magazine *see* Jr. High Ministry Magazine **1239**
Groupwork. (UK ISSN 0951-824X) **4407**, 4022
Grove. (UK) **3802**
Grove City College Alumni Bulletin. (US) **1313**
Grovvarelederen. (DK) **152**
Grow Dahlias with Us. (UK) **2129**
Grow Letter. (US) **2129**
Grower. (US ISSN 0745-1784) **179**
Grower. (CN ISSN 0017-4777) **2129**
Grower. (UK ISSN 0017-4785) **2129**
†Grower. (AT ISSN 0046-6476) **5201**
Grower Talks Magazine. (US ISSN 0276-9433) **2129**
Growing (Nashville). (US ISSN 0162-4512) **4239**
Growing Business. (US) **667**
Growing Child. (US) **1238**
Growing Child Research Review. (US ISSN 0737-0318) **1238**
†Growing Edge. (US ISSN 0741-4498) **5201**
Growing Edge Magazine. (US ISSN 1043-2906) **2129**, 94
Growing From Seed *see* Focus on Plants **5193**
Growing Native Plants. (AT) **504**
Growing Older *see* Australian Journal on Ageing **2270**
Growing Parent Newsletter. (US ISSN 0193-8037) **1238**
Growing Point. (UK ISSN 0046-6506) **4128**, 1255, 2759
Growing Together. (US) **1238**
Growing Up. *see* Hun Boloh Bagaasaa **1637**
Growing Without Schooling. (US ISSN 0745-5305) **1636**, 1238
Growl. (US) **1313**
Growth. (SA ISSN 0258-7173) **667**
Growth. (AT ISSN 0085-1280) **1077**
Growth *see* Growth, Development & Aging **3101**
Growth and Change. (US ISSN 0017-4815) **1077**
Growth, Development & Aging. (US ISSN 1041-1232) **3101**, 440, 2273
Growth Factors. (US ISSN 0897-7194) **572**
Growth Factors *see* Growth Factors & Cytokines **3185**
Growth Factors & Cytokines. (UK ISSN 0964-7554) **3185**, 3253
Growth Fund Guide. (US ISSN 0017-4831) **948**
Growth of Crystals. (US ISSN 0072-7814) **1210**
Growth Promoting Hormones. (UK ISSN 0143-4268) **477**, 3253, 3320
▼Growth Regulation. (UK ISSN 0956-523X) **3253**
†Growth Stock Advisory. (US) **5201**
Growth Stock Outlook. (US) **948**
†Growth Stock Report. (US) **5201**
Grubensicherheit *see* Arbeit und Sicherheit **3478**
Grudnaya Khirurgiya/Chest Surgery. (RU ISSN 0017-4866) **3379**
Grue Magazine. (US ISSN 0897-9707) **3011**
Gruene Blaetter. (GW) **4844**
Gruene Demokraten *see* Umfeld **3931**
Das Gruene Jahrbuch. (GW ISSN 0935-5405) **3711**
†Die Gruenen. (GW) **5201**
Gruenstift (Berlin). (GW ISSN 0178-1421) **1488**, 440, 2487
Gruenstift (Rattingen). (GW) **1956**
Grumman Aerospace Horizons *see* Grumman Horizons **53**
Grumman Horizons. (US) **53**
†Grundbegriffe der Modernen Biologie. (GW ISSN 0085-1299) **5201**
Grundbesitz. (GW) **4149**

Das Grundeigentum. (GW) **619**, 300, 4149
Grundig Report. (GW) **1893**
Grundlagen der Exakten Naturwissenschaften. (GW) **4311**
Grundlagen der Germanistik. (GW) **2816**
Grundlagen der Landtechnik *see* Landtechnik **184**
Grundlagen und Fortschritte der Lebensmitteluntersuchung *see* Grundlagen und Fortschritte der Lebensmitteluntersuchung und Lebensmitteltechnologie **2072**
Grundlagen und Fortschritte der Lebensmitteluntersuchung und Lebensmitteltechnologie. (GW ISSN 0341-0498) **2072**
Grundlagen und Praxis des Bank- und Boersenwesens. (GW) **783**, 948
Grundlagen und Praxis des Wirtschaftsrechts. (GW ISSN 0533-3407) **2710**
Grundlagenstudien aus Kybernetik und Geisteswissenschaft. (GW ISSN 0723-4899) **1441**, 4311
Grundlehren der Mathematischen Wissenschaften. (US) **3037**
Grundlehren der Mathematischen Wissenschaften in Einzeldarstellungen *see* Grundlehren der Mathematischen Wissenschaften **3037**
Grundriss der Sozialwissenschaft. (GW) **4373**
Grundschule. (GW ISSN 0533-3431) **1750**
Die Grundschulzeitschrift. (GW) **1750**
Grundtvig Studier. (DK) **1374**
†Grupo Andino. (PE) **5201**
Grupo de Investigacao Arqueologica do Norte. Trabalhos. (PO) **273**
Grupo Espanol de la Union Interparlamentaria. Boletin de Informacion. (SP) **3958**
Grupo I N I (Resumen de Actividades). (Instituto Nacional de Industria) (SP) **1077**
Gruppe Berliner Mondbeobachter. Protokoll der Sitzung. (GW) **364**
Gruppe und Spiel. (GW ISSN 0341-6879) **1750**
Gruppendynamik. (GW ISSN 0046-6514) **4022**, 4436
Gruppenpsychotherapie und Gruppendynamik. (GW ISSN 0017-4947) **3337**
Gruppenpsychotherapie und Gruppendynamik. Beihefte. (GW ISSN 0085-1302) **4023**
Gruppo Micologico "G. Bresadola". Bollettino *see* Rivista di Micologia **516**
Grusavisen. (DK ISSN 0109-9051) **619**
Gruss Aus. (GW) **257**
Gruss aus der Weltweiten Brueder-Unitaet - Daheim und Draussen. (GW ISSN 0177-1817) **4239**
Gruss der Grossheppacher Schwesternschaft. (GW) **4180**
Gruvarbetaren. (SW) **3484**
Gryphon Theatre News. (CN) **4633**
Guacharo. (VE ISSN 0583-774X) **1567**
Guadeloupe Economique. (GP) **816**
Guadeloupe 2000. (GP) **3897**
Guajana. (PR ISSN 0017-498X) **2994**
Guam. Department of Commerce. Monthly Food Index. (GU) **2085**, 13
Guam. Department of Commerce. Occasional Paper. (GU) **835**
Guam. Department of Commerce. Quarterly Economic and Social Indicators *see* Guam. Department of Commerce. Quarterly Economic Review **999**
Guam. Department of Commerce. Quarterly Economic Review. (GU) **999**
Guam. Department of Commerce. Statistical Abstract *see* Guam Annual Economic Review **867**
Guam. Department of Revenue and Taxation. Report. (GU ISSN 0072-7873) **1096**
Guam Annual Economic Review. (GU) **867**

Guam Economic Annual Review *see* Guam Annual Economic Review **867**
†Guam Recorder. (GU ISSN 0046-6522) **5201**
†Guam Trade with the United States and Foreign Countries. (GU) **5201**
Guanabara: O Balanco Economico. (BL) **867**
Guang de Shijie/World of Light. (CC) **3852**
Guang Tongxin Jishu. (CC) **1336**
Guang yu Ying/Light and Shadow. (CC) **327**
Guangdianzi - Jiguang/Photoelectron - Laser. (CC) **3852**
Guangdong. (HK) **783**
Guangdong Dianshi/Guangdong Television. (CC) **1374**
Guangdong Dizhi/Guangdong Geology. (CC) **1567**
Guangdong Duiwai Jingmao/Guangdong Foreign Economics and Trade. (CC) **910**
Guangdong Education. *see* Guangdong Jiaoyu **1636**
Guangdong Finance. *see* Guangdong Jinrong **783**
Guangdong Foreign Economics and Trade. *see* Guangdong Duiwai Jingmao **910**
Guangdong Geology. *see* Guangdong Dizhi **1567**
Guangdong Gongxueyuan Xuebao/ Guangdong Institute of Engineering. Journal. (CC) **1823**
Guangdong Huabao/Guangdong Pictorial. (CC) **2182**, 3791
Guangdong Institute of Engineering. Journal. *see* Guangdong Gongxueyuan Xuebao **1823**
Guangdong Institute of Nationalities. Journal. *see* Guangdong Minzu Xueyuan Xuebao **4373**
Guangdong Jiage Yanjiu/Guangdong Price Research. (CC) **667**
Guangdong Jiaoyu/Guangdong Education. (CC) **1636**
Guangdong Jinrong/Guangdong Finance. (CC) **783**
Guangdong Medical Science. *see* Guangdong Yixue **3101**
Guangdong Minzu Xueyuan Xuebao/ Guangdong Institute of Nationalities. Journal. (CC) **4373**, 4311
Guangdong Pictorial. *see* Guangdong Huabao **2182**
Guangdong Price Research. *see* Guangdong Jiage Yanjiu **667**
Guangdong Shehui Kexue/Guangdong Social Science. (CC) **4373**
Guangdong Shizhi. (CC) **2338**
Guangdong Social Science. *see* Guangdong Shehui Kexue **4373**
Guangdong Television. *see* Guangdong Dianshi **1374**
Guangdong Yixue/Guangdong Medical Science. (CC) **3101**
Guanggao Shijie/Advertising World. (CC) **32**
Guanghua *see* Sinorama **2219**
Guangming Ribao Suoyin/Index to the Guangming Ribao. (CC) **2578**
Guangpuxue yu Guangpu Fenxi/ Spectroscopy and Spectral Analysis. (CC ISSN 1000-0593) **3852**
Guangxi Audit. *see* Guangxi Shenji **1096**
Guangxi Huabao/Guangxi Pictorial. (CC) **2182**
Guangxi Literature. *see* Guangxi Wenxue **2920**
Guangxi Nianjian/Guangxi Yearbook. (CC) **1781**
Guangxi Pictorial. *see* Guangxi Huabao **2182**
Guangxi Plants. *see* Guangxi Zhiwu **504**
Guangxi Shenji/Guangxi Audit. (CC) **1096**
Guangxi Shuiwu/Guangxi Taxation. (CC) **1096**
Guangxi Statistics. *see* Guangxi Tongji **4573**
Guangxi Taxation. *see* Guangxi Shuiwu **1096**
Guangxi Tongji/Guangxi Statistics. (CC) **4573**
Guangxi Traditional Chinese Medicine. *see* Guangxi Zhongyi Yao **3101**

Guangxi Wenxue/Guangxi Literature. (CC) **2920**
Guangxi Yearbook. *see* Guangxi Nianjian **1781**
Guangxi Zhiwu/Guangxi Plants. (CC) **504**
Guangxi Zhongyi Yao/Guangxi Traditional Chinese Medicine. (CC) **3101**
Guangxian yu Dianlan/Optical Fibre and Cable. (CC) **1893**, 3852
Guangxue Xuebao/Acta Optica Sinica. (CC ISSN 0253-2239) **3852**
Guangxue Yiqi/Optical Instruments. (CC) **2522**, 3852
Guangzhou Civil Aviation. *see* Guangzhou Minhang **4673**
Guangzhou Economics. *see* Guangzhou Jingji **667**
Guangzhou Education. *see* Guangzhou Jiaoyu **1636**
Guangzhou Institute of Traditional Chinese Medicine. Journal. *see* Guangzhou Zhongyi Xueyuan Xuebao **3101**
Guangzhou Jiaoyu/Guangzhou Education. (CC) **1636**
Guangzhou Jingji/Guangzhou Economics. (CC) **667**
Guangzhou Literature. *see* Guangzhou Wenyi **2921**
Guangzhou Minhang/Guangzhou Civil Aviation. (CC) **4673**
Guangzhou Pharmacy. *see* Guangzhou Yiyao **3727**
Guangzhou Wenyi/Guangzhou Literature. (CC ISSN 0257-022X) **2921**
Guangzhou Yiyao/Guangzhou Pharmacy. (CC) **3727**
Guangzhou Zhongyi Xueyuan Xuebao/ Guangzhou Institute of Traditional Chinese Medicine. Journal. (CC) **3101**
Guanli Gongcheng Xuebao. (CC) **1823**
Guanli Shijie/Administrative World. (CC) **1011**
Guanli yu Xiaoyi/Management and Benefit. (CC ISSN 1004-5414) **1011**
Guarantor. (US) **4149**
Guard. *see* Straz **2024**
Guard the North. (CN) **3011**
Guardia Costiera. (IT) **4728**
Guardian. (IE) **2202**
Guardian. (CN) **2583**
Guardian. (US ISSN 0017-5021) **3897**
Guardian. (AT) **3897**
Guardian Engel. (GW) **1298**, 1374
Guardian Gazette *see* Law Society's Guardian Gazette **2646**
Guardian Magazine. (BR) **2921**
▼Guardianship and Conservatorship in Massachusetts. (US) **2715**
Guards Magazine. (UK ISSN 0017-503X) **3459**
The Guardsman. (US) **1313**
Guatemala! *see* Report on Guatemala **3970**
Guatemala. Banco Nacional de Desarrollo Agricola. Memoria. (GT) **152**, 867
Guatemala. Direccion General de Estadistica. Departamento de Estudios Especiales y Estadisticas Continuas. Produccion, Venta y Otros Ingresos de la Encuesta Anual de la Industria Manufacturera Fabril *see* Guatemala. Direccion General de Estadistica. Encuesta de la Industria Manufacturera Fabril **4573**
Guatemala. Direccion General de Estadistica. Encuesta de la Industria Manufacturera Fabril. (GT) **4573**
Guatemala. Instituto Nacional de Estadistica. Anuario Estadistico. (GT) **4573**
Guatemala. Instituto Nacional de Estadistica. Boletin Estadistico. (GT ISSN 0017-5048) **4573**
Guatemala. Instituto Nacional de Estadistica. Directorio Nacional de Establecimientos Industriales. (GT) **719**
Guatemala. Instituto Nacional de Sismologia, Vulcanologia, Meteorologia e Hidrologia. Boletin. (GT) **1545**

GUATEMALA

Guatemala en Cifras see Guatemala. Instituto Nacional de Estadistica. Anuario Estadistico **4573**
Guatemala Filatelica. (GT ISSN 0046-6549) **3753**
Guatemala Pediatrica. (GT ISSN 0017-5064) **3320**
Guatemalteco see Diario de Centro America **4058**
Guckloch. (GW) **4265**
Gudian Wenxue Zhishi. (CC) **2921**
Gudian Wenxue Zhishi/Classic Literature Knowledge. (CC) **2921**
Gudok. (RU) **4710, 980**
Guelph Dairy Research Report. (CN) **200**
Guerin Sportivo. (IT) **4473**
Guerin Sportivo Mese. (IT) **4518, 4692**
Guernsey Breeders' Journal. (US ISSN 0017-5110) **217**
Guernsey Breeders' Journal. (UK) **217**
Guerres Mondiales et Conflits Contemporains. (FR ISSN 0984-2292) **2311**
Guest Author. (US ISSN 0160-6565) **2921**
Guest Informant. (US) **4802**
Guest Informant - Atlanta. (US) **4802**
Guest Informant - Boston. (US) **4802**
Guest Informant - Chicago. (US) **4802**
Guest Informant - Houston. (US) **4802**
Guest Informant - Kansas City. (US) **4802**
Guest Informant - New Orleans. (US) **4802**
Guest Informant - Orlando. (US) **4802**
Guest Informant - Puerto Rico. (US) **4802**
Guest Informant - The Florida Gold Coast. (US) **4802**
Guest Informant - Twin Cities. (US) **4802**
Guesthouses, Farmhouses and Inns in Britain see Inspected Bed & Breakfast in Britain **4772**
Guetertransport in Seeverkehr. (GW) **4728**
Gueterverkehr. (GW ISSN 0017-5137) **4745**
Gugong Bowuyuan Yuankan/Palace Museum. Journal. (CC) **273**
Gugong Tongxun Yingwen Shuangyuekan see National Palace Museum Bulletin **3530**
Gugong Wenwu Yuekan see National Palace Museum. Monthly of Chinese Art **3530**
Gugong Wenxian see Ch'ing Documents **5165**
Gugong Xueshu Jikan see National Palace Museum Research Quarterly **3530**
Gugong Zhanlan Tongxun see National Palace Museum. Newsletter **3530**
Guia. (DR) **910**
Guia a las Resenas de Libros de y sobre Hispanoamerica. see Guide to Reviews of Books from and about Hispanic America **4128**
Guia Aerea de Mexico y Centro-America. (MX) **4673**
Guia Aerea y Maritima. (PE) **4769, 4650**
Guia Aerea y Maritima de Venezuela C.A. (VE) **4650, 4769**
Guia Aeronautico. (BL ISSN 0017-5145) **4673, 4769**
Guia Argentina de Trafico Aereo. (AG) **4673**
Guia Automotriz. (MX) **4650**
Guia Automotriz de Venezuela/ Venezuelan Automotive Guide. (VE) **4692**
Guia Bolivia. (BO) **867**
Guia Brasil. (BL) **4769**
†Guia Bursatil. (SP) **5201**
†Guia Camping. (BL) **5201**
Guia Cocina. (SP) **2446**
Guia da Embalagem. (BL) **3648**
Guia das Editoras Brasileiras see Guia dos Editores Associados **4128**
Guia das Livrarias e Pontos de Venda de Livros no Brasil. (BL) **4128**
Guia de Audio. (AG) **4460**
Guia de Centros Educativos Catolicos. (SP ISSN 0211-4410) **1694**
Guia de Congresos Medicos Jano. (SP ISSN 0214-4689) **3101**

Guia de Editores y de Libreros de Espana. (SP ISSN 0072-7903) **4128**
Guia de la Industria Alimentaria. (MX) **2072**
Guia de la Industria: Automotriz. (MX) **4692**
Guia de la Industria del Caucho. (AG ISSN 0533-4500) **4291**
Guia de la Industria: Equipo y Aparatos.(MX) **3017**
Guia de la Industria: Equipo y Materiales. (MX) **3017**
Guia de la Industria: Hule, Plasticos y Resinas. (MX) **3862**
Guia de la Industria: Hulera. (MX) **4291**
Guia de la Industria: Laboratorios de Especialades y Control. (MX) **2522**
Guia de la Industria: Plasticos y Resinas. (MX) **3862**
Guia de la Industria Quimica: Productos Quimicos. (MX) **1853**
Guia de la Industria: Republica del Paraguay. (PY) **1137**
Guia de la Moda del Calzado. (SP) **4361**
Guia de los Caballos Verificados en Espana. (SP ISSN 0085-1337) **4534**
Guia de Material de Laboratorio. (SP) **2522, 3259**
Guia de Reuniones Cientificas y Tecnicas en la Argentina. (AG ISSN 0301-7567) **3392**
Guia del Comercio y de la Industria (Year). (SP) **816**
Guia del Comercio y de la Industria de Madrid see Guia del Comercio y de la Industria (Year) **816**
Guia del Envase y Embalaje. (MX) **3648**
Guia del Equipamiento Hospitalario. (SP) **2522, 2461, 3101**
Guia del Plastico. (AG) **3862**
Guia del Sol. (CU) **4769**
Guia do Estudante. (BL) **1694, 1707**
Guia do Laboratorio. (BL) **1853**
Guia do Porto de Lisboa. (PO) **4728**
Guia dos Editores Associados. (BL) **4128, 1137**
Guia Economico e Industrial do Estado de Minas Gerais. (BL) **3484**
Guia Financiera. (UY) **783**
Guia General de las Industrias Azulejeras y Auxiliares de Espana. (SP) **1137, 1164**
Guia Geral de Produtos Quimicos. (BL) **1853**
Guia Industrial de Venezuela. (VE) **667**
Guia Industrial Mexicana. (MX) **1137**
†Guia Internacional de Investigaciones sobre Mexico. (MX) **5201**
Guia Internacional de Trafico. (AG) **4769**
Guia Internacional de Trafico - Division Viajes see Guia Internacional de Trafico **4769**
Guia Oficial de Centro-America. (HO) **4769**
Guia Panrotas. (BL ISSN 0102-3225) **4769**
Guia Quatro Rodas. Brazil. (BL ISSN 0533-473X) **4769**
Guia Quatro Rodas. Camping. (BL) **4769, 4547**
Guia Quatro Rodas. Rio de Janeiro. (BL) **4769**
Guia Quatro Rodas. Rodoviario. (BL) **4769**
Guia Quatro Rodas. Sao Paulo. (BL) **4769**
Guia Quatro Rodas. Sul. (BL) **4769**
Guia - Revista Pratica. (PO) **4844**
Guia Rural. (BL) **94**
Guia Silber. Directorio de Instituciones Chilenas. (CL) **1137**
†Guia Sul. (BL) **5201**
†Guia Turistica de Caracas, Litoral y Venezuela. (VE) **5201**
Guia Turistica de Rosario y Sante Fe. (AG) **4769**
Guia Venezolana de Publicidad y Mercadeo. (VE) **32, 1040**
†Guias Bibliograficas. (PE) **5201**
Guida. (IT) **2631**
Guida ai Punti di Credito/Guide to the Establishments. (IT) **2474**

Guida all'Abbigliamento Italiano. (IT) **1285**
Guida all'Industria Italiana della Gomma/Guide to the Italian Rubber Industry. (IT) **4291**
Guida all'Industria Italiana della Maglieria e della Calzetteria. (IT) **4619**
Guida allo Spettacolo see Nuova Guida Cinematografica **3515**
Guida Camping d'Italia. (IT ISSN 0072-792X) **4547**
Guida Cucina see Guidacucina **2447**
Guida del Mercato Ristretto. (IT) **948**
Guida della Stampa Periodica Italiana. (IT) **401**
Guida delle Regioni d'Italia. (IT) **1137**
Guida di Veterinaria e Zootecnia. (IT ISSN 0391-1918) **4810**
Guida Eurocamping Europa. (IT) **4769**
Guida Eurocamping Italia e Corsica. (IT) **4769**
Guida Monaci. Annuario Sanitario see Annuario Sanitario Italiano **4097**
Guida T V see Nuova Guida T V **1377**
Guida Verde. (IT) **2129**
Guida Viaggi. (IT) **4769**
Guidacucina. (IT) **2447**
Guidance and Assessment Review see Selection and Development Review **1027**
Guidance and Control. (US ISSN 1057-493X) **53**
Guidance & Counselling. (CN) **1636**
†Guidance Clinic. (US ISSN 0146-1168) **5202**
Guidance of Infants/Yoji-No-Shido. (JA) **1636**
Guide. see Al-Murshid **2173**
Guide. see Al-Murshid **4778**
Guide (Hagerstown). (US ISSN 0017-5226) **4283, 1255**
Guide A for Preschool Teachers see Preschool Bible Teacher A **4247**
Guide a l'Usage des Amateurs de Livres Syndicat National de la Librairie Ancienne et Moderne. Repertoire des Membres **4137**
Guide A P A. (IT) **4769**
†Guide & Directory of Port of Yokohama. (JA) **5202**
Guide - Annuaire de l'Equipement Agricole. (FR) **162**
Guide Annuaire des H L M see Annuaire H L M **2483**
Guide Annuaire Etancheite. (FR) **619**
Guide Annuaire Joints et Facades. (FR) **619**
Guide Annuaire Officiel du Complexe de Rungis GUIDOR see GUIDOR **2092**
▼Guide Annuel (Year) Salons Expositions Congres. (CN) **3392**
Guide Annuel des S A M U et S M U R de France. (FR ISSN 0992-6739) **3308**
Guide Astrologique. (FR) **358**
Guide B for Preschool Teachers see Preschool Bible Teacher B **4247**
Guide Bounty de la Grossesse see Bounty Pregnancy Guide **3290**
Guide Bounty des Soins au Nourisson see Bounty Infant Care Guide **3319**
Guide Bureaux Montreal. see Montreal Office Guide **625**
Guide C for Preschool Teachers see Preschool Bible Teacher C **4247**
Guide de France. (FR ISSN 0750-4152) **1298, 1255**
Guide de l'Eau. (FR) **4824**
Guide de l'Equipement et de l'Outillage. (FR) **4692**
Guide de l'Habitat et de l'Amenagement Rural see Guide de l'Habitat et du Developpement Local **2487**
Guide de l'Habitat et du Developpement Local. (FR) **2487**
Guide de l'Investisseur Industriel au Senegal. (SG) **1077**
Guide de la Chimie International. (FR) **1177**
Guide de la Famille. (FR) **1684**
†Guide de la Jeune Maman. (FR) **5202**
Guide de la Parfumerie/General Directory of the Perfume and Cosmetic Industry. (FR ISSN 0072-7989) **1137, 375**
Guide de la Route: L'Ontario. (CN ISSN 0838-0023) **4769**

Guide de la Route: La Floride. (French translation of: American Automobile Association, Florida TourBook) (CN ISSN 0838-0015) **4769**
▼Guide de la Route: Le Maine, le New Hampshire, et le Vermont. (CN) **4769**
Guide de la Route: Les Provinces de l'Atlantique et le Quebec. (CN) **4769**
Guide de Subventions et Bourses. see Medical Research Council of Canada. Grants and Awards Guide **3127**
Guide Demographie de l'Afrique. see Demographic Handbook for Africa **3981**
†Guide des Acheteurs: Horlogerie, Bijouterie et Branches Annexes/ Buyers' Guide: Watch Industry, Jewellery and Allied Trades. (SZ) **5202**
Guide des Affaires Franco-Canadiennes. (FR) **816**
Guide des Banques de Donnees Factuelles Francaises sur les Materiaux. (FR) **1879, 401**
Guide des Banques de Donnees Professionelles (Videotex et ASCII). (FR) **1450**
Guide des Declarations Fiscales. (FR) **751**
Guide des Futurs Epoux. (FR) **4436**
Guide des Industries. (UA) **667**
Guide Dog News. (US) **3711, 2293**
Guide du Cadeau et des Arts de la Table. (FR ISSN 0396-4299) **2281**
Guide du Cheval Arabe en France. (FR) **4534**
Guide du Contribuable. (BE) **1505**
Le Guide du Contribuable Canadien. (CN) **1096**
Guide du Diffuseur. see Presenter's Handbook **4783**
Guide du Directeur de Tournees de Spectacles. see Tour Organizers' Handbook **4789**
Guide du Feu. (FR ISSN 0337-5781) **2033**
Guide du Tourisme Nigerien. see Nigeria Tourist Guide **4780**
Guide du Transport. (CN) **4650**
Guide du Transport par Camion. (CN) **4745**
Guide Economique de la Tunisie. (TI ISSN 0330-9290) **1137**
Guide Emer see Guide Europeen de l'Amateur d'Art, de l'Antiquaire et du Bibliophile **328**
Guide Europeen de l'Amateur d'Art, de l'Antiquaire et du Bibliophile. (FR ISSN 0066-3069) **328**
Guide Europeen des Produits Logiciels see Centre d'Information des Utilisateurs de Progiciel. Catalogue **825**
Guide Europeen des Progiciels see Centre d'Information des Utilisateurs de Progiciel. Catalogue **825**
Guide for Biblical Studies. (US) **4239**
Guide for Buyers of Quality Hardwoods. (US) **1137**
Guide for Expectant Parents. (US) **3292**
Guide for New Planners. (US) **1707**
Guide for Planning Educational Facilities. (US ISSN 0072-8101) **1727**
Guide for the Care and Use of Laboratory Animals. (US) **3259**
The Guide: Gay Travel, Entertainment, Politics, and Sex. (US) **2453, 3942**
Guide i Jylland. (DK ISSN 0106-3022) **4769**
Guide International du Voyage. see International Travel Guide **4772**
▼Guide Lines (Red Rock). (US ISSN 1057-6193) **1065**
Guide Lines (Yorktown Hts.). (US) **3711, 2293**
†Guide Magazine (Denver). (US) **5202**
Guide Magazine (Seattle). (US) **2453, 3397, 3942, 4844**
Guide Musical see Scherzo - Guide Musical **3579**
Guide National de Prescription des Medicaments. (FR) **3727**
Guide Naturiste Internationale. see International Naturist Guide **4549**

Guide News. (US) **2226**
Guide Officiel Camping - Caravaning. (FR) **4547**
Guide Parlementaire Canadien. *see* Canadian Parliamentary Guide (Year) **3878**
Guide Patrol. (UK) **1255**
Guide Post. (US ISSN 0017-5269) **2793**
Guide Pratique de l'Entrepreneur du Batiment et des Travaux Publics. (FR) **1866**
Guide Professionel du Minitel. (FR) **401**
Guide Ressources. (CN ISSN 0827-7982) **3594**
Guide Rosenwald: Annuaire Medical. (FR) **3101**
Guide Rosenwald: Annuaire Medical et Pharmaceutique *see* Guide Rosenwald: Annuaire Medical **3101**
Guide Routier et Touristique: Madagascar, Reunion, Maurice, Comores et Seychelles. (MG) **4770**
Guide to A P R S Member Studios *see* Guide to Recording in the UK **1137**
Guide to Accredited Camps (Year). (US ISSN 1046-5774) **4547**
Guide to Afro-American Resources. (US) **2003**
Guide to Agricultural Production in Malawi. (MW) **94**
Guide to Alternative Periodicals. (US) **4394, 2890**
Guide to American Directories. (US ISSN 0533-5248) **401**
Guide to American Educational Directories. (US) **1677**
Guide to American Scientific and Technical Directories. (US ISSN 0094-4505) **4614, 401, 4356**
Guide to Architecture Schools in North America. (US ISSN 0092-7856) **300**
Guide to Arkansas Funding Sources. (US) **1011, 4062, 4407**
Guide to Astronomy. *see* Tenmon Gaido **370**
Guide to Available Technologies. (US) **4599, 3675**
Guide to Biotechnology Products and Instruments. (US) **489, 2522**
Guide to Britain's Best Holidays *see* Britain's Best Holidays - A Quick Reference Guide **4754**
†Guide to C O P A Recognized Accrediting Bodies. (US) **5202**
Guide to Campus Recruiting. (AT) **1694, 3627**
Guide to Caravan and Camping Holidays. (UK ISSN 0267-3355) **4770, 4547**
Guide to Charleston's Islands Magazine.(US) **4770**
Guide to Christian Camps *see* Official Guide to Christian Camps & Conference Centers **4193**
Guide to Collections of Manuscripts Relating to Australia. (AT ISSN 0725-9107) **2328, 401**
Guide to College Courses in Film and Television. (US ISSN 0072-8284) **3511, 1684**
Guide to College Programs in Hospitality & Tourism. (US) **1694**
Guide to Communication Services *see* Planning Guide X-1 **1365**
Guide to Computer Law. (US) **1395, 2631**
Guide to Computer Living. (US) **1395**
Guide to Craft Supplies in New South Wales and the Australian Capital Territory. (AT ISSN 1030-4479) **355, 1137**
Guide to Cruising the Chesapeake Bay. (US) **4524, 4770**
Guide to Current Literature in Environmental Health Engineering and Science. (II ISSN 0252-7979) **401**
Guide to Danish Libraries. *see* Biblioteksvejviser **2748**
Guide to Departments of Anthropology (Year) *see* A A A Guide (Year) **232**
Guide to Departments of Geography in the United States and Canada *see* Guide to Departments of Geography in the United States and Canada - A A G Membership Directory **2252**

Guide to Departments of Geography in the United States and Canada - A A G Membership Directory. (US) **2252, 1694**
Guide to Departments of History (Year) *see* Directory of History Departments and Organizations (Year) **1693**
Guide to Departments of Sociology, Anthropology and Archaeology in Universities and Museums in Canada/Annuaire des Departementes de Sociologie, d'Anthropologie et d'Archeologie des Universites et des Musees du Canada. (CN ISSN 0316-1854) **1707**
Guide to Design Criteria for Metal Structures *see* Guide to Stability Design Criteria for Metal Structures **5202**
Guide to Dialog Searching *see* Searching Dialog: The Complete Guide **2784**
Guide to Doctoral Programs in Business and Management. (US) **1694**
†Guide to East Africa. (UK) **5202**
Guide to Electronics Industry in India. (II) **1771, 1137**
Guide to Employment Law and Regulation. (US) **980**
Guide to Employment Law and Regulation - O S H A. (US) **980, 2710**
†Guide to Engineered Materials. (US) **5202**
Guide to Exhibitions in the World. (JA) **401**
The Guide to Export Finance. (UK) **910**
▼Guide to Federal Funding for Anti-Drug Programs. (US) **1536, 1515**
Guide to Federal Funding for Education.(US ISSN 0275-8393) **1728, 1096**
†Guide to Federal Income Taxes for Savings Institutions. (US) **5202**
Guide to Film, Television and Communication Studies in Canada. (CN) **3511**
Guide to Florida Writers. (US) **1137, 2570**
Guide to Four-Year College Databook *see* Chronicle Four-Year College Databook **1692**
Guide to Four-Year Colleges *see* Peterson's Guide to Four-Year Colleges (Year) **1696**
Guide to Free Computer Materials. (US) **1395**
Guide to Gardening. *see* Engei Gaido **2125**
▼Guide to Government Contracting. (US) **4062**
Guide to Government in Hawaii. (US ISSN 0072-8454) **4062**
Guide to Government-Loan Films. (US) **3511, 3459**
Guide to Government-Loan Films Volume 1: the Civilian Agencies. (US ISSN 0072-8462) **3520**
Guide to Graduate Degree Programs in Architectural History. (US) **300**
Guide to Graduate Departments of Sociology. (US ISSN 0091-7052) **4436, 1707**
Guide to Graduate Education in Speech - Language Pathology and Audiology.(US) **1694, 2287**
Guide to Graduate Study in Botany for the United States and Canada. (US ISSN 0072-8500) **1694, 504**
Guide to Graduate Study in Political Science. (US ISSN 0091-9632) **1694**
Guide to Grants and Fellowships in Linguistics. (US) **2816**
†Guide to Greece. (UK) **5202**
Guide to Heavy Goods Vehicle Test and Licences. (UK) **4692**
Guide to Hospitality and Tourism Education *see* Guide to College Programs in Hospitality & Tourism **1694**
Guide to In-Career Training Courses for Civil Engineers. (UK ISSN 0261-5207) **1866**
Guide to Indian Chemical Plants and Equipment. (II) **1853**
Guide to Indian Periodical Literature. (II ISSN 0017-5285) **401**

Guide to Industrial and Office Real Estate Markets *see* Comparative Statistics of Industrial Office Real Estate Markets **4147**
Guide to International Arbitration and Arbitrators (Year). (US) **2723, 910**
Guide to International Commerce Law. (US) **2723, 910**
Guide to International Investing. (CN) **948**
Guide to International Journals & Periodicals. (UK) **401**
Guide to International Periodicals *see* International Periodicals and Reference Works **2578**
Guide to Intra L A T A Communications Services *see* Planning Guide 2. Intra-L A T A Telecommunications Rates and Services **1365**
Guide to Japanese Taxes. (JA ISSN 0072-8551) **1096**
Guide to Key British Enterprises I and II.(US) **1137**
Guide to Leading Twin Cities Companies. (US) **836**
Guide to Literary Agents and Art - Photo Reps. (US ISSN 1055-6087) **4128, 328**
Guide to Management Improvement Projects in Local Government. (US) **4088**
Guide to Manuscripts Relating to Australia *see* Guide to Collections of Manuscripts Relating to Australia **2328**
Guide to Microforms in Print. Author - Title. (GW ISSN 0164-0747) **401, 2759, 4128**
Guide to Microforms in Print. Subject. (GW ISSN 0163-8386) **401**
Guide to Microforms in Print. Supplement. (GW ISSN 0164-0739) **401**
Guide to Military-Loan Films *see* Guide to Government-Loan Films **3511**
Guide to Minority Resources *see* Guide to Afro-American Resources **2003**
Guide to Muscle Cars. (US) **4692**
Guide to Mutual Funds. (US) **948, 783**
Guide to National Bibliographical Information Centres. (UN ISSN 0072-8608) **2759**
Guide to National Endowment for the Arts. (US) **328**
Guide to Nebraska State Agencies. (US ISSN 0091-0716) **4062**
Guide to Networking Services. (US) **1363**
Guide to New Zealand Income Tax Practice *see* Staples' Guide to New Zealand Income Tax Practice **1106**
Guide to Norwegian Statistics. *see* Norway. Statistisk Sentralbyraa. Vejviser i Norsk Statistikk **4582**
Guide to Obtaining Minority Business Directories. (US) **1137**
Guide to Over 100 Properties. (UK ISSN 0269-0934) **1488**
†Guide to Party Booking. (UK) **5202**
Guide to Pension and Profit Sharing Plans: Taxation, Selection and Design. (US) **1096**
Guide to Periodicals and Newspapers in the Public Libraries of Metropolitan Toronto. (CN ISSN 0315-7288) **401**
Guide to Petroleum Statistical Information. (US) **3705**
Guide to Planning, Selecting and Managing Remote Computing Services. (CN) **1395**
Guide to Port Entry (Year). (UK) **4728**
Guide to Postgraduate Degrees, Diplomas and Courses in Medicine. (UK ISSN 0265-2730) **1707**
Guide to Private English Language Schools in the U.K. for Overseas Students *see* Schools **1697**
Guide to Products and Services of Member Companies. (US) **3407**
Guide to Professional Bodies in Malawi. (MW) **1781**
Guide to Programs in Linguistics *see* Directory of Programs in Linguistics **2811**

Guide to Publishers and Related Industries in Japan *see* Directory of the Japanese Publishing Industry **4126**
Guide to Radio Electronics and Components Trade and Industry in India *see* Guide to Electronics Industry in India **1771**
Guide to Recording in the UK. (UK) **1137, 3553, 4460**
Guide to Reference Books. (US ISSN 0072-8624) **401**
Guide to Reference Books for School Media Centers. (US) **2793, 401**
Guide to Reference Material *see* Walford's Guide to Reference Material **416**
Guide to Religious Careers for Catholic Men and Women *see* Guide to Religious Ministries for Catholic Men and Women **4265**
Guide to Religious Ministries for Catholic Men and Women. (US) **4265**
Guide to Reprints. (US ISSN 0072-8667) **401**
Guide to Restoration Experts *see* Care and Repair **609**
Guide to Reviews of Books from and about Hispanic America/Guia a las Resenas de Libros de y sobre Hispanoamerica. (PR) **4128, 2003**
Guide to Sales and Use Taxes (Year). (US) **1096**
Guide to Scientific Instruments *see* Guide to Biotechnology Products and Instruments **489**
Guide to Small Business Computing and Distributed Processing. (CN) **1450, 1460**
Guide to Social Science and Religion in Periodical Literature. (US ISSN 0017-5307) **4212, 13, 4394**
Guide to Software Productivity Aids. (US) **1477**
Guide to Sources of Financial Aid for Osteopathic Medical Students *see* Selected Sources of Financial Aid for Osteopathic Medical Students **1716**
Guide to Sources of International Population Assistance. (UN) **3982**
Guide to Sourcing American Made Apparel. (US) **1285**
Guide to Special Issues and Indexes of Periodicals. (US) **13**
Guide to Springfield. (US) **2252, 836**
†Guide to Stability Design Criteria for Metal Structures. (US) **5202**
Guide to State and Federal Resources for Economic Development. (US ISSN 0894-4202) **867**
Guide to Steam Trains in the British Isles *see* British Coal Guide to Steam Trains in the British Isles **4708**
Guide to Summer Camps and Summer Schools. (US ISSN 0072-8705) **1694**
Guide to Teaching Yourself Chinese. *see* Zhongwen Zixue Zhidao **2854**
▼Guide to Texas Workers' Compensation Reform. (US) **2631, 1065**
Guide to the American Left. (US ISSN 8756-0208) **3897**
Guide to the American Occult. (US ISSN 0888-0433) **3669, 401**
Guide to the American Right. (US ISSN 8756-0216) **3897**
Guide to the Antique Shops of Britain (Year). (UK) **257**
Guide to the Classification of Steel Industry Products in the U K Customs Tariff. (UK) **3425**
Guide to the Coalfields. (UK ISSN 0072-8713) **3484**
Guide to the Essentials of a Modern Medical Practice Act. (US ISSN 0888-6768) **3101**
Guide to the Establishments. *see* Guida ai Punti di Credito **2474**
Guide to the Evaluation of Educational Experiences in the Armed Services. (US ISSN 0732-3034) **1728**
Guide to the Food Regulations in the U.K. (UK) **2631, 2072**
Guide to the Gay Northeast *see* The Guide: Gay Travel, Entertainment, Politics, and Sex **2453**

6234 GUIDE

Guide to the Italian Rubber Industry. see Guida all'Industria Italiana della Gomma **4291**
Guide to the Motor Industry of Japan. (JA) **4692**
Guide to the Port of Yokohama. (JA) **4728**
Guide to the Queen Charlottes. (US) **4770**
Guide to the Recommended Country Inns of Arizona, New Mexico, and Texas. (US) **4770, 2474**
Guide to the Recommended Country Inns of New England. (US ISSN 0093-4585) **2474**
Guide to the Recommended Country Inns of the Midwest. (US) **4770, 2474**
Guide to the Recommended Country Inns of the Rocky Mountain Region. (US) **4770, 2474**
Guide to the Recommended Country Inns of the South. (US) **4770, 2474**
Guide to the Recommended Country Inns of the West Coast. (US) **4770, 2474**
Guide to the Recommended Inns of the Mid-Atlantic States. (US) **4770, 2474**
Guide to the Social Services. (UK ISSN 0072-8756) **4407**
†Guide to the Sources of the History of Africa. (NE) **5202**
Guide to the Toronto Region's Top Employers. (CN) **667, 3627**
Guide to the Use of Insecticides and Fungicides in South Africa see Guide to the Use of Pesticides and Fungicides in the Republic of South Africa **179**
Guide to the Use of Pesticides and Fungicides in the Republic of South Africa. (SA) **179**
Guide to Tourist Homes and Guest Houses see Bed and Breakfast U S A **4753**
Guide to Training Opportunities for Industrial Development. (AU) **930**
Guide to U N C T A D Publications. (UN ISSN 0255-9358) **719**
Guide to U S G S Geologic and Hydrologic Maps. (US ISSN 0891-4915) **1545, 1790, 3688**
†Guide to U S Government Directories. (US) **5202**
Guide to U S Government Publications. (US ISSN 0092-3168) **13, 401**
Guide to U S Government Statistics. (US ISSN 0434-9067) **4573**
Guide to United States Treaties in Force. (US ISSN 0736-5713) **2699, 2723**
Guide to Venture Capital Sources see Pratt's Guide to Venture Capital Sources **960**
†Guide to Whirlpool Baths. (US) **5202**
Guide to Women's Art Organizations. (US) **328, 4844**
Guide to World Commodity Markets. (US) **910**
†Guide to Your Child's Development. (US) **5202**
Guide Touristique. see Tourist Guide **5291**
Guide Touristique Europeen pour Israelites/European Travel Guide for Jews. (BE) **2003**
Guidebook of United States Coins. (US ISSN 0072-8829) **3599**
Guidebook on Industrial Safety. (JA) **3617**
Guidebook - State of Ohio, Department of Natural Resources, Division of Geological Survey see Ohio. Division of Geological Survey. Guidebook **1576**
Guidebook to California Taxes. (US ISSN 0072-8837) **1096**
Guidebook to Fair Employment Practices. (US ISSN 0196-7975) **2631**
Guidebook to Florida Taxes. (US ISSN 0093-8637) **1096**
Guidebook to Illinois Taxes. (US ISSN 0072-8845) **1096**
Guidebook to Labor Relations. (US ISSN 0072-8853) **980, 2631**
Guidebook to Massachusetts Taxes. (US ISSN 0072-8861) **1096**
Guidebook to Michigan Taxes. (US ISSN 0072-887X) **1096**
Guidebook to New Jersey Taxes. (US ISSN 0072-8888) **1096**
Guidebook to New York Taxes. (US ISSN 0072-8896) **1096**
Guidebook to North Carolina Taxes. (US ISSN 0091-1186) **1096**
Guidebook to Ohio Taxes. (US ISSN 0091-4010) **1096**
Guidebook to Pennsylvania Taxes. (US ISSN 0072-890X) **1096**
Guidebook to the European Adhesives Industry. (UK) **1137, 1177**
Guidebook to Wisconsin Taxes. (US ISSN 0093-8645) **1096**
Guideline see Trends (Alexandria) **1498**
GuideLines. (US) **1363, 1040**
Guidelines. (AT ISSN 0156-6717) **2793, 13**
Guidelines for Health Supervision II. (US) **2461, 3101**
Guidelines for Improving Practice. Architects and Engineers Professional Liability. (US ISSN 0091-8245) **300, 1823**
Guidelines for Industrial Investors in Kenya see Kenya: The Gateway to Africa **1142**
Guidelines for Perinatal Care. (US) **3292, 2461**
Guidelines for Teachers. (UK ISSN 0072-8918) **1750**
Guidelines Letter. (US) **300**
Guidelines Magazine see Writers' Guidelines Magazine **2577**
Guidepost. (US ISSN 0017-5323) **3627**
Guideposts. (US ISSN 0017-5331) **4180**
Guides Pratiques. (BE) **1505**
Guides to European Taxation: Taxation in European Socialist Countries. (NE) **1096**
Guides to European Taxation: Taxation of Companies in Europe. (NE) **1096**
▼Guides to European Taxation: Taxation of Individuals in Europe. (NE) **1096**
Guides to European Taxation: Taxation of Patent Royalties, Dividends, Interest in Europe. (NE) **1096**
Guides to European Taxation: Taxation of Private Investment Income. (NE) **1096**
Guides to European Taxation: Value Added Taxation in Europe. (NE) **1096**
Guiding. (UK ISSN 0265-2706) **1238**
Guiding in Australia. (AT ISSN 0159-0340) **1255, 1238**
Guidon see Norwich Guidon **1319**
GUIDOR. (Guide Annuaire Officiel du Complexe de Rungis) (FR) **2092, 1137**
Guild: a Sourcebook of American Craft Artists see Guild: A Sourcebook of Artists and Artisans **328**
Guild: A Sourcebook of Artists and Artisans. (US) **328**
Guild and City Gazette. (UK) **1313**
Guild Digest (Year). (AT) **3747**
Guild News. (UK) **53, 4673**
Guild Notes see National Lawyers Guild. Guild Notes **2657**
Guild of Agricultural Journalists Year Book. (UK) **94, 2570**
Guild of Air Pilots and Air Navigators. Journal. (UK) **53**
Guild of Book Workers. Newsletter. (US) **4128**
Guild of Book Workers Journal. (US ISSN 0434-9245) **4128, 4000**
Guild of British Newspaper Editors Guild Journal. (UK) **2570**
Guild of Carillonneurs in North America (San Antonio) Bulletin see G C N A Bulletin **3552**
Guild of Freemen of the City of London.(UK) **2364**
Guild of Industrial, Commercial, and Institutional Accountants. Journal. (CN) **751**
Guild Reporter. (US ISSN 0017-5404) **2583, 2570**
Guilder. (US) **2287, 4102**
Guildhall Poets. (UK) **2994**
Guildnotes. (US) **328, 3553**
Guilfoyle Report. (US) **3791, 1488**
Guilin Dianzi Gongye Xueyuan Xuebao/ Guilin Institute of Electronic Industry. Journal. (CC ISSN 1001-7437) **1771**
Guilin Institute of Electronic Industry. Journal. see Guilin Dianzi Gongye Xueyuan Xuebao **1771**
Guimaraes. Arquivo Municipal "Alfredo Pimenta." Boletim de Trabalhos Historicos. (PO) **2407**
Guineenne. (GV) **4844**
Guiniguada. (SP ISSN 0213-0610) **1684, 1750**
Guinness Book of Records. (US ISSN 1057-4557) **1781**
Guinness Book of World Records see Guinness Book of Records **1781**
Guinness Globe. (UK) **381**
Guion. (CK) **2183**
Guion. (SP ISSN 0017-5455) **3459**
Guis de Viajes. (MX) **4770**
Guisuanyan Tongbao/Chinese Silicate Society. Bulletin. (CC ISSN 1001-1625) **1213**
Guisuanyan Xuebao/Chinese Silicate Society. Journal. (CC ISSN 0454-5648) **1213**
Guitar and Mandolin. (US ISSN 0270-9325) **3553**
Guitar Extra. (US) **3553**
Guitar for the Practicing Musician. (US ISSN 0738-937X) **3553**
Guitar International. (UK ISSN 0958-6342) **3553**
Guitar Player. (US ISSN 0017-5463) **3553**
Guitar Review. (US ISSN 0017-5471) **3553**
Guitar School. (US) **3553**
Guitar World. (US) **3553**
Guitarist. (UK) **3553**
Guitarra Magazine. (US) **3553**
Guizhou Historical Studies. see Guizhou Wenshi Congkan **2338**
Guizhou Minzu Yanjiu/Study of Guizhou Nationalities. (CC) **3637, 240**
Guizhou Shehui Kexue (Jingji Ban)/ Social Sciences in Guizhou (Economics Edition). (CC) **867, 4373**
Guizhou Shehui Kexue (Wen-Shi-Zhe Ban)/Social Sciences in Guizhou (Literature, History, Philosophy Edition). (CC) **4373**
Guizhou Wenshi Congkan/Guizhou Historical Studies. (CC ISSN 1000-8705) **2338**
Gujarat Agricultural University Research Journal. (II ISSN 0250-5193) **94**
Gujarat Chamber of Commerce and Industry. Annual Report. (II) **816**
Gujarat Chamber of Commerce and Industry. Bulletin. (II) **816**
Gujarat Industrial Development Corporation. Annual Report. (II) **1077**
Gujarat Labour Gazette. (II ISSN 0017-5501) **980**
Gujarat Law Reporter. (II ISSN 0017-551X) **2631**
Gujarat Law Times. (II ISSN 0017-5528) **2631**
Gujarat Research Society. Journal. (II) **4311**
Gujarat Revenue Tribunal Law Reporter. (II ISSN 0017-5536) **2631**
Gujarat State Financial Corporation. Annual Report. (II ISSN 0533-649X) **1096**
Guji Zhengli Yanjiu Xuekan. (CC) **2759, 2338**
Gujian Yuanlin Jishu/Traditional Chinese Architecture and Gardens. (CC ISSN 1000-7237) **300**
Gujizhui Dongwu Xuebao/Vertebrate Palasiatica. (CC ISSN 1000-3118) **3657, 583**
Gukjesaenghwal/International Life. (KN) **3958**
Gulcher see Radio Free Rock **3576**
Gulden Passer/Compas d'Or. (BE) **4128**
Guldsmedebladet. (DK ISSN 0017-5544) **2564**
Guldsmedstidningen. (SW ISSN 0282-4175) **2564**
Gulf and Caribbean Fisheries Institute. Annual Proceedings. (US ISSN 0072-9019) **2042**
Gulf Coast. (US) **2226**
Gulf Coast Cattleman. (US ISSN 0017-5552) **217**
Gulf Coast Conference Proceedings. (US) **2407**
Gulf Coast Fisherman. (US ISSN 0164-3746) **4547**
Gulf Coast Golfer. (US) **4506**
Gulf Coast Historical Review. (US ISSN 0892-9025) **2311**
Gulf Coast Oil World. (US ISSN 0884-7967) **3688**
▼Gulf Coast PetroProcess Directory. (US) **3688, 1853**
Gulf Coast Plumbing - Heating - Cooling News. (US ISSN 0046-659X) **2299**
Gulf Coast Retail Grocer. (US) **2092**
Gulf Coast Singles Association Monthly Book see Southeast Singles Association Monthly Publication **4364**
Gulf Construction see Gulf Construction & Saudi Arabia Review **619**
Gulf Construction & Saudi Arabia Review. (BA) **619, 1866**
Gulf Directory. (BA) **1137**
†Gulf Guide & Diary. (UK) **5202**
Gulf Handbook. (US) **2429**
Gulf News. (TS) **667**
Gulf of Mexico Drilling Report. (US) **3688**
Gulf of Mexico Field Development Locator. (US) **3688**
Gulf of Mexico Index see Gulf of Mexico Summary Report - Index **3688**
Gulf of Mexico Newsletter. (US ISSN 1058-5885) **3688**
Gulf of Mexico Rig Locator. (US) **3688**
Gulf of Mexico Summary Report see Gulf of Mexico Summary Report - Index **3688**
Gulf of Mexico Summary Report - Index. (US) **3688**
Gulf Panorama. (BA) **2173**
▼Gulf Reconstruction Report. (US ISSN 1055-744X) **3459, 667**
Gulf Shipping and Transport see Shipping & Transport News International **4739**
Gulf States Newsletter. (UK ISSN 0953-5411) **3959, 667**
Gulf T V. (SU) **1374**
Gulf Times. (QA) **2210**
▼Gulf Tourism Directory. (BA) **4770**
Gulf Weekly. (TS) **2220**
†Gulf Wings. (CN ISSN 0319-2776) **5202**
Gulfshore Life. (US) **2226**
Gull. (US ISSN 0164-971X) **564**
▼Gullet. (UK ISSN 0952-0643) **3101**
Gulliver. (GW ISSN 0344-242X) **2816, 2921, 4844**
Gullsmedkunst. (NO ISSN 0046-6603) **2564**
Gumbinner Heimatbrief. (GW) **2055, 2364**
Gummi, Asbest, Kunstoffe see Gummi, Fasern, Kunststoffe **4291**
Gummi, Fasern, Kunststoffe. (GW) **4291**
Gummibereifung. (GW ISSN 0017-5609) **4291**
Gumpoldskirchner Nachrichten. (AU) **4088**
Gun & Accessories Mart. (UK) **2436**
Gun Dog. (US ISSN 0279-5086) **4547, 3711**
Gun List. (US ISSN 0894-8119) **257**
Gun Report. (US ISSN 0017-5617) **2436, 4473**
Gun Show Calendar. (US ISSN 0896-6001) **257, 4547**
Gun Talk. (CN ISSN 0017-5625) **2436**
Gun Tests. (US ISSN 1042-6450) **4547**
Gun Traders Guide. (US) **4473**
Gun Week see New Gun Week **4481**
Gun World. (US ISSN 0017-5641) **4473**
Gun World Annual. (US) **4547**

Gun World Hunting Guide see Gun World Annual **4547**
†Gung-Ho. (US ISSN 0279-4268) **5202**
Gunma Daigaku Kyoikugakubu Kiyo. Shizen Kagaku Hen/Gunma University. Faculty of Education. Science Reports. (JA ISSN 0017-5668) **4311**
Gunma Journal of Liberal Arts and Sciences. (JA ISSN 0367-4061) **2507**
Gunma Reports on Medical Sciences/ Gunma Repoto. (JA ISSN 0386-0760) **3101**
Gunma Repoto. see Gunma Reports on Medical Sciences **3101**
Gunma Symposia on Endocrinology. (JA ISSN 0533-6724) **3253**
Gunma University. Faculty of Education. Annual Report: Cultural Science Series. (JA ISSN 0386-4294) **2507**
Gunma University. Faculty of Education. Science Reports. see Gunma Daigaku Kyoikugakubu Kiyo. Shizen Kagaku Hen **4311**
Gunma University, Faculty of Education. Annual Report: Art, Technology, Health & Physical Education, and Science of Human Living Series. (JA ISSN 0533-6627) **1707**, 328, 4599
Gunn Salute. (US ISSN 0738-4866) **2153**
Gunneria. (NO ISSN 0332-8554) **273**, 440, 504
Guns. (US ISSN 0017-5676) **4473**
Guns & Ammo. (US ISSN 0017-5684) **4548**, 2436
†Guns and Ammo Annual. (US ISSN 0072-906X) **5202**
Guns Australia. (AT ISSN 0157-1729) **4473**
Guns Guide see Cord Sportfacts Guns Guide **5172**
Guns Magazine see Guns **4473**
Guns Review. (UK ISSN 0017-5692) **2436**, 4473
Gunsite Gossip. (US) **4473**
Gunzo. (JA) **2921**
Guo Ji Dian Li Gong Ye see Electricity for China **5185**
Guo Ji Dian Zi Gong Ye see International Electronics for China **5216**
Guo Moruo Xuekan. (CC ISSN 1003-7225) **419**
Guoji Chanye Jingji Jishu. (CC) **910**
Guoji Dianzi Shangqing see Electronic News for China **1768**
Guoji Dizhen Dongtai/Recent Developments of World Seismology. (CC) **1590**
Guoji Dizhen Dongtai/International Seismology Development. (CC ISSN 0253-4975) **1590**
Guoji Gongyunshi Yanjiu/Research in the History of the International Communist Movement. (CC) **3959**
Guoji Hangkong/International Aviation. (CC ISSN 1000-4009) **54**
Guoji Jingji Hezuo/International Economic Cooperation. (CC) **930**, 910
Guoji Jingmao Xiaoxi/Information - International Trade & Economics. (US) **910**, 867
Guoji Jingmao Xiaoxi Bao/International Trade News. (CC) **910**
Guoji Jingmao Xiaoxi Bao. Shuangbian Jingmao Zhuankan/International Trade News Supplement. (CC) **910**
Guoji Jinrong Daokan/World Finance Herald. (CC) **783**
Guoji Keji Jiaoliu/International Science and Technology Exchange. (CC) **4311**, 4599
Guoji Laogong Tongxun/International Labor Bulletin. (CC) **980**
Guoji Maoyi/International Trade. (CC) **910**
Guoji Maoyi Wenti/International Trade Journal. (CC ISSN 1002-4670) **910**
Guoji Nisha Yanjiu. see International Silt Research **1545**

Guoji Rencai Jiaoliu/International Exchange of Personnel. (CC ISSN 1001-0114) **1722**
Guoji Shangbao/International Commerce. (CC) **910**
Guoji Shangbao Yuekan/International Commerce Monthly. (CC) **910**
Guoji Shangye yu Guanli/International Commerce and Management. (CC) **910**
Guoji Shichang/International Market. (CC ISSN 1001-5450) **910**
Guoji Wenti Yanjiu/International Studies.(CC ISSN 0452-8832) **3959**, 867
Guoji Xiangqi/Chess. (CC) **4473**
Guoji Zhanwang/International Prospect. (CC ISSN 0452-8778) **3959**
Guoli Taiwan Daxue Nongxueyuan Yanjiu Baogao see National Taiwan University. College of Agriculture. Memoirs **109**
Guoli Taiwan Daxue Shehui Xuekan see National Taiwan University Journal of Sociology **4443**
Guoli Taiwan Daxue Yixueyuan Yanjiu Baogao see National Taiwan University. College of Medicine. Memoirs **3134**
Guomin Jingji Dongxiang Tongji Jibao - Zhonghua Minguo Taiwan Diqu see China, Republic. Executive Yuan. Directorate-General of Budget, Accounting & Statistics. Quarterly National Economic Trends, Taiwan Area **851**
Guowai Dizhi/Geology Abroad. (CC) **1567**
Guowai Dizhi Keji/Foreign Geology Science and Technology. (CC) **1567**
Guowai Hangkong Wenzhai/Foreign Aeronautics Abstracts. (CC ISSN 1002-6614) **66**, 13
Guowai Jiguang/Foreign Lasers. (CC) **3852**
Guowai Keji Dongtai/Foreign Science and Technology Development. (CC) **4311**, 4599
Guowai Keji Ziliao Mulu - Cehuixue/ Foreign Science and Technology Literature Catalogue - Survey. (CC) **2268**, 401
Guowai Keji Ziliao Mulu - Dizhixue/ Foreign Science and Technology Catalogue - Geology. (CC) **1551**, 1567
Guowai Naihuo Cailiao. (CC ISSN 1000-7563) **3407**
Guowai Nongxue - Nongye Qixiang/ Foreign Agriculture - Agricultural Meteorology. (CC ISSN 1000-6427) **95**
Guowai Shehui Kexue/Social Science Abroad. (CC) **4373**
Guowai Shehui Kexue Kuaibao/Foreign Social Science Bulletin. (CC ISSN 1000-4785) **4373**
Guowai Shehui Kexue Lunwen Suoyin/ Foreign Social Science Dissertation Index. (CC) **4394**, 13
Guowai Sichou/Foreign Silk. (CC) **4619**
Guowai Waiyu Jiaoxue/Foreign Language Teaching in Foreign Countries. (CC) **2816**, 1636
Guowai Xumu Keji/Foreign Animal Husbandry Science and Technology. (CC) **217**, 4810
Guowai Yixue (Erkexue Fence)/Foreign Medical Sciences (Pediatrics). (CC) **3320**
Guowai Yixue (Fuchan Kexue Fence)/ Foreign Medical Sciences (Gynecology & Obstetrics). (CC) **3292**
Guowai Yixue (Huxi Xitong Fence)/ Foreign Medical Sciences (Respiratory Diseases). (CC) **3365**
Guowai Yixue (Jihua Shengyu Fence)/ Foreign Medical Sciences (Birth Control). (CC ISSN 1001-3490) **596**
Guowai Yixue (Jishengbing Fence)/ Foreign Medical Science (Parasitosis). (CC ISSN 1001-1072) **552**
Guowai Yixue (Linchuang Fangshexue Fence)/Foreign Medical Sciences (Clinical Radiology). (CC) **3358**

Guowai Yixue (Linchuang Shengwu Huaxue yu Jianyan Fence)/Foreign Medical Science (Clinical Biochemistry and Inspection). (CC) **3101**
Guowai Yixue (Shuxue yu Xueyexue Fence)/Foreign Medical Science (Blood Transfusion and Blood). (CC) **3272**
Guowai Yixue (Yaoxue Fence)/Foreign Medical Sciences (Pharmacology). (CC) **3727**
Guowai Yixue - Neikexue Fence/Foreign Medical Science - Internal Medicine. (CC) **3102**
Guowai Yiyao (Kangshengsu Fence)/ World Notes on Antibiotics. (CC ISSN 1001-8751) **3727**
Guowai Yiyao - Zhiwuyao Fence/World Notes on Herbal Medicine. (CC ISSN 1001-6856) **3727**
Guowai Youqi Kantan. (CC ISSN 1001-5825) **1567**, 3688
Guowai Yuyanxue. (US) **2816**, 1707
Guowai Zaozhi/Paper Manufacturing in Foreign Countries. (CC ISSN 1001-3911) **3663**
Gupta Gavesana. (CE) **358**
Gurin Pawa/Green Power. (JA ISSN 0389-0988) **2101**
Gurmat Sagar. (II) **4214**
Guru Malaysia. (MY) **1636**, 2583
Guru Nanak Commemorative Lectures. (II) **4214**
Gushengwu Xue Wenzhai. (CC ISSN 1001-4306) **3657**
Gushengwu Xuebao/Acta Palaeontologica Sinica. (CC ISSN 0001-6616) **3657**
Gushi Daguan. (CC) **2921**
Gushi Dawang. (CC) **2921**, 1255
Gushi Jia/Story Teller. (CC) **2921**
Gushi Lin. (CC ISSN 1002-2554) **2921**
Gushi Shijie. (CC) **2921**
Gushihui/Storyteller. (CC ISSN 0257-0238) **2921**
†Guss Produkte. (GW ISSN 0177-9796) **5202**
Gussrohr - Technik. (GW) **2299**
Gustav - Adolf - Blatt. (GW ISSN 0017-5730) **4180**
Gustav Freytag Blaetter. (GW) **2921**
Gusto. (AU ISSN 1013-9478) **2072**
Gut. (UK ISSN 0017-5749) **3268**
Gut Essen/Eats & Treats. (GW) **2474**, 4770
Gut Speisen und Reisen. (GW) **2474**
Gute Besserung. (GW) **4180**
Gute Fahrt. (GW ISSN 0017-5765) **4692**
Gute Jugendbuch see Jugendbuchmagazin **1240**
Gute Nachrichten. (AU ISSN 0017-5781) **2173**
†Gute Reise. (SZ ISSN 0017-579X) **5202**
Die Gute Tat. (GW ISSN 0017-5803) **4407**
Der Gute Wille. (GW) **4407**, 980
Guten Tag. (GW ISSN 0172-4525) **2189**
Le Gutenberg. (SZ ISSN 0017-5811) **2583**, 4000
†Gutenberg. (FR) **5202**
†Gutenberg & Family. (US) **5202**
Gutenberg - Gesellschaft. Kleine Drucke.(GW ISSN 0933-6230) **4001**, 2311, 4128
Gutenberg - Jahrbuch. (GW ISSN 0072-9094) **4001**
Guter Rat. (GW ISSN 0017-582X) **2447**
Guthrie Journal. (US ISSN 0882-696X) **3102**
Guti Dianzixue Yanjiu yu Jinzhan. (CC ISSN 1000-3819) **1771**, 1893
Guti Lixue Xuebao. (CC ISSN 0254-7805) **3843**
Gutmann Knife Journal. (US) **4473**
Guts. (US) **2921**
Guyana. Geology & Mines Commission. Annual Report. (GY) **1567**
Guyana. Geology & Mines Commission. Mineral Resources Pamphlet. (GY) **1567**
Guyana. Hydrometeorological Service. Annual Climatological Data Summary.(GY) **3436**

GYNECOLOGY

Guyana. National Insurance Board. Annual Report: Guyana National Insurance Scheme. (GY) **2546**
Guyana. Statistical Bureau. Annual Account Relating to External Trade. (GY ISSN 0533-991X) **910**
Guyana Association of Medical Technologists. Newsletter. (GY) **3259**
Guyana Association of Professional Engineers see G A P E **1822**
†Guyana Business. (GY ISSN 0017-5854) **5202**
Guyana Information Bulletin. (GY) **3897**
Guyana Institute for Social Research and Action see G I S R A **5198**
Guyana Journal. (GY ISSN 0046-6654) **3897**
Guyana Library Association Bulletin. (GY) **2759**
Guyana Science Teachers' Association. Newsletter. (GY) **4311**, 1750
Guyana Sugar Corporation. Annual Reports and Accounts. (GY) **179**
Guyana Trade Directory. (UK) **1137**
Guyanese National Bibliography. (GY) **402**
Guybau News see Guymine News **3484**
Guymine News. (GY) **3484**
Guys. (US) **2453**
Guy's Hospital Gazette. (UK ISSN 0017-5870) **2461**
▼Guzarish. (IR) **667**
▼Guzarish-i Film. (NP) **3511**, 1374
Gwechall. (FR ISSN 0220-276X) **2364**, 273
Gwent Family History Society. Journal. (UK ISSN 0262-4672) **2153**
Y Gwyddonydd. (UK ISSN 0017-5897) **4311**
Gwynmercian. (US) **1313**
Gyden. (DK ISSN 0109-2111) **1707**
Gyermekgyogyaszat. (HU ISSN 0017-5900) **3320**
†Gym Coach. (AT) **5202**
†Gym Dandies. (US ISSN 0887-1027) **5202**
Gymnase. (GW) **1255**
Gymnasieskolen. (DK ISSN 0017-5927) **1636**
Gymnasiet Laerere i Billedkunst see G L B **1635**
Gymnasium. (GW ISSN 0017-5943) **1277**
Gymnasium Helveticum. (SZ ISSN 0017-5951) **1636**
Das Gymnasium in Bayern. (GW) **1636**
Gymnast Magazine. (UK) **4474**
Gymnastics. see Ticao **4495**
Gymnastics Guide see N A G W S Guide. Gymnastics **5241**
†Gymnastics Today. (US ISSN 0895-2914) **5202**
Gymnastics World see International Gymnast Magazine **4476**
Gymnastik. (DK ISSN 0108-3678) **4474**
Gymnastika see Sportovni a Moderni Gymnastika **5282**
Gymnastikk og Turn. (NO ISSN 0017-596X) **4474**
Gymnastikledaren see Svensk Gymnastik **4493**
Gymnica. (IT) **4474**
Der Gynaekologe. (GW ISSN 0017-5994) **3292**
Gynaekologische Praxis. (GW ISSN 0341-8677) **3292**
Gynaekologische Rundschau. (SZ ISSN 0017-6001) **3292**
Gynaika. (GR) **4844**
▼GynComp. (GW ISSN 0938-6467) **3292**
Gynecologic and Obstetric Investigation. (SZ ISSN 0378-7346) **3292**
Gynecologic Oncology. (US ISSN 0090-8258) **3292**
Gynecological Tumors--Diagnosis, Treatment see I C R D B Cancergram: Gynecological Tumors - Diagnosis, Treatment **3175**
Gynecologie. (FR ISSN 0301-2204) **3293**
Gynecology - Obstetrics. see Berichte Gynaekologie - Geburtshilfe **3166**

Gyobyo Kenkyu/Fish Pathology. (JA ISSN 0388-788X) **583**
Gyogyszereszet. (HU ISSN 0017-6036) **3727**
Gyoko Kensetsu Gijutsu Kenkyu Happyokai Koenshu/Proceedings of Fishing Port Engineering. (JA) **1866**
†Gyorsindex - Epites. (HU ISSN 0209-9853) **5202**
†Gyorsindex - Szamitastechnika, Automatizalas. (HU ISSN 0133-9966) **5202**
Gypsum Products see Canada. Statistics Canada. Gypsum Products **637**
Gypsy. (US ISSN 0176-3148) **2921**, 2867
Gypsy Lore Society. Journal. (US ISSN 0017-6087) **240**, 2921
Gypsy Lore Society. Newsletter. (US ISSN 0731-4841) **240**, 2055, 2816, 4373
Gypsy Lore Society. Publications. (US ISSN 8756-7245) **240**, 2055, 2311, 2816
GyroScope. (US ISSN 0279-6694) **1298**
H see H L M Aujourd'hui **2487**
H A C Techline. (Historical Aircraft Corporation) (US) **54**, 2436, 3397, 4673
H A H R see Hispanic American Historical Review **2408**
H A L O Newsletter. (Homophile Association of London Ontario) (CN) **2453**
H A L - P C Newsletter see H A L - P C User Journal **1469**
H A L - P C User Journal. (Houston Area League of P C Users, Inc.) (US) **1469**, 1460
H A N D S (Hawaiian Aloha Needs Deaf Spirit) see Ka Kuli O'Hawai'i **2288**
H A N O W Herald. (Houston Area National Organization for Women) (US) **4844**
H A P P I see Household & Personal Products Industry **1854**
†H & S Reports. (Haskins & Sells) (US ISSN 0017-6117) **5202**
H & V News. (UK) **2299**
H B Modelbouw en Techniek see H B Modelbouw Magazine **2436**
H B Modelbouw Magazine. (NE ISSN 0922-2170) **2436**
H B S A Newsletter. (Historical Breechloading Smallarms Association) (UK) **257**, 3459
H B S A Occasional Papers see H B S A Newsletter **257**
H B S Case Bibliography see H B S Catalog of Teaching Materials **719**
H B S Catalog of Teaching Materials. (Harvard University, Graduate School of Business Administration) (US ISSN 1042-654X) **719**
H C E A Exhibitors Advisory Council's Action Memo. (Healthcare Convention & Exhibitors Association) (US) **3392**, 3102
H C F A Manuals see Health Care Financing Administration Manuals **2462**
H C I Abstracts see Abstracts in Human - Computer Interaction **1403**
H C I M A Quarterly Bibliography of Hotel and Catering Management. (Hotel Catering and Institutional Management Association) (UK ISSN 0144-7580) **2482**, 402
H C J Communications Report. (CY ISSN 0256-5935) **3959**, 1040, 1636
H C L Authority File (Microfiche Edition). (Hennepin County Library) (US) **2759**
H C M State Institute of Public Administration. (II) **4062**
H C V C Newsletter see Historical Commercial News **257**
H D K Info. (Hochschule der Kunste Berlin) (GW) **328**, 300, 3553, 4633
H D Newsletter. (Hilda Doolittle) (US ISSN 1040-4015) **2921**
▼H D T V Report. (High Definition Television) (US ISSN 1055-9280) **1374**, 1893

H D T V World Review see H D World Review **1374**
▼H D World Review. (US ISSN 1055-6931) **1374**, 1893
H E A Advocate. (Houston Education Association) (US) **1636**
H E A G Journal. (Hessische Elektrizitaets AG) (GW) **1893**
H E A P Journal. (Health Education Association of the Philippines) (PH) **4102**
H E C Forum. (Hospital Ethics Committee) (NE ISSN 0956-2737) **2461**, 3767
H E P see Humor Events & Possibilities **2868**
H E R A - Bulletin. (GW) **3819**, 1866
H E R D S A Green Guide. (Higher Education Research and Development Society of Australasia) (AT ISSN 0813-524X) **1707**, 1750
H E R D S A News. (Higher Education Research and Development Society of Australasia) (AT ISSN 0157-1826) **1636**, 1707
H E R P I C C Pothole Gazette. (Highway Extension and Research Program, Indiana Counties and Cities) (US) **4719**
H E R S Newsletter. (Hysterectomy Educational Resources & Services) (US ISSN 0892-628X) **4844**, 596, 4407, 4835
H F see Health & Fitness **3802**
H F D - Retailing Home Furnishings. (US ISSN 0162-9158) **2559**
H G. (US) **2551**, 2129, 2559
H G V Driver's Handbook see Truck Driver's Handbook **4704**
H.G. Wells Society Newsletter. (UK ISSN 0306-5480) **2921**
H H I see Heilbronner Hochschul-Informationen **5204**
H H L A Report. (Hamburger Hafen- und Lagerhaus-Aktiengesellschaft) (GW) **4728**
H I A S Reporter. (US) **4407**
H I A S Statistical Abstract. (US) **3992**
H I C S S see Hawaii International Conference on System Sciences. Proceedings **1437**
†H I F P A Guide to Hispanic Cultural World. (Hispanic Institute for the Performing Arts) (US ISSN 1040-6654) **5202**
H I V Funding Watch. (Human Immunodeficiency Virus) (US) **3219**
H I V O S - Informatie Bulletin see H I V O S - Projectbericht **930**
H I V O S - Projectbericht. (Humanistisch Instituut voor Ontwikkelingssamenwerking) (NE ISSN 0169-0337) **930**
H I V Prevention News. (Human Immunodeficiency Virus) (US) **3219**, 3185
†H K F E Newsletter. (Hong Kong Futures Exchange Ltd.) (HK) **5202**
H K I Report see Insight (New York, 1978) **2293**
H K P C Electronics Bulletin. (Hong Kong Productivity Council) (HK) **1771**
H K Staff. (HK ISSN 1012-7887) **1065**
H K T see Handelskammartidningen **816**
†H L A Journal. (Hawaii Library Association) (US) **5202**
H L B Newsletter. (US ISSN 0887-3712) **3259**, 3208, 3272, 3365
H L D I Injury and Collision Loss Experience. (Highway Loss Data Institute) (US) **4692**
H L H, Heizung, Lueftung, Klima, Haustechnik. (GW) **2299**
H L H, Zeitschrift fuer Heizung, Lueftung, Klimatechnik, Haustechnik see H L H, Heizung, Lueftung, Klima, Haustechnik **2299**
H L I Canadian Report. (Human Life International in Canada Inc.) (CN) **3982**, 4265, 4407
H L I Reports. (Human Life International) (US ISSN 0899-2673) **3982**, 4265, 4407

H L I Reports. (Human Life International in Canada Inc.) (CN) **3982**, 4265, 4407
H L I Reports - Canada see H L I Reports **3982**
H L I Sister Lucille's Special Canadian Report see H L I Canadian Report **3982**
H L M Aujourd'hui. (FR) **2487**
H L Q Wellness Calendar see H L Q Wellness Directory **3214**
H L Q Wellness Directory. (US) **3214**
H L Z. (GW) **1636**
H L Z see Hessische Lehrerzeitung **1728**
H M see Heavy Metal **3012**
H M A T. (Hot Mix Asphalt Technology) (US) **4719**
H M C R I. (Hazardous Materials Control Research Institute) (US) **1984**, 1956
H M C R I Focus. (Hazardous Materials Control Research Institute) (US) **1984**, 1956, 4102
H M C R I Forum see H M C R I Focus **1984**
H M Customs and Excise Official V A T Guides. (UK) **1096**
H M D - Theorie und Praxis der Wirtschaftsinformatik. (GW) **1395**
H.M. Heavy Metal & Hard Rock. (IT) **3553**, 4460
H M K Kirche see H M K Kurier **4180**
H M K Kurier. (Hilfsaktion Maertyrerkirche e.V.) (GW) **4180**, 3942
H M O Magazine. (Health Maintenance Organization) (US ISSN 1050-9038) **2532**
H M O Practice. (US ISSN 0891-6624) **3102**
H M Q see Health Management Quarterly **2462**
H N O (Berlin). (Hals-, Nasen-, Ohren-Heilkunde) (GW ISSN 0017-6192) **3314**
H N O (Cologne). (Deutsche Berufsverband der Hals-, Nasen-, Ohrenaerzte e.V.) (GW ISSN 0341-9746) **3314**
H N O - Nachrichten. (GW) **3314**
H N O - Praxis. (Hals, Nasen, Ohren) (GW ISSN 0323-5033) **3314**
H O B - Die Holzbearbeitung. (GW ISSN 0018-3822) **4599**
H O R E S C A - Informations. (Federation Nationale des Hoteliers, Restaurateurs et Cafetiers du Grand-Duche de Luxembourg) (LU) **2474**, 4770
H P A see Helvetica Physica Acta **3819**
H P A Bulletin (Hospital Physicists Association) see Scope (York) **3830**
H P A C Techlit Selector. (Heating Piping Air Conditioning) (US) **1930**
H P B Surgery. (US ISSN 0894-8569) **3379**
H P Chronicle. (Hewlett-Packard) (US ISSN 0892-2829) **1460**
H P Chronicle - Europe. (US ISSN 0895-0342) **1469**
H P Design and Automation see Workstation Magazine **1402**
H P Design & Manfacturing see Workstation **1424**
H P Energia Trasporti see H P Trasporti **4719**
H P L C: Advances and Perspectives. (High-Performance Liquid Chromatography) (US ISSN 0270-8531) **1205**
H.P.O. Notes see Transit Postmark Collector **3758**
H P Professional. (US) **1460**
H P R see Hungarian Press Review and Economic News **5207**
H P Trasporti. (IT ISSN 0391-2019) **4719**
H P V News. (International Human-Powered-Vehicle Association) (US ISSN 0898-6894) **4474**
H Q see High Quality **4001**
H R C. (Journal of High Resolution Chromatography) (GW) **1205**
H R C and C C see H R C **1205**
H R D I Advisory. (Human Resources Development Institute) (US) **980**, 3627

H R Focus. (US) **1065**
H R I - Buyers Guide. (Hotels, Restaurants, Institutions) (US) **2072**, 200, 217
H R I S Abstracts see Highway Research Abstracts **4664**
H.R. Macmillan Lectureship in Forestry. (CN ISSN 0072-9140) **2101**
H R Magazine. (Human Resources) (US) **1065**
H R Planning Newsletter. (US ISSN 0733-0332) **1065**
H R Power see H R Update **826**
H R Reporter. (Human Resource) (US ISSN 0741-6997) **1065**, 980
H R S P Review. (Association of Human Resource Systems Professionals) (US) **1065**
H R Update. (US) **826**, 1065
H S A Happenings. (Homeschoolers' Support Association) (US) **1636**
H S Aktuell. (Heinrich /Schmid GmbH und Co.) (GW) **328**
H S B International. (NE ISSN 0923-666X) **4728**
†H S Dent Business Forecast. (US) **5202**
H S I Bulletin. (Heliconia Society International) (US) **2129**
H S L see H S L A **2921**
H S L A. (Hebrew University Studies in Literature and the Arts) (IS) **2921**
H S U Brand. (Hardin - Simmons University) (US ISSN 0017-6249) **1313**
H S U S News. (Humane Society of the United States) (US ISSN 1059-1621) **231**
H S V - Journal. (Hamburger Sport -Verein e.V.) (GW) **4474**
H S V - Post see H S V - Journal **4474**
H - Scoop. (US) **1460**, 1469, 1477
H T A Advocate see H E A Advocate **1636**
H T F S Digest. (UK) **1853**
H T H Poolife see Poolife **4483**
H T M see Haerterei-Technische Mitteilungen **3407**
H T W Praxis. (Hauswirtschaft Textilarbeit Werken) (GW) **2447**
†H U D Newsletter. (U.S. Department of Housing and Urban Development) (US ISSN 0017-6311) **5202**
H U L Notes see Harvard University Library Notes **2759**
H U P. (US) **328**
H V A C Product News. (Heating, Ventilating, Air Conditioning) (US) **2299**
H V A C ProfitMaker. (US ISSN 0899-9791) **1011**
†H V A C Red Book of Heating, Ventilating and Air Conditioning Equipment. (UK) **5202**
H V A Current Awareness Bulletin. (Health Visitors' Association) (UK ISSN 0262-172X) **3278**, 3802
H V - Journal. (GW ISSN 0936-9856) **836**
H V Magazine. (AU) **667**
†H V V Extra. (Hessischer Volkshochschulverband) (GW ISSN 0932-8300) **5202**
H V V Rundschreiben. (Hessischer Volkshochschulverband) (GW ISSN 0932-8297) **1684**
H V W P in Action. (Hospitalized Veterans Writing Project, Inc.) (US) **2921**, 3459
H W W Retail Banking Products Survey see Retail Banking Products Survey: At Call Deposits **797**
H W W Retail Banking Products Survey see Retail Banking Products Survey: Term Deposits **797**
H W W Retail Banking Products Survey see Retail Banking Products Survey: Continuing Credit **797**
H W W Retail Banking Products Survey see Retail Banking Products Survey: Term Loans **797**
H W W Retail Banking Products Survey see Retail Banking Products Survey: Credit Cards **797**
H W W Weekly Rates Update see Weekly Rates Update: At Call Deposits **803**

H W W Weekly Rates Update see Weekly Rates Update: Term Deposits **803**
H Z see Holzarbeiter-Zeitung **2584**
H Z Deutsches Wirtschaftsblatt. (GW) **667**
Ha Tikvah see Tikvah **2026**
Den Haag. (NE) **4088**
Haagse Jazz Club. (NE ISSN 0017-632X) **3553**
Ha'am. (US) **2003**
Haandarbejde Trin for Trin. (DK) **3591**
Haandarbejdets Fremme/Danish Handcraft Guild. (DK ISSN 0107-1769) **3591**
Haandarbejdets Fremme. Aarets Korssting. (DK ISSN 0107-9611) **328**
Haandarbejdets Fremme. Kalender see Haandarbejdets Fremme. Aarets Korssting **328**
Haandbog for Boerne- og Ungdominstitutioner see Haandbogen Daginstitutioner **4407**
Haandbog for Boerne- og Ungdominstitutioner. Daginstitutioner see Haandbogen Daginstitutioner **4407**
Haandbog for Bygningsindustrien. (DK) **619**
Haandbog for Social og Sundhedssektor. (DK) **4407**
Haandbog for Studerende ved H D Studiet i Organisation see Handelshoejskolen i Koebenhavn. Institut for Organisation og Arbejdssociologi. H D Studiet i Organisation **980**
Haandbog for Studerende ved Landbohoejskolen see Kongelige Veterinaer- og Landbohoejskole. Haandbog **103**
Haandbogen Daginstitutioner. (DK) **4407**, 1238
Haandvaerket and Maskinen. (DK ISSN 0105-9416) **355**
Haandvaerkets Dagblad see Licitationen **622**
Haandvaerkshistorisk Tidsskrift. (DK ISSN 0109-4564) **328**
Habelts Dissertationsdrucke. Reihe Aegyptologie. (GW) **2429**
Habelts Dissertationsdrucke. Reihe Alte Geschichte. (GW ISSN 0072-9175) **2311**
Habelts Dissertationsdrucke. Reihe Germanistik. (GW) **2921**
Habelts Dissertationsdrucke. Reihe Klassische Archaeologie. (GW ISSN 0072-9183) **273**
Habelts Dissertationsdrucke. Reihe Klassische Philologie. (GW ISSN 0072-9191) **2816**
Habelts Dissertationsdrucke. Reihe Kunstgeschichte. (GW ISSN 0072-9205) **328**
Habelts Dissertationsdrucke. Reihe Mittelalterliche Geschichte. (GW ISSN 0072-9213) **2311**
▼Habersham Review. (US) **2921**
Habiletes Loisirs. (CN) **2283**, 2436
Habilitative Mental Healthcare Newsletter. (US ISSN 1057-3291) **3337**, 1736
Habinjan. (NE ISSN 0017-6346) **2003**, 4223
Habit. (SW ISSN 0017-6362) **1291**, 4619
Habitabec Montreal. (CN ISSN 0700-5040) **2487**, 4149
Habitabec Quebec. (CN ISSN 0844-2487) **2487**, 4149
Habitat see Habitat Australia **1489**
Habitat (London). (UK ISSN 0028-9043) **4312**
Habitat Australia. (AT ISSN 0310-2939) **1489**
Habitat - Calabria. (IT) **3436**, 1598
Habitat Happenings see Habitat World **2488**
Habitat International. (US ISSN 0197-3975) **1957**, 1974
Habitat News see U N C H S Habitat News **2497**
Habitat Ufficio. (IT ISSN 1120-236X) **2551**, 1058
Habitat World. (US ISSN 0890-958X) **2488**, 4407

Habitation. (SZ ISSN 0017-6419) **300**
Habitation Moderne. see Modernes Wohnen **2554**
Habitations a Loyer Modere Actualites H L M see Actualites H L M **2482**
Habitations a Loyer Modere Annuaire H L M see Annuaire H L M **2483**
Habitats et Societes Urbaines en Egypte et au Soudan. (FR) **2333**
Habitechut. (IS) **3617**
Habone. (FR ISSN 0292-7993) **2003**, 4223
Hacettepe Bulletin of Medicine-Surgery - Hacettepe Tip Cerrahi Bulteni see Hacettepe Medical Journal **3379**
Hacettepe Bulletin of Natural Sciences and Engineering. (TU) **3037**, 4573
†Hacettepe Bulletin of Social Sciences and Humanities. (TU ISSN 0441-6058) **5202**
Hacettepe Dis Hekimligi Fakultesi Dergisi. see Hacettepe Faculty of Dentistry. Journal **3234**
Hacettepe Faculty of Dentistry. Journal/Hacettepe Dis Hekimligi Fakultesi Dergisi. (TU) **3234**
Hacettepe Fen ve Muhendislik Bilimleri Dergisi. (TU ISSN 0072-9221) **4312**, 1823
Hacettepe Medical Journal/Hacettepe Tip Dergisi. (TU) **3379**
Hacettepe Sosyal ve Beseri Bilimler Dergisi see Hacettepe Bulletin of Social Sciences and Humanities **5202**
Hacettepe Tip Dergisi. see Hacettepe Medical Journal **3379**
Hacettepe Universitesi. Dis Hekimligi Fakultesi. Dergisi see Hacettepe Faculty of Dentistry. Journal **3234**
Hacettepe University. Institute of Population Studies. Turkish Population and Health Survey. (TU) **3982**
Hacia la Luz. (AG ISSN 0017-6478) **2293**, 2921
Hacienda Publica Espanola. (SP ISSN 0210-1173) **1096**
Hack'd. (US) **4518**
Hackney Horse Society Year Book. (UK) **4534**
Hackney Journal. (US ISSN 0046-6700) **4534**
Hackney Stud Book. (UK) **4534**
Al-Hadaf. (TS) **4534**, 4474
Hadarim. (IS ISSN 0333-7588) **2994**
Hadashot. (US) **3553**, 328, 1530
Hadashot Arkheologiyot. (IS) **273**
Hadashot Kupot Holim. (IS) **2533**, 980, 3102
Hadashot Mehachaim Hadatiyim Beisrael. (IS ISSN 0017-6508) **4223**
Hadashot Sapanut Veteufah - Yidion. (IS) **4728**, 4673
Hadassah Career Counseling Institute. Annual Report for the Year. (IS) **3627**
Hadassah Career Guidance Institute. Annual Report for the Year see Hadassah Career Counseling Institute. Annual Report for the Year **3627**
Hadassah Headlines. (US) **2003**, 4844
Hadassah Magazine. (US ISSN 0017-6516) **2003**, 1298
Haderslav Stifts Arbog see Haderslev Stiftsbog **2364**
Haderslev Stiftsbog. (DK) **2364**
Hadoar. (US ISSN 0017-6524) **2867**
Hadorom. (US ISSN 0017-6532) **4223**
Hadracha Digest. (IS) **1636**
Hadtortenelmi Kozlemenyek. (HU ISSN 0017-6540) **3459**, 2311
▼Haeckel Buecherei. (GW ISSN 0936-8515) **1567**
Haelsa. (SW ISSN 0345-4797) **3606**
Haematologia. (HU ISSN 0017-6559) **3272**
Haematologica. (IT ISSN 0390-6078) **3272**
†Haematologica Latina. (IT ISSN 0017-6575) **5202**
Haematologie und Bluttransfusion. (US ISSN 0440-0607) **3272**

Haemophilia Society of Victoria. Newsletter. (AT) **3272**
Haemostaseologie. (GW ISSN 0720-9355) **3272**
Haemostasis. (SZ ISSN 0301-0147) **3208**
Haent i Veckan. (SW ISSN 0345-4843) **2218**
Haerterei-Technische Mitteilungen. (GW ISSN 0341-101X) **3407**
Haesten/Horse. (SW ISSN 0345-486X) **4534**
Haeusliche Pflege. (GW ISSN 0935-8234) **3388**
Hafenbautechnische Gesellschaft. Jahrbuch. (US ISSN 0340-4838) **1866**
†Haffkine Institute. Bulletin. (II) **5202**
Hafnia: Copenhagen Papers in the History of Art. (DK ISSN 0085-1361) **328**
Haga. (FR) **1255**
Hagemi/Encouragement. (JA ISSN 0017-6605) **3102**
Hagskyrslur Islands/Statistics of Iceland.(IC ISSN 0254-4733) **4573**
Hagstrom Map and Travel Newsletter. (US) **4770**, 2252
Hagtidindi. (IC ISSN 0019-1078) **4573**
Hague Academy of International Law. Collected Courses. see Academie de Droit International de la Haye. Recueil des Cours **2719**
Hague Conference on Private International Law. Actes et Documents/Hague Conference on Private International Law. Documents and Proceedings. (NE ISSN 0072-9272) **2723**
Hague Conference on Private International Law. Documents and Proceedings. see Hague Conference on Private International Law. Actes et Documents **2723**
Haha Huabao/Haha Pictorial. (CC) **1255**
Haha Pictorial. see Haha Huabao **1255**
Hahnemannian Homoeopathic Sandesh.(II ISSN 0379-8151) **3214**
Hai. (IO) **1256**
Hai Ou/Sea Gull Literature. (CC) **2921**
Hai Wai Wen Chai Pan Yueh K'an. see Overseas Digest Semimonthly **5254**
Hai Yan. (CC) **2921**
Haifa University. Institute for Study and Research of the Kibbutz and the Cooperative Idea. Discussion Papers. (IS) **830**
Haight Ashbury Literary Journal. (US) **2921**
Haight Ashbury Newspaper. (US) **4407**
Haiguan Tongji/Customs Statistics. (CC) **719**, 1096, 4573
Haiku Headlines. (US) **2994**
Haiku Highlights see Dragonfly **2992**
†Haiku Review. (US) **5202**
Haiku Zasshi Zo. (US) **2994**, 2868
Haileybrian. (UK) **1313**
Hainan Finance. see Hainan Jinrong **783**
Hainan Jinrong/Hainan Finance. (CC) **783**
Hainan Jishu Jingji Xinxi. (CC) **667**
Hainan Medical Science. see Hainan Yixue **3102**
Hainan Yixue/Hainan Medical Science. (CC) **3102**
Hair. (SZ) **373**
Hair. (UK) **373**
†Hair. (US) **5202**
Hair & Beauty. (UK ISSN 0017-6702) **373**
Hair & Beauty. (JA) **373**
Hair Fashion and Style see Your Hair **374**
Hair Fashion de Mexico. (MX) **373**
Hair Fashions Magazine see Hairtell **373**
†Hair International. (HK) **5202**
Hair International News. (US) **373**
Hairdressers' Journal see Hairdressers' Journal International **373**
Hairdressers' Journal International. (UK) **373**

Hairenik. (US ISSN 0017-677X) **2868**
Hairtell. (AT) **373**, 1291
Haiteny, Haisorata, Hairaha. (MG) **2868**
Haiti. Conseil National de Developpement et de Planification. Plan Annuel et Budget de Developpement see Haiti. Secretaire d'Etat du Plan. Plan Annuel et Budget de Developpement **895**
Haiti. Institut Haitjen de Statistique. Bulletin Trimestriel de Statistique. (HT ISSN 0017-6788) **4573**
Haiti. Secretaire d'Etat du Plan. Plan Annuel et Budget de Developpement. (HT) **895**
Haiti News. (US) **930**, 3959
Haiti Observateur. (HT) **2197**
Haiti Philately. (US) **3753**
Haiti Progres. (HT) **2197**
†Haiti Report. (US ISSN 0163-7770) **5202**
Haiti Sante. (HT) **3802**
Haiti Times. (HT) **2197**
Haixia/Strait. (CC) **2921**
Haiyang/Oceans. (CC) **1604**
Haiyang Huanjing Kexue. (CC) **1957**
Haiyang Jishu/Ocean Technology. (CC ISSN 1003-2029) **1604**
Haiyang Kexue/Marine Sciences. (CC ISSN 1000-3096) **1604**
Haiyang Shijie/Oceanic World. (CC ISSN 1001-5043) **1604**
Haiyang Tongbao. (CC ISSN 1001-6392) **1604**
Haiyang Wenzhai. (CC ISSN 1001-0157) **1604**
Haiyang Xinxi. (CC) **1604**
Haiyang Xuebao. (CC ISSN 0253-4193) **1604**
Haiyang yu Hai'andai Kaifa/Ocean and Coast Exploitation. (CC) **1604**
Haiyang yu Huzhao. (CC) **1605**, 1598
Haiyang Yubao. (CC) **1605**
Haiyang Yuye/Marine Fisheries. (CC ISSN 1004-2490) **2042**
Haizi Tiandi/Children's World. (CC) **1238**
Hajj. (SU) **4218**
Hajozasi Szakirodalmi Tajekoztato/Shipping Abstracts. (HU ISSN 0231-1941) **4664**, 13
Hakenkreuz see Military Collectors News **2438**
Hakim Fashion Eyewear Magazine. (CN) **1291**, 3852
Hakko Kenkyujo Hokoku. see Institute for Fermentation, Osaka. Research Communications **553**
Hakkokogaku. (JA ISSN 0385-6151) **552**
Hakku. (FI ISSN 0017-6796) **3459**, 1823
Hakluyt Society. Works in the Ordinary Series. Second Series. (UK ISSN 0072-9396) **2311**
Hakodate Kogyo Koto Senmon Gakko Kiyo. see Hakodate Technical College. Research Reports **4599**
Hakodate Technical College. Research Reports/Hakodate Kogyo Koto Senmon Gakko Kiyo. (JA) **4599**
Hakomi Forum. (US ISSN 0884-5808) **4023**
Hakubutsukan Dayori/Saito Ho-on Kai Museum of Natural History. News. (JA ISSN 0289-4092) **4312**
Hakubutsukan Kenkyu/Museum Studies. (JA ISSN 0911-9892) **3524**
Hakusan/Hakusan Nature Conservation Center. News. (JA ISSN 0388-4732) **1489**
Hakusan Nature Conservation Center. News. see Hakusan **1489**
Hakusan Nature Conservation Center, Ishikawa Prefecture. Annual Report. see Ishikawa-ken Hakusan Shizen Hogo Senta Kenkyu Hokoku **1490**
Hakuyo Kogyo. (JA) **4728**
Halaszat/Fishing. (HU ISSN 0133-1922) **2042**
Halbjaehrliches Verzeichniss Taschenbuecher. (GW ISSN 0342-507X) **402**
Halcyon. (US ISSN 0198-6449) **2507**

Hale Heritage. (US) 2153
Half Tones to Jubilee. (US) 2994
Hali. (UK ISSN 0142-0798) 355, 257, 4619
Halichot. (IS) 4223
Halifax Board of Trade. Business Directory. (CN) 1137
Halifax Board of Trade. Commercial News. (CN ISSN 0046-6735) 816
Halifax Board of Trade. Industrial Development Profile. (CN) 1137
Halifax Nuclear Disarmament Group. Bulletin see Halifax Nuclear Disarmament Group Newsletter 3959
Halifax Nuclear Disarmament Group Newsletter. (UK) 3959
Halifax Wildlife Association. The Four Seasons. (CN ISSN 0046-6743) 2177
Hall of Fame News. (US) 4474
Halle News. (UK) 3553
Halle Year Book. (UK) 3554
Hallelujah! (CN) 4283
Hallesche Studien zur Geschichte der Sozialdemokratie. (GW ISSN 0138-1091) 2364
Hallo! (IT) 1256
Hallo! Taxi. (GW) 4692
Hals-, Nasen-, Ohren-Heilkunde Berlin) see H N O (Berlin) 3314
Hals, Nasen, Ohren Praxis see H N O - Praxis 3314
Halsbury's Laws of England Annual Abridgment. (UK ISSN 0308-4388) 2731
Halsbury's Laws of England Monthly Review. (UK ISSN 0307-9821) 2731
Halton Business Journal. (CN) 667
†Halton Business Report. (CN) 5202
Halton Farm News. (CN ISSN 0704-9226) 95
De Halve Maen. (US ISSN 0017-6834) 2407, 2003
Ham Journal. (JA ISSN 0388-2306) 1356
†Ham Radio Magazine. (US ISSN 0148-5989) 5202
Ham Radio Today. (UK ISSN 0269-8269) 1356
Hamagshimim Journal. (US) 2003
Hambai Kakushin. (JA) 4128
Hambone. (US ISSN 0733-6616) 2921
Hambro Company Guide. (UK ISSN 0144-2015) 783
Hambro Corporate Register see Abthul Andersen Corporate Register 643
Hambro Euromoney Directory see Merrill Lynch - Euromoney Directory 1145
Hamburg Fuehrer. (GW) 2189
Hamburg in Zahlen. (GW ISSN 0017-6877) 4573
Hamburg-Mannheimer-Stiftung fuer Informationsmedizin. Schriftenreihe. (GW) 3102
Hamburg Nachrichten. (GW) 1011
Hamburg - Norddeutschland von Hinten.(GW) 2453, 4770
Hamburg the Quick Port. (GW) 4728
Hamburger Beitraege fuer Russischlehrer. (GW ISSN 0072-9515) 2816
Hamburger Beitraege zur Archaeologie. (GW ISSN 0341-3152) 273
Hamburger Beitraege zur Friedenforschung und Sicherheitspolitik. (GW) 3959
Hamburger Beitraege zur Numismatik. (GW ISSN 0072-9523) 3599
Hamburger Export-Woche. (GW ISSN 0017-6931) 910
Hamburger Hafen - Nachrichten. (GW ISSN 0341-0862) 4728
Hamburger Hafen-Nachrichten und Schiffsabfahrten see Hamburger Hafen - Nachrichten 4728
Hamburger Hafen- und Lagerhaus- Aktiengesellschaft Report see H H L A Report 4728
Hamburger Historische Studien. (GW ISSN 0072-9558) 2311
Hamburger Jahrbuch fuer Musikwissenschaft. (GW) 3554
Hamburger Jahrbuch fuer Wirtschafts- und Gesellschaftspolitik. (GW ISSN 0072-9566) 4312

Hamburger Lehrerzeitung see H L Z 1636
Hamburger Monatszahlen see Hamburg in Zahlen 4573
Hamburger Philologische Studien. (GW ISSN 0072-9582) 2816
Hamburger Phonetische Beitraege see Beitraege zur Phonetik und Linguistik 2805
Hamburger Sport - Mitteilungen. (GW ISSN 0017-6982) 4474
Hamburger Sport - Verein e.V. Journal see H S V - Journal 4474
Hamburger Studien zur Philosophie. (GW ISSN 0072-9604) 3767
Hamburger Top Info for Visitors. (GW) 4770
▼Hamburger Unizeitung. (GW) 1313
Hamburger Wasserwerke. Fachliche Berichte. (GW) 4824
Hamburger Wirtschaft. (GW) 816
Hamburgische Geschichts- und Heimatblaetter. (GW) 2364
Hamburgisches Museum fuer Voelkerkunde. Mitteilungen. (GW ISSN 0072-9469) 240
Hamburgisches Zoologisches Museum und Institut. Mitteilungen. (GW ISSN 0072-9612) 583
Hamdard Foundation. Report. (PK) 4218
Hamdard Islamicus. (PK ISSN 0250-7196) 4218
Hamdard Medicus. (PK ISSN 0250-7188) 3102
Hameenmaa. (FI) 2364
Hamersky & Allied Families Newsletter. (US ISSN 0882-4150) 2153
Hameshek Hashitufi. (IS) 831
Hamevaser. (US ISSN 0017-7040) 4223, 2003
Hamilton Alumni Review. (US ISSN 0017-7067) 1313
Hamilton Business Report. (CN) 667
Hamilton Report. (CN) 667
Hamilton This Month. (CN) 2177
Hamlet Studies. (II ISSN 0256-2480) 2921
Hamline Law Review. (US ISSN 0198-7364) 2631
Hammer. (SI) 3897
▼Hammers. (US) 2994
Hamore. (FR ISSN 0046-676X) 1751, 2003
Hampden-Sydney Poetry Review. (US) 2994
Hampden-Sydney Tiger. (US) 1313
Hampshire Down Sheepbreeders Association. Flock Book Handbook. (UK) 217
▼Hampshire East. (US) 2226
Hampshire Family Historian. (UK ISSN 0306-6843) 2153
Hampshire Farmer. (UK ISSN 0017-7121) 95
Hampshire Field. Proceedings see Hampshire Field Club and Archaeological Society Proceedings 273
Hampshire Field Club and Archaeological Society Proceedings. (UK ISSN 0142-8950) 273, 2364
†Hampshire Poets. (UK) 5202
Hampstead Clinic. Bulletin see Anna Freud Centre. Bulletin 3330
Hampton Script. (US) 1313
Hampton Style. (US) 4149
Han Sheng. see Echo 2219
Hanako. (JA) 1505
Hand see Journal of Hand Surgery: British Volume 3380
Hand Clinics. (US ISSN 0749-0712) 3308
Hand in Hand. (GW) 1636
Hand in Hand. (CN) 3278
Hand Papermaking. (US ISSN 0887-1418) 3663, 355
Hand Vol Pluis. (NE ISSN 0017-7148) 2994
Handai Kyojiba/Osaka University. Faculty of Science. Report on Research and Development in High Magnetic Field Laboratory. (JA) 3819, 1893
†Handakten fuer die Standesamtliche Arbeit. (GW ISSN 0438-5004) 5203

Handarbeit. (GW ISSN 0017-7156) 3591
Handarbeiten und Hauswirtschaft see H T W Praxis 2447
Handasah. (IS) 1823
Al-Handasah. (LE ISSN 0987-8467) 1823, 619
Handasah ve-Adrikhalut see Handasah 1823
Handasat Michonote. (IS) 1823
Handbal. (NE ISSN 0017-7180) 4506
Handball. (US ISSN 0046-6778) 4506
Handball (Dortmund). (GW) 4506
Handball (Raugsdorf). (GW ISSN 0138-1296) 4506
Handball Magazin. (GW ISSN 0178-2983) 4506
Handball und Faustball in Oesterreich. (AU ISSN 0072-9698) 4474
Handballtraining. (GW ISSN 0172-2476) 4506
Handbells. (US ISSN 8756-7407) 3554, 4239
Handboek van de Nederlandse Pers en Publiciteit/Manual of the Dutch Press and Publicity. (NE ISSN 0440-1875) 32
Handbog for Kvaeghold. (DK ISSN 0900-8012) 217
†Handbog i Sociallovgivning. (DK ISSN 0901-0602) 5203
Handbok Baenda. (IC ISSN 0251-1940) 95
Handboll. (SW) 4506
Handbook and Directory of Crematoria see Directory of Crematoria 1129
Handbook Commercial Law see International Handbook on Commercial Arbitration 2725
Handbook for Internal Auditors. (US) 751
Handbook for No-Load Fund Investors. (US ISSN 0736-6264) 948
Handbook for Recruiting Minority College Students see C C D M Minority Student Recruitment Guide 1701
Handbook of Adult Education in Scotland see Scottish Handbook of Adult and Continuing Education 1686
Handbook of Advertising and Marketing Services. (US) 32, 1040
▼Handbook of American Business History. (US) 895
Handbook of Aroma Research. (NE) 2072
Handbook of Basic Economic Statistics. (US ISSN 0017-7199) 719
Handbook of Basic Statistics of Maharashtra State. (II ISSN 0072-9728) 4573
Handbook of Business Finance and Capital Sources. (US ISSN 0163-4615) 1096
Handbook of Canadian Consumer Markets. (CN ISSN 0225-4190) 1505, 1040
Handbook of Circulation Management. (US) 4129
Handbook of Commercial Roofing Systems. (US) 619
†Handbook of Common Poisonings in Children. (US) 5203
Handbook of Communications Systems Management. (US) 1350
▼Handbook of Comparative Economic Policies. (US ISSN 1054-7681) 895
Handbook of Composites. (NE) 1226
Handbook of Connecticut Corporation Statutes. (US) 2710
Handbook of Corporate Finance. (US) 783
Handbook of Degree and Advanced Courses in Institutes-Colleges of Higher Education, Colleges of Education, Polytechnics, University Departments of Education. (UK) 1694, 1707
Handbook of Denominations in the U.S. (US ISSN 0072-9787) 4180
Handbook of Endotoxin. (NE) 3727
Handbook of Engineering Education. (II) 1694, 1707, 1823
Handbook of Environmental Chemistry. (US) 1177, 1957

Handbook of Existing & New Chemical Substances. (JA) 1177
Handbook of Experimental Pharmacology. (US ISSN 0171-2004) 3727
Handbook of Exploration Geochemistry. (NE) 1567
†Handbook of Food Preparation. (US ISSN 0278-906X) 5203
▼Handbook of Hyperlipidemia. (US) 3175, 3208
Handbook of Indian Pumps for Irrigation. (II) 162, 179
Handbook of Industrial Statistics. (UK) 719, 4573
Handbook of Inflammation. (NE ISSN 0167-5567) 3102
Handbook of International Documentation and Information. see Handbuch der Internationalen Dokumentation und Information 2759
Handbook of Korea. (KO) 4770
Handbook of Labor Force Data for Selected Areas of Oklahoma. (US) 980
Handbook of Latin American Studies: A Selected and Annotated Guide to Recent Publications. (US ISSN 0072-9833) 2328
Handbook of Live Animal Transport. (US) 4650, 95, 1137, 3711
Handbook of Living Will Laws see Refusal of Treatment Legislation (Year) 2671
Handbook of M I S Management. (US) 1011, 826
Handbook of Magazine Production. (US) 4129, 1040
Handbook of Magazine Publishing. (US) 4129
Handbook of Manufacturing Automation and Integration. (US) 1413
Handbook of Medical Education. (II) 1694, 1707, 3102
Handbook of Medical Treatment. (US ISSN 0072-9841) 3102
Handbook of Medicinal Feed Additives. (UK ISSN 0956-8220) 206
Handbook of National Development Plans. (UK) 930
Handbook of Natural Toxins. (US) 3102, 3727
Handbook of Nuclear Safeguards. (JA) 1805
Handbook of Ocular Therapeutics and Pharmacology see Ocular Therapeutics and Pharmacology 3302
Handbook of Oklahoma Employment Statistics. (US) 719
Handbook of Organizations Involved in Soviet-American Relations. (US ISSN 1049-3999) 3959
Handbook of Paper Science. (NE) 3663
Handbook of Papua and New Guinea see Papua New Guinea Handbook 4782
Handbook of Plasma Physics. (NE) 3819
Handbook of Powder Technology. (NE) 1866
▼Handbook of Practice Treatment. (UK) 3102
Handbook of Private Schools. (US ISSN 0072-9884) 1694
Handbook of Psychology and Health Series. (US) 4023, 3802
Handbook of Science and Technology. see Kwahak Kisul Yoram 4603
Handbook of Securities of the United States Government and Federal Agencies and Related Money Market Instruments see Handbook of United States Government and Federal Agency and Related Money Market Instruments 948
Handbook of Sensory Physiology. (US ISSN 0072-9906) 3102
Handbook of Strata-Bound and Stratiform Ore Deposits. (NE) 1567
Handbook of Systems Management. (US) 826, 1011
Handbook of the Indian Cotton Textile Industry. (II ISSN 0436-7316) 4619
Handbook of the Nations. (US ISSN 0194-3790) 3959

Handbook of the Northern Wood Industries. (SW ISSN 0072-9922) **2115**
Handbook of the Spinal Cord. (US) **3102**
Handbook of United States Coins. (US ISSN 0072-9949) **3599**
Handbook of United States Government and Federal Agency and Related Money Market Instruments. (US) **948**
Handbook of Women Workers *see* Time of Change: Handbook on Women Workers **995**
Handbook on Ferromagnetic Materials. (NE) **3407, 3819**
Handbook on Injectable Drugs. (US) **3727**
Handbook on Semiconductors. (NE) **1771**
Handbook on the Physics and Chemistry of Rare Earths. (NE) **3819, 1177, 1567**
Handbook on the Physics and Chemistry of the Actinides. (NE) **3819, 1177**
Handbook on the U.S. - German Tax Convention *see* Handbook on the 1989 Double Taxation Convention Between the Federal Republic of Germany and the United States of America **1096**
Handbook on the 1989 Double Taxation Convention Between the Federal Republic of Germany and the United States of America. (NE) **1096**
Handbook on U S Luminescent Stamps.(US ISSN 0072-9981) **3753**
Handbooks in Economics. (NE) **895**
†Handbooks in Maritime Archaeology. (UK ISSN 0260-5570) **5203**
Handbooks of Physiology. (US ISSN 0072-9876) **572**
Handbuch der Datenbanken fuer Naturwissenschaft, Technik, Patente. (GW ISSN 1444, 3675, 4312, 4599
Handbuch der Deutschen Aktiengesellschaften. (GW) **668**
Handbuch der Finanzstatistik. (GW ISSN 0172-360X) **4080**
Handbuch der Grossunternehmen. (GW ISSN 0073-0068) **1077**
Handbuch der Internationalen Dokumentation und Information/ Handbook of International Documentation and Information. (GW ISSN 0340-1332) **2759**
Handbuch der Internationalen Kautschukindustrie/International Rubber Directory/Manuel International de Caoutchouc. (SZ ISSN 0073-0076) **4291**
Handbuch der Internationalen Kunststoffindustrie/International Plastics Directory/Manuel International des Plastiques. (SZ ISSN 0073-0084) **3862**
Handbuch der Justiz. (GW) **2631**
Handbuch der Modernen Datenverarbeitung *see* H M D - Theorie und Praxis der Wirtschaftsinformatik **1395**
Handbuch der Oeffentlichen Bibliotheken. (GW ISSN 0301-9225) **2759**
Handbuch der Oesterreichischen Sozialversicherung. (AU) **2546, 4573**
Handbuch der Oologie. (GW) **564**
Handbuch der Orientalistik. (NE) **3637, 273, 2429**
Handbuch der Orientalistik. 1. Abteilung. Der Nahe und der Mittlere Osten. (NE ISSN 0169-9423) **2429, 3638**
Handbuch der Orientalistik. 2. Abteilung. Indien. (NE ISSN 0169-9377) **3638, 2338**
Handbuch der Orientalistik. 3. Abteilung. Indonesien, Malaysia und die Philippinen. (NE ISSN 0169-9571) **3638, 2338**
Handbuch der Orientalistik. 4. Abteilung. China. (NE ISSN 0169-9520) **3638, 2338**
Handbuch der Orientalistik. 5. Abteilung. Japan. (NE ISSN 0921-5239) **3638, 2338**

Handbuch der Orientalistik. 7. Abteilung. Kunst und Archaeologie. (NE ISSN 0169-9474) **3638, 328**
Handbuch der Orientalistik. 8. Abteilung. Handbook of Uralic Studies. (NE) **3638, 2816**
Handbuch der Steuerveranlagungen: Einkommensteuer, Koerperschaftsteuer, Gewerbesteuer, Umsatzsteuer. (GW) **1097**
Handbuch der Technischen Dokumentation und Bibliographie *see* Handbuch der Internationalen Dokumentation und Information **2759**
Handbuch der Wirtschaftsdatenbanken. (GW) **1444, 867**
Handbuch des Bauherrn. (GW ISSN 0017-7202) **619**
Handbuch des Berliner Sports. (GW ISSN 0174-1209) **4474**
Handbuch des Bremer Sports. (GW ISSN 0174-1217) **4474**
Handbuch des Hamburger Sports. (GW ISSN 0174-1195) **4474**
Handbuch des Sports in Hessen. (GW ISSN 0174-1187) **4474**
Handbuch fuer das Gesundheitswesen in Schleswig-Holstein. (GW) **3102, 1137**
Handbuch fuer den Werbenden Buch- und Zeitschriftenhandel. (GW ISSN 0073-0165) **4129**
Handbuch fuer die Druckindustrie Berlin. (GW ISSN 0073-0173) **4001**
Handbuch fuer die Sanitaetsberufe Oesterreich. (AU ISSN 0073-0181) **3102**
Handbuch Holz. (GW ISSN 0518-0147) **2115**
Handbuch Oeffentlicher Verkehrsbetriebe. (GW ISSN 0073-019X) **4650**
▼Handbuch Stil und Etikette. (GW) **2189**
†Handbuch zur Deutschen Militaergeschichte. (GW) **5203**
Handchirurgie. (GW ISSN 0046-6794) **3379**
Handchirurgie - Mikrochirurgie - Plastische Chirurgie. (GW ISSN 0722-1819) **3379**
Der Handel. (GW ISSN 0017-7229) **836**
†Handel. (GW) **5203**
Handel Wewnetrzny. (PL ISSN 0438-5403) **836**
Handel Zagraniczny/Foreign Trade. (PL ISSN 0017-7245) **910**
Handelingen der Staten-Generaal. (NE ISSN 0017-7253) **836**
Handels - Compass. (AU) **1137**
Handels-Magazin F S B und Fachblatt fuer Selbstbedienung. (GW) **1040**
Handels- og Soefartsmuseet paa Kronborg. Aarbog. (DK ISSN 0085-1418) **4728**
Handelsbestyreren. (NO ISSN 0332-8066) **1011**
Handelsblatt. (LU) **668**
Handelsblatt. (GW ISSN 0017-7296) **836**
Handelshochschule Leipzig. Wissenschaftliche Zeitschrift. (GW ISSN 0323-3545) **668, 826, 2475, 4573**
Handelshoejskolen i Aarhus. Institut for Erhvervs- og Samfundsbeskrivelse. Skriftserie C. (DK ISSN 0106-4363) **668**
Handelshoejskolen i Aarhus. Institut for Finansiering og Kreditvaesen. Kompendium D. (DK ISSN 0105-4058) **783**
†Handelshoejskolen i Aarhus. Institut for Markedsoekonomi. Skriftserie E. (DK ISSN 0105-533X) **5203**
Handelshoejskolen i Aarhus. Skriftserie. (DK ISSN 0106-8490) **4573**
Handelshoejskolen i Koebenhavn. Center for Uddannelses Forskning. Arbejdsnote. (DK ISSN 0900-2472) **668, 1636**
Handelshoejskolen i Koebenhavn. Center for Uddannelsesfroskning. Rapport *see* Center of Educational Research. Copenhagen Business School. Report **655**

Handelshoejskolen i Koebenhavn. Institut for Organisation og Arbejdssociologi. H D Studiet i Organisation. (DK ISSN 0107-4458) **980**
†Handelshoejskolen i Koebenhavn. Institut for Trafik-, Turist- og Regionaloekonomi. Publikation. (DK) **5203**
Handelskammartidningen. (SW ISSN 0345-4495) **816**
Handelskammer Finnland-Schweiz. Bulletin. (SZ) **816**
Handelslaget *see* Assa **829**
†Handelsministeriets Energiforskningsprogram. (DK) **5203**
Handelsnytt. (SW ISSN 0017-7326) **2583, 836**
Handelspartner. (GW ISSN 0721-0477) **816**
Handelsrechtliche Entscheidungen. (AU) **2710**
Handelsregister Oesterreich *see* Firmenbuch Oesterreich **1135**
Handelsregistertidning. *see* Kaupparekisterilehti **3676**
Handelsskolen. (DK) **668, 1751**
Handelsvertreter und Handelsmakler *see* H V - Journal **836**
Handelswoche. (GW ISSN 0863-4084) **836**
Handelswoche - Konsum-Genossenschafter *see* Handelswoche **836**
Handes Amsorya. (AU ISSN 0017-7377) **2816, 3638**
Handgun Control. Semi-Annual Progress Report. (US) **2631, 4102**
Handgun Illustrated. (US) **4474**
Handgun Quarterly. (US) **257**
Handgunner: Britain's Foremost Firearms Journal. (UK ISSN 0260-8693) **4474**
Handhaaf. (SA) **2216**
Handicap Idraet. (DK ISSN 0106-3197) **2283**
Handicap Idrett. (NO) **2283, 1736**
Handicap Information *see* Handicap Idraet **2283**
Handicap News. (US ISSN 0896-131X) **2283, 4407**
Handicap - Nyt. (DK ISSN 0904-8081) **4407**
Handicapped Americans Report *see* Report on Disability Programs **4417**
Handicapped Funding Directory. (US ISSN 0733-4753) **2283, 1736, 4407**
Handicapped Requirements Handbook. (US ISSN 0194-7818) **2284, 980**
Handicraft - Hobby Index. (US ISSN 0730-6466) **357**
Handikapp - Reflex. (SW ISSN 0348-8071) **3337**
Handleren. (DK ISSN 0108-6987) **668**
Handling. (GW ISSN 0343-8759) **1413**
Handling and Packaging Product Information Cards. (UK) **3648**
Handling and Shipping Management *see* Transportation & Distribution **4658**
Handling and Shipping Managements Presidential Issue *see* Transportation & Distribution Presidential Issue **5292**
†Handling Chemicals Safely. (NE) **5203**
Handling Child Custody Cases. (US) **2717, 1238, 4436**
Handling Equipment Directory (Year). (UK) **3018, 1137, 1930**
Handling Pregnancy and Birth Cases. (US) **2717, 596, 4835**
Handloader. (US ISSN 0017-7393) **2436**
Handmade Accents. (US ISSN 0894-0924) **355**
Hands On. (AT ISSN 1033-7814) **1536**
Hands On! (Cambridge). (US ISSN 0743-0221) **1636, 1689**
Hands On (Rabun Gap). (US) **2055, 1751**
Hands On Electronics *see* Popular Electronics **1776**
Handsatzletter. (GW) **4001, 4129**

Das Handwerk. (GW) **4599**
Handwerk - Volkskunst - Kunsthandwerk *see* Schweizer Heimatwerk: Handwerk - Volkskunst - Kunsthandwerk **357**
Handwerken Ariadne *see* Ariadne **3590**
Handwierk. (LU) **2584**
Handworker. (US) **3591**
Handwoven. (US ISSN 0198-8212) **355**
Handy Shipping Guide. (UK ISSN 0017-7423) **4728**
Handy - Whitman Index of Public Utility Construction Costs. (US) **1097**
Hang Gliding. (US) **4548, 54**
Hang Hai. (CC ISSN 1000-0356) **4728**
Hanghai Jishu/Ocean Shipping Technology. (CC) **4728**
Hanghai Keji Dongtai. (CC ISSN 1000-4688) **4728**
Hanging Loose. (US ISSN 0440-2316) **2994**
Hangkong Dang'an/Aeronautics Archives. (CC) **54, 2759**
Hangkong Gongyi Jishu. *see* Aeronautical Manufacturing Technology **43**
Hangkong Moxing/Model Airplane. (CC ISSN 1000-6885) **54**
Hangkong Xuebao/Acta Aeronautica et Astronautica Sinica. (CC ISSN 1000-6893) **54**
Hangkong Zhishi/Aerospace Knowledge.(CC ISSN 1000-0119) **54, 4673**
Hangkong Zhizao Gongcheng/Aviation Production Engineering. (CC ISSN 1001-1765) **54**
Hangtian/Astronautics. (CC ISSN 1000-7474) **54**
Hangtian Jishu yu Minpin. (CC) **54**
Han'guk Baksa mit Soksa Hagwi Nonmun Ch'ongmongnok/List of Theses for the Doctor's and Master's Degree in Korea. (KO) **1677**
Hanguk Energy Yeonguso Hwibo. *see* K A E R I Journal **1806**
Hanguk Sahoehak/Korean Journal of Sociology. (KO) **4436**
Hanguk Sinmun Pangsong Yongam. *see* Korean Press Annual **2572**
Hanguk Tonggye Yongam. *see* Korea Statistical Yearbook **4577**
Hangzhou Daxue Xuebao (Shehui Kexue Ban)/Hangzhou University. Journal (Social Science Edition). (CC) **4373**
Hangzhou Daxue Xuebao (Ziran Kexue Ban)/Hangzhou University. Journal (Natural Science Edition). (CC ISSN 0253-3618) **4312**
Hangzhou Normal College. Journal (Social Science Edition). *see* Hangzhou Shifan Xueyuan Xuebao (Shehui Kexue Ban) **4373**
Hangzhou Shifan Xueyuan Xuebao (Shehui Kexue Ban)/Hangzhou Normal College. Journal (Social Science Edition). (CC) **4373, 3767**
Hangzhou University. Journal (Natural Science Edition). *see* Hangzhou Daxue Xuebao (Ziran Kexue Ban) **4312**
Hangzhou University. Journal (Social Science Edition). *see* Hangzhou Daxue Xuebao (Shehui Kexue Ban) **4373**
Hanjie/Welding. (CC ISSN 1001-1382) **3429**
Hanjie Xuebao/Journal of Welding. (CC ISSN 0253-360X) **3429**
Hankuk Ch'ulpan Yongam. *see* Korean Publications Yearbook **4131**
Hannan's Local and District Criminal Courts Practice. (AT ISSN 0727-7938) **2713**
Hannover Extra *see* Niespulver **2877**
Hannover Vorschau. (GW) **2868**
Der Hannoveraner. (GW) **4534**
Hannoversche Geographische Arbeiten. (GW) **2252**
Hannoversche Geschichtsblaetter. (GW ISSN 0342-1104) **2364**
Hannoversche Land- und Forstwirtschaftliche Zeitung. (GW ISSN 0017-7466) **95, 2101**
Hannoversches Pferd *see* Der Hannoveraner **4534**

Hanover News. (US ISSN 0017-7482) 2533
Hans Kelsen - Institut. Schriftenreihe. (AU) 2631
Hans - Pfitzner - Gesellschaft. Mitteilungen. (GW ISSN 0440-2863) 3554, 419
Hansa. (GW ISSN 0017-7504) 4728
Hanseatische Wertpapierboerse Hamburg. Amtliche Kursblatt. (GW) 668
Hansenologia Internationalis. (BL ISSN 0100-3283) 3219, 3248
Hansestadt Luebeck Travemuende Aktuell. (GW) 4770
Hanshoku Gijutsu. see Animal Reproduction Techniques 210
Hansische Geschichtsblaetter. (GW ISSN 0073-0327) 2364
Hanson's Latin America Letter. (US ISSN 0017-7539) 910
Hanyu Xuexi/Studying Chinese. (CC) 2816, 1751
Hanyu Xuexi see Xue Hanyu 2853
Hanzai Shinrigaku Kenkyu. see Japanese Journal of Criminal Psychology 4026
Hanzaigaku Zasshi. see Acta Criminologiae et Medicae Legalis Japonica 1509
Hanzi Wenhua/Chinese Culture. (CC ISSN 1001-0661) 2507, 2921
Hao Ertong/Good Children. (CC) 1256
Haor. (US) 2004
Hap Jones Motorcycle Blue Book see Motorcycle Blue Book 4519
Hapdong Yongam see Korea Annual 1142
Happenings. (CN ISSN 0844-5753) 2759
Happiness. see Jargalan 2447
Happiness. see Xingfu 4858
Happiness Holding Tank. (US ISSN 0046-6832) 2994
Happy Computer. (GW) 1469
Happy Day Diary see Day One Diary 4173
Happy Home. (NR) 4844, 2212
Happy Home and Family Health see Happy Home 4844
Happy Times. (US) 4239
Happy Wanderer see Worldwide Travel Planner 5307
Al-Haqq. see Droit 2620
Al-Haqq - Shari'ah wa Qanun. (TS) 2731, 4218
Al-Harakah. (MY) 3897
Harambee. (KE) 831
Haratch. (FR) 2004
Harbin Chuanbo Gongcheng Xueyuan Xuebao/Harbin Institute of Shipping Engineering. Journal. (CC ISSN 1000-1875) 4728
Harbin Gongye Daxue Xuebao/Harbin University of Engineering. Journal. (CC ISSN 0367-6234) 1823
Harbin Institute of Shipping Engineering. Journal. see Harbin Chuanbo Gongcheng Xueyuan Xuebao 4728
Harbin Kexue Jishu Daxue Xuebao/ Harbin University of Science and Technology. Journal. (CC ISSN 1000-5897) 4312
Harbin Medicine. see Harbin Yiyao 3727
Harbin Normal University. Journal of Natural Sciences. see Harbin Shifan Daxue Ziran Kexue Xuebao 4312
Harbin Shifan Daxue Ziran Kexue Xuebao/Harbin Normal University. Journal of Natural Sciences. (CC ISSN 1000-5617) 4312
Harbin University of Engineering. Journal. see Harbin Gongye Daxue Xuebao 1823
Harbin University of Science and Technology. Journal. see Harbin Kexue Jishu Daxue Xuebao 4312
Harbin Yiyao/Harbin Medicine. (CC ISSN 1001-8131) 3727
Harbinger (Detroit). (US) 1636
Harbinger File. (US) 1957, 1790
Harbor Branch News. (US) 1605, 1707, 1823, 1957
Harbor Review. (US) 2994
Harbour and Shipping. (CN ISSN 0017-7636) 4728
Harbour Review. (US) 2921

Hard and Soft Ware. (CL) 1453, 1477
Hard Hat News. (US) 619, 3018
†Hard Money Digest. (US) 5203
Hard Rock Video. (US) 1385, 3554
Hard Row to Hoe. (US) 2921
Hardboiled see Hardboiled Detective 2985
Hardboiled Detective. (US) 2985
Harden Murrumburrah Express. (AT) 2172
Harden Newsletter. (US) 2153
▼Hardhat (Indianapolis). (US) 619
Hardhat (Oklahoma City). (US ISSN 0193-0400) 619
Hardin County Historical Quarterly. (US ISSN 8755-6073) 2408
Hardin - Simmons University Brand see H S U Brand 1313
Hards Family Newsletter. (UK) 2153
Hardsyssels Aarbog. (DK ISSN 0046-6840) 2364
Hardware Age "Who Makes It" Buyers' Guide. (US) 1137, 642
Hardware Age "Who Makes It" Directory see Hardware Age "Who Makes It" Buyers' Guide 1137
Hardware Age Who's Who. (US) 1137
Hardware and Building (Year) see Building, Hardware and Housewares (Year) 606
Hardware and Farm Equipment see Western Retailer 165
Hardware and Garden Review. (UK ISSN 0266-0539) 642, 2129
†Hardware Merchandiser. (US ISSN 0017-7709) 5203
Hardware Merchandising. (CN ISSN 0017-7717) 642, 1040
Hardware Product News Show Guide see Show Guide 643
Hardware Retailer News. (AT) 642
Hardware Review see Hardware and Garden Review 642
Hardware Source Guide. (US) 1453, 1460, 1469
Hardware Today. (UK) 642
Hardware Trade. (US) 642
Hardware Trade Journal see D I Y Week 641
▼Hardwood Expressions. (US) 2115
Hardwood Floors. (US) 639, 2551
Hardy Plant Bulletin. (UK) 2129
Hardy Plant Directory see The Plant Finder 2143
Hardy Plant Society. Bulletin see Hardy Plant Bulletin 2129
Hardy Plant Society. News Letter. (UK) 2129
Hardy Plant Society of Oregon. Bulletin. (US) 2129
Hareem. (II) 4844
Harford Business Ledger. (US) 668
Hargrove Newsletter. (US) 2153
Harian Creative Press see What's Cooking in Congress 2975
Haricot. (AT) 3388, 4407
Harja. (DK ISSN 0105-1660) 273
Harley Women. (US ISSN 0893-6447) 4518
Harlow and Bishop's Stortford Citizen. (UK) 2194
Harlow and Bishop's Stortford Gazette see Harlow and Bishop's Stortford Citizen 2194
Harlow Report: Geographic Information Systems. (US ISSN 1043-6146) 826
Harmonic Research. (US) 948
Harmonika International. (GW ISSN 0938-6629) 3554
Harmonika-Revue see Harmonika International 3554
Harmoniously United. see Pupukahi 3468
Harmonizer. (US ISSN 0017-7849) 3554
Harmonologia - Studies in Music Theory. (US) 3554
†Harmony (Harmony). (US ISSN 0099-0604) 5203
Harmony (San Francisco). (US ISSN 0896-243X) 3942, 2868, 4180
†Harness Horse. (US ISSN 0017-7857) 5203
Harness Racer. (AT) 4534
†Harold C. Mack Symposium. Proceedings. (US) 5203

Harold L. Lyon Arboretum Lecture. (US) 504
Harold Wells Gulf Coast Fisherman see Gulf Coast Fisherman 4547
Harp & Hound. (US) 3711
Harp-Strings. (US) 2921
Harper-Grace Hospitals, Pharmacy and Therapeutics Newsletter see Harper Hospital, Pharmacy & Therapeutics Newsletter 3728
Harper Hospital, Pharmacy & Therapeutics Newsletter. (US) 3728
Harpers & Queen. (UK ISSN 0141-0547) 4844
Harper's Bazaar. (US ISSN 0017-7873) 1291, 2226
Harper's Bazaar en Espanol. (US ISSN 0890-9598) 1291, 4844
Harper's Bazaar France see Harper's Bazaar France and Italy 1291
Harper's Bazaar France and Italy. (FR) 1291
Harper's Bazaar International. (IT) 1291
Harper's Bazaar Italia see Harper's Bazaar International 1291
Harper's Bazaar - Switzerland. (SZ) 1291
Harpers Directory of the Wine and Spirit Trade see Harpers Wine and Spirit Annual 381
Harper's Gran Bazaar. (IT) 2559
Harpers Guide to Sports Trade. (UK ISSN 0073-0416) 4474, 1138
Harper's Magazine. (US ISSN 0017-789X) 2226
Harpers Sports see Harpers Sports & Leisure 4548
Harpers Sports & Leisure. (UK ISSN 0263-8134) 4548, 2738
Harpers Wine and Spirit Annual. (UK) 381
Harpers Wine and Spirit Gazette. (UK ISSN 0017-7903) 381
Harpsichord and Fortepiano. (UK) 3554
Harriman Institute Forum. (US ISSN 0896-114X) 2868, 3959
Harrington Family Miscellany. (UK ISSN 0307-0298) 2153
Harris Auction Galleries. Collectors' Auction. (US ISSN 0093-1047) 3524
Harris Illinois Industrial Directory (Year). (US ISSN 0734-3256) 1138
Harris Indiana Industrial Directory (Year). (US ISSN 0888-8175) 1138
Harris Kentucky Industrial Directory (Year). (US ISSN 0887-4255) 1138
Harris Maryland Industrial Directory (Year). (US ISSN 0070-5802) 1138
Harris Michigan Industrial Directory (Year). (US ISSN 0888-8167) 1138
Harris Missouri Directory of Manufacturers. (US ISSN 0895-2469) 1138, 3484
Harris Ohio Industrial Directory (Year). (US ISSN 0888-8140) 1138
Harris Pennsylvania Industrial Directory (Year). (US) 1138
Harris Poll. (US ISSN 0273-1037) 4457, 13
Harris Sound of Business see Sound of Business 884
Harris West Virginia Manufacturing Directory (Year). (US ISSN 0887-4247) 1138
Harrison Post. (US) 3459
Harrisonburg-Rockingham Historical Society Newsletter. (US) 2153
Harrison's Inland Revenue Index to Tax Cases. (UK) 1097
Harrow and Wembley Observer Series. (UK) 2194
Harrowsmith. (CN ISSN 0381-6885) 95, 4436
Harrowsmith (U.S. Edition) see Harrowsmith Country Life 2129
Harrowsmith Country Life. (US ISSN 1049-4618) 2129
Harry Browne's Special Reports. (US) 948, 867
Harry S. Truman Research Institute for the Advancement of Peace. Reprint Series. (IS) 402, 4373

Harry S. Truman Research Institute, Jerusalem. Occasional Papers see Harry S. Truman Research Institute for the Advancement of Peace. Reprint Series 402
Harsunan Nijeriya. (NR) 2816
Hart County Historical Society Quarterly.(US) 2408
Hart Crane Newsletter see Visionary Company: A Magazine of the Twenties 348
Hart Forum. (US) 2153
The Hartford Agent. (US ISSN 0017-7962) 2533
Hartford Business. (US) 668
Hartford College for Women. Chronicle. (US) 1313
Hartford Monthly. (US) 2226
Hartmannbund in Baden - Wuerttemberg. (GW) 4102, 4407
Harumfrodite see Fortitudine 3458
Harvard A I D S Institute Series on Gene Regulation of Human Retroviruses. (US) 3102, 543, 3219
Harvard Advocate. (US ISSN 0017-8004) 2921
Harvard Architecture Review. (US ISSN 0194-3650) 300
Harvard Armenian Texts and Studies. (US ISSN 0073-0459) 2429, 3638
Harvard BlackLetter Journal. (US) 2631, 3942
†Harvard Boersen. (DK ISSN 0107-7724) 5203
Harvard Books in Biophysics. (US ISSN 0073-0475) 485
Harvard Business Review. (US ISSN 0017-8012) 668
Harvard Business Review Catalog (Year). (US) 719
Harvard Business School. Annual Report. (US) 668
Harvard Business School. Baker Library. Core Collection, an Author and Subject Guide see Harvard Business School. Publishing Division. Core Collection, An Author and Subject Guide 719
†Harvard Business School. Baker Library. Current Periodical Publications in Baker Library. (US) 5203
†Harvard Business School. Baker Library. Kress Library of Business and Economics. Publications. (US) 5203
Harvard Business School. Baker Library. Recent Additions to Baker Library. (US) 719
Harvard Business School. Baker Library. Working Papers in Baker Library. (US ISSN 0364-6645) 668, 2759
Harvard Business School. Bulletin. (US ISSN 0017-8020) 668, 1707
Harvard Business School. Publishing Division. Core Collection, An Author and Subject Guide. (US ISSN 1044-2111) 719
Harvard Celtic Colloquium. Proceedings.(US) 2816, 2364, 2921
Harvard Civil Rights - Civil Liberties Law Review. (US ISSN 0017-8039) 2702, 3942
Harvard College Economist. (US ISSN 0197-7636) 999, 783, 895
Harvard Contemporary China Series. (US) 2338
Harvard Dental Alumni Bulletin. (US ISSN 0046-6891) 3234
Harvard Dental Bulletin. (US) 3234
Harvard Divinity Bulletin. (US ISSN 0017-8047) 1313, 4180
Harvard East Asian Monographs. (US ISSN 0073-0483) 2338
Harvard East Asian Series. (US ISSN 0073-0491) 2338
Harvard Economic Studies. (US ISSN 0073-0505) 668
Harvard Educational Review. (US ISSN 0017-8055) 1636
Harvard English Studies. (US ISSN 0073-0513) 2921, 2816
Harvard Environmental Law Review. (US ISSN 0147-8257) 2631
Harvard - Espansione. (IT) 668
Harvard Health Letter. (US ISSN 1052-1577) 3802

Harvard Historical Monographs. (US ISSN 0073-0521) **2311**
Harvard Historical Studies. (US ISSN 0073-053X) **2311**
Harvard Holland Review. (NE ISSN 0168-9444) **668**
Harvard Human Rights Journal. (US) **3942**, **2702**
Harvard Human Rights Yearbook. (US) **3942**, **2702**
Harvard International Law Journal. (US ISSN 0017-8063) **2723**
Harvard International Review. (US ISSN 0739-1854) **3959**, **910**, **2723**
Harvard Iranian Series. (US) **2429**
Harvard Journal of Asiatic Studies. (US ISSN 0073-0548) **3638**
Harvard Journal of Law and Public Policy. (US ISSN 0193-4872) **2631**, **4062**
Harvard Journal on Legislation. (US ISSN 0017-808X) **2631**
Harvard Judaic Monographs. (US) **2004**, **4223**
Harvard l'Expansion. (FR) **668**
Harvard Lampoon. (US ISSN 0017-8098) **1313**
Harvard Law Bulletin. (US ISSN 1053-8186) **1313**, **2631**
Harvard Law Record. (US ISSN 0017-8101) **2631**
Harvard Law Review. (US ISSN 0017-811X) **2631**
Harvard Law School Bulletin see Harvard Law Bulletin **1313**
Harvard Librarian. (US ISSN 0073-0564) **2759**
Harvard Library Bulletin. (US ISSN 0017-8136) **2759**
Harvard Magazine. (US ISSN 0095-2427) **2868**
Harvard Medical Alumni Bulletin. (US ISSN 0191-7757) **1313**, **3102**
Harvard Medical School Health Letter see Harvard Health Letter **3802**
Harvard Middle Eastern Studies. (US ISSN 0073-0580) **2429**
Harvard Political Review. (US ISSN 0090-1032) **3897**
Harvard Publications in Music. (US ISSN 0073-0629) **3554**
Harvard Review. (US ISSN 0888-983X) **2507**
Harvard Semitic Monographs. (US ISSN 0073-0637) **2817**, **4180**
Harvard Semitic Series see Harvard Semitic Studies **2429**
Harvard Semitic Studies. (US) **2429**
Harvard Studies in American-East Asian Relations. (US) **2338**
Harvard Studies in Business History. (US ISSN 0073-067X) **895**
Harvard Studies in Classical Philology. (US ISSN 0073-0688) **2817**, **1277**
Harvard Studies in Comparative Literature. (US ISSN 0073-0696) **2921**
Harvard Studies in Romance Languages. (US ISSN 0073-0718) **1277**
Harvard Studies in Urban History. (US) **2488**
Harvard Theological Review. (US ISSN 0017-8160) **4180**
Harvard Theological Studies. (US ISSN 0073-0726) **4180**
†Harvard Ukrainian Research Institute. Minutes of the Seminar in Ukrainian Studies. (US ISSN 0362-8078) **5203**
Harvard Ukrainian Studies. (US ISSN 0363-5570) **2004**, **2364**
Harvard University. Center for International Affairs. Annual Report. (US ISSN 0073-0734) **3959**
Harvard University. Computation Laboratory. Mathematical Linguistics and Automatic Translation; Report to National Science Foundation. (US ISSN 0073-0769) **2759**
Harvard University. Graduate School of Business Administration. Program for Management Development. Publication. (US ISSN 0073-0785) **1011**
Harvard University. Graduate School of Education. Bulletin. (US ISSN 0046-6905) **1636**, **1313**

Harvard University. Museum of Comparative Zoology. Department of Mollusks. Occasional Papers on Mollusks. (US ISSN 0073-0807) **583**
Harvard University. Russian Research Center. Studies. (US ISSN 0073-0831) **2365**
Harvard University Catalog of Teaching Materials see H B S Catalog of Teaching Materials **719**
Harvard University Gazette. (US ISSN 0364-7692) **1313**
Harvard University Graduate School of Design News see G S D News **300**
Harvard University Library Notes. (US ISSN 1050-2408) **2759**
Harvard Women's Law Journal. (US ISSN 0270-1456) **2631**, **4859**
Harvard - Yenching Institute. Monograph Series. (US ISSN 0073-084X) **2338**, **2817**, **2921**
Harvard - Yenching Institute. Studies. (US ISSN 0073-0858) **2338**
Harvard - Yenching Library Bibliographical Series. (US) **402**, **2202**
HarvardManager. (GW ISSN 0174-335X) **1011**
Harvest. (CN) **95**
Harvest. (PP) **179**
Harvest. (UK ISSN 0266-4771) **4023**
Harvest (Lakeville-Middleboro). (US) **95**, **381**
Harvest. (Salem). (US) **2994**
Harvest. (Southboro). (US) **3669**
Harvest: A Literary Magazine. see Shou Huo **2959**
Harvest Book Series. (US ISSN 0146-5414) **4436**, **668**, **2055**, **2311**
Harvest: Jahangirnagar Studies in Literature. (BG) **2922**
Harvest Moon. (UK) **3669**
Harvest News. (US) **4436**
Harvest Semi-monthly. (CH ISSN 0017-8195) **95**
Harvest States Journal. (US) **95**, **831**
Harvester. (II ISSN 0017-8225) **95**, **1823**
Harvester. (US) **2922**, **328**
Harvests. (US) **2129**
Harvests Newsletter. (US) **2129**
Harvey for Loving People. (US) **3397**
Harvey Lectures. (US ISSN 0073-0874) **3102**
Harvey on Industrial Relations & Employment Law. (UK) **980**, **2710**
Haryana Agricultural University. Journal of Research. (II ISSN 0379-4008) **95**, **4373**, **4810**
Haryana Cooperation. (II ISSN 0017-8233) **831**
Haryana Electricity. (II ISSN 0046-6913) **1893**
Haryana Health Journal. (II ISSN 0017-8241) **4102**
Haryana Journal of Education. (II ISSN 0017-825X) **1636**
Haryana Labour Journal. (II ISSN 0046-6921) **980**
Haryana Veterinarian. (II ISSN 0033-4359) **4810**
Harz - Zeitschrift. (GW ISSN 0073-0882) **2365**
Hashalom. (SA) **2004**
Hashi/Bridges in Japan. (JA) **1866**
▼Al-Hashulchan. (IS) **2072**
Haskins & Sells Reports see H & S Reports **5202**
Hassadeh/Field. (IS ISSN 0017-8314) **95**
Hassei, Seicho, Bunka. see Development, Growth and Differentiation **436**
Hastings Center Report. (US ISSN 0093-0334) **3102**, **440**, **3767**
Hastings Communications and Entertainment Law Journal (Comm - Ent). (US) **2631**, **1374**, **1395**
Hastings Constitutional Law Quarterly. (US ISSN 0094-5617) **2706**
Hastings Herald. (US ISSN 0898-543X) **2153**
Hastings Historian. (US) **2408**
Hastings International and Comparative Law Review. (US ISSN 0149-9246) **2723**

Hastings Law Journal. (US ISSN 0017-8322) **2632**
Hastings Women's Law Journal. (US) **2632**
Hat Life Yearbook & Directory. (US) **1285**
Hata'asiyah Be-Yisra. see Surveys and Development Plans of Industry in Israel **1085**
Hatcher Review. (UK ISSN 0309-5118) **2365**, **2153**
Hatcheries and Dealers Participating in the National Poultry Improvement Plan. (US ISSN 0082-9722) **217**
Hatchet see G W Hatchet **1312**
Hattori Botanical Laboratory. Journal/ Hattori Shokubutsu Kenkyujo Hokoku. (JA ISSN 0073-0912) **504**
Hattori Shokubutsu Kenkyujo Hokoku. see Hattori Botanical Laboratory. Journal **504**
Hauenstein Verlag. Mitteilungsblatt see Ring-Post **2882**
Haul Down and Ease Off. (US) **54**, **3459**
Haulage Manual. (UK) **4745**
▼Haunt of Fear. (US) **3011**
Haunted Journal. (US) **2994**
Haunts. (US ISSN 1043-3503) **3012**
Hauptverband der Gewerblichen Berufsgenossenschaften e.V. see Die B G **2527**
Hauptverband der Oesterreichischen Sparkassen. Jahresbericht. (AU) **783**
Das Haus. (GW) **2551**, **300**
▼Haus & Wohnung. (GW) **2488**
Haus Echo. (GW) **2475**
Haus Tech. (SZ) **2299**
Haus und Grund. (GW ISSN 0017-8403) **619**
Haus- und Grundbesitz. (GW) **4149**
Der Haus- und Grundeigentuemer. (GW) **4149**
Hausarzt in Hessen. (GW ISSN 0934-3164) **3102**
Hausarzt in Thueringen. (GW) **3102**
Hausbesitzer A B C. (GW ISSN 0930-6692) **2632**
Die Hausfrau. (US ISSN 0017-842X) **2004**
Haushaltungsrechnungen/Budgets des Menages. (SZ) **719**
Hauskurier see Beiersdorf Journal **1072**
Hausnachrichten. (AU) **980**
Haustechnische Rundschau. (GW ISSN 0344-2330) **2299**, **619**
Haustex. (GW) **2559**
Hauswirtschaft Textilarbeit Werken Praxis see H T W Praxis **2447**
Hauswirtschaftliche Bildung. (GW ISSN 0342-5088) **2447**
▼Haut Decor. (US) **2551**
Haut-Parleur. (FR ISSN 0337-1883) **1356**
Der Hautarzt. (GW ISSN 0017-8470) **3248**
Hautes Etudes du Monde Greco-Romain. (SZ ISSN 0073-0939) **1277**, **2817**
Hautes Etudes Islamiques et Orientales d'Histoire Comparee. (SZ ISSN 0073-0947) **2429**
Hautes Etudes Medievales et Modernes.(SZ ISSN 0073-0955) **2365**
Hautes Etudes Numismatiques. (SZ ISSN 0073-0963) **3599**
Hautes Etudes Orientales. (SZ ISSN 0073-0971) **3638**
Hautfreund. (GW ISSN 0933-7385) **3248**
Hautnah. (GW ISSN 0930-7109) **3248**
Have You Heard. (US) **3982**
Havebladet. (DK ISSN 0017-8497) **2129**
Havekunst see Landskab **2133**
Haven. (DK ISSN 0017-8500) **2129**
Haven. (BE) **4710**
Haven Amsterdam. (NE) **4728**
Havenloods. (NE ISSN 0017-8519) **2868**
Havennieuws. (NE) **4728**
Haverhill and District Archaeological Group. Journal. (UK ISSN 0144-3968) **273**

Haverhill and District Archaeological Group. Newsletter see Haverhill and District Archaeological Group. Journal **273**
Havre see Escale **4727**
Havre Port. (FR) **4728**
Havsfiskelaboratoriet. Meddelande. (SW ISSN 0374-8030) **2042**
Hawa'a/Eve. (UA) **4844**
Hawaii. Commission on Judicial Discipline. Annual Report. (US) **2632**
Hawaii. Criminal Injuries Compensation Commission. Annual Report. (US ISSN 0098-5708) **1515**
Hawaii. Department of Business and Economic Development. Annual Report. (US) **1077**
Hawaii. Department of Education. Educational Directory: State & District Office. (US ISSN 0092-1777) **1636**
Hawaii. Department of Education. Office of Business Services. Public and Private School Enrollment. (US) **1636**
Hawaii. Department of Education. Office of Library Services. Annual Report see Hawaii. State Public Library System. Annual Report **2759**
Hawaii. Department of Health. Division of Mental Health. Children's Health Services see Hawaii. Department of Health. Waimano Training School and Hospital Division (Report) **2461**
Hawaii. Department of Health. Mental Health Services for Children and Youth. (US ISSN 0362-6296) **4407**, **1238**, **4102**
Hawaii. Department of Health. Research and Statistics Office. R & S Report. (US ISSN 0093-3481) **3992**, **3811**
Hawaii. Department of Health. Waimano Training School and Hospital Division (Report). (US) **2461**, **4407**
Hawaii. Department of Planning and Economic Development. Annual Report see Hawaii. Department of Business and Economic Development. Annual Report **1077**
Hawaii. Insurance Division. Report of the Insurance Commissioner of Hawaii. (US ISSN 0073-1110) **2533**
Hawaii. Legislative Auditor. Special Reports. (US) **4062**, **1097**
Hawaii. Legislative Reference Bureau. Report. (US ISSN 0073-1277) **4062**
Hawaii. Office of the Ombudsman. Report. (US ISSN 0073-1137) **4088**
Hawaii. State Commission on the Status of Women. Annual Report. (US ISSN 0092-9190) **4844**, **2632**
Hawaii. State Judiciary. Annual Report. (US) **2632**
Hawaii. State Public Library System. Annual Report. (US) **2759**
†Hawaii. State Public Library System. L S C A Annual Program. (Library Services and Construction Act) (US ISSN 0095-4721) **5203**
Hawaii (Year). (US) **4770**
Hawaii A F L - C I O News see Hawaii A F L - C I O Nupepa **2584**
Hawaii A F L - C I O Nupepa. (US) **2584**
Hawaii Annual Economic Report. (US ISSN 1043-6685) **867**
Hawaii Annual Economic Review see Hawaii Annual Economic Report **867**
Hawaii Bar Journal. (US) **2632**
Hawaii Beverage Guide. (US ISSN 0017-8543) **381**
Hawaii Business. (US) **867**
Hawaii Buyer's Guide. (US) **1138**
Hawaii Catholic Herald. (US) **4265**
†Hawaii Conference on High Energy Physics. (US) **5203**
Hawaii Dental Association. Transactions. (US ISSN 0073-1021) **3234**
Hawaii Dental Journal. (US) **3234**
Hawaii Drive Guides. (US) **4770**
Hawaii Health Messenger. (US ISSN 1053-9662) **4102**

Hawaii Health Planning News. (US) 4102
Hawaii High Tech Journal. (US) 4599
Hawaii Hotel Network. (US) 4770
Hawaii Institute of Geophysics. Technical Reports and Special Publications see School of Ocean and Earth Science and Technology. Reports and Special Publications 1594
Hawaii Institute of Geophysics. Yearbook see School of Ocean and Earth Science and Technology. Yearbook 1594
Hawaii Institute of Marine Biology. Technical Reports. (US ISSN 0073-1331) 440
Hawaii International Conference on System Sciences. Proceedings. (US ISSN 0073-1129) 1437
Hawaii Investor. (US) 948
Hawaii Library Association Journal see H L A Journal 5202
†Hawaii Library Association Newsletter. (US) 5203
Hawaii Literary Review see Hawaii Review 2922
Hawaii Magazine. (US ISSN 0892-0990) 4770
Hawaii Medical Journal. (US ISSN 0017-8594) 3102
Hawaii on 35 Dollars a Day see Hawaii on 60 Dollars a Day 4770
Hawaii on 60 Dollars a Day. (US) 4770
Hawaii Orchid Journal. see Na Okika O Hawaii 2134
Hawaii Realtor Journal. (US) 4149
Hawaii Review. (US ISSN 0093-9625) 2922
Hawaii: The Big Island, a Paradise Guide. (US) 4770
Hawaii: The Big Island Update. (US ISSN 1042-8046) 4770
Hawaii Topical Conference in Particle Physics. Proceedings see Hawaii Conference on High Energy Physics 5203
Hawaii TourBook see Tourbook: Hawaii 4790
Hawaii Visitors Bureau. Annual Research Report. (US ISSN 0066-412X) 4770
Hawaii Weekly Weather & Crop Bulletin.(US) 3436, 179
Hawaiian Acquisition List. (US) 402
Hawaiian Airlines Magazine. (US) 4802
Hawaiian Church Chronicle. (US ISSN 0274-7154) 4239
Hawaiian Entomological Society. Proceedings. (US ISSN 0073-134X) 533
Hawaiian Express Magazine. (US ISSN 1051-0621) 2226
Hawaiian Historical Society. Annual Report. (US) 2344
Hawaiian Island Home. (US) 2551
Hawaiian Journal of History. (US ISSN 0440-5145) 2344
Hawaiian Newsletter. (US) 2226
Hawaiian Philatelist. (US) 3753
Hawaiian Planters' Record. (US ISSN 0073-1358) 179
Hawaiian Shell News. (US ISSN 0017-8624) 583
Hawaiian Sugar Manual. (US) 179
Hawaiian Sugar Planters' Association Experiment Station. Annual Report. (US ISSN 0073-1366) 179
Hawaii's International Festival of the Pacific. (US) 816
Hawaii's National Gay Community News. (US) 2453, 1636, 3102, 4407
▼Hawk. (US) 3397
Hawk. (UK) 3459, 54
†Hawk Migration Association of North America. Journal. (US) 5203
Hawk Migration Association of North America. Newsletter see Hawk Migration Sudies 564
Hawk Migration Association of North America. Proceedings of Hawk Migration Conference. (US) 564, 1489
Hawk Migration Sudies. (US) 564, 1489

Hawk Mountain News. (US) 564, 1489
Hawk Reporter. (US) 1313
Hawkeye (Des Moines). (US) 4239
Hawkeye (La Plata). (US) 1313
Hawkeye Engineer. (US) 1823
Hawkeye Heritage. (US ISSN 0440-5234) 2154
Hawkfrendz. (UK) 2868
Hawliyah Kulliyah al-Tarbiyyah/ Educational Journal. (TS) 1636
Haworth Series in International Business. (US ISSN 1041-2565) 910
Haworth Series in Marketing. (US ISSN 1048-8464) 1040
Hay & Forage Grower. (US) 206, 152
Hay Guetron. (AG ISSN 0017-8640) 4283
Hay Roe's Paper Tree Letter see Paper Tree Letter 2116
Al-Haya al-Tijariya. see Bahrain Chamber of Commerce and Industry. Commerce Review 808
†El-Hayam. (IS) 5203
Hayastanyaitz Yegeghetzy see Bema 4280
Hayat. (II) 3897
Hayden's Ferry Review. (US ISSN 0887-5170) 2994
Haydn Society Newsletter. (UK) 3554
Haydn - Studien. (GW ISSN 0440-5323) 3554, 419
Hayes and Becker Information Sciences Series see Information Sciences Series 5213
Hayes Directory of Dental Supply Houses. (US ISSN 0073-1404) 3234
Hayes Directory of Medical Supply Houses. (US) 2461
Hayes Directory of Physician and Hospital Supply Houses see Hayes Directory of Medical Supply Houses 2461
Hayes Druggist Directory. (US ISSN 0073-1420) 3728
Hayes Historical Journal. (US ISSN 0364-5924) 2408
Hayes Maze see Hayes of America Herald 2154
Hayes of America Herald. (US ISSN 0736-9557) 2154
Hayling Island Magazine see Holiday Islander 4770
Hayling Islander see Holiday Islander 4770
Haynes Alloys Digest. (US) 3429
Haynes Family Association. Chronicle. (US ISSN 0885-4823) 2154
Haynes High Performance Alloys Digest see Haynes Alloys Digest 3429
Hayreniky Dzayn. (AI) 2868
Hazard Monthly. (US ISSN 0742-6410) 1273, 1957, 4102
Hazard Prevention. (US ISSN 0743-8826) 4102
Hazardous Cargo Bulletin. (UK ISSN 0143-6864) 4650
†Hazardous Cargo Contacts. (GW) 5203
†Hazardous Chemicals Information Annual. (US) 5203
Hazardous Commodity Handbook. (US) 1984, 1957, 4745
Hazardous Materials Control. (US ISSN 0895-3260) 1984
Hazardous Materials Control Research Institute see H M C R I 1984
Hazardous Materials Control Research Institute Focus see H M C R I Focus 1984
Hazardous Materials Management. (CN ISSN 0843-9303) 1984
Hazardous Materials Newsletter. (US ISSN 0889-3454) 4102, 3617
Hazardous Materials Training Bulletin for Supervisors see O S H A Training Bulletin for Supervisors 1964
Hazardous Materials Transportation. (US ISSN 0197-3177) 1985, 1957, 4650
Hazardous Substance Advisor see Environment Advisor 1984
Hazardous Substances. (UK) 3617
▼Hazardous Substances & Public Health. (US) 1985, 4102

Hazardous Waste & Hazardous Materials. (US ISSN 0882-5696) 1985, 1823, 1957
Hazardous Waste and Toxic Torts Law and Strategy. (US) 2632, 1985, 2533, 4102
Hazardous Waste Business. (US) 1985
Hazardous Waste Consultant. (US ISSN 0738-0232) 1985, 1823, 4102
Hazardous Waste Hotline see Environmental Hotline (Albuquerque) 1951
Hazardous Waste Litigation Reporter. (US ISSN 0275-0244) 2632
Hazardous Waste Management see Environmental Waste Management 1984
Hazardous Waste Management & Business Opportunities Newsletter. (US ISSN 1055-3495) 1985, 1011
Hazardous Waste Management Handbook. (CN ISSN 0711-7140) 1985
Hazardous Waste News. (US ISSN 0275-374X) 1985
Hazardous Waste Report. (US ISSN 0271-2601) 4102, 1985
Hazards. (UK ISSN 0267-7296) 3617, 4102
▼Hazelden News and Professional Update. (US) 1536
Hazell's Guide to the Judiciary & the Courts with the Holborn Law Society's Bar List. (UK) 2632
Hazell's Guide to the Judiciary and the Courts with the Holborn Law Society's Bar List by Chambers see Hazell's Guide to the Judiciary & the Courts with the Holborn Law Society's Bar List 2632
Hazmat News. (US) 1985
HazMat Transport. (US) 1985, 4650
HazMat World. (US ISSN 0898-5685) 1985
HazTech News. (US) 1985
He Jishu. (CC ISSN 0253-3219) 1805
He Kexue yu Gongcheng/Chinese Journal of Nuclear Science and Engineering. (CC ISSN 0258-0918) 1805
He - She Directory. (US) 3397, 4844
Head & Neck. (US ISSN 1043-3074) 3379
Head and Neck Surgery see Head & Neck 3379
†Head, Heart, Hands & Health in Virginia. (US ISSN 0017-8713) 5203
Head Office at Home. (CN) 668
Head Start Services to Handicapped Children see U.S. Department of Health and Human Services. Annual Report to the Congress of the United States on Services Provided to Handicapped Children in Project Head Start 5295
Head Teachers Review. (UK ISSN 0017-873X) 1636
Head to Toe. (CN) 3102
Headache. (US ISSN 0017-8748) 3338
▼Headache Quarterly. (US) 3102
Headlight. see Hooflig 2584
Headline Focus see World Newsmap of the Week - Headline Focus 2266
Headliner. (NZ) 948
Headlines see Profile (Los Angeles) 821
Headlines. (NR ISSN 0189-3963) 2212
Headlines. (US) 3102
Headlines (Leicester). (UK) 1728
Headlines (London). (UK ISSN 0954-9021) 2570
Headmaster U.S.A. see Private School Quarterly 1656
Headmasters Association Review see Secondary Heads Association Review 5275
Headpiece. (US) 1285, 3066
Headpress. (UK) 328
Headquarters Detective. (US) 2985
Headquarters Heliogram. (US) 2408, 3459
Headquarters News see Amax News 3477
Headwaters Review. (US) 2994

Headway. (US ISSN 1044-7377) 4474, 3802, 4844
Headwear Institute of America. Newsletter. (US) 1285, 1291
Healing Currents. (US) 3802
Healing Hand. (UK ISSN 0017-8829) 4180
Healing Thoughts. (US) 4283
Health. see Eruul Mend 3801
Health. (Il ISSN 0017-8861) 3802
Health. (US ISSN 0279-3547) 3802
Health. see Jiankang 3804
Health/Sihhah. (JO) 4102
Health. (NZ ISSN 0017-887X) 4102
Health. see Suc Khoe 4113
Health Action. (Il ISSN 0970-471X) 2461, 3102
Health Action Newsletter. (US) 3102
Health Affairs. (US ISSN 0278-2715) 4102, 2533
Health and Beauty. see Ygia k Omorfia 3811
Health and Beauty Formulary see For Formulation Chemists Only 375
Health & Beauty Guide. (UK) 3802, 373
Health & Beauty Salon. (UK) 373
Health and Efficiency. (UK ISSN 0017-8888) 3802
Health & Environment Digest. (US ISSN 0893-6242) 1957, 3802
Health & Fitness. (US) 3802, 3395, 4835
Health and Fitness (Bicester). (UK ISSN 0264-2549) 3802
Health and Fitness (London). (UK) 3802
Health and Healing. (UK) 3803
▼Health & Healing. (US) 3803, 3102
Health and Health Care in New York City: Local, State, and National Perspectives. (US ISSN 0889-0331) 2461
Health and Homoeopathy. (UK) 3214
Health and Hygiene. (UK ISSN 0140-2986) 4102
Health & Medical Horizons. (US) 3803, 3102
Health and Medicine see Health - P A C Bulletin 4103
Health and Nutrition Update. (CN ISSN 0831-8530) 3338
Health and Personal Social Services Statistics. (UK) 4102
Health and Physical Education/Hoken Taiiku Kyoshitsu. (JA ISSN 0018-3350) 1637, 3803
Health and Physical Education Project Newsletter. (UK) 3803
Health and Population: Perspectives and Issues. (Il) 596
Health and Safety at Work. (AT) 4102, 2033
Health and Safety Concepts see Health and Safety at Work 4102
Health and Safety in Industry and Commerce. (UK) 3617
Health and Safety Information Bulletin see Health, Safety Environment Bulletin 4103
Health & Safety Monitor. (UK) 3617, 2632
Health & Safety Newsline. (UK ISSN 0142-5021) 4102, 1893, 1930, 2033
Health and Safety Officer's Handbook. (UK ISSN 0954-5972) 3617
Health and Safety Product Information Cards see Health and Safety Specifier 4102
Health and Safety: Quarries. (UK ISSN 0263-3094) 3617, 3484
Health and Safety Science Abstracts. (US ISSN 0892-9351) 4117, 13, 3623, 4102
Health and Safety Specifier. (UK) 4102
Health & Social Service Journal. (UK ISSN 0300-8347) 2461, 4407
Health and Social Service Manpower in Alberta see Inventory of Health & Social Service Personnel 4409
Health and Social Service Personnel Working in Alberta see Health and Social Service Workforce in Alberta 4102
Health and Social Service Workforce in Alberta. (CN) 4102, 4407

Health and Social Services Workforce in Alberta see Inventory of Health & Social Service Personnel 4409
Health and Social Work. (US ISSN 0360-7283) 4407, 4102
Health and Society see Milbank Quarterly 3907
Health and Strength see Sport & Fitness 3809
Health & Wealth Guardian. (US) 3102
Health and Welfare Directory see Human Services Directory 4408
Health and Welfare Libraries Quarterly. (UK ISSN 0305-9340) 2760, 2475
Health and Welfare Statistics in Japan see Japan. Ministry of Health and Welfare. Statistics and Information Department. Handbook of Health and Welfare Statistics 4117
Health & You. (US ISSN 0898-3569) 3803
Health Aspects of Pesticides: Abstract Bulletin see Pesticides Abstracts 1974
Health at Work. (AT ISSN 1033-1425) 3617, 3803
Health Buildings Library Bulletin. (UK) 2461, 1866
Health Bulletin. (UK ISSN 0374-8014) 3103, 2461
Health Business. (US) 3103
Health Care. see Hoken no Kagaku 3803
†Health Care (Don Mills). (CN ISSN 0226-5788) 5203
Health Care Articles. (US) 3803
Health Care Competition Week. (US ISSN 0886-2095) 2462, 1040, 4102
Health Care Costs. (US) 867, 2462
▼Health Care Facility. Management. (US) 2462, 4407
Health Care Financing Administration Manuals. (US) 2462, 2533
Health Care Financing Notes. (US) 2533
Health Care Financing Review. (US ISSN 0195-8631) 3103, 4407
Health Care for Women, International. (US ISSN 0739-9332) 4835, 3293, 4844
Health Care in Canada see Health Care (Don Mills) 5203
Health Care Information Service. see Informationsdienst Krankenhauswesen 2466
Health Care Labor Manual. (US ISSN 0197-3738) 2462, 980, 2632
Health Care Labor Review see Health Care Labor Manual 2462
Health Care Management see International Journal of Health Care Quality Assurance 3110
Health Care Management Review. (US ISSN 0361-6274) 2462, 1011
Health Care Marketer see Hospital Revenue Report 1040
Health Care Newsletter. (US) 3617, 2462
Health Care Product News see Health CareSystems 5203
Health Care Strategic Management. (US ISSN 0742-1478) 2462, 3803
Health Care Supervisor. (US ISSN 0731-3381) 3278
Health Care Supervisors Journal see Health Care Supervisor 3278
Health Care Systems see Healthcare Information Management 2463
†Health Care Viewpoint. (US) 5203
†Health Career News. (US) 5203
Health Career Post. (CN ISSN 0828-203X) 2462, 3103, 3278, 3627
Health Care's Hospital Products & Technology. (CN) 2462
†Health CareSystems. (US) 5203
Health Commission of Victoria. Annual Report see Victoria. Health Department. Annual Report 2470
Health Communication. (US ISSN 1041-0236) 4103
Health Confidential. (US) 3803
Health Consciousness. (US) 3594, 3606, 3803
Health Consequences of Smoking. (US ISSN 0098-311X) 1536, 3103

Health Consultant. see Jiankang Guwen 3804
Health Devices. (US ISSN 0046-7022) 3259, 2462, 4103
Health Devices Alerts. (US ISSN 0163-0458) 3175
▼Health Devices Inspection & Preventive Maintenance System. (US) 3103
Health Devices Sourcebook. (US ISSN 0278-3452) 3103, 2462, 3175
▼Health Diet & Nutrition. (US ISSN 1055-8241) 3606
Health Digest. (US) 3103
Health Digest. see Jiankang Wenzhai 4106
▼Health Economics. (UK ISSN 1057-9230) 3103
Health Education Association of the Philippines Journal see H E A P Journal 4102
Health Education Focal Points see Focal Points 5193
Health Education Index. (UK ISSN 0140-3273) 3811, 13
Health Education Journal. (UK ISSN 0017-8969) 3803, 3395, 4835
Health Education Monographs see Health Education Quarterly 3103
Health Education News. (UK) 3803, 4103
Health Education Quarterly. (US ISSN 0195-8402) 3103
Health Education Research. (UK ISSN 0268-1153) 4407, 3103
Health Estate Journal. (UK ISSN 0957-7742) 2462
Health Exchange. (US ISSN 0742-8081) 3103
†Health Express. (UK) 5203
Health Express (Cleveland). (US) 3803
Health Express (Las Vegas). (US) 3606
Health Facilities Directory (Sacramento). (US ISSN 0361-2929) 4407, 4103
Health Facilities Energy Report. (US ISSN 0272-8443) 2462, 1489, 1790
Health Facilities in Southern New York: A Guide to Inpatient, Outpatient, and Long-Term Care. (US ISSN 0888-7039) 2462
Health Facilities Management. (US ISSN 0899-6210) 2462
Health Food Trader see Natural Food Trader 3609
Health Foods Business. (US ISSN 0149-9602) 3606, 2072
Health for All see Here's Health 3803
Health for Children. see Shoni no Hoken 1244
†Health for Life. (US ISSN 0046-7057) 5203
Health for the Millions. (II) 3606
Health Freedom News. (US) 4103
Health Funds Development Letter. (US ISSN 0193-7928) 2462
Health Gazette. see Jiankang Bao 3804
Health Grants & Contracts Weekly. (US ISSN 0194-2352) 4062, 4103
Health Guidance. see Jiankang Zhinan 3805
†Health Highlights. (US) 5203
Health in Day Care: A Manual for Health Professionals. (US) 3320
Health in Wisconsin. (US ISSN 0146-2768) 4103
Health in Work Place. (CN) 3617
Health Index. (US) 3175, 13
Health Industry Buyers Guide. (US) 3103
Health Industry Today. (US ISSN 0745-4678) 3103
▼Health Information and Libraries. (HU ISSN 0864-991X) 2760, 3103
Health Information Bulletin. (KE) 4103, 3219
Health Information Service. (UK ISSN 0268-5973) 3103
Health Information System. (KE) 3103
†Health Insurance Medical Records Risk Management Report. (US ISSN 0883-6671) 5203
Health Insurance Underwriter. (US ISSN 0017-9019) 2533
Health Insurance Viewpoints see Health Care Viewpoint 5203

Health Journal. (US) 3803
Health Labor Relations Alert. (US) 3103, 1011
Health Labor Relations Reports. (US ISSN 0148-4761) 2462, 981
Health Law Digest. (US) 2632, 3803
Health Law in Canada. (CN ISSN 0226-8841) 3264
Health Law Journal of Ohio. (US ISSN 1043-6081) 2632, 3803
Health Lawyer. (US ISSN 0736-3443) 2632, 3103
Health Lawyers News Report. (US) 2632, 3103
Health Legislation and Regulation. (US ISSN 0899-8965) 3103, 2632, 4103
Health Letter (Washington). (US ISSN 0882-598X) 3103, 1505, 4103
Health Libraries Review. (UK ISSN 0265-6647) 2760
Health Life. (JA) 1684
Health Maintenance Organization Magazine see H M O Magazine 2532
Health Management Quarterly. (US ISSN 0891-3250) 2462
Health Manager's Update. (US) 3103
Health Manpower Management. (UK ISSN 0955-2065) 1011, 3278
Health Marketing Quarterly. (US ISSN 0735-9683) 4103
†Health Matrix. (US) 5203
Health News (Toronto). (CN ISSN 0821-3925) 3103
Health News & Review. (US) 3606
Health News Daily. (US ISSN 1042-2781) 3103
Health Now. (UK ISSN 0144-4948) 3606, 3395, 4835
Health-O-Gram. (US) 3253
Health of America's Children. (US ISSN 0899-4137) 4103
†Health of Kansas Chart Book. (US ISSN 0276-606X) 5203
Health of the Rep Newsletter. (US) 3803
Health Organizations of the U.S., Canada and the World. (US ISSN 0440-5609) 3103, 4103
Health - P A C Bulletin. (Health Policy Advisory Center) (US) 4103, 3103
Health Personnel in Canada/Personnel de la Sante au Canada. (CN) 3103
Health, Physical Education and Recreation Microform Publications Bulletin. (US ISSN 0090-5119) 3811, 4498
Health Physics. (US ISSN 0017-9078) 3104, 3803
Health Physics Research Abstracts. (UN ISSN 0085-1450) 4117, 13
Health Physics Society. Newsletter. (US ISSN 0073-1498) 3358, 3104
Health Planning and Manpower Report see Health Professions Report 1637
Health Plus. (US) 3617
Health Policy. (NE ISSN 0168-8510) 4103, 1637
Health Policy Advisory Center Health - P A C Bulletin see Health - P A C Bulletin 4103
Health Policy & Biomedical Research: The Blue Sheet. (US ISSN 0162-3605) 3104
Health Policy and Planning. (UK ISSN 0268-1080) 4103
Health Policy Series. (US) 3803
Health Policy Week. (US) 4103
Health Professions News and Notes. (US) 1313
Health Professions Report. (US ISSN 0888-9465) 1637, 981, 4103
Health Progress. (US ISSN 0882-1577) 2462
Health Promotion. (CN ISSN 0833-7594) 4103
Health Promotion see Health Promotion International 4103
Health Promotion International. (UK) 4103
Health Psychology. (US ISSN 0278-6133) 4023, 3104, 4103
†Health Reporter. (US) 5203
Health Reports. (CN ISSN 0840-6529) 3811
†Health Resources. (US) 5203
†Health Review. (US) 5203

Health, Safety Environment Bulletin. (UK) 4103
Health Science. (US ISSN 0883-8216) 3803
Health Sciences Information in Canada: Associations/Information en Sciences de la Sante au Canada: Associations. (CN) 3104
Health Sciences Information in Canada: Libraries/Information en Sciences de la Sante au Canada: Bibliotheques. (CN) 3104
Health Sciences Serials. (US ISSN 0162-0843) 3175
Health Series see Health & Fitness 3802
Health Service Abstracts. (UK) 4426, 4117
Health Service Buyers Guide. (UK ISSN 0140-5748) 2462
Health Service Journal. (UK ISSN 0952-2271) 1011, 2462
Health Services Administration Education. (US ISSN 0160-4961) 1694
Health Services Journal. see Yobo Igaku 3163
Health Services Journal see C O H S E Journal 4099
Health Services Management. (UK ISSN 0953-8534) 2462
Health Services Management Research.(UK ISSN 0951-4848) 3104, 4103
Health Services Manpower Review see Health Manpower Management 1011
Health Services Research. (US ISSN 0017-9124) 3104, 4103
Health Shopper. (US) 3803
Health, Society and Culture. (US ISSN 0891-7795) 4436, 3803
Health Statistics. see Norway. Statistisk Sentralbyraa. Helsestatistikk 4118
†Health Student. (UK) 5203
Health Systems Management. (US ISSN 0361-0195) 4103, 2462
†Health Technology. (US ISSN 0891-1924) 5203
Health Technology Management. (US) 3104, 4599
Health Technology Trends. (US ISSN 1041-6072) 2462, 2522
Health Texas. (US) 2462
Health Through Martial Arts. see Wushu Jianshen 4497
Health Trends. (UK ISSN 0017-9132) 3104, 4103
Health, United States. (US ISSN 0361-4468) 4407
Health Update. (US) 3803, 1505
Health Values. (US ISSN 0147-0353) 3803
Health Victory Bulletin. (US) 3197
Health Visitor. (UK ISSN 0017-9140) 3278
Health Visitors' Association Current Awareness Bulletin see H V A Current Awareness Bulletin 3278
Health Wage Monitor. (US) 3104, 3627
Health Watch. (CN) 3606, 3803
†Health Watch. (US) 5204
Health World. (US ISSN 0888-7330) 3606
HealthAction. (US) 4103
Healthcare Advertising Review. (US ISSN 8756-4513) 32, 4103
Healthcare Community Relations & Marketing Letter. (US ISSN 0894-9980) 3104, 1040
Healthcare Convention & Exhibitors Association Exhibitors Advisory Council's Action Memo see H C E A Exhibitors Advisory Council's Action Memo 3392
Healthcare Employment News. (US) 3803
Healthcare Environmental Management System. (US) 3104
Healthcare Environmental Services. (US) 2462, 1957
Healthcare Executive. (US ISSN 0883-5381) 2463
Healthcare Financial Management. (US ISSN 0735-0732) 2463
▼Healthcare Foodservice Magazine. (US) 2072, 2463

HEALTHCARE FOODSERVICE

Healthcare Foodservice Who's Who. (US) **1138**, **2072**, **3606**
Healthcare Forum Journal. (US ISSN 0899-9287) **2463**
Healthcare Fund Raising Newsletter. (US) **2463**
Healthcare Hazardous Materials Management. (US) **2463**, **3617**
Healthcare Informatics. (US) **3225**
Healthcare Information Management. (US) **2463**, **1011**, **1363**, **1395**
Healthcare Management Team Letter. (US ISSN 0891-9267) **1011**, **3803**
Healthcare Marketing see Healthcare Marketing and Hospital National Account Management **5204**
Healthcare Marketing Abstracts. (US ISSN 0891-5016) **2470**, 13
†Healthcare Marketing and Hospital National Account Management. (US) **5204**
Healthcare Marketing and Management Report. (US) **3803**
Healthcare Marketing Report. (US) **3803**
Healthcare New Orleans. (US) **3803**, **3606**
Healthcare Productivity Report see Strategies for Healthcare Excellence **2469**
Healthcare Technology & Business Opportunities. (US) **3104**, 668
Healthcare Trends and Transition. (US) **3627**, 3104
Healthdocs. (US) **2760**, 3104
HealthFacts. (US ISSN 0738-811X) **3104**, 4103
Healthline. (US ISSN 0736-7929) **4103**
†Healthright. (AT ISSN 0725-1688) **5204**
Healthscan see HealthSpan **1011**
Healthsharing. (CN ISSN 0226-1510) **4835**, 596, 4844
HealthSpan. (US ISSN 0883-0452) **1011**, **2463**, **2632**
Healthstate. (US) **3104**, **3234**
Healthways. (US ISSN 0897-9251) **3606**
†Healthweek. (US) **5204**
Healthwire. (US) **3278**
Healthy Children's Pictorial. see Jiankang Shaonian Huabao **3804**
†Healthy Companies. (US) **5204**
Healthy Family. (JA) **3803**
Healthy Heart. (US) **3208**
Healthy Kids: Birth - 3. (US ISSN 1063-0945) **1238**, **3803**
▼Healthy Kids: 4-10 Years. (US ISSN 1062-4236) **1238**, **3803**
Healthy Life News. (AT) **3606**, 4103
†Healthy Man. (US) **5204**
Healthy Times. (US) **3803**, **3606**
Healthy World. see Jiankang Tiandi **3804**
Hear Our Wings. (CN) **1736**, 1751
Hear This. (US ISSN 0017-9175) **1313**
Heard Heritage. (US ISSN 0149-5046) **2154**, 4436
†Heard Journal. (US ISSN 0886-4969) **5204**
Heard Museum Newsletter. (US) **3524**, 328
†Hearing. (UK ISSN 0263-7324) **5204**
Hearing Aid Journal see Hearing Journal **2287**
Hearing Aid Journal. (II ISSN 0971-0949) **2287**
Hearing Conservation News see Spectrum (Des Moines) **2289**
Hearing Health. (US) **2287**
Hearing Instruments. (US ISSN 0092-4466) **2287**
Hearing Journal. (US ISSN 0745-7472) **2287**
Hearing News. see Kuuloviesti **2288**
Hearing Rehabilitation Quarterly. (US ISSN 0360-9278) **2287**
Hearing Research. (NE ISSN 0378-5955) **3314**
Hearing Research Developments. (US) **2287**
Hearsay. (CN) **2632**
Hearsay. (AT) **2734**
▼Hearsay Handbook. (US) **2632**
Heart see Clinical Science **3089**

Heart & Circulation. (GW ISSN 0179-342X) **3208**
Heart and Lung. (US ISSN 0147-9563) **3278**
▼Heart & Soul. (US) **2994**
Heart and Stroke Foundation of Canada. Annual Report. (CN) **3208**
Heart and Vessels. (JA ISSN 0910-8327) **3208**
Heart and Wings Journal see Emergence: Journal for Evolving Consciousness **5186**
Heart Care. (Il ISSN 0046-7111) **3208**
Heart Failure. (US ISSN 8755-7673) **3208**
Heart of America Aquarium Society News. (US ISSN 0193-1997) **3711**
Heart of Texas Records. (US ISSN 0093-9854) **2154**
Heartbeat (Nashville). (US) **4239**
HeartBeat (New York). (US) **3208**
Heartbeat (Orlando). (US ISSN 0194-8032) **596**, 4835
Heartbeat (San Francisco). (US) **3208**
Heartbeat of St. Joseph's Hospital see Heartbeat of St. Joseph's Medical Center **2463**
Heartbeat of St. Joseph's Medical Center. (US) **2463**
Hearth & Home. (US) **1790**, 1040, 2559
Hearthstone Collection of Folklore, Nostalgia and History. (US) **2055**, 257
Heartland Adventures. (US) **4770**
Heartland Boating. (US ISSN 1042-1009) **4525**
Heartland Critiques. (US) **2868**, 2983, 4129, 4844
†Heartland Journal (Madison). (US ISSN 0887-2597) **5204**
Heartland Journal (Mason City). (US) **95**
Heartland Retailer. (US) **2299**
Heartland U.S.A. (US) **3398**
▼Heartlands Today. (US) **2922**
Heartline. (US ISSN 8755-5271) **3208**
Hearts Aflame. (US ISSN 0893-536X) **4265**, 1256
Heartsong Review. (US ISSN 0889-5252) **3554**, 3594
Heat. (US) **3398**, 2454
Heat Dynamics Engineering. see Reneng Dongli Gongcheng **1938**
Heat Engineering. (US ISSN 0017-9329) **1823**
Heat Processing Digest. (US) **3407**
Heat Pump Technology Conference Proceedings. (US) **1930**
Heat Recovery Systems & C H P. (US ISSN 0890-4332) **3841**
Heat Shock Proteins. (UK ISSN 0950-0510) **477**, 3308
Heat Transfer and Fluid Flow Digest see H T F S Digest **1853**
Heat Transfer & Fluid Flow Service Digest. (UK) **1853**
Heat Transfer Engineering. (US ISSN 0145-7632) **1853**, 1930
Heat Transfer - Japanese Research. (US ISSN 0096-0802) **1930**, 3841
Heat Transfer - Soviet Research. (US ISSN 0440-5749) **1930**, 3841
Heat Treating. (US ISSN 0017-9345) **3407**
Heat Treatment. see Traitement Thermique **3422**
Heat Treatment of Metals. see Jinshu Rechuli **1918**
Heat Treatment of Metals. (UK ISSN 0305-4829) **3408**
Heathen. (UK) **4283**
Heathenzine. (US) **2994**
Heather News. (US ISSN 1041-6838) **2129**
Heather Society. Bulletin. (UK ISSN 0440-5757) **2129**
Heather Society. Yearbook. (UK ISSN 0440-5757) **2129**, 504
†Heating, Air Conditioning & Plumbing Products. (US) **5204**
Heating and Air Conditioning Journal. (UK ISSN 0307-7950) **2299**
Heating & Plumbing Monthly Inc. Ventilation. (UK ISSN 0265-7899) **2299**

Heating and Ventilating Engineer. (UK) **2299**
Heating and Ventilating Engineer and Journal of Air Conditioning see Heating and Ventilating Engineer **2299**
Heating and Ventilating News see H & V News **2299**
Heating and Ventilating Products see Heating, Ventilating & Plumbing **2300**
Heating and Ventilating Research Association. Laboratory Reports see B S R I A Application Guides **2297**
Heating and Ventilating Research Association. Technical Notes see B S R I A Technical Notes **2297**
Heating and Ventilating Review. (UK ISSN 0017-9396) **2300**
Heating - Piping - Air Conditioning. (US ISSN 0017-940X) **2300**
Heating Piping Air Conditioning Techlit Selector see H P A C Techlit Selector **1930**
Heating, Plumbing, Air Conditioning. (CN ISSN 0017-9418) **2300**
Heating, Plumbing, Air Conditioning Buyers' Guide. (CN ISSN 0382-6996) **2300**
Heating, Ventilating, Air Conditioning Product News see H V A C Product News **2299**
Heating, Ventilating and Air Conditioning Year Book see The Specifier's Guide to Heating, Ventilating, Air Conditioning, and Refrigeration **2303**
Heating, Ventilating & Plumbing. (UK ISSN 0265-4571) **2300**
Heaven Bone. (US ISSN 1042-5381) **2994**
Heavy Construction News. (CN ISSN 0017-9426) **619**
Heavy-Duty Distribution see Truck Parts & Service **4749**
Heavy Duty Trucking. (US ISSN 0017-9434) **4745**
Heavy Horse see Heavy Horse World **4534**
Heavy Horse World. (UK ISSN 0951-2640) **4534**
†Heavy-Ion Reactions. (US ISSN 8756-1964) **5204**
Heavy Metal. (US) **3012**
Heavy Metal Thunder. (US) **3554**
Heavy Truck Salesman see Truck Sales & Leasing Magazine **4749**
Heavyside Building Materials. (UK ISSN 0956-5035) **619**
Hebai University. Journal. see Hebei Daxue Xuebao **4373**
Die Hebamme. (GW ISSN 0932-8122) **3293**
Hebbel - Jahrbuecher. (GW ISSN 0073-1560) **2922**
Hebbel - Mensch und Dichter im Werk. (AU) **2922**
Hebdo Canada see Reportage Canada **2178**
Hebdo de la Blanchisserie - Teinturerie see Hebdo-Tex **1281**
Hebdo-Tex. (FR) **1281**
Hebdocuir. (FR ISSN 0399-5461) **2736**
Hebei Academic Journal. see Hebei Xuekan **4373**
Hebei Academy of Medical Sciences. Journal. see Hebei Yixue Yuan Xuebao **3104**
Hebei Accounting. see Hebei Caikuai **751**
Hebei Caijing Xueyuan Xuebao/Hebei Institute of Finance and Economics. Journal. (CC) **783**
Hebei Caikuai/Hebei Accounting. (CC) **751**
Hebei Ceramics. see Hebei Taoci **1164**
Hebei Chemical Engineering. see Hebei Huagong **1177**
Hebei Commerce. see Hebei Shangye Yanjiu **836**
Hebei Daxue Xuebao/Hebai University. Journal. (CC ISSN 1000-1565) **4373**
Hebei Education. see Hebei Jiaoyu **1637**
Hebei Engineering Institute. Journal. see Hebei Gongxueyuan Xuebao **1823**
Hebei Faxue. (CC) **2632**

Hebei Gongxueyuan Xuebao/Hebei Engineering Institute. Journal. (CC) **1823**
Hebei Huabao/Hebei Pictorial. (CC) **2182**
Hebei Huagong/Hebei Chemical Engineering. (CC) **1177**
Hebei Institute of Finance and Economics. Journal. see Hebei Caijing Xueyuan Xuebao **783**
Hebei Jiaoyu/Hebei Education. (CC) **1637**
Hebei Literature. see Hebei Wenxue **2922**
Hebei Nongye Daxue Xuebao/Hebei University of Agriculture. Journal. (CC ISSN 1000-1573) **95**
Hebei Normal University. Journal (Natural Science Edition). see Hebei Shifan Daxue Xuebao (Ziran Kexue Ban) **4312**
Hebei Normal University. Journal (Social Science Edition). see Hebei Shifan Daxue Xuebao (Shehui Kexue Ban) **4373**
Hebei Pictorial. see Hebei Huabao **2182**
Hebei Shangye Yanjiu/Hebei Commerce. (CC) **836**
Hebei Shifan Daxue Xuebao (Shehui Kexue Ban)/Hebei Normal University. Journal (Social Science Edition). (CC ISSN 1000-5587) **4373**
Hebei Shifan Daxue Xuebao (Ziran Kexue Ban)/Hebei Normal University. Journal (Natural Science Edition). (CC ISSN 1000-5854) **4312**
Hebei Taoci/Hebei Ceramics. (CC) **1164**
Hebei Traditional Medicine. see Hebei Zhongyi **3104**
Hebei University of Agriculture. Journal. see Hebei Nongye Daxue Xuebao **95**
Hebei Wenxue/Hebei Literature. (CC ISSN 1000-9663) **2922**
Hebei Xuekan/Hebei Academic Journal. (CC ISSN 1003-7071) **4373**
Hebei Yixue Yuan Xuebao/Hebei Academy of Medical Sciences. Journal. (CC ISSN 1000-1581) **3104**
Hebei Yiyao/Journal of Hebei Medicine. (CC) **3728**
Hebei Zhongyi/Hebei Traditional Medicine. (CC) **3104**
Hebetim. (IS) **3897**
Hebezeuge und Foerdermittel. (GW ISSN 0017-9442) **1866**
Hebraeische Beitraege zur Wissenschaft des Judentums. (GW ISSN 0175-7016) **4223**
Hebrew Annual Review. (US) **2922**, 2507
Hebrew Christian. (UK ISSN 0017-9477) **4180**
Hebrew Computational Linguistics. (IS ISSN 0792-3252) **2817**
Hebrew Journal. (CN) **2004**
Hebrew Studies. (US ISSN 0146-4094) **2817**, 2922, 4223
Hebrew Union College Annual. (US ISSN 0360-9049) **2004**, 4223
Hebrew Union College Annual Supplements. (US ISSN 0275-9993) **2004**, 4223
Hebrew Union College - Jewish Institute of Religion. Chronicle. (US) **4223**
Hebrew University. News. (US) **1313**
Hebrew University of Jerusalem. Authority for Research and Development. Current Research. (IS ISSN 0333-6964) **4373**
Hebrew University of Jerusalem. Bi-weekly - Dushavuon see Hebrew University of Jerusalem. Monthly **1313**
†Hebrew University of Jerusalem. Department of Atmospheric Sciences. List of Contributions. (IS) **5204**
Hebrew University of Jerusalem. Folklore Research Center. Studies. (IS ISSN 0075-3661) **2055**
Hebrew University of Jerusalem. Lionel Cohen Lectures. (IS ISSN 0075-9740) **2632**
Hebrew University of Jerusalem. Monthly/Kav P'nim. (IS) **1313**
Hebrew University of Jerusalem. News see Hebrew University. News **1313**

Hebrew University Studies in Literature and the Arts see H S L A **2921**
Hecate. (AT ISSN 0311-4198) **4859**
Hechizos. (US) **3669**
Hechos de Mascara. (AG) **2584**, 3511
Heckners Hefte fuer Textverarbeitung. (GW) **1058**
▼Hectarea. (SP) **217**
Hed ha-Ulpan. (IS) **1684**
Hed Hachinuch. (IS ISSN 0017-9493) **1637**
Hed Hagan. (IS ISSN 0334-2263) **1637**
Heddle. (CN) **3591**
Hedei Din. (IS) **2632**
Hedeselskabets Tidsskrift. (DK ISSN 0017-9507) **2101**, 1957, 4824
Hedmark Slektshistorielags Tidsskrift. (NO ISSN 0046-7170) **2154**
Heemkring Okegem. Annalen. (BE) **2365**
Heemkring Okegem. Mededelingen. (BE) **2365**
Heemschut. (NE ISSN 0017-9515) **300**
Heenayana. (II) **2922**
Heer. (GW ISSN 0342-3867) **3459**
Hefte fuer Ostasiatische Literatur. (GW ISSN 0933-8721) **2922**, 2817
Hefte zur Unfallheilkunde. (US ISSN 0085-1469) **3308**
Hegel Society of America. Proceedings. (US) **3767**
Hegel Society of Great Britain. Bulletin. (UK) **3768**
Hegel - Studien. (GW ISSN 0073-1587) **3768**
Hegel - Studien Beihefte. (GW ISSN 0440-5927) **3768**
Hehai Daxue Xuebao/Hehai University. Journal. (CC ISSN 1000-1980) **4373**
Hehai University. Journal. see Hehai Daxue Xuebao **4373**
Hehua Dian. (CC) **2922**
He-Huaxue yu Fangshe Huaxue/Journal of Nuclear Chemistry and Radio Chemistry. (CC ISSN 0253-9950) **1805**, 1177
Heidegger Studies. (GW ISSN 0885-4580) **3768**
Heidelberg Science Library. (US ISSN 0073-1595) **4312**
Heidelberger Akademie der Wissenschaften. Mathematisch-Naturwissenschaftliche Klasse. Sitzungsberichte. (US ISSN 0371-0165) **4312**
Heidelberger Althistorische Beitraege und Epigraphische Studien. (GW ISSN 0930-1208) **2311**
Heidelberger Amtsanzeiger. (GW) **4088**
Heidelberger Arbeitsbuecher. (US ISSN 0073-1633) **4312**, 4599
Heidelberger Jahrbuecher. (US ISSN 0073-1641) **4312**, 4599
Heidelberger Rechtsvergleichende und Wirtschaftsrechtliche Studien. (GW) **2632**
Heidelberger Rechtswissenschaftliche Abhandlungen. Neue Folge. (GW ISSN 0073-165X) **2632**
Heidelberger Sociologica. (GW ISSN 0073-1676) **4436**
Heidelberger Studien zur Naturkunde der Fruehen Neuzeit. (GW ISSN 0935-6576) **4312**
Heidelberger Taschenbuecher. (US ISSN 0073-1684) **4312**, 4599
Heidem. (IS) **2507**
Heights see Cathedral **2568**
The Heights. (US ISSN 0017-9590) **1313**
Die Heilberufe. (GW ISSN 0017-9604) **3104**
†Heilbronner Hochschul-Informationen. (GW) **5204**
Das Heilige Band. (GW ISSN 0017-9612) **2004**
Heiliger Dienst. (AU ISSN 0017-9620) **4180**
Heilkunst. (GW ISSN 0017-9639) **3214**
Heilongjiang Chengshi Jinrong/Heilongjiang Urban Finance. (CC) **783**

Heilongjiang Daxue Ziran Kexue Xuebao/Heilongjiang University. Journal of Natural Sciences. (CC ISSN 1001-7011) **4312**
Heilongjiang Education. see Heilongjiang Jiaoyu **1637**
Heilongjiang Finance. see Heilongjiang Jingrong **783**
Heilongjiang Huabao. (CC) **2182**
Heilongjiang Institute of Commerce. Journal. see Heilongjiang Shangxueyuan Xuebao **836**
Heilongjiang Jiaoyu/Heilongjiang Education. (CC ISSN 0438-9050) **1637**
Heilongjiang Jingrong/Heilongjiang Finance. (CC ISSN 1001-0432) **783**
Heilongjiang Library. see Heilongjiang Tushuguan **2760**
Heilongjiang Shangxueyuan Xuebao/Heilongjiang Institute of Commerce. Journal. (CC ISSN 1001-6066) **836**
Heilongjiang Traditional Chinese Medical Science. see Heilongjiang Zhongyiyao **3104**
Heilongjiang Tushuguan/Heilongjiang Library. (CC ISSN 1001-5604) **2760**
Heilongjiang University. Journal of Natural Sciences. see Heilongjiang Daxue Ziran Kexue Xuebao **4312**
Heilongjiang Urban Finance. see Heilongjiang Chengshi Jinrong **783**
Heilongjiang Zhongyiyao/Heilongjiang Traditional Chinese Medical Science. (CC ISSN 1000-9906) **3104**
Heilpraxis - Magazin. (GW ISSN 0177-8617) **3214**
Heim Gallery Catalogues. (UK) **3524**
Heim und Anstalt. (GW ISSN 0176-9243) **2072**, 3104, 4103
Heim und Anstalt see S K A V - Fachblatt **4418**
†Heim und Farbe. (GW) **5204**
Heim und Garten. (GW) **2130**
Heim und Herd see Bauspar-Journal **603**
Heim und Hobby. (GW) **2447**, 2551
Heim und Welt. (GW) **4844**, 2189
Heima Er Bezt. (IC ISSN 0017-9698) **2198**
Heimarbeiterverband der Konfektions- und Wascheindustrie. Appell. (SZ) **1285**
Die Heimat. (GW ISSN 0017-9701) **2365**
Heimat am Inn. (GW) **2365**
Heimat Dortmund. (GW ISSN 0932-9757) **4088**
Heimat im Weinland. (AU) **2365**
Heimat und Welt. (AU) **402**
Heimat - Zeitung Roemerstaedter Laendchen. (GW ISSN 0017-9752) **2365**
Heimatblaettle. (GW ISSN 0935-364X) **2365**
Heimatbogen der Gemeinde Schnelldorf.(GW) **2365**
Heimatbrief der Stadt Germersheim. (GW) **2365**, 2055
Heimatbriefe der Stadt Pirmasens. (GW) **4088**
Heimatbuch des Kreises Viersen. (GW) **2311**
Heimatgemeinschaft Eckernfoerde. Jahrbuch. (GW ISSN 0179-8790) **2189**
Heimatgruss. (GW ISSN 0440-6230) **2365**
Heimatjahrbuch Kreis Ahrweiler. (GW) **2922**, 273, 2189
Heimatjahrbuch Landkreis Alzey-Worms.(GW) **2189**
Heimatkunde, Kulturpflege, Stadtgeschichte. (AU) **2365**
Heimatkundliche Nachrichten. (AU) **2365**
Heimatkundliches Beiblatt see Heimat im Weinland **2365**
Heimatkundliches Jahrbuch fuer den Kreis Segeberg. (GW) **2365**
Heimatland see Literatur aus Oesterreich **2933**
Heimatland Lippe. (GW ISSN 0017-9787) **2189**
Heimatleben. (SZ) **2365**

Das Heimatmuseum Alsergrund. (AU ISSN 0017-9809) **2365**
Heimatpflege in Westfalen. (GW ISSN 0933-6346) **1957**
Der Heimatpfleger. (GW ISSN 0177-2538) **2055**, 1530, 3554
Heimatrecht. (GW) **2055**, 2004
Heimatschutz/Sauvegarde. (SZ ISSN 0017-9817) **1489**, 300
Heimatstimmen aus dem Kreis Olpe. (GW ISSN 0177-2899) **2365**
Heimdal. (FR ISSN 0336-030X) **2365**, 240, 2252
Heimen. (NO ISSN 0017-9841) **2365**
Heimevernsbladet. (NO ISSN 0017-985X) **3193**
Die Heimstatt. (GW ISSN 0017-9868) **4407**
Heimtex. (GW ISSN 0017-9876) **2551**
Heimwerkstatt Vereinigt mit Magazin fuer Heim und Ausbau see Magazin fuer Heimwerker **5230**
Hein Annual Checklist Statutes see Hein Checklist of Statutes **2632**
Hein Checklist of Statutes. (US) **2632**
Heine-Jahrbuch. (GW ISSN 0073-1692) **2922**
Heine Saekularausgabe: Werke-Briefwechsel-Lebenszeugnisse. (GW) **2922**, 2994
Heinrich /Schmid GmbH und Co. Aktuell see H S Aktuell **328**
Heir Lines. (US) **2154**
Heisey News. (US ISSN 0731-8014) **257**, 1164
Heizung Klima. (SZ) **2300**
Heizung und Lueftung/Chauffage et Ventilation. (SZ) **2300**
Hej see Cystisk Fibrose **3092**
Hejnal Mariacki. (PL ISSN 0017-9914) **4265**
†Hel. (DK ISSN 0107-3575) **5204**
Hel Achau. (UK ISSN 0260-1753) **2154**
Heladeria Internacional. (SP ISSN 0213-1021) **2088**, 152
Helan Medical Magazine. (II ISSN 0017-9922) **3104**, 3803
Helen Keller National Center for Deaf-Blind Youths and Adults Nat - Cent News see Nat - Cent News **2294**
Helensburgh Advertiser. (UK) **2194**
Helesestatistikk see Norway. Statistisk Sentralbyraa. Helsestatistikk **4118**
Helfende Haende. (GW) **4407**, 4239
Helferin des Artzes see Die Arzthelferin **3275**
Helgolaender Meeresuntersuchungen. (GW ISSN 0174-3597) **1605**
Heliand Korrespondenz. (GW) **4265**
Helice. (MX) **54**
Helicon. (II) **2994**
†Helicon Nine. (US ISSN 0197-3371) **5204**
Heliconia Society International Bulletin see H S I Bulletin **2129**
Heliconian see American Comparative Literature Association Newsletter **2893**
Helicopter Annual. (US ISSN 0739-5728) **4674**
Helicopter Association International. Operations Update. (US) **4674**
Helicopter Association International. Preliminary Accident Reports and Technical Notes. (US) **54**, 4674
Helicopter International Magazine. (UK) **54**, 3459
Helicopter News. (US ISSN 0363-8227) **54**
Helicopter Safety. (US ISSN 0898-8145) **54**
Helicopter Safety Bulletin see Helicopter Safety **54**
Helicopter World. (UK ISSN 0262-0448) **4674**
Helicopters Magazine Canada. (CN) **4674**
Helictite. (AT ISSN 0017-9973) **1567**, 440, 583, 1598, 1957
HeliData see HeliData News **54**
HeliData News. (UK) **54**
Helikon. (IT ISSN 0017-9981) **1277**
Helikon. (HU ISSN 0017-999X) **2922**
Helinium. (BE ISSN 0018-0009) **273**
Helio. (US) **1811**
Heliogram (Bridgeport). (US ISSN 0887-168X) **3369**

Helios. (DR) **2868**
Helios (Lubbock). (US ISSN 0160-0923) **2922**
Heliport Development Guide. (US) **4674**, 54
Helix. (AT ISSN 0155-9044) **2922**, 2994
▼Hellas. (US ISSN 1044-5331) **2994**
Hellenews. (GR) **668**
Hellenic-American Chamber of Commerce. Newsletter. (US ISSN 0018-0025) **816**
Hellenic American Society. Journal see Journal of the Hellenic Diaspora **2010**
Hellenic Canadian Chronicles. (CN) **2004**
Hellenic Dental Association. Journal. see Elliniki Odontiatriki Omospondia. Enemerotiko Deltio **3232**
Hellenic Hamilton News. (CN) **2004**
Hellenic Herald see Greek Herald **2003**
Hellenic Industrial Development Bank. Investment Guide. (GR) **948**
Hellenic Journal. (US) **2004**, 3959
Hellenic News. (CN ISSN 0821-7270) **2004**
Hellenic Philatelic Society of Great Britain. Bulletin. (UK) **3753**
Hellenic Photography Selections. (GR ISSN 1011-1638) **3791**
Hellenic Postman. (UK) **2004**
Hellenic Stomatological Annals see Hellenic Stomatological Review **3234**
Hellenic Stomatological Review. (GR) **3234**
Hellenic Times. (US) **2004**
Hellenic Veterinary Medical Society. Bulletin/Deltio tis Ellinikis Ktiniatrikis Eterias. (GR ISSN 0257-2354) **4810**
Hellenika. (GW ISSN 0018-0084) **2922**, 2507
Hellenike Mathematike Hetaireia. Deltion. see Greek Mathematical Society. Bulletin **3037**
Heller Helper. (US ISSN 0882-5882) **2154**
Heller Report on Education Technology and Telecommunications Markets. (US) **1728**
Hello! (UK) **2194**
Hello Again. (US) **1298**
Hello Israel. (IS) **4770**
Hello, Welcome. see Ahlan Wasahlan **4801**
Helmantica. (SP ISSN 0018-0114) **2507**
Helminthologia. (CS) **583**
Helminthological Abstracts. (UK ISSN 0957-6789) **138**, 13, 465
Helminthological Abstracts. Series A: Animal and Human Helminthology see Helminthological Abstracts **138**
Helminthological Abstracts. Series B: Plant Nematology see Nematological Abstracts **140**
Helminthological Society of Washington. Journal. (US ISSN 1049-233X) **583**
Helminthological Society of Washington. Proceedings see Helminthological Society of Washington. Journal **583**
The Helper. (US) **3219**
†Helping Each Other. (US) **5204**
Helping Hand in Bible Study. (US) **4239**
Helping Out in the Outdoors. (US ISSN 8756-310X) **1138**, 3627, 4548
Helping the Homeless see Public Assistance Report **4417**
Helps for Students of History. (UK ISSN 0073-1714) **1751**
Helse. (DK ISSN 0018-0149) **3803**
Helse og Sosial Forum. (NO) **4436**
Helsenytt. (NO ISSN 0018-0157) **2273**
†Helses Boerneblad. (DK ISSN 0108-934X) **5204**
Helsetjenesten. Fagtidsskriftet. (NO) **2463**
Helsingfors Stads. Statistikcentral Kvartalsoeversikt. see Helsingin Kaupungin Tilastokeskuksen Neljannesvuosikatsaus **4573**

Helsingfors Universitets Biblioteks Skrifter. *see* Helsingin Yliopiston Kirjaston. Julkaisuja **2760**
Helsingin Kauppakorkeakoulu. Julkaisusarja A. Vaeitoeskirjoja. (FI) **1707**
Helsingin Kauppakorkeakoulu. Julkaisusarja B. Tutkimuksia. (FI) **668**
Helsingin Kauppakorkeakoulu. Julkaisusarja D. Laitosjulkaisuja. (FI ISSN 0356-8164) **719**
Helsingin Kauppakorkeakoulu. Julkaisusarja E. Selvityksiae. (FI) **668**
Helsingin Kauppakorkeakoulu. Julkaisusarja F. Tyopapereita. (FI ISSN 0358-2973) **668**
Helsingin Kaupungin Tilastokeskuksen Neljannesvuosikatsaus/Helsingfors Stads. Statistikcentral Kvartalsoeversikt. (FI ISSN 0357-3362) **4573**
Helsingin Kaupungin Tilastollinen Vuosikirja. (FI ISSN 0785-8736) **4573**
Helsingin Kaupunki Tilastolunen Vuosikirja *see* Helsingin Kaupungin Tilastollinen Vuosikirja **4573**
Helsingin Laakarilehti. (FI ISSN 0437-2468) **3104**
Helsingin Sanomat, Kuukausiliite. (FI ISSN 0780-0096) **2186**
Helsingin Yliopiston Kirjaston. Julkaisuja/Helsingfors Universitets Biblioteks Skrifter/Helsinki University Library. Publications. (FI ISSN 0355-1350) **2760**
Helsingoer Bymuseum. Aarbog *see* Helsingoer Kommunes Museer. Aarbog **3524**
Helsingoer Kommunes Museer. Aarbog. (DK ISSN 0108-0393) **3524**
Helsingoer som Fotografen saa det. (DK ISSN 0106-5440) **3524**
Helsinki University Library. Publications. *see* Helsingin Yliopiston Kirjaston. Julkaisuja **2760**
Helsinki Watch. (US) **3942**
Helsinki Watch Report. (US) **3942**
Helter Skelter. (US) **2994**
Helvetia Alphorn *see* Tell **3758**
Helvetia Herald *see* Tell **3758**
Helvetica Chimica Acta. (SZ ISSN 0018-019X) **1177**
Helvetica Chirurgica Acta. (SZ ISSN 0018-0181) **3379**
Helvetica Odontologica Acta *see* Schweizer Monatsschrift fuer Zahnmedizin **3242**
Helvetica Odontologica Acta. Supplementum *see* Schweizer Monatsschrift fuer Zahnmedizin **3242**
Helvetica Paediatrica Acta *see* European Journal of Pediatrics **3320**
Helvetica Physica Acta. (SZ ISSN 0018-0238) **3819**
Hematologic Pathology. (US ISSN 0886-0238) **3272**
Hematological Oncology. (UK ISSN 0278-0232) **3272**
Hematology and Transfusiology. *see* Gematologiya i Transfusiologiya **3272**
Hematology - Oncology Clinics of North America. (US ISSN 0889-8588) **3197**
Hematology Reviews and Communications. (US ISSN 0882-8083) **3272**
Hematology Series. (US) **3272**
Hembygden. (SW ISSN 0346-9018) **1530**, 2055, 3554
Hemecht. (LU ISSN 0018-0270) **2311**
Hemel en Dampkring *see* Zenit **371**
Hemel Hempstead Business Directory. (UK ISSN 0957-1043) **1138**
Hemi-Sync Journal. (US) **3859**
Hemijska Industrija/Chemical Industry. (YU ISSN 0367-598X) **1854**
Hemijski Pregled/Chemical Review. (YU ISSN 0440-6826) **1178**
Hemingway Newsletter. (US ISSN 0739-7801) **2922**
Hemingway Review. (US ISSN 0276-3362) **2922**

Hemisphere. (US ISSN 0898-3038) **3959**
Hemispheres. (PL ISSN 0239-8818) **4373**
Hemlock Quarterly. (US ISSN 0742-5376) **3104**, 2632, 4407
†Hemlocks and Balsams. (US ISSN 0737-7169) **5204**
Hemmets Journal. (SW ISSN 0018-0327) **2447**
Hemmets Vaen. (SW ISSN 0018-0335) **4180**
Hemmets Veckotidning. (SW ISSN 0345-4630) **2218**
Hemmings Motor News. (US) **4692**, 257
Hemming's Vintage Auto Almanac. (US ISSN 0363-4639) **257**
Hemochromatosis Awareness. (US ISSN 0883-2285) **3104**, 543
Hemoglobin. (US ISSN 0363-0269) **3272**
Hemophilia Today. (CN ISSN 0046-7251) **3272**
Hempstead County Historical Society. Journal. (US) **2408**
Hemvaernet. (SW ISSN 0018-0351) **3459**
Hen House Herald *see* National Poultry News **221**
Henan Daxue Xuebao (Shehui Kexue Ban)/Henan University. Journal (Social Science Edition). (CC ISSN 1000-5242) **2507**
Henan Daxue Xuebao (Ziran Kexue Ban)/Henan University. Journal (Natural Science Edition). (CC ISSN 1000-2472) **4312**
Henan Huabao. (CC) **2182**, 3791
Henan Normal University. Journal (Natural Science Edition). *see* Henan Shifan Daxue Xuebao (Ziran Kexue Ban) **4312**
Henan Normal University. Journal (Social Science Edition). *see* Henan Shifan Daxue Xuebao (Shehui Kexue Ban) **4373**
Henan Shifan Daxue Xuebao (Shehui Kexue Ban)/Henan Normal University. Journal (Social Science Edition). (CC ISSN 1000-2359) **4373**
Henan Shifan Daxue Xuebao (Ziran Kexue Ban)/Henan Normal University. Journal (Natural Science Edition). (CC ISSN 1000-2367) **4312**
Henan University. Journal (Natural Science Edition). *see* Henan Daxue Xuebao (Ziran Kexue Ban) **4312**
Henan University. Journal (Social Science Edition). *see* Henan Daxue Xuebao (Shehui Kexue Ban) **2507**
Henderson Community College Literary Magazine. (US) **2994**, 2868
Henderson Heritage. (US) **2154**
Hendes Verden. (DK) **4844**
Heng Ngan. (LS) **836**
Hengelsport Nieuws. (NE) **4548**
Hengstenboek. (NE) **4534**
Henkel - Referate. (GW ISSN 0720-941X) **1178**
Henkel Referate, Excerpts of Henkel Research Papers *see* Henkel - Referate **1178**
Henley Centre for Forecasting. Costs & Prices. (UK ISSN 0305-9928) **867**
†Henley Centre for Forecasting. Director's Guide to the E E C Economies. (UK) **5204**
Henley Centre for Forecasting. Director's Guide to the U.K. Economy *see* Henley Centre for Forecasting. Director's Report **783**
Henley Centre for Forecasting. Director's Report. (UK ISSN 0952-5467) **783**, 867
Hennepin County Library Authority File (Microfiche Edition) *see* H C L Authority File (Microfiche Edition) **2759**
Hennepin County Library Cataloging Bulletin. (US ISSN 0732-894X) **2760**
†Hennepin Reporter. (US ISSN 0018-0386) **5204**
Henning C L E Reporter *see* Lawyer Hiring & Training Report **2646**
Henoch. (IT) **2817**, 3768

Henong Xuebao. (CC) **95**, 1790
Henri Frankfort Foundation. Publications. (NE) **1277**
Henry County Historicalog. (US) **2154**, 2408
Henry - D R U Nytt. (Danmarks Retsforbunds Ungdom) (DK ISSN 0903-9295) **2868**
Henry Ford Hospital Medical Journal. (US ISSN 0018-0416) **2463**, 3104
Henry George Newsletter. (US ISSN 0734-4031) **1313**
Henry James Review. (US ISSN 0273-0340) **2922**
Henry Martyn Institute of Islamic Studies. Bulletin. (II ISSN 0970-4698) **4218**, 3638
Henry's Auktionen. (GW) **257**, 328, 2564
Henston Veterinary Vade Mecum (Large Animals). (UK ISSN 0268-4276) **4810**
Henston Veterinary Vade Mecum (Small Animals). (UK ISSN 0268-4268) **4810**, 3711
Hepato-Gastroenterology. (GW ISSN 0172-6390) **3268**
Hepatology (St. Louis). (US ISSN 0270-9139) **3105**
Her Majesty's Consuls List. (UK) **3897**
Her Own Words. (US ISSN 0898-0241) **2922**, 2311, 4844
Her World. (SI ISSN 0046-7278) **4844**
Her World. (MY) **4844**
Her World Annual. (SI ISSN 0217-1058) **4844**
Hera. (US) **4844**, 2454, 3803
Herald. *see* Kirykas **985**
The Herald. (UK) **1536**
Herald. (BG) **2174**
Herald. (PK ISSN 0018-0467) **2213**
Herald. *see* Visnyk **2888**
Herald. (AT ISSN 0815-9904) **3943**
Herald *see* C W I Herald **4167**
Herald/Visnyk. (CN) **4283**
Herald (Conroe). (US ISSN 0730-6520) **2154**
Herald Business Review. (US) **668**
Herald Caravanning Guide. (AT ISSN 0085-1477) **4548**, 4770
Herald Motel Guide. (AT ISSN 0085-1485) **2475**
Herald of Christian Science. (Danish edition: Kristen Videnskabs Herold) (US ISSN 0018-0475) **4283**
Herald of Health. (II ISSN 0018-0491) **3803**
Herald of His Coming. (US) **4180**
Herald of Holistic Health Newsletter *see* Nutrition & Dietary Consultant **3610**
Herald of Library Science. (II ISSN 0018-0521) **2760**
Herald of the Serbian Orthodox Church in Western Europe. (UK) **4283**
Herald Times. (SA) **2004**
Heraldika. (CS ISSN 0139-5009) **2154**
Heraldique au Canada. *see* Heraldry in Canada **2154**
Heraldisch - Genealogische Gesellschaft Adler. Jahrbuch. (AU ISSN 0073-1897) **2154**
Heraldiske Studier. (DK ISSN 0109-3061) **2154**
El Heraldo Catolico. (US ISSN 0746-4185) **4265**
Heraldo Cristiano. (CU ISSN 0864-0270) **4239**
Heraldo de Broward. (US) **2004**
Heraldo de Caldas. (CK) **3897**
Heraldo de Chicago. (US) **2004**
Heraldo de la Ciencia Cristiana *see* Herald of Christian Science **4283**
Heraldo Episcopal. (CU) **4180**
Heraldry in Canada/Heraldique au Canada. (CN ISSN 0441-6619) **2154**
Heraut van de Christelijke Wetenschap *see* Herald of Christian Science **4283**
†Herb Basket. (US ISSN 8750-1090) **5204**
The Herb Companion. (US ISSN 1040-581X) **2130**
Herb Quarterly. (US ISSN 0163-9900) **2130**

Herb, Spice and Medicinal Plant Digest. (US ISSN 1048-3160) **2130**
Herba Hungarica *see* Journal of Medicinal and Aromatic Plants **507**
Herba Polonica. (PL ISSN 0018-0599) **504**, 3214
Herbage Abstracts. (UK ISSN 0018-0602) **138**, 13
†Herbal Kitchen. (US) **5204**
HerbalGram. (US ISSN 0899-5648) **504**, 2004, 3728
Herbarist. (US) **2130**
Herbarium News. (US ISSN 0731-7824) **504**
†Herbergen der Christenheit. (GW ISSN 0437-3014) **5204**
Herbert Read Series. (UK ISSN 0073-1927) **2922**
Herbertia. (US ISSN 8756-9418) **504**, 2130
Hercules Moderno. (MX) **3803**
Hercynia. (GW ISSN 0018-0637) **4312**
Hercynica. (FR ISSN 0982-3816) **1567**, 3484
Herd Book for Angora Goats in Australia. (AT ISSN 0310-2971) **217**
Herd Book of Hereford Cattle. (UK ISSN 0073-1943) **217**
Herder Correspondence *see* Month **4270**
Herder - Korrespondenz. (GW ISSN 0018-0645) **4265**
Here and Now. (CN ISSN 0085-1493) **4023**
Here Is Your Indiana Government. (US) **816**
Here, There and Everywhere *see* Good Day Sunshine **3553**
Hereditas. (SW ISSN 0018-0661) **543**, 524
Hereditas. *see* Yichuan **547**
Hereditas-Genetiskt Arkiv *see* Hereditas **543**
Heredity. (UK ISSN 0018-067X) **543**
Heredity and Disease. *see* Yichuan yu Jibing **3163**
Hereford. (DK ISSN 0108-9692) **2365**
Hereford Breed Journal. (UK ISSN 0073-1951) **217**
Herefordbladet *see* Hereford **2365**
Hereford's Americas. (US) **4650**
Hereford's North America *see* Hereford's Americas **4650**
Hereford's Worldwide. (UK ISSN 0951-9637) **4674**
Herefordshire Family History Society. Journal. (UK ISSN 0260-1044) **2154**
Herefordshire Farmer. (UK ISSN 0018-0688) **95**
Here's Health. (UK ISSN 0018-0696) **3803**, 3606
Heresies. (US ISSN 0146-3411) **4859**, 328
Herforder Jahrbuch; Beitraege zur Geschichte der Stadt des Kreises und des Stiftes Herford. (GW) **2365**
Herforder Jahrbuch; Beitraege zur Geschichte der Stadt und des Stiftes Herford *see* Herforder Jahrbuch; Beitraege zur Geschichte der Stadt des Kreises und des Stiftes Herford **2365**
Herion - Informationen. (GW ISSN 0440-7059) **1924**, 3018, 4599
Herisson. (FR) **2868**
Heritage. (SI) **328**, 2004, 2338, 3524
Heritage. *see* Morasha **2014**
L'Heritage. (US) **2154**
Heritage *see* Heritage of Zimbabwe **2333**
Heritage. (UK ISSN 0260-4957) **2365**
Heritage (Carson). (US ISSN 0895-0792) **2004**
Heritage (Chicago). (US) **2004**
Heritage (Cooperstown). (US ISSN 0883-1513) **2408**
Heritage (Lagos, 1981). (NR ISSN 0189-255X) **2004**
Heritage (Lagos, 1984). (NR ISSN 0794-3415) **2004**, 2333
Heritage (Lawrenceville). (US ISSN 8756-5242) **2408**
Heritage (Roseville). (US) **2226**

Heritage (Waltham). (US ISSN 0732-0914) **4223**
Heritage and Arts. *see* Turath wa Funun **2059**
Heritage and History. (US) **2408**
Heritage Australia. (AT ISSN 0728-6422) **2344, 1489**
Heritage: British Life and Countryside. (UK) **2194**
Heritage Canada *see* Canadian Heritage **5161**
Heritage Foundation. Issue Bulletins. (US) **3897**
†Heritage Holidays and Visits in Britain. (UK) **5204**
Heritage Interpretation *see* Interpretation Journal **1959**
Heritage Lectures. (US ISSN 0272-1155) **4062**
Heritage Link. (CN ISSN 0820-2893) **2177**
Heritage News. (AT ISSN 0313-6701) **300, 273, 1489, 1957**
Heritage News. (CN) **2177**
Heritage Newsletter *see* Heritage News **300**
Heritage Newsletter. (US) **2408**
†Heritage of Sociology. (US ISSN 0073-1986) **5204**
Heritage of Stone. (US) **2154**
Heritage of Vermilion County. (US ISSN 0018-0718) **2408**
Heritage of Zimbabwe. (RH) **2333**
Heritage Outlook. (UK ISSN 0261-1988) **1957, 1489**
Heritage Quest. (US ISSN 0886-0262) **2154**
Heritage Record Series. (CN ISSN 0701-9556) **402, 3536**
Heritage Review. (US ISSN 0162-8267) **2004**
Heritage Rose Letter. (US) **2130**
Heritage Seeker. (US) **2154**
Heritage Seekers. (CN ISSN 0707-0780) **2154**
Heritage - Southwest Jewish Press. (US ISSN 0018-0726) **2004**
†Herizon Newsletter. (US) **5204**
Herkenning (The Hague). (NE) **4180**
Herkenning (The Hague, 1948). (NE ISSN 0018-0734) **54, 1336**
Herkimer County Historical Society. (US) **2408**
Hermaea. (GW) **2922**
Hermathena. (IE ISSN 0018-0750) **2507**
Hermeneus. (NE) **2311**
Hermeneutic Commentaries. (US ISSN 1043-5735) **3768**
Hermeneutics of Art. (US ISSN 0899-9856) **328**
Hermeneutische Untersuchungen zur Theologie. (GW ISSN 0440-7180) **4180**
Hermes. (JA ISSN 0910-3023) **2507**
Hermes. (GW ISSN 0018-0777) **2817, 1277**
Hermes Americanus. (US ISSN 0741-1286) **1277**
Hermes - Einzelschriften. (GW ISSN 0341-0064) **2817, 1277**
The Hermetic Journal. (UK ISSN 0141-6391) **4283, 3669, 3768**
†Hermetika. (GW ISSN 0723-8673) **5204**
Herne in Zahlen. Jahresheft (Year). (GW) **719, 867, 4088**
Herne in Zahlen. Vierteljahresberichte. (GW) **719, 868, 4088**
Hernhutter Suriname Zending. (NE) **4180**
Herning - Bogen. (DK ISSN 0108-8017) **2365**
Herodote. (FR ISSN 0333-8487) **2252, 2922**
Herold (Berlin). (GW ISSN 0018-0793) **2154**
Herold der Christlichen Wissenschaft *see* Herald of Christian Science **4283**
Herold der Wahrheit. (US ISSN 0300-8851) **4284**
Herold Export - Adressbuch von Oesterreich *see* Austria Export Herold **1122**
Heron. (NE ISSN 0046-7316) **1866, 619**
Heron. (JA ISSN 0387-9348) **2922, 2817**

Heron Newsletter. (AT) **4525**
Herpeticulturist. (CN ISSN 0832-7009) **583**
Herpetofauna. (AT ISSN 0725-1424) **583**
Herpetologica. (US ISSN 0018-0831) **583**
Herpetological Association of Africa. Journal. (SA ISSN 0441-6651) **583**
Herpetological Journal. (UK ISSN 0268-0130) **583**
Herpetological Review. (US ISSN 0018-084X) **583**
Herr Schmidt. (GW ISSN 0933-5498) **2189**
Hertfordshire Countryside. (UK ISSN 0306-672X) **2194**
Hertfordshire Countryside Illustrated *see* Hertfordshire Countryside **2194**
Hertfordshire Farmer. (UK) **95**
Hertfordshire People. (UK ISSN 0309-913X) **2154**
Hertha. (SW ISSN 0018-0912) **4844, 3943**
†Hertz Travel Guide. (US) **5204**
Hervey Bay Fraser Island Sun *see* Hervey Bay Observer **2172**
Hervey Bay Observer. (AT) **2172**
Hervey Families of America Bulletin. (US) **2154**
Hervormd Arnhem. (NE ISSN 0018-0920) **4239**
Hervormd Nederland. (NE ISSN 0018-0939) **4239**
Hervormd Wageningen. (NE ISSN 0018-0947) **4239**
Hervormde Teologiese Studies. (SA ISSN 0259-9422) **4180**
Die Hervormer. (SA ISSN 0259-949X) **4239**
Herz. (GW ISSN 0340-9937) **3208**
Herz Kreislauf. (GW ISSN 0046-7324) **3208**
Herz und Gefaesse. (GW ISSN 0720-0730) **3208**
Herz und Gesundheit. (GW) **3208**
Herzl Institute Bulletin. (US ISSN 0744-1444) **2004**
Herzogia. (GW ISSN 0018-0971) **504**
▼Herzschrittmachertherapie und Elektrophysiologie. (GW ISSN 0938-7412) **3208**
Hesperia. (US ISSN 0018-098X) **274, 1277**
▼Hesperia. (IT) **1277**
Hesperis - Tamuda. (MR ISSN 0018-1005) **3638, 2311**
Hesperus Review. (II) **2994**
Hesse. Minister fuer Landesentwicklung, Umwelt, Landwirtschaft und Forsten. Ernten, Maerkte, Preise *see* Hesse. Minister fuer Landwirtschaft, Forsten. Ernten, Maerkte, Preisen **152**
Hesse. Minister fuer Landwirtschaft, Forsten. Ernten, Maerkte, Preisen. (GW) **152, 2092**
Hessen. Kommunalverwaltung. Fundstelle. (GW) **4088**
Hessen. Minister fuer Landesentwicklung, Umwelt, Landwirtschaft und Forsten. Mitteilungen. Land und Umwelt *see* Blick ins Hessenland **79**
Hessen - Report. (GW) **4088**
Hessische Beitraege zur Geschichte der Arbeiterbewegung. (GW ISSN 0018-1099) **2365, 2584**
Hessische Bibliographie. (GW) **402**
Hessische Blaetter fuer Volks- und Kulturforschung. (GW) **2004, 240, 2055**
Hessische Blaetter fuer Volksbildung. (GW ISSN 0018-103X) **1684**
Hessische Blaetter fuer Volkskunde *see* Hessische Blaetter fuer Volks- und Kulturforschung **2004**
Hessische Elektrizitaets AG Journal *see* H E A G Journal **1893**
Hessische Familienkunde. (GW ISSN 0018-1064) **2154**
Hessische Faunistische Briefe. (GW ISSN 0721-6874) **583, 533**
Hessische Floristische Briefe. (GW ISSN 0439-0687) **504**
Hessische Gross- und Aussenhandel *see* Grosshandel-Aussenhandel **910**

Hessische Jugend. (GW ISSN 0018-1099) **1256**
Hessische Kreiszahlen. (GW) **4573**
Hessische Lehrerzeitung. (GW) **1728**
Hessische Staatsarchiv Darmstadt. Repertorien. (GW) **2365**
Hessische Staedte- und Gemeinde-Zeitung. (GW) **2488**
Hessische Stiftung Friedens- und Konfliktforschung. Mitteilungen. (GW) **3959, 4436**
Hessischer Verkehrsspiegel. (GW) **4710**
Hessischer Volkshochschulverband Extra *see* H V V Extra **5202**
Hessischer Volkshochschulverband Rundschreiben *see* H V V Rundschreiben **1684**
Hessisches Aerzteblatt. (GW) **3105**
Hessisches Jahrbuch fuer Landesgeschichte. (GW ISSN 0073-2001) **2365**
Hessisches Pfarrblatt. (GW) **4239**
Hessisches Staatsarchiv. Mitteilungen. (GW) **2365, 2329**
Hestia. (GW) **3768**
Het. (RM) **2215**
Het. (CS) **2922**
▼Heteroatom Chemistry. (GW ISSN 1042-7163) **1213**
Heterocera Sumatrana. (GW ISSN 0724-1348) **533**
Heterocycles. (JA ISSN 0385-5414) **1218**
†Heterocyclic Chemistry. (UK ISSN 0144-8773) **5204**
▼Heterodoxy. (US) **3897**
Heterofonia. (MX ISSN 0018-1137) **3554**
Heti Vilaggazdasag. (HU ISSN 0139-1682) **668**
Hevesi Szemle. (HU ISSN 0133-7564) **2365**
Hevra u-Revaha. *see* Society and Welfare **4421**
Hewlett-Packard Chronicle *see* H P Chronicle **1460**
Hewlett-Packard Journal. (US ISSN 0018-1153) **1460**
Hexagon. (US ISSN 0164-6109) **1178**
Hey Lady. (US ISSN 0018-1188) **2994**
Heydon - Hayden - Hyden Families Quarterly. (US ISSN 0737-7258) **2154**
Heythrop Journal. (UK ISSN 0018-1196) **4181, 3768**
Hezi Kexue *see* Nuclear Science Journal **3849**
Hi Class Living. (US) **2226**
Hi Fi Aarbogen. (DK ISSN 0441-5833) **3554**
Hi-Fi & Elektronik. (DK) **4460, 1893**
Hi-Fi and Video Revyen. (DK ISSN 0108-4658) **4460, 1385**
Hi-Fi Answers *see* Audiophile **4459**
Hi Fi Buyers' Review. (US) **4460**
Hi-Fi Choice. (UK) **4460**
Hi-Fi for Pleasure *see* Which Compact Disc & Hi-Fi for Pleasure **4462**
Hi-Fi News and Record Review. (UK ISSN 0142-6230) **3554**
†Hi-Fi Now! (UK) **5204**
Hi-Fi Revyen *see* Hi-Fi and Video Revyen **4460**
Hi-Fi Stereo. (IT) **4460, 3554**
Hi-Fi Vision. (SZ) **4460, 1893, 2436**
▼Hi Hello Salut. (GW) **2817, 1751**
Hi-Res. (US ISSN 0742-6747) **1419**
Hi-Rise. (CN ISSN 0715-5948) **2177**
Hi-Tech Alert for the Professional Communicator *see* Social Science Monitor **5278**
Hi-Tech Buyers Guide. (US) **1040**
†Hi-Tech Terror. (US) **5204**
Hi-Tension News. (US ISSN 0018-1242) **1893**
Hiaka Khronika. (GR ISSN 1105-0225) **2365, 274, 2055, 2817**
Hiba Kagaku/Hiba Society of Natural History. Journal. (JA ISSN 0389-5491) **4312**
Hiba Society of Natural History. Journal. *see* Hiba Kagaku **4312**
Hiballer Forest Magazine. (CN ISSN 0708-2169) **2101**
Hiballer Magazine *see* Hiballer Forest Magazine **2101**

†Hibiscus. (US ISSN 0748-3015) **5204**
Hibou. (CN ISSN 0709-9177) **1256**
Hibou. (FR) **1256**
Hibueras. (HO ISSN 0046-7359) **2180**
HiCall. (US ISSN 0018-120X) **4284, 1256**
†Hickenia. (AG ISSN 0325-3732) **5204**
†Hickory Stump. (US) **5204**
Hid. (YU) **2365**
Hidalguia. (SP ISSN 0018-1285) **2154**
Al-Hidayah. (BA) **4218**
Hidden History. (UK) **3669**
▼The Hidden Job Market. (US) **1138**
Hidden Springs Review. (US) **2994**
Hidden Valley Journal. (US) **2154**
Hide and Leather Bulletin. (US ISSN 0018-1293) **2736, 4361**
Hideaways Guide. (US ISSN 0741-1952) **4770**
Hideaways Newsletter. (US) **4770**
Hides and Skins. (UK ISSN 0142-1891) **2736, 1040**
Hides, Skins and Footwear Indusrty in O E C D Countries - Industrie des Cuirs et Peaux et de la Chaussure dans les Pays de l'O C D E *see* Footwear, Raw Hides and Skins, and Leatther Industry in O E C D Countries **5195**
Hidrologiai Kozlony. (HU ISSN 0018-1323) **4825, 1957**
Hidrologija i Meteorologija. *see* Hydrology and Meteorology **3436**
Hidrotehnica. (RM) **4825, 1924**
Hidrotehnica, Gospodarirea Apelor, Meteorologia *see* Hidrotehnica **4825**
Hidrotehnicka Bibliografija. (YU ISSN 0018-1358) **4835**
Hier en Ginder. (NE) **4181**
Hier et Aujourd'hui. *see* Omaly sy Anio **2334**
Hierro *see* Venezuela. Ministerio de Energia y Minas. Anuario Estadistico Minero **3502**
Hiersemanns Bibliographische Handbuecher. (GW ISSN 0170-2408) **402**
Hifi. (FI ISSN 0357-0738) **4460**
HiFi & Video Markt. (GW) **4460, 1385**
HiFi Exklusiv. (GW) **4460**
HiFi-Markt *see* HiFi & Video Markt **4460**
Hifi Musique. Revue des Disques et de la Haute Fidelite. (BE) **3554**
Hifi & Musik. (SW ISSN 0346-0576) **4460, 3554**
Hifi Stereo. (FR ISSN 0337-1891) **4460**
HiFi Stereophonie *see* Stereoplay **3582**
HiFi Stereopraxis *see* Stereoplay **3582**
HiFi und TV. (GW ISSN 0343-4206) **1374, 1356**
HiFi Vision. (GW ISSN 0178-6156) **3554**
Hifu. *see* Skin Research **3249**
Hifuka Kiyo. *see* Acta Dermatologica **3245**
Hifuka No Rinsho. *see* Clinical Dermatology **3246**
Higashi Taisetsu Museum of Natural History. Bulletin. *see* Kamishihoro-cho Higashi Taisetsu Hakubutsukan Kenkyu Hokoku **4319**
Higdon Family Newsletter. (US) **2154**
Higginson Journal. (US ISSN 0164-145X) **2994**
Higginson Journal of American Poetry *see* Higginson Journal **2994**
High Adventure. (US ISSN 0190-3802) **1256, 4284, 4548**
†High Country. (US ISSN 0018-1420) **5204**
High Country News. (US ISSN 0191-5657) **2570, 1957**
High Definition Television Report *see* H D T V Report **1374**
High Energy Chemistry. (English translation of: Khimiya Vysokikh Energii) (US ISSN 0018-1439) **1226**
High Energy Particle Physics *see* Physics and Applications **3827**

HIGH ENERGY

High Energy Physics and Nuclear Physics. (English translation of: Gaoneng Wuli yu He-wuli) (US ISSN 0899-9996) **3847**
High Energy Physics Index/Hochenergiephysik-Index. (GW ISSN 0018-1447) **3837**, 13
High Fashion. (JA) **1291**
High Fidelity. (DK) **3554**
High Fidelity. (UK) **4460**
High Fidelity see Stereo Review **4462**
High Flight. (CN ISSN 0708-4331) **54**, 3459
High Frequency Broadcasting Schedule. (UN) **1356**
High Gear. (US) **54**, 3018
High Life. (UK) **4802**
†High - Low Report. (US ISSN 0191-2283) **5204**
High Magazine see High Mountain Sports **4548**
High Mountain Sports. (UK ISSN 0962-2667) **4548**
High Performance. (US ISSN 0160-9769) **328**
High-Performance Liquid Chromatography see H P L C: Advances and Perspectives **1205**
High Performance Liquid Chromatography. (UK ISSN 0261-4707) **3259**
High-Performance Liquid Chromatography Advances and Perspectives see H P L C: Advances and Perspectives **1205**
High-Performance Mopar. (US ISSN 1040-0044) **4692**
High Performance Optometry. (US ISSN 0894-5810) **3301**
High Performance Plastics. (UK ISSN 0264-7753) **3862**
High Performance Polymers. (UK ISSN 0954-0083) **1218**
High-Performance Pontiac. (US ISSN 0745-5941) **4692**
†High Performance Systems. (US) **5204**
High Performance Textiles. (UK ISSN 0144-5871) **4619**
High Plains Journal. (US ISSN 0018-1471) **95**
High Plains Literary Review. (US ISSN 0888-4153) **2922**
High Points. (US ISSN 0018-148X) **1637**
High Pressure Research. (US ISSN 0895-7959) **3843**
High Profits from Rare Coin Investment. (US) **3599**, 948
High-Purity Substances. (English translation of: Vysokochistye Veshchestva) (US) **1178**
High Quality. (GW ISSN 0177-2945) **4001**
High Reliability & Military Components Guide. (US ISSN 0899-8531) **3459**, 1893
High Roller. (US) **2760**
High School Journal. (US ISSN 0018-1498) **1637**
High School News Service Report see Profile (Norfolk) **3468**
High School Psychology Teacher. (US) **4023**, 1751
High School Rage. (CN) **1256**
†High School Sports. (US) **5204**
High Schools Statistics in Punjab. (PK) **1677**
High-Scope Extensions. (US ISSN 0892-5135) **1751**
High-Scope Resource. (US ISSN 0887-2007) **1751**
High Score. (GW) **2189**
High Society. (US) **3398**
High Society Book of Lingerie. (US) **3398**
High Society's Private Letters. (US) **3398**
†High Solids Coatings. (US ISSN 0146-4752) **5204**
High Speed Diesel Report see High Speed Diesels & Drives **1930**
High Speed Diesels & Drives. (US ISSN 1041-5416) **1930**
High Speed Rail Yearbook. (US) **4710**
High-Speed Surface Craft see Fast Ferry International **4727**
High Spots. (US ISSN 0885-2138) **783**

High Standards see High Standards in Productivity and Performance **5204**
†High Standards in Productivity and Performance. (US) **5204**
High - Tc Update. (US ISSN 1048-1141) **3819**, 1178, 3408
High Tech Ceramics News. (US ISSN 1045-2397) **1164**
High Tech Growth Forecaster. (US) **948**
High Tech Investor (Barrington). (US ISSN 0736-427X) **948**, 4599
†High Tech Investor (Elkview). (US) **5204**
High Tech Lifestyles. (US) **2226**
†High-Tech Manager's Bulletin. (US) **5204**
†High-Tech Marketing. (US ISSN 0743-4294) **5204**
High-Tech Materials Alert. (US ISSN 0741-0808) **4599**, 1413
High Tech Separations News. (US ISSN 1046-039X) **1205**, 4599
High Tech Tomorrow. (US) **4599**
High Technology and Other Growth Stocks. (US) **948**, 826
†High Technology Business. (US ISSN 0895-8432) **5204**
High Technology Careers. (US ISSN 0749-2960) **3627**, 54
†High Technology Export & Import. (US) **5204**
High Technology Law Journal. (US ISSN 0885-2715) **2632**, 4599
High Technology P R News. (US) **32**
High Technology Report. (JA) **1823**
High Temperature. (English translation of: Teplofizika Vysokikh Temperatur) (US) **3841**
High Temperature Materials and Processes. (UK ISSN 0334-1704) **1917**
High Temperature Science. (US ISSN 0018-1536) **1226**
High Temperature Technology see Materials at High Temperature **1920**
High Temperatures - High Pressures. (UK ISSN 0018-1544) **3841**, 1226, 1823
High Voltage. (US) **3554**
High Volume Printing. (US ISSN 0737-1020) **4001**
Higher Education. (NE ISSN 0018-1560) **1707**
Higher Education. (US ISSN 0882-4126) **1707**
Higher Education Abstracts. (US ISSN 0748-4364) **1708**, 13, 402, 4573
Higher Education and National Affairs. (US ISSN 0018-1579) **1708**
Higher Education and School Life see American Education **5134**
Higher Education Daily see Education Daily **1628**
Higher Education in China. see Zhongguo Gaodeng Jiaoyu **1721**
Higher Education in Europe. (UN ISSN 0379-7724) **1708**
Higher Education in the United Kingdom. (UK ISSN 0306-1744) **1708**
Higher Education Management. (FR ISSN 1013-851X) **1708**
Higher Education Opportunities for Minorities and Women: Annotated Selections. (US) **1708**, 4844
Higher Education Policy. (UK ISSN 0952-8733) **1708**
▼Higher Education Product Companion. (US) **1689**, 1708
Higher Education Quarterly. (UK ISSN 0951-5224) **1708**
Higher Education Research and Development. Research Papers. (AT ISSN 0729-4360) **1637**, 1708
Higher Education Research and Development Society of Australasia Green Guide see H E R D S A Green Guide **1707**
Higher Education Research and Development Society of Australasia News see H E R D S A News **1636**
Higher Education Review. (UK ISSN 0018-1609) **1708**
▼Highland Booknews. (II) **4844**

Highland Family History Society Journal.(UK ISSN 0262-6659) **2154**
Highland Heritage. (CN ISSN 0707-2554) **2154**
Highlander. (II ISSN 0376-9569) **2252**, 328, 2338
Highlander (Barrington). (US ISSN 0161-5378) **2004**
Highlander (Highland). (US) **1313**
Highlands Field Station Report. (KE) **2488**
Highlands Voice. (US ISSN 0161-9896) **1489**, 1957
Highlights. (BG) **596**
Highlights. (CN) **1505**
Highlights. (II ISSN 0018-1625) **2199**
Highlights. see MeBrookdale **5233**
†Highlights (Charlottesville). (US) **5204**
Highlights (Edwardsville). (US) **2488**
Highlights for Children. (US ISSN 0018-165X) **1256**
Highlights of Agricultural and Food Research in Ontario. (CN) **95**
Highlights of Agricultural Research. (US ISSN 0018-1668) **95**
Highlights of Agricultural Research in Ontario see Highlights of Agricultural and Food Research in Ontario **95**
†Highlights of Industrial Relations Literature. (CN ISSN 0714-4571) **5204**
Highlights of State Unemployment Compensations Laws. (US ISSN 0730-7624) **2734**, 2533
Highroller see High Roller **2760**
†HighTech. (GW ISSN 0933-9280) **5205**
Hightech Italia. (IT) **4599**
Highway. (UK ISSN 0018-1676) **2584**
Highway. (SA ISSN 0018-1684) **4239**
Highway. (SI ISSN 0439-1292) **4692**
†Highway. (AT ISSN 0046-7383) **5205**
Highway and Heavy Construction see Highway & Heavy Construction Products **1866**
Highway & Heavy Construction Products. (US) **1866**, 4719
Highway & Vehicle - Safety Report. (US ISSN 0161-0325) **4650**
Highway Builder. (US ISSN 0018-1692) **1866**, 619
Highway Code. (UK) **4719**, 2632
Highway Common Carrier Newsletter. (US ISSN 0018-1706) **4745**
Highway Engineering in Australia. (AT ISSN 0046-7391) **1867**
Highway Extension and Research Program Pothole Gazette see H E R P I C C Pothole Gazette **4719**
Highway Loss Data Institute Injury and Collision Loss Experience see H L D I Injury and Collision Loss Experience **4692**
Highway Mail. (SA ISSN 0018-1722) **2216**
Highway Planning Notes. (US ISSN 0073-2176) **1867**
Highway Reporter. (SA) **2216**
Highway Research Abstracts. (US) **4664**, 13, 1844
Highway Research Record. (II ISSN 0970-2598) **1867**, 4719
Highway Safety Directions. (US) **4719**
Highway Safety Highlights see Highway Safety Directions **4719**
Highway Safety Improvement Programs see U.S. Department of Transportation. Highway Safety Stewardship Report **4722**
Highways. (UK) **1867**
Highways. (US) **4548**
Highways. Current Literature see Transportation. Current Literature **4667**
Highways and Transportation. (UK ISSN 0265-6868) **1867**, 4719
Higiena i Zdraveopazvane. (BU ISSN 0018-8247) **4103**
Higiene y Sanidad Animal see Spain. Instituto Nacional de Investigaciones Agrarias. Comunicaciones: Serie: Higiene y Sanidad **226**
Hika. (US ISSN 0018-179X) **2994**

Hikaku Gijutsu. see Leather Technology **2737**
Hikaku Ho Kenkyu/Comparative Law Journal. (JA ISSN 0439-1365) **2632**
Hikaku Kagaku. see Leather Chemistry **2737**
Hikakuho Zasshi. see Comparative Law Review **2614**
†Al-Hikma. (PK ISSN 0065-5627) **5205**
Hikobia. (JA ISSN 0046-7413) **505**
Hikuin. (DK ISSN 0105-8118) **2365**, 274
Al-Hilal. (UA ISSN 0378-4010) **2922**
Al-Hilal Al-Dawli. (UK ISSN 0952-6145) **4218**
†Hilandar Bulletin. (US) **5205**
Hilberg - Easley Report. (US) **54**
Hilda Doolittle Newsletter see H D Newsletter **2921**
Hildebrandt Report. (US) **2632**, 1011, 1040
Hildesheimer Blindenmission. (GW) **2293**
Hildy's Ford Blue Book. (US) **4692**
Hilf Mit! (GW) **831**
Hilfsaktion Maertyrerkirche e.V. Kurier see H M K Kurier **4180**
Hilgardia. (US ISSN 0073-2230) **95**
Hilite. (SA) **816**
Hill and Holler. (US) **2922**
Hill & Redman: Landlord & Tenant. (UK) **4149**, 2632
Hill Topic. (US) **3338**
Hillcole Group Papers. (UK) **1751**
Hillel Gate. (US ISSN 0018-1862) **2004**, 4223
Hillel Guide to Jewish Life on Campus (Year). (US) **1313**, 1256, 2005, 4223
†Hilliard History. (US ISSN 0890-0612) **5205**
Hillsdale Magazine. (US) **1314**
Hillside Hospital Journal see Hillside Journal of Clinical Psychiatry **5205**
†Hillside Journal of Clinical Psychiatry. (US ISSN 0193-5216) **5205**
Hilltop. (US) **1314**
Hilprecht: Sammlung. (GW ISSN 0232-3001) **3638**
Hilton Colombia. (CK) **2475**
Hilton Greece. (GR) **2475**
Hilton Head Islander see Islander **4773**
Hilton - Holland Life. (NE) **2475**
†Hilton Horizon. (HK) **5205**
Hilton International (U.K.) Magazine. (UK) **2475**, 4770
Himachal Agricultural Newsletter. (II ISSN 0018-1889) **95**
Himachal Journal of Agricultural Research. (II ISSN 0970-0595) **95**, 4810
Himalaya see Journal of Himalayan Studies and Regional Development **1961**
Himalayan Culture. (NP) **3638**
Himalayan Economist. (NP) **668**
Himalayan Geology. (II ISSN 0379-5101) **1567**
Himalayan Institute Quarterly Guide. (US ISSN 0891-6144) **3768**, 3803
†Himalayan International Institute. Eleanor N. Dana Laboratory. Research Bulletin. (US ISSN 0276-4148) **5205**
Himalayan Journal. (II) **4548**
Himalayan News see Himalayan Institute Quarterly Guide **3768**
Himalayan Observer. (II ISSN 0046-7456) **2199**
Himalayan Plant Journal. (II ISSN 0970-2326) **2130**
Himalayan Review. (NP) **2252**
Himavanta. (II ISSN 0018-1897) **4548**, 274
Himmat/Courage. (II ISSN 0018-1900) **3897**
Himmel & Erde. (GW ISSN 0722-8252) **3897**
Das Himmelsjahr. (GW ISSN 0439-1551) **364**
Himpunan Nelayan Seluruh Indonesia. Dewan Pimpanan Pusat. Laporan Kegiatan. see Fisherman Union of Indonesia. Central Governing Board. Annual Report **2040**

Hind Mazdoor Sabha. Report of the Annual Convention. (II ISSN 0073-2273) **2584**
Hindemith - Jahrbuch/Annales Hindemith. (GW) **3554**
Hindi Folklore *see* Lokabritta: Hindi Folklore **2056**
Hindi Kahani. (II) **2922**
Hindsight G C S E Modern History Review. (UK ISSN 0958-3637) **2311**
Hindu. (MF) **4217**
Hindu Astronomical and Mathematical Text Series. (II ISSN 0073-2281) **3037**
Hindu - Christian Studies Bulletin. (CN) **4181**
Hindu International Edition. (II) **2199**
Hindu Regeneration. (II) **4217**
Hindu Text Information *see* Asian Religious Studies Information **5139**
Hinduism Today. (US ISSN 0896-0801) **4217**
Hindustan Antibiotics Bulletin. (II ISSN 0018-1935) **3728**
Hindustan Chamber Review. (II ISSN 0018-1943) **816**
Hindustan Latex. Annual Reports. *see* Hindustan Latex. Varshika Riporta **3862**
Hindustan Latex. Varshika Riporta/ Hindustan Latex. Annual Reports. (II) **3862**, **1178**
Hindustani Zaban. (II ISSN 0378-3928) **2817**, **2922**
Hine's Directory of Insurance Adjusters. (US) **2533**
Hine's Insurance Counsel. (US) **2632**, **2533**
Hinman Heritage. (US ISSN 0885-2367) **2154**
Hinshitsu Kanri/Total Quality Control. (JA ISSN 0018-1951) **1011**
Hinterland. (BE ISSN 0018-1978) **4728**
†Hinterland. (IT) **5205**
Hints for Job Hunters. (AT) **3627**, **1684**
Hints to Potato Growers. (US ISSN 0018-1986) **179**
Ha-Hinukh ha-Meshutaf. (IS ISSN 0334-4568) **1637**
Hinweis. (GW) **2533**, **668**, **2632**
Hinyokika Kiyo. *see* Acta Urologica Japonica **3386**
▼Hip Pathology. (IT ISSN 1120-7000) **3105**
Hipodromo. (VE) **4474**
Hippo. (US ISSN 1050-6802) **2922**
▼Hippocampus. (US ISSN 1050-9631) **3105**
Hippocrates. (US ISSN 0892-2977) **3105**
Hippocrates News. (US ISSN 0893-0627) **3606**, **2072**, **2130**, **3803**
Hippologisk Tidsskrift. (DK ISSN 0018-201X) **4534**
Hira-Gana Times. (JA) **2207**
Hiradastechnika. (HU ISSN 0018-2028) **1336**, **1893**
Hiram Poetry Review. (US ISSN 0018-2036) **2994**
Hire Trading *see* Consumer Credit **773**
Hiring & Firing. (CN) **1065**
Hirosaki Daigaku Igakubu Eiseigaku Kyoshitsu Gyosekishu. (JA ISSN 0910-0377) **3105**, **3208**
Hirosaki Daigaku Nogakubu Gakujutsu Hokoku. *see* Hirosaki University. Faculty of Agriculture. Bulletin **95**
Hirosaki Daigaku Rika Hokoku. *see* Hirosaki University. Faculty of Science. Science Reports **4312**
Hirosaki Medical Journal. (JA ISSN 0439-1721) **3105**, **440**
Hirosaki University. Faculty of Agriculture. Bulletin/Hirosaki Daigaku Nogakubu Gakujutsu Hokoku. (JA ISSN 0073-229X) **95**
Hirosaki University. Faculty of Science. Science Reports/Hirosaki Daigaku Rika Hokoku. (JA ISSN 0367-6439) **4312**
Hiroshima Daigaku Genbaku Hoshano Igaku Kenkyujo Nenpo. *see* Hiroshima University. Research Institute for Nuclear Medicine and Biology. Proceedings **3358**

Hiroshima Daigaku Igaku Zasshi. (JA ISSN 0018-2087) **3105**
Hiroshima Daigaku Kogakubu Kenkyu Hokoku. *see* Hiroshima University. Faculty of Engineering. Bulletin **1823**
Hiroshima Daigaku Rika Kiyo, Chishitsugaku to Kobutsugaku. *see* Hiroshima University. Journal of Science. Series C. Geology and Mineralogy **1567**
Hiroshima Daigaku Rika Kiyo, Dobutsugaku. *see* Hiroshima University. Journal of Science. Series B. Division 1: Zoology **583**
Hiroshima Daigaku Rika Kiyo, Shokubutsugaku. *see* Hiroshima University. Journal of Science. Series B. Division 2. Botany **505**
Hiroshima Daigaku Seibutsu Seisan Gakubu Kiyo. (JA ISSN 0387-7647) **200**, **217**, **2042**, **2072**
Hiroshima Daigaku Shigaku Zasshi. *see* Hiroshima University Dental Society. Journal **3234**
Hiroshima Igaku. *see* Hiroshima Medical Association. Journal **3105**
Hiroshima Journal of Medical Sciences. (JA ISSN 0018-2052) **3105**
Hiroshima Mathematical Journal. (JA ISSN 0018-2079) **3037**
Hiroshima Medical Association. Journal/ Hiroshima Igaku. (JA ISSN 0018-2044) **3105**
Hiroshima University. Department of Geology. Geological Report. (JA ISSN 0073-2303) **1567**
Hiroshima University. Faculty of Engineering. Bulletin/Hiroshima Daigaku Kogakubu Kenkyu Hokoku. (JA ISSN 0018-2060) **1823**
Hiroshima University. Faculty of Engineering. Memoirs. (JA ISSN 0073-2311) **1823**
Hiroshima University. Faculty of Integrated Arts and Sciences. Science Reports. *see* Kiso, Kankyo Kagaku Kenkyu **1962**
Hiroshima University. Journal of Science. Series B. Division 1: Zoology/Hiroshima Daigaku Rika Kiyo, Dobutsugaku. (JA ISSN 0368-4113) **583**
Hiroshima University. Journal of Science. Series B. Division 2. Botany/ Hiroshima Daigaku Rika Kiyo, Shokubutsugaku. (JA ISSN 0075-4366) **505**
Hiroshima University. Journal of Science. Series C. Geology and Mineralogy/Hiroshima Daigaku Rika Kiyo, Chishitsugaku to Kobutsugaku. (JA ISSN 0075-4374) **1567**, **3484**
Hiroshima University. Laboratory for Amphibian Biology. Scientific Report. (JA) **584**, **440**
Hiroshima University. Research Institute for Nuclear Medicine and Biology. Proceedings/Hiroshima Daigaku Genbaku Hoshano Igaku Kenkyujo Nenpo. (JA ISSN 0073-232X) **3358**
Hiroshima University Dental Society. Journal/Hiroshima Daigaku Shigaku Zasshi. (JA ISSN 0046-7472) **3234**
Hirschmannbrief. (GW) **4548**
†His Dominion. (CN ISSN 0229-7175) **5205**
His Salt Shaker *see* Christian Alert **4169**
Hisla. (PE) **895**
Hispalis Medica. (SP ISSN 0018-2125) **3105**
Hispamerica. (US ISSN 0363-0471) **2922**, **2868**
Hispania. (SP ISSN 0018-2141) **2365**
Hispania. (SP ISSN 0018-2133) **2817**, **1637**
Hispania Antiqua. (SP ISSN 1130-0515) **2365**
Hispania Sacra. (SP ISSN 0018-215X) **4181**, **2311**
Hispanic. (US) **2005**
Hispanic American Arts. (US ISSN 0738-5625) **328**, **3554**, **4633**

Hispanic American Family Magazine. (US) **4437**, **1238**
Hispanic American Historical Review. (US ISSN 0018-2168) **2408**
Hispanic American Periodicals Index. (US ISSN 0361-5502) **2329**
▼Hispanic Americans Information Directory. (US) **2005**
Hispanic Arts *see* A H A! Hispanic Arts News **309**
Hispanic Business Magazine. (US ISSN 0199-0349) **668**, **2005**
Hispanic Engineer. (US ISSN 1058-269X) **1823**, **3627**
Hispanic Entrepreneur. (US) **668**
Hispanic Focus. (US) **2030**
Hispanic Institute for the Performing Arts Guide to Hispanic Cultural World *see* H I F P A Guide to Hispanic Cultural World **5202**
Hispanic Issues. (US ISSN 0893-2395) **2408**
Hispanic Journal. (US ISSN 0271-0986) **2005**
Hispanic Journal of Behavioral Sciences.(US ISSN 0739-9863) **4023**, **2005**
Hispanic Link Weekly Report. (US) **2005**
Hispanic Literature. (US) **2005**
Hispanic Market News. (US) **2092**
Hispanic Media & Markets. (US) **32**
Hispanic Resource Directory. (US) **2005**
Hispanic Review. (US ISSN 0018-2176) **2817**, **2922**
Hispanic Student - U S A. (US) **2005**, **1256**
Hispanic Texts. (UK) **2817**
Hispanic Times Magazine. (US ISSN 0892-1369) **3628**, **2005**
Hispanic U S A Magazine. (US) **2005**
Hispanic Yellow Pages (McLean). (US) **1138**
Hispanic Yellow Pages (Stone Mountain). (US) **1138**
El Hispano. (US ISSN 0018-2184) **2005**
Hispano Americano. (MX ISSN 0018-2192) **2210**
Hispanofila. (US ISSN 0018-2206) **2923**, **2868**
Hispanorama. (GW ISSN 0720-1168) **2923**, **1637**, **2817**, **2868**
Hispo. (SZ) **2365**, **3897**
Hissu Aminosan Kenkyu. *see* Research Committee of Essential Amino Acids. Reports **482**
Histadrut Nachrichten *see* Labour in Israel **2586**
†Histamine Receptors. (UK ISSN 0143-4209) **5205**
The Histochemical Journal. (UK ISSN 0018-2214) **524**
Histochemistry. (GW ISSN 0301-5564) **477**, **524**
Histoire. (FR ISSN 0182-2411) **2311**
Histoire au Pays de Matane *see* Au Pays de Matane **2399**
Histoire de l'Horticulture au Canada. *see* Canadian Horticultural History **2124**
Histoire de la Pensee. (FR ISSN 0073-2362) **4312**
Histoire des Idees et Critique Litteraire. (SZ ISSN 0073-2397) **2923**
Histoire des Sciences et des Techniques. (FR ISSN 1141-4588) **4312**
Histoire des Sciences et des Techniques. (US ISSN 0761-1102) **4312**
Histoire du Theatre au Canada. *see* Theatre History in Canada **4641**
Histoire Economie et Societe. (FR ISSN 0752-5702) **895**
Histoire en Savoie. (FR ISSN 0046-7510) **2365**
Histoire et Biologie *see* Histoire et Nature **4312**
Histoire et Civilisation Arabe. (FR ISSN 0073-2400) **2429**
Histoire et Civilisation du Livre. (SZ ISSN 0073-2419) **2312**
Histoire et Defense. (FR ISSN 0765-0531) **3459**, **2365**
Histoire et Maquettisme. (FR) **2436**, **2312**, **3459**
Histoire et Mesure. (FR ISSN 0982-1783) **2312**

HISTORIAS 6249

Histoire et Nature. (FR) **4312**
Histoire et ses Representations. (FR ISSN 0766-1827) **2366**
Histoire et Theorie. (FR) **2366**
Histoire Sociale/Social History. (CN ISSN 0018-2257) **2312**, **4437**
Histopathology. (UK ISSN 0309-0167) **3197**
Historia. (GW ISSN 0018-2311) **2312**
Historia. (SA ISSN 0018-229X) **2312**
Historia. (BL ISSN 0101-9074) **2312**
Historia. (IT) **2366**
Historia. (CL ISSN 0073-2435) **2408**
Historia. (AG ISSN 0326-1352) **2408**, **2868**
Historia (Budapest). (HU ISSN 0139-2409) **2366**
Historia. Einzelhriften. (GW ISSN 0341-0056) **2312**
Historia Archaeologica. (CI) **274**, **2366**
Historia de Espana en el Mundo Moderno. Estudios. (SP) **2366**
Historia de la Musica Pop Espanola. (SP) **3554**
Historia de las Geociencias en Venezuela. Boletin. (VE ISSN 0258-3135) **1567**
Historia del Derecho Espanol. Anuario. (SP ISSN 0304-4319) **2632**, **2366**
Historia 16. (SP) **2312**
Historia Economica. (SP ISSN 0212-6109) **868**, **895**, **3897**
Historia Grafica de Catalunya Dia a Dia.(SP) **2366**
Historia Hospitalium. (GW ISSN 0440-9043) **2463**, **2312**
Historia Ilustrada. (MX) **2210**
Historia Mathematica. (US ISSN 0315-0860) **3037**
Historia Medicinae Veterinariae. (DK ISSN 0105-1423) **4810**
Historia Mexicana. (MX ISSN 0185-0172) **2408**
Historia Militar del Paraguay. (PY) **2408**, **3459**
Historia Moderna e Contemporanea *see* Universidade do Parana. Setor de Ciencias Humanas, Letras e Artes. Departamento de Historia. Boletim **2325**
†Historia Natural y Pro Natura. (GT ISSN 0018-2346) **5205**
Historia Scientiarum. (JA ISSN 0285-4821) **4312**
Historia Sztuki. (PL ISSN 0083-4270) **328**
Historia Universal. (SP) **2312**
Historia y Cultura. (PE ISSN 0073-2486) **2408**
Historia y Cultura. (BO) **2408**
Historia y Filosofia de la Ciencia. Serie Mayor. Encuadernada. (SP ISSN 0073-2494) **4312**
Historia y Filosofia de la Ciencia. Serie Menor. Rustica. (SP ISSN 0073-2508) **4312**
Historia y Vida. (SP ISSN 0018-2354) **2312**
Historiae Musicae Cultores Bibliotheca. (IT ISSN 0073-2516) **3554**
Historiae Scientiarum Elementa. (GW ISSN 0073-2532) **4312**
Historiallinen Aikakauskirja. (FI ISSN 0018-2362) **2312**
Historiallinen Arkisto. (FI ISSN 0073-2540) **2366**
Historiallinen Kirjasto. (FI ISSN 0359-3223) **2312**
Historiallisia Tutkimuksia. (FI ISSN 0073-2559) **2366**
Historian. (UK ISSN 0265-1076) **2312**
Historian *see* Nottinghamshire Historian **2378**
Historian (Athens) *see* Chinese Historian **3636**
The Historian (Tempe). (US ISSN 0018-2370) **2312**
Historian Aitta. (FI ISSN 0439-2183) **2312**
Historian's Bicentennial Newsletter *see* Pacific Northwest Forum **2418**
Historian's Digest. (US) **4181**, **2408**
Historians of Early Modern Europe. (US ISSN 0883-3559) **2366**, **4181**
Historias. (MX) **2312**

Historias Biblicas para Preescolares: Alumnos. (US ISSN 0890-3247) **4239**, 1256
Historias Biblicas para Preescolares: Maestros. (US ISSN 0890-3158) **4239**, 1256
Historic Bethlehem. Newsletter. (US) **2408**
Historic Brass Society Journal. (US ISSN 1045-4616) **3554**
Historic Brass Society Newsletter. (US ISSN 1045-4594) **3554**
†Historic Country House Hotels: Great Britain. (US) **5205**
Historic Deerfield Quarterly. (US) **3524**
Historic Documents. (US ISSN 0892-080X) **2408**, **3897**
Historic Environment. (AT ISSN 0726-6715) **1957**, 300
Historic Genealogical Magazine. (US) **2408**
Historic Guelph. (CN ISSN 0709-5562) **2408**, 300, 419
Historic Hawaii Magazine. (US) **2408**, 300
Historic Hawaii News see Historic Hawaii Magazine **2408**
Historic House. (UK ISSN 0260-8707) **300**
Historic Houses, Castles and Gardens see Historic Houses, Castles and Gardens in Great Britain and Ireland **2366**
Historic Houses, Castles and Gardens in Great Britain and Ireland. (UK) **2366**
Historic Houses in New England see S P N E A's Historic Houses in New England **306**
Historic Kansas City Foundation Gazette. (US) **2408**, 300
Historic Kern. (US ISSN 0018-2397) **2408**
▼Historic Landmarks of Black America.(US) **2005**
Historic Madison. Journal. (US ISSN 0361-574X) **2408**
Historic Nantucket. (US ISSN 0439-2248) **2408**
Historic New Orleans Collection Newsletter. (US ISSN 0886-2109) **2408**
Historic Palestine Series. (CN) **2005**, **3959**
Historic Places in New Zealand see New Zealand Historic Places **2345**
Historic Preservation. (US ISSN 0018-2419) **300**
Historic Register. (US) **2409**
Historic St. Mary's City Newsletter see A Brief Relation **2400**
Historic Schaefferstown Record. (US) **2409**, **2055**
Historic Society of Lancashire and Cheshire. Transactions. (UK ISSN 0140-332X) **2366**
Historic Textiles of India. (II) **4619**
Historica. (IT ISSN 0018-2427) **2312**, **2868**
Historica. (CS ISSN 0440-9205) **2366**
Historica. (PE ISSN 0376-4052) **2409**
Historica. (FR) **3459**, **2312**
Historical Abstracts. Part A: Modern History Abstracts, 1450-1914. (US ISSN 0363-2717) **2329**, 13, **3937**
Historical Abstracts. Part B: Twentieth Century Abstracts, 1914 to the Present. (US ISSN 0363-2725) **2329**, 13, **3937**
Historical Aircraft Corporation Techline see H A C Techline **54**
Historical and Geographical Review of Northwest China. see Xibei Shi-Di **2343**
Historical and Philosophical Society of Ohio. Bulletin see Queen City Heritage **2420**
Historical Archaeology. (US ISSN 0440-9213) **274**
Historical Archives. see Lishi Dang'an **2340**
Historical Arms Series. (US ISSN 0440-9221) **257**
Historical Association, London. General Series. (UK) **2312**

Historical Association of Southern Florida. Update see South Florida History Magazine **2423**
Historical Association of Tanzania. Papers. (TZ ISSN 0440-9264) **2333**
Historical Association of Zimbabwe. Local Series Pamphlets. (RH) **2333**
Historical Aviation Album. (US ISSN 0018-2443) **54**
▼Historical Biology. (US ISSN 0891-2963) **3657**, 240, 440
Historical Breechloading Smallarms Association. Journal. (UK ISSN 0305-0440) **3459**
Historical Breechloading Smallarms Association Newsletter see H B S A Newsletter **257**
†Historical Chart Book. (US) **5205**
Historical Commercial News. (US) **257**
Historical Contributions. see Povijesni Prilozi **2319**
Historical Ecology. see Historicka Ekologie **440**
Historical Firearms Society of South Africa. Journal/Historiese Vuurwapenvereniging van Suid-Afrika. Tydskrif. (SA ISSN 0018-2451) **257**
Historical Firearms Society of South Africa. Newsletter/Historiese Vuurwapenvereniging van Suid Afrika. Nuusbrief. (SA) **257**
Historical Footnotes (St. Louis). (US ISSN 0360-9030) **4239**
Historical Footnotes (Stonington). (US ISSN 0886-5272) **2409**
Historical Geography see Historical Geography Newsletter **2252**
Historical Geography Newsletter. (US ISSN 0160-1725) **2252**
Historical Geography Research Series. (UK ISSN 0143-683X) **2252**
Historical Guides to the World's Periodicals and Newspapers. (US ISSN 0742-5538) **2570**
Historical Harpsichord Series. (US) **3554**
Historical Highlights. (US) **4239**
Historical Journal. (UK ISSN 0018-246X) **2312**
Historical Journal. see Historicky Casopis **2313**
†Historical Journal. (AT ISSN 0311-8924) **5205**
Historical Journal Mizoram. (II) **2338**
Historical Journal of Film, Radio and Television. (UK ISSN 0143-9685) **2312**, 1356, 1374, 3511
Historical Journal of Japan/Shigaku Zasshi. (JA ISSN 0018-2478) **2338**
Historical Journal of Massachusetts. (US ISSN 0276-8313) **2409**
Historical Journal of Western Massachusetts see Historical Journal of Massachusetts **2409**
Historical Linguistics. see Historische Sprachforschung **2817**
Historical Material of Chinese Science and Technology. see Zhongguo Keji Shiliao **4353**
Historical Material on Publishing. see Chuban Shiliao **4125**
Historical Materials of New Literature. see Xin Wenxue Shiliao **2978**
Historical Messenger. (US) **4240**, **2312**
Historical Metallurgy. (UK ISSN 0142-3304) **3408**
Historical Methods. (US ISSN 0161-5440) **2312**, **3897**, **4373**, **4437**
Historical Museum of Hokkaido. Annual Report. see Hokkaido Kaitaku Kinenkan Kenkyu Nenpo **3524**
Historical New Hampshire. (US ISSN 0018-2508) **2409**
Historical News. (NZ ISSN 0439-2345) **2344**
Historical Performance. (US ISSN 0898-8587) **3554**
†Historical Periodicals Directory. (US) **5205**
Historical Plant Cost and Annual Production Expenses for Selected Electric Plants see Electric Plant Costs & Power Production Expenses **616**

†Historical Problems: Studies and Documents. (UK ISSN 0073-2621) **5205**
Historical Records of Australian Science.(AT) **4312**
Historical Records of the New Culture. see Xin Wenhua Shiliao **2343**
Historical Reflections/Reflexions Historiques. (US ISSN 0315-7997) **2312**
Historical Research. (UK ISSN 0950-3471) **2312**
Historical Research. see Lishi Yanjiu **2317**
Historical Research for Higher Degrees in the United Kingdom. Part 1: Theses Completed. (UK ISSN 0268-6716) **2313**
Historical Research for Higher Degrees in the United Kingdom. Part 2: Theses in Progress. (UK ISSN 0268-6724) **2313**
Historical Research for University Degrees in the United Kingdom. Part 1: Theses Completed see Historical Research for Higher Degrees in the United Kingdom. Part 1: Theses Completed **2313**
Historical Research for University Degrees in the United Kingdom. Part 2: Theses in Progress see Historical Research for Higher Degrees in the United Kingdom. Part 2: Theses in Progress **2313**
Historical Review. see Tortenelmi Szemle **2324**
Historical Review. (NZ ISSN 0018-2516) **2344**
Historical Review of Berks County. (US ISSN 0018-2524) **2409**
Historical Roller Skating Overview. (US ISSN 0896-1379) **4474**
Historical Science. see Ryoksagwahak **2321**
Historical Social Research/Historische Sozialforschung. (GW ISSN 0172-6404) **2366**, **3897**, **4437**
Historical Society of Carroll County Newsletter see Carroll County History Journal **2402**
Historical Society of Ghana. Transactions. (GH ISSN 0073-2648) **2313**
Historical Society of Haddonfield. Bulletin. (US ISSN 0018-2532) **2409**
Historical Society of Montgomery County. Bulletin. (US) **2409**
Historical Society of Nigeria. Journal. (NR ISSN 0018-2540) **2313**
Historical Society of Rockland County News. (US) **2409**
Historical Society of South Australia. Guidesheet. (AT) **402**
Historical Society of South Australia. Journal. (AT ISSN 0312-9640) **2344**, 300
Historical Society of South Australia Newsletter. (AT) **2344**, 300
Historical Society of the Church in Wales. Journal. (UK) **4240**, **2366**
Historical Society of the Presbyterian Church of Wales. Journal. (UK) **4240**, **2366**
Historical Statistics of the Gas Industry. (US ISSN 0073-2656) **3705**
Historical Statistics of the United States.(US ISSN 0073-2664) **4573**
Historical Studies see Australian Historical Studies **2307**
Historical Studies. see Studi Storici **2323**
Historical Studies. (IE ISSN 0075-0743) **2366**
Historical Studies (Pakistan) Series. (PK) **2338**
Historical Studies in Irish Science and Technology. (IE) **4313**, **2313**, **4599**
Historical Studies in the Physical and Biological Sciences. (US ISSN 0890-9997) **4313**
Historical Studies in the Physical Sciences. (US) **4313**
Historical Tidings. (US) **2154**
Historical Time Capsules of Monroe County. (US) **2409**, **2154**
Historicalog. (US) **2409**

Historicka Demografie. (CS ISSN 0323-0937) **2366**, **3982**
Historicka Ekologie/Historical Ecology. (CS ISSN 0862-3090) **440**
Historicka Geografie. (CS ISSN 0323-0988) **2366**
Historicke Studie. (CS ISSN 0440-9515) **2366**
Historicky Casopis/Historical Journal. (CS ISSN 0018-2575) **2313**
Historie. (DK ISSN 0046-7561) **2313**
Historie a Vojenstvi. (CS ISSN 0018-2583) **3459**, **2313**
Historie og Samtidsorientering. (DK) **2313**, 1751
Historiens et Geographes. (FR ISSN 0046-757X) **2313**, 1637, **2252**
Historiese Vuurwapenvereniging van Suid Afrika. Nuusbrief. see Historical Firearms Society of South Africa. Newsletter **257**
Historiese Vuurwapenvereniging van Suid-Afrika. Tydskrif. see Historical Firearms Society of South Africa. Journal **257**
Historijski Arhiv Rijeka. Vjesnik. (CI ISSN 0353-9520) **2366**, 668, **2632**
Historijski Arhiv u Rijeci i Pazinu. Vjesnik see Historijski Arhiv Rijeka. Vjesnik **2366**
Historijski Pregled see Nastava Povijesti **2377**
Historiografia y Bibliografia Americanista. (SP) **2409**, **2329**
†Historiographer. (US ISSN 0018-2591) **5205**
Historiographia Linguistica. (NE ISSN 0302-5160) **2817**, **2313**, **3768**
Historisch-Demographische Mitteilungen/Communications de Demographie Historique/Review of Historical Demography. (HU ISSN 0134-0050) **3982**
Historisch Jaarboek Vlaardingen. (NE) **2366**
Das Historisch-Politische Buch. (GW ISSN 0018-2605) **2313**, **3897**
Historische Bibliographie. (GW ISSN 0933-5420) **2329**
Historische Documenten van de Wetenschappen. (BE) **4313**
Historische Forschungen. (GW ISSN 0440-9558) **2313**
Historische Grundwissenschaften in Einzeldarstellungen. (GW ISSN 0930-6404) **2313**
Historische Kommission zu Berlin. Einzelveroeffentlichungen. (GW ISSN 0067-5857) **2313**
Historische Mitteilungen. (GW ISSN 0936-5796) **2313**
Historische Sozialforschung. see Historical Social Research **2366**
Historische Sprachforschung/Historical Linguistics. (GW ISSN 0935-3518) **2817**
Historische Studien. (GW) **2366**
Historische und Paedagogische Studien.(GW ISSN 0723-3264) **2313**, 1637
Historische Vereniging Vlaardingen. Tijdschrift see Historisch Jaarboek Vlaardingen **2366**
Historische Zeitschrift. (GW ISSN 0018-2613) **2313**
Historischer Verein der Pfalz. Mitteilungen. (GW ISSN 0073-2680) **2366**
Historischer Verein des Kantons Bern. Archiv. (SZ) **2366**, **2154**
Historischer Verein des Kantons St. Gallen. Neujahrsblatt. (SZ) **2366**
Historischer Verein Dillingen an der Donau. Jahrbuch. (GW ISSN 0073-2699) **2366**
Historischer Verein Eichstaett. Sammelblatt. (GW ISSN 0936-5869) **2366**
Historischer Verein fuer das Fuerstentum Liechtenstein. Jahrbuch.(LH) **2366**, **274**
Historischer Verein fuer Niederbayern. Verhandlungen. (GW) **2366**
Historischer Verein fuer Steiermark. Zeitschrift. (AU) **2366**
Historisches Jahrbuch. (GW ISSN 0018-2621) **2313**

Historisches Jahrbuch der Stadt Graz. (AU ISSN 0440-9728) **2366**
Historisches Jahrbuch der Stadt Linz. (AU ISSN 0440-9736) **2366**
Historisches Magazin-Geschichte. (SZ) **2366**
Historisk Aarbog for Felsted Sogn. (DK ISSN 0109-2138) **2367**
Historisk Aarbog for Skive og Omegn. (DK ISSN 0107-721X) **2367**
Historisk Aarbog fra Randers Amt. (DK ISSN 0108-4100) **2367**
Historisk Arbog for Thy og Vester Hanherred. (DK ISSN 0904-6267) **2367**
Historisk Arbog fra Roskilde Amt. (DK) **2367**
Historisk Arkiv for Broerup og Omegn. Aarsskrift. (DK ISSN 0109-0674) **2367**
Historisk Forening for Vaerloese Kommune. Arsskrift. (DK ISSN 0108-6804) **2367**
Historisk Samfund for Aarhus Stift. Aarboeger. (DK) **2367**
Historisk Samfund for Hoeje-Taastrup Kommune. Meddelelser. (DK ISSN 0109-2944) **2367**
Historisk Samfund for Praesto Amt. Aarbog. (DK ISSN 0107-6868) **2367**
Historisk Samfund for Soenderjylland. Skrifter. (DK ISSN 0109-9264) **2367**
Historisk Samfund for Soro Amt. Arbog.(DK) **2367**
Historisk Tidskrift. (SW ISSN 0345-469X) **2367**
Historisk Tidskrift foer Finland. (FI ISSN 0046-7596) **2367**
Historisk Tidsskrift. (NO ISSN 0018-263X) **2367**
Historisk-Topografisk Selskab for Gjentofte Kommune. Meddelelser see Gentofte-Bogen **5199**
Historiska och Litteraturhistoriska Studier. (FI ISSN 0073-2702) **2507**
Historiska Samfundet i Abo. Skrifter Utgivna. (FI ISSN 0356-1496) **2367**
Historiske Meddelelser om Koebenhavn.(DK) **2367**
History. (UK ISSN 0018-2648) **2313**
History and Anthropology. (US ISSN 0275-7206) **240**, **2313**
History and Applied Linguistics. (US) **2313**, **2817**
†History and Archaeology Review. (UK ISSN 0269-9591) **5205**
History and Computing. (UK ISSN 0957-0144) **1395**
History and Law Series. (UK) **2367**, **2632**
History and Literature. see Rekishi to Bungaku **5268**
History & Memory. (US) **2313**
History and Personalities. see Rekishi to Jinbutsu **2320**
History and Philosophy of Logic. (UK ISSN 0144-5340) **3768**
History and Philosophy of the Life Sciences. (UK ISSN 0391-9714) **440**, **3768**
History and Social Science Teacher see Canadian Social Studies: History and Social Science Teacher **1746**
History and Technology. (US ISSN 0734-1512) **2313**, **4599**
History and Theory. (US ISSN 0018-2656) **2313**, **3768**
History and Travel. see Rekishi to Tabi **4784**
History Book Club Review. (US ISSN 0018-2664) **4129**, **2313**
History House Newsletter. (US) **2154**
History Imprints see News in Tennessee History **2416**
History in Africa. (US ISSN 0361-5413) **2333**
History in Malawi. (MW) **2333**
History in Zambia. (ZA) **2329**
History News (Nashville). (US ISSN 0363-7492) **2409**
History News Dispatch. (US) **2409**
History of Agriculture. (II ISSN 0378-7524) **95**
History of Anthropology. (US) **240**

History of Anthropology Newsletter. (US ISSN 0362-9074) **240**
History of Art Research Reports see Sponsored Research in the History of Art **345**
History of Arts. see Meishu Shilun **335**
History of Economic Thought Newsletter. (UK ISSN 0440-9884) **895**
History of Education. (UK ISSN 0046-760X) **1637**
History of Education Quarterly. (US ISSN 0018-2680) **1637**
History of Education Review. (AT) **1637**
History of Education Society Bulletin. (UK ISSN 0018-2699) **1637**, **2313**
History of European Ideas. (US ISSN 0191-6599) **2367**
History of Geography Newsletter. (US) **2252**
History of Higher Education Annual. (US ISSN 0737-2698) **1708**
History of Historiography. see Storia della Storiografia **2389**
History of Mathematics. (US ISSN 0899-2428) **3037**
History of Nursing Bulletin see History of Nursing Journal **3278**
History of Nursing Journal. (UK ISSN 0960-2348) **3278**, **2313**
History of Philosophy Quarterly. (US ISSN 0740-0675) **3768**
History of Photography. (UK ISSN 0308-7298) **3792**
History of Political Economy. (US ISSN 0018-2702) **895**
History of Political Thought. (UK ISSN 0143-781X) **3897**, **2313**
▼History of Psychiatry. (UK ISSN 0957-154X) **3338**
†History of Psychoanalysis. (US ISSN 0734-9831) **5205**
History of Religions. (US ISSN 0018-2710) **4181**, **2313**
History of Science. (UK ISSN 0073-2753) **4313**
History of Sciences and Technology. see Dejiny Ved a Techniky **4306**
History of Sociology: An International Review. (US ISSN 0190-2067) **4437**
History of Technology. (UK ISSN 0307-5451) **4599**
History of the Aztec Club of 1847. (US) **2409**
History of the Chinese Communist Party. see Zhonggong Dangshi **3936**
History of the Human Sciences. (UK ISSN 0952-6951) **4373**
History of Universities. (UK ISSN 0144-5138) **1708**, **2367**
History: Reviews of New Books. (US ISSN 0361-2759) **4129**
History Studies. see Lishi Xuexi **2317**
History Studies. see Shixue Yanjiu **2322**
History Studies Collection. see Shizhi Wencui **2322**
History Teacher. (US ISSN 0018-2745) **2313**, **1637**
History Teachers Association of New South Wales. Newsletter. (AT ISSN 0085-1558) **1751**, **2313**
History Teaching. see Lishi Jiaoyue **2317**
History Teaching Review see History Teaching Review Yearbook **2313**
History Teaching Review Yearbook. (UK) **2313**
History Today. (UK ISSN 0018-2753) **2314**, **2868**
History Workshop. (UK ISSN 0309-2984) **2314**, **3897**
Historygram. (US) **2409**
Historyka; Studia Metodologiczne. (PL ISSN 0073-277X) **2367**
Hit Parader. (US ISSN 0162-0266) **3554**
Hitachi Review. (JA ISSN 0018-277X) **1771**
Hitachi Zosen Giho. see Hitachi Zosen Technical Review **1823**
Hitachi Zosen News. (JA ISSN 0439-2795) **1012**

Hitachi Zosen Technical Review/Hitachi Zosen Giho. (JA ISSN 0018-2788) **1823**
Hitchhiker. (US) **2760**
Hitotsubashi Journal of Arts and Sciences. (JA ISSN 0073-2788) **4313**, **2507**
Hitotsubashi Journal of Commerce and Management. (JA ISSN 0018-2796) **1012**
Hitotsubashi Journal of Economics. (JA ISSN 0018-280X) **669**
Hitotsubashi Journal of Law and Politics. (JA ISSN 0073-2796) **2632**, **3897**
Hitotsubashi Journal of Social Studies. (JA ISSN 0073-280X) **4374**
Hitotsubashi Review/Hitotsubashi Ronso. (JA ISSN 0018-2818) **669**, **4374**
Hitotsubashi Ronso. see Hitotsubashi Review **669**
Hitotsubashi University Research Series. Sciences. see Shizen Kagaku Kenkyu (Tokyo) **4343**
Hitsaustekniikka - Svetsteknik. (FI) **3429**
Hivi. (JA) **4460**
Hiwa Kagaku Hakubutsukan Kenkyu Hokoku/Hiwa Museum for Natural History. Miscellaneous Reports. (JA ISSN 0285-5615) **4313**, **3524**
Hiwa Museum for Natural History. Miscellaneous Reports. see Hiwa Kagaku Hakubutsukan Kenkyu Hokoku **4313**
Hiwar. see Debate **3890**
Hiya. (TS) **4844**
Hiyoshi Review of Natural Science. see Keio Gijuku Daigaku Hiyoshi Kiyo. Shizen Kagaku **4319**
Hjaert-Lungfonden. (SW) **3365**
Hjaerta Kaerl Lungor see Hjaert-Lungfonden **3365**
Hjelpepleieren. (NO ISSN 0332-7841) **3278**
Hjemkundskab. (DK ISSN 0106-0279) **2447**, **1751**
Hjemmet. (DK ISSN 0046-7626) **2185**
Hjemmet. (NO ISSN 0018-2842) **2213**
Hjemmevaernsbladet. (DK) **3459**
Hjerteforeningen. (DK ISSN 0105-9785) **3208**
Hjerteforeningens Motionsblad see Motionsbladet **3210**
Hjertenyt. (DK ISSN 0108-8904) **3208**
Hjukrun. (IC ISSN 0250-4731) **3278**
Hjukrunarfelag Islands. Timarit see Hjukrun **3278**
Hlas Ludu. (YU ISSN 0018-2869) **2239**
Ho-sei Kenkyu. see Journal of Law and Politics **2639**
▼Ho To Do It Manuals for School and Public Librarians. (US) **2760**, **1637**
Hoard's Dairyman. (US ISSN 0018-2885) **200**
Hob-Nob. (US) **2923**, **2436**
Hob-Nob Annual see Hob-Nob **2923**
Hobart Paperbacks. (UK ISSN 0309-1783) **895**
Hobart Papers. (UK ISSN 0073-2818) **669**
Hobbes Studies. (NE ISSN 0921-5891) **3768**, **895**
Hobbs Family Association Newsletter. (US) **2154**
Hobby. (AG ISSN 0046-7650) **2437**
Hobby. (GW ISSN 0721-9903) **2437**
Hobby Bookwatch. (US) **3459**
Hobby - Business World. (US) **1097**, **2437**
†Hobby Electronics. (UK) **5205**
Hobby Greenhouse. (US ISSN 1040-6212) **2130**
Hobby Magazine der Technik. (GW) **1893**
Hobby Merchandiser. (US ISSN 0744-1738) **2437**
Hobby Merchandiser Annual Trade Directory. (US) **2437**, **3591**
Hobbyindeks for Boernebiblioteker. (DK) **2444**
Hobbyist Sourcebook. (US ISSN 1045-0602) **2437**

HOCHSCHULE 6251

Hobe. (RW) **1256**
Hobel und Span. (GW) **355**
Hobetsu-choritsu Hakubutsukan Kenkyu Hokoku/Hobetsu Museum. Bulletin. (JA ISSN 0912-7798) **3657**, **1567**
Hobetsu Museum. Bulletin. see Hobetsu-choritsu Hakubutsukan Kenkyu Hokoku **3657**
Hobo Stew Review. (US) **2995**
Hobo Times. (US ISSN 1055-3967) **4710**, **2437**
Hobson's Engineering Casebook. (UK) **1867**, **1893**, **1930**
Hobstar. (US) **257**, **1164**
Hoc Tap see Tap Chi Cong San **3929**
Hoch- und Niedrigwasserzeiten fuer die Deutsche Bucht und deren Flussgebiete. (GW ISSN 0172-8253) **1605**
Hoch- und Tiefbau. (GW ISSN 0342-5169) **619**
Hoch und Tiefbau see Schweizer Bauwirtschaft **631**
Hochdruck. (GW ISSN 0721-1465) **3208**
Hochenergiephysik-Index. see High Energy Physics Index **3837**
Hochschulbuecher fuer Mathematik. (GW ISSN 0073-2842) **3037**
Hochschulbuecher fuer Physik. (GW ISSN 0073-2850) **3819**
Hochschule Bremen. Fachbereich Wirtschaft. Veranstaltungsverzeichnis.(GW) **1637**
Hochschule der Kunste Berlin Info see H D K Info **328**
Hochschule fuer Architektur und Bauwesen Weimar. Wissenschaftliche Zeitschrift. (GW ISSN 0509-9773) **300**
†Hochschule fuer Bauwesen Cottbus. Wissenschaftliche Zeitschrift. (GW ISSN 0138-2098) **5205**
Hochschule fuer Bodenkultur in Wien. Dissertationen see Universitaet fuer Bodenkultur in Wien. Dissertationen **126**
Hochschule fuer Maschinenbau Karl-Marx-Stadt. Wissenschaftliche Zeitschrift see Technische Hochschule Karl-Marx-Stadt. Wissenschaftliche Zeitschrift **1837**
Hochschule fuer Musik Koeln. Journal. (GW ISSN 0936-2940) **3554**
†Hochschule fuer Oekonomie "Bruno Leuschner" Berlin. Wissenschaftliche Zeitschrift. (GW ISSN 0067-5954) **5205**
Hochschule fuer Seefahrt Warnemuende-Wustrow. Wissenschaftliche Beitraege see Hochschule fuer Seefahrt Warnemuende-Wustrow. Wissenschaftliche Zeitschrift **4728**
Hochschule fuer Seefahrt Warnemuende-Wustrow. Wissenschaftliche Zeitschrift. (GW ISSN 0323-8725) **4728**, **1374**, **2042**
†Hochschule fuer Verkehrswesen "Friedrich List". Bibliographie Verkerswesen. (GW ISSN 0233-0016) **5205**
Hochschule fuer Verkehrswesen "Friedrich List". Verkehrswissenschaft Aktuell - Wissenschaftliche Zeitschrift.(GW) **4719**
Hochschule fuer Verkehrswesen "Friedrich List". Wissenschaftliche Zeitschrift see Hochschule fuer Verkehrswesen "Friedrich List". Verkehrswissenschaft Aktuell - Wissenschaftliche Zeitschrift **4719**
Hochschule St. Gallen fuer Wirtschafts- und Sozialwissenschaften. Forschungsinstitut fuer Absatz und Handel. Schriftenreihe see Forschungsinstitut fuer Absatz und Handel. Schriftenreihe **835**
Hochschule St. Gallen fuer Wirtschafts- und Sozialwissenschaften. Schriftenreihe des Managementzentrums see Schriftenreihe des Managementzentrums **690**

HOCHSCHULE

Hochschule St. Gallen fuer Wirtschafts- und Sozialwissenschaften. Veroeffentlichungen. Schriftenreihe Betriebswirtschaft. (SZ) **1012**
Hochschulfuhrer. (GW) **1823**, 1708
Hochschuljournal Essen see Essener Universitaetsberichte **4309**
Hochschulsport. (GW) **4474**, 1314, 3803
Das Hochschulwesen. (GW ISSN 0018-2974) **1637**
Hochtaunusblaetter. (GW ISSN 0938-4731) **2367**
Hochzeit. (GW ISSN 0720-7301) **3067**
Hocken Lecture. (NZ) **240**, 2344
Hockey. (SW ISSN 0345-4347) **4474**
Hockey Association. Official Handbook. (UK ISSN 0085-1566) **4506**
Hockey Card Price Guide see The Sport Americana Hockey Card Price Guide **2442**
Hockey Circle. (AT ISSN 0018-2982) **4474**
Hockey Digest. (US ISSN 0046-7693) **4474**
Hockey Digest. (UK ISSN 0950-9550) **4506**
Hockey Field see Hockey Digest **4506**
Hockey Guide. (US ISSN 0278-4955) **4474**
Hockey Illustrated. (US) **4474**
Hockey News. (CN ISSN 0018-3016) **4474**
Hockey Register. (US ISSN 0090-2292) **4506**
Al-Hoda see New Al-Hoda **2016**
Hodowla Roslin, Aklimatyzacja i Nasiennictwo. (PL ISSN 0018-3040) **95**
Hoechstrichterliche Finanzrechtsprechung. (GW ISSN 0018-3059) **2633**
Hoefchen-Briefe see Pflanzenschutz-Nachrichten Bayer **188**
Hoefslag. (NE ISSN 0046-7715) **4534**
Die Hoehle. (AU ISSN 0018-3091) **1568**
Hoehlenpost. (SZ ISSN 0018-3105) **1568**
Hoehnea. (BL ISSN 0073-2877) **505**
Hoeje-Tastrup Kommunes Lokalhistoriske Arkiv. Aarskrift. (DK ISSN 0900-2596) **2367**
Hoejskolebladet. (DK ISSN 0018-3334) **1708**
Hoer Zu. (GW ISSN 0018-3113) **2189**, 4770
Hoerakustik. (GW ISSN 0933-1980) **3859**
Hoerbuchverzeichnis. (GW) **2293**
Hoerelsen. (DK ISSN 0018-4934) **2287**
Hoergeraete-Akustiker see Hoerakustik **3859**
Hoergeschaedigte Kinder. (GW ISSN 0018-3121) **2287**, 1736
Hoergeschaedigten-Paedagogik. (GW ISSN 0342-4898) **2287**
Hoeruebersicht International. (GW ISSN 0179-1869) **1356**
Hofklatsch. (GW) **1708**, 1238, 2437
Hofmannsthal-Blaetter. (GW ISSN 0441-6813) **2868**
Hofmannsthal-Forschungen. (GW) **2868**
Hofstra Chronicle see Chronicle (Hempstead) **1307**
Hofstra Law Review. (US ISSN 0091-4029) **2633**
Hofstra University Yearbook of Business. (US ISSN 0073-2907) **669**
†Hog Call Fanletter. (US) **5205**
Hog Extra see Hogs Today **217**
Hog Farm Management. (US ISSN 0018-3180) **217**
†Hog Guide. (CN ISSN 0018-3199) **5205**
Hog Marketplace Quarterly. (CN ISSN 0380-3651) **217**
Hog Producer. (US) **217**
Hogaku/Journal of Law and Political Science. (JA ISSN 0385-5082) **2633**, 3897
Hogaku Kenkyu/Journal of Law, Politics, and Sociology. (JA) **2633**, 3897

Hogaku Kyokai Zasshi. see Jurisprudence Association. Journal **2641**
Hogaku Shinpo. see Chuo Law Review **2612**
Hogan Family Association Research Quarterly. (US) **2154**
Hogar. (EC ISSN 0018-3210) **4844**
Hogar Cristiano. (US ISSN 0018-3229) **4240**
Hogar y Moda. (SP ISSN 0046-7723) **4844**, 2447
Hogar y Vida. (MX) **2447**
Hogs Today. (US) **217**
▼Hoh Ineed/Ironic Laugh. (MP) **2868**
Hohe Bruecke. (AU ISSN 0018-3245) **2868**
Hohenheimer Arbeiten. (GW ISSN 0340-9783) **96**
Hohenloher Freilandmuseum Mitteilungen. (GW) **3524**
Hohenloher Leben. (GW) **2189**
Hohenzollerische Heimat. (GW ISSN 0018-3253) **2367**
Hoigaku no Jissai to Kenkyu/Research and Practice in Forensic Medicine. (JA ISSN 0289-0755) **3264**
Hoiku No Tomo. (JA ISSN 0018-327X) **4407**
Hoja del Lunes de Lugo. (SP ISSN 0018-3296) **2217**
Hoja del Lunes de Orense. (SP ISSN 0018-330X) **2217**
Hoja del Mar see Mar **1607**
Hoja Trinitaria. (SP) **4265**
Hojas de Frijol. (CK) **96**
Hojas de Frijol para America Latina see Hojas de Frijol **96**
Hojas de Poesia. (AG) **2995**
Hojas Literarias Ilustradas. (AG) **2923**, 328, 4633
Hojin Kigyo no Jittai see Zeimu Tokei Kara Mita Hojin Kigyo no Jittai **1112**
Hok see Hoogstratens Oudheidkundige Kring. Geschiedenis **2367**
Hoken Kanri Senta Dayori. (JA ISSN 0912-1420) **4104**, 1684
Hoken no Kagaku/Health Care. (JA ISSN 0018-3342) **3803**
Hoken Taiiku Kyoshitsu. see Health and Physical Education **1637**
Hokenfu no Kekkaku Tenbo/Review of Tuberculosis for Public Health Nurse.(JA ISSN 0018-3369) **3278**
Hokenfu Zasshi/Japanese Journal for Public Health Nurse. (JA ISSN 0047-1844) **3278**
Hokenjo Un'ei Hokoku see Japan. Ministry of Health and Welfare. Statistics and Information Department. Report on Activities of Public Health Centers **3176**
Hokkaido Daigaku Oyo Denki Kenkyujo Gijutsu Hokoku/Hokkaido University. Research Institute of Applied Electricity. Technical Bulletin. (JA ISSN 0286-3189) **1893**
Hokkaido Daigaku Oyo Denki Kenkyujo Hokoku see Hokkaido Daigaku Oyo Denki Kenkyujo Gijutsu Hokoku **1893**
Hokkaido Daigaku Rigakubu Kaiso Kenkyujo Obun Hokoku. see Hokkaido University. Institute of Algological Research. Scientific Papers **1605**
Hokkaido Daigaku Shokubai Kagaku Kenkyu Center Nenpo. see Hokkaido University. Catalysis Research Center. Annual Report **1226**
Hokkaido Dental Association. Journal/ Hokkaido Shika Ishikaishi, Doshikai Tsushin. (JA ISSN 0073-2915) **3234**
Hokkaido Eiyo Syokuryo Gakkaishi/ Hokkaido Society of Food and Nutrition. Journal. (JA ISSN 0285-1806) **200**, 2072
Hokkaido Fisheries Experimental Station. Journal. see Hokusuishi Dayori **2042**
Hokkaido Fisheries Experimental Station. Scientific Reports. see Hokkaidoritsu Suisan Shikenjo Kenkyu Hokoku **2042**
Hokkaido Journal of Medical Science. (JA) **3105**

Hokkaido Journal of Orthopedic & Traumatic Surgery/Hokkaido Seikei Saigai Geka Zasshi. (JA ISSN 0018-3377) **3308**
Hokkaido Kaitaku Kinenkan Kenkyu Nenpo/Historical Museum of Hokkaido. Annual Report. (JA ISSN 0287-9433) **3524**, 2338
Hokkaido Kogai Boshi Kenkyujo Ho. see Hokkaido Research Institute for Environmental Pollution. Report **1977**
Hokkaido Kogyo Kaihatsu Shikenjo Gijutsu. see Japan. Government Industrial Development Laboratory, Hokkaido. Technical Data **4601**
Hokkaido Kogyo Kaihatsu Shikenjo Hokoku. see Japan. Government Industrial Development Laboratory, Hokkaido. Reports **4601**
Hokkaido Kogyo Kaihatsu Shikenjo Nenpo/Government Industrial Development Laboratory, Hokkaido. Annual Report. (JA) **1077**
Hokkaido Kyoiku Daigaku Kiyo. Dai-1-Bu, A. Jinbun Hen/Hokkaido University of Education. Journal. Section 1 A. Humanities. (JA ISSN 0386-4472) **2507**
Hokkaido Kyoiku Daigaku Kiyo. Dai-1-Bu, B. Shakai Kagaku Hen/Hokkaido University of Education. Journal. Section 1 B. Social Science. (JA ISSN 0386-4480) **4374**
Hokkaido Kyoiku Daigaku Kiyo. Dai-1-Bu, C. Kyoikugaku Hen/Hokkaido University of Education. Journal. Section 1 C. Education. (JA ISSN 0386-4499) **1637**
Hokkaido Kyoiku Daigaku Kiyo. Dai-2-Bu, A. Sugaku, Butsuri, Kagaku, Kogaku- Hen/Hokkaido University of Education. Journal. Section 2 A. Mathematics, Physics, Chemistry, Engineering. (JA ISSN 0367-5939) **3037**, 1178, 1823, 3819
Hokkaido Kyoiku Daigaku Kiyo. Dai-2-Bu, B. Seibutsugaku, Chigaku, Nogaku- Hen/Hokkaido University of Education. Journal. Section 2 B. Biology, Geology, and Agriculture. (JA ISSN 0018-3393) **440**, 96, 1568
Hokkaido Kyoiku Daigaku Kiyo. Dai-2-Bu, C. Katei, Taiiku- Hen/Hokkaido University of Education. Journal. Section 2 C. Home Economics, Teacher Training for School Health and Physical Education. (JA ISSN 0386-4901) **2447**, 3803
Hokkaido Kyoiku Daigaku Taisetsuzan Shizen Kyoiku Kenkyu Shisetsu Kenkyu Hokoku/Hokkaido University of Education. Taisetsuzan Institute of Science. Reports. (JA ISSN 0386-4464) **4313**
Hokkaido Librarians Study Circle. Bulletin. see Hokkaido Toshokan Kenkyukai. Kaiho **2760**
Hokkaido Mathematical Journal. (JA ISSN 0385-4035) **3037**
Hokkaido National Agricultural Experiment Station. Research Bulletin. see Hokkaido Nogyo Shikenjo Kenkyu Hokoku **96**
Hokkaido National Agricultural Experiment Station. Soil Survey Report. see Hokkaido Nogyo Shikenjo Dojo Chosa Hokoku **5205**
Hokkaido no Shizen/Nature in Hokkaido. (JA ISSN 0286-0627) **1489**
†Hokkaido Nogyo Shikenjo Dojo Chosa Hokoku/Hokkaido National Agricultural Experiment Station. Soil Survey Report. (JA ISSN 0073-2923) **5205**
Hokkaido Nogyo Shikenjo Kenkyu Hokoku/Hokkaido National Agricultural Experiment Station. Research Bulletin. (JA ISSN 0018-3415) **96**
Hokkaido Research Institute for Environmental Pollution. Report/ Hokkaido Kogai Boshi Kenkyujo Ho. (JA) **1977**
Hokkaido Salmon Hatchery. Technical Report. (JA) **2042**

Hokkaido Seikei Saigai Geka Zasshi. see Hokkaido Journal of Orthopedic & Traumatic Surgery **3308**
Hokkaido Shika Ishikaishi, Doshikai Tsushin. see Hokkaido Dental Association. Journal **3234**
Hokkaido Society of Food and Nutrition. Journal. see Hokkaido Eiyo Syokuryo Gakkaishi **200**
Hokkaido Toshokan Kenkyukai. Kaiho/ Hokkaido Librarians Study Circle. Bulletin. (JA ISSN 0018-3431) **2760**
Hokkaido University. Catalysis Research Center. Annual Report/Hokkaido Daigaku Shokubai Kagaku Kenkyu Center Nenpo. (JA) **1226**, 1212
Hokkaido University. Catalysis Research Center. Annual Report see Hokkaido University. Catalysis Research Center. Annual Report **1226**
Hokkaido University. Economic Journal. (JA ISSN 0916-4650) **669**
Hokkaido University. Faculty of Agriculture. Journal. (JA ISSN 0018-344X) **96**
Hokkaido University. Faculty of Engineering. Memoirs. (JA ISSN 0368-9379) **1823**
Hokkaido University. Faculty of Fisheries. Bulletin. (JA ISSN 0018-3458) **2042**
Hokkaido University. Faculty of Fisheries. Data Record of Oceanographic Observations and Exploratory Fishing/Kaiyo Chosa Gyogyo Shiken Yoho. (JA ISSN 0439-3511) **1605**, 2042
Hokkaido University. Faculty of Fisheries. Memoirs. (JA ISSN 0018-3466) **2042**
Hokkaido University. Faculty of Science. Journal. Series 4: Geology and Mineralogy. (JA ISSN 0018-3474) **1568**, 3484
Hokkaido University. Faculty of Science. Journal. Series 5: Botany. (JA ISSN 0368-2145) **505**
Hokkaido University. Faculty of Science. Journal. Series 6: Zoology. (JA ISSN 0368-2188) **584**
Hokkaido University. Faculty of Science. Journal. Series 7: Geophysics. (JA ISSN 0441-067X) **1590**
Hokkaido University. Institute of Algological Research. Scientific Papers/Hokkaido Daigaku Rigakubu Kaiso Kenkyujo Obun Hokoku. (JA) **1605**, 505
Hokkaido University. Institute of Immunological Science. Bulletin. (JA) **3365**, 3185
†Hokkaido University. Research Institute of Applied Electricity. Monograph Series. (JA ISSN 0439-3465) **5205**
Hokkaido University. Research Institute of Applied Electricity. Technical Bulletin. see Hokkaido Daigaku Oyo Denki Kenkyujo Gijutsu Hokoku **1893**
Hokkaido University. Urakawa Seismological Observatory. Bulletin. (JA) **1568**
Hokkaido University of Education. Journal. Section 1 A. Humanities. see Hokkaido Kyoiku Daigaku Kiyo. Dai-1-Bu, A. Jinbun Hen **2507**
Hokkaido University of Education. Journal. Section 1 B. Social Science. see Hokkaido Kyoiku Daigaku Kiyo. Dai-1-Bu, B. Shakai Kagaku Hen **4374**
Hokkaido University of Education. Journal. Section 1 C. Education. see Hokkaido Kyoiku Daigaku Kiyo. Dai-1-Bu, C. Kyoikugaku Hen **1637**
Hokkaido University of Education. Journal. Section 2 A. Mathematics, Physics, Chemistry, Engineering. see Hokkaido Kyoiku Daigaku Kiyo. Dai-2-Bu, A. Sugaku, Butsuri, Kagaku, Kogaku- Hen **3037**
Hokkaido University of Education. Journal. Section 2 B. Biology, Geology, and Agriculture. see Hokkaido Kyoiku Daigaku Kiyo. Dai-2-Bu, B. Seibutsugaku, Chigaku, Nogaku- Hen **440**

Hokkaido University of Education. Journal. Section 2 C. Home Economics, Teacher Training for School Health and Physical Education. see Hokkaido Kyoiku Daigaku Kiyo. Dai-2-Bu, C. Katei, Taiiku-Hen **2447**
Hokkaido University of Education. Taisetsuzan Institute of Science. Reports. see Hokkaido Kyoiku Daigaku Taisetsuzan Shizen Kyoiku Kenkyu Shisetsu Kenkyu Hokoku **4313**
Hokkaido Wakkanai Fisheries Experimental Station. Annual Report. (JA) **2042**
†Hokkaido Wakkanai Fisheries Experimental Station. Collected Reprints. (JA ISSN 0385-1362) **5205**
Hokkaidoritsu Suisan Shikenjo Hokoku see Hokkaidoritsu Suisan Shikenjo Kenkyu Hokoku **2042**
Hokkaidoritsu Suisan Shikenjo Kenkyu Hokoku/Hokkaido Fisheries Experimental Station. Scientific Reports. (JA ISSN 0914-6830) **2042**, 477, 505
Hokkaishi News. (JA) **1077**
Hokke Bunka Kenkyu. see Institute for the Comprehensive Study of Lotus Sutra. Journal **4214**
Hokkyokusei Hoikakuho/Polaris Almanac for Azimuth Determination. (JA ISSN 0389-7605) **4664**, 371, 2268
Hokouk. (AF) **2633**, 3897
Hokubei Hochi. see North American Post **2017**
Hokudai Economic Papers see Hokkaido University. Economic Journal **669**
Hokuriku Journal of Zootechnical Science. (JA ISSN 0285-3760) **584**
Hokuriku no Denki to Kogyo/Electricity and Industry in Hokuriku. (JA) **1799**
Hokusuishi Dayori/Hokkaido Fisheries Experimental Station. Journal. (JA ISSN 0914-6849) **2042**
Hokusuishi Geppo see Hokusuishi Dayori **2042**
Holarctic Ecology see Ecography **1948**
Holas Crakvy/Voice of the Church. (US) **4216**
Hold Pusten. (NO ISSN 0332-9410) **3358**
Holding. (IT) **669**
Holdsworth Law Review. (UK ISSN 0260-5864) **2633**
▼Hole. (CN ISSN 1180-1670) **2923**
Holiday. (BG) **2174**
Holiday. (GW) **4770**, 2475
Holiday Guide see Children Welcome! Family Holiday Guide **4757**
Holiday Haunts in Great Britain. (UK ISSN 0073-3016) **4770**
Holiday Hints Handbook. (UK) **4770**
Holiday Inn Live. (GW ISSN 0931-5179) **2475**
Holiday Islander. (UK) **4770**
Holiday Western Australia. Travel News.(AT) **4770**
Holiday Which? (UK) **4770**
▼Holidaymaker. (SA) **4770**
Holidays & Business Travel. (UK) **4770**, 669
Holidays and Travel see Holidays & Business Travel **4770**
Holidays at the Kindergarten. (RU) **1256**, 3554
Holidays in Britain. (UK ISSN 0073-3024) **4771**
Holidays in Romania. (RM ISSN 0018-3555) **4771**
Holidays in Wales see Wales Best Holidays **4796**
Holiness Digest. (US ISSN 1040-8584) **4240**
†Holistic Health News. (US) **5205**
▼Holistic Life/Vida Holistica. (US ISSN 1060-2615) **3214**
Holistic Living. (US) **3594**, 3606
Holistic Medicine. (US ISSN 0898-6029) **3214**
Holistic Medicine see Journal of Interprofessional Care **3215**
Holistic Nursing Practice. (US) **3278**
Holland Camping. (NE) **4548**

Holland Exports. (NE ISSN 0073-3032) **911**
Holland Herald. (NE ISSN 0018-3563) **2211**, 4771
Holland - Schweiz. (SZ) **816**
Holland Shipbuilding see H S B International **4728**
Holland Shipping and Trading see Holland's Export Magazine **911**
Holland U S A (Closter). (US) **911**, 816
Holland - U S A (New York). (US) **817**
Holland - U S A and Netherlands News see Holland - U S A (New York) **817**
†Holland Windsurfing. (NE) **5205**
Hollandia News see Windmill Herald: Central East Canada **2029**
Holland's Export Magazine. (NE) **911**, 4728
Hollands Maandblad. (NE ISSN 0018-3601) **2868**
Hollandse Krant. (CN) **2005**
Hollfelder Blaetter. (GW) **2189**
Hollingsworth Register. (US ISSN 0018-3636) **2155**
Hollins Critic. (US ISSN 0018-3644) **2868**
Hollis Press & Public Relations Annual. (UK ISSN 0073-3059) **1040**, 32
Hollow Spring Review of Poetry. (US ISSN 0147-2631) **2995**
Holly Letter see Holly Society Journal **2130**
Holly Society Journal. (US ISSN 0738-2421) **2130**
Holly Society of America. Proceedings see Holly Society Journal **2130**
Hollywood Acting Coaches and Teachers Directory. (US) **1751**, 1374, 3511, 4633
Hollywood Canada Magazine. (CN) **2177**
Hollywood Drama-Logue see Drama-Logue **3507**
†Hollywood Magazine. (US) **5205**
Hollywood Philatelist. (US) **3753**
Hollywood Reporter. (US ISSN 0018-3660) **3511**, 4633
Hollywood Reporter Studio Blu-Book Directory. (US ISSN 0278-419X) **3511**, 1374
Hollywood Studio Magazine see Hollywood Then & Now **3511**
Hollywood Stuntmen's Hall of Fame News. (US) **3511**
Hollywood Then & Now. (US) **3511**
Holm Conference on Electrical Contacts (Proceedings) see Electrical Contacts: I E E E Holm Conference on Electrical Contacts (Proceedings) **1887**
Holmes Group Forum. (US) **1728**, 1751
Holocaust and Genocide Studies. (US ISSN 8756-6583) **2367**
Holocaust Studies Annual. (US ISSN 0738-0739) **2367**, 2005, 3943
▼The Holocene. (UK) **274**
Hologram. (CN) **3105**
†Hologramm. (GW) **5205**
Holography Directory see Museum of Holography. Directory & Buyers' Guide **3855**
Holos Practice Report. (US) **3105**, 4023
Holstebro Museum. Aarsskrift. (DK ISSN 0107-6752) **2367**
Holstein Friesian Journal. (UK ISSN 0954-6219) **217**
Holstein Journal. (CN ISSN 0710-1309) **200**
Holstein Latinoamericano see Lechero Latinoamericano **5226**
Holstein News see Ohio News **202**
Holstein World. (US ISSN 0199-4239) **200**
Holsteiner Pferd see Pferde **4536**
Holston Pastfinder. (US ISSN 0887-3135) **2155**, 2314
Holt Advisory. (US ISSN 1047-9791) **669**
Holt Happenings. (US) **2155**
Holy Cross. Newsletter. (US ISSN 0018-3725) **4240**
Holy Land. (IS) **4265**, 2429, 4218, 4223
Holy Land Postal History. (IS ISSN 0333-6875) **3753**, 1352
Holy Places of Palestine. (IS) **4181**, 2429, 4771

Holz Aktuell. (GW ISSN 0724-6471) **2101**
Holz als Roh- und Werkstoff. (GW ISSN 0018-3768) **639**
Holz im Handwerk. (AU ISSN 0018-3776) **2559**
Holz-Kunststoff. (GW ISSN 0933-4580) **639**
Holz-Kunststoff-Moebelfertigung see Holz-Kunststoff **639**
Holz - Kurier. (AU ISSN 0018-3784) **2115**, 2101, 3018
Holz Praxis. (GW) **639**
Holz und Elfenbein see Drechseln **355**
Holz- und Kunststoffverarbeitung see Holz- und Moebelindustrie **2559**
Holz- und Moebelindustrie. (GW) **2559**
Holz-Zentralblatt. (GW ISSN 0018-3792) **2115**
Holzarbeiter-Zeitung. (GW ISSN 0018-3806) **2584**, 639
Holzauge. (GW) **2868**, 1314
Holzbau - Report. (GW ISSN 0723-4856) **639**, 669, 2633
Holzforschung. (GW ISSN 0018-3830) **2115**, 2101
Holzforschung und Holzverwertung. (AU ISSN 0018-3849) **2115**
Holzpreisstatistik/Statistique des Prix des Bois. (SZ) **2112**
Die Holzschwelle. (GW ISSN 0018-3865) **2115**
Holztechnologie. (GW ISSN 0018-3881) **2115**
Die Holzzucht. (GW ISSN 0437-7168) **2101**
Hombre de Mundo. (US) **3398**, 2210
Hombre y Ambiente. (EC) **4437**
Hombre y Trabajo. (CU) **981**
Hombre y Trabajo. (MX) **4104**, 981, 3105
Home. (US ISSN 0278-2839) **300**, 619, 2551
Home. (IT) **2551**
Home Altar. (US) **4181**
Home & Away. (US ISSN 8750-5649) **4771**, 4692
Home & Away Minnesota. (US) **4771**
Home & Away Ohio. (US) **4771**
Home & Condo. (US) **4149**, 2488
Home and Country. (UK) **4844**, 2447
Home & Decor. (SI) **2559**
Home and Family. see Hus & Hibyli **2552**
Home and Family. (UK ISSN 0018-3946) **4181**
Home and Freezer Digest. (UK ISSN 0305-8751) **2447**
Home and Garden Supply Merchandiser Green Book see Garden Supply Retailer Green Book **2127**
Home & Holiday International. (US) **2552**
Home and School. (UK ISSN 0305-1536) **1637**
Home & Studio Recording. (UK) **4460**
Home & Studio Recording. (US ISSN 0896-7172) **4461**
Home Builder Magazine. (CN ISSN 0840-4348) **619**
Home Builder Network. (US) **619**
†Home Builders Journal. (TZ ISSN 0856-0366) **5205**
†Home Business Advisor. (US ISSN 0893-7621) **5205**
†Home Business Monthly. (US) **5205**
†Home Business News. (US) **5205**
Home Care Services, Day Care Establishments, Day Services - Scotland. (UK ISSN 0260-5295) **4407**
†Home Care Services in New York State. (US) **5205**
Home Center Magazine see Home Improvement Center **619**
†Home Center Products Report. (US) **5205**
Home Computer Compendium see Micropendium **1471**
Home Computer Magazine. (US ISSN 0747-055X) **1460**
Home Computer Review. (US) **1469**, 1460
Home Computers - Software. (UK) **1469**, 1477
†Home Computing Weekly. (UK) **5205**
Home Cooking. (US) **4844**, 2447
Home Decor. (UK) **3653**, 2447

HOME MINIATURIST 6253

Home Decorating Ideas see Woman's Day Home Decorating Ideas **2556**
Home Economics. see Economie Familiale **2446**
Home Economics see New Home Economics **2448**
Home Economics Association of Australia. Journal. (AT ISSN 0158-6912) **2447**
Home Economics Association of Victoria. Newsletter. (AT) **2447**, 3606, 4619
Home Economics Education Association. Newsletter see Home Economics Educator **1637**
Home Economics Educator. (US) **1637**, 2447
Home Economics, Housing and Nutrition. Bulletins. (US) **2447**, 2488, 3606
Home Economics, Housing and Nutrition. Report Series. (US) **2447**, 2488, 3606
Home Economics, Housing and Nutrition. Special Reports. (US) **2447**, 2488, 3606
†Home Economics in Institutions Granting Bachelors or Higher Degrees. (US ISSN 0073-3105) **5205**
Home Economics Research Journal. (US ISSN 0046-7774) **2447**
Home Economics Yearbook see Homec - Home Economics Yearbook **2447**
Home Education Magazine. (US ISSN 0888-4633) **1751**
Home Energy. (US ISSN 0896-9442) **1790**
Home Entertainment see Television: the New Era **5288**
†Home Equity Lending Service. (US) **5205**
Home Equity Lines of Credit Report. (US ISSN 1051-4902) **783**
Home Farm. (UK ISSN 0264-8873) **96**, 2130, 2447
Home Fashion Textiles see Home Fashions Magazine **2559**
Home Fashions Magazine. (US ISSN 0896-7962) **2559**, 4619
Home Finders Guidebook. (US) **4149**, 2488
Home Front. (SA) **3459**
Home Furnishings see Home Furnishings Review **2559**
Home Furnishings Review. (US) **2559**, 2552
†Home Furnishings Survey. (UK) **5205**
†Home Goods Retailing. (CN ISSN 0018-4055) **5205**
Home Graphic/Katei-Gaho. (JA) **2447**
Home Health Care. (CN) **3105**
Home Health Care Dealer. (US) **2463**
Home Health Care Merchandising. (CN) **3728**
Home Health Care Services Quarterly. (US ISSN 0162-1424) **2463**
Home Health Line. (US) **3804**
†Home Health Management Advisor. (US) **5205**
Home Healthcare Business see Home Healthcare Nurse **3105**
Home Healthcare Nurse. (US ISSN 0884-741X) **3105**, 3804
Home Help. (UK) **2293**
Home Hygiene Report see Household Cleaning: UK & European Trends and Forcasts to 1995 **1040**
Home Improvement Center. (US ISSN 1045-9367) **619**
Home Improvement Guides. (UK) **619**
Home Journal. (HK) **2552**
Home Keyboard Review. (UK) **3554**
Home Leaguer see Sally Ann **4852**
Home Life. (US ISSN 0018-4071) **4240**, 1238
Home Lighting & Accessories. (US ISSN 0162-9077) **2559**
Home Loan Affordability in Australia. (AT ISSN 0816-6153) **4160**, 2500
Home Magazine's Best Kitchen & Bath. (US) **619**
Home Mechanix. (US ISSN 8755-0423) **2501**
†Home Microwave. (US) **5205**
Home Miniaturist. (UK ISSN 0143-554X) **2437**

HOME MISSIONS

Home Missions see Missions U S A 4244
Home-Mixer see Feeds and Feeding 206
Home Office Computing. (US ISSN 0899-7373) 1469, 1460
Home Office List of Publications. (UK ISSN 0143-3237) 4129, 4062
▼Home Office Opportunities. (US) 1115
Home Organist & Keyboard Update. (UK) 3554
Home Planet News. (US) 2995
Home Planner. (US) 619
Home Plans. (US) 2552
Home Plans to Build. (US ISSN 0899-4366) 300
Home Power. (US ISSN 1050-2416) 1790
Home Quarterly. (UK) 2447
Home Renovator. (CN) 619
Home-Run Business Newsletter. (US) 1115
Home Satellite TV see Camcorder Report 1384
Home School Gazette. (US) 2570, 1637, 4181
Home School Researcher. (US ISSN 1054-8033) 1637, 1751
†Home Schooler's Weekly. (US) 5205
Home Shop Machinist. (US ISSN 0744-6640) 3018
Home Shopping Investor. (US ISSN 0890-1155) 948, 1374
Home Studio Recording see Home & Studio Recording 4460
†Home Study. (UK ISSN 0441-7445) 5205
†Home Sweet Home. (US) 5205
Home Textiles International. (US) 4619
Home Textiles Today. (US ISSN 0195-3184) 4619
Home Video Publisher see Video Marketing News 1056
Home Viewer Magazine. (US) 1374
Home Workplace. (CN) 669
Homebuilder. (US) 619
Homebuilt Aircraft see Plane and Pilot 60
Homebuyer's Guide - Dallas - Fort Worth. (US) 4149
HomeBuyer's Guide - Florida Gulf Coast.(US) 4149
Homebuyers Guide Magazine. (US) 4150
Homec - Home Economics Yearbook. (UK) 2447
Homecare. (US) 3279, 1040
Homecare News. (US) 3279
Homecare Rental-Sales see Homecare 3279
Homefinders Guide. (US) 4150
Homelife. (PH ISSN 0115-2971) 2213, 4265
Homelife. (UK) 2274
Homemakers Network Newsletter. (US) 4844, 2447
Homemakers's Magazine/Madame au Foyer. (CN ISSN 0018-4209) 2447
Homemarket Trends. (US) 2559
Homen see Playboy 3399
†Homeopathic Digest. (US) 5205
Homeopathic Herald. (II ISSN 0377-4902) 3214
Homeopathie Francaise. (FR ISSN 0018-4225) 3214
Homeostasis in Health & Disease. (US ISSN 0960-7560) 3338
Homeostasis Quarterly. (US) 3253
†HomeOwner. (US ISSN 0195-2196) 5206
Homeowners' Guide. (CN) 4150
†Homeowner's Guide to Glass. (US) 5206
Homeowners How-To Magazine see HomeOwner 5206
Homes Abroad. (UK ISSN 0956-3091) 4150, 4771
Homes and Cottages. (CN) 2552
Homes and Gardens. (UK ISSN 0018-4233) 2552, 2130
Homes and Ideas Magazine. (CN) 2552
Homes & Real Estate Magazine - Billings, Montana. (US ISSN 1052-4703) 4150

Homes & Real Estate Magazine - Great Falls, Montana. (US ISSN 1052-4711) 4150
Homes and Travel Abroad see Homes Abroad 4150
Homes for the Aged. see Netherlands. Centraal Bureau voor de Statistiek. Statistiek van de Bejaardenoorden 4426
Homes Magazine. (CN) 4150
Homes Overseas. (UK ISSN 0018-4241) 4150
Homeschoolers' Support Association Happenings see H S A Happenings 1636
Homeschoolers' Voice see H S A Happenings 1636
Homeservice Stations Outside the Tropical Bands. (DK ISSN 0109-9140) 1356
Homestake Mining. Update. (US) 3484, 981
Homestay Australia see Homestay Eastern Australia 4771
Homestay Eastern Australia. (AT) 4771
Homestead Hotline. (US) 4845
Homesteader. (US) 2155
Homestyle Affairs. (US) 3398
Homestyles Home Plans. (US ISSN 0897-621X) 619
Hometown - Overseas Chinese. see Fujian Qiao Bao 2002
HomeWork. (US) 1115
HomeWorld Business. (US) 2560
Homicide in California. (US ISSN 0098-8537) 1515, 1525
Homiletic and Pastoral Review. (US ISSN 0018-4268) 4265
Homiletic Service see Celebrate 4260
Homiletica. (SP ISSN 0439-4208) 4181
Homiletische Monatshefte. (GW ISSN 0018-4276) 4181
Homily Helps. (US) 4181
Homily Service. (US ISSN 0732-1872) 4181
Homin Ukrainy/Ukrainian Echo. (CN ISSN 0018-4284) 2005
Homines. (PR) 4374
Homing World Stud Book. (UK ISSN 0073-3164) 4474
Hominids, Oh! (CN) 2923
Homme. (FR ISSN 0439-4216) 240
Homme et l'Architecture. (FR ISSN 1147-7105) 301
Homme et la Nature. see Man and Nature 2317
Homme Libre. (FR ISSN 0018-4314) 4023, 3897
Homme Nouveau. (FR ISSN 0018-4322) 4181
Hommes et Commerce. (FR ISSN 0223-5846) 1077
Hommes et Commerce - Horizons et Conjoncture see Hommes et Commerce 1077
Hommes et Fonderie. (FR ISSN 0018-4357) 3408
Hommes et la Terre. (FR ISSN 0073-3202) 2314
Hommes et les Lettres. (FR) 2923
Hommes et Migrations. (FR ISSN 0223-3290) 4437, 3982
Hommes et Terres du Nord. (FR ISSN 0018-439X) 2252
Hommes Volants. (FR ISSN 0018-4411) 54
Homo. (GW ISSN 0018-442X) 240
Homo. (FR ISSN 0563-9743) 4437
Homo- en Lesbiennekrant. (BE) 2454
Homo Faber. (IT ISSN 0439-4291) 981
Homo Sociologicus. (SP) 4437
Homobevrijding. (NE) 3943
Homoeopathic Heritage. (II ISSN 0970-6038) 3214
Homoeopathic World. (II ISSN 0046-7812) 3214
†Homoeopathie Caracteristique. (BE) 5206
Homoeopathisch Tijdschrift. (NE) 3215
Homoeopathy. (II ISSN 0046-7820) 3215
Homoeopathy. (UK) 3215
Homoeopathy Today see Health and Homoeopathy 3214

Homogeneous Catalysis in Organic and Inorganic Chemistry see Catalysis by Metal Complexes 1217
Homokrant see Homo- en Lesbiennekrant 2454
Homophile Association of London Ontario Newsletter see H A L O Newsletter 2453
Homosexual Information Center. Newsletter. (US) 2454, 3943
Hon. (JA) 2923
Hon Viet Magazine. (US) 2005
Honcho. (US) 3398, 2454
Honcho Overload. (US) 3398, 2454
Hondenwereld. (NE ISSN 0018-4527) 3711
Honduras. Congreso Nacional. Boletin. (HO) 4062
Honduras. Consejo Superior de Planificacion Economica. Plan Operativo Anual. Sector Industrial. (HO) 669
Honduras. Consejo Superior de Planificacion Economica. Plan Operativo Anual. Sector Turismo. (HO) 4771, 669
Honduras. Corte Suprema de Justicia. Gaceta Judicial. (HO ISSN 0016-3791) 2633
Honduras. Secretaria de Trabajo y Prevision Social. Boletin de Estadisticas Laborales. (HO) 4407
Honduras. Universidad Nacional Autonoma. Revista de la Universidad.(HO) 1637
Honduras (Year). (HO) 2180
Honduras al Dia. (HO) 2180
Honduras en Cifras. (HO) 4573
Honduras Pediatricia. (HO ISSN 0018-4535) 3321
Honduras Rotaria. (HO) 1298
Hone Report. (US) 948
Honest Ulsterman. (UK ISSN 0018-4543) 2923, 2868, 2995
Honey. (UK ISSN 0018-4551) 2194
Honey. (CE) 2447
Honey Market News. (US) 152, 96
Honeyguide. (RH ISSN 0018-456X) 564
†Honeywell Bull Source Magazine. (US) 5206
Honeywell Instrumentatie Nieuws. (NE ISSN 0020-4358) 2522
Honeywell Monthly see The Bulletin (Austin) 1458
Honeywell Source Magazine see Honeywell Bull Source Magazine 5206
Hong Dou. (CC) 2923
Hong Kong. Annual Digest of Statistics. (HK) 4573
Hong Kong. Building Development Department. Building Statistics. (HK) 4062, 619
Hong Kong. Census and Statistics Department. Consumer Price Index. Annual Report. (HK) 4573, 719
Hong Kong. Census and Statistics Department. Consumer Price Index. Report. (HK) 4573, 719
Hong Kong. Census and Statistics Department. Director of Audits. Report. (HK) 4573, 751
Hong Kong. Census and Statistics Department. Energy Statistics (Ten Year Span). (HK) 1799
Hong Kong. Census and Statistics Department. General Household Survey Labour Force Characteristics. (HK) 719, 4573
Hong Kong. Census and Statistics Department. Labour Force Survey Report see Hong Kong. Census and Statistics Department. General Household Survey Labour Force Characteristics 719
Hong Kong. Census and Statistics Department. Monthly Survey of Retail Sales. Report. (HK) 4573, 719
Hong Kong. Census and Statistics Department. Quarterly Business Survey Report see Hong Kong. Census and Statistics Department. Report on Quarterly Business Survey 720

Hong Kong. Census and Statistics Department. Quarterly Report of Wages, Salaries and Employee Benefits Statistics. Volume 1 see Hong Kong. Census and Statistics Department. Report on Half-Yearly Survey of Wages, Salaries and Employee Benefits. Volume 1 719
Hong Kong. Census and Statistics Department. Report on Half-Yearly Survey of Wages, Salaries and Employee Benefits. Volume 1. (HK) 719, 4573
Hong Kong. Census and Statistics Department. Report on Quarterly Business Survey. (HK) 720
Hong Kong. Census and Statistics Department. Salaries and Employee Statistics. Report. Managerial and Professional Employees (Excluding Top Management). (HK) 720, 4573
Hong Kong. Census and Statistics Department. Shipping Statistics. (HK) 4664, 4573, 4728
Hong Kong. Census and Statistics Department. Trade Index Numbers. (HK) 720, 911
Hong Kong. Census and Statistics Department. Wholesale, Retail and Import - Export Trades, Restaurants and Hotels. Survey. (HK) 720, 2482
Hong Kong. Census and Statistics Department. Yearbook (Year). (HK) 720
Hong Kong. Civil Aviation Department. Director's Annual Report. (HK) 4674
Hong Kong. Commissioner of Banking. Annual Report. (HK) 720, 783
Hong Kong. Estimates of Gross Domestic Product. (HK) 720, 4573
Hong Kong. Government Publication Centre. Economic Background. (HK) 999
Hong Kong. Government Publication Centre. Economic Prospects. (HK) 999
Hong Kong. Government Publication Centre. Economic Report. (HK) 999
Hong Kong. Government Publication Centre. Inquiry Reports. (HK) 4062
Hong Kong. Law Reform Commission. Report. (HK) 2731, 4062
Hong Kong. Legislative Council. Finance Committee. Report. (HK) 4063
Hong Kong. Legislative Council. Proceedings. (HK) 4063
Hong Kong. Legislative Council. Public Works Sub-Committee. Report. (HK) 4063
Hong Kong. Public Service Commission. Chairman's Report. (HK) 4063
Hong Kong. Royal Observatory. Climatological Note see Hong Kong. Royal Observatory. Technical Note 3436
Hong Kong. Royal Observatory. Daily Weather Chart. (HK) 3436
Hong Kong. Royal Observatory. Historical Publications. (HK) 3436
Hong Kong. Royal Observatory. Meteorological Results - Part III. (HK) 3436
Hong Kong. Royal Observatory. Monthly Weather Summary. (HK) 3436
Hong Kong. Royal Observatory. Occasional Paper. (HK) 3436
Hong Kong. Royal Observatory. Rainfall Chart. (HK) 3436
Hong Kong. Royal Observatory. Technical Memoirs. (HK) 3436
Hong Kong. Royal Observatory. Technical Note. (HK) 3436
Hong Kong. Royal Observatory. Technical Notes (Local). (HK) 3436
Hong Kong. Standing Commission on Civil Service Salaries and Conditions of Service. Civil Service Pay. (HK) 4063
Hong Kong. Television Advisory Board. Annual Report. (HK) 4063, 1374
Hong Kong. Urban Council. Proceedings. (HK) 4063
Hong Kong: A Review of (Year). (HK) 2338
Hong Kong Airline Timetable. (HK) 4674

Hong Kong and Guangzhou Visitor see Hong Kong Visitor 4771
Hong Kong Annual Report. (HK) 868
Hong Kong Apparel. (HK) 1285, 1291
Hong Kong Architects & Designers Catalogue. (HK) 301, 619
Hong Kong Bargain Guide to Factory Outlets see Hong Kong Directory to 10,000 Exporters & Importers 1040
Hong Kong Builder Directory. (HK) 619
Hong Kong Business. (HK) 669
Hong Kong Business Today see Hong Kong Business 669
†Hong Kong Cable. (US) 5206
Hong Kong Catholic Church Directory/Hsiang-Kang T'ien Chu Chiao Shou Ts'e. (HK ISSN 0073-3210) 4265
Hong Kong Computer Expo (Year) see Computer Expo (Year): Exhibition Guide 3391
Hong Kong Countdown: Perspectives on Change. (HK ISSN 0257-3636) 3959, 911
Hong Kong Customs. see Xianggang Fengqing 4456
Hong Kong Directory to 10,000 Exporters & Importers. (US) 1040
Hong Kong Economic Papers. (HK ISSN 0018-4578) 669
Hong Kong Economic Trends. (HK) 720, 868, 4573
Hong Kong Economic Yearbook. (HK) 669
Hong Kong Electronics. (HK) 2215
Hong Kong Engineer. (HK) 1823
Hong Kong Enterprise. (HK ISSN 0018-4586) 1285, 642, 2281
Hong Kong Export Credit Insurance Corporation. Annual Report. (HK) 783
Hong Kong External Trade. (HK) 720, 911
Hong Kong for the Business Visitor. (HK) 4771, 669
Hong Kong Futures Exchange Ltd. Newsletter see H K F E Newsletter 5202
▼Hong Kong Garments and Accessories. (HK) 4619
Hong Kong General Chamber of Commerce. Annual Report. (HK) 817
Hong Kong General Chamber of Commerce Bulletin. (HK) 817
Hong Kong Gifts & Premiums. (HK) 2281
Hong Kong Government Gazette. (HK) 4063
Hong Kong Guide - Streets and Places. (HK) 4771
Hong Kong Household. (HK) 642, 2281
▼Hong Kong I.T. Focus. (HK) 1423
Hong Kong in Figures. (HK) 4573
Hong Kong Industrialist. (HK) 836
Hong Kong Interbank Directory. (HK) 783
▼Hong Kong International Book Fair (Year): Fair Catalogue. (HK) 4129
Hong Kong Jewellery and Watches see Hong Kong Jewellery Bi-Annual 2564
Hong Kong Jewellery and Watches see Hong Kong Watches & Clocks 2564
Hong Kong Jewellery Annual see Hong Kong Jewellery Bi-Annual 2564
Hong Kong Jewellery Bi-Annual. (HK) 2564
Hong Kong Jewellery Magazine. (HK) 2564
Hong Kong Law Journal. (HK ISSN 0378-0600) 2633
Hong Kong Library Association. Journal.(HK ISSN 0073-3237) 2760
Hong Kong Manager. (HK ISSN 0018-4594) 1012
Hong Kong Manufacturers and Exporters Register. (HK ISSN 0073-3245) 1138
Hong Kong Medical Association. Journal. (HK ISSN 1010-8424) 3105
Hong Kong Monthly Digest of Statistics.(HK ISSN 0300-418X) 4573

Hong Kong Narcotics Report. (HK) 1536
Hong Kong Nursing Journal/Hsiang Kang Hu Li Tsa Chih. (HK ISSN 0073-3253) 3279
Hong Kong Overall Merchandise Trade. (HK) 817
†Hong Kong Port Services Index (Year). (HK) 5206
Hong Kong Productivity Council and Centre Annual Report see Hong Kong Productivity Council Annual Report 1077
Hong Kong Productivity Council Annual Report. (HK) 1077
Hong Kong Productivity Council Electronics Bulletin see H K P C Electronics Bulletin 1771
Hong Kong Productivity News. (HK) 1077
Hong Kong Progress. (HK) 817
Hong Kong Psychological Society. Bulletin. (HK ISSN 0379-4490) 4023
Hong Kong Revenue Legislation. (AT) 2633, 911
Hong Kong Review of Overseas Trade. (HK) 911
Hong Kong Social and Economic Trends. (HK) 868, 4437
Hong Kong Streets and Places see Hong Kong Guide - Streets and Places 4771
Hong Kong Tatler. (HK) 2197
Hong Kong Toys. (HK) 2281
Hong Kong Trade Statistics. (HK) 720, 911
Hong Kong Trade Statistics. Summary see Hong Kong External Trade 720
Hong Kong Trader. (HK) 836
Hong Kong Travel Bulletin. (HK ISSN 0018-4616) 4771
Hong Kong Visitor. (HK) 4771, 2197, 2252
Hong Kong Watches & Clocks. (HK) 2564
Hong Qi - Red Flag see Qiu Shi 4383
Hong Yan. (CC) 2923
Honger en Dorst see Emmaus 4434
†HongKongiana. (HK ISSN 0379-5853) 5206
Hongloumeng Xuekan/Studies on a Dream of Red Mansions. (CC) 2923
"Hongloumeng" Yanjiu. (CC ISSN 1001-277X) 2923
Hongwai Yanjiu/Infrared Research. (CC) 3852
Hongwai yu Haomibo Xuebao/Journal of Infrared and Millimetre Wave. (CC) 3853
Honi Soit. (AT) 1314
Honismeret. (HU ISSN 0324-7627) 2367
Honismereti Hirado see Honismeret 2367
Honneur et Fidelite. (CM ISSN 0046-7855) 3459
Honolulu. (US ISSN 0441-2044) 2226
Honolulu Employee Journal. (US) 4088, 981
Honourable Artillery Company Journal. (UK ISSN 0046-7863) 3459
Honourable Company of Master Mariners. Journal. (UK ISSN 0018-4675) 4728
Honpo Kogyo no Susei/Mining Yearbook of Japan. (JA) 3484
Hontanar. (AG ISSN 0073-327X) 402
Hoof Beats. (US ISSN 0018-4683) 4534
Hoof Print. (US) 4534
Hoofdlijnen. (NE ISSN 0018-4705) 3338, 3259
Hooflig/Headlight. (SA) 2584, 4710
Hoofstrikes Newsletter. (US) 231, 2995
Hoogovens Groep Bulletin. (NE) 1823, 3408
The Hoogsteder Mercury. (NE ISSN 0169-1198) 328
Hoogsteder-Naumann Mercury see The Hoogsteder Mercury 328
Hoogstratens Oudheidkundige Kring. Geschiedenis. (BE) 2367, 274
The Hook. (US ISSN 0736-9220) 3459
Hook, Line & Sinker. (US) 2042

Hooked on Crochet! (US ISSN 0893-1879) 3591, 355
Hooked on Fishing. (US) 4548
†Hooker's Icones Plantarium. (UK) 5206
Hooks and Lines. (US) 4548, 4845
†Hooks Family Chronicles. (US ISSN 0886-3601) 5206
Hoop - N B A Today. (National Basketball Association) (US ISSN 0749-5285) 4506
†Hoosharar. (US ISSN 0018-4721) 5206
Hoosharar - Mioutune. (US ISSN 0275-3065) 4407, 1637
Hoosier Banker. (US ISSN 0018-473X) 784
Hoosier Challenger. (US) 2923
Hoosier Farmer. (US ISSN 0018-4748) 96
Hoosier Genealogist. (US ISSN 0018-4756) 2155
Hoosier Independent. (US ISSN 0018-4764) 3688
Hoosier Journal of Ancestry. (US ISSN 0147-1228) 2155
Hoosier Legionnaire. (US ISSN 0018-4772) 3459, 1298
Hoosier Outdoors. (US ISSN 0018-4780) 4548
Hoosier Purchasor. (US ISSN 0018-4799) 1040
Hoosier Schoolmaster. (US ISSN 0018-4810) 1637
Hooters. (US) 3398
▼Hoover's Handbook of World Business. (US ISSN 1055-7199) 1138
Hope. see Al-Manaal 1738
Hope. see Xiwang 4392
Hope Health Letter. (US ISSN 0891-3374) 3804, 3617, 4104
Hope News. (US) 4104
Hopeful Day. see Getroster Tag 4239
Hopfen - Rundschau. (GW ISSN 0018-4845) 179
Hopital a Paris. (FR ISSN 0018-4861) 2463
L'Hopital Belge/Belgisch Ziekenhuis. (BE) 2463
†Hopitaux Civils et Militaires. Gazette. (FR ISSN 0018-487X) 5206
Hopkins News-Letter. (US) 1314
Hopkins Quarterly. (CN ISSN 0094-9086) 2995
Hoppe-Seyler's Zeitschrift fuer Physiologische Chemie see Biological Chemistry Hoppe-Seyler 474
Hoppea. (GW ISSN 0340-4196) 505
Hoppenstedt Boersenfuehrer. (GW ISSN 0171-5658) 784
Hoppenstedt Charts. (GW) 784, 948
Hoppenstedt Kurstabellen - Kursanalysen. (GW ISSN 0174-1284) 948
Hoppenstedt-Monatskurstabellen see Hoppenstedt Kurstabellen - Kursanalysen 948
Hoppenstedt Stock Guide Germany. (GW ISSN 0933-3169) 948
Hoppenstedt Vademecum der Investmentfonds. (GW ISSN 0073-3342) 948
Hoppenstedt Versicherungs-Jahrbuch. (GW ISSN 0073-3350) 2533
†Hopper. (NE) 5206
Hoppo Kagaku Chosa Hokoku/Human Culture and Environmental Studies in Northern Hokkaido. (JA) 1957
Hoppo Sangyo Eisei/Journal of Northern Occupational Health. (JA ISSN 0911-3363) 3617
Hopscotch. (US) 1256
Hor-Tasy. (US) 2923
Hor Yezh. (FR ISSN 0769-0088) 2868
Hora. (US ISSN 0741-9384) 1530
Hora de Poesia. (SP ISSN 0212-9442) 2995
Hora del Hombre. (PE) 2868
Horace M. Albright Conservation Lectureship. (US ISSN 0073-3369) 1489, 2101
Horeca see Missets Horeca 2478
Horeca News (Brussels, 1971). (BE) 2072, 2475
HoReCo. (SP) 2475
Die Horen. (GW ISSN 0018-4942) 2923

HORMONES 6255

Horesca - Informations. (LU) 2475
Horim Ve Yeladim. (IS) 1238
Horison. (IO) 2923
Horison see International Horisont 983
Horisont. (FI ISSN 0439-5530) 2923, 1298, 4633
Horizon. (SA) 2216
†Horizon. (IE) 5206
Horizon. Bulletin Bibliographique O R S T O M Oceanographie Hydrobiologie. (FR ISSN 1142-2505) 1551, 402, 1605
Horizon. Bulletin Bibliographique O R S T O M Sante. (FR ISSN 0998-478X) 3614, 402
Horizon. Bulletin Bibliographique O R S T O M Science de la Terre. (FR ISSN 0998-4771) 1551, 402, 1568
Horizon. Bulletin Bibliographique O R S T O M Sciences du Monde Vegetal et Animal. (FR ISSN 1142-2521) 138, 402
Horizon. Bulletin Bibliographique O R S T O M Sciences Economiques et Sociales. (FR ISSN 1142-2513) 720, 402
Horizon. Bulletin Bibliographique O R S T O M Sciences et Techniques Fondamentales Sciences de l'Ingenieur. (FR ISSN 1142-253X) 1844, 402
Horizon (Montreal). (CN) 1314
Horizon (Neptune). (US) 2274, 4240
Horizon (Salt Lake City). (US) 1314
Horizon (Tuscaloosa). (US ISSN 0018-4977) 2868, 328
Horizon (Vancouver). (CN ISSN 0315-8527) 1751
Horizon Air Magazine. (US ISSN 1050-2440) 4802
Horizon Armenian Weekly. (CN) 2005
Horizon International. (UG) 868
Horizon Jeunesse see Getting There 1255
Horizons see Grumman Horizons 53
Horizons. (FR) 96
Horizons. see Afaq 1733
Horizons. (IS ISSN 0334-3774) 2252
Horizons. (UK ISSN 0959-1362) 3321
Horizons (Columbus). (US) 4063
Horizons (Elmwood Park). (US) 355
Horizons (Montreal). (CN ISSN 0704-2965) 2177
Horizons (Torrance). (US) 54
Horizons (Villanova). (US ISSN 0360-9669) 4265
Horizons Beyond. (US) 2923
Horizons in Biblical Theology. (US ISSN 0195-9085) 4181
Horizons Interculturels see Intercultural Horizons 2508
Horizons Unlimited. (PH ISSN 0018-5019) 1637
Horizons Unlimited. (US) 4240
Horizons West. (US) 2923
Horizont. (HU ISSN 0139-1380) 1298, 2760, 3524, 4633
Horizont. (CS) 2868
†Horizont (Berlin). (GW ISSN 0046-791X) 5206
Horizont (Cologne). (GW ISSN 0724-0279) 3959
Horizont (Muenchen). (GW) 2239
Horizonte. (PO) 3804, 4474
Horizonte Empresarial. (SP ISSN 0212-0607) 868
Horizontes. (PR ISSN 0018-5027) 2507
Horizontes (Paterson). (US) 2923, 3792
Horizontes (San Francisco). (US) 2005
Hori onti. (AA) 4313, 1256
Ho. no. and Metabolic Research. (GW ISSN 0018-5043) 3254
Hormone Research. (SZ ISSN 0301-0163) 3254
Hormones and Behavior. (US ISSN 0018-506X) 3254
Hormones in Cancer-Related Biology - Non-Steroid Hormones see I C R D B Cancergram: Hormones in Cancer-Related Biology - Non-Steroid Hormones 5208

HORMONES

Hormones in Cancer-Related Biology - Steroid Hormones see I C R D B Cancergram: Hormones in Cancer-Related Biology - Steroid Hormones **5208**
Hormoon see Organorama **5253**
Horn & Whistle. (US) **2409**
Horn Book Magazine. (US ISSN 0018-5078) **4129**, 1238
Horn Call. (US ISSN 0046-7928) **3554**
Horn Call Annual. (US) **3555**
Horn of Africa. (US ISSN 0161-4703) **2252**
Horn Speaker. (US ISSN 0898-6959) **257**, 1356, 4461
Horna Nitra. (CS) **2367**
Hornbill. (II ISSN 0441-2370) **440**
Hornero. (AG ISSN 0073-3407) **564**
Hornet. (US ISSN 0018-5086) **1314**
Horns of Plenty. (US ISSN 0896-9965) **2868**, 2995
Hornsey Historical Society. Bulletin. (UK ISSN 0955-8071) **2367**
Hornsey Historical Society. Occasional Papers. (UK) **2367**
Hornsmatch. (US) **217**
Horological Institute of Japan. Journal. see Nihon Tokei Gakkaishi **2565**
Horological Review see Retail Jeweller **2565**
Horological Times. (US ISSN 0145-9546) **2564**
Horoscope. (FR) **358**
Horoscope. (UK) **358**
Horoscope Guide. (US ISSN 8750-3042) **358**
Horoscope Quotidien Eclair. (CN ISSN 0018-5124) **358**
Horoscopo Capricho. (BL) **358**
▼Horreyati/My Liberty. (UA) **2185**
Horror Fiction Newsletter. (US ISSN 1049-0310) **3012**, 2923
Horror Show. (US ISSN 0748-2914) **3012**
Horror: The Illustrated Book of Fears. (US) **3012**
Horse. see Haesten **4534**
†Horse Action. (US) **5206**
Horse and Horseman. (US ISSN 0094-3355) **4534**
Horse and Hound. (UK ISSN 0018-5140) **4534**
Horse and Pony (Peterborough). (UK) **4534**
Horse & Rider. (UK) **4535**
Horse & Rider. (US ISSN 0018-5159) **4535**
Horse and Rider All-Western Yearbook see Horse & Rider's Rodeo Action **5206**
†Horse & Rider's Rodeo Action. (US) **5206**
Horse Brass. (UK) **2437**, 4710
†Horse Care. (US ISSN 0162-8127) **5206**
Horse Chronicle. (CN ISSN 0847-9984) **4535**
Horse Digest see International Saddlery and Apparel Journal **4535**
Horse Illustrated. (US ISSN 0145-9791) **4535**
Horse Industry Directory. (US ISSN 0890-233X) **4535**
Horse Industry Directory of Canada. (CN ISSN 0828-4679) **1138**, 4535
Horse Lover's. (US) **4535**
Horse Owners and Breeders Tax Manual. (US) **4535**, 751, 948, 1097
Horse Racing Quiz Book. (UK) **4535**
Horse Sense see Canadian Horseman **4533**
Horse Sheets. (US) **4535**
Horse Show. (US) **4535**
†Horse Woman. (US) **5206**
Horse Women see Horse Woman **5206**
Horse World. (US ISSN 0018-5191) **4535**
Horsefeathers see Directions for Utah Libraries **2754**
Horseless Carriage Gazette. (US ISSN 0018-5213) **257**, 4518, 4692
†Horseman. (US ISSN 0018-5221) **5206**
Horseman and Fair World. (US ISSN 0018-523X) **4535**
†Horseman's Service Directory and Desk Reference. (US) **5206**
Horsemen's Journal. (US ISSN 0018-5256) **4535**
HorsePlay. (US ISSN 0092-6353) **4535**
Horsepower. (CN ISSN 0840-6715) **4535**
Horses. (US ISSN 0046-7936) **4535**
Horses All. (CN ISSN 0225-4913) **4535**
Horses Magazine. (CN) **4535**
Horses to Follow. (UK) **4535**
Horseshoe. (UK) **4474**
Horsetrader. (US ISSN 0018-5264) **4535**
Hort West. (CN ISSN 0847-9763) **2130**
Horticulteur see Le Producteur Horticole **5262**
Horticulteurs et Maraichers Romands. (SZ) **2130**
Horticultura. (SP) **2130**
Horticultural Abstracts. (UK ISSN 0018-5280) **2141**, 13
Horticultural and Coffee Research Institute. Annual Report. Part 3. Rhodes Experimental Station see Zimbabwe. Coffee Research Institute. Annual Report. Part 2. Nyanga Experimental Station **197**
Horticultural and Viticultural Science. see Gradinarska i Lozarska Nauka **2128**
Horticultural Guide to Australian Plants.(AT) **2130**
Horticultural Handbooks. (US) **2130**
Horticultural Magazin Yugoslavie. see Hortikultura **2131**
Horticultural News. (US ISSN 0886-5779) **2130**
Horticultural Produce and Practice see AgLink Leaflets **68**
Horticultural Research see Crop Research **174**
Horticultural Research International. (UK ISSN 0963-3235) **179**, 2130
Horticultural Research International. (NE ISSN 0441-7461) **1138**, 2130
Horticultural Reviews. (US ISSN 0163-7851) **2130**
Horticultural Societies' Newsletter. (CN) **2130**
Horticultural Society of Ethiopia. Bulletin. (ET) **2130**
Horticultural Society of New York. Newsletter. (US) **2130**
Horticulture. see Gartenbau **2127**
Horticulture. (US ISSN 0018-5329) **2130**
Horticulture. see Kertgazdasag **2133**
Horticulture. see Zahradnictvi **2141**
Horticulture and Coffee Research Institute. Annual Report. Part 1. Horticultural Research Centre see Horticulture Research Institute. Annual Report. Part 1. Horticultural Research Centre **179**
Horticulture and Coffee Research Institute. Annual Report. Part 2. Coffee Research Station see Coffee Research Institute. Annual Report. Coffee Research Station **173**
Horticulture and Forestry. Bulletins. (US) **2130**, 2101
Horticulture and Forestry. Report Series.(US) **2130**, 2101
Horticulture and Forestry. Southern Cooperative Series Bulletins. (US) **2130**, 2101
Horticulture and Forestry. Special Reports. (US) **2130**, 2102
Horticulture Francaise. (FR ISSN 0395-8531) **2130**
Horticulture in N.Z. (Wellington) see Royal New Zealand Institute of Horticulture. Newsletter **2138**
Horticulture in New Zealand (Lincoln). (NZ ISSN 1170-1803) **2130**
Horticulture News. (NZ) **2130**
Horticulture Research Institute. Annual Report. Part 1. Horticultural Research Centre. (RH) **179**
Horticulture Week. (UK) **2130**
HortIdeas. (US ISSN 0742-8219) **2131**
Hortikultura/Horticultural Magazin Yugoslavie. (CI ISSN 0018-5337) **2131**
†Hortline. (US) **5206**
HortScience. (US ISSN 0018-5345) **2131**
▼HortTechnology. (US) **2131**
Hortus. (UK ISSN 0950-1657) **2131**
Horus. (GW) **2293**
Horyzonty Techniki. (PL ISSN 0137-8813) **4599**
Hoseasons Boating Holidays. (UK) **4525**, 4771
Hoseasons Holiday Boats and Bungalows Hire see Hoseasons Boating Holidays **4525**
Hoseasons Holiday-Homes in U.K. (UK) **4771**
Hoshasen Ikushujo Kenkyu Hokoku. see Acta Radiobotanica et Genetica **426**
Hoshi. (JA) **364**
Hoshi no Techo. (JA ISSN 0389-2131) **364**
Hoshi no Tomo/Friend of Stars. (JA ISSN 0389-0341) **365**
Hoshruba Da'ijist. (PK) **2923**
Hosiery and Textile Journal. (II ISSN 0018-5388) **1285**, 4619
Hosiery and Underwear. (US ISSN 0018-5396) **4619**
Hosiery News. (US ISSN 0742-8065) **1285**
Hosiery Newsletter see Hosiery News **1285**
Hosiery Report Weekly. (II) **4619**
Hosiery Statistics. (US) **1288**
Hosiery Trade Journal see Knitting International **4621**
▼Hospice. (US) **4407**, 2463
Hospice Care Newsletter see Hospice Today **4407**
Hospice Journal. (US ISSN 0742-969X) **2463**
Hospice Letter. (US ISSN 0913-6681) **2463**
Hospice Today. (US) **4407**, 3105
Hospimedica. (US ISSN 0898-7270) **2463**
Hospitaal Beampte. see Hospital Official **5206**
Hospitaalnuus. see Hospital News **2465**
Hospitais Civis de Lisboa. Boletim Clinico. (PO ISSN 0046-8037) **3105**, 2463
Hospital. see Byoin **2459**
El Hospital (Cincinnati). (US ISSN 0018-5485) **3105**, 2463
Hospital Administration. see Byoin Kanri **2459**
Hospital Administration. (II ISSN 0018-5531) **2463**
Hospital Administration see Hospital & Health Services Administration **2463**
Hospital Admitting Monthly. (US) **2463**
Hospital and Community Psychiatry. (US ISSN 0022-1597) **3338**, 2463
Hospital and Health Administration see Australian Hospital **2459**
†Hospital and Health Service Purchasing. (UK ISSN 0300-5461) **5206**
Hospital & Health Services Administration. (US ISSN 8750-3735) **2463**
†Hospital & Health Services News & Appointment Review. (UK) **5206**
Hospital and Health Services Review see Health Services Management **2462**
Hospital & Health Services Yearbook Australia. (AT) **2463**
Hospital and Healthcare Australia. (AT ISSN 0813-7471) **2464**
Hospital Association of New York State. News. (US ISSN 0018-5574) **2464**
Hospital Aviation see Journal of Air Medical Transport **4675**
Hospital Blue Book (Official National Edition). (US ISSN 1047-6903) **2464**
Hospital Blue Book (Official Southern Edition). (US ISSN 1047-6911) **2464**
Hospital Brief. (AT ISSN 0817-5675) **2464**
Hospital Building and Engineering see Hospital Development **2464**
Hospital Buildings Library Bulletin see Health Buildings Library Bulletin **2461**
Hospital Capital Formation and Reorganization Report see Hospital Capital Formation Management Letter **5206**
†Hospital Capital Formation Management Letter. (US) **5206**
†Hospital Care of Children and Youth. (US) **5206**
†Hospital Caterer. (UK) **5206**
Hospital Chronicle. (US) **2464**
Hospital Consultants and Specialists Association Year Book. (UK) **2464**
Hospital Contracts Manual. (US) **2464**
Hospital Cost Management and Accounting. (US) **2464**
Hospital de Ninos. Revista. (AG ISSN 0521-517X) **3321**, 2464
Hospital Development. (UK ISSN 0300-5720) **2464**
Hospital Doctor. (UK ISSN 0262-3145) **3105**, 2464
▼Hospital Editors' Idea Exchange. (US ISSN 1046-1647) **2464**, 2570
Hospital Employee Health. (US ISSN 0744-6470) **2464**, 981, 3617
Hospital Engineering Association of Japan. Journal/Byoin Setsubi. (JA) **2464**
Hospital Entrepreneur's Newsletter see Hospital Strategy Report **2465**
Hospital Equipment see Hospital Engineering Association of Japan. Journal **2464**
Hospital Equipment & Supplies. (UK ISSN 0018-5620) **2464**
Hospital Equipment and Supplies Directory (Year). (AT ISSN 0159-9100) **2464**
Hospital-Escola Sao Camilo e Sao Luis. Boletim. (BL) **2464**
Hospital Ethics. (US ISSN 8756-8519) **2464**, 3768
Hospital Ethics Committee Forum see H E C Forum **2461**
Hospital Food & Nutrition Focus. (US) **2464**, 2072
Hospital for Joint Diseases. Bulletin see Hospital for Joint Diseases Orthopaedic Institute. Bulletin **3308**
Hospital for Joint Diseases Orthopaedic Institute. Bulletin. (US ISSN 0018-5647) **3308**
Hospital for Sick Children, Toronto. Research Institute. Annual Report. (CN ISSN 0082-5034) **3105**, 2464, 3321
Hospital Formulary. (US ISSN 0098-6909) **3728**
Hospital Fund Raising Newsletter see Healthcare Fund Raising Newsletter **2463**
†Hospital Gift Shop Management. (US) **5206**
Hospital Guest Relations Report see Hospital Patient Relations Report **2465**
Hospital Hazardous Materials Management see Healthcare Hazardous Materials Management **2463**
Hospital Home Health. (US ISSN 0884-8521) **2464**
Hospital Infantil de Mexico. Boletin Medico. (MX ISSN 0539-6115) **2464**, 3321
Hospital Infection Control. (US ISSN 0098-180X) **2464**, 3105
Hospital Law see Journal of Health and Hospital Law **3115**
Hospital Law Manual. Administrators. (US) **2633**, 2464
Hospital Law Manual. Attorneys. (US) **2633**, 2464
Hospital Law Manual and Quarterly Service see Hospital Law Manual. Attorneys **2633**
Hospital Law Newsletter. (US) **2464**, 2633
Hospital Literature Index. (US ISSN 0018-5736) **2470**, 13
▼Hospital Litigation Reporter. (US ISSN 1048-5201) **2464**, 2633
Hospital Management. (IT) **2464**

Hospital Management International. (UK ISSN 0953-9743) **2464**, 1012
Hospital Management Review. (US ISSN 0737-903X) **2464**, 1012
Hospital Marketing and Public Relations. (US) **2464**, 32, 1040
Hospital Materials Management. (US ISSN 0888-3068) **2465**, 1012
Hospital Materiel Management Quarterly. (US ISSN 0192-2262) **2465**
Hospital Medical Practice. (UA ISSN 0046-8010) **3105**, 2465
Hospital Medicine. *see* Medecine Hospitaliere **2467**
Hospital Medicine. (US ISSN 0441-2745) **3105**, 2465
Hospital News/Hospitaalnuus. (SA) **2465**
Hospital News *see* Hospital News Delaware Valley **2465**
Hospital News Delaware Valley. (US) **2465**, 3279
Hospital News Downtown Toronto *see* Hospital News - Toronto and Region **2465**
Hospital News Greater Toronto *see* Hospital News - Toronto and Region **2465**
Hospital News of Minnesota. (US) **2465**
Hospital News - S W Ontario. (CN) **2465**
Hospital News - Toronto and Region. (CN) **2465**
†Hospital Official/Hospitaal Beampte. (SA) **5206**
Hospital Patient Relations Report. (US ISSN 0899-8957) **2465**
Hospital Peer Review. (US ISSN 0149-2632) **2465**
Hospital Personnel Administration *see* Human Resources Administrator **2466**
Hospital Pharmacist Report. (US) **3728**, 2465
Hospital Pharmacy. (US ISSN 0018-5787) **3728**, 2465
Hospital Pharmacy *see* White Sheet **3746**
Hospital Pharmacy Director's Monthly Management Series. (US ISSN 0739-957X) **3728**, 3279
Hospital Pharmacy in Ontario. (CN) **3728**, 2465
Hospital Pharmacy News. (US) **3728**
Hospital Pharmacy Service Instant Up-Date. (US ISSN 0739-9561) **3728**, 2465
Hospital Physician. (US ISSN 0018-5795) **3105**, 2465
Hospital Podiatrist. (US) **3379**, 2465
Hospital Practice. (US ISSN 8750-2836) **3106**, 2465
Hospital Practice (Edicion Espanola). (SP ISSN 0213-4845) **3106**, 2465
Hospital Product Comparison System. (US) **2465**
Hospital Product Line Report. (US) **2465**
†Hospital Products & Technology. (CN ISSN 0823-6798) **5206**
Hospital Psiquiatrico de la Habana. Revista. (CU ISSN 0138-7103) **3338**
Hospital Public Relations *see* Hospital Marketing and Public Relations **2464**
Hospital Purchasing - Hospitaalaankope *see* Hospital News **2465**
Hospital Purchasing Management *see* Hospital Materials Management **2465**
Hospital Purchasing News. (US ISSN 0279-4799) **2465**
Hospital R.S.A. (SA ISSN 0018-5833) **2465**
Hospital Revenue Report. (US ISSN 1052-8733) **1040**, 3804
Hospital Risk Control. (US) **2465**, 1012, 2633
Hospital Risk Management. (US ISSN 0199-6312) **2465**, 1012
Hospital Safety Information Service. (US ISSN 0276-2323) **2465**, 3617
Hospital Security and Safety Management. (US ISSN 0745-1148) **1526**, 2465

Hospital Statistics *see* A H A Hospital Statistics (Year) **2470**
Hospital Strategy Report. (US) **2465**
Hospital Supervisor's Bulletin. (US ISSN 0018-585X) **2465**
Hospital Technology Series. (US) **2465**, 4599
Hospital Therapy *see* P & T **3737**
Hospital Topics. (US ISSN 0018-5868) **2465**
Hospital Trustee *see* Leadership in Health Services **2467**
Hospital Update. (UK ISSN 0305-4136) **2465**, 3106
▼Hospital Update. (SA) **2465**, 3106
Hospital Vargas. Archivos. (VE ISSN 0018-5884) **3106**, 2465
Hospital Worker. (UK) **2465**, 2584
Hospitalia. (BE ISSN 0018-5914) **2465**
Hospitalier. (FR ISSN 0018-5922) **2465**
Hospitalis. (SZ ISSN 0018-5930) **2466**
Hospitalisation Nouvelle. (FR ISSN 0751-5766) **2466**
Hospitalisation Privee. (FR ISSN 0439-6162) **2466**
L'Hospitalite. (CN ISSN 0704-6359) **2475**
Hospitality. (HU) **2088**, 2475
Hospitality. (UK ISSN 0144-3704) **2475**
Hospitality and Convention News *see* Hospitality Foodservice **2475**
Hospitality & Tourism Educator. (US) **1684**, 2475, 4771
Hospitality Beverage. (AT) **381**
Hospitality Buyers Guide *see* Hospitality Industry Suppliers Index **2475**
Hospitality Education and Research Journal. (US ISSN 0741-5095) **2475**
Hospitality Foodservice. (AT) **2475**, 2072
Hospitality Index. (US) **2482**, 2085, 4799
Hospitality Industry Suppliers Index. (AT ISSN 0817-0398) **2475**
Hospitality Law. (US ISSN 0889-5414) **2475**, 2633
Hospitality Lodging *see* Lodging Hospitality **2477**
Hospitality Management. (US) **2475**
Hospitality Manager. (US) **1138**, 2475
Hospitality Scene *see* Hospitality Management **2475**
Hospitalized Veterans Writing Project, Inc. Action *see* H V W P in Action **2921**
Hospitals. (US ISSN 0018-5973) **2466**
Hospitals and Healthcare International *see* Hospimedica **2463**
Hospital's Medicare Policy & Payment Report. (US) **3106**
HospitAlta. (CN ISSN 0821-2015) **2466**
Hospiz-Kurier *see* V C H Kurier **2481**
Hospodar. (US ISSN 0018-599X) **2005**, 2226
Hospodarske Dejiny/Economic History. (CS ISSN 0231-7540) **2368**
Host Magazine. (AT) **2072**
Hostel Travel. (AT) **4771**
†Hosteling. (US) **5206**
†Hosteling Holidays. (US) **5206**
Hosteller. (AT ISSN 0157-3977) **4771**
Hostelling. (AT ISSN 0725-8968) **4771**
Hostelling News *see* Triangle **4794**
Hostelling North America. (US) **4771**
Hosteni/Aiguillon. (AA) **2570**
HostEx Show Guide. (CN) **2475**
Hot! (US) **3555**
Hot Air. (UK ISSN 0952-7974) **4803**
Hot Beverages: The International Market *see* Hot Drinks: The International Market **381**
Hot Bike. (US ISSN 0046-8045) **4518**
Hot Boat. (US ISSN 0892-8320) **4525**
Hot Buttoneer. (US ISSN 8755-8734) **1040**
Hot Car *see* Performance Car **4699**
Hot Dog. (US) **1256**

Hot Dog Press. (JA) **3398**
Hot Drinks: The International Market. (UK) **381**
Hot Flash. (US) **4845**, 4835
Hot Flashes. (US) **2923**
Hot Graphics. (UK) **4007**
Hot Letters. (US) **3398**, 4845
Hot Line. (US) **619**
Hot Line Construction Equipment Monthly Update. (US ISSN 1047-4382) **619**
Hot Line Farm Equipment Guide. (US ISSN 1047-725X) **162**
Hot Line News. (US) **3555**
Hot Mix Asphalt Technology *see* H M A T **4719**
Hot Off the Computer. (US ISSN 0737-8076) **1456**, 1460
Hot Picks. (US) **4129**
Hot Rod. (US ISSN 0018-6031) **4692**, 4474
Hot Rod and Custom U.K. *see* Custom Car **4688**
†Hot Rod Performance Boats. (US) **5206**
†Hot Shots (New York). (US) **5206**
Hot Shots (San Diego). (US ISSN 0885-6117) **2454**
Hot Springs Gazette. (US) **4548**
▼Hot Stuf. (US) **2454**
Hot Talk. (US) **3398**
†Hot Tips. (US ISSN 0898-7521) **5206**
Hot Truck *see* Sport Truck **4748**
Hot Water Review. (US ISSN 0278-4173) **2995**
Hot Wire. (US ISSN 0747-8887) **4845**, 4437
HotAds International. (UK) **32**
Hotel. (JA) **4771**
Hotel Amenities in Canada. (CN ISSN 0835-4170) **2475**
Hotel & Catering Gazette. (RH) **2475**
Hotel and Catering Review. (IE) **2475**
Hotel and Motel Management. (US ISSN 0018-6082) **2475**
Hotel and Motel Red Book. (US ISSN 0073-3490) **2475**
Hotel & Resort Industry. (US ISSN 0149-3639) **2475**
Hotel & Tourism Development Report. (II) **4771**
Hotel and Travel Index. (US ISSN 0162-9972) **2475**, 4771
Hotel & Travel Index - A B C International Edition. (US) **2475**
▼Hotel Business. (US) **2475**
Hotel Catering and Institutional Management Association Quarterly Bibliography of Hotel and Catering Management *see* H C I M A Quarterly Bibliography of Hotel and Catering Management **2482**
Hotel Domani. (IT) **2475**
Hotel Gazette of South Australia. (AT ISSN 0018-6139) **2475**
Hotel Guide to Turkey *see* Turkey: Hotels - Camping **2481**
†Hotel Magazine Network. (US) **5206**
Hotel Management/Hotel Ryokan. (JA) **2475**
Hotel Mosaik. (GW) **2475**
Hotel - Motel Security and Safety Management. (US ISSN 8750-5126) **1526**, 2475
Hotel og Restaurant *see* Hotel Restaurant og Fritid **2476**
Hotel Restaurant. (GW ISSN 0018-621X) **2475**
Hotel - Restaurant. (IT) **2476**
†Hotel, Restaurant & Catering Selector. (SA) **5206**
Hotel, Restaurant and Catering Supplies. (UK ISSN 0142-1824) **2072**
Hotel Restaurant og Fritid. (DK) **2476**
Hotel Ryokan. *see* Hotel Management **2475**
Hotel Specification International. (UK) **2476**, 301, 2552
Hotel und Gastgewerbe. (SZ ISSN 0035-9920) **2476**, 2072
Hotel und Gastgewerbe Rundschau *see* Hotel und Gastgewerbe **2476**
Hotel & Touristik. (AU) **2476**, 4771
Hotel und Touristik-Magazin *see* Hotel & Touristik **2476**
Hotel und Touristik Revue. (SZ) **2476**, 4771

HOUSE BEAUTIFUL'S   6257

Hotel Update Newsletter. (US) **2476**
Hotel Voice. (US) **2584**
Hotelarz. (PL ISSN 0137-7612) **2476**
Hoteles de Colombia. (CK ISSN 0018-6279) **2476**
Hotelier. (GW ISSN 0018-6287) **2476**
Hotelier. (CN) **2476**
Hotelier. *see* Mlonai **2478**
Hotelier & Caterer (Cape Town). (SA ISSN 0018-6295) **2476**
Hotelier & Caterer (Nairobi). (KE) **2476**
Hotelier and Caterer Buyer's Guide *see* Hotelier & Caterer (Cape Town) **2476**
Hoteliers Information. Journal. (UK) **2476**
Hotell og Restaurant. (NO) **2476**
Hotellerie *see* Food & Beverage **2474**
L'Hotellerie. (FR) **2476**
Hotelnews. (BL ISSN 0018-6333) **2476**
Hotels. (US ISSN 1047-2975) **2476**, 2072
Hotels and Restaurants International *see* Hotels **2476**
Hotels and Restaurants of Britain. (UK) **2476**
Hotels & Tourism: Latin American Industrial Report. (US) **4771**
Hotels Association of Saskatchewan. Newsletter. (CN) **2476**
Hotels de la France. (FR) **2476**
Hotels, Motels and Guest Houses in New Providence and Paradise Island *see* Hotels, Motels and Guesthouses and Restaurants: New Providence, Paradise Island and Grand Bahama **4771**
Hotels, Motels and Guesthouses and Restaurants: New Providence, Paradise Island and Grand Bahama. (BF) **4771**
Hotels, Restaurants, Institutions Buyers Guide *see* H R I - Buyers Guide **2072**
Hotelsko-Turisticki Adresar *see* Yugoslavia: Hotel and Tourist Directory **2482**
Hotetsu Rinsho. *see* Practice in Prosthodontics **3240**
Hotline (Falls Church). (US) **3897**, 4063
Hotline (Kansas City). (US) **1058**
Hotline (Stony Brook). (US ISSN 0895-3171) **1238**, 2570, 2633
Hotline Magazine. (US) **2072**
Hotline on Object-Oriented Technology. (US ISSN 1044-4319) **1430**
Hotlines. (UK ISSN 0951-614X) **1256**, 1536
HotShoe International. (UK) **32**
Les Houches Summer School Proceedings. (NE) **3819**
Al Houda. (CM) **4218**
Houghton Star. (US) **1314**
Houille Blanche. (FR ISSN 0018-6368) **4825**
Houjyou. (JA ISSN 0911-6494) **96**, 2131
Hounds. (UK) **4535**, 4548
Hounds and Hunting. (US ISSN 0018-6384) **3711**
Hourly Precipitation Data. (US) **3436**
House & Bungalow. (UK ISSN 0018-6392) **301**, 2552
House and Garden *see* H G **2551**
House & Garden (London). (UK ISSN 0043-5759) **2552**, 2131
House and Garden Gardening Guide *see* Gardening **2127**
House & Home *see* Canadian House & Home **2445**
House & Home. (JA) **2552**
House and Home/Huis en Tuis. (SA) **2560**
House Beautiful. (US ISSN 0018-6422) **2552**, 301, 2560
House Beautiful. (UK) **2560**
†House Beautiful's Building & Remodeling Products Annual Buyer's Guide. (US) **5206**
House Beautiful's Building Manual. (US ISSN 0018-6430) **619**
House Beautiful's Colonial Homes *see* Colonial Homes **610**

HOUSE BEAUTIFUL'S

House Beautiful's Home Building. (US) **619**, **2552**
House Beautiful's Home Decorating see House Beautiful's Home Remodeling & Decorating **2552**
House Beautiful's Home Remodeling see House Beautiful's Home Remodeling & Decorating **2552**
House Beautiful's Home Remodeling & Decorating. (US) **2552**
House Beautiful's Houses and Plans. (US ISSN 0073-3571) **301**
House Beautiful's Kitchens - Baths. (US) **2552**
House Builder. (UK ISSN 0951-1334) **619**
House Buyer. (UK ISSN 0018-6473) **4150**
†House Ear Institute. Progress Report. (US ISSN 0197-3657) **5206**
†House Ear Institute. Research Bulletin. (US) **5206**
▼House, Home & Garden. (US) **2226**
House - Lifestyle of the Island. (US) **2226**
House Magazine of Parliament. (UK) **4063**
House Plan Favorites. (US) **2552**
Houseboat Association of America. Newsletter. (US) **4525**
Houseboat Magazine. (US) **4525**
Housebuilding Today. (UK ISSN 0955-3991) **620**
Household & Personal Products Industry. (US ISSN 0090-8878) **1854**, **375**, **3649**
Household Appliance. see Jiayong Dianqi **1079**
Household Brigade Magazine see Guards Magazine **3459**
Household Chemical Market see Household Cleaning: UK & European Trends and Forcasts to 1995 **1040**
Household Cleaning Report see Household Cleaning: UK & European Trends and Forcasts to 1995 **1040**
Household Cleaning: UK & European Trends and Forcasts to 1995. (UK) **1040**
Households see New Zealand. Department of Statistics. Population Census: Families **3994**
Houseleeks see Sempervivum Society. Newsletter **2139**
Houseplant Forum see Houseplant Magazine **2131**
Houseplant Magazine. (US ISSN 1061-4079) **2131**
Houser Hunters Directory. (US) **2155**
†Houser Hunters: Family of Charles Franklin Houser. (US) **5206**
Houser Hunters Index of Houser Family Researchers. (US) **2155**
†Houser Hunters Newsletter. (US) **5206**
Housewares. (UK ISSN 0264-8563) **2560**
†Housewares. (US ISSN 0162-8836) **5206**
Housewares Canada. (CN ISSN 0829-9889) **2560**, **1040**
Housewares Show Stoppers (A.M. and P.M. Editions). (US) **2447**, **2560**
Housewife - Writer's Forum. (US ISSN 1056-0815) **2995**, **4845**
Housewives and Living. (JA) **4845**
Housewives' Handy Hints, Small Businesswoman's Newsletter. (US) **3591**, **4845**
Housing Abstracts (H A B S). (UK ISSN 0952-8156) **2500**
Housing Activity in Hawaii see Construction in Hawaii **612**
Housing Affairs Letter. (US ISSN 0018-6554) **2488**
Housing Aid see Adviser **4397**
†Housing America. (US) **5206**
Housing and Community Development News see California Communities **2484**
Housing and Development Reporter. (US ISSN 0091-5939) **2488**
Housing & Finance - Jamaica. (JM) **2488**, **868**
Housing and Planning Bulletin see Housing and Planning Review **2488**
†Housing and Planning References. (US ISSN 0018-6570) **5206**

Housing and Planning Review. (UK) **2488**
Housing and Population Census of Mauritius. (MF) **2488**, **3982**
Housing and Society. (US ISSN 0888-2746) **2488**
Housing and Urban Development Digest see Urban Perspectives **2498**
Housing and Urban Planning in Sweden. Annual Report/Svenska Bostaeder. Aarsredovisning. (SW) **2488**
Housing Associations Weekly. (UK) **2488**
Housing Authority Journal. (US ISSN 0018-6627) **2488**
▼Housing Cheap or on a Budget Newsletter. (US) **1505**, **4150**
Housing Construction Catalogue. (UK) **620**
Housing Corporation. Quarterly Review. (UK ISSN 0260-4094) **2488**
Housing Economics. (US ISSN 1056-5140) **868**, **2488**, **4150**
Housing Finance. (UK ISSN 0955-3800) **4150**, **784**, **2488**
Housing Finance Company of Kenya. Annual Report and Accounts. (KE) **2488**, **784**
Housing Finance Fact Book (Year). (UK) **4150**, **720**, **784**
Housing Finance International. (US) **784**
†Housing Finance Review. (US ISSN 0276-4415) **5206**
Housing in South Africa/Behuising in Suid-Afrika. (SA) **2488**
Housing Information Digest. (UK ISSN 0267-0054) **2500**
Housing Law Bulletin. (US ISSN 0277-8491) **2488**
Housing Law Reports. (UK) **2633**, **2488**
Housing Market Report. (US ISSN 0363-4744) **2488**
Housing Market Statistics. (US ISSN 1056-5132) **720**, **2500**, **4573**
Housing Matters. (US) **2488**
▼Housing Policy Debate. (US ISSN 1051-1482) **2488**, **4150**
Housing Products and Costing Guide see Housing Victoria - Tasmania **620**
Housing Research Review/Behuisingsnavorsingsoorsig. (SA) **2488**
Housing Review. (UK ISSN 0018-6651) **2488**
Housing Studies. (UK ISSN 0267-3037) **2488**
▼Housing Survey of Japan (Year). (JA) **2500**, **4573**
Housing the Elderly Report. (US ISSN 1050-3234) **2488**, **2274**, **4407**
Housing Times. (II) **2488**
Housing Units in Connecticut. Annual Summary see Connecticut Housing Production and Permit Authorized Construction **611**
Housing Vacancies and Homeownership see Current Housing Reports: Housing Vacancies **2486**
Housing Vacancies and Homeownership Annual Statistics see Current Housing Reports: Housing Vacancies **2488**
Housing Victoria see Housing Victoria - Tasmania **620**
Housing Victoria - Tasmania. (AT) **620**, **2488**
Housing Year Book. (UK ISSN 0264-5181) **2488**
Housman Society Journal. (UK ISSN 0305-926X) **2923**
Houston Area League of P C Users, Inc. User Journal see H A L - P C User Journal **1469**
Houston Area National Organization for Women Herald see H A N O W Herald **4844**
Houston Business Briefs. (US) **868**
Houston Business Journal. (US) **868**, **3688**
Houston Education Association Advocate see H E A Advocate **1636**
Houston Geological Society. Bulletin. (US ISSN 0018-6686) **1568**
Houston Heights Tribune. (US) **2226**
Houston Home and Garden see Houston Metropolitan **2560**

Houston Journal of International Law. (US ISSN 0194-1879) **2633**, **911**
Houston Journal of Mathematics. (US ISSN 0362-1588) **3037**
Houston Law Review. (US ISSN 0018-6694) **2633**
Houston Living see Houston Living Housing Guide **4150**
Houston Living Housing Guide. (US) **4150**, **2488**
Houston Medical Journal see Houston Medicine **3106**
Houston Medicine. (US ISSN 0889-0358) **3106**
Houston Metropolitan. (US) **2560**, **2131**
Houston Monthly Magazine. (US ISSN 0272-8060) **4771**
Houston Oil Directory. (US) **3688**, **1138**
▼Houston People. (US) **2227**
Houston Petroleum Industry. (US) **3688**, **1138**
Houston Post Index. (US ISSN 0893-2476) **2578**
Houston Press. (US) **2227**
Houston Retail Grocer see Gulf Coast Retail Grocer **2092**
Houston Review: History and Culture of the Gulf Coast. (US ISSN 0272-4030) **2409**, **4437**
Houston Sarmatian see Sarmatian Review **2022**
Houston Symphony Magazine. (US) **3555**
Houston, Texas. Museum of Fine Arts Bulletin. (US ISSN 0018-6708) **3524**
Houston Tribune. (US) **2227**
Houstonian. (US) **1314**
Houtadresboek. (NE) **2115**
Het Houtblad. (NE ISSN 0923-5574) **639**, **2115**
Houthandel en Nijverheid. (BE) **2102**
†Houtim. (SA ISSN 0367-6447) **5206**
Houtland. (BE) **2368**, **2055**
Houtnieuws see Courrier du Bois **2114**
Houtwereld. (NE ISSN 0018-6732) **2115**
Houtwerker. see Woodworker **641**
†Houvast. (NE) **5206**
Hovercraft Bulletin. (UK ISSN 0144-3755) **54**
Hoverfoil News. (UK ISSN 0018-6767) **4728**, **1823**
Hovering Craft and Hydrofoil see Fast Ferry International **4727**
How. (US ISSN 0886-0483) **2501**, **4001**
†How(ever). (US) **5206**
†How(ever). (US) **5207**
How and Where Directory. (AT) **2793**
How to Avoid Financial Tangles. (US) **1012**, **784**
How to Be Your Own Publisher Update. (US ISSN 0738-7415) **4129**, **1115**
How to Buy and Sell Business Opportunities. (US) **948**, **4150**
How to Do It Manuals for Librarians. (US) **2760**
How to Double Your Income. (US ISSN 0277-0334) **373**, **1115**
How to Evaluate Education Programs see Report on Education Research **1658**
How to Find Anyone Anywhere. (US) **1515**
How to Find Company Intelligence in State Documents. (US) **669**, **1138**
How to Find Information About Companies. (US ISSN 0278-372X) **669**, **1138**
How to Find Information About Japanese Companies and Industries see Asian Markets **900**
How to Find Negligence and Misrepresentations in Financial Statements see Fraud, Window Dressing and Negligence in Financial Statements **2628**
†How to Get Help for Kids. (US ISSN 0275-4819) **5207**
How to Invest in Brazil. (BL) **949**
How to Live in Britain. (UK) **4407**
How to Prepare Witnesses for Trial. (US) **2633**

How to Start Your Own Business with 2000 to 5000 Dollars. (NP) **1115**
Howard Florey Institute of Experimental Physiology & Medicine. Annual Report and Notice of Meeting. (AT ISSN 0314-6162) **3106**
Howard Historian. (US ISSN 0886-9103) **2155**
Howard Journal of Communications. (US) **1336**
Howard Journal of Criminal Justice. (UK ISSN 0265-5527) **1515**
Howard Journal of Penology and Crime Prevention see Howard Journal of Criminal Justice **1515**
Howard Law Journal. (US ISSN 0018-6813) **2633**
Howard University Alumni News. (US) **1314**
Howling Dog. (US ISSN 0888-3521) **2923**
Howling Manstra. (US) **2923**
How's Business Annual. (US) **32**, **4001**
Hoy. (CL ISSN 0716-3460) **2868**
Hoy Dia. (UK ISSN 0018-6856) **2817**, **1751**
Hoy en Italia see Vida Italiana **4795**
Hoy es Historia. (UY) **2409**
Hoyan. (US ISSN 0270-3602) **4374**
Hozon Kagaku/Science for Conservation. (JA ISSN 0287-0606) **1489**
Hp 1 Modellbahn. (GW ISSN 0941-3480) **2437**
Hrvatska Domovina see That's Yugoslavia **3930**
Hrvatska Revija. (SP ISSN 0018-6902) **2868**, **328**
Hrvatska Sloboda. (AT ISSN 0818-0954) **3943**, **2005**
Hrvatski Katolicki Glasnik. (US ISSN 0018-6910) **4265**
Hrvatski Obrtnik. (CI) **1115**
Hrvatski Planinar/Croatian Mountaineer.(CI ISSN 0354-0650) **4474**
Hrvatski Put/Croatian Way. (CN ISSN 0702-3855) **3897**
Hsiang Kang Hu Li Tsa Chih. see Hong Kong Nursing Journal **3279**
Hsiang-Kang Tien Chu Chiao Shou Ts'e. see Hong Kong Catholic Church Directory **4265**
Hsiao Shuo Ch'uang Tso. see Novelistic Works **2944**
Hsien Cheng Ssu Ch'ao. (CH) **3897**, **2633**
Hsin Ju Chia/New Confucians. (CH ISSN 0018-6937) **3768**
Hu Li Tsa Chih. see Journal of Nursing **3280**
Hua de Yuanye/Prairie of Flowers. (US) **2923**
Hua Jen. see Life Overseas **2197**
Huabei Dizhen Kexue. (CC) **1590**
Huabei Nongxue Bao/North China Agriculture Journal. (CC ISSN 1000-7091) **96**
Huacheng. (CC ISSN 1000-789X) **2923**, **2995**
Huadong Gongxueyuan Xuebao/East China Institute of Engineering. Journal. (CC ISSN 1001-5159) **1823**
Huadong Shifan Daxue Xuebao (Jiaoyu Ban)/East China Normal University. Journal (Education Edition). (CC ISSN 1000-5560) **1637**
Huadong Shifan Daxue Xuebao (Zhexue Shehui Kexue Ban)/East China Normal University. Journal. (Social Science Edition). (CC ISSN 1000-5579) **4374**, **3688**
Huadong Shifan Daxue Xuebao (Ziran Kexue Ban)/East China Normal University. Journal (Natural Science Edition). (CC ISSN 1000-5641) **4313**
Huagong Jixie/Chemical Engineering and Machinery. (CC ISSN 0254-6094) **1854**, **3018**
Huagong Yejin/Journal of Engineering Chemistry and Metallurgy. (CC) **1854**, **3408**
Huagong zhi You/Friend of Chemical Industry. (CC) **1178**, **3688**
Hualang/Gallery. (CC ISSN 1000-4815) **328**

Huamu Penjing/Flowers, Trees & Potted Landscapes. (US) **2131**
Huan Bohai Jingji Liaowang/Economic Outlook for the Bohai Bay. (CC) **669**
Huan Qiu/Globe. (CC) **3959**, 2868
Huanan Dizhen/South-China Seismology. (CC) **1590**
Huanan Ligong Daxue Xuebao (Ziran Kexue Ban)/South-China University of Science and Engineering. Journal (Natural Science Edition). (CC ISSN 1000-565X) **4313**, 4599
Huanan Shifan Daxue Xuebao (Shehui Kexue Ban)/South-China Normal University. Journal (Social Science Edition). (CC ISSN 1000-5455) **4374**
Huanan Shifan Daxue Xuebao (Ziran Kexue Ban)/South-China Normal University. Journal (Natural Science Edition). (CC ISSN 1000-5463) **4313**
Huang Bohai Haiyang. (CC ISSN 1000-7199) **1605**
Huang He/Yellow River. (CC ISSN 1000-4823) **2923**
Huang Kuan. see Crown **2219**
Huang Pu. (CC) **2182**
Huang Shan/Yellow Mountain. (CC) **2252**
Huang Zhong. (CC) **3555**
Huangjin Shidai/Golden Times. (CC) **2182**
Huanjing Daobao/Environment Herald. (CC) **1957**
Huanjing Huaxue/Journal of Environmental Chemistry. (CC ISSN 0254-6108) **1178**, 1957
Huanjing Kexue. (CC ISSN 0250-3301) **1957**
Huanjing Kexue Xuebao/Acta Scientiae Circumstantiae. (CC ISSN 0253-2468) **1957**
Huanjing Wuran yu Fangzhi/Environmental Pollution and Prevention. (CC ISSN 1001-3865) **1957**
Huanjing Yaogan/Remote Sensing of Environment. (CC ISSN 1000-3312) **2252**, 4359
Huanjing yu Jiankang Zazhi/Journal of Environment and Health. (CC ISSN 1001-5914) **1957**, 4104
Huanqiu Yinmu Huakan/Global Screen Pictorial. (CC) **3511**
Huaqiao Daxue Xuebao (Shehui Kexue Ban)/Huaqiao University. Journal (Social Science Edition). (CC) **4374**
Huaqiao Daxue Xuebao (Ziran Kexue Ban)/Huaqiao University. Journal (Natural Science Edition). (CC ISSN 1000-5013) **4313**
Huaqiao University. Journal (Natural Science Edition). see Huaqiao Daxue Xuebao (Ziran Kexue Ban) **4313**
Huaqiao University. Journal (Social Science Edition). see Huaqiao Daxue Xuebao (Shehui Kexue Ban) **4374**
†Huaren Shijie. (CC) **5207**
Huaren zhi Sheng/Voice of the Chinese.(CC) **2182**
Huashi/Fossils. (CC ISSN 1000-3185) **3657**
Huaxi. (CC ISSN 1002-686X) **2923**, 1256, 2995
Huaxi Kouqiang Yixue Zazhi/West China Journal of Stomatology. (CC ISSN 1000-1182) **3234**
Huaxi Yike Daxue Xuebao/West China University of Medical Sciences. Journal. (CC ISSN 0257-7712) **3106**, 440, 3728
Huaxi Yixue/West China Medical Journal. (CC ISSN 1002-0179) **3106**
Huaxia Gushengwu. see Palaeontologia Cathayana **3659**
Huaxia Kaogu. (CC) **274**
Huaxia Mingren/China's Famous People. (US) **419**
Huaxue Fanying Gongcheng yu Gongyi. (CC ISSN 1001-7631) **1178**
Huaxue Gongchengshi/Chemical Engineers. (CC) **1854**
Huaxue Jiaoxue/Chemistry Teaching. (CC) **1178**, 1637
Huaxue Tongbao/Chemistry Bulletin. (CC ISSN 0441-3776) **1178**

Huaxue Wuli Xuebao/Journal of Chemical Physics. (CC) **3819**, 1178
Huaxue Xuebao/Acta Chimica Sinica. (CC ISSN 0567-7351) **1178**
Huaxue yu Nianhe/Chemistry and Binding. (CC) **1854**, 3688
Huazhong Ligong Daxue Xuebao/Central-China University of Science and Engineering. Journal. (CC ISSN 1000-8616) **4313**, 4599
Huazhong Shifan Daxue Xuebao (Shehui Kexue Ban)/Central-China Normal University. Journal (Social Science Edition). (CC ISSN 1000-2456) **4374**
Huazhong Shifan Daxue Xuebao (Ziran Kexue Ban)/Central-China Normal University. Journal (Natural Science Edition). (CC ISSN 1000-1190) **4313**
Hub. (CN) **2177**
Hub Rail see Harness Horse **5203**
Hubbard School System Office of Curriculum and Instruction. Digest Newsletter see Insight (Hubbard) **1639**
Hubbub. (US ISSN 1047-0158) **2995**
Hubei Caikuai. (CC) **784**
Hubei Caishui. (CC) **1097**
Hubei Fangzhi. (CC) **2570**, 4129
Hubo Kexue/Lake Science. (CC) **1545**
Huda al-Islam. (JO) **4218**
Hudebni Nastroje. (CS ISSN 0323-1283) **3555**
Hudebni Rozhledy. (CS ISSN 0018-6996) **3555**
Hudebni Veda/Musicology. (CS ISSN 0018-7003) **3555**
Hudobny Archiv. (CS) **3555**
Hudobny Zivot. (CS) **3555**
Hudson Center Journal. (US) **328**
▼Hudson County Magazine. (US) **2227**
Hudson Family Association. Bulletin. (US) **2155**
†Hudson Forum. (US ISSN 0193-4791) **5207**
Hudson Home Magazine see Home **300**
Hudson Institute Briefing Paper. (US) **3959**
Hudson Institute Report. (US) **3959**
Hudson Letter. (FR ISSN 0242-3502) **3959**
Hudson Opinion. (US) **4063**
Hudson Review. (US ISSN 0018-702X) **2868**
Hudson Valley Business Journal. (US) **669**
Hudson Valley G R E E N Times. (US ISSN 0888-661X) **1957**, 1790
Hudson Valley Magazine. (US ISSN 0191-9288) **2227**
Hudson Valley Regional Review. (US ISSN 0742-2075) **1314**
Hudsoniana see Hudson Family Association. Bulletin **2155**
Hudson's Newsletter Directory see Hudson's Subscription Newsletter Directory **2570**
Hudson's State Capitals. (US ISSN 0885-1328) **1138**
Hudson's Subscription Newsletter Directory. (US ISSN 1046-8110) **2570**
Hudson's Washington News Media Contacts Directory. (US ISSN 0441-389X) **2570**
Huebner Foundation Monograph. (US) **2533**
Huenefeld Report. (US) **4129**
Hueso Humero. (PE) **2923**, 328
†Der Huettenmann. (GW) **5207**
Hufeland - Journal. (GW ISSN 0179-7581) **3106**, 440
Hug! (DK ISSN 0106-4959) **2868**, 2185
Hugang Jingji/Shanghai Harbor Economy. (CC) **669**
Hughes and Woodley on Patents. (CN) **3675**
Hughes Family Letter. (US ISSN 0747-5675) **2155**
Hughes on Copyright and Industrial Design. (CN) **3675**
Hughes on Trademark. (CN) **3675**

Hughes Report see Management Report **988**
Huginn and Muninn. (IC) **3669**, 3768
Huguenot Society of Great Britain and Ireland. Proceedings. (UK) **2368**, 2155
Huguenot Society of Great Britain and Ireland. Quarto Series. (UK) **2368**, 2155
Huguenot Society of London. Proceedings see Huguenot Society of Great Britain and Ireland. Proceedings **2368**
Huguenot Society of London. Quarto Series see Huguenot Society of Great Britain and Ireland. Quarto Series **2368**
Huguenot Trails. (CN ISSN 0441-6910) **2409**, 2155, 4240
Huila. (CK) **2409**
Huis en Tuis. see House and Home **2560**
Huis van Geluk see Path of Truth **4286**
Huisarts en Wetenschap. (NE ISSN 0018-7070) **3106**
Huisgenoot. (SA ISSN 0018-7089) **2216**
Huismuziek. (NE ISSN 0018-7097) **3555**
Huizer Kerkblad. (NE ISSN 0018-7119) **4181**
Hukerikar Memorial Lecture Series. (II ISSN 0419-0432) **669**
Al-Hukm al-Shabi al-Mahalli. see People's Local Government Journal **5256**
Hukum dan Pembangunan. (IO ISSN 0125-9687) **2633**
Hulbert Financial Digest. (US) **949**
Hule Mexicano y Plasticos. (MX ISSN 0018-7127) **4291**, 3862
Hule, Plasticos y Resinas (Annual) see Guia de la Industria: Hule, Plasticos y Resinas **3862**
Hulequipo. (MX) **4291**
Hull City Council. Civic News. (UK) **4088**
†Hull Monographs on South-East Asia. (NE) **5207**
Hull Papers in Politics. (UK ISSN 0142-7377) **3897**
Hullfire. (UK) **1314**
Human & Experimental Toxicology. (UK) **1982**, 3728
▼Human Antibodies and Hybridomas. (US ISSN 0956-960X) **3185**, 3197
Human Behavior and Environment. (US) **4023**
Human Biology (Detroit). (US ISSN 0018-7143) **440**
Human Biology (New York) see American Journal of Human Biology **427**
Human Capital. (US) **1065**, 1012
Human Communication and Its Disorders. (US) **1736**, 2817
Human Communication Canada see Journal of Speech Language Pathology and Audiology **1737**
Human Communication Research. (US ISSN 0360-3989) **1336**, 2817
Human - Computer Interaction (Hillsdale). (US ISSN 0737-0024) **1395**, 4023
Human - Computer Interaction (Norwood). (US) **1417**
Human Concern Newspaper. (UK) **3293**
Human Culture and Environmental Studies in Northern Hokkaido. see Hoppo Kagaku Chosa Hokoku **1957**
Human Design. (IT ISSN 0046-8150) **328**, 301, 4599
Human Development. (SZ ISSN 0018-716X) **4023**, 3293, 3321
Human Development (Hartford). (US ISSN 0197-3096) **4023**, 4240
Human Development (Norwood). (US) **4023**
Human Digest. (US) **4023**
The Human Ecologist. (US ISSN 8755-7878) **1957**, 1489, 1505
Human Ecology. Annual Report. (US) **4374**, 3606
Human Ecology (New York). (US ISSN 0300-7839) **241**

Human Ecology (Park Ridge). (US ISSN 0046-8169) **2466**, 4104
Human Ecology & Energy Balancing Scientist. (US ISSN 1045-2729) **3106**, 3606, 3804
Human Ecology Balancing Scientist see Human Ecology & Energy Balancing Scientist **3106**
Human Ecology Forum. (US ISSN 0018-7178) **4374**, 1314, 1957
Human Environment see Industrial Engineer **1926**
Human Environment in Sweden see Viewpoint Sweden **2218**
Human Ergology Society. Newsletter. see Jinrui Dotai Gakkai Kaiho **3821**
Human Ethology Newsletter. (US ISSN 0739-2036) **241**, 440
Human Events. (US ISSN 0018-7194) **3897**
Human Evolution. (IT ISSN 0393-9375) **241**, 440
▼Human Evolution, Behavior, and Intelligence. (US) **543**, 4023
Human Factors. (US ISSN 0018-7208) **1823**, 4023
Human Factors & Aviation Medicine. (US ISSN 0898-5723) **54**, 3106
Human Factors and Aviation Medicine Bulletin see Human Factors & Aviation Medicine **54**
Human Factors Society Annual Meeting. Proceedings. (US ISSN 0163-5182) **4023**, 1823
Human Factors Society Bulletin. (US ISSN 0438-1629) **1823**, 4023
Human Gene Mapping. (SZ ISSN 0378-9861) **543**, 3259
▼Human Gene Therapy. (US ISSN 1043-0342) **543**
Human Genetics. (GW ISSN 0340-6717) **544**
Human Genetics. Supplement. (US ISSN 0172-7699) **544**
Human Genetics, Informational and Educational Materials. Supplement. (US ISSN 0197-8160) **3219**
†Human Genome. (UK ISSN 0952-0325) **5207**
▼Human Genome Abstracts. (US ISSN 1045-4470) **465**, 469, 477, 544
Human Geography/Jimbun-Chiri. (JA ISSN 0018-7216) **2252**, 3982
Human Heredity. (SZ ISSN 0001-5652) **544**
Human Immunodeficiency Virus Funding Watch see H I V Funding Watch **3219**
Human Immunodeficiency Virus Prevention News see H I V Prevention News **3219**
Human Immunology. (US ISSN 0198-8859) **3185**
Human Industrial Design. (AU ISSN 0018-7224) **4599**
Human Inquiries see Review of Existential Psychology and Psychiatry **4044**
†Human Intelligence International Newsletter. (US ISSN 0741-5745) **5207**
Human Issue see New Kent Quarterly **2942**
Human Kindness Foundation Newsletter.(US) **4181**, 1515, 4437
Human Learning see Applied Cognitive Psychology **4011**
Human Life International. Letter Dr. Report see Human Life International. Special Report **3982**
Human Life International. Special Report. (US ISSN 0899-420X) **3982**, 4265
Human Life International in Canada Inc. Canadian Report see H L I Canadian Report **3982**
Human Life International in Canada Inc. Reports see H L I Reports **3982**
Human Life International Reports see H L I Reports **3982**
Human Life Issues. (US) **3768**, 596, 4104, 4437
†Human Life Matters. (UK ISSN 0951-1172) **5207**
Human Life Review. (US ISSN 0097-9783) **4437**

HUMAN MEDICINE

Human Medicine. see Ningen Igaku 3609
Human Mosaic. (US ISSN 0018-7240) 241, 274
Human Movement Science. (NE ISSN 0167-9457) 3106, 3804, 4023
▼Human Nature. (US ISSN 1045-6767) 4374, 440, 4023, 4437
Human Nutrition. (US ISSN 0886-6848) 3606
Human Nutrition. Applied Nutrition see Journal of Human Nutrition and Dietetics 3608
Human-Oekologie see Uebersee-Museum, Bremen. Veroeffentlichungen. Reihe E: Human-Oekologie 4455
Human Organization. (US ISSN 0018-7259) 241, 4374
Human Parasitic Diseases. (NE) 3219
Human Pathology. (US ISSN 0046-8177) 3106
Human Performance. (US ISSN 0895-9285) 4023
Human Physiology. (English translation of: Fiziologiya Cheloveka) (US ISSN 0362-1197) 572
Human Potential. (US) 4023, 4437
Human Potential Magazine. (UK ISSN 0955-4815) 4023, 1637
Human Potential Resources see Human Potential Magazine 4023
Human Power. (US ISSN 0898-6908) 4474
Human Psychopharmacology: Clinical and Experimental. (UK ISSN 0885-6222) 3338, 3728
Human Quest. (US) 4181, 4437
Human Relations. (US ISSN 0018-7267) 4374
Human Relations News of Chicago. (US ISSN 0018-7283) 4437
Human Reproduction. (UK ISSN 0268-1161) 3293, 3254, 3728
Human Research Report. (US ISSN 0885-0615) 3259, 2633
Human Resource. (CN) 1012, 981
Human Resource Computers in H R Management see Computers in H R Management 825
▼Human Resource Development Quarterly. (US ISSN 1044-8004) 1066
Human Resource Developments in the Middle East and North Africa see Arab World Almanac 1744
Human Resource Executive. (US) 1066
Human Resource Information Network Update. (US) 4143
Human Resource Management. (US ISSN 0090-4848) 1012
Human Resource Management Australia see Asia Pacific Human Resource Management 1062
Human Resource Management News. (US) 1066, 981
▼Human Resource Management Review. (US ISSN 1053-4822) 1066
Human Resource Management Yearbook. (UK) 1066
Human Resource Manager's Legal Reporter. (US) 981
Human Resource Planning. (US) 1066
Human Resource Professional. (US) 1066
Human Resource Reporter see H R Reporter 1065
Human Resources Abstracts. (US ISSN 0099-2453) 4457, 13, 3897, 4437
Human Resources Administrator. (US) 2466, 4104
Human Resources Development Institute Advisory see H R D I Advisory 980
†Human Resources Journal. (HK) 5207
Human Resources Magazine see H R Magazine 1065
Human Resources Management. (US) 981, 1066
Human Resources Management Ideas and Trends Newsletter. (US) 1012
Human Resources Management in Canada. (US) 1066, 2710
Human Resources Management - O S H A Compliance. (US) 3617
†Human Resources Management Reporter. (US) 5207
Human Resources Policies and Practices. (US) 1066
Human Resources Professional. (CN) 1066
Human Resources Research Organization. Professional Papers. (US ISSN 0073-3873) 4063
Human Resources Update. (US) 1066
Human Retroviruses see I C R D B Cancergram: Human Retroviruses 5208
Human Rights. (US ISSN 0046-8185) 3943, 2702
Human Rights. see Huniy Erh 3943
Human Rights Act of British Columbia. (CN) 3943
Human Rights Bulletin. (UN ISSN 0251-7019) 3943
Human Rights Bulletin (New York). (US) 3943
Human Rights Council Decisions. (CN) 3943
Human Rights Internet Reporter. (CN ISSN 0275-049X) 3943
Human Rights Law Journal. (GW ISSN 0174-4704) 2706, 3943
Human Rights Newsletter. (UN ISSN 1014-4986) 3943
Human Rights Organizations & Periodicals Directory. (US ISSN 0098-0579) 1138, 3937, 3943
Human Rights Quarterly. (US ISSN 0275-0392) 4437, 2702
Human Rights Resources. (US) 3943, 4407
Human Rights Review see Human Rights Law Journal 2706
Human Rights Watch. (US) 3943
▼Human Rights Watch World Report. (US ISSN 1054-948X) 3943
▼Human Rights Worldwide. (GW ISSN 1015-5945) 3943
Human Science. (II ISSN 0970-3411) 241
Human Sciences Research Council. Annual Report. (SA) 2507, 4374
Human Sciences Research Council. Bulletin. News for the Human Sciences/Raad vir Geesteswetenskaplike Navorsing. Bulletin. Nuus vir die Geesteswetenskappe. (SA ISSN 1017-6136) 4374, 2507
†Human Sciences Research Council. Compass. (SA) 5207
Human Sciences Research Council. Research Bulletin - Raad vir Geesteswetenskaplike Navorsing. Navorsingsbulletin see Human Sciences Research Council. Bulletin. News for the Human Sciences 4374
Human Serve Campaign Newsletter. (US) 4408, 3943
†Human Services (Woodhaven). (US ISSN 0745-2616) 5207
Human Services Directory. (US) 4408
Human Services in the Rural Environment. (US ISSN 0193-9009) 4408
Human Services Reporter. (US ISSN 0164-6079) 4408
Human Settlement Issues. (CN) 2488, 4374
Human Settlements Situation and Related Trends and Policies. (DK ISSN 0108-562X) 2489
Human Sexuality. (UK ISSN 0142-811X) 572, 2454, 4845
Human Sexuality. (US ISSN 0883-1289) 4023, 440, 2454, 4845
Human Side of Supervision. (US) 981, 1066
Human Stress Current Advances in Research see Human Stress: Current Selected Research 4023
Human Stress: Current Selected Research. (US ISSN 0885-1174) 4023, 1238, 4437
Human Studies. (NE ISSN 0163-8548) 3768, 4437
Human Systems Management. (NE ISSN 0167-2533) 1012
Human Toxicology see Human & Experimental Toxicology 1982
Humana Civilitas. (US ISSN 0742-115X) 2368
Humana Hospital - Michael Reese News. (US) 2466
Humane Gesellschaft. (GW) 3897
Humane Innovations and Alternatives. (US) 3259
Humane Innovations and Alternatives in Animal Experimentation: A Notebook see Humane Innovations and Alternatives 3259
Humane Medicine. (CN ISSN 0828-7090) 3106
†Humane Produktion, Humane Arbeitsplaetze. (GW ISSN 0172-8334) 5207
Humane Society of the United States News see H S U S News 231
Humane Studies Review. (US) 3768, 4374
Humanidad. (PR ISSN 0441-4144) 4408
Humanidades. (GT ISSN 0018-7356) 2508
Humanidades. (BL ISSN 0102-9479) 2508
†Humanidades. (PO) 5207
Humanisme. (FR ISSN 0018-7364) 1298
Humanisme et Entreprise. (FR ISSN 0018-7372) 981, 1066
Humanist. (DK ISSN 0107-9573) 2508
Der Humanist. (GW) 3768
Humanist. (NE ISSN 0025-9489) 3768
Humanist. (US ISSN 0018-7399) 3768, 2868
Humanist see New Humanist 3774
Humanist in Canada. (CN ISSN 0018-7402) 3768, 4284
Humanist News. (UK) 3768
Humanist Newsletter see Humanist News 3768
Humanist Outlook. (II ISSN 0018-7429) 3768
Humanist Post. (AT) 3768
The Humanist Sociologist. (US) 4437
Humanist Viewpoints. (AT) 2508
Humanistic Judaism. (US ISSN 0441-4195) 4223
The Humanistic Psychologist. (US ISSN 0887-3267) 4023
Humanistic Psychology Review see Saybrook Review 4045
Humanistica Lovaniensia. (BE ISSN 0774-2908) 1277
Humanistica Lovaniensia. Supplementa. (BE) 1277
Humanistisch Instituut voor Ontwikkelingssamenwerking Projectbericht see H I V O S - Projectbericht 930
Humanistische Union. Mitteilungen. (GW ISSN 0046-824X) 3768
Humanitas. (IT ISSN 0018-7461) 2868
Humanitas. (PL ISSN 0137-9666) 4374
Humanitas (New Jersey) see New Jersey Humanities 2512
Humanities. (US ISSN 0018-7526) 2508
Humanities, Christianity and Culture. (JA ISSN 0073-3938) 4181
Humanities Computing Yearbook. (UK) 2520, 2508
Humanities Education. (US ISSN 0882-5475) 2508, 1751
Humanities in the South. (US ISSN 0018-7577) 1637
Humanities Index. (US ISSN 0095-5981) 2520, 13
Humanities Journal see Humanities Education 2508
Humanities Research Centre Bulletin. (AT ISSN 0312-5041) 2508
Humanities Research Council of Canada. Bulletin see Canadian Federation for the Humanities. Bulletin 2504
Humanities Research Council of Canada. Report see Canadian Federation for the Humanities. Annual Report 5161
Humanities Review. (II) 2508
Humanity & Society. (US ISSN 0160-5976) 4437
Humanizacja Pracy/Humanization of Work. (PL ISSN 0137-3013) 981
Humanization of Work. see Humanizacja Pracy 981
Humanomics. (UK ISSN 0828-8666) 895
Humanspace Books. Newsletter. (US) 2454, 3669, 4845
Humboldt (Portuguese Edition). (GW ISSN 0018-7623) 2868, 328
Humboldt (Spanish Edition). (GW ISSN 0018-7615) 2868
Humboldt Journal of Social Relations. (US ISSN 0160-4341) 4374
Humboldt Society Newsletter. (US ISSN 0898-2805) 2454, 440, 1545, 1957
Humboldt - Universitaet zu Berlin. Universitaetsbibliothek. Schriftenreihe. (GW ISSN 0522-9898) 2760
Humboldt - Universitaet zu Berlin. Wissenschaftliche Zeitschrift: Reihe Gesellschaftswissenschaft see Humboldt - Universitaet zu Berlin. Wissenschaftliche Zeitschrift: Reihe Geistes- und Sozialwissenschaft 4313
Humboldt - Universitaet zu Berlin. Wissenschaftliche Zeitschrift: Reihe Geistes- und Sozialwissenschaft. (GW) 4313, 4374
Humboldtiana see Bibliographia Humboldtiana 2503
Hume News see C S R Construction News 1862
Hume Studies. (CN ISSN 0319-7336) 3768
Humerus. (US) 2923
Hummer Trail and Touring Guide. (US) 4548
Humm's Guide to the Florida Keys. (US) 4771
Humor. (AG) 2868
Humor. (GW ISSN 0933-1719) 4374, 4023, 4437
Humor and Cartoon Markets. (US ISSN 1043-240X) 4129, 328
Humor Events & Possibilities. (US) 2868
Humor Graphic. (IT) 2868
Humphrey Family Quarterly. (US) 2155
Humphreys County Historical Society. Publication. (US) 2409
Humpty Dumpty's Magazine. (US ISSN 0273-7590) 1256
Humsafar. (TH) 4803
Hun Boloh Bagaasaa/Growing Up. (MP) 1637
Huna London. (UK ISSN 0951-8045) 1356
Huna Work. (US) 3768
Hunan Literature. see Hunan Wenxue 2923
Hunan Normal University. Journal (Natural Science Edition). see Hunan Shifan Daxue Xuebao (Ziran Kexue Ban) 4313
Hunan Normal University. Journal (Social Science Edition). see Hunan Shifan Daxue Xuebao (Shehui Kexue Ban) 4374
Hunan Shifan Daxue Xuebao (Shehui Kexue Ban)/Hunan Normal University. Journal (Social Science Edition). (CC ISSN 1000-2529) 4374
Hunan Shifan Daxue Xuebao (Ziran Kexue Ban)/Hunan Normal University. Journal (Natural Science Edition). (CC ISSN 1000-2537) 4313
Hunan Wenxue/Hunan Literature. (CC ISSN 0439-8106) 2923
Hunde Haltung Zucht Sport. (SZ) 3711
Hunden. (DK) 3711
Hundsport. (NO) 3711
Die Hundewelt. (GW ISSN 0018-7682) 3711
Hundsport. (SW ISSN 0018-7690) 3711
Hungarian Academy of Sciences. Central Research Institute for Physics. Yearbook/Magyar Tudomanyos Akademia. Kozponti Fizikai Kutato Intezet. Evkonyv. (HU ISSN 0133-5502) 3819, 1178

Hungarian Academy of Sciences. Research Institute for Agricultural Economics. Bulletin see Research Institute for Agricultural Economics. Bulletin 157
Hungarian Academy of Sciences. Research Institute for Microbiology. Proceedings. see Magyar Tudomanyos Akademia. Mikrobiologiai Kutato Intezet. Proceedings 554
Hungarian Agricultural Engineering. (HU) 96
Hungarian Agricultural Review. (HU ISSN 0018-7712) 138, 13
Hungarian Agriculture. see Magyar Mezogazdasag 106
Hungarian Aluminum. see Magyar Aluminium 3412
Hungarian Archives of America. see Amerikai Magyar Levelestar 2348
Hungarian Book Review. see Magyar Konyvszemle 4132
†Hungarian Book Review. (HU ISSN 0324-3451) 5207
†Hungarian Building Bulletin. (HU ISSN 0018-7720) 5207
Hungarian Building Industry. see Magyar Epitoipar 623
Hungarian Business Herald. (HU) 817
†Hungarian Cinema. (HU) 5207
Hungarian Co-operation. (HU ISSN 0439-9056) 831
Hungarian Digest. (HU ISSN 0209-5386) 2198
Hungarian Economic Literature. see Magyar Kozgazdasagi Irodalom 728
▼Hungarian Economic Review. (HU ISSN 1215-2439) 868
Hungarian Economy. (HU ISSN 0133-0365) 669
Hungarian Folklore Bibliography. see Magyar Neprajzi Bibliografia 2056
Hungarian Graphic Arts. see Magyar Grafika 4002
Hungarian Historical Review. see Magyar Tortenelmi Szemle 2374
Hungarian Journal of Chemistry. see Magyar Kemiai Folyoirat 1183
Hungarian Journal of Industrial Chemistry. (HU ISSN 0133-0276) 1178, 1854
Hungarian Journal of Physics. see Magyar Fizikai Folyoirat 3824
▼Hungarian Journal of Viticulture and Enology. (HU ISSN 0866-6083) 179
Hungarian Language. see Magyar Nyelv 2828
†Hungarian Law Review. (HU ISSN 0441-4411) 5207
Hungarian Library and Information Science Abstracts. (HU ISSN 0046-8304) 2793, 13
Hungarian Library Literature. see Magyar Konyvtari Szakirodalom Bibliografiaja 2794
Hungarian Life. see Magyar Elet 2012
Hungarian Medical Bibliography. (HU ISSN 0441-4438) 3175
Hungarian Medical Journal see Therapia Hungarica 3157
Hungarian Music News see Hungarian Music Quarterly 3555
Hungarian Music Quarterly. (HU ISSN 0238-9401) 3555
Hungarian Observer. (HU ISSN 0238-9932) 2198
Hungarian P.E.N/P.E.N. Hongrois. (HU ISSN 0439-9080) 2923
Hungarian Pedagogy. see Magyar Pedagogia 1646
Hungarian People. see Magyarsag 2013
Hungarian Philosophical Review. see Magyar Filozofiai Szemle 3772
†Hungarian Press Review and Economic News. (HU) 5207
Hungarian Psychological Review. see Magyar Pszichologiai Szemle 4035
Hungarian Purist. see Magyar Nyelvor 2828
Hungarian R and D Abstracts. Science and Technology. (HU ISSN 0237-0808) 4356, 13, 4614
Hungarian Review see Hungarian Digest 2198
Hungarian Science. see Magyar Tudomany 4323

Hungarian Scout Magazine. see Magyar Cserkesz 1299
Hungarian Stock Market Courier. see Tozsde Kurir 966
Hungarian Studies. (HU ISSN 0236-6568) 2508, 4374
Hungarian Studies Newsletter. (US ISSN 0194-164X) 2817, 2923
Hungarian Tomorrow. see Magyar Holnap 2013
†Hungarian Trade Journal. (HU ISSN 0238-602X) 5207
Hungarian Trade Union News. (HU ISSN 0018-778X) 2584
Hungarian Traumatology, Orthopaedy and Restorative Surgery. see Magyar Traumatologia, Orthopedia es Helyreallito-Sebeszet 3310
Hungarian University of Physical Education. Review. (HU) 4474
Hungarian Water Supply. see Magyar Vizgazdalkodas 1924
Hungarian Word. see Amerikai Magyar Szo 1991
Hungarika Informacio. (HU ISSN 0238-0196) 402
†Hungarika Irodalmi Szemle. (HU ISSN 0133-7505) 5207
Hungarofilm Bulletin see Hungarian Cinema 5207
†Hungaropress Economic Information. (HU) 5207
Hungary see Magyarorszag 4578
Hungary. Central Statistical Office. Yearbook of Agricultural Statistics. see Hungary. Kozponti Statisztikai Hivatal. Mezogazdasagi Elelmiszeripari Statisztikai Evkonyv 138
Hungary. Kozponti Statisztikai Hivatal. A Kiskereskedem es a Fogyasztasi Szolgalt see Hungary. Kozponti Statisztikai Hivatal. Belkereskedelm 720
†Hungary. Kozponti Statisztikai Hivatal. Agazati Kapcsolatok Merlege. (HU ISSN 0209-6919) 5207
Hungary. Kozponti Statisztikai Hivatal. Belkereskedelm. (HU ISSN 0866-1146) 720
Hungary. Kozponti Statisztikai Hivatal. Belkereskedelmi Statisztikai Evkonyv see Hungary. Kozponti Statisztikai Hivatal. Belkereskedelm 720
Hungary. Kozponti Statisztikai Hivatal. Beruhazasi, Epitoipari, Lakasepitesi Evkonyu. (HU) 638
Hungary. Kozponti Statisztikai Hivatal. Beruhazasi, Epitoipari, Lakasepitesi Zsebkonyv. (HU ISSN 0139-3510) 638
Hungary. Kozponti Statisztikai Hivatal. Demografiai Evkonyv. (HU ISSN 0073-4020) 3992, 3982
†Hungary. Kozponti Statisztikai Hivatal. Epitoipari Arak Alakulasa. (HU ISSN 0237-0298) 5207
Hungary. Kozponti Statisztikai Hivatal. Foglalkoztatottsag es Kereseti Aranyok. (HU ISSN 0133-543X) 720, 981
Hungary. Kozponti Statisztikai Hivatal. Gazdasag es Statisztika. (HU ISSN 0239-1589) 720
Hungary. Kozponti Statisztikai Hivatal. Haztartasstatisztika. (HU ISSN 0439-9285) 2450
Hungary. Kozponti Statisztikai Hivatal. Idegenforgalmi Evkonyv. (HU ISSN 0230-4414) 4799
Hungary. Kozponti Statisztikai Hivatal. Ipari es Epitoipari Statisztikai Ertesito see Hungary. Kozponti Statisztikai Hivatal. Gazdasag es Statisztika 720
Hungary. Kozponti Statisztikai Hivatal. Ipari Zsebkonyv. (HU ISSN 0133-8684) 720
Hungary. Kozponti Statisztikai Hivatal. Iparstatisztikai Evkonyv. (HU ISSN 0209-4002) 720, 1077
Hungary. Kozponti Statisztikai Hivatal. Kozlekedesi Evkonyv. (HU ISSN 0237-8280) 4664, 4719
Hungary. Kozponti Statisztikai Hivatal. Kozlekedesi Posta es Tavkozlesi see Hungary. Kozponti Statisztikai Hivatal. Kozlekedesi Evkonyv 4664

Hungary. Kozponti Statisztikai Hivatal. Kulkereskedelmi Statisztikai Evkonyv.(HU ISSN 0139-3634) 720
Hungary. Kozponti Statisztikai Hivatal. Lakasstatisztikai Evkonyu see Hungary. Kozponti Statisztikai Hivatal. Beruhazasi, Epitoipari, Lakasepitesi Evkonyu 638
Hungary. Kozponti Statisztikai Hivatal. Mezogazdasagi Elelmiszeripari Statisztikai Evkonyv/Hungary. Central Statistical Office. Yearbook of Agricultural Statistics. (HU) 138
Hungary. Kozponti Statisztikai Hivatal. Mezogazdasagi Elelmiszeripari Statisztikai Zsebkonyv. (HU ISSN 0238-7891) 138
Hungary. Kozponti Statisztikai Hivatal. Mezogazdasagi Statisztikai Evkonyv see Hungary. Kozponti Statisztikai Hivatal. Mezogazdasagi Elelmiszeripari Statisztikai Evkonyv 138
Hungary. Kozponti Statisztikai Hivatal. Mezogazdasagi Statisztikao Zsebkonyu see Hungary. Kozponti Statisztikai Hivatal. Mezogazdasagi Elelmiszeripari Statisztikai Zsebkonyv 138
Hungary. Kozponti Statisztikai Hivatal. Nemzetkozi Statisztikai Evkonyv. (HU ISSN 0441-4713) 4573
Hungary. Kozponti Statisztikai Hivatal. Statisztikai Evkonyv. (HU ISSN 0073-4039) 4574
Hungary. Kozponti Statisztikai Hivatal. Statisztikai Havi Kozlemenyek. (HU ISSN 0018-781X) 4574
Hungary. Kozponti Statisztikai Hivatal. Statisztikai Szemle. (HU ISSN 0039-0690) 4574
Hungary. Kozponti Statisztikai Hivatal. Szamitastechnikai Statisztikai Evkonyv see Hungary. Kozponti Statisztikai Hivatal. Szamitastechnikai Statisztikai Zsebkonyv 1404
Hungary. Kozponti Statisztikai Hivatal. Szamitastechnikai Statisztikai Zsebkonyv. (HU) 1404
Hungary. Kozponti Statisztikai Hivatal. Teruleti Statisztika. (HU ISSN 0018-7828) 4574
Hungary. Kozponti Statisztikai Hivatal. Teruleti Statisztikai Evkonyv. (HU ISSN 0303-5344) 4574
Hungary. Kozponti Statisztikai Hivatal. Tudomanyos Kutatas es Fejlesztes. (HU) 4356
Hungary. Kozponti Statisztikai Hivatal. Vizgazdalkodasi Statisztikai Zsebkonyv. (HU ISSN 0209-7915) 4835
Hunger Notes. (US ISSN 0740-1116) 3606
Hungry Mind Review. (US ISSN 0887-5499) 4129, 2923
▼Hungry Mind Review Children's Book Supplement. (US) 4129, 1238
Huniy Erh/Human Rights. (MP) 3943
Hunt. (US) 4548
Hunt Institute for Botanical Documentation. Bulletin. (US) 505, 328
Hunt Magazine. (US) 4548
Hunter & Sport Horse. (US ISSN 1057-8501) 4535
Hunter Education Instructor. (US) 4548
Hunter Magazine. (US) 1314
Hunter Mountain News. (US) 4548
Hunter Region Economic Indicators. (AT ISSN 1030-0856) 720
Hunter Region Quarterly Economic Indicators see Hunter Region Economic Indicators 720
Hunter Safety Instructor see Hunter Education Instructor 4548
Hunter Valley Research Foundation. Monographs. (AT ISSN 0085-1663) 1489
Hunter Valley Research Foundation. Working Papers. (AT ISSN 0729-5030) 4574, 868, 4825
Hunterdon Historical Newsletter. (US ISSN 0018-7852) 2155, 2409
Hunter's Hill Trust Journal. (AT ISSN 0310-0111) 1489

HUSTLER LETTERS 6261

Hunter's Horn. (US ISSN 0018-7860) 4548
Huntia. (US ISSN 0073-4071) 505
Hunting see Petersen's Hunting 4553
Hunting and Fishing. see Pol'ovnictvo a Rybarstvo 4553
Hunting Annual see Sports Afield Special Publications 5282
Hunting Annual (Los Angeles). (US) 4548
Hunting Annual (New York) see Field & Stream Hunting Annual 4546
Hunting Group Review. (UK ISSN 0018-7887) 2194, 54, 3688
Hunting Guns by Outdoor Life & Jim Carmichel. (US) 4548
†Hunting House News. (US) 5207
Hunting Ranch Business. (US) 4548
Hunting Report: Edition II - For Birdshooters and Waterfowlers. (US ISSN 1053-4466) 4548
The Hunting Report for Big Game Hunters. (US ISSN 1052-4746) 4548
Hunting Retriever. (US ISSN 8750-6629) 3711
†Huntington Historical Society. Quarterly. (US) 5207
Huntington Library, Art Collections, and Botanical Gardens. Calendar. (US) 3525
Huntington Library, Art Gallery and Botanical Gardens. Collections see Huntington Library, Art Collections, and Botanical Gardens. Calendar 3525
Huntington Library Quarterly. (US ISSN 0018-7895) 2924
Huntsville Historical Review. (US ISSN 1048-3152) 2409
Hunyin yu Jiating/Marriage & Family. (US) 3067, 1238
Huon News. (AT ISSN 0018-7909) 2131
Hurdy Gurdy. (US ISSN 0191-6785) 3555
Huron Church News. (CN ISSN 0018-7917) 4240
Huron College Alphomega see Huron University Alphomega 1314
Huron Soil and Crop News. (CN) 179
Huron University Alphomega. (US) 1314
Huronia Business Journal. (CN) 868
Huronia Lifestyle. (CN) 2177
Hurra Juventus. (IT ISSN 0018-7933) 4474
Hurricane Alice. (US ISSN 0882-7907) 4845
Hurriyyati see Horreyati 2185
Hurtigmetode-nyt see Mikrobiologi-Nyt 4813
Hus & Hibyli/Home and Family. (IC) 2552, 2560
Husbyggaren. (SW ISSN 0018-7968) 620
Husdjur. (SW ISSN 0046-8339) 217, 200
†Huseierens Magasin. (NO ISSN 0333-3329) 5207
Huset Ude og Inde see Interieur 2552
Huset Vaart. (NO ISSN 0018-7976) 2560
Husfreyjan. (IC ISSN 0018-7984) 4845
Husholdningsarbejdet. (DK ISSN 0108-786X) 2447
Husipar. (HU ISSN 0018-800X) 2072
Husitsky Tabor. (CS) 2368
Huskers Illustrated. (US) 4506, 1314
Husmandshjemmet see Landbrugsmagasinet 104
Husmoderen. (DK) 2447
Husmorbladet. (NO ISSN 0018-8034) 4845, 1238, 2447
Husserl Studies. (NE ISSN 0167-9848) 3768
Husserliana. (NE ISSN 0439-9714) 3769
Hustler. (US ISSN 0149-4635) 3398
Hustler Busty Beauties. (US) 3398
Hustler Erotic Video Guide. (US) 3398, 1385
Hustler Fantasies. (US) 3398
Hustler Humor. (US ISSN 0199-5405) 3398
†Hustler Letters Magazine. (US) 5207

Husumer Monatshefte. (GW ISSN 0343-5555) 4771
Hutmacher-, Modisten- und Schirmmacher-Zeitung. (AU ISSN 0018-8050) 1285
Hutnicke Listy. (CS ISSN 0018-8069) 3408
Hutnik see Hutnik - Wiadomosci Hutnicze 3408
Hutnik. (CS) 3408
Hutnik - Wiadomosci Hutnicze. (PL) 3408
Hutoipar. (HU ISSN 0018-8085) 2072, 2300
Hutsuliya. (US) 2005, 2314
Huttlinger's Energy Reports. (US) 1790
Huttlinger's Natural Gas Bulletin. (US) 3688
Huttlinger's Oil Report. (US) 3688
Huttlinger's Pipeline Report. (US) 3688, 620
†Hutton's Building Products Catalog. (US) 5207
†Hutton's Mechanical Products Catalog.(US) 5207
†Hutton's Plumbing, Heating, Cooling Catalog. (US) 5207
▼Huul' Dzuyn Medeele/Legal Information. (MP) 2633
Huul' Yos/Legality. (MP) 2633
Huwat al-Funoun. see Arts Amateurs 316
Huxford Genealogical Society. Magazine.(US ISSN 0747-8445) 2155
Huxley Institute - C S F Newsletter see Health and Nutrition Update 3338
†Hvalraadets Skrifter/Scientific Results of Marine Biological Research. (NO ISSN 0073-4128) 5207
Hvar Observatory Bulletin. (CI ISSN 0351-2657) 365, 1590
Hvem, Hvad, Hvor. (DK ISSN 0106-4177) 3897
Hvidovre Lokalhistorie. (DK ISSN 0902-3046) 2368
Hvidvare-Nyt. (DK ISSN 0018-8107) 1893
▼Hwup! (US) 2995
†Hyatt Magazine. (US) 5207
†Hyatt's P C News Report. (US ISSN 0740-4859) 5207
Hybrid Circuit Technology. (US ISSN 0747-1599) 1893
Hybrid Circuits. (UK ISSN 0265-3028) 4599
Hybrid Microelectronics Review. (US) 1771
Hybrid Microelectronics Symposium. (Papers). (UK ISSN 0073-4136) 1771
Hybridoma. (US ISSN 0272-457X) 3185
Hydata - News and Views. (US) 4825
Hydraulics & Pneumatics. (US ISSN 0018-814X) 1924, 1930
Hydraulics and Pneumatics. (JA ISSN 0385-3780) 1924
Hydro-electric Power. see Shuili Fadian 4828
Hydro-Presse. (CN) 1893
Hydro Review. (US) 1802
Hydrobiologia. (NE ISSN 0018-8158) 440
Hydrobiological Bulletin see Netherlands Journal of Aquatic Ecology 449
Hydrobiological Journal. (English translation of: Gidrobiologicheskii Zhurnal) (US ISSN 0018-8166) 441, 1598, 2042
Hydrobiology. (BU ISSN 0324-0924) 441
Hydrocarbon and Byproduct Reserves. (CN) 3688, 1568
Hydrocarbon Processing. (US ISSN 0018-8190) 3688, 1854
Hydrocarbons Reserve Tape. (CN) 3688, 1568
Hydroelectric Plants Data Base. (US) 1802, 1790
Hydrogeology and Engineering Geology. see Shuiwen Dizhi Gongcheng Dizhi 1600
Hydrographic Journal. (UK ISSN 0309-7846) 1605, 1598
Hydrological Processes: An International Journal. (UK ISSN 0885-6087) 1598

Hydrological Science and Technology. (US ISSN 0887-686X) 4825, 1598, 1823, 1957
Hydrological Sciences Bulletin see Hydrological Sciences Journal 1598
Hydrological Sciences Journal/Journal des Sciences Hydrologiques. (UK ISSN 0262-6667) 1598
Hydrological Yearbook of Israel/Shenaton Hidrologi Le-Yisrael. (IS ISSN 0073-4217) 1598
Hydrological Yearbook of Surface Waters. The Oder Basin and the Rivers of the Coast Region Between the Oder and the Vistula. see Rocznik Hydrologiczny Wod Powirzchniowych. Dorzecze Odry i Rzeki Przymorza Miedzy Odra i Wisla 1600
Hydrological Yearbook of Surface Waters. The Vistula Basin and the Rivers of the Coast Region East of the Vistula River. see Rocznik Hydrologiczny Wod Powierzchniowych. Dorzecze Wisly i Rzeki Przymorza na Wschod od Wisly 1600
Hydrologie Continentale. (FR ISSN 0246-1528) 4825, 1598
Hydrology and Meteorology/Hidrologija i Meteorologija. (BU ISSN 0018-1331) 3436
Hydrolysis and Wood Chemistry U.S.S.R. (English translation of: Gidroliznaya i Lesokhimicheskaya Promyshlennost') (US ISSN 0730-8124) 1178, 2115
Hydrometallurgy. (NE ISSN 0304-386X) 3408
Hydrometeorologicky Ustav. Vyrocni Zprava. (CS) 3436
Hydrometeorologicky Ustav, Bratislava. Zbornik Prac. (CS) 3436
Hydrometric Yearbook. see Rocznik Hydrometryczny 1600
Hydronymia Europaea. (GW ISSN 0176-8123) 2924
Hydronymia Germaniae. (GW ISSN 0441-5302) 2252
Hydroplus. (FR) 4825
Hydroponic Society of Victoria. Newsletter. (AT) 2131
Hydroponic - Soilless Grower see Soilless Grower 2139
Hydrosoft see Advances in Water Resources 4821
Hydrotechnical Construction. (English translation of: Gidrotekhnicheskoe Stroietl'stvo) (US ISSN 0018-8220) 1867
Hydrotechnical Transactions. see Rozprawy Hydrotechniczne 4828
Hydrowire. (US) 1803
Hygie. (FR) 4104, 3804
Hygien och Miljoe see Kommun-Aktuelt 4089
Hygiene & Medizin. (GW ISSN 0172-3790) 3106
Hygiene and Sanitation. see Gigiena i Sanitariya 3802
Hygienic Community Network News. (US) 3804
Hygienist. (UK ISSN 0018-8263) 3804
Hyman Blumberg Symposium Series. (US) 1637, 4023
Hymn. (US ISSN 0018-8271) 3555, 4181
Hymn Society of Great Britain and Ireland. (UK) 3555
Hymnologiske Meddelelser. (DK ISSN 0106-4940) 4240, 3555, 4265
Hymy. (FI ISSN 0355-4317) 2186
Hymylehti see Hymy 2186
Hyogo Ika Daigaku Igakkai Zasshi. (JA ISSN 0385-7638) 3106
Hyogo Kyoiku Daigaku Kenkyu Kiyo. Dai-3-Bunsatsu. Shizenkei Kyoiku, Seikatsu Kenkokei Kyoiku/Hyogo University of Teacher Education Journal. Series 3: Natural Science, Practical Life Studies. (JA ISSN 0911-6230) 4313, 1751
Hyogo University of Teacher Education Journal. Series 3: Natural Science, Practical Life Studies. see Hyogo Kyoiku Daigaku Kenkyu Kiyo. Dai-3-Bunsatsu. Shizenkei Kyoiku, Seikatsu Kenkokei Kyoiku 4313

Hyologisk Tidsskrift Svinet. (DK ISSN 0106-1933) 217
Hyomen Gijutsu. (JA ISSN 0915-1869) 1212, 1854
Hypatia. (US ISSN 0887-5367) 4859
Hyper Activities. (AT ISSN 0810-6398) 1736
Hyperbaric Medicine Newsletter see Pressure (Bethesda) 3144
Hyperbaric Oxygen Review see Journal of Hyperbaric Medicine 4317
Hyperfine Interactions. (SZ ISSN 0304-3843) 3819
Hyperguide des Hypermarches see Annuaire des Hypermarches 1121
Hyperion (Austin). (US ISSN 0018-8328) 2995
Hypermedia. (UK ISSN 0955-8543) 1395, 1336
HyperNexus. (US) 1417, 1638
†Hypersensitivity. (UK ISSN 0142-8497) 5207
Hypertension. (US ISSN 0194-911X) 3208
Hypertension. (UK ISSN 0143-117X) 3208
Hyphen. (II ISSN 0018-8336) 2199
Hyphen. (MM) 2368
Hypnotherapy Today. (US ISSN 0882-8652) 3274, 4023
Hypomnemata. (GW ISSN 0085-1671) 1277, 3769
†Hypothalamus. (UK ISSN 0142-8683) 5207
Hyresgaesten. (SW ISSN 0018-8360) 2489, 2633, 4150
Hyria. (IT ISSN 0393-9367) 4374
Hysterectomy Educational Resources & Services Newsletter see H E R S Newsletter 4844
Hyundae Munhak. (KO) 2924
H2O. (NE) 4825
H4 - H8 C A G E Publication, Sec. A: U.S. and Canada see H4 - H8 Commercial and Government Entity Publication, Section A: U.S. and Canada 3476
H4 - H8 C A G E Publication, Sec. B: C A G E Code see H4 - H8 Commercial and Government Entity Publication, Section B: C A G E Code 3476
H4 - H8 C A G E Publication, Sec. C: NATO Manufacturers see H4 - H8 Commercial and Government Entity Publication, Section C: NATO Manufacturers 3476
H4 - H8 C A G E Publication, Sec. D: NATO C A G E see H4 - H8 Commercial and Government Entity Publication, Section D: NATO C A G E 3476
H4 - H8 Commercial and Government Entity Publication, Section A: U.S. and Canada. (US) 3476
H4 - H8 Commercial and Government Entity Publication, Section B: C A G E Code. (US) 3476
H4 - H8 Commercial and Government Entity Publication, Section C: NATO Manufacturers. (US) 3476
H4 - H8 Commercial and Government Entity Publication, Section D: NATO C A G E. (US) 3476
I A. (Industrial Archeology) (US ISSN 0160-1040) 4599
I A A E Journal see S A E - Australasia 4701
I A A F Newsletter. (International Agricultural Aviation Foundation) (US) 179
I A A H Newsletter. (International Association for Adolescent Health) (AT ISSN 0819-9558) 3106
I A A O Update. (International Association of Assessing Officers) (US) 4150
I A B Aktuell. (Institut fuer Arbeitsmarkt- und Berufsforschung) (GW ISSN 0933-2286) 981, 1066
I A B S E Congress Report. (International Association for Bridge and Structural Engineering) (SZ) 1867
I A B S E Periodica - Bulletin see Structural Engineering International 1874
I A B S E Periodica - Journal see Structural Engineering International 1874

I A B S E Periodica - Proceedings see Structural Engineering International 1874
I A B S E Periodica - Structures see Structural Engineering International 1874
I A B S E Periodica - Surveys see Structural Engineering International 1874
I A B S E Report. (International Association for Bridge and Structural Engineering) (SZ) 1867
I A C C Newsletter see Indo - U S Business 817
I A C P - B J A Policy Issues. (International Association of Chiefs of Police, Inc.) (US) 1515
I A C P Law Enforcement Legal Review see Law Enforcement Legal Review 1517
I A C P News. (International Association of Chiefs of Police, Inc.) (US) 1515
I A C P Training Key. (International Association of Chiefs of Police, Inc.) (US) 1515
I A D A Bulletin. (Independent Automotive Damage Appraisers Association) (US) 2533, 4692
†I A D A Watch Line. (Independent Automotive Damage Appraisers Association) (US) 5207
I A E A Film Catalog see I A E A Library Film Catalog 3837
I A E A Library Film Catalog. (International Atomic Energy Agency) (UN ISSN 0534-7319) 3837
I A E A Technical Documents Series. (International Atomic Energy Agency) (UN) 1805
I A E I News. (International Association of Electrical Inspectors) (US ISSN 0020-5974) 1893
I A E S T E Annual Report see International Association for the Exchange of Students for Technical Experience. Annual Report 1722
I A F C On Scene. (International Association of Fire Chiefs) (US) 2033, 4104
I A F - Information. (Interessengemeinschaft der mit Auslaendern Verheirateten Frauen e.V.) (GW) 4845
I A G A News. (International Association of Geomagnetism and Aeronomy) (UK ISSN 0536-1095) 1590
I A I A Bulletin see Impact Assessment Bulletin 4600
I A J R C Journal. (International Association of Jazz Record Collectors) (US ISSN 0098-9487) 3555
I A L A Bulletin. see A I S M. Bulletin 4723
I A L Directory of Industrial and Business Market Reports. (UK) 720
I A L News. (International Association of Laryngectomees) (US ISSN 0300-6883) 1736, 3106
I A L Plastics Yearbook. (UK) 3862, 1138
I A M C R Newsletter. (International Association for Mass Communications Research) (NE ISSN 0925-7950) 1336
†I A M P News Bulletin. (International Association of Meteorology and Atmospheric Physics) (AU) 5207
I.A.M.R. Reports. (Institute of Applied Manpower Research) (II ISSN 0418-5633) 981
I A M S Newsletter. (Institute for Archaeo-Metallurgical Studies) (UK ISSN 0261-068X) 274
I A P A Bulletin. (International Association of Physicians in Audiology) (UK ISSN 0262-6853) 3314
I A P A News. (Inter American Press Association) (US ISSN 0018-8409) 2570
I A P N H Newsletter. (International Association of Professional Natural Hygienists) (US) 3606, 3804
I.A.P. Professional Photography in Australia see Professional Photography in Australia 3796
I A Q C Circle Report see A Q P Report 1001

I A Quarterly Journal. (Ileostomy Association of Great Britain & Ireland) (UK) **3197**
I A R C Annual Report *see* I A R C Biennial Report **3197**
I A R C Biennial Report. (International Agency for Research on Cancer) (FR ISSN 0250-8613) **3197**
I A R C Monographs on the Evaluation of Carcinogenic Risks to Humans. (International Agency for Research on Cancer) (UN) **3197**
I A R C Scientific Publications. (International Agency for Research on Cancer) (UN ISSN 0300-5038) **3197**
tl A R U S Occasional Papers. (International Association for Regional and Urban Statistics) (NE) **5207**
I A S Bulletin. (Iowa Academy of Science) (US ISSN 0075-0344) **4313**
I A S E R Discussion Papers *see* N R I Discussion Papers **4380**
I A S E R Monographs *see* N R I Monographs **4380**
I A S E R Special Publications *see* N R I Special Publications **4380**
I A S L Conference Proceedings. (International Association of School Librarianship) (US ISSN 0257-3229) **2760**, 1638
I A S L I C Bulletin. (Indian Association of Special Libraries and Information Centres) (II ISSN 0018-8441) **2760**
I A S L I C Newsletter. (Indian Association of Special Libraries and Information Centres) (II ISSN 0018-845X) **2760**
I A S L I C Special Publication. (Indian Association of Special Libraries and Information Centres) (II ISSN 0073-6279) **2760**
I A S L I C Technical Pamphlets. (Indian Association of Special Libraries and Information Centres) (II ISSN 0073-6260) **2760**
I A S L Newsletter. (International Association of School Librarianship) (US ISSN 0085-2015) **2760**
I A S M H F Newsletter. (International Association of Sports Museums and Halls of Fame) (US) **3525**, 4475
I A S News. (US ISSN 0882-2751) **3959**
I A S P Explorer. (International Association of Space Philatelists) (US) **3753**, 54
I A S P Newsletter. (International Association of Scholarly Publishers) (NO ISSN 0333-3620) **1708**
I A S S I S T Newsletter *see* I A S S I S T Quarterly **2760**
I A S S I S T Quarterly. (International Association for Social Science Information Services and Technology) (US ISSN 0739-1137) **2760**, 2797, 4394
I A S T E D. International Conference Proceedings. (International Association of Science and Technology for Development) (CN) **1407**, 3338
I A T A Annual Report. (International Air Transport Association) (CN) **4674**
I A T A Dangerous Goods Regulations. (International Air Transport Association) (CN) **4674**
I A T A Live Animals Regulations. (International Air Transport Association) (CN) **4674**
I A T A News Review *see* I A T A Review **4674**
I A T A Publications and Training Material Available to the Public. (International Air Transport Association) (SZ) **4674**
I A T A Review. (International Air Transport Association) (CN ISSN 0376-642X) **4674**
I A T S S Research. (International Association of Traffic and Safety Sciences) (JA ISSN 0386-1104) **4692**
I A T U L Proceedings *see* I A T U L Quarterly **2760**

I A T U L Quarterly. (International Association of Technological Universities Libraries) (UK ISSN 0950-4117) **2760**, 1823, 4313
I A V Informationen. (Internationalen Aerosol - Verband) (SZ) **1178**
I A W A Bulletin. (International Association of Wood Anatomists) (NE ISSN 0254-3915) **505**, 2115
I A W A Publications *see* I A W A Bulletin **505**
tl A W C M Bulletin. (International Association of Wiping Cloth Manufacturers) (US) **5207**
I A W P C Technical Annual. (Indian Association for Water Pollution Control) (II) **1957**
I Aller Vaeder *see* Friluftsliv **4547**
tl Am News. (US) **5207**
I & C. (Ideology and Consciousness) (UK) **4374**
tl & C S Buyers' Guide. (US) **5207**
I & L. (Ideologies and Literature) (US ISSN 0161-9225) **2924**
I and N Reporter. (Immigration and Naturalization) (US ISSN 0018-8514) **3982**
I and S M *see* Iron & Steelmaker **3410**
I & T T *see* X I I I Magazine **1346**
I B A C International Update. (International Business Aviation Council) (US) **54**, 4674
I B A Commercial - Ag Lending Letter. (Illinois Bankers Association) (US) **784**
I B A Law Watch. (Illinois Bankers Association) (US) **2633**, 784
tl.B.A. News. (International Bartenders Association) (IT ISSN 0018-8530) **5207**
I B A Report. (International Baseball Association) (US) **4506**
I B A Review. (International Bauxite Association) (JM) **3485**
tl B A Technical Review. (Independent Broadcasting Authority) (UK ISSN 0308-423X) **5207**
I B C A M Journal. (Institute of British Carriage and Automobile Manufacturers) (UK) **4692**
I B C D: International Business Conditions Digest. (US ISSN 0738-3398) **868**
I B C - Donoghue's Money Fund Report.(US ISSN 0197-7091) **949**, 784
I B C's Money Market Insight. (US ISSN 1043-285X) **949**
I B C's Quarterly Report on Money Fund Performance. (US) **949**
I B E A S. (Instituto Boliviano de Estudio y Accion Social) (BO ISSN 0018-8581) **4437**
I B E D O C Information Newsletter *see* Educational Innovation and Information **1721**
I-B-E-S *see* Institutional Brokers Estimate System **785**
I B E W - A F L - C I O. Local 1470 Journal. (International Brotherhood of Electrical Workers, A F L - C I O) (US ISSN 0018-859X) **2584**, 1893
I B E W Journal. (International Brotherhood of Electrical Workers, A F L - C I O) (US ISSN 0897-2826) **2584**, 1893
I B F A N News. (International Baby Food Action Network) (US ISSN 0889-4000) **1238**, 930, 3606, 4104
I B F News. (International Bicycle Fund) (US) **4518**
tl.B. Flash-Edition Batiment. (BE ISSN 0018-8603) **5207**
I B G E Indicators. *see* Indicadores I B G E **5212**
tl B I D. (Journal of International Biomedical Information and Data) (UK ISSN 0260-0765) **5207**
I B I D (International Bibliography, Information, Documentation) *see* International Bibliography: Publications of Intergovernmental Organizations **403**
I B I-I C C Newsletter *see* I B I Newsletter **5208**
I B I Newsletter *see* InterMedia **1375**
tl B I Newsletter. (Intergovernmental Bureau for Informatics) (IT) **5208**

I B I S (Briefing Service). (International Benefits Information Service) (US ISSN 0018-8611) **981**
I B I S Review. (International Benefits Information Service) (US) **2533**, 4408
I B I T Arquivos *see* Arquivos Brasileiros de Tuberculose e Doencas do Torax **3364**
I.B. Informacja Biezaca. (PL ISSN 0033-2321) **3175**, 13
I B J Monthly Report. (Industrial Bank of Japan) (JA) **868**
I B L A. (Institut des Belles Lettres Arabes) (TI ISSN 0018-862X) **3638**, 2924
I B M & Compatibles User Group News.(US) **2705**, 1477
I B M Computer Today. (UK) **1395**
I B M - D E C *see* Network Computing (Cedar Knolls) **5244**
I B M Journal of Research and Development. (International Business Machines Corp.) (US ISSN 0018-8646) **1395**
I B M Monitor *see* I B M Nieuws **1453**
I B M Nachrichten. (GW ISSN 0018-8662) **1395**
I B M Nieuws. (NE) **1453**
I B M - P C Index. (US ISSN 0741-2355) **1404**, 13
I B M P C Update *see* Macintosh Update **1461**
I B M Quarterly. (AT) **1395**
tl B M Research Symposia Series. (US ISSN 0085-2082) **5208**
I B M Systems Journal. (International Business Machines Corp.) (US ISSN 0018-8670) **1437**, 1395
I B M UK News. (UK) **1396**
I B M User. (UK ISSN 0261-3654) **1444**
I B Magazette *see* Magazette **1470**
I B N. (Internationale Bodensee & Boot Nachrichten) (GW ISSN 0020-921X) **4525**
I B Nachrichten. (Oesterreichisches Institut fuer Bauforschung) (AU ISSN 0018-8697) **620**
I B R/Internationale Bibliographie der Rezensionen Wissenschaftlicher Literatur. (International Bibliography of Book Reviews of Scholarly Literature) (GW ISSN 0020-918X) **4356**
I B R O Monograph Series *see* International Brain Research Organization Monograph Series **3339**
I B R R *see* Index to Book Reviews in Religion **4213**
I B S A Bulletin. (Indigenous Bulb Growers Association of South Africa) (SA) **2131**
I B S Aktuell. (Interessenvereins des Bayerische Staatsopernpublikums e.V.) (GW) **3555**
I B W A News. (International Bottled Water Association) (US) **381**
I B W A Technical Bulletin. (International Bottled Water Association) (US) **381**
I B Z *see* Internationale Bibliographie der Zeitschriftenliteratur aus allen Gebieten des Wissens **403**
I B - 1. Informacja Biezaca. (PL) **3106**
I B - 2. Informacja Biezaca. (PL) **3106**, 4104
I-bunpi Kenkyukai Kiroku *see* I-bunpi Kenkyukaishi **3254**
I-bunpi Kenkyukaishi/Japanese Society of Gastric Secretion Research. Proceedings. (JA ISSN 0289-2057) **3254**, 441
I Byen's Spiseguide. (DK ISSN 0107-8313) **2476**
I C *see* Index Chemicus **1201**
I C A A. International Institutes on the Prevention and Treatment of Alcoholism. Papers. (International Congress on Alcoholism and Addictions) (SZ) **1536**
I C A A. Publications. (International Congress on Alcoholism and Addictions) (SZ) **1536**
I C A A C Program and Abstracts *see* Interscience Conference on Antimicrobial Agents and Chemotherapy. Program and Abstracts **553**

I C A A News. (Insulation Contractors Association of America) (US) **620**, 2300
I C A A News. (International Congress on Alcoholism and Addictions) (SZ) **1536**
I C A B A. (UK) **3959**
I C A Bulletin. (Insurance Council of Australia Inc.) (AT) **2533**
I C A C. Commissioner's Annual Report. (Independent Commission Against Corruption) (HK) **4063**
I C A C H. (Instituto de Ciencias y Artes de Chiapas) (MX ISSN 0536-2571) **328**, 4313
I C A E News. (International Council for Adult Education) (CN ISSN 0834-9789) **1684**, 4845
I C A Executive Search Newsletter. (International Classified Advertising (I C A)) (FR ISSN 0752-4676) **3628**, 1012
I C A Informa. (Instituto Colombiano Agropecuario) (CK ISSN 0046-9920) **96**
I C A - Kuriren. (SW ISSN 0345-5068) **2447**
I C A Letter. (International Carwash Association) (US) **4692**, 669
I C A M. (VE) **2924**, 2995
I C A M Annuaire. (Institut Catholique d'Arts et Metiers de Lille) (FR ISSN 0066-8982) **1823**
I C A Monthly Bulletin. (Institute of Contemporary Arts) (UK) **328**, 4633
I C A Newsletter. (International Communication Association) (US ISSN 0018-876X) **1336**
I C A O Bulletin *see* I C A O Journal **54**
I C A O Circulars. (International Civil Aviation Organization) (UN ISSN 0074-2481) **4674**
I C A O Journal. (International Civil Aviation Organization) (UN) **54**
I C A R Newsletter. (Interstate Cinderellans and Revenuers Educational Club) (US) **3753**
I C A Regional Bulletin. (International Cooperative Alliance) (II) **831**
I C A Review. (International Chiropractors Association) (US) **3215**
I C A S A L S Newsletter. (International Center for Arid and Semiarid Land Studies) (US ISSN 0018-8808) **96**, 1489, 2252, 4825
I C A S News *see* World Airshow News **65**
I C A T U Review. (International Confederation of Arab Trade Unions) (SY ISSN 0018-8816) **2584**
I C A Trade Journal. (International Ceramic Association) (US) **1138**, 1164
I C Alternate Sources & Replacements D.A.T.A. Digest. (US ISSN 1049-2682) **1771**, 1138
I C A's Newsletter. (International Credit Association) (US ISSN 0885-6788) **1505**
I C B. (International Communication Bulletin) (US ISSN 0018-8824) **2570**, 1638
I C B Magazine. (UK) **784**
I C B P Monographs. (International Council for Bird Preservation) (UK) **564**
I C B P Newsletter *see* World Birdwatch **568**
I C B P Parrot Working Group Meeting. Proceedings *see* I C B P Technical Publications **564**
I C B P Technical Publications. (International Council for Bird Preservation) (UK) **564**
I C B Review (Institute of Canadian Bankers) *see* Canadian Banker **770**
I C C A Congress Series. (International Council for Commercial Arbitration) (NE) **2710**
I C C A D *see* I E E E International Conference on Computer-Aided Design. Proceedings **1421**
I C C A Journal. (International Computer Chess Association) (NE ISSN 0920-234X) **1419**
I C C A's Newsletter *see* I C A's Newsletter **1505**

I C C D see I E E E International Conference on Computer Design. V L S I in Computers & Processors. Proceedings **1418**

I C C E see I E E E International Conference on Consumer Electronics. Digest of Technical Papers **1772**

I C C E T Annual Report. (Imperial College of Science and Technology) (UK) **1957**

I C C N - Outpatient Care. (US) **2466**

I C C Nederland. Publicaties. (NE) **817**

I C C V see International Conference on Computer Vision. Proceedings **1441**

I C C V - Internal Conference on Computer Vision. (US) **1407**

I C C W News Bulletin. (Indian Council for Child Welfare) (II ISSN 0018-8867) **4408**, 1238

I C D.A.T.A. Flash Service. (US) **1771**

I C D C News. (Industrial and Commercial Development Corporation) (KE) **836**

I C D L see International Conference on Conduction and Breakdown in Dielectric Liquids. Conference Record **1900**

I C D Letterette. (International College of Dentists) (US ISSN 0018-8875) **3234**

I C D Newsletter see I C D Letterette **3234**

I C E A Bulletin de Liaison. (Institut Canadien d'Education des Adultes) (CN) **1684**

†I.C.E.A. Cahiers. (Institut Canadien d'Education des Adultes) (CN ISSN 0018-8891) **5208**

I C E A Newsletter see Community Education International **1683**

I C E C A P Report. (Integrated Circuit Engineering Corporation) (US) **1772**

I C E L References. (International Council on Environmental Law) (GW) **1974**, 2699

I C E List of Members. (Institution of Civil Engineers) (UK) **1867**

I C E M Review. (International Council for Educational Media) (FR) **1638**

I C E N. (Israel Commercial Economic Newsletter) (IS ISSN 0792-3465) **836**

I C E S Cooperative Research Report/ Rapport des Recherches Collectives. (DK ISSN 1017-6195) **1605**, 1957, 2042

I C E S Fisheries Statistics/Bulletin Statistique des Peches Maritimes. (DK ISSN 1018-1571) **2051**, 4574

I C E S Identification Leaflets for Diseases and Parasites of Fish and Shellfish/Fiches d'Identification des Maladies et Parasites des Poissons, Crustaces et Mollusques. (DK ISSN 0109-2510) **584**, 1957, 2043

I C E S Identification Leaflets for Plankton/Fiches d'Identification du Plancton. (DK ISSN 0109-2529) **584**, 2043

I C E S Journal of Marine Science. (UK ISSN 1054-3139) **1605**, 2043

I C E S Marine Science Symposia/Actes du Symposium. (DK ISSN 0906-060X) **1605**, 1957, 2043

I C E S Oceanographic Data Lists see I C E S Oceanographic Data Lists and Inventories **1605**

I C E S Oceanographic Data Lists and Inventories. (DK ISSN 0106-6935) **1605**

I C E V H Educator. (International Council for Education of the Visually Handicapped) (US) **1736**, 2293

I C E Yearbook see I C E List of Members **1867**

I C F A Instrumentation Bulletin. (International Committee for Future Accelerators) (GW) **2522**

I C F Bugle. (International Crane Foundation) (US) **564**

I C F Quarterly. (Industrial Christian Fellowship) (UK ISSN 0018-8913) **4284**

†I C F T U Economic & Social Bulletin. (International Confederation of Free Trade Unions) (BE ISSN 0018-8921) **5208**

I C F T U - O R I T Inter-American Labor News. (Organizacion Regional Interamericana de Trabajadores) (MX) **2584**

I C H C A Quarterly Bulletin. (International Cargo Handling Coordination Association) (UK) **4664**, 13

I C H P E R Congress Proceedings. (International Council on Health, Physical Education and Recreation) (US) **3804**, 3106

I C H P E R Congress Reports see I C H P E R Congress Proceedings **3804**

I C H R Newsletter. (Indian Council of Historical Research) (II ISSN 0376-9682) **2338**

I C I A S F Record see International Congress on Instrumentation in Aerospace Simulation Facilities. Record **56**

I C I D Bulletin. (International Commission on Irrigation and Drainage) (II ISSN 0579-5427) **96**, 4825

I C I Spectrum. (Imperial Chemical Industries) (CN) **1077**

I C J Bibliography. (International Court of Justice) (UN) **2699**, 402, 2724

†I C J C Newsletter. (International Council of Jews from Czechoslovakia) (UK) **5208**

I C L A Bulletin. (International Comparative Literature Association) (US ISSN 0887-3615) **2924**

I C L A R M Bibliographies. (International Center for Living Aquatic Resources Management) (PH ISSN 0115-5997) **2051**

I C L A R M Conference Proceedings. (International Center for Living Aquatic Resources Management) (PH ISSN 0115-4435) **2043**, 584

I C L A R M Newsletter see N A G A: I C L A R M Quarterly **2046**

I C L A R M Studies and Reviews. (International Center for Living Aquatic Resources Management) (PH ISSN 0115-4389) **2043**

I C L A R M Technical Reports. (International Center for Living Aquatic Resources Management) (PH ISSN 0115-5547) **2043**

I C L A R M Translations. (International Center for Living Aquatic Resources Management) (PH ISSN 0115-4141) **2043**

†I C L A S Bulletin. (International Council for Laboratory Animal Science) (GW ISSN 0333-2241) **5208**

I C L C see International Contact Lens Clinic **3301**

I C L Technical Journal. (UK ISSN 0142-1557) **1396**

I C L Today. (UK ISSN 0268-5957) **827**

I C M A Abstracts Bulletin see Management Accounting Research **728**

I C M A Newsletter. (International City - County Management Association) (US ISSN 0047-0651) **4088**

†I C M C Newsletter/C I C M Informations/Boletin Informativo. (International Catholic Migration Commission) (SZ) **5208**

I C M E (Cars). (UK) **4692**

I C M E (Heavy Commercial Vehicles). (UK) **4692**

I C M E (Light Commercial Vehicles). (UK) **4692**

I C M Monthly Dispatch see I O M Monthly Dispatch **3982**

†I C M Monthly Dispatch for the Press. (Intergovernmental Committee for Migration) (SZ) **5208**

I C M R Annals. (International Center for Medical Research) (JA ISSN 0287-1785) **3106**

I C M R Bulletin. (Indian Council of Medical Research) (II ISSN 0377-4910) **3107**

I C Master. (US ISSN 0894-6809) **1772**

I C N-U C L A Symposium on Molecular Biology Proceedings see U C L A Symposium on Molecular Biology Proceedings **527**

I.C. Nachrichten. (Institutum Canarium) (AU) **274**

I C O C. (Istanbul Chamber of Commerce) (TU) **817**

I C O - Iconographisk Post. (SW ISSN 0106-1348) **328**, 4181

I C O Library Monthly Entries - Coffeeline. (International Coffee Organization) (UK ISSN 0144-6800) **2072**, 2085

I C O M News. (International Council of Museums) (FR ISSN 0018-8999) **3525**

I C P. (IT ISSN 0390-2358) **1854**

I C P A Quarterly. (International Commission for the Prevention of Alcoholism and Drug Dependency) (UN) **1536**

I C P A Quarterly Bulletin see I C P A Quarterly **1536**

I C P Administrative and Accounting Software. (International Computer Program) (US) **1450**

I C P Banking Software see Banking Software Review **805**

I C P E A C. Abstracts of Contributed Papers and Invited Papers see International Conference on the Physics of Electronic and Atomic Collisions. Abstracts of Contributed Papers and Invited Papers **3847**

I C P Manufacturing Software. (International Computer Program) (US) **1451**

I C P S R Bulletin. (Inter-University Consortium for Political and Social Research) (US) **4374**, 3898

I C R A F Newsletter and Agroforestry Review see Agroforestry Today **74**

I C R D B Cancergram: Acute and Chronic Leukemia - Diagnosis, Treatment see I C R D B Cancergram: Leukemia and Multiple Myeloma - Diagnosis, Treatment **3175**

I C R D B Cancergram: Antitumor and Antiviral Agents - Experimental Therapeutics, Toxicology, Pharmacology. (International Cancer Research Data Bank) (US) **1982**, 13, 3197, 3728

I C R D B Cancergram: Antitumor and Antiviral Agents - Mechanism of Action. (International Cancer Research Data Bank) (US) **3175**, 13, 3197

I C R D B Cancergram: Breast Cancer - Diagnosis, Treatment, Preclinical Biology. (International Cancer Research Data Bank) (US) **3175**, 13, 3197

I C R D B Cancergram: C N S Malignancies - Diagnosis, Treatment. (International Cancer Research Data Bank) (US) **3175**, 13, 3197

I C R D B Cancergram: Cancer Detection and Management - Biological Markers. (US) **3175**, 13, 3197

I C R D B Cancergram: Cancer Detection and Management - Diagnostic Radiology. (US) **3175**, 13, 3198, 3358

I C R D B Cancergram: Cancer Detection and Management - Nuclear Medicine. (US) **3175**, 13, 3198, 3358

†I C R D B Cancergram: Cancer Research Techniques and Applications. (US) **5208**

†I C R D B Cancergram: Cell Biology - Cell Kinetics. (US) **5208**

†I C R D B Cancergram: Cell Biology - Cytogenetics. (US) **5208**

†I C R D B Cancergram: Cell Biology - Growth Regulation and Differentiation. (US) **5208**

I C R D B Cancergram: Cell Biology - Kinetics see I C R D B Cancergram: Cell Biology - Cell Kinetics **5208**

†I C R D B Cancergram: Chemical Carcinogenesis - Aromatic Hydrocarbons and Heterocyclic Analogs. (US) **5208**

†I C R D B Cancergram: Chemical Carcinogenesis - Azo Dyes, Aryl Amines, and Related Compounds. (US) **5208**

†I C R D B Cancergram: Chemical Carcinogenesis - Miscellaneous Agents. (US) **5208**

†I C R D B Cancergram: Chemical Carcinogenesis - Nitroso Compounds.(US) **5208**

†I C R D B Cancergram: Clinical Cancer Immunology and Biological Therapy. (US) **5208**

I C R D B Cancergram: Clinical Treatment of Cancer - Radiation Therapy. (US) **3175**, 13, 3198, 3358

I C R D B Cancergram: Colorectal Cancer - Diagnosis, Treatment. (US) **3175**, 13, 3198

I C R D B Cancergram: Cytology - Techniques, Applications see I C R D B Cancergram: Cancer Research Techniques and Applications **5208**

†I C R D B Cancergram: D N A Tumor Viruses in Non-Primate Systems. (US) **5208**

†I C R D B Cancergram: Dietary Aspects of Carcinogenesis. (US) **5208**

I C R D B Cancergram: Endocrine Tumors - Diagnosis, Treatment, Pathophysiology. (US) **3175**, 13, 3198, 3254

†I C R D B Cancergram: Environmental and Occupational Carcinogenesis. (US) **5208**

†I C R D B Cancergram: Genetic Aspects of Carcinogenesis. (US) **5208**

I C R D B Cancergram: Genitourinary Cancers - Diagnosis, Treatment. (US) **3175**, 13, 3198, 3388

I C R D B Cancergram: Gynecological Tumors - Diagnosis, Treatment. (US) **3175**, 13, 3198, 3293

†I C R D B Cancergram: Hormones in Cancer-Related Biology - Non-Steroid Hormones. (US) **5208**

†I C R D B Cancergram: Hormones in Cancer-Related Biology - Steroid Hormones. (US) **5208**

†I C R D B Cancergram: Human Retroviruses. (US) **5208**

†I C R D B Cancergram: Immunobiology and Cancer - Functional Aspects of Cell-Mediated Immunity. (US) **5208**

†I C R D B Cancergram: Immunobiology and Cancer - Humoral Immunity. (US) **5208**

†I C R D B Cancergram: Immunobiology and Cancer - Identification and Characterization of Immune Cells. (US) **5208**

†I C R D B Cancergram: Immunobiology and Cancer - Tumor-Associated Antigens. (US) **5208**

†I C R D B Cancergram: Immunology and Cancer - The Major Histocompatibility Complex. (US) **5208**

I C R D B Cancergram: Leukemia and Multiple Myeloma - Diagnosis, Treatment. (US) **3175**, 13, 3198, 3272

I C R D B Cancergram: Lung Cancer - Diagnosis, Treatment. (US) **3175**, 13, 3198, 3365

I C R D B Cancergram: Lymphomas - Diagnosis, Treatment. (US) **3175**, 13, 3198

†I C R D B Cancergram: Mechanisms of Carcinogenesis - Activation and Metabolism of Carcinogens. (US) **5208**

†I C R D B Cancergram: Mechanisms of Carcinogenesis - Macromolecular Alteration and Repair. (US) **5208**

†I C R D B Cancergram: Mechanisms of Carcinogenesis - Oncogenic Transformation. (US) **5208**

I C R D B Cancergram: Melanoma and Other Skin Cancer - Diagnosis, Treatment. (US) **3175**, 13, 3198, 3248

†I C R D B Cancergram: Metastasis. (US) **5208**

†I C R D B Cancergram: Modification of Carcinogenesis. (US) **5208**

†I C R D B Cancergram: Molecular Biology - Cyclic Nucleotides. (US) **5209**

†I C R D B Cancergram: Molecular Biology - D N A. (US) **5209**

†I C R D B Cancergram: Molecular Biology - Proteins, Polypeptides, Amino Acids. (US) **5209**

†I C R D B Cancergram: Molecular Biology - R N A. (US) **5209**

I C R D B Cancergram: Neoplasia of the Head and Neck - Diagnosis, Treatment. (US) **3175,** 13, 3198

†I C R D B Cancergram: Organ Site Carcinogenesis - Gastrointestinal Tract and Pancreas. (US) **5209**

†I C R D B Cancergram: Organ Site Carcinogenesis - Kidney and Urinary Tract. (US) **5209**

†I C R D B Cancergram: Organ Site Carcinogenesis - Liver. (US) **5209**

†I C R D B Cancergram: Organ Site Carcinogenesis - Lymphatic and Hematopoietic Tissues. (US) **5209**

†I C R D B Cancergram: Organ Site Carcinogenesis - Mammary Gland. (US) **5209**

†I C R D B Cancergram: Organ Site Carcinogenesis - Reproductive Tract. (US) **5209**

†I C R D B Cancergram: Organ Site Carcinogenesis - Respiratory Tract. (US) **5209**

†I C R D B Cancergram: Organ Site Carcinogenesis - Skin. (US) **5209**

I C R D B Cancergram: Pediatric Oncology. (US) **3175,** 13, 3198, 3321

†I C R D B Cancergram: R N A Viruses Associated with Cancer. (US) **5209**

†I C R D B Cancergram: Radiation Carcinogenesis. (US) **5209**

I C R D B Cancergram: Rehabilitation and Supportive Care. (US) **3175,** 13, 3198

I C R D B Cancergram: Sarcomas and Related Tumors - Diagnosis, Treatment. (US) **3175,** 13, 3198

†I C R D B Cancergram: Short-Term Test Systems for Carcinogenicity and Mutagenicity. (US) **5209**

†I C R D B Cancergram: Structural and Functional Aspects of Cell Membranes. (US) **5209**

I C R D B Cancergram: Upper Gastrointestinal Tumors - Diagnosis, Treatment. (US) **3175,** 13, 3198, 3268

†I C R D B Cancergram: Viral Immunology. (US) **5209**

†I C R D B Cancergram: Virus Studies in Humans and Other Primates. (US) **5209**

I C R R Annual Report. (Institute for Cosmic Ray Research) (JA) **365,** 3436

I C R R Hokoku. (Institute for Cosmic Ray Research) (JA) **365**

I C R R Report. (Institute for Cosmic Ray Research) (JA) **365**

I.C.R. Scientific Report *see* Fox Chase Cancer Center. Scientific Report **3197**

I C R W Occasional Paper Series. (International Center for Research on Women) (US) **4845**

I C Replacement and Alternate Source Guide D.A.T.A. Book *see* I C Alternate Sources & Replacements D.A.T.A. Digest **1771**

I C S A Newsletter. (International Christian Studies Association) (US ISSN 1051-2772) **4181,** 4374

I C S D *see* International Conference on Conduction and Breakdown in Solid Dielectrics. Proceedings **1900**

I C S I D Review: Foreign Investment Law Journal. (International Center for Settlement of Investment Disputes) (US ISSN 0258-3690) **949,** 2633

I C S Newsletter. (International Catacomb Society) (US) **328,** 274, 4181

I C S S R Journal of Abstracts and Reviews: Economics. (Indian Council of Social Science Research) (II ISSN 0250-9695) **720**

I C S S R Journal of Abstracts and Reviews: Geography. (Indian Council of Social Science Research) (II ISSN 0250-9687) **2268**

I C S S R Journal of Abstracts and Reviews: Political Science. (Indian Council of Social Science Research) (II ISSN 0250-9660) **3937**

I C S S R Journal of Abstracts and Reviews: Sociology & Social Anthropology. (Indian Council of Social Science Research) (II) **254,** 13, 4457

I C S S R Newsletter. (Indian Council of Social Science Research) (II ISSN 0018-9049) **4374**

I C S S R Research Abstracts Quarterly. (Indian Council of Social Science Research) (II ISSN 0376-4206) **4394,** 13

I C S S R Union Catalogue of Social Science Periodicals. (Indian Council of Social Science Research) (II) **4395,** 402

I C S S R Union Catalogue of Social Science Periodicals - Serials *see* I C S S R Union Catalogue of Social Science Periodicals **4395**

▼I C S T I Forum. (International Council for Scientific and Technical Information) (FR) **2760**

I C S U AB News *see* I C S U Newsletter **4313**

I C S U Bulletin *see* I C S U Newsletter **4313**

I C S U Newsletter. (International Council of Scientific Unions) (FR) **4313**

I C-Stats: Forecasts, Analysis & Trends. (US) **720,** 868

I C Stockmarket Letter. (Investors Chronicle) (UK) **949**

I C T A Directory. (Institute of Certified Travel Agents) (US) **4771**

I C T A News. (Institute of Certified Travel Agents) (US) **4771**

I C T P Series in Theoretical Physics. (SI) **3819**

I C Update Master *see* I C Master **1772**

I C-Wissen Buerokommunikation. (GW ISSN 0724-4681) **1058**

I C Y R A N A Directory. (Intercollegiate Yacht Racing Association of North America) (US) **4525**

▼I C 2 Management and Management Science Series. (US ISSN 1058-5036) **1012**

I - D. (UK ISSN 0262-3579) **1291**

I D. (Ingenieurs Diplomes) (FR ISSN 0536-1362) **1823**

I D. (Information Display) (US) **2797,** 2760

I D A. (TU) **911**

†I D A F News Notes. (International Defense and Aid Fund for Southern Africa) (US) **5209**

†I.D.A. Journal. (International Desalination Association) (US) **5209**

I D A Newsletter. (International Desalination Association) (US) **4825**

I D A Working Papers. (Institute for Development Anthropology) (US) **241**

The I D B. (Inter-American Development Bank) (US) **784,** 930

I D C *see* Industrie du Cuir **2736**

I D C Impact. (Industrial Development Corporation) (BB) **930**

I D C Japan Report. (International Data Corporation) (US) **1424**

I D Checking Guide (Year). (US ISSN 1041-5793) **1515**

I D E. (Informacion de Envase y Embalaje) (SP ISSN 0300-4171) **3649**

†I D E A. (IT) **5209**

I.D.E.A. *see* Uusi Elektroniikka **5299**

†I D E A Monographs. (Institute for Development of Educational Activities, Inc.) (US ISSN 0073-8697) **5209**

†I D E A Occasional Papers. (Institute for Development of Educational Activities, Inc.) (US ISSN 0073-8700) **5209**

I.D.E.A.S. (Interiors, Design, Environment, Arts, Structures) (US ISSN 0161-1895) **2552**

I D E A S Bulletin. (Investment Diversification & Economic Analysis Ltd.) (UK) **949**

I D E A Today. (International Dance-Exercise Association) (US) **3804**

†I D E E S. (Innovations, Demarches, Experiences dans l'Enseignement Superieur) (CN ISSN 0382-0769) **5209**

I D E Occasional Papers Series. (Institute of Developing Economies) (JA ISSN 0537-9202) **669,** 1077

I D E S T *see* Index Documentation - Economie - Science - Technique **721**

I.D.E. Symposium Proceedings. (Institute of Developing Economies) (JA) **930**

I D F Bulletin. (International Diabetes Federation) (BE ISSN 0306-4980) **3254**

I D F Directory. (International Diabetes Federation) (BE) **3254**

†I D F Journal. (Israel Defense Forces) (IS ISSN 0333-8428) **5209**

I D F News Bulletin. (International Diabetes Federation) (BE) **3254**

I D G - Bulletin. (Information and Documentation Centre for the Geography of the Netherlands) (NE) **2252**

I D Handbook of Foodservice Distribution (Year). (Institutional Distribution) (US ISSN 0731-518X) **1138,** 2072

I D I Cronache *see* Chronica Dermatologica **3246**

I D - Informationsdienst fuer die Personalabteilung. (GW ISSN 0173-0665) **1012**

I D: International Design Magazine. (US ISSN 0192-3021) **2552,** 301, 3649, 4599

I D Magazine of International Design *see* I D: International Design Magazine **2552**

I D N - Infectious Diseases Newsletter. (US ISSN 0278-2316) **3219**

I D O C Internazionale. (International Documentation and Communication Center) (IT) **4395**

I D P Report. (Information and Data Base Publishing Report) (US ISSN 0197-0178) **1444**

I D R. (Industrie Diamanten Rundschau) (GW) **3485**

I D R A Newsletter. (Intercultural Development Research Association) (US) **1751**

I D R C Reports. (International Development Research Centre) (CN ISSN 0315-9981) **930**

I D S Briefs. (Incomes Data Services Ltd.) (UK) **981**

I D S Bulletin. (Institute of Development Studies) (UK ISSN 0265-5012) **930,** 4437

I D S Discussion Paper. (Institute of Development Studies) (UK ISSN 0308-5864) **930,** 4437

I D S European. (Incomes Data Services Ltd.) (UK) **981**

I D S International Report *see* I D S European **981**

I D S Research Reports. (Institute of Development Studies) (UK ISSN 0141-1314) **930,** 4437

I D Systems. (US ISSN 0892-676X) **827,** 1413

I D Systems Buyers Guide. (US) **827,** 1138, 1413

I E A - N E A Advocate. (Illinois Education Association, National Education Association) (US) **1638,** 2584

I E A - N E A Reporter *see* I E A Reporter (Year) **1638**

I E A Reporter (Year). (Idaho Education Association) (US) **1638**

I E C A Report. (International Erosion Control Association, Inc.) (US ISSN 0733-8910) **1489,** 3485

I E C Bulletin. (International Electrotechnical Commission) (SZ ISSN 0018-9138) **1893,** 3446

I E C Catalogue of Publications. (International Electrotechnical Commission) (SZ) **1772,** 402

I E C E C *see* Intersociety Energy Conversion Engineering Conference. Proceedings **1806**

I E C Newsletter. (International Evangelism Crusades) (US) **4181**

I E C O N: International Conference on Industrial Electronics, Control and Instrumentation. Proceedings. (US) **2522**

I E E Conference Publication Series. (Institution of Electrical Engineers) (UK ISSN 0537-9989) **1893**

I E E E. Orlando Section Monthly. (Institute of Electrical and Electronics Engineers) (US) **1894**

I E E E - A E S C O N. Aerospace and Electronics System Conference. Record. (Institute of Electrical and Electronics Engineers, Inc.) (US) **1894,** 55

I E E E - A E S S Dayton Chapter Symposium. (Aerospace and Electronic Systems Society, Dayton Section) (US) **55**

I E E E - A I A A Digital Avionics Systems Conference. Proceedings. (US) **55**

I E E E - A S S P Magazine *see* I E E E - Signal Processing Magazine **3859**

I E E E Acoustics, Speech and Signal Processing Magazine *see* I E E E - Signal Processing Magazine **3859**

I E E E Aerospace and Electronic Systems Magazine. (US ISSN 0885-8985) **1772,** 55

I E E E Aerospace Applications Conference. Digest. (US) **55**

I E E E Almanack. (US ISSN 0018-9154) **1894**

I E E E Annals of the History of Computing. (US ISSN 1058-6180) **1396**

I E E E Antennas and Propagation Magazine. (US ISSN 1045-9243) **1894**

I E E E Antennas and Propagation Society. International Symposium Digest *see* I E E E Antennas and Propagation Magazine **1894**

I E E E Applied Power Electronics Conference and Exposition. Conference Proceedings. (US) **1772**

I E E E Bipolar Circuits and Technology Meeting *see* Bipolar Circuits and Technology Meeting. Proceedings **1764**

I E E E - C H M T International Electronic Manufacturing Technology Symposium. (US) **1894,** 1917

I E E E Careers Conference. Conference Record. (US) **1894,** 3628

I E E E Cement Industry Technical Conference. Record. (US) **620**

I E E E Circuits and Devices Magazine. (US ISSN 8755-3996) **1772**

I E E E Communications Magazine. (US ISSN 0163-6804) **1894**

I E E E Computer *see* Computer **1391**

I E E E Computer Applications in Power.(US ISSN 0895-0156) **1894**

I E E E Computer Graphics and Applications. (US ISSN 0272-1716) **1421**

I E E E Computer Society Conference on Computer Vision and Pattern Recognition. Proceedings. (Institute of Electrical and Electronics Engineers, Inc.) (US) **1421**

I E E E Computer Society International Conference *see* CompCon: I E E E Computer Society International Conference **1390**

I E E E Computer Society International Conference on Computer Languages *see* International Conference on Computer Languages. Proceedings **1430**

I E E E Computer Society Workshop on Computer Vision *see* I C C V - Internal Conference on Computer Vision **1407**

I E E E Computer Society Workshop on Visual Languages. (US) **2856**

I E E E Computer Society's International Computer Software & Applications Conference. Proceedings. *see* C O M P S A C **1476**

†I E E E Conference on Computer Workstations. Proceedings. (US) **5209**

Title

I E E E Conference on Decision and Control. Proceedings. (US) **4599**
I E E E Conference on Human Factors and Power Plant. Conference Record.(US) **1805, 1894, 4104**
I E E E Conference on U S Technology Policy. Proceedings *see* Conference on U S Technology Policy. Proceedings **4595**
▼I E E E Conference on Visualization. (US) **1421**
I E E E Control Systems Magazine. (US ISSN 0888-0611) **1894**
I E E E Custom Integrated Circuits Conference. Proceedings. (US) **1894**
I E E E Design & Test of Computers. (US ISSN 0740-7475) **1418**
I E E E Electrical Insulation Magazine. (US ISSN 0883-7554) **1894**
I E E E Electron Device Letters. (US ISSN 0741-3106) **1772, 1790**
††I E E E ElectroTechnology Review. (US ISSN 0748-9196) **5209**
I E E E Engineering in Medicine and Biology Magazine. (US ISSN 0739-5175) **469, 3107, 4599**
I E E E Engineering in Medicine and Biology Society. Conference *see* I E E E Engineering in Medicine and Biology Society. International Conference **3225**
I E E E Engineering in Medicine and Biology Society. International Conference. (US) **3225**
I E E E Engineering Management Review. (US ISSN 0360-8581) **1824, 1012, 1894**
I E E E Expert. (US ISSN 0885-9000) **1418, 1477**
I E E E Gallium Arsenide Integrated Circuit Symposium. Technical Digest *see* Ga As I C Symposium **1771**
I E E E Grid. (US) **1894**
I E E E Industrial Electronics Society Conference *see* I E C O N: International Conference on Industrial Electronics, Control and Instrumentation. Proceedings **2522**
I E E E Infocom. Proceedings. (US) **1350**
I E E E Instrumentation and Measurement Technology Conference. Proceedings. (US) **2522, 3446**
I E E E International Conference on Acoustics, Speech and Signal Processing. Proceedings. (US) **1894**
I E E E International Conference on Acoustics, Speech and Signal Processing. Record *see* I E E E International Conference on Acoustics, Speech and Signal Processing. Proceedings **1894**
I E E E International Conference on Communications. Conference Record.(US ISSN 0536-1486) **1337**
I E E E International Conference on Computer-Aided Design. Proceedings.(US) **1421**
I E E E International Conference on Computer Design. V L S I in Computers & Processors. Proceedings. (US) **1418**
I E E E International Conference on Consumer Electronics. Digest of Technical Papers. (US) **1772**
I E E E International Conference on Engineering in the Ocean Environment. Record *see* Oceans. Conference Record **1832**
I E E E International Conference on Plasma Science. I E E E Conference Record-Abstracts. (US ISSN 0730-9244) **1894**
I E E E International Conference on Robotics and Automation. Proceedings. (US) **1413, 1407**
I E E E International Conference on Systems, Man, and Cybernetics. Proceedings. (US) **1441**
I E E E International Conference on Tools for A I. (US) **1408**
I E E E International Electronic Manufacturing Technology Symposium *see* I E E E - C H M T International Electronic Manufacturing Technology Symposium **1894**

I E E E International Semiconductor Laser Conference. Conference Digest.(US) **3853**
I E E E International Solid State Circuits Conference. Digest of Technical Papers. (US ISSN 0193-6530) **1772**
I E E E International Symposium on Circuit Theory. Symposium Digest. Summaries of Papers *see* I E E E International Symposium on Circuits and Systems. Proceedings **1772**
I E E E International Symposium on Circuits and Systems. Proceedings. (US ISSN 0277-674X) **1772**
I E E E International Symposium on Electrical Insulation. I E E E Conference Record. (US) **1894**
I E E E International Symposium on Electromagnetic Compatibility. (US ISSN 0190-1494) **1894**
I E E E International Symposium on Information Theory. Abstracts of Papers. (US ISSN 0271-4655) **1456**
I E E E International Symposium on Intelligent Control. Proceedings. (US) **1408, 1413**
▼I E E E Journal of Microelectromechanical Systems. (US ISSN 1057-7157) **1894**
I E E E Journal of Oceanic Engineering. (US ISSN 0364-9059) **1895, 1605, 1824**
I E E E Journal of Quantum Electronics. (US ISSN 0018-9197) **1772, 3853**
I E E E Journal of Robotics and Automation *see* I E E E Transactions on Robotics and Automation **1413**
I E E E Journal of Solid State Circuits. (US ISSN 0018-9200) **1895**
I E E E Journal on Selected Areas in Communications. (US ISSN 0733-8716) **1337, 1895**
▼I E E E - L T S: The Magazine of Lightwave Telecommunications Systems. (US ISSN 1055-6877) **1895, 1337**
I E E E - M T T - S International Microwave Symposium. Digest. (Microwave Theory and Techniques Society) (US ISSN 0149-645X) **1895**
I E E E - M T T - S International Microwave Symposium. Digest of Technical Papers *see* I E E E - M T T - S International Microwave Symposium. Digest **1895**
I E E E Micro. (US ISSN 0272-1732) **1460, 1469**
▼I E E E Microwave and Guided Wave Letters. (US ISSN 1051-8207) **1895, 3819**
I E E E Microwave and Millimeter-Wave Monolithic Circuits Symposium. Digest of Papers. (US) **1895**
I E E E Military Communications Conference. Conference Record. (US) **1895**
I E E E Military Communications Conference. Proceedings *see* I E E E Military Communications Conference. Conference Record **1895**
I E E E National Aerospace and Electronics Conference. Proceedings. (US ISSN 0547-3578) **55**
I E E E National Radar Conference. Proceedings. (US) **1895, 1337**
I E E E Network. (US ISSN 0890-8044) **1427**
I E E E Pacific Rim Conference on Communications, Computers and Signal Processing. Conference Proceedings. (US) **1350**
I E E E Particle Accelerator Conference. Proceedings. (US) **1895, 3819**
I E E E Photonics Technology Letters. (US ISSN 1041-1135) **3853, 1895**
I E E E Photovoltaic Specialists Conference. Conference Record. (US ISSN 0160-8371) **1895**
I E E E Position Location and Navigation Symposium. Record. (US) **1895, 1337**
I E E E Potentials. (US ISSN 0278-6648) **1895, 1708**

I E E E Power Electronics Specialists Conference. Record. (US ISSN 0275-9306) **55**
I E E E Power Engineering Review. (US ISSN 0272-1724) **1895**
I E E E Power Engineering Society. Summer Meeting. Preprints. (US) **1895**
I E E E Power Engineering Society. Winter Meeting. Preprints. (US ISSN 0073-9154) **1895**
I E E E Power Processing and Electronics Specialists Conference. Record *see* I E E E Power Electronics Specialists Conference. Record **55**
I E E E Professional Communication Society Conference. Record *see* International Professional Communication Conference. Conference Record **1895**
I E E E Publications Bulletin. (US ISSN 0046-8371) **1844, 1772, 1895**
I E E E Pulsed Power Conference. Digest of Technical Papers. (US) **1802, 1790**
I E E E Region 5 Conference. Record. (US ISSN 0073-9197) **1895**
I E E E Semiconductor Manufacturing. Transactions. (US ISSN 0894-6507) **1895**
I E E E Semiconductor Thermal and Temperature Measurement Symposium. Proceedings. (US) **1895, 3841**
I E E E - Signal Processing Magazine. (US ISSN 1053-5888) **3859**
I E E E Software. (US ISSN 0740-7459) **1477**
I E E E Solid-State Sensor and Actuator Workshop. Technical Digest. (US) **1896**
I E E E Solid-State Sensor Workshop *see* I E E E Solid-State Sensor and Actuator Workshop. Technical Digest **1896**
I E E E Southeastcon (Region 3 Conference) Record. (US) **1896**
I E E E Spectrum. (US ISSN 0018-9235) **1896**
I E E E Student Papers. (US ISSN 0362-4536) **1896**
I E E E Symposium on Mass Storage Systems. Digest of Papers. (US) **1396, 827, 1058**
I E E E Symposium on Research in Security and Privacy. Proceedings. (US ISSN 0278-7032) **1434, 1526**
I E E E Symposium on Security and Privacy. Proceedings *see* I E E E Symposium on Research in Security and Privacy. Proceedings **1434**
I E E E Technical Activities Guide. (US ISSN 0278-520X) **1896**
I E E E Technical Papers Presented at the A S M E - I E E E Joint Railroad Conference (1989) *see* A S M E - I E E E Joint Railroad Conference. I E E E Technical Papers **4707**
I E E E Technology and Society Magazine. (US ISSN 0278-0097) **4599, 1896**
I E E E Transactions on Acoustics, Speech and Signal Processing *see* I E E E Transactions on Signal Processing **1897**
I E E E Transactions on Aerospace and Electronic Systems. (US ISSN 0018-9251) **1896, 55**
I E E E Transactions on Antennas and Propagation. (US ISSN 0018-926X) **1896**
▼I E E E Transactions on Applied Superconductivity. (US ISSN 1051-8223) **1772, 3819**
I E E E Transactions on Automatic Control. (US ISSN 0018-9286) **1896, 1413**
I E E E Transactions on Biomedical Engineering. (US ISSN 0018-9294) **469, 3107**
I E E E Transactions on Broadcasting. (US ISSN 0018-9316) **1374**
I E E E Transactions on Circuit Theory *see* I E E E Transactions on Circuits and Systems Part 2: Analog and Digital Signal Processing **1772**

I E E E Transactions on Circuits and Systems *see* I E E E Transactions on Circuits and Systems Part 1: Fundamental Theory and Applications **1772**
I E E E Transactions on Circuits and Systems *see* I E E E Transactions on Circuits and Systems Part 2: Analog and Digital Signal Processing **1772**
▼I E E E Transactions on Circuits and Systems for Video Technology. (US ISSN 1051-8215) **1772, 1385**
I E E E Transactions on Circuits and Systems Part 1: Fundamental Theory and Applications. (US ISSN 1057-7122) **1772, 1896**
I E E E Transactions on Circuits and Systems Part 2: Analog and Digital Signal Processing. (US ISSN 1057-7130) **1772, 1896**
I E E E Transactions on Communications. (US ISSN 0090-6778) **1337**
I E E E Transactions on Components, Hybrids and Manufacturing Technology. (US ISSN 0148-6411) **1772, 1896**
I E E E Transactions on Computer-Aided Design of Integrated Circuits and Systems. (US ISSN 0278-0070) **1779**
I E E E Transactions on Computers. (US ISSN 0018-9340) **1396**
I E E E Transactions on Consumer Electronics. (US ISSN 0098-3063) **1772**
I E E E Transactions on Education. (US ISSN 0018-9359) **1896, 1638**
I E E E Transactions on Electrical Insulation. (US ISSN 0018-9367) **1896**
I E E E Transactions on Electromagnetic Compatibility. (US ISSN 0018-9375) **1773**
I E E E Transactions on Electron Devices. (US ISSN 0018-9383) **1773**
I E E E Transactions on Energy Conversion. (US ISSN 0885-8969) **1802, 1896**
I E E E Transactions on Engineering Management. (US ISSN 0018-9391) **1896**
I E E E Transactions on Geoscience and Remote Sensing. (US ISSN 0196-2892) **1896, 1545**
I E E E Transactions on Industrial Electronics. (US ISSN 0278-0046) **1773**
I E E E Transactions on Industry Applications. (US ISSN 0093-9994) **1897, 4599**
I E E E Transactions on Information Theory. (US ISSN 0018-9448) **1456**
I E E E Transactions on Instrumentation and Measurement. (US ISSN 0018-9456) **3446**
I E E E Transactions on Knowledge & Data Engineering. (US ISSN 1041-4347) **1897**
I E E E Transactions on Magnetics. (US ISSN 0018-9464) **1897**
I E E E Transactions on Medical Imaging. (US ISSN 0278-0062) **3107**
I E E E Transactions on Microwave Theory and Techniques. (US ISSN 0018-9480) **1897**
▼I E E E Transactions on Neural Networks. (US ISSN 1045-9227) **1408, 1897**
I E E E Transactions on Nuclear Science. (US ISSN 0018-9499) **1897, 1805**
▼I E E E Transactions on Parallel and Distributed Systems. (US ISSN 1045-9219) **1427, 1897**
I E E E Transactions on Pattern Analysis and Machine Intelligence. (US ISSN 0162-8828) **1421**
I E E E Transactions on Plasma Science. (US ISSN 0093-3813) **3819**
I E E E Transactions on Power Delivery. (US ISSN 0885-8977) **1897**
I E E E Transactions on Power Electronics. (US ISSN 0885-8993) **1773**

I E E E Transactions on Power Systems.(US ISSN 0885-8950) **1802,** 1790
I E E E Transactions on Professional Communication. (US ISSN 0361-1434) **1897,** 2570
I E E E Transactions on Reliability. (US ISSN 0018-9529) **1897**
I E E E Transactions on Robotics and Automation. (US ISSN 1042-296X) **1413,** 1408
I E E E Transactions on Signal Processing. (US ISSN 1053-587X) **1897,** 1441
I E E E Transactions on Software Engineering. (US ISSN 0098-5589) **1477**
I E E E Transactions on Sonics and Ultrasonics *see* I E E E Transactions on Ultrasonics, Ferroelectrics and Frequency Control **3859**
I E E E Transactions on Systems, Man and Cybernetics. (US ISSN 0018-9472) **1441**
I E E E Transactions on Ultrasonics, Ferroelectrics and Frequency Control.(US ISSN 0885-3010) **3859**
I E E E Transactions on Vehicular Technology. (US ISSN 0018-9545) **1897,** 4650
I E E E Translation Journal on Magnetics in Japan. (US ISSN 0882-4959) **1897**
I E E E Trends in Electronics Conference. Proceedings *see* T E N C O N (I E E E Region 10 Conference). Proceedings **1401**
I E E E Vehicular Technology Conference. Record. (US ISSN 0098-3551) **4692**
I E E E Working Conference on Current Measurement. Proceedings. (US) **1605,** 1897
I E E E Workshop on Automotive Applications of Electronics (Publication). (US) **4707**
I E E E Workshop on Intelligent Control. Proceedings *see* I E E E International Symposium on Intelligent Control. Proceedings **1408**
†I E E E Workshop on Languages for Automation (Proceedings). (US) **5209**
▼I E E E Workshop on Visual Motion. (US) **1421**
I E E - Industrie, Elektrik und Elektronik.(GW ISSN 0722-6179) **1897**
I E E News *see* I E E Review **1898**
I E E Proceedings Part A: Covering Reviews, Physical Science, Measurement and Instrumentation, Management and Education *see* I E E Proceedings Part A: Covering Science, Measurement and Technology **1898**
I E E Proceedings Part A: Covering Science, Measurement and Technology. (Institution of Electrical Engineers) (UK) **1898**
I E E Proceedings Part B: Electric Power Applications. (UK ISSN 0143-7038) **1898**
I E E Proceedings Part C: Generation, Transmission and Distribution. (UK ISSN 0143-7046) **1898**
I E E Proceedings Part D: Control Theory and Applications. (UK ISSN 0143-7054) **1898,** 1408
I E E Proceedings Part E: Computers and Digital Techniques. (UK ISSN 0143-7062) **1453,** 1396
I E E Proceedings Part F: Communications, Radar and Signal Processing *see* I E E Proceedings Part F: Radar and Signal Processing **1898**
I E E Proceedings Part F: Radar and Signal Processing. (UK ISSN 0956-375X) **1898**
I E E Proceedings Part G: Circuits, Devices and Systems. (UK ISSN 0956-3768) **1898**
I E E Proceedings Part G: Electronic Circuits and Systems *see* I E E Proceedings Part G: Circuits, Devices and Systems **1898**

I E E Proceedings Part H: Microwaves, Antennas & Propagation. (UK ISSN 0950-107X) **1898**
I E E Proceedings Part H: Microwaves, Optics and Antennas *see* I E E Proceedings Part H: Microwaves, Antennas & Propagation **1898**
I E E Proceedings Part I: Communications, Speech and Vision. (UK ISSN 0956-3776) **1898**
I E E Proceedings Part I: Solid-State and Electron Devices *see* I E E Proceedings Part I: Communications, Speech and Vision **1898**
I E E Proceedings Part J: Optoelectronics. (Institution of Electrical Engineers) (UK ISSN 0267-3932) **3853,** 1898
I E E Review. (UK) **1898,** 1337
I E F Information. (Institut for Europaeisk Folkelivsforskning) (DK ISSN 0105-0532) **4437**
I E G Directory of Sponsorship Marketing. (International Events Group, Inc.) (US ISSN 0894-0649) **1040**
I E G Sponsorship Report. (International Events Group, Inc.) (US) **1040**
I E I C E Transactions - Denshi Joho Tsushin Gakkai Ronbunshi (E) *see* I E I C E Transactions on Communications Electronics Information and Systems **1773**
I E I C E Transactions on Communications Electronics Information and Systems. (Institute of Electronics, Information and Communication Engineers) (JA ISSN 0917-1673) **1773,** 1337
I E M T *see* I E E E - C H M T International Electronic Manufacturing Technology Symposium **1894**
I E N - Europe. (Industrial Engineering News) (BE) **1925**
I E N - Europe (International Equipment News) *see* I E N - Europe **1925**
I E N: Industrial Equipment News. (US ISSN 0019-8285) **1041,** 3018
I E N Pubblicazione. (Istituto Elettrotecnico Nazionale Galileo Ferraris) (IT ISSN 0018-957X) **1773**
I.E.N.S. Press Handbook *see* Indian & Eastern Newspaper Society Press Handbook **2571**
I E News: Aerospace. (Institute of Industrial Engineers) (US) **55,** 3392
I E News: Health Services *see* Society for Health Systems. Journal **3622**
†I E News: Process Industries. (Institute of Industrial Engineers) (US) **5209**
I E News: Utilities. (Institute of Industrial Engineers) (US) **1867**
I E S A Information. (International Society for Electrosleep and Electroanaesthesia) (AU ISSN 0539-0230) **3338**
I E S Lighting Handbook. (Illuminating Engineering Society) (US ISSN 0073-5469) **1898**
†I.E.S. Lighting Review. (Illuminating Engineering Society of Australia) (AT ISSN 0018-9618) **5209**
I E S News *see* X I I I Magazine **1346**
I E S Newsletter. (Institute of Ecosystem Studies) (US) **1957,** 505, 2131
I E S Proceedings. (Institution of Environmental Sciences) (UK ISSN 0260-4833) **1957**
I E T E Technical Review. (Institution of Electronics and Telecommunication Engineers) (II ISSN 0256-4602) **1337,** 1824
I E X E Newsletter *see* I I E X E Newsletter **1824**
I F *see* Informatore Fitopatologico **506**
I F *see* Die Industriefeuerung **3689**
I F A Annual Report. (International Federation of Accountants) (US) **751**
I F A C Proceedings *see* I F A C Symposia Series **1930**
I F A C Symposia Series. (International Federation of Automatic Control) (US ISSN 0962-9505) **1930**
I F A Congress Seminar Series. (International Fiscal Association) (NE) **1097**

I F A Cooperator. (Intermountain Farmers Association) (US) **96**
I F A N Bulletin. Serie A: Sciences Naturelles. (Institut Fondamental d'Afrique Noire) (SG ISSN 0018-9634) **4313**
I F A N Bulletin. Serie B: Sciences Humaines. (Institut Fondamental d'Afrique Noire) (SG ISSN 0018-9642) **2508**
I F A Newsletter. (International Federation of Accountants) (US) **751**
I F A P Bulletin *see* Safety W A **3621**
I F A P Newsletter. (International Federation of Agricultural Producers) (FR) **96**
I F A R Reports. (International Foundation for Art Research, Inc.) (US ISSN 8756-7172) **329,** 1515
I F A Seminar Series. (International Fiscal Association) (NE) **2724**
I F A Technical Conference. Proceedings. (International Fertilizer Industry Association) (FR) **179**
I F A W P C A Newsletter. (International Federation of Asian and Western Pacific Contractors' Associations) (PH) **620,** 1824
I F C A T I Directory *see* I T M F Directory **4619**
I F C E P Journal *see* Asian Economic and Social Review **4366**
I F C O Journal. (International Fan Club Organization) (US) **1298**
I F C O News. (Interreligious Foundation for Community Organization) (US ISSN 0047-1305) **4408**
I F D A Dossier. (International Foundation for Development Alternatives) (UN ISSN 0254-3036) **3959,** 930
I F E F, Austria Sekcio. Bulteno. (Federacio Esperantista Fervojista) (AU ISSN 0005-0504) **4710,** 2817
I F E P P Informations. (Institut de Formation et d'Etudes Psycho-Sociologiques et Pedagogiques) (FR ISSN 0046-9688) **4023,** 4374
I F E S Review. (International Fellowship of Evangelical Students) (UK) **4181**
I F H O H Journal. (International Federation of the Hard of Hearing) (NE ISSN 0255-0326) **2288,** 1736, 3314
I F H P News Sheet *see* Prospect **2494**
I F I Fabricare News. (International Fabricare Institute) (US ISSN 0161-8040) **1281**
I F I P Transactions A: Computer Science and Technology. (International Federation for Information Processing) (NE ISSN 0926-5473) **1396,** 1418
I F I P Transactions B: Applications in Technology. (NE ISSN 0926-5481) **1396,** 1418
I F I P Transactions C: Communications Systems. (NE ISSN 0926-549X) **1350,** 1396, 1418
I F J Information. (International Federation of Journalists) (BE) **2570**
I F L A Annual. (International Federation of Library Associations and Institutions) (GW ISSN 0074-5987) **2760**
I F L A Communications. (International Federation of Library Associations and Institutions) (NE ISSN 0109-5366) **2793**
I F L A Directory. (International Federation of Library Associations and Institutions) (NE ISSN 0074-6002) **2760**
I F L A Journal. (GW ISSN 0340-0352) **2761**
I F L A News *see* I F L A Journal **2761**
I F L A Publications. (GW ISSN 0344-6891) **2761**
†I F L - Mitteilungen. (Institut fuer Leichtbau und Oekonomische Verwendung von Werkstoffen) (GW ISSN 0018-9693) **5209**
I F L Nieuws. (International Friendship League) (NE ISSN 0018-9707) **1298,** 4771

I F M A News. (International Facility Management Association) (US ISSN 0747-6221) **1012**
I F M A News. (Interdenomination Foreign Mission Association of North America, Inc.) (US ISSN 0018-9723) **4181**
I F M A World. (International Foodservice Manufacturers Association) (US) **2072**
I F M R Publications. (Institute for Financial Management and Research) (II) **1012**
I F M - S E I Bulletin. (International Falcon Movement - Socialist Educational International) (AU ISSN 0018-9715) **1638,** 3898
I F M T Magazine. (International Fashion Model & Talent) (US ISSN 1045-0629) **1291,** 373
I F O *see* Information fuer Ormesheim **4089**
I F O A M *see* Oekologie und Landbau **112**
I F O Digest. (GW ISSN 0170-7663) **669**
I F O Forschungsberichte der Abteilung Entwicklungslaender. (GW) **669**
I F O Institut fuer Wirtschaftsforschung. Studien zu Handels- und Dienstleistungsfragen. (GW ISSN 0170-5695) **669**
I F O Konjunkturperspektiven. (GW) **669**
I F O Mitteilungen der Abteilung Entwicklungslaender. (GW) **930**
I F O Schnelldienst. (GW ISSN 0018-974X) **669**
I F O Spiegel der Wirtschaft. (GW ISSN 0170-3617) **868**
I F O Studien. (GW ISSN 0018-9731) **669**
I F O Studien zur Entwicklungsforschung. (GW) **669**
I F P A A W News. (International Federation of Plantation, Agricultural and Allied Workers) (SZ) **981**
I F P A A W Snips *see* I F P A A W News **981**
I F P A Quarterly *see* Fire Photographers Journal **3790**
I F P R A Bulletin. (International Federation of Park and Recreation Administration) (UK ISSN 1012-7720) **4548**
I F P R I Report. (International Food Policy Research Institute) (US) **152**
I F P R I Research Report. (International Food Policy Research Institute) (US) **152,** 2072
I F P T E Outlook. (International Federation of Professional and Technical Engineers) (US) **981,** 1824
I F R. (Instrument Flight Rule) (US ISSN 0894-6620) **55**
I F R Newsletter *see* I F R Robotics Newsletter **1408**
I F R Refresher. (US) **55**
I F R Robotics Newsletter. (International Federation of Robotics) (SW) **1408**
I F R T Report. (Intellectual Freedom Round Table) (US) **2761**
†I.F. Stone's Weekly. (US ISSN 0018-9758) **5209**
I F T Basic Symposium Series. (International Food Technology) (US) **2072**
I F T E C Informations *see* Institut Europeen de Formation des Techniciens des Circuits Imprimes. Informations **1773**
†I.F.T. Journal. (International Foundation for Telemetering) (US ISSN 0095-1021) **5209**
I F U. (Institut fuer Umformtechnik) (US) **4599**
I F U Annual Report. (Industrialiserings Fonden for Udviklingslandene) (DK ISSN 0901-6171) **930**
I F U's Participation in Joint Ventures *see* I F U Annual Report **930**
I G A Grocergram. (Independent Grocers Alliance) (US ISSN 0018-9766) **2092**
I G A R S S *see* International Geoscience and Remote Sensing Symposium Digest **2253**

I G

I G C C Newsletter. (Institute on Global Conflict and Cooperation) (US) **3959**

I G E News. (International Guiding Eyes) (US) **3711, 2293**

I G F - Journal. (International Graphical Federation) (BE ISSN 0018-9782) **4001, 4129**

I G Medien Forum. (GW) **4129, 4001**

I G O Report. (Intergovernmental Organizations) (US) **911**

†I G P C Philatelic Report. (Inter-Governmental Philatelic Corporation) (US) **5209**

I G U Bulletin/Bulletin de l'U G I. (International Geographical Union) (CN ISSN 0018-9804) **2252**

I G W M C Ground Water Modeling Newsletter. (International Ground Water Modeling Center) (US ISSN 0741-8507) **1598, 4825**

I Guide see Golden Keys Magazine **4768**

I H G Newsletter. (Independent Hospital Group) (UK) **2466**

I H J Bulletin. (International House of Japan, Inc.) (JA ISSN 0285-2608) **3959**

I H K Aktuell. (Industrie- und Handelskammer zu Luebeck) (GW) **817**

I H K Lippe Info. (Industrie- und Handelskammer Lippe zu Detmold) (GW) **817**

I H K Magazin. (Industrie- und Handelskammer fuer die Pfalz) (GW) **817**

I H K Wuppertal. Wirtschaftliche Mitteilungen. (Industrie- und Handelskammer Wuppertal) (GW ISSN 0018-9839) **817**

I H N News. (International Handicapper's Net) (US ISSN 1042-4334) **2284, 2437**

I H R Newsletter. (Institute for Historical Review) (US) **2314**

I H 3 P A Newsletter see Poker Tips **4483**

I Hsing see First Line **2993**

I I A S A Annual Report. (International Institute for Applied Systems Analysis) (AU) **1437**

I I A S Newsletter. (Indian Institute of Advanced Study) (II) **1708**

I I A S Occasional Papers. (Indian Institute of Advanced Study) (II) **1708, 2508**

I I A Today. (Institute of Internal Auditors, Inc.) (US ISSN 0744-1223) **751**

I I C. (International Review of Industrial Property and Copyright Law) (GW ISSN 0018-9855) **3675**

I I C A. Documentacao. (Instituto de Investigacao Cientifica de Angola) (AO ISSN 0018-9863) **4356**

I I C Abstracts see Art and Archaeology Technical Abstracts **351**

I I C I T News. (International Institute of Connector and Interconnection Technology, Inc.) (US) **1773**

I I C S Reporter. (International Interactive Communications Society) (US ISSN 1047-5346) **1350, 1689**

I I E. Revista. (Instituto de Investigaciones Economicas) (BO ISSN 0034-9283) **669**

I I E P Occasional Papers. (International Institute for Educational Planning) (UN ISSN 0074-6401) **1722**

I I E P Research Reports. (International Institute for Educational Planning) (UN) **1722**

I I E P Seminar Papers. (International Institute for Educational Planning) (UN) **1722, 930**

I I E Transactions. (Institute of Industrial Engineers) (US) **1925**

I I E X E Newsletter. (Institution of Incorporated Executive Engineers) (UK ISSN 0266-2450) **1824**

I.I. Grekov Annals of Surgery. see Vestnik Khirurgii im. I.I. Grekova **3385**

I I L S Bulletin see Labour and Society **5225**

I I M C Bulletin. (Indian Institute of Mass Communication) (II) **1337**

I I P A Newsletter. (Indian Institute of Public Administration) (II) **4063**

I I P Monitor. (International Institute for Peace) (AU ISSN 1017-6861) **3959**

I I P Occasional Paper. (International Institute for Peace) (AU) **3959**

I I P S Newsletter. (International Institute for Population Sciences) (!I) **3982**

†I.I.R.B. (BE ISSN 0018-9898) **5209**

I I R B Winter Congress Proceedings see International Institute for Sugar Beet Research. Reports of the Winter Congress **181**

I I R R Report. (International Institute of Rural Reconstruction) (US ISSN 1011-8721) **930, 1077**

I I T C Bulletin. (Indian International Trade Center) (II ISSN 0019-4980) **911**

I I T C Directory. (Indian International Trade Center) (II ISSN 0073-6546) **911**

I I T Chicago - Kent Law Review see Chicago - Kent Law Review **2612**

†I I T Tecnologia. (Instituto de Investigaciones Tecnologicas) (CK ISSN 0049-3201) **5209**

I J A. Research Reports. (Institute of Jewish Affairs) (UK ISSN 0257-6406) **2005, 3943**

†I J A L Native American Texts Series. (International Journal of American Linguistics) (US ISSN 0361-3399) **5209**

†I J B - Bulletin. (Internationale Jugendbibliothek) (GW) **5209**

I J B F see International Annual Bibliography of Festschriften **403**

I J B K see Internationale Jahresbibliographie der Kongressberichte **3395**

I J B - Report. (Internationale Jugendbibliothek) (GW) **2924, 1256**

I J D B see International Journal of Development Banking **932**

I J D L. (International Journal of Dravidian Linguistics) (II ISSN 0378-2484) **2817**

I J S B see International Journal of Sport Biomechanics **4476**

I J S N see International Journal of Sport Nutrition **3607**

I K. (GW ISSN 0173-6612) **836**

I K K Stuttgart Aktuell. (GW) **2533**

I K O Newsletter see N I K H E F. K Bulletin **3825**

I K Z - Haustechnik. (GW) **2300**

I-Kwadraat - Elektrotechniek - Electronica. (NE) **1898**

I-Kwadraat - Werktuigbouwkunde. (NE) **1824**

I L A Newsletter. (International Law Association) (US ISSN 0190-5821) **2724**

I L A Practitioner's Notebook. (International Law Association) (US) **2724**

I L A R News. (Institute of Laboratory Animal Resources) (US ISSN 0018-9960) **3259, 584**

I L A Reporter. (Illinois Library Association) (US ISSN 0018-9979) **2761**

I L B Information. (Institut fuer Landwirtschaftliche Bauforschung) (GW) **96**

I L C A Annual Report. (International Livestock Centre for Africa) (UN ISSN 0255-0040) **217**

I L C A Bulletin. (UN ISSN 0255-0008) **217**

I L C A Newsletter. (UN ISSN 0255-0024) **218**

I L C A Proceedings. (UN) **218**

I L C A Programme and Budget. (UN) **218**

I L C A Reporter. (International Labor Communications Association) (US) **2570**

I L C A Research Report. (International Livestock Centre for Africa) (UN) **218**

I L C O Praxis. (GW ISSN 0724-8016) **3198, 4408**

I.L.C. Quarterly see Liszt Saeculum **3561**

I L E. (Industrias Lacteas Espanolas) (SP) **200**

†I L E A Contact. (Inner London Education Authority) (UK ISSN 0306-1981) **5209**

I L G A Bulletin. (International Lesbian and Gay Association) (BE ISSN 0281-627X) **2454, 3943, 4845**

I L O Information. (International Labour Office) (UN ISSN 0379-1734) **981**

I L O Judgements of the Administrative Tribunal. (International Labour Office) (UN ISSN 0378-7362) **2633**

I L O Publications. (International Labour Office) (UN ISSN 0378-5904) **720**

I L P A Reporter see I L C A Reporter **2570**

I L P E S Cuadernos. (Instituto Latinamericano y del Caribe de Planificacion Economica y Social) (UN ISSN 0020-4080) **999, 4437**

I L P Magazine. (Independent Labour Publications) (UK ISSN 0951-2187) **3898**

I L R Paperbacks. (New York State School of Industrial and Labor Relations) (US ISSN 0070-0177) **981**

I L R Report. (US ISSN 0736-6396) **981**

I L R Review see Industrial and Labor Relations Review **982**

I L S A Journal of International Law. (International Law Students Association) (US) **2633, 1708**

I L S I Human Nutrition Reviews. (US) **3606**

I L S M H News. (International League of Societies for Persons with Mental Handicap) (BE) **4024, 3338**

I Laisve/Toward Freedom. (US) **2005, 3898**

I Love Cats. (US ISSN 0899-9570) **3711**

I Love New York Skiing and Winter Adventures. (US) **4548**

I Love New York: The Finger Lakes Travel Guide. (US) **4771**

I M see Italia Missionaria **1256**

I M see Inside Music **3556**

I M A Bulletin. (International MIDI Association) (US) **3555**

I M A Bulletin (Inter Monastic Aid) see A I M Monastic Bulletin **4254**

I M A C A Directory. (International Mobile Air Conditioning Association) (US) **4692**

I M A C S Annals on Computing and Applied Mathematics. (SZ ISSN 1012-2435) **3064**

I M A C S News see Mathematics and Computers in Simulation **1435**

I M A Journal of Applied Mathematics. (Institute of Mathematics and its Applications) (UK ISSN 0272-4960) **3037**

I M A Journal of Mathematical Control & Information. (Institute of Mathematics and its Applications) (UK ISSN 0265-0754) **3037**

I M A Journal of Mathematics Applied in Business and Industry. (Institute of Mathematics and its Applications) (UK ISSN 0953-0061) **3037**

I M A Journal of Mathematics Applied in Medicine & Biology. (UK ISSN 0265-0746) **3037, 441, 3107**

I M A Journal of Mathematics in Management see I M A Journal of Mathematics Applied in Business and Industry **3037**

I M A Journal of Numerical Analysis. (UK ISSN 0272-4979) **3037**

I M A Trattorista see Macchine e Motori Agricoli - I M A il Trattorista **163**

I M A Volumes in Mathematics and its Applications. (US) **3037**

I M C H Newsletter. (Institute of Maternal and Child Health) (PH) **1238, 3982**

I M C Journal. (International Information Management Congress) (US ISSN 0019-0012) **2797**

†I M C Journal. (International Medical Centers) (US) **5209**

I M C O News see I M O News **4728**

I M D A Journal see Instruments India **2523**

I.M.E. see Rivista di Meccanica International Edition **3419**

I M F News. (International Metalworkers Federation) (SZ) **3408**

I M F Survey. (International Monetary Fund) (UN ISSN 0047-083X) **720, 13**

†I M G - T N O Research Institute for Environmental Hygiene. Annual Report. (NE) **5209**

I M H E. (Informacion de Maquinas - Herramienta Equipos y Accesorios) (SP ISSN 0210-1777) **3018**

I M I E S A Journal see Institution of Municipal Engineers of Southern Africa. Journal **2489**

†I M I S Council Newsletter. (US) **5210**

▼I M - Internal Medicine for the Specialist. (US ISSN 0273-6608) **3268**

I M J. (Irish Marketing Journal Ltd.) (IE) **1041**

I M J Appointments see Irish Medical News **3111**

I M L S Gazette. (UK ISSN 0267-2928) **3107**

I M M Abstracts see I M M Abstracts and Index **3499**

I M M Abstracts and Index. (Institution of Mining and Metallurgy) (UK) **3499, 13, 1551, 3425**

I M M Bulletin see Minerals Industry International **3489**

I M M E Boletin. (Instituto de Materiales y Modelos Estructurales) (VE ISSN 0020-3971) **1867, 1164**

I M N Auction Report see Black Book Auction Report **3016**

I M O News. (International Maritime Organization) (UN) **4728**

†I M P A C T. (Information for Managers on Personnel and Current Trends in Human Resources) (US) **5210**

I M P O see Chilton's Industrial Maintenance & Plant Operation **1005**

†I M P O Distributor News. (US) **5210**

I M R A News. (Industrial Marketing Research Association) (UK) **1041, 868, 1012**

I M Report see N C S Integrated Manufacturing **1936**

I M S A Arrow. (International Motorsports Association) (US) **4475**

I M S A Yearbook. (International Motor Sports Association) (US) **4475**

I M S Bulletin. (Institute of Materials Science) (US ISSN 0019-0063) **1917**

I M S Lecture Notes. Monograph Series. (Institute of Mathematical Statistics) (US) **3037**

I M S Newsletter. (International Marine Science) (UN) **1605, 441**

I M T C see I E E E Instrumentation and Measurement Technology Conference. Proceedings **2522**

I M T Swiatowid. (Ilustrowany Magazyn Turystyczny) (PL) **4771**

I M U Canberra Circular. (International Mathematical Union) (AT ISSN 0311-0621) **3037**

I Magazine see Atlantic States Insurance **2527**

I N A D E S Documentation. (Institut Africain pour le Developpement Economique et Social) (IV) **402**

I N A I L Notiziario Statistico. (Istituto Nazionale per l'Assicurazione Contro gli Infortuni sul Lavoro) (IT ISSN 0021-2539) **2546**

I N A Vjesnik Industrije Nafte. (CI) **3688, 669, 1178**

I N - Argomenti e Immagini di Design. (IT) **301**

I N C Hebdo Consommateurs Actualites. (Institut National de la Consommation) (FR) **1505**

I N D A Association of the Nonwoven Fabrics Industry. I N D A - Tec Symposium Papers. (US) **4619**

I N D A C. (Indianapolis Athletic Club) (US ISSN 0019-3569) **1298**

I N E S Informations see Institut d'Etudes Slaves Informations **2508**

†I N E T Up-Date. (US) **5210**

I N F. (Information Nederland France) (NE ISSN 0921-2701) **817, 911** tI N F A A Rapport. (Aabenraa Proevecenter for Ny Informationsteknologi) (DK) **5210**

I N F A Press and Advertisers Year Book. (India News and Feature Alliance) (II ISSN 0073-4284) **32, 2466**

I N F F O - Flash. (FR ISSN 0397-3301) **1012**

I N F O. (US ISSN 0019-0136) **2793**

I N F O Journal. (International Fortean Organization) (US ISSN 0019-0144) **4313**

I N F O P A K Konstrukt *see* Construction Alert **611**

I N F O P A K Management. (SA) **1012**

I N F O P A K Manufacturing. (SA) **4599**

I N F O R Journal/C O R S. (CN ISSN 0315-5986) **1451**

▼I N F O R M: International News on Fats, Oils & Related Materials. (US) **477**

I N I R E B Informa *see* Instituto de Ecologia. Informa **442**

I N I S Atomindex. (UN ISSN 0004-7139) **3837, 13**

I N I S Newsletter. (UN ISSN 0047-0856) **2761**

I N I S Reference Series. (UN) **2761, 1805**

I N I S T - Info. (Institut de l'Information Scientifique et Technique) (FR ISSN 0992-0692) **4313**

I N P R E K O R R. (Internationale Pressekorrespondenz) (GW ISSN 0177-6657) **3898**

I N R Ads *see* I N R O Ads **231**

I N R O Ads. (International Network for Religion and Animals) (US) **231, 4181**

I N R S Bulletin de Documentation. (Institut National de Recherche et de Securite pour la Prevention des Accidents du Travail et des Maladies Professionnelles) (FR ISSN 0335-0274) **3617**

I N R S Lettre d'Information sur la Recherche *see* Lettre d'Information sur la Recherche Hygiene et Securite **3619**

I N S. (International Stationery) (SP) **3663**

tI N S A Bulletin. (PL) **5210**

I N S D O C. Russian Scientific and Technical Publications. Accessions List. (Indian National Scientific Documentation Centre) (II ISSN 0304-534X) **4356, 4614**

I N S D O C Union Catalogue Series. (Indian National Scientific Documentation Centre) (II ISSN 0073-6627) **402**

I N S E E. Cadrage. (Institut National de la Statistique et des Etudes Economiques) (FR) **720**

I N S E E. Cadrage et I N S E E Resultats Consommations et Modes de Vie. (Institut National de la Statistique et des Etudes Economiques) (FR ISSN 0998-4852) **721**

I N S E E. Cadrage et I N S E E Resultats Demographie et Societe. (Institut National de la Statistique et des Etudes Economiques) (FR ISSN 0998-4860) **721**

I N S E E. Cadrage et I N S E E Resultats Economie Generale. (FR ISSN 0998-4828) **721**

I N S E E. Cadrage et I N S E E Resultats Emplois Revenus. (FR ISSN 0998-4844) **721**

I N S E E. Cadrage et I N S E E Resultats Systeme Productif. (FR ISSN 0998-4836) **721**

I N S E E. Etudes. (FR ISSN 1140-5252) **721**

I N S E E. Methodes. (FR ISSN 1142-3080) **721**

I N S E E. Premiere. (FR ISSN 0997-3192) **721**

I N S E E. Resultats. (FR) **721**

I N S E E - Infos. (FR ISSN 0998-4402) **669**

tI N S E E Premiers Resultats. (FR ISSN 0758-7724) **5210**

I N S I V U M E H Boletin *see* Guatemala. Instituto Nacional de Sismologia, Vulcanologia, Meteorologia e Hidrologia. Boletin **1545**

I N S Newsline. (Intravenous Nurses Society) (US) **3279**

I N S Reporter *see* I and N Reporter **3982**

I N S T R A W News. (International Research and Training Institute for the Advancement of Women) (UN) **4845**

I N S Update *see* I N S Newsline **3279**

I N T E L E C *see* International Telecommunications Energy Conference. Proceedings **1375**

tI N T I. (Instituto Nacional de Tecnologia Industrial) (AG ISSN 0325-934X) **5210**

I N T Informativo. (Instituto Nacional de Tecnologia) (BL ISSN 0019-0233) **4313, 4599**

I N T V Newsletter. (Association of Independent Television Stations, Inc.) (US) **1374, 2633**

I N U F A Katalog. (SZ) **4745**

I N U F A Rundschau *see* Transport Rundschau **4748**

I Nostri Monumenti Storici. *see* Unsere Kunstdenkmaeler **308**

I O C C C Annual Statistical Bulletin *see* International Office of Cocoa, Chocolate and Sugar Confectionery. Annual Statistical Bulletin **2088**

I.O. Evans Studies in the Philosophy & Criticism of Literature. (US ISSN 0271-9061) **2924**

I O I News. (International Ocean Institute) (MM) **1605**

I O I Occasional Papers *see* International Ocean Institute. Occasional Papers **1606**

I O J Nachrichten *see* I O J Newsletter **2570**

I O J Newsletter. (International Organization of Journalists) (CS) **2570**

I O L and Ocular Surgery News *see* Ocular Surgery News **3382**

I O L R Collected Reports. (Israel Oceanographic and Limnological Research Ltd.) (IS ISSN 0333-5194) **4825**

I O L T A Update. (Commission on Interest on Lawyers' Trust Accounts) (US) **2633**

I O M A's G I C - B I C Yields and Market Report (Guranteed Investment Contracts - Bank Investment Contracts) *see* I O M A's Report on Defined Contribution Plan Investing **784**

▼I O M A's Report on Controlling Law Firms Costs. (US ISSN 1060-5924) **2710, 1012**

I O M A's Report on Defined Contribution Plan Investing. (Institute of Management and Administration) (US) **784**

▼I O M A's Report on Managing 401K Plans. (US ISSN 1059-2741) **784, 1066, 2710**

I O M A's Report on Reducing Benefits Costs. (US ISSN 1056-7984) **751**

I O M Monthly Dispatch. (International Organization for Migration) (SZ) **3982**

I O Management Zeitschrift. (SZ ISSN 0019-9281) **1012**

I O O C. Information Sheet *see* C O I. Hoja de Informacion **171**

I O P Short Meetings Series. (Institute of Physics) (UK ISSN 0269-8986) **3841**

I P A Aktuell. (GW) **1515**

I P A Bulletin. (International Psychohistorical Association) (US) **4024, 2314**

I P A - Forschung und Praxis. (Fraunhofer-Institute fuer Produktionstechnik und Automatisierung) (US) **1824**

I P A Newsletter *see* PlayRights **1243**

I P A Review. (Institute of Public Affairs) (AT ISSN 1030-4177) **670**

I P A S E Biblioteca Informa. (Instituto de Previdencia e Assistencia dos Servidores do Estado) (BL ISSN 0019-0276) **2793**

I P Asia. (HK ISSN 1011-3649) **3675**

I P B Joernaal. *see* I P M Journal **1012**

I P C C *see* International Professional Communication Conference. Conference Record **1338**

I P C Monographs. (Institute of Philippine Culture) (PH ISSN 0073-9537) **4437**

I P C Papers. (Institute of Philippine Culture) (PH ISSN 0073-9545) **4437**

I P C Poverty Research Series. (Institute of Philippine Culture) (PH) **4437, 4408**

I P C R. Annual Reports of Research Activities. *see* Rikagaku Kenkyujo Kenkyu Nenpo **3839**

I P C R Accelerator Progress Report *see* Riken. Accelerator Progress Report **3850**

tI P C R Cyclotron Technical Report. (Institute of Physical and Chemical Research) (JA) **5210**

I P C Report. (International Procurement Committee) (US) **2633**

I P C Reprints. (Institute of Philippine Culture) (PH) **4437, 241**

I P C S Bulletin *see* I P M S Bulletin **4063**

I P D Cahier/P A I D Reports. (Institut Panafricain pour le Developpement) (CM ISSN 0256-4912) **931**

I P D Working Papers. (Interuniversity Programme in Demography) (BE) **3992**

I P E A Estudos para o Planejamento. (Instituto de Planejamento Economico e Social) (BL) **1077**

I P E A Relatorios de Pesquisa. (Instituto de Planejamento Economico e Social) (BL) **4437, 868**

I P E A Serie Monografica. (Instituto de Planejamento Economico e Social) (BL) **868, 1077**

I P E A Serie P N P E. (Programa Nacional de Pesquisa Economica) (BL) **670, 868**

I P E F Journal. (Instituto de Pesquisas e Estudos Florestais) (BL ISSN 0100-4557) **2102**

I P E - Industrial and Production Engineering *see* E P E **1928**

I P E Journal *see* Institute of Public Enterprise. Journal **1014**

I P E N Z Proceedings Annual Conference (Year). (Institution of Professional Engineers, New Zealand) (NZ) **1824**

I P F C Report *see* Indo-Pacific Fishery Commission. Report **2043**

I P I Bulletin. (International Potash Institute) (SZ) **179**

I P I R I Journal. (Indian Plywood Industries Research Institute) (II ISSN 0046-9033) **2115**

I P I Report. (International Press Institute) (UK ISSN 0019-0314) **2570**

I P I Research Topics. (International Potash Institute) (SZ) **179**

I P Information. (Dansk Institut for Personaleraadgivning) (DK ISSN 0109-2987) **1066**

I P L E Lighting Journal *see* Lighting Journal **1902**

I P M A News. (International Personnel Management Association) (US) **1066**

tI P M Digest. (Institute of Personnel Management) (UK ISSN 0019-0330) **5210**

I P M Journal/I P B Joernaal. (Institute of Personnel Management) (SA) **1012**

I P M Manpower Journal *see* I P M Journal **1012**

I P M Practitioner. (Integrated Pest Management) (US ISSN 0738-968X) **96, 533, 2131, 4104**

I P M S Bulletin. (Institution of Professionals, Managers and Specialists) (UK ISSN 0958-5222) **4063**

I.P.M.S. Magazine *see* I.P.M.S. (UK) Magazine **2437**

I.P.M.S. (UK) Magazine. (International Plastic Modellers Society (UK)) (UK) **2437**

I.P. Mark. (Informacion de Publicidad y Marketing) (SP) **1041, 32**

I P N - Blaetter. (Institut fuer die Paedagogik der Naturwissenschaften) (GW ISSN 0179-5775) **4313, 1751, 1957**

tI P N L. (Individual Psychology News Letter) (GW ISSN 0445-9121) **5210**

I P N Marketing News. (Independent Publishers Network) (US) **1041, 4129**

I P O Annual Progress Report. (Institute for Perception Research) (NE ISSN 0921-2566) **2817, 4024**

I P P A Newsletter. (Indonesian Planned Parenthood Association) (IO) **597**

I P P F Annual Report. (International Planned Parenthood Federation) (UK) **597**

tI P P F Co-operative Information Service. (International Planned Parenthood Federation) (UK ISSN 0309-6904) **5210**

I P P F in Action *see* I P P F Annual Report **597**

I P P F Medical Bulletin. (International Planned Parenthood Federation) (UK ISSN 0019-0357) **597**

I P P L Newsletter *see* International Primate Protection League Newsletter **1489**

I P R A Newsletter. (International Peace Research Association) (US) **3959**

I P R A Review *see* International Public Relations Review **33**

I P: Revista da Industria de Panificacao/Baking Industry Review. (BL) **2088**

I P S F News Bulletin. (International Pharmaceutical Students Federation) (NE ISSN 0019-039X) **3728**

I P S R - R I S P *see* International Political Science Review **3961**

I P S S Bulletin. (Institute of Political and Social Studies) (II ISSN 0019-0403) **3898, 4374**

I P T C News. (International Press Telecommunications Council) (UK) **1363**

I P T C Newsletter *see* I P T C News **1363**

I P T O Bulletin *see* Pets Europe **3713**

tI.P.V.D.F. Boletim Mensal. (Instituto de Pesquisa Veterinarias Desiderio Finamor) (BL ISSN 0019-0411) **5210**

I P W Berichte. (Internationale Politik und Wirtschaft) (GW ISSN 0046-970X) **3898, 895**

tI P W Forschungshefte. (Institut fuer Internationale Politik und Wirtschaft der D.D.R.) (GW ISSN 0323-3901) **5210**

I P Z Information. Reihe S: Subversion. (Institut fuer Politologische Zeitfragen) (SZ) **3898**

I-Punkt. (GW) **981**

I.Q.S. (Institut Quimic de Sarria) (SP ISSN 0210-508X) **1178**

I R A Bulletin. (Individual Retirement Account) (US) **949**

I R A Compliance Manual. (US) **1097**

I R A - Individual Retirement Account Stocks. (US ISSN 0892-6018) **949**

I R A L. (International Review of Applied Linguistics in Language Teaching) (GW ISSN 0019-042X) **2817, 1751**

I R A Reporter. (US) **949**

I R B: A Review of Human Subjects Research. (Institutional Review Board) (US ISSN 0193-7758) **3259**

I R B Revista. (Instituto de Resseguros do Brasil) (BL ISSN 0019-0446) **2533**

I R C I H E Bulletin. (International Referral Centre for Information Handling Equipment) (CI ISSN 0351-0123) **2761**
I R C Special Publication. (Indian Roads Congress) (II) **4719**
I.R.C. Weekly Newsletter. (AT) **2633**
†I.R. Concepts. (US ISSN 0019-0454) **5210**
I R E Transactions on Circuit Theory see I E E E Transactions on Circuits and Systems Part 2: Analog and Digital Signal Processing **1772**
†I R F Newsletter. (International Religious Foundation, Inc.) (US ISSN 0887-1043) **5210**
†I.R.I. Journal. (Institution of the Rubber Industry) (UK ISSN 0019-0462) **5210**
I R I Notizie see Holding **669**
I R I S see Integrated Risk Information System (for Microcomputers) **1958**
I R P I: International Reinforced Plastics Industry. (UK ISSN 0261-5487) **3862**
I R R A Newsletter. (Industrial Relations Research Association) (US ISSN 0019-0500) **981**
I R R I Annual Report see I R R I Program Report **206**
I R R I Program Report. (International Rice Research Institute) (PH) **206**
I R R I Reporter. (International Rice Research Institute) (PH ISSN 0115-2467) **206**
I R R I Research Highlights. (International Rice Research Institute) (PH ISSN 0115-1142) **206**
I R R I Research Paper Series. (International Rice Research Institute) (PH ISSN 0115-3862) **206**
I R S A Items. (International Rural Sociology Association) (AT) **4437**
I R S Letter Rulings. (Internal Revenue Service) (US ISSN 0148-1940) **1097, 751**
I R S Memoranda and Letter Rulings. (US) **1097**
I R S Practice Alert. (US) **1097**
I R S Publications. (US) **1097**
I R T see Energy News Brief **1788**
I R T Communication Quarterly. (Institute for Research on Teaching) (US ISSN 0274-6530) **1638**
I R T Notes and News. (Institute for Research on Teaching) (US) **1751**
I R T S Gold Medal Annual see I R T S Gold Medal Journal **1374**
I R T S Gold Medal Journal. (International Radio and Television Society, Inc.) (US) **1374, 1356**
I S. (Interservice) (US ISSN 0273-7485) **3460, 1041, 1298, 2092**
I S A Bulletin/Conseillers aux Etudiants Etrangers. Bulletin. (International Student Advisers) (CN) **1722**
I S A Directory of Instrumentation. (Instrument Society of America) (US ISSN 0272-8141) **2522**
I S A G A Newsletter. (International Simulation and Gaming Association) (US) **4437**
I S A M Newsletter see Institute for Studies in American Music. Newsletter **3556**
I S A P see Index to South African Periodicals **4141**
I S A S Lunar and Planetary Symposium. Proceedings. (Institute of Space and Astronautical Science) (JA) **365**
I S A S Nyusu. (Institute of Space and Astronautical Science) (JA ISSN 0285-2861) **365**
I S A S Research Note. (Institute of Space and Astronautical Science) (JA) **365**
I S A Transactions. (Instrument Society of America) (US ISSN 0019-0578) **1824**
I S A Update. (Interactive Services Association) (US) **1350, 1363**
I S Analyzer. (US) **1350**
I S B A Journal. (Indiana School Boards Association) (US ISSN 0019-0586) **1728**

I S B A News. (Illinois State Bar Association) (US) **2633**
I S B C see Index to Scientific Book Contents **4356**
I S B N Review. (International Standard Book Number) (GW ISSN 0342-4634) **4129, 2761**
I S C A Quarterly. (International Society of Copier Artists) (US ISSN 0741-2940) **329, 2761**
I S C E T Update. (International Society of Certified Electronics Technicians) (US) **1773**
I S C Newsletter. (International Society of Cryptozoology) (US ISSN 0741-5362) **584**
I S C O Careers Bulletin see Careers Cop: I S C O Careers Bulletin **1620**
I S Capacity Management Handbook Series. (Information Systems) (US) **1451**
I S D D Current Awareness Bulletin. (Institute for the Study of Drug Dependence) (UK) **1540, 3747**
I S D N see Integrated Service Digital Network **1427**
I S D N Handbook and Buyers Guide. (Integrated Services Digital Network) (US) **1337**
I S D N News. (Integrated Services Digital Network) (US ISSN 0899-9554) **1351**
I S D N Report. (Integrated Service Digital Network) (US) **1363**
I S D N User Magazine. (Integrated Services Digital Network) (US) **1351, 1363**
I S D S Bulletin see I S D S Register (Microfiche Edition) **402**
I S D S Register (Microfiche Edition). (International Serials Data System) (FR ISSN 0257-2222) **402**
I S D S Register (Tape Edition). (International Serials Data System) (FR ISSN 0256-8888) **402**
I S E A Communique. (Iowa State Education Association) (US ISSN 0019-0624) **1638**
▼I S E A S Current Economic Affairs Series. (Institute of Southeast Asian Studies) (SI ISSN 0218-2114) **670**
▼I S E A S Environment and Development Series. (Institute of Southeast Asian Studies) (SI) **1957**
I S E C Monograph. (Institute for Social and Economic Change) (II) **868**
I S E Firms and Members. (International Stock Exchange) (UK) **949**
I S E G R Occasional Papers see I S E R Occasional Papers **4374**
I S E G R Research Notes see I S E R Research Notes **670**
I S E R Occasional Papers. (Institute of Social and Economic Research) (US) **4374, 868**
I S E R Reprint Series. (Institute of Social and Economic Research) (JA) **670**
I S E R Research and Policy Papers. (Institute of Social and Economic Research) (CN ISSN 0828-6868) **4437, 868**
I S E R Research Notes. (Institute of Social and Economic Research) (US) **670, 4374**
I S G E Transactions. (International Society for Geothermal Engineering, Inc.) (US) **1802, 1790**
I S H I Occasional Papers in Social Change. (Institute for the Study of Human Issues) (US) **4437, 3898**
I S I Atlas of Science: Animal and Plant Sciences see Research Reviews in Animal and Plant Sciences **5269**
I S I Atlas of Science: Biochemistry see Research Reviews in Biochemistry **5269**
I S I J International. (Iron and Steel Institute of Japan) (JA ISSN 0915-1559) **3408, 1917**
†I S I Online News. (Institute for Scientific Information) (US ISSN 0892-094X) **5210**
I S I R I Yearbook. (Institute of Standards and Industrial Research of Iran) (IR) **3446**
†I S I S Bulletin. (Indian Society for Information Science) (II) **5210**

The I S I S Magazine. (Independent Schools Information Service) (UK) **1694, 1238**
I S I S News see The I S I S Magazine **1694**
I S I S Report see I S R I Report **1489**
I S K C O N World Review. (International Society for Krishna Consciousness) (US ISSN 0748-2280) **4284**
I S L A. (Information Services on Latin America) (US ISSN 0046-8401) **2409**
▼I S L A: A Journal of Micronesian Studies. (GU) **2344**
I S L E Rassegna Parlamentare (Istituto di Studi Legislativa) see Rassegna Parlamentare **2670**
I S L I C Bulletin. (Israel Society of Special Libraries and Information Centers) (IS ISSN 0021-2318) **2761**
I S M A Occasional Papers. (Institute for the Study of Man in Africa) (SA ISSN 0073-893X) **241**
I S M A Papers. (Institute for the Study of Man in Africa) (SA ISSN 0073-8921) **241**
I S M A Technical Conference. Proceedings see I F A Technical Conference. Proceedings **179**
I S M E C Bulletin see I S M E C: Mechanical Engineering Abstracts **1844**
I S M E C: Mechanical Engineering Abstracts. (Information Service in Mechanical Engineering) (US ISSN 0896-7113) **1844, 13**
I S Magazine. (UK) **1012**
I S N A Matters. (Islamic Society of North America) (US) **4218**
I S N A Newsletter see Journal of Nuclear Agriculture and Biology **183**
I S O Bulletin (English Edition). (International Organization for Standardization) (SZ ISSN 0303-805X) **3446, 2761**
I S O Catalogue. (International Organization for Standardization) (SZ ISSN 0303-3309) **3446**
I S O Information see Organ Building Periodical **3572**
I S O International Standards. (International Organization for Standardization) (SZ) **3446**
I S O Memento. (International Organization for Standardization) (SZ ISSN 0536-2067) **3446**
I S O S C. International Congress. Proceedings. (International Society of Soilless Culture) (NE) **1568, 179**
I S O World see Micro Marketworld **1433**
▼I S P News. (InfoSecurity Product) (US) **1526**
I S P R A Courses on Nuclear Engineering and Technology Series. (US ISSN 0275-7575) **1805**
I S P R S Journal of Photogrammetry and Remote Sensing. (International Society for Photogrammetry and Remote Sensing) (NE ISSN 0924-2716) **2252**
I S P T International Journal of Educational Sciences. (Institute for Studies in Psychological Testing) (II) **1638**
I S P T Journal of Research in Educational & Psychological Measurement. (Institute for Studies in Psychological Testing) (II ISSN 0251-0146) **1638, 4024**
I S P T Quarterly Bulletin. (Institute for Studies in Psychological Testing) (II) **4024**
I S Q see Information Standards Quarterly **4130**
I S R see Index to Scientific Reviews **4356**
I S R see Indian Synthetic & Rayon **4620**
I S R I Report. (Institute of Scrap Recycling Industries) (US) **1489**
I S R: Intelligent Systems Report. (US ISSN 0897-3466) **1408**
I S R - Interdisciplinary Science Reviews. (UK ISSN 0308-0188) **4313**

I S R Newsletter see Institute for Social Research. Newsletter **4375**
I S S A. Committee on Provident Funds. Reports. (International Social Security Association) (SZ ISSN 0255-7592) **2533**
I S S A. Social Security Documentation. Caribbean Series. (International Social Security Association) (SZ ISSN 0254-0576) **2533**
I S S A Access. (Information Systems Security Association) (US) **1434**
I S S A Today. (International Sanitary Supply Association, Inc.) (US) **4104**
I S S Directory of Overseas Schools. (International Schools Services, Inc.) (US) **1694**
I S S H P see Index to Social Sciences & Humanities Proceedings **4375**
I S S L S see International Symposium on Subscriber Loop and Services. Proceedings **1900**
▼I S S N Compact. (International Standard Serial Number) (FR ISSN 1018-4783) **402**
I S S U P Bulletin see University of Pretoria. Institute for Strategic Studies. Bulletin **1274**
I S S U P Strategic Review see Strategic Review for Southern Africa **1274**
I S T A Advocate. (Indiana State Teachers Association) (US) **1638**
I S T A News Bulletin. (International Seed Testing Association) (SZ ISSN 0019-0713) **179**
I S T A T. Notiziario see Italy. Istituto Centrale di Statistica. Notiziario **724**
I S T C Banner see I S T C Phoenix **3408**
I S T C Phoenix. (Iron and Steel Trades Confederation) (UK) **3408, 620**
I S T E Update. (International Society for Technology in Education) (US ISSN 1040-4694) **1638, 1417**
I S T F News. (International Society of Tropical Foresters) (US ISSN 0276-2056) **2102**
I S T F Noticias see I S T F News **2102**
I S T P see Index to Scientific & Technical Proceedings **4356**
I S U C C Newsletter see I S U Computation Center Newsletter **1396**
I S U Computation Center Newsletter. (Iowa State University) (US) **1396**
I S U Constitution. (International Skating Union) (SZ) **4475**
I S U Regulations. (International Skating Union) (SZ) **4475**
I S W N E Newsletter. (International Society of Weekly Newspaper Editors) (US) **2571**
I T see Informatore Tessile **1285**
I T A A Compensation and Non-Cash Benefits Surveys. (Information Technology Association of America) (US) **1066**
I T A A Membership Directory. (Information Technology Association of America) (US) **1451, 1477**
I T A A New Products and Services Guide. (Information Technology Association of America) (US) **1477**
I T A A Newsletter. (International Textile and Apparel Association) (US) **1285**
I T A A Proceedings. (International Textile and Apparel Association) (US) **1288**
I T A A Software Industry Reports. (Information Technology Association of America) (US) **1477**
I T A A Special Publications. (International Textile and Apparel Association) (US) **1285**
†I T A - Engenharia. (Instituto Tecnologico de Aeronautica) (BL ISSN 0019-0772) **5210**
▼I T A Series. (Income Tax Act) (CN) **1097**
†I T C C Review. (International Technical Cooperation Centre) (IS ISSN 0047-1216) **5210**
I T C Desktop see Desktop Communications **1459**
I T C Journal. (NE ISSN 0303-2434) **2252, 1545, 1957**
I T C N. Informacion Tecnico Cientifico Naval. (CU) **3460**

I T D see Izotoptechnika, Diagnosztika **3359**
I T E A Journal of Test and Evaluation. (International Test & Evaluation Association) (US) **4599**
I T E Journal. (Institute of Transportation Engineers) (US ISSN 0162-8178) **4719**
I T E M. (Interference Technology Engineers Master) (US ISSN 0190-0943) **1898**
I T E S T Bulletin. (Institute for Theological Encounter with Science and Technology) (US) **4181**, 4599
I T E S T Conference Proceedings. (Institute for Theological Encounter with Science and Technology) (US) **4181**, 4599
I T F News. (International Transport Workers' Federation) (UK) **2584**, 4650
I T F Newsletter see I T F News **2584**
I T F Newsletter. (International Tremor Foundation) (US) **3338**
I T Focus (INSPEC, Section D) see Key Abstracts - Business Automation **1404**
I T G Journal. (International Trumpet Guild) (US) **3555**
I T I News see Professional Translator and Interpreter **2835**
†I T Intelligence. (Information Technology) (UK ISSN 0268-3954) **5210**
I T - Invaliditiyoe. (FI ISSN 0356-7249) **4408**
I T L Review of Applied Linguistics. (BE ISSN 0019-0829) **2817**, 1638
I T M see Intelligent Tutoring Media **1408**
I T M F. Country Statements. (International Textile Manufacturers Federation) (SZ) **4619**
I T M F Directory. (International Textile Manufacturers Federation) (SZ) **4619**
I T Magazine. (Irish Tatler) (IE) **2202**, 3067
I T N see International Television News **1375**
I T Novine. (YU ISSN 0019-0837) **1824**
I T P A Letters see Lettre des I T P A **105**
I T R. (International Transport Revue) (AU ISSN 0019-0845) **4745**
I T Review see Information Technology Review **1447**
I T S Bulletin see I T S Review **4650**
I T S Review. (Institute of Transportation Studies) (US ISSN 0192-3994) **4650**
I T U Review. (International Typographical Union) (US ISSN 0019-0853) **2584**, 4001
I T V A (UK) see I V C A Magazine **3511**
†I: The First Person. (US ISSN 1047-5249) **5210**
I to Cho/Stomach and Intestine. (JA ISSN 0536-2180) **3268**
I U A E S Commission on Urgent Anthropological Research. Newsletter.(AU) **241**
I U B Libraries. Faculty Newsletter. (Indiana University Libraries) (US) **2761**
I U B S Newsmagazine see Biology International: I U B S Newsmagazine **432**
I U C C Bulletin see University Computing **1401**
I U C N Bulletin. (International Union for Conservation of Nature and Natural Resources) (SZ ISSN 0020-9058) **1489**
I U D Digest. (Industrial Union Department) (US ISSN 0199-3704) **2584**
I U E News. (International Union of Electronic, Electrical, Salaried, Machine and Furniture Workers, A F L - C I O) (US ISSN 0019-0861) **2584**, 4599
I U F R O News. (International Union of Forestry Research Organizations) (AU) **2102**

I U F R O World Series. (International Union of Forestry Research Organizations) (AU ISSN 1016-3263) **2102**
I U G G Chronicle. (International Union of Geodesy and Geophysics) (FR ISSN 0047-1259) **1590**, 2253
I U I Yearbook. (Industriens Utredningsinstitut) (FI) **670**
I U O M A Magazine. (International Union of Mail Artists) (NE) **329**, 2924
I U P I W Views. (International Union of Petroleum & Industrial Workers) (US) **3688**
I U P Stress and Health Series. (International Universities Press, Inc.) (US) **3338**
I U S S P Newsletter/U I E S P Bulletin de Liaison. (International Union for the Scientific Study of Population) (BE ISSN 0771-2022) **3983**, 597
I U S S P Papers/U I E S P Documents de l'Union. (International Union for the Scientific Study of Population) (BE) **3983**, 597
I U S Y Bulletin see I U S Y Newsletter **3898**
I U S Y Newsletter. (International Union of Socialist Youth) (AU) **3898**
I V C A Magazine. (International Visual Communications Association) (UK ISSN 0952-7419) **3511**, 1374
I V I E Update. (UK) **1385**
I V I S Newsletter. (International Visitors Information Service) (US) **2227**
I V L - Nytt. (Institutet foer Vatten- och Luftvaardsforskning) (SW ISSN 0019-0896) **1957**
I V L - Referat. (Institutet foer Vatten- och Luftvaardsforskning) (SW ISSN 0283-1511) **1958**
I V S. (Index of Veterinary Specialists) (SA ISSN 0019-0918) **4820**, 13
I V U N News. (International Ventilator Users Network) (US) **3107**
I V V O - D L O Jaarverslag see Instituut voor Veevoedingsonderzoek. Jaarverslag **219**
I W see Israelitisches Wochenblatt fuer die Schweiz **2007**
I W F A Yearbook. (International Women's Fishing Association) (US) **4548**, 4845
I W G I A Boletin. (International Work Group for Indigenous Affairs) (DK ISSN 0107-556X) **241**
I W G I A Documento see I W G I A Documents **241**
I W G I A Documents. (International Work Group for Indigenous Affairs) (DK ISSN 0105-4503) **241**, 2005, 3943
I W G I A Newsletter. (International Work Group for Indigenous Affairs) (DK ISSN 0105-6387) **241**, 2005, 3943
I W G I A Yearbook. (International Work Group for Indigenous Affairs) (DK) **241**, 2005, 3943
I W I Monthly see I W I Newsletter **2571**
I W I Newsletter. (Illinois Writers, Inc.) (US) **2571**, 2924
I W K. (Internationale Wissenschaftliche Korrespondenz zur Geschichte der Deutschen Arbeiterbewegung) (GW ISSN 0046-8428) **2584**, 2368, 3898
I W L - Umweltbrief. (Institut fuer Gewerbliche Wasserwirtschaft und Luftreinhaltung e.V.) (GW ISSN 0179-3462) **1489**, 1958
I W P C Newsletter see Institution of Water and Environmental Management. Newsletter **4825**
†I W R A Newsletter. (International Water Resources Association) (US) **5210**
I W R B News. (International Waterfowl and Wetlands Research Bureau) (UK) **584**, 1958
I W - Report. (GW ISSN 0342-6319) **3018**, 1178, 1898
I W S A Year Book. (International Water Supply Association) (UK) **4825**
I W Trends. (GW) **868**
I Z see Informatore Zootecnico **218**

I Z A. (Illustrierte Zeitschrift fuer Arbeitssicherheit) (SZ) **3617**, 2584, 4104
Iade. (AG ISSN 0019-0934) **1898**, 1374
Iaderna Energiia/Nuclear Energy. (BU ISSN 0204-6989) **1805**
I'anson Times. (UK) **2155**
Iasi Polytechnic Magazine. (RM ISSN 1013-5278) **1824**
Iatrika Pepragmena. (GR ISSN 0019-0942) **3107**
Iatriki. (GR ISSN 0019-0950) **3107**
Iatrofon. (US) **3107**
Ibaraki Daigaku Kyoikugakubu Kiyo. Shizen Kagaku/Ibaraki University. Faculty of Education. Bulletin. Natural Sciences. (JA ISSN 0386-7668) **4313**
Ibaraki Daigaku Rigakubu Kiyo. Sugaku. see Ibaraki University. Faculty of Science. Bulletin. Series A: Mathematics **3037**
Ibaraki University. Faculty of Education. Bulletin. Natural Sciences. see Ibaraki Daigaku Kyoikugakubu Kiyo. Shizen Kagaku **4313**
Ibaraki University. Faculty of Science. Bulletin. Series A: Mathematics/ Ibaraki Daigaku Rigakubu Kiyo. Sugaku. (JA ISSN 0579-3068) **3037**
Ibarske Novosti. (YU ISSN 0019-0977) **2239**
Ibda/Innovation. (UA) **2924**, 329, 2995
Iberian Studies. (UK ISSN 0307-3262) **4375**, 2368
Iberica. (US) **2368**
†Ibero-American Bureau of Education. Information and Publications Department Series V: Technical Seminars and Meetings. (SP ISSN 0536-2512) **5210**
Ibero-Americana see Nordic Journal on Latin American Studies **2329**
Ibero-Amerikanisches Archiv. (GW ISSN 0340-3068) **2409**
Ibero-Romania. (GW ISSN 0019-0993) **2817**
Iberoamericana. (GW ISSN 0342-1864) **2869**, 2817
Iberoamericana Pragensia. (CS) **2409**
Ibidem: Glendon College Student Handbook. (CN) **1638**
Ibiden Company. Annual Report. (JA) **1178**, 1164
Ibis. (UK ISSN 0019-1019) **564**
Ibsenaarboken see Contemporary Approaches to Ibsen **2908**
Ibykus. (GW ISSN 0720-8782) **2995**, 3898, 4313
ICACH see I C A C H **328**
ICarbS. (US ISSN 0360-8409) **2761**
Icare. (FR ISSN 0018-8786) **55**
Icaro. (BL) **4803**
Icarus. (US ISSN 0019-1035) **365**
Icarus. (IE ISSN 0019-1027) **2924**, 329
▼Icarus (New York). (US ISSN 1054-1381) **2869**
Icarus File. (US) **3107**, 4408
Icarus Review. (US) **2924**
Ice. (UK ISSN 0019-1043) **1568**
Ice Cap News. (US ISSN 0019-1051) **3753**
Ice Cream & Frozen Confectionery. (UK ISSN 0019-106X) **2088**
Ice Cream Reporter. (US ISSN 0897-3261) **2088**
Ice Hockey Magazine. (JA) **4475**
Ice Hockey Rule Book. (US ISSN 0732-8117) **4475**
Ice News. (US) **2300**
†Ice River. (US) **5210**
Ice River - A Journal of Speculative Writing see Ice River **5210**
Ice River - A Quarterly Review and Market Tabloid for Speculative Writing, Fantastic Art and Electronic Music see Ice River **5210**
Ice Skating Institute of America. Newsletter. (US) **4475**
Icecap see I C E C A P Report **1772**
Iceland. Landsbokasafn Islands. Arbok see Iceland. Landsbokafn Islands. Arbok. Nyr Flokkur **2761**
Iceland. Landsbokasafn Islands. Arbok see Islensk Bokaskra **2794**

Iceland. Landsbokasafn Islands. Arbok. Nyr Flokkur. (IC) **2761**
Iceland. Statistical Bureau. Statistical Bulletin see Central Bank of Iceland. Economic Statistics **710**
Iceland Review. (IC ISSN 0019-1094) **2198**
▼Icelandic - American Society of New York. Society News. (US) **2005**
Icelandic National Bibliography. see Islensk Bokaskra **2794**
Icelandic Scientific Society. Occasional Papers. see Visindafelag Islendinga. Rit **4351**
Icengelo. (ZA) **4181**
Ich Schreibe. (GW ISSN 0445-1821) **2924**
▼Ichnos. (US ISSN 1042-0940) **441**, 241
Ichnusa. (IT) **2205**
Ichthyologia see Acta Biologica Iugoslavica. Serija E: Ichthyologia **576**
▼Ichthyological Exploration of Freshwaters. (GW ISSN 0936-9902) **584**
Ichthyosis Focus. (US) **3248**
Ici New York. (FR) **2227**, 4771
Ici Renault see Autoworld **4684**
Icomos Information. (IT) **301**
Icon Newsletter. (US) **1430**, 1477
▼Icones Orchidacearum. (MX ISSN 0188-4018) **505**
Icones Plantarum Africanarum. (SG ISSN 0073-4403) **505**
Iconographia Franciscana. (IT) **4265**, 329
Iconography of Religions. (NE) **329**, 4181
Iconography of Religions. Section 2, New Zealand. (NE) **329**, 4284
Iconography of Religions. Section 5, Australia. (NE ISSN 0169-8087) **329**, 4284
Iconography of Religions. Section 7, Africa. (NE ISSN 0169-8230) **329**, 4284
Iconography of Religions. Section 8, Arctic Peoples. (NE ISSN 0169-9628) **329**, 4284
Iconography of Religions. Section 9, South America. (NE ISSN 0921-0334) **329**, 4284
Iconography of Religions. Section 10, North America. (NE ISSN 0169-8184) **329**, 4284
Iconography of Religions. Section 11, Ancient America. (NE ISSN 0169-9970) **329**, 4284
Iconography of Religions. Section 12, East and Central Asia. (NE ISSN 0169-9725) **329**, 4214
Iconography of Religions. Section 13, Indian Religions. (NE ISSN 0169-8133) **329**, 4214
Iconography of Religions. Section 14, Iran. (NE ISSN 0169-9873) **329**, 4284
Iconography of Religions. Section 15, Mesopotamia and the Near East. (NE ISSN 0169-8036) **329**, 4284
Iconography of Religions. Section 16, Egypt. (NE ISSN 0169-8338) **329**, 4284
Iconography of Religions. Section 17, Greece and Rome. (NE ISSN 0169-9822) **329**, 4284
Iconography of Religions. Section 19, Ancient Europe. (NE ISSN 0169-9679) **329**, 4284
Iconography of Religions. Section 20, Manichaeism. (NE ISSN 0169-8435) **329**, 4284
Iconography of Religions. Section 21, Mandaeism. (NE ISSN 0169-9776) **329**, 4284
Iconography of Religions. Section 22, Islam. (NE ISSN 0169-8389) **329**, 4218
Iconography of Religions. Section 23, Judaism. (NE ISSN 0169-8281) **329**, 4223
Iconography of Religions. Section 24, Christianity. (NE ISSN 0169-992X) **329**, 4181
Iconography of Religions. Supplement. (NE) **330**, 4181
Ictesad. (IQ) **868**

6272 IDAHO. DEPARTMENT

Idaho. Department of Education. News and Reports. (US ISSN 1049-2437) **1638**
Idaho. Department of Employment. Annual Planning Report see Idaho. Department of Employment. Idaho Demographic Profile **981**
Idaho. Department of Employment. Idaho Demographic Profile. (US) **981**
Idaho. Department of Fish and Game. Federal Aid Investigation Projects. Progress Reports and Publications. (US ISSN 0073-4527) **1489, 2043**
Idaho. Department of Health and Welfare. Annual Summary of Vital Statistics. (US ISSN 0362-9279) **4117, 4426, 4574**
Idaho. Department of Health and Welfare. Bureau of Research and Statistics. Quarterly Welfare Statistical Bulletin see Idaho. Department of Health and Welfare. Research and Statistics Section. Quarterly Welfare Statistical Bulletin **4426**
Idaho. Department of Health and Welfare. Research and Statistics Section. Quarterly Welfare Statistical Bulletin. (US) **4426, 4104**
†Idaho. Department of Labor and Industrial Services. Annual Report. (US ISSN 0362-3912) **5210**
Idaho. Geological Survey. Bulletin. (US ISSN 0734-3825) **1568, 3485**
Idaho. Geological Survey. Information Circular. (US) **1568, 3485**
Idaho. Geological Survey. Technical Report. (US) **1568**
Idaho. State Board for Vocational Education. Annual Descriptive Report of Program Activities for Vocational Education see Idaho. State Division of Vocational Education. Annual Performance Report **1684**
Idaho. State Division of Vocational Education. Annual Performance Report. (US) **1684**
Idaho. State Superintendent of Public Instruction. Annual Report. State of Idaho Johnson-O'Malley Program. (US ISSN 0093-7223) **1638, 2005**
Idaho Agricultural Statistics. (US ISSN 0094-1271) **138**
†Idaho Beverage Analyst. (US) **5210**
Idaho Business Review. (US) **670**
Idaho Cattleman. (US) **218**
Idaho Cities. (US) **4088**
Idaho Clean Water. (US) **1977, 1598, 4825**
Idaho Department of Highways. Highway Information see Idaho Transportation Department. Highway Information **4719**
Idaho Education Association. Proceedings. (US ISSN 0073-4497) **1638**
Idaho Education Association Reporter (Year) see I E A Reporter (Year) **1638**
Idaho Educational Directory. (US) **1695**
Idaho Employment. (US ISSN 0536-2733) **981**
Idaho Farmer - Stockman. (US ISSN 1041-1682) **96, 218**
Idaho Grain. (US) **206**
Idaho Law Review. (US ISSN 0019-1205) **2633**
Idaho Librarian. (US ISSN 0019-1213) **2761**
Idaho Manufacturing Directory. (US) **1138**
Idaho, Montana, Wyoming TourBook see Tourbook: Idaho, Montana, Wyoming **4790**
Idaho Museum of Natural History. Occasional Papers. (US ISSN 0196-7703) **3525, 4314**
Idaho Museum of Natural History. Special Publication. (US) **3525**
Idaho Occupation Wage Survey. (US) **868, 981**
†Idaho Peace Officer. (US) **5210**
Idaho Pharmacist. (US ISSN 0019-1221) **3728**
Idaho: The University Magazine. (US ISSN 0160-5305) **1708**

Idaho Transportation Department. Highway Information. (US ISSN 0019-1175) **4719, 1867**
Idaho Wheat see Idaho Grain **206**
Idaho Wildlife. (US) **1489**
Idaho Wildlife Review see Idaho Wildlife **1489**
Idaho Yesterdays. (US ISSN 0019-1264) **2409**
Al-Idarah al-Aamah. (SU) **4063**
Al-Idarah wal-Tanmiyah/Administration and Development. (TS) **4063**
Al Idari. (LE) **1012**
Al-Idari. (MK) **4063**
Ide. (NO ISSN 0046-8517) **3898**
Ide-nyt Hus og Have til Villa - Raekkehuse see Ide-nyt: Til Lejligheder i Etagebebyggelse **2552**
Ide-nyt Til Lejligheder see Ide-nyt: Til Lejligheder i Etagebebyggelse **2552**
Ide-nyt: Til Lejligheder i Etagebebyggelse. (DK ISSN 0109-4505) **2552**
Ide-Nyt: Til Villa, Raekkehuse og Jordbrugere. (DK ISSN 0906-0952) **2552, 2131**
Ide og Form see Forming i Skolen **326**
Idea. (JA ISSN 0019-1299) **32**
Idea Factory. (US ISSN 0891-3978) **1751**
Idea Ink. (US) **2869, 4265**
Idea Liberale. (IT) **3898**
Idea Magazin. (SZ) **3392**
Idea Schweiz see Idea Magazin **3392**
Idea Source Guide. (US ISSN 0019-1310) **1041**
Idea-Spektrum. (GW) **4240**
Idea Today. (US ISSN 1040-8282) **3804, 4475**
Ideal Education. (II ISSN 0019-1353) **1638**
Ideal Home. (UK ISSN 0019-1361) **2552**
Ideal Home Plans. (US) **2552**
▼Ideal Traveller. (US ISSN 1055-8314) **4771**
Ideal Woman/Obaa Sima. (GH) **4845, 2192**
Idealistic Studies. (US ISSN 0046-8541) **3769**
Ideals. (US ISSN 0019-137X) **2995**
Ideas. (II ISSN 0301-9101) **2409**
Ideas/Afkar. (JO) **2869**
Ideas (Coral Gables). (US) **2560**
Ideas (Reston). (US ISSN 0896-1441) **32**
Ideas (Tokyo). (JA) **330**
Ideas & Action. (US ISSN 0894-024X) **981, 2584, 4437**
Ideas and Action Bulletin. (UN ISSN 0445-2216) **152**
Ideas and Information about Development Education. (US ISSN 1040-6352) **1722, 3959**
Ideas and Productions. (UK ISSN 0264-4940) **2869**
Ideas and Solutions. (US) **1077, 1066**
Ideas Bulletin see I D E A S Bulletin **949**
Ideas en Arte y Tecnologia. (AG ISSN 0326-3878) **4600**
Ideas en Ciencias Sociales. (AG ISSN 0326-386X) **4375**
Ideas for Better Living. (US) **2552**
Ideas for Joint Ventures. (HU) **949**
†Ideas in Sound. (US) **5210**
Ideas Newsletter see Ideas (Reston) **32**
Ideas para Su Hogar. (US) **2447**
Ideas Unlimited. (US) **2571**
Ideas y Valores see Revista Ideas y Valores **3779**
†Ideasworth. (US) **5210**
Ideele Import Informatie. (NE) **911**
Ideen Archiv. (GW ISSN 0176-859X) **32**
Idees de ma Maison. (CN ISSN 0840-8130) **2552**
Idees pour Tous see Idees pour Tous - Speciale Hebdo **5210**
†Idees pour Tous - Speciale Hebdo. (FR) **5210**
Idegenforgalmi Statisztika see Hungary. Kozponti Statisztikai Hivatal. Idegenforgalmi Evkonyv **4799**
Ideggyogyaszati Szemle. (HU ISSN 0019-1442) **3338**
Ideje. (YU) **1256**

Idengaku Zasshi. see Japanese Journal of Genetics **544**
†Identification Journal. (US ISSN 0747-962X) **5210**
Identification News. (US ISSN 0019-1450) **1515**
Identified Sources of Supply. (US) **3446**
Identity. (US ISSN 0899-3483) **32**
Identity. (IS ISSN 0333-838X) **2924**
Ideologia y Politica. (PE) **3898**
Ideologies and Literature see I & L **2924**
Ideology and Consciousness see I & C **4374**
Ideology Front. see Sixiang Zhanxian **4386**
Ideology of Madness. (US) **2995**
Idesia. (CL ISSN 0073-4675) **96**
Idillio. (IT) **2983**
Idiom. (AT ISSN 0046-8568) **1751, 2817**
Idiom 23. (AT) **2995**
Idioms and Phrases Index. (US) **2817**
The Idler. (CN ISSN 0828-1289) **2177**
Idnadurinn. (IC) **981**
Ido-Letro see Ido-Vivo **2818**
Ido-Vivo. (UK) **2818, 1337**
Idol of My Heart Elvis Presley Fan Club Newsletter. (US) **1298, 3555**
Idraetshistorisk Aarbog. (DK ISSN 0900-8632) **4475**
Idraetsliv. (DK ISSN 0109-3835) **4475**
Idrijski Razgledi. (XV ISSN 0019-1523) **2869**
Idrotecnica. (IT) **4825**
Idrottsbladet. (SW) **4475**
Idryma Meleton Chersonesou Aimou. Ekdoseis. see Institute for Balkan Studies. Publications **2368**
Ie. (US) **330**
Ie-no-Hikari/Light of Home. (JA) **96**
Ievanhel's'kyi Holos. (CN ISSN 0383-2538) **4284, 2005**
Ife African Studies. (NR) **2333**
Ife Journal of Agriculture. (NR) **96**
Ifjumunkas. (RM) **2584**
Iftah ya Simsim. (KU) **1256**
Igaku Hyoron/Japana Medicina Revuo. (JA ISSN 0019-1574) **3107**
Igaku no Ayumi. (JA ISSN 0039-2359) **3107**
Igaku Seibutsugaku Kenkyu Kiyo. see Acta Medica et Biologica **3070**
Igaku to Fukuin/Medicine and Gospel. (JA ISSN 0019-1582) **3107, 4181**
Igaku to Seibutsugaku/Medicine and Biology. (JA ISSN 0019-1604) **3107, 441**
Igaku Toshokan. (JA ISSN 0445-2429) **2761, 3107**
Igakushi Kenkyu/Studies on History of Medicine. (JA ISSN 0019-1612) **3107**
Igaz Szo see Lato **2931**
Igbo Philosophy. (NR) **241**
Igea Medica. (IT) **3107**
Igeret. (US) **2005, 4223**
Igeret Lechinuch. (IS ISSN 0536-3535) **1638**
Igiene e Sanita Pubblica. (IT ISSN 0019-1639) **4104**
Igiene Mentale. (IT ISSN 0019-1647) **4024, 4104**
Igiene Moderna. (IT ISSN 0019-1655) **3804**
Igitte. (GW) **4845**
Igitur Revista Literaria. (AG ISSN 0019-1663) **2924**
Iglesia de Sevilla. (SP) **4265**
Iglesia Evangelica del Rio de la Plata. Revista Parroquial. (AG ISSN 0019-1671) **4240**
Iglesia - Mundo. (SP) **4181**
Igloos see Revue Quart Monde **4418**
Ignis see Kyrkogarden **2119**
Igo. see Go **4473**
Igra. (IS) **2924**
Igud Yotzei Sin. Bulletin. (IS) **2005**
Iheringia. Serie Antropologia. (BL ISSN 0073-4691) **241**
Iheringia. Serie Botanica. (BL ISSN 0073-4705) **505**
Iheringia. Serie Geologia. (BL ISSN 0073-4713) **1568**

Iheringia. Serie Miscelanea. (BL ISSN 0102-3314) **505, 584**
Iheringia. Serie Zoologia. (BL ISSN 0073-4721) **584**
Ihos. see Sound & Hi Fi **3581**
Ihr Arzt an Sie. (GW) **3107**
Ihre Ferienwohnung. (GW) **4771**
Ihre Kette. (GW) **32**
Ihsa'iyah-i Amual-i Sadirati-i Afghanistan. see Export Statistics of Afghanistan **715**
Ihsa'iyah-i Amual-i Varidati-i Afghanistan. see Imports Statistics of Afghanistan **721**
Ihsa'iyyat Dubai lil-Tijarah al-Kharijiyyah. see Dubai External Trade Statistics **713**
III - Vs Review. (UK ISSN 0961-1290) **1773**
Ija Webonere. (TZ ISSN 0019-171X) **4240**
Ijo Tennko Kanshi Hokoku see Monthly Report on Climate System **3439**
Ikai Jiho. (JA ISSN 0019-1728) **3107**
Ikakikai Gaku Zasshi/Journal of Medical Instruments. (JA ISSN 0019-1736) **2522, 3107**
Ikarie. (CS) **3012**
Ikenga. (NR) **2005**
Ikomayama Uchu Kagakukan Nyusu. (JA) **3525, 55, 365**
Ikon. (US) **2995**
Ikon - Ricerche sulla Comunicazione. (IT) **1337**
Ikonenkalender. (GW) **330**
Ikonomiceska Misal. (BU ISSN 0013-2993) **670**
Ikoyeneakos Thesavros/Family Treasure. (GR) **2447**
Ikutoku Kogyo Daigaku Kenkyu Hokoku. B Rikogaku Hen/Ikutoku Technical University. Research Reports. Part B. Science and Technology. (JA ISSN 0386-1163) **4600, 4314**
Ikutoku Technical University. Research Reports. Part B. Science and Technology. see Ikutoku Kogyo Daigaku Kenkyu Hokoku. B Rikogaku Hen **4600**
Il. (FR) **3398**
Al-I'lamiyyah/Information. (TS) **2761, 1374**
Ilanga Lethu see Sedibeng **2295**
Ile de France a la Page. (FR ISSN 0984-4724) **721**
Ile de la Reunion. Gazette. (RE) **2169**
Ileostomy Association of Great Britain & Ireland Quarterly Journal see I A Quarterly Journal **3197**
†Iliff Review. (US ISSN 0019-1795) **5210**
†Ill-la-Mo Searcher. (US) **5210**
Iller ve Belediyeler. (TU) **4088**
Illiana Genealogist. (US ISSN 0019-1809) **2155, 2409**
Illiana Spirit. (US) **2227**
Illinois. Administrative Office of Illinois Courts. Annual Report to the Supreme Court of Illinois. (US ISSN 0536-3713) **2633**
Illinois. Board of Higher Education. Directory of Higher Education. (US ISSN 0094-8322) **1708**
†Illinois. Board of Higher Education. Statewide Space Survey. (US ISSN 0362-5524) **5210**
Illinois. Community College Board. Annual Report. (US) **1708**
Illinois. Community College Board. Biennial Report see Illinois. Community College Board. Annual Report **1708**
Illinois. Community College Board. Data and Characteristics. (US) **1708**
Illinois. Department of Commerce and Community Affairs. Bi-monthly Economic Data Summary. (US) **670**
Illinois. Department of Commerce and Community Affairs. Monthly Economic Data Sheets see Illinois. Department of Commerce and Community Affairs. Bi-monthly Economic Data Summary **670**
Illinois. Department of Conservation. Outdoor Highlights. (US) **1489, 2102**

Illinois. Department of Public Instruction. Annual State of Education Message see Illinois. State Board of Education. Annual Report **1638**
Illinois. Division of Air Pollution Control. Annual Air Quality Report. (US) **1977**
Illinois. Housing Development Authority. Annual Report. (US ISSN 0090-3248) **2489**
Illinois. Judicial Inquiry Board. Report. (US ISSN 0093-8939) **3943**
Illinois. Junior College Board. Annual Report see Illinois. Community College Board. Annual Report **1708**
Illinois. Legislative Reference Bureau. Legislative Synopsis and Digest. (US) **2634**
Illinois. Natural History Survey. Biological Notes. (US ISSN 0073-490X) **441**
Illinois. Natural History Survey. Bulletin. (US ISSN 0073-4918) **441**
Illinois. Natural History Survey. Circular. (US ISSN 0073-4926) **441**
Illinois. Natural History Survey. Reports.(US) **1489, 2409, 4314**
Illinois. Natural History Survey. Special Publication. (US ISSN 0888-9546) **441**
Illinois. State Board of Education. Annual Report. (US ISSN 0147-2860) **1638**
Illinois. State Geological Survey. Bulletins. (US ISSN 0073-5051) **1568**
Illinois. State Geological Survey. Circulars. (US ISSN 0073-506X) **1568**
Illinois. State Geological Survey. Educational Series. (US ISSN 0073-5078) **1568**
Illinois. State Geological Survey. Environmental Geology. (US) **1568**
Illinois. State Geological Survey. Environmental Geology Notes see Illinois. State Geological Survey. Environmental Geology **1568**
Illinois. State Geological Survey. Guidebook Series. (US ISSN 0073-5094) **1568**
Illinois. State Geological Survey. Industrial Mineral Notes see Illinois Minerals **3485**
Illinois. State Geological Survey. Mineral Economic Briefs see Illinois Minerals **3485**
Illinois. State Library, Springfield. Publications of the State of Illinois. (US ISSN 0191-1058) **3937**
Illinois. State Museum. Handbook of Collections. (US ISSN 0445-3387) **330**
Illinois. State Museum. Inventory of the Collections. (US ISSN 0095-2893) **3525, 4314**
Illinois. State Museum. Popular Science Series. (US ISSN 0360-0297) **4314**
Illinois. State Museum. Reports of Investigations. (US ISSN 0360-0270) **4314**
Illinois. State Museum. Research Series. Papers in Anthropology. (US ISSN 0095-2915) **241**
Illinois. State Museum. Scientific Papers Series. (US ISSN 0445-3395) **4314, 274, 441, 2409**
Illinois. State Museum. Story of Illinois Series. (US ISSN 0360-0289) **4314**
Illinois Advance. (US ISSN 0745-1539) **2288**
Illinois Agri-News. (US) **96**
Illinois Alumni News see Illinois Quarterly **1314**
Illinois Antiquity. Quarterly Newsletter. (US) **274**
Illinois Attorney General's Report and Opinions. (US) **2634**
Illinois Audubon. (US) **1489**
Illinois Aviation. (US) **4674**
Illinois Banker. (US ISSN 0019-185X) **784**
Illinois Bankers Association Commercial - Ag Lending Letter see I B A Commercial - Ag Lending Letter **784**
Illinois Bankers Association Law Watch see I B A Law Watch **2633**

Illinois Banknews. (US) **784**
Illinois Baptist. (US ISSN 0019-1868) **4240**
Illinois Bar Journal. (US ISSN 0019-1876) **2634**
Illinois Beef. (US) **218**
Illinois Benedictine Magazine. (US) **1314**
Illinois Beverage Journal. (US ISSN 0019-1892) **381**
Illinois Biological Monographs. (US ISSN 0073-4748) **441**
Illinois Birds and Birding. (US) **564**
Illinois Braille Messenger (Braille Edition). (US) **2293**
Illinois Braille Messenger (Inkprint Edition). (US ISSN 0019-1906) **2293**
Illinois Building News. (US ISSN 0019-1914) **620, 2115**
Illinois Business Review. (US ISSN 0019-1922) **670**
Illinois Career Education Journal see Illinois Vocational Education Journal **3628**
Illinois Classical Studies. (US ISSN 0363-1923) **1277**
Illinois County and Township Official. (US ISSN 0019-1949) **4088**
Illinois Courts Bulletin. (US ISSN 0019-1957) **2634**
Illinois Criminal Law. (US) **2713**
Illinois Criminal Procedure. (US) **2713**
Illinois Criminal Trial Evidence. (US) **2713**
Illinois Dealer Directory and Buyer's Guide. (US) **620**
Illinois Dental Journal. (US ISSN 0019-1973) **3234**
Illinois Directory and Suppliers Listing see Illinois Dealer Directory and Buyer's Guide **620**
Illinois Economic Summary see Illinois. Department of Commerce and Community Affairs. Bi-monthly Economic Data Summary **670**
Illinois Education Association, National Education Association Advocate see I E A - N E A Advocate **1638**
▼Illinois Employment Law Letter. (US ISSN 1049-9385) **2710, 981**
Illinois Engineer. (US ISSN 0019-2015) **1824**
Illinois English Bulletin. (US ISSN 0019-2023) **1751**
Illinois Entertainer. (US) **3555**
▼Illinois Environmental Law Letter. (US) **2634**
Illinois Facts. (US ISSN 1041-2778) **1781**
Illinois Farmers Fastline see Farmers Fastline: Illinois Edition **91**
Illinois FarmWeek. (US) **96, 2634**
Illinois Food Service News. (US) **2476**
Illinois Geographical Society. Bulletin. (US ISSN 0019-2031) **2253**
▼Illinois Golfer's Travel Guide. (US) **4506, 4771**
Illinois Gross State Product. (US) **1077**
Illinois Guard Chronicle. (US) **3460**
Illinois Historical Journal. (US ISSN 0748-8149) **2409**
Illinois History. (US ISSN 0019-2058) **2409, 1256**
Illinois, Indiana, Ohio TourBook see Tourbook: Illinois, Indiana, Ohio **4790**
Illinois Insurance. (US ISSN 0094-7660) **2533**
Illinois Issues. (US ISSN 0738-9663) **4088**
Illinois Journal of Mathematics. (US ISSN 0019-2082) **3038**
Illinois Labor History Society Reporter. (US ISSN 0085-1728) **981, 2584**
Illinois Legal Times. (US) **2634**
Illinois Libertarian. (US) **3898**
Illinois Libraries. (US ISSN 0019-2104) **2761**
Illinois Library Association Reporter see I L A Reporter **2761**
Illinois Limitations Manual. (US) **2634**
Illinois Magazine. (US ISSN 0148-3390) **2410, 1489, 2227, 4771**
Illinois Manufacturers Directory. (US ISSN 0160-3302) **1138**

Illinois Master Plumber Magazine. (US ISSN 0019-2112) **2300**
Illinois Medical Journal see Illinois Medicine **3107**
Illinois Medicine. (US) **3107**
Illinois Medieval Monograph Series. (US) **2368**
Illinois Minerals. (US) **3485, 1568**
Illinois Minerals Notes see Illinois Minerals **3485**
Illinois Mining Institute. Proceedings. (US) **3485**
Illinois Municipal Review. (US ISSN 0019-2139) **4088**
Illinois Music Educator. (US ISSN 0019-2147) **3555**
Illinois Notes. (US) **2761**
Illinois Park and Recreation Quarterly see Illinois Parks & Recreation **4548**
Illinois Parks & Recreation. (US ISSN 0019-2155) **4548, 1489**
Illinois Petroleum. (US) **3688, 1568**
Illinois Pharmacist. (US ISSN 0195-2099) **3728**
Illinois Police Association. Official Journal. (US ISSN 0019-2171) **1515**
Illinois Postal Historian. (US) **3753**
Illinois Property Tax Statistics. (US) **721, 1097**
Illinois Publisher. (US) **2571**
Illinois Quarterly. (US) **1314**
Illinois Racing News. (US) **4535**
Illinois Reporter. (US) **784**
Illinois Research. (US ISSN 0019-2201) **96**
Illinois Runner. (US) **4475**
Illinois Rural Electric News. (US) **1898**
Illinois School Board Journal. (US ISSN 0019-221X) **1728**
Illinois School Research and Development. (US ISSN 0163-822X) **1751**
Illinois Schools Journal. (US ISSN 0019-2236) **1638**
Illinois Services Directory. (US ISSN 0092-3818) **1138**
Illinois Short Fiction. (US) **2924**
▼Illinois Soybean Farmer. (US) **96**
Illinois Speech and Theatre Association. Journal. (US) **1337, 1751**
Illinois State Academy of Science. Transactions. (US ISSN 0019-2252) **4314**
Illinois State and Regional Economic Data Book. (US ISSN 0093-9552) **868**
Illinois State Bar Association. Legislative Bulletin. (US) **2634**
Illinois State Bar Association. Tort Trends see Tort Trends Newsletter **2686**
Illinois State Bar Association News see I S B A News **2633**
Illinois State Genealogical Society Quarterly. (US ISSN 0046-8622) **2155**
Illinois State University Alumni Today see Illinois State University Today **1314**
Illinois State University Today. (US) **1314**
Illinois Studies in Anthropology. (US ISSN 0073-5167) **241**
Illinois T E S O L - B E Newsletter. (Illinois Teachers of English to Speakers of Other Languages - Bilingual Education) (US) **2818**
Illinois Teacher for Contemporary Roles see Illinois Teacher of Home Economics **5210**
†Illinois Teacher of Home Economics. (US ISSN 0739-148X) **5210**
Illinois Teachers of English to Speakers of Other Languages - Bilingual Education Illinois T E S O L - B E Newsletter see Illinois T E S O L - B E Newsletter **2818**
Illinois Technograph. (US) **1824**
Illinois Tort Law. (US) **2634**
†Illinois Travel and Recreation Guide. (US) **5210**
▼Illinois Trials. (US) **2634**
Illinois Truck News. (US ISSN 0019-2309) **4745**
Illinois Trucker. (US) **4745**

Illinois University. Department of Urban and Regional Planning. Research Bureau. Newsletter see Planning and Public Policy **2494**
Illinois Vocational Education Journal. (US ISSN 0279-0491) **3628**
Illinois Wildlife. (US ISSN 0019-2317) **1489**
Illinois Word see The Word **1779**
Illinois Writers, Inc. Newsletter see I W I Newsletter **2571**
Illinois Writers Review. (US ISSN 0733-9526) **2869**
Illuminating Engineering Institute of Japan. Journal/Shomei Gakkai Shi. (JA ISSN 0019-2341) **1898**
Illuminating Engineering Society. Journal. (US ISSN 0099-4480) **1899**
Illuminating Engineering Society. Transactions see Lighting Research and Technology **1902**
Illuminating Engineering Society Lighting Handbook see I E S Lighting Handbook **1898**
Illuminating Engineering Society of Australia Lighting Review see I.E.S. Lighting Review **5209**
Illuminations. (UK ISSN 0736-4725) **2995**
Illuminotecnica. (IT ISSN 0019-2384) **1899, 2552**
Illustrated Buyers Guide to Exhibits. (US ISSN 1054-1934) **1041, 32, 1115**
Illustrated Directory of Handicapped Products. (US) **1138, 3107**
†Illustrated Guide to the Protozoa. (US) **5210**
Illustrated London News. (UK ISSN 0019-2422) **2194**
Illustrated News. see Kepes Ujsag **2198**
Illustrated Weekly of India. (II ISSN 0019-2430) **2199**
Illustration in Japan. (JA) **330**
Illustration 63. (GW ISSN 0019-2457) **330**
Illustratofiat. (IT) **4692**
Illustrator. (US ISSN 0019-2465) **330, 1638**
The Illustrator Collectors News. (US) **2437**
†Illustrators. (UK ISSN 0307-319X) **5210**
†Illustrators Despatch. (UK ISSN 0260-8324) **5210**
Illustrators: The Annual of American Illustration. (US ISSN 0073-5477) **330**
Illustrazione Italiana. (IT) **2205**
†Illustrerad Motor Sport. (SW ISSN 0019-249X) **5210**
Illustreret Videnskab. (DK ISSN 0109-2456) **4314**
Illustrierte Historische Hefte. (GW) **2314**
Illustrierte Neue Welt. (AU) **2005, 2173**
Illustrierte Rundschau der Gendarmerie see Illustrierte Rundschau der Oesterreichischen Gendarmerie **1515**
Illustrierte Rundschau der Oesterreichischen Gendarmerie. (AU) **1515**
Illustrierte Zeitschrift fuer Arbeitssicherheit see I Z A **3617**
†Illustrierter Motorsport. (GW ISSN 0442-3054) **5210**
Ilmailu. (FI ISSN 0019-252X) **55**
Ilmatieteen Laitoksen Toimituksia - Finnish Meteorological Institute Contributions see Finnish Meteorological Institute. Contributions **3435**
Ilmatieteen Laitos. Geofysikaalisia Julkaisuja. see Finnish Meteorological Institute. Geophysical Publications **1589**
Ilmatieteen Laitos. Ilmansuojelun Julkaisuja. see Finnish Meteorological Institute. Publications on Air Quality **1977**
Ilmatieteen Laitos. Meteorologisia Julkaisuja/Finnish Meteorological Institute. Publications. (FI ISSN 0782-6109) **3436**
Ilmi A'ino. (PK) **4141**

ILMU ALAM

Ilmu Alam. (MY ISSN 0126-7000) **2253**
Ilocos Review. (PH ISSN 0019-2538) **2344**, 2924
Ilustrovana Politika. (YU ISSN 0019-2570) **2239**
Ilustrowany Magazyn Turystyczny Swiatowid see I M T Swiatowid **4771**
Im Gespraech. (GW ISSN 0721-2097) **3898**
Im Heiligen Dienst. (GW ISSN 0938-3190) **4265**
Im Lande der Bibel. (GW ISSN 0019-2597) **4181**
Imafronte see Universidad de Murcia. Imafronte. Departamento de Historia del Arte **347**
Image see Virginia P H C Image **2304**
Image. (CN) **2552**
Image see Image: Journal of Nursing Scholarship **3279**
Image. (Il) **3638**, 2924
Image. (GW ISSN 0176-8565) **4182**
Image (Fort Worth). (US) **620**, 3943
Image (Liverpool). (UK) **330**, 1314
Image (London). (UK) **3792**
Image (Rochester, 1952). (US ISSN 0536-5465) **3792**, 3511
Image and Vision Computing. (UK ISSN 0262-8856) **1422**
Image de la Mauricie. (CN) **1505**
Image File. (US ISSN 0743-7617) **2410**
Image: Journal of Nursing Scholarship. (US ISSN 0743-5150) **3279**, 1708
Image Magazine. (US ISSN 0748-1780) **2924**
Image Processing. (UK) **670**, 4600
▼Image Systems. (US) **1435**
Image Technology Journal of the B K S T S. (British Kinematograph Sound and Television Society) (UK ISSN 0950-2114) **3511**, 1374
Image Understanding. (US ISSN 0748-0059) **1414**
Image World. (US ISSN 8756-6664) **3628**, 4001, 4129
Imagen. (PN) **2005**
Imagen. (PR ISSN 0890-6548) **2215**
Imagen y Sonida see Eikonos **3508**
Imagenes. (UY) **2238**
†Imagenes. (PR) **5210**
Imagenes de la Fe. (SP) **4265**
Imagery Today. (US ISSN 1041-8377) **4024**, 2924
†Images. (US) **5210**
Images du Mois. (FR) **4265**
▼Images of Nashville. (US) **2227**
Imagezine. (US) **330**
Imagination. (GW ISSN 1010-8386) **402**
Imagination, Cognition and Personality. (US ISSN 0276-2366) **4024**, 3669
▼Imagination Magazine. (US) **2924**
Imagine. (CN ISSN 0709-8855) **3012**
Imaging. see Bildgebung **3357**
Imaging Abstracts. (UK ISSN 0896-100X) **3798**, 13
Imaging and Monitoring News see Medical Imaging and Monitoring **3126**
▼Imaging Business Report. (US ISSN 1050-7019) **4007**
Imaging Guidelines. (AT) **3107**
Imaging on Campus. (US ISSN 0893-1925) **3792**
Imaging Service Bureau News. (US ISSN 1055-8098) **1451**
Imaging Supplies Annual. (US) **4007**
Imaging Technology Report. (US ISSN 1041-4320) **4600**
Imaging Update. (US) **1422**
Imago. (AT) **2995**
Imago. (AG) **3338**, 4024
Imago Mvndi. (UK ISSN 0308-5694) **2253**
Imago Musicae. (US ISSN 0255-8831) **3555**, 2410
Al-Imarat fil-Ajwa/Emirates in Flight. (TS) **4803**
Imb see Catalogo Guida dell'Imballaggio (Year) **3648**
Imballaggio. (IT ISSN 0019-2708) **3649**

Imballaggio News. (IT) **3649**
Imbat. (US) **3555**
Imbila. (ZA) **2240**
Imbongi. (SA ISSN 0019-2716) **1314**, 4182
Imbongi Yenkosi. (SA ISSN 0378-4088) **4240**
Imboniselo. (SA ISSN 0019-008X) **4284**
Imbottigliamento. (IT ISSN 0392-792X) **3649**, 381
Imera. (PE) **1917**
Imfama (Braille Edition). (SA) **2293**
Imfama (Inkprint Edition). (SA ISSN 0019-2724) **2293**
Imfama (Tape Edition). (SA) **2293**
Imkerfreund. (GW ISSN 0019-2732) **96**
Immagine. (IT) **3511**
Immagine Riflessa. (IT) **2924**
Immanuel. (IS ISSN 0302-8127) **4182**
Immediate Impact. (US) **1337**
Immenstaader Heimatblaetter. (GW) **2368**, 2055
Immer Gruen. (GW) **4240**
Immergruene Blaetter. (GW) **2131**, 505
Immigrant Communities & Ethnic Minorities in the United States & Canada. (US ISSN 0749-5951) **3983**, 241, 2005
Immigrants & Minorities. (UK ISSN 0261-9288) **3983**, 2005
Immigration and Nationality Law & Practice. (UK) **2702**, 2005
Immigration and Nationality Law Review. (US ISSN 0149-9807) **2702**, 3983
Immigration and Naturalization Reporter see I and N Reporter **3982**
Immigration Briefings. (US ISSN 0897-6708) **3983**, 2702
Immigration Digest. (US ISSN 0899-5400) **3983**, 2155
Immigration Highlights. (CN) **3992**
Immigration History Newsletter. (US ISSN 0579-4374) **3983**, 2314
Immigration Journal. (US ISSN 0884-3244) **2702**, 4437
Immigration Law Report. (US ISSN 0731-5767) **2702**, 3983
Immigration Law Reporter. Second Series. (CN ISSN 0835-3808) **3983**, 2702
†Immigration Management Alert. (US) **5211**
Immigration Newsletter. (US ISSN 0145-3416) **2724**
Immigration Policy & Law. (US ISSN 0892-547X) **3983**
Immigration Report. (US) **2702**, 3898, 3983
Immobilia. (SZ) **4150**
Immobilien-Berater. (GW) **4150**
Immobilien Verwaltung Heute. (GW) **4150**
Immobilien Wirtschaft Heute. (GW) **4150**
The Immortalist. (US) **3259**
Immunitaet und Infektion. (GW ISSN 0340-1162) **3185**
Immunizations/Vaccinations/Vacunaciones. (FR ISSN 1011-8624) **3175**
†Immuno-Advance. (JA ISSN 0285-0796) **5211**
Immuno-analyse et Biologie Specialisee. (FR ISSN 0923-2532) **441**
Immunoassay. (UK ISSN 0142-8128) **3259**
Immunobiology. (GW ISSN 0171-2985) **3185**
Immunobiology and Cancer - Functional Aspects of Cell-Mediated Immunity see I C R D B Cancergram: Immunobiology and Cancer - Functional Aspects of Cell-Mediated Immunity **5208**
Immunobiology and Cancer - Humoral Immunity see I C R D B Cancergram: Immunobiology and Cancer - Humoral Immunity **5208**

Immunobiology and Cancer - Identification and Characterization of Immune Cells see I C R D B Cancergram: Immunobiology and Cancer - Identification and Characterization of Immune Cells **5208**
Immunobiology and Cancer - Tumor-Associated Antigens see I C R D B Cancergram: Immunobiology and Cancer - Tumor-Associated Antigens **5208**
†Immunodeficiency. (UK ISSN 0266-6340) **5211**
Immunodeficiency Reviews. (US ISSN 0893-5300) **3185**
Immunogenetics. (GW ISSN 0093-7711) **3185**, 544
Immunohistochemistry. (UK ISSN 0142-8136) **525**, 552, 3259
Immunologia Clinica. (IT) **3185**
Immunologia Clinica e Sperimentale see Immunologia Clinica **3185**
Immunologia Polska. (PL ISSN 0324-8534) **3185**
†Immunologic Receptors. (UK ISSN 0268-1587) **5211**
Immunologic Research. (SZ ISSN 0257-277X) **3185**
Immunological and Molecular Probes see Journal of Immunoassay **3731**
Immunological Investigations. (US ISSN 0882-0139) **3185**
Immunological Reviews. (DK ISSN 0105-2896) **3185**
Immunologiya/Immunology. (RU ISSN 0206-4952) **3186**
Immunology see A P M I S **424**
Immunology. (UK ISSN 0019-2805) **3186**
Immunology. see Immunologiya **3186**
Immunology Abstracts. (US ISSN 0307-112X) **3176**, 13
†Immunology: An International Series of Monographs and Treatises. (US ISSN 0092-6019) **5211**
Immunology and Allergy Clinics of North America. (US ISSN 0889-8561) **3186**
Immunology and Allergy Practice. (US ISSN 0194-7508) **3186**
Immunology and Cancer - the Major Histocompatibility Complex see I C R D B Cancergram: Immunology and Cancer - The Major Histocompatibility Complex **5208**
Immunology and Cell Biology. (AT ISSN 0818-9641) **3186**, 441
▼Immunology and Infectious Diseases. (UK ISSN 0959-4957) **3219**, 3186
Immunology Letters. (NE ISSN 0165-2478) **3186**
Immunology Series. (US) **3186**
Immunology Today. (UK ISSN 0167-4919) **3186**
†Immunology Tribune. (US ISSN 0271-3284) **5211**
▼ImmunoMethods. (US ISSN 1058-6687) **3186**
†Immunoparasitology. (UK ISSN 0264-9551) **5211**
Immunopharmacology. (NE ISSN 0162-3109) **3186**, 3728
Immunopharmacology and Immunotoxicology. (US ISSN 0892-3973) **3728**
†Immunosuppression. (UK ISSN 0264-956X) **5211**
Immunotherapy see International Journal of Immunotherapy **3187**
Imono. see Japan Foundrymen's Society. Journal **3410**
Imono Daijesuto. see Casting Digest **3404**
Impact see Impact on Instructional Improvement **1638**
Impact see Living in Thailand **2220**
Impact. (FR) **3511**
Impact. (PH ISSN 0300-4155) **4375**, 3898, 4182
Impact (Athens). (US ISSN 0749-1573) **96**
Impact (Austin). (US) **3338**, 4024
Impact (Columbia). (US ISSN 0019-2856) **1638**
Impact (Dundas). (AT ISSN 0310-0316) **1012**
†Impact (Evanston). (US) **5211**

Impact (London). (UK ISSN 0046-8703) **2869**
Impact (Nepean). see Algonquin Times **1303**
Impact (New York). (US) **381**
Impact (New York, 1983) see The U S Non-Alcoholic Beverage Market: Impact Databank Review and Forecast **5293**
Impact (North Fitzroy). (AT ISSN 0706-5914) **4408**
Impact (North York). (CN) **1314**
Impact (Omaha). (US) **3107**, 1708
Impact (Rockville). (US) **1363**
†Impact (San Francisco). (US) **5211**
Impact (Sydney). (AT) **4408**
Impact (Washington). (US ISSN 0162-4989) **4692**, 1505, 2634
Impact (Westport). (US) **4408**, 1238
Impact (Wheaton). (US ISSN 0019-2821) **4240**
Impact AgBioBusiness see Impact AgBioIndustry **179**
▼Impact AgBioIndustry. (UK) **179**
Impact American Beer Market Review and Forecast see The U S Beer Market: Impact Databank Review and Forecast **386**
Impact American Distilled Spirits Market Review and Forecast see The U S Distilled Spirits Market: Impact Databank Review and Forecast **386**
Impact American Wine Market Review and Forecast see The U S Wine Market: Impact Databank Review and Forecast **386**
Impact Assessment Bulletin. (US) **4600**
Impact: Forum of the Student National Education Association see S N E A Impact: The Student Voice of the United Teaching Profession **1660**
Impact International. (US ISSN 0268-8212) **381**
Impact International Directory see Impact World Directory **1139**
Impact Journal. (US ISSN 0162-1300) **1505**
Impact News see Ofari's Bi-Monthly **2018**
Impact Newsletter see Impact (New York) **381**
Impact of Computing in Science and Engineering. (US ISSN 0899-8248) **1879**, 3064
Impact of Federal Expenditures on California see Defense Spending in the 1990s: Impact on California **859**
Impact of Science on Society. (UN ISSN 0019-2872) **4314**, 4437
Impact of Travel on State Economies. (US ISSN 0730-9813) **4772**
Impact on Instructional Improvement. (US) **1638**
Impact Pump News Patents. (US ISSN 1056-1536) **3018**, 1854, 2300, 3675
Impact Pump Patents see Impact Pump News Patents **3018**
Impact Pumps, Pumps-Compressors see Impact Pump News Patents **3018**
†L'Impact Suisse. (SZ) **5211**
Impact Valves see Impact Valves News and Patents **3675**
Impact Valves News and Patents. (US ISSN 1056-1544) **3675**, 1854, 1930, 2300
Impact: Wine and Spirits Newsletter see Impact (New York) **381**
▼Impact World Directory. (US) **1139**, 381
†Impact Yearbook. (US ISSN 0749-7946) **5211**
Impacto. (MX ISSN 0019-2880) **2210**
Impacto Internacional. (EC) **2185**
Impacto Latin News. (US) **2005**
†Impacto Socialista. (DR) **5211**
Impacts. (FR ISSN 0019-2899) **2508**
Impaired Driving & Breathalyzer Law. (CN) **2634**
Imparcial. (AG ISSN 0019-2902) **2170**
Impartial Citizen. (US ISSN 0738-9116) **2006**, 3943, 3959
Impegno Settanta. (IT ISSN 0046-8711) **2869**

Imperial Cancer Research Fund. Scientific Report. (UK ISSN 0306-4905) **3198**
Imperial Chemical Industries Spectrum see I C I Spectrum **1077**
Imperial College of Science and Technology Annual Report see I C C E T Annual Report **1957**
Imperial Oil Limited. Review see Imperial Oil Review **3688**
Imperial Oil Review/Revue de l'Imperiale. (CN ISSN 0700-5156) **3688**
▼Imperial Quarterly. (CN ISSN 1188-0066) **2368**, 330
Imperial War Museum, London. Department of Printed Books. Accessions List. (UK) **3476**
Imperial War Museum Review. (UK ISSN 0951-3094) **3525**, 3460
Impermeabilizzare see Specializzata **632**
Impetus. (US ISSN 1044-7490) **330**, 2869, 2995, 3398, 4845
Impex Guide: Import and Export. (JA) **911**
Impianti see Innovazione: Impianti e Produzione **1825**
Impianti Attrezzature Sportive e Ricreative see Sport e Citta **4489**
Impianti Sport. (IT) **4475**
Impiantistica Italiana. (IT ISSN 0394-1582) **3018**, 2300
L'Impianto Elettrico. (IT ISSN 0394-5634) **1899**
▼Implant Dentistry. (US) **3234**
Implanter. (II) **831**
Implantologist see International Journal of Oral Implantology **3235**
Implants in Ophthalmology. (SI ISSN 0218-0367) **3301**
Implement & Tractor. (US ISSN 0019-2953) **162**, 3018
Implement & Tractor Product File. (US ISSN 0073-5566) **162**
Implement & Tractor Red Book. (US ISSN 0073-5574) **162**
Import Automotive Parts & Accesories. (US ISSN 0199-4468) **4692**
Import - Export Directory. (US) **911**
Import - Export Newsletter. (US) **911**
▼Import - Export Opportunities Bulletin.(US) **911**
Import Insights. (US) **381**
Import of Marine Products by Country. (JA) **1041**
Import Service. (US) **4692**
Import Statistical Schedule of Japan (Year). (JA) **911**
Import Trade Control: Handbook of Rules and Procedures. (II ISSN 0536-9983) **911**
Import Trade Control Policy. (II ISSN 0536-9061) **911**
ImportCar & Truck. (US ISSN 0735-7877) **4692**
Imported Cars, Light Trucks & Vans Service & Repair. (US) **4693**, 4745
Imported Crude Oil and Petroleum Products. (US) **3688**, 1790, 4574
†Importers and Exporters Trade Promotion Guide. (US ISSN 0073-5604) **5211**
Importfile. (CN ISSN 0383-6304) **911**
Importing and Consulting. see Yinjin yu Zixun **970**
Imports of the Republic of China. (CH) **911**
Imports Statistics of Afghanistan/ Ihsa'iyah-i Amual-i Varidati-i Afghanistan. (AF) **721**, 4574
Importweek. (CN ISSN 0045-494X) **911**
Impossibility - Challenger. (US) **4475**
Imposte Dirette Erariali e l'Iva see Rassegna Tributaria **1104**
Impot Federal Direct, Rendement et Cotes par Tete de la Periode de Taxation. see Direkte Bundessteuer, Steuerertraege und Kopfquoten der Veranlagungsperiode **713**
Impot Federal Direct - Statistique de la Periode de Taxation (Year). see Direkte Bundessteuer - Statistik der Veranlagungsperiode (Year) **713**

Imprecor see International Viewpoint **3900**
Imprempres. (SP) **3663**, 330
Imprenditorialita. (IT) **670**
Imprensa Oficial do Estado do Rio de Janeiro. (BL) **4063**
Impresa Pubblica. (IT ISSN 0019-3003) **4088**, 4063
L'Impresa Pubblica Municipalizzazione. (IT) **4088**
Impresor. (MX) **4001**, 2571
Impresor Internacional see Impresor **4001**
Impressionen. (GW ISSN 0931-5187) **2476**
Impressions. (FR) **4001**
Impressions (New York). (US) **1291**
Impressions (New York, 1976). (US) **330**, 2338
Imprimase. (VE) **4001**
Imprimatur. Jahrbuch fuer Buecherfreunde. Neue Folge see Imprimatur. Neue Folge **4001**
Imprimatur. Neue Folge. (GW) **4001**
Imprimerie Francaise. (FR) **4001**
Imprimerie Syndicaliste. (FR) **2584**, 4129
Imprimis. (US ISSN 0277-8432) **2508**
Imprint. (CN) **1314**
Imprint. (II ISSN 0019-3046) **2199**
Imprint. (NZ ISSN 0019-3054) **2584**, 4001
Imprint (Brooklyn Heights). (US ISSN 0277-7061) **4001**, 2410
Imprint (New York). (US ISSN 0019-3062) **3279**
Imprints. (US) **2155**
Impromtu. (US) **3555**
Improved Oil-Recovery Field Reports see Enhanced Oil-Recovery Field Reports **3685**
Improvement District Manual. (CN) **4088**
Improvement of Agriculture. see Nogyo no Kairyo **5248**
Improving College and University Teaching see College Teaching **1703**
Improving Urban Mobility see Directory of Research, Development and Demonstration Projects **5181**
Impuestos. (AG) **1097**
Impuls. (GW) **1012**, 2533
Impulse see M 5 V Magazine **334**
Impulse see Bundesinfo - Impulse **1250**
Impulse. (II ISSN 0027-4690) **2199**
Impulse. (US ISSN 0732-2402) **2761**
Impulse. (SA) **4314**
Impulse (Giessen). (GW) **4182**
Impulse aus Wissenschaft und Forschung. (AU) **4314**
Impulse Foods see Food Trade Review **2070**
Imroze. (CN) **2006**
IMS Monitor Report see Marketletter **3734**
IMS Pharmaceutical Marketletter see Marketletter **3734**
Imvaho. (RW) **4063**
In Between. (US) **1351**
In Brief. (US) **330**
In Brief see Ceram Research News **1162**
In Britain. (UK ISSN 0019-3143) **4772**
In Business (Emmaus). (US ISSN 0190-2458) **1115**
In Business (Madison). (US ISSN 0192-7450) **836**, 1012
In Business Now. (UK) **1115**, 1077
In Business Windsor. (CN) **670**
In Cinema. (US) **3511**
In Common. (UK ISSN 0962-3507) **1238**
In Common see Common Cause Magazine **3880**
In Common. (US ISSN 0363-5058) **4182**
In Context. (US ISSN 0741-6180) **2924**, 1256
In Cornwall Magazine. (UK ISSN 0951-8932) **2194**, 4772
In Dance. (US ISSN 0883-9956) **1531**
In de Rechte Straat/En la Calle Recta. (NE ISSN 0019-3151) **4182**

In de Waagschaal. (NE ISSN 0019-316X) **4182**, 3898
In Defense of the Alien. (US ISSN 0275-634X) **3983**
†In Delaware. (US ISSN 1041-6056) **5211**
In Depth (New York). (US ISSN 0885-7229) **981**, 1066, 2634
▼In Depth (Washington). (US ISSN 1055-9809) **3959**, 2634
†In Design. (IT) **5211**
In die Welt - Fuer die Welt. (GW) **4182**
In Dublin. (IE ISSN 0790-6862) **2203**
In Duck Country see From Duck Country **1488**
In English see In English Magazine **2203**
In English Magazine. (IS) **2203**
In Famiglia. (IT ISSN 0019-3186) **4265**
In Fashion. (US) **1291**
In-Fisherman. (US ISSN 0276-9905) **4548**
In-Fisherman Angling Adventures see In-Fisherman Angling Adventures Travel Guide **4548**
In-Fisherman Angling Adventures Travel Guide. (US ISSN 1048-4892) **4548**
In-Fisherman - Walleye Guide. (US) **4548**
†In Flight with Air Zimbabwe. (RH) **5211**
In Focus see Entertainment Worker **2582**
In Focus (Los Angeles). (US) **3511**, 330, 1374, 2006
In Focus (New York). (US) **2293**, 1256
In Focus (Washington). (US) **2102**
In Gear. (US) **4475**
In Good Taste. (US) **2072**
In Health see Health **3802**
In-House. (US) **2489**
In House. (US) **2571**
In House Graphics. (US ISSN 0883-6973) **4001**
▼In House Hort. (US) **2131**
In Iure Praesentia. (IT) **2634**
In Kuerze Erscheinen see Soon to Appear **412**
In Leder. (GW ISSN 0178-5052) **2736**
In Motion (Annapolis). (US ISSN 0889-6208) **3511**, 1385
In Motion (Eureka). (US) **4475**, 4772
In Moto. (IT) **4518**
In Ontario. (CN ISSN 0225-1701) **2533**
In Other Words. (US) **4182**, 2818
In-Pak. (DK ISSN 0106-9403) **3649**, 3018
†In Paradise. (US) **5211**
In Performance see Inside the Black Hills **4634**
In-Plant Printer & Electronic Publisher. (US) **4001**
In-Plant Reproductions. (US) **4001**, 4129
In-Plant Reproductions and Electronic Publishing see In-Plant Reproductions **4001**
In Pocket. (JA) **2924**
In Practice. (UK ISSN 0263-841X) **4810**
In Print. (US) **2571**
In Process. (US ISSN 1060-6734) **330**
In Public Service see P E D Forum **2587**
In-Register Newsletter. (US) **4001**, 1041
In Review see S E R I Science and Technology in Review **1811**
In - S I T E Magazine. (Society of Incentive Travel Executives) (US) **4772**
In Sachen Spiel und Feier. (GW) **4634**, 2437
In Search of a Song. (US) **1256**, 2924
In Search of the Guibord-Chopp Family. (US) **2155**
In Season. (US) **4240**
In-Short. (US ISSN 0046-8762) **3365**
In-Side Harlem. (US ISSN 1050-2882) **2006**
In-Site. (CN) **620**

INCHIESTA 6275

In - Site. (US) **2131**
In Situ. (ZA) **301**
In Situ. (US ISSN 0146-2520) **1824**
In-Stat Electronics Report. (US) **1773**
†In Step. (US) **5211**
In Step with N S D A. (US) **620**
In Stride. (US) **4535**
In Summary. (CN ISSN 0228-2518) **4375**, 4437
In Technology. (US) **670**, 4600
In Terris. (PE ISSN 0300-4031) **2995**
In the Anacostia Watershed. (US) **4825**, 1958
In the Driver's Seat. (CN ISSN 0702-5785) **4693**
In the Field. (US ISSN 1051-4546) **4314**
In the Groove. (US) **257**, 3555
In the Mainstream. (US ISSN 0888-9724) **3943**, 1066
In the Making. (UK ISSN 0309-3298) **831**, 4437
In the Middle. (CN ISSN 0823-695X) **1638**
In the Van see American Mover **4743**
In the Wind. (US) **4693**
In Theory Only. (US ISSN 0360-4365) **3555**
In These Times. (US ISSN 0160-5992) **3898**
In Touch (Austin). (US) **2293**, 2761, 4408
In Touch (Chicago). (US) **2924**, 2006
In Touch (Glouchester). (CN ISSN 0848-1733) **3804**
†In Touch (Indianapolis). (US) **5211**
In Touch (London). (UK ISSN 0308-7212) **911**
In Touch (Pinner). (UK ISSN 0019-3283) **4182**
In Touch (Reigate). (UK) **2293**
In Touch (Toronto). (CN) **2293**, 4182
In Touch for Health. (US) **3804**, 3215
In Touch for Men. (US ISSN 0744-8341) **2454**
In Touch with What's Happening. (CN) **2177**
In Transit. (US ISSN 0019-3291) **2584**, 4650
In Tune. (US) **4182**
In Unity. (AT ISSN 0728-6503) **4408**
†In View. (US) **5211**
In Vitro Cellular and Developmental Biology see In Vitro Cellular & Developmental Biology - Animal **552**
In Vitro Cellular and Developmental Biology see In Vitro Cellular & Developmental Biology - Plant **552**
In Vitro Cellular & Developmental Biology - Animal. (US) **552**, 544, 3198
In Vitro Cellular & Developmental Biology - Plant. (US ISSN 1054-5476) **552**, 544, 3198
In Vitro Toxicology. (US ISSN 0888-319X) **1982**, 525, 3728
In Vivo. (US ISSN 0733-1398) **3107**, 670
In Vivo. (GR ISSN 0258-851X) **3259**
In Your Hands. (US ISSN 0019-3321) **4223**
Inazucar. (DR) **179**
†Inborn Errors of Metabolism. (UK ISSN 0142-8691) **5211**
Inbound Logistics. (US) **4651**
Inbound - Outbound. (US ISSN 1042-6116) **1041**
Inc. (US ISSN 0162-8968) **1115**
Inc. (JA) **1115**
Incant. (UK) **1314**
Incentive. (IT) **670**
Incentive (Akron). (US) **1041**
Incentive and Agenda see British Airways Executive **4671**
Incentive Journal. (GW ISSN 0933-7849) **1041**, 3392
Incentive Marketing see Incentive (Akron) **1041**
Incentive Taxation. (US) **2489**, 868
Incentives for Better Books in Pakistan see Literary Prizes in Pakistan **2933**
Incept. (UK) **2995**
Inches. (US) **3398**, 2454
Inchiesta. (IT ISSN 0046-8819) **4408**, 3898

INCIDENCA RAKA

Incidenca Raka v Sloveniji/Cancer Incidence in Slovenia. (XV ISSN 0079-9580) **3198**
Incidenza. (IT ISSN 0019-3410) **2205**
InCider see InCider - A Plus **1469**
InCider - A Plus. (US ISSN 1054-6456) **1469**, 1460
InCite. (AT ISSN 0158-0876) **2761**
▼Incognita. (NE ISSN 0923-7135) **2508**
Incognita. (IT) **2995**
Income and Fees of Accountants in Public Practice. (US) **751**
Income & Safety. (US ISSN 0891-1215) **949**
Income and Wealth Series see Review of Income and Wealth **1000**
†Income, Employment, Estate and Gift Tax Provisions: Internal Revenue Code. (US) **5211**
Income, Estate and Gift Tax Provisions: Internal Revenue Code see Income, Employment, Estate and Gift Tax Provisions: Internal Revenue Code **5211**
Income - Expense Analysis: Apartments see Income - Expense Analysis: Conventional Apartments **4150**
Income - Expense Analysis: Conventional Apartments. (US ISSN 0194-1941) **4150**, 620
Income - Expense Analysis: Federally Assisted Apartments. (US) **4150**, 620
Income - Expense Analysis: Office Buildings, Downtown and Suburban. (US) **4150**
Income - Expense Analysis: Shopping Centers, Open and Enclosed. (US) **4150**, 620
Income - Expense Analysis: Suburban Office Buildings see Income - Expense Analysis: Office Buildings, Downtown and Suburban **4150**
Income in Sales - Marketing Management. (US) **981**, 1041
Income Investor Perspectives. (US) **949**
Income Opportunities. (US ISSN 0019-3429) **949**
Income Plus. (US ISSN 1046-1736) **1115**
Income Stocks. (US ISSN 0895-2183) **949**
Income Tax Act Series see I T A Series **1097**
Income Tax and Family Law Handbook. (CN) **1097**, 2717
Income Tax Handbook. (SA) **1097**
†Income-Tax Journal. (II ISSN 0019-3437) **5211**
Income Tax Regulations (Chicago). (US) **1097**
Income Tax Reports. (II ISSN 0019-3453) **1097**
Income Tax Service. (SA) **1097**
Income Taxation: Accounting Methods and Periods. (US) **1097**
Income Taxation in Canada. (US) **1097**
Income Taxation of Natural Resources. (US) **1097**, 2634
Incomes Data Focus. (UK) **981**
Incomes Data Report. (UK ISSN 0019-3461) **981**
Incomes Data Services Ltd. Briefs see I D S Briefs **981**
Incomes Data Services Ltd. European see I D S European **981**
Incomes Data Studies. (UK) **981**
Incomes Data Top Pay Unit Review. (UK) **981**
Incompatex. (FR) **3728**
Inconnu. (FR ISSN 0338-8190) **3669**
Inconscio e Cultura. (IT ISSN 0391-3198) **4024**
InContact. (US) **1238**
Incontri. (IT) **96**
Incontri Linguistici. (IT) **2818**
L'Incontro. (IT ISSN 0019-3496) **3959**
L'Incontro delle Genti. (IT) **330**, 2508, 3898
Incorporated Brewers Guild Directory. (UK) **381**
Incorporated Law Society of Sri Lanka. Annual Report. (CE ISSN 0073-5728) **2634**

Incorporated Law Society of Sri Lanka. Journal. (CE ISSN 0073-5736) **2634**
Incorporated Linguist see Linguist **2826**
Incorporated Society of Musicians Handbook see Incorporated Society of Musicians Yearbook **3555**
Incorporated Society of Musicians Yearbook. (UK ISSN 0951-6220) **3555**
Incorporated Society of Organ Builders. Journal. (UK ISSN 0073-5744) **3555**
Incorporates (in 1989) Managing the Information System Resource see Auerbach Information Management Series **1455**
Increase. (US ISSN 0274-5569) **4240**
Increase Your Sales Volume. (NE) **1041**
▼Incredible Edible Munch. (US) **2447**, 2006
Incremental Motion Control Systems and Devices Newsletter. (US) **1414**
Incunabula Graeca. (IT ISSN 0073-5752) **1277**
Ind-Africana: Collected Research Papers on Africa. (II) **4375**
Ind Dak. (II) **3753**
Indac see I N D A C **1298**
Indagationes Mathematicae. (NE ISSN 0019-3577) **3038**
Indagine Congiunturale Liguria. (IT) **2476**
Indagine Statistica Nazionale. (IT) **4574**
Indagini e Prospettive. (IT) **3898**, 2924, 4438
Indeks Biologi dan Pertanian de Indonesia. see Indonesian Biological and Agricultural Index **138**
Indeks Madjalah Ilmiah Indonesia. see Index of Indonesian Learned Periodicals **402**
Indeks Majalah Malaysia. see Malaysian Periodicals Index **16**
Indeks Persidangan Malaysia. see Index to Malaysian Conferences **3395**
Indeks Suratkhabar Malaysia. (MY ISSN 0126-9062) **2578**, 13
Independence. see Niepodleglosc **2377**
Independence County Chronicle. (US) **2410**
Independent. see Anexartitos **2184**
Independent see Western Sunday Independent **2196**
Independent (Arlington). (US) **4129**, 2869
Independent (Durango). (US) **1314**
The Independent (St. Louis). (US) **1425**
Independent (Washington, 1956). (US) **1708**
Independent (Washington, 1978). (US) **2088**
Independent Accounting International. Update. (US) **751**
Independent Adjuster. (US ISSN 0019-3658) **2533**
Independent Agent. (US ISSN 0002-7197) **2533**
Independent Atlantic Sun. (US) **1314**
Independent Automotive Damage Appraisers Association Bulletin see I A D A Bulletin **2533**
Independent Automotive Damage Appraisers Association Watch Line see I A D A Watch Line **5207**
Independent Bakers Association Newsletter. (US) **2088**
Independent Banker. (US ISSN 0019-3674) **784**
†Independent Broadcasting Authority. Annual Report and Accounts. (UK ISSN 0309-0175) **5211**
Independent Broadcasting Authority Technical Review see I B A Technical Review **5207**
Independent Business. (US) **670**, 1012
Independent Commission Against Corruption Commissioner's Annual Report see I C A C. Commissioner's Annual Report **4063**
Independent Computer Commodore Magazine see Det Nye Computer **1463**

Independent Consulting Engineer. (UK) **931**, 1139, 1824
Independent Education. (AT ISSN 0310-7175) **1708**, 1728, 1751
Independent Energy. (US ISSN 1043-7320) **1790**, 1958, 3688
Independent Farmer and Rancher see Record-Farm and Ranch **116**
Independent Film and Video Monthly. (US ISSN 0731-5198) **3512**, 1385
Independent Film Journal see Film Journal **3509**
Independent Florida Alligator. (US ISSN 0889-2423) **1314**
Independent Food Retailer. (AT) **2072**, 2088, 2092, 4643
Independent Gasoline Marketing. (US) **3688**, 4063
Independent Grocer. (UK ISSN 0261-524X) **2092**
Independent Grocers Alliance Grocergram see I G A Grocergram **2092**
†Independent Higher Education. (US ISSN 0734-6735) **5211**
Independent Hospital Group Newsletter see I H G Newsletter **2466**
Independent Image see Northamptonshire Image **2195**
†Independent Investor. (US ISSN 1042-3346) **5211**
Independent Journal of Philosophy/Revue Independante de Philosophie. (US ISSN 0378-4789) **3769**
Independent Labour Publications Magazine see I L P Magazine **3898**
Independent Lesson Sermon Quarterly. (US) **4182**
Independent Life-Styles. (US) **2274**
Independent Liquid Terminals Association. Directory of Bulk Liquid and Storage Facilities. (US) **3689**, 1139
Independent Liquid Terminals Association. Directory of Suppliers of Goods & Services. (US) **3689**, 1139
Independent Liquid Terminals Association. Newsletter. (US) **3689**
Independent Living. (US) **4408**, 3338
Independent Living. (AT ISSN 0815-2276) **4408**
Independent Living and Health Care Today see Independent Living **4408**
Independent National Edition. (CN) **1958**, 2571, 3898, 4772
Independent Phonefacts see Phonefacts **1365**
Independent Power see Independent Energy **1790**
Independent Power Report. (US) **1791**, 2634
Independent Publishers Network Marketing News see I P N Marketing News **1041**
†Independent Publishers Trade Report. (US ISSN 0898-784X) **5211**
Independent Publishing Report. (US) **2571**, 2924, 4129
Independent Republic Quarterly. (US ISSN 0046-8843) **2410**
Independent Review. (US) **2869**
Independent Scholar. (US) **3628**
Independent Scholars of Asia Newsletter. (US) **2006**
Independent School. (US ISSN 0145-9635) **1638**
Independent School Bulletin see Independent School **1638**
Independent Schools Association of the Southwest. Membership List. (US ISSN 0073-5779) **1695**
Independent Schools Careers Organisation Careers Cop: I S C O Careers Bulletin see Careers Cop: I S C O Careers Bulletin **1620**
Independent Schools Information Service Magazine see The I S I S Magazine **1694**
Independent Schools of the United Kingdom. (UK) **1695**
Independent Schools Yearbook: Boys & Co-Ed. (UK) **1728**
Independent Schools Yearbook: Boys Schools see Independent Schools Yearbook: Boys & Co-Ed **1728**
Independent Schools Yearbook: Girls Schools. (UK) **1728**

Independent Sector. Annual Report. (US) **4408**
Independent Sector. Update. (US) **1638**, 4408, 4574
▼Independent Senior. (CN) **2274**
Independent Shavian. (US ISSN 0019-3763) **2924**, 4634
Independent Small Press Review. (US ISSN 1051-1261) **4129**
Independent Solicitor. (UK ISSN 0265-2501) **2634**
The Independent Study Catalog: N U C E A's Guide to Independent Study Through Correspondence Instruction. (US ISSN 0733-6020) **1695**
Independent Taiwan. (US) **3943**
Independent Telco News. (US ISSN 1051-3124) **1363**
▼Independent Television. (US) **1374**
Independent Thinker. (US) **949**
†Independent Trucker. (CN) **5211**
Independent Zimbabwe. (RH) **2240**
Index Actorum Romanorum Pontificum.(VC) **4265**
Index and Abstract Directory. (US ISSN 1041-1321) **14**
Index and Directory of Industry Standards. (US ISSN 3446**, 1824
Index and Directory of U.S. Industry Standards see Index and Directory of Industry Standards **3446**
Index Asia Series in Humanities. (II) **3646**, 14
Index Chemicus. (US ISSN 0891-6055) **1201**, 14
†Index Chemicus Registry System. (US ISSN 0019-3828) **5211**
†Index de References: Inventaire des Stations Hydrometriques. (CN) **5211**
Index der Rechtsmittelentscheidungen und des Schrifttums. (AU) **2699**
Index - Digest Bulletin. (US) **1097**, 2634
Index Documentation - Economie - Science - Technique. (MR ISSN 0851-0016) **721**, 14, 4356, 4614
Index Filicum. (UK) **441**
Index: Foreign Broadcast Information Service Daily Reports: Africa Sub-Sahara. (US) **3937**, 14
Index: Foreign Broadcast Information Service Daily Reports: Asia and Pacific see Index: Foreign Broadcast Information Service Daily Reports: East Asia **3937**
Index: Foreign Broadcast Information Service Daily Reports: China. (US ISSN 0271-1761) **3937**, 14
Index: Foreign Broadcast Information Service Daily Reports: East Asia. (US) **3937**, 14
Index: Foreign Broadcast Information Service Daily Reports: Eastern Europe. (US ISSN 0731-4116) **3937**, 14
Index: Foreign Broadcast Information Service Daily Reports: Latin America. (US ISSN 0278-1360) **3937**, 14
Index: Foreign Broadcast Information Service Daily Reports: Middle East and Africa see Index: Foreign Broadcast Information Service Daily Reports: Near East and South Asia **3937**
Index: Foreign Broadcast Information Service Daily Reports: Near East and South Asia. (US) **3937**, 14
Index: Foreign Broadcast Information Service Daily Reports: People's Republic of China see Index: Foreign Broadcast Information Service Daily Reports: China **3937**
Index: Foreign Broadcast Information Service Daily Reports: South Asia see Index: Foreign Broadcast Information Service Daily Reports: Africa Sub-Sahara **3937**
Index: Foreign Broadcast Information Service Daily Reports: Soviet Union. (US ISSN 0731-3276) **3937**, 14
Index: Foreign Broadcast Information Service Daily Reports: Western Europe. (US) **3937**, 14
Index Hepaticarum. (GW ISSN 0073-5787) **465**, 14, 505
Index India. (II ISSN 0019-3844) **3646**, 14

Index Indiana. (II ISSN 0250-7595) 14
Index Indo-Asiaticus. (II ISSN 0019-3852) 3646, 14
Index Internationalis Indicus. (II) 3646, 14
Index Islamicus. (UK ISSN 0306-9524) 402
Index Kewensis. (UK) 441
Index Library. (UK) 2793
Index Medicus. (US ISSN 0019-3879) 3176, 14
Index Medicus Iugoslavicus. see Bibliografija Medicinske Periodike Jugoslavije 3166
Index Medicus Latinoamericano. (BL ISSN 0100-4743) 3176, 14
Index New Zealand. (NZ ISSN 0113-6526) 14
Index Nominum. (GW) 3728
Index of American Periodical Verse. (US ISSN 0090-9130) 2982, 14
†Index of Art in the Pacific Northwest. (US ISSN 0085-1760) 5211
Index of Articles on Jewish Studies/Reshimat Ma'amarim be-Mada'e ha-Yahadut. (IS ISSN 0073-5817) 2030, 14, 4212
Index of Biology, Agriculture and Agro Economy see Indonesian Biological and Agricultural Index 138
Index of Current B C Regulations. (CN ISSN 0701-760X) 2634
Index of Current Medical Literature in the U S S R. (RU ISSN 0206-0515) 3176
Index of Current Research on Pigs. (UK ISSN 0568-2800) 138, 14
Index of Economic Articles in Journals and Collective Volumes. (US ISSN 0536-647X) 721, 14
Index of English Literary Manuscripts. (UK) 2982
Index of Federal Specifications, Standards and Commercial Item Descriptions. (US) 3446
Index of Federal Specifications, Standards, and Handbooks see Index of Federal Specifications, Standards and Commercial Item Descriptions 3446
Index of Fungi. (UK ISSN 0019-3895) 466, 14, 505
Index of Indonesian Learned Periodicals/Indeks Madjalah Ilmiah Indonesia. (IO ISSN 0216-6216) 402
†Index of Industrial Relations Literature.(CN ISSN 0226-1537) 5211
Index of Insurance and Employee Benefits Proceedings. (US) 2533
Index of Libyan Periodicals. (LY) 402
Index of Mathematical Papers. (US ISSN 0019-3917) 3062, 14
Index of Patents Issued from the United States Patent and Trademark Office. (US ISSN 0362-0719) 3679
†Index of Psychoanalytic Writings. (US ISSN 0073-5884) 5211
Index of Publications of the Geological Survey of Canada see Canada. Geological Survey. Index of Publications of the Geological Survey of Canada 1550
Index of Reviews in Organic Chemistry. (UK ISSN 0536-6518) 1201, 14
Index of Specifications and Standards see U.S. Department of Defense. Index of Specifications and Standards 3449
Index of the Minneapolis Star and Tribune. (US) 2578, 14
Index of Trademarks Issued from the U.S. Patent and Trademark Office. (US ISSN 0099-0809) 3679
Index of Trademarks Issued from the United States Patent Office see Index of Trademarks Issued from the U.S. Patent and Trademark Office 3679
Index of Veterinary Specialists see I V S 4820
Index of Veterinary Specialities. (UK ISSN 0019-3941) 4820, 14
Index of Veterinary Specialties. (AT ISSN 1033-2863) 4820, 14
Index of Wholesale Prices in India. (II) 836

Index on Censorship. (UK ISSN 0306-4220) 2869
Index Port see Industrial India 1078
Index S V P. (FR) 1077
Index Seminum. (IS) 505
Index to Black Periodicals. (US) 2030, 14
Index to Book Reviews in Religion. (US ISSN 0887-1574) 4213, 14
†Index to Book Reviews in the Humanities. (US ISSN 0073-5892) 5211
Index to Business Reports. (UK ISSN 0266-0180) 721, 911
Index to Canadian Legal Periodical Literature. (CN ISSN 0316-8891) 2699
Index to Chemical Regulations. (US) 1202, 14
Index to Chinese Legal Periodicals. (CH ISSN 0259-3793) 2699, 14
Index to Chinese Periodicals. (CH ISSN 0378-0112) 14
Index to Chinese Periodicals - Humanities and Social Sciences see Index to Chinese Periodicals 14
Index to Chinese Periodicals - Science and Technology see Index to Chinese Periodicals 14
Index to Countertrade (Year). (US) 911, 949
Index to Craft Journals. (AT) 357, 14
Index to Current Urban Documents. (US ISSN 0046-8908) 2500, 14, 4080
▼Index to Dance Periodicals. (US ISSN 1058-6350) 1532, 14
Index to Dental Literature. (US ISSN 0019-3992) 3176, 14
Index to Ecology see Science and Computer Literacy Audiovisuals 1457
Index to Federal Tax Articles (Supplement). (US ISSN 0149-6166) 721, 14
Index to Foreign Legal Periodicals. (US ISSN 0019-400X) 2699, 14
Index to Free Periodicals. (US ISSN 0147-5630) 14
Index to Government Regulation see Index to Chemical Regulations 1202
Index to Hebrew Periodicals. (IS ISSN 0334-2921) 402, 14
Index to Hebrew Periodicals (Microfiche Edition). (IS) 402, 14
Index to How to Do It Information. (US ISSN 0073-5930) 14
Index to Indian Economic Journals. (II ISSN 0019-4026) 721, 14
Index to Indian Legal Periodicals. (II ISSN 0019-4034) 2699, 14
Index to International Public Opinion. (US ISSN 0193-905X) 3959, 4375
Index to International Statistics. (US ISSN 0737-4461) 4574
†Index to Legal Books. (US ISSN 0000-104X) 5211
Index to Legal Periodicals. (US ISSN 0019-4077) 2699, 14
Index to Malaysian Conferences/Indeks Persidangan Malaysia. (MY ISSN 0127-4880) 3395, 14
Index to Marquis Who's Who Books. (US) 4129
Index to Micrographics Equipment Evaluations see Micrographics and Optical Storage Equipment Review 2773
Index to New England Periodicals. (US ISSN 0163-0466) 14
Index to Periodical Articles By and About Blacks see Index to Black Periodicals 2030
Index to Periodical Articles Related to Law. (US ISSN 0019-4093) 2699, 14
Index to Periodicals of the Church of Jesus Christ of Latter-Day Saints. (US ISSN 0073-5981) 4213
Index to Philippine Periodicals. (PH ISSN 0073-599X) 402
Index to Plant Chromosome Numbers. (NE ISSN 0073-6007) 505

Index to Post-1944 Periodical Articles on Political, Economic and Social Problems. see Bibliographie Courante d'Articles de Periodiques Posterieurs a 1944 sur les Problemes Politiques, Economiques et Sociaux 5148
Index to Reproductions in Art Periodicals. (US ISSN 0893-0139) 352, 14
Index to Reviews of Bibliographical Publications. (US ISSN 0161-4029) 402
Index to Scientific & Technical Proceedings. (US ISSN 0149-8088) 4356, 14, 4614
Index to Scientific Book Contents. (US) 4356
Index to Scientific Papers. see Maqalah-namah-i 'Ulum 4357
Index to Scientific Reviews. (US ISSN 0360-0661) 4356, 14
▼Index to Selected Canadian Provincial Publications. (CN) 4080
Index to Social Sciences & Humanities Proceedings. (US ISSN 0191-0574) 4375, 2508
Index to South African Periodicals. (SA ISSN 0379-0584) 4141, 14
Index to Spanish Science and Technology. see Indice Espanol de Ciencia y Tecnologia 4356
Index to Statistics Canada Surveys and Questionnaires. (CN ISSN 0843-6142) 4574
Index to Thai Periodical Literature. (TH ISSN 0125-5827) 4395, 14
Index to the American Banker. (US) 721, 14
Index to the Boston Globe. (US ISSN 0741-5281) 2578, 14
Index to the Christian Science Monitor see Christian Science Monitor Index 2577
Index to the Code of Federal Regulations. (US ISSN 0198-9014) 4080, 14, 4063
Index to the Denver Post see Denver Post Index 2578
Index to the Detroit News see Detroit News Index 2578
Index to the Guangming Ribao. see Guangming Ribao Suoyin 2578
Index to the Houston Post see Houston Post Index 2578
Index to the Los Angeles Times see Los Angeles Times Index 2578
Index to the National Assembly Debates. see Kukhoe Hoeuirok Saegin 4081
Index to the National Observer. (US) 2578, 14
Index to the New Orleans Times-Picayune see New Orleans Times-Picayune Index 2578
Index to the St. Louis Post-Dispatch see St. Louis Post-Dispatch Index 2579
Index to the St. Paul Pioneer Press. (US) 2578, 14
Index to the St. Paul Pioneer Press and Dispatch see Index to the St. Paul Pioneer Press 2578
Index to the San Francisco Chronicle see San Francisco Chronicle Index 2579
▼Index to the Sporting News. (US) 4498, 14
Index to the U.S. Patent Classification. (US) 3679
Index to Theses Accepted for Higher Degrees in the Universities of Great Britain and Ireland. (UK ISSN 0073-6066) 2761
Index to U.S. Government Periodicals. (US ISSN 0098-4604) 15
Index to USA Today see U S A Today Index 2579
Index to Who's Who Books see Index to Marquis Who's Who Books 4129
Index Translationum. (UN ISSN 0073-6074) 2793
Index Veterinarius. (UK ISSN 0019-4123) 4820, 15
Indexer. (UK ISSN 0019-4131) 15
Indexing and Abstracting Society of Canada. Bulletin. (CN ISSN 0227-1338) 15
India. Cardamom Board. Annual Report.(II) 180

India. Central Board of Revenue. Central Excise Manual. (II ISSN 0073-6120) 1097
India. Central Statistical Organisation. National Accounts Statistics: Sources and Methods. (II) 721, 999
India. Central Statistical Organization. Annual Report. (II) 4574
India. Central Statistical Organization. Annual Survey of Industries/Udyogen Ka Varshika Sarvekshana. (II ISSN 0073-6139) 721
India. Central Statistical Organization. Monthly Abstract of Statistics. (II ISSN 0019-4174) 4574
India. Central Statistical Organization. National Accounts Statistics. (II) 721, 999
India. Central Statistical Organization. Sample Surveys of Current Interest in India. Report see India. Central Statistical Organization. Annual Report 4574
India. Central Statistical Organization. Statistical Abstract. (II ISSN 0073-6155) 4574
India. Central Vigilance Commission. Report. (II ISSN 0073-6171) 4063
India. Committee on Science and Technology. Annual Report see India. Department of Science & Technology. Annual Report 4314
India. Department of Atomic Energy. Annual Report. (II ISSN 0073-618X) 1805
India. Department of Culture. Demands for Grants/Samskriti Vibhaga Ki Anudanom Ki Mangem. (II) 1728
India. Department of Economic Affairs. Budget Division. Key to the Budget Documents. (II) 4063
India. Department of Labour and Employment. Annual Report see India. Ministry of Labour. Annual Report 981
India. Department of Labour and Employment. Library. Documentation of Labour see India. Ministry of Labour. Bulletin of Current Awareness 721
India. Department of Power. Report. (II) 1791, 4063
India. Department of Publication. Publications. (II) 402
India. Department of Rural Development. Administrative Intelligence Division. Progress Report on Small Farmers Development Agency Programme. (II) 138, 4574
India. Department of Rural Development. Administrative Intelligence Division. Some Special Programmes of Rural Development. Statistics. (II) 138, 4574
India. Department of Science & Technology. Annual Report. (II ISSN 0085-1779) 4314, 4600
India. Department of Science and Technology. Research and Development Statistics. (II) 4356, 4614
India. Department of Space. Annual Report. (II ISSN 0376-5466) 55
India. Directorate of Jute Development. Jute Development Journal. (II ISSN 0970-3497) 4619
India. Finance Department. Budget of the Central Government. (II) 1097
India. Labour Bureau. Pocket Book of Labour Statistics. (II) 721
India. Meteorological Department. Memoirs. (II) 3436
India. Ministry of Agriculture. Bulletin on Commercial Crops Statistics. (II) 138, 180, 4574
India. Ministry of Agriculture. Bulletin on Food Statistics. (II ISSN 0536-8502) 138, 218
India. Ministry of Agriculture. Directorate of Economics and Statistics. Bulletin of Agriculture Prices. (II) 138
India. Ministry of Education and Social Welfare. Department of Education. Report see India. Ministry of Human Resource Development. Department of Education. Report 1638

INDIA. MINISTRY

India. Ministry of Education and Social Welfare. Department of Social Welfare. Documentation Service Bulletin. (II) **4395, 15**
India. Ministry of Education and Social Welfare. Provisional Statistics of Education in the States. (II ISSN 0579-6105) **1677**
India. Ministry of Finance. Budget see India. Finance Department. Budget of the Central Government **1097**
India. Ministry of Finance. Finance Library. Weekly Bulletin. (II ISSN 0019-4204) **784**
India. Ministry of Heavy Industry. Report. (II) **670**
India. Ministry of Home Affairs. Vital Statistics Division. Causes of Death: a Survey see India. Ministry of Home Affairs. Vital Statistics Division. Survey of Causes of Death (Rural) **3992**
India. Ministry of Home Affairs. Vital Statistics Division. Sample Registration Bulletin. (II) **3992, 4574**
India. Ministry of Home Affairs. Vital Statistics Division. Survey of Causes of Death (Rural). (II) **3992, 4574**
India. Ministry of Human Resource Development. Department of Education. Report. (II) **1638**
India. Ministry of Labour. Annual Report. (II) **981**
India. Ministry of Labour. Bulletin of Current Awareness. (II) **721**
India. Monthly Abstract of Statistics. (II) **721**
India. National Geophysical Research Institute. Observatories' Data. (II) **1590**
†India. Office of the Comptroller and Auditor-General. Report: Union Government (Posts and Telegraphs). (II ISSN 0536-7506) **5211**
India. Office of the Registrar General. Newsletter see India. Ministry of Home Affairs. Vital Statistics Division. Sample Registration Bulletin **3992**
India. Parliament. Public Accounts Committee. Report on the Accounts. (II ISSN 0445-6831) **4063**
India. Production of Selected Industries in India. (II) **836**
India (Republic) Ministry of Shipping and Transport. Statistics of Water Transport Industries see Water Transport Statistics of India **4668**
India. Supreme Court. Unreported Judgments. (II) **2634**
India. Textiles Committee. Consumer Purchases of Textiles. (II ISSN 0970-9800) **4619**
India. Tobacco Board. Annual Report. (II) **4643**
India. Union Public Service Commission Report. (II ISSN 0073-6236) **4063**
India. Zoological Survey. Annual Report.(II ISSN 0537-0744) **584**
India. Zoological Survey. Newsletter. (II) **584**
India. Zoological Survey. Records. (II) **584**
India: a Reference Annual. (II ISSN 0073-6090) **403**
India Abroad. (US ISSN 0046-8932) **2006, 2338**
India and Pakistan Wool, Hosiery and Fabrics see Directory of Wool, Hosiery and Fabrics **4618**
India and World Affairs: an Annual Bibliography. (II) **2329, 3937**
India Calling. (II ISSN 0019-4158) **1356**
India Calling. (CN) **2006**
India Cultures. (II) **4438**
India Cultures Quarterly see India Cultures **4438**
India Currents. (US ISSN 0896-095X) **2006, 2227**
†India Energy. (UK ISSN 0957-2384) **5211**
India International Centre Quarterly. (II ISSN 0376-9771) **3959, 868, 2199**
India Magazine. (II) **2199**
India News. (US ISSN 0019-4212) **3898, 868**

India News and Feature Alliance Press and Advertisers Year Book see I N F A Press and Advertisers Year Book **32**
India Office Library and Records Oriental Collections Newsletter see O I O C Newsletter **3642**
India Perspectives. (II) **2199**
India Post. (UK ISSN 0952-7729) **3753**
India Quarterly. (II ISSN 0019-4220) **3960**
India Today. (II ISSN 0537-0922) **2199**
India Today and Tomorrow. (II ISSN 0019-4239) **911**
India Transport Statistics see Pocket Book of Transport Statistics of India **4666**
India - West. (US ISSN 0883-721X) **2006**
India Who's Who. (II ISSN 0073-6244) **419**
The Indian (Loudonville). (US) **1314**
Indian Academy of Applied Psychology. Journal. (II ISSN 0019-4247) **4024**
Indian Academy of Geoscience. Journal. (II) **1545**
Indian Academy of Mathematics. Journal. (II ISSN 0970-5120) **3038**
Indian Academy of Philosophy. Journal. (II ISSN 0019-4271) **3769**
Indian Academy of Sciences. Proceedings. Animal Sciences see Journal of Biosciences **443**
Indian Academy of Sciences. Proceedings. Chemical Sciences. (II ISSN 0253-4134) **1178**
Indian Academy of Sciences. Proceedings. Earth and Planetary Sciences. (II ISSN 0253-4126) **1545**
Indian Academy of Sciences. Proceedings. Mathematical Sciences. (II ISSN 0253-4142) **3038**
Indian Academy of Sciences. Proceedings. Plant Sciences see Journal of Biosciences **443**
Indian Academy of Wood Science. Journal. (II) **2115**
Indian Administrative and Management Review see Indian Review of Management and Future **1012**
Indian Advocate. (II ISSN 0019-4301) **2634**
Indian Affairs. (US ISSN 0046-8967) **3943, 2006**
Indian Agriculture in Brief. (II ISSN 0084-781X) **96**
Indian Agriculturist. (II ISSN 0019-4336) **97**
Indian Airman and Spaceman. (II) **55**
Indian and Eastern Engineer. (II ISSN 0019-4352) **1824**
Indian & Eastern Newspaper Society Press Handbook. (II) **2571, 4001**
Indian & Eastern Pharmacy. (II ISSN 0019-4360) **3728**
Indian and Foreign Review. (II ISSN 0019-4379) **2869**
Indian and Inuit Supporter see Native Issues **2015**
Indian and World Arts & Crafts. (II ISSN 0970-8413) **330**
Indian Anthropological Society. Journal. (II ISSN 0019-4387) **241**
Indian Anthropologist. (II ISSN 0970-0927) **241**
Indian Architect. (II ISSN 0019-4409) **301, 2489**
Indian Architects Directory. (II ISSN 0256-4017) **301, 1139**
Indian Archives. (II ISSN 0046-8975) **2761, 2338**
Indian - Artifact Magazine. (US ISSN 0736-265X) **2410, 2006, 2055**
Indian Arts & Crafts Association Newsletter. (US) **2006, 355**
Indian Association for Environmental Management. Journal. (II) **1958**
Indian Association for Water Pollution Control Technical Annual see I A W P C Technical Annual **1957**
Indian Association of American Studies. Papers. (II) **2410**

Indian Association of Occupational Medicine. Journal see Indian Journal of Industrial Medicine **3108**
Indian Association of Physiotherapists. Journal. (II) **3107**
Indian Association of Special Libraries and Information Centres Bulletin see I A S L I C Bulletin **2760**
Indian Association of Special Libraries and Information Centres Newsletter see I A S L I C Newsletter **2760**
Indian Association of Special Libraries and Information Centres Special Publication see I A S L I C Special Publication **2760**
Indian Association of Special Libraries and Information Centres Technical Pamphlets see I A S L I C Technical Pamphlets **2760**
Indian Astronomical Ephemeris. (II) **365**
Indian Author. (II) **2924**
Indian Aviation. (II ISSN 0019-4417) **55**
Indian Awareness Center Newsletter. (US) **2006**
Indian Bank Today and Tomorrow. (II) **784**
Indian Bar Review. (II) **2634**
Indian Bee Journal. (II ISSN 0019-4425) **97, 533**
Indian Biography. (II) **419**
Indian Biologist. (II ISSN 0302-7554) **441**
Indian Biophysical Society. Proceedings.(II) **485**
Indian Book Industry. (II ISSN 0019-4433) **4129**
†Indian Book Review Digest. (CN ISSN 0709-9010) **5211**
Indian Book Review Supplement. (II ISSN 0019-4441) **4129, 2761**
Indian Books. (II ISSN 0019-445X) **4141**
Indian Books in Print. (II ISSN 0971-1589) **403**
Indian Botanical Reporter. (II ISSN 0254-4091) **505**
Indian Bradshaw. (II) **4710, 4674**
Indian Bureau of Mines. Bulletin of Mineral Information. (II ISSN 0027-0261) **3499**
Indian Bureau of Mines. Documentation Notes. (II) **3499, 15**
Indian Cashew Journal. (II ISSN 0019-4484) **2072**
Indian Cement Industry Deskbook. (II) **620**
Indian Cement Review. (II) **1077**
Indian Ceramic Society. Transactions. (II ISSN 0371-750X) **1164**
Indian Ceramics. (II ISSN 0019-4492) **1164**
Indian Chemical Directory. (II ISSN 0073-6295) **1854, 1178**
Indian Chemical Engineer. (II ISSN 0019-4506) **1854**
Indian Chemical Society. Journal. (II ISSN 0019-4522) **1178**
Indian Chemicals and Pharmaceuticals Statistics. (II) **3748**
Indian Church History Review. (II ISSN 0019-4530) **4182, 2338**
Indian Cocoa, Arecanut & Spices Journal. (II) **2072**
Indian Coconut Journal. (II) **97**
Indian Coffee. (II ISSN 0019-4549) **2072**
Indian Concrete Journal. (II ISSN 0019-4565) **620**
Indian Construction. (II) **620**
Indian Cooperative Review. (II ISSN 0019-4581) **831**
Indian Cotton Mills Federation Journal. (II ISSN 0019-459X) **4619**
Indian Cotton Textile Industry; Annual Statistical Bulletin. (II) **4628**
Indian Council for Child Welfare. Annual Report. (II) **4408, 1256**
Indian Council for Child Welfare News Bulletin see I C C W News Bulletin **4408**
Indian Council of Historical Research. Annual Report. (II ISSN 0304-7032) **2338**
Indian Council of Historical Research Newsletter see I C H R Newsletter **2338**

Indian Council of Medical Research Bulletin see I C M R Bulletin **3107**
Indian Council of Social Research. Annual Report. (II ISSN 0256-4491) **4375**
Indian Council of Social Science Research Journal of Abstracts and Reviews: Economics see I C S S R Journal of Abstracts and Reviews: Economics **720**
Indian Council of Social Science Research Journal of Abstracts and Reviews: Geography see I C S S R Journal of Abstracts and Reviews: Geography **2268**
Indian Council of Social Science Research Journal of Abstracts and Reviews: Political Science see I C S S R Journal of Abstracts and Reviews: Political Science **3937**
Indian Council of Social Science Research Journal of Abstracts and Reviews: Sociology & Social Anthropology see I C S S R Journal of Abstracts and Reviews: Sociology & Social Anthropology **254**
Indian Council of Social Science Research Newsletter see I C S S R Newsletter **4374**
Indian Council of Social Science Research Research Abstracts Quarterly see I C S S R Research Abstracts Quarterly **4394**
Indian Council of Social Science Research Union Catalogue of Social Science Periodicals see I C S S R Union Catalogue of Social Science Periodicals **4395**
Indian Crusader. (US) **2006**
Indian Dairyman. (II ISSN 0019-4603) **200**
Indian Defence Review. (II ISSN 0970-2512) **3460**
Indian Dental Association. Journal. (II ISSN 0019-4611) **3234**
Indian Deoiled Cakes Exporters' Performance Monitor. (II) **138, 721**
Indian Dissertation Abstracts. (II ISSN 0250-9709) **4395, 15**
Indian Drugs. (II ISSN 0019-462X) **3728**
Indian Drugs and Pharmaceuticals Industry. (II ISSN 0019-4638) **3728**
Indian Economic and Social History Review. (US ISSN 0019-4646) **4375, 895, 2338**
Indian Economic Diary. (II ISSN 0019-4654) **868**
Indian Economic Journal. (II ISSN 0019-4662) **670**
Indian Economic Review. (II ISSN 0019-4670) **670**
Indian Education. (II ISSN 0019-4689) **1638**
Indian Education (Agra). (II) **1708**
Indian Education Abstracts. (II ISSN 0019-4697) **1677, 15**
Indian Education Annual Report see Idaho. State Superintendent of Public Instruction. Annual Report. State of Idaho Johnson-O'Malley Program **1638**
Indian Educational Review. (II ISSN 0019-4700) **1638**
Indian Electronics Directory. (II ISSN 0377-7340) **1773**
Indian Energy Abstracts see T I D E **1796**
Indian Energy and Power Update. (II) **1791**
Indian Engineering & Industries Register see Engineering Times Annual Directory **1821**
Indian Engineering Exporter. (II ISSN 0019-4719) **1824**
Indian Export Bulletin. (II) **911**
Indian Export Service Bulletin see Indian Export Bulletin **911**
Indian Export Trade Journal. (II ISSN 0019-4735) **911**
Indian Export Year Book. (II) **911**
Indian Export Year Book. (II) **911**
Indian Farm Mechanization. (II ISSN 0019-4778) **162**
Indian Farmer Times. (II) **97**
Indian Farming. (II ISSN 0019-4786) **97**

Indian Fertiliser Industry Deskbook. (II) 180
Indian Fertiliser Statistics. (II) 138, 180
Indian Films. (II ISSN 0377-7359) 3512
Indian Fisheries Abstracts. (II ISSN 0970-6879) 2051
Indian Fishery Handbook. (II) 2043
Indian Forest Bulletin (New Series). (II ISSN 0073-635X) 2102
Indian Forest Leaflets (New Series). (II ISSN 0073-6368) 2102
Indian Forest Records (New Series) Botany. (II ISSN 0073-6376) 505
Indian Forest Records (New Series) Composite Wood. (II ISSN 0073-6384) 2115
Indian Forest Records (New Series) Entomology. (II ISSN 0073-6392) 533
Indian Forest Records (New Series) Forest Management and Mensuration. (II) 2102
Indian Forest Records (New Series) Forest Pathology. (II ISSN 0073-6406) 2102
Indian Forest Records (New Series) Logging. (II ISSN 0073-6414) 2115
Indian Forest Records (New Series) Mycology see Indian Forest Records (New Series) Forest Pathology 2102
Indian Forest Records (New Series) Silviculture. (II ISSN 0073-6422) 2102
Indian Forest Records (New Series) Statistical. (II ISSN 0073-6430) 2112
Indian Forest Records (New Series) Timber Mechanics. (II ISSN 0073-6449) 2115
Indian Forest Records Wood Anatomy. (II ISSN 0442-6827) 2115
Indian Forest Records Wood Technology see Indian Forest Records Wood Anatomy 2115
Indian Forester. (II ISSN 0019-4816) 2102, 97
Indian Foundry Journal. (II ISSN 0379-5446) 3408
Indian Geographical Journal. (II ISSN 0019-4824) 2253
Indian Geographical Studies. (II) 2253
Indian Geologists' Association. Bi-Annual Bulletin. (II) 1568
Indian Geoscience Association. Journal see Indian Academy of Geoscience. Journal 1545
Indian Geotechnical Journal. (II ISSN 0046-8983) 1545
Indian Granite Exporters' Performance Monitor. (II) 3499, 721
Indian Health Trends and Services. (US ISSN 0885-9914) 4104, 3983
Indian Heart Journal. (II ISSN 0019-4832) 3209
Indian Highways. (II ISSN 0376-7256) 1867
Indian Historical Review. (II ISSN 0376-9836) 2338
Indian History and Culture. Series. (II) 2338, 2006
Indian Homoeopathic Gazette. (II ISSN 0019-4867) 3215
Indian Horizons. (II) 2338, 2924, 3638
Indian Horticulture. (II ISSN 0019-4875) 2131
Indian Hosiery Directory. (II) 1285, 1139
Indian Hotelkeeper & Traveler. (II) 2476
Indian Institute of Advanced Study. Transactions and Monographs. (II ISSN 0073-6465) 2508
Indian Institute of Advanced Study Newsletter see I I A S Newsletter 1708
Indian Institute of Advanced Study Occasional Papers see I I A S Occasional Papers 1708
Indian Institute of Advanced Study, Simla. Bulletin see I I A S Newsletter 1708
Indian Institute of Bankers. Journal. (II ISSN 0019-4921) 784

Indian Institute of Foreign Trade. Report. (II ISSN 0073-6473) 911
Indian Institute of History of Medicine. Bulletin (Madras). (II) 3107
Indian Institute of History of Medicine. Bulletin (New Delhi). (II ISSN 0304-9558) 3107
Indian Institute of Mass Communication. Annual Report. (II) 1337
Indian Institute of Mass Communication Bulletin see I I M C Bulletin 1337
Indian Institute of Metals. Proceedings. (II) 3408
Indian Institute of Metals. Transactions. (II ISSN 0019-493X) 3408
Indian Institute of Public Administration Newsletter see I I P A Newsletter 4063
Indian Institute of Public Opinion. Monthly Public Opinion Surveys. (II) 3898, 4375
Indian Institute of Public Opinion. Quarterly Economic Report. (II ISSN 0019-4948) 868
Indian Institute of Road Transport. Monthly Bulletin. (II ISSN 0019-4956) 4651
Indian Institute of Science. Journal. (II ISSN 0019-4964) 4314, 1824
Indian Institute of Sugarcane Research, Lucknow. Annual Report. (II ISSN 0073-649X) 180
†Indian Institute of Technology, Bombay. Series. (II ISSN 0073-6503) 5211
Indian Institute of Technology, Madras. Annual Report. (II ISSN 0073-6511) 4600
Indian Institute of Technology, Madras. Ph.D. Dissertation Abstracts. (II) 4614, 15
Indian Institute of Tropical Meteorology. Annual Report. (II ISSN 0250-6017) 3436
Indian Institute of Tropical Meteorology. Contributions. (II ISSN 0252-1075) 3436
Indian Institute of Tropical Meteorology. Research Report see Indian Institute of Tropical Meteorology. Contributions 3436
Indian Institute of World Culture. Annual Report. (II) 2508
Indian Institute of World Culture. Bulletin. (II ISSN 0251-1630) 2508
Indian Institute of World Culture. Transactions. (II ISSN 0019-4972) 2199
Indian International Trade Center Bulletin see I I T C Bulletin 911
Indian International Trade Center Directory see I I T C Directory 911
Indian Investment Centre. Monthly Newsletter. (II ISSN 0019-4999) 868
Indian Jewry. (IS) 2006
Indian Journal of Acarology see Journal of Acarology 534
Indian Journal of Adult Education. (II ISSN 0019-5006) 1684
Indian Journal of Aerospace Medicine. (II ISSN 0970-6666) 3107
Indian Journal of Agricultural Chemistry.(II ISSN 0367-8229) 180
Indian Journal of Agricultural Economics. (II ISSN 0019-5014) 152
▼Indian Journal of Agricultural Engineering. (II) 97
Indian Journal of Agricultural Research. (II ISSN 0367-8245) 97
Indian Journal of Agricultural Sciences. (II ISSN 0019-5022) 97
Indian Journal of Agronomy. (II ISSN 0537-197X) 97
Indian Journal of American Studies. (II ISSN 0019-5030) 2410, 2924
Indian Journal of Anaesthesia. (II ISSN 0019-5049) 3191
Indian Journal of Animal Health. (II ISSN 0019-5057) 4810
Indian Journal of Animal Nutrition. (II ISSN 0970-3209) 218, 4810
Indian Journal of Animal Production and Management. (II ISSN 0970-1524) 218
Indian Journal of Animal Research. (II ISSN 0367-6722) 218, 4810

Indian Journal of Animal Sciences. (II) 4810
Indian Journal of Applied Linguistics. (II ISSN 0379-0037) 2818
Indian Journal of Applied Psychology. (II ISSN 0019-5073) 4024
Indian Journal of Behaviour. (II ISSN 0970-0897) 4024
Indian Journal of Biochemistry and Biophysics. (II ISSN 0301-1208) 477
Indian Journal of Botany. (II ISSN 0250-829X) 505
Indian Journal of Cancer. (II ISSN 0019-509X) 3198
Indian Journal of Chemistry. Section A: Inorganic, Physical, Theoretical and Analytical Chemistry. (II ISSN 0376-4710) 1178
Indian Journal of Chemistry. Section B: Organic and Medicinal Chemistry. (II ISSN 0376-4699) 1178
Indian Journal of Chest Diseases and Allied Sciences. (II ISSN 0377-9343) 3107
Indian Journal of Clinical Psychology. (II ISSN 0303-2582) 4024
Indian Journal of Colo-Proctology. (II ISSN 0970-0935) 3268, 3379
Indian Journal of Commerce. (II ISSN 0019-512X) 836
Indian Journal of Communication Arts. (II) 1337
Indian Journal of Criminology. (II ISSN 0376-9844) 1515
Indian Journal of Cryogenics. (II ISSN 0379-0479) 3841
Indian Journal of Dairy Science. (II ISSN 0019-5146) 200
Indian Journal of Dermatology. (II ISSN 0019-5154) 3248
Indian Journal of Dermatology, Venereology and Leprology. (II ISSN 0378-6323) 3248, 3219
Indian Journal of Earth Sciences. (II ISSN 0379-5128) 1545
Indian Journal of Ecology. (II ISSN 0304-5250) 1958
Indian Journal of Economics. (II ISSN 0019-5170) 670
Indian Journal of Engineering Mathematics. (II ISSN 0304-9884) 3038, 1824
Indian Journal of Engineers. (II ISSN 0376-9852) 1824
Indian Journal of Engineers. Annual Foundry Number. (II ISSN 0073-6554) 1824
Indian Journal of Environmental Health. (II) 4104, 1958
Indian Journal of Environmental Protection. (II ISSN 0253-7141) 1958
Indian Journal of Experimental Biology. (II ISSN 0019-5189) 441
Indian Journal of Extension Education. (II ISSN 0537-1996) 1684
Indian Journal of Fibre & Textile Research. (II) 4619
Indian Journal of Fisheries. (II ISSN 0537-2003) 2043, 584
Indian Journal of Forensic Sciences. (II ISSN 0970-1982) 3264
Indian Journal of Forestry. (II ISSN 0250-524X) 2102
Indian Journal of Gastroenterology. (II ISSN 0254-8860) 3268
Indian Journal of Genetics and Plant Breeding. (II ISSN 0019-5200) 544, 505
Indian Journal of Geology. (II ISSN 0970-1354) 1568, 3408, 3485
Indian Journal of Gerontology. (II ISSN 0019-5219) 2274
Indian Journal of Helminthology. (II ISSN 0019-5227) 3219
Indian Journal of Heredity. (II ISSN 0374-826X) 544, 97, 1218
▼Indian Journal of Heterocyclic Chemistry. (II) 1178
Indian Journal of History of Science. (II ISSN 0019-5235) 4314, 2314, 4600
Indian Journal of Home Science. (II ISSN 0970-2733) 2447
Indian Journal of Homoeopathic Medicine. (II ISSN 0019-5243) 3215

INDIAN JOURNAL 6279

Indian Journal of Homoeopathy see Indian Journal of Homoeopathic Medicine 3215
Indian Journal of Horticulture. (II ISSN 0019-5251) 2131
Indian Journal of Hospital Pharmacy. (II ISSN 0019-526X) 3728
Indian Journal of Industrial Medicine. (II ISSN 0019-5278) 3108, 3617
Indian Journal of Industrial Relations. (II ISSN 0019-5286) 982
Indian Journal of International Law. (II ISSN 0019-5294) 2724
Indian Journal of Labour Economics. (II ISSN 0019-5308) 982
Indian Journal of Leprosy. (II ISSN 0254-9395) 3219
Indian Journal of Library Science. (II) 2761
Indian Journal of Malariology. (II ISSN 0367-8326) 3108
Indian Journal of Marine Sciences. (II ISSN 0379-5136) 1605, 441
Indian Journal of Marketing. (II ISSN 0019-5316) 1041
Indian Journal of Marketing Geography. (II ISSN 0970-1095) 2253, 895
Indian Journal of Medical Photography. (II) 3792, 441, 3108
Indian Journal of Medical Research. (II ISSN 0019-5340) 3108
Indian Journal of Medical Research. Supplement. (II ISSN 0367-9012) 3108
Indian Journal of Medical Sciences. (II ISSN 0019-5359) 3108
Indian Journal of Mental Retardation. (II ISSN 0019-5375) 3338
Indian Journal of Mushrooms. (II ISSN 0970-2970) 2131
Indian Journal of Mycology and Plant Pathology. (II ISSN 0303-4097) 552
Indian Journal of Natural Rubber Research. (II ISSN 0970-2431) 4291
Indian Journal of Nematology. (II ISSN 0303-6960) 97, 552
Indian Journal of Nutrition and Dietetics.(II ISSN 0022-3174) 3607
Indian Journal of Occupational Health. (II ISSN 0019-5391) 3617
Indian Journal of Occupational Therapy. (II ISSN 0445-7706) 3108
Indian Journal of Ophthalmology. (II ISSN 0301-4738) 3301
Indian Journal of Orthopaedics. (II ISSN 0019-5413) 3308
Indian Journal of Otolaryngology. (II ISSN 0019-5421) 3314
Indian Journal of Pathology and Bacteriology see Indian Journal of Pathology & Microbiology 3108
Indian Journal of Pathology & Microbiology. (II) 3108, 552
Indian Journal of Pediatrics. (II ISSN 0019-5456) 3321
▼Indian Journal of Petroleum Geology. (II) 3689
Indian Journal of Pharmaceutical Education. (II ISSN 0019-5464) 3728
Indian Journal of Pharmaceutical Sciences. (II ISSN 0250-474X) 3728
Indian Journal of Pharmacology. (II ISSN 0253-7613) 3728
Indian Journal of Pharmacy see Indian Journal of Pharmaceutical Sciences 3728
Indian Journal of Photography. (II) 3792
Indian Journal of Physical Anthropology and Human Genetics. (II ISSN 0378-8156) 241, 544
Indian Journal of Physics and Proceedings of the Indian Association for the Cultivation of Science. (II ISSN 0019-5480) 3819, 4314
Indian Journal of Physiology and Pharmacology. (II ISSN 0019-5499) 572, 3728
Indian Journal of Plant Physiology. (II ISSN 0019-5502) 505
Indian Journal of Plastic Surgery. (II ISSN 0970-0358) 3379
Indian Journal of Political Science. (II ISSN 0019-5510) 3898

Indian Journal of Politics. (II ISSN 0303-9951) **3898**
Indian Journal of Power and River Valley Development. (II ISSN 0019-5537) **4825**, 1899
Indian Journal of Psychiatry. (II ISSN 0019-5545) **3338**
▼Indian Journal of Psychological Development. (II) **4024**
Indian Journal of Psychological Medicine. (II ISSN 0253-7176) **3338**
Indian Journal of Psychometry and Education. (II ISSN 0046-9009) **4024**, 1638
Indian Journal of Public Administration. (II ISSN 0019-5561) **4063**
Indian Journal of Public Health. (II ISSN 0019-557X) **4104**
Indian Journal of Pure and Applied Mathematics. (II ISSN 0019-5588) **3038**
Indian Journal of Pure & Applied Physics. (II ISSN 0019-5596) **3820**
Indian Journal of Quantitative Economics. (II ISSN 0970-1532) **931**
Indian Journal of Radio & Space Physics. (II ISSN 0367-8393) **365**, 3436
Indian Journal of Radiology. (II ISSN 0019-560X) **3358**
Indian Journal of Regional Science. (II ISSN 0046-9017) **4375**
Indian Journal of Rural Technology. (II ISSN 0970-7867) **4600**, 931
Indian Journal of Science and Industry. Section A see Indian Journal of Agricultural Research **97**
Indian Journal of Sericulture. (II ISSN 0445-7722) **4619**
Indian Journal of Social Science. (US) **4375**
Indian Journal of Social Science Research see Indian Journal of Social Science **4375**
Indian Journal of Social Sciences. (II ISSN 0376-9879) **4375**
Indian Journal of Social Work. (II ISSN 0019-5634) **4408**, 4375
Indian Journal of Sociology. (II ISSN 0019-5642) **4438**
Indian Journal of Soil Conservation. (II) **180**
Indian Journal of Surgery. (II ISSN 0019-5650) **3379**
Indian Journal of Technical Education. (II) **4600**
Indian Journal of Technology. (II ISSN 0019-5669) **4314**
Indian Journal of Textile Research see Indian Journal of Fibre & Textile Research **4619**
Indian Journal of the History of Medicine see Indian Institute of History of Medicine. Bulletin (Madras) **3107**
Indian Journal of Theology. (II ISSN 0019-5685) **4182**
Indian Journal of Theoretical Physics. (II ISSN 0019-5693) **3820**
Indian Journal of Training & Development. (II) **1066**, 3628
Indian Journal of Tuberculosis. (II ISSN 0019-5707) **3365**
Indian Journal of Veterinary Anatomy. (II ISSN 0971-1937) **4810**, 3108
Indian Journal of Veterinary Surgery. (II ISSN 0254-4105) **4820**
Indian Journal of Zoology. (II ISSN 0302-7562) **584**
Indian Jute Mills Association. Annual Summary of Jute and Gunny Statistics. (II ISSN 0073-6562) **4619**
Indian Jute Mills Association. Loom and Spindle Statistics. (II ISSN 0073-6570) **4620**
Indian Labour Journal. (II ISSN 0019-5723) **982**
Indian Law Institute. Journal. (II ISSN 0019-5731) **2634**
Indian Law Reporter. (US ISSN 0097-1154) **2634**, 2006
Indian Law Reports. (II) **2634**
Indian Leader. (US) **1314**, 2006
Indian Leather. (II ISSN 0019-574X) **2736**

Indian Leather Technologists' Association. Journal. (II ISSN 0019-5758) **2736**
Indian Library and Information Science Indexes Series. (II) **2793**
Indian Library Association. Bulletin. (II ISSN 0019-5782) **2761**
Indian Library Association. Journal see Indian Library Association. Bulletin **2761**
Indian Library Movement. (II ISSN 0377-7367) **2761**
Indian Library Science Abstracts. (II ISSN 0019-5790) **2793**, 15
Indian Life. (CN ISSN 0226-9317) **2006**, 4284
Indian Linguistics. (II ISSN 0378-0759) **2818**
Indian Linguistics Monograph Series. (II ISSN 0073-6589) **2818**
Indian Literary Index. (II) **2890**
Indian Literature. (II ISSN 0019-5804) **2924**
Indian Literature in Environmental Engineering. (II) **1974**, 489, 1844
Indian Lutheran. (II) **4240**
Indian Malay Movie News see Indian Movie News **3512**
Indian Management. (II ISSN 0019-5812) **1012**
Indian Management Abstracts. (II ISSN 0019-5820) **721**, 15
Indian Manager. (II ISSN 0046-9025) **1012**
Indian Mathematical Society. Journal. (II ISSN 0019-5839) **3038**
Indian Medical Association. Journal. (II ISSN 0019-5847) **3108**
Indian Medical Forum. (II ISSN 0019-5855) **3108**
Indian Medical Gazette. (II ISSN 0019-5863) **3379**, 3108
†Indian Medical Record. (II ISSN 0019-5898) **5211**
Indian Medicine/Indiyan Medisin. (II) **3215**
Indian Merchants' Chamber. Journal. (II ISSN 0019-5901) **836**
Indian Mineralogist. (II ISSN 0019-5928) **3485**, 1568
Indian Minerals. (II ISSN 0019-5936) **3485**
Indian Minerals Year Book. (II ISSN 0445-7897) **3485**
Indian Mining & Engineering Journal. (II ISSN 0019-5944) **3485**, 1824
Indian Motion Picture Almanac. (II) **3512**
Indian Mountaineer. (II) **4548**
Indian Movie News. (SI) **3512**
Indian Museum Bulletin. (II ISSN 0019-5987) **3525**
Indian Music Journal. (II ISSN 0019-5995) **3555**, 1638
Indian Musicological Society. Journal. (II ISSN 0251-012X) **3555**, 1531, 2055
Indian Muslim Relief Committee. Annual Report. (US) **4218**
Indian National Bibliography. (II ISSN 0019-6002) **403**
Indian National Science Academy. Biographical Memoirs of Fellows. (II) **419**, 4314
Indian National Science Academy. Bulletin. (II ISSN 0378-6242) **4314**
Indian National Science Academy. Proceedings. (II ISSN 0073-6600) **4314**
Indian National Science Academy. Year Book. (II ISSN 0073-6619) **4314**
Indian National Scientific Documentation Centre Russian Scientific and Technical Publications. Accessions List see I N S D O C. Russian Scientific and Technical Publications. Accessions List **4356**
Indian National Scientific Documentation Centre Union Catalogue Series see I N S D O C Union Catalogue Series **402**
Indian News from the Americas. (MX ISSN 0185-6278) **241**
Indian Observer. (II) **2199**
Indian Ocean Centre for Peace Studies. Briefing Papers. (AT ISSN 1037-7131) **3898**, 2344

Indian Ocean Centre for Peace Studies. Monographs. (AT) **3898**, 2344
Indian Ocean Centre for Peace Studies. Occasional Papers. (AT ISSN 1037-7123) **3898**, 2344
Indian Ocean Fishery Commission. Report of the Session see F A O Fisheries Reports **2039**
Indian Ocean Newsletter see Indian Ocean Review **3898**
Indian Ocean Newsletter. (FR ISSN 0294-6475) **3960**, 868
Indian Ocean Review. (AT ISSN 1031-2331) **3898**, 2344
Indian Odonatology. (II) **533**
Indian Optometric Association. Journal see Optometry Today **3304**
Indian Orchid Journal. (II) **2131**
The Indian P.E.N. (II ISSN 0019-6053) **2924**
Indian Pediatrics. (II ISSN 0019-6061) **3321**
Indian Perfumer. (II ISSN 0019-607X) **375**
Indian Periodicals Record see Journal of Indexing & Reference Work **2794**
Indian Petrochemical Industry Deskbook. (II) **3689**
Indian Petroleum and Natural Gas Statistics. (II) **3705**, 4574
Indian Petroleum and Petrochemicals Statistics see Indian Petroleum and Natural Gas Statistics **3705**
Indian Pharmaceutical Directory. (II) **3728**
Indian Pharmaceutical Guide. (II ISSN 0073-6635) **3729**
Indian Philosophical Annual. (II ISSN 0376-4109) **3769**
Indian Philosophical Quarterly. (II ISSN 0376-415X) **3769**
Indian Phytopathological Society. Bulletin. (II ISSN 0537-2410) **505**
Indian Phytopathology. (II ISSN 0367-973X) **505**
Indian Plywood Industries Research Institute Journal see I P I R I Journal **2115**
Indian Police Journal. (II ISSN 0537-2429) **1515**
Indian Potato Association. Journal. (II ISSN 0970-8235) **180**, 552
Indian Poultry Industry Yearbook. (II ISSN 0970-9738) **218**, 4810
Indian Poultry Review. (II ISSN 0019-6150) **218**, 4810
The Indian Practitioner. (II ISSN 0019-6169) **3108**, 4104
Indian Press. (II ISSN 0445-801X) **2571**, 4001
Indian Press Index. (II ISSN 0019-6177) **2578**, 15
Indian Print & Paper. (II ISSN 0019-6185) **4001**, 3663
Indian Progress. (US ISSN 0019-6193) **2006**
Indian Psychological Abstracts. (II ISSN 0250-9679) **4051**, 15
Indian Psychological Review. (II) **4024**
Indian Publisher and Bookseller. (II ISSN 0019-6223) **4129**
Indian Pulp and Paper. (II ISSN 0019-6231) **3663**
Indian Pulp & Paper Industry Deskbook.(II) **3663**
Indian Radio Amateur. (II ISSN 0019-624X) **1356**
Indian Railway Gazette. (II ISSN 0019-6258) **4710**
Indian Railway Technical Bulletin. (II ISSN 0019-6266) **4710**
Indian Railways. (II ISSN 0019-6274) **4710**
Indian Railways Safety Performance - A Review. (II) **4710**
Indian Railways Yearbook. (II ISSN 0376-9909) **4664**
Indian Records. (II ISSN 0302-6744) **4461**, 3555
Indian Review. (II ISSN 0019-6304) **2869**
†Indian Review (Chicago). (US) **5211**
Indian Review of Life Sciences. (II) **441**
Indian Review of Management and Future. (II) **1012**
Indian Rice Exporters' Performance Monitor. (II) **2085**, 721

Indian Roads Congress. Highway Research Board Bulletin. (II ISSN 0376-4788) **4719**
Indian Roads Congress. Journal. (II ISSN 0258-0500) **4719**
Indian Roads Congress Special Publication see I R C Special Publication **4719**
Indian Rubber & Plastics Age. (II ISSN 0019-6312) **4292**, 3862
Indian Rubber Statistics. (II ISSN 0073-6651) **4294**, 4292
Indian School of International Studies see Jawaharlal Nehru University. School of International Studies Series **4377**
Indian School of Mines. Annual Report. (II ISSN 0304-1158) **3485**
Indian Science Abstracts. (II ISSN 0019-6339) **4356**, 15
Indian Science Congress Association. Proceedings. (II ISSN 0085-1817) **4314**
Indian Science Cruiser. (II ISSN 0970-4256) **4314**
Indian Science Index. Ser.B Calcutta: Pre-modern Period. (II) **4614**, 15, 4356
Indian Seafoods. (II ISSN 0019-6347) **2043**
Indian Shipping. (II) **4728**
Indian Shipping and Shipbuilding. (II) **4728**
Indian Silk. (II ISSN 0019-6355) **4620**
Indian Silk and Rayon see Indian Synthetic & Rayon **4620**
Indian Society for Information Science Bulletin see I S I S Bulletin **5210**
Indian Society of Agricultural Statistics. Journal. (II ISSN 0019-6363) **138**
Indian Society of Desert Technology. Transactions. (II ISSN 0970-3918) **1568**
Indian Society of Desert Technology and University Centre of Desert Studies. Transactions see Indian Society of Desert Technology. Transactions **1568**
Indian Society of Earthquake Technology. Bulletin. (II ISSN 0019-6371) **1867**, 1568
Indian Society of Gastroenterology. Proceedings of the Annual Conference. (II) **3268**
Indian Society of International Law. Publications. (II ISSN 0073-6678) **2724**
Indian Society of Soil Science. Journal. (II ISSN 0019-638X) **97**
Indian Society of Statistics and Operations Research. Journal. (II ISSN 0250-9636) **4574**, 1414
Indian Sociological Bulletin see International Journal of Contemporary Sociology **4438**
Indian Spices. (II ISSN 0019-6401) **911**, 180
Indian Spices Exporters' Performance Monitor. (II) **2085**, 721
Indian Statistical Institute. Annual Report. (II ISSN 0073-6686) **4574**
Indian Statistical Institute. Documentation Research and Training Centre. D R T C Annual Seminar. (II ISSN 0067-3439) **2761**
Indian Statistical Institute. Documentation Research and Training Centre. D R T C Refresher Seminar. (II) **2761**
Indian Statistical Institute. Econometric and Social Sciences Series. Research Monographs. (II ISSN 0073-6694) **4375**
Indian Statistical Institute. Lecture Notes. (II) **4574**
Indian Statistical Institute. Library. Bibliographic Series. (II ISSN 0073-6708) **403**
Indian Statistical Institute. Research and Training School. Publications see Indian Statistical Institute. Lecture Notes **4574**
Indian Statistical Institute. Statistics and Probability Series. Research Monographs. (II ISSN 0073-6716) **4574**

Indian Statistical Series. (II ISSN 0073-6724) **4574**
Indian Steel Age. (II ISSN 0019-641X) **3408**
Indian Stratigraphy. (II) **1568**
Indian Sugar. (II ISSN 0019-6428) **180**
Indian Surveyor. (II) **1867**
Indian Synthetic & Rayon. (II) **4620**
Indian Tea Exporters' Performance Monitor. (II) **2085,** 721
Indian Textile Annual & Directory. (II ISSN 0537-2666) **4620**
Indian Textile Bulletin. (II ISSN 0970-0870) **4620**
Indian Textile Journal. (II ISSN 0019-6436) **4620**
Indian Thought. (NE ISSN 0924-8986) **3769**
Indian Tobacco see Tobacco News **4645**
†Indian Tobacco Journal. (II ISSN 0970-4981) **5211**
Indian Trade Journal. (II ISSN 0019-6444) **836**
Indian Trader, Inc. (US ISSN 0046-9076) **2006**
Indian Vacuum Society. Bulletin. (II ISSN 0970-2334) **3820**
Indian Vegetarian Congress Quarterly. (II ISSN 0019-6460) **3607,** 2072
Indian Verse. (II) **2995**
Indian Veterinary Journal. (II ISSN 0019-6479) **4810**
Indian Veterinary Medical Journal. (II ISSN 0250-5266) **4810**
Indian Veterinary Research Institute. Annual Report. (II ISSN 0304-7067) **4810**
Indian Welding Journal. (II ISSN 0046-9092) **3429**
Indian Witness. (II ISSN 0019-6487) **4240**
Indian Worker. (II) **2584**
Indian Writer. (II) **2924,** 2995
Indian Yearbook of International Affairs. (II ISSN 0537-2704) **3960,** 2338
Indian Youth of America Newsletter. (US) **1238,** 2006, 4408
Indiana. (GW ISSN 0341-8642) **241,** 274, 2410
Indiana. (II ISSN 0019-6509) **2199**
Indiana. Agricultural Experiment Station. Inspection Report. (US ISSN 0073-6783) **97**
Indiana. Agricultural Experiment Station. Research Bulletin. (US ISSN 0073-6791) **97**
Indiana. Council on Vocational Education. Annual Report see Indiana. Indiana Commission on Vocational and Technical Education **1751**
Indiana. Department of Employment and Training Services. County Employment Patterns. (US) **982**
Indiana. Department of Employment and Training Services. Covered Employment and Payrolls. (US) **982**
Indiana. Department of Employment and Training Services. Labor Force Estimates. (US) **982**
†Indiana. Department of Employment and Training Services. Monthly Summary of Unemployment Insurance Activities. (US) **5211**
Indiana. Department of Employment and Training Services. Non - M S A Establishment Employment. (US) **982**
†Indiana. Department of Employment and Training Services. Some Significant Statistics about Unemployment Insurance. (US) **5211**
Indiana. Department of Employment and Training Services. Unemployment Insurance Claims by Area. (US) **2546,** 721
Indiana. Department of Employment and Training Services. Unemployment Insurance Payments by Industry. (US) **2546,** 721
Indiana. Department of Environmental Management. Annual Report. (US) **1958**
Indiana. Department of Public Welfare. Semi-Annual Statistical Series. (US ISSN 0019-6576) **4426**

Indiana. Environmental Management Board. Annual Report see Indiana. Department of Environmental Management. Annual Report **1958**
Indiana. Geological Survey. Annual Report of the State Geologist. (US ISSN 0362-3513) **1568**
Indiana. Indiana Commission on Vocational and Technical Education. (US) **1751**
Indiana. State Advisory Council for Vocational Technical Education. Annual Report see Indiana. Indiana Commission on Vocational and Technical Education **1751**
Indiana Academy of Science. Monograph. (US ISSN 0073-6759) **4314**
Indiana Academy of Science. Proceedings. (US ISSN 0073-6767) **4314**
Indiana Agri-News. (US) **97**
Indiana Alumni Magazine. (US ISSN 0019-6517) **1314**
Indiana Audubon Quarterly. (US ISSN 0019-6525) **564**
Indiana Automotive Directory see Automotive Contact Directory. Indiana **4683**
Indiana Beef. (US) **218**
Indiana Beverage Journal. (US ISSN 0274-547X) **382**
Indiana Business. (US ISSN 0273-7930) **868**
Indiana Business Review. (US ISSN 0019-6541) **670**
Indiana Contractor. (US) **2300**
Indiana Covered Bridge Society. Newsletter. (US ISSN 0019-655X) **2410,** 2437
Indiana Daily Student. (US) **1314**
Indiana Dental Association. Journal. (US ISSN 0019-6568) **3234**
Indiana Directory of International Business Services. (US) **911**
Indiana Directory of Music Teachers. (US ISSN 0742-2490) **3556,** 1638
▼Indiana Employment Law Letter. (US ISSN 1053-6191) **2710,** 982
Indiana Employment Review. (US) **982**
Indiana English. (US) **2924,** 1751, 2818
▼Indiana Environmental Law Letter. (US ISSN 1053-6183) **2634,** 1958
Indiana Facts. (US ISSN 0893-2298) **1781**
Indiana Farmers Fastline see Farmers Fastline: Indiana Edition **91**
Indiana Freemason. (US ISSN 0019-6622) **1298**
▼Indiana Golfer's Travel Guide. (US) **4506,** 4772
Indiana Herald. (US ISSN 0019-6630) **2227**
Indiana Historical Collections. (US ISSN 0073-6880) **2410**
Indiana Historical Society. Prehistory Research Series. (US ISSN 0073-6899) **274**
Indiana Historical Society. Publications. (US ISSN 0073-6902) **2410**
Indiana Historical Society News. (US ISSN 1047-708X) **2410**
†Indiana History Bulletin. (US ISSN 0019-6649) **5211**
Indiana History Resource Series. (US) **2410**
Indiana Horizons. (US) **2227**
Indiana International Trade Directory see Indiana Directory of International Business Services **911**
Indiana Issues. (US) **4063**
Indiana Jewish Historical Society. Newsletter. (US) **2006**
Indiana Jewish Post and Opinion. (US) **2006**
†Indiana Labor Market Letter. (US) **5212**
Indiana Law Journal. (US ISSN 0019-6665) **2634**
Indiana Law Review. (US ISSN 0046-9106) **2634**
Indiana Legislative Insight. (US) **4063**
Indiana Libraries. (US ISSN 0275-777X) **2762**
Indiana Magazine of History. (US ISSN 0019-6673) **2410**

Indiana Manufacturers Directory. (US ISSN 0735-2417) **1139**
Indiana Medicine. (US ISSN 0746-8288) **3108**
Indiana Musicator. (US ISSN 0273-9933) **3556,** 1751
Indiana Pharmacist. (US) **3729**
Indiana Plumbing - Heating - Cooling Contractor see Indiana Contractor **2300**
Indiana Prairie Farmer. (US ISSN 0162-7104) **97**
Indiana Professional Engineer. (US) **1824**
Indiana Public Management see Indiana University. School of Public and Environmental Affairs. Review **4063**
Indiana Publisher. (US ISSN 0019-6711) **2571**
Indiana Reading Quarterly. (US ISSN 0019-672X) **1751**
†Indiana Report. (US) **5212**
Indiana Review. (US ISSN 0738-386X) **2924**
Indiana Runner. (US) **4475**
Indiana Rural News - Electric Consumer see Electric Consumer **1801**
Indiana School Boards Association Journal see I S B A Journal **1728**
Indiana School Directory. (US) **1695**
Indiana Secondary School Administrators. Newsletter. (US) **1728**
Indiana State Board of Health Bulletin. (US ISSN 0019-6754) **4104**
Indiana State Plan for Vocational Education. see Indiana State Plan for Vocational-Technical Education. (Fiscal Year) **1684**
Indiana State Plan for Vocational-Technical Education. (Fiscal Year). (US) **1684**
Indiana State Teachers Association Advocate see I S T A Advocate **1638**
Indiana State University. Department of Geography and Geology. Professional Paper. (US ISSN 0073-6937) **2253**
Indiana Statesman. (US ISSN 0019-6789) **1314**
†Indiana Studies in Higher Education. (US) **5212**
Indiana Theory Review. (US ISSN 0271-8022) **3556**
Indiana Truck Exchange see Indiana Trucker **4745**
Indiana Trucker. (US) **4745**
Indiana Underwriter. (US) **2533**
Indiana University. Department of Geography. Geographic Monograph Series. (US ISSN 0073-6953) **2253**
Indiana University. Department of Geography. Occasional Publication. (US ISSN 0073-6961) **2253**
Indiana University. Research Institute for Inner Asian Studies. Uralic and Altaic Series. (US ISSN 0073-7097) **2818**
Indiana University. School of Library and Information Science. Alumni Newsletter see Vibrations **2790**
Indiana University. School of Public and Environmental Affairs. Review. (US) **4063**
Indiana University Art Museum. Bulletin.(US) **3525**
†Indiana University Bookman. (US ISSN 0019-6800) **5212**
Indiana University Libraries Libraries. Faculty Newsletter see I U B Libraries. Faculty Newsletter **2761**
Indiana University Mathematics Journal.(US ISSN 0022-2518) **3038,** 1930
Indianapolis Athletic Club see I N D A C **1298**
Indianapolis Business Journal. (US ISSN 0274-4929) **836**
Indianapolis District Dental Society. Newsletter. (US) **3234**
Indianapolis Monthly. (US ISSN 0195-2900) **2227**
Indianapolis Museum of Art. Newsletter see Indianapolis Museum of Art. Previews Magazine **3525**
Indianapolis Museum of Art. Previews Magazine. (US) **3525**

INDICE ESPANOL 6281

Indianapolis Museum of Art. Quarterly Magazine see Indianapolis Museum of Art. Previews Magazine **3525**
Indianist Yearbook. see Anuario Indigenista **235**
India's Production, Exports, and Internal Consumption of Coir. (II) **911**
Indica. (II ISSN 0019-686X) **3638**
Indicadores de Comercio Exterior. (CL ISSN 0716-2405) **911**
Indicadores de la Fuerza de Trabajo. (VE) **721**
†Indicadores del Sector Financiero. (MX) **5212**
Indicadores Economicos Mensuales de Puerto Rico/Monthly Economic Indicators of Puerto Rico. (PR) **868**
†Indicadores I B G E/I B G E Indicators. (Fundacao Instituto Brasileiro de Geografia e Estatistica) (BL ISSN 0101-8353) **5212**
Indicateur see Indicator **1824**
Indicateur Bertrand see Indicateur Bertrand Paris - Banlieu **4150**
Indicateur Bertrand Mediterranee see Indicateur Bertrand Midi - Mediterranee **4150**
Indicateur Bertrand Midi - Mediterranee.(FR) **4150**
Indicateur Bertrand Montagne. (FR) **4150**
Indicateur Bertrand Ouest see Indicateur Bertrand Ouest - Sud-Ouest **4150**
Indicateur Bertrand Ouest - Sud-Ouest. (FR) **4150**
Indicateur Bertrand Paris - Banlieu. (FR) **4150**
Indicateur Bertrand Rhone-Alpes. (FR) **4150**
†Indicateur Industriel. (SZ) **5212**
Indicateur Universel des P T T. (FR ISSN 0019-6908) **1353,** 1363
Indicateurs Telematiques. (FR) **4574**
Indicator. (US ISSN 0019-6924) **1178**
Indicator. (CN ISSN 0828-7198) **1824**
Indicator S A Issue Focus see Indicator S A Report **4375**
Indicator S A Report. (SA) **4375**
Indicator South Africa. (SA ISSN 0259-188X) **4375**
Indicatore Cartario see Cellulosa e Carta **2114**
†Indicatore Grafico. (IT ISSN 0019-6967) **5212**
Indicators see Adhesive Trends **4291**
Indicators for the Telegram Retransmission System (TRS) - Telex Identification Codes. (UN) **1363**
L'Indice. (IT ISSN 0393-3903) **4129,** 403
Indice Agricola Colombiano. (CK ISSN 0073-7151) **138**
Indice de Contenidos - Serie 1: Ciencias de la Informacion. (AG ISSN 0327-2915) **2762**
Indice de la Literatura Dental en Castellano. (AG ISSN 0325-0679) **3176,** 3234
Indice de la Literatura Dental Periodica en Castellano y Portugues see Indice de la Literatura Dental en Castellano **3176**
Indice de Precios al Consumidor. (EC ISSN 0019-7025) **721**
Indice de Precios al Consumidor. (ES) **721**
Indice de Precios al Consumidor para Familias Obreras en Puerto Rico. (PR ISSN 0019-7017) **4574**
Indice des Loyers. see Mietpreiserhebung **2500**
Indice des Prix de Gros. see Grosshandelspreisindes **719**
Indice Espanol de Ciencia y Tecnologia/Index to Spanish Science and Technology. (SP ISSN 0210-9409) **4356,** 4614
Indice Espanol de Ciencias Sociales. Series A: Psychology and Educational Sciences. (SP ISSN 0213-019X) **4051,** 1677
Indice Espanol de Ciencias Sociales. Series B: Economics, Sociology and Political Science. (SP ISSN 0213-0521) **721,** 3937, 4457

INDICE ESPANOL

Indice Espanol de Ciencias Sociales. Series C: Law. (SP ISSN 0213-4683) **2699**
Indice Espanol de Ciencias Sociales. Series D: Science and Scientific Information. (SP ISSN 0214-1086) **4356**, 2793
Indice Espanol de Ciencias Sociales. Series E: Urban Planning. (SP ISSN 1130-3700) **2500**
Indice Espanol de Ciencias Sociales. Series F: Philosophy see Indice Espanol de Humanidades. Series D: Philosophy **3787**
Indice Espanol de Humanidades see Indice Espanol de Humanidades. Series A: Art **352**
Indice Espanol de Humanidades see Indice Espanol de Humanidades. Series B: Historical Sciences **2329**
Indice Espanol de Humanidades see Indice Espanol de Humanidades. Series C: Linguistics and Literature **2855**
Indice Espanol de Humanidades. Series A: Art. (SP) **352**
Indice Espanol de Humanidades. Series B: Historical Sciences. (SP ISSN 1130-099X) **2329**
Indice Espanol de Humanidades. Series C: Linguistics and Literature. (SP ISSN 1130-1163) **2855**, 2982
Indice Espanol de Humanidades. Series D: Philosophy. (SP ISSN 1130-9105) **3787**
Indice General de Publicaciones Periodicas Cubanas. (CU ISSN 0864-1382) **15**
Indice Historico Espanol. (SP ISSN 0537-3522) **2329**, 290
Indice Industrial - Anuario de la Industria Uruguaya. (UY) **1077**
Indice Medico Espanol. (SP ISSN 0019-7068) **3176**, 15
Indice Penale. (IT ISSN 0019-7084) **1515**
L'Indice Pensable. (CN) **1314**
Indices de Precios: Petroleo y Acero. (CU) **722**, 15
Indices des Prix a la Consommation see New Caledonia. Institut Territorial de la Statistique et des Etudes Economiques. Indices des Prix la Consommation **731**
Indices et Index du B T P see New Caledonia. Institut Territorial de la Statistique et des Etudes Economiques. Indices et Index du B T P **638**
†Indices Naturwissenschaftlich-Medizinischer Periodica bis 1850. (GW ISSN 0340-8094) **5212**
Indices of Urban Land Prices and Construction Cost of Wooden Houses in Japan. (JA ISSN 0073-7186) **4150**
Indices Verborum Linguae Mongoliae Monumentis Traditorum. (HU ISSN 0073-7194) **2818**, 3638
Indici Mensili Pirola. (IT) **868**
Indien. (GW ISSN 0046-9149) **3960**, 868
Indienrundbrief. (GW ISSN 0934-5175) **931**
Indigenous Bulb Growers Association of South Africa Bulletin see I B S A Bulletin **2131**
Indigenous World/Mundo Indigena. (US) **2924**
Individual Bank Reports. (US) **722**
Individual Computer. see Ordinateur Individuel **1399**
Individual Employment Rights. (US) **982**
Individual Homes. (UK) **620**, 2552
Individual Investor. (US) **949**
Individual Investor's Guide to Computerized Investing. (US) **949**, 1460
Individual Investor's Guide to Investment Publications. (US) **949**
▼Individual Investor's Guide to Low-Load Insurance Products. (US) **949**, 2533
Individual Investor's Guide to No-Load Mutual Funds. (US) **949**, 1460

Individual Investor's Microcomputer Resource Guide. see Individual Investor's Guide to Computerized Investing **949**
Individual Liberty. (US) **3898**, 3769
Individual Psychology. (US ISSN 0277-7010) **4024**
Individual Psychology News Letter. (GW ISSN 0019-7157) **4024**
Individual Psychology News Letter see I P N L **5210**
Individual Psychology Reporter. (US ISSN 0888-4595) **4024**, 3338
Individual Retirement Account Bulletin see I R A Bulletin **949**
Individualist. (US ISSN 0034-0030) **3769**, 3898, 4438
†Individualized Portfolios. (US) **5212**
Individually Paced or Self Teaching Instruction Source Book. (US) **403**
†Indiviualitaet. (GW ISSN 0179-7565) **5212**
Indiyan Medisin. see Indian Medicine **3215**
Indo-American Chamber of Commerce. Newsletter. (II) **817**
Indo-Asia. (GW ISSN 0019-719X) **3898**, 3638
Indo-British Review. (II ISSN 0019-7211) **2338**, 3960
Indo-Burma Petroleum Company. Annual Report. (II) **3689**
Indo-Canadian. (CN ISSN 0019-722X) **2177**
Indo Canadian Times. (CN ISSN 0708-949X) **2006**
Indo Caribbean World. (CN) **2006**
Indo-China Philatelist. (US) **3753**
Indo-Iran Journal. (II ISSN 0042-9740) **3898**, 3638
Indo-Iranian Journal. (NE ISSN 0019-7246) **3638**, 2818
Indo-Iranica. (II ISSN 0378-0856) **2924**, 3960
Indo-Israel. (II) **3960**
Indo-Korean Friendship. (II) **3960**
†Indo-Malayan Zoology. (NE ISSN 0168-6259) **5212**
†Indo-Pacific Fisheries Council. Regional Studies. (UN ISSN 0537-3654) **5212**
Indo-Pacific Fishery Commission. Report. (UN) **2043**
Indo-Pacific Fishes. (US ISSN 0736-0460) **584**
†Indo-Pacific Mollusca. (US ISSN 0073-7240) **5212**
Indo Pak Community Voice. (CN) **2006**
Indo - U S Business. (II) **817**
Indochina Digest. (US) **3960**
Indochina Issues. (US ISSN 0738-4548) **3960**
Indochina Newsletter. (US) **3960**
Indogaku Bunkkyogaku Kenkyu. see Journal of Indian and Buddhist Studies **4215**
Indogermanische Forschungen. (GW ISSN 0019-7262) **2818**
Indologica Taurinensia. (NE) **3638**
Indological Studies. (II) **2925**, 2818
Indonesia. Central Bureau of Statistics. Economic Indicator Bulletin. (IO ISSN 0126-2319) **722**, 999
†Indonesia. Centre for Scientific Documentation and Information. Annual Report/Indonesia. Pusat Dokumentasi dan Informasi Ilmiah. Laporan Tahunan. (IO) **5212**
Indonesia. Departemen Penerangan. Siaran Umum. (IO) **4063**
Indonesia. Directorate General of Protestant Affairs. Annual Report. see Indonesia. Direktorat Jenderal Bimbingan Masyarakat Kristen-Protestan Laporan Tahunan **4240**
Indonesia. Direktorat Jenderal Bimbingan Masyarakat Kristen-Protestan Laporan Tahunan/Indonesia. Directorate General of Protestant Affairs. Annual Report. (IO) **4240**
Indonesia. Direktorat Perumahan Rakjat. Laporan Kerdja. (IO) **2489**
Indonesia. Export by Commodity, Country of Destination and Port of Export. (IO ISSN 0126-3714) **911**

Indonesia. Import by Commodity and Country of Origin. (IO ISSN 0126-4419) **912**
Indonesia (Ithaca). (US ISSN 0019-7289) **3638**
Indonesia. Lembaga Pertahanan Nasional. Ketahanan Nasional. (IO ISSN 0303-4992) **3460**
Indonesia. Lembaga Pertahanan Nasional. National Resilience. (IO ISSN 0216-3217) **3460**
Indonesia. National Scientific Documentation Center. Annual Report see Indonesia. Centre for Scientific Documentation and Information. Annual Report **5212**
Indonesia. Pusat Dokumentasi dan Informasi Ilmiah. Laporan Tahunan. see Indonesia. Centre for Scientific Documentation and Information. Annual Report **5212**
Indonesia. Social Welfare Indicators see Indonesia. Welfare Indicators **4574**
Indonesia. Welfare Indicators. (IO) **4574**
Indonesia Letter. (HK ISSN 0019-7297) **868**, 3898
Indonesia Magazine. (IO) **2202**
Indonesia Oil Statistics/Statistik Perminyakan Indonesia. (IO) **3705**, 4574
Indonesia Statistics. (IO ISSN 0376-9984) **722**, 4574
Indonesia Today. (IO) **2202**
Indonesian Acquisitions List/Daftar Pengadaan Bahan Indonesia. (AT ISSN 0310-6659) **403**
Indonesian Association for Secure Contraception. Journal. see Mantap: Majalah Ilmaih P K M I **3294**
Indonesian Biological and Agricultural Index/Indeks Biologi dan Pertanian de Indonesia. (IO) **138**, 15, 466
Indonesian Commercial Newsletter. (IO ISSN 0377-0001) **836**
Indonesian Economy. (AT ISSN 0815-0478) **868**
Indonesian Financial Statistics. see Statistik Ekonomi-Keuangan Indonesia **739**
Indonesian Importers Directory. (IO ISSN 0216-1052) **1139**, 912
Indonesian Indicator see Prisma **2202**
Indonesian Journal of Bioanthropology/Berkala Bioanthropologi Indonesia. (IO ISSN 0216-7204) **242**, 441
Indonesian Journal of Geography. (IO ISSN 0024-9521) **2253**
Indonesian Journal of Industrial Hygiene, Occupational Health-Safety and Social Security/Majalah Higene Perusahaan, Kesehatan-Keselamatan Kerja, dan Jaminan Sosial. (IO) **3617**
Indonesian Journal of Public Health/Majalah Kesehatan Masyarakat Indonesia. (IO ISSN 0216-3527) **4104**
Indonesian National Bibliography. see Bibliografi Nasional Indonesia **390**
Indonesian Planned Parenthood Association Newsletter see I P P A Newsletter **597**
Indonesian Public Health Association. Journal see Indonesian Journal of Public Health **4104**
Indonesian Quarterly. (IO ISSN 0304-2170) **3898**, 3960
Indonesian Review of International Affairs. (IO ISSN 0046-9173) **3960**
Indonesian Statistics on Trade of Forest Products. (IO) **2102**
Indonesian Studies. (AT ISSN 0813-4820) **3960**, 2338, 3638
Indonesian Sugar Research Center. Annual Report. see Pusat Penelitian Perkebunan Gula Indonesia. Annual Report **190**
Indonesian Sugar Research Center. Bulletin. see Pusat Penelitian Perkebunan Gula Indonesia. Bulletin **190**
Indonesian Sugar Research Center. News. see Pusat Penelitian Perkebunan Gula Indonesia. Berita **190**

Indonesian Sugar Research Center. Prosiding. see Pusat Penelitian Perkebunan Gula Indonesia. Prosiding **190**
Indonesian Women's Congress. Bulletin - Kongres Wanita Indonesia. Berita see Kowani News **4846**
Indoor Air Quality Update. (US ISSN 1040-5313) **301**, 4104
†Indoor Citrus & Rare Fruit Society. Newsletter. (US) **5212**
Indoor Comfort News. (US) **2300**
▼Indoor Environment. (SZ ISSN 1016-4901) **3186**
Indoor Garden. (US ISSN 8750-4081) **2131**
Indoor Pollution Law Reporter. (US) **2634**, 1977, 4104
▼Indoor Pollution Litigation Reporter. (US ISSN 1053-024X) **2634**, 1977
Indoor Pollution News. (US ISSN 0896-8594) **1489**, 2634
†Indos. (YU ISSN 0353-0973) **5212**
Indranil. (II ISSN 0300-4007) **2869**
Indsatsen mod Ungdomsarbejdsloesheden. (DK ISSN 0109-4319) **982**
Indsearch see Industrial Herald **1078**
Induced Abortion: A World Review. (US) **3983**, 4835
Indus. (PK ISSN 0537-4715) **4825**
†Indusafe. (UK) **5212**
Industri-Noticias. (MX) **670**
Industria. (PN) **670**
Industria. (Confederacion de Camaras Industriales de los Estados Unidos Mexicanos) (MX) **836**
Industria. (GT ISSN 0019-7408) **1077**
Industria see Industria: Rivista di Economia Politica Industriale **1077**
Industria Alimentaria. (MX ISSN 0187-7658) **2072**
Industria Alimentaria. (AG ISSN 0326-9000) **2073**
Industria Alimenticia. (CU ISSN 0019-7459) **2073**
Industria Alimenticia. (US) **2073**
Industria and Mundo Turistico see Industria Turistica **4772**
Industria & Produtividade. (BL ISSN 0019-7718) **4600**
Industria Aseguradora Colombiana. Estadisticas Anuales. (CK) **2546**
Industria Automobilistica Mondiale. (IT) **4664**
Industria Avicola. (US ISSN 0019-7467) **218**
Industria Azucarera. (AG ISSN 0325-0326) **2073**
Industria Boliviana. (BO) **1077**
Industria Conserve. (IT ISSN 0019-7483) **2073**
Industria Conservera. (SP) **2073**
Industria Cotoniera. (IT ISSN 0019-7491) **4620**
†Industria dei Farmaci. (IT ISSN 0446-0243) **5212**
L'Industria dei Laterizi. (IT) **620**
Industria del Mobile. (IT ISSN 0019-753X) **2560**
Industria del Petrolio in Italia. (IT ISSN 0073-7275) **3689**
Industria della Carta. (IT ISSN 0019-7548) **3663**
Industria della Gomma. (IT ISSN 0019-7556) **4292**
L'Industria delle Costruzioni. (IT) **620**, 301, 1867
Industria do Norte. (PO ISSN 0019-7572) **670**
Industria e Desenvolvimento. (BL ISSN 0019-7602) **1077**
Industria Espanola. (SP) **1077**
Industria Farmaceutica. (SP ISSN 0213-5574) **3729**
Industria Grafica see Industria Grafica y Artes Graficas **4001**
Industria Grafica y Artes Graficas. (US ISSN 1054-2434) **4001**, 3649
Industria Internacional. (SP ISSN 0210-1815) **1077**
Industria Internacional see Industry International **5212**
Industria Italiana dei Laterizi see L'Industria dei Laterizi **620**
Industria Italiana del Cemento. (IT ISSN 0019-7637) **620**

INDUSTRIAL MACHINERY 6283

Industria Italiana del Ciclo e del Motociclo. Annuario. (IT ISSN 0073-7291) **4693**
Industria Lechera. (AG ISSN 0046-9181) **200**
Industria Lemnului. (RM) **2102**
Industria Lombarda. (IT ISSN 0019-7661) **1077**
Industria Meccanica see Industria Mercato **1930**
Industria Meccanica. (IT) **1930**
Industria Mercato. (IT ISSN 0393-599X) **1930, 3018**
Industria Minera. (SP ISSN 0210-2307) **3485**
Industria Mineraria. (IT ISSN 0391-1586) **3485**

Industria Naval. (AG) **4728**
†Industria Oggi. (IT) **5212**
Industria Orafa Italiana. (IT) **2564**
Industria Peruana. (PE) **1077**

Industria Petrolera en Mexico. (MX ISSN 0187-487X) **3689, 3705**
Industria Porcina. (US) **218**
Industria Quimica. (SP) **1854**
Industria Quimica en Cifras. (SP) **1202, 1179, 1854**
Industria Quimica en Mexico. (MX ISSN 0187-4888) **1854**
Industria Quimica Espanola. Repertorio/Spanish Chemical Industry. Directory.(SP) **1139**
Industria: Rivista di Economia Politica Industriale. (IT) **1077**
Industria Saccarifera Italiana. (IT ISSN 0019-7734) **2073**
Industria Siderurgica en Mexico. (MX) **3408**
Industria Textil Sud Americana. (AG ISSN 0019-7742) **4620**
Industria Toscana. (IT ISSN 0019-7769) **1077**
Industria Turistica. (US ISSN 0019-7777) **4772**
Industria Venezolana. (VE) **670**
Industrial Abstracts for Tanzania. (TZ ISSN 0251-2459) **4614, 15**
Industrial Accident Law Bulletin. (US ISSN 8755-8270) **3617, 2634**
Industrial Accident Prevention Association. Annual Report. (CN ISSN 0073-7305) **3617**
†Industrial Accident Prevention Association. Guide to Safety. (CN ISSN 0073-7313) **5212**
Industrial Accident Prevention Bulletin see R S P A Bulletin **4111**
Industrial Accountant. (PK ISSN 0019-7793) **751**
Industrial Aerodynamics Abstracts. (UK ISSN 0019-7823) **1844, 15**
Industrial Aids in the UK - A Businessman's Guide see Government Funding for United Kingdom Business: A Complete Guide to Sources, Grants and Applicable Procedures **867**
Industrial and Business Directory Kerala (Year). (II) **1139**
Industrial and Commercial Development see Development **5179**
Industrial and Commercial Development Corporation. Annual Report and Accounts. (KE) **836**
Industrial and Commercial Development Corporation News see I C D C News **836**
Industrial and Commercial Photography see Commercial Photography **3789**
Industrial and Commercial Power Systems and Electrical Space Heating and Air Conditioning Joint Technical Conference. Record see Industrial and Commercial Power Systems Technical Conference **1899**
Industrial and Commercial Power Systems Technical Conference. (US) **1899**
Industrial & Commercial Property - Windsor - Essex. (CN) **4150, 620**
Industrial and Commercial Training. (UK ISSN 0019-7858) **1066, 1012**
▼Industrial and Corporate Change. (UK ISSN 0960-6491) **895**

Industrial and Engineering Chemistry Fundamentals see Industrial & Engineering Chemistry Research **1854**
Industrial and Engineering Chemistry Process Design and Development see Industrial & Engineering Chemistry Research **1854**
Industrial and Engineering Chemistry Product Research and Development see Industrial & Engineering Chemistry Research **1854**
Industrial & Engineering Chemistry Research. (US ISSN 0888-5885) **1854**
Industrial and Labor Relations Bibliography Series. (US ISSN 0070-0142) **722**
Industrial and Labor Relations Report see I L R Report **981**
Industrial and Labor Relations Review. (US ISSN 0019-7939) **982**
Industrial and Scientific Instruments. (UK) **2522**
Industrial and Technological Information of Yokkaichi City. see Sangyo Gijutsu Joho Yokkaichi **4608**
Industrial & Trade Directory. (KE) **1139, 670**
Industrial Arbitration Reports, New South Wales. (AT ISSN 0155-2589) **982**
Industrial Archaeology. (UK ISSN 0019-7971) **4600**
Industrial Archeology see I A **4599**
Industrial Arts and Vocational Education see Industrial Education **1708**
Industrial Arts Education see Technology Design Education **1761**
Industrial Automation Outlook see Manufacturing Automation **1045**
Industrial Automation Products & Technology. (CN) **1414**
Industrial Bank of Japan Monthly Report see I B J Monthly Report **868**
Industrial Bank of Korea, Seoul. Annual Report (Year). (KO) **784**
Industrial Bank of Kuwait. Annual Report. (KU) **784**
Industrial Bank of Sudan. Board of Directors. Annual Report. (SJ ISSN 0073-7356) **784**
Industrial Bioprocessing. (US ISSN 1056-7194) **1218, 1791, 1854**
Industrial Brochure & Literature Digest. (CN) **670**
Industrial Buildings - Windsor - Essex see Industrial & Commercial Property - Windsor - Essex **4150**
Industrial Bulletin see Industrial Product Bulletin **4600**
Industrial Cases Reports. (UK ISSN 0306-2163) **2710, 982**
Industrial Ceramic - C I News see Industrial Ceramics **1164**
Industrial Ceramics. (IT) **1164**
†Industrial Chemical News. (US ISSN 0273-9313) **5212**
Industrial Christian Fellowship Quarterly see I C F Quarterly **4284**
Industrial-Commercial Real Estate Managers' Directory see U S Real Estate Register **4159**
Industrial Communications. (US ISSN 0737-0415) **1363, 670**
Industrial Computing. (UK ISSN 0268-7860) **1396**
Industrial Computing. (US) **1424**
Industrial Construction. see Gongye Jianzhu **618**
Industrial Consultancy. (II) **4600**
Industrial Corrosion. (UK ISSN 0265-0584) **1917, 3408**
Industrial Corrosion Abstracts. (UK ISSN 0955-7040) **3425, 1844, 1974**
Industrial Courier. (II ISSN 0019-8099) **1077**
Industrial Court Reporter. (II ISSN 0019-8102) **982, 2710**
Industrial Crisis Quarterly. (NE ISSN 0921-8106) **1013, 1958, 4104**
▼Industrial Crops and Products. (NE ISSN 0926-6690) **180, 544, 3729**
Industrial Design Abstracts. see Ipari Formatervezesi Szakirodalmi Tajekoztato **1845**

Industrial Development. (PK) **1077**
Industrial Development Abstracts. (United Nations Industrial Development Organization) (UN ISSN 0378-2654) **722, 15**
Industrial Development Act, 1982, Annual Report. (UK) **670**
Industrial Development and the Social Fabric. (US) **670**
Industrial Development Bank. Annual Report and Balance Sheet/Bank al-Inma al-Sinai. Annual Report and Balance Sheet. (JO) **784**
Industrial Development Bank Limited. Annual Report and Accounts. (KE) **784**
Industrial Development Bank of India. Annual Report. (II ISSN 0073-7372) **784**
Industrial Development Bank of Turkey. Annual Statement. (TU ISSN 0073-7402) **784**
Industrial Development Corporation Impact see I D C Impact **930**
†Industrial Development in the Tennessee Valley Region. (US ISSN 0882-9454) **5212**
Industrial Development News - Asia and the Pacific see Industry and Technology Development News - Asia and the Pacific **931**
Industrial Diamond Abstracts see Industrial Diamond Review **4600**
Industrial Diamond Review. (UK ISSN 0019-8145) **4600, 1824**
Industrial Directory and Brand Names Index of Malawi see Associated Chambers of Commerce and Industry of Malawi. Industrial and Trade Directory **1122**
Industrial Directory of South Carolina see South Carolina Industrial Directory **1153**
Industrial Directory of Wales see Wales Business Directory (Cardiff) **1158**
Industrial Distribution. (US ISSN 0019-8153) **1041**
Industrial Education. (US ISSN 0091-8601) **1708, 4600**
Industrial Educational and Research Foundation. Dialogues see Foundation for Business Responsibilities. Dialogues **666**
Industrial Egypt. (UA ISSN 0019-820X) **1077**
Industrial Energy Bulletin. (US) **1791**
Industrial Energy Conservation. (US) **1799**
Industrial Engineer. (AT) **1926**
Industrial Engineering. (US ISSN 0019-8234) **1926, 1414, 1460, 1879**
Industrial Engineering: A Series of Reference Books & Textbooks. (US) **1926**
Industrial Engineering and Management.(II ISSN 0019-8242) **1926, 1013**
†Industrial Engineering News. (BE) **5212**
Industrial Engineering News Europe see I E N - Europe **1925**
Industrial Enterprise. (II ISSN 0019-8269) **1077**
Industrial Equipment News. (UK ISSN 0019-8277) **1041, 3018**
Industrial Equipment News. (NZ ISSN 0113-9371) **1824**
Industrial Equipment News Korea. (KO) **3018**
Industrial Equipment News Product Information Service. (UK) **1077**
†Industrial Equipment Selector. (SA) **5212**
Industrial Exchange & Mart. (UK) **3018, 32**
Industrial Expansion. (II) **1077**
Industrial Fabric Products Review. (US ISSN 0019-8307) **4620**
Industrial Fabric Products Review Buyer's Guide. (US ISSN 0019-8307) **4620**
Industrial Fasteners. (UK) **1917, 1824**
Industrial Finishing see Finishing **3653**
Industrial Finishing. (US ISSN 0019-8323) **3654**
Industrial Finishing and Surface Coatings see Finishing **3653**

Industrial Finishing Buyer's Guide. (US) **3654**
Industrial Fire World. (US) **2033**
†Industrial Forestry Association. Newsletter. (US) **5212**
Industrial Gloucestershire. (UK) **817**
Industrial Goods Distribution in Japan. (JA) **1139**
Industrial Groupings in Japan. (JA) **836**
Industrial Growth in Tennessee, Annual Report see Economic Growth in Tennessee, Annual Report **1075**
Industrial Handling & Storage. (UK) **3018, 4651**
Industrial Health. (JA ISSN 0019-8366) **3617**
Industrial Health & Hazards Update. (US ISSN 0890-3018) **4104, 1958, 2634, 3108**
Industrial Health and Safety see Health & Safety Newsline **4102**
Industrial Health Foundation. Engineering Series. Bulletins. (US ISSN 0073-7496) **3617**
Industrial Health Foundation. Legal Series Bulletins. (US ISSN 0073-750X) **3617, 2634**
Industrial Health Foundation. Management Series. (US) **3617**
Industrial Health Foundation. Medical Series. Bulletins. (US ISSN 0073-7518) **3617, 3108**
Industrial Health Foundation. Nursing Series. Bulletins. (US ISSN 0073-7526) **3618, 3279**
Industrial Heating. (US ISSN 0019-8374) **3841**
Industrial Herald. (II ISSN 0377-0036) **1078**
Industrial Heritage Magazine. (UK ISSN 0265-5071) **3485, 4651**
Industrial Hygiene and Occupational Diseases. see Gigiena Truda i Professional'nye Zabolevaniya **3617**
Industrial Hygiene Digest. (US ISSN 0019-8382) **3623, 15**
Industrial Hygiene Foundation. Chemical-Toxicological Series. Bulletin see Chemical-Toxicological Series. Bulletins **3616**
Industrial Hygiene News. (US ISSN 0147-5401) **3618**
Industrial India. (II ISSN 0019-8412) **1078**
Industrial Institute for Economic and Social Research. Current Research Projects see Industrial Institute for Economic and Social Research. Yearbook **895**
Industrial Institute for Economic and Social Research. Yearbook. (SW ISSN 0283-8974) **895**
Industrial Institute of Electronics. Proceedings. see Przemyslowy Instytut Elektroniki. Prace **1777**
Industrial Investment Hong Kong. (HK) **949**
Industrial Japan see Dentsu Japan Marketing - Advertising Yearbook **30**
Industrial Jetting Report. (UK ISSN 0264-8644) **4600**
Industrial Laboratory. (English translation of: Zavodskaya Laboratoriya) (US ISSN 0019-8447) **4600**
Industrial Laser Annual Handbook. (US) **3853, 1179**
Industrial Laser Review. (US) **3853**
Industrial Launderer. (US ISSN 0046-9211) **1281**
Industrial Law: Federal. (AT) **2710**
Industrial Law Journal. (UK ISSN 0305-9332) **982, 2710**
Industrial Law Journal. (SA ISSN 0258-249X) **2710**
Industrial Literature Review. (US) **722, 403**
Industrial Location Handbook. see Kogyo Ritchi Handobukku **5224**
Industrial Locations in Canada. (CN ISSN 0073-7569) **1078**
Industrial Locomotive. (UK) **4710**
Industrial Lubrication & Tribology. (UK ISSN 0036-8792) **1930**
Industrial Machine Trader. (US ISSN 1047-4374) **3018, 1041**
Industrial Machinery: Latin American Industrial Report. (US) **3018**

INDUSTRIAL MACHINERY

Industrial Machinery News. (US ISSN 0019-8455) **3018**
Industrial Maintenance. (UK) **3618, 1824**
Industrial Maintenance Repair and Overhaul News. (CN ISSN 0830-8810) **1917**
Industrial Management. (US ISSN 0019-8471) **1013**
Industrial Management Abstracts. see Vallalatszervezesi es Ipargazdasagi Szakirodalmi Tajekoztato **743**
Industrial Management & Data Systems.(UK ISSN 0007-6929) **827, 1444**
Industrial Market Place. (US) **3018**
Industrial Marketing. see Seisanzai **1053**
Industrial Marketing Digest. (UK ISSN 0950-9038) **1041**
Industrial Marketing Management. (US ISSN 0019-8501) **1041**
Industrial Marketing Research Association News see I M R A News **1041**
Industrial Mathematics. (US ISSN 0019-8528) **3038, 3843, 4600**
▼Industrial Metrology. (NE ISSN 0921-5956) **3446**
Industrial Microbiology. see Gongye Weishengwu **552**
Industrial Minerals. (US ISSN 0019-8544) **3485**
Industrial Minerals Directory - World Guide to Producers and Processors. (US ISSN 0269-1701) **3485**
Industrial News see Hong Kong Industrialist **836**
Industrial News see Confederation of Western Australian Industry. Confederation Report **976**
Industrial News (Iaeger). (US) **670**
Industrial News (Montrose). (US ISSN 0745-8088) **1414**
Industrial Nottinghamshire. (UK ISSN 0019-8579) **817**
Industrial Participation see Involvement of Participation **984**
Industrial Past see Industrial Heritage Magazine **3485**
†Industrial Philippines. (PH ISSN 0019-8587) **5212**
Industrial Photography. (US ISSN 0019-8595) **3792**
Industrial Policy Developments in O E C D Countries see Industrial Policy in O E C D Countries **869**
Industrial Policy in O E C D Countries. (FR) **869**
Industrial Process Products and Technology. (CN) **1078**
Industrial Product Bulletin. (US) **4600**
Industrial Product Ideas. (CN ISSN 0820-6759) **1078, 3408**
Industrial Production see Statistical Office of the European Communities. Industrial Production **4587**
Industrial Production Index. (US) **722**
Industrial Production Survey see Cyprus. Department of Statistics and Research. Industrial Statistics **712**
Industrial Products & Services. (CN) **1078**
Industrial Products Finder. (II) **1139, 3018, 4600**
Industrial Progress. (US ISSN 0019-8617) **4600**
Industrial Promotion Trends in the States see From the State Capitals. Economic Development **1076**
Industrial Property. (UN ISSN 0019-8625) **3675**
†Industrial Property Law. Annual. (UK) **5212**
Industrial Property, Statistics B see Industrial Property, Statistics B. Part 1 - Patents **3679**
Industrial Property, Statistics B see Industrial Property, Statistics B. Part 2 - Trademarks and Service Marks, Utility Models, Industrial Designs, Varieties of Plants, Microorganisms **3680**
Industrial Property, Statistics B. Part 1 - Patents/Propriete Industrielle, Statistiques B. Partie 1 - Brevets. (UN ISSN 1013-8374) **3679**
Industrial Property, Statistics B. Part 2 - Trademarks and Service Marks, Utility Models, Industrial Designs, Varieties of Plants, Microorganisms/ Propriete Industrielle, Statistiques B. Partie 2 - Marques de Produits et des Services, Modeles d'Utilit. (UN ISSN 1013-8382) **3680**
Industrial Property - Windsor - Essex see Industrial & Commercial Property - Windsor - Essex **4150**
Industrial Prospect. see Gongye Zhanwang **4598**
Industrial Puerto Rico. (PR ISSN 0019-8633) **1078**
Industrial Pump & Valve. (US) **3018**
Industrial Purchasing Agent. (US ISSN 0019-8641) **1041**
Industrial Real Estate Guide. (US) **4150**
Industrial Real Estate Market Survey see Comparative Statistics of Industrial Office Real Estate Markets **4147**
Industrial Relations. (UK ISSN 0019-8676) **982**
Industrial Relations. see Relations Industrielles **992**
Industrial Relations and Management Letter. (AT) **982, 1066**
Industrial Relations Europe. (UK) **982**
Industrial Relations Journal. (UK ISSN 0019-8692) **982**
Industrial Relations Journal of South Africa. (SA ISSN 0258-7181) **982, 4375**
Industrial Relations Law Journal. (US ISSN 0145-188X) **982, 2710**
Industrial Relations Law Reports. (UK ISSN 0307-5591) **982, 2634**
Industrial Relations Legal Information Bulletin. (UK ISSN 0307-5540) **983, 2635**
Industrial Relations Legislation in Canada/Relations Industrielles au Canada. (CN) **983**
Industrial Relations Research Association. Annual Research Volume. (US) **983**
Industrial Relations Research Association. Proceedings of the Annual Meeting. (US) **983**
Industrial Relations Research Association. Proceedings of the Annual Spring Meeting. (US) **983**
Industrial Relations Research Association. Proceedings of the Annual Winter Meeting see Industrial Relations Research Association. Proceedings of the Annual Meeting **983**
Industrial Relations Research Association Newsletter see I R R A Newsletter **981**
Industrial Relations Review and Report.(UK ISSN 0046-9246) **983**
Industrial Relations Service Bureau. Public Sector Arbitration Awards see Public Sector Arbitration Awards **992**
Industrial Relations Service Bureau's Wisconsin Employment Relations Commission, Reporter see Wisconsin. Employment Relations Commission. Reporter **997**
Industrial Reports. (AT ISSN 0728-8417) **2710, 670**
Industrial Research in United Kingdom. (UK ISSN 0263-7952) **1078**
Industrial Researcher. (II) **670**
Industrial Review see C Z I Industrial Review **653**
Industrial Review. (SA) **1078**
Industrial Review. see Viomichaniki Epitheorissis **1086**
Industrial Review of Japan see Japan Economic Almanac **1079**
Industrial Road Transport see Freight **4650**
Industrial Robot. (UK ISSN 0143-991X) **1408, 1414**
Industrial Robots International see Advanced Manufacturing Technology **1411**
Industrial Safety see Industrial Safety Data File **3618**
†Industrial Safety & Health Bulletin. (II ISSN 0019-8765) **5212**
Industrial Safety Chronicle. (II ISSN 0301-4746) **3618**
Industrial Safety Data File. (UK ISSN 0262-3226) **3618**
Industrial Sewing Machine Times see Clothing Machinery Times **3016**
†Industrial Sewing News. (US) **5212**
Industrial Situation in India. (II) **1078**
Industrial Society see I S Magazine **1012**
Industrial Society. Handbook and Diary. (UK) **1078**
Industrial Specialties News. (CN ISSN 0835-5134) **1179**
Industrial Statistics. Vol.1. see Norway. Statistisk Sentralbyraa. Industristatistikk. Vol.1 **731**
Industrial Statistics. Vol.2. see Norway. Statistisk Sentralbyraa. Industristatistikk. Vol.2 **731**
Industrial Statistics Yearbook. (UN ISSN 0257-7208) **722**
Industrial Structure of Rajasthan. (II ISSN 0073-7666) **1078**
Industrial Teacher Education Directory. (US) **1709, 4600**
Industrial Technology. (UK) **1824**
†Industrial Technology and Machine Tools. (AT) **5212**
Industrial Television News see International Television News **1375**
Industrial Times. (II ISSN 0019-8803) **4600**
Industrial Training/Sangyo Kunren. (JA ISSN 0036-438X) **1013**
Industrial Trends. (EI ISSN 0258-1922) **722, 4574**
†Industrial Tyne & Wear. (UK) **5212**
Industrial Vehicles. see Sangyo Sharyo **4701**
Industrial Ventilation; a Manual of Recommended Practice. (US ISSN 0569-4043) **2300, 3618**
Industrial Wales see Progress Wales **821**
Industrial Waste Conference, Purdue University, Lafayette, Indiana. Proceedings. (US ISSN 0073-7682) **1985**
▼Industrial Water Treatment. (US) **4825**
Industrial Week. see Teollisuusviikko **1085**
Industrial Welder. (II ISSN 0377-7391) **3429**
Industrial West. (US ISSN 0743-3271) **4600**
Industrial Worker. (US ISSN 0019-8870) **983**
Industrial World. (US ISSN 0019-8889) **4600**
Industrial World en Espanol see Industrial World **4600**
Industrial World's Metalworking Edition. (US) **3408**
Industrialiserings Fonden for Udviklingslandene Annual Report see I F U Annual Report **930**
†Industrialist/Sinai. (IQ ISSN 0046-9270) **5212**
Industrias do Arroz no Rio Grande do Sul. (BL) **152**
Industrias Lacteas Espanolas see I L E **200**
Industrias Pesqueras. (SP ISSN 0212-7202) **671, 4600**
Industriatheque. (FR) **403**
Industrie see Industrie Magazine **912**
Industrie. (AU ISSN 0019-896X) **1078**
Industrie Advertenties see Annonces de l'Industrie **1002**
Industrie Alimentari. (IT ISSN 0019-901X) **2073**
Industrie-Anzeiger. (GW ISSN 0019-9036) **4600**
Industrie-Ausruestungs-Magazin. (GW ISSN 0174-7215) **3018**
Industrie Camerounaise. (CM) **1078**
Industrie Ceramique. (FR) **1165**
Industrie Cimentiere Belge/Belgische Cementnijverheid. (BE) **620**
Industrie-Compass Oesterreich. (AU ISSN 0073-7712) **1139**
Industrie de l'Information. (FR ISSN 0754-1996) **2797**
Industrie de la Manutention dans les Ports Francais. (FR ISSN 0073-7720) **4728**
Industrie delle Bevande. (IT ISSN 0390-0541) **382**
Industrie der Steine und Erden. (GW ISSN 0341-3489) **3485**
Industrie des Cercueils. see Canada. Statistics Canada. Coffin and Casket Industry **5159**
Industrie des Corsets et Soutiens-Gorge. see Canada. Statistics Canada. Foundation Garment Industry **5159**
Industrie des Lampes Electriques et des Abat-Jour. see Canada. Statistics Canada. Electric Lamp and Shade Manufacturers **5159**
Industrie des Meubles de Bureau. see Canada. Statistics Canada. Office Furniture Manufacturers **5160**
Industrie des Pates et Papiers dans les Pays Membres de l'O C D E. see Pulp and Paper Industry in O E C D Member Countries **3666**
Industrie des Plastiques Moderne et Elastomeres see Plastiques Modernes et Elastomeres **3867**
Industrie Diamanten Rundschau see I D R **3485**
Industrie du Cuir. (FR ISSN 0980-1367) **2736**
Industrie du Livre au Canada. see Book Trade in Canada **4122**
Industrie Elektrik und Elektronik see I E E - Industrie, Elektrik und Elektronik **1897**
Industrie Europeenne. (FR) **1078, 931**
Industrie Flash. (SZ) **671**
Industrie Francaise des Moteurs a Combustion Interne. (FR ISSN 0073-7747) **4693**
Industrie Hoteliere. (FR) **2476**
Industrie Lackierbetrieb. (GW ISSN 0019-9109) **3654**
Industrie Laitiere Suisse see Producteur de Lait **203**
Industrie Magazine. (BE ISSN 0772-4942) **912**
Industrie Meister. (GW) **1078**
Industrie Minerale see Industrie Minerale Mines et Carrieres **3485**
Industrie Minerale. Techniques see Industrie Minerale Mines et Carrieres. Techniques **3485**
Industrie Minerale Mines et Carrieres. (FR) **3485**
Industrie Minerale Mines et Carrieres. Techniques. (FR ISSN 0766-1207) **3485**
Industrie Nouvelles. (CN) **1078**
Industrie Sante. (FR ISSN 0154-8867) **3729**
Industrie Service. (GW ISSN 0174-6146) **1078**
Industrie Spiegel see Messe Industriespiegel **1047**
Industrie Textile. (FR ISSN 0019-9176) **4620**
Industrie Textile. see Sanaet El-Nassig **4623**
Industrie- und Handels-Kurier see Handelspartner **816**
Industrie- und Handelskammer Frankfurt am Main. Mitteilungen. (GW ISSN 0019-8986) **817**
Industrie- und Handelskammer fuer die Pfalz Magazin see I H K Magazin **817**
Industrie- und Handelskammer Hannover-Hildesheim. Yearbook - Information Kommentare see Industrie- und Handelskammer Hannover-Hildesheim. Yearbook - Statistics **817**
Industrie- und Handelskammer Hannover-Hildesheim. Yearbook - Statistics. (GW) **817**
Industrie- und Handelskammer Lippe zu Detmold Lippe Info see I H K Lippe Info **817**
Industrie- und Handelskammer Luneburg - Wolfsburg. Mitteilungen. (GW) **817**
Industrie- und Handelskammer Reutlingen. Mitteilungen see Wirtschaft - Neckar - Alb **824**
Industrie- und Handelskammer Wuppertal Wuppertal. Wirtschaftliche Mitteilungen see I H K Wuppertal. Wirtschaftliche Mitteilungen **817**

Industrie- und Handelskammer zu Aachen. Wirtschaftliche Nachrichten. (GW) **817**
Industrie- und Handelskammer zu Duesseldorf. Schnelldienst. (GW) **817**
Industrie- und Handelskammer zu Luebeck Aktuell *see* I H K Aktuell **817**
Der Industrie- und Handelsvertreter. (GW ISSN 0019-9214) **1078**
Industrieabwaesser. (GW ISSN 0073-7755) **1924**
Industriearchaeologie. (SZ ISSN 0253-8539) **4772**, **330**
Industriebau. (GW ISSN 0935-2023) **620**
Industriebedarf. (GW ISSN 0172-7117) **3018**
Industrieel Eigendom. (NE ISSN 0019-9249) **3675**
Die Industriefeuerung. (GW ISSN 0341-3756) **3689**, **1791**
Industriegesellschaft und Recht. (GW) **2710**
Industriegewerkschaft Chemie - Papier - Keramik. Umschau *see* Gewerkschaftliche Umschau **3663**
Industriegewerkschaft Druck und Papier. Schriftenreihe fuer Betriebsrate *see* Industriegewerkschaft Medien. Schriftenreihe fuer Betriebsrate **4129**
Industriegewerkschaft Medien. Schriftenreihe fuer Betriebsrate. (GW) **4129**, **4001**
Industriekaufmann *see* I K **836**
Industriel de Cote d'Ivoire. (IV ISSN 0019-9230) **869**
Industriel sur Bois. (SZ) **640**, **2560**
Industriell Datateknik. (SW ISSN 0349-8476) **1396**
Industrielle Obst- und Gemueseverwertung. (GW ISSN 0367-939X) **180**
Industriemagazin *see* Top Business **1029**
Industriemeister Nachrichten. (GW ISSN 0019-9303) **1013**
Industriens Utredningsinstitut Yearbook *see* I U I Yearbook **670**
Industries Alimentaires et Agricoles. (FR) **2073**, **97**
Industries de l'Alimentation Animale *see* Revue de l'Alimentation Animale **208**
Industries Directory, Capitals. (II ISSN 0073-7763) **1139**
Industries Directory, Delhi. (II ISSN 0073-7771) **1139**
Industries Directory, Northern India. (II ISSN 0073-7798) **1139**
Industries et Developpement International. (FR) **931**
Industries et Techniques *see* Industries et Techniques Francaises **4600**
Industries et Techniques Francaises. (FR ISSN 0537-5819) **4600**
Industries in Transition. (US ISSN 0885-0003) **1078**, **949**
Industries Mecaniques. (FR ISSN 0019-9370) **1930**, **3018**
Industries Nautiques. (FR ISSN 0019-9389) **4525**
Industries of Japan. (JA ISSN 0446-1266) **1078**
Industriethemen. (GW) **1879**
Industrija Secera. (YU) **2073**
Industrijska Istrazivanja. (YU ISSN 0019-9419) **1078**
Industrijski Proizvodi. (YU) **722**
†IndustriScope. (US ISSN 0094-1352) **5212**
Industriscope (Richmond) *see* IndustriScope **5212**
Industristatistikk. Vol.2 *see* Norway. Statistisk Sentralbyraa. Industristatistikk. Vol.2 **731**
Industrivern-Nytt. (NO) **3618**, **1273**
Industry. *see* Al-Sina'ah **691**
The Industry. (US) **2227**
†Industry. (US ISSN 0019-9435) **5212**
Industry Analysis in the Federal Government *see* Who Knows About Industries and Markets **699**
Industry & Commerce. (IE) **836**
Industry and Development. (GW) **912**

Industry and Development. (UN ISSN 0250-7935) **931**
Industry and Environment. (UN ISSN 0378-9993) **1958**
Industry and Higher Education. (UK ISSN 0950-4222) **1709**, **1078**
Industry and Society *see* Bulletin of the European Communities **848**
Industry and Technology Development News - Asia and the Pacific. (UN ISSN 0252-4481) **931**
Industry Applications Society. I E E E - I A S Annual Meeting. Conference Record. (US ISSN 0197-2618) **1899**
Industry Forecast. (US) **869**
Industry Group Market Values. (US) **949**
Industry Group Market Values and Shares Outstanding *see* Industry Group Market Values **949**
Industry in East Africa. (KE ISSN 0073-781X) **1078**
Industry in Kenya. (KE) **1078**
Industry International. (UK) **1078**
†Industry International. (US) **5212**
Industry News *see* Sports Industry News **4492**
Industry News Briefs *see* F M I Issues Bulletin **2091**
Industry Norms and Key Business Ratios. Desk Top Edition. (US) **869**
Industry Norms and Key Business Ratios. Library Edition *see* Industry Norms and Key Business Ratios. Desk Top Edition **869**
Industry Northwest. (UK ISSN 0264-4932) **1078**
Industry of Free China. (CH ISSN 0019-946X) **671**
Industry Price Indexes. (CN ISSN 0700-2033) **722**
Industry Pulse. (US) **1363**
Industry Review. (US) **722**, **949**, **4574**
Industry Review. (AT ISSN 1035-4107) **912**
Industry Statistics (Year). (US) **4664**, **4693**, **4745**
Industry Study *see* Retirement Housing Industry **5269**
Industry Surveys *see* Standard and Poor's Industry Surveys **964**
Industry Week. (US ISSN 0039-0895) **1013**
Industry Woman *see* Industry World **382**
Industry World. (US) **382**, **1041**
Indvandreren. (DK ISSN 0109-2421) **4438**
Inedita. (PE) **2410**
Inf-Inn *see* Informazione Innovativa **1958**
InFact Medical School Information System. (US ISSN 0073-5639) **3108**
†Infact Update. (US) **5212**
Infame Turba. (MX ISSN 0186-7067) **2925**
Infancia e Juventude. (PO ISSN 0870-6565) **4408**, **1238**, **2635**
Infancia y Sociedad. (SP) **1238**, **2635**
Infansis - Textile. (GR) **4620**
Infant Behavior and Development. (US ISSN 0163-6383) **4024**, **3321**
Infant Mental Health Journal. (US ISSN 0163-9641) **3321**, **4024**
Infant Pictorial. *see* Yinger Huabao **1271**
Infant Projects. (UK ISSN 0269-9524) **1638**
Infant Screening. (US ISSN 0886-1315) **3321**, **3338**
▼Infant - Toddler Intervention. (US ISSN 1053-5586) **3321**
Infanteria. (PE ISSN 0019-9524) **3460**
Infantry. (US ISSN 0019-9532) **3460**
Infantry Journal. (II ISSN 0019-9540) **3460**
Infants and Young Children. (US ISSN 0896-3746) **3321**, **1238**
Infants to Teens Wear Buyers. (US ISSN 0019-9559) **1285**
Infanzia. (IT ISSN 0390-2420) **1239**, **4024**
Infanzia Psicoanalisi e Istituzioni. (IT) **4024**

Infectiologie du Praticien. (FR) **3219**
Infection. (GW ISSN 0300-8126) **3108**
Infection and Immunity. (US ISSN 0019-9567) **3186**, **552**
Infection Control *see* Infection Control & Hospital Epidemiology **3219**
Infection Control & Hospital Epidemiology. (US ISSN 0899-823X) **3219**
†Infection Control Canada. (CN ISSN 0833-076X) **5212**
Infection Control Yearbook. (UK) **3279**, **3108**
Infections in Medicine. (US ISSN 0749-6524) **3219**
Infections in Surgery *see* Complications in Surgery **3377**
▼Infectious Agents and Disease. (US) **3220**, **552**
Infectious Disease Alert. (US ISSN 0739-7348) **3220**
Infectious Disease News. (US) **3220**, **3108**
Infectious Disease Practice. (US ISSN 0162-6493) **3108**
†Infectious Disease Reviews. (US ISSN 0090-6549) **5212**
Infectious Diseases in Children. (US ISSN 1044-9779) **3321**
▼Infectious Diseases in Clinical Practice. (US) **3108**
Infectious Wastes News. (US) **1985**, **3108**
Infektionen und Klinikhygiene. (GW ISSN 0178-9090) **3108**
Infektions Klinik. (GW ISSN 0934-8379) **3220**, **552**
Infertility. (US ISSN 0160-7626) **3293**
Infini. (FR) **2869**
Infinite Onion. (US) **2925**
Infinity Limited. (US ISSN 1050-7280) **2925**, **330**
L'Infirmiere Auxiliaire. (CN ISSN 0822-8558) **3279**
Infirmiere Canadienne *see* Canadian Nurse - L'Infirmiere Canadienne **3276**
Infirmiere Francaise *see* Infirmiere Magazine **3108**
Infirmiere Magazine. (FR) **3108**
Infirmiers. (FR) **2466**
Inflammation. (US ISSN 0360-3997) **3108**
▼Inflammopharmacology. (NE ISSN 0925-4692) **3729**, **3108**
†Inflation Monitor. (CN ISSN 0824-801X) **5212**
Inflation Survival Letter *see* Personal Finance **959**
Inflight *see* Accent (Ogden) **4669**
†Influence. (CN) **5212**
Info. (UK) **817**
Info *see* Verband Angestellter Akademiker und Leitender Angestellter der Chemischen Industrie. Info **824**
Info *see* Nursing Info (Fredericton) **3284**
†Info (Iowa City). (US) **5212**
Info (Nordman). (US) **4548**, **3711**
Info A A U. (Amateur Athletic Union of the United States) (US ISSN 0279-9863) **4475**
Info A C C S. *see* C H A C Info **2459**
Info A L S. (CN) **3338**
Info A M P *see* M A P News **4412**
Info About Info. (US) **2762**
Info - Affaires. (CN) **671**
Info Canada. (CN) **1451**, **827**
Info D B *see* InfoDB **1444**
Info D G A. (Delegation Generale pour l'Armement) (FR) **3460**
Info Dechets. Environment et Technique.(FR ISSN 0241-7375) **1958**
Info for Amiga Users. (US) **1469**
Info Franchise Newsletter. (US ISSN 0147-5924) **1115**
Info Germany *see* Canadian German Trade **849**
Info Holz und Kunststoff. (GW) **330**
Info III. (US) **97**
Info - Infogettable. (GW) **1256**
Info-Line. (US) **1684**, **1066**, **1751**
Info-Log Magazine. (CN ISSN 0847-4915) **1433**
Info M I V B. *see* Info S T I B **5212**

INFORMACION COMERCIAL 6285

Info Magazine. (US) **4710**
Info-mat Magazine. (US) **1460**
Info-Nature. (RE) **1489**
Info-Nursing. (BE) **3279**
Info Outlook (Year). (CN ISSN 0828-525X) **1013**, **2762**
Info P C. (FR ISSN 0981-6402) **1396**
Info-Pilote. (FR) **55**
Info Presse Canada *see* Info Presse Communications **32**
Info Presse Communications. (CN) **32**, **1041**, **4129**
Info Renault Vehicules Industriels *see* Virages **4705**
†Info S T I B/Info M I V B. (BE) **5212**
Info-Sourds Journal. (BE) **2288**
†Info-Tex. (DK ISSN 0901-4233) **5212**
Info 64 *see* Info (Iowa City) **5212**
Infocab. (AT ISSN 0725-5489) **2869**
Infochem. (US) **1854**
▼Infoclub. (RM) **1396**
Infocus (Emporia). (US) **2762**
Infocus (Philadelphia). (US) **1430**, **1437**
Infocus (Portland). (US) **827**
Infocus Newsletter. (AT ISSN 0157-3942) **2006**, **3943**, **4408**
InfoDB. (US ISSN 0891-6004) **1444**
Infodont *see* Det Ny Infodont **5250**
Infofish Fullnet: Globefish Highlight. (MY) **2043**
Infofish Fullnet: Trade News. (MY) **2043**
Infofish International. (MY ISSN 0127-2012) **2043**
Infografik. (GW) **352**
L'Infomane. (CN) **1314**
Infomatics. (UK ISSN 0260-7247) **1451**
Infomediary. (NE ISSN 0169-2763) **2762**, **1456**
Infomedica. (NE) **3260**
Infomet. (US) **3408**
Infonetics. (US) **1460**
Infonews *see* Info Magazine **4710**
Infoperspectives. (US ISSN 0733-9305) **1433**, **1425**
Infopost. (GW) **3460**, **1256**
Infopro: The Directory. (US) **1460**, **1469**, **1477**
Infoquim *see* Infochem **1854**
Inforcadre. (BE) **983**, **1013**
Inforespace. (BE) **55**
Inform. (CN) **1314**
Inform. (SA) **1456**
Inform *see* Consumer Choice **1503**
Inform. (UK) **2762**
InForm (Saratoga Springs). (US) **355**
Inform (Silver Spring). (US ISSN 0892-3876) **1456**, **1013**
Inform-Action. (CN ISSN 0822-5109) **2818**, **1751**
Inform - Letter *see* Inform Quarterly Newsletter **3264**
Inform Quarterly Newsletter. (US) **3264**
Inform Reports. (US ISSN 0275-522X) **1958**
▼Inform Special Reports. (US ISSN 1050-8953) **1958**
†Informa. (SA ISSN 0250-1910) **5212**
†Informacao Cultural. (PO) **5212**
Informacao Economica. (PO) **869**
Informacao Psiquiatrica. (BL ISSN 0101-4331) **3338**
Informacao Semanal C A C E X *see* Carteria de Comercion Exterior. Informacao Semanal **5162**
Informacio-Elektronika. (HU ISSN 0019-9753) **1451**
Informacion. (MX) **1337**, **4651**
Informacion Agricola Panamena. (PN) **97**
Informacion Arqueologica. (SP ISSN 0210-489X) **274**
Informacion C E L C I T *see* Tercer Rostro **5289**
Informacion Cientifica y Tecnologica. (MX ISSN 0185-0261) **4314**, **4600**
Informacion Comercial Espanola. (SP) **836**
Informacion Comercial Espanola. Boletin Economico. (SP) **836**

Informacion Comercial Espanola. Boletin Semanal see Informacion Comercial Espanola. Boletin Economico 836
Informacion Comercial Espanola. Cuadernos Economicos. (SP) 869
Informacion Construccion. (CU) 620
†Informacion Cultural. (SP) 5213
Informacion de Envase y Embalaje see I D E 3649
Informacion de Maquinas - Herramienta Equipos y Accesorios see I M H E 3018
Informacion de Patentes. (CU) 3675
Informacion de Publicidad y Marketing Mark see I.P. Mark 1041
Informacion Economica. Boletin. see Extebank Monthly Economic Report 5190
Informacion Express. Serie: Apicultura. (CU ISSN 0138-7685) 218
Informacion Express. Serie: Arroz. (CU ISSN 0138-7731) 180
Informacion Express. Serie: Avicultura. (CU ISSN 0138-7383) 218
Informacion Express. Serie: Cafe y Cacao. (CU ISSN 0138-7634) 180
Informacion Express. Serie: Citricos y Otros Frutales. (CU ISSN 0138-743X) 180
Informacion Express. Serie: Economia y Organizacion del Trabajo Agropecuario. (CU ISSN 0138-7480) 152
Informacion Express. Serie: Forestales. (CU ISSN 0138-6735) 2102
Informacion Express. Serie: Ganado Equino. (CU ISSN 0138-7537) 218
Informacion Express. Serie: Ganado Porcino. (CU ISSN 0138-7588) 218
Informacion Express. Serie: Genetica y Reproduccion. (CU ISSN 0138-6832) 584
Informacion Express. Serie: Mechanizacion Agropecuaria. (CU ISSN 0138-7332) 162
Informacion Express. Serie: Pastos y Forrajes. (CU ISSN 0138-6786) 207
Informacion Express. Serie: Plantas Medicinales y Flores. (CU) 505
Informacion Express. Serie: Proteccion de Plantas. (CU ISSN 0138-7286) 180
Informacion Express. Serie: Riego y Drenaje. (CU) 180
Informacion Express. Serie: Rumiantes. (CU ISSN 0138-7081) 218
Informacion Express. Serie: Suelos y Agroquimica. (CU ISSN 0138-7030) 180
Informacion Express. Serie: Tabaco. (CU ISSN 0138-7138) 180
Informacion Express. Serie: Veterinaria. (CU ISSN 0138-7235) 4810
Informacion Express. Serie: Viandas, Hortalizas y Granos. (CU ISSN 0138-7189) 180
Informacion Iberoamericana. (SP) 4089
Informacion Juridica. (CU) 2635
Informacion Laboral. (CU) 983
Informacion Politica y Economica. (BO) 869, 3898
Informacion Tecnico Economica. (SP) 671, 3663
Informaciones Danesas see Danish Journal 2185
Informaciones Economicas Belgas. (SP) 817
Informaciones Especiales. (CU) 4314
Informaciones Geograficas. (CL ISSN 0716-0364) 2253
Informacionn Agropecuaria. (SP) 218
Informacja Biezaca see I B - 1. Informacja Biezaca 3106
Informacoes Economicas. (BL) 152
Informacoes F I P E. (Fundacao Instituto de Pesquisas Economicas) (BL) 671, 784
Informador. (US ISSN 0019-9869) 2006
Informador. (MX) 2115
Informador das Construcoes. (BL) 620
Informador de la Construccion y de la Industria. (VE) 620
Informal Logic. (CN ISSN 0824-2577) 3769

Informare. (IT) 4728
Informart Magazine. (US) 1460
Informat. (SA ISSN 0256-4106) 2762
Informat. (BE) 4063
▼Informat (International Edition). (SA ISSN 1018-3310) 2762
†L'Informateur Agricole. (CN) 5213
Informateur de la Quinzaine. (FR ISSN 0019-9893) 2187
L'Informateur des Affaires Monteregiennes. (CN) 671
Informateur des Assurances. (UA) 784
Informateur O P T I M A. see O P T I M A Newsletter 512
Informatic. (UK) 1447
Informatic Assistance. (BE) 1396
Informatica. (US) 2797
Informatica. (CL ISSN 0716-0658) 2797, 1456
Informatica e Diritto. (IT) 2762, 2635
Informatica ed Enti Locali. (IT) 4089
Informatica Museologica. (CI ISSN 0350-2325) 3525
Informatica Oggi see Informatica Oggi e UNIX 1416
Informatica Oggi e UNIX. (IT) 1416, 1451
Informatica Oggi Settimanale. (IT) 1451
Informatics Abstracts see Referativnyi Zhurnal. Informatika 2795
Informatics Week. (GR) 1396
Informatie. (NE ISSN 0019-9907) 2797
▼Informatie en Automatisering - Vakmatig. (NE ISSN 0927-2011) 4083, 4089
Informatie Management/Information Management. (NE) 1451
Informatieblad 2112. (NE) 3556
Informatierecht. (NE ISSN 0920-3745) 2635
Informatii de Comert Exterior. (RM) 912
Informatik. (GW) 1396
Informatik. (GW ISSN 0019-9915) 2762, 1456
Informatik-Fachberichte. (US ISSN 0343-3005) 1396
Informatik - Forschung und Entwicklung.(GW ISSN 0178-3564) 1456
Informatik - Kybernetic - Rechentechnik. Schriftenreihe see Informatik - Kybernetik - Rechentechnik 1441
Informatik - Kybernetik - Rechentechnik.(GW) 1441
Informatik-Spektrum. (GW ISSN 0170-6012) 2797
Informatika. (YU ISSN 0019-9923) 2762
Informatika es Tudomanyelemzes. (HU ISSN 0230-4619) 2762, 4314
Information. (GR) 1013
Information see Office Life 1452
Information. see Al-I'lamiyyah 2761
†Information. (GW ISSN 0171-6913) 5213
Information (Poughkeepsie) see InForm (Saratoga Springs) 355
†Information about the Oil Industry - for the Oil Industry. (UK ISSN 0019-9931) 5213
Information Access see Answers 2743
Information Age see Journal of Strategic I T 1434
Information Age. (HK) 1451
Information Agricole. (FR ISSN 0019-994X) 97
Information and Behavior. (US ISSN 0740-5502) 1337
Information and Computation. (US ISSN 0890-5401) 1414
Information and Computer. (CH) 1424
Information and Control. see Xinxi yu Kongzhi 1416
Information and Data Base Publishing Report see I D P Report 1444
Information & Decision Technologies. (NE ISSN 0923-0408) 1437
Information and Documentation see Journal of Information Processing and Managements 2765
Information and Documentation Centre for the Geography of the Netherlands Bulletin see I D G - Bulletin 2252

Information & Interactive Services Report. (US) 4143
Information and Library Manager see Logistics Information Management 2771
Information and Management. (NE ISSN 0378-7206) 1445, 1451
Information and Referral. (US ISSN 0278-2383) 4408
Information and Software Technology. (UK ISSN 0950-5849) 1451, 1445
Information and Word Processing Report see Office Automation Report 1482
Information Broker. (US) 2762
Information Bulletin see Hydrographic Journal 1605
Information Bulletin for Catholic Rural Organizations. (IT) 97, 4266
Information Bulletin - Library of Congress see U.S. Library of Congress. Information Bulletin 2788
Information Bulletin on Variable Stars. (HU ISSN 0374-0676) 365
Information Cardiologique. (FR ISSN 0220-2476) 3209
†Information Center. (US ISSN 0883-315X) 5213
Information Center Quarterly see Information Center 5213
Information Centres in the Northern Territory. List. (AT ISSN 1037-6399) 2762
Information Chicago. (US ISSN 0196-3643) 912
Information Circular on Radiation Techniques and Their Applications to Insect Pests. (UN) 3358
Information Circular - State of Washington, Department of Natural Resources, Division of Geology and Earth Resources see Washington (State). Department of Natural Resources. Division of Geology and Earth Resources. Information Circular 3497
Information, Computer and Communications Policy. (FR) 931
Information Consommation. (FR) 1505
Information Construction. (CN ISSN 0713-6919) 620
Information Dechets see Info Dechets. Environment et Technique 1958
Information Dentaire. (FR ISSN 0020-0018) 3234
Information Design Journal. (UK ISSN 0142-5471) 2762
Information Development. (UK ISSN 0266-6669) 2762
Information Dietetique. (FR ISSN 0020-0034) 3607
Information Display. (US ISSN 0020-0042) 2797, 2762
Information Display see I D 2797
Information Drum Corps see Parades & Pageantry 3573
Information du Technicien Biologiste. (FR ISSN 0989-8735) 3260, 441
Information du Vehicule. (FR) 836
Information e Technology. (IT) 1058
Information Eaux. (FR ISSN 0012-9003) 4825
Information Economics and Policy. (NE ISSN 0167-6245) 671
†Information Economique. (MQ) 5213
Information Economique Africaine. (TI ISSN 0020-0050) 869
Information Eisenbahn. (GW) 4664, 15, 4710
Information en Sciences de la Sante au Canada: Associations. see Health Sciences Information in Canada: Associations 3104
Information en Sciences de la Sante au Canada: Bibliotheques. see Health Sciences Information in Canada: Libraries 3104
Information Exchange. (US) 3321, 3264
Information Exchange Bulletin see Entourage 3336
†Information Executive. (US ISSN 1041-9098) 5213
Information Fiscale et Sociale. (FR) 1013

Information for Civic Education. see Informationen zur Politischen Bildung 3898
Information for Foreign Students Intending to Study at an Austrian Institution of Higher Learning. see Information fuer auslaendische Studienbewerber an oesterreichischen Hochschulen 1709
Information for Forskningsbiblioteker see Nyt fra Nyhavn 2777
Information for Librarians in Agriculture and Food Industry. see Mezogazdasagi es Elelmiszeripari Konyvtarosok Tajekoztatoja 107
Information for Managers on Personnel and Current Trends in Human Resources see I M P A C T 5210
Information for Overseas Students and Their Families. (AT ISSN 0816-3960) 1314
Information from Czechoslovakia. (CS) 2184
Information from the Peace Movement of the German Democratic Republic. (GW ISSN 0020-0085) 3960
Information fuer auslaendische Studienbewerber an oesterreichischen Hochschulen/Information for Foreign Students Intending to Study at an Austrian Institution of Higher Learning. (AU ISSN 0020-0077) 1709
Information fuer den G M B H - Geschaeftsfuehrer. (GW ISSN 0723-4929) 4129
Information fuer die Truppe. (GW ISSN 0443-1243) 3460
Information fuer Ormesheim. (GW) 4089, 3898
†Information G. (GW ISSN 0046-9343) 5213
Information Geographique. (FR ISSN 0020-0093) 2253
Information Hippique. (FR) 4535
Information Historique. (FR ISSN 0046-9351) 2314
Information Hotline. (US ISSN 0360-5817) 2762
Information Immobiliere. (FR ISSN 0046-936X) 4151
†Information Industry Alert. (US ISSN 1049-9326) 5213
Information Industry Bulletin. (US ISSN 0883-5772) 4143, 1424
Information Industry Directory. (US) 1425
Information Industry Directory Supplement. (US) 1425
Information Industry Factbook. (US) 2762, 4130
Information Intelligence Online Libraries and Microcomputers see Online Libraries and Microcomputers 2799
Information Intelligence Online Newsletter see Online Newsletter 1428
Information - International Trade & Economics. see Guoji Jingmao Xiaoxi 910
Information Juive. (FR ISSN 0020-0107) 2006, 4223, 4408
Information Legislative Service. (US) 1638
Information Litteraire. (FR ISSN 0020-0123) 2925
Information - Logiciel see Info-Log Magazine 1433
Information Malaysia. (MY) 2338
Information Management. see Informatie Management 1451
Information Management (Sioux City). (US ISSN 0197-6524) 1013
Information Management Directory see Information Management Year Book 1451
Information Management for Rehabilitation Administrators. (US) 1013
Information Management Journal. (UK) 1451, 1445
Information Management, Policies and Services. (US) 2762
Information Management Report. (UK ISSN 0961-7612) 2797, 1351, 2762
†Information Management Review. (US) 5213

Information Management Sourcebook. (US) **2762**
Information Management: Strategies, Systems, and Technologies. (US) **1451**
Information Management Year Book. (UK) **1451**
Information Market see X I I I Magazine **1346**
Information Market of Science and Technology. see Keji Qingbao Shichang **2767**
†Information Marketing News. (US) **5213**
Information Media & Technology. (UK ISSN 0266-6960) **1337**
Information Medizin. (GW ISSN 0931-2358) **3108**
†Information Moscow, Western Edition. (US) **5213**
Information Nederland France see I N F **817**
Information News and Sources see Information Hotline **2762**
Information nicht nur fuer Studieanfaenger see Wo Geht's Lang **1720**
Information North. (CN ISSN 0315-2561) **4315**, 2253
Information om Rehabilitering. (SW ISSN 0020-0174) **2284**
Information om Skolen i Norden see Skolen i Norden **1663**
Information on Environmental Pollution in Foreign Countries. (JA) **1985**
Information on Microcomputers. see Wei Jisuanji Xinxi **1465**
Information on Parana. (BL) **869**
Information on Psychological Sciences. see Xinli Kexue Tongxun **4050**
Information on the Court of Justice of the European Communities see Reports of Cases Before the Court of Justice of the European Communities **2672**
Information Ouvrieres. (FR) **2869**
Information Pamphlet - Department of Employment and Social Services (Baltimore) see Maryland. Department of Human Resources. Information Pamphlet **5232**
Information-Part 2-Reports - Bibliographies see Information Reports and Bibliographies **2793**
†Information Peking (Beijing). (US) **5213**
Information Philosophie. (GW) **3769**
Information Pictorial. see Xinxi Huabao **2183**
Information Please Sports Almanac (Year). (US ISSN 1046-4980) **4475**
Information Processing & Management.(US ISSN 0306-4573) **2762**
Information Processing Association of Israel. National Conference on Data Processing. Proceedings. (IS ISSN 0073-7879) **1456**, 2797
Information Processing Letters. (NE ISSN 0020-0190) **1451**
Information Processing Report. (UK) **1482**, 1456
Information Processing Society of Japan. Journal. see Joho Shori **1452**
Information Processing Society of Japan. Transactions. (JA ISSN 0387-5806) **1451**
Information Proche-Orient. (CN) **2869**, 3960
Information Psychiatrique. (FR) **3338**
Information Report. (US ISSN 0733-8961) **403**
Information Reports and Bibliographies. (US ISSN 0360-0971) **2793**
Information Research News. (UK) **2762**
Information Resources Management Journal. (US ISSN 1040-1628) **1013**, 2762
Information Retrieval & Library Automation. (US) **2798**, 1456
Information Retrieval and Library Automation Newsletter see Information Retrieval & Library Automation **2798**
Information Returns Guide. (US) **1097**

Information Routiere et Touristique. (FR) **4745**, 4772
Information Science. see Qingbao Kexue **1457**
Information Science Abstracts. (US ISSN 0020-0239) **2793**, 15
Information Science: Theory and Application. see Qingbao Lilun yu Shijian **2780**
Information Sciences. (US ISSN 0020-0255) **1456**
Information Sciences for Agriculture. see Zemedelska Informatika **2791**
†Information Sciences Series. (US) **5213**
Information Scientist see Journal of Information Science **2766**
Information Searcher. (US ISSN 1055-3916) **1690**, 2798
Information Series on Agricultural Economics see Giannini Foundation of Agricultural Economics. Information Series **152**
Information Series - Tennessee State Board of Vocational Education see Tennessee. State Board for Vocational Education. Information Series **1742**
Information Service. (UK) **97**, 620
Information Service in Mechanical Engineering Mechanical Engineering Abstracts see I S M E C: Mechanical Engineering Abstracts **1844**
Information Service of the European Communities. Documentation Europeenne - Serie Agricole see Documentation Europeenne - Serie Agricole **87**
Information Service of the European Communities. Documentation Europeenne - Serie Syndical et Ouvriere see Documentation Europeenne - Serie Syndicale et Ouvriere **977**
Information Service of the European Communities. Newsletter on the Common Agricultural Policy. (EI ISSN 0073-7895) **152**
Information Service of the European Communities. Trade Union News. (EI ISSN 0073-7909) **2584**
Information Services & Use. (NE ISSN 0167-5265) **2763**
Information Services on Latin America see I S L A **2409**
†Information Sharing Index. (US) **5213**
Information Society. (US ISSN 0197-2243) **1456**, 2798
Information Solutions. (CN ISSN 0824-3514) **1013**, 1041, 2763
Information Sources (Year). (US ISSN 0734-9637) **1396**, 1337, 3675, 4130
Information Standards Quarterly. (US ISSN 1041-0031) **4130**, 2763
Information Strategy. (US ISSN 0743-8613) **1013**, 1451
Information System Engineering. see Xinxi Xitong Gongcheng **1346**
†Information Systems (Carol Stream). (US) **5213**
Information Systems (Tarrytown). (US ISSN 0306-4379) **2798**, 1445
Information Systems Capacity Management Handbook Series see I S Capacity Management Handbook Series **1451**
Information Systems News see Information Week **1445**
▼Information Systems Research. (US) **1456**
Information Systems Security Association Access see I S S A Access **1434**
▼Information Systems Spending. (US) **1452**, 1041
Information Technology & Learning. (UK) **1690**
Information Technology and Libraries. (US ISSN 0730-9295) **2798**, 1456
Information Technology and People. (US ISSN 0959-3845) **2798**
Information Technology and Public Policy. (UK ISSN 0266-8513) **2763**

Information Technology Association of America Compensation and Non-Cash Benefits Surveys see I T A A Compensation and Non-Cash Benefits Surveys **1066**
Information Technology Association of America Membership Directory see I T A A Membership Directory **1451**
Information Technology Association of America New Products and Services Guide see I T A A New Products and Services Guide **1477**
Information Technology Association of America Software Industry Reports see I T A A Software Industry Reports **1477**
†Information Technology, Computer & Communications. Hardware Index. (UK) **5213**
Information Technology Digest. (US) **1396**
▼Information Technology, Education and Society. (AT ISSN 1037-616X) **1456**, 1638
†Information Technology for Development. (UK ISSN 0268-1102) **5213**
Information Technology Index. (AT ISSN 1036-0352) **1452**, 1477
Information Technology Intelligence see I T Intelligence **5210**
Information Technology Intelligence (Luton). (UK) **1337**, 1396
Information Technology Management. (AT) **1059**, 1351, 1363, 1374
Information Technology Notes. (UK ISSN 0953-4458) **5213**
Information Technology Review. (UK) **1447**, 1456
Information Technology Series. (US) **1456**
▼Information, Theory and Society. (AT ISSN 1033-6273) **4438**
Information Times. (US) **2798**, 1337, 3675, 4130
Information Today. (US ISSN 8755-6286) **2798**, 2763
Information Transports. (FR ISSN 0020-0298) **4651**
†Information und Dokumentation: Annotierte Titelliste. (GW ISSN 0138-5739) **5213**
Information und Meinung. (AU) **2571**
†Information Veterinaire. (CN ISSN 0581-3263) **5213**
Information Week. (US) **1445**
Information World. see Xinxi Shijie **2791**
Information World Review. (UK ISSN 0950-9879) **1351**
Informationdienst Verkehr. (GW ISSN 0931-1688) **4651**
Informationen. (GW) **3960**
Informationen aus der Wirtschaft. (AU) **784**
Informationen aus Kassel see Information **5213**
Informationen aus Orthodontie und Kieferorthopaedie. (GW ISSN 0020-0336) **3234**
Informationen - Bildung, Wissenschaft. (GW ISSN 0343-7868) **1638**
Informationen Deutsch als Fremdsprache. (GW ISSN 0724-9616) **1709**, 2818
Informationen fuer das Gas- und Wasserfach see Gussrohr - Technik **2299**
Informationen fuer den Biologieunterricht. (GW) **441**
Informationen fuer den Verkaufs Innendienst. (GW) **1041**
Informationen fuer die Fischwirtschaft. (GW ISSN 0020-0344) **2043**
Informationen fuer die Frau. (GW ISSN 0020-0352) **4845**
Informationen fuer die Lippische Wirtschaft see I H K Lippe Info **817**
Informationen fuer die Museen in der DDR. (GW ISSN 0138-1989) **3525**
Informationen fuer die Wirtschaft. (GW) **817**
▼Informationen fuer Einelternfamilien. (GW ISSN 0938-0124) **4438**
Informationen fuer Mitarbeiter und Vereine. (GW) **4475**

INFORMATIONS 6287

Informationen fuer Regensburger Studentinnen und Studenten. (GW) **1709**
Informationen fuer Steuerberatende Berufe. (GW) **784**
Informationen Jugendliteratur und Medien-Jugendschriften-Warte. (GW ISSN 0937-6755) **1247**
Informationen ueber die Fischwirtschaft des Auslandes. (GW ISSN 0020-0379) **2043**
Informationen ueber Jugendarbeit und Jugendpolitik im Landkreis Muenchen. (GW) **4408**, 1239
Informationen zu Aktuellen Fragen der Sozial- und Wirtschaftpolitik. (AU ISSN 0083-6125) **3898**
Informationen zum Arbeitslosenrecht und Sozialhilferecht. (GW ISSN 0179-8863) **4408**, 3628
Informationen zum Religionsunterricht see Religion Heute: Supplement **1658**
Informationen zur Ausstellungsplanung. (GW) **3525**, 330
Informationen zur Beruflichen Bildung. (GW) **3628**
Informationen zur Deutschdidaktik. (AU ISSN 0721-9954) **1639**, 2818
Informationen zur Modernen Stadtgeschichte (I M S). (GW ISSN 0340-1774) **2489**, 4089
Informationen zur Orts-, Regional- und Landesplanung see D I S P **2486**
Informationen zur Politischen Bildung/ Information for Civic Education. (GW ISSN 0046-9408) **3898**, 1639
Informationen zur Raumentwicklung. (GW ISSN 0303-2493) **2489**
†Informationen zur Soziologische Forschung in der D.D.R. (GW ISSN 0020-0395) **5213**
Informationen zur Stadtentwicklung Ludwigshafen. (GW) **4089**
Informations. (GW) **983**
Informations Aeronautiques see Informations Aeronautiques et Spatiales **55**
Informations Aeronautiques et Spatiales.(FR) **55**
Informations Annuelles de Caryosystematique et Cytogenetique.(FR ISSN 0073-7917) **505**, 544
Informations C N C see Centre National de la Cinematographie. Bulletin d'Information **3505**
Informations Canadiennes. (FR ISSN 0020-0433) **817**
Informations - Chimie. (FR ISSN 0020-045X) **1179**
Informations Chimie Hebdo. (FR) **1179**
Informations Couverture Plomberie. (FR) **2300**
†Informations d'Ile de France. (FR ISSN 0396-9975) **5213**
Informations du Caoutchouc et des Plastiques. (FR ISSN 0247-3518) **4292**, 3862
Informations du Commerce Exterieur. (BE ISSN 0770-3058) **912**
Informations et Nouveautes Techniques/Ettela'at Va Tazeha-Ye Fanni. (IR) **4315**
Informations F.N.A.I.M. (Federation Nationale des Agents Immobiliers et Administrateurs de Biens-Syndics d'Immeubles) (FR) **4151**
Informations Laitieres. (FR ISSN 0046-9432) **200**
Informations pour Jounalistes d'Entreprise - Informatie voor Bedrijfsjournalisten see Redactuel **2575**
Informations Rapides de l'Administration Francaise. (FR ISSN 0020-0492) **419**, 4063
Informations Recentes sur les Comptes Nationaux des Pays en Developpement/Latest Information on National Accounts of Developing Countries. (FR ISSN 0252-2683) **931**
Informations Sociales. (FR ISSN 0046-9459) **4408**
Informations Speciales. (FR) **2635**
Informations U F O L E P-U S E P. (FR) **3804**

INFORMATIONS

Informations V S I G. see V S I G - Mitteilungen **924**
†Informationsaufnahme und Informationsverarbeitung im Lebenden Organismus. (GW ISSN 0344-4430) **5213**
†Informationsblaetter zu Nachbarwissenschaften der Ur- und Fruehgeschichte. (GW) **5213**
Informationsbrief Auslaenderrecht. (GW ISSN 0174-2108) **2724**
Informationsbrief fuer Fuehrungskraefte in der Chemischen Industrie. (GW) **1854**
Informationsbulletin Kurdistan. (GW) **2006**
Informationsdienst Bibliothekswesen see Dokumentationsdienst Bibliothekswesen **2756**
Informationsdienst des Deutschen Rates der Europaeischen Bewegung see Europaeisches Forum **3956**
Informationsdienst fuer Betriebsraete, Vertrauensleute und Funktionstraeger. (GW) **983**
†Informationsdienst fuer den K F Z-Zubehoer und Ersatzteile-Fachhandel.(GW ISSN 0342-4960) **5213**
Informationsdienst fuer Sachverstaendige. (GW) **671**
Informationsdienst Gross- und Aussenhandel. (GW) **912**, 1041
Informationsdienst Krankenhauswesen/Health Care Information Service. (GW ISSN 0341-0595) **2466**, 3279
Informationsdienst Laerm. (GW ISSN 0344-7758) **1844**, 15, 3820
Informationsdienst Suedliches Afrika. (GW ISSN 0721-5088) **931**, 3960
†Informationsdienst Uebersetzungen. (GW) **5213**
Informationsdienst zur Auslaenderarbeit.(GW ISSN 0721-1295) **3628**
Informationstechnik - I T. (GW ISSN 0179-9738) **1396**
Informationstidsskrift for Social- og Sundhedssektor see Nyhedsinformation for Social-, Sygehus- og Sundhedssektor **4118**
†Informationszentrum Haut. (GW ISSN 0930-6803) **5213**
Informatique & Bureautique. (CN ISSN 0227-8332) **827**
Informatique Canadienne. see Canadian Information Processing **1448**
Informatique et Etudes Medievales. see Computers and Medieval Data Processing **5170**
Informatique et Sciences Juridiques. (FR ISSN 0181-110X) **2705**, 2520, 4458
Informativo Alamar. (UY) **4729**
Informativo Bamerindus. (BL ISSN 0020-0654) **784**
Informativo del Maiz. (PE) **180**
Informativo Fasecolda see Informativo Tecnico **2533**
Informativo Industrial. (PN) **2584**
Informativo Juridico. (CK ISSN 0120-1875) **2533**, 2635
Informativo Legal Rodrigo. (PE) **2635**, 3943
Informativo Medico. (SP) **3108**
†Informativo R N. (BL) **5213**
Informativo Tecnico. (CK) **2533**
▼Informatization and the Public Sector.(NE ISSN 0925-5052) **1337**, 4063
Informatization White Paper. (JA) **1396**
Informatologia. (CI) **2763**
Informatologia Yugoslavica see Informatologia **2763**
Informator Archeologiczny. (PL ISSN 0085-1876) **274**
Informator Nauki Polskiej. (PL ISSN 0537-667X) **4315**
Informatore. (IT) **2205**
Informatore Agrario. (IT ISSN 0020-0689) **97**
Informatore Botanico Italiano. (IT ISSN 0020-0697) **505**
Informatore dei Commercianti. (IT) **817**, 4772
Informatore di Urio. (IT) **4266**, 1684

Informatore Farmaceutico. (IT ISSN 0073-7984) **3729**
Informatore Fitopatologico. (IT ISSN 0020-0735) **506**, 97
Informatore Industriale. (IT) **1078**
Informatore Medico-Sociale. (IT ISSN 0020-0743) **3108**
Informatore Pirola. (IT) **1066**, 1097
Informatore Tessile. (IT) **1285**
Informatore Turistico. (IT ISSN 0020-076X) **4772**
Informatore Zootecnico. (IT ISSN 0020-0778) **218**
Informatory Regionalne. (PL) **2169**
Informatsionno-Izmeritel'naya Tekhnika. (KR) **1899**
Informatyka. (PL ISSN 0542-9951) **3038**
Informazione Elettronica. (IT) **1773**
Informazione Filosofica. (IT) **3769**
Informazione Industriale. (IT ISSN 0020-0786) **1078**
Informazione Innovativa. (IT) **1958**, 4104
Informazione Mediterranea. (IT ISSN 0020-0794) **869**, 784
Informazione Radio TV. (IT ISSN 0300-3973) **1374**, 1356
Informazioni Aziendali e Professionali. (IT) **1013**
Informazioni di Parapsicologia see Quaderni Gnosis **3671**
Informazioni e Orientamenti. (IT) **32**
Informazioni e Studi Vivaldiani. (IT ISSN 0393-2915) **419**, 3556
Informazioni S U N I A. (Sindicato Unitario Nazionale Inquilini Assegnatari) (IT) **2489**
Informazioni Sociali. (IT ISSN 0020-0816) **4408**
Informazioni sui Farmaci. (IT) **3729**
†Informe. (MX ISSN 0185-4399) **5213**
Informe Agropecuario. (BL ISSN 0100-3364) **97**
Informe Anual de las Actividades de las Unidades Operativas de Salud en el Programa de Planificacion Familiar del Ministerio de Salud. (EC) **597**
Informe Anual del Programa de Pastos Tropicales. (CK ISSN 0120-2391) **97**
Informe CIAT. see C I A T Report **81**
Informe Conjuntural. (BL ISSN 0101-6377) **869**
Informe de Operacion de las Principales Empresas Productoras y Distribuidoras de Energia Electrica de Costa Rica. (CR ISSN 0074-0047) **1899**
Informe Demografico. (BL ISSN 0100-7173) **3983**, 2253
Informe Economico. (SP) **869**
Informe Economico de Aragon. (SP ISSN 0211-5468) **817**
Informe Economico Regional. (SP ISSN 0211-8734) **817**
Informe Economico y Financiero. (CL ISSN 0716-243X) **784**
Informe Latinoamericano. (UK ISSN 0263-5372) **869**, 3898
Informe S E A T. (SP) **912**
Informe Sobre Chile. (CL) **4574**
Informe sobre el Comercio y el Desarrollo see Trade and Development Report **922**
†InforMed. (US ISSN 0730-6636) **5213**
Informed Enophile see Wine Investor: Buyers' Guide **387**
Informer. (UK ISSN 0020-0840) **2995**, 2925
†Informer (Eau Claire). (US) **5213**
Informer (Plainview). (US) **2284**
Informer (San Rafael). (US) **3753**
Informer and Texas Freeman. (US) **2006**
Informes. (PE) **3899**
Informes Conjunturais da Agropecuaria do Nordeste. (BL) **152**
Informes de la Construccion. (SP ISSN 0020-0883) **620**
Informes Especiales. (UK ISSN 0266-2914) **949**, 784
Informobili see Macchine Accessori Componenti **2560**
Informobili Middle East see Forwood International **5196**

Inform'optique. (FR ISSN 0758-5756) **3853**
Informs. (International Business Forms Industries, Inc.) (US ISSN 0278-9841) **671**
Inforpress Centroamericana. (GT ISSN 0252-8754) **3899**, 671
Infos Federales. (FR) **4651**, 4063
InfoSecurity Product News see I S P News **1526**
InfoSFera. (LI) **3012**
Infosystems see Information Systems (Carol Stream) **5213**
†Infotec China. (HK) **5213**
Infotecture. (FR ISSN 0241-2640) **805**
Infoterm Series. (International Information Centre for Terminology, Vienna) (GW) **2818**, 2763
Infoterra. (UN ISSN 0252-3213) **1958**, 931
InfoText. (US) **1363**
Infowat see W A T C O M News **1455**
InfoWorld. (US ISSN 0199-6649) **1461**, 1424
Info3 Extra. (GW ISSN 0936-546X) **4375**
†Infrared and Millimeter Waves. (US) **5213**
Infrared Physics. (US ISSN 0020-0891) **3853**
Infrared Research. see Hongwai Yanjiu **3852**
Infrared Society of Japan. Proceeding. (JA ISSN 0386-8044) **3841**, 3853, 4600
Infrared Spectroscopy Abstracts see Laser Raman & Infrared Spectroscopy Abstracts **3837**
Infusion. (US ISSN 0160-757X) **3109**, 3729
Infusions-Journal. (GW ISSN 0720-0722) **3109**, 3176
Infusionstherapie. (SZ ISSN 1011-6966) **3607**
Infusionstherapie und Klinische Ernaehrung - Forschung und Praxis see Infusionstherapie **3607**
▼Ing. (GW ISSN 0863-4831) **1824**
Ingegnere. (IT ISSN 0020-0905) **1824**
Ingegneri Architetti Construttori. (IT) **1867**, 301, 620
Ingegneri e Architetti Svizzeri. see Schweizer Ingenieur und Architekt **306**
Ingegneri E Costruttori. (IT) **620**
†Ingegneria. (IT ISSN 0035-6263) **5213**
Ingegneria Ambientale. (IT ISSN 0394-5871) **4104**, 4825
Ingegneria Ambientale Inquinamento e Depurazione see Ingegneria Ambientale **4104**
Ingegneria Ambientale Inquinamento e Depurazione Quaderni see Ingegneria Ambientale Quaderni **4104**
Ingegneria Ambientale Quaderni. (IT) **4104**, 4825
Ingegneria Elettronica. (IT) **1773**
Ingegneria Ferroviaria. (IT ISSN 0020-0956) **4710**
Ingegneria Sanitaria see Ingegneria Sanitaria Ambientale **4104**
Ingegneria Sanitaria Ambientale. (IT) **4104**
Ingenera y Arquitectura. (PN) **1867**, 301
▼Ingenieria. (CR) **1824**
Ingenieria. Boletin Informativo. see Ingenieria e Investigacion **1824**
Ingenieria Agronomica. (MX) **98**
Ingenieria Civil. (CU ISSN 0020-1022) **1867**
Ingenieria Civil/Civil Engineering. (MX) **1867**
Ingenieria de Costos. (MX) **1013**
Ingenieria e Industria. (AG ISSN 0020-1030) **1824**
Ingenieria e Investigacion. (CK ISSN 0120-5609) **1824**
Ingenieria Electronica, Automatica y Comunicaciones. (CU) **1773**
Ingenieria Energetica. (CU) **1791**, 1899
Ingenieria Estructural. (CU) **1930**
Ingenieria Hidraulica. (CU) **1924**
Ingenieria Hidraulica en Mexico. (MX ISSN 0186-4076) **4825**

Ingenieria Industrial. (CU) **1824**
Ingenieria Mecanica y Electrica. (MX) **1930**, 1899
Ingenieria Naval. (SP ISSN 0020-1073) **4729**
Ingenieria Petrolera. (MX) **3689**
Ingenieria Quimica. (SP ISSN 0210-2064) **1854**
Ingenieria Quimica. (AG) **1854**
Ingenieria Sanitaria. (AG ISSN 0446-2424) **4104**
Ingeniero Latinoamericano. (CK) **1825**
Ingenieros. (CL ISSN 0716-4610) **1825**
De Ingenieur. (NE ISSN 0020-1146) **1825**
Der Ingenieur. (AU) **1825**, 620, 1899
Ingenieur-Archiv/Archive of Applied Mechanics. (GW ISSN 0020-1154) **1825**
Ingenieur - Constructeur. (FR) **1867**
Der Ingenieur der Deutschen Bundespost. (GW ISSN 0020-1170) **1825**, 1353
Ingenieur Digest see Innovation **5213**
Ingenieur et Industrie. (BE ISSN 0775-2962) **1825**
Ingenieurbauten. (US ISSN 0172-8008) **1867**
Ingenieurs de l'Automobile. (FR ISSN 0020-1200) **4693**
Ingenieurs de la Vie. (FR) **180**, 2073
Ingenieurs Diplomes see I D **1823**
Ingenieurs et Architectes Suisses. see Schweizer Ingenieur und Architekt **306**
Ingenieurs et Architectes Suisses. (SZ ISSN 0251-0979) **1867**, 301
Ingenieurs Nieuws see De Ingenieur **1825**
De Ingenieurskrant. (NE ISSN 0923-1919) **1825**
Ingenieurwissenschaftliche Bibliothek/Engineering Science Library. (US ISSN 0173-0274) **1825**
Ingenioer see Ingenioer - Hvorfor, Hvordan **1825**
Ingenioer - Hvorfor, Hvordan. (DK) **1825**
Ingenioer - Nytt/Engineering News. (NO ISSN 0332-611X) **1825**
Ingenioer- og Bygningsvaesen see Ingenioeren **1825**
Ingenioeren/Danish Engineer's Weekly. (DK) **1825**, 620
Ingenioeren Indkoebsbog. (DK ISSN 0446-2491) **1078**, 1139
Ingenioerens Ugeblad see Ingenioeren **1825**
Ingeniurs Informatie see De Ingenieurskrant **1825**
Ingenjoersnytt. see Tekniikka & Talous **4612**
Inglewood Public Library Quarterly Report. (US ISSN 0020-1308) **2763**
†Inglis Lecture. (US ISSN 0073-800X) **5213**
Ingot. (CN ISSN 0707-8013) **3408**
Ingram's Magazine. (US) **671**
Ingrid. (GW) **4845**
Inhalation Toxicology. (US ISSN 0895-8378) **1982**, 3729
Inheritance, Estate and Gift Tax Reports, Home State. (US) **1097**
▼Initial. (GW) **2869**
Initial Decisions and Board Opinions and Orders in Safety. (US) **4674**, 2635
†Initial Public Offerings Annual. (US ISSN 1053-7163) **5213**
Initiation. Serie Textes, Bibliographies. (FR ISSN 0073-8034) **403**
Initiation a la Linguistique. Serie A. Lectures. (FR ISSN 0073-8018) **2818**
Initiation a la Linguistique. Serie B. Problemes et Methodes. (FR ISSN 0073-8026) **2818**
Initiations et Etudes Africaines see Institut Fondamental d'Afrique Noire. Initiations et Etudes Africaines **2333**
Initiativ. (SW ISSN 0282-4655) **1115**
Initiative. (AU) **1256**
Initiative. (CN ISSN 0827-4789) **4408**
†Initiative and Referendum: The Power of the People! (US) **5213**

Initiatives see Employment Initiatives 978
Initiatives. (US) 1728, 4845
Iniziativa Europea see Sinistra Europea 3972
Iniziativa Isontina. (IT ISSN 0020-1359) 869, 4375
Injury. (UK ISSN 0020-1383) 3308
Injury Control for Children and Youth. (US) 3321
Injury Valuation Reports and Special Research Reports. (US ISSN 0020-1391) 2635, 2533
▼Injuve. (SP ISSN 1130-4618) 1256
†Ink (Buffalo). (US) 5213
Ink (Chicago). (US) 1139, 32
Ink & Gall. (US ISSN 0894-0479) 355, 4001
Ink and Print see Ink & Print International 4001
Ink & Print International. (UK) 4001
Ink W E L. (Women's Electoral Lobby A.C.T.) (AT) 4845, 3899
Inkasso-Praxis. (SZ) 949
Inkblot. (US) 2925
Inking. (UK) 1314
Inkling. (UK) 1684
Inkling see Writers' Journal (N. St. Paul) 2977
Inkling Literary Journal see Writers' Journal (N. St. Paul) 2977
Inklings. (UK ISSN 0143-9871) 4001
Inklusief. (NE ISSN 0041-2562) 1239
Inkshed - Poetry and Fiction. (UK ISSN 0951-0427) 2995
Inksherds. (US) 274
Inkslinger's Review see Continental Newstime 852
Inkstone. (CN ISSN 0714-2870) 2995, 2869, 3638
Inkworld. (II ISSN 0377-0087) 2584, 2571
Inland. (US ISSN 0020-1456) 2227
Inland Africa see A I M International 4161
Inland Architect. (US ISSN 0020-1472) 301
Inland Bird Banding Newsletter see North American Bird Bander 565
Inland Business Magazine. (US) 836
Inland Empire. (US) 2227
Inland Empire Manufacturers Guide see Inland Northwest Manufacturers Directory 1139
Inland Farmer-Stockman. (US ISSN 1041-2719) 218
Inland Messenger. (US) 2763
Inland Northwest Manufacturers Directory. (US) 1139
Inland Northwest Manufacturers Guide see Inland Northwest Manufacturers Directory 1139
Inland Register. (US ISSN 0020-1510) 4266
Inland Revenue Clearances. (UK) 1097
Inland Revenue Official Tax Guides. (UK) 1097
Inland Revenue Practices and Concessions. (UK) 1097
Inland River Guide. (US) 4729
Inland River Record. (US) 4729
Inland Seas. (US ISSN 0020-1537) 2410, 4729
Inland Waterways Guide. (UK) 4729
Inlet. (US ISSN 0085-1884) 2925
▼InLine. (US) 4548
Inlogov Informs. (Institute of Local Government Studies) (UK ISSN 0958-4021) 4089
Inmarin Magazine. (US) 2227
Inmun Kwahak. see Journal of Humanistic Studies 2509
Inmunologia. (SP ISSN 0213-9626) 3186
†Inmunologika. (SP) 5213
†Inmusic. (US ISSN 1047-2363) 5213
Inn Business. (CN ISSN 0821-7610) 2476
Inn Business Review Newsletter. (US) 2476, 4772
The Inn Guide. (US ISSN 0895-2965) 2476
Inn Places (Year). (US) 2454, 4772
Inn Review Newsletter see Inn Business Review Newsletter 2476

Inn Room Magazine. (US) 4803
Inn Touch. (US) 2476
Inner Circle Letter. (US ISSN 0894-7902) 2437
Inner City News. (US) 2006
Inner Horizons. (US ISSN 0897-229X) 4266
Inner Journeys. (US) 3594
Inner London Education Authority Contact see I L E A Contact 5209
Inner Mongolian Normal University. Journal (Natural Science Edition). see Nei Menggu Shifan Daxue Xuebao (Ziran Kexue Ban) 4329
Inner Mongolian Social Sciences. see Nei Menggu Shehui Kexue 4381
Inner Mongolian University. Journal (Natural Science Edition). see Nei Menggu Daxue Xuebao (Ziran Kexue Ban) 4329
Inner Mongolian University. Journal (Social Science Edition). see Nei Menggu Daxue Xuebao (Shehui Kexue Ban) 4381
Inner Mongolian Women. see Nei Menggu Funu 4849
Inner Paths. (US ISSN 0149-6026) 3594, 4182
Inner Search. (CN) 2925
Inner - View. (US) 4772
Inner Voice. (US ISSN 1062-9491) 2102, 1958
Inner Woman see New Times (Seattle) 3595
Innere Medizin. (GW ISSN 0303-4305) 3109
Innergy News. (US) 3669
Innes Clan Society Newsletter see Bullrush 2146
Innes Review. (UK ISSN 0020-157X) 4266, 2314
Innews see Inside Dining 2073
Innis Herald. (CN) 1314
†Innisfail Canegrower. (AT ISSN 0020-1588) 5213
Innisfree. (US) 2995, 2925
Innkeeping World. (US ISSN 0746-6498) 2476
Innominate. (AT ISSN 0020-1618) 1314
▼Innovating. (US ISSN 1053-2587) 1751, 4408
Innovation. (IS ISSN 0334-3847) 1078, 1013
Innovation see Educational Innovation and Information 1721
Innovation. (US) 1825
Innovation. see Ibda 2924
Innovation. (AU) 4375, 4600
Innovation. (FR) 4600
Innovation. (CN) 4600, 4315
†Innovation. (GW) 5213
Innovation and Employment. (FR) 3628
Innovation & Management. (GW ISSN 0863-2790) 3675
Innovation and Technology Transfer. (EI ISSN 0255-0806) 2763, 3392
Innovation et Produits Nouveaux see Telecommunications 1344
▼Innovations. (US) 4315
▼Innovations & Ideas. (US ISSN 1059-2091) 4315
†Der Innovations-Berater. (GW ISSN 0721-4405) 5213
Innovations, Demarches, Experiences dans l'Enseignement Superieur see I D E E S 5209
†Innovations in Polymers - Engineering Plastics. (US ISSN 1045-1889) 5213
Innovations in Relocation Management. (US) 4745
Innovations-Nachrichten. (GW) 4601, 4315
Innovative Business Technologies. (GR) 1059
Innovative Graduate Programs Directory. (US ISSN 0363-2601) 1709
Innovative Higher Education. (US ISSN 0742-5627) 1709
Innovative Municipal Programs (Year). (US) 4089
Innovative Products. (US ISSN 1058-8523) 3675, 1078
Innovative Products Letter see Innovative Products 3675

Innovator (Ann Arbor). (US ISSN 0046-9572) 1639
Innovator (University Park). (US ISSN 0888-8469) 1314
Innovator's Digest. (US ISSN 0890-300X) 4315
†Innovators Directory. (AT) 5213
Innovazione: Impianti e Produzione. (IT) 1825
Innowacje see Przeglad Techniczny, Innowacje 4607
Innsbruck. Statistisches Jahrbuch. (AU) 4574
Innsbrucker Beitraege zur Musikwissenschaft. (AU) 3556
Innsbrucker Universitaetsreden. (AU) 1709
Inorganic Chemistry. (US ISSN 0020-1669) 1213
Inorganic Chemistry Concepts. (US ISSN 0172-7966) 1213
Inorganic Materials. (English translation of: Izvestiya Akademii Nauk S.S.S.R., Seriya Neorganicheskie Materialy) (US ISSN 0020-1685) 1213, 1854, 3408
Inorganic Syntheses Series. (US ISSN 0073-8077) 1226
Inorganica Chimica Acta. (SZ ISSN 0020-1693) 1213
Inozemna Filolohija. (KR. ISSN 0320-2372) 2818
Inpatient Hospital Use in New York City (Year). (US ISSN 0894-8151) 2470, 2466
Inpharma. (NZ ISSN 0156-2703) 3729
Inpho. (GW ISSN 0019-0179) 3792
Inpho Oesterreich. (AU ISSN 0020-1707) 3792
Inprekorr see I N P R E K O R R 3898
†Inprint. (AT ISSN 0314-285X) 5213
Input. (US) 1751, 1239
Inqabayokulinda. (SA ISSN 0019-0241) 4284
Inquiline Worldwide Home Exchanges and Rentals. (US) 4151, 4772
Inquilino. see Tenant 2497
Inquinamento. (IT ISSN 0001-4982) 1958
Inquirer. (UK ISSN 0020-1723) 4182
Inquiry. (NO ISSN 0020-174X) 3769, 4375
Inquiry (Chicago). (US ISSN 0046-9580) 3109
Inquiry & Analysis. (US) 1639, 2635
Inquiry into Economic Problems. see Jingji Wenti Tansuo 672
Inquiry into the Future. (KO) 2338
Inquisitor. (II ISSN 0046-9599) 1256
Inriatheque. (Institut National de Recherche en Informatique et en Automatique) (FR ISSN 0756-7677) 1452
Ins and Outs. (NE ISSN 0167-3696) 2869
†Insaat Muhendisleri Odasi. Teknik Bulten. (TU ISSN 0300-2721) 5213
Al-Insaf. (LY) 2429, 2333
Insatsukai/Printing World. (JA ISSN 0020-1766) 4001
Inscape (Pasadena). (US ISSN 0094-2715) 2995
Inschriften Griechischer Staedte aus Kleinasien. (GW) 274
INSEAD Address Book. (UK ISSN 0304-4270) 1013
Insect & fungus Damage to Cultural Properties. see Bunkazai no Chu-kin-gai 529
Insect Biochemistry see Insect Biochemistry and Molecular Biology 533
Insect Biochemistry and Molecular Biology. (US ISSN 0965-1748) 533
Insect Chemoreception. see Khemoretseptsiya Nasekomykh 535
Insect Control Guide. (US) 180
Insect Science and Its Application. (KE ISSN 0191-9040) 533
Insect World. (US ISSN 1043-6057) 533
Insecta Matsumurana. (JA ISSN 0020-1804) 533
Insecta Mundi. (US ISSN 0749-6737) 533

INSIDE KUNG

Insectarium. (JA) 533
Insectes Sociaux/Social Insects. (SZ ISSN 0020-1812) 533
Insecticide and Acaricide Tests. (US ISSN 0276-3656) 533
Insecticide Product Guide. (US ISSN 8756-1530) 1854
Insectimes. (US) 533
Insectivorous Plant Society. Journal. see Shokuchu Shokubutsu Kenkyukai Kaishi 517
Insects Are People Too. (US) 2995
Insects of Micronesia. (US ISSN 0073-8115) 533
Insects of Virginia. (US ISSN 0098-1222) 534
Insegnamento della Matematica e delle Scienze Integrate. (IT) 3038, 1751
Insel-Almanach. (GW ISSN 0443-2460) 2925
Inseminacao Artificial. (BL) 218
Inside see Focus 1706
Inside. (GW) 2560
Inside (Helena, MT). (US) 4063, 2489
Inside (Philadelphia). (US ISSN 0199-7602) 2006
Inside A H S C A. (US) 3591, 355
Inside Advertising and Media see Adbrief 26
Inside Al-Anon. (US ISSN 1054-1438) 1536
Inside Alabama Politics. (US ISSN 0884-030X) 4063, 3899
Inside Arkansas see Arkansas Journal 1072
Inside Bahrain. (BA) 2173
Inside Bluegrass. (US) 3556
†Inside Books. (US) 5213
Inside Canberra. (AT ISSN 0046-9629) 3899
Inside Chess. (US ISSN 0896-8195) 4475
Inside Chicago. (US) 2227
Inside China Mainland. (CH ISSN 0250-961X) 3960, 2182
†Inside Cycling. (US) 5213
Inside D.O.E. (Department of Energy) see Inside Energy With Federal Lands 1791
▼Inside D O S. (US ISSN 1049-5320) 1477
Inside D P M A. (Data Processing Management Association) (US) 1452
Inside Defense Electronics. (US) 3460, 1899
Inside Detective. (US ISSN 0020-1847) 2985
Inside Dining. (AT) 2073, 2476
†Inside Drug Law. (US ISSN 0747-6213) 5214
Inside E P A see Inside E P A Weekly Report 1958
Inside E P A Weekly Report. (US) 1958
Inside Energy With Federal Lands. (US ISSN 0278-2227) 1791
Inside F.E.R.C. (US ISSN 0163-948X) 1791
Inside F E R C's Gas Market Report. (US) 3689
Inside F M S. (US) 1414, 3025
Inside Freelance. (US) 1422
†Inside Green. (CN) 5214
Inside Guide. (CN ISSN 1188-6803) 784
Inside Hockey. (CN) 4475
▼Inside Hollywood. (US) 3512
Inside Housing. (UK ISSN 0950-3358) 2489
Inside HyperCard. (US) 1469, 1477
▼Inside I V H S. (US ISSN 1054-2647) 4719
Inside Impact. (US) 32
Inside Indonesia. (AT ISSN 0814-1185) 3960, 931
Inside Information. (UK) 2763, 1456
Inside International. (US) 4535
Inside Issues. (US) 4151, 2476
†Inside Joke. (US) 5214
Inside Karate. (US) 4475
Inside Kenya Today. (KE ISSN 0020-1863) 2208
Inside Kung Fu. (US ISSN 0199-8501) 4475
Inside Kung Fu Presents Tae Kwon Do. (US) 4475

Inside Litigation. (US ISSN 0890-7315) **2635**
Inside M S. (US) **3338**, 4438
Inside Market Data. (US ISSN 1047-2908) **805**, 1469
Inside Media. (US) **32**, 4130
Inside Michigan Politics. (US ISSN 1052-8857) **4064**, 671, 3899
▼Inside Microsoft BASIC. (US ISSN 1047-6067) **1430**, 1477
▼Inside Microsoft C. (US ISSN 1047-6075) **1477**
Inside Microsoft Windows. (US) **1477**, 1469
Inside Microsoft Works. (US ISSN 1046-9648) **1469**
Inside Mortgage Finance. (US) **949**
Inside Music. (US) **3556**, 4182
Inside N R C. (US ISSN 0194-0252) **1805**
Inside Negotiations. (US) **983**
†Inside Out. (UK) **5214**
Inside - Outside. (II ISSN 0970-1761) **2552**
Inside P R. (US) **32**
Inside Print see Inside Media **32**
Inside Product News see Law Enforcement Product News **1518**
Inside Quattro Pro. (US ISSN 1053-1467) **1477**
Inside QuickBasic. (US ISSN 1055-0577) **1477**, 1469
Inside R & D. (US ISSN 0300-757X) **4601**
Inside Radio. (US) **1356**, 1013
Inside Retailing. (AT) **1078**
Inside San Francisco State University. (US) **1314**, 2869
▼Inside Self-Storage. (US) **1115**
Inside Sports. (US ISSN 0195-3478) **4475**
Inside Tennis. (US) **4506**
Inside Texas Running. (US) **4549**
Inside Textiles. (US ISSN 0733-8244) **4620**
Inside the Administration see Inside the White House **4064**
Inside the Army. (US) **3460**
Inside the Black Hills. (US) **4634**
Inside the Navy. (US) **3460**
Inside the Pentagon. (US) **3460**
Inside the White House. (US) **4064**
Inside Tracks. (CN) **3556**
Inside Travel News. (US) **4772**
Inside Tucson Business. (US) **671**
Inside Turbo C see Inside Turbo C Plus Plus **1477**
Inside Turbo C Plus Plus. (US) **1477**
Inside Turbo Pascal. (US ISSN 1045-6775) **1477**
Inside U S A Volleyball. (US ISSN 1059-8227) **4506**
Inside U S Trade. (US) **912**
Inside VisualBasic. (US) **1477**, 1469
Inside Waste. (US) **1985**
Inside WaU. (US) **2763**
Inside Word. (US ISSN 0893-9349) **1469**
▼Inside Word for Windows. (US ISSN 1049-0795) **1482**, 1477
▼Inside WordPerfect. (US ISSN 1046-9656) **1482**, 1477
Inside Wrestling. (US) **4475**
†Inside 1 2 3 - G. (US) **5214**
Inside 1-2-3 Release 3. (US ISSN 1052-2662) **1469**, 1477
Insider see Scottish Business Insider **799**
Insiders. (US ISSN 0730-2908) **949**
Insiders Baseball Fact-Book. (US ISSN 0731-8162) **4506**
†Insiders Baseball Fact-Book Extra. (US ISSN 0731-8146) **5214**
†Insider's Box Office Report Annual. (US) **5214**
Insiders' Chronicle. (US ISSN 0162-5152) **949**
Insider's Letter. (US) **1690**
Insider's Report. (US) **2584**, 1639
Insiders Ski Letter. (US) **4549**
Insiders Sportsletter. (US) **4475**, 1374
Insieme. (CN) **2006**
Insieme (Rome). (IT ISSN 0020-1871) **1505**
Insieme nella Valle see Insieme nella Valle e Accademia Internationale Arte Lettere Scienze Dafni **2925**

Insieme nella Valle e Accademia Internationale Arte Lettere Scienze Dafni. (IT) **2925**, 1273, 2995
Insight see Franklin's Insight **947**
Insight. (NR ISSN 0020-1936) **2212**
Insight see Wisconsin **2238**
Insight. (US) **3279**
†Insight. (AT ISSN 0811-4188) **5214**
Insight (Akron). (US) **2763**
Insight (Atlanta). (US) **3392**, 3109
Insight (Chatsworth). (US ISSN 0884-4925) **2635**, 2533
Insight (Fresno). (US) **1314**
Insight (Hagerstown). (US ISSN 0020-1944) **4240**, 1256
Insight (Hubbard). (US) **1639**
†Insight (London, 1978). (UK ISSN 0144-8871) **5214**
Insight (London, 1984). (UK) **1066**
Insight (New York, 1978). (US) **2293**
Insight (Regina) see Third Degree (Regina) **1326**
Insight (Schaumburg) see National Society to Prevent Blindness. Member News **2295**
Insight (Toronto). (CN) **2293**, 4182
Insight (Wallington) see Community Care **4402**
Insight (Washington). (US ISSN 1051-4880) **2227**
Insight and Opinion see Insight Publication **2192**
Insight Magazine. (NR ISSN 0794-7968) **3595**
Insight on Collectables. (CN ISSN 0833-4447) **330**, 2281
Insight Publication. (GH) **2192**
†Insight: Soviet Jews. (UK ISSN 0307-353X) **5214**
Insights. (CN ISSN 0073-8123) **1639**
InSights (Herndon). (US ISSN 0747-007X) **4475**
Insights (Morristown). (US) **3669**
Insights (Washington, 1977). (US) **4408**
Insights (Washington, 1988). (US) **2763**
Insights for Preachers. (US) **4182**
Insights into Open Education. (US) **1751**
Insights into Preaching see Insights for Preachers **4182**
Insinooriuutiset see Tekniikka & Talous **4612**
Insite. (CN ISSN 0020-2029) **1639**
Insite (Year). (US) **2073**
Insolvency Bulletin. (CN) **671**, 950
Insolvency Intelligence. (UK ISSN 0950-2645) **2635**
Insolvency Law & Practice. (UK ISSN 0267-0771) **2635**
Insound. (CN) **2293**, 4182
InSpain. (SP) **4772**
INSPEC. Section A see Physics Abstracts **3838**
INSPEC Matters. (UK ISSN 0266-1616) **4359**, 1899
INSPEC, Section B. see Electrical & Electronics Abstracts **1843**
INSPEC, Section C. see Computer & Control Abstracts **1403**
INSPEC Thesaurus. (UK) **4359**, 1899
Inspected Bed & Breakfast in Britain. (UK) **4772**, 4693
Inspector General Brief. (US) **3460**
Inspel. (GW ISSN 0019-0217) **2763**
Inst-Ed-News see Institute of Education News **1639**
Instalaciones Deportivas. (SP ISSN 0212-8519) **620**
Installateur. (FR ISSN 0020-207X) **2300**
L'Installateur. (SZ) **2300**
Installateur. (SZ) **2300**
Installateur Sanitaire see L'Installateur **2300**
Installatie. (NE ISSN 0020-2096) **2300**
Installatie Journaal. (NE) **1899**
Installatietechniek see Intech **2300**
Installation & Cleaning Specialist. (US ISSN 0192-1657) **2560**
Installation News. (US ISSN 0887-2287) **1337**, 1899, 4693
Installations Nyt. (DK ISSN 0105-9629) **1899**
Installations Nyts Leverandoerregister. (DK) **1899**

L'Installatore Italiano. (IT ISSN 0020-2118) **2300**, 4601
Instalment Credit Report. (US ISSN 1041-6390) **785**
Instandhaltung. (GW ISSN 0170-6993) **3018**
Instant. (GW ISSN 0174-6944) **3792**
Instant & Small Commercial Printer. (US) **4002**
Instant Record. (UK ISSN 0260-9363) **3792**
Instant Replay. (US) **1385**
†Instantanes Criminologiques. (FR ISSN 0020-2134) **5214**
Instantanes Medicaux. (FR ISSN 0020-2142) **3109**
Instauration. (US ISSN 0277-2302) **3983**
Instead. (AT ISSN 0313-3249) **1728**, 1709
Instead of a Magazine. (US) **2869**
Institucion Fernan-Gonzalez. Boletin. (SP ISSN 0211-8998) **2314**, 330, 3769, 4375
Institucion Principe de Viana. Coleccion Historia. (SP) **2368**
Instituciones Europeas. (SP) **3899**
Institut Africain pour le Developpement Economique et Social Documentation see I N A D E S Documentation **402**
†Institut Agricola Catala de Sant Isidre. Butlleti. (SP) **5214**
Institut Agricola Catala de Sant Isidre. Calendari del Pages. (SP) **98**
Institut Appert. Bulletin Analytique Cie. (FR ISSN 0243-5314) **15**
Institut Archeologique du Luxembourg. Annales. (BE) **274**
Institut Archeologique du Luxembourg. Bulletins. (BE ISSN 0020-2177) **274**, 330, 2055, 2314
Institut Archeologique Liegeois. Bulletin. (BE) **274**
Institut Botanic de Barcelona. Treballs. (SP ISSN 0210-8062) **506**
Institut Canadien d'Education des Adultes Bulletin de Liaison see I C E A Bulletin de Liaison **1684**
Institut Canadien d'Education des Adultes Cahiers see I.C.E.A. Cahiers **5208**
Institut Canadien de l'Information Scientifique et Technique. Rapport Annuel. see Canada Institute for Scientific and Technical Information. Annual Report **4303**
Institut Canadien de Recherches sur les Femmes. Bulletin. see Canadian Research Institute for the Advancement of Women. Newsletter **4838**
Institut Catholique d'Arts et Metiers de Lille Annuaire see I C A M Annuaire **1823**
Institut Catholique de Paris. Annuaire. (FR) **4266**
Institut Catholique de Paris. Nouvelles see Institut Catholique de Paris. Revue **2187**
Institut Catholique de Paris. Revue. (FR) **2187**, 2925, 4182
Institut Collegial Europeen. Actes des Colloques de Loches. (FR) **1639**
Institut d'Amenagement et d'Urbanisme de la Region d'Ile de France. Cahiers.(FR ISSN 0153-6184) **2489**
Institut d'Economie Regionale Bourgogne-Franche-Comte. Cahiers. (FR ISSN 0153-4459) **869**
Institut d'Elevage et de Medecine Veterinaire des Pays Tropicaux. Rapport d'Activite. (FR ISSN 0246-2303) **4810**
Institut d'Emission d'Outre Mer, Paris. Rapport d'Activite. (FR ISSN 0073-8247) **931**
Institut d'Ethnologie. Archives et Documents, Micro Edition. Sciences Humaines. (FR ISSN 0248-3912) **242**
Institut d'Ethnologie. Archives et Documents, Micro Edition. Sciences Naturelles. (FR ISSN 0248-3807) **441**
Institut d'Etudes du Developpement. Cahiers. (SZ) **931**
Institut d'Etudes Slaves Informations. (FR ISSN 0980-3637) **2508**

Institut d'Etudes Slaves, Paris. Bibliotheque Russe. (FR ISSN 0078-9976) **2925**
Institut d'Etudes Slaves, Paris. Collection de Grammaires. (FR ISSN 0078-9984) **2818**
Institut d'Etudes Slaves, Paris. Collection de Manuels. (FR ISSN 0078-9992) **2818**
Institut d'Etudes Slaves, Paris. Collection Historique. (FR ISSN 0079-0001) **2368**
Institut d'Etudes Slaves, Paris. Documents Pedagogiques. (FR ISSN 0300-2594) **2818**
Institut d'Etudes Slaves, Paris. Lexiques.(FR ISSN 0154-0157) **2818**
Institut d'Etudes Slaves, Paris. Textes. (FR ISSN 0079-001X) **2925**
Institut d'Etudes Slaves, Paris. Travaux. (FR ISSN 0079-0028) **2925**, 2368, 2818
Institut de Formation et d'Etudes Psycho-Sociologiques et Pedagogiques Informations see I F E P P Informations **4023**
Institut de Formation et de Recherche Demographiques. Annales. (CM) **3983**
Institut de l'Information Scientifique et Technique Info see I N I S T - Info **4313**
Institut de la Communaute Europeenne pour les Etudes Universitaires. Recherche see Recherches Universitaires sur l'Integration Europeenne **1715**
Institut de Linguistique de Louvain. Bibliotheque des C I L L. (BE) **2818**
Institut de Linguistique de Louvain. Cahiers. (BE ISSN 0771-6524) **2818**
Institut de Linguistique de Lund. Travaux. (SW) **2818**
Institut de Readaptation de Montreal. Bulletin. (CN) **3109**, 4408
Institut de Recherche du Cafe, du Cacao et Autres Plantes Stimulantes. Rapport d'Activite. (FR ISSN 0762-1418) **98**
Institut de Recherche du Cafe et du Cacao. Rapport d'Activite see Institut de Recherche du Cafe, du Cacao et Autres Plantes Stimulantes. Rapport d'Activite **98**
Institut de Recherche et d'Histoire des Textes, Paris. Documents, Etudes et Repertoires. (FR ISSN 0073-8212) **2925**
Institut de Recherches Juridiques, Politiques et Sociales de Strasbourg. Faculte de Droit et de Science Politique. Annales. (FR) **2635**
Institut de Recherches Marxistes see Pensee (Paris) **3914**
Institut de Science Financiere et d'Assurances. Bulletin des Actuaires Diplomes. (FR ISSN 0007-4438) **2533**
Institut de Speologie Emil Racovitza. Travaux. (RM ISSN 0065-0498) **1590**
Institut der Deutschen Wirtschaft. Forum. (GW) **1013**, 869, 895
Institut der Deutschen Wirtschaft. Gewerkschaftsreport. (GW ISSN 0084-9782) **2584**
Institut der Deutschen Wirtschaft. Vortragsreihe see Institut der Deutschen Wirtschaft. Forum **1013**
†Institut des Actuaires Francais. Bulletin Trimestriel. (FR ISSN 0020-2223) **5214**
Institut des Belles Lettres Arabes see I B L A **3638**
†Institut des Etudes Occitanes. Publications. (FR ISSN 0073-8263) **5214**
Institut des Hautes Etudes de l'Amerique Latine. Collection des Travaux et Memoires. (FR ISSN 0993-5878) **2410**, 3899, 4375
Institut des Hautes Etudes Scientifiques, Paris. Publications Mathematiques. (FR ISSN 0073-8301) **3038**
Institut des Recherches Marxistes. Issues. (FR) **671**, 3899

INSTITUT NATIONAL 6291

Institut des Recherches Marxistes. Recherches Internationales. (FR ISSN 0294-3069) **3960,** 3899
Institut des Sciences Agronomiques du Rwanda. Departement des Productions Animales. Compte Rendu des Travaux. (RW) **218**
Institut des Sciences Agronomiques du Rwanda. Departement des Productions Vegetales. Compte Rendu des Travaux. (RW) **98**
Institut des Sciences Nucleaires Grenoble. Rapport d'Activite. (FR) **1805**
Institut Dominicain d'Etudes Orientales du Caire. Melanges. (BE ISSN 0575-1330) **2429,** 3638
Institut du Moyen-Age Grec et Latin. Cahier *see* Universite de Copenhague. Institut du Moyen-Age Grec et Latin. Cahiers **2393**
Institut Europeen de Formation des Techniciens des Circuits Imprimes. Informations. (SZ ISSN 0153-9930) **1773**
Institut "Finanzen und Steuern." Gruene Briefe. (GW ISSN 0067-9941) **785,** 1097
Institut "Finanzen und Steuern." Schriftenreihe. (GW ISSN 0067-995X) **785,** 1097
Institut Fondamental d'Afrique Noire. Catalogues et Documents. (SG ISSN 0070-2617) **2333**
Institut Fondamental d'Afrique Noire. Initiations et Etudes Africaines. (SG ISSN 0070-2625) **2333**
†Institut Fondamental d'Afrique Noire. Memoires. (SG ISSN 0070-2633) **5214**
Institut Fondamental d'Afrique Noire Bulletin. Serie A: Sciences Naturelles *see* I F A N Bulletin. Serie A: Sciences Naturelles **4313**
Institut Fondamental d'Afrique Noire Bulletin. Serie B: Sciences Humaines *see* I F A N Bulletin. Serie B: Sciences Humaines **2508**
†Institut for Afsaetningsoekonomi. Nyt. (DK ISSN 0108-1489) **5214**
Institut for Finansiering og Kreditvaesen. Kompendium. (DK) **785**
Institut for Graenseregionsforskning. Arbejdspapir. (DK ISSN 0106-8628) **869**
Institut Forestier National de Petawawa. Revue de Programme *see* Canada. Petawawa National Forestry Institute. Program Review **2097**
Institut Francais d'Archeologie Orientale du Caire. Bulletin. (UA ISSN 0255-0962) **274**
Institut Francais d'Etudes Andines. Bulletin/Instituto Frances de Estudios Andinos. Boletin. (PE ISSN 0303-7495) **4375**
Institut Francais d'Etudes Andines. Travaux. (PE) **242,** 1568, 2410
Institut Francais d'Indologie. Publications *see* Institut Francais de Pondichery. Departement d'Indologie. Publications **3638**
Institut Francais de Pondichery. Departement d'Indologie. Publications. (II ISSN 0073-8352) **3638**
▼Institut Francais de Pondichery. Departement de Sciences Sociales. Publications. (II) **4375**
Institut Francais de Pondichery. Publications du Departement d'Ecologie. (II) **4315**
Institut Francais de Pondichery. Section Scientifique et Technique. Travaux. *see* Institut Francais de Pondichery. Publications du Departement d'Ecologie **4315**
Institut Francais de Pondichery. Section Scientifique et Technique. Travaux. Hors Serie *see* Institut Francais de Pondichery. Publications du Departement d'Ecologie **4315**
Institut Francais de Recherche pour l'Exploitation de la Mer (IFREMER) France. IFREMER. Centre de Brest. Colloques. Actes *see* France. IFREMER. Centre de Brest. Colloques. Actes **1604**
Institut Francais de Recherche pour l'Exploitation de la Mer (IFREMER) France. IFREMER. Centre de Brest. Publications. Serie: Rapports Economiques et Juridiques *see* France. IFREMER. Centre de Brest. Publications. Serie: Rapports Economiques et Juridiques **1604**
Institut Francais des Sciences Administratives. (Publications). (FR) **1013**
Institut Francais du Petrole. Collection Colloques et Seminaires. (FR ISSN 0073-8360) **3689**
Institut Francais du Petrole. Rapport Annuel. (FR ISSN 0073-8379) **3689**
Institut Francais du Petrole. Revue. (FR) **3689**
Institut fuer Allgemeine Botanik und Botanischer Garten. Mitteilungen. (GW ISSN 0344-5615) **506**
Institut fuer Angewandte Geodaesie. Mitteilungen. (GW ISSN 0071-9196) **2253**
Institut fuer Asienkunde. Schriften. (GW ISSN 0073-8387) **3638**
Institut fuer Auslandsbeziehungen. Mitteilungen *see* Zeitschrift fuer Kulturaustausch **3978**
Institut fuer Bautechnik. Mitteilungen. (GW ISSN 0172-3006) **621,** 301
Institut fuer den Wissenschaftlichen Film. Publikationen zu Wissenschaftlichen Filmen. Sektion Biologie. (GW ISSN 0073-8417) **3512,** 441
Institut fuer den Wissenschaftlichen Film. Publikationen zu Wissenschaftlichen Filmen. Sektion Voelkerkunde *see* Publikationen zu Wissenschaftlichen Filmen. Sektion Ethnologie **3516**
Institut fuer die Paedagogik der Naturwissenschaften Blaetter *see* I P N - Blaetter **4313**
Institut fuer Europaeische Geschichte, Mainz. Veroeffentlichungen. Abteilung Universalgeschichte. Beihefte. (GW ISSN 0170-365X) **2314**
Institut fuer Europaeische Geschichte, Mainz. Veroeffentlichungen. Abteilung Universalgeschichte und Abteilung fuer Abendlaendische Religionsgeschichte. (GW) **4182,** 2314
Institut fuer Europaeische Geschichte, Mainz. Veroeffentlichungen. Abteilung Universitaetsgeschichte und Abteilung fuer Abendlaendische Religionsphilosophie *see* Institut fuer Europaeische Geschichte, Mainz. Veroeffentlichungen. Abteilung Universalgeschichte und Abteilung fuer Abendlaendische Religionsgeschichte **4182**
Institut fuer Europaeische Geschichte, Mainz. Vortraege. Abteilung Universalgeschichte und Abteilung fuer Abendlaendische Religionsgeschichte. (GW) **4182**
Institut fuer Europaeische Geschichte, Mainz. Vortraege. Abteilung Universalgeschichte und Abteilung fuer Abendlaendische Religionsphilosophie *see* Institut fuer Europaeische Geschichte, Mainz. Vortraege. Abteilung Universalgeschichte und Abteilung fuer Abendlaendische Religionsgeschichte **4182**
Institut fuer Finanzwissenschaft und Steuerrecht. Gelbe Briefe. (AU) **1097,** 785
Institut fuer Finanzwissenschaft und Steuerrecht. Mitteilungsblatt. (AU) **1098,** 785
Institut fuer Gegenwartsvolkskunde. Mitteilungen. (AU) **2055**
†Institut fuer Gesellschaftspolitik. Mitteilungen. (AU ISSN 0046-9696) **5214**
Institut fuer Gewerbliche Wasserwirtschaft und Luftreinhaltung e.V. Umweltbrief *see* I W L - Umweltbrief **1489**
†Institut fuer Iberoamerika-Kunde. Schriftenreihe. (GW ISSN 0073-8948) **5214**
Institut fuer Internationale Politik und Wirtschaft der D.D.R. Forschungshefte *see* I P W Forschungshefte **5210**
Institut fuer Internationales Recht und Internationale Beziehungen. Schriftenreihe. (SZ) **2724**
Institut fuer Landeskunde. Rundbrief *see* Informationen zur Raumentwicklung **2489**
Institut fuer Landwirtschaftliche Bauforschung Information *see* I L B Information **96**
Institut fuer Leichtbau und Oekonomische Verwendung von Werkstoffen Mitteilungen *see* I F L - Mitteilungen **5209**
Institut fuer Oesterreichische Geschichtsforschung. Mitteilungen. (AU ISSN 0073-8484) **2368**
Institut fuer Ostrecht. Studien. (GW ISSN 0073-8492) **2635**
Institut fuer Politologische Zeitfragen Information. Reihe S: Subversion *see* I P Z Information. Reihe S: Subversion **3898**
Institut fuer Raumordnung. Informationen *see* Informationen zur Raumentwicklung **2489**
Institut fuer Reaktorsicherheit der Technischen Ueberwachungs-Vereine. Taetigkeitsbericht *see* Gesellschaft fuer Reaktorsicherheit. Jahresbericht **1822**
Institut fuer Stadtbauwesen. Veroeffentlichungen. (GW ISSN 0341-5805) **4719,** 1958
Institut fuer Textiltechnik der Rheinisch-Westfaelischen Technischen Hochschule Aachen. Mitteilungen. (GW) **4620**
Institut fuer Theoretische Chemie. Universitaet Stuttgart. Arbeitsbericht. (GW) **1179**
Institut fuer Wasserwirtschaft, Hydrologie und Landwirtschaftlichen Wasserbau. Mitteilungen. (GW ISSN 0343-8090) **4825,** 1598
Institut fuer Wirtschafts- und Sozialgeography Discussion Papers *see* W S G Discussion Papers **2266**
Institut fuer Wissenschaft und Kunst. Mitteilungen. (AU ISSN 0020-2320) **1709**
Institut Geographique du Congo. Rapport *see* Institut Geographique du Zaire. Rapport Annuel **2253**
Institut Geographique du Zaire. Rapport Annuel. (ZR ISSN 0443-3173) **2253**
Institut Geographique National. Bulletin d'Information. (FR ISSN 0427-2218) **2268**
Institut Henri Poincare. Annales: Analyse Non Lineaire. (FR ISSN 0294-1449) **3038,** 3820
Institut Henri Poincare. Annales. Probabilites et Statistiques. (FR ISSN 0246-0203) **3038**
Institut Henri Poincare. Annales. Section A: Physique Theorique. (FR ISSN 0020-2339) **3820,** 3038
Institut Henri Poincare. Annals. Section A: Theoretical Physics *see* Institut Henri Poincare. Annales. Section A: Physique Theorique **3820**
Institut Henri Poincare. Groupe d'Etude d'Analyse Ultrametrique. Exposes. (FR) **3038**
Institut Historique Belge de Rome. Bibliotheque. (BE ISSN 0073-8522) **2368**
Institut Historique Belge de Rome. Bulletin. (BE ISSN 0073-8530) **2368**
Institut Historique et Archeologique Neerlandais de Stamboul. Publications. (NE ISSN 0073-8549) **2429**
Institut International d'Administration Publique. Annee Administrative *see* Institut International d'Administration Publique. Dossiers et Debats **4064**
Institut International d'Administration Publique. Dossiers et Debats. (FR) **4064**
Institut International d'Etudes Sociales. Serie des Conferences Publiques *see* International Institute for Labour Studies. Public Lecture Series **5217**
Institut International du Froid. Bulletin/ International Institute of Refrigeration. Bulletin. (FR ISSN 0020-6970) **2300**
Institut International du Froid. Comptes Rendus de Reunions de Commissions/International Institute of Refrigeration. Proceedings of Commision Meetings. (FR ISSN 0074-6541) **2300**
Institut International J. Maritain. Notes et Documents. (IT ISSN 0393-6503) **3899,** 3769
Institut Jules Destree. Collection: Connaitre la Wallonie *see* Connaitre la Wallonie **2357**
Institut Jules Destree. Collection: Etudes et Documents *see* Institut Jules Destree. Etudes et Documents **2368**
Institut Jules Destree. Collection: Figures de Wallonie *see* Figures de Wallonie **2361**
Institut Jules Destree. Etudes et Documents. (BE ISSN 0073-8557) **2368**
†Institut Mediterraneen des Transports Maritimes. (FR) **5214**
Institut Michel Pacha. Annales. (FR ISSN 0073-8565) **572**
Institut National de la Consommation Hebdo Consommateurs Actualites *see* I N C Hebdo Consommateurs Actualites **1505**
Institut National de la Recherche Agronomique de Tunisie. Annales. (TI ISSN 0365-4761) **98**
Institut National de la Recherche Agronomique de Tunisie. Documents Techniques. (TI ISSN 0020-238X) **98**
Institut National de la Statistique et des Etudes Economiques. Service Departemental de la Guyane. Bulletin Trimestriel de Statistiques. (FG ISSN 0751-7599) **722**
Institut National de la Statistique et des Etudes Economiques Cadrage et I N S E E Resultats Consommations et Modes de Vie *see* I N S E E. Cadrage et I N S E E Resultats Consommations et Modes de Vie **721**
Institut National de la Statistique et des Etudes Economiques Cadrage et I N S E E Resultats Demographie et Societe *see* I N S E E. Cadrage et I N S E E Resultats Demographie et Societe **721**
Institut National de la Statistique et des Etudes Economiques Cadrage *see* I N S E E. Cadrage **720**
Institut National de la Statistique et des Etudes Economiques Note de Conjoncture de l'I N S E E *see* Note de Conjoncture de l'I N S E E **682**
Institut National de Preparation Professionnelle. Cahier. (ZR) **983**
Institut National de Recherche en Informatique et en Automatique. Collection Didactique. (FR) **1452**
Institut National de Recherche en Informatique et en Automatique. Rapports de Recherche. (FR ISSN 0249-6399) **1396**
Institut National de Recherche en Informatique et en Automatique Inriatheque *see* Inriatheque **1452**
Institut National de Recherche et de Securite pour la Prevention des Accidents du Travail et des Maladies Professionnelles Bulletin de Documentation *see* I N R S Bulletin de Documentation **3617**
†Institut National de Recherche Scientifique. Rapport pour l'Annee. (RW) **5214**
Institut National des Appellations d'Origine. Bulletin. (FR) **382**
Institut National des Appellations d'Origine des Vins et Eaux-de-Vie. Bulletin *see* Institut National des Appellations d'Origine. Bulletin **382**
Institut National des Langues et Civilisations Orientales. Bulletin des Etudes Africaines. (FR) **2818**

Title

INSTITUT NATIONAL

Institut National des Statistiques. Communique Hebdomadaire see Nationaal Instituut voor de Statistiek. Weekbericht **4580**

Institut National Genevois. Acts. (SZ) **2508**

Institut National pour l'Etude et la Recherche Agronomique. Rapport Annuel. (ZR) **98**

Institut Oceanographique. Annales. (FR ISSN 0078-9682) **1605**

Institut Oceanographique. Bulletin. (MC ISSN 0304-5722) **1605**

Institut Oceanographique. Memoires. (MC ISSN 0304-5714) **1605**

Institut of National History, Skopje. Review. see Institut za Nacionalna Istorija, Skopje. Glasnik **2368**

Institut Panafricain pour le Developpement. Annuaire des Anciens Etudiants see Institut Panafricain pour le Developpement. Travaux d'Etudiants. Bulletin Analytique **931**

Institut Panafricain pour le Developpement. Centre d'Etudes et de Recherches Appliquees. Evaluation du Seminaire sur la Methodologie du Management des Projets. (CM) **931**, 1013

Institut Panafricain pour le Developpement. Centre de Formation au Management des Projets. Bilan des Activites. (CM) **931**, 1013

Institut Panafricain pour le Developpement. Travaux d'Etudiants. Bulletin Analytique. (CM) **931**

Institut Panafricain pour le Developpement. Travaux Manuscrits. (CM) **152**, 931

Institut Panafricain pour le Developpement Cahier see I P D Cahier **931**

▼Institut Pasteur. Annales. Actualites. (FR ISSN 0924-4204) **552**, 477, 544

Institut Pasteur. Annales. Immunologie see Research in Immunology **3188**

Institut Pasteur. Annales. Microbiologie see Research in Microbiology **557**

Institut Pasteur. Annales. Virologie see Research in Virology **3223**

Institut Pasteur. Bulletin. (FR ISSN 0020-2452) **3220**, 552

Institut Pasteur d'Algerie. Archives. (AE ISSN 0020-2460) **3220**, 553

Institut Pasteur de Bangui. Rapport Annuel see Institut Pasteur de Bangui. Rapport Bisannuel **3109**

Institut Pasteur de Bangui. Rapport Bisannuel. (CX) **3109**

Institut Pasteur de Dakar. Rapport sur le Fonctionnement Technique. (SG) **553**

Institut Pasteur de Lyon. Revue. (FR ISSN 0020-2487) **553**, 3220

Institut Pasteur de Madagascar. Archives. (MG ISSN 0020-2495) **553**, 3220

Institut Pasteur de Tunis. Archives. (TI ISSN 0020-2509) **3220**, 441

Institut Pasteur Hellenique. Archives. (GR ISSN 0004-6620) **3220**, 553

Institut Phytopathologique Benaki. Annales. (GR ISSN 0365-5814) **98**, 180

Institut po Istoriia na B K P. Izvestiia. (BU ISSN 0324-0282) **2368**, 3899

Institut pour la Recherche Scientifique en Afrique Centrale Chronique de l'I R S A C see Chronique de l'I R S A C **4305**

Institut Provincial d'Etudes et Recherches Bibliotheconomiques. Memoires. (BE) **403**, 2763, 2925

Institut Quimic de Sarria see I.Q.S **1178**

Institut Regional pour les Constructions Scolaires en Afrique. Lettre. see Regional Educational Building Institute for Africa. Letter **1658**

Institut Royal Belge du Petrole. Annales/Koninklijk Belgisch Petroleum Instituut. Annalen. (BE ISSN 0020-2185) **3689**

Institut Royal des Sciences Naturelles de Belgique. Bulletin. Serie Biologie. (BE ISSN 0374-6429) **441**, 1958

Institut Royal de Sciences Naturelles de Belgique. Bulletin. Serie Entomologie. (BE ISSN 0374-6232) **534**

Institut Royal des Sciences Naturelles de Belgique. Bulletin. Serie Sciences de la Terre. (BE ISSN 0374-6291) **1568**

Institut Royal des Sciences Naturelles de Belgique. Documents de Travail. see Koninklijk Belgisch Instituut voor Natuurwetenschappen. Studiedocumenten **445**

Institut Royal du Patrimoine Artistique. Bulletin/Koninklijk Instituut voor het Kunstpatrimonium. Bulletin. (BE ISSN 0085-1892) **330**

Institut Technique de l'Aviculture. Tendances des Marches. (FR ISSN 0398-8287) **152**, 218

Institut Technique du Batiment et des Travaux Publics. Annales. (FR ISSN 0020-2568) **621**

Institut Teknologi Mara. Laporan Tahunan. see Mara Institute of Technology. Annual Report **1711**

Institut Teoreticheskoi Astronomii. Byulleten' (RU ISSN 0002-3302) **365**

Institut Vodnogo Transporta, Leningrad. Gidrotekhnicheskaya Laboratoriya. Materialy. (RU) **1924**

Institut za Arhitekturu i Urbanizam Srbije. Zbornik Radova. (YU) **301**, 2489

Institut za Istrazivanje i Razvoj Obrazovanja. Bibliograija see Republicki Zavod za Unaprejivanje Vaspitanja i Obrazovanja. Bibliografija **1679**

Institut za Javno Upravo. Vestnik. (CI ISSN 0350-0365) **2635**, 4064

Institut za Kriminoloska i Socioloska Istrazivanja. Zbornik. (YU ISSN 0350-2694) **1515**, 4438

Institut za Marksisticne Studije. Vestnik see Slovenska Akademija Znanosti in Umetnosti. Filozofski Vestnik **3781**

Institut za Medunarodnu Politiku i Privredu. Bilten Dokumentacije. (YU) **3937**, 722

Institut za Nacionalna Istorija, Skopje. Glasnik/Institut of National History, Skopje. Review. (XN ISSN 0583-4961) **2368**

Institut zur Erforschung der Europaeischen Arbeiterbewegung. Mitteilungsblatt. (GW ISSN 0173-2471) **2584**, 983, 2368, 3960

Instituta et Monumenta. Serie I: Monumenta. (IT ISSN 0073-8611) **3556**

Instituta et Monumenta. Serie II: Instituta. (IT ISSN 0392-629X) **3556**

The Institute (New York). (US) **1899**

Institute for Agricultural Research According to the Torah. Monthly Bulletin. (IS) **98**, 4223

Institute for American Universities. Newsletter. (FR) **1722**, 1315

Institute for Archaeo-Metallurgical Studies Newsletter see I A M S Newsletter **274**

Institute for Balkan Studies. Publications/Idryma Meleton Chersonesou Aimou. Ekdoseis. (GR ISSN 0073-862X) **2368**

Institute for Briquetting and Agglomeration. Proceedings. (US) **3485**

Institute for Canadian-American Relations (Papers) see Annual Canadian-American Seminar. Proceedings **5136**

Institute for Comparative Studies of Culture. Annals. (JA ISSN 0563-8186) **4375**

Institute for Comparative Studies of Culture. Publications see Institute for Comparative Studies of Culture. Annals **4375**

Institute for Consciousness and Music Newsletter see Crescendo (Garrett Park) **5174**

Institute for Contemporary Studies. Letter. (US) **4409**, 4438

Institute for Defence Studies and Analyses. Journal. (II ISSN 0020-2606) **1273**, 3460

Institute for Defence Studies and Analyses. Strategic Analyses. (II) **1273**, 3460

Institute for Defence Studies and Analyses. Strategic Digest. (II) **1273**, 3460

Institute for Development Anthropology Working Papers see I D A Working Papers **241**

Institute for Development of Educational Activities, Inc. Monographs see I D E A Monographs **5209**

Institute for Development of Educational Activities, Inc. Occasional Papers see I D E A Occasional Papers **5209**

Institute for East - West Security Studies. Annual Report. (US) **3960**

Institute for Economic & Financial Research. Economic Reports. (US) **671**, 785

Institute for Fermentation, Osaka. Research Communications/Hakko Kenkyujo Hokoku. (JA ISSN 0073-8751) **553**

Institute for Financial Management and Research Publications see I F M R Publications **1012**

Institute for Grassland and Animal Production, England (Berkshire) see A F R C Institute of Grassland and Environmental Research (UK). Annual Report **165**

Institute for Historical Review Newsletter see I H R Newsletter **2314**

Institute for Horticultural Plant Breeding. Annual Report. Research Projects. see Instituut voor de Veredeling van Tuinbouwgewassen. Jaarverslag. Projecten van Onderzoek **5215**

Institute for Management Education and Development. Report. (IO) **1013**

Institute for Migration, Turku. Migration Studies see Migration Institute. Migration Studies **3985**

Institute for Orgonomic Science. Annals.(US) **572**, 3339

†Institute for Palestine Studies. Arabic Annual Documentary Series. (LE) **5214**

†Institute for Palestine Studies. Arabs Under Israeli Occupation Series. (LE) **5214**

†Institute for Palestine Studies. I.P.S. Papers Series. (LE) **5214**

†Institute for Palestine Studies. International Annual Documentary Series. (LE ISSN 0073-8808) **5214**

Institute for Palestine Studies. Israeli Knesset Series. (LE) **2429**

Institute for Palestine Studies. Monograph Series. (LE ISSN 0073-8816) **2429**

Institute for Palestine Studies. Zionist Congress Series. (LE) **2429**

Institute for Perception Research Annual Progress Report see I P O Annual Progress Report **2817**

Institute for Petroleum Research and Geophysics, Holon, Israel. Report. (IS ISSN 0073-8832) **3689**, 1590

†Institute for Psychoanalysis. Newsletter. (US) **5214**

Institute for Research in Children's Literature. Bulletin. see Instituut vir Navorsing in Kinder- en Jeuglektuur. Bulletin **5215**

Institute for Research on Teaching Notes and News see I R T Notes and News **1751**

Institute for Rewriting Indian History. Annual Report and General Meeting Invitation see Rewriting Indian and World History **2341**

Institute for Scientific Co-operation with Developing Countries. Economics. (GW ISSN 0341-616X) **931**

Institute for Scientific Information Online News see I S I Online News **5210**

Institute for Sea Training. Journal. (JA ISSN 0386-1198) **4729**

Institute for Social and Economic Change Monograph see I S E C Monograph **868**

Institute for Social Research. Newsletter. (US ISSN 0020-2622) **4375**

Institute for Socioeconomic Studies. Journal. (US ISSN 0364-0779) **3899**

Institute for Studies in American Music. Monographs. (US) **3556**

Institute for Studies in American Music. Newsletter. (US ISSN 0145-8396) **3556**

Institute for Studies in Psychological Testing International Journal of Educational Sciences see I S P T International Journal of Educational Sciences **1638**

Institute for Studies in Psychological Testing Journal of Research in Educational & Psychological Measurement see I S P T Journal of Research in Educational & Psychological Measurement **1638**

Institute for Studies in Psychological Testing Quarterly Bulletin see I S P T Quarterly Bulletin **4024**

Institute for the Certification of Computer Professionals. Annual Report. (US ISSN 0098-2431) **1396**, 1424

Institute for the Comprehensive Study of Lotus Sutra. Journal/Hokke Bunka Kenkyu. (JA) **4214**

Institute for the Study of Drug Dependence Current Awareness Bulletin see I S D D Current Awareness Bulletin **1540**

Institute for the Study of Earth and Man Newsletter. (US) **274**, 1545

Institute for the Study of Human Issues Occasional Papers in Social Change see I S H I Occasional Papers in Social Change **4437**

Institute for the Study of Labor and Economic Crisis. Occasional Papers see Global Options Dateline **3896**

Institute for the Study of Man in Africa Occasional Papers see I S M A Occasional Papers **241**

Institute for the Study of Man in Africa Papers see I S M A Papers **241**

Institute for Theological Encounter with Science and Technology Bulletin see I T E S T Bulletin **4181**

Institute for Theological Encounter with Science and Technology Conference Proceedings see I T E S T Conference Proceedings **4181**

Institute Jean Vigo. Archives. (FR) **3512**

Institute News. (UK) **3729**, 1013

Institute of Actuaries. Journal. (UK ISSN 0020-2681) **2533**

†Institute of Actuaries Students' Society. Journal. (UK ISSN 0020-269X) **5214**

Institute of Administration and Commerce of South Africa. Journal. (SA) **1013**

Institute of Administrative Management. Journal. (UK ISSN 0951-5062) **1013**

Institute of Agricultural Engineering, Bet Dagan. Scientific Activities. (IS) **162**

Institute of Animal Technicians. Journal see Animal Technology **4806**

Institute of Applied Manpower Research Reports see I.A.M.R. Reports **981**

Institute of Art Education. Journal see Australian Art Education **318**

Institute of Asian Studies. Journal. (II ISSN 0970-2814) **4438**, 3638, 3769

Institute of Bankers in Ireland. Journal see Banking Ireland **766**

Institute of Bankers in Pakistan. Council. Report and Accounts. (PK ISSN 0073-8999) **785**

Institute of Bankers of Sri Lanka. Journal. (CE) **3628**, 785

Institute of Brewing. Journal (London). (UK ISSN 0046-9750) **382**, 98

Institute of British Carriage and Automobile Manufacturers Journal see I B C A M Journal **4692**

Institute of British Geographers. Transactions. (UK ISSN 0020-2754) **2253**

Institute of Burial and Cremation Administration. Journal. (UK ISSN 0020-2762) **2119**

Institute of Carpenters Journal. (UK) **640**

Institute of Certified Financial Planners. Journal see Journal of Financial Planning **952**

Institute of Certified Financial Planners Today see C F P Today **1004**

Institute of Certified Travel Agents Directory see I C T A Directory **4771**

Institute of Certified Travel Agents News see I C T A News **4771**

Institute of Chartered Accountants in Australia. Annual Report and Accounts. (AT) **751**

Institute of Chartered Accountants in England and Wales. Exposure Drafts and Financial Reporting Standards. (UK) **751**

Institute of Chartered Accountants in England and Wales. Exposure Drafts and Statements of Standard Accounting Practice see Institute of Chartered Accountants in England and Wales. Exposure Drafts and Financial Reporting Standards **751**

†Institute of Chartered Accountants in England and Wales. Management Information Series. (UK ISSN 0073-9030) **5214**

†Institute of Chartered Accountants in England and Wales. Quarterly Taxation Bulletin. (UK ISSN 0143-5205) **5214**

Institute of Chartered Accountants in England and Wales. Tax Digest. (UK ISSN 0260-6496) **1098**

Institute of Chartered Accountants in England and Wales. Technical Bulletin see Institute of Chartered Accountants in England and Wales. Update **751**

Institute of Chartered Accountants in England and Wales. Update. (UK) **751**

Institute of Chartered Accountants of Alberta. C A Monthly Statement. (CN) **751**

Institute of Chartered Accountants of Alberta. Monthly Statement see Institute of Chartered Accountants of Alberta. C A Monthly Statement **751**

Institute of Chartered Accountants of British Columbia. Communications. (CN) **751**, **1337**

Institute of Chartered Accountants of Scotland. Official Directory. (UK ISSN 0073-9057) **751**

Institute of Chartered Accountants of Sri Lanka. Journal. (CE) **751**

Institute of Chartered Financial Analysts. Seminar Proceedings see Association for Investment Management and Research. Seminar Proceedings **759**

Institute of Chartered Shipbrokers. Reference Book and List of Members (Year). (UK ISSN 0267-2006) **4729**

Institute of Clerk of Works of Great Britain Incorporated. Year Book. (UK ISSN 0073-9073) **621**

Institute of Commerce, London. Magazine see Business Education International **834**

Institute of Consulting Engineers. Journal. (II ISSN 0020-2800) **1825**

Institute of Contemporary Arts Monthly Bulletin see I C A Monthly Bulletin **328**

Institute of Cornish Studies. Cornish Studies. (UK) **2006**

Institute of Cornish Studies. Special Bibliography see Institute of Cornish Studies. Cornish Studies **2006**

Institute of Cost and Management Accountants. Framework Series in Accounting see Chartered Institute of Management Accountants. Framework Series In Accounting **749**

Institute of Cost and Management Accountants. Occasional Papers Series see Chartered Institute of Management Accountants. Occasional Papers Series **749**

Institute of Developing Economies. Annual Report. (JA) **931**

Institute of Developing Economies. Library Bulletin/Ajia Keizai Shiryo-Geppo. (JA ISSN 0020-2827) **2763**, **3899**

Institute of Developing Economies Occasional Papers Series see I D E Occasional Papers Series **669**

Institute of Developing Economies Symposium Proceedings see I.D.E. Symposium Proceedings **930**

Institute of Development Management. Report of the Activities of the Institute. (TZ) **1013**

Institute of Development Studies. Annual Report. (UK) **931**, **4438**

Institute of Development Studies. Commissioned Studies. (UK ISSN 0263-5402) **931**, **4438**

Institute of Development Studies. Development Bibliography Series. (UK ISSN 0955-0569) **722**

Institute of Development Studies Bulletin see I D S Bulletin **930**

Institute of Development Studies Discussion Paper see I D S Discussion Paper **930**

Institute of Development Studies Research Reports see I D S Research Reports **930**

Institute of Diving. Newsletter. (US) **4475**, **3525**

Institute of Early American History and Culture. News Letter. (US ISSN 0020-2843) **2410**

Institute of Economic Affairs. Occasional Papers. (UK ISSN 0073-909X) **671**

Institute of Economic Affairs. Research Monographs. (UK ISSN 0073-9103) **671**

Institute of Economic Geography, India. Journal. (II) **671**

Institute of Economic Growth, Delhi. Census Studies. (II ISSN 0070-3311) **3983**

Institute of Economic Research. Journal.(II ISSN 0020-2851) **671**

Institute of Economic Research. Publications on Demography. (II) **3983**

Institute of Economic Research. Publications on Economics. (II) **671**

Institute of Economic Research. Publications on Family Planning. (II) **597**

Institute of Ecosystem Studies Newsletter see I E S Newsletter **1957**

Institute of Education. Handbook. (AT) **1695**, **1709**

▼Institute of Education News. (AT) **1639**

Institute of Electrical and Electronics Engineers. Proceedings. (US ISSN 0018-9219) **1899**

Institute of Electrical and Electronics Engineers, Inc. Aerospace and Electronics System Conference. Record see I E E E - A E S C O N. Aerospace and Electronics System Conference. Record **1894**

Institute of Electrical and Electronics Engineers, Inc. Computer Society Conference on Computer Vision and Pattern Recognition. Proceedings see I E E E Computer Society Conference on Computer Vision and Pattern Recognition. Proceedings **1421**

Institute of Electrical and Electronics Engineers Orlando Section Monthly see I E E E. Orlando Section Monthly **1894**

Institute of Electrical Inspectors. I.E.I. Journal. (AT ISSN 0046-9807) **1899**

Institute of Electrolysis. List of Qualified Operators. Syllabus Prospectus. (UK) **373**

Institute of Electronics and Communication Engineering of Japan. Transactions see Institute of Electronics, Information and Communication Engineers. Transactions (Section A) **1773**

Institute of Electronics and Communication Engineers of Japan. Journal - Denshi Tsushin Gakkaishi see Institute of Electronics, Information and Communications Engineers. Journal **1774**

Institute of Electronics, Information and Communication Engineers. Transactions (Section A)/Denshi Joho Tsushin Gakkai Ronbunshi (A). (JA ISSN 0913-5707) **1773**, **1374**

Institute of Electronics Information and Communication Engineers. Transactions (Section B) see Institute of Electronics, Information and Communication Engineers. Transactions (Section B-I) **1773**

Institute of Electronics Information and Communication Engineers. Transactions (Section B) see Institute of Electronics, Information and Communication Engineers. Transactions (Section B-II) **1773**

Institute of Electronics, Information and Communication Engineers. Transactions (Section B-I)/Denshi Joho Tsushin Gakkai Ronbunshi (B-I) .(JA ISSN 0915-1877) **1773**, **1374**

Institute of Electronics, Information and Communication Engineers. Transactions (Section B-II)/Denshi Joho Tsushin Gakkai Ronbunshi (B-II) . (JA ISSN 0915-1885) **1773**, **1374**

Institute of Electronics Information and Communication Engineers. Transactions (Section C) see Institute of Electronics, Information and Communication Engineers. Transactions (Section C-I) **1773**

Institute of Electronics Information and Communication Engineers. Transactions (Section C) see Institute of Electronics, Information and Communication Engineers. Transactions (Section C-II) **1774**

Institute of Electronics, Information and Communication Engineers. Transactions (Section C-I)/Denshi Joho Tsushin Gakkai Ronbunshi (C-I) .(JA ISSN 0915-1893) **1773**, **1374**

Institute of Electronics, Information and Communication Engineers. Transactions (Section C-II)/Denshi Joho Tsushin Gakkai Ronbunshi (C-II) . (JA ISSN 0915-1907) **1774**, **1374**

Institute of Electronics, Information and Communication Engineers. Transactions (Section D) see Institute of Electronics, Information and Communication Engineers. Transactions (Section D-I) **1437**

Institute of Electronics, Information and Communication Engineers. Transactions (Section D) see Institute of Electronics, Information and Communication Engineers. Transactions (Section D-II) **1437**

Institute of Electronics, Information and Communication Engineers. Transactions (Section D-I)/Denshi Joho Tsushin Gakkai Ronbunshi (D-I) .(JA ISSN 0915-1915) **1437**, **1374**, **1899**

Institute of Electronics, Information and Communication Engineers. Transactions (Section D-II)/Denshi Joho Tsushin Gakkai Ronbunshi (D-II) . (JA ISSN 0915-1923) **1437**, **1374**, **1414**, **1899**

Institute of Electronics, Information and Communication Engineers Transactions on Communications Electronics Information and Systems see I E I C E Transactions on Communications Electronics Information and Systems **1773**

Institute of Electronics, Information and Communications Engineers. Journal/ Denshi Joho Tsushin Gakkaishi. (JA ISSN 0913-5693) **1774**, **1337**

Institute of Energy. Journal. (UK ISSN 0144-2600) **1791**, **3689**

Institute of Energy. Report and Accounts see Institute of Energy. Journal **1791**

Institute of Engineers & Technicians Journal. (UK) **1930**

Institute of Environmental Sciences. Annual Meeting. Proceedings. (US ISSN 0073-9227) **1958**, **441**, **1825**

Institute of Environmental Sciences. Journal. (US ISSN 1052-2883) **1958**, **1825**

Institute of Environmental Sciences. Tutorial Series. (US ISSN 0073-9251) **1958**, **441**, **1825**

Institute of European Studies - Institute of Asian Studies News from I E S - I A S see News from I E S - I A S **1723**

Institute of Ferrous Metallurgy. Transactions. see Instytut Metalurgii Zelaza. Prace **3409**

Institute of Field and Garden Crops. Scientific Activities. (IS) **180**

Institute of Finance Management. Prospectus. (TZ) **785**

†Institute of Food Research - Bristol Laboratory Biennial Report. (UK) **5214**

Institute of Forest Genetics, Suwon, Korea. Research Report. (KO ISSN 0073-9294) **2102**

Institute of Freight Forwarders. Yearbook see British International Freight Association. Yearbook **4708**

Institute of Freshwater Research, Drottningholm. Report see Nordic Journal of Freshwater Research **2046**

Institute of Gas Technology. Annual Report. (US) **3689**

Institute of Gas Technology. Director's Report see Institute of Gas Technology. Annual Report **3689**

Institute of Geological Sciences, London. Statistical Summary of the Mineral Industry see World Mineral Statistics **3502**

Institute of Geoscience. Annual Report. (JA) **1590**

Institute of Grocery Distribution. Economic Bulletin see Institute of Grocery Distribution. Economic Commentary. Bulletin **2092**

Institute of Grocery Distribution. Economic Commentary. Bulletin. (UK ISSN 0954-1683) **2092**

Institute of Grocery Distribution. Economics and Finance. Bulletin see Institute of Grocery Distribution. Economic Commentary. Bulletin **2092**

Institute of Guidance Counsellors. Journal. (IE ISSN 0332-3641) **3628**

Institute of Health Education. Journal. (UK ISSN 0307-3289) **3109**, **1736**, **3804**, **4104**

Institute of Health Sciences. Quarterly Medical News Bulletin. (MK) **3109**

Institute of Hospital Engineering. Journal see Health Estate Journal **2462**

Institute of Human Sciences. Review see Urban and Social Change Review **4423**

Institute of Indian Geographers. Transactions. (II ISSN 0970-9851) **2253**

†Institute of Industrial Engineers. Facilities Planning and Design Division. Monograph Series. (US) **5214**

Institute of Industrial Engineers. Fall Industrial Engineering Conference. Proceedings see Institute of Industrial Engineers. Industrial Engineering Conference. Proceedings **1926**

Institute of Industrial Engineers. Industrial Engineering Conference. Proceedings. (US) **1926**

†Institute of Industrial Engineers. Operations Research Division. Monograph Series. (US) **5214**

INSTITUTE

Institute of Industrial Engineers News: Aerospace *see* I E News: Aerospace **55**
Institute of Industrial Engineers News: Process Industries *see* I E News: Process Industries **5209**
Institute of Industrial Engineers News: Utilities *see* I E News: Utilities **1867**
Institute of Industrial Engineers Transactions *see* I I E Transactions **1925**
Institute of Internal Auditors, Inc. Today *see* I I A Today **751**
Institute of International Law and International Relations. Contributions to the Study of Comparative and International Law/Prinosi za Poredbeno Proucavanje Prava i Medunarodno Pravo. (CI ISSN 0351-2800) **2724**
Institute of Jewish Affairs Research Reports *see* I J A. Research Reports **2005**
Institute of Laboratory Animal Resources News *see* I L A R News **3259**
Institute of Local Government Studies Inlogov Informs *see* Inlogov Informs **4089**
Institute of Management and Administration Report on Defined Contribution Plan Investing *see* I O M A's Report on Defined Contribution Plan Investing **784**
Institute of Management Consultants. Yearbook. (UK ISSN 0260-373X) **1013**
Institute of Marine Engineers. Technical Reports *see* Marine Management Holdings. Transactions **4665**
Institute of Maritime and Tropical Medicine in Gdynia. Bulletin. *see* Instytut Medycyny Morskiej i Tropikalnej w Gdyni. Bulletin **3220**
Institute of Maternal and Child Health Newsletter *see* I M C H Newsletter **1238**
Institute of Mathematical Geography. Monograph Series. (US) **3038, 2253**
Institute of Mathematical Sciences, Madras. Reports. (II) **3038, 3820**
Institute of Mathematical Statistics. Bulletin. (US ISSN 0146-3942) **3038**
Institute of Mathematical Statistics Lecture Notes. Monograph Series *see* I M S Lecture Notes. Monograph Series **3037**
Institute of Mathematics and its Applications. Bulletin. (UK ISSN 0950-5628) **3038**
Institute of Mathematics and Its Applications. Proceedings. (UK) **3038**
Institute of Mathematics and its Applications Journal of Applied Mathematics *see* I M A Journal of Applied Mathematics **3037**
Institute of Mathematics and its Applications Journal of Mathematics Applied in Business and Industry *see* I M A Journal of Mathematics Applied in Business and Industry **3037**
Institute of Mathematics and its Applications Journal of Mathematical Control & Information *see* I M A Journal of Mathematical Control & Information **3037**
Institute of Measurement and Control. Transactions. (UK ISSN 0142-3312) **2522, 3447**
Institute of Medical Laboratory Sciences. Gazette *see* I M L S Gazette **3107**
Institute of Medical Laboratory Sciences, London. Annual Report. (UK) **3260**
Institute of Medicine. Journal. (NP ISSN 0259-0972) **3109**
Institute of Medicine of Chicago. Proceedings. (US ISSN 0091-746X) **3109**
Institute of Mennonite Studies Series. (US ISSN 0073-9456) **4284**
Institute of Metal Finishing. Transactions. (UK ISSN 0020-2967) **3408**
Institute of Metals and Materials Australasia. Proceedings. (AT) **3408**

Institute of Meteorology and Water Management. Reports. *see* Instytut Meteorologii i Gospodarki Wodnej. Wiadomosci **3436**
Institute of Meteorology and Water Management. Research Papers Series: Hydrology and Oceanology. *see* Instytut Meteorologii i Gospodarki Wodnej. Materialy Badawcze. Seria: Hydrologia i Oceanologia **1598**
Institute of Meteorology and Water Management. Research Papers Series: Meteorology. *see* Instytut Meteorologii i Gospodarki Wodnej. Materialy Badawcze. Seria: Meteorologia **3436**
Institute of Meteorology and Water Management. Research Papers Series: Water Engineering. *see* Instytut Meteorologii i Gospodarki Wodnej. Materialy Badawcze. Seria: Inzynieria Wodna **1924**
Institute of Meteorology and Water Management. Research Papers Series: Water Management and Water Protection. *see* Instytut Meteorologii i Gospodarki Wodnej. Materialy Badawcze. Seria: Gospodarka Wodna i Ochrona Wod **1598**
Institute of Mine Surveyors of South Africa. Journal/Instituut van Mynopmeters van Suid-Afrika. Joernaal. (SA ISSN 0020-2983) **3485**
Institute of Mining and Metallurgy. Transactions: Metallurgical Series. *see* Vysoka Skola Banska. Sbornik Vedeckych Praci: Rada Hutnicka **3423**
Institute of Modern Russian Culture Newsletter. (US ISSN 0738-7105) **2006, 4438**
Institute of Municipal Administration *see* Q I M A **4093**
Institute of Muslim Minority Affairs. Journal. (UK ISSN 0266-6952) **2429**
Institute of Nature Education in Shiga Heights. Bulletin. *see* Shiga Shizen Kyoiku Kenkyu Shisetsu Kenkyu Gyoseki **1548**
Institute of Navigation. Journal *see* Journal of Navigation **4730**
Institute of Navigation. National Technical Meeting Proceedings. (US) **55**
Institute of Navigation. Proceedings of the Annual Meeting. (US) **4729**
Institute of Noetic Sciences. Newsletter *see* Institute of Noetic Sciences. Quarterly Bulletin **4315**
Institute of Noetic Sciences. Quarterly Bulletin. (US ISSN 0897-1013) **4315**
Institute of Noise Control Engineering. Journal. (JA ISSN 0386-8761) **3859**
Institute of Nuclear Agriculture. Annual Report. (BG) **98**
Institute of Nuclear Materials Management. Proceedings of Annual Meeting. (US ISSN 0073-9472) **1805, 1825**
Institute of Nuclear Power Operations. Review. (US) **1805**
Institute of Occupational Health. Proceedings. (UK) **3618**
Institute of Oceanographic Sciences. Annual Report *see* Institute of Oceanographic Sciences. Deacon Laboratory. Annual Report **1605**
Institute of Oceanographic Sciences. Deacon Laboratory. Annual Report. (UK) **1605**
Institute of Outdoor Advertising. Newsletter. (US) **32**
Institute of Outdoor Drama Newsletter *see* U S Outdoor Drama **4642**
Institute of Paper Chemistry. Abstract Bulletin *see* Institute of Paper Science and Technology. Abstract Bulletin **3668**
Institute of Paper Chemistry. Keyword Index to Abstract Bulletin *see* Institute of Paper Science and Technology. Keyword Index to Abstract Bulletin **5214**

Institute of Paper Science and Technology. Abstract Bulletin. (US) **3668, 15**
†Institute of Paper Science and Technology. Bibliographic Series. (US) **5214**
Institute of Paper Science and Technology. Graphic Arts Bulletin. (US) **4007, 15**
†Institute of Paper Science and Technology. Keyword Index to Abstract Bulletin. (US) **5214**
Institute of Patent Attorneys of Australia. Annual Proceedings. (AT) **3675, 2635**
Institute of Personnel Management Digest *see* I P M Digest **5210**
Institute of Personnel Management Journal *see* I P M Journal **1012**
Institute of Physical and Chemical Research. List of Papers. *see* Rikagaku Kenkyujo Kenkyu Happyo Ronbun Mokuroku **3839**
Institute of Physical and Chemical Research. Reports. *see* Rikagaku Kenkyujo Hokoku **3830**
Institute of Physical and Chemical Research. Scientific Papers. (JA ISSN 0020-3092) **3820, 1179**
Institute of Physical and Chemical Research Cyclotron Technical Report *see* I P C R Cyclotron Technical Report **5210**
Institute of Physics, London. Conference Series. Proceedings. (UK ISSN 0305-2346) **3820**
Institute of Physics Short Meetings Series *see* I O P Short Meetings Series **3841**
Institute of Phytopathological Research. Communications. *see* Instituut voor Plantenziektenkundig Onderzoek. Mededeling **5215**
Institute of Plant Breeding and Acclimatization. Bulletin. *see* Instytut Hodowli i Aklimatyzacji Roslin. Biuletyn **181**
Institute of Plant Protection. Scientific Activities. (IS) **180**
Institute of Political and Social Studies Bulletin *see* I P S S Bulletin **3898**
Institute of Primate Research. Annual Report. (KE) **544, 584**
Institute of Psychophysical Research. Proceedings. (UK ISSN 0073-9561) **4024**
Institute of Public Administration, Dublin. Administration Yearbook and Diary. (IE ISSN 0073-9596) **4064**
Institute of Public Administration, Dublin. Annual Report. (IE ISSN 0073-9588) **4064**
Institute of Public Administration, Khartoum. Occasional Papers. (SJ ISSN 0073-9618) **4064**
Institute of Public Administration, Khartoum. Proceedings of the Annual Round Table Conference. (SJ ISSN 0073-9626) **4064**
Institute of Public Administration of Canada. Bulletin *see* Public Sector Management **4071**
Institute of Public Affairs Review *see* I P A Review **670**
Institute of Public Enterprise. Journal. (II) **1014, 1078**
Institute of Public Health. Annual Report/Kokuritsu Koshu Eisei-in Nenpo. (JA) **4104**
Institute of Public Health. Bulletin/Kokuritsu Koshu Eisei-in Kenkyu Hokoku. (JA ISSN 0020-3106) **4104**
Institute of Qualified Private Secretaries. Career Secretary. (UK ISSN 0268-8387) **1059, 1014**
Institute of Qualified Private Secretaries. Journal *see* Institute of Qualified Private Secretaries. Career Secretary **1059**
Institute of Race Relations. Annual Report. (UK) **4438**
Institute of Rail Transport. Journal. (II ISSN 0020-3114) **4710**
Institute of Refractories Engineers. Journal. (UK ISSN 0269-6924) **1165**
Institute of Refrigeration. Proceedings. (UK) **2300**

Institute of Revenues, Rating and Valuation Monthly *see* R R V Monthly **4155**
Institute of Science Technology. Bulletin.(UK ISSN 0020-3130) **4601**
Institute of Scrap Recycling Industries Report *see* I S R I Report **1489**
Institute of Secretariat Training and Management. Annual Report. (II ISSN 0304-7083) **1066**
Institute of Social and Economic Research. Reports. (US) **671, 4375**
Institute of Social and Economic Research Reprint Series *see* I S E R Reprint Series **670**
Institute of Social and Economic Research Research and Policy Papers *see* I S E R Research and Policy Papers **4437**
Institute of Social, Economic and Government Research. Reports *see* Institute of Social and Economic Research. Reports **671**
Institute of Soils & Water. Scientific Activities. (IS) **180**
Institute of Southeast Asian Studies. Annual Report. (SI) **2338**
Institute of Southeast Asian Studies. Annual Review *see* Southeast Asian Affairs **3927**
Institute of Southeast Asian Studies. Current Issues Seminar Series. (SI) **2338**
Institute of Southeast Asian Studies. Field Reports Series. (SI ISSN 0217-7099) **4375**
Institute of Southeast Asian Studies. Library. Accessions List. (SI ISSN 0046-984X) **3646, 2329**
Institute of Southeast Asian Studies. Library Bulletin. (SI ISSN 0217-0914) **2794**
Institute of Southeast Asian Studies. Local History and Memoirs. (SI) **2339**
Institute of Southeast Asian Studies. Monographs Series. (SI) **4375**
Institute of Southeast Asian Studies. Occasional Paper. (SI ISSN 0073-9731) **4376**
Institute of Southeast Asian Studies. Proceedings of International Conferences. (SI) **869**
Institute of Southeast Asian Studies. Research Notes and Discussion Series. (SI ISSN 0129-8828) **4376**
Institute of Southeast Asian Studies Current Economic Affairs Series *see* I S E A S Current Economic Affairs Series **670**
Institute of Southeast Asian Studies Environment and Development Series *see* I S E A S Environment and Development Series **1957**
Institute of Space and Astronautical Science. Report. (JA ISSN 0285-6808) **365**
Institute of Space and Astronautical Science. Report. Special Publication. (JA ISSN 0288-433X) **365**
Institute of Space and Astronautical Science Lunar and Planetary Symposium. Proceedings *see* I S A S Lunar and Planetary Symposium. Proceedings **365**
Institute of Space and Astronautical Science Nyusu *see* I S A S Nyusu **365**
Institute of Space and Astronautical Science Research Note *see* I S A S Research Note **365**
Institute of Standards and Industrial Research of Iran Yearbook *see* I S I R I Yearbook **3446**
Institute of Statistical Mathematics. Annals. (JA ISSN 0020-3157) **3038, 4574**
Institute of Statistical Mathematics. Annual Report. *see* Monbu-sho Tokei Suri Kenkyujo Nenpo **5239**
Institute of Swimming Teachers & Coaches Directory of Membership. (UK) **1139, 4475**
Institute of Town Planners, India. Journal. (II ISSN 0537-9679) **2489**

Institute of Town Planners, India. Newsletter. (II) **2489**
Institute of Trading Standards Administration Monthly Review *see* Trading Standards Review **1055**
Institute of Traditional Cultures, Madras. Bulletin. (II) **242**
Institute of Transportation Engineers Journal *see* I T E Journal **4719**
Institute of Urban Studies Newsletter. (CN) **2489**, 1958, 2253, 3899
Institute of Vitreous Enamellers. Bulletin and Proceedings *see* Vitreous Enameller **1167**
Institute on Advanced Tax Planning for Real Property Transactions. (US) **1098**, 2635, 4151
Institute on Global Conflict and Cooperation Newsletter *see* I G C C Newsletter **3959**
Institute on Labor Law. Labor Law Developments. Annual Proceeding *see* Labor Law Institute **2643**
Institute on Oil and Gas Law and Taxation. Proceedings. (US) **3689**, 2635
Institute on Planning, Zoning and Eminent Domain. Proceedings. (US ISSN 0730-3009) **2635**, 4151
†Institute on Pluralism and Group Identity. Working Paper Series. (US) **5214**
Institute Scholar. (US ISSN 0196-5603) **3769**
Institute T N O for Building Materials and Building Structures. Annual Report *see* T N O Building and Construction Research. Annual Report **634**
Institute Today *see* C F P Today **1004**
Institutet foer Metallforskning. Forskningsverksamheten. (SW ISSN 0015-7953) **3408**
Institutet foer Vatten- och Luftvaardsforskning Nytt *see* I V L - Nytt **1957**
Institutet foer Vatten- och Luftvaardsforskning Referat *see* I V L - Referat **1958**
Instituteur. *see* Mesuesi **1647**
Institution Analysis. (US) **3899**
Institution of Chemical Engineers. Transactions *see* Process Safety and Environmental Protection **1186**
Institution of Chemical Engineers. Transactions *see* Chemical Engineering Research & Design **1850**
Institution of Chemists (India). Journal. (II ISSN 0020-3254) **1179**, 3260
Institution of Chemists (India). Proceedings. (II ISSN 0369-8599) **1179**, 3260
†Institution of Civil Engineers. Proceedings. Part 1: Design and Construction. (UK ISSN 0307-8353) **5214**
†Institution of Civil Engineers. Proceedings. Part 2: Research and Theory. (UK ISSN 0307-8361) **5214**
Institution of Civil Engineers List of Members *see* I C E List of Members **1867**
Institution of Diesel and Gas Turbine Engineers. Transactions. (UK) **1930**
Institution of Electrical Engineers. Proceedings *see* I E E Proceedings Part A: Covering Science, Measurement and Technology **1898**
Institution of Electrical Engineers Conference Publication Series *see* I E E Conference Publication Series **1893**
Institution of Electrical Engineers Proceedings Part A: Covering Science, Measurement and Technology *see* I E E Proceedings Part A: Covering Science, Measurement and Technology **1898**
Institution of Electrical Engineers Proceedings Part J: Optoelectronics *see* I E E Proceedings Part J: Optoelectronics **3853**
Institution of Electronic and Radio Engineers. Journal *see* Electronics & Communication Engineering Journal **1768**

Institution of Electronics and Telecommunication Engineers. Journal. (II ISSN 0377-2063) **1337**, 1825
Institution of Electronics and Telecommunication Engineers. Students' Journal. (II ISSN 0970-1664) **1337**, 1825
Institution of Electronics and Telecommunication Engineers Technical Review *see* I E T E Technical Review **1337**
Institution of Engineering Designers Official Reference Book and Buyers Guide. (UK ISSN 0261-7641) **1825**
Institution of Engineers (India). Aerospace Engineering Division. Journal. (II ISSN 0257-3423) **55**
Institution of Engineers (India). Agricultural Engineering Division. Journal. (II ISSN 0257-3431) **180**, 98
Institution of Engineers (India). Architectural Engineering. (II ISSN 0257-344X) **1867**, 301
Institution of Engineers (India). Bulletin. (II ISSN 0020-3343) **1825**
Institution of Engineers (India). Chemical Engineering Division. Journal. (II ISSN 0020-3351) **1854**
Institution of Engineers (India). Civil Engineering Division. Journal. (II ISSN 0373-1995) **1867**
Institution of Engineers (India). Computer Engineering Division. Journal. (II) **1879**
Institution of Engineers (India). Electrical Engineering Division. Journal. (II ISSN 0020-3386) **1899**
Institution of Engineers (India). Electronics and Telecommunication Engineering Division. Journal. (II ISSN 0020-3378) **1774**, 1363, 1374
Institution of Engineers (India). Environmental Engineering Division. Journal. (II ISSN 0251-110X) **4105**, 1958, 4825
Institution of Engineers (India). Hindi Section. Journal. (II) **1825**
Institution of Engineers (India). Interdisciplinary Panels and General Engineering. Journal *see* Institution of Engineers (India). Interdisciplinary Panels Journal **1825**
Institution of Engineers (India). Interdisciplinary Panels Journal. (II ISSN 0970-9843) **1825**
Institution of Engineers (India). Marine Engineering Division. Journal. (II) **1924**
Institution of Engineers (India). Mechanical Engineering Division. Journal. (II ISSN 0020-3408) **1930**
Institution of Engineers (India). Metallurgy & Material Science Division. Journal. (II ISSN 0257-4411) **3409**
Institution of Engineers (India). Mining Engineering Division. Journal. (II ISSN 0257-442X) **3485**, 3409
▼Institution of Engineers (India). Panorama. (II) **1825**
Institution of Engineers (India). Production Engineering Division. Journal. (II ISSN 0257-6708) **1825**
Institution of Engineers (India). Students' Journal *see* Institution of Engineers (India). Technicians' Journal **1825**
Institution of Engineers (India). Technicians' Journal. (II) **1825**
Institution of Engineers (India). Textile Engineering Division. Journal. (II ISSN 0257-4438) **4620**
Institution of Engineers. Technical Journal. (BG ISSN 0073-9200) **1825**
Institution of Engineers. Year Book. (BG ISSN 0073-9219) **1825**
Institution of Engineers and Shipbuilders in Scotland. Transactions. (UK ISSN 0020-3289) **4729**

Institution of Engineers, Australia. Brisbane Division. Technical Papers *see* Institution of Engineers, Australia. Queensland Division. Technical Papers **1825**
Institution of Engineers, Australia. Chemical Engineering Transactions *see* Chemical Engineering in Australia **1850**
Institution of Engineers, Australia. General Engineering Transactions *see* Institution of Engineers, Australia. Transactions. Multi-Disciplinary Engineering **1826**
Institution of Engineers, Australia. Mechanical and Chemical Engineering Transactions *see* Institution of Engineers, Australia. Transactions. Mechanical Engineering **1930**
Institution of Engineers, Australia. National Conference Publications. (AT) **1825**
Institution of Engineers, Australia. Queensland Division. Technical Papers. (AT) **1825**
Institution of Engineers, Australia. Transactions. Civil Engineering. (AT ISSN 0159-2068) **1867**
Institution of Engineers, Australia. Transactions. Mechanical Engineering. (AT ISSN 0727-7369) **1930**
Institution of Engineers, Australia. Transactions. Multi-Disciplinary Engineering. (AT ISSN 0812-3314) **1826**
Institution of Engineers, Bangladesh. Journal. (BG ISSN 0379-4318) **1826**
Institution of Engineers, Jamaica. Journal. (JM ISSN 0046-9882) **1826**
Institution of Engineers, Malaysia. Bulletin. (MY) **1826**
Institution of Engineers, Malaysia. Journal. (MY ISSN 0538-0057) **1826**
Institution of Engineers of Ireland. Register of Chartered Engineers and Members. (IE) **1826**
Institution of Engineers of Ireland. Transactions. (IE ISSN 0073-9790) **1826**
Institution of Engineers, Sri Lanka. Members Directory. (CE) **1826**
Institution of Engineers, Sri Lanka. Newsletter. (CE) **1826**
Institution of Engineers, Sri Lanka. Transactions. (CE) **1826**
Institution of Engineers, Sri Lanka. Year Book *see* Institution of Engineers, Sri Lanka. Members Directory **1826**
Institution of Environmental Sciences Proceedings *see* I E S Proceedings **1957**
Institution of Fire Engineers Quarterly *see* Fire Engineers Journal **2032**
Institution of Gas Engineers. Journal *see* Gas Engineering & Management **3687**
Institution of Gas Engineers. Proceedings. (UK ISSN 0367-7850) **3689**
Institution of Incorporated Executive Engineers Newsletter *see* I I E X E Newsletter **1824**
Institution of Marine Technologists. Journal. (II ISSN 0020-3475) **4729**
Institution of Mechanical Engineers (India) Engineer - I.M.E. News *see* Engineer - I.M.E. News **1929**
Institution of Mechanical Engineers. Proceedings *see* Institution of Mechanical Engineers. Proceedings. Part D: Journal of Automobile Engineering **4693**
Institution of Mechanical Engineers. Proceedings. Part A: Journal of Power and Energy. (UK) **1930**
Institution of Mechanical Engineers. Proceedings. Part A: Journal of Power Engineering *see* Institution of Mechanical Engineers. Proceedings. Part A: Journal of Power and Energy **1930**

INSTITUTION 6295

Institution of Mechanical Engineers. Proceedings. Part B: Journal of Engineering Manufacture. (UK ISSN 0954-4054) **1931**
Institution of Mechanical Engineers. Proceedings. Part B: Management and Engineering Manufacture *see* Institution of Mechanical Engineers. Proceedings. Part B: Journal of Engineering Manufacture **1931**
Institution of Mechanical Engineers. Proceedings. Part C: Journal of Mechanical Engineering Science. (UK) **1931**
Institution of Mechanical Engineers. Proceedings. Part C: Mechanical Engineering Science *see* Institution of Mechanical Engineers. Proceedings. Part C: Journal of Mechanical Engineering Science **1931**
Institution of Mechanical Engineers. Proceedings. Part D: Journal of Automobile Engineering. (UK ISSN 0954-4070) **4693**, 1931
Institution of Mechanical Engineers. Proceedings. Part D: Transport Engineering *see* Institution of Mechanical Engineers. Proceedings. Part D: Journal of Automobile Engineering **4693**
Institution of Mechanical Engineers. Proceedings. Part E: Journal of Process Mechanical Engineering. (UK ISSN 0954-4089) **1931**
Institution of Mechanical Engineers. Proceedings. Part F: Journal of Rail and Rapid Transit. (UK ISSN 0954-4097) **4710**, 1931
Institution of Mechanical Engineers. Proceedings. Part G: Journal of Aerospace Engineering. (UK ISSN 0954-4100) **55**, 1931
Institution of Mechanical Engineers. Proceedings. Part H: Journal of Engineering in Medicine. (UK ISSN 0954-4119) **469**, 1931, 3109
Institution of Mining and Metallurgy. Bulletin and Transactions. Section A: Mining Industry *see* Institution of Mining and Metallurgy. Transactions. Section A: Mining Industry **3485**
Institution of Mining and Metallurgy. Bulletin and Transactions. Section B: Applied Earth Sciences *see* Institution of Mining and Metallurgy. Transactions. Section B: Applied Earth Sciences **3485**
Institution of Mining and Metallurgy. Bulletin and Transactions. Section C: Mineral Processing and Extractive Metallurgy *see* Institution of Mining and Metallurgy. Transactions. Section C: Mineral Processing & Extractive Metallurgy **3485**
Institution of Mining and Metallurgy. Transactions. Section A: Mining Industry. (UK ISSN 0371-7844) **3485**, 3409
Institution of Mining and Metallurgy. Transactions. Section B: Applied Earth Sciences. (UK ISSN 0371-7453) **3485**, 1545, 3409
Institution of Mining and Metallurgy. Transactions. Section C: Mineral Processing & Extractive Metallurgy. (UK ISSN 0371-9553) **3485**, 3409
Institution of Mining and Metallurgy Abstracts and Index *see* I M M Abstracts and Index **3499**
Institution of Mining Engineers. Transactions *see* Mining Engineer **3490**
Institution of Municipal Engineers of Southern Africa. Journal. (SA ISSN 0257-1978) **2489**
Institution of Nuclear Engineers. Journal *see* Nuclear Engineer **1832**
Institution of Professional Engineers. Transactions. Civil Engineering Section. (NZ ISSN 0111-9508) **1867**
Institution of Professional Engineers. Transactions. Electrical, Mechanical and Chemical Engineering Section. (NZ ISSN 0111-946X) **1899**, 1854, 1931

6296 INSTITUTION

Institution of Professional Engineers, New Zealand Proceedings Annual Conference (Year) see I P E N Z Proceedings Annual Conference (Year) **1824**
Institution of Professionals, Managers and Specialists Bulletin see I P M S Bulletin **4063**
Institution of Radio and Electronics Engineers. Monitor. (AT) **1375, 1899**
Institution of Railway Signal Engineers. Proceedings. (UK ISSN 0073-9839) **4710**
Institution of Structural Engineers. Sessional Yearbook and Directory of Members. (UK) **1867**
Institution of Structural Engineers. Yearbook see Institution of Structural Engineers. Sessional Yearbook and Directory of Members **1867**
Institution of the Rubber Industry Journal see I.R.I. Journal **5210**
Institution of Water and Environmental Management. Journal. (UK ISSN 0951-7359) **4825**
Institution of Water and Environmental Management. Newsletter. (UK) **4825, 1958**
Institution U Q A M. Transactions. (CN) **1315**
Institutional Brokers Estimate System. (US) **785**
Institutional Distribution. (US ISSN 0020-3572) **2073**
Institutional Distribution Handbook of Foodservice Distribution (Year) see I D Handbook of Foodservice Distribution (Year) **1138**
Institutional Investor. (US ISSN 0020-3580) **950**
Institutional Investor International Edition. (US) **950**
Institutional Research Magazine. (US) **785**
Institutional Review Board Review of Human Subjects Research see I R B: A Review of Human Subjects Research **3259**
Institutions, Etc. see Augustus **4398**
Institutions of Engineers, Australia. Civil Engineering Transactions see Institution of Engineers, Australia. Transactions. Civil Engineering **1867**
Institutions of Engineers, Australia. Mechanical Engineering Transactions see Institution of Engineers, Australia. Transactions. Mechanical Engineering **1930**
Instituto Adolfo Lutz. Revista. (BL ISSN 0073-9855) **477, 553**
†Instituto Agricola Catalan de San Isidro. Revista. (SP ISSN 0046-9890) **5214**
Instituto Agronomico do Sul. Escola de Agronomia Eliseu Maciel. Arquivos de Entomologia. Serie A & Serie B. (BL ISSN 0020-3629) **534**
Instituto Americano de Estudios Vascos. Boletin. (AG ISSN 0020-3637) **2410, 2006**
Instituto Antartico Chileno. Contribution. Serie Cientifica. (CL ISSN 0073-9871) **2410**
Instituto Antartico Chileno. Publicacion see Instituto Antartico Chileno. Contribution. Serie Cientifica **2410**
Instituto Argentino de Ciencias Genealogicas. Boletin Interno. (AG ISSN 0579-3599) **2155**
Instituto Bacteriologico de Chile. Boletin see Instituto de Salud Publica de Chile. Boletin **4105**
Instituto Barraquer. Anales. (SP ISSN 0020-3645) **3301**
Instituto Biologico. Arquivos. (BL ISSN 0020-3653) **4810**
Instituto Biologico da Bahia. Boletim. (BL ISSN 0020-3661) **441**
Instituto Boliviano de Estudio y Accion Social see I B E A S **4437**
Instituto Botanico A.J. Cavanilles. Anales see Jardin Botanico de Madrid. Anales **506**
Instituto Brasil - Estados Unidos. Boletim. (BL ISSN 0020-367X) **1639, 330, 3556, 4634**

Instituto Brasileiro do Cafe. Departamento Economico. Anuario Estatistico do Cafe. (BL) **382**
Instituto Brasileiro do Cafe. Departamento Economico. Anuario Estatistico do Cafe. see Instituto Brasileiro do Cafe. Departamento Economico. Anuario Estatistico do Cafe **382**
Instituto Brasileiro do Cafe. Grupo Executivo de Racionalizacao de Cafeicultura. Relatorio do Gerca. (BL) **382**
Instituto Butantan. Memorias. (BL ISSN 0073-9901) **584**
Instituto Caro y Cuervo. Boletin see Thesaurus **2847**
Instituto Caro y Cuervo. Noticias Culturales. (CK ISSN 0020-370X) **2925, 330**
Instituto Caro y Cuervo. Publicaciones. (CK) **2508**
Instituto Caro y Cuervo. Seminario Andres Bello. Cuadernos. (CK) **2818**
Instituto Caro y Cuervo. Serie Bibliografica. (CK ISSN 0073-991X) **403**
Instituto Caro y Cuervo. Serie Granada Entreabierta. (CK) **2925**
Instituto Caro y Cuervo. Serie Minor. (CK ISSN 0073-9928) **2925, 2818**
Instituto Centroamericano de Administracion Publica. Serie 100. Aspectos Humanos de la Administracion. (CR ISSN 0073-9944) **4064**
Instituto Centroamericano de Administracion Publica. Serie 200. Ciencia de la Administracion. (CR ISSN 0073-9952) **4064**
Instituto Centroamericano de Administracion Publica. Serie 300: Investigacion. (CR ISSN 0073-9960) **4064**
Instituto Centroamericano de Administracion Publica. Serie 400: Economia y Finanzas. (CR ISSN 0073-9979) **4064**
Instituto Centroamericano de Administracion Publica. Serie 600: Informes de Seminarios. (CR ISSN 0073-9995) **4064**
Instituto Centroamericano de Administracion Publica. Serie 700: Materiales de Informacion. (CR ISSN 0074-0004) **4064**
Instituto Centroamericano de Administracion Publica. Serie 800: Metodologia de la Administracion. (CR ISSN 0074-0012) **4064**
Instituto Centroamericano de Administracion Publica. Serie 900: Misceláneas. (CR ISSN 0074-0020) **4064**
Instituto Centroamericano de Investigacion y Tecnologia Industrial Revista I C A I T I see Revista I C A I T I **4607**
Instituto Colombiano Agropecuario. Boletin Tecnico. (CK ISSN 0538-0391) **98**
†Instituto Colombiano Agropecuario. Catalogo de Publicaciones Periodicas. (CK) **5214**
Instituto Colombiano Agropecuario. Revista I C A. (Instituto Colombiano Agropecuario) (CK ISSN 0018-8794) **98, 441, 4810**
Instituto Colombiano Agropecuario. Temas Didacticos see I C A Informa **96**
Instituto Colombiano Agropecuario Informa see I C A Informa **96**
Instituto Colombiano Agropecuario Instituto Colombiano Agropecuario. Revista I C A see Instituto Colombiano Agropecuario. Revista I C A **98**
Instituto Colombiano de Cultura. Gaceta. (CK) **4376**
Instituto Costarricense de Turismo. Memoria Anual. (CR) **4772**
Instituto Cultural Italo-Brasileiro. Caderno. (BL) **3960**
Instituto Cultural Peruano Norteamericano. Boletin see Instituto Cultural Peruano Norteamericano. Newsletter **1639**

Instituto Cultural Peruano Norteamericano. Newsletter. (PE) **1639**
Instituto de Biologia Marinha e Oceanografia. Trabalhos see Universidade Federal de Pernambuco. Departamento de Oceanografia. Centro de Tecnologia. Trabalhos Oceanograficos **458**
Instituto de Cardiologia de Mexico. Archivos. (MX ISSN 0020-3785) **3209**
Instituto de Censores Jurados de Cuentas de Espagna. Revista Technica. (SP) **751**
Instituto de Ciencia Politica Rafael Bielsa. Anuario. (AG ISSN 0074-0063) **3899**
Instituto de Ciencias para la Familia. (SP) **2635, 1639**
Instituto de Ciencias y Artes de Chiapas see I C A C H **328**
Instituto de Credito Agricola y Pecuario. Boletin Mensual. (VE) **139**
Instituto de Credito Agricola y Pecuario. Informe Annual. (VE) **869**
Instituto de Credito Oficial Memoria del Grupo I C O see Memoria del Grupo I C O **1101**
Instituto de Cultura Puertorriquena. Revista. (PR ISSN 0020-3815) **2508**
Instituto de Derecho Privado. Boletin. (VE ISSN 0020-3823) **2635**
Instituto de Desarrollo Urbano Noticiero I.D.U.N. see Noticiero I.D.U.N **2493**
Instituto de Ecologia. Informa. (MX) **442**
Instituto de Ecologia. Nota Tecnica. (MX) **2115**
Instituto de Economia y Producciones Ganaderas del Ebro. Comunicaciones.(SP ISSN 0374-8189) **98**
Instituto de Economia y Producciones Ganaderas del Ebro. Trabajos. (SP ISSN 0375-3417) **98**
Instituto de Estudios Andinos. Cuadernos. (PE) **4438**
Instituto de Estudios Andinos. Trabajo de Campo. (PE) **242**
Instituto de Estudios Asturianos. Boletin.(SP ISSN 0020-384X) **2368, 2818**
Instituto de Estudios Aymaras. Boletin. (PE ISSN 0258-8536) **4376**
Instituto de Estudios de Administracion Local. Catedra Calvo Sotelo. Conferencias. (SP) **4089**
Instituto de Estudios de Administracion Local. Oficina Tecnica de la O I C I. Boletin de Informacion see Informacion Iberoamericana **4089**
Instituto de Estudios de Administracion Local. Secretariado Iberoamericano de Municipios. Boletin de Informacion see Informacion Iberoamericana **4089**
Instituto de Estudios Economicos sobre la Realidad Argentina y Latinoamericana. Estudios. (AG) **869**
Instituto de Estudios Gerundenses. Anales. (SP ISSN 0211-2329) **2006**
Instituto de Estudios Gerundenses. Serie Monografica. (SP ISSN 0211-2477) **2006**
Instituto de Estudios Giennenses Boletin. (SP ISSN 0561-3590) **2368**
Instituto de Estudios Madrilenos. Anales.(SP ISSN 0584-6374) **2508**
Instituto de Estudios Medicos y Biologicos. Boletin see Estudios Medicos y Biologicos. Boletin **3096**
Instituto de Estudios Peruanos. Analisis Economico. (PE) **869**
Instituto de Estudios Peruanos. Coleccion Minima. (PE) **4438**
Instituto de Estudios Peruanos. Documentos de Trabajo. (PE) **242, 2818, 3899, 4438**
Instituto de Estudios Peruanos. Estudios de la Sociedad Rural. (PE) **4438**
Instituto de Estudios Peruanos. Historia Andina. (PE) **2410**

Instituto de Estudios Peruanos. Miscelanea. (PE) **242**
Instituto de Estudios Peruanos. Proyecto de Estudios Etnologicos del Valle de Chancay. Monografia. (PE) **242**
Instituto de Estudios Politicos. Boletin. (SP ISSN 0020-3866) **3899**
Instituto de Estudios Tarraconenses Ramon Berenguer IV. Publicacion. (SP ISSN 0534-3364) **2368**
Instituto de Estudios Tarraconenses Ramon Berenguer IV. Seccion de Estudios Juridicos. Publicacion. (SP) **2635**
Instituto de Filosofia, Ciencias y Letras. Cuadernos. (UY) **2508**
Instituto de Filosofia del Derecho. Boletin Informativo. (VE) **2635**
Instituto de Fomento Pesquero. Boletin Cientifico see Serie Investigacion Pesquera **2048**
Instituto de Geografia. Annales see Anales de Geografia **2241**
Instituto de Geografia e Historia Militar do Brasil. Revista. (BL ISSN 0020-3890) **2410, 3460**
Instituto de Higiene e Medicina Tropical. Anais. (PO ISSN 0303-7762) **4105, 3220**
Instituto de Investigacao Agronomica de Angola. Divisao de Meteorologia Agricola. Anuario. (AO) **3436, 98**
Instituto de Investigacao Agronomica de Angola. Relatorio. (AO ISSN 0078-2254) **98**
Instituto de Investigacao Agronomica de Angola. Serie Cientifica. (AO ISSN 0078-2262) **98**
Instituto de Investigacao Agronomica de Angola. Serie Tecnica. (AO ISSN 0078-2270) **98**
Instituto de Investigacao Agronomica de Mocambique. Centro de Documentacas Agraria. Memorias. (MZ ISSN 0077-1791) **98**
Instituto de Investigacao Agronomica de Mocambique. Comunicacoes see Agronomia Mocambicana **74**
Instituto de Investigacao Cientifica de Angola. Bibliograficas Tematicas. (AO ISSN 0074-008X) **4356**
Instituto de Investigacao Cientifica de Angola. Boletim. (AO ISSN 0020-3912) **4315**
Instituto de Investigacao Cientifica de Angola. Memorias e Trabalhos. (AO ISSN 0074-0098) **4315**
Instituto de Investigacao Cientifica de Angola. Relatorios e Communicacoes.(AO ISSN 0003-343X) **4315**
Instituto de Investigacao Cientifica de Angola Documentacao see I I C A. Documentacao **4356**
Instituto de Investigacao Cientifica Tropical. Anuario de Actividades. (PO) **4315**
Instituto de Investigacao Cientifica Tropical. Centro de Estudos de Historia e Cartografia Antiga. Studia. (PO ISSN 0870-0028) **2314, 2253**
Instituto de Investigacao Cientifica Tropical. Centro de Estudos de Historia e Cartografia Antiga. Serie Separatas. (PO ISSN 0870-6735) **2314, 2253**
Instituto de Investigacao Cientifica Tropical. Comunicacoes. Serie de Ciencias Agrarias. (PO ISSN 0871-1763) **98**
Instituto de Investigacao Cientifica Tropical. Comunicacoes. Serie de Ciencias Biologicas. (PO ISSN 0871-1755) **442**
Instituto de Investigacao Cientifica Tropical. Comunicacoes. Serie de Ciencias da Engenharia Geografica. (PO ISSN 0871-1747) **2253**
Instituto de Investigacao Cientifica Tropical. Comunicacoes. Serie de Ciencias da Terra. (PO ISSN 0871-1798) **1545**
Instituto de Investigacao Cientifica Tropical. Comunicacoes. Serie de Ciencias Etnologicas e Etnomuseologicas. (PO ISSN 0871-178X) **2007**

INSTITUTO NACIONAL 6297

Instituto de Investigacao Cientifica Tropical. Comunicacoes. Serie de Ciencias Historicas, Economicas e Sociologicas. (PO ISSN 0871-1771) **2314**, 4376
Instituto de Investigacao Cientifica Tropical. Estudos de Historia e Cartografia Antiga - Memorias. (PO ISSN 0870-015X) **2368**, 2253
Instituto de Investigacao Cientifica Tropical. Index Seminum Quae Hortus et Musaeum Agricolum Tropicum. (PO) **2141**
Instituto de Investigacao Cientifica Tropical. Memorias. (PO ISSN 0870-0036) **4315**
Instituto de Investigacao Cientifica Tropical. Plano de Actividades. (PO) **4315**
Instituto de Investigacao Cientifica Tropical. Relatorio de Actividades. (PO) **4315**
Instituto de Investigacion Textil y de Cooperacion Industrial. Boletin INTEXTER. (SP ISSN 0212-6699) **4620**
Instituto de Investigacion Textil y de Cooperacion Industrial. Boletin *see* Instituto de Investigacion Textil y de Cooperacion Industrial. Boletin INTEXTER **4620**
Instituto de Investigaciones Economicas. Revista. (BO) **895**
Instituto de Investigaciones Electricas. Informe Anual. (MX) **1899**
Instituto de Investigaciones Electricas Boletin I I E *see* Boletin I I E **1883**
Instituto de Investigaciones Pecuarias Revista *see* Instituto de Zoonosis e Investigacion Pecuaria Revista **4811**
Instituto de Investigaciones Tecnologicas Tecnologia *see* I I T Tecnologia **5209**
Instituto de Investigaciones Veterinarias. Boletin *see* Veterinaria Tropical **4817**
Instituto de la Demanda Interna. Opina. (CU) **1505**
Instituto de la Ingenieria de Espana. Hoja Informativa. (SP) **1868**
Instituto de la Patagonia. Anales. Social Sciences. (CL ISSN 0716-6478) **2410**, 442
Instituto de Matematica Beppo Levi. Cuadernos. (AG ISSN 0326-0690) **3038**
Instituto de Medicina Tropical de Sao Paulo. Revista. (BL ISSN 0036-4665) **3220**
Instituto de Numismatica e Historia de San Nicolas de los Arroyos. Boletin. (AG ISSN 0325-7622) **3599**, 2410
Instituto de Nutricion de Centro America y Panama (INCAP). Informe Anual. (UN ISSN 0533-4179) **3607**
Instituto de Pesca, Sao Paulo. Boletim. (BL ISSN 0046-9939) **2043**
Instituto de Pesca, Sao Paulo. Boletim. Serie de Divulgacao. (BL) **2043**
†Instituto de Pesquisa Agropecuaria do l'Este. Pesquisa e Experimentos. Comunicado Tecnico. (BL ISSN 0046-9947) **5214**
Instituto de Pesquisa Veterinarias Desiderio Finamor Boletim Mensal *see* I.P.V.D.F. Boletim Mensal **5210**
Instituto de Pesquisas Veterinarias Desiderio Finamor. Boletim. (BL) **4810**
Instituto de Pesquisas Zootecnicas "Francisco Osorio". Anuario Tecnico. (BL ISSN 0100-2546) **218**, 207
Instituto de Planejamento Economico e Social Estudos para o Planejamento *see* I P E A Estudos para o Planejamento **1077**
Instituto de Planejamento Economico e Social Relatorios de Pesquisa *see* I P E A Relatorios de Pesquisa **4437**
Instituto de Planejamento Economico e Social Serie Monografica *see* I P E A Serie Monografica **868**
Instituto de Previdencia e Assistencia dos Servidores do Estado Biblioteca Informa *see* I P A S E Biblioteca Informa **2793**
Instituto de Resseguros do Brasil. Assessoria de Comunicacao Social. Relatorio do Exercicio *see* Instituto de Resseguros do Brasil. Secretaria Geral da Presidencia. Relatorio do Exercicio **5214**
†Instituto de Resseguros do Brasil. Secretaria Geral da Presidencia. Relatorio do Exercicio. (BL ISSN 0100-5790) **5214**
Instituto de Resseguros do Brasil Revista *see* I R B Revista **2533**
Instituto de Salud Publica de Chile. Boletin. (CL ISSN 0716-1387) **4105**, 553
Instituto de Tecnologia de Alimentos. Coletanea. (BL ISSN 0100-350X) **2073**, 3607
Instituto de Tecnologia de Alimentos. Estudos Economicos. Alimentos Processados. (BL ISSN 0100-4964) **2073**, 2092
Instituto de Tecnologia de Alimentos. Instrucoes Praticas. (BL ISSN 0074-0144) **2073**, 3607
Instituto de Tecnologia de Alimentos. Instrucoes Tecnicas. (BL ISSN 0074-0152) **2073**, 3607
Instituto de Zoologia "Dr. Augusto Nobre". Publicacoes. (PO ISSN 0020-4021) **584**
Instituto de Zoonosis e Investigacion Pecuaria Revista. (PE ISSN 0020-3963) **4811**
Instituto de Zootecnia. Facultad de Veterinaria. Catalogo de Publicaciones. (SP) **4811**, 218
Instituto del Mar del Peru. Boletin. (PE ISSN 0378-7699) **2043**
Instituto del Mar del Peru. Informe. (PE ISSN 0378-7702) **2043**
Instituto do Desenvolvimento Economico-Social do Para. Anuario Estatistico do Estado do Para. (BL) **4574**
Instituto do Desenvolvimento Economico-Social do Para. Boletim de Pesquisa Emprego e Desemprego na Regiao Metropolitana de Belem. (BL) **983**
Instituto do Desenvolvimento Economico-Social do Para. Comercio Varejista. (BL) **869**
Instituto do Desenvolvimento Economico-Social do Para. Indicadores da Socio-Economia Paraense. (BL) **869**
Instituto do Desenvolvimento Economico-Social do Para. Indicadores Setoriais. (BL) **1078**
Instituto do Desenvolvimento Economico-Social do Para. Indice do Custo de Vida. (BL) **869**
Instituto do Desenvolvimento Economico-Social do Para. Para Agrario. (BL) **98**
Instituto do Desenvolvimento Economico-Social do Para Para Desenvolvimento. (BL) **869**, 931
Instituto do Patrimonio Historico e Artistico Nacional. Publicacoes. (BL) **2508**
Instituto dos Advogados de S. Paulo. Revista. (BL) **2635**
Instituto Ecuatoriano de Ciencias Naturales. Contribuciones. (EC ISSN 0010-7972) **4315**, 1489
Instituto Ecuatoriano de Seguridad Social. Boletin. Normas Resoluciones y Jurisprudencias. (EC) **2533**
Instituto Espanol de Oceanografia. Boletin. (SP ISSN 0074-0195) **1606**
Instituto Espanol de Oceanografia. Monografias. (SP ISSN 0214-1949) **1606**
Instituto Espanol de Oceanografia. Publicaciones Especiales. (SP ISSN 0214-7378) **1606**
Instituto Espanol del Envase y Embalaje. B I U. Boletin Informativo Urgente *see* I D E **3649**
Instituto Estadual de Hematologia Arthur de Siqueira Cavalcanti. Boletim *see* Instituto Estadual de Hematologia Arthur de Siqueira Cavalcanti. Revista **3272**
Instituto Estadual de Hematologia Arthur de Siqueira Cavalcanti. Revista. (BL ISSN 0103-3263) **3272**
†Instituto Florestal. Boletim Tecnico. (BL ISSN 0100-3151) **5214**
Instituto Forestal Latinoamericano de Investigacion y Capacitacion. Boletin Bibliografico. *see* Bibliografia Forestal Latinoamericana **2111**
Instituto Frances de Estudios Andinos. Boletin. *see* Institut Francais d'Etudes Andines. Bulletin **4375**
Instituto Gemologico Espanol. Boletin. (SP ISSN 0210-7228) **2155**
Instituto Geografico Agustin Codazzi. Informe de Labores. (CK) **2253**
Instituto Historico e Geografico Brasileiro. Revista. (BL ISSN 0101-4366) **2410**
Instituto Historico e Geografico de Juiz de Fora. (BL ISSN 0020-4218) **2410**, 2253
Instituto Historico e Geografico do Espirito Santo. Revista. (BL) **2314**, 2253
Instituto Hondureno de Seguridad Social. Departamento de Estadistica y Procesamiento de Datos. Anuario Estadistico. (HO ISSN 0074-0233) **2533**
Instituto Indigenista Interamericano Serie de Ediciones Especiales. (MX) **242**
Instituto Ingenieros Civiles de Espana. Boletim Informativo *see* Instituto de la Ingenieria de Espana. Hoja Informativa **1868**
Instituto Interamericano de Ciencias Agricolas de la O E A. Documentos Oficiales *see* Instituto Interamericano de Cooperacion para la Agricultura - O E A. Documentos Oficiales **98**
Instituto Interamericano de Cooperacion para la Agricultura - O E A. Documentos Oficiales. (CR) **98**
Instituto Interamericano de Etnomusicologia y Folklore. Revista *see* Centro para las Culturas Populares y Tradicionales. Boletin **3544**
Instituto Interamericano del Nino. Boletin. (US ISSN 0020-4056) **1239**
Instituto Interamericano del Nino. Educacion Especial. Informes Tecnicos. (UY) **4409**, 1736
Instituto Interamericano del Nino. Estadistica e Informatica. Informes Tecnicos. (UY) **4409**, 4574
Instituto Interamericano del Nino. Juridico Social. Informes Tecnicos. (UY) **4438**, 2635
Instituto Interamericano del Nino. Publicaciones sobre Servicio Social *see* Instituto Interamericano del Nino. Servicio Social. Informes Tecnicos **4409**
Instituto Interamericano del Nino. Registro Civil. Informes Tecnicos. (UY) **4409**
Instituto Interamericano del Nino. Servicio Social. Informes Tecnicos. (UY) **4409**
Instituto Internacional de Historia del Derecho Indiano. Actas y Estudios. (SP) **2699**
Instituto Joaquim Nabuco de Pesquisas Sociais. Serie Monografias *see* Fundacao Joaquim Nabuco. Serie Monografias **4372**
Instituto Latinamericano y del Caribe de Planificacion Economica y Social Cuadernos *see* I L P E S Cuadernos **999**
Instituto Linguistico de Verano. Documentos de Trabajo. (PE) **2818**
†Instituto Linguistico de Verano. Serie Sintactica. (CK) **5214**
Instituto Linguistico de Verano en Colombia. Bibliografia. (CK) **2855**
Instituto Medico "Sucre". Revista. (BO) **3109**
†Instituto Mexicano del Petroleo. Boletin Informativo. (MX ISSN 0186-3266) **5214**
Instituto Mexicano del Petroleo. Revista.(MX ISSN 0538-1428) **3689**
Instituto Mexicano del Seguro Social. Boletin Estadistico. (MX) **4105**
Instituto Mexicano del Seguro Social. Boletin sobre Morbilidad Hospitalaria.(MX) **4105**
Instituto Mexicano del Seguro Social. Boletin sobre Mortalidad. (MX) **4105**
Instituto Mexicano del Seguro Social. Boletin sobre Motivos de Consulta. (MX) **4105**
Instituto Nacional de Administracion Publica. Biblioteca. Boletin Informativo *see* Instituto Nacional de Administracion Publica. Servicio de Biblioteca y Documentacion. Boletin de Informacion Bibliografica **4081**
Instituto Nacional de Administracion Publica. Servicio de Biblioteca y Documentacion. Boletin de Informacion Bibliografica. (SP) **4081**
Instituto Nacional de Antropologia. Cuadernos *see* Instituto Nacional de Antropologia y Pensamiento Latinoamericano. Cuadernos **242**
Instituto Nacional de Antropologia e Historia. Coleccion Cientifica. (MX ISSN 0076-7611) **242**
Instituto Nacional de Antropologia e Historia. Series Cientifica *see* Instituto Nacional de Antropologia e Historia. Coleccion Cientifica **242**
Instituto Nacional de Antropologia y Pensamiento Latinoamericano. Cuadernos. (AG) **242**, 274
Instituto Nacional de Astrofisica, Optica y Electronica. Boletin. (MX) **365**, 1899
Instituto Nacional de Cancerologia de Mexico. Revista. (MX ISSN 0076-7131) **3198**
Instituto Nacional de Colonizacao e Reforma Agraria. Coordenadoria Regional do Parana. Sinopse do Cooperativismo No Parana. (BL) **831**
Instituto Nacional de Colonizacao e Reforma Agraria. Procuradoria Geral. Boletim. Pareceres. (BL) **2635**
Instituto Nacional de Deportes, Educacion Fisica y Recreacion Boletin Cientifico-Tecnico I N D E R - Cuba *see* Boletin Cientifico-Tecnico I N D E R - Cuba **3800**
Instituto Nacional de Estadistica, Geografia e Informatica Catalogo (Year) Productos del I N E G I *see* Catalogo (Year) Productos del I N E G I **8**
Instituto Nacional de Estadistica, Geografia e Informatica Gaceta Informativa I N E G I *see* Gaceta Informativa I N E G I **866**
Instituto Nacional de Industria Grupo I N I (Resumen de Actividades) *see* Grupo I N I (Resumen de Actividades) **1077**
Instituto Nacional de Investigacao Cientifica. C E G. Memorias. (Centro de Estudos Geograficos) (PO) **2253**
Instituto Nacional de Investigacao Cientifica. Textos Classicos. (PO) **3769**
Instituto Nacional de Investigacao Cientifica. Textos de Linguistica. (PO) **2818**
Instituto Nacional de Investigacao Cientifica. Textos Humanisticos Portugueses. (PO) **2508**
Instituto Nacional de Investigacao das Pescas. Publicacoes Avulsas. (PO ISSN 0870-0435) **584**, 2043
Instituto Nacional de Investigacion y Desarrollo Pesquero. Memoria. (AG ISSN 0325-6987) **2043**
Instituto Nacional de Investigacion y Desarrollo Pesquero. Revista. (AG ISSN 0325-6375) **2043**
Instituto Nacional de Investigacion y Desarrollo Pesquero. Serie Contribuciones. (AG ISSN 0325-6790) **2043**
Instituto Nacional de Investigaciones Forestales. Boletin Divulgativo. (MX ISSN 0185-2361) **534**, 2102
Instituto Nacional de Investigaciones Forestales. Boletin Tecnico. (MX ISSN 0185-2310) **534**, 2102

Title

6298 INSTITUTO NACIONAL

Instituto Nacional de Investigaciones Forestales. Catalogo. (MX ISSN 0185-4445) **2102**
Instituto Nacional de Investigaciones Forestales. Ciencia Forestal. (MX ISSN 0185-2418) **2102**
Instituto Nacional de Investigaciones Forestales. Publicacion Especial. (MX ISSN 0185-2566) **534,** 2102
Instituto Nacional de Investigaciones Geologico Mineras. Informe Anual de Actividades. (CK) **1568**
Instituto Nacional de Investigaciones Geologico Mineras. Publicaciones Geologicas Especiales del Ingeominas. (CK) **1568**
Instituto Nacional de Investigaciones sobre Recursos Bioticos. Nota Tecnica *see* Instituto de Ecologia. Nota Tecnica **2115**
Instituto Nacional de Medicina Legal de Colombia. Revista. (CK) **3265,** 2635
Instituto Nacional de Seguridad e Higiene en el Trabajo. Boletin Bibliografico *see* E R G A. Bibliografico **3623**
Instituto Nacional de Seguros Memoria Anual. (CR) **2533**
Instituto Nacional de Tecnologia Agropecuaria. Estacion Experimental Regional Agropecuaria. Boletin de Divulgacion Tecnica. (AG ISSN 0325-1772) **98**
Instituto Nacional de Tecnologia Industrial *see* I N T I **5210**
Instituto Nacional de Tecnologia Informativo *see* I N T Informativo **4313**
Instituto Oswaldo Cruz, Rio de Janeiro. Memorias. (BL ISSN 0074-0276) **442**
Instituto Panamericano de Geografia e Historia. Boletin Aereo. (MX ISSN 0020-4188) **2253,** 2410
Instituto para el Desarrollo de Ejecutivos en la Argentina. Noticias *see* Instituto para el Desarrollo de Ejecutivos en la Argentina. Revista **1014**
Instituto para el Desarrollo de Ejecutivos en la Argentina. Revista. (AG ISSN 0325-9064) **1014**
Instituto Peruano de Derecho Agrario. Cuadernos Agrarios. (PE) **98,** 2635
Instituto Peruano de Polemologia. (PE) **3899**
Instituto Politecnico Nacional. Escuela Nacional de Ciencias Biologicas. Anales. (MX ISSN 0365-1932) **477**
Instituto Politecnico Nacional. Escuela Nacional de Ciencias Biologicas. Boletin Bibliografico. (MX ISSN 0185-0997) **466**
Instituto Rio Grandense do Arroz. Custo de Producao do Arroz. (BL) **152**
Instituto Superior de Agronomia. Anais. (PO ISSN 0365-2971) **98,** 2073
†Instituto Superior de Estudios Eclesiasticos. Libro Anual. (MX) **5214**
Instituto Tecnologico de Aeronautica Engenharia *see* I T A - Engenharia **5210**
Instituto Tecnologico de Santo Domingo. Biblioteca. Boletin de Analiticas. (DR) **4601**
Instituto Tecnologico de Santo Domingo. Boletin. (DR) **1709**
Instituto Tecnologico de Santo Domingo. Documentos. (DR ISSN 0378-956X) **4315**
Instituto Teconologico de Santo Domingo. Biblioteca. Boletin de Adquisiciones. (DR) **403**
†Instituto Teologico del Uruguay. Cuadernos. (UY) **5214**
Instituto Teologico del Uruguay Monsenor Mariano Soler. Libro Anual.(UY) **4182**
Instituto y Observatorio de Marina. Almanaque Nautico *see* Real Instituto y Observatorio de la Armada. Almanaque Nautico **368**
Instituto y Observatorio de Marina. Boletin Astronomico *see* Real Instituto y Observatorio de la Armada. Boletin Astronomico **368**
Instituto y Observatorio de Marina. Efemerides Astronomicas *see* Real Instituto y Observatorio de la Armada. Efemerides Astronomicas **368**
Instituto y Observatorio de Marina. Observaciones Meteorologicas, Magneticas y Sismicas. Anales *see* Real Instituto y Observatorio de la Armada. Observaciones Meteorologicas, Magneticas y Sismicas. Anales **1593**
Instituttet for Matematisk Statistik og Operationsanalyse. Working Paper *see* Technical University of Denmark. Institute of Mathematical Statistics and Operations Research. Research Reports **4590**
Institutul Agronomic Cluj-Napoca. Buletinul *see* Institutul Agronomic Cluj-Napoca. Buletinul. Seria Agricultura **98**
Institutul Agronomic Cluj-Napoca. Buletinul. Seria Agricultura. (RM ISSN 0557-465X) **98,** 2131
Institutul Agronomic Cluj-Napoca. Buletinul. Seria Agricultura se Horticultura *see* Institutul Agronomic Cluj-Napoca. Buletinul. Seria Agricultura **98**
Institutul Agronomic Cluj-Napoca. Buletinul. Seria Zootehnie si Medicina Veterinara. (RM ISSN 0557-4668) **218,** 4811
Institutul Agronomic Ion Ionescu de la Brad. Lucrari Stiintifice. Seria Agronomie. (RM ISSN 0379-8364) **98**
Institutul Agronomic Ion Ionescu de la Brad. Lucrari Stiintifice. Seria Horticultura. (RM ISSN 0379-8372) **2131**
Institutul Agronomic Ion Ionescu de la Brad. Lucrari Stiintifice, Seria Zootechnie - Medicina Veterinaria. (RM ISSN 0075-3513) **218,** 4811
Institutul Astronomic din Bucuresti. Anuarul *see* Centrul de Astronomie si Stiinte Spatiale. Anuarul Astronomic **363**
Institutul Astronomic din Bucuresti. Observations Solaires *see* Centre de l'Astronomie et des Sciences Spatiales. Observations Solaires **363**
Institutul de Arheologie - Cluj-Napoca. Anuarul. (RM) **274,** 2368
Institutul de Arheologie - Iasi. Anuarul. (RM) **274,** 2368
Institutul de Cercetare si Productie Pentru Cultura si Industrializarea Sfeclei de Zahar si a Substantelor Dulci-Fundulea. Lucrari Stiintifice. Sfecla si Zahar. (RM) **180**
Institutul de Cercetari pentru Cereale si Plante Tehnice. Laborator Sfecla de Zahar. Anale. Lucrari Stiintifice. (RM) **181**
Institutul de Cercetari Pentru Cultura Cartofului si Sfeclei de Zahar, Brasov. Anale. Cartoful *see* Institutul de Cercetare si Productie Pentru Cultura si Industrializarea Sfeclei de Zahar si a Substantelor Dulci-Fundulea. Lucrari Stiintifice. Sfecla si Zahar **180**
Institutul de Cercetari pentru Protectia Plantelor. Analele/Research Institute for Plant Protection. Annals. (RM) **98,** 534, 553, 584
Institutul de Cercetari si Productie a Cartofului, Brasov. Anale. Lucrari Stiintifice *see* Institutul de Cercetare si Productie Pentru Cultura si Industrializarea Sfeclei de Zahar si a Substantelor Dulci-Fundulea. Lucrari Stiintifice. Sfecla si Zahar **180**
Institutul de Fizica Atomica. Sesiunea Stiintifica Anuala de Comunicari; Program si Rezumate. (RM) **3847**
Institutul de Geologie si Geofizica. Anuarul. (RM) **1568**
Institutul de Geologie si Geofizica. Dari de Seama ale Sedintelor. (RM ISSN 0068-306X) **1590**
Institutul de Geologie si Geofizica. Studii Tehnice si Economice. (RM) **1568**
Institutul de Istorie si Arheologie "A.D. Xenopol" - Iasi. Anuarul *see* Institutul de Arheologie - Iasi. Anuarul **274**
Institutul de Istorie si Arheologie - Cluj-Napoca. Anuarul *see* Institutul de Arheologie - Cluj-Napoca. Anuarul **274**
Institutul de Mine Petrosani. Lucrari Stiintifice *see* Universitatea Tehnica Petrosani. Lucrari Stiintifice **1583**
Institutul de Studii Cercetari si Proiectari Pentru Gospodarirea Apelor. Studii de Economia Apelor. (RM) **4825**
Institutul de Studii si Proiectari Energetice. Buletinul. (RM ISSN 1220-4145) **1791,** 1899
Institutul de Subingineri Oradea. Lucrari Stiintifice Seria Biologic. (RM) **442**
Institutul de Subingineri Oradea. Lucrari Stiintifice Seria Chimie. (RM) **1179**
Institutul de Subingineri Oradea. Lucrari Stiintifice Seria Educatie Fizica si Sport. (RM) **4475**
Institutul de Subingineri Oradea. Lucrari Stiintifice: Seria Fizica. (RM) **3820**
Institutul de Subingineri Oradea. Lucrari Stiintifice: Seria Geografie. (RM) **2253**
Institutul de Subingineri Oradea. Lucrari Stiintifice: Seria Istorie. (RM) **2314**
Institutul de Subingineri Oradea. Lucrari Stiintifice: Seria Lingvistica. (RM) **2818**
Institutul de Subingineri Oradea. Lucrari Stiintifice: Seria Literatura. (RM) **2925**
Institutul de Subingineri Oradea. Lucrari Stiintifice: Seria Matematica. (RM) **3039**
Institutul de Subingineri Oradea. Lucrari Stiintifice: Seria Pedagogie, Psihologie, Metodica. (RM) **4024,** 1639
Institutul de Subingineri Oradea. Lucrari Stiintifice: Seria Stiinte Sociale. (RM) **4376**
Institutul Geologie si Geofizica. Memoire. (RM ISSN 0020-4234) **1545**
Institutul Politehnic Bucuresti. Buletin Stiintific/Polytechnical Institute of Bucharest. Scientific Bulletin. (RM) **4601**
Institutul Politehnic "Gheorghe Asachi" din Iasi. Buletinul. Sectia I: Mecanica Matematica, Fizica. (RM) **3039,** 3820, 3843
Institutul Politehnic "Gheorghe Asachi" din Iasi. Buletinul. Sectia VII: Textile, Pielarie. (RM ISSN 0253-1119) **4620,** 2736
Institutul Politehnic Iasi. Buletinul. Sectia I: Matematica, Mecanica Teoretica, Fizica *see* Institutul Politehnic "Gheorghe Asachi" din Iasi. Buletinul. Sectia I: Mecanica Matematica, Fizica **3039**
Institutul Politehnic Iasi. Buletinul. Sectia II: Chimie *see* Institutului Politehnic Din Iasi. Buletinul. Sectia II: Chimie. Si Inginerie Chimica **1179**
Institutul Politehnic Iasi. Buletinul. Sectia III: Electrotehnica, Electronica, Automatizari *see* Institutului Politehnic Din Iasi. Buletinul. Sectia III: Electrotehnica, Energetica, Electronica, Automatizari **1899**
Institutul Politehnic Iasi. Buletinul. Sectia IV: Mecanica Tehnica *see* Institutului Politehnic Din Iasi. Buletinul. Sectia IV: Constructii de Masini **1917**
Institutul Politehnic Iasi. Buletinul. Sectia V: Constructi. Arhitectura. *see* Institutului Politehnic Din Iasi. Buletinul. Sectia V: Constructi, Imbunatatiri Funciare **621**
Institutul Politehnic Iasi. Buletinul. Sectia VI: Imbunatatiri Funciare *see* Institutului Politehnic Din Iasi. Buletinul. Sectia VI: Imbunatatiri Funciare **1826**
Institutul Politehnic Iasi. Buletinul. Sectia VII: Textile, Pielarie *see* Institutul Politehnic "Gheorghe Asachi" din Iasi. Buletinul. Sectia VII: Textile, Pielarie **4620**
†Institutul Politehnic Iasi. Buletinul. Sectia VIII. Stiinte Social-Economice. (RM) **5215**
Institutul Politehnic "Traian-Vuia". Buletinul Stiintific si Tehnic. (RM) **1826**
Institutul Politihnic Bucuresti. Buletin *see* Institutul Politehnic Bucuresti. Buletin Stiintific **4601**
Institutului Politehnic Din Iasi. Buletinul. Sectia II: Chimie. Si Inginerie Chimica.(RM ISSN 0254-7104) **1179,** 1854
Institutului Politehnic Din Iasi. Buletinul. Sectia III: Electrotehnica, Energetica, Electronica, Automatizari. (RM ISSN 0258-9109) **1899**
Institutului Politehnic Din Iasi. Buletinul. Sectia IV: Constructii de Masini. (RM ISSN 1011-2855) **1917,** 1931
Institutului Politehnic Din Iasi. Buletinul. Sectia V: Constructi, Imbunatatiri Funciare. (RM) **621,** 301, 1868, 1924
Institutului Politehnic Din Iasi. Buletinul. Sectia VI: Imbunatatiri Funciare. (RM) **1826**
Institutum Canarium Nachrichten *see* I.C. Nachrichten **274**
Institutum Canarium Yearbook. Almogaren. (AU) **274,** 242
Instituut van Mynopmeters van Suid-Afrika. Joernaal. *see* Institute of Mine Surveyors of South Africa. Journal **3485**
†Instituut vir Navorsing in Kinder- en Jeuglektuur. Bulletin/Institute for Research in Children's Literature. Bulletin. (SA) **5215**
Instituut voor Bodemvruchtbaarheid. Jaarverslag. (NE ISSN 0434-6785) **181**
Instituut voor Cultuurtechniek en Waterhuishouding. Jaarverslag *see* Dienst Landbouwkundig Onderzoek. Staring Centrum, Instituut voor Onderzoek van het Landelijke Gebied. Jaarverslag **176**
†Instituut voor Cultuurtechniek en Waterhuishouding. Mededeling. Nieuwe Serie. (NE) **5215**
Instituut voor Cultuurtechniek en Waterhuishouding. Rapporten. Nieuwe Serie *see* Dienst Landbouwkundig Onderzoek. Staring Centrum, Instituut voor Onderzoek van het Landelijk Gebied. Rapporten **176**
Instituut voor Cultuurtechniek en Waterhuishouding. Reports *see* Agricultural Research Department. Winand Staring Centre for Integrated Land, Soil and Water Research. Reports **166**
†Instituut voor Cultuurtechniek en Waterhuishouding. Technical Bulletins. New Series. (NE) **5215**
†Instituut voor de Veredeling van Tuinbouwgewassen. Jaarverslag. Projecten van Onderzoek/Institute for Horticultural Plant Breeding. Annual Report. Research Projects. (NE) **5215**
Instituut voor Hygiene en Epidemiologie. Zwavel-Rook Meetnet *see* Studie van de Luchtkwaliteit in Belgie. Zwavel-Rook Meetnet **4113**
†Instituut voor Plantenziektenkundig Onderzoek. Mededeling/Institute of Phytopathological Research. Communications. (NE ISSN 0019-0349) **5215**
Instituut voor Planteziektenkundig Onderzoek. Jaarverslag/Research Institute for Plant Protection. Annual Report. (NE ISSN 0074-0446) **181**
Instituut voor Pluimveeonderzoek Het Spelderholt. Jaarverslag *see* Centrum voor Onderzoek en Voorlichting voor de Pluimveehouderij "Het Spelderholt". Jaarsverlag **214**
Instituut voor Rassenonderzoek van Landbouwgewassen. Mededelingen *see* Centrum voor Rassenonderzoek en Zaadtechnologie. Mededelingen **172**
Instituut voor Veevoedingsonderzoek. Jaarverslag. (NE) **219**

Title

Instituut voor Veevoedingsonderzoek. Jaarverslag see Instituut voor Veevoedingsonderzoek. Jaarverslag **219**
Instruction Delivery Systems. (US ISSN 0892-4872) **1690**
Instructional Cassette Recordings Catalog see Music & Musicians: Instructional Cassette Recordings Catalog (Large Print Edition) **2285**
Instructional Science. (NE ISSN 0020-4277) **1639**, 4024, 4376
Instructions Nautiques. (FR ISSN 0223-534X) **4729**
Instructor. (US ISSN 1049-5851) **1639**
Instructor. (UK) **4693**
Instructor and Teacher see Instructor **1639**
▼Instruktiv. (GW) **2534**
Instrument Flight Rule see I F R **55**
Instrument Review see Control and Instrumentation **1413**
Instrument Society of America Directory of Instrumentation see I S A Directory of Instrumentation **2522**
Instrument Society of America Transactions see I S A Transactions **1824**
Instrumenta Lexicologia Latina. Series A & B. (BE) **1277**, 4182
Instrumentalist. (US ISSN 0020-4331) **3556**, 1639
Instrumentation & Automation News. (US) **2522**
Instrumentation and Control Engineering. (English translation of: Journal of Instrumentation and Control) (UK ISSN 0959-8286) **1931**
Instrumentation and Control Engineering in Japan see Instrumentation and Control Engineering **1931**
Instrumentation and Control Systems. (US) **2523**
Instrumentation Bulletin see I C F A Instrumentation Bulletin **2522**
Instrumentation for the Process Industries. (US) **2523**
Instrumentation in the Aerospace Industry see International Instrumentation Symposium **56**
Instrumentation in the Chemical and Petroleum Industries. (US ISSN 0074-0551) **2523**, 1854
Instrumentation in the Food and Pharmaceutical Industries. (US) **2523**, 2073
Instrumentation in the Food Industry see Instrumentation in the Food and Pharmaceutical Industries **2523**
Instrumentation in the Mining and Metallurgy Industries. (US ISSN 0361-3070) **3409**
Instrumentation in the Power Industry. (US ISSN 0074-056X) **2523**
Instrumentation in the Pulp and Paper Industry. (US ISSN 0361-4719) **3663**
Instrumentation Newsletter. (US) **2523**
Instrumentation Symposium for the Process Industries see Instrumentation for the Process Industries **2523**
Instrumentation Systems. (FR) **2523**
Instrumentenbau Report. (GW ISSN 0936-014X) **3556**, 355
Instrumentos y Controles Internacionales. (US) **2523**
Instruments and Control Systems Buyers' Guide see I & C S Buyers' Guide **5207**
Instruments and Experimental Techniques. (English translation of: Pribory i Tekhnika Eksperimenta) (US ISSN 0020-4412) **2523**
Instruments India. (II ISSN 0047-0376) **2523**
Instrumenty od A do Z. (PL) **3556**
Instytut Automatyki Systemow Energetycznych. Prace. (PL ISSN 0084-2788) **1899**, 1418
Instytut Badan Jadrowych. Zaklad Radiobiologii i Ochrony Zdrowia. Prace Doswiadczalne. (PL ISSN 0074-0640) **3358**, 485, 4105
Instytut Badania Prawa Sadowego. Zeszyty Naukowe. (PL) **1515**

Instytut Badawczy Drog i Mostow. Prace. (PL) **1826**, 4719
Instytut Baltycki Gdansk. Komunikaty. (PL ISSN 0137-5253) **2368**, 274
Instytut Elektrotechniki. Prace. (PL ISSN 0032-6216) **1899**
Instytut Geologiczny. Biuletyn. Geology of Poland. (PL ISSN 0138-0389) **1568**
Instytut Gornictwa Naftowego i Gazownictwa. Prace. (PL ISSN 0209-0724) **3689**
†Instytut Gospodarki Wodnej. Prace. (PL ISSN 0074-0586) **5215**
Instytut Hodowli i Aklimatyzacji Roslin. Biuletyn/Institute of Plant Breeding and Acclimatization. Bulletin. (PL ISSN 0373-7837) **181**
†Instytut Lacznosci. Prace. (PL ISSN 0020-451X) **5215**
Instytut Maszyn Matematycznych. Prace Naukowo-Badawcze. (PL ISSN 0209-1593) **1441**
Instytut Medycyny Morskiej i Tropikalnej w Gdyni. Bulletin/Institute of Maritime and Tropical Medicine in Gdynia. Bulletin. (PL) **3220**
Instytut Medycyny Morskiej w Gdansku. Biuletyn - Institute of Marine Medicine in Gdansk. Bulletin see Instytut Medycyny Morskiej i Tropikalnej w Gdyni. Bulletin **3220**
Instytut Medycyny Pracy. Zeszyty Metodyczno-Organizacyjne. (PL) **3109**
Instytut Medycyny Pracy w Przemysle Wlokienniczym i Chemicznym. Zeszyty Metodyczno-Organizacyjne see Instytut Medycyny Pracy. Zeszyty Metodyczno-Organizacyjne **3109**
†Instytut Metali Niezelaznych. Prace. (PL ISSN 0137-589X) **5215**
Instytut Metalurgii Zelaza. Prace/Institute of Ferrous Metallurgy. Transactions. (PL ISSN 0137-9941) **3409**
Instytut Meteorologii i Gospodarki Wodnej. Materialy Badawcze. Seria: Gospodarka Wodna i Ochrona Wod/Institute of Meteorology and Water Management. Research Papers Series: Water Management and Water Protection. (PL ISSN 0239-6238) **1598**, 1958
Instytut Meteorologii i Gospodarki Wodnej. Materialy Badawcze. Seria: Hydrologia i Oceanologia/Institute of Meteorology and Water Management. Research Papers Series: Hydrology and Oceanology. (PL ISSN 0239-6297) **1598**, 1606
Instytut Meteorologii i Gospodarki Wodnej. Materialy Badawcze. Seria: Inzynieria Wodna/Institute of Meteorology and Water Management. Research Papers Series: Water Engineering. (PL ISSN 0239-6254) **1924**, 1868
Instytut Meteorologii i Gospodarki Wodnej. Materialy Badawcze. Seria: Meteorologia/Institute of Meteorology and Water Management. Research Papers Series: Meteorology. (PL ISSN 0239-6262) **3436**
Instytut Meteorologii i Gospodarki Wodnej. Oddzial Morski w Gdyni. Materialy. Warunki Srodowiskowe Polskiej Strefy Poludniowego Baltyku.(PL) **1606**, 1958
Instytut Meteorologii i Gospodarki Wodnej. Oddzial Morski w Gdyni. Materialy. Zlodzenie Polskiej Strefy Przybrzeznej. (PL) **1606**
Instytut Meteorologii i Gospodarki Wodnej. Wiadomosci/Institute of Meteorology and Water Management. Reports. (PL ISSN 0208-6263) **3436**, 4826
Instytut Meteorologii i Gospodarki Wodnej Gazeta Obserwatora I M G W see Gazeta Obserwatora I M G W **3435**
Instytut Naftowy. Prace see Instytut Gornictwa Naftowego i Gazownictwa. Prace **3689**
Instytut Obrobki Skrawaniem. Przeglad Dokumentacyjny. (PL) **1844**, 15, 3425

Instytut Obrobki Skrawaniem. Zeszyty Naukowe. (PL ISSN 0020-4528) **1917**, 3018
Instytut Ochrony Roslin. Biuletyn. (PL ISSN 0020-448X) **99**
Instytut Sadownictwa i Kwiaciarstwa w Skierniewicach. Prace. Seria B: Rosliny Ozdobne/Ornamental Plants. (PL ISSN 0208-5925) **2131**
Instytut Sadownictwa i Kwiaciarstwa w Skierniewicach. Seria A: Prace Doswiadczalne z Zakresu Sadownictwa/Fruit Research. (PL ISSN 0208-5933) **2131**
Instytut Techniki Budowlanej. Prace see Prace Instytutu Techniki Budowlanej. Kwartalnik **1872**
Instytut Technologii Drewna. Prace. (PL ISSN 0032-6240) **640**, 2115
Instytut Tele- i Radiotechniczny. Prace. (PL ISSN 0032-6259) **1375**, 1356, 1899
Instytut Transportu Samochodowego. Zeszyty Naukowe. (PL) **4651**
Instytut Zachodni. Studium Niemcoznawcze. (PL ISSN 0239-7846) **2368**
Instytut Zootechniki. Roczniki Naukowe Zootechniki/Annals of Animal Science. (PL ISSN 0137-1657) **219**, 544, 1958
Insula. (SP ISSN 0020-4536) **403**
Insulation Contractors Association of America News see I C A A News **620**
Insulation Handbook. (UK) **621**, 2033
Insulation Journal. (UK) **621**, 2033
Insulation Outlook see Outlook (Alexandria, 1953) **627**
Insulin and Glucagon. (UK ISSN 0142-8144) **3254**
Insurance. Seimei Hoken Tokei-go see Statistics of Life Insurance Business in Japan **2547**
Insurance. Songai Hoken Tokubetsu Tokei-go see Statistics of Japanese Non-Life Insurance Business **2547**
Insurance Adjuster see Claims **2530**
Insurance Advocate. (US ISSN 0020-4587) **2534**
Insurance Age. (UK ISSN 0142-6265) **2534**
Insurance Almanac; Who, What, When and Where in Insurance. (US ISSN 0074-0675) **2534**
Insurance and Banking Record see Insurance Record of Australia & New Zealand **2535**
Insurance and Employee Benefits Literature. (US) **2546**
Insurance and Financial Review. (US ISSN 0736-0126) **2534**
Insurance and Financial Services Careers. (US) **3628**, 785, 2534
Insurance & Liability Reporter. (US) **2534**
Insurance and Risk Management. (US ISSN 0892-5887) **2534**, 950
Insurance and Technology. (US ISSN 1054-0733) **2547**
Insurance Anti-Trust and Tort Reform Report see Mealey's Litigation Report: Punitive Damages and Tort Reform **2703**
Insurance Broker. (AT) **2534**
Insurance Brokers' Monthly see Brokers' Monthly & Insurance Adviser **2528**
Insurance Case Law Digest. (CN) **2635**, 2534
Insurance Company Profile. (PH) **2534**
Insurance Conference Planner. (US ISSN 0193-0516) **3392**, 2534
Insurance Council of Australia Inc. Bulletin see I C A Bulletin **2533**
Insurance Counsel Journal see Defense Counsel Journal **2701**
Insurance Directory and Year Book. (UK ISSN 0074-0691) **2534**
Insurance Directory of New Zealand. (NZ) **2534**
Insurance Facts. (US ISSN 0074-0713) **2546**
Insurance Facts and Figures see Insurance Statistics (Years) **2546**
Insurance Field. (US ISSN 0020-4684) **2534**
Insurance Forum. (US ISSN 0095-2923) **2534**

Insurance in Australia. (AT) **2534**
Insurance in Australia and New Zealand see Insurance in Australia **2534**
Insurance in China. see Zhongguo Baoxian **2545**
Insurance in Finland. (FI ISSN 0356-9993) **2534**
Insurance Industry Litigation Reporter. (US ISSN 0887-7858) **2635**
Insurance Industry Newsletter. (US) **2534**
Insurance Institute for Highway Safety. Status Report. (US ISSN 0018-988X) **4105**, 4719
Insurance Institute of Canada. Newsletter see Insurance Institute of Canada. Perspectives **2534**
Insurance Institute of Canada. Perspectives. (CN) **2534**
Insurance Institute of India. Journal. (II) **2534**
Insurance Institute of Ontario. Newsletter see In Ontario **2533**
Insurance Journal. (BG) **2534**
▼Insurance Law & Practice. (UK ISSN 0962-1385) **2635**, 2534
Insurance Law Anthology. (US ISSN 0892-4422) **2534**, 2635
†Insurance Law Briefings. (US) **5215**
Insurance Law Citations. (US) **2635**, 2534
Insurance Law Journal. (AT ISSN 1030-2379) **2635**, 2534
Insurance Law Monthly. (UK) **2534**
Insurance Law Reports: Fire & Casualty.(US ISSN 0020-4730) **2534**, 2635
Insurance Law Reports: Life, Health & Accident. (US) **2534**, 2635
Insurance Literature see Insurance and Employee Benefits Literature **2546**
Insurance Litigation Reporter. (US ISSN 0195-1858) **2635**, 2534
Insurance Magazine's Green Book of Convention Planning see Insurance Conference Planner **3392**
Insurance Mail. (UK ISSN 0020-4773) **2534**
Insurance Marketing Insider. (US ISSN 0892-1458) **2534**, 1041
Insurance Marketplace. (US ISSN 0538-2629) **2534**
Insurance: Mathematics & Economics. (NE ISSN 0167-6687) **2534**, 3039
Insurance Periodicals Index. (US ISSN 0074-073X) **2546**, 15
Insurance Product News. (US) **2534**
Insurance Pulse. (US) **2535**
Insurance Record. (US ISSN 0020-4803) **2535**
Insurance Record of Australia & New Zealand. (AT ISSN 0725-4644) **2535**
Insurance Regulatory Information System Ratio Results. (US) **2546**, 2699, 4574
Insurance Report and Statistics of Fiji. (FJ) **2546**
Insurance Review. (PK ISSN 0020-4811) **2535**
Insurance Review. (RH) **2535**
Insurance Review (New York). (US ISSN 0749-8667) **2535**
Insurance Review (Stamford) see Insurance and Financial Review **2534**
Insurance Sales see Life & Health Insurance Sales **2536**
Insurance Settlements Journal. (US ISSN 1052-7249) **2635**, 2535
Insurance Software Review see Insurance and Technology **2547**
Insurance South Magazine. (US) **2535**
Insurance Statistics (Years). (UK ISSN 0950-3668) **2546**
Insurance Statistics of Fiji see Insurance Report and Statistics of Fiji **2546**
Insurance Systems Bulletin. (UK ISSN 0268-1935) **2547**
Insurance Times. (US ISSN 0888-4935) **2535**
InsuranceWeek. (US ISSN 0020-4846) **2535**
Insurgent Sociologist see Critical Sociology **2863**
Intair. (CN) **1505**, 4674
Intanda News. (ZA ISSN 0020-4854) **2240**

Intech. (NE) **2300**
InTech. (US ISSN 0192-303X) **2523**
Integracion Economica Socialista. (CU) **869**
Integracion en Cifras. (GT) **3899**
Integracion Financiera. (CK) **869**
Integracion Latinoamericana/Latin American Integration. (AG ISSN 0325-1675) **931**
Integral. (SP ISSN 0210-0134) **99, 1489, 3804**
Integral. (US) **3556, 3769**
Integral Equations and Operator Theory.(SZ ISSN 0378-620X) **3039**
†Integral Light. (US) **5215**
Integral Yoga. (US ISSN 0161-1380) **4284**
Integral'noe Issledovanie Indiviudal'nosti.(RU) **4024**
Integrated Bar of the Philippines. Journal. (PH ISSN 0115-138X) **2636**
Integrated Circuit Engineering Corporation Report see I C E C A P Report **1772**
Integrated Circuits International. (UK ISSN 0263-6522) **1416**
Integrated Circuits Microprocessor I C's D.A.T.A. Digest see Microprocessor I C's D.A.T.A. Digest **1462**
▼Integrated Ferroelectrics. (US ISSN 1058-4587) **1899**
Integrated Manufacturing Systems. (UK ISSN 0957-6061) **3025, 1414**
Integrated Manufacturing Technology. (US) **1931**
▼Integrated Messaging News. (US ISSN 1056-1412) **1351**
†Integrated Networks Update. (US) **5215**
Integrated Online Library Systems. Meeting Proceedings. (US) **2798**
Integrated Pest Management for Stored Grains (Year). (US) **207, 181**
Integrated Pest Management Practitioner see I P M Practitioner **96**
Integrated Risk Information System (for Microcomputers). (US) **1958**
Integrated Rural Development. Publications. (IS ISSN 0333-9874) **3983, 931**
Integrated Service Digital Network. (US ISSN 0735-1844) **1427**
Integrated Service Digital Network Report see I S D N Report **1363**
Integrated Services Digital Network Handbook and Buyers Guide see I S D N Handbook and Buyers Guide **1337**
Integrated Services Digital Network News see I S D N News **1351**
Integrated Services Digital Network User Magazine see I S D N User Magazine **1351**
Integrated Voice - Data P B X's. (US) **1454**
Integrated Waste Management. (US) **1985, 1791**
Integrateducation see Equity & Excellence **1632**
Integration. (NE ISSN 0167-9260) **1454, 1899**
Integration. (GW ISSN 0720-5120) **3960, 4315**
Integrative Physiological and Behavioral Science. (US) **4024, 442**
Integrative Psychiatry. (US ISSN 0735-3847) **3339**
Integrative Therapie. (GW ISSN 0342-6831) **4025**
Integrity International. (CN ISSN 0712-7685) **3595**
Integro. (SZ) **4409, 4105**
†Intel Yellow Pages. (US) **5215**
Intellect. (FR ISSN 0181-9445) **2437**
The Intellectual Activist. (US ISSN 0730-2355) **3769**
Intellectual Property - Copyright. (AT) **3675**
Intellectual Property Decisions. (UK ISSN 0141-7584) **912, 2724**
Intellectual Property in Australia: Patents, Designs & Trademarks. (AT) **3675**
Intellectual Property in Business (Briefing and Review). (UK ISSN 0955-2197) **2724, 671**

Intellectual Property Journal. (CN ISSN 0824-7064) **2636, 3675**
Intellectual Property Journal. (AT ISSN 1034-3032) **2636**
Intellectual Property Law. (US ISSN 0892-2365) **2636**
Intellectual Property Law Review. (US ISSN 0193-4864) **3675**
Intellectual Property Newsletter. (UK ISSN 0141-9749) **912, 2724**
▼Intellectual Property Protection in Asia. (US) **2724**
Intellectual Property Reports. (AT ISSN 0812-2024) **2636**
Intellectuals' Rendezvous. (Il) **2199**
Intelligence. see Zhili **2183**
Intelligence (Norwood). (US ISSN 0160-2896) **4025**
Intelligence and National Security. (UK ISSN 0268-4527) **3899, 3460**
▼Intelligence Briefs (Irregular). (US) **3960**
▼Intelligence Briefs (Monthly). (US) **3960**
Intelligence Digest (Cheltenham) see Intelligence Digest - A Review of World Affairs **3899**
†Intelligence Digest (Edinburgh). (UK) **5215**
Intelligence Digest - A Review of World Affairs. (UK) **3899, 671**
Intelligence Digest Briefing Paper see Intelligence Digest Strategic Briefing Paper **3899**
Intelligence Digest Strategic Briefing Paper. (UK) **3899**
Intelligence Informatique. see Computational Intelligence **1390**
Intelligence Newsletter. (FR ISSN 0762-8374) **3460, 1515**
Intelligence Report see Richard C. Young's Intelligence Report **961**
Intelligence Report (Washington) see National Security Law Report **2657**
Intelligence Survey. (AT ISSN 0047-0406) **3899**
Intelligence: The Future of Computing. (US ISSN 1042-4296) **827**
†Intelligent Buildings Conference Proceedings. (US) **5215**
Intelligent Decisions. (US) **1337**
Intelligent Instruments & Computers. (US ISSN 0889-8308) **4359, 1418**
†Intelligent Mac. (US) **5215**
Intelligent Network News. (US ISSN 1042-6930) **1338**
Intelligent Software. (US) **1408, 1430**
Intelligent Systems see TechScan Newsletter **828**
▼Intelligent Tutoring Media. (US ISSN 0957-9133) **1408**
Intendance et Syndicalisme. (FR) **2584**
Intensiv- und Notfallbehandlung. (GW) **3109**
Intensivbehandlung see Intensiv- und Notfallbehandlung **3109**
Intensive Agriculture. (Il ISSN 0020-4919) **99**
Intensive & Critical Care Digest. (UK ISSN 0265-5241) **3109**
Intensive Care Medicine. (GW ISSN 0342-4642) **3109**
Intensive Care Nursing. (UK ISSN 0266-612X) **3279**
Intensive Care World. (UK ISSN 0266-7037) **3109**
Intensive Caring Unlimited. (US) **1239, 2466, 3279, 4845**
†Intensive Therapy & Clinical Monitoring. (UK ISSN 0264-7494) **5215**
Intensivmedizin see Intensivmedizin und Notfallmedizin **3109**
Intensivmedizin und Notfallmedizin. (GW ISSN 0175-3851) **3109**
Inter. (IS) **3899**
†Inter. (CN ISSN 0020-4927) **5215**
Inter Alia. (US ISSN 0092-6086) **2636**
Inter American Press Association. Committee on Freedom on the Press. Report. (US ISSN 0579-6695) **3899, 2571**
Inter American Press Association. Minutes of the Annual Meeting. (US) **2571**
Inter American Press Association News see I A P A News **2570**

Inter Architecture. (UK ISSN 0954-8580) **301, 2552**
Inter Auto Ecoles de France - Inter Auto Route. (FR ISSN 0020-5001) **1639, 4693**
Inter Divisas. (SP) **785**
Inter - Industry Study of the New Zealand Economy. (NZ ISSN 0110-7321) **722, 4575**
†Inter - Mecanique du Batiment. (CN) **5215**
Inter Regions. (FR ISSN 0240-9925) **1078**
Inter Universites. (CN) **1315**
Inter-Acao. (BL ISSN 0101-7136) **1709**
Interact. (US ISSN 0279-2664) **1452**
†Interact (Wyndmoor). (US ISSN 1041-911X) **5215**
Interacta. (AT) **1751, 330**
Interacting with Computers. (UK ISSN 0953-5438) **1396**
Interaction see Teacher's Interaction **1667**
Interaction (Canberra). (AT ISSN 0818-6286) **4409**
Interaction (New York). (US) **1014, 4025**
Interaction (Washington, 1981). (US ISSN 8756-6281) **1958**
†Interactions. (US) **5215**
▼Interactions of Man & Animals. (US) **2982, 403**
Interactive Computing see Executive Computing **826**
Interactive Healthcare Newsletter. (US ISSN 1048-0501) **3225**
▼Interactive Learning Environments. (US ISSN 1049-4820) **1690**
Interactive Learning International. (UK ISSN 0748-5743) **1690, 1751**
Interactive Media International. (UK) **1447**
Interactive Services Association Update see I S A Update **1350**
Interactive Update. (UK ISSN 0953-8771) **1351, 1375**
Interactive Video Courseware Catalogue (Year). (UK) **1385**
Interactive Video Yearbook (Year). (UK) **1385**
Interactivity Report see Information & Interactive Services Report **4143**
Interafrican Committee for Hydraulic Studies. Liaison Bulletin. (UV) **4826, 1598**
Inter-African Conference of the Mechanisation of Agriculture Meeting.(NG ISSN 0534-4794) **162**
Inter-African Conference on Co-Operative Societies Meeting. Reunion.(NG ISSN 0534-4697) **831**
Inter-African Conference on Food and Nutrition. Programa e Informacoes. (NG ISSN 0534-4700) **3607**
Inter-African Conference on Food and Nutrition. Report. (NG ISSN 0538-2785) **3607**
Inter-African Conference on Industrial Commercial and Agricultural Education Meeting. (NG ISSN 0534-4727) **1722**
Inter-African Conference on Medical Co-Operation. Meeting. (NG ISSN 0534-4735) **3109**
Inter-African Conference on Social Science Meeting. (NG ISSN 0534-4751) **4376**
Inter-African Conference on the Treatment of Offenders. Meetings. Reunion. (NG ISSN 0534-4816) **1515**
Inter-African Forestry Conference. Conference Forestiere Interafricaine (Communications). (NG ISSN 0534-4824) **2102**
Inter-African Labour Conference Reports, Recommendations and Conclusions. (NG ISSN 0538-2807) **983**
Inter-African Phyto-Sanitary Bulletin see African Journal of Plant Protection **166**
†Interafrique Presse. (FR ISSN 0020-5125) **5215**
Interagency Power Group Briefs. (US) **1791**

†Interaktie. (NE) **5215**
Inter-American Arbitration. (CN) **2636**
Inter-American Bar Association. Conference Proceedings. (US) **2636**
Inter-American Bar Association. Letter to Members. (US) **2636**
Inter-American Center of Tax Administrators. Informativo - Newsletter. (AG) **1098**
†Inter-American Centre for Agricultural Documentation and Information. Documentacion e Informacion Agricola. (CR ISSN 0301-438X) **5215**
Interamerican Children's Institute. Report of the General Director. (UY) **4409, 1256**
Inter-American Commission of Women. News Bulletin. (US ISSN 0538-2912) **4845**
Inter-American Commission of Women. Noticiero. (US ISSN 0538-2920) **4845**
Inter-American Commission of Women. Special Assembly. Final Act/Comision Interamericana de Mujeres. Asamblea Extrarodinaria. Acta Final. (US ISSN 0074-0764) **3943**
Inter-American Conference on Indian Life. Acts - Congresos Indigenistas Interamericanos. Acta see Congresos Indigenistas Interamericanos. Actas **237**
Inter-American Council for Education, Science, and Culture. Final Report. (US ISSN 0074-0829) **1639, 4315**
Inter-American Council of Commerce and Production. Uruguayan Section. Publicaciones. (UY ISSN 0538-3048) **931**
Inter-American Development Bank see The I D B **784**
Inter-American Development Bank. Annual Report. (US) **785, 931**
Inter-American Development Bank. Board of Governors. Anales (de la) Reunion see Inter-American Development Bank. Board of Governors. Proceedings of the Meeting **785**
Inter-American Development Bank. Board of Governors. Proceedings of the Meeting. (US ISSN 0074-0861) **785, 931**
Inter-American Development Bank. Informe Anual see Inter-American Development Bank. Annual Report **785**
Inter-American Development Bank. Institute for Latin American Integration. Annual Report. (AG ISSN 0538-3110) **931**
Inter-American Development Bank. Statement of Loans see Inter-American Development Bank. Annual Report **785**
Inter-American Economic Affairs. (US ISSN 0020-4943) **912, 931**
Inter-American Economic and Social Council. Final Report of the Annual Meeting at the Ministerial Level. (US ISSN 0074-0918) **2410, 4376**
Inter-American Foundation. Annual Report. (US) **931**
Inter-American Foundation. Journal see Grassroots Development **930**
Inter-American Institute for Cooperation on Agriculture. Executive Committee. Yearly Meeting Report. (CR) **99**
Inter-American Institute for Cooperation on Agriculture. Informe Anual. (CR) **99**
Inter-American Institute of Agricultural Sciences. Bibliografias see Inter-American Centre for Agricultural Documentation and Information. Documentacion e Informacion Agricola **5215**
Inter-American Institute of Agricultural Sciences. Center for Training and Research. Bibliotecologia y Documentacion see Inter-American Centre for Agricultural Documentation and Information. Documentacion e Informacion Agricola **5215**

INTERNAL MEDICINE 6301

Inter-American Institute of Agricultural Sciences. Informe Anual see Inter-American Institute for Cooperation on Agriculture. Informe Anual **99**
Inter-American Institute of Agricultural Sciences. Technical Advisory Council. Junta Directiva. Reunion Anual. Resoluciones y Documentos see Inter-American Institute for Cooperation on Agriculture. Executive Committee. Yearly Meeting Report **99**
Inter-American Law Review. (US) **2724**
Inter-American Legal Materials. (US) **2724**
Inter-American Music Review. (US ISSN 0195-6655) **3556**
InterAmerican Opportunities Briefing. (US ISSN 1055-9299) **931, 3960**
Inter-American Review of Bibliography/ Revista Interamericana de Bibliografia. (US ISSN 0250-6270) **2520, 2982, 4395**
Interamerican Society for Tropical Horticulture. Proceedings. (US ISSN 0254-2528) **2131**
Inter-American Tropical Tuna Commission. Annual Report/ Comision InterAmericana del Atun Tropical. Informe Anual. (US ISSN 0074-1000) **2043**
Inter-American Tropical Tuna Commission. Bulletin/Comision Interamericana del Atun Tropical. Boletin. (US ISSN 0074-0993) **2043**
Inter-American Tropical Tuna Commission. Data Report. (US ISSN 0538-3609) **2043**
Inter-American Tropical Tuna Commission. Quarterly Report/ Comision Interamericana del Atun Tropical. Informe Trimestral. (US ISSN 1048-6259) **2043**
Inter-American Tropical Tuna Commission. Special Report. (US) **2043**
Inter-American Yearbook on Human Rights. see Anuario Interamericano de Derechos Humanos **2719**
Interamericana. (PR) **1315**
Interarma Military News. (IT) **3460**
Interavia A B C see International A B C Aerospace Directory **55**
Interavia: Aerospace Review. (UK) **55, 1899**
Interavia Air Letter. (UK ISSN 0020-5176) **55**
Interavia Space Directory. (UK) **55**
Interbehaviorist. (US ISSN 8755-612X) **4025, 3769**
Interben. (US) **2535**
Interbloc. (FR ISSN 0242-3960) **3279**
Interbrick see Tile & Brick International **1166**
InterCamara. (GW ISSN 0940-2330) **817**
Inter-Cambio. (MX ISSN 0020-5192) **817**
Intercambio. (BL) **4409**
Intercambio Internacional. (MX) **912**
Intercede (Manchester). (UK ISSN 0260-4019) **1736**
Interceram. (GW ISSN 0020-5214) **1165**
Intercessor. (CN) **32, 4182**
Interchange. (CN ISSN 0826-4805) **1639**
Interchange. (AT ISSN 0047-0430) **4182**
Interchange. (US) **4182**
Interchange. (UK ISSN 0144-3488) **4409**
Interchange (Portland). (US ISSN 0047-0457) **1639**
Interchange (Rockville). (US) **2584, 4651**
Interchange Customer Newsletter. (US) **2227**
Inter-Church Committee on Human Rights in Latin America. Newsletter. (CN ISSN 0226-661X) **3943**
Interciencia. (VE ISSN 0378-1844) **4315**
Inter-City Wage & Salary Differentials. (US) **983**
Intercogui. (SP) **785**

Intercollegiate Review. (US ISSN 0020-5249) **2869, 4376**
Intercollegiate Yacht Racing Association of North America Directory see I C Y R A N A Directory **4525**
Intercom. (CN ISSN 0315-9892) **671, 1751**
Inter-Com. (US) **2007**
Intercom. (CN ISSN 0383-6061) **4240**
Intercom (New York, 1960?). (US) **4223, 4315**
Intercom (Washington, 1971). (US ISSN 0047-0414) **2763**
Intercom Technical Bulletin see Orange Seed Technical Bulletin **2778**
Intercompany Announcements see Opera America Newsline **3572**
Intercon. (Spanish edition of: Vademecum) (SP) **3109**
Intercon. (UK ISSN 0264-0961) **4182**
Intercontainer. (SZ) **4710**
†Intercontinental Press. (US) **5215**
Intercontinental Press Combined with Imprecor see Intercontinental Press **5215**
Inter-Corporate Ownership. (CN ISSN 0575-8823) **836**
▼Intercultural Communication Studies. (US ISSN 1057-7769) **4438**
Intercultural Development Research Association Newsletter see I D R A Newsletter **1751**
Intercultural Horizons. (CN ISSN 0827-1569) **2508, 2007**
Intercultural Studies. (US) **2818, 4438**
Interculture. (CN ISSN 0828-797X) **2508, 2007**
Interdenomination Foreign Mission Association of North America, Inc. News see I F M A News **4181**
Interdenominational Theological Center, Atlanta. Journal. (US ISSN 0092-6558) **4182**
Interdependence see Terra Una **4205**
InterDependent. (US ISSN 0094-5072) **3960**
Interdisciplinair Tijdschrift voor Taal en Tekstwetenschap see T T T
Interdisciplinair Tijdschrift voor Taal-en Tekstwetenschap **2847**
Interdisciplinaria. (AG ISSN 0325-8203) **4025, 4376**
Interdisciplinaria Monographs. (AG ISSN 0326-1913) **4025**
Interdisciplinarite Etudes Philosophiques et Litteraires. (FR ISSN 3769, 2925
Interdisciplinary Studies in Alcohol Use and Abuse. (US) **1536**
Interdisciplinary Topics in Gerontology. (SZ ISSN 0074-1132) **2274**
†Interdiscipline. (II ISSN 0020-5338) **5215**
Interdisziplinaere Beitraege zur Kriminologischen Forschung. (GW ISSN 0937-0773) **1515**
†L'Interdit. (CN) **5215**
Intereconomics. (GW ISSN 0020-5346) **912**
Interesse. (AU ISSN 0020-5362) **4409, 3899**
Interessement du Personnel a l'Entreprise. (FR) **1066**
Interessengemeinschaft der mit Auslaendern Verheirateten Frauen e.V. Information see I A F - Information **4845**
Interessenvereins des Bayerische Staatsopernpublikums e.V. Aktuell see I B S Aktuell **3555**
Interest Rate Service. (UK ISSN 0308-9002) **785**
Interest Rates Survey. (AT ISSN 0813-6491) **785**
L'Interet. (CN) **1315**
Interets Prives. (FR ISSN 0153-9884) **950**
Interex Press. (US) **1461**
Interexpress. (US) **1452**
†Interfaccia. (IT ISSN 0393-4470) **5215**
Interface. (JA ISSN 0387-9569) **1397**
Interface. (SZ ISSN 0257-3849) **1751, 1298**
Interface. (NE ISSN 0303-3902) **3556**

Interface. (BE ISSN 0770-4720) **4266**
Interface. (IS ISSN 0334-1100) **4315**
†Interface. (NZ ISSN 0113-3462) **5215**
Interface. Banking Industry see Banking Software Review **805**
Interface (Bethesda). (US ISSN 0020-5419) **1397, 4105**
Interface (Chicago). (US ISSN 0270-6717) **2763, 1736, 3109**
Interface (Montreal) see Association Canadienne-Francaise pour l'Avancement des Sciences. Interface **4300**
Interface (Sacramento). (US) **1397, 1515**
Interface (Santa Cruz) see Interface: the Computer Education Quarterly **1690**
Interface (Trenton). (US) **4409**
Interface I Cs D.A.T.A. Book see Interface I Cs D.A.T.A. Digest **1774**
Interface I Cs D.A.T.A. Digest. (US ISSN 1057-4522) **1774**
Interface: the Computer Education Quarterly. (US ISSN 0163-6626) **1690, 1417**
Interfaces. (US ISSN 0092-2102) **1014**
Interfaces: Linguistics, Psychology and Health Therapeutics. (US) **2819, 3109, 4025, 4376**
Interfaith Action see Interfaith Impact **4409**
Interfaith Center to Reverse the Arms Race Challenge see R A R Challenge **5266**
Interfaith Impact. (US) **4409**
†Interfaith Women's News & Network. (US ISSN 0892-6719) **5215**
Interfax. (SP) **785**
Interference. (FR ISSN 0154-5604) **2925**
Interference Technology Engineers Master see I T E M **1898**
Interferences, Arts, Lettres. (FR ISSN 0074-1140) **2925, 330**
Interferon. (US ISSN 0276-1076) **553**
Interflo. (US ISSN 0748-4631) **912**
Interfolk. (FR ISSN 0339-3275) **2055**
Interfraternity Bulletin. (US) **1315**
Interfraternity Research and Advisory Council. Bulletin see Interfraternity Bulletin **1315**
Intergeo-Bulletin. (FR ISSN 0396-5880) **2253**
Intergovernmental Bureau for Informatics Newsletter see I B I Newsletter **5208**
Intergovernmental Committee for Migration Monthly Dispatch for the Press see I C M Monthly Dispatch for the Press **5208**
Intergovernmental Council of Copper Exporting Countries. Quarterly Review. (FR) **912, 3409**
Intergovernmental Council of Copper Exporting Countries. Statistical Bulletin. (FR) **3499**
Intergovernmental Oceanographic Commission. Technical Series. (UN ISSN 0074-1175) **1606**
Intergovernmental Organizations Report see I G O Report **911**
Intergovernmental Perspective. (US ISSN 0362-8507) **3899**
Inter-Governmental Philatelic Corporation Philatelic Report see I G P C Philatelic Report **5209**
Inter-hemispheric Education Resource Center. Bulletin. (US ISSN 0891-2688) **3960, 3943**
Interieur. (DK) **2552, 2560**
Interim see Mensa Bulletin **1299**
Interim (Las Vegas). (US ISSN 0888-2452) **2925**
Interinvest Review and Outlook. (US) **950**
Interior. (UK) **4620**
Interior Construction. (US ISSN 0888-0387) **621**
Interior Cost Data (Year) see Means Interior Cost Data (Year) **624**
Interior Decorators' Handbook. (US) **2552**
Interior Design. (UK ISSN 0020-5494) **2552**

Interior Design. (US ISSN 0020-5508) **2552**
Interior Design. see Shinei Sheji **2555**
Interior Design Buyers Guide. (US) **1139, 2552**
Interior Design Market. (US) **2560**
Interior Design Ontario. (CN ISSN 0836-3803) **2552**
Interior Designer's Handbook. (UK) **2553**
Interior Landscape Industry. (US ISSN 0742-1648) **2131, 2553**
Interior Textiles see L D B Interior Textiles **2560**
Interiors (New York, 1978) see Interiors: For the Contract Design Professional **2553**
Interiors & Sources. (US) **2560**
Interiors, Design, Environment, Arts, Structures see I.D.E.A.S **2552**
Interiors: For the Contract Design Professional. (US ISSN 0164-8470) **2553**
Interiors Magazine. (AT) **2553, 2560**
Interiors Quarterly. (UK) **2553**
Interiorscape. (US ISSN 0744-8635) **2553**
Interkantonale Kontrollstelle fuer Heilmittel. Monatsbericht/Office Intercantonal de Controle de Medicaments. Bulletin Mensuel/ Ufficio Intercantonale di Controllo dei Medicamenti. Bollettino Mensile. (SZ ISSN 0026-9212) **3109, 3729**
Interkulturell. (GW ISSN 0935-0993) **1639**
Interlanguage Studies Bulletin see Second Language Research **2840**
Interleaf. (US ISSN 0892-9793) **3753**
Interlending and Document Supply. (UK ISSN 0264-1615) **2763**
Interlingua Institute Newsletter see Lingua e Vita **2825**
Interlit. (US ISSN 0020-5575) **4182, 1375**
†Interlocking Concrete Paving Review. (AT) **5215**
▼Interlog Quarterly Review. (CN) **2115**
Intermagazine. (NE) **671, 4772**
†InterMarket. (US) **5215**
Intermarket Association of Advertising Agencies. Newsletter. (US) **32**
InterMedia. (UK ISSN 0309-118X) **1375**
Intermediair. (NE ISSN 0020-5605) **785**
Intermediaire des Chercheurs et Curieux. (FR ISSN 0020-5613) **2314, 2869**
Intermediaire des Genealogistes/ Middelaar Tussen de Genealogische Navorsers. (BE ISSN 0020-5621) **2155**
Intermedica Post. (GW) **932, 3804**
Intermission (Alexandria). (US) **4634**
Intermission (Buena Park). (US) **3556**
Intermodal Age. (US) **4651**
Intermodal Asia. (HK ISSN 1015-2253) **4729**
Intermodal Reporter. (US) **4651**
Intermountain Catholic. (US ISSN 0273-6187) **4266**
Intermountain Contractor. (US ISSN 0020-5656) **621**
Intermountain Farmer see I F A Cooperator **96**
Intermountain Farmers Association Cooperator see I F A Cooperator **96**
Intermountain Food Retailer see Intermountain Retailer **2092**
Intermountain Jewish News. (US ISSN 0047-0511) **2007, 4223**
Intermountain Retailer. (US) **2092**
Intern. (AU) **33**
Intern. (GW) **640**
Intern. (GW ISSN 0177-8722) **2535**
Internacia Esperanto-Muzeo en Wien. Informilo see La Dua Jarcento. Informilo **2811**
Internal Auditing. (US) **752**
Internal Auditing Alert. (US) **752**
Internal Auditor. (US ISSN 0020-5745) **752**
Internal Medicine/Naika. (JA) **3109**
Internal Medicine. see Zentralblatt Innere Medizin **5309**

6302 INTERNAL MEDICINE

Internal Medicine Alert. (US ISSN 0195-315X) **3109**
Internal Medicine News see Internal Medicine News & Cardiology News **3109**
Internal Medicine News & Cardiology News. (US ISSN 0274-5542) **3109**
▼Internal Medicine Resident. (US) **3110**
Internal Medicine World Report. (US) **3110**
Internal Memoranda of the IRS see I R S Memoranda and Letter Rulings **1097**
Internal Publications Directory. (US) **4130**
Internal Revenue Bulletin. (US ISSN 0020-5761) **1098**
Internal Revenue Code. (US ISSN 0163-7177) **1098**
Internal Revenue Code of 1986 as Amended. (US) **1098**
Internal Revenue Manual - Audit and Administration. (US) **1098**
Internal Revenue Service Letter Rulings see I R S Letter Rulings **1097**
Internal Trade of Iran. (IR ISSN 0074-1213) **836**
Internasjonal Politikk. (NO ISSN 0020-577X) **3960**
Internation Center for Tropical Agriculture. Bean Program Annual Report see Bean Program Annual Report **78**
Internation Directory of Fruit Juices. see Annuaire International des Jus de Fruits **377**
International A B C Aerospace Directory.(UK) **55**
International Abstracts in Operations Research. (UK ISSN 0020-580X) **1404, 15**
International Academy of Indian Culture. Report see International Academy of Indian Culture. Satapitaka Series **2339**
International Academy of Indian Culture. Satapitaka Series. (II ISSN 0074-123X) **2339**
International Academy of Legal Medicine and of Social Medicine. (Congress Reports). (IT ISSN 0074-1248) **3265**
International Academy of Preventive Medicine. Journal see Journal of Applied Nutrition **3608**
International Academy of Trial Lawyers. Bulletin see International Academy of Trial Lawyers. Journal **2636**
International Academy of Trial Lawyers. Journal. (US) **2636**
International Accounting Bulletin. (IE) **752**
†International Actuarial Congress. Transactions. (SZ ISSN 0074-1264) **5215**
International Advances in Nondestructive Testing. (US ISSN 0140-072X) **1917**
International Advertiser. (US ISSN 0885-3363) **33**
†International Advertising Association. Intelligence Summary. (US) **5215**
†International Advertising Association Airletter. (US) **5215**
International Aerial Lift Review. (AU) **1078**
International Aerial Lift Review. see Internationale Seilbahn-Rundschau **4651**
International Aerospace Abstracts. (US ISSN 0020-5842) **66, 15**
International Affairs. (UK ISSN 0020-5850) **3960**
International Affairs. (RU ISSN 0130-9641) **3961**
International Affairs Bulletin. (SA ISSN 0258-7270) **3961**
International Affiliation of Independent Accounting Firms. Update see Independent Accounting International. Update **751**
International African Bibliography. (UK ISSN 0020-5877) **403**
International African Library. (UK) **2333**
▼International Agency and Distribution Agreements. (US) **2724**

International Agency for Research on Cancer Biennial Report see I A R C Biennial Report **3197**
International Agency for Research on Cancer Monographs on the Evaluation of Carcinogenic Risks to Humans see I A R C Monographs on the Evaluation of Carcinogenic Risks to Humans **3197**
International Agency for Research on Cancer Scientific Publications see I A R C Scientific Publications **3197**
International Agricultural Aviation Foundation Newsletter see I A A F Newsletter **179**
International Agricultural Development. (UK ISSN 0261-4413) **99**
International Agrophysics. (HU ISSN 0236-8722) **181, 485**
International Air Review. (US) **4674**
International Air Safety Seminar Proceedings. (US ISSN 0270-5176) **55**
International Air Show Guide. (NE) **4674**
International Air Transport Association. Annual General Meeting. Reports and Proceedings. (CN) **4674**
International Air Transport Association. Annual Report see International Air Transport Association. Annual General Meeting. Reports and Proceedings **4674**
International Air Transport Association. Industry Automation and Finance Services Department. Publications see I A T A Publications and Training Material Available to the Public **4674**
International Air Transport Association. Monthly International Statistics. (SZ) **4664**
International Air Transport Association Annual Report see I A T A Annual Report **4674**
International Air Transport Association Dangerous Goods Regulations see I A T A Dangerous Goods Regulations **4674**
International Air Transport Association Live Animals Regulations see I A T A Live Animals Regulations **4674**
International Air Transport Association Publications and Training Material Available to the Public see I A T A Publications and Training Material Available to the Public **4674**
International Air Transport Association Review see I A T A Review **4674**
International Air Transport Newsletter. (US) **3618, 4674**
International Airforwarder and Agents Association. Update. (US) **4710**
International Alban Berg Society Newsletter. (US) **3556**
International Alliance of Theatrical Stage Employes and Moving Picture Machine Operators of the United States and Canada. Official Bulletin. (US ISSN 0020-5885) **2584, 3512**
International Amateur Basketball Federation. Official Report of the World Congress see International Basketball Federation. Official Report of the World Congress **4507**
International Anatomical Congress. Proceedings. (RU ISSN 0074-1353) **3110, 442**
†International and Comparative Broadcasting. (US) **5215**
International and Comparative Law Quarterly. (UK ISSN 0020-5893) **2724**
International and Intercultural Communication Annual. (US) **1338**
International and National Meeting Events. see Empresa Brasileira de Turismo. Calendario de Congresos Nacionais y Internacionais **3392**
International Anesthesiology Clinics. (US ISSN 0020-5907) **3191**
International Angiology. (IT ISSN 0392-9590) **3272**
International Angler. (US ISSN 0257-1420) **4549**
International Animated Film Association. Bulletin see A S I F A News **3503**

International Annals of Adolescent Psychiatry. (US) **3339**
International Annals of Criminology. see Annales Internationales de Criminologie **1510**
International Annual Bibliography of Congress Proceedings. see Internationale Jahresbibliographie der Kongressberichte **3395**
International Annual Bibliography of Festschriften. (GW) **403**
International Annual of Oral History. (US) **2314**
International Antique Airplane Digest. (US) **56, 257**
International Arbitration Report. (US ISSN 0886-0114) **2724, 912**
International Archery Federation. Bulletin Officiel. (UK ISSN 0074-137X) **4475**
International Archives of Allergy and Applied Immunology see International Archives of Allergy and Immunology **3186**
International Archives of Allergy and Immunology. (SZ ISSN 1018-2438) **3186**
†▼International Archives of Heat and Mass Transfer. (US ISSN 1044-5102) **5215**
International Archives of Occupational and Environmental Health. (GW ISSN 0340-0131) **3618**
International Archives of Pharmacology. see Archives Internationales de Pharmacodynamie et de Therapie **3718**
International Archives of the History of Ideas. see Archives Internationales d'Histoire des Idees **3761**
International Art Post. (CN) **330, 1353, 3753**
International Arthurian Society. Bibliographical Bulletin/Societe Internationale Arthurienne. Bulletin Bibliographique. (CN ISSN 0074-1388) **2982, 2060**
International Arthurian Society. Newsletter. (CN) **2925, 2055**
International Arts Manager. (UK) **330, 1014**
International Assessor see Assessment Digest **4145**
International Association for Adolescent Health Newsletter see I A A H Newsletter **3106**
International Association for Bridge and Structural Engineering. Final Report (of Congress) see I A B S E Congress Report **1867**
International Association for Bridge and Structural Engineering. Reports of the Working Commissions see I A B S E Report **1867**
International Association for Bridge and Structural Engineering Congress Report see I A B S E Congress Report **1867**
International Association for Bridge and Structural Engineering Report see I A B S E Report **1867**
International Association for Byzantine Studies. Bulletin d'Information et de Coordination. (GR ISSN 0571-5857) **2368, 2429**
International Association for Cereal Chemistry. Congress Proceedings see International Association for Cereal Science and Technology. Congress Proceedings **2073**
International Association for Cereal Science and Technology. Congress Proceedings. (AU) **2073**
International Association for Child Psychiatry and Allied Professions. Yearbook see International Association of Child and Adolescent Psychiatry and Allied Professions. Yearbook **5215**
International Association for Classical Archaeology. Proceedings of Congress. (IT ISSN 0074-1469) **274, 1277**
International Association for Cross-Cultural Psychology. International Conference. Selected Papers. (NE) **4025**

International Association for Dental Research. Abstracts of the General Meeting. (US ISSN 0534-669X) **3234**
International Association for Educational and Vocational Information. Studies and Reports. (FR) **1639, 3628**
International Association for Hydraulic Research. Congress Proceedings. (NE ISSN 0074-1477) **1924**
International Association for Mass Communications Research. Letter from the President see I A M C R Newsletter **1336**
International Association for Mass Communications Research. Monographs. (NE) **1338**
International Association for Mass Communications Research Newsletter see I A M C R Newsletter **1336**
International Association for Mathematical Geology. Journal see Mathematical Geology **1572**
International Association for Plant Tissue Culture. Newsletter. (IT) **506**
International Association for Regional and Urban Statistics Occasional Papers see I A R U S Occasional Papers **5207**
International Association for Scientific Study of Mental Deficiency. Proceedings of International Congress. (UK ISSN 0085-2007) **3339**
International Association for Shell and Spatial Structures. Bulletin. (SP ISSN 0304-3622) **1868**
International Association for Social Science Information Services and Technology Quarterly see I A S S I S T Quarterly **2760**
International Association for the Advancement of Educational Research. Congress Reports see World Association for Educational Research. Congress Reports **1672**
International Association for the Advancement of Modelling and Simulation Techniques in Enterprises News see A M S E News **3063**
International Association for the Development of Consciousness. Information Bulletin. (IS) **3769, 4182**
International Association for the Exchange of Students for Technical Experience. Annual Report. (FR ISSN 0538-4427) **1722**
International Association for the Fantastic in the Arts Newsletter. (US) **330**
International Association for the Physical Science of the Ocean. Proces-Verbaux. (US) **1606**
International Association for the Physical Sciences of the Ocean. Publications Scientifique. (US) **1606**
International Association for the Protection of Industrial Property Japanese Group. Journal (International Edition) see A.I.P.P.I. Japanese Group. Journal (International Edition) **3672**
International Association for the Study of Organized Crime. Update see Criminal Organizations **1513**
International Association of Agricultural Information Specialists. Quarterly Bulletin. (NE) **139, 2794**
International Association of Agricultural Librarians and Documentalists. Quarterly Bulletin see International Association of Agricultural Information Specialists. Quarterly Bulletin **139**
International Association of Assessing Officers. News Bulletin see I A A O Update **4150**
International Association of Assessing Officers Update see I A A O Update **4150**
International Association of Book Trade Consultants Report. (US ISSN 0896-6508) **4130, 1041**
International Association of Buddhist Studies. Journal. (US ISSN 0193-600X) **4214**

International Association of Chain Stores. Congress Report see International Center for Companies of the Food Trade and Industry. Congress Report **1041**

International Association of Chiefs of Police, Inc. News see I A C P News **1515**

International Association of Chiefs of Police, Inc. Policy Issues see I A C P - B J A Policy Issues **1515**

International Association of Chiefs of Police, Inc. Training Key see I A C P Training Key **1515**

†International Association of Child and Adolescent Psychiatry and Allied Professions. Yearbook. (US) **5215**

International Association of Clothing Designers. Bulletin. (US) **1291**

International Association of Clothing Designers. Convention Yearbook. (US) **1291**

International Association of Clothing Designers. Industry Resources Book. (US) **1292**

International Association of Clothing Designers. Technology and Productivity Resources Directory. (US) **1292**

International Association of Cooking Professionals Commentary see International Association of Culinary Professionals Commentary **2073**

International Association of Culinary Professionals Commentary. (US) **2073**

International Association of Democratic Lawyers. Congress Report. (BE ISSN 0074-1604) **2636**

International Association of Dentistry for Children. Journal see International Journal of Paediatric Dentistry **3235**

International Association of Electrical Inspectors. News-Bulletin see I A E I News **1893**

International Association of Electrical Inspectors News see I A E I News **1893**

International Association of Engineering Geology. Bulletin. (FR ISSN 0074-1612) **1568, 1868**

International Association of Fire Chiefs On Scene see I A F C On Scene **2033**

International Association of Fish and Wildlife Agencies. Proceedings of the Convention. (US ISSN 0161-3332) **1489**

International Association of French Studies. Cahiers. (FR ISSN 0571-5865) **2925**

International Association of Geodesy. Central Bureau for Satellite Geodesy. Bibliography. (GR) **2268**

International Association of Geodesy. Central Bureau for Satellite Geodesy. Information Bulletin. (GR ISSN 0081-0312) **2253**

International Association of Geodesy. Commission Permanente des Marees Terrestres. Marees Terrestres Bulletin d'Information. (BE ISSN 0542-6766) **1590, 2253**

International Association of Geomagnetism and Aeronomy News see I A G A News **1590**

International Association of Jazz Record Collectors Journal see I A J R C Journal **3555**

International Association of Jewish Lawyers and Jurists. Bulletin. (IS) **2636**

International Association of Labour History Institutions. Bibliographische Information. (SZ) **722**

International Association of Laryngectomees News see I A L News **1736**

International Association of Law Libraries. Directory. (US) **2763**

International Association of Liberal Religious Women. Newsletter. (US) **4182**

International Association of Literary Critics. Revue. (FR ISSN 0242-035X) **4130**

International Association of Logopedics and Phoniatrics. Reports of Congress. (SZ ISSN 0074-1655) **3339**

International Association of Meteorology and Atmospheric Physics. Report of Proceedings of General Assembly. (AU ISSN 0074-1663) **3436**

International Association of Meteorology and Atmospheric Physics News Bulletin see I A M P News Bulletin **5207**

International Association of Milk Control Agencies. Proceedings of Annual Meetings. (US ISSN 0074-1671) **200**

International Association of Museums of Arms and Military History. Congress Reports. (GW ISSN 0074-168X) **3525, 3460**

International Association of Performing Arts Libraries and Museums. Congress Proceedings. (FR) **330, 2763**

International Association of Personnel in Employment Security. News. (US ISSN 0020-6008) **983**

International Association of Physical Education and Sports for Girls and Women. Proceedings of the International Congress. (JA ISSN 0074-1728) **4475**

International Association of Physicians in Audiology Bulletin see I A P A Bulletin **3314**

International Association of Plumbing and Mechanical Officials. Directory of Research Recommendations see Directory of Plumbing Research Recommendations **2298**

International Association of Professional Natural Hygienists Newsletter see I A P N H Newsletter **3606**

International Association of Pupil Personnel Workers. Journal. (US ISSN 0020-6016) **1639, 1239**

International Association of Quality Circles. Annual Conference and Resource Mart Transactions see Association for Quality and Participation. Annual Conference and Resource Mart Transactions **1003**

International Association of Residential and Community Alternatives. Journal.(US) **1515**

International Association of Scholarly Publishers Newsletter see I A S P Newsletter **1708**

International Association of School Librarianship Conference Proceedings see I A S L Conference Proceedings **2760**

International Association of School Librarianship Newsletter see I A S L Newsletter **2760**

International Association of Science and Technology for Development International Conference Proceedings see I A S T E D. International Conference Proceedings **1407**

International Association of Space Philatelists Explorer see I A S P Explorer **3753**

International Association of Sports Museums and Halls of Fame Newsletter see I A S M H F Newsletter **3525**

International Association of State Lotteries. (Reports of Congress). (SZ ISSN 0074-1744) **1098**

International Association of Technological Universities Libraries Quarterly see I A T U L Quarterly **2760**

International Association of Thalassotherapy. Congress Reports. (FR ISSN 0074-1760) **3110**

International Association of Theoretical and Applied Limnology. Communications/Internationale Vereinigung fuer Theoretische und Angewandte Limnologie. Mitteilungen.(GW ISSN 0538-4680) **1598, 442**

International Association of Theoretical and Applied Limnology. Proceedings/ Internationale Vereinigung fuer Theoretische und Angewandte Limnologie. Verhandlungen. (GW ISSN 0368-0770) **1598, 442, 1606**

International Association of Traffic and Safety Sciences Research see I A T S S Research **4692**

International Association of Universities. Bulletin see Higher Education Policy **1708**

International Association of Wiping Cloth Manufacturers Bulletin see I A W C M Bulletin **5207**

International Association of Wood Anatomists Bulletin see I A W A Bulletin **505**

International Association of Workers for Maladjusted Children. Congress Report see International Association of Workers for Troubled Children and Youth. Congress Reports **1736**

International Association of Workers for Troubled Children and Youth. Congress Reports. (FR) **1736**

International Association of Zoo Educators. Journal. (US ISSN 1040-5208) **1489, 1722**

International Association of Zoo Educators. Newsletter see International Association of Zoo Educators. Journal **1489**

International Association on the Artificial Prolongation of the Human Specific Lifespan. Official Journal see Rejuvenation **2278**

International Associations see Transnational Associations **3974**

International Astronautical Federation (I A F). International Congress. Invited Papers see International Development in Space Station and Space Technologies **56**

International Astronomical Union. Central Bureau for Astronomical Telegrams. Circular. (US ISSN 0081-0304) **365**

International Astronomical Union. General Assembly. Highlights. (NE) **365**

International Astronomical Union. General Assembly. Proceedings see International Astronomical Union. General Assembly. Highlights **365**

International Astronomical Union. Minor Planet Center. Minor Planet Circulars - Minor Planets and Comets. (US ISSN 0736-6884) **365**

International Astronomical Union. Proceedings of Symposia. (NE ISSN 0074-1809) **365**

International Astronomical Union. Transactions. (NE ISSN 0080-1372) **365**

International Astronomical Union. Transactions and Highlights see International Astronomical Union. Transactions **365**

International Atomic Energy Agency. Annual Report. (UN ISSN 0085-2023) **1805, 1826**

International Atomic Energy Agency. Bulletin. (UN ISSN 0020-6067) **1805, 1826**

International Atomic Energy Agency. Legal Series. (UN ISSN 0074-1868) **2636, 1805**

International Atomic Energy Agency. Nuclear Power Reactors in the World. (UN) **1806, 1826**

International Atomic Energy Agency. Panel Proceedings Series. (UN ISSN 0074-1876) **1806, 1826**

International Atomic Energy Agency. Power Reactors in Member States see International Atomic Energy Agency. Nuclear Power Reactors in the World **1806**

International Atomic Energy Agency. Proceedings Series. (UN ISSN 0074-1884) **1806, 1826**

International Atomic Energy Agency. Radiation Data for Medical Use; Catalogue see Radiation Dosimetry Data: Catalogue **3361**

International Atomic Energy Agency. Safety Series. (AU) **1806, 1826**

International Atomic Energy Agency. Safety Series. (UN ISSN 0074-1892) **4105**

International Atomic Energy Agency. Technical Directories. (UN ISSN 0074-1906) **1806, 1826**

International Atomic Energy Agency. Technical Report Series. (UN ISSN 0074-1914) **1806, 1826**

International Atomic Energy Agency Library Film Catalog see I A E A Library Film Catalog **3837**

International Atomic Energy Agency Technical Documents Series see I A E A Technical Documents Series **1805**

International Auction Records. (US ISSN 0074-1922) **330**

International Audio Review. (US) **3859**

International Authors and Writers Who's Who. (UK ISSN 0143-8263) **419, 2925**

International Auto Statistics. see Das Auto-International-in Zahlen **4680**

International Automotive Review. (UK ISSN 0261-2267) **4693**

International Aviation. see Guoji Hangkong **54**

International Aviation News. (UK) **4674, 56**

International Baby Food Action Network News see I B F A N News **1238**

International Baccalaureate Organisation. Annual Bulletin. (SZ) **1639**

International Bacclaureate Office. Annual Bulletin see International Baccalaureate Organisation. Annual Bulletin **1639**

International Back Pain News. (UK) **3110**

International Badminton Federation. Annual Handbook see International Badminton Federation. Annual Statute Book **4475**

International Badminton Federation. Annual Statute Book. (UK ISSN 0255-4437) **4475**

International Bahama Life. (BF) **4772**

International Bandsman see British Bandsman **3542**

International Banjo. (US ISSN 0272-2062) **3556**

†International Banking & Financial Law Bulletin. (UK ISSN 0266-3147) **5215**

International Banking: Government Relations Status Report. (US) **785**

International Bar Journal see International Bar News **2724**

International Bar News. (UK ISSN 0143-7453) **2724**

International Bartenders Association News see I.B.A. News **5207**

International Baseball Association Report see I B A Report **4506**

International Basketball Federation. Official Report of the World Congress. (GW) **4507**

International Bauxite Association Review see I B A Review **3485**

International Bear News. (US) **584, 1489, 1958**

International Beekeeping Congress. Reports. (RM ISSN 0074-2007) **99**

International Behavioural Scientist. (II ISSN 0020-613X) **4025**

International Benefits Information Service Briefing Service) see I B I S (Briefing Service) **981**

International Benefits Information Service Review see I B I S Review **2533**

International Beverage News see International Bottler and Packer **382**

International Bibliography of Anthropology see International Bibliography of the Social Sciences. Social and Cultural Anthropology **254**

International Bibliography of Austrian Philosophy/Internationale Bibliographie zuer Oesterreichischen Philosophie. (NE) **3787**

International Bibliography of Book Reviews of Scholarly Literature see I B R **4356**

International Bibliography of Cropping Systems. (PH) 139
International Bibliography of Economics see International Bibliography of the Social Sciences. Economics 722
International Bibliography of Historical Demography/Bibliographie Internationale de la Demographie Historique. (BE ISSN 0255-0849) 3992, 403
International Bibliography of Historical Sciences. (GW ISSN 0074-2015) 2329
International Bibliography of Periodical Literature from all Fields of Knowledge. see Internationale Bibliographie der Zeitschriftenliteratur aus allen Gebieten des Wissens 403
International Bibliography of Political Science see International Bibliography of the Social Sciences. Political Science 3938
International Bibliography of Rice Research. (PH ISSN 0074-2031) 139
†International Bibliography of Selected Police Literature. (UK) 5215
International Bibliography of Sociology see International Bibliography of the Social Sciences. Sociology 4457
International Bibliography of Special Directories. see Internationale Bibliographie der Fachadressbuecher 403
International Bibliography of Structural Engineering. (IE) 1844
International Bibliography of Studies on Alcohol. (US ISSN 0074-204X) 1540
International Bibliography of the Book Trade and Librarianship. see Fachliteratur zum Buch- und Bibliothekswesen 2757
International Bibliography of the Forensic Sciences. (US ISSN 0098-2393) 3176
†International Bibliography of the History of Religions/Bibliographie International de l'Histoire des Religions. (NE ISSN 0538-5105) 5215
International Bibliography of the Social Sciences. Economics. (UK ISSN 0085-204X) 722
International Bibliography of the Social Sciences. Political Science. (UK ISSN 0085-2058) 3938
International Bibliography of the Social Sciences. Social and Cultural Anthropology. (UK ISSN 0085-2074) 254, 15, 403
International Bibliography of the Social Sciences. Sociology. (UK ISSN 0085-2066) 4457
International Bibliography on Burns. (US ISSN 0090-0575) 3176
International Bibliography: Publications of Intergovernmental Organizations. (US ISSN 0256-1042) 403
International Bicycle Fund News see I B F News 4518
International Bio-Sciences Monographs. (II ISSN 0253-7206) 442
International Biodeterioration. (UK ISSN 0265-3036) 490
†International Biodeterioration Symposium. Proceedings. Biodeterioration of Materials. (US) 5215
International Biological Programme Series. (UK) 442
International Biometeorological Congress. Proceedings see Biometeorology; Proceedings 3433
International Biometeorological Congress. Summaries and Reports Presented to the Congress. (NE ISSN 0074-2082) 442
International Biophysics Congress. Abstracts. (US) 466, 15
International Bioscience Series. (II ISSN 0971-1716) 506
International Biotechnology Directory see Biotechnology Directory (Year) 1123
International Biotechnology Laboratory. (US ISSN 0888-7225) 490, 3260

International Bluegrass. (US) 3556, 1375
International Boat Industry. (UK ISSN 0020-6172) 4525
International Boehringer Mannheim. Symposia. (US ISSN 0173-0282) 3209
International Bonds Service. (UK) 785
International Bonsai. (US ISSN 0198-9561) 2131
†International Book Collectors Almanac. Newsletter. (US ISSN 0741-9953) 5215
International Book Trade Directory. (GW ISSN 0344-6190) 4141, 4130
International Books in Print. (GW ISSN 0170-9348) 403
International Bottled Water Association News see I B W A News 381
International Bottled Water Association Technical Bulletin see I B W A Technical Bulletin 381
International Bottler and Packer. (UK) 382, 3649, 3862
International Boundary Study. (US ISSN 0502-0034) 2253, 2724
International Bowhunter. (US ISSN 0739-0696) 4549
International Brain Dominance Review. (US ISSN 1046-5448) 3339, 1639
International Brain Research Organization Monograph Series. (US ISSN 0361-0462) 3339
International Brewer's Directory. (SZ ISSN 0074-9796) 382
International Bridge Conference. Proceedings. (US) 1868
International Bridge, Tunnel and Turnpike Association. Report of the Annual Meeting. (US) 4719
International Broadcast Engineer. (UK ISSN 0020-6229) 1375
International Brotherhood of Electrical Workers, A F L - C I O Journal see I B E W Journal 2584
International Brotherhood of Electrical Workers, A F L - C I O Local 1470 Journal see I B E W - A F L - C I O. Local 1470 Journal 2584
International Buddhist Center. Monthly Guide see International Buddhist Meditation Center. Monthly Guide 4214
International Buddhist Meditation Center. Monthly Guide. (US) 4214
International Building Science & Construction Abstracts. (IE) 638
International Building Science & Construction Abstracts see International Building Science & Construction Abstracts 638
International Building Services Abstracts. (UK ISSN 0140-4237) 2304, 15
International Bulk Journal. (UK ISSN 0260-1087) 4710
International Bulletin for Photographic Documentation of the Visual Arts see Visual Resources Association Bulletin 349
International Bulletin of Bibliography on Education Annual Summary see B I B E Annual Summary 1674
International Bulletin of Bibliography on Education Quarterly Bulletin see B I B E Quarterly Bulletin 1674
International Bulletin of Missionary Research. (US ISSN 0272-6122) 2763, 4240
International Bulletin of Sports Information. (NE ISSN 0378-4037) 4476
International Bulletin on Atomic and Molecular Data for Fusion. (UN) 1806
International Bureau of Education. Bulletin. (UN) 1677
International Bureau of Fiscal Documentation. Annual Report. (NE ISSN 0074-2104) 1098
International Business. (US ISSN 1060-4073) 912
International Business and Financial Outlook. (US) 869
International Business and Management see Business Week - China 652

International Business Aviation Council International Update see I B A C International Update 54
International Business Directory of Iran. (IR) 1139
International Business Forms Industries, Inc. Informs see Informs 671
International Business Lawyer. (UK ISSN 0309-7676) 2724
International Business Machines Corp. Journal of Research and Development see I B M Journal of Research and Development 1395
International Business Machines Corp. Systems Journal see I B M Systems Journal 1437
International Business Opportunities Service. (US) 912
International Business Perspectives see Global Business Issues 5200
†International Business Regulations Report. (US) 5216
International Business Report. (SA) 912
International Businessmen's Who's Who.(UK) 1139
International Butane - Propane Newsletter. (US) 3689
International Buyers Guide of the Music, Record and Tape Industry see Billboard's International Buyer's Guide of the Music-Record-Tape Industry 3541
†International C A D - C A M - C A E Software Products Database. (US) 5216
International C A D - C A M Software Directory see International C A D - C A M - C A E Software Products Database 5216
The International C D - R O M Report. (CN) 1477
International Cable. (US) 1375
International Callbook. (US) 1356
International Camellia Journal. (US) 2131
International Camellia Society. Mid-Year Newsletter. (US) 2132
International Canada see International Perspectives 3961
International Cancer News see U I C C Magazine 5293
International Cancer Research Data Bank Cancergram: Antitumor and Antiviral Agents - Experimental Therapeutics, Toxicology, Pharmacology see I C R D B Cancergram: Antitumor and Antiviral Agents - Experimental Therapeutics, Toxicology, Pharmacology 1982
International Cancer Research Data Bank Cancergram: Antitumor and Antiviral Agents - Mechanism of Action see I C R D B Cancergram: Antitumor and Antiviral Agents - Mechanism of Action 3175
International Cancer Research Data Bank Cancergram: Breast Cancer - Diagnosis, Treatment, Preclinical Biology see I C R D B Cancergram: Breast Cancer - Diagnosis, Treatment, Preclinical Biology 3175
International Cancer Research Data Bank Cancergram: C N S Malignancies - Diagnosis, Treatment see I C R D B Cancergram: C N S Malignancies - Diagnosis, Treatment 3175
International Capital Markets Review. (US) 785
International Cargo Crime Prevention see Commercial Crime International 1512
International Cargo Handling Coordination Association. Buyers' Guide to Manufacturers. (UK ISSN 0954-5964) 4729
International Cargo Handling Coordination Association Quarterly Bulletin see I C H C A Quarterly Bulletin 4664
International Carpet Bulletin. (UK ISSN 0268-2966) 2553
International Carwash Association Letter see I C A Letter 4692
International Catacomb Society Newsletter see I C S Newsletter 328

†International Catalogue of Films, Filmstrips and Slides on Public Education About Cancer. (SZ) 5216
International Catalogue of Films for Public Education About Cancer see International Catalogue of Films, Filmstrips and Slides on Public Education About Cancer 5216
International Catalogue of Occupational Safety and Health Films. (UN ISSN 0074-2147) 3623
International Cataloguing see International Cataloguing and Bibliographic Control 2763
International Cataloguing and Bibliographic Control. (GW ISSN 1011-8829) 2763
International Catholic Committee of Nurses and Medico Social Assistants News - Nouvelles - Nachrichten see C I C I A M S News - Nouvelles - Nachrichten 3276
†International Catholic Migration Commission. Annual Report/ Commission Internationale Catholique pour les Migrations. Rapport Annuel/ Comision Catolica Internacional de Migration. Informe Anual. (SZ) 5216
International Catholic Migration Commission Newsletter see I C M C Newsletter 5208
International Catholic Movement for Intellectual Cultural Affairs. Proceedings of the Plenary Assembly see Pax Romana 5256
†International Cellular Plastics Conference. Proceedings. (US ISSN 0579-5400) 5216
International Cement Review. (UK ISSN 0959-6038) 621
International Center for Arid and Semiarid Land Studies Newsletter see I C A S A L S Newsletter 96
International Center for Companies of the Food Trade and Industry. Congress Report. (FR) 1041, 2073
International Center for Companies of the Food Trade and Industry Communication see C I E S Communication 2062
International Center for Economic Growth. Newsletter. (US) 869
International Center for Living Aquatic Resources Management Bibliographies see I C L A R M Bibliographies 2051
International Center for Living Aquatic Resources Management Conference Proceedings. see I C L A R M Conference Proceedings 2043
International Center for Living Aquatic Resources Management Quarterly see N A G A: I C L A R M Quarterly 2046
International Center for Living Aquatic Resources Management Studies and Reviews see I C L A R M Studies and Reviews 2043
International Center for Living Aquatic Resources Management Technical Reports see I C L A R M Technical Reports 2043
International Center for Living Aquatic Resources Management Translations see I C L A R M Translations 2043
International Center for Medical Research Annals see I C M R Annals 3106
International Center for Research on Women Occasional Paper Series see I C R W Occasional Paper Series 4845
International Center for Settlement of Investment Disputes Review: Foreign Investment Law Journal see I C S I D Review: Foreign Investment Law Journal 949
International Center of Medieval Art. Newsletter. (US) 330
†International Centre for Heat & Mass Transfer. Bulletin. (US ISSN 0888-6911) 5216
International Centre for Mechanical Sciences. Courses and Lectures. (US) 1931

INTERNATIONAL COMPUTER 6305

International Centre for Settlement of Investment Disputes. Annual Report. (US ISSN 0074-2163) **950,** 2724
International Centre for Settlement of Investment Disputes News from I C S I D *see* News from I C S I D **958**
International Centre for Theoretical Physics. Annual Report. (UN ISSN 0304-7091) **3820**
International Centre for Theoretical Physics. Report *see* International Centre for Theoretical Physics. Annual Report **3820**
International Centre of Insect Physiology and Ecology. Annual Report. (KE) **534,** 1489
International Ceramic Association Trade Journal *see* I C A Trade Journal **1138**
International Ceramic Congress. Proceedings. (FR ISSN 0074-218X) **1165**
International Ceramic Directory. (UK) **1165**
International Chain of Industrial and Technical Advertising Agencies. Proceedings. (US) **33**
International Chemical Engineering. (US ISSN 0020-6318) **1854**
International Chemical Worker *see* Chemical Worker **2581**
International Chemicals Today *see* Chemicals Today **1851**
International Child Health: A Digest of Current Information. (FR ISSN 1016-8699) **3321**
International Children's Centre. Paris. Report of the Director-General to the Executive Board. (FR ISSN 0538-5490) **4438,** 1239
International Children's Rights Monitor. (SZ ISSN 0259-3696) **3943,** 1239
International Chinese Snuff Bottle Society. Journal. (US ISSN 0734-5534) **258,** 330
International Chiropractors Association Review *see* I C A Review **3215**
International Choral Bulletin. (US ISSN 0896-0968) **3556**
†International Christian Digest. (US ISSN 0890-4081) **5216**
International Christian Studies Association Newsletter *see* I C S A Newsletter **4181**
International Christian University. Language Research Bulletin. (JA) **2819**
International Chromatography Guide *see* Journal of Chromatographic Science **1206**
International Church Music Review. *see* Rivista Internazionale di Musica Sacra **3578**
International City - County Management Association Newsletter *see* I C M A Newsletter **4088**
International Civil Aviation Organization. Aeronautical Agreements and Arrangements. Annual Supplement. (UN ISSN 0074-221X) **4674**
International Civil Aviation Organization. Air Navigation Plan. Africa - Indian Ocean Region. (UN ISSN 0074-2287) **56**
International Civil Aviation Organization. Air Navigation Plan. Caribbean and South American Regions. (UN ISSN 0074-2295) **56**
International Civil Aviation Organization. Air Navigation Plan. Middle East and Asia Regions. (UN ISSN 1014-0034) **56**
International Civil Aviation Organization. Air Navigation Plan. Middle East and South East Asia Regions *see* International Civil Aviation Organization. Air Navigation Plan. Middle East and Asia Regions **56**
International Civil Aviation Organization. Air Navigation Plan. North Atlantic, North American and Pacific Regions. (UN ISSN 0074-2325) **56**
International Civil Aviation Organization. Airworthiness Committee. Report of Meeting. (UN ISSN 0074-2244) **56**
International Civil Aviation Organization. All-Weather Operations Panel. Report of Meeting. (UN ISSN 0074-2333) **56**
International Civil Aviation Organization. Assembly. Report and Minutes of the Legal Commission. (UN ISSN 0074-2368) **4674**
International Civil Aviation Organization. Assembly. Report of the Economic Commission. (UN ISSN 0074-2376) **4674**
International Civil Aviation Organization. Assembly. Report of the Technical Commission. (UN ISSN 0074-2384) **56**
International Civil Aviation Organization. Assembly. Resolutions. (UN ISSN 0074-235X) **4674**
International Civil Aviation Organization. Automated Data Interchange Systems Panel. Report of Meeting. (UN ISSN 0074-2252) **56**
International Civil Aviation Organization. Council. Annual Report. (UN) **4674**
International Civil Aviation Organization. Digests of Statistics. Series AT. Airport Traffic. (UN ISSN 0074-2422) **4664,** 4674
International Civil Aviation Organization. Digests of Statistics. Series F. Financial Data. (UN ISSN 0074-2430) **4664,** 4674
International Civil Aviation Organization. Digests of Statistics. Series FP. Fleet, Personnel *see* International Civil Aviation Organization. Digests of Statistics. Series FP. Fleet, Personnel, Commercial Air Carriers **4664**
International Civil Aviation Organization. Digests of Statistics. Series FP. Fleet, Personnel, Commercial Air Carriers. (UN) **4664,** 4674
International Civil Aviation Organization. Digests of Statistics. Series R. Civil Aircraft on Register. (UN ISSN 0074-2457) **4664,** 4674
International Civil Aviation Organization. Digests of Statistics. Series T. Airline Traffic *see* International Civil Aviation Organization. Digests of Statistics. Series T. Traffic, Commercial Air Traffic **4664**
International Civil Aviation Organization. Digests of Statistics. Series TF. Traffic by Flight Stage. (UN ISSN 1014-0093) **4664,** 4674
International Civil Aviation Organization. Digests of Statistics. Series T. Traffic, Commercial Air Traffic. (UN ISSN 1014-0077) **4664,** 4674
International Civil Aviation Organization. Digests of Statistics. Series TF. Traffic Flow *see* International Civil Aviation Organization. Digests of Statistics. Series TF. Traffic by Flight Stage **4664**
International Civil Aviation Organization. Index of I C A O Publications. Annual Cumulation. (UN ISSN 0074-249X) **4664,** 66
International Civil Aviation Organization. Legal Committee. Minutes and Documents (of Sessions). (UN ISSN 0074-2503) **4675**
International Civil Aviation Organization. Library Information: Recent Accessions and Selected Articles. (UN) **66,** 403
†International Civil Aviation Organization. Obstacle Clearance Panel. Report of Meeting. (UN ISSN 0074-252X) **5216**
†International Civil Aviation Organization. (Panel On) Application of Space Techniques Relating to Aviation. Report of Meeting. (UN ISSN 0074-2228) **5216**
†International Civil Aviation Organization. Sonic Boom Committee. Report of the Meeting. (UN) **5216**
†International Civil Aviation Organization. Visual Aids Panel. Report of Meeting. (UN ISSN 0074-2589) **5216**
International Civil Aviation Organization Circulars *see* I C A O Circulars **4674**
International Civil Aviation Organization Journal *see* I C A O Journal **54**
International Civil Defence *see* International Civil Defence Journal **1273**
International Civil Defence Journal/ Revue Internationale de Protection Civile/Revista Internacional de Proteccion Civil. (SZ) **1273**
International Civil Engineering Abstracts.(IE ISSN 0332-4095) **1845,** 15
International Claim Association Proceedings. (US) **2535**
International Classification. (GW ISSN 0340-0050) **2763**
International Classified Advertising (I C A) Executive Search Newsletter *see* I C A Executive Search Newsletter **3628**
International Clean Air Congress. Proceedings. (US ISSN 0085-2090) **1977**
International Clinical Nutrition Review. (AT ISSN 0725-7090) **3607**
International Clinical Products Review *see* European Clinical Laboratory **3259**
International Clinical Psychopharmacology. (UK) **4025,** 3729
International Coal. (US) **3485,** 912
International Coal Letter. (BE) **1799**
International Coal Report. (UK ISSN 0260-4299) **3486**
International Coal Review. (US) **3486**
International Coal Testing Conference. (US ISSN 0740-5162) **1569**
International Cocoa Organization. Annual Report. (UK) **2073**
International Cocoa Organization. Quarterly Bulletin of Cocoa Statistics. (UK ISSN 0308-4469) **181,** 152
International CODEN Directory. (US ISSN 0364-3670) **2764**
International Coffee Organization Library Monthly Entries - Coffeeline *see* I C O Library Monthly Entries - Coffeeline **2072**
International Collection of Contract Design. (UK) **2553**
International Collection of Interior Design. (UK) **2553**
International College of Dentists. European Section. Newsletter. (UK) **3234**
International College of Dentists Letterette *see* I C D Letterette **3234**
†International College of Psychosomatic Medicine. Proceedings of the Congress. (SZ) **5216**
International College of Surgeons. Journal *see* International Surgery **3379**
†International Combat Arms. (US) **5216**
International Comet Quarterly. (US ISSN 0736-6922) **365**
International Commerce. *see* Guoji Shangbao **910**
International Commerce and Management. *see* Guoji Shangye yu Guanli **910**
International Commerce Monthly. *see* Guoji Shangbao Yuekan **910**
International Commercial Bank of China. Annual Report. (CH) **785**
International Commercial Bank of China. Monthly Economic Survey. (CH) **869**
International Commission for the Conservation of Atlantic Tunas. Collective Volume of Scientific Papers. (SP) **2043**
International Commission for the Conservation of Atlantic Tunas. Data Record. (SP) **2043**
International Commission for the Conservation of Atlantic Tunas. Newsletter. (SP) **2043**
International Commission for the Conservation of Atlantic Tunas. Report. (SP ISSN 0377-368X) **584,** 1489
International Commission for the Conservation of Atlantic Tunas. Statistical Bulletin. (SP) **2051,** 4575
International Commission for the Prevention of Alcoholism and Drug Dependency Quarterly *see* I C P A Quarterly **1536**
International Commission for the Southeast Atlantic Fisheries. Collection of Scientific Papers. (SP) **2044**
International Commission for the Southeast Atlantic Fisheries. Statistical Bulletin. (SP) **2051,** 4575
International Commission for Uniform Methods of Sugar Analysis. Report of the Proceedings of the Session (Year). (UK) **2073**
International Commission of Jurists. Bulletin *see* International Commission of Jurists. Review **2724**
International Commission of Jurists. Journal *see* International Commission of Jurists. Review **2724**
International Commission of Jurists. Review. (SZ ISSN 0020-6393) **2724**
International Commission of Maritime History. Colloques. Actes. (FR) **4729**
International Commission of Sugar Technology. Proceedings of the General Assembly. (GW ISSN 0074-2708) **2073**
International Commission on Irrigation and Drainage. Congress Reports. (II ISSN 0074-2732) **1924,** 99
International Commission on Irrigation and Drainage. Report. (II ISSN 0538-5768) **4826,** 99
International Commission on Irrigation and Drainage Bulletin *see* I C I D Bulletin **96**
International Commission on Large Dams. Bulletin. (FR ISSN 0534-8293) **1868**
International Commission on Large Dams. Transactions. (FR ISSN 0074-4115) **1868**
International Commission on Radiological Protection. Annals. (US ISSN 0146-6453) **3358**
International Commission on Trichinellosis. Proceedings. (PL ISSN 0074-3356) **3220**
International Committee for Future Accelerators Instrumentation Bulletin *see* I C F A Instrumentation Bulletin **2522**
International Committee for Historical Science. Bulletin d'Information. (FR ISSN 0074-2783) **2314**
†International Committee for Standardization in Hematology. Symposia. (GW) **5216**
International Committee of Onomastic Sciences. Congress Proceedings. (BE ISSN 0074-2791) **2819**
International Committee of the Red Cross. Annual Report - Rapport d'Activite - Informe de Actividad - Taetigkeitsbericht. (SZ) **4409**
International Committee on Urgent Anthropological and Ethnological Research. Bulletin. (AU ISSN 0538-5865) **242**
International Communication Association Newsletter *see* I C A Newsletter **1336**
International Communication Bulletin *see* I C B **2570**
International Communications in Heat and Mass Transfer. (US ISSN 0735-1933) **1931**
International Communications Report. (UK) **1452,** 1414
International Communicator. (US ISSN 1057-5235) **3234**
▼International Company and Commercial Law Review. (UK ISSN 0958-5214) **2724**
International Comparative Literature Association Bulletin *see* I C L A Bulletin **2924**
International Comparative Statistics Centering on the Japanese Economy *see* Comparative Economic and Financial Statistics Japan and Other Major Countries **711**
International Computer Chess Association Journal *see* I C C A Journal **1419**
International Computer Law Adviser. (US ISSN 0893-2859) **1397,** 1338, 2636

Title

International Computer Program Administrative and Accounting Software *see* I C P Administrative and Accounting Software **1450**
International Computer Program Manufacturing Software *see* I C P Manufacturing Software **1451**
International Computer Update. (US ISSN 0897-411X) **1445**, 827, 1452
International Computer Vision Directory *see* International Computer Vision Products Database **5216**
†International Computer Vision Products Database. (US) **5216**
International Confederation for Agricultural Credit. Assembly and Congress Reports. (SZ ISSN 0074-2856) **152**
International Confederation of Arab Trade Unions Review *see* I C A T U Review **2584**
International Confederation of Free Trade Unions. World Congress Reports. (BE ISSN 0074-2872) **2584**
International Confederation of Free Trade Unions Economic & Social Bulletin *see* I C F T U Economic & Social Bulletin **5208**
International Confederation of Societies of Authors and Composers. (FR ISSN 0074-2899) **3675**
International Conference for the Sociology of Religion *see* International Society for the Sociology of Religion **4183**
International Conference of Agricultural Economists. Proceedings. (UK ISSN 0074-2902) **152**
International Conference of Building Officials. Analysis of Revisions to the Uniform Building Code *see* International Conference of Building Officials. Analysis of Revisions to the (Year) Uniform Codes **621**
International Conference of Building Officials. Analysis of Revisions to the (Year) Uniform Codes. (US) **621**
International Conference of Building Officials. Building Department Administration. (US) **621**
International Conference of Building Officials. Code Changes Committee. Annual Report. (US ISSN 0579-3769) **621**
International Conference of Building Officials. Dwelling Construction Under the Uniform Building Code. (US) **621**
International Conference of Building Officials. Evaluation Reports. (US) **621**, 2489
International Conference of Building Officials. One and Two Family Dwelling Code *see* Council of American Building Officials. One and Two Family Dwelling Code **614**
International Conference of Building Officials. Plan Review Manual. (US) **621**
International Conference of Building Officials. Uniform Building Code. (US ISSN 0082-7584) **621**
International Conference of Building Officials. Uniform Code for the Abatement of Dangerous Buildings. (US) **621**
International Conference of Building Officials. Uniform Fire Code. (US) **621**
International Conference of Building Officials. Uniform Housing Code. (US ISSN 0501-1213) **621**
International Conference of Building Officials. Uniform Mechanical Code. (US) **621**
International Conference of Building Officials. (Year) Accumulative Supplement to the Uniform Codes and Related Publications. (US) **621**
International Conference of Building Officials. (Year) Supplement to the Uniform Codes and Related Publications *see* International Conference of Building Officials. (Year) Accumulative Supplement to the Uniform Codes and Related Publications **621**

International Conference of Ethiopian Studies. Proceedings. (ET ISSN 0074-2945) **2333**
International Conference of Insurance Regulatory Officials. Proceedings. (US) **2535**, 2636
International Conference of Orientalists in Japan. Transactions. (JA ISSN 0538-6012) **3638**, 2314, 2508
International Conference of Social Security Actuaries and Statisticians. Reports. (SZ ISSN 0444-1583) **2535**
International Conference of Social Work. Conference Proceedings. (US ISSN 0074-2961) **4409**
International Conference of Social Work. Japanese National Committee. Progress Report *see* Japanese Report to the International Council on Social Welfare **4410**
International Conference on Acoustics. Reports. (CN ISSN 0074-400X) **3859**
International Conference on Aerospace Computers in Rockets and Spacecraft. Proceedings. (FR) **67**, 56
International Conference on Atomic Physics. Proceedings *see* Atomic Physics **5140**
International Conference on Cloud Physics. Proceedings. (CN ISSN 0074-3011) **3436**
International Conference on Communications. Conference Record *see* I E E E International Conference on Communications. Conference Record **1337**
International Conference on Computer Communications. (Proceedings). (US) **1447**
International Conference on Computer Languages. Proceedings. (US) **1430**, 1477
International Conference on Computer Vision. Proceedings. (US) **1441**, 1414
International Conference on Computer Workstations. Proceedings *see* I E E E Conference on Computer Workstations. Proceedings **5209**
†International Conference on Computers and Applications. (US) **5216**
International Conference on Computing Fixed Points with Applications. Proceedings. (US) **3039**
International Conference on Conduction and Breakdown in Dielectric Liquids. Conference Record. (US) **1900**
International Conference on Conduction and Breakdown in Solid Dielectrics. Proceedings. (US) **1900**
International Conference on Cosmic Rays. (Proceedings). (Ii ISSN 0074-3046) **3847**
International Conference on Data Engineering (Proceedings). (US) **1418**
International Conference on Data Processing in the Field of Social Security. Reports. (SZ ISSN 0251-7469) **2535**
International Conference on Distributed Computing Systems. Proceedings. (US) **1437**
International Conference on Education. Final Report/Conference International de l'Education. Rapport Final. (UN) **1639**
International Conference on Education. Proceedings *see* International Conference on Education. Final Report **1639**
†International Conference on Electron and Ion Beam Science and Technology. Abstracts. (US ISSN 0534-8676) **5216**
International Conference on Fertilizers. Proceedings. (UK) **181**
International Conference on Fluid Sealing. Proceedings. (UK ISSN 0074-3089) **1931**
International Conference on Information Systems. Proceedings. (US) **1437**
International Conference on Infrared and Millimeter Waves. Conference Digest. (US) **3853**, 1900

International Conference on Large High Voltage Electric Systems. Proceedings. (FR ISSN 0074-3151) **1900**
International Conference on Lasers. Proceedings. (US ISSN 0190-4132) **3853**
International Conference on Lead. Proceedings. (UK ISSN 0074-316X) **3409**
International Conference on Lighthouses and Other Aids to Navigation. Reports. (FR ISSN 0538-6128) **4729**
International Conference on Liquefied Natural Gas. Papers. (US) **3689**
International Conference on Liquefied Natural Gas. Proceedings *see* International Conference on Liquefied Natural Gas. Papers **3689**
International Conference on Livestock and Poultry in the Tropics (Proceedings). (US) **219**
International Conference on Oral Biology. Proceedings. (US ISSN 0074-3216) **3234**
International Conference on Parallel Processing. Proceedings. (US ISSN 0190-3918) **1452**
International Conference on Pattern Recognition. Proceedings. (US) **1422**
International Conference on Piagetian Theory and the Helping Professions. Proceedings. (US) **1639**, 1736
International Conference on Plasma Science. Conference Record Abstracts *see* I E E E International Conference on Plasma Science. I E E E Conference Record-Abstracts **1894**
International Conference on Pressure Surges. Proceedings. (UK ISSN 0140-2080) **1931**
International Conference on Radar (Publication) *see* International Radar Conference. Record **1338**
International Conference on Robotics. Proceedings *see* I E E E International Conference on Robotics and Automation. Proceedings **1413**
International Conference on Software Engineering. Proceedings. (US ISSN 0270-5257) **1477**
International Conference on Synthetic Fibrinolytic--Thrombolytic Agents. Proceedings *see* Progress in Chemical Fibrinolysis and Thrombolysis **5263**
International Conference on the Physics of Electronic and Atomic Collisions. Abstracts of Contributed Papers and Invited Papers. (US) **3847**
International Conference on the Physics of Electronic and Atomic Collisions. Papers *see* International Conference on the Physics of Electronic and Atomic Collisions. Abstracts of Contributed Papers and Invited Papers **3847**
International Conference on the Protection of Pipes. Proceedings. (US) **1826**
International Conference on the Structural Design of Asphalt Pavements. Proceedings. (US ISSN 0074-3348) **4719**
International Conference on Thermoelectric Energy Conversion. Proceedings. (US) **1900**
International Conference on Vehicle Structural Mechanics. Proceedings. (US) **4693**
International Conference on Very Large Data Bases. Proceedings. (US ISSN 0730-9317) **1445**
International Conference on Wafer Scale Integration. (US) **1408**
International Congress Calendar. (GW ISSN 0538-6349) **3392**
International Congress for Byzantine Studies. Acts/Congres International des Etudes Byzantines. Actes. (GR ISSN 0074-3542) **2368**, 2429
International Congress for Cybernetics. Proceedings. Actes. (BE ISSN 0074-3380) **1441**

International Congress for Papyrology. Proceedings. (UK ISSN 0074-3429) **274**
International Congress for Stereology. Proceedings. (GW ISSN 0074-3437) **1917**
International Congress for the Study of Pre-Columbian Cultures of the Lesser Antilles. Proceedings. (CN ISSN 0538-6381) **242**
International Congress of Angiology. Proceedings. (IT ISSN 0074-347X) **3209**
International Congress of Comparative Law. Israel Reports. (IS) **2636**
International Congress of Entomology. (UK ISSN 0074-364X) **534**
†International Congress of Graphoanalysts. Proceedings. (US ISSN 0534-9044) **5216**
International Congress of Hematology. Proceedings. (US ISSN 0074-3682) **3272**
International Congress of Histochemistry and Cytochemistry. Proceedings. (FI ISSN 0074-3690) **477**, 525
International Congress of Historical Sciences. Proceedings *see* Etudes Historiques **2310**
†International Congress of History of Medicine. Proceedings. (GW ISSN 0074-3704) **5216**
International Congress of Home Economics. Report. (FR ISSN 0074-3712) **2447**
International Congress of Linguists. Proceedings. (NE ISSN 0074-3755) **2819**
†International Congress of Microbiology. Proceedings. (GW) **5216**
International Congress of Nephrology. Abstracts of Reports and Communications. (GR ISSN 0074-3771) **3388**
International Congress of Occupational Therapy. Proceedings. (AT ISSN 0074-3828) **3618**
International Congress of Parasitology. Proceedings. (IT ISSN 0074-3860) **584**
International Congress of Pharmaceutical Sciences. Proceedings. (NE ISSN 0074-3879) **3729**
International Congress of Primatology. Proceedings. (GW ISSN 0074-3895) **242**, 584
International Congress of Psychology. Proceedings. (GW ISSN 0085-2112) **4025**
International Congress of Radiology. (Reports). (FI ISSN 0074-3933) **3358**
International Congress of Sugarcane Technologists. Proceedings. (IO ISSN 0074-3968) **2073**
International Congress of the Transplantation Society. Proceedings *see* Transplantation Today **5291**
International Congress of Verdi Studies. Proceedings. (IT) **3556**
International Congress on Alcoholism and Addictions. Proceedings. (SZ) **1536**
International Congress on Alcoholism and Addictions International Institutes on the Prevention and Treatment of Alcoholism. Papers *see* I C A A. International Institutes on the Prevention and Treatment of Alcoholism. Papers **1536**
International Congress on Alcoholism and Addictions News *see* I C A A News **1536**
International Congress on Alcoholism and Addictions Publications *see* I C A A. Publications **1536**
International Congress on Alcoholism and Drug Dependence. Proceedings *see* International Congress on Alcoholism and Addictions. Proceedings **1536**
International Congress on Animal Reproduction. Proceedings. (SW) **4811**

INTERNATIONAL DIGEST

International Congress on Animal Reproduction and Artificial Insemination. Proceedings see International Congress on Animal Reproduction. Proceedings **4811**

International Congress on Archives. Proceedings see Archivum **2744**

International Congress on Clinical Chemistry. Abstracts. (AU ISSN 0074-4042) **477, 3729**

International Congress on Clinical Chemistry. Papers. (FI ISSN 0074-4069) **477, 3729**

International Congress on Combustion Engines. Proceedings. (UK ISSN 0074-4077) **1931**

International Congress on Instrumentation in Aerospace Simulation Facilities. Record. (US ISSN 0730-2010) **56**

International Congress on Metallic Corrosion. (Proceedings). (CN ISSN 0074-4123) **3409**

International Congress on Mushroom Science. Proceedings see Mushroom Science **510**

International Congress on Technology and Technology Exchange. Proceedings. (US ISSN 1045-585X) **1826, 4601**

International Congress on the History of Art. Proceedings. (FR ISSN 0074-4190) **330**

†International Congress on Women in Music. Newsletter. (US) **5216**

International Congress Science Series. (BE ISSN 0538-6772) **3392**

International Congress Series. (NE ISSN 0531-5131) **3393, 4315**

International Congresses on Tropical Medicine and Malaria. (Proceedings). (NE ISSN 0074-4212) **3220**

International Connector for Jewish Singles. (US) **4362, 2007**

†International Conservative Insight. (CN ISSN 0831-4268) **5216**

International Construction. (UK ISSN 0020-6415) **1868, 621**

International Construction Law Review. (UK ISSN 0265-1416) **2724, 621**

†International Construction Week. (US ISSN 0149-5585) **5216**

†International Construction Week: Africa Construction Business Report. (US) **5216**

†International Construction Week: Asia Construction Business Report. (US ISSN 0278-2448) **5216**

†International Construction Week: Latin America Construction Business Report. (US ISSN 0278-2456) **5216**

†International Construction Week: Mideast Construction Business Report. (US ISSN 0278-2464) **5216**

International Consumer Directory. (UK) **1505**

International Contact Lens Clinic. (US ISSN 0892-8967) **3301**

International Contact - Photo, Video, Lab Technology. (GW ISSN 0939-8619) **3792, 1385**

International Container Directory. (US) **3649**

▼International Contributions to Labour Studies. (UK) **869**

†International Control Products Database. (US) **5216**

†International Convocation on Immunology. Papers. (SZ ISSN 0074-4220) **5216**

International Cooperation. see Kokusai Kyoryoku **3964**

†International Cooperative Alliance. Congress Report. (SZ ISSN 0074-4247) **5216**

International Cooperative Alliance. Cooperative Series. (II ISSN 0074-4255) **831**

†International Cooperative Alliance. Documentation Bulletin for Southeast Asia. (II) **5216**

International Cooperative Alliance Regional Bulletin see I C A Regional Bulletin **831**

International Copper Information Bulletin. (UK ISSN 0309-2216) **3425**

International Corporate Taxation. (US) **1098**

International Corporate Yellow Book. (US ISSN 1058-2894) **1139**

International Corporate 1000 see International Corporate Yellow Book **1139**

International Corporate 1000 Yellow Book see International Corporate Yellow Book **1139**

International Correspondence. (US) **3899**

International Correspondence Society of Obstetrics and Gynecology. Collected Letters. (US ISSN 0443-9058) **3293**

International Correspondent Banker see I C B Magazine **784**

International Cost Forecasting Service Review see D R I - McGraw-Hill Cost and Price Review: International Focus **859**

International Cotton Advisory Committee. Quarterly Statistical Bulletin see Cotton. Part 2: World Statistics **4628**

International Cotton Industry Statistics. (SZ ISSN 0538-6829) **4628, 4575**

International Cotton Industry Statistics. Supplement see International Textile Machinery Shipment Statistics **4628**

†International Cotton-System Fibre Consumption Statistics. (SZ) **5216**

International Council for Adult Education News see I C A E News **1684**

International Council for Bird Preservation. British Section. Report. (UK ISSN 0074-4263) **564**

International Council for Bird Preservation. Proceedings of Conferences. (UK ISSN 0074-4271) **564**

International Council for Bird Preservation Monographs see I C B P Monographs **564**

International Council for Bird Preservation Technical Publications see I C B P Technical Publications **564**

International Council for Commercial Arbitration Congress Series see I C C A Congress Series **2710**

International Council for Distance Education. Bulletin. (UK ISSN 0264-0201) **1639, 1684**

International Council for Education of the Visually Handicapped Educator see I C E V H Educator **1736**

International Council for Educational Media Review see I C E M Review **1638**

International Council for Health, Physical Education and Recreation. Journal. (US) **3804**

†International Council for Laboratory Animal Science. Proceedings of the Symposium. (GW) **5216**

International Council for Laboratory Animal Science Bulletin see I C L A S Bulletin **5208**

International Council for Research in Agroforestry. Annual Report. (KE) **99**

International Council for Scientific and Technical Information Forum see I C S T I Forum **2760**

International Council for the Exploration of the Sea see I C E S Journal of Marine Science **1605**

†International Council for the Exploration of the Sea. Annales Biologiques. (DK ISSN 0106-1003) **5216**

International Council for the Exploration of the Sea. Bulletin Hydrographique see I C E S Oceanographic Data Lists and Inventories **1605**

International Council for the Exploration of the Sea. Bulletin Statistique see I C E S Fisheries Statistics **2051**

International Council for the Exploration of the Sea. Cooperative Research Report see I C E S Cooperative Research Report **1605**

International Council for the Exploration of the Sea. Rapports et Procès-Verbaux des Reunions see I C E S Marine Science Symposia **1605**

International Council for Traditional Music. Bulletin. (US ISSN 0739-1390) **3556**

International Council of Aircraft Owner and Pilot Association Bulletin. (US) **56**

International Council of Jews from Czechoslovakia Newsletter see I C J C Newsletter **5208**

†International Council of Kinetography Laban. Proceedings. (CN ISSN 1013-4468) **5216**

International Council of Museums News see I C O M News **3525**

International Council of Scientific Unions. Year Book. (FR ISSN 0074-4387) **4315**

International Council of Scientific Unions Newsletter see I C S U Newsletter **4313**

International Council on Archives. Committee on Conservation and Restoration. Committee on Archival Reprography (Bulletin). (SP ISSN 0255-3139) **2764**

International Council on Archives. East and Central Africa Regional Branch. General Conference Proceedings. (BS) **2764**

International Council on Archives. Microfilm Committee. Bulletin see International Council on Archives. Committee on Conservation and Restoration. Committee on Archival Reprography (Bulletin) **2764**

International Council on Archives Journal see E S A R B I C A Journal **2756**

International Council on Environmental Law References see I C E L References **1974**

International Council on Health, Physical Education and Recreation Congress Proceedings see I C H P E R Congress Proceedings **3804**

International Countermeasures Handbook. (US ISSN 0145-2584) **3460**

▼International Counterterrorism & Security. (US ISSN 1047-8779) **1526, 3961**

International Country Risk Guide. (UK ISSN 0278-6680) **785**

International Court of Justice. Yearbook.(UN ISSN 0074-445X) **2724**

International Court of Justice Bibliography see I C J Bibliography **2699**

International Crane Foundation Bugle see I C F Bugle **564**

International Credit Association Newsletter see I C A's Newsletter **1505**

International Crop Improvement Association. Production Publication see Association of Official Seed Certifying Agencies. Report of Acres Applied for Certification by Seed Certifying Agencies **169**

International Crude Oil and Product Prices. (CY ISSN 1010-1179) **3689**

International Cruise and Ferry Review. (UK ISSN 0957-7696) **4729, 4772**

International Cryogenic Materials Conferences see Advances in Cryogenic Engineering **3840**

International Cryogenics Monograph Series. (US ISSN 0538-7051) **3841**

International Currency Report. (US ISSN 0738-8888) **912**

International Currency Review. (UK ISSN 0020-6490) **785**

▼International Current Awareness Services. Anthropology. (UK ISSN 0960-1511) **254, 15**

▼International Current Awareness Services. Economics. (UK ISSN 0960-152X) **722**

▼International Current Awareness Services. Political Science. (US ISSN 0960-1538) **3938**

▼International Current Awareness Services. Sociology. (UK ISSN 0960-1546) **4458**

International Customs Journal/Bulletin International des Douanes. (BE ISSN 0074-4476) **1098, 912**

International Cycle Sport. (UK ISSN 0020-6504) **4518, 4549**

International Dairy Federation. Annual Bulletin/Federation Internationale de Laiterie. Bulletin Annuel. (BE ISSN 0250-5118) **200**

International Dairy Federation. Annual Memento/Federation Internationale de Laiterie. Memento Annuel. (BE ISSN 0538-7078) **200**

International Dairy Federation. Catalogue of I D F Publications/Federation Internationale Laitiere. Catalogue des Publications. (BE ISSN 0538-7086) **139**

International Dairy Federation. International Standard/Federation Internationale de Laiterie. Norme Internationale. (BE ISSN 0538-7094) **200**

International Dairy Federation. Newsletter/Federation Internationale de Laiterie. Newsletter. (BE ISSN 1011-9027) **200**

▼International Dairy Journal. (UK ISSN 0958-6946) **200**

International Dance-Exercise Association Today see I D E A Today **3804**

International Data Corporation Japan Report see I D C Japan Report **1424**

International Data Networks News see Integrated Service Digital Network **1427**

International Data Series. Selected Data on Mixtures. Series A. Thermodynamic Properties of Non-reacting Binary Systems of Organic Substances. (US) **1226, 1218**

International Defense and Aid Fund for Southern Africa News Notes see I D A F News Notes **5209**

International Defense Directory. (UK ISSN 0256-7822) **3460**

†International Defense Images. (US) **5216**

†International Defense Intelligence. (US) **5216**

International Defense Review. (UK ISSN 0020-6512) **3460**

International Dental Journal. (UK ISSN 0020-6539) **3234**

International Desalination Association Journal see I.D.A. Journal **5209**

International Desalination Association Newsletter see I D A Newsletter **4825**

International Design Yearbook. (JA) **330**

International Designer. (US) **1292**

International Designs Bulletin. (UN ISSN 0250-7730) **3675**

International Development Abstracts. (UK ISSN 0262-0855) **2268, 15**

International Development in Space Station and Space Technologies. (US) **56**

International Development Networker. (US) **932**

International Development Research Centre. Annual Report/Centre de Recherches pour le Developpement International. Rapport Annuel. (CN ISSN 0704-7584) **671**

International Development Research Centre Reports see I D R C Reports **930**

International Development Resource Books. (US ISSN 0738-1425) **869**

†International Development Review. (US) **5216**

International Diabetes Federation. Triennial Report. (BE) **3254**

International Diabetes Federation Bulletin see I D F Bulletin **3254**

International Diabetes Federation Directory see I D F Directory **3254**

International Diabetes Federation News Bulletin see I D F News Bulletin **3254**

International Digest of Health Legislation. (UN ISSN 0020-6563) **4105, 2636**

6308 INTERNATIONAL DIRECTORIES

International Directories in Print *see* Directories in Print **399**
International Directory I Cs and Discrete Semiconductors D.A.T.A. Digest *see* International Semiconductor Directory I Cs & Discrete Semiconductors D.A.T.A. Digest: Master Type Locator **1774**
International Directory of Arts. (GW ISSN 0074-4565) **330**
International Directory of Arts (Year). (US) **330**, 1139
International Directory of Brands and Their Companies. (US ISSN 1050-8376) **3675**
International Directory of Centers for Asian Studies. (HK) **1139**, 1695, 3638
International Directory of Children's Literature. (US) **4141**, 1247
International Directory of Corporate Affiliations. (US) **1139**
International Directory of Corporate Affiliations: Non-U S Parent Companies. (US) **1139**, 912
International Directory of Corporate Affiliations: U S Parent Companies. (US) **1139**, 912
International Directory of Eighteenth-Century Studies/Repertoire International des Dix-Huitiemistes. (UK) **2508**
International Directory of Exhibiting Artists. (UK) **352**
International Directory of Film and T V Documentation Centers. (US) **3520**, 1348
▼The International Directory of Government. (UK ISSN 0956-0998) **4064**
International Directory of Importers. (US) **1139**, 912
International Directory of Importers: Africa. (US) **1139**, 912
International Directory of Importers: Asia - Pacific. (US) **1140**, 912
International Directory of Importers: Europe. (US) **1140**, 912
International Directory of Importers: Middle East. (US) **1140**, 912
International Directory of Importers: North America. (US) **1140**, 912
International Directory of Importers: South - Central America. (US) **1140**, 912
International Directory of Investigators in Psychopharmacology. (US) **3729**
International Directory of Little Magazines and Small Presses. (US ISSN 0092-3974) **4141**, 403
International Directory of Marine Scientists. (UN) **442**, 1606
International Directory of New and Renewable Energy. (UN) **1140**, 1791
International Directory of News Libraries Including Buyers' Guide (Year) *see* International Directory of News Libraries Including Finding **2764**
International Directory of News Libraries Including Finding. (US ISSN 0889-0919) **2764**
International Directory of Non-Official Statistics Sources. (UK) **722**, 912
International Directory of Nuclear Utilities. (US ISSN 0742-5821) **1806**
International Directory of Philosophy and Philosophers. (US ISSN 0074-4603) **3769**
International Directory of Prisoners Aid Agencies. (US ISSN 0538-7191) **1515**, 4409
International Directory of Private Presses. (US) **1140**, 4002
International Directory of Psychic Sciences. (US) **3669**
International Directory of Public Refrigerated Warehouses. (US) **2300**
International Directory of Published Market Research *see* Marketsearch **729**
International Directory of Specialized Cancer Research and Treatment Establishments *see* U I C C International Directory of Cancer Institutes and Organizations **3202**
International Directory of the Nonwoven Fabrics Industry. (US ISSN 0095-683X) **4620**
International Directory of 16MM Film Collectors. (US ISSN 0074-462X) **3512**
International Disability Studies *see* Disability and Rehabilitation **3094**
International Display Research Conference. Conference Record. (US) **1900**
International Distribution & Handling Review. (UK ISSN 0141-9501) **1931**
International District Heating Association. Proceedings. (US ISSN 0074-4638) **2301**
International Documentary. (US ISSN 0742-5333) **3512**, 242
International Documentation and Communication Center Internazionale *see* I D O C Internazionale **4395**
International Documentation on Macedonia. (SZ) **3943**, 2368
International Documents on Palestine *see* Institute for Palestine Studies. International Annual Documentary Series **5214**
International Doll World. (US) **2437**
International Dostoevsky Society Bulletin *see* Dostoevsky Studies **2912**
International Double Reed Society (Publication) *see* Double Reed **3549**
International Dredging Abstracts *see* World Ports and Harbours Abstracts **4668**
International Dredging Review. (US ISSN 0737-8181) **1924**, 1868, 3486
International Drug Device Regulatory Monitor. (US) **3729**, 375
International Drug Regulatory Monitor *see* International Drug Device Regulatory Monitor **3729**
International Drug Report. (US ISSN 0148-4648) **1515**, 1536
International Drug Therapy Newsletter. (US ISSN 0020-6571) **3110**, 3729
International Dyer, Textile Printer, Bleacher and Finisher. (UK ISSN 0020-658X) **4620**, 1281
International E-22 Class Newsletter *see* International Etchells Class Newsletter **4525**
International E-22 Class Yearbook *see* International Etchells Class Yearbook **4525**
International Earth Rotation Service. Annual Report. (FR) **365**
International Earth Rotation Service. Monthly Bulletin. (FR) **365**
International Earth Rotation Service. Monthly Notes *see* International Earth Rotation Service. Monthly Bulletin **365**
International Earth Rotation Service. Special Bulletin C. (FR) **365**
International Earth Rotation Service. Special Bulletin D. (FR) **365**
International Earth Rotation Service. Technical Notes. (FR) **366**
International Earth Rotation Service. Weekly Bulletin A. (US) **366**
International Economic Association. Proceedings of the Conferences and Congresses. (UK ISSN 0074-4646) **671**
International Economic Cooperation. *see* Guoji Jingji Hezuo **930**
International Economic Indicators. *see* Internationale Wirtschaftszahlen **723**
▼International Economic Insights. (US ISSN 1050-8481) **869**, 895
International Economic Journal. (KO) **870**
International Economic Review. (US ISSN 0020-6598) **671**
International Economic Scoreboard. (US ISSN 0270-045X) **870**
International Economics and Trade. *see* Duiwai Jingmao **905**
International Economy. (US) **913**
International Education. (US ISSN 0160-5429) **1722**
International Education Forum. (US ISSN 1053-1750) **1728**, 1722
International Education Magazine/Magazine de l'Education Internationale. (CN ISSN 0827-0678) **1722**
International Educator. (US ISSN 1044-3509) **1722**, 1751, 3628
International Egg Commission. Market Review Situation & Outlook Report. (UK ISSN 0020-661X) **2073**
International Egg Commission. Monthly Chick Placement Bulletin. (UK) **2073**
International Egg Commission. Monthly News Bulletin *see* International Egg Commission. Monthly News Letter **2073**
International Egg Commission. Monthly News Letter. (UK) **2073**
International Egg Commission. Six-Monthly Statistical Bulletin. (UK ISSN 0020-6628) **2073**
International Electrical and Mechanical Catalogue. (UK) **1900**
InterNational Electrical Testing Association Technical Papers *see* N E T A Technical Papers **1904**
InterNational Electrical Testing Association World *see* N E T A World **1904**
International Electricity Catalogue *see* International Electrical and Mechanical Catalogue **1900**
International Electrochemical Progress. (US ISSN 0741-1413) **1212**
International Electron Devices Meeting. I E D M Technical Digest. (US ISSN 0163-1918) **1774**
†International Electronics for China. (UK ISSN 0267-9299) **5216**
International Electronics Packaging Society. (Publication). (US) **1774**
International Electrotechnical Commission. Repertoire - Directory. (SZ) **1900**
International Electrotechnical Commission. Yearbook - Annuaire. (SZ ISSN 0074-4697) **1900**
International Electrotechnical Commission Bulletin *see* I E C Bulletin **1893**
International Electrotechnical Commission Catalogue of Publications *see* I E C Catalogue of Publications **1772**
▼International Employment Gazette. (US ISSN 1058-0506) **983**
International Employment Hotline. (US ISSN 0748-8890) **3628**, 932, 1722, 4772
International Employment Opportunities Digest. (US ISSN 0890-2305) **3628**
International Encyclopedia of Food and Nutrition *see* Progress in Food & Nutrition Science **3611**
International Endodontic Journal. (UK ISSN 0143-2885) **3235**
International Energy Annual. (US) **1791**
International Energy Biweekly Statistical Review *see* International Energy Statistical Review **3705**
International Energy Statistical Review. (US ISSN 0163-3724) **3705**
International Engineering Directory. (US ISSN 0074-5774) **1826**
International Environment and Safety. (UK ISSN 0141-4836) **1959**, 4105
International Environment Reporter. (US ISSN 0149-8738) **1959**
International Environmental Affairs. (US ISSN 1041-4665) **1959**
International Environmental Outlook. (UK ISSN 0960-8869) **1959**
International Equipment News. Europe *see* Industrial Engineering News **5212**
International Erosion Control Association, Inc. Report *see* I E C A Report **1489**
International Estate Planning. (US) **950**, 1098
International Estimate Series. (US) **3961**
International Etchells Class Newsletter. (US) **4525**
International Etchells Class Yearbook. (US) **4525**
International Eucharist Congress. Proceedings. (VC ISSN 0074-5782) **4266**
International European Conference on High Energy Physics. Proceedings. (SZ) **3847**
International Evangelism Crusades Newsletter *see* I E C Newsletter **4181**
International Events Group, Inc. Directory of Sponsorship Marketing *see* I E G Directory of Sponsorship Marketing **1040**
International Events Group, Inc. Sponsorship Report *see* I E G Sponsorship Report **1040**
†International Exchange of Information on Current Criminological Research Projects in Member States. (FR ISSN 0252-063X) **5216**
International Exchange of Personnel. *see* Guoji Rencai Jiaoliu **1722**
International Executive. (US ISSN 0020-6652) **913**, 870
International Executive Search Newsletter *see* I C A Executive Search Newsletter **3628**
International Executive Summary *see* T M A World Alert **4645**
International Expert Systems Conference Proceedings *see* Advanced Information Systems. Proceedings **1406**
†International Eye. (US) **5216**
International Eye Foundation - Society of Eye Surgeons. Newsletter *see* Eye to Eye **3300**
International Fabricare Institute Fabricare News *see* I F I Fabricare News **1281**
International Facility Management Association News *see* I F M A News **1012**
†International Fact Book on Direct Marketing. (US) **5217**
International Falcon Movement - Socialist Educational International Bulletin *see* I F M - S E I Bulletin **1638**
International Family Planning Perspectives. (US ISSN 0190-3187) **597**, 3293
International Fan Club Organization Journal *see* I F C O Journal **1298**
International Farm Machinery Abstracts. *see* Bulletin Bibliographique International du Machinisme Agricole **5154**
International Fashion Group. Annual Report. (US) **1292**, 1014, 4845
International Fashion Group. Bulletin. (US) **1292**, 1014, 4845
International Fashion Group. Newsletter.(US) **1292**, 1014, 4845
International Fashion Model & Talent Magazine *see* I F M T Magazine **1291**
International Federation for Documentation. P-Notes. (NE ISSN 0378-7656) **2764**
International Federation for Documentation. Proceedings of Congress *see* International Federation for Information and Documentation. Proceedings of Congress **2764**
International Federation for Documentation Report Series *see* F I D - C R Report Series **5190**
International Federation for Home Economics - Federation Internationale pour l'Economie Familiale. Bulletin. *see* Economie Familiale **2446**
International Federation for Housing and Planning. Directory. (NE) **2489**
International Federation for Housing and Planning. Yearbook *see* International Federation for Housing and Planning. Directory **2489**
International Federation for Information and Documentation. Proceedings of Congress. (NE) **2764**
International Federation for Information Processing Transactions A: Computer Science and Technology *see* I F I P Transactions A: Computer Science and Technology **1396**

Title

INTERNATIONAL HISTORY 6309

International Federation for Medical Psychotherapy. Congress Reports. (SZ ISSN 0074-5847) **3339**
International Federation of Accountants Annual Report *see* I F A Annual Report **751**
International Federation of Accountants Newsletter *see* I F A Newsletter **751**
International Federation of Advertising Agencies. Newsletter. (US) **33**
International Federation of Agricultural Producers. General Conference Proceedings. (FR ISSN 0074-5863) **99**
International Federation of Agricultural Producers Newsletter *see* I F A P Newsletter **96**
International Federation of Asian and Western Pacific Contractors' Associations. Proceedings of the Annual Convention. (PH ISSN 0074-588X) **3393**
International Federation of Asian and Western Pacific Contractors' Associations Newsletter *see* I F A W P C A Newsletter **620**
International Federation of Associations of Textile Chemists and Colorists. Reports of Congress. (IT ISSN 0074-5898) **4620**, 1281
International Federation of Automatic Control. Newsletter. (AU) **1414**
International Federation of Automatic Control Symposia Series *see* I F A C Symposia Series **1930**
International Federation of Catholic Universities. General Assembly. Report. (FR ISSN 0579-3866) **1709**
International Federation of Clinical Chemistry. Journal. (US) **477**, 3729
International Federation of Commercial Clerical and Technical Employees. Newsletter *see* International Federation of Commercial Clerical, Professional and Technical Employees. Newsletter **2585**
International Federation of Commercial Clerical, Professional and Technical Employees. Newsletter. (SZ) **2585**
International Federation of European Contractors of Building and Public Works Review *see* Entreprise Europeenne **617**
International Federation of Fruit Juice Producers. Proceedings. Berichte. Rapports *see* International Federation of Fruit Juice Producers. Rapport Annuel d'Activite **2073**
International Federation of Fruit Juice Producers. Proceedings of Congress. Compte-Rendu du Congres. (FR ISSN 0074-5952) **382**
International Federation of Fruit Juice Producers. Rapport Annuel d'Activite.(FR) **2073**
International Federation of Gynaecology and Obstetrics. Journal *see* International Journal of Gynaecology and Obstetrics **3293**
International Federation of Journalists and Travel Writers. Official List/ Repertoire Officiel. (BE ISSN 0074-5979) **4772**, 2571
International Federation of Journalists Information *see* I F J Information **2570**
International Federation of Library Associations and Institutions Annual *see* I F L A Annual **2760**
International Federation of Library Associations and Institutions Directory *see* I F L A Directory **2760**
International Federation of Library Associations and Institutions. Section of Art Libraries. Newsletter. (NE ISSN 0261-152X) **2764**, 330
International Federation of Library Associations and Institutions Communications *see* I F L A Communications **2793**
International Federation of Medical Students' Associations. Minutes and Reports of the General Assembly. (NE ISSN 0074-6037) **3110**
International Federation of Operational Research Societies. Airline Group (A G I F O R S) Proceedings. (US ISSN 0538-7442) **4675**
International Federation of Organic Agriculture Movements. Bulletin. (US ISSN 0195-0304) **99**
International Federation of Park and Recreation Administration Bulletin *see* I F P R A Bulletin **4548**
International Federation of Plantation, Agricultural and Allied Workers. Report of the Secretariat to the I F P A A W World Congress. (SZ ISSN 0538-7477) **152**, 2585
International Federation of Plantation, Agricultural and Allied Workers News *see* I F P A A W News **981**
International Federation of Prestressing. Congress Proceedings. (UK ISSN 0074-6045) **1868**
International Federation of Professional and Technical Engineers Outlook *see* I F P T E Outlook **981**
International Federation of Robotics Robotics Newsletter *see* I F R Robotics Newsletter **1408**
International Federation of Secondary Teachers. International Bulletin *see* F I P E S O Newsletter **1633**
International Federation of Shipmasters Associations. Annual Report. (UK) **4729**
International Federation of Shipmasters Associations. Newsletter. (UK) **4729**
International Federation of the Hard of Hearing Journal *see* I F H O H Journal **2288**
International Fellowship of Evangelical Students Review *see* I F E S Review **4181**
International Fertilizer Correspondant. (SZ) **181**
International Fertilizer Industry Association Technical Conference. Proceedings *see* I F A Technical Conference. Proceedings **179**
International Fiber Journal. (US ISSN 1049-801X) **4620**, 1213
International Fiber Science and Technology Series. (US) **1218**, 4601
International Fiction Review. (CN ISSN 0315-4149) **2925**
International Field Hockey Rules *see* Rules of the Game of Field Hockey **4486**
International File of Micrographics Equipment and Accessories. *see* Micrographics and Optical Storage Equipment Review **2773**
International Film and T.V. Yearbook *see* Screen International Film and T.V. Yearbook **3517**
International Film Guide. (UK ISSN 0074-6053) **3512**
International Finance Corporation. Report. (UN ISSN 0074-6061) **785**
International Financial Law Review. (UK ISSN 0262-6969) **2724**, 785
International Financial News Survey *see* I M F Survey **720**
International Financial Statistics. (UN ISSN 0020-6725) **722**
International Financial Statistics Yearbook. (UN ISSN 0250-7463) **722**
International Financier. (US) **785**, 950
International Financing Review. (UK ISSN 0953-0223) **785**
International Fire & Security Product News. (UK) **2033**
International Fire Chief *see* I A F C On Scene **2033**
International Fire Fighter. (US) **2033**
International Fire Security Safety News *see* International Fire & Security Product News **2033**
International Fireball. (UK) **4525**
International Fiscal Association. Yearbook. (NE) **2724**
International Fiscal Association Congress Seminar Series *see* I F A Congress Seminar Series **1097**
International Fiscal Association Seminar Series *see* I F A Seminar Series **2724**
International Flight Attendants Association Newsletter. (US) **4675**
International Flight Information Manual. (US) **56**
International Flying Farmer. (US ISSN 0020-675X) **99**, 56
International Folk Music Council. Internationale Arbeitstagung der Study Group on Folk Musical Instruments. (SW) **3556**
International Folk Music Council. Yearbook *see* Yearbook for Traditional Music **3587**
International Folklore Bibliography. *see* Internationale Volkskundliche Bibliographie **2060**
International Food Directory. (US) **2073**, 1140
International Food Marketing and Technology. (GW) **2073**, 1041
International Food Policy Research Institute Report *see* I F P R I Report **152**
International Food Policy Research Institute Research Report *see* I F P R I Research Report **152**
▼International Food Safety News. (UK ISSN 0960-9784) **2074**, 4105
International Food Technology Basic Symposium Series *see* I F T Basic Symposium Series **2072**
International Foodservice Manufacturers Association World *see* I F M A World **2072**
International Football Book. (UK ISSN 0074-610X) **4507**
International Fortean Organization Journal *see* I N F O Journal **4313**
International Forum. (MY ISSN 0020-6784) **4409**
International Forum on Information and Documentation. (RU ISSN 0304-9701) **2764**
International Forum on Traffic Records Systems Proceedings. (US) **4719**
International Foundation Directory. (US) **1722**
International Foundation Employee Benefits Journal *see* Employee Benefits Journal **977**
International Foundation for Art Research, Inc. Reports *see* I F A R Reports **329**
International Foundation for Development Alternatives Dossier *see* I F D A Dossier **3959**
International Foundation for Telemetering Conference Proceedings (ITC-USA) *see* International Telemetering Conference **1338**
International Foundation for Telemetering Journal *see* I.F.T. Journal **5209**
International Foundation of Employee Benefit Plans. Digest. (US ISSN 0146-1141) **983**, 2535
International Foundry Congress. Papers and Communications. (US ISSN 0074-6118) **3409**
International Franchise Association. Quarterly Legal Bulletin *see* Franchising World **1039**
International Franchising and Distribution Law. (UK ISSN 0950-365X) **2725**
International Freedom Review *see* Terra Nova **3973**
International Freighting Weekly. (UK ISSN 0032-5007) **4651**
International Frequency List. (UN) **1375**
International Frequency List. Preface. (UN) **1375**
International Friendship and Good Will Bulletin. (US) **4409**, 3961
International Friendship League. Newsletter *see* Friendship News **1298**
International Friendship League Nieuws *see* I F L Nieuws **1298**
†International Frozen Food Association. Bulletin Board. (US) **5217**
International Fruit World. (SZ ISSN 0250-944X) **2074**, 181
International Fund Monitor. (US) **950**
International Fur Fashion Review. (CN ISSN 0823-6976) **2736**, 1292
International Gamblers Club Newsletter.(CN) **4476**, 4535
International Gas Bearing Symposium. Proceedings. (UK) **1931**
International Gas Research Conference. Proceedings. (US ISSN 0736-5721) **3689**, 1791
International Gas Technology Highlights.(US ISSN 0276-4040) **3689**
International Gas Turbine and Aeroengine Technology Report. (US) **3018**, 1917
International Gas Union. Proceedings of Conferences *see* International Gas Union. Proceedings of World Gas Conferences **3689**
International Gas Union. Proceedings of World Gas Conferences. (SZ) **3689**
†International Gemological Symposium Proceedings. (US) **5217**
International Geneva Yearbook. (SZ) **3961**, 2725
International Geographical Union Bulletin *see* I G U Bulletin **2252**
International Geology Review. (US ISSN 0020-6814) **1569**
International Geophysics Series. (US ISSN 0074-6142) **1590**
International Geoscience and Remote Sensing Symposium Digest. (US) **2253**, 1338, 1452, 1545
†International Gifts News. (UK) **5217**
International Glass-Metal Catalog. (US ISSN 0147-300X) **1165**
International Gold Mining Newsletter. (UK) **3486**
International Golf Directory *see* Golf Index **4505**
International Grafik. (DK ISSN 0020-6830) **331**
International Graphical Federation. Report of Activities. (BE ISSN 0074-6177) **2585**
International Graphical Federation Journal *see* I G F - Journal **4001**
International Grassland Congress. Proceedings. (RU ISSN 0074-6185) **181**
International Gravimetrique Bureau. Bulletin d'Information. (FR) **1590**
International Green Book. (US ISSN 0074-6193) **1140**
International Ground Water Modeling Center Ground Water Modeling Newsletter *see* I G W M C Ground Water Modeling Newsletter **1598**
International Gueterkursbuch. (CS) **4710**
International Guide. (CN) **4772**, 2476
International Guide to Psi-Periodicals *see* Whole Again Resource Guide **4396**
International Guide to Scientific Instruments & Chemicals. (UK) **2523**, 1179
International Guiding Eyes. Newsletter *see* I G E News **3711**
International Guiding Eyes News *see* I G E News **3711**
International Guild for Infant Survival Newsletter. (US) **3321**
International Gymnast *see* International Gymnast Magazine **4476**
International Gymnast Magazine. (US ISSN 0276-1041) **4476**
International Halfway House Association. Newsletter *see* International Association of Residential and Community Alternatives. Journal **1515**
International Handbook of Resources for the Educators of Adults *see* Resources for Educators of Adults **1686**
International Handbook of Universities *see* International Handbook of Universities and Other Institutions of Higher Education **1709**
International Handbook of Universities and Other Institutions of Higher Education. (UK ISSN 0074-6215) **1709**
International Handbook on Commercial Arbitration. (NE) **2725**
International Handicapper's Net News *see* I H N News **2284**
†International Heat Transfer Conference.(US) **5217**
International History of Mammalogy. (NE) **584**

Title

International History Review. (CN ISSN 0707-5332) **2314**

International Home and Private Poker Players Newsletter. (US) **4476**

International Hop Growers Convention. Report of Congress. (XV ISSN 0074-6223) **207**

International Horisont. (DK ISSN 0901-2605) **983**

International Horn Society. Directory. (US) **3556**

International Horn Society. Newsletter. (US) **3556**

International Horticultural Congress. Proceedings. (NE ISSN 0074-6231) **2132**

International Hospital Equipment. (BE) **3110**

International Hospital Federation. Official Handbook see Hospital Management International **2464**

International Hotel Guide. (FR ISSN 0074-624X) **2477**

International House of Japan, Inc. Bulletin see I H J Bulletin **3959**

International Human-Powered-Vehicle Association News see H P V News **4474**

International Humanist. (CN ISSN 0925-1375) **3769**

International Humanist and Ethical Union. Proceedings of the Congress. (CN ISSN 0074-6258) **3769**

International Hydrographic Bulletin. (MC ISSN 0020-6938) **1606**, 1598

International Hydrographic Conference. Reports of Proceedings. (MC ISSN 0074-6274) **1606**, 1598

International Hydrographic Organization. Yearbook. (MC) **1606**, 1598

International Hydrographic Review. (MC ISSN 0020-6946) **1606**, 1545, 1598

International Hydrological Programme: Operational Hydrological Programme: Yearbook Federal Republic of Germany and Berlin (West). see Internationales Hydrologisches Programm: Operationelles Hydrologisches Programm: Jahrbuch Bundesrepublik Deutschland und Berlin (West) **1598**

†International I E E E Conference on Ada Applications and Environments. (US) **5217**

International I E E E V L S I Mutilevel Interconnection Conference. Proceedings. (US) **1900**

International I S B N Publishers' Directory see Publishers' International I S B N Directory **4142**

International Imaging Source Book. (US) **2794**

International Immunology. (UK ISSN 0953-8178) **3186**

International Income Tax Rules of the United States. (US) **1098**, 2725

International Index to Film Periodicals. (UK ISSN 0000-0388) **3520**, 15

International Index to Television Periodicals. (UK ISSN 0143-5663) **1348**, 1375

International Individual Taxation. (US) **1098**

International Industrial Biotechnology see Genetic Engineer and Biotechnologist **469**

International Industrial Opportunities. (US) **913**

International Industrial Sensor Directory see International Industrial Sensor Products Database **5217**

†International Industrial Sensor Products Database. (US) **5217**

International Information and Word Processing Report see Information Processing Report **1482**

International Information Centre for Terminology, Vienna Infoterm Series see Infoterm Series **2818**

International Information, Communication and Education. (II ISSN 0970-1850) **2764**

International Information Management Congress Journal see I M C Journal **2797**

International Information Report. (US ISSN 0748-206X) **403**

▼International Information Systems. (US) **1456**

International Institute for Applied Systems Analysis Annual Report see I I A S A Annual Report **1437**

International Institute for Educational Planning Occasional Papers see I I E P Occasional Papers **1722**

International Institute for Educational Planning Research Reports see I I E P Research Reports **1722**

International Institute for Educational Planning Seminar Papers see I I E P Seminar Papers **1722**

International Institute for Labour Studies. Bibliography Series. (UN) **722**, 983

†International Institute for Labour Studies. Public Lecture Series. (UN) **5217**

International Institute for Labour Studies. Research Series. (UN) **983**

International Institute for Land Reclamation and Improvement. Annual Report. (NE ISSN 0074-6428) **181**

International Institute for Land Reclamation and Improvement. Bibliography. (NE ISSN 0074-6436) **139**

International Institute for Land Reclamation and Improvement. Publication. (NE ISSN 0074-6452) **181**

International Institute for Peace Monitor see I I P Monitor **3959**

International Institute for Peace Occasional Paper see I I P Occasional Paper **3959**

International Institute for Population Sciences. Director's Report. (II) **3983**

International Institute for Population Sciences Newsletter see I I P S Newsletter **3982**

International Institute for Population Studies. Newsletter see I I P S Newsletter **3982**

International Institute for Sugar Beet Research. Reports of the Winter Congress. (BE ISSN 0074-6460) **181**

International Institute of Administrative Sciences. Reports of the International Congress. (BE ISSN 0074-6479) **4064**

International Institute of Connector and Interconnection Technology. Annual Connector Symposium. Proceedings. (US) **1900**

International Institute of Connector and Interconnection Technology, Inc. News see I I C I T News **1773**

International Institute of Fisheries Economics and Trade Newsletter. (US) **2044**

International Institute of Ibero-American Literature. Congress Proceedings. Memoria. (US ISSN 0074-6495) **2925**

International Institute of Public Finance. Papers and Proceedings. (GW ISSN 0074-6533) **1098**

International Institute of Refrigeration. Bulletin. see Institut International du Froid. Bulletin **2300**

International Institute of Refrigeration. Proceedings of Commision Meetings. see Institut International du Froid. Comptes Rendus de Reunions de Commissions **2300**

International Institute of Rural Reconstruction Report see I I R R Report **930**

International Institute of Seismology and Earthquake Engineering. Bulletin. (JA ISSN 0074-655X) **1591**, 1868

International Institute of Seismology and Earthquake Engineering. Individual Studies by Participants at I I S E E. (JA) **1591**, 1868

International Institute of Seismology and Earthquake Engineering. Year Book. (JA ISSN 0074-6614) **1591**, 1868

International Institute of Synthetic Rubber Producers. Annual Meeting Proceedings. (US ISSN 0146-3977) **4292**

International Institute of Tropical Agriculture. Annual Program Reports Series. (NR) **99**

International Institute of Tropical Agriculture. Annual Report see International Institute of Tropical Agriculture. Annual Program Reports Series **99**

International Institute of Tropical Agriculture. Annual Report and Research Highlights. (NR) **99**

International Institute of Tropical Agriculture. Research Highlights see International Institute of Tropical Agriculture. Annual Report and Research Highlights **99**

International Institute on the Prevention and Treatment of Addictions. Selected Papers. (SZ ISSN 0254-2536) **1536**

International Institute on the Prevention and Treatment of Drug Dependence. Selected Papers see International Institute on the Prevention and Treatment of Addictions. Selected Papers **1536**

International Instrumentation & Controls. (US) **2523**

International Instrumentation Symposium. (US ISSN 0277-7576) **56**, 1917

International Insurance Monitor. (US ISSN 0020-6997) **2535**

International Interactions. (US ISSN 0305-0629) **3961**

International Interactive Communications Society Reporter see I I C S Reporter **1350**

†International Interdisciplinary Seminar on Piagetian Theory and Its Implications for the Helping Professions. Proceedings. (US ISSN 0192-5318) **5217**

International Intertrade Index. (US ISSN 0020-7004) **722**, 15

International Investing Update. (CN) **950**, 913

International Investment Banking Report. (UK) **671**

International Investment Guide see Global Trends **947**

International Investor's Directory. (US ISSN 1040-6921) **1140**, 950

International Iron and Steel Institute. Report of Conference Proceedings. (BE ISSN 0074-6630) **3409**

International Joint Conference on Artificial Intelligence. Advance Papers of the Conference. (US) **1408**

International Joseph Martin Kraus-Gesellschaft. Mitteilungen. (GW ISSN 0723-9769) **3556**, 2368

International Journal. (US ISSN 0020-7039) **2437**

International Journal. (CN ISSN 0020-7020) **3961**

International Journal for Artificial Intelligence in Engineering see Artificial Intelligence in Engineering **1407**

International Journal for Biosocial Research see International Journal of Biosocial and Medical Research **3607**

International Journal for Communication Design. see Novum Gebrauchsgraphik **36**

International Journal for Housing Science and Its Applications. (US ISSN 0146-6518) **2489**

International Journal for Hybrid Microelectronics. (US ISSN 0277-8270) **1774**

International Journal for Numerical and Analytical Methods in Geomechanics.(UK ISSN 0363-9061) **1545**, 1868

International Journal for Numerical Methods in Engineering. (UK ISSN 0029-5981) **1826**, 3039

International Journal for Numerical Methods in Fluids. (UK ISSN 0271-2091) **1924**, 1879

International Journal for Parasitology. (US ISSN 0020-7519) **3220**, 553

International Journal for Philosophy of Religion. (NE ISSN 0020-7047) **4182**, 3769

International Journal for the Advancement of Counselling. (NE ISSN 0165-0653) **1640**

▼International Journal for the Psychology of Religion. (US ISSN 1050-8619) **4182**, 4025

International Journal for the Semiotics of Law. (UK ISSN 0952-8059) **2636**, 2819

International Journal for Vitamin and Nutrition Research. (SZ ISSN 0300-9831) **3729**, 3607

▼International Journal in Computer Simulation. (US ISSN 1055-8470) **1414**

International Journal of Acarology. (US ISSN 0164-7954) **534**

International Journal of Accounting Education and Research. (UK ISSN 0020-7063) **752**, 1709

International Journal of Adaptive Control and Signal Processing. (UK ISSN 0890-6327) **1900**

International Journal of Adhesion and Adhesives. (UK ISSN 0143-7496) **3862**, 1854

International Journal of Adolescence and Youth. (UK ISSN 0267-3843) **1256**, 1239

International Journal of Adolescent Medicine and Health. (UK ISSN 0334-0139) **3321**

International Journal of Adult Orthodontics and Orthognathic Surgery. (US ISSN 0742-1931) **3235**, 3379

International Journal of Advanced Manufacturing Technology. (UK ISSN 0268-3768) **1931**, 3018

International Journal of Advertising. (UK ISSN 0265-0487) **33**, 1041

International Journal of African Historical Studies. (US ISSN 0361-7882) **2333**

International Journal of Aging & Human Development. (US ISSN 0091-4150) **2274**

▼International Journal of Algebra and Computation. (SI ISSN 0218-1967) **3039**, 3064

International Journal of Ambient Energy.(UK ISSN 0143-0750) **1791**, 1811, 1812

International Journal of American Linguistics. (US ISSN 0020-7071) **2819**

International Journal of American Linguistics Native American Texts Series see I J A L Native American Texts Series **5209**

International Journal of Andrology. (UK ISSN 0105-6263) **3388**

International Journal of Andrology. Supplement. (UK ISSN 0106-1607) **3388**

International Journal of Anthropology. (IT ISSN 0393-9383) **242**

▼International Journal of Antimicrobial Agents. (NE ISSN 0924-8579) **553**

▼International Journal of Applied Electromagnetics in Materials. (NE ISSN 0925-2096) **1900**, 1931

International Journal of Applied Engineering Education. (GW ISSN 0742-0269) **1826**, 1640

International Journal of Applied Pneumatics. (UK) **1931**, 3018

International Journal of Approximate Reasoning. (US ISSN 0888-613X) **1408**

International Journal of Arbitration. (II ISSN 0020-7098) **2636**

▼International Journal of Artificial Intelligence Tools. (SI ISSN 0218-2130) **1408**

International Journal of Artificial Organs.(IT ISSN 0391-3988) **3110**, 3260

▼International Journal of Arts Medicine.(US ISSN 1057-4263) **3110**, 331

▼International Journal of Aviation Psychology. (US ISSN 1050-8414) **56**, 4025

International Journal of Bank Marketing.(UK ISSN 0265-2323) **786**, 1041

International Journal of Behavioral Development. (UK ISSN 0165-0254) **4025**
▼International Journal of Bifurcations and Chaos in Applied Sciences and Engineering. (SI ISSN 0218-1274) **1826**
International Journal of Bio-Medical Computing. (IE ISSN 0020-7101) **3226**, 442
International Journal of Biochemistry. (US ISSN 0020-711X) **477**
International Journal of Biological Macromolecules. (UK ISSN 0141-8130) **477**
International Journal of Biological Markers. (IT ISSN 0393-6155) **442**
International Journal of Biometeorology.(GW ISSN 0020-7128) **3436**, 442, 3110
International Journal of Biosocial and Medical Research. (US ISSN 1044-811X) **3607**, 4025, 4438
International Journal of Bulk Solids Storage in Silos. (UK ISSN 0265-5918) **1854**
International Journal of Cancer. (US ISSN 0020-7136) **3198**
International Journal of Cardiac Imaging. (NE ISSN 0167-9899) **3209**
International Journal of Cardiology. (NE ISSN 0167-5273) **3209**
International Journal of Career Management. (UK ISSN 0955-6214) **3628**, 1014
International Journal of Cell Cloning. (US ISSN 0737-1454) **560**
International Journal of Cement Composites and Lightweight Concrete see Cement and Concrete Composites **609**
International Journal of Chemical Kinetics. (US ISSN 0538-8066) **1226**
International Journal of Childbirth Education. (US ISSN 0887-8625) **3293**, 3321
International Journal of Circuit Theory & Applications. (UK ISSN 0098-9886) **1900**
International Journal of Climatology. (UK ISSN 0899-8418) **3436**, 4826
International Journal of Clinical and Experimental Hypnosis. (US ISSN 0020-7144) **3274**
International Journal of Clinical Monitoring and Computing. (NE ISSN 0167-9945) **3191**, 3226
International Journal of Clinical Neuropsychology. (US ISSN 0197-3681) **3339**, 4025
International Journal of Clinical Pharmacology Research. (SZ ISSN 0251-1649) **3729**
International Journal of Clinical Pharmacology, Therapy and Toxicology. (GW ISSN 0174-4879) **3729**, 1982
International Journal of Clothing Science and Technology. (UK ISSN 0955-6222) **1285**
International Journal of Coal Geology. (NE ISSN 0166-5162) **1569**, 3486
▼International Journal of Cognitive Education & Mediated Learning. (UK ISSN 0957-4964) **1640**
International Journal of Colorectal Disease. (GW ISSN 0179-1958) **3379**
▼International Journal of Communication. (II) **1338**
International Journal of Comparative and Applied Criminal Justice. (US ISSN 0192-4036) **1515**
International Journal of Comparative Psychology. (US ISSN 0889-3667) **4025**
International Journal of Comparative Sociology. (NE ISSN 0020-7152) **4438**
▼International Journal of Computational Geometry and Applications. (SI ISSN 0218-1959) **3065**
†International Journal of Computer Aided V L S I Design. (US) **5217**

International Journal of Computer Applications in Technology. (SZ ISSN 0952-8091) **1477**, 1456
International Journal of Computer Integrated Manufacturing. (UK ISSN 0951-192X) **827**, 1416, 1422
International Journal of Computer Mathematics. (US ISSN 0020-7160) **3065**
International Journal of Computer Vision. (US ISSN 0920-5691) **1437**
▼International Journal of Conflict Management. (US ISSN 1044-4068) **1014**, 3899
International Journal of Construction Maintenance & Repair. (UK ISSN 0959-5090) **621**
International Journal of Construction Management and Technology see Construction Management and Economics **613**
International Journal of Contemporary Sociology. (FI ISSN 0019-6398) **4438**
International Journal of Continuing Engineering Education. (SZ ISSN 0957-4344) **1826**, 1684
International Journal of Control. (UK ISSN 0020-7179) **1826**
International Journal of Cosmetic Science. (UK ISSN 0142-5463) **375**
International Journal of Critical Sociology. (II ISSN 0377-0141) **4438**
International Journal of Cross-Cultural Consumer Behavior see International Journal of International Consumer Marketing **1506**
▼International Journal of Damage Mechanics. (US ISSN 1056-7895) **1931**
International Journal of Dermatology. (US ISSN 0011-9059) **3248**
International Journal of Development Banking. (II ISSN 0970-1044) **932**, 786
International Journal of Developmental Neuroscience. (US ISSN 0736-5748) **3339**
International Journal of Digital and Analog Cabled Systems see International Journal of Digital & Analog Communication Systems **1900**
International Journal of Digital & Analog Communication Systems. (UK) **1900**
International Journal of Disability, Development and Education. (AT) **1736**, 2284
International Journal of Dravidian Linguistics see I J D L **2817**
International Journal of Early Childhood.(US ISSN 0020-7187) **1239**
International Journal of Eating Disorders. (US ISSN 0276-3478) **3607**, 4025
International Journal of Eclectic Psychotherapy see Journal of Integrative and Eclectic Psychotherapy **4030**
International Journal of Ecology and Environmental Sciences. (II ISSN 0377-015X) **1959**
International Journal of Economic and Social History. see Quaderni Internazionali di Storia Economica e Sociale **2382**
International Journal of Educational Development. (UK ISSN 0738-0593) **1640**
International Journal of Educational Management. (UK ISSN 0951-354X) **1014**
▼International Journal of Educational Reform. (US ISSN 1056-7879) **1640**
International Journal of Educational Research. (US ISSN 0883-0355) **1722**
International Journal of Educational Sciences. (II ISSN 0252-8576) **1640**
International Journal of Educology. (AT ISSN 0818-0563) **1684**, 1640

International Journal of Electrical Engineering Education. (UK ISSN 0020-7209) **1900**, 1751
International Journal of Electrical Power and Energy Systems see Electrical Power and Energy Systems **5185**
International Journal of Electronics. (UK ISSN 0020-7217) **1774**
▼International Journal of Energy - Environment - Economics. (US ISSN 1054-853X) **1791**, 870, 1959
International Journal of Energy Research. (UK ISSN 0363-907X) **1791**
International Journal of Energy Systems.(CN ISSN 0226-1472) **1791**, 4315, 4601
International Journal of Engineering Fluid Mechanics. (US ISSN 0893-3960) **1226**, 1854, 1931
International Journal of Engineering Science. (US ISSN 0020-7225) **1826**
▼International Journal of Environment and Pollution. (SZ ISSN 0957-4352) **1977**, 1489
International Journal of Environmental and Analytical Chemistry. (US ISSN 0306-7319) **1206**, 1959
▼International Journal of Environmental Health Research. (UK ISSN 0960-3123) **1959**
International Journal of Environmental Studies. Sections A & B. (US ISSN 0020-7233) **1959**, 2489, 4376
International Journal of Epidemiology. (UK ISSN 0300-5771) **3110**, 4105
International Journal of Ergonomics see International Journal of Industrial Ergonomics **1827**
International Journal of Estuarine and Coastal Law. (UK ISSN 0268-0106) **2725**
International Journal of Experimental Pathology. (UK ISSN 0959-9673) **3110**
International Journal of Expert Systems.(US) **1408**
International Journal of Fatigue. (UK ISSN 0142-1123) **1917**
International Journal of Fertility. (US ISSN 0020-725X) **3110**, 442
International Journal of Flexible Manufacturing Systems. (US ISSN 0920-6299) **1917**, 1931
International Journal of Food Microbiology. (NE ISSN 0168-1605) **466**
International Journal of Food Science and Technology. (UK ISSN 0950-5423) **2074**
International Journal of Forecasting. (NE ISSN 0169-2070) **672**
▼International Journal of Foundations of Computer Science. (SI ISSN 0129-0541) **1430**, 1477
International Journal of Fracture. (NE ISSN 0376-9429) **1917**
International Journal of Fracture Mechanics see International Journal of Fracture **1917**
International Journal of Game Theory. (GW ISSN 0020-7276) **3039**, 895, 3899
International Journal of General Systems. (US ISSN 0308-1079) **1437**
▼International Journal of Genome Research. (SI ISSN 0218-1932) **544**
International Journal of Geographical Information Systems. (UK ISSN 0269-3798) **2268**
International Journal of Geriatric Psychiatry. (UK ISSN 0885-6230) **2274**, 3339
International Journal of Global Energy Issues. (SZ ISSN 0954-7118) **1791**, 1489
International Journal of Government Auditing/Revue Internationale de la Verification des Comptes Publics/Revista Internacional de Entidades Fiscalizadoras Superiores. (US ISSN 0047-0724) **4064**
International Journal of Group Psychotherapy. (US ISSN 0020-7284) **4025**, 3339

International Journal of Group Tensions.(US ISSN 0047-0732) **4025**, 3899, 4438
International Journal of Gynaecology and Obstetrics. (IE ISSN 0020-7292) **3293**
▼International Journal of Gynecological Cancer. (US ISSN 1048-891X) **3293**, 3198
International Journal of Gynecological Pathology. (US) **3293**
International Journal of Health Care Quality Assurance. (UK ISSN 0952-6862) **3110**
International Journal of Health Planning and Management. (UK ISSN 0749-6753) **4409**
▼International Journal of Health Sciences. (NE ISSN 0924-2287) **3110**
International Journal of Health Services.(US ISSN 0020-7314) **4105**
International Journal of Heat and Fluid Flow. (US ISSN 0142-727X) **3841**, 1931
International Journal of Heat and Mass Transfer. (US ISSN 0017-9310) **1932**, 3820
International Journal of Hematology. (NE ISSN 0925-5710) **3272**
International Journal of High Speed Computing. (SI ISSN 0129-0533) **1454**, 1430, 1477
▼International Journal of High Speed Electronics. (SI ISSN 0129-1564) **1774**
International Journal of High Technology Ceramics see European Ceramic Society. Journal **1163**
International Journal of Holistic Health and Medicine see Health World **3606**
International Journal of Hospitality Management. (US ISSN 0278-4319) **4772**, 2477
International Journal of Human-Computer Interaction. (US ISSN 1044-7318) **4458**
▼International Journal of Human Factors in Manufacturing. (US ISSN 1045-2699) **1414**, 1078, 4025
▼International Journal of Human Resources Management. (UK ISSN 0958-5192) **1066**
International Journal of Humanities and Peace. (US ISSN 1042-4032) **2508**, 1959
International Journal of Hydrogen Energy. (US ISSN 0360-3199) **1791**, 3820
International Journal of Hyperthermia. (UK ISSN 0265-6736) **3198**
International Journal of Imaging Systems and Technology. (US ISSN 0899-9457) **3820**
International Journal of Immunopathology and Pharmacology.(IT) **3186**, 3729
International Journal of Immunopharmacology. (US ISSN 0192-0561) **3729**, 3187
International Journal of Immunotherapy.(SZ ISSN 0255-9625) **3187**
International Journal of Impact Engineering. (US ISSN 0734-743X) **1826**
▼International Journal of Indian Studies. (CN ISSN 0847-3471) **3638**, 2508, 4376
International Journal of Industrial Ergonomics. (NE ISSN 0169-8141) **1827**, 1078, 1879
International Journal of Industrial Organization. (NE ISSN 0167-7187) **983**, 895
International Journal of Information and Library Research. (UK ISSN 0953-556X) **2764**
International Journal of Information and Management Sciences. (CH ISSN 1017-1819) **1014**, 722, 1447
International Journal of Information Management. (UK ISSN 0268-4012) **1456**, 1338, 2764, 4376

▼International Journal of Information Resource Management. (UK ISSN 0956-4225) **1014**, 2764
International Journal of Infrared and Millimeter Waves. (US ISSN 0195-9271) **3853**
International Journal of Insect Morphology and Embryology. (US ISSN 0020-7322) **534**
International Journal of Institutional Management in Higher Education see Higher Education Management **1708**
International Journal of Instructional Media. (US ISSN 0092-1815) **1752**, 4601
International Journal of Intelligence and Counterintelligence. (US ISSN 0885-0607) **3899**, 1526
▼International Journal of Intelligent and Cooperative Information Systems. (SI ISSN 0218-2157) **1456**
International Journal of Intelligent Systems. (US ISSN 0884-8173) **1408**
▼International Journal of Intelligent Systems in Accounting, Finance & Management. (US ISSN 1055-615X) **827**, 752, 805
International Journal of Intercultural Relations. (US ISSN 0147-1767) **4438**
International Journal of Invertebrate Reproduction and Development see Invertebrate Reproduction and Development **534**
International Journal of Islamic and Arabic Studies. (US ISSN 0740-5375) **2429**
International Journal of Korean Studies. (KO ISSN 0303-3007) **2339**
International Journal of Law and Psychiatry. (US ISSN 0160-2527) **2636**, 3339
International Journal of Law and the Family. (UK ISSN 0950-4109) **2717**
International Journal of Legal Information. (US ISSN 0731-1265) **2764**, 2636
International Journal of Legal Medicine. (GW ISSN 0937-9827) **3265**
International Journal of Leprosy and Other Mycobacterial Diseases. (US ISSN 0148-916X) **3220**
International Journal of Lexicography. (UK ISSN 0950-3846) **2819**
International Journal of Lifelong Education. (UK ISSN 0260-1370) **1684**
▼International Journal of Logistics Management. (UK) **1014**
International Journal of Machine Tool Design and Research see International Journal of Machine Tools & Manufacture **3018**
International Journal of Machine Tools & Manufacture. (US ISSN 0890-6955) **3018**, 1932
International Journal of Man-Machine Studies. (UK ISSN 0020-7373) **1441**
International Journal of Management. (UK ISSN 0813-0183) **1014**, 752
International Journal of Manpower. (UK ISSN 0143-7720) **983**
International Journal of Maritime History. (CN ISSN 0843-8714) **4729**, 2410
International Journal of Mass Emergencies and Disasters. (US) **4438**, 4105
International Journal of Mass Spectrometry and Ion Processes. (NE ISSN 0168-1176) **3853**
International Journal of Materials & Product Technology. (SZ ISSN 0268-1900) **4601**
International Journal of Mathematical Education in Science and Technology.(UK ISSN 0020-739X) **3039**
▼International Journal of Mathematics. (SI ISSN 0129-167X) **3039**
International Journal of Mathematics and Mathematical Sciences. (II ISSN 0161-1712) **3039**, 3820

International Journal of Mechanical Engineering Education. (UK ISSN 0306-4190) **1827**
International Journal of Mechanical Sciences. (US ISSN 0020-7403) **1917**
International Journal of Mental Health. (US ISSN 0020-7411) **4025**, 4105
▼International Journal of Methods in Psychiatric Research. (UK ISSN 1049-8931) **3339**
International Journal of Microcirculation: Clinical & Experimental. (US ISSN 0167-6865) **3110**
International Journal of Micrographics & Optical Technology. (US ISSN 0958-9961) **2798**, 1445
International Journal of Micrographics and Video Technology see International Journal of Micrographics & Optical Technology **2798**
▼International Journal of Microwave and Millimeter-Wave Computer Aided Engineering. (US ISSN 1050-1827) **1879**, 1422
International Journal of Middle East Studies. (UK ISSN 0020-7438) **3638**
International Journal of Mineral Processing. (NE ISSN 0301-7516) **3486**, 3409
International Journal of Mini and Microcomputers. (CN ISSN 0702-0481) **1466**, 1461
International Journal of Mining and Geological Engineering see Geotechnical and Geological Engineering **3484**
International Journal of Modelling & Simulation. (CN ISSN 0228-6203) **1918**
International Journal of Modern Physics A. (SI ISSN 0217-751X) **3820**
International Journal of Modern Physics B. (SI ISSN 0217-9792) **3820**
▼International Journal of Modern Physics C: Physics and Computers. (SI ISSN 0129-1831) **3820**, 4359
International Journal of Multiphase Flow.(US ISSN 0301-9322) **1932**, 3820
International Journal of Museum Management and Curatorship see Museum Management and Curatorship **3529**
International Journal of Music Education. (UK ISSN 0255-7614) **3556**, 1640
International Journal of Mycology and Lichenology. (GW ISSN 0723-3353) **506**
International Journal of Nautical Archeology. (UK ISSN 1057-2414) **274**
International Journal of Nautical Archeology and Underwater Exploration see International Journal of Nautical Archeology **274**
International Journal of Neonatal and Later Screening see Screening **3326**
▼International Journal of Network Management. (UK ISSN 1055-7148) **1338**, 1900
International Journal of Neural Network.(US) **1408**
International Journal of Neural Systems.(SI ISSN 0129-0657) **3820**, 1408
International Journal of Neurology. (UY ISSN 0020-7446) **3339**
International Journal of Neuroscience. (US ISSN 0020-7454) **3339**, 477
International Journal of Non-Linear Mechanics. (US ISSN 0020-7462) **1918**, 3039
▼International Journal of Nonlinear Optical Physics. (SI ISSN 0218-1991) **3853**
International Journal of Numerical Modelling: Electronic Networks, Devices and Fields. (UK ISSN 0894-3370) **1879**, 3039
International Journal of Nursing Studies.(US ISSN 0020-7489) **3279**

International Journal of Obesity. (UK ISSN 0307-0565) **3607**, 3804
International Journal of Obstetric Anesthesia. (UK ISSN 0959-289X) **3191**
International Journal of Offender Therapy and Comparative Criminology. (US ISSN 0306-624X) **1515**, 3339
▼International Journal of Offshore and Polar Engineering. (US ISSN 1053-5381) **1932**, 1606, 3689
International Journal of Operations and Production Management. (UK ISSN 0144-3577) **1014**
▼International Journal of Optical Computing. (UK ISSN 1047-8507) **1397**, 1900, 3853
International Journal of Optical Sensors see International Journal of Optoelectronics **3853**
International Journal of Optoelectronics. (UK ISSN 0952-5432) **3853**
International Journal of Oral & Maxillofacial Implants. (US ISSN 0882-2786) **3235**
International Journal of Oral & Maxillofacial Surgery. (DK ISSN 0901-5027) **3235**, 3379
International Journal of Oral History see International Annual of Oral History **2314**
International Journal of Oral Implantology. (US) **3235**
International Journal of Oral Surgery see International Journal of Oral & Maxillofacial Surgery **3235**
†International Journal of Orthodontics. (US) **5217**
▼International Journal of Osteoarchaeology. (UK ISSN 1047-482X) **242**
▼International Journal of P I X E. (SI ISSN 0129-0835) **3847**, 1206
International Journal of Paediatric Dentistry. (UK ISSN 0960-7439) **3235**
International Journal of Pancreatology. (US ISSN 0169-4197) **3254**, 3198, 3268
International Journal of Parallel Programming. (US ISSN 0885-7458) **1430**
International Journal of Partial Hospitalization. (US ISSN 0272-4308) **4409**
International Journal of Pattern Recognition and Artificial Intelligence.(SI ISSN 0218-0014) **1422**
International Journal of Pediatric Nephrology see Child Nephrology and Urology **3387**
International Journal of Pediatric Otorhinolaryngology. (NE ISSN 0165-5876) **3315**, 3321
International Journal of Peptide & Protein Research. (DK ISSN 0367-8377) **478**, 3110
International Journal of Periodontics & Restorative Dentistry. (GW) **3235**
International Journal of Periodontics & Restorative Dentistry. (US ISSN 0198-7569) **3235**, 3379
International Journal of Personal Construct Psychology. (US ISSN 0893-603X) **4025**
International Journal of Pharmaceutical Technology & Product Manufacture. (UK ISSN 0260-6267) **3729**
International Journal of Pharmaceutics. (NE ISSN 0378-5173) **3729**
International Journal of Pharmacognosy.(NE ISSN 0925-1618) **3730**
▼International Journal of Pharmacy Practice. (UK) **3730**
International Journal of Physical Distribution & Logistics Management.(UK ISSN 0960-0035) **4745**
International Journal of Physical Distribution and Materials Management see International Journal of Physical Distribution & Logistics Management **4745**

International Journal of Physical Education/Internationale Zeitschrift fuer Sportpaedagogik. (GW ISSN 0341-8685) **1752**, 3804, 4476
International Journal of Plant Sciences. (US) **506**
International Journal of Plasticity. (US ISSN 0749-6419) **1918**
International Journal of Political Economy. (US ISSN 0891-1916) **3899**
International Journal of Politics see International Journal of Political Economy **3899**
International Journal of Politics, Culture, and Society. (US ISSN 0891-4486) **3961**
International Journal of Politics, Culture, and State see International Journal of Politics, Culture, and Society **3961**
International Journal of Polymeric Materials. (US ISSN 0091-4037) **1854**, 1218
International Journal of Powder Metallurgy. (US ISSN 0888-7462) **3409**
International Journal of Powder Metallurgy and Powder Technology see International Journal of Powder Metallurgy **3409**
International Journal of Pressure Vessels and Piping. (UK) **1932**
International Journal of Primatology. (US ISSN 0164-0291) **584**
International Journal of Production Economics. (NE ISSN 0925-5273) **1827**, 1014, 1078, 1879
International Journal of Production Research. (UK ISSN 0020-7543) **1079**, 1827
International Journal of Project Management. (UK ISSN 0263-7863) **827**, 1014
International Journal of Prosthodontics. (US ISSN 0893-2174) **3235**
International Journal of Psychiatry in Medicine. (US ISSN 0091-2174) **3339**, 4025
International Journal of Psycho-Analysis.(UK ISSN 0020-7578) **4025**
International Journal of Psychology/ Journal International de Psychologie. (UK ISSN 0020-7594) **4025**
International Journal of Psychophysiology. (NE ISSN 0167-8760) **4026**
International Journal of Psychosomatics.(US ISSN 0884-8297) **3110**, 3235, 3730, 4026
International Journal of Public Administration. (US ISSN 0190-0692) **4064**
International Journal of Public Opinion Research. (UK ISSN 0954-2892) **4376**, 3899
International Journal of Public Sector Management. (UK ISSN 0951-3558) **1014**
International Journal of Purchasing & Materials Management. (US) **1042**
International Journal of Qualitative Studies in Education. (UK ISSN 0951-8398) **1640**
International Journal of Quality & Reliability Management. (UK ISSN 0265-671X) **1014**
International Journal of Quantum Chemistry. (US ISSN 0020-7608) **1179**
International Journal of Quantum Chemistry. Symposium see International Symposium on Atomic, Molecular and Solid-State Theory, Collision Phenomena and Computational Methods. Proceedings **1179**
International Journal of Radiation Applications and Instrumentation. Part A: Applied Radiation and Isotopes. (US ISSN 0883-2889) **3847**, 3260, 3358
International Journal of Radiation Applications and Instrumentation. Part B: Nuclear Medicine and Biology. (US ISSN 0883-2897) **3359**, 442, 1806

INTERNATIONAL LIFE   6313

International Journal of Radiation Applications and Instrumentation. Part C: Radiation Physics and Chemistry. (US) 3847, 1179
International Journal of Radiation Applications and Instrumentation. Part D: Nuclear Tracks and Radiation Measurements. (US) 3847
International Journal of Radiation Applications and Instrumentation. Part E: Nuclear Geophysics. (UK ISSN 0886-0130) 1591, 1806
International Journal of Radiation Biology. (UK ISSN 0020-7616) 3198, 485, 3820, 4315
International Journal of Radiation: Oncology - Biology - Physics. (US ISSN 0360-3016) 3848, 3359
▼International Journal of Radioactive Materials Transport. (UK ISSN 0957-476X) 4651, 3649
International Journal of Rapid Solidification. (UK ISSN 0265-0916) 3409, 1932
International Journal of Refractory and Hard Metals see International Journal of Refractory Metals & Hard Materials 3409
International Journal of Refractory Metals & Hard Materials. (UK ISSN 0958-0611) 3409
International Journal of Refrigeration. (UK ISSN 0140-7007) 2301
International Journal of Refugee Law. (UK ISSN 0953-8186) 3961, 2702, 3943
International Journal of Rehabilitation Research. (UK ISSN 0342-5282) 3110, 1736
International Journal of Remote Sensing. (UK ISSN 0143-1161) 1545, 2253, 2523
International Journal of Research in Marketing. (NE ISSN 0167-8116) 1042
International Journal of Retail & Distribution Management. (UK ISSN 0959-0552) 1042
International Journal of Retailing see International Journal of Retail & Distribution Management 1042
†International Journal of Reviews in Library and Information Science. (US ISSN 0740-5138) 5217
▼International Journal of Risk and Safety in Medicine. (NE ISSN 0924-6479) 3111
International Journal of Robotics and Automation. (CN ISSN 0826-8185) 1414
International Journal of Robotics Research. (US ISSN 0278-3649) 1408, 1879
▼International Journal of Robust and Nonlinear Control. (UK ISSN 1049-8923) 1900
International Journal of Rock Mechanics and Mining Sciences & Geomechanics Abstracts. (US ISSN 0148-9062) 3499, 15
†International Journal of Roofing Technology. (US) 5217
International Journal of Rumanian Studies. (NE) 2368
▼International Journal of S T D & A I D S. (UK ISSN 0956-4624) 3220
International Journal of Satellite Communications. (UK ISSN 0737-2884) 1338
International Journal of Science and Technology. (US) 4315
International Journal of Science Education. (UK ISSN 0950-0693) 1640, 4315
▼International Journal of Service Industry Management. (UK) 1014, 1079
International Journal of Short Term Psychotherapy. (UK) 4026
International Journal of Sign Linguistics.(UK ISSN 0959-6402) 2819, 2288
International Journal of Slavic Linguistics and Poetics. (US ISSN 0538-8228) 2819, 2925
International Journal of Small Group Research see Small Group Research 4046

International Journal of Social Economics. (UK ISSN 0306-8293) 672, 4438
International Journal of Social Education. (US ISSN 0889-0293) 4376, 1640
International Journal of Social Psychiatry. (UK ISSN 0020-7640) 3339
International Journal of Sociology. (US ISSN 0020-7659) 4438
International Journal of Sociology and Social Policy. (UK ISSN 0144-333X) 4438, 4376
International Journal of Sociology of Agriculture and Food. see Revista Internacional de Sociología sobre Agricultura y Alimentos 4447
International Journal of Sociology of the Family. (II) 4438
▼International Journal of Software Engineering and Knowledge Engineering. (SI ISSN 0218-1940) 1478
International Journal of Solar Energy. (US ISSN 0142-5919) 1811
International Journal of Solids and Structures. (US ISSN 0020-7683) 3843
International Journal of Special Education. (CN) 1736
International Journal of Sport Biomechanics. (US ISSN 0740-2082) 4476, 572
▼International Journal of Sport Nutrition. (US ISSN 1050-1606) 3607, 3371
International Journal of Sport Psychology. (IT ISSN 0047-0767) 4476, 3371, 4026
International Journal of Sports Cardiology. (IT ISSN 0393-6066) 3209
International Journal of Sports Medicine.(GW ISSN 0172-4622) 3371, 4476
International Journal of Structures. (II ISSN 0253-4754) 1868
International Journal of Supercomputer Applications. (US ISSN 0890-2720) 1478
International Journal of Surface Mining see International Journal of Surface Mining and Reclamation 3486
International Journal of Surface Mining and Reclamation. (NE) 3486, 3409, 3689
International Journal of Systematic Bacteriology. (US ISSN 0020-7713) 553
▼International Journal of Systems Automation. (US ISSN 1055-8462) 1414
International Journal of Systems Research see Systems Research 1837
International Journal of Systems Science. (UK ISSN 0020-7721) 1827
International Journal of Technology & Aging. (US ISSN 0891-4478) 2274
International Journal of Technology and Design Education. (UK ISSN 0957-7572) 1752, 4601
International Journal of Technology Assessment in Health Care. (UK ISSN 0266-4623) 3260
International Journal of Technology Management. (SZ ISSN 0267-5730) 4601, 1014
International Journal of the Addictions. (US ISSN 0020-773X) 1536
International Journal of the History of Sport. (UK ISSN 0952-3367) 4476, 2314
International Journal of the Sociology of Language. (GW ISSN 0165-2516) 2819, 4438
International Journal of the Sociology of Law. (UK ISSN 0194-6595) 2636, 4438
International Journal of Theoretical Physics. (US ISSN 0020-7748) 3820
International Journal of Therapeutic Communities. (UK ISSN 0196-1365) 3339, 4507

International Journal of Thermophysics. (US ISSN 0195-928X) 3841
International Journal of Translation. (II ISSN 0970-9819) 2819
International Journal of Transport Economics/Rivista Internazionale di Economica dei Trasporti. (IT ISSN 0391-8440) 4651
International Journal of Tropical Agriculture. (II ISSN 0254-8755) 99
International Journal of Tropical Plant Diseases. (II ISSN 0254-0126) 506
International Journal of Turbo and Jet Engines. (IS ISSN 0334-0082) 56
International Journal of Turkish Studies.(US ISSN 0272-7919) 2429, 2253
International Journal of University Adult Education. (CN) 1684
International Journal of Urban and Regional Research. (UK ISSN 0309-1317) 2489
International Journal of Value-Based Management. (US ISSN 0895-8815) 1014
International Journal of Vehicle Design. (SZ ISSN 0143-3369) 4651, 1932, 4601
International Journal of Water Resources Development. (UK ISSN 0790-0627) 4826
International Journal of Wine Marketing.(UK ISSN 0954-7541) 382
International Journal on Drug Policy. (UK) 3961, 1536, 3730
International Journal on Policy and Information see International Journal of Information and Management Sciences 1014
International Journal on the Unity of the Sciences. (US ISSN 0896-2294) 4315
International Journal on World Peace. (US ISSN 0742-3640) 3961
International Jugglers Association Newsletter see Juggler's World Magazine 2437
International Kierkegaard Newsletter. (DK ISSN 0108-3104) 3769
International Labmate. (UK ISSN 0143-5140) 3260, 2523
International Labor Affairs Report. (US) 817
International Labor and Working Class History. (US ISSN 0147-5479) 983, 2314
International Labor Bulletin. see Guoji Laogong Tongxun 980
International Labor Communications Association Reporter see I L C A Reporter 2570
International Laboratory. (US ISSN 0010-2164) 1206
International Laboratory Conference. Reports to the Conference and Record of Proceedings. (UN ISSN 0074-6681) 983
International Labour Documentation. (UN ISSN 0020-7756) 722, 15
International Labour Law Reports. (NE) 2636, 983
International Labour Office. Labour Law Documents. (UN ISSN 1014-7071) 984, 2636
International Labour Office. Legislative Series see International Labour Office. Labour Law Documents 984
International Labour Office. Official Bulletin see International Labour Office. Official Bulletin. Series A 984
International Labour Office. Official Bulletin see International Labour Office. Official Bulletin. Series B 984
International Labour Office. Official Bulletin. Series A. (UN ISSN 0378-5882) 984
International Labour Office. Official Bulletin. Series B. (UN ISSN 0378-5890) 984
International Labour Office. Social and Labour Bulletin see Social and Labour Bulletin 993

International Labour Office. Special Report of the Director-General on the Application of the Declaration Concerning the Policy of Apartheid of the Republic of South Africa. (UN ISSN 0538-8333) 3944
International Labour Office Information see I L O Information 981
International Labour Office Judgements of the Administrative Tribunal see I L O Judgements of the Administrative Tribunal 2633
International Labour Office Publications see I L O Publications 720
†International Labour Reports. (UK ISSN 0266-2140) 5217
International Labour Review. (UN ISSN 0020-7780) 984
†International Latitude Observatory of Mizusawa. Proceedings. (JA ISSN 0536-3403) 5217
†International Latitude Observatory of Mizusawa. Publications. (JA ISSN 0386-0779) 5217
International Law and Trade Perspective. (US) 2725
International Law Association. American Branch. Proceedings. (US) 2725
International Law Association. Reports of Conferences. (UK ISSN 0074-6738) 2725
International Law Association Newsletter see I L A Newsletter 2724
International Law Association Practitioner's Notebook see I L A Practitioner's Notebook 2724
International Law News. (US ISSN 0047-0813) 2725, 3961
International Law Perspective see International Law and Trade Perspective 2725
International Law Practicum. (US ISSN 1041-3405) 2725
International Law Reporter. (II ISSN 0300-4058) 2725
International Law Reports. (UK) 2725, 2636, 3961
International Law Students Association Journal of International Law see I L S A Journal of International Law 2633
International Lawyer. (US ISSN 0020-7810) 2725
International Lawyers' Newsletter. (US ISSN 0738-9728) 2636
International Leadership. (US) 3961
International Leads. (US ISSN 0892-4546) 2764, 3961
International League for Human Rights. Annual Report. (US ISSN 0363-9347) 3944
International League for the Rights of Man. Annual Report see International League for Human Rights. Annual Report 3944
International League of Societies for Persons with Mental Handicap. News see I L S M H News 4024
International League of Societies for Persons with Mental Handicap News see I L S M H News 4024
International League of Women Composers. Newsletter. (US ISSN 0748-5735) 3557
International Leather Guide. (UK ISSN 0955-5080) 2736
International Lecture Series in Computer Science. (US) 1397
International Legal Materials. (US ISSN 0020-7829) 2725
International Legal Practitioner. (UK ISSN 0309-7684) 2725
International Lesbian and Gay Association Bulletin see I L G A Bulletin 2454
International Lesson Annual. (US) 4183
International Library and Information Review. (UK ISSN 1057-2317) 2764
International Library Movement. (II ISSN 0970-0048) 2764
International Library Review see International Library and Information Review 2764
International Licensing. (UK ISSN 0020-7845) 4601, 3675
International Life. see Gukjesaenghwal 3958

INTERNATIONAL LIGHTING

International Lighting Review. (NE ISSN 0020-7853) **621**, 1900, 1959, 2553
International Lilac Society. Newsletter see Lilacs Quarterly Journal **2133**
†International Limousin Journal. (US) **5217**
International Linguistic Association. Monograph. (US ISSN 0074-6797) **2819**
International Linguistic Association. Special Publications. (US ISSN 0074-6800) **2819**
International Listening Guide. (GW ISSN 0178-9287) **1356**
International Literary and Artistic Association. Proceedings and Reports of Congress. (FR ISSN 0074-6819) **2508**
International Literary Market Place. (US ISSN 0074-6827) **4130**
▼International Litigation Procedure. (UK) **2725**
International Livestock Centre for Africa Annual Report see I L C A Annual Report **217**
International Livestock Centre for Africa Research Report see I L C A Research Report **218**
International Living. (US ISSN 0277-2442) **4772**
International Logic Review. see Rassegna Internazionale di Logica **3778**
International Logistics Symposium Proceedings see Society of Logistics Engineers. Proceedings **4609**
International Logo Exchange see Logo Exchange **1691**
International Loss Control Review. (US) **1014**
International Magnetics Conference. Digests of the Intermag Conference. (US) **3820**
International Mail Manual. (US) **1353**
International Management. (UK ISSN 0020-7888) **1014**
†International Management (Arabic Edition)/Alam Al-Idarah. (UK) **5217**
International Management Development Review. (UK ISSN 0266-7908) **1014**, 786
International Map Dealers Association. Directory of Suppliers. (US) **1140**, 2253
International Map Dealers Association Newsletter see Map Report **2256**
International Marine Business Journal. (US) **4525**, 672
International Marine Science Newsletter see I M S Newsletter **1605**
International Maritime Committee. Documentation see C M I News Letter **4725**
International Maritime Committee. Documentation see C M I Year Book **4725**
International Maritime Committee News Letter see C M I News Letter **4725**
†International Maritime Law Seminar. Publication. (CN) **5217**
International Maritime Organization News see I M O News **4728**
International Market. see Guoji Shichang **910**
International Market Alert. (US ISSN 1051-8061) **950**
International Market Guide - Continental Europe see Market Guide Continental Europe **955**
International Market Review. (CN) **786**, 870, 913
†International Marketing Communications Newsletter. (US) **5217**
International Marketing Data and Statistics. (UK ISSN 0308-2938) **723**
International Marketing Review. (UK ISSN 0265-1335) **1042**
International Markets for Meat. (UN) **219**
International Materials Review. (UK ISSN 0950-6608) **3409**
International Mathematical News. (AU ISSN 0020-7926) **3039**
International Mathematical Union Canberra Circular see I M U Canberra Circular **3037**

International Measurement Confederation Acta I M E K O see Acta I M E K O **3445**
International Media Guide. Consumer Magazines Worldwide. (US ISSN 0730-5257) **41**, 4664
International Media Guide. Newspapers Worldwide. (US) **41**
International Media Guides. Business - Professional Publications Edition. (US) **41**
International Media Law. (UK ISSN 0263-6395) **2725**, 1338
International Medical Advances Now! see Health & Wealth Guardian **3102**
International Medical Centers Journal see I M C Journal **5209**
▼International Medical Device and Diagnostic Industry. (US) **2523**
†International Medical Newsletter. (BE) **5217**
International Medical Who's Who see Medical Sciences International Who's Who **420**
International Medieval Bibliography. (UK ISSN 0020-7950) **2329**
International Medieval Bibliography. Annual Subject Guide see International Medieval Bibliography **2329**
International Meeting of Animal Nutrition Experts. Proceedings. (SP ISSN 0074-6959) **219**
International Meeting on Cattle Diseases. Reports. see World Buiatrics Congress **4819**
International Meeting Place. (UK ISSN 0268-5671) **4772**
International Melodic Scribble see The Last Ever Melodic Scribble **2996**
▼International Merger Law: Events and Commentary. (US ISSN 1053-4660) **2725**, 913
International Metals Review see International Materials Review **3409**
International Metalworkers' Congress. Reports. (SZ ISSN 0074-6983) **3409**
International Metalworkers Federation News see I M F News **3408**
International Meteorological Institute in Stockholm. Annual Report. (SW ISSN 0349-0068) **3436**
†International Micro News. (US) **5217**
International Microfilm Source Book see International Imaging Source Book **2794**
†International Microform Journal of Legal Medicine and Forensic Sciences. (US) **5217**
International Micrographics Source Book see International Imaging Source Book **2794**
International MIDI Association Bulletin see I M A Bulletin **3555**
International Migration. (SZ ISSN 0020-7985) **3983**
International Migration Digest see International Migration Review **3983**
International Migration Newsletter see International Newsletter on Migration **3983**
International Migration Review. (US ISSN 0197-9183) **3983**, 2007, 4376
International Mineralogical Association. Proceedings of Meetings. (GW ISSN 0074-7017) **3486**
International Mining see Engineering & Mining Journal **3483**
International Mobile Air Conditioning Association Directory see I M A C A Directory **4692**
†International Molders' and Allied Workers' Journal. (US ISSN 0020-8019) **5217**
International Monetary Agreements Acts. Annual Report. (AT ISSN 0818-6316) **786**, 2636
International Monetary Fund. Annual Report of the Executive Board. (UN ISSN 0250-7498) **786**
International Monetary Fund. Annual Report of the Executive Directors see International Monetary Fund. Annual Report of the Executive Board **786**

International Monetary Fund. Annual Report on Exchange Arrangements and Exchange Restrictions. (UN ISSN 0250-7366) **786**
International Monetary Fund. Annual Report on Exchange Restrictions see International Monetary Fund. Annual Report on Exchange Arrangements and Exchange Restrictions **786**
International Monetary Fund. Balance of Payments Statistics. (UN ISSN 0252-3051) **723**, 913, 999
International Monetary Fund. Government Finance Statistics Yearbook. (UN ISSN 0250-7374) **723**
International Monetary Fund. Occasional Papers. (UN ISSN 0251-6365) **786**
International Monetary Fund. Pamphlet Series. (UN ISSN 0538-8759) **786**
International Monetary Fund. Selected Decisions of the Executive Directors and Selected Documents see International Monetary Fund. Selected Decisions of the International Monetary Fund and Selected Documents **786**
International Monetary Fund. Selected Decisions of the International Monetary Fund and Selected Documents. (UN ISSN 0094-1735) **786**
International Monetary Fund. Staff Papers. (UN ISSN 0020-8027) **786**
International Monetary Fund. Summary Proceedings of the Annual Meeting of the Board of Governors. (UN ISSN 0074-7025) **786**
International Monetary Fund. World Economic and Financial Surveys. (UN ISSN 0258-7440) **786**, 932
International Monetary Fund Survey see I M F Survey **720**
†International Monograph Series on Early Child Care. (US ISSN 0140-668X) **5217**
International Monographs on Advanced Biology and Biophysics. (II ISSN 0074-7033) **442**, 485
International Monographs on Advanced Chemistry. (II ISSN 0074-7041) **1179**
International Monographs on Advanced Mathematics and Physics. (II ISSN 0074-705X) **3039**, 3820
International Monographs on Studies in Indian Economics. (II ISSN 0074-7068) **672**
International Motion Picture Almanac. (US ISSN 0074-7084) **3512**
International Motor Business. (UK ISSN 0267-8225) **4693**
International Motor Sports Association Yearbook see I M S A Yearbook **4475**
International Motorsports Association Arrow see I M S A Arrow **4475**
International Museum of Cultures. Publication. (US ISSN 0895-9897) **242**
International Music Council. German Committee. Referate Informationen see Musikforum - Referate und Informationen des Deutschen Musikrates **3568**
International Musician. (US ISSN 0020-8051) **3557**, 2585
International Musician & Recording World. (UK) **3557**, 4461
International Narcotic Conference. Report: Proceedings of Annual Conference see International Drug Report **1515**
International Narcotic Enforcement Officers Association. Annual Conference Report see Narc Officer **2656**
International Narcotic Enforcement Officers Association Directory. (US) **1515**, 1536
International Narcotics Control Board. Report for (Year). (UN ISSN 0257-3717) **3730**, 1536, 4105
International Narcotics Control Board. Statistics on Psychotropic Substances for (Year). (UN) **3748**, 1540, 4117

International Naturist Guide/ Internationaler FKK-Reisefuehrer/ Guide Naturiste Internationale. (GW ISSN 0074-7122) **4549**
International Navigation Congress. Papers. (BE) **4729**
International Navigation Congress. Proceedings. (BE) **4729**
†International Netsuke Collectors Society Journal. (US ISSN 0095-2591) **5217**
International Network for Religion and Animals Ads see I N R O Ads **231**
International New Product Newsletter. (US ISSN 1046-7211) **1079**
International New Product Report. (UK) **2092**, 1042
†International Newsletter. (SW ISSN 0308-762X) **5217**
International Newsletter of Maritime History. (CN ISSN 0835-6955) **4729**
International Newsletter on Chemical Education. (UK ISSN 0306-7696) **1179**, 1640
International Newsletter on Migration. (CN ISSN 0383-2767) **3983**
International Newspaper Advertising and Marketing Executives. Sales and Idea Book. (US) **33**, 1042
International Notices to Airmen. (US ISSN 0364-6742) **56**
International Nuclear Information System Newsletter see I N I S Newsletter **2761**
International Nursing Index. (US ISSN 0020-8124) **3176**, 15
International Nursing Review. (SZ ISSN 0020-8132) **3279**
International Obesity Newsletter see Obesity & Health **3611**
International Ocean Institute. Occasional Papers. (MM) **1606**
International Ocean Institute. Pacem in Maribus. Proceedings. (MM) **1606**
International Ocean Institute News see I O I News **1605**
International Oceanographic Tables. (UN ISSN 0538-8880) **1606**
International Odd Fellow and Rebekah. (US) **1298**
International Office of Cocoa and Chocolate and the International Sugar Confectionery Manufacturers' Association. Periodic Bulletin see International Office of Cocoa, Chocolate and Sugar Confectionery. Annual Statistical Bulletin **2088**
International Office of Cocoa, Chocolate and Sugar Confectionery. Annual Statistical Bulletin. (BE) **2088**
International Office of Cocoa, Chocolate and Sugar Confectionery. Report of the General Assembly. (BE) **2088**
International Offshore Craft Conference. Proceedings. (UK) **4729**
International Offshore Financial Centres.(AT) **913**, 3689
International Offshore Rig Owners Directory. (US ISSN 1058-6008) **3690**
International Oil and Gas Development Yearbook. (US) **3690**, 1569
International Oil News see International Oil News: Suppliers Edition **1140**
International Oil News see International Oil News: Management Edition **3690**
International Oil News: Management Edition. (US) **3690**
International Oil News: Suppliers Edition.(US) **1140**, 3690
International Oil Scouts Association. Official Newsletter see International Oil Scouts Association. Official Publication **3690**
International Oil Scouts Association. Official Publication. (US ISSN 0277-6812) **3690**, 1569
International Oil Scouts Association Directory. (US) **1140**, 1569, 3690
International Olympic Academy. Report of the Sessions. (GR ISSN 0074-7181) **4476**
International Olympic Lifter. (US) **4476**
International Ombudsman Institute. Newsletter. (CN ISSN 0229-2181) **2636**

INTERNATIONAL PRESS 6315

International Ombudsman Institute. Occasional Paper Series. (CN) **2636**
†International Ombudsman Institute Bibliography. (CN) **5217**
International Omega Association. Proceedings of Annual Meeting. (US ISSN 0278-9396) **56,** 4729
International Omega Association Newsletter. (US) **4675,** 1827, 4729
International Online Information Meeting (Proceedings). (UK) **1427**
International Operating Engineer. (US ISSN 0020-8159) **2585**
International Ophthalmology. (NE ISSN 0165-5701) **3301**
International Ophthalmology Clinics. (US ISSN 0020-8167) **3301**
International Optical Year Book. (UK) **3301**
International Organization. (US ISSN 0020-8183) **3961**
International Organization for Cooperation in Health Care. General Assembly. Report. (BE) **3111**
International Organization for Medical Cooperation. General Assembly. Report *see* International Organization for Cooperation in Health Care. General Assembly. Report **3111**
International Organization for Migration. Annual Report. (SZ) **3983**
International Organization for Migration. Annual Review *see* International Organization for Migration. Annual Report **3983**
International Organization for Migration Monthly Dispatch *see* I O M Monthly Dispatch **3982**
International Organization for Standardization Bulletin (English Edition) *see* I S O Bulletin (English Edition) **3446**
International Organization for Standardization Catalogue *see* I S O Catalogue **3446**
International Organization for Standardization International Standards *see* I S O International Standards **3446**
International Organization for Standardization Memento *see* I S O Memento **3446**
International Organization of Consumers Unions. Proceedings. (NE ISSN 0538-8988) **1505**
International Organization of Journalists Newsletter *see* I O J Newsletter **2570**
International Organization of Plant Biosystematists. Newsletter. (SZ ISSN 0254-8844) **506,** 525
International Organizations (Year). (US) **1140**
International Organizing Committee of World Mining Congresses. Report *see* World Mining Congress. Report **3498**
International Orthopaedics. (GW ISSN 0341-2695) **3308**
International P.E.N. Bulletin of Selected Books *see* P E N International **2982**
International P.E.N. Congress. Report. (UK ISSN 0074-722X) **2925**
International Pacific Halibut Commission (U.S. and Canada). Annual Report. (US ISSN 0074-7238) **2044**
International Pacific Halibut Commission (U.S. and Canada). Scientific Reports.(US ISSN 0074-7246) **2044**
International Pacific Halibut Commission (U S and Canada). Technical Reports. (US ISSN 0579-3920) **2044**
International Packaging Abstracts. (UK ISSN 0260-7409) **3652,** 15
International Paper Board Industry. (US ISSN 0020-8191) **3649,** 3663
▼International Parallels. (US ISSN 1055-3649) **1505**
International Partners in Prayer Trumpeting News. (US ISSN 0743-5614) **4183**
International Patent Litigation. (US) **3676**
▼International Patent Litigation. Supplement. (US) **3676**
International Peace Research Association Newsletter *see* I P R A Newsletter **3959**
International Peace Research Newsletter *see* I P R A Newsletter **3959**
†International Peace Studies Newsletter.(US) **5217**
International Peat Journal. (FI ISSN 0782-7784) **442,** 478
†International Pediatric Association. Bulletin. (FR ISSN 0245-9337) **5217**
International Pediatric Association. Proceedings of Congress. (FR ISSN 0074-7300) **3321**
International Pentecostal Holiness Advocate. (US ISSN 0031-4900) **4284**
International Periodicals and Reference Works. (US ISSN 0742-3985) **2578,** 403
The International Permaculture Solutions Journal. (US ISSN 1046-8366) **442,** 1959
▼International Personal Tax Planning Encyclopedia. (US) **1098**
International Personnel Management Association. Personnel News *see* I P M A News **1066**
International Personnel Management Association News *see* I P M A News **1066**
International Perspectives. (CN ISSN 0381-4874) **3961**
International Pest Control. (UK ISSN 0020-8256) **534,** 181, 4105
International Petroleum Abstracts. (UK ISSN 0309-4944) **3705,** 15
International Petroleum Encyclopedia. (US ISSN 0148-0375) **3690**
International Petroleum Finance. (US ISSN 0193-9270) **3690,** 786
International Petroleum Industry. (US) **3690,** 1140
International Pharmaceutical Abstracts. (US ISSN 0020-8264) **3748,** 15
International Pharmaceutical Students Federation News Bulletin *see* I P S F News Bulletin **3728**
International Pharmacy Journal. (GW ISSN 1010-0423) **3730**
International Philatelic Federation. General Assembly. Proces-Verbal. (SZ ISSN 0074-7343) **3753**
International Philatelic Press Club. Report to Members. (US) **3753**
International Philosophical Bibliography. *see* Repertoire Bibliographique de la Philosophie **3788**
International Philosophical Quarterly. (US ISSN 0019-0365) **3769**
International Phoenix Conference on Computers and Communications. Proceedings *see* Phoenix Conference on Computers and Communications. Conference Proceedings **1351**
International Phonetic Association. Journal. (UK ISSN 0025-1003) **2819**
International Photo Technik *see* Photo Technik International **3795**
International Photographer. (US ISSN 0020-8299) **3792**
International Planned Parenthood Federation. Library Bulletin *see* I P P F Co-operative Information Service **5210**
International Planned Parenthood Federation Annual Report *see* I P P F Annual Report **597**
International Planned Parenthood Federation Co-operative Information Service *see* I P P F Co-operative Information Service **5210**
International Planned Parenthood Federation Medical Bulletin *see* I P P F Medical Bulletin **597**
International Plant Propagators' Society. Combined Proceedings of Annual Meetings. (US ISSN 0538-9143) **2132**
International Plant Protection Center. Infoletter. (US ISSN 0145-6288) **181**
International Plastic Modellers Society (UK) UK) Magazine *see* I.P.M.S. (UK) Magazine **2437**
International Plastics Directory. *see* Handbuch der Internationalen Kunststoffindustrie **3862**
International Poetry. (US) **2995**
International Polar Motion Service. Annual Report. *see* International Earth Rotation Service. Annual Report **365**
†International Police Association. Meeting of the International Executive Council. (UK ISSN 0579-5567) **5217**
†International Police Association. Travel Scholarships. (UK ISSN 0579-6881) **5217**
International Policy Report. (US ISSN 0738-6508) **3961**
International Political Economy Yearbook. (US) **3899,** 932
International Political Science Abstracts/ Documentation Politique Internationale. (NO ISSN 0020-8345) **3938,** 15
International Political Science Association. Circular *see* Participation **3914**
International Political Science Association. World Conference. Proceedings *see* International Political Science Association. World Congress **3899**
International Political Science Association. World Congress. (NO) **3899**
International Political Science Review/ Revue Internationale de Science Politique. (UK ISSN 0192-5121) **3961**
International Politik *see* Review of International Affairs **3970**
International Polymer Processing. (GW ISSN 0930-777X) **3862**
International Polymer Science and Technology. (UK ISSN 0307-174X) **3863,** 1179
International Popular Bridge Monthly. (UK ISSN 0951-1555) **4476**
International Population Conference. Proceedings. (BE ISSN 0074-9338) **3983,** 597
International Population Data. (US) **3984**
International Portland Review *see* Portland Review Magazine **2949**
International Post. (II) **3961**
International Potash Institute. Colloquium. Proceedings. (SZ ISSN 0074-7491) **181**
International Potash Institute. Congress Proceedings. (SZ) **181**
International Potash Institute. Congress Report *see* International Potash Institute. Congress Proceedings **181**
International Potash Institute Bulletin *see* I P I Bulletin **179**
International Potash Institute Research Topics *see* I P I Research Topics **179**
International Poultry Trade Show Guide.(US) **219**
International Powder & Bulk Solids Abstracts. (UK ISSN 0266-2922) **1845,** 1854
International Power Generation. (UK ISSN 0141-1918) **1900**
†International Power Systems. (US) **5217**
International President's Bulletin. (US ISSN 0161-9314) **2585**
International Press Cutting Service: Advertising, Marketing, Sales Executive's Report. (II) **33,** 1042
International Press Cutting Service: Ceramics - Porcelain - Refractory - Cement - Glass. (II ISSN 0047-0902) **1165**
International Press Cutting Service: Chemical Process Engineering. Drugs - Pharmaceuticals. (II ISSN 0047-0910) **1855,** 3730
International Press Cutting Service: Computer World - Data Processing - Accounting. (II) **1452,** 752
International Press Cutting Service: Dyestuff Industry and Chemicals. (II ISSN 0047-0929) **1281,** 1855
International Press Cutting Service: Electronics and Electricals Industry. (II ISSN 0047-0937) **1774**
International Press Cutting Service: Export Opportunities - New Addresses - Handlooms. (II) **913**
International Press Cutting Service: Fermented Wines, Liqueurs, Brandy, Gin, Rum, Whisky, Beer and Alcoholic Drinks. (II ISSN 0047-0945) **382**
International Press Cutting Service: Import - Export - Licenses. (II ISSN 0047-0953) **913**
International Press Cutting Service: Jute, Gunny, Hessian, Burlap, Coir. (II ISSN 0047-0961) **4620**
International Press Cutting Service: Labour Welfare - Industrial Legislation and Personnel Management. (II ISSN 0047-097X) **984,** 1066
International Press Cutting Service: Leather - Hides - Skin - Footwear. (II ISSN 0047-0988) **2736**
International Press Cutting Service: List of Industrial Licences Issued. (II) **3676**
International Press Cutting Service: Machine Tool and Iron Steel Industry.(II ISSN 0047-0996) **3018,** 3409
International Press Cutting Service: Mines & Minerals (Coal and Ores). (II ISSN 0047-1003) **3486**
International Press Cutting Service: Modern Plastics and Engineering. (II ISSN 0047-0899) **3863**
International Press Cutting Service: Non-Ferrous Metals - Aluminium. (II ISSN 0047-1011) **3409**
International Press Cutting Service: Oils (Vegetable) Fats - Soap - Animalfeed.(II ISSN 0047-102X) **1218**
International Press Cutting Service: Paint - Colour - Varnish - Inks. (II) **3654**
International Press Cutting Service: Paper - Pulp - Board - Straw. (II ISSN 0047-1038) **3663**
International Press Cutting Service: Petroleum - Petrochemicals - Fertilisers - Agricultural Chemistry. (II ISSN 0047-1046) **3690**
International Press Cutting Service: Plywood - Timber - Particle Board. (II ISSN 0047-1054) **2115**
International Press Cutting Service: Processed Food Products - Spices. (II ISSN 0047-1151) **2074**
International Press Cutting Service: Rubber and Rubber Technology. (II ISSN 0047-1062) **4292**
International Press Cutting Service: Scientific Instruments, Laboratory Equipment & Chemicals. (II ISSN 0047-1070) **2523,** 3260
International Press Cutting Service: Sugar - Gur - Khandasari. (II ISSN 0047-1089) **2074**
International Press Cutting Service: Taxation - Finance - Company Law. (II ISSN 0047-1097) **1098,** 786
International Press Cutting Service: Tea and Coffee News. (II ISSN 0047-1100) **2074**
International Press Cutting Service: Technical News Report. (II) **4601**
International Press Cutting Service: Tender Notifications (Indian & Global). (II ISSN 0047-1127) **913**
International Press Cutting Service: Textile News. (II ISSN 0047-1119) **4620**
International Press Cutting Service: Tobacco News. (II ISSN 0047-1135) **4643**
International Press Cutting Service: Weekly Energy - Ecology - Pollution Report. (II) **1791,** 1959
International Press Cutting Service: Wheat & Wheat Products (Rice - Food Grains). (II ISSN 0047-1143) **207,** 2074
International Press Institute. Survey *see* World Press Freedom Review **2577**
International Press Institute Report *see* I P I Report **2570**
International Press Journal. (US ISSN 0020-837X) **2571**
International Press Telecommunications Council News *see* I P T C News **1363**

Title

International Primate Protection League Newsletter. (US ISSN 1040-3027) **1489**
International Prisoners Aid Association. Newsletter. (US ISSN 0020-8396) **4409**, 1515
International Problems. (IS ISSN 0020-840X) **3961**, 2725
International Process Technology Abstracts. (UK ISSN 0266-2930) **1845**, 1855
International Procurement Committee Report *see* I P C Report **2633**
International Product Alert. (US) **2074**, 382, 1505, 3649
International Production Cost Comparison. (SZ) **4620**
International Professional Communication Conference. Conference Record. (US) **1338**
International Programmable Controllers Directory *see* International Control Products Database **5216**
International Progress in Urethanes. (US ISSN 0147-0671) **3863**, 1218
†International Property Review. (UK ISSN 0267-744X) **5217**
International Prospect. *see* Guoji Zhanwang **3959**
†International Psychic Register. (US ISSN 0147-782X) **5217**
†International Psycho-Analytical Association. Monograph. (US) **5217**
International Psychohistorical Association Bulletin *see* I P A Bulletin **4024**
International Psychologist. (US ISSN 0047-116X) **4026**
International Public Relations Review. (UK ISSN 0269-0357) **33**, 3961
International Public Relations Review *see* Public Relations Quarterly **37**
International Publishers Association. Proceedings of Congress. (SZ ISSN 0074-7556) **4130**
International Publishing Newsletter *see* B P Report **4121**
International Pulp & Paper Directory. (US ISSN 0097-2509) **3663**, 1140
†International Q C Forum. (US) **5217**
International Quarterly. (UK) **3486**
†International Quarterly of Analytical Chemistry. (TU ISSN 0259-8388) **5217**
International Quarterly of Antibiotic Research. (TU ISSN 0259-8396) **478**
International Quarterly of Cancer Research. (TU ISSN 0259-840X) **3198**
International Quarterly of Community Health Education. (US ISSN 0272-684X) **4105**
International Quarterly of Entomology. (TU ISSN 0256-6672) **534**
International Quarterly of Materials Science. (TU ISSN 0259-8418) **1827**, 1918
International Quarterly of Virology. (TU ISSN 0259-8426) **553**
International Quarterly Review of South African Gold Shares *see* International Quarterly **3486**
International Radar Conference. Record.(US) **1338**, 56, 1900
International Radio and Television Society, Inc. Gold Medal Journal *see* I R T S Gold Medal Journal **1374**
International Radio Consultative Committee. Plenary Assembly. Proceedings. (UN) **1356**
International Rail Statistics. (FR) **4664**
International Railway Journal *see* International Railway Journal and Rapid Transit Review **4710**
International Railway Journal and Rapid Transit Review. (US ISSN 0744-5326) **4710**
International Railway Progress *see* Developing Railways **4709**
International Railway Statistics. Statistics of Individual Railways. (FR ISSN 0074-7580) **4664**, 4710
International Railway Traveler. (US ISSN 0891-7655) **4772**, 4710
International Rare Book Prices - Early Printed Books. (UK) **4141**

International Rare Book Prices - Literature. (UK) **4141**, 2982
International Rare Book Prices - Modern First Edition. (UK) **4141**, 2982
International Rare Book Prices - Sciences & Medicine. (UK) **4141**, 3176, 4356
International Rare Book Prices - The Arts & Architecture. (UK) **4141**, 309, 352
International Rare Book Prices - Voyages, Travel & Exploration. (UK) **4141**, 4799
International Rare Book Prices - 19th Century Literature *see* International Rare Book Prices - Literature **4141**
International Real Estate Journal. (US ISSN 8755-6138) **4151**
International Rebekah News *see* International Odd Fellow and Rebekah **1298**
International Records News. (IT) **3557**
International Reference Annual for Building and Equipment of Sports, Tourism, Recreation Installations. (FR ISSN 0074-7645) **4476**
International Referral Centre for Information Handling Equipment Bulletin *see* I R C I H E Bulletin **2761**
International Refractories Handbook & Directory. (UK) **1165**, 1140
International Regional Science Review. (US ISSN 0160-0176) **4376**
International Register of Telegraphic and Trade Addresses *see* Marconi's International Register **1145**
International Registry of Organization Development Professionals and Organization Development Handbook.(US) **1066**, 4026
International Rehabilitation Review. (US ISSN 0020-8477) **3111**
International Reinforced Plastics Conference. Papers and Proceedings. *see* Reinforced Plastics. Composite Papers **3868**
International Relations. (UK ISSN 0047-1178) **3961**
International Relations: Studies of the P I S M. (Polski Instytut Spraw Miedzynarodowych) (PL) **3961**
International Reliability Physics Symposium. Proceedings *see* Reliability Physics **3838**
International Religious Foundation, Inc. Newsletter *see* I R F Newsletter **5210**
International Report (Irvine). (US ISSN 0740-669X) **3962**
International Reporter. (II ISSN 0020-8493) **2199**
International Reports. (UK ISSN 0020-8507) **786**
International Rescue Committee Annual Report. (US ISSN 0538-9461) **4409**
International Research and Information Association. Survey. (AT ISSN 0312-0627) **3899**
International Research and Training Institute for the Advancement of Women News *see* I N S T R A W News **4845**
International Research Center for Energy and Economic Development. Occasional Papers. (US) **1791**, 932
International Research Centers Directory. (US ISSN 0278-2731) **1640**
International Review. (US) **597**
International Review for Business Education/Revue Internationale pour l'Enseignement Commercial/ Internationale Zeitschrift fuer Kaufmaennisches Bildungswesen/ Rivista Internazionale per la Cultura Commerciale/Revista Internacional la Ensenanza Comercial. (DK ISSN 0035-354X) **672**, 1752
International Review for the Sociology of Sport. (UN) **4439**
International Review of Administrative Sciences. (UK ISSN 0020-8523) **4064**, 1014
International Review of African American Art. (US ISSN 0145-8116) **331**, 2007, 2925

International Review of Applied Economics. (UK ISSN 0269-2171) **672**
International Review of Applied Linguistics in Language Teaching *see* I R A L **2817**
International Review of Applied Psychology *see* Applied Psychology **4011**
International Review of Child Neurology Series. (US) **3339**, 3321
International Review of Children's Literature and Librarianship. (UK ISSN 0269-0500) **2764**
International Review of Computers, Technology and the Law *see* International Computer Law Adviser **1397**
International Review of Contemporary Law. (BE ISSN 0048-7473) **2636**
International Review of Criminal Policy. (UN ISSN 0074-7688) **1516**
International Review of Cytology. (US ISSN 0074-7696) **525**
▼International Review of Economics and Finance. (US) **870**, 786
International Review of Education/ Internationale Zeitschrift fuer Erziehungswissenschaft/Revue Internationale de Pedagogie. (NE ISSN 0020-8566) **1640**
†International Review of Ergonomics: Current Trends in Human Factors Research and Practice. (UK ISSN 0269-5839) **5217**
International Review of Experimental Pathology. (US ISSN 0074-7718) **3111**
▼International Review of Financial Analysis. (US) **786**
International Review of Food and Wine *see* Food & Wine **2068**
International Review of Industrial and Organizational Psychology. (UK ISSN 0886-1528) **4026**
International Review of Industrial Property and Copyright Law *see* I I C **3675**
International Review of Law and Economics. (US ISSN 0144-8188) **2636**, 672
†International Review of Mental Imagery. (US ISSN 0741-0131) **5217**
International Review of Mission. (SZ ISSN 0020-8582) **4183**
International Review of Modern Sociology. (II) **4439**
International Review of Natural Family Planning *see* International Review **597**
International Review of Neurobiology. (US ISSN 0074-7742) **3339**
International Review of Nuclear Physics.(SI) **3848**
International Review of Psychiatry. (UK ISSN 0954-0261) **3339**
International Review of Psycho-Analysis.(UK ISSN 0306-2643) **4026**
International Review of Research in Mental Retardation. (US ISSN 0074-7750) **3339**, 1736
▼International Review of Retail, Distribution and Consumer Research.(UK ISSN 0959-3969) **1042**
International Review of Social History. (NE ISSN 0165-0629) **2314**
▼International Review of Strategic Management. (UK ISSN 1047-7918) **1014**
International Review of the Aesthetics and Sociology of Music. (CI ISSN 0351-5796) **3557**
International Review of the Red Cross. (SZ ISSN 0020-8604) **2725**, 4409
▼International Review of Victimology. (UK ISSN 0269-7580) **1516**, 4409
International Reviews in Immunology. (US ISSN 0883-0185) **3187**
International Reviews in Physical Chemistry. (UK ISSN 0144-235X) **1227**
International Rice Commission. Newsletter. (UN ISSN 0538-9550) **181**

International Rice Research Institute Program Report *see* I R R I Program Report **206**
International Rice Research Institute Reporter *see* I R R I Reporter **206**
International Rice Research Institute Research Highlights *see* I R R I Research Highlights **206**
International Rice Research Institute Research Paper Series *see* I R R I Research Paper Series **206**
International Rice Research Newsletter. (PH ISSN 0115-0944) **207**
International Rider and Driver *see* Horse and Horseman **4534**
International Right of Way. (US) **2636**
International Risk Control Review *see* International Loss Control Review **1014**
International Risk Management Advisor.(US) **786**, 913
International Road Congresses. Proceedings. (FR ISSN 0074-7815) **4719**, 1868
International Road Federation. World Road Statistics. (US) **4664**
International Road Haulage by United Kingdom Registered Vehicles. (UK ISSN 0262-6195) **4745**
International Robotics Industry Directory *see* International Robotics Product Database **1408**
International Robotics Product Database. (US) **1408**
International Robotics Yearbook *see* World Yearbook of Robotics and C I M Research and Development **1411**
International Round Table. (US) **913**, 786, 1140
International Rubber Digest. (UK ISSN 0020-8655) **4292**
International Rubber Directory. *see* Handbuch der Internationalen Kautschukindustrie **4291**
International Rubber Forum. (UK) **4292**
International Rubber Study Group. Summary of Proceedings of the Group Meetings and Assemblies. (UK ISSN 0074-7823) **4292**
International Rural Housing Journal. *see* Revista Internacional de Vivienda Rural **5270**
International Rural Sociology Association Items *see* I R S A Items **4437**
International S A M P E Technical Conference Series. I S T C Preprint Series. (Society for the Advancement of Material and Process Engineering) (US) **1918**
International Saddlery and Apparel Journal. (US) **4535**, 1292
International Sanitary Supply Association, Inc. Today *see* I S S A Today **4104**
International Savings Banks Institute. Report. (SZ) **786**
International School of Physics "Enrico Fermi". Italian Physical Society. Proceedings. (US) **3820**
International Schools Services, Inc. Directory of Overseas Schools *see* I S S Directory of Overseas Schools **1694**
International Science and Technology Exchange. *see* Guoji Keji Jiaoliu **4311**
†International Science Review Series. (US ISSN 0074-7866) **5217**
International Scientific Council for Trypanosomiasis Research and Control. (KE) **4811**
International Scrap Directory. (US) **3409**
International Sculpture *see* Sculpture **343**
International Sculpture Conference. Proceedings. (US ISSN 0363-5937) **331**
International Seaweed Symposium. Proceedings. (NO ISSN 0074-7874) **506**, 1606
International Securities Regulation Report. (US ISSN 0896-3010) **950**, 2710
International Security. (US ISSN 0162-2889) **3962**

INTERNATIONAL STUDIES 6317

International Security Directory. (UK ISSN 0074-7890) **1526**, 4064, 4105
†International Security News Clipping Service. (US) **5218**
International Security Review. (UK ISSN 0141-8017) **1526**
International Sedimentological Congress. Guidebook. (GW ISSN 0074-7904) **1569**
International Seed Testing Association News Bulletin *see* I S T A News Bulletin **179**
International Seismological Centre. Bulletin. (UK ISSN 0020-8671) **1591**
International Seismological Centre. Regional Catalogue of Earthquakes. (UK ISSN 0034-334X) **1591**
International Seismology Development. *see* Guoji Dizhen Dongtai **1590**
International Semiconductor Directory I Cs & Discrete Semiconductors D.A.T.A. Digest: Master Type Locator.(US ISSN 1048-6607) **1774**
International Seminar on Digital Processing of Analog Signals (Proceedings) *see* International Zurich Seminar on Digital Communications. (Proceedings) **1454**
International Semiotic Spectrum. (CN ISSN 0825-0456) **2509**, 3769, 4376
International Serials Data System Register (Microfiche Edition) *see* I S D S Register (Microfiche Edition) **402**
International Serials Data System Register (Tape Edition) *see* I S D S Register (Tape Edition) **402**
International Series of Monographs on Chemistry. (US) **1179**
International Series of Monographs on Physics. (US) **3820**
†International Series on the Quality of Working Life. (US) **5218**
International Sharing. (US ISSN 1011-8713) **932**
International Shipbuilding Progress. (NE ISSN 0020-868X) **4729**
International Silk Association. Bulletin *see* International Silk Association. Monthly Newsletter **4620**
International Silk Association. Monthly Newsletter. (FR ISSN 0290-8271) **4620**
International Silt Research/Guoji Nisha Yanjiu. (CC ISSN 1001-6279) **1545**
International Simulation and Gaming Association Newsletter *see* I S A G A Newsletter **4437**
International Sinatra Society Newsletter.(US) **1298**, 3557
International Skating. (IT) **4549**
International Skating Union. Ice Dancing Regulations. (SZ ISSN 0539-0168) **4476**
International Skating Union. Minutes of Congress. (SZ ISSN 0535-2479) **4476**
International Skating Union Constitution *see* I S U Constitution **4475**
International Skating Union Regulations *see* I S U Regulations **4475**
International Ski Federation Bulletin *see* F I S Bulletin **4545**
International Skyline. (CN ISSN 0823-1931) **1338**, 3962
International Small Business Journal. (UK ISSN 0266-2426) **1115**
International Social Science Journal. (UK ISSN 0020-8701) **4376**
International Social Science Review. (US ISSN 0278-2308) **4376**
International Social Security Association. Reports of the General Assemblies of the ISSA. (SZ ISSN 0251-1339) **2535**
International Social Security Association. Studies and Research. (SZ) **2535**
International Social Security Association. Technical Reports of Assemblies *see* International Social Security Association. Reports of the General Assemblies of the ISSA **2535**
International Social Security Association Bulletin *see* International Social Security Review **2535**
International Social Security Association Committee on Provident Funds. Reports *see* I S S A. Committee on Provident Funds. Reports **2533**
International Social Security Association Social Security Documentation. Caribbean Series *see* I S S A. Social Security Documentation. Caribbean Series **2533**
International Social Security Review. (SZ ISSN 0020-871X) **2535**
International Social Work. (UK ISSN 0020-8728) **4409**
International Socialism. (UK) **2869**, 3899
International Society for Animal Rights Report. (US) **231**
International Society for Applied Cardiovascular Biology. (SZ ISSN 1016-4723) **3209**
International Society for British Genealogy and Family History. Newsletter. (US ISSN 0736-8054) **2155**
International Society for Electrosleep and Electroanaesthesia Information *see* I E S A Information **3338**
International Society for Geothermal Engineering, Inc. Transactions *see* I S G E Transactions **1802**
International Society for Krishna Consciousness World Review *see* I S K C O N World Review **4284**
International Society for Labor Law and Social Legislation. United States National Committee. Bulletin *see* Comparative Labor Law Journal **2614**
International Society for Photogrammetry and Remote Sensing Journal of Photogrammetry and Remote Sensing *see* I S P R S Journal of Photogrammetry and Remote Sensing **2252**
International Society for Rock Mechanics. Congress. Proceedings. (PO ISSN 0074-848X) **1868**, 1569
International Society for Rock Mechanics. News. (PO ISSN 0539-0281) **1868**
International Society for Soil Mechanics and Foundation Engineering. Proceedings. (MX ISSN 0074-3313) **1868**
International Society for Technology in Education Update *see* I S T E Update **1638**
International Society for the Sociology of Religion. (IT) **4183**, 4439
International Society for the Study of Time. Proceedings *see* Study of Time **370**
International Society of Applied Biology. Biological Memoirs. (II ISSN 0379-8097) **442**
International Society of Bassists. Journal. (US ISSN 0892-0532) **3557**
International Society of Blood Transfusion. Proceedings of the Congress. (FR ISSN 0074-8528) **3272**, 3209
International Society of Certified Electronics Technicians Update *see* I S C E T Update **1773**
International Society of Certified Employee Benefits Specialists. Newsbriefs. (US ISSN 0731-4531) **1067**
International Society of Citriculture. Proceedings. (US) **99**, 3393
International Society of Copier Artists Quarterly *see* I S C A Quarterly **329**
International Society of Criminology. Bulletin. (FR ISSN 0539-032X) **1516**
International Society of Criminology. Rapports Quinquennaux. (FR) **1516**
International Society of Cryptozoology Newsletter *see* I S C Newsletter **584**
†International Society of Internal Medicine. Congress Proceedings. (SZ ISSN 0074-8544) **5218**
International Society of Organbuilders Organ Building Periodical *see* Organ Building Periodical **3572**
International Society of Orthopaedic Surgery and Traumatology. Proceedings of Congresses *see* International Orthopaedics **3308**
International Society of Parametric Analysts. Conference Proceedings. (US) **752**, 3039
International Society of Performing Arts Administrators. Forum. (US) **3557**
International Society of Plant Morphologists. Yearbook. (II ISSN 0539-0346) **506**
International Society of Soil Science. Bulletin. (AU ISSN 0374-0447) **181**
International Society of Soilless Culture International Congress. Proceedings *see* I S O S C. International Congress. Proceedings **1568**
▼International Society of Toronto for Hungarian Church History. Newsletter/M E T E M. Hirek. (CN ISSN 1183-6350) **2369**, 4183
International Society of Tropical Foresters News *see* I S T F News **2102**
International Society of Urology. Reports of Congress. (FR ISSN 0074-8579) **3388**
International Society of Weekly Newspaper Editors Newsletter *see* I S W N E Newsletter **2571**
International Society of Women Airline Pilots Newsletter. (US) **56**, 4845
International Sociological Review. (US) **4439**
International Sociology. (UK ISSN 0268-5809) **4439**
International Softball Congress (Year) Official Yearbook and Guide *see* International Softball Congress (Year) World Championship Guide **4507**
International Softball Congress (Year) World Championship Guide. (US) **4507**
International Solar Energy Intelligence Report. (US) **1811**
International Solid Fuel Buyer's Guide Directory. (US ISSN 0277-870X) **1792**
International Soroptimist. (UK) **1298**, 4315
†International Space Business Review. (US) **5218**
International Spectator. (IT ISSN 0393-2729) **3899**, 3962
International Spectrum. (US ISSN 1050-9070) **827**
▼International Spirits Market Report. (US) **382**
International Standard Book Number Review *see* I S B N Review **4129**
International Standard Serial Number Compact *see* I S S N Compact **402**
International Stationery. (IT) **1059**
International Stationery *see* I N S **3663**
International Statistical Handbook of Urban Public Transport/Recueil International de Statistiques des Transports Publics Urbains/ Internationales Statistik-Handbuch fuer den Oeffentlichen Stadtverkehr. (BE ISSN 0378-1968) **4664**
International Statistical Institute. Bulletin. Proceedings of the Biennial Sessions. (NE ISSN 0074-8609) **4575**
International Statistical Institute. Comparative Studies. Cross-National Summaries *see* International Statistical Institute. Comparative Studies. Cross-National Summaries and E C E Reports **4575**
International Statistical Institute. Comparative Studies. Cross-National Summaries and E C E Reports. (NE) **4575**
International Statistical Review. (NE ISSN 0306-7734) **4575**
International Status Report on Plastics Industry Worldwide. (UK) **3863**, 672
International Steel Statistics - Australia. (UK ISSN 0952-5831) **3425**
International Steel Statistics - Australia and New Zealand *see* International Steel Statistics - Australia **3425**
International Steel Statistics - Austria. (UK ISSN 0952-584X) **3425**
International Steel Statistics - Belgium, Luxembourg. (UK ISSN 0952-5858) **3425**
International Steel Statistics - Brazil. (UK ISSN 0952-5866) **3425**
International Steel Statistics - Canada. (UK ISSN 0952-5874) **3425**
International Steel Statistics - Denmark. (UK ISSN 0960-2372) **3426**
International Steel Statistics - Denmark and Greece *see* International Steel Statistics - Denmark **3426**
International Steel Statistics - Eastern European Countries, Turkey and Yugoslavia. (UK ISSN 0952-6056) **3426**
International Steel Statistics - Finland. (UK ISSN 0952-5890) **3426**
International Steel Statistics - France. (UK ISSN 0952-5904) **3426**
International Steel Statistics - Germany, Federal Republic. (UK ISSN 0952-5912) **3426**
International Steel Statistics - Greece. (UK ISSN 0960-2380) **3426**
International Steel Statistics - Irish Republic. (UK ISSN 0952-5920) **3426**
International Steel Statistics - Italy. (UK ISSN 0952-5939) **3426**
International Steel Statistics - Japan. (UK ISSN 0952-5947) **3426**
International Steel Statistics - Korea (South). (UK ISSN 0952-603X) **3426**
International Steel Statistics - Netherlands. (UK ISSN 0952-6005) **3426**
International Steel Statistics - Norway. (UK ISSN 0952-6013) **3426**
International Steel Statistics - Portugal. (UK ISSN 0958-4951) **3426**
International Steel Statistics - Selected Asian and African Countries. (UK ISSN 0958-515X) **3426**
International Steel Statistics - Selected Asian Countries *see* International Steel Statistics - Selected Asian and African Countries **3426**
International Steel Statistics - Selected Central and South American Countries. (UK ISSN 0952-6102) **3426**
International Steel Statistics - Spain. (UK ISSN 0958-4943) **3426**
International Steel Statistics - Spain and Portugal *see* International Steel Statistics - Spain **3426**
International Steel Statistics - Summary Tables. (UK ISSN 0952-6803) **3426**
International Steel Statistics - Sweden. (UK ISSN 0952-6048) **3426**
International Steel Statistics - Switzerland. (UK ISSN 0952-6099) **3426**
International Steel Statistics - U S A. (UK ISSN 0952-6811) **3427**
International Steel Statistics - United Kingdom. (UK ISSN 0307-7608) **3427**
International Stock Exchange. Quality of Market Companies Book. (UK) **950**
International Stock Exchange. Quality of Markets Quarterly. (UK) **950**
International Stock Exchange Fact Sheet Monthly. (UK) **950**
International Stock Exchange Firms and Members *see* I S E Firms and Members **949**
International Straits of the World. (NE) **3962**, 2254
International Structural Engineering Abstracts *see* International Building Science & Construction Abstracts **638**
International Student Advisers Bulletin *see* I S A Bulletin **1722**
International Studies. *see* Kokusai Kenkyu **3944**
International Studies. *see* Guoji Wenti Yanjiu **3959**
International Studies. (US ISSN 0020-8817) **3962**, 2637

Title

International Studies. Nordic Seminar on Human Rights. Proceedings. (NE ISSN 0903-9961) **2637**, **3944**
†International Studies in Education. (UN) **5218**
International Studies in Global Change. (US) **2509**
International Studies in Philosophy. (US ISSN 0270-5664) **3769**
International Studies in Planning. (US) **2489**
International Studies in Sociology and Social Anthropology. (NE ISSN 0074-8684) **4439**, **4376**
▼International Studies in Sociology of Education. (UK ISSN 0962-0214) **1752**
International Studies in the Philosophy of Science. (UK) **3769**
International Studies in the Philosophy of Science - the Dubrovnik Papers see International Studies in the Philosophy of Science **3769**
International Studies Newsletter see International Studies **3962**
International Studies Notes. (US ISSN 0094-7768) **3962**
International Studies of Management and Organization. (US ISSN 0020-8825) **1015**
International Studies on Human Rights. (NE) **3944**
International Studies Quarterly. (US ISSN 0020-8833) **3962**
International Sugar Council. Statistical Bulletin see International Sugar Organization Statistical Bulletin **2085**
International Sugar Journal see Sugar Cane **122**
International Sugar Journal. (UK ISSN 0020-8841) **2074**
International Sugar Journal Buyer's Guide see Sugar Industry Journal Buyer's Guide **2082**
†International Sugar Organization. Annual Report. (UK ISSN 0074-8706) **5218**
International Sugar Organization. Sugar Year Book. (UK) **2074**
International Sugar Organization Statistical Bulletin. (UK ISSN 0020-885X) **2085**, **4575**
International Surgery. (IT ISSN 0020-8868) **3379**
International Survey of Business Expectations. (US) **932**
†International Swimmer. (AT ISSN 0020-8876) **5218**
International Swimming Hall of Fame Headlines. (US) **4476**, **3525**
International Swimming Hall of Fame News see International Swimming Hall of Fame Headlines **4476**
International Symposia on Asian Studies. Proceedings. (HK) **3639**
International Symposia on the Pharmacology of Thermoregulation. (SZ ISSN 1013-9222) **3730**, **1227**
International Symposium on Acoustical Imaging. Proceedings see Acoustical Imaging **3858**
International Symposium on Atherosclerosis. Proceedings. (US ISSN 0074-8765) **3209**
International Symposium on Atomic, Molecular and Solid-State Theory, Collision Phenomena and Computational Methods. Proceedings.(US) **1179**
International Symposium on Automated Cartography. Proceedings. (US) **2254**
International Symposium on Canine Heartworm Disease. Proceedings. (US) **4811**
International Symposium on Cell Biology and Cytopharmacology. Proceedings see Advances in Cytopharmacology **5131**
International Symposium on Chemical Reaction Engineering. Proceedings. (US ISSN 0071-3112) **1855**
International Symposium on Circuits and Systems see I E E E International Symposium on Circuits and Systems. Proceedings **1772**

International Symposium on Combustion. Proceedings see Symposium (International) on Combustion **1230**
International Symposium on Computer Architecture. Conference Proceedings. (US) **1416**
International Symposium on Computer-Assisted Cartography. Proceedings see International Symposium on Automated Cartography. Proceedings **2254**
International Symposium on Computer Hardware Description Languages. Proceedings. (US) **1454**
International Symposium on Concrete Roads. Reports. (BE) **1868**
International Symposium on Crop Protection. Proceedings. (BE ISSN 0368-9697) **181**
International Symposium on Discharges and Electrical Insulation (Proceedings) see International Symposium on Discharges and Electrical Insulation in Vacuum. Proceedings **1900**
International Symposium on Discharges and Electrical Insulation in Vacuum. Proceedings. (US) **1900**
†International Symposium on Dredging Technology. Proceedings. (UK ISSN 0140-1769) **5218**
International Symposium on Earthquake Countermeasures. Proceedings. (US) **1868**
International Symposium on Fault-Tolerant Computing. Digest of Papers. (US ISSN 0731-3071) **1397**
International Symposium on Jet Cutting Technology. Proceedings. (UK ISSN 0306-2732) **1932**, **1924**
International Symposium on Laboratory Animals see International Council for Laboratory Animal Science. Proceedings of the Symposium **5216**
International Symposium on Mini and Microcomputers. Proceedings. (CN) **1466**, **1461**
International Symposium on Multiple-Valued Logic. Proceedings. (US ISSN 0195-623X) **1418**
International Symposium on Quantum Biology and Quantum Pharmacology. Proceedings. (US ISSN 0731-0358) **442**, **3730**
International Symposium on Regional Development. Papers and Proceedings. (JA ISSN 0074-8897) **2489**
†International Symposium on Silicon Materials Science and Technology. Proceedings. (US ISSN 0091-391X) **5218**
International Symposium on Subscriber Loop and Services. Proceedings. (US) **1900**
International Symposium on Switching Arc Phenomena. Proceedings. (PL) **1827**
International Symposium on the Aerodynamics and Ventilation of Vehicle Tunnels. Proceedings. (UK) **1868**, **4651**
International Symposium on the Chemistry of Cement. Proceedings. (JA) **1179**
International Symposium on Wastewater Treatment. (CN) **4826**, **1959**
International Symposium on Wave and Tidal Energy. Proceedings. (UK) **1792**, **1803**
International Symposium on Wind Energy Systems. Proceedings. (UK) **1812**
International Symposium on Wound Ballistics. Proceedings. (SW) **3265**, **1516**
International System Safety Conference. Proceedings. (US) **4105**
International Talent and Touring Directory see Billboard's International Talent and Touring Directory **3541**
International Tax and Business Lawyer. (US ISSN 0741-4269) **2725**, **1098**

International Tax and Duty Free Buyers' Index. (UK ISSN 0262-7310) **1140**, **913**
International Tax Digest. (UK ISSN 0955-498X) **1098**
International Tax-Free Trade Buyers Guide & Directory. (UK ISSN 0263-5488) **913**
International Tax-Free Trader & Duty-Free World. (UK ISSN 0306-6045) **913**
International Tax Journal. (US ISSN 0097-7314) **1098**
International Tax News. (UK) **1098**
International Tax Planning Manual. (US) **1098**
International Tax Planning Manual. (AT) **1098**, **913**
International Tax Report. (UK ISSN 0300-1628) **1098**
International Tax Review. (UK) **913**, **1098**
International Tax Systems and Planning Techniques. (UK) **1098**
International Tax Treaties of All Nations. Series A. (US ISSN 0892-1032) **2725**, **1098**
International Tax Treaties of All Nations. Series B. (US ISSN 0892-1040) **2725**, **1098**
International Taxation Series. (US) **1098**, **2725**, **3690**
International Teamster. (US ISSN 0020-8892) **2585**
International Technical Communication Conference Proceedings see Society for Technical Communication. Annual Conference Proceedings **1342**
International Technical Cooperation Centre Review see I T C C Review **5210**
International Telcom Directory. (US) **1363**
International Telecommunication Union. Booklets. (UN) **1338**
International Telecommunication Union. Central Library. List of Annuals/Union Internationale des Telecommunications. Bibliotheque Centrale. Listes des Publications Annuelles/Union Internacional de Telecomunicaciones. Biblioteca Central. Lista de Publicaciones Anuales. (UN) **1348**
International Telecommunication Union. Central Library. List of Periodicals/Union Internationale des Telecommunications. Bibliotheque Centrale. Liste des Periodique/Union International de Telcommunicaciones. Biblioteca Central. Lista de Revistas. (UN) **1348**
International Telecommunication Union. Central Library. List of Recent Acquisitions/Union Internationale des Telecommunications. Bibliotheque Centrale. Liste des Acquisitions Recentes/Union Internacional de Telecomunicaciones. Biblioteca Central. Lista de Adquisiciones Recientes. (UN) **1348**
International Telecommunication Union. List of Telegraph Offices Open for International Service. (UN ISSN 0074-9044) **1363**
International Telecommunication Union. Operational Bulletin. (UN ISSN 0047-1224) **1363**
International Telecommunication Union. Report on the Activities. (UN ISSN 0085-2201) **1363**
International Telecommunication Union. Seminars. (UN) **1338**
International Telecommunications Energy Conference. Proceedings. (US ISSN 0275-0473) **1375**
†International Teleconferencing Symposium (Proceedings). (US) **5218**
International Telegraph and Telephone Consultative Committee. Plans. (UN) **1363**
International Telegraph and Telephone Consultative Committee. Plenary Assembly. Proceedings. (UN) **1363**
International Telegraph and Telephone Consultative Committee Red Books see C C I T T Red Books **1361**

International Telemetering Conference. (US ISSN 0884-5123) **1338**
International Telephone Directory of T D D Users (Year). (US) **2288**, **1363**
International Telephone Energy Conference. Proceedings see International Telecommunications Energy Conference. Proceedings **1375**
International Television Almanac see International Television & Video Almanac **1375**
International Television & Video Almanac. (US) **1375**, **1385**
International Television News. (US) **1375**
International Television Symposium and Technical Exhibition, Montreux. Symposium Record. (SZ ISSN 0082-0776) **1375**
International Telex Directory. International Service. (AT ISSN 0310-8031) **1363**
International Tennis Weekly. (US) **4507**
International Terrorism Newsletter. (US ISSN 0738-9191) **3962**, **1516**
International Test & Evaluation Association Journal of Test and Evaluation see I T E A Journal of Test and Evaluation **4599**
International Test Commission. Bulletin. (UK ISSN 0379-2439) **4026**
International Test Conference. Proceedings. (US) **1454**, **1397**
International Textile and Apparel Association Newsletter see I T A A Newsletter **1285**
International Textile and Apparel Association Proceedings see I T A A Proceedings **1288**
International Textile and Apparel Association Special Publications see I T A A Special Publications **1285**
†International Textile Machinery. (UK ISSN 0074-9087) **5218**
International Textile Machinery Shipment Statistics. (SZ) **4628**, **4575**
International Textile Manufacturers Federation Country Statements see I T M F. Country Statements **4619**
International Textile Manufacturers Federation Directory see I T M F Directory **4619**
International Textile Manufacturing. (SZ) **4620**
International Textile Reports. see Melliand Textilberichte (English Edition) **4621**
International Textiles Interior see Interior **4620**
International Theatre Institute of the United States. Newsletter. (US) **4634**
International Thermal Spraying Conference. Preprint of Papers. (US) **3429**
International Third World Studies - Journal and Review. (US) **3962**, **3393**
International Tijdschrift voor Spel en Speelgoed. see Revue Internationale des Jeux et Jouets **2282**
International Tin Council. Monthly Statistical Summary. (UK) **3409**, **3427**
International Tin Council. Quarterly Statistical Bulletin. (UK) **3427**
International Tin Council. Statistical Yearbook see Tin Statistics **3428**
International Tin Research Council. Annual Report see International Tin Research Institute. Annual Report **3409**
International Tin Research Institute. Annual Report. (UK) **3409**
International Tourism Reports. (UK ISSN 0269-3747) **4772**
International Track & Field Annual. (US) **4476**
International Tracts in Computer Studies. (UI) **1397**
International Trade. see Guoji Maoyi **910**
International Trade Alert. (US) **913**

International Trade and Development Statistics. Handbook/Statistiques du Commerce International et du Development. Manuel. (UN ISSN 0251-9461) **723**, **913**, **932**
International Trade and Investment Letter. (US ISSN 0890-4251) **913**, **950**
†International Trade and Transport. (US) **5218**
International Trade Conference of Workers of the Building, Wood and Building Materials Industries. (Brochure). (FI) **621**, **2585**
International Trade Directory of Sri Lanka and Maldives. (CE) **1140**
International Trade Fairs and Exhibitions Directory. (TS) **817**
International Trade Finance. (UK) **786**, **913**
International Trade Forum. (UN ISSN 0020-8957) **913**
International Trade Journal. see Guoji Maoyi Wenti **910**
International Trade Journal. (US ISSN 0885-3908) **913**
International Trade Law and Practice. see Droit et Pratique du Commerce International **2722**
International Trade Names Directory see International Directory of Brands and Their Companies **3675**
International Trade News. see Guoji Jingmao Xiaoxi Bao **910**
International Trade News Supplement. see Guoji Jingmao Xiaoxi Bao. Shuangbian Jingmao Zhuankan **910**
International Trade Perspective see International Law and Trade Perspective **2725**
International Trade Practice. (US) **913**
International Trade Reporter Current Reports. (US ISSN 0748-0172) **913**
International Trade Reporter Decisions. (US ISSN 0748-0709) **913**, **2725**
International Trade Reporter Export Reference Manual. (US ISSN 1043-5670) **913**
International Trade Reporter Import Reference Manual. (US ISSN 1043-5662) **913**
International Trade Reporter Reference File see International Trade Reporter Import Reference Manual **913**
International Trade Review. (II ISSN 0020-8981) **913**
International Trade Statistics Yearbook. (UN ISSN 1010-447X) **723**, **4575**
†International Trade Union Conference for Action Against Apartheid. Resolution. (CS) **5218**
International Trade Winds. (CH) **913**
International Tradeshow Directory. (GW) **1140**, **1042**, **3393**
International Transport Journal-Overseas Digest. see Internationale Transport-Zeitschrift **4651**
International Transport Journal - Overseas Digest. (SZ) **4651**
International Transport Revue see I T R **4745**
International Transport Workers' Federation News see I T F News **2584**
International Transport Workers' Federation Report on Activities. (UK ISSN 0539-0915) **2585**, **4651**
International Travel and Health: Vaccination Requirements and Health Advice. (UN) **4105**
International Travel Briefing Service see Pinkerton Eye on Travel **4782**
▼International Travel Guide/Guide International du Voyage. (CN) **4772**
International Travel News. (US) **4772**
International Travelweek see Travelweek **4794**
International Tree Crops. (AT ISSN 1032-7290) **2102**
International Tree Crops Journal. (UK ISSN 0143-5698) **2102**, **99**
International Tremor Foundation Newsletter see I T F Newsletter **3338**
International Trends in General Thoracic Surgery. (US) **3379**

International Trends in Manufacturing Technology. (US) **4601**, **1079**, **3018**
International Trends in Oil and Gas. (US) **3690**
International Trombone Association. Journal. (US ISSN 0145-3513) **3557**
International Trombone Association Series. (US ISSN 0363-5708) **3557**
International Trumpet Guild Journal see I T G Journal **3555**
International Tug Convention Proceedings. (UK) **4729**
International Typographical Union. Bulletin see Typographical Journal **2590**
International Typographical Union Review see I T U Review **2584**
International U F O Reporter. (US ISSN 0730-174X) **56**
International Understanding. (II) **3962**, **870**
International Understanding at School. (UN ISSN 0047-1240) **1640**
International Underwater System Design. (UK ISSN 0267-1085) **1606**, **4601**
†International Union Against Cancer. Manual/Union Internationale Contre le Cancer. Manuel. (SZ ISSN 0074-9192) **5218**
International Union Against Cancer International Calendar of Meetings on Cancer see U I C C International Calendar of Meetings on Cancer **3394**
International Union Against Cancer International Directory of Cancer Institutes and Organizations see U I C C International Directory of Cancer Institutes and Organizations **3202**
International Union Against Cancer Technical Report Series see U I C C Technical Report Series **5293**
International Union against Tuberculosis. Conference Proceedings. (FR) **3365**
International Union against Tuberculosis and Lung Disease. Bulletin see Tubercle and Lung Disease **3367**
International Union for Conservation of Nature and Natural Resources. Proceedings of the General Assembly. (SZ ISSN 0074-929X) **1489**
International Union for Conservation of Nature and Natural Resources Bulletin see I U C N Bulletin **1489**
International Union for Inland Navigation. Annual Report. (BE ISSN 0074-9311) **4651**
International Union for Moral and Social Action Bulletin Trimestriel see U.I.A.M.S. Bulletin Trimestriel **4422**
International Union for Moral and Social Action Informations see U.I.A.M.S. Informations **3930**
International Union for the Scientific Study of Population Newsletter see I U S S P Newsletter **3983**
International Union for the Scientific Study of Population Papers see I U S S P Papers **3983**
International Union for Vacuum Science, Technique and Applications. News Bulletin. (US ISSN 0020-9066) **3821**
International Union of Alpine Associations. Bulletin/Union Internationale des Associations d'Alpinisme. Bulletin. (SZ) **4772**, **4549**
International Union of Anthropological and Ethnological Sciences Newsletter.(UK ISSN 0074-3496) **242**
International Union of Biological Sciences. General Assemblies. Proceedings. (FR ISSN 0445-1333) **442**
International Union of Biological Sciences. Reports of General Assemblies see International Union of Biological Sciences. General Assemblies. Proceedings **442**

International Union of Biological Sciences Biology International: I U B S Newsmagazine see Biology International: I U B S Newsmagazine **432**
International Union of Bricklayers and Allied Craftsmen. Journal. (US ISSN 0362-3696) **2585**, **621**
International Union of Building Societies and Savings Associations. Congress Proceedings see International Union of Housing Finance Institutions. Congress Proceedings **786**
International Union of Consumers Unions Newsletter see World Consumer **1508**
International Union of Crystallography. Abstracts of the Triennial Congress. (DK ISSN 0074-9389) **1210**
International Union of Electronic, Electrical, Salaried, Machine and Furniture Workers, A F L - C I O News see I U E News **2584**
International Union of Food and Allied Workers' Associations. Meeting of the Executive Committee. I. Documents of the Secretariat. II. Summary Report. (SZ ISSN 0579-8299) **2585**, **2074**
International Union of Food and Allied Workers' Associations. News Bulletin. (SZ ISSN 0020-9074) **2585**, **2074**
International Union of Forestry Research Organizations. Congress Proceedings. (AU ISSN 0074-9400) **2102**
International Union of Forestry Research Organizations News see I U F R O News **2102**
International Union of Forestry Research Organizations World Series see I U F R O World Series **2102**
International Union of Geodesy and Geophysics. Monograph. (CN ISSN 0539-1016) **2254**, **1591**, **2254**
International Union of Geodesy and Geophysics. Proceedings of the General Assembly. (FR ISSN 0074-9419) **1591**, **2254**
International Union of Geodesy and Geophysics Chronicle see I U G G Chronicle **1590**
International Union of Housing Finance Institutions. Congress Proceedings. (US) **786**
International Union of Latin Notaries. Proceedings of Congress. (IT ISSN 0074-9435) **4064**
International Union of Liberal Christian Women. Newsletter see International Association of Liberal Religious Women. Newsletter **4182**
†International Union of Local Authorities. Reports of Congress. (NE ISSN 0074-9443) **5218**
International Union of Mail Artists Magazine see I U O M A Magazine **329**
International Union of Petroleum & Industrial Workers Views see I U P I W Views **3688**
International Union of Public Transport. Technical Reports of the Congresses.(BE) **4651**
International Union of Public Transport Biblio-Express see U I T P Biblio-Express **4668**
International Union of Radio Science. Proceedings of General Assemblies. (BE ISSN 0074-9516) **1357**
International Union of Radio Science Information Bulletin see U R S I Information Bulletin **1360**
International Union of School and University Health and Medicine. Congress Reports. (BE ISSN 0074-9524) **1640**, **3111**, **4105**
International Union of Socialist Youth Newsletter see I U S Y Newsletter **3898**
International Union of Students. African Bulletin. (CS) **2169**
International Union of Students. Congress and Executive Committee Meetings Resolutions. (CS) **1709**

International Union of Students. Congress Resolutions see International Union of Students. Congress and Executive Committee Meetings Resolutions **1709**
International Union of Students. Secretariat Reports. (CS) **3900**
International Union of Students. Sport Bulletin. (CS ISSN 0038-7789) **4476**, **1709**
International Union of Tenants. International Information. (SW ISSN 0345-5440) **2489**
International Union of Theoretical and Applied Mechanics. Symposia. (US) **1827**
International Union of Tramways, Light Railways and Motor Omnibuses. Review see Public Transport International **4655**
International Universities Press, Inc. Stress and Health Series see I U P Stress and Health Series **3338**
International University Collegiate Sports Report. (US ISSN 0748-9668) **4476**, **1315**
International University Foundation Directory. (US) **1709**, **1722**
International University Foundation Report. (US) **1709**, **1722**
International University Newsletter. (US) **1709**
International University Poetry Quarterly. (US ISSN 0748-9676) **2995**
International Urology and Nephrology. (HU ISSN 0301-1623) **3388**
▼International V A T Monitor. (NE) **1098**, **913**
International Vegetarian Health Food Handbook see Vegetarian Handbook **3612**
International Vending Buyer's Guide and Directory. (US) **1042**
International Ventilator Users Network News see I V U N News **3107**
International Venture Capital Network. (US) **786**
▼International Video Journal of Engineering Research. (UK ISSN 1052-9268) **1827**
International Videotex Teletext News see Information & Interactive Services Report **4143**
International Videovue Magazine. (CN) **1385**
International Viewpoint. (FR ISSN 0294-2925) **3900**
International Violin and Guitar Makers Association. Journal. (US) **3557**
International Visitors Information Service Newsletter see I V I S Newsletter **2227**
International Visual Communications Association Magazine see I V C A Magazine **3511**
International Visual Literacy Association. Annual Conference Readings. (US) **1752**, **1690**
International Voice Systems Review. (US) **1338**
International Water Conference. Proceedings. (US ISSN 0074-9575) **4826**, **1924**
International Water Power and Dam Construction. (UK ISSN 0306-400X) **4826**, **1868**
International Water Report. (US) **4826**
International Water Resources Association Newsletter see I W R A Newsletter **5210**
International Water Supply Association Year Book see I W S A Year Book **4825**
International Water Supply Congress. Proceedings see Water Supply **4833**
International Waterfowl and Wetlands Research Bureau News see I W R B News **584**
International Wealth Success Newsletter.(US ISSN 0047-1275) **914**
International Welding Engineering. (GW ISSN 0930-9241) **3429**, **621**, **1827**
International Whaling Commission. Annual Reports. (UK ISSN 0143-8700) **2044**, **584**, **1489**

International Whaling Commission. Report see International Whaling Commission. Annual Reports **2044**
International Whaling Commission. Special Issues. (UK ISSN 0255-2760) **442**, **1489**
International Wheat Council. Market Report. (UK) **152**, **207**
International Wheat Council. Record of Shipments Wheat and Wheat Flour (Year). (UK) **99**
International Wheat Council. Report for Crop Year. (UK) **99**
International Wheat Council. Review of the World Grains Situation see International Wheat Council. Report for Crop Year **99**
International Wheat Council. Secretariat Papers. (UK ISSN 0539-1326) **99**
International Wheat Council. Shipments of Wheat and Wheat Flour see International Wheat Council. Record of Shipments Wheat and Wheat Flour (Year) **99**
International Who's Who. (UK ISSN 0074-9613) **419**
International Who's Who in Art and Antiques. (UK) **331**, **258**, **419**
International Who's Who in Community Service. (UK) **4409**
International Who's Who in Education. (UK) **1640**, **419**
International Who's Who in Energy and Nuclear Sciences see Energy and Nuclear Sciences International Who's Who **1787**
†International Who's Who in Engineering. (UK) **5218**
International Who's Who in Medicine. (UK) **419**
International Who's Who in Music and Musicians' Directory. (UK ISSN 0307-2894) **3557**
International Who's Who in the Arab World. (UK ISSN 0261-0310) **419**
International Who's Who in Water Supply see I W S A Year Book **4825**
International Widescreen. (UK) **3792**, **3859**
International Wildlife. (US ISSN 0020-9112) **1490**
International Wildlife (Canadian Edition). (CN) **1490**
International Wine and Food Society Journal see World Gastronomy **388**
▼International Wine Market Report. (US) **382**
International Women's Fishing Association Yearbook see I W F A Yearbook **4548**
International Women's Tribune Center. Newsletter see Tribune **4854**
†International Women's Writing Guild Yearbook. (US) **5218**
International Woodworker see Woodworker **2591**
International Woodworking Magazine. (US) **640**
International Work Group for Indigenous Affairs Boletin see I W G I A Boletin **241**
International Work Group for Indigenous Affairs Documents see I W G I A Documents **241**
International Work Group for Indigenous Affairs Newsletter see I W G I A Newsletter **241**
International Work Group for Indigenous Affairs Yearbook see I W G I A Yearbook **241**
International Workcamp Directory. (US) **1722**
International Workcamp Listing (Year). (US) **932**, **4409**
†International Workshop on Nude Mice. Proceedings. (GW) **5218**
International Workshop on Petri Nets and Performance Models. (US) **1418**
International Workshop on Software Specification and Design (Proceedings). (US) **1478**
International Wrist Watch. (US) **2564**
International Year Book and Statesmen's Who's Who. (UK ISSN 0074-9621) **419**, **3900**

International Yearbook of Adult Education. see Internationales Jahrbuch der Erwachsenenbildung **1684**
International Yearbook of Educational and International Technology see International Yearbook of Educational & Training Technology **1752**
International Yearbook of Educational & Training Technology. (UK) **1752**
†International Yearbook of Organizational Democracy. (US) **5218**
International Yearbook of Rural Planning. (UK) **2489**
International Yearbook of Serials Librarianship. (US) **2764**, **2798**
†International Yearbook of the Underwater World/Annuaire International du Monde Sous-Marin. (FR ISSN 0074-9648) **5218**
International Yoga Guide. (US ISSN 0277-092X) **3769**, **4214**
International Zakendoen. (NE) **914**
†International Zinc & Galvanising Survey. (US ISSN 0264-9438) **5218**
International Zoo News. (UK ISSN 0020-9155) **584**
International Zoo Yearbook. (UK ISSN 0074-9664) **584**
International Zurich Seminar on Digital Communications. (Proceedings). (US) **1454**
International Zurich Seminar on Integrated Systems for Speech, Video and Data Communications. Proceedings see International Zurich Seminar on Digital Communications. (Proceedings) **1454**
†Internationale-Agrar-Industriezeitschrift.(GW ISSN 0863-1840) **5218**
†Internationale Aufgaben der D G D. (GW ISSN 0172-3146) **5218**
Internationale Beitraege zur Markt-, Meinungs- und Zukunftsforschung. (GW) **1042**
Internationale Berg- und Seilbahn-Rundschau see Internationale Seilbahn-Rundschau **4651**
Internationale Beziehungen. (GW ISSN 0936-5184) **3900**
Internationale Bibellektionen. (US) **4183**
Internationale Bibliographie der Fachadressbuecher/International Bibliography of Special Directories. (GW ISSN 0074-9672) **403**
Internationale Bibliographie der Rezensionen Wissenschaftlicher Literatur. see I B R **4356**
Internationale Bibliographie der Zeitschriftenliteratur aus allen Gebieten des Wissens/International Bibliography of Periodical Literature from all Fields of Knowledge. (GW ISSN 0020-9201) **403**
Internationale Bibliographie zuer Oesterreichischen Philosophie. see International Bibliography of Austrian Philosophy **3787**
Internationale Bibliographie zur Deutschen Klassik 1750-1850. (GW) **403**
Internationale Bodensee & Boot Nachrichten see I B N **4525**
Der Internationalen Gesellschaft fuer Geschichte der Pharmazie. Veroeffentlichungen. Neue Folge. (GW ISSN 0074-9729) **3730**
Internationale Gesellschaft fuer Urheberrecht. Schriftenreihe. (AU) **2637**
Internationale Gesellschaft fuer Urheberrecht. Yearbook. (AU ISSN 0539-1512) **3676**
Internationale Jahresbibliographie der Kongressberichte/International Annual Bibliography of Congress Proceedings. (GW ISSN 0933-1905) **3395**
Internationale Jugendbibliothek Bulletin see I J B - Bulletin **5209**
Internationale Jugendbibliothek Report see I J B - Report **2924**
Internationale Katholische Zeitschrift. (GW ISSN 0341-8693) **4266**

Internationale Kirchliche Zeitschrift. (SZ ISSN 0020-9252) **4183**
Internationale Licht Rundschau see Internationale Lighting Review **621**
Internationale Politik und Wirtschaft. (GW) **3962**
Internationale Politik und Wirtschaft Berichte see I P W Berichte **3898**
Internationale Pressekorrespondenz see I N P R E K O R R **3898**
Internationale Revue der Gesamten Hydrobiologie. (GW ISSN 0020-9309) **442**
Internationale Revue fuer Sociale Sicherheit see International Social Security Review **2535**
Internationale Schulbuchforschung. (GW ISSN 0172-8237) **1752**
Internationale Seilbahn-Rundschau/International Aerial Lift Review. (AU) **4651**
Internationale Spectator. (NE ISSN 0020-9317) **2726**, **932**
Internationale Stiftung Mozarteum. Mitteilungen. (AU ISSN 0020-9325) **3557**
Internationale Transport-Zeitschrift/Journal pour le Transport International/International Transport Journal-Overseas Digest. (SZ ISSN 0020-9341) **4651**, **4729**
Internationale Transport Zeitschrift. (SZ) **4651**
Internationale Vereinigung fuer Theoretische und Angewandte Limnologie. Mitteilungen. see International Association of Theoretical and Applied Limnology. Communications **1598**
Internationale Vereinigung fuer Theoretische und Angewandte Limnologie. Verhandlungen. see International Association of Theoretical and Applied Limnology. Proceedings **1598**
Internationale Vereinigung zur Foerderung des Studiums der Hegelschen Philosophie. Veroeffentlichung see Hegel - Studien Beihefte **3768**
Internationale Volkskundliche Bibliographie/International Folklore Bibliography/Bibliographie Internationale D'Ethnologie. (GW ISSN 0074-9737) **2060**
Internationale Wirtschaft. (AU ISSN 0020-935X) **914**
Internationale Wirtschafts-Briefe. (GW ISSN 0020-9368) **1099**, **2710**
Internationale Wirtschaftszahlen/International Economic Indicators. (GW) **723**
Internationale Wissenschaftliche Korrespondenz zur Geschichte der Deutschen Arbeiterbewegung see I W K **2584**
Internationale Zeitschrift fuer Erziehungswissenschaft. see International Review of Education **1640**
Internationale Zeitschrift fuer Infusionstherapie, Klinische Ernaehrung und Transfusionsmedizin see Infusionstherapie **3607**
Internationale Zeitschrift fuer Kaufmaennisches Bildungswesen. see International Review for Business Education **672**
Internationale Zeitschrift fuer Kirchenmusik. see Rivista Internazionale di Musica Sacra **3578**
Internationale Zeitschrift fuer Sportpaedagogik. see International Journal of Physical Education **1752**
Internationalen Aerosol - Verband Informationen see I A V Informationen **1178**
†Internationaler Arzt- und Spitalbedarf. (SZ) **5218**
Internationaler Entomologischer Verein. Mitteilungen. (GW) **534**
Internationaler FKK-Reisefuehrer. see International Naturist Guide **4549**
Internationaler Holzmarkt. (AU ISSN 0020-9422) **640**

Internationaler Verband der Stadt-, Sport- und Mehrzwerkhallen Informationsdienst see V D S M - Informationsdienst **3394**
Internationaler Verband Forstlicher Forschungsanstalten. Weltkongress Berichtswerk. (AU) **2102**
Internationaler Verband fuer Oeffentliches Verkehrswesen. Technische Berichte zu den Internationalen Kongressen see International Union of Public Transport. Technical Reports of the Congresses **4651**
Internationaler Weltkongress der U F O-Forscher. Dokumentarbericht. (GW ISSN 0579-6938) **56**
Internationales Afrikaforum. (GW ISSN 0020-9430) **3962**
Internationales Archiv fuer Sozialgeschichte der Deutschen Literatur. (GW ISSN 0340-4528) **2925**
Internationales Asienforum. (GW ISSN 0020-9449) **3962**
Internationales Bibliotheks-Handbuch/World Guide to Libraries. (GW ISSN 0000-0221) **2764**
Internationales Biographisches Archiv see Internationales Biographisches Archiv - Personen Aktuell **419**
Internationales Biographisches Archiv - Personen Aktuell. (GW) **419**
Internationales Bodensee-Jahrbuch der Sportschiffahrt. (GW) **4525**
Internationales Bodensee Regatta Programm. (GW) **4525**
Internationales Diplomatisches Magazin. see Diplomatic Observer **3955**
Internationales Energie Forum. (GW ISSN 0170-6640) **1792**
Internationales Firmenregister der Brauindustrie, Malzerien, Brennereien, Mineralwasser und Erfrischungsgetranke see International Brewer's Directory **382**
Internationales Freies Wort. (AU ISSN 0020-9473) **3900**
Internationales Gewerbearchiv. (GW ISSN 0020-9481) **1115**
Internationales Handbuch see Internationales Handbuch - Laender Aktuell **3962**
Internationales Handbuch fuer Rundfunk und Fernsehen. (GW ISSN 0535-4358) **1375**, **1357**
Internationales Handbuch - Laender Aktuell. (GW) **3962**, **2254**
Internationales Handbuch - Zeitarchiv. (GW) **2314**
Internationales Hydrologisches Programm: Operationelles Hydrologisches Programm: Jahrbuch Bundesrepublik Deutschland und Berlin (West)/International Hydrological Programme: Operational Hydrological Programme: Yearbook Federal Republic of Germany and Berlin (West). (GW ISSN 0344-5259) **1598**
Internationales Jahrbuch der Erwachsenenbildung/International Yearbook of Adult Education. (GW ISSN 0074-9818) **1684**
Internationales Jahrbuch fuer Geschichts und Geographieunterricht see Internationale Schulbuchforschung **1752**
Internationales Jahrbuch fuer Kartographie. (GW ISSN 0341-0986) **2254**
Internationales Journal fuer Paradontologie & Restaurative Zahnheilkunde see International Journal of Periodontics & Restorative Dentistry **3235**
†Internationales Recht und Diplomatie. (GW ISSN 0020-9503) **5218**
Internationales Sauna - Archiv. (GW ISSN 0178-7764) **3804**
Internationales Statistik-Handbuch fuer den Oeffentlichen Stadtverkehr. see International Statistical Handbook of Urban Public Transport **4664**
Internationales Verkehrswesen. (GW ISSN 0020-9511) **4719**, **4710**
Internationales Verlagsadressbuch mit I S B N - Register see Publishers' International I S B N Directory **4142**

Internationales Verzeichnis der Wirtschaftsverbaende/World Guide to Trade Associations. (GW ISSN 0302-2196) **1140**
Internationales Waffen-Magazin. (SZ) **4476**, 1526
†Internationally Speaking. (UK) **5218**
Internationella Studier. (SW ISSN 0020-952X) **3962**
▼Internetworking: Research and Experience. (UK ISSN 1049-8915) **1427**
Internewsletter Afrique. (US) **3962**, 870
Interni. (IT) **2560**
Der Internist. (GW ISSN 0020-9554) **3111**
Internist. (SA) **3111**
Internist: Health Policy in Practice. (US) **3111**, 870
Internistische Praxis. (GW ISSN 0020-9570) **3111**
Die Internistische Welt. (GW ISSN 0344-4201) **3111**
Internist's Compendium of Drug Therapy. (US ISSN 0276-4342) **3730**
Internist's Intercom. (US ISSN 0164-6419) **3111**
Internships. (US ISSN 0272-5460) **3628**, 1067
Interp Central Clearinghouse Newsletter.(US ISSN 0890-1538) **1959**, 1490, 3525, 4772
Inter-Parliamentary Bulletin. (SZ ISSN 0020-5079) **3962**
Inter-Parliamentary Union. Conference Proceedings see Inter-Parliamentary Union. Summary Records of the Inter-Parliamentary Conferences **3962**
Inter-Parliamentary Union. Series: "Reports and Documents". (SZ ISSN 0579-8337) **3900**
Inter-Parliamentary Union. Summary Records of the Inter-Parliamentary Conferences. (SZ) **3962**
Interphila. (GW ISSN 0535-4455) **3753**, 3599
Interplanetary News. (UK ISSN 0020-9597) **56**
Interplastics. (IT ISSN 0392-3800) **3863**
Interplay. (US) **2925**, 331
Interplay of Phonology, Morphology and Syntax see Chicago Linguistic Society. Papers from the Regional Meetings **2809**
▼Interpol - Moskva. (RU) **2985**, 1516
Interpressgrafik see Interpressgraphic **4002**
Interpressgraphic. (CS) **4002**
Interpretation (Flushing). (US ISSN 0020-9635) **3900**, 4183
Interpretation (Richmond). (US ISSN 0020-9643) **4183**
Interpretation Journal. (UK) **1959**
Interpretations see Arthurian Interpretations **2896**
Interpretazioni. (IT) **3769**
Interprete. (SZ ISSN 0047-1291) **2819**, 1640
Interprete. (IT) **2925**
El Interprete. (US ISSN 0162-4342) **4240**
El Interprete: Maestros. (US ISSN 0740-0063) **4240**
Interpreter (Nashville). (US ISSN 0020-9678) **4240**
Interpreter (Sacramento). (US ISSN 0742-4876) **2819**
Interpreter Releases. (US ISSN 0020-9686) **3984**, 2637
Interpreter Views see Views (Silver Spring) **2289**
▼Interpretive Perspectives on Education and Policy. (US) **1640**, 4439
Interrace Magazine. (US ISSN 1047-5370) **2007**
Interracial Books for Children Bulletin. (US ISSN 0146-5562) **4130**, 1256, 2007, 4439
Inter-Religio. (HK) **4183**
Interreligious Foundation for Community Organization News see I F C O News **4408**
Interrogatories, Documents and Admissions. (US) **2637**

Interrupt see Interexpress **1452**
Interscena. (CS) **4634**
Interscholastic Athletic Administration. (US) **1728**
Inter-School & Inter-Varsity Christian Fellowship. (JM ISSN 0020-5087) **4183**
Inter-School and Inter-Varsity Christian Fellowship of the West Indies see Inter-School & Inter-Varsity Christian Fellowship **4183**
Inter-Science. (PH) **4315**
Interscience Conference on Antimicrobial Agents and Chemotherapy. Program and Abstracts. (US ISSN 0733-6373) **553**
Intersections. (US ISSN 0095-6945) **1959**, 4439
Intersections (Montreal, 1987). (CN ISSN 0836-0839) **1722**
▼Intersections (Montreal, 1990). (CN) **301**
Interservice see I S **3460**
Intersezioni. (IT ISSN 0393-2451) **4315**
Inter-Society Color Council News. (US ISSN 0731-2911) **3853**
Intersociety Energy Conversion Engineering Conference. Proceedings.(US ISSN) **1806**, 1792
Interspace - Link Confidential Newsletter. (US) **56**
Interspecies Newsletter. (US) **584**, 2819
Interstandox. (GW) **3654**, 4693
Interstandox Extra. (GW) **3654**, 4693
Interstate. (US ISSN 0363-9991) **2925**
Interstate Cinderellans and Reveneurs Educational Club Newsletter see I C A R Newsletter **3753**
Interstate Commission on the Potomac River Basin. Proceedings. (US ISSN 0535-4676) **4826**, 1959
Interstate Commission on the Potomac River Basin. Technical Reports. (US) **1959**
Interstate Information Report. (US ISSN 0884-8394) **4745**
Interstate Manufacturers and Industrial Directory Buyers Guide. (US) **1140**
Interstate Natural Gas Association of America Washington Report. (US) **3690**, 1792
Interstate Natural Gas Association of America Weekly Report see Interstate Natural Gas Association of America Washington Report **3690**
Interstate Oil Compact Commission. Committee Bulletin see Interstate Oil Compact Commission. Compact & Committee Bulletin **3690**
Interstate Oil Compact Commission. Compact & Committee Bulletin. (US ISSN 1046-2333) **3690**
Interstate Oil Compact Commission Annual Report. (US) **3690**
Interstate Tax Report. (US ISSN 0731-5651) **1099**
Interstellar Bulletins see Huginn and Muninn **3669**
Intertax. (NE ISSN 0165-2826) **914**, 1099
†Inter-Technic. (BE) **5218**
Intertelex see Interfax **785**
Intertitres see Libertitres **2169**
Inter-Transport. (SP ISSN 0213-3091) **4651**
Interuniversitair Centrum voor Hedendaagse Geschiedenis. Medeelingen. see Centre Interuniversitaire d'Histoire Contemporaine. Cahiers **2356**
Inter-University Case Program. Case Study. (US ISSN 0074-106X) **4064**
Interuniversity Centre for European Studies. Bulletin. (CN ISSN 0319-1095) **2369**
Interuniversity Centre for European Studies. International Colloquium Proceedings. (CN) **2369**
Interuniversity Centre for European Studies. Research Report. (CN) **2369**
Inter-University Consortium for Political and Social Research. Annual Report. (US ISSN 0074-1078) **3900**

Inter-University Consortium for Political and Social Research. Guide to Resources and Services. (US ISSN 0362-8736) **4376**
Inter-University Consortium for Political and Social Research Bulletin see I C P S R Bulletin **4374**
Intervac U S. (US) **4772**
Interval International Traveler. (US) **4772**
Intervalle. (Arbeitskreis Musik in der Jugend) (GW ISSN 0579-8353) **3557**
InterVarsity. (US) **4240**, 1728
Intervencao Social. (PO) **4439**
Intervenor. (CN) **1959**, 2637
Interventi Classensi. (IT) **331**, 2314, 2925, 3769
Intervention. (CN ISSN 0047-1321) **4409**
Intervention in School and Clinic. (US) **1737**, 4026
†Interventional Radiology. (UK ISSN 0954-3317) **5218**
Interventions Chirurgicales et Traitements. see Canada. Statistics Canada. Surgical Procedures and Treatments **5160**
Interview. (GW ISSN 0932-9358) **2189**
Interview (New York). (US ISSN 0149-8932) **2227**
Interview - International Consulting Engineer see Independent Consulting Engineer **931**
Intervirology. (SZ ISSN 0300-5526) **553**
Interviu. (SP) **2217**
InterVue. (US) **1424**
Interweave see Handwoven **355**
Interzone. (UK ISSN 0264-3596) **3012**, 2925
Intestinal Function. (UK ISSN 0261-4995) **3268**
†Intestinal Malfunction. (UK ISSN 0261-4723) **5218**
Inti. (US ISSN 0732-6750) **2925**
Intimate Apparel see Body Fashions - Intimate Apparel **1283**
Intimate Fashion News. (US) **1285**
Intimate Fashion News Directory. (US) **1292**
Intimate Story. (US ISSN 0020-9813) **2983**
Intimita see Intimita della Famiglia **3512**
Intimita della Famiglia. (IT) **3512**
Intimite. (FR) **4845**
Intisari/Digest. (IO) **950**
Into the Blue. (AT) **4549**
Into the Courts. (US) **2454**, 3944
Intractable Pain Society of Great Britain and Ireland. Journal see Pain Society of Great Britain and Ireland. Journal **3138**
Intramurale Gezondheidszorg. (NE) **2466**
Intramuros. (FR) **301**
†Intrapreneurial Excellence. (US) **5218**
Intravenous Nurses Society Newsline see I N S Newsline **3279**
Intravenous Therapy News. (US) **3209**
Intrigue. (US) **1526**, 3962
Intro Singles Club. (US) **4362**
Introduction to C A S E. (US) **1478**
Introduction to Gravitation Chemistry. (US) **1179**
Introduction to Mail Order. (US) **1115**, 33
Introduction to the Constitution of India.(II) **2706**
Introduction to the Korean Securities Market. (KO) **950**
Introduktsiya i Akklimatyzatsiya Rastenii. (KR ISSN 0235-0904) **506**
Intrus. (UV) **2869**
Inuit see Inuit Tusaataat **4439**
Inuit Art Quarterly. (CN ISSN 0831-6708) **331**, 355
Inuit Tusaataat. (GL ISSN 0906-5504) **4439**, 442, 2007
Inuktitut. (CN ISSN 0020-9872) **2410**, 2055
Invalid Children's Aid Association Year Book see Invalid Children's Aid Nationwide Year Book **4409**
Invalid Children's Aid Nationwide Year Book. (UK) **4409**, 1239

Invalide Belge. (BE) **3460**
Invalidensport see Behindertensport **3370**
†Invandrarfraagor. Aarsbok. (SW ISSN 0280-8773) **5218**
Invandrarrapport. (SW ISSN 0345-5505) **3984**, 2007, 4439
†Invandrartidningen (Monthly). (SW ISSN 0349-554X) **5218**
Invandrartidningen (Weekly). (SW ISSN 0345-4991) **2218**
Invandrerinformasjon see Mosaikk **2015**
Invasion and Metastasis. (SZ ISSN 0251-1789) **525**
Invatamintul Liceal si Tehnic Profesional. (RM) **1640**
Invatamintul Profesional si Tehnic see Invatamintul Liceal si Tehnic Profesional **1640**
Invent. (US ISSN 1040-3485) **4601**, 4315
Inventaire des Archives Historiques/Inventaris van het Historisch Archief. (BE) **2333**
Inventaire General des Monuments et des Richesses Artistiques de la France. (FR ISSN 0075-0018) **301**, 331, 3525
Inventaires Economiques et Industriels Regionaux see Kompass Regionaux **676**
Inventare Nichtstaatlicher Archive. (GW ISSN 0535-5079) **403**
Inventari dei Manoscritti delle Biblioteche d'Italia. (IT ISSN 0075-0026) **2794**
Inventaria Archaeologica. (GW) **274**
Inventaria Archaeologica Belgique. (GW ISSN 0075-0034) **274**
Inventaria Archaeologica Ceskoslovensko. (GW ISSN 0075-0042) **274**
Inventaria Archaeologica Denmark. (GW ISSN 0075-0050) **274**
Inventaria Archaeologica Deutschland. (GW ISSN 0075-0069) **275**
Inventaria Archaeologica Espana. (GW ISSN 0075-0077) **275**
Inventaria Archaeologica France. (GW ISSN 0075-0085) **275**
Inventaria Archaeologica Great Britain. (GW ISSN 0075-0093) **275**
Inventaria Archaeologica Italia. (GW ISSN 0075-0107) **275**
Inventaria Archaeologica Jugoslavija. (GW ISSN 0075-0115) **275**
Inventaria Archaeologica Norway. (GW ISSN 0075-0123) **275**
Inventaria Archaeologica Oesterreich. (GW ISSN 0075-0131) **275**
Inventaria Archaeologica Pologne. (GW ISSN 0075-014X) **275**
Inventaria Archaeologica The Netherlands. (GW) **275**
Inventaria Archaeologica Ungarn. (GW ISSN 0075-0158) **275**
Inventario. (IT ISSN 0392-6095) **2925**
Inventaris van het Historisch Archief. see Inventaire des Archives Historiques **2333**
▼Inventing and Patenting Sourcebook. (US) **3676**
Invention Intelligence. (II ISSN 0970-0056) **4316**, 3676
Inventiones Mathematicae. (GW ISSN 0020-9910) **3039**
Inventions and Improvement Suggestions. see Vynalezy a Zlepsovaci Navrhy **3679**
Inventiva. (IT) **4601**, 1806, 4316
Inventor. (UK ISSN 0579-8388) **3676**
Inventories of Natural Gas Liquids & Liquified Refinery Gases. (US) **3690**
Inventors Clubs of America. News. (US) **4316**
Inventors' Digest. (US ISSN 0883-9859) **3676**
Inventor's Gazette. (US ISSN 0899-8841) **3676**
Inventory (Directory) of Holding Companies, Subsidiaries, and Other Companies Affiliated with Selected U S Utilities. (US) **1802**
Inventory of Health & Social Service Personnel. (CN) **4409**, 4105

INVENTORY

Inventory of Marriage and Family Literature. (US ISSN 0094-7814) **4458**, 3067
Inventory of Population Projects in Developing Countries Around the World. (UN ISSN 0363-5155) **3984**
Inventory of Retired U S Steam - Electric Plants. (US) **1901**, 1792
Inventory of Water Resources Research in Australia. (AT) **1598**
Inventory Reduction Report. (US ISSN 1049-9849) **1059**
Invenzione. (IT) **2983**
Inverness Courier. (UK ISSN 0020-9929) **2194**
Inverse Problems. (UK ISSN 0266-5611) **3065**, 1418, 1879
Inversiones, Venezuela. (VE) **950**
Inversionista Mexicano. (MX) **950**
Invertebrate Neurobiology. (UK ISSN 0261-4952) **572**, 585
Invertebrate Reproduction and Development. (IS ISSN 0168-8170) **534**
Invertebrate Taxonomy. (AT ISSN 0818-0164) **442**
Invertebres see Annales de Paleontologie (Vert - Invert) **3656**
Inverted - A Horn. (US ISSN 0894-7910) **2227**
Invest in Ecuador see Invierta en el Ecuador **952**
Invest Yourself see Volunteer! (Newton, 1944) **4423**
Investbanka. (YU) **787**
Investbanka. Annual Report. (YU) **787**
InvesTech Market Analyst. (US ISSN 0896-4157) **950**
InvesTech Mutual Fund Advisor. (US ISSN 0896-4165) **950**
Investering i Produktion see National Agency of Industry and Trade. Annual Reports (Year) **1081**
InvesText Advisor. (US ISSN 0893-4274) **1445**
InvesText News see InvesText Advisor **1445**
Investicije. (YU) **723**
Investicni Vystavba. (CS ISSN 0020-9937) **621**, 2489
Investigacion Agraria. Economia. (SP ISSN 0213-635X) **152**
Investigacion Agraria. Produccion y Proteccion Vegetales. (SP ISSN 0213-5000) **181**
Investigacion Agraria. Produccion y Sanidad Animales. (SP ISSN 0213-5035) **219**
▼Investigacion Agraria. Sistemas y Recursos Forestales. (SP) **2103**
Investigacion Bibliotecologica. (MX ISSN 0187-358X) **2764**
Investigacion Clinica. (VE ISSN 0535-5133) **3111**
Investigacion e Informacion Textil y de Tensioactivos. (SP ISSN 0302-5268) **4620**
Investigacion en la Escuela. (SP) **1640**
Investigacion Pesquera. (SP ISSN 0020-9953) **2044**
Investigacion y Ciencia. (Spanish translation of: Scientific American) (SP ISSN 0210-136X) **4316**, 4601
Investigacion y Educacion en Enfermeria. (CK ISSN 0120-5307) **3279**
Investigacion y Progreso Agropecuario Carillanca. (CL) **99**
Investigacion y Progreso Agropecuario Kampenaike. (CL) **99**
Investigacion y Progreso Agropecuario La Platina. (CL ISSN 0716-5331) **99**
Investigacion y Progreso Agropecuario Quilamapu. (CL ISSN 0716-6052) **99**
Investigacion y Progreso Agropecuario Remehue. (CL ISSN 0716-5951) **99**
Investigacion y Tecnica del Papel. (SP) **3663**
Investigaciones Economicas. Revista. (SP ISSN 0210-1521) **672**
Investigaciones en la Seguridad Social. see Current Research in Social Security **2530**

Investigaciones en Sociologia. (AG ISSN 0020-9961) **4439**
Investigaciones Geograficas. (MX) **2254**
Investigaciones Historicas. (SP ISSN 0210-9425) **2369**
Investigate. (US) **950**
Investigational New Drugs. (US ISSN 0167-6997) **3730**
Investigations in Fish Control see U.S. Fish and Wildlife Service. Investigations in Fish Control **2050**
Investigative Ophthalmology see Investigative Ophthalmology & Visual Science **3301**
Investigative Ophthalmology & Visual Science. (US ISSN 0146-0404) **3301**
Investigative Radiology. (US ISSN 0020-9996) **3359**
Investigative Reporters & Editors Journal. (US ISSN 0164-7016) **2571**
Investigative Reports. (US) **2571**
Investigator. (AT ISSN 0021-0013) **2345**
†Investigator. (US) **5218**
Investigator's International All-in-One Directory of the Investigative Industry.(US) **1516**, 1140
†Investing. (US) **5218**
Investing for Beginners. (UK) **950**
Investing in Crisis. (US ISSN 0740-3666) **950**
Investing in Real Estate. (US ISSN 0734-5860) **4151**
Investing, Licensing and Trading Conditions Abroad: Asia - Pacific. (US) **914**, 950
Investing, Licensing and Trading Conditions Abroad: Europe - Middle East - Africa. (US) **914**, 950
Investing, Licensing & Trading Conditions Abroad: Global Edition. (US ISSN 0021-003X) **914**, 950
Investing, Licensing and Trading Conditions Abroad: Latin America. (US) **914**, 950
Investir. (FR ISSN 0759-7673) **787**
Investire. (IT) **950**
Investment Action Newsletter see Trendex **966**
Investment Advice/Toshi Sodan. (JA) **950**
Investment Adviser. (AT) **950**, 4151
Investment Advisors Equity Characteristics. (US) **951**
Investment Advisors Equity Performance see Investment Advisors Equity Characteristics **951**
Investment Advisory Service see Fleet Street Letter **946**
Investment Africa. (UN) **932**
†Investment Analyst. (UK ISSN 0021-0048) **5218**
Investment Analysts Journal/Beleggingsontleders Tydskrif. (SA) **951**
Investment and Construction. see Touzi yu Jianshe **966**
Investment and Development Bank of Malawi. Annual Report and Accounts.(MW) **787**
Investment & Marketing. (PK ISSN 0021-0064) **1042**, 951
Investment & Tax Shelter Blue Book. (US) **951**, 1099
Investment Bulletin see A I C Investment Bulletin **937**
Investment Coin Review. (US ISSN 8750-4502) **951**, 3599
Investment Column Quarterly. (US ISSN 0739-6449) **951**
†Investment Companies. (US ISSN 0075-0271) **5218**
Investment Company Institute. Annual Report. (US) **951**
Investment Consultation see Investment Advice **950**
Investment Dealers' Digest. (US ISSN 0021-0080) **951**
Investment Digest. (US) **951**
Investment Diversification & Economic Analysis Ltd. Bulletin see I D E A S Bulletin **949**
Investment Economics/Toshi Keizai. (JA) **951**
Investment Executive. (CN ISSN 0840-9137) **951**

Investment Fund Index - Investment Trusts. (UK ISSN 0954-2485) **951**
Investment Horizons. (US) **951**
Investment International. (UK ISSN 0950-6195) **951**
Investment Limited Partnerships Handbook. (US) **951**, 1099, 2710
Investment Limited Partnerships Law Report. (US ISSN 0893-1364) **2710**, 951, 1099
Investment Management. (UK) **787**, 951
Investment Management and Study. see Touzi Guanli yu Yanjiu **966**
Investment Management Weekly. (US) **951**
†Investment Monthly. (US) **5218**
Investment News. (KE) **951**, 672
Investment Newsletter see Investor **951**
Investment Notes. (US) **951**
Investment Opportunities. (UK ISSN 0262-4257) **951**
Investment Opportunities in the Philippines. (PH) **951**, 1079
Investment Performance Digest. (US) **672**
Investment Projects in the Hunter Region. (AT ISSN 0725-3850) **951**
Investment Promotion Newsletter see Investment Africa **932**
Investment Quality Trends. (US ISSN 0021-0110) **951**
Investment Reporter. (CN ISSN 0700-5539) **951**
Investment Reporter. (US) **951**
Investment Research. see Touzi Yanjiu **966**
Investment Sources and Ideas see S I E (Year) Guide to Investment Services **962**
Investment Strategies: How to Create Your Own & Make it Work for You. (CN) **951**
Investment Strategy. (US) **951**
†Investment Trust Directory (Year). (UK ISSN 0953-8453) **5218**
Investment Trust Year Book see Investment Trust Directory (Year) **5218**
Investment - U S A see Foreign Investment in the U S **666**
Investment Vision see Worth **969**
Investments and Credit Corporation of Oyo State. Industrial Directory. (NR) **1140**
Investor. (TH ISSN 0021-0153) **951**
Investor Guide. (US) **951**
†Investor Relations (San Francisco). (US) **5218**
†Investor Relations (Washington). (US) **5218**
Investor Relations Newsletter. (US) **951**, 33
†Investor Relations Report. (US) **5218**
Investor Relations Update. (US) **951**
Investor Responsibility Research Center. Annual Report. (US) **951**
Investor's Business Daily. (US) **951**
The Investor's Choice. (JM) **951**
Investors Chronicle (London). (UK) **723**, 951
Investors Chronicle (London, 1860). (UK ISSN 0261-3115) **951**
Investors Chronicle and Stock Exchange Gazette see Investors Chronicle (London, 1860) **951**
Investors Chronicle Hillier Parker Rent Index. (UK ISSN 0143-6473) **4151**
Investors Chronicle Stockmarket Letter see I C Stockmarket Letter **949**
Investor's Daily. (US) **952**
▼Investor's Digest of Canada. (CN ISSN 0047-1356) **952**
The Investor's Edge. (US) **952**
Investor's Guide see Facts Investors Guide **945**
▼Investor's Guide. (CN) **952**
Investor's Guide to Football Cards. (US) **4507**, 952
Investors' Guide to Hungary. (HU ISSN 0865-6746) **952**
Investor's Guide to Low-Cost Mutual Funds. (US) **952**
Investors' Guide to Nepal. (NP) **952**

Investors' Guide to the Economic Climate of Singapore. (SI ISSN 0129-5276) **952**, 817
Investors Guide to the Stockmarket. (UK) **952**
Investor's Hotline. (US) **952**
Investors Intelligence. (US) **952**
Investors Update. (US) **952**
Invierta en el Ecuador. (EC) **952**
Invisible City. (US ISSN 0147-4936) **2995**, 2869
†Invision. (UK) **5218**
Invitation. (US) **4218**
Invitation to Comment see Exposure Draft (Accounting Standards) **750**
Invited Lectures on the Middle East at the University of Texas at Austin. (US ISSN 0742-1133) **2429**
▼InVitro Diagnostika Nachrichten. (GW ISSN 0938-0922) **3111**
Involvement of Participation. (UK) **984**
†Inward Light. (US ISSN 0021-0250) **5218**
Inyan-Chaddash. (IS ISSN 0334-7397) **1256**
Inzenerna Geologiia i Khidrogeologiia. (BU ISSN 0204-7934) **1546**
Inzhener - Naftyanik see Neftyanik (Moscow, 1974) **3706**
Inzhenerno-Fizicheskii Zhurnal. (RU) **1827**
Inzicht. (NE ISSN 0021-0307) **1640**
Inzinierske Stavby/Civil Engineering. (CS ISSN 0021-0277) **1868**
Inzynieria Chemiczna see Inzynieria Chemiczna i Procesowa **1855**
Inzynieria Chemiczna i Procesowa. (PL) **1855**
Inzynieria i Aparatura Chemiczna. (PL ISSN 0368-0827) **1855**
Inzynieria i Budownictwo. (PL ISSN 0021-0315) **1868**
Io. (US ISSN 0021-0331) **242**, 2926, 3669, 4507
Io e il Mio Bambino. (IT) **4845**
Io e Mio Figlio. (IT) **4845**
Ion Exchange and Solvent Extraction. (US ISSN 0092-0193) **1227**
Ion-Selective Electrode Reviews see Selective Electrode Reviews **3830**
Ionian. (US ISSN 0021-0358) **1315**
Ionnye Rasplavy i Tverdye Elektrolity. (KR ISSN 0234-4483) **1214**
▼Ionosfera. (KR) **1546**
Ionospheric Data at Showa Station (Antarctica). (JA ISSN 0389-8237) **3436**
Ionospheric Data in Japan/Denriso Geppo. (JA ISSN 0021-0382) **3437**
Iota. (UK) **2926**
Iowa. Bureau of Labor. Occupational Injuries and Illnesses Survey see Iowa. Division of Labor. Occupational Injuries and Illnesses Survey **3618**
Iowa. College Student Aid Commission. Annual Data Digest Report. (US) **1728**
Iowa. College Student Aid Commission. Annual Report see Iowa. College Student Aid Commission. Annual Data Digest Report **1728**
Iowa. Crop and Livestock Reporting Service. Weather and Field Crops see Iowa Agricultural Statistics **5218**
Iowa. Department of Job Service. Annual Report. (US ISSN 0149-449X) **984**
†Iowa. Department of Public Instruction. Summary of Federal Programs. (US ISSN 0091-8962) **5218**
Iowa. Division of Labor. Occupational Injuries and Illnesses Survey. (US) **3618**
Iowa. Employment Security Commission. Annual Report see Iowa. Department of Job Service. Annual Report **984**
Iowa A E C News see Iowa R E C News **1901**
Iowa Academy of Science. Journal. (US ISSN 0896-8381) **4316**
Iowa Academy of Science. Proceedings see Iowa Academy of Science. Journal **4316**
Iowa Academy of Science Bulletin see I A S Bulletin **4313**
Iowa Advocate. (US ISSN 0578-6533) **2637**
†Iowa Agri-News. (US) **5218**

†Iowa Agricultural Statistics. (US) **5218**
Iowa Agriculture and Home Economics Experiment Station. Research Bulletin. (US ISSN 0097-3416) **99, 2447, 3821**
Iowa Agriculture and Home Economics Experiment Station. Special Report. (US ISSN 0097-5125) **100**
Iowa Agriculturist. (US) **100**
Iowa Alumni Review. (US) **1315**
Iowa Appetizer. (US) **2477**
Iowa Archeological Society. Journal. (US ISSN 0535-5729) **275**
Iowa Archeological Society. Newsletter. (US ISSN 0578-655X) **275**
Iowa Architect. (US ISSN 0021-0439) **301**
Iowa Bankruptcy. (US) **2710**
Iowa Bird Life. (US ISSN 0021-0455) **564**
Iowa Cattleman. (US) **219**
Iowa City Magazine. (US) **2227**
Iowa Civil Rights Commission. Annual Report. (US) **3944**
Iowa Civil Rights Commission. Case Reports. (US) **3944**
Iowa Commerce. (US) **837**
Iowa Comprehensive State Plan for Substance Abuse (Year). (US) **1537**
Iowa Comprehensive State Plan for Substance Abuse Prevention: Annual Performance Report *see* Iowa Comprehensive State Plan for Substance Abuse (Year) **1537**
Iowa Congress of Parents and Teachers Iowa P T A Bulletin *see* Iowa P T A Bulletin **1640**
Iowa County. (US ISSN 0892-3795) **4089**
Iowa County Farmer. (US) **100**
Iowa Criminal Law Bulletin. (US) **1516, 2713**
Iowa Dental Journal. (US ISSN 0021-0498) **3235**
Iowa Detailed Report of Vital Statistics *see* Vital Statistics of Iowa **3996**
Iowa Educational Leadership. (US) **1752**
Iowa Engineer. (US ISSN 0021-0501) **1827**
Iowa English Bulletin. (US ISSN 0444-4663) **1752**
Iowa English Bulletin - Yearbook *see* Iowa English Bulletin **1752**
Iowa Facts. (US ISSN 0895-8092) **1781**
Iowa Farm Bureau Spokesman. (US ISSN 0021-051X) **100**
Iowa Farm - Business *see* Agribusiness (Des Moines) **70**
Iowa Farmer Today. (US) **100**
Iowa Farmers Fastline *see* Farmers Fastline: Iowa Edition **91**
Iowa Food Dealer *see* Iowa Grocer **2092**
Iowa Genealogical Society. Surname Index. (US ISSN 0090-905X) **2155**
Iowa Geographer *see* Geographical Perspectives **2250**
Iowa Geological Survey. Reports of Investigations *see* Iowa Geological Survey Bureau. Reports of Investigations **1569**
Iowa Geological Survey Bureau. Reports of Investigations. (US) **1569**
Iowa Grocer. (US) **2092**
Iowa Idea. (US) **3900**
Iowa Image. (US) **4845**
Iowa International Directory *see* Directory of Exporters **1130**
Iowa Journal of Optometry. (US) **3301**
Iowa Journal of Social Work *see* Social Development Issues **4419**
Iowa Journal of Speech Communication.(US ISSN 0886-1943) **1737, 1338**
Iowa Law Review. (US ISSN 0021-0552) **2637**
Iowa Legionnaire. (US ISSN 0021-0560) **1298**
Iowa Legislative News Service Bulletin. (US) **4064**
Iowa Limitations Manual. (US) **2732**
Iowa Manufacturers Register. (US ISSN 0737-7940) **1140**
Iowa Matrimonial Law. (US) **2718**

Iowa Media Message. (US) **2764, 1640**
Iowa Medical Society. Journal *see* Iowa Medicine **3111**
Iowa Medicine. (US ISSN 0746-8709) **3111**
Iowa Middle Level Educators Bulletin. (US) **1752**
Iowa Music Educator. (US ISSN 0021-0609) **3557, 1640**
†Iowa Nurses' Association. Bulletin. (US ISSN 0075-0387) **5218**
Iowa Official Register. (US) **3938, 4081, 4575**
Iowa Oil Spout. (US) **3690**
Iowa P T A Bulletin. (Iowa Congress of Parents and Teachers) (US ISSN 0021-0617) **1640**
Iowa Parent. (US) **1239**
Iowa Parks & Recreation. (US) **1490, 4549**
Iowa Petroleum Distributor Newsletter. (US) **3690**
Iowa Pharmacist. (US) **3730**
Iowa Pleading and Causes of Action. (US) **2637**
Iowa Police Journal. (US ISSN 0021-0633) **1516**
Iowa Pork Producer. (US) **219**
Iowa Pork Today. (US ISSN 1043-9676) **219, 2074**
Iowa R E C News. (US ISSN 0162-2412) **1901, 100**
Iowa Review. (US ISSN 0021-065X) **2926**
Iowa School Board Dialogue. (US ISSN 0021-0668) **1728**
Iowa Science Teachers Journal. (US ISSN 0021-0676) **4316, 1752**
Iowa Sierran. (US) **1298, 1490, 1959, 4549**
Iowa Smoke-Eater. (US) **2033**
Iowa State Archaeologist. Report. (US ISSN 0085-2252) **275**
Iowa State Daily. (US) **1315**
Iowa State Education Association Communique *see* I S E A Communique **1638**
Iowa State University. Engineering Research Institute. Engineering Research Report. (US ISSN 0075-0433) **1827**
Iowa State University. Statistical Laboratory. Annual Report. (US) **3062, 3039, 4575**
Iowa State University Computation Center Newsletter *see* I S U Computation Center Newsletter **1396**
Iowa State University Veterinarian. (US ISSN 0099-5851) **4811**
Iowa Stater. (US) **1315**
Iowa Summary of Vital Statistics *see* Vital Statistics of Iowa **3996**
Iowa Trucking Lifeliner. (US) **4745**
Iowa Woman. (US ISSN 0271-8227) **2926, 4845**
Iowan. (US ISSN 0021-0722) **2227**
Ipargazdasag. (HU ISSN 0021-0749) **1079**
Ipargazdasagi Szemle. (HU ISSN 0133-6452) **1079**
Ipari Formatervezesi Szakirodalmi Tajekoztato/Industrial Design Abstracts. (HU ISSN 0231-195X) **1845, 4614**
Iparmuveszet. *see* Ars Decorativa **3521**
†L'Ippogrifo. (IT) **5219**
Ipsissima Verba. (US) **2926, 2995**
Ipswich and Suffolk Directory of Industry and Commerce *see* Suffolk Business Directory **1154**
Iqbal Review. (PK ISSN 0021-0773) **3770**
Iqbaliat *see* Iqbal Review **3770**
Iqra/Read. (TS) **1256**
Al-Iqtisad al-Islami/Islamic Economy. (TS) **870, 4218**
Al-Iqtisad wal-Tijarah/Economy and Commerce. (TS) **914**
Iran. (UK ISSN 0578-6967) **2430**
Iran. Geological Survey. Report. (IR ISSN 0075-0484) **1569**
Iran. Ministry of Economy. Bureau of Statistics. Series. (IR) **723**
Iran. Ministry of Economy. Internal Wholesale Trade Statistics. (IR) **723**

Iran. Ministry of Economy. International Trade Statistics. (IR) **723**
Iran. Ministry of Economy. Report on Commencement and Operation Permits for Industrial Establishments.(IR ISSN 0578-6959) **1079**
†Iran. Ministry of Industries and Mines. Trends in Industrial and Commercial Statistics. (IR) **5219**
Iran al-Islam fi Mir'a al-Ihsa' *see* Statistical Reflection of the Islamic Republic of Iran **4588**
Iran Almanac and Book of Facts. (IR ISSN 0075-0476) **2202**
Iran Dar A'inah-i Amar *see* Statistical Reflection of the Islamic Republic of Iran **4588**
Iran Exports *see* Iran Exports & Imports Magazine **914**
Iran Exports & Imports Magazine. (IR) **914**
Iran Management Association. Management Bulletin. (IR) **1015**
Iran Monitor. (US) **914, 1079**
Iran Nameh. (US) **2430**
Iran Oil Journal. (IR ISSN 0021-079X) **3690**
Iran Oil News. (IR) **3690**
Iran Petrole *see* Iran Oil Journal **3690**
Iran Philatelic Study Circle Bulletin. (UK) **3753**
Iran Post. (US) **2202**
Iran Press Digest (Economic). (IR) **672**
Iran Press Digest (Political). (IR) **3900**
Iran Times International. (US) **2007**
Iran Trade and Industry. (IR ISSN 0021-0803) **837, 1079**
Iran Trade & Industry Annual Review. (IR) **870**
Iran Yearbook *see* Kayhan Yearbook **2430**
Iranama. (CE) **3900**
Iranian Assets Litigation Reporter. (US ISSN 0277-2922) **2726**
†Iranian Cinema. (IR) **5219**
Iranian Dental Association. Bulletin. *see* Jame'e Dandanpezeshki Iran. Namah-i **3235**
Iranian Dental Association. Journal - Jame'e-Ye Dandanpezeshkan-e Iran. Majalleh *see* Majda **3237**
Iranian Industrial Statistics. (IR ISSN 0075-0506) **723**
Iranian Journal of Agricultural Sciences. (IR) **100**
Iranian Journal of Linguistics. *see* Majaliah-i Zabanshinasi **2828**
Iranian Journal of Medical Sciences. (IR ISSN 0253-0716) **3111**
Iranian Journal of Physics. *see* Majallah-i Fizik **3824**
Iranian Journal of Plant Pathology/Bimarihaye Guiahi. (IR ISSN 0006-2774) **506, 100, 534**
Iranian Journal of Public Health/Majalle-Ye Behdasht-e Iran. (IR ISSN 0304-4556) **4105**
Iranian Mathematical Society. Bulletin/Anjoman-i Riyazi-i Iran. Buletan-i. (IR) **3039**
Iranian Mineral Statistics. (IR ISSN 0075-0514) **3486**
Iranian National Bibliography. (IR ISSN 0075-0522) **403**
Iranian National Film Quarterly *see* Filmkhane-ye Melli-e Iran. Name-ye **3509**
Iranian Studies. (US ISSN 0021-0862) **3639**
Iranica Antiqua. (BE ISSN 0021-0870) **275, 3639**
Iranica Antiqua Supplementa. (BE ISSN 0169-877X) **275, 3639**
Iranistische Mitteilungen. (GW) **3639**
Iraq. (UK ISSN 0021-0889) **275, 3639**
Iraq. Central Statistical Organization. Annual Abstract of Statistics. (IQ) **4575**
Iraq. Central Statistical Organization. Monthly Bulletin of Foreign Trade Statistics *see* Iraq. Central Statistical Organization. Quarterly Bulletin of Foreign Trade Statistics **723**
Iraq. Central Statistical Organization. Quarterly Bulletin of Foreign Trade Statistics. (IQ) **723**

Iraq. Central Statistical Organization. Results of the Industrial Survey of Large Establishments in Iraq. (IQ) **723**
Iraq. Central Statistical Organization. Statistical Pocket Book. (IQ) **4575**
Iraq. Central Statistical Organization. Summary of Foreign Trade Statistics.(IQ ISSN 0021-0900) **723**
Iraq. Ministry of Education. Al-Mu'allem al-Jadid. (IQ) **1640, 2869**
Iraq. Ministry of Information. Information Series. (IQ) **4064**
Iraq. Ministry of Oil. Bulletin *see* Iraq Oil News **3690**
Iraq. Weekly Gazette of the Republic of Iraq *see* Waqai al-Iraqiya **2693**
Iraq Government Gazette. (IQ) **4064**
Iraq Natural History Museum. Bulletin. (IQ) **4316**
Iraq Natural History Museum. Publication. (IQ) **4316, 442**
Iraq Natural History Research Center and Museum. Bulletin *see* Iraq Natural History Museum. Bulletin **4316**
Iraq Natural History Research Centre and Museum. Publications *see* Iraq Natural History Museum. Publication **4316**
Iraq News Bulletin. (II ISSN 0047-1429) **2430**
Iraq Oil News. (IQ) **3690**
Iraqi Chemical Society. Journal. (IQ ISSN 0379-8321) **1179**
Iraqi Journal of Agricultural Sciences "ZANCO" *see* University of Salahaddin. College of Agriculture. Scientific Journal "ZANCO **127**
Iraqi Journal of Science. (IQ) **4316**
Iraqi Medical Professions' Association. Journal. (IQ ISSN 0021-0927) **3111**
Iraqi National Bibliography. (IQ) **403**
Irebun. *see* Eleven **4503**
Iredell County Tracks (NC). (US ISSN 0740-5006) **2155**
Ireland. (IE) **2203**
Ireland. Central Statistics Office. Advance Estimate of Output, Input and Income Arising in Agriculture. (IE ISSN 0791-301X) **139**
Ireland. Central Statistics Office. Age-by-Duration Analysis of the Live Register *see* Ireland. Central Statistics Office. Live Register Age by Duration Analysis **724**
Ireland. Central Statistics Office. Agricultural Input Price Index. (IE ISSN 0791-3346) **139**
Ireland. Central Statistics Office. Agricultural Input Price Indices *see* Ireland. Central Statistics Office. Agricultural Input Price Index **139**
Ireland. Central Statistics Office. Agriculture - June Survey - Provisional Results. (IE ISSN 0791-3141) **139**
Ireland. Central Statistics Office. Agriculture Output Price Index. (IE ISSN 0791-3354) **139**
Ireland. Central Statistics Office. Agriculture Output Price Indices *see* Ireland. Central Statistics Office. Agriculture Output Price Index **139**
Ireland. Central Statistics Office. Analysis of External Trade by Ports. (IE ISSN 0791-3451) **723**
Ireland. Central Statistics Office. Analysis of the Live Register According to Area of Residence *see* Ireland. Central Statistics Office. Live Register Area Analysis **724**
Ireland. Central Statistics Office. Balance of International Payments. (IE ISSN 0791-3370) **723, 1099**
Ireland. Central Statistics Office. Banking, Insurance and Building Societies. Employment and Earnings. (IE ISSN 0791-3168) **723**
Ireland. Central Statistics Office. Building and Construction: Average Earnings and Hours Worked. (IE ISSN 0791-2951) **638, 723**

6324 IRELAND. CENTRAL

Ireland. Central Statistics Office. Building and Construction. Monthly Index of Employment in Private Firms with 5 or More Persons Engaged. (IE ISSN 0791-2943) **638**, 723
Ireland. Central Statistics Office. Building and Construction Planning Permissions. (IE ISSN 0791-2978) **638**, 723
Ireland. Central Statistics Office. Building Employment Index *see* Ireland. Central Statistics Office. Building and Construction. Monthly Index of Employment in Private Firms with 5 or More Persons Engaged **638**
Ireland. Central Statistics Office. Census of Building and Construction *see* Ireland. Central Statistics Office. Census of Building and Construction. Results for Private Firms with 20 or More Persons Engaged **638**
Ireland. Central Statistics Office. Census of Building and Construction. Results for Private Firms with 20 or More Persons Engaged. (IE ISSN 0791-296X) **638**, 723
Ireland. Central Statistics Office. Census of Industrial Production. (IE ISSN 0790-6080) **723**, 4575
Ireland. Central Statistics Office. Census of Industrial Production. Overall Results for Industrial Enterprises. (IE ISSN 0791-2897) **723**
Ireland. Central Statistics Office. Census of Industrial Production. Overall Results for Industrial Establishments.(IE ISSN 0790-6099) **723**
Ireland. Central Statistics Office. Consumer Price Index. (IE ISSN 0791-3303) **1042**, 723
Ireland. Central Statistics Office. Distribution of Cattle and Pigs by Size of Herd. (IE ISSN 0790-7729) **139**
Ireland. Central Statistics Office. Economic Series *see* Ireland. Stationery Office. Economic Series **724**
Ireland. Central Statistics Office. Estimated Numbers and Expenditures of Visitors to Ireland and Irish Visitors Abroad *see* Ireland. Central Statistics Office. Tourism and Travel **724**
Ireland. Central Statistics Office. External Trade Provisional Figures. (IE ISSN 0791-3478) **723**
Ireland. Central Statistics Office. Hire Purchase and Credit Sales Inquiry. (IE ISSN 0791-3389) **787**, 723, 1042
Ireland. Central Statistics Office. Industrial Disputes. (IE ISSN 0791-329X) **723**, 984
Ireland. Central Statistics Office. Industrial Earnings and Hours Worked. (IE ISSN 0791-2900) **723**
Ireland. Central Statistics Office. Industrial Employment. (IE ISSN 0791-2919) **723**
Ireland. Central Statistics Office. Industrial Employment Earnings and Hours Worked *see* Ireland. Central Statistics Office. Industrial Employment **723**
Ireland. Central Statistics Office. Industrial Employment Earnings and Hours Worked *see* Ireland. Central Statistics Office. Industrial Earnings and Hours Worked **723**
Ireland. Central Statistics Office. Industrial Employment Earnings and Hours Worked: Details for Supplementary N A C E Sub-Sectors. (IE ISSN 0791-2927) **723**
Ireland. Central Statistics Office. Industrial Employment Earnings and Hours Worked: Details for Supplementary N A C E Sub-Groups *see* Ireland. Central Statistics Office. Industrial Employment Earnings and Hours Worked: Details for Supplementary N A C E Sub-Sectors **723**
Ireland. Central Statistics Office. Industrial Production Index. (IE ISSN 0790-5130) **723**
Ireland. Central Statistics Office. Industrial Turnover Index. (IE ISSN 0791-2889) **723**
Ireland. Central Statistics Office. Labour Force. Mid-April Estimates. (IE ISSN 0791-3184) **724**
Ireland. Central Statistics Office. Labour Force, Preliminary Estimates. (IE ISSN 0791-3176) **724**
Ireland. Central Statistics Office. Labour Force Survey. (IE ISSN 0791-0533) **724**
Ireland. Central Statistics Office. Labour Force Survey. First Results *see* Ireland. Central Statistics Office. Labour Force Survey **724**
Ireland. Central Statistics Office. Live Register Age by Duration Analysis. (IE ISSN 0791-394X) **724**, 984
Ireland. Central Statistics Office. Live Register Area Analysis. (IE ISSN 0791-3206) **724**, 984
Ireland. Central Statistics Office. Live Register, Monthly Flow Analysis. (IE ISSN 0791-3192) **724**
Ireland. Central Statistics Office. Live Register Statement. (IE) **724**, 984
Ireland. Central Statistics Office. Monthly Live Register Statement *see* Ireland. Central Statistics Office. Live Register Statement **724**
Ireland. Central Statistics Office. Motor Registrations - Provisional Results. (IE ISSN 0791-3435) **724**
Ireland. Central Statistics Office. Number and Weight of Pigs Slaughtered at Bacon Factories. (IE ISSN 0791-3044) **139**
Ireland. Central Statistics Office. Particulars of Vehicles Registered and Licensed for First Time. (IE ISSN 0791-3427) **724**
Ireland. Central Statistics Office. Particulars of Vehicles Registered and Licensed for the First Time. (IE ISSN 0444-5147) **4664**
Ireland. Central Statistics Office. Pig Enumeration *see* Ireland. Central Statistics Office. Pig Survey **139**
Ireland. Central Statistics Office. Pig Slaughterings *see* Ireland. Central Statistics Office. Number and Weight of Pigs Slaughtered at Bacon Factories **139**
Ireland. Central Statistics Office. Pig Survey. (IE ISSN 0791-3079) **139**
Ireland. Central Statistics Office. Pig Survey - August. (IE ISSN 0791-3095) **139**
Ireland. Central Statistics Office. Preliminary Estimate of Output, Input and Income in Agriculture. (IE ISSN 0791-3028) **139**
Ireland. Central Statistics Office. Production of Butter and Separated Milk Powder *see* Ireland. Central Statistics Office. Production of Milk and Milk Products **139**
Ireland. Central Statistics Office. Production of Milk and Milk Products. (IE ISSN 0791-3036) **139**
Ireland. Central Statistics Office. Quarterly Report on Births, Deaths and Marriages and on Certain Infectious Diseases *see* Ireland. Central Statistics Office. Quarterly Report on Vital Statistics **3992**
Ireland. Central Statistics Office. Quarterly Report on Vital Statistics. (IE) **3992**
Ireland. Central Statistics Office. Retail Sales Index. (IE ISSN 0791-315X) **1042**, 724
Ireland. Central Statistics Office. Road Freight Transport Survey. (IE ISSN 0790-9934) **724**
Ireland. Central Statistics Office. Statistics of Port Traffic. (IE ISSN 0791-346X) **4664**
Ireland. Central Statistics Office. Strikes or Lock-outs Reported during the Quarter *see* Ireland. Central Statistics Office. Industrial Disputes **723**
Ireland. Central Statistics Office. Tourism and Travel. (IE) **724**
Ireland. Central Statistics Office. Tourism and Travel Quarterly. (IE ISSN 0791-3656) **724**
Ireland. Central Statistics Office. Wholesale Price Index. (IE ISSN 0791-3311) **724**, 1042
Ireland. Department of Agriculture and Fisheries. Annual Report *see* Ireland. Department of Agriculture. Annual Report **100**
Ireland. Department of Agriculture. Annual Report. (IE) **100**
Ireland. Department of Social Welfare. Statistical Information on Social Welfare. (IE) **4409**
Ireland (Eire) Central Statistics Office. Advertising Agencies Inquiry *see* Ireland (Eire) Central Statistics Office. Business of Advertising Agencies. Results for Respondents to Inquiry **41**
Ireland (Eire) Central Statistics Office. Agricultural Output *see* Ireland (Eire) Central Statistics Office. Estimated Output, Input and Income Arising in Agriculture **100**
Ireland (Eire) Central Statistics Office. Agriculture - June Survey - Final Estimates. (IE ISSN 0791-3524) **139**, 219
Ireland (Eire) Central Statistics Office. Business of Advertising Agencies *see* Ireland (Eire) Central Statistics Office. Business of Advertising Agencies. Results for Respondents to Inquiry **41**
Ireland (Eire) Central Statistics Office. Business of Advertising Agencies. Results for Respondents to Inquiry. (IE ISSN 0791-3516) **41**
Ireland (Eire) Central Statistics Office. December Livestock Survey. (IE ISSN 0791-3133) **219**
Ireland (Eire) Central Statistics Office. Estimated Output, Input and Income Arising in Agriculture. (IE ISSN 0791-3001) **100**
Ireland (Eire) Central Statistics Office. Hire - Purchase and Credit Sales *see* Ireland. Central Statistics Office. Hire Purchase and Credit Sales Inquiry **787**
Ireland (Eire) Central Statistics Office. June Survey - Final Estimates *see* Ireland (Eire) Central Statistics Office. Agriculture - June Survey - Final Estimates **139**
Ireland (Eire) Central Statistics Office. Livestock Enumeration *see* Ireland (Eire) Central Statistics Office. December Livestock Survey **219**
Ireland (Eire) Central Statistics Office. National Income and Expenditure. (IE ISSN 0075-0603) **724**, 999, 1099
Ireland (Eire) Central Statistics Office. Trend of Employment and Unemployment. (IE ISSN 0075-0638) **724**
Ireland (Eire) Central Statistics Office. Tuarascail Ar Staidreamh Beatha - Report on Vital Statistics. (IE ISSN 0075-062X) **4575**
Ireland (Eire) Department of Finance. Financial Statement of the Minister for Finance. (IE ISSN 0075-0670) **1099**
Ireland. Stationery Office. Economic Series. (IE ISSN 0790-8407) **724**
Ireland. Stationery Office. Statistical Abstract. (IE ISSN 0790-8970) **4575**
Ireland. Stationery Office. Statistical Bulletin. (IE ISSN 0790-8334) **4575**
▼Ireland (Year). (US) **4772**
Ireland (Year). (US) **4772**
Ireland Department of Education. Liosta de Iar-Bhunscoileanna Aitheanta - List of Recognised Post-Primary Schools.(IE ISSN 0075-0662) **1695**
Ireland of the Welcomes. (IE ISSN 0021-0943) **4772**
Ireland Ports & Shipping Handbook. (UK ISSN 0260-924X) **4729**, 1140
†Ireland Today. (IE) **5219**
Ireland's Own. (IE ISSN 0021-0951) **2203**
Irenikon. (BE ISSN 0021-0978) **4183**
Irian: Bulletin of Irian Jaya. (IO ISSN 0304-2189) **242**, 2819
Iridis. (US) **3669**
Iris. (AT) **1277**
Iris. (FR ISSN 0291-2066) **2926**
Iris. (BL) **3792**, 3512, 4461
Iris: A Journal About Women. (US ISSN 0896-1301) **4845**, 2007, 2509, 2869
Iris and Res Novissimae *see* Iris **1277**
Iris Eireannach an Oideachais. *see* Irish Journal of Education **1640**
Iris Oifigiuil. (IE) **4064**
Iris- und Lilien *see* Der Staudengarten **2139**
Iris Year Book. (UK ISSN 0075-0700) **2132**
Irish Advocate *see* Advocate (New York) **1989**
Irish Agricultural and Creamery Review *see* Dairy Executive **198**
Irish Agricultural Organization Society. Annual Report *see* Irish Cooperative Organization Society. Annual Report **100**
Irish America Magazine. (US ISSN 0884-4240) **2007**, 3900, 4439
Irish Ancestor. (IE ISSN 0047-1437) **2155**, 2369
†Irish Archaeological Research Forum. (UK) **5219**
Irish Architect. (IE) **301**
Irish Archives. (IE) **2764**
Irish Archives Bulletin *see* Irish Archives **2764**
Irish Arts Review. (UK ISSN 0790-178X) **331**, 301, 3525
Irish Astronomical Journal. (UK ISSN 0021-1052) **366**
Irish Bacon News. (IE ISSN 0047-1445) **2074**
Irish Bank Officials Association Newsheet. (IE ISSN 0790-066X) **787**
Irish Banking Review. (IE ISSN 0021-1060) **787**
Irish Baptist. (UK) **4240**
Irish Baptist Historical Society. Journal. (UK ISSN 0075-0727) **4240**
Irish Bee-Keeper. (IE ISSN 0021-1079) **100**
Irish Biblical Association. Proceedings. (IE ISSN 0332-4427) **4183**
Irish Biblical Studies. (UK ISSN 0268-6112) **4183**
Irish Bird Report *see* Irish Birds **564**
Irish Birds. (IE ISSN 0332-0111) **564**
Irish Booklore - New Series *see* Linen Hall Review **2872**
Irish Building Services News. (IE ISSN 0791-0878) **621**
Irish Bystander. (IE) **2203**
Irish Catholic. (IE) **4266**
Irish Catholic Directory. (UK ISSN 0075-0735) **4266**
Irish Christian Study Centre. Journal. (UK ISSN 0264-6579) **4183**
Irish Colleges of Physicians and Surgeons. Journal. (UK ISSN 0374-8405) **3111**
Irish Computer. (IE ISSN 0332-0197) **1461**, 1397, 1424, 1433
Irish Cooperative Organization Society. Annual Report. (IE ISSN 0790-4568) **100**
Irish Countrywoman *see* Irish Woman **1298**
Irish Countrywomen's Association: An Grianan Programme *see* Adult Education College: An Grianan Programme **1614**
Irish Creamery Managers' Association. Creamery Directory and Diary *see* Dairy Executive. Directory and Diary **198**
†Irish Creek Cousins Newsletter. (US) **5219**
▼Irish Criminal Law Journal. (IE ISSN 0791-539X) **2713**
Irish Dental Association. Journal. (IE ISSN 0021-1133) **3235**
Irish Drama Selections. (UK ISSN 0260-7964) **4634**, 2926
Irish Echo. (US ISSN 0192-1215) **2007**
Irish Economic and Social History. (IE ISSN 0332-4893) **2369**
Irish Electrical Industries Review. (IE ISSN 0021-1141) **1375**

Title

Irish Engineers see Engineers Journal 1821
Irish Equipment News. (IE ISSN 0047-1453) 3018
▼Irish European Law Journal. (IE ISSN 0791-5403) 2637
Irish Exporter. (IE) 914
Irish Family History see Irish Genealogy 2155
Irish Family Links see Irish Heritage Links 2155
Irish Family Names Society News Letter.(US) 2155, 2369
Irish Farmers' Journal. (IE ISSN 0021-1168) 100
Irish Farmers Monthly. (IE ISSN 0332-2408) 100
Irish Field. (IE ISSN 0021-1184) 4535
Irish Fisheries Investigations. Series A: Freshwater. (IE) 2044, 442
Irish Fisheries Investigations. Series B: Marine. (IE) 2044, 442
Irish Folk Music Studies. (IE) 3557
Irish Forestry. (IE ISSN 0021-1192) 2103
Irish Genealogy. (US) 2155
Irish Geography. (IE ISSN 0075-0778) 2254
Irish Georgian Society. Bulletin. (IE ISSN 0021-1206) 301
Irish Hardware and Allied Trader. (IE ISSN 0047-1461) 642
Irish Hare. (UK ISSN 0260-986X) 1490
Irish Heating and Ventilating News. (IE) 2301
Irish Herald. (US) 2007
Irish Heritage Links. (UK) 2155
Irish Historical Studies. (IE ISSN 0021-1214) 2369
Irish History Workshop/Saotharlann Staire Eireann. (IE ISSN 0332-3633) 2369
The Irish in America. (US) 4266
Irish in Britain Directory. (UK ISSN 0260-650X) 2007
Irish Journal of Agricultural and Food Research. (IE) 100
†Irish Journal of Agricultural Economics and Rural Sociology. (IE ISSN 0021-1249) 5219
Irish Journal of Agricultural Research see Irish Journal of Agricultural and Food Research 100
Irish Journal of Earth Sciences. (IE ISSN 0790-1763) 1546, 1569
Irish Journal of Education/Iris Eireannach an Oideachais. (IE ISSN 0021-1257) 1640
†Irish Journal of Environmental Science.(IE ISSN 0332-1665) 5219
Irish Journal of Food Science and Technology. (IE ISSN 0332-0375) 2074
Irish Journal of Medical Sciences. (IE ISSN 0021-1265) 3111
Irish Journal of Psychiatry. (IE ISSN 0790-1186) 3340
Irish Journal of Psychological Medicine. (IE ISSN 0790-9667) 3340, 4026
Irish Journal of Psychology. (IE ISSN 0303-3910) 4026
Irish Journal of Psychotherapy and Psychosomatic Medicine see Irish Journal of Psychological Medicine 3340
Irish Jurist. (IE ISSN 0021-1273) 2637
Irish Law Reports Monthly. (IE ISSN 0332-3293) 2637, 4064
Irish Law Times and Solicitors' Journal. (IE ISSN 0021-1281) 2637
Irish Library. see An Leabharlann 2768
Irish Link. (AT ISSN 0814-5482) 2155
Irish Literary Studies. (UK ISSN 0140-895X) 2926
Irish Literary Supplement. (US ISSN 0733-3390) 2926, 2007
Irish Marketing Journal Ltd. see I M J 1041
Irish Medical Association. Journal see Irish Medical Journal 3111
Irish Medical Journal. (IE ISSN 0332-3102) 3111
Irish Medical News. (IE) 3111

Irish Medical Organization see Irish Medical Journal 3111
Irish Medical Times. (UK ISSN 0047-147X) 3111
Irish Messenger of the Sacred Heart see Sacred Heart Messenger 4275
Irish Motor Industry. (IE ISSN 0376-7221) 4693
Irish Music and Dance Association Newsletter. (US) 3557, 1531, 2055
Irish Naturalists' Journal. (UK ISSN 0021-1311) 4316
Irish People. (IE) 3900
Irish People (New York). (US) 2007
Irish Philosophical Journal. (UK ISSN 0266-9080) 3770
Irish Play Series. (US ISSN 0075-0816) 2926
Irish Plumbing and Heating Engineer see Irish Heating and Ventilating News 2301
Irish Political Review. (UK) 3900
Irish Political Studies. (IE ISSN 0790-7184) 3900
Irish Post. (UK) 2869
Irish Printer. (IE ISSN 0790-2026) 4002
Irish Purchasing Journal. (IE) 1042
Irish Radio and Electrical Journal see Irish Electrical Industries Review 1375
Irish Review. (UK ISSN 0790-7850) 2869
Irish Sea Fisheries Board. Annual Report. see Bord Iascaigh Mhara. Tuarascail Agus Cuntaisi 2037
Irish Skipper. (IE) 2044, 4729
Irish Slavonic Studies. (IE ISSN 0260-2067) 2369, 2926
Irish Stamp News. (IE ISSN 0332-317X) 3753
Irish Statistical Bulletin see Ireland. Stationery Office. Statistical Bulletin 4575
Irish Statistical Survey see Ireland (Eire) Central Statistics Office. National Income and Expenditure 724
Irish Studies. (US ISSN 1043-5743) 2369, 2007
Irish Studies in Britain. (UK ISSN 0260-8154) 2369, 2007
Irish Studies in International Affairs. (IE ISSN 0332-1460) 3962, 932
Irish Studies Series. (US) 2926
Irish Sword. (IE ISSN 0021-1389) 3460, 2314
Irish Tatler Magazine see I T Magazine 2202
Irish Terrier Club of America. Newsletter. (US) 3711
Irish Theological Quarterly. (IE ISSN 0021-1400) 4183
Irish University Review. (IE ISSN 0021-1427) 2509
Irish Veterinary Journal. (IE ISSN 0368-0762) 4811
Irish Veterinary News. (IE ISSN 0332-236X) 4811
Irish Voice. (US) 2007, 3900
Irish Water Spaniel Club of America. Newsletter. (US) 3711
Irish Weekly Examiner. (IE) 2203
Irish Wolfhound Quarterly. (US ISSN 0164-8675) 3711
Irish Woman. (IE) 1298
Irodalom - Szocializmus. (HU ISSN 0075-0824) 2926, 3900
Irodalomelmelet Klasszikusai. (HU ISSN 0075-0832) 2926
Irodalomtortenet/Literary History. (HU ISSN 0021-1478) 2926
Irodalomtorteneti Fuzetek. (HU ISSN 0075-0840) 2926
Irodalomtorteneti Konyvtar. (HU ISSN 0075-0859) 2926
Irodalomtorteneti Kozlemenyek/Literary History Communications. (HU ISSN 0021-1486) 2926
Irohin Yoruba. (NR ISSN 0021-1494) 2212
Iron. (UK ISSN 0140-7597) 2926, 331
Iron Age. (US ISSN 0897-4365) 3409
Iron Age: Metal Producer see Iron Age 3409
†Iron & Manganese Ores Survey. (US ISSN 0140-8402) 5219

Iron and Steel. see Gangtie 3407
Iron and Steel. Annual Statistics for the United Kingdom see U K Iron and Steel Industry. Annual Statistics 3428
Iron and Steel Engineer. (US ISSN 0021-1559) 3409
Iron and Steel Institute of Japan. Transactions see I S I J International 3408
Iron and Steel Institute of Japan International see I S I J International 3408
Iron and Steel International see Steel Times International 3421
Iron & Steel Journal of India. (II ISSN 0021-1613) 3409
Iron & Steel Society. Ironmaking Proceedings. (US) 3409
Iron & Steel Society. Mechanical Working and Steel Processing Conference Proceedings. (US) 3409
Iron & Steel Society. Process Technology Conference Proceedings. (US) 3409
Iron & Steel Society. Transactions. (US) 3410
Iron and Steel Statistical Yearbook. (EI) 3427, 4575
Iron and Steel Trades Confederation Phoenix see I S T C Phoenix 3408
Iron and Steel Works of the World. (US ISSN 0075-0875) 3410
Iron & Steelmaker. (US) 3410, 3486
Iron Game History. (US) 4507
Iron Horse. (US) 4518
Iron Horse Yearbook. (US) 4518
Iron Metabolism. (UK ISSN 0142-8152) 478, 3272, 3607
Iron Mountain Review. (US) 2926
Iron Ore Databook. (US ISSN 0950-2548) 3410
Iron, Steel see Iron & Steel Journal of India 3409
Ironcaster see Metalcaster 1021
Ironic Blood. (US ISSN 0895-7762) 3273
Ironic Laugh. see Hoh Ineed 2868
Ironmaking and Steelmaking. (UK ISSN 0301-9233) 3410
IronMan. (US ISSN 0047-1496) 3804, 4476
†Ironwood. (US ISSN 0047-150X) 5219
Ironworker. (US ISSN 0021-163X) 2585, 3410
Iroquois Indian Museum. Museum Notes. (US) 3525
Iroquois Stalker. (US ISSN 0743-7579) 2155, 2410
▼Irrevocable Trusts. (US) 2637
Irrigating Potatoes. (US) 181
Irrigation and Drainage. see Meliorace 107
Irrigation and Drainage Abstracts. (UK ISSN 0306-7327) 139, 15, 4835
Irrigation and Drainage Systems. (NE ISSN 0168-6291) 162
Irrigation and Power. (II ISSN 0021-1664) 4826, 100, 1901
Irrigation and Power Abstracts. (II ISSN 0021-1672) 4835, 15, 139
†Irrigation Association. Management Bulletin. (US) 5219
Irrigation Association. Membership Directory and Buyers' Guide. (US) 162, 1140
Irrigation Association. Technical Conference Proceedings. (US ISSN 0160-7499) 181
Irrigation Engineering. (US) 162
Irrigation Engineering and Maintenance see Irrigation Journal (Van Nuys) 182
Irrigation Journal (Clearwater). (US) 182
Irrigation Journal (Van Nuys). (US ISSN 0047-1518) 182, 4826
Irrigation News. (US) 182, 162
Irrigation News. (UK ISSN 0265-5136) 4826, 100, 1490
†Irrigation Newsletter. (US) 5219
Irrigation Research Institute, Lahore. Report. (PK) 4826
Irrigation Science. (GW ISSN 0342-7188) 100, 4826, 5219
Irrigazione see Irrigazione e Drenaggio 4826

ISLAMIC ECONOMY 6325

Irrigazione e Drenaggio. (IT ISSN 0021-1680) 4826, 100
Irshad al-Zirai. (SY) 100
Iryo (Year). (JA ISSN 0910-6030) 3111
Is see Transient 2970
Is it in Force? (UK) 2637
Isaac Asimov's Science Fiction Magazine. (US ISSN 0162-2188) 3012
Isam see Le Nurb 1319
Ischia Mondo. (IT) 4772
Iscor News/Yskornuus. (SA ISSN 0019-0594) 3410
Iseljenicki Kalendar. (CI ISSN 0543-1077) 2205
Iselya. (US) 506
Isenkram-Goer-det-Selv - Byggemarkedet. (DK ISSN 0107-9263) 642
Isha L'isha Newsletter. (IS) 4845, 2007
Isha I'Isha - Woman to Woman see Isha L'isha Newsletter 4845
Ishikawa-ken Hakusan Shizen Hogo Senta Kenkyu Hokoku/Hakusan Nature Conservation Center, Ishikawa Prefecture. Annual Report. (JA ISSN 0286-8660) 1490
Ishmael. (US) 2926, 331
Ishraqah. (UA) 1728
Ishraqat Jeel. (TS) 4218, 4845
Isika Mianakavy. (MG) 4266
Isis. (UK) 1315
Isis. (US ISSN 0021-1753) 4316, 2314
Isis International Women's Book Series. (PH) 4859
Isis International Women's Journal see Isis International Women's Book Series 4859
†Isizwe. (SA) 5219
Iskatel. (RU ISSN 0130-6634) 1256, 2983
Iskcon Review. (US ISSN 0886-6910) 4284
Iske ha-Bituah be-Yisrael. see Israel. Central Bureau of Statistics. Insurance in Israel 2546
Iskos. (FI ISSN 0355-3108) 275
Iskra. (CN ISSN 0021-1761) 4216, 2007
Iskusstvo. (RU ISSN 0021-177X) 331
Iskusstvo Kino. (RU ISSN 0021-1788) 3512
Isla see I S L A: A Journal of Micronesian Studies 2344
Al-Islaam. (NE ISSN 0021-180X) 4218, 3639
Al-Islah/Reform. (TS) 4218
Der Islam. (GW ISSN 0021-1818) 3639, 2314, 4219
Al Islam. (RE ISSN 0151-7163) 4219
Islam. (IT) 4219
Al-Islam. (PK) 4219
Islam and the Modern Age. (II ISSN 0021-1826) 4219, 331, 2926
Islam and the Modern World. (BG ISSN 0379-4032) 4219
Islam Aujourd'hui. see Islam Today 4219
Islam Cagrisi. (IR) 4219, 2869
Islam et Societes au Sud du Sahara. (FR ISSN 0984-7685) 2333, 3900, 4219
Islam International. (NP ISSN 8755-8912) 3900, 4219
Islam Nachrichten. (GW) 4219
Islam Today/Islam Aujourd'hui. (MR ISSN 0851-1128) 4219
Islamabad Journal of Sciences. (PK ISSN 0304-5218) 4316
▼Islami Bayrlayk. (IR) 4219, 2869
Islamic Academy of Sciences. Journal. (TU ISSN 1016-3360) 4316, 3111
Islamic Art and Architecture. (US ISSN 0742-1125) 331, 301, 2430
Islamic Book Review Index. (GW ISSN 0724-2263) 4213
Islamic Culture. (II ISSN 0021-1834) 3639, 4219
Islamic Development Bank. Annual Report. (SU) 787
Islamic Economy. see Al-Iqtisad al-Islami 870

6326 ISLAMIC EDUCATION

Islamic Education. (PK ISSN 0578-8056) **1640**, 3639
Islamic Horizons. (US ISSN 8756-2367) **4219**
Islamic Philosophy, Theology and Science. (NE ISSN 0169-8729) **4219**, 3770
Islamic Quarterly. (UK ISSN 0021-1842) **3639**, 4219
Islamic Society of North America Matters *see* I S N A Matters **4218**
Islamic Standard. *see* Al-Liwa' al-Islami **4219**
Islamic Studies. (PK ISSN 0578-8072) **4219**
Islamic University of Imam Muhammad Ibn Saud. Research Center. Journal. *see* Jami'at al-Imam Muhammad Ibn Sa'ud al-Islamiyyah. Markaz al-Buhuth. Majallah **4219**
Islamiyyat. (MY ISSN 0126-5636) **3639**
Island. (US ISSN 0894-3494) **2007**, 2055
Island (Lantzville). (CN ISSN 0227-0773) **2926**, 3792
Island - Berichte der Gesellschaft der Freunde Islands Hamburg. (GW) **2198**
Island - Ear. (US) **3557**, 3512
Island Escapes. (US) **4772**
Island Grower. (CN ISSN 0827-2824) **2132**
Island Life. (US) **4773**
Island Magazine. (CN ISSN 0384-8175) **2410**
Island Magazine. (AT ISSN 0156-8124) **2926**
Island Parent Magazine. (CN ISSN 0838-5505) **1505**, 1256
Island Properties Report. (US ISSN 0882-1879) **4151**
Island Sun. (VB ISSN 0257-3563) **2239**
Islander. (US ISSN 1051-7898) **4773**
Islands. (US ISSN 0745-7847) **2254**
Islands. (NZ ISSN 0110-0858) **2926**, 331
Islands Business *see* Islands Business Pacific **672**
Islands Business Pacific. (FJ) **672**
Islands Magazine *see* Guide to Charleston's Islands Magazine **4770**
Islands' Sounder. (US) **4773**
Islandside. (CN) **2177**
Islas. (CU ISSN 0047-1542) **1315**
Isle of Man Natural History and Antiquarian Society. Proceedings. (UK) **2314**, 4316
Islensk Bokaskra/Icelandic National Bibliography. (IC ISSN 0254-1378) **2794**
Islensk Hljodritaskra/Bibliography of Icelandic Sound Recordings. (IC ISSN 0254-4067) **403**, 3557
Islenzk Sagnabloed *see* Skirnir **2960**
Hid Islenzka Fornleifafelag. Arbok. (IC ISSN 0256-8462) **2369**, 275
†Ismael Reed and Al Young's Quilt. (US ISSN 0277-593X) **5219**
▼Isokinetics and Exercise Science. (US ISSN 0959-3020) **3371**, 3308, 3804
†Isolare. (IT) **5219**
Isotech Journal of Thermometry. (UK) **3447**
Isotope and Radiation Research. (UA ISSN 0021-1907) **3359**
Isotope Geoscience *see* Chemical Geology. Isotope Geoscience Section **1557**
Isotope News. (JA ISSN 0285-5518) **478**, 1179, 3111, 3821
Isotope Technics, Diagnostics. *see* Izotoptechnika, Diagnosztika **3359**
Isotopenpraxis. (GW ISSN 0021-1915) **1179**, 3821
Isotopes in Organic Chemistry. (NE) **1218**
Isotype Titles *see* Zidis **5309**
Isozymes: Current Topics in Biological and Medical Research. (US ISSN 0160-3787) **442**
Ispat (Chittagong). (BG) **3410**
Ispat (Kushtia). (BG) **2174**
Ispat Vihangam. *see* B S P Magazine **3402**
Israel. (DK ISSN 0021-194X) **3900**
Israel. Antiquities Authority. Atiqot (English Series). (IS) **275**
Israel. Antiquities Authority. Atiqot (Hebrew Series). (IS) **275**
Israel. Atomic Energy Commission. Annual Report. (IS ISSN 0333-5771) **1806**
Israel. Atomic Energy Commission. I A - Reports. (IS ISSN 0075-0980) **1806**
Israel. Central Bureau of Statistics. Agricultural Statistics Monthly *see* Israel. Central Bureau of Statistics. Agricultural Statistics Quarterly **139**
Israel. Central Bureau of Statistics. Agricultural Statistics Quarterly. (IS ISSN 0334-2573) **139**, 4575
Israel. Central Bureau of Statistics. Annual Foreign Trade Statistics. (IS) **724**
Israel. Central Bureau of Statistics. Causes of Death. (IS ISSN 0075-0999) **3992**, 4575
Israel. Central Bureau of Statistics. Construction in Israel/Ha-Binui Be-Yisrael. (IS ISSN 0069-9195) **621**
Israel. Central Bureau of Statistics. Criminal Statistics. (IS ISSN 0075-1006) **1525**
Israel. Central Bureau of Statistics. Diagnostic Statistics of Hospitalized Patients. (IS ISSN 0075-1014) **4409**, 2466
Israel. Central Bureau of Statistics. Foreign Trade Statistics Quarterly *see* Israel. Central Bureau of Statistics. Annual Foreign Trade Statistics **724**
Israel. Central Bureau of Statistics. Immigration to Israel. (IS ISSN 0302-816X) **3992**
Israel. Central Bureau of Statistics. Industry and Crafts Survey. (IS ISSN 0578-8420) **724**, 1115
Israel. Central Bureau of Statistics. Inputs in Research and Development in Academic Institutions. (IS) **1677**
Israel. Central Bureau of Statistics. Insurance in Israel/Iske ha-Bituah be-Yisrael. (IS ISSN 0074-0705) **2546**
Israel. Central Bureau of Statistics. Israel's Foreign Trade/Sehar Huts Shel Yisrael. (IS ISSN 0075-1421) **724**
Israel. Central Bureau of Statistics. Judicial Statistics. (IS ISSN 0075-1030) **2699**
Israel. Central Bureau of Statistics. Labour Force Surveys. (IS ISSN 0075-1049) **724**
Israel. Central Bureau of Statistics. Monthly Bulletin of Statistics. (IS ISSN 0021-1982) **4575**
Israel. Central Bureau of Statistics. Monthly Price Statistics. (IS ISSN 0021-2008) **724**
Israel. Central Bureau of Statistics. Motor Vehicles. (IS ISSN 0075-1057) **4664**
Israel. Central Bureau of Statistics. New Statistical Projects and Publications in Israel. (IS ISSN 0334-3278) **4575**, 403
Israel. Central Bureau of Statistics. Projections of Population in Judea, Samaria and Gaza Area up to 2002.(IS ISSN 0334-9721) **3992**
Israel. Central Bureau of Statistics. Quarterly Statistics of the Administered Territories. (IS) **4575**
Israel. Central Bureau of Statistics. Road Accidents with Casualties. (IS) **4665**
Israel. Central Bureau of Statistics. Schools and Kindergartens. (IS ISSN 0075-1065) **1677**
Israel. Central Bureau of Statistics. Staff in Universities. (IS ISSN 0333-600X) **1677**, 4575
Israel. Central Bureau of Statistics. Statistical Abstract of Israel/Shenaton Statisti le-Yisrael. (IS ISSN 0081-4679) **4575**
Israel. Central Bureau of Statistics. Students in Academic Institutions *see* Israel. Central Bureau of Statistics. Students in Universities **1677**
Israel. Central Bureau of Statistics. Students in Universities. (IS) **1677**
Israel. Central Bureau of Statistics. Suicides and Attempted Suicides. (IS) **3992**, 4575
Israel. Central Bureau of Statistics. Survey of Housing Conditions. (IS ISSN 0075-109X) **2489**
Israel. Central Bureau of Statistics. Survey on Research and Development in Industry. (IS ISSN 0333-9793) **724**
Israel. Central Bureau of Statistics. Tourist Hotels. (IS ISSN 0333-7715) **2482**
Israel. Central Bureau of Statistics. Vital Statistics. (IS ISSN 0075-1111) **3992**, 4575
Israel. Commissioner for Complaints from the Public (Ombudsman). Annual Report. (IS) **4064**
Israel. Department of Antiquities and Museums. Archaeological Newsletter - Hadashot Arkheologiyot *see* Hadashot Arkheologiyot **273**
Israel. Department of Customs and Excise. Yalkut *see* Israel. Department of Customs and V A T. Yalkut **1099**
Israel. Department of Customs and V A T. Yalkut. (IS) **1099**
Israel. Department of Surveys. Cartographic Papers *see* Survey of Israel. Cartographic Papers **2263**
Israel. Department of Surveys. Geodetic Papers. (IS ISSN 0075-1138) **2254**
Israel. Department of Surveys. Photogrammetric Papers *see* Survey of Israel. Photogrammetric Papers **2263**
Israel. Environmental Protection Service. Ekhut ha-Svivah be-Yisrael. Luakh Shnati *see* Israel. Ministry of the Environment. Misrad Le-Ichut ha-Svivah. Doch Shnati **1959**
Israel. Geological Survey. Bibliography Series. (IS) **1551**, 15
Israel. Geological Survey. Bulletin. (IS ISSN 0075-1200) **1569**
Israel. Geological Survey. Current Bibliography of Middle East Geology. (IS ISSN 0334-3510) **1569**
Israel. Geological Survey. Current Research. (IS ISSN 0333-6425) **1569**
Israel. Government Press Office. Daily News and Editorial Survey. (IS) **2203**
†Israel. Government Press Office. Newspapers and Periodicals Appearing in Israel. (IS ISSN 0078-0448) **5219**
Israel. Government Press Office. Weekly News Bulletin *see* Israel. Government Press Office. Daily News and Editorial Survey **2203**
Israel. Knesset. Divrei ha-Knesset. (IS ISSN 0012-4249) **3900**
Israel. Knesset. Finance Committee. Data on Activities. *see* Israel. Knesset. Va'adat ha-Kesafim Misparim al Va'adat ha-Kesafim **1099**
Israel. Knesset. ha-Va'ada le-Inyanei Bikoret ha-Medina. Sikumeha ve-Hatsa'oteha shel ha-Va'ada le-Inyanei Bikoret ha-Medina le-Din ve-Kheshbon shel Mevaker ha-Medina. (IS) **4089**
Israel. Knesset. Va'adat ha-Kesafim Misparim al Va'adat ha-Kesafim/ Israel. Knesset. Finance Committee. Data on Activities. (IS) **1099**
Israel. Meteorological Service. Monthly Agroclimatological Bulletin *see* Israel. Meteorological Service. Monthly Agroclimatological Report **3437**
Israel. Meteorological Service. Monthly Agroclimatological Report. (IS ISSN 0333-7936) **3437**, 100
Israel. Meteorological Service. Rainfall Season. (IS) **3437**, 4826
Israel. Meteorological Service. Series B: Observational Data. Annual Rainfall Summary. (IS ISSN 0075-126X) **3437**
Israel. Meteorological Service. Series B: Observational Data. Annual Weather Report. (IS ISSN 0075-1286) **3437**
Israel. Meteorological Service. Series B: Observational Data. Monthly Weather Report. (IS ISSN 0021-2261) **3437**
Israel. Meteorological Society. Meteorologia Be-Israel. (IS) **3437**
Israel. Ministry of Agriculture. Department of Fisheries. Bamidgeh *see* Israeli Journal of Aquaculture - Bamidgeh **2044**
Israel. Ministry of Agriculture. Department of Fisheries. Dayig u-Midgeh be-Yisrael - Fisheries and Fishbreeding in Israel. (IS ISSN 0011-7110) **2044**
Israel. Ministry of Communications. Statistics/Israel. Misrad ha-Tikshoret. Statistikah. (IS ISSN 0075-1308) **1353**
Israel. Ministry of Education and Culture. Department of Antiquities and Museums. Atiqot (English Series) *see* Israel. Antiquities Authority. Atiqot (English Series) **275**
Israel. Ministry of Education and Culture. Department of Antiquities and Museums. Atiqot (Hebrew Series) *see* Israel. Antiquities Authority. Atiqot (Hebrew Series) **275**
Israel. Ministry of Health. Division of Epidemiology. Infectious Diseases Surveillance. (IS) **4105**
Israel. Ministry of Health. Division of Epidemiology. Weekly Epidemiological Record. (IS) **4105**
Israel. Ministry of Justice. Patent Office. Patents and Designs Journal. (IS ISSN 0021-2326) **3676**
Israel. Ministry of Labour and Social Affairs. Department of International Relations. The Press on Welfare. (IS) **4410**
Israel. Ministry of Labour. Registrar of Cooperative Societies. Report on the Cooperative Movement in Israel. (IS ISSN 0080-1313) **831**
Israel. Ministry of Social Welfare. Department of International Relations. The Press on Welfare *see* Israel. Ministry of Labour and Social Affairs. Department of International Relations. The Press on Welfare **4410**
Israel. Ministry of the Environment. Misrad Le-Ichut ha-Svivah. Doch Shnati. (IS) **1959**
Israel. Ministry of the Interior. City and Region - Ir ve Ezor. (IS ISSN 0302-8267) **2489**, 1959
Israel. Misrad ha-Tikshoret. Statistikah. *see* Israel. Ministry of Communications. Statistics **1353**
Israel. Rural Planning and Development Authority. Agricultural and Rural Development Report *see* Israel. Rural Planning and Development Authority. Agricultural and Rural Economic Report **100**
Israel. Rural Planning and Development Authority. Agricultural and Rural Economic Report. (IS) **100**
Israel. Tourism News. Information Letter *see* Israel Information Letter **4773**
Israel Academy of Sciences and Humanities. Section of Humanities. Proceedings. (IS ISSN 0578-9230) **2509**, 4601
Israel Academy of Sciences and Humanities. Section of Sciences. Proceedings. (IS ISSN 0333-6190) **4316**
Israel Advertising. (IS) **33**
Israel Air Force Magazine. *see* Bitaon Heyl ha-Avir **49**
Israel Annual Conference on Aviation and Astronautics. Proceedings. (IS ISSN 0075-0972) **56**
Israel au Travail *see* Labour in Israel **2586**
Israel Aussenhandel. (IS) **914**
Israel Bibliophiles Newsletter. (IS) **4002**
Israel Book News. (IS ISSN 0333-953X) **4130**, 2007, 4223
Israel Book Trade Directory. (IS ISSN 0333-6018) **4130**, 4002

Title

Israel Book Trades Directory: A Select List see Israel Book Trade Directory **4130**
Israel Book World see Israel Book News **4130**
†Israel Business. (IS ISSN 0334-3898) **5219**
Israel Business and Investors' Report see Israel Business **5219**
Israel Business Directory see Israel Advertising **33**
Israel C P A. (IS) **752**
Israel Chemist. (IS ISSN 0792-4275) **1179**
Israel Commercial Economic Newsletter see I C E N **836**
Israel Customs Import Duty Tariff Rates and Purchase Tax. English Translation and Amendments. (IS) **870**
Israel Dance see Israel Dance Quarterly **1531**
Israel Dance Quarterly. (IS) **1531**
Israel Defense Forces Journal see I D F Journal **5209**
Israel Diamonds. (IS ISSN 0021-2016) **2564**
Israel Economist. (IS ISSN 0021-2040) **672**
Israel Environment Bulletin. (IS ISSN 0334-3804) **1959**
Israel Exploration Journal. (IS ISSN 0021-2059) **275**, 3639
Israel Exploration Society. Bulletin see Kadmoniot **276**
Israel Export and Trade Journal see Israel Aussenhandel **914**
Israel Export Directory. (IS ISSN 0075-1154) **914**
Israel Export Journal. (IS) **914**
Israel Film Centre. Information Bulletin. (IS) **3512**
Israel Film Industry Directory. (IS) **3512**
Israel Gerontological Society. Information Bulletin/Ha-Agudah ha-Israelit le-Gerontologyah. Yedion. (IS ISSN 0047-1577) **2274**
Israel Government Year Book. (IS) **4064**
Israel Horizons. (US ISSN 0021-2083) **3900**, 3962
Israel Information Letter. (IS) **4773**
Israel Institute for Biological Research. Scientific Activities. (IS) **442**
Israel Institute of Animal Science. Scientific Activities. (IS) **3260**, 4811
Israel Institute of Horticulture. Scientific Activities. (IS) **2132**
Israel Institute of Packaging. Packaging Directory. (IS) **1140**, 3649
Israel Investor see Israel Advertising **33**
Israel Journal of Botany. (IS ISSN 0021-213X) **506**
Israel Journal of Chemistry. (IS ISSN 0021-2148) **1179**
Israel Journal of Earth Sciences. (IS ISSN 0021-2164) **1546**, 1569
Israel Journal of Entomology. (IS ISSN 0075-1243) **534**
Israel Journal of Mathematics. (IS ISSN 0021-2172) **3039**
Israel Journal of Medical Sciences. (IS ISSN 0021-2180) **3112**
▼Israel Journal of Obstetrics & Gynecology. (IS ISSN 0792-4569) **3293**
Israel Journal of Physiotherapy. (IS ISSN 0021-2199) **3112**
Israel Journal of Psychiatry and Related Sciences. (IS ISSN 0333-7308) **3340**
Israel Journal of Technology. (IS ISSN 0021-2202) **4601**
Israel Journal of Veterinary Medicine. (IS ISSN 0334-9152) **4811**
Israel Journal of Zoology. (IS ISSN 0021-2210) **585**
Israel - Land and Nature see Eretz **2203**
Israel Law Review. (IS ISSN 0021-2237) **2637**
Israel Medical Association. Quarterly Medical Review. (IS) **3112**
Israel Medical Association. Quarterly Review. see Israel Medical Association. Quarterly Medical Review **3112**

Israel Money see Israel Advertising **33**
Israel Museum Journal. (IS ISSN 0333-7499) **3525**
Israel Museum News see Israel Museum Journal **3525**
Israel News Bulletin. (IS) **2203**
Israel Numismatic Journal. (IS ISSN 0021-2288) **3599**
Israel Oceanographic and Limnological Research. Biennial Report. (IS ISSN 0304-7423) **1606**
Israel Oceanographic and Limnological Research. Triennial Report see Israel Oceanographic and Limnological Research. Biennial Report **1606**
Israel Oceanographic and Limnological Research Ltd. Collected Reports see I O L R Collected Reports **4825**
Israel Oriental Studies. (NE ISSN 0334-4401) **3639**
Israel - People and Land. see Yisrael-Am ve-Eretz **5308**
Israel Pharmaceutical Journal/Ha-Rokeach ha-Ivri/Association Pharmaceutique d'Israel. Journal. (IS ISSN 0017-7865) **3730**
Israel Philatelist. (US) **3753**
Israel Physical Society. Annals. (IS ISSN 0309-8710) **3821**
†Israel Ports Authority. Annual Report. (IS) **5219**
Israel Quarterly of Psychology. (IS ISSN 0334-6080) **4026**
Israel Scene. (IS ISSN 0199-7424) **2203**
†Israel Securities Review. (US ISSN 0147-4316) **5219**
Israel Shipping and Aviation Research Institute. Yidion see Hadashot Sapanut Veteufah - Yidion **4728**
Israel Shipping Research Institute. Journal see Sapanut **4737**
Israel Social Science Research. (IS ISSN 0334-133X) **4376**
Israel Society for Rehabilitation of the Disabled. Annual. (IS ISSN 0075-1383) **1737**, 2284
Israel Society of Special Libraries and Information Centers Bulletin see I S L I C Bulletin **2761**
Israel Studies. (IS) **4376**, 3900
Israel Studies in Musicology. (IS ISSN 0334-2026) **3557**
†Israel Tax Law Letter. (IS) **5219**
Israel Today see National Jewish News **2015**
Israel Tourist Statistics/Tayarut be-Yisrael. (IS ISSN 0075-1405) **4799**
Israel Travel News. (IS) **4773**
Israel und Palaestina. (GW ISSN 0175-7024) **3900**, 3962
Israel Women's Network. Newsletter. (IS) **4845**
Israel Women's Network. Yidion. (IS) **4845**
Israel Yearbook see Israel Yearbook and Almanac (Year) **2203**
Israel Yearbook and Almanac (Year). (IS) **2203**
Israel Yearbook on Human Rights. (IS ISSN 0333-5925) **3944**, 2637
†Israeli Democracy (English Edition). (IS) **5219**
Israeli Democracy (Hebrew Edition). (IS) **3900**
Israeli Family Planning Association. Bulletin. (IS) **597**
Israeli Folk Dance Clearinghouse Calendar. (US) **2007**
Israeli Journal of Aquaculture - Bamidgeh. (IS ISSN 0792-156X) **2044**
Israeli Map Collectors Society. Journal. (IS ISSN 0792-318X) **2437**
Israeli Tax Review. see Rivaon ha-Yisraeli l'Misim **1105**
Israelitische Kultusgemeinde Fuerth see Nachrichten fuer den Juedischen Buerger Fuerths **2015**
Israelitisches Wochenblatt fuer die Schweiz/Revue Juive. (SZ ISSN 0021-2342) **2007**
Israels Aussenhandel. (IS ISSN 0578-9427) **817**, 932
Israel's Banking System. (IS ISSN 0334-2093) **787**
Israelske Ambassade. Information. (DK ISSN 0108-3783) **3962**

Issledovania po Teorii Algorifmov i Matematicheskoi Logike. (RU ISSN 0302-9085) **3770**, 3039
Issledovanie, Konstruirovanie i Raschet Rezbovykh Soedinenii. (RU) **1827**
Issledovaniya v Oblasti Khimii Redkozemel'nykh Elementov. (RU) **1546**, 1214
Issue. (US ISSN 0047-1607) **2869**
The Issue (St. Laurent). (CN) **1315**
†Issue (Toronto). (CN) **5219**
Issue Brief. (US) **2489**
Issue One. (UK ISSN 0266-111X) **2995**, 2926
Issues. (AT ISSN 0814-303X) **2764**
Issues and Concepts in the Postmodern Theory of Education. (US ISSN 1058-1634) **1640**
Issues and Innovations see Banking Issues and Innovations in Products, Marketing and Technology **766**
Issues & Observations. (US) **1684**, 1015
Issues & Studies. (CH ISSN 1013-2511) **3962**, 3639
†Issues for Bank Counsel. (US) **5219**
†Issues in Accountability. (UK) **5219**
Issues in Accounting Education. (US ISSN 0739-3172) **752**, 1640
Issues in Bank Regulation. (US ISSN 0164-7725) **787**
Issues in Biblical Archaeology. (US) **275**, 4183
Issues in Biomedicine. (SZ ISSN 1010-8408) **442**, 3112
†Issues in Canadian Social Policy/ Politique Sociale au Canada. (CN) **5219**
Issues in Comprehensive Pediatric Nursing. (US ISSN 0146-0862) **3279**, 3321
Issues in Cooperation and Power see New Studies on the Left **2876**
Issues in Ego Psychology. (US ISSN 0097-6555) **4026**, 3340
Issues in Higher Education. (US) **1709**
Issues in Integrative Studies. (US) **1640**
Issues in International Business. (US) **914**
Issues in Language Education. (US) **2819**, 1641
Issues in Law and Medicine. (US ISSN 8756-8160) **2637**, 3112
Issues in Mental Health Nursing. (US ISSN 0161-2840) **3279**, 3340, 4026
Issues in Race and Education. (UK ISSN 0308-3233) **1641**, 2007
Issues in Radical Therapy see New Studies on the Left **2876**
Issues in Reproductive and Genetic Engineering. (US ISSN 0958-6415) **544**, 4845
Issues in Science and Technology. (US ISSN 0748-5492) **4316**, 4601
Issues in Southeast Asian Security. (SI) **3962**
Issues in the Islamic Movement. (CN ISSN 0266-6421) **4219**, 4213
Issues in Writing. (US ISSN 0897-0696) **2571**, 1709
Issues Management Letter see Executive Trend Watch **5189**
Issues of the American Council for Judaism see American Council for Judaism. Issues **4221**
Istanbul Chamber of Commerce see I C O C **817**
Istanbul Chamber of Commerce. Economic Report. (TU) **817**
Istanbul Chamber of Commerce. Magazine. (TU) **818**
Istanbul: Handbook for Tourists see Istanbul Key **4773**
Istanbul Key. (TU) **4773**
Istanbul Medical Faculty. Medical Bulletin/Istanbul Tip Fakultesi. Mecmuasi. (TU ISSN 0374-1656) **3112**
Istanbul Ticaret. (TU) **818**
Istanbul Ticaret Odasi Mecumusai - Istanbul Chamber of Commerce. Journal see I C O C **817**
Istanbul Tip Fakultesi. Mecmuasi. see Istanbul Medical Faculty. Medical Bulletin **3112**

ISTITUTO ITALIANO 6327

Istanbul Universitesi. Istanbul Tip Fakultesi. Mecmuasi see Istanbul Medical Faculty. Medical Bulletin **3112**
Istanbul Universitesi. Orman Fakultesi. Dergisi/University of Istanbul. Faculty of Forestry. Review/Universitat Istanbul. Forstlichen Fakultaet. Zeitschrift/Universite d'Istanbul. Faculte Forestiere. Revue. (TU) **2103**
Istanbuler Mitteilungen. (GW ISSN 0341-9142) **275**, 3639
Istanbuler Mitteilungen. Beihefte. (GW ISSN 0418-9701) **2430**, 275
Istarski Mozaik. (CI ISSN 0021-2415) **2869**
Istina. (FR ISSN 0021-2423) **4183**
Istituto Centrale per la Patologia del Libro. Bollettino. (IT ISSN 0391-5972) **404**
Istituto Comeliana di Lugano. Collectio Monographica Minor. (IT) **4316**
Istituto di Architettura e Urbanistica. Rassegna. (IT ISSN 0021-2458) **301**, 2489
Istituto di Diritto Romano. Bollettino. (IT) **2637**
Istituto di Filologia Greca. Bollettino. (IT) **2819**
Istituto di Filologia Greca. Bollettino. Supplementi. (IT) **2819**
Istituto di Fisica dell'Atmosfera, Rome. Bibliografia Generale. (IT ISSN 0075-1901) **3444**
Istituto di Fisica dell'Atmosfera, Rome. Contributi Scientifici: Pubblicazioni di Fisica dell'Atmosfera e di Meteorologia. (IT ISSN 0075-191X) **3437**
Istituto di Fisica dell'Atmosfera, Rome. Pubblicazioni Didattiche. (IT ISSN 0075-1928) **3437**
Istituto di Fisica dell'Atmosfera, Rome. Pubblicazioni Scientifiche. (IT ISSN 0075-1936) **3437**
Istituto di Fisica dell'Atmosfera, Rome. Pubblicazioni Varie. (IT ISSN 0075-1944) **3437**
Istituto di Fisica dell'Atmosfera, Rome. Rapporti Interni Provvisori Adiffusione Limitata. (IT ISSN 0075-1952) **3437**
Istituto di Fisica dell'Atmosfera, Rome. Rapporti Scientifici. (IT ISSN 0075-1960) **3437**
Istituto di Fisica dell'Atmosfera, Rome. Rapporti Tecnici. (IT ISSN 0075-1979) **3437**
Istituto di Musica "Vincenzo Amato". Quaderni. (IT) **3557**
Istituto di Patologia del Libro "Alfonso Gallo." Bollettino see Istituto Centrale per la Patologia del Libro. Bollettino **404**
Istituto di Scienze Religiose in Trento. Pubblicazioni. (IT) **4266**
Istituto di Storia dell'Architettura. Quaderni. (IT) **301**
Istituto di Studi e Documentazioni sull'Est Europeo. Serie Giuridica. (IT) **672**
Istituto di Studi Romani. Rassegna d'Informazioni see Istituto Nazionale di Studi Romani. Rassegna d'Informazioni **2509**
Istituto e Museo di Storia della Scienza. Biblioteca. (IT ISSN 0075-1499) **4316**
Istituto Elettrotecnico Nazionale Galileo Ferraris Pubblicazioni see I E N Pubblicazioni **1773**
Istituto Ellenico di Studi Bizantini e Postbizantini, Venice. Biblioteca. (IT ISSN 0075-1502) **2369**, 2430
Istituto Giapponese di Cultura, Rome. Annuario. (IT ISSN 0080-391X) **2369**, 2509, 4376
Istituto Giapponese di Cultura, Rome. Notiziario. (IT ISSN 0080-3928) **2339**
Istituto Gramsci Piemontese. Materiali. (IT) **3900**
Istituto Internazionale di Studi Liguri. Collezione di Monografie Preistoriche e Archeologiche. (IT ISSN 0530-9867) **275**
Istituto Italiano degli Attuari. Giornale. (IT ISSN 0021-2482) **2535**

6328 ISTITUTO ITALIANO

†Istituto Italiano di Cultura. Bulletin. (US ISSN 0020-4064) **5219**
Istituto Italiano di Idrobiologia. Memorie.(IT ISSN 0374-9118) **442**
Istituto Italiano di Navigazione. Atti. (IT) **56**, 4651
Istituto Italiano di Numismatica. Annali. (IT ISSN 0578-9923) **3600**
Istituto Italiano per gli Studi Storici. Annali. (IT ISSN 0578-9931) **2314**
Istituto Lombardo Accademia di Scienze e Lettere. Rendiconti. A. (IT ISSN 0021-2504) **4316**
Istituto Mobiliare Italiano. Annual Report. (IT ISSN 0075-1529) **672**
Istituto Nazionale della Previdenza Sociale. Atti Ufficiali. (IT ISSN 0021-2520) **2535**
Istituto Nazionale di Archeologia e Storia dell'Arte. Rivista. (IT) **275**, 331
Istituto Nazionale di Studi Romani. Rassegna d'Informazioni. (IT) **2509**
Istituto Nazionale di Studi sul Rinascimento. Atti di Convegni. (IT) **2369**
Istituto Nazionale di Studi sul Rinascimento. Studi e Testi. (IT) **2369**
Istituto Nazionale per l'Assicurazione Contro gli Infortuni sul Lavoro Notiziario Statistico see I N A I L Notiziario Statistico **2546**
Istituto Nazionale per la Storia del Movimento di Liberazione in Italia. Notizie e Documenti. (IT) **2369**
Istituto Nazionale per lo Studio della Congiuntura. Rapporto Semestrale. (IT) **870**
Istituto Orientale di Napoli. Annali see Istituto Universitario Orientale di Napoli. Annali **3639**
Istituto per la Documentazione Giuridica. Bibliografia. Diritto Civile. (IT ISSN 0392-7571) **2699**
Istituto per la Documentazione Giuridica. Bibliografia. Diritto Internazionale. (IT) **2699**
Istituto Ricerche Pesca Marittima. Quaderni. (IT ISSN 0393-3571) **2044**, 1606
Istituto Siciliano di Studi Bizantini e Neoellenici. Monumenti. (IT) **331**, 2369
Istituto Siciliano di Studi Bizantini e Neoellenici. Quaderni. (IT ISSN 0075-1545) **2369**
Istituto Siciliano di Studi Bizantini e Neoellenici. Testi e Monumenti. Testi.(IT ISSN 0075-1553) **2369**
Istituto Sieroterapico Milanese. Bollettino. (IT ISSN 0021-2547) **3187**, 553
Istituto Sperimentale per il Tabacco. Annali. (IT) **4643**
Istituto Sperimentale per l'Enologia Asti. Annali. (IT ISSN 0374-5791) **382**
Istituto Sperimentale per la Cerealicoltura. Annali. (IT ISSN 0374-535X) **207**
Istituto Sperimentale per la Floricoltura. Annali. (IT ISSN 0304-0550) **182**
Istituto Sperimentale per la Selvicoltura. Annali. (IT ISSN 0390-0010) **2103**
Istituto Sperimentale Talassografico di Trieste. Pubblicazione. (IT ISSN 0082-6456) **1606**
Istituto Storico Artistico Orvietano. Bollettino. (IT ISSN 0391-8211) **2369**
Istituto Storico e di Cultura dell'Arma del Genio. Bollettino. (IT ISSN 0021-2555) **3460**, 1827
Istituto Storico Italo-Germanico in Trento. Annali/Italienisch-Deutschen Historischen Instituts in Trento. Jahrbuch. (IT ISSN 0392-0011) **2369**
Istituto Superiore di Sanita. Annali. (IT ISSN 0021-2571) **4105**, 3112, 4811
Istituto Superiore di Sanita. Rendiconti see Istituto Superiore di Sanita. Annali **4105**
Istituto Tecnico. (IT ISSN 0021-258X) **1641**

Istituto Universitario Navale. Facolta di Scienze Nautiche. Naples. Annali. (IT) **4729**, 1546
Istituto Universitario Orientale. Annali. (IT) **2007**, 2819
Istituto Universitario Orientale. Dipartimento di Filosofia e Politica. Quaderni. (IT) **3770**
Istituto Universitario Orientale. Dipartimento di Scienze Sociali. Quaderni. (IT) **4376**
Istituto Universitario Orientale di Napoli. Annali. (IT) **3639**
†Istituto Universitario Orientale di Napoli. Annali. Sezione Germanica. (IT ISSN 0077-2763) **5219**
Istituto Universitario Orientale di Napoli. Annali. Sezione Romanza. (IT) **2926**, 2819
Istituto Universitario Orientale di Napoli. Dipartimento di Studi Letterari e Linguistici dell' Occidente. Annali: Filiogia Germanica. (IT) **2819**, 2926
Istituto Universitario Orientale di Napoli. Dipartimento di Studi Letterari e Linguistici dell' Occidente. Annuali: Studi di Anglistica. (IT) **2926**, 2819
Istituto Universitario Orientale di Napoli. Dipartimento di Studi Letterari e Linguistici dell' Occidente. Annuali: Studi Tedeschi. (IT) **2926**, 2819
Istituto Universitario Orientale di Napoli. Seminario di Studi del Mondo Classico. Annali. Sezione Linguistica. (IT) **1277**, 3639
Istituzioni Culturali Piemontesi. Pubblicazioni. (IT) **4634**
Istmo. (MX ISSN 0021-261X) **2210**
†Isto Cito Patologia. (IT ISSN 0391-7452) **5219**
Istochnikovedenie Otechestvennoi Istorii.(RU) **2369**
Istoricheski Pregled. (BU ISSN 0323-9748) **2315**
Istoricheskie Zapiski. (RU) **2315**
Istorie si Civilizatie. (RM ISSN 0075-1626) **2315**
Istorija. (XN) **2369**
Istorija. (LI ISSN 0202-3261) **2369**
Istorijski Glasnik. (YU ISSN 0021-2644) **2315**
Istorijski Zapisi. (YU ISSN 0021-2652) **2315**
Istoriko-Matematicheskie Issledovaniya. (RU) **3039**
Istoriya i Istoriki. (RU) **2369**
Istoriya i Obshtestvoznanie. (BU ISSN 0204-9260) **2369**, 3900
Istoriya i Osnovi na Komunizma see Istoriya i Obshtestvoznanie **2369**
Istoriya Narodnogo Gospodarstva ta Ekonomichnoi Dumki Ukrainskoi R.S.R. (RU ISSN 0320-4421) **895**
Istoriya S.S.S.R. (RU ISSN 0021-2660) **2369**
Istorychni Doslidzhennya. Istoriya Zarubizhnykh Krayin. (KR ISSN 0135-2202) **2315**
Istorychni Doslidzhennya. Vitchyznyana Istoriya. (KR ISSN 0135-2210) **2315**
Istra. (CI) **2926**, 331
Istruzione Tecnica see Istruzione Tecnica e Professionale **1641**
Istruzione Tecnica e Professionale. (IT ISSN 0535-899X) **1641**
It. (AT) **4549**
It Goes on the Shelf. (US) **3012**, 2926
It Starts in the Classroom. (US ISSN 0021-2717) **1641**, 33
It-Torca. (MM ISSN 0021-2725) **2585**
Italcommerce. (CN) **818**
Italdoc. (IT ISSN 0021-2733) **2205**
Italia. (IS) **2007**
Italia. (IT) **3792**
Italia Africa Medio Oriente. (IT) **3962**, 914, 932
Italia Agricola. (IT ISSN 0021-275X) **100**
Italia Contemporanea. (IT ISSN 0392-3568) **2369**, 3900
Italia Cooperativa. (IT ISSN 0021-) **831**, 4439
†L'Italia del Legno. (IT) **5219**
Italia del Popolo. (IT) **3900**

L'Italia Dialettale. (IT ISSN 0085-2295) **2819**
Italia e l'Europa. (IT) **2726**
Italia Forestale e Montana. (IT ISSN 0021-2776) **2103**
Italia Francescana. (IT) **3770**
L'Italia Grafica. (IT) **4002**
Italia Missionaria. (IT ISSN 0021-2806) **1256**, 4266
Italia Nostra. (IT ISSN 0021-2822) **3525**, 301, 1490
Italia Nostra. Sezione di Trento. Bollettino. (IT) **1959**, 1273, 3984
L'Italia Scacchistica. (IT ISSN 0021-2849) **4476**
Italia sul Mare. (IT ISSN 0021-2857) **4525**
Italia Turistica. (IT) **4773**
Italia Viaggia. (IT) **4773**
Italia Viva. (IT) **3900**, 2205
Italian Administrative Directory. see Annuario Amministrativo Italiano **4053**
Italian American Business. (IT ISSN 0021-2873) **818**
Italian American Chamber of Commerce of Chicago. Bulletin. (US ISSN 0021-2903) **818**
Italian-American Digest. (US) **2007**
Italian Americana. (US ISSN 0096-8846) **2007**
Italian-Australian Bulletin of Commerce. (AT ISSN 0047-1658) **818**, 914
Italian Books and Periodicals see Libri e Riviste d'Italia **4131**
Italian Books in Print. see Catalogo dei Libri in Commercio **397**
Italian Building and Construction. (IT ISSN 0393-8069) **621**
Italian Cars - Classic & Sport. (US) **4693**
Italian Chamber of Commerce for Great Britain. Information Bulletin. (UK) **818**
Italian Communists. (IT) **3900**
Italian Design Fashion. (IT ISSN 1120-6268) **1292**
Italian Echo see The Echo **2000**
†Italian Economic Survey. (IT ISSN 0021-2911) **5219**
Italian Fashion Report. (IT) **1292**
Italian General Review of Dermatology. (IT ISSN 0021-292X) **3248**
Italian Goldsmith in the World. see Orafo Italiano nel Mondo **2565**
Italian Journal. (US ISSN 0894-1793) **2369**
Italian Journal of Biochemistry. (IT ISSN 0021-2938) **478**
Italian Journal of Food Science. (IT ISSN 1120-1770) **2074**
Italian Journal of Gastroenterology. (IT ISSN 0392-0623) **3269**
Italian Journal of Neurological Sciences. (IT) **3340**
Italian Journal of Orthopaedics and Traumatology. (IT ISSN 0390-5489) **3308**
Italian Journal of Psychiatry and Behavioural Sciences. (IT) **3340**
Italian Journal of Psychology. see Giornale Italiano di Psicologia **4022**
Italian Journal of Sports Traumatology see Journal of Sports Traumatology and Related Research **3372**
†Italian Journal of Surgical Sciences. (IT ISSN 0392-3525) **5219**
Italian Journal of Zoology. Monographs. see Monitore Zoologico Italiano. Monografie **5239**
Italian Medieval and Renaissance Studies. (IT) **2369**
Italian Politics. (UK ISSN 0952-3243) **672**, 2369, 3900
Italian Private English Language Schools & Italian Language Schools for Overseas & Italy. (UK) **1695**, 2819
Italian Quarterly (New Brunswick). (US) **2926**, 2007
Italian Sanitary Directory. see Annuario Sanitario Italiano **4097**
Italian Studies. (UK ISSN 0075-1634) **2926**
Italian Technology. (IT) **4601**
Italian Toys. (IT) **2281**
Italian Trade-Marks. see Siglario Italiano **3678**
†Italian Trade Topics. (US ISSN 0021-2997) **5219**

Italian Tribune News. (US) **2007**
Italian Voice/Voce Italiana. (CN) **2007**, 33
Italian Voice/Voce Italiana. (US) **2007**
Italian Wines & Spirits (U K Edition). (IT) **382**
Italian Wines & Spirits (U S and Canada Edition). (IT) **382**
Italian Yearbook of International Law. (IT) **2726**
Italianist. (UK ISSN 0261-4340) **2370**, 2926
Italianistica. (IT) **2926**
Italic Handwriting Newsletter. (US) **1752**, 355
Italica (Madison). (US ISSN 0021-3020) **2926**, 1641, 2819
Italics see Decorating Products Trends Advisory **2550**
Italienisch. (GW ISSN 0171-4996) **2819**
Italienisch-Deutschen Historischen Instituts in Trento. Jahrbuch. see Istituto Storico Italo-Germanico in Trento. Annali **2369**
Italienische Studien. (AU) **2926**, 2370, 2819
Italiken Emborikon Epimelitirion. Journal. (GR) **818**
L'Italo Americano Newspaper. (US) **2007**
Italy. (IT) **33**
Italy. Azienda Autonoma delle Ferrovie dello Stato. Informazioni Doc. (IT ISSN 0021-3128) **4710**
Italy. Centro per la Statistica Aziendale. Index. (IT ISSN 0021-3101) **724**, 4575
Italy. Direzione Generale delle Fonti di Energia e delle Industrie di Base. Bilanci Energetici. (IT ISSN 0075-1650) **1792**
Italy. Istituto Centrale di Statistica. Annuario delle Statistiche Culturali see Italy. Istituto Centrale di Statistica. Statistiche Culturali **4141**
Italy. Istituto Centrale di Statistica. Annuario di Statistica Agraria see Italy. Istituto Centrale di Statistica. Statistiche dell'Agricoltura, Zootecnia e Mezzi di Produzione. Annuario **100**
Italy. Istituto Centrale di Statistica. Annuario di Statistica Forestale see Italy. Istituto Centrale di Statistica. Statistiche Forestali **2112**
Italy. Istituto Centrale di Statistica. Annuario di Statistiche del Lavoro see Italy. Istituto Centrale di Statistica. Statistiche del Lavoro **3992**
Italy. Istituto Centrale di Statistica. Annuario di Statistiche Demografiche see Italy. Istituto Centrale di Statistica. Statistiche Demografiche **3992**
Italy. Istituto Centrale di Statistica. Annuario di Statistiche Industriali see Italy. Istituto Centrale di Statistica. Statistiche Industriali **724**
Italy. Istituto Centrale di Statistica. Annuario di Statistiche Meteorologiche see Italy. Istituto Centrale di Statistica. Statistiche Meteorologiche **3444**
Italy. Istituto Centrale di Statistica. Annuario di Statistiche Sanitarie see Italy. Istituto Centrale di Statistica. Statistiche Sanitarie **4117**
Italy. Istituto Centrale di Statistica. Annuario Statistico del Commercio Interno e del Turismo see Italy. Istituto Centrale di Statistica. Statistiche del Commercio Interno **724**
Italy. Istituto Centrale di Statistica. Annuario Statistico dell' Assistenza e della Previdenza Sociale see Italy. Istituto Centrale di Statistica. Statistiche dell' Assistenza e della Previdenza Sociale **4410**
Italy. Istituto Centrale di Statistica. Annuario Statistico della Navigazione Marittima see Italy. Istituto Centrale di Statistica. Statistiche della Navigazione Marittima **4665**

Italy. Istituto Centrale di Statistica. Annuario Statistico della Zootecnia, della Pesca e della Caccia see Italy. Istituto Centrale di Statistica. Statistiche della Zootecnia, della Pesca e della Caccia **139**
Italy. Istituto Centrale di Statistica. Bollettino Mensile di Statistica. (IT ISSN 0021-3136) **4575**
Italy. Istituto Centrale di Statistica. Indicatori Mensili. (IT ISSN 0390-6620) **4575**
Italy. Istituto Centrale di Statistica. Notiziario. (IT) **724**
Italy. Istituto Centrale di Statistica. Statistica Annuale del Commercio con l'Estero see Italy. Istituto Centrale di Statistica. Statistica Annuale del Commercio con l'Estero. Tomo 1 **724**
Italy. Istituto Centrale di Statistica. Statistica Annuale del Commercio con l'Estero see Italy. Istituto Centrale di Statistica. Statistica Annuale del Commercio con l'Estero. Parte 1-6 Tomo 2 **724**
Italy. Istituto Centrale di Statistica. Statistica Annuale del Commercio con l'Estero. Parte 1-6 Tomo 2. (IT ISSN 0390-6566) **724**, **914**, **4575**
Italy. Istituto Centrale di Statistica. Statistica Annuale del Commercio con l'Estero. Tomo 1. (IT ISSN 0390-6558) **724**, **914**, **4575**
Italy. Istituto Centrale di Statistica. Statistica Mensile del Commercio con L'Estero see Italy. Istituto Centrale di Statistica. Statistica Trimestrale del Commercio con L'Estero **724**
Italy. Istituto Centrale di Statistica. Statistica Trimestrale del Commercio con L'Estero. (IT) **724**, **914**, **4575**
Italy. Istituto Centrale di Statistica. Statistiche Culturali. (IT) **4141**
Italy. Istituto Centrale di Statistica. Statistiche del Commercio Interno. (IT) **724**, **837**, **4575**
Italy. Istituto Centrale di Statistica. Statistiche del Lavoro. (IT) **3992**
Italy. Istituto Centrale di Statistica. Statistiche dell'Agricoltura, Zootecnia e Mezzi di Produzione. Annuario. (IT) **100**
Italy. Istituto Centrale di Statistica. Statistiche dell' Assistenza e della Previdenza Sociale. (IT) **4410**
Italy. Istituto Centrale di Statistica. Statistiche della Navigazione Marittima. (IT) **4665**, **4575**, **4729**
Italy. Istituto Centrale di Statistica. Statistiche della Zootecnia, della Pesca e della Caccia. (IT) **139**
Italy. Istituto Centrale di Statistica. Statistiche Demografiche. (IT) **3992**, **4575**
Italy. Istituto Centrale di Statistica. Statistiche Forestali. (IT) **2112**
Italy. Istituto Centrale di Statistica. Statistiche Giudiziarie. (IT) **2699**, **4575**
Italy. Istituto Centrale di Statistica. Statistiche Industriali. (IT) **724**, **4575**
Italy. Istituto Centrale di Statistica. Statistiche Meteorologiche. (IT) **3444**, **4575**
Italy. Istituto Centrale di Statistica. Statistiche Sanitarie. (IT) **4117**
Italy. Istituto di Studi sulla Ricerca e Documentazione Scientifica. Note di Bibliografia e Documentazione Scientifica. (IT) **2765**
Italy. Istituto Nazionale per lo Studio della Congiuntura. Quaderni Analitici. (IT ISSN 0075-1987) **1079**
†Italy. Laboratorio di Idrobiologia. Bollettino di Pesca Piscicoltura e Idrobiologia. (IT ISSN 0006-6753) **5219**
Italy. Ministero dei Trasporti e dell'Aviazione Civile. Azienda Autonoma delle Ferrovie dello Stato. Bollettino Statistico Mensile. (IT ISSN 0021-3144) **4665**

Italy. Ministero del Bilancio e della Programmazione Economica. Relazione Generale Sulla Situazione Economica del Paese. (IT ISSN 0075-1995) **870**
Italy. Ministero del Lavoro e della Previdenza Sociale. Notiziario Mensile. Statistiche del Lavoro. (IT) **724**
Italy. Ministero dell'Industria del Commercio e dell'Artigianato. (IT) **3705**
Italy. Ministero della Pubblica Istruzione. Annali della Pubblica Istruzione. (IT ISSN 0003-4584) **1641**, **1752**
Italy. Officio della Proprieta Letteraria, Artistica e Scientifica. Bollettino. (IT) **3676**
Italy. Scuola di Guerra. Biblioteca. Bollettino. (IT ISSN 0036-9845) **2765**, **3460**
Italy (Year). (US) **4773**
Italy & Switzerland Stamp Catalogue. (UK ISSN 0142-9825) **3753**
Italy Canada Trade. (CN ISSN 0021-3098) **818**
Italy - Documents and Notes. (IT ISSN 0021-3063) **3900**
Italy Italy. (IT) **4773**
Italy's Contribution to the Promotion of World Wide Prosperity. (IT) **914**
Itawamba Settlers. (US ISSN 0737-7932) **2155**, **2410**
Itch. (NE) **2454**
Itek News see Item **1115**
Item. (IT) **1115**
▼Item Processing Report. (US ISSN 1048-5120) **1452**
Items. (US ISSN 0049-0903) **4376**
Iterarte. (IT) **331**
Ithaca College Quarterly. (US) **1315**
Ithaca Women's Anthology. (US) **2995**, **4845**
Ithrottabladid. (IC ISSN 1017-3579) **4476**
Itihas. (II ISSN 0970-812X) **2339**, **2765**
Itihasa Samiti Patrika. see Bangladesh Itihas Samiti. Journal **2337**
Itineraires. (FR ISSN 0021-3187) **2869**
Itinerario. (IT ISSN 0393-5469) **2205**
Itinerario. (NE ISSN 0165-1153) **2315**
Itinerarium. (PO ISSN 0021-3209) **4266**, **2315**, **3770**
Itinerary (Bayonne). (US ISSN 0743-5223) **4773**, **4410**
Itinerary (Bowling Green) see Mid-American Review **2874**
Itogi Nauki i Tekhniki. Organizatsiya i Bezopasnost' Dorozhnogo Dvizheniya.(RU ISSN 0234-4742) **4719**
Itogi Nauki i Tekhniki: Algebra - Topologiya - Geometriya. (RU ISSN 0202-7445) **3039**
Itogi Nauki i Tekhniki: Astronomiya. (RU ISSN 0202-0742) **366**
Itogi Nauki i Tekhniki: Avtomobil'nyi i Gorodskoi Transport. (RU ISSN 0202-7844) **1868**, **4719**
Itogi Nauki i Tekhniki: Biofizika see Itogi Nauki i Tekhniki: Biofizika Membran **485**
Itogi Nauki i Tekhniki: Biofizika Membran. (RU ISSN 0234-2979) **485**
Itogi Nauki i Tekhniki: Biologicheskaya Khimiya. (RU ISSN 0202-795X) **478**
Itogi Nauki i Tekhniki: Dvigateli Vnutrennego Sgoraniya. (RU ISSN 0202-7542) **1932**
Itogi Nauki i Tekhniki: Elektricheskie Apparaty. (RU ISSN 0202-8301) **1901**
Itogi Nauki i Tekhniki: Elektricheskie Stantsi i Seti. (RU) **1901**
Itogi Nauki i Tekhniki: Elektricheskie Stantsii, Seti i Sistemy see Itogi Nauki i Tekhniki: Elektricheskie Stantsi i Seti **1901**
Itogi Nauki i Tekhniki: Elektrokhimiya. (RU ISSN 0202-8093) **1212**
Itogi Nauki i Tekhniki: Elektronika. (RU) **1774**
Itogi Nauki i Tekhniki: Elektrosvyaz'. (RU ISSN 0130-6804) **1338**

Itogi Nauki i Tekhniki: Fiziologiya Cheloveka i Zhivotnykh. (RU ISSN 0134-2673) **572**
Itogi Nauki i Tekhniki: Genetika Cheloveka. (RU ISSN 0301-391X) **544**
Itogi Nauki i Tekhniki: Geodeziya i Aeros'emka. (RU ISSN 0202-0726) **2254**
Itogi Nauki i Tekhniki: Geografiya Zarubezhnykh Stran. (RU ISSN 0202-7208) **2254**
Itogi Nauki i Tekhniki: Geokhimiya - Mineralogiya - Petrografiya. (RU ISSN 0202-7348) **1569**, **3486**
Itogi Nauki i Tekhniki: Geomagnetizm i Vysokie Sloi Atmosfery. (RU ISSN 0202-7275) **1591**
Itogi Nauki i Tekhniki: Gidrogeologiya. Inzhenernaya Geologiya. (RU ISSN 0202-7356) **1598**
Itogi Nauki i Tekhniki: Issledovanie Kosmicheskogo Prostranstva. (RU ISSN 0202-0734) **366**
Itogi Nauki i Tekhniki: Kartografiya. (RU ISSN 0202-7240) **2254**
Itogi Nauki i Tekhniki: Khimiya i Tekhnologiya Vysokomolekulyarnykh Soedinenii. (RU ISSN 0202-8069) **1855**
Itogi Nauki i Tekhniki: Kinetika. Kataliz. (RU ISSN 0202-7968) **1227**
Itogi Nauki i Tekhniki: Korroziya i Zashchita ot Korrozii. (RU ISSN 0202-7976) **3410**
Itogi Nauki i Tekhniki: Kristallokhimiya. (RU ISSN 0202-7984) **1210**
Itogi Nauki i Tekhniki: Matematicheskii Analiz. (RU ISSN 0202-7453) **3039**
Itogi Nauki i Tekhniki: Mekhanika Zhidkosti i Gaza. (RU ISSN 0202-781X) **1932**
Itogi Nauki i Tekhniki: Mestorozhdeniya Goryuchikh Poleznykh Iskopaemykh. (RU ISSN 0302-542X) **1569**
Itogi Nauki i Tekhniki: Metallovedenie i Termicheskaya Obrabotka. (RU ISSN 0202-7739) **3410**
Itogi Nauki i Tekhniki: Metallurgicheskaya Teplotekhnika. (RU ISSN 0202-7755) **3410**
Itogi Nauki i Tekhniki: Metallurgiya Tsvetnykh Metallov. (RU ISSN 0202-7747) **3410**
Itogi Nauki i Tekhniki: Molekulyarnaya Biologiya. (RU ISSN 0202-7070) **443**
Itogi Nauki i Tekhniki: Obogashchenie Poleznykh Iskopaemykh. (RU ISSN 0202-7437) **3486**
Itogi Nauki i Tekhniki: Obshchaya Geologiya. (RU ISSN 0202-7372) **1569**
Itogi Nauki i Tekhniki: Obshchie Problemy Biologii. (RU ISSN 0203-5405) **443**
Itogi Nauki i Tekhniki: Okhrana Prirody i Vosproizvodstvo Prirodnykh Resursov. (RU ISSN 0202-7321) **1959**
Itogi Nauki i Tekhniki: Onkologiya. (RU ISSN 0202-7127) **3198**, **443**
Itogi Nauki i Tekhniki: Organicheskaya Khimiya. (RU ISSN 0137-0251) **1218**
Itogi Nauki i Tekhniki: Organizatsiya Upravleniya Transportom. (RU ISSN 0134-7799) **4651**
Itogi Nauki i Tekhniki: Problemy Geometrii. (RU ISSN 0202-7461) **3039**
Itogi Nauki i Tekhniki: Promyshlennyi Transport. (RU ISSN 0202-7909) **4651**
Itogi Nauki i Tekhniki: Protsessy i Apparaty Khimicheskoi Tekhnologii. (RU ISSN 0202-8018) **1855**
Itogi Nauki i Tekhniki: Radiotekhnika. (RU ISSN 0202-0769) **1357**
Itogi Nauki i Tekhniki: Rastenievodstvo. (RU ISSN 0202-716X) **506**
Itogi Nauki i Tekhniki: Razrabotka Mestorozhdenii Tverdykh Poleznykh Iskopaemykh. (RU ISSN 0202-7410) **3486**

Itogi Nauki i Tekhniki: Razrabotka Neftyanykh i Gazovykh Mestorozhdenii. (RU ISSN 0202-7429) **3690**
Itogi Nauki i Tekhniki: Rudnye Mestorozhdeniya. (RU ISSN 0202-7380) **3486**
Itogi Nauki i Tekhniki: Svarka. (RU ISSN 0202-778X) **3429**
Itogi Nauki i Tekhniki: Tekhnicheskaya Kibernetika. (RU ISSN 0130-6774) **1441**
Itogi Nauki i Tekhniki: Teoriya Veroyatnostej - Matematicheskaya Statistika-Teoreticheskaya Kibernetika. (RU ISSN 0202-7488) **3039**, **1441**
Itogi Nauki i Tekhniki: Truboprovodnyi Transport. (RU ISSN 0202-7917) **1932**
Itogi Nauki i Tekhniki: Vodnyi Transport.(RU ISSN 0202-7879) **4729**
Itogi Nauki i Tekhniki: Vozdushnyi Transport. (RU ISSN 0202-7887) **4675**
Itogi Nauki i Tekhniki: Zoologiya Pozvonochnykh. (RU ISSN 0202-702X) **585**
It's a Math Math World see Math Math World **3045**
It's Happening. (US ISSN 0098-7549) **1641**
†It's Ntertainment. (UK) **5219**
It's Our World. (US) **1257**, **4266**
Itsuu Kenkyujo Nenpo. see Itsuu Laboratory, Tokyo. Annual Report **1218**
Itsuu Laboratory, Tokyo. Annual Report/ Itsuu Kenkyujo Nenpo. (JA ISSN 0075-2010) **1218**
Al-Ittihad. (TS) **2220**
Ittihad al-Baridi al-Arabi/Arab Postal Union. Review. (TS) **1353**
Ittihad al-Sinaat al-Misriyah. Year Book/ Federation of Egyptian Industries. Year Book. (UA) **1140**
Al-Ittihad al-Usbu'i. (TS) **2220**
Al Ittihadi/Unionist. (SJ) **2169**
Itto Suijunten Kensoku Seika Shuroku. (JA) **2268**
Iugoslavica Physiologica et Pharmacologica Acta see Acta Biologica Iugoslavica. Serija C: Iugoslavica Physiologica et Pharmacologica Acta **425**
Iura. (IT ISSN 0021-3241) **2637**
Ius Canonicum. (SP ISSN 0021-325X) **4183**
Ius Icclesiae. (IT) **4266**, **2637**
Ius Romanum Medii Aevi. (IT ISSN 0075-2037) **2637**
Iustitia. (IT ISSN 0021-3268) **2637**, **4266**
Ivoire. Dimanche. (IV ISSN 0047-1674) **2169**
Ivory Coast. Direction de la Statistique. Bulletin Mensuel de Statistiques. (IV) **4081**
Ivory Coast. Direction des Investissements. Budget Special d'Investissement et d'Equipement. Rapport de Presentation. (IV) **952**
Ivory Coast. Direction des Mines et de la Geologie. Rapport Provisoire sur les Activities du Secteur. (IV) **3486**, **1569**
Ivory Coast. Direction du Budget Special d'Investissement et d'Equipment. Rapport de Presentation du Budget Special d'Investissement et d'Equipment. (IV) **4065**
Ivory Coast. Ministere de l'Agriculture. Statistiques Agricoles. (IV) **139**
Ivory Coast. Ministere de l'Economie, des Finances et du Plan. Comptes de la Nation. (IV) **1099**
Ivory Coast. Ministere de l'Economie et des Finances. Etudes Economiques et Financieres see Revue Economique et Financiere Ivoirienne **883**
Ivy Journal. (US ISSN 0882-4142) **2132**
Ivy Leaf. (US ISSN 0021-3276) **1315**
Iwa-To-Yuki/Rock and Snow. (JA) **4549**
Iwatani Naoji Foundation. Research Report. see Iwatani Naoji Kinen Zaidan Kenkyu Hokokusho **4316**

Iwatani Naoji Kinen Zaidan Kenkyu Hokokusho/Iwatani Naoji Foundation. Research Report. (JA ISSN 0287-3532) **4316**

Iwate Daigaku Kogakubu Kenkyu Hokoku. see Iwate University. Faculty of Engineering. Technology Reports **1827**

Iwate Daigaku Kyoikugakubu Kenkyu Nenpo. see Iwate University. Faculty of Education. Annual Report **4377**

Iwate Horticulture Experiment Station. Bulletin. (JA ISSN 0388-4449) **182**, 100

Iwate Igaku Zasshi/Iwate Medical Association. Journal. (JA ISSN 0021-3284) **3112**

Iwate Ika Daigaku Kyoyobu Nenpo. see Iwate Medical University School of Liberal Arts & Sciences. Annual Report **4316**

Iwate Ika Daigaku Shigaku Zasshi. see Iwate Medical University. Dental Journal **3235**

Iwate Medical Association. Journal. see Iwate Igaku Zasshi **3112**

Iwate Medical University. Dental Journal/Iwate Ika Daigaku Shigaku Zasshi. (JA ISSN 0385-1311) **3235**

Iwate Medical University School of Liberal Arts & Sciences. Annual Report/Iwate Ika Daigaku Kyoyobu Nenpo. (JA ISSN 0385-4132) **4316**, 2509, 4376

Iwate University. Faculty of Education. Annual Report/Iwate Daigaku Kyoikugakubu Kenkyu Nenpo. (JA ISSN 0367-7370) **4377**, 1752, 2926, 4316

Iwate University. Faculty of Engineering. Technology Reports/Iwate Daigaku Kogakubu Kenkyu Hokoku. (JA ISSN 0085-2325) **1827**

†Iwate University. Mountains Land Use Research Laboratory. Bulletin. (JA) **5219**

Iwate University Forests. Bulletin. (JA ISSN 0286-4339) **2103**

IX. (GW) **1397**, 1445

Ixtapa & Zihuatanejo (Year). (US) **4773**

Iyakuhin Sogo Sayo Kenkyu/Research on Drug Actions and Interactions. (JA) **3730**, 2466

Iyo Denshi to Seito Kogaku (Nihon M-E Gakkai Zasshi). see Japanese Journal of Medical Electronics and Biological Engineering **3112**

Iyo Kizai Kenkyujo Hokoku. see Tokyo Medical and Dental University. Institute for Medical and Dental Engineering. Reports **3157**

Iyunei Mishpat. see Tel Aviv University. Law Review **2684**

Iyunim B'bikoret Hamedina. (IS) **3900**

Iyunim B'minhal Hachinuch. (IS) **1728**

Iyyun. (IS ISSN 0021-3306) **3770**

Iz Istorii Estestvoznaniya i Tekhniki Pribaltiki. see Contributions to the History of Natural Sciences and Technology in the Baltic **4306**

Iz Starog i Novog Zagreba. (CI) **301**, 331

Al-Izaa wal-Television/Radio and Television. (UA) **1375**, 1357

†Izard County Historian. (US) **5219**

Izgradnja/Construction. (YU ISSN 0350-5421) **1868**, 621

Izmeritel'naya Tekhnika. (RU ISSN 0021-3349) **2523**

Izmir Chamber of Commerce. Bulletin. (TU) **818**

Izmir Chamber of Commerce Review/Izmir Ticaret Odasi Dergisi. (TU ISSN 0021-3357) **818**

Izmir Ticaret Odasi Dergisi. see Izmir Chamber of Commerce Review **818**

Izobrazitel'noe Iskusstvo Belorussii. (BW) **2927**

Izobretatel' i Ratsionalizator. (RU ISSN 0130-1802) **3676**

Izotoptechnika see Izotoptechnika, Diagnosztika **3359**

Izotoptechnika, Diagnosztika/Isotope Technics, Diagnostics. (HU ISSN 0865-0497) **3359**, 443

Izraz. (BN ISSN 0021-3381) **2927**

Izsledovaniia po Bulgarska Istoriia. (BU) **2370**

Izsledovaniya za Istoriiata na Bulgarskiya Narod. (BU) **2370**

Izumi. (GW ISSN 0937-2008) **3639**

Izvestiia po Khimiia. (BU ISSN 0324-1130) **1179**

Izvestiya na Darzhavnite Arkhivi. (BU ISSN 0323-9780) **2370**, 3900

Izvestiya na Muzeite ot Iugoiztochna Bulgariya. (BU ISSN 0204-403X) **275**, 2370

Izvestiya na Muzeite ot Iuzhna Bulgariya. (BU ISSN 0204-4072) **275**, 2370

Izvestiya na Narodnata Biblioteka Kiril i Metodii i na Biblioekata na Sofiiskiya Universitet Kliment Okhridski see Narodna Biblioteka Kiril i Metodii. Izvestiya **2377**

Izvestiya Vysshikh Uchebnykh Zavedenii. Seriya Energetika. (BW ISSN 0579-2983) **1792**

Izvestiya Vysshikh Uchebnykh Zavedenii. Seriya Fizika. (RU ISSN 0021-3411) **3821**

Izvestiya Vysshikh Uchebnykh Zavedenii. Seriya Geologiya i Razvedka. (RU ISSN 0016-7762) **1569**, 1591, 3486

Izvestiya Vysshikh Uchebnykh Zavedenii. Seriya Matematika. (RU ISSN 0021-3446) **3039**, 1932

Izvestiya Vysshikh Uchebnykh Zavedenii. Seriya Priborostroenie. (RU ISSN 0021-3454) **2523**

Izvestiya Vysshikh Uchebnykh Zavedenii. Seriya Radioelektronika. (KR ISSN 0021-3470) **1357**, 1774

Izvestiya Vysshikh Uchebnykh Zavedenii. Seriya Radiofizika. (RU ISSN 0021-3462) **3821**, 1901

Izvestiya Vysshikh Uchebnykh Zavedenii. Seriya Tekhnologiya Legkoi Promyshlennosti. (KR ISSN 0021-3489) **1827**

Izvestiya Vysshikh Uchebnykh Zavedenii. Seriya Tekhnologiya Tekstil'noi Promyshlennosti. (RU ISSN 0021-3497) **4621**

Izvori Srpskog Prava/Sources de Droit Serbe/Serbische Rechtsquellen. (YU) **2637**

I'91. (CS ISSN 0862-9382) **2765**, 4601

J A C E P see Annals of Emergency Medicine **3306**

J A C G Newsletter. (Jersey Atari Computer Group) (US) **1469**, 1427, 1461

J A C Newsletter. (US) **2074**

J A C S Volunteer. (Joint Action in Community Services, Inc.) (US) **3628**, 4410

J A C T Review. (Joint Association of Classical Teachers) (UK ISSN 0268-0181) **1277**, 1752

J A C T Themes. (Joint Association of Classical Teachers) (UK) **1277**

J A D News. (Judicial Administration Division) (US) **2637**

J A E see Journal of Architectural Education **302**

J A E R I Report. (Japan Atomic Energy Research Institute) (JA) **1806**, 404

J A E R I Reports. List. (Japan Atomic Energy Research Institute) (JA) **1806**

J A E R I Reports Abstracts/Genken Kenkyu Seika Shorokusyu. (Japan Atomic Energy Research Institute) (JA ISSN 0385-6437) **3837**, 15, 1806

J A G Bulletin see Air Force Law Review **2596**

J A G Law Review see Air Force Law Review **2596**

J A I A. (Australian-Indonesian Association of Victoria) (AT ISSN 0812-7131) **2202**, 2007

J A I E see Journal of Artificial Intelligence in Education **1690**

J A L A see Joint Acquisitions List of Africana **254**

J A L S. (US) **3557**

J A M A en Colombia. (Journal of the American Medical Association) (SP) **3112**

J A M A en Espanol. (SP) **3112**

J A M A en Venezuela. (SP) **3112**

J A M A - France. (FR) **3112**

J A M A: The Journal of the American Medical Association. (US ISSN 0098-7484) **3112**

J A M A: The Journal of the American Medical Association (Italian Edition). (IT ISSN 0393-554X) **3112**

J A M I F. (Journal Association des Medecins Israelites de France) (FR ISSN 0299-3953) **3112**

J A M R I Report. (Japan Maritime Research Institute) (JA ISSN 0913-5480) **4729**

J A N A C see Association of Nurses in A I D S Care. Journal **3218**

J A N E S see Ancient Near Eastern Society. Journal **3633**

J A O A: Journal of the American Osteopathic Association. (US ISSN 0098-6151) **3215**

J A P C A see Air & Waste Management Association. Journal **1942**

J A P I C Weekly Bulletin. (Japan Pharmaceutical Information Center) (JA ISSN 0915-163X) **3730**

†J A P O S Bulletin. (Journalists, Authors, Poets on Stamps) (US ISSN 0278-436X) **5219**

J A R A see Academy of Rehabilitative Audiology. Journal **3312**

J A R Q see Japan Agricultural Research Quarterly **100**

J A S A. Journal of the American Statistical Association. (US ISSN 0162-1459) **4575**

J A S I S see American Society for Information Science. Journal **2742**

J A S N A News. (CN) **2927**

J A S O see Anthropological Society of Oxford. Journal **234**

J A S S A. (AT ISSN 0313-5934) **952**, 787

J A T A: Journal of the American Telemarketing Association. (US) **1042**, 1363

J & K Research Biannual. (Jammu and Kashmir) (II) **2509**

J & W Telefax International. International Facsimile Directory. (GW) **1363**

J & W Telex International. International Telex and Teletex Directory. (GW) **1363**

J & W Travel International. (GW) **1363**, 2477

J B I A Directory. (Japan Book Importers Association) (JA) **1140**

J B I Journal. (Jamaica Bauxite Institute) (JM ISSN 0254-5241) **3486**

J B M see Jornal Brasileiro de Medicina **3113**

†J.B. Speed Art Museum Bulletin. (US ISSN 0021-356X) **5219**

J C A H P O Outlook. (Joint Commission on Allied Health Personnel in Ophthalmology) (US) **3301**, 3628

J C A Janaru see J C A Journal **914**

J C A Journal. (Japan Commercial Arbitration Association) (JA ISSN 0386-3042) **914**

J C C A (Journal of the Canadian Chiropractic Association) see Canadian Chiropractic Association. Journal **3213**

J C C Circle. (Jewish Community Centers Association of North America) (US) **4223**, 4410

J C C E see Journal of Computing in Childhood Education **1690**

J.C.H.R. News Letter. (Jamaica Council of Human Rights) (JM) **3944**, 2637

J C I News. (Junior Chamber International) (US) **1298**

J C I Transactions. (Japan Concrete Institute) (JA) **621**

J C L C see Journal of Criminal Law & Criminology **1516**

J C M S T see Journal of Computers in Mathematics and Science Teaching **3065**

J C M T - U K I R T Newsletter. (United Kingdom Infrared Telescope) (UK ISSN 0963-2700) **366**

J C P S Congressional District Fact Book. (Joint Center for Political Studies, Inc.) (US ISSN 0888-8957) **3900**, 4065

J.C. Poggendorff: Biographisch-Literarisches Handwoerterbuch der Exakten Naturwissenschaften. (GW) **4316**

J C R see Journal of Consumer Research **1042**

J C S E see Journal of Comparative Sociology and Ethics **4439**

J C S S Studies. (Jaffee Center for Strategic Studies) (IS) **3900**

J C S U News. (Johnson C. Smith University) (US) **1315**

J C T. (US) **1752**

J C T: Journal of Coatings Technology. (US ISSN 0361-8773) **3654**

J. Cross Executive Alert. (US) **1015**

J D. (IT ISSN 0393-800X) **3235**

J D C - Brookdale Institute of Gerontology and Human Development in Israel. Annual Report.(IS) **2274**

J D C - Brookdale Institute of Gerontology and Human Development in Israel. Discussion Papers. (IS ISSN 0334-9012) **2274**

J D C - Brookdale Institute of Gerontology and Human Development in Israel. International Forum. (IS ISSN 0334-9101) **2274**

J D C - Brookdale Institute of Gerontology and Human Development in Israel. Special Series.(IS ISSN 0334-908X) **2274**

J D Journal. (John Deere) (US) **162**, 152

J D P A see Journal of Dental Practice Administration **3236**

J D Q: Journal Dentaire du Quebec. (CN ISSN 0845-9320) **3235**

†J E B Theatre. (BE) **5219**

J E E see Journal of Electronic Engineering **1901**

J E E: Japan Electronic Engineering see Journal of Electronic Engineering **1901**

J E G P: Journal of English and Germanic Philology. (US ISSN 0363-6941) **2819**, 2927

J E I. (Journal of Economic Issues) (US ISSN 0021-3624) **895**

J E I see Journal of the Electronics Industry **1775**

J E I Council Report see J E I Report **914**

J E I Report. (Japan Economic Institute) (US ISSN 0744-6489) **914**

J E M see Jurnal Ekonomi Malaysia **871**

†J.E.M. (Jeunes en Marche) (FR ISSN 0021-583X) **5219**

J E M H see Journal of Educational Multimedia and Hypermedia **1690**

J E M S. (Journal of Emergency Medical Services) (US ISSN 0197-2510) **3112**

J E N. (Journal of Emergency Nursing) (US ISSN 0099-1767) **3279**

J E O L News: Analytical Instrumentation. (JA ISSN 0385-4418) **2523**, 3260

J E O L News - Analytical Instruments: Application see J E O L News: Analytical Instrumentation **2523**

J E O L News: Electron Optics Instrumentation. (JA ISSN 0385-4426) **2523**, 3260

J E O L News - Electron Optics Instruments - Application see J E O L News: Electron Optics Instrumentation **2523**

J E P: A B P see Journal of Experimental Psychology: Animal Behavior Processes **4029**

J E P: GEN see Journal of Experimental Psychology: General **4029**

J E P: H P P see Journal of Experimental Psychology: Human Perception and Performance **4029**

J E P: L M C see Journal of Experimental Psychology: Learning, Memory, and Cognition **4029**

J E T see Journal of Education for Teaching **1710**

J E T A I see Journal of Experimental & Theoretical Artificial Intelligence 1409

J E T: Journal of Educational Thought/ Revue de la Pensee Educative. (CN ISSN 0022-0701) 1641

J E T P Letters. (English translation of: Pis'ma v Zhurnal Eksperimental'noi i Teoreticheskoi Fiziki) (US ISSN 0021-3640) 3821

J E T R O China Newsletter see China Newsletter 903

J E T S Report. (Junior Engineering Technical Society) (US) 1827, 1752

J F I T News. (UK ISSN 0956-3393) 1430, 1397

J G E see Journal of General Education 1642

J G R: Journal of Geophysical Research. (US ISSN 0148-0227) 3437

J G R: Journal of Geophysical Research: Atmosphere. (US) 3437

J G R: Journal of Geophysical Research: Oceans. (US) 1591

J G R: Journal of Geophysical Research: Planets. (US) 366

J G R: Journal of Geophysical Research: Solid Earth. (US) 1591

J G R: Journal of Geophysical Research: Solid Earth and Planets see J G R: Journal of Geophysical Research: Planets 366

J G R: Journal of Geophysical Research: Solid Earth and Planets see J G R: Journal of Geophysical Research: Solid Earth 1591

J G R: Journal of Geophysical Research: Space Physics. (US ISSN 0196-6928) 1591

J. Gruber's Hagers-Town Town and Country Almanack. (US) 1781, 358

J I C S T Online Information System. (Japanese Information Center of Science and Technology) (US) 4359, 4083

J I L A Data Center. Report. (Joint Institute for Laboratory Astrophysics) (US) 3848

J I L A Information Center. Report see J I L A Data Center. Report 3848

J I L B see Northwestern Journal of International Law & Business 2727

J.I.P.D.E.C. Report see Japan Computer Quarterly 1397

J I R A Robot News. (JA) 1408

J I S Computerized Bibliography. (US) 404

J I S T A. (Journal of the Indian Scientific Translators Association) (II ISSN 0253-8776) 2819

J I T see Journal of Information Technology 2766

J J N Special. see J J N Supesharu 3279

J J N Supesharu/J J N Special. (JA ISSN 0912-3741) 3279

J.K. Lasser Tax Institute. Monthly Tax Service. (US) 1099

J.K. Lasser's Your Income Tax. (US ISSN 0084-4314) 1099

J.K. Lasser's Your Income Tax, Professional Edition. (US ISSN 0075-2061) 1099

J L A News. (Jamaica Library Association) (JM) 2765

J L B Smith Institute of Ichthyology. Ichthyological Bulletin. (SA ISSN 0073-4381) 585

J L B Smith Institute of Ichthyology. Special Publication. (SA ISSN 0075-2088) 585

†J L C Educator. (Jewish Labor Committee) (US) 5219

J L C Review see Jewish Labor Committee Review 2008

J L I S see Journal of Library and Information Science 2766

▼J M A Management News. (Japan Management Association) (JA) 1015

†J M A Newsletter. (Japan Management Association) (JA) 5219

J M B see Journal of Motor Behavior 4031

J M B A see Marine Biological Association of the United Kingdom. Journal 447

J M C I: Journal of Molecular and Cellular Immunology. (US ISSN 0724-6803) 3187

†J M E A Newsletter. (Japan Machinery Exporters' Association) (JA) 5219

J M I S see Journal of Management Information Systems 1016

J M P S see Moscow Physical Society. Journal 3825

J M P T: Journal of Manipulative and Physiological Therapeutics. (US) 3215, 3308

J M R see Journal of Materials Research 3822

J N C I see National Cancer Institute. Journal 3200

J N F Illustrated. (Jewish National Fund) (IS ISSN 0021-3705) 4065

J N K V V News. (Jawaharlal Nehru Krishi Vishwa Vidyalaya) (II ISSN 0021-3713) 100, 4811

J N K V V Research Journal. (Jawaharlal Nehru Krishi Vishwa Vidyalaya) (II ISSN 0021-3721) 100

J N M A see Nepal Medical Association. Journal 3134

J N M M see Journal of Nuclear Materials Management 1806

J N R R see Journal of Natural Rubber Research 4292

J O. (Junge Ortskrankenkasse) (GW) 2535

J O G N N. (Journal of Obstetric, Gynecologic and Neonatal Nursing) (US ISSN 0884-2175) 3279, 3293

J O G N Nursing see J O G N N 3279

▼J O I C E. (Journal of International and Comparative Economics) (GW ISSN 0940-4821) 914, 895

J O I C F P News. (Japanese Organization for International Cooperation in Family Planning, Inc.) (JA ISSN 0911-0755) 597

J O I S see J I C S T Online Information System 4359

†J O L A Technical Communications. (Journal of Library Automation) (US ISSN 0021-3748) 5219

J O M. (US ISSN 1047-4838) 3410

J O N A see Journal of Nursing Administration 3280

J O N O M A S see Journal of Neurological and Orthopaedic Medicine & Surgery 3380

J O P S O M. (Journal of Preventive and Social Medicine) (BG) 4105, 3112

J O T. (Journal fuer Oberflaechentechnik) (GW ISSN 0940-8789) 3018, 1827, 3410

J O T S see Elysium: Journal of the Senses 3594

J O T T see Journal of Translation and Textlinguistics 2821

J P. (FI ISSN 0781-7177) 1257, 4183

J P C Newsletter. (Joint Planning Commission, Lehigh - Northampton Counties) (US) 2490

J P C Planner see J P C Newsletter 2490

J P E N: Journal of Parenteral and Enteral Nutrition. (US ISSN 0148-6071) 3607

J P G Letter. (Japan Publications Guide Service) (JA ISSN 0387-3927) 4130, 15

J P I - Jugend Presse Informationen. (GW) 1257, 3900

J P K E. Journal of Post Keynesian Economics see Journal of Post Keynesian Economics 871

J P M A see Pakistan Medical Association. Journal 3139

J P S. (Journal of the Polynesian Society) (NZ ISSN 0032-4000) 242, 275

J P S see Journal of the Philosophy of Sport 4477

J.P.T. Journal of Paint Technology see J C T: Journal of Coatings Technology 3654

J P T: Journal of Petroleum Technology.(US ISSN 0149-2136) 3690

J P 4 Mensile di Aeronautica. (IT ISSN 0394-3437) 57

J. Paul Getty Museum Journal. (US ISSN 0362-1979) 3525, 331

J Q: Journalism Quarterly. (US ISSN 0196-3031) 2571

J R S see Journal of Raman Spectroscopy 1207

†J S A C Grapevine. (Joint Strategy and Action Committee) (US ISSN 0364-4103) 5219

J S A E Review. (Society of Automotive Engineers of Japan, Inc.) (JA ISSN 0389-4304) 4693

J S A S see Society for Armenian Studies. Journal 2024

The J S E Handbook. (Johannesburg Stock Exchange) (SA) 952

J S E P see Journal of Sport and Exercise Psychology 4033

J S I F Report see Boken Report 4617

J S L see Jawaharal Nehru University. School of Languages. Journal 2820

J S L P A - R O A see Journal of Speech Language Pathology and Audiology 1737

J S M see Journal of Sport Management 4477

J S M E Bulletin see J S M E International Journal 1932

J S M E International Journal. (Japan Society of Mechanical Engineers) (JA ISSN 0913-185X) 1932

J S M E Journal. (Japan Society of Mechanical Engineers) (JA ISSN 0021-4728) 1932

J S N International. (JA) 1285

J S R see Journal of Sport Rehabilitation 3372

J T see Journal du Textile 4621

J T A Community News Reporter. (Jewish Telegraphic Agency) (US) 2007, 3900, 4223

J T A Daily News Bulletin. (US ISSN 0021-3772) 2007

J T A Weekly News Digest. (Jewish Telegraphic Agency) (US ISSN 0021-6763) 3900

J T T E see Journal of Technology and Teacher Education 1691

J U G Newsletter. (Jefferson State Computer Users Group) (US) 1427, 1461, 1469

J U M A. (GW ISSN 0940-4961) 1641

J U S. (IT ISSN 0022-6955) 2637

J U S E K. (SW ISSN 1100-620X) 2637

J W B Circle see J C C Circle 4223

J.W. Dawes Family Newsletter. (US) 2155

J W Plus. (Jewellery World Ltd.) (CN) 2564

J.W.V.A. Bulletin. (Jewish War Veterans Association) (US ISSN 0021-3799) 2007

†J-20. (Juventud Siglo XX) (SP) 5219

J - 22 Magazine. (US) 4525

Ja. (GW ISSN 0342-6505) 4183

Ja, Das Wort Fuer Alle. (GW ISSN 0342-6513) 4183

Jaarbericht "Ex Oriente Lux" see Vooraziatisch-Egyptisch Genootschap "Ex Oriente Lux". Jaarbericht 2343

Jaarboek: Aardmagnetisme. see Belgium. Institut Royal Meteorologique. Annuaire: Magnetisme Terrestre 3433

Jaarboek Achterhoek en Liemers. (NE) 2370

Jaarboek der Schone Kunsten/ Algemeen Jaarboek der Schone Kunsten. (BE ISSN 0066-3174) 331

Jaarboek Eindhoven. (NE) 4575

Jaarboek van de Openbare Gasvoorziening. (NE) 3690, 1792

Jaarboek voor Munt- en Penningkunde. (NE) 3600

Jaarboek: Zonnestraling. see Belgium. Institut Royal Meteorologique. Annuaire: Rayonnement Solaire 3433

Jaarstatistiek van de Bevolking see Netherlands. Centraal Bureau voor de Statistiek. Jaarstatistiek van de Bevolking 3993

Jaarverslag S C - D L O see Dienst Landbouwkundig Onderzoek. Staring Centrum, Instituut voor Onderzoek van het Landelijke Gebied. Jaarverslag 176

Jabalpur Law Journal. (II ISSN 0448-1054) 2637

Jabberwocky. (UK ISSN 0305-8182) 2927

Jabberwocky. (US) 2995

Jabega. (SP) 2217

Jacaranda Review. (US ISSN 1042-7082) 2995

Jacetania. (SP ISSN 0021-3810) 4773

J'Achete Mieux. (SZ) 1505

Jacht en Natuurbeheer. (BE) 1490, 4549

Jack and Jill. (UK) 1257

Jack and Jill (Inkprint Edition). (US ISSN 0021-3829) 1257

Jack Anderson Confidential see Jack Anderson First Alert 952

Jack Anderson First Alert. (US) 952

Jack Hutslar's Sport Scene see Jack Hutslar's Weekly News 4476

Jack Hutslar's Weekly News. (US) 4476, 1239, 1641, 3804

Jack Knight Air Log & A F A News. (US) 3753

†Jack London Newsletter. (US ISSN 0021-3837) 5219

Jack Miller's CommonWealth Letters see CommonWealth Letters 4147

Jack O'Dwyer's Newsletter. (US) 33

Jack-Pine Warbler. (US ISSN 0021-3845) 564

Jackie. (UK) 1257

Jackpotunities. (US) 2437

Jackson and Byron Local Courts (Civil Claims) Practice. (AT ISSN 0727-7954) 2702

Jackson County Chronicles. (US) 2410

Jackson Financial Letter. (US) 952

Jackson Laboratory Annual Report see Jackson Laboratory Scientific Report 544

Jackson Laboratory News see Jax 544

Jackson Laboratory Scientific Report. (US) 544, 3112

Jackson Letter see Jackson Financial Letter 952

†Jacksoniana. (US ISSN 0738-6648) 5219

Jacksonville Advocate Free Press see Jacksonville Free Press 2008

Jacksonville Business Journal. (US) 672

Jacksonville Free Press. (US) 2008, 3944

Jacksonville Genealogical Society. Magazine. see Jacksonville Genealogical Society Quarterly 2155

Jacksonville Genealogical Society Quarterly. (US ISSN 0149-6867) 2155

Jacksonville Magazine. (US ISSN 0021-3861) 818

Jacksonville Medicine Bulletin see Jacksonville Medicine Journal 3112

Jacksonville Medicine Journal. (US) 3112

†Jacksonville Poetry Quarterly. (US) 5219

Jacksonville Today. (US ISSN 0885-4769) 2227

Jacob Blaustein Lectures in International Affairs. (US ISSN 0075-2142) 3962

Jacob Marschak Interdisciplinary Colloquium on Mathematics in the Behavioral Sciences. (US ISSN 0160-7146) 1015

†Jacobean Drama Studies. (AU) 5219

Jacobete. (UK) 2370

†Jacobs' County Court Practice. (AT ISSN 0727-7946) 5220

Jacob's Ladder. (US) 2156

Jacob's Well. (US) 4266

Jacobsen's Fats & Oils Bulletin. (US ISSN 0021-387X) 2074

Jadavpur Journal of Comparative Literature. (II ISSN 0448-1143) 2927

Jade Biweekly Magazine. (CH) 2219

Jadeed Science. (PK ISSN 0021-3888) 4316

Jaderna Energie/Nuclear Energy. (CS ISSN 0448-116X) 1806

Jaegaren see Metsastaja 1491
Jaeger. (DK) 4549
Jaeger. (GW ISSN 0720-4523) 4549
Jaegerblatt. (GW ISSN 0021-3896) 57
Jaeger's Intertravel. (GW ISSN 0075-2150) 4773
Jaegerzeitung. (IT) 4549
Jaehrliche Aegyptologische Bibliographie. see Annual Egyptological Bibliography 2327
Jaernhandlaren. (SW ISSN 0021-552X) 1042, 642
Jaffna Medical Journal. (CE) 3112
Jag. (US ISSN 0021-390X) 3900, 3770
Jagat (Hindi) Monthly. (II) 2200
Jagat Weekly. (II) 2200
Jagd in Bayern. (GW) 4549
Jagd und Jaeger in Rheinland-Pfalz. (GW ISSN 0021-3926) 4549
Der Jagdgebrauchshund. (GW ISSN 0021-3942) 4549
Der Jagdspaniel. (GW ISSN 0021-3950) 3711, 4476
†Jagger Journal. (SA ISSN 0256-0070) 5220
Jagriti. (II ISSN 0447-2500) 1115
Jagriti. (FJ ISSN 0021-3969) 2008
Jagt og Fiskeri. (DK ISSN 0021-3977) 4549
Jagthunden. (DK) 4549, 3711
Jaguar Torque see Jaguars West 4693
Jaguars West. (AT) 4693
Jahan-e-Nau. (BG) 2174
Jahane Nao. (BG) 2339
Jahangirnagar Review. Part C. (BG) 2509
Jahnamamu (Oriya). (II) 1257
Jahrbuch Arbeit und Technik. (GW ISSN 0938-152X) 4316, 4601
Jahrbuch Chemische Rundschau. (SZ) 1179
Jahrbuch der Absatz- und Verbrauchsforschung. (GW ISSN 0021-3985) 1042
Jahrbuch der Auktionspreise fuer Buecher, Handschriften und Autographen. (GW) 3525, 2765, 4130
Jahrbuch der Bayerischen Staatsoper. (GW) 3557, 4634
Jahrbuch der Berliner Museen. (GW ISSN 0075-2207) 3525
Jahrbuch der Bibliotheken, Archive und Informationseinrichtungen der Deutschen Demokratischen Republik.(GW ISSN 0075-2215) 2765
Jahrbuch der Bibliotheken, Informationsstellen und Archive der D D R see Jahrbuch der Bibliotheken, Archive und Informationseinrichtungen der Deutschen Demokratischen Republik 2765
Jahrbuch der Buerokommunikation. (GW ISSN 0932-3635) 724, 1059
Jahrbuch der Bundesrepublik Deutschland. (GW ISSN 0931-4938) 4377
Jahrbuch der Deutschdidaktik. (GW ISSN 0173-6469) 2927, 2820
Jahrbuch der Deutschen Bibliotheken. (GW ISSN 0075-2223) 2765
Jahrbuch der Erzdioese Wien. (AU) 4266
Jahrbuch der Europaeischen Erdoelindustrie. see European Petroleum Yearbook 3685
Jahrbuch der Export- und Versandtleiter.(GW ISSN 0075-224X) 914
Jahrbuch der Fachanwaelte fuer Steuerrecht. (GW) 1099
Jahrbuch der Getraenke und Fluessigen Nahrmittel. see Annuaire des Boissons et des Liquides Alimentaires 5136
Jahrbuch der Hessischen Kirchengeschichtlichen Vereinigung. (GW) 4183
†Jahrbuch der Historischen Forschung in der Bundesrepublik Deutschland. (GW ISSN 0341-9177) 5220
Jahrbuch der Jagdheit. (GW) 1239
Jahrbuch der Koelner Jugendpresse. (GW) 2571

Jahrbuch der Luftfahrt und Raumfahrt see Reuss Jahrbuch der Luft- und Raumfahrt 61
Jahrbuch der Milchwirtschaft. (GW ISSN 0721-4332) 200
Jahrbuch der Oeffentlichen Meinung see Allensbacher Jahrbuch der Demoskopie 4428
Jahrbuch der Oesterreichischen Wirtschaft. (AU) 870
Jahrbuch der Philatelie see Briefmarken-Magazin 3750
Jahrbuch der Psychoanalyse. (GW ISSN 0075-2363) 4026
Jahrbuch der Schleiff-, Hon-, Laepp- und Poliertechnik see Jahrbuch Schleiffen, Honen, Laeppen und Polieren, Verfahren und Maschinen 1932
Jahrbuch der Stadt Weinsberg. (GW) 2189
Jahrbuch der Wehrtechnik. (GW ISSN 0075-2428) 3460
Jahrbuch der Werbung/Advertisers Annual. (GW ISSN 0932-6251) 3525
Jahrbuch des Baltischen Deutschtums. (GW ISSN 0075-2436) 2370
Jahrbuch des Eisenbahnwesens. (GW ISSN 0075-2479) 4710
Jahrbuch des Kameramanns. (GW ISSN 0075-2509) 3512
Jahrbuch des Kreises Dueren. (GW ISSN 0342-5835) 2189
Jahrbuch des Oeffentlichen Rechts der Gegenwart. (GW ISSN 0075-2517) 2706
Jahrbuch des Schwalm-Eder-Kreises (Year). (GW ISSN 0932-822X) 2370
Jahrbuch des Sozialrechts der Gegenwart. (GW) 4410, 2637
Jahrbuch des Sports. (GW ISSN 0448-1445) 4476
Jahrbuch des Vereins fuer Niederdeutsche Sprachforschung. (GW ISSN 0083-5617) 2820
Jahrbuch Deutsch Als Fremdsprache. (GW ISSN 0342-6300) 1709, 2820
Jahrbuch Deutscher Dichtung. (GW) 2995
Jahrbuch Elektrotechnik. (GW ISSN 0722-0340) 1901
Jahrbuch fuer Antike und Christentum. (GW ISSN 0075-2541) 4183
Jahrbuch fuer Bergbau, Energie, Mineraloel und Chemie. (GW) 3486
Jahrbuch fuer Berlin-Brandenburgische Kirchengeschichte. (GW ISSN 0075-2568) 4183
†Jahrbuch fuer Betriebswirte. (GW) 5220
Jahrbuch fuer Biotechnologie. (GW ISSN 0930-9152) 485, 443, 560, 4316
Jahrbuch fuer Blindenfreunde. (GW) 2293, 1737, 3301
Jahrbuch fuer Brandenburgische Kirchengeschichte see Jahrbuch fuer Berlin-Brandenburgische Kirchengeschichte 4183
Jahrbuch fuer Christliche Sozialwissenschaften. (GW ISSN 0075-2584) 4439, 4183
Jahrbuch fuer das Bayerische Transportgewerbe. (GW) 4710
Jahrbuch fuer das Elektrohandwerk (Year). (GW ISSN 0344-6581) 1774
Jahrbuch fuer den Kreis Pinneberg. (GW ISSN 0448-150X) 2370
Jahrbuch fuer den Oesterreichischen Tierarzt. (AU ISSN 0075-2606) 4811
Jahrbuch fuer die Geschichte Mittel- und Ostdeutschlands. (GW) 2370
Jahrbuch fuer die Kirche von Wien see Jahrbuch der Erzdioese Wien 4266
Jahrbuch fuer Eisenbahnliteratur see Dumjahn's Jahrbuch fuer Eisenbahnliteratur 4709
Jahrbuch fuer Elektromaschinenbau und Elektronik (Year). (GW) 1901
†Jahrbuch fuer Entwicklungspsychologie. (GW) 5220
Jahrbuch fuer Fraenkische Landesforschung. (GW ISSN 0446-3943) 2370, 3984

Jahrbuch fuer Fremdenverkehr. (GW ISSN 0075-2649) 4773
Jahrbuch fuer Fuehrungs Kraefte des Rechnungswesens. (GW) 752
Jahrbuch fuer Geschichte. (GW ISSN 0448-1526) 2370
Jahrbuch fuer Geschichte der USSR und der Volksdemokratischen Laender Europas see Geschichte der Sozialistischen Laender Europas. Jahrbuch 2363
Jahrbuch fuer Geschichte des Feudalismus. (GW ISSN 0138-4856) 2370
Jahrbuch fuer Geschichte von Staat, Wirtschaft und Gesellschaft Lateinamerikas. (GW ISSN 0075-2673) 2410
Jahrbuch fuer Internationale Germanistik. (SZ) 2927
Jahrbuch fuer Internationales Recht see German Yearbook of International Law 2723
Jahrbuch fuer Lehrer. (GW) 1641
Jahrbuch fuer Liturgik und Hymnologie. (GW ISSN 0075-2681) 4183, 3557
Jahrbuch fuer Musikalische Volks- und Voelkerkunde. (GW ISSN 0075-2703) 3557, 2055
Jahrbuch fuer Neue Politische Oekonomie. (GW ISSN 0722-5369) 895
Jahrbuch fuer Numismatik und Geldgeschichte. (GW ISSN 0075-2711) 3600
Jahrbuch fuer Opernforschung. (GW ISSN 0724-8156) 3557
Jahrbuch fuer Optik und Feinmechanik. (GW ISSN 0075-272X) 3853
Jahrbuch fuer Ostdeutsche Volkskunde. (GW ISSN 0075-2738) 2055, 242
Jahrbuch fuer Ostrecht. (GW ISSN 0075-2746) 2637
Jahrbuch fuer Praktiker des Rechnungswesens see Jahrbuch fuer Fuehrungs Kraefte des Rechnungswesens 752
Jahrbuch fuer Psychologie, Psychotherapie, und Medizinische Anthropologie see Zeitschrift fuer Klinische Psychologie und Psychotherapie 3356
Jahrbuch fuer Regionalgeschichte. (GW ISSN 0085-2341) 2370
Jahrbuch fuer Regionalwissenschaft. (GW ISSN 0173-7600) 4316
Jahrbuch fuer Salesianische Studien. (GW ISSN 0075-2754) 4266
Jahrbuch fuer Sozialwissenschaft. (GW ISSN 0075-2770) 724, 404
Jahrbuch fuer Soziologie und Sozialpolitik. (GW ISSN 0138-435X) 4439, 4377
Jahrbuch fuer Vergleichende Sozialforschung. (GW ISSN 0177-4093) 4439
Jahrbuch fuer Volkskunde und Kulturgeschichte. Neue Folge. (GW ISSN 0138-4503) 2055
Jahrbuch fuer Volksliedforschung. (GW ISSN 0075-2789) 3557
Jahrbuch fuer Westdeutsche Landesgeschichte. (GW ISSN 0170-2025) 2370
Jahrbuch fuer Westfaelische Kirchengeschichte. (GW) 2370, 4183
Jahrbuch fuer Wirtschaftsgeschichte. (GW ISSN 0075-2800) 895
Jahrbuch fuer Zeitgeschichte. (AU) 2370
†Jahrbuch Internationale Politik und Wirtschaft. (GW ISSN 0304-2197) 5220
Jahrbuch Kreis Euskirchen. (GW) 2509
Jahrbuch Kunststoffe: Plastics. (SZ) 3863
Jahrbuch Landkreis Kassel. (GW) 2370, 2509
Jahrbuch Mission. (GW ISSN 0931-248X) 4183
Jahrbuch Oberflaechentechnik (Year). (GW ISSN 0075-2819) 3410
Jahrbuch Peters. (GW ISSN 0323-8105) 3557
Jahrbuch Precision. (SZ) 1418

†Jahrbuch Schienenverkehr. (GW ISSN 0177-5529) 5220
Jahrbuch Schleiffen, Honen, Laeppen und Polieren, Verfahren und Maschinen. (GW) 1932
Jahrbuch Schweisstechnik. (GW) 4601, 3410
Jahrbuch Stahl. (GW ISSN 0724-8482) 3410
Jahrbuch Sucht. (GW) 1537
Jahrbuch Zucht. (GW) 4535
Jahrbuch zur Frage der Suchtgefahren see Jahrbuch Sucht 1537
†Jahrbuch zur Geschichte Dresdens. (GW) 5220
Jahrbuch zur Geschichte und Gesellschaft des Vorderen und Mittleren Orients see Jahrbuch fuer Vergleichende Sozialforschung 4439
Jahrbuecher der Deutschen Sporthochschule Koeln see Brennpunkte der Sportwissenschaft 4467
Jahrbuecher fuer Geschichte Osteuropas. (GW ISSN 0021-4019) 2370
Jahrbuecher fuer Nationaloekonomie und Statistik. (GW ISSN 0021-4027) 725
Jahrbuecher fuer Statistik und Landeskunde von Baden-Wuerttemberg. (GW) 4576
Jahresbericht see European Free Trade Association. Annual Report 906
Jahresbericht der Bayerischen Bodendenkmalpflege. (GW ISSN 0075-2835) 2315
Jahresbericht der Landesforstverwaltung. (GW) 2112
Jahresbericht ueber die Deutsche Fischwirtschaft. (GW ISSN 0075-2851) 2044
Jahresbibliographie Massenkommunikation. (GW) 1348, 404
Jahresschrift fuer Mitteldeutsche Vorgeschichte. (GW ISSN 0075-2932) 2370
Jahresverzeichnis der Deutschen Hochschulschriften see Jahresverzeichnis der Hochschulschriften der D D R, der B R D und Westberlins 1677
Jahresverzeichnis der Hochschulschriften der D D R, der B R D und Westberlins. (GW ISSN 0323-455X) 1677, 15
Jahresverzeichnis der Musikalien und Musikschriften. (GW ISSN 0075-2959) 3588
Jai Hind. (II) 2200
Jail and Prisoner Law Bulletin. (US ISSN 0739-0998) 1516, 2713
J'Aime Lire. (FR) 4183, 1257
Jain Journal. (II ISSN 0021-4043) 4214
Jakarta Business Directory. (IO) 1140
Jakarta Metropolitan Buyers' Guide. (IO) 1140
Jakata Magazine. (GP) 2239
Jake Bernstein's Letter of Long Term Trends. (US) 952
Jakt-Fiske. (NO) 4476
Jakt-Fiske-Friluftsliv see Jakt-Fiske 4476
Jakt och Jaegare. (SW) 4549
Jaktjournalen. (SW) 4549
Jaktmaker och Fiskevatten. (SW ISSN 0021-406X) 4549
Jalons. (FR ISSN 0184-8100) 2995
Jam Rag. (US) 3557
†Jam to-Day. (US ISSN 0362-8302) 5220
Jama'at al-Ta'rikh al-Tabi'i. Nashrat/ Emirates Natural History Group Bulletin. (TS) 4316
Al-Jamahiriya. (LY) 2209
Jamaica. Department of Statistics. Demographic Statistics see Statistical Institute of Jamaica. Demographic Statistics 3995
Jamaica. Ministry of Construction (Works). Jamaica Budget (Year). (JM) 621, 2490
Jamaica. Ministry of Pensions and Social Security. Report see Jamaica. Ministry of Social Security. Report 2535

Jamaica. Ministry of Social Security. Report. (JM) **2535**
Jamaica. National Insurance Scheme. Annual Reports *see* Jamaica. Ministry of Social Security. Report **2535**
Jamaica Agricultural Society. Minutes of the Half-Yearly Meeting. (JM) **100**
Jamaica Bauxite Institute Journal *see* J B I Journal **3486**
Jamaica Beat. (JM) **2239**
Jamaica Chamber of Commerce Journal. (JM ISSN 0021-4094) **818**
Jamaica Churchman. (JM ISSN 0047-1720) **4240**
Jamaica Council of Human Rights News Letter *see* J.C.H.R. News Letter **3944**
Jamaica Dental Association. Newsletter. (JM) **3235**
Jamaica Industrial Review *see* News Review **1081**
Jamaica Journal. (JM ISSN 0021-4124) **2239**
Jamaica Law Journal *see* West Indian Law Journal **2694**
Jamaica Library Association. Bulletin. (JM) **2765**
Jamaica Library Association News *see* J L A News **2765**
Jamaica Midwives Association. Newsletter. (JM) **3293**
▼Jamaica Naturalist. (JM ISSN 1018-1261) **585**, **1490**
Jamaica Pictorial. (JM) **3557**, **2927**, **4634**
Jamaica Port News. (JM) **4730**
Jamaica Public Health. (JM ISSN 0021-4132) **4106**
Jamaican Association of Sugar Technologists. Proceedings. (JM) **182**
Jamaican Bar Association. Annual Report. (JM) **2637**
Jamaican Exporter. (JM) **914**
Jamaican Geographer. (JM ISSN 1017-4753) **2254**
Jamaican Geographical Society Newsletter *see* Jamaican Geographer **2254**
Jamaican Historical Review. (JM) **2411**
Jamaican Journal of Science and Technology. (JM ISSN 1016-2054) **4317**
†Jamaican Manufacturer. (JM) **5220**
Jamaican National Bibliography. (JM ISSN 0075-2991) **404**
Jamaican Nurse. (JM ISSN 0021-4140) **3279**
†Jamaican Packaging Directory. (JM) **5220**
Jamaican Weekly Gleaner. (JM ISSN 0021-4159) **2239**
Jamana. (ML) **2169**
Jame'e Dandanpezeshki Iran. Namah-i/Iranian Dental Association. Bulletin. (IR) **3235**
James Arthur Lecture on the Evolution of the Human Brain. (US) **544**, **3340**
James Cook University of North Queensland. Department of Geography. Monograph Series. (AT) **2254**
James Dickey Newsletter. (US ISSN 0749-0291) **2927**, **419**
James Hardie 1000 *see* The Great Race **4473**
James Hogg Society. Newsletter *see* Studies in Hogg and His World **2965**
James Joyce Broadsheet. (UK ISSN 0143-6333) **2927**
James Joyce Foundation Newsletter *see* James Joyce Newestlatter **2927**
James Joyce Literary Supplement. (US ISSN 0899-3114) **2927**
James Joyce Newestlatter. (US) **2927**
James Joyce Quarterly. (US ISSN 0021-4183) **2927**
James Martin Productivity Series. (US) **1478**
James Nicholas Education Newsletter. (AT) **1728**, **1752**, **4439**
James White Review. (US ISSN 0891-5393) **2454**, **2927**
Jamestown College. Alumni & Friends. (US) **1315**

Jamhour - Al-Jadid. (LE) **3900**
Jami'at al-Azhar. Kulliyyat al-Lughah al-Arabiyyah bil-Mansurah. Majallah/Al-Azhar University. Arabic Language Faculty in Mansoura. Journal. (UA) **2820**
Jami'at al-Azhar. Kulliyyat al-Lughah al-Arabiyyah bil-Manufiyyah. Majallah/Al-Azhar University. Arabic Language Faculty in Menoufia. Journal. (UA) **2820**
Jami'at al-Azhar. Kulliyyat al-Lughah al-Arabiyyah bil-Zagazig. Majallah/Al-Azhar University. Arabic Language Faculty in Zagazig. Journal. (UA) **2820**
Jami'at al-Azhar. Kulliyyat Usul al-Din wal-Da'wah al-Islamiyyah bi-Tanta. Majallah/Al-Azhar University. Faculty of Islamic Theology in Tanta. Journal.(UA) **4219**
Jami'at al-Imam Muhammad Ibn Sa'ud al-Islamiyyah. Markaz al-Buhuth. Majallah/Islamic University of Imam Muhammad Ibn Saud. Research Center. Journal. (SU) **4219**
Jami'at al-Imarat al-Arabiyyah al-Muttahidah. Kulliyyat al-Aadaab. Majallah/United Arab Emirates University. Faculty of Arts. Journal. (TS) **2509**
Jami'at al-Imarat al-Arabiyyah al-Muttahidah. Kulliyyat al-Ulum. Majallah. *see* United Arab Emirates University. Faculty of Science. Journal **4349**
Jami'at al-Imarat al-Arabiyyah al-Muttahidah. Majallah/United Arab Emirates University. Journal. (TS) **2509**, **4317**
Jami'at al-Manufiyyah. Kulliyyat al-Tarbiyyah. Majallah/Menoufia University. Faculty of Education. Journal. (UA) **1641**
Jami'at Assiut. Kulliyyat al-Tarbiyyah. Majallah/Assiut University. Faculty of Education. Journal. (UA) **1641**
Jami'at Qatar. Al-Taqrir al-Ihsa'i al-Sanawi lil-Aam al-Jami'i/University of Qatar. Annual Statistical Report for the School Year. (QA) **1677**, **1728**
Jami'at Tanta. Kulliyyat al-Adab. Majallah/Tanta University. Faculty of Literature. Journal. (UA) **2927**
Jami'at Umm al-Qura. Kulliyyat al-Lughah al-Arabiyyah. Muhadarat al-Mawsim al-Thaqafi. (SU) **2820**
Jami'i. (TS) **1315**
Jaminraitu. (II) **2995**
Jammu and Kashmir. Directorate of Economics and Statistics. Digest of Statistics. (II) **4576**
Jammu and Kashmir. Legislative Council. Committee on Privileges. Report. (II ISSN 0448-2433) **3900**
Jammu and Kashmir Law Reporter. (II) **2637**
Jammu & Kashmir Minerals Limited. Annual Report. (II ISSN 0304-7164) **3486**
Jammu and Kashmir Research Biannual *see* J & K Research Biannual **2509**
Jamstec. (JA) **1546**
Jan Corporation. Facts & Info. (JA) **4693**
Jana Sangh Patrika. (II ISSN 0021-4205) **3901**
Janakavi. (CE) **3901**
Janaman. (II ISSN 0021-4213) **3901**
Janashakti News Weekly. (II) **2927**
Janasudha Daily. (II) **2869**, **3512**
Janasudha Monthly. (II) **2870**, **3512**
Janasudha Weekly. (II) **2870**, **3512**
Janata. (II ISSN 0021-4221) **3901**
Jane Austen Society of North America News *see* J A S N A News **2927**
Jane's A F V Retrofit Systems. (UK) **3460**
Jane's A F V Systems *see* Jane's A F V Retrofit Systems **3460**
Jane's Airport and A T C Equipment. (UK) **4675**, **57**
Jane's Airport Equipment *see* Jane's Airport and A T C Equipment **4675**
Jane's Airport Review. (UK ISSN 0954-7649) **4675**
Jane's All the World Aircraft. (UK ISSN 0075-3017) **57**

Jane's Armour and Artillery. (UK ISSN 0143-9952) **3460**
Jane's Avionics. (UK) **57**
Jane's Battlefield Air Defence *see* Jane's Land-Based Air Defence **3461**
Jane's Battlefield Surveillance. (UK) **3461**, **57**
Jane's C 3 I *see* Jane's C 3 I Systems **3461**
Jane's C 3 I Systems. (Command, Control, Communications & Intelligence) (UK) **3461**, **57**
Jane's Containerisation Directory. (UK) **4710**
Jane's Defence Weekly. (UK ISSN 0265-3818) **3461**
Jane's Fighting Ships. (UK ISSN 0075-3025) **3461**, **4730**
Jane's Freight Containers *see* Jane's Containerisation Directory **4710**
Jane's High-Speed Marine Craft. (UK) **4730**
Jane's High-Speed Marine Craft and Air Cushion Vehicles *see* Jane's High-Speed Marine Craft **4730**
Jane's Infantry Weapons. (UK ISSN 0306-3410) **3461**
Jane's Intelligence Review. (UK) **3461**
Jane's Land-Based Air Defence. (UK) **3461**
Jane's Military Communications. (UK ISSN 0144-0004) **3461**
Jane's Military Logistics *see* Jane's Military Vehicles and Logistics **3461**
Jane's Military Training Systems. (UK) **3461**
Jane's Military Vehicles and Logistics. (UK) **3461**
Jane's N B C Protection Equipment. (UK) **3461**
Jane's NATO Handbook. (UK ISSN 0958-126X) **3461**
Jane's Naval Weapon System. (UK) **3461**
Jane's Radar and E-W Systems. (UK) **3461**, **1338**, **1901**
Jane's Radar and Electronic Warfare. (UK) **3461**
Jane's Security & Co-In Equipment. (UK) **3461**
Jane's Soviet Intelligence Review *see* Jane's Intelligence Review **3461**
Jane's Spaceflight Directory *see* Interavia Space Directory **55**
Jane's Underwater Warfare Systems. (UK) **3461**
Jane's Urban Transport Systems. (UK) **4651**
Jane's World Airlines. (UK) **4675**
Jane's World Railways. (UK ISSN 0075-3084) **4710**
Janitsjarn. (NO) **3557**
Janmabhoomi. (II) **2200**
Janmabhoomi Khagol Siddha Sukshma Nirayana Bharatiya Panchang (Gujarati Edition). (II) **359**
▼Janmabhoomi Khagol Siddha Sukshma Nirayana Bharatiya Panchang (Hindi Edition). (II) **359**
Janmabhoomi Panchang. (II) **359**
Janmabhoomi Pravasi. (II) **2200**
Janmabhumi. (NP) **2211**
Jano "Medicina y Humanidades". (SP ISSN 0210-220X) **3112**
Janomot Bengali Newsweekly. (UK) **2008**
Jantantra. (II ISSN 0021-423X) **2870**
January Bulletin. (UK) **2132**
Janus *see* Aurora (Madison) **3010**
Janus. (NE ISSN 0021-4264) **4317**, **3112**, **4601**
†Januz Direct Marketing Letter. (US ISSN 0162-9107) **5220**
Japan. Annual Report on National Life. (JA) **870**
Japan. Chiba National Institute of Animal Industry. Annual Report *see* Japan. Ibaraki National Institute of Animal Industry. Annual Report **219**
Japan. Chiba National Institute of Animal Industry. Bulletin *see* Japan. Ibaraki National Institute of Animal Industry. Bulletin **219**
Japan. Electro Technical Laboratory. Summaries of Reports. (JA ISSN 0388-080X) **1901**, **1827**
Japan. Finance Department. Quarterly Bulletin of Financial Statistics *see* Financial Statistics of Japan **716**

JAPAN. MINISTRY 6333

Japan. Forestry and Forest Products Research Institute. Annual Report/Norinsho Ringyo Shikenjo Nenpo. (JA) **2103**
Japan. Forestry and Forest Products Research Institute. Bulletin. (JA) **2103**
Japan. Government Chemical Industrial Research Institute, Tokyo. Reports *see* Japan. National Chemical Laboratory for Industry. Journal **1179**
Japan. Government Forest Experiment Station. Kyushu Branch. Annual Report/Ringyo Shikenjo Kyushu Shijo Nenpo. (JA ISSN 0557-0395) **2103**
Japan. Government Forest Experiment Station, Tokyo. Annual Report *see* Japan. Forestry and Forest Products Research Institute. Annual Report **2103**
Japan. Government Industrial Development Laboratory, Hokkaido. Reports/Hokkaido Kogyo Kaihatsu Shikenjo Hokoku. (JA ISSN 0441-0734) **4601**
Japan. Government Industrial Development Laboratory, Hokkaido. Technical Data/Hokkaido Kogyo Kaihatsu Shikenjo Gijutsu. (JA) **4601**
Japan. Government Industrial Research Institute, Nagoya. Technical News. (JA ISSN 0027-7614) **4601**
Japan. Hokuriku National Agricultural Experiment Station. Bulletin. (JA ISSN 0439-3600) **182**, **152**
Japan. Ibaraki National Institute of Animal Industry. Annual Report/Nippon Ibaraki Chikusan Shikenjo Nenpo. (JA ISSN 0289-4238) **219**
Japan. Ibaraki National Institute of Animal Industry. Bulletin/Nippon Ibaraki Chikusan Shikenjo. Chikusan Shikenjo Kenkyu Hokoku. (JA) **219**
Japan. Information Science and Technology Association. Journal/Joho no Kagaku to Gijutsu. (JA ISSN 0913-3801) **2765**
Japan. Institute of Population Problems. Annual Report. (JA) **3984**
Japan. Institute of Statistical Mathematics. Research Reports, General Series. *see* Tokei Suri Kenkyujo Kenkyu Ripoto **3058**
Japan. Kaijo Hoan-cho. Suiro-bu. Suiro Yoho/Japan. Maritime Safety Agency. Hydrographic Department. Hydrographic Bulletin. (JA ISSN 0021-4485) **1598**
Japan. Management and Coordination Agency. Statistics Bureau. Employment Status Survey. (JA) **725**, **4576**
Japan. Maritime Safety Agency. Hydrographic Department. Hydrographic Bulletin. *see* Japan. Kaijo Hoan-cho. Suiro-bu. Suiro Yoho **1598**
Japan. Maritime Safety Agency. Hydrographic Department. Notices to Mariners/Suiro Tsuho. (JA ISSN 0447-3728) **4730**
Japan. Maritime Safety Agency. Hydrographic Department. Report of Hydrographic Research. (JA ISSN 0373-3602) **1546**
Japan. Meteorological Agency. Mean Maps. Long Range Weather Forecasting *see* Japan Meteorological Agency. Monthly Report on Climate System **3437**
Japan. Meteorological Agency. Monthly Report/Kisho-cho Geppo Zenkoku Kishchyo. (JA ISSN 0448-374X) **3437**
Japan. Ministry of Agriculture and Forestry. Annual Report. *see* Japan. Norin-sho Nenpo **100**
Japan. Ministry of Agriculture, Forestry and Fisheries. National Food Research Institute. Report. (JA ISSN 0301-9780) **2074**, **100**
Japan. Ministry of Agriculture, Forestry and Fisheries. National Research Institute of Agricultural Engineering. Abstracts from Research Reports. (JA ISSN 0386-5126) **162**, **1827**

JAPAN. MINISTRY

Japan. Ministry of Agriculture, Forestry and Fisheries. National Research Institute of Agricultural Engineering. Bulletin. (JA ISSN 0549-5725) **163**, **1827**

Japan. Ministry of Agriculture, Forestry and Fisheries. National Research Institute of Agricultural Engineering. Technical Report. (JA ISSN 0287-0029) **163**, **1827**

Japan. Ministry of Agriculture, Forestry and Fisheries. National Veterinary Assay Laboratory. Annual Report. (JA ISSN 0388-7421) **4811**

Japan. Ministry of Health and Welfare. Statistics and Information Department. Handbook of Health and Welfare Statistics. (JA ISSN 0911-8403) **4117**, **4426**, **4576**

Japan. Ministry of Health and Welfare. Statistics and Information Department. Monthly Report on Vital Statistics. (JA ISSN 0385-969X) **4576**

Japan. Ministry of Health and Welfare. Statistics and Information Department. Report on Activities of Public Health Centers. (JA ISSN 0911-8411) **3176**, **4576**

Japan. Ministry of Health and Welfare. Statistics and Information Department. Report on Survey of National Medical Care Insurance Services. (JA ISSN 0911-8454) **2547**, **4576**

Japan. Ministry of Health and Welfare. Statistics and Information Department. Report on Survey of Occupational Statistics on Vital Events. (JA ISSN 0911-8527) **3632**, **4576**

Japan. Ministry of Health and Welfare. Statistics and Information Department. Report on Survey of Public Assistance. (JA ISSN 0448-4002) **4426**, **4576**

Japan. Ministry of Health and Welfare. Statistics and Information Department. Report on Survey of Socio-Economic Aspects on Vital Events. (JA ISSN 0448-3960) **725**, **4395**, **4576**

Japan. Ministry of Health and Welfare. Statistics and Information Department. Report on Survey of Social Welfare Institutions. (JA ISSN 0448-4029) **4426**, **4576**

Japan. Ministry of Health and Welfare. Statistics and Information Department. Statistical Report on Communicable Diseases. (JA ISSN 0911-8489) **3176**, **4576**

Japan. Ministry of Health and Welfare. Statistics and Information Department. Statistical Report on Food Poisonings. (JA ISSN 0911-8497) **3176**, **4576**

Japan. Ministry of Health and Welfare. Statistics and Information Department. Statistical Report on Public Health Administration and Services/Eisei Gyosei Gyomu Hokoku. (JA ISSN 0448-3952) **4117**, **4576**

Japan. Ministry of Health and Welfare. Statistics and Information Department. Statistical Report on Social Welfare Administration and Services. (JA ISSN 0448-4010) **4426**, **4576**

Japan. Ministry of Health and Welfare. Statistics and Information Department. Vital Statistics. (JA ISSN 0075-3270) **4576**

Japan. Ministry of Labour. Yearbook of Labour Statistics. (JA) **725**

Japan. National Chemical Laboratory for Industry. Journal/Kagaku Gijutsu Kenkyujo Hokoku. (JA ISSN 0388-3213) **1179**

Japan. National Food Research Institute. News. (JA) **2074**

Japan. National Institute for Educational Research. Newsletter. (JA ISSN 0385-1990) **1641**

Japan. National Institute of Agrobiological Resources. Bulletin. (JA ISSN 0911-6575) **443**

Japan. National Institute of Animal Health. Annual Report. see Japan. Norin-sho Kachiku Eisei Shikenjo Nenpo **5220**

Japan. National Institute of Animal Health. Bulletin/Norin Suisan-sho Kachiku Eisei Shikenjo Kenkyu Hokoku. (JA ISSN 0388-2403) **4811**

Japan. National Institute of Genetics, Mishima. Annual Report/Nippon Mishima Kokuritsu Idengaku Kenkyujo. Nenpo. (JA ISSN 0077-4995) **544**

Japan. National Museum News. (JA ISSN 0040-8948) **3525**

†Japan. Norin-sho Kachiku Eisei Shikenjo Nenpo/Japan. National Institute of Animal Health. Annual Report. (JA ISSN 0453-0535) **5220**

Japan. Norin-sho Nenpo/Japan. Ministry of Agriculture and Forestry. Annual Report. (JA ISSN 0446-5458) **100**, **2103**

Japan. Pocket Size Statistics of Sugar Products. (JA) **2085**, **4576**

Japan. Society of Sea Water Science. Bulletin. (JA ISSN 0369-4550) **1606**, **1212**, **1901**

Japan (Year) see Japan: An International Comparison **4576**

Japan Academy. Proceedings see Japan Academy. Proceedings. Series A: Mathematical Sciences **3040**

Japan Academy. Proceedings. Series A: Mathematical Sciences/Nippon Gakushiin Kiyo A. (JA ISSN 0386-2194) **3040**

Japan Academy. Proceedings. Series B: Physical and Biological Sciences/Nippon Gakushiin Kiyo B. (JA ISSN 0386-2208) **4317**

Japan Advertising Federation. Aims and Organization. (JA) **33**

Japan Agricultural Coop News see Zenchu Farm News **833**

Japan Agricultural Research Quarterly. (JA ISSN 0021-3551) **100**

Japan Air Cleaning Association. Journal.(JA) **1959**

Japan Air Self Defense Force. Aeromedical Laboratory. Reports. see Koku Igaku Jikkentai Hokoku **3120**

Japan Aktuell. (GW) **2207**

Japan-America Society of Washington. Bulletin. (US ISSN 0021-4299) **3962**, **2008**, **3639**

Japan: An International Comparison. (JA ISSN 0389-3502) **4576**, **2207**

†Japan and America. (US) **5220**

Japan & Korea Stamp Catalogue. (UK ISSN 0142-9906) **3753**

Japan and the World Economy. (NE ISSN 0922-1425) **914**, **895**, **999**

Japan Annual Reviews in Electronics, Computers & Telecommunications. Amorphous Semiconductor Technologies & Devices. (JA ISSN 0167-5036) **1774**, **1351**

†Japan Anti-Tuberculosis Association. Reports on Medical Research Problems/Kekkaku Yobokai Kenkyu Gyoseki. (JA ISSN 0075-3165) **5220**

Japan Architect. (International edition of: Shinkenchiku). (JA ISSN 0021-4302) **301**

Japan Association for Philosophy of Science. Annals. (JA ISSN 0453-0691) **4317**, **3770**

Japan Association for Philosophy of Science. Journal. see Kagaku Kisoron Kenkyu **4319**

Japan Astronomical Study Association. Monthly Bulletin. see Nihon Tenmon Kenkyukai Kansoku Geppo **371**

Japan Atomic Energy Research Institute Report see J A E R I Report **1806**

Japan Atomic Energy Research Institute Reports. List see J A E R I Reports. List **1806**

Japan Atomic Energy Research Institute Reports Abstracts see J A E R I Reports Abstracts **3837**

Japan Auto Abstracts. (JA) **4665**, **4693**

Japan Automotive News. (JA ISSN 0021-4329) **4693**

▼Japan Avenue. (US) **2227**

Japan Aviation Directory. (JA ISSN 0286-0635) **1140**, **57**

Japan Banana Importers Association. Annual Report of Banana Statistics. (JA) **139**

Japan Banana Importers Association. Monthly Bulletin of Banana Statistics.(JA) **139**

Japan Bioindustry Letters. (JA) **490**

Japan Book Importers Association Directory see J B I A Directory **1140**

Japan Broncho-Esophagological Society. Journal. see Nihon Kikan Shokudoka Gakkai Kaiho **3366**

†Japan Business. (US ISSN 0895-6731) **5220**

Japan Business Directory. see Diamond's Japan Business Directory (Year) **1128**

Japan Business Law Guide. (AT) **672**, **2637**

Japan Business Law Letter. (JA) **672**

Japan Camera Trade News. (JA ISSN 0021-4345) **3792**

Japan Census of Manufactures: Report by Commodities. (JA ISSN 0075-3289) **1079**

Japan Center for Economic Research. Center Paper Series. (JA ISSN 0075-3238) **870**

Japan Chemical Annual. (JA ISSN 0075-319X) **1855**

Japan Chemical Directory (Tokyo, 1963). (JA ISSN 0075-3203) **1855**

Japan Chemical Industry Association. Annual Report. (JA) **1855**

Japan Chemical Industry Association Monthly. see Nikkakyo Geppo **1857**

Japan Chemical Week. (JA ISSN 0047-1755) **1855**

†Japan Chemistry. (US ISSN 0895-674X) **5220**

Japan Christian Activity News. (JA ISSN 0021-4353) **4183**

Japan Christian Quarterly. (JA ISSN 0021-4361) **4183**

Japan Commercial Arbitration Association. Quarterly. (JA ISSN 0452-3385) **914**

Japan Commercial Arbitration Association Journal see J C A Journal **914**

▼Japan Company Datafile. (JA) **1140**

Japan Company Handbook. First Section. (JA ISSN 0288-9307) **1141**

Japan Company Handbook. Second Section. (JA) **1141**

Japan Comparative Education Society. Bulletin. (JA ISSN 0289-405X) **1641**

Japan Computer Quarterly. (JA ISSN 0388-0494) **1397**

†Japan Computer Technology and Applications Abstracts. (US ISSN 0890-1406) **5220**

†Japan Computers. (US ISSN 0895-6715) **5220**

Japan Concrete Institute Transactions see J C I Transactions **621**

Japan Congress on Materials Research. Proceedings/Zairyo Kenkyu Rengo Koenkai Ronbunshu. (JA ISSN 0368-3141) **1918**

Japan Cotton Statistics and Related Data. (JA ISSN 0447-5321) **4628**

Japan Dental Association. Journal/Nihon Shika Ishikai Zasshi. (JA ISSN 0047-1763) **3235**

Japan Diabetes Society. Journal/Tonyobyo. (JA ISSN 0021-437X) **3254**

Japan Diabetic Society. Journal see Japan Diabetes Society. Journal **3254**

▼Japan Digest. (UK ISSN 0960-1473) **3962**

Japan Directory. (JA ISSN 0075-322X) **1141**

Japan Directory of Professional Associations. (JA ISSN 0287-9530) **4130**

Japan Drug Industry Review see Pharma Japan Yearbook **3737**

Japan Echo. (JA) **2339**

Japan Economic Almanac. (JA) **1079**, **870**

Japan Economic Daily. (US ISSN 0734-0575) **870**, **787**

Japan Economic Institute Report see J E I Report **914**

Japan Economic Journal see The Nikkei Weekly **682**

Japan Economic Research Center. Center Paper Series see Japan Center for Economic Research. Center Paper Series **870**

Japan Electronics (Gardena). (US ISSN 0888-904X) **1774**, **1879**

†Japan Electronics (Washington). (US ISSN 0895-6723) **5220**

Japan Electronics Almanac. (JA) **1774**, **914**

Japan Electronics Buyers' Guide. (JA) **1141**, **1901**

Japan Electronics Tec Report see Japan Electronics (Gardena) **1774**

Japan Electronics Today News see Nikkei High Tech Report **5248**

†Japan Energy. (US ISSN 0895-6774) **5220**

Japan English Books in Print see Japan English Publications in Print **404**

Japan English Magazine Directory see Japan English Publications in Print **404**

Japan English Publications in Print. (JA ISSN 0910-7908) **404**

Japan Federation of Composers. Catalogue of Publications. (JA) **3588**

Japan Forum. (UK ISSN 0955-5803) **3963**

Japan Foundation Annual Report. (JA) **2509**

Japan Foundation Newsletter. (JA ISSN 0385-2318) **3639**, **2207**

Japan Foundrymen's Society. Journal/Imono. (JA ISSN 0021-4396) **3410**

Japan Free Press. (JA ISSN 0912-6317) **2207**

Japan Fruit Growers Cooperative Association. Fruit Statistics in Japan. (JA) **139**

Japan Gas Association. Journal. see Nihon Gasu Kyokaishi **3693**

Japan Graphic Arts. (JA ISSN 0072-548X) **331**

Japan Harvest. (JA ISSN 0021-440X) **4240**

Japan Hearing-Handicap News Paper. (JA) **2288**

Japan High Tech Review see East Asia High Tech Review **4597**

Japan Hotel Guide. (JA ISSN 0446-6217) **2477**

Japan Industrial and Technology Bulletin see New Technology Japan **3021**

Japan Industrial Safety and Health Association. Annual Report. (JA) **3618**

Japan Industrial Safety and Health Association. International Cooperation Department. Guidebook on Occupational Health. (JA) **3618**

Japan Industrial Safety and Health Association. International Cooperation Department. Occupational Health. (JA) **3618**

Japan Industrial Safety and Health Association. International Cooperation Department. Safety. (JA) **3618**

Japan Industrial Safety and Health Association. International Cooperation Department. Yearbook of Industrial Safety and Health. (JA) **3618**

Japan Industrial Safety and Health Association. Research and Survey Division. Yearbook of Industrial Safety see Japan Industrial Safety and Health Association. International Cooperation Department. Yearbook of Industrial Safety and Health **3618**

Japan Information Resources in the United States. (JA) **2207**

Japan Institute of Insect Damage to Cultural Properties. Journal see Bunkazai no Chu-kin-gai **529**

Japan Institute of Labour. Journal. see Nihon Rodo Kyokai Zasshi **990**

Japan Institute of Metals. Bulletin/Nihon Kinzoku Gakkai Kaiho. (JA ISSN 0021-4426) **3410**

Japan Institute of Metals. Journal/ Nippon Kinzoku Gakkaishi. (JA ISSN 0021-4876) **3410**
Japan Institute of Metals. Transactions see Materials Transactions, J I M **3413**
Japan Institute of Navigation. Journal/ Nihon Kokai Gakkai Ronbunshu. (JA ISSN 0388-7405) **4730**, 57, 1606, 4317
Japan Insurance News. (JA ISSN 0910-4534) **2535**
Japan International Cooperation Agency. Organization and Functions. (JA) **932**
▼Japan International Journal. (JA) **2207**
Japan Journal of Applied Mathematics. (JA ISSN 0910-2043) **3040**
Japan Journal of Educational Technology. (JA ISSN 0385-5236) **4601**
Japan Journal of Logopedics and Phoniatrics. see Onsei Gengo Igaku **3316**
Japan Labour Bulletin. (JA ISSN 0021-4469) **984**
Japan Letter. (HK ISSN 0379-2889) **870**, 3639
Japan Lumber Journal. (JA ISSN 0021-4477) **2115**
Japan Machinery Exporters' Association Newsletter see J M E A Newsletter **5219**
Japan Management Association Management News see J M A Management News **1015**
Japan Management Association Newsletter see J M A Newsletter **5219**
†Japan Manufacturing. (US ISSN 0895-6685) **5220**
Japan Map Center News/Chizu Senta Nyusu. (JA ISSN 0302-0231) **2254**
Japan Marine Science and Technology Center. Annual Report. (JA) **1546**
Japan Marine Science and Technology Center. Technical Reports. (JA ISSN 0387-382X) **1546**
Japan Maritime Daily. see Nihon Kaiji Shinbun **2573**
Japan Maritime Research Institute. Bulletin. see Kaiji Sangyo Kenkyujoho **4730**
Japan Maritime Research Institute Report see J A M R I Report **4729**
†Japan Materials. (US ISSN 0895-6707) **5220**
†Japan Materials News. (US) **5220**
Japan Meat Processing Journal. (JA ISSN 0386-2372) **2074**
Japan Medical and Pharmaceutical Directory see Medical Companies Guide to Japan **3748**
Japan Medical Journal. (JA ISSN 0385-9215) **3112**
Japan Medical News. (JA ISSN 0021-4515) **3112**
Japan Medical Review. (US ISSN 0914-0255) **3112**, 1042
Japan Metal Bulletin. (JA ISSN 0021-4523) **3410**, 3486
Japan Meteorological Agency. Agricultural Meteorology. Annual Report. (JA ISSN 0368-5942) **3437**, 100
Japan Meteorological Agency. Annual Report/Kisho-cho Nenpo Zenkoku Kishohyo. (JA ISSN 0448-3758) **3437**
Japan Meteorological Agency. Monthly Report on Climate System. (JA) **3437**
Japan Meteorological Agency. Report of Magnetic Pulsations. (JA) **1591**
Japan Meteorological Agency. Seismological Bulletin/Jishin Geppo. (JA ISSN 0446-5059) **1591**
Japan Meteorological Agency. Technical Report. (JA ISSN 0447-3868) **1591**
Japan Meteorological Agency. Volcanological Bulletin/Kazan Hokoku. (JA ISSN 0447-3892) **1591**
Japan Missionary Bulletin. (JA ISSN 0021-4531) **4183**
Japan Motor Industry. (JA) **4693**

Japan News. (UK ISSN 0307-3033) **4184**
Japan Notebook. (US ISSN 1053-4997) **2008**
Japan Optics. (JA) **3301**
Japan Orthodontic Society. Journal/ Nihon Kyosei Shika Gakkai Zasshi. (JA ISSN 0021-454X) **3235**
†Japan Periodicals. (JA) **5220**
Japan Pesticide Information. (JA ISSN 0368-265X) **182**
Japan Petroleum and Energy Trends. (JA ISSN 0916-2623) **3690**
Japan Petroleum and Energy Weekly see Japan Petroleum and Energy Trends **3690**
Japan Petroleum Weekly see Japan Petroleum and Energy Trends **3690**
Japan Pharma Insight. (JA) **3730**
Japan Pharmaceutical Information Center. Information see J A P I C Weekly Bulletin **3730**
Japan Pharmaceutical Information Center Weekly Bulletin see J A P I C Weekly Bulletin **3730**
Japan Pharmaceutical Reference. (JA ISSN 0917-7825) **3730**
†Japan Philately. (JA) **5220**
Japan Pictorial. (JA) **2207**
Japan Plastics Age. (JA ISSN 0021-4582) **3863**
Japan Plastics Journal. see Nihon Purasuchikkusu Shinpo **3864**
Japan Political Research. (US) **3901**
Japan Port Information. (JA) **4730**
Japan Precious Metals and Watch News. see Nippon Kikinzoku Tokei Shinbun **2565**
Japan Press Weekly: News & Comments. (JA ISSN 0287-7112) **2207**
Japan Printing Art Annual. see Nihon Insatsu Nenkan **4003**
Japan Printing News. see Nippon Insatsu Shinbun **4003**
Japan Publications Guide Service Letter see J P G Letter **4130**
Japan Publishers Directory. (JA) **4130**
Japan Pulp and Paper. (JA) **3663**
Japan Quarterly. (JA ISSN 0021-4590) **2870**
Japan Radiation Research Society. Journal see Journal of Radiation Research **3360**
Japan Refrigeration and Air Conditioning News. see Nihon Reito Reibo Shinbun **2302**
Japan Register of Merchants, Manufacturers and Shippers see Standard Trade Index of Japan **1154**
Japan Report see Japan - U S Business Report **914**
Japan Report (Arlington). (US) **870**, 3901
Japan Report (New York). (US ISSN 0021-4604) **2207**
Japan Report: Science and Technology. (US) **4317**, 4601
Japan Research Association for Textile End-Uses. Journal. see Sen'i Seihin Shohi Kagaku **4623**
Japan Science and Technology. see Nihon no Kagaku to Gijutsu **4330**
Japan Sea Regional Fisheries Research Laboratory. Bulletin/Nihonkai-ku Suisan Kenkyujo Kenkyu Hokoku. (JA ISSN 0021-4620) **2044**
†Japan Socialist Review. (JA ISSN 0021-4655) **5220**
Japan Society. Review. (UK) **3963**
Japan Society for Aeronautical and Space Sciences. Journal/Nihon Koku Uchu Gakkai-shi. (JA ISSN 0021-4663) **57**
Japan Society for Aeronautical and Space Sciences. Transactions. (JA ISSN 0549-3811) **57**
Japan Society for Bioscience, Biotechnology, and Agrochemistry. Journal. see Nippon Nogeikaggaku Kaishi **491**
Japan Society for Cancer Therapy. Journal. (JA ISSN 0021-4671) **3198**
Japan Society for Cancer Therapy. Proceedings of the Congress. (JA ISSN 0075-3327) **3198**

Japan Society for Comparative Endocrinology. Proceedings. (JA ISSN 0913-9036) **3254**, 443
Japan Society for Composite Materials. Transactions. (JA ISSN 0385-2571) **1918**, 1827
Japan Society for Heat Treatment. Journal. see Netsu Shori **3416**
Japan Society for Precision Engineering. International Journal. (JA ISSN 0916-782X) **2523**
Japan Society for Simulation Technology. Journal. (JA ISSN 0285-9947) **1435**, 1879, 4359
Japan Society for Technology of Plasticity. Journal/Sosei to Kako. (JA ISSN 0038-1586) **4601**, 1932, 3821
Japan Society for the History of Industrial Technology. Annual Conference. Proceedings. see Nihon Sangyo Gijutsushi Gakkai Nenkai Koen Gaiyoshu **4615**
Japan Society of Air Pollution. Journal/ Taiki Osen Kenkyu. (JA ISSN 0039-9000) **1977**
Japan Society of Civil Engineers. Journal/Doboku Gakkaishi. (JA ISSN 0021-468X) **1868**
Japan Society of Civil Engineers. Proceedings. see Doboku Gakkai Ronbunshu **1864**
Japan Society of Civil Engineers. Proceedings of the Annual Conference. see Doboku Gakkai Nenji Koenkai Koen Gaiyoshu **1864**
Japan Society of Industrial and Technical Education. Bulletin. (JA) **1752**
Japan Society of Library Science. Annals/Toshokan Gakkai Nenpo. (JA ISSN 0040-9650) **2765**
Japan Society of London. Bulletin see Japan Society. Review **3963**
Japan Society of Mechanical Engineers. Transactions. see Nihon Kikai Gakkai Ronbunshu **1936**
Japan Society of Mechanical Engineers International Journal see J S M E International Journal **1932**
Japan Society of Mechanical Engineers Journal see J S M E Journal **1932**
Japan Society of Plant Taxonomists. News. see Syokubutsu Bunrui Gakkai Nyusu **518**
Japan Society of Plant Taxonomists. Proceedings/Nihon Shokubutsu Bunrui Gakkai Kaiho. (JA ISSN 0911-6052) **506**
Japan Society of Precision Engineering. Bulletin see Japan Society for Precision Engineering. International Journal **2523**
Japan Spinners' Association. Monthly Report. see Nihon Boseki Geppo **4622**
Japan Statistical Association. Annual Report on the Internal Migration in Japan Derived from the Basic Resident Registers. (JA ISSN 0286-1410) **3993**
Japan Statistical Association. Annual Report on the Labour Force Survey. (JA ISSN 0289-1301) **725**, 984
Japan Statistical Association. Annual Report on the Retail Price Survey. (JA) **725**
Japan Statistical Association. Annual Report on the Unincorporated Enterprise Survey. (JA ISSN 0448-7141) **725**
Japan Statistical Society. Journal. see Nihon Tokei Gakkaishi **731**
Japan Steel Works Technical News. (JA) **3410**
Japan Steel Works Technical Review. see Nihon Seikosho Giho **3416**
Japan Sugar Yearbook. (JA) **2074**
Japan T A P P I Journal/Kami Pa Gikyoshi. (Japan Technical Association of the Pulp and Paper Industry) (JA ISSN 0022-815X) **3663**
Japan Technical Association of the Pulp and Paper Industry Japan T A P P I Journal see Japan T A P P I Journal **3663**
†Japan Technology Series. (US) **5220**

†Japan Telecommunications. (US ISSN 0895-6766) **5220**
Japan Telecommunications Review see N T T Review **1340**
Japan Textile Industry. Directory. see Sen-i Kougyo Yoran **4628**
Japan: the Official Guide see New Official Guide: Japan **4779**
Japan Times. (JA ISSN 0289-1956) **2207**
†Japan Times Directory. (JA) **5220**
Japan - Tin in Tinplate. (UK) **3410**
Japan Trade Center Information Service. Monthly Economic Report. (US) **870**
Japan Trade Directory (Year)/Nihon Boeki Shinkokai. (JA) **1141**
Japan Typography Annual/Nihon Taipogurafi Nenkan. (JA) **4002**
Japan - U S Business Report. (US ISSN 0888-5702) **914**
Japan Update. (JA ISSN 0912-3474) **672**, 870
Japan Water Works Association. Journal see Water Japan **4832**
Japan Welding Society. Journal/Yosetsu Gakkaishi. (JA ISSN 0021-4787) **3429**
Japan Welding Society. Transactions. (JA ISSN 0385-9282) **3410**
Japan Wood Research Society. Journal/ Mokuzai Gakkaishi. (JA ISSN 0021-4795) **2115**
Japan 21st. (JA) **1079**
Japana Medicina Revuo. see Igaku Hyoron **3107**
Japanese-American Yellow Pages. (US) **1141**
†Japanese Anaesthesia Journals Review. (NE ISSN 0169-1066) **5220**
Japanese Antarctic Research Expedition Data Reports. (JA ISSN 0075-3343) **1546**
Japanese Antarctic Research Expedition, 1956-1962. Scientific Reports. Series B: Meteorology see National Institute of Polar Research. Memoirs. Series B: Meteorology **3439**
Japanese Antarctic Research Expedition, 1956-1962. Scientific Reports. Series C: Earth Sciences. see National Institute of Polar Research. Memoirs. Series C: Earth Sciences **1547**
Japanese Antarctic Research Expedition, 1956-1962. Scientific Reports. Series D: Oceanography see National Institute of Polar Research. Memoirs. Series D: Oceanography **1608**
Japanese Antarctic Research Expedition, 1956-1962. Scientific Reports. Series E. Biology see National Institute of Polar Research. Memoirs. Series E: Biology and Medical Science **448**
Japanese Antarctic Research Expedition, 1956-1962. Scientific Reports. Series F: Logistic see National Institute of Polar Research. Memoirs. Series F: Logistics **4326**
Japanese Antarctic Research Expedition, 1956-1962. Scientific Reports. Special Issue see National Institute of Polar Research. Memoirs. Special Issue **1547**
Japanese Archives of Internal Medicine/ Naikahokan. (JA ISSN 0021-4809) **3112**
Japanese Association of Groundwater Hydrology. Journal see Journal of Groundwater Hydrology **1599**
Japanese Association of Physical Medicine, Balneology, and Climatology. Journal. see Nihon Onsen Kiko Butsuri Igakkai Zasshi **3136**
Japanese Association of Refrigeration. Transactions. (JA ISSN 0910-0040) **2301**
Japanese Biochemical Society. Journal. see Seikagaku **482**
Japanese Books in Print (Year). (JA) **404**
Japanese Bulletin of Art Therapy. (JA ISSN 0916-6688) **331**, 4026
Japanese Business. see Jitsugyo No Nihon **673**

JAPANESE CANADIAN

Japanese Canadian Citizens Association of Greater Vancouver. Bulletin. (CN ISSN 1182-0225) **2207**, 2339

Japanese Chamber of Commerce and Industry of Hawaii. Newsbulletin. (US) 818

Japanese Circulation Journal/Nihon Junkankigakushi. (JA ISSN 0047-1828) **3209**

Japanese Circulation Journal Supplement. (JA) **3209**

Japanese City Guide. (US) **4773**

Japanese Collagen Club. Proceedings of the Annual Meeting see Japanese Matrix (Collagen) Club. Proceedings of the Annual Meeting **3113**

Japanese Communist Party. Central Committee. Bulletin: Information for Abroad. (JA ISSN 0007-4683) **3901**

Japanese Companies in the U.K. see Britain's Top Japanese-Owned Companies **1124**

Japanese Cosmetic Science Society. Journal. (JA ISSN 0287-1238) **375**

Japanese Economic Indicators. see Nihon Keizai Shihyo **875**

Japanese Economic Studies. (US ISSN 0021-4841) **672**

Japanese Finance and Industry: Quarterly Survey. (JA) **787**, 1079

†Japanese Flower Arranging. (US ISSN 1041-5912) **5220**

Japanese Forestry Society. Journal/Nihon Ringakkaishi. (JA ISSN 0021-485X) **2103**

Japanese Guide to Hawaii. (US) **4773**

Japanese Heart Journal. (JA ISSN 0021-4868) **3209**

Japanese Hospital Directory. see Byoin Yoran **2459**

Japanese Industry and Technology. Digest. (JA) **4601**

Japanese Information Center of Science and Technology Online Information System see J I C S T Online Information System **4359**

Japanese Investment in U S Real Estate (Western Region) see Japanese Investment in U S Real Estate Review **952**

Japanese Investment in U S Real Estate Review. (US ISSN 0898-9761) **952**, 4151

Japanese Journal for Midwives. see Josanpu Zasshi **3293**

Japanese Journal for Public Health Nurse. see Hokenfu Zasshi **3278**

Japanese Journal of Allergology/Arerugi.(JA ISSN 0021-4884) **3187**

Japanese Journal of Animal Reproduction see Journal of Reproduction and Development **4811**

Japanese Journal of Antibiotics. (JA ISSN 0368-2781) **3112**, 3730

Japanese Journal of Applied Entomology and Zoology/Nihon Oyo Dobutsu Konchu Gakkaishi. (JA ISSN 0021-4914) **534**, 585

Japanese Journal of Applied Physics. (JA ISSN 0021-4922) **3821**, 1827

Japanese Journal of Applied Statistics. see Oyo Tokeigaku **4582**

Japanese Journal of Bacteriology. (JA ISSN 0021-4930) **3220**

Japanese Journal of Behavior Therapy. see Kodo Ryoho Kenkyu **4034**

Japanese Journal of Behaviormetrics. see Kodo Keiryogaku **4034**

Japanese Journal of Biometeorology. see Nihon Seikisho Gakkai Zasshi **3440**

Japanese Journal of Breeding. (JA ISSN 0536-3683) **544**

Japanese Journal of Cancer Clinics/Gan No Rinsho. (JA ISSN 0021-4949) **3198**

Japanese Journal of Cancer Research. (JA ISSN 0910-5050) **3199**

Japanese Journal of Child & Adolescent Psychiatry/Jido Seinen Seishin Igaku to Sono Kinsetsu Ryoiki. (JA ISSN 0289-0968) **3340**

Japanese Journal of Clinical and Experimental Medicine/Rinsho to Kenkyu. (JA ISSN 0021-4965) **3260**

Japanese Journal of Clinical Dermatology/Rinsho Hifuka. (JA ISSN 0021-4973) **3248**

Japanese Journal of Clinical Medicine/Nippon Rinsho. (JA ISSN 0047-1852) **3112**

Japanese Journal of Clinical Nutrition/Rinsho Eiyo. (JA ISSN 0485-1412) **3607**

Japanese Journal of Clinical Oncology. (JA ISSN 0368-2811) **3199**

Japanese Journal of Clinical Ophthalmology. (JA ISSN 0370-5579) **3301**

Japanese Journal of Clinical Radiology/Rinsho Hoshasen. (JA) **3359**

Japanese Journal of Clinical Urology. see Rinsho Hinyokika **3389**

Japanese Journal of Criminal Psychology/Hanzai Shinrigaku Kenkyu. (JA ISSN 0017-7547) **4026**

Japanese Journal of Crop Science/Nihon Sakumotsu Gakkai Kiji. (JA) **182**

Japanese Journal of Dermatology: Series A/Nihon Hifuka Gakkai Zasshi.(JA ISSN 0021-499X) **3248**

Japanese Journal of Dermatology: Series B/Nihon Hifuka Gakkai Zasshi.(JA) **3248**

Japanese Journal of Ecology/Nippon Seitai Gakkaishi. (JA ISSN 0021-5007) **1959**, 443

Japanese Journal of Education of the Handicapped. see Shitai Fujiyu Kyoiku **1741**

Japanese Journal of Educational Psychology. (JA ISSN 0021-5015) **4026**, 1641

Japanese Journal of Entomology. (JA) **534**

Japanese Journal of Ethnology/Minzokugaku Kenkyu. (JA ISSN 0021-5023) **242**

†Japanese Journal of Experimental Medicine. (JA ISSN 0021-5031) **5220**

Japanese Journal of Genetics/Idengaku Zasshi. (JA ISSN 0021-504X) **544**

Japanese Journal of Health and Human Ecology. (JA ISSN 0368-9395) **443**

Japanese Journal of Human Genetics/Jinrui Idengaku Zasshi. (JA ISSN 0021-5074) **544**

Japanese Journal of Hygiene/Nihon Eiseigaku Zasshi. (JA ISSN 0021-5082) **3804**

Japanese Journal of Ichthyology. (JA ISSN 0021-5090) **585**, 2044

Japanese Journal of Industrial Health/Sangyo Igaku. (JA ISSN 0047-1879) **3618**

Japanese Journal of Legal Medicine/Nippon Hoigaku Zasshi. (JA ISSN 0047-1887) **3265**

Japanese Journal of Leprosy. (JA ISSN 0386-3980) **3220**

Japanese Journal of Limnology/Rikusui Gaku Zasshi. (JA ISSN 0021-5104) **1599**

Japanese Journal of Mathematics. (JA ISSN 0289-2316) **3040**

Japanese Journal of Medical Electronics and Biological Engineering/Iyo Denshi to Seito Kogaku (Nihon M-E Gakkai Zasshi). (JA ISSN 0021-3675) **3112**

Japanese Journal of Medical Mycology. (JA ISSN 0583-0516) **553**, 3187

Japanese Journal of Medical Science and Biology. (JA ISSN 0021-5112) **3113**, 443

Japanese Journal of Medicine. (JA ISSN 0021-5120) **3113**

Japanese Journal of Nuclear Medicine. see Kaku Igaku **3360**

Japanese Journal of Nursing. (JA ISSN 0389-8326) **3279**

Japanese Journal of Nursing Arts. see Kango Gijutsu **3281**

Japanese Journal of Nursing Education. see Kango Kyoiku **3281**

Japanese Journal of Nursing Research. see Kango Kenkyu **3281**

Japanese Journal of Nursing Science. see Kango Tenbo **3281**

Japanese Journal of Nutrition/Eiyogaku Zasshi. (JA ISSN 0021-5147) **3607**

Japanese Journal of Ophthalmology. (JA ISSN 0021-5155) **3301**

Japanese Journal of Ornithology. (JA) **564**

Japanese Journal of Parasitology/Kiseichugaku Zasshi. (JA ISSN 0021-5171) **3220**

Japanese Journal of Pediatric Medicine. see Shoni Naika **3326**

Japanese Journal of Pharmacognosy. see Shoyakugaku Zasshi **3743**

Japanese Journal of Pharmacology. (JA ISSN 0021-5198) **3730**

Japanese Journal of Physical Fitness see Japanese Journal of Physical Fitness and Sports Medicine **3804**

Japanese Journal of Physical Fitness and Sports Medicine. (JA ISSN 0039-906X) **3804**, 3371

Japanese Journal of Physical Therapy. see Rigaku Ryoho Janaru **3216**

Japanese Journal of Physiology. (JA ISSN 0021-521X) **572**, 3113

Japanese Journal of Plastic & Reconstructive Surgery/Keisei Geka. (JA ISSN 0021-5228) **3379**

Japanese Journal of Primary Care see Primary Care **3144**

Japanese Journal of Psychiatry and Neurology. (JA ISSN 0912-2036) **3340**

Japanese Journal of Psychology. see Shinrigaku Kenkyu **4046**

Japanese Journal of Psychosomatic Medicine. see Shinshin-Igaku **3354**

Japanese Journal of Rehabilitation Medicine. see Rihabiriteshon Igaku **3149**

Japanese Journal of Religious Studies. (JA ISSN 0304-1042) **4215**, 3639

Japanese Journal of Rheumatology. (NE ISSN 0169-1163) **3369**

Japanese Journal of Sanitary Zoology/Eisei Dobutsu. (JA ISSN 0424-7086) **585**, 4106, 4811

Japanese Journal of Soil Science and Plant Nutrition. see Nippon Dojo Hiryogaku Zasshi **186**

Japanese Journal of Thoracic Surgery/Kyobu Geka. (JA ISSN 0021-5252) **3379**

Japanese Journal of Toxicology and Environmental Health. see Eisei Kagaku **1981**

Japanese Journal of Tribology. (English translation of: Tribologist) (US ISSN 1045-7828) **1932**, 3018

Japanese Journal of Tropical Agriculture/Nettai Nogyo. (JA ISSN 0021-5260) **101**

Japanese Journal of Tropical Medicine and Hygiene. (JA ISSN 0304-2146) **3221**

Japanese Journal of Urology/Nihon Hinyokika Gakkai Zasshi. (JA ISSN 0021-5287) **3388**

Japanese Journal of Veterinary Research. (JA ISSN 0047-1917) **4811**

Japanese Journal of Veterinary Science see Journal of Veterinary Medical Science **4812**

Japanese Journal of Zootechnical Science see Animal Science and Technology (Japan) **210**

Japanese Junior Red Cross. see Seishonen Sekijuji **4112**

Japanese Language. see Riyu Zhishi **2838**

Japanese Lifestyle - U S A see LifeStyle - U S A **2012**

Japanese Literature. see Nihon Bungaku **2943**

Japanese Literature Today. (JA) **2927**

Japanese Matrix (Collagen) Club. Proceedings of the Annual Meeting. (JA) **3113**, 443

Japanese Medical Researchers Directory. (JA) **3113**

Japanese Motor Business. (UK ISSN 0266-898X) **4693**

Japanese Musicological Society. Journal. see Ongaku Gaku **3571**

Japanese National Bibliography Weekly List/Nihon Zenkoku Shoshi. (JA ISSN 0385-3292) **404**

Japanese Neurochemical Society. Bulletin. see Shinkei Kagaku **3354**

Japanese Nursing Association Research Report. (JA ISSN 0911-0844) **3279**, 3628

Japanese Organization for International Cooperation in Family Planning, Inc. News see J O I C F P News **597**

Japanese Orthopaedic Association. Journal/Nippon Seikei Geka Gakkai Zasshi. (JA ISSN 0021-5325) **3308**

▼Japanese Overseas Investments. (JA) **1141**

Japanese Pelagic Investigation on Fur Seals. (JA) **443**, 585

Japanese Periodicals Index. Humanities and Social Science Section. see Zasshi Kiji Sakuin. Jinbun Shakai Hen **2520**

Japanese Periodicals Index. Science and Technology/Zasshi Kiji Sakuin. Kagaku Gijutsu Hen. (JA ISSN 0514-2253) **4356**, 4614

Japanese Philately. (US ISSN 0146-0994) **3753**

Japanese Poultry Science. see Nihon Kakin Gakkaishi **222**

The Japanese Press. (JA) **2571**, 2207

Japanese Problems. see Riben Wenti **883**

Japanese Psychological Research. (JA ISSN 0021-5368) **4026**

Japanese Psychological Review. see Shinrigaku Hyoron **4046**

Japanese Religions. (JA ISSN 0448-8954) **4184**

Japanese Report to the International Council on Social Welfare. (JA) **4410**

Japanese Scholarly Works in English. (US) **2927**

Japanese Scientific Monthly. see Gakujutsu Geppo **4310**

Japanese Singapore Visitor see Singapore Visitor **4786**

Japanese Slavic & East European Studies. (JA ISSN 0389-1186) **2820**

Japanese Society for Horticultural Science. Journal/Engei Gakkai Zasshi. (JA ISSN 0013-7626) **2132**

Japanese Society for Public Administration. Annals. see Nippon Gyosei Kenkyu Nenpo **4068**

Japanese Society for Strength and Fracture of Materials. Journal. (JA ISSN 0286-4010) **1918**, 1827

Japanese Society of Gastric Secretion Research. Proceedings. see I-bunpi Kenkyukaishi **3254**

Japanese Society of Grassland Science. Journal/Nippon Sochi Gakkai-shi. (JA ISSN 0447-5933) **182**

Japanese Society of Internal Medicine. Journal/Nihon Naika Gakkai Zasshi. (JA ISSN 0021-5384) **3113**

Japanese Society of Lubrication Engineers. Journal see Tribologist **1940**

Japanese Society of Nutrition and Food Science. Journal/Nippon Eiyo Shokuryo Gakkaishi. (JA ISSN 0287-3516) **3607**

Japanese Society of Printing Science and Technology. Bulletin. (JA) **4002**

Japanese Society of Printing Science and Technology. Bulletin (Overseas Edition). (JA) **4002**

Japanese Society of Scientific Fisheries. Bulletin/Nippon Suisan Gakkaishi. (JA ISSN 0021-5392) **2044**

Japanese Society of Soil Mechanics and Foundation Engineering. Journal/Doshitsu Kogakkai Ronbun Hokokushu. (JA ISSN 0385-1621) **1868**

Japanese Society of Starch Science. Journal/Denpun Kagaku. (JA ISSN 0021-5406) **2074**

Japanese Society of Tribologists. Journal see Tribologist **1940**

Japanese Society of Tribologists. Journal. International Edition see Tribologist. International Edition **5292**
Japanese Sociological Review/ Shakaigaku Hyoron. (JA ISSN 0021-5414) **4439**
Japanese Stomatological Society. Journal. see Nihon Kokuka Gakkai Zasshi **3238**
Japanese Studies. (US) **2008**
Japanese Studies in German Language and Literature/Japanische Studien zur Deutschen Sprache und Literatur.(SZ ISSN 0721-3719) **2927**, 2820
Japanese Sword Society of the U S Bulletin. (US) **258**
Japanese Sword Society of the U S Newsletter. (US) **258**
Japanese Technical Abstracts see Japan Technology Series **5220**
Japanese Technology Review see Japanese Technology Reviews: Biotechnology (Section E) **490**
Japanese Technology Review see Japanese Technology Reviews: Computers and Communication (Section B) **1351**
Japanese Technology Review see Japanese Technology Reviews: Electronics (Section A) **1774**
Japanese Technology Review see Japanese Technology Reviews: Manufacturing Engineering (Section D) **1827**
Japanese Technology Review see Japanese Technology Reviews: New Materials (Section C) **4602**
Japanese Technology Reviews: Biotechnology (Section E). (US ISSN 1058-7330) **490**
Japanese Technology Reviews: Computers and Communication (Section B). (US ISSN 1058-7306) **1351**
Japanese Technology Reviews: Electronics (Section A). (US ISSN 1058-7292) **1774**
Japanese Technology Reviews: Manufacturing Engineering (Section D). (US ISSN 1058-7322) **1827**
Japanese Technology Reviews: New Materials (Section C). (US ISSN 1058-7314) **4602**
▼Japanese Telecommunications. (US) **1338**
Japanese Weekly on Pharmacy and Chemistry/Yakugyo Shinbun. (JA ISSN 0021-5201) **3730**, 1179
Japaninfo. (GW ISSN 0931-3230) **914**, 4602
Japanische Fachtexte. (GW ISSN 0934-9995) **3639**
Japanische Studien zur Deutschen Sprache und Literatur. see Japanese Studies in German Language and Literature **2927**
Japanophile. (US) **3639**
Japan's Bicycle Guide. (JA ISSN 0446-6667) **4518**
†Japan's Economy and Japan - U S Trade. (JA) **5220**
Japan's Iron and Steel Industry. (JA ISSN 0075-3475) **3410**
Japan's Timber Consuming Industries. (JA) **2115**
Japanwirtschaft. (GW) **870**, 3639
Jaque. (SP) **4476**
Jardim Botanico do Rio de Janeiro. Arquivos. (BL ISSN 0103-2550) **506**, 2103, 2132
Jardin Botanico de Madrid. Anales. (SP ISSN 0211-1322) **506**
Jardin Botanico Nacional. Revista. (CU ISSN 0253-5696) **506**
Jardin Botanico Nacional "Dr. Rafael M. Moscoso." Boletin. (DR) **507**
Jardin Botanique de Montreal. Annuelles et Legumes: Resultats des Cultures d'Essai see Jardin Botanique de Montreal. Legumes: Resultats des Cultures d'Essai **2132**
Jardin Botanique de Montreal. Legumes: Resultats des Cultures d'Essai. (CN) **2132**

Jardin Botanique National de Belgique. Bulletin/Nationale Plantentuin van Belgie. Bulletin. (BE ISSN 0303-9153) **507**
Jardin des Modes. (FR) **1292**
Jardin Familial see Jardin Familial de France **2132**
Jardin Familial de France. (FR ISSN 0240-5024) **2132**
Jardineries see Jardineries Vegetal **2132**
Jardineries Vegetal. (FR) **2132**
Jardins de France. (FR ISSN 0021-5481) **2132**
Jargalan/Happiness. (MP) **2447**
Jaridah al-Rasmiyah li-Jumhuriyat al-Sudan al-Dimuqratiyah. see Democratic Republic of the Sudan Gazette **4058**
Al-Jaridah al-Rasmiyyah li-Dawlat al-Imarat al-Arabiyyah al-Muttahidah/ United Arab Emirates. Official Gazette. (TS) **4065**
Al-Jaridah al-Rasmiyyah li-Hukumat Dubai see Dubai. Hukumat Dubai. Al-Jaridah al-Rasmiyyah **4059**
Al-Jaridah al-Rasmiyyah li-Imarat Abu Dhabi see Abu Dhabi. Al-Jaridah al-Rasmiyyah **4052**
Jarlibro. (NE ISSN 0075-3491) **2820**, 4439
Jarmuvek, Mezogazdasagi Gepek. (HU ISSN 0021-5511) **1932**, 163, 4651
Jaslok Hospital & Research Centre. Bulletin. (II ISSN 0379-1653) **3113**
Jasoosi Duniya. (II) **2200**
Jasper County Missouri Journal. (US) **2156**, 2411
Jaszkunsag. (HU ISSN 0448-9144) **2927**, 331, 4439
Jatros Dermatologie. (GW ISSN 0932-8661) **3248**, 3176
Jatros Gynaekologie. (GW ISSN 0177-9109) **3293**, 3176
Jatros H N O. (GW ISSN 0930-8318) **3315**, 3176
Jatros Neurologie - Psychiatrie. (GW ISSN 0178-7535) **3340**, 3176
Jatros Orthopaedie. (GW ISSN 0930-8326) **3308**, 3176
Jatros Paediatrie. (GW ISSN 0177-9095) **3321**, 3176
Jatros Urologie. (GW ISSN 0178-7527) **3388**, 3176
Jatuli. (FI) **2370**
Jauna Gaita. (CN ISSN 0448-9179) **331**, 2927, 2995, 3557
La Jaune et la Rouge. (FR ISSN 0021-5554) **4602**
Jaunimo Gretos. (LI ISSN 0132-6562) **1257**
Javanan Emrooz. (IR) **1257**
Javaneh. (IR) **2202**
Javelin Class Association Yearbook. (US) **4525**
Javelin Class Association Yearbook. Supplement. (US) **4525**
Javeriana. (CK ISSN 0021-5562) **3901**, 870
Javisko. (CS) **4634**
Jawaharal Nehru University. School of Languages. Journal. (II ISSN 0377-0648) **2820**, 2870
Jawaharlal Nehru Krishi Vishwa Vidyalaya News see J N K V V News **100**
Jawaharlal Nehru Krishi Vishwa Vidyalaya Research Journal see J N K V V Research Journal **100**
Jawaharlal Nehru University. School of International Studies Series. (II ISSN 0075-3548) **4377**
Jawetz, Melnick & Adelberg's Medical Microbiology. (US) **553**
Al-Jawhara. (QA) **4845**
Jax. (US ISSN 0021-5570) **544**
Jax Fax Travel Marketing Magazine. (US ISSN 0279-7984) **4773**
Jay Schabacker's Mutual Fund Buying Guide. (US) **952**
Jay Schabacker's Mutual Fund Investing.(US ISSN 8756-5161) **952**
Jaybee. (US ISSN 0010-7646) **2437**
Jaycees Magazine. (US) **1298**
Jayne Mansfield Collector's Guide. (US) **419**, 2437

Jayne Mansfield Fan Club Newsletter. (US) **419**
Jazdectvo. (CS) **4535**
Al-Jazirah. (TS) **4476**
Jazykovedne Studie. (CS ISSN 0448-9241) **2820**
Jazykovedny Casopis. (CS ISSN 0021-5597) **2820**
Jazz. (PL ISSN 0021-5600) **3557**
Jazz. (SZ) **3557**
Jazz Archivist. (US) **3558**
Jazz Club Karlsruhe e.V. (GW) **3558**
Jazz Down Under. (AT) **3558**
Jazz Educators Journal. (US ISSN 0730-9791) **3558**
Jazz Festivals and Related Major Jazz Events. Directory. (DK ISSN 0900-064X) **3558**
Jazz Forum. (PL ISSN 0021-5635) **3558**
Jazz Hot. (FR ISSN 0021-5643) **3558**
Jazz in the Midlands. (UK) **3558**
Jazz Interactions. (US ISSN 8756-6540) **3558**, 1298
Jazz Journal International. (UK ISSN 0140-2285) **3558**
Jazz Magazine. (FR ISSN 0021-566X) **3558**
†Jazz Music News. (UK) **5220**
Jazz Newsletter. (US) **3558**
Jazz Nu. (NE ISSN 0166-7025) **3558**
Jazz Passion. (SZ) **3558**
Jazz Podium. (GW ISSN 0021-5686) **3558**
Jazz Research. see Jazzforschung **3558**
Jazz - Rhythm and Blues see Jazz **3557**
Jazz Times. (UK ISSN 0021-5716) **3558**
Jazz World. (US) **3558**
Jazz World Index see Jazz World **3558**
Jazz Zeitung. (GW) **3558**
Jazzband. (AG) **3558**
Jazzforschung/Jazz Research. (AU ISSN 0075-3572) **3558**
Der Jazzfreund. (GW ISSN 0021-5724) **3558**
Jazziz. (US) **3558**
Jazzletter. (US ISSN 0890-6440) **3558**, 2411
Jazzline. (AT) **3558**
Jazzline. (US ISSN 8756-6540) **3558**
Jazzmen's Reference Book. (US) **3558**
Jazznytt. (SW) **3558**
Jazzologist. (US) **3558**
JazzTimes. (US ISSN 0272-572X) **3558**
Je Crois. (CN ISSN 0021-5740) **4266**
Je Lis Deja. (FR) **1257**
Je Me Petit Debrouille see Les Debrouillards **1253**
Je Me Souviens. (US ISSN 0195-7384) **2156**
Jean-Paul-Gesellschaft. Jahrbuch. (GW ISSN 0075-3580) **2927**
Jean Rhys Review. (US ISSN 0889-759X) **2927**
Jeannette. (FR ISSN 0750-3806) **1257**
Jeansflash. (US) **4621**, 1285
▼Jeanswear. (NE) **1285**
Jebat. (MY) **2339**
J'Ecris. (FR ISSN 0981-9185) **2927**
Jedefrau & Jedermann. (GW) **4439**
Jedermann see Jedefrau & Jedermann **4439**
Jedinstvo. (YU ISSN 0021-5775) **2239**
Jednota. (CI ISSN 0021-5791) **2008**
Jednota/Union. (US) **2008**, 4266
Jednota Kalendar see Kalendar Jednota **5223**
Jednota Klasickych Filologu Prague. Zpravy. (CS) **2370**
Jednotna Skola. (CS ISSN 0021-5805) **1641**, 4026
Jee: Film & T V Fortnightly. (II) **3512**, 1375
Jee: Film Fortnightly see Jee: Film & T V Fortnightly **3512**
Jeevadhara. (II ISSN 0970-1117) **4266**
Jeevak. (II) **3113**

Jeevan Jauban. (II ISSN 0021-5813) **3804**, 4410
Jeffe Report on Computer Graphics for Design. (US) **1422**
Jefferson. (SW ISSN 0345-5653) **3558**
Jefferson Business: New Orleans see New Orleans Business **681**
Jefferson Medical College Alumni Bulletin. (US ISSN 0021-5821) **3113**
Jefferson State Computer Users Group Newsletter see J U G Newsletter **1427**
Jeffries Report. (US ISSN 0734-4589) **1470**, 1461
Jeg Arbejder Med. (DK ISSN 0105-8347) **2156**
Jehovah's Witnesses Yearbook. (US ISSN 0075-3602) **4284**
Jeiwa Kenkyu/Peace Studies. (JA ISSN 0385-0749) **3901**
Jelenkor. (HU ISSN 0447-6425) **2870**
Jelita. (MY) **1292**
Jemna Mechanika a Optika/Fine Mechanics and Optics. (CS ISSN 0447-6441) **3843**, 3853
JEN, Journal of Emergency Nursing see J E N **3279**
†Jena Review/Jenaer Rundschau. (GW ISSN 0448-9497) **5220**
†Jenaer Beitraege zur Parteigeschichte. (GW ISSN 0138-3604) **5220**
Jenaer Rundschau. see Jena Review **5220**
Jenga. (TZ ISSN 0021-5872) **1079**
†Jenks Southeastern Business Letter. (US ISSN 0731-9444) **5220**
†Jennings Magazine. (UK ISSN 0268-5000) **5220**
▼Jenny Craig's Your Body, Your Health.(US) **3804**, 4845
Jeopardy. (US ISSN 0021-5880) **2927**, 331, 2995
Jepara. Shrimp Culture Research Centre. Bulletin see Brackishwater Aquaculture Development Centre. Bulletin **2037**
Jerfair News. (IS) **4130**
Jericho. (FR ISSN 1156-5977) **4130**
Jern- og Maskinindustrien. (DK) **1827**, 3018
Jernal Antropoloji dan Sosioloji see Jurnal Antropologi dan Sosiologi **4441**
Jernal Sains Malaysia. see Malaysian Journal of Science **4323**
Jernal Undang-Undang. see Journal of Malaysian and Comparative Law **2640**
Jernbanen. (DK ISSN 0107-3702) **4710**
Jernvare Bygg Hobby see Jernvarehandleren **642**
Jernvarehandleren. (NO) **642**, 1179
Jerome Lectures. (US ISSN 0075-3610) **2315**
Jerome Schneider's Offshore Moneyletter. (US) **787**
Jersey. (UK ISSN 0021-5929) **219**
Jersey. (SP) **4621**
Jersey at Home. (UI ISSN 0446-7310) **200**, 219
Jersey Atari Computer Group Newsletter see J A C G Newsletter **1469**
Jersey Herd Book and Members Directory. (UK) **219**
Jersey Holiday Post. (UI) **4773**
Jersey Jazz. (US ISSN 0740-5928) **3558**
Jersey Journal. (US ISSN 0021-5953) **219**
Jersey Journeys. (US) **2411**, 1641
Jersey Publisher see In Print **2571**
Jersey Sierran. (US) **1490**, 1959, 2637, 4549
Jersey Woman Magazine see New Jersey Woman Magazine **4849**
Jerusalem al-Fajr see Al-Fajr Jerusalem Palestinian Weekly **3957**
Jerusalem Conference on Accountancy. (IS) **752**
Jerusalem Historical Medical Publications see Koroth (Jerusalem) **3177**

JERUSALEM INSTITUTE

Jerusalem Institute for Israel Studies. Discussion Papers - Research Series *see* Israel Studies **4376**
Jerusalem Journal of International Relations. (IS ISSN 0363-2865) **3963**, 2203
Jerusalem Letter - Viewpoints. (IS ISSN 0334-4096) **2008**
Jerusalem Post (International Edition). (IS) **2203**
Jerusalem Post Literary Supplement *see* Israel Book News **4130**
▼Jerusalem Report. (IS ISSN 0792-6049) **2210**
Jerusalem Star *see* Star **2208**
Jerusalem Studies in Arabic and Islam. (IS ISSN 0334-4118) **4219**
Jerusalem Studies in Jewish Thought. (IS) **4223**, 3770
Jerusalem Symposia on Quantum Chemistry and Biochemistry. (NE ISSN 0075-3696) **1227**
Jerusalem Urban Studies. (IS) **4439**, 2490
Jerusalem Voice. (IS) **2203**
Jessup's Land Titles Office Practice S.A.(AT) **2637**, 4151
Jesuit Bulletin. (US) **4266**
Jesuits and Friends. (UK) **4266**
Jesus. (IT) **2205**
Jesus Caritas. (IT) **4266**
Jesus Liebt Kinder. (GW) **4240**, 1257
Jesus Maestro. (SP) **1257**, 4184
Jet. (US ISSN 0021-5996) **2227**, 2008
Jet Cadet *see* R-A-D-A-R **1263**
Jet Cargo News. (US ISSN 0021-6003) **4675**, 1042
Jet Lag Magazine. (US) **3558**
Jet Set. (MX) **2870**
JeTrader. (US) **4675**
JetSkier Magazine *see* JetSports Magazine **4525**
JetSports Magazine. (US) **4525**
Jetstream Air News. (SZ) **4675**, 4773
Jetzt. (GW ISSN 0342-6386) **4266**, 4845
Jeu. (CN ISSN 0382-0335) **4634**
Jeune Afrique. (FR ISSN 0021-6089) **3963**, 932
Jeune Cinema. (FR) **3512**
Jeune Cinema et Theatre. *see* Young Cinema and Theatre **3519**
Jeune Garde *see* Lutte Ouvriere **2873**
Jeune Revolutionnaire *see* Information Ouvrieres **2869**
Jeunes. (FR ISSN 0021-6135) **4476**, 1257
Jeunes Agriculteurs. (FR) **101**
Jeunes Annees. (FR ISSN 0021-6143) **1257**
Jeunes Avocats. (FR ISSN 0021-6151) **2637**
Jeunes des Auberges. (FR ISSN 0021-616X) **4773**
Jeunes en Marche *see* J.E.M **5219**
Jeunesse du Monde. *see* World Youth **1271**
Jeunesse du Quart Monde. (FR ISSN 0396-7360) **1257**
Jeunesse du Vietnam *see* Vietnam Youth **1269**
Jeunesses Litteraires de France. (FR) **2927**
Jeux et Jouets. (CN ISSN 0713-4118) **2281**
Jeux et Jouets *see* Revue Internationale des Jeux et Jouets **2282**
Jevrejski Pregled. (YU ISSN 0021-6240) **2008**, 4223
†Jewel. (US) **5220**
Jewelers' Book Club Catalog. (US) **2566**
Jewelers' Book Club News. (US) **2564**, 2566
Jewelers, Inc. (US) **2564**
Jewellers Association of Australia. Federal Newsletter *see* Jewellers Association of Australia. National Newsletter **2564**
Jewellers Association of Australia. National Newsletter. (AT) **2564**
Jewellers' Reference Book. (UK) **2564**
Jewellery. (UK) **2565**
†Jewellery, Curios, Arts & Crafts (Year) (SA) **5220**
Jewellery News Asia. (HK) **2565**
Jewellery Time. (NZ) **2565**

Jewellery World. (CN ISSN 0823-1346) **2565**
Jewellery World. (AT ISSN 0811-2274) **2565**
Jewellery World Ltd. Plus *see* J W Plus **2564**
The Jewelry Appraiser. (US) **2565**, 2535
▼Jewelry Buyers. (US) **2565**, 1042
Jewelry Fashion Guide. (US) **2565**
Jewelry Making, Gems and Minerals. (US ISSN 0274-8193) **2437**, 3486
Jewelry Newsletter International. (US ISSN 0738-7261) **2565**
Jewelry Workers' Bulletin. (US ISSN 0021-6291) **2585**
Jewish Action. (US ISSN 0447-7049) **4223**
Jewish Affairs. (SA ISSN 0021-6313) **2008**, 2870
Jewish Affairs. (US ISSN 0021-6305) **3901**, 4223
Jewish Bible Quarterly. (IS ISSN 0792-3910) **4184**, 4223
Jewish Book Annual. (US ISSN 0075-3726) **4223**
Jewish Book World. (US) **2870**
Jewish Boston. (US ISSN 0085-2368) **2008**
Jewish Boston and New England Jewry *see* Jewish Boston **2008**
Jewish Braille Institute of America. Directory of Services. (US) **2293**
Jewish Braille Review. (US ISSN 0021-6321) **2293**, 4223
Jewish Chicago. (US) **2008**
Jewish Chronicle. (UK ISSN 0021-633X) **2870**, 4223
Jewish Chronicle (Yonkers). (US) **2870**, 4223
Jewish Civic Press. (US ISSN 0021-6348) **2008**, 4223
Jewish Civilization: Essays and Studies. (US ISSN 0191-3034) **2008**
†Jewish Commentary. (AT) **5220**
Jewish Community Centers Association of North America Circle *see* J C C Circle **4223**
Jewish Current Events. (US ISSN 0021-6380) **2008**, 1257, 1641, 4223
Jewish Currents. (US ISSN 0021-6399) **2008**
Jewish Defense League Iton. (US) **2008**, 3901
Jewish Defense League Newsletter *see* Jewish Defense League Iton **2008**
Jewish Denominations in America. (US) **4223**
Jewish Directory *see* Jewish Directory of Greater Toronto **2008**
Jewish Directory of Greater Toronto. (CN) **2008**
Jewish Echo. (UK) **2008**
Jewish Education. (US ISSN 0021-6429) **1641**, 4223
Jewish Educational Statistics. (IS) **1677**, 2030
Jewish Executive. (US) **2008**
Jewish Exponent. (US ISSN 0021-6437) **2008**
Jewish Federation News. (US) **2008**
Jewish Federations, Welfare Funds and Community Councils Directory *see* Directory of Jewish Federations, Welfare Funds and Community Councils **4404**
Jewish Frontier. (US ISSN 0021-6453) **2008**, 3901
Jewish Gazette. (UK ISSN 0021-6461) **2008**
Jewish Genealogical Society of Philadelphia. Chronicles. (US ISSN 0893-2921) **2156**
Jewish Guardian. (US) **4223**, 2008
Jewish Guild for the Blind. Newsletter. (US) **2293**
Jewish Guild of the Blind. Guild News *see* Jewish Guild for the Blind. Newsletter **2293**
Jewish Herald. (SA ISSN 0021-647X) **2008**
Jewish Herald-Voice. (US ISSN 0021-6488) **2008**
Jewish Heritage Libraries. Ethnic Studies Institute. Year End Report. (US) **2008**

Jewish Historical Society of England. Annual Report and Accounts for the Session. (UK ISSN 0306-7998) **2370**, 4223
Jewish Historical Society of England. Bulletin. (UK) **2370**, 4223
Jewish Historical Society of England. Report and Balance Sheet *see* Jewish Historical Society of England. Annual Report and Accounts for the Session **2370**
Jewish Historical Society of England. Transactions *see* Jewish Historical Studies. Transactions **2370**
Jewish Historical Society of New York. Publications. (US) **2008**
Jewish Historical Society of Western Canada. Annual Publication *see* Jewish Life and Times **2009**
Jewish Historical Studies. Transactions. (UK) **2370**, 4223
Jewish History. (IS ISSN 0334-701X) **2008**
Jewish Home. *see* Yiddishe Heim **4227**
Jewish Information and Referral Service Directory. (US) **2008**
Jewish Intelligentsia in the USSR *see* Jews of the Soviet Union **4224**
Jewish Journal of San Antonio. (US) **2008**, 4223
Jewish Journal of Sociology. (UK ISSN 0021-6534) **4439**, 4223
Jewish Jurisprudence Series. (US ISSN 0276-1432) **2638**, 4223
Jewish Labor Committee Educator *see* J L C Educator **5219**
Jewish Labor Committee Review. (US) **2008**, 984
Jewish Language Review. (US ISSN 0333-8347) **2820**, 2008, 4223
Jewish Law Annual. (US ISSN 0169-8354) **2638**, 4223
Jewish Law Annual Supplements. (NE ISSN 0169-8400) **2638**, 2008
Jewish Law in Context. (US ISSN 1045-6015) **2638**, 4223
Jewish Leader. (US) **2009**
Jewish Ledger. (US ISSN 0021-6550) **2009**
†Jewish Librarians Task Force. Newsletter. (US) **5220**
▼Jewish Linguistic Studies. (US ISSN 0792-559X) **2820**, 2009
Jewish Museum of Greece. Newsletter. (GR) **3525**
†Jewish Music Notes. (US) **5220**
Jewish National Fund Illustrated *see* J N F Illustrated **4065**
Jewish Observer. (US ISSN 0021-6615) **4223**
Jewish Peace Fellowship Newsletter *see* Shalom **3947**
Jewish Population Series. (IS) **3984**, 4410
Jewish Post *see* Jewish Post and News **2009**
Jewish Post and News. (CN) **2009**
Jewish Post and Opinion *see* National Jewish Post and Opinion **2015**
Jewish Press (Brooklyn). (US ISSN 0021-6674) **2009**, 4223
Jewish Press (Omaha). (US ISSN 0021-6666) **2009**
Jewish Proclaimer. (US) **4223**, 2009
Jewish Quarterly. (UK) **2009**, 2870
Jewish Quarterly Review. (US ISSN 0021-6682) **4224**
Jewish Radical. (US ISSN 0047-200X) **3901**
Jewish Record. (US) **2009**
Jewish Review (1983). (UK) **4224**
Jewish Samizdat. (IS) **2009**
Jewish Science Interpreter. (US) **4224**
Jewish Singles *see* Jewish Singles Magazine (Newton) **4362**
Jewish Singles Magazine (Bloomfield). (US) **4362**, 2009
Jewish Singles Magazine (Newton). (US) **4362**, 2009
Jewish Social Studies. (US ISSN 0021-6704) **4377**, 2009, 4224
Jewish Social Work Forum. (US ISSN 0021-6712) **4410**
Jewish Spectator. (US ISSN 0021-6720) **4224**, 2009
Jewish Standard. (CN ISSN 0021-6739) **2009**, 2177, 4224

Jewish Standard. (US ISSN 0021-6747) **2009**
Jewish Star (Birmingham). (US) **2009**
Jewish Star (San Francisco). (US) **2009**
Jewish Star - Holyland Features *see* Jewish Star (Birmingham) **2009**
Jewish Studies. (US) **2009**
Jewish Studies. (IS) **4224**
Jewish Telegraph. (UK ISSN 0021-6755) **2009**, 4224
Jewish Telegraphic Agency Community News Reporter *see* J T A Community News Reporter **2007**
Jewish Telegraphic Agency Weekly News Digest *see* J T A Weekly News Digest **3900**
Jewish Times. (CN) **2009**
Jewish Times (Boston) *see* Boston Jewish Times **1994**
Jewish Times (Huntingdon Valley). (US) **2009**
Jewish Tradition. (SA) **4224**, 2009
Jewish Transcript. (US ISSN 0021-678X) **2009**, 4224
Jewish Travel Guide. (UK ISSN 0075-3750) **4773**
Jewish Tribune. (UK) **2009**
Jewish Vanguard. (UK ISSN 0021-6801) **2870**
Jewish Vegetarian. (UK ISSN 0021-681X) **3607**, 3804
Jewish Vegetarians. (US) **3607**
Jewish Vegetarians of New York *see* Jewish Vegetarians **3607**
Jewish Veteran. (US ISSN 0047-2018) **3461**, 2009
Jewish Voice. (US ISSN 0021-6828) **4224**
Jewish War Veterans Association Bulletin *see* J.W.V.A. Bulletin **2007**
Jewish Week. (US ISSN 0745-5356) **2009**
Jewish Week and American Examiner *see* Jewish Week **2009**
Jewish Weekly News. (US ISSN 0021-6860) **2009**, 4224
Jewish Western Bulletin. (CN ISSN 0021-6879) **2009**
Jewish Woman's Review *see* F.W.Z. Review **2001**
Jewish World. (US ISSN 0199-4441) **2009**, 2571
Jewish World. (IS) **2009**
Jewish Year Book. (UK ISSN 0075-3769) **4224**
Jews and Jewish Topics in Soviet and East European Publications *see* Jews and Jewish Topics in the Soviet Union and Eastern Europe **3944**
Jews and Jewish Topics in the Soviet Union and Eastern Europe. (IS) **3944**, 2370
Jews and the Jewish People. (IS ISSN 0021-6895) **3901**
Jews and the Jewish People - Jewish Samizdat. (IS ISSN 0334-438X) **2009**, 2509
Jews for Jesus Newsletter. (US ISSN 0740-5901) **4224**
Jews of the Soviet Union. (IS ISSN 0334-0953) **4224**, 3944
Jez. (YU ISSN 0021-6917) **2870**
Jezik. (CI ISSN 0021-6925) **2820**
Jezik in Slovstvo. (XV ISSN 0021-6933) **2820**, 1752, 2927
Jezsenyegyelnij Bjuletiny *see* Weekly Bulletin **2198**
Jezyk Polski. (PL ISSN 0021-6941) **2820**
Jezyk Rosyjski *see* Jezyki Obce w Szkole **1641**
Jezyki Obce w Szkole. (PL ISSN 0446-7965) **1641**, 2820
Jezykoznawstwo Stosowane/Applied Linguistics. (PL ISSN 0137-1444) **2820**
Ji You/Chinese Philatelic Magazine. (CC ISSN 0529-0325) **3753**
Jiamusi Medical Institute. Journal. *see* Jiamusi Yixueyuan Xuebao **3113**
Jiamusi Yixueyuan Xuebao/Jiamusi Medical Institute. Journal. (CC ISSN 1001-7321) **3113**
Jian yu Mei/Strength & Beauty. (US) **3804**
Jianchuan Zhishi. (CC ISSN 1000-7148) **4730**, 3461

Jianghai Xuekan/Journal of Jianghai Academia. (CC ISSN 1000-856X) 4377
Jianghai Xuekan (Jingji Shehui Ban) see Jianghai Xuekan 4377
Jianghai Xuekan (Wen-Shi-Zhe Ban) see Jianghai Xuekan 4377
Jianghan Archaeology. see Jianghan Kaogu 275
Jianghan Forum. see Jianghan Luntan 4377
Jianghan Kaogu/Jianghan Archaeology. (CC ISSN 1001-0327) 275
Jianghan Luntan/Jianghan Forum. (CC) 4377
Jianghuai Forum. see Jianghuai Luntan 4377
Jianghuai Luntan/Jianghuai Forum. (CC) 4377
Jiangnan. (CC ISSN 1001-6694) 2927
Jiangsu Baoxian/Jiangsu Insurance. (CC) 2535
Jiangsu Chuanbo. (CC ISSN 1001-5388) 4730
Jiangsu Economic Inquiry. see Jiangsu Jingji Tantao 895
Jiangsu Gaojiao/Jiangsu Higher Education. (CC) 1709
Jiangsu Higher Education. see Jiangsu Gaojiao 1709
Jiangsu Huakan/Jiangsu Journal of Painting. (CC) 331
Jiangsu Insurance. see Jiangsu Baoxian 2535
Jiangsu Jingji Tantao/Jiangsu Economic Inquiry. (CC) 895
Jiangsu Journal of Agricultural Sciences. see Jiangsu Nongye Xuebao 101
Jiangsu Journal of Painting. see Jiangsu Huakan 331
Jiangsu Library. Journal. see Jiangsu Tushuguan Xuebao 2765
Jiangsu Linye Keji. (CC ISSN 1001-7380) 2103
Jiangsu Music. see Jiangsu Yinyue 3558
Jiangsu Nongye Xuebao/Jiangsu Journal of Agricultural Sciences. (CC ISSN 1000-4440) 101
Jiangsu Traditional Chinese Medicine. see Jiangsu Zhongyi 3113
Jiangsu Tushuguan Xuebao/Jiangsu Library. Journal. (CC) 2765
Jiangsu Yinyue/Jiangsu Music. (CC) 3558
Jiangsu Zhongyi/Jiangsu Traditional Chinese Medicine. (CC ISSN 0529-0414) 3113
Jiangxi Chengshi Jinrong/Jiangxi Urban Finance. (CC) 787
Jiangxi Cultural Relics. see Jiangxi Wenwu 275
Jiangxi Gongye Daxue Xuebao/Jiangxi Industrial University. Journal. (CC ISSN 1000-5803) 4602
Jiangxi Huabao/Jiangxi Pictorial. (CC) 2182
Jiangxi Industrial University. Journal. see Jiangxi Gongye Daxue Xuebao 4602
Jiangxi Institute of Education. Journal. see Jiangxi Jiaoyu Xueyuan Xuebao 1641
Jiangxi Jiaoyu Xueyuan Xuebao/Jiangxi Institute of Education. Journal. (CC) 1641
Jiangxi Kexue/Jiangxi Science. (CC) 4317
Jiangxi Library Journal. see Jiangxi Tushuguan Xuebao 2765
Jiangxi Normal University. Journal (Natural Science Edition). see Jiangxi Shifan Daxue Xuebao (Ziran Kexue Ban) 4317
Jiangxi Normal University. Journal (Social Science Edition). see Jiangxi Shifan Daxue Xuebao (Shehui Kexue Ban) 4377
Jiangxi Pictorial. see Jiangxi Huabao 2182
Jiangxi Science. see Jiangxi Kexue 4317
Jiangxi Shifan Daxue Xuebao (Shehui Kexue Ban)/Jiangxi Normal University. Journal (Social Science Edition). (CC ISSN 1000-579X) 4377

Jiangxi Shifan Daxue Xuebao (Ziran Kexue Ban)/Jiangxi Normal University. Journal (Natural Science Edition). (CC ISSN 1000-5862) 4317
Jiangxi Tushuguan Xuekan/Jiangxi Library Journal. (CC) 2765
Jiangxi Urban Finance. see Jiangxi Chengshi Jinrong 787
Jiangxi Wenwu/Jiangxi Cultural Relics. (CC) 275
Jiankang/Health. (CC ISSN 1002-297X) 3804
Jiankang Bao/Health Gazette. (US) 3804, 3113, 3607
Jiankang Guwen/Health Consultant. (CC) 3804
Jiankang Shaonian Huabao/Healthy Children's Pictorial. (CC) 3804, 1257
Jiankang Tiandi/Healthy World. (CC) 3804
Jiankang Wenzhai/Health Digest. (CC) 4106
Jiankang zhi You/Friend of Health. (CC) 3805
Jiankang Zhinan/Health Guidance. (CC) 3805
Jianzhu/Architecture. (CC) 301
Jianzhu Gongren/Construction Workers.(CC ISSN 0412-0787) 622
Jianzhu Guanli Xiandaihua/Construction Management Modernization. (CC ISSN 1001-019X) 622, 1015
Jianzhu Jiegou/Architectural Structure. (CC) 301
Jianzhu Jiegou Xuebao/Journal of Building Structures. (CC) 622
Jianzhu Jingji. (CC) 672, 301
Jianzhu Jishu/Architectural Technology. (CC ISSN 1000-4726) 622, 301
Jianzhu Jixie/Architectural Machinery. (CC ISSN 1001-554X) 3018, 301
Jianzhu Kexue/Building Science. (CC ISSN 1002-8528) 1868
Jianzhu Xuebao/Architectural Journal. (CC ISSN 0529-1399) 302
Jiaocai Tongxun/Bulletin of Teaching Material. (CC ISSN 1001-5469) 1709
Jiaotong Huanbao (Shuiyun Ban)/ Environmental Protection in Transportation (Water Transport Edition). (CC) 1959
Jiaotongbu Shanghai Chuanbo Yunshu Kexue Yanjiusuo Xuebao. (CC ISSN 1000-4696) 4730
Jiaoxue yu Yanjiu/Teaching and Research. (CC ISSN 0257-2826) 1752
Jiaoyu Kexue/Science of Education. (CC) 1641
Jiaoyu Pinglun/Education Review. (CC) 1641
Jiaoyu Yanjiu/Educational Research. (CC) 1641, 1737
Jiaoyu yu Zhiye/Education and Occupation. (CC) 1684
Jiaoyu Zhanwang/Educational Prospects. (CC) 1641
Jiaoyu Ziliao yu Tushuguan Xue see Journal of Educational Media and Library Sciences 2765
Jiashi Yuan. (CC) 4693
Jiating/Family. (CC) 2447, 1239, 3398, 4845
Jiating Shenghuo Zhinan/Family Life Guide. (CC) 2448
Jiating Yixue/Family Medicine. (CC ISSN 1001-0203) 3113
Jiating - Yu'er. (CC) 4377
Jiayong Dianqi/Household Appliance. (CC ISSN 1002-5626) 1079
Jibi Inkoka Rinsho. see Practica Otologica Kyoto 3316
Jibi Inkoka, Tokeibu Geka/ Otolaryngology - Head and Neck Surgery. (JA ISSN 0914-3491) 3315
Jibi to Rinsho see Otologia Fukuoka - Jibi to Rinsho 3316
Jicarilla Chieftain. (US ISSN 0021-695X) 2009
Jichu Yixue yu Linchuang/Basic Medical Science and Clinics. (CC) 3113
Jidische Schtudies. (GW ISSN 0720-6666) 2820, 2927

Jido Seinen Seishin Igaku to Sono Kinsetsu Ryoiki. see Japanese Journal of Child & Adolescent Psychiatry 3340
Jidosha Gijutsu/Society of Automotive Engineers of Japan. Journal. (JA ISSN 0385-7298) 4693
Jidosha Gijutsu Kyokai Kaiho see Jidosha Gijutsu 4693
Jidosha Gijutsukai Ronbunshu/Society of Automotive Engineers of Japan. Transactions. (JA ISSN 0287-8321) 4693
Jidosha Hoyu Sharyosu. (JA ISSN 0910-9684) 4576
Jidosha Kogaku/Automobile Engineering. (JA) 4693, 1932
Jiefang Ribao Suoyin/Liberation Daily. Index. (US) 2578
Jiefangjun Bao/Liberation Army Daily. (US) 3462
Jiefangjun Huabao/P L A Pictorial. (CC ISSN 0009-3823) 3462
Jiefangjun Shenghuo/Life of P L A Soldiers. (US) 3462
Jiefangjun Wenyi/Literature and Art of People's Liberation Army. (CC) 2927, 3462
Jiegou Gongchengshi/Structure Engineers. (CC) 1869
Jiegou Huaxue/Journal of Structural Chemistry. (CC ISSN 0254-5861) 1180
Jiepouxue Zazhi/Journal of Anatomy. (CC ISSN 1001-1633) 443
Jihad. (IR) 2870
Jihad see Comunita Islamica 4218
Jihocesky Sbornik Historicky. (CS) 2370, 3901
Jiinasa. (Il ISSN 0377-743X) 2339
Jikeikai Medical Journal. (JA ISSN 0021-6968) 3113
Jikken Dobutsu. see Experimental Animals 3259
Jilin Caimao Xueyuan Xuebao/Jilin Institute of Finance and Trade. Journal. (CC ISSN 1001-4586) 787, 914, 2710
Jilin Daxue Ziran Kexue Xuebao/Jilin University. Journal of Natural Science. (CC ISSN 0529-0279) 4317
Jilin Huabao/Jilin Pictorial. (CC) 2182
Jilin Institute of Finance and Trade. Journal. see Jilin Caimao Xueyuan Xuebao 787
Jilin Nongye Daxue Xuebao/Jilin University of Agriculture. Journal. (CC ISSN 1000-5684) 101
Jilin Pictorial. see Jilin Huabao 2182
Jilin Traditional Chinese Medicine. see Jilin Zhongyiyao 3113
Jilin University. Journal of Natural Science. see Jilin Daxue Ziran Kexue Xuebao 4317
Jilin University of Agriculture. Journal. see Jilin Nongye Daxue Xuebao 101
Jilin Zhongyiyao/Jilin Traditional Chinese Medicine. (CC) 3113, 3730
Jim Highland's Fund Switch. (US) 952
Jim Rennie's Sports Letter. (CN) 4476
Jimbun-Chiri. see Human Geography 2252
Jimmie Rodgers Memorial Association Newsletter see Old Time Country 3571
Jimu Kanri. see Administrative Management 1001
Jin Dun/Golden Shield. (CC) 2638
Jin to Toseki. (JA ISSN 0385-2156) 3113, 3388
Jin Yaoshi/Golden Key. (CC) 2927
Jinan Liyi Xuebao/Jinan University. Journal: Medical & Natural Science and Technology Edition. (CC) 4317, 3113
Jinan University. Journal: Medical & Natural Science and Technology Edition. see Jinan Liyi Xuebao 4317
Jinan University. Journal (Philosophy & Social Sciences Edition). see Jinan Xuebao (Zhexue Shehui Kexue Ban) 3770
Jinan Xuebao (Zhexue Shehui Kexue Ban)/Jinan University. Journal (Philosophy & Social Sciences Edition). (CC ISSN 1000-5072) 3770, 4377

Jinbun see Zinbvn 2519
Jinbun Gakuho. see Journal of Social Sciences and Humanities 2509
Jinbun Shizen Kagaku Ronshu/Journal of Humanities and Natural Sciences. (JA ISSN 0495-8012) 2509, 4377
Jindai Shi Yanjiu/Studies on Modern Chinese History. (CC) 2339
Jing Bao Journal. (US) 3462
Jing Mao Shijie/Economic and Trade World. (CC) 672
Jingdezhen Ceramics. see Jingdezhen Taoci 1165
Jingdezhen Ceramics Institute. Journal. see Jingdezhen Taoci Xueyuan Xuebao 1165
Jingdezhen Taoci/Jingdezhen Ceramics.(CC) 1165
Jingdezhen Taoci Xueyuan Xuebao/ Jingdezhen Ceramics Institute. Journal. (CC ISSN 1000-2278) 1165
Jingji Cankao/Economic Information. (CC) 672, 870
Jingji Daobao see Economic Reporter 861
Jingji Dili/Economic Geography. (CC ISSN 1000-8462) 2254, 870
Jingji Fazhi. (CC) 2710, 672
Jingji Gaige/Economic Reform. (CC ISSN 1000-7989) 895, 870, 4065
Jingji Gongzuo Tongxun. (CC) 672
Jingji Guanli/Economic Management. (CC ISSN 1002-5766) 1015
Jingji Juece Bao/Economic Policymaking. (US) 895, 4065
Jingji Kexue/Economic Science. (CC) 672
Jingji Lilun yu Jingji Guanli/Economic Theory & Business Management. (US) 1015, 895
Jingji Luntan/Economic Tribune. (CC) 672
Jingji Ribao. (CC) 870
Jingji Shi/Economist. (CC) 672
Jingji Shijie - Nanfang/Economic World - South. (CC) 672
Jingji Tizhi Gaige/Reformation of Economic System. (CC) 999
Jingji Wenti/Economic Issues. (CC) 672
Jingji Wenti Tansuo/Inquiry into Economic Problems. (US) 672, 895
Jingji Yanjiu/Economic Research. (CC ISSN 0577-9154) 896
Jingji yu Falu see Economy and Law 894
Jingji yu Guanli/Economics and Management. (CC) 1015
Jingji yu Guanli Yanjiu/Research on Economics and Management. (CC ISSN 1000-7636) 1015, 870
Jingji yu Jianmei. (CC) 4476
Jingji yu Shehui Fazhan/Economics and Social Development. (CC ISSN 1000-8330) 673
Jingji Yuce yu Xinxi/Economic Forecast and Information. (CC) 673
Jingji Zongheng. (CC) 673
Jingjixue Dongtai. (CC) 673
Jingjixue Jia/Economist. (CC) 673
Jingjixue Wenzhai/Economics Abstracts.(US) 725
Jingtan Fengyun. (CC ISSN 1001-0459) 2985
Jingu Chuanqi/Modern and Ancient Legends. (CC) 2055, 2927
Jingwu. (CC) 4477
Jingxi Shiyou Huagong/Specialty Petrochemicals. (CC ISSN 1003-9384) 3690
Jingying yu Guanli. (CC) 1015
Jinko Dotai Shakai Keizaimen Chosa Hokoku see Japan. Ministry of Health and Welfare. Statistics and Information Department. Report on Survey of Socio-Economic Aspects on Vital Events 725
Jinko Dotai Tokei see Japan. Ministry of Health and Welfare. Statistics and Information Department. Vital Statistics 4576

JINKO DOTAI

Jinko Dotai Tokei Geppo, Gaisu see Japan. Ministry of Health and Welfare. Statistics and Information Department. Monthly Report on Vital Statistics **4576**

Jinko Mondai Kenkyu/Journal of Population Problems. (JA ISSN 0387-2793) **3984**

Jinmin Chugoku/Renmin Zhongguo/ People's China. (CC ISSN 0449-0312) **2182**

Jinri Keji/Science and Technology Today. (CC) **4317, 4602**

Jinri Shenghuo/Today's Life. (CC) **2182, 3792**

Jinrong Shibao/Financial Times. (US) **787, 870**

Jinrong Yanjiu/Banking and Finance Studies. (CC ISSN 0529-2794) **787**

Jinrong yu Jingji/Finance and Economics. (CC) **673**

Jinrui Dotai Gakkai Kaiho/Human Ergology Society. Newsletter. (JA ISSN 0913-7785) **3821, 443, 984**

Jinrui Idengaku Zasshi. see Japanese Journal of Human Genetics **544**

Jinshan. (CC) **2927**

Jinshu Kexue yu Gongyi/Metallurgical Science and Techniques. (CC ISSN 1001-0181) **3410**

Jinshu Rechuli/Heat Treatment of Metals. (CC ISSN 0254-6051) **1918, 1932, 3410**

Jinshu Xuebao. (CC ISSN 0412-1961) **3410**

Jinshu Zaisheng. (CC ISSN 1001-4446) **3410**

Jintian/Today. (CC) **2182**

Jintian. see Today Literary Magazine **2969**

Jintu Xuekan. (CC) **2765**

Jinyang Journal. see Jinyang Xuekan **4377**

Jinyang Wenyi. (CC ISSN 0257-2915) **2927**

Jinyang Xuekan/Jinyang Journal. (CC ISSN 1000-2987) **4377**

Jinzhan/Progress. (CC) **4317**

Jinzhan: Guoji Maoyi yu Keji Jiaoliu/ Progress: International Exchange in Trade, Science and Technology. (CC ISSN 1002-1221) **914, 4602**

Jiqiren/Robot. (CC) **1414**

Jishin Geppo. see Japan Meteorological Agency. Seismological Bulletin **1591**

Jishu Jingji Xinxi. (CC) **673**

Jishu Jingji yu Guanli Yanjiu. (CC) **1015**

Jishu Kaifa yu Yinjin/Exploration and Import of Technology. (CC ISSN 1002-283X) **4602**

Jissen Shogaiji Kyoiku. see Practical Education for the Handicapped **1739**

Jisuan Jiegou Lixue Jiqi Yingyong/ Journal of Computational Structural Mechanics and Applications. (CC ISSN 1000-3401) **1932**

Jisuan Shuxue/Mathematica Numerica Sinica. (CC ISSN 0254-7791) **3040**

Jisuanji Gongcheng/Computer Engineering. (CC ISSN 1000-3428) **1418**

Jisuanji Jiao yu Xue/Computer in Teaching and Learning. (CC) **1690**

Jisuanji Shidai/Computer Age. (CC) **1397**

Jisuanji Xuebao. (CC ISSN 0254-4164) **1482, 1416, 1427**

Jisuanji Yanjiu yu Fazhan/Computer Research and Development. (CC ISSN 1000-1239) **1418, 1454, 1478**

Jisuanji Yingyong yu Ruanjian/ Computer Applications and Software. (CC ISSN 1000-386X) **1397, 1478**

Jisuanji yu Yingyong Huaxue/ Computers and Applied Chemistry. (CC ISSN 1001-4160) **4359, 1408**

Jisuberi/Landslides. (JA ISSN 0285-2926) **1591**

Jisunu. (BO) **2571**

Jitsugyo no Burajiru. see Seleçoes Economicas **935**

Jitsugyo No Nihon/Japanese Business. (JA) **673**

Jitsumu Hyomen Gijutsu see Hyomen Gijutsu **1212**

Jiu Shi Nian Dai. see The Nineties Monthly **2197**

Jiwan Dhara. (II ISSN 0021-6976) **2571**

Jixie Gongcheng Cailiao. (CC ISSN 1000-3738) **3018**

Jixie Gongcheng Xuebao. (CC ISSN 0577-6686) **1932**

Jixie Kexue yu Jishu. (CC ISSN 1001-0513) **3019**

Jixie Sheji yu Yanjiu. (CC) **3019**

Jixie Zhizao. see Chinamac Journal **3016**

Jixie Zhizao. (CC ISSN 1000-4998) **3019**

Jiyou Bolan/Philately Vision. (CC) **3753**

Jiyou Yanjiu/Philately Research. (CC) **3753**

Jiyu Sekai. see Free World **3895**

Jizhe Yaolan/Journalists Cradle. (CC) **2571**

Jizni Morava. (CS ISSN 0449-0436) **2370**

Jnanadhara. (II ISSN 0021-700X) **2927**

Jo-Koso Geppo. see Aerological Data of Japan **3432**

Joachim-Junglus-Gesellschaft der Wissenschaften, Hamburg. Veroeffentlichungen. (GW) **4317**

Job Catalog. (US ISSN 0278-5706) **3628**

Job Creation. (US) **984**

Job Express. (US ISSN 1041-1828) **1397, 3628**

Job Express Registry. (US) **3628, 1531**

Job Finder. (US) **3628**

Job Market. (US) **3628**

Job Openings for Economists. (US) **3628, 673**

Job Prospector: New England Edition. (US) **3628**

Job Safety & Health (Washington). (US ISSN 0149-7510) **3618**

Job Safety Consultant. (US ISSN 1040-4198) **3618**

Job Seeker. (US) **3628**

Job Service North Dakota. Annual Report. (US) **984**

Job Service North Dakota. Biennial Report to the Governor. (US) **984**

Job Service Openings and Starting Wages Reports. (US) **3628**

Job Shop Technology. (US) **1067**

Jobarat see Cimbora **1252**

†Jobber Executive. (US ISSN 1047-2312) **5220**

Jobber News. (CN ISSN 0021-7050) **4693**

Jobber Retailer. (US ISSN 0148-5792) **4693**

Jobber Topics see Jobber Topics Reports **4693**

Jobber Topics Reports. (US) **4693**

†Jobless Newsletter. (US ISSN 0738-0208) **5220**

JobMart. (US) **3628**

Jobs, Careers and Further Studies see Smart Start **3631**

Jobs for Philosophers. (US) **3628, 3770**

▼Jobs From Recyclables Possibility Newsletter. (US) **3628**

†Jobs in Print. (US) **5220**

▼Jobs in Recessionary Times Possibility Newsletter. (US ISSN 1053-654X) **3628**

Jobs in the 'Gap' Year. (UK) **3629**

†Jobs Today. (US ISSN 1040-9300) **5221**

▼Jobson's Cheers. (US) **382**

Jobson's Investment Digest of Australia and New Zealand see Jobson's Year Book of Public Companies **952**

Jobson's Liquor Handbook. (US ISSN 1046-8250) **382**

Jobson's Mining Year Book. (AT ISSN 0075-3777) **3486**

Jobson's Quarterly. (AT ISSN 0813-7455) **952, 1792, 3486**

Jobson's Wine Marketing Handbook. (US) **382**

Jobson's Year Book of Public Companies. (AT ISSN 0075-3785) **952**

Jochi Daigaku Sugaku Kokyuroku/ Sophia Kokyuroku in Mathematics. (JA ISSN 0914-3378) **3040**

Jockey Club. (AG ISSN 0021-7115) **4535**

Jocks. (UK ISSN 0951-5143) **3559, 4461**

Jodesa. (II) **3462**

Jodhpur Management Journal. (II) **1015**

Jodrell Laboratory. Notes. (UK) **507**

▼Joe Franklin's Nostalgia. (US ISSN 1047-0476) **3512, 2411**

Joe Magazine. (KE) **2208**

Joe Scott's the Political Animal. (US ISSN 0747-5659) **3901**

Joedisk Orientering. (DK ISSN 0021-7131) **2009, 4224**

†Joedisk Revy. (DK ISSN 0107-7333) **5221**

Joedisk Samfund see Joedisk Orientering **2009**

Joekull. (IC ISSN 0449-0576) **1569, 1591, 1599**

Joel Sater's Antiques and Auction News see Antiques and Auction News **255**

Joernaal vir Eietydse Geskiedenis. see Journal for Contemporary History **3963**

Joetsu Kyoiku Daigaku Kenkyu Kiyo. Dai-3-Bunsatsu. Shizenkei Kyoiku, Seikatsu Kenkokei Kyoiku/Joetsu University of Education. Bulletin. 3. Natural Sciences and Human Living. (JA ISSN 0911-9639) **4317**

Joetsu University of Education. Bulletin. 3. Natural Sciences and Human Living. see Joetsu Kyoiku Daigaku Kenkyu Kiyo. Dai-3-Bunsatsu. Shizenkei Kyoiku, Seikatsu Kenkokei Kyoiku **4317**

Joeygram see Calliope (Baltimore) **4631**

Jogasz Szovetsegi Ertekezesek. (HU) **2638**

Jogging. (IT) **4361**

Jogging Magazine see Running **3808**

Jogo Aberto. (BL) **4477**

Jogtudomanyi Kozlony/Law Sciences Review. (HU ISSN 0021-7166) **2638**

Johann Wilhelm Klein. (AU ISSN 0021-7174) **2293, 1641**

Johann Wolfgang Goethe Universitaet. Studienfuehrer. (GW ISSN 0302-5926) **1709**

Johann Wolfgang Goethe Universitaet. Vorlesungsverzeichnis. (GW) **1709**

†Johann-Wolfgang-Goethe-Universitaet, Frankfurt. Ostasiatische Seminar. Veroeffentlichungen. Reihe A. Suedostasienkunde. (GW ISSN 0532-596X) **5221**

†Johann-Wolfgang-Goethe-Universitaet, Frankfurt. Ostasiatische Seminar. Veroeffentlichungen. Reihe B: Ostasienkunde. (GW) **5221**

Johannes Gutenberg-Universitaet Mainz. Forschungsmagazin. (GW ISSN 0178-4757) **4317**

Johannes-Kepler-Hochschule Linz. Dissertationen see Johannes-Kepler-Universitaet Linz. Dissertationen **4317**

Johannes-Kepler-Universitaet Linz. Dissertationen. (AU ISSN 0259-0689) **4317**

Johannes Schwalm Historical Association. Journal. (US) **2411**

Johannesburg Gold & Metal Mining Advisor. (US) **3486**

Johannesburg Historical Foundation. Journal see Between the Chains **2331**

Johannesburg Public Library. Annual Report. (SA) **2765**

Johannesburg Stock Exchange. Handbook see The J S E Handbook **952**

Johannesburg Stock Exchange Handbook see The J S E Handbook **952**

Johannesburg Stock Exchange Monthly Bulletin. (SA ISSN 0075-7182) **952**

Johannesburg - West Rand Directory. (SA) **1141**

†John Alexander Monograph Series on Various Phases of Thoracic Surgery. (US ISSN 0075-3815) **5221**

John & Mable Ringling Museum of Art. (US) **3525**

John Birch Society. Bulletin. (US ISSN 0449-0754) **3963**

John Clare Society Journal. (UK) **2928, 2995**

John Deere Journal see J D Journal **162**

John Deutsch Institute for the Study of Economic Policy. Discussion Paper Series. (CN ISSN 0840-5425) **896**

John Deutsch Institute for the Study of Economic Policy. Policy Forum Series. (CN) **896**

John Deutsch Institute for the Study of Economic Policy. Roundtable Series. (CN) **896**

John Deutsch Institute for the Study of Economic Policy. Walwyn Lecture Series. (CN) **896**

John Deutsch Roundtable on Economic Policy see John Deutsch Institute for the Study of Economic Policy. Roundtable Series **896**

John Donne Journal: Studies in the Age of Donne. (US ISSN 0738-9655) **2928**

John E. Bryan Gardening Newsletter. (US) **2132**

John Grooms Newsletter. (UK) **4410**

†John Herling's Labor Letter. (US ISSN 0021-7190) **5221**

John Howard Society of Alberta Reporter. (CN) **1516, 2638**

John Liner Letter. (US ISSN 0021-7204) **2535**

John Liner Review. (US) **2535, 952**

John Macmurray Studies. (US ISSN 1044-5757) **4184**

John Marshall Law Review. (US ISSN 0270-854X) **2638**

John Milton Adult Lessons Quarterly. (US) **4184, 2293**

John Milton Magazine. (US) **2293, 4184**

John Milton Sunday School Quarterly. see John Milton Adult Lessons Quarterly **4184**

John Milton Talking Book see John Milton Talking Book Magazine **2293**

John Milton Talking Book Magazine. (US) **2293, 4184**

John Naisbitt's Trend Letter. (US ISSN 0883-136X) **870**

John Rylands Library. Bulletin see John Rylands University Library of Manchester. Bulletin **2509**

John Rylands University Library of Manchester. Bulletin. (UK ISSN 0301-102X) **2509, 2765**

John T. Reed's Real Estate Investor's Monthly. (US ISSN 0887-1922) **4151, 952**

Johns Hopkins A P L Technical Digest. (Applied Physics Laboratory) (US ISSN 0270-5214) **3821, 1827**

Johns Hopkins Health After 50. (US) **2274**

Johns Hopkins Hospital School of Nursing. Alumni Magazine. (US ISSN 0002-6700) **3279**

Johns Hopkins Magazine. (US ISSN 0021-7255) **1315**

Johns Hopkins Oceanographic Studies. (US ISSN 0075-3858) **1606**

Johns Hopkins Studies in Atlantic History and Culture. (US) **2411**

Johns Hopkins Studies in the History of Technology. (US) **4602**

Johns Hopkins Symposia in Comparative History. (US ISSN 0075-3874) **2315**

†Johns Hopkins University. Population Information Program. Population Reports. Arabic Edition. (US ISSN **5221**

Johns Hopkins University. Population Information Program. Population Reports. English Edition. (US ISSN 0887-0241) **3984**

Johns Hopkins University. Population Information Program. Population Reports. French Edition. (US ISSN 0887-025X) **3984**

Johns Hopkins University. Population Information Program. Population Reports. Portuguese Edition. (US ISSN 0887-0276) **3984**
Johns Hopkins University. Population Information Program. Population Reports. Spanish Edition. (US ISSN 0887-0268) **3984**
Johns Hopkins University Studies in Geology. (US ISSN 0075-3890) **1569**
Johns Hopkins University Studies in Historical and Political Science. (US ISSN 0075-3904) **2315, 3901**
Johnson C. Smith Newsletter. (US) **1315**
Johnson C. Smith University News see J C S U News **1315**
Johnson County Genealogist. (US) **2156**
Johnson Herald. (US) **2156**
†Johnson Journal. (US ISSN 8755-1721) **5221**
†Johnson Outboards Boating. (US ISSN 0271-2040) **5221**
Johnson Redbook Service Weekly Comments. (US) **870, 952**
Johnson Reporter. (CN ISSN 0731-8979) **2156**
Johnson Safari Wait-a-Bit Newsletter see Martin & Osa Johnson Safari Museum Wait-a-Bit News **3527**
Johnson Survey see America's Fastest Growing Companies **938**
Johnsonia. (US ISSN 0075-3920) **585**
Johnsonian News Letter. (US ISSN 0021-728X) **2928, 2315**
Johnson's Investment Company Charts. (US) **952**
Joho Kanri. see Journal of Information Processing and Managements **2765**
Joho Kodo Kagaku Kenkyu/Studies in Information and Behavioral Sciences. (JA ISSN 0385-1478) **2509**
Joho no Kagaku to Gijutsu. see Japan. Information Science and Technology Association. Journal **2765**
Joho Shori/Information Processing Society of Japan. Journal. (JA ISSN 0447-8053) **1452**
Al-Johrah Fashion. (SU) **1292**
Johrath Al-Araies. (SU) **1292**
Johrath Al-Khalig. (SU) **1292**
Join Us...Costa Rica Awaits You. (CR ISSN 1018-1253) **4773**
†Joining and Materials. (UK) **5221**
Joint Acquisitions List of Africana. (US ISSN 0021-731X) **254, 2329, 3938**
Joint Action in Community Services, Inc. Volunteer see J A C S Volunteer **3628**
Joint Association of Classical Teachers. Bulletin. (UK ISSN 0267-8349) **1277, 1752**
Joint Association of Classical Teachers Review see J A C T Review **1277**
Joint Association of Classical Teachers Themes see J A C T Themes **1277**
Joint Association Survey on Drilling Costs. (US) **3706**
Joint Automatic Control Conference. Record see American Control Conference. Conference Proceedings **1881**
Joint Center for Housing Studies of M I T and Harvard University. Joint Center Review. (US) **2490**
Joint Center for Political Studies. New and Recent Books. (US) **3901**
Joint Center for Political Studies, Inc. Congressional District Fact Book see J C P S Congressional District Fact Book **3900**
Joint Center for Urban Studies. Publications. (US ISSN 0075-3947) **2490**
Joint Commission on Allied Health Personnel in Ophthalmology. Annual Report. (US) **3301**
Joint Commission on Allied Health Personnel in Ophthalmology Outlook see J C A H P O Outlook **3301**
†Joint Commission Perspectives. (US ISSN 0277-8327) **5221**
Joint Committee for Church Music in Ireland. Newsletter. (IE) **3559**

Joint Committee on Mineral Resources in Greenland. Annual Report. (DK) **3486**
Joint Conference of the I E E E Computer and Communications Societies see I E E E Infocom. Proceedings **1350**
†Joint Endeavor. (US) **5221**
Joint F A O - W H O Codex Alimentarius Commission. Report of the Session. (UN ISSN 0449-122X) **4106, 2074**
Joint Financial Management Improvement Program. Annual Report. (US) **1015**
Joint Forum for Philippine Progress News. (US) **932, 915**
Joint Governmental Salary and Benefits Survey: Arizona. (US) **725, 984**
Joint Governmental Salary Survey: Arizona see Joint Governmental Salary and Benefits Survey: Arizona **725**
Joint Institute for Laboratory Astrophysics Data Center. Report see J I L A Data Center. Report **3848**
†Joint Meeting of the Members of the Consultative Assembly of the Council of Europe and of the Members of the European Parliamentary Assembly. Official Report of Debates. (EI ISSN 0447-8452) **5221**
Joint Nuclear Research Center, Ispra, Italy. Annual Report. (EI) **1806**
Joint Planning Commission, Lehigh - Northampton Counties Newsletter see J P C Newsletter **2490**
Joint Strategy and Action Committee Grapevine see J S A C Grapevine **5219**
▼Joint Venture Digest. (US) **952**
Joint Ventures in the Soviet Union. (US) **2726, 915**
Joint Ventures: Structuring Alternatives. (US) **2710, 673**
Joint Ventures with International Partners. (US) **2726, 915**
▼Joint Ventures with the Soviet Union. (US) **2726, 932**
JOJO. (Journal der Fachjournalisten) (GW) **2571**
Jojoba Happenings. (US ISSN 0746-3766) **182, 507**
Joken Hansha see Neurosciences **3348**
Jokesmith. (US ISSN 0749-4351) **2870, 1338, 2765**
Jokook Tongil. (KN) **3901**
Joliet Catholic Explorer see New Catholic Explorer **4270**
La Jolla Magazine. (US ISSN 0893-1151) **2227**
Jolly. (IT) **4361**
Jolson Journal. (US) **3559**
Jolson Journalette. (US) **3559**
Jomar. (SP) **915**
Jomar B O N N. (SP) **1115**
†Jonah Hex. (DK) **5221**
Jonathan. (US) **1298**
Jones County Historical Review. (US) **2411, 2055**
Jones Journeys. (US) **2156**
†Jones of America. (US) **5221**
Jones of Virginia Letter. (US) **2156**
Jonesreport for Shopping Center Marketing. (US ISSN 0889-485X) **33, 1042**
Jong Dae see Young Ideas **4290**
Jonge Kampvechter see Wyzer **4290**
Jonge Kerk. (NE ISSN 0021-7395) **4184, 1257**
Jonquil. (US ISSN 0744-3943) **1298, 4410**
Jord og Myr. (NO ISSN 0332-5229) **101, 2103**
Jord og Viden. (DK ISSN 0906-7043) **101**
Jordan/Urdon. (JO) **2208**
Jordan. Department of Statistics. Agricultural Statistical Yearbook and Agricultural Sample Survey. (JO) **101**
Jordan. Department of Statistics. Annual Statistical Yearbook. (JO ISSN 0075-4013) **4576**
Jordan. Department of Statistics. Construction Statistics. (JO) **638**

Jordan. Department of Statistics. Employment Survey for Establishments Engaging Five Persons or More. (JO) **725, 984**
Jordan. Department of Statistics. External Trade Statistics. (JO ISSN 0075-4021) **725**
Jordan. Department of Statistics. Industrial Survey. (JO) **725**
Jordan. Department of Statistics. Internal Trade Survey. (JO) **725**
†Jordan. Department of Statistics. Monthly Bulletin of External Trade Statistics. (JO) **5221**
Jordan. Department of Statistics. National Accounts. (JO ISSN 0449-1513) **999**
Jordan. Ministry of Tourism and Antiquities. Tourist Arrivals in Numbers. (JO) **4799**
Jordan. Ministry of Tourism and Antiquities. Travel Statistics see Jordan. Ministry of Tourism and Antiquities. Tourist Arrivals in Numbers **4799**
†Jordan (Washington). (US ISSN 0164-4777) **5221**
†Jordan Economy in Figures. (JO ISSN 0449-1491) **5221**
▼Jordan Issues and Perspectives. (US) **2208**
Jordan Magazine see Jordan (Washington) **5221**
Jordan Medical Journal/Majallat al-Tibbiyya al-Urdaniyya. (JO ISSN 0446-9283) **3113**
Jordan University Newsletter/Anba al-Jamiah. (JO) **1709, 1315**
Jordanian National Bibliography. (JO) **404, 2430**
Jordan's Regional Directories of Key Business Prospects - Yorkshire and Humberside (Year). (UK) **1141, 837**
Jordbrug. (DK ISSN 0108-884X) **101**
Jordbrug Oestjylland (Midt): Samtlige Landbrug, Skovbrug og Gartnerier. (DK ISSN 0107-6108) **101, 2103**
Jordbruksekonomiska Meddelanden/ Journal of Agricultural Economics. (SW ISSN 0021-7441) **153**
Jordbruksstatistikk see Norway. Statistisk Sentralbyraa. Jordbruksstatistikk **141**
Jordemodern. (SW ISSN 0021-7468) **3293**
†Jorden Runt. (SW ISSN 0021-7476) **5221**
Jornada. (CN) **2009**
Jornada Deportiva. (SP) **4477**
Jornadas Nacionales de Derecho Aeronautico y Espacial. Trabajos. (AG) **4675, 57, 2638**
Jornal Arquiteto see Cadernos Brasileiros de Arquitetura **296**
Jornal Arquiteto see Projeto **1083**
Jornal Brasileiro de Ginecologia. (BL ISSN 0368-1416) **3293**
Jornal Brasileiro de Medicina. (BL ISSN 0047-2077) **3113**
Jornal Brasileiro de Neurologia see Revista Brasileiro de Neurologia **3353**
Jornal Brasileiro de Psiquiatria. (BL ISSN 0047-2085) **3340**
Jornal da A P E C see Associacao Portuguesa de Empresas Cinematograficas. Jornal **3503**
Jornal da F U N A I. (Fundacao Nacional do Indio) (BL) **3944, 2009**
Jornal das Ciencias Medicas. (PO) **3113**
Jornal de Contabilidade. (PO ISSN 0870-8789) **752**
Jornal de Letras. (BL ISSN 0047-2093) **2870**
†Jornal de Pediatria. (BL ISSN 0021-7557) **5221**
Jornal de Pneumologia. (BL ISSN 0102-3586) **3365**
Jornal de Psicologia. (PO ISSN 0870-4783) **4026**
Jornal do Exercito. (PO ISSN 0447-8819) **3462**
Jornal do Medico. (PO ISSN 0021-7573) **3113**
Jornal do Noticias Embalagem Vende. (BL) **1042**

Jornal do Professor de 1o Grau. (BL) **1641**
Jornal dos Transportes. (BL) **4651**
Jornal Portugues. see Portuguese Journal **2020**
Josai Daigaku Kenkyu Nenpo. Shizen Kagaku Hen/Josai University Bulletin of Liberal Arts. Natural Science, Health and Physical Education. (JA ISSN 0914-9775) **2509, 3805, 4317**
Josai Shika Daigaku Kiyo see Meikai University School of Dentistry. Journal **3237**
Josai University Bulletin of Liberal Arts. Natural Science, Health and Physical Education. see Josai Daigaku Kenkyu Nenpo. Shizen Kagaku Hen **2509**
Josanpu Zasshi/Japanese Journal for Midwives. (JA ISSN 0047-1836) **3293, 3279**
Jose. (BL) **2870**
Josef-Albers-School. Almanach. (GW) **2928**
Joseph & Mary Ray Reunions Newsletter. (US) **2156**
Joseph Haas Gesellschaft. Mitteilungensblatt. (GW ISSN 0446-9577) **3559**
Joseph I. Lubin Memorial Lectures. (US) **673**
Josephinum Newsletter. (US ISSN 0021-759X) **4266**
Josephinum Review see Josephinum Newsletter **4266**
Josephite Harvest. (US ISSN 0021-7603) **4184**
Joslin Diabetes Center Newsletter see Joslin Magazine **3254**
Joslin Magazine. (US) **3254**
Joslyn Art Museum Members' Calendar see Joslyn News **3525**
Joslyn News. (US) **3525**
Jots from the Point. (US) **2156**
Jottings. (US) **2293, 4284**
Jouets et Jeux. (FR ISSN 0075-4056) **2281**
Jouko. (FI) **2370**
Jounal of Friction. see Mocaxue Xuebao **3844**
Jour et la Nuit see Horizon (Montreal) **1314**
Journal (Columbus). (US ISSN 1045-084X) **2928, 3792**
Journal (Oak Park) see Michigan Society for Respiratory Therapy. Journal **3366**
Journal Africain de Genetique see African Journal of Genetics **539**
Journal American Rhododendron Society. (US ISSN 0745-7839) **2132**
Journal Anglican. see Anglican Journal **4229**
Journal Annuel de la Societe Historique de la Vallee de la Chateauguay. see Chateauguay Valley Historical Society Annual Journal **2402**
Journal Asiatique. (FR ISSN 0021-762X) **3639**
Journal Association des Medecins Israelites de France see J A M I F **3112**
Journal Barreau. (CN ISSN 0833-921X) **2638**
Journal Canadien d'Anesthesie. see Canadian Journal of Anaesthesia **3191**
Journal Canadien d'Ophtalmologie. see Canadian Journal of Ophthalmology **3299**
Journal Canadien de Botanique. see Canadian Journal of Botany **499**
Journal Canadien de Chimie. see Canadian Journal of Chemistry **1171**
Journal Canadien de Chirurgie. see Canadian Journal of Surgery **3376**
Journal Canadien de Mathematiques. see Canadian Journal of Mathematics **3031**
Journal Canadien de Microbiologie. see Canadian Journal of Microbiology **550**
Journal Canadien de Physiologie et Pharmacologie. see Canadian Journal of Physiology and Pharmacology **570**

Journal Canadien de Physique. see Canadian Journal of Physics **3815**
Journal Canadien de Zoologie. see Canadian Journal of Zoology **580**
Journal Canadien des Sciences de la Terre. see Canadian Journal of Earth Sciences **1542**
Journal Canadien des Techniques en Radiation Medicale. see Canadian Journal of Medical Radiation Technology **3357**
Journal Contents in Quantitative Methods. (UK ISSN 0142-5951) **725**, **1015**, **4576**
Journal d'Acoustique. (FR ISSN 0988-4319) **3859**
Journal d'Administration des Communes Rurales. (FR) **4089**
†Journal d'Agriculture Traditionnelle et de Botanique Appliquee. (FR ISSN 0183-5173) **5221**
Journal d'Analyse Mathematique. (IS ISSN 0021-7670) **3040**
Journal d'Echographie et de Medecine par Ultrasons. (FR ISSN 0245-5552) **3113**
Journal d'Economie Medicale. (FR ISSN 0294-0736) **3113**, **1505**
Journal d'Ergotherapie. (FR ISSN 0249-6550) **3113**
Journal d'O.R.L. see Archives of Otolaryngology **3077**
Journal d'Urologie. (FR ISSN 0248-0018) **3388**
Journal de Biologie Buccale. (FR ISSN 0301-3952) **3235**
Journal de Chimie Physique et de Physico-Chimie Biologique. (FR ISSN 0021-7689) **1227**, **478**
Journal de Chirurgie. (FR ISSN 0021-7697) **3379**
Journal de Commerce. (HT) **837**
Journal de Conchyliologie. (AT ISSN 0021-7719) **585**
Journal de Droit Fiscal. (BE) **2638**
Journal de Genetique Humaine see Genetic Counseling **542**
Journal de Gynecologie Obstetrique et Biologie de la Reproduction. (FR ISSN 0368-2315) **3293**
Journal de l'Affiche. (FR) **33**
Journal de l'Annee. (FR ISSN 0449-4733) **1781**
Journal de l'Histoire Economique et Sociale de l'Orient. see Journal of the Economic and Social History of the Orient **2339**
Journal de l'Hotellerie. (FR) **2477**
Journal de l'Ile de la Reunion. (RE ISSN 0395-8876) **2169**
Journal de la Construction de la Suisse Romande. (SZ ISSN 0021-776X) **622**
Journal de la Corse Agricole. (FR ISSN 0021-7778) **101**
Journal de la Formation Continue. (FR) **1684**
Journal de la Librairie. (BE) **2765**
Journal de la Maison. (FR) **2553**
Journal de la Marine Marchande see Journal de la Marine Marchande et du Transport Multimondal **4730**
Journal de la Marine Marchande et de la Navigation Aerienne see Journal de la Marine Marchande et du Transport Multimondal **4730**
Journal de la Marine Marchande et du Transport Multimondal. (FR ISSN 0983-0537) **4730**
Journal de Linguistique Arabe. see Zeitschrift fuer Arabische Linguistik **2853**
Journal de Mathematiques et de Physique Appliquees. see Zeitschrift fuer Angewandte Mathematik und Physik **3062**
Journal de Mathematiques Pures et Appliquees. (FR ISSN 0021-7824) **3040**
Journal de Mecanique see European Journal of Mechanics B - Fluids **3843**
Journal de Mecanique Appliquee see European Journal of Mechanics B - Fluids **3843**
Journal de Mecanique Theorique et Appliquee see European Journal of Mechanics A - Solids **3843**

Journal de Mecanique Theorique et Appliquee see European Journal of Mechanics B - Fluids **3843**
Journal de Medecine de Lyon. (FR ISSN 0021-7883) **3113**
Journal de Medecine de Strasbourg. (FR ISSN 0021-7905) **3113**
Journal de Medecine et de Chirurgie Pratiques. (FR ISSN 0021-7913) **3379**
Journal de Medecine Legale see Journal de Medecine Legale Droit Medical **3265**
Journal de Medecine Legale Droit Medical. (FR ISSN 0249-6208) **3265**, **1982**
Journal de Medecine Nucleaire et Biophysique. (FR ISSN 0992-3039) **3359**, **485**
Journal de Mickey. (FR ISSN 0767-8088) **1257**
Journal de Microscopie et de Spectroscopie Electroniques see Microscopy Microanalysis Microstrucures **3855**
Journal de Monaco. (MC) **4065**
Journal de Mycologie Medicale. (FR ISSN 1156-5233) **507**, **3113**
Journal de Pediatrie see A J D C: American Journal of Diseases of Children **3317**
Journal de Pharmacie Clinique. (FR ISSN 0291-1981) **3730**
Journal de Pharmacie de Belgique. (FR ISSN 0047-2166) **3730**
Journal de Physiologie. (FR ISSN 0021-7948) **572**, **3113**
Journal de Physique see Journal de Physique I **3821**
Journal de Physique I. (FR) **3821**
Journal de Physique II. (FR) **3821**
Journal de Physique III. (FR) **3821**, **1827**
Journal de Physique IV. (FR) **3821**
†Journal de Psychiatrie Biologique et Therapeutique. (FR) **5221**
Journal de Radiologie. (FR ISSN 0227-9363) **3359**
Journal de Readaptation Medicale. (FR ISSN 0242-648X) **1737**
Journal de Tanger. (MR ISSN 0047-2174) **2169**
Journal de Therapie Comportamentale et Cognitive. (FR ISSN 1155-1704) **3340**
Journal de Touring Secours. (BE) **4773**
Journal de Toxicologie Clinique et Experimentale. (FR ISSN 0753-2830) **1982**, **3113**
Journal de Traumatologie du Sport. (FR ISSN 0762-915X) **3371**
Journal Dentaire du Quebec see J D Q: Journal Dentaire du Quebec **3235**
Journal der Fachjournalisten JOJO see JOJO **2571**
Journal des Africanistes. (FR ISSN 0399-0346) **242**, **275**
Journal des Amis du Progres de l'Afrique Noire. (IV) **3944**
Journal des Associations Patronales. see Schweizerische Arbeitgeber-Zeitung **993**
Journal des Beaux-Arts see Art and Culture **313**
Journal des Caisses d'Epargne. (FR ISSN 0047-2182) **787**
Journal des Combattants. (FR ISSN 0021-8014) **3462**
Journal des Comites d'Enterprises. (FR) **1015**
Journal des Communautes see Information Juive **2006**
Journal des Communes. (FR ISSN 0021-8030) **4089**
Journal des Electriciens. (FR ISSN 0337-8500) **1901**
Journal des Finances. (FR ISSN 0021-8049) **787**
Journal des Horticulteurs et Maraichers Romands. see Horticulteurs et Maraichers Romands **2130**
Journal des Instituteurs et des Institutrices. (FR ISSN 0021-8073) **1641**
Journal des Juges de Paix. (BE) **2638**
Journal des Lettres et de l'Audiovisuel. (FR) **2928**, **1375**
Journal des Maires. (FR) **4089**

Journal des Maires et des Conseils Municipaux. (FR) **4089**
Journal des Maladies Vasculaires. (FR ISSN 0398-0499) **3209**
Journal des Marques de Commerce. see Trade Marks Journal **3678**
Journal des Menageres. (FR) **2448**
Journal des Notaires et des Avocats. (FR) **2638**
Journal des Oiseaux. (FR) **564**
Journal des Orphelins de Guerre. (FR) **4410**
Journal des Pates et Papiers. (CN ISSN 0830-887X) **3663**
Journal des Poetes. (BE) **2996**
Journal des Sciences de la Nutrition. see Zeitschrift fuer Ernaehrungswissenschaft **3613**
Journal des Sciences Hydrologiques. see Hydrological Sciences Journal **1598**
Journal des Sciences Medicales de Lille.(FR ISSN 0021-8111) **3113**
Journal des Telecommunications see Telecommunication Journal **1343**
Journal des Tribunaux. (BE ISSN 0021-812X) **2638**
Journal des Tribunaux du Travail. (BE) **2638**
Journal du Batiment et des Travaux Publics. (FR) **1869**, **622**
Journal du Chasseur. (FR) **4549**
Journal du Chauffage et du Sanitaire. (FR) **622**
Journal du Droit International. (FR ISSN 0021-8170) **2726**
Journal du Fermier et du Metayer. (FR ISSN 0446-9739) **101**
Journal du Mineur. (FR ISSN 0397-1511) **2585**, **3486**
Journal du Nord-Ouest. (CN ISSN 0380-2051) **2571**
Journal du Patissier. (FR) **2088**
Journal du Sport. (CN) **4477**
Journal du Textile. (FR ISSN 0021-8197) **4621**, **1285**
Journal du Travail Temporaire et des Services. (FR ISSN 0184-0584) **1067**
Journal Europeen de Combinatoire. see European Journal of Combinatorics **3035**
Journal Europeen de Dermatologie/ European Journal of Dermatology. (FR) **3248**
Journal Europeen de Pathologie Forestiere. see European Journal of Forest Pathology **2099**
†Journal Europeen de Radiotherapie. (FR ISSN 0243-1203) **5221**
Journal Europeen des Urgences/ European Journal of Emergencies. (FR ISSN 0993-9857) **3113**
Journal Export. (YU ISSN 0021-8227) **915**
Journal Fee-Based Information Services see Information Broker **2762**
Journal for Anthroposophy. (US ISSN 0021-8235) **4284**
Journal for Biomedical Engineering. see Shengwu Yixue Gongchengxue Zazhi **3153**
Journal for Contemporary History/ Joernaal vir Eietydse Geskiedenis. (SA ISSN 0258-2422) **3963**, **2315**
Journal for Contemporary History and International Relations see Journal for Contemporary History **3963**
Journal for Corporate Growth. (US ISSN 1048-1648) **787**, **952**
Journal for Creative Change. (US) **4026**, **4184**
Journal for Ethnomusicology. (US) **3559**, **3365**
Journal for General Philosophy of Science/Zeitschrift fuer Allgemeine Wissenschaftstheorie. (NE ISSN 0925-4560) **4317**, **2509**, **3770**
Journal for Geography - Tydskrif vir Aardrykskunde see South African Geographer **2263**
Journal for Higher Education Management. (US) **1709**
Journal for Humanistic and Transpersonal Education see Wholistic Education **1672**
Journal for Juridical Science/Tydskrif vir Regswetenskap. (SA ISSN 0258-252X) **2638**

Journal for Photogrammetrists & Surveyors. (GW) **1869**
Journal for Quality and Participation. (US ISSN 1040-9602) **1067**
Journal for Research in Mathematics Education. (US ISSN 0021-8251) **3040**, **1752**
Journal for Social Work Education in Africa see A S W E A Journal for Social Work Education in Africa **4397**
Journal for Specialists in Group Work. (US ISSN 0193-3922) **4026**
Journal for Students of V C E Political and International Studies. (AT) **4377**
Journal for Students of Year 12 Politics see Journal for Students of V C E Political and International Studies **4377**
Journal for Studies in Economics and Econometrics/Tydskryf vir Studies in Ekonomie en Ekonometrie. (SA ISSN 0379-6205) **896**
Journal for the Cultivation of Mathematics. see Casopis pro Pestovani Matematiky **3032**
Journal for the Education of the Gifted. (US ISSN 0162-3532) **1737**
Journal for the History of Arabic Science. (SY ISSN 0379-2927) **4317**
Journal for the History of Astronomy. (UK ISSN 0021-8286) **366**
Journal for the Scientific Study of Religion. (US ISSN 0021-8294) **4184**, **4439**
Journal for the Study of Consciousness.(US ISSN 0090-2586) **3770**, **3595**
Journal for the Study of Judaism in the Persian, Hellenistic and Roman Period. (NE ISSN 0047-2212) **4224**
Journal for the Study of Religion. (SA ISSN 1011-7601) **4184**
Journal for the Study of the New Testament. (UK ISSN 0142-064X) **4184**
Journal for the Study of the New Testament. Supplement Series. (UK ISSN 0143-5108) **4184**
Journal for the Study of the Old Testament. (UK ISSN 0309-0892) **4184**
Journal for the Study of the Old Testament. Supplement Series. (UK ISSN 0309-0787) **4184**
Journal for the Theory of Social Behaviour. (UK ISSN 0021-8308) **4026**, **3770**, **4377**
Journal for Transport Science. see Tijdschrift voor Vervoerswetenschap **4657**
Journal for Vocational Special Needs Education. (US ISSN 0195-7597) **1737**, **1684**, **1752**
Journal for Water and Waste Water Research. see Zeitschrift fuer Wasser- und Abwasserforschung **4834**
Journal for Weavers, Spinners & Dyers. (UK ISSN 0267-7806) **4621**, **1281**
Journal Forestier Suisse. see Schweizerische Zeitschrift fuer Forstwesen **2107**
Journal Francais d'Amerique. (US ISSN 0195-2889) **2187**, **2227**
Journal Francais d'Ophtalmologie. (FR ISSN 0181-5512) **3301**
Journal Francais d'Orthoptique. (FR ISSN 0240-7914) **3301**
Journal Francais d'Oto-Rhino-Laryngologie see Journal Francais d'Oto-Rhino-Laryngologie - Audiophonologie - Chirurgie Maxillo-Faciale **3315**
Journal Francais d'Oto-Rhino-Laryngologie - Audiophonologie - Chirurgie Maxillo-Faciale. (FR) **3315**
Journal Francais de Biophysique et Medecine Nucleaire see Journal de Medecine Nucleaire et Biophysique **3359**
Journal Frankfurt. (GW) **2189**
Journal fuer Betriebswirtschaft. (AU) **1015**
Journal fuer die Frau. (GW) **1292**

Journal fuer die Reine und Angewandte Mathematik. (GW ISSN 0075-4102) **3040**
Journal fuer Hirnforschung. (GW ISSN 0021-8359) **3340**, 443
Journal fuer Mathematik-Didaktik. (GW ISSN 0173-5322) **3040**, 1641
Journal fuer Oberflaechentechnik see J O T **3018**
Journal fuer Ornithologie. (GW ISSN 0021-8375) **564**
Journal fuer Praktische Chemie. (GW ISSN 0021-8383) **1180**
Journal fuer Signalaufzeichnungsmaterialien see Journal of Information Recording Materials **3792**
Journal fuer Sozialforschung see S W S - Rundschau **4385**
Journal fuer Sozialforschung. (AU ISSN 0025-8822) **4439**
Journal fuer U F O - Forschung. (GW ISSN 0723-7766) **57**, 1299, 4317
Journal fuer Unterhaltungskunst. (GW ISSN 0863-1611) **4634**
Journal Geschichte see G - Geschichte mit Pfiff **2311**
Journal Guadeloupeen see Magazine Gwadloupeyen **2239**
Journal Historique des Bernier. (CN ISSN 0021-8006) **2156**
Journal Holdings in the National Capital Area. (US ISSN 0893-5386) **2765**
Journal Holdings in the Washington-Baltimore Area see Journal Holdings in the National Capital Area **2765**
Journal Industriel du Quebec. (CN ISSN 0831-0122) **622**
Journal International de Psychologie. see International Journal of Psychology **4025**
Journal International des Sciences de la Vigne et du Vin. (FR ISSN 1151-0285) **182**
Journal McIlvanea see McIlvainea **509**
Journal Medical Libanais. see Lebanese Medical Journal **3122**
Journal Michigan Pharmacist. (US ISSN 1045-6481) **3730**
Journal: News of the Blood Programme in Canada. (CN ISSN 0715-8602) **3273**
Journal of Abdominal Surgery. (US ISSN 0021-8421) **3379**
Journal of Abnormal Child Psychology. (US ISSN 0091-0627) **4026**
Journal of Abnormal Psychology. (US ISSN 0021-843X) **4026**
Journal of Abstracts in International Education. (US ISSN 0094-2383) **1677**, 15
Journal of Academic Librarianship. (US ISSN 0099-1333) **2765**
Journal of Acarology. (II) **534**
Journal of Accidental Medicine see Orthopaedic and Traumatic Surgery **3310**
Journal of Accountancy. (US ISSN 0021-8448) **752**
Journal of Accounting and E D P see Financial & Accounting Systems **1450**
Journal of Accounting and Economics. (NE ISSN 0165-4101) **752**, 870
Journal of Accounting and Public Policy.(US ISSN 0278-4254) **752**, 1099
Journal of Accounting, Auditing & Finance. (US ISSN 0148-558X) **752**
Journal of Accounting Education. (US ISSN 0748-5751) **752**, 1709
Journal of Accounting Literature. (US ISSN 0737-4607) **752**
Journal of Accounting Research. (US ISSN 0021-8456) **752**
Journal of Accounting Research. Supplement. (US) **752**
Journal of Acoustic Emission. (US ISSN 0730-0050) **3859**, 3843
Journal of Acquired Immune Deficiency Syndromes. (US ISSN 0894-9255) **3221**
Journal of Ad-Jective Contagion see Plague Watch **2879**
Journal of Addictions & Offender Counseling. (US ISSN 1055-3835) **1516**, 4410

Journal of Addictive Diseases. (US ISSN 1055-0887) **1537**
Journal of Adhesion. (US ISSN 0021-8464) **3821**, 1227, 3863
Journal of Adhesion Science and Technology. (NE ISSN 0169-4243) **3863**, 1855, 4292
Journal of Adolescence. (UK ISSN 0140-1971) **1239**
Journal of Adolescent Chemical Dependency. (US ISSN 0896-7768) **1537**, 1239
Journal of Adolescent Health. (US ISSN 1054-139X) **3114**, 1239
Journal of Adolescent Health Care see Journal of Adolescent Health **3114**
Journal of Adolescent Research. (US ISSN 0743-5584) **1239**, 1641, 4026
Journal of Adult Education. (TZ ISSN 0856-1109) **1685**
Journal of Advanced Nursing. (UK ISSN 0309-2402) **3280**
Journal of Advanced Transportation. (US ISSN 0197-6729) **4652**, 1827
Journal of Advancement in Medicine. (US ISSN 0894-5888) **3114**
Journal of Adventist Education. (US ISSN 0021-8480) **4284**
Journal of Advertising. (US ISSN 0091-3367) **33**
Journal of Advertising Research. (US ISSN 0021-8499) **33**
Journal of Aeromedical Society of India see Indian Journal of Aerospace Medicine **3107**
Journal of Aerosol Medicine. (US ISSN 0894-2684) **3365**
Journal of Aerosol Science. (US ISSN 0021-8502) **3649**, 1855
Journal of Aerospace Engineering. (US ISSN 0893-1321) **1869**, 57
Journal of Aesthetic Education. (US ISSN 0021-8510) **1641**, 3770
Journal of Aesthetics and Art Criticism. (US ISSN 0021-8529) **331**, 3559, 3770
Journal of Affective Disorders. (NE ISSN 0165-0327) **3340**
Journal of African Civilizations. (US ISSN 0270-2495) **242**, 275, 2333
Journal of African Earth Sciences (and the Middle East). (US ISSN 0899-5362) **1569**
▼Journal of African Economies. (UK ISSN 0963-8024) **870**
Journal of African History. (UK ISSN 0021-8537) **2333**, 242, 275
Journal of African Languages and Linguistics. (US ISSN 0167-6164) **2820**
Journal of African Law. (UK ISSN 0021-8553) **2638**
Journal of African Religion and Philosophy. (UG) **4184**, 3770
Journal of African Studies/Afurika Kenkyu. (JA ISSN 0065-4140) **2333**
†Journal of African Studies. (US ISSN 0095-4993) **5221**
▼Journal of Afroasiatic Languages. (NE ISSN 0894-9824) **2820**
Journal of Aged Care see Clinical Gerontologist **2271**
Journal of Aging and Health. (US ISSN 0898-2643) **2274**
Journal of Aging and Judaism see Journal of Psychology and Judaism **4032**
Journal of Aging & Social Policy. (US ISSN 0895-9420) **2274**, 4439
Journal of Aging Studies. (US ISSN 0890-4065) **2274**
Journal of Agricultural and Environmental Ethics. (CN) **3770**, 101
Journal of Agricultural and Food Chemistry. (US ISSN 0021-8561) **182**
Journal of Agricultural & Food Information. (US ISSN 1049-6505) **101**, 2074
Journal of Agricultural Economics. see Jordbruksekonomiska Meddelanden **153**
Journal of Agricultural Economics. (UK ISSN 0021-857X) **153**

Journal of Agricultural Economics. see Nogyo Keizai Kenkyu **155**
Journal of Agricultural Economics Research. (US ISSN 1043-3309) **153**
Journal of Agricultural Education. (US ISSN 1042-0541) **1642**, 101
Journal of Agricultural Engineering. (II ISSN 0256-6524) **101**, 1827
Journal of Agricultural Engineering Research. (UK ISSN 0021-8634) **182**
Journal of Agricultural Entomology. (US ISSN 0735-939X) **534**, 101
Journal of Agricultural Ethics see Journal of Agricultural and Environmental Ethics **3770**
Journal of Agricultural Lending. (US) **787**, 101
Journal of Agricultural Machinery. see Nongye Jixie Zazhi **163**
Journal of Agricultural Meteorology/Nogyo Kisho. (JA ISSN 0021-8588) **3437**, 101
Journal of Agricultural Research see Pakistan Journal of Agricultural Research **113**
Journal of Agricultural Research of China. (CH ISSN 0376-477X) **101**
Journal of Agricultural Science. (UK ISSN 0021-8596) **101**
Journal of Agricultural Science in Finland. (FI ISSN 0782-4386) **101**
Journal of Agricultural Taxation and Law. (US) **1099**, 101
Journal of Agriculture and Water Research. Plant Production. (IQ ISSN 1012-3474) **101**, 4826
Journal of Agriculture and Water Resources Research. Animal Production. (IQ ISSN 1012-3466) **101**, 4826
Journal of Agriculture and Water Resources Research. Soil and Water Resources. (IQ ISSN 1012-3482) **101**, 4826
Journal of Agriculture of Western Australia. (AT ISSN 0021-8618) **101**
Journal of Agronomic Education. (US ISSN 0094-2391) **182**, 1752
Journal of Agronomy and Crop Science/Zeitschrift fuer Acker- und Pflanzenbau. (GW ISSN 0931-2250) **183**
Journal of Air Law and Commerce. (US ISSN 0021-8642) **2638**
Journal of Air Medical Transport. (US) **3114**, 57
Journal of Air Medical Transport. (US ISSN 1046-9095) **4675**, 3209, 3280, 3308
Journal of Air Traffic Control. (US ISSN 0021-8650) **57**
Journal of Aircraft. (US ISSN 0021-8669) **57**
Journal of Alabama Archaeology. (US ISSN 0449-2153) **275**
Journal of Alcohol and Drug Education. (US ISSN 0090-1482) **1537**
Journal of Alcohol, Drugs and other Psychotropic Substances/Tijdschrift voor Alcohol, Drugs en Andere Psychotrope Stoffen. (NE ISSN 0378-2778) **1537**
Journal of Algebra. (US ISSN 0021-8693) **3040**
▼Journal of Algebraic Geometry. (US ISSN 1056-3911) **3040**
Journal of Algorithms. (US ISSN 0196-6774) **3065**
Journal of Allergy and Clinical Immunology. (US ISSN 0091-6749) **3187**
Journal of Allied Health. (US ISSN 0090-7421) **4106**
Journal of Alloys and Compounds. (SZ ISSN 0925-8388) **3411**, 1180, 3821
Journal of Ambulatory Care Management. (US ISSN 0148-9917) **2466**
Journal of Ambulatory Care Marketing. (US ISSN 0886-9723) **3308**
Journal of Ambulatory Monitoring. (UK ISSN 0951-1830) **3209**
Journal of American College Health. (US ISSN 0744-8481) **3805**, 1709

Journal of American Culture. (US ISSN 0191-1813) **2055**
Journal of American Drama and Theatre. (US ISSN 1044-937X) **4634**, 2928
Journal of American Ethnic History. (US ISSN 0278-5927) **2010**, 2411
Journal of American Folklore. (US ISSN 0021-8715) **2056**
▼Journal of American Health Policy. (US ISSN 1055-324X) **3114**
Journal of American History. (US ISSN 0021-8723) **2411**
Journal of American Indian Education. (US ISSN 0021-8731) **2010**, 1642
Journal of American Indian Family Research. (US ISSN 0730-6148) **2010**, 2156
Journal of American Indian Family Research Monthly Newsletter. (US ISSN 1040-6581) **2010**, 2156
†Journal of American Insurance. (US ISSN 0021-874X) **5221**
Journal of American Studies. (UK) **2411**
▼Journal of Analytic Social Work. (US ISSN 1052-9950) **4410**
Journal of Analytical and Applied Pyrolysis. (NE ISSN 0165-2370) **1180**
Journal of Analytical Atomic Spectrometry. (UK ISSN 0267-9477) **1206**
Journal of Analytical Chemistry of the U S S R. (English translation of: Zhurnal Analiticheskoi Khimii) (US ISSN 0021-8766) **1206**
Journal of Analytical Toxicology. (US ISSN 0146-4760) **1982**, 3730
Journal of Anatomy. (UK ISSN 0021-8782) **443**, 3114
Journal of Anatomy. see Jiepouxue Zazhi **443**
Journal of Ancient and Medieval Studies. (US) **2315**, 2156
Journal of Ancient History. see Vestnik Drevnei Istorii **2325**
Journal of Ancient Indian History. (II ISSN 0075-4110) **2339**
Journal of Andrology. (US ISSN 0196-3635) **3114**
Journal of Animal Breeding and Genetics/Zeitschrift fuer Tierzuechtung und Zuechtungsbiologie. (GW ISSN 0044-3581) **219**
Journal of Animal Ecology. (UK ISSN 0021-8790) **443**, 585
Journal of Animal Morphology and Physiology. (II ISSN 0021-8804) **585**, 572
Journal of Animal Physiology and Animal Nutrition/Zeitschrift fuer Tierphysiologie, Tierernaehrung und Futtermittelkunde. (GW ISSN 0044-3565) **585**
Journal of Animal Science. (US ISSN 0021-8812) **219**, 544, 572
Journal of Animal Science. Supplement. Biennial Symposium on Animal Reproduction. (US) **220**, 544, 572
Journal of Anthropological Archaeology. (US ISSN 0278-4165) **242**, 275
Journal of Anthropological Research. (US ISSN 0091-7710) **243**
Journal of Anthropology at McMaster see Nexus **246**
Journal of Antibiotics. (JA ISSN 0021-8820) **3114**, 3730
Journal of Antibiotics. Series A see Journal of Antibiotics **3114**
Journal of Antimicrobial Chemotherapy. (UK ISSN 0305-7453) **3221**
Journal of Anxiety Disorders. (UK ISSN 0887-6185) **4026**, 3340
Journal of Aphidology. (II ISSN 0970-3810) **183**, 534
Journal of Apicultural Research. (UK ISSN 0021-8839) **101**
▼Journal of Applied Aquaculture. (US ISSN 1045-4438) **2044**, 443
Journal of Applied Bacteriology. (UK ISSN 0021-8847) **553**
Journal of Applied Behavior Analysis. (US ISSN 0021-8855) **4027**

Journal of Applied Behavioral Science. (US ISSN 0021-8863) **4027**, **4439**
▼Journal of Applied Biomaterials. (US ISSN 1045-4861) **3260**, **2638**
Journal of Applied Business Research. (US ISSN 0892-7626) **673**
†Journal of Applied Cardiology. (UK ISSN 0883-2935) **5221**
Journal of Applied Chemistry of the U S S R. (English translation of: Zhurnal Prikladnoi Khimii) (US ISSN 0021-888X) **1855**
Journal of Applied Communication Research. (US ISSN 0090-9882) **1338**
Journal of Applied Corporate Finance. (US ISSN 0898-4484) **787**
Journal of Applied Cosmetology. (IT ISSN 0392-8543) **3248**
Journal of Applied Crystallography. (DK ISSN 0021-8898) **1210**
Journal of Applied Developmental Psychology. (US ISSN 0193-3973) **4027**
Journal of Applied Ecology. (UK ISSN 0021-8901) **443**
Journal of Applied Ecology. see Yingyong Shengtai Xuebao **1972**
Journal of Applied Econometrics. (UK ISSN 0883-7252) **3040**, **3062**
Journal of Applied Electrochemistry. (UK ISSN 0021-891X) **1212**, **1855**
Journal of Applied Entomology/Zeitschrift fuer Angewandte Entomologie. (GW ISSN 0044-2240) **534**, **585**
▼Journal of Applied Fire Science. (US ISSN 1044-4300) **2033**
Journal of Applied Geophysics. (NE ISSN 0926-9851) **1591**, **3486**
Journal of Applied Gerontology. (US ISSN 0733-4648) **2274**
Journal of Applied Ichthyology/Zeitschrift fuer Angewandte Ichthyologie. (GW ISSN 0175-8659) **585**
Journal of Applied Mathematics and Mechanics. (English translation of: Prikladnaya Matematika i Mekhanika) (US ISSN 0021-8928) **1918**, **3040**
Journal of Applied Mathematics and Physics. see Zeitschrift fuer Angewandte Mathematik und Physik **3062**
Journal of Applied Mathematics in Higher Education. see Gaoxiao Yingyong Shuxue Xuebao **3036**
Journal of Applied Mechanics. (US ISSN 0021-8936) **1933**
Journal of Applied Mechanics and Technical Physics. (English translation of: Zhurnal Prikladnoi Mekhaniki i Tekhnicheskoi Fiziki) (US ISSN 0021-8944) **1918**, **3821**
Journal of Applied Medicine/Oyo Igaku. (JA) **3114**
Journal of Applied Medicine. (II ISSN 0377-0400) **3114**
Journal of Applied Metalworking see Journal of Materials Shaping Technology **3411**
Journal of Applied Meteorology. (US ISSN 0733-3021) **3437**
Journal of Applied Nutrition. (US ISSN 0021-8960) **3608**
Journal of Applied Oncology. see Shiyong Zhongliu Zazhi **3202**
Journal of Applied Oncology. see Shiyong Zhongliuxue Zazhi **3202**
Journal of Applied Philosophy. (UK ISSN 0264-3758) **3770**
Journal of Applied Phycology. (NE ISSN 0921-8971) **553**, **443**
Journal of Applied Physics. (US ISSN 0021-8979) **3821**, **1827**
Journal of Applied Physiology. (US ISSN 8750-7587) **572**, **3114**
Journal of Applied Physiology: Respiratory, Environmental and Exercise Physiology see Journal of Applied Physiology **572**
Journal of Applied Pneumatics see International Journal of Applied Pneumatics **1931**
Journal of Applied Polymer Science. (US ISSN 0021-8995) **1855**

Journal of Applied Polymer Science. Symposia. (US ISSN 0570-4898) **1855**
Journal of Applied Probability. (UK ISSN 0021-9002) **3040**
Journal of Applied Psychology. (US ISSN 0021-9010) **4027**
Journal of Applied Rabbit Research. (US ISSN 0738-9760) **585**, **220**
Journal of Applied Recreation Research.(CN ISSN 0843-9117) **4773**, **4549**
Journal of Applied Rehabilitation Counseling. (US ISSN 0047-2220) **4410**
Journal of Applied Sciences. see Yingyong Kexue Xuebao **4353**
Journal of Applied Social and Economic Sciences see Confrontation - Change Review **656**
Journal of Applied Social Psychology. (US ISSN 0021-9029) **4027**, **4377**
Journal of Applied Spectroscopy. (English translation of: Zhurnal Prikladnoi Spektroskopii) (US ISSN 0021-9037) **3854**, **1206**
Journal of Applied Sport Psychology. (US ISSN 1041-3200) **3371**, **4027**
Journal of Applied Sports Science Research. (US) **3371**
Journal of Applied Statistics. (UK ISSN 0266-4763) **4576**, **3040**
Journal of Applied Systems Analysis see European Journal of Information Systems **1456**
Journal of Applied Toxicology. (UK ISSN 0260-437X) **1982**, **3730**
Journal of Approximation Theory. (US ISSN 0021-9045) **3040**
Journal of Aquaculture in the Tropics. (II ISSN 0970-0846) **2044**
Journal of Aquatic Animal Health. (US ISSN 0899-7659) **2044**
▼Journal of Aquatic Ecosystem Health. (NE ISSN 0925-1014) **1960**, **4826**
▼Journal of Aquatic Food Product Technology. (US ISSN 1049-8850) **2074**, **2044**
Journal of Aquatic Plant Management. (US ISSN 0146-6623) **507**, **2132**
Journal of Aquatic Products. see Shuichan Xuebao **2049**
Journal of Arab Affairs. (US ISSN 0275-3588) **3963**
Journal of Arabic Linguistics. see Zeitschrift fuer Arabische Linguistik **2853**
Journal of Arabic Literature. (NE ISSN 0085-2376) **2928**, **3639**
Journal of Arachnology. (US ISSN 0161-8202) **535**
Journal of Arboriculture. (US ISSN 0278-5226) **2132**
Journal of Archaeological Science. (UK ISSN 0305-4403) **276**
Journal of Archaeology in Andhra Pradesh. (II) **276**
Journal of Architectural and Planning Research. (US ISSN 0738-0895) **302**
Journal of Architectural Education. (US ISSN 0149-2993) **302**
Journal of Arid Environments. (UK ISSN 0140-1963) **2254**, **1960**
Journal of Arizona History. (US ISSN 0021-9053) **2411**
†Journal of Art. (US) **5221**
Journal of Art and Design Education. (UK ISSN 0260-9991) **331**
Journal of Art History/Bijutsu Shi. (JA ISSN 0021-907X) **331**, **2315**
Journal of Art Studies/Bijutsu Kenkyu. (JA ISSN 0021-9088) **331**
Journal of Arthroplasty. (US ISSN 0883-5403) **3309**
Journal of Artificial Intelligence in Education. (US ISSN 1043-1020) **1690**, **1408**
Journal of Arts Management and Law. (US ISSN 0733-5113) **2638**
Journal of Asia Electronics Union. (JA ISSN 0385-0447) **1774**
Journal of Asian and African Affairs. (US ISSN 1044-2979) **3639**, **2333**, **3963**

Journal of Asian and African Studies. (NE ISSN 0021-9096) **4439**, **243**
Journal of Asian Culture. (US ISSN 0162-6795) **3639**
▼Journal of Asian Economics. (US ISSN 1049-0078) **870**
Journal of Asian History. (GW ISSN 0021-910X) **2339**, **2430**
Journal of Asian-Pacific & World Perspectives. (US ISSN 0148-611X) **4377**
▼Journal of Asian Pacific Communication. (UK ISSN 0957-6851) **1338**, **2820**
Journal of Asian Studies. (US ISSN 0021-9118) **3639**
Journal of Asiatic Studies. (KO ISSN 0021-9126) **3639**
Journal of Assisted Reproduction and Genetics. (US) **3293**
Journal of Asthma (New York). (US ISSN 0277-0903) **3365**
Journal of Astrological Studies. (US ISSN 0085-2384) **359**
Journal of Astronautical Sciences. (US ISSN 0021-9142) **57**
Journal of Astrophysics and Astronomy.(II ISSN 0250-6335) **366**
Journal of Athletic Training. (US) **3371**
Journal of Atmospheric and Oceanic Technology. (US ISSN 0739-0572) **3437**, **1606**
Journal of Atmospheric and Terrestrial Physics. (US ISSN 0021-9169) **1591**
Journal of Atmospheric Chemistry. (NE ISSN 0167-7764) **1180**, **3437**
Journal of Audiovisual Media in Medicine. (UK ISSN 0140-511X) **3114**, **443**
Journal of Australian Direct Marketing. (AT) **1042**
Journal of Australian Political Economy. (AT ISSN 0156-5826) **870**, **896**
Journal of Australian Studies. (AT ISSN 0314-769X) **2345**
Journal of Autism and Developmental Disorders. (US ISSN 0162-3257) **3340**, **4027**
Journal of Autoimmunity. (UK ISSN 0896-8411) **3187**
Journal of Automated Reasoning. (NE ISSN 0168-7433) **1414**, **1409**, **1430**
Journal of Automatic Chemistry. (UK ISSN 0142-0453) **4359**
Journal of Automotive Engineering see Automotive Engineer **4683**
Journal of Autonomic Pharmacology. (UK ISSN 0144-1795) **3731**
▼Journal of Back and Musculoskeletal Rehabilitation. (US ISSN 1053-8127) **3309**, **3215**, **3372**
Journal of Bacteriology. (US ISSN 0021-9193) **553**
Journal of Baha'i Studies. (CN ISSN 0838-0430) **4184**
Journal of Ballistics. (US ISSN 0146-4140) **1933**, **1180**
Journal of Baltic Studies. (US ISSN 0162-9778) **2370**
Journal of Band Research. (US ISSN 0021-9207) **3559**
Journal of Bank Accounting & Auditing. (US ISSN 0895-853X) **752**, **787**
Journal of Bank Cost & Management Accounting. (US) **787**, **752**
Journal of Bank Taxation. (US) **787**, **1099**
Journal of Banking and Finance. (NE ISSN 0378-4266) **787**
Journal of Banking and Finance - Law and Practice. (AT ISSN 1034-3040) **787**, **2710**
Journal of Basic and Clinical Physiology and Pharmacology. (US) **3731**
Journal of Basic Microbiology. (GW ISSN 0233-111X) **554**
Journal of Basic Writing. (US ISSN 0147-1635) **1752**
Journal of Beckett Studies. (UK ISSN 0309-5207) **2928**, **4634**
Journal of Behavior Therapy and Experimental Psychiatry. (US ISSN 0005-7916) **3340**, **4027**
Journal of Behavioral Decision Making. (UK ISSN 0894-3257) **1015**

Journal of Behavioral Economics. (US ISSN 0090-5720) **896**
▼Journal of Behavioral Education. (US ISSN 1053-0819) **4027**
Journal of Behavioral Medicine. (US ISSN 0160-7715) **3340**, **4027**
Journal of Beliefs and Values. (UK) **4184**, **1642**
Journal of Bible and Religion see American Academy of Religion. Journal **4162**
Journal of Biblical Literature. (US ISSN 0021-9231) **4184**
Journal of Bioactive and Compatible Polymers. (US ISSN 0883-9115) **478**
Journal of Biochemical and Biophysical Methods. (NE ISSN 0165-022X) **478**, **485**
Journal of Biochemical Toxicology. (GW ISSN 0887-2082) **1982**, **478**
Journal of Biochemistry. (JA ISSN 0021-924X) **478**
Journal of Biocommunication. (US ISSN 0094-2499) **3114**
Journal of Biodynamic Psychology. (UK ISSN 0143-1218) **4027**
Journal of Bioelectricity. (US ISSN 0730-823X) **485**
Journal of Bioenergetics and Biomembranes. (US ISSN 0145-479X) **486**, **3805**
Journal of Bioengineering see Annals of Biomedical Engineering **468**
Journal of Biogeography. (UK ISSN 0305-0270) **2254**, **443**
Journal of Biological Chemistry. (US ISSN 0021-9258) **478**
Journal of Biological Education. (UK ISSN 0021-9266) **443**, **1642**
Journal of Biological Photography. (US ISSN 0274-497X) **443**, **3792**
Journal of Biological Physics. (NE ISSN 0092-0606) **486**
Journal of Biological Regulators and Homeostatic Agents. (IT ISSN 0393-974X) **443**
Journal of Biological Response Modifiers see Journal of Immunotherapy **3116**
Journal of Biological Rhythms. (US ISSN 0748-7304) **3340**
Journal of Biological Science Research. (IQ ISSN 1012-344X) **443**
Journal of Biological Sciences. (II ISSN 0021-9282) **443**
Journal of Biological Standardization see Biologicals **431**
Journal of Bioluminescence and Chemiluminescence. (UK ISSN 0884-3996) **1227**, **478**, **1206**
Journal of Biomaterials Applications. (US ISSN 0885-3282) **3863**
Journal of Biomaterials Science. Polymer Edition. (NE ISSN 0920-5063) **1219**
Journal of Biomechanical Engineering. (US ISSN 0148-0731) **469**, **1827**, **3114**
Journal of Biomechanics. (US ISSN 0021-9290) **4106**
Journal of Biomedical Engineering. (UK ISSN 0141-5425) **469**, **3114**
Journal of Biomedical Materials Research. (US ISSN 0021-9304) **490**, **3114**
Journal of Biomedical Measurement Informatics and Control see Computer Methods & Programs in Biomedicine **3225**
▼Journal of Biomolecular N M R. (NE ISSN 0925-2738) **478**, **486**, **1227**
▼Journal of Biopharmaceutical Statistics. (US ISSN 1054-3406) **3731**, **478**
Journal of Biosciences. (II ISSN 0250-5991) **443**
Journal of Biosocial Science. (UK ISSN 0021-9320) **544**, **3984**, **4439**
Journal of Biotechnology. (NE ISSN 0168-1656) **490**
Journal of Black Psychology. (US ISSN 0095-7984) **4027**, **2010**
Journal of Black Sacred Music see Black Sacred Music **3541**
Journal of Black Studies. (US ISSN 0021-9347) **4377**, **1642**, **2010**

Journal of Bone and Joint Surgery: American Volume. (US ISSN 0021-9355) **3309**
Journal of Bone and Joint Surgery: British Volume. (UK ISSN 0301-620X) **3309**
Journal of Bone and Mineral Research. (US ISSN 0884-0431) **3309**
Journal of Borderland Research. (US) **3669**, 4317
Journal of Borderland Studies. (US ISSN 0886-5655) **3963**, 915, 2254
▼Journal of British Commonwealth Philately. (US) **3753**
Journal of British Music Therapy. (UK ISSN 0951-5038) **1737**, 3559, 4027
Journal of British Podiatric Medicine. (UK) **3379**
Journal of British Studies. (US ISSN 0021-9371) **2370**
Journal of Broadcasting and Electronic Media. (US ISSN 0883-8151) **1375**, 1642
Journal of Bryology. (UK ISSN 0373-6687) **507**
Journal of Building Research. (IQ ISSN 1012-3423) **1869**
Journal of Building Structures. see Jianzhu Jiegou Xuebao **622**
Journal of Burn Care and Rehabilitation.(US ISSN 0273-8481) **3114**, 3309
Journal of Business see Journal of Business Issues **673**
Journal of Business (Chicago). (US ISSN 0021-9398) **673**
Journal of Business (Spokane). (US) **787**, 1042, 1115
Journal of Business Administration. (CN ISSN 0021-941X) **1015**
Journal of Business and Economic Perspectives. (US) **673**
Journal of Business and Economic Statistics. (US ISSN 0735-0015) **725**, 870, 4576
Journal of Business and Economic Studies. (US) **673**
Journal of Business and Economics see D L S U Business & Economics Review **658**
Journal of Business & Finance Librarianship. (US ISSN 0896-3568) **2765**, 673
Journal of Business & Industrial Marketing. (US ISSN 0885-8624) **1042**
Journal of Business & Psychology. (US ISSN 0889-3268) **4027**, 673
Journal of Business & Social Studies. (NR ISSN 0331-8583) **673**, 4439
Journal of Business and Technical Communication. (US ISSN 1050-6519) **673**, 1338
Journal of Business Communication. (US ISSN 0021-9436) **1015**, 1338
Journal of Business Ethics. (NE ISSN 0167-4544) **673**
Journal of Business Finance & Accounting. (UK ISSN 0306-686X) **753**, 673
Journal of Business Forecasting Methods and Systems. (US ISSN 0278-6087) **673**
Journal of Business Issues. (US) **673**
Journal of Business Law. (UK ISSN 0021-9460) **2710**, 673
Journal of Business Logistics. (US) **1042**, 1015, 1397
Journal of Business Research. (US ISSN 0148-2963) **673**
Journal of Business Strategy. (US ISSN 0275-6668) **1015**
▼Journal of Business-to-Business Marketing. (US ISSN 1051-712X) **1042**
Journal of Business Venturing. (US ISSN 0883-9026) **673**
†Journal of Byelorussian Studies. (UK ISSN 0075-4161) **5221**
Journal of California and Great Basin Anthropology. (US ISSN 0191-3557) **243**
Journal of California Anthropology see Journal of California and Great Basin Anthropology **243**

Journal of California Taxation. (US) **1099**
Journal of Canadian Art History/Annales d'Histoire de l'Art Canadien. (CN ISSN 0315-4297) **331**, 302
Journal of Canadian Fiction. (CN ISSN 0047-2255) **2928**
Journal of Canadian Petroleum Technology. (CN ISSN 0021-9487) **3690**
Journal of Canadian Poetry. (CN ISSN 0705-1328) **2996**
Journal of Canadian Studies/Revue d'Etudes Canadiennes. (CN ISSN 0021-9495) **2509**, 4377
Journal of Cancer Education. (UK ISSN 0885-8195) **3199**
Journal of Cancer Research and Clinical Oncology. (GW ISSN 0171-5216) **3199**
Journal of Carbohydrate Chemistry. (US ISSN 0732-8303) **1180**
Journal of Cardiac Rehabilitation see Journal of Cardiopulmonary Rehabilitation **3209**
Journal of Cardiac Surgery. (US ISSN 0886-0440) **3209**
Journal of Cardiopulmonary Rehabilitation. (US ISSN 0883-9212) **3209**
Journal of Cardiothoracic and Vascular Anesthesia. (US ISSN 1053-0770) **3191**, 3209, 3315
Journal of Cardiothoracic Anesthesia see Journal of Cardiothoracic and Vascular Anesthesia **3191**
Journal of Cardiovascular and Pulmonary Technology. (US ISSN 0893-2972) **3209**
▼Journal of Cardiovascular Electrophysiology. (US ISSN 1045-3873) **3209**
Journal of Cardiovascular Management. (US) **3209**
Journal of Cardiovascular Nursing. (US ISSN 0889-4655) **3209**, 3280
Journal of Cardiovascular Pharmacology. (US ISSN 0160-2446) **3731**, 3209
Journal of Cardiovascular Surgery. (IT ISSN 0021-9509) **3210**, 3379
Journal of Cardiovascular Technology. (US ISSN 1043-4356) **3210**, 3260
Journal of Cardiovascular Ultrasonography see Journal of Cardiovascular Technology **3210**
Journal of Career Development. (US ISSN 0894-8453) **3629**, 1737
Journal of Career Planning & Employment. (US ISSN 0884-5352) **3629**, 1067, 1709
Journal of Caribbean History. (BB ISSN 0047-2263) **2411**
Journal of Caribbean Studies. (US ISSN 0190-2008) **2010**, 2411
Journal of Cash Management. (US ISSN 0731-1281) **787**
Journal of Catalysis. see Cuihua Xuebao **1213**
Journal of Catalysis. (US ISSN 0021-9517) **1227**
Journal of Cataract and Refractive Surgery. (US ISSN 0886-3350) **3301**
Journal of Cell Biology. (US ISSN 0021-9525) **525**
Journal of Cell Science. (UK ISSN 0021-9533) **560**, 525
Journal of Cellular Biochemistry. (US ISSN 0730-2312) **525**, 478
Journal of Cellular Physiology. (US ISSN 0021-9541) **572**, 3114
Journal of Cellular Plastics. (US ISSN 0021-955X) **3863**
▼Journal of Celtic Linguistics. (UK ISSN 0962-1377) **2820**
Journal of Central Asia. (PK) **276**, 243, 2339
Journal of Cereal Science. (UK ISSN 0733-5210) **207**
Journal of Cerebral Blood Flow and Metabolism. (US ISSN 0271-678X) **3340**, 478
▼Journal of Chemical and Biochemical Kinetics. (US ISSN 1058-5834) **1180**, 478

Journal of Chemical and Engineering Data. (US ISSN 0021-9568) **1180**, 1855
Journal of Chemical Dependency Treatment. (US ISSN 0885-4734) **1537**
Journal of Chemical Ecology. (US ISSN 0098-0331) **1960**, 1180
Journal of Chemical Education. (US ISSN 0021-9584) **1180**, 1709
Journal of Chemical Education: Software. Series A. (US ISSN 1050-4281) **1690**, 1180, 1478, 1677
Journal of Chemical Education: Software. Series B. (US ISSN 1050-429X) **1690**, 1180, 1478, 1677
Journal of Chemical Education: Software. Series C. (US ISSN 1050-4303) **1690**, 1180, 1478, 1677
Journal of Chemical Education: Software. Special Issue Series. (US ISSN 1050-6942) **1690**, 1180, 1478, 1677
Journal of Chemical Engineering of Japan. (JA ISSN 0021-9592) **1855**
Journal of Chemical Industry and Engineering. (CC ISSN 1000-9027) **1855**, 1180
Journal of Chemical Information and Computer Sciences. (US ISSN 0095-2338) **4360**, 1397
Journal of Chemical Neuroanatomy. (UK ISSN 0891-0618) **3341**
Journal of Chemical Physics. see Huaxue Wuli Xuebao **3819**
Journal of Chemical Physics. (US ISSN 0021-9606) **3821**, 1227
Journal of Chemical Research. (UK ISSN 0308-2342) **1180**
Journal of Chemical Technology and Biotechnology. (UK ISSN 0268-2575) **490**, 1855
Journal of Chemical Thermodynamics. (UK ISSN 0021-9614) **1227**
▼Journal of Chemical Vapor Deposition.(US ISSN 1056-7860) **1210**
Journal of Chemicals and Allied Industries. (II ISSN 0021-9622) **1180**
Journal of Chemistry. see Chemicke Listy **1173**
Journal of Chemometrics. (UK ISSN 0886-9383) **1206**
Journal of Cherokee Studies. (US ISSN 0146-2962) **2411**, 2010
▼Journal of Child and Adolescent Group Therapy. (US ISSN 1053-0800) **3341**, 3321
Journal of Child and Adolescent Psychiatric and Mental Health Nursing. (US ISSN 0897-9685) **3280**, 1239, 3341
▼Journal of Child and Adolescent Psychopharmacology. (US ISSN 1044-5463) **3341**, 3321, 3731
▼Journal of Child and Family Studies. (US) **4027**
Journal of Child and Youth Care. (CN ISSN 0840-982X) **1239**
Journal of Child Care see Journal of Child and Youth Care **1239**
Journal of Child Language. (UK ISSN 0305-0009) **1239**
Journal of Child Law. (UK ISSN 0955-4475) **2718**, 1239
Journal of Child Neurology. (US ISSN 0883-0738) **3341**, 3114
Journal of Child Psychology & Psychiatry & Allied Disciplines. (US ISSN 0021-9630) **4027**, 3341
Journal of Child Psychotherapy. (UK ISSN 0075-417X) **4027**
▼Journal of Child Sexual Abuse. (US ISSN 1053-8712) **4410**
Journal of Childhood Communication Disorders. (US ISSN 0735-3170) **1737**, 1239
†Journal of Children in Contemporary Society. (US ISSN 0276-6256) **5221**
Journal of Chinese Art History see Soochow University Journal of Chinese Art History **5279**

Journal of Chinese Communist Party History. see Zhong Gong Dangshi Yanjiu **3936**
Journal of Chinese Education. see Zhongguo Jiaoyu Xuekan **1673**
Journal of Chinese Law. (US ISSN 1041-7567) **2638**, 3639
Journal of Chinese Linguistics. (US ISSN 0091-3723) **2820**
Journal of Chinese Linguistics Monograph Series. (US) **2820**
Journal of Chinese Pharmacology. see Zhongguo Yiyao Xuebao **3746**
Journal of Chinese Pharmacy. see Zhongguo Yiyao **3746**
†Journal of Chinese Physics. (English translation of: Wuli Xuebao) (US ISSN 1044-8357) **5221**
Journal of Chinese Religions. (CN ISSN 0737-769X) **4215**, 3639
Journal of Chinese Social and Economic History. see Zhongguo Shehui Jingjishi Yanjiu **2343**
Journal of Chinese Studies. (US) **3639**
Journal of Chiropractic. (US ISSN 0744-9984) **3215**
Journal of Christian Camping. (US ISSN 0021-9649) **4549**
Journal of Christian Education. (AT ISSN 0021-9657) **4184**, 1642
Journal of Christian Education of the African Methodist Episcopal Church. (US) **4241**, 1642
Journal of Christian Jurisprudence. (US ISSN 0741-6075) **2638**, 4184
Journal of Christian Nursing. (US ISSN 0743-2550) **3280**, 4184
Journal of Christian Reconstruction. (US ISSN 0360-1420) **4184**
Journal of Chromatographic Science. (US ISSN 0021-9665) **1206**
Journal of Chromatography. (NE ISSN 0021-9673) **1206**
Journal of Chromatography - Biomedical Applications. (NE ISSN 0378-4347) **1180**, 478
Journal of Chromatography Library. (NE) **1206**
Journal of Chronic Diseases see Journal of Clinical Epidemiology **3114**
Journal of Church and State. (US ISSN 0021-969X) **4184**, 2638, 3901
▼Journal of Circuits, Systems and Computers. (SI ISSN 0218-1266) **1828**, 1454
Journal of Civil and Hydraulic Engineering. (CH ISSN 0253-3804) **1869**
Journal of Civil Defense. (US ISSN 0740-5537) **1273**
Journal of Civil Engineering see Journal of Civil and Hydraulic Engineering **1869**
Journal of Civil Procedure/Minji Sosho Zasshi. (JA ISSN 0075-4188) **2702**
Journal of Classical Studies. see Seiyo Kotengaku Kenkyu **1280**
Journal of Classification. (US ISSN 0176-4268) **3040**, 2765, 4027
Journal of Classroom Interaction. (US ISSN 0749-4025) **1642**
▼Journal of Clean Technology and Environmental Sciences. (US ISSN 1052-1062) **1977**, 1985
Journal of Climate. (US ISSN 0894-8755) **3437**
Journal of Climate and Applied Meteorology see Journal of Applied Meteorology **3437**
Journal of Climate and Applied Meteorology see Journal of Climate **3437**
Journal of Climatology see International Journal of Climatology **3436**
Journal of Clinical and Experimental Gerontology. (US ISSN 0192-1193) **2274**
Journal of Clinical and Experimental Neuropsychology. (NE ISSN 0168-8634) **3341**, 4027
Journal of Clinical and Experimental Pathology. see Linchuang yu Shiyan Binglixue Zazhi **3122**
Journal of Clinical and Hospital Pharmacy see Journal of Clinical Pharmacy and Therapeutics **3731**

JOURNAL

Journal of Clinical & Laboratory Immunology. (UK ISSN 0141-2760) **3187**
Journal of Clinical and Radiological Anatomy. Anatomica Clinica see Surgical and Radiologic Anatomy **575**
Journal of Clinical Anesthesia. (US ISSN 0952-8180) **3191**
Journal of Clinical Anesthesiology. see Linchuang Mazuixue Zazhi **3191**
Journal of Clinical Apheresis. (US ISSN 0733-2459) **3388**
Journal of Clinical Child Psychology. (US ISSN 0047-228X) **4027**, 1239
Journal of Clinical Computing. (US ISSN 0090-1091) **3226**
Journal of Clinical Dermatology. see Linchuang Pifuke Zazhi **3249**
Journal of Clinical Endocrinology and Metabolism. (US ISSN 0021-972X) **3254**
Journal of Clinical Engineering. (US ISSN 0363-8855) **469**, 3114
Journal of Clinical Epidemiology. (US ISSN 0895-4356) **3114**
▼Journal of Clinical Ethics. (US ISSN 1046-7890) **3114**, 2638
Journal of Clinical Gastroenterology. (US ISSN 0192-0790) **3269**
Journal of Clinical Hypertension see American Journal of Hypertension **3204**
Journal of Clinical Immunoassay. (US ISSN 0736-4393) **3187**
Journal of Clinical Immunology. (US ISSN 0271-9142) **3187**
Journal of Clinical Investigation. (US ISSN 0021-9738) **3114**
Journal of Clinical Laboratory Analysis. (US ISSN 0887-8013) **3260**
Journal of Clinical Laser Medicine & Surgery. (US ISSN 1044-5471) **3359**, 3379
Journal of Clinical Microbiology. (US ISSN 0095-1137) **554**
Journal of Clinical Monitoring. (US ISSN 0748-1977) **3114**
Journal of Clinical Neuro-Ophthalmology. (US ISSN 0272-846X) **3301**
Journal of Clinical Neurophysiology. (US ISSN 0736-0258) **3341**
Journal of Clinical Nutrition and Gastroenterology. (SP) **3269**, 3608
Journal of Clinical Oncology. (US ISSN 0732-183X) **3199**, 525, 3359, 3731
Journal of Clinical Orthodontics. (US ISSN 0022-3875) **3235**
Journal of Clinical Pathology. (UK ISSN 0021-9746) **3115**
Journal of Clinical Pediatric Dentistry. (US ISSN 1053-4628) **3235**, 3321
Journal of Clinical Pediatrics/Rinsho Shoni Igaku. (JA ISSN 0035-550X) **3321**
Journal of Clinical Periodontology. (DK ISSN 0303-6979) **3235**
Journal of Clinical Pharmacology. (US ISSN 0091-2700) **3115**
Journal of Clinical Pharmacology and New Drugs see Journal of Clinical Pharmacology **3731**
Journal of Clinical Pharmacy and Therapeutics. (UK ISSN 0269-4727) **3731**
Journal of Clinical Practice in Sexuality. (US) **3115**
Journal of Clinical Psychiatry. (US ISSN 0160-6689) **3341**
▼Journal of Clinical Psychoanalysis. (US) **4027**
Journal of Clinical Psychology. (US ISSN 0021-9762) **4027**
Journal of Clinical Psychopharmacology.(US ISSN 0271-0749) **3731**
Journal of Clinical Reading: Research and Programs. (US) **1752**
Journal of Clinical Research and Drug Development see Journal of Clinical Research and Pharmacoepidemiology **3731**

Journal of Clinical Research and Pharmacoepidemiology. (US ISSN 1047-0336) **3731**
Journal of Clinical Ultrasound. (US ISSN 0091-2751) **3859**, 3115
Journal of Cluster Science. (US ISSN 1040-7278) **1180**
Journal of Coal Quality. (US) **3486**
Journal of Coastal Research. (US ISSN 0749-0208) **1606**, 1569
Journal of Coated Fabrics. (US ISSN 0093-4658) **4621**, 1180, 3654, 3863
Journal of Coated Fibrous Materials see Journal of Coated Fabrics **4621**
Journal of Coatings Technology see J C T: Journal of Coatings Technology **3654**
Journal of Cognitive Neuroscience. (US ISSN 0898-929X) **3341**, 4027
Journal of Cognitive Psychotherapy. (US ISSN 0889-8391) **4027**
Journal of Cognitive Rehabilitation. (US) **1737**
Journal of Cold Regions Engineering. (US ISSN 0887-381X) **1869**
Journal of Collective Chemistry and Physics. (UK) **1227**
Journal of Collective Negotiations in the Public Sector. (US ISSN 0047-2301) **984**, 4065
Journal of College Admissions. (US ISSN 0734-6670) **1728**
Journal of College and Adult Reading. (US) **1685**
▼Journal of College & University Foodservice. (US ISSN 1053-8739) **2074**
Journal of College and University Law. (US ISSN 0093-8688) **2638**
Journal of College and University Student Housing. (US) **1710**, 1315
Journal of College Radio. (US ISSN 0010-1133) **1357**
Journal of College Science Teaching. (US ISSN 0047-231X) **1710**, 4317
Journal of College Student Development. (US ISSN 0897-5264) **1710**
Journal of College Student Psychotherapy. (US ISSN 8756-8225) **4028**
Journal of Colloid and Interface Science.(US ISSN 0021-9797) **1227**
Journal of Combinatorial Theory see Journal of Combinatorial Theory. Series A **3040**
Journal of Combinatorial Theory see Journal of Combinatorial Theory. Series B **3040**
Journal of Combinatorial Theory. Series A. (US ISSN 0097-3165) **3040**
Journal of Combinatorial Theory. Series B. (US ISSN 0095-8956) **3040**
Journal of Combinatorics, Information & System Sciences. (II ISSN 0250-9628) **3040**
Journal of Commerce. (CN ISSN 0021-9819) **837**
Journal of Commerce. (TH ISSN 0125-0566) **870**
Journal of Commerce and Commercial. (US ISSN 0361-5561) **837**
Journal of Commerce and Industry see Journal of Commerce, Industry & Transportation **837**
Journal of Commerce Import Bulletin. (US) **915**
Journal of Commerce, Industry & Transportation. (LB) **837**, 1079, 4652
Journal of Commerce Transportation Telephone Tickler see Transportation Telephone Tickler **1156**
Journal of Commercial Bank Lending. (US ISSN 0021-986X) **788**
Journal of Common Market Studies. (UK ISSN 0021-9886) **3901**, 673
Journal of Commonwealth & Comparative Politics. (UK ISSN 0306-3631) **3963**
Journal of Commonwealth Literature. (UK ISSN 0021-9894) **2928**

Journal of Commonwealth Political Studies see Journal of Commonwealth & Comparative Politics **3963**
Journal of Communicable Diseases. (II ISSN 0019-5138) **3221**
Journal of Communication. (US ISSN 0021-9916) **1338**, 2571, 4028
Journal of Communication between Rural Communities and Towns/ Noson to Toshi o Musubu. (JA ISSN 0913-6134) **153**, 2585
Journal of Communication Disorders. (US ISSN 0021-9924) **4028**, 3341
Journal of Communication Inquiry. (US ISSN 0196-8599) **1338**
Journal of Communist Studies. (UK ISSN 0268-4535) **3901**
Journal of Community and Applied Social Psychology. (UK ISSN 1052-9284) **4028**, 4439
†Journal of Community Communications. (US ISSN 0194-2158) **5221**
Journal of Community Education. (UK ISSN 0263-5909) **1685**
Journal of Community Gardening. (US) **2132**
Journal of Community Health. (US ISSN 0094-5145) **3115**, 4106
Journal of Community Health Nursing. (US ISSN 0737-0016) **3280**
Journal of Community Nursing see Journal of District Nursing **3280**
Journal of Community Psychology. (US ISSN 0090-4392) **4028**, 4439
Journal of Comparative Administration see Administration and Society **4052**
▼Journal of Comparative and International Law. (US ISSN 1053-6736) **2726**
Journal of Comparative Economics. (US ISSN 0147-5967) **674**
Journal of Comparative Family Studies. (CN ISSN 0047-2328) **4439**
Journal of Comparative Literature and Aesthetics. (II ISSN 0252-8169) **2928**
The Journal of Comparative Neurology. (US ISSN 0021-9967) **3341**
Journal of Comparative Pathology. (UK ISSN 0021-9975) **4811**
Journal of Comparative Physical and Education Sport. (GW ISSN 1010-8262) **4477**, 3805
Journal of Comparative Physiology. A: Sensory, Neural, and Behavioral Physiology. (GW ISSN 0340-7594) **572**
Journal of Comparative Physiology. B: Biochemical, Systematic, and Environmental Physiology. (GW ISSN 0174-1578) **572**
Journal of Comparative Physiology. B. Systematic and Environmental Physiology see Journal of Comparative Physiology. B: Biochemical, Systematic, and Environmental Physiology **572**
Journal of Comparative Psychology. (US ISSN 0735-7036) **4028**
Journal of Comparative Sociology and Ethics. (CN) **4439**, 4184
Journal of Comparative Sociology and Religion see Journal of Comparative Sociology and Ethics **4439**
Journal of Compensation and Benefits. (US) **1067**
Journal of Complexity. (US ISSN 0885-064X) **3065**
†Journal of Compliance in Health Care. (US ISSN 0887-6509) **5221**
Journal of Composite Materials. (US ISSN 0021-9983) **1918**
Journal of Composites Technology and Research. (US ISSN 0884-6804) **1933**
Journal of Computational and Applied Mathematics. (NE ISSN 0377-0427) **3041**
Journal of Computational Chemistry. (US ISSN 0192-8651) **1181**
Journal of Computational Mathematics. (CC ISSN 0254-9409) **3041**
Journal of Computational Physics. (US ISSN 0021-9991) **3840**

Journal of Computational Structural Mechanics and Applications. see Jisuan Jiegou Lixue Jiqi Yingyong **1932**
Journal of Computer-Aided Molecular Design. (NE ISSN 0920-654X) **1181**, 1422, 1445
Journal of Computer and System Sciences. (US ISSN 0022-0000) **1397**, 1437
Journal of Computer Assisted Learning. (UK ISSN 0266-4909) **1417**, 1690
Journal of Computer-Assisted Microscopy. (US ISSN 1040-7286) **1435**, 560
Journal of Computer Assisted Tomography. (US ISSN 0363-8715) **3359**
Journal of Computer-Based Instruction. (US ISSN 0098-597X) **1417**
Journal of Computer Documentation. (US ISSN 0163-5956) **1456**
Journal of Computer Information Systems. (US ISSN 0887-4417) **1417**, 1437, 1452, 1690
▼Journal of Computer Security. (NE ISSN 0926-227X) **1434**
Journal of Computers in Mathematics and Science Teaching. (US ISSN 0731-9258) **3065**, 1752, 4317, 4360
†Journal of Computing and Society. (US ISSN 1044-0755) **5221**
Journal of Computing in Childhood Education. (US ISSN 1043-1055) **1690**, 1239
Journal of Computing in Civil Engineering. (US ISSN 0887-3801) **1879**, 1869
Journal of Conchology. (UK ISSN 0022-0019) **585**
Journal of Confederate History. (US ISSN 0897-0475) **3462**
Journal of Conflict Resolution. (US ISSN 0022-0027) **4377**, 3963
Journal of Constitutional & Parliamentary Studies. (II ISSN 0022-0043) **3901**
Journal of Constitutional Law see Legal History **2648**
Journal of Construction Engineering and Management. (US ISSN 0733-9364) **1869**
Journal of Constructional Steel Research. (UK ISSN 0143-974X) **1869**
Journal of Consulting and Clinical Psychology. (US ISSN 0022-006X) **4028**, 3341
Journal of Consulting Psychology see Journal of Consulting and Clinical Psychology **4028**
Journal of Consumer Affairs. (US ISSN 0022-0078) **1505**
Journal of Consumer Lending see Credit Card Management **774**
Journal of Consumer Marketing. (US ISSN 0736-3761) **1042**
Journal of Consumer Policy. (NE ISSN 0168-7034) **1505**, 999
▼Journal of Consumer Psychology. (US ISSN 1057-7408) **33**
Journal of Consumer Research. (US ISSN 0093-5301) **1042**
Journal of Consumer Studies & Home Economics. (UK ISSN 0309-3891) **1505**
Journal of Contaminant Hydrology. (NE ISSN 0169-7722) **1599**
Journal of Contemplative Psychotherapy. (US ISSN 0894-8577) **4028**
†Journal of Contemporary African Studies. (SA ISSN 0258-9001) **5221**
Journal of Contemporary Art. (US ISSN 0897-2400) **331**
Journal of Contemporary Asia. (PH ISSN 0047-2336) **2172**
Journal of Contemporary Ethnography. (US ISSN 0891-2416) **4440**, 243
Journal of Contemporary Health Law and Policy. (US ISSN 0882-1046) **3115**, 2638
Journal of Contemporary History. (UK ISSN 0022-0094) **2315**, 3901

▼Journal of Contemporary Hospitality Management. (UK ISSN 0954-9234) **2477**
Journal of Contemporary Law. (US ISSN 0097-9937) **2638**
Journal of Contemporary Psychotherapy. (US ISSN 0022-0116) **4028**, 3341
Journal of Contemporary Roman Dutch Law. see Tydskrif vir Hededaagse Romeins-Hollandse Reg **2687**
Journal of Continuing Education in Nursing. (US ISSN 0022-0124) **3280**
Journal of Continuing Education in Obstetrics and Gynecology see Ob-Gyn Digest (Year) **5251**
†Journal of Continuing Education in the Health Profession. (US ISSN 0894-1912) **5221**
Journal of Continuing Higher Education.(US ISSN 0737-7363) **1685**
Journal of Continuing Medical Education International. (US) **3115**
Journal of Contract Law. (AT ISSN 1030-7230) **2638**
Journal of Controlled Release. (NE ISSN 0168-3659) **478**, 3731
Journal of Cooperative Education. (US ISSN 0022-0132) **1642**
Journal of Cooperative Extension see Journal of Extension **1642**
Journal of Coordination Chemistry. Sections A & B. (US ISSN 0095-8972) **1181**
▼Journal of Coptic Studies. (BE ISSN 1016-5584) **2430**, 4184
Journal of Corporate Accounting and Finance. (US ISSN 1044-8136) **753**
Journal of Corporate Taxation. (US ISSN 0094-0593) **1099**
Journal of Corporation Law. (US ISSN 0360-795X) **2710**
Journal of Correctional Education. (US ISSN 0022-0159) **1642**, 1516
Journal of Cost Analysis. (US) **753**
Journal of Cost Management. (US) **674**
Journal of Cost Management for the Manufacturing Industry see Journal of Cost Management **674**
Journal of Counseling & Development. (US ISSN 0748-9633) **3629**
Journal of Counseling Psychology. (US ISSN 0022-0167) **4028**
Journal of Country Music. (US ISSN 0092-0517) **3559**
Journal of Couples Therapy. (US ISSN 0897-4446) **4028**, 3398, 4845
Journal of Court Reporting. (US) **2638**
Journal of Cranio and Maxillofacial Surgery see Journal of Cranio-Maxillo-Facial Surgery **3380**
Journal of Cranio-Maxillo-Facial Surgery.(UK ISSN 1010-5182) **3380**
Journal of Craniofacial Genetics and Developmental Biology. (DK ISSN 0270-4145) **544**
▼Journal of Craniofacial Surgery. (US ISSN 1049-2275) **3380**
Journal of Craniomandibular Disorders. (US ISSN 0890-2739) **3236**, 3115
Journal of Craniomandibular Practice see Cranio: Journal of Craniomandibular Practice **3091**
Journal of Creative Behavior. (US ISSN 0022-0175) **1642**, 4028
Journal of Crime & Justice. (US ISSN 0735-648X) **1516**, 2638
Journal of Criminal Justice. (US ISSN 0047-2352) **2639**, 1516
▼Journal of Criminal Justice Education.(US ISSN 1051-1253) **1516**, 1642
Journal of Criminal Law/Keiho Zasshi. (JA ISSN 0022-0191) **2713**, 1516
Journal of Criminal Law. (UK ISSN 0022-0183) **2713**
Journal of Criminal Law & Criminology. (US ISSN 0091-4169) **1516**, 2713
Journal of Critical Analysis. (US ISSN 0022-0213) **3770**, 1642

Journal of Critical Care. (US ISSN 0883-9441) **3115**, 3210, 3309
Journal of Critical Illness. (US ISSN 1040-0257) **3115**
Journal of Croatian Studies. (US ISSN 0075-4218) **2370**, 2870
Journal of Cross-Cultural Gerontology. (NE ISSN 0169-3816) **2275**, 243
Journal of Cross-Cultural Psychology. (US ISSN 0022-0221) **4028**, 4440
Journal of Crustacean Biology. (US ISSN 0278-0372) **585**
Journal of Cryosurgery see Ophthalmic Surgery **3382**
Journal of Crystal and Molecular Structure see Journal of Crystallographic and Spectroscopic Research **1211**
Journal of Crystal Growth. (NE ISSN 0022-0248) **1211**
Journal of Crystallographic and Spectroscopic Research. (US ISSN 0277-8068) **1211**
▼Journal of Culinary Practice. (US ISSN 1052-9241) **2074**, 2477
Journal of Cultural Economics. (US) **870**
Journal of Cultural Geography. (US) **2254**, 243
Journal of Cultural Sciences/Bunka Kagaku Kiyo. (JA ISSN 0521-7903) **2509**
Journal of Cultural Sciences see Tokushima Daigaku Gakugei Kiyo **2516**
Journal of Cuneiform Studies. (US ISSN 0022-0256) **276**, 3639
Journal of Current Laser Abstracts. (US ISSN 0022-0264) **3837**, 15
Journal of Current Podiatric Medicine. (US ISSN 0893-2034) **3380**
Journal of Curriculum and Supervision. (US ISSN 0882-1232) **1752**
Journal of Curriculum Studies. (UK ISSN 0022-0272) **1752**
Journal of Curriculum Theorizing see J C T **1752**
▼Journal of Cutaneous Aging & Cosmetic Dermatology. (US ISSN 0894-0061) **3248**, 2275
Journal of Cutaneous Pathology. (DK ISSN 0303-6987) **3248**
Journal of Cyclic Nucleotide and Protein Phosphorylation Research see Second Messengers and Phosphoproteins **455**
Journal of Cytology see Xibao Shengwuxue Zazhi **527**
Journal of Cytology and Genetics. (II ISSN 0253-7605) **545**, 3115
▼Journal of D N A Sequencing and Mapping. (US ISSN 1042-5179) **545**
Journal of Dairy Research. (UK ISSN 0022-0299) **200**
Journal of Dairy Science. (US ISSN 0022-0302) **200**
Journal of Danish Archaeology. (DK ISSN 0108-464X) **276**
Journal of Data and Computer Communications. (US) **1447**
Journal of Data Collection see Applied Marketing Research **1033**
▼Journal of Database Administration. (US ISSN 1047-9430) **1445**
†Journal of Decorative and Propaganda Arts. (US ISSN 0888-7314) **5221**
Journal of Defense and Diplomacy see Defense & Diplomacy **5178**
▼Journal of Democracy. (US ISSN 1045-5736) **3901**
Journal of Demography/Warasarn Prachakornsatr. (TH ISSN 0857-2143) **3984**
Journal of Dendrology. (SA) **507**, 2103
Journal of Dental Education. (US ISSN 0022-0337) **3236**, 1752
Journal of Dental Health. see Koku Eisei Gakkai Zasshi **3237**
Journal of Dental Hygiene. (US ISSN 1043-254X) **3236**
Journal of Dental Hygiene. (JA ISSN 0285-0508) **3236**
Journal of Dental Practice Administration. (US ISSN 0741-8620) **3236**

Journal of Dental Research. (US ISSN 0022-0345) **3236**
Journal of Dental Technics. see Shika Giko **3242**
Journal of Dentistry. (UK ISSN 0300-5712) **3236**
Journal of Dentistry for Children. (US ISSN 0022-0353) **3236**, 3321
Journal of Dermatologic Surgery and Oncology. (US ISSN 0148-0812) **3380**, 3199, 3248
▼Journal of Dermatological Science. (NE ISSN 0923-1811) **3248**
Journal of Dermatological Treatment. (UK ISSN 0954-6634) **3248**
Journal of Design History. (UK ISSN 0952-4649) **331**, 2553
▼Journal of Design Manufacturing. (UK ISSN 0962-4694) **1933**
Journal of Detergents and Collective Chemistry and Physics see Journal of Collective Chemistry and Physics **1227**
Journal of Developing Areas. (US ISSN 0022-037X) **932**, 3901, 4440
Journal of Developing Societies. (NE) **4377**, 2509
Journal of Development Administration. (CE ISSN 0047-2360) **4065**
Journal of Development and Administrative Studies. (NP) **896**
Journal of Development Economics. (NE ISSN 0304-3878) **932**
Journal of Development Policy Studies. see Kaihatsu Ronshu **871**
Journal of Development Studies. (UK ISSN 0022-0388) **932**, 3901, 4440
Journal of Developmental and Behavioral Pediatrics. (US) **3321**
Journal of Developmental and Comparative Immunology see Developmental and Comparative Immunology **3184**
Journal of Developmental and Physical Disabilities. (US) **2284**
Journal of Developmental Education. (US ISSN 0738-9701) **1710**
Journal of Developmental Physiology. (UK ISSN 0141-9846) **3293**, 3115
Journal of Developmental Reading see Journal of Reading **1643**
Journal of Dharma. (II ISSN 0253-7222) **4184**
Journal of Diabetes and Its Complications. (US ISSN 1056-8727) **3254**
Journal of Diabetic Complications see Journal of Diabetes and Its Complications **3254**
Journal of Diagnostic Medical Sonography. (US ISSN 8756-4793) **3115**, 3293
Journal of Dialectics of Nature. see Ziran Bianzhengfa Tongxun **4354**
Journal of Differential Equations. (US ISSN 0022-0396) **3041**
Journal of Differential Geometry. (US ISSN 0022-040X) **3041**
Journal of Direct Marketing. (US ISSN 0892-0591) **1043**
▼Journal of Disability Policy Studies. (US ISSN 1044-2073) **2639**, 3115
Journal of Dispersion Science and Technology. (US ISSN 0193-2691) **1227**
Journal of Distance Education. (CN ISSN 0830-0445) **1685**, 1752
Journal of District Nursing. (UK ISSN 0263-4465) **3280**
Journal of Divorce see Journal of Divorce & Remarriage **3067**
Journal of Divorce & Remarriage. (US ISSN 1050-2556) **3067**, 4440
Journal of Documentation. (UK ISSN 0022-0418) **2765**
Journal of Documentation Project Management. (US ISSN 0891-5865) **1397**
Journal of Dramatic Theory and Criticism. (US) **4634**
Journal of Drug Development. (UK ISSN 0952-9500) **3731**
Journal of Drug Education. (US ISSN 0047-2379) **1537**, 1642
Journal of Drug Issues. (US ISSN 0022-0426) **1537**

Journal of Drug Research see Journal of Drug Research of Egypt **3731**
Journal of Drug Research of Egypt. (UA ISSN 0085-2406) **3731**
Journal of Dufu Studies. see Dufu Yanjiu Xuekan **2864**
Journal of Dynamic Systems, Measurement and Control. (US ISSN 0022-0434) **1918**, 1933, 3447
Journal of Dynamics and Differential Equations. (US ISSN 1040-7294) **3041**
Journal of Early Adolescence. (US ISSN 0272-4316) **1239**, 4028, 4440
Journal of Early Intervention. (US) **1737**, 1239, 1752
Journal of Early Southern Decorative Arts. (US ISSN 0098-9266) **332**
Journal of Earth Sciences. (JA ISSN 0022-0442) **1546**
Journal of Earth Sciences see Irish Journal of Earth Sciences **1546**
Journal of East and West Studies/Tongso Yongu. (KO) **3901**
Journal of East Asiatic Studies. (PH ISSN 0022-0450) **3639**
Journal of Ecclesiastical History. (UK ISSN 0022-0469) **4185**, 2315
Journal of Ecology. (UK ISSN 0022-0477) **444**
Journal of Ecology. see Shengtaixue Zazhi **1968**
Journal of Econometrics. (SZ ISSN 0304-4076) **674**
Journal of Economic Affairs see Economic Affairs **660**
Journal of Economic and International Relations. (HK) **870**, 3901
Journal of Economic & Social Measurement. (NE ISSN 0747-9662) **725**, 4576
Journal of Economic and Taxonomic Botany. (II) **507**
Journal of Economic Behavior & Organization. (NE ISSN 0167-2681) **674**
Journal of Economic Dynamics and Control. (NE ISSN 0165-1889) **896**
Journal of Economic Education. (US ISSN 0022-0485) **674**, 1753
Journal of Economic Entomology. (US ISSN 0022-0493) **535**
†Journal of Economic Growth. (US ISSN 0897-1862) **5221**
Journal of Economic History. (UK ISSN 0022-0507) **896**
Journal of Economic Issues see J E I **895**
Journal of Economic Literature. (US ISSN 0022-0515) **725**, 15
Journal of Economic Perspectives. (US) **870**
Journal of Economic Psychology. (NE ISSN 0167-4870) **1043**, 4028
Journal of Economic Reflections. (TZ) **674**
Journal of Economic Studies. (US ISSN 0144-3585) **674**
Journal of Economic Surveys. (UK ISSN 0950-0804) **674**
Journal of Economic Theory. (US ISSN 0022-0531) **896**
Journal of Economics. (II) **674**
Journal of Economics. see Keizaigaku Ronshu **676**
Journal of Economics (New York) see Journal of Economics - Zeitschrift fuer Nationaloekonomie **674**
Journal of Economics (Vermillion). (US ISSN 0361-6576) **674**
Journal of Economics and Business. (US ISSN 0148-6195) **674**
Journal of Economics - Zeitschrift fuer Nationaloekonomie. (US ISSN 0931-8658) **674**
Journal of Ecumenical Studies. (US ISSN 0022-0558) **4185**
Journal of Education (Boston). (US ISSN 0022-0574) **1642**
Journal of Education and Psychology. (II ISSN 0022-0590) **1642**, 4028
Journal of Education Finance. (US ISSN 0098-9495) **1728**
Journal of Education for Business. (US ISSN 0883-2323) **674**, 1710
Journal of Education for Library and Information Science. (US ISSN 0748-5786) **2765**, 1753

JOURNAL

Journal of Education for Teaching. (UK ISSN 0260-7476) **1710**
Journal of Education in Museums. (UK ISSN 0260-9126) **3525**
Journal of Education Policy. (UK ISSN 0268-0939) **1728**
Journal of Educational Administration. (UK ISSN 0022-0639) **1728**
Journal of Educational Administration and History. (UK ISSN 0022-0620) **1728**, 2315
▼Journal of Educational and Psychological Consultation. (US ISSN 1047-4412) **1642**, 4028
Journal of Educational Computing Research. (US ISSN 0735-6331) **1690**
Journal of Educational Management. (PH) **1729**, 1015
Journal of Educational Measurement. (US ISSN 0022-0655) **1642**
Journal of Educational Media and Library Sciences. (CH ISSN 1013-090X) **2765**, 1642
Journal of Educational Media Sciences see Journal of Educational Media and Library Sciences **2765**
Journal of Educational Modules for Materials Science and Engineering see Journal of Materials Education **1828**
▼Journal of Educational Multimedia and Hypermedia. (US ISSN 1055-8896) **1690**
Journal of Educational Planning and Administration. (National Institute of Educational Planning and Administration) (II) **1729**
Journal of Educational Psychology. (US ISSN 0022-0663) **4029**
Journal of Educational Public Relations.(US ISSN 0741-3653) **1338**, 1642
Journal of Educational Research. (US ISSN 0022-0671) **1642**
Journal of Educational Research/Jurnal Pendidikan. (MY ISSN 0126-6020) **1642**
Journal of Educational Research and Extension. (II ISSN 0022-068X) **1642**, 1806
Journal of Educational Statistics. (US ISSN 0362-9791) **1677**
Journal of Educational Techniques and Technologies. (US ISSN 0891-2521) **2820**, 1753
Journal of Educational Technology Systems. (US ISSN 0047-2395) **1690**, 1417
Journal of Educational Television. (UK ISSN 0260-7417) **1375**, 1753
Journal of Educational Therapy. (UK ISSN 0952-4339) **1737**
Journal of Efficiency. (II) **1015**
Journal of Egyptian Archaeology. (UK ISSN 0307-5133) **276**
Journal of Elasticity. (NE ISSN 0374-3535) **1918**, 1869, 1933
Journal of Elastomers and Plastics. (US ISSN 0095-2443) **3863**
Journal of Elder Abuse & Neglect. (US ISSN 0894-6566) **2275**
Journal of Electoral Record and Comment see Representation **3921**
Journal of Electrical and Electronics Engineering, Australia. (AT ISSN 0725-2986) **1901**
Journal of Electroanalytical Chemistry and Interfacial Electrochemistry. (SZ ISSN 0022-0728) **1206**
Journal of Electrocardiology. (US ISSN 0022-0736) **3210**
Journal of Electromagnetic Waves and Applications. (NE ISSN 0920-5071) **3821**, 1901
▼Journal of Electromyography and Kinesiology. (US ISSN 1050-6411) **444**, 572
Journal of Electron Microscopy. (JA ISSN 0022-0744) **560**, 554, 3115
Journal of Electron Microscopy Technique see Journal of Microscopy Research and Technique **444**
Journal of Electron Spectroscopy and Related Phenomena. (NE ISSN 0368-2048) **3854**
Journal of Electronic Defense. (US ISSN 0192-429X) **3462**

Journal of Electronic Engineering. (JA ISSN 0385-4507) **1901**
▼Journal of Electronic Imaging. (US) **3854**
Journal of Electronic Materials. (US ISSN 0361-5235) **1774**, 1918
▼Journal of Electronic Testing. (US ISSN 0923-8174) **1901**
Journal of Electronics. (CC ISSN 0217-9822) **1774**
Journal of Electronics and Computer Research. (IQ ISSN 1012-3385) **1775**, 1397
▼Journal of Electronics Manufacturing. (UK ISSN 0960-3131) **1775**
Journal of Electrophysiological Techniques see Brain Research Bulletin **3332**
Journal of Electrophysiological Technology. (UK ISSN 0307-5095) **486**, 2523
†Journal of Electrophysiology. (US ISSN 0892-1059) **5221**
Journal of Electrostatics. (NE ISSN 0304-3886) **1901**
Journal of Electrotopography. (US) **3821**, 1546
Journal of Embryology and Experimental Morphology see Development **436**
Journal of Emergency Medical Services see J E M S **3112**
Journal of Emergency Medicine. (US ISSN 0736-4679) **3115**
Journal of Emergency Nursing see J E N **3279**
Journal of Emergency Surgery and Intensive Care. (IT) **3380**
Journal of Employment Counseling. (US ISSN 0022-0787) **3629**
Journal of Endocrinological Investigation. (IT ISSN 0391-4097) **3254**
Journal of Endocrinology. (UK ISSN 0022-0795) **3254**
Journal of Endodontics. (US ISSN 0099-2399) **3236**
Journal of Endourology. (US ISSN 0892-7790) **3388**
Journal of Energetic Materials. (US ISSN 0737-0652) **3821**
Journal of Energy and Development. (US ISSN 0361-4476) **1792**, 932
Journal of Energy and Natural Resources Law. (NE ISSN 0264-6811) **2639**, 1792
Journal of Energy Engineering. (US ISSN 0733-9402) **1869**
Journal of Energy Law and Policy see Journal of Energy, Natural Resources and Environmental Law **1792**
Journal of Energy, Natural Resources and Environmental Law. (US ISSN 1053-377X) **1792**, 1960, 2639
▼Journal of Energy R & D in Southern Africa. (SA) **1792**
Journal of Energy Resources Technology. (US ISSN 0195-0738) **1792**, 1933
†Journal of Engineering & Applied Sciences. (US ISSN 0191-9539) **5221**
†Journal of Engineering & Computer Applications. (US) **5221**
Journal of Engineering and Technology Management. (NE ISSN 0923-4748) **1015**, 1079, 1828
Journal of Engineering Chemistry and Metallurgy. see Huagong Yejin **1854**
▼Journal of Engineering Design. (UK ISSN 0954-4828) **1828**
Journal of Engineering for Gas Turbines and Power. (US ISSN 0742-4795) **1933**
Journal of Engineering for Industry. (US ISSN 0022-0817) **1933**
Journal of Engineering Materials and Technology. (US ISSN 0094-4289) **1918**, 1933
Journal of Engineering Mathematics. (NE ISSN 0022-0833) **1828**, 3041
Journal of Engineering Mechanics. (US ISSN 0733-9399) **1869**

Journal of Engineering Physics. (English translation of: Inzhenerno-Fizicheskii Zhurnal) (US ISSN 0022-0841) **1828**, 3822
Journal of Engineering Physics. see Tehnicka Fizika **3833**
†Journal of Engineering Production. (II ISSN 0251-1770) **5221**
Journal of Engineering Research. (KO) **1828**
Journal of Engineering Sciences see King Saud University. Journal. Engineering Sciences **1829**
Journal of English Linguistics. (US ISSN 0075-4242) **2820**
Journal of English Studies. (NR ISSN 0189-6652) **2821**
Journal of Enterostomal Therapy. (US ISSN 0270-1170) **3380**
Journal of Entomological Research. (II ISSN 0378-9519) **535**
Journal of Entomological Science. (US ISSN 0749-8004) **535**
Journal of Entomology (A) see Physiological Entomology **537**
▼Journal of Entrepreneurship. (US) **1015**
Journal of Environment and Health. see Huanjing yu Jiankang Zazhi **1957**
Journal of Environmental Biology. (II ISSN 0254-8704) **1960**
Journal of Environmental Chemistry. see Huanjing Huaxue **1178**
Journal of Environmental Economics and Management. (US ISSN 0095-0696) **1960**
Journal of Environmental Education. (US ISSN 0095-8964) **1960**
Journal of Environmental Engineering. (US ISSN 0733-9372) **1960**, 1869
Journal of Environmental Health. (US ISSN 0022-0892) **1960**, 4106
Journal of Environmental Horticulture. (US ISSN 0738-2898) **102**, 507
Journal of Environmental Law. (UK ISSN 0952-8873) **1960**, 2639
Journal of Environmental Management. (UK ISSN 0301-4797) **1960**
Journal of Environmental Pathology and Toxicology see Journal of Environmental Pathology, Toxicology and Oncology **1982**
Journal of Environmental Pathology, Toxicology and Oncology. (US ISSN 0731-8898) **1982**, 4106
▼Journal of Environmental Permitting. (US ISSN 1058-1367) **1960**
Journal of Environmental Planning and Management. (UK ISSN 0964-0568) **2490**, 1960
▼Journal of Environmental Polymer Degradation. (US) **478**, 1855
Journal of Environmental Psychology. (UK ISSN 0272-4944) **4029**
Journal of Environmental Quality. (US ISSN 0047-2425) **1960**, 183
Journal of Environmental Radioactivity. (UK ISSN 0265-931X) **1960**, 486
▼Journal of Environmental Regulation. (US ISSN 1055-758X) **1960**, 2639
Journal of Environmental Science and Health. Part A: Environmental Science and Engineering. (US ISSN 0360-1226) **1961**, 4106
Journal of Environmental Science and Health. Part B: Pesticides, Food Contaminants, and Agricultural Wastes. (US ISSN 0360-1234) **1961**, 102, 4106
Journal of Environmental Science and Health. Part C: Environmental Carcinogenesis and Ecotoxicology Reviews. (US ISSN 0882-8164) **1982**, 1961, 3199
Journal of Environmental Science and Health. Part C: Environmental Carcinogenesis Review see Journal of Environmental Science and Health. Part C: Environmental Carcinogenesis and Ecotoxicology Reviews **1982**
Journal of Environmental Sciences see Institute of Environmental Sciences. Journal **1958**
Journal of Environmental Sciences. (CC ISSN 1001-0742) **1961**

Journal of Environmental Systems. (US ISSN 0047-2433) **1961**
Journal of Enzyme Inhibition. (US ISSN 8755-5093) **478**
Journal of Epidemiology & Community Health. (UK ISSN 0141-7681) **3115**, 4106
Journal of Epidemiology and Community Medicine see Journal of Epidemiology & Community Health **3115**
Journal of Epilepsy. (US ISSN 0896-6974) **3341**
Journal of Equine Medicine and Surgery see Equine Practice **4809**
Journal of Equine Veterinary Science. (US ISSN 0737-0806) **4811**
Journal of Erie Studies. (US ISSN 0090-1938) **2411**
Journal of Esthetic Dentistry. (CN) **3236**, 3341
▼Journal of Esthetic Dentistry (Edicion Espanola). (SP) **3236**
Journal of Ethical Studies. (US ISSN 1010-7304) **3770**
Journal of Ethiopian Studies. (ET ISSN 0022-0922) **2333**, 4377
†Journal of Ethnic Studies. (US ISSN 0091-3219) **5221**
Journal of Ethnic Studies - Treatises and Documents see Razprave in Gradivo **2020**
Journal of Ethnobiology. (US ISSN 0278-0771) **444**, 243, 276
Journal of Ethnopharmacology. (IE ISSN 0378-8741) **3731**
▼Journal of Euromarketing. (US ISSN 1049-6483) **1043**, 915
Journal of European Business. (US ISSN 1044-002X) **674**
Journal of European Economic History. (IT ISSN 0391-5115) **896**
Journal of European Industrial Training. (UK ISSN 0309-0590) **1015**
Journal of European Integration. see Revue d'Integration Europeenne **3971**
Journal of European Social Policy. (UK) **3963**
Journal of European Studies. (UK ISSN 0047-2441) **2370**
Journal of European Studies. (PK ISSN 0258-9680) **2371**, 276, 332, 4185
Journal of Evidence Photography. (US) **3792**, 3265
Journal of Evolutionary Biochemistry and Physiology. (English translation of: Zhurnal Evolyutsionnoi Biokhimii i Fiziologii) (US ISSN 0022-0930) **478**, 572
Journal of Evolutionary Biology. (SZ ISSN 1010-061X) **545**, 507
▼Journal of Evolutionary Economics. (US ISSN 0936-9937) **896**
Journal of Evolutionary Psychology. (US ISSN 0737-4828) **4029**, 2928
Journal of Experiential Education (Boulder). (US ISSN 1053-8259) **1753**
Journal of Experimental and Clinical Hematology. (US ISSN 0029-4810) **3273**
Journal of Experimental & Theoretical Artificial Intelligence. (UK ISSN 0952-813X) **1409**
Journal of Experimental Animal Science/Zeitschrift fuer Versuchstierkunde. (GW ISSN 0044-3697) **3260**
Journal of Experimental Biology. (UK ISSN 0022-0949) **444**
Journal of Experimental Botany. (UK ISSN 0022-0957) **507**
Journal of Experimental Child Psychology. (US ISSN 0022-0965) **4029**, 1239
Journal of Experimental Education. (US ISSN 0022-0973) **1753**
Journal of Experimental Marine Biology and Ecology. (NE ISSN 0022-0981) **444**
▼Journal of Experimental Mathematics.(US ISSN 1058-6458) **3041**
Journal of Experimental Medicine. (US ISSN 0022-1007) **3260**
†Journal of Experimental Pathology. (US ISSN 0730-8485) **5222**

Journal of Experimental Psychology see Journal of Experimental Psychology: General **4029**
Journal of Experimental Psychology: Animal Behavior Processes. (US ISSN 0097-7403) **4029**
Journal of Experimental Psychology: General. (US ISSN 0096-3445) **4029**
Journal of Experimental Psychology: Human Perception and Performance.(US ISSN 0096-1523) **4029**
Journal of Experimental Psychology: Learning, Memory, and Cognition. (US ISSN 0278-7393) **4029**
Journal of Experimental Research in Personality see Journal of Research in Personality **4033**
Journal of Experimental Social Psychology. (US ISSN 0022-1031) **4029**, **4440**
Journal of Experimental Zoology. (US ISSN 0022-104X) **586**
▼Journal of Exposure Analysis and Environmental Epidemiology. (US ISSN 1053-4245) **1961**, **3115**
Journal of Extension. (US ISSN 0022-0140) **1642**
Journal of Extra-Corporeal Technology. (US ISSN 0022-1058) **3115**
Journal of Family and Economic Issues. (US) **4029**
Journal of Family and Social Welfare Law see Journal of Social Welfare and Family Law **2718**
Journal of Family History. (US ISSN 0363-1990) **4440**
Journal of Family Issues. (US ISSN 0192-513X) **4440**
Journal of Family Law. (US ISSN 0022-1066) **2718**, **4440**
Journal of Family Planning Studies see Journal of Population and Health Studies **597**
Journal of Family Practice. (US ISSN 0094-3509) **3115**
Journal of Family Psychology. (US ISSN 0893-3200) **4029**
Journal of Family Psychotherapy. (US ISSN 0897-5353) **4029**, **3341**
Journal of Family Therapy. (UK ISSN 0163-4445) **3341**, **4029**, **4440**
Journal of Family Violence. (US ISSN 0885-7482) **1516**, **4440**
Journal of Family Welfare. (II ISSN 0022-1074) **597**
Journal of Feminist Family Therapy. (US ISSN 0895-2833) **4859**, **4029**
Journal of Feminist Studies in Religion. (UK ISSN 8755-4178) **4859**, **4185**
Journal of Fermentation and Bioengineering. (JA ISSN 0922-338X) **469**, **490**
Journal of Fermentation Technology see Journal of Fermentation and Bioengineering **469**
Journal of Ferrocement. (TH ISSN 0125-1759) **622**
Journal of Fibrinolysis see Fibrinolysis **3259**
Journal of Field Archaeology. (US ISSN 0093-4690) **276**
Journal of Field Ornithology. (US ISSN 0273-8570) **565**
Journal of Film and Video. (US ISSN 0742-4671) **3512**, **1385**
Journal of Finance. (US ISSN 0022-1082) **788**
Journal of Financial and Quantitative Analysis. (US ISSN 0022-1090) **1016**
Journal of Financial Economics. (SZ ISSN 0304-405X) **674**
Journal of Financial Education. (US ISSN 0093-3961) **788**, **1710**
▼Journal of Financial Intermediation. (US ISSN 1042-9573) **870**
Journal of Financial Management and Analysis. (II ISSN 0970-4205) **788**, **870**
Journal of Financial Planning. (US ISSN 1040-3981) **952**, **753**, **1099**
Journal of Financial Planning Today. (US) **788**
Journal of Financial Research. (US ISSN 0270-2592) **674**, **788**

Journal of Financial Services Research. (US ISSN 0920-8550) **788**, **952**, **2535**, **4151**
Journal of Fire Sciences. (US ISSN 0734-9041) **2033**
Journal of Fish Biology. (UK ISSN 0022-1112) **586**
Journal of Fish Diseases. (UK ISSN 0140-7775) **2044**
Journal of Fisheries & Aquaculture. (PH ISSN 0115-690X) **586**
Journal of Fixed Income. (US ISSN 1059-8596) **953**
Journal of Fluency Disorders. (US ISSN 0094-730X) **4030**, **4440**
Journal of Fluid Control. (US ISSN 8755-8564) **1933**, **3843**
Journal of Fluid Mechanics. (UK ISSN 0022-1120) **1924**, **3822**
Journal of Fluids and Structures. (UK ISSN 0889-9746) **1828**
Journal of Fluids Engineering. (US ISSN 0098-2202) **1924**
▼Journal of Fluorescence. (US ISSN 1053-0509) **1214**, **1181**
Journal of Fluorine Chemistry. (SZ ISSN 0022-1139) **1214**
Journal of Foetal Medicine. (IT ISSN 0392-9507) **3293**
Journal of Folklore Research. (US ISSN 0737-7037) **2056**
Journal of Food and Agricultural Info see Journal of Agricultural & Food Information **101**
Journal of Food and Nutrition see Australian Journal of Nutrition and Dietetics **3603**
Journal of Food Biochemistry. (US ISSN 0145-8884) **2074**
Journal of Food Composition and Analysis. (US ISSN 0889-1575) **2075**, **1181**
Journal of Food Distribution Research. (US ISSN 0047-245X) **2075**, **1043**
Journal of Food Engineering. (UK ISSN 0260-8774) **2075**
Journal of Food Process Engineering. (US ISSN 0145-8876) **2075**
Journal of Food Processing and Preservation. (US ISSN 0145-8892) **2075**
▼Journal of Food Products Marketing. (US ISSN 1045-4446) **2075**, **1043**
Journal of Food Protection. (US ISSN 0362-028X) **4106**, **200**, **2075**
Journal of Food Quality. (US ISSN 0146-9428) **2075**
Journal of Food Safety. (US ISSN 0149-6085) **2075**
Journal of Food Science. (US ISSN 0022-1147) **2075**
Journal of Food Science and Technology. (II ISSN 0022-1155) **2075**
Journal of Food Science and Technology. see Nippon Shokuhin Kogyo Gakkaishi **2078**
Journal of Food Technology see International Journal of Food Science and Technology **2074**
Journal of Foodservice Systems. (US ISSN 0196-4283) **2075**
Journal of Foot Surgery. (US ISSN 0449-2544) **3380**
Journal of Foraminiferal Research. (US ISSN 0096-1191) **3658**
Journal of Forecasting. (UK ISSN 0277-6693) **1016**, **4440**
Journal of Foreign Economics and Trade. see Duiwai Jingji Maoyi **905**
Journal of Foreign Language. see Waiguoyu **2851**
Journal of Foreign Languages. see Waiyu Xuekan **2851**
Journal of Forensic Sciences. see Fayixue Zazhi **3264**
Journal of Forensic Sciences. (US ISSN 0022-1198) **3265**
Journal of Forest History see Forest & Conservation History **2099**
Journal of Forestry. (US ISSN 0022-1201) **2103**
Journal of Forth Application and Research. (US ISSN 0738-2022) **1430**

Journal of Free Radicals in Biology and Medicine see Free Radical Biology & Medicine **485**
▼Journal of French Language Studies. (UK ISSN 0959-2695) **2821**, **1753**
†Journal of Freshwater. (US ISSN 0276-0142) **5222**
Journal of Freshwater Ecology. (US ISSN 0270-5060) **1599**, **1961**
Journal of Fuel Chemistry and Technology. see Ranliao Huaxue Xuebao **1859**
Journal of Fukien History. (CH ISSN 0022-1228) **2339**, **3639**
Journal of Functional Analysis. (US ISSN 0022-1236) **3041**
▼Journal of Functional Programming. (UK ISSN 0956-7968) **1430**
Journal of Further and Higher Education. (UK ISSN 0309-877X) **1710**
Journal of Fusion Energy. (US ISSN 0164-0313) **1806**
The Journal of Futures Markets. (US ISSN 0270-7314) **953**
Journal of Gambling Behavior see Journal of Gambling Studies **3341**
Journal of Gambling Studies. (US ISSN 1050-5350) **3341**, **4477**
Journal of Gandhian Studies. (II) **3901**, **3770**
Journal of Garden History. (UK ISSN 0144-5170) **2132**
Journal of Gas Chromatography see Journal of Chromatographic Science **1206**
Journal of Gastroenterology and Hepatology. (AT ISSN 0815-9319) **3269**
Journal of Gastronomy. (US ISSN 0747-7368) **382**
Journal of Gay & Lesbian Psychotherapy. (US ISSN 0891-7140) **2454**, **3341**, **4030**, **4410**
▼Journal of Gay & Lesbian Social Services. (US ISSN 1053-8720) **4410**, **2454**
Journal of Gem Industry. (II ISSN 0022-1244) **2565**
Journal of Gemmology. (UK) **2565**
Journal of Gemmology and Proceedings of the Gemmological Association of Great Britain see Journal of Gemmology **2565**
Journal of General and Applied Microbiology. (JA ISSN 0022-1260) **554**
Journal of General Chemistry of the U S S R. (English translation of: Zhurnal Obshchei Khimii) (US ISSN 0022-1279) **1181**
Journal of General Education. (US ISSN 0021-3667) **1642**
Journal of General Internal Medicine. (US ISSN 0884-8734) **3115**
Journal of General Management. (UK ISSN 0306-3070) **1016**
Journal of General Medicine. (II ISSN 0970-566X) **3115**
Journal of General Microbiology. (UK ISSN 0022-1287) **554**
▼Journal of General Orthodontics. (US ISSN 1048-1990) **3236**
Journal of General Physiology. (US ISSN 0022-1295) **572**, **3115**
Journal of General Practice see New Zealand General Practice **3135**
Journal of General Psychology. (US ISSN 0022-1309) **4030**
Journal of General Virology. (UK ISSN 0022-1317) **554**
▼Journal of Genetic Counseling. (US) **4030**
Journal of Genetic Psychology. (US ISSN 0022-1325) **4030**, **545**
Journal of Genetics. (II ISSN 0022-1333) **545**
Journal of Genetics & Breeding. (IT ISSN 0394-9257) **102**, **545**
Journal of Geochemical Exploration. (NE ISSN 0375-6742) **1546**
Journal of Geodynamics. (UK ISSN 0264-3707) **1591**, **1569**
Journal of Geography. see Chigaku Zasshi **1542**
Journal of Geography. (US ISSN 0022-1341) **2254**, **1642**

JOURNAL 6349

Journal of Geography in Higher Education. (UK ISSN 0309-8265) **2254**, **1710**
Journal of Geography of Health. see Cahiers de Geographie de la Sante **3085**
Journal of Geological Education. (US ISSN 0022-1368) **1569**, **1710**
Journal of Geological Sciences: Anthropozoic. see Sbornik Geologickych Ved: Antropozoikum **1579**
Journal of Geological Sciences: Applied Geophysics. see Sbornik Geologickych Ved: Uzita Geofyzika **1594**
Journal of Geological Sciences: Economic Geology, Mineralogy. see Sbornik Geologickych Ved: Loziskova Geologie, Mineralogie **1579**
Journal of Geological Sciences: Geology. see Sbornik Geologickych Ved: Geologie **1579**
Journal of Geological Sciences: Hydrogeology, Engineering Geology. see Sbornik Geologickych Ved: Hydrogeologie, Inzenyrska Geologie **1600**
Journal of Geological Sciences: Paleontology. see Sbornik Geologickych Ved: Paleontologie **3660**
Journal of Geological Sciences: Technology, Geochemistry. see Sbornik Geologickych Ved: Technologie, Geochemie **1579**
Journal of Geology. (US ISSN 0022-1376) **1569**
Journal of Geomagnetism and Geoelectricity. (JA ISSN 0022-1392) **1569**, **1591**
Journal of Geometry. (SZ ISSN 0047-2468) **3041**
Journal of Geometry and Physics. (NE ISSN 0393-0440) **3041**, **3822**
Journal of Geophysics. see Geofizicheskii Zhurnal **1589**
Journal of Geosciences/Osaka-shiritsu Daigaku Rigakubu Chigaku Kiyo. (JA ISSN 0449-2560) **1546**
Journal of Geotechnical Engineering. (US ISSN 0733-9410) **1869**, **1569**
Journal of Geriatric Drug Therapy. (US ISSN 8756-4629) **3731**, **2275**
Journal of Geriatric Psychiatry. (US ISSN 0022-1414) **3341**, **2275**
Journal of Geriatric Psychiatry and Neurology. (US) **2275**, **3341**
Journal of German - American Studies see Yearbook of German - American Studies **2978**
Journal of Gerontological Nursing. (US ISSN 0098-9134) **2275**, **3280**
Journal of Gerontological Social Work. (US ISSN 0163-4372) **2275**
Journal of Gerontology. see Laonianxue Zazhi **2275**
Journal of Glaciology. (UK ISSN 0022-1430) **1569**
Journal of Glaciology and Geocryology. see Bingchuan Dongtu **1587**
Journal of Glass Studies. (US ISSN 0075-4250) **355**
▼Journal of Glaucoma. (US ISSN 1057-0829) **3302**
▼Journal of Global Business. (US ISSN 1053-7287) **674**
Journal of Global Marketing. (US ISSN 0891-1762) **1043**, **915**
▼Journal of Global Optimization. (NE ISSN 0925-5001) **4360**, **1879**
Journal of Government and Political Studies. (II ISSN 0251-3056) **3901**
Journal of Graph Theory. (US ISSN 0364-9024) **3041**
Journal of Graphic Science of Japan. see Zugaku Kenkyu **351**
Journal of Graphoanalysis. (US ISSN 0022-1449) **4030**
Journal of Great Lakes Research. (US ISSN 0380-1330) **1961**, **1599**
Journal of Ground Water see Ground Water **1598**
Journal of Groundwater Hydrology/ Chikasui Gakkaishi. (JA ISSN 0913-4182) **1599**

Journal of Group Psychotherapy, Psychodrama & Sociometry. (US ISSN 0731-1273) **4030**, **4440**
Journal of Growth. *see* Seicho **248**
Journal of Guidance, Control, and Dynamics. (US ISSN 0731-5090) **57**
†Journal of Guitar Acoustics & Technology. (US) **5222**
Journal of Gynaecological Endocrinology. (IT) **3254**, **3294**
Journal of Gynecologic Surgery. (US ISSN 1042-4067) **3294**, **3254**, **3380**
Journal of Halacha and Contemporary Society. (US ISSN 0730-2614) **2010**, **2639**
Journal of Hand Surgery: American Volume. (US ISSN 0363-5023) **3380**
Journal of Hand Surgery: British Volume. (UK ISSN 0266-7681) **3380**
Journal of Hand Therapy. (US ISSN 0894-1130) **3115**
▼Journal of Hard Materials. (UK ISSN 0954-027X) **1918**, **3822**
Journal of Hazardous Materials. (NE ISSN 0304-3894) **1855**, **984**
Journal of Head Trauma Rehabilitation. (US ISSN 0885-9701) **3309**
Journal of Health Administration Education. (US ISSN 0735-6722) **2466**, **1710**
Journal of Health & Healing. (US ISSN 1044-2790) **3805**, **3115**
Journal of Health and Hospital Law. (US) **3115**, **2639**
Journal of Health and Human Resources Administration. (US ISSN 0160-4198) **2466**, **4106**
Journal of Health and Physical Education *see* Taiiku no Kagaku **1760**
Journal of Health and Safety. (UK ISSN 0954-576X) **3618**
Journal of Health and Social Behavior. (US ISSN 0022-1465) **4440**
Journal of Health & Social Policy. (US ISSN 0897-7186) **4410**, **4106**
Journal of Health Care Chaplaincy. (US ISSN 0885-4726) **3805**, **4185**
▼Journal of Health Care for the Poor and Underserved. (US ISSN 1049-2089) **3116**
Journal of Health Care Marketing. (US ISSN 0737-3252) **1043**, **3805**
Journal of Health Economics. (NE ISSN 0167-6296) **4106**, **2466**
Journal of Health Education. (US ISSN 1055-6699) **1753**, **3805**
Journal of Health Information & Medical Records Officers. (UK) **3116**, **2466**
Journal of Health, Physical Education and Recreation. *see* Taiiku no Kagaku **1760**
Journal of Health Politics, Policy and Law. (US ISSN 0361-6878) **3116**, **2466**, **2639**, **3901**
Journal of Health Science. (US) **3608**, **3805**
Journal of Healthcare Materiel Management. (US ISSN 0889-2482) **2466**
Journal of Healthcare Protection Management. (US) **2466**, **1526**
Journal of Heart and Lung Transplantation. (US ISSN 1053-2498) **3380**
Journal of Heart Transplantation *see* Journal of Heart and Lung Transplantation **3380**
Journal of Heat Transfer. (US ISSN 0022-1481) **1933**
Journal of Heat Treating. (US ISSN 0190-9177) **3411**
Journal of Hebei Medicine. *see* Hebei Yiyao **3728**
Journal of Hellenic Studies. (UK ISSN 0075-4269) **1277**, **2821**
Journal of Helminthology. (UK ISSN 0022-149X) **3221**
Journal of Hepatology. (NE ISSN 0168-8278) **3269**
▼Journal of Herbs, Spices & Medicinal Plants. (US ISSN 1049-6475) **2132**, **3116**

Journal of Heredity. (US ISSN 0022-1503) **545**
Journal of Herpetology. (US ISSN 0022-1511) **586**
Journal of Heterocyclic Chemistry. (US ISSN 0022-152X) **1219**
Journal of High Pressure Institute of Japan. *see* Atsuryoku Gijutsu **1815**
Journal of High Resolution Chromatography *see* H R C **1205**
▼Journal of High Speed Networks. (NE ISSN 0926-6801) **1427**
▼Journal of High Technology Management Research. (US ISSN 1047-8310) **827**, **1016**, **1043**
Journal of Higher Education. (US ISSN 0022-1546) **1710**
Journal of Higher Education. (II ISSN 0252-0397) **1710**
▼Journal of Himalayan Geology. (II ISSN 0970-0951) **1570**
Journal of Himalayan Studies and Regional Development. (II ISSN 0250-8346) **1961**, **932**
Journal of Hispanic Philology. (US ISSN 0147-5460) **2928**, **2821**
Journal of Hispanic Policy. (US ISSN 0892-6115) **2010**, **3901**
Journal of Hispanic Politics *see* Journal of Hispanic Policy **2010**
Journal of Histochemistry and Cytochemistry. (US ISSN 0022-1554) **525**
Journal of Historic Madison, Inc. of Wisconsin *see* Historic Madison. Journal **2408**
Journal of Historical Geography. (UK ISSN 0305-7488) **2254**
Journal of Historical Research. (II ISSN 0022-1562) **2315**
Journal of Historical Research. *see* Majallah-i Tahqiqat-i Tarikhi **2430**
Journal of Historical Review. (US ISSN 0195-6752) **2315**
Journal of Historical Science. *see* Shixue Yuekan **2322**
Journal of Historical Sociology. (UK ISSN 0952-1909) **4440**
Journal of Historiography. *see* Shixueshi Yanjiu **2322**
Journal of History. (PH) **2339**
Journal of History and Political Science *see* Journal of Political Science **3902**
Journal of History of Science. *see* Kagakushi Kenkyu **4319**
Journal of Histotechnology. (US ISSN 0147-8885) **4602**, **2315**
Journal of Holistic Nursing. (US) **3280**
▼Journal of Home & Consumer Horticulture. (US ISSN 1054-4682) **2132**
Journal of Home Economics. (US ISSN 0022-1570) **2448**
Journal of Home Economics of Japan. *see* Nihon Kasei Gakkaishi **2449**
Journal of Home Health Care Practice. (US ISSN 0897-8018) **2466**
Journal of Homoeopathic Medicine *see* Indian Journal of Homoeopathic Medicine **3215**
Journal of Homosexuality. (US ISSN 0091-8369) **2454**, **4440**
Journal of Horticultural Science. (UK ISSN 0022-1589) **2132**
Journal of Hospital Infection. (UK ISSN 0195-6701) **3221**
Journal of Hospital Marketing. (US ISSN 0883-7570) **1043**, **2466**
Journal of Hospital Supply, Processing and Distribution *see* Journal of Healthcare Materiel Management **2466**
▼Journal of Hospitality & Leisure Marketing. (US ISSN 1050-7051) **2477**, **1043**, **2738**
Journal of Hospitality Education *see* Hospitality Education and Research Journal **2475**
Journal of Housing. (US ISSN 0272-7374) **2490**
▼Journal of Housing Economics. (US ISSN 1051-1377) **2490**
Journal of Housing for the Elderly. (US ISSN 0276-3893) **2275**
▼Journal of Housing Research. (US ISSN 1052-7001) **2490**, **4151**
▼Journal of Human Ecology. (II ISSN 0970-9274) **1961**, **243**, **545**

Journal of Human Ergology. (JA ISSN 0300-8134) **984**, **3116**
Journal of Human Evolution *see* Human Evolution **241**
Journal of Human Evolution. (UK ISSN 0047-2484) **545**
Journal of Human Hypertension. (UK ISSN 0950-9240) **3210**
Journal of Human Lactation. (US ISSN 0890-3344) **3294**, **3608**
Journal of Human Movement Studies. (UK ISSN 0306-7297) **4030**, **3116**
▼Journal of Human Muscle Performance. (US ISSN 1053-2137) **3372**
Journal of Human Nutrition and Dietetics. (UK ISSN 0952-3871) **3608**
Journal of Human Resources. (US ISSN 0022-166X) **1067**, **984**
Journal of Human Stress *see* Behavioral Medicine **4013**
Journal of Humanistic Education and Development. (US ISSN 0735-6846) **1642**
Journal of Humanistic Psychology. (US ISSN 0022-1678) **4030**
Journal of Humanistic Studies/Inmun Kwahak. (KO ISSN 0537-7137) **2509**
Journal of Humanities. (MW) **2509**
Journal of Humanities. *see* Renwen Zazhi **2513**
Journal of Humanities and Natural Sciences. *see* Jinbun Shizen Kagaku Ronshu **2509**
Journal of Hungarian Veterinary Science. *see* Magyar Allatorvosok Lapja **4812**
Journal of Hydraulic Engineering. *see* Shuili Xuebao **1925**
†Journal of Hydraulic Engineering (Bristol). (US ISSN 1051-2705) **5222**
Journal of Hydraulic Engineering (New York). (US ISSN 0733-9429) **1869**, **1924**
Journal of Hydraulic Research. (NE ISSN 0022-1686) **1924**, **4826**
Journal of Hydrobiology. (II ISSN 0970-3594) **444**
Journal of Hydrodynamics. (CC ISSN 1000-4874) **3822**
Journal of Hydrology. (NE ISSN 0022-1694) **1599**
Journal of Hydrology. (NZ ISSN 0022-1708) **1599**
Journal of Hygiene, Epidemiology, Microbiology and Immunology. (CS ISSN 0022-1732) **3116**, **3187**, **4106**
Journal of Hygienic Chemistry *see* Eisei Kagaku **1711**
Journal of Hyperbaric Medicine. (US ISSN 0884-1225) **4317**, **3116**
Journal of Hypertension. (US ISSN 0263-6352) **3176**, **3210**
Journal of I M W M Observer. *see* Gazeta Obserwatora I M G W **3435**
Journal of Ichthyology. (English translation of: Voprosy Ikhtiologii) (US ISSN 0032-9452) **586**
▼Journal of Ideas. (US ISSN 1049-6335) **4317**
Journal of Imaging Science. (US) **3792**, **1828**
Journal of Imaging Technology. (US ISSN 0747-3583) **3792**, **1828**
Journal of Immunoassay. (US ISSN 0197-1522) **3731**
Journal of Immunogenetics *see* European Journal of Immunogenetics **541**
Journal of Immunological Methods. (NE ISSN 0022-1759) **3187**
Journal of Immunology. (US ISSN 0022-1767) **3187**
Journal of Immunotherapy. (US ISSN 1053-8550) **3116**
Journal of Imperial and Commonwealth History. (UK ISSN 0308-6534) **2315**
Journal of In Vitro Fertilization and Embryo Transfer *see* Journal of Assisted Reproduction and Genetics **3293**

Journal of Inclusion Phenomena *see* Journal of Inclusion Phenomena & Molecular Recognition in Chemistry **1227**
Journal of Inclusion Phenomena & Molecular Recognition in Chemistry. (NE ISSN 0923-0750) **1227**
Journal of Independent Social Work. (US ISSN 0883-7562) **4410**
Journal of Indexing & Reference Work. (II) **2794**
Journal of India Folkloristics. (II) **2056**
Journal of Indian and Buddhist Studies/Indogaku Bunkkyogaku Kenkyu. (JA ISSN 0019-4344) **4215**
Journal of Indian Education. (II) **1642**
Journal of Indian History. (II ISSN 0022-1775) **2339**
Journal of Indian Museums. (II) **3526**
Journal of Indian Philosophy. (NE ISSN 0022-1791) **3770**, **3639**
Journal of Indian Psychology. (II ISSN 0379-3885) **4030**
Journal of Indian Writing in English. (II ISSN 0302-1319) **2928**
Journal of Indigenous Studies. (CN ISSN 0838-4711) **243**
▼Journal of Individual Employment Rights. (US ISSN 1055-7512) **984**, **2639**
Journal of Indo-European Studies. (US ISSN 0092-2323) **4377**
Journal of Indo-European Studies Monograph Series. (US ISSN 0895-7258) **4377**
Journal of Indonesian Demography/Majalah Demografi Indonesia. (IO ISSN 0126-0251) **3984**
Journal of Industrial Aerodynamics *see* Journal of Wind Engineering and Industrial Aerodynamics **1934**
Journal of Industrial Affairs. (UK ISSN 0143-084X) **674**
Journal of Industrial Economics. (UK ISSN 0022-1821) **675**
Journal of Industrial Engineering. (II) **1926**
Journal of Industrial Engineering *see* Industrial Engineering **1926**
†Journal of Industrial Irradiation Technology. (US ISSN 0735-7923) **5222**
Journal of Industrial Microbiology. (NE ISSN 0169-4146) **490**, **554**
Journal of Industrial Relations. (AT ISSN 0022-1856) **984**
Journal of Industrial Teacher Education. (US ISSN 0022-1864) **1710**, **4602**
Journal of Industry *see* South Australia in Business **822**
Journal of Industry and Commerce. (AT ISSN 0314-7592) **1079**
Journal of Industry and Management. *see* Sangyo Keiei Kenkyujoho **1027**
Journal of Industry and Trade. (II ISSN 0022-1880) **1079**
Journal of Industry Furnace. *see* Gongye Lu **1917**
Journal of Infection. (UK ISSN 0163-4453) **3221**
Journal of Infectious Diseases. (US ISSN 0022-1899) **3221**
Journal of Inferential and Deductive Biology. (US ISSN 0883-1394) **444**
Journal of Information & Optimization Sciences. (II ISSN 0252-2667) **3041**, **1457**
▼Journal of Information Ethics. (US) **2639**, **2765**
▼Journal of Information Networking. (UK) **1457**
Journal of Information Processing. (JA ISSN 0387-6101) **1452**
Journal of Information Processing and Cybernetics. (GW ISSN 0863-0593) **1441**, **1452**
Journal of Information Processing and Managements/Joho Kanri. (JA ISSN 0021-7298) **2765**
Journal of Information Recording Materials. (GW ISSN 0863-0453) **3792**
Journal of Information Science. (NE ISSN 0165-5515) **2766**, **1338**, **2798**, **4130**
▼Journal of Information Systems. (UK ISSN 0959-2954) **1457**

Journal of Information Systems Management. (US ISSN 0739-9014) **2798**
▼Journal of Information Systems Security. (US) **1434**
Journal of Information Technology. (UK ISSN 0268-3962) **2766**
Journal of Information Technology for Teacher Education. (UK ISSN 0962-029X) **1753**
▼Journal of Information Technology Management. (US ISSN 1042-1319) **1457**
Journal of Infrared and Millimetre Wave. see Hongwai yu Haomibo Xuebao **3853**
Journal of Inherited Metabolic Disease. (UK) **573**
Journal of Inherited Metabolic Disease. (NE ISSN 0141-8955) **3321**
▼Journal of Inorganic and Organometallic Polymers. (US ISSN 1053-0495) **1219**, **1214**
Journal of Inorganic Biochemistry. (US ISSN 0162-0134) **479**, **1214**
Journal of Inorganic Materials. see Wuji Cailiao Xuebao **1215**
Journal of Insect Behavior. (US ISSN 0892-7553) **535**
Journal of Insect Physiology. (US ISSN 0022-1910) **535**
Journal of Institutional and Theoretical Economics. (GW ISSN 0932-4569) **3901**, **896**
Journal of Instructional Development see Educational Technology Research & Development **1748**
Journal of Instructional Psychology. (US ISSN 0094-1956) **1643**, **4030**
Journal of Insurance Medicine. (US ISSN 0743-6661) **2536**, **3116**
Journal of Insurance Regulation. (US) **2536**, **2639**
Journal of Insurance Science. (JA) **2536**
Journal of Integrative and Eclectic Psychotherapy. (MX) **4030**, **3341**
Journal of Intellectual Disability Research. (UK) **3341**, **4410**
Journal of Intelligence Studies. (US) **3963**
Journal of Intelligent and Robotic Systems. (NE ISSN 0921-0296) **1409**
▼Journal of Intelligent Manufacturing. (UK ISSN 0956-5515) **1414**, **1409**
▼Journal of Intelligent Material Systems and Stuctures. (US ISSN 1045-389X) **4317**
Journal of Intelligent Systems. (UK ISSN 0334-1860) **1441**
Journal of Intensive Care Medicine. (US ISSN 0885-0666) **3116**
Journal of Intensive English Studies. (US ISSN 0899-885X) **2821**, **1753**
Journal of Interamerican Studies and World Affairs. (US ISSN 0022-1937) **3963**
Journal of Intercultural Studies. (JA ISSN 0388-0508) **4377**
Journal of Interdisciplinary Cycle Research. (NE ISSN 0022-1945) **4318**
Journal of Interdisciplinary Economics. (UK ISSN 0260-1079) **675**
Journal of Interdisciplinary History. (US ISSN 0022-1953) **2315**, **2509**
Journal of Interdisciplinary Studies. (US ISSN 0890-0132) **4377**
Journal of Interferon Research. (US ISSN 0197-8357) **3116**
Journal of Interior Design Education and Research. (US ISSN 0147-0418) **2553**, **1753**
▼Journal of Interlibrary Loan & Information Supply. (US ISSN 1042-4458) **2766**
Journal of Intermountain Archeology. (US) **276**
Journal of Internal Medicine. (UK ISSN 0954-6820) **3116**
Journal of International Affairs. (US ISSN 0022-197X) **3963**
Journal of International Affairs. (KO) **3963**
Journal of International and Comparative Economics see J O I C E **914**

Journal of International Arbitration. (SZ ISSN 0255-8106) **2726**, **984**
Journal of International Banking Law. (UK ISSN 0267-937X) **2710**, **788**
Journal of International Biomedical Information and Data see I B I D **5207**
Journal of International Business Law see University of Pennsylvania Journal of International Business Law **2730**
Journal of International Business Studies. (US ISSN 0047-2506) **675**
Journal of International Consumer Marketing. (US ISSN 0896-1530) **1506**, **915**, **1043**
Journal of International Development: Policy, Economics, & International Relations. (UK ISSN 0954-1748) **4377**, **3901**
Journal of International Economics. (NE ISSN 0022-1996) **675**
Journal of International Financial Management and Accounting. (UK ISSN 0954-1314) **788**, **753**
▼Journal of International Financial Markets, Institutions & Money. (US ISSN 1042-4431) **788**, **1016**
Journal of International Food & Agribusiness Marketing. (US ISSN 0897-4438) **153**
Journal of International Franchising & Distribution Law. (UK) **675**, **2477**, **2710**
Journal of International Law and Diplomacy. see Kokusaiho Gaiko Zasshi **2726**
Journal of International Marketing & Marketing Research. (UK ISSN 1010-7347) **1043**
Journal of International Medical Research. (UK ISSN 0300-0605) **3116**
Journal of International Money and Finance. (UK ISSN 0261-5606) **788**
Journal of International Student Personnel. (US ISSN 0273-3382) **1722**, **4440**
Journal of International Studies see Guoji Wenti Yanjiu **3959**
Journal of International Studies. (JA ISSN 0910-5476) **3963**
Journal of Interpersonal Violence. (US ISSN 0886-2605) **1516**, **4030**, **4440**
†Journal of Interpretation (Derwood). (US) **5222**
†Journal of Interpretation (Rockville). (US ISSN 0882-7893) **5222**
Journal of Interprofessional Care. (UK) **3215**, **3341**
Journal of Interventional Cardiology. (US ISSN 0896-4327) **3210**
Journal of Interventional Radiology. (UK ISSN 0268-0882) **3359**
Journal of Intravenous Nursing. (US ISSN 0896-5846) **3280**
Journal of Intravenous Therapy. (US ISSN 0194-1658) **3280**
Journal of Invasive Cardiology. (US ISSN 1042-3931) **3210**
Journal of Invertebrate Pathology. (US ISSN 0022-2011) **535**
Journal of Investigative Dermatology. (US ISSN 0022-202X) **3248**
Journal of Investigative Surgery. (US ISSN 0894-1939) **3380**
Journal of Iraqi Dissertation Abstracts. Part A: Humanities and Social Sciences. (IQ ISSN 1012-3377) **2509**
Journal of Iraqi Dissertation Abstracts. Part B: Science and Engineering. (IQ ISSN 1012-3490) **1828**
Journal of Irish Archaeology. (IE ISSN 0268-537X) **276**
Journal of Irish Literature. (US ISSN 0047-2514) **2928**
Journal of Irreproducible Results. (US ISSN 0022-2038) **4318**
Journal of Irrigation and Drainage. (US ISSN 0733-9437) **1870**, **I02**
▼Journal of Islamic Studies. (UK ISSN 0955-2340) **4219**, **243**

Journal of J.J. Group of Hospitals and Grant Medical College. (II ISSN 0022-2054) **3116**, **2466**
Journal of J A S T R O. (US ISSN 1040-9564) **3359**
Journal of Japanese Botany/Shokubutsu Kenkyu Zasshi. (JA ISSN 0022-2062) **507**
Journal of Japanese Fine Arts Swords. see Token Bijutsu **347**
Journal of Japanese Scientists. see Nihon no Kagakusha **4330**
Journal of Japanese Studies. (US ISSN 0095-6848) **3639**, **2339**
Journal of Japanese Studies. see Riben Wenti Yanjiu **3643**
Journal of Japanese Trade and Industry.(UK ISSN 0285-9556) **871**
Journal of Jazz Studies see Annual Review of Jazz Studies **5136**
Journal of Jewish Communal Service. (US ISSN 0022-2089) **4440**
Journal of Jewish Music and Liturgy. (US ISSN 0197-0100) **3559**, **4224**
Journal of Jewish Studies. (UK ISSN 0022-2097) **4224**
Journal of Jewish Thought and Philosophy. (US ISSN 1053-699X) **4224**
Journal of Jianghai Academia. see Jianghai Xuekan **4377**
Journal of Jurisprudence. see Faxue Zazhi **2625**
Journal of Juristic Papyrology. (PL ISSN 0075-4277) **2639**, **276**
Journal of Juvenile and Family Courts see Juvenile and Family Court Journal **2718**
Journal of Juvenile Law. (US ISSN 0160-2098) **2639**
Journal of Kansas Pharmacy. (US ISSN 0194-5106) **3731**
Journal of Karyopathology. see Saibokaku Byorigaku Zasshi **3202**
Journal of Kerala Studies. (II ISSN 0377-0443) **2339**
▼Journal of Knot Theory and Its Ramifications. (SI ISSN 0218-2165) **3041**
Journal of Labelled Compounds and Radiopharmaceuticals. (UK ISSN 0362-4803) **1206**
Journal of Labor Economics. (US ISSN 0734-306X) **753**
Journal of Labor Hygiene in Iron and Steel Industry. see Tekko Rodo Eisei **3422**
Journal of Labor Research. (US ISSN 0195-3613) **984**, **2585**
Journal of Laboratory and Clinical Medicine. (US ISSN 0022-2143) **3260**
Journal of Land Use and Environmental Law. (US ISSN 0892-4880) **1961**, **2639**
Journal of Language and Social Psychology. (UK ISSN 0261-927X) **4030**, **4440**
Journal of Laryngology and Otology. (UK ISSN 0022-2151) **3315**
Journal of Laser Applications. (US ISSN 1042-346X) **3854**
Journal of Latin American Lore. (US ISSN 0360-1927) **2056**, **2928**
Journal of Latin American Studies. (UK ISSN 0022-216X) **2411**, **3901**
Journal of Law & Commerce. (US ISSN 0733-2491) **2710**, **915**
Journal of Law and Economics. (US ISSN 0022-2186) **2639**, **675**
Journal of Law and Education. (US ISSN 0275-6072) **2639**, **1643**
†Journal of Law and Ethics in Dentistry.(US ISSN 0894-8879) **5222**
Journal of Law and Health. (US) **2639**, **3116**
Journal of Law and Political Science. see Hogaku **2633**
Journal of Law and Politics. see Daito Hogaku **2617**
Journal of Law and Politics/Ho-sei Kenkyu. (JA ISSN 0387-2882) **2639**, **3901**
Journal of Law and Religion. (US ISSN 0748-0814) **2639**, **4185**

Journal of Law and Society. (UK ISSN 0263-323X) **2639**
Journal of Law, Economics, and Organization. (US ISSN 8756-6222) **2639**, **896**
Journal of Law, Politics, and Sociology. see Hogaku Kenkyu **2633**
Journal of Law Reform see University of Michigan Journal of Law Reform **2690**
Journal of Learning Disabilities. (US ISSN 0022-2194) **1737**, **3116**, **4030**
Journal of Legal Education. (US ISSN 0022-2208) **2639**, **1643**
Journal of Legal History. (UK ISSN 0144-0365) **2639**, **2315**
Journal of Legal Medicine. (US ISSN 0194-7648) **3116**, **2639**
Journal of Legal Pluralism and Unofficial Law. (US ISSN 0732-9113) **2639**
Journal of Legal Studies. (US ISSN 0047-2530) **2640**
Journal of Legislation. (US ISSN 0146-9584) **2640**
Journal of Leisurability. (CN ISSN 0711-222X) **1737**
Journal of Leisure Research. (US ISSN 0022-2216) **2738**, **4549**
Journal of Leukocyte Biology. (US ISSN 0741-5400) **3116**
Journal of Lexicographical Studies. see Cishu Yanjiu **2809**
Journal of Libertarian Studies. (US ISSN 0363-2873) **4378**
Journal of Librarianship see Journal of Librarianship and Information Science **2766**
Journal of Librarianship and Information Science. (UK ISSN 0961-0006) **2766**
Journal of Library Administration. (US ISSN 0193-0826) **2766**
Journal of Library & Information Science/Tushuguanxue yu Zixun Kexue. (CH ISSN 0363-3640) **2766**
Journal of Library and Information Science. (II ISSN 0970-714X) **2766**
Journal of Library Automation Technical Communications see J O L A Technical Communications **5219**
Journal of Light & Visual Environment. (JA ISSN 0387-8805) **3854**, **1901**
Journal of Light Construction. (US ISSN 1040-5224) **622**
Journal of Lightwave Technology. (US ISSN 0733-8724) **3854**
Journal of Linguistics. (UK ISSN 0022-2267) **2821**
Journal of Lipid Mediators. (NE ISSN 0921-8319) **3116**
Journal of Lipid Research. (US ISSN 0022-2275) **479**
Journal of Liposome Research. (US ISSN 0898-2104) **3731**
Journal of Liquid Chromatography. (US ISSN 0148-3919) **1181**
Journal of Literary Semantics. (GW ISSN 0341-7638) **2821**, **2928**
Journal of Literary Studies/Tydskrif vir Literatuurwetenskap. (SA ISSN 0256-4718) **2928**, **2870**
Journal of Literature, History and Philosophy. see Wen Shi Zhe **2518**
Journal of Lithotripsy & Stone Disease. (US ISSN 1040-2152) **3116**
▼Journal of Logic and Computation. (UK ISSN 0955-792X) **1409**
Journal of Logic Programming. (US ISSN 0743-1066) **1431**
Journal of Long-Term Care Administration. (US ISSN 0093-4445) **2466**, **3116**
Journal of Loss Prevention in the Process Industries. (UK ISSN 0950-4230) **1855**
Journal of Low Frequency Noise and Vibration. (UK ISSN 0263-0923) **3859**
Journal of Low Temperature Physics. (US ISSN 0022-2291) **3841**
Journal of Lubrication Technology see Journal of Tribology **3691**
Journal of Luminescence. (NE ISSN 0022-2313) **3854**, **486**, **1181**

Journal of Machinery Manufacture and Reliability. (English translation of: Mashinovedenie) (US ISSN 1052-6188) **1414**, 1933
Journal of Macroeconomics. (US ISSN 0164-0704) **999**
Journal of Macromarketing. (US ISSN 0276-1467) **1043**
Journal of Macromolecular Science: Part A - Chemistry see Journal of Macromolecular Science: Part A - Pure and Applied Chemistry **1219**
Journal of Macromolecular Science: Part A - Pure and Applied Chemistry. (US ISSN 1060-1325) **1219**
Journal of Macromolecular Science: Part B - Physics. (US ISSN 0022-2348) **3822**, 1219
Journal of Macromolecular Science: Part C - Reviews in Macromolecular Chemistry and Physics. (US ISSN 0736-6574) **1219**
Journal of Magnetic Resonance. (US ISSN 0022-2364) **3822**
▼Journal of Magnetic Resonance Imaging. (US) **3359**, 3822
Journal of Magnetism and Magnetic Materials. (NE ISSN 0304-8853) **3822**
Journal of Maharashtra Agricultural Universities. (II ISSN 0378-2395) **102**
Journal of Malaysian and Comparative Law/Jernal Undang-Undang. (MY ISSN 0126-6322) **2640**
Journal of Maltese Studies. (MM ISSN 0075-4285) **2371**
Journal of Mammalogy. (US ISSN 0022-2372) **586**, 444
Journal of Management. (US ISSN 0149-2063) **1016**
Journal of Management and Communication see Institute News **3729**
Journal of Management Consulting. (NE ISSN 0168-7778) **1016**
Journal of Management Development. (UK ISSN 0262-1711) **1016**
Journal of Management Education. (US ISSN 1052-5629) **1016**, 1753
Journal of Management in Engineering. (US ISSN 0742-597X) **1828**
Journal of Management in Practice see Journal of Management Systems **1016**
Journal of Management Information Systems. (US ISSN 0742-1222) **1016**, 3901
▼Journal of Management Inquiry. (US ISSN 1056-4926) **1016**
Journal of Management Studies. (GH ISSN 0022-2399) **1016**
Journal of Management Studies. (UK ISSN 0022-2380) **1016**
Journal of Management Systems. (US ISSN 1041-2808) **1016**
Journal of Managerial Issues. (US ISSN 1045-3695) **1016**
Journal of Managerial Psychology. (UK ISSN 0268-3946) **1016**, 4030
Journal of Manipulative and Physiological Therapeutics see J M P T: Journal of Manipulative and Physiological Therapeutics **3215**
Journal of Manual Medicine. (GW ISSN 0935-6339) **3117**
Journal of Manufacturing. (US ISSN 1041-4673) **1437**, 1828
Journal of Manufacturing and Operations Management. (US ISSN 0890-2577) **1016**, 1079
Journal of Manufacturing Systems. (UK ISSN 0278-6125) **1438**, 1828
Journal of Marine Resource Economics see Marine Resource Economics **5232**
Journal of Marine Science see Northeast Gulf Science **1609**
Journal of Marine Systems. (NE ISSN 0924-7963) **1607**
Journal of Marital and Family Therapy. (US ISSN 0194-472X) **4030**, 3067, 4410, 4440
Journal of Maritime Law and Commerce. (US ISSN 0022-2410) **2735**, 4730
Journal of Marketing. (US ISSN 0022-2429) **725**, 15

Journal of Marketing and Public Policy see Journal of Public Policy & Marketing **1043**
▼Journal of Marketing Channels. (US ISSN 1046-669X) **1043**
Journal of Marketing Education. (US ISSN 0273-4753) **1043**, 1753
Journal of Marketing for Higher Education. (US ISSN 0884-1241) **1043**, 1710
Journal of Marketing for Mental Health see Journal of Nonprofit & Public Sector Marketing **1043**
Journal of Marketing Management. (UK ISSN 0267-257X) **1043**
Journal of Marketing Research. (US ISSN 0022-2437) **1043**
Journal of Marriage and the Family. (US ISSN 0022-2445) **4440**, 3067
Journal of Mass Media Ethics. (US ISSN 0890-0523) **1338**, 4030
▼Journal of Materials Chemistry. (UK ISSN 0959-9428) **1181**
Journal of Materials Education. (US ISSN 0738-7989) **1828**
Journal of Materials Engineering. (US ISSN 0931-7058) **3411**, 1792
Journal of Materials for Energy Systems see Journal of Materials Engineering **3411**
Journal of Materials in Civil Engineering: Properties, Applications, Durability. (US ISSN 0899-1561) **1870**
Journal of Materials Processing Technology. (NE ISSN 0924-0136) **1933**, 1435, 1879, 3019
Journal of Materials Research. (US ISSN 0884-2914) **3822**
Journal of Materials Science. (UK ISSN 0022-2461) **1918**
Journal of Materials Science Letters. (UK ISSN 0261-8028) **1919**
Journal of Materials Science: Materials in Electronics. (UK ISSN 0957-4522) **1919**
Journal of Materials Science: Materials in Medicine. (UK ISSN 0957-4530) **1919**, 3117
Journal of Materials Shaping Technology. (US ISSN 0931-704X) **3411**
Journal of Maternal and Child Health see Maternal & Child Health **3322**
Journal of Maternal - Fetal Investigation.(US) **3294**
Journal of Mathematical Analysis and Applications. (US ISSN 0022-247X) **3041**
Journal of Mathematical and Physical Sciences. (II ISSN 0047-2557) **3041**, 3822
Journal of Mathematical Behavior. (US ISSN 0732-3123) **3041**
Journal of Mathematical Biology. (GW ISSN 0303-6812) **444**, 3041
Journal of Mathematical Chemistry. (SZ ISSN 0259-9791) **1181**, 3041
Journal of Mathematical Economics. (NE ISSN 0304-4068) **896**, 3041
▼Journal of Mathematical Imaging and Vision. (US ISSN 0924-9907) **3065**
Journal of Mathematical Physics. (US ISSN 0022-2488) **3822**, 3041
Journal of Mathematical Psychology. (US ISSN 0022-2496) **4030**, 3041
Journal of Mathematical Sociology. (US ISSN 0022-250X) **4440**, 3062
▼Journal of Mathematical Systems, Estimation and Control. (US ISSN 1052-0600) **3065**
Journal of Mathematics. (JA ISSN 0075-4293) **3041**
Journal of Mathematics and Physics see Studies in Applied Mathematics **3056**
Journal of Mayan Linguistics. (US ISSN 0195-475X) **2821**
Journal of Mechanical Design. (US ISSN 1050-0472) **1933**
Journal of Mechanical Engineering Science see Institution of Mechanical Engineers. Proceedings. Part C: Journal of Mechanical Engineering Science **1931**

Journal of Mechanical Working Technology see Journal of Materials Processing Technology **1933**
Journal of Mechanisms, Transmissions and Automation in Design see Journal of Mechanical Design **1933**
Journal of Media Law and Practice. (UK ISSN 0144-0373) **2640**, 1339
Journal of Medical and Applied Malacology. (US ISSN 1053-6388) **554**
Journal of Medical and Pharmaceutical Marketing. (NR ISSN 0331-0124) **1043**, 3117, 3731
Journal of Medical & Veterinary Mycology. (UK ISSN 0268-1218) **3221**
Journal of Medical Education see Academic Medicine **3069**
Journal of Medical Engineering & Technology. (UK ISSN 0309-1902) **3117**
Journal of Medical Entomology. (US ISSN 0022-2585) **3221**, 535
Journal of Medical Ethics. (UK ISSN 0306-6800) **3117**
Journal of Medical Genetics. (UK ISSN 0022-2593) **545**, 3117
Journal of Medical Humanities. (US ISSN 1041-3545) **3117**, 3770
Journal of Medical Humanities and Bioethics see Journal of Medical Humanities **3117**
Journal of Medical Imaging see European Journal of Radiology **3358**
Journal of Medical Instruments. see Ikakikai Gaku Zasshi **2522**
Journal of Medical Microbiology. (UK ISSN 0022-2615) **3117**
Journal of Medical Practice Management. (US) **3117**
Journal of Medical Primatology. (DK ISSN 0047-2565) **586**
Journal of Medical Systems. (US ISSN 0148-5598) **3226**
Journal of Medical Technology. see Rinsho Kensa **3263**
Journal of Medical Virology. (US ISSN 0146-6615) **3117**
Journal of Medicinal and Aromatic Plants. (HU) **507**, 102
Journal of Medicinal Chemistry. (US ISSN 0022-2623) **3732**
Journal of Medicine (Clinical, Experimental and Theoretical). (US) **3117**
Journal of Medicine and Philosophy. (NE ISSN 0360-5310) **3117**, 3770
Journal of Medieval and Renaissance Studies. (US ISSN 0047-2573) **2509**, 332, 2315, 2928
Journal of Medieval History. (NE ISSN 0304-4181) **2371**
Journal of Medieval Indian Literature. (II) **2928**
▼Journal of Mediterranean Studies. (UK) **2430**, 243
Journal of Membrane Biology. (GW ISSN 0022-2631) **525**
Journal of Membrane Science. (NE ISSN 0376-7388) **1227**, 479
Journal of Memory and Language. (US ISSN 0749-596X) **1643**
Journal of Mennonite Studies. (CN ISSN 0824-5053) **4241**
Journal of Mental Deficiency Research see Journal of Intellectual Disability Research **3341**
▼Journal of Mental Health. (UK ISSN 0963-8237) **3341**
Journal of Mental Health Administration.(US ISSN 0092-8623) **4106**, 4410
Journal of Mental Health Counseling. (US ISSN 1040-2861) **4030**
Journal of Mental Imagery. (US ISSN 0364-5541) **4030**, 2928
Journal of Metallurgy, Part A & B see Jinshu Xuebao **3410**
Journal of Metals see J O M **3410**
Journal of Metamorphic Geology. (US ISSN 0263-4929) **1570**
Journal of Meteorological Research. (JA) **3437**
Journal of Meteorology. (UK ISSN 0307-5966) **3437**

Journal of Microbial Biotechnology. (II ISSN 0256-8551) **490**, 554
Journal of Microbiological Methods. (NE ISSN 0167-7012) **554**, 490
Journal of Microbiology. see Weishengwu Xue Zazhi **558**
Journal of Microbiology, Epidemiology and Immunobiology. see Zhurnal Mikrobiologii, Epidemiologii i Immunobiologii **559**
Journal of Microcolumn Separations. (US ISSN 1040-7685) **1206**
Journal of Microcomputer Applications. (UK ISSN 0745-7138) **1461**
Journal of Microcomputer Systems Management. (US ISSN 1043-6464) **1461**, 1016
Journal of Microencapsulation. (UK ISSN 0265-2048) **3732**, 3117
Journal of Micrographics/Maikuro Shashin. (JA) **3792**
▼Journal of Micromechanics and Microengineering. (US ISSN 0960-1317) **1933**
Journal of Micronutrient Analysis see Food Chemistry **1177**
Journal of Microphotography see Journal of Micrographics **3792**
Journal of Microscopy. (UK ISSN 0022-2720) **560**
Journal of Microscopy Research and Technique. (US ISSN 1059-910X) **444**
Journal of Microsurgery. (US) **3380**, 3260
Journal of Microwave. see Weibo Xuebao **1779**
Journal of Microwave Power. (US ISSN 0022-2739) **1901**
Journal of Middle Atlantic Archaeology. (US ISSN 0883-9697) **276**
Journal of Military History. (US ISSN 0899-3718) **3462**, 2411
Journal of Mind and Behavior. (US ISSN 0271-0137) **4030**, 3770
Journal of Mineralogy and Geology. see Casopis pro Mineralogii a Geologii **1557**
Journal of Mineralogy, Petrology and Economic Geology. (JA ISSN 0914-9783) **1570**, 3486
Journal of Mines, Metals and Fuels. (II ISSN 0022-2755) **3486**, 3411
▼Journal of Ministry in Addiction & Recovery. (US ISSN 1053-8755) **4185**, 1537
Journal of Minority Aging. (US) **2275**, 2010, 4410
Journal of Minority Literature. see Minzu Wenxue **2939**
Journal of Mississippi History. (US ISSN 0022-2771) **2411**
Journal of Modern African Studies. (UK ISSN 0022-278X) **3901**, 675
Journal of Modern Greek Studies. (US ISSN 0738-1727) **2371**, 2010
Journal of Modern Hellenism. (US ISSN 0743-7749) **2010**, 2371
Journal of Modern History. (US ISSN 0022-2801) **2315**
Journal of Modern Optics. (UK ISSN 0950-0340) **3854**
Journal of Molecular and Cellular Cardiology. (UK ISSN 0022-2828) **3210**
Journal of Molecular Biology. (UK ISSN 0022-2836) **525**
Journal of Molecular Catalysis. (SZ ISSN 0304-5102) **1228**
Journal of Molecular Electronics see Advanced Materials for Optics and Electronics **1211**
Journal of Molecular Evolution. (US ISSN 0022-2844) **545**
Journal of Molecular Graphics. (US ISSN 0263-7855) **1422**, 554
Journal of Molecular Liquids. (NE ISSN 0167-7322) **1228**
Journal of Molecular Neuroscience. (US ISSN 0895-8696) **3342**, 554
Journal of Molecular Recognition. (UK ISSN 0952-3499) **479**
Journal of Molecular Spectroscopy. (US ISSN 0022-2852) **3854**, 1206
Journal of Molecular Structure. (NE ISSN 0022-2860) **1181**
Journal of Molecular Structure: Theochem. (NE ISSN 0166-1280) **1181**

Journal of Molluscan Studies. (UK ISSN 0260-1230) **586**
Journal of Monetary Economics. (NE ISSN 0304-3932) **788**
Journal of Money, Credit & Banking. (US ISSN 0022-2879) **788**
Journal of Moral Education. (UK ISSN 0305-7240) **3770**
Journal of Mormon History. (US ISSN 0094-7342) **4284**
Journal of Morphology. (US ISSN 0362-2525) **444**, 3117
Journal of Motor Behavior. (US ISSN 0022-2895) **4031**, 1643
Journal of Motor Vehicle Law. (CN ISSN 0840-7754) **2640**, 4652
Journal of Motorcycle Technology. *see* Motuoche Jishu **4697**
▼Journal of Multi-Criteria Decision Analysis. (UK ISSN 1057-9214) **1017**
Journal of Multicultural Counseling and Development. (US ISSN 0883-8534) **4031**, 1067, 2010
Journal of Multicultural Librarianship *see* MultiCultural Review **4443**
▼Journal of Multicultural Social Work. (US ISSN 1042-8224) **4440**
Journal of Multilingual & Multicultural Development. (UK ISSN 0143-4632) **2821**, 1722, 4440
▼Journal of Multinational Financial Management. (US ISSN 1042-444X) **915**, 1017
Journal of Multivariate Analysis. (US ISSN 0047-259X) **3041**
▼Journal of Muscle Foods. (US ISSN 1046-0756) **2075**, 3608
Journal of Muscle Research and Cell Motility. (UK ISSN 0142-4319) **3117**, 573, 3372
Journal of Muscle Shoals History. (US ISSN 0094-8039) **2411**
Journal of Musculoskeletal Medicine. (US ISSN 0899-2517) **3309**, 3369, 3372
▼Journal of Musculoskeletal Pain. (US ISSN 1058-2452) **3309**, 3215, 3369
Journal of Museums & Archaeology. *see* Wen Bo **3535**
Journal of Music Scores *see* S C I Journal of Music Scores **3579**
Journal of Music Theory. (US ISSN 0022-2909) **3559**
Journal of Music Therapy. (US ISSN 0022-2917) **3559**, 1737
Journal of Musicological Research. (US ISSN 0141-1896) **3559**
Journal of Musicology. (US ISSN 0277-9269) **3559**
Journal of Mycology *see* Mycologia **510**
Journal of N I H Research. (National Institutes of Health) (US ISSN 1043-609X) **3117**
▼Journal of Narrative and Life History. (US ISSN 1053-6981) **2928**
Journal of Narrative Technique. (US ISSN 0022-2925) **2928**
Journal of Natal and Zulu History. (SA) **2333**
Journal of National Cultures *see* San Yue San **2956**
Journal of National Defense. *see* Shin Boei Ronshu **3471**
Journal of Natural & Physical Sciences. (II ISSN 0970-3799) **4318**, 1546
Journal of Natural History. (UK ISSN 0022-2933) **444**
Journal of Natural Hygiene. (US ISSN 0884-0946) **4106**
Journal of Natural Products. (US ISSN 0163-3864) **3732**
Journal of Natural Resources. *see* Ziran Ziyuan Xuebao **1549**
Journal of Natural Rubber Research. (MY ISSN 0127-7065) **4292**
Journal of Natural Science. (JA ISSN 0075-4307) **4318**
Journal of Natural Sciences and Mathematics. (PK ISSN 0022-2941) **4318**, 1181, 3041, 3822
Journal of Navigation. (UK ISSN 0373-4633) **4730**, 57
Journal of Near-Death Studies. (US ISSN 0891-4494) **4031**

Journal of Near Eastern Studies. (US ISSN 0022-2968) **276**, 2821
Journal of Negro Education. (US ISSN 0022-2984) **1643**, 2010
Journal of Nematology. (US ISSN 0022-300X) **586**
Journal of Nervous and Mental Disease.(US ISSN 0022-3018) **3342**
Journal of Network Management. (US ISSN 1041-8334) **1427**
†Journal of Neural Network Computing. (US ISSN 1049-2976) **5222**
Journal of Neural Transmission. (US ISSN 0300-9564) **3342**
Journal of Neural Transmission. Supplement. (US ISSN 0303-6995) **3342**
Journal of Neuro-Oncology. (US ISSN 0167-594X) **3199**
Journal of Neurobiology. (US ISSN 0022-3034) **573**, 3342
Journal of Neurochemistry. (US ISSN 0022-3042) **479**, 3342
Journal of Neurocytology. (UK ISSN 0300-4864) **525**
Journal of Neuroendocrinology. (UK ISSN 0953-8194) **3342**, 3254
Journal of Neurogenetics. (US ISSN 0167-7063) **3342**
▼Journal of Neuroimaging. (US ISSN 1051-2284) **3342**, 3359
Journal of Neuroimmunology. (NE ISSN 0165-5728) **3342**, 3187
Journal of Neurolinguistics. (US ISSN 0911-6044) **3342**, 2821
Journal of Neurologic Rehabilitation. (US ISSN 0888-4390) **3342**
Journal of Neurological and Orthopaedic Medicine & Surgery. (US ISSN 0890-6599) **3380**, 3309
Journal of Neurological Sciences *see* Journal of Neurosurgical Sciences **3380**
Journal of Neurology/Zeitschrift fuer Neurologie. (GW ISSN 0340-5354) **3342**
Journal of Neurology, Neurosurgery and Psychiatry. (UK ISSN 0022-3050) **3342**, 3380
Journal of Neuropathology and Experimental Neurology. (US ISSN 0022-3069) **3342**
Journal of Neuropathology and Psychiatry. S.S. Korsakov. *see* Zhurnal Nevropatologii i Psikhiatrii im. S.S. Korsakova **3356**
Journal of Neurophysiology. (US ISSN 0022-3077) **573**, 3342
Journal of Neuropsychiatry and Clinical Neurosciences. (US ISSN 0895-0172) **3342**
Journal of Neuroradiology - Journal de Neuroradiologie. (FR ISSN 0150-9861) **3359**
Journal of Neuroscience. (US ISSN 0270-6474) **3342**
Journal of Neuroscience Methods. (NE ISSN 0165-0270) **3343**
Journal of Neuroscience Nursing. (US ISSN 0888-0395) **3280**
Journal of Neuroscience Research. (US ISSN 0360-4012) **3343**
Journal of Neurosurgery. (US ISSN 0022-3085) **3343**, 3380
Journal of Neurosurgical Anesthesiology. (US ISSN 0898-4921) **3191**, 3380
Journal of Neurosurgical Problems. *see* Voprosy Neirokhirurgii **3386**
Journal of Neurosurgical Sciences. (IT) **3380**, 3343
Journal of Neurotrauma. (US ISSN 0897-7151) **3309**, 3343
Journal of New Generation Computer Systems. (GW ISSN 0863-0445) **1441**
Journal of New Jersey Poets. (US ISSN 0363-4205) **2996**
▼Journal of New York Taxation. (US) **1099**
Journal of New Zealand Literature. (NZ ISSN 0112-1227) **2928**
Journal of Newspaper and Periodical History. (US ISSN 0265-5942) **4130**, 2766
Journal of Nichiren Buddhism. (US) **4215**

Journal of Non-Crystalline Solids. (NE ISSN 0022-3093) **3822**
Journal of Non-Equilibrium Thermodynamics. (GW ISSN 0340-0204) **3841**
Journal of Non-Newtonian Fluid Mechanics. (NE ISSN 0377-0257) **3843**
Journal of Non-White Concerns in Personnel and Guidance *see* Journal of Multicultural Counseling and Development **4031**
Journal of Nondestructive Evaluation. (US ISSN 0195-9298) **1919**
▼Journal of Nonlinear Biology. (US) **486**, 479, 3041
▼Journal of Nonlinear Science. (US ISSN 0938-8974) **3822**
Journal of Nonmetals and Semiconductors *see* Semiconductors and Insulators **1778**
Journal of Nonprofit & Public Sector Marketing. (US ISSN 1049-5142) **1043**
Journal of Nonverbal Behavior. (US ISSN 0191-5886) **4031**
Journal of Northeast Asian Studies. (US ISSN 0738-7997) **2339**
Journal of Northern Luzon. (PH ISSN 0115-2408) **4440**, 243, 1643, 2315
Journal of Northern Occupational Health. *see* Hoppo Sangyo Eisei **3617**
Journal of Northwest Atlantic Fishery Science. (CN ISSN 0250-6408) **2045**
Journal of Notarial Acts and Recordkeeping Practices. (US) **2640**
Journal of Nuclear Agriculture and Biology. (II ISSN 0379-5489) **183**, 444, 1806
Journal of Nuclear Biology and Medicine. (IT) **3359**, 444
Journal of Nuclear Chemistry and Radio Chemistry. *see* He-Huaxue yu Fangshe Huaxue **1805**
Journal of Nuclear Materials. (NE ISSN 0022-3115) **3848**, 1828
Journal of Nuclear Materials Management. (US ISSN 0893-6188) **1806**
Journal of Nuclear Medicine. (US ISSN 0161-5505) **3359**
Journal of Nuclear Medicine and Allied Sciences *see* Journal of Nuclear Biology and Medicine **3359**
Journal of Nuclear Medicine Technology.(US ISSN 0091-4916) **3360**
Journal of Nuclear Science and Technology/Nihon Genshiryoku Gakkai Obun Ronbunshi. (JA ISSN 0022-3131) **3848**, 1828
Journal of Number Theory. (US ISSN 0022-314X) **3042**
▼Journal of Numerical Linear Algebra with Applications. (SI ISSN 0129-3281) **3042**
Journal of Nurse-Midwifery. (US ISSN 0091-2182) **3294**, 3280
Journal of Nursing/Hu Li Tsa Chih. (CH ISSN 0047-262X) **3280**
Journal of Nursing Administration. (US ISSN 0002-0443) **3280**
Journal of Nursing Care *see* Licensed Practical Nurse **3281**
Journal of Nursing Education. (US ISSN 0022-3158) **3280**, 1710
Journal of Nursing Quality Assurance. (US ISSN 0889-4647) **3280**
Journal of Nursing Staff Development. (US ISSN 0882-0627) **3280**
Journal of Nutrition. (US ISSN 0022-3166) **3608**
Journal of Nutrition. *see* Yingyang Xuebao **3613**
Journal of Nutrition Education. (US ISSN 0022-3182) **3608**
Journal of Nutrition for the Elderly. (US ISSN 0163-9366) **2275**, 3608
Journal of Nutrition, Growth and Cancer. (US ISSN 0736-8283) **3608**, 3117
▼Journal of Nutrition in Recipe & Menu Development. (US ISSN 1055-1379) **3608**

Journal of Nutritional Biochemistry. (US ISSN 0955-2863) **3608**
▼Journal of Nutritional Immunology. (US ISSN 1049-5150) **3187**, 3608
▼Journal of Nutritional Medicine. (UK ISSN 0955-6664) **3608**
Journal of Nutritional Science and Vitaminology. (JA ISSN 0301-4800) **3608**
Journal of Nutritional Sciences. *see* Zeitschrift fuer Ernaehrungswissenschaft **3613**
†Journal of Obesity and Weight Regulation. (US ISSN 0731-4361) **5222**
Journal of Object-Oriented Programming. (US ISSN 0896-8438) **1431**
Journal of Obstetric, Gynecologic and Neonatal Nursing *see* J O G N N **3279**
Journal of Obstetrics and Gynaecology of India. (II ISSN 0022-3190) **3294**
Journal of Obstetrics and Gynaecology of the British Commonwealth *see* British Journal of Obstetrics & Gynaecology **3290**
Journal of Obstetrics and Gynecology of the Republic of China. (CH) **3294**
Journal of Occupational Accidents and Safety Science **3621**
Journal of Occupational and Organizational Psychology. (UK ISSN 0963-1798) **4031**
Journal of Occupational Behaviour *see* Journal of Organizational Behaviour **4031**
Journal of Occupational Health and Safety: Australia and New Zealand. (AT ISSN 0815-6409) **3618**
Journal of Occupational Medicine. (US ISSN 0096-1736) **3117**, 3618
Journal of Occupational Psychology *see* Journal of Occupational and Organizational Psychology **4031**
▼Journal of Occupational Rehabilitation. (US ISSN 1053-0487) **3118**
Journal of Oceanography. (JA ISSN 0916-8370) **1607**
Journal of Ocular Pharmacology. (US ISSN 8756-3320) **3302**, 2275, 3732
Journal of Offender Counseling *see* Journal of Addictions & Offender Counseling **1516**
Journal of Offender Counseling, Services and Rehabilitation *see* Journal of Offender Rehabilitation **1516**
Journal of Offender Rehabilitation. (US ISSN 1050-9674) **1516**, 4410
Journal of Official Statistics. (SW ISSN 0282-423X) **4576**
Journal of Offshore Mechanics and Arctic Engineering. (US ISSN 0892-7219) **1933**
Journal of Oil and Gas Accountancy *see* Oil & Gas Finance and Accounting **3695**
Journal of Oilseeds Research. (II ISSN 0970-2776) **183**, 507, 535
Journal of Oman Studies. (MK ISSN 0378-8180) **2430**, 4318
Journal of Oman Studies Special Report.(MK ISSN 0379-0703) **2430**, 4318
Journal of Oncology. *see* Deutsche Zeitschrift fuer Onkologie **3196**
Journal of One-Name Studies. (UK ISSN 0262-4842) **2156**, 2821, 3984
Journal of Onomastic Studies. *see* Nouvelle Revue d'Onomastique **2832**
Journal of Operating Theatre Male and Female Nurses *see* Interbloc **3279**
Journal of Operations Management. (US ISSN 0272-6963) **1017**
Journal of Operative Dentistry *see* Operative Dentistry **3239**
Journal of Operator Theory. (RM) **3042**
Journal of Ophthalmic Nursing & Technology. (US ISSN 0744-7132) **3280**, 3302
Journal of Optical Communication. (GW ISSN 0173-4911) **1339**

Journal of Optics/Nouvelle Revue d'Optique. (FR ISSN 0150-536X) **3854**
Journal of Optics. (II ISSN 0970-0374) **3854**
Journal of Optimization Theory and Applications. (US ISSN 0022-3239) **3062**
Journal of Optometric Education see Optometric Education **3304**
Journal of Optometric Vision Development. (US ISSN 0149-886X) **3302**
Journal of Oral and Maxillofacial Surgery. (US ISSN 0278-2391) **3236**, 3380
Journal of Oral Implantology. (US ISSN 0160-6972) **3236**
Journal of Oral Pathology see Journal of Oral Pathology & Medicine **3236**
Journal of Oral Pathology & Medicine. (DK ISSN 0904-2512) **3236**
Journal of Oral Rehabilitation. (UK ISSN 0305-182X) **3236**
Journal of Oral Surgery see Journal of Oral and Maxillofacial Surgery **3236**
Journal of Organic Chemistry. (US ISSN 0022-3263) **1219**
Journal of Organic Chemistry of the U S S R. (English translation of: Zhurnal Organicheskoi Khimii) (US ISSN 0022-3271) **1219**
Journal of Organizational Behavior Management. (US ISSN 0160-8061) **4031**
Journal of Organizational Behaviour. (UK ISSN 0894-3796) **4031**, 4440
Journal of Organizational Change Management. (UK ISSN 0953-4814) **1017**
▼Journal of Organizational Computing. (US ISSN 1054-1721) **827**
Journal of Organometallic Chemistry. (SZ ISSN 0022-328X) **1219**
Journal of Organometallic Chemistry Library. (NE) **1181**
Journal of Orgonomy. (US ISSN 0022-3298) **3343**, 3822
Journal of Oriental Research. (II ISSN 0022-3301) **3639**
Journal of Oriental Studies. (HK ISSN 0022-331X) **3639**
Journal of Orthomolecular Medicine. (CN) **3343**
Journal of Orthomolecular Psychiatry see Journal of Orthomolecular Medicine **3343**
Journal of Orthopaedic and Sports Physical Therapy. (US ISSN 0190-6011) **3372**, 3118, 3309, 4477
Journal of Orthopaedic Research. (US ISSN 0736-0266) **3309**
Journal of Orthopaedic Rheumatology. (UK ISSN 0951-9580) **3369**, 3309
Journal of Orthopaedic Surgery. (FR) **3309**
Journal of Orthopaedic Trauma. (US ISSN 0890-5339) **3309**
Journal of Orthopedic Surgical Techniques. (UK ISSN 0334-0236) **3380**, 3309
Journal of Osteopathic Medicine. (US) **3309**
Journal of Osteopathic Sports Medicine. (US ISSN 0893-3871) **3372**
Journal of Otolaryngology. (CN ISSN 0381-6605) **3315**
Journal of Otolaryngology. (AT) **3315**
Journal of Otolaryngology of Japan/Nihon Jibi Inkoka Gakkai Kaiho. (JA ISSN 0030-6622) **3315**
†Journal of Our Time. (CN ISSN 0381-6524) **5222**
Journal of Outdoor Education. (US ISSN 0022-3336) **1643**
Journal of Pacific History. (AT ISSN 0022-3344) **2345**
Journal of Pacific Studies. (FJ ISSN 1011-3029) **4378**
Journal of Packaging Technology. (US ISSN 0892-029X) **3649**
Journal of Paediatric Dentistry see International Journal of Paediatric Dentistry **3235**
Journal of Paediatrics and Child Health.(AT ISSN 1034-4810) **3322**

Journal of Paediatrics, Obstetrics and Gynaecology. (HK) **3294**, 3322
Journal of Pain and Symptom Management. (US ISSN 0885-3924) **3191**, 573, 3280
Journal of Paleolimnology. (NE ISSN 0921-2728) **3658**, 444, 1961
Journal of Paleontology. (US ISSN 0022-3360) **3658**
Journal of Palestine Studies. (US ISSN 0377-919X) **2430**
Journal of Palestine Studies. see Majallat al-Dirasat al-Filastiniyya **2430**
Journal of Palliative Care. (CN ISSN 0825-8597) **3118**, 2466
Journal of Palynology. (II ISSN 0022-3379) **507**, 102
Journal of Pan African Studies. (US ISSN 0888-6601) **4378**, 2010, 3770, 3901
Journal of Parallel and Distributed Computing. (US ISSN 0743-7315) **1397**
Journal of Parametrics. (US ISSN 1015-7891) **753**, 3042
Journal of Parapsychology. (US ISSN 0022-3387) **3669**
Journal of Parasitology. (US ISSN 0022-3395) **3221**, 554
Journal of Parenteral and Enteral Nutrition. (US) **3608**
Journal of Parenteral Science and Technology. (US ISSN 0279-7976) **3732**
Journal of Park and Recreation Administration. (US ISSN 0735-1968) **4549**, 1017, 1490
Journal of Partial Differential Equations.(US ISSN 1000-940X) **3042**
Journal of Partnership Taxation. (US ISSN 0749-4513) **1099**
Journal of Pascal, Ada, & Modula-2. (US ISSN 0747-1351) **1431**
Journal of Pascal and Ada see Journal of Pascal, Ada, & Modula-2 **1431**
Journal of Pastoral Care. (US ISSN 0022-3409) **4185**, 4031
Journal of Pastoral Practice. (US ISSN 0196-9072) **4185**
Journal of Pastoral Psychotherapy see Journal of Religion in Psychotherapy **4185**
Journal of Pathology. (UK ISSN 0022-3417) **3118**
Journal of Peace & Justice Studies. (US) **3902**
Journal of Peace Research. (UK ISSN 0022-3433) **3963**
Journal of Peasant Studies. (UK ISSN 0306-6150) **4440**, 675
Journal of Pedagogics. see Pedagogiekjoernaal **1654**
Journal of Pediatric & Perinatal Nutrition. (US ISSN 8756-6206) **3322**, 3294, 3608
Journal of Pediatric Endocrinology. (UK ISSN 0334-018X) **3254**, 3322
Journal of Pediatric Endocrinology. (IS) **3254**, 3322
Journal of Pediatric Gastroenterology and Nutrition. (US ISSN 0277-2116) **3269**, 3322, 3608
Journal of Pediatric Health Care (Philadelphia). (US) **3322**
Journal of Pediatric Health Care (St. Louis). (US ISSN 0891-5245) **3322**
Journal of Pediatric Nursing. (US ISSN 0882-5963) **3280**, 3322
Journal of Pediatric Ophthalmology see Journal of Pediatric Ophthalmology and Strabismus **3302**
Journal of Pediatric Ophthalmology and Strabismus. (US ISSN 0191-3913) **3302**
Journal of Pediatric Orthopedics. (US ISSN 0271-6798) **3309**, 3322
Journal of Pediatric Psychology. (US ISSN 0146-8693) **4031**
Journal of Pediatric Surgery. (US ISSN 0022-3468) **3380**, 3294, 3322
Journal of Pediatrics. (US ISSN 0022-3476) **3322**
Journal of Pediatrics for the New-born. see Xinsheng Erke Zazhi **3327**
Journal of Pedodontics see Journal of Clinical Pediatric Dentistry **3235**

Journal of Pension Planning and Compliance. (US ISSN 0148-2181) **1099**, 984
Journal of Performance of Constructed Facilities. (US ISSN 0887-3828) **1870**
Journal of Perinatal and Neonatal Nursing. (US ISSN 0893-2190) **3280**
Journal of Perinatal Medicine. (GW ISSN 0300-5577) **3294**
Journal of Perinatology. (US ISSN 0743-8346) **3294**, 3322
Journal of Periodontal Research. (DK ISSN 0022-3484) **3236**
†Journal of Periodontal Research. Supplementum. (DK ISSN 0075-4331) **5222**
Journal of Periodontology. (US ISSN 0022-3492) **3237**
Journal of Personality. (US ISSN 0022-3506) **4031**
Journal of Personality and Clinical Studies. (II ISSN 0970-1206) **4031**
Journal of Personality and Social Psychology. (US ISSN 0022-3514) **4031**
Journal of Personality Assessment. (US ISSN 0022-3891) **4031**
Journal of Personality Disorders. (US ISSN 0885-579X) **4031**
Journal of Personnel Evaluation in Education. (US ISSN 0920-525X) **1643**, 1067
Journal of Pesticide Reform. (US ISSN 0893-357X) **1961**, 4106
Journal of Pesticide Science. (JA ISSN 0385-1559) **4106**, 183
Journal of Petroleum Geology. (UK ISSN 0141-6421) **3690**
Journal of Petroleum Marketing. (US) **3691**
Journal of Petroleum Research. (IQ ISSN 1012-3369) **3691**
Journal of Petroleum Science and Engineering. (NE ISSN 0920-4105) **3691**, 1570, 1828
Journal of Petroleum Technology see J P T: Journal of Petroleum Technology **3690**
Journal of Petrology. (UK ISSN 0022-3530) **1570**
Journal of Pharmaceutical and Biomedical Analysis. (US ISSN 0731-7085) **3732**
Journal of Pharmaceutical and Medical Sciences. (NR ISSN 0331-0604) **3732**, 3118
▼Journal of Pharmaceutical Care in Pain & Symptom Control. (US ISSN 1056-4950) **3732**
Journal of Pharmaceutical Marketing and Management. (US ISSN 0883-7597) **3732**, 1017, 1043
▼Journal of Pharmaceutical Medicine. (UK ISSN 0958-0581) **3732**
Journal of Pharmaceutical Science and Technology/Yakuzaigaku. (JA ISSN 0372-7629) **3732**
Journal of Pharmaceutical Sciences. (US ISSN 0022-3549) **3732**
Journal of Pharmacobio-Dynamics. (JA ISSN 0386-846X) **3732**, 479
Journal of Pharmacoepidemiology. (US ISSN 0896-6966) **3732**, 4106
Journal of Pharmacokinetics and Biopharmaceutics. (US ISSN 0090-466X) **3732**
Journal of Pharmacologic Analysis. see Yaowu Fenxi Zazhi **3746**
Journal of Pharmacological and Toxicological Methods. (US ISSN 1056-8719) **1982**, 479
Journal of Pharmacological Methods see Journal of Pharmacological and Toxicological Methods **1982**
Journal of Pharmacology. see Farmacoterapia **3726**
Journal of Pharmacology and Experimental Therapeutics. (US ISSN 0022-3565) **3733**
Journal of Pharmacology and Immunotoxicology see Journal of Pharmacology and Immunopharmacology and Immunotoxicology **3728**
Journal of Pharmacy and Pharmacology. (UK ISSN 0022-3573) **3733**

▼Journal of Pharmacy Teaching. (US ISSN 1044-0054) **3733**, 1753
Journal of Pharmacy Technology. (US ISSN 8755-1225) **3733**
Journal of Phase Equilibria. (US ISSN 1054-9714) **3411**
Journal of Phenomenological Psychology. (US ISSN 0047-2662) **4032**
Journal of Phi Rho Sigma see Phi Rho Sigma. Journal **1321**
Journal of Philippine Development. (PH ISSN 0115-9143) **1099**, 153, 837
Journal of Philippine Librarianship. (PH ISSN 0022-359X) **2766**
Journal of Philippine Statistics. (PH ISSN 0022-3603) **4576**
Journal of Philology. see Listy Filologicke **2827**
Journal of Philosophical Logic. (NE ISSN 0022-3611) **3770**
Journal of Philosophical Research. (US ISSN 1053-8364) **3770**
Journal of Philosophy. (US ISSN 0022-362X) **3770**
Journal of Philosophy of Education. (UK ISSN 0309-8249) **3770**
Journal of Phonetics. (UK ISSN 0095-4470) **2821**
Journal of Photochemistry see Journal of Photochemistry and Photobiology, A: Chemistry **1228**
Journal of Photochemistry and Photobiology, A: Chemistry. (SZ ISSN 1010-6030) **1228**, 3792
Journal of Photochemistry and Photobiology, B: Biology. (SZ ISSN 1011-1344) **479**
Journal of Photographic Science. (UK ISSN 0022-3638) **3792**
Journal of Phycology. (US ISSN 0022-3646) **507**
Journal of Physical and Chemical Reference Data. (US ISSN 0047-2689) **1181**, 3822
Journal of Physical Chemistry. (US ISSN 0022-3654) **1228**
Journal of Physical Education, Recreation and Dance. (US ISSN 0730-3084) **4477**, 1753
Journal of Physical Oceanography. (US ISSN 0022-3670) **1607**
Journal of Physical Organic Chemistry. (UK ISSN 0894-3230) **1228**, 1219
Journal of Physics A: Mathematical and General. (UK ISSN 0305-4470) **3822**
Journal of Physics and Chemistry of Niigata. see Niigata Rikagaku **3825**
Journal of Physics B: Atomic, Molecular and Optical Physics. (UK ISSN 0953-4075) **3822**
Journal of Physics, Chemistry and Earth Science. see Rikagakkaishi **4336**
Journal of Physics: Condensed Matter. (UK ISSN 0953-8984) **3822**
Journal of Physics D: Applied Physics. (UK ISSN 0022-3727) **3822**, 1828
Journal of Physics E: Scientific Instruments see Measurement Science and Technology **2524**
Journal of Physics Engineering/Fizik Muhendisligi Dergisi. (TU) **3823**, 1828
Journal of Physics F: Metal Physics see Journal of Physics: Condensed Matter **3822**
Journal of Physics G: Nuclear and Particle Physics. (UK ISSN 0954-3899) **3848**, 3823
Journal of Physics G: Nuclear Physics see Journal of Physics G: Nuclear and Particle Physics **3848**
Journal of Physics and Chemistry of Solids. (US ISSN 0022-3697) **3823**, 1181
Journal of Physics of the Earth. (JA ISSN 0022-3743) **1591**
Journal of Physiology. (UK ISSN 0022-3751) **573**, 3118
Journal of Phytopathology/Phytopathologische Zeitschrift. (GW ISSN 0931-1785) **507**
Journal of Pidgin and Creole Languages. (NE ISSN 0920-9034) **2821**

Journal of Pineal Research. (DK ISSN 0742-3098) **3343**
Journal of Place Names. *see* Diming Congkan **2246**
Journal of Planar Chromatography - Modern T L C. (GW ISSN 0933-4173) **1206**, **1228**, **3733**
Journal of Plankton Research. (UK ISSN 0142-7873) **444**, **1607**
Journal of Planning. *see* Zeitschrift fuer Planung **701**
Journal of Planning and Environment Law. (UK ISSN 0307-4870) **2640**, **1961**, **2490**
Journal of Planning Education and Research. (US ISSN 0739-456X) **2490**
Journal of Planning Literature. (US ISSN 0885-4122) **2490**
Journal of Plant Anatomy and Morphology. (II ISSN 0256-436X) **507**
Journal of Plant and Machinery. (II ISSN 0449-5721) **3019**
Journal of Plant Foods *see* Food Science **3606**
Journal of Plant Growth Regulation. (US ISSN 0721-7595) **507**
Journal of Plant Nutrition. (US ISSN 0190-4167) **507**
Journal of Plant Nutrition and Soil Science. *see* Zeitschrift fuer Pflanzenernaehrung und Bodenkunde **468**
Journal of Plant Physiology. (GW ISSN 0176-1617) **508**
Journal of Plantation Crops. (II ISSN 0304-5242) **183**
Journal of Plasma Physics. (UK ISSN 0022-3778) **3823**
Journal of Plastic Film and Sheeting. (US ISSN 8756-0879) **3863**
Journal of Poetry Therapy. (US ISSN 0889-3675) **2996**, **4032**
Journal of Police and Criminal Psychology. (US ISSN 0882-0783) **1516**
Journal of Police Science and Administration. (US ISSN 0090-9084) **1516**
Journal of Policy Analysis and Management. (US ISSN 0276-8739) **4065**, **3902**
Journal of Policy History. (US ISSN 0898-0306) **2411**
Journal of Policy Modeling. (US ISSN 0161-8938) **3902**
Journal of Polish Science. (PL) **4318**
Journal of Political Economy. (US ISSN 0022-3808) **675**, **3902**
Journal of Political Economy. *see* Keizaigaku Kenkyu **676**
Journal of Political Economy. *see* Politicka Ekonomie **685**
Journal of Political Science. (PK) **3902**, **2339**
Journal of Political Science (Clemson). (US ISSN 0098-4612) **3902**
Journal of Political Studies. (II ISSN 0047-2700) **3902**
Journal of Politics. (US ISSN 0022-3816) **3902**
Journal of Polygraph Science. (US) **1516**
Journal of Polymer Engineering. (IS ISSN 0334-6447) **1855**
Journal of Polymer Materials. (II ISSN 0970-0838) **1219**
Journal of Polymer Science. Part A: Polymer Chemistry. (US ISSN 0887-624X) **1219**
Journal of Polymer Science. Part B: Polymer Physics. (US ISSN 0887-6266) **1219**
Journal of Polymer Science. Part C: Polymer Letters *see* Journal of Polymer Science. Part B: Polymer Physics **1219**
Journal of Polymer Science. Part C: Polymer Letters *see* Journal of Polymer Science. Part A: Polymer Chemistry **1219**
Journal of Polymer Science. Polymer Chemistry Edition *see* Journal of Polymer Science. Part A: Polymer Chemistry **1219**

Journal of Polymer Science. Polymer Physics Edition *see* Journal of Polymer Science. Part B: Polymer Physics **1219**
Journal of Polymer Science. Polymer Symposia Edition. (US ISSN 0360-8905) **1219**
Journal of Polymorphous Perversity. (US ISSN 0737-1195) **4032**, **3343**
Journal of Popular Culture. (US ISSN 0022-3840) **2928**, **2056**
Journal of Popular Film and Television. (US ISSN 0195-6051) **3512**
Journal of Popular Literature. (US) **2928**
Journal of Population and Health *see* Journal of Population and Health Studies **597**
Journal of Population and Health Studies. (KO) **597**
Journal of Population Economics. (US ISSN 0933-1433) **3984**
Journal of Population Problems. *see* Jinko Mondai Kenkyu **3984**
Journal of Population Research *see* Health and Population: Perspectives and Issues **596**
Journal of Portfolio Management. (US ISSN 0095-4918) **953**
Journal of Post Anesthesia Nursing. (US ISSN 0883-9433) **3280**, **3191**
Journal of Post Keynesian Economics. (US ISSN 0160-3477) **871**
Journal of Postgraduate Medicine. (II ISSN 0022-3859) **3118**
Journal of Potassium Research. (II ISSN 0257-4993) **3411**
Journal of Potatoes. *see* Malingshu Zazhi **184**
Journal of Powder & Bulk Solids Technology. (UK ISSN 0147-698X) **1856**
Journal of Power Sources. (SZ ISSN 0378-7753) **1901**
Journal of Power Sources Technology *see* Dianyuan Jishu **1885**
Journal of Practical Approaches to Developmental Handicap. (CN ISSN 0707-7807) **1737**, **1239**
Journal of Practical Civil Defence. (UK ISSN 0264-4525) **1273**
Journal of Practical Diabetes. (JA ISSN 0289-4947) **3254**
Journal of Practical Gynecology and Obstetrics. *see* Shiyong Fuke yu Chanke Zazhi **3296**
Journal of Practical Internal Medicine. *see* Shiyong Neike Zazhi **3153**
Journal of Practical Nursing. (US ISSN 0022-3867) **3280**
Journal of Practical Pediatrics. *see* Shiyong Erke Zazhi **3326**
Journal of Practical Surgery. *see* Shiyong Waike Zazhi **3384**
Journal of Pragmatics. (NE ISSN 0378-2166) **2821**, **1339**, **1409**
†Journal of Pre-Raphaelite & Aesthetic Studies. (CN ISSN 0835-7099) **5222**
Journal of Prehistoric Religion. (SW ISSN 0283-8486) **276**, **1277**
Journal of Prehospital Medicine *see* Prehospital and Disaster Medicine **3143**
Journal of Pressure Vessel Technology. (US ISSN 0094-9930) **1933**
Journal of Prevention *see* Journal of Primary Prevention **4032**
Journal of Preventive and Social Medicine *see* J O P S O M **4105**
†Journal of Preventive Psychiatry and Allied Disciplines. (US ISSN 1049-6343) **5222**
▼Journal of Pricing Management. (US) **1043**
Journal of Primary Prevention. (US ISSN 0278-095X) **4032**
Journal of Prison and Jail Health. (US ISSN 0731-8332) **3118**, **1516**
Journal of Private Enterprise. (US ISSN 0890-913X) **1643**
▼Journal of Process Control. (UK ISSN 0959-1524) **1452**
Journal of Product Innovation Management. (US ISSN 0737-6782) **1079**
Journal of Production Agriculture. (US) **102**

Journal of Productivity Analysis. (US ISSN 0895-562X) **1079**
Journal of Products Liability. (US ISSN 0363-0404) **2640**, **1828**, **3118**
Journal of Professional Issues in Engineering *see* Journal of Professional Issues in Engineering and Practice **1870**
Journal of Professional Issues in Engineering and Practice. (US ISSN 1052-3928) **1870**
Journal of Professional Nursing. (US ISSN 8755-7223) **3280**
Journal of Professional Services Marketing. (US ISSN 0748-4623) **1043**
▼Journal of Programming Language Design and Implementation. (UK ISSN 0963-9306) **1431**
Journal of Progressive Human Services.(US ISSN 1042-8232) **4410**, **3902**
Journal of Projective Techniques and Personality Assessment *see* Journal of Personality Assessment **4031**
▼Journal of Promotion Management. (US ISSN 1049-6491) **33**, **1017**
▼Journal of Property Finance. (UK ISSN 0958-868X) **4151**
Journal of Property Management. (US ISSN 0022-3905) **4151**
Journal of Property Tax Management. (US ISSN 1041-4797) **1099**
Journal of Property Valuation and Investment. (UK) **4151**
Journal of Propulsion and Power. (US ISSN 0748-4658) **57**
Journal of Propulsion Technology. *see* Tuijin Jishu **63**
Journal of Prosthetic Dentistry. (US ISSN 0022-3913) **3237**
Journal of Prosthetic Dentistry (Edizione Italiana). (IT) **3237**
Journal of Prosthetics and Orthotics. (US ISSN 1040-8800) **3118**
Journal of Protective Coatings and Linings. (US ISSN 8755-1985) **3654**
Journal of Protein Chemistry. (US ISSN 0277-8033) **1219**, **479**
Journal of Protozoology. (US ISSN 0022-3921) **586**
Journal of Psychiatric Education *see* Academic Psychiatry **3327**
Journal of Psychiatric Nursing and Mental Health Services *see* Journal of Psychosocial Nursing and Mental Health Services **3281**
Journal of Psychiatric Research. (US ISSN 0022-3956) **3343**
Journal of Psychiatry and Law. (US ISSN 0093-1853) **2640**, **3343**
Journal of Psychiatry and Neuroscience.(CN ISSN 1180-4882) **3343**
Journal of Psychoactive Drugs. (US ISSN 0279-1072) **1537**, **3343**, **3733**, **4032**
Journal of Psychoanalytic Anthropology *see* Journal of Psychohistory **4032**
Journal of Psychoeducational Assessment. (US ISSN 0734-2829) **4032**, **1737**
Journal of Psychohistory. (US ISSN 0145-3378) **4032**, **2315**
Journal of Psycholinguistic Research. (US ISSN 0090-6905) **2821**, **4032**
Journal of Psychological Researches. (II ISSN 0022-3972) **4032**
Journal of Psychology. (US ISSN 0022-3980) **4032**
Journal of Psychology and Christianity. (US ISSN 0733-4273) **4032**, **4185**
Journal of Psychology & Human Sexuality. (US ISSN 0890-7064) **4032**
Journal of Psychology and Judaism. (US ISSN 0700-9801) **4032**, **4224**
Journal of Psychology and Theology. (US ISSN 0091-6471) **4032**, **4185**
Journal of Psychopathology and Behavioral Assessment. (US ISSN 0882-2689) **4032**
Journal of Psychopharmacology. (UK) **3733**, **4032**

JOURNAL 6355

Journal of Psychophysiology. (GW ISSN 0269-8803) **4032**, **3343**
Journal of Psychosocial Nursing and Mental Health Services. (US ISSN 0279-3695) **3281**, **4410**
Journal of Psychosocial Oncology. (US ISSN 0734-7332) **3199**
Journal of Psychosomatic Obstetrics and Gynaecology. (UK ISSN 0167-482X) **3294**
Journal of Psychosomatic Research. (US ISSN 0022-3999) **3343**
Journal of Psychotherapy and the Family *see* Journal of Family Psychotherapy **4029**
▼Journal of Psychotherapy Integration. (US ISSN 1053-0479) **3343**
▼Journal of Psychotherapy Practice and Research. (US ISSN 1055-050X) **3343**
Journal of Public Communication and Membership Directory *see* G C Government Communications **2570**
Journal of Public Economics. (SZ ISSN 0047-2727) **675**
Journal of Public Finance and Public Choice. *see* Economia delle Scelte Pubbliche **1093**
Journal of Public Health Dentistry. (US ISSN 0022-4006) **3237**, **4106**
Journal of Public Health Medicine. (UK ISSN 0957-4832) **4410**, **4106**
Journal of Public Health Policy. (US ISSN 0197-5897) **4106**, **1537**, **2466**
Journal of Public Health Practice. *see* Koshu Eisei **4107**
Journal of Public Policy. (UK ISSN 0143-814X) **4378**
Journal of Public Policy & Marketing. (US) **1043**
▼Journal of Public Relations Research.(US ISSN 1042-1408) **33**
Journal of Pulp & Paper Science. (CN ISSN 0826-6220) **3663**
Journal of Purchasing and Materials Management *see* International Journal of Purchasing & Materials Management **1042**
Journal of Pure and Applied Algebra. (NE ISSN 0022-4049) **3042**
Journal of Pure and Applied Sciences/Temel ve Uygulamali Bilmler Dergisi. (TU ISSN 0022-4057) **4318**, **4602**
Journal of Pure and Applied Ultrasonics.(II ISSN 0256-4637) **3859**, **486**
Journal of Quality Technology. (US ISSN 0022-4065) **1919**, **1017**
Journal of Quantitative Anthropology. (NE ISSN 0922-2995) **243**, **290**
Journal of Quantitative Criminology. (US ISSN 0748-4518) **1516**
Journal of Quantitative Spectroscopy and Radiative Transfer. (US ISSN 0022-4073) **3854**
Journal of Quaternary Science. (UK ISSN 0267-8179) **4318**, **276**, **444**, **1546**
Journal of Racial Affairs. *see* Tydskrif vir Rasse - Aangeleenthede **4455**
Journal of Radiation Curing *see* Radiation Curing - Journal of Radiation Curing **1186**
Journal of Radiation Research. (JA) **3360**
Journal of Radioanalytical and Nuclear Chemistry *see* Journal of Radioanalytical and Nuclear Chemistry. Articles **1207**
Journal of Radioanalytical and Nuclear Chemistry *see* Journal of Radioanalytical and Nuclear Chemistry. Letters **1207**
Journal of Radioanalytical and Nuclear Chemistry. Articles. (SZ) **1207**
Journal of Radioanalytical and Nuclear Chemistry. Letters. (SZ) **1207**
Journal of Radiological Protection. (UK ISSN 0952-4746) **1806**, **1961**, **3360**
Journal of Radiology and Physical Therapy. *see* Kanazawa Irigaku Sosho **5223**
Journal of Raman Spectroscopy. (UK ISSN 0377-0486) **1207**

Journal of Range Management. (US ISSN 0022-409X) **445**, 102, 1490

Journal of Raptor Research. (US ISSN 0892-1016) **565**

Journal of Rare Earths. (CC ISSN 1002-0721) **3411**

Journal of Rational-Emotive and Cognitive-Behavior Therapy. (US ISSN 0894-9085) **4032**

Journal of Rational-Emotive Therapy see Journal of Rational-Emotive and Cognitive-Behavior Therapy **4032**

Journal of Reading. (US ISSN 0022-4103) **1643**

Journal of Reading Behavior. (US ISSN 0022-4111) **2821**, 1643

Journal of Reading, Writing, and Learning Disabilities International. (US ISSN 0748-7630) **1737**, 1257, 2821

†Journal of Real Estate Development. (US ISSN 0887-5812) **5222**

Journal of Real Estate Finance and Economics. (US ISSN 0895-5638) **4151**, 788, 2490

Journal of Real Estate Research. (US ISSN 0896-5803) **4151**

Journal of Real Estate Taxation. (US ISSN 0093-5107) **4151**, 1099

Journal of Receptor Research. (US ISSN 0197-5110) **3118**

Journal of Reconstructive Microsurgery.(US ISSN 0743-684X) **3381**

Journal of Recreational Mathematics. (US ISSN 0022-412X) **3042**, 4477

Journal of Reform Judaism see C C A R Journal **4222**

Journal of Refractive Surgery see Refractive & Corneal Surgery **3383**

Journal of Refugee Studies. (UK ISSN 0951-6328) **3944**, 3984

Journal of Regional and Local Studies. (UK) **2371**, 4378

Journal of Regional Criticism. (US) **332**, 2870, 3042

Journal of Regional Policy. (IT ISSN 0394-3933) **2726**, 788

Journal of Regional Science. (US ISSN 0022-4146) **2490**

Journal of Regression Therapy. (US ISSN 1054-0830) **4032**, 3595

Journal of Regulatory Economics. (NE ISSN 0922-680X) **871**

Journal of Rehabilitation. (US ISSN 0022-4154) **4410**, 3118

Journal of Rehabilitation Administration.(US ISSN 0148-3846) **1017**, 3118

Journal of Rehabilitation R and D see Journal of Rehabilitation Research and Development **3309**

Journal of Rehabilitation Research and Development. (US ISSN 0748-7711) **3309**, 1828

Journal of Rehabilitation Sciences. see Tijdschrift voor Revalidatiewetenschappen **1742**

Journal of Reinforced Plastics & Composites. (US ISSN 0731-6844) **1919**, 3863

Journal of Religion. (US ISSN 0022-4189) **4185**

Journal of Religion and Aging see Journal of Religious Gerontology **2275**

Journal of Religion and Health. (US ISSN 0022-4197) **4185**

Journal of Religion & Psychical Research. (US ISSN 0731-2148) **3670**, 4185

Journal of Religion and the Applied Behavioral Sciences see Journal for Creative Change **4026**

Journal of Religion in Africa/Religion en Afrique. (NE ISSN 0022-4200) **4185**

Journal of Religion in Psychotherapy. (US ISSN 1045-5876) **4185**

Journal of Religious and Intellectual History. see Zeitschrift fuer Religions- und Geistesgeschichte **4211**

▼Journal of Religious & Theological Information. (US ISSN 1047-7845) **4185**

Journal of Religious Education see Journal of Christian Education of the African Methodist Episcopal Church **4241**

Journal of Religious Education of the African Methodist Episcopal Church see Journal of Christian Education of the African Methodist Episcopal Church **4241**

Journal of Religious Ethics. (US ISSN 0384-9694) **4185**

Journal of Religious Gerontology. (US ISSN 1050-2289) **2275**, 4185

Journal of Religious History. (AT ISSN 0022-4227) **4185**, 2315

The Journal of Religious Studies. (Il ISSN 0047-2735) **4185**

Journal of Religious Studies. (US ISSN 0193-3604) **4185**

Journal of Religious Thought. (US ISSN 0022-4235) **4185**

▼Journal of Renal Nutrition. (US) **3608**, 3388

Journal of Reprints Affecting Women's Rights & Opportunities see Journal of Reprints of Documents Affecting Women **4845**

Journal of Reprints for Antitrust Law & Economics. (US ISSN 0022-4243) **2640**, 675

Journal of Reprints of Documents Affecting Women. (US ISSN 0362-062X) **4845**, 984, 2640

Journal of Reproduction and Development. (JA) **4811**

Journal of Reproduction and Fertility. (UK ISSN 0022-4251) **573**

Journal of Reproduction and Fertility (India). (Il) **445**, 3118

Journal of Reproductive Immunology. (IE ISSN 0165-0378) **3187**, 3294

Journal of Reproductive Medicine. (US ISSN 0024-7758) **3294**

Journal of Research and Development in Education. (US ISSN 0022-426X) **1643**

Journal of Research in Ayurveda and Siddha. (Il) **3118**, 243

Journal of Research in Childhood Education. (US ISSN 0256-8543) **1643**, 1239

Journal of Research in Crime and Delinquency. (US ISSN 0022-4278) **1516**

Journal of Research in Indian Medicine see Journal of Research in Ayurveda and Siddha **3118**

Journal of Research in Music Education.(US ISSN 0022-4294) **3559**, 1753

Journal of Research in Personality. (US ISSN 0092-6566) **4033**

Journal of Research in Pharmaceutical Economics. (US ISSN 0896-6621) **3733**, 871

Journal of Research in Reading. (UK ISSN 0141-0423) **1643**

Journal of Research in Science Teaching. (US ISSN 0022-4308) **4318**, 1643

Journal of Research in Singing see Journal of Research in Singing and Applied Vocal Pedagogy **3559**

Journal of Research in Singing and Applied Vocal Pedagogy. (US) **3559**

▼Journal of Research on Adolescence. (US ISSN 1050-8392) **1239**, 4033

Journal of Research on Computing in Education see Journal of Research on Computing in Teacher Education **1691**

Journal of Research on Computing in Teacher Education. (US) **1691**, 1417

Journal of Research on the Lepidoptera.(US ISSN 0022-4324) **535**

Journal of Research Property. (UK ISSN 0959-9916) **2490**

Journal of Resource Management and Technology. (US ISSN 0745-6999) **1961**

Journal of Respiratory Diseases. (US ISSN 0194-259X) **3365**

▼Journal of Restaurant & Foodservice Marketing. (US ISSN 1052-214X) **2477**, 1043, 2075

Journal of Retail Banking. (US ISSN 0195-2064) **788**

Journal of Retailing. (US ISSN 0022-4359) **1044**

Journal of Rheology. (US ISSN 0148-6055) **3844**

Journal of Rheumatology. (CN ISSN 0315-162X) **3369**

Journal of Risk and Insurance. (US ISSN 0022-4367) **2536**

Journal of Risk and Uncertainty. (US ISSN 0895-5646) **675**, 4033

Journal of Robotic Systems. (US ISSN 0741-2223) **1409**, 1414

Journal of Rock Mechanics and Engineering. see Yanshi Lixue yu Gongcheng Xuebao **3846**

Journal of Roman Archaeology. (US) **276**

Journal of Roman Studies. (UK ISSN 0075-4358) **1277**

Journal of Roman Studies Monograph Series. (UK ISSN 0951-6549) **1277**

Journal of Roofing Technology see International Journal of Roofing Technology **5217**

Journal of Root Crops. (Il ISSN 0378-2409) **183**

Journal of Rural and Small Schools. (US ISSN 0890-9520) **1643**

Journal of Rural Community Psychology. (US ISSN 0276-2285) **4033**

Journal of Rural Cooperation. (IS ISSN 0377-7480) **831**, 153

Journal of Rural Development. (Il ISSN 0970-3357) **3902**, 4441

Journal of Rural Development and Administration (PARD). (PK ISSN 0047-2751) **4065**

Journal of Rural Engineering and Development. see Zeitschrift fuer Kulturtechnik und Landentwicklung **1876**

Journal of Rural Health. (US ISSN 0890-765X) **3118**, 4106, 4441

Journal of Rural Studies. (US ISSN 0743-0167) **4441**, 2254

Journal of Russian and East European Psychiatry. (US) **3343**

Journal of Russian and East European Psychology. (US) **4033**

Journal of Russian Studies see Rusistika **2839**

Journal of Safety Research. (US ISSN 0022-4375) **4652**, 4773

Journal of San Diego History. (US ISSN 0022-4383) **2411**

Journal of School Health. (US ISSN 0022-4391) **4106**, 1643

▼Journal of School Leadership. (US ISSN 1052-6846) **1729**

Journal of School Psychology. (US ISSN 0022-4405) **4033**

Journal of School Psychology. see Psykologisk Paedagogisk Raadgivning **4043**

Journal of Science and Mathematics Education in Southeast Asia. (MY ISSN 0126-7663) **1753**, 3042, 4318

Journal of Science and Technology. (PK) **4318**, 4602

▼Journal of Science Education and Technology. (US ISSN 1059-0145) **1643**, 4318

Journal of Science Education in Japan. see Kagaku Kyoiku Kenkyu **4319**

Journal of Science of Labour. see Rodo Kagaku (Kawasaki, 1924) **3621**

Journal of Science Policy and Research Management. see Kenkyu Gijutsu Keikaku **1017**

Journal of Scientific and Industrial Research. (Il ISSN 0022-4456) **4318**

Journal of Scientific Computing. (US ISSN 0885-7474) **4360**

Journal of Scientific Exploration. (US ISSN 0892-3310) **4318**, 3670

Journal of Scientific Research. (Il ISSN 0253-7230) **586**

Journal of Scientific Research in Plants & Medicines. (Il ISSN 0253-7249) **3733**, 3118, 4318

Journal of Secondary Education see Michigan Association of Secondary School Principals' Bulletin **1648**

Journal of Security Administration. (US ISSN 0195-9425) **1526**

Journal of Security Administration and Private Police see Journal of Security Administration **1526**

Journal of Sedimentary Petrology. (US ISSN 0022-4472) **1546**

Journal of Seed Technology. (US ISSN 0146-3071) **102**

Journal of Seismology. see Dizhen **1588**

Journal of Semantics. (UK ISSN 0167-5133) **2821**, 1409

Journal of Semi-Custom I Cs see Microelectronics Journal **1775**

Journal of Semitic Studies. (UK ISSN 0022-4480) **4224**, 2821, 4219

Journal of Sensory Studies. (US ISSN 0887-8250) **3343**, 2075, 3608

Journal of Separation Process Technology. (UK ISSN 0260-6275) **1856**

Journal of Sericultural Science of Japan/Nippon Sanshigaku Zasshi. (JA ISSN 0037-2455) **535**, 102, 4621

Journal of Services Marketing. (US ISSN 0887-6045) **1044**

Journal of Sex. (UK) **4441**

Journal of Sex & Marital Therapy. (US ISSN 0092-623X) **4033**

Journal of Sex Education and Therapy. (US ISSN 0161-4576) **1643**, 3805, 4033

Journal of Sex Research. (US ISSN 0022-4499) **4033**, 3118, 4441

Journal of Sexual Liberty. (US) **2702**, 2454, 3902

Journal of Shellfish Research. (US ISSN 0730-8000) **586**

Journal of Ship Production. (US ISSN 8756-1417) **4730**

Journal of Ship Research. (US ISSN 0022-4502) **4730**

Journal of Shipping, Customs, and Transport Law. (Il ISSN 0377-0494) **2735**, 4652

▼Journal of Shoulder and Elbow Surgery. (US) **3381**

Journal of Sikh Studies. (Il ISSN 0379-8194) **3640**

Journal of Sinological Studies/ Shinagaku Kenkyu. (JA) **3640**

Journal of Slovenia Medical Society. see Zdravstveni Vestnik **3164**

Journal of Small Animal Practice. (UK ISSN 0022-4510) **4811**

Journal of Small Business - Canada. (CN ISSN 0820-957X) **1115**

▼Journal of Small Business Finance. (US) **1115**, 788

Journal of Small Business Management.(US ISSN 0047-2778) **1116**

▼Journal of Small Exotic Animal Medicine. (US) **4811**

▼Journal of Small Fruit & Viticulture. (US ISSN 1052-0015) **183**

▼Journal of Smoking-Related Disorders. (UK ISSN 0959-2431) **3118**

Journal of Smooth Muscle Research. (JA ISSN 0374-3527) **3118**, 3372

Journal of Social Administrative Pharmacy. (SW ISSN 0281-0662) **3733**

Journal of Social and Clinical Psychology. (US ISSN 0736-7236) **4033**

Journal of Social and Personal Relationships. (UK ISSN 0265-4075) **4033**

Journal of Social Behavior and Personality. (US ISSN 0886-1641) **4033**, 4378

Journal of Social Development. (BG) **4410**

Journal of Social Development in Africa.(RH ISSN 1012-1080) **4410**

▼Journal of Social Distress and the Homeless. (US ISSN 1053-0789) **4411**

Journal of Social History. (US ISSN 0022-4529) **4441**, 2315

Journal of Social Issues. (US ISSN 0022-4537) **4033**, 4441

Journal of Social Philosophy. (US ISSN 0047-2786) **3771**
Journal of Social Policy. (UK ISSN 0047-2794) **4441**
Journal of Social, Political and Economic Studies. (US ISSN 0278-839X) **3902**
Journal of Social, Political and Economic Studies Monograph Series. (US ISSN 0895-724X) **3902**
Journal of Social Psychology. (US ISSN 0022-4545) **4033**
Journal of Social Research. (II) **243**
Journal of Social Science. (JA ISSN 0454-2134) **4378**
Journal of Social Sciences. (II ISSN 0449-3168) **4378**
Journal of Social Sciences and Humanities/Jinbun Gakuho. (JA) **2509**, **4378**
Journal of Social Service Research. (US ISSN 0148-8376) **4411**
Journal of Social Studies. (BG) **4378**
Journal of Social Studies Research. (US) **1753**
Journal of Social Welfare and Family Law. (UK) **2718**, **4411**
Journal of Social Work and Human Sexuality. (US ISSN 0276-3850) **4411**
Journal of Social Work and Policy in Israel. (IS ISSN 0334-9977) **4411**
Journal of Social Work Education. (US) **4411**, **1643**
Journal of Social Work Practice. (UK ISSN 0265-0533) **4411**, **1239**, **1537**
Journal of Society for Health Systems see Society for Health Systems. Journal **3622**
Journal of Sociology and Social Welfare.(US ISSN 0191-5096) **4441**, **4411**
Journal of Software. see Ruanjian Xuebao **1479**
Journal of Software Maintenance. (UK ISSN 1040-550X) **1478**
▼Journal of Software Testing, Verification and Reliability. (UK ISSN 0960-0833) **1478**
Journal of Soil and Water Conservation. (US ISSN 0022-4561) **183**, **4826**
Journal of Soil and Water Conservation in India. (II ISSN 0022-457X) **1490**, **102**, **4826**
Journal of Soil Biology and Ecology. (II ISSN 0970-1370) **445**, **535**, **586**
Journal of Soil Conservation see Australian Journal of Soil and Water Conservation **170**
Journal of Soil Science. (UK ISSN 0022-4588) **183**
Journal of Solar Energy Engineering. (US ISSN 0199-6231) **1811**
Journal of Solar Energy Research. (IQ ISSN 0256-7911) **1811**
Journal of Solid State Chemistry. (US ISSN 0022-4596) **1228**
Journal of Solution Chemistry. (US ISSN 0095-9782) **1228**
Journal of Sound and Vibration. (UK ISSN 0022-460X) **3859**
Journal of Sources in Educational History. (UK ISSN 0140-671X) **1643**
Journal of South African Law. see Tydskrif vir die Suid-Afrikaanse Reg **2687**
Journal of South American Earth Sciences. (UK ISSN 0895-9811) **1546**
Journal of South Asian and Middle Eastern Studies. (US ISSN 0149-1784) **2430**, **2339**
Journal of South Asian Literature. (US ISSN 0091-5637) **2929**
Journal of South-East Asian Earth Sciences. (US ISSN 0743-9547) **1570**
Journal of Southeast Asia Business. (US ISSN 1055-2073) **871**, **4378**
Journal of Southeast Asian History see Journal of Southeast Asian Studies **2339**
Journal of Southeast Asian Studies. (SI ISSN 0022-4634) **2339**, **3640**, **3902**

Journal of Southern African Studies. (UK ISSN 0305-7070) **4378**
Journal of Southern History. (US ISSN 0022-4642) **2411**
Journal of Southwest Georgia History. (US ISSN 0739-1943) **2411**
Journal of Soviet Laser Research. (US ISSN 0270-2010) **1828**, **3823**
Journal of Soviet Mathematics. (US ISSN 0090-4104) **3042**
Journal of Soviet Military Studies. (UK ISSN 0954-254X) **3462**, **2371**
▼Journal of Soviet Nationalities. (US ISSN 1043-7916) **3902**, **2010**
Journal of Space Astronomy Research. (IQ ISSN 1012-3431) **366**
Journal of Space Law. (US ISSN 0095-7577) **2726**, **57**
Journal of Space Technology and Science. (JA ISSN 0911-551X) **57**
Journal of Spacecraft and Rockets. (US ISSN 0022-4650) **57**
Journal of Spaceflight. see Yuhang Xuebao **65**
Journal of Special Education Technology. (US ISSN 0162-6434) **1737**, **1417**, **1691**
Journal of Spectrum. see Bopuxue Zazhi **3852**
Journal of Speculative Philosophy. (US ISSN 0891-625X) **3771**
†Journal of Speech and Hearing Disorders. (US ISSN 0022-4677) **5222**
Journal of Speech and Hearing Research. (US ISSN 0022-4685) **3343**, **3315**
Journal of Speech Language Pathologists and Audiologists see Journal of Speech Language Pathology and Audiology **1737**
Journal of Speech Language Pathology and Audiology/Revue d'Orthophonie et d'Audiologie. (CN ISSN 0848-1970) **1737**, **2821**
Journal of Spelean History. (US ISSN 0022-4693) **1570**, **2315**
Journal of Spinal Disorders. (US ISSN 0895-0385) **3309**, **3381**
†Journal of Spiritual and Natural Healing. (US) **5222**
Journal of Sport and Exercise Psychology. (US ISSN 0895-2779) **4033**, **3372**, **4477**
Journal of Sport and Social Issues. (US ISSN 0193-7235) **4477**, **4441**
Journal of Sport Behavior. (US ISSN 0162-7341) **4477**, **4033**
Journal of Sport History. (US ISSN 0094-1700) **4477**
Journal of Sport Management. (US ISSN 0888-4773) **4477**, **1017**
▼Journal of Sport Rehabilitation. (US ISSN 1056-6716) **3372**, **1737**
Journal of Sports Medicine and Physical Fitness. (IT ISSN 0022-4707) **3372**, **3805**
Journal of Sports Philately. (US ISSN 0447-953X) **3753**
Journal of Sports Sciences. (UK ISSN 0264-0414) **4477**, **3372**
Journal of Sports Traumatology and Related Research. (IT ISSN 1120-3137) **3372**, **3309**
Journal of Staff Development. (US ISSN 0276-928X) **1753**
Journal of Staffing and Recruitment. (US ISSN 1044-0038) **1067**
Journal of Stained Glass. (UK) **355**
Journal of State and Administration. (II) **3902**, **4065**
Journal of State Government. (US ISSN 0039-0097) **3902**, **4065**
Journal of State Taxation. (US ISSN 0744-6713) **1099**
Journal of Statistical Computation and Simulation. (US ISSN 0094-9655) **1435**, **3065**, **4576**
Journal of Statistical Physics. (US ISSN 0022-4715) **3823**
Journal of Statistical Planning and Inference. (NE ISSN 0378-3758) **4576**, **3042**
Journal of Statistical Research. (BG) **4576**
Journal of Steroid Biochemistry see Journal of Steroid Biochemistry and Molecular Biology **479**

Journal of Steroid Biochemistry and Molecular Biology. (US ISSN 0960-0760) **479**
Journal of Stored Products Research. (US ISSN 0022-474X) **183**
Journal of Strain Analysis see Journal of Strain Analysis for Engineering Design **1919**
Journal of Strain Analysis for Engineering Design. (UK ISSN 0309-3247) **1919**
Journal of Strategic and Systemic Therapies. (CN ISSN 0711-5075) **4033**, **3343**
▼Journal of Strategic Change. (UK ISSN 1057-9265) **1017**
Journal of Strategic I T. (UK ISSN 0960-3395) **1434**
Journal of Strategic Studies. (UK ISSN 0140-2390) **3462**
Journal of Stratigraphy. see Dicengxue Zazhi **1559**
Journal of Structural Biology. (US ISSN 1047-8477) **445**
Journal of Structural Chemistry. see Jiegou Huaxue **1180**
Journal of Structural Chemistry. (English translation of: Zhurnal Strukturnoi Khimii) (US ISSN 0022-4766) **1181**
Journal of Structural Engineering. (US ISSN 0733-9445) **1870**
Journal of Structural Engineering. (II ISSN 0970-0137) **1870**, **1933**
Journal of Structural Geology. (US ISSN 0191-8141) **1570**
Journal of Structural Learning. (US ISSN 0022-4774) **4033**, **1753**
Journal of Structural Mechanics see Mechanics of Structures and Machines **1935**
Journal of Studies in Technical Careers. (US ISSN 0163-3252) **1710**, **3629**
Journal of Studies in the Bhagavadgita. (CN ISSN 0706-6449) **4217**
Journal of Studies on Alcohol. (US ISSN 0096-882X) **1537**
Journal of Studies on Alcohol. Supplement. (US ISSN 0363-468X) **1537**
Journal of Substance Abuse. (US ISSN 0899-3289) **1537**
Journal of Substance Abuse Treatment. (US ISSN 0740-5472) **1537**
Journal of Sung-Yuan Studies. (US) **3640**
Journal of Sunology. (CH) **3640**
Journal of Supercomputing. (US ISSN 0920-8542) **1397**
Journal of Superconductivity. (US ISSN 0896-1107) **3844**
Journal of Supervision and Training in Ministry. (US ISSN 0160-7774) **4185**
Journal of Supramolecular Structure and Cellular Biochemistry see Journal of Cellular Biochemistry **525**
Journal of Surgical Oncology. (US ISSN 0022-4790) **3381**, **3199**
Journal of Surgical Practice. (US ISSN 0161-9721) **3381**
Journal of Surgical Research. (US ISSN 0022-4804) **3381**
Journal of Surveying. see Cehui Tongbao **2244**
Journal of Surveying Engineering. (US ISSN 0733-9453) **1870**
▼Journal of Sustainable Agriculture. (US ISSN 1044-0046) **1490**
▼Journal of Sustainable Forestry. (US ISSN 1054-9811) **2103**
Journal of Swimming Research. (US ISSN 0747-5993) **4477**
Journal of Symbolic Computation. (UK ISSN 0747-7171) **3065**
Journal of Symbolic Logic. (US ISSN 0022-4812) **3771**, **3042**
Journal of Synthetic Lubrication. (UK ISSN 0265-6582) **3691**, **1181**
Journal of System Engineering. see Xitong Gongcheng Xuebao **1840**
Journal of Systems and Software. (US ISSN 0164-1212) **1478**, **1438**
▼Journal of Systems Engineering and Electronics/Xitong Gongcheng yu Dianzi Jishu. (CC ISSN 1001-506X) **57**

▼Journal of Systems Integration. (NE ISSN 0925-4676) **1438**
Journal of Taiwan Fisheries Research. (CH ISSN 1018-7324) **2045**
Journal of Taiwan Museum. (CH ISSN 0256-257X) **3526**
Journal of Tamil Studies. (II ISSN 0022-4855) **2821**
Journal of Tanmiat al-Rafidain see Tanmiat al-Rafidain **4075**
Journal of Taxation. (US ISSN 0022-4863) **1099**
Journal of Taxation of Estates and Trusts. (US) **1099**
Journal of Taxation of Exempt Organizations. (US) **1099**
Journal of Taxation of Investments. (US) **1099**, **953**
Journal of Taxation of S Corporations. (US) **1100**, **953**
Journal of Teacher Education. (US ISSN 0022-4871) **1710**
Journal of Teaching in International Business. (US ISSN 0897-5930) **1643**, **915**
Journal of Teaching in Physical Education. (US ISSN 0273-5024) **3805**, **1753**
Journal of Teaching in Social Work. (US ISSN 0884-1233) **1753**, **4411**
Journal of Teaching Practice. (AT ISSN 1030-407X) **1753**, **1643**
Journal of Technical Physics. (PL ISSN 0032-9576) **3859**
Journal of Technical Writing and Communication. (US ISSN 0047-2816) **1643**, **1828**
Journal of Technology. (II ISSN 0047-2824) **1828**
▼Journal of Technology and Teacher Education. (US ISSN 1059-7069) **1691**
▼Journal of Technology Education. (US ISSN 1045-1064) **1691**
▼Journal of Technology in Mathematics. (US ISSN 1055-789X) **3042**
Journal of Technology Transfer. (US ISSN 0892-9912) **4602**
Journal of Telecommunication Networks see Advances in Telecommunications Networks Series **5131**
Journal of Terramechanics. (US ISSN 0022-4898) **3019**
Journal of Testing and Evaluation. (US ISSN 0090-3973) **1919**
Journal of Texture Studies. (US ISSN 0022-4901) **2075**, **3608**
Journal of Thanatology see Advances in Thanatology **4009**
Journal of the Aerospace Sciences see A I A A Journal **42**
Journal of the Air & Waste Management Association see Air & Waste Management Association. Journal **1942**
Journal of the Alleghenies. (US ISSN 0276-7449) **2411**
Journal of the American Animal Hospital Association see American Animal Hospital Association Journal **4805**
Journal of the American Chemical Society see American Chemical Society. Journal **1169**
Journal of the American College of Cariology see American College of Cardiology. Journal **3203**
Journal of the American Medical Association Colombia see J A M A en Colombia **3112**
Journal of the American Medical Women's Association see American Medical Women's Association. Journal **3075**
Journal of the American Musical Instrument Society see American Musical Instrument Society. Journal **3538**
Journal of the American Portuguese Society see American Portuguese Society. Journal **4752**
Journal of the Association of Nurses in AIDS Care see Association of Nurses in A I D S Care. Journal **3218**
Journal of the Astronautical Sciences see Journal of Astronautical Sciences **57**
Journal of the Atmospheric Sciences. (US ISSN 0022-4928) **3438**

Journal of the Australian War Memorial.(AT ISSN 0729-6274) **3462**, 2345, 3526
Journal of the Autonomic Nervous System. (NE ISSN 0165-1838) **3343**
Journal of the British Fire Services Association and Industrial Fire Protection Association see British Fire Services Association. Journal **2031**
Journal of the Bromeliad Society see Bromeliad Society. Journal **498**
Journal of the C P P C C. see Renmin Zhengxie Bao **4072**
Journal of the Chemical Society. Chemical Communications. (UK ISSN 0022-4936) **1181**
▼Journal of the Coin Laundry and Drycleaning Industry. (US) **1281**, 4621
Journal of the Early Republic. (US ISSN 0275-1275) **2411**
Journal of the Earth and Space Physics.(IR) **3823**
Journal of the East Africa Natural History Society and National Museum. (KE ISSN 0012-8317) **445**, 4318
Journal of the Economic and Social History of the Orient/Journal de l'Histoire Economique et Sociale de l'Orient. (NE ISSN 0022-4995) **2339**, 896, 3640
Journal of the Electronics Industry. (JA ISSN 0385-4515) **1775**
Journal of the European Ceramic Society see European Ceramic Society. Journal **1163**
Journal of the Experimental Analysis of Behavior. (US ISSN 0022-5002) **4033**
Journal of the Fantastic in the Arts. (US) **2870**
Journal of the Franklin Institute see Franklin Institute. Journal **4310**
Journal of the Freshman Year Experience. (US ISSN 1053-203X) **1710**
Journal of the Graduate Music Students at the Ohio State University. (US ISSN 0364-2216) **3559**
Journal of the Gulf and Arabian Peninsula Studies/Majallat Dirasat al-Khalij Wa-al Jazirah al-Arabiyah. (KU) **2430**
Journal of the Hellenic Diaspora. (US ISSN 0364-2976) **2010**
Journal of the History of Biology. (NE ISSN 0022-5010) **445**, 2315
Journal of the History of Collections. (UK ISSN 0954-6650) **3526**
Journal of the History of Ideas. (US ISSN 0022-5037) **2509**, 2315
Journal of the History of Mathematics, Japan. see Sugakushi Kenkyu **3057**
Journal of the History of Medicine and Allied Sciences. (US ISSN 0022-5045) **3118**, 2315
Journal of the History of Philosophy. (US ISSN 0022-5053) **3771**, 2315
▼Journal of the History of Sexuality. (US ISSN 1043-4070) **4441**
Journal of the History of Sociology see History of Sociology: An International Review **4437**
Journal of the History of the Behavioral Sciences. (US ISSN 0022-5061) **4034**, 2316
Journal of the I E S see Institute of Environmental Sciences. Journal **1958**
Journal of the Illuminating Engineering Society see Illuminating Engineering Society. Journal **1899**
Journal of the Indian Medical Profession. (II ISSN 0022-507X) **3118**
Journal of the Indian Scientific Translators Association see J I S T A **2819**
Journal of the Institute for Socioeconomic Studies see Institute for Socioeconomic Studies. Journal **3899**
Journal of the Interdenominational Theological Center see Interdenominational Theological Center, Atlanta. Journal **4182**

Journal of the Italian Psychoanalytical Society. see Rivista di Psicoanalisi **4045**
Journal of the Japanese and International Economies. (US ISSN 0889-1583) **915**
Journal of the Japanese Association of Mineralogists, Petrologists and Economic Geologists. see Journal of Mineralogy, Petrology and Economic Geology **1570**
Journal of the Japanese Group of A.I.P.P.I. International Edition see A.I.P.P.I. Japanese Group. Journal (International Edition) **3672**
Journal of the Korean Society for Microbiology. see Taehan Misaengmul Hakhoe Chi **558**
▼Journal of the Learning Sciences. (US) **1643**, 4034
Journal of the Legal Profession. (US) **2640**
Journal of the Less-Common Metals see Journal of Alloys and Compounds **3411**
Journal of the London Society see London Society. Journal **2491**
Journal of the Mechanical Behavior of Materials. (UK ISSN 0334-8938) **3411**
Journal of the Mechanics and Physics of Solids. (US ISSN 0022-5096) **3844**
Journal of the Medical Sciences/Berkala Ilmu Kedokteran. (IO ISSN 0126-1312) **3118**
Journal of the Midwest History of Education Society see Midwest History of Education Society. Journal **1648**
Journal of the Milking Shorthorn and Illawarra Breeds. (US ISSN 0145-8264) **220**
Journal of the Moscow Patriarchate. see Russkaya Pravoslavnaya Tserkov'. Moskovskaya Patriarkhiya. Zhurnal **4217**
Journal of the Multihandicapped Person see Journal of Developmental and Physical Disabilities **2284**
Journal of the National Cancer Institute see National Cancer Institute. Journal **3200**
Journal of the National Cancer Institute. Monographs see National Cancer Institute. Journal. Monographs **3200**
Journal of the Neurological Sciences. (NE ISSN 0022-510X) **3344**
Journal of the Oil Technologists' Association of India (Bombay) see Oil Technologists' Association of India. Journal **1220**
Journal of the Operational Research Society see Operational Research Society. Journal **1399**
†Journal of the Oslo City Hospitals. (NO ISSN 0030-6207) **5222**
Journal of the Philosophy of Sport. (US ISSN 0094-8705) **4477**, 3771
Journal of the Polynesian Society see J P S **242**
Journal of the Predmore, Pridemore, Pridmore, Prigmore Association. (US) **2156**
Journal of the Royal Artillery. (UK ISSN 0022-5134) **3462**
Journal of the Science of Food and Agriculture. (UK ISSN 0022-5142) **102**, 2075
Journal of the Short Story in English. (FR ISSN 0294-0442) **2929**
Journal of the Society of Glass Technology see Glass Technology **1167**
Journal of the Southwest. (US ISSN 0894-8410) **2411**, 243
Journal of the Strong Arm. (US ISSN 0738-1735) **2156**
Journal of the Textile Machinery Society of Japan see Textile Machinery Society of Japan. Journal **4625**
Journal of the Violin Society of America see Violin Society of America. Journal **3586**
Journal of the Walters Art Gallery. (US ISSN 0083-7156) **332**
Journal of the Warburg and Courtauld Institutes. (UK ISSN 0075-4390) **2509**

Journal of the Washington Academy of Sciences see Washington Academy of Sciences. Journal **4351**
Journal of the West. (US ISSN 0022-5169) **2412**, 2254
Journal of the Western Society of Periodontology. Periodontal Abstracts see Western Society of Periodontology. Journal. Periodontal Abstracts **3182**
Journal of Theological Studies. (UK ISSN 0022-5185) **4186**
Journal of Theology. (US ISSN 0361-1906) **4241**
Journal of Theology for Southern Africa.(SA ISSN 0047-2867) **4186**
Journal of Theoretical Biology. (UK ISSN 0022-5193) **445**
Journal of Theoretical Graphics and Computing. (US ISSN 1040-7847) **1422**
Journal of Theoretical Politics. (UK ISSN 0951-6298) **3902**
Journal of Theoretical Probability. (US ISSN 0894-9840) **3042**
Journal of Theoretical Psychology. (US ISSN 0887-252X) **4034**
Journal of Therapeutic Horticulture. (US) **2132**
Journal of Therapy/Chiryo. (JA ISSN 0022-5207) **3118**
Journal of Thermal Analysis. (UK) **1207**
Journal of Thermal Analysis. (HU ISSN 0368-4466) **1228**
Journal of Thermal Biology. (US ISSN 0306-4565) **486**
Journal of Thermal Insulation. (US ISSN 0148-8287) **1828**, 2301
▼Journal of Thermal Science/Rekexue Xuebao. (CC) **3841**
Journal of Thermal Stresses. (US ISSN 0149-5739) **1933**
Journal of Thermophysics and Heat Transfer. (US ISSN 0887-8722) **3823**
Journal of Thermoplastic Composite Materials. (US ISSN 0892-7057) **3863**
Journal of Third World Studies. (US ISSN 8755-3449) **2316**, 3963
Journal of Thoracic and Cardiovascular Surgery. (US ISSN 0022-5223) **3381**
Journal of Thoracic Imaging. (US) **3118**
Journal of Thought. (US ISSN 0022-5231) **4378**, 2509
Journal of Time Series Analysis. (UK ISSN 0143-9782) **4602**
Journal of Tissue Culture Methods. (US ISSN 0271-8057) **554**, 545, 3199
Journal of Tosoh Research/Tosoh Kenkyu Hokoku. (JA ISSN 0914-3106) **1856**
Journal of Tourism. see Luyou Xuekan **4775**
Journal of Toxicology and Environmental Health. (US ISSN 0098-4108) **1982**, 3199, 3733, 4106
Journal of Toxicology: Clinical Toxicology. (US ISSN 0731-3810) **1982**, 3733
Journal of Toxicology: Cutaneous and Ocular Toxicology. (US ISSN 0731-3829) **3733**, 1982, 3248, 3302
Journal of Toxicology: Toxin Reviews. (US ISSN 0731-3837) **3733**, 1983
Journal of Trace and Microprobe Techniques. (US ISSN 0733-4680) **1207**
Journal of Trace Elements and Electrolytes in Health and Disease. (GW ISSN 0931-2838) **479**, 3118
The Journal of Trace Elements in Experimental Medicine. (US ISSN 0896-548X) **3260**, 445
Journal of Traditional Acupuncture. (US) **3118**, 3640
Journal of Traditional Chinese Medicine. see Zhongyi Zazhi **3165**
Journal of Traffic Medicine. (SW ISSN 0345-5564) **3309**, 4719

Journal of Traffic Safety Education. (US) **4693**, 4106
Journal of Training & Practice in Professional Psychology. (US ISSN 0895-7673) **4034**
Journal of Transcultural Nursing. (US ISSN 1043-6596) **3281**
Journal of Translation and Textlinguistics. (US) **2821**, 1710, 4186
Journal of Transpersonal Psychology. (US ISSN 0022-524X) **4034**
Journal of Transport Economics and Policy. (UK ISSN 0022-5258) **4652**
Journal of Transport History. (UK ISSN 0022-5266) **4652**, 2316
Journal of Transport Management. (II ISSN 0970-4736) **4652**
Journal of Transportation Engineering. (US ISSN 0733-947X) **4652**, 1870
Journal of Transportation Medicine. (JA ISSN 0022-5274) **3310**
Journal of Trauma. (US ISSN 0022-5282) **3310**
Journal of Traumatic Stress. (US ISSN 0894-9867) **4034**
▼Journal of Travel & Tourism Marketing. (US ISSN 1054-8408) **4773**
Journal of Travel Research. (US ISSN 0047-2875) **4773**
Journal of Tribology. (US ISSN 0742-4787) **3691**, 1933
Journal of Tropical Ecology. (UK ISSN 0266-4674) **1961**
Journal of Tropical Forest Science. (MY ISSN 0128-1283) **2103**
Journal of Tropical Geography see Singapore Journal of Tropical Geography **2262**
Journal of Tropical Medicine and Hygiene. (UK ISSN 0022-5304) **3221**, 4106
Journal of Tropical Pediatrics. (UK ISSN 0142-6338) **3322**
Journal of Tropical Pediatrics and Environmental Child Health see Journal of Tropical Pediatrics **3322**
Journal of Tropical Plants. see Redai Zuowu Xuebao **516**
Journal of True Education see Journal of Adventist Education **4284**
Journal of Tumor Marker Oncology. (US ISSN 0886-3849) **3199**
Journal of Turbomachinery. (US ISSN 0889-504X) **1934**
Journal of Turkish Studies/Turkluk Bilgisi Arastirmalari. (US) **2430**
Journal of Typographic Research see Visible Language **1345**
Journal of U F O Studies. (US ISSN 0730-5478) **57**
Journal of U O E H see University of Occupational and Environmental Health. Journal **3622**
Journal of Ukrainian Studies. (CN ISSN 0228-1635) **2929**, 4378
Journal of Ultrasound in Medicine. (US ISSN 0278-4297) **3119**, 3859
Journal of Ultrastructure and Molecular Structure Research see Journal of Structural Biology **445**
Journal of Undergraduate Mathematics. (US ISSN 0022-5339) **3042**
Journal of Undergraduate Research in Physics. (US ISSN 0731-3764) **3823**
Journal of University Libraries. see Daxue Tushuguan Xuebao **2754**
Journal of Urban Affairs. (US ISSN 0735-2166) **2490**
Journal of Urban Analysis and Public Management. (US) **2490**
Journal of Urban & Contemporary Law. (US ISSN 8756-0801) **2640**
▼Journal of Urban and Cultural Studies. (US ISSN 1054-1802) **4441**
Journal of Urban Economics. (US ISSN 0094-1190) **675**
Journal of Urban History. (US ISSN 0096-1442) **2316**
Journal of Urban Planning and Development. (US ISSN 0733-9488) **2490**, 1870
Journal of Urology. (US ISSN 0022-5347) **3388**

Journal of V L S I and Computer Systems see Advances in V L S I and Computer Systems **5131**
▼Journal of V L S I Signal Processing. (US ISSN 0922-5773) **1447,** 1431
Journal of Vacuum Science and Technology. Part A. Vacuum, Surfaces and Films. (US ISSN 0734-2101) **3823**
Journal of Vacuum Science and Technology. Part B. Microelectronics Processing and Phenomena. (US ISSN 0734-211X) **3823**
Journal of Valuation see Journal of Property Valuation and Investment **4151**
Journal of Value Inquiry. (NE ISSN 0022-5363) **3771**
▼Journal of Vascular and Interventional Radiology. (US) **3360**
Journal of Vascular Medicine and Biology. (US ISSN 1042-5268) **3210,** 445
Journal of Vascular Research. (SZ ISSN 1018-1172) **479,** 573
Journal of Vascular Surgery. (US ISSN 0741-5214) **3381,** 3210
Journal of Verbal Learning and Verbal Behavior see Journal of Memory and Language **1643**
Journal of Vertebrate Paleontology. (US ISSN 0272-4634) **3658**
▼Journal of Vestibular Research: Equilibrium and Orientation. (US ISSN 0957-4271) **573,** 3119
Journal of Veterinary and Animal Sciences. (II ISSN 0971-0701) **4811**
Journal of Veterinary and Comparative Oncology see Journal of Veterinary Oncology **5222**
Journal of Veterinary Dentistry. (US ISSN 0898-7564) **4811**
Journal of Veterinary Diagnostic Investigation. (US ISSN 1040-6387) **4811**
▼Journal of Veterinary Emergency and Critical Care. (US ISSN 1056-6392) **4811,** 3310
Journal of Veterinary Internal Medicine. (US ISSN 0891-6640) **4812**
Journal of Veterinary Medical Education.(US ISSN 0748-321X) **4812,** 1710
Journal of Veterinary Medical Science. (JA ISSN 0916-7250) **4812**
Journal of Veterinary Medicine. Series A.(GW ISSN 0931-184X) **4812**
Journal of Veterinary Medicine. Series B.(GW ISSN 0931-1793) **4812**
†Journal of Veterinary Oncology. (US ISSN 0748-0512) **5222**
Journal of Veterinary Pharmacology and Therapeutics. (UK ISSN 0140-7783) **3733,** 4812
Journal of Veterinary Surgery see Veterinary Surgery **4819**
Journal of Vibration, Acoustics, Stress and Reliability in Design see Journal of Vibration and Acoustics **1934**
Journal of Vibration and Acoustics. (US ISSN 1048-9002) **1934**
Journal of Vinyl Technology. (US ISSN 0193-7197) **3863**
Journal of Virological Methods. (NE ISSN 0166-0934) **554**
Journal of Virology. (US ISSN 0022-538X) **554**
Journal of Vision Rehabilitation. (US) **3302**
▼Journal of Visual Communication and Image Representation. (US ISSN 1047-3203) **1422,** 1351
Journal of Visual Impairment & Blindness. (US ISSN 0145-482X) **2293,** 1643
▼Journal of Visual Languages and Computing. (UK ISSN 1045-926X) **2856**
Journal of Visual Literacy. (US ISSN 1051-144X) **1753,** 1691
Journal of Visual-Verbal Languaging see Journal of Visual Literacy **1753**
▼The Journal of Visualization and Computer Animation. (UK ISSN 1049-8907) **1422**
Journal of Vocational Behavior. (US ISSN 0001-8791) **4034**

Journal of Vocational Education Research. (US ISSN 0739-3369) **1753**
▼Journal of Vocational Rehabilitation. (US ISSN 1052-2263) **3618**
Journal of Voice. (US ISSN 0892-1997) **3315**
Journal of Volcanology and Geothermal Research. (NE ISSN 0377-0273) **1592,** 1570
Journal of Volunteer Administration. (US ISSN 0733-6535) **4411**
†Journal of Water Borne Coatings. (US ISSN 0163-4526) **5222**
Journal of Water Borne Coatings Buyer's Guide see Journal of Water Borne Coatings **5222**
Journal of Water Resources. (IQ) **1599,** 4826
Journal of Water Resources Planning and Management. (US ISSN 0733-9496) **1870**
Journal of Waterway, Port, Coastal, and Ocean Engineering. (US ISSN 0733-950X) **1870,** 1607
Journal of Weather Modification. (US ISSN 0739-1781) **3438**
Journal of Welding. see Hanjie Xuebao **3429**
Journal of West African Languages. (US ISSN 0022-5401) **2821**
Journal of West Indian Literature. (BB ISSN 0258-8501) **2929**
▼Journal of Wilderness Medicine. (UK ISSN 0953-9859) **3372,** 4549
Journal of Wildlife Diseases. (US ISSN 0090-3558) **4812,** 1490
Journal of Wildlife Management. (US ISSN 0022-541X) **1490**
Journal of Wind Energy Technology. (US ISSN 0884-0318) **1812**
Journal of Wind Engineering and Industrial Aerodynamics. (NE ISSN 0167-6105) **1934**
▼Journal of Wine Research. (UK ISSN 0957-1264) **183,** 382
▼Journal of Women and Aging. (US ISSN 0895-2841) **4860,** 2275
Journal of Women and Religion. (US ISSN 0888-5621) **4846,** 4186
Journal of Women's History. (US ISSN 1042-7961) **4860,** 2316
Journal of Wood Chemistry and Technology. (US ISSN 0277-3813) **1181**
▼Journal of Workers Compensation. (US) **2536,** 984
Journal of World Education. (DK) **1644**
Journal of World Forest Resource Management. (UK ISSN 0261-4286) **2103**
▼Journal of World History. (US ISSN 1045-6007) **2316**
Journal of World Prehistory. (US ISSN 0892-7537) **276,** 243, 2254
Journal of World Trade. (SZ ISSN 0022-5444) **2726,** 915, 2640
Journal of X-Ray Science and Technology. (US ISSN 0895-3996) **3823,** 1828
Journal of Xiangtan Mining Institute. see Xiangtan Kuangye Xueyuan Xuebao **3498**
Journal of Youth and Adolescence. (US ISSN 0047-2891) **1239**
Journal of Youth Services in Libraries. (US ISSN 0894-2498) **2766**
Journal of Yugoslav Foreign Trade. (YU ISSN 0022-5452) **915**
Journal of Yugoslav Pomology. see Jugoslovensko Vocarstvo **2132**
Journal of Zoo and Wildlife Medicine. (US ISSN 1042-7260) **4812**
Journal of Zoo Animal Medicine see Journal of Zoo and Wildlife Medicine **4812**
Journal of Zoological Research. (II ISSN 0253-7273) **586**
Journal of Zoology. (UK ISSN 0952-8369) **586**
Journal Officiel de Guinee. (GV ISSN 0533-5701) **4065**
Journal Officiel de la Cote d'Ivoire. (IV) **4065**
Journal Officiel de la Republique de Djibouti. (FT) **4065**

Journal Officiel de la Republique Democratique de Madagascar. see Gazetim-panjakan'ny Repoblika Demokratika Malagasy **4061**
Journal Officiel de la Republique du Cameroun. (CM) **4065**
Journal Officiel de la Republique du Niger. (NG) **4065**
Journal Officiel de la Republique du Senegal. (SG) **4065**
Journal Officiel de la Republique Gabonaise. (GO) **4065**
Journal Officiel de la Republique Populaire du Benin. (DM) **4065**
Journal Officiel de la Republique Rwandaise. (RW) **4065**
Journal Officiel du Burkina. (UV) **4065**
Journal - Ohio School Boards Association see Ohio School Boards Association. Journal **1730**
Journal on Computing. (US) **1397**
Journal on Numerical Methods and Computer Applications. see Shuzhi Jisuan yu Jisuanji Yingyong **4360**
Journal Parlementaire. (MR) **4065**
Journal Philatelique de Berne. see Berner Briefmarken-Zeitung **3750**
Journal pour le Transport International. see Internationale Transport-Zeitschrift **4651**
Journal Pratique de Droit Fiscal. (BE) **2640**
Journal Quebec Quilles. (CN) **4507**
Journal R P F see R P F **2302**
Journal Record. (US) **675,** 2640
Journal S O G C. (Society of Obstetricians and Gynecologists of Canada) (CN) **3294**
Journal Suisse d'Apiculture. (SZ) **102**
Journal Suisse de Pharmacie. see Schweizerische Apotheker-Zeitung **3742**
Journal Suisse des Bouchers-Charcutiers. see Schweizerische Metzger-Zeitung **2081**
Journal Suisse des Employes de Commerce. see Schweizerische Kaufmaennische Zeitung **1053**
Journal Suisse des Entrepreneurs. see Schweizer Bauwirtschaft **631**
Journal Suisse des Horlogers et des Bijoutiers-Orfevres. see Schweizerische Uhrmacher- und Goldschmiede-Zeitung **2566**
Journal Trimestriel d'Agriculture Internationale. see Zeitschrift fuer Auslaendische Landwirtschaft **130**
Journal Vinicole Suisse. see Schweizerische Weinzeitung **385**
Journal Watch. (US ISSN 0896-7210) **3119**
Journalen. Lokal- og Kulturhistorisk Tidsskrift. (DK ISSN 0906-1614) **2371**
Journalen Sykepleien. (NO ISSN 0802-9776) **3281**
Journalism. see Demosiografiki **2569**
Journalism Abstracts. (US ISSN 0075-4412) **2578**
Journalism and Mass Communication Directory. (US ISSN 0895-6545) **2571,** 1695
Journalism and Writing. see Xinwen yu Xiezuo **2577**
Journalism Career and Scholarship Guide. (US) **2571,** 1695
Journalism Career Guide for Minorities. (US) **3629,** 2571
Journalism Educator. (US ISSN 0022-5517) **2571,** 1710
Journalism History. (US ISSN 0094-7679) **2571**
Journalism Monographs. (US ISSN 0022-5525) **2571**
Journalism Research Materials. see Xinwen Yanjiu Ziliao **2577**
Journalism Scholarship Guide see Journalism Career and Scholarship Guide **2571**
Journalism Yearbook. (IS ISSN 0334-2948) **2571**
Der Journalist. (GW ISSN 0022-5576) **2572**
Journalist. (NE ISSN 0022-555X) **2572**
Journalist. (UK ISSN 0022-5541) **2572**
Journalist. see Setguulch **2575**
Journalist. see Novinar **5250**

JUDARNA 6359

Journaliste de Tourisme. see Travel Journalist **4792**
Journaliste Democratique see Democratic Journalist **2568**
Journalisten. (SW ISSN 0022-5592) **2572**
Journalisten. (NO) **2572**
Journalisten. see Sanomalehtimies **2575**
†Journalisten - Handbuch. (GW) **5222**
Journalisten Jahrbuch. (GW ISSN 0176-9707) **2572,** 1339
Journalistenhandbuch Entwicklungspolitik. (GW) **932**
Journalists. see Xinwen Jizhe **2577**
Journalists, Authors, Poets on Stamps Bulletin see J A P O S Bulletin **5219**
Journalists Cradle. see Jizhe Yaolan **2571**
Journalist's Handbook. (UK ISSN 0269-1736) **2572,** 1375
Journals in Translation. (UK ISSN 0950-9747) **404**
Journals of Dissent and Social Change. (US) **4458,** 3938
Journals of Gerontology. (US ISSN 0022-1422) **2275**
Journee de Medecine Physique et de Reeducation. (FR ISSN 0755-3951) **1737**
Journee de Reeducation see Journee de Medecine Physique et de Reeducation **1737**
Journee des Fruits & Legumes. (FR ISSN 0022-5622) **183**
Journee Vinicole. (FR ISSN 0022-5649) **382**
▼Journee Vinicole International Newsletter. (FR) **382**
Journees Annuelles de Diabetologie de l'Hotel Dieu. (FR ISSN 0075-4439) **3255**
Journees Biochimiques Latines. Rapports. (IT ISSN 0075-4447) **479**
Journees de la Societe de Legislation Comparee. (FR ISSN 0756-3825) **2640**
Journees de Strasbourg. (FR) **366**
Journees Parisiennes de Pediatrie. (FR ISSN 0399-029X) **3322**
Journey (Antioch). (US) **675**
Journey (Brisbane). (AT ISSN 0314-6235) **4241**
Journey (Kansas City). (US) **1710**
Journey (St. Louis). (US) **1257,** 4241
The Journeyman Roofer and Waterproofer. (US) **622**
▼Journeymen. (US) **3398**
†Jovenes "A" (Student Edition). (US) **5222**
Jovenes Agricultores. (SP) **102,** 1257
Joy & Light. (UK ISSN 0022-5703) **4284**
†Joy of Herbs. (US) **5222**
Joyas & Joyeros. (SP ISSN 0213-120X) **2565**
▼Joyce Studies Annual. (US ISSN 1049-0809) **2929,** 419
Joyful Woman. (US ISSN 0164-4882) **4241,** 4846
Jr. High Ministry Magazine. (US) **1239,** 1257, 4186
Jr. Rider. (CN ISSN 0380-3554) **4535**
Juben/Play Scripts. (CC ISSN 0578-0659) **4634**
Jubilation. (US) **3559,** 1299
Jubilee. (US ISSN 0893-1607) **4241,** 1517
Jubilee International. (US) **4186,** 1517
Juco Review. (US ISSN 0047-2956) **4477,** 1644
Jucunda Laudatio. (IT ISSN 0022-5711) **3559**
Judaica. (SZ ISSN 0022-572X) **4224**
Judaica Bohemiae. (CS ISSN 0022-5738) **2010,** 4186
Judaica Book News. (US ISSN 0022-5754) **4130,** 2010, 4224
Judaica Iberoamericana. (CL) **2010,** 243
Judaica Librarianship. (US ISSN 0739-5086) **2766,** 2010
Judaica Philatelic Journal. (US) **3754**
Judaism. (US ISSN 0022-5762) **4224,** 2870
Judarna i Sovjet. (SW) **3944,** 2010

JUDEAN

Judean. (SA ISSN 0022-5770) **3462**
Judean Desert Studies. (IS ISSN 0075-4501) **276**
Judges' Journal. (US ISSN 0047-2972) **2732**
Judge's Retirement System. Annual Financial Report and Report of Operations. (US) **871**, 953
Judicatura. (UY) **2732**
Judicature. (US ISSN 0022-5800) **2732**, 4378
Judicial Conduct Reporter. (US ISSN 0193-7367) **2732**
Judicial Council Report to the Governor and Legislature. (US) **2640**
Judicial Interim Release: Bail Manual. (CN) **2713**, 1517
Judicial Staff Directory. (US) **2640**, 4065
Judicial Statistics see Michigan. State Court Administrator. Annual Report **2700**
Judo. (NE) **4477**
Judo. (UK ISSN 0022-5819) **4477**
Judo. (FR) **4477**
Judo & Wrestling. see Roudao yu Shuaijiao **4486**
Judo Journal. (US) **4477**
Judo-Koerier see Budo Koerier **4467**
Judo Regionale. (IT) **4477**
Judson Cameo. (US) **1315**
Judy see Judy and Tracy **1239**
Judy and Tracy. (UK) **1239**
Juedische Gemeindezeitung Frankfurt. Amtliches Organ. (GW) **2010**
Juedische Rundschau Maccabi. (SZ) **3902**, 2010
Jugabheri. (BG) **2174**
Jugend Beruf Gesellschaft. (GW ISSN 0342-0175) **1239**, 4411
Jugend Film Fernsehen see Medien & Erziehung **1376**
Jugend in Wien. (AU) **1257**
Jugend und Kultur. (RM) **332**, 2929
Jugend und Technik see Vision & Technik **5301**
Jugendbuchmagazin. (GW ISSN 0177-4247) **1240**
Jugendbuecher zum Thema. (GW) **1257**, 2371
Jugenddorf-Zeitung see Klinge **4411**
Jugendherberge. (GW ISSN 0022-5932) **4773**, 1240
Jugendherbergs-Verzeichnis. (GW ISSN 0075-4528) **2255**
Jugendherbergswerk. (GW) **1240**
Jugendhilfe. (GW ISSN 0022-5940) **4411**, 1240
Jugendliteratur. (SZ) **1240**
Jugendmagazin see J U M A **1641**
Jugendnachrichten. (GW) **1722**, 1240
†Jugendpolitik. (GW) **5222**
Jugendpost see Rasant **1263**
Jugendpressedienst des V N J. (GW) **1257**, 1961
Jugendpressereport. (GW) **1257**, 2572
Jugendwohl. (GW ISSN 0022-5975) **4411**, 1240
Juggler's World Magazine. (US) **2437**, 4477
Juggs. (US ISSN 0734-4309) **3398**
Jugi - Ajiste see Ticket **4789**
Jugoslavenska Akademija Znanosti i Umjetnosti. Historijski Institut, Dubrovnik. Anali. (CI ISSN 0449-3648) **2371**
Jugoslavenska Akademija Znanosti i Umjetnosti. Razred za Prirodne Znanosti. Rad. (CI ISSN 0351-3297) **1570**, 445
Jugoslavenska Akademija Znanosti i Umjetnosti. Zavod za Provijesne Znanosti. Radovi. (CI ISSN 0351-6709) **2371**
Jugoslavenska Ginekologija i Opstetricija see Yugoslav Gynecology and Perinatology **3297**
Jugoslavenska Medicinska Biokemija. (CI ISSN 0352-1311) **573**, 1181
Jugoslavia Fervojisto. (YU ISSN 0022-6025) **2821**
Jugoslavija. (YU ISSN 0022-6033) **2239**
Jugoslavija-Wirtschaft. (GW ISSN 0723-1296) **915**

Jugoslawische Touristenzeitung/Yugoslav Tourist News. (YU ISSN 0022-605X) **4773**
Jugoslovenska i Inostrana Dokumentacija Zastite na Radu. (YU ISSN 0022-6068) **985**
Jugoslovenska Revija za Kriminologiju i Krivicno Pravo. (YU ISSN 0022-6076) **1517**, 2640
Jugoslovenska Revija za Medjunarodno Pravo. (YU ISSN 0022-6084) **2726**
Jugoslovenski Istorijski Casopis. (YU) **2316**, 2371
Jugoslovenski Pregled. (YU ISSN 0022-6114) **2239**
Jugoslovensko Bankarstvo. (YU) **788**
Jugoslovensko Vinogradarstvo i Vinarstvo. (YU ISSN 0022-6130) **382**
Jugoslovensko Vocarstvo/Journal of Yugoslav Pomology. (YU ISSN 0350-2155) **2132**
Juguetecnica. (SP ISSN 0214-7122) **2437**
Juguetes. (AG) **2281**
Juguetes y Juegos de Espana. (SP ISSN 0022-6157) **2281**
Juguetes y Juegos de Espana Express. (SP) **2281**
Juigaku Kenkyu see Japanese Journal of Veterinary Research **4811**
Juilliard Journal. (US) **3559**, 1531
Juilliard Performance Guides. (US) **3559**
Juke Blues. (UK) **3559**
Jukebox Collector. (US ISSN 1053-6884) **2437**, 3559
Jukebox Collector Newsletter see Jukebox Collector **2437**
Jukic. (BN ISSN 0350-6398) **4186**, 3771
Jul i Familien. (DK) **1257**, 4186
Jul i Frederikssund. (DK ISSN 0107-5446) **2371**
Jul i Lejre. (DK ISSN 0108-2965) **2371**
Jul i Skive see Skive-egnens Jul **2386**
Julegaven. (DK ISSN 0905-1678) **2929**
Julehaeftet, Vanfoeres Jul. (DK) **4411**
Julehilsen. (DK ISSN 0107-8887) **1644**
Juli-Magazin. (GW) **3393**, 3944
Julia. (IT) **4361**
Julius C. Stevens Annual Lectures in Education. (LB) **1644**
Jumbo Cross. (UK ISSN 0267-9442) **4477**
Jumbo Flash Report. (US) **953**, 788
Jumbo Rate News. (US ISSN 8756-2332) **788**, 953
Jumin Katsudo. (JA) **1961**
Jump Cut. (US ISSN 0146-5546) **3512**, 1339, 3792
Jumping Pouch Newsletter. (US) **220**
Jun Ma/Steed. (CC) **2929**
Junction. (US) **2996**
Juncture Recognition. (US) **953**
Jund Oman. (MK) **3462**
Al-Jundi. (TS) **3462**
Jundi Shapur University. Faculty of Medicine. Library Bulletin/Daneshgah-e Jondishapur. Daneshkade-Ye Pezeski. Bultan-e Ketabkhaneh. (IR) **2766**, 3119
Jundui Zhuanye Ganbu. (CC) **1067**, 3462
Der Junge Elektro-techniker. (GW) **1753**, 1257, 1901
Junge Elektrohandwerk see Der Junge Elektro-techniker **1753**
Junge Familie. (GW) **3322**, 1240, 2281
Der Junge Florist. (GW ISSN 0022-6262) **2142**
Junge Freiheit. (GW ISSN 0932-660X) **2870**
Junge Gemeinde. (AU ISSN 0022-6289) **4186**, 1257
†Junge Generation. (GW ISSN 0022-6297) **5222**
Der Junge Kaufmann. (AU ISSN 0022-6300) **1044**
Junge Kaufmann. (SZ) **1044**
Junge Kirche. (GW ISSN 0022-6319) **4186**, 4441
Junge Liberale Bayern. Forum. (GW) **3902**

Der Junge Metall-Facharbeiter. (GW) **3411**
Junge Metallhandwerker see Der Junge Metall-Facharbeiter **3411**
Junge Ortskrankenkasse see J O **2535**
Junge Radio-, Fernseh- und Industrie-Elektroniker. (GW ISSN 0343-9003) **1357**, 1375, 1775
Junge Sammler. (GW ISSN 0022-6343) **3754**, 1257
Junge Wirtschaft see Unternehmer **1030**
Junge Wissenschaft. (GW) **4318**
Junges Forum. (GW ISSN 0171-9386) **2371**, 3902
Junghandwerker im Kraftfahrzeug Betrieb see Autofachmann **4681**
Jungle. (II ISSN 0047-2999) **4773**, 1490
Jungscharhelfer. (GW ISSN 0022-6467) **4186**, 1257
Juni. (GW ISSN 0931-2854) **2189**
Juni see Juni Druzi **5222**
†Juni Druzi. (UK) **5222**
Junindex. (PE) **3395**, 725
Junior. (SZ ISSN 0022-6475) **1257**
Junior. (IT) **4361**
Junior Authors and Illustrators Series. (US) **2572**, 332, 1240
Junior Bookshelf. (UK ISSN 0022-6505) **4130**, 1240, 2766
Junior Bowler see Y A B A Framework **4515**
Junior Chess. (AT) **4477**
Junior Citizen. (US) **1240**
Junior Clubhouse. (AT ISSN 1030-0287) **4241**, 1257
Junior College Journalist see Community College Journalist **2568**
Junior Editor. (US) **2996**, 1257
Junior Education. (UK ISSN 0309-3484) **1644**
Junior Education Special see Junior Projects **1644**
Junior Electronics/Shoho No Rajio. (JA) **1257**, 1901
Junior Engineering Technical Society Report see J E T S Report **1827**
Junior Farmer and 4-H Enthusiast see Enthusiast **5187**
Junior Fashion International see Junior Fashion Record **1292**
Junior Fashion Record. (UK) **1292**
†Junior Friends. (UK ISSN 0960-720X) **5222**
Junior Growth Stocks. (US) **953**
Junior High Magazine Abstracts. (US ISSN 1045-5493) **1677**, 15
Junior High School Library Catalog. (US) **2766**
Junior Keynotes. (US ISSN 0022-6629) **3559**
Junior Land. (JA) **1257**
Junior League Newsline. (US) **4411**, 1299
Junior League Review. (US) **4411**, 1299
Junior Musician see Young Musicians **3587**
Junior Naturalist. (AT) **1490**
Junior Post. (II) **2200**
Junior Projects. (UK ISSN 0269-9532) **1644**
Junior Scholastic. (US ISSN 0022-6688) **1257**, 1644
Junior Science/Kodomo No Kagaku. (JA) **1257**, 4318
Junior Scientist. (II) **1753**, 4318
Junior State Report see Junior Statement **1257**
Junior Statement. (US) **1257**
Junior Statesman. (II) **3902**
Junior Teacher see Bible Searchers Teacher **4231**
Junior Topics. (AT) **1644**
Junior Trails. (US ISSN 0022-6718) **4284**, 1257
Junior Vikatan. (II) **1257**
†Junk Journal. (US ISSN 0892-791X) **5222**
Junkan Asu no Kagaku Gijutsu/News of Science and Technology of Tomorrow. (JA) **4602**, 4318
Junkanoo. (UK) **4241**, 1257
Junkanoo. (BF) **4634**, 2929, 3559
Junki Yonkam. see Electrical Yearbook **1889**
Junon. (JA) **4846**

Junta de Estudios Historicos de Mendoza. Revista. (AG ISSN 0076-6380) **2412**
Junta de Investigacao Cientifica Tropical. Centro de Estudos de Historia e Cartografia Antiga. Studia Memoria see Instituto de Investigacao Cientifica Tropical. Centro de Estudos de Historia e Cartografia Antiga. Studia **2314**
Junta de Investigacoes Cientifica do Ultramar. Memorias see Instituto de Investigacao Cientifica Tropical. Memorias **4315**
Junta Nacional da Marinha Mercante. Boletim see Portugal. Direccao Geral de Marinha do Comercio. Boletim **4736**
Juntendo Igaku. see Juntendo Medical Journal **3119**
Juntendo Medical Journal/Juntendo Igaku. (JA ISSN 0022-6769) **3119**
Juntendo University. Medical Ultrasonics Research Center. Annual Report. (JA ISSN 0075-4579) **3119**
Juprecu. (CU ISSN 0864-0254) **4186**, 1257
Jura. (GW ISSN 0170-1452) **2640**
Jureco. (MG) **2640**, 871
†Juri-Social. (FR ISSN 0154-8840) **5222**
Jurid-Tip. (GW) **4693**
Juridica. (MX) **2640**
Juridical Review. (UK ISSN 0022-6785) **2640**, 3902
Juridiska Foereningen i Finland. Tidskrift. (FI ISSN 0040-6953) **2640**
Jurimetrics Journal. (US ISSN 0022-6793) **2640**, 1397, 1644
Juris. (US ISSN 0022-6807) **2641**
Juriscivel do S T F. (Supremo Tribunal Federal) (BL) **2641**
Jurisdiction in Civil Actions. (US) **2702**
Jurisdiction Journal see Jurisdiction Journal & Sovereign Review **5222**
†Jurisdiction Journal & Sovereign Review. (US) **5222**
Jurisfemme. (CN ISSN 0835-0892) **2641**, 4846
Jurisprudence Association. Journal/Hogaku Kyokai Zasshi. (JA ISSN 0022-6815) **2641**
Jurisprudence Automobile. (FR ISSN 0022-6823) **2536**
Jurisprudence des Jurisdictions du Travail de Bruxelles see Jurisprudence du Droit Social **2641**
Jurisprudence du Droit Social. (BE) **2641**
Jurisprudence du Port d'Anvers. (BE ISSN 0022-6831) **2735**
Jurisprudence in China. see Zhongguo Faxue **2697**
Jurisprudence Logement. (CN) **2641**
Jurisprudencia Aragonesa. (SP) **2641**
Jurisprudencia Argentina. (AG ISSN 0326-1190) **2641**
Jurisprudencia e Doutrina. (BL ISSN 0022-684X) **2641**
▼Jurisprudentie voor Gemeenten. (NE ISSN 0924-4824) **2641**, 3944, 4065
Jurist. (US ISSN 0022-6858) **2641**, 4266
Juristat. (CN ISSN 0715-271X) **2699**
Juriste. (CN ISSN 0829-5476) **2641**, 1710
Juristen see Juristen og Oekonomen **2641**
Juristen og Oekonomen. (DK) **2641**, 675
Juristenzeitung. (GW ISSN 0022-6882) **2641**
Juristische Abhandlungen. (GW ISSN 0449-4342) **2641**
Juristische Blaetter. (US ISSN 0022-6912) **2641**
Juristische Neuerscheinungen. (GW) **2699**
Juristische Rundschau. (GW ISSN 0022-6920) **2641**
Juristische Schulung. (GW ISSN 0022-6939) **2641**
Juristkontakt. (NO ISSN 0332-7590) **2641**
Juristnytt. see Lakimiesuutiset **2643**
Jurnal Antropologi dan Sosiologi. (MY ISSN 0126-9518) **4441**, 243

Jurnal Ekonomi Malaysia. (MY ISSN 0127-1962) **871**
Jurnal Fizik Malaysia. (MY ISSN 0128-0333) **3823**
Jurnal Pendidikan. *see* Journal of Educational Research **1642**
Jurnal Pengurusan. (MY ISSN 0127-2713) **1017**
Jurnal Penyelidikan M A R D I. *see* M A R D I Research Journal **106**
Jurnal Perubatan U K M. (Penerbit Universiti Kebangsaan Malaysia) (MY ISSN 0127-1075) **3119**
Jurnal Psikologi Malaysia. (MY ISSN 0127-8029) **4034**
†Jurnal Sains Institut Penyelidikan Getah Malaysia. (MY ISSN 0126-6136) **5222**
Jurnal Veterinar Malaysia. (MY) **4812**
Jurope. (GW) **1257**
Jurutera. (MY) **1856**, 1870, 1934
The Jury. (CN) **2713**
▼Jury Selection, 2-E. (US) **2641**
Jus. (PE) **2641**
Jus Gentium. (IT ISSN 0022-6963) **2726**, 3963
Jussens Venner. (NO ISSN 0022-6971) **2641**
Just a Bite. (UK) **2477**
†Just B'twx Us: An Interlibrary Loan Information Bulletin. (US) **5222**
Just Compensation. (US ISSN 0738-6494) **2641**
Just for Laughs. (US) **4634**
Just for You. (US) **2466**
Just Go! (US) **4773**
Just Grand. (CN) **2177**
Just Horsin' Around. (US) **4536**
Just Seventeen. (UK) **1257**
▼Just Wages. (CN) **4846**
Justice. (US ISSN 0022-7013) **2585**, 1285
Justice. *see* Al-Adalah **2594**
Justice. (MQ) **3902**
Justice (Sainte-Foy). (CN ISSN 0707-8501) **2641**
Justice and the J.P. (AT) **1517**, 1644, 2641
Justice - Directory of Services/Justice - Repertoire des Services. (CN ISSN 0225-4115) **1517**
Justice Expenditure and Employment Data in the U.S. *see* Justice Expenditure and Employment in the U.S **1517**
Justice Expenditure and Employment in the U.S. (US) **1517**
Justice in America Series. (US) **2641**, 1517
Justice in Urban America Series *see* Justice in America Series **2641**
Justice Institute of British Columbia. Annual Report. (CN) **1710**, 2641
Justice of the Peace. (UK ISSN 0141-5859) **2714**, 4089
Justice of the Peace Reports. (UK ISSN 0264-3731) **2641**
Justice Populaire. *see* Drejtesia Popullore **2620**
Justice Quarterly. (US ISSN 0741-8825) **1517**, 2641
Justice - Repertoire des Services. *see* Justice - Directory of Services **1517**
Justice Report/Actualites Justice. (CN ISSN 0823-9436) **1517**, 4411
Justice System Journal. (US ISSN 0098-261X) **2641**
Justice Times. (US) **1100**
Justice Trends. (AT ISSN 0157-6011) **3944**
Justices Act and Summary Offences N S W *see* Criminal Practice & Procedure N S W **2713**
Justices' Clerk. (UK) **2641**
Justicia. (US ISSN 0195-3737) **2585**, 1285
Justicia. (NA ISSN 0022-7056) **2641**
Justicia Social. (AG) **985**, 896
Justicia Uruguaya. (UY) **2641**
Justinian. (AT ISSN 0157-5317) **2641**
Justitiele Verkenningen. (NE ISSN 0167-5850) **1525**, 15, 2699
Justiz in Zahlen. (GW) **2699**, 4576
Justiz-Ministerial-Blatt fuer Hessen. (GW ISSN 0022-7064) **2641**
JustPeace. (UK ISSN 0306-7645) **4186**, 3963

Justuf. (GW ISSN 0941-6781) **2641**, 1710
†Justus-Liebig-Universitaet Giessen-Lahn. Arbeitskreis fuer Wildbiologie und Jagdwissenschaft. Schriften. (GW) **5222**
Justus Liebigs Annalen der Chemie *see* Liebigs Annalen der Chemie **1183**
Jusur. (US ISSN 0888-9007) **2430**, 4219
Juta - State Library Index to the Government Gazette. (SA) **4081**, 15
Jutaku Sangyo Handbook. (JA) **2490**
Jutaku Sangyo Handobukku *see* Jutaku Sangyo Handbook **2490**
Juta's Tax Service. (SA) **1100**
Jute and Jute Fabrics - Bangladesh. (BG) **4621**
Jute and Jute Fabrics - Pakistan *see* Jute and Jute Fabrics - Bangladesh **4621**
Jutland Archaeological Society. Publications. *see* Jysk Arkaeologisk Selskabs. Skrifter **2371**
Jutro Polski/Poland of Tomorrow. (UK ISSN 0022-7137) **2010**
Juvenile and Adult Correctional Departments, Institutions, Agencies, and Paroling Authorities of the United States and Canada. (US ISSN 0190-2555) **1517**
Juvenile and Family Court Journal. (US ISSN 0161-7109) **2718**, 1240, 1517
Juvenile and Family Court Newsletter. (US ISSN 0162-9859) **2718**, 1240, 1517
Juvenile and Family Law Digest. (US ISSN 0279-2257) **2718**, 1240
Juvenile Justice Digest. (US ISSN 0094-2413) **1517**, 2641
Juvenile Law Reports. (US ISSN 0276-9603) **2718**, 1517
Juvenile Merchandising. (US ISSN 0022-7161) **2560**, 1257
Juvenile Miscellany. (US) **1240**, 2766
Juvenile Philately. *see* Shaonian Jiyou **3757**
Juvenile Press. *see* Shaonian Bao **1265**
Juvenile Science. *see* Shaonian Kexue **1265**
Juvenile Scientific Pictorial. *see* Shaonian Kexue Huabao **1265**
†Juventud. (AG ISSN 0022-7196) **5222**
Juventud del Mundo. *see* World Youth **1271**
Juventud Panadera. (SP ISSN 0022-7218) **2088**
Juventud Rebelde. (CU) **1240**, 2184
Juventud Siglo XX 20 *see* J-20 **5219**
Juventud Tecnica. (CU ISSN 0449-4555) **4602**
Juying Yuebao/Drama & Film Monthly. (CC) **4634**, 3512
Juzen Igakkai Zasshi/Juzen Medical Society. Journal. (JA ISSN 0022-7226) **3119**
Juzen Medical Society. Journal. *see* Juzen Igakkai Zasshi **3119**
Juznoslovenski Filolog. (YU ISSN 0350-185X) **2822**
Juzuojia/Playwright. (CC ISSN 1001-3768) **4634**
Jyoti Chitra. (II) **2200**
Jyotsana. (II) **2200**
Jysk Arkaeologisk Selskabs. Skrifter/ Jutland Archaeological Society. Publications. (DK ISSN 0107-2854) **2371**, 276
Jysk Landbrug *see* Dansk Landbrug **86**
Jyvaskyla Studies in Computer Science, Economics and Statistics. (FI ISSN 0357-9921) **1397**, 827
Jyvaskyla Studies in Education, Psychology and Social Research. (FI ISSN 0075-4625) **1644**, 4034
Jyvaskyla Studies in the Arts. (FI ISSN 0075-4633) **332**, 2929
Jyvaskylan Yliopisto. Department of Physics. Research Report *see* University of Jyvaskyla. Department of Physics. Preprints **3834**
Jyvaskylan Yliopisto. Matematiikan Laitos. Report. (FI ISSN 0075-4641) **3042**

K A B. (Katholischen Arbeiternehemer-Bewegung Deutschlands) (GW ISSN 0175-5161) **4266**
K A C Research Series. (Kampsville Archaeological Center) (US) **276**
K A E R I Journal/Hanguk Energy Yeonguso Hwibo. (Korea Atomic Energy Research Institute) (KO) **1806**
K A F P Journal. (Kentucky Academy of Family Physicians) (US ISSN 0090-5089) **3119**
K A G P Journal *see* K A F P Journal **3119**
K A H P E R D Journal. (Kentucky Association for Health, Physical Education, Recreation and Dance) (US) **1738**, 3805
K A H P E R Journal *see* K A H P E R D Journal **1738**
†K.A.M. (Keepers of the Ancient Mysteries) (US) **5222**
K.A.M. Newsletter *see* K.A.M **5222**
K A P T Union Patrika. (Kerala Aided Primary Teachers' Union) (II) **1644**
K & C. (BE ISSN 0022-7277) **332**, 1375, 3512, 4634
K B D *see* Australian Key Business Directory **1122**
K B M - Kantoormarkt. (NE) **1059**
K B S - Rapporter. (SW ISSN 0022-7293) **2490**, 1870
K B S Technical Regulations. *see* K B S Tekniska Foereskrifter **2490**
K B S Tekniska Foereskrifter/K B S Technical Regulations. (SW) **2490**, 622, 1870
K C C I Quarterly Review. (Korea Chamber of Commerce and Industry) (KO) **818**
K C C Kennel Gazette *see* V C A Kennel Gazette **3714**
K C Computer User. (US) **1461**
K C M S Bulletin. (Medical Society County of Kings) (US ISSN 0886-4772) **3119**
K C Nyt. (Foreningen af Kommunale Chefer (KC)) (DK) **4089**
K C T S Magazine *see* K C T S - Nine **2227**
K C T S - Nine. (US ISSN 1050-513X) **2227**, 1375
K D B Report. (Korea Development Bank) (KO) **675**, 788, 871, 999
K D D (Year). (Kokusai Denshin Denwa Co. Ltd.) (JA) **1363**
K E A News. (Kentucky Education Association) (US ISSN 0164-3959) **1644**
K E A Publications *see* K E A Research Publications **1677**
K E A Research Publications. (Kentucky Education Association) (US) **1677**
K E M *see* Konstruktion Elemente Maschinenbau **1829**
K E M - European Design Engineering. (GW ISSN 0174-7312) **1828**
K E P C O Annual Review. (Korea Electric Power Corporation) (KO) **1901**
K E S. (Kommunikation und E D P Security) (GW ISSN 0177-4565) **1339**
K F A Intern. (Kernforschungsanlage) (GW ISSN 0722-0456) **4318**
K F F Medlemsblad *see* Ledarforum **831**
K F T *see* Kraftfahrzeugtechnik **4694**
K F Z Anzeiger. (GW ISSN 0341-9681) **4745**
K F Z Betrieb *see* K F Z Betrieb Unternehmermagazin **4694**
K F Z Betrieb Aktuelle Wochenzeitung. (GW) **4694**
K F Z Betrieb Unternehmermagazin. (GW) **4694**
K F Z Werkstaette *see* K F Z Wirtschaft **4694**
K F Z Wirtschaft. (AU) **4694**
K F Z Zeitschrift fuer den Nachwuchs des Kraftfahrzeuhandwerks. (GW ISSN 0343-9011) **4694**
†K G S - N C I C Newsletter. (Kentucky Geological Survey) (US) **5222**
K I *see* Kuenstliche Intelligenz **1409**
K I *see* K I - Klima, Kaelte, Heizung **2301**

K: REVISTA   6361

K I A Occasional Papers. (Kenya Institute of Administration) (KE ISSN 0075-5761) **4065**
K I K. (Kunst in Koeln) (GW) **3526**, 332
K I - Klima, Kaelte, Heizung. (Klima und Kaelteingenieur) (GW ISSN 0172-1984) **2301**
K I P H Bulletin. (Korean Institute for Population and Health) (KO) **597**
K I R D I Annual Report and Statement of Accounts. (Kenya Industrial Research and Development Institute) (KE) **837**
K - International Ceramics Magazine *see* Keramikos International Ceramics Magazine **1165**
K J E S *see* Kakatiya Journal of English Studies **2929**
K J Z T News. (US) **1299**
K K A *see* Kueche in Krankenhaus und Altenheim **2076**
†K K C Brief. (Keizai Koho Center) (JA ISSN 0289-890X) **5222**
K K - die Kaelte und Klimatechnik. (GW ISSN 0343-2246) **2301**
K K H Journal. (Kaufmaennische Krankenkasse Hauptverwaltung) (GW ISSN 0932-1055) **3805**
K K H Nachrichten. (Kaufmaennische Krankenkasse Hauptverwaltung) (GW) **2536**
K L A Bulletin. (Korean Library Association) (KO ISSN 0022-7358) **2766**
K L A Bulletin *see* Kentucky Libraries **2767**
K L A G E. (Koelner Linguistische Arbeiten - Germanistik) (GW ISSN 0939-9275) **2822**
K L A Newsletter. (Kansas Library Association) (US) **2766**
K L G: Kritisches Lexikon zur Deutschsprachigen Gegenwartsliteratur. (GW) **2929**
K L M Literatuuroverzicht. (NE ISSN 0022-7366) **66**, 16
K L M News. (NE ISSN 0022-7374) **4675**
K L M Windmill. (US) **4803**
K L O E Impulse. (Katholische Lehrerschaft Oesterreichs) (AU) **1644**
†K M D Plannyt. (Kommunedata) (DK ISSN 0107-2692) **5222**
K M - Die Katholischen Missionen. (GW) **4266**
K M I Buerowirtschaft - Lehre und Praxis. (GW ISSN 0178-594X) **1059**
K M T *see* Kyrkomusikernas Tidning **3560**
K M U Monthly Newsletter *see* K M U News Report **1901**
K M U News Report. (Kansas Municipal Utilities, Inc.) (US) **1901**
K Mitteilungen. (GW ISSN 0451-1646) **3863**
K N A A S News *see* Kenya National Academy for Advancement of Arts and Sciences. Newsletter **4320**
K.N.G.M.G. Nieuwsbrief. (Koninklijk Nederlands Geologisch Mijnbouwkundig Genootschap) (NE ISSN 0165-7720) **1570**
K N V Ber *see* Voetbal Totaal **4514**
K O. (Knock Out) (US) **4477**
K O A Directory Road Atlas and Camping Guide. (Kampgrounds of America, Inc.) (US) **1141**, 4549
K O W A N I News. (Kongres Wanita Indonesia) (IO) **4846**, 2202
K Oe B *see* Katholische Oeffentliche Buecherei **2766**
K OE F F - Bladet - I N *see* Koeffbladet - I N **1079**
K P B S on Air. (US) **1375**, 1357
K P T News Bulletin. (Karachi Port Trust) (PK) **4730**
K: Plastic und Kautschuk Zeitung. (GW ISSN 0177-0608) **3863**
K R P. (Kostenrechnungspraxis) (GW ISSN 0931-9077) **1017**, 1538
K R S Jugoslavije/Carsus Jugoslaviae. (CI ISSN 0454-5478) **1570**, 1599
K: Revista de Poesia. (VE ISSN 0047-3030) **2996**

K S B Technische Berichte. (Klein, Schanzlin und Becker Aktiengesellschaft) (GW ISSN 0179-8715) **1828**
K S Bulletin. (Foreningen af Katolske Skoler i Danmark) (DK ISSN 0109-3886) **1729, 4266**
K S M E Journal. (Korean Society of Mechanical Engineers) (KO) **1934**
K S M Review. (Kerjasama Serbaguna Malaysia) (MY) **102**
K T B L - Schriften. (Kuratorium fuer Technik und Bauwesen in der Landwirtschaft e.V.) (GW) **102**
K T S - Zeitschrift fuer Insolvensrecht, Konkurs, Treuhand, Sanierung. (GW) **2642**
K - Theory. (NE ISSN 0920-3036) **3042**
K U L I M U. (Kunst, Literatur & Music) (GW) **2929, 2996**
K und L Magazin. (GW ISSN 0931-3117) **2301**
K und R see Keramische Rundschau Klima und Raum **355**
K V I C Annual Report. (Khadi and Village Industries Commission) (II) **1116**
K V P News. (CN ISSN 0022-7439) **3360**
K W Heute see Kloeckner Werke Heute **3411**
K W M Newsletter. (Kendall Whaling Museum) (US) **3526**, 332, 1607, 2412
K Z and Veteranfly Klubben see Veteranfly Klubben **64**
Ka Kuli O'Hawai'i. (US) **2288**
Kaapse Bibliotekaris. see Cape Librarian **2751**
De Kaarsvlam. (NE ISSN 0022-7463) **359**
Kabaare. (GH) **2192**
Kabaaru. (ML) **2010**
†Kabalarian Courier. (CN ISSN 0319-1648) **5222**
Kabar. (IO ISSN 0216-0269) **597**
Kabar. (AT ISSN 0311-0419) **3963**
Kabar Cocos. (AT) **2171**
Kabbalah. (IS ISSN 0334-6994) **4224**, 3771
Kabbalist. (UK) **3670**
Kabel & Satellit. (GW ISSN 0177-9249) **1375**
Kabel- og Liniemesteren. (DK) **1901**
Kablan Veboneh/Contractor and Builder.(IS) **622**
Kabul Mojala. (AF) **3771**, 2929
Kach Nazar. (US) **2929**
Kachiku Eisei Shikenjo Nenpo see Japan. Norin-sho Kachiku Eisei Shikenjo Nenpo **5220**
Kachina Talk see Security News (Los Angeles) **799**
Kacic. (CI ISSN 0453-0578) **2371**, 4186
Kadambini. (II) **2200**
Kadarot. (IS) **1165**
Kader Info see Inforcadre **983**
Kadima. (YU ISSN 0022-748X) **2870**, 4224
Kadmoniot. (IS ISSN 0033-4839) **276**, 3640
Kadmos. (GW ISSN 0022-7498) **276**
Kadrovi i Rad see Organizacija i Kadrovi **1068**
Kaduna State. Ministry of Works. Report. (NR) **4065**
Kaduna State Statistical Yearbook. (NR) **4576**
Kaelte see K K - die Kaelte und Klimatechnik **2301**
Kaelte Klima Aktuell. (GW ISSN 0722-4605) **2301**
Kaerntner Bauer. (AU) **102**, 2103
Kaerntner Gemeindeblatt. (AU ISSN 0022-7552) **4089**
Kaerntner Heimatleben. (AU ISSN 0022-7560) **2056**
Kaerntner Jaeger. (AU) **4549**
Kaerntner Landes-Zeitung. (AU ISSN 0022-7579) **4089**
Kaerntner Museumsschriften. (AU ISSN 0022-7587) **3526**, 2316
†Kaerntner Naturschutzblaetter. (AU ISSN 0022-7595) **5222**
Kaffa. (ET) **2075**
Kafka Society of America. Journal. (US ISSN 0894-6388) **2929**

Kafka Society of America. Newsletter see Kafka Society of America. Journal **2929**
Kagaku/Science. (JA ISSN 0022-7625) **4318**
Kagaku Asahi/Scientific Asahi. (JA ISSN 0368-4741) **4318**
Kagaku Gijutsu Bunken Sabisu/Science and Technology Information Service. (JA ISSN 0022-7633) **4318**, 4602
Kagaku Gijutsu Bunken Sokuho. Butsuri, Oyobutsuri-hen. see Current Bibliography on Science and Technology: Pure and Applied Physics **3837**
Kagaku Gijutsu Bunken Sokuho. Denki Kogaku-hen. see Current Bibliography on Science and Technology: Electronics and Electrical Engineering **1842**
Kagaku Gijutsu Bunken Sokuho. Doboku, Kenchiku Kogaku Hen/ Current Bibliography on Science and Technology: Civil Engineering and Architecture. (JA ISSN 0022-7641) **1845**, 16, 309
Kagaku Gijutsu Bunken Sokuho. Enerugi-hen. see Current Bibliography on Science and Technology: Energy **1798**
Kagaku Gijutsu Bunken Sokuho. Genshiryoku Kogaku-hen. see Current Bibliography on Science and Technology: Nuclear Engineering **1842**
Kagaku Gijutsu Bunken Sokuho. Kagaku, Kagaku Kogyo-hen (Gaikoku-hen). see Current Bibliography on Science and Technology: Chemistry and Chemical Engineering (Foreign) **1200**
Kagaku Gijutsu Bunken Sokuho. Kankyo Kogai-hen. see Current Bibliography on Science and Technology: Environmental Pollution **1973**
Kagaku Gijutsu Bunken Sokuho. Kanri Shisutemu Gijutsu-hen. see Current Bibliography on Science and Technology: Management Science and Systems Engineering **712**
Kagaku Gijutsu Bunken Sokuho. Kikai Kogaku-hen. see Current Bibliography on Science and Technology: Mechanical Engineering **1842**
Kagaku Gijutsu Bunken Sokuho. Kinzoku Kogaku, Kozan Kogaku, Chikyu no Kagaku-hen. see Current Bibliography on Science and Technology: Earth Science, Mining and Metallurgy **1550**
Kagaku Gijutsu Bunken Sokuho. Raifusaiensu Hen. see Current Bibliography on Science and Technology: Life Sciences **464**
Kagaku Gijutsu Bunken Sokuho Kagaku. Kagaku Kogyo-hen (Kokunai-hen). see Current Bibliography on Science and Technology: Chemistry and Chemical Engineering (Japanese) **1200**
Kagaku Gijutsu Bunken Toyama/ Toyama Science and Technical Documents. (JA ISSN 0022-765X) **4614**, 2794, 4356
Kagaku Gijutsu-cho Nenpo. (JA) **4602**, 4318
Kagaku Gijutsu Foramu Hokokusho. (JA) **4614**, 4318
Kagaku Gijutsu Hakusho/White Paper of Science and Technology in Japan. (JA) **4602**, 4318
Kagaku Gijutsu Hakusho no Aramashi. (JA) **4602**, 4318
Kagaku Gijutsu Kenkyu Chosa Hokoku/ Report on the Survey of Research and Development. (JA) **4602**
Kagaku Gijutsu Kenkyu Chosa Kekka no Gaiyo. (JA) **4602**
Kagaku Gijutsu Kenkyujo Hokoku. see Japan. National Chemical Laboratory for Industry. Journal **1179**
Kagaku Gijutsu Shinko Choseihi Nyusu. (JA) **4602**, 4318
Kagaku Gijutsu Shinko Choseihi Shiken Kenkyu Jisshi Keikaku. (JA) **4602**, 4318

Kagaku Keisatsu Kenkyujo Hokoku Bohan Shonen Hen/National Research Insititute of Police Science. Report. Research on Prevention of Crime and Delinquency. (JA ISSN 0451-1999) **1517**
Kagaku Keisatsu Kenkyujo Hokoku Hokagaku Hen/National Research Institute of Police Science. Report. Research of Forensic Science. (JA ISSN 0285-7960) **3265**
Kagaku Keisatsu Kenkyujo Hokoku Kotsu Ken/National Research Institute of Police Science. Report. Research on Traffic Safety and Regulation. (JA ISSN 0451-2006) **4694**
Kagaku Keisatsu Kenkyujo Nenpo/ National Research Institute of Police Science. Annual Report. (JA ISSN 0453-0667) **1517**
†Kagaku Keisatsu Kenkyujo Shiryo/ National Research Institute of Police Science. Data. (JA ISSN 0453-0675) **5222**
Kagaku Kisoron Kenkyu/Japan Association for Philosophy of Science. Journal. (JA ISSN 0022-7668) **4319**
Kagaku Koenkai Koen Yoshi. (JA) **3823**, 1181
Kagaku Kogaku/Chemical Engineering. (JA ISSN 0022-7676) **1856**
Kagaku Kogaku Ronbunshu. (JA) **1856**
Kagaku Kogyo Nippo/Chemical Daily. (JA) **1182**, 1856
†Kagaku Kojo/Chemical Factory. (JA ISSN 0451-2030) **5223**
Kagaku Kyoiku Kenkyu/Journal of Science Education in Japan. (JA ISSN 0386-4553) **4319**, 1644
Kagaku Land. (JA) **1257**
Kagaku Saron. (JA ISSN 0386-183X) **4319**
Kagaku Shinbun/Science News. (JA) **4319**
Kagaku Shoho/Chemical Abstracts. (JA ISSN 0386-2143) **1202**, 16
Kagaku Tetsugaku/Philosophy of Science. (JA ISSN 0289-3428) **4319**
Kagaku to Kogyo (Osaka)/Science and Industry. (JA ISSN 0368-5918) **4602**, 1828, 4319
Kagaku to Kogyo (Tokyo)/Chemistry and Chemical Industry. (JA ISSN 0022-7684) **1182**, 1856
Kagakushi Kenkyu/Journal of History of Science. (JA ISSN 0022-7692) **4319**
Kagami. (GW) **2870**
Kagan Census of Cable and Pay TV. (US ISSN 0732-2283) **1375**
Kagawa Daigaku Kyoikugakubu Kenkyu Hokoku. Dai-2-Bu/Kagawa University. Faculty of Education. Memoirs. Part 2. (JA ISSN 0389-3057) **4319**, 1644
Kagawa Prefecture Agricultural Experiment Station. Bulletin. (JA ISSN 0374-8804) **102**
Kagawa University. Faculty of Education. Memoirs. Part 2. see Kagawa Daigaku Kyoikugakubu Kenkyu Hokoku. Dai-2-Bu **4319**
Kagoshima Daigaku. Nankanen Shiryo Senta. Hokoku/Kagoshima University. Reference Center of the Scientific Researches for the Southwest Pacific Area. Reports. (JA ISSN 0287-7791) **1607**
Kagoshima Daigaku Igaku Zasshi/ Medical Journal of Kagoshima University. (JA ISSN 0368-5063) **3119**
Kagoshima Daigaku Kyoikugakubu Kenkyu Kiyo. Shizen Kagaku Hen/ Kagoshima University. Faculty of Education. Bulletin. Natural Science. (JA ISSN 0389-6692) **4319**, 1644
Kagoshima Daigaku Nogakubu Kiyo. see Kagoshima University. Faculty of Agriculture. Memoirs **102**

Kagoshima Daigaku Rigakubu Kiyo. Chigaku, Seibutsugaku/Kagoshima University. Faculty of Science. Reports. Earth Sciences and Biology. (JA ISSN 0385-4019) **1546**, 445
Kagoshima Daigaku Rigakubu Kiyo. Sugaku, Butsurigaku, Kagaku/ Kagoshima University. Faculty of Science. Reports. Mathematics, Physics, Chemistry. (JA ISSN 0385-4027) **4319**, 1182, 3042, 3823
Kagoshima-ken Nogyo Kisho Geppo/ Monthly Report of Agricultural Meteorology, Kagoshima Prefecture. (JA ISSN 0022-7706) **3438**, 102
Kagoshima-kenritsu Tanki Daigaku Kiyo. Shizen Kagaku Hen/Kagoshima Prefectural Junior College. Bulletin. Natural Sciences. (JA ISSN 0286-1208) **4319**
Kagoshima Prefectural Junior College. Bulletin. Natural Sciences. see Kagoshima-kenritsu Tanki Daigaku Kiyo. Shizen Kagaku Hen **4319**
Kagoshima University. Faculty of Agriculture. Memoirs/Kagoshima Daigaku Nogakubu Kiyo. (JA ISSN 0453-0853) **102**
Kagoshima University. Faculty of Education. Bulletin. Natural Science. see Kagoshima Daigaku Kyoikugakubu Kenkyu Kiyo. Shizen Kagaku Hen **4319**
Kagoshima University. Faculty of Science. Reports. Earth Sciences and Biology. see Kagoshima Daigaku Rigakubu Kiyo. Chigaku, Seibutsugaku **1546**
Kagoshima University. Faculty of Science. Reports. Mathematics, Physics, Chemistry. see Kagoshima Daigaku Rigakubu Kiyo. Sugaku, Butsurigaku, Kagaku **4319**
Kagoshima University. Reference Center of the Scientific Researches for the Southwest Pacific Area. Reports. see Kagoshima Daigaku. Nankanen Shiryo Senta. Hokoku **1607**
Kahane. (US) **2010**
Kahertaja. (FI ISSN 0022-7714) **373**
Kahtou see Kahtou Native News **2010**
Kahtou Native News. (CN) **2010**
Kai. (GR) **2196**
Kaibogaku Zasshi. see Acta Anatomica Nipponica **425**
Kaichu Koen Kenkyujo Kenkyu Hokoku. see Marine Park Research Stations. Bulletin **4323**
Kaifa Bao/Development News. (CC) **871**
Kaigai Gijutsu Hairaito/Technology Highlight. (JA ISSN 0022-7730) **4602**
Kaigai Gijutsu Kyoryoku see Kokusai Kyoryoku **3964**
Kaigai Kagaku Gijutsu Shiryo Geppo. see National Diet Library. Monthly List of Foreign Scientific and Technical Publications **4615**
Kaigai Keizai Kyoryoku Kikin Nenpo. see Overseas Economic Cooperation Fund. Annual Report **933**
Kaigai Kogyo Jijo Chosa Hokokusho: Indo, Pakisutan, Banguradesshu. see Report of Overseas Mining Investigation: India, Pakistan, Bangladesh **3494**
Kaigai Kogyo Jijo Chosa Hokokusho: Madagasukaru, Suwajirando. see Report of Overseas Mining Investigation: Madagascar, Swaziland **3494**
Kaigai Sato Joho. see World Sugar News **196**
Kaigaki Kagaku Gijutsu Joho Shiryo. see Scientific and Technical Information in Foreign Countries **4341**
Kaigan Kogaku Koenkai Ronbunshu/ Proceedings of the Japanese Conference on Coastal Engineering. (JA) **1870**
Kaihatsu Ronshu/Journal of Development Policy Studies. (JA ISSN 0288-089X) **871**, 932, 1961
Kaiji Sangyo Kenkyujoho/Japan Maritime Research Institute. Bulletin. (JA ISSN 0286-9152) **4730**

Kaijo Hoan-cho. Suiro-bu Kansoku Hokoku. Eisei Sokuchi Hen/Data Report of Hydrographic Observations. Series of Satellite Geodesy. (JA ISSN 0914-5753) **1592**, **4730**
Kaijo Hoan-cho. Suiro-bu Kansoku Hokoku. Tenmon Sokuchi Hen/Data Report of Hydrographic Observations. Series of Astronomy and Geodesy. (JA ISSN 0287-2633) **1592**, **366**
Kaikuja Hameesta. (FI) **2371**
Kailash. (NP) **2339**, **2056**, **3902**, **4441**
Kaimana. (US) **2870**
Kainai News. (CN ISSN 0047-3081) **2010**
Kairi. (TR) **2870**
Kairos. (US ISSN 0277-710X) **2870**
Kairos. (FR ISSN 1148-9227) **3771**
Kairos. (AU ISSN 0022-7757) **4186**
Kairuigaku Zasshi. see Venus: Japanese Journal of Malacology **593**
Kaiserswerther Mitteilungen. (GW ISSN 0022-779X) **4186**
Kaiserzeit. (US) **2371**, **3462**
Kaisha Shikiho. (JA) **1141**
†Kaissa. (GR) **5223**
Kaiun/Shipping. (JA ISSN 0022-7803) **4730**
Kaiyo Chosa Gyogyo Shiken Yoho. see Hokkaido University. Faculty of Fisheries. Data Record of Oceanographic Observations and Exploratory Fishing **1605**
Kaiyo Jiho/Current Oceanography. (JA ISSN 0385-2687) **1546**, **1607**
Kaiyo Kaihatsu Ronbunshu/Proceedings of the Ocean Development Symposium. (JA) **1870**
Kajian Veterinar see Kajian Veterinar Malaysia **5223**
†Kajian Veterinar Malaysia. (MY ISSN 0126-9437) **5223**
Kakao und Zucker. (GW ISSN 0022-7838) **2088**
Kakatiya Journal of English Studies. (II) **2929**
Kaks Plus. (FI ISSN 0355-4252) **2186**, **1240**
Kakteen - Sukkulenten. (GW) **508**
Kakteen und Andere Sukkulenten. (GW ISSN 0022-7846) **508**
Kaktusbluete. (GW) **1240**, **4773**
Kaktusy. (CS ISSN 0862-4372) **2133**
Kaku Igaku/Japanese Journal of Nuclear Medicine. (JA ISSN 0022-7854) **3360**
Kakyevole. (GH ISSN 0022-7862) **4065**
Kalaallit Nunaani Aalisakkanik Misissuinerit. Ukiumoortumik Nalunaarusiaq. (DK ISSN 0905-5215) **2045**
Kalaallit Nunaat. see Groenland (Copenhagen) **4572**
Kalai Magal. (II) **2929**
Kalaikathir. (II ISSN 0022-7870) **4319**
Kalakalpam. (II ISSN 0047-3103) **1531**
†Kalakshetra Quarterly. (II) **5223**
Kalamanakaranaya. (CE) **1017**
Kalamazoo College Quarterly. (US ISSN 8750-5746) **1315**
Kalami Rishate. (II) **2996**
Kalamies. (FI ISSN 0085-2449) **2045**
Kalantar. (BG) **2174**
Kalapaikkaopas see Suomen Kalapaikkaopas **4557**
Kalapatra. (II) **2870**
Kalastaja. (FI ISSN 0357-8682) **2045**
Kalatdlit Nunane Inuit. see Groenlands Befolkning **3982**
Kalatdlitnunane Augtitagssanik Atortugssiagssiat Pivdlugit. Faellesraadet Naluaerut see Joint Committee on Mineral Resources in Greenland. Annual Report **3486**
Kalava Ha Sahityaya. (CE) **2929**, **332**
Kalayaan see Mosaik **2214**
Kalba Vilnius. (LI) **1375**
Kalbos Kultura. (LI ISSN 0022-7900) **2822**
Kalbotyra/Linguistics. (LI ISSN 0202-330X) **2822**
Kaldron. (US) **2996**, **332**

Kale. (TZ) **2316**
Kale Memorial Lectures see R.B.R.R. Kale Memorial Lectures **3921**
Kaleidoscope. see Wanhuatong Lianhuan Huabao **1270**
Kaleidoscope. (CH ISSN 1016-4162) **2870**
Kaleidoscope. (CN) **3322**, **2466**
Kaleidoscope. (PL) **4803**
Kaleidoscope. (Akron). (US ISSN 0748-8742) **2929**, **332**, **1738**, **4411**
Kaleidoscope (Asheville) see Blue Banner **1305**
Kaleidoscope (Birmingham). (US) **1315**
Kaleidoscope (Madison). (US) **1644**
Kaleidoscope Canada see Projection (Montreal) **2020**
Kaleidoscope: Current World Data. (US) **3963**
†Kalejdoskop Techniki. (PL ISSN 0137-8856) **5223**
Kalendar - Al'manakh Novoho Shliakhu/New Pathway Almanac. (CN) **2010**
†Kalendar Jednota. (US) **5223**
Kalendar Odborara. (CS) **2585**, **3393**
Kalendarz Slowa Bozego. (PL ISSN 0860-410X) **4266**
Kalender fuer den Biogarten. (GW ISSN 0931-380X) **2133**
Kalevalaseuran Vuosikirja. (FI ISSN 0355-0311) **2929**
Kali und Steinsalz. (GW) **3486**
Kalikasan. (PH ISSN 0115-0553) **445**
Al-Kalima. (YE) **2870**
†Kalininskii Nauchno-issledovatel'skii Institut Tekstil'noi Promyshlennosti. Nauchno-issledovatel'skie Trudy. (UR) **5223**
Kalis' Shopping Center Leasing Directory. (US ISSN 0899-8930) **4151**, **1141**
Kalkala Umischar. (IS) **675**
Kalkandu. (II) **2200**
Kalki. (US ISSN 0022-7994) **2929**
Kalki. (II) **2929**
†Kalki. (FR) **5223**
Kalle Anka och Co. (SW) **1258**
Kalliope. (US ISSN 0735-7885) **2929**, **4846**
Kalmia. (US ISSN 0453-1388) **508**
Kalnirnay. (II) **359**, **2448**
Kalori. (AT ISSN 0047-312X) **332**
Kaltio. (FI) **2870**
Kalulu. (MW) **2929**, **243**
Kaluvabala. (II) **4846**
Kalyan. (II ISSN 0022-8028) **4186**
Kalyani. (CE) **2510**, **4378**
Kamaq Maki. (PE) **2412**, **332**
Kamar Dagang dan Industri di Jawa Barat. Daftar Anggota. see Chamber of Commerce and Industry in West Java. Member List **811**
Kamarat. (CS) **1258**
Kamer van Koophandel en Fabrieken voor Amsterdam. Jaarrede. (NE) **818**
Kamer van Koophandel en Fabrieken voor Eemland. Kamer van Koophandel. (NE) **818**
Kamer van Koophandel en Nijverheid van Antwerpen. Bulletin see Chambre de Commerce et d'Industrie d'Anvers. Bulletin **812**
Kamera see Technikon Forum **1717**
Kamera. (DK) **3792**
Kamera und Schule see Medien Aktiv **3793**
Kamerad Tier. (AU ISSN 0022-8117) **3711**
Kameradschaft der Wiener Panzer-Division. Mitteilungsblatt. (AU ISSN 0029-974X) **3462**
Kameradschaftsbund Sechste Panzerdivision. Nachrichtenblatt. (GW) **3462**
Kameralehti. (FI ISSN 0022-8133) **3792**
Kami Pa Gikyoshi. see Japan T A P P I Journal **3663**
Kami Parupu Tokei Geppo/Paper & Pulp Statistical Monthly. (JA ISSN 0022-8168) **3663**
Kami Parupu Tokei Nenpo/Yearbook of Pulp and Paper Statistics. (JA ISSN 0453-1515) **3663**

Kami Ryutsu Tokei Geppo. see Monthly Statistics of Paper Distribution **3668**
Kamishihoro-cho Higashi Taisetsu Hakubutsukan Kenkyu Hokoku/ Higashi Taisetsu Museum of Natural History. Bulletin. (JA) **4319**, **3526**
Kamm und Schere. (GW ISSN 0022-8176) **373**
Kammer Nachrichten. (AU ISSN 0022-8184) **818**
Kampanje! (NO ISSN 0022-8214) **1044**
Kampeer en Caravankampioen. (NE) **4773**
Kampeertoerist. (BE ISSN 0775-8545) **4549**
Kampf dem Krieg. (AU ISSN 0022-8230) **3963**
Kampgrounds of America, Inc. Directory Road Atlas and Camping Guide see K O A Directory Road Atlas and Camping Guide **1141**
Kampioen. (NE ISSN 0022-8265) **4773**
Kampsville Seminars in Archeology. (US) **276**
Kamratposten. (SW ISSN 0022-8273) **1258**
Kan Anders. (NE ISSN 0925-5893) **3963**, **1961**, **4441**
Kanada Kurier. (CN) **2010**
Kanadai Magyarsag/Canadian Hungarians. (CN ISSN 0022-8281) **2010**, **2177**
Kanadske Listy/Canadian Pages. (CN) **2010**
Kanadski Srobobran. (CN) **2010**
Kanadsky Slovak/Canadian Slovak. (CN ISSN 0047-3154) **2010**
Kanagawa Association of Psychiatry. Journal. see Kanagawa-ken Seishin Igakkaishi **3344**
Kanagawa Dental College. Bulletin. (JA ISSN 0385-1443) **3237**
Kanagawa Horticultural Experiment Station. Bulletin. (JA ISSN 0374-8731) **2133**
Kanagawa-ken Hakubutsukan Kyokai Kaiho/Kanagawa-ken Museum Gazette. (JA) **3526**
Kanagawa-ken Museum Gazette. see Kanagawa-ken Hakubutsukan Kyokai Kaiho **3526**
Kanagawa-ken Seishin Igakkaishi/ Kanagawa Association of Psychiatry. Journal. (JA ISSN 0288-9617) **3344**
Kanagawa-kenritsu Hakubutsukan Kenkyu Hokoku. Shizen Kagaku/ Kanagawa Prefectural Museum. Bulletin. Natural Science. (JA ISSN 0453-1906) **4319**, **3526**
Kanagawa-kenritsu Shizen Hogo Senta Hokoku. (JA ISSN 0914-8744) **1490**
Kanagawa Medical Association. Journal see Kanagawa Medical Prefecture Association. Journal **3119**
Kanagawa Medical Prefecture Association. Journal. (JA) **3119**
Kanagawa Odontological Society. Journal. see Kanagawa Shigaku **3237**
Kanagawa Prefectural Museum. Bulletin. Natural Science. see Kanagawa-kenritsu Hakubutsukan Kenkyu Hokoku. Shizen Kagaku **4319**
Kanagawa Shigaku/Kanagawa Odontological Society. Journal. (JA ISSN 0454-8302) **3237**
Kanagawa Shizenshi Shiryo/Natural History Report of Kanagawa. (JA ISSN 0388-9009) **4319**
Kanagawa University. Institute for Humanities Research. Bulletin. (JA ISSN 0287-7082) **2510**
Kanagawa University. Institute of Humanities. Bulletin see Kanagawa University. Institute for Humanities Research. Bulletin **2510**
Kanak. (BG) **2174**
†Kanan. (PE) **5223**
Kanara Chamber of Commerce & Industry Journal. (II ISSN 0300-4074) **818**
Kanarienfreund. (GW) **565**, **3711**
Kanaski Srbobran/Canadian Serbian. (CN ISSN 0022-829X) **2010**

Kanava. (FI ISSN 0355-0303) **2870**
Kanazawa Daigaku Kogakubu Kiyo/ Kanazawa University. Faculty of Technology. Memoirs. (JA ISSN 0022-832X) **4602**
Kanazawa Daigaku Kyoikugakubu Kiyo. Jinbun, Shakai Kyoiku Kagaku. see Kanazawa University. Faculty of Education. Bulletin: Humanities, Social and Educational Sciences **1644**
Kanazawa Daigaku Kyoikugakubu Kiyo. Shizen Kagaku Hen/Kanazawa University. Faculty of Education. Bulletin. Natural Sciences. (JA ISSN 0387-0995) **4319**
Kanazawa Daigaku Kyoyobu Ronshu. Shizen Kagaku Hen/Kanazawa University. College of Liberal Arts. Annals of Science. (JA ISSN 0302-0479) **4319**
Kanazawa Daigaku Rigakubu Ronbun Oyobi Chosho Mokuroku/Kanazawa University. Faculty of Science. List of Publications. (JA) **4356**
Kanazawa Daigaku Rika Hokoku. see Kanazawa University. Science Reports **4319**
†Kanazawa Irigaku Sosho/Journal of Radiology and Physical Therapy. (JA ISSN 0022-8311) **5223**
Kanazawa University. College of Liberal Arts. Annals of Science. see Kanazawa Daigaku Kyoyobu Ronshu. Shizen Kagaku Hen **4319**
Kanazawa University. Faculty of Education. Bulletin: Humanities, Social and Educational Sciences/ Kanazawa Daigaku Kyoikugakubu Kiyo. Jinbun, Shakai Kyoiku Kagaku. (JA) **1644**
Kanazawa University. Faculty of Education. Bulletin. Natural Sciences. see Kanazawa Daigaku Kyoikugakubu Kiyo. Shizen Kagaku Hen **4319**
Kanazawa University. Faculty of Law and Literature. Studies and Essays. (JA ISSN 0453-1981) **2929**, **2642**
Kanazawa University. Faculty of Science. List of Publications. see Kanazawa Daigaku Rigakubu Ronbun Oyobi Chosho Mokuroku **4356**
Kanazawa University. Faculty of Technology. Memoirs. see Kanazawa Daigaku Kogakubu Kiyo **4602**
Kanazawa University. Science Reports/ Kanazawa Daigaku Rika Hokoku. (JA ISSN 0022-8338) **4319**
Kancha Kexue Jishu/Science and Technology of Prospecting. (CC ISSN 1001-3946) **3486**
Kanchan Prabha. (II) **2200**
Kandang Kerbau Hospital Bulletin see Singapore Journal of Obstetrics & Gynaecology **3296**
Kandelaar. (NE ISSN 0022-8354) **1644**, **4186**
Kane County Marketing Directory. (US) **1141**
Kane's Beverage Week. (US ISSN 0882-2573) **382**
Kang Fu/Rehabilitation. (CC) **3119**
Kangaroo. (AT ISSN 1036-3262) **2870**
Kango/Nursing. (JA ISSN 0022-8362) **3281**
Kango Gakusei/Nurse Student. (JA ISSN 0385-5988) **3281**
Kango Gijutsu/Japanese Journal of Nursing Arts. (JA ISSN 0449-752X) **3281**
Kango Kenkyu/Japanese Journal of Nursing Research. (JA ISSN 0022-8370) **3281**
Kango Kyoiku/Japanese Journal of Nursing Education. (JA ISSN 0047-1895) **3281**
Kango Tenbo/Japanese Journal of Nursing Science. (JA ISSN 0385-549X) **3281**
Kangogaku Zasshi/Nursing Magazine. (JA ISSN 0387-351X) **3281**
Kanguka. (RW) **2169**
Kangura. (RW) **2169**
Kanhistique. (US ISSN 0738-9736) **258**
Kanina. (CR ISSN 0378-0473) **2929**, **332**

Kankan. (BG) 2174
Kankyo Gijutsu/Environmental Conservation Engineering. (JA ISSN 0388-9459) 1961
Kankyo Mondai Shinpojumu Koen Ronbunshu/Symposium on Environmental Problems. Proceedings. (JA) 1870, 1961
Kano-Bulletin see Kano-Sport 4525
Kano-Sport. (NE) 4525
Kano State Courier. (NR) 2212
Kano State of Nigeria Gazette. (NR) 4065, 2642
Kano State Statistical Year Book. (NR) 4576
†Kano Studies. (NR ISSN 0567-4840) 5223
Kanon. (AU ISSN 0259-0727) 2642, 4186
Kanot-Nytt. (SW ISSN 0022-8397) 4525
Kansai Daigaku Keizai Ronshu. see Kansai University Economic Review 675
Kansai Daigaku Kogaku Kenkyu Hokoku. see Kansai University Technology Reports 4602
Kansai Ika Daigaku. Zasshi. see Kansai Medical University. Journal 3119
Kansai Medical University. Journal/ Kansai Ika Daigaku. Zasshi. (JA) 3119
Kansai Shizen Kagaku. (JA ISSN 0285-3205) 4319
Kansai University Economic Review/ Kansai Daigaku Keizai Ronshu. (JA ISSN 0449-7554) 675
Kansai University Review of Law and Politics. (JA ISSN 0388-886X) 2642, 3902
Kansai University Technology Reports/ Kansai Daigaku Kogaku Kenkyu Hokoku. (JA ISSN 0453-2198) 4602
Kansainvalinen Automatkailu see Autolla Ulkomaille 4753
Kansallis-Osake-Pankki. Economic Review. (FI ISSN 0022-8419) 675
Kansallis-Osake-Pankki. Taloudellinen Katsaus. (FI ISSN 0355-0044) 675
Kansantaloudellinen Aikakauskirja/ Finnish Economic Journal. (FI ISSN 0022-8427) 675
Kansas! (US ISSN 0022-8435) 2227
Kansas. Department of Health and Environment. Annual Summary of Vital Statistics. (US) 3984
†Kansas. Juvenile Justice Information Center. Annual Report. (US) 5223
Kansas. Legislative Research Department. Report on Kansas Legislative Interim Studies. (US ISSN 0270-4331) 3902
Kansas. State Board of Agriculture. Annual Report with Farm Facts. (US) 102
Kansas. State Board of Agriculture. Report see Kansas. State Board of Agriculture. Annual Report with Farm Facts 102
Kansas. State Conservation Commission. Conservation in Kansas see Conservation in Kansas 1486
Kansas. Water Office. Annual Report on Water-Related Studies-Research in Kansas. (US) 4826
Kansas. Water Office. Fact Sheet. (US) 4826
Kansas. Water Office. Semi-Annual Report on Water-Related Studies-Research in Kansas. see Kansas. Water Office. Annual Report on Water-Related Studies-Research in Kansas 4826
Kansas Academy of Science. Transactions. (US ISSN 0022-8443) 4319, 4034
Kansas Agriculture Report see Kansas. State Board of Agriculture. Annual Report with Farm Facts 102
Kansas Alumni Magazine. (US ISSN 0745-3345) 1315
Kansas Anthropological Association. Journal see The Kansas Anthropologist 243
Kansas Anthropological Association Newsletter. (US) 243, 276

The Kansas Anthropolotist. (US) 243, 276
Kansas Banker. (US ISSN 0022-8478) 788
Kansas Bar Association. Journal. (US ISSN 0022-8486) 2642
Kansas Beverage News. (US ISSN 0022-8494) 382
Kansas Business News. (US ISSN 0199-3607) 871
Kansas Citian. (US ISSN 0274-9912) 818
Kansas City Business Journal. (US) 871
▼Kansas City Commerce. (US) 1044
Kansas City Genealogist. (US ISSN 0451-3991) 2156
Kansas City Grocer. (US ISSN 0022-8516) 2092
Kansas City Grocer Annual Food Industry Directory. (US) 2092
Kansas City Jewish Chronicle. (US ISSN 0022-8524) 2010
Kansas City Labor Beacon. (US) 985
Kansas City Live! (US) 2227
Kansas City Magazine. (US ISSN 0193-2020) 2227
†Kansas City Medical Guide. (US) 5223
Kansas City Squire. (US) 2227
Kansas Corn Performance Tests. (US) 207
Kansas Country Living. (US ISSN 0091-9586) 102
Kansas Dental Association. Journal. (US) 3237
Kansas Directory of Commerce. (US) 1141, 837
Kansas Electric Farmer see Kansas Country Living 102
Kansas Engineer. (US ISSN 0022-8559) 1828
Kansas Entomological Society. Journal. (US ISSN 0022-8567) 535
▼Kansas Facts. (US ISSN 1051-7138) 1781
Kansas Farm Bureau News. (US ISSN 0022-8575) 102
Kansas Farmer. (US) 220
Kansas Farmers Fastline see Farmers Fastline: Kansas Edition 162
Kansas Food Dealers Bulletin. (US ISSN 0022-8605) 2092, 200
Kansas Food News. (US) 2075
Kansas Geological Survey. Bulletin. (US) 1570
Kansas Geological Survey. Chemical Quality Series. (US) 1570
Kansas Geological Survey. Educational Series. (US) 1570
Kansas Geological Survey. Energy Resources Series. (US) 1792, 1546
Kansas Geological Survey. Geology Series. (US) 1570
Kansas Geological Survey. Ground Water Series. (US) 1599
Kansas Geological Survey. Subsurface Geology Series. (US) 1570
Kansas Golf. (US) 4507
Kansas Government Journal. (US ISSN 0022-8613) 4089
Kansas Grain Sorghum Performance Tests see Kansas Sorghum Performance Tests. Grain & Forage 207
Kansas History. (US ISSN 0149-9114) 2412
Kansas Horseman. (US) 4536
Kansas Insurance. (US ISSN 0194-634X) 2536
▼Kansas - Iowa Environmental Law Letter. (US) 2642
Kansas Journal of Sociology see Mid-American Review of Sociology 4443
†Kansas Justice Information System. Resource Directory (Year). (US) 5223
Kansas Library Association Newsletter see K L A Newsletter 2766
Kansas Living. (US) 102
Kansas Medical Society. Journal see Kansas Medicine 3119
Kansas Medicine. (US ISSN 8755-0059) 3119
Kansas Municipal Utilities, Inc. News Report see K M U News Report 1901

Kansas Music Review. (US ISSN 0022-8702) 3559, 1753
Kansas Nurse. (US ISSN 0022-8710) 3281
Kansas Oil Marketer. (US) 3691
Kansas Optometric Journal. (US) 3302
Kansas Ornithological Society. Bulletin. (US ISSN 0022-8729) 565
Kansas Precancel News. (US) 3754
Kansas Publisher. (US ISSN 0022-8737) 2572, 4002
Kansas Quarterly. (US ISSN 0022-8745) 2510
Kansas Restaurant. (US ISSN 0022-8753) 2477, 2075
Kansas Review. (US ISSN 1043-7657) 2156
Kansas Sorghum Performance Tests. Grain & Forage. (US) 207
Kansas Speech - Language - Hearing Association Journal. (US) 1738, 4106
Kansas State Engineer. (US ISSN 0047-3189) 1828
Kansas State Teachers College Alumni Association. Alumni News see Spotlight (Emporia) 1325
Kansas State University. Computing Activities Newsletter see Kansas State University. Computing and Telecommunications Newsletter 1397
Kansas State University. Computing and Telecommunications Newsletter. (US) 1397
Kansas State University. Food and Feed Grain Institute. Technical Assistance in Grain Storage, Processing and Marketing, and Agribusiness Development. (US) 207
Kansas State University. Library Bibliography Series. (US ISSN 0075-4951) 404
Kansas Stockman. (US ISSN 0022-8826) 220
Kansas Teacher. (US ISSN 0022-8834) 1644
Kansas Transporter see Mid-America Transporter 4746
Kansas Water Plan. (US) 4826
Kansas Water Resources Research Institute. Annual Report. (US ISSN 0160-2659) 4826
Kansas Weekly Journal. (US) 2227
Kansas Wildflower Society Newsletter. (US) 2133
Kansas Wildlife see Kansas Wildlife & Parks 1490
Kansas Wildlife & Parks. (US) 1490, 4549
Kansas Works. (US) 675
Kansas 4-H Journal. (US) 102, 1299
Kansatieteellinen Arkisto. (FI ISSN 0355-1830) 243
Kansokujo Kisho Nenpo/Annual Report of Climatological Stations. (JA) 3438
Kant Studien. (GW ISSN 0022-8877) 3771
Kantil. (SP) 2929
Kantinen. (DK ISSN 0022-8885) 1299, 2075
Kantoor en Efficiency. (NE ISSN 0022-8893) 1059
Kantoor Revue. (NE) 1059, 1414
Kantoor - School - Huis. (NE ISSN 0022-8907) 1059
Kantu. (PE) 332
Kantu Shuohua/Picture Talk. (CC) 1258
Kanu Sport. (GW ISSN 0022-8923) 4525
Kaogu/Archaeology. (CC ISSN 0453-2899) 276
Kaogu Xuebao/Acta Archaeologica Sinica. (CC ISSN 0453-2902) 276
Kaogu yu Wenwu/Archaeology and Cultural Relics. (CC ISSN 1000-7830) 277
Kaohsiung Journal of Medical Sciences. (CH ISSN 0257-5655) 3119, 3733
Kapital. (NO ISSN 0332-5423) 1017
Kappa Delta Epsilon Current see The Current of Kappa Delta Epsilon 1309
Kappa Delta Pi Record. (US ISSN 0022-8958) 1644

Kappa Gamma Pi News. (US) 1710, 4266
Kappa Kappa Iota Bulletin see Kappa Kappa Iota Newsletter 1644
Kappa Kappa Iota Newsletter. (US) 1644, 1299
Kappa Pi International Honorary Art Fraternity. Sketch Book see Sketch Book 344
Kappa Tau Alpha. Newsletter. (US) 2572
Kapper en Kapsels. (BE) 373
▼Kar va Tawsi'ah/Labour and Development. (IR) 4411
Karachi. Chamber of Commerce and Industry. Annual Report. (PK ISSN 0075-5079) 818
Karachi. Chamber of Commerce and Industry. Guide for Industrial Investment in Pakistan. (PK) 953
Karachi. Chamber of Commerce and Industry. News Bulletin. (PK) 818
Karachi. Chamber of Commerce and Industry. Pattern of Foreign Trade of Pakistan. (PK) 915
Karachi. Chamber of Commerce and Industry. Report see Karachi. Chamber of Commerce and Industry. Annual Report 818
Karachi Journal of Science. (PK ISSN 0250-5363) 4319
Karachi Port Trust. Year Book of Information, Port of Karachi, Pakistan. (PK ISSN 0075-5109) 4652
Karachi Port Trust News Bulletin see K P T News Bulletin 4730
Karakul. (SX) 220
Karala Sabdam. (II) 2200
Karamu. (US ISSN 0022-8990) 2929
Karat see Cursillo 4173
Karate. (FR) 4477
Karate and Oriental Arts. (UK ISSN 0022-9008) 4477, 3640, 4773
†Karate Budokan International Anniversary. (MY) 5223
†Karate Forum. (US) 5223
Karate Illustrated see Karate - Kung Fu Illustrated 4477
Karate International. (US) 4477
Karate - Kung Fu Illustrated. (US ISSN 0888-031X) 4477
Karayollari Teknik Bulteni. (TU ISSN 0022-9024) 1870
Kardio. (GW ISSN 0724-9187) 3119, 3210
Kardiologia Polska. (PL ISSN 0022-9032) 3210
Kardiologiya/Cardiology. (RU ISSN 0022-9040) 3210
†Karger Biobehavioral Medicine Series. (SZ ISSN 0254-5373) 5223
†Karger Continuing Education Series. (SZ ISSN 0254-1270) 5223
Karibu. (KE) 4773
†Karikazo. (US ISSN 0164-2537) 5223
Karinca. (TU) 831
Karjala. (FI) 2371
†Karjatalous. (FI ISSN 0047-3251) 5223
Karka/Land. (IS ISSN 0302-6248) 2490
Karl August Forster Lectures. (GW ISSN 0340-5419) 445
†Karl Marx Universitaet, Leipzig. Wissenschaftliche Zeitschrift. (GW) 5223
Karl-May-Gesellschaft. Jahrbuch. (GW ISSN 0300-1989) 2929
Karl-May-Gesellschaft. Mitteilungen. (GW) 2929
Karlebynejden. (FI ISSN 0783-6864) 2371
Karlovacki Tjednik. (CI ISSN 0022-9059) 2870
Karlsbader Zeitung. (GW) 2010, 2371
Karlsruher Bote. (GW) 2929, 2996
Karlsruher Greif. (GW) 2536
Karlsruher Juristische Bibliographie. (GW ISSN 0453-3283) 2699
Karmasangsthaan. (II) 2200
Al-Karmil. (IS) 2929, 2010
Karnaphuli Shipping News. (BG) 4730
Karnatak Granthalaya. (II ISSN 0022-9083) 2766

Karnatak University. College of Education. Journal. (II ISSN 0022-4979) **1644**
Karnatak University, Dharwad, India. Journal. Humanities. (II ISSN 0075-515X) **2510**
Karnatak University, Dharwad, India. Journal. Science. (II ISSN 0075-5168) **4319**
Karnatak University, Dharwad, India. Journal. Social Sciences. (II ISSN 0075-5176) **4378**
Karnataka. Department of Tourism. Annual Report. (II) **4774**, **4065**
Karnataka. Finance Department. Annual Report. (II) **1100**
Karnataka Consumer Voice. (II) **1506**
Karnataka Medical Journal. (II ISSN 0377-9378) **3119**
Karolinska Institute. Nobel Conference Series. (US) **3119**
Karpaten Jahrbuch. (GW) **2371**
Die Karpatenpost. (GW ISSN 0022-9105) **2011**
Karpathos. (US) **2011**
Karrosseri Bladet. (DK) **4694**
Karst in China. see Zhongguo Yanrong **1586**
Karstenia. (FI ISSN 0453-3402) **508**
Kart and Superkart Magazine. (UK) **4518**
Kart og Plan. (NO ISSN 0047-3278) **2255**
Kart Sport. (US) **4694**
Kartei der Praktischen Medizin. (GW ISSN 0022-9113) **3176**, **16**
Kartei fuer das Gesamte Brauwesen. (GW) **382**
Karter News. (US ISSN 0096-3216) **4694**
Karthago. (FR ISSN 0453-3429) **277**
Karting. (UK ISSN 0022-913X) **4694**
Kartkowy Katalog Nowosci. (PL ISSN 0324-8003) **404**
Kartofel' i Ovoshchi. (RU ISSN 0022-9148) **183**
Kartoffel Nyt. (DK ISSN 0106-9276) **183**
Der Kartoffelbau. (GW ISSN 0022-9156) **183**
Kartoflexmarkt. (NE) **3649**
Kartograficheskaya Letopis'. (RU) **2255**
Kartographische Nachrichten. (GW ISSN 0022-9164) **2255**, **3792**
Kartographisches Taschenbuch. (GW) **2255**
Kartonnagemarkt see Kartoflexmarkt **3649**
Karty Dokumentacyjne/Documentation Cards. (PL ISSN 0022-9172) **2794**, **16**
Karuna: A Journal of Buddhist Meditation. (CN) **4215**, **3595**
Karunungan. (PH ISSN 0116-7073) **3771**
Karuzela. (PL) **2870**
Karys. (US ISSN 0022-9199) **3462**
Kaseki. see Fossils **3657**
Kasem Libie. (GH) **2192**
Kasetsart Journal. (TH ISSN 0075-5192) **102**
Kasetsart University, Bangkok, Thailand. Faculty of Fisheries. Notes. (TH ISSN 0125-7978) **2045**
Kashmir Affairs. (II ISSN 0022-9210) **3640**
Kashmir Report. (US) **2011**
Kashrus. (US) **2075**, **1506**, **2011**
▼Kashrus Faxletter. (US) **2075**, **2011**
Kashrus Newsletter see Kashrus **2075**
Kashrut Guide. (SA) **4224**, **2011**
Kashshafat al-Imarat/Emirates Boy Scouts. (TS) **1299**, **4549**
Kasikorn. (TH) **102**
Kasityo ja Teollisuus, (FI ISSN 0022-9229) **1116**
Kasmera. (VE ISSN 0075-5222) **3119**
Kasruth Directory. (CN) **2075**, **1141**
Kassei. see Energetic Life **1683**
Kassel Kulturell. (GW ISSN 0936-5133) **332**, **4634**
Kasseler Sonntagsblatt. (GW ISSN 0022-9245) **4186**
Kasseler Statistik. (GW ISSN 0451-4874) **4081**
Kastner & Oehler Firmen Zeitung. (AU ISSN 0022-9253) **1079**

Kasturi. (II ISSN 0022-9261) **2200**
Kasvatus. (FI ISSN 0022-927X) **1644**
Kataliku Pasaulis. (LI) **4266**
Kataliz i Katalizatory. (KR ISSN 0453-3585) **1182**
Katallagete. (US ISSN 0022-9288) **4186**, **3944**
Katalog Ceskoslovenskych Znamek see Ceskoslovensko **3750**
Katalog Fauny Pasozytniczej Polski. (PL ISSN 0075-5230) **586**
Katalog Fauny Polski. (PL ISSN 0453-3623) **586**
Katalog for Boerne- og Skolebiblioteker see Katalog for Skolebiblioteker. Titelkatalog **404**
Katalog for Skolebiblioteker. Emnekatalog see Katalog for Skolebiblioteker. Skolebibliotekarens **404**
Katalog for Skolebiblioteker. Forfatterkatalog see Katalog for Skolebiblioteker. Skolebibliotekarens **404**
Katalog for Skolebiblioteker. Skolebibliotekarens. (DK) **404**, **1644**
Katalog for Skolebiblioteker. Titelkatalog. (DK ISSN 0106-7583) **404**, **1644**
Katalog Knjiga Jugoslovenskih Izdavaca.(YU) **404**
Katalog Polskich Drukow Muzycznych 1800-1963. (PL) **3588**
Katalog Radiatsionnykh Dannykh/ Catalogue of Solar Radiation Data. (RU) **3438**
Katalog Slovenskych Plagatov see Slovenska Narodna Bibliografia Seria G: Grafika **352**
Katalog Stranih Serijskih Publikacija u Bibliotekama Jugoslavije. (YU ISSN 0352-132X) **404**
Katalog Tekucih Stranih Publikacija u Bibliotekama Jugoslavije see Katalog Stranih Serijskih Publikacija u Bibliotekama Jugoslavije **404**
Katalog Zabytkow Sztuki w Polsce. (PL ISSN 0075-5257) **332**
Katanalotis/Consumer. (CY) **1506**
Katastrophenschutz Aktuell see Schutz Aktuell **2034**
Katechetische Blaetter. (GW ISSN 0341-0013) **4266**, **1753**
Katedra. (CI ISSN 0022-9296) **1315**
Katei-Ban Hyakka Series. see All of Housing **2482**
Katei-Gaho. see Home Graphic **2447**
Katei Seikatsu. (JA) **1644**
Katera i Yakhty. (RU ISSN 0022-930X) **4525**
Kateri. (CN ISSN 0315-8020) **4186**, **419**
Kates Kin. (US ISSN 0741-2045) **2156**
Katha-Sahitya. (II ISSN 0022-9318) **2929**
Kathargo. Collection Epigraphique see Karthago **277**
Katherine Asher Engel Lectures. (US ISSN 0075-5265) **2510**
Katholiek Documentatie Centrum. Archieven see Katholiek Documentatie Centrum. Sleutels **5223**
Katholiek Documentatie Centrum. Jaarboek. (NE) **4266**
Katholiek Documentatie Centrum. Publicaties. (NE) **4267**
†Katholiek Documentatie Centrum. Sleutels. (NE) **5223**
Katholische Bildung. (GW) **4267**
Katholische Frau see Frau im Leben **4843**
Katholische Frauenbewegung Oesterreichs. Fuehrungsblatt. (AU ISSN 0022-9377) **4267**
Katholische Gedanke see Renovatio **4274**
Katholische Hochschuljugend Oesterreichs - Blaetter see Wiener Blaetter **1330**
Katholische Lehrerschaft Oesterreichs Impulse see K L O E Impulse **1644**
Katholische Oeffentliche Buecherei. (GW ISSN 0931-4458) **2766**, **4267**
Katholische Universitaet Eichstaett. Vorlesungsverzeichnis. (GW) **1695**

Katholischen Arbeiternehemer-Bewegung Deutschlands see K A B **4266**
Katholischen Militaerbischof fuer die Deutsche Bundeswehr. Verordnungsblatt. (GW) **4267**
Katholischen Missionen see K M - Die Katholischen Missionen **4266**
Katholischer Arbeitskreis fuer Zeitgeschichtliche Fragen. Informationsdienst. (GW ISSN 0176-5493) **4186**
Katholischer Berufsverband fuer Pflegeberufe. Mitteilungsblatt. (GW) **3119**, **4267**
Katholischer Digest. (GW ISSN 0177-2872) **4267**
Katholisches Leben und Kirchenreform im Zeitalter der Glaubensspaltung. (GW ISSN 0170-7302) **4267**
Katib al-Filastini. (LE) **3963**, **2430**
Katilolehti/Tidskrift foer Barnmorskor. (FI ISSN 0022-9415) **3294**
Katipo. (NZ ISSN 0022-9423) **1353**
Katolicki Uniwersytet Lubelski. Wydzial Filozoficzny. Rozprawy. (PL) **3771**
Katolicki Uniwersytet Lubelski. Wydzial Historyczno-Filologiczny. Rozprawy. (PL) **2316**, **2822**
Katolicki Uniwersytet Lubelski. Wydzial Nauk Spolecznych. Rozprawy. (PL) **4378**
Katolicki Uniwersytet Lubelski. Wydzial Teologiczno-Kanoniczny. Rozprawy. (PL) **4267**
Katolicki Uniwersytet Lubelski. Zeszyty Naukowe. (PL ISSN 0044-4405) **4267**, **1644**
Katolicky Sokol see Slovak Catholic Falcon **2023**
Katolikus Magyarok Vasarnapja. see Catholic Hungarians' Sunday **2197**
Katolikus Magyarok Vasarnapja/Catholic Hungarians' Sunday. (US) **4267**, **2011**, **4186**
†Katolikus Szemle. (IT ISSN 0022-9431) **5223**
Katolsk Orientering. (DK) **4267**
Katolski Posol. (GW ISSN 0138-2543) **4267**
Katorikku Kenkyu. (JA ISSN 0387-3005) **4267**
Katso. (FI ISSN 0355-2969) **1375**, **1357**
†Kattegat-Skagerrak-Projectet. Meddelelser. (DK ISSN 0280-8463) **5223**
Katuah. (US) **1490**, **2011**
Katunob. (US) **243**
Katunob: Occasional Publications in Mesoamerican Anthropology. (US) **243**
†Katxa - Ta. (CK) **5223**
Katzen Extra. (GW ISSN 0176-4853) **3711**
Katzenschutz Korrespondenz. (GW) **231**
Kauai, a Paradise Guide. (US) **4774**
Kauai Update. (US ISSN 0898-1418) **4774**
Kauchuk i Rezina. (RU ISSN 0022-9466) **4292**
Kaufhaus und Warenhaus. (GW ISSN 0022-9474) **837**
Kaufmaennische Krankenkasse Hauptverwaltung Journal see K K H Journal **3805**
Kaufmaennische Krankenkasse Hauptverwaltung Nachrichten see K K H Nachrichten **2536**
Kaufmaennische Schule. (GW ISSN 0724-7613) **1644**
Kaukas. (LI) **3012**
Kaukomieli. (FI) **2371**
Kauneus ja Terveys. (FI ISSN 0047-3308) **373**
Kaunis Koti see Avotakka **2548**
Kauperts Deutschland Reisefuehrer. (GW) **4774**
Kauperts Deutschland Staedte-, Hotel-, und Reisefuehrer see Kauperts Deutschland Reisefuehrer **4774**
Kauppa ja Koti see Terassi **2186**
Kauppakamarilehti. (FI) **818**
Kauppalehti. (FI ISSN 0451-5560) **675**
Kaupparekisteri see Kaupparekisterilehti **3676**

Kaupparekisterilehti/ Handelsregistertidning. (FI) **3676**
Kauppias see Kehittyvae Kauppa **1044**
Kautschuk und Gummi. Kunststoffe. (GW ISSN 0022-9520) **4292**
Kav P'nim. see Hebrew University of Jerusalem. Monthly **1313**
Kaviamuthu. (II ISSN 0022-9539) **2200**
Kavita. (II ISSN 0022-9547) **2996**
Kavitha. (US) **2996**
Kavithamandalam. (II) **2996**
Kavya Bharati. (II) **2996**
Kawa to Hakimono/Leather & Footwears. (JA) **2737**, **4361**
Kawakeb. (UA) **3512**
Kawasaki Igakkai Shi. (JA ISSN 0386-5924) **3119**
Kawasaki Medical Journal. (JA ISSN 0385-0234) **3119**
Kawasaki Steel Bulletin. (JA ISSN 0916-6211) **3411**
Kawasaki Steel Technical Report. (JA ISSN 0388-9475) **3411**
Kaya Tao. (PH ISSN 0115-6292) **4441**, **243**, **4034**
Kayhan (Turkish Edition). (IR) **2011**, **2870**
Kayhan Andishe/World of Religion. (IR) **4219**
Kayhan Arabi. (IR ISSN 0885-8187) **2011**, **2870**
Kayhan-e Bacheha/Children's World. (IR ISSN 0022-9563) **1258**
Kayhan Farhangi/World of Culture. (IR) **2870**
Kayhan-i Hava'i. (IR ISSN 1044-6141) **2011**, **2870**
Kayhan International. (IR ISSN 0885-8160) **2870**
Kayhan Varzeshi. (IR) **4477**
Kayhan Yearbook. (IR) **2430**, **4576**
Kaytannon Maamies. (FI ISSN 0022-9571) **103**
Kazakhskii Nauchno-Issledovatel'skii Institut Onkologii i Radiologii. Trudy. (KZ ISSN 0075-529X) **3360**, **3199**
Kazaliste. (CI) **4634**
Kazan Hokoku. see Japan Meteorological Agency. Volcanological Bulletin **1591**
Kazanskii Gosudarstvennyi Pedagogicheskii Institut. Voprosy Istorii, Teorii Muzyki i Muzykal'nogo Vospitaniya. Sbornik. (RU) **3559**
Kazanskii Universitet. Sbornik Aspirantskikh Rabot: Teoriya Plastin i Obolochek. (RU) **1828**
Ke-Ji Ribao/Science & Technology Daily. (CC) **4319**, **4602**
Ke Xue. (Chinese translation of: Scientific American) (CC ISSN 1002-1299) **4319**, **4602**
Keadaan Angkatan Kerja di Indonesia: Angka Sementara. see Labour Force Situation in Indonesia: Preliminary Figures **726**
Keadilan. (IO) **2642**
Keats - Shelley Journal. (US ISSN 0453-4387) **2996**
Keats - Shelley Memorial Bulletin see Keats - Shelley Review **2929**
Keats - Shelley Review. (UK) **2929**
Kecheng - Jiaocai - Jiaofa/Curriculum, Materials, Methods. (CC ISSN 1000-0186) **1753**
Keel ja Kirjandus. (ER ISSN 0131-1441) **2822**, **2930**
Keemat. (II) **1506**
Keep America Beautiful see Vision (Stamford) **1971**
Keep on Truckin' News. (US) **4745**
Keep Tahoe Blue. (US) **1961**
Keeper's Log. (US ISSN 0883-0061) **2316**, **1870**
Keepers of the Ancient Mysteries see K.A.M **5222**
Keepers' Voice. (US) **1526**
Keepin' Track of Vettes see Corvette Fever **4688**
Keeping Ancient Rome Alive. (US) **2316**
Keeping Posted see Reform Judaism **4226**
Keeping Posted with N C S Y. (National Conference of Synagogue Youth) (US ISSN 0022-9644) **4224**, **1240**
Keeping the Trust. (US) **4411**, **4106**

6366 KEEPING TRACK

Keeping Track. (CN) **4710**
Keeping You Posted. (US ISSN 0361-8668) **4241**
Keepsake (Davis). (US ISSN 0075-5311) **2766**
†Keepsake (Scottsdale). (US) **5223**
Keepsake Calendar. (US) **3591**, 355
Keesing's Contemporary Archives see Keesing's Record of World Events **3938**
Keesing's Record of World Events. (UK ISSN 0950-6128) **3938**, 16
Keesing's Special Reports. (US) **3963**, 871
Keezette. (US) **3711**
Kegan Media Index. (US ISSN 0893-2700) **725**, 953
Kegeln und Bowling. (GW) **4507**
Kehakultuur see Spordiilm **4489**
Kehilwenyane. (SA ISSN 0022-9687) **4267**
Kehittyva Yritys. (FI ISSN 0358-0628) **1017**
Kehittyva Yritysjohto see Kehittyva Yritys **1017**
Kehittyvae Kauppa. (FI ISSN 0783-5167) **1044**
Kehrwieder. (GW ISSN 0176-473X) **4730**
Keidanren Geppo. (JA ISSN 0453-4484) **675**
Keidanren Keizai Shiryo. (JA) **871**
Keidanren Pamphlet. (JA) **871**
Keidanren Pocket Series. (JA) **871**
Keidanren Review. (JA ISSN 0022-9695) **675**
Keidanren Shuho. (JA) **871**
Keiei Kagaku - Management Science see Opereshonzu Risachi **1023**
Keihatsu. see Enlightenment **1683**
Keiho Zasshi. see Journal of Criminal Law **2713**
Keikinzoku Kogyo Tokei Nenpo/Light Metal Statistics in Japan. (JA ISSN 0451-6001) **3427**
Keilor Messenger. (AT) **2172**
Keilschrifttexte aus Boghazkoi. (GW) **277**, **2822**, **3640**
Keilschrifturkunden aus Boghazkoei. (GW ISSN 0075-532X) **2339**, 277
Keio Business Review. (JA ISSN 0453-4557) **676**
Keio Economic Studies. (JA ISSN 0022-9709) **676**
Keio Engineering Reports see Keio Science and Technology Reports **4319**
Keio Gijuku Daigaku Hiyoshi Kiyo. Shizen Kagaku/Hiyoshi Review of Natural Science. (JA ISSN 0911-7237) **4319**
Keio Gijuku Daigaku Rikogakubuho. (JA) **4602**, 4319
Keio Journal of Medicine. (JA ISSN 0022-9717) **3119**
Keio Monographs of Business and Commerce. (JA ISSN 0075-5346) **676**
Keio Science and Technology Reports. (JA ISSN 0286-4215) **4319**
Keio University. Faculty of Science and Technology. Department of Mathematics. Research Report. (JA) **3042**
Keiraku Shinryo. (JA) **3119**, 2293, 3640
Keiryo Kokugogaku/Mathematical Linguistics. (JA ISSN 0453-4611) **2822**, 3042
Keisanki Tokeigaku/Bulletin of the Computational Statistics of Japan. (JA ISSN 0914-8930) **4576**, 3042
Keisei Geka. see Japanese Journal of Plastic & Reconstructive Surgery **3379**
Keizai Kagaku/Economic Science. (JA ISSN 0022-9725) **676**
Keizai Kenkyu/Economic Review. (JA ISSN 0022-9733) **676**
Keizai Koho Center Brief see K K C Brief **5222**
Keizai Ohrai/Economic Review. (JA) **676**
Keizai Riron - Economic Theory see Wakayama Economic Review **1031**
Keizai Ronso. see Economic Review **661**

Keizai Shirin/Economic Review (Tokyo, 1925). (JA ISSN 0022-9741) **676**
Keizai Shushi. see Studies in Economic Science **693**
Keizaigaku Kenkyu/Journal of Political Economy. (JA ISSN 0022-975X) **676**
Keizaigaku Ronsan/Economic Journal. (JA ISSN 0453-4778) **676**
Keizaigaku Ronshu/Journal of Economics. (JA ISSN 0022-9768) **676**
Keizaijin. (JA) **676**
Keizaikai. (JA) **676**
Keji Chuban/Science and Technology Publishing. (CC ISSN 1001-5272) **4130**
Keji Daobao/Science and Technology Herald. (CC ISSN 1000-7857) **4319**, 4602
Keji Fazhan yu Gaige/Science and Technology Development and Reform. (CC) **4378**
Keji Guanli Yanjiu. (CC ISSN 1000-7695) **4319**
Keji Jinbu yu Duice. (CC ISSN 1001-7348) **4319**, 4602
Keji Kaifa Dongtai/Science and Technology Exploration Trend. (CC) **4319**, 4602
Keji Qingbao Gongzuo/Science and Technology Information. (CC ISSN 1000-4467) **2766**
Keji Qingbao Shichang/Information Market of Science and Technology. (CC) **2767**
Keji Yingyu Xuexi/Learning English for Science & Technology. (CC) **2822**, 1753, 4319, 4602
Keji yu Fazhan/Science, Technology and Development. (CC) **4320**, 4602
Kekkaku/Tuberculosis. (JA ISSN 0022-9776) **3365**
Kekkaku No Kenkyu see Hokkaido University. Institute of Immunological Science. Bulletin **3365**
Kekkaku Yobokai Kenkyu Gyoseki. see Japan Anti-Tuberculosis Association. Reports on Medical Research Problems **5220**
Keleti Tanulmanyok/Oriental Studies. (HU ISSN 0133-6193) **3640**
Kelk - Review of Art and Literature. see Kilk - Mahnamah-i Adabi va Hunari **2930**
Kelley Blue Book Reporter see Auto Age **4679**
Kellon - Haukiputaan Kotiseutujulkaisu. (FI) **2371**
†Kelly - Grimes Buyers Guide For Word Processing. (US) **5223**
†Kelly's Automated Office & Business Equipment Directory. (UK ISSN 0950-6160) **5223**
Kelly's Business Directory. (UK ISSN 0269-9265) **1141**
Kelly's Business Link. (UK ISSN 0269-9281) **1141**, 1079
Kelly's Export Services. (UK) **1141**, 915
Kelly's London Business Link. (UK ISSN 0955-7113) **1141**, 1339
Kelly's Manufacturers and Merchants Directory see Kelly's Business Directory **1141**
Kelly's Oil & Gas Industry Directory. (UK) **1141**, 3691
Kelly's Post Office London Business Directory. (UK ISSN 0266-3791) **1141**
Kelly's Post Office London Directory see Kelly's Post Office London Business Directory **1141**
Kelly's United Kingdom Exports see Kelly's United Kingdom Exports Directory **1141**
Kelly's United Kingdom Exports Directory. (UK ISSN 0268-3105) **1141**
Kelsey Review. (US ISSN 0451-6338) **2930**
Kelso Courier. (US) **2412**
Keltia. (FR ISSN 0022-9792) **3771**, 2011
Keltic Fringe. (US ISSN 1057-7475) **2011**
Keltica. (US ISSN 0192-1207) **2371**, 2011
Keluarga. (IO) **2448**, 4846

Kelvin News/Kelvinnuus. (SA) **4320**, 4602
Kelvinnuus. see Kelvin News **4320**
†Kema Scientific & Technical Reports. (NE ISSN 0167-8590) **5223**
†Kemble Occasional. (US) **5223**
Die Kemenate. (GW) **2156**
Kemia - Kemi/Finnish Chemistry. (FI ISSN 0355-1628) **1856**, 1182
Kemiai Kozlemenyek. (HU) **1182**
Kemian Teollisuus see Kemia - Kemi **1856**
Kemija u Industriji. (CI ISSN 0022-9830) **1182**
Kemikalikauppias. (FI) **375**
Kemisk Analyse af Mineraler og Bjergarter. (DK ISSN 0105-9386) **1182**, 3486
Kemisk Tidskrift. (SW ISSN 0039-6605) **1182**, 1828
Kemisten. see Kemisti **1182**
Kemisti/Kemisten. (FI ISSN 0022-9865) **1182**
Kemistin Kalenteri. (FI ISSN 0356-7818) **1182**
Kemixon Reporter. (SP ISSN 0022-9873) **1182**, 3733
Kempe's Engineers Year-Book. (UK ISSN 0075-5400) **1828**
Kemphaan. (NE ISSN 0022-9881) **4694**
Kempinski Journal. (GW) **2477**
Kemps Estate Agents Yearbook and Directory see Kemps Property Industry Yearbook **5223**
Kemps Film and Television Year Book (International) see Kemps International Film and Television Year Book **3512**
Kemps International Film and Television Year Book. (UK) **3512**
Kemps International Music and Recording Industry Yearbook see Kemps International Music Book **3559**
Kemps International Music Book. (UK) **3559**
Kemps Production Diary. (UK) **3512**, 1375, 1385
†Kemps Property Industry Yearbook. (UK) **5223**
Ken Chun Ni. (CC) **2930**
Ken uw Dorp en uw Familie: Tijdschrift van de Heemkundige Kring. (BE) **2371**
Kena. (MX) **2210**
Kena. (VE) **4846**
Kenchiku Bunka. see Architecture Culture **293**
Kenchiku Techo/Architect. (JA) **302**
Kendall Whaling Museum Newsletter see K W M Newsletter **3526**
Kenga Jone. (AA) **2056**
Kenkaalusikka. (FI ISSN 0355-6999) **4361**
Kenko Hoken Shinbun see Sukoyaka Kenpo **2544**
Kenko Kyoiku/Public Health Education. (JA ISSN 0022-9938) **4106**, 3805
Kenko na Kurashi/Longer and Healthier Life. (JA ISSN 0022-9946) **3805**
Kenkyu Gijutsu Keikaku/Journal of Science Policy and Research Management. (JA ISSN 0914-7020) **1017**, 4320, 4603
Kenkyu Jitsuyoka Hokoku. see Musashino Electrical Communication Laboratories Technical Journal **1364**
Kenkyu Joseikin Jukyusha Kenkyu Hokokushu. (JA) **1644**
Kenkyu Shuroku. (JA) **1644**
Kenkyujoho - Musashi Kogyo Daigaku Genshiryoku Kenkyujo see Musashi Kogyo Daigaku. Genshiryoku Kenkyujo. Kenkyujoho **1807**
Kenkyuseika Yoshisyu see J A E R I Reports Abstracts **3837**
Kennebec. (US) **2930**, 2996
Kennedy Institute of Bioethics. Scope Note see Kennedy Institute of Ethics. Scope Note **3119**
†Kennedy Institute of Ethics. Newsletter.(US) **5223**
Kennedy Institute of Ethics. Scope Note.(US) **3119**, 3771
▼Kennedy Institute of Ethics Journal. (US ISSN 1054-6863) **3771**

Kennedy's Career Strategist. (US ISSN 0891-2572) **3629**
Kennel and Cattery Management. (UK) **3711**
Kennel Club Yearbook. (UK) **3711**
Kennel Control Council Gazette Dogs see Victorian Canine Association Gazette Dogs **3714**
Kennel Gazette. (UK ISSN 0022-9962) **3711**
Kennel Review. (US ISSN 0164-4289) **3711**
Kenneth J. Gerbino Investment Letter see Smart Investing **963**
Kennis en Methode. (NE ISSN 0165-1773) **4320**, 3771
Kennis Systemen/Expert Systems. (NE) **1447**
Kenpo Nyusu. (JA ISSN 0022-989X) **2536**
Kenrail. (KE) **4652**
Kensa to Gijutsu/Modern Medical Laboratory. (JA ISSN 0301-2611) **3260**
Kensetsu Kogaku Kenkyujo Hokoku/Construction Engineering Research Institute Foundation Report. (JA ISSN 0453-5146) **1919**, 1546, 1961
Kensetsu Kogyo Bukka Chingin Geppo/Monthly Report of Price and Wage in Construction Engineering. (JA ISSN 0022-9997) **1870**, 622
Kent Archaeological Review. (UK ISSN 0023-0014) **277**
Kent Archaeological Society. Newsletter.(UK) **277**
Kent Collector. (US ISSN 0163-1861) **332**
Kent Farmer. (UK ISSN 0023-0022) **103**
Kent Life. (UK ISSN 0023-0030) **2194**
Kent Messenger. (UK ISSN 0023-0049) **2194**
Kent Monograph Series. (UK ISSN 0141-2264) **277**
Kent News see Monitor (Luton) **4604**
Kent Review see Process Instrumentation Review **4606**
Kent State Research Papers in Archaeology. (US) **277**
Kentron Epistemonikon Ereunon. Epeteris/Cyprus Research Centre. Annual. (CY ISSN 0071-0954) **1278**
Kentuckiana Purchasor. (US ISSN 0023-0073) **1044**
Kentucky. Adjutant-General's Office. Report. (US) **3462**, 2412
Kentucky. Cabinet for Human Resources. Vital Statistics Report. (US) **4118**, 4577
Kentucky. Council of Economic Advisors. Annual Report see Commonwealth of Kentucky. Annual Economic Report (Year) **656**
Kentucky. Council on Higher Education. Origin of Kentucky College and University Enrollments see Kentucky College and University Origin of Enrollments **1677**
Kentucky. Court of Justice. Annual Report see Kentucky. Court of Justice. Biennial Report **5223**
†Kentucky. Court of Justice. Biennial Report. (US) **5223**
Kentucky. Department of Child Welfare. Annual Report see Kentucky. Department of Human Resources. Annual Report **4411**
Kentucky. Department of Human Resources. Annual Report. (US) **4411**
Kentucky Academy of Family Physicians Journal see K A F P Journal **3119**
Kentucky Academy of Science. Transactions. (US ISSN 0023-0081) **4320**
Kentucky Accountant see Bottom Line (Louisville) **748**
Kentucky Afield. (US) **4089**, 1490
Kentucky Agricultural Statistics. (US) **139**
Kentucky Ancestors. (US ISSN 0023-0103) **2156**, 2412

Kentucky Annual Vital Statistics Report see Kentucky. Cabinet for Human Resources. Vital Statistics Report 4118
Kentucky Archivist. (US) 2412
Kentucky Association for Health, Physical Education, Recreation and Dance Journal see K A H P E R D Journal 1738
Kentucky Attorney General Opinions. (US ISSN 0748-9080) 2642
Kentucky Banker. (US ISSN 0023-0111) 788
Kentucky Bench & Bar. (US ISSN 0164-9345) 2642
Kentucky Beverage Journal. (US ISSN 0023-012X) 382
Kentucky Business Ledger. (US ISSN 0192-642X) 676
Kentucky Cattleman and Horseman. (US) 220
Kentucky Checklist of State Publications. (US ISSN 1054-2841) 404
Kentucky City. (US ISSN 0453-5677) 4089
Kentucky Civil War Round Table. Bulletin. (US ISSN 0023-0146) 2412
Kentucky Coal Journal see The Coal Journal 3481
Kentucky College and University Degrees and other Formal Awards (Year). (US) 1677, 16
Kentucky College and University Enrollments (Year). (US) 1677, 16
Kentucky College and University Origin of Enrollments. (US) 1677
Kentucky Council on Higher Education. Council Report see Kentucky Council on Higher Education. Executive Council Report 1710
Kentucky Council on Higher Education. Executive Council Report. (US) 1710
Kentucky Dental Association. Journal. (US ISSN 0744-396X) 3237
Kentucky Deskbook of Economic Statistics see Kentucky Economic Statistics 725
Kentucky Directory of Black Elected Officials. (US) 4065, 2011, 3944
Kentucky Directory of Manufacturers. (US ISSN 0075-5494) 1141
†Kentucky Directory of Selected Industrial Services. (US ISSN 0363-5198) 5223
Kentucky Economic Outlook see University of Kentucky. Center for Business and Economic Research. Review & Perspective 887
Kentucky Economic Statistics. (US) 725
Kentucky Economy: Review and Perspective see University of Kentucky. Center for Business and Economic Research. Review & Perspective 887
Kentucky Education Association News see K E A News 1644
Kentucky Education Association Research Publications see K E A Research Publications 1677
Kentucky Education News see K E A News 1644
▼Kentucky Employment Law Letter. (US ISSN 1052-4371) 2642, 985
Kentucky Engineer. (US ISSN 0746-2255) 1829
Kentucky English Bulletin. (US ISSN 0023-0197) 2822, 1644
Kentucky Explorer. (US ISSN 0890-8362) 2412, 2255, 4774
▼Kentucky Facts. (US ISSN 1046-834X) 1781
Kentucky Farm Bureau News. (US ISSN 0023-0200) 103
Kentucky Farmer. (US ISSN 0023-0219) 103
Kentucky Farmers Fastline see Farmers Fastline: Kentucky Edition 91
Kentucky Folklore Record see Southern Folklore 2058
Kentucky Geological Survey. Guidebook to Geological Field Trips. (US ISSN 0075-5575) 1570
Kentucky Geological Survey. Series 11. Annual Report. (US) 1570
Kentucky Geological Survey. Series 11. Bulletin. (US ISSN 0075-5559) 1570
Kentucky Geological Survey. Series 11. County Report. (US ISSN 0075-5567) 1570
Kentucky Geological Survey. Series 11. Information Circular. (US ISSN 0075-5583) 1570
Kentucky Geological Survey. Series 11. Map and Chart Series. (US) 1570
Kentucky Geological Survey. Series 11. Report of Investigations. (US ISSN 0075-5591) 1570
Kentucky Geological Survey. Series 11. Reprints. (US ISSN 0075-5605) 1570
Kentucky Geological Survey. Series 11. Special Publication. (US ISSN 0075-5613) 1571
Kentucky Geological Survey. Series 11. Thesis Series. (US ISSN 0075-5621) 1571
Kentucky Geological Survey Newsletter see K G S - N C I C Newsletter 5222
Kentucky Happy Hunting Ground see Kentucky Afield 4089
Kentucky Heritage. (US) 2412
Kentucky Historical Society. Bulletin. (US) 2412
Kentucky Historical Society. Register. (US ISSN 0023-0243) 2412
Kentucky Horizons. (US) 4065
Kentucky Index. (US) 2301
†Kentucky International Trade Directory.(US) 5223
Kentucky Jewish Post and Opinion. (US) 2011
Kentucky Journal. (US) 4065, 3902
Kentucky Journal of Commerce and Industry. (US) 837
Kentucky Labor News. (US ISSN 0023-0251) 2585
Kentucky Law Journal. (US ISSN 0023-026X) 2642
Kentucky Libraries. (US ISSN 0732-5452) 2767
Kentucky Living. (US) 2227, 1901
Kentucky Local Debt Report. (US ISSN 0095-1498) 1100
The Kentucky Manufacturer. (US) 676, 1079
Kentucky Manufacturers Register. (US ISSN 0741-9031) 1141
Kentucky Medical Association. Journal. (US ISSN 0023-0294) 3119
Kentucky Monthly Checklist see Kentucky Checklist of State Publications 404
Kentucky Nurse. (US) 3281
Kentucky Nurse Association Newsletter see Kentucky Nurse 3281
Kentucky Oil and Gas Association. Technical Sessions. Proceedings see Kentucky Geological Survey. Series 11. Special Publication 1571
Kentucky Pharmacist. (US ISSN 0194-567X) 3733
Kentucky Plumbing & Heating Index. (US) 2301
†Kentucky Poetry Review. (US ISSN 0889-647X) 5223
Kentucky Prairie Farmer. (US) 183
Kentucky Press. (US ISSN 0023-0324) 2572
Kentucky Queries. (US ISSN 0899-1359) 2156
Kentucky Review. (US ISSN 0191-1031) 2510
Kentucky School Directory. (US ISSN 0091-0775) 1695
Kentucky State Bar Journal see Kentucky Bench & Bar 2642
Kentucky State University Around & About K S U see Around & About K S U 1304
Kentucky, Tennessee TourBook see Tourbook: Kentucky, Tennessee 4790
Kenya. Central Bureau of Statistics. Agricultural Census (Large Farm Areas). (KE ISSN 0300-2373) 139, 4577
Kenya. Central Bureau of Statistics. Development Estimates. (KE) 725, 1079, 4577
Kenya. Central Bureau of Statistics. Directory of Industries. (KE) 1141
Kenya. Central Bureau of Statistics. Economic Survey. (KE) 871
Kenya. Central Bureau of Statistics. Employment and Earnings in the Modern Sector. (KE) 725, 4577
Kenya. Central Bureau of Statistics. Estimates of Recurrent Expenditures.(KE) 726, 1079, 4577
Kenya. Central Bureau of Statistics. Estimates of Revenue Expenditures. (KE) 726, 1079, 4577
Kenya. Central Bureau of Statistics. Migration and Tourism Statistics. (KE) 4799
Kenya. Central Bureau of Statistics. Register of Manufacturing Firms. (KE) 726
Kenya. Central Bureau of Statistics. Social Perspectives see Social Perspectives 4449
Kenya. Central Bureau of Statistics. Statistical Abstract. (KE) 726
Kenya. Central Bureau of Statistics. Surveys of Industrial Production. (KE) 726, 1079, 4577
Kenya. Commissioner of Customs and Excise. Annual Trade Report. (KE) 915
Kenya. Court of Appeal. Digest of Decisions of the Court. (KE) 2642
Kenya. Dairy Board. Annual Report. (KE ISSN 0453-5944) 200
Kenya. Government Printing and Stationery Department. Catalogue of Government Publications. (KE) 404
Kenya. Maize and Produce Board. Report see Kenya. National Cereals and Produce Board. Annual Report 183
Kenya. Ministry of Agriculture. Central Development and Marketing Unit. Yields, Costs, Prices. (KE) 153
Kenya. Ministry of Agriculture. Scientific Research Division. Annual Report. (KE) 103
Kenya. Ministry of Economic Planning and Development. Economic Survey see Kenya. Central Bureau of Statistics. Economic Survey 871
Kenya. Ministry of Economic Planning and Development. Estimates of Revenue Expenditures see Kenya. Central Bureau of Statistics. Estimates of Revenue Expenditures 726
Kenya. Ministry of Economic Planning and Development. Statistics Division. Development Estimates see Kenya. Central Bureau of Statistics. Development Estimates 725
Kenya. Ministry of Economic Planning and Development. Statistics Division. Estimates of Recurrent Expenditures see Kenya. Central Bureau of Statistics. Estimates of Recurrent Expenditures 726
Kenya. Ministry of Economic Planning and Development. Statistics Division. Statistical Abstract see Kenya. Central Bureau of Statistics. Statistical Abstract 726
Kenya. Ministry of Education. Annual Report. (KE ISSN 0075-5869) 1644
Kenya. Ministry of Education Newsletter.(KE) 1644
Kenya. Ministry of Education, Science and Technology Newsletter see Kenya. Ministry of Education Newsletter 1644
Kenya. Ministry of Finance and Economic Planning. Budget Speech see Kenya. Ministry of Finance and Planning. Budget Speech by Minister for Finance and Planning 4065
Kenya. Ministry of Finance and Economic Planning. Statistics Division. Register of Manufacturing Firms see Kenya. Central Bureau of Statistics. Register of Manufacturing Firms 726
Kenya. Ministry of Finance and Economic Planning. Statistics Division. Register of Manufacturing Firms see Kenya. Central Bureau of Statistics. Directory of Industries 1141
Kenya. Ministry of Finance and Planning. Budget Speech by Minister for Finance and Planning. (KE) 4065
Kenya. Ministry of Finance and Planning. Plan Implementation Report. (KE) 4065
Kenya. Ministry of Health and Housing. Annual Report see Kenya. Ministry of Housing. Annual Report 2490
Kenya. Ministry of Health. Annual report. (KE) 3119
Kenya. Ministry of Housing. Annual Report. (KE) 2490
Kenya. Ministry of Information and Broadcasting. Annual Report. (KE) 2333
Kenya. Ministry of Information, Broadcasting and Tourism. Annual Report see Kenya. Ministry of Information and Broadcasting. Annual Report 2333
Kenya. Ministry of Tourism and Wildlife. Wildlife Conservation and Management Department. Newsletter. (KE) 1490
Kenya. National Cereals and Produce Board. Annual Report. (KE) 183
Kenya. National Housing Corporation. Annual Report. (KE) 2490
Kenya. National Irrigation Board. Reports and Accounts. (KE ISSN 0075-5915) 183
Kenya. National Library Service Board. Annual and Audit Report. (KE ISSN 0075-5923) 2767
Kenya. Office of the District Commissioner. Annual Report. (KE) 4065
Kenya. Public Accounts Committee. Annual Report. (KE ISSN 0075-5931) 4065
Kenya. Public Service Commission. Annual Report. (KE ISSN 0075-594X) 4411
Kenya. Wheat Board. Report see Kenya. National Cereals and Produce Board. Annual Report 183
Kenya Agricultural Research Institute. Veterinary Research Department. Annual Report. (KE) 4812
Kenya Association of Manufacturers. Industrial Index and Members List see Kenya Association of Manufacturers. Members List and International Standard Industrial Classification 1141
Kenya Association of Manufacturers. Members List and International Standard Industrial Classification. (KE) 1141, 1079
Kenya Builder. (KE) 622
Kenya Business Spotlight. (KE) 871
Kenya Coffee. (KE) 2075, 183
Kenya Commercial Bank. Director's Report and Accounts and Executive Chairman's Statement. (KE) 788
Kenya Conservatoire of Music. Newsletter. (KE) 3560
Kenya Education Journal. (KE ISSN 0023-0413) 1644
Kenya Education Review. (KE) 1710
Kenya Employer. (KE) 985
Kenya Engineer. (KE) 1829
Kenya Enterprise see Industrial & Trade Directory 1139
Kenya Export Directory. (KE) 915
Kenya Export News. (KE) 915
Kenya Farmer. (KE ISSN 0023-0421) 103
Kenya Fisheries Reports. (KE) 2045
Kenya Gazette. (KE) 4065
Kenya Gazette Supplement. (KE) 4065
Kenya Industrial Research and Development Institute Annual Report and Statement of Accounts see K I R D I Annual Report and Statement of Accounts 837
†Kenya Institute of Administration. Journal. (KE ISSN 0065-1966) 5223
Kenya Institute of Administration Occasional Papers see K I A Occasional Papers 4065
Kenya Journal of Science and Technology. Series A: Physical and Chemical Sciences see Kenya Journal of Sciences. Series A: Physical and Chemical Sciences 4320

Kenya Journal of Science and Technology. Series B: Biological Sciences see Kenya Journal of Sciences. Series B: Biological Sciences **445**
Kenya Journal of Sciences. Series A: Physical and Chemical Sciences. (KE) **4320**, **4603**
Kenya Journal of Sciences. Series B: Biological Sciences. (KE) **445**
Kenya Leo. (KE) **2208**
Kenya Library Association Chairman's Annual Report see Maktaba **2772**
†Kenya Medical Abstracts. (KE) **5223**
Kenya Medical Research Institute. Proceedings of the Annual Medical Research Conferences see Kenya Medical Research Institute. Proceedings of the Annual Medical Scientific Conference **3119**
Kenya Medical Research Institute. Proceedings of the Annual Medical Scientific Conference. (KE ISSN 1010-576X) **3119**
Kenya Meteorological Department. Annual Report. (KE) **3438**
Kenya Museum Society. Chairman's Report. (KE) **3526**
Kenya National Academy for Advancement of Arts and Sciences. Annual Report see Kenya National Academy of Sciences. Annual Report **4320**
Kenya National Academy for Advancement of Arts and Sciences. Foundation Lectures. (KE) **2510**
Kenya National Academy for Advancement of Arts and Sciences. Newsletter. (KE) **4320**, **4603**
Kenya National Academy for Advancement of Arts and Sciences. Proceedings. (KE) **2510**
Kenya National Academy for Advancement of Arts and Sciences. Research Information Circulars. (KE) **2333**
Kenya National Academy of Sciences. Annual Report. (KE) **4320**, **332**
Kenya National Bibliography. (KE) **2794**
Kenya National Chamber of Commerce and Industry. Annual Report see Kenya National Chamber of Commerce and Industry. Trade and Industry Guide **818**
Kenya National Chamber of Commerce and Industry. Trade and Industry Guide. (KE) **818**
Kenya National Council of Social Services. Annual Report. (KE) **4411**
Kenya National Library Services. Classified Accession List of Books Added to Stock. (KE) **2794**
Kenya National Trading Corporation. Annual Report. (KE) **837**
Kenya Newsletter. (KE ISSN 0454-949X) **2208**
Kenya Nursing Journal. (KE ISSN 0301-0333) **3281**
Kenya Past and Present. (KE) **2333**, **4320**
Kenya Police Review. (KE ISSN 0023-0448) **1517**
Kenya Record. (KE) **2208**
Kenya Review. (KE) **871**
Kenya Society for the Blind. Annual Report and Accounts. (KE) **2293**
Kenya Statistical Digest. (KE ISSN 0453-6002) **4577**
Kenya Tea Development Authority. Annual Report and Accounts. (KE) **2075**
Kenya: The Gateway to Africa. (KE) **1142**, **953**
Kenya Times. (KE) **2208**
Kenya Tourist Development Corporation. Report and Accounts. (KE) **4774**
Kenya Uhuru Factbook. (KE) **2333**
Kenya Uhuru Yearbook see Kenya Uhuru Factbook **2333**
Kenya Veterinarian. (KE) **4812**
Kenya Weekly News. (KE ISSN 0023-0472) **3902**, **103**
Kenya Yearbook. (UK) **871**
Kenya Yetu. (KE) **2169**
Kenyan Periodicals Directory. (KE) **2794**

Kenyatta University College. Bureau of Educational Research. Research Projects. (KE) **1710**
Kenyatta University College. Directory of Research. (KE) **1710**
Kenyon Review. (US ISSN 0163-075X) **2930**
Kep- es Hangtechnika. (HU ISSN 0023-0480) **3854**, **1339**
Kepes Ifjusag. (YU) **2371**
Kepes Ujsag/Illustrated News. (HU) **2198**
Kepi Blanc. (FR) **3462**
Kerala (India). Board for Prevention and Control of Water Pollution. Annual Report. (II) **1961**
Kerala Academy of Biology. Journal. (II) **445**
Kerala Aided Primary Teachers' Union Union Patrika see K A P T Union Patrika **1644**
Kerala; an Economic Review. (II ISSN 0453-7440) **871**
Kerala Archives Bulletin. (II) **2339**
Kerala Archives Newsletter see Kerala Archives Bulletin **2339**
Kerala Co-Operative Journal. (II) **831**
Kerala Commerce and Industry see Vyavasaya Keralam **841**
Kerala Express. (CN) **2011**
Kerala Homoeo Journal. (II ISSN 0300-3957) **3215**
Kerala Industry. (II ISSN 0047-3359) **1079**
Kerala Journal of Veterinary Science see Journal of Veterinary and Animal Sciences **4811**
Kerala Law Journal. (II ISSN 0023-0510) **2642**
Kerala Law Times. (II ISSN 0023-0529) **2642**
Kerala Medical Journal. (II ISSN 0301-4827) **3119**
Kerala Sabha. (II ISSN 0047-3367) **4284**
Kerala Sree. (II ISSN 0023-0537) **2200**
Keralasabdam. (II) **3902**
†Keramik Boutique. (GW) **5223**
†Keramik Creativ. (GW) **5223**
Keramik-Freunde der Schweiz. Mitteilungsblatt/Amis Suisses de la Ceramique. Bulletin. (SZ ISSN 0023-0553) **355**
Keramik und Glas. (GW) **831**
Keramikos International Ceramics Magazine. (IT ISSN 1120-2394) **1165**
Keramische Rundschau Klima und Raum. (AU) **355**
Keramische Zeitschrift. (GW ISSN 0023-0561) **1165**, **332**
Keraulophon. (US ISSN 0735-8660) **3560**
Al-Kerazeh. (UA) **4186**, **2011**
Kerby News for Seniors. (CN) **2275**
Kerem Shlomo. (US) **4224**
Kereskedelmi Partenr Magyarorszag. see Business Partner Hungary **652**
Keretapi. (MY ISSN 0047-3375) **4711**
Kerista Book Series see Utopia 2 **3597**
Kerjasama Serbaguna Malaysia Review see K S M Review **102**
Kerk en Vrede. (NE) **4186**, **3964**
Kerkblad. (SA ISSN 0023-0596) **4241**
Kerkbode. (SA) **4241**
Kerkbode van Gereformeerde Kerken in Noord en Zuid-Holland see Kerkbode van Nederlands Gereformeerde Kerken **4186**
Kerkbode van Nederlands Gereformeerde Kerken. (NE) **4186**
Kerkhistorische Bijdragen. (NE ISSN 0169-8451) **4186**
Kern County Dental Society Newsletter see Kern County Dental Society Occlusal Register **3237**
Kern County Dental Society Occlusal Register. (US) **3237**
Kern Institute, Leiden. Memoirs. (NE ISSN 0169-8907) **3640**
Kernaktief see Nuclear Active **5250**
Kernenergie. (GW ISSN 0023-0642) **1806**
Kernforschungsanlage Intern see K F A Intern **4318**

Kernforschungszentrum Karlsruhe. Ergebnisbericht ueber Forschung und Entwicklung. (GW ISSN 0171-3191) **1806**, **1829**
Kerngetallen-Testbeeloen. (NE ISSN 0169-5126) **953**
Kerngetallen van Nederlandse Effecten. (NE ISSN 0023-0669) **953**
Kerntechnik. (GW ISSN 0932-3902) **1806**
Kerouac Connection. (UK) **2930**
Kerr Report see Mobilehome Parks Report **4152**
Kerrang! (UK ISSN 0262-6624) **3560**
Kerry Archaeological and Historical Society. Journal. (IE ISSN 0085-2503) **277**
Kerry Blueprints. (US) **3711**
Kerry Hill Flock Book Society. Flock Book. (UK) **220**
Kerry Magazine. (IE) **277**
Kershner Kinfolk. (US ISSN 0736-0886) **2156**
Kerteszet es Szoleszet/Gardening and Viniculture. (HU ISSN 0023-0677) **2133**
Kertgazdasag/Horticulture. (HU ISSN 0133-3410) **2133**
Kerugma. (NE ISSN 0023-0685) **4186**
Kerygma. (CN ISSN 0023-0693) **4186**
Kerygma und Dogma. (GW ISSN 0023-0707) **4186**
Kesatuan Bulletin. (SI ISSN 0047-3383) **1711**
†Kesher (Jerusalem). (IS) **5223**
Kesher Elektronika Machshavim. (IS) **1339**, **3462**
Keshev. (IS) **2371**
Keski-Suomi. (FI ISSN 0355-1393) **2371**
Keste Damena/Rainbow. (ET ISSN 0047-3391) **2186**
Kestrel Chapbook Series. (US) **2930**
Ketch Pen. (US ISSN 0889-2857) **220**
Ketsueki Jigyo no Genkyo. (JA) **3120**
Kettenwirk-Praxis. (GW ISSN 0047-3405) **4621**
Kettering Report see Connections (Dayton) **3881**
Kettering Review. (US ISSN 0748-8815) **4378**
Keuka Connection. (US) **1315**
Keuken. (NE ISSN 0023-0731) **2477**, **2075**, **2448**
Keuken & Interieur Magazine. (NE) **2560**
Keuken Magazine. (NE) **2560**
Keur. (SA) **2216**
Kevo Subarctic Research Institute. Reports. (FI ISSN 0453-7831) **445**, **1546**, **1961**, **2255**
Kevren. (UK ISSN 0140-7562) **3902**, **2870**
Kew Bulletin. (UK ISSN 0075-5974) **508**
Kew Bulletin. Additional Series. (UK ISSN 0075-5982) **508**
Kew Magazine. (UK ISSN 0265-3842) **2133**, **1490**
Kew Record of Taxonomic Literature (Year). (UK) **508**
Kew Record of Taxonomic Literature Relating to Vascular Plants. (UK) **508**, **466**
Kexue see Ke Xue **4319**
Kexue/Science. (CC ISSN 0368-6396) **4320**
Kexue/Science. (CC) **4320**
†Kexue Bolan/Science Panorama. (CC ISSN 1000-3088) **5223**
Kexue Daguanyuan/Grand View Garden of Science. Journal. (CC) **4320**
Kexue Dui Shehui de Yingxiang/Science Impact on Society. (CC ISSN 0254-8763) **4378**, **4320**
Kexue Fazhan see Republic of China. National Science Council Monthly **4335**
Kexue Huabao/Science Pictorial. (CC ISSN 0454-0905) **4320**
Kexue Jishu Yanjiu Chengguo Gongbao/ Bulletin of Scientific and Technological Achievements. (CC) **4320**, **4603**

Kexue Jishu yu Bianzhengfa/Science, Technology, and Dialectics. (CC ISSN 1003-5680) **4320**, **3771**, **4603**
Kexue Shehui Zhuyi/Scientific Socialism.(CC ISSN 1001-3210) **4378**
Kexue Shijie/Scientific World. (CC) **4320**
Kexue Shiyan/Scientific Experiments. (CC) **4320**
Kexue Tongbao. (CC ISSN 0023-074X) **4320**
Kexue Tongbao (Foreign Language Edition) see Chinese Science Bulletin **4305**
Kexue yu Shenghuo/Science and Life. (CC) **4320**
Kexue yu Wenhua/Science & Culture. (CC ISSN 1000-3398) **4320**
Kexue Zhifu Yu Shenghuo/Science Prosperity and Life. (CC ISSN 1001-4284) **4320**, **103**
The Key. (CN) **2177**
Key (Battleground). (US) **33**, **1044**
Key (Los Angeles) see Key Magazine. This Week in Los Angeles and Southern California **4774**
Key (Philadelphia). (US ISSN 0023-0766) **2227**
Key - A Guide to College and Careers. (US) **1695**, **3629**
Key Abstracts - Advanced Materials. (UK ISSN 0950-4753) **3837**, **3868**
Key Abstracts - Antennas & Propagation. (UK ISSN 0950-4761) **1348**, **1357**
Key Abstracts - Artificial Intelligence. (UK ISSN 0950-477X) **1404**, **1845**
Key Abstracts - Business Automation. (UK) **1404**, **1339**
Key Abstracts - Communications Technology see Key Abstracts - Telecommunications **1348**
Key Abstracts - Computer Communications and Storage. (UK ISSN 0950-4788) **1404**, **1454**
Key Abstracts - Computing in Electronics & Power. (UK ISSN 0950-4796) **1404**, **1879**
Key Abstracts - Electrical Measurements and Instrumentation see Key Abstracts - Electronic Instrumentation **1775**
Key Abstracts - Electronic Circuits. (UK ISSN 0306-557X) **1775**, **16**
Key Abstracts - Electronic Instrumentation. (UK ISSN 0950-480X) **1775**, **16**
▼Key Abstracts - Factory Automation. (UK ISSN 0960-6572) **1404**, **1414**
Key Abstracts - High-Temperature Superconductors. (UK ISSN 0953-1262) **3837**, **1212**
▼Key Abstracts - Human-Computer Interaction. (UK ISSN 0964-0150) **1404**, **1441**
Key Abstracts - Industrial Power and Control Systems see Key Abstracts - Robotics & Control **1405**
Key Abstracts - Machine Vision. (US ISSN 0952-7052) **1404**, **1454**
Key Abstracts - Measurements in Physics. (UK ISSN 0950-4818) **3449**, **16**, **2525**
Key Abstracts - Microelectronics & Printed Circuits. (UK ISSN 0952-7060) **1775**, **16**
Key Abstracts - Microwave Technology. (UK ISSN 0952-7079) **1775**, **16**
▼Key Abstracts - Neural Networks. (UK ISSN 0964-0169) **1405**, **16**, **1427**
Key Abstracts - Optoelectronics. (UK ISSN 0950-4826) **3837**, **1348**, **3854**
Key Abstracts - Physical Measurements and Instrumentation see Key Abstracts - Measurements in Physics **3449**
Key Abstracts - Power Systems & Applications. (UK ISSN 0950-4834) **1845**, **1802**, **1901**
Key Abstracts - Power Transmission and Distribution see Key Abstracts - Power Systems & Applications **1845**

Key Abstracts - Robotics & Control. (UK ISSN 0950-4842) **1405**, 1845
Key Abstracts - Semiconductor Devices. (UK ISSN 0950-4850) **1775**, 16
Key Abstracts - Software Engineering. (UK ISSN 0950-4869) **1405**, 1478
Key Abstracts - Systems Theory *see* Key Abstracts - Artificial Intelligence **1404**
Key Abstracts - Telecommunications. (UK ISSN 0950-4877) **1348**, 1339
Key & B P M Annual Guide to Dance Music. (US) **3560**, 1531
Key British Enterprises. (UK ISSN 0142-5048) **676**
Key Business Ratios. (UK) **676**
†Key Cardiology. (US ISSN 0899-8019) **5223**
Key Engineering Materials. (SZ) **3411**, 1165
Key Family Newsletter. (US) **2156**
Key Horizons. (US) **2275**
Key International Guide. (US ISSN 0895-3163) **2454**, 4774
Key, Lock and Lantern. (US ISSN 0271-3241) **258**, 4711
Key Magazine. Carmel & Monterey Peninsula. (US) **4774**
Key Magazine. This Week in Chicago. (US ISSN 0040-6279) **4774**
Key Magazine. This Week in Los Angeles and Southern California. (US) **4774**, 2477
Key Magazine. This Week in Pittsburgh.(US) **2228**
Key Magazine. This Week in San Francisco. (US) **4774**
Key Neurology and Neurosurgery. (US ISSN 0886-8018) **3344**, 3381
The Key-Note (Westminster). (US) **3560**, 2437
Key Notes *see* One to One **4193**
†Key Notes. (NE) **5223**
Key Obstetrics and Gynecology. (US) **3176**, 3294
†Key of the Middle East. (CY) **5223**
Key Ophthalmology. (US ISSN 0886-8026) **3302**
Key Players in the Japanese Electronics Industry *see* Structure of the Japanese Electronics Industry **1778**
Key Reporter. (US ISSN 0023-0804) **1315**
Key Statistical Indicators for National Health Service Management in Wales.(UK ISSN 0264-6714) **4118**, 2470
Key; The Newsletter that Helps You Make More Money from Your Mail Order Advertising *see* Key (Battleground) **33**
Key to Calgary *see* Where Calgary **4797**
Key to Cayman. (CJ) **4774**
Key to Christian Education. (US ISSN 0023-0839) **1644**, 4186
Key to Economic Science. (NE ISSN 0165-4748) **726**, 16
Key to Kingston. (CN ISSN 0710-9628) **4774**
Key to Toronto *see* Where Toronto **4797**
Key to Vancouver *see* Where Vancouver **1508**
Key to Victoria *see* Where Victoria **1508**
Key Vive. (AT) **3560**
†Key West Review. (US ISSN 1041-5254) **5223**
Key Word in Context Northern Titles: K W I C Index *see* Northern Titles: K W I C Index **3938**
Key World Index of Wildlife Research. (SZ) **4356**, 16, 586
Keyan Guanli/Science Research Management. (CC ISSN 1000-2995) **4320**, 1017
Keyboard. (US ISSN 0730-0158) **3560**
Keyboard Classics. (US ISSN 0273-9526) **3560**
Keyboard Player. (UK ISSN 0269-3836) **3560**
Keyboard Teacher. (US) **3560**
Keyboard World. (US ISSN 0199-3313) **3560**
Keyhole. (US) **2156**

†Keynote: A Magazine for the Musical Arts. (US) **5223**
Keynoter. (US) **1299**
Keynotes. (UK) **2930**
Keynotes (Dallas). (US) **1527**
Keynotes (Manhattan). (US) **2275**, 2228
Keynotes (New Orleans). (US ISSN 0277-0792) **2767**
Keynotes (Trenton). (US) **2491**
Keys Guide. (US) **4774**
Keys of Peter. (UK) **4267**
Keys to the Fauna of the U S S R. (NE) **586**
Keystone. (CN) **1315**
Keystone *see* Orange Seed Technical Bulletin **2778**
Keystone A A A Motorist. (US) **4694**, 4774
Keystone Coal Industry Manual. (US) **1142**, 3486
†Keystone Folklore. (US ISSN 0149-8444) **5224**
Keystone - Jersey Truck Exchange. (US) **4745**
Keystone - Jersey Trucker *see* Keystone - Jersey Truck Exchange **4745**
Keystone Motorist *see* Keystone A A A Motorist **4694**
Keystone News Bulletin. (US) **3486**
Keystone Schoolmaster Newsletter. (US) **1729**, 1711
Keystoner. (US) **3754**
Keystrokes. (US) **4130**, 2930
Keyways. (UK ISSN 0262-4478) **642**
Keyword Index to Serial Titles. (UK ISSN 0143-9553) **2794**, 16
Keywords. (US ISSN 0197-7342) **1478**
Kfar Chabad. (IS) **4224**
Khabarovskii Gosudarstvennyi Pedagogicheskii Institut. Voprosy Istorii Dal'nego Vostoka. (RU) **2371**
Khad Patrika. (II ISSN 0023-1010) **183**
Khadi and Village Industries Commission Annual Report *see* K V I C Annual Report **1116**
Khadi Gramodyog. (II ISSN 0023-1029) **153**, 1079
Khadya Vigyan. (II ISSN 0023-1037) **2075**
Khaleej Times. (TS) **676**
Al-Khalij. (TS) **2210**
Al-Khalij al-Arabi/Arab Gulf. (IQ) **2430**
Al-Khalij al-Jadid. (QA) **2211**
Khamsin. (UK ISSN 0338-0181) **3902**
Khao Setthakit Kan-Kaset/Agricultural Economic News. (TH ISSN 0023-1053) **201**
Khar'kovskii Gosudarstvennyi Universitet. Filologiya. (KR) **2822**
Khar'kovskii Gosudarstvennyi Universitet. Matematika i Mekhanika. (KR) **3042**
Khar'kovskii Gosudarstvennyi Universitet. Radiofizika i Elektronika. (KR) **1901**
Khartoum Law Review. (SJ) **2642**
Khartoum University Press. Classified List of Publications. (SJ) **404**
Khasmik Poetry Quarterly. (AT) **2996**
Khatoon Mashriq. (II ISSN 0023-107X) **3591**
▼Khavaran. (IR) **2870**
Khel Bharati. (II) **4478**
Khel ki Dunya. (PK) **4478**
Khela. (II) **4478**
Khemoretseptsiya Nasekomykh/Insect Chemoreception. (LI ISSN 0206-3441) **535**
Kheti. (II ISSN 0023-1088) **103**
Khilauna. (II ISSN 0023-1096) **1258**
Khimicheskaya Promyshlennost' (RU ISSN 0023-110X) **1856**
Khimicheskaya Tekhnologiya. (KR ISSN 0368-556X) **1856**
Khimicheskie Volokna. (RU ISSN 0023-1118) **3863**
Khimicheskoe i Neftyanoe Mashinostroenie/Chemical and Oil Industry. (RU ISSN 0023-1126) **1856**, 3019, 3691
Khimiko-farmatsevticheskii Zhurnal. (RU ISSN 0023-1134) **3733**, 1182
Khimiya Drevesiny. (LV ISSN 0201-7474) **1182**

Khimiya i Tekhnologiya Topliv i Masel. (RU ISSN 0023-1169) **3691**, 1829
Khimiya i Tekhnologiya Vody. (KR ISSN 0204-3556) **1182**
Khimiya i Zhizn' (RU ISSN 0023-1142) **1182**
Khimiya Prirodnykh Soedinenii. (UZ ISSN 0023-1150) **1220**
Khimiya Tverdogo Topliva. (RU ISSN 0023-1177) **1856**, 1182, 2301
Khimiya v Sel'skom Khozyaistve. (RU ISSN 0023-1185) **103**, 1182
Khirurgiya/Surgery. (RU ISSN 0023-1207) **3381**
Khlebopekarnaya i Konditerskaya Promyshlennost' *see* Khleboprodukty **207**
Khleboprodukty. (RU ISSN 0235-2508) **207**, 2088
Khliborob Ukrainy. (KR ISSN 0023-1223) **183**
Khlopkovodstvo. (RU ISSN 0023-1231) **184**
Khoa Hoc Ky Thuat Kinh Te The Gioi/ World Science, Technology and Economy. (VN) **4320**, 4603
Khoa Hoc va Doi Song/Science and Life.(VN) **4320**
Khoj. (GW ISSN 0937-2105) **3640**
Khoj Darpan. (II) **2056**, 2930
Kholodil'naya Tekhnika. (RU ISSN 0023-124X) **2301**
Khosana. (US) **4441**, 2339
Khozyain (Minsk). (BW ISSN 0131-6311) **103**
Khozyain (Moscow). (RU ISSN 0235-2613) **103**
Khryses Selides Esthitikis/Aesthetic Golden Pages. (GR) **376**
Khudozhnik. (RU ISSN 0023-1258) **332**
Khurasan. (IR) **2870**
Khvurjin. (IR) **2202**
Ki-es-Ki. *see* C E A Handbook **1619**
Kibaru. (ML) **2011**
Kibbutz (Efal). (IS) **831**
Kibbutz (Tel Aviv). (IS ISSN 0334-2182) **4441**
Kibbutz Journal (New York). (US) **831**
Kibbutz Planning Bulletin. (IS) **2491**
Kibbutz Studies. (IS ISSN 0333-6379) **985**, 831, 3984
Kibernetika. (KR ISSN 0023-1274) **1441**
Kibernetika i Vychislitel'naya Tekhnika. (KR ISSN 0454-9910) **1441**, 1414
Kick Illustrated *see* Inside Karate **4475**
Kick it Over. (CN ISSN 0823-6526) **3903**, 1961, 4846
Kick Off. (CN) **4507**
Kick to Corruption. (II ISSN 0023-1282) **2870**
Kicker - Sportmagazin. (GW ISSN 0023-1290) **4478**
Kickoff. (US) **4507**
Kicks. (US ISSN 0199-6657) **3560**
Kid City. (US) **1258**
†Kidma. (IS ISSN 0334-2212) **5224**
Kidney. (US ISSN 0023-1304) **3388**
▼Kidney (New York, 1992). (US) **3388**
Kidney Diseases. (US) **3388**
†Kidney Diseases. (UK ISSN 0142-8705) **5224**
Kidney International. (US ISSN 0085-2538) **3388**
Kidney International. Supplement. (US ISSN 0098-6577) **3388**
Kidney Research Fund Newsletter *see* Kidney Research News **3389**
Kidney Research News. (UK) **3389**
Kids. (GW) **1285**, 1240
Kids Computer Connector. (US) **1470**, 1258, 1461
Kids Discover. (US) **1258**
Kids Fashions Magazine. (US ISSN 0362-6660) **1292**
Kids, Kids, Kidz. (US) **1240**
Kid's Korner! (US) **1258**
Kids Lib News. (US) **1240**
▼Kids Rhyme Newsletter. (US) **1258**
Kids Toronto. (CN ISSN 0826-9696) **1240**
Kids Tribute. (CN) **1240**
Kid's World Almanac of Records & Facts. (US) **1258**

KidSports. (US ISSN 1054-7002) **1258**, 4478
Kidstuff. (US ISSN 0278-632X) **1258**, 2767
Kiel. (GW ISSN 0936-6547) **2189**
Kiel Discussion Papers. *see* Kieler Diskussionsbeitraege **871**
Kiel Working Papers. *see* Kieler Arbeitspapiere **871**
Kieler Arbeitspapiere/Kiel Working Papers. (GW ISSN 0342-0787) **871**
Kieler Diskussionsbeitraege/Kiel Discussion Papers. (GW ISSN 0455-0420) **871**
Kieler Milchwirtschaftliche Forschungsberichte. (GW ISSN 0023-1347) **201**
Kieler Studien. (GW ISSN 0340-6989) **915**
Kielikeskusuutisia/Lanuage Centre News. (FI) **2822**
Kiels Feine Adressen. (GW) **2189**, 373
Kierkegaardiana. (DK ISSN 0075-6032) **3771**, 4186
Kierkegaard's Writings. (US) **3771**
Kihara Institute for Biological Research. Report. *see* Kihara Seibutsugaku Kenkyujo. Seiken Jiho **545**
Kihara Institute for Biological Research. Wheat Information Service. (JA ISSN 0510-3517) **508**
Kihara Seibutsugaku Kenkyujo. Seiken Jiho/Kihara Institute for Biological Research. Report. (JA ISSN 0080-8539) **545**
Kiiv. (KR ISSN 0208-0710) **2870**
Kijk op het Noorden/Outlook on the North. (NE ISSN 0023-1363) **871**
Kikai Gijutsu/Mechanical Engineering. (JA ISSN 0451-9396) **1934**
Kikai Sekkei. *see* Machine Design **1934**
Kikaika Nogyo/Farming Mechanization. (JA ISSN 0023-1371) **163**
Kikan Togyo Shiho/Quarterly Information of Sugar Industry. (JA ISSN 0023-138X) **2076**
Kilimo News. (KE) **103**
▼Kilk - Mahnamah-i Adabi va Hunari/ Kelk - Review of Art and Literature. (IR ISSN 1017-415X) **2930**
Kilkenny People Newspaper. (IE) **2203**
†Killer Cells and Cytotoxicity. (UK ISSN 0261-4731) **5224**
Kim. *see* Trefle **1268**
Kimball Family Association Newsletter *see* Connections: Kimball Family Association Newsletter **2148**
Kimia. (MY) **1182**
Kimika. (PH ISSN 0115-2130) **1182**
Kimya Muhendisligi. (TU ISSN 0023-1428) **1856**
Kimya ve Sanayi. (TU) **1182**
Kin. (CN ISSN 0023-1436) **1299**
Kin Kollecting. (US) **2156**
Kina. (CC ISSN 1000-9329) **2182**
Kina Information. (DK ISSN 0108-2612) **871**
Kinaadman/Wisdom. (PH ISSN 0115-6012) **3640**
Kincskereso. (HU ISSN 0133-3755) **1258**
Das Kind. (GW) **1240**, 1753, 4034
Kind en Ziekenhuis. (NE) **3322**
Kind en Zondag. (NE ISSN 0023-1444) **4186**
Kind News Jr. (US ISSN 1050-821X) **1258**, 1961
Kind News Sr. (US ISSN 1050-9542) **1258**, 1961
Kind News 1 *see* Kind News Jr **1258**
Kind News 2 *see* Kind News Sr **1258**
Kindai Eiga. (JA ISSN 0023-1460) **3512**
Kindai Judo. (JA) **4478**
Kinder. (GW) **1240**, 2281, 3322
Kinder Jugend Film Korrespondenz. (GW ISSN 0721-8486) **1258**, 3512
Kinder- und Jugendbuecher. (GW) **1258**
Kinderaerztliche Praxis. (GW ISSN 0023-1495) **3322**
Der Kinderarzt. (GW ISSN 0340-5877) **3176**, 16
Kinderbrief aus der Weltmission *see* Bremer Missionsschiff **5152**

6370 KINDERGARTEN

Kindergarten und Mission. (GW) **1240**
Kindergesundheit. (GW ISSN 0724-3618) **1240, 3322**
Kindergottesdienst/Lass mich Hoeren. (GW ISSN 0341-7190) **4186**
Kinderkrankenschwester. (GW) **3281, 3322**
Kinderschutz Aktuell. (GW ISSN 0930-0775) **4411, 4441**
Kinderverzorging/Jeugdverzorging. (NE) **1240**
Kindex. (US ISSN 0733-8937) **2699, 1247**
Kindheit. (GW ISSN 0170-625X) **1240, 4034**
Kindness Magazine see Monkey Kindness Magazine **231**
Kindred Spirit see Chiron Review **2990**
Kindred Spirits. (CN ISSN 0823-8367) **2156**
Kinematics and Physics of Celestial Bodies. (English translation of: Kinematika i Fizika Nebesnykh Tel) (US ISSN 0884-5913) **366, 3823**
Kinematografija u Srbiji see Kinematografija u Srbiji - Uporedo S F R J **3513**
Kinematografija u Srbiji - Uporedo S F R J. (YU) **3513**
Kinematograph. (GW) **3513**
Kinesiology and Medicine for Dance. (US) **1531, 1753**
Kinesiology for Dance see Kinesiology and Medicine for Dance **1531**
Kinesis. (US ISSN 0023-1568) **3771, 2454**
Kinesis. (CN ISSN 0317-9095) **4846**
Kinesis Report see Kinesis **3771**
Kinesitherapie Actualite. (FR) **3120**
Kinesitherapie Scientifique. (FR ISSN 0023-1576) **3120**
Kinetics and Catalysis. (English translation of: Kinetika i Kataliz) (US ISSN 0023-1584) **1228**
▼Kinetoscopio. (CK ISSN 0121-3776) **3513**
Kinfolks and Connections of Alexander County, N.C. (US) **2156**
King. (IT) **1292, 3398**
King Abdul Aziz University. Faculty of Earth Sciences. Bulletin. (SU) **1546**
King Abdul Aziz University. Faculty of Marine Science. Journal. (SU) **445**
King County Medical Society. Bulletin. (US) **3120**
King Faisal Center for Research and Islamic Studies. Manuscript Catalogue. see Markaz al-Malik Faisal lil-Buhuth wal-Dirasat al-Islamiyyah. Fihris al-Makhtutat **3647**
King Faisal Center for Research and Islamic Studies. Newsletter. (SU) **4219, 2430**
King Island News. (AT) **33, 676**
King Pole Circus Magazine. (UK) **4634**
King Saud University. College of Science. Journal see King Saud University. Journal. Sciences **4320**
King Saud University. Journal. Administrative Sciences. (SU ISSN 1018-3582) **676**
King Saud University. Journal. Agricultural Sciences. (SU ISSN 1018-3590) **103**
King Saud University. Journal. Architecture and Planning. (SU ISSN 1018-3604) **2491**, 302
King Saud University. Journal. Arts. (SU ISSN 1018-3612) **332, 2930**
King Saud University. Journal. Educational Sciences. (SU ISSN 1018-3620) **1644**
King Saud University. Journal. Engineering Sciences. (SU ISSN 1018-3639) **1829**
King Saud University. Journal. Sciences.(SU ISSN 1018-3647) **4320**
King Sized Cracked. (US) **2871**
Kingbird. (US ISSN 0023-1606) **565**
Kingdom Digest. (US ISSN 0023-1614) **4186**
Kingdom Overseas see Now (London, 1970) **4245**
Kingfisher. (US) **2930**
†Kingia. (AT ISSN 0819-1247) **5224**
Kingpin. (UK) **4478**

King's Coal Export Report. (US) **3487, 1792**
King's Coal Export Week see King's Coal Export Report **3487**
King's Coalstats. (US) **3487, 1792**
Kings College Law Journal. (UK) **2642**
Kings Counsel see Kings College Law Journal **2642**
Kings County Historical and Archival Society, Inc.. Newsletter. (CN) **2156**
Kings County Historical Society. Newsletter see Kings County Historical and Archival Society, Inc.. Newsletter **2156**
King's Gazette. (UK ISSN 0085-2546) **3120, 2466**
King's Gulf Grain Guide. (US ISSN 0885-5811) **207**
King's International Coal Trade. (US ISSN 0749-9043) **3487, 1792**
King's Midwest Gas see King's North American Gas **3691**
King's North American Gas. (US) **3691, 1792**
King's Northern Coal. (US ISSN 0749-1719) **3487, 1792**
Kings of Tomorrow Series. (UK ISSN 0075-6083) **419**
Kings Pointer. (US) **1315, 4730**
King's Southern Coal. (US ISSN 0749-1697) **3487, 1792**
King's Tennessee Valley News. (US ISSN 0749-1727) **1044, 1792**
†King's Theological Review. (UK ISSN 0143-5922) **5224**
King's Western Coal. (US ISSN 0749-1700) **3487, 1792**
Kingsman. (US ISSN 0023-1649) **1315**
Kingsman. (UK ISSN 0140-0991) **3462**
†Kingston Law Review. (UK ISSN 0453-8854) **5224**
Kinheart Connection. (US) **4846**
Kinheart Quarterly see Kinheart Connection **4846**
Kinisi. see Motion **4778**
Kinki Chugoku Agricultural Research/ Kinki Chugoku Nogyo Kenkyu. (JA) **103**
Kinki Chugoku Nogyo Kenkyu. see Kinki Chugoku Agricultural Research **103**
Kinki Daigaku Kyushu Kogakubu Kenkyu Hokoku. Rikagaku Hen/Kinki University. Faculty of Engineering (Kyushu). Reports. Science and Technology Section. (JA ISSN 0288-738X) **1829**
Kinki Daigaku Rikogakubu Kenkyu Hokoku/Kinki University. Faculty of Science and Technology. Journal. (JA ISSN 0386-4928) **4320, 4603**
Kinki Daigaku Yakugakubu Kiyo. see Kinki University. Bulletin of Pharmacy **3733**
Kinki Nogyo Josei Hokoku. see Annual Review of Agriculture in Kinki District **76**
Kinki Shokubutsu Dokokai Kaishi. (JA) **508**
Kinki University. Bulletin of Pharmacy/ Kinki Daigaku Yakugakubu Kiyo. (JA ISSN 0023-1657) **3733**
Kinki University. Faculty of Engineering (Kyushu). Reports. Science and Technology Section. see Kinki Daigaku Kyushu Kogakubu Kenkyu Hokoku. Rikagaku Hen **1829**
Kinki University. Faculty of Science and Technology. Journal. see Kinki Daigaku Rikogakubu Kenkyu Hokoku **4320**
Kino. (PL ISSN 0023-1673) **3513**
Kino. (CS) **3513**
†Kino-Film. (SZ) **5224**
Kino-Film mit Werbung Heute see Kino-Film **5224**
Kino; Filme der Bundesrepublik Deutschland. (GW) **3513**
Kino; German Film. (GW) **3513**
Kino News. (GW) **3513**
Kino News Oesterreich. (GW) **3513**
Kino - Nouvelles. (CN ISSN 0709-8227) **3120**
Kinoizkustvo. (BU ISSN 0323-9993) **3513**
Kinolehti. (FI) **3513**
Kinomagazin. (GW) **3513**

Kinomekhanik. (RU ISSN 0023-1681) **3513**
Kinoschriften. (AU) **3513**
Kinotechnik. (PL ISSN 0023-169X) **3513**
Kinship. (US ISSN 0023-1703) **4411, 4186**
Kintu. (II) **2871**
Kinyamateka. (RW) **676**
Kin'yu Keizai see Ryugin Keizai Report **883**
Kin'yu Zaisei Jijo/Financial Economist Weekly. (JA) **788**
Kinzoku Hyomen Gijutsu see Hyomen Gijutsu **1212**
Kinzoku Zairyo Gijutsu Kenkyujo Obun Kenkyu Hokoku. see National Research Institute for Metals. Transactions **3416**
Kiongozi/Leader. (TZ) **4267**
Kiosk. (US) **2996**
Kiosk og Service. (DK ISSN 0903-9287) **1044**
Kioskejer-Bladet see Kiosk og Service **1044**
Kipepeo. (TZ ISSN 0856-1982) **1258**
Kipling Journal. (UK ISSN 0023-1738) **2930**
Kiplinger Agriculture Letter. (US ISSN 0023-1746) **103**
Kiplinger California Letter. (US ISSN 0453-9249) **953**
Kiplinger Florida Letter. (US ISSN 0023-1754) **953**
Kiplinger Tax Letter. (US ISSN 0023-1762) **1100**
Kiplinger Texas Letter. (US ISSN 0279-8484) **953**
Kiplinger Washington Letter. (US ISSN 0023-1770) **953**
Kiplinger's Personal Finance. (US ISSN 1056-697X) **1506**
Kir - Ou - Kirk. (US ISSN 0017-6613) **2930**
Kirajagat. (BG) **4478**
Kiran. (PK) **2930**
Kirche. (AU ISSN 0023-1789) **4267**
Kirche im Osten. (GW) **4241**
Kirche im Sozialismus see Uebergaenge **5294**
Kirche in Marburg. (GW) **4267**, **4186**
Kirche und Konfession. (GW) **4186**
Kirche und Recht. (AU ISSN 0259-0735) **2642, 4186**
Kirche und Schule. (GW) **4267**
Der Kirchenchor. (GW ISSN 0023-1800) **3560**
Kirchenmusikalische Mitteilungen. (GW ISSN 0174-2116) **3560, 4267**
Kirchenmusikalische Nachrichten. (GW ISSN 0939-4761) **3560, 4186**
Kirchenmusikalisches Jahrbuch. (GW ISSN 0075-6199) **3560**
Der Kirchenmusiker. (GW ISSN 0023-1819) **3560, 4186**
Kirchenzeitung fuer das Erzbistum Koeln. (GW) **4267**
Kirchenzeitung fuer die Dioezese Augsburg. (GW) **4267**
Kirchliche Zeitgeschichte. (GW ISSN 0932-9951) **2371, 2412, 4187**
Kirchlicher Dienst in der Arbeitswelt. (GW ISSN 0178-8906) **4241, 985**
Kirchliches Amtsblatt fuer das Bistum Essen. (GW ISSN 0023-1827) **4187**
Kirchliches Amtsblatt fuer das Bistum Trier. (GW) **4187**
Kirchliches Jahrbuch fuer die Evangelische Kirche in Deutschland. (GW ISSN 0075-6210) **4241**
†Kiribati Report. (US) **5224**
Kirin Brewery Company. Annual Report.(JA) **382**
Kirin Brewery Company, Tokyo. Research Laboratory. Report see Technical Report of Kirin **386**
Kirjakauppalehti. (FI ISSN 0047-343X) **4131**
Kirjapainotaito - Graafikko. (FI ISSN 0017-2731) **4002**
Kirjastolehti. (FI ISSN 0023-1843) **2767**
Kirjeshakki. (FI ISSN 0358-1071) **4478**
Kirke og Kultur. (NO ISSN 0023-186X) **4187, 2871**

Kirkefondets Aarbog. (DK ISSN 0107-9824) **4187**
Kirkegaardslederen. (DK ISSN 0107-9123) **2119**
†Kirkehistoriske Samlinger. (DK ISSN 0450-3171) **5224**
Kirkens Undervisning. (DK ISSN 0900-1433) **4187**
Kirkia. (RH ISSN 0451-9930) **508**
Kirkintilloch & Bishopbriggs Herald. (UK) **2194**
Kirkus Reviews. (US ISSN 0042-6598) **4131, 1240**
Kirolak. (SP) **4478**
Kirtlandia. (US ISSN 0075-6245) **4321**
Kiruna Geophysical Data. (SW ISSN 0453-9478) **1592**
Kiruna Geophysical Institute. Annual Report see Swedish Institute of Space Physics. Annual Report **1595**
Kiruna Geophysical Institute. Preprint see Swedish Institute of Space Physics. Preprint **5286**
Kiruna Geophysical Institute. Scientific Report see Swedish Institute of Space Physics. Scientific Report **1595**
Kiruna Geophysical Institute. Technical Report see Swedish Institute of Space Physics. Technical Report **1595**
Kiruna Gephysical Institute. Software Report see Swedish Institute of Space Physics. Software Report **1595**
Kiryat Sefer. (IS ISSN 0023-1851) **404, 4224**
Kirykas/Herald. (CY) **985**
Kis Epito. (CS) **1258**
Kisafim. (IS) **871**
Kisan World. (II) **103**
Kiseichugaku Zasshi. see Japanese Journal of Parasitology **3220**
Kiserletes Orvostudomany. (HU ISSN 0023-1878) **3260**
Kishavaraz. (IR) **103**
Kisho-cho Geppo Zenkoku Kishchyo. see Japan. Meteorological Agency. Monthly Report **3437**
Kisho-Cho Kansoku Gijutsu Shiryo/ Technical Data Series. (JA) **3438**
Kisho-cho Nenpo Zenkoku Kishohyo. see Japan Meteorological Agency. Annual Report **3437**
Kisho-cho Obun Iho. see Geophysical Magazine **1589**
Kisho-cho Obun Kaiyo Hokoku. see Oceanographical Magazine **1609**
Kisho Shushi. see Meteorological Society of Japan. Journal **3438**
Kishore Bangla. (BG) **1258**
Kiso, Kankyo Kagaku Kenkyu/Hiroshima University. Faculty of Integrated Arts and Sciences. Science Reports. (JA ISSN 0285-6905) **1962, 4321**
Kiss. (IT) **2983**
†Kiss Rocks. (US) **5224**
Kiswahili. (TZ ISSN 0856-048X) **2822, 2011, 2930**
Kit Car. (US ISSN 0883-5705) **2437, 4694**
Kit Car Illustrated. (US) **4694**
Kita Nihon Byogaichu Kenkyu Kaiho/ Society of Plant Protection of North Japan. Annual Report. (JA ISSN 0368-623X) **184**
Kita Nippon Byogaichu Kenkyukai Nempo see Kita Nihon Byogaichu Kenkyu Kaiho **184**
Al-Kitab al-Arabi Fi Aam/Arab Book Annual. (AE ISSN 0066-5630) **4141**
Kitab al-Hilal. (UA) **2185**
Kitab el Yom. (UA) **2185**
Kitab-i Muqavamat. (IR) **3462**
Kitakami City Museum. Bulletin. see Kitakami-shiritsu Hakubutsukan Kenkyu **4321**
Kitakami-shiritsu Hakubutsukan Kenkyu/Kitakami City Museum. Bulletin. (JA ISSN 0386-0655) **4321, 3526**
Kitakanto Igaku. see Kitakanto Medical Journal **3120**
Kitakanto Medical Journal/Kitakanto Igaku. (JA ISSN 0023-1908) **3120**

Kitakyushu Museum of Natural History. Bulletin. see Kitakyushu-shiritsu Shizenshi Hakubutsukan Kenkyu Hokoku **4321**
Kitakyushu-shiritsu Shizenshi Hakubutsukan Kenkyu Hokoku/ Kitakyushu Museum of Natural History. Bulletin. (JA ISSN 0387-964X) **4321**, 3526
Kitano Hospital Journal of Medicine. (JA ISSN 0023-1916) **3120**
Kitasato Archives of Experimental Medicine. (JA ISSN 0023-1924) **445**
Kitchen. see Kouzina **2448**
Kitchen. see L'Ambiente Cucina **2548**
Kitchen & Bath Business. (US ISSN 0730-2487) **622**
Kitchen and Bath Concepts see Qualified Remodeler **629**
Kitchen & Bath Design News. (US) **2553**, 2560
Kitchen Bath Specialist. (US) **622**
Kitchen Plans. (US) **2553**
Kitchen Sink Pipeline. (US) **4131**
Kitchen Times. (US) **2448**, 2477
Kitchens. (UK ISSN 0260-1745) **622**
Kitchens & Bathrooms. (UK) **2553**, 2560
Kitchin's Road Transport Law. (UK ISSN 0308-8987) **2642**, 4745
Kite Tales see KiteLines **4549**
KiteLines. (US ISSN 0192-3439) **4549**
Kitimat-Kemano Ingot see Ingot **3408**
Kitorogia. see Cytologia **524**
Kitplanes. (US ISSN 0891-1851) **57**, 2437
Kitte Shumi. (JA) **3754**
Kiva. (US ISSN 0023-1940) **277**, 2011, 2412
Kivun see Emet **4222**
Kiwanis Magazine. (US ISSN 0162-5276) **1299**
Kiyup Kyungyung/Business Management. (KO) **1017**
Kizito. (UG ISSN 0023-1975) **1258**, 4187
Kjelberg och S A B Schriften see Svetsaren **3430**
Kjemi. (NO ISSN 0023-1983) **1182**, 3411
Kjoepmannen. (NO) **1044**
Kjoettbransjen. (NO ISSN 0332-7078) **2093**
Kjoleteknikk og Fryserinaering see Scan Ref **2303**
Klagenfurt. (AU ISSN 0023-2017) **4089**
Klagenfurter Beitraege zur Philosophie. (AU ISSN 0259-0743) **3771**
Klang & Ton. (GW ISSN 0933-0097) **4461**
Klank en Weerklank. (NE ISSN 0030-3836) **3560**
Klappe Auf. (GW) **4634**
Klapper see Diepzee **2911**
Klar und Wahr see Plain Truth **4287**
Klare Blick see ZeitBild **3978**
Klarinette see Oboe - Klarinette - Fagott **3571**
Klasgids. (SA) **2930**
Klasings Bootsmarkt International; Yachten und Boote Zubehoer, Ausruestung, Motoren. (GW ISSN 0075-627X) **4525**
Klassekampen. (DK ISSN 0023-2025) **3903**
Klassifikationsschema der Schulstatistik/Schema de Classification de la Statistique Scolaire. (SZ) **1729**
Klassische Homeopathie see Zeitschrift fuer Klassische Homoeopathie **3216**
Klaus Groth Gesellschaft. Jahresgaben. (GW ISSN 0453-9842) **2822**, 2930
Der Klecks. (GW) **1644**
Klei, Glas, Keramiek. (NE) **1165**
Klein, Schanzlin und Becker Aktiengesellschaft Technische Berichte see K S B Technische Berichte **1828**
Kleinbrennerei. (GW ISSN 0341-2067) **383**
Kleine Aarde. (NE ISSN 0166-3704) **2133**
Kleine Aegyptische Texte. (GW ISSN 0343-1088) **3640**

Kleine Bibliographische Reihe. (GW ISSN 0941-6617) **404**
Het Kleine Brouwersblad. (BE) **383**
†Kleine Chorzeitung. (SZ ISSN 0023-2068) **5224**
Kleine Deutsche Prosadenkmaeler des Mittelalters. (GW ISSN 0075-6318) **2930**
Kleine Historische Reihe. (GW ISSN 0937-9835) **404**
Kleine Museumshefte. (GW ISSN 0075-6326) **3526**
Kleine Naturwissenschaftliche Bibliothek.(GW ISSN 0232-346X) **2767**
Kleintier-Praxis. (GW ISSN 0023-2076) **4812**
Kleinviehzuechter. (SZ) **220**
Kleio. (IT) **1278**
Kleio. (SA ISSN 0023-2084) **2316**, 4131
Kleio. (NE ISSN 0165-6449) **2371**, 676, 1753
Kleist-Jahrbuch. (GW ISSN 0722-8899) **2930**
Kleronomia. (GR) **4284**
Kleur. (NE ISSN 0169-0930) **3654**
Klex - Das Junge Magazin see Topic Klex - Das Junge Magazin **1268**
Kliatt Young Adult Paperback Book Guide. (US ISSN 0199-2376) **4131**
Klick. (GW) **1258**
Klik. (GR) **2196**
Klima-Eilinformation. (GW) **3438**
Klima und Kaelteingenieur Klima, Kaelte, Heizung see K I - Klima, Kaelte, Heizung **2301**
Klimaatbeheersing. (NE ISSN 0165-5523) **2301**
Klimat i Gidrografiya Zabaikal'ya. (RU) **3438**
Klimatologische Werte. (GW) **3438**
Klinge. (GW) **4411**, 1240
Klinicheskaya Meditsina/Clinical Medicine. (RU ISSN 0023-2149) **3120**
Klinika Oczna. (PL ISSN 0023-2157) **3302**
Klinikarzt. (GW ISSN 0341-2350) **3120**
Klinikkalender. (GW) **3120**
Klinische Chemie. (GW ISSN 0173-6647) **3120**, 1182
Klinische Monatsblaetter fuer Augenheilkunde und Augenarztliche Fortbildung. (GW ISSN 0023-2165) **3302**
▼Klinische Neuroradiologie. (GW ISSN 0939-7116) **3360**, 3344
Klinische Paediatrie. (GW ISSN 0300-8630) **3322**
Klinische Psychologie und Psychopathologie. (GW ISSN 0343-9429) **4034**
Klinische und Experimentelle Urologie. (GW ISSN 0174-2752) **3389**
Klinische Wochenschrift see Clinical Investigation **3089**
Klinisches Labor. (GW ISSN 0941-2131) **3260**
Kliniske Tandteknikere. (DK ISSN 0109-2294) **3237**
Klio. (GW ISSN 0075-6334) **2316**
Klip. (DK ISSN 0904-4159) **3513**, 1375
Kloeckner-Werke AG Kloeckner Werke Heute see Kloeckner Werke Heute **3411**
Kloeckner Werke Heute. (Kloeckner-Werke AG) (GW ISSN 0937-6186) **3411**, 1934, 3863
Das Kloecknerhaus. (GW ISSN 0937-6178) **1079**
Kloeverbladet. (SW ISSN 0281-1278) **1258**, 1240
Klok en Klepel. (NE ISSN 0023-2181) **3560**
Klopfzeichen. (GW) **3120**
Klub see Klub i Khudozhestvennaya Samodeyatel'nost **2585**
Klub i Khudozhestvennaya Samodeyatel'nost' (RU) **2585**
Klubb Nachrichten. (GW) **4478**
Klubnachrichten. (GW) **4478**
Klucze do Oznaczania Owadow Polski. (PL ISSN 0075-6350) **535**
Klueter Blaetter. (GW ISSN 0023-2211) **2871**

Die Kluge Hausfrau. (GW ISSN 0023-222X) **2190**
Kluger Mann Baut Selbst see Heim und Hobby **2447**
Kmecki Glas. (XV ISSN 0023-2238) **103**
Kmetianum. (CS) **2371**
Knack. (BE) **2871**
Knafaim. (IL ISSN 0792-4836) **58**
Knanayamithram. (II ISSN 0254-6205) **1258**, 4187
Knarr, Knerr, Knorr Family Newsletter. (US) **2156**
Knave. (UK ISSN 0265-1289) **3398**
Kneipp Blaetter. (GW ISSN 0023-2254) **3805**
Knife & Fork. (US) **2477**, 2228
Kniga Issledovaniya. (RU) **4131**, 2371
Knight. see Vytis **1302**
Knight Letter. (US ISSN 0454-8973) **2156**
Knight's Industrial Reports see Managerial Law **988**
Knight's Local Government and Magisterial Reports see Knight's Local Government Reports **2642**
Knight's Local Government Reports. (UK ISSN 0140-3281) **2642**, 4065
Knights of Malta. Bulletin see Order of St. John. Bulletin **1308**
Knigi Belorusskoi S.S.R/Byelorussian Books. (BW ISSN 0235-3393) **404**
Kniha. (CS) **4131**
Knihovna. (CS ISSN 0139-5335) **2767**, 2371
Knihovnictvi a Bibliografie. (CS) **404**
Knijevni Jivot. (RM) **2930**
Knip. (NE ISSN 0023-2289) **4846**
†Knipplus. (NE) **5224**
Knitovations. (US ISSN 0084-1234) **4621**
Knitstats. (UK ISSN 0260-8855) **4628**, 4577
Knitters. (US ISSN 0747-9026) **3591**
Knitting and Haberdashery Review see Knitting & Haberdashery: the Needlecrafts Review **4621**
Knitting & Haberdashery: the Needlecrafts Review. (UK) **4621**
Knitting and Sewing Machine Times. (UK) **3019**, 1286
Knitting International. (UK ISSN 0266-8394) **4621**
Knitting Technique. (GW ISSN 0177-4875) **4621**, 3591
Knitting Times. (US ISSN 0023-2300) **1286**
Knitting Times Buyers' Guide (Year). (US) **1142**
Knitting Times Buyers' Guide and Knitwear Apparel Directory see Knitting Times Buyers' Guide (Year) **1142**
†Knitting Times Yearbook. (US ISSN 0085-2562) **5224**
Knitting with Simplicity see Simplicity Knitting **5277**
Knitting World. (US ISSN 0194-8083) **3591**
Knitwear Employers Association. Bulletin. (US) **1286**, 985, 1044
Knives (Year). (US ISSN 0277-0725) **2437**
Knives Illustrated. (US) **2437**
Knizhnoe Obozrenie. (RU ISSN 0023-2378) **4131**
Knizna Kultura see Kniha **4131**
†Kniznice a Vedecke Informacie. (CS ISSN 0322-807X) **5224**
Kniznicny Zbornik. (CS ISSN 0075-6369) **2767**
Knjigovodstvo. (YU ISSN 0023-2394) **753**
Knjizevna Kritika. (YU) **2930**, 2316, 3771
Knjizevna Rec. (YU ISSN 0350-4115) **2510**
Knjizevna Smotra. (CI ISSN 0455-0463) **2930**
Knjizevne Novine. (YU ISSN 0023-2416) **2871**
Knjizevni Glasnik Mohorjeve Druzbe. (XV) **4131**
Knjizevnost. (YU ISSN 0023-2408) **2930**, 2871
Knjizevnost i Jezik. (YU) **2822**, 2930

KOBE UNIVERSITY 6371

Knjiznica. (XV ISSN 0023-2424) **2767**, 2794
Knjiznicarske Novice. (XV ISSN 0353-9237) **2767**
Knock Out see K O **4477**
Knotty Problems of Baseball. (US ISSN 0075-6385) **4507**
Know Atlanta. (US) **2228**
Know More About Oil World Statistics. (UK ISSN 0141-4305) **3691**
†Know Your Training Films. (UK) **5224**
Know Your World Extra. (US ISSN 0163-4844) **1258**, 1644
†Knowhow. (IS ISSN 0792-2035) **5224**
Knowledge. (US ISSN 0738-8640) **2871**, 4321
Knowledge Acquisition. (UK ISSN 1042-8143) **1409**
Knowledge and Life. see Zhishi yu Shenghuo **2183**
Knowledge and Policy. (US ISSN 0897-1986) **4378**, 3771
Knowledge and Society. (US ISSN 0278-1557) **4441**, 2510
Knowledge-Based Systems. (UK ISSN 0950-7051) **1409**
Knowledge-Based Systems Management Review. (UK ISSN 0954-9072) **827**
Knowledge: Creation, Diffusion, Utilization. (US ISSN 0164-0259) **1339**
Knowledge Engineering Review. (UK ISSN 0269-8889) **1409**
Knowledge in Society see Knowledge and Policy **4378**
Knowledge is Power. see Zhishi Jiushi Liliang **4353**
Knowledge of Literature and History. see Wenshi Zhishi **4392**
Knox Alumnus. (US) **1315**
Knox County Illinois Genealogical Society. Quarterly. (US ISSN 0741-7284) **2156**
Knox Now and the Knox Alumnus see Knox Alumnus **1315**
Koala Club News. (US) **587**
Kobe Daigaku Daigakuin Shizen Kagaku Kenkyuka Kiyo. A. see Kobe University. Graduate School of Science and Technology. Memoirs. Series A **4603**
Kobe Daigaku Daigakuin Shizen Kagaku Kenkyuka Kiyo B/Kobe University. Graduate School of Science and Technology. Memoirs. Series B. (JA ISSN 0287-6515) **4321**, 4603
Kobe Daigaku Igakubu Kiyo/Kobe University. Medical Journal. (JA ISSN 0075-6431) **3120**
Kobe Economic and Business Research Series. (JA ISSN 0075-6415) **676**
Kobe Economic and Business Review. (JA ISSN 0075-6407) **676**
Kobe Journal of Mathematics. (JA ISSN 0289-9051) **3042**
Kobe Journal of Medical Sciences. (JA ISSN 0023-2513) **3120**
Kobe Kaiyo Kishodai Iho/Kobe Marine Observatory. Bulletin. (JA ISSN 0368-5969) **1607**, 3438
Kobe Marine Observatory. Bulletin. see Kobe Kaiyo Kishodai Iho **1607**
Kobe Plant Protection and Plant Quarantine Information/Kobe Shokubutsu Boeki Joho. (JA ISSN 0023-2521) **184**
Kobe Shokubutsu Boeki Joho. see Kobe Plant Protection and Plant Quarantine Information **184**
Kobe Tokiwa College. Bulletin. see Kobe Tokiwa Tanki Daigaku Kiyo **4321**
Kobe Tokiwa Tanki Daigaku Kiyo/Kobe Tokiwa College. Bulletin. (JA ISSN 0389-9578) **4321**
Kobe University. Faculty of Agriculture. Science Reports. (JA ISSN 0452-2370) **103**, 445
Kobe University. Graduate School of Science and Technology. Memoirs. Series A/Kobe Daigaku Daigakuin Shizen Kagaku Kenkyuka Kiyo. A. (JA ISSN 0287-6507) **4603**
Kobe University. Graduate School of Science and Technology. Memoirs. Series B. see Kobe Daigaku Daigakuin Shizen Kagaku Kenkyuka Kiyo B **4321**

KOBE UNIVERSITY

Kobe University. Medical Journal. see Kobe Daigaku Igakubu Kiyo **3120**
Kobe University. School of Business Administration. Annals. (JA ISSN 0085-2570) **1017**
Kobe University Economic Review. (JA ISSN 0454-1111) **676**
Kobe University Law Review. International Edition. (JA ISSN 0075-6423) **2642**
Kobe University of Mercantile Marine. Review. Part 1. Studies in Humanities and Social Science. (JA) **2510**, 4378
Kobe University of Mercantile Marine. Review. Part 2. Maritime Studies, and Science and Engineering. (JA ISSN 0450-609X) **4321**, 1829
Kobe Women's University. Faculty of Home Economics. Bulletin. (JA ISSN 0389-584X) **2448**
Kobenhavns Statistiske Aarbog. (DK ISSN 0106-3839) **4577**
Kobenhavns Universitet. Sociologisk Institut. Afhandling. (DK ISSN 0900-9922) **4441**
Kobie Revista de Bellas Artes y Ciencias: Serie Antropologia Cultural. (SP ISSN 0214-7939) **243**, 2056
Kobie Revista de Bellas Artes y Ciencias: Serie Bellas Artes. (SP ISSN 0214-7955) **332**
Kobie Revista de Bellas Artes y Ciencias: Serie Ciencias Naturales. (SP ISSN 0214-6967) **4321**, 1571
Kobie Revista de Bellas Artes y Ciencias: Serie Paleoanthropologia. (SP ISSN 0214-7971) **243**, 277
Kobieta i Zycie. (PL ISSN 0023-2548) **4846**
Kobisena. (II) **2996**
Koblenzer Behoerden Spiegel. (GW) **4089**
Koblenzer Geographisches Kolloquium. (GW) **2255**, 1546, 1644, 3903
The Korbin Letter. (US ISSN 0271-1990) **2930**, 1240, 4131
Kobunkazai no Kagaku/Scientific Papers on Japanese Antiques and Art Crafts. (JA ISSN 0368-6272) **258**, 332
Kobunshi/Polymers. (JA) **1220**, 1856
Kobunshi Kako. see Polymer Application **1858**
Kobunshi Ronbunshu. (JA ISSN 0386-2186) **1220**, 1856
Kobus. (ZA ISSN 1015-5546) **1490**
Kochen mit Mikrowelle. (GW) **2448**
Kochen und Geniessen. (GW) **2076**
Kocherburgbote. (GW) **2190**
Kochi Daigaku Gakujutsu Kenkyu Hokoku. Shizen Kagaku/Kochi University. Research Reports. Natural Science. (JA ISSN 0389-0244) **4321**
Kochi Daigaku Kyoikugakubu Kenkyu Hokoku. Dai-3-Bu/Kochi University. Faculty of Education. Bulletin. Series 3. (JA ISSN 0389-0449) **1645**, 4321
Kochi Daigaku Rigakubu Kiyo. Sugaku. see Kochi University. Faculty of Science. Memoirs. Series A, Mathematics **3042**
Kochi Gakuen College. Bulletin. (JA ISSN 0389-4088) **1695**
Kochi Joshi Daigaku Kiyo. Shizen Kagaku Hen/Kochi Women's University. Bulletin. Series of Natural Sciences. (JA ISSN 0452-2486) **4321**
Kochi University. Agricultural Science. Research Reports. (JA ISSN 0389-0473) **103**, 445
Kochi University. Earthquake Observatory. Seismological Bulletin. (JA) **1592**
Kochi University. Faculty of Agriculture. Memoirs. (JA ISSN 0450-6219) **103**, 1829
Kochi University. Faculty of Education. Bulletin. Series 3. see Kochi Daigaku Kyoikugakubu Kenkyu Hokoku. Dai-3-Bu **1645**

Kochi University. Faculty of Science. Memoirs. Series A, Mathematics/Kochi Daigaku Rigakubu Kiyo. Sugaku. (JA ISSN 0389-0252) **3042**
Kochi University. Research Reports. Natural Science. see Kochi Daigaku Gakujutsu Kenkyu Hokoku. Shizen Kagaku **4321**
Kochi Women's University. Bulletin. Series of Natural Sciences. see Kochi Joshi Daigaku Kiyo. Shizen Kagaku Hen **4321**
Kochniano Anees/Anees for Children. (AF ISSN 0023-2572) **1258**, 1645
Kochpraxis und Gemeinschaftsverpflegung. (GW ISSN 0450-6235) **2477**
Kodai Mathematical Journal. (Tokyo Kogyo Daigaku) (JA ISSN 0386-5991) **3042**
Kodak Laboratory Chemicals Bulletin see Eastman Fine Chemicals News **1218**
Kodak Laboratory Chemicals News see Eastman Fine Chemicals News **1218**
Kodak Tech Bits. (US) **3792**
Kodaly Envoy. (US) **3560**
Kodaly Society of Canada. Alla Breve. (CN ISSN 1180-1344) **3560**
Kodaly Society of Canada. Notes see Kodaly Society of Canada. Alla Breve **3560**
Kodikas - Code - Ars Semeiotica. (NE ISSN 0171-0834) **1339**, 332
Kodin Kuvalehti. (FI ISSN 0023-2610) **2186**
Kodintekniikka. (FI ISSN 0783-4632) **1357**
Kodix Nomikou Vematos. (GR) **2642**
Kodo Keiryogaku/Japanese Journal of Behaviormetrics. (JA ISSN 0385-5481) **4034**, 4441
Kodo Ryoho Kenkyu/Japanese Journal of Behavior Therapy. (JA ISSN 0910-6529) **4034**
Kodomo No Kagaku. see Junior Science **1257**
Koebenhavn Boligkommissionen. Aarsberetning. (DK ISSN 0573-9799) **2491**
Koebenhavns Fondsboers. Aarsrapport/Copenhagen Stock Exchange. Annual Report. (DK) **953**
Koebenhavns Havneblad/Port of Copenhagen Review. (DK ISSN 0023-2629) **4730**
Koebenhavns Kommuneskole. (DK) **1645**
Koebenhavns Universitet. Datalogisk Institut. Rapport. (DK ISSN 0107-8283) **1691**, 1397
†Koebenhavns Universitet. Geografisk Centralinstitut. Laboratorium for Geomorfologi. (DK ISSN 0106-3618) **5224**
Koebenhavns Universitet. Geologisk Centralinstitut. Aarsberetning. (DK ISSN 0906-0294) **1571**
Koebenhavns Universitet. Institut for Anvendt og Matematisk Lingvistik. Skrifter. (DK ISSN 0106-8563) **2822**, 3042
Koebenhavns Universitet. Institut for Filmvidenskab. Skrifter see Filmvidenskabeligt Arbog **3510**
Koebenhavns Universitet. Institut for Filmvidenskab. Skrifter see Saerrakke **3517**
Koebenhavns Universitet. Institut for Filmvidenskab. Skrifter see Sekvens **3517**
Koebenhavns Universitet. Institut for Religionshistorie. Skrifter. (DK ISSN 0105-4821) **4187**
Koebenhavns Universitet. Institut for Samfundsfag og Forvaltning. Forskningrapport. (DK ISSN 0900-274X) **3903**
Koebenhavns Universitet. Institut for Social Medicin. Publikationer. (DK ISSN 0105-4139) **3120**
Koebenhavns Universitet. Meddelelser see Universitetsavisen **1719**
Koebenhavns Universitet. Oekonomiske Institut. Memo. (DK ISSN 0574-0045) **676**

Koebenhavns Universitet. Retsvidenskabeligt Institut B. Studier.(DK ISSN 0108-9811) **2642**
Koebenhavns Universitet. Sociologisk Institut. Arbejdspapir. (DK ISSN 0900-9876) **4441**
Koebenhavns Universitet. Statistiske Institut. Afhandlinger. Graa Serie see Universitetets Statistiske Institut. Research Report **4591**
Koebenhavns Universitets Slaviske Institut. Rapporter. (DK ISSN 0107-3265) **2822**
Koebenhavnske Kirkefondets Aarbog see Kirkefondets Aarbog **4187**
Koebstadforeningens Tidsskrift see Danske Kommuner **4086**
Koebstadmuseet Den Gamle By. (DK ISSN 0105-9254) **2371**
Koedbranchen. (DK) **2076**
Koedoe. (SA ISSN 0075-6458) **1490**
Koedoe. Monographs. (SA ISSN 0075-6466) **1490**
Koeffbladet - I N. (NO) **1079**
Koege Museum. (DK ISSN 0107-931X) **3526**
Koege Museum. Aarbog see Koege Museum **3526**
Koehler Rundschau. (GW) **33**, 3663
Koehlers Flottenkalender. Jahrbuch fuer Schiffahrt und Haefen. (GW ISSN 0075-6474) **4730**, 3462
Koeln. (GW ISSN 0075-6482) **2255**
Koeln. Verkehrsamt. Monatsvorschau. (GW) **4774**
Koeln - Bonns Feine Adressen. (GW ISSN 0178-5540) **2190**, 373
▼Koeln Kontakter. (GW) **3560**
Koeln - Reise - Report. (GW) **4774**
Koeln - Rheinland von Hinten. (GW) **2454**, 4774
Koeln Sarasvati Series. (GW ISSN 0722-1789) **3640**
Koelner Arbeiten zum Bibliotheks- und Dokumentationswesen. (GW ISSN 0721-7587) **2767**
Koelner Behoerden Spiegel. (GW) **4089**
Koelner Beitraege zur Musikforschung. (GW) **3560**
Koelner Jahrbuch fuer Vor- und Fruehgeschichte. (GW ISSN 0075-6512) **277**
Koelner Kongress Report. (GW) **3393**, 4774
Koelner Linguistische Arbeiten - Germanistik see K L A G E **2822**
Koelner Museums Bulletin. (GW ISSN 0933-257X) **3526**
Koelner Romanistische Arbeiten. (SZ ISSN 0075-6520) **2510**
Koelner Statistische Nachrichten. (GW ISSN 0933-632X) **4577**
Koelner Statistische Nachrichten. Sonderhefte. (GW ISSN 0933-632X) **4081**
Koelner Vortraege zur Sozial- und Wirtschaftsgeschichte. (GW) **2371**
Koelner Zeitschrift fuer Soziologie und Sozialpsychologie. (GW ISSN 0023-2653) **4441**
Koelner Zoo. Zeitschrift. (GW) **587**
Koeltechniek see Koude Magazine **2301**
Koenigsteiner Woche. (GW) **2190**
Koepfe des 20. Jahrhunderts. (GW ISSN 0454-1383) **419**
Koepmannen. (SW ISSN 0023-2688) **837**, 1044
Koepmannen. (FI ISSN 0023-3862) **1044**
Koerelaereren. (DK) **4694**
Koerier. (NE) **3754**, 1258
Koerpererziehung. (GW ISSN 0323-4916) **3805**
Koers. (SA ISSN 0023-270X) **2510**
Koettbranschen. (SW ISSN 0047-3510) **2076**, 220
Kogai Chosa Hokokusho/Report of Environmental Pollution in Meguro Ward. (JA) **1962**
Kogai Kenkyu. see Research on Environmental Disruption **1967**
Kogan Page Mature Students Handbook. (UK) **1685**
Kogiken Nyusu. see N A L News **59**
▼Kognitionswissenschaft. (GW) **4034**

Kogyo Gijutsuin. Biseibutsu Kogyo Gijutsu Kenkyujo. Kenkyu Hokoku/Fermentation Research Institute. Report. (JA ISSN 0368-5365) **554**, 479
†Kogyo Ritchi Handobukku/Industrial Location Handbook. (JA) **5224**
Kogyo Zairyo/Engineering Materials. (JA ISSN 0452-2834) **1919**
Kohaszati es Onteszeti Szakirodalmi Tajekoztato/Metallurgy and Foundry Abstracts. (HU ISSN 0231-0708) **3427**, 16
Kohle und Heizoel. (GW ISSN 0023-2742) **3487**
Koho Kenkyu. see Public Law Review **2669**
Koihap'nuah. (US) **2011**, 1258
Koiramme - Vaara Hundar. (FI ISSN 0355-7235) **3711**
Kojo Kanri/Factory Management. (JA ISSN 0023-2777) **1017**
Kokai/Navigation. (JA ISSN 0450-660X) **4730**
Kokalos. (IT ISSN 0392-0887) **277**, 2316
Kokka/Essences of Japan. (JA ISSN 0023-2785) **332**
Kokogaku Zasshi. see Archaeological Society of Japan. Journal **263**
▼Kokopelli Notes. (US) **2930**
Kokoro to Shakai/Mind and Society. (JA ISSN 0023-2807) **4034**, 4106
Koks i Khimiya. (RU ISSN 0023-2815) **1220**
Koks, Smola, Gaz. (PL ISSN 0023-2823) **3487**, 3691
Koku Eisei Gakkai Zasshi/Journal of Dental Health. (JA ISSN 0023-2831) **3237**
Koku Fan. see Aero Fan **2433**
Koku Gijutsu/Aircraft Engineering. (JA ISSN 0023-284X) **58**
Koku Igaku Jikkentai Hokoku/Japan Air Self Defense Force. Aeromedical Laboratory. Reports. (JA ISSN 0023-2858) **3120**
Koku Joho/Aireview. (JA ISSN 0450-6669) **2437**
Kokubungaku Kenkyu Shiryokan Kiyo. see National Institute of Japanese Literature. Bulletin **2941**
Kokudo Chiri-in Hokoku. see Geographical Survey Institute, Tokyo. Bulletin **2250**
Kokugakuin Hogaku. see Kokugakuin University. Faculty of Law and Politics. Journal **3903**
Kokugakuin Keizaigaku. see Kokugakuin University Economic Review **676**
Kokugakuin University. Faculty of Law and Politics. Journal/Kokugakuin Hogaku. (JA ISSN 0454-1723) **3903**, 2642
Kokugakuin University Economic Review/Kokugakuin Keizaigaku. (JA ISSN 0288-6340) **676**
Kokunai Iyakuhin Fukusayo Ichiran/List of Adverse Reactions to Drugs. (JA) **3733**
Kokuritsu Eisei Shikenjo Chosa Geppo. see National Institute of Hygienic Sciences. Monthly Report **4108**
Kokuritsu Eiyo Kenkyujo Hokoku - National Institute of Nutrition. Annual Report see Kokuritsu Kenko Eiyo Kenkyujo Hokoku **3608**
Kokuritsu Gan Senta Nenpo. see National Cancer Center. Annual Report **3200**
Kokuritsu Gan Senta, Tokyo. Collected Papers. see National Cancer Center Research Institute. Collected Papers **3200**
Kokuritsu Kagaku Hakubutsukan Kenkyu Hokoku. A Rui: Dobutsugaku. see National Science Museum. Bulletin. Series A: Zoology **589**
Kokuritsu Kagaku Hakubutsukan Kenkyu Hokoku. B Rui: Shokubutsugaku. see National Science Museum. Bulletin. Series B: Botany **511**
Kokuritsu Kagaku Hakubutsukan Kenkyu Hokoku. E Rui, Rikogaku. see National Science Museum. Bulletin. Series E: Physical Sciences and Engineering **1831**

Kokuritsu Kagaku Hakubutsukan Nenpo. (JA) **3526**, **4321**
Kokuritsu Kagaku Hakubutsukan Senpo/National Science Museum. Memoirs. (JA ISSN 0082-4755) **4321**
Kokuritsu Kagaku Hakubutsukan Kenkyu Hoku. D Rui: Jinruigaku. *see* National Science Museum. Bulletin. Series D: Anthropology **246**
Kokuritsu Kenko Eiyo Kenkyujo Hokoku/National Institute of Health and Nutrition. Annual Report. (JA ISSN 0368-5209) **3608**
Kokuritsu Kokkai Toshokan. Refarensu. *see* National Diet Library. Reference **2657**
Kokuritsu Kokkai Toshokan Geppo/ National Diet Library. Monthly Bulletin. (JA ISSN 0027-9153) **2767**
Kokuritsu Kokkai Toshokan Nenpo/ National Diet Library. Annual Report. (JA ISSN 0385-325X) **2767**
Kokuritsu Kokugo Kenkyujo Nenpo. *see* National Language Research Institute. Annual Report **2830**
Kokuritsu Koshu Eisei in Kenkyu Hokoku. *see* Institute of Public Health. Bulletin **4104**
Kokuritsu Koshu Eisei in Nenpo. *see* Institute of Public Health. Annual Report **4104**
Kokuritsu Tama Kenkyujo Nenpo/ National Institute for Leprosy Research Annual Report. (JA ISSN 0454-2029) **3221**
Kokuritsu Tenmondai Nyusu. (JA ISSN 0915-8863) **366**
Kokuritsu Tenmondai Obun Hokoku. *see* National Astronomical Observatory. Publications **367**
Kokuritsu Tokushu Kyoiku Sogo Kenkyujo Kenkyu Kiyo. *see* National Institute of Special Education. Bulletin **1739**
Kokusai Denshin Denwa Co. Ltd. Year) *see* K D D (Year) **1363**
Kokusai Kenkyu/International Studies. (JA ISSN 0910-0156) **3944**
Kokusai Koryu. (JA ISSN 0385-230X) **2011**, **2207**, **3640**
Kokusai Kyoryoku/International Cooperation. (JA ISSN 0285-7928) **3964**
Kokusaiho Gaiko Zasshi/Journal of International Law and Diplomacy. (JA ISSN 0023-2866) **2726**
Kokutetsu Chuo Hoken Kanrijoho. (JA) **4106**, **3120**, **3618**
Kokuritsu Kokkai Toshokan. Sanko Shosi Kenkyu/National Diet Library. Reference Service and Bibliography. (JA ISSN 0385-3306) **2767**
†Kokyo Shiken Kenkyu Kikan Kadai Annai. Kagaku Gijutsu Tema Hen. (JA) **5224**
Kokyo Sokuryo no Kiroku. (JA) **2268**
Kokyo to Junkan. (JA ISSN 0452-3458) **3365**
Kokyuki Shikkan Kekkaku Bunken no Shoroku Sokuho. *see* Abstracts of the Current Literature on Respiratory Diseases and T B **5129**
Kol Atar. (IS) **1490**
Kol Boro Park. *see* Boro Park Voice **1994**
Kol ha-T'nuah/Voice of the Movement. (US ISSN 0742-5031) **2011**, **4224**
Kol Necei Milchama. (IS) **4411**, **2011**
Kola. (CN ISSN 0835-2445) **2930**, **3944**
Koldfax. (US) **2301**
Kolding Bogen. (DK ISSN 0901-8077) **2371**
Koleinu. (UK) **4224**, **1258**, **3964**
†Kolenu. (US) **5224**
Koleopterologische Rundschau. (AU ISSN 0075-6547) **445**
Kolloidnyi Zhurnal. (RU ISSN 0023-2912) **1228**, **3823**
Kolloquium ueber Spaetantike und Fruehmittelalterliche Skulptur. (GW ISSN 0075-6563) **332**
Kolorisztikai Ertesito/Coloristical Review. (HU ISSN 0023-2939) **1856**, **1182**, **3654**
Kolossal. (IT) **2983**

Kolot. (IS ISSN 0333-8584) **4224**
Kolping Banner. (US) **1299**, **4267**
Kolpingblatt. (GW ISSN 0023-2947) **4411**
Kol'tsa. (RU) **3062**
Komal Patra. (II ISSN 0023-2963) **1258**
Komatsu City Museum. Memoirs. *see* Komatsu-shiritsu Hakubutsukan Kenkyu Kiyo **4321**
Komatsu-shiritsu Hakubutsukan Kenkyu Kiyo/Komatsu City Museum. Memoirs. (JA ISSN 0288-7975) **4321**, **3526**
Komba. (KE) **1490**
Komba Rundschau. (GW) **4411**
Komby. (NE) **1258**
Komeet *see* N K B **4779**
Komercijalist. (YU ISSN 0350-1019) **837**
Komise pro Dejiny Zavodu v C S S R. Zpravodaj. (CS) **2372**
Komise pro Dejiny Zavodu v C S S R. Zpravy *see* Komise pro Dejiny Zavodu v C S S R. Zpravodaj **2372**
Komisija za Ispitivanje S-Uredjaja. Bilten. (CI ISSN 0350-7696) **1901**
Komisja Historyczna Przy Komitecie Centralnym Zwiazku Mlodziezy Socjalistycznej. Biuletyn *see* Pokolenia **2380**
Komisja Nauk Pedagogicznych. Rocznik. (PL) **1645**
Komitee Zuidelijk Afrika. Angola Komitee. Facts and Reports *see* Komitee Zuidelijk Afrika. Facts and Reports **2333**
Komitee Zuidelijk Afrika. Facts and Reports. (NE) **2333**
Komiteen mod Dyreforsoeg, Fonden til Sygdomsbekaempelse uden Dyreforsoeg *see* Dyrenes Ret **4809**
Komitet' Ukrainstsiv Kanady. Biuleten' *see* Ukrainian Canadian Congress. Bulletin **2027**
Komma. (NE) **3903**, **4441**
Kommandobruecke *see* Schiff und Hafen - Kommandobruecke **4737**
Kommission der Europaeischen Gemeinschaft Informationen fuer die Schule *see* E G Informationen fuer die Schule **1626**
Kommission fuer Geschichtliche Landeskunde in Baden-Wuerttemberg. Veroeffentlichungen. Reihe A. Quellen. (GW ISSN 0067-2831) **2372**
Kommission fuer Geschichtliche Landeskunde in Baden-Wuerttemberg. Veroeffentlichungen. Reihe B: Forschungen. (GW ISSN 0521-9884) **2372**
Kommission fuer Neuere Geschichte Oesterreichs. Veroeffentlichungen. (AU) **2372**
▼Kommission fuer Oekologie. Rundgespraeche. (GW ISSN 0938-5851) **1962**
Kommun-Aktuelt/Municipal News. (SW ISSN 0347-5484) **4089**
Kommunal Katalog. (SZ) **622**
Kommunal Litteratur. (SW ISSN 0349-5426) **2982**, **16**
Kommunal Litteraturtjaenst *see* Kommunal Litteratur **2982**
Kommunal Skoltidning *see* Kommun-Aktuelt **4089**
Kommunal Tidende *see* Danske Kommuner **4086**
Kommunal Tidskrift *see* Kommun-Aktuelt **4089**
Kommunalarbetaren. (SW) **985**
Kommunalteknik. *see* Kunnallistekniikka **2491**
Kommunaltjaenstemannen. (SW) **985**, **4089**
Kommunalwirtschaft. (GW ISSN 0450-7169) **1829**
Kommunalwissenschaftliche Dissertationen. (GW ISSN 0340-1170) **2491**
Kommune. (GW ISSN 0723-7669) **3903**
Kommunedata Plannyt *see* K M D Plannyt **5222**
Kommunen. (DK) **4089**
†Kommuneplanorientering. (DK ISSN 0106-7362) **5224**

Kommunication and E D P Security *see* K E S **1339**
Kommunikation. (GW) **985**
Kommunikation und Politik. (GW) **2572**
Kommunismus und Klassenkampf *see* Kommune **3903**
Kommunist. (RU ISSN 0023-3099) **3903**
Kommunist Belorussii. (BW ISSN 0023-3102) **3903**
Kommunist Ukrainy. (KR ISSN 0023-3110) **3903**
Kommunisti Tochikiston. (TK ISSN 0023-3129) **3903**
Kommunisticheskaya Partiya Sovetskogo Soyuza. Vysshaya Partiinaya Shkola. Uchenye Zapiski. (RU) **3903**
Komondor Komments. (US) **3711**
Kompass. (GW ISSN 0342-0809) **2536**, **3487**
Kompass Alimentation *see* Kompass Professionnels **1142**
Kompass Australia. (AT) **1142**
Kompass Belgium. (BE) **1142**
Kompass Belgium - Luxembourg *see* Kompass Belgium **1142**
Kompass Buyers Guides *see* Kompass Industrial Sections **1142**
Kompass Danmark. (DK ISSN 0075-661X) **1142**
Kompass France *see* La France de l'Industrie et ses Services **1135**
Kompass Holland. (NE ISSN 0075-6660) **1142**
Kompass Industrial Sections. (UK) **1142**
Kompass Italia. (IT ISSN 0075-6687) **1142**
Kompass Maroc. (MR ISSN 0075-6695) **1142**
Kompass Norge. (NO ISSN 0075-6709) **1142**
Kompass Professionnels. (FR) **1142**, **2076**
Kompass Regionaux. (FR) **676**
Kompass Register *see* Kompass Register Australia **1142**
Kompass Schweiz - Liechtenstein. (SZ ISSN 0075-6717) **1142**
Kompass Select Denmark. Business Services *see* Kompass Select Export. Business Services **915**
Kompass Select Denmark. Chemicals *see* Kompass Select Export. Chemical Industry **915**
Kompass Select Denmark. Construction *see* Kompass Select Export. Building Construction, Contractors **915**
Kompass Select Denmark. Electrical and Electronic Equipment *see* Kompass Select Export. Electrical and Electronic Equipment **915**
Kompass Select Denmark. Food and Beverages *see* Kompass Select Export. Food Industry **915**
Kompass Select Denmark. Furniture *see* Kompass Select Export. Furniture **915**
Kompass Select Denmark. Instruments *see* Kompass Select Export. Scientific and Industrial Instruments, Watch Industry **915**
Kompass Select Denmark. Machinery *see* Kompass Select Export. Machine Industry **915**
Kompass Select Denmark. Metal *see* Kompass Select Export. Metal Products **915**
Kompass Select Denmark. Paper and Printing *see* Kompass Select Export. Paper Industry, Graphic Arts **915**
Kompass Select Denmark. Plastics and Rubber *see* Kompass Select Export. Rubber Industry, Plastics Industry **915**
Kompass Select Denmark. Textiles, Clothing and Footwear *see* Kompass Select Export. Textiles, Clothing and Footwear **915**
Kompass Select Denmark. Transport Equipment *see* Kompass Select Export. Transport Equipment **916**
Kompass Select Denmark. Wood *see* Kompass Select Export. Wood Industry **916**

Kompass Select Export. Building Construction, Contractors. (DK ISSN 0106-1135) **915**
Kompass Select Export. Business Services. (DK ISSN 0106-1100) **915**
Kompass Select Export. Chemical Industry. (DK ISSN 0106-1119) **915**
Kompass Select Export. Electrical and Electronic Equipment. (DK ISSN 0106-1143) **915**
Kompass Select Export. Food Industry. (DK ISSN 0106-1151) **915**
Kompass Select Export. Furniture. (DK ISSN 0106-116X) **915**
Kompass Select Export. Machine Industry. (DK ISSN 0106-1186) **915**
Kompass Select Export. Metal Products. (DK ISSN 0106-1194) **915**
Kompass Select Export. Paper Industry, Graphic Arts. (DK ISSN 0106-1208) **915**
Kompass Select Export. Rubber Industry, Plastics Industry. (DK ISSN 0106-1216) **915**
Kompass Select Export. Scientific and Industrial Instruments, Watch Industry. (DK ISSN 0106-1178) **915**
Kompass Select Export. Textiles, Clothing and Footwear. (DK ISSN 0106-1224) **915**
Kompass Select Export. Transport Equipment. (DK ISSN 0106-1232) **916**
Kompass Select Export. Wood Industry. (DK ISSN 0106-1240) **916**
Kompass Special Services. (FR) **1142**
Kompass Sverige. (SW ISSN 0075-6725) **1142**
▼Kompass Taiwan. (CH) **1142**
Kompass Textile et Habillement. (FR) **1142**, **1286**
Kompass U.K. Management Register *see* Kompass U.K. Regional Sales Guide (Year) **1142**
Kompass U.K. Regional Sales Guide (Year). (UK) **1142**, **1017**
Kompass United Kingdom. (UK) **1142**
Kompleksnoe Ispol'zovanie Mineral'nogo Syr'ya. (RU) **1571**
Kompositsionnye Polimernye Materialy. (KR ISSN 0203-3275) **1228**
Kompost. (GW) **1258**, **2871**
Komsomol'skaya Zhizn' (RU ISSN 0130-2469) **1258**
Komuna (Belgrade). (YU ISSN 0023-3161) **2491**
Komuna (Kikinda). (YU ISSN 0023-1398) **2239**
Komuna Esperanto-Gazeto *see* Fenomeno **2814**
Komunikacyjna *see* Lekarz Kolejowy **3122**
Komunikasi. (IO ISSN 0023-3188) **2871**
Komunikaty Mazursko-Warminskie. (PL ISSN 0023-3196) **2372**
Komunist. (YU ISSN 0023-320X) **3903**
The Kon-Lin Letter. (US) **953**
Konan Daigaku Kiyo. Rigaku Hen/ Konan University. Memoirs. Science Series. (JA ISSN 0452-4160) **4321**
Konan University. Memoirs. Science Series. *see* Konan Daigaku Kiyo. Rigaku Hen **4321**
Koncar Strucne Informacije. (CI ISSN 0350-5537) **1902**
Koncize. (GW) **3393**, **4774**
Konditor *see* Der Neue Konditor **2089**
Konditor Zeitung. (AU ISSN 0023-2432) **2076**
Konditorei und Cafe. (GW ISSN 0023-3234) **2088**
Kondratieff Wave Analyst. (US) **788**
Konepajamies. (FI ISSN 0023-3277) **3411**
Koneviesti. (FI ISSN 0355-0729) **3019**
Konevodstvo i Konnyi Sport. (RU ISSN 0023-3285) **4536**
Konfekturehandleren. (DK ISSN 0047-3553) **2088**

6374 KONFERENSIE

Konferensie van Suid-Afrikaanse Opmeters. Verrigtinge. see Conference of South African Surveyors. Proceedings **1864**
Kongelig Dansk Hof- og Statskalender; Statshaandbog for Kongeriget Danmark. (DK ISSN 0085-2589) **4065**
Kongelige Bibliotek. Fagbibliografer. (DK ISSN 0105-5046) **404**
Kongelige Bibliotek. Magasin. (DK) **2767**
Kongelige Bibliotek. Publikumsorienteringer. (DK ISSN 0105-3167) **2767**
Kongelige Bibliotek. Specialhjaelpemidler. (DK ISSN 0105-8215) **404**
Kongelige Bibliotek og Universitetsbiblioteket. Magasin see Kongelige Bibliotek. Magasin **2767**
Kongelige Danske Videnskabernes Selskab. Biologiske Skrifter. (DK ISSN 0366-3612) **445**, **1546**
Kongelige Danske Videnskabernes Selskab. Historisk - Filosofiske Meddelelser. (DK ISSN 0106-0481) **2510**
Kongelige Danske Videnskabernes Selskab. Historisk - Filosofiske Skrifter. (DK ISSN 0023-3307) **2510**
Kongelige Danske Videnskabernes Selskab. Matematisk - Fysiske Meddelelser. (DK ISSN 0023-3323) **3042**, **3823**
Kongelige Danske Videnskabernes Selskab. Oversigt over Selskabets Virksomhed. Annual Report. (DK ISSN 0368-7201) **2510**
Kongelige Norske Videnskabers Selskab. Arsberetning see Kongelige Norske Videnskabers Selskab. Forhandlinger **4321**
Kongelige Norske Videnskabers Selskab. Forhandlinger. (NO ISSN 0368-6302) **4321**, **2510**
Kongelige Norske Videnskabers Selskab. Museet. Miscellanea see Gunneria **273**
Kongelige Norske Videnskabers Selskab. Skrifter/Royal Norwegian Society of Sciences. Publications. (NO ISSN 0368-6310) **4321**, **2510**
Kongelige Norske Videnskabers Selskab Museet. Rapport. Botanisk Serie see Universitetet i Trondheim. Vitenskapsmuseet. Rapport. Botanisk Serie **519**
Kongelige Veterinaer- og Landbohoejskole. Haandbog. (DK ISSN 0109-4998) **103**, **4812**
Kongelige Veterinaer- og Landbohoejskole. Jordbrugsteknisk Institut. Meddelelse. (DK ISSN 0106-8237) **103**
Kongelige Veterinaer og Landbohoejskole. Skovbruginstitutet. Meddelelser. (DK ISSN 0106-8261) **4812**, **103**
Kongetsu no Nogyo/Agricultural Chemicals Monthly. (JA ISSN 0023-334X) **184**
Konggan/Space. (KO) **302**, **332**
Kongjian Kexue Xuebao/Chinese Journal of Space Science. (CC ISSN 0254-6124) **58**
Kongqi Donglixue Xuebao. (CC ISSN 0258-1825) **3844**
Kongres ha-Tsiyoni. Hahlatot/World Zionist Organization. Zionist Congress. (IS) **3903**
Kongres Wanita Indonesia Kowani News see Kowani News **4846**
Kongres Wanita Indonesia News see K O W A N I News **4846**
Kongresa Libro. (NE ISSN 0083-3851) **3393**
Kongressbericht Bundesschulmusikwoche see Bundesschulmusikwoche **3543**
†Kongresstermindienst: Naturwissenschaftlich-technische Veranstaltungen im Sozialistischen Ausland. (GW ISSN 0233-2264) **5224**
Kongzhi Lilun yu Yingyong. (CC) **1829**
Kongzhi yu Juece. (CC ISSN 1001-0920) **1829**

Kongzi Yanjiu/Studies on Confucius. (CC) **3771**, **3640**, **4215**
Koninklijk Belgisch Instituut voor Natuurwetenschappen. Studiedocumenten/Institut Royal des Sciences Naturelles de Belgique. Documents de Travail. (BE) **445**, **587**
Koninklijk Belgisch Petroleum Instituut. Annalen. see Institut Royal Belge du Petrole. Annales **3689**
Koninklijk Instituut voor de Tropen. A O Bulletin see Royal Tropical Institute. Bulletin **118**
Koninklijk Instituut voor de Tropen. Afdeling Plattelandsontwikkeling. Landendocumentatie see Koninklijk Instituut voor de Tropen. Landenreeks **2255**
Koninklijk Instituut voor de Tropen. Klein Repertorium. (NE) **2329**, **2345**
Koninklijk Instituut voor de Tropen. Landenreeks. (NE ISSN 0922-4939) **2255**
Koninklijk Instituut voor de Tropen. Survey see Koninklijk Instituut voor de Tropen. Survey of Activities **2255**
Koninklijk Instituut voor de Tropen. Survey of Activities. (NE) **2255**
Koninklijk Instituut voor het Kunstpatrimonium. Bulletin. see Institut Royal du Patrimoine Artistique. Bulletin **330**
Koninklijk Instituut voor Taal-, Land- en Volkenkunde. Bibliographical Series. (NE ISSN 0074-0462) **2855**, **254**, **404**
Koninklijk Instituut voor Taal-, Land- en Volkenkunde. Translation Series. (NE ISSN 0074-0470) **243**
Koninklijk Instituut voor Taal-, Land- en Volkenkunde. Verhandelingen. (NE) **243**
Koninklijk Instituut vor de Tropen. Annotated Bibliographies Series. (NE ISSN 0924-9745) **139**, **404**, **726**
Koninklijk Museum voor Midden-Afrika. Annalen. Reeks in 8. Economische Wetenschappen. see Musee Royal de l'Afrique Centrale. Annales. Serie in 8. Sciences Economiques **155**
Koninklijk Museum voor Midden-Afrika. Annalen. Reeks in 8. Geologische Wetenschappen. see Musee Royal de l'Afrique Centrale. Annales. Serie in 8. Sciences Geologiques **1573**
Koninklijk Museum voor Midden-Afrika. Annalen. Reeks in 8. Historische Wetenschappen. see Musee Royal de l'Afrique Centrale. Annales. Serie in 8. Sciences Historiques **2334**
Koninklijk Museum voor Midden-Afrika. Annalen. Reeks in 8. Menselijke Wetenschappen. see Musee Royal de l'Afrique Centrale. Annales. Serie in 8. Sciences Humaines **2511**
Koninklijk Museum voor Midden-Afrika. Annalen. Reeks in 8. Zoologische Wetenschappen. see Musee Royal de l'Afrique Centrale. Annales. Serie in 8. Sciences Zoologiques **588**
Koninklijk Museum voor Midden-Afrika. Economische Documentatie. see Musee Royal de l'Afrique Centrale. Documentation Economique **680**
Koninklijk Museum voor Midden-Afrika. Zoologische Documentatie. see Musee Royal de l'Afrique Centrale. Documentation Zoologique **588**
Koninklijk Nederlands Geologisch Mijnbouwkundig Genootschap. Verhandelingen. (NE ISSN 0075-6741) **1571**, **3487**
Koninklijk Nederlands Geologisch Mijnbouwkundig Genootschap Nieuwsbrief see K.N.G.M.G. Nieuwsbrief **1570**
Koninklijk Nederlandsch Genootschap voor Geslacht- en Wapenkunde. Werken Uitgegeven. (NE) **2156**
Koninklijke Academie voor Nederlandse Taal- en Letterkunde. Jaarboek. (BE ISSN 0770-7762) **2822**, **2930**
Koninklijke Academie voor Nederlandse Taal- en Letterkunde. Verslagen en Mededelingen. (BE ISSN 0770-786X) **2930**, **2822**

Koninklijke Academie voor Overzeese Wetenschappen. Mededelingen der Zittingen. see Academie Royale des Sciences d'Outre-Mer. Bulletin des Seances **4296**
Koninklijke Automobiel Club van Belgie Royal Auto see R A C B Royal Auto **4700**
Koninklijke Belgische Marine Academie. Mededelingen. see Academie Royale de Marine de Belgique. Communications **4723**
Koninklijke Bibliotheek Albert I. Driemaandelijks Informatie Bulletin see Bibliotheque Royal Albert 1er. Bulletin Trimestriel d'Information **2748**
Koninklijke Bibliotheek Albert I. Aangekondigde Publikaties. see Bibliotheque Royale Albert 1er. Publications Annoncees **2748**
Koninklijke Bibliotheek Albert I. Jaarverslag see Bibliotheque Royale Albert 1er. Rapport Annuel **2748**
Koninklijke Commissie voor de Uitgave der Oude Wetten en Verordeningen van Belgie. Handelingen. see Commission Royale des Anciennes Lois et Ordonnances de Belgique. Bulletin **2309**
Koninklijke Commissie voor Toponymie en Dialectologie. Handelingen. see Commission Royale de Toponymie et de Dialectologie. Bulletin **2809**
Koninklijke Geschied- en Oudheidkundige Kring van Kortrijk. Handelingen/Cercle Royal Historique et Archeologique de Courtrai. Memoires. (BE) **2372**
Koninklijke Kring voor Oudheidkunde Letteren en Kunst van Mechelen. Handelingen. (BE) **2372**, **277**
Koninklijke Musea voor Kunst en Geschiedenis. Bulletin. see Musees Royaux d'Art et d'Histoire. Bulletin **2376**
Koninklijke Musea voor Schone Kunsten van Belgie. Bulletin. see Musees Royaux des Beaux-Arts de Belgique. Bulletin **3528**
Koninklijke Nederlandsche Voetbalbond Voetbal Totaal see Voetbal Totaal **4514**
Koninklijke Nederlandse Akademie van Wetenschappen. Afdeling Letterkunde. Verhandelingen. Nieuwe Reeks. (NE ISSN 0065-5511) **2510**
Koninklijke Nederlandse Akademie van Wetenschappen. Afdeling Natuurkunde. Verhandelingen. Tweede Reeks. (NE ISSN 0065-552X) **4321**
Koninklijke Nederlandse Akademie van Wetenschappen. Series A, Mathematical Sciences. Proceedings see Indagationes Mathematicae **3038**
Koninklijke Nederlandse Akademie van Wetenschappen. Series C: Biological and Medical Sciences. Proceedings see Royal Netherlands Academy of Sciences. Proceedings **4336**
Koninklijke Nederlandse Oudheidkundige Bond. Bulletin. (NE) **277**, **2372**
Koninklijke Officiers Schermbond. Kos-Gebeuren. (NE ISSN 0047-3561) **4478**
Koninklijke Oudheidkundige Kring van Antwerpen. Jaarboek. (BE) **277**
Koninklijke Shell-Post see Shell-Post **3701**
Konjunktur. (AU) **1079**
Konjunktur von Morgen. (GW ISSN 0023-3439) **1079**
Konjunkturdienst see Konjunktur **1079**
Konjunkturindikatoren. (GW ISSN 0722-0227) **676**
Konjunkturlaget. (SW ISSN 0023-3463) **1079**
Konjunkturni Barometar. (YU ISSN 0023-3471) **1080**
Konjunkturperspektiven see I F O Konjunkturperspektiven **669**
Konjunkturpolitik. (GW ISSN 0023-3498) **1080**
Konjunkturspiegel see B A W - Monatsbericht **844**

Konkreet. (NE ISSN 0023-3501) **4478**
Konkret. (GW) **2190**
Konkuriito Jaanaru see Konkuriito Kogaku **622**
Konkuriito Kogaku/Concrete Journal. (JA ISSN 0387-1061) **622**
Konkurs, Treuhand- und Schiedsgerichtswesen see K T S - Zeitschrift fuer Insolvensrecht, Konkurs, Treuhand, Sanierung **2642**
Konkursbuch. (GW) **3771**, **2510**
Konkylien. (DK ISSN 0900-2855) **4846**, **4730**
Konnyaku News. (JA) **153**
Konpyuta Repoto. see Computer Report **1392**
Konradsblatt. (GW) **4267**
Konsertnytt. (SW ISSN 0023-3560) **3560**
†Konservativ Heute. (GW) **5224**
Konservatorium Nuus. (SA ISSN 0023-3579) **3560**
Konsonanz. (SZ ISSN 0023-3595) **1044**
†Konstanzer Blaetter fuer Hochschulfragen. (GW ISSN 0452-4918) **5224**
Konsthistorisk Tidskrift. (SW ISSN 0023-3609) **332**
Der Konstrukteur. (GW ISSN 0344-4570) **622**
Konstruktion. (GW ISSN 0720-5953) **3019**
Konstruktion Elemente Maschinenbau. (GW ISSN 0342-7102) **1829**
Konstruktion, Entwicklung und Design see Konstruktion & Elektronik **622**
Konstruktion & Elektronik. (GW ISSN 0177-7459) **622**
Konstruktionsbuecher. (US ISSN 0075-6768) **622**
Konstruktionspraxis. (GW ISSN 0937-4167) **1919**
†Konstruktorsko-Tekhnologicheskii Institut Avtomatizatsii Avtomobilestroeniya. Sbornik Trudov. (UR) **5224**
Konsulentordningen. (DK ISSN 0109-3533) **676**
Konsum Oesterreich. (AU) **1506**
Konsument. (AU) **1506**
De Konsument. (LU) **1506**
Konsumentinformation see Kuluttajatietoa **5225**
Konsumentombudsmannen see Konsumentraett och Ekonomi **1506**
Konsumentraett och Ekonomi/ Consumer Law and Economics. (SW ISSN 0347-6154) **1506**
Konsumentverket see Konsumentraett och Ekonomi **1506**
Konsumgenossenschaft see Konsum Oesterreich **1506**
Kontak. (SA) **1142**, **4089**
Kontaks. (PH) **1142**
Kontakt. (AU) **1258**
▼Kontakt. (RU) **1315**
†Kontakt. (GW ISSN 0323-6021) **5224**
Kontakt (Copenhagen, 1948). (DK ISSN 0105-0982) **3964**
†Kontakt (Copenhagen, 1977). (DK ISSN 0108-5190) **5224**
Kontakt (Esslingen am Neckar). (GW ISSN 0176-246X) **985**, **1339**
Kontakt Drei und Zwanzig. (AU ISSN 0023-3676) **4267**
Kontakt met Denemarken see Contact with Denmark **2357**
Kontakt mit Daenemark see Contact with Denmark **2357**
Kontakt und Reflexionen see Kontakt **1258**
Kontakte. (SZ) **3344**
Kontakte (Darmstadt). (GW ISSN 0172-8717) **1182**
Kontakten. (SW ISSN 0345-6471) **2218**
Kontaktkalender. (DK ISSN 0108-4291) **916**
Die Kontaktlinse. (GW ISSN 0721-5096) **3302**
Kontakto. (NE ISSN 0023-3692) **1258**, **2822**
Kontekst. (RU) **2930**
Konteksten. (NE ISSN 0168-6682) **4441**, **2822**

Kontiki see Anderschume - Kontiki 2451
†Kontinent. (GW) 5224
▼Kontinenz. (GW ISSN 0006-3304) 3269
Kontorbladet. (DK ISSN 0026-8631) 1059
Kontorsvaerlden. (SW ISSN 0023-3722) 1059
Kontrapunkt see I G Medien Forum 4129
Kontrapunkte. (GW) 1258, 1240
Kontraste Impuls. (GW ISSN 0344-5984) 4267
Kontrolle. (GW ISSN 0724-1070) 1829
Kontrollen med Konsummaelkprodukter see Rapport om Kontrollen med Konsummaelkprodukter 1084
†Kontrollraadet foer Betongvaror. Meddelande. (SW ISSN 0075-6776) 5224
Kontur. (AU ISSN 0023-3757) 332
Kontynenty. (PL ISSN 0023-3765) 3903
Kontyu see Japanese Journal of Entomology 534
Konyv es Konyvtar/Book and Library. (HU ISSN 0139-1305) 2767
†Konyvtari es Dokumentacios Szakirodalom/Library and Documentation Literature Abroad. (HU ISSN 0454-3491) 5224
†Konyvtari es Informatikai Kozponti Gyarapodasi Jegyzek/Central Accessioning List about Library and Information Science. (HU ISSN 0236-5200) 5224
Konyvtari Expressz see Konyvtari Levelezo 2767
Konyvtari Figyelo see Konyvtari Figyelo. Uj Folyam 2767
Konyvtari Figyelo. Uj Folyam/Library Review. New Series. (HU) 2767
†Konyvtari Kiadvanyok. (HU ISSN 0209-8393) 5224
Konyvtari Levelezo/Library Postcard. (HU ISSN 0865-1329) 2767
Konyvtaros. (HU) 2767
Konzert Almanach. (GW ISSN 0721-5398) 3560
Koodal Historical Series. (II) 2316
Kooks Magazine. (US) 3595, 4284
Kooperatie: orgaan van de Federatie der Belgische Kooperaties FEBECOOP see Cooperation 829
Kooperation see Agrar-Inform 5132
Kooperationen. (DK ISSN 0023-382X) 831
Kooperatoeren. (SW ISSN 0023-3846) 831
Kootenay Business Journal. (CN) 676
Kootenay Business Magazine. (CN) 1116
Kootenay Review. (CN) 2178
Koppeling. (NE ISSN 0023-3870) 4711
Kora Africaine. see African Kora 1248
Al-Kora wal-Malaeb/Soccer and Playgrounds. (UA) 4478
Korabostroene i Koraboplavane/Shipbuilding and Shipping. (BU) 4730
Koranyi Sandor Tarsasag. Tudomanyos Ulesek. (HU ISSN 0075-6792) 3120
Korea. (KN) 4774
Korea (Republic). Economic Planning Board. Yearbook of Migration Statistics see Korea (Republic). National Statistical Office. Annual Report on the Internal Migration Statistics 3993
Korea (Republic). National Bureau of Statistics. Annual Report on the Family Income and Expenditure Survey see Korea (Republic). National Statistical Office. Annual Report on the Family Income and Expenditure Survey 726
Korea (Republic). National Bureau of Statistics. Annual Report on the Price Survey see Korea (Republic). National Statistical Office. Annual Report on the Price Survey 726

Korea (Republic). National Bureau of Statistics. Population and Housing Census Report see Korea (Republic). National Statistical Office. Population & Housing Census Report 3993
Korea (Republic). National Bureau of Statistics. Report on Mining and Manufacturing Survey see Korea (Republic). National Statistical Office. Report on Mining and Manufacturing Survey 3500
†Korea (Republic). National Bureau of Statistics. Wholesale and Retail Trade Census Report/Tosomaeup Census Bogo Seo. (KO ISSN 0075-6857) 5224
Korea (Republic). National Statistical Office. Annual Report on Current Industrial Production Survey. (KO) 1080
Korea (Republic). National Statistical Office. Annual Report on the Economically Active Population Survey. (KO) 726, 985
Korea (Republic). National Statistical Office. Annual Report on the Family Income and Expenditure Survey. (KO) 726
Korea (Republic). National Statistical Office. Annual Report on the Internal Migration Statistics. (KO) 3993, 4577
Korea (Republic). National Statistical Office. Annual Report on the Price Survey/Mulga Yonbo. (KO) 726
Korea (Republic). National Statistical Office. Population & Housing Census Report. (KO) 3993, 4577
Korea (Republic). National Statistical Office. Report on Mining and Manufacturing Survey. (KO) 3500, 16, 726
Korea (Republic). Office of Rural Development. Agricultural Research Report see Korea (Republic). Office of Rural Development. Research Report 103
Korea (Republic). Office of Rural Development. Research Report. (KO) 103
Korea & World Affairs. (KO) 3964
Korea Annual. (KO) 1142
Korea Atomic Energy Research Institute Journal see K A E R I Journal 1806
Korea Automotive Review. (US ISSN 0890-9156) 4694
†Korea Bi-weekly Report. (US) 5224
Korea Bulletin. (DK ISSN 0108-8467) 3964
Korea Chamber of Commerce and Industry. News see K C C I Quarterly Review 818
Korea Chamber of Commerce and Industry Quarterly Review see K C C I Quarterly Review 818
Korea Development Bank. Monthly Economic Review. (KO ISSN 0017-744X) 871
Korea Development Bank: Its Functions and Activities. (KO ISSN 0075-6806) 788
Korea Development Bank Report see K D B Report 675
Korea Directory. (KO ISSN 0075-6814) 1142
Korea Electric Power Corporation Annual Review see K E P C O Annual Review 1901
Korea Exchange Bank. Monthly Review. (KO ISSN 0023-3889) 788
Korea Film Catalog. (KO) 3513
Korea Herald. (KO ISSN 0023-3897) 2209
Korea High Tech Review see East Asia High Tech Review 4597
Korea Journal. (KO ISSN 0023-3900) 2209
▼The Korea Letter. (HK ISSN 1016-2658) 3964, 916
Korea Newsreview. (KO ISSN 0146-9657) 871
Korea Non-Life Insurance. (KO) 2536
Korea Non-Life Insurance Industry see Korea Non-Life Insurance 2536
Korea Observer. (KO ISSN 0023-3919) 3640
Korea Policy Series. (KO) 3903, 871

Korea Research Society for Dental Materials. Journal. (KO ISSN 0023-3927) 3237
Korea Shipping Gazette. (KO) 4730
Korea Social Work College. Research Institute for Special Education. Journal/Kwang-Eung Yeo. (KO) 1738
†Korea Statistical Korea/Tonggye Suchup. (KO ISSN 0081-4806) 5224
Korea Statistical Yearbook/Hanguk Tonggye Yongam. (KO ISSN 0075-6873) 4577
Korea Stock Exchange. Fact Book. (KO) 953
Korea Times. (KO ISSN 0023-3935) 2209
Korea Times Toronto. (CN) 2011
Korea Today. (KO ISSN 0047-3596) 2255
Korea Today. (KN) 3903
Korea Trade. (KO ISSN 0023-3943) 916
Korea Trade & Business. (KO) 916, 676
Korea Update. (US) 3944, 3640, 3964
Korea Weekly Report see Korea Bi-weekly Report 5224
Korean Affairs Report. (US) 871, 3903
Korean Arts. see Choson Yesul 321
Korean Astronomical Society. Journal. (KO) 366
Korean Book Journal. see Ch'ulpan Moonwha 4125
Korean Buddhism. (KO) 4215
Korean Business Journal. (KO ISSN 0023-396X) 1017
Korean Business Review. (KO) 676
Korean Chemical Society. Bulletin. (KO) 1182, 1856
Korean Chemical Society. Journal/Daehan Hwahak Hoe Jee. (KO) 1182, 1856
Korean Chinese Education. see Zhongguo Chaoxianzu Jiaoyu 1673
Korean Culture. (US ISSN 0270-1618) 2011
Korean Dental Association. Journal. (KO) 3237
Korean Economic Journal/Kyongje Nonjip. (KO ISSN 0023-3978) 676
Korean Fisheries Society. Bulletin. (KO) 2045
Korean Forestry Society. Journal. (KO) 2103
Korean Institute for Population and Health Bulletin see K I P H Bulletin 597
Korean Institute of Metals. Journal. (KO) 3411
Korean Journal. (CN ISSN 0700-3226) 2011
Korean Journal of Animal Sciences. (KO ISSN 0367-5807) 220, 201, 207
Korean Journal of Applied Entomology. (KO) 184
Korean Journal of Biochemistry. (KO ISSN 0378-8512) 479
Korean Journal of Botany. (KO ISSN 0583-421X) 508
Korean Journal of Breeding. (KO ISSN 0250-3360) 220, 184, 2103, 2133
Korean Journal of Dermatology. (KO ISSN 0494-4739) 3248
Korean Journal of Entomology. (KO) 535
Korean Journal of Genetics. (KO) 545, 3199
Korean Journal of International Law. (KO ISSN 0023-3994) 2726
Korean Journal of International Relations. (KO) 3964
Korean Journal of International Studies. (KO ISSN 0377-0451) 3903
Korean Journal of Mycology. (KO ISSN 0253-651X) 508
Korean Journal of Parasitology. (KO ISSN 0023-4001) 3221
Korean Journal of Pharmacognosy. (KO ISSN 0253-3073) 479, 508
Korean Journal of Pharmacology/Taehan Yangnihak Chapchi. (KO ISSN 0377-9459) 3733
Korean Journal of Physiology. (KO ISSN 0300-4015) 573

KORROSION 6375

Korean Journal of Plant Protection see Korean Journal of Applied Entomology 184
Korean Journal of Public Health/Bo Kun Hak Non Zip. (KO ISSN 0023-401X) 4106
Korean Journal of Sociology. see Hanguk Sahoehak 4436
Korean Journal of Zoology. (KO ISSN 0440-2510) 587
Korean Library Association Bulletin see K L A Bulletin 2766
Korean Literature. see Choson Munhak 2905
Korean Medical Abstracts. (KO ISSN 0047-360X) 3176, 16
Korean Medical Association. Journal. (KO ISSN 0023-4028) 3120
Korean Nature. (KN ISSN 0023-4036) 1490
Korean Neuropsychiatric Association. Journal. (KO ISSN 1015-4817) 3344
Korean Nurse/Taehan Kanho. (KO ISSN 0047-3618) 3281
Korean Otolaryngological Society. Journal. (KO) 3315
Korean Periodicals Index. see Chonggi Kanhaengmul Kisa Saegin 8
Korean Philately. (US) 3754
Korean Press. (KO) 2572
Korean Press Annual/Hanguk Sinmun Pangsong Yongam. (KO) 2572, 1339
Korean Publications Yearbook/Hankuk Ch'ulpan Yongam. (KO ISSN 0075-6881) 4131
Korean Reconstruction Bank. Monthly Review. (KO) 871, 788
Korean Research Bulletin. (US) 3903
Korean Review. (US ISSN 0163-0229) 3964
Korean Scholarship Association in Japan. Science Report. see Chosen Shogakkai Gakujutsu Ronbunshu 3032
Korean Scientific Abstracts. (KO ISSN 0023-4052) 4356, 16, 4614
Korean Scientific Information. see Chosen Gakujutsu Tsuho 4614
Korean Social Science Journal. (KO) 4378
Korean Society of Mechanical Engineers Journal see K S M E Journal 1934
Korean Sources (Year). (KO) 1142
Korean Stamps. (KN ISSN 0452-5914) 3754, 2871
Korean Studies. (US ISSN 0145-840X) 3640
Korean Trade Directory. (KO) 1142
Korean Trade Unions. (KN ISSN 0454-4196) 2585
Korean Traders Association. Statistical Yearbook of Foreign Trade. (KO) 726, 916, 4577
Korean Traders Association. Statistics of Foreign Trade. (KO) 726, 916
Korean Women. (KN) 3903, 4846
Korean Youth and Students. (KN) 1240
Koreana. (KO) 3903, 3640
Koreansk Journal. (SW ISSN 0023-4079) 3964
Kornik, Poland. Instytut Dendrologii i Pomologii. Prace see Arboretum Kornickie 495
Kornyezetvedelmi Szakirodalmi Tajekoztato/Environmental Control Abstracts. (HU ISSN 0231-0716) 1974, 16
Korosi Csoma Kiskonyvtar. (HU ISSN 0075-6911) 2339, 2822
Koroth (Haifa). (IS ISSN 0023-4109) 3120
Koroth (Jerusalem). (IS) 3177
Koroze a Ochrana Materialu. (CS ISSN 0452-599X) 1856, 1934
Korp-Motion see Prima Liv 4484
Korps Komando see Mari Jo 3463
Korrespondent. (UZ) 2572
Korrespondenz. (GW) 1258
Korrespondenz Abwasser. (GW ISSN 0341-1478) 1962, 4826
Korrespondenzblatt Evangelischer Schulen und Heime. (GW) 1645, 4187
†Korrosion. (GW ISSN 0233-0741) 5224

Korrozios Figyelo. (HU ISSN 0133-2546) **3654**, 1182, 1856
Kort Sagt. (DK ISSN 0902-7270) **2767**
Kortars. (HU ISSN 0023-415X) **2871**
Kortbegrip van Landboustatistieke. see South Africa. Department of Agriculture and Fisheries. Division of Economic Services. Abstract of Agricultural Statistics **143**
Korunk. (RM) **2056**
Korunk Tudomanya. (HU ISSN 0075-6946) **4321**, 4603
Kos. (IT ISSN 0393-2095) **3120**
Kosciuszko Foundation Monthly Newsletter see Kosciuszko Foundation Newsletter **2011**
Kosciuszko Foundation Newsletter. (US) **2011**
Kosei Tokei Yoran see Japan. Ministry of Health and Welfare. Statistics and Information Department. Handbook of Health and Welfare Statistics **4117**
Kosher Directory. (US) **2011**, 4224
Kosher Gourmet Magazine. (US ISSN 0888-4811) **2076**, 2011
Koshien University. College of Business Administration and Information Science. Bulletin. (JA ISSN 0913-5545) **827**
Koshien University. Department of Nutrition. Bulletin. (JA ISSN 0913-5537) **3608**
Koshu Eisei/Journal of Public Health Practice. (JA ISSN 0368-5187) **4107**
Kosmetik International. (GW ISSN 0342-2976) **376**, 373
Kosmetik Journal. (GW ISSN 0342-2968) **376**
Kosmetik Report. (GW) **376**
Kosmetikerinnen-Fachzeitung - Parfuemerie Journal see Kosmetik International **376**
Kosmetikjahrbuch. (GW) **376**
Kosmicheskaya Biologiya i Aviakosmicheskaya Meditsna/Space Biology and Aerospace Medicine. (RU ISSN 0321-5040) **3120**
Kosmicheskaya Nauka i Tekhnika. (KR) **366**
Kosmicheskie Issledovaniya. (RU ISSN 0023-4206) **58**
Kosmicheskie Issledovaniya na Ukraine see Kosmicheskaya Nauka i Tekhnika **366**
Kosmischer Beobachter see Meridian **3595**
Kosmobiologie see Meridian **3595**
Kosmon News see Kosmon Voice **4284**
Kosmon Unity. (UK) **4284**
Kosmon Voice. (US ISSN 0882-4606) **4284**
Kosmorama. (DK ISSN 0023-4222) **3513**
Kosmos. (US ISSN 0047-3650) **359**
Kosmos. (PL) **445**
Kosmos. (DK ISSN 0107-7902) **4187**
Kosmos. (GW ISSN 0023-4230) **4321**
Kosmos. Series A. Biologia see Kosmos **445**
Kosmos Tis Psychis/World of Soul. (GR ISSN 0023-4257) **3670**
Kosmoskyna. (FI ISSN 0785-2517) **3012**, 2930
Kosmosophie. (GW ISSN 0454-448X) **3771**
Kost og Allergi Nyt. (DK ISSN 0904-3764) **3120**, 3608
Kosten en Financiering van de Gezondheidzorg in Nederland/Cost of Health Care in the Netherlands. (NE ISSN 0075-6954) **4107**, 4411
Kostenrechnungspraxis see K R P **1017**
Koster. (RU) **1259**
Kotai Butsuri/Solid State Physics. (JA ISSN 0454-4544) **3844**
Kotaigun Seitaigaku no Kenkyu. see Researches on Population Ecology **3987**
Kothari's Economic and Industrial Guide of India see Kothari's Industrial Directory of India **1142**

Kothari's Economic Guide and Investor's Handbook of India see Kothari's Industrial Directory of India **1142**
Kothari's Industrial Directory of India. (II) **1142**, 953, 1080
Kothari's World of Reference Works. (II ISSN 0075-6970) **404**
Koti. (FI ISSN 0355-1555) **103**
Kotilaakari. (FI) **4107**
Kotiliesi. (FI ISSN 0023-4281) **2448**, 4846
Kotimaisen Tyon Liitto. Tuotantouutiset. (FI) **837**
Kotiseutu. (FI ISSN 0047-3677) **243**
Kotiseutukuvauksia Lounais-Haemeestae. (FI) **2372**
Kotitalous. (FI ISSN 0047-3685) **2448**
Kotiteollisuus - Vaar Hoemsleojd see Taito **357**
Kotonoura. (JA) **3526**, 4321
Kouakou. (FR ISSN 0765-1376) **1259**
Koude Magazine. (NE) **2301**
Koululainen/Pupil. (FI ISSN 0357-2714) **1259**, 1645
Kouzina/Kitchen. (UK) **2448**
Kovach Tire Report. (US) **4694**, 4292
Kovel's Antiques and Collectibles Price List. (US) **258**
Kovel's Antiques Price List see Kovel's Antiques and Collectibles Price List **258**
Kovels' Bottle Price List. (US) **2437**
Kovel's Complete Bottle Price List see Kovels' Bottle Price List **2437**
Kovels on Antiques and Collectibles. (US ISSN 0741-6091) **258**, 1165
Kovoexport. (CS) **818**
Kovoexport-Investa see Kovoexport **818**
Kovove Materialy/Metal Materials. (CS ISSN 0023-432X) **3411**
Kowan Gijutsu Kenkyujo. Gaido/Port and Harbour Research Institute. Guide. (JA) **4730**, 1870
Kowani News. (Kongres Wanita Indonesia) (IO) **4846**
Kozarstvi/Leather Industry. (CS ISSN 0023-4338) **2737**, 4361
Kozgazdasagi Ertekezesek. (HU ISSN 0075-6989) **676**
Kozgazdasagi Szemle/Economic Review. (HU ISSN 0023-4346) **676**
Kozharska i Obuvna Promishlenost. (BU) **2737**, 4361
Kozhevenno-Obuvnaya Promyshlennost' (RU ISSN 0023-4354) **4361**, 2737
Kozlekedestudomanyi Szemle. (HU ISSN 0023-4362) **4652**
Kozmos. (CS) **366**
Kozoktatas. (RM) **1645**
Kozuti Kozlekedesi Szakirodalmi Tajekoztato/Road Transport Abstracts. (HU ISSN 0231-0724) **4665**
The Kpelle Messenger. (LB) **2169**
Kpodoga. (GH) **2192**
Kracht van Omhoog. (NE ISSN 0023-4389) **4187**
Kraevye Zadachi dlya Differentsial'nykh Uravnenii. (UZ) **3042**
Kraft fuer den Tag. (GW) **4187**
Kraftfahrervereinigung Deutscher Beamter E.V. K V D B Mitteilungen see Auto und Reise **4753**
Kraftfahrt-Bundesamt. Mitteilungen. Ergaenzungshefte. (GW) **4694**
Kraftfahrt-Bundesamt. Statistische Mitteilungen. (GW ISSN 0341-468X) **4694**
Kraftfahrzeug Anzeiger see K F Z Anzeiger **4745**
Kraftfahrzeugtechnik. (GW ISSN 0023-4419) **4694**
Kraftfahrzeugvermieter see Der Autovermieter **4684**
Kraftfornytt see Gaardbrukeren **93**
Kraftfutter. (GW ISSN 0023-4427) **184**
Krafthand. (GW ISSN 0023-4435) **4603**
Kraftverkehr see Lastauto Omnibus **4694**
Kraftverkehrs Handbuch. (GW) **4652**

Kraje Socjalistyczne. (PL ISSN 0860-2220) **4441**
†Krajske Kulturni Stredisko v Hradci Kralove. Komentovana Vyroci. (CS) **5224**
Krajske Muzeum v Teplicich. Zpravy a Studie see Regionalni Muzeum v Teplicich. Zpravy a Studie **2382**
Krajske Vlastivedne Muzeum v Olomouci. Zpravy see Vlastivedne Muzeum v Olomouci. Zpravy **2394**
Krak. (DK) **1142**
Krake see Jugendpressedienst des V N J **1257**
Krakow Dawniej i Dzis. (PL ISSN 0075-7020) **2372**
Krakowskie Studia Prawnicze. (PL ISSN 0023-4478) **2642**
Kraks TransportKatalog. (DK ISSN 0108-8335) **4652**
Kranich. (GW) **1645**
Kranjcan. (XV) **4089**
Krankendienst. (GW ISSN 0023-4486) **2466**, 3281, 4411
Krankengymnastik. (GW ISSN 0023-4494) **3120**
Das Krankenhaus. (GW ISSN 0340-3602) **2466**
Krankenhaus-Apotheke see Krankenhauspharmazie **3733**
Krankenhaus-Hygiene & Infektionsverhuetung. (GW ISSN 0720-3373) **2467**
Krankenhaus Kalender. (GW) **2467**
Krankenhaus Technik. (GW ISSN 0720-3977) **2467**
Krankenhaus-Umschau. (GW ISSN 0023-4508) **2467**
Krankenhausarzt. (GW ISSN 0023-4516) **2467**
Krankenhauspharmazie. (GW ISSN 0173-7597) **3733**
▼Krankenhauspsychiatrie. (GW ISSN 0937-289X) **4034**
Krankenpflege/Soins Infirmiers. (SZ) **3281**
Krankenpflege. (GW ISSN 0002-1008) **3281**
Die Krankenversicherung. (GW ISSN 0301-4835) **2536**
Krant see Fama **2916**
Krantai. (LI) **2209**
Krasoslovni Zbornik. see Acta Carsologica **1540**
Krasy Slovenska/Beauties of Slovakia. (CS) **2184**
Kratylos. (GW ISSN 0023-4567) **2822**, 2930
Kraus-Hefte. (GW ISSN 0342-4626) **2930**
Kraut und Rueben. (GW ISSN 0178-0166) **2133**, 3609
Krcki Zbornik. (CI) **2372**, 2255, 2642, 2930
Kreatif Jaarbook. (BE) **4131**
Kredietbank. Bulletin Mensuel. see Kredietbank. Monthly Bulletin **788**
Kredietbank. Hebdomadaire see Kredietbank. Weekberichten **789**
Kredietbank. Monthly Bulletin/ Kredietbank. Bulletin Mensuel. (BE) **788**
Kredietbank. Weekberichten. (BE ISSN 0772-3318) **789**
Kredietbank. Weekly Bulletin see Kredietbank. Weekberichten **789**
Kredit und Kapital. (GW ISSN 0023-4591) **789**
Kreditpraxis. (GW ISSN 0172-7400) **753**
Kredittmarked Statistikk see Norway. Statistisk Sentralbyraa. Kredittmarked Statistikk **731**
Krefeld. Amt fuer Statistik und Stadtentwicklung. Statistisches Jahrbuch. (GW) **4577**
Krefeld Immigrants and their Descendants. (US) **2156**
Kreisamtsblatt des Landkreises und Landratsamtes Kronach. (GW) **4089**
Kreishandwerkerschaft Moenchengladbach. Mitteilungsblatt. (GW) **1116**
Kreispostille. (GW) **4089**
Kreisstandardzahlen Nordrhein-Westfalen. (GW) **4577**
Krejl. (DK ISSN 0107-6701) **2372**
Kreolische Bibliothek. (GW ISSN 0720-9983) **2822**

Kresge Art Museum Bulletin. (US ISSN 0887-9222) **332**
Kresge Foundation. Annual Report. (US) **3526**
Krestanska Revue. (CS ISSN 0023-4613) **4187**
▼Krest'yanskie Vedomosti. (RU) **153**
▼Kresy. (PL ISSN 0867-1125) **2930**
Kridangan. (II ISSN 0023-4621) **4478**
Kridla Vlasti see Letectvi a Kosmonautika **58**
Krieg und Literatur/War and Literature. (GW ISSN 0935-9060) **2372**
Kriegbaum Heritage. (US) **2157**
Der Kriegsblinde. (GW ISSN 0023-463X) **2293**
Kriegsgraeberfuersorge. (GW ISSN 0023-4648) **3462**
Kriegsopfer- und Behinderten. Rundschau. (GW) **4441**, 3903
Der Kriegsruf. (GW) **4241**
Krigshistorisk Tidsskrift. (DK ISSN 0454-5230) **2372**
†Krikos. (UK ISSN 0023-4656) **5224**
Krikos Ton Vathmoforon. (GR ISSN 0023-4664) **1259**, 1299
Krila Armije. (YU ISSN 0023-4672) **3462**, 58
Kriminal Journalen. (NO ISSN 0800-0484) **2985**
Kriminalforsorgens Aarsberetning. (DK ISSN 0904-1990) **1517**
Der Kriminalist. (GW) **1517**
Kriminalistik. (GW ISSN 0023-4699) **1517**
Kriminalistik und Forensische Wissenschaften. (GW ISSN 0023-4702) **1517**
Kriminalitaet und ihre Verwalter. (GW ISSN 0340-823X) **1517**
†Kriminalsoziologische Bibliographie. (AU ISSN 0255-3678) **5224**
Kriminalstatistik see Norway. Statistisk Sentralbyraa. Kriminalstatistikk **1525**
Kriminalwissenschaftliche Abhandlungen. (GW ISSN 0454-5265) **1517**
Kriminologie. Abhandlungen ueber abwegiges Sozialverhalten. (GW ISSN 0075-7144) **1517**
Kriminologische Gegenwartsfragen. (GW ISSN 0075-7136) **1517**
Kriminologisches Journal. (GW ISSN 0341-1966) **1517**
Krishak Jagat. (II ISSN 0970-8650) **103**
Krishak Samachar. (II ISSN 0023-4710) **103**
Krishanu. (II ISSN 0023-4737) **2930**
Krishi Sameeksha. (II) **932**
Krishnachura. (II ISSN 0023-4745) **2930**
Krishnamurti Foundation. Bulletin. (II ISSN 0047-3693) **4215**
Krisis. (NE ISSN 0168-275X) **3771**
Krisis. (GW ISSN 0178-7691) **3903**, 2316
Kristall und Technik see Crystal Research and Technology **1210**
Kristallografiya. (RU ISSN 0023-4761) **1211**
†Kristaus Karaliaus Laivas/Ship of Christ the King. (US ISSN 0023-477X) **5224**
Kristdemokraten. (SW ISSN 0284-9941) **3903**
Kristelig Fagforening. Medlemsblad. (DK ISSN 0109-2057) **2585**
Kristelig Fagforening, Kristelig Funktionaer-Organisation. Medlemsblad see Kristelig Fagforening. Medlemsblad **2585**
Kristelig Fagforening, Kristelig Funktionaer-Organisation. Medlemsblad see Kristelig Funktionaer-Organisation. Medlemsblad **2585**
Kristelig Funktionaer-Organisation. Medlemsblad. (DK ISSN 0109-1131) **2585**
Kristen Vetenskaps Herold (ISSN 0145-7543) see Herald of Christian Science **4283**
Kristiansand Museum. Aarbok. (NO ISSN 0333-3124) **445**
Kristo see Moto **2240**

Kristofer Lehmkuhl Forelesning. (NO ISSN 0452-7208) **677**
Kritik. (MY) **2871**
†Kritik der Buergerlichen Ideologie. (GW ISSN 0138-3612) **5224**
Kritika. (HU ISSN 0023-4818) **2930**
Kritikon Litterarum. (GW ISSN 0340-9767) **2822**, 2930
Kritische Berichte. (GW ISSN 0340-7403) **332**
Kritische Justiz. (GW ISSN 0023-4834) **3944**, 2642
Kritische Medizin im Argument. (GW ISSN 0341-0943) **3120**, 4107, 4411
Kritische Studien zur Geschichtswissenschaft. (GW) **2316**
Kritische Vierteljahresschrift fuer Gesetzgebung und Rechtswissenschaft. (GW ISSN 0179-2830) **2642**
Krmiva. (CI ISSN 0023-4850) **207**
Kroatische Berichte. (GW ISSN 0179-5961) **2011**
Kroeber Anthropological Society. Papers. (US ISSN 0023-4869) **243**
Kroghs Lovinformation. (DK ISSN 0108-7878) **2642**
Kroghs Register see Kroghs Lovinformation **2642**
Krokodil. (RU ISSN 0023-4877) **2871**
Krolikovodstvo i Zverovodstvo. (RU ISSN 0023-4885) **220**
Kronika. (XV ISSN 0023-4923) **2372**, 277, 3792
Kronika Wielkopolski. (PL ISSN 0137-3102) **2372**, 3903
Kronos. (SA ISSN 0259-0190) **2333**, 277, 2157
Kronos. (US ISSN 0361-6584) **2510**
Kroppsoeving. (NO ISSN 0333-0141) **1645**
Krotkofalowiec Polski. (PL) **1357**
Krske Skofije. Zbornik. see Diozese Gurk. Jahrbuch **4262**
Krug. (IS) **2203**
Krugozor. (RU ISSN 0454-5508) **2215**
Kruidenier see Foodmagazine **2092**
Kruidenier/Epicier. (BE ISSN 0046-2357) **2093**
Kruistocht. (NE) **4187**
Krul's Maandblad voor Stoom- en Chemische Wasserijen, Ververijen en Wassalons. (NE ISSN 0023-4958) **1281**, 4621
Krygshistoriese Tydskrif. see Military History Journal **3464**
Kryl'ya Rodiny/Wings of the Motherland. (RU ISSN 0130-2701) **58**
Krymskaya Astrofizicheskaya Observatoriya. Izvestiya. (RU) **366**
Kryptadia: Journal of Erotic Folklore. (FR ISSN 0075-7160) **2056**
Krystalinikum. (CS ISSN 0454-5524) **1571**
Krzepniecie Metali i Stopow. (UK ISSN 0208-9386) **3411**
Ksiazka w Dawnej Kulturze Polskiej. (PL ISSN 0075-7179) **2510**
Ksiaznica Slaska. (PL) **2767**
Ksiegarz. (PL) **4131**
Ktema. (FR ISSN 0221-5896) **2339**, 1278
Ktemata. (BE) **2930**
Ku Kung Wen Hsien. see Ch'ing Documents **5165**
Kuala Lumpur Stock Exchange. Companies Handbook. (MY ISSN 0126-7558) **953**
Kuan Kuang Tzu Liao. see Monthly Report on Tourism - Republic of China **4800**
Kuang Chiao Ching. see Wide Angle **2197**
Kuangchan yu Dizhi/Minerals and Geology. (CC ISSN 1001-5663) **3411**, 1571
Kuangshan Celiang/Mine Prospecting. (CC ISSN 1001-358X) **3487**, 2255
Kuangshan Dizhi. (CC ISSN 1001-5892) **3487**, 1571
Kuangshan Jishu/Mining Technology. (CC ISSN 1001-5809) **3487**

Kueche. (GW ISSN 0344-4376) **2477**, 2076
Kueche in Krankenhaus und Altenheim. (GW) **2076**, 2467
Kuechenplaner. (GW ISSN 0722-9917) **2553**
Kuechenprofi. (GW) **2560**
Kuensel (Dzongkha Edition). (BT) **871**
Kuensel (English Edition). (BT) **872**
Kuensel (Nepali Edition). (BT) **872**
Die Kuenstlergilde. (GW) **332**, 2585
Kuenstliche Intelligenz. (GW ISSN 0933-1875) **1409**
Die Kueste. (GW ISSN 0452-7739) **1607**, 1829, 1962
Kuka Kukin On/Who's Who in Finland. (FI) **419**
Kukhoe Hoeuirok Saegin/Index to the National Assembly Debates. (KO) **4081**, 3938
Kukhoe Tosogwanbo/National Assembly Library Review. (KO ISSN 0027-8572) **2767**
Kukhoebo/National Assembly Review. (KO ISSN 0027-8580) **3903**
Kuki Shawa Kenkyu. (JA) **366**, 3438
Kukuruza. (RU ISSN 0023-5040) **184**
Kulanu. (IS ISSN 0334-648X) **1259**
▼Kulde. (NO ISSN 0801-7093) **2301**
†Kulfoldi Kozgazdasagi Irodalmi Szemle. Series A. (HU ISSN 0237-0840) **5224**
†Kulfoldi Kozgazdasagi Irodalmi Szemle. Series B. (HU ISSN 0237-0859) **5225**
†Kulfoldi Magyar Nyelvu Kiadvanyok. (HU ISSN 0133-333X) **5225**
Kulgazdasag. (HU ISSN 0324-4202) **818**
KuLiMu see K U L I M U **2929**
Das Kulissenmagazin. (GW) **4634**
Kulisy. (PL ISSN 0023-5083) **2214**
Kulisy Polonii. (CN) **2011**
Kulisy Sportu. (CN) **2011**, 4478
Kuljetus. (FI ISSN 0023-5091) **4652**
Kullagertidningen. (SW ISSN 0347-1748) **1934**
Kulleraugen. (GW ISSN 0171-5208) **3513**
Kulleraugen - Materialsammlung. (GW ISSN 0174-2582) **3513**
Kulliyah. see Middle East Forum **5237**
Kulloja/Workers. (KN) **2585**
Kulpolitika/Foreign Affairs. (HU ISSN 0133-0616) **3964**
Kultaseppien Lehti. (FI ISSN 0085-2600) **2565**
Kultur im Heim see Neues Wohnen **2554**
Kultur Journal. (GW ISSN 0938-619X) **2011**
Kultur og Samfund. (DK ISSN 0107-3591) **2510**
Kultur un Lebn. (US ISSN 0023-513X) **2011**
Kultur und Freizeit. (GW ISSN 0323-5017) **332**
Kultur und Gesellschaft. (GW) **2316**, 4378
Kultur- und Stadtnachrichten aus Weitra. (AU) **2316**, 2437, 4577
Kultur und Technik. (GW ISSN 0344-5690) **3526**, 332, 4603
Kultur Vorschau Europa/Cultural Preview. (GW ISSN 0342-1716) **3903**
Kultur Vorschau International. (GW ISSN 0935-6436) **2190**
Kultura. (FR ISSN 0023-5148) **2871**
Kultura. (PL ISSN 0023-5156) **2871**
Kultura. (YU ISSN 0023-5164) **4442**, 2510
Kultura i Spoleczenstwo. (PL ISSN 0023-5172) **2871**
Kul'tura i Zhizn/Culture and Life. (RU ISSN 0023-5199) **3964**
Kul'tura i Zhyttya. (KR ISSN 0023-5180) **2871**
Kultura Popullore. (AA ISSN 0257-6082) **2056**
Kultura Slova/Culture of the Word. (CS ISSN 0023-5202) **2822**
Kul'tura Slova. (KR ISSN 0201-419X) **2930**
Kulturberichte aus Niederoesterreich. (AU ISSN 0023-5121) **332**, 4321, 4603

Kulturberichte aus Tirol. (AU ISSN 0023-5210) **2173**
Kulturchronik. (GW ISSN 0724-343X) **332**
Kulturen see Kulturens Vaerld **3526**
Kulturen Zivot/Cultural Life. (XN ISSN 0047-3731) **2871**
Kulturens Vaerld. (SW ISSN 0282-5902) **3526**
Kulturgeografiske Haefter. (DK ISSN 0106-5866) **2255**, 4378
Kulturgeografiske Haefters Skriftserie. (DK ISSN 0108-3945) **2255**
Kulturgeografiske Skrifter. (DK ISSN 0023-5245) **2255**
Kulturna Bastina. (CI ISSN 0351-0557) **2316**
Kulturni Radnik. (CI ISSN 0023-5253) **2510**, 3771
Kulturni Zivot. (YU ISSN 0023-5261) **2239**
Kulturnopoliticky Kalendar. (CS) **3393**, 4774
Kulturos Barai. (LI) **2209**
Kulturpflanze. (GW ISSN 0075-7209) **508**, 545
Kulturpolitik. (GW) **2871**
Kulturrevolution. (GW) **3903**
Kultus und Unterricht. (GW ISSN 0933-7776) **1729**
Kultuur see Wending **2212**
Kultuur ja Elu/Culture and Life. (ER ISSN 0134-5605) **2011**, 419, 2056, 3964
†Kuluttajatietoa. (FI ISSN 0359-9329) **5225**
Kumamoto Daigaku Kogakubu Kenkyu Hokoku. see Kumamoto University. Faculty of Engineering. Technical Reports **1829**
Kumamoto Daigaku Kogakubu Kiyo. see Kumamoto University. Faculty of Engineering. Memoirs **1829**
Kumamoto Daigaku Kyoikugakubu Kiyo. Shizen Kagaku/Kumamoto University. Faculty of Education. Memoirs. Natural Science. (JA ISSN 0454-6148) **4321**
Kumamoto Daigaku Kyoyobu Kiyo. Shizen Kagaku Hen/Kumamoto University. Faculty of General Education. Memoirs. Natural Sciences. (JA ISSN 0286-5769) **4321**
Kumamoto Daigaku Taishitsu Igaku Kenkyujo Hokoku/Kumamoto University. Institute of Constitutional Medicine. Report. (JA) **3120**
Kumamoto Daigaku Taishitsu Igaku Kenkyujo Hokoku. see Kumamoto University. Institute of Constitutional Medicine. Bulletin **3121**
Kumamoto Igakkai Zasshi/Kumamoto Medical Society. Journal. (JA) **3120**
Kumamoto Journal of Mathematics. (JA ISSN 0914-675X) **3042**, 1182, 3823
Kumamoto Journal of Science. Mathematics see Kumamoto Journal of Mathematics **3042**
Kumamoto Medical Journal. (JA ISSN 0023-5326) **3120**
Kumamoto Medical Society. Journal. see Kumamoto Igakkai Zasshi **3120**
Kumamoto Prefecture. Monthly Report. (JA) **3438**
Kumamoto University. Department of Geology. Journal. (JA) **1571**
Kumamoto University. Department of Physics. Physics Reports. (JA ISSN 0303-4070) **3823**
Kumamoto University. Faculty of Education. Memoirs. Natural Science. see Kumamoto Daigaku Kyoikugakubu Kiyo. Shizen Kagaku **4321**
Kumamoto University. Faculty of Engineering. Memoirs/Kumamoto Daigaku Kogakubu Kiyo. (JA ISSN 0023-5334) **1829**
Kumamoto University. Faculty of Engineering. Technical Reports/Kumamoto Daigaku Kogakubu Kenkyu Hokoku. (JA ISSN 0023-5296) **1829**

Kumamoto University. Faculty of General Education. Memoirs. Natural Sciences. see Kumamoto Daigaku Kyoyobu Kiyo. Shizen Kagaku Hen **4321**
Kumamoto University. Institute of Constitutional Medicine. Bulletin/Kumamoto Daigaku Taishitsu Igaku Kenkyujo Hokoku. (JA ISSN 0023-530X) **3121**
Kumamoto University. Institute of Constitutional Medicine. Bulletin. Supplement. (JA ISSN 0075-7217) **3121**
Kumamoto University. Institute of Constitutional Medicine. Report. see Kumamoto Daigaku Taishitsu Igaku Kenkyujo Hokoku **3120**
Kumar. (II ISSN 0023-5342) **332**, 1259, 1645, 2930
▼Kumquat Meringue. (US) **2996**
Kumudam. (II) **2200**
Kun Lun/Army Literature. (CC) **2930**, 3462
Kunapipi. (II) **2931**, 2822
Kunchong Xuebao/Acta Entomologica Sinica. (CC ISSN 0454-6296) **535**
Kunchong Zhishi/Entomological Knowledge. (CC ISSN 0452-8255) **536**
Kundalini. (II) **4187**
Die Kunde. (GW ISSN 0342-0736) **277**
Kundu. (AT) **1315**
†Kung Fu. (DK) **5225**
Kung Kao Po/Catholic Chinese Weekly. (HK) **4267**
Kungliga Humanistiska Vetenskapssamfundet i Lund. Aarsberattelse. see Societe Royale de Lettres de Lund. Bulletin **2961**
Kungliga Krigsvetenskapsakademien. Handlingar och Tidskrift. (SW ISSN 0023-5369) **3462**
Kungliga Skogs- och Lantbruksakademiens Tidskrift/Royal Swedish Academy of Agriculture and Forestry. Journal/Academie Royale d'Agriculture et de Sylviculture de Suede. Annales. (SW ISSN 0023-5350) **103**, 2103
Kungliga Vetenskapsakademien. Bidrag till Kungliga Vetenskapsakademiens Historia. (SW ISSN 0081-9956) **4321**
Kungliga Vitterhets Historie och Antikvitets Akademien. Aarsbok. (SW ISSN 0083-6796) **2372**
Kungliga Vitterhets Historie och Antikvitets Akademien. Antikvariskt Arkiv. (SW ISSN 0083-6737) **332**, 277
Kungliga Vitterhets Historie och Antikvitets Akademien. Filologiskt Arkiv. (SW ISSN 0083-6745) **2822**
Kungliga Vitterhets Historie och Antikvitets Akademien. Handlingar. Antikvariska Serien/Royal Academy of Letters, History and Antiquities. Proceedings. Antiquarian Series. (SW ISSN 0083-6761) **2372**
Kungliga Vitterhets Historie och Antikvitets Akademien. Handlingar. Filologisk-Filosofiska Serien/Royal Academy of Letters, History and Antiquities. Proceedings. Philological-Philosophical Series. (SW ISSN 0083-677X) **2822**, 3771
Kungliga Vitterhets Historie och Antikvitets Akademien. Handlingar. Historiska Serien/Royal Academy of Letters, History and Antiquities. Proceedings. Historical Series. (SW ISSN 0083-6788) **2372**
Kungliga Vitterhets Historie och Antikvitets Akademien. Historiskt Arkiv. (SW ISSN 0083-6753) **2372**
Kuni no Shiken Kenkyu Gyomu Keikaku.(JA) **4614**, 4356
Kunitachi College of Music. Memoirs. see Kunitachi Ongaku Daigaku Kenkyu Kiyo **3560**
Kunitachi Ongaku Daigaku Kenkyu Kiyo/Kunitachi College of Music. Memoirs. (JA) **3560**

KUNNALLISTEKNIIKKA/KOMMUNALTEKNIK

Kunnallistekniikka/Kommunalteknik. (FI ISSN 0023-5385) **2491**, 302, 1871
Die Kunst. (GW) **333**, 302, 3526
Kunst. *see* Art **5138**
Kunst am Bau. (GW) **302**, 333, 622, 2491
Kunst & Antiquitaeten. (GW ISSN 0341-4159) **333**
Das Kunst-Bulletin. (SZ) **333**
†Kunst des Orients/Art of the Orient. (GW ISSN 0023-5393) **5225**
Kunst & Antiekrevue. (NE ISSN 0165-3687) **258**
Kunst en Museumjournaal. (NE ISSN 0924-5251) **333**, 3526
Kunst in Koeln *see* K I K **3526**
Kunst-Katalog: Auktionen. (AU ISSN 0075-7241) **333**
Kunst, Literatur & Music *see* K U L I M U **2929**
Kunst og Kultur. (NO ISSN 0023-5415) **333**
Kunst og Museum. (DK ISSN 0454-6520) **333**
Kunst und Altertum am Rhein. (GW ISSN 0075-725X) **277**
Kunst und das Schoene Heim *see* Die Kunst **333**
Kunst und Handwerk. (GW ISSN 0454-6539) **333**, 355
Kunst und Kirche. (AU ISSN 0023-5431) **333**
†Kunst und Literatur. (GW ISSN 0023-544X) **5225**
Kunst und Stein. (SZ ISSN 0023-5458) **333**
Kunst und Unterricht. (GW ISSN 0170-6225) **333**
Kunstavisen. (DK ISSN 0107-6957) **333**
†Kunstblatt. (GW) **5225**
Kunstchronik. (GW ISSN 0023-5474) **3526**
Kunsterziehung. (GW ISSN 0451-0887) **1753**, 333
Der Kunsthandel. (GW ISSN 0023-5504) **333**
†Kunsthandwerk in Europa. (GW) **5225**
Kunsthistorische Sammlungen in Wien. Jahrbuch. (AU ISSN 0075-2312) **333**
Kunsthistorisches Institut in Florenz. Mitteilungen. (IT) **333**, 2316
Kunstjahrbuch der Stadt Linz. (AU) **333**
Kunstmuseets Aarsskrift. (DK ISSN 0107-8933) **333**
Kunstmuseum Bern. Mitteilungen *see* Berner Kunstmitteilungen **319**
Kunstnachrichten. (SZ ISSN 0023-5512) **333**
Kunstpreis-Jahrbuch. (GW ISSN 0174-352X) **333**, 258
Kunstreport. (GW ISSN 0172-7265) **333**, 3526
Kunststof en Rubber. (NE ISSN 0167-9597) **3863**
Kunststof Magazine. (NE) **3863**
Kunststoff Industrie und ihre Helfer. (GW ISSN 0075-7276) **3863**
Kunststoff Journal. (GW ISSN 0047-3766) **3863**
Kunststoff-Magazin-Prodoc. (GW) **1182**
Kunststoff-Produkte *see* Kunststoff- und Kautschuk-Produkte **3863**
Kunststoff Rundschau *see* Kunststoffberater **3863**
Kunststoff- und Kautschuk-Produkte. (GW) **3863**
Kunststoffberater. (GW ISSN 0172-6374) **3863**
Kunststoffe. (GW ISSN 0023-5563) **3863**
▼Kunststoffe Europe. (GW ISSN 0938-9849) **3863**
Kunststoffe - German Plastics. (GW ISSN 0723-0192) **3863**
Kunststoffe im Lebensmittelverkehr. (GW ISSN 0075-7292) **3863**
Kunststoffe - Plasticos *see* Plasticos Universales **3865**
Kunststoffe - Plastics. (SZ ISSN 0023-5598) **3864**
Kunststofftechnik *see* Kunststoffberater **3863**
Kunststunde. (GW) **333**, 1753

Das Kunstwerk. (GW ISSN 0023-561X) **333**
†Kunterbunt. (GW ISSN 0138-5569) **5225**
Kuoku/Quark. (JA ISSN 0286-9500) **4321**
Kupat-Holim. Information Series: Special Studies and Surveys on Medical Manpower Sociology and Medical Economics. (IS) **4107**
Kupat Holim. Information Series: Special Studies on Medical Manpower and Sociology *see* Kupat-Holim. Information Series: Special Studies and Surveys on Medical Manpower Sociology and Medical Economics **4107**
Kupat-Holim Yearbook. (IS ISSN 0301-4843) **4107**
Kup's Komments *see* Health Consciousness **3594**
Kurashi no Sekkei. *see* Planning for Living **2449**
Kurashiki Museum of Natural History. Bulletin. *see* Kurashiki-shiritsu Shizenshi Hakubutsukan Kenkyu Hokoku **4321**
Kurashiki-shiritsu Shizenshi Hakubutsukan Kenkyu Hokoku/Kurashiki Museum of Natural History. Bulletin. (JA ISSN 0913-1566) **4321**, 3526
Kurashiki-shiritsu Shizenshi Hakubutsukanpo. (JA ISSN 0913-1558) **3526**, 4321
Kuratorium fuer Technik und Bauwesen in der Landwirtschaft e.V. Schriften *see* K T B L - Schriften **102**
Kuratorium fuer Verkehrssicherheit. Kleine Fachbuchreihe. (AU ISSN 0075-7306) **4719**
Kurbad *see* Der Deutsche Badebetrieb **3801**
Kurdish Times. (US ISSN 0885-386X) **2202**, 2011, 2220
Kurenai: Japanese Embroidery Journal. (US) **3591**
Kurhessische Wirtschaft *see* Wirtschaft Nordhessen **824**
Kurier (Duesseldorf). (GW ISSN 0170-768X) **1357**
Der Kurier (Liesborn). (GW) **4187**, 3903
Kurinikaru Sutadi/Clinical Study. (JA ISSN 0388-5585) **3281**
Kurinji Quarterly. (II) **2931**
▼Kuriosum. (SZ) **2437**
Kuriren. (FI) **2186**
Kurjournal - Bad Toelz. (GW) **4774**, 4107
Kurortologija i Fizioterapija. (BU ISSN 0368-7066) **3805**
Kursblatt der Amtlich Nicht Notierten Wertpapiere - Geregelter Freiverkehr an der Wiener Boerse *see* Kursblatt der Wiener Wertpapierboerse - Geregelter Freiverkehr **953**
Kursblatt der Wiener Wertpapierboerse - Geregelter Freiverkehr. (AU) **953**
Kursbuch. (GW ISSN 0023-5652) **2190**
Kursbuch der Deutschen Museums - Eisenbahnen. (GW) **4711**
†Kursbuch-Textil (Year). (GW) **5225**
Kursprogramm Spiel und Theater. (GW) **4634**
Kurt-Schwitters-Almanach. (GW ISSN 0723-6638) **333**
Kurt Weill Newsletter. (US ISSN 0899-6407) **3560**
Kurtrierisches Jahrbuch. (GW ISSN 0452-9081) **2372**
Kurtziana. (AG ISSN 0075-7314) **508**
Kurukshetra. (II ISSN 0023-5660) **4089**
†Kurukshetra. (CE) **5225**
Kurukshetra Law Journal. (II) **2642**
Kuruma no Techo/Big Car Life. (JA ISSN 0286-4312) **4694**
Kurume Igakkai Zasshi. *see* Kurume Medical Association. Journal **3121**
Kurume Medical Association. Journal/Kurume Igakkai Zasshi. (JA) **3121**
Kurume Medical Journal. (JA ISSN 0023-5679) **3121**
Kurve. (GW) **4518**

Kurzauszuege aus dem Schrifttum fuer das Eisenbahnwesen *see* Information Eisenbahn **4664**
Kurzberichte aus der Bauforschung. (GW ISSN 0178-7578) **309**
Kurzeitung Gronenbach. (GW) **4774**
Kurzwelle Aktuell. (GW) **33**, 1375
Kuschitische Sprachstudien/Cushitic Language Studies. (GW ISSN 0721-4340) **2822**
Kusegongbo. (KO) **4187**
Kushiro City Museum. Memoirs. *see* Kushiro-shiritsu Hakubutsukan Kiyo **4321**
Kushiro-shiritsu Hakubutsukan Kiyo/Kushiro City Museum. Memoirs. (JA ISSN 0912-1897) **4321**, 3526
Kuspi. (FI ISSN 0023-5717) **3237**
Kustbon. (SW ISSN 0345-6706) **2011**
Kusunoki Noho. (JA ISSN 0023-5725) **103**
Kutatas - Fejlesztes *see* Kutatasszervezesi Tajekoztato **4322**
Kutatasszervezesi Tajekoztato/Bulletin of Research Management. (HU ISSN 0866-5192) **4322**
Kutlwano/Mutual Understanding. (BS ISSN 0023-5733) **3903**, 4065
Kuukausikatsaus Suomen Ilmastoon/Maanadsoeversikt oever Finlands Klimat. (FI ISSN 0303-2485) **3438**
Kuuloviesti/Hearing News. (FI ISSN 0023-5741) **2288**, 4411
▼Kuumba. (US ISSN 1049-328X) **2454**, 2011, 2996
Kuunika. (MW) **4241**
†Kuvasz Newsletter. (US) **5225**
Kuwait. Central Statistical Office. Annual Bulletin for Prices and Index Numbers *see* Kuwait. Central Statistical Office. Monthly Bulletin for Consumer Prices and Index Numbers **726**
Kuwait. Central Statistical Office. Annual Statistical Abstract. (KU) **4577**
Kuwait. Central Statistical Office. Monthly Bulletin for Consumer Prices and Index Numbers. (KU) **726**, 999
Kuwait. Central Statistical Office. Monthly Digest of Statistics *see* Kuwait. Central Statistical Office. Annual Statistical Abstract **4577**
Kuwait Advertising Age. (KU) **33**
Kuwait al-Youm. (KU ISSN 0023-575X) **4065**
Kuwait & Gulf Economic and Financial Bulletin. (KU) **872**
Kuwait Bulletin of Marine Science. (KU ISSN 0250-362X) **2045**, 446, 587
Kuwait Economic and Financial Bulletin *see* Kuwait & Gulf Economic and Financial Bulletin **872**
Kuwait Institute for Scientific Research. Annual Research Report. (KU ISSN 0250-4065) **4322**
Kuwait Investment Company (Report). (KU) **789**
Kuwait Medical Association. Journal. (KU ISSN 0023-5776) **3121**
Kuwait University. Conference on Algebra and Geometry. Proceedings. (KU) **3043**
Kuwaiti. (KU ISSN 0023-5792) **3691**
Kuwaiti Digest. (KU) **2209**
▼Kuzbass-Inform. (RU) **677**
Kuznechno-shtampovochnoe Proizvodstvo. (RU ISSN 0023-5806) **3412**
Kvaekartidskrift. (SW ISSN 0345-6005) **4284**
Kvaellsstunden. (SW ISSN 0023-5822) **2218**
Kvakera Esperantisto. (UK ISSN 0023-5814) **4187**
Kvantovaya Elektronika. (KR ISSN 0368-7155) **1902**, 3823
Kvasny Prumysl/Fermentation Industry. (CS ISSN 0023-5830) **2076**
Kvety. (CS ISSN 0023-5849) **2184**
†Kvinder. (DK ISSN 0900-2073) **5225**
Kvinder, Kvinder. (DK ISSN 0108-1888) **2454**, 4846
†Kvinder paa Tinder. (DK ISSN 0109-0356) **5225**

Kvindestudier ved A U C. Aarbog. (Aalborg Universitetscenter) (DK ISSN 0108-3961) **4846**
Kvinner og Klaer/Women & Clothes. (NO ISSN 0023-5857) **4846**
Kvinnobulletinen. (SW) **4846**
▼Kvintessentsiya. (RU) **3237**
Kwahak Dong-A. (KO) **4322**
Kwahak Kisul Yoram/Handbook of Science and Technology. (KO) **4603**
Kwahakgwa Kwahakgoneop. (KN) **1182**, 1856
Kwahakwon Tongbo/Bulletin of the Academy of Sciences. (KN) **4322**
Kwan Um Zen School Newsletter. (US) **4215**, 3595
Kwang-Eung Yeo. *see* Korea Social Work College. Research Institute for Special Education. Journal **1738**
Kwansei Gakuin Daigaku Rigakubu Tsushin. (JA ISSN 0911-8233) **1315**, 4322
Kwara News. (NR) **2212**
Kwartaalschrift voor Directieve Therapie en Hypnose. (NE ISSN 0167-238X) **4034**, 3274
Kwartalnik Architektury i Urbanistyki. (PL ISSN 0023-5865) **302**, 2491
Kwartalnik Geologiczny/Geological Quarterly. (PL ISSN 0023-5873) **1571**
Kwartalnik Historii i Teorii Ruchu Zawodowego. (PL ISSN 0860-9357) **2372**, 985
Kwartalnik Historii Kultury Materialnej. (PL ISSN 0023-5881) **2372**, 277
Kwartalnik Historii Nauki i Techniki/Quarterly Journal of the History of Science and Technology. (PL ISSN 0023-589X) **4322**, 4603
Kwartalnik Historii Prasy Polskiej. (PL ISSN 0137-2998) **2572**, 2316
Kwartalnik Historii Ruchu Zawodowego *see* Kwartalnik Historii i Teorii Ruchu Zawodowego **2372**
Kwartalnik Neofilologiczny. (PL ISSN 0023-5911) **2822**, 2931
Kwartalnik Opolski. (PL ISSN 0023-592X) **2316**
Kwartalnik Pedagogiczny. (PL ISSN 0023-5938) **1645**
Kxe6s Verein Chess Society. Advisory Board Record. (US ISSN 0148-057X) **4478**
Kxe6s Verein Newsletter. (US ISSN 0148-0561) **4478**
Kybernetes. (UK ISSN 0368-492X) **1441**, 1438
Kybernetik *see* Biological Cybernetics **1440**
Kybernetika/Cybernetics. (CS ISSN 0023-5954) **1442**
Kykies in die Verlede. *see* Looking Back **2333**
Kyklos. (SZ ISSN 0023-5962) **872**
Kymppi. (FI ISSN 0023-5989) **789**
Kyobu Geka. *see* Japanese Journal of Thoracic Surgery **3379**
Kyodo to Hakubutsukan. (JA ISSN 0288-9102) **3526**
Kyodo to Kagaku/Nature and Science. (JA ISSN 0912-6449) **4322**
Kyoiku Hyoron/Educational Review. (JA ISSN 0023-5997) **1645**
Kyoiku Kenkyu/Educational Studies. (JA ISSN 0452-3318) **1645**, 2822
Kyoiku-No-Mori. *see* Forest of Education **1634**
Kyoiku Ongaku, Chugaku Koko-ban/Educational Music, Junior High and High School. (JA ISSN 0388-7502) **3560**, 1753
Kyoiku Ongaku, Shogaku-ban/Educational Music, Elementary School. (JA ISSN 0388-7480) **3560**, 1753
Kyoiku Shinrigaku Nenpo/Annual Report of Educational Psychology in Japan. (JA ISSN 0452-9650) **4034**, 1645
Kyoka Kyoiku Kenkyu. (JA) **1753**
Kyokuchi/Polar News. (JA ISSN 0023-6004) **4322**
Kyongje Nonjip. *see* Korean Economic Journal **676**
Kyorin Igakkai Zasshi/Kyorin Medical Society. Journal. (JA ISSN 0368-5829) **3121**, 2275

Kyorin Medical Society. Journal. see Kyorin Igakkai Zasshi **3121**
Kyoshin Kiroku. see Strong-Motion Earthquake Records in Japan **1595**
Kyoto Business Directory. (JA) **818**
Kyoto College of Pharmacy. Scientific Journal. see Gakujutsu Zasshi **3727**
Kyoto Daigaku. Reichorui Kenkyujo Nenpo/Kyoto University. Primate Research Institute. Annual Report. (JA ISSN 0286-4568) **243, 446, 3121**
Kyoto Daigaku Abuyama Jishin Kansoku Hokoku. see Kyoto University. Abuyama Seismological Observatory. Seismological Bulletin **1592**
Kyoto Daigaku Bosai Kenkyujo Kiyo. see Kyoto University. Disaster Prevention Research Institute. Bulletin **4107**
Kyoto Daigaku Genshi Enerugi Kenkyujo Iho/Kyoto University. Institute of Atomic Energy. Bulletin. (JA ISSN 0368-5039) **1806**
Kyoto Daigaku Genshi Enerugi Kenkyujo Kenkyu Hokoku. see Kyoto University. Institute of Atomic Energy. Technical Reports **1807**
Kyoto Daigaku Kekkaku Kyobu Shikkan Kenkyujo Kiyo. see Kyoto University. Chest Disease Research Institute. Bulletin **3365**
Kyoto Daigaku Kenkyusho. see Kyoto University. Institute for Chemical Research. Bulletin **1182**
Kyoto Daigaku Kogakubu Kiyo. see Kyoto University. Faculty of Engineering. Memoirs **1829**
Kyoto Daigaku Nogakubu Kiyo. see Kyoto University. College of Agriculture. Memoirs **104**
Kyoto Daigaku Ogata Keisanki Senta Eibun Repoto. see Kyoto University. Data Processing Center. Report **1452**
Kyoto Daigaku Rigakubu Sugaku Kiyo. see Kyoto University. Journal of Mathematics **3043**
Kyoto Daigaku Shokuryo Kagaku Kenkyusho Hokoku/Kyoto University. Research Institute for Food Science. Bulletin. (JA ISSN 0451-1476) **103**
Kyoto Daigaku Suri Kaiseki Kenkyujo Kiyo. see Research Institute for Mathematical Sciences. Publications **3052**
Kyoto Daigaku Uirusu Kenkyujo Nenkan Kiyo. see Kyoto University. Institute for Virus Research. Annual Report **554**
Kyoto-furitsu Daigaku Gakujutsu Hokoku. Rigaku Seikatsu Kagaku/Kyoto Prefectural University. Scientific Reports: Natural Science and Living Science. (JA) **4322**
Kyoto-furitsu Daigaku Gakujutsu Hokoku: Jinbun/Kyoto Prefectural University. Scientific Reports: Humanities. (JA ISSN 0075-7381) **2510**
Kyoto-furitsu Daigaku Gakujutsu Hokoku Nogaku. see Kyoto Prefectural University. Scientific Reports: Agriculture **104**
Kyoto-furitsu Ika Daigaku Zasshi. see Kyoto Prefectural University of Medicine. Medical Society. Journal **3121**
Kyoto Institute of Technology. Faculty of Engineering and Design. Memoirs. (JA ISSN 0911-0305) **4322, 4603**
Kyoto Kyoiku Daigaku Kiyo. B. Shizen Kagaku/Kyoto University of Education. Bulletin. Series B: Mathematics and Natural Science. (JA ISSN 0023-6101) **3043, 4322**
Kyoto Prefectural University. Scientific Reports: Agriculture/Kyoto-furitsu Daigaku Gakujutsu Hokoku Nogaku. (JA ISSN 0075-7373) **104**
Kyoto Prefectural University. Scientific Reports: Humanities. see Kyoto-furitsu Daigaku Gakujutsu Hokoku: Jinbun **2510**

Kyoto Prefectural University. Scientific Reports: Natural Science and Living Science. see Kyoto-furitsu Daigaku Gakujutsu Hokoku. Rigaku Seikatsu Kagaku **4322**
Kyoto Prefectural University of Medicine. Medical Society. Journal/Kyoto-furitsu Ika Daigaku Zasshi. (JA ISSN 0023-6012) **3121**
†Kyoto Review. (JA ISSN 0388-0532) **5225**
Kyoto Sangyo Daigaku Ronshu. Shizen Kagaku Keiretsu/Acta Humanistica et Scientifica Universitatis Sangio Kyotiensis. Natural Science Series. (JA ISSN 0287-7902) **4322**
Kyoto Shobo/Fire Prevention. (JA ISSN 0023-6020) **2033**
Kyoto University. Abuyama Seismological Observatory. Seismological Bulletin/Kyoto Daigaku Abuyama Jishin Kansoku Hokoku. (JA ISSN 0454-7659) **1592**
Kyoto University. Chest Disease Research Institute. Bulletin/Kyoto Daigaku Kekkaku Kyobu Shikkan Kenkyujo Kiyo. (JA ISSN 0009-3378) **3365**
Kyoto University. College of Agriculture. Memoirs/Kyoto Daigaku Nogakubu Kiyo. (JA) **104**
Kyoto University. Data Processing Center. Report/Kyoto Daigaku Ogata Keisanki Senta Eibun Repoto. (JA) **1452**
Kyoto University. Department of Astronomy. Contributions. (JA ISSN 0388-0230) **366**
Kyoto University. Disaster Prevention Research Institute. Bulletin/Kyoto Daigaku Bosai Kenkyujo Kiyo. (JA ISSN 0454-7675) **4107**
Kyoto University. Faculty of Engineering. Memoirs/Kyoto Daigaku Kogakubu Kiyo. (JA ISSN 0023-6063) **1829**
Kyoto University. Faculty of Science. Memoirs. Series of Biology. (JA ISSN 0454-7802) **446**
Kyoto University. Faculty of Science. Memoirs. Series of Geology and Mineralogy. (JA ISSN 0454-7810) **1571, 3487**
Kyoto University. Faculty of Science. Memoirs. Series of Physics, Astrophysics, Geophysics and Chemistry. (JA ISSN 0368-9689) **4322**
Kyoto University. Institute for Chemical Research. Bulletin/Kyoto Daigaku Kenkyusho. (JA ISSN 0023-6071) **1182**
Kyoto University. Institute for Virus Research. Annual Report/Kyoto Daigaku Uirusu Kenkyujo Nenkan Kiyo. (JA ISSN 0075-7357) **554**
Kyoto University. Institute of Atomic Energy. Bulletin. see Kyoto Daigaku Genshi Enerugi Kenkyujo Iho **1806**
Kyoto University. Institute of Atomic Energy. Research Activities. (JA ISSN 0386-0752) **1807**
Kyoto University. Institute of Atomic Energy. Technical Reports/Kyoto Daigaku Genshi Enerugi Kenkyujo Kenkyu Hokoku. (JA) **1807**
Kyoto University. Journal of Mathematics/Kyoto Daigaku Rigakubu Sugaku Kiyo. (JA ISSN 0023-608X) **3043**
Kyoto University. Kwasan and Hida Observatories. Contributions. (JA ISSN 0388-2349) **366**
Kyoto University. Primate Research Institute. Annual Report. see Kyoto Daigaku. Reichorui Kenkyujo Nenpo **243**
Kyoto University. Research Activities in Civil Engineering and Related Fields. (JA ISSN 0075-7365) **1871**
Kyoto University. Research Institute for Food Science. Bulletin. see Kyoto Daigaku Shokuryo Kagaku Kenkyusho Hokoku **103**
Kyoto University. Research Reactor Institute. Annual Reports. (JA ISSN 0454-9244) **4322, 1214, 1792, 1807**
Kyoto University Economic Review. (JA ISSN 0023-6055) **677**

Kyoto University of Education. Bulletin. Series B: Mathematics and Natural Science. see Kyoto Kyoiku Daigaku Kiyo. B. Shizen Kagaku **3043**
Kyowa Engineering News. (JA ISSN 0285-2969) **1829, 2523**
Kyowa Hakko Kogyo. Annual Report. (JA) **33, 333**
Kyoyo Ronshu. see Review on Liberal Arts **2514**
Kyoyuk Tarjo/Educational Materials. (KO) **1753**
Kypria/Cypriot Woman. (CY) **4846**
Kypriakai Spoudai. see Society of Cypriot Studies. Bulletin **2388**
Kypriakos Logos. (CY) **2372**
Kypros. (CY ISSN 0023-611X) **2184**
Kyriakatika Nea. see Greek Sunday News **4283**
Kyriatikis Ores/Sunday Hours. (CY) **2184**
Kyriokos see U U W F Journal **4854**
Kyrkans Tidning. (SW ISSN 0280-4603) **4187**
Kyrkofoerfattningar. (SW ISSN 0023-6136) **4187**
Kyrkogarden. (SW ISSN 0282-0595) **2119**
Kyrkohistorisk Aarsskrift. (SW ISSN 0085-2619) **4187**
Kyrkomusikernas Tidning. (SW ISSN 0281-286X) **3560, 4187**
Kyrn. (FR ISSN 0395-1081) **2187**
Kytoesavut. (FI ISSN 0454-8086) **2372**
Kyung-Young Shinmun/Management News. (KO) **1017**
Kyushu American Literature. (JA ISSN 0454-8132) **2931**
Kyushu Daigaku Daigakuin Sogo Rikogaku Kenkyuka Hokoku/Kyushu University. Engineering Sciences Reports. (JA ISSN 0388-1717) **1829**
Kyushu Daigaku Kogaku Shuho. see Kyushu University. Faculty of Engineering. Technology Reports **1829**
Kyushu Daigaku Kogakubu Kiyo. see Kyushu University. Faculty of Engineering. Memoirs **1829**
Kyushu Daigaku Kyoyobu Sugaku Zasshi/Kyushu University. College of General Education. Mathematical Reports. (JA ISSN 0287-9980) **3043**
Kyushu Daigaku Nogakubu Kiyo. see Kyushu University. Faculty of Agriculture. Journal **104**
Kyushu Daigaku Nogakubu Suisangakka Gyosekishu/Kyushu University. Contributions from the Department of Fisheries and the Fishery Research Laboratory. (JA ISSN 0453-0314) **2045**
Kyushu Daigaku Oyo Rikigaku Kenkyujo Shoho. see Kyushu University. Research Institute for Applied Mechanics. Bulletin **1919**
Kyushu Daigaku Rigakubu Kenkyu Hokoku Chikyu-Wakusei-Kagaku. see Kyushu University. Department of Earth and Planetary Sciences. Science Reports **1571**
Kyushu Daigaku Rigakubu Kiyo A. Sugaku. see Kyushu University. Faculty of Science. Memoirs. Series A: Mathematics **3043**
Kyushu Daigaku Rigakubu Kiyo C. Kagaku. see Kyushu University. Faculty of Science. Memoirs. Series C: Chemistry **1182**
Kyushu Daigaku Rigakubu Kiyo D. Chikyuwakusei Kagaku. see Kyushu University. Faculty of Science. Memoirs. Series D: Earth and Planetary Sciences **1546**
Kyushu Daigaku Rigakubu Shimabara Jishin Kazan Kansokujo Kenkyu Hokoku/Kyushu University. Faculty of Science. Shimabara Earthquake and Volcano Observatory. Sciences Reports. (JA ISSN 0916-2259) **1592**
Kyushu Hematological Society. Journal/Kyushu Ketsueki Kenkyu Dokokai-Shi.(JA ISSN 0451-1611) **3273**

KYUSHU UNIVERSITY 6379

Kyushu Institute of Technology. Bulletin: Humanities, Social Sciences/Kyushu Kogyo Daigaku Kenkyu Hokoku: Jinbun-Shakai-Kagaku. (JA ISSN 0453-0349) **2510, 4378**
Kyushu Institute of Technology. Bulletin: Mathematics, Natural Science/Kyushu Kogyo Daigaku Kenkyu Hokoku. Shizen Kagaku. (JA ISSN 0454-8221) **3043, 4322**
Kyushu Institute of Technology. Bulletin: Science and Technology/Kyushu Kogyo Daigaku Kenkyu Hokoku: Kogaku. (JA ISSN 0453-0357) **4603, 4322**
Kyushu Institute of Technology. Memoirs: Engineering. (JA ISSN 0369-0512) **1829**
Kyushu Ketsueki Kenkyu Dokokai-Shi. see Kyushu Hematological Society. Journal **3273**
Kyushu Kogyo Daigaku Kenkyu Hokoku. Shizen Kagaku. see Kyushu Institute of Technology. Bulletin: Mathematics, Natural Science **3043**
Kyushu Kogyo Daigaku Kenkyu Hokoku: Jinbun-Shakai-Kagaku. see Kyushu Institute of Technology. Bulletin: Humanities, Social Sciences **2510**
Kyushu Kogyo Daigaku Kenkyu Hokoku: Kogaku. see Kyushu Institute of Technology. Bulletin: Science and Technology **4603**
Kyushu Kogyo Gijutsu Shikenjo Nenpo/Government Industrial Research Institute, Kyushu. Annual Report. (JA) **1080**
Kyushu Neuro-Psychiatry/Kyushu Shinkei Seishin Igaku. (JA ISSN 0023-6144) **3344**
Kyushu Shinkei Seishin Igaku. see Kyushu Neuro-Psychiatry **3344**
Kyushu University. College of General Education. Mathematical Reports. see Kyushu Daigaku Kyoyobu Sugaku Zasshi **3043**
Kyushu University. Contributions from the Department of Fisheries and the Fishery Research Laboratory. see Kyushu Daigaku Nogakubu Suisangakka Gyosekishu **2045**
Kyushu University. Department of Earth and Planetary Sciences. Science Reports/Kyushu Daigaku Rigakubu Kenkyu Hokoku Chikyu-Wakusei-Kagaku. (JA ISSN 0385-8278) **1571, 3658, 3691**
Kyushu University. Department of Geology. Science Reports see Kyushu University. Department of Earth and Planetary Sciences. Science Reports **1571**
Kyushu University. Engineering Sciences Reports. see Kyushu Daigaku Daigakuin Sogo Rikogaku Kenkyuka Hokoku **1829**
Kyushu University. Faculty of Agriculture. Journal/Kyushu Daigaku Nogakubu Kiyo. (JA ISSN 0023-6152) **104**
Kyushu University. Faculty of Engineering. Memoirs/Kyushu Daigaku Kogakubu Kiyo. (JA ISSN 0023-6160) **1829**
Kyushu University. Faculty of Engineering. Technology Reports/Kyushu Daigaku Kogaku Shuho. (JA ISSN 0023-2718) **1829**
Kyushu University. Faculty of Science. Memoirs. Series A: Mathematics/Kyushu Daigaku Rigakubu Kiyo A. Sugaku. (JA ISSN 0373-6385) **3043**
Kyushu University. Faculty of Science. Memoirs. Series C: Chemistry/Kyushu Daigaku Rigakubu Kiyo C. Kagaku. (JA ISSN 0085-2635) **1182**
Kyushu University. Faculty of Science. Memoirs. Series D: Earth and Planetary Sciences/Kyushu Daigaku Rigakubu Kiyo D. Chikyuwakusei Kagaku. (JA ISSN 0023-6179) **1546**
Kyushu University. Faculty of Science. Memoirs. Series D: Geology see Kyushu University. Faculty of Science. Memoirs. Series D: Earth and Planetary Sciences **1546**

Kyushu University. Faculty of Science. Shimabara Earthquake and Volcano Observatory. Sciences Reports. see Kyushu Daigaku Rigakubu Shimabara Jishin Kazan Kansokujo Kenkyu Hokoku **1592**

Kyushu University. Institute of Tropical Agriculture. Bulletin/Nettai Nogaku Kenkyu. (JA) **104**

Kyushu University. Research Institute for Applied Mechanics. Abstracts of Papers. (JA) **1845**, 16, 1919

Kyushu University. Research Institute for Applied Mechanics. Bulletin/ Kyushu Daigaku Oyo Rikigaku Kenkyujo Shoho. (JA ISSN 0030-7734) **1919**

Kyushu University. Research Institute for Applied Mechanics. Reports/Oyo Rikigaku Kenkyujo Obun Hokoku. (JA ISSN 0023-6195) **1919**

L A C M A Physician. (Los Angeles County Medical Association) (US ISSN 0162-7163) **3121**

L A C U N Y Journal see Urban Academic Librarian **2790**

L A C U S Forum. (Linguistic Association of Canada and the United States) (US ISSN 0195-377X) **2822**

L A Co-ops and the Shared Housing Networker. (US) **4411**, 2491

L.A. Commercial News see W C N Commercial News **924**

L A D O C. (Latin American Documentation) (PE ISSN 0360-3350) **3903**

L A E News. (Louisiana Association of Educators) (US ISSN 0162-3052) **1645**

L A I F S Journal. (Los Angeles International Fern Society) (US) **2133**

L A I G News. (Library Association) (UK) **2767**

L A M A Manager. (US) **2642**, 1017

L A M P. (Literature Analysis of Microcomputer Publications) (US) **1405**, 16

L A M P Lighter. (Standing Committee on Legal Assistance for Military Personnel) (US ISSN 1044-8756) **3462**

L A M Y A Revista Mensual. (Liga de Almaceneros Minoristas y Afines) (AG ISSN 0023-6217) **2076**

L A N. (US ISSN 0898-0012) **1427**

L A N A Nyt. (Lokalhistoriske Arkiver i Nordjyllands Amt) (DK ISSN 0108-7711) **2372**

L A N Book see L A N Component Directory **1427**

L A N Component Directory. (US) **1427**, 1461

▼L A N Computing. (Local Area Network) (US) **1427**

L A N D see Living Among Nature Daringly **2133**

L A N e Telecomunicazioni. (Local Area Network) (IT) **1351**

L A N Newsletter see Local Area Networks **1427**

L A N Product News. (Local Area Network) (US) **1427**

▼L A N Reporter. (Local Area Network) (US ISSN 1051-4066) **1454**, 1478

L A N S A. (Latin American Bank Note Society) (US ISSN 0308-8677) **3600**

L A N Software Directory. (Local Area Network) (US) **1438**, 1425

L A N Technology. (Local Area Network) (US ISSN 1042-4695) **1461**

L A N Times. (Local Area Network) (US ISSN 1040-5917) **1470**

L A Parent. (US ISSN 0740-3437) **1240**, 2448, 4846

L A R C Medical see Lille Medical **3122**

L A R C Newsletter. (Radcliffe College, Lesbian Alumni) (US) **2454**, 4846

L A R F Report. Annual. (Latin American Reserve Fund) (CK) **677**, 789, 872

†L A R U Studies. (Latin American Research Unit) (CN ISSN 0704-1217) **5225**

†L A R U Working Paper. (Latin American Research Unit) (CN) **5225**

L A Resources. (US) **3595**, 3805

L A S A Forum. (Latin American Studies Association) (US ISSN 0890-7218) **4378**, 2412

L A S I E. (Library Automated Systems Information Exchange) (AT ISSN 0047-3774) **2767**

L A S L Newsletter. (Louisiana Association of School Librarians) (US) **2767**

L A S P A U Informativo. (Latin American Scholarship Program of American Universities, Inc.) (US) **1722**

L A Sports Profiles. (Los Angeles) (US) **4478**

L.A. Style. (US ISSN 0895-3465) **2228**

L A T I S see Landscape Architecture Technical Information Series **302**

L A Trade Union News see Employment News **2582**

L A W G Letter. (Latin American Working Group) (CN ISSN 0316-3393) **3964**, 932

†L.A. W I S P. (Southern California Women Strike for Peace) (US) **5225**

L A Weekly. (US) **2228**

L.A. West. (US) **2228**

L.A.X. Magazine. (US) **1422**

L Ae S. (Litteratur, Aestetik, Sprog) (DK ISSN 0109-5390) **2931**, 2822

L'Agent 03 see Le Pont **2779**

L'Annee Automobile. see Automobile Year **4682**

L B A Banker see Louisiana Banker **789**

L B A Info. (Luftfahrt - Bundesamt) (GW) **4675**

L B I News. (Leo Baeck Institute) (US ISSN 0023-625X) **2316**, 2931

L B L Research Review. (Lawrence Berkeley Laboratory) (US ISSN 0882-1305) **4322**

L B M A O Reporter. (Lumber & Building Materials Association of Ontario) (CN ISSN 0380-0326) **622**, 2115

L B Monthly see Long Beach Monthly **2228**

†L C A Quarterly. (Lawyers for the Creative Arts) (US) **5225**

L C and You. (Lori Chapman and Company) (US ISSN 8755-4313) **1292**, 373

L C Folk Archive Finding Aid. (U.S. Library of Congress) (US ISSN 0736-4903) **2767**, 2056

L C Folk Archive Reference Aid. (U.S. Library of Congress) (US ISSN 0736-4911) **2767**, 2056

L C - G C. (Liquid and Gas Chromatography) (US ISSN 0888-9090) **1207**

L C - G C International. (Liquid and Gas Chromatography) (US ISSN 0895-5441) **1207**

L C I E Informations. (Laboratoire Central des Industries Electriques) (FR ISSN 0220-9535) **1902**

L C L see Laboratory Computer Letter **3226**

L C - Liquid Chromatography and H P L C Magazine see L C - G C **1207**

L C Science Tracer Bullet. (U.S. Library of Congress) (US ISSN 0090-5232) **4356**

L D A Newsbriefs. (Learning Disabilities Association of America) (US) **1738**

L D & A. (Lighting Design & Application) (US ISSN 0360-6325) **1902**, 2553, 3854

L D B Interior Textiles. (US ISSN 0892-743X) **2560**

L D V Bogen see D V Bogen **4649**

L E A. (Libros de Edicion Argentina) (AG ISSN 0326-226X) **4131**

L E A F Lines. (Women's Legal Education and Action Fund) (CN) **2642**, 4846

L E & W see Literature East and West **2934**

L.E. Beacon. (Lupus Erythematosus) (US) **3369**, 4835

L E I F - Life and Education in Finland. (FI) **1685**

L E P see Library of Exact Philosophy **4322**

L E R S Monograph Series. (Laboratoires d'Etudes et de Recherches Synthelabo) (US) **3121**

L E S Nouvelles. (Licensing Executives Society (U.S. & Canada), Inc.) (US ISSN 0047-4576) **3676**

L F L Reports: (Libertarians for Life) (US ISSN 0882-116X) **597**, 4846

L G A Nachrichten. (Landesverband des Bayerischen Gross- und Aussenhandels) (GW) **837**

L G A Rundschau. (Landesgewerbeanstalt Bayern) (GW ISSN 0023-6268) **1080**

L.G. Argomenti. (Letteratura Giovanile Argomenti) (IT) **2871**

L G L C Newsletter. (Libertarians for Gay and Lesbian Concerns) (US) **2931**, 2454

L.G.M. see Local Government Management **4090**

†L G M Mededelingen. (NE ISSN 0023-6276) **5225**

L G S N: Lesbian and Gay Studies Newsletter. (US) **2454**, 2931

L H A T Bulletin. (League of Historic American Theatres) (US) **302**, 4634

L H R T Newsletter. (Library History Round Table) (US ISSN 0737-4984) **2767**, 2316

L I A S: Sources and Documents Relating to the Early Modern History of Ideas. (NE ISSN 0304-0003) **2316**, 2931, 3771

L I B E R News Sheet see European Research Library Cooperation **2757**

L I F see Nytt Lif **1293**

†L.I.F.E. Newsletter. (League for International Food Education) (US) **5225**

L I M R A's Marketfacts. (Life Insurance Marketing and Research Association (LIMRA)) (US ISSN 0889-0986) **2536**

L I N K Line. (Library and Information Network) (US ISSN 0735-8407) **597**, 1240, 1645, 3393

L I N K S. (US ISSN 0163-2205) **1738**

L I O N. (Living in the Ozarks Newsletter) (US) **2871**

L I P Newsletter. (Lesbian Interest Press) (US) **2454**, 3944, 4846

L I P P see Library Insights, Promotion & Programs **2770**

L I R I Monthly Circular see L I R I Quarterly Review **2737**

L I R I Quarterly Review. (Leather Industries Research Institute) (SA) **2737**

L I R I Research Bulletin. (Leather Industries Research Institute) (SA ISSN 0085-2724) **2737**

L I R I Technical Bulletin. (Leather Industries Research Institute) (SA) **2737**

L I R S Bulletin. (Lutheran Immigration and Refugee Service) (US) **4241**, 2642

L I R S Information Bulletin see L I R S Bulletin **4241**

L I S L see Amsterdam Studies in the Theory and History of Linguistic Science. Series 5: Library and Information Sources in Linguistics **2855**

▼L I S P and Symbolic Computation. (US ISSN 0892-4635) **1422**

†L I S T. (Library and Information Services Today) (US ISSN 0075-9821) **5225**

L I T A Newsletter. (Library and Information Technology Association) (US ISSN 0196-1799) **2798**, 1457

▼L I T: Literature Interpretation Theory.(US ISSN 1043-6928) **2931**

L'Indice Suisse des Prix a la Consommation. see Landesindex der Konsumentenpreise **726**

†L K B News. (SW) **5225**

L K B News with Science Tools see L K B News **5225**

L L A see Luggage, Leathergoods & Accessories **2737**

L L A Bulletin. (Louisiana Library Association) (US ISSN 0024-6867) **2768**

L L B A see Linguistics and Language Behavior Abstracts **2855**

L L S E E see Linguistic & Literary Studies in Eastern Europe **2826**

L M I Review. (US) **985**

L M l'Industria del Legno e del Mobile. (IT) **2560**

L M News. (Lawson Mardon Group Ltd.) (CN) **3649**

L M P see Letters in Mathematical Physics **3823**

L M S - Laboratory Equipment Buyers Guide. (Laboratory Marketing Spectrum) (SA) **3260**

L M S - Laboratory Marketing Spectrum. (SA ISSN 1013-1205) **3261**, 1044

L M S - Lingua. (Riksfoereningen foer Laerarna i Moderna Spraak) (SW ISSN 0023-6330) **2822**, 1645

L M T A News. (Louisiana Motor Transport Association, Inc.) (US) **4745**

†L N A C Almanac. (Librarians for Nuclear Arms Control) (US) **5225**

▼L N G Observer. (US ISSN 1053-6949) **3691**

L O A P L see Langues Orientales Anciennes Philologie et Linguistique **2824**

L O Bladet. (Landsorganisationen i Danmark) (DK ISSN 0105-032X) **2585**

L O G A. (Local Government Annotations) (UK ISSN 0023-6349) **4081**, 16

L O K Report. (GW ISSN 0344-7146) **4711**

L O K Report Reisefuehrer. (GW ISSN 0170-4621) **4711**

L O M A Bulletin see L O M A Line **3691**

L O M A Line. (Louisiana Oil Marketers Association) (US) **3691**, 1044

L O M A Literature on Modern Art see Artbibliographies Modern **351**

L.O.M.A. Resource. (Life Office Management Association, Inc.) (US) **2536**

L O Tidningen. (Landsorganisationen i Sverige) (SW ISSN 0346-895X) **2585**

L O - Ungdoms Blad. (Lands Organisation) (DK ISSN 0904-0919) **4442**

L P E A HeartBeat. (Luis Palau Evangelistic Association) (US) **4241**, 1722

L P - Gas. (US ISSN 0024-7103) **3691**

L P - Gas Market Facts see Propane Industry Profile **3707**

L P Gas Review. (UK ISSN 0309-3077) **3691**

L P I Technical Report. (Lunar and Planetary Institute) (US) **366**, 1546

L P N Association of British Columbia Newsletter. (Licensed Practical Nurses of British Columbia) (CN) **3281**

L P T Journal. (Leder Pelz Textil) (GW ISSN 0048-3176) **2737**

L P T V Reporter. (Low Power T V) (US) **1375**

L R A's Economic Notes. (Labor Research Association) (US ISSN 0895-5220) **985**

L R C Employment Bulletin see Labour Resourcer **987**

L R D Book of Wage Rates, Hours and Holidays see Bargaining Report **973**

L R D G Bulletin see Learning Resources Journal **1711**

L R D G Newsletter see Learning Resources News **1711**

L R E Project Exchange. (Law-Related Education) (US ISSN 0734-0990) **2642**, 1240

L R E Report. (Law-Related Education) (US ISSN 0731-9711) **2643**, 1240

L R I Guides to Management. Monographs. (Leadership Resources Inc.) (US) **1017**
L R T News *see* L T News **4652**
L S A. (Libre Service Actualites) (FR ISSN 0024-2632) **1044**
L S A Bulletin. (Linguistic Society of America) (US ISSN 0023-6365) **2822**
L S A Newsletter. (Leisure Studies Association) (UK) **2738, 4478, 4774**
▼L S A - Zip. (US) **985**
†L S E Magazine. (London School of Economics and Political Science) (UK ISSN 0023-639X) **5225**
†L.S.E. Quarterly. (London School of Economics) (UK ISSN 0269-9710) **5225**
L S I Zhizhao yu Ceshi. (CC) **2523**
L S L. (Leder, Schuhe, Lederwaren) (GW ISSN 0024-0192) **2737, 4361**
L S T Nyt. (DK ISSN 0904-5198) **3121, 3609**
L S U Alumni News *see* L S U Magazine **1315**
L S U Engineering News. (Louisiana State University) (US ISSN 0023-6411) **1315, 1829**
L S U Forestry Notes. (Louisiana State University) (US) **2103**
L S U Magazine. (Louisiana State University) (US) **1315**
L S U Wood Utilization Notes. (US ISSN 0076-1109) **2115**
L T *see* Lebensmittel-Technologie **2076**
L T A Handbook. (Lawn Tennis Association) (UK) **4507**
L T C B Research. (Long Term Credit Bank of Japan Ltd.) (JA ISSN 0287-2404) **1080**
L T C Paper *see* Land Tenure Center. Paper **153**
L T L O *see* Letter to Libraries Online **2798**
L T News. (London Regional Transport) (UK) **4652**
†L T P. (UK ISSN 0262-575X) **5225**
L U A C Forum. (Life Underwriters Association of Canada) (CN ISSN 0380-3147) **2536**
L U Journal. (GW ISSN 0179-4744) **163**
L U Week2 *see* Agora **1302**
L'udove Noviny. (HU) **2198**
†L V. (US) **5225**
L V M W Nieuws. (Landelijke Vereniging van Maatschappelijk Werkers) (NE) **4411**
L V R - Report. (Landschaftsverband Rheinland) (GW) **2190**
L V S Bladet *see* Specialarbejderskolen **1687**
L W B Dokumentation. Report. (Lutheran World Federation - Geneva) (GW ISSN 0174-1764) **4241**
L W V Info. (Landeswohlfahrtsverband Hessen) (GW) **4411**
La Crosse Economic Indicators *see* La Crosse - Winona Business and Economic Review **872**
La Crosse - Winona Business and Economic Review. (US) **872**
La Fayette. (US) **2157**
La Leche League News *see* New Beginnings (Franklin Park) **1241**
La-Mathil (American Edition). (US) **2823, 2011**
La Sentinelle *see* El Centinela **4232**
Laakintavoimistelija *see* Fysioterapia **3100**
Lab Animal. (US ISSN 0093-7355) **3261**
Lab-Compact Service. (GW) **3261**
Lab Data. (US) **3447**
Lab Hotline. (US) **3261**
Lab Instrumenten. (NE ISSN 0368-7368) **3261**
Lab Lines. (AT) **1753**
Lab Products International. (BE) **3261**
Lab Report. (US ISSN 1045-7313) **3121**
Lab Report for Physicians Newsletter *see* Lab Report **3121**
Lab Talk. (AT ISSN 0159-2033) **1753, 4322**
Lab Waste and Hazards Management *see* Hazardous Waste News **1985**

†Labeling Requirements for Consumer Packages of Fresh Fruits and Vegetables. (US) **5225**
Labels and Labelling *see* Labels and Labelling International **3649**
Labels and Labelling International. (UK ISSN 0143-2192) **3649**
Labeo. (IT ISSN 0023-6462) **2643**
Labirinto. (IT) **4478**
Labmedica. (US ISSN 1054-0970) **3261**
Labo. (GW ISSN 0344-5208) **3261**
Labo - Pharma Problems et Techniques *see* S T P Pharma Sciences **3742**
Labor. (IT ISSN 0023-6489) **985**
Labor. *see* Lao Dong **987**
Labor *see* Labor Press and Information **2585**
Labor. *see* Lao Dong **2586**
Labor (Year). (BE) **985, 4066**
Labor and Development. (TG) **985**
▼Labor and Employment in Connecticut. (US) **985, 2643**
▼Labor & Employment in Massachusetts. (US) **985, 2643**
Labor and Employment in New York. (US) **985, 2643**
Labor & Employment Law. (US ISSN 0193-5739) **985, 2643**
▼Labor and Employment Law Anthology. (US ISSN 0892-4449) **2643, 2585**
Labor and Investments. (US) **2585, 953**
Labor and Working Class History Newsletter *see* International Labor and Working Class History **983**
Labor Arbitration and Dispute Settlements. (US) **2643**
Labor Arbitration Awards. (US ISSN 0023-6500) **985**
Labor Arbitration in Government. (US ISSN 0047-3839) **985**
Labor College Review. (AT) **3903**
Labor Force and Nonagricultural Employment Estimates. (US) **726, 985, 4577**
Labor Force in Idaho. (US) **985**
Labor Force in Idaho and Basic Economic Data for Idaho *see* Basic Economic Data for Idaho **847**
Labor Force in Idaho and Basic Economic Data for Idaho *see* Labor Force in Idaho **985**
Labor Herald. (US) **985**
Labor History. (US ISSN 0023-656X) **985**
Labor in Perspective *see* Labor and Development **985**
Labor Law Institute. (US) **2643, 985**
Labor Law Journal. (US ISSN 0023-6586) **2643, 985**
Labor Law Reports. (US) **2643, 2585**
Labor Law Reports: Summary. (US) **985, 2643**
Labor Lawyer. (US ISSN 8756-2995) **2643**
Labor Leader. (US ISSN 0023-6594) **2585**
Labor Letter. (US) **985, 2643**
Labor - Management Relations Analysis.(US ISSN 1043-5506) **985**
Labor Market and Labor Market Policy. *see* Arbejdsmarkedet og Arbejdsmarkedspolotik **5137**
Labor-Medizin. (GW) **3261**
Labor News. (US ISSN 1053-7023) **985**
Labor Newsletter. (US) **986**
Labor Notes. (US ISSN 0275-4452) **986**
Labor Occupational Health Program Monitor. (US) **3618**
Labor Organization Newsletter *see* Labor Newsletter **986**
The Labor Page. (US) **2585**
Labor Paper. (US) **986, 2585**
Labor Policy and Practice *see* B N A Policy and Practice Series **1063**
Labor Press and Information. (BE) **2585**
Labor Rates for the Construction Industry *see* Means Labor Rates for the Construction Industry **624**
Labor Relations and Employment *see* Labor & Employment Law **985**
Labor Relations and Public Policy Series. (US) **986**

Labor Relations Forms and Agreements.(US ISSN 0731-4612) **1067, 753**
Labor Relations Guide *see* Guide to Employment Law and Regulation **980**
Labor Relations in Maine. (US) **986, 2643**
Labor Relations Reference Manual. (US ISSN 1043-5506) **986**
Labor Relations Reporter *see* B N A Labor Relations Reporter **972**
Labor Relations Today. (US) **986**
Labor Relations Week. (US ISSN 0891-4141) **986**
Labor Research Association Economic Notes *see* L R A's Economic Notes **985**
Labor Research Report (Albany) *see* New York (State) Department of Labor. Division of Research and Statistics. Labor Research Report **731**
Labor Research Review. (US) **986**
Labor Safety. *see* Munkavedelem **3619**
Labor Science of China. *see* Zhongguo Laodong Kexue **998**
Labor Service Bulletin. *see* Laodong Fuwu Tongxun **1067**
Labor Studies Journal. (US ISSN 0160-449X) **986**
Labor Times. (AT ISSN 0819-9825) **3903**
Labor Today. (US ISSN 0023-6640) **2586**
Labor Trade Action *see* Labor (Year) **985**
Labor Trends. (US) **986, 1067**
Labor Unity. (US ISSN 0271-5848) **2586**
Labor Voice. (AT) **3903**
Labor World. (US ISSN 0023-6667) **2586**
Laboratoire Central des Industries Electriques Informations *see* L C I E Informations **1902**
Laboratoires d'Etudes et de Recherches Synthelabo Monograph Series *see* L E R S Monograph Series **3121**
Laboratoires des Ponts et Chaussees. Bulletin de Liaison *see* France. Laboratoires des Ponts et Chaussees. Bulletin de Liaison **1865**
Laboratoriet *see* Tidskriften Laboratoriet **3263**
†Laboratorio. (SP ISSN 0023-6691) **5225**
Laboratorio *see* Il Nuovo Laboratorio **5250**
Laboratorio di Scienze dell'Uomo. (IT) **4442**
Laboratorio di Tecnologia della Pesca. Quaderni *see* Istituto Ricerche Pesca Marittima. Quaderni **2044**
Laboratorio Musica. (IT) **3561**
Laboratorio Nacional de Engeharia Civil. Boletim de Informacao Tecnica. (PO ISSN 0870-9149) **1871**
Laboratorios de Especialidades y Control. (MX) **3261**
Laboratorium Praktijk/Laboratory Magazine. (NE) **3261, 2523**
Laboratoriums Medizin. (GW ISSN 0342-3026) **3261**
Laboratornoe Delo/Laboratory Technique. (RU ISSN 0023-6748) **3121, 3261**
†Laboratory and Research Methods in Biology and Medicine. (US ISSN 0160-8584) **5225**
Laboratory Animal Science. (US ISSN 0023-6764) **3261**
Laboratory Animals. (UK ISSN 0023-6772) **3261**
Laboratory Animals. Buyers Guide. (UK) **3261**
Laboratory Buyers Guide. (CN) **3261**
Laboratory Computer Letter. (US ISSN 0738-8772) **3226, 1461, 1470**
Laboratory Digest (Washington). (US) **1183**
Laboratory Equipment. (US ISSN 0023-6810) **3261**
Laboratory Equipment Digest. (UK ISSN 0023-6829) **3261**
Laboratory Equipment Directory. (UK ISSN 0141-8963) **2523**

LABOUR EDUCATION 6381

Laboratory Equipment Directory and Buyers Guide *see* Laboratory Equipment Directory **2523**
†Laboratory Equipment Index. (UK ISSN 0308-8367) **5225**
†Laboratory Equipment International. (UK) **5225**
Laboratory Hazards Bulletin. (UK ISSN 0261-2917) **3618**
†Laboratory Immunology. (US) **5225**
▼Laboratory Information Management. (NE ISSN 0925-5281) **3261, 2768**
Laboratory Investigation. (US ISSN 0023-6837) **3261**
Laboratory Magazine. *see* Laboratorium Praktijk **3261**
Laboratory Management *see* Diagnostics & Clinical Testing **5180**
Laboratory Marketing Spectrum Laboratory Equipment Buyers Guide *see* L M S - Laboratory Equipment Buyers Guide **3260**
Laboratory Medicine. (US ISSN 0007-5027) **3121, 3261**
▼Laboratory Medicine Abstract and Comment. (US ISSN 1050-9658) **3177, 3261**
Laboratory Microcomputer. (UK ISSN 0262-2955) **1461**
Laboratory News. (AT) **3261**
Laboratory News. (UK ISSN 0266-7169) **3261**
†Laboratory Planning & Design. (US ISSN 1040-7677) **5225**
Laboratory Practice. (UK ISSN 0023-6853) **3261, 4322**
Laboratory Product News. (CN ISSN 0047-3855) **3261**
Laboratory Regulation Manual. (US) **3262, 2643**
▼Laboratory Regulation News. (US ISSN 1048-0706) **3262, 2643**
Laboratory Robotics and Automation. (GW ISSN 0895-7533) **1414**
Laboratory Technique. *see* Laboratornoe Delo **3121**
Laboratory Techniques in Biochemistry and Molecular Biology. (NE ISSN 0075-7535) **479, 446, 3262**
Laboratory Times. (US) **3262**
▼Laboratory Yellow Pages. (CN) **1142, 3262**
Laboreo. (SP ISSN 0210-1718) **163**
Laborer. (US ISSN 0023-6888) **2586**
Labores del Hogar. (SP ISSN 0047-3863) **3591**
LaborPraxis. (GW ISSN 0344-1733) **3262**
Labor's Heritage. (US ISSN 1041-5904) **986**
Laborscope. (SZ) **3262**
Labour. (UA) **986**
Labour/Travail. (CN ISSN 0700-3862) **986, 2412, 2586**
Labour Advocate. (GY) **986**
Labour and Development. *see* Kar va Tawsi'ah **4411**
Labour and Industrial Cases. (II) **986, 2643**
Labour & Ireland. (UK ISSN 0260-6615) **3903**
Labour and National Insurance/Avoda Ubituach Leumi. (IS ISSN 0005-2299) **986, 2536**
†Labour and Society. (UN ISSN 0378-5408) **5225**
Labour & Trade Union Review. (UK ISSN 0953-3494) **2586, 3903**
Labour Arbitration. (CN ISSN 0821-2635) **2643, 2586**
Labour Arbitration Cases. (CN ISSN 0023-690X) **986**
Labour Bulletin. (II) **986**
Labour Bulletin of Current Awareness *see* India. Ministry of Labour. Bulletin of Current Awareness **721**
Labour, Capital and Society/Travail, Capital et Societe. (CN ISSN 0706-1706) **4378**
Labour Chronicle. (II) **986**
Labour Code of Pakistan. (PK) **986**
Labour Comment (Cork). (IE ISSN 0790-1712) **3903**
Labour Directory (Victoria) *see* B.C. Labour Directory **972**
Labour Education. (UN ISSN 0378-5467) **986, 1685**

6382 LABOUR FOCUS

Labour Focus on Eastern Europe. (UK) 986
Labour Force and Migration Survey. (CY) 3993, 4577
Labour Force Situation in Indonesia: Preliminary Figures/Keadaan Angkatan Kerja di Indonesia: Angka Sementara. (IO) 726, 4577
Labour Force Survey. (CN) 726
The Labour Force, Victoria. (AT ISSN 1030-536X) 726, 4577
Labour Gazette. (II ISSN 0023-6934) 986
Labour History. (AT ISSN 0023-6942) 986, 2316
Labour History Review. (UK ISSN 0961-5652) 986, 2316
Labour in Israel. (IS ISSN 0023-6969) 2586
Labour in the Public Sector Undertakings: Basic Information. (II ISSN 0377-077X) 986
Labour Law. see Rodo Ho 993
†Labour Law Cases. (PK) 5225
†Labour Law in New Zealand. (AT) 5225
Labour Law Journal. (II ISSN 0023-6977) 2643, 987
Labour Legislation in Nova Scotia. (CN ISSN 0383-3372) 987, 2643
Labour-Management Relations Series. (UN ISSN 0538-8325) 987
Labour Organizations in Nova Scotia. (CN ISSN 0383-3437) 2586
Labour Party. Campaign Briefing. (UK ISSN 0260-3810) 3903
Labour Research. (UK ISSN 0023-7000) 987
Labour Research Department. Fact Service. (UK ISSN 0047-388X) 987
Labour Resourcer. (AT ISSN 0725-0290) 987, 872, 2586, 3618
†Labour Review. (UK ISSN 0140-1270) 5225
Labour Safety in Industry. see Bezopasnost' Truda v Promyshlennosti 3615
Labour Standards in Canada - Normes du Travail au Canada see Employment Standards Legislation in Canada 978
Labour Statistics. (CY) 726
Labour Statistics Report see Labour Statistics 726
Labour Student. (UK) 3904
Labour Topics/Sujets se Rapportant au Travail. (CN ISSN 0704-8874) 987, 726
Labour World. (II ISSN 0023-7035) 987
Labrador Quarterly. (US) 3711
Labrador Retriever Club of Wales. Yearbook. (UK ISSN 0260-5627) 3711
Labranza. (SP) 220
Labrys. (IT) 4187
Labyrinth. (US) 4846
†Labyrinth. (AT ISSN 0155-2856) 5225
Labyrinthos. (IT) 333, 302, 2316, 2931
Lace & Crafts. (US) 3591
Lace Crafts Quarterly see Lace & Crafts 3591
Lacerta. (NE ISSN 0023-7051) 587
Lacito Documents Afrique. (FR ISSN 0754-2445) 2823, 243
Lacito Documents Asie - Austronesie. (FR ISSN 0751-4875) 2823, 243
Lacito Documents Eurasie. (FR ISSN 0751-4883) 2823, 243
Lackawanna Jurist. (US ISSN 0023-7078) 2643
Lackawanna - Wayne - Pike - Susquehanna Farm & Home News. (US ISSN 0093-4909) 104
Lacombe News see Canadian Lacombe Breeders Association. Newsletter 214
▼Lacoonte. (IT) 3771
Lacrosse. (US ISSN 0194-7893) 4478
Lacrosse see Lacrossetalk 4507
Lacrossetalk. (UK ISSN 0023-7086) 4507
Lacsa's World. (US) 3964

†Lactation Review. (US ISSN 0362-3173) 5225
Lactuca. (US ISSN 0896-8705) 2996
Lada. (BU) 1292
Lada'at. (IS ISSN 0023-7094) 1259, 4322
Ladenbau see Architektur und Ladenbau 294
Ladies Birthday Almanac. (US) 2228
Ladies Home Journal (Inkprint Edition). (US ISSN 0023-7124) 4846, 2448
▼Ladies' Home Journal Parent's Digest.(US) 4846, 2448
Ladies Magazine/Shih Nu Tsa Chih. (US) 1292
Lading Meizhou Yanjiu/Latin American Studies. (CC) 4378, 2412
Ladinia. (IT) 2011
LADOC see L A D O C 3903
Ladue Public Schools Bulletin. (US ISSN 0023-7140) 1645
Ladugaardsfoermannen. (SW ISSN 0023-7159) 220
The Lady. (TH) 373
Lady. (UK ISSN 0023-7167) 2194
Lady see Lady International 4846
Lady. (US) 4846
Lady Golfer's Handbook. (UK) 4507
Lady International. (GW ISSN 0343-3366) 4846
Lady Moda. (IT) 1292
▼Ladybug. (US ISSN 1051-4961) 1259
Lady's Circle. (US ISSN 0023-7191) 4846
Lady's Circle Patchwork Quilts. (US) 3591, 355
Ladyslipper Catalog and Resource Guide of Records, Tapes, Compact Discs and Videos by Women. (US) 4846, 1385, 3513, 3561
Ladysmith Directory. (SA ISSN 0378-9268) 1142
Laegeforeningens Medicinfortegnelse. (DK ISSN 0106-1275) 3733
Laegeforeningens Vejviser. (DK) 3121
Laegekredsforeningen Fyns Amt see Fynske Laeger 3100
Laegemiddelkataloget. (DK ISSN 0105-287X) 3733
Laegen. (DK) 3121
Laegestillinger og Sengepladser paa Institutioner. (DK ISSN 0107-1165) 2467
Laekartidningen. (SW ISSN 0023-7205) 3121
Laeknabladid. (IC ISSN 0023-7213) 3121
Laenderbank Boerse see Laenderbank Boerse Aktuell 953
Laenderbank Boerse Aktuell. (AU) 953
Laengden af Offentlige Veje. (DK ISSN 0109-6044) 4719
Laeraren/Teacher. (FI ISSN 0356-7842) 1645
Laerarhoegskolan i Moelndal. Pedagogiska Institutionen. Rapport see Goeteborgs Universitet. Institutionen foer Praktisk Pedagogik. Rapport 1750
Laerarinnornas Missionsfoerening. Meddelande till L M F. see Laerarnas Missionsfoerening. Meddelande till L M F 4187
Laerarnas Missionsfoerening. Meddelande till L M F. (SW ISSN 0345-7842) 4187
Laerarnas Tidning. (SW ISSN 1101-2633) 1645
Laerartidningen - Svensk Skoltidning see Laerarnas Tidning 1645
Laes om. (DK ISSN 0107-4636) 1247
Lafayette Business Digest. (US ISSN 1048-2822) 872
Lafayette Magazine. (US) 1316
Laff-Letter. (US) 2228
Lag och Avtal. (SW ISSN 0349-7143) 987, 2643
Lagebericht aus Australien. (GW) 3964, 872
†Lagena. (VE ISSN 0023-7256) 5225
Lagertechnik. (GW) 1044
Lagniappe Letter. (US ISSN 1040-3175) 916, 789
Lagniappe Quarterly Monitor. (US ISSN 1040-3183) 932

Lagniappe Quarterly Report see Lagniappe Quarterly Monitor 932
Lago. (VE ISSN 0047-3898) 1490
Lagos Education Review. (NG ISSN 0331-9237) 1645
Lagos Librarian. (NR ISSN 0047-3901) 2768
Lagos State Today. (NR) 2212
Lagos Weekend. (NR ISSN 0023-7272) 2212
Lagrimal Trifurca. (AG ISSN 0023-7280) 2931, 2996
Laguna Magazine see California Riviera Magazine 2222
Lahabili Tsugu. (GH) 2192
Lahaina News. (US) 2228
Lahavot. (IS) 2203
Lahore Chamber of Commerce & Industry. Weekly Chamber Circular. (PK) 818
Lai Rang Ying Nang. see Yunnan Huabao 2183
Laienspieler see Spiel und Theater 4638
Laiks. (US) 2011
Laings' Review of Private Healthcare (Year). (UK ISSN 0953-9050) 1143, 2467
La'Inyan. (US) 2011
†Lair. (US) 5225
Laisha/For Women. (IS) 4846
▼Laissez - Faire. (UK ISSN 0963-6633) 3964
Laissez Faire Books Free Market Catalog. (US) 3904
Laissez Faire Free Market Catalog see Laissez Faire Books Free Market Catalog 3904
Le Lait. (FR ISSN 0023-7302) 201, 446
Lait et Nous. (BE ISSN 0770-2515) 201
Lakaskultura. (HU ISSN 0047-391X) 2553
Lake and Reservoir Management. (US) 4826
Lake Biwa Study Monographs. (JA ISSN 0289-3363) 1599
Lake Carriers' Association. Annual Report. (US ISSN 0075-7748) 4730
Lake Chelan History Notes. (US) 2412
▼Lake County Heritage. (US) 2412
†Lake County Historical Quarterly. (US) 5225
▼Lake County Marketing Directory. (US) 1143
Lake Effect. (US ISSN 0887-4492) 2871, 2228
Lake Life Magazine. (US) 4525
Lake Michigan Sailing see Sailing 4528
Lake Oconee Living see Lake Oconee Magazine 2228
Lake Oconee Magazine. (US) 2228
Lake Science. see Hubo Kexue 1545
†Lake Street Review. (US ISSN 0889-6410) 5225
Lake Superior Magazine. (US ISSN 0890-3050) 2412, 3793, 4774
Lake Superior Port Cities see Lake Superior Magazine 2412
Lakeland Boating. (US ISSN 0744-9194) 4525, 4478
Lakeland Dialect. (UK) 2823
Lakelander. (US) 3711
Lakewoods Astrological Guides. (US) 359
Lakimies. (FI ISSN 0023-7353) 2643
Lakimiesuutiset/Juristnytt. (FI ISSN 0023-7361) 2643
Lakokrasochnye Materialy i ikh Primenenie. (RU ISSN 0023-737X) 3654
Lakonika. (GR) 2372
Lakroan'i Madagasikara. (MG) 4267
Lal-Baugh. (II ISSN 0023-7388) 2133
Lalana. (TH) 2220
Lalbhai Dalpatbhai Institute of Indology. Publications. (II) 3640
Lalit Kala. (II ISSN 0458-6506) 333
Lalit Kala Contemporary. (II ISSN 0023-7396) 333
Lalita see Priya 3516
LaLoggia's Special Situation Report and Stock Market Forecast. (US) 953
Lamalif. (MR) 2871

Lamar Journal of the Humanities. (US ISSN 0275-410X) 2510
Lamar Lecture Series. (US ISSN 0075-7772) 2316, 2931
Lamaze Parents' Magazine. (US) 3294
Lambda. (CN) 1316
Lambda Alpha Journal of Man. (US ISSN 0047-3928) 243
Lambda Book Report. (US ISSN 1048-9487) 2454, 2871, 4131
Lambda Financial Advisor. (US) 953, 2454
Lambda Rising Book Report see Lambda Book Report 2454
Lambda Rising News. (US) 2454
Lambda Update. (US) 2454, 2643
Lambert's Worldwide Government Directory see Worldwide Government Directory 4078
Lamborghini Review. (IT) 4694
Lamb's Pastures. (US ISSN 0883-7708) 2157
Lambton Leader. (CN) 1316
Lamco News. (LB) 3487
Lamed Leshonkha. (IS ISSN 0333-9688) 2823
Lamiera. (IT ISSN 0391-5891) 3412
Lammergeyer. (SA ISSN 0075-7780) 1490
Lamp. (AT ISSN 0047-3936) 3281
Lamp (New York). (US ISSN 0023-7418) 3691, 1792
Lampada see Nursing Standard 3284
Lampas. (NE) 2931
Lampetten see Lys 1902
LampPost. (US) 4066
Lamy Associations. (FR) 1116
Lamy Contrats Internationaux. (FR) 916, 2726
Lamy - Dehove. (FR) 2076
Lamy Droit Commercial. (FR) 2710, 677
Lamy Droit de l'Informatique. (FR) 2643, 4603
Lamy Droit du Financement. (FR) 789
Lamy Droit Economique. (FR) 2643, 677
Lamy Financements des Entreprises. (FR) 789
Lamy Fiscal. (FR) 2643, 789
Lamy Protection Sociale. (FR) 2710, 677
Lamy Social. (FR) 2643, 677
Lamy Societe Commerciales. (FR) 2711, 789
Lamy Societes Commerciales - Formulaire. S.A. a Conseil d'Administration. (FR) 1017
Lamy Societes Commerciales - Formulaire. S.A. a Directoire. (FR) 1017
Lamy Societes Commerciales - Formulaire. S.A.R.L. (FR) 1017
Lamy Societes Commerciales - Formulaire. Societes autres que S.A.R.L. et S.A. Regroupements de Societes. (FR) 1017
Lamy Transport Tome 1. (FR) 2726, 2735, 4652
Lamy Transport Tome 2. (FR) 2726, 2735, 4652
Lamy Transport Tome 3. (FR) 2726, 2735, 4652
Lan Dun. (CC) 2643
LAN Technology see L A N Technology 1461
Lancashire and Cheshire Antiquarian Society. Newsletter. (UK) 2372
Lancashire Constabulary Journal. (UK) 1517
Lancashire Dialect Society. Journal. (UK ISSN 0075-7799) 2823
Lancashire Farmer. (UK) 104
Lancashire Life. (UK ISSN 0023-7469) 2194
Lancashire Magazine. (UK) 2194
Lancaster County Biz. (US) 677
Lancaster County Connections. (US ISSN 0748-1071) 2157
Lancaster County Historical Society. Journal. (US ISSN 0023-7477) 2412, 2157
Lancaster Diocesan Directory. (UK) 4267
Lancaster Farming. (US ISSN 0023-7485) 104
Lancaster Independent Press. (US) 2871

Lance. (CN ISSN 0023-7493) **1316**, 2871
Lancet. (UK ISSN 0140-6736) **3121**
Lancet (Edicion Espanola). (SP ISSN 0212-0151) **3121**
Lancet (Edition Francaise). (FR ISSN 0923-7577) **3121**
Lancet (Edizione Italiana). (IT ISSN 0393-0637) **3121**
Lancet (North American Edition). (US ISSN 0099-5355) **3121**
Lancia Enthusiast. (US) **4694**
Lanciana. (US ISSN 0023-7515) **4694**
Lancillotto e Nausica. (IT) **4478**
Lancz Letter. (US) **953**
Land. (AT ISSN 0023-7523) **104**
Land. (SW ISSN 0023-7531) **104**
The Land. (US) **104**
Land. see Karka **2490**
Land Aktuell. (GW ISSN 0340-7837) **3904**, 104, 4267
Land an der Miesa. (GW) **2372**, 2157
Land and Liberty. (UK ISSN 0023-7574) **4151**, 1100
Land and Life. (US) **2011**, 2203, 4412
Land and Minerals Surveying. (UK ISSN 0265-4210) **1871**, 3487
Land and Property-Auctions see Valuer **4159**
Land and Value. see Mekarkaiin Vearcham **4152**
Land & Water. (US ISSN 0192-9453) **1490**, 1962
Land and Water Conservation Fund Grants Manual. (US) **1490**, 4549
Land and Water Development see Land & Water **1490**
Land and Water Law Review. (US ISSN 0023-7612) **2643**, 2735
Land Bank Journal. (II) **789**
Land Compensation Reports. (CN ISSN 0380-4208) **2643**
Land-Consumerpart. (SW) **104**
Land Degradation and Rehabilitation. (UK ISSN 0898-5812) **1546**
Land Development Law Reporter. (US ISSN 0739-6376) **4151**, 2643
Land Development Studies see Journal of Research Property **2490**
Land Economics. (US ISSN 0023-7639) **153**, 1962
Land Economics Monographs. (US ISSN 0075-7837) **153**
Land- en Tuinbouwonderwijs. (NE) **104**
Land-Konsumentdelen see Land-Consumerpart **104**
†Land - L E A F. (US) **5225**
Land Lantbruk. (SW) **104**
Land Letter. (US ISSN 0890-7625) **1491**
Land Line Magazine. (US ISSN 0279-6503) **4745**
Land Link. (AT) **1491**, 1962
Land Management and Environmental Law Report. (UK) **2643**, 1962
▼Land O'Lakes Collection of Classic Recipes Cookbook. (US) **2448**
†Land Opportunity Review. (US ISSN 0889-0498) **5225**
Land Reform, Land Settlement and Cooperatives/Reforme Agraire, Colonisation et Cooperatives Agricoles/Reforma Agraria, Colonizacion y Cooperativas. (UN ISSN 0047-3952) **153**, 4442
Land Rig Newsletter. (US) **3691**
Land Rights News. (AT) **3944**, 4066
Land Tenure Center. Paper. (US ISSN 0084-0793) **153**
Land Tenure Center. Research Paper. (US ISSN 0084-0815) **153**
Land un Sproch. see Cahiers du Bilinguisme **2808**
Der Land- und Forstwirtschaftliche Betrieb. (AU ISSN 0023-7558) **2103**
Land Use & Environment Law Review. (US ISSN 0192-8309) **1962**
Land Use Digest. (US ISSN 0023-768X) **2491**
▼Land Use Forum. (US ISSN 1058-7012) **2643**, 4151
Land Use Law and Zoning Digest. (US ISSN 0094-7598) **4151**, 2643
Land Use Law Report. (US) **2491**, 2643

†Land Use Planning. (CN) **5225**
Land Use Planning Report see Land Use Law Report **2491**
Land Use Policy. (UK ISSN 0264-8377) **2491**
Land van Valkenburg. (NE ISSN 0023-7698) **2211**
Land Worker see Landworker **105**
Landas. (PH ISSN 0116-4856) **4187**
Landbauforschung Voelkenrode. (GW ISSN 0458-6859) **184**, 153
Landbode. (BE) **104**
Landbode (Groningen). (NE) **104**
Landbode (The Hague). (NE ISSN 0023-7736) **104**
Landboforeningernes Driftsoekonomiske Virksomhed, Regnskabsresultater, Kalenderaar see Regnskabsstatistik-Landbrug **157**
Landbohistorisk Tidsskrift. (DK) **2372**, 104
Landbote. (AU ISSN 0023-7744) **104**, 2103
Landbote. (GW) **2572**
Landbouw-Economisch Bericht. (NE ISSN 0169-3255) **153**
Landbouw-Economisch Instituut. Maandblad Prijsstatistiek. (NE ISSN 0166-8072) **153**
Landbouw-Economisch Instituut. Prijsstatistiek see Landbouw-Economisch Instituut. Maandblad Prijsstatistiek **153**
Landbouw Service. see Agro-Service **73**
Landbouwcijfers. (NE ISSN 0168-4019) **139**
Landbouwdocumentatie see Agriloper **73**
Landbouweekblad. (SA ISSN 0023-7779) **104**
Landbouwleven see Sillon Belge **119**
†Landbouwmaand. (NE) **5225**
Landbouwmechanisatie. (NE ISSN 0023-7795) **163**
Landbouwproefstation Suriname. Jaarverslag/Agricultural Experiment Station Suriname. Annual Report. (SR) **104**
Landbovirke. (DK) **104**
Landbrug Fyn. (DK ISSN 0108-2744) **104**
Landbrugets Maskinoversigt. (DK ISSN 0107-461X) **163**
Landbrugets Oekonomi see Denmark. Jordbrugsoekonomiske Institut. Landbrugets Oekonomi **658**
Landbrugets Organisationshaandbog. (DK ISSN 0108-4003) **104**
Landbrugets Samraad for Forskning og Forsoeg. Kortlaegning see Denmark. Landbrugsministeriet, Forskningssekretariatet, Kortlaegning **87**
Landbrugets Samraad for Forskning og Forsoeg. Ramme planer see Denmark. Landbrugsministeriet, Forskningssekretariatet, Rammeplaner **87**
Landbrugsaarbog. (DK ISSN 0302-4946) **104**
Landbrugseksporten. (DK ISSN 0106-3812) **916**
Landbrugsmagasinet. (DK) **104**
Landbrugsregnskaber see Driftsoekonomi **659**
Landbrugsregnskabsstatistik see Denmark. Statens Jordbrugsoekonomiske Institut. Serie A: Landbrugets Regnskabsstatistik **149**
Landbrukets Aarbok. Jordbruk, Hagebruk, Skogbruk. (NO ISSN 0075-7853) **2103**, 104
Landbrukstidende. (NO ISSN 0023-7833) **104**
Landdros. see Magistrate **2651**
Landeigenaar. (NE) **4151**
Landelijke Vereniging van Maatschappelijk Werkers Nieuws see L V M W Nieuws **4411**
Lander's Herald. (US) **2228**
†Landers Landing. (US ISSN 0739-134X) **5226**
Landes-Trost. (GW) **2190**
Landesamtsblatt fuer das Burgenland. (AU ISSN 0023-7876) **4066**
Landesgesetzblatt fuer das Land Salzburg. (AU ISSN 0023-7884) **4089**

Landesgewerbeanstalt Bayern Rundschau see L G A Rundschau **1080**
Landeshauptstadt Innsbruck. Statistischer Vierteljahresbericht. (AU) **4577**
Landeshauptstadt Kiel. Vierteljahresberichte. (GW) **4081**
Landeshauptstadt Stuttgart. Amtsblatt. (GW) **4066**
Landesindex der Konsumentenpreise/L'Indice Suisse des Prix a la Consommation. (SZ) **726**
Landesinnung der Bayerischen Toepfer. Mitteilungen. (GW) **1165**
Landeskonservator Rheinland. Arbeitsheft. (GW) **302**
Landeskunde von Niederoesterreich. Jahrbuch. (AU) **2372**
Landeskundliche Luftbildauswertung im Mitteleuropaeischen Raum see Fernerkundung in Raumordung und Stadtebau **2247**
Landeskundliche Vierteljahrsblaetter. (GW ISSN 0458-6905) **2373**
Landesmuseum fuer Kaernten. Buchreihe. (AU ISSN 0007-280X) **3526**, 2316, 3600
Landesmuseum fuer Naturkunde zu Muenster in Westfalen. Abhandlungen see Westfaelischen Museum fuer Naturkunde. Abhandlungen **4352**
Landesmuseum fuer Vorgeschichte, Dresden. Kleine Schriften. (GW ISSN 0232-5446) **2316**
Landesmuseum fuer Vorgeschichte, Dresden. Veroeffentlichungen. (GW ISSN 0070-7201) **3526**, 2373
Landesmuseum fuer Vorgeschichte, Halle. Veroeffentlichungen. (GW ISSN 0072-940X) **3526**, 2373
Landesmuseum Joanneum. Abteilung fuer Botanik. Mitteilungen. (AU) **508**
Landesmuseum Joanneum. Abteilung fuer Geologie, Palaeontologie und Bergbau. Mitteilungen see Landesmuseum Joanneum. Abteilung fuer Geologie und Palaeontologie. Mitteilungen **3658**
Landesmuseum Joanneum. Abteilung fuer Geologie und Palaeontologie. Mitteilungen. (AU) **3658**, 1571, 3487
Landesmuseum Joanneum. Abteilung fuer Zoologie. Mitteilungen. (AU) **587**
Landesverband der Tonkuenstler und Musiklehrer. Mitteilungsblatt. (GW ISSN 0047-3979) **3561**
Landesverband des Bayerischen Gross- und Aussenhandels Nachrichten see L G A Nachrichten **837**
Landesverband des Hotel- und Gaststaettengewerbes in Baden-Wuerttemberg. Mitteilungen. (GW) **2477**
Landesverband des Westfalisch - Lippischen Einzelhandels. Einzelhandels - Report. (GW) **837**
Landesverbander Schausteller und der Markkaufleute Niedersachsen - Nord und Bremen. Marktbericht. (GW) **677**
Landesverein fuer Hoehlenkunde in der Steiermark. Mitteilungen. (AU) **1571**
Landesversicherungsanstalt Hessen. Nachrichten. (GW ISSN 0023-7922) **2536**
Landesversicherungsanstalt Wuerttemberg. Mitteilungen. (GW ISSN 0340-3270) **4412**
Landeswohlfahrtsverband Hessen Info see L W V Info **4411**
Landeszentralbank in Hessen. Vierteljahresberichte. (GW) **789**
Landfall. (NZ ISSN 0023-7930) **2871**
Landfrauen Taschenkalender. (GW) **153**
Landinspektoeren. (DK ISSN 0105-4570) **2255**
Landis and Gyr Review see Landis und Gyr Mitteilungen **5226**
†Landis und Gyr Mitteilungen. (SZ ISSN 0023-7949) **5226**
Landjugend. (AU ISSN 0023-7957) **1259**
Der Landkreis. (GW ISSN 0342-2259) **2491**, 4066

Landkreis Kronach. Amtsblatt see Kreisamtsblatt des Landkreises und Landratsamtes Kronach **4089**
Landkreises Birkenfeld. Heimatkalender.(GW ISSN 0174-4631) **2373**
Landline in Australia. (AT ISSN 0310-320X) **4151**, 872, 2491
Landlord Remedies in Florida. (US) **2644**, 4151
Landlord - Tenant Relations Report. (US ISSN 1050-3196) **2491**
Landlord vs Tenant - N Y C. (US ISSN 0883-0746) **4151**, 2644
Landman see Mielies (Bothaville) **107**
Landmarc see Coal Local **3481**
Landmark. (CN ISSN 0843-459X) **2133**
The Landmark (Hartford). (US) **258**, 302
Landmark (New Berlin). (US ISSN 0458-6972) **2412**
Landmark Briefs and Arguments of the Supreme Court of the United States: Constitutional Law. Supplement. (US) **2706**
▼Landmark Studies. (US ISSN 1053-931X) **277**, 4187
†Landmarks. (CN ISSN 0715-1489) **5226**
Landmarks Observer. (US) **2412**, 302
Landmaschinen - Handwerk - Handel. (AU ISSN 0023-7973) **163**
Landmaschinen Rundschau. (GW ISSN 0047-3995) **163**
Landoekonomisk Aarbog see Landbrugsaarbog **104**
Landoekonomisk Oversigt. (DK ISSN 0107-7163) **139**
Landolt-Boernstein Numerical Data and Functional Relationships in Science and Technology. New Series. see Landolt-Boernstein, Zahlenwerte und Funktionen aus Naturwissenschaften und Technik. Neue Serie. Group 1: Nuclear Physics **3848**
Landolt-Boernstein, Zahlenwerte und Funktionen aus Naturwissenschaften und Technik. Neue Serie. Group 1: Nuclear Physics/Landolt-Boernstein Numerical Data and Functional Relationships in Science and Technology. New Series. (US ISSN 0075-7888) **3848**
Landolt-Boernstein, Zahlenwerte und Funktionen aus Naturwissenschaften und Technik. Neue Serie. Group 2: Atomic Physics. (US ISSN 0075-7918) **3848**
Landolt-Boernstein, Zahlenwerte und Funktionen aus Naturwissenschaften und Technik. Neue Serie. Group 3: Crystal Physics. (US ISSN 0075-787X) **3823**, 1211
Landolt-Boernstein, Zahlenwerte und Funktionen aus Naturwissenschaften und Technik. Neue Serie. Group 4: Macroscopic and Technical Properties of Matter. (US ISSN 0075-7926) **4603**
Landolt-Boernstein, Zahlenwerte und Funktionen aus Naturwissenschaften und Technik. Neue Serie. Group 5: Geophysics. (US ISSN 0075-790X) **1592**
Landolt-Boernstein, Zahlenwerte und Funktionen aus Naturwissenschaften und Technik. Neue Serie. Group 6: Astronomy. (US ISSN 0075-7896) **366**
Landowner. (US) **4151**
Landpostmagazin. (GW) **104**
Lands Organisation Ungdoms Blad see L O - Ungdoms Blad **4442**
Landsbladet. (DK ISSN 0455-2741) **104**
Landsbrugsraadets Meddelelser see Raadsnyt **156**
Landscape. (US ISSN 0023-8023) **2255**, 3984
Landscape & Garden Contractor. (UK) **2133**
Landscape & Irrigation. (US ISSN 0745-3795) **184**, 4826
Landscape and Turf Industry see Southern Golf - Landscape & Resort Management **2133**
Landscape and Urban Planning. (NE ISSN 0169-2046) **1491**, 1962

LANDSCAPE ARCHITECTURAL

Landscape Architectural Review/Revue d'Architecture de Paysage. (CN ISSN 0228-6963) **302**, 1491
Landscape Architecture. (US ISSN 0023-8031) **302**, 2133
Landscape Architecture News Digest. (US ISSN 0023-754X) **302**
Landscape Architecture Technical Information Series. (US ISSN 0195-5764) **302**
Landscape Australia. (AT ISSN 0310-9011) **2133**
Landscape Contractor. (US ISSN 0194-7257) **2133**, 302
Landscape Design. (UK ISSN 0020-2908) **302**, 2133
Landscape Design. (US) **2133**
Landscape Ecology. (NE ISSN 0921-2973) **1962**
Landscape History. (UK ISSN 0143-3768) **2373**, 104, 302
Landscape Industry International. (UK ISSN 0266-9455) **2133**
Landscape Issues. (UK ISSN 0265-9786) **302**
Landscape Journal. (US ISSN 0277-2426) **302**, 2133
Landscape Management. (US) **184**
Landscape Management Golf Daily. (US) **2133**, 4507
Landscape Research. (UK ISSN 0142-6397) **302**, 2133
†Landscape Southern Africa. (SA) **5226**
Landscaping Homes & Gardens. (US) **2133**, 302
†Landscentralen for Undervisningsmidler. Baandcentralen. Baandkatalog. (DK ISSN 0106-7737) **5226**
Landschaft und Stadt see Naturschutz und Landschaftsplanung **303**
Landschaftsarchitektur. (GW ISSN 0323-3162) **302**
Landschaftspflege und Naturschutz in Thueringen. (GW ISSN 0323-8253) **1491**
Landschaftsverband Rheinland Report see L V R - Report **2190**
Landschaftsverband Westfalen-Lippe see Volkskuendlichen Kommission fuer Westfalen. Schriften **2059**
Landschaftsverband Westfalen-Lippe. Mitteilungen des Landesjugendamtes.(GW ISSN 0937-7123) **4412**, 1240
†Landshavneplanbidrag. (DK ISSN 0108-7231) **5226**
Landskab. (DK ISSN 0023-8066) **2133**, 302
Landslides. see Jisuberi **1591**
Landsorganisationen i Danmark Bladet see L O Bladet **2585**
Landsorganisationen i Sverige. Yttranden till Offentlig Myndighet. (SW) **2586**
Landsorganisationen i Sverige Tidningen see L O Tidningen **2585**
Landssmband Idnadarmanna. Frettabref see Idnadurinn **981**
Landstingsvaerlden. (SW ISSN 0282-4485) **4089**
Landsudvalget for Fjerkrae. Meddelelse. (DK ISSN 0105-9882) **220**
Landtechnik. (GW) **184**
†Landtechnik. (GW) **5226**
Landtechnische Schriftenreihe. (AU) **104**
Das Landvolk. (GW ISSN 0023-8104) **104**
Landwehr's Who's Who in America's Restaurants see Who's Who in America's Restaurants **1782**
Landwirt see Suedtiroler Landwirt **122**
Die Landwirtschaft. (AU ISSN 0047-4010) **104**, 2103
Landwirtschaft Aktuell. (LU) **104**
Landwirtschaft Schweiz. (SZ) **104**
Landwirtschaftliche Blaetter. (AU) **104**
Landwirtschaftliche Forschung see Agribiological Research **70**
Landwirtschaftliche Literatur der Tschechoslowakei see Agricultural Literature of Czechoslovakia **132**
Landwirtschaftliche Mitteilungen. (AU) **105**
Landwirtschaftliche Wildhaltung see Wildhaltung **130**

Landwirtschaftliche Wochenblatt Westfalen-Lippe: Ausgabe B. (GW) **105**
Landwirtschaftliche Zeitschrift Rheinland. (GW ISSN 0023-8163) **105**
Landwirtschaftlicher Taschenkalender. (GW) **153**
Landwirtschaftlicher Taschenkalender fuer Weser - Ems. (GW) **105**
Landwirtschaftliches Wochenblatt Westfalen-Lippe: Ausgabe A. (GW ISSN 0342-765X) **105**
Landwirtschaftliches Zentralblatt. Abteilung 1: Landtechnik see Agroselekt. Reihe 1: Landtechnik **132**
Landwirtschaftliches Zentralblatt. Abteilung 2: Pflanzliche Produktion see Agroselekt. Reihe 2: Pflanzenprodunktion **132**
Landwirtschaftliches Zentralblatt. Abteilung 3: Tierzucht, Tierernaehrung, Fischerei see Agroselekt. Reihe 3: Tierproduktion **133**
Landwirtschaftliches Zentralblatt. Abteilung 4: Veterinaermedizin see Agroselekt. Reihe 4: Veterinaermedizin **4820**
Landwirtschaftsblatt Weser-Ems. (GW ISSN 0047-4029) **105**
Landworker. (UK) **105**, 2586
Lane Studies in Regional Government. (US) **4066**
Lanelines. (US) **4478**, 1753
Lang Classical Studies. (US ISSN 0891-4087) **1278**
Lang Van. (CN ISSN 0832-1922) **2011**
Langaa. (DK ISSN 0109-0178) **2373**
Langage et Societe. (FR ISSN 0181-4095) **4442**, 2823
Langages. (FR) **2823**
Lange Reihen der vierteljaehrlichen volkswirtschaftlichen Gesamtrechnung. (GW) **872**
Langenbecks Archiv fuer Chirurgie. (GW ISSN 0023-8236) **3381**
Langenscheidts Sprach-Illustrierte. (GW ISSN 0023-8252) **2823**, 1645
Der Langfristige Kred1t. (GW ISSN 0342-0930) **789**
Langmuir. (US ISSN 0743-7463) **1228**
Langniappe Forecasting Report (year). (US) **872**
Langouste. (FR ISSN 0991-9953) **333**
Langston Hughes Review. (US ISSN 0737-0555) **2931**, 2011
Language (Baltimore). (US ISSN 0097-8507) **2823**
▼Language Acquisition. (US ISSN 1048-9223) **2823**, 4034
Language and Cognitive Processes. (UK ISSN 0169-0965) **2823**, 4034
Language & Communication. (US ISSN 0271-5309) **2823**, 1339
Language and Computers. (NE) **2856**
Language and Culture. (JA) **2823**, 243, 2931
Language and Education. (UK ISSN 0950-0782) **2823**, 1753
▼Language and Educational Processes.(US) **1754**, 2823
▼Language and Ideology. (US) **3904**, 2823
Language and Language Behavior Abstracts see Linguistics and Language Behavior Abstracts **2855**
Language and Learning for Human Service Professions. (US) **1754**
Language and Literature. (US ISSN 1057-6037) **2823**, 2931
Language and Society/Langue et Societe. (CN ISSN 0709-7751) **4066**, 4442
Language and Speech. (UK ISSN 0023-8309) **2823**, 3121
Language and Style. (US ISSN 0023-8317) **2823**
Language Arts. (US ISSN 0360-9170) **1645**
Language Association of Eastern Africa. Journal. (KE) **2823**
Language, Culture and Curriculum. (UK ISSN 0790-8318) **2823**, 4442

Language Forum. (II ISSN 0253-9071) **2823**, 2931
Language Forum Monograph Series. (II ISSN 0254-0207) **2823**, 2931
Language in Society. (UK ISSN 0047-4045) **2823**
Language International. (NE ISSN 0923-182X) **2823**
Language Learning. (US ISSN 0023-8333) **2824**, 1645
Language Learning Journal. (UK ISSN 0957-1736) **2824**, 1645, 4461
▼Language Maintenance. (US) **2824**
Language Monthly see Electric Word **1430**
Language of Dance. (US ISSN 0888-1286) **1531**
▼Language of Defense. (US ISSN 1050-7310) **3463**
Language Problems and Language Planning. (NE ISSN 0272-2690) **2824**
Language Quarterly. (US) **2824**, 1645, 2931
Language Research/Ohak Yon'gu. (KO ISSN 0254-4474) **2824**
Language Sciences. (UK ISSN 0388-0001) **2824**, 4034, 4442
Language, Speech and Hearing Services in Schools. (US ISSN 0161-1461) **1738**, 2288
Language Teacher. (UK) **2824**, 1645
Language Teaching. (UK ISSN 0261-4448) **2855**, 16, 1677
Language Teaching & Studies. see Yuyan Jiaoxue yu Yanjiu **2853**
Language Teaching in Middle School. see Zhongxue Yuwen Jiaoxue **2854**
Language Technology see Electric Word **1430**
Language Testing. (UK ISSN 0265-5322) **2824**
Language Variation and Change. (UK ISSN 0954-3945) **2824**
▼Languages of Design. (NE ISSN 0927-3034) **2856**, 352, 1409, 2931
Langue et Cultures. (SZ ISSN 0085-2678) **2824**
Langue et Societe. see Language and Society **4066**
Langue Francaise. (FR ISSN 0023-8368) **2824**
†Langue Internationale. (FR ISSN 0085-2686) **5226**
Langues du Cameroun. (CM) **2824**
Langues et Civilisations a Tradition Orale. (FR ISSN 0240-2041) **2824**, 243
Langues et Cultures Africaines. (FR ISSN 0755-9305) **2824**, 243
Langues et Cultures du Pacifique. (FR ISSN 0750-2036) **2824**, 243
Langues et Styles. (FR ISSN 0457-1320) **2931**, 2824
Langues Modernes. (FR ISSN 0023-8376) **2824**, 2931
Langues Orientales Anciennes Philologie et Linguistique. (BE ISSN 0987-7738) **2824**
Laniera. (IT) **4621**
Lanioturdus Ornithologische Arbeitsgruppe Mitteilungen. (SX) **565**
Lanka Guardian. (CE) **2871**
Lankian Surveyor. (CE) **1829**
Lanqiu/Basketball. (CC ISSN 1000-3460) **4507**
Lansing Labor News. (US ISSN 0023-8384) **2586**
Lansky: Bibliotheksrechtliche Vorschriften. (GW ISSN 0175-6524) **2768**, 2644
Lantarbetaren. (SW) **105**
†Lantbruksnytt. (SW ISSN 0345-7001) **5226**
Lantern. (SA ISSN 0023-8422) **1645**, 333, 4322
Lantern. (US ISSN 0023-8414) **2293**
Lantern Light. (AT) **2293**
Lanternino. (IT ISSN 0393-7445) **3122**, 2316
Lantern's Core. (US ISSN 0047-4053) **2768**
Lanthanide and Actinide Research. (NE ISSN 8755-5301) **1214**
Lantmaestaren. (SW ISSN 0023-8430) **105**

Lantman och Andelsfolk. (FI ISSN 0355-0680) **105**, 831
Lantmannen. (SW ISSN 0023-8449) **105**
Lantmannen Svenskt Land see Lantmannen **105**
Lanuage Centre News. see Kielikeskusuutisia **2822**
Lao Dong/Labor. (VN) **987**
Lao Dong/Labor. (LS) **2586**
Lao Youth. see Noum Lao **1241**
Laodong Fuwu Tongxun/Labor Service Bulletin. (CC) **1067**
Laographike Kypros. (CY) **2056**
Laographikon Archeion. Epeteris see Akademia Athenon. Kentron Erevnes tis Hellenikis Laographias. Epeteris **2052**
Laomedon Review. (CN ISSN 0382-8824) **2931**
Laonian Jiaoyu/Education for the Elderly. (CC) **1685**
Laonianxue Zazhi/Journal of Gerontology. (CC) **2275**
Laoren Shijie/Old People's World. (CC) **2275**
Laoren Tiandi/Elderly World. (CC) **2275**
Laos. (LS) **4774**
Lapeer Legacy. (US ISSN 8756-7067) **2157**
Lapidary Journal. (US ISSN 0023-8457) **2437**, 2565
Lapidus Letter. (US ISSN 0742-7972) **3463**
Lapis. (GW ISSN 0176-1285) **3487**, 2565
Lapis. (IT) **4846**, 3805
Laporan Ketua Odit Negara. Kerajaan Persekutuan. (MY) **872**
Lapsen Mailma/Child's World. (FI ISSN 0786-0188) **4412**, 1240
Lapset Ja Yhteiskunta see Lapsen Mailma **4412**
Laptop Buyer's Guide. (US) **1470**
Lara Lamont. (SA ISSN 0023-8481) **3513**
Lares. (IT ISSN 0023-8503) **2056**
Lares. Biblioteca. (IT ISSN 0075-8019) **2056**
Large Animal Veterinarian. (US) **220**, 4812
▼Large Animal Veterinary Report. (US) **4812**
Large Employers Directory of Metropolitan St. Louis. (US) **1143**, 818
†Large Mixed Retailing. (UK ISSN 0263-4228) **5226**
Large Pack see Better Beagling **3708**
Large-Print Scores and Books Catalog see Music & Musicians: Large-Print Scores and Books Catalog (Large Print Edition) **2285**
Large Scale Systems: Theory and Applications see Information & Decision Technologies **1437**
Large Stores Directory. (UK ISSN 0260-6526) **1143**, 837
Largo Consumo. (IT ISSN 0392-131X) **2093**
Lariat. (US ISSN 0047-4088) **4536**
Larkspur Report see New West Notes **3910**
Larry Abraham's Insider Report. (US) **953**, 896
Laryngo- Rhino- Otologie. (GW ISSN 0935-8943) **3315**
Laryngologie, Rhinologie, Otologie und ihre Grenzgebiete Vereinigt mit Monatsschrift fuer Ohrenheilkunde see Laryngo- Rhino- Otologie **3315**
Laryngoscope. (US ISSN 0023-852X) **3315**
Las Polski. (PL ISSN 0023-8538) **2103**
Las Vegas see L V **5225**
Las Vegas Business Press. (US) **677**
Las Vegas Insider. (US ISSN 0271-0145) **4774**, 2477, 4478
Las Vegas Israelite. (US) **2012**
Las Vegas Kidz Magazine. (US) **1240**
Las Vegas Singles Lifestyle. (US) **4362**
Lasca's World. (US) **4803**
Laser. (UK) **4603**, 4322
†Laser. (US) **5226**
Laser and Applications see Lasers & Optronics **3855**

Laser and Particle Beams. (UK ISSN 0263-0346) **3854**
▼Laser and Technology. (IT ISSN 1121-0656) **3262**, **3854**
†Laser Applications. (US) **5226**
▼Laser Applicazioni Industriali, Tecnologie, Mercati. (IT) **3854**
Laser Chemistry. (US ISSN 0278-6273) **3854**
Laser Disc Newsletter. (US ISSN 0749-5250) **4603**
Laser Focus see Laser Focus World **3855**
Laser Focus - Electro Optics Buyers' Guide see Laser Focus World Buyers' Guide **3855**
Laser Focus World. (US ISSN 1043-8092) **3855**
Laser Focus World Buyers' Guide. (US) **3855**, **1228**
Laser Medicine and Surgery News and Advances see Journal of Clinical Laser Medicine & Surgery **3359**
Laser Nursing. (US ISSN 0888-6075) **3281**
▼Laser Physics (Soviet). (US ISSN 1054-660X) **3855**
Laser Quest. (US) **2523**, **1645**
Laser Raman & Infrared Spectroscopy Abstracts. (UK ISSN 0309-5320) **3837**, **16**
Laser Raman Spectroscopy Abstracts see Laser Raman & Infrared Spectroscopy Abstracts **3837**
Laser Report. (US ISSN 0023-8600) **3855**
†Laser Research. (US ISSN 0741-5222) **5226**
Laser Science and Technology. (US) **3855**
Laser Sinica. see Zhongguo Jiguang **3858**
Laser Therapy. (UK ISSN 0898-5901) **3122**
Laser und Optoelektronik. (GW ISSN 0722-9003) **3855**
Laserdisk Professional see C D - R O M Professional **2796**
Laserjet Journal. (US) **4002**
Laserlog Reporter. (US) **3561**
Lasermedizin. (GW ISSN 0938-765X) **3262**
Lasers (Year) see International Conference on Lasers. Proceedings **3853**
Lasers and Light in Ophthalmology. (NE ISSN 0922-5307) **3302**
Lasers & Optronics. (US ISSN 0733-303X) **3855**, **1902**
▼Lasers in Engineering. (US ISSN 0898-1507) **3855**
Lasers in Graphics: Electronic Publishing in the 80's. Conference Proceedings see Lasers in Graphics: Electronic Publishing in the 90's. Conference Proceedings **4002**
Lasers in Graphics: Electronic Publishing in the 90's. Conference Proceedings. (US) **4002**
Lasers in Medical Science. (UK ISSN 0268-8921) **3122**, **3855**
▼Lasers in Medicine. (NE) **3177**, **3262**
Lasers in Opthalmology see Lasers and Light in Ophthalmology **3302**
Lasers in Surgery and Medicine. (US ISSN 0196-8092) **3381**, **3855**
Lasers in the Life Sciences. (US ISSN 0886-0467) **3855**, **446**
†Last Day Messenger. (US ISSN 0023-8635) **5226**
The Last Ever Melodic Scribble. (UK) **2996**
Last Month's Newsletter. (US) **1299**
Last Resort. (US) **1754**, **1240**
Last Word. (US) **1829**
Lastauto Omnibus. (GW ISSN 0023-866X) **4694**
Lastauto Omnibus Katalog. (GW) **4745**
Lastbilen. (SW ISSN 0023-8678) **4745**
Lastebilen. (NO ISSN 0023-8686) **4745**
Lastechniek. (NE ISSN 0023-8694) **3429**
Lastijdschrift. see Revue de la Soudure **3430**

Latah County Genealogical Society. Quarterly. (US ISSN 0747-6663) **2157**
Latah Legacy. (US) **2412**, **2056**
Late Imperial China. (US ISSN 0884-3236) **2339**
Late Model Digest. (US) **4478**
Latein und Griechisch in Berlin. (GW ISSN 0723-6050) **1278**, **1754**
Lateinamerika. (GW ISSN 0458-7944) **4442**, **2412**
Lateinamerika (Hamburg). (GW) **2412**
Lateinamerika Anders. (AU) **3964**
Lateinamerika Nachrichten. (GW ISSN 0174-6324) **932**, **2012**, **3964**
Lateinamerika Pressespiegel. (AU) **2572**
Later Years. (US ISSN 0892-6921) **2275**
Lateranum. (VC) **4187**
The Latest and Best of T E S S. (US) **1478**, **1691**
Latest Information on National Accounts of Developing Countries. see Informations Recentes sur les Comptes Nationaux des Pays en Developpement **931**
Latest Jokes. (US ISSN 0887-6991) **2871**
†Latest Literature in Family Planning. (UK ISSN 0308-8774) **5226**
Latham Letter. (US) **4412**, **231**
Lathrop Report on Newspaper Indexes. (US) **2578**, **16**
Latienda. (SP) **153**
Latin America and Caribbean Contemporary Record. (US ISSN 0736-4148) **3964**
Latin America and Caribbean Review see Americas Review **843**
Latin America Commodities Report see Latin American Economy and Business **916**
Latin America Evangelist. (US) **4241**
Latin America in Books. (US ISSN 0738-7113) **404**, **2012**
Latin America Letter. (II) **3904**
Latin America Market Guide. (US) **953**, **1143**
Latin America Regional Reports - Brazil.(UK ISSN 0143-5272) **872**, **3904**
Latin America Regional Reports - Caribbean. (UK ISSN 0143-523X) **872**, **3904**
Latin America Regional Reports - Mexico & Central America. (UK ISSN 0143-5264) **872**, **3904**
Latin America Report. (US) **872**, **3904**
Latin America Update. (US ISSN 0738-601X) **3964**
Latin America Weekly Report. (UK ISSN 0143-5280) **872**, **3904**
▼Latin American Antiquity. (US ISSN 1045-6635) **277**
Latin American Applied Research. (AG ISSN 0327-0793) **1183**, **1856**, **3844**
Latin American Art. (US ISSN 1042-9808) **333**
Latin American Bank Note Society see L A N S A **3600**
Latin American Books Newsletter. (II ISSN 0023-8740) **4141**
Latin American Bulletin/Boletin de America Latina. (CS) **2217**, **2412**
Latin American Documentation see L A D O C **3903**
Latin American Economic Report see Latin American Economy and Business **916**
Latin American Economy and Business. (UK ISSN 0960-8702) **916**
Latin American Food Production Conference Summary Report see World Food Production Conference Summary Report **5307**
Latin American Historical Dictionaries Series. (US) **2412**
Latin American Import - Export Directory. (CR) **1143**
Latin American Index. (US ISSN 0090-9416) **3938**, **726**
Latin American Indian Literatures Journal. (US ISSN 0888-5613) **2931**, **2012**
Latin American Integration. see Integracion Latinoamericana **931**

Latin American International Food Industry Directory. (US) **2076**
Latin American Jewish Studies Newsletter. (US ISSN 0738-1379) **2412**, **2012**
Latin American Journal of Chemical Engineering and Applied Chemistry. see Revista Latinoamericana de Ingenieria Quimica y Quimica Aplicada **5270**
Latin American Literary Review. (US ISSN 0047-4134) **2931**
Latin American Metal Mechanic & Electronic Industry Directory. (US) **3019**, **837**
Latin American Mining Letter. (UK ISSN 0959-8219) **3487**
Latin American Monograph and Document Series. (US) **4378**, **2510**
Latin American Monographs. (US ISSN 0075-8108) **4379**
Latin American Music Review/Revista de Musica Latino Americana. (US ISSN 0163-0350) **3561**
Latin American Perspectives. (US ISSN 0094-582X) **4379**, **3904**
Latin American Post. (CN) **3754**
Latin American Regional Reports - Andean Group. (UK ISSN 0143-5248) **872**, **3904**
Latin American Regional Reports - Southern Cone. (UK ISSN 0143-5256) **872**, **3904**
Latin American Report. (US ISSN 0895-3503) **4225**, **2412**
Latin American Research Review. (US ISSN 0023-8791) **4379**
Latin American Research Unit Studies see L A R U Studies **5225**
Latin American Research Unit Working Paper see L A R U Working Paper **5225**
Latin American Reserve Fund Report. Annual see L A R F Report. Annual **677**
Latin American Scholarship Program of American Universities, Inc. Informativo see L A S P A U Informativo **1722**
Latin American Special Reports. (UK ISSN 0264-2867) **953**, **789**
Latin American Studies. (US) **2012**
Latin American Studies. see Lading Meizhou Yanjiu **4378**
Latin American Studies Association Forum see L A S A Forum **4378**
▼Latin American Studies in Asia. (II) **2510**
Latin American Studies in the Universities and Polytechnics of the United Kingdom. (UK ISSN 0956-9006) **2329**, **404**
Latin American Studies in the Universities of the United Kingdom see Latin American Studies in the Universities and Polytechnics of the United Kingdom **2329**
Latin American Studies Working Papers.(US) **4379**
Latin American Textile Industry Directory. (US) **4621**
Latin American Theatre Review. (US ISSN 0023-8813) **4634**, **2931**
Latin American Times. (UK) **916**, **3964**
Latin American Working Group Letter see L A W G Letter **3964**
Latin and Greek Texts. (UK ISSN 0951-7391) **1278**
Latin Chamber of Commerce. Directorio Comercial. (US) **818**
Latin Liturgy Association Newsletter. (US) **4267**, **1278**
Latin Men. (US) **3398**, **2454**
Latin Teaching see J A C T Review **1277**
Latin Women. (US) **3398**
Latina. (JA) **3561**
Latina et Graeca. (CI ISSN 0350-414X) **2373**
Latinamerican Press. (PE) **4187**
Latinamerica Press see Noticias Aliadas **4192**
Latinitas. (VC ISSN 0023-883X) **2824**, **1278**
▼Latino Studies Journal. (US) **3964**, **2012**
Latinoamerica. (US) **4379**

IL LAVORATORE 6385

Latinograma. (US) **2012**
▼Latinomineria. (CL) **3487**
Latinskaya Amerika see Evropa i Amerika **2406**
▼Latitudes South. (US ISSN 1052-1011) **4774**
Latium. (IT) **2373**
Latman's The Copyright Law. (US) **3676**
Lato. (RM) **2931**
Latomistica. (IT) **2316**
Latomus. (BE ISSN 0023-8856) **1278**
Latte. (IT ISSN 0392-6060) **201**
†Latter-Day Sentinel. (US) **5226**
†Latter - Day Woman. (US ISSN 0889-9185) **5226**
Latvian Collector. (US) **3754**
Latvian News Digest. (US) **3904**
†Latviesu Valodas Kulturas Jautajumi. (UR ISSN 0201-8039) **5226**
Latvija Amerika. (CN ISSN 0023-8902) **2012**
Latvija Sodien. (US ISSN 0093-8920) **2012**
Latvijas P.S.R. Preses Hronika. (LV ISSN 0023-8910) **404**
Latvijas P.S.R. Zinatnu Akademijas. Vestis. see Akademiya Nauk Latviiskoi S.S.R. Izvestiya **4298**
Latvju Maksla. (US ISSN 0362-7047) **333**, **2012**
Latvju Muzika. (US) **3561**
Laubach Literacy International Annual Report. (US) **1685**, **1722**
Lauda Air Magazine. (AU) **2190**
Laugh Factory. (US) **2871**
Laugh Lovers News see Sarcastics Anonymous and Laugh Lovers News **2883**
Laugh-Makers. (US) **2437**, **4634**
†Laughing Bear. (US ISSN 0363-2164) **5226**
Laughing Bear Newsletter. (US ISSN 1056-0327) **4131**
Laughing Matters. (US ISSN 0731-1788) **4034**
Laundry and Cleaning News. (UK ISSN 0142-9442) **1281**
Laundry & Cleaning News International.(UK ISSN 0261-4421) **1281**
Laundry News. (US ISSN 0164-5765) **1281**
Laurel Messenger. (US ISSN 0023-8988) **2157**, **2412**
Laurel of Phi Kappa Tau. (US ISSN 0023-8996) **1316**
Laurel Review (Maryville). (US ISSN 0023-9003) **2931**
Laurels see French American Review **2918**
Laurence Scott Engineering Bulletin. (UK ISSN 0023-6381) **1902**, **1829**
Laurentian University. Gazette. (CN ISSN 0226-7934) **1316**
Laurentians: Mountains of Fun North of Montreal. see Les Laurentides **4774**
Laurentians: Spring - Summer - Fall Edition. (CN) **4774**
Laurentianum. (IT ISSN 0023-902X) **4267**
Les Laurentides/Laurentians: Mountains of Fun North of Montreal. (CN ISSN 0829-8033) **4774**
Laurentius. (GW ISSN 0175-8152) **4131**, **2768**
Laurentius Sonderhefte. (GW ISSN 0930-9950) **4131**, **2768**
Laurier Campus. (CN ISSN 0700-5105) **1316**
Lauriston S. Taylor Lecture Series. (US ISSN 0277-9196) **4107**
Lava. (GW ISSN 0863-3746) **1259**
Laval Administration. (CN ISSN 0023-9038) **1017**
Laval Theologique et Philosophique. (CN ISSN 0023-9054) **4187**, **3771**
Lavender Band. (US ISSN 0023-9062) **3237**
Lavender Line. (US) **2157**
Lavender Morning. (US) **2454**, **4846**
Lavender Prairie News. (US) **2454**, **4846**
†Laventhol and Horwath Perspective. (US ISSN 0147-2208) **5226**
▼Laverna. (GW) **1278**
Il Lavoratore Elettrico. (IT) **1792**, **4412**

IL LAVORO

Il Lavoro. (IT) **2586**
Lavoro e Diritto. (IT ISSN 1120-947X) **2586, 2644**
Lavoro e Sicurezza Sociale. (IT) **987**
Lavoro e Sindacato. (IT ISSN 0390-0991) **987**
Lavoro e Societa. (IT) **677, 3904, 4442**
Lavoro Informazione. (IT) **987**
Lavoro Italiano. (IT ISSN 0023-9089) **2586**
Lavoro Neuropsichiatrico. (IT ISSN 0023-9097) **3344**
Lavoura. (BL ISSN 0023-9135) **105**
Lavoura Arrozeira. (BL ISSN 0023-9143) **105**
Lavra & Oficina. (AO) **2510**
Law see A D L Law Report **2593**
Law & Anthropology. (AU ISSN 0259-0816) **2644, 243**
Law & Business Directory of Bankruptcy Attorneys (Year). (US) **1143, 677, 2644**
Law & Business Directory of Corporate Counsel. (US) **2711**
Law and Computer Technology see Law - Technology **2705**
Law and Contemporary Problems. (US ISSN 0023-9186) **2644**
▼Law and Critique. (UK ISSN 0957-8536) **2644**
Law and Ethics Series. (US) **2644**
Law and History Review. (US ISSN 0738-2480) **2644, 2412**
Law and Human Behavior. (US ISSN 0147-7307) **2644, 4034**
Law & Inequality. (US ISSN 0737-089X) **2644, 3944**
Law and International Affairs. (BG) **2644**
Law & Justice. (UK) **2644, 3771, 4187**
Law and Legal Information Directory. (US ISSN 0740-090X) **2644, 2734**
†Law and Legislation in Israel. (US) **5226**
Law and Legislation in the German Democratic Republic. (GW ISSN 0458-8460) **2644, 3904**
Law & Life. see Falu yu Shenghuo **2624**
†Law and Mental Health. (US ISSN 0890-5037) **5226**
Law and Order. (US ISSN 0023-9194) **1517**
Law & Order. see Fazhi Jianshe **2625**
Law and Philosophy. (NE ISSN 0167-5249) **2644, 3771**
Law and Philosophy Library. (NE) **2644, 3771**
Law & Policy. (UK ISSN 0265-8240) **2644, 3904**
Law and Policy in International Business. (US ISSN 0023-9208) **2726, 677**
Law and Political Review. (KO) **2644, 3904**
Law and Practice. see Faxue yu Shijian **2625**
Law and Progress. (Il ISSN 0377-0850) **2644**
Law and Psychology Review. (US ISSN 0098-5961) **2644, 4034**
Law and Social Inquiry. (US ISSN 0897-6546) **2644, 4379**
Law & Society Review. (US ISSN 0023-9216) **2644, 4379, 4442**
Law and State. (GW ISSN 0341-6151) **2726, 3904**
Law & Tax Review. (UK ISSN 0262-7647) **2644**
Law & Women Series. (US) **2644, 4846**
Law and You. (BL) **818, 2644**
Law Bibliography. see Rechtsbibliographie **2700**
Law Books in Print. (US ISSN 0075-8221) **405, 2644**
Law Books in Review. (US ISSN 0886-0408) **2699, 16**
Law Books Published. (US ISSN 0023-9240) **2699**
Law, Computers, and Artificial Intelligence. (UK ISSN 0962-9580) **2644, 1397**
Law Council of Australia. Law Council Newsletter see Australian Law News **2602**

Law Development Commission. Annual Report. (ZA) **2645**
Law Enforcement Legal Reporter. (US) **2645**
Law Enforcement Legal Review. (US) **1517**
Law Enforcement News. (US ISSN 0364-1724) **1517**
Law Enforcement Product News. (US) **1518**
Law Enforcement Technology. (US ISSN 0747-3680) **1518**
Law Firm Profit Report. (US) **2645, 1017**
▼Law Firms Yellow Book. (US ISSN 1054-4054) **1143, 2645**
Law for Business. (UK ISSN 0954-2809) **2711, 677**
The Law Forum. (US) **2645**
Law Group Docket. (US) **3944**
Law Guardian see Law Society's Guardian Gazette **2646**
Law in Context. (AT ISSN 0811-5796) **2645**
Law in Eastern Europe. (NE ISSN 0075-823X) **2726**
Law in Society. (NR ISSN 0458-8592) **2645**
Law Institute Journal. (AT ISSN 0023-9267) **2645**
Law Librarian. (UK ISSN 0023-9275) **2768, 2645**
Law Librarian's Bulletin Board. (US) **2645, 2768**
Law Library Association of Maryland News. (US) **2768, 2645**
Law Library Information Reports. (US ISSN 0268-8336) **2645, 2768**
Law Library Journal. (US ISSN 0023-9283) **2768, 2645**
Law, Medicine & Health Care. (US ISSN 0277-8459) **3265, 2645**
Law Notes see Barrister (Chicago) **2604**
Law Notes. (UK ISSN 0141-5867) **2645**
The Law of Advertising. (US) **2645, 33**
Law of Associations: An Operating Legal Manual for Executives and Counsel. (US) **2645, 4412**
Law of Bank Deposits, Collections and Credit Cards (Supplement). (US) **789, 2645**
Law of Evidence in Washington. (US) **2645**
Law of Macau Statistical Information System. see Legislacao do Sistema de Informacao Estatistica de Macau **4577**
Law of Probation and Parole. (US) **2645, 1518**
▼Law of Products Liability. (US) **2645**
Law of Stamp Duties in Queensland. (AT ISSN 0725-6892) **2645**
Law of Weight & Measures. (UK) **2645**
▼Law Office Computing. (US ISSN 1055-128X) **2705**
Law Office Economics & Management. (US ISSN 0458-8630) **2705**
†Law Office Guide in Computers (Year) Directory. (US) **5226**
Law Office Guide to Small Computers. (US) **1461, 2645**
Law Office Information Service. (US ISSN 0164-5390) **2699, 405**
Law Office Management and Administration Report. (US ISSN 0735-4843) **2645**
Law Office Management Journal. (CN ISSN 0843-7076) **2645**
Law Office Technology Review. (US ISSN 1047-6482) **2705, 2645**
Law Officer's Bulletin. (US ISSN 0145-6571) **1518**
Law Practice Management. (US ISSN 1045-9081) **2645, 1017**
Law Quadrangle Notes. (US) **1316, 2645**
Law Quarterly. (PK) **2645**
Law Quarterly Review. (UK ISSN 0023-933X) **2645**
Law Referencer. (Il) **2645**
Law Reform Commission of Saskatchewan. Annual Report and Review. (CN ISSN 0839-4539) **2645**

Law Reform Commission of Saskatchewan. Yearly Review see Law Reform Commission of Saskatchewan. Annual Report and Review **2645**
Law-Related Education Project Exchange see L R E Project Exchange **2642**
Law-Related Education Report see L R E Report **2643**
▼Law Relating to Banker and Customer in Australia. (AT) **2645, 789, 2711**
Law Relating to Trade Descriptions. (UK) **2645**
Law Reports: Appeal Cases. (UK ISSN 0265-122X) **2645**
Law Reports: Chancery and Family Division. (UK ISSN 0265-1211) **2718**
Law Reports of Tanzania. (TZ) **2645**
Law Reports: Queen's Bench Division. (UK ISSN 0264-1127) **2646**
Law Reprints: Trade Regulation Series. (US) **916, 2726**
Law Review. see Pravny Obzor **2667**
Law Review Journal. (US ISSN 0734-1938) **2646**
Law School Administrator's Journal. (US ISSN 0741-1170) **2646**
Law School Journal. (US ISSN 0737-2590) **2646**
Law School Record. (US) **2646, 1711**
Law Sciences Review. see Jogtudomanyi Kozlony **2638**
Law, Society, and Policy. (US) **2646**
Law Society Digest. (KE) **2646**
Law Society Gazette. (CN ISSN 0023-9364) **2646**
Law Society Journal. (AT ISSN 0023-9372) **2646**
Law Society of Scotland. Journal (Year) .(UK ISSN 0458-8711) **2646**
Law Society of South Australia. Bulletin. (AT) **2646**
Law Society of Upper Canada. Special Lectures. (CN ISSN 0316-5310) **2646**
Law Society's Gazette. (UK ISSN 0023-9380) **2646**
Law Society's Guardian Gazette. (UK) **2646**
Law Teacher. (UK ISSN 0306-9400) **2646, 1754**
Law Teacher's Journal. (US ISSN 0741-1197) **2646**
Law - Technology. (US ISSN 0278-3916) **2705**
Law Thesaurus. (Il ISSN 0023-9399) **2646**
▼Law Times. (CN ISSN 0847-5083) **2646**
Law Tools, Materials, Contacts. (US) **2646**
Law Weekly. (Il) **2646**
Lawasia. (AT ISSN 0047-4207) **2726**
Lawdocs. (US) **2768, 2646**
†Lawn & Garden Marketing. (US ISSN 0091-4665) **5226**
Lawn & Garden Trade. (CN ISSN 0705-212X) **1044, 2133**
Lawn and Landscape Maintenance. (US ISSN 1046-154X) **2133**
Lawn Care Industry. (US ISSN 0160-6042) **2133**
Lawn Care Industry Show Extra. (US) **2133, 677**
Lawn, Garden, Outdoor Living see Lawn & Garden Marketing **5226**
†Lawn Servicing. (US ISSN 0746-9152) **5226**
Lawn Tennis Association Handbook see L T A Handbook **4507**
Lawrence Berkeley Laboratory. Catalog of Research Projects. (US) **4322, 3823**
Lawrence Berkeley Laboratory. Materials and Chemical Sciences Division. Annual Report. (US) **1919**
Lawrence Berkeley Laboratory. Materials and Molecular Research Division. Annual Report see Lawrence Berkeley Laboratory. Materials and Chemical Sciences Division. Annual Report **1919**
Lawrence Berkeley Laboratory. Research Highlights see Lawrence Berkeley Laboratory. Catalog of Research Projects **4322**

Lawrence Review of Natural Products see Lawrence Review of Natural Products Newsletter **3734**
Lawrence Review of Natural Products Monograph System see Lawrence Review of Natural Products Newsletter **3734**
Lawrence Review of Natural Products Newsletter. (US) **3734**
Lawrence Technological University Magazine. (US) **1316**
Lawrenceville Bulletin see Lawrentian **1316**
Lawrentian. (US) **1316**
Lawrie's Durban Street Directory see Lawrie's Durban Street Directory & Information Guide **1143**
Lawrie's Durban Street Directory & Information Guide. (SA) **1143**
Laws of England Annual Abridgment see Halsbury's Laws of England Annual Abridgment **2731**
Laws of Kenya. Supplement. (KE) **2646**
Laws of the People's Republic of China.(CC) **2646**
Lawson Letters. (US ISSN 0748-1691) **2157**
Lawson Mardon Group Ltd. News see L M News **3649**
Lawyer. (NR ISSN 0023-9437) **2646**
Lawyer. (Il) **2646**
Lawyer. see Pravnik **2667**
Lawyer Hiring & Training Report. (US ISSN 0739-1706) **2646, 1067**
Lawyer - Pilots Bar Association Journal. (US) **58, 2646**
Lawyer Referral Network. (US ISSN 0887-7777) **2646**
Lawyers Alert. (US ISSN 0278-9817) **2646**
Lawyers' and Accountants' Guide to Purchase - Sale of Small Business. (US) **2646, 753**
Lawyers and Legal System. see Lushi yu Fazhi **2651**
Lawyers' Arbitration Letter. (US) **2646**
Lawyers' Arbitration Letter and the Digest of Court Decisions see Lawyers' Arbitration Letter **2646**
Lawyer's Committee on Nuclear Policy Newsletter. (US) **2646, 3964**
Lawyers for the Arts Newsletter. (US) **2646**
Lawyers for the Creative Arts Quarterly see L C A Quarterly **5225**
Lawyer's Guide to the Texas Deceptive Trade Practices Act. (US) **2646**
Lawyers Job Bulletin Board. (US) **2646**
Lawyers Letter. (US ISSN 0740-0519) **2647**
Lawyers' Medical Digest. (US) **2647, 3122**
Lawyer's Microcomputer see Lawyer's P C **2705**
Lawyers Monthly Catalog. Government Documents from Official and Commercial Sources. (US ISSN 1049-7978) **2699**
Lawyer's P C. (US ISSN 0740-0942) **2705, 1461**
Lawyer's Phone Book (Year). (CN ISSN 0317-8668) **2647**
Lawyers Practice Manual N.S.W. (AT) **2647**
Lawyers Practice Manual Victoria. (AT) **2647**
Lawyers Professional Liability Update. (US) **2647**
Lawyers' Recreation. (Il ISSN 0023-9488) **2647**
Lawyer's Register by Specialties and Fields of Law. (US ISSN 0883-2412) **2647**
Lawyer's Remembrancer. (UK ISSN 0142-7490) **2647**
Lawyers Tax Alert see Research Institute Lawyers Tax Alert **5269**
Lawyers' Title Guaranty Funds Newsletter. (US ISSN 0361-3763) **2647**
Lawyers Title News. (US) **4151**
The Lawyers Weekly. (CN ISSN 0830-0151) **2647**
Laxton's Building Price Book. (UK) **622**
Laxton's National Building Price Book see Laxton's Building Price Book **622**
Lazio. (IT ISSN 0023-9526) **3904**

Lazio Ieri e Oggi. (IT ISSN 0047-4231) **4774**
Lazy Man's Guide to Holidays Afloat. (UK ISSN 0075-8272) **4525**
Le Depanneur *see* Alimentation au Quebec **2090**
Le Rail *see* Het Spoor **4715**
Le Rail et le Monde *see* Le Rail **4713**
Lea. (CK) **405**, 2931
Lea Magazine. (US) **2012**
An Leabharlann/Irish Library. (UK ISSN 0023-9542) **2768**
Lead Abstracts *see* Leadscan **3427**
Lead and Zinc. *see* Namari to Aen **3416**
Lead and Zinc Statistics. (UK ISSN 0023-9577) **3427**
▼Lead Belly Letter. (US ISSN 1056-5329) **3561**
Leader. (AT) **105**
The Leader. (IE) **1240**
Leader. *see* Kiongozi **4267**
Leader (Anderson). (US ISSN 1041-4460) **4187**
Leader (Coral Gables) *see* J C I News **1298**
Leader in Action. (US ISSN 8755-2620) **1645**, 1339, 3393, 3904
Leader in the Church School Today. (US) **4241**, 1645
Leaders. (US ISSN 0194-3510) **916**, 3964
†Leaders' Digest. (US) **5226**
Leader's Legal Tech Newsletter. (US ISSN 0738-0186) **2647**, 2705
Leadership. (UG ISSN 0047-424X) **4187**
Leadership (Carol Stream). (US ISSN 0199-7661) **4241**
Leadership (Fairfield). (US) **1017**
Leadership (Reston). (US) **1645**
Leadership (Washington). (US ISSN 0195-9204) **1017**
Leadership and Organization Development Journal. (UK ISSN 0143-7739) **1018**
†Leadership Directions. (US) **5226**
Leadership in Health Services. (CN) **2467**
▼Leadership Quarterly. (US ISSN 1048-9843) **1018**, 3904, 4034, 4442
Leadership Reports. (US) **1729**
Leadership Resources Inc. Guides to Management. Monographs *see* L R I Guides to Management. Monographs **1017**
Leadership Today *see* Alpha (New Malden) **4228**
Leading European Banks. (SZ) **789**
Leading Notes. (UK ISSN 0960-6297) **3561**
Leadline. (CN ISSN 0705-6931) **333**
Leads. (CN ISSN 0834-3586) **872**, 1044
Leads *see* International Leads **2764**
Leadscan. (UK ISSN 0950-1584) **3427**, 16
†Leaf & Leisure. (US) **5226**
Leaflet (Boston). (US) **2133**
Leaflet (Lexington). (US ISSN 0023-964X) **2824**, 1754
Leaflets of St. Francis. *see* Listy Sv. Frantiska **5228**
League. *see* Sandara **2022**
League for International Food Education Newsletter *see* L.I.F.E. Newsletter **5225**
League of Canadian Poets. Newsletter *see* Museletter **2998**
League of Historic American Theatres Bulletin *see* L H A T Bulletin **302**
League Sentinel. (UK) **3964**
†Leaking Underground Storage Tank Newsletter/Bulletin Reservoirs Souterrains Non Etanches. (CN ISSN 0832-7580) **5226**
Leaping. (AT ISSN 0726-626X) **1531**, 4241, 4267
†Learn & Play. (US) **5226**
Learn Canoeing! (US) **4525**, 1080
Learned Publishing: A L P S P Bulletin. (Association of Learned and Professional Society Publishers) (UK) **4131**
Learning. (UK) **1645**
Learning. (CN ISSN 0381-1387) **1685**

Learning (Year). (US ISSN 0090-3167) **1645**
Learning A I D S. (US) **405**, 3221
Learning All Together. (UK) **4241**
Learning and Individual Differences. (US ISSN 1041-6080) **4034**, 1645
▼Learning and Instruction. (US ISSN 0959-4752) **1645**
Learning and Memory. (UK ISSN 0143-7534) **3344**, 2275
Learning and Motivation. (US ISSN 0023-9690) **1645**, 4034
Learning Chinese. *see* Xue Hanyu **2853**
Learning Connection *see* Adult & Continuing Education Today **1681**
Learning Disabilities Association of America Newsbriefs *see* L D A Newsbriefs **1738**
Learning Disabilities Focus *see* Learning Disabilities Research and Practice **1738**
Learning Disabilities Research *see* Learning Disabilities Research and Practice **1738**
Learning Disabilities Research and Practice. (US) **1738**, 1240, 1754
Learning Disability Quarterly. (US ISSN 0731-9487) **1738**
Learning Edge. (US ISSN 0896-8756) **1754**, 1240, 1259
Learning English for Science & Technology. *see* Keji Yingyu Xuexi **2822**
Learning English in Britain *see* Learning Languages in Europe **1695**
Learning Exchange News. (US) **1754**
Learning for Living *see* British Journal of Religious Education **4166**
Learning French. *see* Fayu Xuexi **2813**
Learning German. *see* Deyu Xuexi **2810**
Learning Independently. (US) **1685**
Learning Japanese. *see* Riyu Xuexi **2838**
Learning Languages in Europe. (UK ISSN 0953-2617) **1695**
Learning Resources Journal. (UK ISSN 0268-2125) **1711**
Learning Resources News. (UK ISSN 0955-0631) **1711**
Learning Russian. *see* Eyu Xuexi **2813**
Learning Together with Under 5's. (UK) **4241**
Learning Together with 5-7's. (UK) **4187**
Learning Together with 7-11's. (UK) **4187**, 1645
Learning Together with 11-14's. (UK ISSN 0308-356X) **4187**
Learning Traveler. U S College-Sponsored Programs Abroad: Academic Year *see* Academic Year Abroad **1721**
Learning Traveler. Vacation Study Abroad *see* Vacation Study Abroad **1724**
Lear's. (US ISSN 0897-0149) **4846**
Leasehold Law. (UK) **2647**
Leasing Digest *see* Asset Finance and Leasing Digest **938**
Leasing Sourcebook. (US ISSN 1045-2508) **789**
Leather. (UK ISSN 0023-9739) **2737**
Leather & Footwears. *see* Kawa to Hakimono **2737**
†Leather and Shoes. (US ISSN 0023-9747) **5226**
†Leather Buyers Guide and Leather Trade Marks. (US ISSN 0075-8345) **5226**
Leather Chemistry/Hikaku Kagaku. (JA ISSN 0018-1811) **2737**
Leather Crafters Journal. (US ISSN 1056-4225) **355**, 2737
Leather Craftsman *see* Leather Crafters Journal **355**
▼Leather Goods International. (PK) **2737**
Leather Guide *see* International Leather Guide **2736**
Leather Industries of America. Newsbreak. (US) **2737**
Leather Industry. *see* Kozarstvi **2737**
Leather: Latin American Industrial Report. (US) **2737**
Leather Manufacturer. (US ISSN 0023-9763) **2737**

Leather Manufacturer's Directory. (US) **1143**, 2737
Leather Science. (II ISSN 0023-9771) **2737**
Leather Science Abstracts. (II) **2738**, 16
Leather Technology/Hikaku Gijutsu. (JA ISSN 0018-1803) **2737**
Leather Today. (US ISSN 0884-660X) **2737**, 1286
†Leather Today Additions. (US) **5226**
Leathergoods *see* Fashion Extras **1290**
Leatherneck. (US ISSN 0023-981X) **3463**
Leathers. (II ISSN 0023-9828) **2737**
Leaven (Franklin Park). (US ISSN 8750-2011) **1240**
Leaven (Washington) *see* Bread for the World Newsletter **4400**
Leaves of Twin Oaks. (US ISSN 0023-9836) **4442**
Leba. (PO ISSN 0870-0044) **277**
Lebanese Industrial and Commercial Directory/Annuaire des Professions au Liban. (LE ISSN 0075-8353) **1143**
Lebanese Journal of Political Science. (LE) **3904**
Lebanese Medical Journal/Journal Medical Libanais. (LE ISSN 0023-9852) **3122**
Lebanon. Direction Centrale de la Statistique. Bulletin Statistique Mensuel. (LE ISSN 0023-9860) **4577**
Lebanon. Direction Centrale de la Statistique. Comptes Economiques. (LE ISSN 0075-837X) **726**
Lebanon. Direction Centrale de la Statistique. Recueil de Statistiques Libanaises. (LE ISSN 0075-8388) **4577**
Lebanon. Service de Statistique Generale. Bulletin Statistique Mensuel *see* Lebanon. Direction Centrale de la Statistique. Bulletin Statistique Mensuel **4577**
Lebanon News (Arabic Edition). (US ISSN 1043-5913) **3964**
Lebanon News (English Edition). (US ISSN 0742-9665) **3964**
▼Lebanon Report. (LE) **3964**, 872, 2430, 3640
LeBaron Russell Briggs Prize Honors Essays in English. (US ISSN 0075-8396) **2931**
Leben *see* Leben und Umwelt **1491**
Leben. (SZ) **4187**
Leben und Erziehen. (GW ISSN 0047-4274) **1240**, 2190
Leben und Gesundheit *see* Prima Vita **3807**
Leben und Umwelt. (GW ISSN 0303-4283) **1491**
Leben und Weg. (GW ISSN 0724-3820) **4412**
Lebende Sprachen. (GW ISSN 0023-9909) **2824**, 1646
Lebendige Erde. (GW ISSN 0023-9917) **105**, 446
Lebendige Katechese. (GW ISSN 0171-4171) **4267**
Lebendige Seelsorge. (GW) **4034**
Lebendige Seelsorge und Lebendige Katchese. (GW) **4187**
Lebendige Zelle. (GW ISSN 0931-8887) **4267**
Lebendiges Darmstadt. (GW) **3526**, 4634
Lebendiges Darmstadt. Stadtfuehrer Gastronomie und Unterhaltung. (GW) **2076**
Lebendiges Zeugnis. (GW ISSN 0023-9941) **4267**
Lebensabend. (GW) **4412**
Lebensbilder aus Schwaben und Franken. (GW) **419**
Lebenshilfe Aktuell. (GW) **1738**
Lebenshilfe Zeitung. (GW) **1738**
Lebensmittel & Getraenke. *see* Danmark Export: Food & Beverages **905**
Lebensmittel aus Polen *see* Food from Poland **5195**
Lebensmittel-Grosshandel - Susswaren-Zeitung *see* Food and Nonfood **2091**
Lebensmittel Markt. (GW) **1080**

Lebensmittel Praxis. (GW ISSN 0023-9992) **2093**, 2076
Lebensmittel - Revue - Alimentaire. (SZ) **2076**
Lebensmittel-Technologie. (SZ ISSN 0256-6575) **2076**
Lebensmittel und Biotechnologie. (AU ISSN 0254-9298) **2076**, 220, 1183
Lebensmittel und Gerichtliche Chemie *see* Lebensmittelchemie **2076**
Lebensmittel Zeitung. (GW ISSN 0342-9512) **2076**
Lebensmittelchemie. (GW) **2076**, 3265
Lebensmittelhaendler *see* Der Lebensmittelkaufmann **2093**
Lebensmittelhandel *see* Lebensmittel - Revue - Alimentaire **2076**
Lebensmittelindustrie. (GW ISSN 0024-0028) **2076**
Der Lebensmittelkaufmann. (AU ISSN 0047-4282) **2093**
Lebensmittelpost *see* Der Lebensmittelkaufmann **2093**
Lebensmittelreport. (GW ISSN 0935-865X) **2076**
Lebensmitteltechnik. (GW ISSN 0047-4290) **2076**
Lebensschutz. (AU) **3805**
Lebensversicherungsmedizin *see* Versicherungsmedizin **3161**
Leber Magen Darm. (GW ISSN 0300-8622) **3269**
Leblanc Bell. (US) **3561**, 1646
Lebns Fragn. (IS) **3904**
†Lebone la Kgalalelo. (SA) **5226**
Lebone la Kgalalelo Isibani Sobu Ngcwele *see* Lebone la Kgalalelo **5226**
Il Leccio. (IT) **2871**
Lecciones de Historia Juridica. (AG) **2647**, 2316
Lecciones y Ensayos. (AG) **2647**, 2726
†Lechero Latinoamericano. (US) **5226**
Lectins. (UK ISSN 0143-4217) **479**, 508, 3734
Lector. (US ISSN 0732-8001) **4131**, 2824, 2931
Lectura y Vida. (US ISSN 0325-8637) **2824**, 1754
Lecturas. (SP ISSN 0047-4304) **2217**
Lecturas de Economia. (CK ISSN 0120-2596) **896**, 872
Lecture et Tradition. (FR ISSN 0024-0125) **2931**, 3904
Lecture Notes in Bio-Organic Chemistry.(US) **1220**
Lecture Notes in Biomathematics. (US ISSN 0341-633X) **3043**, 446
Lecture Notes in Chemistry. (US ISSN 0342-4901) **1183**
Lecture Notes in Computer Science. (US ISSN 0302-9743) **1397**
Lecture Notes in Control and Information Sciences. (US ISSN 0170-8643) **2768**
Lecture Notes in Economics and Mathematical Systems. (US ISSN 0075-8442) **3043**, 677
Lecture Notes in Engineering. (US ISSN 0176-5035) **1829**
Lecture Notes in Mathematics. (US ISSN 0075-8434) **3043**
Lecture Notes in Mathematics. (CN) **3043**
Lecture Notes in Medical Informatics. (US ISSN 0172-7788) **3122**
†Lecture Notes in Numerical and Applied Analysis. (NE) **5226**
Lecture Notes in Physics. (US ISSN 0075-8450) **3823**
Lecture Notes in Physics. (SI) **3823**
Lecture Notes in Psychology. *see* Lehr- und Forschungstexte Psychologie **4034**
Lecture Notes in Pure and Applied Mathematics. (US ISSN 0075-8469) **3043**
Lecture Notes in Statistics. (US) **4577**
Lecture Notes on Coastal and Estuarine Studies. (US ISSN 0724-5890) **1607**
Lecture Notes Series on Computing. (SI) **1397**
Lectures. (IT) **2931**, 2373

LECTURES

▼Lectures and Course Notes in Chemistry. (SI) **1183**
Lectures da Roland Barthes see Lectures **2931**
Lectures Francaises. (FR ISSN 0024-0133) **3904**
†Lectures in Anaesthesiology. (UK ISSN 0267-0003) **5226**
Lectures in Applied Mathematics. (US ISSN 0075-8485) **3043**
Lectures in Commercial Diplomacy see The World Economy **700**
Lectures in Development Economics. (PK) **932**
Lectures in Economics: Theory, Institutions, Policy. (NE) **896**
Lectures in Heterocyclic Chemistry. (US ISSN 0090-2268) **1220**
Lectures on Mathematics in the Life Sciences. (US ISSN 0075-8523) **3043**, 446
Lectures on the History of Religions. New Series. (US ISSN 0075-8531) **4187**
†Ledarbladet Samspel. (SW ISSN 0345-7044) **5226**
Ledarforum. (SW ISSN 0024-015X) **831**
▼Ledelse i Dag. (DK ISSN 0905-8966) **1018**
Ledelse og Erhvervsoekonomi. (DK ISSN 0902-3704) **677**
Ledelse og Erhvervsoekonomi see Ledelse og Erhvervsoekonomi **677**
Das Leder. (GW ISSN 0024-0176) **2737**
Leder. Kursuskatalog. (DK ISSN 0109-9299) **1685**
Leder Echo. (GW ISSN 0024-0184) **2737**
Leder Pelz Textil Journal see L P T Journal **2737**
Leder, Schuhe, Lederwaren see L S L **2737**
Leder- und Haeutemarkt. (GW ISSN 0342-7641) **2737**
Lederforum. (NO) **1240**
Lederskab og Loensomhed. (DK) **1018**
Lederwaren-Report. (GW ISSN 0024-0214) **2737**, 1292
Lederwaren-Zeitung see In Leder **2736**
Ledge Poetry & Fiction Magazine. (US) **2931**
Ledge Poetry and Prose Magazine see Ledge Poetry & Fiction Magazine **2931**
Lediga Platser. (SW ISSN 0024-0230) **3629**
Ledoeje-Smoerum Historisk Forening og Arkiv. (DK ISSN 0109-0712) **2373**
Lee County Genealogical Society Newsletter see Gleanings (Keokuk) **2153**
†Lee County Historical Society. Historical Yearbook. (US) **5226**
Lee Howard Newsletter. (US) **4131**
Lee Living. (US) **2228**
The Leech. (SA ISSN 0377-9696) **3122**
Leeds. Chamber of Commerce and Industry. Classified Trade Directory of Members see Leeds. Chamber of Commerce and Industry. Directory **818**
Leeds. Chamber of Commerce and Industry. Directory. (UK) **818**, 1143
Leeds African Studies Bulletin. (UK ISSN 0024-0249) **2012**
Leeds and Yorkshire Topic see Yorkshire Topic **2196**
Leeds Arts Calendar. (UK ISSN 0024-0257) **3526**
Leeds Citizen. (UK) **987**
Leeds Journal. (UK ISSN 0024-0273) **818**
†Leeds Medieval Studies. (UK ISSN 0140-8089) **5226**
Leeds Naturalists' Club and Scientific Association. Newsletter. (UK ISSN 0260-1036) **4322**
Leeds Philosophical and Literary Society. Proceedings. Literary and Historical Section. (UK ISSN 0024-0281) **2931**, 2316
Leeds Philosophical and Literary Society. Proceedings. Scientific. (UK) **4322**

Leeds Student. (UK ISSN 0041-6975) **1316**
Leeds Studies in English. (UK ISSN 0075-8566) **2931**, 2824
Leeds Studies in English and Kindred Languages see Leeds Studies in English **2931**
Leeds Texts and Monographs. New Series. (UK ISSN 0075-8574) **2931**, 2824
Leeds Weekly Citizen see Leeds Citizen **987**
Leeftijd. (NE) **2276**
Leerwohnungszaehlung 1. Juni (Year)/Logements Vacants Denombres au 1er Juin (Year). (SZ) **638**
Lefsetz Letter. (US ISSN 0892-1830) **3561**
Left. (UK ISSN 0024-0303) **2871**
Left. (IE) **3904**, 1259, 3944
Left Business Observer. (US ISSN 1042-0134) **677**
Left Court. (US) **3904**
Left Curve. (US ISSN 0160-1857) **2871**
Left Index. (US ISSN 0733-2998) **3938**
Lefthander. (US) **1299**, 573
Lefthander Magazine see Lefthander **1299**
Leg Show. (US ISSN 0734-4295) **3398**
Leg Show Presents High-Heeled Women. (US) **3398**
Lega Contadina. (IT) **105**
Lega Navale. (IT ISSN 0024-032X) **4730**
Legacies in Time. (US) **2996**
Legacy (Herkimer). (US) **2412**
Legacy (Nashville). (US) **2996**, 333
Legacy (University Park). (US ISSN 0748-4321) **2931**, 4860
Legal Action. (UK) **2647**
Legal Aid New Brunswick Annual Report/Aide Juridique Nouveau Brunswick Rapport Annuel. (CN ISSN 0381-2049) **2734**
Legal Almanac Series see Oceana's Legal Almanacs, Second Series **2735**
Legal & Commercial Looseleaf Services Available in Australia. (AT) **2699**
Legal & General Gazette. (UK) **2647**
Legal Aspects of International Organization. (NE) **2726**
†Legal Aspects of Medical Practice. (US ISSN 0190-2350) **5226**
Legal Aspects of Selling and Buying. (US) **2647**, 1044
Legal Assistance Newsletter see L A M P Lighter **3462**
Legal Assistant Management Association. Directory. (US) **2647**, 1018
Legal Assistant Management Newsletter see L A M A Manager **2642**
Legal Assistant Today. (US ISSN 1051-3663) **2647**
Legal Assistants Update. (US ISSN 0272-1961) **2647**
Legal Beagle see Liberator **3398**
Legal Bibliography Journal. (US ISSN 0741-1189) **2647**
Legal Briefs for Architects, Engineers, and Contractors see Legal Briefs for the Construction Industry **5226**
†Legal Briefs for the Construction Industry. (US ISSN 0730-952X) **5226**
Legal Bulletin. (CK ISSN 0458-9564) **2647**, 1018
†Legal Bulletin (Chicago). (US) **5226**
▼Legal Business. (UK ISSN 0958-4609) **2647**, 677
Legal Connection: Corporations and Law Firms. (US ISSN 0270-3424) **2647**, 677, 2711
†Legal Contents. (US ISSN 0279-5787) **5226**
Legal Costs N S W. (AT) **2647**
Legal Costs Victoria. (AT) **2647**
Legal Daily. see Fazhi Ribao **2625**
Legal Eagles News see Lawyer - Pilots Bar Association Journal **58**
Legal Economics see Law Practice Management **2645**
The Legal Edge. (US) **2647**
Legal Education Newsletter see Syllabus **2684**

Legal Executive. (UK ISSN 0024-0362) **2647**
Legal Handbook for Architects, Engineers and Contractors. (US ISSN 0887-1183) **2647**, 302
Legal Handbook for Small Business. (US) **2647**, 1116
Legal History. (II ISSN 0377-0907) **2648**
Legal History Review. see Tijdschrift voor Rechtsgeschiedenis **2686**
Legal Information. see Huul' Dzuyn Medeele **2633**
Legal Information Alert. (US ISSN 0883-1297) **2699**, 2648, 2768
Legal Information Management Index. (US ISSN 0747-9298) **2699**, 2768, 2794
Legal Information Management Reports.(US) **2648**, 2768
†Legal Information Service Reports. (CN ISSN 0225-2287) **5226**
Legal Insights for Managers. (US) **2648**, 1018, 2711
Legal Intelligencer. (US) **2648**
Legal Issues see Legal Issues of European Integration **2727**
Legal Issues, Government Programs & the Elderly (Florida). (US) **2734**, 2276, 4066
Legal Issues of European Integration. (NE) **2727**
Legal Journals Index. (UK) **2699**, 16
Legal - Legislative Reporter. News Bulletin. (US ISSN 0458-9599) **987**, 2648
Legal Looseleafs in Print. (US ISSN 0275-4088) **2648**, 405
Legal Management. (US ISSN 1043-7355) **2648**, 1018
Legal Medicine. see Zentralblatt Rechtsmedizin **3182**
Legal Medicine. (US ISSN 0197-9981) **3265**
Legal Medicine: Legal Dynamics of Medical Encounters. (US) **3122**, 2648, 3265
Legal Memorandum see N A S S P Legal Memorandum **1729**
Legal Newsletter see A E Legal Newsletter **2593**
Legal Newsletter see Organization of American States. Legal Newsletter **2664**
Legal Newsletters in Print. (US ISSN 8755-416X) **2700**, 405
Legal Notes (Washington) see Legislative Update (Washington) **789**
Legal Notes for Education. (US ISSN 0093-397X) **2648**, 1729
Legal Notes for Insurance. (US ISSN 0094-0623) **2536**
Legal Outlook. see Fazhi Liaowang **1514**
Legal Periodicals in English. (US) **2700**
Legal Plan Letter. (US ISSN 0886-6678) **2648**, 1506
▼Legal Planning for the Elderly in Massachusetts. (US) **2648**
Legal Professional see Legal Assistant Today **2647**
Legal Publishing Preview. (US ISSN 0000-1279) **2648**, 4131
▼Legal Quarterly Digest of Mine Safety and Health Decisions. (US) **3487**, 2648, 3122
Legal Reference Services Quarterly. (US ISSN 0270-319X) **2768**, 2648
Legal Reformer. (US) **3904**
Legal Reporter. (AT ISSN 0159-2483) **2648**
Legal Research Journal. (US ISSN 0146-0382) **2648**
Legal Resource Index. (US ISSN 0272-9296) **2700**, 16
Legal Resources for the Mentally Disabled: A Directory of Lawyers and Other Specialists. (US) **3344**, 2648
Legal Rights of Children. (US) **3944**, 1240
Legal Service Bulletin. (AT ISSN 0817-3516) **2648**
Legal Services Monthly see Legal Services Occasional **5226**
†Legal Services Occasional. (US) **5226**
Legal Studies. (UK ISSN 0261-3875) **2648**

Legal Studies Forum. (US ISSN 0894-5993) **2648**, 2871
Legal System and Civilization. see Fazhi yu Wenming **2625**
Legal Times. (US) **2648**
Legal Video Review. (US) **2648**, 1385, 1646
Legal Writing Journal. (US ISSN 0732-4529) **2648**
Legalidad Socialista. (CU) **3904**
Legalita e Giustizia. (IT) **2648**
Legality. see Huul' Yos **2633**
Legend. (TS) **4694**
Legend of Jennie Lee. (US) **1299**, 3398
Legend Series Muscle Cars of the '60s see Legend Series: Muscle Cars of the '60s - '70s **4694**
Legend Series: Muscle Cars of the '60s - '70s. (US ISSN 0898-5820) **4694**, 258
Legendes et Rumeurs. (FR ISSN 1159-098X) **2056**
Legends Sports Memorabilia. (US) **4507**
Legerkoerier. (NE ISSN 0024-0389) **3463**
Leggere Donna. (IT) **4846**
Leggi. (IT ISSN 0024-0400) **2648**
Legi-Social. (FR ISSN 0223-4726) **953**, 2648
Legioen van Maria. (NE ISSN 0024-0427) **4187**
Legion. (UK ISSN 0144-6533) **1299**
Legion. (CN ISSN 0024-0435) **3463**
Legionair. (AT ISSN 0024-0451) **4694**
Legionnaires Disease - Update Service. (UK) **3221**
Legipresse. (FR) **2648**
Legiscon Statehouse Report. (US) **4066**
Legislacao do Sistema de Informacao Estatistica de Macau/Law of Macau Statistical Information System. (MH) **4577**
Legislacao Federal e Marginalia. (BL ISSN 0024-158X) **2648**
Legislacion Comunidades Autonomas. (SP) **2648**
Legislacion Comunidades Europeas. (SP) **2648**
Legislacion Economica Argentina/Argentine Economic Legislation. (AG) **2648**
Legislation en Matiere d'Emploi see Employment Standards Legislation in Canada **978**
Legislative Advisory. (US) **2648**
Legislative Alert. (US) **2649**, 4412
Legislative and Regulatory Update. (US) **789**, 2649
Legislative & Socio-Economic Issues in Focus see Legislative Issues in Focus **5226**
Legislative Conference Reporter see P S C Clarion **1714**
Legislative Finance Papers. (US) **4066**
Legislative Gazette. (US) **4066**
Legislative Information Alert see Government and Politics Alert **4061**
†Legislative Issues in Focus. (US) **5226**
Legislative Monitor see Professional Monitor **5262**
Legislative Network for Nurses. (US) **3281**, 2649
Legislative Reporter. (US) **2536**
Legislative Research Checklist see State Government Research Checklist **4074**
Legislative Scene. (US) **1067**, 2649
Legislative Studies Quarterly. (US ISSN 0362-9805) **3904**, 4066
Legislative Trends. (US ISSN 0457-3633) **2700**, 4081
Legislative Update (Dallas). (US) **3904**
Legislative Update (Washington). (US) **789**, 2649
Legislator. (II ISSN 0024-0508) **3904**
Legislatve Memoranda. (US) **2477**, 2076, 2649
Legislazione e Normativa delle Costruzioni. (IT) **622**, 2649
Legislazione Italiana. (IT ISSN 0024-0524) **2649**
Legkaya Atletika. (RU ISSN 0024-4155) **4478**

Il Legno (Milan). (IT) 2560
Legon Journal of the Humanities. (GH) 2510
†Leguas. (SP) 5227
Legume Research. (II ISSN 0250-5371) 184
Lehel Aktuell. (GW) 3904
Lehigh Alumni Bulletin. (US) 1316
Lehigh County Historical Society. Proceedings. (US) 2412
Lehigh Valley Motor Club News see A A A Motorist 4678
Lehr- und Forschungstexte Psychologie/ Lecture Notes in Psychology. (US) 4034
Lehrbogen fuer Kunsterzeihung see Lernhilfen fuer Bildende Kunst 334
Lehrbuecher und Monographien zur Didaktik der Mathematik. (GW) 3043, 1646
Lehre und Praxis des Handballspiels see Handballtraining 4506
Lehren und Lernen. (GW) 1646
Lehrer-Briefe zur Verkehrserziehung see Praxis Verkehrserziehung 1655
Lehrer der Welt see Educadores del Mundo 1627
Lehrer im Berufsfeld Koerperpflege. (GW ISSN 0723-7928) 373
Lehrer in Friseurklassen see Lehrer im Berufsfeld Koerperpflege 373
Lehrerinnen- und Lehrerkalender. (GW) 1646
Lehrerjournal Grundschulmagazin. (GW) 1754
Lehrerjournal Hauptschulmagazin. (GW) 1754
Lehrermagazin Sonderschulmagazin. (GW ISSN 0930-696X) 1754
Lehrerzeitung Baden-Wuerttemberg. (GW ISSN 0170-4605) 1646
Lehrhilfen fuer den Sportunterricht. (GW ISSN 0342-2461) 1754, 3805
Lehrmittel Aktuell see Lehrmittel Aktuell - Lehrmittel Computer 1729
Lehrmittel Aktuell - Lehrmittel Computer. (GW) 1729
Lei see Glamour 4844
Leibniz Newsletter. (UK ISSN 0266-0598) 3771
Leica-Fotografie International. (GW ISSN 0024-0621) 3793
Leicester & County Chamber of Commerce & Industry Directory see Leicestershire Chamber of Commerce & Industry Directory 818
Leicester and County Chamber of Commerce Journal see City and County 813
Leicester Literary & Philosophical Society. Transactions. (UK ISSN 0141-3511) 2931, 3771
Leicester Longwool Sheepbreeders' Association. Flock Book. (UK) 220
Leicester Topic. (UK ISSN 0140-6981) 2194
Leicestershire Archaeological and Historical Society. Transactions. (UK ISSN 0140-3990) 277, 2373
Leicestershire Business Today. (UK) 677, 1018
Leicestershire Chamber of Commerce & Industry Directory. (UK) 818
Leicestershire Family History Circle. Newsletter see Leicestershire Family History Society. Newsletter 2157
Leicestershire Family History Society. Newsletter. (UK ISSN 0262-7574) 2157
Leicestershire Farmer see Leicestershire, Northamptonshire & Rutland Farmer 105
Leicestershire Historian. (UK ISSN 0024-0664) 2316, 2157
Leicestershire, Northamptonshire & Rutland Farmer. (UK ISSN 0306-0160) 105
Leichhardt Historical Journal. (AT ISSN 0155-4840) 2345
Leichtathlet. (GW ISSN 0323-4134) 4478
Leichtathletik. (GW ISSN 0047-4355) 4549
Leichter Leben. (GW) 2190
Leiden Botanical Series. (NE ISSN 0169-8508) 508
Leidinggeven & Organiseren. (NE ISSN 0169-281X) 1018
Leidraad. (NE ISSN 0168-1850) 140

Leidse Germanistische en Anglistische Reeks. (NE ISSN 0169-8559) 2931
Leidse Juridische Reeks. (NE ISSN 0169-8605) 2649
†Leidse Kunsthistorische Reeks. (NE ISSN 0169-8575) 5227
Leidse Romanistische Reeks. (NE ISSN 0169-8656) 2825, 2931
Leipuri. (FI ISSN 0024-0699) 2088
Leipzig aus Vergangenheit und Gegenwart. (GW) 2373
▼Leipziger Behoerden Spiegel. (GW) 4089
Leipziger Messejournal. (GW) 34
Leipziger Sportwissenschaftliche Beitraege. (GW) 4478
Leirinta ja Retkeily see Matkailu 4775
Leisha. (IS) 4846
†Leishmaniasis. (UK ISSN 0952-0333) 5227
Leistungssport. (GW ISSN 0341-7387) 4478
Leisure and Fitness. (UK) 2738, 4478
Leisure Arts. (US) 2437, 2738
Leisure Beverage Insider Newsletter. (US ISSN 1040-3736) 383
Leisure Futures. (UK ISSN 0263-7774) 2739, 789
Leisure Industry Digest see Leisure Industry Report 2739
Leisure Industry Report. (US) 2739, 3561, 4478
Leisure Information Quarterly. (US) 2739, 4442
Leisure Information Service. Fund Development and Revenue Source Report see Recreation Executive Report 2739
Leisure Intelligence. (UK) 2739
Leisure Lines. (US) 2739
Leisure Management. (UK ISSN 0266-9102) 2739, 2437, 4478
Leisure Manager. (UK ISSN 0267-3754) 2739, 1491, 4066, 4549
Leisure Ontario see Leisure World 2739
Leisure Painter. (UK ISSN 0024-0710) 333
Leisure, Recreation and Tourism Abstracts. (UK ISSN 0261-1392) 4799, 16, 2739
Leisure Sciences. (US ISSN 0149-0400) 2739, 4478
Leisure Studies. (UK ISSN 0261-4367) 2739, 4442, 4478
Leisure Studies Association Newsletter see L S A Newsletter 2738
†Leisure Time Electronics. (US) 5227
Leisure World. (CN) 2739, 4694, 4774
Leisure World Golden Rain News. (US) 2228
Leisureguide - Atlanta see Guest Informant - Atlanta 4802
Leisureguide - Boston see Guest Informant - Boston 4802
Leisureguide - Chicago see Guest Informant - Chicago 4802
Leisureguide - Houston see Guest Informant - Houston 4802
Leisureguide - Kansas City see Guest Informant - Kansas City 4802
†Leisureguide - Louisville. (US) 5227
†Leisureguide - Milwaukee. (US) 5227
Leisureguide - New Orleans see Guest Informant - New Orleans 4802
Leisureguide - Orlando see Guest Informant - Orlando 4802
Leisureguide - Puerto Rico see Guest Informant - Puerto Rico 4802
Leisureguide - The Florida Gold Coast see Guest Informant - The Florida Gold Coast 4802
Leisureguide - Twin Cities see Guest Informant - Twin Cities 4802
LeisureWays. (CN) 2178
Der Leitende Angestellte. (GW ISSN 0024-0737) 1067
Leitende Maenner der Wirtschaft see Leitende Maenner und Frauen der Wirtschaft 1018
Leitende Maenner und Frauen der Wirtschaft. (GW) 1018, 419
Leithead Family Newsletter. (UK ISSN 0262-4435) 2157

†Leitung und Planung von Wissenschaft und Technik. (GW ISSN 0138-2845) 5227
Vi Lejere. (DK) 4151
Lejeunia. (BE ISSN 0457-4184) 508
Lekarske Prace. (CS ISSN 0075-8736) 3122
Lekarsky Obzor. (CS) 3122, 3734
Lekarz Kolejowy. (PL) 3122
Lekarz Wojskowy. (PL ISSN 0024-0745) 3122
Leket. (IS) 2931
Lemon Aid Bulletin - Auto Conseils see Lemon Aid Magazine 4694
Lemon Aid Magazine. (CN ISSN 0834-2423) 4694, 1506
†Lemon File. (US) 5227
Lemon Times. (US) 4694, 1506
Lemouzi. (FR ISSN 0024-0761) 2373, 2825
Lempert Report. (US) 1044
Len i Konoplya. (RU ISSN 0024-418X) 184
Lendemains. (GW ISSN 0170-3803) 2871, 4442
Lender Liability Law and Litigation. (US) 2649, 789
Lender Liability Law Report. (US) 2649, 789
Lender Liability Litigation Reporter. (US ISSN 1042-5764) 2649, 789
Lender Liability News. (US ISSN 0898-7645) 2649, 789
†Lending for the Commercial Banker. (US) 5227
Lengas. (FR ISSN 0153-0313) 2825
Lengo/Target. (TZ ISSN 0039-9655) 4188
Length of Stay by D R G and Payment Source. (Diagnosis Related Group) (US) 2470, 2467
Length of Stay by Diagnosis & Operation, United States. (US) 2471, 4577
Length of Stay by Diagnosis & Operation, United States, North Central Region. (US) 2471, 4577
Length of Stay by Diagnosis & Operation, United States, Northeastern Region. (US) 2471, 4577
Length of Stay by Diagnosis & Operation, United States, Southern Region. (US) 2471, 4577
Length of Stay by Diagnosis & Operation, United States, Western Region. (US) 2471, 4577
Length of Stay by Diagnosis & Operation, United States see Length of Stay by Diagnosis & Operation, United States 2471
Length of Stay by Diagnosis, United States, North Central Region see Length of Stay by Diagnosis & Operation, United States, North Central Region 2471
Length of Stay by Diagnosis, United States, Northeastern Region see Length of Stay by Diagnosis & Operation, United States, Northeastern Region 2471
Length of Stay by Diagnosis, United States, Southern Region see Length of Stay by Diagnosis & Operation, United States, Southern Region 2471
Length of Stay by Diagnosis, United States, Western Region see Length of Stay by Diagnosis & Operation, United States, Western Region 2471
Length of Stay by Operation, United States see Length of Stay by Diagnosis & Operation, United States 2471
Length of Stay by Operation, United States, North Central Region see Length of Stay by Diagnosis & Operation, United States, North Central Region 2471
Length of Stay by Operation, United States, Northeastern Region see Length of Stay by Diagnosis & Operation, United States, Northeastern Region 2471

Length of Stay by Operation, United States, Southern Region see Length of Stay by Diagnosis & Operation, United States, Southern Region 2471
Length of Stay by Operation, United States, Western Region see Length of Stay by Diagnosis & Operation, United States, Western Region 2471
Lengua y Sociedad. (PE) 2825
Lenguaje. (CK ISSN 0120-3479) 2825
Lenguaje y Ciencias. (PE ISSN 0024-0796) 2825
Lenguajes. (AG) 2825
▼Leningrad Mathematical Journal. (US ISSN 1048-9924) 3043
Leningrad News see St. Petersburg News 4785
Leningrad University Mechanics Bulletin. (English translation of: Vestnik Leningradskogo Universiteta: Mekhanika) (US ISSN 0883-623X) 3844
Leningradskaya Panorama. (RU) 622, 302
Leningradskii Universitet. Uchenye Zapiski. Seriya Geologicheskikh Nauk.(RU ISSN 0459-0805) 1571
Leningradskii Universitet. Vestnik. Seriya Biologiya. (RU ISSN 0321-186X) 446
Leningradskii Universitet. Vestnik. Seriya Ekonomika, Filosofiya i Pravo. (RU ISSN 0024-0818) 677, 2649, 3771
Leningradskii Universitet. Vestnik. Seriya Fizika i Khimiya. (RU ISSN 0024-0826) 3823, 1183
Leningradskii Universitet. Vestnik. Seriya Geologiya i Geografiya. (RU ISSN 0024-0834) 1571, 2255
Leningradskii Universitet. Vestnik. Seriya Istoriya, Yazyk i Literatura. (RU ISSN 0024-0842) 2316, 2825
Leningradskii Universitet. Vestnik. Seriya Matematika, Mekhanika i Astronomiya. (RU ISSN 0024-0850) 3043, 366
Leninyan Ugiov. (AI ISSN 0130-8114) 3904
Lennox News. (US) 2301
Lens. (IE) 3793
Lens and Eye Toxicity Research. (US ISSN 1042-6922) 3302, 1983
The Lenshade. (US) 3793
Lentil Abstracts see Lentils 140
Lentils. (UK ISSN 0961-3501) 140, 105
Lentsoe la Basotho. (LO) 2169
Lenzinger Berichte. (AU ISSN 0024-0907) 4621
Leo Baeck Institut. Bulletin. (GW ISSN 0024-0915) 2316
Leo Baeck Institute. Year Book. (UK ISSN 0075-8744) 2316
Leo Baeck Institute News see L B I News 2316
Leobener Gruene Hefte. Neue Folge. (AU ISSN 0259-0751) 3487, 2316
Leodiensian. (UK ISSN 0024-0923) 1316
Leodium. (BE) 2373, 333
Leon. Boletin de Informacion Municipal. (SP) 4089
Leonard Horwin Collection. (CN) 2012, 3964
Leonardo. (GW ISSN 0935-1108) 302
Leonardo. (IT ISSN 0075-8760) 1646
Leonardo: Art Science and Technology. (US ISSN 0024-094X) 334
▼Leonardo Music Journal. (US ISSN 0961-1215) 3561, 334
Leonard's Annual Index of Art Auctions. (US ISSN 0733-5342) 334, 677
Leone. (US ISSN 0024-0958) 1299
Leopoldianum. (BL ISSN 0101-9635) 1339
Leopoldina. (GW ISSN 0323-4444) 4322
Lepidoptera. (DK ISSN 0075-8787) 536
Lepidopterists' Society. Journal. (US ISSN 0024-0966) 536

Lepidopterists' Society. Memoirs. (US ISSN 0075-8795) **536**
Lepidopterological Society of Japan. Journal. *see* Yadoriga **539**
Lepidopterological Society of Japan. Transactions. (JA ISSN 0024-0974) **536**
Leppro *see* Japanese Journal of Leprosy **3220**
Leprologia. (AG ISSN 0024-1016) **3221**
Leprosy Mission in Action *see* New Day **3222**
Leprosy Mission, London. Annual Report. (UK ISSN 0075-8809) **4188**
Leprosy Review. (UK ISSN 0305-7518) **3221**
Ler Historia. (PO ISSN 0870-6182) **2373**, **4379**
Lernen Foerdern. (GW ISSN 0720-8316) **1738**
Lernen in Deutschland. (GW ISSN 0173-0614) **1646**
Lernen Konkret. (GW ISSN 0722-1843) **1646**
Lernfeld Betrieb. (GW) **677**
Lernhilfen fuer Bildende Kunst. (GW ISSN 0932-7959) **334**
Les. (CS) **2103**, **4826**
Les. (XV ISSN 0024-1067) **2115**
Les Commandes, la Production, les Chiffres d'Affaires et les Stocks dans l'Industrie et le Secteur Principal de la Construction. *see* Auftrags-, Produktions-, Umsatz- und Lagerverhaeltnisse in der Industrie und im Bauhauptgewerbe **702**
Lesbenrundbrief. (AU) **2454**, **4846**
LesbenStich. (GW) **2454**, **4846**
Lesbia Magazine. (FR) **2455**
Lesbian and Gay Counselling News. (AT) **2455**, **4034**, **4412**, **4442**
Lesbian & Gay Teacher's Association Newsletter. (US) **2455**, **1646**
Lesbian Center News. (US) **2455**, **4846**
Lesbian Community News. (US) **2455**, **4846**
Lesbian Connection. (US) **2455**, **3944**, **4846**
Lesbian Ethics. (US ISSN 8755-5352) **2455**, **3771**, **4846**
Lesbian Feminist. (US) **4846**, **2455**
Lesbian - Gay Law Notes. (US ISSN 8755-9021) **2649**, **2455**
Lesbian Herstory Archives Newsletter. (US) **2455**, **2458**, **4637**
Lesbian Interest Press Newsletter *see* L I P Newsletter **2454**
Lesbian News. (US ISSN 0739-1803) **2455**, **4846**
†Lesbian Position. (US) **5227**
Lesbians Rising. (US) **2455**, **4846**
Lesbisch Archivaria. (NE) **2458**, **4858**
Lesbisch Informatieboekje. (NE) **2455**
Lesedi Ja Molemirui. (SA) **105**
Leselinyana la Lesotho. (LO) **4188**
Leseplan Jahreslosung. (GW) **4267**
Lesestunde mit dem Grossen Freizeit-Programm. (GW ISSN 0024-1083) **4131**
Leshonenu. (IS ISSN 0334-3626) **2825**
Leshonenu La'am. (IS ISSN 0024-1091) **2825**
Lesko's Info - Power Newsletter. (US) **1427**, **1351**, **1457**, **1461**
Leslie and Britts: Motor Vehicle Law in N.S.W. (AT) **2649**, **2536**
Leslie L. Schaffer Lectureship in Forest Science. (CN ISSN 0836-0618) **2103**
Lesnaya Promyshlennost' (RU) **2115**
Lesnicka Prace/Forestry. (CS) **2103**
Lesnicke Drevarske a Pol'ovnicke Muzeum. Zbornik. (CS) **2373**, **2103**
Lesnicky Casopis/Forestry Journal. (CS) **2104**
Lesnictvi/Forestry. (CS ISSN 0024-1105) **2104**
Lesnoe Khozyaistvo. (RU ISSN 0024-1113) **2104**
†Lesotho. Bureau of Statistics. Half-Yearly Statistical Bulletin. (LO) **5227**

Lesotho. Ministry of Education and Culture. Annual Report of the Permanent Secretary *see* Lesotho. Ministry of Education, Sports and Culture. Annual Report of the Permanent Secretary **1646**
Lesotho. Ministry of Education, Sports and Culture. Annual Report of the Permanent Secretary. (LO) **1646**
Lesotho. Ministry of Foreign Affairs. Diplomatic and Consular List. (LO ISSN 0460-2099) **3964**
Lesotho. Ministry of Water, Energy and Mining. Hydrological Yearbook. (LO) **1599**
Lesotho. Treasury. Report on the Finances and Accounts. (LO ISSN 0075-8817) **1100**
Lesotho Bank. Annual Report. (LO) **789**
Lesotho Catholic Directory. (LO) **1143**, **4267**
Lesotho Law Journal. (LO ISSN 0255-6472) **2649**
Lesotho National Development Corporation. Newsletter. (LO) **872**
Lesotho Today. (LO) **2169**
Lesovedenie. (RU ISSN 0024-1148) **2104**
Lessico Intellettuale Europeo. (IT ISSN 0075-8825) **2825**
Lessing Yearbook. (US ISSN 0075-8833) **2931**
Lesson Plans Plus *see* Educational Computing Chronicle **5184**
Lessons of Mastership. (RU) **3561**
Lest We Forget. (US ISSN 0887-2856) **2412**
†Let It Rock. (UK) **5227**
Letaasiyan. (IS) **677**
Letecky Obzor. (CS ISSN 0457-5792) **4675**
Letectvi a Kosmonautika. (CS ISSN 0024-1156) **58**
Lethaia. (NO ISSN 0024-1164) **3658**
Lethbridge Historical Society Newletter. (CN ISSN 0838-7249) **2412**
Lethbridge Magazine. (CN ISSN 0821-5278) **2178**
Letizia. (IT) **2983**
Letopis. Reihe B. Geschichte. (GW ISSN 0522-5078) **2373**
Letopis. Reihe C. Volkskunde. (GW ISSN 0522-5086) **2373**
Letopis' Gazetnykh Statei. (RU ISSN 0024-1172) **405**
Letopis Matice Srpske. (YU ISSN 0025-5939) **2932**
Letopis na Periodichna Pechat *see* Létopis na Statiite ot Bulgarskite Spisaniia i Sbornitsi **405**
Letopis na Periodichna Pechat *see* Letopis na Statiite ot Bulgarskite Vestnitsi **405**
Letopis na Statiite ot Bulgarskite Spisaniia i Sbornitsi/Articles from Bulgarian Journals and Collections. (BU ISSN 0324-0398) **405**
Letopis na Statiite ot Bulgarskite Vestnitsi/Articles from Bulgarian Newspapers. (BU ISSN 0324-0347) **405**
Letopis Pamatnika Slovenskej Literatury *see* Literarno - Muzejny Letopis **2933**
Letopis' Pechati B.S.S.R. (BW ISSN 0130-9218) **2768**
Letopis' Pechatnykh Proizvedenii Izobrazitel'nogo Iskusstva. (RU ISSN 0024-1199) **334**, **4002**
Letopis' Zhurnal'nykh Statei. (RU ISSN 0024-1202) **405**
Letra Grande, Arte y Literatura. (DR) **334**, **2932**
Letras. (MX ISSN 0024-1210) **2982**
Letras (Caracas). (VE) **2825**
Letras da Provincia. (BL ISSN 0047-441X) **2871**
Letras de Buenos Aires. (AG ISSN 0326-2928) **2932**, **2996**
Letras de Deusto. (SP ISSN 0210-3516) **2511**, **3771**
Letras de Hoje. (BL ISSN 0047-4428) **2825**
Letras de Nicaragua. (NQ) **2996**
Letras del Ecuador. (EC) **2932**, **334**
Letras Femeninas. (US ISSN 0277-4356) **2932**, **4846**

Letras Potosinas. (MX ISSN 0024-1245) **2932**
Der Letroner. (GW) **987**
Let's Be Human. (US) **3944**
Let's Dance. (US ISSN 0024-1253) **1531**
Let's Find Out. (US ISSN 0024-1261) **1259**, **1646**
Let's Find Out. (AT) **1754**
Let's Go: The Budget Guide to Europe. (US ISSN 0163-4585) **4774**
Let's Go: The Budget Guide to Greece, Israel and Egypt - Including Cyprus & Turkish Coast. (US) **4774**
Let's Go: The Budget Guide to Italy. (US ISSN 0192-2920) **4774**
Let's Go: U S A. (US) **4774**
Let's Live. (US ISSN 0024-1288) **3805**, **3609**
Let's Love Oita. (JA) **2207**
Let's Make it Official. (US) **4478**
Let's Play Hockey. (US) **4478**
Let's Play Softball. (US) **4507**
†Let's Pray Together. (US ISSN 0740-9613) **5227**
Let's Square Dance. (UK ISSN 0301-8881) **1531**
Let's Talk Business Niagara. (CN) **677**
Letter (Bradenton) *see* Root Directory **1474**
Letter Bomb. (US) **1353**, **334**
Letter Exchange. (US ISSN 0882-3804) **2932**, **1353**
Letter from Evans. (US) **3561**
Letter from Plymouth Rock. (US) **4188**
Letter from Taize. (FR ISSN 0750-3695) **4284**
Letter of Credit Update. (US ISSN 0883-0487) **2649**, **1100**
Letter of the L A A. (Library Association of Alberta) (CN ISSN 0705-4890) **2768**
Letter to Friends Around the World. (FR) **4412**
Letter to Libraries. (US) **2768**
▼Letter to Libraries Online. (US ISSN 1059-3195) **2798**
Lettera dall'Italia. (IT ISSN 0393-6457) **2205**
Lettera Internazionale. (IT) **4442**
Letterato. (IT ISSN 0024-130X) **2871**
Letteratura Giovanile Argomenti *see* L.G. Argomenti **2871**
Letterature. (IT) **2932**
Letterature d'America. (IT) **2932**
Lettere d'Affari. (IT ISSN 0024-1326) **726**, **4577**
Lettere Italiane. (IT ISSN 0024-1334) **2932**
Lettere Italiane. Biblioteca. (IT ISSN 0075-8892) **2932**
Lettere Italiane. Saggi. (IT) **2932**
Letterheads. (US) **334**
Letters *see* Live Letters **2935**
Letters from Limerick. (US) **2996**
Letters in Mathematical Physics. (NE ISSN 0377-9017) **3823**, **3043**
Letters Magazine (Teaneck). (US ISSN 0279-1250) **3398**
Letters of Credit. (US) **2649**, **789**
Letters of Credit Report. (US ISSN 0886-0459) **789**, **2649**
Letters of Intent and Other Precontractual Documents. (US) **2649**
Letterstick. (AT ISSN 0727-5854) **4241**
Lettore di Provincia. (IT ISSN 0024-1350) **2932**
Lettre Ada. (FR ISSN 0981-0455) **1431**
Lettre Afrique Energies. (FR ISSN 0754-5215) **3691**, **1902**, **3487**
†Lettre aux Educateurs. (FR ISSN 0397-0167) **5227**
Lettre Confidentielle des Transports. (FR ISSN 0756-8037) **4675**, **4711**, **4730**
†Lettre Culturelle. (FR) **5227**
▼Lettre d'Excel. (FR) **1478**
Lettre d'Information Metaux. (FR ISSN 0181-1223) **3412**
Lettre d'Information sur la Recherche Hygiene et Securite. (FR) **3619**
Lettre d'Intergeo. (FR ISSN 0220-0546) **2255**
▼Lettre de dBASE. (FR) **1478**

Lettre de l'Audiovisuel. (FR) **1339**
Lettre de l'Energie. (FR) **1807**
Lettre de l'Environnement. (FR) **1962**
Lettre de l'Expansion. (FR) **1080**, **789**
†Lettre de l'Informatique Medicale. (FR) **5227**
Lettre de l'Intelligence Artificielle. (FR ISSN 0767-4910) **1409**
Lettre de l'Ocean Indien *see* Indian Ocean Newsletter **3960**
Lettre de L'U N I D I R. *see* U N I D I R Newsletter **3974**
Lettre de la Surete de Fonctionnement. (FR) **1398**, **1879**
▼Lettre de Paradox. (FR) **1478**
Lettre de Solagral *see* Courrier de la Planete **149**
▼Lettre de Windows. (FR) **1478**
▼Lettre de Word. (FR) **1478**
Lettre des I T P A. (FR) **105**
Lettre du Continent. (FR) **3964**
Lettre du Moniteur *see* Urbapress **635**
Lettre du Musicien. (FR ISSN 0766-916X) **3561**
Lettre du Psychiatre. (FR ISSN 0223-9434) **3344**
Lettre du Sponsoring et du Mecenat. (FR ISSN 0298-9239) **1044**, **34**, **1339**
Lettre Europeenne. *see* European Insight **906**
Lettre Financiere. (FR) **789**
Lettre Hebdo des Cuisinistes, des Bainistes et des Electromenagistes. (FR) **2448**
Lettre Informatique et Collectivites Locales. (FR) **4083**
Lettre International. (GW) **2932**
Lettre Medicale. (FR ISSN 0153-4742) **3122**
Lettre Micro-Informatique. (FR) **1461**
Lettre 101. (FR) **1080**
Lettres. (FR ISSN 0024-1369) **2932**
Les Lettres Albanaises. (AA) **2932**
Lettres Botaniques. (FR ISSN 0181-1797) **508**
Lettres des Elus Locaux. (FR) **1018**
Lettres Eoliennes/Eolika Grammata. (GR) **2932**, **334**
Lettres et Cultures de Langues Francaises. (FR) **2932**, **2316**
Lettres Medievales. (FR) **2932**
Lettres Quebecoises. (CN ISSN 0382-084X) **2932**
Les Lettres Romanes. (BE ISSN 0024-1415) **2932**
Lettrisme. (FR ISSN 0024-1423) **2932**
Lettuce Club. (JA) **2448**
Lettura Stenografica. (IT ISSN 0024-1431) **1659**
Letture. (IT ISSN 0024-144X) **4634**, **3513**
Letture Classensi. (IT ISSN 0459-1623) **2932**
Letture Drammatiche *see* Cineschedario - Letture Drammatiche **3506**
Letture Trentine e Altoatesine. (IT) **2205**
Letunk. (YU ISSN 0350-4158) **2871**
Letzeburger Bauer. (LU) **105**
Letzeburger Sonndesblad. (LU) **4267**
Leucocytes. (UK ISSN 0142-8160) **3187**
Leukemia. (US ISSN 0887-6924) **3177**
Leukemia and Lymphoma. (US ISSN 1042-8194) **3273**, **3199**
Leukemia and Multiple Myeloma - Diagnosis, Treatment *see* I C R D B Cancergram: Leukemia and Multiple Myeloma - Diagnosis, Treatment **3175**
Leukemia Research. (US ISSN 0145-2126) **3273**
†Leukemia Research. (UK ISSN 0261-474X) **5227**
Leukemia Society of America. Society News. (US) **3199**
Leumi Review. (IS ISSN 0334-9160) **872**
Leuven Notes in Mathematical and Theoretical Physics. Series A, Mathematical Physics. (BE) **3823**, **3043**

▼Leuven Notes in Mathematical and Theoretical Physics. Series B, Theoretical Particle Physics. (BE) **3824**
Leuvense Bijdragen. (BE ISSN 0024-1482) **2825**
Levage Actualite. (FR ISSN 1158-0038) **622**
Levant. (UK ISSN 0075-8914) **277**
Levant. (IS ISSN 0992-0757) **2932**
Levant - Cahiers de l'Espace Mediterraneen. (FR) **2932**
Levant Morgenland. (FR ISSN 0024-1490) **4188**, 3640
Levantamento Sistematico da Producao Agricola/Systematic Survey of Agricultural Production. (BL ISSN 0103-443X) **153**, 140
Levante. (IT ISSN 0024-1504) **3964**
Levante Agricola. (SP ISSN 0457-6039) **184**
Levantina. (IS ISSN 0334-3715) **587**
Levelezesi Sakkhirado. (HU ISSN 0230-5151) **4478**
Leveltari Kozlemenyek/Archival Communications. (HU ISSN 0024-1512) **2317**
Leveltari Szemle. (HU ISSN 0457-6047) **2373**
†Leven en Gezondheid. (NE) **5227**
Levend Land. (BE) **105**
Levend Woord/Living Word. (NE ISSN 0024-1547) **4284**
Levende Billeder. (DK ISSN 0108-5697) **3513**, 1375
Levende Natur. (DK ISSN 0108-7991) **446**, 1491
Levende Natuur. (NE ISSN 0024-1520) **4322**
Leverandoerhaandbogen (Hellerup) see Grafisk Leverandoerhaandbog **4000**
Leverandoerhaandbogen (Skovlunde). (DK) **3649**
Leveranstidningen Entreprenad. (SW ISSN 0345-7133) **622**
Levevilkaar i Danmark/Living Conditions in Denmark. (DK ISSN 0900-2499) **4577**
Leviathan. (US) **2012**
Leviathan. (GW ISSN 0340-0425) **4379**
Levnedsmiddelbladet see Levnedsmiddelbladet - Supermarkedet **2093**
Levnedsmiddelbladet - Supermarkedet/Foodstuff Magazine - The Supermarket. (DK ISSN 0105-6654) **2093**, 3649
Lewis Carroll Society of North America. Chapbook. (US) **2982**
Lewis County Historical Society Journal. (US ISSN 0895-500X) **2412**
Lewis J. Smith Association Newsletter. (US) **2157**
Lewis Letter on Cable Marketing. (US) **1375**, 1044
Lewis Letter on Energy Communication.(US) **1792**, 34, 1018
Lewiston Poetry. (US) **2996**
Lex. (US ISSN 0047-4452) **1316**, 1518
Lex. (IT ISSN 0024-1598) **2649**
Lex Collegii. (US ISSN 0749-9078) **1711**, 2649
Lex Review. (US) **1316**, 1518
Lex Vitae. (US) **2649**, 4846
Lexicographica. (GW ISSN 0175-6206) **2825**
Lexikon Buerotechnik see New **1059**
Lexikon des Steuer- und Wirtschaftsrechts. (GW ISSN 0171-0826) **2649**, 872, 1100
Lexington Philharmonic Society Newsletter see Upbeat. Lexington Philharmonic Society Newsletter **3585**
Lexington School for the Deaf. Parents' Newsletter. see Sounds of Lexington **2289**
Lexington Theological Quarterly. (US ISSN 0160-8770) **4188**
Lexique Trilingue de l'Eau. (FR) **4826**
Lexis. (PE ISSN 0254-9239) **2825**, 2932
Lexport. (IT) **2737**
Ley. (AG ISSN 0024-1636) **2649**
Leyes de la Republica de Nicaragua. (NQ) **2649**

†Leyes Economicas de los Paises Miembros. (PE) **5227**
Leykor Guide to Brighter Motoring. (SA) **4694**
†Leyte-Samar Studies. (PH ISSN 0024-1679) **5227**
Lhasa Apso Reporter. (US ISSN 0273-8333) **3711**
Lhasa Bulletin. (US) **3711**
Li Jiang/Li River. (CC) **2932**
Li River. see Li Jiang **2932**
†Liability & Insurance Bulletin. (US ISSN 0889-4469) **5227**
Liability Reporter. (US ISSN 0271-5481) **2702**, 1518
Liaison. (CN ISSN 0227-227X) **334**, 3561, 4634
Liaison. (FR) **2293**, 2932
Liaisons. (FR ISSN 0024-1717) **1518**
Les Liaisons Financieres. (FR) **789**
Liaisons Juridiques et Fiscales. (FR) **2649**, 789
Liaisons Sociales. (FR ISSN 0024-1725) **987**, 4412
Liaisons Transports Equipement. (FR ISSN 0180-7811) **4652**
Al Liamm. (FR ISSN 0024-1733) **2932**, 2996
Liane Newsletter. (AT ISSN 0811-5400) **2104**
Liangshi Wenti Yanjiu/Food Problems Research. (CC) **2076**
Lianheguo Jishi/United Nations Chronicle. (CC) **3964**
Lianhuan Huabao/Picture Stories. (CC) **2572**, 3793
Lianhuanhua Yishu/Art of Pictorial Stories. (CC) **334**, 2932
Liaoning Dizhi/Liaoning Geology. (CC ISSN 1000-6273) **1571**
Liaoning Economic Weekly. see Liaoning Jingji Bao **872**
Liaoning Economics. see Liaoning Jingji **677**
Liaoning Education. see Liaoning Jiaoyu **1646**
Liaoning Forestry Technology. see Liaoning Linye Keji **2104**
Liaoning Geology. see Liaoning Dizhi **1571**
Liaoning Huabao/Liaoning Pictorial. (CC ISSN 0457-6306) **2182**
Liaoning Jiaoyu/Liaoning Education. (CC) **1646**
Liaoning Jingji/Liaoning Economics. (CC) **677**
Liaoning Jingji Bao/Liaoning Economic Weekly. (CC) **872**
Liaoning Journal of Traditional Chinese Medicine. see Liaoning Zhongyi Zazhi **3122**
Liaoning Linye Keji/Liaoning Forestry Technology. (CC ISSN 1001-1714) **2104**
Liaoning Normal University. Journal (Natural Science Edition). see Liaoning Shifan Daxue Xuebao (Ziran Kexue Ban) **4322**
Liaoning Pictorial. see Liaoning Huabao **2182**
Liaoning Qingnian/Liaoning Youth. (CC) **1259**
Liaoning Shifan Daxue Xuebao (Ziran Kexue Ban)/Liaoning Normal University. Journal (Natural Science Edition). (CC) **4322**
Liaoning Youth. see Liaoning Qingnian **1259**
Liaoning Zhongyi Zazhi/Liaoning Journal of Traditional Chinese Medicine. (CC ISSN 1000-1719) **3122**, 3734
Liaowang/Outlook. (CC ISSN 8755-9358) **2182**
Liat Islander. (AQ) **4675**, 2228, 4774
Lib Ed. (UK ISSN 0267-8500) **1646**
Libelle. (BE ISSN 0024-175X) **4847**
Liber. (FR) **2871**
Liber Academiae Kierkegaardiensis Annuarius. (DK ISSN 0106-8989) **3772**
Liberaal Reveil. (NE) **2872**
Liberal. (DK ISSN 0047-4460) **3904**
▼Liberal. (RU) **3904**
Liberal Catholic. (UK ISSN 0024-1792) **4284**
Liberal Debat see Ung og Fri **2887**

Liberal Democrat News. (UK ISSN 0954-5735) **3904**
Liberal Democrat News. (UK ISSN 0954-5735) **3904**
Liberal Education. (US ISSN 0024-1822) **1711**
Liberal Party Organisation. Liberal News see Liberal Democrat News **3904**
Liberal Review. (CE) **3904**
Liberal Star. (JA) **3904**
Liberal Ungdom. (SW ISSN 0024-1857) **3904**
Liberalt Perspektiv see Populist **2880**
Liberation! see Liberation and Marxism **3904**
Liberation. (UK ISSN 0024-1873) **3944**, 3964
Liberation. (CN) **4241**
Liberation and Marxism. (US ISSN 1051-7871) **3904**
Liberation Army Daily. see Jiefangjun Bao **3462**
†Liberation Bulletin. (US) **5227**
Liberation Daily. Index. see Jiefang Ribao Suoyin **2578**
Liberation News Service. (UK ISSN 0024-1903) **2872**
Liberation Path. see Vyzvol'nyi Shlyakh **2888**
Liberation War. (II ISSN 0047-4495) **2872**
Liberator. (US ISSN 1040-3760) **3398**, 2649
†Liberator. (UK) **5227**
Liberia. Bureau of Economic Research and Statistics. Annual Report to the President on the Operation and Activities see Liberia. Office of National Planning. Annual Report to the President on the Operation and Activities **4066**
Liberia. Department of State. Newsletter. (LB ISSN 0300-2241) **3964**
Liberia. General Services Agency. Annual Report. (LB) **4412**
Liberia. Institute of Public Administration. Annual Report. (LB) **4066**
Liberia. Ministry of Action for Development and Progress. Annual Report. (LB) **4066**
Liberia. Ministry of Agriculture. National Rice Production Estimates see Liberia. Ministry of Agriculture. Production Estimates of Major Crops **140**
Liberia. Ministry of Agriculture. Production Estimates of Major Crops.(LB) **140**
Liberia. Ministry of Agriculture. Statistical Handbook. (LB) **140**
Liberia. Ministry of Commerce, Industry and Transportation. Annual Report. (LB) **1080**, 4652
Liberia. Ministry of Finance. Annual Report. (LB ISSN 0304-727X) **1100**
Liberia. Ministry of Foreign Affairs. Annual Report. (LB) **3964**
Liberia. Ministry of Health and Social Welfare. Annual Report. (LB) **4107**
Liberia. Ministry of Information, Cultural Affairs & Tourism. Annual Report to the Session of the Legislature. (LB) **4774**
Liberia. Ministry of Justice. Annual Report to the Legislature. (LB) **2649**
Liberia. Ministry of Labour, Youth & Sports. Annual Report. (LB) **4412**, 1240
Liberia. Ministry of Lands and Mines. Annual Report see Liberia. Ministry of Lands, Mines and Energy. Annual Report **1871**
Liberia. Ministry of Lands, Mines and Energy. Annual Report. (LB) **1871**, 3487
Liberia. Ministry of Local Government, Rural Development & Urban Reconstruction. Annual Report. (LB ISSN 0304-730X) **4090**
Liberia. Ministry of National Defense. Annual Report. (LB) **3463**
Liberia. Ministry of Planning and Economic Affairs. Annual Report to the People's Redemption Council. (LB) **1080**

Liberia. Ministry of Planning and Economic Affairs. Annual Report to the Session of the Legislature of the Republic of Liberia see Liberia. Ministry of Planning and Economic Affairs. Annual Report to the People's Redemption Council **1080**
Liberia. Ministry of Planning and Economic Affairs. Government Accounts. (LB) **1100**
Liberia. Ministry of Public Works. Annual Report. (LB ISSN 0304-7326) **4066**
Liberia. Office of Fiscal Policy and Planning. Finance Bulletin see Finance Bulletin **866**
Liberia. Office of National Planning. Annual Report to the President on the Operation and Activities. (LB) **4066**
Liberia Baptist Missionary and Educational Convention. Yearbook. (LB) **4241**
Liberia Ministry of Posts and Telecommunications. Annual Report. (LB) **1339**
Liberia: Political, Economics and Social Monthly. (LB) **2169**
Liberian Economic and Management Review. (LB) **677**, 1018
Liberian Law Journal. (LB ISSN 0024-1970) **2649**
Liberian Naturalist see U L Science and Technology Magazine **4349**
Liberian Philatelic Society Journal. (US) **3754**
Liberian Philatelic Society Newsletter see Liberian Philatelic Society Journal **3754**
Liberian Shipping Journal. (UK) **4730**
Liberian Star. (LB) **2169**
Liberian Studies Journal. (US ISSN 0024-1989) **4379**
Liberian Studies Monograph Series. (US) **4379**
Liberian Studies Research Working Papers. (US) **4379**
Liberian Trade Directory. (LB) **1143**
Liberian Trade Topics and Newsletter and Forecasts. (LB) **819**
▼Liberta de Ahorros. (US) **2012**
Liberta di Educazione. (IT) **1646**
Libertad de Expresion. (PN) **1339**
Libertarian Alliance. Background Briefings. (UK ISSN 0267-7121) **3904**
Libertarian Alliance. Cultural Notes. (UK ISSN 0267-677X) **3904**, 3944
Libertarian Alliance. Economic Notes. (UK ISSN 0267-7164) **872**
Libertarian Alliance. Foreign Policy Perspectives. (UK ISSN 0267-6761) **3904**
Libertarian Alliance. Historical Notes. (UK ISSN 0267-7105) **2373**
Libertarian Alliance. Legal Notes. (UK ISSN 0267-7083) **2649**
Libertarian Alliance. Personal Perspectives. (UK ISSN 0267-7156) **3905**
Libertarian Alliance. Philosophical Notes.(UK ISSN 0267-7091) **3772**
Libertarian Alliance. Political Notes. (UK ISSN 0267-7059) **3905**
Libertarian Alliance. Psychological Notes. (UK ISSN 0267-7172) **4034**
Libertarian Alliance. Scientific Notes. (UK ISSN 0267-7067) **3905**, 4379
Libertarian Alliance. Sociological Notes. (UK ISSN 0267-7113) **4442**
Libertarian Alliance. Study Guides. (UK ISSN 0267-7180) **3905**
Libertarian Alliance. Tactical Notes. (UK) **3905**
Libertarian Alliance. World Reports. (UK) **3905**
Libertarian Connection see Connection (Alexandria) **2862**
Libertarian Digest. (US ISSN 0272-5959) **2872**
†Libertarian E-Mail Directory. (US ISSN 0893-2115) **5227**
Libertarian Forum. (US ISSN 0047-4517) **3905**
Libertarian News. (UK ISSN 0267-6788) **3905**
Libertarian Party News. (US) **3905**

Libertarian Reprints. (UK ISSN 0267-6796) 3905
Libertarian Student. (UK ISSN 0267-7199) 3905
Libertarians for Gay and Lesbian Concerns Newsletter see L G L C Newsletter 2931
Libertarians for Life Reports: see L F L Reports 597
Libertas. (GW ISSN 0341-9762) 3964, 872
Libertas Mathematica. (US ISSN 0278-5307) 3043
Libertas Review. (US) 2872
Liberte. (CN ISSN 0024-2020) 2996, 2872
▼Libertitres. (FR) 2169
Liberty (Hagerstown). (US ISSN 0024-2055) 4188
Liberty (Port Townsend). (US ISSN 0894-1408) 2872, 896, 3772, 3905
Liberty & Justice. (JA) 2649
Liberty and the Publick Good. (US ISSN 0894-251X) 2872
Liberty at Bay. (US) 872, 3964
Liberty Bell. (US ISSN 0145-7667) 3905
Liberty Lowdown see Spotlight (Washington) 3927
†Liberty News. (IE ISSN 0790-5068) 5227
Liberty Report. (US) 2872
Libido. (US) 2932
Libiya al-Qadimat. see Libya Antiqua 2430
Libra. (UK) 753
Librairie Suisse. see Schweizer Buchhandel 4136
Librarian of West Pomerania. see Bibliotekarz Zachodniopomorski 2747
Librarians. see Tushuguan Yuan 2787
Librarians' Christian Fellowship Newsletter. (UK ISSN 0308-5473) 2768, 4131, 4241
Librarians for Nuclear Arms Control Almanac see L N A C Almanac 5225
Librarians' Guide to Back Issues of International Periodicals see International Periodicals and Reference Works 2578
Librarian's Handbook. (UK) 2768
Librarians' Handbook. (US ISSN 0093-1888) 2794
Librarian's World. (US ISSN 0739-0297) 2768, 4131
Librarianship. see Bibliotekarstvo 2747
Libraries & Culture. (US ISSN 0894-8631) 2768, 2412
Libraries and Resources Centres in the Northern Territory. List see Information Centres in the Northern Territory. List 2762
Libraries Directory. (UK) 1143, 2768
Libraries in the United Kingdom & the Republic of Ireland. (UK) 1143, 2768
Libraries, Museums and Art Galleries Year Book see Libraries Directory 1143
Libraries of Maine; Directory and Statistics. (US ISSN 0092-833X) 1143, 2768
Libraries Today/Gendai no Toshokan. (JA) 2768
Libraries Unlimited Newsletter. (US) 2768
Libraries Yearbook see Libraries Directory 1143
Librarium. (SZ ISSN 0024-2152) 4131
Library. (UK ISSN 0024-2160) 2768
Library Acquisitions: Practice and Theory. (US ISSN 0364-6408) 2769
Library Administration and Management. (US ISSN 0888-4463) 2769
Library Administrator's Digest. (US ISSN 0746-6129) 2769, 1646, 4066
Library & Archival Security. (US ISSN 0196-0075) 2769, 1527
Library & Archives News. (US) 2317, 2012, 2373

Library and Documentation Literature Abroad. see Konyvtari es Dokumentacios Szakirodalom 5224
Library and Information Activists Record. (UK) 2769
Library and Information Assistant. (UK ISSN 0957-7912) 2769
Library and Information Network Line see L I N K Line 597
Library and Information News. (UK) 2769
Library and Information Research News.(UK ISSN 0141-6561) 2769
Library and Information Science. (JA ISSN 0373-4447) 2769
Library & Information Science Abstracts.(UK ISSN 0024-2179) 2794, 16
†Library and Information Science Annual. (US) 5227
Library and Information Science Education Statistical Report. (US) 2794, 1677, 4577
Library & Information Science Research.(US ISSN 0740-8188) 2769
Library and Information Science Update.(CN ISSN 0820-0521) 2794
Library and Information Service. see Tushu Qingbao Gongzuo 2787
Library and Information Service of Western Australia. Newsletter. (AT) 2769
Library and Information Services Today see L I S T 5225
Library and Information Technology Association Newsletter see L I T A Newsletter 2798
Library Association. Industrial Group Newsletter see L A I G News 2767
Library Association. Rare Books Group. Newsletter see Rare Books Newsletter 2780
Library Association. University, College and Research Section. Newsletter. (UK ISSN 0144-056X) 2769
Library Association. Yearbook. (UK ISSN 0075-9066) 2769
Library Association News see L A I G News 2767
Library Association Newsletter. see Ghaqda Bibljotekarji 2759
Library Association of Alberta. Newsletter. (CN) 2769
Library Association of Alberta. Occasional Papers see Library Association of Alberta. Newsletter 2769
Library Association of Alberta Letter of the L A A see Letter of the L A A 2768
Library Association of Barbados. Bulletin. (BB) 2769
Library Association of Barbados. Occasional Newsletter see Update (Bridgetown) 2790
Library Association of China. Newsletter.(CH ISSN 0254-4784) 2769
Library Association of Trinidad and Tobago. Bulletin. (TR ISSN 0521-9590) 2769
Library Association Record. (UK ISSN 0024-2195) 2769
Library Automated Systems Information Exchange see L A S I E 2767
†Library Automation News. (US) 5227
†Library Bibliographies and Indexes. (US) 5227
The Library Bookseller. (US ISSN 0024-2217) 4131
Library Catalog of the Metropolitan Museum of Art. (US) 3536, 352
Library Chronicle (Austin). (US ISSN 0024-2241) 2769
Library Circle. see Tushuguan Jie 2787
Library Company of Philadelphia. Annual Report. (US ISSN 0160-922X) 2769
Library Company of Philadelphia. Occasional Miscellany. (US ISSN 0734-3698) 2413, 2769, 3526
Library Computer Systems & Equipment Review. (US) 2798, 1461
Library Conservation News. (UK ISSN 0265-041X) 1491, 2769

Library Cooperation News. see Toshokan Kyoryoku Tsushin 2787
Library Currents. (US ISSN 0741-4188) 2769
Library Developments. (US ISSN 0145-5397) 2769
Library Equipment Report. (UK ISSN 0269-963X) 2769
Library Footnotes. (CN ISSN 0838-360X) 2769
Library Government Documents and Information Conference. Proceedings. see Government Documents and Information Conference. Proceedings 5200
Library Herald. (II ISSN 0024-2292) 2770
Library Hi Tech Bibliography. (US ISSN 1040-4333) 2798
Library Hi Tech Journal. (US ISSN 0737-8831) 2798
Library Hi Tech News. (US ISSN 0741-9058) 2798
Library History. (UK ISSN 0024-2306) 2770, 2317
Library History Review. (II ISSN 0378-7508) 2770
Library Hotline. (US ISSN 0740-736X) 2770
Library Imagination Paper. (US ISSN 0197-5587) 2770
Library Insights, Promotion & Programs. (US ISSN 0196-1977) 2770
Library Issues. (US ISSN 0734-3035) 2770
Library Journal. see Biblioteksbladet 2747
Library Journal. (US ISSN 0363-0277) 2770, 4131
Library Journal/Toshokan Zasshi. (JA ISSN 0385-4000) 2770
Library Journal. see Tushuguan Xuekan 2787
Library Lectures see Louisiana State University. Library Lectures 2771
Library Life. (NZ ISSN 0110-4373) 2770
Library Lines. (CN) 2770, 4188
†Library Link. (UK ISSN 0263-3612) 5227
Library Lit. (US ISSN 0085-2767) 2794, 16
Library Literature. (US ISSN 0024-2373) 2794, 16
Library Literature in India Series. (II) 2770
Library Management. (UK ISSN 0143-5124) 2770
Library Management Bulletin see Library Management Quarterly 2770
Library Management Quarterly. (US ISSN 0271-3306) 2770
Library Materials Guide. (US) 2770
Library Matters. (US) 2770
†Library Media Output. (US) 5227
Library Micromation News see Library Technology News 2799
Library Mosaics. (US ISSN 1054-9676) 2770
Library News (Atlanta). (US) 2770
Library News (Chicago). (US) 2770
Library News for Zoos and Aquariums. (US) 2770, 587
Library of Analytical Psychology Series. (US) 4034
Library of Anthropology. (US ISSN 0141-1012) 244
†Library of Congress. (US ISSN 0162-6426) 5227
Library of Congress Classification Schedules: A Cumulation of Additions and Changes. (US) 2794
Library of Congress Professional Association. Newsletter see Insights (Washington, 1988) 2763
Library of Congress Publications in Print see U.S. Library of Congress. Library of Congress Publications in Print 2796
Library of Exact Philosophy. (US ISSN 0075-9104) 4322
Library of Great Painters. (US) 334
Library of Jewish Law and Ethics. (US) 4225
Library of Law and Contemporary Problems. (US ISSN 0075-9120) 2649, 4379
Library of Peasant Studies. (UK) 2012

Library of Religious Philosophy. (US) 4188
Library of the Economists. (US) 677, 4131
Library of Theoria. (SW) 3772
Library of Ukrainian Studies. see Naukove Tovarystvo Imeni Shevchenka. Biblioteka Ukrainoznavstva 2377
Library Outreach Reporter. (US ISSN 0895-1179) 2770
Library P R News. (US ISSN 0164-9566) 2770, 34
Library Personnel News. (US ISSN 0891-2742) 2770, 1067
Library Pointes. (US) 2770
Library Postcard. see Konyvtari Levelezo 2767
Library Progress. (II ISSN 0970-1052) 2770
Library Quarterly. (US ISSN 0024-2519) 2771
Library Research see Library & Information Science Research 2769
▼Library Research in Asia, Africa & Australia. (AT) 2771, 3640
Library Resources & Technical Services.(US ISSN 0024-2527) 2771
Library Resources for the Blind and Physically Handicapped (Large Print Edition). (US ISSN 0364-1236) 2771, 2294
Library Resources in Scotland see Scottish Library and Information Resources 2783
Library Review. (UK ISSN 0024-2535) 2771
Library Review. (US ISSN 0041-9788) 2771
Library Review. New Series. see Konyvtari Figyelo. Uj Folyam 2767
Library School Review see Great Plains Libraries 5201
Library Science Abstracts see Library & Information Science Abstracts 2794
Library Science with a Slant to Documentation see Library Science with a Slant to Documentation and Information Studies 2798
Library Science with a Slant to Documentation and Information Studies. (II ISSN 0024-2543) 2798
Library Selections see Ontario. Ministry of Labour. Library. Infolink 733
Library Service News. (US ISSN 0024-2551) 2771, 1316
Library Service of Western Australia. Newsletter see Library and Information Service of Western Australia. Newsletter 2769
†Library Service to the People of New York State: A Long Range Plan. (US) 5227
Library Services and Construction Act Hawaii. State Public Library System. L S C A Annual Program see Hawaii. State Public Library System. L S C A Annual Program 5203
Library Software Review. (US ISSN 0742-5759) 1478, 1461, 1691, 2798
Library Systems Newsletter. (US ISSN 0277-0288) 2798
Library Talk. (US ISSN 1043-237X) 2771
Library Technology News. (UK ISSN 0964-7627) 2799, 1461
Library Technology Reports. (US ISSN 0024-2586) 2771
Library Times International. (US ISSN 0743-4839) 2771
Library Trends. (US ISSN 0024-2594) 2771
Library Trustees Foundation of New York State. Newsletter. (US ISSN 0047-4541) 2771
Library Video Magazine. (US ISSN 0895-2248) 2771
Library Workstation and P C Report see Academic and Library Computing 2796
Library Workstation Report see Academic and Library Computing 2796
Library Yearbook/Toshokan Nenkan. (JA) 2771

LIFETIME NUCLEAR 6393

Libre Service Actualites see L S A **1044**
Libreria. (IT ISSN 0024-2640) **4131**
Libreria. (SP ISSN 0024-2659) **4131**
Libreria Svizzera. see Schweizer Buchhandel **4136**
Libri. (DK ISSN 0024-2667) **2771**
Libri e Riviste d'Italia. (IT ISSN 0024-2683) **4131**
Libri Oncologici. (CI) **3199**
Libri Rari. (IT) **4141**
Libriper. (IT) **2872**
Libro Chileno en Venta. (CL) **405**
Libro di Casa. (IT) **2553**
Librorama Internacional. (SP) **405**
†Libros. (CK) **5227**
Libros de Edicion Argentina see L E A **4131**
Libros de Iniciacion Filosofica. (SP) **3772**
Libros de Mexico. (MX ISSN 0186-2243) **4131**, **2932**
Libros en Venta en Hispanoamerica y Espana. (PR) **405**
Libros Espanoles en Venta. (SP ISSN 0377-0974) **405**
Libros Paraguayos. (PY ISSN 0257-3555) **2932**, **2982**
Libros y Material de Ensenanza. (SP ISSN 0075-9201) **1646**
LibSat. (CN ISSN 0712-6115) **2771**
Libya. Census and Statistics Department. Agricultural Census. (LY) **140**
Libya. Census and Statistics Department. External Trade Statistics.(LY ISSN 0075-9228) **726**
Libya. Census and Statistics Department. General Population Census. (LY ISSN 0075-9236) **3993**, **3984**
Libya. Census and Statistics Department. Industrial Census. (LY ISSN 0075-9244) **726**
Libya. Census and Statistics Department. Monthly Cost of Living Index for Tripoli Town. (LY ISSN 0023-1630) **4577**
Libya. Census and Statistics Department. Report of the Annual Survey of Large Manufacturing Establishments. (LY ISSN 0075-9252) **726**
Libya. Census and Statistics Department. Report of the Annual Survey of Petroleum Mining Industry.(LY ISSN 0075-9260) **3706**
Libya. Census and Statistics Department. Report of the Annual Survey of Units Providing Technical Services to the Petroleum Mining Industry. (LY) **3706**
Libya. Census and Statistics Department. Report of the Survey of Licensed Construction Units. (LY ISSN 0075-9279) **638**
Libya. Census and Statistics Department. Statistical Abstract. (LY ISSN 0075-9287) **4577**
Libya. Census and Statistics Department. Statistical Handbook of the Libyan Arab Jamahiriya. (LY) **726**
Libya. Census and Statistics Department. Vital Statistics of the Socialist People's Libyan Arab Jamahiriya. (LY) **726**
Libya. Census and Statistics Department. Wholesale Prices in Tripoli Town. (LY ISSN 0075-9295) **726**
Libya Antiqua/Libiya al-Qadimat. (LY ISSN 0459-2980) **2430**, **2333**
Libya Past and Present Series. (UK) **4774**
Libyan Journal of Agriculture. (LY ISSN 1010-3740) **105**
Libyan Journal of Sciences. (LY ISSN 0368-7481) **4322**
Libyen Bulletin. (DK ISSN 0108-3236) **3965**
Licensed and Catering News. (UK) **383**
Licensed Practical Nurse. (US) **3281**

Licensed Practical Nurses of British Columbia Association of British Columbia Newsletter see L P N Association of British Columbia Newsletter **3281**
Licensed Product Marketing. (UK) **1044**, **34**
Licensee. (UK ISSN 0024-2802) **383**
Licensee Name Index to Non-Government Master Frequency Data Base. (US) **1348**
Licensing Book. (US) **3676**, **1044**
†Licensing Business Yearbook. (US) **5227**
Licensing, Countersigning and Surplus Line Laws. (US ISSN 0742-5120) **2536**
Licensing Executives Society (U.S. & Canada), Inc. Nouvelles see L E S Nouvelles **3676**
Licensing Industry Newsletter see Licensing Letter **3676**
†Licensing International. (US) **5227**
Licensing Journal. (US ISSN 0890-135X) **3676**
Licensing Law and Business Report. (US ISSN 0162-5764) **2711**
Licensing Law Handbook. (US ISSN 0731-5783) **2649**, **916**, **4603**
Licensing Laws N S W: Liquor Act & Regulations. (AT) **2649**, **383**
Licensing Letter. (US ISSN 8755-6235) **3676**, **1044**
Licensing Scope. (US) **34**, **1044**
Licensing Today. (US) **3676**, **1044**
Lichamelijke Opvoeding. (NE ISSN 0024-2810) **1754**, **4478**
Lichen. see Raiken **515**
Lichenologist. (UK ISSN 0024-2829) **508**
Licht. (GW) **1902**
Licht Journaal. (NE) **1902**, **2553**
Licht und Leben. (GW ISSN 0047-4584) **4241**
Lichtbogen. (GW ISSN 0024-2845) **1183**
Lichtenberg-Jahrbuch. (GW) **419**, **2932**, **3772**, **3824**
Lichtenrader Rundschau. (GW ISSN 0932-318X) **2190**
Lichtentaler Pfarrnachrichten. (AU) **4267**
Der Lichtgang. (GW) **2056**
†Lichthoeve. (NE) **5227**
Lichtstrahlen. (GW) **4241**
Lichtvisie see Licht Journaal **1902**
†Lichtwark-Stiftung. Veroeffentlichung. (GW) **5227**
Licitationen. (DK ISSN 0024-287X) **622**
Lick Observatory. Publications. (US ISSN 0075-9325) **366**
Licki Vjesnik. (CI ISSN 0350-2562) **2872**
Licking Lantern. (US ISSN 0748-1012) **2157**
Licni Dohoci. (YU ISSN 0300-2535) **726**
Lide a Zeme/People and Countries. (CS ISSN 0024-2896) **2255**
El Lider Bautista. (US ISSN 0890-0590) **4241**
Lieb Frauen Bote. (IT) **4267**
Liebfrauen Kalender. (GW) **4241**
Liebigs Annalen der Chemie. (GW ISSN 0170-2041) **1183**
Liechtenstein. Botanisch-Zoologische Gesellschaft Liechtenstein Sargans-Werdenberg. Bericht. (LH) **446**
Liechtenstein Economy see Economy of the Principality of Liechtenstein **5184**
Liechtenstein - Fuerstentum im Herzen Europas see Liechtenstein - Principality in the Heart of Europe **2373**
Liechtenstein Politische Schriften. (LH) **3905**
Liechtenstein - Principality in the Heart of Europe. (LH) **2373**
Liechtenstein - Principaute au Coeur de l'Europe see Liechtenstein - Principality in the Heart of Europe **2373**
Liechtenstein - Un Principato nel Cuore dell'Europa see Liechtenstein - Principality in the Heart of Europe **2373**

Liechtensteinische Industrie- und Handelskammer. Annual Report. (LH) **819**
Liechtensteinische Industrie- und Handelskammer. Bulletin. (LH) **819**
Lied und Chor. (GW ISSN 0024-290X) **3561**
Lieferkatalog fuer Krankenhaus, Arzt, Apotheke und Labor. (AU) **3122**
Liefern und Leisten. (GW) **1143**
Le Lien. (SY) **4188**
Lien des Freres Mennonites. (CN) **4284**
Lien Entre Meres et Peres de Pretres. (FR ISSN 0024-2926) **4267**
Lien Ho Wen Hsueh. see Unitas **2887**
Lien Ho Yueh K'an. (CH) **2872**
Lien Horticole. (FR ISSN 0293-6852) **2133**
Lien Informatique. (FR) **2771**
Lier en Boog. (NE ISSN 0925-8191) **334**, **3772**
▼Lies of Our Times. (US) **2572**, **4442**
Liesinger Pfarrblatt see Kontakt Drei und Zwanzig **4267**
Lietuviu Dienos/Lithuanian Days. (US ISSN 0024-2950) **2012**
Lietuviu Kalbotyros Klausimai/Problems of Lithuanian Linguistics. (LI ISSN 0130-0172) **2825**
Lietuviu Tautos Praeitis/Lithuanian Historical Review. (US ISSN 0091-4347) **2373**
Lietuvos Fizikos Rinkinys. see Litovskii Fizicheskii Sbornik **3824**
Lietuvos Mokslu Akademija. Lietuvos Matematikos Rinkinys. see Litovskii Matematicheskii Sbornik **3043**
Lietuvos T.S.R. Mokslu Akademijos Darbai. A Serija. Visuomenes Mokslai. see Akademiya Nauk Litovskoi S.S.R. Trudy. Seriya A. Obshchestvennye Nauki **5133**
Lietuvos T.S.R. Mokslu Akademijos Darbai. B Serija. Chemija, Technika, Fizine Geografija. see Akademiya Nauk Litovskoi S.S.R. Trudy. Seriya B. Khimiya, Tekhnika, Fizicheskaya Geografiya **5133**
Lietuvos T.S.R. Mokslu Akademijos Darbai. C Serija. Biologijos Mokslai. see Akademiya Nauk Litovskoi S.S.R. Trudy. Seriya C. Biologicheskie Nauki **5133**
Lieux de l'Enfance. (FR) **1240**
Life see Ren Sheng **598**
Life (New York). (US ISSN 0024-3019) **2228**
Life and Breath of Brooklyn - Fresh Air News see In-Short **3365**
Life and Companions. see Rensheng yu Banlu **4384**
Life and Environment. see Seikatsu to Kankyo **1968**
Life and Health. (HK) **3805**
Life & Health Insurance Sales. (US ISSN 1053-2838) **2536**
Life and Home see Tampa Bay Life **2236**
Life & School/Zhyttia i Shkola. (US) **2012**
Life and Thought. see Zycie i Mysl **3787**
Life and Times see Journey (Brisbane) **4241**
Life and Work. (UK ISSN 0024-306X) **4241**
Life and Worship see Music and Liturgy **3564**
Life Association News. (US ISSN 0024-3078) **2536**
Life Begins at 50's see Choice **2271**
Life Chemistry Reports. (US ISSN 0278-6281) **1183**
Life Communications. (US) **34**, **2536**
Life Consultation. see Rensheng Zixun **1264**
Life - Creation. see Shenghuo - Chuangzao **2183**
Life Cycle. (SA) **4518**
Life Docket. (US) **2649**, **4847**
Life in Action Magazine. (US) **3772**, **4322**
Life Indeed. (UK) **4241**
Life Insurance Business in Taiwan (Year). (CH) **2536**
Life Insurance Fact Book. (US ISSN 0075-9406) **2536**

Life Insurance in the United Kingdom see Insurance Statistics (Years) **2546**
Life Insurance International. (IE) **2536**
Life Insurance Marketing and Research Association (LIMRA) Marketfacts see L I M R A's Marketfacts **2536**
Life Insurance Planning. (US ISSN 0024-3132) **2536**
Life Insurance Selling. (US ISSN 0024-3140) **2536**
Life-Line. (US ISSN 1059-6593) **3344**, **1738**
Life Lines. (US) **2537**
Life of P L A Soldiers. see Jiefangjun Shenghuo **3462**
Life Office Management Association. Annual Conference. Proceedings of Concurrent Sessions see L.O.M.A. Resource **2536**
Life Office Management Association, Inc. Resource see L.O.M.A. Resource **2536**
Life Overseas/Hua Jen. (HK) **2197**
†Life Rates & Data. (US) **5227**
Life Renewed. see Obnovljeni Zivot **4193**
Life Science. see Seitai no Kagaku **455**
▼Life Science Book Review. (US) **466**, **405**
†Life Science Lab Products. (US) **5227**
▼Life Science Network News. (US) **466**, **16**, **3177**
Life Sciences (1973). (US ISSN 0024-3205) **4323**
Life Support Systems see International Journal of Artificial Organs **3110**
Life Support Technology see Precision Machinery **1410**
Life Today. (US) **2276**
Life Underwriters Association of Canada Forum see L U A C Forum **2536**
Life Underwriters Association of the City of New York. Bulletin see New York City Association of Life Underwriters **2539**
Lifeboat. (UK ISSN 0024-3086) **4525**
Lifeglow. (US) **4188**, **2294**
Lifeline. (UK) **4284**
Lifeline (Cornwall) see Writer's Lifeline **4139**
LifeLine (Kingston). (CN) **2537**
Lifeline (Westport) see Impact (Westport) **4408**
Lifeliner (Des Moines) see Iowa Trucking Lifeliner **4745**
Lifeliner (Riverside). (US ISSN 0047-4630) **2157**
†Lifelines (New York). (US) **5227**
Lifelines (Saskatoon). (CN) **3805**, **1754**
Lifelines (Toronto). (CN ISSN 0834-3543) **3805**, **3609**
Lifelong Education Network. (UN) **1646**
Lifelong Learning see Adult Learning **1681**
Lifeprints. (US) **2294**, **987**
†Lifestyle (Newbury). (UK) **5227**
Lifestyle. Northern California. (US) **4362**
Lifestyle and London Living. (UK) **4151**, **953**
Lifestyle Apparel News. (US) **1292**
Lifestyle Asia. (PH) **2213**
Lifestyle Characteristics of Sporting Goods Consumers. (US) **4498**, **726**
Lifestyle Magazine. (JM) **2239**
Lifestyle Market Analyst. (US) **1044**
Lifestyle Southern California. (US) **4362**
▼LifeStyle - U S A. (US) **2012**
Lifestyle Zip Code Analyst. (US) **1044**, **34**
Lifestyles: Family and Economic Issues see Journal of Family and Economic Issues **4029**
Lifestyles Magazine. (CN) **4152**
Lifestyles Pittsburgh see Pittsburgh Singles' Lifestyles **4363**
Lifestyles Season. (AT ISSN 1033-0186) **3595**, **1491**
Lifestyles 5749. (CN) **2178**
Lifetime. (US) **2537**
Lifetime Nuclear Plant Capitalization and O & M Summary Data. (US) **1902**, **1807**

LIFETIMES

Lifetimes. (US ISSN 0194-4312) **2537**
Liffey Valley News see Cill Dara and Liffey Valley News **2202**
Lift. (UK) **3122**, **3281**
Lift Equipment. (US) **3019**
Lifting & Transportation International. (US) **4745**, 622
Liftoff. (US) **2511**
Liftouts. (US) **4131**, 2932, 2996
Liga de Almaceneros Minoristas y Afines Revista Mensual see L A M Y A Revista Mensual **2076**
Ligament see Aktiviteitensektor. Maandblad **4397**
Ligament see Maandblad Aktiviteitensektor **4442**
Ligand Quarterly see Journal of Clinical Immunoassay **3187**
Ligand Review. (US ISSN 0197-4041) **3187**
Ligature. (US ISSN 0738-9302) **4002**
Die Ligdraer. (SA ISSN 0024-3272) **4242**
Light. (US ISSN 0456-0434) **987**, 1792
Light. see Goleuad **4239**
Light. see Svitlo **4276**
Light. see Svit **4289**
Light (London, 1881). (UK ISSN 0047-4649) **3670**
Light (London, 1969). (UK ISSN 0047-4657) **4188**
Light (Wheaton). (US) **2294**, 1738, 3302, 4412
Light Aircraft Manufacturers Association. Newsletter. (US) **4675**
Light and Life. (US ISSN 0024-3299) **4242**
Light and Life. (UK) **4242**
Light and Life. (AT) **4242**
Light and Shade. (US) **3793**
Light and Shadow. see Guang yu Ying **327**
Light: Annual Report. (US) **2294**
Light Bearer. (US) **3670**, 359, 2056, 4188
▼Light Design and Technology. (IT) **3855**
Light Horse see Horse & Rider **4535**
Light in the East News see Dein Reich Komme **4174**
Light - Lines. (US) **3670**
Light Metal Age. (US ISSN 0024-3345) **3412**
Light Metal Statistics in Japan. see Keikinzoku Kogyo Tokei Nenpo **3427**
Light Music. see Qing Yinyue **3575**
Light of Consciousness. (US ISSN 1040-7448) **4188**, 3772
Light of Home. see Ie-no-Hikari **96**
Light of Life. (II ISSN 0970-2571) **4188**
Light of the Moon. (UK ISSN 0024-3361) **2294**
Light of the Word. see Svjetlo Rijeci **4276**
Light Plane Maintenance. (US ISSN 0278-8950) **58**, 4675
Light Plane World see E A A Experimenter **51**
Light Railway News. (AT ISSN 0155-2260) **4711**, 3487
Light Railways. (AT ISSN 0727-8101) **4711**, 3487
Light Steam Power see Steam Power **1939**
Light Truck Guide see Carguide **4687**
Light Year. (US ISSN 0743-913X) **2932**
†Lighted Pathway. (US ISSN 0737-8173) **5227**
†Lighter/Briquet. (CN ISSN 0024-340X) **5227**
Lighthouse (Auburn). (US ISSN 0887-4328) **2932**
Lighthouse Magazine see Lighthouse (Auburn) **2932**
Lighting Design & Application see L D & A **1902**
Lighting Dimensions. (US ISSN 0191-541X) **302**, 2553, 3513, 4634
Lighting Equipment News. (UK ISSN 0024-3418) **2560**, 1080, 1902
Lighting in Australia. (AT ISSN 0728-5639) **1902**

Lighting Journal. (UK ISSN 0950-4559) **1902**, 1871
Lighting Magazine. (CN) **1080**, 1044, 1902
Lighting Research and Technology. (UK ISSN 0024-3426) **1902**
Lighting Review. (CH) **1044**, 1902
Lightning Strikes. (US) **3561**
Lightning Sword. (US) **2996**
Light's List of Literary Magazines (Year). (UK) **2890**, 405, 2982
Lights of Homeland. see Teviskes Ziburiai **2026**
Lightwave. (US ISSN 0741-5834) **1339**
Lightweight Concrete Information Sheets. (US ISSN 0075-9457) **622**
Lightworks. (US ISSN 0161-4223) **334**, 3793
Lignes. (FR ISSN 0988-5226) **2187**
Ligue Internationale Contre la Concurrence Deloyale. Annuaire. (FR ISSN 0459-3871) **916**
Ligue Internationale Contre la Concurrence Deloyale. Communication. (FR ISSN 0459-388X) **1080**
Ligue Suisse de Litterature pour la Jeunesse. Rapport Annuel. see Schweizerischer Bund fuer Jugendliteratur. Jahresbericht **1265**
Ligue Urbaine et Rurale Cahiers. (FR) **1962**, 2491
Liguori Editore. Monografie. (IT) **2932**
Liguorian. (US ISSN 0024-3450) **4268**
Liguria. (IT) **2205**
Liguria Territorio e Civilta. (IT) **2255**
Liguria Tre see Liguria Tre - Rapporto Annuale **819**
Liguria Tre - Rapporto Annuale. (IT) **819**
Liikearkisto. (FI ISSN 0356-7850) **677**
Liikearkistoyhdistys. Julkaisuja. (FI) **677**
Liiketaloudellinen Aikakauskirja/Finnish Journal of Business Economics. (FI ISSN 0024-3469) **677**
Liikuntakasvatus. (FI ISSN 0355-7073) **3805**, 1754
Lijstenboek. (BE) **4131**
Likas-Yaman. (PH ISSN 0115-835X) **1491**
Likembe. (ZR) **3561**
Likha. (PH ISSN 0115-6144) **2932**
Likutim. (US ISSN 0792-0873) **2294**
Lilac Hinge. (US) **3754**
Lilacs Quarterly Journal. (US) **2133**
LiLi. (Zeitschrift fuer Literaturwissenschaft und Linguistik) (GW ISSN 0049-8653) **2825**, 2932
LiLi. Beihefte. (Zeitschrift fuer Literaturwissenschaft und Linguistik) (GW) **2825**, 2932
Liliput Review. (US) **2932**
Lilith. (US ISSN 0146-2334) **4847**, 2012
Lille Chirurgical. (FR ISSN 0024-3493) **3381**
Lille Medical. (FR ISSN 0981-1095) **3122**
Lilloa. (AG ISSN 0075-9481) **508**
Lilun Wuli. see Communications in Theoretical Physics **3816**
Lilun yu Xiandaihui/Theory and Modernization. (CC) **4379**
Lily of the Mohawks. (US) **4268**
Lima. (GW) **1316**
Lima Times. (PE) **2213**
Limba Romana/Romanian Language. (RM ISSN 0024-3523) **2825**
Limba si Literatura. (RM ISSN 0583-8045) **2825**
Limberlost Review. (US ISSN 0743-2909) **2996**
Lime Green Bulldozers (and Other Related Species). (US) **2996**
†Limerence Forum. (US) **2932**
Limestone. (US ISSN 0899-5966) **2932**, 2996
Limicola. (GW ISSN 0932-9153) **565**
Limit. (US) **3905**
Limited Mobility & Immobilized Patient Products. (US) **2467**
Limited Partners Letter. (US ISSN 0163-0652) **953**, 1100

Limited Partnership Investment Review. (US) **1100**
Limits in the Seas. (US ISSN 0092-6426) **2735**
Limnetica. (SP ISSN 0213-8409) **1599**
†Limnobios. (AG ISSN 0325-7592) **5227**
Limnologica. (GW ISSN 0075-9511) **1599**
Limnological Society of Southern Africa. Journal see Southern Africa Journal of Aquatic Sciences **1600**
Limnology and Oceanography. (US ISSN 0024-3590) **1599**, 1607
Limonadier de Paris. (FR ISSN 0024-3612) **2477**
Limosa. (NE ISSN 0024-3620) **565**
Limousin Elevage. (FR) **220**
Limousin Leader. (CN) **220**
Limousin Magazine. (FR) **2187**, 4774
Limousin-Marche Magazine see Limousin Magazine **2187**
Limousin World. (US) **220**
Limousine & Chauffeur. (US ISSN 8750-7374) **4694**, 1044
Limousine Nyt. (DK ISSN 0900-050X) **220**
Limpieza Inform. (SP) **1282**
Linacre Quarterly. (US ISSN 0024-3639) **3122**
Linchuang Huicui/Clinical Focus. (CC) **3122**
Linchuang Mazuixue Zazhi/Journal of Clinical Anesthesiology. (CC) **3191**
Linchuang Pifuke Zazhi/Journal of Clinical Dermatology. (CC ISSN 1000-4963) **3249**
Linchuang yu Shiyan Binglixue Zazhi/ Journal of Clinical and Experimental Pathology. (CC ISSN 1001-7399) **3122**
Lincoln Center Calendar of Events. (US) **4634**
Lincoln College. Agricultural Economics Research Unit. Discussion Paper see Lincoln University. Agribusiness and Economics Research Unit. Discussion Paper **154**
Lincoln College. Agricultural Economics Research Unit. Research Report see Lincoln University. Agribusiness and Economics Research Unit. Research Report **154**
Lincoln College. Department of Horticulture. Bulletin. (NZ ISSN 0069-3820) **2133**
†Lincoln College. Farmers' Conference. Proceedings. (NZ ISSN 0069-3839) **5227**
Lincoln County Tennessee Pioneers. (US) **2157**, 2413
Lincoln Herald. (US ISSN 0024-3671) **2413**
†Lincoln Institute of Land Policy. Basic Concept Series. (US) **5227**
Lincoln Library Bulletin. (US ISSN 0024-3698) **2771**
Lincoln Longwool Sheep Breeders' Association. Annual Flock Book. (UK) **220**
Lincoln Memorial Association Newsletter. (US) **2413**, 420, 3463
Lincoln Review. (US ISSN 0192-5083) **2012**
Lincoln University. Agribusiness and Economics Research Unit. Discussion Paper. (NZ ISSN 1170-7607) **154**
Lincoln University. Agribusiness and Economics Research Unit. Research Report. (NZ ISSN 1170-7682) **154**
Lincolnshire Bird Report. (UK ISSN 0261-5525) **565**
†Lincolnshire Family Historian. (UK) **5227**
Lincolnshire Farmer. (UK) **105**
Lincolnshire Farmer & Record see Lincolnshire Farmer **105**
Lincolnshire History and Archaeology. (UK ISSN 0459-4487) **277**, 2373
Lincolnshire Information. Employment. (UK ISSN 0262-1452) **987**
Lincolnshire Life. (UK ISSN 0024-371X) **2194**
Lincolnshire Methodist History Society. Journal. (UK) **4242**, 2373

Lincolnshire Past and Present. (UK ISSN 0960-9555) **277**, 2373
Linde Berichte aus Technik und Wissenschaft. (GW ISSN 0024-3728) **4323**, 4603
Linde Reports on Science and Technology see Linde Berichte aus Technik und Wissenschaft **4323**
Linden Blatt. (GW) **34**
Lindley Lecture. (US ISSN 0075-9554) **3772**
Lindleyana. (US) **2133**
Lindquist - Lepic Market Letter. (US) **954**
†Lindsay Links & Legacy. (US) **5227**
Lindy's A C C Football Annual. (Atlantic Coast Conference) (US) **4507**
Lindy's Big 8 Football Annual. (US) **4507**
Lindy's Big 10 Football Annual. (US) **4507**
Lindy's Pac 10 Football Annual. (US) **4507**
Lindy's Pro Edition Football Annual. (US) **4507**
Lindy's S E C Football Annual. (Southeast Conference) (US) **4507**
†Lindy's Southeastern Recruiting Guide. (US) **5227**
Lindy's Southwest Football Annual. (US) **4507**
Linea see Examen **3893**
Linea Capital. (IT) **677**
Linea d'Ombra. (IT) **2932**
Linea Dura. (AG) **2872**
Linea Estetica. (IT) **334**
Linea Intima. (IT ISSN 0394-8048) **1286**
Linea Veneta nella Cultura Contemporanea. (IT) **2511**
Linea Verde. (IT ISSN 0394-3704) **105**, 872, 2104, 2133
Linea Z. (IT ISSN 0024-3779) **4652**
Lineagrafica. (IT ISSN 0024-3744) **4002**
Lineaires. (FR) **220**
Lineal Industrial Distributors Registers. (US) **1143**
Lineamenti. (IT) **3905**
Linear Algebra and Its Applications. (US ISSN 0024-3795) **3043**
Linear and Multilinear Algebra. (US ISSN 0308-1087) **3043**
Linear I Cs D.A.T.A. Book see Linear I Cs D.A.T.A. Digest **1775**
Linear I Cs D.A.T.A. Digest. (US) **1775**
Lineastruttura. (IT ISSN 0024-3817) **302**, 334
Lineaverde. (IT) **334**
Linen Hall Review. (UK ISSN 0266-1500) **2872**
Linen Supply News see Textile Rental **1282**
Linens, Domestics & Bath - Interior Textile Annual Directory. (US) **2560**
Linens, Domestics and Bath Products see L D B Interior Textiles **2560**
Lines Available Bulletin. (US) **1902**
Lines Review. (UK ISSN 0459-4541) **2996**
Linfield Review. (US) **1316**
Ling Shui. (CC) **2932**
Lingnan Music. see Lingnan Yinyue **3561**
Lingnan Yinyue/Lingnan Music. (US) **3561**
Le Lingot. (CN) **1212**
Lingua. (NE ISSN 0024-3841) **2825**
Lingua. (GW) **2932**
Lingua e Cultura. (PO ISSN 0047-4703) **2825**, 2932
Lingua e Letteratura. (IT) **2933**
Lingua e Literatura. (BL ISSN 0047-4711) **2825**, 2933
Lingua e Stile. (IT ISSN 0024-385X) **2825**, 2933, 3772
Lingua e Vita. (UK) **2825**
▼Lingua Franca. (US ISSN 1051-3310) **1711**
Lingua Nostra. (IT ISSN 0024-3868) **2825**
Lingua Posnaniensis. (PL ISSN 0079-4740) **2825**
Linguaggio Astrale. (IT) **359**
Linguaggio dell'Architettura Romana. (IT) **303**
Linguarum Minorum Documenta Historiographica. (GW ISSN 0341-3225) **2825**, 2317

Lingue del Mondo. (IT ISSN 0024-3876) **2826**
Lingue e Iscrizioni dell'Italia Antica. (IT) **2826**
Le Lingue e le Civilta Straniere Moderne. (IT ISSN 0391-3228) **2826**
Linguist. (UK ISSN 0268-5965) **2826**
Linguiste/Taalkundige. (BE) **2826**
Linguistic Analysis. (US ISSN 0098-9053) **2826**
Linguistic & Literary Studies in Eastern Europe. (US ISSN 0165-7712) **2826**, 2933
Linguistic Association of Canada and the United States Forum see L A C U S Forum **2822**
Linguistic Association of the Southwest. Journal see Southwest Journal of Linguistics **2842**
Linguistic Bibliography/Bibliographie Linguistique. (NE ISSN 0378-4592) **2855**
Linguistic Calculation. (NE) **2826**
Linguistic Circle of Manitoba and North Dakota. Proceedings. (US ISSN 0075-9597) **2826**
Linguistic Inquiry. (US ISSN 0024-3892) **2826**
Linguistic Models. (US) **2826**
Linguistic Notes from La Jolla. (US ISSN 0737-4720) **2826**
Linguistic Review. (US ISSN 0167-6318) **2826**
Linguistic Society of America. Meeting Handbooks. (US ISSN 0075-9600) **2826**
Linguistic Society of America Bulletin see L S A Bulletin **2822**
Linguistic Society of India. Bulletin. (II ISSN 0075-9627) **2826**
Linguistic Society of Japan. Journal/Gengo Kenkyu. (JA ISSN 0024-3914) **2826**
Linguistic Studies. see Nyelvtudomanyi Kozlemenyek **2832**
Linguistica. (XV ISSN 0024-3922) **2826**
Linguistica Biblica. (GW ISSN 0342-0884) **2826**, 4188
Linguistica e Letteratura. (IT) **2826**, 2933
Linguistica Espanola Actual. (SP) **2826**
Linguistica Pragensia. (NE) **2826**, 2933
Linguistica Silesiana. (PL ISSN 0208-4228) **2826**
Linguistica Uralica. (ER) **2826**
Linguistica y Literatura. (CK ISSN 0120-5587) **2826**, 2933
Linguisticae Investigationes see Lingvisticae Investigationes **2827**
Linguistics. see Kalbotyra **2822**
Linguistics. (GW ISSN 0024-3949) **2826**
Linguistics Abstracts. (UK ISSN 0267-5498) **2855**, 2827
Linguistics and Education. (US ISSN 0898-5898) **2827**, 1646
Linguistics and Language Behavior Abstracts. (US ISSN 0888-8027) **2855**, 16
Linguistics and Philosophy. (NE ISSN 0165-0157) **3772**, 2827
Linguistics in Literature see Language and Literature **2823**
Linguistics - National Minorities. see Minzu Yuwen **2829**
Linguistics of the Tibeto-Burman Area. (US ISSN 0731-3500) **2827**
Linguistik Aktuell. (US ISSN 0166-0829) **2827**
Linguistik und Didaktik (Munich) see Sprache und Literatur in Wissenschaft und Unterricht **2843**
Linguistik und Didaktik (Paderborn) see Sprache und Literatur in Wissenschaft **2843**
Linguistique. (FR ISSN 0024-3957) **2827**
Linguistique Balkanique/Balkansko Izikoznanie. (BU ISSN 0324-1653) **2827**
Linguistique et Enseignement. (MG) **2827**, 1754
Linguistique Francaise. Cahiers de. (SZ) **2827**, 1754

Linguistische Arbeiten. (GW ISSN 0344-6727) **2827**
Linguistische Berichte. (GW ISSN 0024-3930) **2827**
Lingvisticae Investigationes. (NE ISSN 0378-4169) **2827**
Lingvisticae Investigationes: Supplementa. (US ISSN 0165-7569) **2827**
Lingvisticheskie Issledovaniya. (RU ISSN 0301-6900) **2827**
Lingvisticke Citanky/Readings in Linguistics. (CS) **2827**
Die Linie. (GW) **1292**
Die Linie. (GW) **4711**
Linieofficeren. (DK ISSN 0024-3973) **3463**
Linington Lineup. (US ISSN 8756-5609) **2933**
The Link. (AT) **4268**, 1259
Link (Ashland). (US ISSN 1040-3469) **2033**
Link (Burnaby). (CN) **1646**, 1316
Link (London, 1966). (UK) **3122**, 3281
Link (London, 1973). (UK) **4847**, 3944
Link (Mississauga) see Check it Out **2752**
Link (Montreal). (CN) **2872**
Link (New York). (US ISSN 0024-4007) **3965**
Link (St. Louis). (US ISSN 1045-9723) **34**
Link (Troy). (US) **34**
Link (Vancouver). (CN) **2012**
Link (Westerville) see Newslink (Westerville) **1471**
Link (Woodland Hills). (US) **3344**, 3281
Link & Visitor. (CN ISSN 0380-4100) **4847**, 4242
Link Disability Journal. (AT ISSN 1034-8883) **4412**, 1506
Link Indian News Magazine. (II) **2200**
Link International: Educational Newsletter. (UK ISSN 0268-8352) **4219**
Link Magazine. (US) **2142**
Link-Up. (US ISSN 0739-988X) **1447**, 1427, 1461, 1470
Link-Up. (AT ISSN 0158-5460) **4412**, 2294
Link-Up: Hiroshima Prefecture News. (JA) **2208**
Linkage. (JA) **1398**
LinkAge. (US) **1414**
▼Linked Ring Letter. (US ISSN 1049-4812) **3793**
Linking Libraries. (US) **2771**
Linking Ring. (US ISSN 0024-4023) **2438**
Linking Up. (US) **1375**
Links. (AT ISSN 0156-1103) **1240**, 1754
LINKS see L I N K S **1738**
Links. (GW ISSN 0024-404X) **3905**
Links see Links: Health and Development Report **3944**
Links (Oxford). (UK ISSN 0261-4014) **932**
Links: Health and Development Report. (US ISSN 0894-3036) **3944**
Links und Rechts der Autobahn. (GW ISSN 0343-4192) **2477**, 4719, 4774
Linksaf. (NE ISSN 0167-093X) **3905**
Linkup see P C Netter Newsletter **1472**
Linnean Society. Biological Journal. (UK ISSN 0024-4066) **446**
Linnean Society. Botanical Journal. (UK ISSN 0024-4074) **508**
Linnean Society. Symposia Series. (US) **446**
Linnean Society. Zoological Journal. (UK ISSN 0024-4082) **587**
Linnean Society of London. Journal see Linnean Society. Zoological Journal **587**
Linnean Society of New South Wales. Proceedings. (AT ISSN 0047-4746) **587**, 1571
Linneana Belgica/Belgian Entomology Journal. (BE ISSN 0024-4090) **536**
Linn's Stamp News. (US ISSN 0161-6234) **3754**

Linn's Weekly Stamp News see Linn's Stamp News **3754**
Linn's World Stamp Almanac. (US ISSN 0146-6887) **3754**
Linq. (AT ISSN 0817-458X) **2933**
Linschoten-Vereeniging. Werken. (NE) **2373**
Linus. (IT) **2872**
Linye Jingji. (CC) **2104**, 677
Linye Jixie/Forestry Machinery. (CC ISSN 1001-4462) **2104**, 3019
Linye Kexue/Scientia Silvae Sinica. (CC ISSN 0459-441X) **2104**
Linye Yuekan/Forestry Monthly. (CC ISSN 1000-839X) **2104**
Linzer Hochschulschriften see Linzer Universitaetsschriften **1711**
Linzer Jahrbuch fuer Kunstgeschichte see Kunstjahrbuch der Stadt Linz **333**
Linzer Theaterzeitung. (AU ISSN 0024-4139) **4634**
Linzer Universitaetsschriften. (US) **1711**
Linzer Woche. (AU ISSN 0024-4147) **4774**
Lion. (IT) **1299**
Lion. (CY) **3463**
The Lion. (UK ISSN 0024-4163) **1299**
Lion & the Unicorn. (US ISSN 0147-2593) **2872**
Lion City see This Week Singapore **4789**
The Lion en Espanol. (US ISSN 0024-4171) **1299**
Lion of Alpha Epsilon Pi. (US) **1299**
Lion of Belfort. (US) **4694**
Lioness. (UK) **3463**
Lionismo. (IT) **1299**
Lip Service. (US ISSN 0893-620X) **2996**
Lipid Technology. (UK ISSN 0956-666X) **479**
Lipids. (US ISSN 0024-4201) **479**
Lipman Report. (US) **1527**
Liposomes. (UK ISSN 0264-9659) **479**, 3734
Lippische Mitteilungen aus Geschichte und Landeskunde. (GW ISSN 0342-0876) **2373**, 4323
Lips (Montclair). (US ISSN 0278-0933) **2996**
Lips (New York). (US) **3398**
Lipscomb Newsletter. (US) **2157**
Lipscombe Report. (AT ISSN 0817-6191) **3691**
Liptov. (CS) **2373**
†Lipunan Journal. (PH ISSN 0459-4835) **5227**
Al-Liqa. (SU) **2220**
Liquid and Gas Chromatography see L C - G C **1207**
Liquid and Gas Chromatography International see L C - G C International **1207**
Liquid Chromatography Abstracts. (UK ISSN 0306-2104) **1202**, 16
Liquid Chromatography Literature - Abstracts and Index. (US ISSN 0147-328X) **1202**, 16
Liquid Chromatography Mass Spectrometry Abstracts. (UK) **1183**, 3824
Liquid Crystals. (UK ISSN 0267-8292) **1211**, 3864
Liquid Gas Carrier Register. (UK ISSN 0305-1803) **3691**, 4730
Liquids Handling. (UK ISSN 0268-9219) **1829**, 3691
Liquified Petroleum Gas Report see Inventories of Natural Gas Liquids & Liquified Refinery Gases **3690**
Liquor Control Law Reports. (US) **1100**, 383
Liquor Handbook see Jobson's Liquor Handbook **382**
Liquor Industry Marketing. (US) **383**
Liquor Laws Victoria. (AT) **2649**, 383
Liquor Licensing Law and Practice N.S.W. (AT) **2649**
Liquor Marketing Yearbook. (AT) **383**
Liquor Reporter. (US) **383**
Liquor Store Magazine see Beverage Dynamics **378**
Liquor Store Monthly. (SA) **383**
Lira. (BN ISSN 0024-4244) **3561**
Lire. (FR) **2933**
Lisa's Kitchen Bi-Weekly. (HK) **2448**

Lisbon. Escola Nacional de Saude de Medicina Tropical. Anais see Instituto de Higiene e Medicina Tropical. Anais **4105**
Liseli la Zambia. (ZA) **2240**
Lishi Daguanyuan. (CC) **2339**
Lishi Dang'an/Historical Archives. (CC) **2340**, 2771
Lishi Jiaoxue/History Teaching. (CC ISSN 0457-6241) **2317**, 1754
Lishi Jiaoxue Wenti. (CC) **2317**, 1754
Lishi Xuexi/History Studies. (CC) **2317**
Lishi Yanjiu/Historical Research. (CC ISSN 0459-1909) **2317**
Lisiak. (CS) **2872**
Lisse. Laboratorium voor Bloembollenonderzoek. Jaarverslag. (NE) **184**
List Bio-Med; Biomedical Serials in Scandinavian Libraries. (SW ISSN 0075-9813) **3177**
†List-O-Tapes. (US ISSN 0024-4309) **5228**
List of Adverse Reactions to Drugs. see Kokunai Iyakuhin Fukusayo Ichiran **3733**
List of American Firms in France see American Chamber of Commerce in France. Directory **806**
List of Approved Hospitals and Recognised House Officer Posts. (UK) **2471**, 2467
List of Books and Articles Catalogued. (SZ) **4081**
List of Bulgarian Foreign Trade Organizations see List of Production and Export - Import Firms and Organizations in Bulgaria **1143**
List of Cables Forming the World Submarine Network. (UN ISSN 0074-9001) **1363**
List of Current Serial Publications Being Received at the University of Puerto Rico Medical Sciences Campus Library. (PR) **3177**
List of Destination Indicators and Telex Identification Codes see Indicators for the Telegram Retransmission System (TRS) - Telex Identification Codes **1363**
List of E C A Documents Issued/Liste des Documents Publies par la C E A.(UN) **932**
List of Goods for the Statistics of Foreign Trade. Supplement. see Netherlands. Centraal Bureau voor de Statistiek. Naamlijsten voor de Statistiek van de Buitenlandse Handel **5244**
List of Grants and Awards Available to American Writers see Grants and Awards Available to American Writers **2920**
List of Hydrobiological Papers of British Fresh Waters. (UK) **1974**, 1599, 1962
List of International Telephone Routes. (UN ISSN 0074-9028) **1364**
List of Italian Stocks. (IT) **954**, 872
List of Journals Abstracted (Year). (NE ISSN 0923-5582) **3177**, 16, 466
List of Journals Indexed in Index Medicus. (US ISSN 0093-3821) **3177**
List of Member Institutions - Federal Saving and Loan Insurance Corporation see Federal Home Loan Bank System. List of Member Institutions **2531**
List of Production and Export - Import Firms and Organizations in Bulgaria. (BU) **1143**
List of Radiocommunication Stations and Radioastronomy Stations see List of Space Radiocommunication Stations and Radioastronomy Stations **1357**
†List of Research Institutes and Scientists in O E C D Member Countries. (FR ISSN 0078-6292) **5228**
List of Scientific and Technical Literature Relating to Thailand. (TH ISSN 0125-4537) **4356**
List of Selected Articles on I C A O and Civil Aviation see International Civil Aviation Organization. Library Information: Recent Accessions and Selected Articles **66**

LIST

List of Serial Title Word Abbreviations. (FR ISSN 0259-000X) **405**
List of Serials and Monographs Indexed for Online Users *see* List of Serials Indexed for Online Users **3177**
List of Serials Indexed for Online Users. (US ISSN 0736-7139) **3177**
List of Shipowners. (UK ISSN 0260-7387) **4730**
List of Space Radiocommunication Stations and Radioastronomy Stations. (UN) **1357**
List of Telecommunication Channels Used for the Transmission of Telegrams. (UN) **1364**
List of Theses for the Doctor's and Master's Degree in Korea. *see* Han'guk Baksa mit Soksa Hagwi Nonmun Ch'ongmongnok **1677**
Listas Argentinas. (AG) **1143**
Liste des Documents Publies par la C E A. *see* List of E C A Documents Issued **932**
Liste des Membres du Corps Diplomatique a Beograd *see* Yugoslavia. Federal Secretariat for Foreign Affairs. Diplomatic List **3978**
Liste des Signaux Distinctifs et Indicatifs Internationaux des Stations Francaises (Navires, Stations Terrestres). (FR) **4731**
Liste des Travaux Arachnologiques *see* Centre International de Documentation Arachnologique. Liste des Travaux Arachnologiques **464**
Liste Officielle des Navires de Mer Belges et de la Flotte de la Force Navale. (BE) **4731**
Liste over Danske Jazzklubber og Huse *see* Liste over Rytmiske Spillesteder i Danmark **3561**
Liste over Loebende Tidsskrifter og Aarboeger paa A B A *see* Arbejderbevaegelsens Bibliotek og Arkiv. Liste over Loebende Tidsskrifter og Aarboeger paa A B A **702**
Liste over Rytmiske Spillesteder i Danmark. (DK ISSN 0109-1212) **3561**
Liste Pharmindex *see* Gelbe Liste Pharmindex **3727**
Listen. (US ISSN 0024-435X) **1537**
Listen. (GW ISSN 0179-7417) **4131**
Listen Real Loud. (US ISSN 0893-8083) **4847**
†Listen to Your Beer. (US) **5228**
Listener. (US) **2288**
†Listener. (UK ISSN 0024-4392) **5228**
Listener, T V and Radio Times. (NZ) **1376**, 1357
▼The Lister. (UK) **1316**
Listing of Aircraft Accidents-Incidents by Make and Model, U.S. Civil Aviation *see* U.S. National Transportation Safety Board. Listing of Aircraft Accidents-Incidents by Make and Model, U.S. Civil Aviation **5296**
Listino Ufficiale della Borsa Valori di Torino. (IT ISSN 0024-4430) **954**
Lists of P A N S Doc Bibliographies *see* Lists of P A S T I C Bibliographies **4614**
Lists of P A S T I C Bibliographies. (Pakistan Scientific and Technological Information Centre) (PK) **4614**
Listy Cukrovarnicke/Sugar Journal. (CS ISSN 0024-4449) **2076**
Listy Filologicke/Journal of Philology. (NE ISSN 0024-4457) **2827**
†Listy Sv. Frantiska/Leaflets of St. Francis. (US ISSN 0024-4465) **5228**
Liszt Saeculum. (SW ISSN 0263-0249) **3561**
Liszt Society. Journal. (UK ISSN 0141-0792) **3561**
Liszt Society, London. Newsletter *see* Liszt Society. Journal **3561**
Litani. (IS) **3463**
†Lite Rate. (US) **5228**
Liteinoe Proizvodstvo. (RU ISSN 0024-449X) **3412**
Liteinoe Proizvodstvo, Metallovedenie i Obrabotka Metallov Davleniem. (RU ISSN 0302-9069) **3412**

Literacy: a Newsletter *see* Adult Education Information Notes **1681**
Literacy Advance. (US ISSN 0047-4142) **1738**
Literacy Link. (AT ISSN 0158-3026) **1685**
Literaire Tijdschriften in Nederland. (NE) **2982**
Literarischer Verein in Stuttgart. Bibliothek. (GW ISSN 0340-7888) **2933**
Literarischer Weihnachtskatalog. (GW) **2872**
†Literarisches Arbeitsjournal. (GW ISSN 0172-0457) **5228**
†Literarisches Sonderheft. (GW ISSN 0323-3766) **5228**
Literarni Archiv. (CS) **2373**
Literarni Mesicnik. (CS ISSN 0300-2446) **2933**
Literarno - Muzejny Letopis. (CS) **2933**, 3561
Literarny Archiv. (CS ISSN 0075-9872) **2933**
Literary Affairs. *see* Shu'un Adabiyyah **2959**
Literary Agent. (US) **4131**, 1018, 2586
Literary Agents of North America. (US) **2933**, 2572, 4131
Literary Agents of North America Marketplace *see* Literary Agents of North America **2933**
Literary and Art Review. *see* Wenyi Pinglun **2889**
Literary and Linguistic Computing. (UK ISSN 0951-1474) **2856**
Literary Arts Hawaii *see* Kaimana **2870**
Literary Cavalcade. (US ISSN 0024-4511) **1259**, 1646, 2933
Literary Center Quarterly *see* Upstream **3008**
▼Literary Creations. (US ISSN 1049-9598) **2996**, 334
Literary Criterion. (II ISSN 0024-452X) **2872**
Literary Criticism Register. (US ISSN 0733-2165) **2982**, 16
Literary Critics. *see* Wenxue Pinglunjia **2975**
Literary Endeavour. (II ISSN 0255-2779) **2933**
▼Literary Gazette International. (Selected English translation of: Literaturnaya Gazeta) (US) **2872**
Literary Half-Yearly. (II ISSN 0024-4554) **2933**
Literary Heritage. *see* Wenxue Yichan **2975**
Literary History. *see* Irodalomtortenet **2926**
Literary History Communications. *see* Irodalomtorteneti Kozlemenyek **2926**
Literary Magazine Review. (US ISSN 0732-6637) **2933**, 2572
Literary Market Place. (US ISSN 0161-2905) **4132**
†Literary Markets. (CN ISSN 0712-4384) **5228**
Literary Monographs. (US ISSN 0075-9902) **2933**
Literary Onomastics Studies. (US ISSN 0160-8703) **2933**
Literary Prizes in Pakistan. (PK ISSN 0075-9929) **2933**
Literary Research: A Journal of Scholarly Method and Technique. (US ISSN 0891-6365) **2933**
Literary Research Newsletter *see* Literary Research: A Journal of Scholarly Method and Technique **2933**
Literary Review. (US ISSN 0024-4589) **2933**
Literary Review. *see* Wenxue Pinglun **2975**
Literary Review and Quarto. (UK ISSN 0144-4360) **2872**
Literary Sketches. (US ISSN 0024-4597) **2933**, 4132
Literary Studies. (II ISSN 0024-4600) **2933**, 2872
Literary Studies in Poland. (PL) **2933**
Literary Taiwan/Wen Hsueh Chieh. (CH) **2933**, 2996
Der Literat. (GW ISSN 0024-4627) **2933**

The Literate Lawyer. (US) **2649**
Literator. (SA ISSN 0258-2279) **2827**, 2933
Literatur. (GW) **2933**
Literatur & Kritik. (AU ISSN 0024-466X) **2933**, 2996
Literatur aus der Bildungsforschung *see* Literaturinformationen aus der Bildungsforschung **1677**
Literatur aus Oesterreich. (AU) **2933**
Der Literatur Bote. (GW ISSN 0930-4010) **2933**
Literatur fuer Leser. (GW ISSN 0343-1657) **2933**
†Literatur im Historischen Prozess (Neue Folge). (GW ISSN 0177-2074) **5228**
Literatur in Bayern. (GW ISSN 0178-6857) **2933**, 2827
Literatur in Wissenschaft und Unterricht.(GW ISSN 0024-4643) **2872**
Literatur-Telegramm. (GW ISSN 0930-2778) **2872**
Literatur um 11. (GW ISSN 0932-4623) **2996**
Literatur und Geschichte. Eine Schriftenreihe. (GW) **2934**
Literatur und Gesellschaft. (GW ISSN 0232-315X) **2934**, 2996
Literatur und Wirklichkeit. (GW ISSN 0075-9937) **2934**
Literatur zum Angewoehnen. (GW ISSN 0938-1767) **2934**
Literatura. (PL) **2934**
Literatura. (HU ISSN 0133-2368) **2934**
Literatura. (LI ISSN 0202-3296) **2934**
Literatura Chilena. (US ISSN 0730-0220) **2934**
Literatura Drevnei Rusi. (RU) **2934**
Literatura Economica. (BL ISSN 0100-655X) **727**, 677
Literatura i Mastatstva. (BW ISSN 0024-4686) **2934**, 334
Literatura ir Menas. (LI) **2872**
Literatura Kajero. (BL ISSN 0024-4694) **2934**, 2827
Literatura Linguistica Anuario L L *see* Anuario L L **2895**
Literatura Ludowa/Folk Literature. (PL ISSN 0024-4708) **2056**
Literatura na Swiecie. (PL) **2934**
Literatura o Sakhalinskoi Oblasti. (RU) **405**
Literatura ob Arkhangel'skoi Oblasti. (RU) **2934**
Literatura Piekna. Adnotowany Rocznik Bibliograficzny. (PL ISSN 0075-9945) **2982**, 405
Literatura Popular em Verso. (BL) **2934**
Literatura v Shkole. (RU ISSN 0130-3414) **2934**, 1754
Literaturas Andinas. (PE) **2934**
Literaturberichte ueber Wasser, Abwasser, Luft und Feste Abfallstoffe.(GW ISSN 0340-4900) **1977**, 4826
Literaturdokumentation zur Arbeitsmarkt- und Berufsforschung. (GW) **727**
Literature. *see* Bungaku **2901**
Literature. *see* Ha-Sifrut **2960**
Literature Abstracts. (American Petroleum Institute) (US) **3706**, 16
Literature Abstracts: Catalysts & Catalysis. (American Petroleum Institute) (US) **1202**, 3691
Literature Analysis of Microcomputer Publications *see* L A M P **1405**
Literature & Art for Juveniles. *see* Shaonian Wenyi **1265**
Literature & Art Gazette. *see* Wenyi Bao **2975**
Literature and Art of People's Liberation Army. *see* Jiefangjun Wenyi **2927**
Literature and Art Studies. *see* Wenyi Yanjiu **2975**
Literature and Belief. (US ISSN 0732-1929) **4188**, 2934
Literature & History. (US ISSN 0306-1973) **2934**, 2373
Literature and Ideology *see* New Literature and Ideology **2876**
Literature & Medicine. (US ISSN 0278-9671) **2934**, 3122

Literature and Patent Abstracts: Oilfield Chemicals. (American Petroleum Institute) (US) **3706**, 16
Literature and Psychology. (US ISSN 0024-4759) **2934**, 4034
Literature and Society in the Seventeenth Century. (NE) **2934**
Literature and the Sciences of Man. (US ISSN 1040-7928) **2934**, 3772
Literature and the Visual Arts: New Foundations. (US ISSN 0888-3890) **2934**, 334
Literature and Theology. (UK ISSN 0269-1205) **2934**, 4188
▼The Literature Base. (AT ISSN 1034-6244) **1259**, 2934
Literature Canadienne Pour la Jeunesse. *see* C C L **4124**
Literature East and West. (US ISSN 0024-4767) **2934**
Literature - Film Quarterly. (US ISSN 0090-4260) **3513**, 2511, 2934
Literature Magazine. *see* Tap Chi Van Hoc **2968**
†Literature, Music, Fine Arts. (GW ISSN 0024-4775) **5228**
Literature of Exclusion in Spain. (US) **2934**
Literature Press. *see* Wenxue Bao **2974**
Literaturen Zbor. (XN ISSN 0024-4791) **2934**
Literaturinformationdienst Schrifttum Bauwesen: Gesamtausgabe. (GW ISSN 0722-060X) **638**, 16
Literaturinformationen aus der Bildungsforschung. (GW) **1677**
Literaturinformationen zur Beruflichen Bildung. (GW ISSN 0172-1658) **3629**
Literaturna Misal. (BU ISSN 0324-0495) **2934**
Literaturna Ukrayina. (KR ISSN 0024-4821) **2872**
Literaturnaya Armeniya. (AI ISSN 0024-483X) **2872**
Literaturnaya Gazeta. (RU ISSN 0024-4848) **2872**
Literaturnaya Osetiya. Literaturno-Khudozhestvennyi i Obshchestvenno-Politicheskii Zhurnal. (RU ISSN 0132-1986) **2872**
Literaturnaya Rossiya. (RU ISSN 0024-4856) **2872**, 334, 2934
Literaturnaya Ucheba. (RU ISSN 0203-5847) **1259**, 1646
Literaturnye Vzaimosvyazi. (GS) **2934**
Literaturnyi Azerbaidzhan. (AJ ISSN 0024-4864) **2934**
†Literaturrundschau. (SZ ISSN 0024-4872) **5228**
Literaturschau "Stahl und Eisen". (GW ISSN 0933-8934) **3412**
Literaturwissenschaftliches Jahrbuch. Neue Folge. (GW ISSN 0075-997X) **2934**
Literatuur- en Dokumentatieoverzicht N I D I-Bibliotheek. (Nederlands Interdisciplinair Demografisch Instituut) (NE) **3993**
Literatuurinformatie Personeelsaangelegenheden *see* Literatuurinformatie Personeelsbeleid en Organisatie **1067**
Literatuurinformatie Personeelsbeleid en Organisatie. (NE ISSN 0921-6154) **1067**, 1018
Literauur-Overzicht Personeelsaangelegenheden *see* Literatuurinformatie Personeelsbeleid en Organisatie **1067**
Literrature d'America. (IT) **2934**
Litfass. (GW) **2934**
Lithiques. (FR ISSN 0769-3397) **303**, 244, 2317
▼Lithium. (UK ISSN 0954-1381) **3344**
†Lithium Therapy Monographs. (SZ ISSN 1011-2928) **5228**
Litho Week. (UK ISSN 0264-732X) **4002**
Lithology and Mineral Resources. (English Translation of: Litologiya i Poleznye Iskopaemye) (US ISSN 0024-4902) **1571**, 3487
Lithophane Collector's Club Bulletin. (US) **3526**, 334
Lithoprinter Week *see* Litho Week **4002**

Lithos. (NE ISSN 0024-4937) **1571,** 3487
Lithuanian Days. *see* Lietuviu Dienos **2012**
Lithuanian Historical Review. *see* Lietuviu Tautos Praeitis **2373**
Lithuanian Mathematical Journal. (English translation of: Akademiya Nauk Litovskoi S.S.R. Litovskii Matematicheskii Sbornik) (US ISSN 0363-1672) **3043**
Lithuanian Mathematical Transactions *see* Lithuanian Mathematical Journal **3043**
Lithuanian Philatelic Society of New York. Bulletin. (US) **3754**
Lithuanian Physics Journal. (English translation of: Lietuvos Fizikos Rinkinys) (US ISSN 1047-4064) **3824, 3855**
Litigating Private Antitrust Actions. (US) **2650**
Litigation. (US ISSN 0097-9813) **2650**
Litigation. (UK ISSN 0263-2160) **2650**
Litigation and Prevention of Insurer Bad Faith. (US) **2650,** 2537
Litigation Committee Newsletter. (US) **2650**
Litigation News. (US ISSN 0147-9970) **2650**
Litigation of Federal Tax Controversies. (US) **1100**
Litigation Under the Federal Freedom of Information Act and Privacy Act *see* Litigation Under the Federal Open Government Laws **2650**
Litigation Under the Federal Open Government Laws. (US) **2650,** 3905
Litigation User Group News. (US) **2705,** 1478
Litis. (BL) **2650**
Litmus. (UK ISSN 0263-4635) **2872**
Litologiya i Paleogeografiya. (RU ISSN 0131-1719) **1546**
Litologiya i Poleznye Iskopaemye. (RU ISSN 0024-497X) **3487**
Litomericko. (CS ISSN 0075-9988) **2373**
Litopys Boykivshchyny. (US) **2012**
Litovskii Fizicheskii Sbornik/Lietuvos Fizikos Rinkinys. (LI ISSN 0024-2969) **3824, 3855**
Litovskii Matematicheskii Sbornik/ Lietuvos Mokslu Akademija. Lietuvos Matematikos Rinkinys. (LI ISSN 0132-2818) **3043**
Littell's Living Age. (US) **2157**
Litterae Communionis. (IT) **4188**
Litterae Numismaticae Vindobonenses. (AU ISSN 0255-2809) **3600,** 2317
Litterae Textuales. (NE ISSN 0169-8702) **2935**
Litteraria. (PL ISSN 0084-3008) **2935**
Litteraria. (CS) **2935**
▼Litteraria Pragensia. (NE) **2935,** 2827
Litteratur, Aestetik, Sprog Ae S *see* L Ae S **2931**
Litteratur paa Indvandrersprog i Danske Folkebiblioteker. (DK ISSN 0108-7215) **2982**
Litterature. (FR ISSN 0047-4800) **2935**
Litterature Canadienne. *see* Canadian Literature **2903**
Litterature Chinoise. (CC ISSN 1000-9132) **2935**
Litterature Comparee au Canada. *see* Comparative Literature in Canada **2907**
Litteratures. (FR ISSN 0563-9751) **2935**
Litteraturtolkninger. (DK ISSN 0107-0916) **2996**
Little Balkans Review. (US ISSN 0271-7735) **334,** 2935
Little Black Book. (US) **1143,** 1165
Little Free Press. (US) **677**
Little Friends. *see* Xiao Pengyou **1271**
Little Lamp. (US ISSN 0460-1297) **4188**
Little Macaque. *see* Xiao Mihou **1271**

Little Red Book *see* Guide to International Journals & Periodicals **401**
Little Red Book, Classified to All Public Transport Fleet Owners and Operators and Vehicle Manufacturers.(UK ISSN 0076-0013) **4652**
Little Review. (US ISSN 0024-5054) **2935,** 2996
Little Richard News. (DK) **3561**
Little Rock Currents *see* Business (Little Rock) **809**
Little Ship. (UK ISSN 0024-5062) **4525**
Little Star. *see* Xiao Xingxing **1271**
Little Things Word Loom. (CN) **1259**
Little Torches. *see* Xiao Huoju **1271**
†Little Word Machine. (UK) **5228**
†Lituanistika v S.S.S.R. Ekonomika. (UR ISSN 0207-1266) **5228**
†Lituanistika v S.S.S.R. Filosofiya i Psikhologiya. (UR ISSN 0202-2001) **5228**
†Lituanistika v S.S.S.R. Iskusstvovedenie. (UR) **5228**
†Lituanistika v S.S.S.R. Istoriya. (UR) **5228**
†Lituanistika v S.S.S.R. Literaturovedenie. (UR ISSN 0207-1274) **5228**
†Lituanistika v S.S.S.R. Pravo. (UR ISSN 0202-2028) **5228**
†Lituanistika v S.S.S.R. Yazykoznanie. (UR ISSN 0202-201X) **5228**
Lituano-Slavica Posnaniensia. (PL ISSN 0860-0066) **2373**
Lituanus. (US ISSN 0024-5089) **2012**
Liturgie, Foi et Culture. (CN) **4268**
Liturgie Konkret. (GW ISSN 0344-9092) **4188**
Liturgiewissenschaftliche Quellen und Forschungen. (GW ISSN 0076-0048) **4188**
Liturgisches Jahrbuch. (GW ISSN 0024-5100) **4188**
Liturgy. (US ISSN 0458-063X) **4188**
Liturgy. (UK ISSN 0309-4308) **4188**
Liturgy 80 *see* Liturgy 90 **4268**
Liturgy 90. (US ISSN 1046-9990) **4268,** 3561
Liuxing Se/Colour in Fashion. (CC) **1292**
Livability Digest. (US ISSN 0278-9485) **2491,** 4774
Livable City. (US) **2511**
Livarski Vestnik. (BX ISSN 0024-5135) **3412**
Livarstvo. (YU ISSN 0352-8936) **3412**
Live. (JA) **1685**
Live. (GW ISSN 0177-8390) **2190**
Live (Springfield). (US ISSN 0190-3845) **4188**
†Live and Let Live. (US) **5228**
Live Animal Trade & Transport Magazine. (US ISSN 1043-1039) **4652,** 105, 1143, 3712
Live in Concert. (GW) **3561**
Live Letters. (US) **2935**
Live Lines. (NZ ISSN 0024-5143) **1902**
Live Rail. (UK ISSN 0142-7326) **4711**
Live Saar. (GW) **2872**
Live Steam. (US ISSN 0364-5177) **2438**
Live Steam Magazine *see* Live Steam **2438**
Liver. (DK ISSN 0106-9543) **3269**
†Liver Function. (UK ISSN 0261-4758) **5228**
Liver Update. (US) **3122**
Liverpool Catholic Directory. (UK) **4268**
Liverpool Classical Monthly. (UK ISSN 0309-3700) **1278**
Liverpool Cotton Association. Weekly Raw Cotton Report. (UK) **837**
Liverpool Cotton Association. Weekly Value Differences Circular. (UK) **837**
Liverpool Family Historian. (UK ISSN 0260-759X) **2157**
Liverpool Family History Society *see* Liverpool Family Historian **2157**
Liverpool Latin Texts *see* Latin and Greek Texts **1278**

Liverpool Law Review. (UK ISSN 0144-932X) **2650**
Liverpool Library - Classic. (US) **3398**
Liverpool Link. (UK ISSN 0266-8750) **4412**
Liverpool Monographs in Hispanic Studies. (UK ISSN 0261-1538) **2935**
Liverpool Newsletter. (UK ISSN 0047-4827) **3905**
Livestock Adviser. (II ISSN 0970-3004) **220,** 3712, 4812
Livestock and Grain Producers *see* N.S.W. Farmers News **221**
Livestock and Meat Prices and Receipts at Certain California and Western Area Markets. (US) **154**
Livestock and Poultry in Latin America. Annual Conference *see* International Conference on Livestock and Poultry in the Tropics (Proceedings) **219**
Livestock: Latin American Industrial Report. (US) **220**
Livestock Market Digest. (US ISSN 0024-5208) **220**
Livestock, Meat and Wool Market News.(US) **220,** 4621
Livestock Producer's Day Report *see* Animal Science Research Report **5136**
Livestock Production Science. (NE ISSN 0301-6226) **220**
Livestock Weekly. (US ISSN 0162-5047) **221**
LiveWell. (US) **3805,** 3199, 3210, 3365
†Living. (SI) **5228**
Living (Dallas - Fort Worth Edition) *see* Dallas - Fort Worth Home Buyer's Guide **4147**
Living (Denver Edition) *see* Denver Housing Guide **4147**
Living (Florida Gulf Coast Edition) *see* Florida Gulf Coast Homebuyer's Guide **4149**
Living (Houston Edition) *see* Houston Living Housing Guide **4150**
Living (Nashville). (US ISSN 0162-4253) **4242**
†Living (Phoenix Edition). (US ISSN 0741-5516) **5228**
Living Among Nature Daringly! (US ISSN 0897-9561) **2133,** 184, 2737, 4549
Living and Loving. (SA) **4847**
Living and Retiring Abroad. (UK) **4774,** 1506
Living Architecture. (DK ISSN 0108-4135) **303**
Living Bird *see* Living Bird Quarterly **565**
Living Bird Quarterly. (US ISSN 0732-9210) **565**
Living Blues. (US ISSN 0024-5232) **3561**
Living Church. (US ISSN 0024-5240) **4242**
Living City. (US ISSN 0193-5968) **4188**
†Living City. (AT ISSN 0047-4835) **5228**
Living Conditions in Denmark. *see* Levevilkaar i Danmark **4577**
Living Earth. (UK ISSN 0954-1098) **184**
Living for Young Homemakers *see* H G **2551**
Living Free. (US) **3595**
Living Guide. (CN) **4152**
Living Healthy. (US) **3269,** 446, 4034
Living Historian. (US) **2413**
Living Historical Farms Bulletin. (US ISSN 0047-4851) **3526,** 105
Living History Association Quarterly. (US) **2317**
Living in Freedom Eternally, Inc. Words of L I F E *see* Words of L I F E **4210**
Living in Japan. (JA ISSN 0913-8102) **2208**
Living in South Carolina. (US ISSN 0047-486X) **2228**
Living in Thailand. (TH) **2220**
Living in the Ozarks Newsletter *see* L I O N **2871**
Living in Venezuela. (VE) **4774,** 819
Living Judaism *see* Manna **4225**
Living Light. (US ISSN 0024-5275) **4268**

The Living Light Philosophy. (US) **4188,** 3772
The Living Museum. (US ISSN 0024-5283) **4323**
Living Off the Land. (US ISSN 0738-7687) **2134**
†Living Physics. (US ISSN 0893-8067) **5228**
Living Prayer. (US ISSN 0890-5568) **4188,** 3772
Living Safety. (CN ISSN 0714-5896) **4107**
Living Stones. (UK ISSN 0951-8347) **4188**
Living Streams. (US) **2935,** 4188
Living - The Denver Housing Guide *see* Denver Housing Guide **4147**
Living Well. (US) **3805**
†Living with Allergies. (US ISSN 0192-995X) **5228**
†Living with Antiques. (AT) **5228**
†Living with Cancer. (US) **5228**
Living with Children. (US ISSN 0456-3271) **1240**
Living with Christ - Complete Edition. (CN ISSN 0703-6752) **4268**
Living with Christ - Sunday Edition. (CN ISSN 0703-6760) **4268**
Living with Preschoolers. (US ISSN 0162-4350) **4242,** 1240
Living with Teenagers. (US ISSN 0162-4261) **4242,** 1241
Living with the Shore. (US) **1962,** 1491, 1607
Living Word. *see* Levend Woord **4284**
Living World. (US ISSN 0896-2154) **4412**
LivingRight. (US) **3199**
Livingston County Agricultural News. (US ISSN 0024-5313) **105**
Livingstone Museum. Research Notes. (ZA) **2333,** 3526
Livornocronaca *see* Livornocronaca - Il Vernacoliere **2872**
Livornocronaca - Il Vernacoliere. (IT) **2872**
Livraisons. (FR) **4132**
Livraria Figueirinhas Catalogo. (PO) **4132**
Livre d'Art Information. (FR) **352**
Livre du Congres l'A F T P V. (FR) **334**
Le Livre et l'Estampe. (BE ISSN 0024-533X) **4132**
Livres. (FR ISSN 0024-5348) **4141**
Livres Canadiens Courants. *see* Current Canadian Books **4126**
Livres Canadiens pour la Jeunesse. *see* Canadian Books for Young People **1247**
Livres d'Aujourd'hui *see* Bulletin Bibliographique Thematique **395**
Livres de France. (FR) **4132**
Livres Disponibles. (FR) **405**
Livres du Mois. (FR) **4132**
†Livres et Auteurs Quebecois. (CN ISSN 0076-0153) **5228**
Livres et des Jeunes. (CN ISSN 0706-795X) **1259**
Livres Hebdo. (FR ISSN 0294-0000) **4141,** 405
Livret de la Quatrieme Section, Ecole Pratique Hautes Etudes. (SZ) **2317**
Livros de Portugal. (PO ISSN 0870-5259) **4132**
Livrustkammaren. (SW ISSN 0024-5372) **3526**
Livs. (SW ISSN 0024-5380) **2076**
Livsmedelsteknik. (SW ISSN 0024-5399) **2076**
Al-Liwa' al-Islami/Islamic Standard. (UA) **4219**
Lixue Jinzhan/Advances in Mechanics. (CC ISSN 1000-0992) **3844**
Lixue Xuebao. (CC ISSN 0459-1879) **3844**
Lixue yu Shijian/Mechanics and Practice. (CC ISSN 1000-0879) **1934,** 3844
Lizi Jiaohuan yu Xifu. (CC ISSN 1001-5493) **1183**
Ljuskultur. (SW) **1902**
Llafur. (UK ISSN 0306-0837) **987**
Llais. (UK) **1316**
Llais Llyfrau/Book News from Wales. (UK ISSN 0024-5437) **4142**
†Llama World Magazine. (US) **5228**
Llamas Magazine. (US ISSN 0887-9923) **587,** 4812
Llan. (UK ISSN 0024-5445) **4188**

Llandaff Diocesan Directory. (UK) **4242**
Llen Cymru. (UK ISSN 0076-0188) **2935**
Llewellyn New Times. (US) **359**
Llewellyn's Astrological Calendar. (US ISSN 0145-8868) **359**
Llewellyn's Moon Sign Book. (US) **359**, **2134**
Lliria. (AA) **277**
Lloyd Aero Boliviano Aboard L A B Airlines *see* Aboard L A B Airlines **4801**
Lloyd Report. (GW) **2537**
Lloyd's A S E A N Shipping Directory. (UK) **4731**
Lloyd's Aviation Law. (US) **58**, **2650**
Lloyds Bank Annual Review. (UK ISSN 0953-5004) **789**
Lloyds Bank Economic Bulletin. (UK) **789**
Lloyds Bank News. (UK) **789**
Lloyds Bank Review Quarterly *see* Lloyds Bank Annual Review **789**
Lloyd's Insurance International. (US) **2537**
Lloyd's International Marine Equipment Guide (Year). (UK) **4731**
Lloyd's Law Reports. (UK ISSN 0024-5488) **2650**, **2711**, **2735**
Lloyd's List International. (UK) **4731**, **677**, **1792**, **2537**
Lloyd's Loading List. (UK ISSN 0144-6681) **4731**, **916**
Lloyd's Log. (UK ISSN 0024-550X) **2537**
Lloyd's Marine Equipment Guide *see* Lloyd's International Marine Equipment Guide (Year) **4731**
Lloyd's Maritime & Commercial Law Quarterly. (UK ISSN 0306-2945) **2735**, **4731**
Lloyd's Maritime Asia. (HK ISSN 1015-227X) **4731**
Lloyd's Maritime Atlas. (UK ISSN 0076-020X) **4731**
Lloyd's Maritime Directory (Year). (UK ISSN 0268-327X) **4731**
Lloyd's Maritime Law Newsletter. (UK ISSN 0268-0696) **2735**, **4731**
Lloyd's Monthly List of Laid up Vessels. (UK ISSN 0266-6189) **4731**
Lloyd's Nautical Year Book. (UK ISSN 0952-5394) **4731**
Lloyd's Passenger Shipping International. (US) **4731**
Lloyd's Ports of the World (Year). (UK ISSN 0266-6197) **4731**
Lloyd's Register of Classed Yachts. (UK ISSN 0261-6688) **4731**
Lloyd's Register of Shipping. Statistical Tables. (UK ISSN 0076-0234) **4731**
Lloyd's Register of Ships. (UK ISSN 0141-4909) **4731**
Lloyd's Register of Yachts *see* Lloyd's Register of Classed Yachts **4731**
Lloyds Register World *see* 100A1 **4742**
Lloyd's Ship Arrest International. (US) **4731**
Lloyd's Ship Manager. (UK ISSN 0265-2455) **4731**
Lloyd's Ship Manager. Shipping News International. (NO) **4731**
Lloyd's Shipping Economist. (UK ISSN 0144-6673) **4731**
Lloyd's Shipping Index. (UK ISSN 0144-4549) **4731**
Lloyd's Survey Handbook. (UK) **4731**
Lloyd's Voyage Record. (UK ISSN 0144-4557) **4732**
Lloyd's Weekly Casualty Reports. (UK ISSN 0047-4908) **2537**, **4732**
Lluvia de Rosas. (SP) **4268**
Lo Gai Saber. (FR) **2827**, **2935**
Lo Nishkach. (IS ISSN 0334-9470) **2373**
Loadstar. (US ISSN 0886-4144) **1461**, **1470**
Loan-a-Home Directory. (US) **1143**, **4152**
Loan Investor. (US) **789**
Loan Officers Legal Alert. (US ISSN 8756-1522) **789**, **2650**
†Loans Closed and Servicing Volume for the Mortgage Banking Industry. (US ISSN 0277-1497) **5228**

LOAPL *see* Langues Orientales Anciennes Philologie et Linguistique **2824**
Lobby. (AT) **3905**
Lobby Press Newsletter. (UK) **2872**, **2996**
▼Lobbying Resource Directory. (US ISSN 1057-0594) **2650**, **4066**
Loblolly. (US ISSN 0361-3577) **2413**
Lobster. (UK) **3905**
Locaguide. (FR ISSN 0990-1159) **622**
Local Agent *see* American Agent and Broker **2526**
Local and Regional Authorities in Europe *see* Council of Europe. Study Series: Local and Regional Authorities in Europe **4086**
Local and Regional Authorities in Europe. Study Series. (FR) **4090**
†Local Area Housing Statistics. (UK) **5228**
Local Area Network *see* L A N **1427**
Local Area Network Computing *see* L A N Computing **1427**
Local Area Network Product News *see* L A N Product News **1427**
Local Area Network Reporter *see* L A N Reporter **1454**
Local Area Network Software Directory *see* L A N Software Directory **1438**
Local Area Network Technology *see* L A N Technology **1461**
Local Area Network Telecomunicazioni *see* L A N e Telecomunicazioni **1351**
Local Area Network Times *see* L A N Times **1470**
Local Area Networking Directory *see* Networking Directory **1428**
Local Area Networks. (US ISSN 1051-1962) **1427**, **1461**, **1470**
Local Authorities in Israel: Financial Data. (IS ISSN 0333-886X) **727**, **1100**
Local Authority Administration *see* Local Authority Management **4090**
Local Authority and Public Service Yearbook. (UK) **4090**
Local Authority Management. (NZ) **4090**
Local Authority Specifiers' Reference Book and Buyers Guide. (UK ISSN 0260-3756) **2491**
Local Climatological Data. (US) **3438**
Local Council Review. (UK ISSN 0308-3594) **4090**
Local Data Record *see* Linking Libraries **2771**
Local Economic Development Information Service. (UK) **4412**, **837**
Local Economy. (UK ISSN 0269-0942) **677**
Local Government. (PK) **4090**
Local Government Administrators' Official Source Book. (UK ISSN 0267-2022) **4090**
▼Local Government and Law. (UK) **4090**, **2650**
Local Government Annotations *see* L O G A **4081**
Local Government Bulletin. (PH ISSN 0024-5526) **4090**
Local Government Chronicle. (UK ISSN 0024-5534) **4090**
Local Government Companion. (UK ISSN 0305-0130) **4090**
†Local Government Employment. (UK ISSN 0957-5111) **5228**
Local Government Finance *see* Public Finance and Accountancy **4093**
Local Government Finances in Maryland. (US ISSN 0085-2821) **1100**
Local Government in Mauritius *see* Association of Urban Authorities. Annual Bulletin **4084**
Local Government in Southern Africa/Plaaslike Regering in Suidelike Afrika. (SA) **4090**
Local Government Index (New South Wales). (AT ISSN 0727-7989) **2700**, **638**
Local Government Law & Practice (New South Wales). (AT ISSN 0727-7830) **2650**
Local Government Management. (AT ISSN 0727-7342) **4090**

Local Government News. (UK) **4090**
†Local Government Newsletter. (NE) **5228**
Local Government Ordinance 70 "Building" (New South Wales). (AT ISSN 0727-7997) **2650**, **623**
Local Government Ordinances Services (New South Wales). (AT ISSN 0727-8004) **2650**
Local Government Planning & Environment Service N S W. (AT) **4066**, **1962**
Local Government Policy Making. (UK) **4090**
Local Government Reports of Australia. (AT ISSN 0076-0242) **4066**
Local Government Review. (UK ISSN 0262-4303) **2650**, **4090**
Local Government Review *see* Local Government Review in Japan **4090**
Local Government Review in Japan. (JA ISSN 0288-7622) **4090**
Local Government Studies. (UK ISSN 0300-3930) **4090**
Local Historian. (UK ISSN 0024-5585) **2373**
Local History *see* Local History Magazine **2373**
Local History Magazine. (UK) **2373**
Local Jewish Historical Society News. (US) **2012**, **2413**
Local Level Experience in Agricultural Development. *see* Mestnyi Proizvodstvennyi Opyt v Sel'skom Khozyaistve **154**
Local Level Experience in the Construction Industry. *see* Mestnyi Proizvodstvennyi Opyt v Stroitel'stve **624**
Local Level Experience in the Manufacturing Industry. *see* Mestnyi Proizvodstvennyi Opyt v Promyshlennosti **1936**
Local Museum *see* Community History **2344**
Local Planet Visibility Report (Year). (US) **366**
Local Population Studies. (UK ISSN 0143-2974) **3984**
Local Preachers Magazine. (UK ISSN 0024-5607) **4242**
Local Rules of the District Courts in Texas. (US) **2650**
Local Rules of the Superior Court: Washington State. (US) **2650**
Local Self-Government. (II ISSN 0024-5615) **4090**, **2491**
Local - State Funding Report. (US ISSN 0741-3173) **1100**, **2491**, **4412**, **4719**
Local Studies *see* Northern Ireland Bibliography **407**
Local Studies Index. (UK ISSN 0269-2317) **2329**, **16**
Local 144 News. (US) **987**, **2467**, **2477**
LocalNetter Newsletter. (US ISSN 0886-2397) **1427**, **1461**
†LocalNetter Update Service. (US) **5228**
Locate! (US) **2255**, **1871**
Locating Gold *see* Locating Gold, Gems, & Minerals **3487**
Locating Gold, Gems, & Minerals. (US) **3487**
Location Actualite. (FR) **623**
Location Production Guide. (US ISSN 1047-9775) **3513**
Location Update. (US) **3513**, **1385**
Locations. (US) **3513**
Locations and Ventes *see* Semaine Immobiliere **4158**
Locations of Industries in Gujarat State. (II ISSN 0076-0269) **1080**
Locations Vacances. (FR ISSN 0024-5674) **4152**
Locator (Silver Spring) *see* Locator of Used Machinery, Equipment & Plant Services **3019**
Locator (Whiting). (US) **4694**
Locator of Used Machinery, Equipment & Plant Services. (US) **3019**
Halochame. (IS ISSN 0334-357X) **3463**, **4412**
Lock *see* Bible of Weather Forecasting **3433**
Locke. (GW ISSN 0724-1429) **4412**
Locke Newsletter. (UK ISSN 0307-2606) **3772**

Lockert Library of Poetry in Translation.(US) **2997**
Lockheed M S C Star. (Lockheed Missiles and Space Co., Inc.) (US) **67**
Lockheed Missiles and Space Co., Inc. Lockheed M S C Star *see* Lockheed M S C Star **67**
†Lockheed Orion Service Digest. (US ISSN 0024-5704) **5228**
Lockheed Reports *see* A S W Log **42**
Locksmith Gazette. (US) **642**
Locksmith Ledger *see* Locksmith Ledger International **642**
Locksmith Ledger International. (US) **642**
Locksmith Ledger - International Directory. (US) **1143**, **642**, **1527**
Locksmith Ledger - Security Guide and Directory *see* Locksmith Ledger - International Directory **1143**
Lockwood - Post's Directory of the Pulp, Paper and Allied Trades. (US) **1143**, **3663**
Lockwood's Directory of the Paper and Allied Trades *see* Lockwood - Post's Directory of the Pulp, Paper and Allied Trades **1143**
Loco-Revue. (FR ISSN 0024-5739) **2438**, **4711**
Locomotive. (US ISSN 0741-8760) **3019**, **1902**
Locomotive & Railway Preservation. (US ISSN 0891-7647) **4711**
Locomotive Engineer Newsletter. (US ISSN 0024-5747) **4711**, **2586**
Locomotive Engineers Journal. (US ISSN 0894-3605) **4711**, **2586**
Locomotive Journal. (UK) **4711**, **2586**
Locomotive Maintenance Officers Association. Annual Proceedings. (US ISSN 0076-0285) **4711**
Locomotive Maintenance Officers Association. Preconvention Report. (US ISSN 0076-0293) **4711**
Locomotive, Railway Carriage *see* Modern Railways **4711**
Locomotives Illustrated. (UK ISSN 0307-1804) **4711**
Locus (Denton). (US ISSN 0898-8056) **2413**
Locus (New York). (US) **3526**
Locus (Oakland). (US ISSN 0047-4959) **3012**
Locus Select. (US) **3526**
Locust Newsletter *see* Migrant Pest Newsletter **185**
Locusta. (ML ISSN 0459-6803) **184**
Lodestone's Australian Oil and Gas Journal *see* Australia's Mining Monthly **3478**
Lodging. (US ISSN 0360-9235) **2477**
Lodging Briefing. (US) **4774**
Lodging Hospitality. (US ISSN 0148-0766) **2477**
Lodiamo Il Signore *see* Celebriamo **3544**
Lodzki Numismatyk. (PL ISSN 0024-5771) **3600**
†Lodzkie Studia Etnograficzne. (PL ISSN 0076-0382) **5228**
Lodzkie Towarzystwo Naukowe. Prace Wydzialu Jezykoznawstwa, Nauki o Literaturze i Filozofii. (PL ISSN 0076-0404) **2935**
Lodzkie Towarzystwo Naukowe. Rozprawy Komisji Jezykowej. (PL ISSN 0076-0390) **2827**
†Lodzkie Towarzystwo Naukowe. Wydzial III Nauk Matematyczno-Przyrodniczych. Prace. (PL ISSN 0076-0412) **5228**
†Lodzkie Towarzystwo Naukowe. Wydzial IV. Nauk Lekarskich. Prace. (PL ISSN 0076-0420) **5228**
†Lodzkie Towarzystwo Naukowe. Wydzial V. Nauk Technicznych. Prace. (PL ISSN 0076-0439) **5228**
Loeb Classical Library. (US) **2935**
Loegumkloster-Studier. (DK ISSN 0106-0430) **2373**
Loennsstatistikk *see* Norway. Statistisk Sentralbyraa. Loennsstatistikk **731**
Loevetann. (NO ISSN 0800-014X) **2455**
Lofty Times. (US) **2491**

Log. (UK ISSN 0024-5798) **58**, **4675**
The Log. (CN) **2178**
Log see Seafarers Log **2589**
Log. (AT ISSN 0815-0052) **4732**
†The Log. (US) **5228**
Log Analyst. (US ISSN 0024-581X) **3691**
The Log and San Diego Log. (US) **4525**
Log Home and Alternative Housing Builder see Builder-Dealer Magazine **605**
Log Home Decor for Builders and Buyers see Muir's Original Log Home Guide for Builders & Buyers **625**
Log Home Guide for Builders and Buyers see Muir's Original Log Home Guide for Builders & Buyers **625**
Log Home Living. (US ISSN 1041-830X) **623**
†Log Homes Design, Construction & Finance Issue. (US ISSN 0894-0355) **5228**
†Log House. (CN ISSN 0315-8756) **5229**
Log In. (GW ISSN 0720-8642) **1691**
Log Magazine see Army Logistician **3452**
Log of Mystic Seaport. (US ISSN 0024-5828) **3527**, **4525**
Log of the Star Class. (US ISSN 0076-0455) **4525**
Log On. (US) **1445**
Log Trucker. (US ISSN 0194-150X) **2115**, **4652**
LOGA-Local Government Abstracts see L O G A **4081**
Logberg-Heimskringla. (CN ISSN 0047-4967) **2872**
Logbook. see Bordbuch **4754**
Logbook (Year). (US) **4507**
Das Logbuch. (GW ISSN 0175-7601) **2438**
Logement et Famille. (FR) **4442**
Logements Vacants Denombres au 1er Juin (Year). see Leerwohnungszaehlung 1. Juni (Year) **638**
Loggen see Loggen Magazine **4732**
Loggen Magazine. (SW) **4732**
Logger and Lumberman. (US ISSN 0192-7124) **2116**
Loggers World. (US ISSN 0047-4983) **2116**
Loggin' Times see Southern Loggin' Times **2117**
Logging & Sawmilling Journal. (CN ISSN 0225-7572) **2116**
Logibase. (CN ISSN 0836-6853) **1143**, **1478**
Logibase: Directory of Quebec Software. (CN ISSN 0847-2165) **1143**, **1478**
Logic and Language Studies. see Luoji yu Yuyan Xuexi **3772**
Logique et Analyse. (BE ISSN 0024-5836) **3772**
Logistica. (IT) **4652**
Logistics and Transportation Review. (CN ISSN 0047-4991) **4652**, **3463**
Logistics Comment. (US) **1044**
Logistics Information Management. (UK ISSN 0957-6053) **2771**
Logistics Spectrum. (US ISSN 0024-5852) **4603**
Logistics Today. (UK ISSN 0262-4354) **1934**, **4652**
Logistik Heute. (GW ISSN 0173-6213) **827**, **1351**, **1438**
Logistik im Unternehmen. (GW ISSN 0930-7834) **1018**
Logistik Spektrum. (GW ISSN 0935-7939) **1414**
Logistiques Magazine. (FR ISSN 0295-4192) **1919**
†Logo and Education Computing Journal. (US ISSN 0743-2445) **5229**
Logo Exchange. (US ISSN 0888-6970) **1691**, **1431**
Logophile. (UK ISSN 0309-6270) **2827**
Logos. (IT ISSN 0024-5887) **3772**
▼Logos. (UK ISSN 0957-9656) **4132**, **2771**
†Logos. (PH ISSN 0076-0471) **5229**
Logos (Argonne). (US) **1829**, **1962**

Logos (Mason City). (US) **1316**
Logos (New York). (US) **4285**, **3772**
Logos (San Antonio). (US) **1316**
Logsdon Connections. (US ISSN 0732-7595) **2157**
Lohn und Gehalt. (GW ISSN 0172-9047) **677**
Lohnunternehmen in Land- und Forstwirtschaft. (GW ISSN 0341-261X) **163**
Loi de l'Impot sur le Revenu du Canada see Loi de l'Impot sur le Revenu du Canada et Reglements **1100**
Loi de l'Impot sur le Revenu du Canada et Reglements. (CN) **1100**
Loisir et Societe/Society and Leisure. (CN ISSN 0705-3436) **2739**, **4442**, **4478**
Loisirama. (BE) **2739**
Loisirs Jeunes. (FR) **4478**
Loisirs Nautiques. (FR ISSN 0047-5017) **4526**
Lojas & Lojistas. (BL) **837**
Lok Magazin. (GW ISSN 0458-1822) **4711**
Lok Rajya. (II ISSN 0024-5917) **1646**, **3944**
▼Lokaal & Mondial - Vakmatig. (NE ISSN 0927-202X) **3965**, **4066**
Lokabritta: Hindi Folklore. (II) **2056**, **244**
Lokal Historie i Skoerping Kommune. (DK ISSN 0108-4690) **2373**
Lokales. (GW) **3905**, **1518**
Lokalhistorie: Hadsund Kommune. (DK ISSN 0109-002X) **2373**
Lokalhistorisk Arkiv, Aalestrup. Aarsskrift. (DK ISSN 0109-6699) **2373**
Lokalhistorisk Arkiv for Fredericia og Omegn. Aarsskrift. (DK ISSN 0900-3126) **2373**
Lokalhistorisk Arkiv, Roedby. Aarsskrift.(DK ISSN 0109-8551) **2373**
Lokalhistorisk Arkiv Stubbekoebing. Aarsskrift. (DK ISSN 0109-2162) **2374**
Lokalhistorisk Forening for Hoerup Sogn. Aarsskrift. (DK ISSN 0109-2839) **2374**
Lokalhistorisk Forening for Sejlflod Kommune. (DK ISSN 0106-9748) **2374**
Lokalhistorisk Forening for Soenderhald Kommune. Aarsskrift. (DK ISSN 0109-4017) **2374**
Lokalhistorisk Journal see Journalen. Lokal- og Kulturhistorisk Tidsskrift **2371**
▼Lokalhistorisk Magasin. (NO ISSN 0802-8931) **2374**
Lokalhistorisk Orientering Hvidovre see Hvidovre Lokalhistorie **2368**
Lokalhistoriske Arkiver i Nordjyllands Amt Nyt see L A N A Nyt **2372**
Lokalhistoriske Arkiver i Vestsjaellands Amt Vulkanen: Ren L A V A see Vulkanen: Ren L A V A **2395**
Lokomotivet. (DK ISSN 0108-9307) **2438**
Lokprabha. (II) **677**
Die Lokrundschau. (GW ISSN 0170-379X) **4711**
Loktantra Samiksha. (II ISSN 0024-595X) **3905**
Lola-Fish. (FR) **2997**
Lola Proceedings. see Lola Saopstenja **1934**
Lola Saopstenja/Lola Proceedings. (YU ISSN 0352-8456) **1934**, **1902**, **3019**
Lolemi! (SA) **4285**
Lolland-Falsters Historiske Samfund. Aarbog. (DK ISSN 0107-8798) **2374**
Lolland-Falsters Landbrugs-Nyt see Storstroems Amts Landbrugs-Nyt **122**
Lolland-Falsters Stiftsmuseums Aarskrift. (DK ISSN 0542-6820) **2374**
Lollipops. (US ISSN 0890-3557) **1754**, **1241**
Loma Weekly Paper. (LB) **4242**
Lombard. (IT) **789**
Londam. (IT) **3122**, **4412**

London. Stock Exchange. Stock Exchange Companies see International Stock Exchange. Quality of Market Companies Book **950**
London. Stock Exchange. Stock Exchange Fact Service see International Stock Exchange Fact Sheet Monthly **950**
London. Stock Exchange. Stock Exchange Quarterly see International Stock Exchange. Quality of Markets Quarterly **950**
London (Year). (US) **4774**
London and Local Advertiser see London Weekly Advertiser **34**
London and Middlesex Archaeological Society. Special Papers. (UK) **277**
London and Middlesex Archaeological Society. Transactions. (UK ISSN 0076-0501) **277**
London and Middlesex Archaeological Society & Surrey Archaeological Society. Joint Publication. (UK) **278**
London and South East Region Advisory Council for Education and Training. Index of Courses. (UK) **1711**, **1695**
†London and South Eastern Regional Advisory Council for Further Education. Bulletin of Special Courses. (UK) **5229**
London and South Eastern Regional Advisory Council for Further Education. Index of Courses see London and South East Region Advisory Council for Education and Training. Index of Courses **1711**
London Archaeologist. (UK ISSN 0024-5984) **278**
†London Bibliography of the Social Sciences. (UK ISSN 0076-051X) **5229**
London Bird Report. (UK ISSN 0141-4348) **565**
London Borough of Hammersmith and Fulham. Review see Streetlife **2885**
London Business Monthly Magazine. (CN) **677**
London Business School. Bibliography of Financial Markets. (UK) **727**, **789**
†London Business School. Journal. (UK) **5229**
London Business School. Small Business Bibliography. (UK) **1116**
London Calling. (UK ISSN 0024-600X) **1357**
London Chamber of Commerce. Annual Review see London Chamber of Commerce and Industry. Annual Review **819**
London Chamber of Commerce and Industry. Annual Report and Annual Directory see London Chamber of Commerce and Industry. Directory **819**
London Chamber of Commerce and Industry. Annual Review. (UK) **819**
London Chamber of Commerce and Industry. Directory. (UK ISSN 0142-9728) **819**
London City Mission Magazine see Span (London) **4202**
London Collector. (US ISSN 0047-5033) **2935**
London College of Music Magazine. (UK) **3561**
London Commerce. (UK) **819**
London Corn Circular. (UK ISSN 0024-6026) **184**
†London Creative Listings (Year). (UK) **5229**
London Currency Report. (UK ISSN 0307-0360) **789**
London Dayori. (UK) **4775**
▼London Defence Studies. (UK) **3463**, **3965**
†London Delegate. (UK) **5229**
London Directory for Trade & Industry. (UK ISSN 0952-8784) **1143**
†London Directory of Industry and Commerce. (UK) **5229**
London Disability News. (UK) **4412**
London Drama Magazine see The Drama Magazine **4632**
London Drinker. (UK ISSN 0144-7866) **383**
London Energy Group Data Book and Diary see Energy Data Book and Diary **1798**

London Energy News. (UK ISSN 0267-1263) **1792**
London Federation of Museum and Art Galleries. Newsletter. (UK ISSN 0260-7743) **3527**
London Gazette. (UK) **2650**
London Gentleman see Lifestyle and London Living **4151**
London German Studies. (UK) **2935**
London Guide see London Magazine Guidebook **4775**
London Hilton Magazine see Hilton International (U.K.) Magazine **2475**
London Journal. (UK ISSN 0305-8034) **2374**, **4442**
London Life for Delegates see London Delegate **5229**
London Magazine. (UK ISSN 0024-6085) **2873**, **2511**
London Magazine (London). (CN) **2178**
London Magazine (London, 1980). (CN) **2178**
London Magazine Guidebook. (CN) **4775**
London Mathematical Society. Bulletin. (UK ISSN 0024-6093) **3044**
London Mathematical Society. Journal. (UK ISSN 0024-6107) **3044**
London Mathematical Society. Lecture Note Series. (UK ISSN 0076-0552) **3044**
London Mathematical Society. Monographs. (US) **3044**
London Mathematical Society. Proceedings. (UK ISSN 0024-6115) **3044**
†London Medicine. (UK) **5229**
London Naturalist. (UK ISSN 0076-0579) **446**
London, Ont. University of Western Ontario Series in Philosophy of Science see University of Western Ontario Series in Philosophy of Science **3785**
London Papers in Regional Science see European Research in Regional Science **2487**
London Philatelist. (UK ISSN 0024-6131) **3754**
London Police Court Mission. Annual Report see Rainer Foundation. Annual Report **1521**
London Port Handbook 1984. (UK ISSN 0260-8839) **4732**, **1143**
London Portrait. (UK) **2194**
London Postal History Group Notebook.(UK) **3754**, **1353**
London Record Society. Publications. (UK ISSN 0085-2848) **2374**
London Regional Transport News see L T News **4652**
London Restaurant Guide (London, 1990). (UK) **2477**
London Review. (UK ISSN 0024-614X) **2935**
London Review of Books. (UK ISSN 0260-9592) **2873**
†London School of Economics and Political Science. Department of Geography. Geographical Papers. (UK ISSN 0076-0641) **5229**
London School of Economics and Political Science Magazine see L S E Magazine **5225**
London School of Economics Monographs on Social Anthropology. (UK ISSN 0077-1074) **244**
London School of Economics Quarterly see L.S.E. Quarterly **5225**
London Shop Surveys see Retail Directory **1052**
London Society. Journal. (UK ISSN 0954-6685) **2491**
▼London Stage 1800-1900: A Documentary Record and Calendar of Performances. (US ISSN 1043-6650) **4634**
London Student. (UK) **1316**
London Studies on South Asia. (UK ISSN 0142-601X) **3640**
London Theatre Index (Year). (UK ISSN 0263-2322) **4634**
London Theatre News. (US) **4634**
London Theatre Record see Theatre Record **4641**
London Weekly Advertiser. (UK ISSN 0958-9600) **34**

6400 LONDON WEEKLY

†London Weekly Diary of Social Events. (UK ISSN 0024-6190) **5229**
London Welshman. *see* Cymro Llundain **2863**
London's Best Bed & Breakfast Hotels. (UK) **4775**
Lone Star *see* Lone Star Humor **2873**
Lone Star Comedy Monthly *see* Lone Star Comedy Service **2873**
Lone Star Comedy Service. (US) **2873**
Lone Star Horse Report. (US ISSN 0892-6271) **4536**
Lone Star Humor. (US) **2873**
Lonely Planet Newsletter *see* Lonely Planet Update **5229**
†Lonely Planet Update. (AT ISSN 1030-5459) **5229**
Lonergan Studies Newsletter. (CN ISSN 0828-184X) **3772, 4188**
Lonergan Workshop. (US ISSN 0148-2009) **4188**
Long Ashton Research Station Annual Report *see* A F R C Institute of Arable Crops Research. Report **165**
Long Ashton Research Station Report *see* A F R C Institute of Arable Crops Research. Report **165**
Long Beach Business Journal. (US) **677**
Long Beach Island Magazine. (US) **2228**
Long Beach Monthly. (US) **2228**
Long Cane News. (US ISSN 0899-644X) **2294**
Long-Distance Letter. (US ISSN 0740-6851) **1364, 677**
Long Island. (US) **678, 2228**
Long Island - Business *see* Long Island Business News **872**
Long Island Business News. (US) **872**
Long Island Catholic. (US ISSN 0024-6255) **4268**
Long Island Fisherman *see* Fisherman **4546**
Long Island Forum. (US ISSN 0024-628X) **2413**
Long Island Goodliving. (US) **2228**
Long Island Historical Journal. (US ISSN 0898-7084) **2413**
Long Island Jewish World. (US ISSN 0199-2899) **2012, 4225**
†Long Island Monthly. (US ISSN 0898-557X) **5229**
Long Island Nightlife. (US) **4362**
Long Island Parenting News. (US) **1241, 3398, 4847**
Long Island Pediatrician *see* New York Pediatrician **3323**
Long Island Poetry Collective. Newsletter. (US) **2997**
Long Island Postal History Society Journal. (US) **3754**
Long Island Power & Sail. (US) **4526**
Long Island Singles Club. Calendar. (US) **4362, 1299**
Long Island Ski. (US) **4549**
Long Island Sound Report *see* Long Island Sound Study Update **1607**
Long Island Sound Study Update. (US) **1607**
Long Island Swingers Magazine. (US) **4362**
Long Island Telephone Tickler for Insurance Men & Women. (US) **2537**
Long Point Bird Observatory Newsletter. (CN ISSN 0317-9575) **565**
Long Point Genealogist. (CN) **2157**
Long Pond Review. (US ISSN 8756-5099) **2935**
Long Range Planning. (US ISSN 0024-6301) **1018**
Long Room. (IE ISSN 0024-631X) **2794**
Long Shot. (US ISSN 0895-9773) **2935**
Long Story. (US ISSN 0741-4242) **2935**
Long Term Care *see* Long Term Care Management **3281**
†Long Term Care. (US) **5229**
Long-Term Care Administrator. (US ISSN 0146-275X) **2467, 2276**
Long Term Care Management. (US) **3281, 2467**
Long Term Care Monitor. (CN ISSN 1180-2189) **2276**

Long Term Credit Bank of Japan Ltd. Research *see* L T C B Research **1080**
Long-Term Economic Forecast. (JA) **872**
Long Term Forecasts (Year). (AT) **678**
Long Term Investing. (US) **954**
Long-Term Score. (US) **954**
Long Trail News. (US) **4549**
Longer and Healthier Life. *see* Kenko na Kurashi **3805**
Longevity. *see* Chang Shou **2271**
Longevity. (US ISSN 0895-8254) **2276**
Longhouse. (US) **2997**
Longman Directory of Local Authorities. (UK) **2650**
Longman Tax Digest. (UK ISSN 0951-7618) **1100**
Longview Current. (US) **1316**
Longwood Graduate Program Seminars. (US) **509, 2134**
Longwood Program Seminars *see* Longwood Graduate Program Seminars **509**
▼The Loogie. (US) **2997**
Look! (UK) **1259, 4242**
Look. (TH) **2220**
Look & Listen. (RH ISSN 0024-6352) **1376**
Look and Listen. (US ISSN 0162-4369) **4242**
Look at Finland. (FI ISSN 0024-6379) **4775, 2186**
Look Back. (US ISSN 1049-4340) **3561**
Look East. (TH) **916**
Look Hear. (UK ISSN 0954-5611) **1754**
Look - in. (UK) **1259**
Look - in Television Annual. (UK) **1376, 1259**
Look Japan. (JA ISSN 0456-5339) **932, 3905**
Look - Listen Opinion Project Report *see* Look - Listen Project Report **1376**
Look - Listen Project Report. (US) **1376**
Look Magazine. (AT ISSN 0817-8445) **3527**
Look Magazine. (HK) **3905**
Look 'n Read. (MW) **2209**
Look Quick. (US) **2997**
LookEast. (TH) **4775**
Looking. (US) **2157**
Looking Ahead. (US ISSN 0747-525X) **999**
Looking Ahead and Projection Highlights *see* Looking Ahead **999**
Looking Back/Kykies in die Verlede. (SA ISSN 0024-6417) **2333**
Looking Fit. (US) **3805**
Looking for Employment in Foreign Countries. (US) **3629**
Looking Forward. (US ISSN 0896-7032) **2276**
Looking into Leadership Series. (US ISSN 0076-0889) **1067**
Lookout. (SP ISSN 0024-6433) **2217**
Lookout (Cincinnati). (US) **4242**
The Lookout (Lansing). (US) **1316**
Lookout (Naples) *see* Lookout - Nonfoods **376**
Lookout (Naples) *see* Lookout - Foods **2076**
Lookout (New York). (US ISSN 0024-6425) **4188, 4732**
Lookout - Foods. (US ISSN 2076, 1080, 1506**
Lookout - Nonfoods. (US ISSN 376, 3734**
Looming. (ER ISSN 0134-4536) **2873**
Loompanics Book Catalog *see* Best Book Catalog in the World **390**
Loon. (US ISSN 0024-645X) **565**
Looney Tunes Magazine. (US) **1259**
Loonfeather. (US ISSN 0734-0699) **2997**
Loose Change. (US ISSN 0278-4114) **4478, 258**
Loose Connections. (US) **3122**
†Loot. (UK ISSN 1044-6436) **5229**
Looys. (US ISSN 0024-6476) **4285**
Lord Dowding Fund for Humane Research. Bulletin. (UK) **231**
Lord's. (MX) **373**
Lore. (IL ISSN 0377-1083) **2935**

Lore. (US ISSN 0024-6492) **3527**
Lore and Language. (UK ISSN 0307-7144) **2827, 244, 2056**
Lorentzia. (AG ISSN 0076-0897) **509**
Lori Chapman and Company You *see* L C and You **1292**
Loris. (CE ISSN 0024-6514) **1491**
Lorma Weekly. (LB) **2169**
Lormatic. (CS) **1414**
Los Angeles. (US ISSN 0024-6522) **2228**
Los Angeles (Year). (US) **4775**
Los Angeles Business Journal. (US ISSN 0194-2603) **872**
Los Angeles Cinematheque. (US) **3513**
Los Angeles Citizen. (US ISSN 0024-6549) **2586**
Los Angeles College of Chiropractic. News & Alumni Report. (US) **3215, 1316**
Los Angeles County Medical Association. Bulletin *see* L A C M A Physician **3121**
Los Angeles County Medical Association Physician *see* L A C M A Physician **3121**
Los Angeles Daily Journal. (US ISSN 0362-5575) **2650**
Los Angeles Foundation of Otology. Progress Report *see* House Ear Institute. Progress Report **5206**
Los Angeles International Fern Society Journal *see* L A I F S Journal **2133**
Los Angeles Lawyer. (US ISSN 0162-2900) **2650**
Los Angeles Loyolan. (US) **1316**
Los Angeles Port and Shipping Handbook. (UK ISSN 0266-0644) **4732, 1143**
Los Angeles Songwriters Showcase Musepaper. (US) **3561**
Los Angeles Sports Profiles *see* L A Sports Profiles **4478**
Los Angeles Times Book Review. (US) **4132**
Los Angeles Times Index. (US ISSN 0742-4817) **2578**
Los Perros del Mundo. (MX) **3712**
Lose Weight Naturally Newsletter. (US) **3609, 3805**
Loss, Grief & Care. (US ISSN 8756-4610) **4034**
†Loss Prevention and Control. (US ISSN 0191-2763) **5229**
†Loss Prevention Newsletter for Distribution Center Executives. (US) **5229**
Loss Prevention Newsletter for Supermarket Executives. (US) **2093, 1527**
Lost and Found Times. (US) **2873**
Lost Generation Journal. (US ISSN 0091-2948) **2935, 334**
Lost in Canada? (US ISSN 0362-4293) **2157**
Lost Palatine. (US) **2157**
Lost Treasure. (US ISSN 0195-2692) **2438**
Losungen. (GW) **4188**
Loteria. (PN ISSN 0024-662X) **2213**
Loto - Quebec. Rapport Annuel. (CN) **1100**
Lotta Contro la Tubercolosi *see* Lotta Contro la Tubercolosi e le Malattie Polmonari Sociali **3365**
Lotta Contro la Tubercolosi e le Malattie Polmonari Sociali. (IT) **3365**
Lottebladet. (NO) **3463**
Lottery Gazette. (IL ISSN 0024-6654) **4478**
Lottery Player's Magazine. (US ISSN 0277-5565) **4478**
Lottoroscopo. (IT ISSN 0024-6662) **4478**
Lotus. (IT ISSN 0076-101X) **303**
Lotus. (US ISSN 8756-7334) **1478, 1461, 1470**
Lotus. (UA ISSN 0002-0664) **2935**
Lotus Bleu. (FR ISSN 0024-6670) **3772**
Lotus International. (IT) **303**
Lotus Lantern International Buddhist Center. Newsletter. (KO) **4215**
Louder Than Bombs. (US) **2997**
Loughborough Occasional Papers in Economics. (UK) **678**
Loughborough Student *see* Fast Forward **1311**

Loughborough University of Technology Gazette. (UK ISSN 0024-6719) **1316**
Louis Braille. (FR ISSN 0024-6727) **2294**
▼Louis Rukeyser's Wall Street. (US) **954**
Louisiana. Department of Agriculture. Analysis of Official Pesticide Samples. Annual Report. (US ISSN 0099-1929) **184**
Louisiana. Department of Public Safety. Summary of Motor Vehicle Accident Reports *see* Louisiana. Department of Public Safety. Summary of Motor Vehicle Traffic Accidents **4107**
Louisiana. Department of Public Safety. Summary of Motor Vehicle Traffic Accidents. (US) **4107**
Louisiana. Geological Survey. Water Resources Bulletin. (US ISSN 0459-8474) **1571**
Louisiana. Polytechnic Institute, Ruston. School of Agriculture and Forestry. Research Bulletin *see* Louisiana Tech University. Division of Life Sciences Research. Research Bulletin **446**
Louisiana. State Board of Nursing. Report (Calendar Year). (US) **3281**
Louisiana Academy of Sciences. Proceedings. (US ISSN 0096-9192) **4323**
Louisiana Administrative Code. (US) **4066, 2650**
Louisiana Agriculture. (US ISSN 0024-6735) **105**
Louisiana Archives and Manuscripts Association. Newsletter. (US) **2771, 2157, 2413**
Louisiana Association of Educators News *see* L A E News **1645**
Louisiana Association of School Librarians Newsletter *see* L A S L Newsletter **2767**
†Louisiana Avent. (US) **5229**
Louisiana Banker. (US ISSN 0895-1640) **789**
Louisiana Baptist Builder. (US ISSN 0024-6743) **4242**
Louisiana Bar Journal. (US ISSN 0459-8881) **2650**
Louisiana Business Survey. (US ISSN 0193-5712) **872**
Louisiana Cancer Reporter. (US ISSN 0459-889X) **3199**
Louisiana Cattleman. (US) **221**
Louisiana Coastal Law Report. (US) **2650, 2045, 2735**
Louisiana Conservationist. (US ISSN 0024-6778) **1491, 4549**
Louisiana Country. (US) **1902**
Louisiana Dental Association. Journal. (US ISSN 0024-6786) **3237**
Louisiana Engineer. (US ISSN 0024-6794) **1829**
Louisiana English Journal. (US ISSN 0456-7463) **2827**
Louisiana Folklore Miscellany. (US ISSN 0459-8962) **2056**
Louisiana Game and Fish. (US ISSN 0744-3692) **4549**
Louisiana Genealogical Register. (US ISSN 0148-7655) **2157**
Louisiana Grocer. (US) **2093**
Louisiana History. (US ISSN 0024-6816) **2413**
Louisiana History Quarterly Newsletter. (US) **2413**
Louisiana Labor Market *see* Louisiana Labor Market Information **987**
Louisiana Labor Market Information. (US) **987**
Louisiana Landlord & Tenant Law. (US) **2650, 4152**
Louisiana Law Review. (US ISSN 0024-6859) **2650**
Louisiana Legal Research. (US) **2650**
Louisiana Library Association Bulletin *see* L L A Bulletin **2768**
Louisiana Literature. (US ISSN 0890-0477) **2935**
▼Louisiana Manufacturers Register. (US ISSN 1053-8992) **1143**
Louisiana Market Bulletin. (US ISSN 0279-8824) **105**
Louisiana Motor Transport Association, Inc. News *see* L M T A News **4745**
Louisiana Municipal Review. (US ISSN 0164-3622) **4090**

Louisiana Oil and Gas Law. (US) **2651**, 3691
Louisiana Oil Marketers Association Line see L O M A Line **3691**
Louisiana Pharmacist. (US ISSN 0192-3838) **3734**
Louisiana Philosophy of Education Journal. (US) **1646**
Louisiana Political Review. (US) **2873**, 2228
Louisiana Register. (US) **4066**, 2651
Louisiana-Revy. (DK ISSN 0024-6891) **334**
▼Louisiana Security Rights in Personal Property. (US) **2651**
Louisiana State Medical Society. Journal. (US ISSN 0024-6921) **3122**
Louisiana State University. Law School. Institute on Mineral Law. Proceedings. (US ISSN 0076-1087) **2651**, 3487
Louisiana State University. Library Lectures. (US ISSN 0085-2759) **2771**
†Louisiana State University. School of Forestry, Wildlife, and Fisheries. Annual Forestry Symposium. Proceedings. (US) **5229**
Louisiana State University. School of Forestry, Wildlife and Fisheries. Research Reports. (US) **2104**, 2045
Louisiana State University Engineering News see L S U Engineering News **1315**
Louisiana State University Forestry Notes see L S U Forestry Notes **2103**
Louisiana State University Magazine see L S U Magazine **1315**
Louisiana Surplus Line Reporter. (US) **2537**
Louisiana Teachers' Tabloid see L A E News **1645**
Louisiana Tech University. Division of Life Sciences Research. Research Bulletin. (US ISSN 0076-1044) **446**
Louisiana Water Resources Research Institute. Annual Report. (US) **4826**, 1599
Louisiana Wrongful Death & Survival Actions. (US) **2651**
Louisville see Louisville Magazine **819**
Louisville Magazine. (US) **819**
Louisville Review. (US ISSN 0148-3250) **2935**
Lounais-Haemeen Kotiseutu ja Museoyhdistys. Vuosikirja. (FI) **2374**
Loupe see Bijou Magazine **5149**
Lourdes - Rosen. (GW) **4268**
Lousiana Life. (US ISSN 0279-6791) **2228**, 4775
Louvain Medical. (BE ISSN 0024-6956) **3122**
Louvain Philosophical Studies. (BE) **3772**
Louvain Studies. (BE ISSN 0024-6964) **4188**
Louveteau. (FR ISSN 0751-5685) **1259**
Lov og Rett. (NO ISSN 0024-6980) **2651**
Lovacki Vjesnik. (CI ISSN 0024-6999) **4478**
Love. (US) **3595**, 3772
†Love Historical and Genealogical Quarterly. (US) **5229**
Love og Bekendtgoerelser m.v. (DK ISSN 0108-9102) **2651**
Lovec. (XV ISSN 0024-7014) **4550**
Lovecraft Studies. (US) **3012**, 2935
Lovejoy's College Guide. (US ISSN 0076-132X) **1695**
Lovejoy's Guidance Digest. (US ISSN 0024-7022) **1695**, 1316
Lover. (NE ISSN 0165-8042) **4847**
Lovetrance News see Lovetrance World **3772**
Lovetrance World. (US) **3772**, 4285
Loving. (UK) **2984**
Loving Brotherhood Newsletter. (US) **2455**, 2935, 3772, 4034
Loving More. (US) **4442**, 3067, 3398, 4847
Lovnoegle. (DK ISSN 0108-0849) **2651**

Lovoe Geomagnetic Observatory Yearbook. (SW ISSN 0076-1354) **1571**
Lovtidende A for Kongeriget Danmark. (DK ISSN 0106-8458) **2651**
Lovtidende B for Kongeriget Danmark. (DK ISSN 0106-8466) **1100**
Lovtidende C for Kongeriget Danmark. (DK ISSN 0106-8474) **2727**
Low Bidder. (US ISSN 0024-7030) **4719**, 623
†Low Cost C A D - C A M Systems. (US) **5229**
Low Country Courier. (US) **2157**
Low Power T V Reporter see L P T V Reporter **1375**
Low-Priced Stock Analyst see Investment Reporter **951**
Low Priced Stock Survey. (US ISSN 0273-7752) **954**
Low Priced Stocks. (US ISSN 0892-984X) **954**
Low - Risk Growth Letter. (US) **954**
Low Temperature Physics. see Fizika Nizkikh Temperatur **3840**
Low Temperature Science. Series A. Physical Science. (JA ISSN 0439-3538) **3841**
Lowdin Symposia see International Symposium on Atomic, Molecular and Solid-State Theory, Collision Phenomena and Computational Methods. Proceedings **1179**
Lowdown. (AT ISSN 0158-099X) **1259**
The Lowdown. (US) **1357**
Lowell Observatory Bulletin. (US ISSN 0024-7057) **366**
Lower Cape Fear Historical Society. Bulletin. (US) **2413**
†Lower Cape Fear Historical Society. Bulletin. (US ISSN 0458-4201) **5229**
Lower Cape Fear Historical Society. Journal see Lower Cape Fear Historical Society. Bulletin **2413**
†Lowfat Lifeline. (US ISSN 0893-3383) **5229**
Lowlands Review. (US) **2935**
Lowrider. (US) **4694**
Lowveld Research Stations. Annual Report. (RH) **105**
Loxton News. (AT) **2172**
Loyal. (GW ISSN 0343-0103) **3463**
Loyal Legion Historical Journal. (US) **2413**
Loyalist Gazette. (CN ISSN 0047-5149) **2413**, 2157
Loyola Law Review. (US) **2651**
Loyola Lecture Series in Political Analysis. (US) **3905**
Loyola Magazine. (US ISSN 1054-7614) **1316**
Loyola News see Link (Montreal) **2872**
Loyola of Los Angeles International and Comparative Law Annual see Loyola of Los Angeles International and Comparative Law Journal **2651**
Loyola of Los Angeles International and Comparative Law Journal. (US ISSN 0277-5417) **2651**
Loyola University of Chicago Law Journal. (US ISSN 0024-7081) **2651**
Lozania. (CK ISSN 0085-2899) **587**
Lozarstvo i Vinarstvo. (BU) **383**, 2134
Lraber Asarakakan Gitutyunneri. (AI ISSN 0024-7111) **2511**, 4323
Lu Chao. (CC) **4775**
Lu Hsing Tsa Chih. see Travelling Magazine **4794**
Lu Ming. (CC) **2935**
Lu Xun Meishu Xueyuan Xuebao see Meiyuan **335**
Lu Xun Studies Monthly. see Lu Xun Yanjiu Yuekan **420**
Lu Xun Yanjiu Yuekan/Lu Xun Studies Monthly. (CC) **420**, 2935
Lua Nova. (BL ISSN 0102-6445) **4442**, 3905
Lubelskie Towarzystwo Naukowe. Wydzial Humanistyczny. Prace. Monografie. (PL ISSN 0208-4996) **2511**
Lubricants World. (US) **3691**, 1080
Lubrication Engineering. (US ISSN 0024-7154) **1934**

Lubrication Science. (UK ISSN 0954-0075) **3841**
Luca. (YU ISSN 0352-4973) **4442**, 3772
Luce (Milan). (IT ISSN 0024-7189) **1902**
La Luce (Turin). (IT) **4242**
Luceafarul. (RM) **2935**
Lucha - Struggle. (US) **4268**, 3965
Lucht en Omgeving. (BE) **1977**
Luchtvaart. (NE) **4675**
Luchtvaartwereld see Luchtvaart **4675**
Luciano Manara. (IT) **2374**, 3463
Lucidity. (US ISSN 0897-6481) **2997**
Luciernaga. (CK) **2935**
Lucina. (IT) **3294**
Lucknow Law Times. (II ISSN 0459-9756) **2651**
Lucknow Librarian. (II ISSN 0024-7219) **2772**
Lucky. (AT ISSN 0816-3642) **1259**, 1646
Lucky. (IT) **2984**
Lucky Mee Family Association. Yearbook. (US) **2157**
Lucky Mee Family Association News & Notes. (US) **2157**
Lucrari de Muzicologie. (RM) **3561**
Lucre-Hatif. (BE) **2935**, 2997
Lud. (PL ISSN 0076-1435) **4442**, 244
Ludas Matyi. (HU) **2873**
Ludas Matyi Evkonyve. (HU ISSN 0133-9214) **1781**
†Ludd's Mill. (UK ISSN 0047-5157) **5229**
Ludorama. (FR) **2281**
Ludwig Boltzmann-Institut fuer Umweltwissenschaften und Naturschutz. Mitteilungen. (AU) **1962**, 1491
Ludwig Feuerbach: Gesammelte Werke. (GW) **3772**
Ludwigsburger Geschichtsblaetter. (GW ISSN 0179-1842) **2374**
Ludwigsteiner Blaetter. (GW) **2190**
Luebecker Wochenspiegel. (GW) **2873**
Lueginsland. (GW) **3905**
Luft og Rumfartsaarbogen. (DK ISSN 0108-4550) **58**
Luft- und Kaeltetechnik. (GW ISSN 0024-7251) **2301**
Luft- und Raumfahrt. (GW ISSN 0173-6264) **58**
Luftfahrt - Bundesamt Info see L B A Info **4675**
Luftfahrt International see Pilot und Flugzeug **4676**
†Lufthansa's Germany. (GW) **5229**
Lufthanseat. (GW) **4675**
Lufthygienischer Monatsbericht. (GW) **1977**
Luftverkehr. (GW) **4775**
Luftverunreinigung. (GW ISSN 0460-2374) **1977**
Luftwaffe. (US ISSN 0015-3699) **58**
Luftwaffen-Forum. (GW) **3463**, 58
Luggage and Travelware Directory and Market Guide see Travelware Resources Directory **1156**
Luggage, Leathergoods & Accessories. (CN ISSN 0836-3862) **2737**
Lugha Yetu. (TZ ISSN 0047-5165) **2827**
Luhua yu Shenghuo. (CC) **2104**
Lui. (FR) **3398**
Lui. (GW) **3398**
Luis Palau Evangelistic Association HeartBeat see L P E A HeartBeat **4241**
Luis Palau Letter. (US) **4188**
Luisa la Santa Tereziaria Domenicana. (IT) **4268**
Luister. (NE ISSN 0024-7286) **4461**
Lukanga News. (ZA) **2240**
▼Lullwater Review. (US ISSN 1051-5968) **2997**
Lumber & Building Materials Association of Ontario Reporter see L B M A O Reporter **622**
Lumber Co-Operator. (US ISSN 0024-7294) **2116**
Lumber Price Index. Inland Index. (US ISSN 0195-9395) **2112**, 2116
Lumber Price Index. P N W Coast Index. (US ISSN 0735-066X) **2104**

Lumber Price Trends. Inland Index see Lumber Price Index. Inland Index **2112**
Lumbering Science. see Senlin Caiyun Kexue **2117**
Lumberjack. (US) **1316**
Lumbermens Red Book. (US) **2116**, 789
Lumea. (RM) **3965**
Lumen. (AT) **1316**
Lumen Vitae. (BE ISSN 0770-2477) **4268**, 1646
Lumiere. (IT) **3513**
Lumiere. (FR ISSN 0024-7332) **4188**
Lumiere du Monde see Solidaires - Lumiere du Monde **4202**
Lumiere et Vie. (FR ISSN 0024-7359) **4189**
Lumieres dans la Nuit. (FR) **58**
Lumina. (YU) **2935**, 334
Luminaires et Eclairage. (FR) **2560**, 1902
†Luminescence. (UK ISSN 0950-0529) **5229**
Luna de Madrid. (SP) **1259**
Lunar and Planetary Information Bulletin. (US) **366**, 1546
Lunar and Planetary Institute Technical Report see L P I Technical Report **366**
†Lunar Entrepreneurs Directory. (US ISSN 0892-7782) **5229**
Lunar Epidecis. see Epidecides Lunaires **364**
Lunarionuovo. (IT) **2935**
Lund Studies in Art History. (SW ISSN 1100-2859) **334**, 2317
Lund Studies in Economics and Management. (SW ISSN 0284-5075) **896**, 1018
Lund Studies in English. (SW ISSN 0076-1451) **2827**
Lund Studies in Geography. Series A. Physical Geography. (SW ISSN 0076-146X) **2255**
Lund Studies in Geography. Series B. Human Geography. (SW ISSN 0076-1478) **446**, 2255
Lund Studies in Geography. Series C. General and Mathematical Geography see Lund Studies in Geography. Series C. General, Mathematical and Regional Geography **5229**
†Lund Studies in Geography. Series C. General, Mathematical and Regional Geography. (SW) **5229**
Lund Studies in International History. (SW ISSN 0076-1494) **2317**
Lund Universitet. Historiska Museet Samt Mynt-och Medaljkabinettet. Meddelanden see Lund Universitet. Historiska Museum. Meddelanden **278**
Lund Universitet. Historiska Museum. Meddelanden. (SW ISSN 0458-4767) **278**
†Lund Universitet. Vaextekologiska - Institutionen. Meddelanden. (SW ISSN 0348-2456) **5229**
Lundberg Letter. (US) **3691**, 954
Lundi. (CN ISSN 0704-7886) **4847**
Lundian. (SW) **2218**
Lundy Collectors Club Philatelic Quarterly. (US) **3754**
Lung. (US ISSN 0341-2040) **3365**
Lung and Respiration. (GW ISSN 0176-1749) **3365**
Lung Biology in Health and Disease. (US) **3365**, 573
Lung Cancer. (NE ISSN 0169-5002) **3199**
Lung Cancer--Diagnosis, Treatment see I C R D B Cancergram: Lung Cancer - Diagnosis, Treatment **3175**
Lunge and Atmung. (GW ISSN 0720-0706) **3365**, 3177
▼Luoghi dell'Anima. (IT) **2936**
Luoji yu Yuyan Xuexi/Logic and Language Studies. (CC) **3772**, 2827
Luomaniya. (RM) **2215**
Luonnon Tutkija. (FI ISSN 0024-7383) **446**
Lupta C F R. (RM) **2586**, 4711
Lupta Intregului Popor. (RM) **3463**
Luptonian. (US ISSN 0099-1791) **2157**

LUPUS ASSOCIATION

Lupus Association of New South Wales. Newsletter. (AT ISSN 1033-2480) **3122,** 1738

Lupus Erythematosus Beacon *see* L.E. Beacon **3369**

Luratha. (BO) **254**

Luren. (US ISSN 0739-0025) **3754**

Lurzer's International Archive. (US ISSN 0893-0260) **34,** 1376

Lusaka. Medical Officer of Health. Annual Report. (ZA) **4107**

Lusaka City Library. Annual Report. (ZA) **2772**

Luscinia. (GW ISSN 0024-7391) **565**

Lushi Shijie. (CC) **2651**

Lushi yu Fazhi/Lawyers and Legal System. (CC ISSN 1001-6376) **2651**

Lusitania Sacra. (PO ISSN 0076-1508) **2374**

Lusitano. (CN ISSN 0707-5324) **2012**

Luso. (MW ISSN 0251-0154) **4356,** 4614

Luso - Americano. (US ISSN 0898-9052) **2012**

Luso - Brazilian Review. (US ISSN 0024-7413) **2873,** 2511

Lust & Gratie. (NE ISSN 0168-8413) **2455,** 2873, 4847

†Der Lustige Grillenfaenger. (GW ISSN 0138-5518) **5229**

Lustracje Dobr Krolewskich XVI-XVIII Wieku. (PL ISSN 0076-1516) **2374**

Lustrum. (GW ISSN 0024-7421) **1278**

The Lute. (UK ISSN 0952-0759) **3561**

Lute Society of America. Journal. (US ISSN 0076-1524) **3561**

Lute Society of America. Newsletter *see* Lute Society of America. Quarterly **3561**

Lute Society of America. Quarterly. (US) **3561**

Luther *see* Luther Alumni: Quarterly **1316**

Luther. (GW ISSN 0340-6210) **4242**

Luther Alumni: Quarterly. (US) **1316**

Luther Family Newsletter. (US ISSN 0896-4602) **2157,** 2413

The Lutheran. (US ISSN 0024-743X) **4242**

Lutheran Almanac *see* Lutheran Church of Australia. Yearbook **4242**

Lutheran Annual. (US) **4242**

Lutheran Church in America. Yearbook *see* Evangelical Lutheran Church in America (Year) **4237**

Lutheran Church of Australia. Yearbook.(AT ISSN 0726-4305) **4242**

Lutheran Church of Central Africa. Statistical Report. (ZA) **4213**

Lutheran Churches in Canada. Directory. (CN ISSN 0316-800X) **1144,** 4242

Lutheran Digest. (US ISSN 0458-497X) **4242**

▼Lutheran Digest (Large Print Edition). (US) **2294,** 4242

Lutheran Education. (US ISSN 0024-7448) **1646,** 4242

Lutheran Forum. (US ISSN 0024-7456) **4242**

Lutheran Forum. Forum Letter. (US ISSN 0046-4732) **4242**

Lutheran Historical Conference. Essays and Reports. (US ISSN 0090-3817) **4242,** 2413

Lutheran Historical Conference Newsletter. (US ISSN 0460-0274) **4242**

Lutheran Historical Society of Eastern Pennsylvania *see* Lutheran Historical Society of Eastern Pennsylvania. Periodical **4242**

Lutheran Historical Society of Eastern Pennsylvania. Periodical. (US) **4242**

Lutheran Hour Sermons. (US) **4242**

Lutheran Immigration and Refugee Service Bulletin *see* L I R S Bulletin **4241**

Lutheran Journal. (US ISSN 0360-6945) **4242**

Lutheran Layman. (US ISSN 0024-7464) **4242**

Lutheran Libraries. (US ISSN 0024-7472) **2772,** 4242

Lutheran Messenger for the Blind. (US ISSN 0024-7480) **2294,** 4242

Lutheran Partners. (US ISSN 0885-9922) **4242**

Lutheran Sentinel. (US ISSN 0024-7510) **4242**

Lutheran Social Services of Illinois Eye on L S S I *see* Eye on L S S I **4405**

Lutheran Spokesman. (US ISSN 0024-7537) **4243**

Lutheran Standard *see* The Lutheran **4242**

Lutheran Theological Journal. (AT ISSN 0024-7553) **4243**

Lutheran Theological Seminary Bulletin. (US) **4243**

Lutheran Witness. (US ISSN 0024-757X) **4243**

Lutheran Witness (Large Print Edition). (US) **4243,** 2294

Lutheran Woman *see* Lutheran Woman Today **4243**

Lutheran Woman Today. (US ISSN 0896-209X) **4243,** 4847

Lutheran Woman's Quarterly. (US) **4243,** 4847

Lutheran World Federation - Geneva Dokumentation. Report *see* L W B Dokumentation. Report **4241**

Lutherische Monatshefte. (GW ISSN 0024-7618) **4243**

Lutherische Theologie und Kirche. (GW ISSN 0170-3846) **4243**

Lutherjahrbuch. (GW) **4243**

Die Lutherkirche. (AU ISSN 0024-7626) **4243**

Luthersk Barntidning. (SW ISSN 0345-7389) **4243**

Luton Commerce and Trade Journal *see* Chiltern Enterprise **813**

Lutra. (NE ISSN 0024-7634) **587**

Lutte. (SG) **3905**

Lutte Contre le Cancer *see* Vivre **3203**

Lutte de Classe. (FR ISSN 0458-5143) **3905**

Lutte Ouvriere. (FR ISSN 0024-7650) **2586**

Lutte Ouvriere. (CN ISSN 0701-8746) **2873**

Lutteur Canadien. *see* Canadian Wrestler **4468**

Luvah. (FR ISSN 0754-927X) **2936,** 2997

Lux. (FR ISSN 0024-7669) **1902**

†Lux. (IT) **5229**

Lux Vera. (FR ISSN 0024-7685) **2294**

▼Luxembourg. Inspection Generale de la Securite Sociale. Apercu sur la Legislation de la Securite Sociale au Grand-Duche de Luxembourg. (LU) **2537**

Luxembourg. Inspection Generale de la Securite Sociale. Rapport General sur la Securite Sociale au Grand-Duche de Luxembourg. (LU) **2547**

Luxembourg. Ministere des Finances. Budget de l'Etat. (LU ISSN 0076-1559) **1100**

Luxembourg. Ministere des Finances. Projet de Loi Concernant le Budget des Recettes et des Depenses de l'Etat. (LU) **1100**

Luxembourg. Service Central de la Statistique et des Etudes Economiques. Annuaire Statistique. (LU ISSN 0076-1575) **727,** 4577

Luxembourg. Service Central de la Statistique et des Etudes Economiques. Annuaire Statistique Retrospectif. (LU) **727,** 4577

Luxembourg. Service Central de la Statistique et des Etudes Economiques. Bulletin du STATEC. (LU ISSN 0076-1583) **727**

Luxembourg. Service Central de la Statistique et des Etudes Economiques. Collection D et M: Definitions et Methodes. (LU ISSN 0076-1591) **727,** 4577

Luxembourg. Service Central de la Statistique et des Etudes Economiques. Cahiers Economiques. Serie A: Economie Luxembourgeoise. (LU ISSN 0070-881X) **727**

Luxembourg. Service Central de la Statistique et des Etudes Economiques. Cahiers Economiques. Serie B: Comptes Nationaux. (LU) **727**

Luxembourg. Service Central de la Statistique et des Etudes Economiques. Cahiers Economiques. Serie C: Apercus sur l'Industrie *see* Luxembourg. Service Central de la Statistique et des Etudes Economiques. Cahiers Economiques. Serie C: Etudes Approfondies sur l'Industrie **727**

Luxembourg. Service Central de la Statistique et des Etudes Economiques. Cahiers Economiques. Serie C: Etudes Approfondies sur l'Industrie. (LU) **727**

Luxembourg. Service Central de la Statistique et des Etudes Economiques. Cahiers Economiques. Serie D: Etudes Diverses *see* Luxembourg. Service Central de la Statistique et des Etudes Economiques. Cahiers Economiques. Serie D: Etudes Methodoligiques et Etudes Diverses **727**

Luxembourg. Service Central de la Statistique et des Etudes Economiques. Cahiers Economiques. Serie D: Etudes Methodoligiques et Etudes Diverses. (LU) **727**

Luxembourg. Service Central de la Statistique et des Etudes Economiques. Collection RP: Recensement de la Population *see* Luxembourg. Service Central de la Statistique et des Etudes Economiques. Collection RP: Recensement de la Population et Mouvement de la Population **3993**

Luxembourg. Service Central de la Statistique et des Etudes Economiques. Collection RP: Recensement de la Population et Mouvement de la Population. (LU) **3993**

Luxembourg. Service Central de la Statistique et des Etudes Economiques. Indicateurs Rapides. (LU ISSN 0019-6916) **727**

Luxembourg. Service Central de la Statistique et des Etudes Economiques. Notes Trimestrielles de Conjoncture. (LU) **872**

Luxembourg Stock Exchange. Annual Report. *see* Societe de la Bourse de Luxembourg. Rapport Annuel **963**

Luxembourg Stock Exchange. Cote Officielle de la Bourse de Luxembourg. (LU) **954**

Luxembourg Stock Exchange. Facts and Figures *see* Societe de la Bourse de Luxembourg. Faits et Chiffres **738**

Luxembourg Stock Exchange. Stock Exchange Statistics. *see* Societe de la Bourse de Luxembourg. Statistiques Boursieres **738**

Luxemburger Auto Revue. (LU) **4694**

Luxemburger Verbraucher - Zeitung. (LU) **1506**

Luxingjia/Travellers. (CC) **4775**

Luxury Home Ideas. (US) **2553,** 4152

Luxury Homes. (US) **2553**

Luyou/Tourism. (CC ISSN 1000-7253) **4775**

Luyou Tiandi/Travelling Scope. (CC) **4775**

Luyou Xuekan/Journal of Tourism. (CC) **4775**

Luz. (AG ISSN 0024-7693) **2873,** 2012, 4225

Luz (Miami). (US) **4442**

Luzerner Kantonsblatt. (SZ) **4090**

Luzifer-Amor. (GW ISSN 0933-3347) **4034**

Lybarger Linkages. (US ISSN 0887-9354) **2157**

Lyboen. (DK ISSN 0107-1238) **2374**

Lychnos-Bibliotek. Studies och Kaellskrifter Udgivna av Laerdomshistoriska Samfundet. Studies and Sources Published by the Swedish History of Science Society. (SW ISSN 0076-163X) **4323**

Lychnos-Laerdomshistoriska Samfundets Aarsbok. Annual of the Swedish History of Science Society. (SW ISSN 0076-1648) **4323**

Lycoming County Historical Society Journal. (US ISSN 0887-543X) **2413**

Lycoming Medicine. (US) **3122**

Lydbogskatalog *see* Gode Lydboeger **401**

Lydhullet *see* Strings and Squares **3582**

Lydia. (GW) **4847**

Lydteknisk Institut. Rapport. (DK ISSN 0105-614X) **3859**

Lying-in *see* Journal of Reproductive Medicine **3294**

Lyle Official Antiques Review. (US) **258,** 334

Lyle Official Arts Review. (US) **334**

Lymphocytes. (UK ISSN 0142-8179) **3187**

Lymphokine and Cytokine Research. (US) **3273**

Lymphokine Research *see* Lymphokine and Cytokine Research **3273**

Lymphokines *see* Growth Factors & Cytokines **3185**

Lymphomas--Diagnosis, Treatment *see* I C R D B Cancergram: Lymphomas - Diagnosis, Treatment **3175**

Lynch International Investment Survey. (US) **954**

Lynch Municipal Bond Advisory. (US) **954**

Lyngby - Bogen. (DK ISSN 0107-7848) **2374**

Lynn - Linn Lineage Quarterly. (US ISSN 0892-418X) **2157**

Lynn's Letter *see* T S Today **3156**

Lynx. (CS ISSN 0024-7774) **587**

Lynx. (US ISSN 1049-4502) **3640,** 2997, 3595

Lynx Play Golf! (US) **4507**

Lyon Chirurgical. (FR ISSN 0024-7782) **3381**

Lyon Mediterranee Medical *see* Lyon Mediterranee Medical - Medecine du Sud Est **3122**

Lyon Mediterranee Medical - Medecine du Sud Est. (FR ISSN 0766-5466) **3122**

Lyonia. (US) **509**

Lyra. (US ISSN 0897-6716) **2873,** 2997

▼The Lyre. (US) **3012**

Lyric. (US ISSN 0024-7820) **2997**

Lyric and Melody Newsletter. (US) **3561**

Lyric Opera News. (US ISSN 0024-7839) **3562**

Lyrical Iowa. (US ISSN 0076-1699) **2997**

Lys. (DK ISSN 0904-7824) **1902,** 1080, 2560, 3855

Lys Rouge. (FR ISSN 0150-4428) **3905**

Lysosomes. (UK ISSN 0142-8187) **480,** 545, 3322

Lysosomes in Biology and Pathology. (NE) **446,** 3123

Lyudyna i Svit. (KR ISSN 0024-7871) **2220**

†Lyzarstvi. (CS ISSN 0323-1445) **5229**

L5 Space Development Conference. Proceedings. (US) **58,** 3393

M. (US) **1292,** 3398

M A A Focus. (Mathematical Association of America) (US) **3044,** 1646

M A A News Bulletin. (Motel Association of Alberta) (CN) **2477**

M A A S Journal of Islamic Science. (Muslim Association for the Advancement of Science) (II) **3640,** 2430, 4219

M A A S Journal of Islamic Studies *see* M A A S Journal of Islamic Science **3640**

M A A Studies in Mathematics *see* Studies in Mathematics (Washington) **3057**

†M A B Fashion Preview. (Menswear Association of Britain) (UK) **5229**

M A C *see* Macchine Accessori Componenti **2560**

·M A C A P Consumer Bulletins. (Major Appliance Consumer Action Panel) (US) **2560**

†M A C azine. (US) **5229**
M A C Flyer. (Military Airlift Command) (US ISSN 0024-788X) **3463**
M A C Gopher. (Minneapolis Athletic Club) (US ISSN 0024-7898) **4478**
M A C Newsletter. (Midwest Archives Conference) (US ISSN 0741-0379) **2772**
M A C S Service Reports. (Mobile Air Conditioning Society) (US) **4694**
M A C Western Advertising News (Media Agencies Clients) see Adweek (Los Angeles) **27**
M A F E S Research Highlights. (Mississippi Agricultural and Forestry Experiment Station) (US ISSN 0091-4460) **105**
▼M A I N. (Media Arts Information Network) (US) **1376, 3513**
M A I N. (Mark-Age Inform-Nations) (US ISSN 0147-1201) **3595**
M A K. (Mladosc, Aktivnosc, Kreativnocs) (YU ISSN 0350-8080) **1259,** 1241
M A L A S Forum. (Midwest Association for Latin American Studies) (US) **2413**
M A L A S Noticias see M A L A S Forum **2413**
M A L D E F Newsletter. (Mexican American Legal Defense and Educational Fund) (US) **2012, 3944**
M A L T Newsletter. (Manitoba Association of Library Technicians) (CN ISSN 0710-3417) **2772**
M A N see Modern Applications News **3415**
M A N A. (Mexican American Women's National Association) (US) **2012, 4847**
M A N Forschen, Planen, Bauen. (GW) **1829**
M A N I P see Manipulacion de Materiales en la Industria **623**
M A N Research, Engineering, Manufacturing see M A N Forschen, Planen, Bauen **1829**
M A N Roland Nachrichten see M A N Roland Revue **3019**
M A N Roland News Extra see M A N Roland Revue **3019**
M A N Roland Revue. (GW) **3019**
M A P A Annual Report. (Omaha - Council Bluffs Metropolitan Area Planning Agency) (US) **4066**
M A P A Community Assistance Report.(US) **4066**
M A P A Log. (Mooney Aircraft Pilots Association) (US ISSN 0199-5243) **58**
M A P A Regional Directory of Public Officials. (US) **4090**
M A P Actualite. (Maghreb Arab Press) (MR) **3905**
M A P Netter. (Manufacturing Automation Protocol) (US ISSN 0888-6989) **1351**
M A P News. (Medical Aid for Palestine) (CN) **4412,** 932, 3123
M A P S Data Base. (US) **1348**
M A P S Newsletter. (Mid-Atlantic Preservation Service) (US) **2772**
M A R see Management Accounting Research **728**
M A R A D (Year). (U.S. Maritime Administration) (US) **4732**
M A R C Newsletter. (Missions Advanced Research & Communication Center) (US) **4189**
M A R D I Report. (Malaysian Agricultural Research & Development Institute) (MY ISSN 0127-4007) **105**
M A R D I Research Journal/Jurnal Penyelidikan M A R D I. (Malaysian Agricultural Research and Development Institute) (MY ISSN 0128-0686) **106**
M A R Gospel Ministries. (Middle Atlantic Regional) (US ISSN 1049-152X) **4189,** 2012
M A R L Newsletter see Rights and Liberties **3947**
M A R T A Rider's Digest. (Metropolitan Atlanta Rapid Transit Authority) (US) **2228,** 4711

M A S B Journal. (Michigan Association of School Boards, Inc.) (US ISSN 0026-2439) **1729**
M A S C A Journal see M A S C A Research Papers in Science and Archaeology **278**
M A S C A Newsletter see M A S C A Research Papers in Science and Archaeology **278**
M A S C A Research Papers in Science and Archaeology. (Museum Applied Science and Culture Archaeology) (US) **278**
M A S C D Newsletter see Focus Magazine (Detroit) **1750**
M A S K C Komondor News. (Middle Atlantic States Komondor Club, Inc.) (US ISSN 0146-9436) **221**
M A S Newsletter. (Maine Archaeological Society, Inc.) (US) **278**
M A S T. (Maritime Anthropological Studies) (NE ISSN 0922-1476) **244**
M A T Y C Journal see Mathematics and Computer Education **3065**
M A Training. (Martial Arts) (US ISSN 0898-4786) **4479**
M A V see Maschinen Anlagen Verfahren **1021**
M A Weapons see M A Training **4479**
M & A Dealmaker. (Mergers and Acquisitions) (US) **954,** 789, 2651
M & A Europe. (Mergers and Acquisitions) (US) **916,** 954
M & A Healthcare Report see M & A Healthcare Sourcebook **954**
M & A Healthcare Sourcebook. (Mergers and Acquisitions) (US) **954,** 678
†M & A Infodienst. (GW ISSN 0723-3078) **5229**
M & A Review. (Mergers and Acquisitions) (US) **916,** 954
M & C. (Meeting & Congressi) (IT) **3393, 4775**
M & C Data Acquisition and Recorder Handbook & Buyers Guide. (US) **2524**
M and C Temperature Handbook and Buyers Guide see M & C Data Acquisition and Recorder Handbook & Buyers Guide **2524**
M & K Congress. (SZ ISSN 0251-0006) **1461**
M & M A - I M A see Macchine e Motori Agricoli - I M A il Trattorista **163**
M & M Magazine see Manufacturing & Management Magazine **3412**
M and M Rapper. (Microcar and Minicar Club) (US ISSN 0888-4641) **4695,** 258
†M & Q Environment. (UK ISSN 0952-4711) **5229**
M & T see Metaal & Techniek **3413**
M & T - Metallhandwerk & Technik. (GW) **623,** 3412
M B see Monti e Boschi **2104**
M B. (Mitteilungsblatt) (IS) **2204**
†M B A. (Masters in Business Administration) (US ISSN 0024-7952) **5229**
M B A A Technical Quarterly. (Master Brewers Association of America) (US ISSN 0024-7960) **383**
M B A News Review see Mortgage Banking **791**
M B B Aktuell. (Messerschmitt-Boelkow-Blohm GmbH) (GW) **58**
M B - Extra. (NE) **1934**
M B H Weekly Commodity Letter. (US) **954**
M B I. (Medico-Biologic Information) (BU ISSN 0324-119X) **3123,** 446
M B I's Indian Industries Annual. (II ISSN 0541-5357) **1080**
M B K - Mission. Nachrichten. (GW) **4243**
M B L Lectures in Biology. (Marine Biological Laboratory) **446**
†M B L Science. (Marine Biological Laboratory) (US) **5229**
M B News. (US ISSN 0192-2491) **334**
M B Produktiertechniek. (NE) **1919,** 1934
M B Q see Montana Business Quarterly **680**

M C. (Ministerio de Comunicaciones) (CU) **1339**
M C. (GW ISSN 0720-4442) **1461**
M C A A Info. (Mason Contractors Association of America) (US) **623**
M C A News. (Michigan Council for the Arts) (US) **334**
M C C Contact. (Mennonite Central Committee) (US) **4285**
M C C News. (Manhattan Christian College) (US) **1316**
M C C Office of Criminal Network Newsletter see Crime and Justice Network Newsletter **1512**
M C C Post. (Mott Community College) (US) **1316**
M C D S Occasional Paper Series. (Malaysian Centre for Development Studies) (MY) **4379**
M C D's Warehousing Distribution Directory. (Motor Carrier Directory) (US) **4745**
M C G Today. (Medical College of Georgia Foundation, Inc.) (US ISSN 0047-6471) **3123**
†M C I. (Marches Contrats Investissements) (FR ISSN 1145-2447) **5229**
M C J A see Midcontinental Journal of Archaeology **278**
M C L C Letters. (Molecular Crystals and Liquid Crystals) (US ISSN 0140-6566) **1211**
M C M : La Storia delle Cose. (Maria Cristina de Montemayor Editore) (IT ISSN 0393-8190) **356**
M C - Microcomputer. (IT) **1461**
M C N: American Journal of Maternal Child Nursing. (US ISSN 0361-929X) **3282**
M C N: Computer Automated Solutions for Design Engineering. (US) **1422**
M C - Nytt. (SW ISSN 0024-7995) **4518**
M C R L - 1 see Master Cross Reference List, Part 1 **4107**
M C R L - 2 see Master Cross Reference List, Part 2 **4107**
M C R L - 3 see Master Cross Reference List, Part 3 **4107**
M C R MikroComputer-Report. (GW) **1461**
M C Revyen. (DK ISSN 0107-0606) **4518**
†M C S. (Music, Computers & Software) (US) **5229**
M C S C C On Cover. (Motor City Stamp and Cover Club) (US) **3754**
M D. (Moebel Interior Design) (GW ISSN 0343-0642) **2553**
†M D A Information. (Museum Documentation Association) (UK ISSN 0309-6653) **5229**
M D A News see M D A Newsmagazine **3123**
M D A Newsmagazine. (Muscular Dystrophy Association, Inc.) (US ISSN 8750-2321) **3123**
M.D. Anderson Cancer Center. Research Report. (US) **3199**
M.D. Anderson Clinical Conferences on Cancer. (US ISSN 0160-2454) **3199**
M.D. Anderson Hospital and Tumor Institute. Research Report see M.D. Anderson Cancer Center. Research Report **3199**
M.D. Anderson Symposia in Fundamental Cancer Research. (US) **3199**
M D C Business Journal. (Management Development Centre) (TR) **678**
M D C News see Productivity News **1025**
M.D. Computing (New York). (US ISSN 0724-6811) **3226,** 1461, 1470
M D D I Reports see Medical Devices, Diagnostics & Instrumentation Reports: The Gray Sheet **3126**
M D E - Managerial and Decision Economics. (UK ISSN 0143-6570) **1018**
M D en Espanol. (MX ISSN 0024-8002) **3123**
M.D.I. see Monografias de Diagnostico por Imagen **3360**
M D I Management Journal. (Management Development Institute) (II ISSN 0970-6623) **1018**

M D L: Mercato del Legno e Derivati. (IT) **2116**
M D Magazine. (US) **3123**
M D - Marketing Digest. (GW) **1044,** 34, 837
M D: Medical Newsmagazine see M D Magazine **3123**
M D R see Morgan Directory Reviews **1146**
M D R T Annual Meeting. Proceedings. (Million Dollar Round Table) (US) **2537**
M D R Watch. (Medical Device Reporting) (US ISSN 0890-7587) **3123,** 1506
M D S. (FI ISSN 0024-8045) **3734**
M D S News. (Massachusetts Dental Society) (US ISSN 0738-4556) **3237**
M E A L Digest see M E A L Tri-Media Digest for Brands Advertisers **34**
M E A L Tri-Media Digest for Brands Advertisers. (Media Expenditure Analysis Ltd.) (UK) **34**
M - E - A - N - I - N - G. (US ISSN 1040-8576) **334**
M E A T. (CN) **3562**
M E A Today. (Montana Education Association) (US) **1646**
M E D I C. (Monthly Ethical Drug Index Complication) (IS) **3748,** 16
M E E D Practical Guide. Jordan. (Middle East Economic Digest Ltd.) (UK) **4775**
M E E D Practical Guide. Qatar. (Middle East Economic Digest Ltd.) (UK) **4775**
†M E E D Practical Guide. U A E. (UK) **5229**
M E E D Profile. (Middle East Economic Digest Ltd.) (UK) **678**
M E E S see Middle East Economic Survey **3692**
M E I Marketing Economics Guide. (Marketing Economics Institute, Ltd.) (US ISSN 0092-4857) **1044**
M E J. (Medical Equipment Journal of Japan) (JA ISSN 0025-8830) **3123**
M E L A Notes. (Middle East Librarians Association) (US ISSN 0364-2410) **2772**
M E L E C O N see Mediterranean Electrotechnical Conference **1903**
M E L U S. (Society for the Study of the Multi-Ethnic Literature of the United States) (US ISSN 0163-755X) **2936,** 2012
M e M Agencias. (Editora /Meio e Mensagem Ltda.) (BL) **1044**
M E M C O News. (Miller Electric Manufacturing Co.) (US) **3429**
M e M Documento. (Editora /Meio e Mensagem Ltda.) (BL) **1044**
M E N see Mining Equipment News **3490**
M E N (Mechanical Engineering News) see Engineering News **1929**
M E N C Soundpost. (Music Educators National Conference) (US ISSN 1056-4039) **3562,** 1754
M E N Economic Weekly. (Middle East News Agency) (UA ISSN 0024-8118) **873**
M E N Weekly Review of World and Arab Affairs see M E N Economic Weekly **873**
M E O Bulletin. (Middle East Observer) (UA) **873**
M E R I P Reports see Middle East Report **2431**
M E R I's Monthly Circular. (Mitsubishi Economic Research Institute) (JA ISSN 0026-6809) **873**
M E R P Memo. (Medical Education Resources Program) (US ISSN 0046-9122) **3123**
M E S Newsletter. (Michigan Entomological Society) (US) **536**
M E T E M. Hirek. see International Society of Toronto for Hungarian Church History. Newsletter **2369**
M E T U Journal of Pure and Applied Sciences see Journal of Pure and Applied Sciences **4318**
M E T U Studies in Development see Studies in Development **1028**
M & O. (NE ISSN 0165-1722) **4442**
†M - F. (UK ISSN 0141-948X) **5229**

M F A Review. (Ministry of Foreign Affairs) (PH) **3965**
M F C News. (US ISSN 0024-8134) **106**
M F D Register. (Milwaukee Fire Department) (US) **4107**
M F E A Mutual Fund Directory see Investor's Guide to Low-Cost Mutual Funds **952**
M F M C Review. (Mississippi Foundation for Medical Care) (US) **3123**
M F M Fototechnik. (GW) **3793**
M F M - Moderne Fototechnik see M F M Fototechnik **3793**
M F O C Newsletter see Fiber Optics Business **1362**
M F V A Brochure. (Manitoba Farm Vacations Association) (CN) **4775**
M G F. (Mens's Guide to Fashion) (US) **1292**, **3398**
M - G Financial Weekly see Media General Financial Weekly **5233**
M G G see Molecular and General Genetics **545**
M G H News. (Massachusetts General Hospital Corp.) (US) **2467**
M G S News see Generations (Winnipeg) **2152**
M G V. (Maandblad Geestelijke Volksgezondheid) (NE) **3344**
M G W Newspaper see Mom Guess What Newspaper **2455**
M: Gentle Men for Gender Justice see Changing Men **3400**
†M H. (Mental Hygiene) (US ISSN 0025-9683) **5229**
M H Builders News see M H - R V Builders News **623**
M H F A Newsletter. (Massachusetts Housing Finance Agency) (US) **2491**
M H H - Info. (Medizinische Hochschule Hannover) (GW) **1316**, **3123**
M H I News. (Material Handling Institute) (US) **3019**
M H L A News. (Manitoba Health Libraries Association) (CN ISSN 0848-9009) **2772**, **3123**
M H L A Newsletter see M H L A News **2772**
M H L S News. (Mid-Hudson Library System) (US ISSN 1049-0760) **2772**
M H Q: The Quarterly Journal of Military History. (US ISSN 1040-5992) **3463**, **2413**
M H - R V Builders News. (US) **623**
M I. (Mladi Istrazivaci Srbije) (YU ISSN 0353-1074) **1646**, **1962**, **4379**
M I. (Montajes e Instalaciones) (SP ISSN 0210-184X) **2301**
M I see Male Insider **3398**
†M I A C Communique. (Music Industries Association of Canada) (CN) **5229**
M I A C Newsletter see M I A C Communique **5229**
M I A P Bulletin see M M I Bulletin **4412**
M I C A Newsletter see Minnesota Dance Newsletter **1531**
†M I C - Alert. (Management Information Corporation) (US) **5229**
M I C C I Digest. (Malaysian International Chamber of Commerce and Industry) (MY) **819**
M I C E Asia see Asian Meetings and Incentives **3390**
M I C - Info. (Management Information Corporation) (US) **1351**
M I C - Tech-Computers. (Management Information Corporation) (US) **1452**, **1466**
▼M I C - Tech - Data Communications. (Management Information Corporation) (US) **1447**
M I C - Tech-Retail and Banking. (Management Information Corporation) (US) **805**, **827**
M I C - Tech-Telecommunications. (Management Information Corporation) (US) **1364**, **1351**
M I C - Tech-Unix. (Management Information Corporation) (US) **1478**
M I Contact see Marconi Instruments Contact **2524**

†M I D I S T Rapport d'Activite (Year). (Mission Interministerielle de l'Information Scientifique et Technique) (FR) **5230**
M I D S Newsletter. (Miscarriage, Infant Death, and Stillbirth) (US) **3294**, **4034**, **4847**
M I E A Notes see Music and Entertainment Industry Educators' Notes **3564**
M I E C Servico de Documentacion. (Movimiento Internacional de Estudiantes Catolicos) (PE) **4268**, **1711**
M I L C O M see I E E E Military Communications Conference. Conference Record **1895**
M I L U S see University of Stockholm. Institute of Linguistics. Monographs **2850**
M I M A G. (AT) **3487**
M I M C Microforms Annual see Microforms Annual **406**
M I M I. (Mini and Microcomputers) (CN ISSN 0226-1480) **1466**, **1461**
M I M S see M I M S Medical Specialities **3177**
M I M S Africa. (UK ISSN 0140-4415) **3734**
M I M S Annual. (AT ISSN 0725-4709) **3734**
M I M S Bi-Monthly. (AT ISSN 1035-5723) **3734**
M I M S Caribbean. (UK) **3734**
M I M S Companion. (SA) **3123**
M I M S Companion. (AT) **3123**
M I M S Desk Reference. (SA ISSN 0076-8847) **3734**
M I M S Disease Index. (AT ISSN 1035-5693) **3177**, **16**
▼M I M S Drugs and Sport. (AT ISSN 1035-5715) **3372**
M I M S Medical Memory Aids see M I M S Companion **3123**
M I M S Medical Specialities. (SA ISSN 0580-6755) **3177**, **16**
M I M S Middle East. (UK ISSN 0302-4172) **3734**
M I M S Reference Manual see M I M S Desk Reference **3734**
M I M S Services Directory. (AT ISSN 1035-5707) **4412**, **2467**
M I N see Media Industry Newsletter **34**
M I N Fax. (Marketing Information Network) (US ISSN 1047-1359) **2491**, **2553**, **4152**
M I N T E K Reports see Mintek Reports **3491**
M I N T E K Research Digest see Mintek Research Digest **3491**
M I P S (Magazine of Intelligent Personal Systems) see Personal Workstation **5257**
M I P S World. (US) **1461**
M I R see Musical Interpretation Research **3566**
M I R A Abstracts see M I R A Automobile Abstracts **4665**
M I R A Automobile Abstracts. (Motor Industry Research Association) (UK ISSN 0309-0817) **4665**, **16**
M I R A Automotive Business Index. (Motor Industry Research Association) (UK) **727**, **16**
M I R S Legislative Report. (Michigan Information and Research Service, Inc.) (US) **4066**, **3905**
M I S Information. (US) **1398**, **2873**
M I S - Motor Im Schnee. (GW ISSN 0178-1529) **4775**
M I S Quarterly. (Management Information Systems) (US ISSN 0276-7783) **1018**, **1398**
M I S Reports. (Management Information Service) (US ISSN 0047-5262) **4090**
†M I S Week. (Management Information Systems) (US ISSN 0199-8838) **5230**
M I T E. (Manufacturing Ideas for Today's Engineers) (US) **1934**, **3412**
M I T S see Materials Information Translations Service **3413**
M I V: Museerne i Viborg Amt. (DK ISSN 0107-9328) **2374**
M Inc. see M **1292**

M J F Growth Stock Advisory. (US) **954**
M L see Guia de Material de Laboratorio **2522**
M L A Directory (Year). (Medical Library Association) (US ISSN 0543-2774) **3123**
M L A Directory of Periodicals. (Modern Language Association of America) (US ISSN 0197-0380) **2982**, **2060**, **2855**
M L A International Bibliography of Books and Articles on the Modern Languages and Literatures. (Modern Language Association of America) (US ISSN 0024-8215) **405**, **16**, **2827**, **2936**
M L A Job Information Lists. (Modern Language Association of America) (US) **3629**, **2827**
M L A News (Chicago). (Medical Library Association) (US ISSN 0541-5489) **3123**, **2772**
M L A News (Raleigh). (Multi-housing Laundry Association) (US) **1282**, **2491**
M L A Newsletter see Music Library Association. Newsletter **3565**
M L A Newsletter (Minneapolis). (Minnesota Library Association) (US) **2772**
M L A Newsletter (New York). (Modern Language Association of America) (US ISSN 0160-5720) **2827**, **2936**
M L B D Newsletter. (Motilal Banarsidass (Delhi)) (II ISSN 0970-1435) **3647**, **405**
M L B Log. (Maritime Lumber Bureau) (CN ISSN 0024-8231) **2116**
M L N. (Modern Language Notes) (US ISSN 0026-7910) **2828**
M L N Bulletin see M L N New Directions **3282**
M L N Bulletin - Newsletter see M L N New Directions **3282**
M L N New Directions. (Minnesota League for Nursing) (US) **3282**
M L Newsletter see M L T A V Newsletter **2828**
M L O. (Medical Laboratory Observer) (US ISSN 0580-7247) **3262**
M L S. (Marketing Library Services) (US ISSN 0896-3908) **2772**, **1044**
M L Seidman Memorial Town Hall Lecture Series. (US ISSN 0076-1729) **3905**
M L T A News. (Modern Language Teachers' Association of New South Wales) (AT ISSN 0310-9674) **2828**
M L T A V Newsletter. (Modern Language Teachers'Association of Victoria) (AT) **2828**, **1754**
M M A Newsletter. see Berita M M A **3081**
M M & M see Medical Marketing & Media **3734**
M M Branchen Handbuch. (Musik Markt) (GW ISSN 0722-9119) **3562**
▼M M C A News. (Montana Motor Carriers Association, Inc.) (US) **4745**
M M G. (Medizin-Mensch-Gesellschaft) (GW ISSN 0340-8183) **3123**, **4107**
M M I Bulletin. (Medicaid Management Institute) (US) **4412**
M M I P see Music Management & International Promotion **3565**
M M I Press Polymer Monograph Series. (US ISSN 0275-7265) **3044**, **3824**
M M I Press Symposium Series. (US ISSN 0195-3966) **3044**, **3824**
M M News. (US) **3123**
M M P see Microform Market Place **2773**
M M R. (US) **1018**
M M S Currency Facts. (Money Market Services International) (US) **790**
M M T C News. (Minerals and Metals Trading Corp. of India Ltd.) (II ISSN 0377-1482) **3487**
M M W see Muenchener Medizinische Wochenschrift **3132**
M - Moderne Metalltechnik. (GW ISSN 0933-8810) **3412**, **1919**

M N A Accent see Minnesota Nursing Accent **3282**
M N I Courant. (NE) **4132**
M O C I. (Moniteur du Commerce International) (FR ISSN 0026-9719) **916**
M O D A Report. (M.O. Dickerson Associates, Inc.) (US) **678**
M O D Contracts Bulletin. (Ministry of Defence) (UK ISSN 0269-0365) **678**, **3463**
M O D News. (Ministry of Defence) (UK ISSN 0951-8053) **678**, **3463**
M.O. Dickerson Associates, Inc. Report see M O D A Report **678**
M O H R News. (Michigan Organization for Human Rights) (US) **3944**, **2455**
M O H R News & Notes see M O H R News **3944**
M O M Magazine. (Mothers and Others for Midwives) (US) **4847**, **3294**
M O N Y News. (Mutual of New York Life Insurance Co.) (US ISSN 0024-8282) **2537**
M O T C's Notebook. (National Organization of Mothers of Twins Clubs, Inc.) (US ISSN 8756-9965) **4847**
M O T S: Mots, Ordinateurs, Textes, Societes. (FR ISSN 0243-6450) **3905**
M P A Bulletin. (Maine Press Association) (US) **2572**
M P A D Today. (Massachusetts Parents Association for the Deaf and Hard of Hearing) (US) **2288**
M P A E A Newsletter. (Mountain Plains Adult Education Association) (US) **1685**
M P A Newsletter of Research. (Magazine Publishers of America) (US) **34**, **1044**, **4132**
†M P and L News. (Mississippi Power and Light) (US) **5230**
M P C see M P C World **1470**
▼M P C World. (Multimedia Personal Computing) (US ISSN 1060-2194) **1470**
M P G Spiegel. (Max-Planck-Gesellschaft zur Foerderung der Wissenschaften) (GW ISSN 0341-7727) **4323**, **4603**
†M P I Buyers Guide. (Meeting Planners International) (US) **5230**
M P I News see L M News **3649**
M P I R G State Watch see Statewatch **1969**
M P L A Newsletter. (Mountain Plains Library Association) (US ISSN 0145-6180) **2772**
M P L Now! (Muncie Public Library) (US) **2772**
M P M see Maquettes Plastique Magazine **5232**
M P M - Mexican Advertising Agencies Directory. see Directorio M P M - Agencias y Anunciantes **31**
M P M - Mexican Audiovisual Media Rates & Data. see Directorio M P M - Medios Audiovisuales **41**
M P M - Mexican Print Media Rates & Data. see Directorio M P M - Medios Impresos **41**
M P - Mikroprozessortechnik see Mikroprozessortechnik **1463**
M P R C Report on Finance, Commerce, Industry: Indonesia. (MY) **873**
M P R C Report on Finance, Commerce, Industry: Indonesia. Supplement. (MY) **873**
M P R C Report on Finance, Commerce, Industry: Singapore. (MY) **873**
M P R C Report on Finance, Commerce, Industry: South East Asia.(MY) **873**
M P R C Report on Finance, Commerce, Industry: Thailand. (MY) **873**
M P R C South East Asia. (MY) **873**
M P S A Newsletter. (Missouri Political Science Association) (US ISSN 0464-1973) **3905**
M P T - Metallurgical Plant and Technology. (GW ISSN 0171-4511) **3412**
M P T Review. (US) **954**, **790**

M P W Bulletin. (Ministry of Public Works) (PH) **4081**
M P Z - Kooperationsprojekt. (Museumspaedagogisches Zentrum) (GW) **3527**, 1646
▼M R. (Menswear Retailing) (US) **1286**, 3398
▼M R (San Francisco). (US) **3824**
M R A A Newsletter. (Marine Retailers Association of America) (US) **4526**, 1044
M R A Research Service Directory. (Marketing Research Association, Inc.) (US) **1044**
M R I Bankers' Guide to Foreign Currency. (Monetary Research International) (US) **790**
M R I Compensation in Mass Retailing, Salaries and Incentives *see* N M R I Compensation in Mass Retailing, Salaries and Incentives **989**
M R Magazine *see* Men's Report **5235**
M R S Bulletin. (Materials Research Society) (US ISSN 0883-7694) **3824**
M R S Newsletter. (Market Research Society) (UK) **1045**, 34
M S A Monthly Bulletin. (Michigan Society of Architects) (US ISSN 0024-8363) **303**
M S A N: Marlowe Society of America Newsletter *see* Marlowe Society of America Newsletter **2937**
M S A News Journal. (Motor Schools Association of G.B.) (UK) **4695**
M S A Newsletter. (Marquetry Society of America, Inc.) (US) **640**
M S B A in Brief. (Minnesota State Bar Association) (US ISSN 0884-1667) **2651**, 4066
M S Biblioteksnyt. (Mellemfolkeligt Samvirke) (DK ISSN 0900-5072) **3965**
M S-Brevet *see* Handikapp - Reflex **3337**
▼M S C Buyer's Reference. (US) **3019**
M S C Kontakte. (Missionaries of Sacred Heart) (GW) **4268**
M S Canada. (Multiple Sclerosis Society of Canada) (CN ISSN 0315-1131) **3188**, 545, 4107
M S D D Digest. (PH) **4412**
M S F Journal. (UK) **2586**, 1829
†M S H D A Housing Trends and Activity. (Michigan State Housing Development Authority) (US) **5230**
M S H D A Review. (State Housing Development Authority) (US) **2491**
M S I Newsletter *see* Marketing Science Institute. Newsletter **1046**
M S L A V A Journal. (Manitoba School Library Audio Visual Association) (CN ISSN 0315-9124) **2772**
M S M C Happenings. (Mount Saint Mary College) (US) **1316**
M S M - The Magazine for Computer Service Managers *see* M S M - The Magazine of Computer Service Management **727**
M S M - The Magazine of Computer Service Management. (US ISSN 0898-5499) **727**, 1018
M S N Newsletter. (Movement Support Network) (US) **2651**
M S News. (Multiple Sclerosis Society) (UK ISSN 0047-5270) **3344**
†M S O. (US) **5230**
M S O A Bulletin. (Mine Surface. Officials' Association of South Africa) (SA) **3487**
M S O A Journal *see* M S O A Bulletin **3487**
M S O S Journal. (Manitoba Society of Seniors) (CN ISSN 0831-3040) **2276**
M S Ontario. (Multiple Sclerosis Society of Canada) (CN ISSN 0707-0934) **3123**
M S P B Digest Service *see* Merit Systems Protection Board Service **988**
M S R *see* Messen - Steuern - Regeln **1830**
M S R B Manual. (Municpal Security Rulemaking Board) (US) **678**
M S R R T Newsletter. (Minnesota Social Responsibilities Round Table) (US) **2772**

M S S. (Master Sermon Series) (US ISSN 0362-0808) **4189**
M S S Bulletin *see* Messenger (London) **3345**
M S S C Exchange. (Metropolitan School Study Council) (US ISSN 0024-8444) **1729**
M S S Liaison. (Missouri Speleological Survey, Inc.) (US) **1571**
M S S Magazine. (US ISSN 0738-9469) **2936**
M S T English Quarterly. (D C S Manila Teachers of Secondary English) (PH ISSN 0047-5289) **1754**
M S T Luft *see* D M U Luft. A **5176**
M S U Alumni Magazine. (US ISSN 0273-6977) **1316**
M S U Exponent *see* Exponent **1311**
M S U Mathematics Newsletter. (Montana State University) (US) **3044**
M S U U Newsletter *see* M S U U Newsletter: Gleanings **4243**
M S U U Newsletter: Gleanings. (Ministerial Sisterhood Unitarian Universalist) (US) **4243**, 4847
▼M S W Management. (US ISSN 1053-7899) **4107**
M S Z: Muenchener Studentenzeitung *see* Asta-Press **1725**
The M Street Journal. (US ISSN 1052-7109) **1357**
The M Street Radio Directory. (US ISSN 1052-7117) **1357**
M T A C Journal *see* Management Journal **1019**
M T A - Fachzeitschrift fuer Technische Assistenten der Medizin. (Medizinisch-Technische Assistenten) (GW ISSN 0930-4622) **3123**, 3262
M T A - Journal *see* M T A - Fachzeitschrift fuer Technische Assistenten der Medizin **3123**
M T A Journal. (AT ISSN 0047-5297) **4695**
M T A Medicina Interna. (Metodos Terapeutico-diagnosticos de Actualidad) (SP ISSN 0212-1514) **3123**
M T A Pediatria. (Metodos Terapeutico-diagnosticos de Actualidad) (SP ISSN 0210-8135) **3322**
†M T A S Municipal Report. (Municipal Technical Advisory Service) (US) **5230**
M T A S Municipal Technical Report *see* M T A S Municipal Report **5230**
M T A Ship by Truck Directory *see* Manitoba Ship by Truck Directory **4746**
M T A Today. (Massachusetts Teachers Association) (US) **1646**
M T B *see* Messtechnische Briefe **1936**
M T Dialog. (Medizin-Technischer) (GW ISSN 0935-137X) **3123**, 4603
M T I A Input. (Metal Trades Industry Association of Australia) (AT) **987**, 3412
M T I A Metal & Engineering Industry Yearbook. (Metal Trades Industry Association of Australia) (AT ISSN 0314-1586) **987**, 3412
M T I A N E G's Export Note Pad *see* M T I A's Engineering Exporter **3412**
M T I A News Bulletin *see* M T I A Input **987**
M T I A's Engineering Exporter. (Metal Trades Industry Association) (AT) **3412**, 916
M T I Reporter. (Madison Teachers, Inc.) (US) **1646**
M T J Recycling Markets. (US) **3649**, 3663
M T L A, the Micropublishers' Trade List Annual *see* Micropublishers' Trade List Annual **406**
M T L Montreal. (CN ISSN 0833-0026) **2178**
M T M (Meddelelser til Medlemmerne) *see* Folkeminder **2054**
†M T M Journal of Methods-Time Measurement. (US ISSN 0024-8509) **5230**
†M T Medical Top. (IT) **5230**
M T P E *see* Machine Tools & Production Engineering **5230**

M T R *see* Manufacturing Review **4603**
M T S Echo. (Manitoba Telephone System) (CN) **1364**
M T S Update. (Manitoba Teachers' Society) (CN) **1646**
M T T. (NO ISSN 0024-8517) **3463**
▼M T Today. (Medical Technologist) (US) **3262**, 3273
†M T U Heute. (Motoren - und Turbinen - Union Heute) (GW ISSN 0935-8080) **5230**
M T Z. (Motortechnische Zeitschrift) (GW ISSN 0024-8525) **4695**
M U C G - Raker. (Macquarie University Caving Group) (AT ISSN 1035-4697) **1571**
M U F O N - International U F O Symposium Proceedings. (Mutual U F O Network, Inc.) (US) **58**
M U F O N - U F O Journal. (Mutual U F O Network, Inc.) (US ISSN 0270-6822) **58**
M U F O N - U F O Symposium Proceedings *see* M U F O N - International U F O Symposium Proceedings **58**
M U G Quarterly *see* M U M P S Computing **1431**
M - U - M. (GW) **1398**, 2438
M U M. (Magic, Unity, Might) (US ISSN 0047-5300) **2438**
M U M P S Computing. (Massachusetts General Hospital Utility Multi-Programming System) (US ISSN 1060-7684) **1431**, 1461, 3226
M U M P S News. (Massachusetts General Hospital Utility Multi-Programming Systems) (US) **1431**, 1461, 3226
M U S E Letter *see* Information Technology & Learning **1690**
M U S T *see* Museum Store **1048**
M und A Info *see* M und A Report **837**
M und A Kalender *see* M und A - Messeplaner International **1144**
M und A - Messeplaner International. (GW ISSN 0932-3317) **1144**, 3393
M und A Report. (GW ISSN 0723-3361) **837**, 819
M und A Tagungsplaner *see* T W Veranstaltungsplaner **3394**
M V *see* Miljoevaern **5237**
M V A Viewpoints. (Minnesota Vocational Association) (US) **1754**
M V M A Motor Vehicle Facts and Figures. (Motor Vehicle Manufacturers Association of the U.S. Inc.) (US ISSN 0146-9932) **4695**
M W *see* Metropolitan Woman **5236**
M W A Annual. (Mystery Writers of America, Inc.) (US) **2985**
M W V - A E V Jahresbericht *see* M W V Jahresbericht **1220**
M W V Jahresbericht. (Mineraloelwirtschafts Verband e.V.) (GW ISSN 0076-891X) **1220**
M.3. (NE ISSN 0166-3917) **1259**, 1646
M 5 V Magazine. (CN) **334**, 2936
Ma Caisse. (CN ISSN 0225-4700) **790**, 1506
MA F L A Newsletter. (Massachusetts Foreign Language Association) (US) **2828**, 1754
Ma Kadai. (IS) **1506**
Maa Bra. (SW) **3805**, 3609
Maadini. (ZR ISSN 0250-538X) **1571**
Ma'agalai Keri'a. (IS ISSN 0334-2867) **2936**, 1259
Maajan - Die Quelle. (SZ ISSN 1011-4009) **2157**, 4225
Maal och Medel. (SW) **2076**
Mal & Maele. (DK) **2828**
Maal og Minne. (NO ISSN 0024-855X) **2828**
Maalarilehti. (FI ISSN 0024-8568) **3654**
Maanadens Standard. (SW) **3447**
Maanadens Stopp. (SW) **2218**
Maanadsjournalen. (SW) **2218**
Maanadsoeversikt oever Finlands Klimat. *see* Kuukausikatsaus Suomen Ilmastoon **3438**
Maanblad voor het Land- en Tuinbouwonderwijs *see* Land- en Tuinbouwonderwijs **104**

MACAO. CENSUS 6405

Maandblad Aktiviteitensektor. (NE ISSN 0168-2857) **4442**
Maandblad Belasting Beschouwingen. (NE ISSN 0005-8335) **1100**
Maandblad Geestelijke Volksgezondheid *see* M G V **3344**
Maandblad Suiker Unie. (NE ISSN 0024-8606) **184**
Maandblad Varkens *see* Varkens **228**
Maandblad voor Accountancy en Bedrijfshuishoudkunde. (NE ISSN 0024-8622) **753**
Maandblad voor Bedrijfsadministratie en Organisatie. (NE ISSN 0024-8630) **1059**
Maandblad voor het Notariaat *see* W P N R **2693**
Maandelikse Bulletin van Ionosferiese Karakteristieke Soos Waargeneem in Johannesburg en Hermanus. *see* Monthly Bulletin of Ionospheric Characteristics Recorded at Johannesburg and Hermanus **1377**
Maandschrift Economie. (NE ISSN 0024-8673) **678**
Maandschrift voor Kindergeneeskunde *see* Tijdschrift voor Kindergeneeskunde **3326**
†Maaneds Boersen. (DK) **5230**
Maanedsmagasinet Erhverv - Nordjylland. (DK ISSN 0900-6028) **1018**, 1059, 1080
Maanit. (IS) **831**
Maankaytto. (FI ISSN 0356-7869) **1871**
Maanmittaus/Surveying. (FI ISSN 0047-5319) **1871**
Maanmittausinsinoori *see* Maankaytto **1871**
Maansiirto/Earthmoving. (FI ISSN 0047-5327) **1871**, 623
Ha-Maapil. (US ISSN 0017-6850) **3905**, 1259
Ma'arachot. (IS ISSN 0464-2147) **3463**
Maarachot Cheimush. (IS) **3463**
Maarakennus ja Kuljetus/Earth Construction and Transport. (FI ISSN 0024-8819) **4745**, 623, 3019
Maarav. (US ISSN 0149-5712) **2828**, 2936
Al-Ma'arif. (PK ISSN 0002-4015) **3640**
Maariv Lanoar. (IS) **2204**
Ma'asef *see* Ya'ad **3935**
Ma'aseh Choshev. (IS) **1452**
Maaseututyovaen Viesti. (FI) **2586**, 106, 2104
Maatalous. (FI ISSN 0024-8827) **106**
Maatschappijbelangen. (NE ISSN 0024-8843) **1080**
Maatskaplike Werk *see* Social Work **4420**
Maatskaplikewerk-Praktyk. *see* Social Work Practice **4225**
Maatstaf. (NE) **2873**
Maba. *see* Expression **1311**
Mabat Lamerpaot. (IS) **3123**
Mabat Shelanu. (IS) **2288**
Mabat Shelanv. *see* Our Review **2288**
Mabua/Fountain. (IS) **2936**, 405, 420, 2997
Mabuey Hanchal. (US) **2012**, 4225
Mabuhay. (PH ISSN 0217-6998) **4803**
Mac - Chicago. (US) **1461**
Mac Diskworld. (US) **1470**, 1478
Mac Intelligencer *see* Intelligent Mac **5215**
▼Mac Publishing and Presentations. (US) **4143**, 1470
Mac Today *see* Macalester Today **1316**
Macalester Today. (US) **1316**
McAlvany Intelligence Advisor. (US) **954**
Macao. Census and Statistics Department. Activities Plan. *see* Macao. Direccao dos Servicos de Estatistica e Censos. Plano de Actividades **4578**
Macao. Census and Statistics Department. Activities Report. *see* Macao. Direccao dos Servicos de Estatistica e Censos. Relatorio de Actividades **4578**

MACAO. CENSUS

Macao. Census and Statistics Department. Balance of Energy. see Macao. Direccao dos Servicos de Estatistica e Censos. Balanco Energetico **1799**

Macao. Census and Statistics Department. Balance of Energy (Annual). see Macao. Direccao dos Servicos de Estatistica e Censos. Balanco Energetico (Anual) **1799**

Macao. Census and Statistics Department. Bibliography Bulletin. see Macao. Direccao dos Servicos de Estatistica e Censos. Boletim Bibliografico **405**

Macao. Census and Statistics Department. C A M Classification of Economic Activities. see Macao. Direccao dos Servicos de Estatistica e Censos. C A M Classificacao das Actividades **727**

Macao. Census and Statistics Department. Census of Informal Accomodation. see Macao. Direccao dos Servicos de Estatistica e Censos. Recenseamento dos Alojamentos Informais **3993**

Macao. Census and Statistics Department. Census of Restaurants, Hotels and Similar Establishments. see Macao. Direccao dos Servicos de Estatistica e Censos. Inquerito aos Restaurantes, Hoteis e Estabelecimentos Similares **2482**

Macao. Census and Statistics Department. Civil Construction in Macao (Annual Report). see Macao. Direccao dos Servicos de Estatistica e Censos. Relatorio Anual da Construcao Civil **4160**

Macao. Census and Statistics Department. Consumer Price Index. see Macao. Direccao dos Servicos de Estatistica e Censos. Indice de Precos no Consumidor **727**

Macao. Census and Statistics Department. Consumer Price Index (Annual Report). see Macao. Direccao dos Servicos de Estatistica e Censos. Indice de Precos no Consumidor (Relatorio Anual) **727**

Macao. Census and Statistics Department. Consumer Price Index Methodology. see Macao. Direccao dos Servicos de Estatistica e Censos. Metodologia do Indice de Precos no Consumidor **728**

Macao. Census and Statistics Department. Demographic Statistics. see Macao. Direccao dos Servicos de Estatistica e Censos. Estatisticas Demograficas **3993**

Macao. Census and Statistics Department. Economic Accounts of Public Sector. see Macao. Direccao dos Servicos de Estatistica e Censos. Contas Economicas do Sector Publico **727**

Macao. Census and Statistics Department. Education Survey. see Macao. Direccao dos Servicos de Estatistica e Censos. Inquerito ao Ensino **1678**

Macao. Census and Statistics Department. Estimation of Resident Population in Macao. see Macao. Direccao dos Servicos de Estatistica e Censos. Estimativas da Populacao Residente em Macau **3993**

Macao. Census and Statistics Department. Gross Domestic Product. see Macao. Direccao dos Servicos de Estatistica e Censos. Estimativas do Produto Interno Bruto **727**

Macao. Census and Statistics Department. Household Expenditure Survey. see Macao. Direccao dos Servicos de Estatistica e Censos. Inquerito as Despesas Familiares **727**

Macao. Census and Statistics Department. II General Census of Housing. see Macao. Direccao dos Servicos de Estatistica e Censos. II Recenseamento Geral a Habitcao **2500**

Macao. Census and Statistics Department. Industrial Survey. see Macao. Direccao dos Servicos de Estatistica e Censos. Inquerito Industrial **727**

Macao. Census and Statistics Department. Monthly Bulletin of External Trade. see Macao. Direccao dos Servicos de Estatistica e Censos. Boletim Mensal do Comercio Externo **727**

Macao. Census and Statistics Department. Monthly Digest of Statistics. see Macao. Direccao dos Servicos de Estatistica e Censos. Boletim Mensal de Estatistica **4578**

Macao. Census and Statistics Department. Population Census. see Macao. Direccao dos Servicos de Estatistica e Censos. Censos da Populacao **3993**

Macao. Census and Statistics Department. Quarterly Retail Survey. see Macao. Direccao dos Servicos de Estatistica e Censos. Inquerito Trimestral ao Comercio a Retalho **727**

Macao. Census and Statistics Department. Retrospective Series of External Trade. see Macao. Direccao dos Servicos de Estatistica e Censos. Series Retrospectivas do Comercio Externo **728**

Macao. Census and Statistics Department. Statistical Data - Transactions Concerning Real Estate and Companies. see Macao. Direccao dos Servicos de Estatistica e Censos. Indicadores Estatisticos - Operacoes sobre Imoveis e Sociedades **4160**

Macao. Census and Statistics Department. Statistics of Fishery. see Macao. Direccao dos Servicos de Estatistica e Censos. Estatisticas da Pesca **2051**

Macao. Census and Statistics Department. Statistics of Justice and Criminality. see Macao. Direccao dos Servicos de Estatistica e Censos. Estatisticas da Justica e da Criminalidade **2700**

Macao. Census and Statistics Department. Statistics of Non Resident Workers Importation. see Macao. Direccao dos Servicos de Estatistica e Censos. Importacao de Mao-de-obra e Renovacao de Contratos de Trabalhadores Nao Residnetes **3993**

Macao. Census and Statistics Department. Survey of Employment and Wages in the Construction Industry. see Macao. Direccao dos Servicos de Estatistica e Censos. Inquerito ao Emprego e Salarios na Construcao Civil **727**

Macao. Census and Statistics Department. Survey of Fishing Vessels. see Macao. Direccao dos Servicos de Estatistica e Censos. Inquerito as Embarcacoes de Pesca **2051**

Macao. Census and Statistics Department. Tourism Statistics. see Macao. Direccao dos Servicos de Estatistica e Censos. Estatisticas do Turismo **4799**

Macao. Census and Statistics Department. Tourism Statistics (Annual Report). see Macao. Direccao dos Servicos de Estatistica e Censos. Estatisticas do Turismo (Relatorio Anual) **4799**

Macao. Census and Statistics Department. Yearbook of External Trade Statistics. see Macao. Direccao dos Servicos de Estatistica e Censos. Anuario Estatistico do Comercio Externo **727**

Macao. Census and Statistics Department. Yearbook of Statistics. see Macao. Direccao dos Servicos de Estatistica e Censos. Anuario Estatistico **4577**

Macao. Direccao dos Servicos de Estatistica e Censos. Anuario Estatistico do Comercio Externo/ Macao. Census and Statistics Department. Yearbook of External Trade Statistics. (MH) **727**, **916**, **4577**

Macao. Direccao dos Servicos de Estatistica e Censos. Anuario Estatistico/Macao. Census and Statistics Department. Yearbook of Statistics. (MH) **4577**

Macao. Direccao dos Servicos de Estatistica e Censos. Balanco Energetico (Anual)/Macao. Census and Statistics Department. Balance of Energy (Annual). (MH) **1799**, **4577**

Macao. Direccao dos Servicos de Estatistica e Censos. Balanco Energetico/Macao. Census and Statistics Department. Balance of Energy. (MH) **1799**, **4577**

Macao. Direccao dos Servicos de Estatistica e Censos. Boletim Bibliografico/Macao. Census and Statistics Department. Bibliography Bulletin. (MH) **405**

Macao. Direccao dos Servicos de Estatistica e Censos. Boletim Mensal do Comercio Externo/Macao. Census and Statistics Department. Monthly Bulletin of External Trade. (MH) **727**, **916**, **4577**

Macao. Direccao dos Servicos de Estatistica e Censos. Boletim Mensal de Estatistica/Macao. Census and Statistics Department. Monthly Digest of Statistics. (MH) **4578**

Macao. Direccao dos Servicos de Estatistica e Censos. C A M Classificacao das Actividades/Macao. Census and Statistics Department. C A M Classification of Economic Activities. (MH) **727**, **837**

Macao. Direccao dos Servicos de Estatistica e Censos. Censos da Populacao/Macao. Census and Statistics Department. Population Census. (MH) **3993**, **4578**

Macao. Direccao dos Servicos de Estatistica e Censos. Contas Economicas do Sector Publico/ Macao. Census and Statistics Department. Economic Accounts of Public Sector. (MH) **727**

Macao. Direccao dos Servicos de Estatistica e Censos. Estatisticas da Pesca/Macao. Census and Statistics Department. Statistics of Fishery. (MH) **2051**, **4578**

Macao. Direccao dos Servicos de Estatistica e Censos. Estatisticas Demograficas/Macao. Census and Statistics Department. Demographic Statistics. (MH) **3993**, **4578**

Macao. Direccao dos Servicos de Estatistica e Censos. Estatisticas da Justica e da Criminalidade/Macao. Census and Statistics Department. Statistics of Justice and Criminality. (MH) **2700**, **4578**

Macao. Direccao dos Servicos de Estatistica e Censos. Estatisticas do Turismo/Macao. Census and Statistics Department. Tourism Statistics. (MH) **4799**, **4578**, **4775**

Macao. Direccao dos Servicos de Estatistica e Censos. Estatisticas do Turismo (Relatorio Anual)/Macao. Census and Statistics Department. Tourism Statistics (Annual Report). (MH) **4799**, **4578**, **4775**

Macao. Direccao dos Servicos de Estatistica e Censos. Estimativas do Produto Interno Bruto/Macao. Census and Statistics Department. Gross Domestic Product. (MH) **727**, **678**, **4578**

Macao. Direccao dos Servicos de Estatistica e Censos. Estimativas da Populacao Residente em Macau/ Macao. Census and Statistics Department. Estimation of Resident Population in Macao. (MH) **3993**, **4578**

Macao. Direccao dos Servicos de Estatistica e Censos. II Recenseamento Geral a Habitacao/ Macao. Census and Statistics Department. II General Census of Housing. (MH) **2500**, **4578**

Macao. Direccao dos Servicos de Estatistica e Censos. Importacao de Mao-de-obra e Renovacao de Contratos de Trabalhadores Nao Residnetes/Macao. Census and Statistics Department. Statistics of Non Resident Workers Importation. (MH) **3993**, **4578**

Macao. Direccao dos Servicos de Estatistica e Censos. Indicadores Estatisticos - Operacoes sobre Imoveis e Sociedades/Macao. Census and Statistics Department. Statistical Data - Transactions Concerning Real Estate and Companies. (MH) **4160**, **4578**

Macao. Direccao dos Servicos de Estatistica e Censos. Indice de Precos no Consumidor/Macao. Census and Statistics Department. Consumer Price Index. (MH) **727**, **837**, **4578**

Macao. Direccao dos Servicos de Estatistica e Censos. Indice de Precos no Consumidor (Relatorio Anual)/Macao. Census and Statistics Department. Consumer Price Index (Annual Report). (MH) **727**, **837**, **4578**

Macao. Direccao dos Servicos de Estatistica e Censos. Inquerito ao Ensino/Macao. Census and Statistics Department. Education Survey. (MH) **1678**, **4578**

Macao. Direccao dos Servicos de Estatistica e Censos. Inquerito ao Emprego e Salarios na Construcao Civil/Macao. Census and Statistics Department. Survey of Employment and Wages in the Construction Industry. (MH) **727**, **987**, **4578**

Macao. Direccao dos Servicos de Estatistica e Censos. Inquerito aos Restaurantes, Hoteis e Estabelecimentos Similares/Macao. Census and Statistics Department. Census of Restaurants, Hotels and Similar Establishments. (MH) **2482**, **2477**, **4578**

Macao. Direccao dos Servicos de Estatistica e Censos. Inquerito as Despesas Familiares/Macao. Census and Statistics Department. Household Expenditure Survey. (MH) **727**

Macao. Direccao dos Servicos de Estatistica e Censos. Inquerito as Embarcacoes de Pesca/Macao. Census and Statistics Department. Survey of Fishing Vessels. (MH) **2051**, **4578**

Macao. Direccao dos Servicos de Estatistica e Censos. Inquerito Industrial/Macao. Census and Statistics Department. Industrial Survey. (MH) **727**, **678**, **4578**

Macao. Direccao dos Servicos de Estatistica e Censos. Inquerito Trimestral ao Comercio a Retalho/ Macao. Census and Statistics Department. Quarterly Retail Survey. (MH) **727**, **837**, **4578**

Macao. Direccao dos Servicos de Estatistica e Censos. Metodologia do Indice de Precos no Consumidor/ Macao. Census and Statistics Department. Consumer Price Index Methodology. (MH) **728**, **837**

Macao. Direccao dos Servicos de Estatistica e Censos. Plano de Actividades/Macao. Census and Statistics Department. Activities Plan.(MH) **4578**

Macao. Direccao dos Servicos de Estatistica e Censos. Recenseamento dos Alojamentos Informais/Macao. Census and Statistics Department. Census of Informal Accomodation. (MH) **3993**, **4578**

Macao. Direccao dos Servicos de Estatistica e Censos. Relatorio Anual da Construcao Civil/Macao. Census and Statistics Department. Civil Construction in Macao (Annual Report). (MH) **4160**, **4578**
Macao. Direccao dos Servicos de Estatistica e Censos. Relatorio de Actividades/Macao. Census and Statistics Department. Activities Report. (MH) **4578**
Macao. Direccao dos Servicos de Estatistica e Censos. Series Retrospectivas do Comercio Externo/Macao. Census and Statistics Department. Retrospective Series of External Trade. (MH) **728**, **678**, **4578**
Macao. Direccao dos Servicos de Estatistica e Censos. Transporte de Mercadorias por Vias de Utilizacao. (MH) **728**, **916**, **4578**
Macao em Numeros/Macao in Figures. (MH) **4578**
Macao in Figures. see Macao em Numeros **4578**
Macarthur Advertiser. (AT) **2873**
MacArtist. (US ISSN 1059-4132) **352**, **1470**
Macau Image. (MH) **916**
Macau Industry. (MH) **678**
MACazine. (US) **1470**, **1431**, **1461**
Maccabi News Bulletin see Maccabi World Union. Newsletter **4479**
Maccabi World Union. Newsletter. (IS) **4479**
McCall's. (US ISSN 0024-8908) **4847**, **1292**, **2448**
McCall's Creative Crafts. (US) **356**
McCall's Needlework & Crafts. (US ISSN 0024-8924) **3591**
McCall's Silver. (US) **2276**, **4847**
McCall's Design Ideas see McCall's Creative Crafts **356**
McCarville - Gray Report see McCarville - Hill Report **4066**
McCarville - Hill Report. (US ISSN 0732-0205) **4066**, **3905**
McCarville Report see McCarville - Hill Report **4066**
Macchine. (IT ISSN 0024-8959) **3019**
Macchine Accessori Componenti. (IT) **2560**
†Macchine del Legno. (IT) **5230**
Macchine e Motori Agricoli see Macchine e Motori Agricoli - I M A il Trattorista **163**
Macchine e Motori Agricoli - I M A il Trattorista. (IT) **163**
McClain County Oklahoma Historical and Genealogical Society. Quarterly. (US) **2157**
Macclesfield Express Advertiser. (UK) **2572**, **34**
McCowm - Colquhoun Quarterly. (US) **2157**
McCrary (McCreary) "Clan" Newsletter. (US) **2157**
McCurry Kith & Kin. (US) **2157**
McCutcheon's Emulsifiers and Detergents - International Edition. (US) **1183**
McCutcheon's Emulsifiers and Detergents - North American Edition. (US ISSN 0145-7055) **1183**
McDonald, Henry and Meek: Australian Bankruptcy Law and Practice. (AT) **2651**
MacDonald Journal. (CN ISSN 0047-5335) **106**, **2448**
McDonald Observatory News see Star Date **370**
Macedon Ranges Telegraph. (AT) **2172**
Macedonia. (US) **2012**
Macedonia. (CN) **2873**
Macedonian Academy of Sciences and Arts. Section of Biological and Medical Sciences. Contributions. see Makedonska Akademija na Naukite i Umetnostite. Oddelenie za Bioloski i Medicinski Nauki. Prilozi **446**
Macedonian Academy of Sciences and Arts. Section of Linguistics and Literary Sciences. Contributions. see Makedonska Akademija na Naukite i Umetnostite. Oddelenie za Lingvistika i Literaturna Nauka. Prilozi **2828**

Macedonian Academy of Sciences and Arts. Section of Mathematical and Technical Sciences. Contributions. see Makedonska Akademija na Naukite i Umetnostite. Oddelenie za Matematicki i Tehnicki Nauki. Prilozi **4323**
Macedonian Academy of Sciences and Arts. Section of Social Sciences. Contributions. see Makedonska Akademija na Naukite i Umetnostite. Oddelenie za Opstestveni Nauki. Prilozi **4379**
Macedonian Life. see Makedoniki Zoi **2196**
Macedonian Review. (XN ISSN 0350-3089) **2936**, **334**, **2012**
Macedonian Tribune. (US ISSN 0024-9009) **1299**, **2012**, **3905**
Macellaio - Salumiere. see Metzger und Wurster **2077**
Macelleria Italiana. (IT ISSN 0024-9017) **2076**
MacEwan Journalist. (CN) **1316**
McGehee Messenger. (US) **2157**
McGill Daily. (CN) **1317**
McGill Dental Review. (CN ISSN 0024-9025) **3237**
McGill Journal of Business see Purple Report **686**
McGill Journal of Education. (CN ISSN 0024-9033) **1646**
McGill Law Journal/Revue de Droit de McGill. (CN ISSN 0024-9041) **2651**
McGill News. (CN ISSN 0024-9068) **1317**
McGill Sub-Arctic Research Papers. (CN ISSN 0076-1982) **2255**
McGill University. Register. (CN ISSN 0226-7586) **2317**
McGill University Graduate School of Library and Information Studies Newsletter. (CN) **1317**
McGill University, Montreal. Axel Heiberg Island Research Reports. (CN ISSN 0076-1850) **1547**
McGill University, Montreal. Centre for Developing-Area Studies. Annual Report. (CN ISSN 0076-1893) **4379**
McGill University, Montreal. Department of Geography. Climatological Research Series. (CN ISSN 0076-1931) **3438**
†McGill University, Montreal. Marine Sciences Centre. Manuscript Report. (CN) **5230**
McGill University, Montreal. Mechanical Engineering Research Laboratories. Report. (CN ISSN 0076-1966) **1934**
McGill University, Montreal. Mechanical Engineering Research Laboratories. Technical Note. (CN ISSN 0076-1974) **1934**
McGill University Savanna Research Project - Savanna Research Series. (CN) **2255**
McGoldrick's Canadian Customs Guide "Harmonized System". (CN ISSN 1183-3246) **916**, **1100**
McGoldrick's Canadian Customs Tariff "Harmonized System" see McGoldrick's Canadian Customs Guide "Harmonized System **916**
McGraw-Hill Yearbook of Science and Technology. (US ISSN 0076-2016) **4323**, **4603**
McGraw-Hill's Biotechnology Newswatch.(US ISSN 0275-3685) **490**
McGraw-Hill's Washington Report on Medicine and Health. (US ISSN 1047-8922) **3123**, **4066**
McGuffey Writer. (US) **1259**
MacGuffin. (US) **2997**
MacGuide Magazine see MacGuide Report **1470**
MacGuide Report. (US) **1470**, **1478**
Mach. (US) **2455**
Machberet Hamenahel. (US) **4225**
▼McHenry County Marketing Directory.(US) **1144**
Machiavelli Studies. (US ISSN 1049-9776) **3905**
Machine and Machinery. (II ISSN 0024-9092) **3019**

†Machine and Tool Blue Book. (US ISSN 0024-9106) **5230**
Machine Building Industry. (II ISSN 0541-6388) **3019**
Machine Cancel Forum. (US) **3754**
Machine Design. (US ISSN 0024-9114) **1934**
Machine Design/Kikai Sekkei. (JA ISSN 0387-1045) **1934**
Machine Intelligence and Pattern Recognition. (NE) **1409**, **1398**
Machine Intelligence Workshop. (UK ISSN 0076-2032) **1409**
Machine Knitting Monthly. (UK ISSN 0269-9761) **3591**
Machine Knitting News. (UK ISSN 0266-8505) **3591**, **1286**
Machine Learning. (US ISSN 0885-6125) **1398**, **1409**
Machine - Mediated Learning. (US ISSN 0732-6718) **1417**, **1754**
Machine Moderne see Techniques et Equipments de Production **3421**
Machine - Outil Produire. (FR ISSN 0758-1874) **3019**
Machine Tool Buyers Guide for Southern Africa. (SA) **3412**
†Machine Tool Engineer. (II ISSN 0541-6434) **5230**
Machine Tool Enterprise. (UK ISSN 0140-9360) **1934**
Machine Tool Selector. (UK) **3019**
†Machine Tools & Production Engineering. (SA) **5230**
Machine Translation. (NE ISSN 0922-6567) **2856**
Machine Vision & Applications. (US ISSN 0932-8092) **1442**, **1830**, **1879**, **4603**
†Machine Vision Product Buyer's Guide.(US) **5230**
Machinery see Machinery and Production Engineering **3019**
Machinery Abstracts. see Gepeszeti Szakirodalmi Tajekoztato **1844**
Machinery & Equipment M R O. (Machinery and Equipment Maintenance Repair Overhaul) (CN ISSN 0831-8603) **3019**, **1934**
Machinery and Equipment Maintenance Repair Overhaul Machinery & Equipment M R O see Machinery & Equipment M R O **3019**
Machinery & Machine Tool Journal. (II ISSN 0047-5351) **3019**
Machinery and Production Engineering. (UK ISSN 0024-919X) **3019**
Machinery and Steel. (AU) **3019**, **3412**
Machinery Buyers' Guide. (UK ISSN 0305-3121) **3019**
Machinery Engineering & Maintenance Technology. (CN) **1934**
†Machinery Japan. (JA) **5230**
†Machinery Korea. (KO) **5230**
Machinery: Latin American Industrial Report. (US) **3019**, **873**
Machinery Market. (UK) **3020**
Machinery Market and the Machinery and Engineering Materials Gazette see Machinery Market **3020**
Machinery Outlook. (US ISSN 8756-923X) **3020**
Machinery Trader. (US) **3020**
Machinery World. (UK) **3020**, **1934**
Machinery's Annual Buyer's Guide see Machinery Buyers' Guide **3019**
Machines and Tooling see Soviet Engineering Research **3023**
Machines Production. (FR ISSN 0047-536X) **3020**
Machining Technology. (US) **3020**
†Machinisme Agricole Tropical. (FR ISSN 0024-9246) **5230**
Machinist. (NE) **1934**, **3020**
Machinist. (US ISSN 0047-5378) **2586**, **3020**
†Al-Machriq. (LE ISSN 0002-4023) **5230**
Machshavim. see Computers **1393**
Machshever. (IS) **4225**
MacII Review. (US) **1470**
McIlvainea. (US ISSN 0099-8400) **509**
Macintosh Business Review. (US ISSN 0899-725X) **1470**
†Macintosh Hands On. (US) **5230**
Macintosh Magazin. (GW ISSN 0934-845X) **1470**

MACROBIOTIC WORLD 6407

Macintosh News see Computer Reseller News **1432**
†Macintosh News. (US) **5230**
Macintosh Product Registry. (US) **1470**
Macintosh Update. (US) **1461**, **1454**, **1478**
McKeever Money Strategy Letter. (US) **954**
McKeever Strategy Letter see McKeever Money Strategy Letter **954**
Mackenzie M A G see Vista **3535**
Mackinac. (US) **1491**, **1962**
McKinsey Quarterly. (US ISSN 0047-5394) **1018**
Mackintosh Yearbook of International Electronics Data see Yearbook of World Electronics Data Vol. 2: America, Japan, Asia-Pacific **1779**
Mackintosh Yearbook of West European Electronics Data see Yearbook of World Electronics Data Vol. 1: West Europe **1779**
McKnight's Long Term Care News. (US) **2276**
Maclean Building Guide see Building Homes & Renovation **606**
McLean Hospital Journal. (US) **2467**
Maclean's. (CN ISSN 0024-9262) **2178**
Macmaailma. (FI ISSN 0786-3683) **1470**
McMahon Heavy Construction Cost Guide. (US ISSN 1050-270X) **623**, **1871**
McMaster Journal of Theology. (CN ISSN 0849-0899) **4189**
McMaster Theological Bulletin see McMaster Journal of Theology **4189**
McMaster University, Hamilton, Ontario. Institute for Materials Research. Annual Report. (CN ISSN 0076-2059) **1920**
†McMaster University Library Research News. (CN ISSN 0024-9270) **5230**
Macmillan Directory of International Advertisers and Agencies see Standard Directory of International Advertisers and Agencies **1154**
McNeese Review. (US ISSN 0885-467X) **2936**, **2413**
†McNeill Memoranda. (US) **5230**
Macomb County Legal News. (US ISSN 0024-9289) **2651**, **678**
Macon Courier. (US) **2012**
Macon Junior College Commuter. (US) **1317**
Macon Magazine. (US) **2228**
Macplas. (IT ISSN 0394-3453) **3864**
Macplas International. (IT) **3864**
Macquarie University Caving Group Raker see M U C G - Raker **1571**
Macquarie University French Monographs. (AT ISSN 0815-7138) **2828**, **1646**
McQuillin Municipal Law Report. (US) **2651**, **4090**
MacRae's Blue Book. (US) **1144**
MacRae's State Industrial Directory: Connecticut - Rhode Island. (US ISSN 0740-2937) **1144**
MacRae's State Industrial Directory: Maine - New Hampshire - Vermont. (US ISSN 0740-2945) **1144**
MacRae's State Industrial Directory: Maryland - District of Columbia - Delaware. (US) **1144**
MacRae's State Industrial Directory: Massachusetts - Rhode Island. (US ISSN 0740-4689) **1144**
MacRae's State Industrial Directory: New Jersey. (US ISSN 0733-3684) **1144**
MacRae's State Industrial Directory: New York State. (US ISSN 0740-2953) **1144**
MacRae's State Industrial Directory: North Carolina - South Carolina - Virginia. (US) **1144**
MacRae's State Industrial Directory: Pennsylvania. (US ISSN 0740-4298) **1144**
MacRae's Virginia State Industrial Directory. (US ISSN 0740-2902) **1144**
Macrobiotic World Directory. (US) **3609**

6408 MACROBIOTICS TODAY

Macrobiotics Today. (US) **3609, 3772**
Macromolecular Chemistry (Oxford). (UK ISSN 0076-2075) **1220**
▼Macromolecular Reports. (US ISSN 1060-1325) **1220**
†Macromolecular Syntheses. (US ISSN 0076-2091) **5230**
Macromolecules. (US ISSN 0024-9297) **1220**
Macrophages. (UK ISSN 0142-8195) **3188**
Mac's Tracs. (US) **2157**
Mac's Year (Year). (UK) **2873**
MacTech Journal. (US ISSN 1052-9128) **1470**
MacTech Quarterly see MacTech Journal **1470**
MacTutor. (US ISSN 8756-8810) **1470**
Macula. (FR) **334**
MACup. (GW ISSN 0935-6282) **1470**
MACup Buyer's Guide. (GW) **1470**
MACup Extra. (GW) **1470**
MacUser. (US ISSN 0884-0997) **1470, 1461**
MacWeek. (US) **1470**
†McWilliams Letter. (US) **5230**
McWinners Magazine. (US) **2936**
MacWorld. (US ISSN 0741-8647) **1470, 1461**
MacWorld Sweden. (SW) **1470, 1461**
Mad. (US ISSN 0024-9319) **2873, 1259**
▼Mad Poets Review. (US) **2997**
▼Mad River. (US ISSN 1054-2655) **2936**
Mad Scientist. (US) **3595, 3670**
Mada. (IS ISSN 0024-9335) **4603, 1259, 4323**
Madagascar. Service Geologique. Rapport d'Activite: Geologie. (MG) **1571**
Madagascar Renouveau. (MG) **2209**
Madagascar; Revue de Geographie. (MG ISSN 0047-5416) **2255**
Madam. (JA ISSN 0024-9343) **1292, 2208**
Madam. (UK ISSN 0024-9351) **2294**
Madame. (GW ISSN 0024-936X) **376, 1292**
Madame au Foyer. see Homemaker's Magazine **2447**
Madame Figaro. (FR) **1292**
Madan. (PO) **278**
Madden Family Newsletter. (US ISSN 0883-556X) **2157**
Maddux Report. (US) **678**
Made in Austria. (AU ISSN 0076-2105) **1144**
Made in Brazil. (BL) **916**
†Made in Europe. Furniture and Interiors. (GW ISSN 0171-6042) **5230**
Made in Europe. General Merchandise. (GW) **916, 1045**
Made in Europe. Technical and Industrial Supply Guide. (GW) **916**
Made in Europe. Technical Equipment Catalog see Made in Europe. Technical and Industrial Supply Guide **916**
Made in Europe Buyers' Guide. (GW ISSN 0172-2182) **916**
Made in Europe - Medical Equipment and Supply Guide. (GW ISSN 0720-597X) **3123, 3262**
▼Made in Hungary Monthly. (HU) **916**
Made in Hungary Special. (HU ISSN 0133-9680) **916**
Made in Hungary Yearbook. (HU ISSN 0209-4401) **916**
Made in Italy. (IT) **916**
Made in the Arab World. (BA) **1144**
Made in Tunisia. (TI) **1144**
Made to Measure. (US) **1286**
Madeira. Servico Regional de Estatistica. Boletim Trimestral de Estatistica. (PO) **4578**
Mademoiselle. (US ISSN 0024-9394) **4847, 1292**
Mademoiselle Gymnast see International Gymnast Magazine **4476**
Madencilik. (TU ISSN 0024-9416) **3487**
Madera y su Uso en la Construccion. (MX) **2116, 623**
Madhuparka. (NP) **2936**

Madhuprapancha. (II ISSN 0970-0919) **106**
Madhuri. (II ISSN 0024-9432) **3513**
Madhya Pradesh. Directorate of Agriculture. Agricultural Statistics. (II ISSN 0304-6184) **140**
Madhya Pradesh Itihasa Parishad. Journal. (II) **3640**
Madhya Pradesh Law Journal. (II ISSN 0024-9459) **2651**
Madhya Pradesh State Agro-Industries Development Corporation Ltd. Annual Report. (II ISSN 0304-7245) **154**
Madhya Pradesh Vikas Varshiki. (II) **2200**
Madhya Pradesh Who's Who. (II) **420, 405**
Madhya Pradesh Yearbook see Madhya Pradesh Vikas Varshiki **2200**
Madison Area's Gay - Lesbian Calendar.(US) **2455, 3393**
Madison Avenue Handbook. (US ISSN 0076-2148) **34**
Madison, Connecticut - A Pictorial Guide. (US) **819**
Madison County Heritage. (US) **2413**
Madison County Musings. (US) **2158**
Madison Gay Lesbian Resource Center. Directory. (US) **1144, 2455, 4847**
Madison Magazine. (US) **2228**
Madison N O W Chapter Newsletter see Equality N O W **4841**
Madison Review. (US) **2997**
Madison Teachers, Inc. Reporter see M T I Reporter **1646**
Madison Waste Conference. Annual Proceedings. (US) **1985, 1871**
Madison's Canadian Lumber Directory. (CN ISSN 0316-6414) **1144, 2116**
Madison's Canadian Lumber Reporter. (CN) **2116**
Madjalah Persatuan Dokter Gigi Indonesia. (IO ISSN 0024-9548) **3237**
Madjalah Pertanian. (IO ISSN 0024-9556) **106**
Madju. (GW) **4243**
Madonna. (IT) **4268**
La Madonna del Divino Amore. (IT) **4268**
†Madonna di Barbana. (IT ISSN 0024-9580) **5230**
Madonna di Castelmonte. (IT ISSN 0024-9599) **4189**
Madoqua. (SX ISSN 1011-5498) **1491, 446**
Madoqua. Series 2 see Madoqua **1491**
Madras. Government Museum. Bulletin. New Series. (II ISSN 0085-2945) **4323**
Madras Agricultural Journal. (II ISSN 0024-9602) **106**
Madras Development Seminar Series. (II) **678**
Madras Information see Tamil Nadu Information **4075**
Madras Institute of Development Studies. Bulletin see Madras Development Seminar Series **678**
Madras Institute of Neurology. Proceedings. (II) **3344**
Madras Journal of Co-operation see Tamil Nadu Journal of Co-operation **832**
Madras Labour Gazette. see Tamil Nadu Labour Journal **994**
Madras Law Journal. (II) **2651**
Madras Law Journal (Criminal). (II) **2651**
Madre. (IT) **4847, 2448**
Madre di Dio. (IT) **4268**
Madre y Maestra. (SP) **4268**
Madrich Legrote Chove. (IS) **954**
Madrid Trans-Port. (SP) **4732**
Madrider Mitteilungen. (GW) **278**
Madrigalisti dell'Italia Centro-Settentrionale. (IT) **3562**
†Madrona. (US ISSN 0047-5432) **5230**
Madrono. (US ISSN 0024-9637) **509**
Maeda Lerofei. (IS ISSN 0334-4169) **3123**
Maeda Venitunim. (IS) **1398**
Maelk & Ost. (DK) **201**
Maelkeproducenten. (DK ISSN 0107-7988) **201**
Maelkeritidende. (DK) **201**

Maend og Mission see Verden Rundt **4208**
Maenner see Maenner Aktuell **2455**
Maenner Aktuell. (GW ISSN 0935-8838) **2455, 3395, 4775**
Maenner Vogue. (GW) **1292, 3398**
Der Maerker. (GW ISSN 0024-9661) **2374**
Maerkische Zeitung. (GW ISSN 0024-967X) **3905**
†Maerkischen Museum. Jahrbuch. (GW) **5230**
Maerklin-Magazin. (GW ISSN 0024-9688) **2438, 4711**
Maerkte im Saarland. (GW ISSN 0177-7491) **1116**
Maestri Friulani. (IT) **1646**
Maestria Industrial. (SP ISSN 0210-0762) **1080**
Maestro. (IT ISSN 0024-9696) **4268, 1646**
Mafeking Mail and Botswana Guardian see The Mail **2216**
Maffra & District Historical Society. Bulletin. (AT ISSN 0811-1197) **2345**
†Magadh University Journal. (II ISSN 0024-9726) **5230**
Magaleti. (IS) **1259**
Al-Magallah al-Qanuniyyah al-Iqtisadiyyah. (UA) **2651, 678**
Magallat al-Dirasat al-Qanuniyyah. (UA) **2651**
Magallat al-Iskandiriyyah li-Tibb al-Asnan. see Alexandria Dental Journal **3227**
Magallat Al-Mohandeseen/Engineer's Magazine. (UA) **1830**
Magallat Gami'at al-Malik al-Sa'ud, al-Adab see King Saud University. Journal. Arts **332**
Magallat Gami'at al-Malik al-Sa'ud, al-Imarat wal-Takhtit see King Saud University. Journal. Architecture and Planning **2491**
Magallat Gami'at al-Malik al-Sa'ud, al-'Ulum see King Saud University. Journal. Sciences **4320**
Magallat Gami'at al-Malik al-Sa'ud, al-'Ulum al-Handasiyyat see King Saud University. Journal. Engineering Sciences **1829**
Magallat Gami'at al-Malik al-Sa'ud, al-'Ulum al-Idariyyat see King Saud University. Journal. Administrative Sciences **676**
Magallat Gami'at al-Malik al-Sa'ud, al-'Ulum al-Tarbawiyyat see King Saud University. Journal. Educational Sciences **1644**
Magallat Gami'at al-Malik al-Sa'ud, al-'Ulum al-Zira'iyyat see King Saud University. Journal. Agricultural Sciences **103**
Magallat Kulliyyat al-Adab see Jami'at Tanta. Kulliyyat al-Adab. Majallah **2927**
Magallat Kulliyyat al-Lughah al-Arabiyyah bil-Manufiyyah see Jami'at al-Azhar. Kulliyyat al-Lughah al-Arabiyyah bil-Manufiyyah. Majallah **2820**
Magallat Kulliyyat al-Lughah al-Arabiyyah bil-Zagazig see Jami'at al-Azhar. Kulliyyat al-Lughah al-Arabiyyah bil-Zagazig. Majallah **2820**
Magallat Kulliyyat Usul al-Din wal-Da'wah al-Islamiyyah bi-Tanta see Jami'at al-Azhar. Kulliyyat Usul al-Din wal-Da'wah al-Islamiyyah bi-Tanta. Majallah **4219**
Magasin d'Horlogerie Specialise. see Uhrenfachgeschaeft **2566**
Magasinet Nu. (DK) **2572**
Magasinet Print see Print **1464**
Magazette. (US ISSN 0897-8921) **1470, 1461**
Magazin. (RM) **4323**
Magazin C S N. (CS) **3447**
Magazin der Tierfreunde. (GW) **3712**
Magazin fuer Amerikanistik. (GW ISSN 0170-2513) **2413, 244**
Magazin fuer Arbeitnehmer - Werk und Leben see Magazin fuer Mitarbeiter - Werk und Leben **2873**
Magazin fuer die Polizei. (GW) **1518**
Magazin fuer Haus und Wohnung. (GW ISSN 0024-9769) **623**

†Magazin fuer Heimwerker. (GW ISSN 0174-5735) **5230**
Magazin fuer Mitarbeiter - Werk und Leben. (GW) **2873**
Magazin fuer Technik und Unterricht. (GW ISSN 0723-7049) **4603**
Magazin Polovnika. (CS ISSN 0541-8836) **4550, 2448, 2936**
Magazin Sammeln see Troedler- und Magazin Sammeln **259**
Magazin Werbung Saar. (GW) **34**
Magazin Wirtschaft. (GW) **819**
Magazine. (LE) **2209**
The Magazine. (US) **4132, 1045**
Magazine Affaires see Magazine Affaires Plus **954**
Magazine Affaires Plus. (CN ISSN 0836-6942) **954, 1100, 3629**
Magazine & Bookseller. (US ISSN 0744-3102) **4132**
The Magazine Antiques. (US ISSN 0161-9284) **258**
Magazine Article Summaries. (US ISSN 1041-1151) **16**
Magazine Avenir. (CN ISSN 0846-5274) **1685, 3629**
Magazine Carguide see Carguide **4687**
Magazine Commercial Polonais see Polish Trade Magazine **919**
Magazine de l'Education Internationale. see International Education Magazine **1722**
Magazine de l'Evenement see L'Evenement **2174**
Magazine des Industries Gourmandes see Magazine Strategies Gourmandes **2089**
Magazine Design and Production. (US ISSN 0882-049X) **4002, 4132**
Magazine for Christian Youth! (US) **4189, 1259**
Magazine for London Living. (UK) **2553**
Magazine Gwadloupeyen. (GP) **2239**
Magazine Index. (US) **4142, 16**
Magazine Issues. (US ISSN 0899-7039) **4132**
Magazine Le Clap. (CN) **1506**
Magazine Litteraire. (FR ISSN 0024-9807) **2936**
Magazine Market Coverage Report. (US) **41**
Magazine Nautique. (CN) **4526**
Magazine Newsletter of Research see M P A Newsletter of Research **34**
Magazine Oesterreich - U S A see Amerikanische Handelskammer in Oesterrich. Newsletter **807**
Magazine of Albemarle County History. (US ISSN 0076-2342) **2413**
Magazine of America's Best Recipes. (US) **2076, 2448**
Magazine of Concrete Research. (UK ISSN 0024-9831) **623**
Magazine of Contemporary History. see Casopis za Suvremenu Povijest **2308**
Magazine of Fantasy and Science Fiction. (US ISSN 0024-984X) **3012**
Magazine of Masonry Construction. (US ISSN 0898-6088) **623**
Magazine of Sigma Chi. (US) **1317**
Magazine of Speculative Poetry. (US ISSN 8755-8785) **2997**
Magazine of Virginia Genealogy. (US ISSN 0743-8095) **2158**
Magazine of Wall Street see Wall Street and U S Business News **968**
Magazine P M E. (CN ISSN 0828-8089) **1116, 790**
Magazine Publishers Association. Newsletter of Circulation. (US) **4132**
Magazine Publishers of America. (US) **4132**
Magazine Publishers of America Newsletter of Research see M P A Newsletter of Research **34**
Magazine Recycling Benelux. (NE) **1080, 1962**
Magazine Ressources Humaines see Magazine Avenir **1685**
Magazine Silver see Silver **259**
Magazine Strategies Gourmandes. (FR) **2089**
Magazine Suisse d'Echecs. see Schweizer Schach-Magazin **4487**
Magazine That's All About Small Business see Profit **686**

Magazine Trend Report. (US) **41**
†Magazine Vivre. (CN) **5230**
†Le Magazine Voyages Plus. (CN ISSN 0838-6838) **5230**
Magazine Week see U K Press Gazette **2576**
Magazines (Washington) see Magazines in Special Media **2285**
Magazines for Libraries. (US ISSN 0000-0914) **405, 2772**
Magazines for School Libraries see Magazines for Young People **405**
Magazines for Young People. (US ISSN 0000-1368) **405, 1259, 2772**
Magazines in Special Media. (US ISSN 0889-6518) **2285, 405**
MagazineWeek. (US ISSN 0895-2124) **4132**
Magazyn Fotograficzny FOTO. (PL ISSN 0324-8453) **3793**
Magazyn Polski. (PL ISSN 0024-9866) **2214**
Magazyn Pomorze, Fakty 1 see Fakty (Year) **2866**
▼Magazyn Wilenski. (LI) **2012**
Magazzini e Trasporti - Logistica see Logistica **4652**
Mage. (US) **3012, 334, 2997**
Magen-Escudo. (VE) **2012**
Maggie's Farm. (AT) **2873**
Maghreb Arab Press Actualite see M A P Actualite **3905**
▼Maghreb Confidentiel. (FR ISSN 1150-4447) **3965**
Maghreb, Machrek, Monde Arabe. (FR ISSN 0336-6324) **3905, 2727, 4379**
Maghreb Review. (UK ISSN 0309-457X) **2334, 3906**
Maghreb Selection. (FR ISSN 0153-4157) **917**
Maghrebi Bengal. (II) **2200**
Magic Carpet. (UK ISSN 0047-5475) **3123**
Magic Cauldron. (US ISSN 0024-9904) **2438**
Magic Changes. (US ISSN 0196-8432) **2936, 334**
Magic Circular. (UK) **2438**
Magic Crochet. (FR ISSN 0246-5957) **3591**
Magic Ink. (UK) **2873**
Magic, Unity, Might see M U M **2438**
▼Magic Valley Ag Weekly. (US) **106**
Magical Blend. (US ISSN 1040-4287) **3595, 334, 2936, 3772**
Magickal Unicorn Messenger. (US) **3670, 3595**
Magill: Ireland's Current Affairs Monthly Magazine. (IE) **2203**
Magill's Cinema Annual. (US) **3513**
Magill's History Annual see Magill's Literary Annual: History and Biography **5230**
Magill's Literary Annual. (US ISSN 0163-3058) **2936, 4132**
†Magill's Literary Annual: History and Biography. (US) **5230**
Magira. (GW) **3012, 334, 2997**
"Magische" Welt. (GW ISSN 0024-9912) **2438, 4634**
Magisterio Espanol. (SP) **1646**
Magistrate/Landdros. (SA ISSN 0024-9971) **2651**
The Magistrate. (UK ISSN 0024-9920) **2651**
Magistrenes Universitetslaererforeningen. Beskrivelse see Universitetslaereren. Beskrivelse **1719**
Maglie Calze Industria. (IT ISSN 0024-9947) **4621**
Maglieria in Italia see R M 1 Maglieria in Italia **1287**
Maglieria Italiana. (IT) **1286**
Magna. (US) **1292**
Magna Graecia. (IT ISSN 0024-9955) **278**
Magnes News. (US) **3527, 2012**
Magnesium see Magnesium and Trace Elements **480**
Magnesium and Trace Elements. (SZ ISSN 1015-3845) **480**
Magnesium Bulletin. (GW ISSN 0172-908X) **1207, 3123**
Magnesium Monthly Review. (US ISSN 0047-5491) **3412**
Magnesium Newsletter. (US ISSN 0891-6942) **3412**

Magnet Marketing. (US) **1045, 34**
Magnetic and Electrical Separation. (US ISSN 1055-6915) **3824, 1902**
Magnetic Resonance Annual see Magnetic Resonance Quarterly **3360**
Magnetic Resonance Imaging. (US ISSN 0730-725X) **3360**
†Magnetic Resonance in Biology. (US) **5230**
Magnetic Resonance in Chemistry. (UK ISSN 0749-1581) **1228**
Magnetic Resonance in Medicine. (US ISSN 0740-3194) **3360, 3824**
Magnetic Resonance Quarterly. (US ISSN 0899-9422) **3360**
Magnetic Resonance Review. (US ISSN 0097-7330) **3824**
Magnetic Separation News see Magnetic and Electrical Separation **3824**
Magnetohydrodynamics. (English translation of: Magnitnaya Gidrodinamika) (US ISSN 0024-998X) **1902**
†Magnetohydrodynamics. (US ISSN 0891-9801) **5230**
Magnets in Your Future. (US ISSN 0887-5707) **1902**
Magnificat. (CN ISSN 0025-0007) **4268**
Magnitnaya Gidrodinamika. (LV ISSN 0025-0015) **1934**
Magnitnoimpul'snaya Obrabotka Metallov. (KR) **1902**
Magnito-Poluprovodnikovye i Elektromashinnye Elementy Avtomatiki. (RU) **1902**
Magnolia (Hammond). (US ISSN 0738-3053) **2134**
Magnolia (Winston-Salem). (US) **2134**
Magnum. (SA) **4550, 4479**
Magnus. (GW ISSN 0936-9090) **2455**
Magon. Serie Scientifique. (LE ISSN 0076-2369) **106**
Magon. Serie Technique. (LE ISSN 0076-2377) **106**
Magpies. (AT ISSN 0817-0088) **1241, 2936**
Maguare. (CK ISSN 0120-3045) **244, 278**
Maguire Bulletin. (UK ISSN 0265-5691) **2158**
Magwa. (GP) **3906**
Magyar Allami Eotvos Lorand Geofizikai Intezet evi Jelentese. see Eotvos Lorand Geophysical Institute of Hungary. Annual Report **1588**
Magyar Allatorvosok Lapja/Journal of Hungarian Veterinary Science. (HU ISSN 0025-004X) **4812**
Magyar Aluminium/Hungarian Aluminum. (HU ISSN 0025-0058) **3412**
Magyar Belorovosi Archivum es Ideggyogyaszati Szemle see Magyar Belorvosi Archivum **3123**
Magyar Belorvosi Archivum. (HU ISSN 0133-5464) **3123**
Magyar Cserkesz/Hungarian Scout Magazine. (US) **1299, 1259**
Magyar Egyhaztorteneti Vazlatok/ Essays in Church History in Hungary.(CN ISSN 0865-5227) **2374, 4189**
Magyar Elet/Hungarian Life. (CN ISSN 0047-5513) **2012**
Magyar Epitoipar/Hungarian Building Industry. (HU ISSN 0025-0074) **623**
Magyar Epitomuveszet. (HU ISSN 0025-0082) **303**
Magyar Evkonyv. (US ISSN 0094-1484) **1781**
Magyar Filozofiai Szemle/Hungarian Philosophical Review. (HU ISSN 0025-0090) **3772**
Magyar Fizikai Folyoirat/Hungarian Journal of Physics. (HU ISSN 0025-0104) **3824**
Magyar Fuzetek. (FR ISSN 0292-7934) **3944**
Magyar Geofizika. (HU ISSN 0025-0120) **1592**
Magyar Grafika/Hungarian Graphic Arts. (HU ISSN 0479-480X) **4002**
Magyar Holnap/Hungarian Tomorrow. (US) **2013**

Magyar Ifjusag. (HU) **1259**
Magyar Irodalom es Irodalomtudomany Bibliografiaja. (HU ISSN 0134-1464) **405**
Magyar Irodalomtortenetiras Forrasai. (HU ISSN 0076-2385) **2936**
Magyar Jog. (HU ISSN 0025-0147) **2651**
Magyar Jog es Kulfoldi Jogi Szemle see Magyar Jog **2651**
Magyar Kemiai Folyoirat/Hungarian Journal of Chemistry. (HU ISSN 0025-0155) **1183**
Magyar Kemikusok Lapja. (HU ISSN 0025-0163) **1183**
▼Magyar Kiadas - Business Week. (US ISSN 0865-8986) **678, 917**
Magyar Konyveszet (Budapest, 1961). (HU ISSN 0133-3496) **405**
Magyar Konyvszemle/Hungarian Book Review. (HU ISSN 0025-0171) **4132, 2772**
Magyar Konyvtari Szakirodalom Bibliografiaja/Hungarian Library Literature. (HU ISSN 0133-736X) **2794, 1405**
†Magyar Konyvtarosok Egyesuletenek Evkonyve. (HU ISSN 0133-1949) **5230**
Magyar Kozgazdasagi Irodalom/ Hungarian Economic Literature. (HU ISSN 0133-0152) **728**
Magyar Kozlony. (HU ISSN 0076-2407) **2374**
Magyar Kulpolitikai Evkonyv. (HU ISSN 0541-9220) **3965**
Magyar Mezogazdasag/Hungarian Agriculture. (HU ISSN 0025-018X) **106**
Magyar Mezogazdasagi Bibliografia. (HU ISSN 0025-0198) **140, 2085, 2112**
†Magyar Munkasmozgalmi Muzeum. Evkonyv. (HU ISSN 0076-2415) **5230**
Magyar Naplo (Toronto, 1966). (CN) **2013**
Magyar Naplo (Toronto, 1979). (CN) **2198**
Magyar Naptar see Magyar Evkonyv **1781**
Magyar Nemzeti Bibliografia see Magyar Nemzeti Bibliografia. Zenemuvek Bibliografiaja **3588**
Magyar Nemzeti Bibliografia. Idoszaki Kiadvanyok Bibliografiaja. (HU ISSN 0231-4592) **405**
Magyar Nemzeti Bibliografia. Idoszaki Kiadvanyok Repertoriuma. (HU ISSN 0133-6894) **406, 2198**
Magyar Nemzeti Bibliografia. Konyvek Bibliografiaja. (HU ISSN 0133-6843) **406**
Magyar Nemzeti Bibliografia. Zenemuvek Bibliografiaja. (HU ISSN 0133-5782) **3588, 406**
Magyar Neprajzi Bibliografia/Hungarian Folklore Bibliography. (HU ISSN 0865-1906) **2056**
Magyar Nok Lapja. (HU ISSN 0029-0963) **4847**
Magyar Noorvosok Lapja. (HU ISSN 0025-021X) **3294**
Magyar Nyelv/Hungarian Language. (HU ISSN 0025-0228) **2828**
Magyar Nyelvor/Hungarian Purist. (HU ISSN 0025-0236) **2828**
Magyar Olajipari Muzeum. Evkonyv. (HU) **3691**
Magyar Onkologia. (HU ISSN 0025-0244) **3199**
Magyar Orvosi Bibliografia. (HU ISSN 0025-0252) **3177**
Magyar Pedagogia/Hungarian Pedagogy. (HU ISSN 0025-0260) **1646**
Magyar Pszichologiai Szemle/Hungarian Psychological Review. (HU ISSN 0025-0279) **4035**
Magyar Radiologia. (HU ISSN 0025-0287) **3360**
Magyar Sebeszet. (HU ISSN 0025-0295) **3381**
Magyar Statisztikai Szemle see Hungary. Kozponti Statisztikai Hivatal. Statisztikai Szemle **4574**
Magyar Statisztikai Zsebkonyv. (HU ISSN 0133-5847) **4578**

Magyar Szo Naptara. (YU ISSN 0541-9344) **1781**
Magyar Textiltechnika. (HU ISSN 0025-0309) **4621**
Magyar Tortenelmi Szemle/Hungarian Historical Review/Revista Historica Hungara. (AG ISSN 0300-3817) **2374**
Magyar Traumatologia, Orthopedia es Helyreallito-Sebeszet/Hungarian Traumatology, Orthopaedy and Restorative Surgery. (HU ISSN 0025-0317) **3310**
Magyar Tudomany/Hungarian Science. (HU ISSN 0025-0325) **4323**
Magyar Tudomanyos Akademia. Agrartudomanyok Osztalya. Monografiasorozat. (HU ISSN 0076-2423) **106**
Magyar Tudomanyos Akademia. Kozponti Fizikai Kutato Intezet. Evkonyv. see Hungarian Academy of Sciences. Central Research Institute for Physics. Yearbook **3819**
Magyar Tudomanyos Akademia. Matematikai es Fizikai Tudomanyok Osztalya. Kozlemenyek see Alkalmazott Matematikai Lapok **3028**
Magyar Tudomanyos Akademia. Mikrobiologiai Kutato Intezet. Proceedings/Hungarian Academy of Sciences. Research Institute for Microbiology. Proceedings. (HU ISSN 0076-2431) **554**
Magyar Tudomanyos Akademia Konvytaranak Kiadvanyai see Magyar Tudomanyos Akademia Konvytaranak Kozlemenyei **4357**
Magyar Tudomanyos Akademia Konvytaranak Kozlemenyei. (HU) **4357, 2794**
Magyar Tudomanyos Akademia Konyvtara Kezirattaranak Katalogusai. (HU ISSN 0541-9492) **406**
Magyar Vizgazdalkodas/Hungarian Water Supply. (HU) **1924, 4826**
Magyar Zene. (HU ISSN 0025-0384) **3562**
Magyarorszag. (HU ISSN 0230-5828) **4578**
Magyarorszag Allatvilaga/Fauna Hungariae. (HU ISSN 0076-2474) **587**
Magyarorszag Kulturfloraja. (HU ISSN 0076-2482) **509**
Magyarorszag Muemleki Topografiaja. (HU ISSN 0076-2490) **334, 2374**
Magyarorszag Regeszeti Topografiaja. (HU ISSN 0076-2504) **278**
Magyarorszag Tajfoldrajza. (HU ISSN 0076-2512) **2255**
Magyarsag/Hungarian People. (US) **2013**
Maha Bodhi. (II ISSN 0025-0406) **4215, 3772**
Mahaffy & Dodson on Road Traffic see Butterworths Road Traffic Service **2607**
Mahagone Bride. (US) **3067**
Mahajanmer Lagna. (II ISSN 0025-0414) **3772**
Maharaja Sawai Man Singh II Memorial Series. (II) **3527**
Maharaja Sayajirao University of Baroda. Department of Archaeology and Ancient History. Archaeology Series. (II ISSN 0076-2520) **278**
Maharaja Sayajirao University of Baroda. Department of History Series. (II ISSN 0464-5030) **2317**
Maharaja Sayajirao University of Baroda. Journal. (II ISSN 0025-0422) **4323, 2511**
Maharashtra. (II ISSN 0025-0392) **2200**
Maharashtra Chamber Patrika. (II) **819**
Maharashtra Co-Operative Quarterly. (II ISSN 0025-0430) **831**
Maharashtra Economic Development Council. Monthly Economic Digest for Business Executives. (II) **873**
Maharashtra Law Journal. (II ISSN 0025-0465) **2651**

MAHARASHTRA QUARTERLY

Maharashtra Quarterly Bulletin of Economics and Statistics. (II ISSN 0025-0481) **728**
Maharashtra State Budget in Brief. (II ISSN 0076-2555) **1100**
Maharashtra State Financial Corporation. Annual Report. (II ISSN 0076-2563) **790**
Maharashtra State Institute of Education. Research Bulletin. (II) **1646**
Mahasagar. (II ISSN 0542-0938) **1607**
Mahenjodaro. (II ISSN 0025-049X) **2936**
Mahinda. (CE) **4215**
Mahjubah. (IR) **4219**, **4847**
Die Mahnung. (GW ISSN 0025-0511) **3944**
Mahogany. (US ISSN 0149-0729) **334**, **2013**
Mahogany. (RH) **4847**
Mahratta. (II ISSN 0076-2571) **2340**
Maia. (IT ISSN 0025-0538) **1278**, **2936**
Maihaugen. (NO ISSN 0333-0974) **2374**, **278**
Maikuro Shashin. *see* Journal of Micrographics **3792**
The Mail. (SA) **2216**
Mail Advertising Service Association International. Computer Survey. (US) **34**, **1398**
Mail Advertising Service Association International. Fringe Benefit Survey. (US) **41**
Mail Advertising Service Association International. Postscripts. (US) **34**
Mail Advertising Service Association International. Quarterly Business Outlook. (US) **41**
Mail Advertising Service Association International. Ratio Survey. (US) **41**
Mail Advertising Service Association International. Sales Personnel Compensation Survey. (US) **41**
Mail Advertising Service Association International. Wage and Salary Survey. (US) **41**
Mail Bag. (US) **565**
Mail-Coach. (NZ ISSN 0542-0997) **3754**
Mail Order Business *see* Mail Order Selling & Small Business World **1045**
Mail Order Business Directory. (US ISSN 0085-2953) **1144**, **1045**
Mail Order Connection *see* Direct Response Specialist **31**
Mail Order Digest. (US) **1045**, **4090**
Mail Order Product *see* Key (Battleground) **33**
Mail Order Product Guide. (US) **1144**, **34**
Mail Order Rounds International *see* Global Opportunities Advertiser **32**
Mail Order Selling & Small Business World. (US) **1045**
†Mail Order Success Newsletter. (US) **5230**
Mail: The Journal of Communication Distribution. (US) **1353**
Mail Trade. (US ISSN 0025-0562) **1045**
Main Economic Indicators. (NP) **873**
Main Event. (US) **3372**
Main Group Metal Chemistry. (IS ISSN 0334-9195) **1183**
Main Group Metal Chemistry. (UK ISSN 0334-7575) **3412**
†Main Hurdman & Cranstoun News Summary. (US) **5230**
†Main Hurdman & Cranstoun Tax Newsletter. (US) **5230**
Main Line. (UK ISSN 0264-7028) **4711**
Main Line Times. (US) **2228**
†Main Street Journal. (US) **5230**
Main Street Memorandum. (US) **4412**
Maine. Arts Commission. Newsletter. (US) **2511**, **334**
Maine. Bureau of Property Taxation. Annual Report. (US) **1100**
Maine. Department of Human Services. Population Estimates for Minor Civil Divisions by County. (US) **3984**
Maine. Department of Human Services. Vital Statistics. (US) **3993**
Maine. Department of Labor. Bureau of Labor Standards. Characteristics of Work-related Injuries & Illnesses. (US) **987**
Maine (Machias). (US) **2228**
Maine. State Library. Special Subject Resources in Maine. (US ISSN 0091-0759) **2772**
Maine Administrative Procedure. (US) **2652**, **4066**
Maine Agricultural Experiment Station. Annual Report. (US) **106**, **446**, **1962**
Maine Agricultural Experiment Station. Miscellaneous Report. (US ISSN 0734-9564) **106**
Maine Agricultural Experiment Station. Technical Bulletin. (US ISSN 0734-9556) **106**
Maine - Anjou International. (CN ISSN 0823-4604) **221**
Maine Antique Digest. (US ISSN 0147-0639) **258**
Maine Archaeological Society, Inc. Newsletter *see* M A S Newsletter **278**
Maine Archeological Society Bulletin. (US) **278**
Maine Bar Journal. (US ISSN 0885-9973) **2652**
Maine Beverage Journal. (US ISSN 0025-0716) **383**
Maine Business Indicators. (US ISSN 0025-0619) **873**
Maine Business Newsletter. (US) **819**
Maine Civil Remedies. (US) **2702**
Maine Coast Fisherman *see* National Fisherman **2046**
Maine Construction Wage Rates. (US) **987**
Maine Cooperative Extension Service. Forestry Facts *see* Yankee Woodlot **2111**
Maine Criminal Practice. (US) **2714**
Maine Enterprise. (US) **678**
Maine Entry. (US) **2772**, **4132**
Maine Environment. (US) **1491**
Maine EnvironNews. (US ISSN 0161-2107) **1962**
Maine Evidence. (US) **2652**
Maine Fish and Wildlife. (US ISSN 0360-005X) **1491**
Maine Geologist. (US) **1571**
†Maine Historical Society. Research Series. (US) **5230**
Maine Historical Society Quarterly. (US ISSN 0163-1152) **2413**
Maine Invites You. (US) **4775**
Maine Jury Instruction Manual. (US) **2652**
Maine Labor Market Digest. (US) **987**
Maine Law Review. (US ISSN 0025-0651) **2652**
Maine Lesbian Feminist Newsletter. (US) **2455**, **4847**
Maine Library Association. Monthly Memo *see* Maine Memo **2772**
†Maine Life Magazine. (US ISSN 0025-0678) **5230**
Maine Manpower *see* Maine Labor Market Digest **987**
Maine Manual on Professional Responsibility. (US) **2652**
Maine Manufacturing Directory. (US) **1144**
Maine Media Directory *see* Burrelle's New England Media Directory (Year) **29**
Maine Memo. (US) **2772**
Maine Motor Transport News. (US) **4745**
Maine, New Hampshire, Vermont TourBook *see* Tourbook: Maine, New Hampshire, Vermont **4790**
Maine Organic Farmer and Gardener. (US ISSN 0891-9194) **106**, **2134**
Maine Potato News. (US) **184**
Maine Press Association Bulletin *see* M P A Bulletin **2572**
Maine Principal. (US) **1729**
Maine Probate Manual. (US) **2715**
Maine Progressive. (US) **3906**, **4442**
Maine Real Estate Guide. (US) **1144**, **4152**
Maine Register: State Yearbook and Legislative Manual. (US) **4090**, **4066**
Maine Scholar. (US) **2936**
Maine Secondary School Principals' Association. Newsletter *see* Maine Principal **1729**
Maine Seine. (US ISSN 0885-307X) **2158**
Maine Sportsman. (US) **4550**
Maine Teacher. (US ISSN 0025-0775) **1646**
Maine Times. (US ISSN 0025-0783) **1962**
†Maine Today Magazine. (US) **5230**
Maine Townsman. (US ISSN 0025-0791) **4090**
Maine Trails. (US ISSN 0047-5548) **1871**
Maine United Methodist. (US ISSN 0745-0273) **4243**
Maine, Vermont and New Hampshire Directory of Manufacturers. (US ISSN 0197-1220) **1145**
Maine Water Utilities Association. Journal. (US ISSN 0025-0805) **4826**
Maine Workers' Compensation Act. (US) **987**, **2652**
Maine Workers Compensation Commission: Appellate Division Decisions. (US) **987**, **2652**
Maineiac Express. (US) **2873**
Mainely Running. (US) **4479**
Mainfraenkische Wirtschaft. (GW) **678**
Mainfraenkisches Jahrbuch fuer Geschichte und Kunst. (GW ISSN 0076-2725) **2374**, **334**
Mainframe Communications Report. (US) **1351**
Mainframe Computing. (US) **1454**
Mainframe Journal *see* Enterprise Systems Journal **1450**
Mainichi Daily News. (JA) **1781**
Mainichi Graphic. (JA ISSN 0025-0813) **2208**
Mainichi Life. (JA) **3805**
Mainland China Monthly. (CH ISSN 0257-9456) **2182**
Mainland China Studies. *see* Chung-Kuo Ta-Lu Yen-Chiu **3880**
Mainline Modeler. (US ISSN 0199-5421) **2438**
Mainly. (UK ISSN 0025-0848) **2936**
Mainly for Seniors - Lambton. (CN) **2276**
Mainly Marketing. (US ISSN 0464-591X) **1045**
Mainosuutiset. (FI ISSN 0025-0864) **34**
Les Mains du C R A L. (SZ) **2288**
Mainstream. (II ISSN 0542-1462) **2200**
†Mainstream (Rutherford). (US) **5230**
Mainstream (Sacramento). (US) **231**
Mainstream (San Diego). (US ISSN 0278-8225) **1738**
†Maintainer. (CN ISSN 0827-5637) **5231**
Maintenance. (FR ISSN 0025-0880) **1018**
Maintenance. (US) **4746**
Maintenance (Newsletter for Professional Truck Driver-Owner) *see* Maintenance **4746**
Maintenance (Newsletter for Professional Truck Equipment Executives) *see* Maintenance **4746**
Maintenance (Newsletter for Professional Truck Equipment Managers) *see* Maintenance **4746**
Maintenance (Newsletter for Professional Truck Equipment Supervisors) *see* Maintenance **4746**
Maintenance and Modernization Supervisor. (US) **2491**
Maintenance Executive. (US) **623**
Maintenance: Managers. (US) **4746**
Maintenance Sales News. (US ISSN 1040-371X) **1045**
Maintenance Supervisor's Bulletin. (US ISSN 0194-5912) **1018**
Maintenance Supplies. (US ISSN 0025-0929) **623**
Maintenance Supplies Annual. (US) **1145**, **623**
Maintenance Supplies Buyers' Guide *see* Maintenance Supplies Annual **1145**
Maintenance Technology. (US ISSN 0899-5729) **4603**
†Maintenance Trends Report. (US) **5231**
Mainzer Geowissenschaftliche Mitteilungen. (GW ISSN 0340-4404) **1572**, **3658**
Mainzer Philosophische Forschungen. (GW ISSN 0076-2776) **3772**
Mainzer Reihe. (GW ISSN 0076-2784) **2936**
Mainzer Romanistische Arbeiten. (GW ISSN 0542-1551) **2828**
Mainzer Studien zur Amerikanistik. (GW ISSN 0170-9135) **2936**, **2828**
Mainzer Studien zur Sprach- und Volksforschung. (GW ISSN 0170-3560) **2828**
Mainzer Zeitschrift. (GW ISSN 0076-2792) **334**, **278**, **2374**
Mairena. (PR) **2997**
Mais. (GW) **184**
Maison de la Chasse et de la Nature. Bulletin d'Information *see* Maison de la Chasse et de la Nature. Revue **4550**
Maison de la Chasse et de la Nature. Revue. (FR) **4550**
Maison de Marie Claire. (FR ISSN 0542-1594) **2187**
Maison - Dieu. (FR ISSN 0025-0937) **4189**, **1646**
Maison et Jardin. (FR ISSN 0025-0945) **2553**
Maison et Jardin Hors Serie. (FR) **2553**
Maison et Travaux. (FR) **623**
Maison Francaise. (FR ISSN 0025-0953) **2553**
Maison Franco-Japonaise. Bulletin. (BE ISSN 0495-7725) **3640**, **2511**, **4379**
Maison Individuelle. (FR) **2553**
Maison Magazine *see* Maison et Jardin Hors Serie **2553**
Maisons d'Enfants et d'Adolescents de France. Album-Annuaire National. (FR ISSN 0076-2814) **1241**, **4107**
Maisons & Decors Mediterranee. (FR ISSN 0180-4561) **2553**
Maitre de Poste Canadien. *see* Canadian Postmaster **2581**
Le Maitre Electricien. (CN ISSN 0025-0988) **1902**
Le Maitre Imprimeur. (CN ISSN 0025-0996) **4002**
Maitre Phonetique *see* International Phonetic Association. Journal **2819**
Maitres. (CN ISSN 0842-9960) **2652**
Maitrise (Edition Chimie). (FR ISSN 1157-6065) **1067**
Maitrise (Edition Generale). (FR ISSN 1157-6049) **1067**
Maitrise (Edition Siderurgie). (FR ISSN 1157-6057) **1067**
Maize. *see* Mielies (Bothaville) **107**
Maize. *see* Mielies (Pretoria) **207**
Maize Abstracts. (UK ISSN 0267-2987) **140**, **16**
Maize News - Mielienuus *see* Mielies (Pretoria) **207**
Maize Quality Protein Abstracts *see* Maize Abstracts **140**
Majalah Administrasi Negara. (IO ISSN 0125-9652) **4066**
Majalah B A T A N. (IO ISSN 0303-2876) **1807**
Majalah Demografi Indonesia. *see* Journal of Indonesian Demography **3984**
Majalah Ekonomis. (IO) **678**
Majalah Fakultas Hukum Universitas Airlangga *see* Yuridika **2696**
Majalah Higene Perusahaan, Kesehatan-Keselamatan Kerja, dan Jaminan Sosial. *see* Indonesian Journal of Industrial Hygiene, Occupational Health-Safety and Social Security **3617**
Majalah Kedokteran Indonesia. (IO ISSN 0377-1121) **3123**
Majalah Kedokteran Surabaya. (IO ISSN 0303-7932) **3123**
Majalah Kesehatan Masyarakat Indonesia. *see* Indonesian Journal of Public Health **4104**
Majalah Perusahaan Gula. (IO ISSN 0541-7406) **4603**
Majalah Universitas Sumatera Utara. *see* University of North Sumatra. Bulletin **1720**
Al-Majalla. (UK ISSN 0261-0876) **2013**

Majalla al-Toubiya al-Arabiya. (SY) 3123
Al-Majallah al-Arabiyyah lil-Idarah/Arab Journal of Administration. (JO ISSN 1010-0709) 4066
Majallah al-Askariyyah. *see* Military Journal 3465
Al-Majallah al-Bahriyyah/Maritime Magazine. (TS) 4732
Al-Majallah al-Ihsa'iyyah al-Misriyyah/ Egyptian Statistical Journal. (UA ISSN 0542-1748) 4578
Al-Majallah al-'Ilmiyyah li-Kulliyyat Usul al-Din wal-Da'wah lil-Zagazig. (UA) 4219
Majallah al-Misriyah li-Ulum al-Aghdhiya. *see* Egyptian Journal of Food Science 3605
Majallah al-Misriyah lil-Nabat. *see* Egyptian Journal of Botany 501
Al-Majallah Al-Misriyyah li-Jirahat al-'Itham. *see* Egyptian Orthopaedic Journal 3307
Al-Majallah al-Tibbiyyah *see* United Arab Emirates. Al-Qiyadah al-Aamah lil-Quwwat al-Musallihah. Majallah al-Tibbiyyah 3159
Majallah-i Fizik/Iranian Journal of Physics. (IR ISSN 0254-9611) 3824, 366, 1754
Majallah-i Tahqiqat-i Tarikhi/Journal of Historical Research. (IR) 2430, 3640
Majallah-i Zabanshinasi/Iranian Journal of Linguistics. (IR ISSN 0259-9082) 2828
Majallah Pantai. *see* Pan T'ai Hsueh Pao 2833
Majallah Perpustakaan Malaysia. (MY ISSN 0126-7809) 2772
Majallat al-Anshittah al-Tarbawiyyah/ Educational Activities Magazine. (TS) 1646
Majallat al-Azhar. (UA) 4219, 1711
Majallat al-Buhuth al-Ta'rikhiyyah. (LY) 2430, 2334
▼Majallat al-Dirasat al-Filastiniyya/ Journal of Palestine Studies. (LE) 2430
Majallat al-Dirasat al-Sudaniyya. (SJ) 2334, 2430
Majallat al-Imarat lil-'Ulum al-Zira'iyyah/ Emirates Journal for Agricultural Sciences. (TS) 106
Majallat al-Shari'ah wal-Qanun. (TS) 2652, 4219
Majallat al-Sihhah al-Nafsiyyah. *see* Psychiatry Journal 3351
Majallat al-Tibbiyya al-Urdaniyya. *see* Jordan Medical Journal 3113
Majallat al-Tijara wal-Sina'a. *see* Trade and Industry 823
Majallat al-Ulum al-Idariyyah wal-Siyasiyyah. *see* Administration and Political Sciences Review 3870
Majallat al-Wahdah al-Iqtisadiyyah al-Arabiyyah/Arab Economic Union Journal. (JO) 896
Majallat Baladiat al-Ain *see* Al-Ain 4052
Majallat Dirasat al-Khalij Wa-al Jazirah al-Arabiyah. *see* Journal of the Gulf and Arabian Peninsula Studies 2430
Majallat Jami'at al-Imarat *see* Jami'at al-Imarat al-Arabiyyah al-Muttahidah. Majallah 2509
Majallat Kulliyyat al-Aadaab *see* Jami'at al-Imarat al-Arabiyyah al-Muttahidah. Kulliyyat al-Aadaab. Majallah 2509
Majallat Kulliyyat al-Tarbiyyah li-Jami'at Assiut *see* Jami'at Assiut. Kulliyyat al-Tarbiyyah. Majallah 1641
Majallat Kulliyyat al-Ulum *see* United Arab Emirates University. Faculty of Science. Journal 4349
Majallat Markaz al-Buhuth *see* Jami'at al-Imam Muhammad Ibn Sa'ud al-Islamiyyah. Markaz al-Buhuth. Majallah 4219
Majalle-Ye Behdasht-e Iran. *see* Iranian Journal of Public Health 4105
Majalle-Ye Behdasht-e Jahan. (Persian translation of: World Health) (IR) 4107
Majalle-Ye Danesh-e Ruz. (IR) 2873

Majalleh Daneshkadeh Pezeshki. *see* Medical Sciences University of Tehran. School of Medicine. Journal 3128
Majalleh Elmi Peseshki Daneshgahe Elome Pezeshki Ahwaz. *see* Ahwaz University of Medical Sciences. Scientific Medical Journal 3072
Majda. (IR) 3237
†Majed. (US) 5231
Majellan. (AT) 4268
Majesty. (UK) 2158
Maji Review. (TZ) 1792, 4826
Majid. (TS) 1259
Majlis Pengeluar-Pengeluar Getah Malaysia. Lapuran Tahunan. *see* Malaysian Rubber Producers' Council. Annual Report 4292
Majma' al-Lughah al-Arabiyyah. Majallah/Arab Language Academy. Journal. (SY ISSN 0002-4031) 2936, 2828
Major Attractions. Annual Diary. (AT) 3562, 4634
Major Banks, Finance and Investment Companies of Continental Europe *see* Major Financial Institutions of Continental Europe (Year) 1145
Major Chemical and Petrochemical Companies of Europe. (UK) 3691, 1183
Major Companies of Europe. (UK) 1145
Major Companies of the Arab World. (UK) 1145
Major Companies of the Far East. (UK ISSN 0267-2251) 1145
†Major Companies of the United States of America (Year). (UK ISSN 0268-2338) 5231
Major Concepts in Politics and Political Theory. (US ISSN 1059-3535) 3906
▼Major Decisions. (US) 1695
Major Development Projects and Proposals in Queensland. (AT) 678, 954
Major Employers Directory. (US) 819
Major Energy Companies of Europe. (UK) 1792, 1145
Major Energy Companies of Western Europe *see* Major Energy Companies of Europe 1792
†Major Energy Statistics. (AT ISSN 0727-260X) 5231
Major European Author Series. (UK) 2936
Major Financial Institutions of Continental Europe (Year). (UK) 1145, 790
†Major Industrial Nations Executive Report. (US) 5231
Major Industrial Research Unit Studies. (US) 1080
▼Major League Baseball Official (Year) Preview. (US) 4507
Major Media Keys *see* Media News Keys 35
Major Studies and Issue Briefs of the Congressional Research Service. (US) 2652
†Major Trading Bank Statistics. (AT) 5231
Makai. (US ISSN 0745-2896) 1607
†Makasiini. (FI ISSN 0356-8202) 5231
Make a Fresh Start (Year) *see* Kogan Page Mature Students Handbook 1685
Make Money. (US) 954
Makedonika. (GR ISSN 0076-289X) 2374, 278, 2056, 2828
Makedoniki Zoi/Macedonian Life. (GR) 2196
Makedonska Akademija na Naukite i Umetnostite. Letopis. (XN ISSN 0580-4981) 4323, 2511
Makedonska Akademija na Naukite i Umetnostite. Oddelenie za Bioloski i Medicinski Nauki. Prilozi/Macedonian Academy of Sciences and Arts. Section of Biological and Medical Sciences. Contributions. (XN ISSN 0351-3254) 446, 3123

Makedonska Akademija na Naukite i Umetnostite. Oddelenie za Lingvistika i Literaturna Nauka. Prilozi/Macedonian Academy of Sciences and Arts. Section of Linguistics and Literary Sciences. Contributions. (XN ISSN 0350-1914) 2828, 2936
Makedonska Akademija na Naukite i Umetnostite. Oddelenie za Matematicki i Tehnicki Nauki. Prilozi/Macedonian Academy of Sciences and Arts. Section of Mathematical and Technical Sciences. Contributions. (XN ISSN 0351-3246) 4323, 3044
Makedonska Akademija na Naukite i Umetnostite. Oddelenie za Opstestveni Nauki. Prilozi/Macedonian Academy of Sciences and Arts. Section of Social Sciences. Contributions. (XN ISSN 0350-1698) 4379
Makedonski Arhivist. (XN ISSN 0350-1728) 2772
Makedonski Folklor. (XN ISSN 0542-2108) 2056
Makedonski Jazik. (XN ISSN 0025-1089) 2828
Makerere Law Journal. (UG) 2652
Makerere Library Publications *see* Makerere University. Library. Makerere Library Publications 2772
Makerere Medical Journal. (UG ISSN 0025-1119) 3123
Makerere Political Review. (UG) 3906
Makerere University. Albert Cook Library. Library Bulletin and Accession List. (UG) 2794, 3177
Makerere University. Department of Geography. Occasional Paper. (UG ISSN 0075-4722) 2255
Makerere University. Faculty of Agriculture. Handbook. (UG ISSN 0075-4730) 106
Makerere University. Faculty of Agriculture. Technical Bulletin. (UG ISSN 0075-4773) 106
Makerere University. Faculty of Education. Handbook. (UG) 1711
Makerere University. Faculty of Law. Handbook. (UG ISSN 0075-4781) 2652
Makerere University. Library. Library Bulletin and Accessions List. (UG ISSN 0047-3138) 406
Makerere University. Library. Makerere Library Publications. (UG ISSN 0075-4854) 2772
Makerere University. Science Faculty. Handbook. (UG) 4323
Makina Muehendisleri Odasi Haftalik Haberler Gazetesi. (TU ISSN 0025-1135) 1934
Making Better Movies *see* Video Maker 1387
Making of the Twentieth Century. (US) 2317
Making Sense. (IE ISSN 0791-0770) 2873
Makintosh. (IS) 4143, 1470
Makromolekulare Chemie. (SZ ISSN 0025-116X) 1220
Makromolekulare Chemie. Macromolecular Symposia. (SZ ISSN 0258-0322) 1220
Makromolekulare Chemie. Rapid Communications. (SZ ISSN 0173-2803) 1220
Makromolekulare Chemie. Short Communications *see* Makromolekulare Chemie. Rapid Communications 1220
Die Makromolekulare Chemie. Supplement. (SZ ISSN 0253-5904) 1220, 1024
Maksvadaya. (CE) 3906
Maktaba. (KE ISSN 0070-7988) 2772
†Maktabat al-Idarah. (SU ISSN 0256-4971) 5231
Maky/Rataplan. (SZ) 1259
Mal-I-Mic News. (CN) 2013
Mal und Bastelstunde. (GW) 1646
Mala Biblioteka Baletowa. (PL ISSN 0076-2989) 1531
Mala Biblioteka Operowa. (PL) 3562
Mala Ukrstenica. (YU ISSN 0025-1178) 4775
Malacoda. (IT) 2511

MALAWI 6411

Malacologia. (US ISSN 0076-2997) 587
Malacological Review. (US ISSN 0076-3004) 587
Malacological Society of Australia. Journal. (AT ISSN 0085-2988) 587
Malacological Society of Japan. Newsletter *see* Chiribotan 580
Maladies Diarrheiques. *see* Diarrhoeal Diseases 3171
Maladies Tranmises Sexuellement au Canada *see* Sexually Transmitted Diseases in Canada 3249
Maladjustment and Therapeutic Education. (UK ISSN 0264-4614) 1738
Maladosts' (BW ISSN 0025-1208) 2873, 1259
Malagasy Republic. Direction Generale de la Banque des Donnees de l'Etat. Bulletin Mensuel de Statistique. (MG) 728
Malagasy Republic. Direction Generale de la Banque des Donnees de l'Etat. Recensement Industriel. (MG) 728, 4578
Malagasy Republic. Direction Generale de la Banque des Donnees de l'Etat. Situation Economique au 1 Janvier (Year). (MG) 917, 954
Malagasy Republic. Ministere de la Production Agricole et du Patrimoine Foncier. Statistiques Agricoles. Annuaire. (MG) 140
Malagasy Republic. Ministere de la Production Agricole et la Reforme Agraire. Statistiques Agricoles. Annuaire *see* Malagasy Republic. Ministere de la Production Agricole et du Patrimoine Foncier. Statistiques Agricoles. Annuaire 140
Malahat Review. (CN ISSN 0025-1216) 2997
Malaimathi. (II) 2200
Malamute Quarterly. (US) 3712
†Malaria. (UK ISSN 0952-0341) 5231
Malattie Cardiovascolari *see* Giornale Italiano di Cardiologia 3208
Malattie del Tessuto Connettivo. *see* Connective Tissue Diseases 3369
Malawi. National Statistical Office. Transport Statistics. (MW) 4665, 4652
Malawi. Accountant General. Report. (MW ISSN 0076-3020) 1100
Malawi. Department of Agricultural Research. Annual Report. (MW) 106
Malawi. Department of Agriculture. Annual Report *see* Malawi. Department of Agricultural Research. Annual Report 106
Malawi. Department of Civil Aviation. Annual Report. (MW ISSN 0076-3055) 4675
Malawi. Department of Forestry and Game. Report. (MW ISSN 0076-3071) 2104, 1491
Malawi. Department of Information. Year in Review *see* Malawi Handbook 2334
Malawi. Department of Taxes. Annual Report of the Commissioner of Taxes. (MW) 1100
Malawi. Department of Veterinary Services and Animal Industry. Annual Report. (MW ISSN 0076-3365) 4812
Malawi. Economic Planning Division. Mid-year Economic Review. (MW) 4066, 1100
Malawi. Fisheries Department. Fisheries Bulletin. (MW) 2045
Malawi. Geological Survey Department. Annual Report. (MW ISSN 0076-311X) 1572
Malawi. Government Printer. Catalogue of Publications. (MW) 4066
Malawi. Malawi Bureau of Standards. Annual Report and Statement of Accounts. (MW) 3447
Malawi. Malawi Bureau of Standards. Library. Additions to the Library. (MW) 3449

MALAWI. METEORLOGICAL

Malawi. Meteorological Services. Totals of Monthly and Annual Rainfall *see* Malawi. Meteorological Department. Totals of Monthly and Annual Rainfall **3438**

Malawi. Meteorological Department. Monthly Summaries. (MW) **3438**

Malawi. Meteorological Department. Totals of Monthly and Annual Rainfall. (MW) **3438**

Malawi. Ministry of Finance. Budget Statement. (MW ISSN 0076-3195) **1100**

Malawi. Ministry of Finance. Financial Statement. (MW) **1100**

Malawi. Ministry of Justice. Annual Report. (MW ISSN 0076-3160) **2652**

Malawi. Ministry of Justice. Laws Amendments. (MW) **2652**

Malawi. Ministry of Local Government. Annual Report. (MW ISSN 0076-3225) **3906**

Malawi. National Library. Annual Report *see* Malawi. National Library Service Board. Annual Report **2772**

Malawi. National Library Service Board. Annual Report. (MW) **2772**

Malawi. National Library Service. Bulletin. (MW) **2772**

Malawi. National Statistical Office. Annual Statement of External Trade. (MW ISSN 0076-325X) **728**

Malawi. National Statistical Office. Annual Survey of Economic Activities.(MW ISSN 0076-3241) **728**

Malawi. National Statistical Office. Balance of Payments. (MW ISSN 0085-3003) **1100**, **917**

Malawi. National Statistical Office. Compendium of Agricultural Statistics *see* Malawi. National Statistical Office. National Sample Survey of Agriculture **140**

Malawi. National Statistical Office. Compendium of Statistics *see* Malawi Statistical Yearbook **4578**

Malawi. National Statistical Office. Household Income and Expenditure Survey. (MW ISSN 0076-3276) **3993**, **4578**

Malawi. National Statistical Office. Monthly Statistical Bulletin. (MW) **4578**

Malawi. National Statistical Office. National Accounts Report. (MW ISSN 0076-3284) **4578**

Malawi. National Statistical Office. National Sample Survey of Agriculture. (MW ISSN 0076-3292) **140**

Malawi. National Statistical Office. Population Census Final Report. (MW ISSN 0076-3306) **3993**

Malawi. National Statistical Office. Reported Employment and Earnings: Annual Report. (MW) **728**

Malawi. National Statistical Office. Tourist Report *see* Malawi Tourism Report **4800**

Malawi. Office of the Auditor General. Report. (MW ISSN 0076-3314) **1100**

Malawi. Police Force. Annual Report. (MW ISSN 0076-308X) **1518**

Malawi. Post Office Savings Bank. Annual Report. (MW ISSN 0076-3322) **790**

Malawi. Registrar of Insurance. Report. (MW ISSN 0076-3349) **2537**

Malawi: A Guide for the Visitor. (MW) **4775**

Malawi Broadcasting Corporation. Annual Report and Statement of Accounts. (MW) **1376**

Malawi Buyers' Guide. (MW) **917**

Malawi Crafts Buyers Guide. (MW) **917**, **356**

Malawi Development Corporation. Annual Report. (MW) **678**

Malawi Economic Report. (MW ISSN 0076-3101) **873**

Malawi Export *see* Malawi Buyers' Guide **917**

Malawi Gazette Supplement Containing Acts. (MW) **4066**

Malawi Gazette Supplement Containing Bills. (MW) **4066**

Malawi Gazette Supplement Containing Regulations, Rules, Etc. (MW) **4066**

Malawi Government Directory. (MW) **4066**

Malawi Government Gazette. (MW) **4066**

Malawi Handbook. (MW) **2334**

Malawi Housing Corporation. Annual Report and Accounts. (MW ISSN 0581-0892) **2491**

Malawi Journal of Science. (MW) **4323**

Malawi Journal of Social Science. (MW) **4379**

Malawi Law Reports. (MW) **2652**

Malawi Mwezi Uno-Malawi This Month *see* Boma Lathu **847**

Malawi National Library Service Board. Staff Newsletter. (MW) **2772**

Malawi News. (MW) **2209**

Malawi Patent Journal and Trade Marks Journal. (MW ISSN 0025-1267) **3676**

Malawi Railways. Annual Reports and Accounts. (MW ISSN 0076-3330) **4711**

Malawi Railways. Directors' Reports and Accounts *see* Malawi Railways. Annual Reports and Accounts **4711**

Malawi Statistical Yearbook. (MW) **4578**

Malawi Tourism Report. (MW) **4800**

Malawi Treaty Series. (MW ISSN 0076-3357) **2727**

Malawi Youth News. (MW) **1259**

Malawian Geographer. (MW) **2255**

Malay. (PH ISSN 0115-6195) **2511**, **4412**

Malay Literature. (MY ISSN 0128-1186) **2936**

Malaya Law Review *see* Singapore Journal of Legal Studies **2679**

Malayalam Literary Survey. (II) **2873**

Malayalee. (CN) **2013**

Malayan Law Journal. (SI ISSN 0025-1283) **2652**

Malayan Nature Journal. (MY ISSN 0025-1291) **4323**

Malaysia. Department of Inland Revenue. Annual Report/Malaysia. Jabatan Hasil Dalam Negeri. Lapuran Tahunan. (MY) **837**

Malaysia. Department of Mines. Statistics Relating to the Mining Industry of Malaysia. (MY ISSN 0126-818X) **3500**, **4578**

Malaysia. Department of Statistics. Annual Bulletin of Statistics Sabah. (MY ISSN 0080-5203) **4578**

Malaysia. Department of Statistics. Annual Statistical Bulletin Sarawak. (MY ISSN 0127-4732) **4579**

Malaysia. Department of Statistics. Handbook of Oil Palm, Cocoa, Coconut and Tea Statistics Malaysia. (MY) **140**

Malaysia. Department of Statistics. Index of Industrial Production, Malaysia. (MY) **728**, **1080**

Malaysia. Department of Statistics. Manufacturing Statistics, Malaysia. (MY) **728**, **1080**

Malaysia. Department of Statistics. Monthly Bulletin of Statistics, Sabah. (MY) **4579**

Malaysia. Department of Statistics. Monthly Rubber Statistics of Malaysia. (MY) **4294**

Malaysia. Department of Statistics. Monthly Statistical Bulletin, Malaysia/Siaran Perangkaan Bulanan Semenanjung Malaysia. (MY) **4579**

Malaysia. Department of Statistics. Monthly Statistical Bulletin, Sarawak. (MY) **4579**

Malaysia. Department of Statistics. Monthly Tin Statistics of Malaysia. (MY) **3500**, **4579**

Malaysia. Department of Statistics. National Accounts Statistics, Malaysia. (MY) **4579**

Malaysia. Department of Statistics. Quarterly Review of Malaysian Population Statistics. (MY) **3993**

Malaysia. Department of Statistics. Rubber Statistics Handbook, Malaysia. (MY) **4294**

Malaysia. Department of Statistics. Statistics Handbook Malaysia *see* Malaysia. Department of Statistics. Yearbook of Statistics **4579**

Malaysia. Department of Statistics. Statistics of External Trade Sarawak. (MY ISSN 0127-0451) **728**

Malaysia. Department of Statistics. Trade Summary Malaysia. (MY) **728**, **917**

Malaysia. Department of Statistics. Vital Statistics, Peninsular Malaysia. (MY ISSN 0127-466X) **3993**, **4579**

Malaysia. Department of Statistics. Vital Statistics Sarawak. (MY ISSN 0126-9267) **3993**

Malaysia. Department of Statistics. Yearbook of Statistics. (MY ISSN 0127-2624) **4579**

Malaysia. Directory of Timber Trade. (MY ISSN 0126-6330) **1145**, **2116**

Malaysia. Geological Survey. Annual Report. (MY ISSN 0127-0559) **1572**

Malaysia. Jabatan Hasil Dalam Negeri. Lapuran Tahunan. *see* Malaysia. Department of Inland Revenue. Annual Report **837**

Malaysia. Kementerian Buroh dan Tenaga Raayat. Monthly Report. (MY) **987**

Malaysia. Kementerian Pertanian. Bahagian Perikanan. Perangkaan Tahunan Perikanan. *see* Malaysia. Ministry of Agriculture. Fisheries Division. Annual Fisheries Statistics **2045**

Malaysia. Meteorological Service. Annual Summary of Meteorological Observations. (MY) **3438**

Malaysia. Meteorological Service. Summary of Observations for Malaysia *see* Malaysia. Meteorological Service. Annual Summary of Meteorological Observations **3438**

Malaysia. Ministry of Agriculture. Fisheries Division. Annual Fisheries Statistics/Malaysia. Kementerian Pertanian. Bahagian Perikanan. Perangkaan Tahunan Perikanan. (MY ISSN 0126-8856) **2045**

Malaysia. Ministry of Agriculture. Technical and General Bulletins. (MY) **106**, **2045**

Malaysia. Ministry of Agriculture. Technical Bulletins *see* Malaysia. Ministry of Agriculture. Technical and General Bulletins **106**

Malaysia. National Population and Family Development Board. Buletin Keluarga. (MY ISSN 0126-8104) **3984**

Malaysia External Trade Statistics. (MY ISSN 0127-8533) **728**

Malaysia in Brief. (MY ISSN 0301-7095) **2340**

†Malaysia in History. (MY ISSN 0047-5610) **5231**

Malaysia Inter-Religious Organisation. Suara. (MY) **4285**

Malaysia Official Year Book. (MY ISSN 0126-6098) **2340**

Malaysia Year Book *see* Information Malaysia **2338**

†Malaysian Accountant. (SI ISSN 0217-717X) **5231**

Malaysian Agricultural Journal. (MY ISSN 0025-1321) **106**

Malaysian Agricultural Research & Development Institute Report *see* M A R D I Report **105**

Malaysian Agricultural Research and Development Institute Research Journal *see* M A R D I Research Journal **106**

Malaysian Building & Construction. (MY) **623**

Malaysian Business. (MY) **678**

Malaysian Centre for Development Studies Occasional Paper Series *see* M C D S Occasional Paper Series **4379**

Malaysian Chamber of Mines. Council Report. (MY) **3487**

Malaysian Chamber of Mines. Yearbook.(MY) **3487**

Malaysian Chinese Association. Annual Report. (MY ISSN 0542-397X) **2340**

Malaysian Digest. (MY ISSN 0047-5629) **3906**

Malaysian Employers Federation Annual Report. (MY) **987**

Malaysian Forester. (MY ISSN 0302-2935) **2104**

Malaysian International Chamber of Commerce and Industry Digest *see* M I C C I Digest **819**

Malaysian Journal of Economic Studies. (MY ISSN 0126-5350) **678**

Malaysian Journal of Family Studies. (MY ISSN 0128-1232) **3984**

Malaysian Journal of Pathology. (MY ISSN 0126-8635) **3124**

Malaysian Journal of Reproductive Health. (MY) **597**, **4847**

Malaysian Journal of Science/Jernal Sains Malaysia. (MY ISSN 0301-0554) **4323**

Malaysian Journal of Tropical Geography. (MY ISSN 0127-1474) **2255**

Malaysian Mathematical Society. Bulletin. (MY ISSN 0126-6705) **3044**

Malaysian Medical Association Berita M M A *see* Berita M M A **3081**

Malaysian Multi-Purpose Cooperative Society. Review *see* K S M Review **102**

Malaysian National Bibliography/Bibliografi Negara Malaysia. (MY ISSN 0126-5210) **2329**

Malaysian Newspaper Index *see* Indeks Suratkhabar Malaysia **2578**

Malaysian Panorama. (MY ISSN 0126-527X) **2210**

Malaysian Periodicals Index/Indeks Majalah Malaysia. (MY ISSN 0126-5040) **16**

Malaysian Philatelist. *see* Pemungut Setem Malaysia **3755**

Malaysian Pineapple. (MY) **106**

Malaysian Rubber Producers' Council. Annual Report/Majlis Pengeluar-Pengeluar Getah Malaysia. Lapuran Tahunan. (MY ISSN 0126-8309) **4292**

Malaysian Rubber Producers' Council. Monthly Statistical Bulletin. (MY ISSN 0126-5865) **4292**

Malaysian Tatler. (MY ISSN 0128-3022) **2210**

Malaysian Technologist. (MY ISSN 0127-6441) **4603**

Malaysian Tin. *see* Timah Malaysia **5290**

†Malaysian Veterinary Journal. (MY ISSN 0126-5652) **5231**

†Malcolm Hulke Studies in Cinema & Television. (US) **5231**

Malcolm X Lovers Network. (US ISSN 1044-9116) **2013**

Malcriado. (US ISSN 0731-0323) **2586**, **1962**

Male - Female Roles. (US) **244**, **3400**, **4442**, **4860**

Male Insider. (US) **3398**, **2455**

Male Monografie Muzyczne. (PL) **3562**

Maledicta. (US ISSN 0363-3659) **2828**

Maledicta Monitor. (US ISSN 1041-8504) **2828**

Maledicta Press Publications. (US ISSN 0363-9037) **2828**

Maler Praxis. (GW) **334**

Das Maler- und Lackiererhandwerk. (GW ISSN 0343-4079) **356**

Der Maler und Lackierermeister. (GW ISSN 0464-7777) **3654**

Maleren. (NO) **3654**, **623**

Malermesteren *see* Danske Malermestre **3653**

Malertidende. (DK) **3654**

Mali. Direction Nationale de la Statistique et de l'Informatique. Annuaire Statistique. (ML) **728**

Mali. Service de la Statistique Generale, de la Comptabilite Nationale et de la Mecanographie. Bulletin Mensuel de Statistique. (ML) **4579**

Mali. Service de la Statistique Generale, de la Comtabilite Nationale et de la Mecanographie. Statistiques Douanieres du Commerce Exterieur. (ML) **728**
Mali Muso. (ML) **4847**
Malingshu Zazhi/Journal of Potatoes. (CC ISSN 1001-0092) **184**
Mallal's Monthly Digest. (SI ISSN 0961-5563) **2652**
Mallas ja Olut. (FI ISSN 0356-3014) **383**
Mallige. (II ISSN 0025-1399) **2200**
Mallorn. (UK ISSN 0308-6674) **2936**
Malopolskie Studia Historyczne see Studia Historyczne **2390**
Malpractice Lifeline see Medical Liability Monitor **2537**
Malpractice Reporter. (US ISSN 0738-1026) **3124, 2652**
Malpractice Reporter. Anesthesiology Edition see Anesthesiology Malpractice Reporter **3075**
Malpractice Reporter. Hospitals Edition. (US ISSN 0738-1956) **3124, 2652**
Malpractice Reporter. Podiatry Edition. (US ISSN 0749-3495) **3124, 2652**
Malta. Central Office of Statistics. Annual Abstract of Statistics. (MM ISSN 0081-4733) **4579**
†Malta. Central Office of Statistics. Census of Agriculture and Fisheries. (MM) **5231**
Malta. Central Office of Statistics. Census of Industrial Production Report. (MM ISSN 0076-3462) **728**
Malta. Central Office of Statistics. Census of Industrial Production. Summary Tables. (MM) **728**
Malta. Central Office of Statistics. Census of Production Report see Malta. Central Office of Statistics. Census of Industrial Production Report **728**
Malta. Central Office of Statistics. Demographic Review. (MM ISSN 0076-3470) **3993, 3984**
Malta. Central Office of Statistics. Economic Survey. (MM) **873**
Malta. Central Office of Statistics. Economic Trends. (MM) **728**
Malta. Central Office of Statistics. Education Statistics. (MM ISSN 0076-3489) **1678**
Malta. Central Office of Statistics. Quarterly Digest of Statistics. (MM ISSN 0025-1437) **4579**
Malta. Office of Statistics. Census of Agriculture see Malta. Central Office of Statistics. Census of Agriculture and Fisheries **5231**
Malta Trade Directory (Year). (MM) **1145**
Malta Trade Statistics. (MM) **917**
Malta Yearbook. (UK ISSN 0542-4550) **3906, 4775**
Maltechnik-Restauro see Restauro **342**
Maltese Directory: Canada. (CN) **2013, 2413**
Maltese Directory: Canada, United States see Maltese Directory: Canada **2013**
Maltese Herald. (AT) **2013**
Maltese Magazine. (US) **3712**
Ma'lumat-i Ihsa'ivi-i Afghanistan. see Statistical Information of Afghanistan **4587**
Malus. (US) **2134**
Malyatko. (KR ISSN 0025-1453) **1647**
Mama Bears News and Notes. (US) **4847**
Mamane. (II) **1647**
†Mambo Occasional Papers. Socio-Economic Series. (RH) **5231**
Mamiru. (JA) **2448**
Mammal Review. (UK ISSN 0305-1838) **587**
Mammalia. (FR ISSN 0025-1461) **587**
Mammalia Depicta. (GW ISSN 0301-2778) **587**
▼Mammalian Genome. (US ISSN 0938-8990) **446**
Mammalian Species. (US ISSN 0076-3519) **587**

▼Mammary Gland. (UK ISSN 0964-7600) **525**
†Mammary Gland. (UK ISSN 0266-6375) **5231**
Mammillaria Journal. (UK ISSN 0464-8072) **2134**
Mammoth Trumpet. (US ISSN 8755-6898) **278**
Man. (UK ISSN 0025-1496) **244**
▼Man! (US ISSN 1056-5175) **3399, 3400**
Man. (NE) **3399**
Man see Magnum **4550**
Man & Environment. (II ISSN 0258-0446) **244, 278, 3658**
Man and Life. (II) **4442**
Man and Nature/Homme et la Nature. (CN ISSN 0824-3298) **2317, 2936, 3772**
Man and Society. see Manusia dan Masyarakat **244**
Man and Work. see Adam Veavoda **3624**
Man and World. (NE ISSN 0025-1534) **3772**
Man at Arms. (US ISSN 0191-3522) **258, 2438**
†Man, Environment, Space and Time. (US) **5231**
Man - Environment Systems. (US ISSN 0025-1550) **1962, 2491**
Man from Mainz and His Descendants. (US ISSN 0890-8192) **2158**
Man in India. (II ISSN 0025-1569) **244**
Man in New Guinea see Research in Melanesia **247**
Man in Southeast Asia. (AT) **244, 4379**
Man in the Northeast. (US ISSN 0191-4138) **244**
Man - Life & Style. (SI) **3399**
†Man-Made Fibers of Japan. (JA) **5231**
Man-Made Textiles in India. (II ISSN 0377-7537) **4621**
Man to Man Guide. (NE) **2455, 4775**
Mana. (FJ ISSN 0379-5268) **2936**
Mana Annual of Creative Writing see Mana **2936**
Al-Manaal/Hope. (TS) **1738**
Manaar al-Islam. (TS) **4219**
Manab Mon. (II ISSN 0025-1615) **4035, 446, 3344, 4379**
Manage. (US ISSN 0025-1623) **1018**
Manage I T. (US ISSN 1047-7926) **1691**
Managed Accounts Reports. (US ISSN 0197-5382) **954**
Managed Care Law Outlook. (US ISSN 1042-4091) **3124, 2467, 2652**
Managed Care Outlook. (US ISSN 0896-6567) **3124, 2467**
Managed Care Report see Managed Care Outlook **3124**
▼Managed Healthcare News. (US) **2467**
Management. (IE ISSN 0025-164X) **1018**
Management. (NZ ISSN 0025-1658) **1018**
Management. (KE) **1018**
Management. (IT) **1018**
Management see Management Journal **1019**
Management (Baltimore). (US ISSN 0565-7199) **1018, 58**
†Management (Los Angeles). (US ISSN 0278-999X) **5231**
Management (Washington). (US ISSN 0198-8557) **1019**
Management Abstracts. (TR) **728, 16**
Management Abstracts see Indian Management **1012**
Management Abstracts see Management News **1019**
Management Accountant. (II ISSN 0025-1674) **753**
Management Accounter. (CN) **753**
Management Accounting. (UK ISSN 0025-1682) **753**
Management Accounting. (US ISSN 0025-1690) **753**
Management Accounting Research. (UK ISSN 1044-5005) **728**
†Management Advisor. (US) **5231**
Management and Benefit. see Guanli yu Xiaoyi **1011**

Management and Coordination Agency. Statistics Bureau. Research Memoir. see Somu-cho. Tokei-kyoku Kenkyu Iho **4586**
Management and Industrial Relations Series. (UK) **1019**
Management and Labour Studies. (II ISSN 0258-042X) **988**
Management and Marketing Abstracts. (UK ISSN 0308-2172) **728, 16**
†Management and Marketing Update. (AT) **5231**
Management Bibliographies & Reviews. (UK) **728**
Management Bibliographies and Reviews. (UK ISSN 0309-0582) **728, 406**
Management Briefs. (US) **2467, 1067**
Management Communication Quarterly. (US ISSN 0893-3189) **1067, 1339**
Management Consultancy - Financial Survey (Year). (UK) **1145, 837, 1019**
Management Consultant International. (IE) **1019**
Management Consulting. (US) **728, 1019**
Management Contents. (US ISSN 0360-2400) **728, 16**
Management dan Usahawan Indonesia. (IO) **1019**
Management Data List (ML): ML - Marine Corps. (US) **3476**
Management Data List (ML): ML - Navy.(US) **3477**
Management Data List Consolidated (ML-C). (US) **3477**
Management Decision. (UK ISSN 0025-1747) **1019**
Management Development. (BG ISSN 0378-7532) **1019**
Management Development Centre Business Journal see M D C Business Journal **678**
Management Development Centre Productivity News see Productivity News **1025**
†Management Development Guide. (US) **5231**
Management Development Institute Management Journal see M D I Management Journal **1018**
Management Development Series. (UN ISSN 0074-6703) **1019**
Management Diary see Management Review **1020**
Management e Informatica. (IT) **1445**
Management Education & Development.(UK ISSN 0047-5688) **1019, 1711**
Management et Secteur Public. see Public Sector Management **4071**
Management Facetten see Leidinggeven & Organiseren **1018**
†Management Guide to N C. (US ISSN 0076-3624) **5231**
Management Heute see Management Heute und Marktwirtschaft **1019**
Management Heute und Marktwirtschaft. (GW ISSN 0302-6671) **1019, 1045**
Management Horizons. (US ISSN 0025-1836) **1019**
Management Ideas. (II ISSN 0025-1771) **1019**
Management in Government. (II ISSN 0047-570X) **4066, 1019**
Management in Nigeria. (NR ISSN 0025-178X) **1019**
Management in Practice see Management Review **1020**
Management Information Corporation Alert see M I C - Alert **5229**
Management Information Corporation Info see M I C - Info **1351**
Management Information Corporation Tech-Computers see M I C - Tech-Computers **1452**
Management Information Corporation Tech - Data Communications see M I C - Tech - Data Communications **1447**
Management Information Corporation Tech-Retail and Banking see M I C - Tech-Retail and Banking **805**

Management Information Corporation Tech-Telecommunications see M I C - Tech-Telecommunications **1364**
Management Information Corporation Tech-Unix see M I C - Tech-Unix **1478**
Management Information Manual see Croner's Executive Companion **1007**
Management Information Service. (II ISSN 0300-2667) **1019**
Management Information Service Reports see M I S Reports **4090**
Management Information Systems Quarterly see M I S Quarterly **1018**
Management Information Systems Week see M I S Week **5230**
Management International Review. (GW ISSN 0025-181X) **1019**
Management Japan. (JA ISSN 0025-1828) **1019**
Management Journal. (UG ISSN 0300-2144) **1019**
Management Letter see Management Horizons **1019**
Management Magazine. (CH) **1019**
Management Matters. (US ISSN 1054-4275) **1019**
†Management Network Perspective. (US) **5231**
Management News. see Kyung-Young Shinmun **1017**
Management News. (UK) **1019**
Management of the California State Water Project. (US ISSN 0090-5968) **4826**
Management of World Wastes. (US ISSN 0745-6921) **1985**
Management Pakistan. (PK) **1019**
Management Policies & Personnel Law.(US) **1019, 2652**
Management Portfolio. (US ISSN 1050-2114) **1019**
Management Praxis. (SZ) **1019**
Management Professionals Association. Events Diary. (II ISSN 0970-0447) **1019**
Management Professionals Association. Journal. (II ISSN 0970-0447) **1020**
Management Quarterly. (US ISSN 0025-1860) **1020, 1902**
Management Report. (US ISSN 0745-4880) **988**
Management Report - General Services Administration see U.S. General Services Administration. Management Report **4423**
Management Research News. (UK ISSN 0140-9174) **1020**
Management Review. (AT ISSN 0313-0835) **1020**
Management Review. (US ISSN 0025-1895) **1020**
Management Review and Digest see Management News **1019**
Management Review & Inventiveness Report. (US) **1020**
Management Science. (US ISSN 0025-1909) **1020**
Management Services. (UK ISSN 0307-6768) **1020**
Management Services & Production Abstracts. (UK ISSN 0952-4614) **728, 16**
Management Solutions see Supervisory Management (New York) **1029**
Management Today. (UK ISSN 0025-1925) **1020**
Management Today. (MX ISSN 0186-5609) **1020**
Management Topics. (UK) **1398, 1020, 1445**
Management Training and Research Centres in India. Directory. (II) **1020**
Management Training Directory. (UK) **1020**
Management und Krankenhaus. (GW) **2467, 1020**
Management & Seminar. (GW ISSN 0939-7795) **1398**
Management Update see A B A Management Update of Personal Trust & Private Banking **757**
Management Update (Denver). (US ISSN 0196-9455) **3124, 1020**
Management Visions. (US) **827, 1020**
†Management Wissen. (GW ISSN 0340-4137) **5231**

MANAGEMENT WISSEN

†Management Wissen Jahrbuch. (GW) 5231
†Management World. (US ISSN 0090-3825) 5231
Manager see Management Today 1020
Manager. (SJ) 1020
Manager Magazin. (GW ISSN 0047-5726) 1020
Manager Update. (UK ISSN 0957-4212) 1020
Managerial Auditing Journal. (UK ISSN 0268-6902) 1020
Managerial Finance. (UK ISSN 0307-4358) 1020
Managerial Law. (UK ISSN 0309-0558) 988, 2652
Manager's Digest. (II) 1020
Manager's Legal Bulletin. (US) 988, 2652
Manager's Magazine. (US ISSN 0025-1968) 2537
Manager's Manual. (US) 790, 1020, 2652
Manager's Memo see Grounds Management Forum 2129
Manager's Notebook see American Productivity & Quality Center. Notebook 1002
Manager's Report. (US) 4152, 1020
Managing (Pittsburgh). (US) 1020
Managing Automation. (US) 1414, 1020
Managing Automation Literature Review. (US) 1415
Managing Corporate Benefit Plans see Corporate Benefit Plans (Year) 5173
Managing Data Networks. (US) 1452
Managing Employee Benefits. (US) 1067
Managing End-User Computing Report. (US) 827
†Managing for Health. (US) 5231
Managing Housing Letter. (US ISSN 0193-6808) 2491
Managing Information Technology. (US) 1452
Managing L A Ns. (US) 1461
†Managing M I S Personnel. (US) 5231
▼Managing Open Systems. (US) 1445, 1438
Managing Print Sales. (US) 4002, 1020
Managing Service Quality. (UK ISSN 0960-4529) 1020
Managing the Florida Condominium. (US) 2652, 4152
Managing the Human Climate. (US ISSN 0277-7398) 34, 1339
Managing the Information Center Resource see Auerbach Information Management Series 1455
Managing the Nation's Public Lands. (US) 4066
Managing the Product Life Cycle, the Essence of Business. (US) 678
Managing Voice Networks. (US) 1364, 1351
Managing Your Accounting and Consulting Practice. (US) 2652, 753, 1020
Manana. (MX ISSN 0034-9844) 2210
El Manana Daily. (US) 2013, 2228
Mananam Publication Series. (US ISSN 0276-0444) 4217
Manas. (II ISSN 0025-1984) 4035
†Manas. (US ISSN 0025-1976) 5231
Manasota Genealogical Society. Newsletter see Cracker Crumbs 2148
†Manassas Review. (US) 5231
Manasseh/Menasheh. (US) 2013
▼Manay Inder/Our Platform. (MP) 3906
Manchester. (US) 2228
Manchester Chamber of Commerce and Industry. Yearbook see Manchester Regional Business Directory 819
Manchester Free Press. (UK ISSN 0306-5030) 2873
The Manchester Geographer. (UK ISSN 0260-5503) 2255
Manchester Guardian Weekly. (UK ISSN 0025-200X) 2194, 2873
†Manchester Medicine. (UK) 5231
Manchester Memoirs. (UK) 3772

Manchester Papers on Development see Journal of International Development: Policy, Economics, & International Relations 4377
Manchester Polytechnic. Department of Library and Information Studies. Occasional Papers. (UK ISSN 0260-8502) 2772
Manchester Regional Business Directory. (UK) 819
Manchester School of Economic and Social Studies. (UK ISSN 0025-2034) 896, 4379
Manchester Teacher. (UK) 1647
Manchester Training Handbooks. (UK ISSN 0260-4388) 1020, 1711
Manchete see Manchete Esportiva 2175
Manchete Esportiva. (BL) 2175
Manchu Language Studies. see Manyu Yanjiu 3640
Manchu Literature. see Manzu Wenxue 2937
Manchu Studies. see Manzu Yanjiu 2013
Mancunion. (UK) 1317
Mandarin Home. (CN) 2553
Mandate. (US ISSN 0360-1005) 2455
Mandate. (CN ISSN 0225-7068) 4189
Mandate "Special". (CN ISSN 0225-7068) 4189
Mandeville's Used Book Price Guide. (US ISSN 1045-5388) 4132
La Mandragore Qui Chante. (SZ ISSN 0076-3748) 2997
Mandurah Telegraph. (AT) 2172
Mandurah Telegraph and Murray Telegraph see Mandurah Telegraph 2172
Mandy. (UK) 1259
Maneapa. (US ISSN 0734-905X) 3754
Maneggiare. (BG) 1020
Manequim. (BL ISSN 0025-2077) 1292, 2448, 3591
Mang Yuan. (CC) 335, 2936
Mang Zhong. (CC) 2936
Mangiarbere Oggi. (IT) 2477
Mangle. (IO) 2202
Mangren Yuekan/Monthly Journal for the Blind. (CC) 2294
Al-Manhal/Fountain. (TS) 1259
Al-Manhal. (SU) 2873
Manhattan Arts. (US) 335
Manhattan Catalogue. (US) 34
Manhattan Christian College News see M C C News 1316
Manhattan College Engineer. (US ISSN 0025-2093) 1830
▼Manhattan Comic News. (US) 2873
Manhattan Cooperator. (US ISSN 0889-9878) 4152, 2553
†Manhattan Directory of Commercial & Industrial Properties. (US ISSN 0095-0688) 5231
Manhattan Inc. see M 1292
†Manhattan Lawyer. (US ISSN 0893-8911) 5231
Manhattan Living. (US) 2228
Manhattan Magazine. (US) 2228
Manhattan Office Buildings: Downtown. (US) 4152
Manhattan Office Buildings: Midtown. (US) 4152
Manhattan Office Buildings: Midtown South. (US) 4152
Manhattan Poetry Review. (US ISSN 0885-9205) 2997
Manhattan Real Estate Exchange. (US) 4152
Manhattan Review. (US ISSN 0275-6889) 2997
Mani di Fata. (IT) 2448
Manica Post. (RH) 2240
Manifold. (UK ISSN 0025-2166) 2997
Manila Journal. (PH) 2213
Manila Review. (PH) 2936, 335
Manioc Bulletin d'Information see Yuca Boletin Informativo 130
Manipulace, Skladovani, Baleni/Material Handling, Storage Packaging. (CS) 3649
Manipulacion de Materiales en la Industria. (SP ISSN 0210-1513) 623, 1045, 3649

Manipulator. (GW ISSN 0178-3556) 335, 2873
Manipur State Kala Akademi. Quarterly Journal. (II) 2936, 2997
Manipur State Museum. Bulletin. (II) 3527
Manitoba. Cooperative Loans and Loans Guarantee Board. Annual Report. (CN) 790
Manitoba. Department of Cooperative Development. Report see Manitoba Cooperative, Consumer and Corporate Affairs. Annual Report 790
Manitoba. Department of Energy and Mines. Production Statistics and Activity Report see Manitoba. Department of Energy and Mines. Production Statistics Report 3706
Manitoba. Department of Energy and Mines. Production Statistics Report. (CN) 3706, 1799
Manitoba. Economic Development Network. Community Profile Information System. (CN) 873
Manitoba. Energy and Mines. Annual Report Series. (CN) 1792, 3487
Manitoba. Environmental Council. Annual Report. (CN ISSN 0380-9803) 1962
Manitoba. Environmental Council. Studies. (CN ISSN 0380-979X) 1962
Manitoba. Environmental Council. Topics. (CN ISSN 0711-8422) 1962
†Manitoba. Health Services Commission. Annual Report. (CN ISSN 0383-3925) 5231
†Manitoba. Health Services Commission. Annual Statistics. (CN) 5231
Manitoba. Horse Racing Commission. Annual Report. (CN ISSN 0317-7262) 4536
Manitoba. Human Rights Commission. Annual Report. (CN ISSN 0383-5588) 3944
Manitoba. Lotteries Commission. Annual Report see Manitoba Lotteries Foundation. Annual Report 4479
Manitoba. Municipal Employees Benefits Board. Annual Report. (CN ISSN 0706-3792) 988
Manitoba. Public Library Services. Newsletter. (CN ISSN 0706-7798) 2772
Manitoba. Water Services Board. Annual Report. (CN ISSN 0318-3912) 4826
Manitoba Agriculture Yearbook. (CN ISSN 0084-3865) 106
Manitoba and Saskatchewan Tax Reports. (CN) 1100
Manitoba Archaeological Quarterly. (CN ISSN 0705-2669) 278
Manitoba Association for Schooling at Home Newsletter. (CN) 1647
Manitoba Association of Library Technicians Newsletter see M A L T Newsletter 2772
Manitoba Beekeeper. (CN ISSN 0708-3483) 106
Manitoba Business Magazine. (CN ISSN 0709-2423) 1021
Manitoba Cancer Treatment and Research Foundation. Report. (CN ISSN 0076-3802) 3199
Manitoba Co-Operator. (CN ISSN 0025-2239) 106
Manitoba Cooperative, Consumer and Corporate Affairs. Annual Report. (CN) 790, 831
Manitoba Credit Unions: Annual Report see Manitoba Cooperative, Consumer and Corporate Affairs. Annual Report 790
Manitoba Crop Insurance Corporation. Annual Report. (CN ISSN 0542-5395) 2537, 184
Manitoba Decisions - Civil and Criminal Cases. (CN ISSN 0380-0008) 2652, 2702, 2714
Manitoba Decisions - Rules and Statute Citator. (CN ISSN 0824-7293) 2652
Manitoba Energy and Mines. Bibliography Series. (CN) 1551
Manitoba Energy and Mines. Economic Geology Paper Series. (CN) 1572

Manitoba Energy and Mines. Educational Series. (CN) 1572
Manitoba Energy and Mines. Geological Paper. (CN) 1572
Manitoba Energy and Mines. Geological Report. (CN) 1572, 3487
Manitoba Energy and Mines. Open File Report Series. (CN) 1572
Manitoba Energy and Mines. Report of Field Activities. (CN) 1572
Manitoba Farm Vacations Association Brochure see M F V A Brochure 4775
Manitoba Geographical Studies. (CN) 2255
Manitoba Health Libraries Association News see M H L A News 2772
Manitoba Highway News. (CN ISSN 0380-4852) 4746
Manitoba Historical Society. Newsletter. (CN) 2413
Manitoba History. (CN ISSN 0226-5036) 2413
Manitoba Labour - Management Review Committee. Annual Report. (CN ISSN 0076-3853) 988
Manitoba Law Journal. (CN ISSN 0076-3861) 2652
Manitoba Library Association. Newsline. (CN ISSN 0700-3684) 2772
Manitoba Library Association Bulletin see Manitoba Library Association. Newsline 2772
Manitoba Living Guide. (CN) 2553
Manitoba Lotteries Foundation. Annual Report. (CN) 4479
Manitoba Medicine. (CN ISSN 0832-6096) 3124
Manitoba Museum of Man and Nature. Annual Report. (CN) 3527
Manitoba Naturalists Society Bulletin. (CN ISSN 0823-2911) 1491, 509, 565, 4550
Manitoba Petroleum Royalty and Tax Information. (CN) 3706
Manitoba Record Society. Publications. (CN ISSN 0076-3896) 2413
Manitoba Reports. (CN) 2652
†Manitoba Restaurant & Foodservices Roster. (CN) 5231
Manitoba School Library Audio Visual Association Journal see M S L A V A Journal 2772
Manitoba Science Teacher. (CN ISSN 0315-9159) 1647, 4323
Manitoba Ship by Truck Directory. (CN ISSN 0713-8776) 4746
Manitoba Social Science Teacher. (CN ISSN 0315-9116) 1754
Manitoba Social Worker. (CN) 4412
Manitoba Society of Seniors Journal see M S O S Journal 2276
Manitoba Spectra. (CN ISSN 0318-2118) 1754
Manitoba Statistical Review. (CN ISSN 0700-2971) 4579
Manitoba Teacher. (CN) 1647
Manitoba Teachers' Society Update see M T S Update 1646
Manitoba Telephone System Echo see M T S Echo 1364
Manitoba Theatre Centre. House Programme. (CN) 4635
†Manitoba Trade Directory. (CN ISSN 0076-390X) 5231
Manitoba Vacation Guide, Canada see Manitoba Vacation Planner 4775
Manitoba Vacation Planner. (CN) 4775
Manitoba - Winnipeg Building & Construction Trades Council Yearbook. (CN) 623
Manitoban. (CN ISSN 0025-2298) 1317
Manitowoc County Historical Society. Occupational Monographs. (US) 2413
Mankato Poetry Review. (US ISSN 0894-2242) 2997
Mankato State Independent see Mankato State Reporter 1317
Mankato State Reporter. (US) 1317
Mankind see T A J A 250
Mankind Quarterly. (US ISSN 0025-2344) 244, 545, 4035
Mankind Quarterly Monograph Series. (US ISSN 0076-4116) 244
Manley Family Newsletter. (US ISSN 0883-7805) 2158
Manliness. see Nanzi Han 3399

†Der Mann Magazin. (GW ISSN 0344-5631) **5231**
Manna. (US ISSN 0886-5957) **2997**
Manna. (JM) **4189**
Manna. (UK) **4225**
Manned Undersea Science and Technology Program see U.S. National Oceanic and Atmospheric Administration. Manned Undersea Science and Technology Program; Report **1839**
Mannenmode. (NE) **1292**
Mannesmann Illustrierte. (GW) **837, 988, 1067**
Mannesmann Kienzle Aktuell. (GW) **678**
†Mannesmann Kienzle Kurier. (GW) **5231**
Mannheimer Berichte. (GW ISSN 0934-9472) **1317**
Mannheimer Hefte. (GW) **4090**
Mannheimer Hefte fuer Schriftvergleichung. (GW ISSN 0172-8563) **1518**
Mannheimer Liedertafel. Mitteilungen. (GW) **1299, 3562**
Mannlicher Collector. (US ISSN 0883-6949) **258**
Mannlif. (IC ISSN 1017-3587) **2198**
Mannus see Volksleben **2326**
Manoa. (US ISSN 1045-7909) **2936, 2997**
Manohar Kahaniyan. (II) **2200**
Manohara. (II) **2200**
Manorama. (II) **2200**
Manorama Weekly. (II) **2873**
Manos Unidas. (SP ISSN 0214-5979) **4412**
Manovella. (IT ISSN 0025-2387) **2438, 4695**
Manpower and Human Resources Studies. (US ISSN 0149-080X) **988**
Manpower and Immigration Review: Quebec Region/Revue de la Main d'Oeuvre: Region du Quebec. (CN ISSN 0380-5107) **988**
Manpower and Unemployment Research see Labour, Capital and Society **4378**
Manpower Demonstration Research Corporation. Annual Report. (US) **988**
Manpower Documentation. (II ISSN 0047-5793) **988**
Manpower Information Service see Employment and Training Reporter **1064**
Manpower Journal. (II ISSN 0542-5808) **988**
Manpower Planning see H R Planning Newsletter **1065**
Manpower Requirements and Cost Control at D P Installations. (US) **1452, 988**
Manpower Review. (PK) **988**
Manpower Services Guide. (AT) **4067**
Manresa. (SP) **4189**
Manscape. (US) **2455, 2984**
†Manscape 2. (US) **5231**
Mansfield Historical Society's Magazine. (AT ISSN 0814-5296) **2345**
Mansralo. (GH) **2192**
†Manstyle. (CN) **5231**
Mantap: Majalah Ilmaih P K M I/ Indonesian Association for Secure Contraception. Journal. (Perkumpulan Kontrasepsi Mantap Indonesia (PKMI)) (IO ISSN 0216-4027) **3294, 3381**
Manthan. (II) **4379**
Mantooth Report. (US) **3906**
Mantova. (IT ISSN 0025-2506) **819**
The Manual. (UK ISSN 0958-3548) **1351**
Manual del Instrumentista. (CU) **1830**
Manual Farmaceutico. (AG) **3734**
Manual for Florida Legal Secretaries. (US) **2652**
Manual Medicine see Journal of Manual Medicine **3117**
Manual of Air Force Law - Amendments.(UK) **2735, 3463**
Manual of Employee Taxation. (UK) **1100**
Manual of Foreign Investment in the United States. (US) **954**

Manual of Materials Handling and Ancillary Equipment see Materials Handling Buyers Guide **1047**
Manual of Military Law - Amendments. (UK) **2735, 3463**
Manual of the Dutch Press and Publicity. see Handboek van de Nederlandse Pers en Publiciteit **32**
Manual-State of Maryland see Maryland Manual **4067**
Manuali di Politica Internazionale. (IT) **3965**
Manuel de l' O T A N see N A T O Handbook **3966**
Manuel International de Caoutchouc. see Handbuch der Internationalen Kautschukindustrie **4291**
Manuel International des Plastiques. see Handbuch der Internationalen Kunststoffindustrie **3862**
Manuel Medicin. (DK ISSN 0107-9190) **3124**
Manuelle Medizin. (GW ISSN 0025-2514) **3124**
Manufactured Home Merchandiser. (US) **2491**
Manufactured Home News. (US) **2491, 4775**
Manufactured Housing Newsletter. (US ISSN 0197-1816) **623, 2491**
Manufactured Housing Quarterly. (US) **2491**
†Manufactured Housing Reporter. (US) **5231**
Manufactured Housing Trade Digest. (US) **623, 2491**
Manufacturer. (NZ ISSN 0113-9320) **678**
Manufacturers Agent. (UK ISSN 0025-2522) **837**
Manufacturers' Agents National Association. Rep Letter. (US) **1080**
Manufacturers & Processors Directory (Pierre) see South Dakota Manufacturers & Processors Directory **1153**
Manufacturers Association of Nigeria. Industrial Directory see Nigeria Industrial Directory **1148**
Manufacturers' Bulletin see A C M Bulletin (N.S.W. Edition) **1071**
Manufacturers' Mart. (US) **1080**
Manufacturers' Monthly. (AT ISSN 0025-2530) **1080**
Manufacturers Representatives of America. Newsline. (US) **1080**
Manufacturers' Sales of Commodities. see Denmark. Danmarks Statistik. Varestatistik for Industri **713**
▼Manufacturier. (CN) **1080**
Manufacturing & Management Magazine. (US) **3412**
†Manufacturing and Materials Handling Index. (UK) **5231**
†Manufacturing & Materials Management. (SA) **5231**
†Manufacturing Applications: The D P Manager's Report. (US) **5231**
Manufacturing Automation. (US ISSN 1060-2712) **1045, 1398, 1830**
Manufacturing Automation Protocol Netter see M A P Netter **1351**
Manufacturing Chemist. (UK ISSN 0262-4230) **1856**
Manufacturing Chemist and Aerosol News. (UK ISSN 0025-2557) **1183, 1856**
Manufacturing Clothier. (UK ISSN 0025-2565) **1286**
Manufacturing Confectioner. (US ISSN 0025-2573) **2089**
Manufacturing Confectioner with International Confectioner see Manufacturing Confectioner **2089**
Manufacturing Engineer. (UK) **1830**
Manufacturing Engineering. (US ISSN 0361-0853) **1830, 3020**
Manufacturing Engineering and Management see Manufacturing Engineering **1830**
Manufacturing Engineering and Materials Processing Series. (US) **1080**
Manufacturing Forum see Technology Education Activity Forum **1761**
Manufacturing Ideas for Today's Engineers see M I T E **1934**
†Manufacturing Investment Outlook. (US ISSN 0896-2529) **5232**

Manufacturing Midwest. (US) **1527, 642**
Manufacturing News in Australia see Factory Management **1075**
†Manufacturing Report. (AT ISSN 1031-296X) **5232**
Manufacturing Research and Technology. (NE) **1080**
Manufacturing Review. (SA) **4603**
Manufacturing Review. (US ISSN 0896-1611) **4603, 1080, 3844**
Manufacturing Survey. (US) **1080**
Manufacturing Systems. (US ISSN 0748-948X) **1080**
†Manufacturing Technology Horizons. (US ISSN 0278-4424) **5232**
Manufaktur see Tekstilforum **4624**
Manuscripta. (US ISSN 0025-2603) **2937**
Manuscripta Geodaetica. (GW ISSN 0340-8825) **1592**
Manuscripta Mathematica. (GW ISSN 0025-2611) **3044**
Manuscripts. (US ISSN 0025-262X) **2438, 4132**
Manuscripts of the Middle East. (BE ISSN 0920-0401) **2430, 3640**
Manuscriptum. (RM) **2937**
Manuscrito. (BL ISSN 0100-6045) **3772**
Manushi. (II ISSN 0257-7305) **4860**
Manusia dan Masyarakat/Man and Society. (MY ISSN 0303-3171) **244, 4442**
Manuskripte. (AU ISSN 0025-2638) **2937, 335**
Manutencion y Almacenaje. (SP ISSN 0025-2646) **3020, 1934**
Manutention Emballages/Behandeling Verpakkingen. (BE) **3649**
†Manutenzione. (IT) **5232**
Manx Life. (UK) **2194**
Manx Star. (UK ISSN 0047-5823) **2194**
Many Hands. (US) **3595**
Manyu Yanjiu/Manchu Language Studies. (CC ISSN 1000-7873) **3640, 244**
Manzu Wenxue/Manchu Literature. (CC) **2937, 3640**
Manzu Yanjiu/Manchu Studies. (CC) **2013**
Mao Zedong Zhexue Sixiang Yanjiu/ Studies in Mao Zedong's Philosophical Thought. (CC) **3772**
Maopi Dongwu Siyang/Breeding of Fur-Bearing Animals. (CC ISSN 1000-7407) **2737**
Maori Education Foundation. Annual Report. (NZ ISSN 0076-4280) **1647**
Map and Landscape. see Chizu no Tomo **2245**
Map Collector. (UK ISSN 0140-427X) **2256**
Map Report. (US) **2256, 4132**
Mapam. (IS) **3906**
†Mapamond. (RM) **5232**
Mapenzi ya Mungu. (KE) **4219**
Mapics the Magazine. (US ISSN 0891-7973) **1478**
Mapinduzi Katika Uandishi see Kipepeo **1258**
Maple Leaf Trot see Trot **4538**
Maple Leaves. (UK ISSN 0951-5283) **3754**
Maple Orchard. (CN ISSN 0827-1755) **1470, 1462**
Maple Syrup Digest. (US) **2076**
Mapline. (US ISSN 0196-0881) **2256, 2413**
Die Mappe. (GW ISSN 0025-2697) **3654**
Le Mappe - Cultura e Societa. (IT) **4442**
Mapping Sciences & Remote Sensing. (US ISSN 0749-3878) **2256**
Map's Companion see Chizu no Tomo **2245**
Maqalah-namah-i 'Ulum/Index to Scientific Papers. (IR) **4357, 16, 1845**
†Maquettes Plastique Magazine. (FR) **5232**
Maquiladora. (MX) **819**
Maquinaria Agricola see Agricola XXI **161**
Maquinas & Metais. (BL ISSN 0025-2700) **3020, 3412**

Mar. (SP) **1607**
Mar. (UK) **2997**
Mar see Mar: Vela e Motor **4526**
Mar. (CL ISSN 0047-5866) **4732**
Mar: Vela e Motor. (BL) **4526**
Mar y Pesca. (CU ISSN 0025-2735) **2045**
Mara Institute of Technology. Annual Report/Institut Teknologi Mara. Laporan Tahunan. (MY) **1711**
Maranatha. (SA) **4285**
Maranatha see Agape **5132**
Marang. (BS) **2937**
Marathon. (IE ISSN 0047-5874) **4479**
Marathon Aktuell. (GW) **4550**
Marathon Running see Running Review **5271**
Marathwada University Journal. (II ISSN 0025-2751) **1711, 2511, 4323**
Marauder Times. (US) **1317**
Maravillas & Cuentos. see Merveilles & Contes **2056**
Marbacher Magazin. (GW) **2937, 2997**
Marble Mart Newsletter. (US) **2438**
Marblehead Magazine. (US) **2228**
Marburger Beitraege zum Blindenbildungswesen see Marburger Beitraege Zur Integration Sehgeschaedigter **2294**
Marburger Beitraege Zur Integration Sehgeschaedigter. (GW) **2294**
Marburger Buecherlisten. (GW) **2294, 1738**
Marburger Gemeinschaftsblatt see Blickpunkte **4231**
Marc N U C O M. (AT ISSN 0810-2333) **406**
Marcellia see Cecidologia Internationale **529**
March of Karnataka. (II) **1081**
Le Marche. (BE) **1021**
Marche. (NG) **2169**
Marche de l'Acier see Steel Market **3421**
†Marche de l'Innovation. (FR ISSN 0153-9019) **5232**
Marche des Dechets Industriels. (FR ISSN 0249-5430) **819**
Marche des Emprunts Internationaux en E C U see Bond Market in Luxembourg Francs and in E C U **706**
Marche des Microserveurs: Realites et Perspectives. (FR) **1462**
Marche du Travail. (CN ISSN 0226-2576) **873**
Marche Europeen du Bateau d'Occasion see Bato Loc International **4522**
Marche Financier de Paris. (FR ISSN 0464-9605) **954**
Marche National des Emprunts Obligataires see Bond Market in Luxembourg Francs and in E C U **706**
Marche Romane. (BE ISSN 0542-6669) **2828, 2937**
Marche Suisse des Machines. (SZ ISSN 0025-2840) **3020**
Marches. (FR) **106**
Marches Africains. (FR) **917**
Marches Agricoles-l'Echo des Halles see Marches **106**
Marches Arabes. (FR) **917**
Marches Asiatiques. (FR) **917**
Marches Contrats Investissements see M C I **5229**
Marches Est-Europeens. (FR) **917**
Marches Etrangers - Auslandmaerkte see L'Exportation en Pratique **864**
Marches Europeens des Fruits et Legumes see F E L Actualites **176**
Marches Latino-Americains. (FR) **917**
Marches Publics. (FR ISSN 0542-6685) **4067**
Marches Tropicaux et Mediterraneens. (FR ISSN 0025-2859) **917**
▼Marcheterritorio. (IT) **4442, 1962**
Marco Polo News. (HK) **4775**
Marcolian. (US ISSN 0025-2867) **1317**
Marcom. (UK) **1879, 4732**
Marconi Instruments Contact. (UK) **2524, 1902**
Marconi Review see G E C Journal of Research **1893**
Marconi's International Register. (US ISSN 0076-4418) **1145, 1364**

Mardon Sensai Va Farhange-e Amme-e Iran. *see* Etnologie et Traditions Populaires de l'Iran **2001**
Mare Balticum. (GW ISSN 0542-6758) **4732**, 2374
Marechal. (FR ISSN 0025-2891) **2374**
Maree de France. (FR ISSN 0025-2905) **2045**
Marelli *see* Ercole Marelli **1891**
Maresianer. (GW) **2190**
Marfleet Society Newsletter. (UK ISSN 0308-6380) **2158**
Marg. (Il ISSN 0025-2913) **335**
Marg Art Magazine *see* Marg **335**
Marga. (CE ISSN 0047-5912) **4379**, 2340
†Marga Institute. Progress Report. (CE) **5232**
Margaret Gee's Media Guide. (AT ISSN 0158-0779) **1145**, 1339
Margin. (Il ISSN 0025-2921) **678**
Margin. (UK ISSN 0950-5091) **2873**
Marginales. (BE ISSN 0025-293X) **2937**
Marginalien. (GW ISSN 0025-2948) **2873**
Marginalita e Societa. (IT) **4412**
Margo's Market Monitor. (US) **954**
Margraf on the Markets *see* On the Markets **958**
Margriet. (NE ISSN 0025-2956) **4847**
Mari *see* Mari-Board Converting News **3649**
Mari Annales de recherches Interdisciplinaires. (FR) **278**, 2828
Mari-Board Converting News. (US) **3649**, 3663
Mari-Board Converting News Espanol. (US) **3649**, 3663
Mari Jo. (IO) **3463**
Mari Sandoz Heritage. (US) **2937**
Maria. (SZ ISSN 0025-2972) **4268**
Maria. (PO) **4847**
†Maria. (CN ISSN 0381-7946) **5232**
Maria Cristina de Montemayor Editore La Storia delle Cose *see* M C M : La Storia delle Cose **356**
Maria Nostra Luce. (IT) **4268**
Mariaberger Brief. (GW) **1738**
Mariaberger Heime. (GW) **1738**
Mariage Quebec. (CN) **4847**
Mariager Aarbog. (DK ISSN 0108-2868) **2374**
Mariages. (FR ISSN 0025-2980) **3067**, 1292
Mariah - Outside *see* Outside (Chicago, 1980) **4553**
Mariahilfer Pfarrbote. (AU ISSN 0025-2999) **4189**
Marian Helpers Bulletin. (US) **4268**
Marian Library Studies. New Series. (US ISSN 0076-4434) **4268**, 2772
Marian Studies. (US ISSN 0464-9680) **4268**
Marianist. (AU ISSN 0025-3014) **4268**
Mariannhill. (AU ISSN 0025-3022) **4189**
Marianum. (IT) **4268**
Marie-Claire. (FR ISSN 0025-3049) **1292**
Marie Claire. (PO) **4847**
Marie Claire 16. (SP) **4847**
Marie Claire - Donnapiu. (IT) **4847**
Marie Claire Japon. (JA) **4847**
Marie Claire - Nederlandse Editie. (NE) **4847**
Marie-France. (FR ISSN 0025-3057) **4847**
Mariemou. (MU ISSN 0047-5920) **4847**, 1260
Marienbad - Tepler Heimatbrief. (GW) **2190**
Marienburger Zeitung. (GW) **2374**
Le Marin. (FR) **2045**, 4732
Marin Sports. (US) **4479**
Marina. (IT) **2984**
Marina. (FI ISSN 0784-5480) **4775**
Marina Dock Age. (US) **4526**
Marina Italiana. (IT ISSN 0025-309X) **4732**
Marina Mercantile. (IT ISSN 0025-3103) **4732**
Marine. (FR) **3463**
Marine Advocate *see* Atlantic Advocate **5140**

Marine Affairs Bibliography. (US ISSN 0226-8361) **2700**, 406
Marine and Aviation Insurance Report. (UK ISSN 0265-8410) **2537**
Marine & Fire Insurance Association of Japan. Fact Book. (JA) **2537**
Marine and Outdoor Trades *see* Marine Trades **4526**
Marine and Petroleum Geology. (UK ISSN 0264-8172) **1572**, 3691
Marine & Recreation News. (US ISSN 0025-312X) **4526**, 4550
Marine Behaviour and Physiology. Sections A & B. (US ISSN 0091-181X) **446**, 2045
Marine Biological Association of India. Journal. (Il ISSN 0025-3146) **446**, 1607
Marine Biological Association of the United Kingdom. Journal. (UK ISSN 0025-3154) **447**
Marine Biological Association of the United Kingdom. Occasional Publications. (UK) **447**
Marine Biological Laboratory Lectures in Biology *see* M B L Lectures in Biology **446**
Marine Biological Laboratory Science *see* M B L Science **5229**
Marine Biological Station of Asamushi. Bulletin. (JA) **447**
Marine Biology. *see* Biologiya Morya **432**
Marine Biology. (GW ISSN 0025-3162) **447**
Marine Biology Research Centre. Bulletin. (LY) **2045**
Marine Biotechnology Abstracts *see* A S F A Marine Biotechnology Abstracts **1549**
Marine Board of Hobart. Annual Report.(AT) **4732**
Marine Bulletin. (US) **1491**, 2045
Marine Business *see* Boating Industry **4523**
Marine Chemistry. (NE ISSN 0304-4203) **1547**, 1183
Marine Conservation News. (US) **1491**, 1607
Marine Corps Gazette. (US ISSN 0025-3170) **3463**
Marine Data Base. (US) **1348**, 1357
Marine Digest *see* Marine Digest and Transportation News **4732**
Marine Digest and Transportation News.(US) **4732**
Marine Ecology. (GW ISSN 0173-9565) **447**
†Marine Ecology. (US) **5232**
Marine Ecology-Progress Series. (GW ISSN 0171-8630) **555**
Marine Engine Guide. (AT) **4732**
Marine Engineering Digest/Revue Technique Maritime. (CN ISSN 0824-734X) **1830**, 1607
Marine Engineering - Log *see* Marine Log **4732**
†Marine Engineering Log Marine Directory. (US) **5232**
Marine Engineers Review. (UK ISSN 0047-5955) **4732**
Marine Environmental Research. (UK ISSN 0141-1136) **1977**, 447, 1607
Marine Equipment Catalog. (US) **4732**
Marine Equipment Directory. (CN) **4732**
Marine Fish Management. (US) **2045**
Marine Fish Monthly. (US ISSN 1045-3555) **447**
Marine Fisheries. *see* Haiyang Yuye **2042**
Marine Fisheries. *see* Morsko Ribarstvo **2046**
Marine Fisheries Review. (US ISSN 0090-1830) **2045**, 1491
Marine Geodesy. (US ISSN 0149-0419) **2256**
Marine Geology. (NE ISSN 0025-3227) **1607**
Marine Geology and Geophysics. *see* Morskaya Geologiya i Geofizika **1608**
Marine Geophysical Researches. (NE ISSN 0025-3235) **1607**, 1592
Marine Geotechnology. (US ISSN 0360-8867) **1607**, 1830
Marine Industry News. (AT) **4732**

Marine Industry Retailer. (US) **1045**, 4732
Marine Invertebrates of Scandinavia. (NO ISSN 0542-6987) **447**, 587
Marine Laws. (US) **2735**, 1607
Marine Librarians' Association Newsletter *see* Maritime Information Association Newsletter **2772**
Marine Log. (US ISSN 0897-0491) **4732**
Marine Mammal News. (US) **587**
Marine Mammal Protection Act of 1972 Annual Report. (US ISSN 0196-4690) **1491**
Marine Mammal Science. (US ISSN 0824-0469) **1607**, 587
Marine Management Holdings. Transactions. (UK) **4665**, 16
Marine Marchand: Etudes et Statistiques *see* Transport Maritime: Etudes et Statistiques **4667**
Marine Marchande *see* Journal de la Marine Marchande et du Transport Multimondal **4730**
Marine Microbial Food Webs. (FR ISSN 0297-8148) **555**, 1599, 1607
Marine Micropaleontology. (NE ISSN 0377-8398) **3658**
Marine Mining. (US ISSN 0149-0397) **3487**
Marine News. (UK ISSN 0025-3243) **4732**
Marine Newsletter. (US) **3619**
Marine Observer. (UK ISSN 0025-3251) **3438**, 1607
Marine Ornithology. (SA ISSN 1018-3337) **565**
Marine Park Research Stations. Bulletin/Kaichu Koen Kenkyujo Kenkyu Hokoku. (JA) **4323**
Marine Parks Journal. (JA ISSN 0910-4496) **447**, 4550
Marine Policy. (UK ISSN 0308-597X) **1608**, 2735
Marine Pollution Bulletin. (US ISSN 0025-326X) **1978**
Marine Pollution Research Titles. (UK ISSN 0264-8059) **1974**, 16, 1551, 1978
Marine Propulsion International. (UK ISSN 0143-3709) **4732**
Marine Radio Station Master File. (US) **1348**, 1357
Marine Recreational Fisheries. (US ISSN 0161-522X) **2045**
Marine Research in Indonesia. (IO ISSN 0079-0435) **1608**
Marine Research Institute. Journal. *see* Rit Fiskideildar **2048**
Marine Resource Bulletin. (US) **2045**, 1608
†Marine Resource Economics. (US) **5232**
Marine Retailers Association of America Newsletter *see* M R A A Newsletter **4526**
Marine-Rundschau. (GW ISSN 0025-3294) **4732**, 3463
†Marine-Rundschau International. (GW ISSN 0720-8103) **5232**
Marine Science Contents Tables. (UN ISSN 0025-3308) **466**, 1551, 2051
Marine Sciences. *see* Haiyang Kexue **1604**
▼Marine Stores Merchandising. (US ISSN 1051-5100) **4526**, 4621
Marine Structures, Design, Construction and Safety. (UK ISSN 0951-8339) **1935**
Marine Technology. (US ISSN 0025-3316) **4732**
Marine Technology Research Abstracts & Index (MATRAX)/Senpaku - Kaiyo Kogaku Gijutsu Bunken Sokuho. (JA ISSN 0286-7427) **4665**
Marine Technology Society Journal. (US ISSN 0025-3324) **1608**, 1830
Marine Textiles. (US ISSN 0885-9949) **4621**
Marine Textiles Buyers' Guide. (US) **4621**
Marine Trades. (CN ISSN 0705-8993) **4526**
Marineblad. (NE ISSN 0025-3340) **3463**
▼MarineFacts. (US ISSN 1052-4282) **4498**, 16, 729, 4526

Marineforum. (GW ISSN 0172-8539) **4732**
Marinehistorisk Tidsskrift. (DK ISSN 0106-5122) **2374**, 3463
The Mariner. (US) **4526**
Mariner's Mirror. (UK ISSN 0025-3359) **2317**, 1608
Mariners Weather Log. (US ISSN 0025-3367) **3438**, 1608
Marines. (US) **3463**
Mario Negri Institute for Pharmacological Research. Monographs. (US ISSN 0085-3100) **3734**
Marion. (NE ISSN 0025-3383) **3591**
Marion Military Institute Bulletin. (US) **3487**
Marion Zimmer Bradley's Fantasy Magazine. (US ISSN 0897-9286) **3012**
Marionnettes et Marionnettistes. *see* Puppenspiel und Puppenspieler **4637**
Maritimas Informacion Comercial. (SP) **4732**
Maritime *see* Maritime Newsletter **4733**
Maritime Abstracts. (US) **4665**, 16, 4732
Maritime Advisor Arbitration Award Digest. (US ISSN 0894-6698) **4732**, 2735
Maritime Advisor Marine Operations Reporter. (US) **4732**, 2735
Maritime Anthropological Studies *see* M A S T **244**
Maritime Association of the Port of New York. Newsletter *see* Maritime Association of the Port of New York - New Jersey. Newsletter **4733**
Maritime Association of the Port of New York - New Jersey. Newsletter. (US) **4733**
Maritime Bank of Israel. Annual Report/ Bank ha-Sapanut le-Yisrael. Annual Report. (IS ISSN 0076-4515) **790**
Maritime China. *see* Zhongguo Haiyun **4742**
Maritime Command Trident. (CN ISSN 0025-3413) **3463**, 58
Maritime Defence. (UK) **3463**
Maritime Defence International *see* Maritime Defence **3463**
Maritime Exchange Bulletin *see* Maritime Association of the Port of New York - New Jersey. Newsletter **4733**
Maritime Farmer and Co-Operative Dairyman. (CN ISSN 0025-343X) **106**, 201
Maritime Food & Beverage. (CN) **2076**, 383
Maritime Guide. (UK ISSN 0264-6420) **4733**
†Maritime History Group Newsletter. (CN) **5232**
Maritime Industries. (CN ISSN 0826-8371) **3691**
Maritime Information Association Newsletter. (UK) **2772**
Maritime Information Review. (NE ISSN 0920-1610) **4733**
Maritime Law Reporter. (US) **2735**
Maritime Law Review. *see* Recht der Schiffahrt **4736**
Maritime Lawyer *see* Tulane Maritime Law Journal **2735**
Maritime Lumber Bureau Log *see* M L B Log **2116**
Maritime Magazine. *see* Al-Majallah al-Bahriyyah **4732**
Maritime Management *see* Shipcare & Maritime Management **4738**
†Maritime Monographs and Reports. (UK ISSN 0307-8590) **5232**
Maritime Newsletter. (US ISSN 0161-9373) **4733**, 2586
Maritime Personal Injury Report. (US ISSN 0894-5713) **4733**, 2735
Maritime Policy and Management. (UK ISSN 0308-8839) **4733**
▼Maritime Report. (CN) **4733**
Maritime Reporter and Engineering News. (US ISSN 0025-3448) **4733**
Maritime Research. Weekly Newsletter. (US) **4665**
Maritime Research Charter Newsletter. (US) **4733**, 917

Maritime Sediments and Atlantic Geology see Atlantic Geology **1555**
†Maritime Story of Southern England. (UK) **5232**
Maritime Studies. (AT ISSN 0726-6472) **4733, 2045, 4526**
Maritime Studies and Management see Maritime Policy and Management **4733**
Maritime Telegraph & Telephone. Bulletin. (CN) **1364**
Maritime Worker. (AT ISSN 0025-3464) **4733, 2586**
Maritimer. (CN ISSN 0704-0652) **2288**
Maritimes. (US ISSN 0025-3472) **1608**
Maritimes Tax Reports. (CN ISSN 0047-5971) **1100**
Marius. (FR) **2873**
Marjolaine. (FR ISSN 0025-3480) **3463**
Marjorie Mayrock Center for Soviet and East European Research. Occasional Papers. (IS) **3965**
Mark. (US ISSN 0735-1240) **2873, 2317**
Mark-Age Inform-Nations see M A I N **3595**
Mark Markkinoinnin Ammattilehti. (FI) **1045, 34**
Mark og Montre. (DK ISSN 0105-0826) **2374**
Mark Siegel and Associates Washington Insider. (US) **3906, 4067**
Mark Twain Journal. (US ISSN 0025-3499) **2937**
Mark Twain Society Bulletin. (US ISSN 0272-6378) **2937**
Markaz al-Malik Faisal lil-Buhuth wal-Dirasat al-Islamiyyah. Fihris al-Makhtutat/King Faisal Center for Research and Islamic Studies. Manuscript Catalogue. (SU) **3647, 406**
Al-Markazi. (MK) **790**
Markeds-bog. (DK ISSN 0107-8305) **1116**
Markedsfoering. (DK) **34, 1045**
Markedsfoering. (NO ISSN 0025-3502) **1045**
Markedskalender see Markeds-bog **1116**
Markee. (US) **3513, 1385**
Marken-Handbuch der Werbung und Etatbetreuung. (GW ISSN 0085-3119) **34**
Marker see Arch **1303**
Marker. (US) **3344**
Markers. (US ISSN 0277-8726) **335, 2119**
Market. see Dzah Dzeel **1038**
Markel. (FR ISSN 0025-3537) **2560, 642**
Market & Waterfront. (CN ISSN 0835-5592) **2178**
Market Bulletin. (PK ISSN 0464-9974) **1081**
Market Bulletin Fruit and Vegetables. (BE) **831, 2134**
Market Charts. (US) **954**
†Market Chronicle. (US ISSN 0360-1773) **5232**
Market Commentary see Canada. Agriculture Canada. Market Outlook and Analysis Division. Policy Branch. Market Commentary **82**
Market Cycle Investing. (US ISSN 0892-3272) **954**
Market-Espresso. (IT ISSN 0391-7398) **837**
Market Express. (US) **954**
Market Facts. (AT ISSN 0818-1152) **4160, 2500**
Market Facts (Northern Territory: Darwin - Alice Springs). (AT) **4160, 2500**
Market Fare see Bill of Fare **2062**
Market Frontier News. (US ISSN 0025-3553) **201**
Market Guide Continental Europe. (US ISSN 0278-6524) **955, 1145**
Market Guide Over-the-Counter Stock Edition. (US) **955, 1506**
▼Market Insight. (US) **4507, 678**
Market Intelligence. (UK) **1045**
Market Intelligence Bulletin. (II) **917**
Market Journal. see Shichang **1053**

Market Logic. (US ISSN 0162-6817) **955**
Market Maker see Market Maker Body Fashions - Intimate Apparel **1293**
Market Maker Body Fashions - Intimate Apparel. (US) **1293**
Market Mania Newsletter. (US) **955**
Market Month. (US) **955**
Market News. (US) **955**
Market Place see Retail Market **1052**
Market Place. (SA) **2216**
Market Profiles. (US) **4152**
Market Progress Executive Report. (CN) **955**
†Market Report for China's Textile and Apparel Industry. (HK) **5232**
Market Research Abstracts. (UK ISSN 0025-3596) **729, 16**
Market Research Europe. (UK ISSN 0308-3446) **1045**
†Market Research Facts and Trends. (CN ISSN 0025-360X) **5232**
Market Research Great Britain. (UK ISSN 0308-3047) **1045**
†Market Research Report. (US) **5232**
Market Research Society. Journal. (UK ISSN 0025-3618) **1045**
Market Research Society. Survey. (UK) **1045**
Market Research Society. Yearbook. (UK ISSN 0076-4523) **1045**
Market Research Society Newsletter see M R S Newsletter **1045**
Market Screen. (US) **955**
▼Market Share in Japan (Year). (JA) **678**
Market Share Reporter. (US) **729**
Market Share Reports. (US) **729**
Market Signals. (US) **955**
Market Statistics Key Plant Directory see Marketing Economics Key Plants **1046**
Market Summary. (HK) **790**
Market Timing Report. (US) **873**
Market Trader see World's Fair **1057**
Market Trends & Prospects for Chemical Products. (UN) **1183**
Market Vane's Bullish Consensus. (US ISSN 0889-7840) **955**
Market Watch. (US ISSN 0277-9277) **383**
†Market Watch. (US) **5232**
Market Weekly. see Shichang Zhoubao **839**
Marketeer. (US) **1045**
†The Marketer. (US) **5232**
Marketers Forum Magazine. (US ISSN 0888-3327) **1116**
Marketfacts see L I M R A's Marketfacts **2536**
Marketing. (BL ISSN 0025-3634) **1045**
Marketing. (CN ISSN 0025-3642) **1045, 34**
Marketing. (UK ISSN 0025-3650) **1045**
Marketing. (YU ISSN 0581-1023) **1045**
Marketing. (GW ISSN 0344-1369) **1045, 34**
Marketing. (NZ ISSN 0111-9044) **1045**
Marketing. (US) **1045**
Marketing Actualidad. (SP) **1045**
Marketing Adult Education. (US) **1685**
Marketing Advents. (US) **1046**
Marketing AdVents. (US) **1046**
†Marketing - Advertising - Research Newsletter. (US) **5232**
Marketing & Advertising Law Reporter see Marketing Law Reporting Service **2653**
Marketing & Distribution Abstracts. (UK ISSN 0305-0661) **729, 17**
Marketing and Management Monthly see Marketology Quarterly **1021**
Marketing and Media Decisions see Media Week **35**
Marketing & Purchasing Management. (II) **1046, 1021**
Marketing and Research Today. (NE ISSN 0923-5957) **1046**
†Marketing Boards in Canada/Offices de Commercialisation au Canada. (CN ISSN 0527-6624) **5232**
Marketing California and Arizona Melons. (US) **154**
Marketing California Apricots. (US) **154**

Marketing California Asparagus. (US) **154**
Marketing California Broccoli. (US) **154**
Marketing California Carrots. (US) **154**
Marketing California Cauliflower. (US) **154**
Marketing California Celery. (US) **154**
Marketing California Cherries. (US) **154**
Marketing California Dried Fruits see Marketing California Dried Fruits: Prunes, Raisins, Dried Apricots & Peaches **5232**
†Marketing California Dried Fruits: Prunes, Raisins, Dried Apricots & Peaches. (US ISSN 0094-2510) **5232**
Marketing California Grapes for Fresh Use. (US) **154**
Marketing California Nectarines, Peaches, and Plums. (US) **154**
Marketing California Onions. (US) **154**
Marketing California Ornamental Crops. (US ISSN 0190-7492) **154**
Marketing California Pears for Fresh Market. (US ISSN 0098-8928) **154**
Marketing California Potatoes, Featuring the Kern District. (US) **154**
Marketing California Selected Fruits. (US) **154**
Marketing California Strawberries. (US) **154**
Marketing California Tomatoes. (US) **154**
Marketing Classes for Adults see Course Trends **1683**
Marketing Communications see Potentials in Marketing **1050**
†Marketing Communications Report. (US) **5232**
Marketing Digest see Marketology Quarterly **1021**
Marketing Economics Guide see M E I Marketing Economics Guide **1044**
Marketing Economics Institute, Ltd. Marketing Economics Guide see M E I Marketing Economics Guide **1044**
Marketing Economics Key Plants. (US ISSN 0098-1397) **1046**
Marketing - Espansione. (IT) **1046**
Marketing Exchange. (US) **1046**
Marketing Flash. (SZ) **1046**
Marketing for Lawyers Newsletter. (US) **2652, 1046**
Marketing Forum see Quarterly Review of Marketing **5265**
Marketing Grocery Products. (US) **2093**
†Marketing Guide. (US ISSN 0093-125X) **5232**
†Marketing - High Tech Trends. (US) **5232**
Marketing in Europe. (UK ISSN 0025-3723) **1046**
Marketing in Nigeria. (NR ISSN 0331-8400) **1046**
Marketing Information Network Fax see M I N Fax **2491**
Marketing Intelligence & Planning. (UK ISSN 0263-4503) **1046**
Marketing Jahrbuch Wein. (GW) **383, 678**
Marketing Journal. (GW ISSN 0025-3774) **1046**
Marketing Law Reporting Service. (CN) **2653, 1046**
Marketing Letter. (AT) **1046**
▼Marketing Letters. (US ISSN 0923-0645) **1046**
Marketing Lettuce from Salinas-Watsonville, Other Central California Districts, and Colorado. (US) **154**
Marketing Library Services see M L S **2772**
Marketing Mix. (SA) **1046**
Marketing New Media. (US ISSN 0743-2178) **1376, 1046**
Marketing News. (US ISSN 0025-3790) **1046**
The Marketing Pulse. (US) **1046, 34**
Marketing Recreation Classes. (US) **1695, 1046**
Marketing Research. (US ISSN 1040-8460) **1046**
Marketing Research Association, Inc. Research Service Directory see M R A Research Service Directory **1044**

MAROC FRUITS 6417

Marketing Research Review. (US ISSN 0885-3312) **1046**
Marketing Research Study of the Housewares Industry. (US) **729, 873, 4579**
Marketing Review. (US) **1046**
Marketing Science. (US ISSN 0732-2399) **1046, 1021**
Marketing Science Institute. Newsletter. (US ISSN 0733-5768) **1046**
Marketing Science Institute. Publications. (US) **1047**
Marketing Science Institute. Research Briefs see Marketing Science Institute. Research Priorities **1047**
Marketing Science Institute. Research Priorities. (US) **1047**
Marketing Selected California Vegetables. (US) **154**
Marketing to Women. (US ISSN 1047-1677) **1047, 4847**
Marketing Treasures. (US ISSN 0895-1799) **2773**
Marketing Trends see A I M - Age of Information Marketing **1032**
†Marketing Trends (Des Plaines). (US) **5232**
Marketing Update. (US ISSN 0732-555X) **729, 17**
Marketing Week. (UK) **1047**
Marketletter. (UK) **3734**
Marketnews. (CN) **1047**
Marketology Quarterly. (II) **1021, 1047**
Marketplace. (SA) **1047**
Marketplace. (US) **4695**
Marketplace Magazine. (US ISSN 1054-2264) **678**
Marketpro. (US) **1462**
Marketpulse. (US) **1047**
†Marketrends. (US) **5232**
Markets Abroad. (US ISSN 0894-3540) **3793, 1047, 1506**
†Markets for Coal and Coal Technologies. (US) **5232**
Markets Year Book. (UK ISSN 0076-4647) **1047**
Marketsearch. (UK) **729**
Marketwatch. (SI) **790**
Das Markgraeflerland. (GW) **2374, 2190**
Markham Business Journal see York Region Business Journal **700**
Markham Month. (CN) **2178**
†Markham Review. (US ISSN 0025-3820) **5232**
Markham - York Region Business Journal see York Region Business Journal **700**
Marking Industry. (US ISSN 0025-3839) **1059**
Marking Products & Equipment. (US) **1059**
Markings. (US) **4189**
Markkinointiviestinta. (FI ISSN 0785-1324) **1047**
Das Markscheidewesen. (GW) **3488**
Marksisticke Teme see Teme **4454**
Markt. (AU ISSN 0025-3863) **1047**
Markt & Technik. (GW ISSN 0344-8843) **1903**
Markt fuer Klassische Automobile und Motorraeder. (GW ISSN 0175-9698) **4695**
Markt Intern. (GW) **1047**
†Markt Kommunikation. (GW) **5232**
Markt und Chance. (GW) **678**
Marktforschungsreport. (GW ISSN 0177-7173) **1047**
Marktgefluester. (GW) **3906**
Marktgilde Gids. (NE) **917**
Marktwirtschaft see Management Heute und Marktwirtschaft **1019**
Markwick Midden. (CN ISSN 0821-3275) **2158**
Marlin. (US ISSN 0749-2006) **4526, 2045**
Marlowe Society of America Newsletter. (US) **2937**
Marmi Graniti Pietre. (IT ISSN 0047-603X) **623, 303**
Marmomacchine. (IT) **3488**
Marmor. (IT ISSN 0393-876X) **335, 303**
†Maroc Agricole. (MR) **5232**
Maroc Business. (MR) **678**
Le Maroc en Chiffres. (MR ISSN 0076-4655) **4579**
Maroc Fruits. (MR) **184**

Maroc Magazine. (MR) 873
Maroc Repression. (FR) 3906
Maroon Tiger. (US) 1317
Marote Hamishtarah. (IS) 1518
Marple's Business Newsletter. (US ISSN 0279-960X) 873
Marquee. (US ISSN 0025-3928) 4635, 303
Marquee (Norwalk). (US ISSN 0364-815X) 3562
Marques Benelux Recueil. see Merkenblad Benelux 3676
Marques Internationales. (UN ISSN 0025-3936) 3676
Marquetarian. (UK ISSN 0025-3944) 2438
Marquetry Society of America, Inc. Newsletter see M S A Newsletter 640
Marquette. (US) 1711
†Marquette Engineer. (US ISSN 0025-3960) 5232
Marquette Journal. (US ISSN 0025-3979) 2937
Marquette Law Review. (US ISSN 0025-3987) 2653
▼Marquette Sports Law Journal. (US ISSN 1057-6029) 4479, 2653
Marquette Today see Marquette 1711
Marquette Tribune. (US ISSN 0025-3995) 1317
Marriage and Divorce Today see Behavior Today 4013
Marriage & Family. see Hunyin yu Jiating 3067
†Marriage & Family. (US ISSN 0276-4512) 5232
Marriage and Family Law Agreements. (US) 2718, 3067, 4442
Marriage and Family Living see Marriage & Family 5232
Marriage & Family Review. (US ISSN 0149-4929) 4442, 3067
Marriage Encounter see Marriage Magazine 3067
Marriage Magazine. (US) 3067, 4412, 4847
Marriage Partnership. (US ISSN 0897-5469) 3067
†Marriott Portfolio. (US) 5232
Marroquineria Espanola. (SP) 2737
Mars en Mercurius. see Mars et Mercure 3463
Mars et Mercure/Mars en Mercurius. (BE) 3463
Mars in Cathedra. (NE ISSN 0025-4029) 3463
Mars-Magazine. (BE ISSN 0025-4037) 642
Marschenrat zur Foerderung der Forschung im Kuestengebiet der Nordsee. Nachrichten. (GW) 4323, 509, 1572, 2256
Marshall County Historical Quarterly. (US) 2413
Marshall Islands Journal. (XE ISSN 0892-2098) 2213
†Marsyas. (US ISSN 0076-4701) 5232
Mart see Revue Municipale 2495
†Mart. (US ISSN 0025-4061) 5232
▼Martha Stewart Living. (US) 2448
Martha's Vineyard Magazine. (US) 2997
Martial Arts. see Wulin 4497
Martial Arts and Fitness see Taekwondo World 4494
Martial Arts Training see M A Training 4479
Martin and Morley Motor Vehicle Law (Queensland). (AT ISSN 0728-5981) 2653, 4719
Martin & Osa Johnson Safari Museum Wait-a-Bit News. (US) 3527, 2773, 3513
Martin Classical Lectures. (US ISSN 0076-471X) 1278
Martin Luther see Evangelischer Bund in Oesterreich. Schriftenreihe 4237
Martin Luther King, Jr. Center for Non-Violent Social Change Newsletter. (US) 3944
Martin Luther King, Jr. Memorial Studies in Religion, Culture and Social Development. (US ISSN 1052-181X) 4189, 2413

Martin-Luther-Universitaet Halle-Wittenberg. Wissenschaftliche Zeitschrift. (GW ISSN 0438-4385) 4442, 2828
Martin-Luther-Universitaett Halle-Wittenberg. Wissenschaftliche Zeitschrift. Mathematisch-Naturwissenschaftliche Reihe. (GW) 3044, 4323
Martin Mystere. (IT) 2985
Martin Newsletter. (US) 2158
Martindale-Hubbell Bar Register of Preeminent Lawyers. (US) 2653
Martindale-Hubbell Law Directory. (US ISSN 0191-0221) 2653
Martindale: the Extra Pharmacopoeia. (UK) 3734
Martin's Annual Criminal Code. (CN ISSN 0527-7892) 2714
Martin's Related Criminal Statutes. (CN ISSN 0710-1805) 2714, 1518
Martlet. (CN) 1317
Marturion. (US ISSN 0047-6064) 4285
Martyrdom and Freedom see Martyrdom and Resistance 2013
Martyrdom and Resistance. (US ISSN 0892-1571) 2013, 2374, 3945
Martyrs' Shrine Message. (CN) 4269, 2317
Maruee. (Il ISSN 0025-4096) 2200
Marvels & Tales. see Merveilles & Contes 2056
Marx Centouno. (IT) 3906
Marx Karoly Kozgazdasagtudomanyi Egyetem: Doktori Ertekezesek see Budapesti Kozgazdasagtudomanyi Egyetem: Doktori Ertekezesek 707
Marx Karoly Kozgazdasagtudomanyi Egyetem Folyoirata. Egyetemi Szemle see Budapesti Kozgazdasagtudomanyi Egyetem Folyoirata. Aula 648
Marx Karoly Kozgazdasagtudomanyi Egyetem Oktatoinak Szakirodalmi Munkassaga see Budapesti Kozgazdasagtudomanyi Egyetem Oktatoinak Szakirodalmi Munkassaga 707
Marx Memorial Library. Quarterly Bulletin see Marx Memorial Library Bulletin 2773
Marx Memorial Library Bulletin. (UK) 2773, 3906
Marxism and the Mass Media. (US ISSN 0098-9509) 1339, 406, 3906
†Marxism Today. (UK ISSN 0025-4118) 5232
Marxismo Oggi. (IT) 3906
†Marxismus a Soucasnost. (CS ISSN 0323-164X) 5232
Marxismus heute. (GW ISSN 0934-649X) 3906
Marxist Criticism. see Critica Marxista 3889
Marxist Veekshanam. (Il ISSN 0025-4134) 3906, 4379
Marxistische Blaetter. (GW ISSN 0542-7770) 3906
Marxistische Studien. (GW ISSN 0171-3698) 4379, 3906
Marxistisk Antropologi. (DK) 244, 3906
Marxistiskt Forum. (SW ISSN 0047-6072) 3906
Mary Wollstonecraft Journal see Women & Literature 2976
Maryknoll see Maryknoll Fathers and Brothers 4269
Maryknoll Fathers and Brothers. (US) 4269
†Maryland. Attorney General. Attorney General's Digest. (US) 5232
Maryland. Correctional Training Commission. Annual Report see Maryland. Police and Correctional Training Commissions. Report to the Governor, the Secretary of Public Safety and Correctional Services, and Members of the General Assembly 1518
†Maryland. Department of Human Resources. Information Pamphlet. (US ISSN 0092-9476) 5232
†Maryland. Department of Legislative Reference. Update. (US) 5232

Maryland. Department of Natural Resources. Annual Activities Report. (US) 1491
Maryland. Division of Correction. Report. (US ISSN 0362-9198) 1518
Maryland. General Assembly. Subject Index to Bills Introduced in the Session. (US) 2653, 406
Maryland. Geological Survey. Archeological Studies. (US) 278
Maryland. Geological Survey. Bulletin. (US ISSN 0076-4779) 1572
Maryland. Geological Survey. Educational Series. (US ISSN 0076-4787) 1572
Maryland. Geological Survey. Information Circular. (US ISSN 0076-4795) 1572
Maryland. Geological Survey. Report of Investigations. (US ISSN 0076-4809) 1572
Maryland. Geological Survey. Water Resources Basic Data Report. (US ISSN 0076-4817) 4826
Maryland. House of Delegates. Journal of Proceedings. Regular Session. (US) 2653
Maryland. Police and Correctional Training Commissions. Report to the Governor, the Secretary of Public Safety and Correctional Services, and Members of the General Assembly. (US) 1518
Maryland. Police Training Commission. Annual Report see Maryland. Police and Correctional Training Commissions. Report to the Governor, the Secretary of Public Safety and Correctional Services, and Members of the General Assembly 1518
Maryland. Senate. Journal of Proceedings. Regular Session. (US) 2653
†Maryland. State Archives. Newsletter. (US) 5232
Maryland. State Department of Legislative Reference. Synopsis of Laws Enacted by the State of Maryland. (US ISSN 0093-0520) 2653
Maryland. State Highway Administration. Traffic Trends. (US ISSN 0094-6265) 4719
The Maryland Agenda. (US) 819
Maryland Air Management Administration. Data Report. (US) 1978
Maryland Air Quality Data Report see Maryland Air Management Administration. Data Report 1978
†Maryland and Delaware Genealogist. (US ISSN 0025-4150) 5233
Maryland Bar Journal. (US ISSN 0025-4177) 2653
Maryland Birdlife. (US ISSN 0147-9725) 565
Maryland Builder. (US) 2492, 623
Maryland Business & Living Journal. (US) 678
Maryland Business Journal see Maryland Business & Living Journal 678
†Maryland C.P.A. Quarterly. (US ISSN 0025-4185) 5233
Maryland Crime Control Directory. (US) 1518
Maryland Crime Report see Maryland Crime Control Directory 1518
Maryland Documents. (US ISSN 0195-3443) 4081
▼Maryland Employment Law Letter. (US ISSN 1049-9377) 2711, 988
Maryland English Journal. (US ISSN 0542-8343) 1754, 2937
Maryland Farmer. (US) 106
Maryland Fruit Grower. (US ISSN 0025-4223) 2134
Maryland Genealogical Society Bulletin. (US ISSN 0542-8351) 2158
Maryland Herpetological Society. Bulletin. (US ISSN 0025-4231) 587
Maryland High-Tech Directory (Year). (US) 4323
Maryland Historian. (US ISSN 0025-424X) 2317

Maryland Historical Magazine. (US ISSN 0025-4258) 2414
Maryland Historical Society. News and Notes. (US) 2414
Maryland Home and Apartment Journal see Maryland Builder 2492
Maryland Horse. (US ISSN 0025-4274) 4536
Maryland Journal of Contemporary Legal Issues. (US) 2653
Maryland Journal of International Law and Trade. (US) 2727, 917
Maryland Labor Market Dimensions. (US) 988
†Maryland Law Forum. (US) 5233
Maryland Law Review. (US ISSN 0025-4282) 2653
Maryland Lawyer's Manual. (US ISSN 0542-836X) 2653
Maryland Magazine. (US ISSN 1040-7936) 2228
Maryland Magazine of Genealogy see Maryland Historical Magazine 2414
Maryland Manual. (US ISSN 0094-4491) 4067
Maryland Master Plumber see Maryland P H C C News & Views 2301
Maryland Medical Journal. (US ISSN 0886-0572) 3124
Maryland Motorist. (US) 4775, 4695
Maryland Music Educator. (US ISSN 0025-4312) 3562, 1647
Maryland Naturalist. (US ISSN 0096-4158) 447, 509, 587
Maryland Nurse. (US ISSN 0047-6080) 3282
Maryland P H C C News & Views. (Maryland Plumbing-Heating-Cooling Contractors, Inc.) (US) 2301
Maryland P T A Bulletin. (US ISSN 0025-4339) 1647
Maryland Pharmacist. (US ISSN 0025-4347) 3734
Maryland Plumbing-Heating-Cooling Contractors, Inc. Maryland P H C C News & Views see Maryland P H C C News & Views 2301
Maryland Poetry Review. (US) 2997
Maryland Purchasor. (US) 1047
Maryland Register. (US ISSN 0360-2834) 4067, 2653
Maryland Register. State Contract Supplement. (US ISSN 0360-2834) 4067, 2653
Maryland Report. (US ISSN 1042-1564) 4067, 679, 3906
Maryland State Chamber of Commerce. Newsletter see The Maryland Agenda 819
Maryland State Dental Association. Journal. (US ISSN 0025-4355) 3237
Maryland Tomorrow. (US) 2492, 3984, 4826
Maryland Travel Scene see Maryland Travelgram 4775
Maryland Travelgram. (US) 4775
Maryland-Washington Beverage Journal.(US) 383
Maryland-Washington-Delaware Beverage Journal see Maryland-Washington Beverage Journal 383
Marynka: Mercados de Mexico en Accion. (MX) 837
Mas. (US ISSN 1046-5634) 2013
Mas Caminos. (MX) 4652
Masa Acher. (IS) 4775
Masada. (CN ISSN 0025-4428) 2013, 3965
Masalah Pendidikan. (MY ISSN 0126-5024) 1647
Masaryk University. Faculty of Sciences. Scripta Biologia. (CS) 447
Masaryk University. Faculty of Sciences. Scripta Chemia. (CS) 1183
Masaryk University. Faculty of Sciences. Scripta Geographia. (CS) 4323
Masaryk University. Faculty of Sciences. Scripta Geologia. (CS) 1572
Masaryk University. Faculty of Sciences. Scripta Mathematica. (CS) 3044
Masaryk University. Faculty of Sciences. Scripta Physica. (CS) 3824
Masarykova Univerzita. Filozoficka Fakulta. Sbornik Praci. A: Rada Jazykovedna. (CS) 2828
Masarykova Univerzita. Filozoficka Fakulta. Sbornik Praci. B: Rada Filozoficka. (CS) 3772

Masarykova Univerzita. Filozoficka Fakulta. Sbornik Praci. C: Rada Historicka. (CS) **2374**
Masarykova Univerzita. Filozoficka Fakulta. Sbornik Praci. D: Rada Literarnevedna. (CS) **2937**
Masarykova Univerzita. Filozoficka Fakulta. Sbornik Praci. E: Rada Archeologicko-Klasicka. (CS) **278**, 1278, 2374
Masarykova Univerzita. Filozoficka Fakulta. Sbornik Praci. F: Rada Umenovedna. (CS) **335**
Masarykova Univerzita. Filozoficka Fakulta. Sbornik Praci. G: Rada Socialnevedna. (CS) **897**, 2586, 4442
Masarykova Univerzita. Filozoficka Fakulta. Sbornik Praci. H: Rada Hudebnevedna. (CS) **3562**
Masarykova Univerzita. Filozoficka Fakulta. Sbornik Praci. I: Rada Pedagogicka - Psychologicka. (CS) **4035**, 1647
Masarykova Univerzita. Filozoficka Fakulta. Sbornik Praci. K: Rada Germanisticko - Anglisticka. (CS) **2828**, 2937
Masarykova Univerzita. Filozoficka Fakulta. Sbornik Praci. L: Rada Romanisticka. (CS) **2828**, 2937
Die Maschine. (GW ISSN 0340-5737) **3020**
Maschine und Werkzeug. (GW ISSN 0025-4452) **3020**
Maschinen & Stahlbau see Machinery and Steel **3019**
Maschinen Anlagen Verfahren. (GW ISSN 0343-043X) **1021**
Maschinen Report International. (AU) **3020**
Maschinen und Stahlbau. (AU) **3020**, 623
Maschinen- und Stahlbauindustrie in Oesterreich see Maschinen und Stahlbau **3020**
Maschinenbau. (SZ) **3020**
Maschinenbau und Fertigungstechnik der U d S S R. (GW ISSN 0025-4487) **3020**
†Maschinenbautechnik. (GW ISSN 0025-4495) **5233**
Maschinenmarkt. (GW ISSN 0341-5775) **3020**
Maschinenschaden. (GW ISSN 0025-4517) **3020**
Maschinenwelt - Elektrotechnik. (AU ISSN 0025-4533) **3020**, 1903
Maschinenwelt und Elektrotechnik see Maschinenwelt - Elektrotechnik **3020**
MascuLines. (US ISSN 0025-4541) **1286**
Mashabei Einosh. (IS ISSN 0792-0970) **1067**, 988
Al-Masha'il. (QA) **1260**
Al-Mash'al/Torch. (QA) **3691**
Mashhad University. Faculty of Letters and Humanities. Journal. (IR) **2937**
Mashinostroitel' (RU ISSN 0025-4568) **3020**
Mashinovedenie. (RU ISSN 0025-4576) **3020**
Mashonaland Chamber of Industries. Annual Report. (RH) **819**
Mashriq. (UK ISSN 0025-4584) **2013**
Mashriq. (US) **2013**
Masiform D. (US) **3012**, 1376
Masihi Avaza. (II ISSN 0376-6608) **4189**
Masinstvo. (YU ISSN 0461-2531) **3020**
Al-Masirah. (BA) **2873**
Mask. (AT ISSN 0726-9072) **1754**, 4635
Maskayu. (MY ISSN 0126-771X) **2116**
Maske und Kothurn. (AU ISSN 0025-4606) **4635**
Maskin - Aktuelt. (DK) **3412**
Maskinbefaelet. (SW ISSN 0025-4622) **4733**
Maskinentreprenoeren. (SW) **623**, 2119, 4107
MaskinKontakt. (SW ISSN 0345-7788) **3020**, 4719
Maskinmesteren. (DK ISSN 0047-6102) **3020**

Maskinstationen see Maskinstationen og Landbrugslederen **163**
Maskinstationen og Landbrugslederen. (DK ISSN 0109-0291) **163**
Al-Maskukat. (IQ ISSN 0002-4058) **3600**
Maslichnye Kul'tury. (RU ISSN 0207-2165) **185**
Mason Clinic. Bulletin see Virginia Mason Clinic Bulletin **3161**
Mason Contractors Association of America Info see M C A A Info **623**
Mason Family Newsletter. (US ISSN 0895-4496) **2158**
†Mason Memories. (US ISSN 0735-4754) **5233**
Masonic World. (US) **1299**
Masonry. (US ISSN 0025-4681) **623**
Masonry Design West. (US) **623**
Masonry Society Journal. (US ISSN 0741-1294) **623**, 1871
Masque. (AT ISSN 0025-469X) **4635**, 1531
†Masque. (UK ISSN 0025-4711) **5233**
Mass Comm Review. (US) **1339**
Mass Culture. see Qunzhong Wenhua **2182**
Mass High Tech. (US ISSN 8750-2100) **4603**
Mass Market Retailers see M M R **1018**
Mass Media in India. (II) **1376**
Mass Retailers' Executive Perquisite Report. (US) **988**
Mass Spectrometry. (UK ISSN 0305-9987) **1183**, 3824
†Mass Spectrometry. (SZ) **5233**
Mass Spectrometry Bulletin. (UK ISSN 0025-4738) **1202**, 17
Mass Spectrometry Reviews. (US ISSN 0277-7037) **3855**
Mass Transit. (US ISSN 0364-3484) **4653**
Massachusetts. Department of Employment and Training. Employment and Wages State Summary. (US) **729**, 988
Massachusetts. Department of Public Health. Annual Report. (US) **4107**
Massachusetts. Division of Employment Security. Employment and Wages in the Establishments Subject to the Massachusetts Employment Security Law. see Massachusetts. Department of Employment and Training. Employment and Wages State Summary **729**
Massachusetts. Division of Fisheries and Game. Annual Report see Massachusetts. Division of Fisheries and Wildlife. Annual Report **1491**
Massachusetts. Division of Fisheries and Wildlife. Annual Report. (US) **1491**
Massachusetts Agricultural Statistics see Massachusetts Agriculture (Year) Annual Report **140**
Massachusetts Agriculture (Year) Annual Report. (US) **140**
Massachusetts Appellate Tax Board Reporter. (US) **1101**
Massachusetts Archaeological Society. Bulletin. (US ISSN 0148-1886) **278**
Massachusetts Archaeological Society. Newsletter. (US) **278**
Massachusetts Association of School Committees Bulletin. (US) **1729**
Massachusetts Attorney Discipline Reports. (US) **2653**
Massachusetts Beverage Journal. (US) **383**
Massachusetts Business and Economic Report. (US) **679**
Massachusetts C P A Review. (US ISSN 0025-4770) **753**
Massachusetts Collections Manual. (US) **2653**, 679
Massachusetts College of Pharmacy. Bulletin. (US ISSN 0025-4789) **3734**, 1317
Massachusetts Collegian see Massachusetts Daily Collegian **1317**
Massachusetts Condominium Law. (US) **2715**
Massachusetts Corporate Tax Manual. (US) **1101**
▼Massachusetts Criminal Defense. (US) **2714**, 1518

Massachusetts Daily Collegian. (US ISSN 0025-4797) **1317**
Massachusetts Dental Society. Journal. (US ISSN 0025-4800) **3237**
Massachusetts Dental Society News see M D S News **3237**
Massachusetts Directory of Manufacturers. (US ISSN 0195-5810) **1145**
Massachusetts Discrimination Law Reporter. (US) **2653**, 2711
▼Massachusetts Employment Law Letter. (US ISSN 1049-2062) **2711**, 988
Massachusetts Facts. (US ISSN 0894-3427) **1781**
Massachusetts Family Law Journal. (US) **2718**
Massachusetts Foreign Language Association MA F L A Newsletter see MA F L A Newsletter **2828**
Massachusetts Foreign Language Bulletin see MA F L A Newsletter **2828**
Massachusetts General Hospital Corp. News see M G H News **2467**
Massachusetts General Hospital Utility Multi-Programming System Computing see M U M P S Computing **1431**
Massachusetts General Hospital Utility Multi-Programming Systems News see M U M P S News **1431**
Massachusetts Golfer. (US) **4507**
Massachusetts Historical Society see N **2415**
Massachusetts Historical Society. Proceedings. (US ISSN 0076-4981) **2414**
Massachusetts Housing Finance Agency. Annual Report. (US ISSN 0076-499X) **2492**
Massachusetts Housing Finance Agency Newsletter see M H F A Newsletter **2491**
Massachusetts Institute of Technology. Flight Transportation Laboratory. F T L Reports see Massachusetts Institute of Technology. Flight Transportation Laboratory. F T L Reports and Memoranda **58**
Massachusetts Institute of Technology. Flight Transportation Laboratory. F T L Reports and Memoranda. (US) **58**, 4675
Massachusetts Institute of Technology. Research Laboratory of Electronics. Quarterly Progress Report see Massachusetts Institute of Technology. Research Laboratory of Electronics. R L E Progress Report **1903**
Massachusetts Institute of Technology. Research Laboratory of Electronics. R L E Progress Report. (US ISSN 0163-9218) **1903**, 1339
Massachusetts Law Review. (US ISSN 0163-1411) **2653**
Massachusetts Lawyer Weekly. (US) **2653**
Massachusetts Magazine. (US) **1711**
Massachusetts Municipal Association Directory. (US ISSN 0361-2090) **4090**
Massachusetts Music News. (US ISSN 0147-2550) **3562**, 1647
Massachusetts Nurse. (US ISSN 0163-0784) **3282**
Massachusetts Nurses Association. Bulletin see Massachusetts Nurse **3282**
Massachusetts Parents Association for the Deaf and Hard of Hearing Today see M P A D Today **2288**
Massachusetts Primer. (US) **1101**
Massachusetts Professional Engineer see New England Engineering Journal **1831**
Massachusetts Review. (US ISSN 0025-4878) **2873**
Massachusetts Sales and Use Tax Manual. (US) **1101**, 2653
Massachusetts Service Directory see George D. Hall's Massachusetts Service Directory **1136**
Massachusetts Spy. (US) **3754**
Massachusetts State Labor Council A F L - C I O Newsletter. (US ISSN 0025-4894) **2586**

Massachusetts Studies in English. (US ISSN 0047-6161) **2937**
Massachusetts Tax Primer see Massachusetts Primer **1101**
Massachusetts Taxpayers Foundation. State Budget Trends. (US) **729**, 4081, 4579
Massachusetts Teachers Association Today see M T A Today **1646**
Massachusetts Wildlife. (US ISSN 0025-4924) **1491**
Massachusetts Workers' Compensation Practice Manual. (US) **2711**, 988
Massachusetts Workers' Compensation Reports. (US) **2711**, 988
Massage and Healing Arts Magazine see Massage Magazine **3805**
Massage Magazine. (US ISSN 1045-4268) **3805**
Massage Therapy Journal. (US ISSN 0895-0814) **3805**, 3372, 3395, 4835
Al-Massar. (UK) **3906**
MassBay Antiques. (US ISSN 0279-8344) **258**
Masscitizen. (US ISSN 8750-8516) **1962**, 1506
Massenet Society. Newsletter. (UK) **3562**
Masseur. (AU) **3124**
Massey Collectors News - Wild Harvest. (US ISSN 0897-215X) **258**
Massey University. Centre for Agricultural Policy Studies. Agricultural Discussion Paper. (NZ) **154**
Massey University. Centre for Agricultural Policy Studies. Agricultural Policy Proceedings. (NZ ISSN 0111-6339) **154**
Massey University. Centre for Agricultural Policy Studies. Agricultural Policy Paper. (NZ ISSN 0110-5558) **154**
Massey University. Centre for Agricultural Policy Studies. Discussion Paper see Massey University. Centre for Agricultural Policy Studies. Agricultural Discussion Paper **154**
Massey University. Department of Accountancy. Discussion Paper Series see Massey University. Division of Accountancy. Discussion Paper Series **753**
Massey University. Department of Accounting and Finance. Discussion Paper Series see Massey University. Division of Accountancy. Discussion Paper Series **753**
Massey University. Division of Accountancy. Discussion Paper Series. (NZ ISSN 0114-5932) **753**, 790
Massimario del Foro Italiano. (IT ISSN 0025-4932) **2653**
Massimario della Giurisprudenza Italiana. (IT ISSN 0025-4940) **2653**
Massimario di Giurisprudenza del Lavoro. (IT ISSN 0025-4959) **2653**
Il Massimo. (IT) **1317**
Massis. (LE ISSN 0025-4975) **4285**, 2873
Mast. (US ISSN 1051-824X) **1353**, 4733
Master see Guerin Sportivo Mese **4518**
Master and the Multitude. (UK) **4189**
Master Baker, Confectioner & Caterer. (UK ISSN 0025-4983) **2089**
Master Baker's Handbook and Buyer's Guide. (UK) **2089**
Master Brewers Association of America. Communications. (US) **383**
Master Brewers Association of America Technical Quarterly see M B A A Technical Quarterly **383**
Master Builders' Journal. (UK ISSN 0025-4991) **623**
†Master Card. (US) **5233**
Master Carriers Journal see Freight Carriers **4744**
Master Cross Reference List, Part 1. (US) **4107**
Master Cross Reference List, Part 2. (US) **4107**
Master Cross Reference List, Part 3. (US) **4107**

6420 MASTER DETECTIVE

Master Detective. (US ISSN 0025-5017) **2985**
Master Drawings. (US ISSN 0025-5025) **335**
Master Economist. (US) **873**
Master Federal Tax Manual. (US) **1101**
Master Frequency Data Base (Frequency Sequence). (US) **1348**
Master Frequency Data Base (Service Group Code Sequence). (US) **1349**
Master Indicator of the Stock Market. (US ISSN 0047-6188) **955**
Master Lock News Today. (US) **642**
Master of Life. (US) **3595**, **3772**
▼Master Painter and Decorations Trade Journal. (AT) **2560**
†Master Performers. (UR) **5233**
Master Photographer see Photo Pro **3795**
Master Plumber. (AT ISSN 0025-5041) **2301**
Master Plumber of South Australia. (AT ISSN 0025-5068) **2301**
Master Sermon Series see M S S **4189**
Master Teacher. (US ISSN 0889-6259) **1647**
Master Thoughts. (US) **4189**
†Masterguide. (US) **5233**
†Masterkey. (US ISSN 0887-6665) **5233**
Masterlink. (CN) **4518**
Masterpieces in the National Gallery of Canada/Chefs-d'Oeuvre de la Galerie Nationale du Canada. (CN ISSN 0383-5391) **335**
Masterplots Annual see Magill's Literary Annual **2936**
Masters Abstracts see Masters Abstracts International **1678**
Masters Abstracts International. (US ISSN 0898-9095) **1678**, **17**
†Master's Education: Route to Opportunities in Contemporary Nursing. (US) **5233**
Master's Education: Route to Opportunities in Modern Nursing see Master's Education: Route to Opportunities in Contemporary Nursing **5233**
Masters in Business Administration see M B A **5229**
Master's Theses in Education. (US ISSN 0076-5112) **1647**
Master's Theses in the Arts and Social Sciences. (US ISSN 0160-8797) **2511**, **1711**, **4379**
▼Master's Theses in the Natural and Technical Sciences. (US ISSN 1053-2110) **4323**
Master's Theses in the Pure and Applied Sciences. (US) **4357**, **4323**
†Masterskaya. (UR) **5233**
Masthead. (US ISSN 0025-5122) **2572**
Masthead. (CN ISSN 0832-512X) **4132**, **2572**
Mastiff Journal. (US) **3712**
Mastika. (MY) **2210**
Masvingo Diary. (RH) **4775**
Maszyny i Ciagniki Rolnicze. (PL ISSN 0465-2592) **107**
Maszyny Przeplywowe. (PL ISSN 0860-3324) **1830**
Mat. (NO) **2477**
Mat och Fest see Femina Maanadens Magasin **4842**
Matangi Tonga. (TO ISSN 0113-0374) **679**, **1962**
Matar Abu Dhabi al-Dawli/Shoptalk - Abu Dhabi Duty Free Guide. (TS) **4775**
Matar Dubai al-Dawli/Dubai International Airport. (TS) **4775**
Matarah. (IS) **4479**
Matatu. (NE ISSN 0932-9714) **2937**, **2334**, **2873**
Match. (GW ISSN 0340-6253) **1183**, **3044**
Match. (US) **3906**
Match Football. (UK) **4507**
Match News. (CN ISSN 0836-7515) **4847**
Match Show Bulletin. (US) **3712**
Match Weekly see Match Football **4507**
Mate Amargo. (UY) **3906**

Mate Postal. (SP) **4479**
Matecon. (IT) **790**, **2537**
Matekon. (US ISSN 0025-1127) **679**, **3044**
Matemaattisten Aineiden Aikakauskirja see Dimensio **3034**
Matematica Aplicada e Computacional/ Computational and Applied Mathematics. (BL ISSN 0101-8205) **3065**
Matematica e la Sua Didattica. (IT) **3044**
Matematicheskaya Fizika see Matematicheskaya Fizika i Nelineinaya Mekhanika **3044**
Matematicheskaya Fizika i Funktsional'nyi Analiz. (KR) **3044**, **3824**
Matematicheskaya Fizika i Nelineinaya Mekhanika. (KR ISSN 0233-7568) **3044**
Matematicheskie Metody i Fiziko-mekhanicheskie Polya. (KR ISSN 0130-9420) **3044**
Matematicheskie Metody v Ekonomike. (LV ISSN 0130-9404) **679**
Matematicheskie Problemy Geofiziki. (RU ISSN 0301-6897) **3065**
Matematicheskie Zametki. (RU ISSN 0025-567X) **3044**
Matematicheskii Sbornik. (RU ISSN 0025-5157) **3044**
Matematicki Vesnik. (YU ISSN 0025-5165) **3044**
Matematicky Casopis see Mathematica Slovaca **3045**
Matematika a Fyzika ve Skole. (CS) **1647**, **3044**, **3824**
Matematika v Shkole. (RU ISSN 0025-5181) **3044**, **1754**
Matematikai Lapok/Mathematical Papers. (HU ISSN 0025-519X) **3044**
Matematyka (Poznan). (PL) **3044**
Matematyka (Warsaw). (PL ISSN 0137-8848) **3045**
Matera. (IT) **819**
Materia Medica Polona. (PL ISSN 0025-5246) **3124**, **3734**
Materiaal, Metodiek, Mededelingen see M.3 **1259**
Material Culture. (US ISSN 0883-3680) **2414**
Material Culture Directories. (US ISSN 0743-7528) **4442**
Material Engineering. see Cailiao Gongcheng **49**
Material Engineering Series. (US) **1935**
Material for Thought. (US) **3772**
Material Handling and Industrial Engineer see American Institute of Industrial Engineers. Material Handling Institute. Proceedings **1925**
Material Handling Education News see M H I News **3019**
Material Handling Engineering. (US ISSN 0025-5262) **3020**, **3649**
Material Handling Engineering Handbook and Directory. (US) **3020**, **3649**
Material Handling Institute News see M H I News **3019**
Material Handling Product News. (US ISSN 0195-2366) **1415**
Material Handling, Storage Packaging. see Manipulace, Skladovani, Baleni **3649**
Material History Bulletin - Bulletin d'Histoire de la Culture Materielle see Material History Review **2317**
Material History Review/Ruvue d'Histoire de la Culture Materielle. (CN ISSN 1183-1073) **2317**
Material Matters. (UK ISSN 0309-7471) **1247**, **2794**
Material Sciences and Engineering see Materials Science and Engineering A: Structural Materials: Properties, Microstructures and Processing **1920**
Material Sciences and Engineering see Materials Science & Engineering B: Solid-State Materials for Advanced Technology **1920**
Material und Markt. (GW ISSN 0939-3684) **34**

Material und Organismen. (GW ISSN 0025-5270) **1207**, **480**
Material und Technik. (GW) **2560**
Materialdienst. (GW ISSN 0721-2402) **4189**
Materialdienst des Konfessionskundlichen Instituts. (GW ISSN 0934-8522) **4269**
Materiale Plastice. (RM ISSN 0025-5289) **3864**
Materialehaandtering og Transport Nyt see Virksomheds Nyt **4660**
Materiales de Construccion. (SP ISSN 0465-2746) **623**
Materiales de la Ciudad. (SP) **2492**
Materiales para la Arqueologia del Peru.(PE) **278**
Materialfluss. (GW ISSN 0170-334X) **4653**
Materiali da Construzione ed Opere Edili Prezzi Indicativi see Materiali da Costruzione Ed Opere Edili Prezzi Informativi **623**
Materiali da Costruzione Ed Opere Edili Prezzi Informativi. (IT) **623**
Materiali e Discussioni per l'Analisi dei Testi Classici. (IT) **1278**
Materiali e Documenti Ticinesi. (SZ ISSN 0088-7714) **2374**, **278**
Materiali per il Vocabolario Neosumerico. Collana. (IT) **3640**
Materiali per Una Storia della Cultura Giuridica. (IT ISSN 0076-5163) **2732**
Materialia Turcica. (GW ISSN 0344-449X) **2430**
Materialien aus der Arbeitsmarkt- und Berufsforschung. (GW ISSN 0177-1426) **988**, **1067**
Materialien aus der Bildungsforschung. (GW ISSN 0173-3842) **1647**
Materialien zum Internationalen Kulturaustausch/Studies in International Cultural Relations. (GW) **3965**, **3640**
Materialien zur Heimerziehung. (GW ISSN 0723-2047) **4412**, **1738**
†Materialien zur Politischen Bildung. (GW ISSN 0340-0476) **5233**
Materialien zur Roemisch-Germanischen Keramik. (GW ISSN 0076-5171) **1165**, **278**
Materialien zur Wirtschafts- und Sozialgeschichte. (AU) **2374**
Materialiensammlung Staedtebau. (GW ISSN 0340-983X) **1871**
Materialoznanie i Tekhnologiia. (BU ISSN 0204-7535) **1920**
Materials and Components in Fossil Energy Applications. (US) **1792**, **3488**, **3691**
Materials and Components in Fossil Energy Applications and E R D A Newsletter see Materials and Components in Fossil Energy Applications **1792**
Materials and Corrosion. see Werkstoffe und Korrosion **3423**
Materials & Design. (UK ISSN 0264-1275) **1920**, **1830**
†Materials & Energy Advantage. (CN ISSN 1180-4246) **5233**
Materials and Manufacture. (UK) **1935**, **3412**, **3429**, **3864**
Materials & Manufacturing Processes. (US ISSN 1042-6914) **1935**
Materials and Plant Protection. (US) **3837**
Materials and Processing Report. (US ISSN 0887-1949) **3412**, **3864**
†Materials and Society. (US ISSN 0146-6399) **5233**
Materials and Structures/Materiaux et Constructions. (UK ISSN 0025-5432) **624**
Materials and Studies for Kassite History. (US ISSN 0146-6798) **2340**
Materials at High Temperature. (UK ISSN 0960-3409) **1920**, **3412**
Materials Australasia. (AT ISSN 0818-3597) **3412**
Materials Business Abstracts see Materials Business Information **3427**
Materials Business Information. (UK) **3427**
Materials Characterization. (US ISSN 1044-5803) **3412**, **1228**

Materials Chemistry and Physics. (SZ ISSN 0254-0584) **1920**, **1183**, **1856**
Materials Edge. (US ISSN 0952-5211) **3864**, **1165**
Materials Engineering. (US ISSN 0025-5319) **1920**
Materials Evaluation. (US ISSN 0025-5327) **1920**
Materials Forum. (AT) **3413**
Materials Handling & Distribution. (AT) **1021**
Materials Handling Buyers Guide. (UK ISSN 0142-114X) **1047**
Materials Handling News. (UK ISSN 0025-5351) **3021**
Materials in Languages of Indonesia. (AT) **2828**
Materials Information Digest Series. (UK) **3413**, **3429**
Materials Information Engineered Materials Search-in-Print Series. (US) **1845**, **3427**
Materials Information Metallurgical Published Search Series see Materials Information Metallurgical Search-in-Print Series **3427**
Materials Information Metallurgical Search-in-Print Series. (US) **3427**, **17**
Materials Information Translations Service. (UK) **3413**
Materials Letters. (NE ISSN 0167-577X) **3824**
Materials Management & Distribution. (CN ISSN 0025-5343) **4653**
▼Materials Management in Health Care. (US) **2467**
Materials Management Journal of India. (II ISSN 0543-0313) **1047**
Materials on Asia - Accession List and Review/Ajia Shiryo Tsuho. (JA ISSN 0913-025X) **406**
Materials on Asia and Africa - Accession List and Review see Materials on Asia - Accession List and Review **406**
Materials Performance. (US ISSN 0094-1492) **1920**
Materials Performance Buyer's Guide see Corrosion Engineer's Source Book **5173**
Materials Processing: Theory and Practices. (NE) **3824**
Materials Protection and Performance see Materials Performance **1920**
Materials Reclamation Weekly. (UK ISSN 0025-5386) **3413**, **1985**
▼Materials Recovery and Recycling Yearbook. (US) **1985**
Materials Research and Engineering/ Reine und Angewandte Metallkunde. (US) **3413**, **1830**
Materials Research Bulletin. (US ISSN 0025-5408) **1211**
Materials Research Centres. (UK) **1920**, **1145**
Materials Research in Science and Engineering at Purdue University. Annual Report see Materials Research in Science and Engineering at Purdue University. Progress Report **5233**
†Materials Research in Science and Engineering at Purdue University. Progress Report. (US ISSN 0079-8126) **5233**
Materials Research Society Bulletin see M R S Bulletin **3824**
Materials Research Society Symposium Proceedings. (US ISSN 0272-9172) **3824**, **1183**, **1830**
Materials Science. (PL ISSN 0137-1339) **1935**
Materials Science and Engineering A: Structural Materials: Properties, Microstructures and Processing. (SZ ISSN 0921-5093) **1920**
Materials Science & Engineering B: Solid-State Materials for Advanced Technology. (SZ ISSN 0921-5107) **1920**, **4603**
Materials Science and Technology. (UK ISSN 0267-0836) **3413**
Materials Science Forum. (SZ ISSN 0255-5476) **3824**, **1228**
Materials Science Monographs. (NE) **1830**

Materials Science of Minerals and Rocks. (NE) **1572**
Materials Science Quarterly *see* Chinese Journal of Materials Science **3404**
Materials Science Reports. (NE ISSN 0920-2307) **3824**
Materials Science Research. (US ISSN 0076-5201) **1920**
Materials Transactions, J I M. (JA ISSN 0916-1821) **3413**
Materialwirtschaft im Unternehmen *see* Materialwirtschaft und Logistik im Unternehmen **1021**
Materialwirtschaft und Logistik im Unternehmen. (GW ISSN 0937-4183) **1021**, **1047**
Materialwissenschaft und Werkstofftechnik. (GW ISSN 0933-5137) **3413**
Materialy Budowlane. (PL) **624**
Materialy do Bibliografii Muzyki Polskiej.(PL) **3589**
Materialy Glyatsiologicheskikh Issledovanii/Data of Glaciological Studies. (RU ISSN 0130-3686) **1592**
Materialy Historyczno-Metodyczne. (PL) **2317**
Materialy i Issledovaniya po Sibirskoi Dialektologii. (RU) **2828**
Materialy i Prace Antropologiczne. (PL ISSN 0076-521X) **244**
Materialy Samizdata. (US ISSN 0177-5332) **3906**, **2572**
Materialy Zachodnio-Pomorskie. (PL ISSN 0076-5236) **2374**, **278**
Materialy Zrodlowe do Dziejow Kosciola W Polsce. (PL ISSN 0076-5244) **4269**
Materiaux et Constructions. *see* Materials and Structures **624**
Materiaux et Techniques. (FR ISSN 0032-6895) **1920**
Materiaux pour l'Etude de l'Asie Orientale Moderne et Contemporaine.(FR ISSN 0293-7107) **2828**
Materiaux pour l'Histoire de notre Temps. (FR ISSN 0769-3206) **2374**, **3906**
Materidouska. (CS ISSN 0025-5440) **1260**
Materie Plastiche ed Elastomeri. (IT ISSN 0025-5459) **3864**
Maternal & Child Health. (UK ISSN 0262-0200) **3322**, **3294**
Maternal and Child Health Data Book *see* Health of America's Children **4103**
Maternal - Child Nursing Journal. (US ISSN 0090-0702) **3282**
Maternal Health News. (CN) **3282**, **597**, **4847**
†Maternidade e Infancia. (BL ISSN 0025-5491) **5233**
Maternity and Mothercraft. (UK) **4848**, **2448**, **4835**
Maternity Matters. (US) **1286**
Math Math World. (AT) **3045**
Math Notebook. (US) **3045**, **1738**
Math Science Network Broadcast. (US) **3045**, **4848**
Mathajothidam. (II) **359**
Mathematica. (RM ISSN 0025-5505) **3045**
†Mathematica Balkanica. (BU ISSN 0205-3217) **5233**
Mathematica Didactica. (GW ISSN 0170-1541) **3045**
Mathematica Japonica. (JA ISSN 0025-5513) **3045**
Mathematica Numerica Sinica. *see* Jisuan Shuxue **3040**
Mathematica Scandinavica. (DK ISSN 0025-5521) **3045**
Mathematica Slovaca. (CS ISSN 0025-5173) **3045**
Mathematicae Notae. (AG ISSN 0025-553X) **3045**
Mathematical and Computer Modelling. (US ISSN 0895-7177) **3045**, **3065**
Mathematical and Physical Society of Egypt. Proceedings. (UA) **3045**, **3824**
Mathematical Approaches to Geophysics. (NE) **1592**, **3045**
Mathematical Association of America Focus *see* M A A Focus **3044**

Mathematical Association of India. Bulletin. (II ISSN 0025-5556) **3045**
Mathematical Association of Tanzania. Bulletin *see* Tanzanian Mathematical Bulletin **3057**
Mathematical Biosciences. (US ISSN 0025-5564) **3045**, **447**
Mathematical Chemistry. (US ISSN 1049-2801) **1183**, **3045**
Mathematical Chronicle *see* New Zealand Journal of Mathematics **3049**
Mathematical Education. (KO) **3045**, **1754**
Mathematical Engineering in Industry. (NE ISSN 0169-121X) **3045**, **1920**
†Mathematical Expositions. (CN ISSN 0076-5333) **5233**
▼Mathematical Finance. (US ISSN 0960-1627) **790**, **3045**
Mathematical Gazette. (UK ISSN 0025-5572) **3045**
Mathematical Geology. (US ISSN 0882-8121) **1572**
Mathematical Intelligencer. (US ISSN 0343-6993) **3045**
Mathematical Journal of Okayama University. (JA ISSN 0030-1566) **3045**
Mathematical Linguistics. *see* Keiryo Kokugogaku **2822**
Mathematical Log. (US ISSN 0025-5580) **3045**
Mathematical Methods in the Applied Sciences. (UK ISSN 0170-4214) **3046**, **4323**
▼Mathematical Modeling (Soviet). (US ISSN 1054-6634) **3065**
Mathematical Modelling *see* Mathematical and Computer Modelling **3045**
▼Mathematical Models and Methods in Applied Sciences. (SI ISSN 0218-2025) **3046**
Mathematical Notes *see* Notas Matematicas **3049**
Mathematical Notes (Princeton). (US) **3046**
Mathematical Papers. *see* Matematikai Lapok **3044**
Mathematical Physics and Applied Mathematics. (NE) **3046**, **3824**
Mathematical Physics Studies. (NE) **3824**, **3046**
Mathematical Pie. (UK ISSN 0025-5602) **3046**, **1647**
Mathematical Population Studies. (US ISSN 0889-8480) **3984**, **3046**
Mathematical Preprints. (CN) **3045**
Mathematical Programming. (NE ISSN 0025-5610) **3065**
Mathematical Programming Symposium, Japan. Proceedings. *see* Suri Keikaku Shinpojumu Ronbunshu **3057**
Mathematical Reports. (US ISSN 0275-7214) **3046**
Mathematical Research. *see* Mathematische Forschung **3047**
Mathematical Reviews. (US ISSN 0025-5629) **3063**, **17**
Mathematical Reviews Annual Index *see* Index of Mathematical Papers **3062**
Mathematical Sciences. *see* Suri Kagaku **3057**
Mathematical Sciences Research Institute Publications. (US) **3046**
Mathematical Scientist. (UK ISSN 0312-3685) **3046**
Mathematical Social Sciences. (NE ISSN 0165-4896) **3046**, **4379**
Mathematical Society of Japan. Journal.(JA ISSN 0025-5645) **3046**
Mathematical Society of Japan. Publications. (JA ISSN 0549-4540) **3046**
Mathematical Spectrum. (UK ISSN 0025-5653) **3046**
▼Mathematical Structures in Computer Science. (UK ISSN 0960-1295) **3065**
Mathematical Studies in Economics and Statistics in the USSR and Eastern Europe *see* Matekon **679**
Mathematical Surveys & Monographs. (US) **3046**

Mathematical Systems in Economics. (GW) **897**, **3046**
Mathematical Systems Theory. (US ISSN 0025-5661) **3046**
Mathematics. *see* Sugaku **3057**
Mathematics Abstracts. *see* Zentralblatt fuer Mathematik und ihre Grenzgebiete **3063**
Mathematics and Computer Education. (US ISSN 0730-8639) **3065**, **1711**, **3046**
Mathematics and Computers in Simulation. (NE ISSN 0378-4754) **1435**, **3065**
Mathematics and Its Applications. (UK ISSN 0543-0941) **3046**
Mathematics and Its Applications. (NE) **3046**
Mathematics and Its Applications: East European Series. (NE) **3046**
Mathematics and Its Applications: Japanese Series. (NE) **3046**
Mathematics and Its Applications: Soviet Series. (NE) **3046**
†Mathematics and Microcomputer Materials Catalog 7-12, Adult. (US) **5233**
Mathematics Bulletin. *see* Shuxue Tongxun **3055**
The Mathematics Education. (II ISSN 0047-6269) **3046**, **1647**
Mathematics Education Library. (NE) **1647**, **3046**, **4035**
Mathematics Education Research Journal. (AT ISSN 1033-2170) **1754**, **3046**
Mathematics for Middle School Students. *see* Zhongxuesheng Shuxue **3062**
†Mathematics in Biology. (US) **5233**
Mathematics in Practice and Cognition. *see* Shuxue de Shijian yu Renshi **3055**
Mathematics in School. (UK ISSN 0305-7259) **3046**, **1754**
Mathematics in Science and Engineering. (US ISSN 0076-5392) **3047**, **1830**
Mathematics Magazine. (US ISSN 0025-570X) **3047**
Mathematics Newsletter. (II) **3047**
Mathematics of Computation. (US ISSN 0025-5718) **3047**
Mathematics of Operations Research. (US ISSN 0364-765X) **1398**, **3047**
Mathematics of the U S S R - Izvestiya. (English translation of: Izvestiya Akademii Nauk SSR Seriya Matematicheskaya) (US ISSN 0025-5726) **3047**
Mathematics of the U S S R - Sbornik. (English translation of: Matematicheskii Sbornik) (US ISSN 0025-5734) **3047**
▼Mathematics Review. (UK ISSN 0957-1280) **3047**
Mathematics Student. (II ISSN 0025-5742) **3047**
†Mathematics Students' Gazette. (AT ISSN 0810-6142) **5233**
Mathematics Teacher. (US ISSN 0025-5769) **3047**, **1754**
Mathematics Teaching. *see* Shuxue Jiaoxue **1759**
Mathematics Teaching. (UK ISSN 0025-5785) **3047**, **1754**
Mathematics Teaching Bulletin. *see* Shuxue Jiaoxue Tongxun **3055**
Mathematics Today. (II) **3047**
Mathematics Tutoring for Junior High School Students. *see* Chuzhongsheng Shuxue Fudao **3032**
Mathematik fuer Naturwissenschaft und Technik. (GW ISSN 0543-100X) **3047**
Mathematik in der Schule. (GW ISSN 0465-3750) **3047**, **1754**
Mathematik Lehren. (GW) **1754**, **3047**
Mathematik und ihre Anwendungen in Physik und Technik. (GW ISSN 0233-1063) **3047**
Mathematika. (UK ISSN 0025-5793) **3047**
Mathematika Sciences *see* Pure and Applied Mathematika Sciences **3051**
Der Mathematikunterricht. (GW ISSN 0025-5807) **3047**, **1754**

†Mathematisch-Naturwissenschaftliche Bibliothek. (GW ISSN 0465-3769) **5233**
Mathematisch-Physikalische Semesterberichte *see* Mathematische Semesterberichte **3047**
Mathematische Annalen. (GW ISSN 0025-5831) **3047**
Mathematische Forschung/ Mathematical Research. (GW) **3047**, **3844**
Mathematische Forschung. Schriftenreihe *see* Mathematische Forschung **3047**
Mathematische Lehrbuecher und Monographien. Abteilung 1: Mathematische Lehrbuecher. (GW ISSN 0076-5422) **3047**, **1754**
Mathematische Lehrbuecher und Monographien. Abteilung 2: Mathematische Monographien. (GW ISSN 0076-5430) **3047**
Mathematische Monographien. (GW ISSN 0543-1042) **3047**
Mathematische Nachrichten. (GW ISSN 0025-584X) **3047**
Mathematische Schuelerbuecherei. (GW ISSN 0076-5449) **3047**
Mathematische Semesterberichte. (GW ISSN 0720-728X) **3047**, **3824**
Der Mathematische und Naturwissenschaftliche Unterricht. (GW ISSN 0025-5866) **3047**
Mathematische Zeitschrift. (GW ISSN 0025-5874) **3048**
Mathematischen Gesellschaft in Hamburg. Mitteilungen. (GW ISSN 0340-4358) **3048**
Mathematischen Seminar Giessen. Mitteilungen. (GW ISSN 0373-8221) **3048**
Mathichon Weekly Review. (TH) **2220**
Mathilda and Terence Kennedy Institute of Rheumatology. Annual Report. (UK) **3369**
Mathilde-Zimmer-Stiftung. Blaetter. (GW) **4189**
Mathitiki Estia. (CY ISSN 0025-5904) **1260**
†Mathmag. (AT ISSN 0810-6150) **5233**
Mathrubhumi Illustrated Weekly. (II) **2200**
Mati. (US) **2997**
Mati. (IS ISSN 0025-5912) **3447**
Matica *see* Nova Matica **2877**
▼Maticne Citanie. Kalendar. (CS) **2184**
Matieres *see* Poetica et Analytica **2834**
Matilda Literary and Art Magazine *see* Matilda Magazine: Literary and Art Magazine **2997**
Matilda Magazine: Literary and Art Magazine. (AT) **2997**, **2937**
Matilda Ziegler Magazine for the Blind. (US ISSN 0025-5955) **2294**
Matkailu/Tourism. (FI) **4775**, **4550**
Matkailumaailma *see* Matkailu **4775**
Matra. (IO) **3399**, **2202**
Matribhoomi/Nepali Weekly. (NP) **2211**
Matrimonial Law Reporter. (II) **2718**
Matrimonial, Overseas Jobs and Real Estate International Newsletter *see* 100 Livelihood Occupations **3631**
Matrimonial Strategist. (US) **2718**
Matrix. (CN ISSN 0318-3610) **2937**
Matrix. (UK ISSN 0307-3335) **3012**, **2937**
Matrix. (GW ISSN 0934-8832) **3124**
Matrix *see* Crosscurrent **5175**
Matrix (Urbana). (US ISSN 8755-7266) **2997**, **3640**
▼Matrix (Washington). (US) **624**, **1879**
Matrix Newsletter. (US) **1398**, **1711**
Matsumoto Dental College Society. Journal. *see* Matsumoto Shigaku **3124**
Matsumoto Shigaku/Matsumoto Dental College Society. Journal. (JA ISSN 0385-1613) **3124**, **3237**
Mattanawcook Observer. (US) **2158**, **2414**
†Mattawa Chronicle. (CN) **5233**
Matter. (US) **356**
Matter of Degree. (UK ISSN 0140-7961) **2256**

6422 MATTER

Matter of Fact: A Digest of Current Facts, with Citations to Sources see Matter of Fact: Statements Containing Statistics on Current Social, Economic and Political Issues 2317
Matter of Fact: Statements Containing Statistics on Current Social, Economic and Political Issues. (US) 2317, 406
The Matthay News. (US ISSN 0360-8484) 3562
Mattoid. (AT) 2937
Maturango Museum Newsletter. (US) 3527
▼Mature Group Traveler. (US) 4775
†Mature Health. (US) 5233
Mature Lifestyles. (US) 2276
Mature Living. (US ISSN 0162-427X) 4243
Mature Outlook. (US ISSN 0742-0935) 2276
Mature Traveler. (US ISSN 1043-2280) 4775
Mature Years. (US ISSN 0025-6021) 2276, 4243
Maturing. (US) 2276
Maturitas. (IE ISSN 0378-5122) 2276
Maturity Magazine. (CN) 2276
Maturity Market Perspectives. (US) 1047, 2276
Maudsley Monographs. (US) 3124
Mauerranker. (GW ISSN 0176-3539) 303, 2492
Maui, a Paradise Guide. (US) 4775
Maui Update. (US ISSN 0895-9390) 4776
Maukef al-Riadi. (SY) 4479
Mauri Ora see New Zealand Natural Sciences 449
Maurice Falk Center for Economic Research in Israel. Report. see Maurice Falk Institute for Economic Research in Israel. Report and Discussion Paper Series 679
Maurice Falk Institute for Economic Research in Israel. Report and Discussion Paper Series. (IS ISSN 0333-7839) 679
†Maurice Rosen's Rare Coin Confidential. (US) 5233
Mauritania. Direction de la Statistique et des Etudes Economiques. Bulletin Mensuel Statistique. (MU ISSN 0543-1433) 4579
Mauritian International. (UK ISSN 0265-44XX) 3906
Mauritiana (Altenburg). (GW ISSN 0233-173X) 4323, 3527
Mauritius. Archives Department. Annual Report. (MF ISSN 0076-5481) 2773
Mauritius. Central Electricity Board. Annual Report. (MF) 1903
Mauritius. Central Statistical Office. Bi-Annual Digest of Statistics. (MF) 4579
Mauritius. Central Statistical Office. Bi-Annual Survey of Employment and Earnings. (MF) 729
Mauritius. Central Statistical Office. Digest of Agricultural Statistics. (MF) 140
Mauritius. Central Statistical Office. Digest of Demographic Statistics. (MF) 3993, 4579
Mauritius. Central Statistical Office. Digest of Educational Statistics. (MF) 1678
Mauritius. Central Statistical Office. Digest of Industrial Statistics. (MF) 729
Mauritius. Central Statistical Office. Digest of Road Transport Statistics. (MF) 4665
Mauritius. Central Statistical Office. External Trade Statistics. (MF) 729
Mauritius. Central Statistical Office. Household Expenditure Survey. (MF) 2450
Mauritius. Central Statistical Office. Housing and Population Census. Analysis Report. (MF) 3993
Mauritius. Central Statistical Office. International Travel and Tourism Statistics. (MF) 4800, 4579

Mauritius. Central Statistical Office. International Travel and Tourism see Mauritius. Central Statistical Office. International Travel and Tourism Statistics 4800
Mauritius. Central Statistical Office. National Accounts of Mauritius. (MF) 729
Mauritius. Central Statistical Office. Quarterly External Trade Statistics see Mauritius. Central Statistical Office. External Trade Statistics 729
Mauritius. Central Statistical Office. Statistical Summary. (MF) 4579
Mauritius. Customs and Excise Department. Annual Report. (MF ISSN 0076-549X) 1101
Mauritius. Director of Audit. Report. (MF ISSN 0543-1565) 1101
Mauritius. Forestry Service. Annual Report. (MF) 2104
Mauritius. Government Fire Services. Annual Report. (MF) 2033
Mauritius. Judicial Department. Annual Report. (MF) 2732
Mauritius. Legislative Assembly. Debates. (MF) 4067
Mauritius. Legislative Assembly. Sessional Paper. (MF ISSN 0076-5503) 4067
Mauritius. Meteorological Services. Report. (MF ISSN 0076-5511) 3438
Mauritius. Ministry for Employment and of Social Security and National Solidarite see Mauritius. Ministry of Social Security. National Solidarity and Reform Institutions 4412
Mauritius. Ministry of Agriculture, Fisheries and Natural Resources. Annual Report. (MF) 107
Mauritius. Ministry of Agriculture, Fisheries and Natural Resources. Technical Bulletin. (MF) 107
Mauritius. Ministry of Co-operatives and Co-operative Development. Annual Report. (MF) 831
Mauritius. Ministry of Finance. Insurance Unit. Controller of Insurance. Report. (MF) 2537
Mauritius. Ministry of Health. Annual Report. (MF) 4107
Mauritius. Ministry of Housing, Lands and Town and Country Planning. Annual Reports. (MF ISSN 0076-552X) 2492
Mauritius. Ministry of Labour and Industrial Relations. Annual Report. (MF) 988
Mauritius. Ministry of Social Security. National Solidarity and Reform Institutions. (MF) 4412
Mauritius. Ministry of Works and Internal Communications. Report. (MF ISSN 0076-5554) 4653, 4067
Mauritius. Ombudsman. Report. (MF) 4067
Mauritius. Posts and Telegraphs Department. Annual Report. (MF) 1353
Mauritius. Public Accounts Committee. Report. (MF ISSN 0076-5562) 1101
Mauritius. Public Service Commission. Report. (MF) 4067
Mauritius. Registrar of Insurance. Annual Report see Mauritius. Ministry of Finance. Insurance Unit. Controller of Insurance. Report 2537
Mauritius. Telecommunications Department. Annual Report. (MF) 1364
Mauritius. Tobacco Board. Annual Report. (MF) 4643
Mauritius Chamber of Agriculture. Annual Report. (MF) 107
Mauritius Chamber of Agriculture. President's Report see Mauritius Chamber of Agriculture. Annual Report 107
Mauritius Chamber of Commerce and Industry. Annual Report. (MF) 819
†Mauritius Chamber of Commerce and Industry. Newsletter. (MF) 5233
Mauritius Directory of the Diplomatic Corps. (MF ISSN 0085-3194) 1145, 3965

†Mauritius Economic Bulletin. (MF) 5233
Mauritius Housing Corporation. Report and Accounts. (MF) 2492
Mauritius Institute of Education. Annual Report. (MF) 1647
Mauritius Institute of Education. Journal.(MF) 1647
Mauritius Police Force. Annual Report. (MF) 1518
Mauritius Police Magazine. (MF) 1518
Mauritius Standards Bureau. Annual Report. (MF) 3447
Mauritius Sugar Industry Research Institute. Advisory Bulletin. (MF) 2077
Mauritius Sugar Industry Research Institute. Annual Report. (MF ISSN 0369-2043) 2077
Mauritius Sugar Industry Research Institute. Occasional Paper. (MF) 2077
Mauritius Times. (MF ISSN 0025-6064) 2169
Mausam. (II ISSN 0252-9416) 3438, 1592
Mausolee. (FR ISSN 0025-6072) 335, 624
Mavbima. (CE) 3906
Mavoschool see Nieuw Zicht 1651
Mavrica/Rainbow. (YU) 1260, 4269
Mawakef Weekly Magazine/Al-Mawaqif. (BA) 2173
Al-Mawakif. (BA) 2173
Al-Mawaqif. see Mawakef Weekly Magazine 2173
Al-Mawarid al-Tabi'iyyah/Natural Resources. (MK) 1491, 3691
Mawazo. (UG ISSN 0047-6293) 4379
†Mawdsley Memoirs. (CN) 5233
Mawqif al-Adabi. (SY) 2937
Max. (IT) 1293
Max. (US ISSN 8756-7644) 3399
Max Euwe-Centrum. Nieuwsbrief. (NE) 4479
Max Freiherr von Oppenheim-Stiftung. Schriften. (GW ISSN 0543-1719) 3640
Max-Planck-Gesellschaft. Jahrbuch. (GW ISSN 0341-0218) 4324, 4379
Max-Planck-Gesellschaft zur Foerderung der Wissenschaften. Jahrbuch. (GW ISSN 0076-5635) 4324
Max-Planck-Gesellschaft zur Foerderung der Wissenschaften Berichte und Mitteilungen. (GW ISSN 0341-7778) 4324
Max-Planck-Gesellschaft zur Foerderung der Wissenschaften Mitteilungen see Max-Planck-Gesellschaft zur Foerderung der Wissenschaften Berichte und Mitteilungen 4324
Max-Planck-Gesellschaft zur Foerderung der Wissenschaften Spiegel see M P G Spiegel 4323
Max-Planck-Institut fuer Auslaendisches Oeffentliches Recht und Voelkerrecht. Fontes see Max-Planck-Institut fuer Auslaendisches Oeffentliches Recht und Voelkerrecht. Fontes Iuris Gentium 2653
Max-Planck-Institut fuer Auslaendisches Oeffentliches Recht und Voelkerrecht. Fontes Iuris Gentium. (GW) 2653
Max-Planck-Institut fuer Europaische Rechtsgeschichte. Veroeffentlichungen. Ius Commune. (GW ISSN 0579-2428) 2653
Max-Planck-Institut fuer Geschichte. Veroeffentlichungen. (GW) 2317
Max-Planck-Institut fuer Metallforschung. Mitteilungen. (GW) 3413
Max-Planck-Institute fuer Europaische Rechtsgeschichte. Veroeffentlichungen. Ius Commune. Sonderhefte. (GW ISSN 0175-6532) 2653
Maxi. (GW) 4848
Maxillofacial and Plastic Surgery. see Chirurgia Maxillofacialis et Plastica 3377
Maxima. (BL) 4848
Maxima. (PO) 4848
Maximaphily. (US) 3754
Maxwell Macmillan Chess Books. (UK) 4479
†May Day! (US) 5233

May Day Pictorial News. (US ISSN 0025-6129) 4733
May Trends. (US ISSN 0025-6137) 1116
Maya. (II) 2200
Ma'yanot. (IS ISSN 0543-1786) 2013
Mayapuri. (II) 3513
Mayaways. (MX) 244
Mayberry Gazette. (US) 1376
Maydaon. (IS ISSN 0333-7685) 1398
Maydica. (IT ISSN 0025-6153) 185
Mayfair. (UK ISSN 0025-6161) 3399
Mayflower Descendant. (US ISSN 8756-3959) 2158
Mayflower Quarterly. (US ISSN 0148-5032) 2158, 2414
Mayflower Warehouseman. (US) 4746
Mayfly. (US) 2997
Mayibuye. (ZA ISSN 0025-6188) 3945
Mayim ve Hashkaiya. (IS) 4827
Maynooth Occasional Papers. (IE) 2256
Maynooth Review. (IE ISSN 0332-4869) 335
Mayo Agricola. (MX) 107
Mayo Alumnus. (US) 3124
Mayo Clinic Health Letter. (US ISSN 0741-6245) 3124
Mayo Clinic Proceedings. (US ISSN 0025-6196) 3124
Mayor see U S Mayor 4095
Mayoreo y Distribucion. (MX) 2093
Mayors' Newsletter. (II) 4090
Mayura. (II) 2200
Mazal U'bracha. (IS) 679
Al-Mazari' (MK) 107
Mazengarb's Industrial Law Bulletin. (NZ ISSN 0111-6770) 2653, 988
Mazengarb's Industrial Law Service. (NZ) 2653, 988
Mazoji Lietuva. (LI) 2209
Mazone Umitbach/Food and Kitchen. (IS ISSN 0334-1488) 2077
Mazputnins. (US ISSN 0025-6218) 2013, 1260
Mazuipin Gongbao see Bulletin on Narcotics 1535
Mbioni. (TZ ISSN 0025-6234) 4379
▼Mbya Guarani. (PY ISSN 1017-2793) 2013, 244
MCC News see Metroline 2455
Md De D C Press News see PressNews 2574
Me. (US ISSN 0272-5657) 335, 2997
Me. (FI ISSN 0025-6269) 831
Me. see Sprout 1665
Me D A L. (Dalhousie Medical Alumni Association) (CN) 1317
Me Magazine. (US) 2997
Me Magazine. (UK ISSN 0956-2486) 4848
Me Naiset. (FI ISSN 0025-6277) 4848
Me Too. (US) 2997
Me'a. (NO) 2045
Mead Art Museum Monographs. (US) 335, 303, 2414, 3527
Meade County Historian. (US) 2414
†Mealey's European Environmental Law Report. (US ISSN 1050-897X) 5233
Mealey's Litigation Report: Asbestos. (US ISSN 0742-4647) 2702, 2537
Mealey's Litigation Report: Asbestos Property Actions. (US ISSN 1040-0192) 2702
Mealey's Litigation Report: Bad Faith. (US ISSN 0893-1011) 2702, 2537
▼Mealey's Litigation Report: Banking Insolvency. (US ISSN 1057-1000) 2702, 790
Mealey's Litigation Report: Insurance. (US ISSN 8755-9005) 2703, 2537
Mealey's Litigation Report: Insurance Insolvency. (US ISSN 1043-8416) 2703, 2537
†Mealey's Litigation Report: Iranian Claims. (US ISSN 0742-4655) 5233
▼Mealey's Litigation Report: Lead. (US) 2703

MEDECINE 6423

Mealey's Litigation Report: Punitive Damages and Tort Reform. (US ISSN 1055-307X) **2703**, 2537
▼Mealey's Litigation Report: Reinsurance. (US) **2703**, 2537
Mealey's Litigation Report: S and L Bailout *see* Mealey's Litigation Report: Banking Insolvency **2702**
Mealey's Litigation Report: Superfund. (US ISSN 0897-3407) **2703**
Mealey's Litigation Report: Tobacco. (US ISSN 0886-0122) **2703**, 4643
Mealey's Reinsurance Report *see* Mealey's Litigation Report: Reinsurance **2703**
Mean Mountain Music. (US) **3562**
▼Mean Streets. (AT ISSN 1035-9761) **2986**
Meander. (PL ISSN 0025-6285) **1278**, 2317, 2828
Meanjin. (AT ISSN 0815-953X) **2874**, 2937
Means Assemblies Cost Data (Year). (US ISSN 0894-4342) **624**
Means Assemblies Costs *see* Means Assemblies Cost Data (Year) **624**
Means Concrete Cost Data (Year). (US) **624**
Means Construction Cost Indexes. (US ISSN 0361-9591) **638**
Means Electrical Cost Data (Year). (US ISSN 0748-7002) **1830**
Means Heavy Construction Cost Data. (US ISSN 0893-5602) **624**
Means Interior Cost Data (Year). (US) **624**, 2553
Means Labor Rates for the Construction Industry. (US) **624**, 988
Means Light Commercial Cost Data (Year). (US ISSN 0896-7601) **624**
Means Mechanical and Electrical Cost Data *see* Means Electrical Cost Data (Year) **1830**
Means Mechanical Cost Data (Year). (US) **624**, 1903
Means Open Shop Building Construction Cost Data (Year). (US) **624**
Means Repair and Remodeling Cost Data (Year). (US) **624**
Means Residential Cost Data. (US ISSN 0738-1239) **624**
Means Site Work and Landscape Cost Data (year). (US) **624**
Means Site Work Cost Data *see* Means Site Work and Landscape Cost Data (year) **624**
Means Square Foot Costs (Year). (US ISSN 0732-815X) **4152**, 624
Me'asef. (IS) **2430**, 988
Measure. (US) **2997**
Measurement. (UK ISSN 0263-2241) **3447**, 1935, 3824
Measurement and Automation News *see* Sira Spotlight **2525**
Measurement and Control. (UK ISSN 0020-2940) **2524**, 3447
Measurement & Control Technology. *see* Cekong Jishu **49**
Measurement and Evaluation in Counseling and Development. (US ISSN 0748-1756) **1647**
Measurement and Inspection Technology *see* Quality Today **3448**
Measurement Chain *see* Sensor Business Digest **1053**
Measurement Science and Technology. (UK ISSN 0957-0233) **2524**, 3824
Measurement Techniques. (English translation of: Izmeritel'naya Tekhnika) (US ISSN 0543-1972) **3447**
Measurements and Control. (US ISSN 0148-0057) **2524**, 1830
Measurements & Control News. (US ISSN 0194-1461) **2524**, 1830
Measurements and Data *see* Measurements and Control **2524**
Meat *see* Meat Industry **2077**
†Meat and Dairy Products. (UK) **5233**
†Meat and Livestock Commission, Bucks, England. Index of Research. (UK ISSN 0076-5716) **5233**
Meat and Livestock Commission, Bucks, England. International Market Survey *see* Meat and Livestock Commission, Bucks, England. International Meat Market Review **221**

Meat and Livestock Commission, Bucks, England. International Meat Market Review. (UK ISSN 0263-2217) **221**
Meat and Poultry. (US ISSN 0892-6077) **2077**
Meat Balances in O E C D Countries. (FR) **140**, 17
Meat Board Reports. (US ISSN 0025-6358) **2077**, 221
Meat Business Magazine. (US) **2077**
▼Meat Focus International. (US ISSN 0961-2076) **221**
Meat Industry. (UK ISSN 0958-5141) **2077**
Meat Industry Digest. (AT) **2077**
Meat Plant Magazine *see* Meat Business Magazine **2077**
Meat Price Report. (US) **955**
Meat Processing. (US ISSN 0025-6390) **2077**
Meat Science. (UK ISSN 0309-1740) **2077**
Meat Science. (JA ISSN 0289-0542) **2077**
Meat Science Institute. Proceedings. (US ISSN 0090-5631) **2077**
Meat Service Report *see* Meat Price Report **955**
Meat Sheet. (US) **221**, 873
Meat Technology. *see* Tehnologija Mesa **227**
Meat Trades Journal. (UK ISSN 0025-6412) **2077**
Meat Trades Journal of Australia *see* Australian Meat Industry Bulletin **2062**
Meath Chronicle. (IE) **2203**
Meatworker. (AT ISSN 0310-6721) **2077**, 2586
†MeBrookdale/Highlights. (IS) **5233**
Mecanica Popular. (US ISSN 0025-6420) **4603**, 2438, 4324
Mecanicien en Prothese Dentaire. (FR) **3237**
Mecanipel. (SP) **2737**
Meccanica Italiana. (IT) **1935**
Meccanica Moderna. (IT ISSN 0393-5558) **1935**
Meccanica Oggi. (IT) **3844**
Meccanizzazione Agricola. (IT ISSN 0392-3983) **163**
Mech. (US ISSN 0025-6471) **3463**
Mechanical and Corrosion Properties *see* Crystal Properties and Preparation **3816**
Mechanical and Corrosion Properties. Series A. Key Engineering Materials *see* Key Engineering Materials **3411**
†Mechanical & Electronic Industries Yearbook of China. (HK ISSN 0258-3038) **5233**
▼Mechanical Buyer and Specifier H V A C - Refrigeration. (CN) **2301**
▼Mechanical Buyer and Specifier Plumbing, Piping and Heating. (CN) **2301**
Mechanical Contractor Literature Showcase. (US) **1935**, 4603
Mechanical Contractors Association of America. Statistical Survey Report. (US) **624**
Mechanical Cost Data *see* Means Mechanical Cost Data (Year) **624**
Mechanical Engineering. *see* Kikai Gijutsu **1934**
Mechanical Engineering. (US ISSN 0025-6501) **1935**
Mechanical Engineering. *see* Polytechnisch Tijdschrift: Werktuigbouw **1937**
Mechanical Engineering & Machine Tool Abstracts. *see* Gepgyartastechnologiai es Szerszamgepipari Szakirodalmi Tajekoztato **1844**
Mechanical Engineering Applications. *see* Oyo Kikai Kogaku **3022**
Mechanical Engineering Bulletin. (II ISSN 0379-5527) **1935**
Mechanical Engineering Journal. *see* Strojniski Vestnik **1939**
Mechanical Engineering Magazine. *see* Strojnicky Casopis **1939**
†Mechanical Engineering News. (US ISSN 0025-651X) **5233**
Mechanical Engineering Series. (US) **1935**

▼Mechanical Engineering Systems. (US) **1879**, 1935
Mechanical Engineering Technology *see* Mechanical Incorporated Engineer **1935**
Mechanical Handling Equipment. *see* Qizhong Yunshu Jixie **1938**
Mechanical Incorporated Engineer. (UK ISSN 0954-6529) **1935**
Mechanical Music. (US) **3562**
Mechanical Systems & Signal Processing. (UK ISSN 0888-3270) **1935**
Mechanics. (US ISSN 0076-5783) **3844**, 1920, 3048
Mechanics, a Writer's Quarterly. (US) **2937**
Mechanics' and Construction Liens in Alaska, Oregon and Washington. (US) **2715**
Mechanics and Mathematical Methods - Series of Handbooks. (NE) **3048**, 3844
Mechanics and Practice. *see* Lixue yu Shijian **1934**
Mechanics: Dynamical Systems. (NE) **3844**
Mechanics of Composite Materials. (English translation of: Mekhanika Kompozitaykh Materialov) (US ISSN 0191-5665) **1856**
Mechanics of Elastic and Inelastic Solids. (NE) **3844**
Mechanics of Materials. (NE ISSN 0167-6636) **1921**
Mechanics of Solids. (English translation of: Akademiya Nauk S.S.S.R. Izvestiya. Mekhanika Tverdogo Tela) (US ISSN 0025-6544) **3844**
Mechanics of Structures and Machines. (US ISSN 0890-5452) **1935**, 3021
Mechanics Research Communications. (US ISSN 0093-6413) **1921**
Mechanik. (PL ISSN 0025-6552) **1935**, 3021
†Mechanik. (AU) **5233**
Mechanika Teoretyczna i Stosowana. (PL ISSN 0079-3701) **1921**, 3844
Mechanine Technologija. *see* Mekhanicheskaya Tekhnologiya **5235**
Mechanism and Machine Theory. (US ISSN 0094-114X) **1935**
Mechanisms of Ageing and Development. (IE ISSN 0047-6374) **2276**
Mechanisms of Carcinogenesis - Activation and Metabolism of Carcinogens *see* I C R D B Cancergram: Mechanisms of Carcinogenesis - Activation and Metabolism of Carcinogens **5208**
Mechanisms of Carcinogenesis - Macromolecular Alterations and Repair *see* I C R D B Cancergram: Mechanisms of Carcinogenesis - Macromolecular Alteration and Repair **5208**
Mechanisms of Carcinogenesis - Oncogenic Transformation *see* I C R D B Cancergram: Mechanisms of Carcinogenesis - Oncogenic Transformation **5208**
Mechanisms of Development. (IE ISSN 0925-4773) **525**
Mechanisms of Inorganic and Organometallic Reactions. (US ISSN 0740-8900) **1214**
Mechanist. (US) **58**, 2586, 4675
Mechanizace Automatizace Administrativy/Mechanization and Automation of Administrative Work. (CS) **1351**
†Mechanizacia. (CS ISSN 0025-6595) **5233**
Mechanizacja i Automatyzacja Gornictwa. (PL ISSN 0208-7448) **3488**, 1935
Mechanization and Automation of Administrative Work. *see* Mechanizace Automatizace Administrativy **1351**
Mechanization in Rural Areas. *see* Nongcun Jixiehua **163**
▼Mechatronics. (US ISSN 0957-4158) **1935**, 1903

▼Mechatronics Systems Engineering. (NE ISSN 0924-3992) **1879**, 1830, 1935
La Meche. (CN) **1317**
Mecklenburg Genealogical Society Quarterly *see* Olde Mecklenburg Genealogical Society Quarterly **2160**
Mecklenburg Times. (US) **2653**
Mecklenburgisches Woerterbuch. (GW) **2829**
Mectronic Buyers Directory. (US) **1145**, 1903
Med. Dent. Magazin. (GW ISSN 0940-2500) **3237**
Med Bil i Europa. (NO) **4776**
Med R-Medizinrecht *see* Medizinrecht **3265**
Med - Report. (GW ISSN 0934-3148) **3124**
Medaglia. (IT ISSN 0392-5439) **3600**
Medailles. (FR ISSN 0025-6625) **2438**
MeDAL *see* Me D A L **1317**
The Medal. (UK ISSN 0263-7707) **3600**, 335
Medal Collector *see* Orders and Medals Society of America. Official Journal **2440**
Medallion. (US ISSN 0890-7595) **2414**
Medborgaren. (SW ISSN 0025-665X) **3906**
Meddelande Armemuseum. Yearbook. (SW) **3527**, 3463
Meddelande fraan Lunds Universitet Historiska Museum. *see* University of Lund. Archeological Institute. Papers. Yearbook **288**
†Meddelanden fraan Svenska Riksarkivet. (SW ISSN 0039-6893) **5233**
Meddelelser fra Ferskvandsfiskerilaboratoriet. (DK) **2045**
Meddelelser fra Sortsafproevningen/ Danish Gazette for Plant Varieties. (DK ISSN 0108-1683) **509**
Meddelelser om Groenland, Bioscience. (DK ISSN 0106-1054) **447**, 1962
Meddelelser om Groenland, Geoscience.(DK ISSN 0106-1046) **1572**
Meddelelser om Groenland, Man & Society. (DK ISSN 0106-1062) **244**, 3124, 4379
Medecin de Famille Canadien. *see* Canadian Family Physician **3086**
Medecin du Quebec. (CN ISSN 0025-6692) **3124**
Medecin Electro-Radiologiste Qualifie de France. (FR) **3360**
Medecin Veterinaire du Quebec. (CN ISSN 0225-9591) **4812**
Medecine Aeronautique et Spatiale. (FR ISSN 0294-0817) **3124**
Medecine Aeronautique et Spatiale - Medecine Subaquatiqe et Hyperbare *see* Medecine Aeronautique et Spatiale **3124**
Medecine - Biologie - Environnement/ Medicine - Biology - Environment/ Geneeskunde - Biologie - Leefmilieu. (BE ISSN 0302-0800) **3200**, 1962
Medecine Clinique et Experimentale. *see* Clinical and Investigative Medicine **3088**
Medecine de l'Homme. (FR ISSN 0543-2243) **3124**
Medecine du Sport. (FR ISSN 0025-6722) **3372**, 3805
Medecine et Armees. (FR ISSN 0300-4937) **3124**
Medecine et Chirurgie Digestives. (FR ISSN 0047-6412) **3269**
Medecine et Chirurgie du Pied. (FR ISSN 0759-2280) **3381**
Medecine et Hygiene. (SZ ISSN 0025-6749) **3124**, 3805
Medecine et Informatique. *see* Medical Informatics **3226**
Medecine et Maladies Infectieuses. (FR) **3222**
Medecine et Nutrition. (FR) **3609**, 3124
Medecine et Travail. (FR ISSN 0025-6757) **3619**

MEDECINE HOSPITALIERE/HOSPITAL

Medecine Hospitaliere/Hospital Medicine. (FR) **2467**, 2586
Medecine Infantile. (FR ISSN 0025-6773) **3322**
Medecine Interne see Revue Roumaine de Medecine Interne **3149**
Medecine Moderne du Canada see Modern Medicine of Canada **5238**
Medecine - Sciences. (FR ISSN 0767-0974) **3125**
Medecine Sociale et Preventive. see Sozial- und Praeventivmedizin **3154**
Medecine Tropicale. (FR ISSN 0025-682X) **3222**
Medecins de Groupe. (FR ISSN 0025-6838) **3125**
Medeconomics. (UK ISSN 0144-4271) **3125**
Mededelingen "Ex Oriente Lux" see Vooraziatisch-Egyptisch Genootschap "Ex Oriente Lux". Mededelingen en Verhandelingen **2343**
Mededelingen over Rijkspersoneelsaangelegenheden Bulletin see R P A Bulletin **4072**
Mededelingenblad van Sobrietas see Verantwoord Levensverkeer **1539**
Medelhavsmuseet. Bulletin. (SW ISSN 0585-3214) **2430**
Medellin. (CK) **4269**
Medequip. (AU ISSN 0253-7419) **3125**
Medexpres. (FR) **4118**, 3177
Media. (HK) **34**, 2572, 4132
†Media A C Tion. (CN) **5233**
Media Agencies Clients Colorado M A C News see Colorado M A C News **29**
Media and Consumer see Columbia Journalism Review **2568**
Media and Marketing see Media **34**
Media & Methods. (US ISSN 0025-6897) **1754**, 1417, 1691
Media and Society Series. (US) **1339**
Media & Values. (US ISSN 0149-6980) **1339**, 4189
†Media Arts. (US ISSN 0889-8928) **5233**
Media Arts Information Network see M A I N **1376**
Media Asia. (SI ISSN 0129-6612) **1339**, 2572, 4132
Media Bulletin. (UK ISSN 0267-5382) **1376**
Media Business Review. (US) **34**, 1047
Media Circle. see Mediya Sakuru **555**
Media Culture and Society. (UK ISSN 0163-4437) **1376**, 4442
Media Data Japan. see Gekkan Media Data **32**
Media Daten see Media Daten: Zeitungen **2578**
Media-Daten Annuals. (GW ISSN 0933-9728) **34**, 4132
Media Daten: Fachzeitschriften. (GW ISSN 0170-4192) **2578**
Media Daten: Radio - T V. (GW ISSN 0935-5936) **1349**
Media Daten: Zeitschriften. (GW ISSN 0170-4176) **2578**
Media Daten: Zeitungen. (GW ISSN 0931-3265) **2578**, 41
Media Development. (GW) **1376**, 4189
Media Digest. (US ISSN 0146-2091) **1754**, 3513
Media Directory. (NZ) **34**, 1047
Media Editorial Profile Edition see Publication Profiles **37**
†Media Exhibitors' Directory for Independent Artists. (US) **5233**
Media Expenditure Analysis Ltd. Tri-Media Digest for Brands Advertisers see M E A L Tri-Media Digest for Brands Advertisers **34**
Media Focus/Mediafokus. (SA ISSN 1016-8206) **2773**, 1647
Media Forum. (IT ISSN 0394-9575) **34**
▼Media Futures. (AT ISSN 1037-3381) **335**
†Media General Financial Weekly. (US ISSN 0279-0734) **5233**
Media General IndustriScope see IndustriScope **5212**
Media Guide (Cleveland). (US) **1376**
Media History Digest. (US ISSN 0195-6779) **1339**

Media in Education & Development. (UK ISSN 0262-0251) **1647**, 1376
Media Inc. (US) **1047**
Media Industry Newsletter. (US ISSN 0024-9793) **34**, 1339
▼Media Info: International Media Directory Japan (Year). (JA ISSN 0912-4160) **1145**, 34
Media Information Australia. (AT ISSN 0312-9616) **1339**, 1376
Media International. (UK ISSN 0266-8688) **35**
Media Law Reporter. (US ISSN 0148-1045) **1339**
Media Letter. (AT) **1339**
Media Letter. (US) **1398**
Media: Library Services Journal see Church Media Library Magazine **2752**
Media Management Monographs see Publishing Trends and Trendsetters **4135**
Media Market Guide. (US) **35**
Media Markt. (BE) **1047**
Media Mergers & Acquisitions. (US ISSN 0895-4550) **1339**, 35, 4132
Media Monitor. (UK) **1339**
†Media Monitor (Ardsley). (US ISSN 0730-3262) **5233**
Media Monitor (Washington). (US) **1340**, 3906, 4379
Media Network Booklist. (NE) **1349**
Media Network Receiver Shopping List. (NE) **1357**, 1775
Media News see Technikon Forum **1717**
Media News Keys. (US ISSN 0033-3913) **35**
Media Newsletter. (US) **35**
Media Ownership in Australia. (AT ISSN 0811-8892) **1145**, 2572
Media People. (US) **1340**
†Media Personnel Directory. (US) **5233**
Media Perspektiven. (GW ISSN 0170-1754) **1376**
Media Plakat. (GW ISSN 0720-3519) **35**
†Media Planning Guide. (US) **5234**
Media Production. (IT) **1376**
Media Profiles: Health Sciences Edition. (US ISSN 0740-1892) **3125**, 1754, 2467, 3282
Media Report see The Marketing Pulse **1046**
Media Report to Women. (US ISSN 0145-9651) **4848**, 1340
Media Reporter. (US) **2455**, 2572
Media Reporter. (UK ISSN 0309-0256) **2572**, 1340
Media Reporter. (PL) **3513**, 1376
†Media Review. (US ISSN 0199-9273) **5234**
Media Review Digest. (US ISSN 0363-7778) **3520**, 17, 3589
Media Scandinavia. (DK ISSN 0076-5821) **35**
Media Selection. (GW ISSN 0934-4217) **917**, 873
Media Spectrum. (GW) **35**
Media Spectrum. (US ISSN 0731-3675) **1755**
Media Sports Business. (US ISSN 0889-0951) **1376**, 4479
Media Studies Journal. (US ISSN 1057-7416) **1376**
†Media User's Newsletter. (US) **5234**
Media Week. (US ISSN 1055-176X) **35**
Media West. (CN) **35**
Mediactive see Immediate Impact **1337**
Mediacult Newsletter. (AU) **1340**
Mediaeval and Modern Breton Series. (IE) **2375**, 2829
Mediaeval and Modern Irish Series. (IE ISSN 0332-4265) **2937**
Mediaeval and Modern Welsh Series. (IE ISSN 0332-4230) **2937**
Mediaeval Philosophical Texts in Translation. (US ISSN 0076-5856) **3772**
Mediaeval Scandinavia. (DK ISSN 0076-5864) **2375**
Mediaeval Scandinavia Supplements. (DK ISSN 0106-102X) **2375**
Mediaeval Sources in Translation. (CN ISSN 0316-0874) **2937**, 2375

Mediaeval Studies. (CN ISSN 0076-5872) **2375**
Mediaeval Studies. (US) **2375**
Mediaevalia. (IT) **335**
Mediaevalia. (US ISSN 0361-946X) **2375**, 335, 2937
Mediaevalia Lovaniensia. Series I. (BE) **2375**
Mediaevalia Philosophica Polonorum. (PL ISSN 0076-5880) **3773**
Mediaevistik. (GW) **2375**
MediaFax see Media Futures **335**
MediaFile. (US) **1340**, 2572
Mediafile. (UK ISSN 0954-3473) **1755**, 2773
Mediafokus. see Media Focus **2773**
Mediagaz. (FR ISSN 0752-5508) **3706**
MediaGuide. (US) **873**, 1340, 3965
Medianite. (US ISSN 0025-6927) **2134**
Medias Pouvoirs. (FR) **2572**, 1376
Mediascene Prevue see Prevue **3516**
▼MediaScope: Market and Media Planner. (US) **35**
Mediatheques Publiques. (FR ISSN 0153-4270) **2773**
Mediation Quarterly. (US ISSN 0739-4098) **4035**, 2653
▼Mediators of Inflammation. (UK ISSN 0962-9351) **3125**
Mediatus. (GW ISSN 0176-5116) **3965**, 1273, 3464
MediaWatch. (US ISSN 1053-8321) **2572**, 3906
Medic see M E D I C **3748**
†Medic Alert Newsletter. (US ISSN 0300-7200) **5234**
Medicaid Directors' Network. (US) **4412**
Medicaid Fraud Report. (US) **2653**, 3125
Medicaid Management Institute Bulletin see M M I Bulletin **4412**
Medicaid Recipient Characteristics and Units of Selected Medical Services. (US ISSN 0098-3616) **4412**, 3125
Medical Abstracts. see Yixue Wenzhai **3182**
Medical Abstracts Newsletter. (US ISSN 0730-7810) **3177**, 3811
Medical Administration Executive. (US) **3125**, 4107
Medical Advertising News. (US) **1047**, 3734
Medical Aid for Palestine News see M A P News **4412**
Medical & Biological Engineering & Computing. (UK ISSN 0140-0118) **470**, 3125
Medical and Biological Illustration see Journal of Audiovisual Media in Medicine **3114**
Medical and Dental Association of Botswana. Journal. (BS) **3125**, 3237
Medical and Health Annual. (US ISSN 0363-0366) **3125**, 3806
Medical and Health Care Books and Serials in Print. (US ISSN 0000-085X) **3177**
Medical & Health Information Directory. (US ISSN 0749-9973) **3806**
Medical and Healthcare Marketplace Guide. (US ISSN 0146-8022) **1145**, 3125
Medical and Pediatric Oncology. (US ISSN 0098-1532) **3200**, 3322
Medical and Pharmaceutical Society for Wakan-Yaku. Journal. (JA ISSN 0289-730X) **3734**
Medical and Radiological Devices Guidance Manual. (US) **4107**, 2653, 3262, 3360
Medical & Veterinary Entomology. (UK ISSN 0269-283X) **536**
Medical Anthropology. (US ISSN 0145-9740) **244**, 3125
Medical Anthropology Quarterly. (US ISSN 0745-5194) **244**, 3125
†Medical Aspects of Human Sexuality. (US ISSN 0025-7001) **5234**
Medical Association of Georgia. Journal. (US ISSN 0025-7028) **3125**
Medical Association of Okayama. Journal. see Okayama Igakkai Zasshi **3137**

Medical Association of Thailand. Journal. (TH ISSN 0025-7036) **3125**
Medical Audit News. (UK ISSN 0959-2903) **753**, 3125
Medical Benefits. (US ISSN 0743-8079) **2547**, 17, 1067, 3125
†Medical Biology. (FI ISSN 0302-2137) **5234**
Medical Book News. (IL ISSN 0025-7060) **3177**
Medical Bulletin see Indian Journal of Medical Sciences **3108**
Medical Business Review. (US) **1021**, 873, 3125
Medical Care. (US ISSN 0025-7079) **3125**, 4107
▼Medical Care International. (US) **3125**
Medical Care Products. (US) **3125**
Medical Care Review. (US ISSN 0025-7087) **4118**, 17, 3177
Medical Care Yearbook see Prevention's Medical Care Yearbook **3144**
Medical Careers in Australia. (AT ISSN 0812-7077) **3125**
Medical Centre Journal. (UK ISSN 0025-7095) **3125**
Medical Checklist. (IL ISSN 0025-7109) **3177**
†Medical China. (HK ISSN 0258-3267) **5234**
Medical China Newsfile. (HK) **3125**
Medical Chronicle. (SA ISSN 0025-7117) **3125**
Medical Client Newsletter. (US) **753**, 3125
Medical Clinics of North America. (US ISSN 0025-7125) **3125**
Medical College and Hospital, Calcutta. Bulletin. (IL ISSN 0025-7133) **3125**
Medical College of Georgia Foundation, Inc. Today see M C G Today **3123**
Medical Communications see A M W A Journal **3069**
Medical Companies Guide to Japan. (JA) **3748**, 3177
Medical Computer Journal see M.D. Computing (New York) **3226**
†Medical Computing. (UK ISSN 0143-4330) **5234**
Medical Conference Series. (JA) **3365**
Medical Corps International. (GW ISSN 0179-1826) **3125**, 3806
Medical Council of Iran. Journal - Nezam Pezeshki-ye Iran. Majalleh see Nizam Pezeshki Jomhuriye Islamiye Iran. Majalleh **3136**
Medical Council of Iran. Publication/ Nezam Pezeshki-Ye Iran. Nashriyeh. (IR) **3125**
Medical Council of the Islamic Republic of Iran. Journal. see Nizam Pezeshki Jomhuriye Islamiye Iran. Majalleh **3136**
Medical Decision Making. (US ISSN 0272-989X) **3125**
†Medical Design and Material. (US) **5234**
Medical Device & Diagnostic Industry. (US ISSN 0194-844X) **2524**
Medical Device Approval Letter. (US ISSN 1060-8338) **3262**, 2524
Medical Device Establishment Registration Master File. (US) **4107**, 2653, 3262
Medical Device Patents Letter. (US) **3676**
Medical Device Problems Report from the D E N: Reports from Medical Device Users. (US) **4107**, 2654, 3262
Medical Device Reporting from the D E N: Reports from Medical Device Manufacturers. (US) **4107**, 2654, 3262
Medical Device Reporting Watch see M D R Watch **3123**
▼Medical Device Technology. (US ISSN 1048-6690) **3125**, 2654
Medical Devices, Diagnostics & Instrumentation Reports: The Gray Sheet. (US ISSN 0163-2426) **3126**, 2524, 2654
Medical Devices Reporter. (US) **3126**
Medical Directory. (UK ISSN 0305-3342) **3126**

Medical Directory of New York State. (US) **3126**
Medical Documentation Update. (US ISSN 0739-6554) **3126**
Medical Dosimetry. (US ISSN 0739-0211) **3360**
Medical Economics. (US ISSN 0025-7206) **3126**
Medical Economics for Surgeons. (US) **3381**
Medical Education. (UK ISSN 0308-0110) **3126**
Medical Education Resources Program Memo see M E R P Memo **3123**
Medical Electronics. (US) **3126**
†Medical Electronics & Communications Abstracts. (UK ISSN 0025-7222) **5234**
Medical Electronics and Data see Medical Electronics **3126**
Medical Electronics and Equipment News. (US) **3126**
Medical Electronics News see Medical Electronics and Equipment News **3126**
Medical Electronics News see Medical Imaging and Monitoring **3126**
Medical Engineering. see Meditsinskaya Tekhnika **3130**
Medical Equipment Designer. (US) **2524**, 3126
Medical Equipment Journal of Japan see M E J **3123**
Medical Equipment Journal of Japan. (JA) **3126**
Medical Essentials Directory - Gastroenterology. (US) **3269**
Medical Ethics Advisor. (US ISSN 0886-0653) **3126**, 2654, 3773
Medical Express. (II) **3126**
Medical Focus. (GW ISSN 0724-8172) **4107**
†Medical Forum. (UK ISSN 0261-3646) **5234**
Medical Gazette. (PK) **3126**
Medical Group Management. Journal. (US ISSN 0025-7257) **3126**, 2467
Medical Group Management Association. Directory. (US ISSN 1040-2330) **3126**, 1021
Medical Group Management Association. International Directory see Medical Group Management Association. Directory **3126**
Medical Group News see Medical Group News & In-Office Testing Advances **5234**
†Medical Group News & In-Office Testing Advances. (US) **5234**
The Medical Herald. (US) **3126**
Medical History. (UK ISSN 0025-7273) **3126**
†Medical Horizons. (UK) **5234**
Medical Humanities Review. (US ISSN 0892-2772) **2511**, 3126
Medical Hypnoanalysis Journal. (US) **3274**, 3344, 4035
Medical Hypotheses. (UK ISSN 0306-9877) **3126**
Medical Imaging. see Yingxiang Yixue **3363**
Medical Imaging and Monitoring. (AT) **3126**
▼Medical Industry Executive. (US) **3126**, 2524
Medical Informatics/Medecine et Informatique. (UK ISSN 0307-7640) **3226**
†Medical Information Systems: Abstracts in Medicine and Key Work Index. (US) **5234**
Medical Information Systems: Anesthesiology see Plexus: Annual Medical Specialty Updates **3180**
†Medical Information Systems: Cardiology. (US) **5234**
†Medical Information Systems: Clinical Pathology. (US) **5234**
†Medical Information Systems: Critical Care and Emergency Medicine. (US) **5234**
†Medical Information Systems: Dermatology. (US) **5234**
†Medical Information Systems: Endocrinology. (US) **5234**
†Medical Information Systems: Gastroenterology. (US) **5234**

†Medical Information Systems: Hematology-Oncology. (US) **5234**
†Medical Information Systems: Infectious Disease. (US) **5234**
†Medical Information Systems: Nephrology. (US) **5234**
†Medical Information Systems: Neurology. (US) **5234**
†Medical Information Systems: Pulmonary. (US) **5234**
†Medical Information Systems: Radiology. (US) **5234**
†Medical Information Systems: Rheumatology. (US) **5234**
†Medical Instrument and Equipment Selector. (SA) **5234**
Medical Instrumentation see Biomedical Instrumentation & Technology **3082**
▼Medical Intelligence. (US) **3226**
Medical Interface. (US ISSN 0896-4831) **3126**
Medical Journal Armed Forces, India. (II) **3126**
Medical Journal of Australia. (AT ISSN 0025-729X) **3126**
Medical Journal of Kagoshima University. see Kagoshima Daigaku Igaku Zasshi **3119**
Medical Journal of Malaysia. (MY ISSN 0300-5283) **3127**
Medical Journal of Zambia. (ZA ISSN 0047-651X) **3127**
Medical Laboratory Directory. (US) **3262**
Medical Laboratory Observer see M L O **3262**
Medical Laboratory Products. (US) **3262**, 2524
Medical Laboratory Sciences. (UK ISSN 0308-3616) **3262**
Medical Laboratory Technology see Medical Laboratory Sciences **3262**
Medical Laboratory World. (UK ISSN 0140-3028) **3262**
Medical Laser Industrial Report. (US) **3855**, 3127
Medical Letter. (Spanish translation of: Medical Letter on Drugs and Therapeutics) (SP) **3734**
Medical Letter on Drugs and Therapeutics. (US ISSN 0025-732X) **3734**
Medical Liability Advisory Service. (US ISSN 0199-1272) **2703**, 2537
Medical Liability Monitor. (US ISSN 0732-9636) **2537**
Medical Liability Reporter. (US ISSN 0199-1833) **2703**, 2537
Medical Librarian. see Orvosi Konyvtaros **2778**
Medical Library Association. Bulletin. (US ISSN 0025-7338) **3127**, 2773
Medical Library Association Directory (Year) see M L A Directory (Year) **3123**
Medical Library Association News (Chicago) see M L A News (Chicago) **3123**
Medical Malpractice: Bases of Liability. (US) **2703**, 3127
Medical Malpractice Defense and Health Care Counsel Directory. (US) **2703**, 3127
Medical Malpractice Defense Attorney and Health Care Counsel Directory see Medical Malpractice Defense and Health Care Counsel Directory **2703**
Medical Malpractice Defense Reporter. (US ISSN 0893-8229) **2703**, 3127
▼Medical Malpractice: Handling Dental Cases, 2-E. (US) **2703**, 3237
Medical Malpractice: Handling Obstetric and Neonatal Cases. (US) **2703**, 3294
Medical Malpractice Law & Strategy. (US) **2703**, 3127
Medical Malpractice Litigation Reporter see Medical Malpractice - Ob-Gyn Litigation Reporter **2703**
Medical Malpractice - Ob-Gyn Litigation Reporter. (US ISSN 1056-4098) **2703**, 3127
Medical Malpractice: Pharmacy Law. (US) **2703**, 3734
Medical Malpractice: Psychiatric Care. (US) **2703**, 3344

Medical Malpractice Reports. (US) **2703**, 3127
Medical Malpractice Verdicts, Settlements & Experts. (US ISSN 0888-658X) **2703**, 3127
Medical Market Place. (AT) **3127**
Medical Marketing & Media. (US ISSN 0025-7354) **3734**, 1047
Medical Meetings. (US ISSN 0093-1314) **3393**
Medical Microbiology and Immunology. (GW ISSN 0300-8584) **3188**
▼Medical Microbiology Letters. (SZ ISSN 1018-4627) **555**, 3127
Medical Mission News. (US) **4269**
Medical Mission Sisters News. (US) **2467**, 4269
Medical Missionary News. (UK ISSN 0025-7370) **4189**
Medical-Moral Newsletter. (US ISSN 0025-7397) **3127**
Medical - Mrs. (US) **4848**
Medical News see Noticias Medicas **3136**
Medical News, Medicine and Law. (II ISSN 0047-6536) **3265**
Medical Office Report. (US ISSN 0895-4313) **3127**, 2537
Medical Oncology & Tumor Pharmacotherapy. (UK ISSN 0736-0118) **3200**, 3127
Medical Parasitology and Parasitic Diseases. see Meditsinskaya Parazitologiya i Parazitarnye Bolezni **3222**
Medical Physics. (US ISSN 0094-2405) **3127**, 3824
Medical Physics Series. (US ISSN 0076-5953) **3127**, 3824
Medical Post. (CN ISSN 0025-7435) **3127**
Medical Practice Management see Journal of Medical Practice Management **3117**
Medical Principles and Practice. (SZ ISSN 1011-7571) **3127**
Medical Problems of Performing Artists. (US ISSN 0885-1158) **3127**, 1531, 3562
Medical Product Development see Healthcare Technology & Business Opportunities **3104**
Medical Product Manufacturing News. (US ISSN 0893-6250) **2524**, 1081
Medical Products Distributors. (US) **1145**, 3127
†Medical Products Marketers Directory. (US) **5234**
Medical Products of Japan. (JA) **3127**, 1145
Medical Products Sales. (US ISSN 0279-4802) **3127**, 1047, 2524
Medical Progress. (HK) **3127**
Medical Progress Through Technology. (NE ISSN 0047-6552) **490**, 470, 3127
Medical Protection Society. Annual Report. (UK ISSN 0076-5961) **3127**
Medical Psychotherapy. (CN ISSN 0835-3069) **4035**
Medical Psychotherapy in International Journal. (US) **4035**
Medical Quarterly. (MW) **3127**
†Medical Radiography and Photography. (US ISSN 0025-746X) **5234**
Medical Radiology. see Meditsinskaya Radiologiya **3360**
Medical Radiology. (US) **3360**
Medical Record Educator see Assembly on Education Network **3079**
▼Medical Record Risks: Claims & Litigation. (US ISSN 1061-4192) **2537**, 2703, 3127
Medical Reference Services Quarterly. (US ISSN 0276-3869) **2773**
Medical Reform. (CN) **3127**
Medical Rehabilitation Review. (US) **3127**
Medical Research Centre, Nairobi. Annual Report. (KE ISSN 0076-5988) **3127**
Medical Research Centres. (UK) **3127**
Medical Research Centres in Ghana: Current Research Projects. (GH) **3127**

Medical Research Council Newsletter/Conseil de Recherches Medicales. Actualites. (CN ISSN 0047-6560) **3127**
Medical Research Council of Canada. Grants and Awards Guide/Guide de Subventions et Bourses. (CN) **3127**
Medical Research Council of Canada. Reference List of Health Science Research in Canada. (CN) **3127**
Medical Research Council of Canada. Report of the President. (CN) **3127**
Medical Research Funding Bulletin. (US) **4412**, 3127
▼Medical Research Funding News. (US) **3128**, 1711
Medical Research in the V.A. (US) **3128**
†Medical Rounds. (US) **5234**
Medical School Admission Requirements, United States and Canada. (US ISSN 0066-9423) **1711**, 3128
Medical Science in Rural China. see Zhongguo Nongcun Yixue **3164**
Medical Science Research. (UK ISSN 0269-8951) **3128**
Medical Sciences Bulletin. (US ISSN 0199-4905) **3734**, 3128
Medical Sciences International Who's Who. (UK) **420**, 3128
Medical Sciences University of Tehran. School of Medicine. Journal/Majalleh Daneshkadeh Pezeshki. (IR) **3128**
†Medical Selfcare. (US ISSN 0162-2285) **5234**
Medical Service see Health Action **2461**
Medical Society County of Kings Bulletin see K C M S Bulletin **3119**
Medical Society of London. Transactions. (UK ISSN 0076-6011) **3128**
Medical Society of the County of Kings and Academy of Medicine of Brooklyn. Bulletin see K C M S Bulletin **3119**
Medical Software Directory. (US) **1478**, 1470, 3226
Medical Staff Law Manual. (US) **2703**, 3128
Medical Staff Leader. (US) **2467**
Medical Staff News see Medical Staff Leader **2467**
Medical Subject Headings (Black Book). (US ISSN 0565-811X) **3128**
Medical Teacher. (UK ISSN 0142-159X) **3128**
Medical Technologist see Medical Technologist and Scientist **3128**
Medical Technologist and Scientist. (UK ISSN 0309-2666) **3128**
Medical Technologist Diary & Classified Buyer's Guide. (UK) **3128**
Medical Technologist Today see M T Today **3262**
Medical Technology. see Rinsho Kensagaku Zasshi **3149**
Medical Technology S A. (SA ISSN 1011-5528) **3262**
Medical Technology Stock Letter. (US) **955**, 3128
Medical Textiles. (UK ISSN 0266-2078) **3128**
Medical Theory and Practice. see Yixue Lilun yu Shijian **3163**
†Medical Times. (US ISSN 0025-7583) **5234**
Medical Trial Technique Quarterly. (US ISSN 0025-7591) **2703**, 3128
Medical Tribune. (IT ISSN 0392-7199) **3128**
Medical Tribune (1980). (US ISSN 0279-9340) **3128**
Medical Tribune and Medical News see Medical Tribune (1980) **3128**
Medical Update. (US) **3806**
Medical Utilization Review. (US ISSN 0734-1970) **3128**
Medical Video Flash. (IT) **3128**
Medical Waste News. (US ISSN 1048-4493) **1985**, 3128
Medical Wire see Wyoming Physicians Newsletter **3163**
Medical World. (UK ISSN 0025-7621) **3128**
Medical World News. (US ISSN 0025-763X) **3128**

MedicalDisc Reporter see Interactive Healthcare Newsletter 3225
Medicamentos de Actualidad - Drugs of Today. (SP) 3734
Medicamundi. (NE ISSN 0025-7664) 3360
Medicare Advisor. (US) 2537, 3128
Medicare and Medicaid Data Book. (US) 2537
Medicare Compliance Alert. (US) 2537, 3128
Medicare Compliance Report see Medicare Compliance Alert 2537
Medicare - Medicaid Guide. (US) 2537
Medicare Review. (US) 2537, 3128
†Medicenter Management. (US ISSN 0892-8185) 5234
Medicina. (AG ISSN 0025-7680) 3128
Medicina. (JA ISSN 0025-7699) 3128
Medicina. (CI ISSN 0025-7729) 3128
Medicina. (BL ISSN 0076-6046) 3128
Medicina Clinica. (SP ISSN 0025-7753) 3129
Medicina Cutanea Ibero-Latino-Americana. (SP ISSN 0210-5187) 3249
Medicina da Pontificia Universidade Catolica do Rio Grande do Sul. Revista. (BL ISSN 0103-2690) 3129
Medicina Danas. (YU ISSN 0025-7796) 3129
Medicina de Empresa. (SP) 3619
Medicina de Hoje. (BL) 3129
Medicina del Lavoro. (IT ISSN 0025-7818) 3619
Medicina Dello Sport. (IT ISSN 0025-7826) 3372
La Medicina di Laboratorio. (IT ISSN 0393-7623) 3262
Medicina do Esporte. (BL) 3372
Medicina e Informatica. (IT) 3226
Medicina e Psyche/Medicine and Mind. (IT ISSN 0394-1531) 3344, 4035
Medicina Geriatrica. (IT ISSN 0391-4844) 2276
Medicina Integral. (SP) 3129
Medicina Intensiva. (SP) 3129
Medicina Interna. Annali Italiani. (IT) 3129
Medicina Moderna Oggi/Modern Medicine Today. (IT ISSN 0394-2627) 3129
Medicina Muncii si Medicina Sociala. (RM) 3129
Medicina Naturale. (IT) 3129
Medicina nei Secoli see Medicina nei Secoli: Arte e Scienza 3129
Medicina nei Secoli: Arte e Scienza. (IT ISSN 0394-9001) 3129
Medicina Oggi. (IT ISSN 0392-4548) 3129
Medicina Ospedaliera Romana. (IT ISSN 0391-7231) 3129, 2467
Medicina Psicosomatica. (IT ISSN 0025-7893) 3344
Medicina Termale e Climatologia. (IT ISSN 0580-9320) 3129
Medicina Thoracalis see Respiration 3366
Medicina Toracica. (IT) 3366
†Medicina Tropical. (SP ISSN 0025-7958) 5234
Medicina y Cirugia. (CR) 3381
Medicina y Deporte. (SP) 3372
Medicinal and Aromatic Plants Abstracts. (II ISSN 0250-4367) 3177, 17
†Medicinal Chemistry. (US ISSN 0076-6054) 5234
▼Medicinal Chemistry Research. (US ISSN 1054-2523) 3129, 447, 1183
Medicinal Research Reviews. (US ISSN 0198-6325) 3734
Medicinal Research Series. (US) 3129
Medicinar. (CI ISSN 0025-7966) 3237
Medicine (Baltimore). (US ISSN 0025-7974) 3129
Medicine and Biology. see Igaku to Seibutsugaku 3107
Medicine and Gospel. see Igaku to Fukuin 3107

Medicine and Health see McGraw-Hill's Washington Report on Medicine and Health 3123
Medicine and Men. see Yaowu yu Ren 3746
Medicine and Mind. see Medicina e Psyche 3344
Medicine and Science in Sports and Exercise. (US ISSN 0195-9131) 3372
Medicine and Sport Science. (SZ ISSN 0254-5020) 3372, 3310
Medicine & Surgery. (II ISSN 0025-8008) 3381
Medicine and War. (UK ISSN 0748-8009) 3129, 3464, 3906
Medicine - Biology - Environment. see Medecine - Biologie - Environnement 3200
Medicine Digest. (UK ISSN 0140-9158) 3129
▼Medicine, Exercise, Nutrition and Health. (US ISSN 1057-9354) 3129, 3609, 3806
Medicine - Health Information Review. (US) 2467, 3129
Medicine International. Middle Eastern Edition. (UK ISSN 0144-0438) 3129
Medicine International. Quarterly Edition.(UK ISSN 0144-0411) 3129
Medicine International. Southern African Edition. (SA ISSN 0260-2334) 3129
Medicine International. U K Edition. (UK ISSN 0144-0403) 3129
Medicine North America. (CN ISSN 0225-3895) 3129
Medicine on the Midway see University of Chicago. Pritzker School of Medicine. Alumni Association. Magazine 1328
Medicinhistorisk Aarsbok see Nordisk Medicinhistorisk Aarsbok 3136
Medicinsk Aarbog. (DK ISSN 0461-6308) 3129
Medicinsk Foedselsstatistik see Medicinsk Foedselsstatistik og Misdannelsesstatistik 3177
Medicinsk Foedselsstatistik og Misdannelsesstatistik. (DK ISSN 0904-1966) 3177
†Medicinsk Forum. (DK ISSN 0025-8040) 5234
Medicinska Misla/Acta Facultatis Medicinae Skopiensis. (XN ISSN 0065-1214) 3130
Medicinski Glasnik. (YU ISSN 0025-8091) 3130
Medicinski Podmladak. (YU ISSN 0369-1527) 3130
Medicinski Pregled. (YU ISSN 0025-8105) 3130
Medicinski Razgledi. (XV ISSN 0025-8121) 3130, 447
Medicintakst. (DK ISSN 0900-4858) 3734
Medico. (PO ISSN 0461-6375) 3130
Medico-Biologic Information see M B I 3123
Medico d'Italia. (IT ISSN 0025-8148) 3130
Medico e Bambino. (IT) 3322
Medico e Paziente. (IT) 3130
Medico Interamericano. (US ISSN 0278-9779) 3130, 2013
Medico-Legal Advisor. (US ISSN 0899-0255) 2703, 3130
†Medico-Legal Bulletin. (US ISSN 0025-8164) 5234
Medico-Legal Expert Testimony. see Sudebnomeditsinskaya Ekspertiza 3266
Medico-Legal Journal. (UK ISSN 0025-8172) 3265
Medico-Legal Society of Sri Lanka. Proceedings. (CE) 3265
Medico-Legal Society of Victoria. Proceedings. (AT ISSN 0047-6595) 2703, 3130
Medico Practico. (SP ISSN 1130-6416) 3130
El Medico, Profesion y Humanidades. (SP) 3130
Medicolegal-Gram. (US) 3265
Medicolegal Library. (US) 2727, 3130
Medicom. (KE) 3130

Medicom Drug Information Newsletter. (US ISSN 0737-3139) 3734
Medicum. (AU) 3130
Medielaererforeningen for Gymnasiet og H F. Meddelelser. (DK ISSN 0903-8981) 3513, 1647
Medien Aktiv. (GW) 3793, 1647
Medien Bulletin. (GW) 1376
Medien Dialog. (GW) 1376, 35, 1047
†Medien Journal. (AU) 5234
Medien-Kritik. (GW ISSN 0176-3849) 1376, 2572
†Medien Memo. (GW ISSN 0937-7417) 5234
Medien & Erziehung. (GW ISSN 0341-6860) 1376, 1260, 1647
Medien und Publicum. (GW ISSN 0932-7886) 2572
Medien und Recht see Medien und Recht International 2654
Medien und Recht International. (AU ISSN 0257-3822) 2654, 1376, 2727
MedienConcret. (GW ISSN 0931-9808) 1340, 1647, 3513
Medienpsychologie. (GW ISSN 0936-7780) 4035, 4442
Medienreport. (GW) 1021, 1047, 1376
Medienwissenschaft. (GW ISSN 0176-4241) 1376, 3513, 4132
Medieval Academy Books. (US) 2375, 335, 2937
Medieval Academy of America. Publications see Medieval Academy Books 2375
Medieval Academy Reprints for Teaching. (CN) 2375, 2511, 2937
Medieval and Early Modern Mysticism. (US ISSN 1056-7917) 4189, 2317
Medieval and Renaissance Authors. (NE ISSN 0169-9059) 2937
Medieval and Renaissance Authors and Texts. (NE ISSN 0925-7683) 2375
Medieval and Renaissance Drama in England. (US ISSN 0731-3403) 4635, 2937
Medieval and Renaissance Texts. (NE ISSN 0169-9105) 2375
Medieval and Renaissance Yearbook. (US ISSN 1048-8588) 2937
Medieval Archaeology. (UK ISSN 0076-6097) 278, 2375
Medieval Architecture & Sculpture in Europe see Courtauld Institute Illustration Archives. Archive 3 323
Medieval English Theatre. (UK ISSN 0143-3784) 4635
Medieval Folklore. (US ISSN 1048-857X) 2056
Medieval Iberian Peninsula. (NE ISSN 0076-6100) 2375
Medieval Music-Drama News see Early Drama, Art, and Music Review 4632
Medieval Prosopography. (US ISSN 0198-9405) 2375
Medievalia et Humanistica. (US ISSN 0076-6127) 2375, 335, 2937, 3773
Medieviste et l'Ordinateur. (FR ISSN 0223-3843) 2330
Medigram. (CN) 35, 3130
Medikament & Meinung. (GW ISSN 0171-3876) 3130, 3735, 4107
Medilab see Labmedica 3261
Medindex. (UK) 2524, 3130
Medio Ambiente. (CL ISSN 0304-8764) 1962
Medio Ambiente en Espana. (SP) 1962
Medioevo. (IT) 3773
Medioevo Romanzo. (IT ISSN 0390-0711) 2937
Medios Audiovisuales. (SP ISSN 0210-7775) 1376, 1647
Medios Publicitarios Mexicanos, S.A. Directorio M P M - Agencias y Anunciantes see Directorio M P M - Agencias y Anunciantes 31
Medios Publicitarios Mexicanos, S.A. Directorio M P M - Medios Audiovisuales see Directorio M P M - Medios Audiovisuales 41

Medios Publicitarios Mexicanos, S.A. Directorio M P M - Medios Impresos see Directorio M P M - Medios Impresos 41
Medipharm. (NR ISSN 0331-4782) 3735, 3130
Medipharm Medical Journal. (NR ISSN 0794-3733) 3130
Medisch Contact. (NE ISSN 0025-8245) 3130
Mediscope. (UK ISSN 0261-7099) 3130
Mediscope. (FR) 3130
Medisoft see Medical Software Directory 1478
Medisom: Anaesthesiology. (BL) 3191
Medisom: Cancer. (BL) 3200
Medisom: Cardiology. (BL) 3210
Medisom: Dermatology. (BL) 3249
Medisom: Gastroenterology. (BL) 3269
Medisom: Gynecology. (BL) 3294
Medisom: Orthopedics. (BL) 3310
Medisom: Otorhinolaryngology. (BL) 3315
Medisom: Rheumatology. (BL) 3369
Meditation see Better World 3593
Meditation. (GW) 4189
Mediterranea. (SP ISSN 0210-5004) 587, 509
Mediterranea. (IT) 4848
Mediterranean Electrotechnical Conference. (US) 1903
Mediterranean Historical Review. (UK ISSN 0951-8967) 2430
Mediterranean Journal of Social Psychiatry. (CI ISSN 0351-4501) 3344
Mediterranean Language and Culture Monograph Series. (GW ISSN 0179-1621) 1278, 2829
Mediterranean Language Review. (GW ISSN 0724-7567) 1278, 2829
Mediterranean Quarterly. (US ISSN 1047-4552) 3965
Mediterranean Social Sciences Network Journal. (MM) 4379
Mediterranean Social Sciences Network Newsletter see Mediterranean Social Sciences Network Journal 4379
Mediterranee. (FR ISSN 0025-8296) 2256, 1547
Mediterranee Immobiliere. (FR) 4152
Mediterranee Medicale. (FR ISSN 0302-9263) 3130
†Mediterraneo. (IT ISSN 0047-6609) 5234
Meditsinskaya Gazeta. (RU ISSN 0025-8318) 3130
Meditsinskaya Parazitologiya i Parazitarnye Bolezni/Medical Parasitology and Parasitic Diseases. (RU ISSN 0025-8326) 3222
Meditsinskaya Radiologiya/Medical Radiology. (RU ISSN 0025-8334) 3360
Meditsinskaya Sestra/Nurse. (RU ISSN 0025-8342) 3282
Meditsinskaya Tekhnika/Medical Engineering. (RU ISSN 0025-8075) 3130
Meditsinskii Zhurnal Uzbekistana. (UZ ISSN 0025-830X) 3130
Medium. (GW ISSN 0025-8350) 1376
Medium. (CN ISSN 0025-8377) 2773, 1755
Medium (New Brunswick). (US) 1317
Medium (New York). (US) 2013, 3513, 3562
Medium Aevum. (UK ISSN 0025-8385) 2937, 2829
▼Medium Companies of Europe. (UK ISSN 0960-1449) 1145, 790
Medium-Term Programme (Years). (NE) 2773
Medium II. (CN) 1317
Medivet. (CU) 4812
Mediya Sakuru/Media Circle. (JA ISSN 0287-5594) 555, 480
Medizin Aktuell. (GW ISSN 0323-5386) 3130
†Medizin Bibliothek Dokumentation. (GW ISSN 0343-1002) 5234
Medizin Heute. (GW ISSN 0179-0404) 3806
Medizin in Berlin (West). (GW ISSN 0721-6076) 2467
Medizin in Recht und Ethik. (GW ISSN 0340-9511) 2703, 3130

Medizin-Mensch-Gesellschaft see M M G 3123
Medizin ohne Nebenwirkungen. (GW ISSN 0939-6292) 3735
Medizin Populaer. (AU) 3130
Medizin-Technischer Dialog see M T Dialog 3123
Medizinhistorisches Journal. (GW ISSN 0025-8431) 3130, 2317
Medizinisch-Orthopaedische Technik. (GW ISSN 0340-5508) 3310
Medizinisch-Technische Assistenten Fachzeitschrift fuer Technische Assistenten der Medizin see M T A - Fachzeitschrift fuer Technische Assistenten der Medizin 3123
Medizinische Akademie "Carl Gustav Carus" Dresden. Schriften. (GW ISSN 0070-721X) 3130
Medizinische Genetik. (GW) 545
Medizinische Hochschule Hannover Info see M H H - Info 1316
Medizinische Informatik und Statistik. (US ISSN 0342-4103) 3130
Medizinische Klinik. (GW ISSN 0723-5003) 3130
Medizinische Kongresse. (GW ISSN 0175-3053) 3393
Medizinische Laenderkunde. Geomedical Monograph Series. (US ISSN 0076-6151) 3130
Medizinische Monatsschrift fuer Pharmazeuten. (GW ISSN 0342-9601) 3131
Medizinische Neuerscheinungen. (GW ISSN 0025-8482) 3177
Der Medizinische Sachverstaendige. (GW ISSN 0025-8490) 3131
Die Medizinische Welt. (GW ISSN 0025-8512) 3131
Medizinischen Universitaet zu Luebeck Focus M U L see Focus M U L 3098
Medizinrecht. (GW ISSN 0723-8886) 3265
Medizinscher Literatur Anzeiger. (GW) 3177
Medizintechnik. (GW ISSN 0344-9416) 3131
Medjimurje. (CI ISSN 0025-8229) 2874
Medjunarodni Problemi. (YU ISSN 0025-8555) 3965
Medlemsavisen. (DK) 3793
Medoc: Index to U S Government Publications in the Medical and Health Sciences. (US ISSN 0097-9732) 3177
Medpro Month. (US) 3131
Medunarodna Politika see Review of International Affairs 3970
Medusa see Agarte 3520
Medway Ports Shipping Handbook. (UK ISSN 0261-281X) 4733, 1145
Medycyna Doswiadczalna i Mikrobiologia. (PL ISSN 0025-8601) 555, 3131
Medycyna Pracy. (PL ISSN 0465-5893) 3131
Medycyna Weterynaryjna. (PL ISSN 0025-8628) 4813
Medycyna Wiejska/Rural Medicine. (PL ISSN 0025-8636) 3131
Medyk/Physician. (PL ISSN 0867-3055) 3131
Meek - Meeks Newsletter. (US) 2158
Meeresforschung/Reports on Marine Research. (GW ISSN 0341-6836) 1608
Meerut University Sanskrit Research see Meerut University Sanskrit Research Journal 4379
Meerut University Sanskrit Research Journal. (II) 4379
†Meet the Lords. (US) 5234
Meeting & Congressi see M & C 3393
▼Meeting Communications. (CN) 3393, 4776
Meeting Ground. (US) 2013, 2414
Meeting in London. (UK) 4776
Meeting Manager. (US ISSN 8750-7218) 3393
Meeting News. (US) 3393
Meeting Place see Meeting Manager 3393
Meeting Planners Alert. (US ISSN 0743-3832) 3393, 679
Meeting Planners Guidebook. (US) 3393, 679

Meeting Planners International Buyers Guide see M P I Buyers Guide 5230
Meetings and Conventions. (US ISSN 0025-8652) 3393
Meetings and Conventions Gavel. (US) 3393
Meetings & Incentive Travel. (CN ISSN 0318-1049) 3393
Meetings Monthly. (CN) 3393
Meetings on Atomic Energy. (UN ISSN 0047-6641) 3393, 1807
Mega Play. (US) 1419
Megadim. (IS ISSN 0334-8814) 4225
Megadrilogica. (CN ISSN 0380-9633) 588, 185
†Megafon. (AG) 5235
Megamot. (IS ISSN 0025-8679) 4442, 4035
Megaphon. (GW) 1260, 1729
Megaphone (Canton). (US ISSN 0025-8687) 1317
Megaphone (Georgetown). (US ISSN 0025-8709) 1317
Megatrends Aktuell see Trendletter Megatrends Aktuell 695
Megavatios. (AG) 1903
Meghalaya Chronicle. (II ISSN 0377-1261) 873
Meghalaya Industrial Development Corporation. Annual Report. (II ISSN 0376-5423) 679
Megiddo Message. (US) 4189
Meglio. (IT ISSN 0025-8717) 2205
Meguro-ku no Kogai/Environmental Pollution in Meguro Ward. (JA) 1962
Megyei es Varosi Statisztikai Ertesito see Hungary. Kozponti Statisztikai Hivatal. Teruleti Statisztika 4574
Mehandesim. (IS) 1830
†Meharri-Dent. (US ISSN 0025-8725) 5235
†Meharry Medical College. School of Dentistry. Proceedings of an Oral Research Seminar. (US) 5235
Mehr Freude Magazin. (GW) 4189, 1260
Mei-kuo Hsin Wen yu Shih Chieh Pao Tao. (Chinese translation of: U S News & World Report) (US) 2228, 3906
Mei Plezant see Volksdans 2059
Mei Shu Chia. see Artist 316
Mei yu Shidai. (CC) 3773
Meidai Uchusan Kenkyushitsu Kiji/Nagoya University. Solar-Terrestrial Environment Laboratory. Cosmic Ray Section. Proceedings. (JA ISSN 0910-0717) 3824
†Meidan Liike/Our Movement. (FI) 5235
Meidan Talo. (FI) 624
Meiden Review. (JA) 1903
Meie Elu/Our Life. (CN ISSN 0047-665X) 2013
Meie Tee. (US ISSN 0025-8768) 2013
Meier-Dudy/Meier's Directory of Exporters and Importers. (GW ISSN 0076-6208) 917
Meieriposten. (NO ISSN 0025-8776) 201
Meier's Directory of Exporters and Importers. see Meier-Dudy 917
Meiguo Yanjiu/American Studies. (CC) 4379
Meiguo Yixuehui Yanke Zazhi. (CC ISSN 1000-0348) 3302
Meijerbergs Arkiv for Svensk Ordforskning. (SW ISSN 0348-7741) 2829
†Meijeriteollisuus. (FI ISSN 0784-1736) 5235
Meijeritieteellinen Aikakauskirja - Finnish Journal of Dairy Science see Finnish Journal of Dairy Science 199
Meiji College of Oriental Medicine. Newsletter. (US) 3131
Meiji Daigaku Kagaku Gijutsu Kenkyujo Hokoku. Sogo Kenkyu/Meiji University. Institute of Science and Technology. Report. Special Project. (JA ISSN 0285-8258) 4603, 4324

Meiji Daigaku Kagaku Gijutsu Kenkyujo Kiyo/Meiji University. Institute of Science and Technology. Memoirs. (JA ISSN 0386-4944) 4603, 4324
Meiji Daigaku Kagaku Gijutsu Kenkyujo Nenpo/Meiji University. Institute of Science and Technology. Annual Report. (JA ISSN 0543-3916) 4603, 4324
Meiji University. Institute of Science and Technology. Annual Report. see Meiji Daigaku Kagaku Gijutsu Kenkyujo Nenpo 4603
Meiji University. Institute of Science and Technology. Memoirs. see Meiji Daigaku Kagaku Gijutsu Kenkyujo Kiyo 4603
Meiji University. Institute of Science and Technology. Report. Special Project. see Meiji Daigaku Kagaku Gijutsu Kenkyujo Hokoku. Sogo Kenkyu 4603
Meijo Daigaku Rikogakubu Kenkyu Hokoku/Meijo University. Faculty of Science and Technology. Reports. (JA ISSN 0386-4952) 4603
Meijo University. Faculty of Science and Technology. Reports. see Meijo Daigaku Rikogakubu Kenkyu Hokoku 4603
Meikai University School of Dentistry. Journal. (JA ISSN 0916-0701) 3237, 3131
Mein Eigenheim. (GW ISSN 0025-8792) 790
Mein Erlebnis. (GW ISSN 0179-8596) 4848
Mein Geheimnis. (GW) 4848
Mein Schicksal. (GW) 4848
Mein Schoener Garten. (US) 2134
Meine Familie und Ich. (GW) 2190
Meine Geschichte. (GW ISSN 0935-8005) 4848
Meine Gesundheit "Reiseapotheke". (GW) 4776, 3735
Meio Ambiente. (BL ISSN 0103-913X) 1962, 1506
Meio & Mensagem. (BL) 35
Meiqi yu Reli/Gas and Heating Power. (CC ISSN 1000-4416) 1903
Meira. (BG) 2997
Meisei Daigaku Kenkyu Kiyo. Rikogakubu/Meisei University. Research Bulletin. Physical Sciences and Engineering. (JA ISSN 0388-130X) 1830, 1183, 3824
Meisei University. Research Bulletin. Physical Sciences and Engineering. see Meisei Daigaku Kenkyu Kiyo. Rikogakubu 1830
Meishu/Art. (CC) 335
Meishu Daguan. (CC) 335
Meishu Gengyun. (CC) 335
Meishu Jie/Air Circle. (CC) 335
Meishu Shilun/History of Arts. (CC) 335
Meishu Yanjiu/Art Research. (CC ISSN 0461-6855) 335
Meishu zhi You/Friend of Fine Arts. (CC) 335
Meister des Puppenspiels. (GW ISSN 0076-6216) 4635
Meister - Zeitung see Industrie Meister 1078
Meisterbetrieb. (GW) 3864, 2116
Meitan Jingji Yanjiu/Coal Economics Study. (CC) 679, 3488
Meitan Qiye Guanli/Coal Industry Management. (CC) 1021
Meitan Xuebao/China Coal Society. Journal. (CC ISSN 0253-9993) 3488
Meiyuan/Centre of Fine Arts Quarterly. (CC ISSN 1003-5605) 335
Mejeri- og Dagligvarehandel. (DK) 201
Mejerbrugets Uge-Nyt. (DK ISSN 0302-833X) 201
Mejeristen. (DK) 201
Mejeritidskrift foer Finlands Svenskbygd.(FI ISSN 0355-0532) 201
Mekarkaiin Vearcham/Land and Value. (IS) 4152
Mekeel's Stamp News. (US ISSN 0025-8857) 3754
Mekevot. see Sources of Contemporary Jewish Thought 2884

MELLEN STUDIES 6427

†Mekhanicheskaya Tekhnologiya/Mechanine Technologija. (UR) 5235
Mekhanika Kompozitnykh Materialov. (LV ISSN 0203-1272) 1935
Mekhanika Polimerov see Mekhanika Kompozitnykh Materialov 1935
Mekhanika Tverdogo Tela. (KR ISSN 0321-1975) 3844
Mekhanizatsiya i Avtomatizatsiya Proizvodstva. (RU ISSN 0025-8873) 1415
Mekhanizatsiya i Elektrifikatsiya. (RU ISSN 0206-572X) 163
Mekhanizatsiya i Elektrifikatsiya Sotsialisticheskogo Sel'skogo Khozyaistva see Mekhanizatsiya i Elektrifikatsiya 163
Mekhanizatsiya Stroitel'stva. (RU ISSN 0025-8903) 1871, 624, 3021
†Mekong Bulletin. (UN ISSN 0252-5348) 5235
Mekong News. (TH) 873
Mela. (UK ISSN 0965-7738) 4848
Melanderia. (US ISSN 0076-6224) 536
Melanesian Journal of Theology. (PP ISSN 0256-856X) 4189
Melanesian Law Journal. (PP ISSN 0254-0657) 2654
Melanges CRAPEL see Universite de Nancy II. Centre de Recherches et d'Applications Pedagogiques en Langues. Melanges 1762
Melanges d'Histoire de l'Architecture. (BE) 303, 335
Melanges de Science Religieuse. (FR ISSN 0025-8911) 4269
Melanoma and Other Skin Cancer - Diagnosis, Treatment see I C R D B Cancergram: Melanoma and Other Skin Cancer - Diagnosis, Treatment 3175
▼Melanoma Research. (UK ISSN 0960-8931) 3200
Melbourne. Port Council News. (AT) 4090, 4413
Melbourne Citymission. Annual Report. (AT ISSN 0728-1897) 4413
Melbourne Cityscope. (AT) 4160
Melbourne College of Advanced Education. Handbook see Institute of Education. Handbook 1695
Melbourne International Philosophy Series see Nijhoff International Philosophy Series 3774
Melbourne Jewish News see Australian Jewish News (Darlinghurst) 1992
Melbourne Journal of Politics. (AT ISSN 0085-3224) 3906
Melbourne Politics Monographs. (AT) 3906
Melbourne Port and Shipping Handbook. (AT ISSN 0267-7350) 1145, 4733
Melbourne Slavonic Studies see Australian Slavonic and East European Studies 2804
Melbourne Star Observer. (AT ISSN 0816-4290) 2455
Melbourne Studies in Education. (AT ISSN 0076-6275) 1647
Melbourne University Law Review. (AT ISSN 0025-8938) 2654
Melbourne Walker see The Walker 4559
Mele. (US ISSN 0025-8954) 2997
Melhores e Maiores. (BL) 1081, 873
Melibea. (PE) 2937
Meliorace/Irrigation and Drainage. (CS) 107
Meliorist. (CN) 1317
Melita Theologica. (MM) 4189, 3773
Melk en Wij see Lait et Nous 201
Melk en Zuivel see Zuivelkoerier 204
Mellemamerika Nyt. (DK ISSN 0904-6089) 2414
Mellemfolkeligt Samvirke Bibliotheksnyt see M S Bibliotheksnyt 3965
Mellemoest Information. Maanedsoversigt. (DK) 3965
Mellen Lives. (US) 420
Mellen Opera Reference Index. (US) 3589
Mellen Poetry Series. (US) 2997
Mellen Studies in Business. (US) 679
Mellen Studies in Education. (US) 1647
Mellen Studies in History. (US) 2317
Mellen Studies in Sociology. (US) 4442

Melliand Textilberichte/Melliand Textile Reports. (GW ISSN 0341-0781) **4621**
Melliand Textilberichte (English Edition)/International Textile Reports. (US ISSN 0198-7275) **4621**
Melliand Textile Reports. *see* Melliand Textilberichte **4621**
Melodie. (CS ISSN 0025-8997) **3562**
Melodie pre Vas. (CS) **3562**
Melodie und Rhythmus. (GW ISSN 0025-9004) **3562**
Melody Maker. (UK ISSN 0025-9012) **3562**
Melos. (GW ISSN 0174-7207) **3562**
Melos *see* N Z: Neue Zeitschrift fuer Musik **3569**
Melpomene Journal. (US) **4835**, **3806**
Melpomene Report *see* Melpomene Journal **4835**
Melsheimer Entomological Series. (US ISSN 0076-6321) **536**
Melts. (English translation of: Rasplavy) (US) **1183**, **3824**
Melus *see* M E L U S **2936**
Melville Society Extracts. (US ISSN 0193-8991) **2937**
Melyepitesi es Vizepitesi Szakirodalmi Tajekoztato/Civil Engineering & Hydraulic Engineering Abstracts. (HU ISSN 0231-0732) **1845**, 17, 1871, 1924
Melyepitestudomanyi Szemle. (HU ISSN 0025-9039) **1871**, **4719**
Member Firm Confidential Statistics Report. (US) **729**
Member Net. (US) **2654**
Memberanda. (US) **1755**
Members Exchange *see* American Medallic Sculpture Association. Members Exchange **311**
Members of the Stock Exchange *see* I S E Firms and Members **949**
Membership Directory - National Association of College Admissions Counselors *see* National Association of College Admissions Counselors. Membership Directory **1712**
Membership Directory of the Golf Course Superintendents Association of America *see* Golf Course Superintendents Association of America. Membership Directory **4505**
Membership Marketer. (US) **1021**, **1047**
Membrane & Separation Technology News. (US ISSN 0737-8483) **490**
Membrane Biochemistry. (US ISSN 0149-046X) **480**, **486**
Membrane Lipids. (UK ISSN 0952-0422) **480**
Membrane Planning Conference (Year). (US) **1183**
Membrane Proteins. (UK ISSN 0143-4233) **480**, **486**, **3131**
▼Membrane Science and Technology Series. (NE) **480**
Membrane Separation Processes. Proceedings. (UK) **1220**
▼Membrane Technology Newsletter. (UK ISSN 0958-2118) **1184**, 1935
Membrane Technology Reviews. (US) **490**
†Membrane Transport Processes. (US ISSN 0160-2462) **5235**
MEMCO News *see* M E M C O News **3429**
Memeler Dampfboot. (GW ISSN 0025-9047) **2013**
Memento de l'Economie Africaine. (FR) **873**
†Memento de l'O.I.V. (Office International de la Vigne et du Vin) (FR ISSN 0085-221X) **5235**
Memento General Tequi Quincaillerie *see* Essor de la Quincaillerie **642**
Memento Pratique des Societes Commerciales. (FR) **2654**
Memes. (UK) **2998**
Memisa Nieuws. (NE ISSN 0025-9063) **3131**
Memminger Geschichtsblaetter. (GW ISSN 0539-2896) **2375**
Memo. (CY) **679**
Memo. (CN) **1067**

Memo *see* Professional Secretary **5262**
Memo (Washington, 1947). (US ISSN 0732-4073) **303**
Memo-Forum. (GW ISSN 0176-5833) **679**
Memo from Belgium. (BE ISSN 0025-908X) **3906**, **873**
†Memo from C O P E. (US ISSN 0032-3160) **5235**
Memo Press: Aktuelle Presse- und Literatur Hinweise mit Kommentar *see* Memopress Ausgabe K **2874**
Memo Press: Aktuelle Presse- und Literatur Hinweise mit Kommentar *see* Memopress Ausgabe D **2874**
Memo to Mailers. (US) **1353**
Memo: To the President. (US ISSN 0047-6692) **1711**
Memoire des Femmes. (FR) **4848**, **420**
Memoires C.E.R.E.S. (Centre d'Etudes, de Recherches et d'Essais Scientifiques du Genie Civil) (BE ISSN 0025-9195) **1871**
Memoires de Photo-Interpretation. (FR ISSN 0076-6364) **3793**
Memoires et Documents Geographie. (FR ISSN 0224-2702) **2256**
Memoires et Documents sur Rome et l'Italie Meridionale. (IT) **2375**
Memoires et Etudes Scientifiques de la Revue de Metallurgie *see* Revue de Metallurgie. Memoires et Etudes Scientifiques **3418**
†Memoires O.R.S.T.O.M. (FR ISSN 0071-9005) **5235**
Memoires Optiques. (FR) **3855**
Memoires Optiques et Systemes. (FR) **1479**
Memoires pour Servir a l'Explication des Cartes Geologiques et Minieres de la Belgique. (BE) **1572**, **3488**
Memoires Suisse de Paleontologie. *see* Schweizerische Palaeontologische Abhandlungen **3660**
Memoirs of the Hourglass Cruises. (US ISSN 0085-0683) **447**, 1608
Memoirs of the Kern Institute *see* Kern Institute, Leiden. Memoirs **3640**
Memoirs on Indian Animal Types. (II) **447**
Memon Alam. (PK ISSN 0025-9144) **1260**
Memopress Ausgabe D. (SZ) **2874**
Memopress Ausgabe K. (SZ) **2874**
Memorabilia Zoologica. (PL ISSN 0076-6372) **588**
Memorandum (St. Paul) *see* University of St. Thomas Magazine **1328**
Memorandum of Books Printed in Mauritius and Registered in the Archives Office. (MF) **406**
Memoria. (IT ISSN 0392-4564) **4848**
Memoria del Grupo I C O. (Instituto de Credito Oficial) (SP) **1101**
Memoria e Historia. (BL) **2414**
Memorial de l'Artillerie Francaise. (FR ISSN 0025-9160) **3464**
Memorial des Percepteurs et Receveurs des Communes. (FR ISSN 0025-9179) **4067**
Memorial University of Newfoundland. Gazette. (CN ISSN 0228-8877) **1317**
Memorial University of Newfoundland. Occasional Papers in Biology. (CN ISSN 0702-0007) **447**
Memorials - Geological Society of America *see* Geological Society of America. Memorials **1563**
Memorias de Historia Antigua. (SP ISSN 0210-2943) **2317**
Memorie di Biologia Marina e di Oceanografia. (IT ISSN 0390-492X) **1608**, 447
Memorie di Scienze Geologiche. (IT) **1572**, 1592, 1599
Memorie Domenicane. (IT) **2317**, **4189**
†Memories. (US ISSN 0898-9184) **5235**
Memory and Cognition. (US ISSN 0090-502X) **4035**
▼Memory Card Systems and Designs. (US) **1416**, 1438
Memory I Cs D.A.T.A. Digest. (US ISSN 1048-2598) **1775**

Memory Lane. (UK ISSN 0266-8033) **3562**
Memphis. (US ISSN 0162-282X) **2228**
Memphis Brooks Museum of Art. Newsletter. (US) **3527**
Memphis Business Journal. (US ISSN 0747-167X) **679**
Memphis Flyer. (US) **2228**
Memphis Health Care News. (US) **3806**, 3609
Memphis Singles *see* Singles Today **4363**
Memphis Star. (US) **3562**, 4635
Memphis State Review. (US ISSN 0732-2968) **2937**
Memphis State University. Anthropological Research Center. Occasional Papers. (US ISSN 0564-8602) **244**
Memphis State University Law Review. (US ISSN 0047-6714) **2654**
▼Men. (US) **3399**
Men and Events *see* State of the Union **1301**
Men and Women of Hawaii. (US ISSN 0461-7398) **420**
Men-Car, Guia de Medios de Transporte Internacional *see* Inter-Transport **4651**
Men of Achievement. (UK ISSN 0306-3666) **420**
Men of the West Coast. (US) **4848**
Men Only. (UK ISSN 0025-9217) **3399**
Menara Perkebunan. (IO ISSN 0125-9318) **107**
Menasheh. *see* Manasseh **2013**
Mencap News. (Mentally Handicapped) (UK) **2284**, 4413
Menckeniana. (US ISSN 0025-9233) **2938**
Mendeleev Chemistry Journal. (English translation of: Zhurnal Vsesoyuznogo Khimicheskogo Obshchestva im. Mendeleeva) (US ISSN 0025-925X) **1184**
▼Mendeleev Communications. (UK ISSN 0959-9436) **1184**
Mendeliana. (AG ISSN 0325-223X) **545**
Mendelssohn Studien. (GW ISSN 0340-8140) **2317**
Mendocino County Historical Society. Newsletter. (US ISSN 0025-9268) **2414**
Menemui Matematik. (MY ISSN 0126-9003) **3048**
Meng Ya. (CC ISSN 0539-323X) **2938**
Menighedsraadenes Blad. (DK) **4189**
Menka Tokei Geppo. *see* Cotton Statistics Monthly **5173**
Menninger Clinic. Bulletin. (US ISSN 0025-9284) **3344**, 4035
Menninger Perspective. (US ISSN 0025-9292) **3344**, 4035
Mennonite. (US ISSN 0025-9330) **4285**
Mennonite Brethren Herald. (CN ISSN 0025-9349) **4285**
Mennonite Central Committee Contact *see* M C C Contact **4285**
Mennonite Family History. (US ISSN 0730-5214) **2158**, 2414
Mennonite Historical Bulletin. (US ISSN 0025-9357) **4285**, 2414
Mennonite History Series. (US ISSN 0076-6429) **4285**
Mennonite Life. (US ISSN 0025-9365) **4285**
Mennonite Mirror. (CN ISSN 0315-8101) **2938**, 4285
Mennonite Quarterly Review. (US ISSN 0025-9373) **4285**
Mennonite Reporter. (CN ISSN 0380-0121) **4243**
Mennonite Review. *see* Mennonitische Rundschau **4285**
Mennonite Yearbook and Directory. (US ISSN 0275-1178) **4285**
Mennonitische Geschichtsblaetter. (GW ISSN 0342-1171) **4243**, 2375
Mennonitische Post. (CN) **2013**
Mennonitische Rundschau/Mennonite Review. (CN ISSN 0025-9314) **4285**
Menora. (CN) **2013**

Menorah. (CK ISSN 0025-939X) **2013**, 4225
Menorah *see* Menorah Review **2013**
Menorah *see* New Menorah: The P'nai or Journal of Jewish Renewal **4225**
Menorah Review. (US) **2013**, 4225
Menores *see* Infancia y Sociedad **1238**
Menores. (PY ISSN 1017-2807) **1247**
Menoufia University. Faculty of Education. Journal. *see* Jami'at al-Manufiyyah. Kulliyyat al-Tarbiyyah. Majallah **1641**
Men's and Boys' Wear Buyers. (US ISSN 0025-9411) **1286**
Men's Apparel News. (US) **1293**, 1286
Men's Art Service. (US ISSN 0025-942X) **35**, 1286
Men's Clip Review *see* Menswear Advertising **1286**
Men's Clothing Retailers. (UK) **1286**, 1293
Men's Club. (JA) **1293**, 2438
Mens en Maatschappij. (NE ISSN 0025-9454) **4443**
Mens en Melodie. (NE ISSN 0025-9462) **3562**
†Mens en Milieu. (NE) **5235**
Mens en Organisatie *see* M & O **4442**
Mens en Wereld *see* Humanist **3768**
Men's Fashion. (GW) **3399**, 1293
Men's Fitness. (US ISSN 0893-4460) **3806**, 4479
Men's Harper's Bazaar *see* Uomo Harper's Bazaar **1295**
Men's Health. (US) **3395**
Men's Health Newsletter. (US) **3395**, 3806
▼Men's Journal. (US) **3399**, 3400
†Men's Life. (US) **5235**
Men's News *see* Men's Apparel News **1293**
†Men's Report. (US) **5235**
†Men's Retailer. (US) **5235**
Men's Wear. (UK ISSN 0025-9519) **1293**
Men's Wear of Canada *see* Manstyle **5231**
Mensa *see* Mensa Magazine **1299**
Mensa Bulletin. (US ISSN 0025-9543) **1299**
Mensa Magazine. (UK) **1299**
Mensa Research Journal. (US) **1647**, 4035
Mensageiro. (CN) **2013**
Mensagem Economica/Economic Message. (BL) **790**
Mensaje. (US) **3906**
Mensaje. (UY) **4225**
Mensaje. (CL ISSN 0716-0062) **4269**
Mensajero. *see* Messenger **367**
Mensajero. (SP ISSN 0211-6561) **4189**
Mensario Estatistico Sul-Rio-Grandense.(BL ISSN 0102-0218) **729**, 17
Der Mensch als Soziales und Personales Wesen. (GW ISSN 0543-4726) **4443**
†Mensch Guten Willens. (GW ISSN 0175-9809) **5235**
Mensch und Arbeit. (AU) **988**
Mensch und Buero. (GW ISSN 0933-8241) **1059**
Mensch und Recht. (SZ) **2727**
Mensch und Tier. (AU) **3712**
Mensch und Ziel. (AU) **3773**
†Menschen Unterwegs. (SZ) **5235**
Das Menschenrecht. (AU ISSN 0025-9616) **3945**
Menschenrechte. (GW ISSN 0171-5976) **3945**
Menschenkinder. (GW ISSN 0176-8204) **1260**
Menschenkinder - Zeitschrift von Kindern und Jugendlichen *see* Menschenkinder **1260**
Mensile del Mezzogiorno. (IT) **873**
Mens's Guide to Fashion *see* M G F **1292**
Mensuel du Medecin Acupuncteur. (FR ISSN 0301-6366) **3131**
Mensuel 25. (BE) **335**, 2938, 2998
Menswear. (AT) **1293**
Menswear Advertising. (US) **1286**

Menswear Association of Britain Fashion Preview see M A B Fashion Preview **5229**
Menswear Magazine. (AT) **1286**
Menswear Retailers of America. Bulletin.(US) **1286, 4621**
Menswear Retailers of America. Financial and Operations Bulletin. (US) **1286, 4621**
Menswear Retailers of America. Market Fashion Bulletin. (US) **1286**
Menswear Retailers of America. Members News Letter. (US) **1286, 837**
Menswear Retailing see M R **1286**
Mental and Developmental Disabilities Directory of Legal Advocates see Legal Resources for the Mentally Disabled: A Directory of Lawyers and Other Specialists **3344**
Mental and Physical Disability Law Reporter. (US ISSN 0883-7902) **2703, 3344**
Mental Capacity: Medical and Legal Aspects of the Aging. (US) **4035, 2276, 2703**
Mental Handicap. (UK ISSN 0261-9997) **3345**
Mental Handicap Bulletin. (UK ISSN 0260-1222) **3345**
Mental Handicap Research. (UK ISSN 0952-9608) **3345**
Mental Health. (US) **4035**
Mental Health. see Psykisk Haelsa **4043**
Mental Health Directory. (US) **4107**
Mental Health in Australia. (AT ISSN 0025-9667) **3345, 4107**
Mental Health in Children. (US) **4035, 3345, 4413**
Mental Health Law News. (US ISSN 0889-017X) **2704, 4035**
Mental Health Law Reporter. (US ISSN 0741-5141) **2704, 4035**
Mental Health Matters. (UK) **4035, 4108**
Mental Health Report. (US ISSN 0191-6750) **4413, 3345**
Mental Health Services for Children and Youth see Hawaii. Department of Health. Mental Health Services for Children and Youth **4407**
Mental Health Statistics for Illinois. (US ISSN 0076-6453) **4413, 4108**
Mental Health Statistics for Wales. (UK ISSN 0260-5252) **3178**
Mental Health Weekly. (US ISSN 1058-1103) **4035, 2654**
Mental Hygiene see M H **5229**
Mental Measurements Yearbook. (US ISSN 0076-6461) **4035, 1755**
†Mental Retardation. (UK ISSN 0143-7550) **5235**
Mental Retardation (Washington). (US ISSN 0047-6765) **1738, 3345**
Mental Retardation and Developmental Disabilities. (US ISSN 0091-6315) **3345**
Mental Retardation and Learning Disability Bulletin see Development Disability Bulletin **3335**
Mental Retardation News see A R C **4396**
Mentalites. see Mentalities **2317**
Mentalites. (FR) **4443**
Mentalites/Mentalities. (NZ ISSN 0111-8854) **2317**
Mentally Handicapped Mencap News see Mencap News **2284**
Mente e Societa. (IT) **4035**
Mentor. (SA ISSN 0025-9713) **1647**
Menzelia. (US) **2134**
La Mer. (JA ISSN 0503-1540) **447, 1184, 1547**
Mer & Bateaux. (FR) **4526**
Meraviglie & Racconti. see Merveilles & Contes **2056**
Merc. (Mercantile Library Association of the City of New York) (US) **4132**
Mercaconsumo. (SP) **107**
Mercado/Business. (AG) **873**
Mercado. (SP) **955**
Mercado Comun Centroamericano. Carta Informativa. (GT) **932**
Mercado Comun Internacional. Notizario Z. (SP) **917**
Mercado da Borracha no Brasil. Boletim Mensual. (BL ISSN 0025-9748) **4294**

Mercado de las Artes Graficas. (MX) **4002**
Mercado de Valores. (MX ISSN 0185-1268) **955**
Mercado Mundial/World Market. (SP ISSN 0539-3728) **917**
Mercados Agricolas see Informacoes Economicas **152**
Mercantile Gazette of New Zealand see New Zealand Mercantile Gazette **838**
Mercantile Library Association of the City of New York Merc see Merc **4132**
Mercato Metalsidurgico. (IT ISSN 0025-9829) **3413**
Mercator see Forum foer Ekonomi och Teknik **1076**
†Le Mercenaire Intelligence Newsletter. (US ISSN 0890-7005) **5235**
Mercer Bulletin. (CN ISSN 0714-6914) **2537**
Mercer Business Magazine. (US ISSN 0194-9101) **819**
Mercer Cluster. (US ISSN 0025-9853) **1317**
Mercer County Board of Realtors. Newsline. (US ISSN 0891-7698) **4152**
Mercer County Heritage. (US) **2414**
Mercer County Historical Society Newsletter see Mercer County Heritage **2414**
Mercer Law Review. (US ISSN 0025-987X) **2654**
†Mercer Memories. (US) **5235**
Mercer Pension Manual. (CN) **988**
Merchandise & Operating Results of Department and Specialty Stores. (US) **1047**
Merchandise Mart Buyers Guide see Merchandise Mart Resource Guide **1047**
Merchandise Mart Resource Guide. (US) **1047, 1145**
†Merchandise Trade with Australia. (NZ) **5235**
Merchandiser. (US) **1506**
Merchant. (NZ ISSN 0113-468X) **1047, 988, 1116**
Merchant and Gould Computer Law Newsletter. (US) **1398, 2654**
Merchant Explorer. (US ISSN 0543-5056) **2375**
Merchant Magazine. (US ISSN 0739-9723) **2116, 624**
Merchant Shipbuilding Return. (UK ISSN 0261-1848) **4733**
Merchantville Stamp Club. Monthly Bulletin. (US) **3754**
†Merchavim. (IS) **5235**
Merchistonian. (UK) **1317**
Mercian Geologist. (UK ISSN 0025-990X) **1572**
Merck Index: An Encyclopedia of Chemicals and Drugs. (US ISSN 0076-6518) **3748**
Merck Manual: A Handbook of Diagnosis and Therapy. (US ISSN 0076-6526) **3131**
Merck Veterinary Manual: A Handbook of Diagnosis and Therapy for the Veterinarian. (US ISSN 0076-6542) **4813**
Mercur. (AU ISSN 0025-9926) **955**
Mercure. (BE ISSN 0025-9934) **2175, 790**
Mercurius. (GW) **1340**
Mercury. (UK) **2142**
†Mercury. (CN) **5235**
Mercury (Glenville). (US) **1317**
Mercury (Los Angeles). (US ISSN 0025-9969) **1299, 4479**
Mercury (San Francisco). (US ISSN 0047-6773) **366**
▼Mercury Rising. (US) **2938**
Meres es Automatika. (HU ISSN 0025-9993) **3447**
Meresugyi Kozlemenyek. (HU ISSN 0026-0002) **3447**
Merger and Acquisition Sourcebook (Year). (US) **679**
Merger Directory. (US) **1145, 679**
Merger Management Report. (US ISSN 0885-8616) **679**
Merger Yearbook: Domestic Edition. (US) **679**
Merger Yearbook: International Edition. (US) **679**

Mergers & Acquisitions. (US ISSN 0026-0010) **679**
Mergers & Acquisitions Consultant. (US) **1021, 790**
Mergers & Acquisitions Dealmaker see M & A Dealmaker **954**
Mergers and Acquisitions Europe see M & A Europe **916**
Mergers and Acquisitions Healthcare Sourcebook see M & A Healthcare Sourcebook **954**
Mergers & Acquisitions Healthcare Sourcebook. (US) **3131**
Mergers and Acquisitions Law Reporter.(US) **2711**
Mergers and Acquisitions Review see M & A Review **916**
Mergers and Corporate Policy. (US ISSN 0273-6357) **679, 955**
†Merging World. (US) **5235**
Meri. (FI ISSN 0356-0023) **1608**
Meri Saheli. (II) **2200**
Merian. (GW ISSN 0026-0029) **2190**
▼Meridian. (IT ISSN 1014-9643) **933, 1260, 3965**
Meridian. (US ISSN 1040-7421) **2256, 2773**
Meridian. (AT ISSN 0728-5914) **2938**
Meridian. (GW) **3595, 486, 4035**
Meridiani. (IT) **4776**
Meridiano. (VE) **4479**
Merigal. (AT ISSN 0725-8739) **1491, 1962, 3712**
Merino Breeders' Journal/Merinotelers Joernaal. (SA ISSN 0026-0045) **221**
Merinotelers Joernaal. see Merino Breeders' Journal **221**
Merit Network News see Michnet News **1427**
Merit Systems Protection Board Service.(US) **988**
Merkaz Haribaz. (IS) **2430**
Merkels' Builders' Pricing and Management Manual. (SA) **624**
Merkenblad Benelux/Marques Benelux Recueil. (NE ISSN 0026-007X) **3676**
Merkur. (GW ISSN 0026-0096) **2874**
Merkur Magazin fuer Volksgesundheit. (AU ISSN 0026-010X) **4108**
Der Merkurstab. (GW ISSN 0935-798X) **3131, 4285**
Merleg. (AU ISSN 0026-0126) **4189, 3773**
Merlyn's Pen. (US ISSN 0882-2050) **1260**
Meroitica. (GW ISSN 0138-3663) **3640**
Merova Technika see Magazin C S N **3447**
Merrill Lynch - Euromoney Directory. (UK ISSN 0306-3933) **1145, 790**
Merrill Lynch Market Letter. (US) **955**
Merrill - Palmer Quarterly. (US ISSN 0026-0150) **4035, 1241, 1647**
Merrimac see M T I Reporter **1646**
Merrimack Valley Business. (US) **679**
Merritt Risk Management Review. (US ISSN 0742-3446) **2537**
Merry-Go-Roundup. (US) **258**
Mersey Ports Handbook (Year). (UK ISSN 0265-1173) **4733, 1145**
Merseyside and North Wales Electricity Board. Report And Accounts. (UK) **1802**
Merseyside Business Survey see Merseyside Economic and Business Prospect **873**
Merseyside Chamber of Commerce and Industry. Directory. (UK ISSN 0302-4148) **819**
Merseyside Economic and Business Prospect. (UK ISSN 0952-0732) **873**
Merseyside Economic Prospect see Merseyside Economic and Business Prospect **873**
Mershon Center Communique see Mershon Memo **3906**
Mershon Center Report Quarterly see Mershon Memo **3906**
Mershon Memo. (US) **3906, 1527**
Mertens Law of Federal Income Taxation: Current Tax Highlights. (US) **1101**

Mertensiella. (GW ISSN 0934-6643) **588**
Merton Annual: Studies in Thomas Merton, Religion, Culture, Literature, and Social Concerns. (US ISSN 0894-4857) **2938, 4189**
Merton Seasonal see The Merton Seasonal: A Quarterly Review **4190**
The Merton Seasonal: A Quarterly Review. (US ISSN 0899-4927) **4190, 2938**
Meru. (JA) **2448**
Merveilles & Contes/Marvels & Tales/ Wunder & Maerchen/Maravillas & Cuentos/Meraviglie & Racconti. (US ISSN 0898-154X) **2056, 2984**
Mervyn Peake Review. (UK ISSN 0309-1309) **3012, 335, 2938**
Mervyn Peake Society Newsletter see Mervyn Peake Review **3012**
Mes Premieres Grilles. (FR ISSN 0396-4914) **2438**
Mesa Connection. (US) **4803**
Mescalito - Sprung in die Unmoeglichkeit. (GW) **3670, 244, 2013**
Il Mese di Caccia. (IT) **4550**
Mese Economico e Finanziario see Le Mois **874**
Mesecni Statisticki Pregled. (YU ISSN 0350-4247) **4579**
Mesemb Study Bulletin. (UK ISSN 0955-8276) **509, 1299, 2134**
Meshek ha-Bakar ve ha-Chalav. (IS) **201**
Meshek Haofote. (IS ISSN 0539-421X) **221**
Mesias. (MX ISSN 0026-0185) **4243**
Mesilot. (IS) **4225**
Ha-Mesivta. (US ISSN 0094-9701) **2654, 4225**
Mesoamerica. (CR) **2414, 3906**
Mesoamerica. (US ISSN 0252-9963) **4379**
Mesoamerican Notes see Notas Mesoamericanas **246**
†Meson. (SA ISSN 0257-1994) **5235**
Mesopotamia. (IT ISSN 0076-6615) **278**
Mesopotamia. (IQ) **4776**
†Mesozoic Research. (NE ISSN 0920-4989) **5235**
Message. (GO) **1647**
Message see Message de l'Ahmadiyyat **4219**
Message see Emergence: Journal for Evolving Consciousness **5186**
Message (Bronx). (US ISSN 0047-679X) **2586, 1364**
Message (Hagerstown). (US ISSN 0026-0231) **4197**
Message d'Extreme-Orient. (BE) **2340**
Message de l'Ahmadiyyat. (MF) **4219**
Message Economique. (MR) **154**
Message Line. (US ISSN 1060-233X) **3200**
Message of the Cross. (US ISSN 0746-0635) **4190**
Message of the Library/Risalat al-Maktaba. (JO ISSN 0257-7739) **2773**
Message of the Open Bible. (US ISSN 0889-4159) **4190**
Message of the Teacher/Risalat al-Mu'allim. (JO ISSN 0040-0505) **1711**
Message Olympique/Olympic Message. (SZ) **4479**
Message Post. (US) **4550, 2492**
Message to the Anglo-Saxon and Celtic Peoples see Wake-up! (Ayrshire) **4209**
Messager. (FR ISSN 0026-024X) **2187**
†Messager de l'Exarchat du Patriarche Russe en Europe Occidentale. (FR ISSN 0026-0266) **5235**
Messager de la Haute Savoie. (FR ISSN 0026-0258) **2187**
Messager du Nord-Ouest. (HT) **2220**
Messager Evangelique. (FR ISSN 0026-0274) **4243**
Messages des P T T. (FR ISSN 0245-6001) **1364**
Messages du Secours Catholique. (FR ISSN 0026-0290) **4269**
Messaggero. see Messenger (Kansas City) **4190**
Messaggero. (AT) **4269, 2013**

Messaggero Avventista. (IT ISSN 0392-6346) **4243**
Messaggero Cappuccino. (IT) **4190**
Messaggero dei Ragazzi. (IT ISSN 0026-0304) **1260**
Messaggero di S. Antonio. (IT ISSN 0026-0312) **4269**
Messe Digest. (GW) **1146**, 642, 1165
Messe Industriespiegel. (GW ISSN 0019-9168) **1047**
Messe- und Kongress-Vorschau/Fairs and Conventions Preview. (GW) **3393**
†Messen Pruefen Automatisieren. (GW) **5235**
Messen - Steuern - Regeln. (GW ISSN 0026-0347) **1830**, 1415
Messenger/Mensajero. (GW ISSN 0722-6691) **367**
Messenger. (CN ISSN 0228-2828) **2013**
Messenger. (SI ISSN 0026-0371) **4285**
The Messenger (Belleville). (US ISSN 0279-3911) **4269**
Messenger (Dunn). (US) **4285**
Messenger (Elgin). (US ISSN 0026-0355) **4285**
Messenger (Grantham). (UK ISSN 0309-3654) **4243**
Messenger (Kansas City)/Messaggero. (US ISSN 0026-0363) **4190**
Messenger (La Porte). (US) **4285**
Messenger (London). (UK) **3345**
Messenger (Omaha). (US) **4243**
▼Messenger (Redding). (US) **4190**
Messenger (Worcester). (US ISSN 0893-0872) **4285**
Messenger of Truth. (US) **4285**
Messenger Reporter. (US) **2538**
Messer und Schere see Der Buechsenmacher und Messer und Schere **641**
Messergebnisse des Zentralen Immissionsmessnetzes. Monatsbericht. (GW ISSN 0720-3934) **1962**
Messerschmitt-Boelkow-Blohm GmbH Aktuell see M B B Aktuell **58**
Messianic Witness. (UK) **4243**
Messidor. (FR ISSN 0026-0401) **4285**
Messing about in Boats. (US) **4526**
Messtechnische Briefe. (GW ISSN 0930-8644) **1936**, 1903, 4603
Messtechnische Briefe fuer Elektrisches Messen Mechanischer Groessen see Messtechnische Briefe **1936**
Mestnyi Proizvodstvennyi Opyt v Promyshlennosti/Local Level Experience in the Manufacturing Industry. (RU ISSN 0202-6309) **1936**, 1792, 3021, 4604
Mestnyi Proizvodstvennyi Opyt v Sel'skom Khozyaistve/Local Level Experience in Agricultural Development. (RU ISSN 0202-6325) **154**, 163, 185, 221
Mestnyi Proizvodstvennyi Opyt v Stroitel'stve/Local Level Experience in the Construction Industry. (RU ISSN 0202-6317) **624**, 1871, 2492, 4604
Mesuesi/Instituteur. (AA) **1647**
Mesures. (FR ISSN 0755-219X) **1415**, 1879
Mesures Regulation Automatisme see Mesures **1415**
Met Golfer. (US) **4507**
Meta. (CN ISSN 0026-0452) **2829**
Metaal & Kunststof. (NE ISSN 0026-0460) **3021**, 1830
Metaal & Techniek. (NE ISSN 0026-0479) **3413**
Metaal Werker. see Metal Worker **5235**
Metaalbewerking see M B Produktiertechniek **1919**
Metabolic Aspects of Cardiovascular Disease. (NE) **3210**
Metabolic Brain Disease. (US ISSN 0885-7490) **3131**
Metabolic, Pediatric and Systemic Ophthalmology. (US ISSN 0882-889X) **3302**

Metabolic, Pediatric and Systemic Ophthalmology (1985) see Metabolic, Pediatric and Systemic Ophthalmology **3302**
Metabolism: Clinical and Experimental. (US ISSN 0026-0495) **3255**, 447
▼Metai. (LI) **2938**
Metal see Carta Metalurgica **1916**
Metal. (DK ISSN 0026-0517) **2586**, 3413
Metal Architecture. (US) **303**, 3413
Metal Building News see Metal Construction News **624**
Metal Building Review. (US ISSN 0026-0525) **624**, 3413
Metal Bulletin. (US ISSN 0026-0533) **3413**
Metal Bulletin Handbook see Metal Bulletin Prices & Data Book **3413**
Metal Bulletin Monthly. (US ISSN 0373-4064) **3413**
Metal Bulletin Prices & Data Book. (US ISSN 0269-1698) **3413**
Metal Casting and Surface Finishing. (AT) **3413**
Metal Center News. (US) **3413**
Metal Construction see Joining and Materials **5221**
Metal Construction News. (US ISSN 0274-8843) **624**, 3413
Metal Detecting see Treasure Hunting **2443**
Metal Distribution. (US ISSN 0098-2210) **3413**
Metal Edge see T V Picture Life - Metal Edge **1381**
Metal Fabricating News. (US ISSN 0026-055X) **3413**
Metal Finishing. (US ISSN 0026-0576) **3413**
Metal Finishing Abstracts see Surface Treatment Technology Abstracts **3428**
Metal Forming. (US ISSN 1040-967X) **3413**
Metal Forming. see Obrobka Plastyczna Metali **3417**
Metal Hammer. (UK) **3562**
Metal Industry (New York) see Metal Finishing **3413**
Metal Ions in Biological Systems. (US) **1214**
Metal Mania. (US) **3562**
Metal Marketing Corporation of Zambia. Annual Report. (ZA) **1047**, 3413
Metal Materials. see Kovove Materialy **3411**
Metal Mining: Latin American Industrial Report. (US) **3488**
Metal News. (II) **3414**
Metal Powder Report. (UK ISSN 0026-0657) **3427**, 17
Metal Resources Circular. (CN) **3488**
Metal Revolution. (US) **3562**
Metal Science and Heat Treatment. (English translation of: Metallovedenie i Termicheskaya Obrabotka Metallov) (US ISSN 0026-0673) **3414**
Metal Stamping see Metal Forming **3413**
Metal Statistics. (US ISSN 0076-6658) **3414**
Metal Statistics (Years). (GW ISSN 0170-9933) **3427**, 4579
Metal Traders of the World. (US ISSN 0143-7607) **3414**
Metal Trades Industry Association Engineering Exporter see M T I A's Engineering Exporter **3412**
Metal Trades Industry Association of Australia Input see M T I A Input **987**
Metal Trades Industry Association of Australia Metal & Engineering Industry Yearbook see M T I A Metal & Engineering Industry Yearbook **987**
Metal Worker. (AT ISSN 0727-1115) **2586**
†Metal Worker/Metaal Werker. (SA ISSN 0026-072X) **5235**
Metalcaster. (US) **1021**, 1047, 3414
Metalektro Profiel. (NE) **3021**, 1903
Metalektro Visie see Metalektro Profiel **3021**

Metales y Maquinas see Metales y Metalurgia **3414**
Metales y Metalurgia. (SP) **3414**, 3021
Metaletter. (US ISSN 0047-6870) **2586**, 3414
Metalforming Digest. (US) **3414**
Metall. (GW ISSN 0026-0746) **3414**
Metall. (AU) **3414**
Metallarbetaren. (SW ISSN 0026-0754) **3414**, 2586
†Metallbericht. (AU ISSN 0047-6889) **5235**
Metalle. (AU ISSN 0026-0762) **3414**
Metallgesellschaft Aktiengesellschaft. Review of the Activities. (GW ISSN 0369-2345) **3414**
Metallhandwerk and Metalltechnik see M & T - Metallhandwerk & Technik **623**
Metallic Materials. (English translation of: Kovove Materialy) (UK ISSN 0264-7303) **1921**, 3414, 3429
Metallix. (US) **3562**
Metalloberflaeche. (GW ISSN 0026-0797) **3414**, 4604
Metallofizika. (KR ISSN 0204-3580) **3414**
Metallography see Materials Characterization **3412**
Metallography & Testing Digest. (US) **3414**
Metallovedenie i Termicheskaya Obrabotka Metallov. (RU ISSN 0026-0819) **3414**
Metallurg. (RU ISSN 0026-0827) **3414**
Metallurgia and Metal Forming see Metallurgia: The Journal of Metals Technology, Metal Forming and Thermal Processing **3414**
La Metallurgia Italiana. (IT ISSN 0026-0843) **3414**
Metallurgia: The Journal of Metals Technology, Metal Forming and Thermal Processing. (UK ISSN 0141-8602) **3414**
†Metallurgical Engineer. (II ISSN 0369-061X) **5235**
Metallurgical Equipment. see Yejin Shebei **3424**
Metallurgical Journal. (English translation of: Hutnicke Listy) (UK ISSN 0951-0869) **3414**
Metallurgical Plantmakers of the World. (US ISSN 0308-7794) **3414**
Metallurgical Science and Techniques. see Jinshu Kexue yu Gongyi **3410**
Metallurgical Transactions see Metallurgical Transactions A - Physical Metallurgy and Materials Science **3414**
Metallurgical Transactions A - Physical Metallurgy and Materials Science. (US ISSN 0360-2133) **3414**, 1830
Metallurgical Transactions B - Process Metallurgy. (US ISSN 0360-2141) **3414**
Metallurgie see Entreprises Rhone Alpes **1075**
Metallurgie. Lexique. (FR) **3414**, 3429
Metallurgist. (English translation of: Metallurg) (US ISSN 0026-0894) **3415**
Metallurgist and Materials Technologist see Metals and Materials **3415**
Metallurgy and Foundry Abstracts. see Kohaszati es Onteszeti Szakirodalmi Tajekoztato **3427**
Metallurgy - Materials Education Yearbook. (US ISSN 0094-5447) **3415**
Metallurgy Transactions see Metallurgical Transactions B - Process Metallurgy **3414**
Metallverarbeitung. (GW ISSN 0026-0908) **3415**
Metalmechanics: Latin American Industrial Report. (US) **3415**
Metals Abstracts. (US ISSN 0026-0924) **3427**, 17
Metals Abstracts Index. (US ISSN 0026-0932) **3427**, 17
Metals Alert. (US) **3488**, 3415
Metals and Castings Australasia see Metal Casting and Surface Finishing **3413**

Metals and Materials. (UK ISSN 0266-7185) **3415**, 1921
Metals and Minerals Review. (II ISSN 0026-0959) **3488**, 3415
Metals Australasia see Materials Australasia **3412**
Metals Economics Group Strategic Report. (CN) **3488**
Metals Forum see Materials Forum **3413**
Metals Industry News. (UK) **3415**
Metals International see World Ceramics & Refractories **1167**
Metals Materials and Processes. (II ISSN 0970-423X) **3415**, 1921
Metals Monitor. (UK) **988**, 3415
Metals Newsletter. (US) **3619**
Metals Price Report - Alloy Steel. (US) **3415**
Metals Price Report - Base Metals. (US) **3415**
Metals Science see Materials Science and Technology **3413**
Metals Society. Digest Series see Materials Information Digest Series **3413**
Metals Society World see Metals and Materials **3415**
Metals Technology see Materials Science and Technology **3413**
Metals Week. (US ISSN 0026-0975) **3488**, 3415
Metals Week Insider Report. (US) **3488**, 3415
Metals Week Price Notification Service. (US) **3488**, 3415
Metalsmith. (US ISSN 0270-1146) **356**, 3415
Metalurgia. (AG) **3415**
Metalurgia A B M see A B M Metalurgia e Materiais **3401**
Metalurgia Moderna. (AG ISSN 0325-0202) **3415**
Metalurgija. (CI ISSN 0543-5846) **3415**, 1207, 1856
Metalworking Digest. (US ISSN 0026-1009) **3415**
Metalworking Digest Literature Review. (US) **3415**
†Metalworking Distributor. (US) **5235**
Metalworking: Engineering and Marketing. (JA) **1921**, 1047
Metalworking Interfaces. (US) **3415**
†Metalworking News. (US ISSN 0891-4036) **5235**
Metalworking Production. (UK ISSN 0026-1033) **3415**, 1936
Metalworking Production & Purchasing.(CN ISSN 0383-090X) **3415**, 3021
Metamedicine see Theoretical Medicine **3156**
Metamorfosi. (IT) **303**
Metamorphic Association Newsletter see Metamorphosis **3670**
Metamorphic Association Newsletter see Metamorphic Association Programme **3670**
Metamorphic Association Programme. (UK) **3670**
Metamorphosis. (UK) **3670**
Metaphilosophy. (UK ISSN 0026-1068) **3773**
Metaphor. (US) **2998**
Metaphor and Symbolic Activity. (US ISSN 0885-7253) **2829**, 2938, 4035
Metaphysical Digest see Neometaphysical Digest **3670**
Metaphysical Fellowship Church. Newsletter. (US) **3773**
Metaphysical Review. (AT ISSN 0814-8805) **2874**, 3514
Metapsichica. (IT ISSN 0026-1076) **3670**, 3595
Metascience Annual. (US) **3670**, 3595
MetaScience Quarterly see Metascience Annual **3670**
Metaux. (FR ISSN 0026-1084) **3415**
Metaux Deformations see R F M **3418**
†"Meteor" Forschungsergebnisse. Reihe C. Geologie und Geophysik. (GW ISSN 0543-5927) **5235**
Meteor News. (US ISSN 0146-9959) **367**
Meteoritics. (US ISSN 0026-1114) **367**

Meteorologica Mundial. Comision de Sistemas Basicos. Informe Final Abreviado de la (No.) Reunion see World Meteorological Organization. Commission for Basic Systems. Abridged Final Report of the (No.) Session 3443
Meteorological and Geoastrophysical Abstracts. (US ISSN 0026-1130) 3444, 17, 371, 1551
Meteorological Magazine. (UK ISSN 0026-1149) 3438
Meteorological Monthly. see Qixiang 3440
Meteorological Society of Japan. Journal/Kisho Shushi. (JA ISSN 0026-1165) 3438
Meteorological Yearbook. see Rocznik Meteorologiczny 3440
Meteorological Yearbook of Finland. Part 1: Climatological Data. (FI ISSN 0076-6747) 3438
Meteorological Yearbook of Finland. Part 2: Precipitation and Snow Cover Data. (FI ISSN 0076-6755) 3438
Meteorological Yearbook of Finland. Part 3. Statistics of Radiosonde Observations 1961-1980. (FI ISSN 0780-7295) 3438
Meteorological Yearbook of Finland. Part 4: Measurements of Radiation and Bright Sunshine see Meteorological Yearbook of Finland. Part 4: 1 Measurements of Solar Radiation 3438
Meteorological Yearbook of Finland. Part 4: Measurements of Radiation and Bright Sunshine see Meteorological Yearbook of Finland. Part 4: 2 Measurements of Sunshine Duration 3439
Meteorological Yearbook of Finland. Part 4: 1 Measurements of Solar Radiation. (FI ISSN 0783-103X) 3438
Meteorological Yearbook of Finland. Part 4: 2 Measurements of Sunshine Duration. (FI ISSN 0783-0556) 3439
Meteorologicke Zpravy. (CS ISSN 0026-1173) 3439
Meteorologie. (FR ISSN 0026-1181) 3439
Meteorologische Abhandlungen. (GW ISSN 0026-1203) 3439
Meteorologische Rundschau see Meteorologische Zeitschrift 3439
Meteorologische Zeitschrift. (GW) 3439, 1592
Meteorologischen Dienstes der D D R. Veroeffentlichungen. (GW ISSN 0138-1105) 3439
Meteorologiske Annaler. (NO) 3439
Meteorologiya i Gidrologiya. (RU ISSN 0130-2906) 3439
Meteorology and Atmospheric Physics. (US ISSN 0177-7971) 3439
Meteorology and Hydrology. (RM) 3439, 1599
Methane Recovery from Landfill Yearbook. (US) 1985, 1792
Method: Journal of Lonergan Studies. (US ISSN 0736-7392) 3773, 4190
Methoden und Verfahren der Mathemathischen Physik. (GW) 3048, 3824
Methodensammlung der Elektronenmikroskopie. (GW ISSN 0076-6771) 560
Methodes Physiques d'Analyse see Analusis 1203
Methodika. (CN ISSN 0932-6510) 4035
Methodika. (GW) 4035
Methodist Church Music Society Bulletin. (UK ISSN 0047-6919) 3562
Methodist College Today. (US) 1317
Methodist Conference. Minutes and Yearbook. (UK) 4243
Methodist Diaries. (UK) 4243
Methodist History. (US ISSN 0026-1238) 4243, 2938
Methodist Homes Quarterly see Horizon (Neptune) 2274
Methodist Recorder. (UK ISSN 0026-1262) 4243
Methodist Theological School in Ohio. Story. (US) 4243, 1647
Methodologia. (IT ISSN 1120-3854) 2829, 4035
Methodology and Science. (NE ISSN 0543-6095) 4324
Methods: A Companion to Methods in Enzymology. (US ISSN 1046-2023) 480
Methods and Achievements in Experimental Pathology. (SZ ISSN 0076-681X) 3131
Methods and Findings in Experimental and Clinical Pharmacology. (SP ISSN 0379-0355) 3735
Methods and Phenomena. (NE) 4324
Methods for the Application of Research Results into Practice. see Metodiky pro Zavadeni Vysledku Vyzkumu do Praxe 5235
Methods in Cell Biology. (US ISSN 0091-679X) 525
Methods in Enzymology. (US ISSN 0076-6879) 480
Methods in Geochemistry and Geophysics. (NE ISSN 0076-6895) 1547, 1592
†Methods in Geomathematics. (NE) 5235
Methods in Microanalysis. (US ISSN 0275-9586) 560
Methods in Organic Synthesis. (UK ISSN 0265-4245) 1220
†Methods in Virology. (US ISSN 0076-6933) 5235
Methods of Biochemical Analysis. (US ISSN 0076-6941) 480, 1207
Methods of Computational Chemistry. (US) 1184, 1856
Methods of Experimental Botany. see Metodicke Prirucky Experimentalni Botaniky 509
Methods of Experimental Physics. (US ISSN 0076-695X) 3825
Methods of Information in Medicine. (GW ISSN 0026-1270) 3131
Methods of Operations Research. see Operations Research - Verfahren 1023
Methods: The Journal of Animal Health Technology see New Methods 4813
†Methyl Transferases. (UK ISSN 0950-0537) 5235
Meticcia. (IT) 2205
Metiers. (FR) 819
Metiers d'Art. (FR) 335
Metiers Graphiques. Bulletin. (LU) 4002
Metlfax. (US ISSN 0026-1297) 3415, 3021
Metmenys. (US ISSN 0543-615X) 2938, 2013
Metodicke Prirucky Experimentalni Botaniky/Methods of Experimental Botany. (CS ISSN 0076-6984) 509
†Metodicky Zpravodaj Cs. Soustavy Vedeckych, Technickych a Ekonomickych Informaci. (CS ISSN 0322-7243) 5235
†Metodiky pro Zavadeni Vysledku Vyzkumu do Praxe/Methods for the Application of Research Results into Practice. (CS ISSN 0026-1319) 5235
Metodistkyrkans i Sverige Aarsbok. (SW ISSN 0543-6206) 4243
Metodologicheski i Istoriografski Problemi na Istoricheskata Nauka. (BU) 2317
Metodos Terapeutico-diagnosticos de Actualidad Medicina Interna see M T A Medicina Interna 3123
Metodos Terapeutico-diagnosticos de Actualidad Pediatria see M T A Pediatria 3322
Metov Tiberia. (IS ISSN 0334-0740) 2317
Metric Fact Sheets. (CN ISSN 0383-9184) 3447
Metric Fastener Standards. (US) 1921
Metric Reporter. (US) 3447
Metric Today. (US ISSN 1050-5628) 3447
Metrika. (GW ISSN 0026-1335) 4579
Metro. (AT ISSN 0312-2654) 1755, 1376, 3514

Metro (Redondo Beach). (US ISSN 0162-6221) 4653
Metro California Media. (US ISSN 0889-2776) 35
Metro Chicago Office Guide. (US) 1059, 4152
Metro Chicago Real Estate. (US) 4152
Metro Courier. (US) 819
Metro Denver see Metro Denver Magazine 819
Metro Denver Magazine. (US) 819
Metro Golf. (US) 4507
†Metro Handbook and Directory of Members (Year). (US ISSN 0887-1973) 5235
†Metro Insights. (US) 5235
Metro Jackson Business. (US) 679
▼Metro Man. (GW ISSN 0940-1849) 2455, 4776
†Metro - Ministry News. (US) 5235
†Metro Monitor. (US) 5235
Metro Monthly. (US) 2228
Metro New York Directory of Manufacturers. (US) 1146
METRO; New York Metropolitan Reference and Research Library Agency. METRO Miscellaneous Publications Series. (US ISSN 0076-7018) 2773
Metro New York Ready-to-Wear. (US) 1286
Metro-Newark see Metro Courier 819
Metro News. (US) 2438
Metro - Orlando Home. (US) 2553
Metro Ottawa Office Guide. (CN) 1059
Metro Parent. (US) 1241
Metro Singles Lifestyles. (US) 4362
Metro Telecaster. (CN) 1376
Metroeconomica. (IT ISSN 0026-1386) 679
▼Metrokids. (US) 1260
Metrolina Singles Datebook see Metrolina Singles Magazine & Datebook 4362
Metrolina Singles Magazine & Datebook. (US) 4362
Metroline. (US) 2455, 4285
Metrologia. (GW ISSN 0026-1394) 3447
Metron. (IT ISSN 0026-1424) 4579
Metronome Magazine. (US) 3562
†MetroNorth. (US) 5235
Metropole see Tout Lyon 2686
Metropolis. (US ISSN 0279-4977) 303, 2554
Metropolitan. (US) 1317
Metropolitan Almanac see Singles Almanac of New York 4363
Metropolitan Area Forecasting Service Review see U S Markets Review: Metropolitan Focus 886
Metropolitan Area Forecasting Study see U S Markets Review: Metropolitan Focus 886
▼Metropolitan Area Networks. (US ISSN 1057-5383) 1340
Metropolitan Atlanta Rapid Transit Authority Rider's Digest see M A R T A Rider's Digest 2228
Metropolitan Beaumont. (US) 2228
Metropolitan Chamber of Commerce and Industry, Dhaka. Chamber News.(BG) 819
Metropolitan College of Technology, Tokyo. Memoirs. see Tokyo-toritsu Koka Tanki Daigaku Kenkyu Hokoku 4612
Metropolitan Education. (US ISSN 0888-868X) 1647
Metropolitan Historic Structures Association. News. (US) 303
Metropolitan Home. (US ISSN 0273-2858) 2554, 2448, 2560
Metropolitan Indianapolis Realtor see Realtor Voice 4157
Metropolitan Life Foundation. Statistical Bulletin see Metropolitan Life Insurance Company. Statistical Bulletin S B 4579
Metropolitan Life Insurance Company. Statistical Bulletin S B. (US ISSN 0741-9767) 4579
Metropolitan Milwaukee Association of Commerce. Economic Studies see Metropolitan Milwaukee Economic Fact Book 873
Metropolitan Milwaukee Economic Fact Book. (US) 873

Metropolitan Museum Journal. (US ISSN 0077-8958) 3527
Metropolitan Museum of Art. Bulletin. (US ISSN 0026-1521) 3527
†Metropolitan Museum of Art. Notable Acquisitions. (US ISSN 0192-6950) 5236
Metropolitan Nashville Board of Education. News and Views. (US ISSN 0026-153X) 1647
Metropolitan Pensioner. (CN ISSN 0026-1556) 4413, 2276
Metropolitan Purchasor. (US ISSN 0192-7973) 1047
Metropolitan School Study Council Exchange see M S S C Exchange 1729
Metropolitan Star see Star (New York, 1945) 2024
Metropolitan Toronto. (CN ISSN 0076-7093) 4090
Metropolitan Toronto Business and Market Guide. (CN ISSN 0829-2558) 679, 1047
Metropolitan Toronto Business Journal. (CN) 837
Metropolitan Toronto Library Board. Annual Report. (CN ISSN 0700-4532) 2773
Metropolitan Toronto Library Board. News see Metropolitan Toronto Reference Library. News 2773
Metropolitan Toronto Reference Library. News. (CN ISSN 0842-9707) 2773
▼Metropolitan Universities. (US ISSN 1047-8485) 1711
Metropolitan Washington Board of Trade News see Greater Washington Board of Trade News 835
Metropolitan Washington D.C. Area Labor Summary. (US) 988
Metropolitan Weekly. (HK) 2197
†Metropolitan Woman. (US) 5236
Metro's Plus Business. (US) 35
MetroSports Magazine. (US) 4479
MetroTrends. (CN) 4152
Metru. (IO) 3514, 3562, 4635
Metsa Ja Puu. (FI ISSN 0026-1602) 2104
Metsanhoitaja. (FI ISSN 0355-7596) 2104
Metsastaja. (FI ISSN 0047-6986) 1491, 4550
Metsastys ja Kalastus. (FI ISSN 0026-1629) 4550
Metsatilastollinen Vuosikirja/Yearbook of Forest Statistics. (FI ISSN 0359-968X) 2104
Metta. (US) 4215
Metzger und Wurster/Boucher - Charcutier/Macellaio - Salumiere. (SZ ISSN 0026-1645) 2077
Der Metzgermeister. (GW ISSN 0005-7088) 2077
Meubel. (NE ISSN 0165-4543) 2560
Meubel Echo see Echo du Meuble 2558
Le Meunier. (CN) 207
Meuse. (AT) 2938, 335
†Mevo. (NE ISSN 0026-1688) 5236
Mex-Am Review see Business Mexico 809
Mexican American Grocers Association. MAGAzine. (US ISSN 0894-8097) 2093
Mexican American Legal Defense and Educational Fund Newsletter see M A L D E F Newsletter 2012
Mexican American Monograph Series. (US) 2013
Mexican American Sun. (US) 2013
Mexican American Women's National Association see M A N A 2012
Mexican Audiovisual Media Rates & Data see Directorio M P M - Medios Audiovisuales 41
Mexican Business and Investment see Inversionista Mexicano 950
†Mexican Forum/El Foro Mexicano. (US ISSN 0730-2584) 5236
Mexican Journal of Behavior Analysis. see Revista Mexicana de Analisis de la Conducta 4045
Mexican Print Media Rates & Data see Directorio M P M - Medios Impresos 41

Mexican Society for Soil Mechanics Meeting. Proceedings. (MX ISSN 0185-402X) **1871**
Mexican Studies/Estudios Mexicanos. (US ISSN 0742-9797) **2511**, 2414
†Mexico. (MX ISSN 0543-7741) **5236**
†Mexico. Archivo General de la Nacion. Boletin. (MX ISSN 0185-1926) **5236**
Mexico. Centro de Informacion Tecnica y Documentacion. Indice Bibliografico.(MX) **406**
Mexico. Centro de Informacion Tecnica y Documentacion. Indice de Articulos sobre Educacion y Adiestramiento. (MX) **1678**, 17
Mexico. Centro de Informacion Tecnica y Documentacion. Indice de Articulos sobre Seguridad e Higiene Industrial. (MX) **2547**, 3623
Mexico. Centro de Informacion Tecnica y Documentacion. Indice de Peliculas.(MX) **3520**
Mexico. Centro de Informacion Tecnica y Documentacion. Indice de Revistas. Seccion de Ciencia y Tecnologia. (MX) **4357**, 4614
Mexico. Centro de Informacion Tecnica y Documentacion. Indice de Revistas. Seccion de Educacion y Comunicacion. (MX) **1678**, 17, 1349
Mexico. Centro de Informacion Tecnica y Documentacion. Indice de Revistas. Seccion de Humanidades y Ciencias Sociales. (MX) **4458**, 17
Mexico. Comision Nacional Bancaria. Boletin Estadistico *see* Mexico. Comision Nacional Bancaria y de Seguros. Boletin Estadistico **790**
Mexico. Comision Nacional Bancaria y de Seguros. Anuario Estadistico de Seguros. (MX) **2547**
Mexico. Comision Nacional Bancaria y de Seguros. Boletin Estadistico. (MX) **790**, 729
Mexico. Departamento de Investigacion de las Tradiciones Populares. Boletin.(MX) **244**, 2056
Mexico. Direccion General de Estadistica. Estadistica Industrial Anual. (MX ISSN 0071-1543) **729**, 4579
†Mexico. Direccion General de Estadistica. Estadistica Industrial Mensual. (MX) **5236**
Mexico. Direccion General de Oceanografia. Calendario Grafico de Mareas. (MX) **1608**
Mexico. Instituto Nacional de Estadistica, Geografia e Informatica. Revista de Estadistica. (MX ISSN 0186-2707) **4579**
Mexico. Instituto Nacional de Investigaciones Forestales, Agricolas y Pecuarias. Folletos de Investigacion *see* Mexico. Instituto Nacional de Investigaciones Forestales y Agropecuarias. Folletos de Investigacion **107**
Mexico. Instituto Nacional de Investigaciones Forestales, Agricolas y Pecuarias. Temas Didacticos *see* Mexico. Instituto Nacional de Investigaciones Forestales y Agropecuarias. Temas Didacticos **107**
Mexico. Instituto Nacional de Investigaciones Forestales y Agropecuarias. Folletos de Investigacion. (MX) **107**, 873
Mexico. Instituto Nacional de Investigaciones Forestales y Agropecuarias. Temas Didacticos. (MX) **107**
Mexico. Secretaria de Educacion Publica. Informe de Labores. (MX) **1647**
†Mexico. Secretaria de Programacion y Presupuesto. (MX ISSN 0076-7492) **5236**
Mexico. Secretaria de Programacion y Presupuesto. Boletin Trimestral de Informacion Economica. (MX) **1101**
Mexico (Year). (US ISSN 0884-1209) **4776**

▼Mexico Business Monthly. (US ISSN 1054-2663) **917**
Mexico City Daily Bulletin. (MX) **4776**, 2477
Mexico; Hechos, Cifras, Tendencias *see* Mexico **5236**
†Mexico Heroico. (MX ISSN 0026-1793) **5236**
Mexico Holstein. (MX) **201**
Mexico Indigena. (MX ISSN 0185-058X) **2492**, 4413
Mexico: Informacion Economica y Social.(MX) **873**
Mexico News. (MX ISSN 0462-1069) **4776**
Mexico Report. (US ISSN 0277-0946) **2210**
Mexico Service. (US ISSN 1044-6303) **955**
Mexico Statistical Data. (MX) **4579**
Mexico Update. (MX) **819**, 2210, 3965
Mexico Vogue. (MX) **1293**, 4848
Mexico West. (US ISSN 0889-7107) **4776**
Mexicon. (GW ISSN 0720-5988) **244**, 278
Meyer's Directory of Genealogical Societies in the U S A & Canada. (US ISSN 0732-3395) **2158**
Meyers Modeblatt. (SZ ISSN 0026-1866) **1293**, 3591
Meying Lao. (LS) **4848**
Meyniana. (GW ISSN 0076-7689) **1572**
Mezhdunarodnaya Politika *see* Review of International Affairs **3970**
Mezhdunarodnaya Zhizn' *see* International Affairs **3961**
Mezhdunarodni Otnosheniya. (BU ISSN 0324-1092) **2375**, 679
Mezhdunarodnyi Agropromyshlennyi Zhurnal. (RU) **107**
Mezhdunarodnyi Obzor Ugolovnoi Politiki *see* International Review of Criminal Policy **1516**
Mezhdunarodnyi Sel'skokhozyaistvennyi Zhurnal *see* Mezhdunarodnyi Agropromyshlennyi Zhurnal **107**
Mezinarodni Vztahy. (CS) **3965**, 679
Mezinarodni Zemedelsko-Prumyslovy Casopis. (CS) **107**
Mezinarodni Zemedelsky Casopis *see* Mezinarodni Zemedelsko-Prumyslovy Casopis **107**
Mezogazdasagi es Elelmiszeripari Konyvtarosok Tajekoztatoja/Information for Librarians in Agriculture and Food Industry. (HU ISSN 0133-4875) **107**
Mezogazdasagi Konyvtarosok Tajekoztatoja *see* Mezogazdasagi es Elelmiszeripari Konyvtarosok Tajekoztatoja **107**
Mezogazdasagi Technika. (HU ISSN 0026-1890) **107**
Mezzalira. (IT) **1506**
Mezzalira Informazioni. (IT) **837**
Mezzogiorno d'Europa *see* Journal of Regional Policy **2726**
Mezzotinto. (GW) **2938**
MGlobal Customer News. (US) **1447**
▼Mi Bebe. (US) **1241**
Mi Mladi. (CI ISSN 0026-1939) **1260**
Mia. (GR) **2196**
Mia. (SP) **4848**
Mia Boutique. (IT) **1293**
La Mia Casa - Mensile di Arredamento. (IT) **2554**
Miami (Year). (US) **4776**
Miami Business Journal *see* South Florida Business Journal **692**
Miami Children's Hospital Journal *see* Revista Internacional de Pediatria **3326**
Miami Jewish Tribune. (US ISSN 0891-6659) **2013**, 4225
Miami Meanderings. (US ISSN 0889-3640) **2158**, 2414
Miami Mensual/Miami Monthly. (US) **2229**
Miami Monthly. *see* Miami Mensual **2229**
Miami Review. (US) **679**
Miami Today. (US) **679**
Miami Valley Dairyman *see* Milk Marketer **201**
Miamian. (US) **1317**
Miasma Philatelist. (US) **3754**

Mibifnim/From Within. (IS ISSN 0046-5178) **154**, 2874
Michael. (IS ISSN 0334-4150) **2013**
Michael. (CN) **4190**
Michael Reese Mirror *see* Humana Hospital - Michael Reese News **2466**
Michael Reese News *see* Humana Hospital - Michael Reese News **2466**
†Michaels on Etiquette. (US ISSN 0889-7042) **5236**
Michael's Thing. (US) **2874**, 4443
Michel-Briefmarken-Kataloge. (GW ISSN 0076-7727) **3754**
Michel-Rundschau. (GW ISSN 0026-198X) **3754**
Michele's Magic Moments. (US) **1299**, 3514
Michelin Green Guide Series: Alpes *see* Michelin Green Guide Series: Alpes du Nord **4776**
Michelin Green Guide Series: Alpes *see* Michelin Green Guide Series: Alpes du Sud **4776**
Michelin Green Guide Series: Alpes du Nord. (FR) **4776**
Michelin Green Guide Series: Alpes du Sud. (FR) **4776**
Michelin Green Guide Series: Alsace et Lorraine (Vosges). (FR) **4776**
Michelin Green Guide Series: Austria. (FR) **4776**
Michelin Green Guide Series: Auvergne. (FR) **4776**
Michelin Green Guide Series: Belgique - Luxembourg. (FR) **4776**
†Michelin Green Guide Series: Belgium - Luxembourg. (FR) **5236**
Michelin Green Guide Series: Berry-Limousin. (FR) **4776**
Michelin Green Guide Series: Bourgogne. (FR) **4776**
Michelin Green Guide Series: Brittany. (FR) **4776**
Michelin Green Guide Series: Burgundy. (FR) **4776**
Michelin Green Guide Series: Canada. (FR) **4776**
Michelin Green Guide Series: Champagne-Ardennes. (FR) **4776**
Michelin Green Guide Series: Chateaux of the Loire. (FR) **4776**
Michelin Green Guide Series: Corse. (FR) **4776**
Michelin Green Guide Series: Cote d'Azur. (FR) **4776**
Michelin Green Guide Series: Dordogne.(FR) **4776**
Michelin Green Guide Series: England, The West Country. (FR) **4776**
Michelin Green Guide Series: Environs de Paris *see* Michelin Green Guide Series: Ile de France **4777**
Michelin Green Guide Series: Flandres, Artois, Picardie. (FR) **4776**
Michelin Green Guide Series: France. (FR) **4776**
Michelin Green Guide Series: French Riviera. (FR) **4776**
Michelin Green Guide Series: Germany. (FR) **4776**
Michelin Green Guide Series: Gorges du Tarn. (FR) **4776**
Michelin Green Guide Series: Great Britain. (FR) **4776**
Michelin Green Guide Series: Greece. (FR) **4777**
Michelin Green Guide Series: Hollande. (FR) **4777**
Michelin Green Guide Series: Ile de France. (FR) **4777**
Michelin Green Guide Series: Italy. (FR) **4777**
Michelin Green Guide Series: Jura. (FR ISSN 0293-9436) **4777**
Michelin Green Guide Series: London. (FR) **4777**
†Michelin Green Guide Series: Londres. (FR) **5236**
Michelin Green Guide Series: Maroc. (FR) **4777**
Michelin Green Guide Series: Mexico. (FR) **4777**
Michelin Green Guide Series: Netherlands. (FR) **4777**
Michelin Green Guide Series: New England. (FR) **4777**

Michelin Green Guide Series: New York (City). (FR) **4777**
Michelin Green Guide Series: Nord de la France *see* Michelin Green Guide Series: Flandres, Artois, Picardie **4776**
†Michelin Green Guide Series: Normandy. (FR) **5236**
Michelin Green Guide Series: Normandy, Cotentin. (FR) **4777**
Michelin Green Guide Series: Normandy, Valley Seine. (FR) **4777**
Michelin Green Guide Series: Paris. (FR) **4777**
Michelin Green Guide Series: Perigord *see* Michelin Green Guide Series: Dordogne **4776**
Michelin Green Guide Series: Perigord-Quercy. (FR) **4777**
Michelin Green Guide Series: Poitou-Vendee-Charentes. (FR) **4777**
Michelin Green Guide Series: Portugal. (FR) **4777**
Michelin Green Guide Series: Provence. (FR) **4777**
Michelin Green Guide Series: Pyrenees *see* Michelin Green Guide Series: Pyrenees Aquitaine **4777**
Michelin Green Guide Series: Pyrenees Aquitaine. (FR) **4777**
Michelin Green Guide Series: Pyrenees Roussillon. (FR) **4777**
Michelin Green Guide Series: Rome. (FR) **4777**
Michelin Green Guide Series: Scotland. (FR) **4777**
Michelin Green Guide Series: Spain. (FR) **4777**
Michelin Green Guide Series: Switzerland. (FR) **4777**
Michelin Green Guide Series: Vallee du Rhone. (FR) **4777**
Michelin Green Guide Series: Vosges *see* Michelin Green Guide Series: Alsace et Lorraine (Vosges) **4776**
Michelin Green Guide Series: Washington, D.C. (FR) **4777**
Michelin Red Guide Series: Benelux. (FR ISSN 0076-7743) **4777**
Michelin Red Guide Series: Camping, France. (FR) **4777**
Michelin Red Guide Series: Deutschland.(FR) **4777**
Michelin Red Guide Series: Espana & Portugal. (FR ISSN 0076-776X) **4777**
Michelin Red Guide Series: Europe, Main Cities. (FR) **4777**
Michelin Red Guide Series: France. (FR ISSN 0076-7778) **4777**
Michelin Red Guide Series: Germany *see* Michelin Red Guide Series: Deutschland **4777**
Michelin Red Guide Series: Great Britain and Ireland. (FR) **4777**
Michelin Red Guide Series: Greater London. (FR) **4777**, 2477
Michelin Red Guide Series: Italy. (FR ISSN 0076-7786) **4778**
Michelin Red Guide Series: Paris. (FR ISSN 0076-7794) **4778**
Micheron Biniya, Energia Vesherutim Nivcharim. (IS) **1792**, 624
Micheron Rechev Veachzakato. (IS) **4695**
Micheron Sherutim Financim Umischariim. (IS) **838**
Michiana Philatelist. (US) **3754**
Michie Library Quarterly. (US) **2773**
Michigan. Advisory Council for Vocational Education. Annual Report *see* Michigan Council on Vocational Eduation. Biennial Evaluation Report (Year) **1738**
Michigan. Civil Rights Commission. Annual Report. (US) **3945**
Michigan. Civil Service Department. Annual Work Force Report. (US) **988**
†Michigan. Department of Commerce. Annual Report. (US) **5236**
Michigan. Department of Commerce. Corporation and Securities Bureau. Securities Bulletin *see* Update (Lansing) **5299**

MICHIGAN WORKERS   6433

Michigan. Department of Conservation. Geological Survey Division. Progress Report *see* Michigan. Geological Survey Division. Report of Investigation **1572**

Michigan. Department of Education. College Admissions and Financial Assistance Handbook *see* Michigan Postsecondary Admissions & Financial Assistance Handbook **1695**

Michigan. Department of Natural Resources. Institute for Fisheries Research. Miscellaneous Publication. (US ISSN 0076-7905) **2045**

Michigan. Department of Social Services. Assistance Payments Statistics. (US) **4413**, **4067**

Michigan. Department of Social Services. Program Statistics. (US ISSN 0093-7835) **4426**

Michigan. Department of Social Services. Public Assistance Statistics *see* Michigan. Department of Social Services. Program Statistics **4426**

Michigan. Department of State Police. Annual Report. (US) **1518**

Michigan. Employment Security Commission. Annual Planning Report. (US) **988**

Michigan. Employment Security Commission. Labor Market Analysis Section. Annual Manpower Planning Report: Detroit Labor Market Area *see* Michigan. Employment Security Commission. Annual Planning Report **988**

Michigan. Geological Survey Division. Bulletin. (US ISSN 0543-8497) **1572**

Michigan. Geological Survey Division. Report of Investigation. (US) **1572**

Michigan. State Court Administrator. Annual Report. (US ISSN 0098-7875) **2700**

Michigan. State Police. Annual Report *see* Michigan. Department of State Police. Annual Report **1518**

Michigan A F L - C I O News. (US ISSN 0026-1998) **2586**

Michigan Academician. (US ISSN 0026-2005) **4324**, **335**, **2511**

Michigan Academy of Science, Arts, and Letters. Academy Letter. (US ISSN 0047-7052) **1711**

Michigan Airway *see* Michigan Society for Respiratory Therapy. Journal **3366**

Michigan: Around and About. (US) **3906**

Michigan Art Fairs. (US) **335**

Michigan Association of School Boards, Inc. Journal *see* M A S B Journal **1729**

Michigan Association of Secondary School Principals' Bulletin. (US ISSN 0026-2013) **1648**

Michigan Association of Speech Communication Journal. (US) **1738**

Michigan Audubon *see* Jack-Pine Warbler **564**

Michigan Audubon Newsletter *see* Jack-Pine Warbler **564**

Michigan Aviation. (US ISSN 0539-8703) **58**

Michigan Banker. (US) **873**

Michigan Banking and Business News *see* Michigan Banker **873**

Michigan Bar Journal. (US ISSN 0164-3576) **2654**

Michigan Beverage News. (US ISSN 0026-2021) **383**

Michigan Botanist. (US ISSN 0026-203X) **509**

Michigan Business *see* Corporate Detroit Magazine **657**

†Michigan Business and Economic Research Bibliography. (US ISSN 0091-9047) **5236**

†Michigan Business Papers. (US ISSN 0076-7840) **5236**

†Michigan Business Reports. (US ISSN 0076-7859) **5236**

†Michigan Business Studies. (US ISSN 0076-7867) **5236**

Michigan Chess. (US) **4479**, 1419

Michigan Christian Advocate. (US ISSN 0026-2072) **4243**

Michigan Christmas Tree Journal. (US) **2104**

Michigan Civil Rights Commission Newsletter. (US ISSN 0047-7087) **3945**, 2704

Michigan Contractor & Builder. (US) **624**, 1830

Michigan Corrections Association Report. (US ISSN 0026-2099) **1518**

Michigan Council for the Arts. Legislative Report. (US) **335**, 2704

Michigan Council for the Arts News *see* M C A News **334**

Michigan Council on Vocational Eduation. Biennial Evaluation Report (Year). (US ISSN 0093-9137) **1738**

Michigan Country Lines. (US) **2229**

Michigan Dairy Line. (US) **201**

Michigan Dental Association. Journal. (US ISSN 0026-2102) **3237**

Michigan Dental Hygienist Association. Bulletin. (US ISSN 0047-7095) **3237**

Michigan Distributors Directory. (US ISSN 0890-4049) **1146**

Michigan Documents. (US ISSN 0026-2110) **406**

Michigan Dry Bean Digest. (US) **107**

†Michigan Economy. (US ISSN 0730-272X) **5236**

▼Michigan Employment Law Letter. (US ISSN 1046-9109) **2711**, 988

Michigan Entomological Society Newsletter *see* M E S Newsletter **536**

Michigan Entomologist *see* Great Lakes Entomologist **533**

▼Michigan Environmental Law Letter. (US ISSN 1046-9192) **2704**, 1962

Michigan Environmental Report. (US ISSN 0747-735X) **1962**

▼Michigan Facts. (US ISSN 1051-7146) **1781**

Michigan Farm News *see* Michigan Farm News - Rural Living **107**

Michigan Farm News - Rural Living. (US) **107**

Michigan Farmer. (US ISSN 0026-2153) **107**

†Michigan Feminist Studies. (US ISSN 1055-856X) **5236**

Michigan Fisherman. (US) **4550**

Michigan Florist. (US ISSN 0026-217X) **2142**

Michigan Food News. (US ISSN 0047-7117) **2077**

Michigan Gazette *see* Bentley Historical Library **2400**

Michigan Geo-Pulse. (US) **1573**

Michigan Germanic Studies. (US ISSN 0098-8030) **2829**, 2938

Michigan Golfer. (US) **4507**

Michigan Golfer's Map & Guide. (US) **4507**, 4778

▼Michigan Golfer's Travel Guide. (US) **4507**, 4778

Michigan Health Educator. (US ISSN 0164-1336) **3806**

Michigan Health Statistics. (US ISSN 0539-7413) **4118**

Michigan Historical Review (Mt. Pleasant). (US ISSN 0439-237X) **2414**, 2874

Michigan History *see* Michigan History Magazine **2414**

Michigan History Magazine. (US) **2414**

Michigan Hospitality *see* Michigan Restaurateur **2477**

Michigan Industry. (US ISSN 0026-2412) **1047**

Michigan Information and Research Service, Inc. Legislative Report *see* M I R S Legislative Report **4066**

†Michigan International Business Studies. (US ISSN 0076-7972) **5236**

†Michigan Investor. (US) **5236**

Michigan Journal of International Law. (US) **2727**, 1518

Michigan Journal of Political Science. (US) **3907**

Michigan Journal of Secondary Education *see* Secondary Education Today **1662**

Michigan Labor Market Review. (US ISSN 0098-0307) **988**

Michigan Law Enforcement Officials Report on Crime *see* Uniform Crime Report for the State of Michigan **1525**

Michigan Law Review. (US ISSN 0026-2234) **2654**

Michigan Lawyers Weekly. (US) **2654**

Michigan Librarian. (US) **2773**

Michigan Librarian Newsletter *see* Michigan Librarian **2773**

Michigan Library Directory. (US) **1146**, 2773

Michigan Library Directory and Statistics *see* Michigan Library Directory **1146**

Michigan Library News *see* Michigan Library Directory **1146**

Michigan Living. (US) **4778**, 4695

Michigan Lutheran. (US) **4243**

†Michigan Magazine Index. (US ISSN 0026-2250) **5236**

Michigan Manpower Review *see* Michigan Labor Market Review **988**

Michigan Manufacturers Directory. (US ISSN 0736-2889) **1047**

Michigan Master Plumber *see* Michigan Master Plumber & Mechanical Contractor **2301**

Michigan Master Plumber & Mechanical Contractor. (US) **2301**, 624

Michigan Mathematical Journal. (US ISSN 0026-2285) **3048**

Michigan Medicine. (US ISSN 0026-2293) **3131**

Michigan Milk Messenger. (US ISSN 0026-2315) **201**

Michigan Monographs in Chinese Studies. (US) **2340**

Michigan Municipal League. Municipal Legal Briefs. (US ISSN 0076-8014) **4091**

Michigan Municipal Review. (US ISSN 0026-2331) **4091**

Michigan Mutual Safety News *see* Amerisure Safety News **4097**

Michigan Natural Resources. (US ISSN 0026-2358) **1491**, 4550

Michigan Nurse. (US ISSN 0026-2366) **3282**

Michigan Oil & Gas News. (US) **3691**

Michigan Optometrist. (US) **3302**

Michigan Organization for Human Rights News *see* M O H R News **3944**

Michigan Osteopathic Journal *see* Triad (Farmington) **3216**

Michigan Out-Of-Doors. (US ISSN 0026-2382) **1492**, 4479

Michigan Papers on South and Southeast Asia. (US) **2340**

Michigan Pharmacist *see* Journal Michigan Pharmacist **3730**

Michigan Police Chiefs Newsletter. (US) **1518**

Michigan Police Journal *see* Michigan Police Chiefs Newsletter **1518**

Michigan Postsecondary Admissions & Financial Assistance Handbook. (US) **1695**

Michigan Quarter Horse Journal. (US) **4536**

Michigan Quarterly Review. (US ISSN 0026-2420) **2874**

Michigan Reading Journal. (US ISSN 0047-7125) **1738**

Michigan Restaurateur. (US ISSN 0161-6447) **2477**, 2077

Michigan Roads and Construction. (US) **1871**

Michigan Runner. (US) **4550**, 3806

Michigan Science in Action *see* Futures (East Lansing) **93**

Michigan Slavic Contributions. (US ISSN 0076-8103) **2938**

Michigan Slavic Materials. (US ISSN 0543-9930) **2938**, 2829

Michigan Slavic Translations. (US) **2938**

Michigan Snowmobiler. (US) **4550**

Michigan Society for Respiratory Therapy. Journal. (US ISSN 0047-7060) **3366**

Michigan Society of Architects Monthly Bulletin *see* M S A Monthly Bulletin **303**

Michigan Sportsman. (US ISSN 0539-8908) **4550**, 1962

Michigan State Employees' Retirement System *see* Michigan State Employees' Retirement System Financial and Statistical Report **988**

Michigan State Employees' Retirement System Financial and Statistical Report. (US ISSN 0092-9212) **988**, 4067

Michigan State Horticultural Society. Annual Report. (US ISSN 0096-7688) **2077**, 1047

Michigan State Housing Development Authority. Annual Report. (US) **2492**

Michigan State Housing Development Authority Housing Trends and Activity *see* M S H D A Housing Trends and Activity **5230**

Michigan State Plan for Vocational Education. (US ISSN 0094-1506) **1685**

Michigan State University. Agricultural Economics Report. (US ISSN 0065-4442) **154**

Michigan State University. Asian Studies Center. Occasional Papers: East Asia Series. (US ISSN 0076-812X) **2340**

Michigan State University. Asian Studies Center. Occasional Papers: South Asia Series. (US ISSN 0076-8138) **2340**

†Michigan State University. Cooperative Extension Service. Annual Report. (US) **5236**

Michigan State University. Institute of Water Research. Annual Report. (US) **4827**

Michigan State University. Institute of Water Research. Technical Reports. (US ISSN 0580-9746) **4827**

Michigan State University. International Networks in Education and Development. Publications. (US) **1648**

Michigan State University. Latin American Studies Center. Monograph Series. (US ISSN 0076-8189) **2414**

Michigan State University. Latin American Studies Center. Research Reports. (US ISSN 0076-8200) **2414**

Michigan State University. Library. Africana: Select Recent Acquisitions. (US ISSN 0147-0604) **406**

Michigan State University. Museum Publications. Anthropological Series. (US) **244**

Michigan State University. Museum Publications. Biological Series. (US ISSN 0076-8227) **447**

Michigan State University. Museum Publications. Cultural Series. (US ISSN 0076-8235) **3527**

Michigan State University. Museum Publications. Folk Art Series. (US) **336**

Michigan State University. Museum Publications. Paleontological Series. (US) **3658**

Michigan State University. National Superconducting Cyclotron Laboratory (Publication). (US) **1807**

Michigan State University. School of Labor and Industrial Relations. Newsletter. (US ISSN 0036-6706) **988**

Michigan State University Alumni Magazine *see* M S U Alumni Magazine **1316**

†Michigan Statistical Abstract. (US ISSN 0076-8308) **5236**

Michigan Studies in the Humanities. (US) **2938**

Michigan Tech Alumnus. (US) **1317**

Michigan Technic. (US ISSN 0026-2471) **1830**

Michigan Times. (US) **1317**

Michigan Today. (US ISSN 0041-9850) **1317**

†Michigan Travel and Recreation Guide.(US) **5236**

Michigan Truck Exchange. (US) **4746**

Michigan, Wisconsin TourBook *see* Tourbook: Michigan, Wisconsin **4790**

Michigan Workers' Comp Digest. (US ISSN 0746-1461) **2538**, 988

6434 MICHIGAN YEARBOOK

Michigan Yearbook of International Legal Studies see Michigan Journal of International Law **2727**
Michigan's Occupational Health. (US ISSN 0026-251X) **3619**
Michigan's Oil and Gas Fields: Annual Statistical Summary. (US ISSN 0085-3429) **3706**
Michkar Chaklaei Beyisrael. (IS ISSN 0334-7532) **107**
Michkarim Begeografiyah Shel Eretz Yisrael/Studies in the Geography in Israel. (IS ISSN 0081-8585) **2256**
Michmanim. (IS ISSN 0334-7311) **278**
Michnet News. (US) **1427**
Mick Family Newsletter. (US) **2158**
Mickery Mouth and Toneel Teatraal see Toneel Teatraal **4642**
Mickey. (BL) **1260**
Mickey Parade. (FR) **1260**
†Mickle Street Review. (US ISSN 0194-1313) **5236**
Micmac News. (CN ISSN 0026-2528) **2014**
Micologia Italiana. (IT ISSN 0390-0460) **509**
Micomlife. (JA ISSN 0285-6425) **1398**
Micomp. (SZ) **201**
Micro see Microprogramming and Microarchitecture Workshop. Proceedings **1462**
Micro see Personal Computer **1464**
Micro see N Z Micro **1471**
Micro Abstracts. (UK ISSN 0958-4668) **1405**
Micro Adventurer. (US) **1422**, **1470**
†Micro and Digital Electronics. (UK) **5236**
▼Micro & Macro Marketing. (IT) **1048**
†Micro-Bibliotheca Anthropos. (GW) **5236**
†Micro Computer College. (GW) **5236**
Micro Computers. see Micro Ordinateurs **5236**
Micro Control Journal. (CN) **3065**, **1454**, **1879**
†Micro Cornucopia. (US ISSN 0747-587X) **5236**
Micro e Personal Computer. (IT) **1462**, **1470**
Micro Extra. (GW ISSN 0172-0899) **1462**
Micro-Gazette. (CN ISSN 0836-3587) **1462**, **1351**
Micro-Library Bulletin. (KO ISSN 0026-2536) **2773**
Micro-Line see Computer Hot Line Weekly (Newsstand Edition) **5170**
Micro M D Journal see Micro M D Newsletter **3226**
Micro M D Newsletter. (US) **3226**
Micro Marketworld. (US ISSN 0746-6765) **1433**
Micro Materials Update. (US) **1470**, **2294**
Micro Medical Newsletter. (US) **3226**, **1462**, **1470**
Micro Money Newsletter. (US ISSN 0742-9398) **1462**, **1433**
Micro Mundo. (BL ISSN 0101-6261) **1462**
Micro News see Irish Computer **1461**
†Micro Ordinateurs/Micro Computers. (FR) **5236**
Micro Publications. Social Science Series. (DK ISSN 0901-0025) **4443**
†Micro Publisher. (US) **5236**
†Micro Software Evaluations. (US ISSN 8755-5794) **5236**
Micro Software Marketing. (US ISSN 0738-6354) **1479**, **1433**, **1462**
Micro-Systems Journal see L A N Technology **1461**
Micro Technology. (UK) **4604**
Micro Ticker Report see Inside Market Data **805**
Micro-to-Host Directory. (US) **1462**, **1454**
Micro User. (UK ISSN 0265-4040) **1462**, **1470**
Micro Verden see P C World **1473**
MicroAge Quarterly. (US) **1466**, **1462**
Microbanker. (US ISSN 0738-7156) **805**, **1462**, **1471**
▼Microbial Biotechnology. (UK ISSN 0964-7562) **555**, **490**

Microbial Ecology. (US ISSN 0095-3628) **555**
Microbial Ecology in Health & Disease. (UK ISSN 0891-060X) **3188**, **555**
Microbial Pathogenesis. (UK ISSN 0882-4010) **555**
Microbiologia. (SP ISSN 0213-4101) **555**
Microbiologica. (IT ISSN 0391-5352) **555**
Microbiological Reviews. (US ISSN 0146-0749) **555**
Microbiological Sciences see Molecular Microbiology **556**
Microbiological Update. (US) **555**
Microbiology see A P M I S **424**
Microbiology. (English translation of: Mikrobiologiya) (US ISSN 0026-2617) **555**
Microbiology Abstracts: Section A. Industrial & Applied Microbiology. (US ISSN 0300-838X) **466**, **17**
Microbiology Abstracts: Section B. Bacteriology. (US ISSN 0300-8398) **466**, **17**
Microbiology Abstracts: Section C. Algology, Mycology and Protozoology. (US ISSN 0301-2328) **466**, **17**
Microbiology and Immunology. (JA ISSN 0385-5600) **555**
Microbiology Series. (US) **555**
Microbios. (US ISSN 0026-2633) **555**, **3131**, **3200**
Microbios Letters see Biomedical Letters **522**
Microbrary. (US) **1462**
Microbyte. (CL ISSN 0716-4777) **1398**
Microcad News see Design Net **1459**
Microcar and Minicar Club Rapper see M and M Rapper **4695**
Microcell News. (US) **1340**
▼Microcell Report. (US ISSN 1048-6976) **1364**
Microchemical Journal. (US ISSN 0026-265X) **560**, **1184**
†Microcirculation. (US) **5236**
Microcirculation, Endothelium and Lymphatics. (US ISSN 0740-9451) **3273**, **480**
Microcomputer Analysis see Integrated Circuits International **1416**
Microcomputer Applications. (CN ISSN 0820-0750) **1462**
Microcomputer Communications. (US) **1462**
Microcomputer Index. (US ISSN 8756-7040) **1405**, **17**, **1462**
Microcomputer Industry Update. (US ISSN 0741-6016) **1405**, **1445**, **1462**, **1471**
MicroComputer Investor. (US) **827**
Microcomputer News International see Integrated Circuits International **1416**
Microcomputer Owner see P C & Office Technology **1463**
Microcomputer Review see Computer Review **1453**
Microcomputer Software Directory - International Directory of Software see Software Users' Year Book **1481**
Microcomputer Software Letter see Business Computer Digest **825**
Microcomputer Systems. see Xiaoxing Weixing Jisuanji Xitong **1466**
Microcomputer User's Year Book see P C Year Book **1464**
Microcomputers. (JA) **1462**
Microcomputers for Information Management. (US) **2799**, **1462**
Microcomputers for Libraries. (US ISSN 0743-0302) **2799**
Microcomputers in Civil Engineering. (UK ISSN 0885-9507) **1880**, **1871**
Microcomputers in Education. (US) **1691**, **1454**, **1462**, **1479**
Microcontamination. (US ISSN 0738-713X) **1775**, **58**, **1398**
Microcosm - Lyrical Ways. (US ISSN 0747-8216) **2874**
Microcritica. (AG ISSN 0026-2676) **3562**, **1531**, **4635**
Microdata Reference Manual from the Call and Income Report. (US) **873**

Microdecision. (HK ISSN 0261-5142) **1462**
Microeconomic Studies. (US) **897**
Microelectronic Engineering. (NE ISSN 0167-9317) **1775**
Microelectronic Manufacturing and Testing see Microelectronics Manufacturing Technology **1775**
†Microelectronic Manufacturing and Testing Desk Manual. (US) **5236**
Microelectronics and Reliability. (US ISSN 0026-2714) **1775**
Microelectronics and Signal Processing. (US) **1775**, **1462**
Microelectronics Journal. (UK ISSN 0026-2692) **1775**
Microelectronics Manufacturing Technology. (US) **1775**
Microfiche Foundation. Newsletter. (NE ISSN 0076-8480) **2773**, **3793**
Microfilaments and Microtubules see Cytoskeleton **524**
Microfilm Newsletter see Micrographics Newsletter **3793**
Microfilmed Newspapers of Finland. see Suomen Sanomalehtien Mikrofilmit **2579**
Microform Market Place. (GW ISSN 0362-0999) **2773**
Microform Review. (GW ISSN 0002-6530) **2773**, **4132**
Microforms Annual. (US ISSN 0270-8523) **406**
†Microgram Newsletter. (US) **5236**
Micrographics and Optical Storage Buyer's Guide. (UK) **3793**
Micrographics and Optical Storage Equipment Review. (US) **2773**
Micrographics Index see Resource Center Index **1061**
Micrographics Market Place. (UK) **729**
Micrographics Newsletter. (US ISSN 0883-9808) **3793**
Micrographics Year Book see Micrographics and Optical Storage Buyer's Guide **3793**
†Micrography. (NE) **5236**
Micrography in Information Systems. see Mikrografija u Informacionim Sistemima **561**
Microgravity News from E S A. (NE) **58**
▼Microgravity Quarterly. (US ISSN 0958-5036) **58**
Microgravity - Science and Technology. (GW ISSN 0938-0108) **58**, **4604**
MicroIndexer. (UK ISSN 0266-4879) **2794**
Microleads Vendor Directory. (US) **1425**, **1471**, **1479**
▼Microlithography World. (US) **1422**
Microlog: Canadian Research Index. (CN ISSN 0839-1289) **17**
Microlog Index see Microlog: Canadian Research Index **17**
Micromath. (UK ISSN 0267-5501) **3048**
Micromegas. (IT) **1722**
Micron and Microscopica Acta. (US ISSN 0739-6260) **560**
Micronesian Independent see Marshall Islands Journal **2213**
Micronesica. (GU ISSN 0026-279X) **447**, **245**
Micronutrient News see Micronutrient News and Information **185**
Micronutrient News and Information. (UK ISSN 0957-4360) **185**
Micropaleontology. (US ISSN 0026-2803) **3658**
Micropaleontology Special Papers. (US ISSN 0160-2071) **3658**
Micropendium. (US ISSN 1043-2299) **1471**, **1462**
Microprocessing and Microprogramming. (NE ISSN 0165-6074) **1462**, **1431**
Microprocessor-Based Systems Engineering. (NE) **1830**, **1462**
Microprocessor I C's D.A.T.A. Digest. (Integrated Circuits) (US ISSN 1049-2445) **1462**
Microprocessor Report. (US ISSN 0899-9341) **1462**
Microprocessors see Microprocessors & Microsystems **1462**
Microprocessors & Microsystems. (UK ISSN 0141-9331) **1462**
Microprofile see Micro Abstracts **1405**

Microprogramming and Microarchitecture Workshop. Proceedings. (US) **1462**, **1431**
Micropsych Network. (US ISSN 0748-2051) **3226**
Micropublishers' Trade List Annual. (US ISSN 0361-2635) **406**
MicroPublishing Report. (US ISSN 0889-9533) **4143**, **1463**
†Micros in Scottish Education. (UK) **5236**
Microscope. (US ISSN 0026-282X) **560**, **1211**, **3265**
Microscope. (UK) **1463**
▼Microscope Book. (US ISSN 1051-404X) **560**
▼Microscope Technology & News. (US) **560**
Microscopia Electronica y Biologia Celular/Electronic Microscopy and Cellular Biology. (AG ISSN 0326-3142) **560**, **555**
Microscopical Society of Canada. Bulletin. (CN ISSN 0383-1825) **560**
Microscopical Society of Canada. Proceedings. (CN) **560**
Microscopy. (UK ISSN 0026-2838) **560**
Microscopy and Analysis. (UK) **561**
†Microscopy and 3D Imaging. (UK ISSN 0268-151X) **5236**
Microscopy Microanalysis Microstrucures. (FR) **3855**, **561**
MicroSistemas see P C World Espana **1473**
Microsoft Networking Journal. (US ISSN 1052-8571) **1438**
Microsoft Systems Journal. (US ISSN 0889-9932) **1431**, **1479**
Microsoft Works in Education. (US) **1417**
Microsoftware News. (US) **1463**, **4091**
†Microsomes. (UK ISSN 0264-9594) **5236**
Microstate Studies. (VI) **4379**
Microsurgery. (US ISSN 0738-1085) **3381**, **3262**
Microsystem Design. (UK ISSN 0269-1477) **1463**
Microsystems. (FR) **1463**, **1452**
Microtables Imports - Exports of O E C D Countries. (Organization for Economic Cooperation and Development) (FR) **917**
Microtecnic. (SZ ISSN 0026-2854) **2524**
Microtimes. (US) **1463**
Microvascular Research. (US ISSN 0026-2862) **3210**
Microview. (CN) **1463**, **827**
Microwave Applications. (US) **1349**
Microwave Journal (International Edition). (US ISSN 0192-6225) **1903**
Microwave Licenses Issued. (US) **1349**
Microwave News. (US ISSN 0275-6595) **4108**
Microwave Power Symposium. Proceedings. (US) **1903**
Microwave Product Digest. (US) **1903**
†Microwave Systems News. (US) **5236**
Microwave Systems News and Communications Technology see Microwave Systems News **5236**
Microwave Times. (US) **2448**, **2077**
Microwave World. (US ISSN 0276-7961) **2077**
▼Microwaves and Food Newsletter. (US) **2077**
Microwaves & R F. (US ISSN 0745-2993) **1903**
Microwaves & R F Product Data Directory. (US) **1903**
Microwaves & R F Product Extra. (US) **1903**
Microwaves Product Data Directory see Microwaves & R F Product Data Directory **1903**
MicroWorld see Faulkner Report on Microcomputers and Software **1460**
Mid-Am Antique Appraisers Association. Newsletter. (US) **258**
Mid-Am Reporter. (US ISSN 0195-5624) **201**
Mid-America. (US ISSN 0026-2927) **2414**
Mid-America Banner. (US) **1081**

Mid-America Commerce & Industry. (US ISSN 0193-2047) **874**
Mid-America Folklore. (US ISSN 0275-6013) **2056**
Mid-America Insurance. (US ISSN 0026-2935) **2538**
Mid-America Transporter. (US) **4746**
Mid-American Journal of Business. (US ISSN 0895-1772) **679**
Mid-American Review. (US ISSN 0747-8895) **2874**
Mid-American Review of Sociology. (US ISSN 0732-913X) **4443**
Mid-Atlantic Apothecary *see* Apothecary **3717**
Mid-Atlantic Archivist. (US ISSN 0738-9396) **2773**
Mid-Atlantic Country Magazine. (US ISSN 0888-1022) **2229**
Mid-Atlantic-Delaware, District of Columbia, Maryland, Virginia, West Virginia TourBook *see* Tourbook: Mid-Atlantic **4790**
Mid - Atlantic Foodservice News. (US) **2477**
Mid-Atlantic Journal of Business. (US ISSN 0732-9334) **679**
Mid-Atlantic Preservation Service Newsletter *see* M A P S Newsletter **2772**
Mid-Atlantic Purchasing *see* P M News **1049**
▼Mid-Canada Airport Business Directory. (CN) **4675**
†Mid-Canada Commerce. (CN) **5236**
Mid Coaster. (US) **2998**
Mid-Continent Bottler. (US) **3649**
Mid-Hudson Genealogical Journal. (US) **2158**
†Mid-Hudson Language Studies. (US ISSN 0272-717X) **5236**
Mid-Hudson Library System News *see* M H L S News **2772**
Mid-Hudson News *see* M H L S News **2772**
Mid-Ohio Review *see* Horizons (Columbus) **4063**
Mid-South Business Journal *see* Business Perspectives **652**
Mid-South Geographer. (US) **2256**
Mid-South Quarterly Business Review *see* Mid-South Business Journal **680**
Mid South Trucking News. (US) **4746**
Mid-Week Petroleum Argus. (UK) **3691**, 1048
†Mid-Week Report. (US ISSN 0734-6506) **5236**
Mid-Zeitschrift fuer Literatur- & Zeitkritik. (GW) **2874**
MidAmerica. (US ISSN 0190-2911) **2938**, 2874
MidAmerica Farmer Grower. (US) **107**
†MidAmerican Outlook. (US) **5237**
Midas Newsletter *see* Monitor Money Review **955**
MidCoaster. (US ISSN 0892-970X) **2938**, 336, 2998
MidContinent Oil World. (US ISSN 0883-7325) **3692**
Midcontinent Petroleum Industry. (US) **3692**, 1146
†Midcontinental. (CN) **5237**
Midcontinental Journal of Archaeology. (US ISSN 0146-1109) **278**
Middelaar Tussen de Genealogische Navorsers. *see* Intermediaire des Genealogistes **2155**
The Midden. (CN ISSN 0047-7222) **278**
Midden Oosten Nieuwsbulletin *see* Afrika - Midden Oosten Bulletin **828**
Middle Ages. (US) **2375**
Middle and Far East Expatriate. (BA) **3629**
Middle Atlantic Perspective. (US) **3131**, 2773
Middle Atlantic Regional Gospel Ministries *see* M A R Gospel Ministries **4189**
Middle Atlantic States Komondor Club, Inc. Komondor News *see* M A S K C Komondor News **221**
The Middle East. (UK ISSN 0305-0734) **2874**, 680

Middle East and Africa *see* U.S. Foreign Broadcast Information Service. Daily Reports: Near East & South Asia **3931**
†Middle East: Abstracts and Index. (US ISSN 0162-766X) **5237**
†Middle East Agribusiness. (UK ISSN 0266-5905) **5237**
Middle East and North Africa (Year). (UK ISSN 0076-8502) **3907**, 874
Middle East and World Construction Directory. (CY) **624**
Middle East and World Construction Industry *see* Middle East and World Construction Directory **624**
Middle East and World Food Directory. (LE) **2077**
Middle East and World Water Directory. (CY) **4827**
†Middle East Annual. (US ISSN 0733-5350) **5237**
Middle East Building Products Catalogue. (UK) **624**
Middle East Business and Banking. (TU) **790**, 874
Middle East Business Intelligence. (UK ISSN 0731-6305) **917**
Middle East Communications. (UK ISSN 0269-9567) **1364**
†Middle East Computing. (UK ISSN 0263-9203) **5237**
Middle East Construction Catalogue - Building Products Edition *see* Middle East Building Products Catalogue **624**
Middle East Contemporary Survey. (US ISSN 0163-5476) **2431**, 3965
Middle East Currency Reports. (UK ISSN 0307-0387) **790**
Middle East Economic Digest. (UK ISSN 0047-7230) **874**
Middle East Economic Digest Ltd. Practical Guide. Jordan *see* M E E D Practical Guide. Jordan **4775**
Middle East Economic Digest Ltd. Practical Guide. Qatar *see* M E E D Practical Guide. Qatar **4775**
Middle East Economic Digest Ltd. Profile *see* M E E D Profile **678**
Middle East Economic Survey. (CY ISSN 0544-0424) **3692**
†Middle East Education & Training. (UK ISSN 0265-5292) **5237**
Middle East Education & Training Buyers Guide. (UK) **1648**
Middle East Electricity. (UK ISSN 0309-4707) **1903**
Middle East Executive Reports. (UK ISSN 0271-0498) **874**
Middle East Express. (LE ISSN 0026-3117) **874**
†Middle East Financial Directory. (UK ISSN 0266-2094) **5237**
Middle East Focus. (CN ISSN 0705-8594) **3907**
Middle East Food. (CY ISSN 0256-7032) **2077**
Middle East Food Trade and Catering Equipment *see* Asia and Middle East Food Trade **5139**
†Middle East Forum/Kulliyah. (LE) **5237**
Middle East Health. (UK ISSN 0309-2003) **4108**
Middle East Insight. (US ISSN 0731-9371) **3965**, 2431
Middle East Institute Newsletter. (US) **3907**
Middle East International. (US ISSN 0047-7249) **3907**
Middle East Journal. (US ISSN 0026-3141) **3965**
Middle East Librarians Association Notes *see* M E L A Notes **2772**
†Middle East Management Review. (UA) **5237**
Middle East Memo. (US) **2014**
Middle East Military Balance (Year). (IS) **3464**
Middle East Monitor. (US ISSN 0026-315X) **3907**
Middle East News Agency Economic Weekly *see* M E N Economic Weekly **873**
Middle East Observer. (UA ISSN 0047-7257) **874**
Middle East Observer Bulletin *see* M E O Bulletin **873**

Middle East Policy. (US) **3965**, 917
Middle East Policy Survey. (US) **3907**
Middle East Record. (IS ISSN 0076-8529) **2431**
Middle East Report. (CN) **2014**
Middle East Report. (US ISSN 0899-2851) **2431**
Middle East Review. (UK ISSN 0305-3210) **874**
Middle East Stamp Catalogue. (UK ISSN 0142-9914) **3754**
Middle East Strategic Studies Quarterly. (UK ISSN 0954-1136) **3464**, 3965
Middle East Studies Association Bulletin.(US ISSN 0026-3184) **4379**, 2431, 3640, 3907
Middle East Trade/Tijjarat al Sharq al Aussat. (UK ISSN 0026-3192) **917**
Middle East Transport. (UK) **4653**, 680
Middle East Transport and Telecommunications *see* Middle East Transport **4653**
Middle East Watch. (US) **3945**
Middle East Watch Report. (US) **3945**
†Middle East Water & Sewage. (UK ISSN 0140-5098) **5237**
Middle Eastern Culture Center, Japan. Bulletin. (GW ISSN 0177-1647) **3641**
Middle Eastern Dancer Magazine. (US ISSN 1041-7591) **1531**
Middle Eastern Studies. (UK ISSN 0026-3206) **3907**, 2317
Middle Income Tax Planning and Shelters *see* Federal Tax Planning **1094**
Middle Management & Professional Compensation Survey (Year). (CN) **3632**
Middle School Chinese. *see* Zhongxue Yuwen **2854**
Middle School Journal. (US ISSN 0094-0771) **1755**
Middle School Science & Technology. *see* Zhongxue Keji **1673**
Middle School Student. *see* Zhongxuesheng **1673**
Middle-School Student Science Education. *see* Zhongxuesheng Kexue Jiaoyu **1673**
▼Middle Schools Directory. (UK) **1695**
Middle Schools Statistics in Punjab. (PK) **1678**
Middle States Association of Colleges and Schools. Proceedings of the Annual Convention. (US) **1711**
Middle States Association of Colleges and Secondary Schools. Proceedings *see* Middle States Association of Colleges and Schools. Proceedings of the Annual Convention **1711**
Middle States Council for the Social Studies. Journal. (US ISSN 0739-8069) **4380**
Middle Tennessee Crossroads. (US) **2414**
Middle Tennessee State University. Business and Economic Research Center. Conference Paper. (US) **874**
Middle Way. (UK ISSN 0026-3214) **4215**
Middlebury Campus. (US) **1317**
Middlebury College Magazine. (US) **1317**
Middlebury College News Letter *see* Middlebury College Magazine **1317**
Middlebury Studies in Russian Language and Literature. (US ISSN 0888-8752) **2829**, 2938
Middlesborough Diocesan Directory. (UK) **4269**
Middlesex Business Magazine. (US) **680**
The Midlesex Business Review. (US) **680**
Middlesex Hospital Journal *see* Bell - U C M S M Students' Magazine **2459**
Middletown Area Historical Society. Newsletter. (US) **2414**
†Mideast File. (US ISSN 0262-818X) **5237**
Mideast Markets. (US ISSN 0098-6461) **680**, 3907
Mideast Monitor. (US ISSN 0888-2460) **2431**, 3907

MidEast Report. (US ISSN 0026-3230) **3965**
Mideastern Campbook. (US ISSN 0734-2705) **4778**, 4550
Midgets & Mini-Sprints Racing News. (US) **4695**
†Midi-Minuit Fantastique. (FR ISSN 0047-7273) **5237**
Midia. (BL) **35**
Midland. (US ISSN 0026-3249) **1317**
Midland Ancestor. (UK ISSN 0307-2851) **2158**
Midland Bank Group Newpaper *see* Midland Group News **790**
Midland Bonsai Society Journal. (UK ISSN 0144-6916) **2134**
†Midland Cardowner. (UK) **5237**
†Midland Cooperator. (US ISSN 0047-7281) **5237**
Midland Genealogical Society. Newsletter. (US) **2158**
Midland Group News. (UK) **790**
Midland History. (UK ISSN 0047-729X) **2375**
†Midland Macromolecular Monographs. (US ISSN 0141-0342) **5237**
Midland News. (SA ISSN 0048-119X) **2216**
Midland Review. (US ISSN 0886-7976) **2938**, 3793
Midlands Business Journal. (US ISSN 0194-4525) **680**
Midlands Industry and Commerce. (UK ISSN 0026-3311) **819**
Midlands Telegraph *see* Sound Telegraph **2172**
▼Midnight Engineering. (US) **1830**
▼Midnight Express. (US) **3012**, 4132
Midnight Graffiti. (US) **3012**
Midnight Horoscope. (US) **359**
Midnight Marquee. (US) **3514**
†Midrange. (US) **5237**
Midrange Computing. (US ISSN 1052-3561) **1466**
Midrange Systems (Delran). (US) **1427**
Midrange Systems (Horsham). (US ISSN 1041-8237) **1466**
Midsouth Political Science Journal. (US) **3907**
Midsouthwest Restaurant. (US) **2477**
Midstream. (US ISSN 0026-332X) **2874**, 3907
†Midway. (US ISSN 1051-7375) **5237**
†Midway Review. (US ISSN 0741-3149) **5237**
Midweek. (UK) **2194**
Midwest Archives Conference Newsletter *see* M A C Newsletter **2772**
Midwest Art Fare. (US) **336**
Midwest Association for Latin American Studies Forum *see* M A L A S Forum **2413**
Midwest Auto Racing Guide *see* National Speedway Directory **4481**
Midwest Automotive & Autobody News. (US) **4695**
Midwest Automotive News *see* Midwest Automotive & Autobody News **4695**
†Midwest Borzoi Club Bulletin. (US) **5237**
Midwest Bowhunter. (US) **4550**
Midwest Bridle and Bit *see* Bit and Bridle **4532**
Midwest Bulletin. (NR) **2212**
Midwest Chaparral. (US ISSN 0026-3346) **2998**
Midwest Clearing Corporation and Midwest Securities Trust Company. Directory of Participants. (US) **1146**, 790
Midwest Conference on Graduate Study and Research. Proceedings *see* Midwestern Association of Graduate Schools. Proceedings of the Annual Meeting **1711**
Midwest Contractor Magazine. (US ISSN 0026-3044) **624**
Midwest Engineer. (US ISSN 0026-3370) **1830**
▼Midwest Environmental Law Letter. (US ISSN 1049-9350) **2654**, 1962
Midwest Farm Exchange - Minnesota. (US) **107**

MIDWEST FISHING

Midwest Fishing by Outdoor Life see Deer and Big Game **4544**
Midwest Flyer Magazine. (US ISSN 0194-5068) **4675**
Midwest Food Service. (US) **2478, 2077**
Midwest Gay Academic Journal see Gay Insurgent **2453**
Midwest Golf News. (US) **4507**
Midwest Historical and Genealogical Register. Quarterly. (US ISSN 0271-8685) **2158**
Midwest History of Education Society. Journal. (US ISSN 0092-2986) **1648**
Midwest Hunter see Hunter & Sport Horse **4535**
Midwest Hunter & Sport Horse see Hunter & Sport Horse **4535**
Midwest Landscaping see Landscape Contractor **2133**
Midwest Law Review. (US) **2654, 680**
Midwest Living. (US ISSN 0889-8138) **2229**
Midwest Messenger see Visions (Overland Park) **1367**
Midwest Middle School Journal see Middle School Journal **1755**
Midwest Modern Language Association. Journal. (US ISSN 0742-5562) **2938**
Midwest Motor Transport News. (US ISSN 0026-3427) **4746**
Midwest Motorist. (US ISSN 0026-3435) **4695, 4778**
Midwest Museum Bulletin. (US) **336, 3527**
Midwest Museums Conference. News Brief. (US) **3527**
Midwest Museums Conference Quarterly see Midwest Museums Conference. News Brief **3527**
MidWest Outdoors. (US) **4550**
Midwest Poetry Review. (US ISSN 0745-8738) **2998**
Midwest Political Consultant. (US) **3907**
Midwest Purchasing Management. (US) **1048**
Midwest Quarterly. (US ISSN 0026-3451) **2511, 3773**
Midwest Racing News. (US ISSN 0047-732X) **4479, 4695**
Midwest Real Estate News. (US ISSN 0893-2719) **4152**
Midwest Research Institute. Annual Report. (US) **4324**
Midwest Retailer. (US) **1048, 2560**
Midwest Stock Exchange Guide. (US) **955**
Midwest Studies in Philosophy. (US ISSN 0363-6550) **3773**
Midwestern Annual see MidAmerica **2938**
Midwestern Archivist. (US) **2317, 2511, 2773, 4380**
Midwestern Association of Graduate Schools. Proceedings of the Annual Meeting. (US) **1711**
Midwestern Dentist. (US ISSN 0026-3478) **3238**
Midwestern Folklore. (US ISSN 0894-4059) **2056**
Midwestern Journal of Language and Folklore see Midwestern Folklore **2056**
Midwestern Miscellany. (US) **2938**
Midwestern State Salvage Guide. (US) **4695**
Midwestern Trucker and Shipper see Nebraska Trucker **4746**
Mid-Western 4-Wheeler. (US) **4695**
Midwife and Health Visitor see Midwife, Health Visitor and Community Nurse **3282**
Midwife, Health Visitor and Community Nurse. (UK ISSN 0306-9699) **3282, 3294**
Midwifery. (UK ISSN 0266-6138) **3282, 3294, 3322**
Midwifery Today see Midwifery Today and Childbirth Education **3294**
Midwifery Today and Childbirth Education. (US) **3294, 4848**
Midwives Chronicle. (UK ISSN 0026-3524) **3295**

Mie Daigaku Kyoikugakubu Kenkyu Kiyo. Shizen Kagaku/Mie University. Faculty of Education. Bulletin. Natural Science. (JA ISSN 0389-9225) **4324**
Mie Daigaku Suisan Kenkyujo Hokoku. see Mie University. Fisheries Research Laboratory. Report **588**
Mie-ken Kogai Senta Nenpo/Mie Prefecture. Environmental Science Institute. Annual Report. (JA) **1962**
Mie Medical Journal. (JA ISSN 0026-3532) **3131**
Mie Prefectural University. Faculty of Fisheries. Bulletin see Mie University. Faculty of Fisheries. Journal **2045**
Mie Prefecture. Environmental Science Institute. Annual Report. see Mie-ken Kogai Senta Nenpo **1962**
Mie University. Faculty of Education. Bulletin. Natural Science. see Mie Daigaku Kyoikugakubu Kenkyu Kiyo. Shizen Kagaku **4324**
Mie University. Faculty of Fisheries. Journal. (JA) **2045**
Mie University. Fisheries Research Laboratory. Report/Mie Daigaku Suisan Kenkyujo Hokoku. (JA) **588**
Mie University Forests. Bulletin. (JA ISSN 0544-1005) **2104**
Miedzynarodowe Czasopismo Rolnicze. (PL ISSN 0026-3540) **107**
Mielies (Bothaville)/Maize. (SA) **107, 2077**
Mielies (Pretoria)/Maize. (SA) **207**
Miesiecznik Franciszkanski. (US ISSN 0300-6158) **4269**
Miesiecznik Literacki. (PL ISSN 0026-3567) **2938**
Mieter Magazin. (GW) **4152**
MieterEcho. (GW) **2492**
Mieterzeitung. (GW) **2492, 4413**
Mietpreiserhebung/Indice des Loyers. (SZ) **2500**
Mietrechtliche Entscheidungen. (AU) **2715**
MietSlg see Mietrechtliche Entscheidungen **2715**
Mieux-Vivre see Mieux-Vivre chez les Aveugles et les Grands Infirmes **2284**
Mieux-Vivre chez les Aveugles et les Grands Infirmes. (FR) **2284, 4413**
Ha-Mifal/Enterprise. (IS ISSN 0017-7059) **1081**
Mifgash. (IS) **2938**
Mify i Real'nost' (RU) **3514**
Migracijske Teme/Migration Themes. (CI ISSN 0352-5600) **4443, 2375**
Migraciones see Migration News **5237**
Migraine News. (UK ISSN 0544-1153) **3345**
Migrant. (US ISSN 0026-3575) **565**
Migrant Education News (Washington State). (US) **1738**
Migrant Pest Newsletter. (UN ISSN 1014-2193) **185**
Migranti-Press. (IT ISSN 0391-5492) **3907, 4190, 4443**
Migrants Formation. (FR ISSN 0335-0894) **3984**
Migrants Nouvelles. (FR ISSN 0397-944X) **3984**
Migration. see Siirtolaisuus **3987**
Migration. (GW ISSN 0721-2887) **4443, 2014**
Migration Action. (AT ISSN 0311-3760) **4443, 4413**
Migration and Intercultural Education in Europe. (UK ISSN 0959-051X) **1648**
Migration Highlights. (CN) **3993**
Migration Institute. Migration Studies. (FI) **3985**
†Migration News. (SZ ISSN 0026-3583) **5237**
Migration Themes. see Migracijske Teme **4443**
Migration Today see Migration World **3985**
Migration Today. (SZ ISSN 0544-1188) **3985**
Migration und Ethnizitaet see Bibliographische Informationen zu Migration und Ethnizitaet **4457**
Migration World. (US) **3985, 2014, 4380**

Migrations. (FR ISSN 0026-3591) **3629, 4443**
Migrations see Migration News **5237**
Migratori Acquatici see Migratori Alati **4550**
Migratori Alati. (IT) **4550**
Migrazione e Caccia. (IT) **565**
Mihira. (CE) **1260**
Mijn Stokpaardje. (NE ISSN 0026-3605) **3754**
Mike. (CN) **1317**
Mikhtav Lehaver. (IS ISSN 0026-363X) **3131**
Mikologiya i Fitopatologiya. (RU ISSN 0026-3648) **447**
Mikro see Mikro P C **1471**
Mikro-Klein Computer see M & K Computer **1461**
Mikro P C. (FI ISSN 0785-9988) **1471**
Mikrobielle Umwelt und Antimikrobielle Massnahmen. (GW) **3131**
Mikrobiologi-Nyt. (DK) **4813,** 3131
Mikrobiologichnyi Zhurnal. (KR ISSN 0201-8462) **555**
Mikrobiologija see Acta Biologica Iugoslavica. Serija B: Mikrobiologija **548**
MikroBitti. (FI ISSN 0781-2078) **1471**
Mikrobiyologi Bulteni Supplement. (TU ISSN 0374-9096) **555**
Mikrochimica Acta. (US ISSN 0026-3672) **1207**
Mikrochimica Acta. Supplement. (US ISSN 0076-8642) **1207**
Mikrochimica et Ichnoanalytica Acta see Mikrochimica Acta **1207**
MikroDatorn. (SW) **1463, 1471**
Mikrodok. (GW) **1463**
Mikroelektronik. (GW ISSN 0931-2714) **1775**
Mikrofauna Marina. (GW ISSN 0176-3296) **447**
Mikrografija u Informacionim Sistemima/Micrography in Information Systems. (YU ISSN 0351-6768) **561**
Mikrokosmos. (GW ISSN 0026-3680) **561, 555**
Mikronyt i Specialundervisningen see Via Datch **1742**
Mikroprozessortechnik. (GW) **1463**
†Mikroskopie. (AU ISSN 0026-3702) **5237**
Mikroszamitogep Magazin see Alaplap **1389**
Mikrowellen and H F - Magazin. (GW ISSN 0722-9488) **1903,** 3464
Mikrowellen and Military Electronics see Mikrowellen and H F - Magazin **1903**
Mikun Vehandasa Bechaklaut. (IS) **163**
Milano Casa Oggi see Casa Oggi **2204**
Milano Finanza. (IT) **955,** 917
Milap Weekly. (US ISSN 0026-3737) **3965**
Milbank Quarterly. (US ISSN 0887-378X) **3907, 4108, 4380**
Milch - Fettwaren - Eier - Handel. (GW ISSN 0026-3761) **2077, 201, 221**
Milch-Marketing. (GW ISSN 0176-5124) **201, 1048**
Milch Post. (GW) **201**
†Milchforschung - Milchpraxis. (GW ISSN 0323-5424) **5237**
Die Milchpraxis und Rindermast. (GW ISSN 0343-0200) **201**
†Milchstrasse. (GW ISSN 0933-0682) **5237**
Milchwirtschaftliche Berichte. (AU) **201**
Milchwissenschaft/Milk Science International. (GW ISSN 0026-3788) **140,** 17
Mildred. (US ISSN 0892-5267) **2874**
Mile Post. (US) **2438, 4695**
Milepost. (US ISSN 0361-1361) **4778**
Miles Alkalizer. (US) **447, 1081**
Miles International Symposium. (US) **525**
†Milestone Car. (US) **5237**
Milestones. (US) **2158**
Milestones. (UK ISSN 0026-380X) **4695**
Milford Historical Society Newsletter. (US ISSN 0540-0694) **2414**

Milford Series. (US ISSN 0163-2469) **2938**
Milieu. (CN ISSN 0380-2760) **1962**
Le Milieu. (CN) **3562**
Milieu en Bedrijf. (BE) **1963, 2654**
Milieudefensie. (NE ISSN 0165-9545) **1492**
▼Milim. (US) **2938**
Militaer-Kuechenchef. (SZ ISSN 0026-3907) **3464, 3609**
Militaer Teknisk Tidskrift. (SW ISSN 0047-7354) **3464**
Militaergeschichte. (GW ISSN 0323-5254) **3464, 2318**
Militaergeschichtliche Mitteilungen. (GW ISSN 0026-3826) **3464, 2318**
Militaerhistorisk Tidskrift. (SW ISSN 0283-8400) **2375, 3464**
Militaerpsykologiske Meddelelser. (NO ISSN 0026-3842) **3464**
Militaerseelsorge. (GW ISSN 0047-7362) **3464, 4269**
Militaert Tidsskrift. (DK ISSN 0026-3850) **3464**
Militaertechnik. (GW ISSN 0047-7346) **3464**
Militaire Spectator. (NE ISSN 0026-3869) **3464**
Militaly. (IT) **3464**
Militancia (Buenos Aires, 1973). (AG) **3907**
Militancia (Buenos Aires, 1986). (AG) **3907**
Militancia: Temas del Socialismo. (MX) **3907**
Militant. (US ISSN 0026-3885) **3907**
Militant. (FR ISSN 0026-3877) **3965**
Militante Comunista. (CU ISSN 0864-2362) **3907**
Militaria. (GW ISSN 0724-3529) **3464**
Militaria Belgica. (BE) **3464**
Military. (US ISSN 1046-2511) **3464**
Military Aircraft and Missile Data Sheets. (UK ISSN 0026-394X) **58, 3464**
Military Aircraft Markings. (UK) **3464, 58**
Military Airlift Command Flyer see M A C Flyer **3463**
▼Military & Aerospace Electronics. (US) **59,** 1903, 3464
Military & Commercial Fiber Business. (US ISSN 0887-2465) **3464, 59**
Military and Diplomats World News. (US) **2014**
Military Balance. (UK ISSN 0459-7222) **3464**
Military Chaplain. (US ISSN 0026-3958) **3464, 4190**
Military Chaplains' Review. (US ISSN 0360-9693) **3464, 4190**
Military Club & Hospitality. (US ISSN 0886-8832) **2077,** 3464
Military Clubs & Recreation. (US ISSN 0192-2718) **3464**
Military Collector & Historian. (US ISSN 0026-3966) **258, 2318, 3464**
Military Collectors News. (US ISSN 0047-7370) **2438, 3464**
†Military Communications. (UK) **5237**
†Military Dealers and Collectors Directory. (US) **5237**
Military Digest. (Il ISSN 0462-4874) **3464**
Military Educators & Counselors Association News. (US) **1711, 3464**
Military Electronic Devices Guide D.A.T.A. Book see High Reliability & Military Components Guide **3459**
Military Engineer. (US ISSN 0026-3982) **1830, 3464**
Military Fiber Optics News see Military & Commercial Fiber Business **3464**
†Military Forum. (US ISSN 0885-1972) **5237**
Military Fuzes. (US) **3464**
▼Military Grocer. (US) **2093**
Military Historical Society. Bulletin. (UK ISSN 0026-4008) **3464, 2318**
Military History. (US ISSN 1060-9490) **2414, 3464**
Military History. (US) **2414, 3464**
†Military History Archives Bulletin. (US) **5237**
Military History Journal/Krygshistoriese Tydskrif. (SA ISSN 0026-4016) **3464, 2318**

MINERAL INDUSTRY 6437

Military History of Texas and the Southwest see Military History of the Southwest **2414**
Military History of the Southwest. (US ISSN 0898-8064) **2414, 3464**
Military History Presents Great Battles. (US) **2414, 3464**
Military History Review see Military **3464**
Military Images. (US ISSN 1040-4961) **3465**
Military Intelligence Critical Attributes. (UK) **3465**
Military Journal/Majallah al-Askariyyah. (JO) **3465**
Military Law Reporter. (US ISSN 0193-3906) **2735**
Military Law Review. (US ISSN 0026-4040) **2735**
Military Lifestyle. (US) **3465, 4848**
Military Lifestyle - Your Ladycom Magazine see Military Lifestyle **3465**
Military Living. (US ISSN 0740-5065) **3465**
Military Living's R & R Report. (US ISSN 0740-5073) **3465, 4778**
†Military Logistics Forum. (US) **5237**
Military Market. (UK ISSN 0026-4067) **3465**
Military Medal Society of South Africa. Journal. (SA) **3600, 3465**
Military Media Review. (US ISSN 0095-635X) **3465**
Military Medical and Pharmaceutical Review. see Vojnosanitetski Pregled **3161**
Military Medicine. (US ISSN 0026-4075) **3131**
Military Microwaves (Year). Proceedings of Conference. (UK) **3465, 1903**
Military Modeler. (US) **3465**
Military Modelling. (UK ISSN 0026-4083) **2438, 3465**
Military Museum, Belgrade. Bulletin. see Vojni Muzej, Belgrade. Vesnik **3475**
Military Operations Research. (US ISSN 0275-5823) **3465**
Military Police. (US ISSN 0895-4208) **3465**
Military Police Journal see Military Police **3465**
Military Portfolio see Military History Archives Bulletin **5237**
Military Psychology. (US ISSN 0899-5605) **4035, 3465**
Military Record of Atomic C B R Happenings see Military Record of Atomic C B R Happenings. Armament Data Sheets **59**
Military Record of Atomic C B R Happenings. Armament Data Sheets. (UK) **59**
Military Research Letter. (US ISSN 0026-413X) **3465**
Military Review. (US ISSN 0026-4148) **3465**
Military Review. see Voennye Znaniya **3474**
Military Revue. see Stratiotiki Epitheorisis **3472**
Military Robotics Newsletter. (US ISSN 0896-0348) **1409, 3465**
Military Robotics Sourcebook. (US) **1409, 3465**
▼Military Simulation and Training. (UK) **3465**
Military Space. (US ISSN 0743-7897) **3465, 59**
Military Specifications and Standard Services Index see Military Specifications and Standards Services Numeric Index **3465**
Military Specifications and Standards Services Numeric Index. (US) **3465**
Military Technology see Military Technology: Miltech **3465**
Military Technology. (US) **3465**
Military Technology: Miltech. (GW) **3465**
Military Travel Guide. (US) **4778, 3465**
Military Travel News. (US) **4778, 3465**
Military Vehicles. (US ISSN 0893-3863) **3465, 4695**
Military Year Book. (II ISSN 0076-8782) **3465**
Militia Christi see Kerk en Vrede **4186**

Miljoe & Teknologi. (DK ISSN 0901-747X) **1963, 4604**
Miljoe-Projekter see Miljoeprojekt **1963**
Miljoemagasinet see Natur og Miljoe **1963**
Miljoprojekt. (DK) **1963**
Miljoeundersoegelser ved Ivigtut. (DK ISSN 0108-8203) **1963**
Miljoeundersoegelser ved Marmorilik. (DK) **1963**
†Miljoevaern. (DK ISSN 0107-8550) **5237**
Milk and Liquid Food Transporter. (US) **4746, 2077**
Milk and Milk Products Balances in O E C D Countries. (FR) **140, 17**
Milk Bar see Food Shop **2070**
Milk Bulletin. (UK ISSN 0309-0809) **201**
Milk Facts. (US ISSN 0740-9222) **201**
Milk Industry. (UK ISSN 0026-4172) **201**
Milk Marketer. (US) **201**
Milk News. (UK ISSN 0047-7400) **201**
Milk Producer. (UK ISSN 0026-4180) **201**
Milk Producer. (SA ISSN 0026-4199) **202**
Milk Products. (UK ISSN 0950-3730) **202**
Milk Reporter see Milk Marketer **201**
Milk Science International. see Milchwissenschaft **140**
Milk Topics. (UK ISSN 0047-7419) **202**
Mill Neck Manor Bulletin. (US) **2288, 1738**
Mill Newsletter see Utilitas **1302**
Mill Report. (US) **4621**
Mill Trade Journal see M T J Recycling Markets **3649**
Millat. (PK) **3907**
Mille Idee per la Donna. (IT) **4848**
Millelibri. (IT) **2773**
Millennium. (IT ISSN 0305-8298) **3965**
Millennium Film Journal. (US) **3514**
Miller Electric Manufacturing Co. News see M E M C O News **3429**
Miller Monitor. (US) **2158**
Miller Notes. (US) **3562, 3527**
Miller of Virginia Letter. (US) **2158**
Millers Antiques Price Guide. (US) **258**
Millesime. (FR ISSN 0076-8812) **1021**
Millimeter. (US ISSN 0164-9655) **3514, 1376**
Millimetro. (IT) **35**
Milling and Baking Industry and Storage Techniques of Grain. see Mlynsko-Pekarensky Prumysl a Technika Skladovani Obili **207**
Milling & Baking News. (US ISSN 0091-4843) **2089, 207**
Milling Directory - Buyers Guide. (US) **1146, 207**
Milling Feed and Farm Supplies. (UK) **207**
Milling Feed and Fertiliser see Milling Feed and Farm Supplies **207**
Milling Flour and Feed. (UK ISSN 0954-4860) **207**
▼Million. (UK ISSN 0960-832X) **2984, 2986, 3012**
Million Dollar Directory Series. (US) **1048**
Million Dollar Project Planned List. (US) **303, 624, 4579**
Million Dollar Round Table Annual Meeting. Proceedings see M D R T Annual Meeting. Proceedings **2537**
Millionaire. (US) **2229**
Mills. see Molens **1492**
Mills Quarterly. (US) **2158**
Mills Stream see Mills Weekly **1317**
Mills Weekly. (US) **1317**
Milltown Studies. (IE ISSN 0332-1428) **4190, 3773**
Millwork Manufacturing. (US) **4621**
Millwork Products Guide. (US) **624**
Milnholm Cross Newsletter. (UK ISSN 0261-3158) **2375, 2158**
Milton Caniff's Steve Canyon Magazine. (US ISSN 0747-1637) **2984**
Milton Chronicles. (US) **2414**

Milton Keynes Business Directory. (UK ISSN 0957-1051) **1146**
Milton Keynes Directory of Business and Buying see Milton Keynes Business Directory **1146**
Milton Quarterly. (US ISSN 0026-4326) **2938**
Milton Society of America. Proceedings. (US ISSN 0540-0961) **2998**
Milton Studies. (US ISSN 0076-8820) **2938**
Milton Traditions see Plantagenet Productions **2948**
Miltronics. (UK ISSN 0144-5243) **3465**
Milu: Wissenschaftliche und Kulturelle Mitteilungen aus dem Tierpark Berlin.(GW ISSN 0076-8839) **588**
Milwaukee Commerce see Milwaukee Commerce Hot-line **838**
Milwaukee Commerce Hot-line. (US) **838**
Milwaukee Community Journal. (US) **2014**
Milwaukee County Historical Society. Historical Messenger see Milwaukee History **2414**
Milwaukee Courier. (US ISSN 0026-4350) **2014**
Milwaukee Engineering. (US) **1830**
Milwaukee Fire Department Register see M F D Register **4107**
Milwaukee Herald. (US) **2014**
Milwaukee History. (US ISSN 0163-7622) **2414**
Milwaukee Labor Press, A F L - C I O. (US) **2586**
Milwaukee Lawyer. (US) **2654**
Milwaukee Magazine. (US) **2229**
Milwaukee Public Schools Staff Bulletin.(US) **1729**
Milwaukee Reader. (US ISSN 0026-4377) **4142**
Milwaukee Star. (US) **2014**
Milwaukee Symphony Orchestra. Encore. (US) **3562**
Milwaukee Symphony Orchestra. Stagebill see Milwaukee Symphony Orchestra. Encore **3562**
Milwaukee Undergraduate Review. (US) **2938**
Mimar. (UK ISSN 0129-8372) **303, 2492**
Mimbar Kabinet Pembangunan. (IO) **2202**
Mime News see Movement Theatre Quarterly **4635**
†Mimesis. (BL) **5237**
Mimi Huabao/Mimi Pictorial. (CC) **1260**
Mimi Pictorial. see Mimi Huabao **1260**
Mimos. (SZ ISSN 0026-4385) **4635**
Mims. (UK) **3131**
Mims Ireland. (UK) **3132**
Mims Magazine. (UK) **3132**
Min Hest. (DK) **1260, 4536**
Min Su/Folk Customs. (CC) **2056, 245, 2014**
†Mina. (IT) **5237**
Minami-Kyushu Daigaku Engeigakubu Kenkyu Hokoku. Shizen Kagaku, Jinbun Shakai Kagaku/Minami Kyushu University. Faculty of Horticulture. Bulletin. Natural Science, Cultural Science, and Social Science. (JA ISSN 0285-211X) **2134, 2511, 4324**
Minami Kyushu University. Faculty of Horticulture. Bulletin. Natural Science, Cultural Science, and Social Science. see Minami-Kyushu Daigaku Engeigakubu Kenkyu Hokoku. Shizen Kagaku, Jinbun Shakai Kagaku **2134**
Minaret Monthly International. (PK) **4219**
Minas Gerais, Brazil. Departamento de Estradas de Rodagem. Servico de Transito. Estatistica de Trafego see Minas Gerais, Brazil. Departamento de Estradas de Rodagem. Servico de Transito. Estatistica de Trafego e Acidentes **4665**
Minas Gerais, Brazil. Departamento de Estradas de Rodagem. Servico de Transito. Estatistica de Trafego e Acidentes. (BL) **4665, 4579**
Minas Gerais Suplemento Literario. (BL) **2938**

Minas Tirith Evening Star. (US) **2938**
Minbar al-Tamrid/Nursing Forum. (TS) **3282**
Mind. (UK ISSN 0026-4423) **3773**
Mind & Language. (UK ISSN 0268-1064) **3773**
▼Mind and Machines. (US ISSN 0924-6495) **1409**
Mind and Society. see Kokoro to Shakai **4034**
†Mind-Body-Health Digest. (US ISSN 0898-3127) **5237**
Mind in Motion. (US ISSN 8756-1549) **2998**
Mind Matters Review. (US) **4035, 680, 1963**
Mind Over Media. (US) **1398**
Mind: The Meetings Index. (US ISSN 0739-5914) **4604, 1830, 3132**
Mind Your Own Business. (UK ISSN 0143-1374) **1059, 827**
Mind Your Own Business at Home. (US ISSN 0277-6820) **1116**
Mindanao Art & Culture. (PH ISSN 0115-6853) **2056, 2340**
Mindanao Journal. (PH ISSN 0115-2742) **4190**
Mindanao Journal of Industrial Education. (PH) **1685, 1648**
Mindanao Mail. (PH ISSN 0300-3906) **2214**
Mindanao State University. U R C Professional Papers. (PH ISSN 0115-7329) **4324**
Mindener Geschichtsverein. Mitteilungen. (GW ISSN 0340-188X) **2375**
Mindener Klinikschriften. (GW ISSN 0179-3799) **3282, 2467, 3132**
Mindolo News Letter see Mindolo World **4190**
Mindolo World. (ZA) **4190**
†Mindprint Review. (US) **5237**
†Mind's Eye. (US) **5237**
Mindszenty Report. (US ISSN 0026-4474) **3907**
Mine. (JA) **4848**
Mine and Quarry. (UK ISSN 0369-1632) **3488**
Mine & Quarry Trader. (US) **3488**
Mine Medical Officers' Association of South Africa. Journal. (SA) **3619**
Mine Medical Officers' Association of South Africa. Proceedings see Mine Medical Officers' Association of South Africa. Journal **3619**
Mine, Petrol si Gaze. (RM) **3692, 3488**
Mine Production of Silver. (US) **3427**
Mine Prospecting. see Kuangshan Celiang **3487**
Mine Regulation and Productivity Report see Coal Week **3481**
Mine Regulation Reporter. (US ISSN 1040-8223) **3488, 3619**
Mine Run. (US) **3488**
Mine Surface Officials' Association of South Africa Bulletin see M S O A Bulletin **3487**
Mine Ventilation Society of South Africa. Journal. (SA ISSN 0026-4504) **3488**
Miner Magazine see Miner Newspaper **3488**
Miner Newspaper. (AT) **3488**
Mineracao Metalurgia. (BL ISSN 0026-4520) **3488, 3415**
Mineral and Electrolyte Metabolism. (SZ ISSN 0378-0392) **3132, 573**
Mineral Facts. (AT) **3488**
Mineral Industry Quarterly. (AT ISSN 0313-6086) **3488**
Mineral Industry Surveys. Aluminum Industry. (US) **3500, 3488**
Mineral Industry Surveys. Antimony. (US) **3500**
Mineral Industry Surveys. Barite. (US) **3500**
Mineral Industry Surveys. Bauxite. (US) **3500**
Mineral Industry Surveys. Bauxite and Aluminum see Mineral Industry Surveys. Bauxite **3500**
Mineral Industry Surveys. Bismuth. (US) **3500**
Mineral Industry Surveys. Boron. (US) **3500**
Mineral Industry Surveys. Bromine. (US) **3500**

MINERAL INDUSTRY

Mineral Industry Surveys. Cadmium. (US ISSN 0193-0044) **3500**
Mineral Industry Surveys. Cement. (US) **3500**
Mineral Industry Surveys. Chromium. (US) **3500**
Mineral Industry Surveys. Clays. (US) **3500**
Mineral Industry Surveys. Cobalt. (US) **3500**
Mineral Industry Surveys. Columbium and Tantalum. (US) **3500**
Mineral Industry Surveys. Copper in the United States. (US) **3500**
Mineral Industry Surveys. Dimension Stone. (US) **3500**
Mineral Industry Surveys. Directory of Peat Producers. (US) **3500**
Mineral Industry Surveys. Directory of Phosphate Rock Producers. (US) **3500**
Mineral Industry Surveys. Directory of Salt Producers. (US) **3500**
Mineral Industry Surveys. Directory of Talc, Pyrophyllite, and Soapstone Mining. (US) **3500**
Mineral Industry Surveys. Directory of U.S. Lime Plants. (US) **3500**
Mineral Industry Surveys. End Uses of Sulfur and Sulfuric Acid. (US) **3500**
Mineral Industry Surveys. Feldspar. (US) **3500**
Mineral Industry Surveys. Fluorspar. (US) **3500**
Mineral Industry Surveys. Gem Stones. (US) **3500**
Mineral Industry Surveys. Gold and Silver. (US) **3500**
Mineral Industry Surveys. Gypsum. (US) **3500**
Mineral Industry Surveys. Gypsum Mines and Calcining Plants in the U.S. (US) **3500**
Mineral Industry Surveys. Industrial Explosives and Blasting Agents. (US) **3501**
Mineral Industry Surveys. Industrial Sand and Gravel Producers in the U.S. (US) **3501**
Mineral Industry Surveys. Iodine. (US) **3501**
Mineral Industry Surveys. Iron and Steel Scrap. (US) **3501**
Mineral Industry Surveys. Kyanite and Related Minerals. (US) **3501**
Mineral Industry Surveys. Lead Industry.(US) **3501**
Mineral Industry Surveys. Lime. (US) **3501**
Mineral Industry Surveys. Lime - Annual, Advance Summary. (US) **3501**
Mineral Industry Surveys. Lime - Annual Preliminary. (US) **3501**
Mineral Industry Surveys. Magnesium. (US) **3501**
Mineral Industry Surveys. Manganese. (US) **3501**
Mineral Industry Surveys. Marketable Phosphate Rock. (US) **3501**
Mineral Industry Surveys. Mercury. (US) **3501**
Mineral Industry Surveys. Molybdenum. (US) **3501**
Mineral Industry Surveys. Nickel. (US) **3501**
Mineral Industry Surveys. Peat. (US) **3501**
Mineral Industry Surveys. Phosphate Rock - Advance Summary. (US) **3501**
Mineral Industry Surveys. Phosphate Rock - Annual Preliminary. (US) **3501**
Mineral Industry Surveys. Phosphate Rock - Crop Year. (US) **3501**
Mineral Industry Surveys. Platinum - Group Metals. (US ISSN 0191-4421) **3501**
Mineral Industry Surveys. Potash - Annual Preliminary. (US) **3501**
Mineral Industry Surveys. Potash - Crop Year. (US) **3501**
Mineral Industry Surveys. Principal Construction Sand and Gravel Producers in the U.S. (US) **3501**
Mineral Industry Surveys. Principal Crushed Stone Producers in the U.S. (US) **3501**
Mineral Industry Surveys. Principal Gem Stones Producers in the U.S. (US) **3501**
Mineral Industry Surveys. Salt. (US) **3501**
Mineral Industry Surveys. Salt - Annual Preliminary. (US) **3501**
Mineral Industry Surveys. Silicon. (US) **3501**
Mineral Industry Surveys. Sodium Compounds. (US) **3501**
Mineral Industry Surveys. Stone - Crushed and Dimension. (US) **3501**
Mineral Industry Surveys. Sulfur. (US) **3501**
Mineral Industry Surveys. Sulfur - Advance Summary. (US) **3502**
Mineral Industry Surveys. Sulfur - Annual Preliminary. (US) **3502**
Mineral Industry Surveys. Tin Industry. (US) **3502**
Mineral Industry Surveys. Titanium. (US) **3502**
Mineral Industry Surveys. Tungsten. (US) **3502**
Mineral Industry Surveys. Vanadium. (US) **3502**
Mineral Industry Surveys. Zinc Industry. (US) **3502**
Mineral Law Newsletter. (US) **3488**, 2654
Mineral News. (US ISSN 0885-4327) **2438**
Mineral Processing and Extractive Metallurgy Review. (US ISSN 0882-7508) **3415**
Mineral Processing and Technology Review see Mineral Processing and Extractive Metallurgy Review **3415**
Mineral Research. (II ISSN 0379-5187) **3488**
Mineral Research and Exploration Institute of Turkey. Bulletin. (TU ISSN 0026-4563) **3488**
†Mineral Resources Engineering. (UK ISSN 0950-6098) **5237**
Mineral Resources Review see Mines and Energy Review, South Australia **3489**
Mineral Review. (PK) **1573**, 3488
Mineral Statistics of India. (II ISSN 0581-0000) **3502**, 3488
Mineral Wealth. (II ISSN 0026-4571) **3488**
Der Mineralbrunnen. (GW) **383**
Minerales. (CL ISSN 0026-458X) **3488**, 1573, 3415
Mineralia Slovaca. (CS ISSN 0369-2086) **3488**
▼Mineralien Welt. (GW ISSN 0939-6640) **3488**
Mineralium Deposita. (GW ISSN 0026-4598) **1573**, 3488
†Mineralocorticoids and Glucocorticoids.(UK ISSN 0142-873X) **5237**
Mineraloel - Mineraloelrundschau. (GW ISSN 0544-2524) **3692**
Mineraloelrundschau see Mineraloel - Mineraloelrundschau **3692**
Mineraloelwirtschafts Verband e.V. Jahresbericht see M W V Jahresbericht **1220**
Mineralogia Polonica. (PL ISSN 0032-6267) **3488**, 1547
Mineralogical Abstracts. (UK ISSN 0026-4601) **3502**
Mineralogical Journal. (JA ISSN 0544-2540) **3489**
Mineralogical Magazine. (UK ISSN 0026-461X) **3489**
Mineralogical Record. (US ISSN 0026-4628) **2438**, 1547
†Mineralogical Society of New South Wales. Journal. (AT) **5237**
Mineralogicheskii Zhurnal. (KR ISSN 0204-3548) **3489**, 1547
Mineralogist see Jewelry Making, Gems and Minerals **2437**
Mineralogy and Petrology. (AU ISSN 0930-0708) **3489**
Minerals and Geology. see Kuangchan yu Dizhi **3411**
Minerals and Materials see Minerals Today **3489**
Minerals and Metallurgical Processing. (US ISSN 0747-9182) **3489**

Minerals and Metals Trading Corp. of India Ltd. News see M M T C News **3487**
Minerals and Rocks. (US ISSN 0343-2181) **1573**, 3489
Minerals and the Environment see Environmental Geochemistry and Health **1951**
Minerals Engineering. (US ISSN 0892-6875) **3489**
Minerals Industry International. (UK ISSN 0955-2847) **3489**, 3415
Minerals Industry Survey. (AT) **3489**
Minerals: Latin American Industry Report. (US) **3489**, 874
Minerals Research Laboratory Bulletin see Minerals Research Laboratory Newsletter **3489**
Minerals Research Laboratory Newsletter. (US) **3489**
Minerals Today. (US) **3489**, 874
Minerax et Fossiles. (FR ISSN 0335-5566) **3658**, 3489
†Minergia. (US ISSN 0890-1392) **5237**
Mineria. (PE ISSN 0026-4679) **3489**
Mineria Chilena. (CL ISSN 0716-1042) **3489**, 3415, 3692
Mineria en Cuba see Revista de Mineria y Geologia **3494**
La Mineria en Mexico. (MX) **3489**
Mineria Pan-Americana. (US) **3489**
Minerios. (BL) **3489**
Minero-Noticias. (MX) **3489**
Mineroeltechnik. (GW ISSN 0341-1893) **3692**
Minerva. (UK ISSN 0026-4695) **1711**, 4324
Minerva. (US ISSN 0736-718X) **3465**, 4848
Minerva Aerospaziale. (IT ISSN 0026-4709) **3132**
Minerva Anestesiologica. (IT ISSN 0026-4717) **3191**
Minerva Angiologica. (IT ISSN 0391-3627) **3210**
Minerva Cardioangiologica. (IT ISSN 0026-4725) **3210**
Minerva Chirurgica. (IT ISSN 0026-4733) **3381**
Minerva Dietologica see Minerva Dietologica e Gastroenterologica **3269**
Minerva Dietologica e Gastroenterologica. (IT ISSN 0391-1993) **3269**
Minerva Endocrinologica. (IT ISSN 0391-1977) **3255**
Minerva Gastroenterologica see Minerva Dietologica e Gastroenterologica **3269**
Minerva Ginecologica. (IT ISSN 0026-4784) **3295**
Minerva Medica. (IT ISSN 0026-4806) **3132**
Minerva Medicolegale. (IT ISSN 0026-4849) **3265**
Minerva Medicopratica. (IT) **3132**
Minerva Mesoterapeutica. (IT) **3132**
Minerva Nefrologica see Minerva Urologica e Nefrologica **3389**
Minerva Nipiologica see Rivista di Pediatria Preventiva e Sociale-Nipiologia **3326**
Minerva Oftalmologica. (IT ISSN 0026-4903) **3302**
Minerva Ortognatodontica. (IT ISSN 0394-168X) **3238**
Minerva Ortopedica see Minerva Ortopedica e Traumatologica **3310**
Minerva Ortopedica e Traumatologica. (IT) **3310**
Minerva Pediatrica. (IT ISSN 0026-4946) **3322**
Minerva Pneumologica. (IT ISSN 0026-4954) **3366**
Minerva Psichiatrica. (IT) **3345**
Minerva Radiologica see Radiologia Medica **3362**
Minerva: Revista de Filologia Clasica. (SP ISSN 0213-9634) **2829**, 1278
Minerva Stomatologica. (IT ISSN 0026-4970) **3238**
Minerva Urologica see Minerva Urologica e Nefrologica **3389**
Minerva Urologica e Nefrologica. (IT) **3389**

Minerva's Bulletin Board. (US ISSN 0897-6104) **3465**, 4848
Mines and Energy Review, South Australia. (AT) **3489**
Mines & Mining Equipment and Service Companies Worldwide (Year). (UK) **3489**, 1146
Mines and Mining Equipment Companies Worldwide see Mines & Mining Equipment and Service Companies Worldwide (Year) **3489**
Mines au Canada - Faits et Chiffres see Mining in Canada - Facts & Figures **3490**
Mines de Potasse. see Canada. Statistics Canada. Manufacturing Industries Division. Potash Mines **5160**
Mines Golden see Mines Magazine **3489**
†Mines in West Virginia. (US) **5237**
Mines Magazine. (US ISSN 0096-4859) **3489**
Mines - Pilier de l'Economie Canadienne see Mining - What Mining Means to Canada **3490**
Mines Safety and Health Commission. Report/Organe Permanent pour la Securite dans les Mines de Houille. Rapport. (EI ISSN 0588-702X) **3489**, 3619
Minetech. (II) **3489**
Minetta Review. (US) **2998**
Mineurs de France. (FR ISSN 0026-5071) **3489**
Mineurs de France: Edition Centre-Midi. (FR ISSN 0989-7577) **3489**
Mineworker/Mynwerker. (SA) **3489**
Minfo. (AT ISSN 0812-0293) **3489**, 1573
Ming Pao Monthly. (HK) **2874**
Ming Ri/Tomorrow. (CC ISSN 1001-6341) **2182**
Ming Studies. (US ISSN 0147-037X) **3641**
Ming Studies Newsletter see Ming Studies **3641**
Mingay's Product Service - Appliances see Mingay's Retail Guide **1903**
Mingay's Product Service - Home Entertainment see Mingay's Retail Guide **1903**
Mingay's Retail Guide. (AT) **1903**, 1376
Mingay's Retailer & Merchandiser. (AT ISSN 0728-9383) **1048**, 1376
Mingren Zhuanji. (CC) **420**
Minguo Chunqiu. (CC) **2318**
Minguo Dang'an/Archives of the Republic of China. (CC ISSN 1000-4491) **2340**, 2773
Mingzuo Xinshang/Best Works of Literature. (CC) **2938**
Minhang Jingji yu Jishu/Civil Aviation Economics and Technology. (CC) **59**
Mini. (GW) **4269**
†Mini. (US) **5237**
Mini and Microcomputers see M I M I **1466**
Mini' App'les. (US) **1471**
Mini Apples see Mini' App'les **1471**
Mini-Break Holidays in Britain see Recommended Short Break Holidays **4784**
Mini Data Report. (SP) **1466**
Mini Lab Focus. (US) **3793**, 1116
Mini License & Keychain Tag Collection Newsletter. (US) **2438**
Mini Micro News. (UK ISSN 0267-131X) **1466**, 1438
Mini Micro Software see P C - Business Software **1479**
Mini - Microcomputer. (NE ISSN 0167-6547) **1466**
Mini-Monitor see Why **4424**
Mini-Storage Messenger. (US ISSN 0273-5822) **624**
Mini Truckin'. (US) **4746**
Mini World. (SR) **2014**
Miniappartamenti. (IT) **2492**, 4152
Miniatura e Arti Minori in Campania. (IT) **336**
Miniaturbahnen see Miniaturbahnen M I B A **2438**
Miniaturbahnen M I B A. (GW ISSN 0723-3841) **2438**, 4711
Miniature Book News. (US ISSN 0026-5128) **2438**, 4132

MINNESOTA POLICE 6439

Miniature Collector. (US ISSN 0199-9184) **2438**, 336
Miniature Donkey Talk. (US ISSN 1058-7063) **221**
Miniature Gazette. (US) **2438**
Miniature Quilts. (US) **3591**
Miniature Rose Growers Bulletin. (US) **2134**
Miniature Wargames. (UK ISSN 0266-3228) **3465**, 2318
Miniatures and Doll Dealer *see* Miniatures Dealer **2438**
Miniatures Catalog. (US) **2438**
Miniatures Dealer. (US) **2438**, 2281
Miniatures Showcase. (US) **2438**
†Minibus. (UK) **5237**
Minicomputer News *see* Mini Micro News **1466**
Minicomputers Reports. (US) **1463**
Minie News. (AT ISSN 0310-3471) **2414**
Minilab Developments. (US) **3793**
MiniMicro Magazin. (GW) **1903**, 1438
†MiniNews. (US) **5237**
Mining Abstracts. *see* Banyaszati Szakirodalmi Tajekoztato **3499**
Mining and Allied Machinery Corporation. Annual Report. (II) **3489**, 3021
Mining & Construction Methods and Equipment. (AT) **3489**
Mining & Energy. (GW) **3490**
Mining and Engineering. (RH) **3490**
Mining and Engineering (Year) *see* Mining and Engineering & Electronics Industries (Year) **3490**
Mining and Engineering & Electronics Industries (Year). (SA ISSN 1017-4249) **3490**, 1146, 1830
Mining and Materials Processing Institute of Japan. Journal. *see* Shigen Sozai **3495**
Mining and Materials Processing Institute of Japan. Metallurgical Review. (JA ISSN 0289-6214) **3415**, 3490
Mining and Metallurgy Quarterly. *see* Rudarsko-Metalurski Zbornik **3495**
▼Mining and Petroleum Legislation Service. (AT) **2654**, 3490, 3692
Mining Annual Review. (UK ISSN 0076-8995) **3490**
Mining Department Magazine. (UK ISSN 0307-9066) **3490**
Mining Directory of Georgia *see* Georgia Geologic Survey. Circular 2. Mining Directory of Georgia **3484**
Mining Engineer. (UK ISSN 0026-5179) **3490**
Mining Engineering. (US ISSN 0026-5187) **3490**
Mining Equipment International *see* World Mining Equipment **3498**
Mining Equipment News. (SA) **3490**
Mining Exploration and Development Review *see* Mining Review **3490**
Mining, Geological and Metallurgical Institute of India. Transactions. (II ISSN 0371-9588) **3490**, 1573, 3415
Mining in British Columbia *see* Engineering and Inspection Annual Report **3483**
Mining in Canada - Facts & Figures. (CN ISSN 0316-2281) **3490**
Mining in Rhodesia *see* Mining in Zimbabwe **3490**
Mining in Zimbabwe. (RH) **3490**
Mining Industry & Trade Annual. (II) **3490**
Mining Industry and Trade Journal *see* Mining Industry & Trade Annual **3490**
†Mining Industry of Idaho. Annual Report. (US) **5237**
Mining Industry Technical Conference. Conference Record. (US) **3490**
Mining Journal. (UK ISSN 0026-5225) **3490**
Mining Legislation: Africa. (US) **2727**, 3490
Mining Legislation: Central America & Caribbean. (US) **2727**, 3490
Mining Legislation: Europe. (US) **2727**, 3490
Mining Legislation: Far East. (US) **2727**, 3490

Mining Legislation: Middle East. (US) **2727**, 3490
Mining Legislation: South America. (US) **2727**, 3490
Mining Magazine. (UK ISSN 0308-6631) **3490**
Mining Mirror. (ZA) **3490**
Mining Mirror. (SA) **3490**
Mining Monthly *see* Australia's Mining Monthly **3478**
Mining News/Mynblad. (SA) **3490**
Mining Newsletter. (US) **3619**, 3490
Mining Quarterly *see* Australia's Mining Monthly **3478**
Mining Record. (US ISSN 0026-5241) **3490**, 1492, 3692
Mining Review. (AT ISSN 0314-4607) **3490**, 1963
Mining Review. (CN ISSN 0711-3277) **3490**
Mining Science and Technology *see* Engineering Geology **1865**
†Mining Sun. (SA) **5237**
Mining Technology. *see* Kuangshan Jishu **3487**
Mining Technology. (UK ISSN 0026-5276) **3490**
Mining - What Mining Means to Canada. (CN ISSN 0317-9508) **3490**
Mining World News. (US) **3491**
Mining World S A *see* S A Mining World **3495**
Mining Year Book *see* Financial Times International Year Books: Mining **3483**
Mining Yearbook of Japan. *see* Honpo Kogyo no Susei **3484**
Ministere de la Jeunesse et des Sport. Bulletin Officiel. (FR) **4479**
Ministere du Loisir de la Chasse et de la Peche. Rapport Annuel. *see* Quebec (Province) Department of Recreation, Fish and Game. Annual Report **4554**
Ministerial Formation. (SZ) **4190**
Ministerial Sisterhood Unitarian Universalist Newsletter: Gleanings *see* M S U U Newsletter: Gleanings **4243**
Ministerialtidende for Kongeriget Danmark. (DK ISSN 0085-3461) **4067**
Ministerialtidende for Kongeriget Danmark. Afdeling A *see* Ministerialtidende for Kongeriget Danmark **4067**
Ministerio de Comunicaciones *see* M C **1339**
Ministerio de Comunicaciones de Cuba. Centro de Informacion de Comunicaciones. Comunicaciones. (CU) **1340**
Ministerio de Cultura. Tablas. (CU) **2184**
Ministerio de Educacao. Faculdade de Ciencias Agrarias do Para. Informe Tecnico. (BL ISSN 0100-9974) **107**
Minister's Manual (Year). (US ISSN 0894-3966) **4190**
Ministries *see* Ministries Today **4190**
†Ministries and Communities. (BE ISSN 1013-4549) **5237**
Ministries Today. (US ISSN 0891-5725) **4190**
Ministry. (US ISSN 0026-5314) **4244**
Ministry of Communication. Tourism Bureau. Annual Report. (CH) **4800**
Ministry of Defence Contracts Bulletin *see* M O D Contracts Bulletin **678**
Ministry of Defence News *see* M O D News **678**
Ministry of Education. Basic Statistics of Education. (KO) **1678**
Ministry of Education. National Science Museum. Institute for Nature Study. Miscellaneous Reports. *see* Shizen Kyoikuen Hokoku **4343**
Ministry of Foreign Affairs Review *see* M F A Review **3965**
Ministry of Public Works Bulletin *see* M P W Bulletin **4081**
Minji Sosho Zasshi. *see* Journal of Civil Procedure **2702**
Minjian Gushi/Folk Tales. (CC) **2056**, 2998

Minjian Wenxue. (CC ISSN 0540-1151) **2057**, 2938
Minjian Wenxue Luntan/Tribune of Folk Literature. (CC) **2057**, 2938
Minjian Wenyi Jikan *see* Chinese Folk Culture **2905**
Minjoong Shinmoon. (CN ISSN 0225-1205) **2014**
†Minkus (Year) Specialized American Stamp Catalog. (US) **5237**
†Minkus Stamp Journal. (US) **5237**
Minne Ha! Ha! (US) **2874**
Minneapolis Athletic Club Gopher *see* M A C Gopher **4478**
Minneapolis Institute of Arts. Annual Report. (US ISSN 0076-9096) **336**
Minneapolis Institute of Arts. Bulletin. (US ISSN 0076-910X) **336**
Minneapolis - St. Paul CityBusiness. (US) **680**
Minneapolis Woman *see* Metropolitan Woman **5236**
Minnesota. Department of Education. Public Library Newsletter. (US ISSN 0026-5438) **2773**
Minnesota. Department of Human Rights. Biennial Report. (US ISSN 0076-9118) **3945**
Minnesota. Department of Jobs and Training. Annual Report. (US) **989**
Minnesota. Department of Jobs and Training. Review of Labor and Economic Conditions. (US) **874**
Minnesota. Department of Natural Resources. Biennial Report. (US ISSN 0090-8177) **1492**
Minnesota. Department of Revenue. Biennial Report. (US ISSN 0095-0645) **1101**
Minnesota. Department of Revenue. Petroleum Division. Annual Report. (US ISSN 0095-3024) **3692**
Minnesota. Department of Taxation. Biennial Report *see* Minnesota. Department of Revenue. Biennial Report **1101**
Minnesota. Geological Survey. Bulletin. (US ISSN 0076-9169) **1573**
Minnesota. Geological Survey. Educational Series. (US ISSN 0544-3083) **1573**, 1648
Minnesota. Geological Survey. Guidebook Series. (US ISSN 0192-6268) **1573**
Minnesota. Geological Survey. Information Circulars. (US ISSN 0544-3105) **1573**
Minnesota. Geological Survey. Report of Investigations. (US ISSN 0076-9177) **1573**
Minnesota (Minneapolis). (US) **1317**
Minnesota. Office of Ombudsman for Corrections. Annual Report. (US ISSN 0094-1409) **1518**
Minnesota Academy of Science. Journal. (US ISSN 0026-539X) **4324**
Minnesota Administrative Procedure. (US) **4067**, 2654
Minnesota Agricultural Economist. (US) **154**
Minnesota Agricultural Experiment Station. Station Bulletin. (US) **107**, 2104
Minnesota Archaeologist. (US ISSN 0026-5403) **278**
Minnesota Arts Directory. (US) **336**, 356
Minnesota Arts Fairs *see* Minnesota Arts Directory **336**
Minnesota Association of Plumbing - Heating - Cooling Contractors Inc. Minnesota P - H - C Contractor *see* Minnesota P - H - C Contractor **2301**
Minnesota Calls. (US) **2229**
Minnesota Chemist. (US ISSN 0026-5411) **1184**
Minnesota Chess Journal. (US) **4479**, 1419
Minnesota Cities. (US ISSN 0148-8546) **4091**
Minnesota Civil Practice. (US) **2704**
Minnesota Clubwoman. (US) **1299**
▼Minnesota Condemnation Law and Practice. (US) **2654**
Minnesota Corporations Practice Manual. (US) **2711**

Minnesota Criminal Law Digest. (US) **2714**
Minnesota Dairy Plants. (US) **202**
Minnesota Dance Newsletter. (US) **1531**
Minnesota Directory of Manufacturers. (US) **1146**
▼Minnesota Employment Law Letter. (US ISSN 1054-6367) **2711**, 989
Minnesota English Journal. (US) **1755**
Minnesota English Newsletter. (US ISSN 0544-3520) **1755**
Minnesota Evidence Trailbook. (US) **2654**
Minnesota Explorer. (US) **4778**
Minnesota Family Law Journal. (US) **2718**
Minnesota Family Law Practice Manual. (US) **2718**
Minnesota Fisheries Investigational Reports. (US) **2045**
Minnesota Fisheries Investigations *see* Minnesota Fisheries Investigational Reports **2045**
Minnesota Food Guide *see* Minnesota Grocer **2093**
Minnesota Genealogical Journal. (US ISSN 0741-3599) **2158**
Minnesota Genealogical Society. Newsletter. (US) **2158**
Minnesota Genealogist. (US ISSN 0581-0086) **2158**
Minnesota Gerontologist. (US) **2276**
Minnesota Government Report. (US) **4067**
Minnesota Grocer. (US) **2093**
Minnesota Guidebook to State Agency Services. (US) **4067**
Minnesota Health Statistics. (US ISSN 0094-5641) **4118**
Minnesota History. (US ISSN 0026-5497) **2414**
Minnesota History News. (US ISSN 0544-358X) **2415**
Minnesota Hockey. (US) **4479**
Minnesota Horticulturist. (US ISSN 0026-5500) **2134**
Minnesota Industrial Minerals Directory. (US ISSN 0272-8583) **3491**
Minnesota Ink *see* Writers' Journal (N. St. Paul) **2977**
Minnesota Insurance. (US) **2538**
†Minnesota Journal. (US ISSN 0741-9449) **5237**
Minnesota Labor Market Review. (US) **989**
Minnesota Law Review. (US ISSN 0026-5535) **2654**
Minnesota League for Nursing New Directions *see* M L N New Directions **3282**
Minnesota Legal Register: Minnesota Tax Court Decisions. (US) **2654**
Minnesota Legal Register: Opinions of the Minnesota Attorney General. (US ISSN 0026-5543) **2654**
Minnesota Legionnaire. (US) **3465**
Minnesota Legislative Manual. (US) **2654**
Minnesota Libraries. (US ISSN 0026-5551) **2774**
Minnesota Library Association Newsletter (Minneapolis) *see* M L A Newsletter (Minneapolis) **2772**
Minnesota Limitations Manual. (US) **2654**
Minnesota Literature. (US ISSN 0890-0566) **2938**
Minnesota Manufacturers Register. (US ISSN 0738-1514) **1146**
Minnesota Mechanics' Liens Practice Manual. (US) **2654**
Minnesota Misdemeanors and Moving Traffic Violations. (US) **2654**
Minnesota Monthly. (US) **2229**
Minnesota Municipalities *see* Minnesota Cities **4091**
Minnesota No-Fault Automobile Insurance. (US) **2538**, 2654
Minnesota Nursing Accent. (US ISSN 0026-5586) **3282**
Minnesota P - H - C Contractor. (Minnesota Association of Plumbing - Heating - Cooling Contractors Inc.) (US) **2301**, 625
Minnesota Parent. (US) **1241**
Minnesota Police Chief. (US) **1518**

6440 MINNESOTA POLICE

Minnesota Police Journal. (US ISSN 0026-5624) **1518**
Minnesota Probate Law Digest. (US) **2654**
Minnesota Real Estate Journal. (US) **4152**
Minnesota Real Estate Law Journal. (US) **2715**
▼Minnesota Residential Real Estate. (US) **2715**
Minnesota Review. (US ISSN 0026-5667) **2939**
Minnesota Rules. (US) **2654, 4067**
Minnesota Rules. Supplement. (US) **2654, 4067**
Minnesota Sales and Use Tax Annual Report Bulletin. (US) **1101**
Minnesota Sales and Use Tax Quarterly Report Bulletin see Minnesota Sales and Use Tax Annual Report Bulletin **1101**
Minnesota Science. (US ISSN 0026-5675) **4324**
Minnesota Smoke-Eater. (US) **2033**
▼Minnesota Soccer Times. (US) **4508**
Minnesota Social Responsibilities Round Table Newsletter see M S R R T Newsletter **2772**
Minnesota Speech and Hearing Association. Newsletter see Minnesota Speech - Language - Hearing Association. Newsletter **3315**
Minnesota Speech - Language - Hearing Association. Newsletter. (US) **3315, 1738**
Minnesota Sports. (US) **4479**
Minnesota Sportsman. (US ISSN 0274-8622) **4550**
Minnesota State Bar Association Brief see M S B A in Brief **2651**
Minnesota State Register. (US ISSN 0146-7751) **2655, 4067**
Minnesota Statutes. (US ISSN 0191-1562) **2655**
Minnesota Statutes. Supplement. (US ISSN 0094-1727) **2655**
Minnesota Statutes on C D - R O M. (US) **2655**
Minnesota Studies in the Philosophy of Science. (US ISSN 0076-9258) **3773, 4324**
Minnesota Symposia on Child Psychology Series. (US ISSN 0076-9266) **4036**
Minnesota Tax Appeals. (US) **1101, 2655**
†Minnesota Tax Journal. (US ISSN 0734-7537) **5238**
Minnesota Technolog. (US ISSN 0026-5691) **1936**
Minnesota Tooling and Machining Association Journal. (US) **1146**
†Minnesota Travel and Recreation Guide. (US) **5238**
Minnesota Vocational Association Viewpoints see M V A Viewpoints **1754**
The Minnesota Volunteer. (US) **1492**
Minnesota Wallaces Farmer. (US) **107**
Minnesota Weather Guide Calendar. (US) **3439**
Minnesota Wildlife Reports. (US) **1492**
▼Minnesota - Wisconsin Golfer's Travel Guide. (US) **4508, 4778**
Minor Matters. (AT) **4695**
Minorities and Women in Business. (US) **1116, 2014**
†Minorities in America. Annual Bibliography. (US ISSN 0748-2302) **5238**
Minorities in Business Insider. (US ISSN 1050-3463) **680**
Minority Aging see Journal of Minority Aging **2275**
Minority Art. see Minzu Yishu **336**
Minority Business Entrepreneur. (US ISSN 1048-0919) **1116, 2014**
Minority Business Today. (US) **1116**
▼Minority Employment Journal. (US) **3629**
Minority Engineer. (US ISSN 0884-1829) **1830, 2014**
Minority Funding Report. (US ISSN 1047-3300) **1729, 2014**
Minority Information Trade Annual. (US) **2030**
Minority M B A. (US) **3629, 680**

Minority Markets Alert. (US ISSN 1041-7524) **1506**
Minority Organizations: A National Directory. (US) **2014**
Minority Rights Group. Newsletter see Outsider **3945**
Minority Rights Group. Reports. (UK ISSN 0305-6252) **3945, 4443**
Minority Student Opportunities in United States Medical Schools. (US ISSN 0085-3488) **3132, 1711**
Minority Suppliers Directory see Minority Suppliers Report and Directory **1146**
Minority Suppliers Report and Directory.(US) **1146**
Minority Today. (US) **2014, 1317**
Minoseg es Megbizhatosag. (HU ISSN 0580-4485) **1081**
Minotaur. (US) **2998**
Minsu Yanjiu/Folk Custom Study. (CC) **4380**
Mint Museum MemberNews. (US) **3527, 336**
Mint Museum Newsletter see Mint Museum MemberNews **3527**
MinTech. (UK ISSN 0955-548X) **3491**
Mintek. Special Publications. (SA) **3491**
Mintek Reports. (SA) **3491**
Mintek Research Digest. (SA ISSN 1010-2582) **3491**
Minulosti Rokycanska. (CS) **2375**
Minulosti Zapadoceskeho Kraje. (CS) **2375**
Minute. (FR ISSN 0996-9640) **3907**
Minute see Minute **3907**
Minute-a-Day Drug Letter see Minute-a-Day Health Newsletter **5238**
†Minute-a-Day Health Newsletter. (US ISSN 0886-876X) **5238**
Minute, le Chardon see Minute **3907**
Minutes of the Annual Meeting of the First Catholic Slovak Union of the United States of America and Canada see First Catholic Slovak Union of America. Minutes of Annual Meeting **4264**
Minutes of the Meetings see A R L Minutes **2740**
Minyong Mei Keji. (CC) **3491**
Minzhu/Democracy. (CC) **3907**
Minzhu yu Fazhi/Democracy & Legal Systems. (CC) **3907, 2655**
Minzhu yu Kexue/Democracy and Science. (CC) **3907**
Minzhu Zhongguo. (FR) **3907**
Minzokugaku Kenkyu. see Japanese Journal of Ethnology **242**
Minzu/Nationalities. (CC) **2014**
Minzu Huabao/Nationality Pictorial. (CC ISSN 0540-1224) **2014, 245, 3641, 3793**
Minzu Jiaoyu see Zhongguo Minzu Jiaoyu **1673**
Minzu Jiaoyu Yanjiu/Studies in the National Minority Education. (CC ISSN 1001-7178) **1648**
Minzu Minjian Yinyue/National and Folk Music. (CC) **3563**
Minzu Tuanjie/Unity of Nationalities. (CC ISSN 0544-2206) **2014, 4380**
Minzu Wenxue/Journal of Minority Literature. (CC ISSN 0257-2850) **2939, 2014**
Minzu Wenxue Yanjiu/Research in National Minority Literature. (CC) **2939, 2014**
Minzu Yanjiu/Study in Nationalities. (CC ISSN 0256-1891) **3641, 245, 2014**
Minzu Yishu/Minority Art. (CC) **336**
Minzu Yuwen/Linguistics - National Minorities. (CC ISSN 0257-5779) **2829**
Minzu Zuojia. (CC) **2939, 2014**
Minzuxue Yanjiusuo Jikan, Zhongyang Yanjiuyuan see Academia Sinica. Institute of Ethnology. Bulletin **232**
Mio Bebe. (IT ISSN 0026-5756) **1241**
Mio Uncinetto. (IT) **3591**
Miorita. (US ISSN 0110-0068) **2014, 4778**
Mir Puteshestvii. (RU ISSN 0868-9547) **4778**

Mira. (II ISSN 0026-5780) **2874, 1648, 3773**
Mirabel Airport Directory. (CN) **4675**
Mirabella. (US) **4848, 1293**
Mirabelle. (UK) **2194**
Miraculous Medal. (US ISSN 0026-5802) **4285**
Mirador. (AG) **680**
Mirador Avicola. (SP) **221**
Mirage. (US) **336, 2998**
▼Miras-i Firhangi. (IR) **278, 2939**
Mircen - Journal of Applied Microbiology & Biotechnology see World Journal of Microbiology and Biotechnology **559**
Mirjam. (SZ) **4269, 4848**
Mirkachton. (IS) **3735, 3132**
Miroir du Centre. (FR ISSN 0026-5810) **108**
Miron. see Gazer **4768**
Mirovaya Ekonomika i Mezhdunarodnye Otnosheniya. (RU ISSN 0026-5829) **680, 3965**
Mirror. (LB) **2169**
The Mirror. (LO) **2169**
Mirror. (GH) **2192**
Mirror. (GY) **2196**
The Mirror/Ching Pao. (HK) **2197**
Mirror. (II ISSN 0026-5845) **2200**
Mirror. (IS) **2204**
Mirror see The Mail **2216**
Mirror. (SI) **2216**
Mirror see R E I D Quarterly **2540**
Mirror see Echo der Liebe **4263**
Mirror. (GW ISSN 0252-2535) **4269**
Mirror (Lancaster). (US ISSN 0738-7237) **2415, 4285**
Mirror (Sheboygan). (US) **1318**
Mirror (Somerset). (US) **1318**
Mirror (Springfield). (US) **4269**
Mirror and Probe. (CE) **3238**
Mirror Class Association of Australia. Constitution-Rules of Measurement see Mirror Class Association of Australia. Yearbook **4526**
Mirror Class Association of Australia. Yearbook. (AT) **4526**
Mirror News Magazine. (US) **2560**
Mirror of Opinion. (SI) **2216**
Mirrors. (US) **2998**
†Misaki Marine Biological Station. Contributions. (JA ISSN 0493-4334) **5238**
Al-Misbah. (IR) **4219**
Miscarriage, Infant Death, and Stillbirth Newsletter see M I D S Newsletter **3294**
Miscel.lania de Textos Medievals. (SP) **2375**
Miscel.lania Zoologica. (SP ISSN 0211-6529) **588**
Miscelanea Comillas. (SP ISSN 0210-9522) **4190, 1648, 3773, 4036**
Miscelanea de Estudios Arabes y Hebraicos. (SP ISSN 0544-408X) **3641**
Miscellanea Bryologica et Lichenologica. see Sentai Chii Zappo **5276**
Miscellanea Byzantina Monacensia. (GW ISSN 0076-9347) **2375, 2939**
Miscellanea Francescana. (VC ISSN 0026-587X) **4269, 2318, 3773**
Miscellanea Musicologica. (CS ISSN 0544-4136) **3563**
Miscellanea Storica della Valdelsa. (IT ISSN 0026-5888) **2375**
Miscellaneous Clothing Industries see Canada. Statistics Canada. Clothing Industries **1288**
Miscellaneous Publications - University of Kansas, Museum of Natural History see University of Kansas. Museum of Natural History. Miscellaneous Publications **459**
Miscellaneous Report - State of Ohio, Department of Natural Resources, Division of Geological Survey see Ohio. Division of Geological Survey. Miscellaneous Report **1576**
Miscellany. (II ISSN 0026-5896) **2939**
Miscellany. (US ISSN 0026-590X) **2939**
Miscellany Magazine. (US) **1318**
Misereor Aktuell. (GW) **933**
Misesu. see Mrs **2448**
Mishbetzet. (IS) **1260**

Mishkafayim. (IS ISSN 0334-9810) **336, 1260**
Mishkan. (IS ISSN 0792-0474) **4225, 4269**
Mishkat. (IR) **4219, 2431**
†Mishkenot Sha'ananim Newsletter. (IS) **5238**
Ha-Mishmar. see Vigil **2028**
Mishpacha. (IS) **4225**
La-Mishpaha. (US) **2829, 4225**
Mishpatim. (IS) **2655**
Mishu Gongzuo. (CC) **1059**
Mishua. (IS ISSN 0542-9943) **2014, 2375**
†Misifrut ha-Hinukh. (IS) **5238**
Misim. (IS) **1101**
Misioneros Javerianos. (SP) **4190**
Misiorama. (SP) **4269**
Misleading Advertising Bulletin. (CN ISSN 0705-6109) **1506**
Misli/Thoughts. (AT) **4285, 2014**
Miss Information's Automotive Calendar of Events. (US) **258, 4695**
Miss Mom - Mister Mom. (US) **1241, 3399, 4848**
†Miss Vogue. (GW) **5238**
Al-Missa/Evening. (UA) **2185**
Misset Horeca Magazine. (BE) **2478**
Misset World Poultry. (NE) **221**
Missets Distrifood. (NE) **2077**
Missets Horeca. (NE ISSN 0026-5950) **2478**
Missets Pakblad. (NE) **3649**
Misset's Vlees en Vleeswaren. (NE) **2077**
Missi. (FR ISSN 0026-5977) **4190**
Missile - Ordinance Letter. (US ISSN 0026-5993) **3466, 59**
Missio Aktuell. (GW) **4269**
Missiology. (US ISSN 0091-8296) **245, 4190**
Mission. (DK) **4190**
Mission. (UK) **4244**
Mission America Newsletter. (US) **4285**
Mission Aviation see Mission Aviation Life Link **4675**
Mission Aviation Life Link. (US) **4675**
Mission de l'Eglise. (FR ISSN 0026-6035) **4190**
Mission Handbook. (US) **4269**
Mission Handbook: North American Protestant Ministries Overseas see Mission Handbook: U S A - Canada Protestant Ministries Overseas **4244**
Mission Handbook: U S A - Canada Protestant Ministries Overseas. (US) **4244**
Mission Intercom. (US) **4269**
Mission Magazine see Mandate "Special **4189**
Mission Messages. (FR ISSN 0026-6124) **4190**
Mission News. see Echo Missionaire **4175**
Mission Outlook. (UK) **4269**
Mission Probe. (AT ISSN 0158-0531) **4190**
†Mission Review. (AT ISSN 0155-2902) **5238**
Mission Statement. (US) **4244**
Mission to Lepers, London. Annual Report see Leprosy Mission, London. Annual Report **4188**
Mission to Military Garrisons Quarterly Record. (UK) **3466, 4190**
Mission Today. (US ISSN 1051-3345) **4244**
Mission Today. (UK) **4269**
Missionari del P.I.M.E. (Pontificio Istituto Missioni Estere) (IT) **4269**
Missionaries of Sacred Heart Kontakte see M S C Kontakte **4268**
Missionary Herald. (UK ISSN 0264-1372) **4244**
Missionary Monthly. (US ISSN 0161-7133) **4190**
Missionary Oblates of Mary Immaculate Missions see O.M.I. Missions **5251**
Missionary Reporter. (US) **4244**
Missionary Society of Saint Paul. Link see The Link **4268**
Missionary Tidings. (US ISSN 1043-0725) **4244**
Missionbeat see Newsbeat **4415**
Missionettes Memos see General Council of the Assemblies of God. Memos **4283**

Missionhurst. (US ISSN 0026-6086) 4269
Missioni Cattoliche see Mondo e Missione 4270
Missioni Domenicane. (IT ISSN 0026-6108) 4269
†Missionland. (UK ISSN 0021-4167) 5238
Missions. (US) 4244
Missions Advanced Research & Communication Center Newsletter see M A R C Newsletter 4189
Missions Advanced Research & Communications Center Christian Handbook (Year) see U K Christian Handbook (Year) 4213
Missions and Missionaries see Mission Today 4269
Missions des Franciscains. (CN ISSN 0700-4192) 4269
Missions Digest and Year Book see Evangelical Baptist Churches in Canada. Fellowship Yearbook 4237
Missions-Etrangeres. (CN ISSN 0026-6116) 4190
Missions, Missionaries and Young Churches see Mission Today 4269
Missions Permanentes Aupres des Nations Unies a Geneve et Orga Principaux des Nations Unies. see Permanent Missions to the United Nations 3969
Missions to Seamen Annual Report. (UK) 4244
Missions to Seamen Handbook see Missions to Seamen Annual Report 4244
Missions U S A. (US ISSN 0279-5345) 4244
Missionsbaneret. (SW ISSN 0026-6132) 4190
Missionsblaetter. (GW ISSN 0179-0102) 4269
Missionsblatt. (GW) 4244
Missionsglocke der Liebenzeller Mission.(GW) 4244
Missionskalender. (GW) 4269
Missionswissenschaftliche Forschungen. (GW ISSN 0076-9428) 4190
Missisquoi Historical Society Reports. (CN) 2158, 2415
Mississauga Business. (CN) 838
Mississauga Business Report Magazine.(CN) 680
Mississippi. (US) 2229
Mississippi. Department of Wildlife Conservation. Annual Report. (US ISSN 0733-2017) 2046, 1492
Mississippi. Department of Wildlife Conservation. Annual Report to the Regular Session of the Mississippi Legislature see Mississippi. Department of Wildlife Conservation. Annual Report 2046
Mississippi. State Board of Architecture. Annual Report. (US) 303
Mississippi Academy of Science. Journal. (US ISSN 0076-9436) 4324, 1830, 3132
Mississippi Agricultural and Forestry Experiment Station Research Highlights see M A F E S Research Highlights 105
Mississippi Banker. (US ISSN 0026-6159) 790
Mississippi Coast. (US) 2229
Mississippi College Law Review. (US ISSN 0277-1152) 2655
Mississippi Congress of Parents and Teachers. Proceedings. (US ISSN 0076-9460) 1729
Mississippi Congress of Parents and Teachers. Yearbook. (US ISSN 0079-9479) 1729
▼Mississippi Construction. (US) 625
Mississippi E P A News see Today in Mississippi 1909
Mississippi Educational Directory. (US ISSN 0092-7899) 1695
Mississippi Farm. Research see M A F E S Research Highlights 105
Mississippi Farm Bureau News. (US ISSN 0026-6205) 108
Mississippi Folklore Register. (US ISSN 0026-6248) 2057
Mississippi Foundation for Medical Care Review see M F M C Review 3123
Mississippi Game & Fish. (US) 4550

Mississippi Geology. (US ISSN 0275-8555) 1573, 3658
Mississippi Grocers' Guide. (US ISSN 0026-6264) 2093
Mississippi History Newsletter. (US) 2415, 303, 336, 2939
Mississippi Kite. (US ISSN 0737-0393) 565
Mississippi Language Crusader. (US ISSN 0026-6272) 2829
Mississippi Law Journal. (US ISSN 0026-6280) 2655
Mississippi Legion-Aire. (US ISSN 0026-6299) 1299, 3466
Mississippi Libraries. (US ISSN 0194-388X) 2774
Mississippi Manufacturers Directory. (US) 1146
Mississippi Marine Resources Council. Annual Report. (US ISSN 0095-6783) 1608
Mississippi Memo Digest. (US) 2014
Mississippi Methodist Advocate see Mississippi United Methodist Advocate 4244
Mississippi Mud. (US) 2939
Mississippi Municipalities. (US ISSN 0026-6337) 4091
Mississippi Music Educator. (US) 3563, 1648
Mississippi N.P.S. Newsletter see Mississippi Native Plant Society Newsletter 2134
Mississippi Native Plant Society Newsletter. (US) 2134, 1492
Mississippi Outdoors. (US ISSN 1041-9306) 1492, 4550
Mississippi Power and Light News see M P and L News 5230
Mississippi Quarterly. (US ISSN 0026-637X) 2874
Mississippi R N. (US ISSN 0026-6388) 3282
Mississippi Rag. (US ISSN 0742-4612) 3563
Mississippi Review. (US ISSN 0047-7559) 2939
Mississippi State Medical Association. Journal. (US ISSN 0026-6396) 3132
Mississippi State University. Forest Products Utilization Laboratory. Information Series. (US ISSN 0076-9509) 2116
Mississippi State University. Forest Products Utilization Laboratory. Research Report. (US ISSN 0026-640X) 2116
Mississippi State University. Social Research Report Series. (US) 4443
Mississippi State University. Sociology Research Report Series see Mississippi State University. Social Research Report Series 4443
†Mississippi State University Abstracts of Theses and Dissertations. (US) 5238
Mississippi State University Alumnus. (US) 1318
Mississippi United Methodist Advocate. (US) 4244
Mississippi Valley Review. (US ISSN 0270-3521) 2939
Mississippi's Business. (US ISSN 0026-6442) 680
Missouri. Department of Agriculture. Daily Market Summary. (US) 108, 221
Missouri. Department of Agriculture. Weekly Market Summary. (US) 108, 221
Missouri. Department of Conservation. Annual Report. (US ISSN 0085-3496) 1492
Missouri. Department of Insurance. Annual Report and Statistical Data. (US) 2538
Missouri. Department of Revenue. Annual Combined Financial Report see Missouri. Department of Revenue. Component Unit Financial Report 1101
Missouri. Department of Revenue. Component Unit Financial Report. (US) 1101
Missouri. Disaster Operations Office. Newsletter see Missouri. Emergency Management Agency. Newsletter 1273

Missouri. Division of Geological Survey and Water Resources. Engineering Geology Series. (US ISSN 0076-9606) 1871
Missouri. Division of Geological Survey and Water Resources. Water Resources Report. (US ISSN 0076-9614) 4827, 1599
Missouri. Division of Highway Safety. Highway Safety Plan. (US) 4720, 4108
Missouri. Division of Insurance. Annual Report and Statistical Data see Missouri. Department of Insurance. Annual Report and Statistical Data 2538
Missouri. Division of Youth Services. Annual Report. (US) 4413
Missouri. Emergency Management Agency. Newsletter. (US ISSN 0197-6672) 1273
Missouri. State Board of Training Schools. Annual Report see Missouri. Division of Youth Services. Annual Report 4413
Missouri Alumnus. (US) 1318
Missouri Annual Campaign Finance Report. (US) 3907
Missouri Archaeological Society. Newsletter see Missouri Archaeological Society. Quarterly 278
Missouri Archaeological Society. Quarterly. (US ISSN 0743-7641) 278
Missouri Archaeological Society. Special Publications. (US ISSN 0735-5467) 278
Missouri Archaeologist. (US ISSN 0076-9576) 279
Missouri Area Labor Trends. (US ISSN 0148-4214) 989
Missouri Beef Cattleman. (US ISSN 0192-3056) 221
Missouri Beverage Journal see Spirits, Wine & Beer Marketing in Missouri 385
Missouri Botanical Garden. Annals. (US ISSN 0026-6493) 509
Missouri Botanical Garden Bulletin. (US ISSN 0026-6507) 2134, 509
Missouri Business. (US) 1116
Missouri Conservationist. (US ISSN 0026-6515) 1492, 4550
Missouri Court Rules Handbook. (US) 2655
Missouri Dental Journal. (US) 3238
Missouri Economic Indicators. (US) 874
▼Missouri Employment Law Letter. (US ISSN 1054-6375) 2655, 989
Missouri Engineer. (US ISSN 0026-6558) 1830
Missouri English Bulletin. (US) 1755
▼Missouri Environmental Law Letter. (US) 2655
▼Missouri Facts. (US ISSN 1056-9596) 1781
Missouri Farm see Small Farm Today 120
Missouri Farm Bureau News. (US ISSN 0026-6574) 108
Missouri Farmers Fastline see Farmers Fastline: Missouri Edition 162
Missouri Folklore Society. Journal. (US ISSN 0731-2946) 2057
Missouri Fox Trotter see The Missouri Fox Trotter Magazine 4479
The Missouri Fox Trotter Magazine. (US) 4479
Missouri Golf. (US) 4508
Missouri Grocer. (US) 2093
†Missouri Handbook Series. (US ISSN 0076-9630) 5238
Missouri Historical Review. (US ISSN 0026-6582) 2415
Missouri Industrial Directory see Harris Missouri Directory of Manufacturers 1138
†Missouri Jewish Post and Opinion. (US ISSN 0746-1291) 5238
Missouri Journal of Research in Music Education. (US ISSN 0085-350X) 3563, 1755
Missouri Law Review. (US ISSN 0026-6604) 2655
Missouri Libraries. (US ISSN 0899-6458) 2774

Missouri Life see Missouri Magazine 2229
†Missouri Literary Frontiers Series. (US ISSN 0076-9649) 5238
Missouri Magazine. (US) 2229
Missouri Manufacturers Register. (US ISSN 0893-2816) 1146
Missouri Medicine. (US ISSN 0026-6620) 3132
Missouri Monthly Vital Statistics. (US) 3993, 4118
Missouri Municipal Review. (US ISSN 0026-6647) 4091
Missouri New and Expanding Manufacturers see Missouri's New and Expanding Industry 1081
Missouri Notary Law Primer. (US) 2655
Missouri Nurse. (US ISSN 0026-6655) 3282
Missouri Oil Jobber see Missouri Pipeline 3692
Missouri Parent-Teacher see Contact (Columbia) 1726
Missouri Pharmacist. (US ISSN 0026-6663) 3735
Missouri Pipeline. (US) 3692
Missouri Political Science Association Newsletter see M P S A Newsletter 3905
Missouri Population Estimates. (US ISSN 0734-032X) 3985
Missouri Press News. (US ISSN 0026-6671) 2572, 35
Missouri Queries. (US ISSN 1041-6552) 2158
Missouri Realtor. (US) 4152
Missouri Record. (US) 2288, 1738
Missouri Restaurant. (US) 2478
Missouri Review. (US ISSN 0191-1961) 2939
Missouri Ruralist. (US ISSN 0026-668X) 108
Missouri School Board. (US ISSN 0026-6698) 1729
Missouri School Music. (US ISSN 0026-6701) 3563, 1648
Missouri Schools. (US ISSN 0745-1237) 1648
Missouri Speech & Theatre Journal. (US) 1340, 4635
Missouri Speech Journal see Missouri Speech & Theatre Journal 1340
Missouri Speleological Survey, Inc. Liaison see M S S Liaison 1571
Missouri Speleology. (US ISSN 0026-671X) 1573
Missouri State and Area Labor Trends see Missouri Area Labor Trends 989
Missouri State Genealogical Association Journal. (US ISSN 0747-5667) 2158
Missouri State Government Documents see Missouri State Government Publications 4081
Missouri State Government Publications. (US ISSN 0091-6633) 4081
†Missouri Tax Review. (US) 5238
Missouri Teamster. (US ISSN 0026-6728) 2586
Missouri Union List of Serial Publications. (US ISSN 0164-0496) 2794
Missouri Veterinarian see Veterinary Medical Review 4818
Missouri Vital Statistics. (US ISSN 0098-1974) 4118
Missouri Wildlife. (US) 1492
Missouri Wine Country Journal. (US) 4778
Missouri's Annual Highway Safety Program see Missouri. Division of Highway Safety. Highway Safety Plan 4720
Missouri's New and Expanding Industry.(US ISSN 0540-4193) 1081
Mistelbach in Vergangenheit und Gegenwart. (AU) 2375
Mistletoe Leaves. (US) 2415
Misul Charyo/National Museum Journal of Arts. (KO ISSN 0540-4568) 336, 3527
Misur Jaryo see Misul Charyo 336
Misure Critiche. (IT ISSN 0392-6397) 2939
Mit Livs Novelle. (DK) 2984

6442 MIT RHEUMA

▼Mit Rheuma Leben. (GW ISSN 0939-219X) **3369**
Mita Gakkai Zasshi/Mita Journal of Economics. (JA ISSN 0026-6760) **680**
Mita Journal of Economics. see Mita Gakkai Zasshi **680**
Die Mitbestimmung. (GW ISSN 0723-5984) **2655**
Mitchell Report. (US) **3754**
Miteinander. (GW) **3132**, 4413
Mitekufat Haeven. (IS) **279**, 245
Mitgliederinformation. (GW) **303**, 625
Mitgliederrundschreiben. (GW) **4479**
Mithila Institute of Post Graduate Studies and Research in Sanskrit Learning. Bulletin. (II ISSN 0026-6787) **2829**, 3641, 3773
Mito Kagaku Gijutsu/Society of Non-Traditional Technology. Journal. (JA ISSN 0914-627X) **4604**
Mitochondria. (UK ISSN 0142-8217) **525**, 480, 3132
Mitre. (CN) **2874**
Mitsubishi Cable Industries Review. see Mitsubishi Densen Kogyo Jiho **1903**
Mitsubishi Densen Kogyo Jiho/ Mitsubishi Cable Industries Review. (JA ISSN 0913-0101) **1903**
Mitsubishi Economic Research Institute Monthly Circular see M E R I's Monthly Circular **873**
Mitsubishi Electric Advance. (JA ISSN 0386-5096) **1903**, 4604
Mitsubishi Heavy Industries Technical Review. (JA ISSN 0026-6817) **4604**
Mitsubishi Juko Giho. (JA ISSN 0387-2432) **4604**
Mitsubishi Technical Bulletin. (JA ISSN 0540-469X) **4604**
†Mitsui Engineering & Shipbuilding Technical Bulletin. (JA) **5238**
Mitsui Zosen Giho/Mitsui Zosen Technical Review. (JA ISSN 0026-6825) **4733**
Mitsui Zosen Technical Review. see Mitsui Zosen Giho **4733**
Mitt Livs Novell. (SW) **2984**
Mitteilungen. see Naukove Tovarystvo Imeni Shevchenka. Zapysky **2016**
Mitteilungen aus Baltischen Leben. (GW ISSN 0026-6833) **2874**
Mitteilungen aus dem Max-Planck-Institut fuer Stroemungsforschung. (GW ISSN 0374-1257) **3844**
Mitteilungen aus dem Max-Planck-Institut fuer Stroemungsforschung und der Aerodynamischen Versuchsanstalt see Mitteilungen aus dem Max-Planck-Institut fuer Stroemungsforschung **3844**
†Mitteilungen aus dem Wissenschaftlichen Bibliothekswesen der DDR. (GW ISSN 0043-6763) **5238**
Mitteilungen aus dem Zoologischen Museum in Berlin. (GW ISSN 0373-8493) **588**
Mitteilungen aus der Arbeitsmarkt- und Berufsforschung. (GW ISSN 0340-3254) **989**
Mitteilungen aus der Gebiete der Lebensmitteluntersuchung und Hygiene/Travaux de Chimie Alimentaire et d'Hygiene. (SZ ISSN 0026-6841) **3609**, 480
Mitteilungen aus der Rheinischen Rinderzucht. (GW ISSN 0026-6868) **221**
Mitteilungen "Berufsbildung". (GW) **819**
Mitteilungen der Arbeitsgemeinschaft fuer Juristisches Bibliotheks- und Dokumentationswesen see Arbeitsgemeinschaft fuer Juristisches Bibliotheks- und Dokumentationswesen. Mitteilungen **2697**
Mitteilungen der Deutschen Patentanwaelte. (GW ISSN 0026-6884) **3676**, 2655
Mitteilungen der Fachhochschule des Bundes. (GW) **4067**
Mitteilungen der Heimstaetten und Landesentwicklungsgesellschaften. (GW) **2492**, 303, 1963
Mitteilungen der Norddeutschen Mission. Bremen. (GW) **4244**

Mitteilungen des Bayerischen Notarvereins, der Notarkasse und der Landesnotarkammer Bayern. (GW) **2655**
Mitteilungen fuer die Archivpflege in Bayern. (GW ISSN 0540-4746) **2318**, 2774
Mitteilungen fuer die Vieh- und Fleischwirtschaft. (GW) **221**
Mitteilungen Meinungen Materialien see Der Deutsche Lehrer im Ausland **2810**
†Mitteilungen P T. (GW ISSN 0323-6315) **5238**
Mitteilungen zur Altenhilfe. (GW ISSN 0933-758X) **2276**
Mitteilungsblatt see M B **2204**
Mitteilungsblatt der Lehrer im Deutschen Friseurhandwerk see Lehrer im Berufsfeld Koerperpflege **373**
Mitteilungsblatt der Sektion Ludwigsburg des D A V. (GW) **4550**
Mitteilungsblatt der Stadt Villach. (AU) **4091**
Mitteilungsblatt des Zivilschutzes. see Feuille Officielle de la Protection Civile **1273**
Mitteilungsblatt fuer Wissenschaftliche Lehrkraefte im Ausland. (GW) **4324**, 1722
Mitteldeutscher Kurier. (GW ISSN 0722-4516) **4443**
Mittellateinische Studien und Texte. (NE ISSN 0076-9754) **2375**
Mittellateinisches Jahrbuch. (GW ISSN 0076-9762) **2376**
Mittelstaendische Unternehmen. (GW ISSN 0930-3618) **1081**
Mittex: Mitteilungen ueber Textilindustrie. (SZ) **4621**
Mittlerer Neckar see Magazin Wirtschaft **819**
Mitzion Tetzeh Torah. M.T.T. (IS ISSN 0541-5632) **4225**, 3773
Mivim. (IS ISSN 0333-7502) **625**
Mix Annual Directory of Recording Industry Facilities and Services. (US) **1146**, 4461
Mix Annual Recording Industry Directory see Mix Annual Directory of Recording Industry Facilities and Services **1146**
Mix Magazine. (US ISSN 0164-9957) **4461**
Mixed Media. (US) **336**, 1648
Mixed Pickles. (US ISSN 0163-5271) **1531**
Mixin' (US) **383**, 2077
Mixing and Separation Technology Abstracts. (UK ISSN 0955-7059) **1845**
Mixture. (NE ISSN 0925-8175) **4644**, 2211
Miyazaki Daigaku Kogakubu Kiyo. see Miyazaki University. Faculty of Engineering. Memoirs **1830**
Miyazaki Daigaku Kyoikugakubu Kiyo. Shizen Kagaku/Miyazaki University. Faculty of Education. Memoirs. Natural Science. (JA ISSN 0285-8576) **4324**
Miyazaki University. Faculty of Education. Memoirs. Natural Science. see Miyazaki Daigaku Kyoikugakubu Kiyo. Shizen Kagaku **4324**
Miyazaki University. Faculty of Engineering. Memoirs/Miyazaki Daigaku Kogakubu Kiyo. (JA ISSN 0540-4924) **1830**
Ha-Mizrah Hehadash/New East. (IS ISSN 0017-7083) **3641**
Mizue. (JA) **336**
Mizz. (UK) **4848**
Mjolkpropagandan see Vaar Naering **3612**
Mkulima wa Kenya see Kenya Farmer **103**
Mlade Rozlety. (CS) **1241**
Mladi Istrazivaci Srbije see M I **1646**
Mladosc, Aktivnosc, Kreativnocs see M A K **1259**
Mladost. (YU ISSN 0026-7031)
Mlezi. (TZ ISSN 0047-7583) **4190**
Mljekarstvo. (CI ISSN 0026-704X) **202**
MLNew Directions see M L N New Directions **3282**

Mloda Polska. (PL ISSN 0866-9791) **2874**
Mlonai/Hotelier. (IS ISSN 0017-7091) **2478**
Mlynsko-Pekarensky Prumysl a Technika Skladovani Obili/Milling and Baking Industry and Storage Techniques of Grain. (CS ISSN 0026-7058) **207**, 2089
Mnansa. (CE) **4036**
Mnemosyne. (NE ISSN 0026-7074) **1278**
Mnemosyne. (GR) **2376**, 279
Mnemosyne. Supplements. (NE ISSN 0169-8958) **1278**
Mo Info. (US ISSN 0884-2205) **2774**
Mo Ju. (CC ISSN 1001-4934) **3429**
Moana: Estudios de Antropologia Oceanica. (UY ISSN 0076-9770) **245**
Moanamesi Was Bokone. see Northern Advertiser **36**
†Mobil. (GW ISSN 0341-5112) **5238**
Mobil Motorist. (US) **4778**
Mobila. (RM ISSN 0026-7104) **2561**, 2554
Il Mobile. (IT ISSN 0026-7112) **2561**
Mobile Air Conditioning Society Service Reports see M A C S Service Reports **4694**
Mobile & Holiday Homes. (UK ISSN 0268-4594) **2492**
Mobile Area Chamber of Commerce Membership Directory and Buyer's Guide. (US) **819**
Mobile - Arredamento Design. (IT) **2561**
Mobile Bay Monthly. (US) **2874**
Mobile Beacon. (US) **2014**
Mobile Communications. (UK ISSN 0953-539X) **1340**
Mobile Communications Business see Mobile Product News **1364**
Mobile Communications Directory. (US) **1340**
Mobile Communications Handbook see R C R Cellular Handbook **1358**
Mobile Communications Handbook see R C R Paging Handbook **1358**
Mobile Data Report: Business Intelligence on Radio-Based Information Networks. (US ISSN 1040-0702) **1340**
Mobile Graduate News and Notes see Health Professions News and Notes **1313**
Mobile Home and Holiday Caravan see Mobile & Holiday Homes **2492**
Mobile Homes and Mobile Home Parks.(US) **2492**, 2715
Mobile Living. (US ISSN 0026-7198) **2492**
Mobile - Manufactured Home Blue Book.(US ISSN 0733-6497) **625**
Mobile - Manufactured Home Merchandiser see Manufactured Home Merchandiser **2491**
Mobile Office. (US) **1059**
Mobile Phone News. (US ISSN 0737-5077) **1364**
†Mobile Plant Design and Components. (UK) **5238**
Mobile Product News. (US ISSN 1044-1190) **1364**
Mobile Public Library Today. (US) **2774**
Mobile Radio Technology. (US) **1357**
▼Mobile Robots and Unmanned Vehicles. (US ISSN 1051-2357) **1409**, 4653
▼Mobile Satellite News (Potomac). (US ISSN 1046-5286) **1364**
Mobile Satellite Reports. (US) **1340**
Mobilehome Parks Report. (US) **4152**
Mobili per Ufficio. (IT) **1059**
Mobilia. (NE ISSN 0165-5302) **2554**
Mobility (Washington). (US ISSN 0195-8194) **4152**, 1067
Mobilizer. (US) **3907**
†Mobius. (AT) **5238**
Mocambique - Informacao Estatistica. (MZ) **4579**
Mocaxue Xuebao/Jounal of Friction. (CC) **3844**, 1228
Moccasin. (US ISSN 0026-7244) **2998**
Mocha see Black Tail **3396**
Moda. (IT) **1293**, 4848

Moda dei Bimbi. (IT ISSN 0026-7252) **1286**
Moda e Bijoux. (IT) **2565**, 1293
Moda e Moda. (PO) **1293**
Moda In. (IT) **1293**
†Moda in Baby. (IT) **5238**
Modal. (FR ISSN 1159-070X) **3563**
Modan Media. see Modern Media **555**
Modapiel. (SP) **4361**
Modasport Intimo see Solointimo International **1287**
Modasport Vacanze. (IT) **1293**
Modaviva. (IT) **1286**
Mode. (HK) **1293**
Mode see Femina Maanadens Magasin **4842**
†Die Mode. (GW ISSN 0026-7279) **5238**
Mode Australia. (AT) **1293**, 4848
Mode Brides. (AT) **3067**, 1293
Mode et Mode. (JA) **1286**
Mode im Verkauf. (GW ISSN 0342-3689) **1286**, 1293
Mode Special. (GW) **1293**
†Model. (US ISSN 0898-4980) **5238**
Model A News. (US) **4695**, 2438
Model Airplane. see Hangkong Moxing **54**
Model Airplane News. (US ISSN 0026-7295) **2438**, 59
Model & Accessories Mart. (UK) **2439**
▼Model & Performer. (US) **1293**, 3514
Model and Toy Collector. (US) **2439**
Model Aviation Canada. (CN ISSN 0317-7831) **2439**
Model Boats. (UK ISSN 0144-2910) **4526**, 2439
Model Builder. (US ISSN 0194-7079) **2439**
▼Model Call. (US) **3629**, 1293
Model Cars. (UK ISSN 0260-762X) **2439**, 4695
Model Engineer. (UK ISSN 0026-7325) **2439**
Model Figure Collector see Model and Toy Collector **2439**
Model for the Preparation of a Guidebook on Medical Discipline. (US ISSN 0888-6792) **3132**
Model Hobby Trader. (UK) **2439**
Model Maker and Model Boats see Model Boats **4526**
Model News. (US) **1293**, 3629
Model Railroader. (US ISSN 0026-7341) **2439**
Model Railways. (UK) **2439**, 4711
Model Retailer. (US ISSN 0191-6904) **1048**, 2439
Model Rocket News. (US) **2439**
Model Rocket News Magazine see Model Rocket News **2439**
Model Ship Builder. (US ISSN 0199-7068) **2439**
Model Shipwright. (UK ISSN 0264-2220) **2439**
†Model Shopper. (US) **5238**
Modelbanen. (DK ISSN 0107-5330) **2439**
Modelbouwer. (NE ISSN 0026-7384) **2439**
Modele Magazine. (FR ISSN 0026-7392) **2439**, 59
Modele Reduit d'Avion. (FR ISSN 0026-7406) **2439**, 59
Modele Reduit de Bateau. (FR ISSN 0026-7414) **2439**, 4733
Modeles Linguistiques. (FR ISSN 0249-6267) **2829**
Modelflyve Nyt. (DK ISSN 0105-6441) **2439**
Modeli Sezona. (RU) **1293**
Modeling and Simulation. (US ISSN 0198-0092) **1435**
Modeling and Simulation on Microcomputers. (US) **1435**, 1463
Modelism - Supliment Tehnium. (RM) **2439**
Modelisme. (FR ISSN 0047-7648) **4695**
Modelist - Konstruktor. (RU ISSN 0131-2243) **1260**, 2439
Modell. (GW ISSN 0540-5203) **2439**
Modell-Eisenbahn. (SZ ISSN 0250-782X) **2439**
Modell Elektronik. (GW) **1775**

Modell Fan. (GW ISSN 0341-5104) **2439**
Modell's Drugs in Current Use and New Drugs. (US) **3735**
Modellbahn Start. (GW ISSN 0938-0213) **2439**
Modellbau Heute. (GW ISSN 0323-312X) **2439**
Modelleisenbahner. (GW ISSN 0026-7422) **2439**
Der Modellhut. (GW ISSN 0723-7839) **1286, 4621**
Modellhut und Accessoires. (GW) **1293**
Modellina. (IT) **1293**
†Modelling and Miniature Crafts. (UK ISSN 0955-1689) **5238**
Modelling, Measurement and Control. (FR) **3065**
▼Modelling of Geo-Biosphere Process. (GW ISSN 0938-9563) **1547, 447**
ModellWerft. (GW ISSN 0170-1819) **2439**
Models in Dermatology. (SZ ISSN 0259-1340) **3249**
Models Mart Directory of Modeling Schools and Agencies USA and Canada see Directory of Model - Talent Agencies and Schools USA and International **1131**
Models of Scientific Thought. (US ISSN 0736-5268) **2829**
Model's Season. (RU ISSN 0132-0793) **1293**
Modeltoget. (DK ISSN 0107-6310) **2439**
Modem Notes. (US ISSN 0741-580X) **1454, 1427, 1471**
Modem User News. (US) **1454**
Modena see Modena Economica **819**
Modena Economica. (IT) **819**
Moderat Debatt. (SW ISSN 0026-7449) **3907**
Moderator. (US) **1318**
Modern Accounting and Auditing Checklists (Supplement). (US) **753**
Modern Africa. (UK) **917**
Modern Age. (US ISSN 0026-7457) **2874, 3907**
Modern Aging Research. (US ISSN 0275-360X) **2276**
Modern Analytical Chemistry. (US) **1207**
Modern and Ancient Legends. see Jingu Chuanqi **2055**
Modern and Contemporary France. (UK ISSN 0267-761X) **2376, 2874**
Modern Animal Husbandry. see Dangdai Xumu **215**
Modern Applications News. (US ISSN 0277-9951) **3415, 1830**
Modern Applications News for Design and Manufacturing see Modern Applications News **3415**
†Modern Approaches to the Diagnosis and Instruction of Multi-Handicapped Children. (NE ISSN 0076-9916) **5238**
Modern Architecture. see Shidai Jianzhu **1873**
Modern Artist. see Dangdai Meisujia **323**
▼Modern Arts Criticism. (US) **336, 420**
Modern Asia see Far East Business **865**
Modern Asian Studies. (UK ISSN 0026-749X) **3641, 3907**
Modern Aspects of Electrochemistry. (US ISSN 0076-9924) **1212**
Modern Athlete and Coach. (AT ISSN 0047-7672) **4550**
Modern Athletics see Athletics Weekly **4465**
Modern Austrian Literature. (US ISSN 0026-7503) **2939**
Modern Baking. (US ISSN 0897-6201) **2089, 1021**
†Modern Banking Checklists (Supplement). (US) **5238**
Modern Beauty Shop see Modern Salon **373**
Modern Biology Series. (US) **447**
Modern Boating. (AT ISSN 0026-752X) **4526**
Modern Brewery Age. (US ISSN 0026-7538) **383**
Modern Brewery Age Blue Book. (US ISSN 0076-9932) **383**

Modern Brewery Age: Magazine Edition.(US) **383**
Modern Brewery Age: Tabloid Edition. (US) **383**
Modern Bride. (US ISSN 0026-7546) **3067**
†Modern British Literature. (US) **5238**
Modern Building Architecture and Engineering in Australia. (AT) **303, 625**
Modern Bulk Transporter. (US ISSN 0031-6431) **4746**
Modern Business Law - Moderne Besigheidreg see South African Mercantile Law Journal **2680**
Modern Casting. (US ISSN 0026-7562) **3415**
Modern Ceylon Studies see Modern Sri Lanka Studies **4380**
Modern Chemical Industry. (CC ISSN 0253-4320) **1856**
Modern China. (US ISSN 0097-7004) **2340, 3641, 4380**
Modern China/Chin Tai Chung-kuo. (CH) **2874**
Modern Chinese Literature. (US ISSN 0190-2369) **2939, 3641**
Modern Churchman. (UK ISSN 0026-7597) **4190**
Modern Civil Aviation. see Xiandai Minhang **65**
Modern Clothes. see Xiandai Fuzhuang **1295**
†Modern Concepts of Cardiovascular Disease. (US ISSN 0026-7600) **5238**
Modern Corporation Checklists (Supplement). (US) **1081**
Modern Courts. (US) **2732**
Modern Daily Necessities. see Xiandai Shenghuo Yongpin **1508**
Modern Dairy. (CN ISSN 0026-7651) **202**
Modern Decoration. see Xiandai Zhuangshi **2556**
†Modern Dental Practice. (US ISSN 0894-7953) **5238**
†Modern Dentalab. (US) **5238**
†Modern Developments in Powder Metallurgy. (US) **5238**
Modern Drama. (CN ISSN 0026-7694) **2939, 4635**
Modern Drummer. (US ISSN 0194-4533) **3563**
†Modern East Asian Studies. (CN) **5238**
Modern Electronics. (US ISSN 0149-2357) **1775**
Modern Elektronik. (SW ISSN 0345-7656) **1775**
Modern Engineering Technology see National Development **4068**
†Modern English Journal/Eigo Kyoiku Jaanaru. (JA) **5238**
Modern English Teacher. (UK ISSN 0308-0587) **2829, 1755**
Modern Enterprise Herald. see Xiandai Qiye Daokan **1031**
Modern Entrepreneurs. see Xiandai Qiyejia **700**
Modern Family. see Xiandai Jiating **2450**
Modern Farming. (UK ISSN 0267-4637) **108**
Modern Farming. see Ukulima Wa Kisasa **125**
Modern Fibres. (II ISSN 0377-1490) **4622**
Modern Fiction Studies. (US ISSN 0026-7724) **2939**
Modern Filologiai Fuzetek. (HU ISSN 0076-9967) **2829**
Modern Fisheries Information. see Xiandai Yuye Xinxi **2050**
Modern Fishing. (AT ISSN 0026-7732) **2046**
Modern Floor Coverings see Floor Covering Business **5193**
Modern Food Service News. (US ISSN 0888-7829) **2077**
Modern Garden Center see Lawn & Garden Marketing **5226**
Modern Geology. (US ISSN 0026-7775) **1573**
Modern Geology. see Xiandai Dizhi **1586**
Modern German Studies. (GW ISSN 0170-3013) **3773**

Modern Gold Coinage (Year). (US) **3600**
Modern Greek Society: A Newsletter see Modern Greek Society: A Social Science Newsletter **2376**
Modern Greek Society: A Social Science Newsletter. (US ISSN 0147-0779) **2376**
Modern Greek Studies Association Bulletin. (US ISSN 0047-7702) **2376, 2829**
Modern Greek Studies Yearbook. (US ISSN 0884-8432) **2014**
Modern Grocer. (US ISSN 0026-7805) **2093**
Modern Grocer en Espanol. (US) **2078**
Modern Grocer Industry Directory. (US) **2078, 1146**
Modern Gymnast see International Gymnast Magazine **4476**
Modern Haiku. (US ISSN 0026-7821) **2998**
Modern Healthcare (Long-Term Care) see Modern Healthcare (Year) **2467**
Modern Healthcare (Short-Term Care) see Modern Healthcare (Year) **2467**
Modern Healthcare (Year). (US ISSN 0160-7480) **2467**
Modern Hebrew Literature. (IS ISSN 0334-4266) **2939**
Modern History Review. (UK ISSN 0956-0726) **2318**
Modern Horse Breeding. (US ISSN 0747-1424) **4536**
Modern Humanities Research Association. Monograph see Modern Humanities Research Association. Publications **2511**
Modern Humanities Research Association. Publications. (UK) **2511**
Modern Images. (US ISSN 0026-7848) **2998**
Modern International Drama. (US ISSN 0026-7856) **4635**
Modern International Relations. see Xiandai Guoji Guanxi **3978**
Modern Jazz. (IT) **3563**
Modern Jeweler. National Executive. (US ISSN 0193-208X) **2565**
Modern Jeweler National. (US ISSN 0744-2513) **2565**
Modern Jewish Masters. (US) **2014**
Modern Jewish Studies Annual. (US ISSN 0270-9406) **2939, 2014**
Modern Journalism. see Savremenna Zhurnalistika **2575**
Modern Judaism. (US ISSN 0276-1114) **4225**
Modern Keyboard. (US) **3563**
Modern Language Association of America Directory of Periodicals see M L A Directory of Periodicals **2982**
Modern Language Association of America International Bibliography of Books and Articles on the Modern Languages and Literatures see M L A International Bibliography of Books and Articles on the Modern Languages and Literatures **405**
Modern Language Association of America Job Information Lists see M L A Job Information Lists **3629**
Modern Language Association of America Newsletter (New York) see M L A Newsletter (New York) **2827**
Modern Language Association of Northern Ireland see N I M L A **2830**
Modern Language Journal. (US ISSN 0026-7902) **2829, 1755**
Modern Language Notes see M L N **2828**
Modern Language Quarterly. (US ISSN 0026-7929) **2939, 2829**
Modern Language Review. (UK ISSN 0026-7937) **2939, 2829**
Modern Language Studies. (US ISSN 0047-7729) **2939, 2829**
Modern Language Teachers' Association of New South Wales News see M L T A News **2828**
Modern Language Teachers'Association of Victoria Newsletter see M L T A V Newsletter **2828**
Modern Languages see Language Learning Journal **2824**
†Modern Law and Society. (GW ISSN 0026-7953) **5238**

MODERN PHILOLOGY 6443

Modern Law Reports, Embodying Cases Decided by the Supreme Court of the Republic of Sri Lanka. (CE) **2655**
Modern Law Review. (UK ISSN 0026-7961) **2655**
Modern Law Science. see Xiandai Faxue **2695**
Modern Leader. see Xiandai Lingdao **3935**
Modern Literary World. see Dangdai Wentan **2910**
Modern Liturgy. (US ISSN 0363-504X) **4190**
Modern Living. (JA) **2448, 2554**
Modern Living at the Home of Gas. (UK) **3692**
Modern Living with Gas see Modern Living at the Home of Gas **3692**
Modern Locomotive Handbook. (US) **4711**
▼Modern Logic. (US ISSN 1047-5982) **3048**
Modern Machine Knitting. (UK ISSN 0957-6673) **3591, 1286**
Modern Machine Shop. (US ISSN 0026-8003) **3021**
Modern Machine Shop N C Guidebook and Directory see N C - C I M Guidebook **3025**
Modern Management. (UK) **1021**
Modern Materials Handling. (US ISSN 0026-8038) **3021**
Modern Materials Handling Casebook Directory. (US) **3021**
Modern Materials Handling Planning Guidebook. (US) **3021**
Modern Maturity. (US ISSN 0026-8046) **2276**
Modern Media/Modan Media. (JA ISSN 0026-8054) **555**
Modern Medical Laboratory. see Kensa to Gijutsu **3260**
Modern Medical Practice see Pharmacy News **3739**
Modern Medicine. (US ISSN 0026-8070) **3132**
Modern Medicine see Modern Medicine of Australia **3132**
Modern Medicine of Australia. (AT ISSN 1030-3782) **3132**
†Modern Medicine of Canada. (CN ISSN 0026-8097) **5238**
†Modern Medicine of Great Britain. (UK ISSN 0026-8100) **5238**
Modern Medicine of Ireland. (UK) **3132**
Modern Medicine of South Africa. (SA) **3132**
Modern Medicine Today. see Medicina Moderna Oggi **3129**
Modern Metals. (US ISSN 0026-8127) **3416**
Modern Methods in Pharmacology. (US ISSN 0732-7218) **3735**
Modern Middle East Series. (US ISSN 0077-0027) **2340, 3641**
Modern Monographs in Analytical Chemistry. (US) **1207**
Modern Mother see Mother **1241**
Modern Motor. (AT ISSN 0026-8143) **4695, 4479**
Modern Neuroradiology Series. (US) **3360**
Modern Neurosurgery. (US) **3381**
Modern Nutrition News. (US) **3609**
†Modern Office. (AT ISSN 0810-9451) **5238**
Modern Office Technology. (US ISSN 0746-3839) **1059, 1452, 1471**
Modern Orthodox Saints. (US) **4285**
Modern Packaging Trends. (II) **3649**
Modern Paint and Coatings. (US ISSN 0098-7786) **3654**
Modern Paint & Coatings Paint Red Book. (US ISSN 0090-5402) **1146, 3654**
Modern Painters. (US) **336**
Modern Pathology. (US ISSN 0893-3952) **3132, 447**
Modern Percussionist see Modern Drummer **3563**
Modern Perfuming. see Perfumeria Moderna **376**
Modern Pharmacology - Toxicology Series. (US ISSN 0098-6925) **3735, 1983**
Modern Philology. (US ISSN 0026-8232) **2829, 2939**

Modern Photography. see Xiandai Sheying **3798**
†Modern Photography. (US ISSN 0026-8240) **5238**
†Modern Photography Video Magazine. (US) **5238**
†Modern Photography's Photo Buying Guide. (US) **5238**
Modern Physics. see Xiandai Wuli Zhishi **3835**
Modern Physics Letter A. (SI ISSN 0217-7323) **3848**
Modern Physics Letter B. (SI ISSN 0217-9849) **3848**
Modern Pictorial. see Xiandai Huabao **2183**
Modern Plastering see Specialist Building Finishes **632**
Modern Plastics. (US ISSN 0026-8275) **3864**
Modern Plastics Encyclopedia. (US ISSN 0085-3518) **3864**
Modern Plastics International. (US ISSN 0026-8283) **3864**
Modern Postal History Journal. (US) **1353**, 2415
Modern Power Systems. (UK ISSN 0260-7840) **1792**
Modern Printing. (CH) **4002**
Modern Problems in Paediatrics see Pediatric and Adolescent Medicine **3324**
Modern Problems of Pharmacopsychiatry. (SZ ISSN 0077-0094) **3345**, 3735
Modern Psychoanalysis. (US ISSN 0361-5227) **4036**
Modern Publicity see World Advertising Review **40**
Modern Purchasing. (CN ISSN 0026-833X) **1048**
Modern Quaternary Research in Southeast Asia. (NE ISSN 0168-6151) **3658**
Modern Railroads see Railway Age **4713**
Modern Railways. (UK ISSN 0026-8356) **4711**
Modern Railways Pictorial see Motive Power Monthly **4711**
Modern Review. (II ISSN 0026-8380) **2200**
▼The Modern Review. (UK ISSN 0964-2323) **2874**
Modern Romances. (US ISSN 0026-8399) **2984**
Modern Salon. (US ISSN 0148-4001) **373**
Modern Schoolman. (US ISSN 0026-8402) **3773**
Modern Screen's Country Music Special.(US) **3563**
†Modern Short Stories. (US) **5238**
Modern Silver Coinage (Year). (US) **3600**
Modern Sri Lanka Studies. (CE) **4380**
Modern Steel Construction. (US ISSN 0026-8445) **625**, 3416
Modern Synthetic Methods. (US ISSN 0176-7615) **1220**
†Modern Technics in Surgery. Abdominal Surgery. (US ISSN 0196-1918) **5239**
†Modern Technics in Surgery. Cardiac - Thoracic Surgery. (US ISSN 0163-7029) **5239**
Modern Technics in Surgery. Head and Neck Surgery. (US ISSN 0271-8219) **3381**
Modern Technics in Surgery. Neurosurgery. (US ISSN 0163-7037) **3381**, 3345
†Modern Technics in Surgery. Plastic Surgery. (US ISSN 0276-9387) **5239**
Modern Technics in Surgery. Urologic Surgery. (US ISSN 0193-8568) **3382**, 3389
Modern Theology. (UK ISSN 0266-7177) **4190**
†Modern Times. (US) **5239**
Modern Tire Dealer. (US ISSN 0026-8496) **4292**, 4695
Modern Tire Dealer Products Catalog see Modern Tire Dealer: Tire, Tools & Equipment Merchandising Guide **4653**

Modern Tire Dealer: Tire, Tools & Equipment Merchandising Guide. (US) **4653**, 4292
Modern Tramway and Light Rail Transit.(UK ISSN 0144-1655) **4711**
Modern Tramway and Rapid Transit Review see Modern Tramway and Light Rail Transit **4711**
Modern Truckstop News. (US) **4746**, 680
Modern Unionist. (AT ISSN 0047-7753) **2586**
Modern Utopian see Communities **829**
Modern Veterinary Practice. (US ISSN 0362-8140) **4813**
†Modern Warfare. (US ISSN 1041-4967) **5239**
Modern Woman. (NR ISSN 0047-7761) **4848**
Modern Woman. (IE ISSN 0790-3855) **4848**
Modern Women. see Xiandai Funu **4858**
Modern Woodmen. (US) **1299**
Modern Woodworking. (US) **3021**
Modern Writers. see Dangdai Zuojia **2910**
Moderna Organizacija see Organizacija in Kadri **1068**
Moderna Spraak. (SW ISSN 0026-8577) **2829**, 2939
Moderne Bil Transport see Moderne Transport **4653**
Moderne Databehandling see Data **1449**
Moderne Fertigung see Fertigung **3017**
Moderne Frau see Petra **4851**
Moderne Geriatrie/Geriatrie Moderne. (NE) **2276**, 3132
▼Moderne Hotel Technik. (GW ISSN 0937-2768) **2478**
Moderne Kontor see Kontorbladet **1059**
Die Moderne Kueche. (GW ISSN 0026-864X) **2561**, 1903, 2448
Moderne Transport. (NO ISSN 0802-5193) **4653**
Moderne Unfallverthutung. (GW) **4108**
†Modernes Hotel. (AU ISSN 0026-8704) **5239**
Modernes Leben-Natuerliches Heilen. (GW ISSN 0340-577X) **3215**
Modernes Wohnen/Habitation Moderne.(SZ ISSN 0026-8712) **2554**
Moderni Rizeni. (CS ISSN 0026-8720) **1021**
Modernisieren. (GW) **625**
Modernization. see Xiandaihua **4613**
†Modern's Market Guide. (US ISSN 0276-0959) **5239**
Modersmaal Selskabet. Aarbog. (DK ISSN 0107-2390) **2829**
Modersmaalet/Mother Tongue. (CN ISSN 0047-7788) **2014**
†Modes de Paris. (FR ISSN 0026-8747) **5239**
Modes et Travaux. (FR ISSN 0026-8739) **1293**
Modesto Peace - Life Center - Stanislaus Safe Energy Committee. Newsletter see Stanislaus Connections **3927**
Modification of Carcinogenesis see I C R D B Cancergram: Modification of Carcinogenesis **5208**
Modis. (BE) **4622**
Modische Linie (Ausgabe B). (GW ISSN 0026-8771) **1293**
Modische Maschen. (GW ISSN 0026-878X) **1293**
Moditalia. (IT) **1286**
Modo. (IT) **4604**, 336
Modul: Schach-Computer-Schach. (AU) **1419**, 4479
Modulo. (IT) **625**, 1871
Modulus. (US ISSN 0191-4022) **303**
Modus. (UK ISSN 0264-9683) **2448**, 1293, 3591
Mody Stran Socializma. (RU ISSN 0320-4650) **1293**
Moebel-Industrie und Ihre Helfer. (GW ISSN 0077-0205) **2561**
Moebel Interior Design see M D **2553**
Moebel-Kultur. (GW ISSN 0047-7796) **2561**
Moebel und Wohnraum. (GW ISSN 0026-8844) **2554**, 2561

Moebelfertigung. (GW) **2561**
Moebelhandleren. (NO ISSN 0333-354X) **2561**
Moebelmarkt. (GW) **2561**
Der Moebelspediteur. (GW ISSN 0047-780X) **4653**
Moebius. (CN ISSN 0225-1582) **2939**
Moebler och Miljoe. (SW ISSN 0345-7737) **2561**
Moeldrup Kommunes Lokalhistoriske Arkiv. Aarsskrift. (DK ISSN 0106-4479) **2376**
Moeletsi Oa Basotho/Counsellor of Basotho. (LO) **4269**
Moeletsi oa Basotho. (LO) **4270**
Moellen. (DK ISSN 0026-8852) **207**, 2376
Moelposen. (DK ISSN 0106-1917) **2376**
Moentsamleren. (DK ISSN 0900-1409) **3600**
Moessbauer Spectroscopy Abstracts. (UK) **3837**, 17
Moesson. (NE ISSN 0165-6546) **3965**
Moethaukpan/Aurora. (BR) **2220**
Moftul Roman. (RM) **2875**
The Mohair Bulletin. (AT) **4622**, 108
The Mohawk. (US ISSN 0740-9699) **2158**
Mohr Kurier. (GW) **4132**
Moin. (GW) **2875**
Le Mois. (SZ ISSN 0304-2162) **874**
Moj Pas. (CI ISSN 0026-8895) **3514**
Moji Shohyoshu. (JA) **3676**
Mokhtarein ya Mobtakerin. (IR) **4604**, 4324
Moko. (II) **2939**, 2829
Moksha Journal. (US ISSN 1051-127X) **3773**
Mokuzai Gakkaishi. see Japan Wood Research Society. Journal **2115**
Mokuzai Kenkyu. see Wood Research **2118**
Molaetsa-Molaetsa. (SA ISSN 0378-410X) **4244**
▼Moldavskii Istoricheskii Zhurnal. (MV) **2318**
Moldavskii Istoricheskii Zhurnal. see Revista de Istorie a Moldovei **2383**
Molders. (JA) **3864**
Molecular and Biochemical Parasitology.(NE ISSN 0166-6851) **556**, 1220
Molecular and Cellular Biochemistry. (US ISSN 0300-8177) **480**, 525
Molecular and Cellular Biology. (US ISSN 0270-7306) **556**
Molecular and Cellular Endocrinology. (IE ISSN 0303-7207) **3255**
▼Molecular and Cellular Neurosciences.(US ISSN 1044-7431) **3345**
Molecular and Cellular Probes. (UK ISSN 0890-8508) **3262**, 1184
Molecular and Chemical Neuropathology. (US ISSN 1044-7393) **3345**
Molecular and General Genetics. (GW ISSN 0026-8925) **545**
Molecular Aspects of Medicine. (US ISSN 0098-2997) **3360**, 3132
Molecular Biology (New York). (English translation of: Molekulyarnaya Biologiya) (US ISSN 0026-8933) **526**, 480
†Molecular Biology (San Diego). (US) **5239**
Molecular Biology and Evolution. (US ISSN 0737-4038) **447**
Molecular Biology and Medicine. (UK ISSN 0735-1313) **3262**, 447
Molecular Biology, Biochemistry and Biophysics. (US ISSN 0077-0221) **526**, 480, 486
Molecular Biology - Cyclic Nucleotides see I C R D B Cancergram: Molecular Biology - Cyclic Nucleotides **5209**
Molecular Biology - D N A see I C R D B Cancergram: Molecular Biology - D N A **5209**
Molecular Biology - Proteins, Polypeptides, Amino Acids see I C R D B Cancergram: Molecular Biology - Proteins, Polypeptides, Amino Acids **5209**

Molecular Biology - R N A see I C R D B Cancergram: Molecular Biology - R N A **5209**
Molecular Biology Reports. (NE ISSN 0301-4851) **526**
Molecular Biotherapy. (US ISSN 0952-8172) **3200**, 480
Molecular Brain Research. (NE ISSN 0169-328X) **3345**, 448
Molecular Carcinogenesis. (US ISSN 0899-1987) **3200**, 556
Molecular Crystals and Liquid Crystals Bulletin see Condensed Matter News **1884**
Molecular Crystals and Liquid Crystals Incorporating Nonlinear Optics see Molecular Crystals and Liquid Crystals Science and Technology. Section A: Molecular Crystals and Liquid Crystals **1211**
Molecular Crystals and Liquid Crystals Incorporating Nonlinear Optics see Molecular Crystals and Liquid Crystals Science and Technology. Section B: Nonlinear Optics **3855**
Molecular Crystals and Liquid Crystals Letters see M C L C Letters **1211**
Molecular Crystals and Liquid Crystals Science and Technology. Section A: Molecular Crystals and Liquid Crystals. (US ISSN 1058-725X) **1211**
Molecular Crystals and Liquid Crystals Science and Technology. Section B: Nonlinear Optics. (US ISSN 1058-7268) **3855**
▼Molecular Crystals and Liquid Crystals Science and Technology. Section C: Molecular Materials. (US ISSN 1058-7276) **1211**
Molecular Crystals and Liquid Crystals Science and Technology. Section D: Display and Imaging. (US ISSN 1058-7284) **3855**
Molecular Endocrinology. (US ISSN 0888-8809) **3255**
▼Molecular Engineering. (NE ISSN 0925-5125) **1856**
Molecular Genetics, Microbiology and Virology. (English translation of: Molekulyarnaya Genetika, Mikrobiologiya i Virusologiya) (US ISSN 0891-4168) **448**
Molecular Immunology. (US ISSN 0161-5890) **480**, 3188
▼Molecular Marine Biology and Biotechnology. (US ISSN 1053-6426) **1608**, 490
Molecular Materials see Molecular Crystals and Liquid Crystals Science and Technology. Section C: Molecular Materials **1211**
Molecular Microbiology. (UK ISSN 0950-382X) **556**
Molecular Neurobiology. (US ISSN 0893-7648) **3345**, 480, 545
▼Molecular Neuropharmacology. (UK ISSN 0959-5244) **3735**
Molecular Pharmacology. (US ISSN 0026-895X) **3735**
▼Molecular Phylogenetics and Evolution. (US ISSN 1055-7903) **545**
Molecular Physics. (UK ISSN 0026-8976) **1229**, 3825
Molecular Plant - Microbe Interactions. (US ISSN 0894-0282) **509**, 545, 556
Molecular Reproduction and Development. (US ISSN 1040-452X) **556**
Molecular Simulation. (US ISSN 0892-7022) **1184**
Molecular Structures and Dimensions. (NE ISSN 0377-2012) **1211**
†Molecular Toxicology. (US) **5239**
Molekulna Biologiia see Uspehi na Moleculiarnata Biologia **459**
Molekulyarnaya Biologiya. (RU ISSN 0026-8984) **526**, 480
Molekulyarnaya Fizika i Biofizika Vodnykh Sistem. (RU) **486**
Molekulyarnaya Genetika, Mikrobiologiya i Virusologiya. (RU ISSN 0208-0613) **545**, 556
Molens/Mills. (NE ISSN 0169-6459) **1492**
Molineria y Panaderia. (SP ISSN 0026-900X) **2089**

Molini d'Italia. (IT ISSN 0026-9018) **207**
Die Molkerei-Zeitung Welt der Milch. (GW ISSN 0043-2512) **202, 2078**
Molkereitechnik. (GW) **202**
Moll Monografies Cientifiques. (SP) **4324**
Moll Monografies d'Historia Local. (SP) **2376**
†Mollusk Farming U S A. (US) **5239**
Molochnoe i Myasnoe Skotovodstvo. (RU ISSN 0026-9034) **221**
Moloda Ukraina/Young Ukraine. (CN ISSN 0026-9042) **1260**
Molodaya Gvardiya. (RU ISSN 0131-2251) **2875**
Molodezhnaya Estrada. (RU ISSN 0132-8816) **1260, 3563, 4635**
Molodoi Kommunist see Perspektivy **3915**
Molula-Qhooa. (SA ISSN 0026-9093) **4285**
†Molybdenum Mosaic. (US) **5239**
Molysulfide Newsletter. (US ISSN 0730-9163) **3416**
Mom Guess What Newspaper. (US) **2455**
Moment. (US ISSN 0099-0280) **2014**
Momento. (VE ISSN 0026-9131) **2238**
Momento. (IT ISSN 0544-7526) **3773**
▼Momento Catolico. (US) **4270**
Momento Economico. (MX) **680**
Momentum. (UK) **2939**
Momentum. (CN) **3399**
Momentum. (SA ISSN 0258-719X) **4653**
Momentum (Rochester). (US) **3238**
Momentum (Washington). (US) **1648, 4270**
Mom's Apple Pie. (US) **4848, 2455**
Momsareew. (SG) **3907**
Mon Bebe. (CN ISSN 0384-0816) **1241, 3806**
Mon-Khmer Studies. (US ISSN 0147-5207) **2829**
Mon Vieux Real. (CN) **1318**
▼Monad. (US) **3012, 2939**
Monarchist Book Review. (UK ISSN 0077-0280) **2329**
Monarchist League Newsletter. (UK) **3908**
Monarchist Newsletter see Monarchist League Newsletter **3908**
Monarchist Press Association. Historical Series. (UK ISSN 0077-0299) **2376**
Monarchy Canada. (CN ISSN 0319-4019) **3908**
Monash Papers on Southeast Asia. (AT) **2340, 3908**
Monash Publications in Geography. (AT ISSN 0313-8410) **2256**
†Monash Review. (AT ISSN 0159-950X) **5239**
Monash University. Careers & Appointments Service. Survey of Graduate Starting Salaries as of 30 April (Year). (AT) **729, 3632**
Monash University. Centre of Policy Studies. Discussion Paper Series. (AT ISSN 0728-5884) **874**
Monash University. Department of Civil Engineering. Civil Engineering Research Report. (AT ISSN 0155-6282) **1871**
Monash University. Department of Geography and Environmental Science. Environmental Papers. (AT) **1963**
Monash University. Department of Geography and Environmental Science. Environmental Reports. (AT) **1963**
Monash University Law Review. (AT ISSN 0311-3140) **2655**
Monastic Studies. (CN ISSN 0026-9190) **4270**
Monastica. (IT) **4270**
Monat. (SZ ISSN 0256-3533) **680**
Monat in Wirtschaft und Finanz see Le Mois **874**
Monatsbericht Angezeigter Flugunfaelle.(GW) **4675**

Monatsbericht der Angezeiten Flugunfalluntersuchungsstelle. (GW ISSN 0343-6594) **4675, 4108**
Monatschrift Deutscher Zahnaerzte see Der Freie Zahnarzt **3233**
Monatshefte. (US) **2829, 1755, 2940**
Monatshefte fuer Chemie/Chemical Monthly. (US ISSN 0026-9247) **1184**
Monatshefte fuer Deutschen Unterricht see Monatshefte **2829**
Monatshefte fuer Evangelische Kirchengeschichte des Rheinlandes. (GW) **4244**
Monatshefte fuer Mathematik. (US ISSN 0026-9255) **3048**
Monatshefte fuer Veterinaermedizin. (GW ISSN 0026-9263) **4813**
Monatsmagazin. (GW) **4778**
Monatsschrift fuer Brauwissenschaft. (GW) **388, 17**
Monatsschrift fuer Deutsches Recht. (GW ISSN 0340-1812) **2655**
Monatsschrift fuer Kriminologie und Strafrechtsreform. (GW ISSN 0026-9301) **1518**
Monatsschrift Kinderheilkunde. (GW ISSN 0026-9298) **3323**
†Monbu-sho Tokei Suri Kenkyujo Nenpo/Institute of Statistical Mathematics. Annual Report. (JA) **5239**
Moncada. (CU) **2184**
Monday see First Monday **3894**
Monday Developments. (US) **4413, 933**
Monday Monitor see Weekly Congressional Monitor **3934**
Monday Morning. (LE) **2209**
Monday Morning. (US ISSN 0360-6171) **4244**
Monday Morning Message. (US) **2561**
Monday Morning Report. (US) **1537**
Monday Report on Retailers. (CN) **1048, 35**
Monday's Free Press. see Eleftherotypia tis Defteras **2865**
Le Monde. (CN ISSN 0839-1416) **221**
Le Monde. (FR ISSN 0026-9360) **2875, 2187, 3908**
Monde Alpin et Rhodanien. (FR ISSN 0758-4431) **245, 2057**
Monde Arabe Economique et les Affaires Internationales. (FR) **874, 3965**
Monde de l'Auto. (CN) **4695**
Monde de l'Education. (FR) **1648**
Monde de l'Electricite. (CN ISSN 0026-9379) **1903**
Monde de la Bible. (FR) **279, 4190**
Monde des Femmes see Women's World **4861**
Monde des Philatelistes. (FR ISSN 0026-9387) **3754**
Monde Diplomatique. (FR ISSN 0026-9395) **3966**
Monde du Camping Car. (FR) **4778, 4653**
Monde du Renseignement see Intelligence Newsletter **3460**
Monde du Rock. (CN ISSN 0823-0498) **3563**
Monde du Travail/World of Labour. (CM) **989**
†Monde et Mineraux. (FR) **5239**
Monde Informatique. (FR ISSN 0242-5769) **1398**
Monde Juif. (FR ISSN 0026-9425) **2014**
Monde Juridique. (CN ISSN 0828-4989) **2732**
Monde Libertaire. (FR ISSN 0026-9433) **3908, 2875**
Monde Porcin see Le Monde **221**
Mondes en Developpment. (BE ISSN 0302-3052) **933**
Mondes et Cultures. (FR ISSN 0221-0436) **4324**
Mondes Hispanophone et Lusophone see Etudes sur les Mondes Hispanophones **2916**
Mondo. (IT) **3908**
Mondo Agricolo. (IT ISSN 0026-9484) **108**
Mondo Archeologico. (IT) **279**
Mondo Bancario. (IT ISSN 0026-9506) **790**

Mondo Barca. (IT) **4526**
Mondo Cinese. (IT) **3641**
Mondo dei Gioielli. (IT ISSN 0392-6079) **2565**
Mondo della Birra. (IT) **383**
Mondo e Missione. (IT ISSN 0026-6094) **4270**
Mondo Economico. (IT ISSN 0026-9522) **874**
Mondo Erre. (IT ISSN 0391-5484) **1260**
Mondo Giudiziario. (IT) **2732**
Mondo Occulto see Nuovo Mondo Occulto **3670**
Mondo Operaio. (IT) **3908**
Mondo Ortodontico. (IT ISSN 0391-2000) **3238**
Mondo Padano. (IT) **819, 3908**
▼Mondo Popolare. (IT) **2057**
Mondo Sommerso. (IT) **1608, 1599, 4479**
Mondo 2000. (US) **3563**
Mondocucina. (IT) **625, 2561**
Mondolegno. (IT) **2116**
Mondoperaio see Mondo Operaio **3908**
Mondoscacchi. (IT) **4479**
Moneda. (PR) **790, 874**
Moneda y Credito. (SP ISSN 0026-959X) **790**
Moneda y Finanzas del Cono Sur. Cuadernos. (AG) **790**
Moneta e Credito. (IT ISSN 0026-9611) **790**
Moneta International. (VB ISSN 0958-1545) **3600**
Monetaria. (MX ISSN 0185-1136) **790**
Monetary and Economic Studies. (JA ISSN 0287-5306) **790**
▼Monetary Policy Statement. (NZ ISSN 1170-4829) **874**
Monetary Research International Bankers' Guide to Foreign Currency see M R I Bankers' Guide to Foreign Currency **790**
Money. (US ISSN 0149-4953) **1506**
Money Affairs. (MX ISSN 0187-7615) **790**
Money and Credit Market. see Denmark. Danmarks Statistik. Penge og Kapitalmarked **712**
Money & Markets. (US ISSN 1047-9821) **874, 955**
The Money Companion: How to Manage Your Money and Achieve Financial Freedom. (CN) **955**
†Money Dynamics Letter. (US) **5239**
Money - Forecast Letter. (US) **955**
Money Fund Safety Ratings see Income & Safety **949**
Money in (Year) see La Monnaie en (Year) **791**
Money Income (in Year) of Families and Persons in the United States see Current Population Reports: Consumer Income. Money Income of Households, Families and Persons in the United States (Year) **998**
Money Japan. (JA) **790**
Money Lines Magazine. (US) **791**
Money Maker see Your Money **1509**
Money Maker's Monthly. (US) **791**
Money Making Magic. (US) **2875**
Money Management. (UK) **791**
Money Management and Unitholder. (UK ISSN 0028-6052) **955, 753**
Money Management Letter. (US) **955, 791**
Money Manager Portfolios. (US) **955**
Money Managers Previews. (US) **955, 1021**
Money Market Directory of Pension Funds and Their Investment Advisors see Money Market Directory of Pension Funds and Their Investment Managers **791**
Money Market Directory of Pension Funds and Their Investment Managers. (US ISSN 0736-6051) **791**
Money Market Fund Survey. (US ISSN 0271-7751) **955**
Money Market Services International Currency Facts see M M S Currency Facts **790**
Money Marketing Unit Trust Index. (UK) **791**
†Money: Markets and Policy. (US) **5239**

Money Matters. (AT) **955**
Money Reporter. (CN ISSN 0709-0579) **955**
Money Saver. (US) **1506, 838**
Money School Monitor see Hone Report **948**
Money Talks. (US) **3600, 3754**
Money Watch Bulletin. (US) **874**
MoneyLetter. (CN ISSN 0703-7163) **955**
Moneypaper. (US ISSN 0745-9858) **955**
▼Moneyplus News. (US) **1116**
Moneysworth. (US ISSN 0026-9646) **1506**
Moneytree. (US ISSN 0162-3451) **2439, 2448**
Moneywise see Financial Post **780**
Moneyworld. (US) **955**
Mongol Nyelvemlektar see Monumenta Linguae Mongolicae Collecta **2830**
Mongol Roman/Mongolian Novel. (MP) **2940**
Mongolia Report. (US) **874, 3908**
Mongolia Society. Occasional Papers. (US ISSN 0077-0396) **2340**
Mongolia Society. Special Papers. (US) **2340**
Mongolia Society Newsletter. New Series. (US) **2340**
Mongolian Agriculture. see Mongolyn Hodoo Aj Ahuy **108**
Mongolian Beauty. see Mongoljin Goo **373**
Mongolian Medical Sciences. see Mongolyn Anagaakh Ukhaan **3132**
Mongolian Novel. see Mongol Roman **2940**
Mongolian Society Bulletin see Mongolian Studies **3641**
Mongolian Studies. (US) **3641**
Mongoljin Goo/Mongolian Beauty. (MP) **373**
Mongolyn Anagaakh Ukhaan/Mongolian Medical Sciences. (MP) **3132**
Mongolyn Hodoo Aj Ahuy/Mongolian Agriculture. (MP) **108**
Moni. (MW) **2209**
Monika. (GW ISSN 0047-7885) **4848**
Monist. (US ISSN 0026-9662) **3773**
Moniteur. (HT) **2197**
Moniteur Architecture - A M C. (FR ISSN 0998-4194) **303**
Le Moniteur de l'Automobile. (BE) **4695**
Le Moniteur des Assurances. (BE) **2538**
Moniteur des Pharmacies et des Laboratoires. (FR ISSN 0026-9689) **3735**
Moniteur des Travaux Publics et du Batiment. (FR ISSN 0026-9700) **1871, 625**
▼Moniteur des Villes. (FR) **1021**
Moniteur du Commerce International see M O C I **916**
▼Moniteur du Commerce International. (BE) **917**
Moniteur du Film en Belgique. (BE) **3514**
Moniteur du Regne de la Justice. (FR ISSN 0026-9727) **3773**
Le Moniteur - Materiels et Chantiers. (FR ISSN 0998-4577) **625, 3021**
Moniteur Officiel du Commerce International see M O C I **916**
Moniteur Professionel de l'Electricite. (FR ISSN 0026-9735) **1903**
Moniteur Valdotain. see Monitore Valdostano **2205**
Moniteur Vinicole. (FR) **383, 185**
Moniteur Vinicole International see Moniteur Vinicole **383**
Monitin. (IS) **2204**
Monitor. (JA) **917**
Monitor. (IT) **1377**
Monitor. (CN) **1463**
Monitor see Ohio Monitor **3620**
Monitor (Abingdon). (UK ISSN 0260-6666) **1398, 1340**
†Monitor (Albany). (US ISSN 0077-040X) **5239**
†Monitor (Arlington). (US ISSN 0882-3944) **5239**
Monitor (Luton). (UK) **4604**
Monitor (Skokie). (US) **625**

MONITOR

Monitor (Stamford). (US ISSN 0895-8777) **4152**
Monitor de la Farmacia y de la Terapeutica. (SP ISSN 0463-1536) **3735**
Monitor Ecclesiasticus. (IT ISSN 0026-976X) **4270**
Monitor Money Marketwatch *see* Monitor Money Review **955**
Monitor Money Review. (AT) **955, 874**
Monitor Month. (US) **1377,** 4190
Monitor - Radio T V. (IT ISSN 0394-0896) **1377,** 1357
Monitor Weekly. (UK ISSN 0262-6845) **2014**
Monitore Valdostano/Moniteur Valdotain. (IT) **2205**
†Monitore Zoologico Italiano. Monografie/Italian Journal of Zoology. Monographs. (IT ISSN 0391-1632) **5239**
Monitore Zoologico Italiano. Supplemento *see* Tropical Zoology **592**
Monitore Zoologico Italiano - Italian Journal of Zoology *see* Ethnology, Ecology & Evolution **582**
Monitoring Information Summary. (UN) **1357**
Monitoring the Future. (US ISSN 0190-9185) **1648,** 1537
Monitoring Times. (US ISSN 0889-5341) **1357**
Monitor's Retail Tenant Directory. (US ISSN 0887-0470) **4152**
Monitor's Weekly Insider. (US) **4152**
Monk. (US ISSN 0899-6059) **4778**
Monkees, Boyce & Hart Photo Fan Club. (US) **1299,** 3514, 3563
Monkey/Monki. (JA ISSN 0026-9794) **588**
Monkey Kindness Magazine. (NE) **231**
Monkeyshines on America. (US) **1260,** 2256, 2415
Monkeyshines on Health and Science. (US) **1260,** 3806
Monki. *see* Monkey **588**
Monmouth Educator. (US ISSN 0026-9808) **1648**
La Monnaie en (Year). (FR) **791**
Monnaies et Medailles. *see* Muenzen und Medaillen **3600**
Monnaies, Prix, Conjoncture. (FR ISSN 0077-0434) **791**
Mono Geo Graphy. (IS) **2256**
Mono Lake Committee Newsletter. (US ISSN 0275-6633) **4827,** 1599, 1963
The Monocacy Valley Review. (US) **2940,** 336, 3793
Monoclonal Antibodies. (US ISSN 1047-871X) **448**
Monoclonal Antibodies. (UK ISSN 0261-4960) **3188,** 3262
Monoclonal Antibody News *see* Monoclonal Antibodies **448**
Monografias Arqueologicas. (SP) **279**
Monografias de Diagnostico por Imagen.(SP) **3360,** 3226
Monografias de Filosofia Juridica y Social/Monographs of Social and Legal Philosophy. (SP ISSN 0077-0442) **2655**
Monografias de Matematica. (BL) **3048**
Monografias de Poblacion y Desarrollo. (BO) **4443**
Monografias de Promocion Femenina. (BO) **4848**
Monografias de Psicologia, Normal y Patologica. (SP ISSN 0077-0469) **4036**
Monografias de Recursos Humanos. (BO) **4443**
Monografias de Sociologia Familiar. (BO) **4443**
Monografias de Zoologia Marina. (NE ISSN 0213-4020) **588**
Monografias em Ciencia da Computacao. (BL) **1398**
Monografias Urbanas. (BO) **2492**
Monografie Biochemiczne. (PL ISSN 0077-0485) **618**
Monografie di Archeologia Libica. (IT ISSN 0077-0493) **279**
Monografie Fauny Polski. (PL) **588**
Monografie Matematyczne. (PL ISSN 0077-0507) **3048**

Monografie Parazytologiczne. (PL ISSN 0540-6722) **4813,** 556
Monografie Psychologiczne. (PL ISSN 0077-0515) **4036**
Monografie Slaskie Ossolineum. (PL ISSN 0077-0523) **2376**
Monografie Slawistyczne. (PL ISSN 0077-0531) **2940,** 2376
Monografie z Dziejow Nauki i Techniki. (PL ISSN 0077-054X) **4324,** 4604
Monografie z Dziejow Oswiaty. (PL ISSN 0077-0558) **1755**
Monografii Matematice. (RM) **3048**
Monograph Series in Finance and Economics *see* New York University. Salomon Center. Monograph Series **793**
Monograph Series on Malaysian Economic Affairs. (MY) **680**
Monograph Series on Mineral Deposits. (GW) **3491**
Monograph Series on Schizophrenia. (US ISSN 0077-0620) **3345**
Monographia Historica Bohemica. (CS ISSN 0231-9136) **2376**
Monographiae Biologicae. (NE ISSN 0077-0639) **448**
Monographien aus dem Gesamtgebiete der Psychiatrie - Psychiatry Series. (US ISSN 0077-0671) **3345**
Monographien zur Angewandten Entomologie. *see* Monographs to Applied Entomology **536**
Monographien zur Geschichte des Mittelalters. (GW ISSN 0026-9832) **2376**
Monographien zur Indischen Archaeologie, Kunst und Philologie. (GW ISSN 0170-8864) **3641**
Monographien zur Philosophischen Forschung. (GW) **3773**
Monographies Reine Elisabeth. (BE) **279,** 2431
Monographs, Advanced Texts and Surveys in Pure and Applied Mathematics. (US) **3048**
Monographs and Studies in Mathematics *see* Monographs, Advanced Texts and Surveys in Pure and Applied Mathematics **3048**
Monographs and Theoretical Studies in Sociology and Anthropology in Honour of Nels Anderson. (NE ISSN 0169-9202) **4443,** 245
Monographs for Teachers of French *see* Macquarie University French Monographs **2828**
Monographs in Allergy. (SZ ISSN 0077-0760) **3188**
Monographs in Anaesthesiology. (NE ISSN 0303-254X) **3191**
Monographs in Clinical Cytology. (SZ ISSN 0077-0809) **3132,** 526
Monographs in Development Anthropology. (US) **245**
Monographs in Developmental Biology. (SZ ISSN 0077-0825) **480**
Monographs in Economic and Social History. (UK) **897,** 4380
Monographs in Electrical and Electronic Engineering. (UK) **1903**
Monographs in Electroanalytical Chemistry and Electrochemistry Series. (US ISSN 0077-0833) **1212,** 1207
Monographs in Epidemiology and Biostatistics. (US) **448**
Monographs in Geography. (UK) **2256**
†Monographs in Geology and Paleontology. (US ISSN 0077-085X) **5239**
Monographs in Human Genetics. (SZ ISSN 0077-0876) **545**
Monographs in International Studies: Africa Series. (US) **2334**
Monographs in International Studies: Latin America Series. (US) **2415**
Monographs in International Studies: Southeast Asia Series. (US) **2340**
†Monographs in Lipid Research. (US ISSN 0094-8950) **5239**
Monographs in Modern Dutch Studies. (UK) **2376,** 2940
Monographs in Modern Languages. (UK) **2830,** 2940
Monographs in Musicology Series. (US) **3563**

Monographs in Neural Sciences. (SZ ISSN 0300-5186) **3345**
Monographs in Neuroscience. (US ISSN 0737-3953) **3345**
Monographs in Nuclear Medicine *see* Nuclear Medicine **3361**
Monographs in Ophthalmology. (NE ISSN 0167-8612) **3302**
Monographs in Oral Science. (SZ ISSN 0077-0892) **3238**
Monographs in Organic Functional Group Analysis *see* Analysis of Organic Materials: an International Series of Monographs **5135**
Monographs in Organizational Behaviour and Industrial Relations. (US) **4380,** 989
Monographs in Paediatrics *see* Pediatric and Adolescent Medicine **3324**
Monographs in Physical Measurement. (US) **1830,** 3825
Monographs in Population Biology. (US ISSN 0077-0930) **3985**
Monographs in Primatology. (US) **448**
Monographs in Psychobiology. (US ISSN 0749-1190) **4036,** 448
Monographs in Regional and Local History. (UK ISSN 0951-8916) **2376**
Monographs in the Economics of Development. (PK ISSN 0544-8433) **933**
Monographs in Virology. (SZ ISSN 0077-0965) **556**
Monographs of Marine Mollusca. (NE ISSN 0162-8321) **588**
Monographs of Social and Legal Philosophy. *see* Monografias de Filosofia Juridica y Social **2655**
Monographs on American Art. (US ISSN 0544-845X) **336**
Monographs on Astronomical Subjects. (US ISSN 0141-1128) **367**
Monographs on Atherosclerosis. (SZ ISSN 0077-099X) **3210**
Monographs on Cryogenics. (US) **1831**
Monographs on Endocrinology. (US ISSN 0077-1015) **3255**
†Monographs on Europe. (US) **5239**
Monographs on Industrial Property and Copyright Law. (NE) **3676,** 2704
Monographs on Infancy. (US) **3323,** 4036
Monographs on Musicology. (US ISSN 0275-5866) **3563**
Monographs on Numerical Analysis. (US) **3048**
Monographs on Oceanographic Methodology. (UN ISSN 0077-104X) **1608**
Monographs on Pathology of Laboratory Animals. (US) **3262**
Monographs on Physical Biochemistry. (US ISSN 0309-0698) **1229,** 480
†Monographs on Plastics Series. (US) **5239**
Monographs on Science, Technology, and Society. (US) **4604,** 4324, 4380
†Monographs on Severely Restricted or Forbidden Advertising Practices. (US) **5239**
Monographs on Soil and Resources Survey. (US) **185,** 1492
Monographs on Soil Survey *see* Monographs on Soil and Resources Survey **185**
Monographs on the Ancient Near East. (US ISSN 0732-6491) **2431**
Monographs on the Fine Arts. (US) **336**
Monographs on the Physics and Chemistry of Materials. (US) **3825,** 1184
Monographs on Theoretical and Applied Genetics. (US ISSN 0341-5376) **545**
Monographs to Applied Entomology/Monographien zur Angewandten Entomologie. (GW ISSN 0077-0698) **536**
Monopoltilsynets Aarsberetning. (DK ISSN 0107-492X) **680**
Monopoly. (UK) **1318**
Monos y Monadas. (PE) **2875**
Monosson on D E C *see* Monosson Report on D E C and I B M **1454**

Monosson Report on D E C and I B M. (US ISSN 1040-0966) **1454**
†Monroe. (US) **5239**
Monroe County Genealogical Society News. (US) **2158**
Monroe Dispatch. (US) **2229**
Monsalvat. (SP ISSN 0210-4083) **3563**
†Monster Trucks. (US) **5239**
Montage. (SW ISSN 0280-9311) **336**
†Montage. (CN) **5239**
▼Montagna. (SZ) **820**
Montagne et Alpinisme. (FR ISSN 0047-7923) **4550**
Montajes e Instalaciones *see* M I **2301**
Montalban. (VE) **2511,** 245
Montan-Berichte *see* B H M. Berg- und Huettenmaennische Monatshefte **3478**
Montana. (US ISSN 0026-9891) **2415**
Montana. Bureau of Mines and Geology. Bulletin. (US ISSN 0077-1090) **1573,** 3491
Montana. Bureau of Mines and Geology. Directory of Mining Enterprises. (US ISSN 0077-1104) **3491**
Montana. Bureau of Mines and Geology. Ground Water Reports *see* Montana. Bureau of Mines and Geology. Bulletin **1573**
Montana. Bureau of Mines and Geology. Memoir. (US ISSN 0077-1120) **1573,** 3491
Montana. Bureau of Mines and Geology. Special Publications. (US ISSN 0077-1139) **1573,** 3491
Montana. Department of Business Regulation. Annual Report *see* Montana. Department of Commerce. Professional and Occupational Licensing Bureau. Public Safety Division. Biennial Report **4067**
Montana. Department of Commerce. Professional and Occupational Licensing Bureau. Public Safety Division. Biennial Report. (US) **4067**
Montana. Department of Social and Rehabilitation Services. Statistical Report. (US ISSN 0091-1143) **4426,** 4579
Montana. Office of the Legislative Auditor. State of Montana Board of Investments. Report on Examination of Financial Statements. (US ISSN 0090-9912) **956,** 4067
Montana Advisory Council for Vocational Education. Annual Report *see* Montana Council on Vocational Education. Annual Report **1755**
Montana AgResearch. (US ISSN 0895-1489) **108**
Montana Agriculture *see* Montana Farm Bureau Spokesman **108**
Montana and the Sky. (US) **4675,** 2492
†Montana Beverage Analyst. (US) **5239**
Montana Business Quarterly. (US ISSN 0026-9921) **680**
Montana Catholic. (US) **4270**
Montana Comprehensive Chemical Dependency Plan. (US) **1538**
Montana Council on Vocational Education. Annual Report. (US) **1755**
Montana Distributor. (US) **2078**
Montana Education Association Today *see* M E A Today **1646**
Montana Farm Bureau Spokesman. (US) **108**
Montana Farmer-Stockman. (US ISSN 1041-1674) **221**
Montana Food Distributor. (US ISSN 0047-7931) **2078**
Montana Forest and Conservation Experiment Station. Biennial Report. (US) **2104,** 1492
†Montana Fourth Estate. (US) **5239**
Montana Land Magazine. (US ISSN 1052-469X) **4152**
Montana Law Review. (US ISSN 0026-9972) **2655**
Montana League of Cities & Towns. Newsletter. (US ISSN 0026-9980) **4091**
Montana Legionnaire. (US ISSN 0026-9999) **1299,** 3466
Montana Library Directory. (US) **2774**

Montana Library Directory, with Statistics of Montana Public Libraries see Montana Library Directory **2774**
Montana Magazine. (US) **2229**
Montana Manufacturers and Products Directory see Montana Manufacturers Directory **1146**
Montana Manufacturers Directory. (US ISSN 1057-6681) **1146**
Montana Motor Carriers Association, Inc. News see M M C A News **4745**
Montana Municipal League. Newsletter see Montana League of Cities & Towns. Newsletter **4091**
Montana Newsletter see Montana League of Cities & Towns. Newsletter **4091**
Montana Oil Journal. (US ISSN 0047-794X) **3692**
Montana Outdoors. (US) **4550**
Montana Post. (US ISSN 0047-7958) **2415**
Montana Public Library Statistics. (US) **2794**
Montana Review. (US) **2940**
Montana Schools. (US) **1648**
Montana State Library News. (US) **2774**
Montana State Library News Update. (US) **2774**
Montana State Plan for Alcohol Abuse and Alcoholism Prevention, Treatment and Rehabilitation see Montana Comprehensive Chemical Dependency Plan **1538**
Montana State University Mathematics Newsletter see M S U Mathematics Newsletter **3044**
Montana Stockgrower. (US ISSN 0047-7990) **221**
Montana Vital Statistics. (US ISSN 0077-1198) **4118**
Montana Water Resources Center. Annual Report. (US) **4827**
Montana Water Resources Center. Technical Reports. (US) **4827**
Montana Water Resources Research Center. Annual Report see Montana Water Resources Center. Annual Report **4827**
Montana Water Resources Research Center. Technical Report see Montana Water Resources Center. Technical Reports **4827**
†Montana Wheat Scoop. (US) **5239**
Montana Wool Grower. (US ISSN 0027-0024) **221**
Montanan. (US) **1318**
Montanaro d'Italia - Monti e Boschi see Monti e Boschi **2104**
Montaneros de Aragon. (SP ISSN 0027-0032) **4479**
Montazhnye i Spetsial'nye Raboty v Stroitel'stve. (RU ISSN 0027-0040) **625**
Montclair Art Museum. Bulletin - Newsletter. (US) **3527**
Monte Carlo Cote d'Azur. (MC) **2187**
Montebello Comet. (US) **2014**
Monterey Bay Area Locale. (US) **791**
Monterey Bay Magazine. (US) **2229**
†Monterey Life. (US) **5239**
Monterey Park Comet. (US) **2014**
Monterey Peninsula Museum of Art News. (US) **336**, **303**, **356**, **1648**
Monte's Mail. (US) **1454**
Montessori News. (US ISSN 0889-6720) **1648**, **3773**
Montessori Observer. (US ISSN 0889-5643) **1648**
Montessori Today. (UK ISSN 0952-8652) **1755**
Montfort. (AU ISSN 0027-0148) **2376**
Montgomery - Bucks Dental Society. Bulletin. (US ISSN 0027-0156) **3238**
Montgomery County Agricultural News. (US) **154**, **163**, **185**, **202**
Montgomery County Genealogical Journal. (US) **2158**
†Montgomeryshire Farmer. (UK) **5239**
Month. (UK ISSN 0027-0172) **4270**
Monthly see Food Industry News **2068**
The Monthly. (US) **2229**

Monthly Abstract of Meteorological Observations of Malaysia. (MY ISSN 0126-8872) **3444**
Monthly Acts Tables & Table of Unrepealed Principal Acts. (AT) **2700**, **4579**
Monthly Art/Gekkan Bijutsu. (JA) **336**
Monthly Asahi. see Gekkan Asahi **2207**
Monthly Benefit Statistics (Chicago) see U.S. Railroad Retirement Board. Monthly Benefit Statistics **996**
Monthly Boy's Champion/Gekkan Shonen-Champion. (JA) **1260**
Monthly Brewing Industry Commentary. (US) **874**, **383**
Monthly Bulletin of Ionospheric Characteristics Recorded at Johannesburg and Capetown see Monthly Bulletin of Ionospheric Characteristics Recorded at Johannesburg and Hermanus **1377**
Monthly Bulletin of Ionospheric Characteristics Recorded at Johannesburg and Hermanus/Maandelikse Bulletin van Ionoferiese Karakteristieke Soos Waargeneem in Johannesburg en Hermanus. (SA) **1377**
Monthly Bulletin of Statistics. see Norway. Statistisk Sentralbyraa. Statistisk Maanedshefte **4582**
Monthly Bulletin of Statistics. see Turkey. Devlet Istatistik Enstitusu. Aylik Istatistik Bulteni **4590**
Monthly Bulletin of the Petroleum and Natural Gas Industry of Indonesia. (IO) **3692**
Monthly Business Failures. (US ISSN 0027-027X) **874**
†Monthly Business Starts. (US) **5239**
Monthly Catalog of United States Government Publications. (US ISSN 0362-6830) **4081**
Monthly Climatic Data for the World. (US ISSN 0027-0296) **3439**
Monthly Commentary on Indian Economic Conditions. (II ISSN 0027-030X) **874**
Monthly Commodity Price News Service/Mulka Jungbo. (KO) **791**
Monthly Completion Report see American Petroleum Institute. Monthly Completion Report **3704**
Monthly Cotton Linters Review. (US ISSN 0027-0318) **155**, **4622**
Monthly Crude Oil Production. (US) **3692**
Monthly Digest of Swedish Statistics. see Sweden. Statistiska Centralbyraan. Allmaan Maanadsstatistik **4590**
Monthly Digest of Tax Articles. (US ISSN 0027-0385) **1101**
Monthly Drilling Completion Report see American Petroleum Institute. Monthly Completion Report **3704**
Monthly Economic Indicators of Bangladesh see Monthly Indicators of Current Economic Situation of Bangladesh **729**
Monthly Economic Indicators of Puerto Rico. see Indicadores Economicos Mensuales de Puerto Rico **868**
Monthly Economic Situation of Bangladesh see Monthly Indicators of Current Economic Situation of Bangladesh **729**
Monthly Education Journal/Gekkan Kyoiku Journal. (JA) **1648**
Monthly Electric Utilities Sales and Revenue Report (E I A - 826). (Energy Information Administration) (US) **1800**, **1802**
Monthly Energy Review. (US ISSN 0095-7356) **1800**, **1792**
Monthly Ethical Drug Index Complication see M E D I C **3748**
Monthly Export Trends. (PK) **820**, **917**
Monthly External Trade Bulletin see Statistical Office of the European Communities. Monthly External Trade Bulletin **739**
Monthly Fern Lesson. (US) **2134**
Monthly Film Bulletin see Sight and Sound **3517**
Monthly Finance Review. (JA ISSN 0388-0605) **791**

Monthly Frozen Food Report see Frozen Food Report **2071**
Monthly Gasoline Stand/Gekkan Gasorin Sutando. (JA ISSN 0016-5069) **3692**
Monthly Gendai see Gekkan Gendai **1011**
Monthly Import Detention List. (US) **4108**, **2727**
Monthly Index to the Financial Times. (UK) **729**, **17**
Monthly Indicators of Current Economic Situation of Bangladesh. (BG) **729**
Monthly Japanese Fencing/Gekkan Kendo Nippon. (JA) **4479**
Monthly Journal for the Blind. see Mangren Yuekan **2294**
Monthly Journal of Gasoline Service Stations/Gekkan Kyusho Nihon. (JA ISSN 0016-5964) **3692**
†Monthly Journal of Scientology. (DK ISSN 0901-2982) **5239**
Monthly Labor Review see U.S. Bureau of Labor Statistics. Monthly Labor Review **742**
Monthly Lesson in Criminal Politics see Criminal Politics **943**
Monthly Letter on Evangelism. (SZ) **4190**
Monthly List of State Publications see U.S. Library of Congress. Monthly Checklist of State Publications **4083**
Monthly Market Statistics. (HK) **791**
Monthly Motor Gasoline Reported by States see U.S. Federal Highway Administration. Monthly Motor Gasoline Reported by States **3707**
Monthly Newspaper Techniques see Newspaper Techniques **4002**
Monthly Planet. (US ISSN 1042-3249) **3966**, **1963**, **3595**
Monthly Pratirodha. (BG) **4067**
Monthly Prescribing Reference. (US ISSN 0883-0266) **3132**, **2655**, **3735**, **4108**
Monthly Price Review. (US ISSN 0566-3628) **2078**, **202**, **221**
Monthly Product Announcement. (US) **3985**
Monthly Production of Crude Oil Allowable, Production and Removal from Leases in the State of Texas see Monthly Crude Oil Production **3692**
Monthly Railway Statistics. (II ISSN 0027-0504) **4665**
Monthly Rainfall Review - Australia. (AT) **3439**
Monthly Record for the Events of the United Arab Emirates. see Al-Sijil al-Shahri li-Ahdath Dawlat al-Imarat al-Arabiyyah al-Muttahidah **4073**
Monthly Record of World Events. see Sijil al-Shahri li-Ahdath al-Alam **3972**
Monthly Report of Agricultural Meteorology. see Oshima-Hiyama Chiho Nogyo Kisho Sokuho **3440**
Monthly Report of Agricultural Meteorology, Kagoshima Prefecture. see Kagoshima-ken Nogyo Kisho Geppo **3438**
Monthly Report of Price and Wage in Construction Engineering. see Kensetsu Kogyo Bukka Chingin Geppo **1870**
Monthly Report of the Iron and Steel Statistics. (JA ISSN 0497-1140) **3427**
Monthly Report on Climate System. (JA) **3439**
Monthly Report on Europe. (BE) **680**
Monthly Report on Tourism - Republic of China/Kuan Kuang Tzu Liao. (CH) **4800**, **4579**, **4778**
Monthly Report to Booksellers see New Age Retailer **3595**
Monthly Review. (US ISSN 0027-0520) **3908**
Monthly Review Dong Suh. (KO) **2209**
Monthly Science Magazine see Sa'insu **4338**
Monthly Smaller Businesses/Gekkan Chusho-Kigyo. (JA) **1116**
Monthly Statistical Bulletin of Bangladesh. (BG ISSN 0377-1555) **4580**

Monthly Statistical Bulletin, Peninsular Malaysia see Malaysia. Department of Statistics. Monthly Statistical Bulletin, Malaysia **4579**
Monthly Statistical Commentary on Indian Economic Conditions see Monthly Commentary on Indian Economic Conditions **874**
Monthly Statistics of Exports and Imports see China, Republic. Ministry of Finance. Department of Statistics. Monthly Statistics of Exports and Imports **711**
Monthly Statistics of Foreign Trade of India. (II ISSN 0027-0547) **729**
Monthly Statistics of Industrial Employment and Labour Costs. see Denmark. Danmarks Statistik. Maanedlig Beskaeftigelses- og Loenstatistik for Industri **712**
Monthly Statistics of Korea. (KO ISSN 0027-0563) **4580**
Monthly Statistics of Paper Distribution/Kami Ryutsu Tokei Geppo. (JA ISSN 0044-0663) **3668**
Monthly Statistics on Agriculture, Forestry and Fisheries/Norin Suisan Tokei Geppo. (JA ISSN 0029-1757) **140**, **2051**, **2112**
Monthly Statutory Rules Tables & Table of Unrevoked Principal Statutory Rules. (AT) **2700**, **4580**
Monthly Stock Charts - Canadian Companies. (CN) **956**
Monthly Summary. (US) **108**, **221**
Monthly Summary of Business Conditions in Southern California. (US ISSN 0027-058X) **874**
Monthly Summary of Jute and Gunny Statistics. (II ISSN 0027-0598) **4628**
Monthly Summary of Texas Natural Gas. (US ISSN 0094-2766) **3692**
Monthly Survey on Current Rolling Stock Production. see Tetsudo Sharyoto Seisan Dotai Tokei Geppo **4667**
Monthly Surveyor Magazine. see Sokuryo **2263**
Monthly Tax Features see Tax Features **1108**
†Monthly Tax Report. (US) **5239**
Monthly Ticket for More Information see Ticket **3473**
Monthly Truck Tonnage Report. (US) **4746**
Monthly Vital Statistics Report see U.S. National Center for Health Statistics. Monthly Vital Statistics Report **3996**
Monthly Weather Review. (US ISSN 0027-0644) **3439**
Monthly Wings. (PK) **59**, **3466**
Monti e Boschi. (IT) **2104**
Montreal Airport Business Directory. (CN) **4675**
Montreal Business Forum. (CN ISSN 0826-8207) **820**
Montreal Business Magazine. (CN) **680**
Montreal Children's Hospital. Children's News see Fax Plus **2461**
Montreal General Hospital News see Generally Speaking **2461**
Montreal Mirror. (CN) **1506**
Montreal Office Guide/Guide Bureaux Montreal. (CN ISSN 0843-6681) **625**
Montreal Office Space Directory. (CN) **4152**
Montreal Options Monthly Strategies see Futures and Options **947**
Montreal Passions. (CN) **2178**
Montreal Port Guide & Directory. (CN) **4733**
Montreal Port Guide & Transportation Register. (CN) **4733**
Montreal Scope. (CN) **2178**
Montreal Women's Directory/Annuaire des Femmes de Montreal. (CN) **1146**, **4848**
Montrose Voice. (US) **2455**, **2229**
Montserrat. Port Authority. Annual Report. (MJ) **4733**
Montserrat. Statistics Office. Digest of Overseas Trade Statistics see Montserrat. Statistics Office. Digest of Statistics **729**
Montserrat. Statistics Office. Digest of Statistics. (MJ) **729**, **917**

Montserrat. Statistics Office. Overseas Trade Report. (MJ) **4580**, 1146
Montserrat. Statistics Office. Tourism Report. (MJ) **4800**
Monument Builder News see M B News **334**
Monument Conservation. see Varstvo Spomenikov **2394**
Monumenta Aegyptiaca. (BE ISSN 0077-1376) **279**, 2431
Monumenta Americana. (GW ISSN 0077-1384) **279**, 2415
▼Monumenta Antiqua Etruriae. (IT) **279**
Monumenta Archaeologica. (US ISSN 0363-7565) **279**
Monumenta Chartae Papyraceae Historiam Illustrantia/Collection of Works and Documents Illustrating the History of Paper. (NE ISSN 0077-1414) **3663**
Monumenta Germaniae Historica. Schriften. (GW ISSN 0080-6951) **2376**
Monumenta Germaniae Historica. Staatsschriften des Spaeteren Mittelalters. (GW ISSN 0340-8035) **2376**
Monumenta Graeca et Romana. (NE ISSN 0169-8850) **336**, 3641
Monumenta Historica Ordinis Minorum Capuccinorum. (IT ISSN 0077-1449) **4270**
Monumenta Historica Societatis Iesu. (IT) **4270**
Monumenta Iuris Canonici. (VC ISSN 0077-1457) **4270**
Monumenta Linguae Mongolicae Collecta. (HU ISSN 0230-8452) **2830**, 3641
Monumenta Musicae in Polonia. Series A: Works by Polish Composers. (PL) **3563**
Monumenta Musicae in Polonia. Series B: Collectanea Musicae Artis. (PL) **3563**
Monumenta Musicae in Polonia. Series B: Fontes Artis Musicae see Monumenta Musicae in Polonia. Series B: Collectanea Musicae Artis **3563**
Monumenta Musicae in Polonia. Series C: Tractatus de Musica. (PL) **3563**
Monumenta Musicae in Polonia. Series D: Bibliotheca Antiqua. (PL) **3563**
Monumenta Nipponica. (JA ISSN 0027-0741) **3641**, 2318
Monumenta Paedagogica. (GW ISSN 0077-1481) **1648**
Monumenta Serica. (GW ISSN 0254-9948) **3641**
Monumenta Serica Monograph Series. (GW ISSN 0179-261X) **3641**, 2340
Monumental Postcard Club Bulletin. (US) **2439**
Monumente Istorice si de Arta. (RM) **3527**
Monumentet/Monuments. (AA ISSN 0253-1607) **245**
Monumenti Etruschi. (IT) **336**
Monumenti Musei e Gallerie Pontificie Museo Gregoriano Etrusco. Cataloghi.(IT) **3527**
Monuments. see Monumentet **245**
†Monuments de la Catalunya Romanica. (SP) **5239**
Monuments Historiques. (FR ISSN 0153-3673) **303**
Monuments of Culture. New Discoveries. see Pamyatniki Kul'tury. Novye Otkrytiya **339**
Monuments of Renaissance Music. (US ISSN 0077-1503) **3563**
†Monuments of Russian Music Art. (UR) **5239**
Monuments of World Musical Science. (RU) **3563**
Moody Street Irregulars. (US ISSN 0196-2604) **2940**
Moody's Bank and Finance Manual. (US ISSN 0545-0152) **791**
Moody's Bank and Finance News Reports. (US) **956**, 791
Moody's Bond Record see Moody's Bond Record and Annual Bond Record Service **956**

Moody's Bond Record and Annual Bond Record Service. (US ISSN 0148-1878) **956**
Moody's Bond Survey. (US ISSN 0027-0822) **956**
Moody's C D see Moody's Company Data **1431**
†Moody's Commercial Paper Record. (US ISSN 0275-0201) **5239**
Moody's Company Data. (US) **1431**, 1479
Moody's Dividend Record see Moody's Dividend Record and Annual Dividend Record **956**
Moody's Dividend Record and Annual Dividend Record. (US) **956**
Moody's Handbook of Common Stocks. (US ISSN 0027-0830) **956**
Moody's Handbook of O T C Stocks. (US ISSN 0276-3516) **956**
Moody's Industrial Manual. (US ISSN 0545-0217) **956**
Moody's Industrial News Reports. (US) **956**
Moody's Industrials see Moody's Industrial News Reports **956**
Moody's International Manual. (US) **956**
Moody's International Manual News Reports. (US) **956**
Moody's International Plus. (US) **956**
Moody's Municipal and Government Manual. (US ISSN 0545-0233) **956**
Moody's Municipal and Government News Reports. (US) **956**
Moody's Municipals and Governments see Moody's Municipal and Government News Reports **956**
Moody's O T C Industrial Manual. (US ISSN 0192-7167) **956**
Moody's O T C Industrial News Reports.(US) **956**
Moody's O T C Industrials see Moody's O T C Industrial News Reports **956**
Moody's O T C Plus see Moody's Company Data **1431**
Moody's O T C Unlisted Manual. (US) **956**
Moody's Public Utility Manual. (US ISSN 0545-0241) **956**
Moody's Public Utility News Reports. (US) **956**
Moody's Transportation see Moody's Transportation News Reports **956**
Moody's Transportation Manual. (US ISSN 0545-025X) **956**
Moody's Transportation News Reports. (US) **956**
Moody's 5000 Plus see Moody's Company Data **1431**
Mool Sarak Ankrey see Basic Road Statistics of India **4662**
Moon and the Planets see Earth, Moon and Planets **364**
Moon Magazine. (UK ISSN 0027-0911) **2294**
Moon Rainbow. (UK ISSN 0047-8083) **2294**, 2288
Moonbi. (AT ISSN 0311-032X) **1492**, 1963
Mooncircles. (US) **4848**, 3670, 4285
Mooney Aircraft Pilots Association Log see M A P A Log **58**
Moonsign Book see Llewellyn's Moon Sign Book **359**
Moonstone Blue, Night Roses. (US) **2998**
Moore Family Inquirer see Richardson Family Researcher and Historical News **2162**
Moore Family Register. (US) **2158**
Moorea. (IE ISSN 0332-4273) **2134**
Moores & Rowland's Tax Guide. (UK ISSN 0267-8829) **1101**
Moores Rowland's Orange & Yellow Tax Guides. (UK) **1101**
Moorlands Review see Prospice **5263**
Moose. (US ISSN 0027-0954) **1299**
Moosehead Review. (CN ISSN 0228-7404) **2998**
†Moot: Thirkill - Threlkeld Family Newsletter. (UK) **5239**
Moottori (Year). (FI ISSN 0359-7636) **4695**
Mopar Muscle. (US) **4695**, 2439
Moral Majority Report see Liberty Report **2872**

Moralia. (SP ISSN 0210-0851) **4270**
Morality and Civilization. see Daode yu Wenming **3890**
Morality in Media see Morality in Media Newsletter **4036**
Morality in Media Newsletter. (US ISSN 0027-1004) **4036**, 1340, 1518
Morasha/Heritage. (US ISSN 1044-6737) **2014**, 2158
Moravian (Bethlehem, 1856). (US ISSN 1041-0961) **4285**
Moravian (Bethlehem, 1912). (US) **1318**
Moravian Message. (UK) **4244**
Moravian Music Foundation. Bulletin see Moravian Music Journal **3563**
Moravian Music Journal. (US ISSN 0278-0763) **3563**
Moravske Zemske Museum. Casopis. Vedy Prirodni see Acta Musei Moraviae - Scientiae Naturales **1540**
Moravske Zemske Museum. Casopis. Vedy Spolecenske see Acta Musei Moraviae - Scientiae Sociales **2347**
Moravskie Numismaticke Zpravy see Acta Musei Moraviae. Supplementum: Folia Numismatica **3597**
Morbidity and Mortality see U.S. Centers for Disease Control. Morbidity and Mortality Weekly Report **4114**
Morbilidad. (UY) **4108**
More see Adult and Continuing Education Newsletter **1681**
More. (US ISSN 0162-4288) **4244**, 1260
More. (JA) **4848**
More. (NZ ISSN 0112-0808) **4848**
More Business. (US) **1048**
More Light Update. (US ISSN 0889-3985) **2455**, 4244
More Magazine see Columbia Journalism Review **2568**
Moreana. (FR ISSN 0047-8105) **2376**, 2655, 4190
Morehouse College Bulletin. (US ISSN 0027-1047) **1318**
Moreland News and Views. (US ISSN 0027-1055) **1648**
Moreshet Derech. (IS ISSN 0334-9748) **4778**
Morgan Directory Reviews. (US ISSN 0899-4560) **1146**, 406
Morgan Gallup Polls. (AT) **4443**
The Morgan Horse. (US ISSN 0027-1098) **4536**
Morgan Index on Airline Travel (Australia). (AT) **4675**
Morgan Index on Beverages Drunk (Australia). (AT) **383**
Morgan Index on TV and Radio. (AT) **1377**, 1357
Morgan Report on Directory Publishing.(US ISSN 0890-9512) **1146**, 4132
Morgannwg. (UK ISSN 0959-4655) **2376**
Morgenrote. (GW) **4191**, 3773
Morgonbris. (SW ISSN 0027-1101) **4848**, 3945
Morison's Company Law Reports. (NZ) **2711**
Mornaricki Glasnik/Navy Journal. (YU ISSN 0027-1136) **3466**
Morning. see Al-Sabah **2208**
Morning Advertiser. (UK) **383**
Morning Calm. (KO) **4778**
†Morning Coffee Chapbook Series. (US ISSN 0882-147X) **5239**
Morning Star. see Avgherinos **1249**
Morning Star/Myojo. (JA) **2208**
Morningland Spiritual Journal. (US) **4215**
Morningstar Mutual Funds. (US) **956**
Morocco. Direction de la Statistique. Bulletin Mensuel des Statistiques. (MR ISSN 0256-9159) **4580**
Morocco. Direction de la Statistique. Etudes Economiques et Statistiques. (MR ISSN 0851-0865) **874**, 729
Morocco. Direction de la Statistique. Indice des Prix a la Production Industrielle, Energetique et Miniere. (MR ISSN 0851-0954) **729**, 1081, 4580

Morocco. Direction de la Statistique. Indice des Prix de Gros. (MR ISSN 0851-0970) **729**, 1081
Morocco. Direction de la Statistique. Indice du Cout de la Vie. (MR ISSN 0851-0962) **729**, 1081, 4580
Morocco. Direction de la Statistique. Population Active Urbaine, Rapport de Synthese. (MR ISSN 0851-092X) **3993**, 4580
Morocco. Direction de la Statistique. Population Active Urbaine, Resultats Detailles. (MR ISSN 0851-6804) **3993**, 4580
Morocco. Direction des Mines et de la Geologie. Activite du Secteur Petrolier see Morocco. Ministere de l'Energie et des Mines. Activite du Secteur Petrolier **3692**
Morocco. Ministere de l'Energie et des Mines. Activite du Secteur Petrolier. (MR) **3692**
Morocco Bound. (AT ISSN 0159-7191) **2439**, 4002
Morocco Tourism. (MR ISSN 0027-1160) **4778**
Morokami. (SA ISSN 0027-1179) **4285**
Morperformance see Performance (Bensalem) **4699**
†Morrell, Morrill Families Association Newsletter. (US ISSN 0889-7247) **5239**
Morris County. (US) **2229**
▼Morris Members. (US ISSN 1059-3705) **2159**
Morris Report. (US) **3712**
Morrison's Company Law in New Zealand. (NZ) **2711**
Morskaya Geologiya i Geofizika/Marine Geology and Geophysics. (LV ISSN 0076-4477) **1608**
Morsko Ribarstvo/Marine Fisheries. (CI ISSN 0027-1209) **2046**
Morskoi Flot. (RU ISSN 0027-1217) **4733**
Morskoi Gidrofizicheskii Zhurnal see Soviet Journal of Physical Oceanography **1611**
Morskoi Sbornik. (RU ISSN 0134-9236) **2376**
Mortgage and Real Estate Executives Report. (US ISSN 0047-813X) **4152**, 957
Mortgage Banker see Mortgage Banking **791**
Mortgage Banking. (US ISSN 0730-0212) **791**, 4152
Mortgage Banking: Financial Statements and Operating Ratios see Financial Statements and Operating Ratios for the Mortgage Banking Industry **781**
Mortgage Banking: Loans Closed and Servicing Volume see Loans Closed and Servicing Volume for the Mortgage Banking Industry **5228**
Mortgage Commentary. (US) **957**
Mortgage Finance Gazette. (UK) **791**, 4152
Mortgage Finance Monthly. (UK) **4153**, 791, 2492
Mortgage Market Insight. (US ISSN 1050-3226) **2492**
Mortgage Marketplace. (US) **957**
Mortgage Product Spotlight. (US) **791**, 4153
Morticians of the Southwest. (US ISSN 0739-0289) **2119**
Morton Arboretum Quarterly. (US ISSN 0027-125X) **509**, 2134
†Morton Prince Digest of Hypnotherapy.(US) **5239**
Mortuary Management. (US ISSN 0027-1268) **2119**
Morze. (PL) **4733**
Mosaic see Human Mosaic **241**
Mosaic see In Touch (Pinner) **4182**
Mosaic (Cambridge). (US ISSN 1046-5596) **2014**
Mosaic (Cleveland). (US) **1318**
Mosaic (St. Petersburg). (US) **3527**, 336
†Mosaic (Washington). (US ISSN 0027-1284) **5239**
Mosaic (Winnipeg, 1967). (CN ISSN 0027-1276) **2940**
Mosaic (Winnipeg, 1984) see Mosaik **2214**
Mosaik. (CN) **2214**

Mosaikk. (NO ISSN 0802-3182) 2015, 4413
Mosasaur. (US ISSN 0736-3907) 3658
Mosca News. (IT) 680, 3908
†Moscow Aviation Institute. Journal. (US ISSN 1044-5129) 5239
▼Moscow Magazine. (RU ISSN 0868-8400) 680
Moscow Mathematical Society. Transactions. (English translation of: Moskovskoe Matematicheskoe Obshchestvo. Trudy) (US ISSN 0077-1554) 3048
Moscow News. (RU ISSN 0027-1306) 3908
▼Moscow Physical Society. Journal. (UK ISSN 0960-0175) 3825
Moscow Society of Naturalists. Biological Series. Bulletin. see Moskovskoe Obshchestvo Ispytatelei Prirody. Biologicheskii Otdel. Byulleten 448
Moscow University Biological Sciences Bulletin. (English translation (in part) of: Moskovskii Universitet. Vestnik. Seriya 6: Biologiya, Pochvovedenie) (US ISSN 0096-3925) 448
Moscow University Chemistry Bulletin. (English translation of: Moskovskii Universitet. Vestnik. Seriya 2: Khimiya) (US ISSN 0027-1314) 1184
Moscow University Computational Mathematics and Cybernetics. (English translation of: Moskovskii Universitet. Vestnik. Seriya 15. Vychislitel'naya Matematika i Kibernetika) (US ISSN 0278-6419) 1442
Moscow University Geology Bulletin. (English translation of: Moskovskii Universitet. Vestnik. Seriya 4: Geologiya) (US ISSN 0145-8752) 1573
Moscow University Mathematics Bulletin. (English translation of: Moskovskii Universitet. Vestnik. Seriya 1: Matematika i Mekhanika) (US ISSN 0027-1322) 3048
Moscow University Mechanics Bulletin. (English translation of: Moscovskii Universitet. Vestnik. Mekhanika) (US ISSN 0027-1330) 3844
Moscow University Physics Bulletin. (English translation of: Moskovskii Universitet. Vestnik. Seriya 3: Fizika, Astronomiya) (US ISSN 0027-1349) 3825
Moscow University Soil Science Bulletin. (English translation (in part) of: Moskovskii Universitet. Vestnik. Seriya 6: Biologiya, Pochvovedenie) (US ISSN 0147-6874) 185
Mosella. (FR ISSN 0047-8164) 2256, 3985
Moshe Dayan Center for Middle Eastern and African Studies. Bulletin. (IS) 2204, 3908
Moshiach Times. (US) 1260, 4225
▼Moskovskii Gosudarstvennyi Tekhnicheskii Universitet. Vestnik. Priborostroenie. (RU ISSN 0236-3933) 2524
Moskovskii Gosudarstviennyi Universitet. Moskovskoe Obshchestvo Ispytatelei Prirody. Otdel Geologicheskii. Byulleten. (RU ISSN 0366-1318) 1573
Moskovskii Institut Stali i Splavov. Nauchnye Trudy. (RU) 3416
Moskovskii Universitet. Biblioteka. Rukopisnaya i Pechatnaya Kniga v Fondakh. (RU) 406
Moskovskii Universitet. Moskovskoe Obshchestvo Ispytatelei Prirody. Geologicheskii Otdel. Byulleten see Moskovskii Gosudarstviennyi Universitet. Moskovskoe Obshchestvo Ispytatelei Prirody. Otdel Geologicheskii. Byulleten 1573
Moskovskii Universitet. Vestnik. Seriya Ekonomika, Filosofiya see Moskovskii Universitet. Vestnik. Seriya 7: Ekonomika 680
Moskovskii Universitet. Vestnik. Seriya Ekonomika, Filosofiya see Moskovskii Universitet. Vestnik. Seriya 8: Filosofiya 3773

Moskovskii Universitet. Vestnik. Seriya Istoricheskie Nauki see Moskovskii Universitet. Vestnik. Seriya 9: Istoriya 2318
Moskovskii Universitet. Vestnik. Seriya 1: Matematika i Mekhanika. (RU) 3048, 3844
Moskovskii Universitet. Vestnik. Seriya 2: Khimiya. (RU) 1184
Moskovskii Universitet. Vestnik. Seriya 3: Fizika, Astronomiya. (RU) 3825, 367
Moskovskii Universitet. Vestnik. Seriya 4: Geologiya. (RU ISSN 0579-9406) 1573
Moskovskii Universitet. Vestnik. Seriya 5: Geografiya. (RU ISSN 0027-1381) 2256
Moskovskii Universitet. Vestnik. Seriya 6: Biologiya, Pochvovedenie. (RU ISSN 0579-9422) 448, 185
Moskovskii Universitet. Vestnik. Seriya 7: Ekonomika. (RU ISSN 0130-0105) 680
Moskovskii Universitet. Vestnik. Seriya 8: Filosofiya. (RU) 3773
Moskovskii Universitet. Vestnik. Seriya 9: Istoriya. (RU ISSN 0130-0083) 2318
Moskovskii Universitet. Vestnik. Seriya 10: Filologiya. (RU) 2830
Moskovskii Universitet. Vestnik. Seriya 11: Zhurnalistika. (RU) 2572
Moskovskii Universitet. Vestnik. Seriya 12: Pravo. (RU ISSN 0027-1357) 2655
Moskovskii Universitet. Vestnik. Seriya 13: Teoriya Nauchnogo Kommunizma. (RU) 3908
Moskovskii Universitet. Vestnik. Seriya 14: Vostokovedenie. (RU) 3641
Moskovskoe Matematicheskoe Obshchestvo. Trudy. (RU) 3048
Moskovskoe Obshchestvo Ispytatelei Prirody. Biologicheskii Otdel. Byulleten/Moscow Society of Naturalists. Biological Series. Bulletin.(RU ISSN 0027-1403) 448, 1573
Moskva. (RU ISSN 0131-2332) 2940
Moslemische Revue. (GW ISSN 0930-7338) 4219
Mosman and Lower North Shore Daily see Mosman Daily 2172
Mosman Daily. (AT) 2172
Mosquito Systematics. (US ISSN 0091-3669) 536
Mossbauer Effect Reference and Data Journal. (US ISSN 0163-9587) 1184, 3825
Mossbauer Spectroscopy Abstracts see Moessbauer Spectroscopy Abstracts 3837
Most/Bridge/Pont/Puente. (CI ISSN 0006-9833) 2940
Al Mostakbal/Future. (FR ISSN 0153-3401) 2015
Mostovi. (YU ISSN 0350-6525) 2830, 2940
Mostre e Musei. (IT ISSN 0394-4271) 336
Mosul University. College of Medicine. Annals. (IQ ISSN 0027-1446) 3132
Mosupa - Tsela. (SA ISSN 0027-1454) 4244
Mot. (GW) 4695
Mot Auto-Kritik see Mot 4695
Mot - Bau. (GW ISSN 0027-1470) 1871, 4720
Mot Brann see Brann og Sikkerhet 2031
Le Mot. (CN) 1318
Motabiala. (GH) 2192
Motadit. (CN) 1318
Motel Association of Alberta News Bulletin see M A A News Bulletin 2477
†Motel - Hotel Insider. (US ISSN 0148-7078) 5239
Motel News. (US) 2478
Motel, Restaurant Voice see Hotel Voice 2584
Moteris. (LI) 4848
Moteur Boat Magazine. (FR) 4526
Moteurs Diesel. (FR) 4695
Moteurs Loisirs. (FR ISSN 0241-8622) 2134

Mother. (UK ISSN 0027-1500) 1241
Mother & Baby. (UK ISSN 0047-8172) 1241
Mother and Child see Journal of Paediatrics, Obstetrics and Gynaecology 3294
Mother and Child. (PK) 4848, 1241, 4413, 4835
Mother Cabrini Messenger. (US ISSN 0027-1527) 4270
Mother Earth News. (US ISSN 0027-1535) 4443, 3773
Mother India. (II ISSN 0027-1543) 2875
Mother Jones. (US ISSN 0362-8841) 2875
Mother Tongue. see Modersmaalet 2014
Mothering. (US ISSN 0733-3013) 3295, 3806, 4835
Motherland. (BG) 2174
Mothers and Others for Midwives Magazine see M O M Magazine 4847
Mothers' Manual see Mothers Today 2448
Mothers' Manual and Baby Post see Mothers Today 2448
Mothers Today. (US) 2448, 1241
Motilal Banarsidass (Delhi) Newsletter see M L B D Newsletter 3647
Motion. (US) 3844
Motion/Kinisi. (GR) 4778
▼Motion Control. (US ISSN 1053-4644) 3844
Motion Picture. (US) 3514
The Motion Picture Guide Annual. (US) 3514
Motion Picture Investor. (US ISSN 0742-8839) 3514
Motion Picture, T V & Theatre Directory.(US ISSN 0580-0412) 1146, 1377, 3514
Motion Pictures Technical Bulletin. (II ISSN 0027-1632) 3514
▼Motions in Federal Court: Civil Practice, 2-E. (US) 2704
Motionsbladet. (DK ISSN 0109-0690) 3210
Motionsgang. (DK ISSN 0107-8976) 4479
Motitalia. (IT) 4518
Motivation and Emotion. (US ISSN 0146-7239) 4036
†Motivational Marketing. (CN) 5239
Motive Power Annual (Year) see Motive Power Review 4711
Motive Power Monthly. (UK) 4711
Motive Power Review. (UK) 4711
Moto. (RH) 2240
Moto. (IT) 4518
Moto Crampons. (FR) 4695
Moto Cross & Enduro. (GW ISSN 0724-7206) 4518
Moto Flash. (FR) 4695
Moto Journal. (CN ISSN 0319-2865) 4518
Moto Journal. (FR) 4695
Moto Revue. (FR ISSN 0047-8180) 4518
Moto Verte. (FR) 4518
Motociclismo. (IT ISSN 0027-1691) 4518
Motociclismo. (SP) 4518
Motocourse. (UK) 4519
Motocross. (UK) 4519
Motocross Action. (US ISSN 0146-3292) 4519
Motoculture Magazine. (FR ISSN 0998-495X) 2134, 2116
†Le Motocycliste. (CN) 5239
Motocyclo Catalogue. (FR ISSN 0077-1570) 4519
Motonautica. (IT) 4526
Motoneigiste Canedien. (CN) 4479
Motor. (NE ISSN 0027-1721) 4519
Motor. (IT) 4675, 4519
Motor see Autocar & Motor 4681
Motor. (DK ISSN 0047-8199) 4695, 4778
Motor. (II ISSN 0027-1713) 4695
Motor. (NO ISSN 0027-173X) 4695
Motor. (SW ISSN 0027-1764) 4695, 4526
Motor. (US ISSN 0027-1748) 4695
Motor. (BE) 4696
Motor. (PO) 4696
†Motor Activity. (UK ISSN 0263-7340) 5239

Motor Age see Chilton's Motor Age 4688
†Motor Agents Association Year Book and Diary. (UK) 5239
Motor & Traffic Law Service - Victoria. (AT) 2704, 4720
Motor Auto Repair Manual. (US) 4696
Motor - Bladet. (DK ISSN 0107-7554) 4519
Motor Boat & Yachting. (UK ISSN 0027-1780) 4526
Motor Boating & Sailing. (US ISSN 0027-1799) 4526
Motor Caravan and Camping see Motorcaravan & Motorhome Monthly 4550
Motor Caravan Monthly see Motor Caravan World 4653
Motor Caravan World. (UK ISSN 0142-0011) 4653, 4550
Motor Caravanner. (UK) 4550, 4653
Motor Carrier Directory Warehousing Distribution Directory see M C D's Warehousing Distribution Directory 4745
Motor Carrier - Freight Forwarder Service. (US) 4746
Motor Carrier Manager. (CN) 4746
Motor Carrier Safety Report. (US) 4746
Motor City Stamp and Cover Club On Cover see M C S C C On Cover 3754
Motor Club News. (US ISSN 0463-6457) 4778, 4696
Motor Crash Estimating Guide. (US) 4696
Motor Cycle News. (UK ISSN 0027-1853) 4519
Motor - Dienst und Erdoel - Nachrichten see Motor und Erdoel 4697
Motor Early Model Crash Estimating Guide. (US ISSN 0160-1644) 4696
Motor Equipment News. (AT) 4696
Motor Fleet Supervision. (US) 1067, 1021, 4746
Motor Freight Controller. (US) 4746
†Motor Handbook. (US ISSN 0094-1514) 5239
Motor Imported Car Crash Estimating Guide. (US ISSN 0164-6346) 4696
†Motor in Canada. (CN ISSN 0027-190X) 5240
Motor Industry Engineer see Motor Industry Management 4665
Motor Industry Journal. (AT) 4696
Motor Industry Management. (UK) 4665, 17
Motor Industry News. (NZ) 4696
†Motor Industry News Digest. (SA) 5240
Motor Industry of Great Britain see Motor Industry of Great Britain (Year) World Automotive Statistics 4696
Motor Industry of Great Britain (Year) World Automotive Statistics. (UK) 4696
Motor Industry of Japan see Automobile Industry - Japan and Toyota 4682
Motor Industry Research Association Automobile Abstracts see M I R A Automobile Abstracts 4665
Motor Industry Research Association Automotive Business Index see M I R A Automotive Business Index 727
Motor Industry Year Book. (NZ) 4653
Motor Italia. (IT ISSN 0027-1926) 4696
Motor Klassik. (GW) 4696
Motor Light Truck & Van Repair Manual. (US) 4696
Motor Light Truck and Van Tuneup and Repair Manual see Motor Light Truck & Van Repair Manual 4696
Motor Magasinet. (DK) 4696
Motor Management see Motor Industry Management 4665
Motor Manual see Australian Motor Manual 4679
Motor - Nachrichten. see Notiziario Motoristico 4698
Motor News. (AT ISSN 0818-5549) 4696
Motor News. see Notiziario Motoristico 4698
Motor News Analysis see Auto Retail Report 4681

6450 DE MOTOR

†De Motor Nytt. (NO) **5240**
Motor Parts & Time Guide. (US ISSN 0077-1716) **4696**
†Motor Racing. (UK ISSN 0268-0831) **5240**
Motor Report International. (UK ISSN 0306-6274) **4696**
Motor Retailer. (UK) **4696**
Motor Revue. (GW) **4696**
Motor Schools Association of G.B. News Journal *see* M S A News Journal **4695**
Motor Service. (US ISSN 0027-1977) **4696**
Motor - Service og Autoteknisk Tidsskrift *see* Auto Bladet **4680**
Motor Ship. (UK ISSN 0027-2000) **4733**
Motor - Soesport. (DK) **4526**
Motor Specifications & Prices. (UK) **4696**, 4665
Motor Sport. (UK ISSN 0027-2019) **4479**, 4696
†Motor Sport Aktuell. (SZ) **5240**
Motor Trade Association of Western Australia. Journal. (AT) **4696**
Motor Trade Executive *see* Motor Retailer **4696**
Motor Trade Journal. (AT ISSN 0027-2035) **4696**
Motor Trader. (AT) **4696**
Motor Trader. (UK ISSN 0027-2043) **4696**
Motor Trader and Fleet Operator. (RH ISSN 0027-2051) **4696**
Motor Traffic in Sweden. (SW ISSN 0077-1619) **4696**
Motor Transport. (UK ISSN 0027-206X) **4746**
Motor Transportation Hi-Lights *see* S C T A Hi-Lights **4747**
Motor Trend. (US ISSN 0027-2094) **4696**
Motor Trend's New Car Buyers' Guide. (US) **4696**
Motor Trend's Road Tests. (US) **4696**
Motor Trend's Sports Cars of the World.(US) **4697**
Motor Trend's Truck and Van Buyers' Guide. (US) **4697**
Motor Truck. (CN ISSN 0027-2108) **4746**
Motor Truck Facts *see* M V M A Motor Vehicle Facts and Figures **4695**
Motor und Erdoel. (AU) **4697**
Motor Vehicle Data Book. (CN ISSN 0316-6198) **4697**
Motor Vehicle Engineering Specifications - Japan. (JA) **4697**
Motor Vehicle Facts & Figures *see* M V M A Motor Vehicle Facts and Figures **4695**
Motor Vehicle Law S.A. (AT) **2704**, 4720
Motor Vehicle Manufacturers Association of the U.S. Inc. Motor Vehicle Facts and Figures *see* M V M A Motor Vehicle Facts and Figures **4695**
Motor Vehicle Reports. (AT ISSN 0813-782X) **2704**
Motor Vehicle Reports. (CN ISSN 0709-5341) **4653**, 2704
Motor Vehicle Safety. (US) **4108**
Motor Vehicle Safety Defect Recall Campaigns (Washington) *see* U.S. National Highway Traffic Safety Administration. Motor Vehicle Safety Defect Recall Campaigns **4704**
Motor Vehicle Statistics of Japan. (JA ISSN 0463-6635) **4697**
Motor World *see* Directions **2212**
▼Motor World. (US ISSN 1055-8233) **4697**
MotorBoat. (US) **4526**
Motorbranschen. (SW ISSN 0027-2140) **4697**
Motorbranschens Registeringsstatistik *see* Motorbranschen **4697**
Motorcaravan & Motorhome Monthly. (UK) **4550**, 4778
Motorcoach Marketer. (US) **4653**
MotorCyclar Allt om M C *see* Allt om M C **4515**
Motorcycle. *see* Motuo Che **4520**
Motorcycle Blue Book. (US ISSN 0091-3774) **4519**
Motorcycle Buyer's Guide *see* Motorcyclist **4519**

Motorcycle Dealer and Trade. (CN ISSN 0705-2030) **4519**
Motorcycle DealerNews *see* DealerNews **4517**
Motorcycle Dealernews Buyers Guide. (US) **4519**, 1506
Motorcycle Dealers' Guide. (SA) **4519**
Motorcycle Enthusiast *see* Enthusiast **4518**
Motorcycle Enthusiast. (UK ISSN 0265-7759) **4519**
†Motorcycle Industry Business Journal. (US) **5240**
Motorcycle Industry Magazine. (US ISSN 0884-626X) **4519**
Motorcycle Japan. (JA) **4519**
Motorcycle Product News. (US ISSN 0164-8349) **4519**
Motorcycle Product News Trade Directory. (US) **1146**, 4519
Motorcycle Red Book. (US) **4519**
Motorcycle Rider. (UK ISSN 0306-1647) **4519**
Motorcycle Road Racer Illustrated. (US) **4519**
Motorcycle Sport. (UK ISSN 0955-9116) **4519**
Motorcyclist. (US ISSN 0027-2205) **4519**, 4778
Motorcyclist's Post. (US ISSN 0164-9256) **4519**
Motoren Nieuws. (NE) **1936**
Motoren - und Turbinen - Union Heute Heute *see* M T U Heute **5230**
Motorfahrzeugbestand in der Schweiz am 30. September (Year)/Effectif des Vehicules a Moteur en Suisse au 30 Septembre (Year). (SZ) **4665**
Motorfoereren. (NO ISSN 0027-2213) **4697**
MotorHome. (US ISSN 0744-074X) **4550**, 4653
Motorhome Life *see* MotorHome **4550**
Motorhome Life and Camper Coachman *see* MotorHome **4550**
Motorhome Magazine. (UK ISSN 0963-7338) **4519**
Motori. (IT ISSN 0393-7666) **4697**
Motorik. (GW ISSN 0170-5792) **3806**, 1755
Motorindia. (II ISSN 0027-223X) **4697**
Motoring. (SI) **4519**
Motoring. (II ISSN 0027-2248) **4697**
Motoring & Leisure. (UK) **4697**, 2739, 4778
†Motoring Life. (IE ISSN 0027-2256) **5240**
Motoring News. (UK ISSN 0027-2264) **4697**
Motoring Review *see* Wheels **4706**
Motoring Today *see* Directions **2212**
Motorist. (UK) **4697**
Motorist *see* A A A Traveler (York) **4750**
Motorist (Seattle). (US ISSN 0899-7578) **4778**, 4697
Motorists Guide to New & Used Car Prices. (UK ISSN 0027-2302) **4697**
Motorland. (US ISSN 0027-2310) **4778**, 4697
Motorliv. (NO ISSN 0027-2337) **4697**
†MotorMadrid. (SP) **5240**
Das Motorrad. (GW ISSN 0027-237X) **4519**
Motorrad Classic. (GW) **4519**
Motorrad Katalog. (GW) **4519**
Motorrad Magazin M O. (GW) **4519**
Motorrad News. (GW) **4519**
Motorrad Oldtimer Katalog. (GW) **4519**
Motorrad, Reisen und Sport. (GW) **4519**
Motorrad Spiegel. (GW) **4519**
Motorrad Szene. (GW) **4519**
Motorrad Test (Year). (GW) **4519**
Motorrad Test Katalog. (GW) **4519**
†Motorrad Touren. (GW) **5240**
Motorradszene Bayern. (GW) **4519**
Motorradtreff Spinner. (GW) **4519**
Motor's Handbook *see* Motor Handbook **5239**
Motorscot. (UK) **4479**, 4697
Motorsports. (US) **4479**
Motorsports Marketing News. (US) **1048**, 4479
Motortechnische Zeitschrift *see* M T Z **4695**

Motosprint. (IT) **4519**
Mototrentino. (IT) **4519**
Mototurismo. (IT) **4520**
Motour *see* A A A Today (Cincinnati) **4750**
Motricite Cerebrale: Readaptation Neurologie du Developpement. (FR ISSN 0245-5919) **3345**
Motrix. (US ISSN 0027-2396) **4697**
Mott Community College Post *see* M C C Post **1316**
Motuo Che/Motorcycle. (CC) **4520**
Motuoche Jishu/Journal of Motorcycle Technology. (CC ISSN 1001-7666) **4697**
Al-Muhandis Al-Arabi. (SY) **1831**
Mould Engineering. (JA) **1831**
Moules et Modeles *see* Moules, Modeles et Maquettes **3021**
Moules, Modeles et Maquettes. (FR ISSN 0297-8717) **3021**
Moun/People. (GP) **3908**
Mount Allison Record. (CN ISSN 0027-2485) **1318**
Mount Buller Guide *see* Mount Buller News **4778**
Mount Buller News. (AT) **4778**, 4550
Mount Carmel. (US) **4191**
Mount Desert Island Biological Laboratory. Bulletin. (US ISSN 0097-0883) **448**
Mount Holyoke Alumnae Quarterly. (US ISSN 0027-2493) **1318**
Mount Magazine. (US) **1318**
Mount St. Helen's and Volcanic Action. (US) **1551**
Mount Saint Mary College Happenings *see* M S M C Happenings **1316**
Mount Saviour Chronicle. (US) **4191**
Mount Sinai Journal of Medicine. (US ISSN 0027-2507) **3132**, 2467
Mount Washington Observatory News Bulletin. (US ISSN 0027-2523) **3439**
†Mount Zion Hospital and Medical Center, San Francisco. Bulletin. (US ISSN 0077-1740) **5240**
Mountain. (UK ISSN 0964-3427) **4550**
Mountain America Truck Trader. (US) **4746**
Mountain and City Biking. (US) **4520**
Mountain and Museum. *see* Yama to Hakubutsukan **3535**
Mountain and Valley. *see* The-Yama-To-Keikoku **4558**
Mountain Bike. (US) **4520**
Mountain Bike Action. (US) **4520**
Mountain Blossoms (Guizhou). *see* Shanhua **2959**
Mountain Call. (US) **2875**
Mountain Club of South Africa. Journal. (SA) **4550**
▼Mountain Constructor & Reclamationist. (US) **625**, 2104
Mountain Diggings. (US) **2415**
Mountain Empire Quarterly. (US) **2159**
Mountain Geologist. (US ISSN 0027-254X) **1573**
†Mountain Life and Work. (US ISSN 0027-2558) **5240**
Mountain Light. (US) **2415**
Mountain Movers. (US ISSN 0164-7253) **4285**
Mountain Path. (II ISSN 0027-2574) **3773**, 4191
Mountain Plains Adult Education Association Newsletter *see* M P A E A Newsletter **1685**
Mountain Plains Journal of Adult Education. (US ISSN 0090-4244) **1685**
Mountain Plains Library Association Newsletter *see* M P L A Newsletter **2772**
Mountain Record. (US ISSN 0896-8942) **4215**
Mountain Research. *see* Shandi Yanjiu **1580**
Mountain Research and Development. (US ISSN 0276-4741) **1547**
Mountain Riders. (US) **4536**
Mountain State Geology. (US ISSN 0163-2825) **1573**
Mountain Times (Killington). (US) **4778**
Mountain Trails. (US) **2256**, 2415
Mountain Visitor. (US ISSN 0027-2612) **4778**, 4550

Mountaineer (Colorado Springs). (US) **3466**
Mountaineer (Seattle). (US ISSN 0027-2620) **4550**, 1492
†Mountainwest Magazine. (US ISSN 0191-9482) **5240**
Mousaion. (SA ISSN 0027-2639) **2774**
Mouse Genome. (UK) **546**
Mouse News Letter *see* Mouse Genome **546**
Mouthpiece. (AT) **1755**, 4191
Mouthpiece (Chicago). (US) **3238**
Mouthpiece (San Mateo). (US) **3238**
Mouton Noir. (CN) **1318**
Mouvement Anti-Utilitariste dans les Science Sociales Revue du M A U S S *see* Revue du M A U S S **4447**
Mouvement Communal. (BE) **4091**
Mouvement de la Population en Suisse. *see* Bevoelkerungsbewegung in der Schweiz **3979**
Mouvement Hotelier et Touristique. (FR) **2478**
Mouvement Naturel de la Population de la Grece. (GR ISSN 0077-6114) **3993**, 3985
Mouvement Social. (FR ISSN 0027-2671) **2318**
Mouvements *see* Nouvelles C E Q **1652**
Movement and Dance. (UK) **1531**
Movement Disorders. (US ISSN 0885-3185) **3345**
Movement Newspaper *see* New Day Herald **3595**
Movement of California Fruits and Vegetables by Rail, Truck, and Air *see* California Fresh Fruit and Vegetable Shipments by Rail, Truck, and Air **4648**
Movement Theatre Quarterly. (US) **4635**
Movements in the Arts. (US ISSN 8756-890X) **336**, 2940, 3563
Movers Journal *see* American Mover **4743**
Movers News. (US) **4746**
Movie. (UK ISSN 0027-268X) **3514**
Movie. (II) **3514**
Movie Collectors World. (US ISSN 0746-0325) **1385**, 2439
Movie Marketing *see* Movie - T V Marketing **3514**
Movie Marketplace. (US) **3514**, 1385
Movie Mirror. (US ISSN 0027-271X) **3514**
Movie Monthly. *see* Dianying Yuebao **3507**
Movie News. (SI ISSN 0027-2736) **3514**
Movie - T V Marketing. (JA ISSN 0047-8288) **3514**, 1377
Movie - T V Marketing Annual Worldwide Television Survey. (JA) **1377**
Movie - T V Marketing Global Motion Picture Year Book. (JA ISSN 0085-3577) **3514**, 1377
Movie - Video Age International. (US ISSN 0278-5013) **3514**, 1385
Movieline. (US ISSN 1055-0917) **3514**
Movies U S A. (US) **3514**
Movietone News. (US) **3514**
Movimento. (IT) **3132**
Movimento di Liberazione in Italia *see* Italia Contemporanea **2369**
Movimento Operaio e Socialista. (IT ISSN 0027-2817) **2376**
Movimiento Internacional de Estudiantes Catolicos Servico de Documentacion *see* M I E C Servico de Documentacion **4268**
Movimiento Natural de la Poblacion de Espana. (SP ISSN 0077-1767) **3993**, 3985
Movimiento Sindical de America Latina y el Caribe. (CU) **989**
Movin' (CN) **4711**
Movin' Out. (US) **4746**
Moving. (SW) **3021**
Moving Finger *see* Aerie **2987**
Moving Food. (US) **2078**
Moving Forward. (US ISSN 1056-7240) **2294**, 1738, 2288
Moving Out. (US ISSN 0047-830X) **4848**

Moving to & Around Alberta. (CN ISSN 0713-8369) **4153**, **4778**
Moving to & Around Maritimes & Newfoundland. (CN ISSN 0228-7153) **4153**, **4778**
Moving to & Around Saskatchewan. (CN) **4153**, **4778**
Moving to & Around Southwestern Ontario. (CN ISSN 0715-8114) **4153**, **4778**
Moving to & Around Toronto & Area. (CN ISSN 0713-8377) **4153**, **4778**
Moving to & Around Vancouver & B.C. (CN ISSN 0713-8407) **4153**, **4778**
Moving to & Around Winnipeg & Manitoba. (CN ISSN 0825-2432) **4153**, **4778**
Moving to Greater Hamilton and the Golden Triangle *see* Moving to Greater Hamilton, C.T.T., Brantford & Niagara **4153**
Moving to Greater Hamilton, C.T.T., Brantford & Niagara. (CN) **4153**
Moving to Montreal/Emmenager a Montreal. (CN ISSN 0702-9225) **4153**
Moving to Ottawa - Hull. (CN ISSN 0226-7837) **4153**, **4778**
Moving to Saskatchewan *see* Moving to & Around Saskatchewan **4153**
Moving to Toronto and Area *see* Moving to & Around Toronto & Area **4153**
Moving to Vancouver and B.C. *see* Moving to & Around Vancouver & B.C **4153**
†Moving Up. (US) **5240**
Movoznavstvo. (KR ISSN 0027-2833) **2830**
Mowia Wieki. (PL ISSN 0580-0943) **2376**
†Moxie. (US) **5240**
▼Moya Moskva. (RU ISSN 0868-5975) **2215**
Le Moyen Age. (BE ISSN 0027-2841) **2376**, **2830**
Moyen-Orient Selection *see* Marches Arabes **917**
Mozambique. Instituto Nacional de Geologia. Boletim Geomagnetico Preliminar. (MZ) **1592**, 1903
Mozambique. Instituto Nacional de Geologia. Boletim Meteorologico para a Agricultura. (MZ) **3439**, 1592
Mozambique. Instituto Nacional de Geologia. Boletim Seismique. (MZ) **1592**
Mozambique. Instituto Nacional de Geologia. Departamento Geofisica Global. Boletim Geomagnetico Preliminar *see* Mozambique. Instituto Nacional de Geologia. Boletim Geomagnetico Preliminar **1592**
Mozambique. Servico Meteorologico. Boletim Meteorologico para a Agricultura *see* Mozambique. Instituto Nacional de Geologia. Boletim Meteorologico para a Agricultura **3439**
Mozambique. Servico Meteorologico. Boletim Seismique *see* Mozambique. Instituto Nacional de Geologia. Boletim Seismique **1592**
Mozambique. Servico Meteorologico. Informacoes de Caracter Astronomico. (MZ) **1592**, 367
Mozambique File. (MZ) **2211**
Mozambique News *see* Mozambique File **2211**
Mozart - Jahrbuch. (GW ISSN 0077-1805) **3563**
Moznayim. (IS ISSN 0027-2892) **2204**
Mpanolotsaina. (MG) **4191**
Mpls. - St. Paul Magazine. (US) **2229**, **4778**
Mr. (FR) **3399**
Mr. Cogito. (US ISSN 0740-1205) **2998**
Mr. Landlord. (US) **4153**
Mrs/Misesu. (JA) **2448**
Mrs. Eagle. (US) **1299**
Ms. (US ISSN 0047-8318) **4860**
MS Outdoors *see* Mississippi Outdoors **1492**
Msafiri. (KE) **4778**
Mss. (US) **2875**

Mt. Juliet - West Wilson Historical Society. Chronicle. (US) **2415**
Mu. (JA) **2986**
Al-Mu'allim. (TS) **1648**
Muanyag es Gumi/Plastics and Rubber.(HU ISSN 0027-2914) **3864**, 4292
Il Mucchio Selvaggio. (IT) **3563**
Muchacha. (CU ISSN 0864-0327) **1260**, 1241
Mucho Mas. (SP) **4848**
†Mucopolysaccharides. (UK ISSN 0142-8748) **5240**
Mudan/Peony. (CC) **2940**
Mudanjiang Medical Institute. Journal. *see* Mudanjiang Yixueyuan Xuebao **3132**
Mudanjiang Yixueyuan Xuebao/ Mudanjiang Medical Institute. Journal.(CC ISSN 1001-7550) **3132**
Muddy Roots. (US) **2159**
Mudfish. (US) **2998**, 336
El Mueble Actual. (SP ISSN 0027-2930) **2554**, 2561
Muecke. (GW ISSN 0930-7818) **1260**
Muecki. (GW ISSN 0932-4755) **1260**
Die Muehle und Mischfuttertechnik. (GW ISSN 0027-2949) **207**
Muehlheimer Monat. (GW) **2190**
Das Muehlrad. (GW ISSN 0723-7286) **2376**
Muehlviertler Heimatblaetter. (AU ISSN 0541-2404) **2376**
Muehlviertler Kulturzeitschrift *see* Muehlviertler Heimatblaetter **2376**
Muelheimer Statistik. (GW ISSN 0173-8895) **4081**
Muell und Abfall. (GW ISSN 0027-2957) **4108**
Mueller Clipper. (US ISSN 0027-2965) **1903**
Muelleria. (AT ISSN 0077-1813) **509**
Muellmagazin. (GW ISSN 0934-3482) **1986**
Muemlekvedelem. (HU ISSN 0541-2439) **303**
Muenchen & Bayern von Hinten. (GW) **2455**, 4778
Muenchen von Hinten *see* Muenchen & Bayern von Hinten **2455**
Muenchener Beitraege zur Mediaevistik und Renaissance-Forschung. (GW ISSN 0930-1127) **1278**, 2376
Muenchener Entomologische Gesellschaft. Mitteilungen. (GW ISSN 0077-1864) **536**
Muenchener Geographische Abhandlungen. (GW) **2256**
Muenchener Indologische Studien. (GW ISSN 0077-1880) **3641**
Muenchener Jahrbuch der Bildenden Kunst. (GW ISSN 0077-1899) **336**
Muenchener Kulturfuehrer mit Theaterplan. (GW) **2190**, 336, 4635
Muenchener Medizinische Wochenschrift. (GW ISSN 0341-3098) **3132**
Muenchener Ostasiatische Studien. (GW ISSN 0170-3668) **3641**
Muenchener Ostasiatische Studien. Sonderreihe. (GW ISSN 0170-3676) **3641**
Muenchener Studien zur Neueren Englischen Literatur/Munich Studies in English Literature. (NE) **2940**
Muenchener Studien zur Sozial- und Wirtschaftsgeographie. (GW ISSN 0077-1902) **2256**
Muenchener Studien zur Sprachwissenschaft. (GW ISSN 0077-1910) **2830**
Muenchener Theologische Zeitschrift. (GW ISSN 0580-1400) **4270**
Muenchener Zeitschrift fuer Balkankunde. (GW ISSN 0170-8929) **2376**, 2431
Muenchens Feine Adressen. (GW ISSN 0178-5516) **2190**, 373
Muenchner Freiheit. (GW) **1318**
Muenchner Geowissenschaftliche Abhandlungen. Reihe A: Geologie und Palaeontologie. (GW ISSN 0177-0950) **3658**, 1573

Muenchner Geowissenschaftliche Abhandlungen. Reihe B: Allgemeine und Angewandte Geologie. (GW ISSN 0931-8739) **1573**, 3491
Muenchner Geowissenschaftliche Abhandlungen. Reihe C: Geographie. (GW ISSN 0931-8747) **2256**
Muenchner Germanistische Beitraege. (GW ISSN 0077-1872) **2940**, 2830
Muenchner Medizinische Wochenschrift en Espanol. (SP) **3132**
Muenchner Philharmoniker. (GW) **3563**
Muenchner Schaukasterl. (GW) **35**
Muenchner Uni Magazin. (GW ISSN 0940-0141) **1318**
Das Muenster. (GW ISSN 0027-299X) **336**
Muenstersche Beitraege zur Antiken Handelsgeschichte. (GW ISSN 0722-4532) **1278**, 279, 2376
Muenstersche Beitraege zur Vor- und Fruehgeschichte. (GW ISSN 0077-2003) **2318**
Muenstersche Beitraege zur Vorgeschichtsforschung *see* Muenstersche Beitraege zur Vor- und Fruehgeschichte **2318**
Muensterschwarzacher Studien. (GW ISSN 0077-2011) **4270**
Muenzautomat. (GW ISSN 0721-6823) **1021**, 4479
Muenzen-Revue. (SZ) **3600**
Muenzen und Medaillen/Monnaies et Medailles. (SZ ISSN 0027-3007) **3600**
Muenzen- und Medaillensammler Berichte. (GW ISSN 0179-3683) **3600**
Muffler Digest *see* Undercar Digest **4704**
Mufti. (AT) **3466**
Mufulira Mirror *see* Mining Mirror **3490**
Muhadarat al-Mawsim al-Thaqafi li-Kulliyyat al-Lughah al-Arabiyyah *see* Jami'at Umm al-Qura. Kulliyyat al-Lughah al-Arabiyyah. Muhadarat al-Mawsim al-Thaqafi **2820**
Muhandis. (IQ) **1831**
Al-Muhandis/Engineer. (BA) **1831**
Al-Muhandis. (TS) **1831**
Muhendis ve Makina. (TU ISSN 0027-304X) **1936**
Muhlenberg Door to Door. (US) **1318**
Muhyiddin Ibn Arabi Society. Journal. (UK ISSN 0266-2183) **4219**
Muir's Original Log Home Guide for Builders & Buyers. (US ISSN 0844-3459) **625**, 1146
Mujer - Fempress. (CL) **4849**
Mujer I L E T *see* Mujer - Fempress **4849**
Mujer y Hogar. (CR) **2448**
Mujeres. (CU ISSN 0581-2011) **4849**
Mujeres. (AG) **4849**
Mujeres y Muchacha. (CU) **3399**, 2984
Mujrim. (II) **2986**
Al-Mujtama. *see* Sudan Society **250**
Al-Mujtama'. (SU) **2211**
Mukai! (SA) **4285**
Mukta. (II ISSN 0027-3104) **2875**
Muktibani. (BG) **2174**
Mulberry Tree Papers. (US ISSN 0896-2618) **1318**
Muldvarpen. (DK ISSN 0109-4599) **3908**
▼Mules and More. (US) **221**
Mulga Wire. (AT ISSN 0157-3381) **3563**
Mulga Yonbo. *see* Korea (Republic). National Statistical Office. Annual Report on the Price Survey **726**
Mulhaq al-Tashri lil-Jaridah al-Rasmiyah li-Jumhuriyat al-Sudan al-Dimuqratiyah *see* Democratic Republic of the Sudan Gazette. Legislative Supplement **4058**
Al-Mulhiq al-Ihsa'i *see* United Arab Emirates. Al-Masraf al-Markazi. Al-Mulhiq al-Ihsa'i **741**
Mulika. (TZ ISSN 0856-0129) **2830**, 2940
Mulino. (IT ISSN 0027-3120) **2875**
Mulka Jungbo. *see* Monthly Commodity Price News Service **791**

MUNCA SANITARIA 6451

Mulot'schen Familienverband. Zeitschrift.(GW) **2159**, 2376, 4244
†Multi Drug Resistance. (UK ISSN 0952-035X) **5240**
Multi-housing Laundry Association News (Raleigh) *see* M L A News (Raleigh) **1282**
†Multi Housing News. (US ISSN 0146-0919) **5240**
Multi - Images. (US ISSN 0893-5440) **35**, 3514
Multi Level Marketing News. (US ISSN 0745-0753) **1048**
Multi Media Reviews Index *see* Media Review Digest **3520**
†Multi - Sport Facility News. (US) **5240**
Multi - User Computing. (UK ISSN 0954-6561) **1445**
▼Multi-year Comparison of Utility Power Purchases from Cogenerators and Independent Power Producers. (US) **1802**
Multicast. (US ISSN 0146-0099) **1377**
Multichannel News. (US ISSN 0276-8593) **1377**
Multicultural Childrens' Literature. (II) **1260**
Multicultural Education Abstracts. (UK ISSN 0260-9770) **1678**, 17
Multicultural Gazette. (CN) **2015**
Multicultural Magazine. (CN) **2015**
▼MultiCultural Review. (US ISSN 1058-9236) **4443**, 2015
Multicultural Teaching. (UK ISSN 0263-0869) **1755**
▼Multidimensional Systems and Signal Processing. (US ISSN 0923-6082) **1438**, 1903
Multihull International. (UK ISSN 0027-3155) **4526**
Multihulls. (US ISSN 0749-4122) **4526**
Multilingua. (GW ISSN 0167-8507) **2830**, 1340
Multilist Realtor. (AT) **4153**
Multimedia & Text Report. (US) **1398**
Multimedia and Videodisc Monitor. (US) **1438**, 1385
Multimedia Computing & Presentations.(US ISSN 1051-953X) **1482**
Multimedia Personal Computing World *see* M P C World **1470**
▼Multimedia Review. (US ISSN 1046-3550) **1457**
Multinational Business. (UK ISSN 0300-3922) **1081**
Multinational Environmental Outlook *see* Greenhouse Effect Report **1956**
Multinational Executive Travel Companion. (US ISSN 0093-7487) **917**, 1340, 4778
Multinational Industrial Relations Series.(US ISSN 0149-0818) **917**
Multinational Monitor. (US ISSN 0197-4637) **918**
Multinational P R Report. (US ISSN 0743-0795) **35**
Multinational Service. (BE) **918**
Multiphase Science and Technology. (US ISSN 0276-1459) **1831**
Multiphase Update. (UK ISSN 0952-6846) **3692**
Multiple Sclerosis Research Report. (US) **3133**
Multiple Sclerosis Society News *see* M S News **3344**
Multiple Sclerosis Society of Canada Canada *see* M S Canada **3188**
Multiple Sclerosis Society of Canada Ontario *see* M S Ontario **3123**
Multistate Corporate Income Tax Guide.(US) **1101**
Multistate Part-Year Nonresident Return Guide. (US) **1101**
Multistate Tax Commission Review. (US) **1101**
Multivariate Behavioral Research. (US ISSN 0027-3171) **4036**
Multivariate Experimental Clinical Research. (US ISSN 0147-3964) **4036**
Munca de Partid. (RM) **3908**
Munca Sanitaria *see* Viata Medicala - Cadre Medii **3288**

MUNCIE PUBLIC

Muncie Public Library Now! see M P L Now **2772**
Mundartfreunde Oesterreichs. Mitteilungen. (AU ISSN 0027-3228) **2830**, 2057
Mundi Medicina. (US) **4191**
Mundo. (US) **2015**
Mundo Agricola. (PO) **108**
El Mundo al Vuelo - Inflight Notes. (CK) **4803**
Mundo Arabe. (AG) **3908**
Mundo Cristiano. (SP ISSN 0027-3252) **4270**
Mundo de los Negocios. (DR) **680**
Mundo del Trabajo Libre see Free Labour World **2583**
Mundo Electronico. (SP ISSN 0300-3787) **1776**
Mundo Eletrico. (BL ISSN 0027-3295) **1903**
Mundo Eletronico. (BL) **1776**
Mundo Estudiantil see World Student News **1672**
Mundo Financiero. (SP ISSN 0300-3884) **791**
Mundo Hispanico. (US ISSN 1051-4147) **2015**
Mundo Indigena. see Indigenous World **2924**
Mundo Israelita. (AG ISSN 0327-5930) **2204**, 2015, 2572, 3908
Mundo Justicialista. (AG) **2655**
Mundo Mecanico. (BL ISSN 0102-0145) **1936**
Mundo Medico. (MX) **3133**
Mundo Negro. (SP) **4191**
Mundo Nuevo. (VE ISSN 0379-6922) **2217**
Mundo Nuevo. (AG ISSN 0027-3333) **2875**
Mundo Policial. (AG ISSN 0030-7955) **1518**
Mundo - Spanish Newspaper. (US) **2015**
Mundo Textil Argentino. (AG) **4622**
Mundus. (GW ISSN 0027-3392) **336**, 4324
Mundus. (IT ISSN 0027-3384) **4132**, 2940
Mundus Arabicus. (US) **2940**
Munger Map Book. (US) **3692**
Munhwao Haksup/Study of Korean Language. (KN) **2830**, 1755
Munibe. (SP ISSN 0027-3414) **4324**
Munich Studies in English Literature. see Muenchener Studien zur Neueren Englischen Literatur **2940**
Municipal Act and Index to Local Government Legislation Manual. (CN) **4091**
Municipal Administration and Engineering see Local Government in Southern Africa **4090**
Municipal Advocate. (US) **4091**
Municipal and Industrial Water and Pollution Control. (CN) **1978**
Municipal and Planning Law Reports (2nd Series). (CN ISSN 0702-7206) **2492**, 2655
Municipal and Public Services Journal see Municipal Journal **4091**
Municipal Association of Tasmania. Session. Minutes of Proceedings. (AT ISSN 0085-3585) **4091**
Municipal Association of Victoria. Minutes of Proceedings of Annual Session. (AT ISSN 0077-2143) **4091**
Municipal Attorney. (US ISSN 0027-3449) **2655**, 4091
Municipal Bond Dealers of the United States see Directory of Municipal Bond Dealers of the United States **944**
†Municipal Bond Interest Record. (US) **5240**
Municipal - County Executive Directory Annual. (US ISSN 0743-6211) **4091**
Municipal Court Review see Court Review **2731**
Municipal Election Calendar. (US) **4091**
Municipal Engineer. see Stads og Havneingenioeren **1837**
Municipal Engineer/Munisipale Ingenieur. (SA ISSN 0047-8369) **1871**
Municipal Engineer. (UK ISSN 0263-788X) **1871**, 2492
Municipal Engineering see Municipal Journal **4091**
Municipal Engineering in Australia. (AT ISSN 0311-354X) **1871**
Municipal Engineers Journal. (US ISSN 0027-3465) **1871**
▼Municipal Environmental Journal. (US ISSN 1058-1332) **1963**
Municipal Executive Directory. (US ISSN 0742-1710) **4091**
Municipal Finance Journal. (US ISSN 0199-6134) **791**
Municipal Journal. (UK ISSN 0143-4187) **4091**
Municipal Law Court Decisions see Municipal Attorney **2655**
Municipal League of King County. Issue Watch. (US) **4091**
Municipal League of Seattle and King County. Municipal News see Municipal League of King County. Issue Watch **4091**
†Municipal Liability Litigation Reporter. (US ISSN 1055-5862) **5240**
Municipal Litigation Reporter. (US ISSN 0278-1301) **4091**
Municipal Maryland. (US) **4091**
Municipal News. see Kommun-Aktuelt **4089**
Municipal Open Line. (CN) **4067**
Municipal Ordinance Review see Municipal Attorney **2655**
Municipal Problems. see Toshi Mondai **4095**
Municipal Reference Library Bulletin/ Bulletin van die Munisipale Naslaanbiblioteek. (SA) **4091**, 2774
Municipal Registered Bond Interest Record see Municipal Bond Interest Record **5240**
Municipal Review see Municipal Review and A M A News **4091**
Municipal Review and A M A News. (UK ISSN 0261-5118) **4091**
Municipal World. (CN ISSN 0027-3589) **4091**
Municipal Year Book. (US ISSN 0077-2186) **4091**
Municipal Year Book. (UK ISSN 0305-5906) **4091**
†Municipal Year Book Directories. (US ISSN 0276-489X) **5240**
Municipal Yearbook see Municipal Year Book **4091**
▼Municipal Yellow Book. (US ISSN 1054-4062) **4091**
Municipalia. (SP) **4091**
Municipalities. see Al-Baladiat **4084**
Municipalities and Corporation Cases. (II ISSN 0377-757X) **2655**, 2711
Municipality. (US ISSN 0027-3597) **4091**
Munipal Security Rulemaking Board Manual see M S R B Manual **678**
Munisipale Ingenieur see Municipal Engineer **1871**
MuniWeek. (US) **957**
†Munka. (HU ISSN 0027-3600) **5240**
Munkaselet. (RM) **2586**
Munkavedelem/Labor Safety. (HU ISSN 0027-3619) **3619**
†Munksgaards Social Aarbog. (DK ISSN 0109-3347) **5240**
Munnpleien. (NO ISSN 0047-8377) **3238**
Munro Eagle. (US) **2159**, 2229
Munson-Williams-Proctor Institute. Bulletin. (US ISSN 0027-3627) **3527**
Al-Muntada. (TS) **2940**
Al-Muntijun. (LY) **4604**
Muntu. (GO ISSN 0768-9403) **2511**
Muon Catalyzed Fusion. (SZ ISSN 0259-9805) **3848**
Muoti & Kauneus. (FI ISSN 0355-192X) **1293**, 2186
Muotisorja see Muoti & Kauneus **1293**
Muoto see Finnish Design Magazine Muoto **299**
Muovi - Plast. (FI ISSN 0788-8430) **3864**
Muoviyhdistys Tiedottaa see Muovi - Plast **3864**
†Muppet Magazine. (US ISSN 0737-6855) **5240**

Muqarnas. (NE ISSN 0732-2992) **336**, 2431
Muqarnas, Supplements. (NE ISSN 0921-0326) **336**, 2431
Mur. (NO ISSN 0332-5733) **625**, 1831
Mur Vivant see Formes et Structures **2487**
Murerhaandbog. (DK ISSN 0108-8602) **625**
Murernes Fagblad see Byg & Trae **607**
Murmesteren. (NO ISSN 0027-3678) **625**
Murmur. (UK ISSN 0047-8385) **3255**
▼Murphy Mates. (US ISSN 1059-3713) **2159**
Murray Grey World. (AT ISSN 0310-9666) **221**
Murray Hill News. (US ISSN 0027-3686) **2229**
Murray Pioneer. (AT) **2875**
Murrelet see Northwestern Naturalist **589**
Al-Murshid/Guide. (BA) **2173**
Al-Murshid/Guide. (QA) **4778**
Murumiwa. (SA ISSN 0378-4126) **4244**
Murzilka. (RU ISSN 0132-1943) **1260**, 1648
Al-Musafir al-Arabi/Arab Traveller. (BA) **4778**
Musashi Institute of Technology. Atomic Energy Research Lab. Bulletin. see Musashi Kogyo Daigaku. Genshiryoku Kenkyujo. Kenkyujoho **1807**
Musashi Kogyo Daigaku. Genshiryoku Kenkyujo. Kenkyujoho/Musashi Institute of Technology. Atomic Energy Research Lab. Bulletin. (JA ISSN 0285-0354) **1807**
Musashino Art University. Bulletin. (JA ISSN 0288-6030) **336**
Musashino Electrical Communication Laboratories Technical Journal/ Kenkyu Jitsuyoka Hokoku. (JA ISSN 0415-3200) **1364**
Musashino Electrical Communication Laboratory. Review of the Electrical Communication Laboratory. (JA ISSN 0029-067X) **1364**
Al-Musawar. (UA) **874**, 2185
Muscadine. (US) **2875**, 2276
Muscle see Muscle & Fitness **3806**
Muscle & Fitness. (US ISSN 0744-5105) **3806**
Muscle & Nerve. (US ISSN 0148-639X) **3133**
†Muscle Biochemistry. (UK ISSN 0261-4766) **5240**
Muscle Car Review. (US) **4697**
Muscle Cars. (US) **4697**, 4479
Muscle Mag International. (CN) **4479**
Muscle Mustangs & Fast Fords. (US ISSN 1054-8912) **4697**
†Muscle Physiology. (UK ISSN 0261-4774) **5240**
Muscle Training Illustrated. (US ISSN 0047-8407) **3806**, 4479
Musclecar Classics. (US ISSN 0899-1421) **4697**
MuscleCars. (US ISSN 0897-0963) **4697**
Musclemag International. (CN) **3806**
Muscular Development. (US ISSN 0047-8415) **3806**, 4479
Muscular Dystrophy Association, Inc. Newsmagazine see M D A Newsmagazine **3123**
Muscular Dystrophy Journal see Search (London, 1957) **3152**
Muse. (NR ISSN 0331-3468) **2940**
†Muse. (US) **5240**
†Muse (Burlington). (US ISSN 0898-2392) **5240**
Muse (Columbia). (US ISSN 0077-2194) **336**, 279
Muse (Ottawa). (CN ISSN 0820-0165) **3527**
Muse (St. John's). (CN) **1318**
Muse Letter see Muse (Burlington) **5240**
Muse News. (AT ISSN 0728-8948) **3527**
Muse - Pie. (US) **2998**
Musealverein Wels. Jahrbuch. (AU) **2376**
†Musee Carnavalet. Bulletin. (FR ISSN 0027-3767) **5240**

†Musee d'Ethnographie de la Ville de Geneve. Bulletin Annuel. (SZ ISSN 0072-0828) **5240**
Musee de l'Homme, Paris. Catalogues. Serie C: Afrique Noire. (FR) **3527**
Musee de l'Homme, Paris. Catalogues. Serie H: Amerique. (FR) **3527**
Musee de l'Homme, Paris. Catalogues. Serie K: Asie. (FR) **3527**
Musee des Beaux-Arts du Canada. Catalogue. Art Canadien. Volume Premier, A - F see National Gallery of Canada. Catalogue. Canadian Art. Volume One, A - F **337**
Musee Ingres. Bulletin. (FR ISSN 0027-3783) **336**
Musee National d'Art Moderne. Cahiers.(FR ISSN 0181-1525) **3528**
Musee National d'Histoire Naturelle, Paris. Memoires. Nouvelle Serie. Serie C. Sciences de la Terre. (FR ISSN 0246-1196) **1547**
†Musee National d'Histoire Naturelle, Paris. Notes et Memoires sur le Moyen-Orient. (FR) **5240**
Musee National de l'Homme. Collection Mercure. Centre Canadien d'Etudes sur la Culture Traditionnelle. Dossiers. see National Museum of Man. Mercury Series. Canadian Centre for Folk Culture Studies. Papers **245**
Musee National de l'Homme. Collection Mercure. Commission Archaeologique du Canada. Dossiers. see National Museum of Man. Mercury Series. Archaeological Survey of Canada. Papers **279**
Musee National de l'Homme. Collection Mercure. Division de l'Histoire. Dossiers. see National Museum of Man. Mercury Series. History Division. Papers **2318**
Musee National de l'Homme. Collection Mercure. Musee Canadien de la Guerre. Dossiers. see National Museum of Man. Mercury Series. Canadian War Museum. Papers **3466**
Musee National de l'Homme. Collection Mercure. Service Canadien d'Ethnologie. Dossiers. see National Museum of Man. Mercury Series. Canadian Ethnology Service. Papers **246**
Musee National de Varsovie. Annuaire. see Muzeum Narodowe w Warszawie. Rocznik **5241**
Musee National de Varsovie. Bulletin. (PL ISSN 0027-3791) **3528**
Musee Royal de l'Afrique Centrale. Annales. Serie in 8. Sciences Economiques/Koninklijk Museum voor Midden-Afrika. Annalen. Reeks in 8. Economische Wetenschappen. (BE) **155**
Musee Royal de l'Afrique Centrale. Annales. Serie in 8. Sciences Geologiques/Koninklijk Museum voor Midden-Afrika. Annalen. Reeks in 8. Geologische Wetenschappen. (BE) **1573**
Musee Royal de l'Afrique Centrale. Annales. Serie in 8. Sciences Historiques/Koninklijk Museum voor Midden-Afrika. Annalen. Reeks in 8. Historische Wetenschappen. (BE) **2334**
Musee Royal de l'Afrique Centrale. Annales. Serie in 8. Sciences Humaines/Koninklijk Museum voor Midden-Afrika. Annalen. Reeks in 8. Menselijke Wetenschappen. (BE) **2511**, 4380
Musee Royal de l'Afrique Centrale. Annales. Serie in 8. Sciences Zoologiques/Koninklijk Museum voor Midden-Afrika. Annalen. Reeks in 8. Zoologische Wetenschappen. (BE) **588**
Musee Royal de l'Afrique Centrale. Archives d'Anthropologie. (BE) **245**
Musee Royal de l'Afrique Centrale. Departement de Geologie et de Mineralogie. Rapport Annuel. (BE) **1574**

MUSEUM 6453

Musee Royal de l'Afrique Centrale. Documentation Economique/ Koninklijk Museum voor Midden-Afrika. Economische Documentatie. (BE) **680**

Musee Royal de l'Afrique Centrale. Documentation Zoologique/Koninklijk Museum voor Midden-Afrika. Zoologische Documentatie. (BE) **588**

Museen der Stadt Koeln. Bulletin *see* Koelner Museums Bulletin **3526**

Museen der Welt. *see* Museums of the World **3529**

Museen in Schleswig-Holstein. (GW ISSN 0720-7883) **3528**

Museerne i Viborg Amt *see* M I V: Museerne i Viborg Amt **2374**

Musees. (CN ISSN 0706-098X) **3528**, 303, 336

Musees de Geneve. (SZ ISSN 0027-3821) **3528**

Musees et Collections Publiques de France. (FR ISSN 0027-383X) **3528**

Musees et Monuments Lyonnais. Bulletin. (FR ISSN 0521-7032) **3528**

Musees Royaux d'Art et d'Histoire. Bulletin/Koninklijke Musea voor Kunst en Geschiedenis. Bulletin. (BE ISSN 0776-1414) **2376**, **3528**

Musees Royaux des Beaux-Arts de Belgique. Bulletin/Koninklijke Musea voor Schone Kunsten van Belgie. Bulletin. (BE ISSN 0027-3856) **3528**

Museet for Fotokunst. Katalog. (DK ISSN 0904-2334) **3793**

Museet for Holbaek og Omegn *see* Museet for Holbaek og Omegn. Aarsberetning **3528**

Museet for Holbaek og Omegn. Aarsberetning. (DK ISSN 0108-917X) **3528**

Musei Civici Veneziani. Bollettino. (IT ISSN 0083-5447) **3528**

Musei Comunali di Roma. Bollettino. (IT) **3528**

Musei e Gallerie d'Italia. (IT ISSN 0027-3872) **3528**

Museika. (IS) **3563**

Museion. (AU ISSN 0077-2208) **2774**

Museletter. (CN) **2998**

Musen to Jikken. *see* Stereo Technic **4462**

Musengau *see* Thema - Das Theatermagazin **4641**

Museo Archeologico di Tarquinia. Materiali. (IT ISSN 0391-9293) **3528**, 279

Museo Argentino de Ciencias Naturales "Bernardino Rivadavia." Instituto Nacional de Investigacion de las Ciencias Naturales. Revista. Botanica.(AG ISSN 0376-2793) **509**

Museo Argentino de Ciencias Naturales "Bernardino Rivadavia." Instituto Nacional de Investigacion de las Ciencias Naturales. Revista. Ecologia.(AG ISSN 0524-9481) **448**

Museo Argentino de Ciencias Naturales "Bernardino Rivadavia." Instituto Nacional de Investigacion de las Ciencias Naturales. Revista. Entomologia. (AG ISSN 0524-949X) **536**

Museo Argentino de Ciencias Naturales "Bernardino Rivadavia." Instituto Nacional de Investigacion de las Ciencias Naturales. Revista. Geologia.(AG ISSN 0027-3880) **1574**

Museo Argentino de Ciencias Naturales "Bernardino Rivadavia." Instituto Nacional de Investigacion de las Ciencias Naturales. Revista. Hidrobiologia. (AG ISSN 0524-9503) **448**

Museo Argentino de Ciencias Naturales "Bernardino Rivadavia." Instituto Nacional de Investigacion de las Ciencias Naturales. Revista. Parasitologia. (AG ISSN 0524-952X) **3222**

Museo Argentino de Ciencias Naturales "Bernardino Rivadavia." Instituto Nacional de Investigacion de las Ciencias Naturales. Revista. Paleontologia. (AG ISSN 0524-9511) **3658**

Museo Argentino de Ciencias Naturales "Bernardino Rivadavia." Instituto Nacional de Investigacion de las Ciencias Naturales. Revista y Comunicaciones. *see* Museo Argentino de Ciencias Naturales "Bernardino Rivadavia." Instituto Nacional de Investigacion de las Ciencias Naturales. Revista. Geologia **1574**

Museo Argentino de Ciencias Naturales "Bernardino Rivadavia." Instituto Nacional de Investigacion de las Ciencias Naturales. Revista. Zoologia.(AG ISSN 0373-9066) **588**

Museo Arqueologico de Valladolid. Monografias. (SP) **279**

Museo Arqueologico Nacional. Catalogos Cientificos. (SP) **279**

Museo Bodoniano. Bollettino. (IT) **3528**

Museo Chileno de Arte Precolombino. Boletin. (CL ISSN 0716-1530) 336, 245, 279

Museo Civico Archeologico Ugo Granafei di Mesagne. Testi e Monumenti. (IT) **3528**, 279

Museo Civico di Storia Naturale di Trieste. Atti. (IT ISSN 0365-1576) **448**, 1547

Museo Civico di Storia Naturale "Giacomo Doria", Genoa. Annali. (IT ISSN 0365-4389) **4324**

Museo Civico di Storia Naturale, Verona. Bollettino. (IT ISSN 0392-0062) **4324**

Museo Civico di Storia Naturale, Verona. Memorie. Serie 2, Part 1: Biologica. (IT) **4324**

Museo Civico di Storia Naturale, Verona. Memorie. Serie 2, Part 2: Abiologica.(IT) **4324**

Museo Civico di Storia Naturale, Verona. Memorie. Serie 2, Part 3: Preistorica.(IT) **4324**

Museo de Arte Colonial de Bogota. Boletin Informativo. (CK) **3528**

Museo de Ciencias Naturales. Boletin. (VE ISSN 0027-3899) **4325**

Museo de Historia Natural de San Rafael. Instituto de Ciencias Naturales. Notas *see* Museo Municipal de Historia Natural de San Rafael. Instituto de Ciencias Naturales. Notas **1574**

Museo de Historia Natural de San Rafael. Revista *see* Museo Municipal de Historia Natural de San Rafael. Revista **4325**

Museo de la Plata. Novedades. (AG) **1547**

Museo del Hombre Dominicano. Boletin.(DR) **245**, 279

Museo del Hombre Dominicano. Papeles Ocasionales. (DR) **245**

Museo del Hombre Dominicano. Serie Catalogos y Memorias. (DR) **3528**, 245

Museo del Hombre Dominicano. Serie Conferencias Pensamiento Dominicano. (DR) **3773**

Museo del Hombre Dominicano. Serie Conferencias sobre el Pensamiento de Pedro Henriquez Urena. (DR) **3773**

†Museo del Hombre Dominicano. Serie Estudio y Arte. (DR) **5240**

Museo del Hombre Dominicano. Serie Investigaciones Antropologicas. (DR) **245**

Museo del Hombre Dominicano. Serie Mesa Redonda Conferencias. (DR) **3528**, 245

Museo del Oro. Boletin. (CK ISSN 0120-7296) **245**

Museo del Prado. Boletin. (SP ISSN 0210-8143) **3528**

Museo dell'Impero Romano. Studi e Materiali *see* Museo della Civilta Romana. Studi e Materiali **3528**

Museo della Civilta Romana. Studi e Materiali. (IT) **3528**

Museo Municipal de Historia Natural de San Rafael. Instituto de Ciencias Naturales. Notas. (AG ISSN 0539-3027) **1574**, 245, 509, 4325

Museo Municipal de Historia Natural de San Rafael. Revista. (AG ISSN 0375-1155) **4325**, 279

Museo Nacional. Revista. (PE) **3528**

Museo Nacional de Antropologia y Arqueologia. Serie: Antropologia Fisica. (PE) **245**

Museo Nacional de Etnografia y Folklore. Avances de Investigacion. (BO) **2057**

†Museo Nacional de Historia Natural. Anales. (UY) **5240**

Museo Nacional de Historia Natural. Boletin. (CL ISSN 0027-3910) **4325**, 245

Museo Nacional de Historia Natural. Comunicaciones Antropologicas. (UY ISSN 0077-1244) **245**

Museo Nacional de Historia Natural. Comunicaciones Botanicas. (UY ISSN 0027-0121) **509**

Museo Nacional de Historia Natural. Comunicaciones Paleontologicas. (UY) **3658**

Museo Nacional de Historia Natural. Comunicaciones Zoologicas. (UY ISSN 0027-0113) **588**

Museo Nacional de Historia Natural. Noticiario Mensual. (CL ISSN 0027-3945) **4325**, 245

Museo Nacional de Historia Natural. Publicacion Ocasional. (CL ISSN 0716-0224) **3528**

Museo Nazionale d'Arte Orientale. Schede. (IT) **3528**, 3641

Museo Regionale di Scienze Naturali, Torino. Bollettino. (IT ISSN 0392-758X) **448**

Museo Risorgimento. Bollettino. (IT ISSN 0523-9478) **2376**

Museo Social Argentino. Boletin *see* Conceptos Boletin **4432**

Museo Trentino del Risorgimento e della Lotta per la Liberta. Bollettino *see* Archivio Trentino di Storia Contemporanea. Museo del Risorgimento e della Lotta per la Liberta. Bollettino **2349**

Museo y Monumento Nacional "Justo Jose de Urquiza". Serie 3. (AG) **3528**

Museogramme. (CN ISSN 0380-4623) **3528**

†Museologia (Florence). (IT) **5240**

†Museologia (Naples). (IT) **5240**

†Museologist. (US ISSN 0027-397X) **5240**

Museology. (US ISSN 0196-0237) **3528**

Le Museon. (BE ISSN 0771-6494) **3641**, 2431

Museu Arxiu de Santa Maria. Fulls. (SP ISSN 0212-9248) **2377**

Museu Bocage. Arquivos. (PO ISSN 0027-3988) **245**

Museu Botanico Municipal. Boletim. (BL) **509**

Museu de Zoologia. Col.leccions. (SP) **588**

Museu Municipal do Funchal. Boletim. (PO ISSN 0870-3876) **588**, 448

Museu Municipal de Antropologia. Cuadernos. (MX ISSN 0076-7158) **245**

Museu Nacional, Rio de Janeiro. Arquivos. (BL ISSN 0080-3111) **4325**, 3528

Museu Nacional, Rio de Janeiro. Boletim. Nova Serie. Antropologia. (BL ISSN 0080-3189) **245**

Museu Nacional, Rio de Janeiro. Boletim. Nova Serie. Botanica. (BL ISSN 0080-3197) **509**

Museu Nacional, Rio de Janeiro. Boletim. Nova Serie. Geologie. (BL ISSN 0080-3200) **1574**

Museu Nacional, Rio de Janeiro. Boletim. Nova Serie. Zoologia. (BL ISSN 0080-312X) **588**

Museu Paraense Emilio Goeldi. Boletim. Nova Serie: Antropologia *see* Museu Paraense Emilio Goeldi. Boletim. Serie Antropologia **245**

Museu Paraense Emilio Goeldi. Boletim. Nova Serie: Botanica *see* Museu Paraense Emilio Goeldi. Boletim. Serie Botanica **509**

Museu Paraense Emilio Goeldi. Boletim. Nova Serie: Geologia. (BL ISSN 0077-2224) **1574**

Museu Paraense Emilio Goeldi. Boletim. Serie Antropologia. (BL) **245**

Museu Paraense Emilio Goeldi. Boletim. Serie Botanica. (BL) **509**

Museu Paraense Emilio Goeldi. Boletim. Serie Ciencias da Terra. (BL ISSN 0103-4278) **1547**

Museu Paraense Emilio Goeldi. Boletim. Serie Zoologia. (BL) **588**

†Museu Paraense Emilio Goeldi. Publicacoes Avulsas. (BL ISSN 0077-2240) **5240**

Museu Paulista. Colecao *see* Universidade de Sao Paulo. Museu Paulista. Colecao. Serie de Etnologia **251**

Museu Paulista. Colecao *see* Universidade de Sao Paulo. Museu Paulista. Colecao. Serie de Arqueologia **288**

Museu Paulista. Colecao *see* Universidade de Sao Paulo. Museu Paulista. Colecao. Serie de Geografia **2264**

Museu Paulista. Colecao *see* Universidade de Sao Paulo. Museu Paulista. Colecao. Serie de Historia **2425**

Museu Paulista. Colecao *see* Universidade de Sao Paulo. Museu Paulista. Colecao. Serie de Numismatica **3602**

Museum *see* Forum der Letteren **2918**

Museum. (UN ISSN 0027-3996) **3528**

Museum. (JA ISSN 0027-4003) **3528**

Museum. (GW ISSN 0341-8634) **3528**

Museum Abstracts. (UK ISSN 0267-8594) **3536**

†Museum Africum. (NR) **5240**

†Museum & Arts Washington. (US ISSN 0884-1918) **5240**

Museum Applied Science and Culture Archaeology Research Papers in Science and Archaeology *see* M A S C A Research Papers in Science and Archaeology **278**

Museum Boymans-van Beuningen. Agenda - Diary. (NE ISSN 0077-2275) **3528**

Museum Briefs *see* University of Missouri, Columbia. Museum of Anthropology. Museum Briefs **252**

Museum Catalog of Publications and Media *see* Catalog of Museum Publications and Media **3536**

Museum Criticum. (IT) **2940**

Museum Documentation Association Information *see* M D A Information **5229**

Museum Ethnographers Group. Newsletter. (UK ISSN 0260-0366) 245, 3528

Museum fuer Ur- und Fruehgeschichte der Bezirke Potsdam, Frankfurt - Oder und Cottbus. Veroeffentlichungen. (GW ISSN 0079-4376) **2318**, 3528

Museum fuer Ur- und Fruehgeschichte Thueringens. Jahreschrift *see* Alt-Thueringen **2348**

Museum fuer Voelkerkunde, Berlin. Veroeffentlichungen. Neue Folge. Abteilung: Afrika. (GW ISSN 0067-5962) **245**, 2334

Museum fuer Voelkerkunde, Berlin. Veroeffentlichungen. Neue Folge. Abteilung: Amerikanische Archaeologie. (GW) **279**

Museum fuer Voelkerkunde, Berlin. Veroeffentlichungen. Neue Folge. Abteilung: Amerikanische Naturvoelker. (GW) **245**, 337

Museum fuer Voelkerkunde, Berlin. Veroeffentlichungen. Neue Folge. Abteilung: Musikethnologie. (GW) **3563**, 245

MUSEUM

Museum fuer Voelkerkunde, Berlin. Veroeffentlichungen. Neue Folge. Abteilung: Suedsee. (GW ISSN 0067-5989) **245,** 2345
Museum fuer Voelkerkunde, Leipzig. Jahrbuch. (GW ISSN 0075-8663) **3528**
Museum fuer Voelkerkunde, Leipzig. Veroeffentlichungen. (GW ISSN 0075-8671) **3528**
Museum Helveticum. (SZ ISSN 0027-4054) **1278,** 279, 2830
Museum Highlights. (US) **3528**
Museum Management and Curatorship. (UK) **3529**
†Museum Methods Manuals. (CN ISSN 0701-9548) **5240**
Museum National d'Histoire Naturelle. Bulletin - Section A (Zoologie et Ecologie Animales). (FR ISSN 0181-0626) **588**
Museum National d'Histoire Naturelle. Bulletin - Section B - Adansonia (Botanique, Phytochimie). (FR ISSN 0240-8937) **510**
Museum National d'Histoire Naturelle. Bulletin - Section C (Sciences de la Terre: Paleontologie, Geologie, Mineralogie). (FR ISSN 0181-0642) **1574**
Museum National d'Histoire Naturelle. Memoires. Nouvelle Serie. Serie B. Botanique. (FR ISSN 0078-9755) **510**
†Museum National d'Histoire Naturelle, Paris. Annuaire. (FR ISSN 0078-9720) **5240**
†Museum National d'Histoire Naturelle, Paris. Archives. (FR ISSN 0078-9739) **5240**
†Museum National d'Histoire Naturelle, Paris. Bibliotheque Centrale. Liste des Periodiques Francais et Etrangers. Supplement. (FR ISSN 0085-476X) **5240**
Museum National d'Histoire Naturelle, Paris. Grands Naturalistes Francais. (FR) **4325**
†Museum National d'Histoire Naturelle, Paris. Laboratoire d'Ethnobotanique. Publications Diverses. (FR) **5240**
Museum National d'Histoire Naturelle, Paris. Memoires. Nouvelle Serie. Serie A. Zoologie. (FR ISSN 0078-9747) **588**
†Museum National d'Histoire Naturelle, Paris. Memoires. Nouvelle Serie. Serie D. Sciences Physico-Chimiques.(FR ISSN 0078-9771) **5240**
Museum News. (US ISSN 0027-4089) **3529,** 2318
Museum News and Views from the Nova Scotia Museum Complex. (CN ISSN 0828-2773) **3529**
Museum News Magazine. see Muzejski Vjesnik **279**
Museum Notes (Providence). (US) **3529**
Museum Notes (Spokane). (US) **3529,** 337, 2415
Museum of African-American History. Newsletter. (US) **2015,** 2415
Museum of Agriculture. Scientifical Works. see Zemedelske Muzeum. Vedecke Prace **131**
Museum of Antiquities of Tel-Aviv-Yafo. Publications. (IS ISSN 0082-2620) **279,** 2256
Museum of Comparative Zoology. Bulletin. (US ISSN 0027-4100) **588**
Museum of Far Eastern Antiquities. Bulletin. (SW ISSN 0081-5691) **3529,** 337, 3641
Museum of Fine Arts, Boston. Journal. (US ISSN 1030-2433) **337,** 3529
Museum of Flight News. (US) **59**
Museum of Holography. Directory & Buyers' Guide. (US) **3855**
Museum of Science Magazine. (US) **3529,** 4325
Museum of Science Newsletter see Museum of Science Magazine **3529**
Museum of the City of New York Quarterly. (US) **3529**
Museum of the Confederacy. Journal. (US) **2415**

Museum of the Fur Trade Quarterly. (US ISSN 0027-4135) **2415,** 2737
Museum of the Great Plains Newsletter.(US) **3529**
Museum of Victoria. Memoirs. (AT ISSN 0814-1827) **588,** 3529
▼Museum of Victoria. Memoirs - Anthropology and History. (AT ISSN 1035-4247) **245,** 2345
Museum of Victoria. Occasional Papers. (AT ISSN 0814-1819) **588,** 3529
†Museum Patavinum. Semestrale. (IT) **5240**
Museum Post Rider. (US) **3754**
Museum Quarterly. (CN ISSN 0822-5931) **3529**
Museum Record. (US) **2159,** 3529
Museum Reporter. (UK ISSN 0954-0423) **3529**
Museum Round-up see British Columbia Museums Association. Museum Round Up **3522**
Museum Store. (US ISSN 1040-6999) **1048,** 3529
Museum Studies. see Hakubutsukan Kenkyu **3524**
†Museum Studies Journal. (US ISSN 0733-0960) **5241**
Museum Talk see Santa Barbara Museum of Natural History. Museum Bulletin **3532**
Museum Year. (US ISSN 0740-0403) **3529,** 337
Museumjournaal see Kunst en Museumjournaal **333**
Museums and Galleries see Museums and Galleries in Great Britain and Ireland **3529**
Museums and Galleries in Great Britain and Ireland. (UK ISSN 0141-6723) **3529**
Museums and Monuments Series. (UN ISSN 0077-233X) **3529**
Museums Association of Australia. Quarterly News. (AT) **3529**
Museums Australia. (AT ISSN 0812-7883) **3529**
Museums Bulletin see Museums Journal **3529**
Museums Calendar see Museums Yearbook **3529**
Museums - Eisenbahn. (GW ISSN 0936-4609) **4711**
Museums Journal. (UK ISSN 0027-416X) **3529**
Museums Newsletter. (II) **3529**
Museums of the World/Museen der Welt. (GW) **3529**
Museums Yearbook. (UK ISSN 0307-7675) **3529**
Museumsforeningen for Laesoe. Litteratur. (DK ISSN 0109-5854) **3529**
Museumskunde. (GW ISSN 0027-4178) **3529**
Museumsnytt. (NO ISSN 0027-4186) **3529,** 4325
Museumspaedagogisches Zentrum Kooperationsprojekt see M P Z - Kooperationsprojekt **3527**
Museumsverband fuer Niedersachsen und Bremen. Mitteilungsblatt. (GW ISSN 0931-4857) **3529**
Al-Mushir/Counselor. (PK ISSN 0254-7856) **4191**
Mushroom. (US ISSN 0740-8161) **2134**
Mushroom Journal. (UK) **2134,** 510
Mushroom News. (US ISSN 0541-3869) **185**
†Mushroom Newswire. (US) **5241**
Mushroom Science. (UK ISSN 0077-2364) **510**
Musi - Key. (US ISSN 0895-1543) **3563**
Music. (IT) **3563**
Music Academy. Conference Souvenir. (II) **3563**
Music Academy. Journal. (II) **3564**
▼Music Access Directory. (US) **3564**
Music Analysis. (UK ISSN 0262-5245) **3564**
Music & Audio Reviews. (US) **3564**
Music & Automata. (UK ISSN 0262-8260) **3564**
▼Music & Computer Educator. (US) **3590,** 1426, 1691
Music and Dance Periodicals. (US) **3589,** 1532

Music and Entertainment Industry Educators' Notes. (US) **3564**
Music & Equipment Mart. (UK) **3564**
Music and Letters. (UK ISSN 0027-4224) **3564**
Music and Life. (UK ISSN 0085-3607) **3564**
Music and Liturgy. (UK ISSN 0305-4438) **3564**
Music and Media - I M Z Bulletin see Music in the Media - I M Z Bulletin **3564**
Music & Musicians: Braille Scores Catalog - Choral (Large Print Edition). (US ISSN 0145-3173) **2285,** 406, 2294, 3589
Music & Musicians: Braille Scores Catalog - Instrumental (Large Print Edition). (US ISSN 0145-3165) **2285,** 406, 2294, 3589
Music & Musicians: Braille Scores Catalog - Organ (Large Print Edition). (US ISSN 0145-3149) **2285,** 406, 2294, 3589
Music & Musicians: Braille Scores Catalog - Piano (Large Print Edition). (US ISSN 0145-3130) **2285,** 406, 2294, 3589
Music and Musicians: Braille Scores Catalog - Vocal (Large Print Edition) see Music & Musicians: Braille Scores Catalog Vocal Part I: Classical (Large Print Edition) **2285**
Music and Musicians: Braille Scores Catalog - Vocal (Large Print Edition) see Music & Musicians: Braille Scores Catalog Vocal Part II: Popular (Large Print Edition) **2285**
Music & Musicians: Braille Scores Catalog Vocal Part I: Classical (Large Print Edition). (US) **2285,** 406, 2294, 3589
Music & Musicians: Braille Scores Catalog Vocal Part II: Popular (Large Print Edition). (US) **2285,** 406, 2294, 3589
Music and Musicians: Braille Scores Catalog - Voice see Music & Musicians: Braille Scores Catalog Vocal Part I: Classical (Large Print Edition) **2285**
Music and Musicians: Braille Scores Catalog - Voice see Music & Musicians: Braille Scores Catalog Vocal Part II: Popular (Large Print Edition) **2285**
Music & Musicians: Instructional Cassette Recordings Catalog (Large Print Edition). (US ISSN 0145-2525) **2285,** 406, 2294, 3589
Music & Musicians: Instructional Disc Recordings Catalog (Large Print Edition). (US ISSN 0145-2517) **2285,** 406, 2294, 3589
†Music & Musicians International. (UK ISSN 0952-2697) **5241**
Music & Musicians: Large-Print Scores and Books Catalog (Large Print Edition). (US) **2285,** 406, 2294, 3589
Music and Musicians: Large Print Scores and Books Catalog for the Blind and Physically Handicapped see Music & Musicians: Large-Print Scores and Books Catalog (Large Print Edition) **2285**
Music and Sound Electronics Retailer see Music and Sound Retailer **3564**
†Music & Sound Output. (US ISSN 0273-8902) **5241**
Music and Sound Retailer. (US ISSN 0894-1238) **3564,** 1048, 4461
Music and the Teacher. (AT ISSN 0047-8431) **1755,** 3564
Music and Video Week see Music Week **3566**
Music and Video Week Directory see Music Week Directory **3566**
Music Article Guide. (US ISSN 0027-4240) **3589,** 17
Music Association of Ireland. Annual Report. (IE) **3564**
Music at the Kindergarten. (RU) **3564,** 1260
Music, Books on Music and Sound Recordings. (US ISSN 0092-2838) **3589,** 2794, 4462
Music Business see Video & Music Business **1056**

Music Business. (UK ISSN 0269-0292) **3564**
†Music Business Contacts. (US) **5241**
Music Cataloging Bulletin. (US ISSN 0027-4283) **2774,** 3564
Music City News. (US ISSN 0027-4291) **3564**
Music Clubs Magazine. (US ISSN 0161-2654) **3564**
Music, Computers & Software see M C S **5229**
Music Connection. (US) **3564**
Music Directory Canada. (CN ISSN 0820-0416) **3564**
Music Educators Journal. (US ISSN 0027-4321) **3564,** 1755
†Music Educators National Conference. Selective Music Lists: Instrumental Solos and Ensembles. (US) **5241**
†Music Educators National Conference. Selective Music Lists: Vocal Solos and Ensembles. (US ISSN 0077-2402) **5241**
Music Educators National Conference Soundpost see M E N C Soundpost **3562**
Music Express. (CN) **3564**
Music File. (UK ISSN 0954-0377) **1755,** 2774, 3564
Music for One Music for All. (CN) **3564**
Music Forum. (US) **3564**
▼Music from China. News/Chang Feng Yue Xun. (US) **3564**
Music in American Life. (US) **3564**
Music in Danish Libraries. see Musikalier i Danske Biblioteker (Quarterly) **2774**
Music in Danish Libraries. see Musikalier i Danske Biblioteker (Annual) **3589**
Music in Germany see Deutsches Musikleben (Year) **3548**
Music in Poland. (PL ISSN 0860-911X) **3564,** 2214
Music-in-Print Series. (US ISSN 0146-7883) **3589,** 17
Music in the Media - I M Z Bulletin. (AU) **3564**
Music in Time. (IS) **3564**
Music Inc. (US) **3564**
Music Index. (US ISSN 0027-4348) **3589,** 17
Music Industries Association of Canada Communique see M I A C Communique **5229**
Music Industry Educators' Notes see Music and Entertainment Industry Educators' Notes **3564**
†Music Industry Products. (US) **5241**
▼Music International. (US ISSN 1048-1400) **3565,** 1531
Music Journal. (UK ISSN 0951-5135) **3565**
The Music Leader. (US ISSN 0027-4372) **3565,** 4244
Music Library Association. Index and Bibliography Series. (US ISSN 0094-6478) **3589**
Music Library Association. Index Series see Music Library Association. Index and Bibliography Series **3589**
Music Library Association. Newsletter. (US ISSN 0580-289X) **3565**
Music Library Association. Notes. (US ISSN 0027-4380) **2774,** 3565
Music Library Association. Technical Reports. (US ISSN 0094-5099) **2774,** 3565
Music Life. (JA) **3565**
Music Life. see Yinyue Shenghuo **3587**
Music Locator see Christian Music Directories: Printed Music **3545**
Music Lover. see Yinyue Aihaozhe **3587**
Music Magazine. (CN ISSN 0705-4009) **3565,** 1260
Music Makers (Nashville). (US ISSN 0162-4377) **4244,** 3565
Music Makers (Redwood City). (US) **3565**
Music Management & International Promotion. (DK ISSN 0108-5328) **3565,** 1021
†Music Mart. (US) **5241**
Music Master see Music Master Catalogue **3565**
Music Master Catalogue. (UK) **3565**
Music Master Labels List. (UK) **3565**

Music McGill. (CN ISSN 0702-9012) 3565
Music News. see Muzikos Zinios 3569
Music News (Washington). (US ISSN 0891-1002) 3565
Music News Bulletin see Union of Bulgarian Composers. News Bulletin 3585
Music News from Prague. (CS ISSN 0027-4410) 3565
Music Now. (US ISSN 0027-4437) 3565
Music O C L C Users Group. Newsletter.(US ISSN 0161-1704) 2774, 3565
Music of the Spheres. (US ISSN 0892-2721) 3595, 337, 3565
Music Paper. (US) 3565
Music Perception. (US ISSN 0730-7829) 3565
Music Reference Collection. (US ISSN 0736-7740) 3589
▼Music Reference Services Quarterly. (US ISSN 1058-8167) 2774, 3565
Music Research/Ongaku Kenkyu. (JA) 3565
Music Research. see Yinyue Yanjiu 3587
Music Research News. (CN ISSN 0700-3838) 3565
▼Music Retailing. (US ISSN 1051-1822) 3565, 1021
Music Review. (UK ISSN 0027-4445) 3565
Music Scene. (SZ) 3565
†Music Scene. (CN ISSN 0380-5131) 5241
Music Study see Yinyue Yanjiu 3587
Music Teacher. (UK ISSN 0027-4461) 3565
Music Teachers' Association of N.S.W. Quarterly Magazine. (AT ISSN 0727-8683) 1755, 3565
Music Teachers Library. (RU) 3565, 1648, 2875
Music Technology. (UK ISSN 0891-7264) 3565, 4461
Music Technology see Home & Studio Recording 4461
†Music Tempo. (US ISSN 0027-447X) 5241
Music Theory Spectrum. (US ISSN 0195-6167) 3565
Music Therapy. (US ISSN 0734-7367) 3565
Music Time. (US ISSN 0164-7180) 3565, 4244
Music Trade in Japan. see Gakki Shoho 3552
Music Trades. (US ISSN 0027-4488) 3565
Music Trades International see Musical World 3567
Music U S A. (US) 3566, 4580
Music Week. (UK ISSN 0265-1548) 3566
Music Week Directory. (UK) 3566
Music World. see Yinyue Tiandi 3587
Music World see Yinyue Shijie 3587
Music World Year Book. (UK ISSN 0077-2453) 3566
Music Yearbook see British Music Yearbook 3543
Musica. (GW ISSN 0027-4518) 3566
Musica. (IT ISSN 0392-5544) 3566
Musica. (CU) 3566
Musica Antiqua. (BE ISSN 0771-7016) 3566
Musica Asiatica. (US ISSN 0140-6078) 3566, 3641
Musica Britannica. (UK ISSN 0580-2954) 3566
Musica, Cinema, Immagine, Teatro. (IT) 3566, 337, 4635
Musica, Cinema, Teatro see Musica, Cinema, Immagine, Teatro 3566
Musica d'Oggi. (IT) 3566
Musica Disciplina. (GW ISSN 0077-2461) 3566
Musica Domani. (IT ISSN 0391-4380) 3566
Musica e Dischi. (IT ISSN 0027-4526) 3566
Musica e Dossier. (IT) 3566
Musica Iberoamericana see Latina
Musica Jazz. (IT ISSN 0027-4542) 3566

Musica Judaica. (US ISSN 0147-7536) 3566, 4225
Musica Medii Aevi. (PL ISSN 0077-247X) 3566
Musica Nova. (JA ISSN 0289-3630) 3566
Musica Sacra. (GW ISSN 0179-356X) 3566
Musica Viva. (IT) 3566
Musicae Sacrae Ministerium. (IT ISSN 0027-4569) 3566
†Musical America. (US ISSN 0735-777X) 5241
Musical America International Directory of the Performing Arts. (US ISSN 0735-7788) 3566
Musical Box Society International. Bulletin see Mechanical Music 3562
Musical Box Society International Technical Journal see Mechanical Music 3562
Musical Creation. see Yinyue Chuangzuo 3587
Musical Denmark. (DK ISSN 0027-4585) 3566
Musical Heritage Review Magazine. (US ISSN 0160-3876) 3566
Musical Instruments of East Africa. (KE) 3566
Musical Interpretation Research. (SW ISSN 0349-988X) 3566, 2511
Musical Mainstream (Large Print Edition). (US ISSN 0364-7501) 2294, 3566
Musical Merchandise Review. (US ISSN 0027-4615) 3566
Musical Opinion. (UK ISSN 0027-4623) 3566
Musical Quarterly. (US ISSN 0027-4631) 3566
Musical Salvationist. (UK ISSN 0027-464X) 4244, 3566
Musical Show. (US ISSN 0027-4658) 4635, 3567
Musical Times. (UK ISSN 0027-4666) 3567
Musical Woman. (US ISSN 0737-0032) 3567, 4849
Musical World. (UK) 3567
Musicalbrande. (IT ISSN 0027-4674) 3567
Musicals. (GW ISSN 0932-7118) 4635, 3567
†Musicanada. (CN ISSN 0700-4745) 5241
▼Musiche del Rinascimento Italiano. (IT) 3567
Musiche Rinascimentali Siciliane. (IT) 3567
Musician. (US ISSN 0733-5253) 3567
Musician. see Muusikko 3568
Musician see Salvationist 4248
Musician. (AT) 4285
Musicien Amateur. see Amateur Musician 3537
Musicien Quebecois. (CN ISSN 0844-479X) 3567
Musick. (CN) 3567
Musick of the Fifes & Drums Series. (US) 3567
MusicMaker. (NE) 3567
Musicologia Espanola. (SP) 3567
Musicologica Neolovaniensia Studia. (BE) 3567
Musicologica Slovaca. (CS ISSN 0581-0558) 3567
Musicological Annual. see Muzikoloski Zbornik 3569
Musicological Society of Australia. Newsletter. (AT ISSN 0155-0543) 3567
Musicological Studies and Documents. (GW ISSN 0077-2496) 3567
Musicological Yearbook. see Arti Musices 3539
Musicology. see Hudebni Veda 3555
Musicology see Musicology Australia 3567
Musicology Australia. (AT ISSN 0814-5857) 3567
Musicology in China. see Zhongguo Yinyuexue 3587
Musicus. (SA ISSN 0256-8837) 3567
Musicworks. (CN ISSN 0225-686X) 3567, 337
Musiikki. (FI ISSN 0355-1059) 3567

Musik - Almanach. (GW ISSN 0930-8954) 3567
Musik & Theater. (SZ) 3567, 1531, 4635
Musik aus der Steiermark. (GW) 3567
Musik Express. (GW) 3567
Musik i Sverige. (SW ISSN 0077-2518) 3567
Musik in Bayern. (GW ISSN 0937-583X) 3567
Musik in der Schule. (GW ISSN 0027-4704) 3567, 1648
Musik - Info. (GW) 3567
†Musik - Information. (GW ISSN 0323-438X) 5241
Musik International. (GW) 3567
Musik - Konzepte. (GW ISSN 0931-3311) 3567
Musik Markt Branchen Handbuch see M M Branchen Handbuch 3562
†Musik Nyt. (DK ISSN 0900-1204) 5241
Musik-, Tanz- und Kunsttherapie. (GW) 3133, 3345
Musik und Bildung. (GW ISSN 0027-4747) 3567
Musik und Gesellschaft. (GW ISSN 0027-4755) 3568
Musik und Gesellschaft. (AU ISSN 0259-076X) 3568, 4443
Musik & Gottesdienst. (SZ ISSN 0027-4763) 3568
Musik und Kirche. (GW ISSN 0027-4771) 3568, 4191
Musikalier i Danske Biblioteker (Annual) /Music in Danish Libraries. (DK ISSN 0085-3623) 3589
Musikalier i Danske Biblioteker (Quarterly)/Music in Danish Libraries.(DK ISSN 0109-0364) 2774
Musikalische Denkmaeler. (GW ISSN 0077-2526) 3568
Musikblatt. (GW ISSN 0172-8989) 3568
Musikbranchens Aarbog. (DK ISSN 0108-0040) 3568
Musikeren. (DK) 3568
Musikern. (SW ISSN 0027-478X) 3568
Musikerziehung. (AU ISSN 0027-4798) 3568
Die Musikforschung. (GW ISSN 0027-4801) 3568
†Musikforum. (GW ISSN 0323-5106) 5241
Musikforum - Referate und Informationen des Deutschen Musikrates. (GW) 3568
Musikhandel. (GW ISSN 0027-481X) 3568
Musikhistorisk Museum og Carl Claudius' Samling. Meddelelser. (DK ISSN 0109-2618) 3568
Musikhistoriska Museets. Skrifter see Musikmuseets Skrifter 3568
Das Musikinstrument. (GW ISSN 0027-4828) 3568
Musikk og Skole. (NO) 3568
Musiklivet - Vaar Saang. (SW ISSN 0027-4836) 3568
Der Musikmarkt. (GW ISSN 0047-8474) 3568
Musikmuseets Skrifter. (SW ISSN 0282-8952) 3568
Musikpaedagogische Bibliothek. (GW) 3568
Musikpsychologie. (GW ISSN 0177-350X) 3568, 4036
Musikrevy. (SW ISSN 0027-4844) 3568
Musikstadt Cologne. (GW) 4778, 3568
MusikTexte. (GW ISSN 0178-8884) 3568
Musiktheorie. (GW ISSN 0177-4182) 3568
Musiktherapeutische Umschau. (GW ISSN 0172-5505) 4036
Musiktidningen. (SW ISSN 0345-7699) 3568
Musiktidningen Musikomanen. (SW) 3568
Musikvejleder for Vejle Amt see Musikvejviser for Vejle Amt 3568
Musikvejviser for Vejle Amt. (DK) 3568
Musikwissenschaft. Beitraege. (GW ISSN 0005-8106) 3568

Musil - Forum. (GW) 2940
MusiMagazine. (CN) 3568
Musique en Jeu. (FR) 3568
Musische Stunde. (GW) 1648
Musizi. (UG ISSN 0541-4385) 4191
Musk - Ox. (CN ISSN 0077-2542) 4325, 2256
Muskoka Focus on Business. (CN) 680
Muskoka Life. (CN) 2178
Muskoka Seniors News. (CN) 2276
Musky Hunter Magazine. (US) 4550
Muslim Africa. (SA ISSN 0027-4860) 4219
Muslim Association for the Advancement of Science Journal of Islamic Science see M A A S Journal of Islamic Science 3640
Muslim Digest. (SA ISSN 0027-4887) 4220
Muslim Educational Quarterly. (UK ISSN 0267-615X) 4220
Muslim Herald. (UK) 4220
Muslim Journal. (US) 4220
Muslim Review. (II ISSN 0027-4895) 4220
Muslim Star. (US) 4220
Muslim Sunrise. (US) 4220
Muslim World. (PK) 3908
Muslim World. (US ISSN 0027-4909) 4220, 2875
Muslim World Book Review. (UK ISSN 0260-3063) 4220
Muslim World League. Journal/Rabitat al-Alam al-Islami. Majallah. (SU) 4220
Al-Muslimun. (UK) 4220
Mustang see Mustang & Fords 258
†Mustang! (Rollingstone). (US) 5241
Mustang & Fords. (US ISSN 0894-5179) 258, 4697
Mustang Illustrated. (US) 4697
Mustang Monthly. (US) 4697
Al-Mustaqbal al-Arabi/Arab Future. (LE) 4380
Mustard and Pepper. (US) 3712
Mustard Seed see On Course 3596
Musteranlagen der Energiewirtschaft. (GW ISSN 0580-3403) 1792
Musterdiktate fuer Kurzschrift, Maschinenschreiben und Phonotypie see Heckners Hefte fuer Textverarbeitung 1058
Musu Gamta. (LI) 1963
Musu Pastoge/Our Haven. (AT) 2015, 2057
Musu Zinios. (US) 2015
Muszaki Egyetemi Konyvtaros/Technical University Librarian. (HU ISSN 0027-3015) 2774
Muszaki-Gazdasagi Magazin/Technical Economic Digest. (HU) 729, 17, 1845
Muszaki-Gazdasagi Tajekoztato see Muszaki-Gazdasagi Magazin 729
Muszaki Konyv Hirado see Muszaki Konyv-Magazin 4604
Muszaki Konyv-Magazin. (HU ISSN 0236-7408) 4604
Muszaki Konyv Ujdonsagok Hiradoja see Muszaki Konyv-Magazin 4604
Muszaki Lapszemle. Kemia Vegyipar - Technical Abstracts. Chemistry, Chemical Industry see Vegyipari Szakirodalmi Tajekoztato 1203
Mut. (GW ISSN 0027-5093) 3908
Mutable Dilemma. (US ISSN 0892-5429) 359
Mutagenesis. (UK ISSN 0267-8357) 546, 480
Mutantia. (AG ISSN 0326-0666) 3595, 3670
Mutation Breeding Newsletter. (UN) 185
Mutation Research. (NE ISSN 0921-8262) 546, 480
Mutation Research - D N A Repair. (NE ISSN 0921-8777) 546, 480
Mutation Research - D N A Repair - Reports see Mutation Research - D N A Repair 546
Mutation Research - D N Aging. (NE ISSN 0921-8734) 546, 480
Mutation Research - Genetic Toxicology Testing. (NE ISSN 0165-1218) 546, 480, 1983
Mutation Research Letters. (NE ISSN 0165-7992) 546, 480

Mutation Research - Reviews in Genetic Toxicology. (NE ISSN 0165-1110) **546**, 480, 1983
Muththaram. (II) **2200**
Mutisia. (CK ISSN 0027-5123) **510**
Mutter. (AU ISSN 0027-5131) **2173**
Mutter und Kind. (GW ISSN 0047-8482) **1241**
Muttersprache. (GW ISSN 0027-514X) **2830**
Mutu. (FR ISSN 0247-6355) **1711**
Mutual Aid. (US ISSN 0734-9998) **4108**, 1021, 1273, 1518, 2033
Mutual Aid Association. Medical Journal.(JA ISSN 0454-7586) **3133**
†Mutual Fund Advantage. (US) **5241**
Mutual Fund Chartist see Mutual Fund Trends **957**
Mutual Fund Charts. (US) **957**
Mutual Fund Fact Book. (US ISSN 0077-2550) **957**
Mutual Fund Forecaster. (US ISSN 8755-9889) **957**
Mutual Fund Letter. (US) **957**
Mutual Fund Monitor. (US) **957**
▼Mutual Fund Performance Report. (US ISSN 1046-8773) **957**
Mutual Fund Profiles. (US) **957**
†Mutual Fund Quarterly. (US) **5241**
Mutual Fund Quarterly Performance Review see Jay Schabacker's Mutual Fund Buying Guide **952**
Mutual Fund Report. (US) **957**
Mutual Fund Source Book. (US ISSN 8755-4151) **957**
Mutual Fund Specialist. (US ISSN 0741-1278) **957**
Mutual Fund Strategies. (US) **957**
Mutual Fund Trends. (US ISSN 0889-0064) **957**
Mutual Fund Values see Morningstar Mutual Funds **956**
Mutual Funds Almanac. (US ISSN 0076-4175) **957**
Mutual Funds Guide. (US ISSN 0027-5182) **957**
Mutual Insurance Bulletin see N A M I C Magazine **2538**
Mutual Magazine. (US ISSN 0740-672X) **4711**
Mutual of New York Life Insurance Co. News see M O N Y News **2537**
Mutual Piper. (US) **2538**, 4132
Mutual U F O Network, Inc. International U F O Symposium Proceedings see M U F O N - International U F O Symposium Proceedings **58**
Mutual U F O Network, Inc. Journal see M U F O N - U F O Journal **58**
Mutual Understanding. see Kutlwano **3903**
Mutualismo. see Mutualite **2538**
Mutualiste du Metro. (FR) **2586**, 4653
Mutualite/Gegenseitigkeit/Mutualismo/Mutuality. (FR ISSN 0027-5239) **2538**
Mutuality. see Mutualite **2538**
†Mutwalisi. (SA) **5241**
Muusikko/Musician. (FI ISSN 0356-7923) **3568**
Muveszettorteneti Ertesito. (HU ISSN 0027-5247) **337**
Muy Interesante. (SP) **4325**
Muzej Brodskog Posavlja. Vijesti. (CI ISSN 0352-1443) **2511**, 3529
Muzejni a Vlastivedna Prace. (CS ISSN 0027-5255) **3529**
Muzejski Vjesnik/Museum News Magazine. (CI ISSN 0350-9370) **279**, 3529
Muzeul de Istorie al Republici Socialiste Romania. Cercetari Arheologice see Muzeul National de Istorie a Romaniei. Cercetari Arheologice **279**
†Muzeul de Istorie al Republicii Socialiste Romania. Cercetari de Conservare si Restaurare a Patrimoniului Muzeal. (RM) **5241**
†Muzeul de Istorie al Republicii Socialiste Romania. Cercetari Istorice.(RM) **5241**

Muzeul de Istorie al Republicii Socialiste Romania. Cercetari Numismatice see Muzeul National de Istorie a Romaniei. Cercetari Numismatice **3600**
Muzeul de Istorie Naturala "Grigore Antipa." Travaux see Travaux du Museum d'Histoire Naturelle "Grigore Antipa **458**
†Muzeul National. (RM) **5241**
Muzeul National de Istorie a Romaniei. Cercetari Arheologice. (RM) **279**
Muzeul National de Istorie a Romaniei. Cercetari Numismatice. (RM) **3600**
†Muzeul si Educatia Socialista. (RM) **5241**
Muzeum. (CS ISSN 0027-5263) **3530**
Muzeum Archeologiczne i Etnograficzne, Lodz. Prace i Materialy. Seria Archeologiczna. (PL ISSN 0458-1520) **279**
Muzeum Archeologiczne i Etnograficzne, Lodz. Prace i Materialy. Seria Etnograficzna. (PL ISSN 0076-0315) **245**, 2015
Muzeum Archeologiczne i Etnograficzne, Lodz. Prace i Materialy. Seria Numizmatyczna i Konserwatorska. (PL ISSN 0208-5062) **3600**
Muzeum Etnograficzne, Wroclaw. Zeszyty Etnograficzne. (PL ISSN 0084-2796) **245**
Muzeum Gornoslaskie w Bytomiu. Rocznik. Seria Archeologia. (PL ISSN 0068-4635) **279**
Muzeum Gornoslaskie w Bytomiu. Rocznik. Seria Etnografia. (PL ISSN 0068-4643) **245**
Muzeum Gornoslaskie w Bytomiu. Rocznik. Seria Historia. (PL ISSN 0068-4651) **2377**
Muzeum Gornoslaskie w Bytomiu. Rocznik. Seria Przyroda. (PL ISSN 0068-466X) **448**
Muzeum Gornoslaskie w Bytomiu. Rocznik. Seria Sztuka. (PL ISSN 0068-4678) **337**
Muzeum Literatury im. Adama Mickiewicza. Blok-Notes. (PL ISSN 0324-8925) **2940**, 3530
Muzeum Militar Central Romania. Studii si Materiale de Muzeografie si Istorie Militara. (RM) **2377**
Muzeum Narodowe w Krakowie. Katalogi Zbiorow/National Museum in Cracow. Catalogues of the Collections. (PL ISSN 0208-8193) **3530**, 337
†Muzeum Narodowe w Warszawie. Rocznik/Musee National de Varsovie. Annuaire. (PL ISSN 0509-6936) **5241**
Muzeum Slovenskeho Narodneho Povstania. Zbornik. (CS) **2377**
Muzeum Ukrajinskej Kultury vo Svidniku. Vedecky Zbornik. (CS) **2377**
Muzica. (RM ISSN 0580-3713) **3568**
Muziek en Dans see Entr'acte **3550**
Muziek en Onderwijs. (NE ISSN 0378-0651) **3569**, 1648
Muziek Expres. (NE ISSN 0027-528X) **3569**, 1260
Muziekbode. (NE) **3569**, 4191
Muziekhandel. (NE ISSN 0027-5301) **3569**
Muzika. (CI ISSN 0027-531X) **3569**, 1648
Muzikoloski Zbornik/Musicological Annual. (XV ISSN 0580-373X) **3569**
Muzikos Zinios/Music News. (US) **3569**
Muzium Brunei. Penerbitan Khas. see Brunei Museum. Special Publication **3522**
Muzsika. (HU ISSN 0027-5336) **3569**
Muzyka. (PL ISSN 0027-5344) **3569**
Muzyka Polska w Dokumentacjach i Interpretacjach. (PL) **3569**
Muzykal'naya Fol'kloristika. (RU) **3569**, 2057
Muzykal'naya Zhizn' (RU ISSN 0027-5352) **3569**

Muzzle Blasts. (US ISSN 0027-5360) **4550**
Muzzleloader. (US ISSN 0274-5720) **4550**
Mvelaphanda see Informa **5212**
Mwana Shaba. (ZR ISSN 0541-4873) **3491**
Mwana Shaba Junior. (ZR) **1260**
Mwendo. (US) **2940**, 2015, 2875
Mwenge. (US) **2015**
My Baby. (AT ISSN 0813-4626) **1241**, 2448
My Baby. see Watashi no Akachan **1245**
My Brother and I. (CN ISSN 0316-8913) **4270**
▼My Bucks Report. (US) **957**, 874
My Career/My Loopbaan. (SA ISSN 0027-5425) **3629**
My Counselor see Counselor (Wheaton) **1252**
My Daily Visitor. (US) **4270**
My Devotions. (US ISSN 0027-5387) **4244**, 1261
My Devotions (Large Print Edition). (US) **2294**, 1261, 4244
My Friend. (US) **4270**, 1241, 1261
My Guy. (UK) **4849**
My Guy Monthly. (UK) **4849**
My Health. see Watashi no Kenko **3810**
My Home and Family. (UK ISSN 0027-5409) **2448**, 2194
†My i Svit/We and the World. (CN ISSN 0027-5417) **5241**
My Lady. see Sayidati **1294**
▼My Legacy. (US) **2998**
My Liberty. see Horreyati **2185**
My Life Depends on You. (FI) **3945**
My Little Salesman Heavy Equipment Catalog. (US) **3021**, 1048
My Little Salesman Truck Catalog. (US ISSN 0192-7027) **4746**, 1048
My Loopbaan. see My Career **3629**
My Own Boss. (US) **1116**, 957
▼My Preschooler. (AT) **1261**, 1648
My Room. see Watashi no Heya **2555**
My Weekly. (UK) **4849**
Myanma Naing Ngan Thuteithana Athin. see Burma Research Society. Journal **4367**
Myawaddy Journal. (BR) **2220**
Myawaddy Magazine. (BR) **2940**
Mycologia. (US ISSN 0027-5514) **510**
Mycologia Helvetica. (SZ ISSN 0256-310X) **510**
Mycologia Memoir. (GW) **510**
Mycological Bulletin see Mycologia **510**
Mycological Papers. (UK ISSN 0027-5522) **510**
Mycological Research. (UK ISSN 0953-7562) **510**
Mycological Society of America Newsletter. (US ISSN 0541-4938) **510**
Mycological Society of Japan. Transactions. (JA ISSN 0029-0289) **510**
Mycologist. (UK ISSN 0269-915X) **510**
Mycology Series. (US) **510**
Mycopathologia. (NE ISSN 0301-486X) **556**, 510
Mycophile. (US ISSN 0027-5549) **510**
Mycorrhiza News. (II ISSN 0970-695X) **510**
Mycoses. (GW ISSN 0027-5557) **3133**
Mycotaxon. (US ISSN 0093-4666) **510**
Mycotoxin Research. (GW ISSN 0178-7888) **556**, 480
Myers Finance and Energy. (US) **957**, 1792
Myers' Finance Review see Myers Finance and Energy **957**
Mykenische Studien. (AU) **1278**
Mynblad. see Mining News **3490**
Mynd. (UK ISSN 0026-4431) **1261**, 1648, 2830
Mynwerker. see Mineworker **3489**
†Myocardium. (UK ISSN 0261-4790) **5241**
Myojo. see Morning Star **2208**
Myopathie. (BE) **3133**
Myosotis. (GW ISSN 0178-0522) **4002**, 4132

Myotis. (GW ISSN 0580-3896) **588**
Myren. see Nemalah **4191**
Myrin Institute for Adult Education Proceedings. (US) **1685**
Myrtia: Revista de Filologia Clasica. (SP ISSN 0213-7674) **2830**, 1278
Myrtle Beach Magazine. (US) **2229**
Mysl Filozoficzna see Studia Filozoficzne **3782**
Mysl Polska/Polish Thought. (UK ISSN 0027-5581) **2875**
Myslivost. (CS ISSN 0323-214X) **1492**, 4550
Mysore. Finance Department. Annual Report see Karnataka. Finance Department. Annual Report **1100**
Mysore Commerce. (II ISSN 0027-559X) **820**
Mysore Journal of Agricultural Sciences.(II ISSN 0047-8539) **108**
Mysore Medical Association. Journal see Karnataka Medical Journal **3119**
Mysore Orientalist. (II ISSN 0580-4396) **3641**
Mysterium. (CK ISSN 0027-5638) **4191**
Mystery & Adventure Series Review. (US) **2984**, 2986
Mystery & Detection Annual. (US ISSN 0000-0302) **2986**
Mystery Notebook. (US) **2986**
Mystery Readers Journal. (US ISSN 1043-3473) **2986**
Mystery Readers of America Journal see Mystery Readers Journal **2986**
Mystery Scene. (US) **2986**
▼Mystery Scene Author's Choice Monthly. (US) **2986**
Mystery Stories/Shosetsu Suiri. (JA) **2986**
†Mystery Time Anthology. (US) **5241**
Mystery Writers of America, Inc. Annual see M W A Annual **2985**
Mystics Quarterly. (US ISSN 0737-5840) **2986**
Mythic Circle. (US) **3012**
Mythic Society. Quarterly Journal. (II ISSN 0047-8555) **2057**, 245, 2340
Mythlore. (US ISSN 0146-9339) **3012**
Mythopoeic Society. Bulletin see Mythprint **3012**
Mythprint. (US ISSN 0146-9347) **3012**
Myyntineuvoja. (FI ISSN 0355-3256) **1081**
M300 and P C Report see Academic and Library Computing **2796**
N. (Massachusetts Historical Society) (US ISSN 0024-8185) **2415**
N. (US ISSN 0893-3472) **4132**, 4143
N A. (Network Africa) (US ISSN 0741-1804) **2511**, 2334
N A see Novas de Alegria **4286**
N A A. (Nordic Archaeological Abstracts) (DK ISSN 0105-6492) **290**, 17
N A A A Newsletter. (National Agricultural Aviation Association) (US) **4675**, 108
N A A C L S News. (National Accrediting Agency for Clinical Laboratory Sciences) (US) **3133**
N A A C O G Newsletter. (N A A C O G: The Organization for Obstetric, Gynecologic, & Neonatal Nurses) (US ISSN 0889-0579) **3282**, 3295
N A A C O G: The Organization for Obstetric, Gynecologic, & Neonatal Nurses Newsletter see N A A C O G Newsletter **3282**
N A A C O G's Women's Health Nursing Scan. (Organization for Obstetric, Gynecologic and Neonatal Nurses) (US ISSN 1055-3533) **3178**, 17, 3282, 4835
N A A C P Annual Report. (National Association for the Advancement of Colored People) (US ISSN 0077-3212) **4443**, 4413
N A A C S News. (National Association of Accredited Cosmetology Schools) (US) **373**
N A A F A Newsletter. (National Association to Advance Fat Acceptance, Inc.) (US) **3609**

N A A F I News. (Navy, Army & Air Force Institutes) (UK ISSN 0027-5662) **3466**
N A A Newsletter see For the Record **53**
N A A Newsletter. (National Archery Association) (US) **4479**
N A A W S Grapevine Newsletter. (North American Association of Wardens and Superintendents) (US) **1518, 1527, 2655**
N A A Where to Stay Book. (National Automobile Association) (US ISSN 0099-0205) **2478**
N A B A Review. (North American Benefit Association) (US ISSN 0027-5689) **1299**
N A B D - Mitteilungen. (Normenausschuss Bibliotheks- und Dokumentationswesen) (GW ISSN 0340-9090) **2774, 406**
N A B E Industry Survey. (National Association of Business Economists) (US) **874, 729, 999**
N A B E News. (National Association of Business Economists) (US) **874, 999**
N A B E Outlook. (National Association of Business Economists) (US) **874, 729, 999**
N A B E Policy Survey. (National Association of Business Economists) (US) **874, 729, 999**
N A B E T News. (National Association of Broadcast Employees and Technicians, A F L - C I O) (US ISSN 0027-5697) **2586, 1377**
N A B J Journal. (National Association of Black Journalists) (US) **2015, 2572**
N A B J Newsletter see N A B J Journal **2015**
N A B P Newsletter. (National Association of Boards of Pharmacy) (US) **3735**
N A B P Quarterly see N A B P Newsletter **3735**
N A B T E Review. (National Association for Business Teacher Education) (US ISSN 0148-5784) **1712, 680**
†N A B W Exchange. (National Association of Bank Women) (US) **5241**
N A C A A News. (National Association of Consumer Agency Administrators) (US ISSN 0739-392X) **1506**
N A C A C Bulletin. (National Association of College Admission Counselors) (US) **1712**
N A C A D A Journal. (National Academic Advising Association) (US ISSN 0271-9517) **1712**
N A C A News. (National Animal Control Association) (US) **3712, 4108**
▼N A C C News. (National Association for Colitis and Crohn's Disease) (UK) **3269**
N A C C Newsletter. (National Association for Colitis and Crohn's Disease) (UK ISSN 0144-6967) **3269**
N A C Calendar of Events. (National Arts Centre) (CN) **1531, 3569, 4635**
N A C - Focus. (Nuclear Assurance Corporation) (US) **1807**
N A C L A Report on the Americas see Report on the Americas **3970**
N A C L O News. (National Association of Canoe Liveries and Outfitters) (US) **4526, 1081**
N A C News see R A S E News **115**
N A C News. (National Accelerator Center) (SA ISSN 0257-2109) **3825**
N A C O News and Views see County News **4086**
N A C T A Journal. (National Association of Colleges and Teachers of Agriculture) (US ISSN 0149-4910) **108, 155**
N A C U F S Journal. (National Association of College and University Food Services) (US) **2078**
N A C U F S Newsletter - Digest see N A C U F S NewsWave **2078**
N A C U F S NewsWave. (National Association of College and University Food Services) (US) **2078**

N A C U F S Technical Bulletin see N A C U F S Journal **2078**
N A C - Update see N A C - Focus **1807**
N A C W Breakthrough (National Association of Commissions for Women) see Women's Rights to Women Leaders **4857**
N A C W P I Journal. (National Association of College Wind & Percussion Instructors) (US ISSN 0027-576X) **3569**
N.A.D.A. Boat Appraisal Guide see N.A.D.A. Small Boat Appraisal Guide **4526**
N.A.D.A. Boat Appraisal Guide see N.A.D.A. Large Boat Appraisal Guide **4526**
N.A.D.A. Large Boat Appraisal Guide. (National Automobile Dealers Association) (US ISSN 1055-1972) **4526**
N.A.D.A. Magazine see Automotive Executive **4683**
N.A.D.A. Mobile Home Appraisal Guide see N.A.D.A. Mobile - Manufactured Housing Appraisal Guide **625**
N.A.D.A. Mobile - Manufactured Housing Appraisal Guide. (National Automobile Dealers Association) (US) **625, 4778**
N.A.D.A. Motorcycle Appraisal Guide see N.A.D.A. Motorcycle - Snowmobile - A T V - Personal Watercraft Appraisal Guide **4520**
N.A.D.A. Motorcycle - Snowmobile - A T V - Personal Watercraft Appraisal Guide. (National Automobile Dealers Association) (US) **4520, 4526**
N.A.D.A. Newsletter see Automotive Executive **4683**
N A D A Official Used Car Guide. (National Automobile Dealers Association) (US) **4697**
N A D A Official Wholesale Used Car Trade-In Guide. (National Automobile Dealers Association) (US) **4697**
N A D A Older Used Car Guide. (National Automobile Dealers Association) (US) **4697**
N A D A Recreation Vehicle Appraisal Guide. (National Automobile Dealers Association) (US ISSN 0092-4601) **4697**
N.A.D.A. Small Boat Appraisal Guide. (National Automobile Dealers Association) (US ISSN 1055-1964) **4526**
N A D C A International Die Casting Congress. Transactions. (North American Die Casting Association) (US) **1921, 3416**
N A D Case Reports. (National Advertising Division) (US) **35**
N A D E Advocate. (National Association of Disability Examiners) (US) **4413, 2538**
N A D L Journal see Trends & Techniques in the Contemporary Dental Laboratory **3243**
N A D S A Annual Conference Directory. (National Association of Dramatic and Speech Arts) (US) **35, 4635**
N A E A News. (National Art Education Association) (US ISSN 0160-6395) **337, 1648**
N A E B Bulletin. (National Association of Educational Buyers) (US) **1755**
N A E B Letter see Current (Washington, 1982) **1372**
N A E C O N see I E E E National Aerospace and Electronics Conference. Proceedings **55**
N A E I R Advantage. (National Association for the Exchange of Industrial Resources) (US) **4413**
N A E I R News see N A E I R Advantage **4413**
N A E M T News. (National Association of Emergency Medical Technicians) (US) **3133**
N A E M T Newsletter see N A E M T News **3133**
N A E N Bulletin. (National Association of Educational Negotiators) (US ISSN 0270-6881) **1729**
N A E P Newsletter. (National Assessment of Educational Progress) (US ISSN 0094-0208) **1648**

N A E R C Winter Assessment (Year). (North American Electric Reliability Council) (US) **1903**
N A F A Annual Reference Book. (National Association of Fleet Administrators, Inc.) (US) **4697**
N A F A Conference Brochure and Reference Book see N A F A Annual Reference Book **4697**
N A F A Fleet Executive. (National Association of Fleet Administrators, Inc.) (US) **4653**
N A F A Fleet Focus. (National Association of Fleet Administrators, Inc.) (US) **4653**
N A F A Newsletter see N A F A Fleet Focus **4653**
N A F E D Marketing Review. (National Agricultural Cooperative Marketing Federation of India Ltd.) (II) **1048**
N A F I Newsletter see Flight Training **52**
N A F I Newsletter. (National Association of Fire Investigators) (US) **2033**
N A F News. (National Agricultural Cooperative Federation) (KO) **155**
N A F O Annual Report. (Northwest Atlantic Fisheries Organization) (CN ISSN 0704-4798) **2046**
N A F O List of Fishing Vessels. (Northwest Atlantic Fisheries Organization) (CN ISSN 0250-7811) **2046**
N A F O Magazine. (National Association of Fire Officers) (UK) **4108**
N A F O Scientific Council Reports. (Northwest Atlantic Fisheries Organization) (CN ISSN 0250-6416) **2046**
N A F O Scientific Council Studies. (Northwest Atlantic Fisheries Organization) (CN ISSN 0250-6432) **2046**
N A F O Statistical Bulletin. (Northwest Atlantic Fisheries Organization) (CN ISSN 0250-6394) **2051**
N A F O Yearbook. (National Association of Fire Officers) (UK) **2033**
N A F S A Directory of Institutions and Individuals in International Educational Exchange. (National Association for Foreign Student Affairs) (US ISSN 0736-4660) **1722**
N A F S A Government Affairs Bulletin. (National Association for Foreign Student Affairs) (US ISSN 0889-9363) **1723, 3966**
N A F S A Newsletter. (National Association for Foreign Student Affairs) (US ISSN 0027-5824) **1648, 3966**
N A F S C O B Bulletin. (National Federation of State Cooperative Banks Ltd.) (II) **791**
N A G A : I C L A R M Quarterly. (International Center for Living Aquatic Resources Management) (PH) **2046, 588**
N A G Newsletter. (Numerical Algorithms Group Ltd.) (UK ISSN 0269-0780) **3048, 1431**
†N A G W S Guide. Gymnastics. (National Association for Girls and Women in Sport) (US ISSN 0363-9282) **5241**
N A G W S Guide. Softball. (National Association for Girls and Women in Sport) (US ISSN 0363-2504) **4508**
†N A G W S Guide. Tennis. (National Association for Girls and Women in Sport) (US ISSN 0272-863X) **5241**
N A G W S Guide. Volleyball. (National Association for Girls and Women in Sport) (US ISSN 0065-7050) **4508**
N A H A M Management Journal. (National Association of Healthcare Access Management) (US ISSN 1057-3526) **2467**
N A H C Report. (National Association for Home Care) (US) **3133**
N A H R O Letter see N A H R O Monitor **2492**

N A H R O Monitor. (National Association of Housing and Redevelopment Officials) (US ISSN 0194-9268) **2492**
N A H S E's Resume. (National Association of Health Services Executives) (US) **4108**
N A I A Handbook. (National Association of Intercollegiate Athletics) (US ISSN 0077-3336) **4480**
N A I A News. (US ISSN 0740-5995) **4480**
N A I A News and Coach see N A I A News **4480**
N A I A Official Records Book see N A I A Official Records Book and Championship Summaries **4480**
N A I A Official Records Book and Championship Summaries. (National Association of Intercollegiate Athletics) (US) **4480**
N A I C Newsletter. (National Association of Insurance Commissioners) (US) **2538, 2655**
N A I F A Convention. Proceedings. (National Association of Independent Fee Appraisers) (US) **4153, 2538**
N A I F A Technical Manual. (National Association of Independent Fee Appraisers) (US) **4153, 2538**
†N A I I Press Samplings. (National Association of Independent Insurers) (US ISSN 0027-5867) **5241**
N.A.I.L.M. Bulletin. (National Association of Institutional Linen Management) (US) **1282**
N.A.I.L.M. News. (National Association of Institutional Linen Management) (US ISSN 0027-5875) **1282**
N A I O P News see Development (Arlington) **615**
N A I R News. (National Association of Independent Resurfacers) (US) **4508, 1081**
N A L G O Annual Report. (National and Local Government Officers Association) (UK ISSN 0077-4456) **4067**
N A L News/Kogiken Nyusu. (National Aerospace Laboratory) (JA ISSN 0023-2726) **59**
N A L P Bulletin. (National Association for Law Placement) (US) **2655**
N A L P Notes see N A L P Bulletin **2655**
N A L S Docket. (National Association of Legal Secretaries) (US) **2655**
N A M A Journal. (National Account Marketing Association) (US) **1048**
N A M A News see N A M A Journal **1048**
N A M B L A Bulletin. (North American Man-Boy Love Association) (US) **2455**
N A M D T. Newsletter. (National Association of Milliners, Dressmakers and Tailors) (US) **1286**
†N A M F Accounting Manual. (National Association of Metal Finishers) (US ISSN 0077-3360) **5241**
N A M F Management Manual. (National Association of Metal Finishers) (US ISSN 0077-3379) **3416**
N A M F Regulatory Compliance Manual. (National Association of Metal Finishers) (US) **3416**
N A M I Advocate. (National Alliance for the Mentally Ill) (US) **3345**
N A M I C Magazine. (National Association of Mutual Insurance Companies) (US) **2538**
N A M I News see N A M I Advocate **3345**
N A M M Members Monthly Bulletin see N A M M Music Retailer News **3569**
N A M M Music Retailer News. (National Association of Music Merchants Inc.) (US ISSN 0027-5913) **3569**
†N A M - N I C Speakers Directory. (National Association of Manufacturers) (US) **5241**
N A M R P Quarterly. (National Apostolate with Mentally Retarded Persons) (US ISSN 0273-9178) **1738**

N A M S B News. (National Association of Men's Sportswear Buyers, Inc.) (US) **1286**

N A M T A News & Views. (National Art Materials Trade Association) (US) **337**

N A N A News (National Aesthetician and Nail Artist Association) see Nail & Beauty Trends **373**

N A N Bulletin. (National Association of Neighborhoods) (US) **2492**

N A O S. (US) **2830, 4191**

N A P C W A Network. (National Association of Public Child Welfare Administrators) (US) **4413**

N A P D Magazine. (National Association of Plastics Distributors) (US) **3864**

†N A P E H E Proceedings. (National Association for Physical Education in Higher Education) (US ISSN 0276-461X) **5241**

N A P E Journal see Communicator (St. John's) **4057**

N A P E T News. (National Association of Photo Equipment Technicians) (US) **3793**

N A P F Pensions Legislation Service. (UK) **2538, 2655**

†N A P Forum. (National Association of the Professions) (US) **5241**

N A P I A Bulletin. (National Association of Public Insurance Adjusters (US ISSN 0027-5964) **2538**

N A P O News. (National Association of Probation Officers) (UK) **1518**

N A P O News/Echo de l'O N A P. (National Anti-Poverty Organization) (CN ISSN 0820-7364) **4413, 1506**

N A P O Newsletter see N A P O News **1518**

N A P S A. Results. (National Appliance Parts Suppliers Association) (US) **2561**

N A P S A C News. (National Association of Parents and Professionals for Safe Alternatives in Childbirth, International) (US ISSN 0192-1223) **3295**

N A P V Newsletter. (National Association of Prison Visitors) (UK ISSN 0306-3313) **1518**

N A R C E A Conference Proceedings. (National Aging Resource Center on Elder Abuse) (US) **4413**

N A R C E A Project Reports. (National Aging Resource Center on Elder Abuse) (US) **4413**

N A R C E A Selected Publications. (National Aging Resource Center on Elder Abuse) (US) **4413**

N A R D A News. (National Association of Retail Dealers of America) (US ISSN 0047-8717) **1021**

N A R D Almanac see N A R D Almanac and Health Guide **1048**

N A R D Almanac and Health Guide. (National Association of Retail Druggists) (US) **1048**

N A R D A's Costs of Doing Business Survey. (National Association of Retail Dealers of America) (US ISSN 0196-3171) **1116**

†N A R D Home Health Care Pharmacy Bulletin. (National Association of Retail Druggists) (US ISSN 0736-5233) **5241**

N A R D Journal. (National Association of Retail Druggists) (US ISSN 0027-5972) **3735**

N A R D Newsletter. (National Association of Retail Druggists) (US ISSN 0162-1602) **3735**

N A R E A Appraisal Guideline. (National Association of Real Estate Appraisers) (US) **4153**

N A R E A Real Estate Appraisal Newsletter. (National Association of Real Estate Appraisers) (US) **4153**

N A R E E News. (National Association of Real Estate Editors) (US) **4153**

N A R F Legal Review. (Native American Rights Fund) (US ISSN 0739-862X) **2015, 2655**

N A R H A News. (North American Riding for the Handicapped Association, Inc.) (US) **4536, 2284**

N A R I Focus. (National Association of the Remodeling Industry) (US) **625**

N A R I Stethoscope. (National Association of Residents and Interns) (US) **957, 2538, 3133**

N A R M C Highlights. (National Association of Regional Media Centers) (US) **3514**

N A R M Sounding Board. (National Association of Recording Merchandisers) (US) **3569**

N A R U C Bulletin see National Association of Regulatory Utility Commissioners. Bulletin **4068**

N A S A Activities see N A S A Magazine **59**

N A S A Facts. (U.S. National Aeronautics and Space Administration) (US ISSN 0077-3093) **59**

N A S A Formal Series Reports. (National Aeronautics and Space Administration) (US) **4325, 59**

N A S A Magazine. (U.S. National Aeronautics and Space Administration) (US) **59**

N A S A Patent Abstracts Bibliography: A Continuing Bibliography. Section 1. Abstracts. (U.S. National Aeronautics and Space Administration) (US) **3680, 17**

N A S A Patent Abstracts Bibliography: A Continuing Bibliography. Section 2. Indexes. (U.S. National Aeronautics and Space Administration) (US) **3680**

N A S A Report to Educators. (U.S. National Aeronautics and Space Administration) (US ISSN 0092-346X) **59, 1755**

N A S A Software Directory. (National Aeronautics and Space Administration) (US) **1479, 1146**

N A S A Tech Briefs see N T I S Tech Notes **4604**

N A S A Technical Memorandum see U.S. National Aeronautics and Space Administration. Technical Memorandum **64**

N A S A - University Conference on Manual Control (Papers). (US ISSN 0077-2623) **59**

N A S B I C News. (National Association of Small Business Investment Companies) (US ISSN 0469-323X) **957, 1116**

N A S C A R News. (National Association for Stock Car Auto Racing, Inc.) (US) **4480**

N A S C A R Newsletter see N A S C A R News **4480**

N A S C O Campus Co-Op Directory see N A S C O Guide to Campus Co-Ops **1146**

N A S C O Guide to Campus Co-Ops. (North American Students of Cooperation) (US) **1146**

N A S C Quarterly. (Numismatic Association of Southern California) (US ISSN 0027-6006) **3600**

N A S D A Q Chief Financial Officer Newsletter see N A S D A Q Financial Executive Journal **957**

N A S D A Q Company Directory see N A S D A Q Fact Book **957**

N A S D A Q Fact Book. (National Association of Securities Dealers Automated Quotations) (US) **957, 791**

▼N A S D A Q Financial Executive Journal. (National Association of Securities Dealers Automated Quotations) (US) **957**

†N A S D A Q Notes. (National Association of Securities Dealers Automated Quotations) (US) **5241**

N A S D A Q Subscriber Bulletin. (US) **957, 791**

N A S D Annual Report. (National Association of Securities Dealers, Inc.) (US) **957, 791**

N A S D Executive Digest see N A S D Notices to Members **957**

†N A S D Executive Digest. (National Association of Securities Dealers, Inc.) (US) **5241**

N A S D Manual. (National Association of Securities Dealers, Inc.) (US) **957**

†N A S D Newsletter. (National Association of Securities Dealers Inc.) (US) **5241**

N A S D Notices to Members. (US) **957, 2655**

N A S D Q Yellow Book. (US ISSN 1058-2886) **1021**

N A S D Regulatory and Compliance Alert. (National Association of Securities Dealers, Inc.) (US) **957, 791, 2655**

N A S F T Showcase. (National Association for Specialty Food Trade, Inc.) (US) **2078, 2093**

N A S I G Newsletter. (North American Serials Interest Group) (US ISSN 0892-1733) **2774**

N A S I S S Newsletter. (National Association of Sailing Instructors and Sailing Schools) (US) **4526**

N A S News Journal see Audubon Activist **1943**

N A S Newsletter. (National Association of School Nurses, Inc.) (US ISSN 1047-4757) **3282**

N A S P A Forum. (National Association of Student Personnel Administrators) (US ISSN 0271-1672) **1318, 1067**

N A S P A Journal. (National Association of Student Personnel Administrators) (US ISSN 0027-6014) **1712**

N A S P A News. (National Systems Programmers Associations) (US) **1431**

N A S S D O C Research Information Series. Acquisition Update. (National Social Science Documentation Centre) (II) **2774**

N A S S D O C Research Information Series. Bibliographic Reprints. (National Social Science Documentation Centre) (II) **406**

N A S S D O C Research Information Series. Conference Alert. (National Social Science Documentation Centre) (II) **3393**

N A S S D O C Research Information Series. Paging Periodical. (National Social Science Documentation Centre) (II) **2794**

†N A S S D O C Research Information Series. Social Science News. (National Social Science Documentation Centre) (II) **5241**

N A S S P Bulletin. (National Association of Secondary School Principals) (US ISSN 0192-6365) **1729**

N A S S P Curriculum Report. (National Association of Secondary School Principals) (US) **1755**

N A S S P Legal Memorandum. (National Association of Secondary School Principals) (US) **1729, 2655**

N A S S P Newsleader. (National Association of Secondary School Principals) (US ISSN 0278-0569) **1729**

N A S S P Newsletter see N A S S P Newsleader **1729**

N A S S P Practitioner. (National Association of Secondary School Principals) (US ISSN 0192-6160) **1729**

N A S S P Tips for Principals. (National Association of Secondary School Principals) (US) **1729**

N A S U W T Career Teacher Journal. (UK) **1648, 2587**

N.A.T.A. Annual Directory. (National Association of Testing Authorities) (AT) **1921**

†N A T A D Newsletter. (National Association of Textile and Apparel Distributors) (US) **5241**

N A T A Journal. (National Association of Temple Administrators) (US) **4225**

N A T A News. (National Association of Testing Authorities) (AT ISSN 0311-662X) **4325, 4604**

N A T A News. (National Air Transportation Association) (US) **4676**

N A T A T's National Community Reporter see N A T a T's Reporter **4091**

N A T a T's Reporter. (US ISSN 0735-9691) **4091, 2492**

N A T E News. (National Association of Temple Educators) (US ISSN 0300-6689) **4225**

N A T F H E Journal. (National Association of Teachers in Further and Higher Education) (UK ISSN 0308-1907) **1712**

N A T I S - News. (National Information System) (UN) **2774**

N A T I S Noticias see N A T I S - News **2774**

N A T I S-Nouvelles see N A T I S - News **2774**

N A T News. (National Association of Theatre Nurses) (UK ISSN 0027-6049) **3282**

N A T O. Annual Economic Colloquia. Proceedings. (BE) **918**

N A T O Advanced Science Institutes Series A: Life Sciences. (North Atlantic Treaty Organization) (US) **448**

N A T O Advanced Science Institutes Series B: Physics. (US) **3825**

N A T O Advanced Science Institutes Series C: Mathematical and Physical Sciences. (North Atlantic Treaty Organization) (NE) **3048, 4325**

N A T O Advanced Science Institutes Series D: Behavioural and Social Sciences. (North Atlantic Treaty Organization) (NE) **4380, 3985, 4108**

N A T O Advanced Science Institutes Series E: Applied Sciences. (North Atlantic Treaty Organization) (NE) **4604**

N A T O Advanced Science Institutes Series F: Computer and Systems Sciences. (North Atlantic Treaty Organization) (NE) **1438**

N A T O Advanced Science Institutes Series G: Ecological Sciences. (North Atlantic Treaty Organization) (NE) **1963**

N A T O Advanced Science Institutes Series H: Cell Biology. (NE) **526**

N A T O Advanced Study Institute. Series H: Cell Biology see N A T O Advanced Science Institutes Series H: Cell Biology **526**

N A T O Advanced Study Institute Series E: Applied Sciences see N A T O Advanced Science Institutes Series E: Applied Sciences **4604**

N A T O Advanced Study Institute Series F: Computer and System Sciences see N A T O Advanced Science Institutes Series F: Computer and Systems Sciences **1438**

N A T O Advanced Study Institute Series G: Ecological Sciences see N A T O Advanced Science Institutes Series G: Ecological Sciences **1963**

N A T O Advanced Study Institutes Series D: Behavioural and Social Sciences see N A T O Advanced Science Institutes Series D: Behavioural and Social Sciences **4380**

N A T O Basic Documents/O T A N Documents Fondamentaux. (BE) **3966**

N A T O Dergisi see N A T O Review **3908**

N A T O Final Communiques/O T A N Communiques Finals. (BE) **3966**

N A T O Flash Bulletin see N A T O News & Views **3514**

N A T O Handbook. (BE ISSN 0549-7175) **3966**

N A T O News & Views. (National Association of Theatre Owners) (US ISSN 0279-120X) **3514, 4635**

N A T O Nyt see N A T O Review **3908**

N A T O Nytt see N A T O Review **3908**

N A T O Review. (North Atlantic Treaty Organization) (BE ISSN 0255-3813) **3908**

N A T O Scientific Publications. Newsletter. (BE ISSN 0255-7134) **4325**

N A T O - Warsaw and Strategies see Western Policies **3934**
N A T O's Nations see N A T O's Sixteen Nations **3966**
N A T O's Sixteen Nations. (North Atlantic Treaty Organization) (GW) **3966**, 3466
N A T P E Programmer. (National Association of Television Program Executives) (US) **1377**
N A T S Journal. (National Association of Teachers of Singing, Inc.) (US ISSN 0884-8106) **3569**, 1648
N A T S News see Contemporary Times **3626**
N A T S O Truckers News. (National Association of Truck Stop Operators) (US) **4746**
N A T T A Newsletter see Renew Newsletter **1795**
N A U I News see Sources (Montclair) **4488**
N A U M D. Office Reports. (National Association of Uniform Manufacturers and Distributors) (US) **1286**, 1048, 1081
N A U M D News. (National Association of Uniform Manufacturers and Distributors) (US) **1286**, 1048, 1081
N A U M D Postal Update. (National Association of Uniform Manufacturers and Distributors) (US) **1286**, 1081
N A U N L U. (Natal Agricultural Union) (SA ISSN 0028-128X) **108**
N A U S Newsletter see U S J **3473**
N A V A S. (Nederlandse Aannemersvereniging van Afbouw- en Stukadoorswerken) (NE) **625**
N A V O Kroniek see N A T O Review **3908**
N A W A News see Women Artists News **350**
N A W C M Bulletin see I A W C M Bulletin **5207**
N A W G A Review. (National-American Wholesale Grocers' Association, Inc.) (US) **2078**
N A W J Counterbalance. (National Association of Women Judges) (US) **2656**, 4849
N A W J News and Announcements see N A W J Counterbalance **2656**
N A W Report. (National Association of Wholesaler - Distributors) (US) **4092**
N A Way Magazine. (Narcotics Anonymous) (US) **1538**, 4108
N A Y S I Resource List. (North American Youth Sport Institute) (US) **4480**, 1241
N A Y W News. (National Association for Young Writers, Inc.) (US) **2940**, 1755
N B see New Builder **626**
†N B A News Report. (National Bankers Association) (US) **5241**
N B A Today see Hoop - N B A Today **4506**
N B C - N F C News. (National Building Code - National Fire Code) (CN ISSN 0848-600X) **625**
N B D C S News. (National Book Development Council of Singapore) (SI ISSN 0129-9239) **4133**
N B E R Macroeconomics Annual. (National Bureau of Economic Research) (US ISSN 0889-3365) **999**
N B I A News. (New Brunswick Institute of Agrologists) (CN ISSN 0848-8851) **108**, 448, 1492, 1963
N B L C Info Bulletin. (Nederlands Bibliotheek en Lektuur Centrum) (NE ISSN 0165-2583) **2774**
N B L Review. (National Bank of Liberia) (LB) **791**
N.B. Naturalist/Naturaliste du N.B. (CN ISSN 0047-9551) **4325**
N B O Abstracts. (National Buildings Organisation) (II ISSN 0027-6138) **638**, 17
N.B. Power News. (CN) **1904**
N B R I Information Sheet. (National Building Research Institute) (SA ISSN 0027-6162) **625**
N B S Handbook see N I S T Handbook **3447**

N B S Special Publication see N I S T Special Publication **3447**
N B T V. (Narrow Bandwidth Television Association) (UK) **1377**
N B W A Handbook. (National Beer Wholesalers Association) (US) **383**, 1048
N B W A Legislative and Regulatory Issues Alert. (National Beer Wholesalers Association) (US) **383**, 1048
N C A A Baseball. (National Collegiate Athletic Association) (US) **4508**, 4498
N C A A Baseball Rules. (National Collegiate Athletic Association) (US ISSN 0736-5209) **4508**
N C A A Basketball. (National Collegiate Athletic Association) (US ISSN 0276-1017) **4508**, 4498
N C A A Basketball Records see N C A A Basketball **4508**
N C A A Directory. (National Collegiate Athletic Association) (US ISSN 0162-1467) **4480**
N C A A Drug Testing Program. (National Collegiate Athletic Association) (US) **4480**, 1538
N C A A Football. (National Collegiate Athletic Association) (US ISSN 0735-5475) **4508**, 4498
N C A A Football Guide see N C A A Football **4508**
N C A A Football Records see N C A A Football **4508**
N C A A Football Rules and Interpretations. (National Collegiate Athletic Association) (US ISSN 0736-5160) **4508**
N C A A Illustrated Basketball Rules see N C A A Men's and Women's Illustrated Basketball Rules **4508**
N C A A Manual see National Collegiate Athletic Association. Manual **4480**
N C A A Men's and Women's Basketball Rules and Interpretations. (National Collegiate Athletic Association) (US) **4508**
N C A A Men's and Women's Cross Country and Track & Field Rules. (National Collegiate Athletic Association) (US ISSN 0736-7783) **4550**
N C A A Men's and Women's Illustrated Basketball Rules. (National Collegiate Athletic Association) (US) **4508**
N C A A Men's and Women's Rifle Rules. (National Collegiate Athletic Association) (US) **4480**
N C A A Men's and Women's Skiing Rules. (National Collegiate Athletic Association) (US ISSN 0741-9279) **4551**
N C A A Men's and Women's Soccer Rules. (National Collegiate Athletic Association) (US) **4508**
N C A A Men's and Women's Swimming and Diving Rules. (National Collegiate Athletic Association) (US ISSN 0736-5128) **4480**
N C A A Men's Basketball Rules and Interpretations see N C A A Men's and Women's Basketball Rules and Interpretations **4508**
N C A A Men's Ice Hockey Rules and Interpretations. (National Collegiate Athletic Association) (US ISSN 0735-9195) **4480**
N C A A Men's Illustrated Basketball Rules see N C A A Men's and Women's Illustrated Basketball Rules **4508**
N C A A Men's Lacrosse Rules. (National Collegiate Athletic Association) (US ISSN 0736-7775) **4508**
N C A A Men's Read-Easy Basketball Rules. (National Collegiate Athletic Association) (US ISSN 0736-5195) **4508**
N C A A Men's Soccer Rules see N C A A Men's and Women's Soccer Rules **4508**
N C A A Men's Water Polo Rules. (National Collegiate Athletic Association) (US ISSN 0734-0508) **4480**

N C A A News. (National Collegiate Athletic Association) (US ISSN 0027-6170) **4480**
N C A A Read-Easy Football Rules. (National Collegiate Athletic Association) (US) **4508**
N C A A Softball. (National Collegiate Athletic Association) (US) **4508**, 4498
N C A A Swimming see N C A A Men's and Women's Swimming and Diving Rules **4480**
N C A A Wrestling Rules. (National Collegiate Athletic Association) (US ISSN 0736-511X) **4480**
N C A C S News see National Coalition News **1649**
N C A Cave Talk. (National Caves Association) (US) **4779**, 1574
N C A E News Bulletin. (North Carolina Association of Educators) (US ISSN 0027-6189) **1648**
N C A H F Newsletter. (National Council Against Health Fraud, Inc.) (US ISSN 0890-3417) **4108**
N C A M P's Technical Report. (National Coalition Against the Misuse of Pesticides) (US) **1963**, 2656
N C A Newsletter. (National Constructors Association) (US) **625**, 989
N C A P News see Journal of Pesticide Reform **1961**
N C A W E News. (National Council of Administrative Women in Education) (US ISSN 0027-6227) **1729**, 4849
N C B Quest. (National Council for Cement and Building Materials) (II ISSN 0970-5600) **625**
N C C E M's Official Monthly Newsletter. (National Coordinating Council on Emergency Management) (US) **4108**
N C - C I M Guidebook. (Numerical Control Computer Integrated Manufacturing) (US) **3025**
N C C M A News see T M A News **800**
N C C P A Newsletter see C M A Newsletter **1306**
N-C Commline see Commline **1446**
N C D C Bulletin. (National Cooperative Development Corporation) (II ISSN 0027-6278) **831**
N C E A Ganley's Catholic Schools in America. (National Catholic Educational Association) (US ISSN 0147-8044) **1695**
N C E A News Bulletin see N C A E News Bulletin **1648**
N C E A Notes. (National Catholic Educational Association) (US ISSN 0550-5682) **1648**, 4270
N C E C A Journal. (National Council on Education for the Ceramic Arts) (US ISSN 0739-1544) **356**
N C E C A News. (National Council on Education for the Ceramic Arts) (US) **356**
N C E C A Newsletter see N C E C A News **356**
N C E E Registration Bulletin see N C E E S Registration Bulletin **1831**
N C E E S Registration Bulletin. (National Council of Examiners for Engineering and Surveying) (US) **1831**, 1871
N C E R T Newsletter. (National Council of Educational Research and Training) (II ISSN 0302-508X) **1648**
N C F E Motivator. (National Center for Financial Education) (US) **791**, 1648
N C Fertigung. (GW) **3416**
N C G A News. (Northern California Golf Association) (US ISSN 0744-1347) **4480**
N C G R Journal. (National Council for Geocosmic Research, Inc.) (US ISSN 0296-5569) **359**
N C G S Open-File Report. (North Carolina Geological Survey) (US) **1574**
N C I Cancer Weekly. (US ISSN 0896-7385) **3200**
N C I Catalyst. (North Conway Institute, Inc.) (US ISSN 0048-0673) **1538**

N C I Fact Book. (National Cancer Institute) (US ISSN 0270-7950) **3200**
N C I Monographs see National Cancer Institute. Journal. Monographs **3200**
N C I V Newsletter. (National Council for International Visitors) (US) **4779**, 4413
N C J R S Document Retrieval Index. (National Criminal Justice Reference Service) (US) **1518**
N C J W Journal. (National Council of Jewish Women) (US ISSN 0161-2115) **4849**, 4225
N C L C Reports: Bankruptcy & Foreclosures. (National Consumer Law Center) (US ISSN 1054-3775) **2656**, 1506
N C L C Reports: Consumer Bankruptcy and Foreclosures Edition see N C L C Reports: Bankruptcy & Foreclosures **2656**
N C L C Reports: Consumer Credit & Usury. (National Consumer Law Center) (US ISSN 0890-2615) **2656**, 1506
N C L C Reports: Debt Collection & Repossessions. (National Consumer Law Center) (US ISSN 0890-2607) **2656**, 1506
N C L C Reports: Deceptive Acts & Warranties. (National Consumer Law Center) (US ISSN 0890-0973) **2656**, 1506
†N C L I S News. (U.S. National Commission on Libraries and Information Science) (US) **5241**
N C M A Magazine see Contract Management **1006**
N C O A Journal. (Non-Commissioned Officers Association) (US) **3466**
N C O A Networks. (National Council on the Aging) (US ISSN 1045-9073) **2276**
N C O A News. (National Campground Owners Association) (US) **4551**, 1021
N C P see Noticias de Cosmetica y de Perfumeria **376**
N C P C Annual Report. (National Crop Protection Center) (PH) **185**
N C P C Quarterly see National Capital Planning Commission. Quarterly Review of Commission Proceedings **2492**
N C P Documenta. (Noticias de Cosmetica y de Perfumeria) (SP) **376**
N C P: Nutrition in Clinical Practice. (US) **3609**
N C - Praxis see C I M - Praxis **1412**
N C R A Yearbook see Journal of College and Adult Reading **1685**
N C R Connection. (US) **1471**, 1463
†N C R L News. (National Chemical Research Laboratory) (SA) **5241**
N C R Monthly see N C R Connection **1471**
N C R P Commentary. (National Council on Radiation Protection and Measurements) (US) **4108**
N C R P News. (National Council on Radiation Protection and Measurements) (US) **4108**
N C R P Report. (National Council on Radiation Protection and Measurements) (US ISSN 0083-209X) **4108**
N C R P Statements. (National Council on Radiation Protection and Measurements) (US) **3360**
N C R P Symposium Proceedings. (National Council on Radiation Protection and Measurements) (US) **4108**
N C R R Update. (National Center for Resource Recovery, Inc.) (US) **1986**
N C R T E Colloquy see N C R T L Special Report **1755**
N C R T L Special Report. (National Center for Research on Teacher Learning) (US ISSN 1054-7673) **1755**, 1729
N C S B C S News. (National Conference of States on Building Codes and Standards, Inc.) (US) **2492**, 625

6460 N.C.S. BULLETIN

N.C.S. Bulletin. (National Chrysanthemum Society) (UK) **2134**

N C S Integrated Manufacturing. (Numerical Control Society - AIMTECH) (US ISSN 0886-1463) **1936**, 1880, 3021

N C S L A Minutes of Annual Meeting. (National Conference of State Liquor Administrators) (US) **4067**, 384

N C S L A Official Directory. (National Conference of State Liquor Administrators) (US) **4067**, 384

N C S L Conference Report. (National Conference of State Legislatures) (US ISSN 0899-5052) **4067**

†N C S L Exchange. (National Civil Service League) (US) **5242**

N C S L Federal Update. (National Conference of State Legislatures) (US ISSN 0898-4298) **4067**

N C S R Bibliography see Zambia. National Council for Scientific Research. N C S R Bibliography **4358**

N C S U Libraries Focus. (North Carolina State University) (US) **2774**

N.C.S. Yearbook. (National Chrysanthemum Society) (UK) **2134**

†N C ShopOwner. (Numerical Control) (US ISSN 0271-1079) **5242**

N C State Economist. (US) **155**, 680

N C T M News Bulletin. (National Council of Teachers of Mathematics) (US ISSN 0277-1365) **1755**, 1712, 3048

N C T V News. (National Coalition on Television Violence) (US ISSN 0739-6767) **1377**

N C U A Watch. (National Credit Union Administration) (US) **791**

N C V O News. (National Council for Voluntary Organisations) (UK ISSN 0955-2170) **4413**

N C W News. (National Council of Women of South Africa) (SA ISSN 0027-6367) **4849**

N D A Pipeline. (New Drug Approval) (US) **3735**, 1146

N.D.A. Quarterly see National Dental Association. Journal **5243**

N D Banner. (US ISSN 0887-0004) **1738**

N D C Boletim Informativo. (Nucleo de Documentacao) (BL) **1712**

N D G S Newsletter. (North Dakota Geological Survey) (US ISSN 0889-3594) **1574**

N D L see Neue Deutsche Literatur **2941**

N.D.L. Library Science Series. see Toshokan Kenkyu Sirizu **2787**

N D R E Publications. (Norwegian Defence Research Establishment) (NO ISSN 0800-4412) **4325**

†N D S P - U P Research Illustrated. (PH) **5242**

N D T International. (Non Destructive Testing) (UK ISSN 0308-9126) **1921**, 4604

N D Z see Neue D E L I W A - Zeitschrift **1793**

N E A A News see Appraisers Standard **312**

N E A Activities in (Year) see O E C D Nuclear Energy Agency Activities in (Year) **1809**

N E A Advocate. (National Education Association of the United States) (US ISSN 0198-8611) **1712**, 2587

N E A Almanac of Higher Education. (National Education Association of the United States) (US ISSN 0743-670X) **1712**, 2587

N E A Grantmaking Programs: Arts Administration Fellows Program. (National Endowment for the Arts) (US) **337**

N E A Grantmaking Programs: Arts in Education. (National Endowment for the Arts) (US) **337**, 1648

N E A Grantmaking Programs: Challenge and Advancement. (National Endowment for the Arts) (US) **2940**, 337, 4635

N E A Grantmaking Programs: Dance. (National Endowment for the Arts) (US) **1531**

N E A Grantmaking Programs: Design Arts. (National Endowment for the Arts) (US) **337**, 303

N E A Grantmaking Programs: Expansion Arts. (National Endowment for the Arts) (US) **337**

N E A Grantmaking Programs: Folk Arts. (National Endowment for the Arts) (US) **337**

N E A Grantmaking Programs: Inter - Arts. (National Endowment for the Arts) (US) **337**

N E A Grantmaking Programs: Literature. (National Endowment for the Arts) (US) **2940**, 2998

N E A Grantmaking Programs: Locals Program. (National Endowment for the Arts) (US) **337**

N E A Grantmaking Programs: Media Arts. (National Endowment for the Arts) (US) **337**

N E A Grantmaking Programs: Museums. (National Endowment for the Arts) (US) **3530**, 337

N E A Grantmaking Programs: Music. (National Endowment for the Arts) (US) **3569**

N E A Grantmaking Programs: Opera - Musical Theater. (National Endowment for the Arts) (US) **4635**, 3569

N E A Grantmaking Programs: States Program. (National Endowment for the Arts) (US) **337**

N E A Grantmaking Programs: Theater. (National Endowment for the Arts) (US) **4635**

N E A Grantmaking Programs: Visual Arts. (National Endowment for the Arts) (US) **337**

N E A Issue Brief. (Nuclear Energy Agency) (FR) **1807**

N E A - N M Advocate see Advocate's Voice **1614**

N E A New York. (National Education Association of New York) (US) **1648**

N E A Now. (National Education Association of the United States) (US ISSN 0744-0154) **1648**

N E A R A Transit Newsletter. (New England Antiquities Research Association) (US) **279**

N E A T E Newsletter. (New England Association of Teachers of English) (US) **2830**, 1755

N E A Today. (National Education Association of the United States) (US ISSN 0734-7219) **1649**

N E A Today: Educational Support Edition. (US) **1729**

N E C News. (Nippon Electric Company) (JA ISSN 0027-6421) **1340**, 1398

N E C Research and Development. (Nippon Electric Co. Ltd.) (JA ISSN 0547-051X) **1904**

N E D A Journal of Development see Journal of Philippine Development **1099**

N E D A Philippine Economic Indicators see Economic Indicators **714**

N E D A Statistical Yearbook of the Philippines see Philippine Statistical Yearbook **734**

N E D O Books and Catalogue. (UK) **730**

▼N E E D I S Initiative. (National Enterprise Education Development and Information Service) (UK) **1685**

N E H G S Nexus. (New England Historic Genealogical Society) (US ISSN 0747-9891) **2159**

N E I Brazil: Noticiario de Equipamentos Industriais. (BL) **3021**

N.E.I.D. Informations. (FR) **384**

N E I - L A see N E I Spanish America: Noticiario de Equipos Industriales **3021**

†N E I News. (Northern Engineering Industries plc.) (UK ISSN 0262-0057) **5242**

N E I S S Data Highlights. (National Electronic Injury Surveillance System) (US) **4108**, 1904

N E I S S News see N E I S S Data Highlights **4108**

N E I Spanish America: Noticiario de Equipos Industriales. (BL) **3021**

N E I Update see Rolls-Royce Worldwide **1835**

N E I W P C C Annual Report. (New England Interstate Water Pollution Control Commission) (US) **1978**

N E I W P C C Water Connection. (New England Interstate Water Pollution Control Commission) (US) **1978**

N E L A Newsletter. (New England Library Association, Inc.) (US ISSN 0027-6448) **2774**

N E M A Bulletin. (National Electrical Manufacturers Association) (US ISSN 0092-5187) **1904**

N E M A Journal see Leading Notes **3561**

N E M A News. (National Electrical Manufacturers Association) (US) **1904**

N E M A Report see N E M A Bulletin **1904**

N E M L A Italian Studies. (Northeast Modern Language Association Conference) (US) **2940**, 2015

N E M S Annual Report. (North of England Museums Service) (UK) **3530**

N E M S News. (North of England Museums Service) (UK ISSN 0267-2618) **3530**

N E N see New Equipment News **4605**

N E O N. (Natal Education - Onderwys in Natal) (SA) **1649**

N E R C News. (Natural Environment Research Council) (UK ISSN 0951-5305) **1963**

N E R C News Journal see N E R C News **1963**

N E S D A Quarterly Newsletter. (National Equipment Servicing Dealers Association) (US) **3021**, 680

N.E.S.F.A. Index: Science Fiction Magazines and Anthologies see N E S F A Index to Short Science Fiction **2982**

N E S F A Index to Short Science Fiction. (New England Science Fiction Association Inc.) (US) **2982**, 17, 3012

†N E S P Newsletter. (US) **5242**

N E T see Nordisk Exlibris Tidsskrift **4133**

N E T A News see N E T A World **1904**

N E T A News. (National Environmental Training Association) (US) **1963**

N E T A Technical Papers. (InterNational Electrical Testing Association) (US) **1904**

N E T A World. (InterNational Electrical Testing Association) (US) **1904**

N E V A C Blad/Dutch Vacuum Society. Journal. (Nederlandse Vacuumvereniging) (NE ISSN 0169-9431) **3825**

N F A see Nachrichten fuer Aussenhandel **957**

N F A A. Bulletin. (National Fashion Accessories Association) (US) **1286**

N F A A. Newsletter. (National Fashion Accessories Association) (US) **1286**

†N F A A Arts Alumni Directory. (National Foundation for Advancement in the Arts) (US) **5242**

†N F A I S Bulletin. (National Federation of Abstracting and Information Services) (US) **5242**

N F A I S Newsletter. (National Federation of Abstracting and Information Services) (US ISSN 0090-0893) **17**

N F A I S Notes. (National Federation of Abstracting and Information Services) (US) **17**

N F A I S Report Series. (National Federation of Abstracting and Information Services) (US) **17**

N F A News, Facts, Actions see News, Facts, Actions **958**

N F C B Legal Handbook for Commercial Stations see Public Radio Legal Handbook **1358**

N F C B News see Community Radio News **1372**

N F C C Members' Bulletin. (National Foundation for Consumer Credit) (US) **791**

N F Digest (National Foundation of Health, Welfare and Pension Plans) see International Foundation of Employee Benefit Plans. Digest **983**

N F E A S Journal see National Forum of Education Administration and Supervision Journal **1730**

N F E Exchange (Non-Formal Education) see I N E T Up-Date **5210**

N F E - W I D Exchange - Asia. Newsletter. (PH ISSN 0115-852X) **1649**, 4380, 4849

†N F E - W I D Exchange - Asia. Occasional Paper. (PH ISSN 0115-8473) **5242**

N F I B. (National Federation of Independent Business) (US ISSN 0195-1513) **1116**

N F I B Quarterly Economic Report for Small Business. (National Federation of Independent Business) (US ISSN 0362-3548) **875**

N F I Bulletin see Hardware Today **642**

N F L Preview (Year) see Football Preview (Year) **4504**

N F Legal Legislative Reporter News Bulletin (National Foundation of Health, Welfare and Pension Plans) see Legal - Legislative Reporter. News Bulletin **987**

N F M - Programma. (Stichting Nederlands Filmmuseum) (NE) **3514**

N F M Programmakrant see N F M - Programma **3514**

▼N F M - Themareeks. (NE) **3514**

N F P A Buyer's Guide. (National Fire Protection Association) (US) **2034**

N F P A Directory and Member Guide see National Fluid Power Association. Directory and Member Guide (Year) **1936**

N F P A: Economics Monthly see N F P A: Statistical Roundup **1048**

N F P A Journal. (National Fire Protection Association) (US ISSN 1054-8793) **2034**

N F P A: Statistical Roundup. (National Forest Products Association) (US) **1048**, 2104, 2116

N F P A Technical Committee. Report. (National Fire Protection Association) (US ISSN 0077-4553) **2034**

N F R A Newsletter. (National Forest Recreaction Association) (US) **1492**, 2104, 2538, 2656

N F R C Roofing Industry Directory. (National Federation of Roofing Contractors) (UK) **625**

N F R C Yearbook see N F R C Roofing Industry Directory **625**

N F S E Journal see National Forum of Special Education Journal **1739**

N F S O Journal (National Federation of Site Operations) see B H & H P A Journal **4753**

N F T see Nordisk Foersaekringstidskrift **2539**

N F T A Annual Report. (Niagara Frontier Transportation Authority) (US) **4653**

†N F T A On the Move. (Niagara Frontier Transportation Authority) (US) **5242**

N F T E J see National Forum Teacher Education Journal **1649**

N F Z; Neue Freie Zeitung. (AU) **3908**

N G Gemeentelijk Magazine. (NE ISSN 0924-4816) **4092**

N G M. (Nouveau Genie Medical) (FR ISSN 0301-6374) **3133**

N G Novine. (Cl) **108**, 1116

N G U Bulletin. (Norges Geologiske Undersoekelse) (NO ISSN 0332-5768) **1574**

N G U Skrifter. (Norges Geologiske Undersoekelse) (NO ISSN 0377-8894) **1574**

N G U Special Publication. (Norges Geologiske Undersoekelser) (NO ISSN 0801-5961) **1574**

N G Z see N G Z Service Manager **2478**

N G Z Service Manager. (Neue Gastronomische Zeitschrift) (GW ISSN 0930-2255) **2478**
N H C A Professional Service Organization Directory. (National Hearing Conservation Association) (US) **2288**
N H D S Newsletter. (New Hampshire Dental Society) (US ISSN 0027-6545) **3238**
N H E L P Health Advocate. (National Health Law Program) (US ISSN 0272-7102) **3806**
N H I F Newsletter. (National Head Injury Foundation) (US) **3310**
†N H K Gijutsu Kenkyu/N H K Technical Journal. (Nippon Hoso Kyokai) (JA ISSN 0027-6553) **5242**
†N H K Giken Geppo/N H K Technical Report. (Nippon Hoso Kyokai) (JA ISSN 0027-6561) **5242**
†N H K Laboratories Note. (Nippon Hoso Kyokai) (JA ISSN 0027-657X) **5242**
N H K Technical Journal. see N H K Gijutsu Kenkyu **5242**
†N H K Technical Monograph. (Nippon Hoso Kyokai) (JA ISSN 0077-2631) **5242**
N H K Technical Report. see N H K Giken Geppo **5242**
N H L A News Report see Health Lawyers News Report **2632**
N H L A Newsletter. (National Hardwood Lumber Association) (US) **2116**
N H L A Newsletter. (New Hampshire Library Association) (US ISSN 0028-5269) **2774**
†N.H.L. Pro Hockey. (CN ISSN 0079-5569) **5242**
†N H Lambda Newsletter. (New Hampshire) (US) **5242**
N H O Hospice News. (National Hospice Organization) (US) **4413, 2468**
N H O President's Letter see N H O Hospice News **4413**
N H P Rapport. (Nordisk Hydrologisk Forening) (DK ISSN 0900-0267) **1599**
N H R A Souvenir Yearbook. (National Hot Rod Association) (US) **4697**
N H R National Newsletter see N W R National Newsletter **4849**
N H S A Journal. (National Head Start Association) (US) **1738**
N H S C News. (National Home Study Council) (US ISSN 0027-6596) **1729**
N H S C Report. (National Home Study Council) (US) **1755**
N H S Economic Review (Year). (National Health Service) (UK) **4067**
N H Z. (Neue Hanauer Zeitung) (GW) **2875**
N.I.A.A.A. - R.U.C.A.S. Alcoholism Treatment Monographs see N I A A A - R U C A S Alcoholism Treatment Series **1538**
N I A A A - R U C A S Alcoholism Treatment Series. (National Institute on Alcohol Abuse and Alcoholism - Rutgers University Center of Alcohol Studies) (US ISSN 0147-0515) **1538**
N I A S - Nytt. (Nordic Institute of Asian Studies) (DK ISSN 0904-4337) **3641**
N I A S Report. (Nordic Institute of Asian Studies) (DK ISSN 0904-597X) **3641**
N I B Annual Report see National Investment Bank, Ghana. Annual Report **792**
N I B R Rapport. (Norsk Institutt for By- og Regionforskning) (NO ISSN 0801-1699) **2492**
N I C E M Index to A V Producers and Distributors. (National Information Center for Educational Media) (US) **3520, 17, 1678**
N I C E M Index to Educational Video Tapes see Film & Video Finder **1676**
N I C E M Index to Environmental Studies - Multimedia see Science and Computer Literacy Audiovisuals **1457**

N I C E M Index to 16mm Educational Films see Film & Video Finder **1676**
N I C E M Index to 35mm Educational Filmstrips see Filmstrip and Slide Set Finder **1676**
N I C E News. (National Information Conference) (US) **1398**
N I C E R Bulletin. (Northern Ireland Council for Educational Research) (UK ISSN 0262-8163) **1649**
N I D A Bulletin. (National Institute of Development Administration) (TH ISSN 0125-5606) **2775**
N I D A Research Monograph see U.S. National Institute on Drug Abuse. Research Monograph Series **1539**
N I D I. Rapport - Report - Bericht - Rapporto. (Nederlands Interdisciplinair Demografisch Instituut) (NE ISSN 0922-7210) **3985**
N I E Journal see Journal of Indian Education **1642**
N I E R. Occasional Paper. (National Institute for Educational Research) (JA) **1649**
N I F Newsletter. (Nordic Institute of Folklore) (FI ISSN 0355-0206) **2057**
N I F P General Series. (National Institute of Health and Family Welfare) (II ISSN 0077-4944) **597**
N I F P Manual Series. (National Institute of Health and Family Welfare) (II ISSN 0077-4952) **597**
N I F P Monograph Series. (National Institute of Health and Family Welfare) (II ISSN 0077-4960) **597**
N I F P Report Series. (National Institute of Health and Family Welfare) (II ISSN 0077-4979) **597**
N I F P Technical Paper Series. (National Institute of Health and Family Welfare) (II ISSN 0077-4987) **597**
N I F Publications. (Nordic Institute of Folklore) (FI) **2057**
N I F Weekly. (National Investment & Finance) (II ISSN 0027-6642) **957**
N I H A E Bulletin see Health and Population: Perspectives and Issues **596**
N I H F W Technical Reports. (National Institute of Health and Family Welfare) (II ISSN 0253-6757) **4413**
N I H Record. (National Institutes of Health) (US) **3133**
N I J Reports. (National Institute of Justice) (US) **1518**
N I K E. (GW) **337**
N I K H E F. Annual Report. (Nationaal Instituut voor Kernfysica en Hoge-Energiefysica) (NE) **3825**
N I K H E F. K Bulletin. (Nationaal Instituut voor Kernfysica en Hoge-Energiefysica) (NE) **3825**
N I M H A N S Journal. (National Institute of Mental Health & Neuro Sciences) (II ISSN 0254-0886) **3345**
N I M L A. (Modern Language Association of Northern Ireland) (UK ISSN 0143-859X) **2830**
N I N. (Nedeljne Informativne Novine) (YU ISSN 0027-6685) **2239**
N I O S H T I C Database. (National Institute for Occupational Safety and Health Technical Information Center) (US) **3619**
N I P H Annals. (National Institute for Public Health) (NO ISSN 0332-5652) **3222, 4108**
N I P R News. (National Institute for Personnel Research) (SA) **4036, 1067**
N I P R Symposium on Antarctic Geosciences. Proceedings. (National Institute of Polar Research) (JA ISSN 0914-2029) **1574**
N I P R Symposium on Antarctic Meteorites. Proceedings. (National Institute of Polar Research) (JA ISSN 0914-5621) **1574**
N I P R Symposium on Polar Biology. Proceedings. (National Institute of Polar Research) (JA ISSN 0914-563X) **448**

N I P R Symposium on Polar Meteorology and Glaciology. Proceedings. (National Institute of Polar Research) (JA ISSN 0914-2037) **1574**
N I P R Symposium on Upper Atmosphere Physics. Proceedings. (National Institute of Polar Research) (JA ISSN 0914-5613) **3825**
N I P S see News in Physiological Sciences **573**
N I R S A Journal. (National Intramural Recreational Sports Association) (US) **4480**
N I S E R Occasional Papers. (Nigerian Institute of Social and Economic Research) (NR) **4380, 680**
N I S S A T Newsletter. (National Information System for Science and Technology) (II ISSN 0970-0188) **4325, 4604**
N I S T Building Science Series. (U.S. National Institute of Standards and Technology) (US ISSN 1049-7579) **625**
N I S T Handbook. (U.S. National Institute of Standards and Technology) (US) **3447**
N I S T Monograph. (U.S. National Institute of Standards and Technology) (US) **3447**
N I S T Newsletter see Con - Science **4595**
N I S T Special Publication. (U.S. National Institute of Standards and Technology) (US ISSN 1048-776X) **3447**
N I S T Technical Note. (U.S. National Institute of Standards and Technology) (US ISSN 1054-013X) **3447**
N I S T Update. (National Institute of Standards and Technology) (US) **680**
N I T A see Journal of Intravenous Nursing **3280**
N I V E Nieuws. (NE) **1021**
N I W O Mededelingen. (Nederlandsche Internationale Wegvervoer Organisatie) (NE) **4653**
†N I W R Information Sheet. (SA) **5242**
N J A O P S Journal. (New Jersey Association of Osteopathic Physicians and Surgeons) (US ISSN 0892-0249) **3215**
N J Audubon. (New Jersey Audubon Society) (US) **565, 4325**
N J E A Review. (New Jersey Education Association) (US ISSN 0027-6758) **1729**
N J Industrial News. (US) **680**
N J Magazine see New Jersey Reporter **2230**
N J N Guide. (New Jersey Network) (US) **1377**
N J S D C Research Bulletin. (New Jersey School Development Council) (US ISSN 0028-5927) **1712**
N J W - Co R see Computerreport der Neue Juristischen Wochenschrift **2705**
N J W - Rechtsprechungs-Report Zivilrecht. (GW ISSN 0179-4043) **2656**
N K B. (Nederlandse Kermisbond) (NE ISSN 0027-6766) **4779**
N.K. Bose Memorial Foundation. Newsletter. (II) **4380**
N K H Nagaoka-shiritsu Kagaku Hakubutsukanpo. (JA) **3530, 4325**
N K K News. (JA ISSN 0388-600X) **1936, 4733**
N L A D A Cornerstone. (National Legal Aid and Defender Association) (US) **2656**
N L A Newsletter see National Librarian **2775**
†N L B A News. (National Licensed Beverage Association) (US) **5242**
N L F - Nytt see NaFo - Nytt **108**
N L G I Spokesman. (National Lubricating Grease Institute) (US ISSN 0027-6782) **3692**
N L N News see Nursing and Health Care **3283**
N L N Nursing Data Book see N L N Nursing Data Review **3282**

NO 6461

N L N Nursing Data Review. (National League for Nursing) (US) **3282**
N L R B Case Handling Manual. (U.S. National Labor Relations Board) (US) **2656**
N M A. (New Music Articles) (AT ISSN 0811-7497) **3569**
N M A Bulletin Board. (Nonprofit Management Association) (US) **1299, 1021**
N - M A G see Vista **3535**
N M A L: Notes on Modern American Literature. (US ISSN 0163-8246) **2940**
N M B see Motel News **2478**
N M F S Fisheries Market News Report. (National Marines Fishery Service) (US ISSN 1055-2766) **2051, 4580**
N M I News see British Maritime Technology News **4725**
N M I - Nordisk Mejeriinformation. (SW ISSN 1101-8399) **202**
N M L Technical Journal. (National Metallurgical Laboratory) (II ISSN 0027-6839) **3416**
N M M A Certification Handbook. (National Marine Manufacturers Association) (US) **4526**
N M - Nordelbische Mission. (GW) **4244**
N M R. (Nuclear Magnetic Resonance) (US ISSN 0170-5989) **3848**
N M R A Newsletter. (National Marine Representatives Association) (US) **838, 1048**
N M R I Compensation in Mass Retailing, Salaries and Incentives. (National Mass Retailing Institute) (US ISSN 0092-5950) **989**
N M R in Biomedicine. (Nuclear Magnetic Resonance) (UK ISSN 0952-3480) **3360**
N M R T Newsletter. (New Members Round Table) (US) **2775**
N N. (Nicht Notierten Deutschen Aktiengesellschaften) (GW) **1146**
N N A National Directory of Weekly Newspapers. (National Newspaper Association) (US) **2573**
▼N N & I - E S R D Product and Service Directory. (Nephrology News and Issues, Inc.) (US) **3389**
N N D C Newsletter. (New Nigeria Development Company Ltd.) (NR) **1081**
N N F A Monitor. (National Nutritional Foods Association) (US) **3609**
N N O Magazine. (Noord - Nederlands Orkest) (NE) **3569**
N: Nude and Natural. (US) **3806**
N O A A National Weather Service. Climate Analysis Center. Average Monthly Weather Outlook see N O A A National Weather Service. Climate Analysis Center. Monthly and Seasonal Weather Outlook **3439**
N O A A National Weather Service. Climate Analysis Center. Monthly and Seasonal Weather Outlook. (U.S. National Oceanic and Atmospheric Administration) (US) **3439**
N O A C A News. (Northeast Ohio Areawide Coordinating Agency) (US) **2492, 4653**
N O A Newsletter. (National Opera Association) (US) **3569**
N O H A News. (Nutrition for Optimal Health Association) (US) **3609, 3188**
N O H U G News. (New Orleans Heath Users Group) (US) **1471, 1427, 1463**
N O I International. (AU) **2940, 337**
N O Kulturberichte see Kulturberichte aus Niederoesterreich **332**
N O L P E Notes. (National Organization on Legal Problems of Education) (US ISSN 0047-8997) **1729, 2656**
N O L P E School Law Reporter. (US ISSN 1059-4094) **2656, 1649**
N O M D A Spokesman. (National Office Machine Dealers Association) (US ISSN 0027-6871) **1059**
N O P A Membership Directory and Buyer's Guide (Year). (National Office Products Association) (US) **1059**

6462 N O

N O P A Office Market Update. (National Office Products Association) (US) **1059**

†N O P A Special Report. (National Office Products Association) (US) **5242**

N O P Political Bulletin see Political Social Economic Review **3917**

N O R C Report. (National Opinion Research Center) (US) **4380**

N O R C Reporter. (National Opinion Research Center) (US ISSN 0147-0124) **4443**

N O R D I N F O Publikation. (Nordiska Samarbetsorganet for Vetenskaplig Information) (FI ISSN 0358-7045) **2775**

N O R M Newsletter. (National Organization for Raw Materials) (US) **918, 875**

N O S A. Fashion Bulletin. (National Outerwear and Sportswear Association) (US) **1286**

N O S A. Production Bulletin. (National Outerwear and Sportswear Association) (US) **1286**

N O S A News. (National Outerwear and Sportswear Association) (US) **1286**

N O S A Update. (National Office Systems Association) (US) **753**

N O S P - Mikro. (Nordisk Samkatalog foer Periodica) (FI ISSN 0357-1955) **406**

N O T E see Notes on Teaching English **2832**

N O W see S F N O W Times **4852**

N O W E L E. (North-Western European Language Evolution) (DK ISSN 0108-8416) **2830**

N O W News (Boston). (National Organization for Women) (US) **4849, 3945**

†N O W Nieuws. (Nederlandse Organisatie van Welzijnswerkers) (NE) **5242**

N O W Notes - Atlanta Chapter see Atlanta N O W News **4837**

N O W San Diego News. (National Organization for Women) (US) **4849**

N O W San Francisco see S F N O W Times **4852**

N O W Schuelerzeitung der Staatlichen Realschule Speyer. (GW) **1261**

N P A - Air Destinations. (US) **4803**

N P A Annual Report. (Nigerian Ports Authority) (NR) **4733**

N P A Bulletin. (Nigerian Ports Authority) (NR ISSN 0794-3008) **4733**

N P A Government Affairs Report see Parking **4699**

N.P.A. Journal. (National Pawnbrokers Association (Inc.)) (UK ISSN 0047-9020) **2565**

N P A News. (Nigerian Ports Authority) (NR ISSN 0547-0730) **4733**

N P A Supplement. (National Pharmaceutical Association) (UK) **3735**

N.P.D.C. Newsletter. (National Poetry Day Committee) (US) **2998**

N P E R see National Public Employment Reporter **989**

N.P.K.S. Processes and Plant Suppliers. World Directory. (UK) **185**

N P L News. (National Physical Laboratory) (UK ISSN 0143-1536) **3825**

N P L Technical Bulletin. (National Physical Laboratory) (II ISSN 0027-6898) **3825**

†N P N Bulletin. (National Petroleum News) (US ISSN 0027-6901) **5242**

N P N Factbook. (National Petroleum News) (US ISSN 0099-4294) **3692**

N P Q see New Perspectives Quarterly **3910**

†N P R L Newsletter. (National Physical Research Institute) (SA) **5242**

N P S E Newsletter - Incentive Report see A I M Newsletter - Incentive Report **1032**

N P T A Management News. (National Paper Trade Association, Inc.) (US ISSN 0739-2214) **3663**

N P U G News. (National Prime Users Group, Inc.) (US ISSN 0895-7754) **1471, 1463**

N P U Supplement see N P A Supplement **3735**

N R A Action. (National Rifle Association of America) (US) **2656, 1518, 4480**

N R A G Papers. (Northern Rockies Action Group, Inc.) (US) **4413**

N R A Journal. (National Rifle Association) (UK) **4551**

N R A News see Restaurants U S A **2479**

N R C A Membership Directory. (National Roofing Contractors Association) (US ISSN 1053-8305) **625**

N R C D Abstracts see Information Media & Technology **1337**

N R C Docket Microfiche. (Nuclear Regulatory Commission) (US) **3837**

N R C P Research Bulletin. (National Research Council of Philippines) (PH ISSN 0115-1304) **4325**

N R C Yearbook. (National Reading Conference, Inc.) (US) **1739**

N R D C Newsline. (Natural Resources Defense Council, Inc.) (US) **4108**

N R E C A - A P P A Legal Reporting Service. (National Rural Electric Cooperative Association) (US ISSN 0362-8833) **2656**

N R G. (US) **2998**

N R I Bibliographies. (National Research Institute) (PP) **406**

N R I Discussion Papers. (National Research Institute) (PP) **4380**

†N R I M S Current Activities. (National Research Institute for Mathematical Sciences) (SA) **5242**

N R I Monographs. (National Research Institute) (PP) **4380**

N R I Special Publications. (National Research Institute) (PP) **4380**

N R M C A Publication. (National Ready Mixed Concrete Association) (US ISSN 0077-5355) **625**

N R O. (Nobeyama Radio Observatory) (JA ISSN 0911-5501) **367**

N R O Gijutsu Hokoku/N R O Technical Report. (Nobeyama Radio Observatory) (JA) **367**

N R O Technical Report. see N R O Gijutsu Hokoku **367**

N R O Yuzazu Mitingu. (Nobeyama Radio Observatory) (JA) **367**

†N R P A Washington Action Report. (National Recreation and Park Association) (US) **5242**

N R R A News. (National Risk Retention Association) (US) **2538**

N R S. (Nouvelle Revue Socialiste) (FR ISSN 0222-4275) **3908**

N R T A Bulletin. (National Retired Teachers Association) (US ISSN 0027-6987) **1649, 2276**

N R Technology see Rubber Developments **4293**

N R W - International. (Nord - Rhein Westfalen) (GW) **989, 3619**

N S A A News. (National Ski Areas Association) (US) **4480**

N S A A Newsletter see N S A A News **4480**

N S A C I News. (North West Suburban Association of Commerce and Industry) (US) **680**

▼N S B E Bridge. (National Society of Black Engineers) (US) **1831, 2015, 3629**

N S B E Journal see N S B E Magazine **1831**

N S B E Magazine. (National Society of Black Engineers) (US) **1831, 1755, 2015**

N.S.C.A. Members Handbook. (National Society for Clean Air and Environmental Protection) (UK ISSN 0140-6787) **1963**

N.S.C.A. Pollution Handbook. (National Society for Clean Air and Environmental Protection) (UK) **1978**

N.S.C.A. Reference Book see N.S.C.A. Pollution Handbook **1978**

N S C Review. (National Science Council of the Republic of China) (CH ISSN 0255-4399) **4325**

N S C Special Publication. (National Science Council of the Republic of China) (CH) **4325**

N S C Symposium Series. (National Science Council of the Republic of China) (CH ISSN 0252-8177) **4325**

N S C T E Monographs. (National Society of College Teachers of Education) (US) **1649**

N.S. Conservation. (Nova Scotia Lands and Forests) (US ISSN 0702-732X) **1492**

N S D C C Newsletter see Nova Scotia Craft News **356**

N S D J A Digest (National Sash and Door Jobbers Association) see Shelter **631**

N S F Bulletin. (U.S. National Science Foundation) (US) **4325, 4067**

N S F R E Journal. (National Society of Fund Raising Executives) (US ISSN 0196-3295) **4413**

N S F R E News. (National Society of Fund Raising Executives) (US ISSN 0890-2828) **4413**

N S G A Circular. (National Sand and Gravel Association) (US ISSN 0077-5673) **1574**

N S G A Retail Focus. (National Sporting Goods Association) (US ISSN 1045-2087) **1048, 4480**

▼N S G A Sports Apparel Diary. (National Sporting Goods Association) (US) **4498, 1288**

N S G A Sports Retailer see N S G A Retail Focus **1048**

N S I Advisory. (National Security Institute) (US ISSN 0882-9667) **3466**

N.S.K. News Bulletin. (JA ISSN 0916-295X) **2573, 4133**

N S L see North Sea Letter **3694**

N S M. (UK) **1649**

N S N A Newsletter see Imprint (New York) **3279**

N S O A Bulletin. (National School Orchestra Association) (US ISSN 0146-9975) **3569**

N S O Monthly Bulletin of Statistics. (National Statistics Office) (PH ISSN 0115-2092) **4580**

N S P A Washington Reporter. (National Society of Public Accountants) (US) **753**

N S P News. (Northern States Power Company) (US) **1792**

N S R A News. (Nuclear Safety Research Association) (JA) **1807**

N S R D S - N B S: National Standard Reference Data Series. (US ISSN 0097-0395) **3447**

N S S A Newsletter. (National Science Supervisors Association) (US) **4325, 1067, 1755**

N S S Bulletin. (National Speleological Society, Inc.) (US ISSN 0146-9517) **1574**

N S S L H A Journal. (National Student Speech Language Hearing Association) (US ISSN 0736-0312) **3315**

N S S News. (National Speleological Society, Inc.) (US ISSN 0027-7010) **1574**

N S T A Annual Safe Transit Conference. Proceedings. (National Safe Transit Association) (US) **3649, 4653**

N S T A Newsletter. (National Spasmodic Torticollis Association) (US ISSN 1040-3671) **3345, 3238**

N S T A Reports. (National Science Teachers Association) (US) **1649, 1261, 4325**

N S T Annual. (MY) **680**

†N S T F Report. (National Scholarship Trust Fund) (US) **5242**

N S U Library. Genealogy Series. (Nicholls State University) (US) **2159**

N S W A M H News. (New South Wales Association for Mental Health) (AT) **3133**

▼N.S.W. Bowls News. (AT) **4508**

N.S.W. Farmers News. (New South Wales) (AT) **221**

N S W Forest Products Association. Prologue Notes. (New South Wales) (AT) **2104**

N.S.W. Freemason. (United Grand Lodge of New South Wales) (AT) **1299**

N.S.W. Golf. (New South Wales Golf Association) (AT) **4508**

N S W Journal of Special Education. (New South Wales Chapter) (AT) **1739**

N.S.W. Realty Auctioneer. (New South Wales) (AT) **4153**

N.S.W. Skindiver. (New South Wales) (AT) **4551, 4480**

N T B see Neue Technik im Buero **5245**

N T C A Exchange. (National Telephone Cooperative Association) (US) **1364, 1377**

N T C A Video Connection see N T C A Video Magazine **1364**

N T C A Video Magazine. (National Telephone Cooperative Association) (US) **1364, 1385**

N T C News. (IT) **4191**

N T C Workshop Report Series. (National Turfgrass Council) (UK) **510, 2134**

N T D see Nordisk Tidskrift foer Doevundervisning **2288**

N T D R A Dealer News. (National Tire Dealers and Retreaders Association, Inc.) (US ISSN 0027-7045) **4292**

N T E U Bulletin. (National Treasury Employees Union) (US ISSN 0279-540X) **2587**

N T I. (Nouvelles Technologies de l'Information) (FR) **4604**

N T I Newsletter. (National Tuberculosis Institute) (II ISSN 0047-9136) **3366**

N T I S Alerts: Administration and Management. (U.S. National Technical Information Service) (US) **4081, 17**

N T I S Alerts: Agriculture & Food. (US) **140, 17, 2085**

N T I S Alerts: Behavior and Society. (US) **4458, 17**

N T I S Alerts: Biomedical Technology & Human Factors Engineering. (US) **3178, 17**

N T I S Alerts: Building Industry Technology. (US) **638, 17**

N T I S Alerts: Business & Economics. (US) **730, 17**

N T I S Alerts: Chemistry. (US) **1202, 17**

N T I S Alerts: Civil Engineering. (US) **1845, 17**

N T I S Alerts: Communication. (U.S. National Technical Information Service) (US) **1349, 17**

N T I S Alerts: Computers, Control & Information Theory. (US) **1405, 17**

N T I S Alerts: Electrotechnology. (US) **1776, 17**

N T I S Alerts: Energy. (US) **1800, 17**

N T I S Alerts: Environmental Pollution & Control. (US) **1974, 17, 1978**

N T I S Alerts: Foreign Technology. (US) **4615, 17**

N T I S Alerts: Government Inventions for Licensing. (US) **4615, 18**

N T I S Alerts: Health Care. (US) **3811, 18**

N T I S Alerts: Library & Information Sciences. (US) **2794, 18**

N T I S Alerts: Manufacturing Technology. (US) **4615, 18, 1415**

N T I S Alerts: Materials Sciences. (US) **1845, 18**

N T I S Alerts: Medicine & Biology. (US) **466, 18, 3178**

N T I S Alerts: Natural Resources & Earth Sciences. (US) **1501, 18, 1551**

N T I S Alerts: Ocean Technology & Engineering. (US) **1551, 18, 1845**

N T I S Alerts: Physics. (US) **3838, 18**

N T I S Alerts: Transportation. (US) **4665, 18**

N T I S Bibliographic Data Base. (U.S. National Technical Information Service) (US) **4143, 1880**

N T I S Digest. (U.S. National Technical Information Service) (US) **2775**

NACIONES UNIDAS 6463

N T I S NewsLine. (U.S. National Technical Information Service) (US) 2775

N T I S Tech Notes. (U.S. National Technical Information Service) (US ISSN 0889-8464) 4604

N T I S Title Index. (U.S. National Technical Information Service) (US) 4615, 3938

N T K - Nuus see S A Co-op 118

N T L News. (National Transient Lodge) (US) 2587

N T M Geschichte der Naturwissenschaften, Technik und Medizin. Schriftenreihe. (GW) 4325

N T Newsletter see Paraphernalia 2778

N T P A Directory see National Trade and Professional Associations of the United States and Labor Unions 1147

N T S A Newsletter. (National Tuberous Sclerosis Association) (US) 3133

N T S B Reporter. (National Transportation Safety Board) (US ISSN 0745-9874) 4676

N T T Review. (Nippon Telegraph and Telephone Corporation) (JA ISSN 0915-2334) 1340

N T T Topics. (Nippon Telegraph & Telephone Company) (US) 1364

N T U C Lifestyle. (SI) 4779

N T Z. (Nachrichtentechnische Zeitschrift) (GW ISSN 0027-707X) 1340

N T Z Archiv see European Transactions on Telecommunications and Related Technologies 1335

N - the Newsletter for Publications. (US) 4133

N U B E News see B I F U Report 760

N U C: D see National Union Catalogue of Library Materials for People with Disabilities 2285

N U C E A News. (National University Continuing Education Association) (US) 1712

N U C: N see National Union Catalogue of Non-Book Materials 407

▼N U C O M 5. (AT ISSN 0729-2562) 406

N U C O S see National Union Catalogue of Serials 407

N U F O I S News. (National U F O Investigation Society) (UK) 59

N U J Freelance Directory. (National Union of Journalists) (UK) 2573

N U K T A. (ZR) 108

N U M M U S. (PO) 3600

N U M U S Numismatica, Medalhistica, Arqueologia see N U M M U S 3600

N U P E Journal. (National Union of Public Employees) (UK) 989

N U P I Notat. (Norsk Utenrikspolitisk Institutt) (NO ISSN 0800-0018) 3966

N U P I Rapport. (Norsk Utenrikspolitisk Institutt) (NO ISSN 0800-000X) 3966

N U Quarter Notes. (Northwestern University) (US ISSN 0093-0288) 3569

N U S Action. (National Union of Students) (UK) 1649

N U S News see N U S Action 1649

N U T Education Review. (National Union of Teachers) (UK ISSN 0951-7855) 1649

N V see Naamloze Vennootschappen 2538

N V. (Neue Verpackung) (GW ISSN 0341-0390) 3650

N V B B Magazine. (Nationale Vereniging voor Beveiliging tegen Brand) (BE) 2034

N.V.B.V. - Info. see F.N.I.B. - Info 3278

N V M W Nieuws see N O W Nieuws 5242

N V R - Informatief. (Nederlandse Vereniging van Rubber- en Kunststoffabrikanten) (NE ISSN 0165-7089) 3864, 2116, 4292

N.V. Vuilafvoer Maatschappij Mededelingen see V A M Mededelingen 1971

N V w Z Rechtsprechungs Report Verwaltungsrecht. (GW ISSN 0934-8603) 2656

N W Aktuell. (Neckarwerke Elektrizitaetsversorgungs AG) (GW) 1904

N W C Market Update. (National Writers Club) (US) 2573

N W C Newsletter. (US) 2573, 2940, 4133

N W D A Executive Newsletter. (National Wholesale Druggists' Association) (US) 3735

N W Europe Petroleum Database. (UK) 3692

N W R National Newsletter. (National Women's Register) (UK ISSN 0952-5335) 4849

N W S A Journal. (National Women's Studies Association) (US ISSN 1040-0656) 4860

N W S Action. (National Women's Studies Association) (US ISSN 1040-0656) 4860

N Y - A B C Employment Letter. (US) 3629, 1340

N Y Auction Advertiser. (US) 1048, 35

N Y C. (New Youth Connections) (US ISSN 0737-285X) 1261

N.Y.C. Parents - F L A G Newsletter. (New York City Parents and Friends of Lesbians and Gays) (US) 2455

N Y C T A Facts & Figures. (New York City Transit Authority) (US) 4653

†N Y City Opera Spotlight. (New York) (US) 5242

N.Y. Civil Liberties. (US ISSN 0746-0201) 3945

N.Y. County Lawyer. (US) 2656

N Y E A Advocate see N E A New York 1648

N Y Eesti Filatelistide Seltsi Bulletaan. (US) 3755

N Y Habitat. (US ISSN 0745-0893) 4153, 2554

N Y L A Bulletin. (New York Library Association) (US ISSN 0027-7134) 2775

N Y L I C Review. (New York Life Insurance Co.) (US ISSN 0027-7142) 2538

†N Y N Y: The Best of New York. (US) 5242

N Y P C Magazine. (New York Personal Computer Inc.) (US) 1471

N Y P C Newsletter see N Y P C Magazine 1471

N Y P I R G Agenda. (New York Public Interest Research Group, Inc.) (US ISSN 1044-3134) 1506

N Y P M A Bulletin. (New York Personnel Management Association) (US ISSN 0027-7150) 1067

†N.Y. Peaceletter. (US) 5242

▼N Y Q see New York Quarterly 2999

N Y Q - New York Queer see Q W 2456

N Y S C A News. (New York School Counselor Association) (US) 1649

N Y S E R Net News. (US) 1427

†N Y S Pesticides Recommends (Redbook). (New York State) (US) 5242

N Y S S A Bulletin see N Y S S A Sphere 3191

N Y S S A Sphere. (New York State Society of Anesthesiologists, Inc.) (US ISSN 0095-2273) 3191

N Y S Waterways Project Magazine see Waterways 3008

N Y School Boards. (US) 1730

N Y State Pharmacist. (US ISSN 0163-1586) 3735

N Y T T S Newsnotes. (New York Turtle and Tortoise Society) (US) 231

N Y Talk. (US) 2229

▼N Y: The City Journal. (US) 3908

†N Y U Alumni News. (US) 5242

N Y U Physician. (New York University Medical Center) (US) 1318

N Y U Today. (New York University) (US) 1318

N.Z.A.R.T. Amateur Radio Callbook. (New Zealand Association of Radio Transmitters, Inc.) (NZ ISSN 0110-5337) 1357, 1377

N Z Agrichemical and Plant Protection Manual. (NZ ISSN 0112-2290) 185

N Z C E R Newsletter. (New Zealand Council for Educational Research) (NZ ISSN 0111-2821) 1649

N Z E I Rourou. (New Zealand Educational Institute) (NZ ISSN 0114-8206) 1649

N Z Electrical Focus. (NZ ISSN 0114-8540) 1904

N Z Family Physician. (NZ ISSN 0110-022X) 3133

N Z Film. (NZ) 3514

†N.Z.H. Maandblad. (Noord-Zuid-Hollandse Vervoer Mij) (NZ ISSN 0027-7193) 5242

N Z Micro. (NZ ISSN 0112-0433) 1471, 1427, 1463

N Z: Neue Zeitschrift fuer Musik. (GW ISSN 0170-8791) 3569

N Z Petroleum Exploration News. (NZ ISSN 0113-0501) 3692

N Z T Committee - Departmental Report Series. (NZ) 4779

N Z T P Catalogue Series see New Zealand Tourism Department. Catalogue Series 407

N Z T P Committee - Departmental Report Series see N Z T Committee - Departmental Report Series 4779

N Z T P Domestic Research Series see New Zealand Tourism Department. Domestic Research Series 4780

N Z T P Economic Research Series see New Zealand Tourism Department. Economic Research Series 682

N Z T P Implications of Tourism Growth Series see New Zealand Tourism Department. Implications of Tourism Growth Series 4780

N Z T P International Visitors Research Series see New Zealand Tourism Department. International Visitors Research Series 4800

N Z T P Marketing Series see New Zealand Tourism Department. Marketing Series 1049

N Z T P Overseas Market Research Series. (NZ ISSN 0112-9724) 4779

N Z T P Product Research Series see New Zealand Tourism Department. Product Research Series 4800

N Z T P Regional Research Series see New Zealand Tourism Department. Regional Research Series 4780

N Z T P Social Research Series see New Zealand Tourism Department. Social Research Series 4444

N Z T P Tourism Incentives Series see New Zealand Tourism Department. Tourism Incentives Series 4780

N Z T P Visitor Statistics Research Series see New Zealand Tourism Department. Visitor Statistics Research Series 4800

N.Z. Truth. (NZ ISSN 0027-7274) 2212

Na Okika O Hawaii/Hawaii Orchid Journal. (US ISSN 0099-8745) 2134, 510

Na Stroikakh Rossii. (RU ISSN 0027-7312) 303, 625

Naa. (NO) 2213

Naaimachine - Nieuws. (NE ISSN 0027-7339) 3021

Naamat. (IS) 4849

Na'Amat Woman. (US ISSN 0888-191X) 4225, 4849

Naamkunde. (BE ISSN 0167-5257) 2830

Naamlooze Venootschap. (NE ISSN 0165-0432) 1021

Naamloze Vennootschappen. (BE) 2538, 680

Naar Lampen Taendes. Fortaellinger see Julegaven 2929

Naar Morgen. (NE ISSN 0027-7355) 2998

Naba Kallol. (II) 2200

Nabokovian. (US) 2940

Nabor Carrillo Lecture Series. Proceedings. (MX ISSN 0185-4011) 1871, 185

Nach der Arbeit. (AU ISSN 0027-7363) 1685

Nachal'naya Shkola. (RU ISSN 0027-7371) 1649

Nachbar G K N. (GW) 1807

Nachbarsprache Niederlaendisch. (GW ISSN 0936-5761) 2830, 2940

Nachrichten aus Chemie, Technik und Laboratorium. (GW ISSN 0341-5163) 1184, 1856

Nachrichten aus dem Karten- und Vermessungswesen see Nachrichten aus dem Karten- und Vermessungswesen. Reihe I: Originalbeitraege 2256

Nachrichten aus dem Karten- und Vermessungswesen see Nachrichten aus dem Karten- und Vermessungswesen. Reihe II: Uebersetzungen 2256

Nachrichten aus dem Karten- und Vermessungswesen. Reihe I: Originalbeitraege. (GW ISSN 0469-4236) 2256

Nachrichten aus dem Karten- und Vermessungswesen. Reihe II: Uebersetzungen. (GW ISSN 0469-4244) 2256

Nachrichten aus den Staatlichen Archiven Bayerns. (GW) 2377

Nachrichten aus der Aerztlichen Mission. (GW ISSN 0027-7398) 4191, 2468, 3806

Nachrichten aus der Basler Mission. (GW) 4244

Nachrichten aus Niedersachsens Urgeschichte. (GW ISSN 0342-1406) 279

Nachrichten der Stadtgemeinde Liezen. (AU) 4092

Nachrichten-Elektronik see Nachrichten - Elektronik und Telematik 1377

Nachrichten - Elektronik und Telematik. (GW) 1377

Nachrichten fuer Aussenhandel. (GW) 957

Nachrichten fuer den Juedischen Buerger Fuerths. (GW) 2015

†Nachrichten fuer Die Zivile Luftfahrt, Deutsche Demokratische Republik. (GW ISSN 0027-7428) 5242

Nachrichten fuer Schoenberg. (GW) 3908

Nachrichten fuer Seefahrer. (GW ISSN 0027-7444) 4733

Nachrichten - Paritaet. (GW ISSN 0937-7425) 4413

Nachrichten zur Mahler Forschung. (AU) 3569

Nachrichtenblatt der Bayerischen Entomologen. (GW) 536

Nachrichtenblatt der Gemeinde Bisingen. (GW) 2190

Nachrichtenblatt der Gemeinde Grosselfingen. (GW) 2190

Nachrichtenblatt des Deutschen Pflanzenschutzdienstes. (GW ISSN 0027-7479) 185

Nachrichtenblatt fuer das Untere Haertsfeld. (GW) 4092

Nachrichtenblatt fuer den Pflanzenschutzdienst in der DDR see Nachrichtenblatt des Deutschen Pflanzenschutzdienstes 185

Nachrichtenblatt fuer die Buersten- und Pinselindustrie see Brossapress-Nachrichtenblatt fuer die Buersten- und Pinselindustrie 3653

Nachrichtenblatt fuer die Gemeinden Sinzheim und Hugelsheim. (GW) 2190

Nachrichtentechnik see Nachrichtentechnik - Elektronik 1340

Nachrichtentechnik. (US ISSN 0342-9148) 2573

Nachrichtentechnik - Elektronik. (GW ISSN 0323-4657) 1340

Nachrichtentechnische Zeitschrift see N T Z 1340

Nacion. (MX ISSN 0027-7509) 3908

Nacion Cubana. (CU) 2184

Nacional Financiera. Annual Report. (MX ISSN 0185-4968) 791

Naciones Unidas. Comision de Derecho Internacional. Anuario see United Nations. International Law Commission Yearbook 2729

Naciones Unidas. Consejo de Seguridad. Documentos Oficiales. Suplemento see United Nations. Security Council. Official Records. Supplement 3975

Naciones Unidas. Origenes, Organizacion, Actividades see Everyone's United Nations 3957

Naciones Unidas Anuario Juridico see United Nations Juridical Yearbook 2730

Naciones Unidas sobre Desarme. Anuario see United Nations Disarmament Yearbook 3473
Nacton Newsletter see Share It 3596
Nada Network. (US) 4191
Nadezhnost' i Dolgovechnost' Mashin i Sooruzhennii. (KR ISSN 0206-3131) 4604
Nadi Abu Dhabi al-Siyahi/Abu Dhabi Tourist Club. (TS) 1300, 4480
Nadi al-Wasl. (TS) 1300, 4480
Nadin-Davis Canadian Sentencing Digest. (CN) 2656
Die Naehrung/Food. (GW ISSN 0027-769X) 3609
Naering i Nord. (NO ISSN 0047-8601) 1081
Naeringsforskning. (SW ISSN 0346-7104) 3609
Naeringsmiddelindustrien. (NO ISSN 0040-7127) 2078
Naeringsrevyen. (NO ISSN 0027-7533) 838
NaFo - Nytt. (Norsk Naturforvalterforbund) (NO) 108
Naft Wal Alam. (IQ) 3692
Nafta. (PL ISSN 0027-7541) 3692
Nafta. (CI ISSN 0027-755X) 3692
Naftika Chronika. (GR ISSN 0047-861X) 4733
Naftiliaki Greek Shipping Review. (GR) 4733
Nag Hammadi Studies. (NE ISSN 0169-9350) 4191
Nagaland Times. (II) 2200
Nagaoka College of Technology. Research Reports/Nagaoka Kogyo Koto Senmon Gakko Kenkyu Kiyo. (JA) 1831, 4325
Nagaoka Kogyo Koto Senmon Gakko Kenkyu Kiyo. see Nagaoka College of Technology. Research Reports 1831
Nagaoka Municipal Science Museum. Bulletin. see Nagaoka-shiritsu Kagaku Hakubutsukan Kenkyu Hokoku 4325
Nagaoka-shiritsu Kagaku Hakubutsukan Kenkyu Hokoku/Nagaoka Municipal Science Museum. Bulletin. (JA ISSN 0285-6085) 4325
Nagaoka Technical College. Research Reports see Nagaoka College of Technology. Research Reports 1831
Nagarjun. (II ISSN 0027-7576) 3133
Nagarlok. (II ISSN 0027-7584) 4092
Nagasaki Daigaku Kyoikugakubu Shizen Kagaku Kenkyu Hokoku/Nagasaki University. Faculty of Education. Science Bulletin. (JA ISSN 0386-443X) 4325
Nagasaki Daigaku Kyoyobu Kiyo. Shizen Kagaku Hen/Nagasaki University. Faculty of Liberal Arts. Bulletin. (JA ISSN 0287-1319) 4325
Nagasaki Igakkai Zasshi/Nagasaki Medical Journal. (JA ISSN 0369-3228) 3133
Nagasaki Medical Journal. see Nagasaki Igakkai Zasshi 3133
Nagasaki University. Faculty of Education. Science Bulletin. see Nagasaki Daigaku Kyoikugakubu Shizen Kagaku Kenkyu Hokoku 4325
Nagasaki University. Faculty of Liberal Arts. Bulletin. see Nagasaki Daigaku Kyoyobu Kiyo. Shizen Kagaku Hen 4325
Nager Sauver. (FR) 4480
Nagoya City University. College of General Education. Bulletin. Natural Science Section. see Nagoya-shiritsu Daigaku Kyoyobu Kiyo. Shizen Kagaku Hen 4326
Nagoya City University. Faculty of Pharmaceutical Science. Annual Report. see Nagoya-shiritsu Daigaku Yakugakubu Kenkyu Nenpo 3735
Nagoya City University. Medical Association. Journal. see Nagoya-shiritsu Daigaku Igakkai Zasshi 3133
Nagoya Daigaku Furukawa Sogo Kenkyu Shiryokan Hokoku/Nagoya University Furukawa Museum. Bulletin. (JA ISSN 0916-6319) 3530, 4325

Nagoya Daigaku Kogakubu Jido Seigyo. see Nagoya University. Faculty of Engineering. Automatic Control Laboratory. Research Reports 1415
Nagoya Daigaku Kogakubu Kiyo. see Nagoya University. Faculty of Engineering. Memoirs 1831
Nagoya Daigaku Kyoyobu Kiyo B. Shizen Kagaku, Shinrigaku/Nagoya University. College of General Education. Research Bulletin B. Natural Science and Psychology. (JA ISSN 0387-4532) 4325, 4036
Nagoya Daigaku Purazuma Kenkyujo Nenpo. see Nagoya University. Institute of Plasma Physics. Annual Review 3825
Nagoya Daigaku Sogo Kenkyu Shiryoukan Houkoku - Nagoya University Museum. Bulletin see Nagoya Daigaku Furukawa Sogo Kenkyu Shiryokan Hokoku 3530
Nagoya Daigaku Uchusan Kenkyushitsu Kiji see Meidai Uchusan Kenkyushitsu Kiji 3824
Nagoya Economics University and Ichimura Gakuen Junior College. Natural Scientific Society. Journal. see Nagoya Keizai Daigaku, Ichimura Gakuen Tanki Daigaku Shizen Kagaku Kenkyukai Kaishi 4325
Nagoya Journal of Medical Science. (JA ISSN 0027-7622) 3133
Nagoya Keizai Daigaku, Ichimura Gakuen Tanki Daigaku Shizen Kagaku Kenkyukai Kaishi/Nagoya Economics University and Ichimura Gakuen Junior College. Natural Scientific Society. Journal. (JA ISSN 0285-4538) 4325
Nagoya Mathematical Journal/Nagoya Sugaku Zasshi. (JA ISSN 0027-7630) 3048
Nagoya Medical Journal. (JA ISSN 0027-7649) 3133
Nagoya Port Statistics Annual/Nagoyako Tokei Nenpo. (JA ISSN 0469-4783) 4665
Nagoya Port Statistics Monthly/Nagoyako Tokei Geppo. (JA ISSN 0027-7592) 4665
Nagoya-shiritsu Daigaku Igakkai Zasshi/Nagoya City University. Medical Association. Journal. (JA ISSN 0027-7606) 3133
Nagoya-shiritsu Daigaku Kyoyobu Kiyo. Shizen Kagaku Hen/Nagoya City University. College of General Education. Bulletin. Natural Science Section. (JA ISSN 0465-7772) 4326
Nagoya-shiritsu Daigaku Yakugakubu Kenkyu Nenpo/Nagoya City University. Faculty of Pharmaceutical Science. Annual Report. (JA ISSN 0369-5611) 3735
Nagoya Sugaku Zasshi. see Nagoya Mathematical Journal 3048
Nagoya University. College of General Education. Research Bulletin B. Natural Science and Psychology. see Nagoya Daigaku Kyoyobu Kiyo B. Shizen Kagaku, Shinrigaku 4325
Nagoya University. Cosmic-Ray Research Laboratory. Report see Nagoya University. Solar-Terrestrial Environment Laboratory. Cosmic Ray Section. Report 371
Nagoya University. Faculty of Engineering. Automatic Control Laboratory. Research Reports/Nagoya Daigaku Kogakubu Jido Seigyo. (JA ISSN 0374-4329) 1415
Nagoya University. Faculty of Engineering. Memoirs/Nagoya Daigaku Kogakubu Kiyo. (JA ISSN 0027-7657) 1831
Nagoya University. Institute of Plasma Physics. Annual Review/Nagoya Daigaku Purazuma Kenkyujo Nenpo. (JA ISSN 0547-1567) 3825
Nagoya University. Institute of Plasma Physics. Technical Reports. (JA) 3825

Nagoya University. Research Institute of Atmospherics. Proceedings - Nagoya Daigaku Kuden Kenkyujo Hokoku see Nagoya University. Solar-Terrestrial Environment Laboratory. Proceedings 3439
Nagoya University. Solar-Terrestrial Environment Laboratory. Cosmic Ray Section. Proceedings. see Meidai Uchusan Kenkyushitsu Kiji 3824
Nagoya University. Solar-Terrestrial Environment Laboratory. Cosmic Ray Section. Report. (JA) 371, 3838
Nagoya University. Solar-Terrestrial Environment Laboratory. Proceedings. (JA) 3439
Nagoya University. Water Research Institute. Annual Report/Suiken Kagaku Kenkyujo Nenpo. (JA) 4827
Nagoya University Furukawa Museum. Bulletin. see Nagoya Daigaku Furukawa Sogo Kenkyu Shiryokan Hokoku 3530
Nagoyako Tokei Geppo. see Nagoya Port Statistics Monthly 4665
Nagoyako Tokei Nenpo. see Nagoya Port Statistics Annual 4665
Nagpur Law Journal see Maharashtra Law Journal 2651
Nagyuzemi Gazdalkodas Kerdesei. (HU ISSN 0077-2658) 108
Nagyvilag. (HU) 2940
Nahar Arab & International. (LE) 680
An-Nahar Arab Report and Memo see Memo 679
Nahda. (KU) 2209
Nahka ja Kenka. (FI) 4326
Nahrungsmittel. (AU ISSN 0027-7703) 2078
Nahverkehr. (GW) 4653
Nahverkehrs Nachrichten. (GW) 4653
Na'i Nasl. (PK) 1318
Naihuo Cailiao. (CC ISSN 1001-1935) 3416
Naika. see Internal Medicine 3109
Naika Oyobi Shonika see Journal of Therapy 3118
Naikahokan. see Japanese Archives of Internal Medicine 3112
Nail & Beauty Trends. (US) 373
Nailm News see N.A.I.L.M. News 1282
▼Nailpro. (US) 376
Nails. (US ISSN 0896-193X) 373
Nairobi Airport. Annual Report. (KE ISSN 0077-2666) 4476
The Nairobi Law Monthly. (KE) 2656
Nairobi Observer. (KE) 2169
Naito Foundation Annual Report. see Naito Kinen Kagaku Shinko Zaidan Kenkyu Hokokushu 4326
Naito Kinen Kagaku Shinko Zaidan Kenkyu Hokokushu/Naito Foundation Annual Report. (JA ISSN 0914-1707) 4326
Naito Zaidan Jiho. (JA ISSN 0911-971X) 4326
Najda Newsletter. (US) 4849, 3966
Nakabat Ul-Muhamin. see Syndicate of Lawyers 2684
Naked Review see Xerotic Ephemera 3009
Nalle Puh. (FI) 1261
Nama Hatta Newsletter. (UK) 4217
Namari to Aen/Lead and Zinc. (JA ISSN 0027-772X) 3416
Namaskaar. (II) 4803
Name Gleaner/Glanure des Noms. (CN ISSN 0700-9445) 2830
Name-Ye 'olum-e Ejtema'i. (IR) 4380
Nameh Sanaat-e-Naft see Iran Oil Journal 3690
Namenkundliche Informationen. (GW) 2830
Namensverzeichnis zum Europaeischen Patentblatt. (GW) 3676
Names. (US ISSN 0027-7738) 2830, 2256
Names and Denominations. see Namn og Nemne 2830
Names in the News. (US) 3938
Names of Africa. see Nomina Africana 2831
Namib Times. (SA ISSN 0027-7746) 2216
Namibia. (SX ISSN 0027-7754) 2015, 3908
Namibia. State Museum. Memoir see Cimbebasia 2505
Namibia Brief. (SX) 933, 3491

Namibia Scientific Society. Journal. (SX) 4380
Namibia Scientific Society. Newsletter. (SX) 4326, 245, 2318
†Namibia Studies Series. (UN) 5242
Namibiana. (SX ISSN 0259-2010) 2334, 245, 2057
Namn och Bygd. (SW ISSN 0077-2704) 2830, 2256
Namn og Nemne/Names and Denominations. (NO ISSN 0800-4684) 2830
Namyn Am'dral see Manay Inder 3906
Nan Feng Chuang/Winds from the South. (CC) 2182
Nan Pei Chi. see The Perspective 2197
NaNa see Nahverkehrs Nachrichten 4653
Nana Film Weekly. (II) 3514
Nana No Pasuporto/Southern Africa Passport. (SA) 4779
Nanak Prakash Patrika. (II ISSN 0027-7770) 4217
Nanba/Sports Graphic Number. (JA) 4480
Nancy's Magazine. (US ISSN 0895-7576) 2511
Nandan. (II) 1241
Nandan Kanan. (II) 3773
†Nande. (PY ISSN 0047-8644) 5242
Nande Reko. (PY ISSN 1012-5507) 2940, 4133
Nanfang Jianzhu/South-China Architecture. (CC ISSN 1000-0232) 303
Nanfang Wentan. (CC) 2940
Nanfang Wenxue/Southern Literature. (CC) 2940
Nanfeng/South Wind. (CC ISSN 0257-2885) 2940
Nanfi Jingguan. see South African Panorama (Chinese Edition) 5280
Nanjing Daxue Xuebao (Zhexue Shehui Kexue Ban)/Nanjing University. Journal (Social Science Edition). (CC ISSN 0257-5892) 4380, 3692
Nanjing Daxue Xuebao (Ziran Kexue Ban)/Nanjing University. Journal (Natural Science Edition). (CC ISSN 0469-5097) 4326, 4604
Nanjing Hangkong Xueyuan Xuebao/Nanjing Institute of Aeronautics. Journal. (CC ISSN 1000-1956) 59
Nanjing Huagong Xueyuan Xuebao/Nanjing Institute of Chemical Engineering. Journal. (CC ISSN 1000-5994) 1857
Nanjing Institute of Aeronautics. Journal. see Nanjing Hangkong Xueyuan Xuebao 59
Nanjing Institute of Chemical Engineering. Journal. see Nanjing Huagong Xueyuan Xuebao 1857
Nanjing Institute of Medical Sciences. Journal. see Nanjing Yixueyuan Xuebao 3133
Nanjing Institute of Traditional Chinese Medicine. Journal. see Nanjing Zhongyi Xueyuan Xuebao 3133
Nanjing Nongye Daxue Xuebao/Nanjing University of Agriculture. Journal. (CC ISSN 1000-2030) 108
Nanjing Normal Universtiy. Journal (Social Science Edition). see Nanjing Shifan Daxue Xuebao (Shehui Kexue Ban) 4380
Nanjing Railway Institute of Medical Sciences. Journal. see Nanjing Tiedao Yixueyuan Xuebao 3133
Nanjing Shehui Kexue/Nanjing Social Sciences. (CC ISSN 1001-8263) 4380
Nanjing Shifan Daxue Xuebao (Shehui Kexue Ban)/Nanjing Normal Universtiy. Journal (Social Science Edition). (CC ISSN 1001-4608) 4380
Nanjing Social Sciences. see Nanjing Shehui Kexue 4380
Nanjing Tiedao Yixueyuan Xuebao/Nanjing Railway Institute of Medical Sciences. Journal. (CC ISSN 1001-7275) 3133
Nanjing University. Journal (Natural Science Edition). see Nanjing Daxue Xuebao (Ziran Kexue Ban) 4326

Nanjing University. Journal (Social Science Edition). see Nanjing Daxue Xuebao (Zhexue Shehui Kexue Ban) **4380**
Nanjing University of Agriculture. Journal. see Nanjing Nongye Daxue Xuebao **108**
Nanjing Yixueyuan Xuebao/Nanjing Institute of Medical Sciences. Journal.(CC ISSN 1000-5331) **3133**
Nanjing Youdian Xueyuan Xuebao. (CC ISSN 1000-1972) **1353**
Nanjing Zhongyi Xueyuan Xuebao/ Nanjing Institute of Traditional Chinese Medicine. Journal. (CC ISSN 1000-5005) **3133**
Nankai Economic Studies. see Nankai Jingji Yanjiu **681**
Nankai Jingji Yanjiu/Nankai Economic Studies. (CC ISSN 1001-4691) **681**
Nankai University. Journal. Philosophy and Social Sciences Edition. see Nankai Xuebao. Zhexue Shehui Kexue Ban **4380**
Nankai Xuebao. Zhexue Shehui Kexue Ban/Nankai University. Journal. Philosophy and Social Sciences Edition. (CC ISSN 1001-4667) **4380**, **3692**
Nankyoku Shiryo/Antarctic Record. (JA ISSN 0085-7289) **2256**
Nanny Times. (US) **1241**, **4036**
▼Nanobiology. (UK ISSN 0958-3165) **556**, **526**
▼Nanostructured Materials. (UK ISSN 0965-9773) **1921**, **1880**
▼Nanotechnology. (UK ISSN 0957-4484) **3825**, **1904**
Nantong Institute of Medical Sciences. Journal. see Nantong Yixueyuan Xuebao **3133**
Nantong Yixueyuan Xuebao/Nantong Institute of Medical Sciences. Journal.(CC ISSN 1000-2057) **3133**
Nantucket Journal. (US) **2229**
Nanya Yanjiu Jikan/South Asian Studies Quarterly. (CC ISSN 1004-1508) **3641**
Nanyang Wenti Yanjiu/Southeast Asian Studies. (CC) **3641**
Nanyang Ziliao Yicong. (CC) **3641**
Nanyuan Xiaoshuo - Novels of Nanyuan see Xiaoshuo Jie **2977**
Nanzan Institute for Religion and Culture. Bulletin. (JA ISSN 0386-720X) **4191**, **3641**
Nanzan University. Nanzan Academic Society. Bulletin. (JA ISSN 0288-500X) **3048**
Nanzi Han/Manliness. (US) **3399**
Napa-Solano Dental Society. District Six. Newsletter see Oracle **3239**
Napa Valley Magazine's Wine Country see Wine Country **387**
Napjaink. (HU ISSN 0547-2075) **2940**, **2875**
Napoleon. (UK ISSN 0027-7827) **2377**
Napoleonic Society of America. Member's Bulletin. (US) **2377**, **420**
Napoli Nobilissima. (IT ISSN 0027-7835) **337**
Napred. (YU ISSN 0027-7843) **2239**
Naprstkovo Muzeum Asijskych, Africkych a Amerikckych Kultur. Annals. (US ISSN 0554-9256) **245**, **2057**
Naqib-i Millat. (PK) **3908**
Nar Nari. (II) **2200**
Nara Igaku Zasshi/Nara Medical Association. Journal. (JA ISSN 0469-5550) **3133**
Nara Joshi Daigaku Hoken Kanri Senta Kiyo see Nara Joshi Daigaku Hoken Kanri Senta Nenpo **4108**
Nara Joshi Daigaku Hoken Kanri Senta Nenpo/Nara Women's University. Health Administration Center. Archives of Health Care. (JA ISSN 0287-9549) **4108**, **1685**
Nara Kyoiku Daigaku Kiyo. Shizen Kagaku/Nara University of Education. Bulletin. Natural Science. (JA ISSN 0547-2407) **4326**
Nara Medical Association. Journal. see Nara Igaku Zasshi **3133**

Nara University of Education. Bulletin. Natural Science. see Nara Kyoiku Daigaku Kiyo. Shizen Kagaku **4326**
Nara Women's University. Health Administration Center. Archives of Health Care. see Nara Joshi Daigaku Hoken Kanri Senta Nenpo **4108**
Naracoorte Herald. (AT) **2172**
Narayanganj Chambers of Commerce & Industry. Chamber News see Metropolitan Chamber of Commerce and Industry, Dhaka. Chamber News **819**
Narc Officer. (US) **2656**, **1518**, **1538**
Narcotic Drugs: Estimated World Requirements for (Year). (UN ISSN 1013-3453) **3811**, **3748**, **4118**
Narcotics and Drug Abuse A to Z. (US ISSN 0094-3991) **1538**
Narcotics Anonymous Way Magazine see N A Way Magazine **1538**
Narcotics Control Digest. (US ISSN 0889-5708) **1518**
Narcotics Demand Reduction Digest. (US ISSN 1043-8572) **1519**
Narcotics Law Bulletin. (US ISSN 8755-8289) **2656**, **1538**
Nargun. (AT) **1574**
Narichten der Fachorganisationen see Bindereport **4121**
Narinkka. (FI ISSN 0355-9106) **2377**
Narod Polski. (US ISSN 0027-7894) **2015**, **1300**
Narodna Armija. (YU ISSN 0027-7908) **3466**
Narodna Banka Jugoslavije. Bilten. (YU ISSN 0351-3211) **791**
Narodna Banka Jugoslavije. Godisnji Izvestaj. (YU ISSN 0352-3314) **875**, **791**
Narodna Biblioteka Kiril i Metodii. Izvestiya. (BU ISSN 0584-0007) **2377**
Narodna in Univerzitetna Knjiznica. Zbornik. (XV ISSN 0350-3569) **2775**
Narodna Kultura. (BU ISSN 0205-1109) **2941**, **303**, **337**
Narodna Odbrana. (YU ISSN 0027-7916) **3466**
Narodna Tvorchist' ta Etnografiya. (KR ISSN 0130-6936) **245**, **2057**
Narodna Umijetnost. (CI ISSN 0547-2504) **2057**, **2015**
Narodne Novine. (YU ISSN 0027-7932) **2239**
Narodne Noviny. (US ISSN 0027-7940) **2015**
Narodni Borac. (BN ISSN 0027-7959) **3466**
Narodni Knihovna. (CS ISSN 0862-7487) **2775**
Narodni List. (CI ISSN 0027-7975) **2875**
Narodni Muzeum. Casopis: Oddil Prirodovedny see Narodni Muzeum v Praze. Casopis: Rada Prirodovedna **3530**
Narodni Muzeum v Praze. Casopis: Rada Historicka. (CS ISSN 0008-7343) **3530**, **2318**
Narodni Muzeum v Praze. Casopis: Rada Prirodovedna. (CS) **3530**
Narodni Muzeum v Praze. Sbornik: Historie see Narodni Muzeum v Praze. Sbornik. Rada A: Historie **2318**
Narodni Muzeum v Praze. Sbornik: Literarni Historie see Narodni Muzeum v Praze. Sbornik. Rada C: Literarni Historie **2775**
Narodni Muzeum v Praze. Sbornik: Prirodni Vedy see Narodni Muzeum v Praze. Sbornik. Rada B: Prirodni Vedy **4326**
Narodni Muzeum v Praze. Sbornik. Rada A: Historie/Acta Musei Nationalis Pragae. (CS ISSN 0036-5335) **2318**
Narodni Muzeum v Praze. Sbornik. Rada B: Prirodni Vedy/Acta Musei Nationalis Pragae. (CS ISSN 0036-5343) **4326**
Narodni Muzeum v Praze. Sbornik. Rada C: Literarni Historie/Acta Musei Nationalis Pragae. (CS ISSN 0036-5351) **2775**

Narodni Technicke Muzeum. Bibliografie. Prameny. (CS) **4615**
Narodni Technicke Muzeum. Catalogues of Collections. (CS) **3530**, **4604**
Narodni Technicke Muzeum. Rozpravy. (CS ISSN 0035-9378) **4604**, **2318**
Narodno Stvaralastvo - Folklor. (YU ISSN 0027-8017) **2057**
Narodnoe Khozyaistvo Altaiskogo Kraya.(RU) **4580**
Narodnoe Obrazovanie. (RU ISSN 0027-8033) **1649**
Narodnostopanski Arkhiv/Archives of National Economy. (BU ISSN 0323-9004) **681**
Narody Azii i Afriki see Narody Azii i Afriki: Istoriya, Ekonomika, Kul'tura **3642**
Narody Azii i Afriki: Istoriya, Ekonomika, Kul'tura. (RU ISSN 0130-6995) **3642**, **2334**, **2340**
Naropa Institute Journal of Psychology see Journal of Contemplative Psychotherapy **4028**
Narradores de Arca. (UY ISSN 0077-2801) **2941**
Narrativa Latinoamericana. (UY ISSN 0077-2844) **2415**, **2941**
Narrow Bandwidth Television Association see N B T V **1377**
Narrow Fabric and Braiding Industry. see Band- und Flechtindustrie **4616**
Narrow Gauge & Short Line Gazette. (US ISSN 0148-2122) **2439**, **4711**
Narrow Gauge News. (UK ISSN 0142-5595) **4711**, **2439**
Narrow Way. (US) **4191**, **4225**
Naryzy z Istoriyi Pryrodoznavstva i Tekhniky see Ocherki po Istorii Estestvoznaniya i Tekhniki **2319**
Nas Chov. (CS ISSN 0027-8068) **221**, **202**
Nas Delavec. (XV) **3945**
Nas Jezik. (YU ISSN 0027-8084) **2830**
Nas Put - Our Way see Hrvatski Put **3897**
Nas Svijet. (BN ISSN 0027-8106) **2875**
Nasa Rec. (YU ISSN 0027-8122) **2239**
Nasa Stampa. (YU ISSN 0027-8149) **2573**
Nasa Zakonitost. (CI ISSN 0027-8165) **2656**
Nasa Zena. (XV) **4849**
†Nase Dejiny. (US) **5242**
Nase Gospodarstvo/Our Economy: Review of Current Problems in Economics. (XV ISSN 0547-3101) **681**
Nase Gradevinarstvo. (YU ISSN 0350-2619) **625**
Nase Liecive Rastliny. (CS) **510**, **3133**
Nase Obcestvo. (XV) **4270**
Nase Planine see Hrvatski Planinar **4474**
Nase Rec/Our Language. (CS ISSN 0027-8203) **2830**
Naselenie. (BU ISSN 0205-0617) **3985**
Nash Notations. (US ISSN 8756-4718) **2159**
Nash on Magistrates' Courts - Victoria. (AT ISSN 0705-3886) **2732**
Nash Times. (US) **4697**
Nasha Meta/Our Aim. (CN) **2015**
Al-Nashra see Al-Arabiyya **2803**
Nashrat A D M A/A D M A Bulletin. (TS) **3692**
Nashrat Al-Iskan wal-Ashghal/Works and Housing Bulletin. (TS) **4067**, **2492**
Nashrat al-Mukhaddirat see Bulletin on Narcotics **1535**
Nashua. (US) **2229**
Nashui Ren. (CC) **1101**
Nashville! see Nashville Business and Lifestyles **681**
Nashville Area Business Directory. (US) **1146**
Nashville Area Guide see Nashville Newcomer Area Guide **2229**
Nashville Business and Lifestyle see Nashville Business and Lifestyles **681**

Nashville Business and Lifestyles. (US ISSN 1052-4215) **681**
Nashville Business Journal. (US) **681**
Nashville Newcomer Area Guide. (US) **2229**
Nashville Scene. (US) **3569**, **4635**
Nashville Tennessee. (NE) **3569**
Nashville Travel Guide. (US) **4779**
Nashville Visitor. (US) **4779**, **2229**
Nashville Visitor's Guide. (US) **4779**
Nashville Women's Alliance. Newsletter. (US) **4849**
Nasi Dani. (BN ISSN 0027-8262) **1649**
Nasi Zbori. (XV ISSN 0027-8270) **3569**
Nasinec. (US ISSN 0744-6594) **2015**
Nasionale Museum, Bloemfontein. Memoirs. see National Museum, Bloemfontein. Memoirs **589**
Nasionale Museum, Bloemfontein. Navorsinge. see National Museum, Bloemfontein. Research **4326**
Nasionale Veiligheid. see National Safety **4108**
Nasjonalregnskapsstatistikk see Norway. Statistisk Sentralbyraa. Nasjonalregnskapsstatistikk **731**
Al-Nasr. (TS) **1300**, **4480**
Nassau and Paradise Island. Tourist News see Nassau Cable Beach and Paradise Island. Tourist News **4779**
Nassau Cable Beach and Paradise Island. Tourist News. (BF) **4779**
Nassau County Dental Society. Bulletin see Nassau County Dental Society. Newsletter **3238**
Nassau County Dental Society. Newsletter. (US) **3238**
Nassau County Historical Society Journal. (US) **2415**
Nassau Herald. (US) **2229**
Nassau Lawyer. (US ISSN 0047-8695) **2656**
Nassau Review. (US ISSN 0077-2879) **2941**
Nassau Weekly. (US) **1318**
Nassauer Gespraeche der Freiherr-vom-Stein-Gesellschaft. (GW ISSN 0176-6023) **4380**
Nassauische Annalen. (GW ISSN 0077-2887) **2377**
Nastava i Vaspitanje. (YU) **1649**, **1755**
Nastava Povijesti. (CI ISSN 0350-6541) **2377**
Nasty Letters. (US) **3399**
Nasty Photos. (US) **3399**
Nasza Przeszlosc. (PL ISSN 0137-3218) **2377**, **4270**
Nasze Drzewa Lesne. Monografie Popularno Naukowe. (PL) **2104**
Nasze Problemy. (PL) **4133**
NAT. Norges Apotekerforenings Tidsskrift see Norges Apotekerforenings Tidsskrift **3736**
Nat - Cent News. (Helen Keller National Center for Deaf-Blind Youths and Adults) (US) **2294**
Nat Ed Newsletter see N Z E I Rourou **1649**
Natal Agricultural Union see N A U N L U **108**
†Natal Business News. (SA) **5242**
Natal Chamber of Industries. Annual Report see Natal Chamber of Industries. Yearbook & Directory **1147**
Natal Chamber of Industries. Yearbook & Directory. (SA) **1147**
Natal Education - Onderwys in Natal see N E O N **1649**
Natal Farmer. (SA) **108**
Natal Museum. Annals/Annale van die Natalse Museum. (SA ISSN 0304-0798) **589**
Natal Museum Journal of Humanities. (SA ISSN 1015-0935) **279**
Natal University Law and Society Review. (SA) **2656**
Natal Wildlife. (SA ISSN 0027-8343) **1492**
Natalia. (SA ISSN 0085-3674) **2334**
Natation. (FR) **4480**
Natchez Trace Traveler. (US ISSN 0738-985X) **2377**
Nathanael Evangelisches Gemeindeblatt.(GW) **4244**

6466 NATHANIEL HAWTHORNE

Nathaniel Hawthorne Journal. (US ISSN 0073-1382) **2941**
Nathaniel Hawthorne Review. (US ISSN 0890-4197) **2941**
Nathaniel Hawthorne Society. Newsletter *see* Nathaniel Hawthorne Review **2941**
Nation. (US ISSN 0027-8378) **2875,** 337
Nation Armee. (FR) **3466**
Nation Djibouti. (FT) **2169**
Nation Europa. (GW ISSN 0027-8408) **2875**
Nation Review. (AT ISSN 0156-8221) **2875**
Nationaal Centrum voor Oudheidkundige Navorsingen in Belgie. Oudheidkundige Repertoria. Reeks A: Bibliografische Repertoria. *see* Centre National de Recherches Archeologiques en Belgique. Repertoires Archeologiques. Serie A: Repertoires Bibliographiques **5163**
Nationaal Instituut voor de Statistiek. Weekbericht. (BE ISSN 0771-0410) **4580**
Nationaal Instituut voor Kernfysica en Hoge-Energiefysica Annual Report *see* N I K H E F. Annual Report **3825**
Nationaal Instituut voor Kernfysica en Hoge-Energiefysica Bulletin *see* N I K H E F. K Bulletin **3825**
Nationaal Natuurhistorisch Museum. Zoologische Bijdragen. (NE) **589**
Nationaal Natuurhistorisch Museum. Zoologische Mededelingen. (NE) **589**
Nationaal Natuurlhistorisch Museum. Zoologische Verhandelingen. (NE) **589**
Nationaal Sport Magazine. (NE) **4480**
The National (Ottawa). (CN) **1904**
National (Ottawa, 1970). (CN ISSN 0709-1370) **1739**
National A I D S Bulletin. (AT ISSN 1030-5289) **3222**
National Academic Advising Association Journal *see* N A C A D A Journal **1712**
National Academy of Arbitrators. Annual Meeting. Proceedings. (US) **989**
National Academy of Design. Annual Exhibition Catalogue. (US) **337**
National Academy of Indian Medicine. Annals. (II) **3133**
National Academy of Medical Sciences. Annals. (II ISSN 0379-038X) **3133**
National Academy of Sciences. Biographical Memoirs. (US ISSN 0077-2933) **420,** 4326
National Academy of Sciences. National Academy of Engineering. National Research Council. Institute of Medicine. News Report *see* National Research Council. Newsreport **4326**
National Academy of Sciences, India. Proceedings. Section A. Physical Sciences. (II ISSN 0369-8203) **4326,** 3825
National Academy of Sciences, India. Proceedings. Section B. Biological Sciences. (II ISSN 0369-8211) **448,** 4326
National Academy of Sciences, India. Science Letters. (II ISSN 0250-541X) **4326**
National Academy of Sciences of the United States of America. Proceedings. (US) **448**
National Accelerator Center News *see* N A C News **3825**
National Account Marketing Association Journal *see* N A M A Journal **1048**
National Accounts. *see* Netherlands. Centraal Bureau voor de Statistiek. Nationale Rekeningen **730**
National Accounts E S A - Aggregates (Years). (EI) **681,** 875
National Accounts of Botswana. (BS ISSN 0302-2056) **999**
National Accounts of O E C D Countries. Volume 1 Main Aggregates. (FR) **730,** 18
National Accounts of O E C D Countries. Volume 2 Detailed Tables. (FR) **730,** 18
National Accounts of the Maltese Islands. (MM ISSN 0077-295X) **1101**
National Accounts Statistics. *see* Norway. Statistisk Sentralbyraa. Nasjonalregnskapsstatistikk **731**
National Accrediting Agency for Clinical Laboratory Sciences News *see* N A A C L S News **3133**
National Acquisitions Group. Newsletter.(UK ISSN 0950-5326) **2775**
National Ad Search. (US ISSN 0744-7140) **3629**
National Adoption Reports. (US) **4413,** 2656
National Adult Video Review. (US) **1385**
National Advertising Agency Network. Management Report. (US) **35,** 1021
National Advertising Agency Network. Staff Report. (US) **35**
▼The National Advocate. (CN) **1712**
National Advocate. (US) **4413,** 1241
National Aeronautic Association For the Record *see* For the Record **53**
National Aeronautical Laboratory. Annual Report. (II ISSN 0077-2976) **59**
National Aeronautical Laboratory. Bibliography Series. (II) **66,** 406
†National Aeronautical Laboratory. Case Studies. (II) **5242**
National Aeronautical Laboratory. Current Scientific and Technical Reports. (II) **59**
National Aeronautical Laboratory. Library Bulletin. (II) **59**
National Aeronautical Laboratory. Recent Book Additions. (II) **66**
National Aeronautical Laboratory. Recent Microfiche Additions. (II) **59**
†National Aeronautical Laboratory. Selected Abstracts from Russian and Other Foreign Scientific Literature. (II) **5242**
National Aeronautical Laboratory. Technical Note. (II ISSN 0077-300X) **59**
National Aeronautical Laboratory Catalogue of N A L Technical Translations *see* Catalogue of N A L Technical Translations **5163**
National Aeronautics and Space Administration Formal Series Reports *see* N A S A Formal Series Reports **4325**
National Aeronautics and Space Administration Software Directory *see* N A S A Software Directory **1479**
National Aerospace Electronics Conference. Proceedings *see* I E E E National Aerospace and Electronics Conference. Proceedings **55**
National Aerospace Laboratory News *see* N A L News **59**
National Aerospace Meeting. Proceedings *see* Institute of Navigation. National Technical Meeting Proceedings **55**
National Afrikan Kalendar of Events and Information *see* Afram Drum **1989**
National Agency of Industry and Trade. Annual Reports (Year)/ Aarsveretninger. (DK) **1081,** 957
National Aging Resource Center on Elder Abuse Conference Proceedings *see* N A R C E A Conference Proceedings **4413**
National Aging Resource Center on Elder Abuse Project Reports *see* N A R C E A Project Reports **4413**
National Aging Resource Center on Elder Abuse Selected Publications *see* N A R C E A Selected Publications **4413**
National Agri-Marketing Association News. (US) **108,** 1048
National Agricultural Aviation Association Newsletter *see* N A A A Newsletter **4675**
National Agricultural Cooperative Federation News *see* N A F News **155**
National Agricultural Cooperative Marketing Federation of India Ltd. Marketing Review *see* N A F E D Marketing Review **1048**
National Agricultural Plastics Association. Proceedings *see* National Agricultural Plastics Congress. Proceedings **3864**
National Agricultural Plastics Congress. Proceedings. (US) **3864,** 108
National Agricultural Research Programme. Project Report. (TZ) **185**
National Agricultural Research Programme. Summary of Programmes *see* National Agricultural Research Programme. Project Report **185**
National Agricultural Society of Ceylon. Journal *see* National Agricultural Society of Sri Lanka. Journal **108**
National Agricultural Society of Sri Lanka. Journal. (CE) **108**
†National Air and Space Museum. Research Report. (US ISSN 0891-1703) **5242**
National Air Quality and Emissions Trends Report. (US) **1978**
National Air Transportation Association. Annual Report. (US) **4676**
National Air Transportation Association. General Aviation Operations. (US) **4676,** 59
National Air Transportation Association. Industry Barometer. (US) **4676**
National Air Transportation Association. Wage and Salary Handbook. (US) **4676**
National Air Transportation Association News *see* N A T A News **4676**
National Airspace System Plan: Facilities, Equipment and Associated Development. (US) **4676**
National Alliance (New York). (US ISSN 0888-1391) **3908**
National Alliance (Washington). (US ISSN 0027-8513) **2587**
National Alliance for Spiritual Growth. Bulletin *see* Within and Beyond **3597**
National Alliance for the Mentally Ill Advocate *see* N A M I Advocate **3345**
National Alliance Report *see* Sales Ways **1053**
National Alopecia Areata Foundation Newsletter. (US) **3249,** 373, 3255
National Amateur. (US ISSN 0027-8521) **2573,** 2439, 4002
National-American Wholesale Grocers' Association, Inc. Review *see* N A W G A Review **2078**
National AMVET. (US ISSN 0027-853X) **3466,** 1300
National and Federal Legal Employment Report. (US ISSN 0733-3285) **1067,** 2656
National and Folk Music. *see* Minzu Minjian Yinyue **3563**
National and Local Government Officers Association Annual Report *see* N A L G O Annual Report **4067**
National Animal Control Association News *see* N A C A News **3712**
National Anti-Poverty Organization News *see* N A P O News **4413**
National Apostolate with Mentally Retarded Persons. Newsletter. (US) **1739**
National Apostolate with Mentally Retarded Persons Quarterly *see* N A M R P Quarterly **1738**
National Appliance Parts Suppliers Association Results *see* N A P S A. Results **2561**
National Archery Association Newsletter *see* N A A Newsletter **4479**
National Archives of Malaysia. Annual Report/Arkib Negara Malaysia. Laporan Tahunan. (MY ISSN 0076-3381) **2340**
National Archives of Zambia. Annual Report. (ZA ISSN 0084-4942) **2775,** 2334
National Archives of Zambia. Calendars of the District Notebooks. (ZA) **2334,** 4067
National Archives of Zambia. Information. (ZA) **2334**
National Archives of Zambia. National Archives Occasional Paper. (ZA) **2334**
National Art Education Association News *see* N A E A News **337**
National Art Materials Trade Association News & Views *see* N A M T A News & Views **337**
National Art Museum of Sport Newsletter *see* Goal Line **4473**
National Arthritis News *see* Arthritis Today **3368**
National Arts Centre Calendar of Events *see* N A C Calendar of Events **1531**
National Arts Guide. (US ISSN 0190-8049) **337**
National Assembly Library Review. *see* Kukhoe Tosogwanbo **2767**
National Assembly Review. *see* Kukhoebo **3903**
National Assessment of Educational Progress. Assessment Reports. (US) **1755**
National Assessment of Educational Progress Newsletter *see* N A E P Newsletter **1648**
National Association for Business Teacher Education Review *see* N A B T E Review **1712**
National Association for Colitis and Crohn's Disease News *see* N A C C News **3269**
National Association for Colitis and Crohn's Disease Newsletter *see* N A C C Newsletter **3269**
National Association for Deaf - Blind and Rubella Handicapped. Newsletter *see* Talking Sense **4422**
National Association for Foreign Student Affairs Directory of Institutions and Individuals in International Educational Exchange *see* N A F S A Directory of Institutions and Individuals in International Educational Exchange **1722**
National Association for Foreign Student Affairs Government Affairs Bulletin *see* N A F S A Government Affairs Bulletin **1723**
National Association for Foreign Student Affairs Newsletter *see* N A F S A Newsletter **1648**
National Association for Girls and Women in Sport Guide. Volleyball *see* N A G W S Guide. Volleyball **4508**
National Association for Home Care Report *see* N A H C Report **3133**
National Association for Law Placement Bulletin *see* N A L P Bulletin **2655**
National Association for Olmsted Parks. Newsletter. (US) **1963,** 1492
National Association for Physical Education in Higher Education Proceedings *see* N A P E H E Proceedings **5241**
National Association for Specialty Food Trade, Inc. Showcase *see* N A S F T Showcase **2078**
National Association for Stock Car Auto Racing, Inc. News *see* N A S C A R News **4480**
National Association for the Advancement of Colored People Annual Report *see* N A A C P Annual Report **4443**
National Association for the Blind, India. Annual Report. (II) **2294**
National Association for the Exchange of Industrial Resources Advantage *see* N A E I R Advantage **4413**
National Association for the Teaching of English. Newsletter. (UK ISSN 0143-4136) **1755,** 2830
National Association for Visually Handicapped. Annual Bulletin. (US) **2294**
National Association for Women Deans, Administrators and Counselors. Journal *see* Initiatives **1728**
National Association for Young Writers, Inc. News *see* N A Y W News **2940**
National Association of Academies of Science. Directory and Proceedings *see* National Association of Academies of Science. Directory, Proceedings and Handbook **4326**
National Association of Academies of Science. Directory, Proceedings and Handbook. (US) **4326**
National Association of Accredited Cosmetology Schools News *see* N A A C S News **373**

Title

NATIONAL ASSOCIATION 6467

National Association of Almshouses. Yearbook and Statement of Accounts.(UK) **4413**

National Association of Animal Breeders. Annual Proceedings. (US ISSN 0077-3255) **202, 221**

National Association of Anorexia Nervosa and Associated Disorders Working Together see A N A D: Working Together **4007**

National Association of Attorneys General Report see A G Report **2593**

National Association of Bank Women Exchange see N A B W Exchange **5241**

National Association of Beverage Importers. Bulletin. (US) **384, 918**

National Association of Beverage Importers. Import Report. (US) **384, 918**

National Association of Beverage Importers. Statistical Report. (US) **388, 918**

National Association of Biology Teachers. News and Views. (US) **448, 1755**

National Association of Black Accountants. News Plus. (US) **753, 2015**

National Association of Black Accountants. Student News Plus. (US) **753, 2015**

National Association of Black Journalists Journal see N A B J Journal **2015**

National Association of Boards of Pharmacy. Proceedings. (US ISSN 0077-3263) **3735**

National Association of Boards of Pharmacy Newsletter see N A B P Newsletter **3735**

National Association of Broadcast Employees and Technicians, A F L - C I O News see N A B E T News **2586**

National Association of Business Economists Industry Survey see N A B E Industry Survey **874**

National Association of Business Economists News see N A B E News **874**

National Association of Business Economists Outlook see N A B E Outlook **874**

National Association of Business Economists Policy Survey see N A B E Policy Survey **874**

National Association of Canoe Liveries and Outfitters News see N A C L O News **4526**

National Association of Career & Guidance Teachers. Journal. (UK) **1730, 1685**

National Association of Chain Drug Stores. Executive Newsletter. (US) **1021, 3735**

National Association of Chain Drug Stores. Legislative News Bulletin see National Association of Chain Drug Stores. Legislative News Letter **3735**

National Association of Chain Drug Stores. Legislative News Letter. (US) **3735**

National Association of Citizens Advice Bureaux News see C A B News **2607**

National Association of Co-op Advertising Professionals. Co-op Newsletter. (US) **35**

National Association of College Admission Counselors Bulletin see N A C A C Bulletin **1712**

National Association of College Admissions Counselors. Membership Directory. (US ISSN 0090-3965) **1712**

National Association of College and University Food Services Journal see N A C U F S Journal **2078**

National Association of College and University Food Services NewsWave see N A C U F S NewsWave **2078**

National Association of College Wind & Percussion Instructors Journal see N A C W P I Journal **3569**

National Association of Colleges and Teachers of Agriculture Journal see N A C T A Journal **108**

National Association of Conservation Districts. Tuesday Letter. (US ISSN 0047-8733) **1492**

National Association of Consumer Agency Administrators News see N A C A A News **1506**

National Association of Counties County News see County News **4086**

National Association of Dealers in Antiques. Bulletin. (US) **258, 1048**

National Association of Disability Examiners Advocate see N A D E Advocate **4413**

National Association of Document Examiners. Journal. (US ISSN 8755-1020) **1519**

National Association of Dramatic and Speech Arts Annual Conference Directory see N A D S A Annual Conference Directory **35**

National Association of Educational Buyers Bulletin see N A E B Bulletin **1755**

National Association of Educational Negotiators Bulletin see N A E N Bulletin **1729**

National Association of Emergency Medical Technicians News see N A E M T News **3133**

National Association of Fashion and Accessory Designers. Newsletter. (US) **1286**

National Association of Fire Investigators Newsletter see N A F I Newsletter **2033**

National Association of Fire Officers Magazine see N A F O Magazine **4108**

National Association of Fire Officers Yearbook see N A F O Yearbook **2033**

National Association of Fleet Administrators, Inc. Annual Reference Book see N A F A Annual Reference Book **4697**

National Association of Fleet Administrators, Inc. Fleet Executive see N A F A Fleet Executive **4653**

National Association of Fleet Administrators, Inc. Fleet Focus see N A F A Fleet Focus **4653**

National Association of Freight Transportation Consultants. Professional Directory. (US) **4712**

National Association of Freight Transportation Consultants. Professional Directory. Supplement. (US) **4712**

National Association of Garage Door Manufacturers. Directory. (US) **625, 1081**

National Association of Garage Door Manufacturers. Newsletter. (US) **625, 1081**

National Association of Health Services Executives Resume see N A H S E's Resume **4108**

National Association of Healthcare Access Management Management Journal see N A H A M Management Journal **2467**

National Association of Home and Workshop Writers Newsletter. (US) **2573, 640**

National Association of Housing and Redevelopment Officials Monitor see N A H R O Monitor **2492**

National Association of Independent Fee Appraisers Convention. Proceedings see N A I F A Convention. Proceedings **4153**

National Association of Independent Fee Appraisers Technical Manual see N A I F A Technical Manual **4153**

National Association of Independent Insurers Press Samplings see N A I I Press Samplings **5241**

National Association of Independent Resurfacers News see N A I R News **4508**

National Association of Independent Schools. Annual Report. (US ISSN 0550-7421) **1649**

National Association of Inspectors and Educational Advisors. Journal. (UK ISSN 0263-9696) **1649**

National Association of Institutional Linen Management Bulletin see N.A.I.L.M. Bulletin **1282**

National Association of Institutional Linen Management News see N.A.I.L.M. News **1282**

National Association of Insurance Commissioners. Compilation of Reports. (US) **2538, 2656**

National Association of Insurance Commissioners. Life and Health Actuarial Report. (US) **2538, 2656**

National Association of Insurance Commissioners. Listing of Companies. (US) **2538, 2656**

National Association of Insurance Commissioners. Proceedings. (US ISSN 0363-0358) **2538, 2656**

National Association of Insurance Commissioners Newsletter see N A I C Newsletter **2538**

National Association of Intercollegiate Athletics Handbook see N A I A Handbook **4480**

National Association of Intercollegiate Athletics Official Records Book and Championship Summaries see N A I A Official Records Book and Championship Summaries **4480**

National Association of Jazz Educators. Newsletter see Jazz Educators Journal **3558**

National Association of Laboratory Schools. Journal. (US) **1649**

National Association of Legal Secretaries Docket see N A L S Docket **2655**

National Association of Manufacturers Speakers Directory see N A M - N I C Speakers Directory **5241**

National Association of Men's Sportswear Buyers, Inc. News see N A M S B News **1286**

National Association of Metal Finishers Accounting Manual see N A M F Accounting Manual **5241**

National Association of Metal Finishers Management Manual see N A M F Management Manual **3416**

National Association of Metal Finishers Regulatory Compliance Manual see N A M F Regulatory Compliance Manual **3416**

National Association of Milliners, Dressmakers and Tailors Newsletter see N A M D T. Newsletter **1286**

National Association of Music Merchants Inc. Music Retailer News see N A M M Music Retailer News **3569**

National Association of Mutual Insurance Companies Magazine see N A M I C Magazine **2538**

National Association of Neighborhoods Bulletin see N A N Bulletin **2492**

National Association of Parents and Professionals for Safe Alternatives in Childbirth, International News see N A P S A C News **3295**

†National Association of Pediatric Nurse Associates and Practitioners. Chapters' Bulletin. (US) **5242**

National Association of Pension Funds. Annual Survey. (UK ISSN 0309-0078) **730**

National Association of Pension Funds. Year Book. (UK) **730**

National Association of Performing Arts Managers and Agents. Newsletter. (US) **4635, 1021, 3262, 3514**

National Association of Pharmaceutical Manufacturers. News Bulletin. (US) **3735**

National Association of Photo Equipment Technicians News see N A P E T News **3793**

National Association of Plastics Distributors Magazine see N A P D Magazine **3864**

National Association of Printers and Lithographers. Special Reports. (US) **4002**

National Association of Prison Visitors Newsletter see N A P V Newsletter **1518**

National Association of Probation Officers News see N A P O News **1518**

National Association of Public Child Welfare Administrators Network see N A P C W A Network **4413**

National Association of Public Insurance Adjusters Bulletin see N A P I A Bulletin **2538**

National Association of Railroad Passengers News. (US ISSN 0739-3490) **4712**

National Association of Real Estate Appraisers Appraisal Guideline see N A R E A Appraisal Guideline **4153**

National Association of Real Estate Appraisers Real Estate Appraisal Newsletter see N A R E A Real Estate Appraisal Newsletter **4153**

National Association of Real Estate Editors News see N A R E E News **4153**

National Association of Real Estate Investment Trusts, Inc. Report see R.E.I.T. Report **4155**

National Association of Realtors. Existing Home Sales see National Association of Realtors. Home Sales **4153**

National Association of Realtors. Home Sales. (US ISSN 0161-5882) **4153**

National Association of Recording Merchandisers Sounding Board see N A R M Sounding Board **3569**

National Association of Regional Councils. News and Notes see National Association of Regional Councils. Regional Reporter **4067**

National Association of Regional Councils. Regional Reporter. (US) **4067**

National Association of Regional Councils. Washington Report see National Association of Regional Councils. Regional Reporter **4067**

National Association of Regional Media Centers Highlights see N A R M C Highlights **3514**

National Association of Regulatory Utility Commissioners. Annual Report on Utility and Carrier Regulation. (US) **4067**

National Association of Regulatory Utility Commissioners. Bulletin. (US ISSN 0027-8645) **4068, 1793**

National Association of Regulatory Utility Commissioners. Proceedings. (US ISSN 0077-3387) **4712**

National Association of Residents and Interns Stethoscope see N A R I Stethoscope **957**

National Association of Retail Dealers of America Costs of Doing Business Survey see N A R D A's Costs of Doing Business Survey **1116**

National Association of Retail Dealers of America News see N A R D A News **1021**

National Association of Retail Druggists Almanac and Health Guide see N A R D Almanac and Health Guide **1048**

National Association of Retail Druggists Home Health Care Pharmacy Bulletin see N A R D Home Health Care Pharmacy Bulletin **5241**

National Association of Retail Druggists Journal see N A R D Journal **3735**

National Association of Retail Druggists Newsletter see N A R D Newsletter **3735**

National Association of Sailing Instructors and Sailing Schools Newsletter see N A S I S S Newsletter **4526**

National Association of Scaffolding Contractors Year Book. (UK) **625**

National Association of School Nurses, Inc. Newsletter see N A S Newsletter **3282**

National Association of Schools of Art and Design. Directory. (US) **1695, 337**

National Association of Schools of Music. Directory. (US ISSN 0547-4175) **3569, 1755**

National Association of Schools of Music. Handbook. (US ISSN 0164-2847) **3569, 1755**

National Association of Schools of Music. Proceedings of the Annual Meeting. (US ISSN 0077-3409) **3569**

6468 NATIONAL ASSOCIATION

National Association of Secondary School Principals. Curriculum Report. see N A S S P Curriculum Report 1755

National Association of Secondary School Principals Bulletin see N A S S P Bulletin 1729

National Association of Secondary School Principals Curriculum Report see N A S S P Curriculum Report 1755

National Association of Secondary School Principals Legal Memorandum see N A S S P Legal Memorandum 1729

National Association of Secondary School Principals Newsleader see N A S S P Newsleader 1729

National Association of Secondary School Principals Practitioner see N A S S P Practitioner 1729

National Association of Secondary School Principals Tips for Principals see N A S S P Tips for Principals 1729

National Association of Secretarial Services. Newsletter. (US) 1059

National Association of Securities Dealers Automated Quotations Fact Book see N A S D A Q Fact Book 957

National Association of Securities Dealers Automated Quotations Financial Executive Journal see N A S D A Q Financial Executive Journal 957

National Association of Securities Dealers Automated Quotations Notes see N A S D A Q Notes 5241

National Association of Securities Dealers, Inc. Annual Report see N A S D Annual Report 957

National Association of Securities Dealers, Inc. Executive Digest see N A S D Executive Digest 5241

National Association of Securities Dealers, Inc. Manual see N A S D Manual 957

National Association of Securities Dealers Inc. Newsletter see N A S D Newsletter 5241

National Association of Securities Dealers, Inc. Regulatory and Compliance Alert see N A S D Regulatory and Compliance Alert 957

National Association of Selective Distributors. Newsletter. (US) 4133

National Association of Small Business Investment Companies News see N A S B I C News 957

National Association of Soil and Water Conservation Districts. Tuesday Letter see National Association of Conservation Districts. Tuesday Letter 1492

National Association of State Park Directors. Annual Information Exchange. (US) 1492

National Association of State Universities and Land-Grant Colleges. Appropriations of State Tax Funds for Higher Education. (US ISSN 0077-3425) 1712

National Association of State Universities and Land-Grant Colleges. Circular Letter. (US) 1712

National Association of State Universities and Land-Grant Colleges. Proceedings. (US ISSN 0077-3433) 1712

National Association of Student Personnel Administrators Forum see N A S P A Forum 1318

National Association of Student Personnel Administrators Journal see N A S P A Journal 1712

National Association of Suggestion Systems. Statistical Report. (US ISSN 0077-3441) 1068

National Association of Summer Sessions. Newsletter see North American Association of Summer Sessions. Newsletter 1319

National Association of Teachers in Further and Higher Education. Technical Journal see N A T F H E Journal 1712

National Association of Teachers in Further and Higher Education Journal see N A T F H E Journal 1712

National Association of Teachers of Singing, Inc. Journal see N A T S Journal 3569

National Association of Television Program Executives Programmer see N A T P E Programmer 1377

National Association of Temple Administrators Journal see N A T A Journal 4225

National Association of Temple Educators News see N A T E News 4225

National Association of Testing Authorities Annual Directory see N.A.T.A. Annual Directory 1921

National Association of Testing Authorities News see N A T A News 4325

National Association of Textile and Apparel Distributors Newsletter see N A T A D Newsletter 5241

National Association of the Professions Forum see N A P Forum 5241

National Association of the Remodeling Industry Focus see N A R I Focus 625

National Association of Theatre Nurses News see N A T News 3282

National Association of Theatre Owners News & Views see N A T O News & Views 3514

National Association of Training Schools and Juvenile Agencies. Proceedings. (US ISSN 0077-3476) 1519, 1739

National Association of Truck Stop Operators Truckers News see N A T S O Truckers News 4746

National Association of Uniform Manufacturers and Distributors News see N A U M D News 1286

National Association of Uniform Manufacturers and Distributors Office Reports see N A U M D. Office Reports 1286

National Association of Uniform Manufacturers and Distributors Postal Update see N A U M D Postal Update 1286

National Association of Watch and Clock Collectors. Bulletin. (US ISSN 0027-8688) 2565, 2439

National Association of Wholesaler - Distributors Report see N A W Report 4092

National Association of Women Artists. Annual Exhibition Catalog. (US) 337

National Association of Women Deans and Counselors. Journal see Initiatives 1728

National Association of Women Judges Counterbalance see N A W J Counterbalance 2656

National Association to Advance Fat Acceptance, Inc. Newsletter see N A A F A Newsletter 3609

†National Astronomical Bulletin. (JA) 5242

National Astronomical Observatory. Annals see National Astronomical Observatory. Publications 367

National Astronomical Observatory. Mizusawa Astrogeodynamics Observatory. Mizusawa Kansoku Center. Technical Report. (JA ISSN 0915-3780) 367, 1592

National Astronomical Observatory. Publications/Kokuritsu Tenmondai Obun Hokoku. (JA ISSN 0915-3640) 367

National Astronomical Observatory. Report. (JA ISSN 0915-6321) 367

National Astronomical Observatory. Reprints. (JA ISSN 0915-0021) 367

▼National Auctions & Sales. (US ISSN 1055-8268) 838, 1048

National Auricula & Primula Society (Northern) Year Book. (UK ISSN 0027-8726) 2134

National Australia Bank Monthly Summary see National Quarterly Summary 792

National Australia Bank Quarterly Summary see National Quarterly Summary 792

National Automobile Association Where to Stay Book see N A A Where to Stay Book 2478

National Automobile Dealers Association Large Boat Appraisal Guide see N.A.D.A. Large Boat Appraisal Guide 4526

National Automobile Dealers Association Mobile - Manufactured Housing Appraisal Guide see N.A.D.A. Mobile - Manufactured Housing Appraisal Guide 625

National Automobile Dealers Association Motorcycle - Snowmobile - A T V - Personal Watercraft Appraisal Guide see N.A.D.A. Motorcycle - Snowmobile - A T V - Personal Watercraft Appraisal Guide 4520

National Automobile Dealers Association Official Used Car Guide see N A D A Official Used Car Guide 4697

National Automobile Dealers Association Official Wholesale Used Car Trade-In Guide see N A D A Official Wholesale Used Car Trade-In Guide 4697

National Automobile Dealers Association Older Used Car Guide see N A D A Older Used Car Guide 4697

National Automobile Dealers Association Recreation Vehicle Appraisal Guide see N A D A Recreation Vehicle Appraisal Guide 4697

National Automobile Dealers Association Small Boat Appraisal Guide see N.A.D.A. Small Boat Appraisal Guide 4526

National Automotive Parts Association. Outlook. (US) 4698

National Awami Party of Bangladesh (in Great Britain). Bulletin. (UK) 3908

National Ballot Issues Monitor. (US) 4068

National Bank of Canada. Economic Review. (CN ISSN 0227-2865) 875, 791

National Bank of Commerce. Annual Report and Accounts. (TZ) 791

National Bank of Egypt. Economic Bulletin. (UA ISSN 0304-274X) 875, 791

National Bank of Ethiopia. Annual Report. (ET) 791

National Bank of Ethiopia. Quarterly Bulletin. (ET ISSN 0027-8750) 791, 875

National Bank of Greece. Annual Report/Ethnike Trapeza tes Hellados. Apologismos. (GR ISSN 0077-3514) 791

National Bank of Kuwait. Annual Report of the Board of Directors and Accounts. (KU) 791

National Bank of Liberia. Annual Report.(LB) 791

National Bank of Liberia. Research Department. Statistical Bulletin. (LB) 792

National Bank of Liberia Review see N B L Review 791

National Bank of Pakistan. Annual Report. (PK) 792

National Bank of Pakistan. Monthly Economic Letter. (PK) 792

National Bank of Pakistan. Report and Statement of Accounts. (PK ISSN 0077-3522) 792

National Bank of Yugoslavia. Annual Report see Narodna Banka Jugoslavije. Godisnji Izvestaj 875

National Bank of Yugoslavia. Quarterly Bulletin see Narodna Banka Jugoslavije. Bilten 791

National Bankers Association News Report see N B A News Report 5241

National Banking Law Review. (CN) 792, 2656

National Banking Review see National Banking Law Review 792

National Bankruptcy Reporter. (US ISSN 0275-0252) 792

†National Barber Styling School Bulletin.(US) 5242

National Bark & Soil Producers Association. Special Regional Releases. (US) 2104

National Baseball Hall of Fame & Museum Yearbook. (US) 4508

National Basic Intelligence Factbook see World Factbook 3977

National Basketball Association Hoop - N B A Today see Hoop - N B A Today 4506

National Basketball Association Official N B A Guide see Official N B A Guide 4509

National Beauty News. (US) 374

National Beauty School Journal see Beauty Education 372

National Beer Wholesalers Association. Beer Perspectives Newsletter. (US) 384, 1048

National Beer Wholesalers Association. Distributor Productivity Report. (US) 384, 1048

National Beer Wholesalers Association Handbook see N B W A Handbook 383

National Beer Wholesalers Association Legislative and Regulatory Issues Alert see N B W A Legislative and Regulatory Issues Alert 383

National Belgian Newsletter. (US) 3712

National Beta Club Journal. (US) 1300

National Beverage Marketing Directory (Year) see Beverage Marketing Directory (Year) 378

National Bible Society of Scotland. Annual Report. (UK ISSN 0077-3557) 4244

National Bibliography of Barbados. (BB ISSN 0256-7709) 406

National Bibliography of Botswana. (BS ISSN 0027-8777) 406, 4142

National Bibliography of Zambia. (ZA) 407

National Billiard News. (US) 4508

National Black Law Journal. (US) 2656, 2015

National Black - Police Association. Newsletter. (US) 1519

National Boat Book. (US ISSN 0363-1354) 4526

National Book Development Council of Singapore News see N B D C S News 4133

National Botanic Gardens. Occasional Papers. (IE ISSN 0790-0422) 510

National Botanic Gardens. Report see National Botanical Institute. Review 510

National Botanic Gardens Glasnevin. Contributions see Glasra 504

National Botanic Gardens, Lucknow. Progress.Report see National Botanic Research Institute, Lucknow. Progress Report 510

National Botanic Research Institute, Lucknow. Progress Report. (II) 510

National Botanical Institute. Review. (SA) 510

National Bowlers Journal and Billiard Revue see Bowlers Journal 4466

National Boycott News. (US) 1506

National Boycott Newsletter see National Boycott News 1506

National Braille Association. Bulletin. (US ISSN 0550-5666) 2294

National Braille Association. General Interest Catalog. (US) 2294

National Braille Association. Music Catalog. (US) 2295, 3569

National Braille Association. Textbook Catalog. (US) 2295

National Braille Press Release. (US) 2295, 4133

National Buckskin Society. Newsletter. (AT) 4536

National Budget of Norway see Norway. Royal Norwegian Ministry of Finance. The Revised National Budget. (Year) 1102

National Budget of Norway see Norway. Royal Norwegian Ministry of Finance. The National Budget. (Year) 1102

National Building Code - National Fire Code News see N B C - N F C News 625

National Building Materials Distributors. Journal. (US) 626

National Building Research Institute. Complete List of N B R I Publications. (SA ISSN 0077-3581) 638

National Building Research Institute Information Sheet see N B R I Information Sheet **625**
National Buildings Construction Corporation. Bulletin. (II ISSN 0255-8165) **626**
National Buildings Organisation. Journal.(II ISSN 0027-8815) **626**
National Buildings Organisation Abstracts see N B O Abstracts **638**
National Bureau of Economic Research. Working Paper. (US) **681**
National Bureau of Economic Research Macroeconomics Annual see N B E R Macroeconomics Annual **999**
National Bureau of Standards Bulletin see N I S T Update **680**
National Bus Trader. (US ISSN 0194-939X) **4653**
National Business Aircraft Association. Maintenance and Operations Bulletin. (US) **4676**, 59
National Business Education Yearbook. (US ISSN 0547-4728) **1756**, 1059
National Business Employment Weekly. (US) **3629**
National Business Review. (NZ ISSN 0110-6813) **875**
National Business Woman. (US ISSN 0027-8831) **4849**, 1021
National Button Bulletin. (US ISSN 0027-884X) **2440**
National C P A Group. Newsletter. (US) **753**
National Cactus and Succulent Journal see British Cactus & Succulent Journal **2123**
National Campground Owners Association News see N C O A News **4551**
National Cancer Center. Annual Report/Kokuritsu Gan Senta Nenpo. (JA) **3200**
National Cancer Center Research Institute. Collected Papers/Kokuritsu Gan Senta, Tokyo. Collected Papers. (JA ISSN 0077-3662) **3200**
†National Cancer Institute. Annual Report. (US ISSN 0195-8690) **5242**
National Cancer Institute. Journal. (US ISSN 0027-8874) **3200**
National Cancer Institute. Journal. Monographs. (US ISSN 1052-6773) **3200**
National Cancer Institute Fact Book see N C I Fact Book **3200**
National Cancer Institute of Canada. Annual Report. (CN ISSN 0077-3689) **3200**
National Candy Wholesaler see Candy Wholesaler **2087**
National Capital Planning Commission. Quarterly Review of Commission Proceedings. (US ISSN 0098-308X) **2492**
National Carousel Association. Carousel Archives see Merry-Go-Roundup **258**
National Catalogue of Heating and Air Conditioning. see Catalogue National du Genie Climatique-Chauffage et Conditionnement d'Air **2298**
National Catholic Almanac see Catholic Almanac **4258**
National Catholic Educational Association Ganley's Catholic Schools in America see N C E A Ganley's Catholic Schools in America **1695**
National Catholic Educational Association Notes see N C E A Notes **1648**
National Catholic Register. (US ISSN 0027-8920) **4270**
National Catholic Reporter. (US ISSN 0027-8939) **4270**
National Cattlemen. (US) **221**
National Caves Association Cave Talk see N C A Cave Talk **4779**
National Center for Agricultural Utilization Research Publications and Patents. (US) **140**, 18
National Center for Financial Education Motivator see N C F E Motivator **791**
National Center for Research on Teacher Learning Special Report see N C R T L Special Report **1755**

National Center for Resource Recovery, Inc. Update see N C R R Update **1986**
National Center for State Courts. Publications. (US) **2732**
National Center for State Courts. Report. (US ISSN 0195-5241) **2732**
National Center for the Study of Collective Bargaining in Higher Education and the Professions. Annual Conference Proceedings. (US ISSN 0742-3667) **1712**, 2587
National Center for the Study of Collective Bargaining in Higher Education and the Professions. Newsletter. (US ISSN 0737-9285) **1712**, 989
National Central Library Bulletin. (CH) **2775**
National Central Library News Bulletin see National Central Library Bulletin **2775**
†National Central University. Bulletin of Geophysics. (CH) **5242**
National Centre for Occupational Health. Annual Report. (SA ISSN 0374-9800) **3619**, 3366
†National Centre for the Performing Arts. Quarterly Journal. (II) **5242**
National Ceramics Quarterly. (SA ISSN 1015-2369) **356**
National Character Laboratory Newsletter. (US) **4036**
National Chemical Research Laboratory News see N C R L News **5241**
National Children's Bureau. Annual Review. (UK ISSN 0302-1998) **1241**
National Chimney Sweep Guild. Newslink. (US) **2034**, 2301
National Chinchilla Breeders of Canada. Bulletin. (CN ISSN 0027-8963) **2737**
National Chrysanthemum Society Bulletin see N.C.S. Bulletin **2134**
National Chrysanthemum Society Yearbook see N.C.S. Yearbook **2134**
National Circle Boat. (US) **4526**
National Civic Review. (US ISSN 0027-9013) **4092**
†National Civil Service League. Annual Report. (US ISSN 0077-3735) **5242**
National Civil Service League Exchange see N C S L Exchange **5242**
National Clergy and Laity Concerned Report see C A L C Report **3952**
National Clothesline. (US) **1282**
National Coal Association. Letter of the Law. (US) **3491**, 2656
National Coal Association. Weekly Statistical Summary. (US) **3491**
National Coalition Against the Misuse of Pesticides Technical Report see N C A M P's Technical Report **1963**
National Coalition News. (US) **1649**
†National Coalition of Gay S.T.D. Services. Official Newsletter. (US) **5242**
National Coalition on Television Violence News see N C T V News **1377**
National Coffee Association News Letter see National Coffee Association of U.S.A. Newsletter **2078**
National Coffee Association of U.S.A. Newsletter. (US) **2078**
National Coil Coaters Association. Product Capability Directory. (US) **1147**
National Coin Operators Reporter. (US) **1048**
National Cold Storage Federation. Directory see Cold Storage & Distribution Federation. Directory **2298**
National Collegiate Athletic Association. Annual Reports. (US ISSN 0077-3794) **4480**
National Collegiate Athletic Association. Convention Proceedings. (US ISSN 0077-3808) **4480**
National Collegiate Athletic Association. Manual. (US ISSN 0077-3816) **4480**

National Collegiate Athletic Association. Proceedings of the Special Convention. (US ISSN 0094-4459) **4480**
National Collegiate Athletic Association Baseball see N C A A Baseball **4508**
National Collegiate Athletic Association Baseball Rules see N C A A Baseball Rules **4508**
National Collegiate Athletic Association Basketball see N C A A Basketball **4508**
National Collegiate Athletic Association Directory see N C A A Directory **4480**
National Collegiate Athletic Association Drug Testing Program see N C A A Drug Testing Program **4480**
National Collegiate Athletic Association Football see N C A A Football **4508**
National Collegiate Athletic Association Football Rules and Interpretations see N C A A Football Rules and Interpretations **4508**
National Collegiate Athletic Association Men's and Women's Basketball Rules and Interpretations see N C A A Men's and Women's Basketball Rules and Interpretations **4508**
National Collegiate Athletic Association Men's and Women's Cross Country and Track & Field Rules see N C A A Men's and Women's Cross Country and Track & Field Rules **4550**
National Collegiate Athletic Association Men's and Women's Illustrated Basketball Rules see N C A A Men's and Women's Illustrated Basketball Rules **4508**
National Collegiate Athletic Association Men's and Women's Rifle Rules see N C A A Men's and Women's Rifle Rules **4480**
National Collegiate Athletic Association Men's and Women's Skiing Rules see N C A A Men's and Women's Skiing Rules **4551**
National Collegiate Athletic Association Men's and Women's Soccer Rules see N C A A Men's and Women's Soccer Rules **4508**
National Collegiate Athletic Association Men's and Women's Swimming and Diving Rules see N C A A Men's and Women's Swimming and Diving Rules **4480**
National Collegiate Athletic Association Men's Ice Hockey Rules and Interpretations see N C A A Men's Ice Hockey Rules and Interpretations **4480**
National Collegiate Athletic Association Men's Lacrosse Rules see N C A A Men's Lacrosse Rules **4508**
National Collegiate Athletic Association Men's Read-Easy Basketball Rules see N C A A Men's Read-Easy Basketball Rules **4508**
National Collegiate Athletic Association Men's Water Polo Rules see N C A A Men's Water Polo Rules **4480**
National Collegiate Athletic Association News see N C A A News **4480**
National Collegiate Athletic Association Read-Easy Football Rules see N C A Read-Easy Football Rules **4508**
National Collegiate Athletic Association Softball see N C A A Softball **4508**
National Collegiate Athletic Association Wrestling Rules see N C A A Wrestling Rules **4480**
National Collegiate Championships. (US ISSN 0190-4329) **4480**
National Commercial & Development Bank. Annual Report and Financial Statements. (DQ) **792**
National Committee for Adoption. Legal Notes see National Council for Adoption. Legal Notes **4413**
National Committee for Adoption. Memo see National Council for Adoption. Memo **4413**
National Committee for the Defence of Peace in the Socialist Republic of Rumania. Information Bulletin see Alliance for Peace in Rumania. Information Bulletin **3871**

National Committee on Science and Technology. Research and Development Statistics see India. Department of Science and Technology. Research and Development Statistics **4356**
National Committee on the Treatment of Intractable Pain. Newsletter. (US) **3134**
National Committee on U.S. China Relations. Highlights of Notes see National Committee on U.S.-China Relations. Notes from the National Committee **3966**
National Committee on U.S.-China Relations. Notes from the National Committee. (US) **3966**
National Communications Forum. Proceedings. (US ISSN 0886-229X) **1340**, 1904
National Communications Union Journal. (UK) **1364**
†National Computer Conference (Proceedings). (US) **5242**
National Computer Security Association. Newsletter. (US) **1434**, 1479
National Computer Security Association. Research Reports. (US) **1434**, 1479
National Conference of C P A Practitioners. Newsletter. (US) **753**
National Conference of Commissioners on Uniform State Laws. Handbook and Proceedings. (US) **2656**
National Conference of Standards Laboratories. Newsletter. (US) **3447**
National Conference of State Legislatures Conference Report see N C S L Conference Report **4067**
National Conference of State Legislatures Federal Update see N C S L Federal Update **4067**
National Conference of State Liquor Administrators Minutes of Annual Meeting see N C S L A Minutes of Annual Meeting **4067**
National Conference of State Liquor Administrators Official Directory see N C S L A Official Directory **4067**
National Conference of State Social Security Administrators. Proceedings.(US) **4413**
National Conference of States on Building Codes and Standards, Inc. News see N C S B C S News **2492**
National Conference of Synagogue Youth Keeping Posted with N C S Y see Keeping Posted with N C S Y **4224**
National Conference on Artificial Intelligence. Proceedings. (US) **1409**
National Conference on Fluid Power. Proceedings. (US ISSN 0160-8428) **1924**, 1936
National Conference on Industrial Hydraulics see National Conference on Fluid Power. Proceedings **1924**
National Conference on Piano Pedagogy. Proceedings. (US) **3569**
National Conference on Safety. Proceedings. (II) **4108**
National Conference on Soviet Jewry. Press Service see Newsbreak (New York) **3945**
National Conference on Weights and Measures. Report. (US ISSN 0077-3964) **3447**
National Congress of American Indians. Bulletin see Sentinel: Bulletin - N C A I News **2023**
National Congress of Jewish Deaf. Quarterly. (US) **2288**, 2015
National Congress of Organizations of the Physically Handicapped, Inc. Bulletin see C O P H Bulletin **3085**
National Consortium for Computer-Based Music Instruction. Newsletter see Association for Technology in Music Instruction Newsletter **3589**
†National Constructor. (AT) **5243**
National Constructors Association Newsletter see N C A Newsletter **625**
National Consultor. (US ISSN 0271-9150) **754**, 1101

National Consumer Law Center Reports: Bankruptcy & Foreclosures *see* N C L C Reports: Bankruptcy & Foreclosures **2656**
National Consumer Law Center Reports: Consumer Credit & Usury *see* N C L C Reports: Consumer Credit & Usury **2656**
National Consumer Law Center Reports: Debt Collection & Reposessions *see* N C L C Reports: Debt Collection & Reposessions **2656**
National Consumer Law Center Reports: Deceptive Acts & Warranties *see* N C L C Reports: Deceptive Acts & Warranties **2656**
National Consumers League Bulletin. (US ISSN 1055-923X) **1507**
National Contract Management Journal (1980). (US) **1021**, 4068
National Convention of Electrical and Electronics Engineers in Israel. Proceedings *see* Convention of Electrical and Electronics Engineers in Israel. Proceedings **1885**
National Cooperative Development Corporation Bulletin *see* N C D C Bulletin **831**
National Cooperative Highway Research Program Reports. (US ISSN 0077-5614) **4720**, 1871
National Cooperative Highway Research Program Research Results Digest. (US ISSN 0547-5554) **4720**, 1871
National Cooperative Highway Research Program Synthesis of Highway Practice. (US ISSN 0547-5570) **4720**, 1871
National Cooperative Transit Research and Development Program. Research Results Digest. (US) **4653**
National Cooperative Transit Research and Development Program Report. (US ISSN 0732-4839) **4653**
National Cooperative Transit Research and Development Program Synthesis of Transit Practice. (US ISSN 0732-1856) **4653**
National Coordinating Council on Emergency Management Official Monthly Newsletter *see* N C C E M's Official Monthly Newsletter **4108**
National Costumers Magazine. (US) **4635**
National Cottonseed Products Association. Trading Rules. (US ISSN 0077-4022) **207**, 1857, 4622
National Council Against Health Fraud, Inc. Newsletter *see* N C A H F Newsletter **4108**
National Council for Adoption. Legal Notes. (US) **4413**, 2718
National Council for Adoption. Memo. (US) **4413**, 2718
National Council for Cement and Building Materials. Annual Report. (II) **626**
National Council for Cement and Building Materials Quest *see* N C B Quest **625**
National Council for Geocosmic Research. Memberletter. (US) **359**
National Council for Geocosmic Research, Inc. Journal *see* N C G R Journal **359**
National Council for Geographic Education. Pacesetter Series. (US) **2256**
National Council for Geographic Education. Topics in Geography. (US) **1756**, 2256
National Council for Geographic Education. Yearbook *see* National Council for Geographic Education. Pacesetter Series **2256**
National Council for Historic Sites and Buildings Quarterly Report *see* Historic Preservation **300**
National Council for International Visitors Newsletter *see* N C I V Newsletter **4779**
National Council for Science & Technology. Directory. (NP) **2775**
National Council for Scientific Research. Annual Report. (LE) **1712**
National Council for Special Education. Conference Reports. (UK) **1756**
National Council for Special Education. Occasional Publications. (UK) **1739**
National Council for the Social Studies. Bulletins. (US ISSN 0077-4049) **4380**
†National Council for the Social Studies. How to Do It Series. (US ISSN 0085-3712) **5243**
National Council for Voluntary Organisations News *see* N C V O News **4413**
National Council for Voluntary Organizations. Annual Report. (UK) **4413**
National Council News. (US ISSN 0738-9159) **3346**, 4413
National Council of Administrative Women in Education News *see* N C A W E News **1729**
National Council of Churches, Bangladesh. Annual Report. (BG) **4285**
National Council of Educational Research and Training Newsletter *see* N C E R T Newsletter **1648**
National Council of Engineering Examiners. Proceedings *see* National Council of Examiners for Engineering and Surveying. Proceedings **1831**
National Council of Examiners for Engineering and Surveying. Proceedings. (US) **1831**, 1871
National Council of Examiners for Engineering and Surveying Registration Bulletin *see* N C E E S Registration Bulletin **1831**
National Council of Jewish Women Journal *see* N C J W Journal **4849**
National Council of La Raza. A I D S Newsletter. (US) **3222**, 4413
▼National Council of La Raza. Ancianos Project Newsletter. (US) **2276**
National Council of La Raza. Poverty Project Newsletter. (US) **4414**
†National Council of Savings Institutions. Annual Report of the President. (US) **5243**
National Council of Savings Institutions. Operations Letter. (US) **792**, 2656
National Council of Savings Institutions. Regulatory Update. (US) **792**, 2656
National Council of Savings Institutions. Trustees & Directors Letter. (US) **792**, 2656
National Council of Savings Institutions. Washington Memo. (US) **792**
National Council of Savings Institutions Directory. (US) **792**
National Council of Social Service. Annual Report *see* National Council for Voluntary Organizations. Annual Report **4413**
National Council of Teachers of Mathematics. Professional Reference Series. (US) **3048**, 1649
National Council of Teachers of Mathematics. Yearbook. (US ISSN 0077-4103) **3048**, 1649
National Council of Teachers of Mathematics News Bulletin *see* N C T M News Bulletin **1755**
National Council of the Churches of Christ in the U.S.A. Biennial Report. (US) **4245**
National Council of the Churches of Christ in the U.S.A. Triennial Report *see* National Council of the Churches of Christ in the U.S.A. Biennial Report **4245**
National Council of the Paper Industry for Air and Stream Improvement. Technical Bulletin. (US) **1978**
National Council of United States Magistrates. Bulletin. (US) **2657**
National Council of Women of Australia. Quarterly Bulletin. (AT ISSN 0047-8792) **3945**
National Council of Women of South Africa News *see* N C W News **4849**
National Council of Wool Selling Brokers of Australia. News Bulletin. (AT) **4622**
National Council on Education for the Ceramic Arts Journal *see* N C E C A Journal **356**
National Council on Education for the Ceramic Arts News *see* N C E C A News **356**
National Council on Family Relations. Report. (US) **4443**
National Council on Family Relations Newsletter *see* National Council on Family Relations. Report **4443**
National Council on Inland Transportation. Newsletter. (UK ISSN 0260-7735) **4720**
National Council on Measurement in Education. Measurement News *see* Educational Measurement: Issues and Practice **1630**
National Council on Measurement in Education. Yearbook *see* Journal of Educational Measurement **1642**
National Council on Radiation Protection and Measurements. Proceedings of the Annual Meeting. (US ISSN 0195-7740) **4108**
National Council on Radiation Protection and Measurements Commentary *see* N C R P Commentary **4108**
National Council on Radiation Protection and Measurements News *see* N C R P News **4108**
National Council on Radiation Protection and Measurements Report *see* N C R P Report **4108**
National Council on Radiation Protection and Measurements Statements *see* N C R P Statements **3360**
National Council on Radiation Protection and Measurements Symposium Proceedings *see* N C R P Symposium Proceedings **4108**
National Council on the Aging Networks *see* N C O A Networks **2276**
National Country Life. (AT) **108**, 2172
National Court Reporters Association. Proceedings of the Annual Convention. (US) **2657**
National Credit Union Administration Watch *see* N C U A Watch **791**
National Creditor - Debtor Review. (CN ISSN 0829-2019) **792**, 1021, 2657
National Cremation *see* Cremationist of North America **2119**
National Crop Protection Center Annual Report *see* N C P C Annual Report **185**
National Croquet Calendar. (US ISSN 1047-6474) **4508**
National Culinary Review. (US) **2078**, 2478
National Custodian *see* Cleaning Management **610**
National Cutting Horse Association. Rule Book. (US) **4536**
National Dahlia Society Annual. (UK ISSN 0077-4189) **2134**
National Dairy Council of Canada. Direction. (CN) **202**
National Dairy Council of Canada. Resume *see* National Dairy Council of Canada. Direction **202**
National Dairy Research Institute. Annual Report. (II ISSN 0301-8407) **202**
National Data Book of Foundations. (US ISSN 0730-1677) **4426**
†National Dating Scene. (US) **5243**
†National Deaf Children's Society. Annual Accounts. (UK) **5243**
National Deaf Children's Society. Annual Report. (UK) **2288**, 1241
National Deaf Children's Society. Directory. (UK) **2288**
National Deaf Children's Society. Yearbook and Annual Accounts *see* National Deaf Children's Society. Annual Report **2288**
National Dean's List. (US ISSN 0191-8133) **1712**
National Defense. (US ISSN 0092-1491) **3466**, 59
National Defense Academy. Digest of Researches by Faculty Members. *see* Boei Daigakko Kyokan Kenkyu Yoroku **3476**
National Defense Academy. Memoirs. Mathematics, Physics, Chemistry, and Engineering/Boei Daigakko Kiyo. Rikogaku Hen. (JA ISSN 0388-4112) **4326**, 4604
National Defense Academy. Scientific and Engineering Reports. *see* Boei Daigakko Rikogaku Kenkyu Hokoku **1816**
National Defense Medical Journal/Boei Eisei. (JA ISSN 0006-5528) **3134**
National Defense Revue. *see* Epitheorisis Ethnikis Amynis **3457**
†National Dental Association. Journal. (US ISSN 0097-1901) **5243**
National Development. (US ISSN 0360-7941) **4068**, 626, 1871
National Development Bank. Annual Report and Accounts. (SL) **792**
National Development Finance Corporation. Monthly Economic Report *see* National Development Finance Corporation. Quarterly Review **875**
National Development Finance Corporation. Quarterly Review. (PK) **875**
National Diary. (II ISSN 0027-9145) **2200**
National Diet Library. Annual Report. *see* Kokuritsu Kokkai Toshokan Nenpo **2767**
National Diet Library. Monthly Bulletin. *see* Kokuritsu Kokkai Toshokan Geppo **2767**
National Diet Library. Monthly List of Foreign Scientific and Technical Publications/Kaigai Kagaku Gijutsu Shiryo Geppo. (JA ISSN 0454-1944) **4615**, 4357
National Diet Library. Newsletter. (JA ISSN 0027-9161) **2775**
National Diet Library. Reference/ Kokuritsu Kokkai Toshokan. Refarensu. (JA ISSN 0034-2912) **2657**
National Diet Library. Reference Service and Bibliography. *see* Kokutritsu Kokkai Toshokan. Sanko Shosi Kenkyu **2767**
National Dipper. (US ISSN 0895-9722) **2078**, 1116
National Directory of Advertising - Print Media (Year). (US) **1147**, 35
National Directory of Alternative Schools. (US) **1695**
▼National Directory of Art & Antiques Buyers & Specialists. (US ISSN 0899-6172) **258**, 337
National Directory of Art Internships. (US) **337**, 1685
National Directory of Arts and Education Support by Business Corporations. (US) **337**
National Directory of Arts Support by Business Corporations *see* National Directory of Arts and Education Support by Business Corporations **337**
National Directory of Arts Support by Private Foundations. (US) **337**
National Directory of Budget Motels. (US) **2478**
National Directory of Bulletin Board Systems. (US ISSN 0884-9536) **1147**, 2775
▼National Directory of Catalogs. (US) **407**
†National Directory of Catholic Higher Education. (US) **5243**
National Directory of Chiropractic. (US) **1147**, 3215
National Directory of College Athletics (Men's Edition). (US ISSN 0547-616X) **4480**
National Directory of College Athletics (Women's Edition). (US ISSN 0739-1226) **4480**
▼National Directory of Corporate Distress Specialists. (US) **1147**
National Directory of Corporate Public Affairs. (US) **681**, 3908
▼National Directory of Courts of Law. (US ISSN 1054-9471) **2732**, 1147
National Directory of Drug Abuse and Alcoholism Treatment and Prevention Programs. (US) **1538**
National Directory of Educational Programs in Gerontology *see* National Directory of Educational Programs in Gerontology and Geriatrics **1147**

Title

National Directory of Educational Programs in Gerontology and Geriatrics. (US) **1147**, 1695, 2276
National Directory of Free Tourist Attractions. (US) **1147**, 4779
National Directory of Grants and Aid to Individuals in the Arts, International. (US) **337**
National Directory of Head Injury Rehabilitation Services. (US) **3310**
National Directory of Internships, Residencies & Registrarships. (AT ISSN 0155-9567) **1147**, 2468, 3629
†National Directory of Landscape Architecture Firms. (US ISSN 0272-247X) **5243**
National Directory of Latin Americanists.(US) **2015**
National Directory of Law Enforcement Administrators and Correctional Agencies see National Directory of Law Enforcement Administrators and Correctional Institutions **1519**
National Directory of Law Enforcement Administrators and Correctional Institutions. (US) **1519**
National Directory of Local Researchers.(US ISSN 0742-9045) **2159**
National Directory of Magazines. (US ISSN 0895-4321) **407**
▼National Directory of Mailing Lists. (US) **407**
National Directory of Minority - Owned Business Firms. (US ISSN 0886-3881) **1147**, 1116
National Directory of Private Social Agencies. (US) **4414**
National Directory of Retirement Facilities. (US ISSN 1053-6825) **2277**
National Directory of Safety Consultants. (US) **1831**, 4108
†National Directory of State Agencies. (US ISSN 0095-3113) **5243**
National Directory of Storytelling. (US) **2941**, 1649
National Directory of Theme Parks and Amusement Areas see Directory of Theme & Amusement Parks **4760**
National Directory of Woman - Owned Business Firms. (US ISSN 0886-389X) **1147**, 4849
National Directory of Women's Athletics see National Directory of College Athletics (Women's Edition) **4480**
National Distribution Directory of Local Cartage-Short Haul Carriers Warehousing see M C D's Warehousing Distribution Directory **4745**
National Doll World see International Doll World **2437**
National Doll World Omnibook see Doll Designs **2435**
National Drag Boat. (US) **4527**
National Dragster. (US) **4698**
National Drillers Buyers Guide. (US ISSN 0279-7739) **4827**, 1599, 3692
National Easter Seal Communicator. (US) **4414**
National Economy. see Undesniy Ediyn Dzasag **840**
National Education see N Z E I Rourou **1649**
National Education Association of New York New York see N E A New York **1648**
National Education Association of the United States. Proceedings of the Annual Meeting see National Education Association of the United States. Proceedings of the Representative Assembly **1649**
National Education Association of the United States. Proceedings of the Representative Assembly. (US) **1649**
National Education Association of the United States Advocate see N E A Advocate **1712**
National Education Association of the United States Almanac of Higher Education see N E A Almanac of Higher Education **1712**

National Education Association of the United States Now see N E A Now **1648**
National Education Association of the United States Today see N E A Today **1649**
National Education Association Rhode Island. Newsline. (US ISSN 0886-9979) **1649**
National Educational Secretary. (US ISSN 0027-9196) **1649**
National Educator. (US) **2229**, 1649
National Electric Reliability Council. Annual Report see North American Electric Reliability Council. Annual Report **1904**
National Electrical Code Report. (US) **1904**
National Electrical Manufacturers Association Bulletin see N E M A Bulletin **1904**
National Electrical Manufacturers Association News see N E M A News **1904**
National Electronic Injury Surveillance System Data Highlights see N E I S S Data Highlights **4108**
National Electronics Conference National Communications Forum. Proceedings see National Communications Forum. Proceedings **1340**
National Electronics Council. Review see National Electronics Review **5243**
†National Electronics Review. (UK ISSN 0305-2257) **5243**
National Employment Listing Service (N E L S) Bulletin. (US) **1519**, 3629
National Employment Listing Service for the Criminal Justice System and Social Services. Bulletin see National Employment Listing Service (N E L S) Bulletin **1519**
National Endowment for the Arts Grantmaking Programs: Arts Administration Fellows Program see N E A Grantmaking Programs: Arts Administration Fellows Program **337**
National Endowment for the Arts Grantmaking Programs: Arts in Education see N E A Grantmaking Programs: Arts in Education **337**
National Endowment for the Arts Grantmaking Programs: Challenge and Advancement see N E A Grantmaking Programs: Challenge and Advancement **2940**
National Endowment for the Arts Grantmaking Programs: Dance see N E A Grantmaking Programs: Dance **1531**
National Endowment for the Arts Grantmaking Programs: Design Arts see N E A Grantmaking Programs: Design Arts **337**
National Endowment for the Arts Grantmaking Programs: Expansion Arts see N E A Grantmaking Programs: Expansion Arts **337**
National Endowment for the Arts Grantmaking Programs: Folk Arts see N E A Grantmaking Programs: Folk Arts **337**
National Endowment for the Arts Grantmaking Programs: Inter - Arts see N E A Grantmaking Programs: Inter - Arts **337**
National Endowment for the Arts Grantmaking Programs: Literature see N E A Grantmaking Programs: Literature **2940**
National Endowment for the Arts Grantmaking Programs: Locals Program see N E A Grantmaking Programs: Locals Program **337**
National Endowment for the Arts Grantmaking Programs: Media Arts see N E A Grantmaking Programs: Media Arts **337**
National Endowment for the Arts Grantmaking Programs: Museums see N E A Grantmaking Programs: Museums **3530**
National Endowment for the Arts Grantmaking Programs: Music see N E A Grantmaking Programs: Music **3569**

National Endowment for the Arts Grantmaking Programs: Opera - Musical Theater see N E A Grantmaking Programs: Opera - Musical Theater **4635**
National Endowment for the Arts Grantmaking Programs: States Program see N E A Grantmaking Programs: States Program **337**
National Endowment for the Arts Grantmaking Programs: Theater see N E A Grantmaking Programs: Theater **4635**
National Endowment for the Arts Grantmaking Programs: Visual Arts see N E A Grantmaking Programs: Visual Arts **337**
National Endowment for the Humanities. Annual Report. (US ISSN 0083-2111) **2511**
National Energy Journal. (US ISSN 0279-4357) **642**, 1793
National Energy Outlook. (JM) **3693**, 1793
National Engineer. (US ISSN 0027-9218) **1936**
National Enquirer. (US ISSN 1056-3482) **2229**
National Enterprise Education Development and Information Service Initiative see N E E D I S Initiative **1685**
National Environmental Enforcement Journal. (US) **1963**, 1527
▼National Environmental Journal. (US) **1963**
National Environmental Training Association News see N E T A News **1963**
National Equine (and Smaller Animals) Defence League. Annual Report. (UK ISSN 0077-4448) **231**
National Equipment Servicing Dealers Association Quarterly Newsletter see N E S D A Quarterly Newsletter **3021**
National Examiner. (US) **2229**
National Export Traffic League. Bulletin. (US) **4712**
†National Fact Book of Savings Institutions. (US ISSN 8756-9043) **5243**
National Faculty Directory. (US ISSN 0077-4472) **1730**
National Faculty Salary Survey by Discipline and Rank in Private Colleges and Universities. (US) **989**, 1712
National Farm Tractor & Implement Blue Book. (US ISSN 0193-7642) **163**
National Farmers' Union Handbook. (UK) **108**
National Farmers Union Washington Newsletter. (US ISSN 0027-9226) **108**
National Fashion Accessories Association Bulletin see N F A A. Bulletin **1286**
National Fashion Accessories Association Newsletter see N F A A. Newsletter **1286**
National Federation Handbook. (US) **4481**
National Federation News. (US) **1730**
National Federation of Abstracting and Information Services Bulletin see N F A I S Bulletin **5242**
National Federation of Abstracting and Information Services Newsletter see N F A I S Newsletter **17**
National Federation of Abstracting and Information Services Notes see N F A I S Notes **17**
National Federation of Abstracting and Information Services Report Series see N F A I S Report Series **17**
National Federation of Building Trades Employers' North Western Region Year Book and Directory. (UK) **626**
National Federation of Catholic Physicians' Guilds. Newsletter. (US) **3134**, 4270
National Federation of Construction Workers' Unions. Zenkensoren. (JA) **626**
National Federation of Flemish Giant Rabbit Breeders. Quarterly Newsletter. (US) **221**

National Federation of Fruit and Potato Trades. Annual Handbook and List of Members. (UK) **108**
National Federation of Fruit & Potato Trades. Federation News. (UK) **108**, 2134
National Federation of Fruit and Potato Trades. News and Views see National Federation of Fruit & Potato Trades. Federation News **108**
National Federation of Independent Business see N F I B **1116**
National Federation of Independent Business. Quarterly Economic Report see N F I B Quarterly Economic Report for Small Business **875**
National Federation of Independent Business Quarterly Economic Report for Small Business see N F I B Quarterly Economic Report for Small Business **875**
National Federation of Painting and Decorating Contractors Year Book. (UK) **2554**
National Federation of Plastering Contractors. Year Book. (UK ISSN 0077-4480) **626**
National Federation of Playgoers Societies. Newsletter. (UK) **4635**
National Federation of Roofing Contractors Roofing Industry Directory see N F R C Roofing Industry Directory **625**
National Federation of Settlements and Neighborhood Centers, News and Round Table see United Neighborhood Centers of America. News & Round Table **4422**
National Federation of State Cooperative Banks Ltd. Bulletin see N A F S C O B Bulletin **791**
National Film and Sound Archive Newsletter. (AT ISSN 0814-6888) **4461**, 1377, 3514
National Film Archive of Iran. Bulletin. (IR) **3514**
National Film Archive of Iran. Quarterly. see Film-khane-ye Melli-e Iran. Name-ye **3509**
National Finances: An Analysis of the Revenues and Expenditures of the Government of Canada. (CN ISSN 0077-4529) **1101**
National Fire and Arson Report. (US) **2034**, 1519, 2657
National Fire Codes see National Fire Protection Association. National Fire Codes **2034**
National Fire Protection Association. National Fire Codes. (US ISSN 0077-4545) **2034**
National Fire Protection Association. National Fire Codes. Subscription Service. (US) **2034**
National Fire Protection Association. National Fire Codes. Supplement see National Fire Protection Association. National Fire Codes. Subscription Service **2034**
National Fire Protection Association Buyer's Guide see N F P A Buyer's Guide **2034**
National Fire Protection Association Journal see N F P A Journal **2034**
National Fire Protection Association Technical Committee. Report see N F P A Technical Committee. Report **2034**
National Fisheries University of Pusan. Institute of Marine Sciences. Contributions. (KO) **448**, 1184, 2046
National Fisheries University of Pusan. Institute of Marine Sciences. Publications see National Fisheries University of Pusan. Institute of Marine Sciences. Contributions **448**
National Fisherman. (US ISSN 0027-9250) **2046**
National Fitness Trade Journal. (US) **1147**
National Five Digit Zip Code and Post Office Directory. (US ISSN 0731-9185) **1353**
National Fluid Power Association. Directory and Member Guide (Year). (US) **1936**
National Fluid Power Association Reporter. (US) **1936**

National Fluoridation News. (US ISSN 0027-9269) **1963, 3238, 3609**
National Food Review. (US ISSN 0161-4274) **155, 2078**
†National Foreign Trade Council. Policy Declaration. (US) **5243**
National Forensic Journal. (US) **1340**
National Forest Products Association Statistical Roundup *see* N F P A: Statistical Roundup **1048**
National Forest Recreation Association Newsletter *see* N F R A Newsletter **1492**
National Forum (Auburn). (US ISSN 0162-1831) **1318, 2229**
National Forum A E R J *see* National Forum of Applied Educational Research Journal **1649**
National Forum of Applied Educational Research Journal. (US ISSN 0895-3880) **1649**
National Forum of Education Administration and Supervision Journal. (US ISSN 0888-8132) **1730, 1021, 1712**
National Forum of Educational Administration and Supervision *see* National Forum of Education Administration and Supervision Journal **1730**
▼National Forum of Instructional Technology Journal. (US) **1691, 1649**
National Forum of Special Education Journal. (US ISSN 1043-2167) **1739**
▼National Forum Teacher Education Journal. (US ISSN 1049-2658) **1649**
National Foundation for Advancement in the Arts. Annual Report. (US) **337, 1531, 2941**
National Foundation for Advancement in the Arts Arts Alumni Directory *see* N F A A Arts Alumni Directory **5242**
National Foundation for Consumer Credit Members' Bulletin *see* N F C C Members' Bulletin **791**
National Foundation for Ileitis and Colitis. Greater New Jersey Chapter. Newsletter *see* Crohn's & Colitis Foundation of America. Greater New Jersey Chapter. Newsletter **3267**
National Foundation for Ileitis and Colitis. Greater New York Chapter. Update *see* Crohn's & Colitis Foundation of America. Greater New York Chapter. Update **3267**
National Four Wheel Drive Association News. (US) **4698**
National Fraternal Clubs News. (US) **1300**
National Free Library of Zimbabwe. Annual Report *see* National Library and Documentation Service. Annual Report **2775**
National Fresh Produce Market, Johannesburg. Annual Report of the Director. (SA) **838**
National Fresh Produce Market, Johannesburg. Annual Trading Results/Jaarliske Handelsyfers. (SA) **155**
†National Front News. (UK) **5243**
National Frozen Food Association Directory. (US) **2078**
National Fund Raiser. (US ISSN 0272-0825) **4414, 1021**
National Future Farmer *see* F F A New Horizons **89**
National Futures and Financial Weekly. (US) **957**
National Futures Association Manual. (US) **958, 2657**
National Galleries of Scotland. Bulletin. (UK ISSN 0953-024X) **3530**
National Galleries of Scotland. News *see* National Galleries of Scotland. Bulletin **3530**
National Gallery, London. Technical Bulletin. (UK ISSN 0140-7430) **337, 3530**
National Gallery of Art. Annual Report. (US ISSN 0091-7222) **337**
National Gallery of Canada. Catalogue. Canadian Art. Volume One, A - F. (CN ISSN 0826-9726) **337**

National Gallery of Zimbabwe. Annual Report and Balance Sheet and Income and Expenditure Account. (RH) **3530**
National Gardener. (US ISSN 0027-9331) **2135**
National Gardening. (US ISSN 0887-8447) **2135, 1048**
National Gardening Survey (Year). (US) **2135, 1048**
National Gay and Lesbian Task Force. Task Force Reports. (US ISSN 0896-3649) **2455, 3945**
National Gay Task Force. Task Force Report *see* National Gay and Lesbian Task Force. Task Force Reports **2455**
National Genealogical Directory. (UK ISSN 0951-9521) **2159**
National Genealogical Society. Newsletter. (US) **2159**
National Genealogical Society Quarterly.(US ISSN 0027-934X) **2159**
National Geographer. (II ISSN 0470-0929) **2256**
National Geographic. (US ISSN 0027-9358) **2257**
National Geographic Books (Series). (US ISSN 0077-4618) **2257**
National Geographic Research *see* National Geographic Research and Exploration **2257**
National Geographic Research and Exploration. (US ISSN 1056-800X) **2257**
National Geographic Society. Special Publications Series *see* National Geographic Books (Series) **2257**
National Geographic Traveler. (US ISSN 0747-0932) **4779**
National Geographic World. (US ISSN 0361-5499) **1261, 2229**
National Geographical Journal of India. (II ISSN 0027-9374) **2257**
National Geophysical Research Institute. Publications. (II ISSN 0073-4144) **1592**
▼National Golf Magazine. (US) **4508**
National Greyhound News. (AT ISSN 0310-589X) **4481, 3712**
National Greyhound Update. (US) **4481**
National Ground Water Association. Briefings. (US ISSN 1051-0214) **1599, 2657**
National Guard. (US ISSN 0163-3945) **3466**
National Guard. (II) **3908**
National Guard Almanac. (US ISSN 0363-8618) **3466**
National Guardian *see* Scottish Licensed Trade Guardian **385**
National Guide to Credit Recommendations for Noncollegiate Courses *see* National Guide to Educational Credit for Training Programs **1730**
National Guide to Educational Credit for Training Programs. (US) **1730**
National Guide to Government. (AT ISSN 1030-6641) **4068**
†National Guild of Catholic Psychiatrists. Bulletin. (US ISSN 0547-7115) **5243**
National Guild of Piano Teachers. Guild Syllabus. (US ISSN 0077-4642) **3570**
National Hairdresser. (UK) **374**
National Hardwood Lumber Association Membership Directory. (US) **1147, 2116**
National Hardwood Lumber Association Newsletter *see* N H L A Newsletter **2116**
National Hardwood Lumber Association Yearbook *see* National Hardwood Lumber Association Membership Directory **1147**
National Hardwood Magazine. (US ISSN 0194-0910) **2116**
National Head Injury Foundation. Catalogue of Educational Materials. (US) **3310**
†National Head Injury Foundation Annual Report. (US) **5243**
National Head Injury Foundation Newsletter *see* N H I F Newsletter **3310**

National Head Start Association Journal *see* N H S A Journal **1738**
National Headache Foundation Newsletter. (US) **3346**
National Health Care Expenditures Study. Data Preview. (US) **4108**
National Health Law Program Health Advocate *see* N H E L P Health Advocate **3806**
National Health Service Economic Review (Year) *see* N H S Economic Review (Year) **4067**
National Hearing Conservation Association Professional Service Organization Directory *see* N H C A Professional Service Organization Directory **2288**
National Heart Foundation of Australia. Annual Report (Year). (AT) **3210**
National Heart Foundation of Australia. Research in Progress. (AT ISSN 0077-4685) **3210**
National Heart News. (AT) **3134, 3210**
National Hereford Hog Annual Newsletter. (US) **221**
National High School Sports Record Book. (US) **4481**
National Historic Communal Societies Association. Newsletter. (US) **2318**
National Hobby News. (US) **2440**
National Hockey League. Guide *see* National Hockey League. Guide & Record Book **4498**
National Hockey League. Guide & Record Book. (CN) **4498, 4508**
National Hockey League. Official Rule Book. (CN) **4481**
National Hog Farmer. (US ISSN 0027-9447) **221**
National Home-Business Report. (US ISSN 0741-5729) **1116, 2440**
National Home Center News. (US ISSN 0192-6772) **626**
National Home Study Council News *see* N H S C News **1729**
National Home Study Council Report *see* N H S C Report **1755**
National Homecare and Hospice Directory. (US) **2468**
National Homeschool Association Newsletter. (US) **1650**
National Honey Market News. (US) **918, 536, 2089**
National Horseman. (US ISSN 0027-9455) **4536**
National Hospice Organization Hospice News *see* N H O Hospice News **4413**
National Hospitality News. (CN) **2478**
National Hot Rod Association Souvenir Yearbook *see* N H R A Souvenir Yearbook **4697**
National Hotelier *see* Hotelier & Caterer (Cape Town) **2476**
National Housing & Rehabilitation Association. Newsletter. (US) **2492**
National Housing and Town Planning Council. Conference and Exhibition Guide. (UK ISSN 0264-9829) **2492**
†National Housing and Town Planning Council. Conference and Exhibition Guide. (UK) **5243**
†National Housing and Town Planning Council. Handbook and Year Book. (UK) **5243**
National Housing Law Project. Law Project Bulletin *see* Housing Law Bulletin **2488**
▼National Housing Register. (US ISSN 1059-3071) **2492, 4068**
National Huguenot Society Proceedings *see* Cross of Languedoc **4235**
National Humanities Center Newsletter. (US ISSN 0196-1721) **2511**
National Hurricane Operations Plan *see* U.S. National Oceanic and Atmospheric Administration. Interdepartmental Committee for Meteorological Services and Supporting Research. National Hurricane Operations Plan **3441**
National Hydro Cephalus Foundation Newsletter *see* Life-Line **3344**
National Hydro Electric Power Corporation. Annual Report. (II) **1803**

National Ice Cream Retailers Association. Yearbook. (US) **1048**
National Impact. Update *see* Interfaith Impact **4409**
National Income Accounts of the Philippines. (PH) **999**
National Income and Product Accounts of the United States, 1929-1982: Statistical Tables. (US ISSN 0361-3895) **730**
National Income in Taiwan Area, Republic of China *see* China, Republic. Executive Yuan. Directorate-General of Budget, Accounting & Statistics. National Income in Taiwan Area, R.O.C **711**
National Income of Iran. (IR ISSN 0572-5941) **875**
National Income of Thailand. (TH) **730**
National Income Statistics of Thailand *see* National Income of Thailand **730**
National Independent Coal Leader. (US ISSN 0192-7329) **3491**
†National Indian Council on Aging. (US) **5243**
National Indian Council on Aging Quarterly *see* Elder Voices **2272**
National Indian Law Library. Catalogue. (US) **2030**
†National Industrial Council of the Printing and Newspaper Industry of South Africa. Monthly Record. (SA) **5243**
National Industrial Research Institute. Report. (KO) **4604, 1831**
National Industrial Transportation League. Notice. (US) **4653**
National Information Center for Children and Youth with Handicaps. News Digest. (US) **2284**
National Information Center for Children and Youth with Handicaps. Transition Summary. (US) **1739, 2775**
National Information Center for Educational Media Index to A V Producers and Distributors *see* N I C E M Index to A V Producers and Distributors **3520**
National Information Center for Educational Media Vocational and Technical Audiovisuals: A Teacher's Sourcebook *see* Vocational and Technical Audiovisuals: A Teacher's Sourcebook **1697**
National Information Center for Educational Media Wellness Media: An Audiovisual Sourcebook *see* Wellness Media: An Audiovisual Sourcebook **3812**
National Information Conference News *see* N I C E News **1398**
National Information Standards Series. (US ISSN 1041-5653) **2775, 4133**
National Information System for Science and Technology Newsletter *see* N I S S A T Newsletter **4325**
National Information System News *see* N A T I S - News **2774**
National Insolvency Review. (CN ISSN 0822-2584) **792, 2657**
National Institute Economic Review. (UK ISSN 0027-9501) **681**
National Institute for Compilation and Translation. Collected Papers on History of China. (CH) **2340, 337**
National Institute for Educational Research. Research Bulletin. (JA ISSN 0085-378X) **1650**
National Institute for Educational Research Occasional Paper *see* N I E R. Occasional Paper **1649**
National Institute for Fusion Science. Research Report. (JA ISSN 0915-6348) **3825**
National Institute for Leprosy Research Annual Report. *see* Kokuritsu Tama Kenkyujo Nenpo **3221**
National Institute for Medical Research. Report. (UK ISSN 0141-2116) **3134**
National Institute for Occupational Diseases. Annual Report *see* National Centre for Occupational Health. Annual Report **3619**

NATIONAL LIBRARY 6473

National Institute for Occupational Safety and Health Technical Information Center Database see N I O S H T I C Database 3619
National Institute for Personnel Research News see N I P R News 4036
National Institute for Public Health Annals see N I P H Annals 3222
†National Institute for the Foodservice Industry. News. (US) 5243
National Institute for Transport and Road Research. Annual Report see South Africa. Division of Roads and Transport Technology. Annual Report 5279
National Institute for Transport and Road Research. Bulletins see South Africa. Division of Roads and Transport Technology. Bulletins 4721
National Institute for Transport and Road Research. P A D Series see South Africa. Division of Roads and Transport Technology. P A D Series 4721
National Institute for Transport and Road Research. Road Statistics see South Africa. Division of Roads and Transport Technology. Transport Statistics 4667
National Institute for Transport and Road Research. Transport Statistics see South Africa. Division of Roads and Transport Technology. Transport Statistics 4667
National Institute for Transport and Road Research. User Manuals for Computer Programs see South Africa. Division of Roads and Transport Technology. User Manuals and Computer Programs 4707
National Institute of Agricultural Botany, Cambridge, England. Annual Report and Accounts. (UK) 185
National Institute of Agricultural Botany, Cambridge, England. Annual Report of the Council and Accounts see National Institute of Agricultural Botany, Cambridge, England. Annual Report and Accounts 185
National Institute of Agricultural Botany, Cambridge, England. Farmers Leaflets. (UK ISSN 0305-1277) 185
National Institute of Agricultural Botany, Cambridge, England. Journal see Plant Varieties and Seeds 189
†National Institute of Agricultural Botany, Cambridge, England. Technical Leaflets. (UK ISSN 0140-4199) 5243
National Institute of Agricultural Botany, Cambridge, England. Vegetable Growers Leaflets. (UK ISSN 0470-1321) 185
†National Institute of Agricultural Sciences, Tokyo. Bulletin. Series H (Farm Management, Land Utilization, Rural Life). (JA ISSN 0077-4863) 5243
National Institute of Agro-Environmental Sciences. Bulletin. see Nogyo Kankyo Gijutsu Kenkyujo Hokoku 110
National Institute of Building Sciences. Annual Report to the President. (US) 626
National Institute of Development Administration Bulletin see N I D A Bulletin 2775
National Institute of Economic and Social Research. Annual Report. (UK ISSN 0077-491X) 4380
National Institute of Economic and Social Research, London. Economic and Social Studies. (UK ISSN 0070-8453) 681, 4380
National Institute of Economic and Social Research, London. Occasional Papers. (UK ISSN 0077-4928) 681
National Institute of Educational Planning and Administration Journal of Educational Planning and Administration see Journal of Educational Planning and Administration 1729

National Institute of Family Planning. Newsletter see Health and Population: Perspectives and Issues 596
National Institute of Health and Family Welfare General Series see N I F P General Series 597
National Institute of Health and Family Welfare Manual Series see N I F P Manual Series 597
National Institute of Health and Family Welfare Monograph Series see N I F P Monograph Series 597
National Institute of Health and Family Welfare Report Series see N I F P Report Series 597
National Institute of Health and Family Welfare Technical Paper Series see N I F P Technical Paper Series 597
National Institute of Health and Family Welfare Technical Reports see N I H F W Technical Reports 4413
National Institute of Health and Nutrition. Annual Report. see Kokuritsu Kenko Eiyo Kenkyujo Hokoku 3608
National Institute of Hygienic Sciences. Bulletin/Eisei Shikenjo Hokoku. (JA ISSN 0077-5002) 4108
National Institute of Hygienic Sciences. Monthly Report/Kokuritsu Eisei Shikenjo Chosa Geppo. (JA) 4108
National Institute of Japanese Literature. Bulletin/Kokubungaku Kenkyu Shiryokan Kiyo. (JA ISSN 0387-3447) 2941
National Institute of Justice. Sponsored Research Programs. (US) 1519
National Institute of Justice - N C J R S Document Retrieval Index (DRI) - Cumulative see N C J R S Document Retrieval Index 1518
National Institute of Mental Health & Neuro Sciences Journal see N I M H A N S Journal 3345
National Institute of Nutrition. Annual Report. (II ISSN 0377-3744) 3609
National Institute of Polar Research. Memoirs. Series A: Aeronomy. (JA ISSN 0386-5517) 3439
National Institute of Polar Research. Memoirs. Series B: Meteorology. (JA ISSN 0386-5525) 3439
National Institute of Polar Research. Memoirs. Series C: Earth Sciences. (JA ISSN 0386-5533) 1547
National Institute of Polar Research. Memoirs. Series D: Oceanography. (JA) 1608
National Institute of Polar Research. Memoirs. Series E: Biology and Medical Science. (JA ISSN 0386-5541) 448, 3134
National Institute of Polar Research. Memoirs. Series F: Logistics. (JA ISSN 0386-555X) 4326
National Institute of Polar Research. Memoirs. Special Issue. (JA ISSN 0386-0744) 1547
National Institute of Polar Research Symposium on Antarctic Geosciences. Proceedings see N I P R Symposium on Antarctic Geosciences. Proceedings 1574
National Institute of Polar Research Symposium on Antarctic Meteorites. Proceedings see N I P R Symposium on Antarctic Meteorites. Proceedings 1574
National Institute of Polar Research Symposium on Polar Biology. Proceedings see N I P R Symposium on Polar Biology. Proceedings 448
National Institute of Polar Research Symposium on Polar Meteorology and Glaciology. Proceedings see N I P R Symposium on Polar Meteorology and Glaciology. Proceedings 1574
National Institute of Polar Research Symposium on Upper Atmosphere Physics. Proceedings see N I P R Symposium on Upper Atmosphere Physics. Proceedings 3825
National Institute of Radiological Sciences. Annual Report. (JA ISSN 0439-5956) 3360

National Institute of Sciences of India. Biographical Memoirs of Fellows see Indian National Science Academy. Biographical Memoirs of Fellows 419
National Institute of Sciences of India. Bulletin see Indian National Science Academy. Bulletin 4314
National Institute of Sciences of India. Yearbook see Indian National Science Academy. Year Book 4314
National Institute of Sericultural and Entomological Science. Bulletin. see Sanshi Konchun Nogyo Gijutsu Kenkyujo Hokoku 537
National Institute of Sericultural and Entomological Science. Miscellaneous Publication. see Sanshi. Konchunogyo Gijutsu Kenkyu Shiryo 537
National Institute of Special Education. Bulletin/Kokuritsu Tokushu Kyoiku Sogo Kenkyujo Kenkyu Kiyo. (JA ISSN 0387-3528) 1739
National Institute of Standards and Technology. Journal of Research. (US ISSN 1044-677X) 3448, 1184, 3048, 3825
National Institute of Standards and Technology Update see N I S T Update 680
National Institute on Alcohol Abuse and Alcoholism - Rutgers University Center of Alcohol Studies Alcoholism Treatment Series see N I A A A - R U C A S Alcoholism Treatment Series 1538
†National Institute Social Services Library. (UK ISSN 0077-4774) 5243
National Institutes of Health Journal of N I H Research see Journal of N I H Research 3117
National Institutes of Health Record see N I H Record 3133
National Instituut voor Kernfysica en Hoge-Energiefysica see N I K H E F. Annual Report 3825
National Insurance Corporation of Tanzania. Annual Report and Accounts. (TZ) 2538
National Insurance Institute, Jerusalem. Annual Survey. (IS) 2547
National Insurance Institute, Jerusalem. Full Actuarial Report. (IS ISSN 0075-1324) 2538
National Insurance Institute, Jerusalem. Statistical Abstracts see National Insurance Institute, Jerusalem. Annual Survey 2547
National Insurance Law Review. (US ISSN 0743-7927) 2657, 2538
National Interest. (US ISSN 0884-9382) 3908, 3966
National Interstate Council of State Boards of Cosmetology. Bulletin. (US) 374
National Intramural Recreational Sports Association. Proceedings. (US) 1712
National Intramural Recreational Sports Association Journal see N I R S A Journal 4480
National Investment & Finance Weekly see N I F Weekly 957
National Investment Bank, Ghana. Annual Report. (GH) 792
National Investment Bank, Ghana. Report of the Directors see National Investment Bank, Ghana. Annual Report 792
National Investor Relations Institute. Annual Report. (US) 958
National Jail and Adult Detention Directory. (US ISSN 0192-8228) 1519
National Jeweler. (US ISSN 0027-9544) 2565
National Jeweler Annual Fashion Guide see National Jeweler's in Style 2565
National Jeweler's in Style. (US) 2565
National Jewish Arts Newsletter. (US) 2015, 337, 3570
National Jewish Monthly see B'nai B'rith International Jewish Monthly 1994
National Jewish News. (US) 2015
National Jewish Post and Opinion. (US ISSN 0888-0379) 2015
National Journal. (US ISSN 0360-4217) 3908

National Junior Horticultural Association. Newsletter. (US ISSN 0077-5088) 2135
▼National Juvenile Detention Directory. (US) 1525
National Juvenile Law Reporter see A B A Juvenile and Child Welfare Law Reporter 1231
National Kidney Foundation. Annual Report. (US ISSN 0077-5096) 3389
National Knife Collector see National Knife Magazine 258
National Knife Magazine. (US) 258
†National Labour Review. (CN ISSN 0835-8087) 5243
National Lampoon. (US ISSN 0027-9587) 2875
National Language Research Institute. Annual Report/Kokuritsu Kokugo Kenkyujo Nenpo. (JA) 2830
National Law Journal. (US ISSN 0162-7325) 2657
†National Law Journal Index. (US) 5243
National Lawyers Guild. Guild Notes. (US ISSN 0148-0588) 2657
National Lawyers Guild Practitioner. (US ISSN 0730-532X) 2657
National Lawyers Guild Referral Directory. (US) 2657
National Leader. (AT) 3908
National League for Nursing. Associate Degree Education for Nursing see Associate Degree Education for Nursing 3276
National League for Nursing Nursing Data Review see N L N Nursing Data Review 3282
National League of Cities. National Municipal Policy see National Municipal Policy 4092
National League of Families of American Prisoners and Missing in Action in Southeast Asia Newsletter. (US) 4414
National Legal Aid and Defender Association Cornerstone see N L A D A Cornerstone 2656
National Legal Aid and Defender Association Directory see Directory of Legal Aid and Defender Offices in the United States and Territories 2619
National Legal Bibliography see Catalog of Current Law Titles 2792
National Legal Bibliography. Part 2. Government Documents from Official and Commercial Sources see Lawyers Monthly Catalog. Government Documents from Official and Commercial Sources 2699
National Librarian. (US ISSN 0191-359X) 2775
National Library and Documentation Service. Annual Report. (RH) 2775
National Library for the Handicapped Child. Newsletter. (UK ISSN 0952-9705) 1739, 4414
National Library News/Bibliotheque Nationale. Nouvelles. (CN ISSN 0027-9633) 2775
National Library of Australia. Annual Report. (AT ISSN 0313-1971) 2775
National Library of Australia. Annual Report of the Council see National Library of Australia. Annual Report 2775
▼National Library of Australia News. (AT ISSN 1035-753X) 2775
National Library of Canada. Annual Report. (CN ISSN 0078-7000) 2775
National Library of Medicine. Audiovisuals Catalog. (US ISSN 0149-9939) 3134
National Library of Medicine. Current Bibliographies in Medicine. (US) 3178
National Library of Medicine. Current Catalog. (US ISSN 0027-9641) 3178
†National Library of Medicine. Current Catalog Proofsheets. (US ISSN 0025-7346) 5243
National Library of Medicine. Literature Search Series see National Library of Medicine. Current Bibliographies in Medicine 3178

6474 NATIONAL LIBRARY

National Library of Medicine. Programs and Services. (US ISSN 0093-0393) **2775**
National Library of Medicine News. (US ISSN 0027-965X) **2775**, **3134**
National Library of Scotland News. (UK ISSN 0950-7086) **2775**
National Library of Wales Journal. *see* Cylchgrawn Llyfrgell Genedlaethol Cymru **2754**
National Library Year-Book. *see* Rocznik Biblioteki Narodowej **2782**
National Licensed Beverage Association News *see* N L B A News **5242**
†National Lifeliner. (CN) **5243**
National Limousine Exchange. (US) **4698**, **1048**
National Liquor News. (AT ISSN 0816-0430) **1507**, **384**
National Liquor Stores Association. News and Views. (US) **384**, **1048**
National List of Advertisers. (CN ISSN 0077-5177) **1147**, **35**
National List of Historic Theatre Buildings. (US) **303**, **4635**
National Locksmith. (US) **1527**
National Loss Prevention. (CN) **1527**, **642**
National Lubricating Grease Institute Spokesman *see* N L G I Spokesman **3692**
National Mall Monitor *see* Monitor (Stamford) **4152**
National Maple Syrup Digest *see* Maple Syrup Digest **2076**
National Marina Survey. (AT ISSN 1030-2425) **4527**
National Marine Bankers Association. Summary Annual Report. (US) **792**, **4527**
National Marine Business Journal. (US) **4527**, **681**
National Marine Manufacturers Association Certification Handbook *see* N M M A Certification Handbook **4526**
National Marine Representatives Association Newsletter *see* N M R A Newsletter **838**
National Marines Fishery Service Fisheries Market News Report *see* N M F S Fisheries Market News Report **2051**
National Maritime Board. (Great Britain) Year Book. (UK ISSN 0077-5185) **4734**
†National Maritime Museum. Occasional Lectures Series. (UK ISSN 0141-1268) **5243**
National Maritime S A R Review *see* On Scene **4735**
National Mass Retailing Institute Compensation in Mass Retailing, Salaries and Incentives *see* N M R I Compensation in Mass Retailing, Salaries and Incentives **989**
National Masters News. (US ISSN 0744-2416) **4551**
National Medical and Dental Association. Bulletin. (US ISSN 0027-9676) **3134**, **3238**
National Medical Association. Journal. (US ISSN 0027-9684) **3134**
National Medical Fellowships Newsletter.(US) **3134**
National Medical Journal of India. (II ISSN 0970-258X) **3134**
National Membership Directory. (US) **1059**, **1147**
National Message. (AT) **3909**
National Message *see* Wake-up! (Ayrshire) **4209**
National Messenger *see* Upper Case **2544**
National Metallurgical Laboratory Technical Journal *see* N M L Technical Journal **3416**
National Migraine Foundation Newsletter *see* National Headache Foundation Newsletter **3346**
National Mirror. (ZA) **1340**
National Missing Persons Report. (US ISSN 1041-3022) **1519**
National Model Railroad Association. Bulletin. (US ISSN 0027-9722) **2440**, **4712**
National Monitor of Education. (US) **1756**

National Mortgage News. (US ISSN 1050-3331) **792**
National Motor Museum Pictorial Guide.(UK) **4698**
National Motorist. (US ISSN 0279-3083) **4779**, **4698**
National Municipal Policy. (US) **4092**
National Museum, Bloemfontein. Annual Report. (SA) **3530**
National Museum, Bloemfontein. Memoirs/Nasionale Museum, Bloemfontein. Memoirs. (SA ISSN 0374-9665) **589**, **4326**
National Museum, Bloemfontein. Research/Nasionale Museum, Bloemfontein. Navorsinge. (SA ISSN 0067-9208) **4326**
National Museum in Cracow. Catalogues of the Collections. *see* Muzeum Narodowe w Krakowie. Katalogi Zbiorow **3530**
National Museum Journal of Arts. *see* Misul Charyo **336**
National Museum of Man. Mercury Series. Archaeological Survey of Canada. Papers/Musee National de l'Homme. Collection Mercure. Commission Archaeologique du Canada. Dossiers. (CN ISSN 0317-2244) **279**
National Museum of Man. Mercury Series. Canadian Centre for Folk Culture Studies. Papers/Musee National de l'Homme. Collection Mercure. Centre Canadien d'Etudes sur la Culture Traditionnelle. Dossiers. (CN ISSN 0316-1897) **245**
National Museum of Man. Mercury Series. Canadian Ethnology Service. Papers/Musee National de l'Homme. Collection Mercure. Service Canadien d'Ethnologie. Dossiers. (CN ISSN 0316-1862) **246**
National Museum of Man. Mercury Series. Canadian War Museum. Papers/Musee National de l'Homme. Collection Mercure. Musee Canadien de la Guerre. Dossiers. (CN ISSN 0316-1919) **3466**
National Museum of Man. Mercury Series. History Division. Papers/Musee National de l'Homme. Collection Mercure. Division de l'Histoire. Dossiers. (CN ISSN 0316-1900) **2318**
National Museum of Modern Art. Annual Report. (JA) **3530**
National Museum of Natural Sciences. Syllogeus *see* Canadian Museum of Nature. Syllogeus **4303**
National Museum of New Zealand. Bulletin. (NZ ISSN 0110-9464) **3530**
National Museum of New Zealand. Miscellaneous Series. (NZ ISSN 0110-1447) **3530**
National Museum of New Zealand Records. (NZ ISSN 0110-943X) **3530**
National Museum of Tanzania. Annual Report. (TZ ISSN 0082-1675) **3530**
National Museum of the Philippines. Annual Report. (PH ISSN 0076-3756) **3530**
†National Museum of the Philippines. Monograph Series. (PH ISSN 0076-3772) **5243**
National Museum of Victoria. Memoirs *see* Museum of Victoria. Memoirs **588**
National Museum of Women in the Arts News *see* Women in the Arts **350**
National Museums, Ottawa: Publications in Natural Science. (CN ISSN 0714-0983) **589**, **510**, **565**
National Music Publishers' Association. Bulletin *see* National Music Publishers' Association. News & Views **3570**
National Music Publishers' Association. News & Views. (US) **3570**
National N O W Times. (US ISSN 0149-4740) **4849**
National Natural Science Foundation of China. Bulletin. *see* Zhongguo Kexue Jijin **4354**
National News. (US) **1377**, **35**

National News Bureau. (US) **2229**
National Newspaper Association National Directory of Weekly Newspapers *see* N N A National Directory of Weekly Newspapers **2573**
National Newspaper Index. (US) **730**, **420**, **4580**
National Notary. (US) **2657**
National Notary Yearbook. (US ISSN 0894-7872) **2657**
National Nutritional Foods Association Monitor *see* N N F A Monitor **3609**
▼National Oceanic and Atmospheric Administration. National Geophysical Data Center. Paleoclimate Publications Series. (US) **3658**, **3439**
National Office Machine Dealers Association Spokesman *see* N O M D A Spokesman **1059**
National Office Products Association Membership Directory and Buyer's Guide (Year) *see* N O P A Membership Directory and Buyer's Guide (Year) **1059**
National Office Products Association Office Market Update *see* N O P A Office Market Update **1059**
National Office Products Association Special Report *see* N O P A Special Report **5242**
National Office Systems Association Update *see* N O S A Update **753**
National Oilseed Processors Association. Yearbook *see* National Oilseed Processors Association. Yearbook and Trading Rules **207**
National Oilseed Processors Association. Yearbook and Trading Rules. (US) **207**
National On-Campus Report. (US ISSN 0300-6646) **1318**, **1712**
National One-Write Systems Association Newsletter *see* N O S A Update **753**
National Online Meeting. Proceedings. (US) **3393**, **2775**
National Opera Association Newsletter *see* N O A Newsletter **3569**
National Opinion Research Center Report *see* N O R C Report **4380**
National Opinion Research Center Reporter *see* N O R C Reporter **4443**
National Order of Women Legislators News & Views. (US) **4849**, **4068**
National Organization for Raw Materials Newsletter *see* N O R M Newsletter **918**
National Organization for River Sports. Currents. (US) **4527**
National Organization for Women Equality N O W! *see* Equality N O W **4841**
National Organization for Women News (Boston) *see* N O W News (Boston) **4849**
National Organization for Women San Diego News *see* N O W San Diego News **4849**
National Organization for Women Times *see* S F N O W Times **4852**
National Organization of Mothers of Twins Clubs, Inc. Notebook *see* M O T C's Notebook **4847**
National Organization on Legal Problems of Education Notes *see* N O L P E Notes **1729**
National Outerwear and Sportswear Association Fashion Bulletin *see* N O S A. Fashion Bulletin **1286**
National Outerwear and Sportswear Association News *see* N O S A News **1286**
National Outerwear and Sportswear Association Production Bulletin *see* N O S A. Production Bulletin **1286**
National Outlook. (AT) **4191**
National P A L Update. (National Police Athletic League) (US) **1261**, **1519**, **4481**
National Packing News. (US) **3650**, **2078**
National Palace Museum. Monthly of Chinese Art. (CH ISSN 1011-9078) **3530**, **337**

National Palace Museum. Newsletter. (CH ISSN 1011-9086) **3530**, **3642**
National Palace Museum Bulletin. (CH ISSN 1011-906X) **3530**
National Palace Museum Quarterly *see* National Palace Museum Research Quarterly **3530**
National Palace Museum Research Quarterly. (CH ISSN 1011-9094) **3530**
National Paper Trade Association, Inc. Management News *see* N P T A Management News **3663**
National Paralegal Employment & Salary Survey. (US) **2657**, **3629**
National Paralegal Reporter. (US) **4849**, **2657**
National Parent - Teacher Association Focus *see* P T A in Focus **5255**
National Parents' Resource Institute for Drug Education, Inc. Quarterly Newsletter *see* P R I D E Quarterly Newsletter **1538**
National Park Guide. (US) **4551**
National Parkinson Foundation. Newsletter *see* Parkinson Report **3349**
National Parks. (US ISSN 0276-8186) **1492**
National Parks Journal. (AT ISSN 0047-9012) **1492**
National Party Platforms. Supplement. (US ISSN 0077-5282) **3909**
National Passive Solar Conference. Proceedings. *see* American Solar Energy Society. Passive Conference. Annual Meeting **1810**
National Pastime. (US ISSN 0734-6905) **4508**
National Patterns of R & D Resources. (US) **4326**
National Patterns of Science and Technology *see* National Patterns of R & D Resources **4326**
National Pawnbrokers Association (Inc.) Journal *see* N.P.A. Journal **2565**
National Peach Council. Proceedings. (US ISSN 0092-2633) **185**
National Perinatal Association. Bulletin. (US) **3134**
National Petroleum News. (US ISSN 0149-5267) **3693**
National Petroleum News Bulletin *see* N P N Bulletin **5242**
National Petroleum News Factbook *see* N P N Factbook **3692**
National Pharmaceutical Association. Journal. (US ISSN 0027-9897) **3735**
National Pharmaceutical Association Supplement *see* N P A Supplement **3735**
National Photographer *see* Professional Photographer **3796**
National Physical Laboratory News *see* N P L News **3825**
National Physical Laboratory Technical Bulletin *see* N P L Technical Bulletin **3825**
National Physical Research Institute Newsletter *see* N P R L Newsletter **5242**
National Piano Manufacturers Association of America. Newsletter. (US) **3570**
National Pig Breeders' Association Herd Book *see* British Pig Association Herd Book **213**
National Pig News. (UK) **108**
National Planning Association Reports. (US) **999**
National Poetry Magazine of the Lower East Side. (US) **2941**
National Police Athletic League National P A L Update *see* National P A L Update **1261**
National Police Review. (US) **1519**
National Political Review *see* Cook Political Report **3882**
National Political Science Review. (US ISSN 0896-629X) **3909**
National Potato Council. Yearbook. (US) **185**
National Poultry News. (US) **221**
National Preservation Office Seminar Papers. (UK) **1492**, **2775**
National Press Club Record. (US ISSN 0027-9927) **2573**, **1300**

National Press Council of the Republic of China Press Council of the Republic of China see Press Council of the Republic of China **2574**
National Prime Users Group, Inc. News see N P U G News **1471**
National Prison Project Journal. (US ISSN 0748-2655) **1519, 3945**
National Prison Project Status Report. (US) **1519, 3945**
National Pro-Life Journal. (US) **4414**
National Productivity Centre, Malaysia. Annual Report see National Productivity Corporation, Malaysia. Annual Report **1022**
National Productivity Corporation, Malaysia. Annual Report/Perbadanan Produktiviti Negara. Laporan Tahunan. (MY) **1022**
National Productivity Review. (US ISSN 0277-8556) **1022**
National Professional Educator Newsletter. (US) **1650**
National Program Letter. (US ISSN 0027-9943) **3909**
National Property Law Digests. (US ISSN 0363-8340) **2657**
National Property Review see National Real Property Review **4153**
National Provincial Bank Review see National Westminster Bank Quarterly Review **792**
National Provisioner. (US ISSN 0027-996X) **2078**
National Psoriasis Foundation. Annual Report. (US ISSN 8756-2243) **3249**
National Psoriasis Foundation. Bulletin. (US ISSN 1040-0060) **3249**
National Psychological Association for Psychoanalysis. Bulletin. (US ISSN 0077-5339) **4036**
National Psychological Association for Psychoanalysis. News and Reviews. (US) **4036**
National Public Accountant. (US ISSN 0027-9978) **754**
National Public Employment Reporter. (US) **989, 1068, 2657**
National Quarterly Summary. (AT) **792, 875**
National Radio Guide. (CN) **1357, 3570**
National Radio Publicity Directory see National Radio Publicity Outlets **1357**
National Radio Publicity Outlets. (US) **1357, 35**
National Railway Bulletin. (US) **4712, 2415**
National Reading Conference, Inc. Yearbook see N R C Yearbook **1739**
National Ready Mixed Concrete Association Publication see N R M C A Publication **625**
National Real Estate Investor. (US ISSN 0027-9994) **4153**
National Real Estate Investor Directory. (US ISSN 0027-9994) **4153**
National Real Property Review. (CN) **4153, 2715**
National Recreation and Park Association Washington Action Report see N R P A Washington Action Report **5242**
National Register of Historic Places in Wisconsin. Newsletter see Wisconsin Preservation: National Register of Historic Places. Newsletter **2427**
National Register of Prominent Americans and International Notables. (US ISSN 0077-5371) **420**
National Rehabilitation Center for the Disabled. Research Bulletin. (JA ISSN 0285-1350) **2284, 1739**
National Rehabilitation Digest see Australian Rehabilitation Digest **3080**
National Relay Conference. Proceedings. (US ISSN 0077-5401) **1904**
National Relocation and Real Estate Directory. (US ISSN 1056-9723) **4153**
National Report for Training and Development. (US) **1022**

National Report on Computers and Health. (US ISSN 0273-4974) **3226**
National Report on Substance Abuse. (US ISSN 0891-5709) **1538**
National Report on Work & Family. (US ISSN 0896-3002) **3629**
National Reporter. (AT) **918**
National Reporter. (CN) **2657**
National Reporter on Legal Ethics and Professional Responsibility. (US) **2657**
National Research Center for Disaster Prevention. Seismological Bulletin. (JA) **1592**
National Research Council. Newsreport. (US) **4326, 1831**
National Research Council. Transportation Research Board. Bibliography. (US ISSN 0148-849X) **4654**
National Research Council, Canada. Associate Committee on Geotechnical Research. Technical Memorandum. (CN ISSN 0077-5428) **1831, 1547**
National Research Council, Canada. Division of Building Research. Bibliography see National Research Council, Canada. Institute for Research in Construction. Bibliography **5243**
National Research Council, Canada. Division of Building Research. Building Practice Note see National Research Council, Canada. Institute for Research in Construction. Building Practice Note **5243**
National Research Council, Canada. Division of Building Research. D B R Paper see National Research Council, Canada. Institute for Research in Construction. Paper **5243**
National Research Council, Canada. Division of Building Research. Proceedings see National Research Council, Canada. Institute for Research in Construction. Proceedings **626**
National Research Council, Canada. Division of Building Research. Research Program see National Research Council, Canada. Institute for Research in Construction. Research Program **626**
National Research Council, Canada. Division of Building Research. Special Technical Publication see National Research Council, Canada. Institute for Research in Construction. Special Technical Publication **5243**
†National Research Council, Canada. Division of Electrical Engineering. Bulletin/Conseil National de Recherches du Canada. Division de Genie Electrique. Bulletin. (CN ISSN 0706-568X) **5243**
National Research Council, Canada. Institute for Aerospace Research. Aeronautical Report (A N Series). (CN) **59**
National Research Council, Canada. Institute for Aerospace Research. Publications List and Supplements. (CN) **66**
National Research Council, Canada. Institute for Mechanical Engineering. Mechanical Engineering Reports. (CN) **1936, 59**
†National Research Council, Canada. Institute for Research in Construction. Bibliography. (CN) **5243**
†National Research Council, Canada. Institute for Research in Construction. Building Practice Note. (CN) **5243**
National Research Council, Canada. Institute for Research in Construction. Proceedings. (CN) **626**
†National Research Council, Canada. Institute for Research in Construction. Paper. (CN) **5243**
National Research Council, Canada. Institute for Research in Construction. Research Program. (CN) **626**

†National Research Council, Canada. Institute for Research in Construction. Special Technical Publication. (CN) **5243**
National Research Council, Canada. National Aeronautical Establishment. Aeronautical Report (L R Series) see National Research Council, Canada. Institute for Aerospace Research. Aeronautical Report (A N Series) **59**
National Research Council, Canada. National Aeronautical Establishment. Mechanical Engineering Reports see National Research Council, Canada. Institute for Mechanical Engineering. Mechanical Engineering Reports **1936**
National Research Council, Canada. National Aeronautical Establishment. Publications List and Supplements see National Research Council, Canada. Institute for Aerospace Research. Publications List and Supplements **66**
▼National Research Council of Canada. Institute for Information Technology. Annual Report. (CN ISSN 1183-9082) **4604**
National Research Council of Canada. N R C Annual Report - Rapport Annuel du C N R C. (CN) **4326**
National Research Council of Canada. Report of the President - Rapport du President see National Research Council of Canada. N R C Annual Report - Rapport Annuel du C N R C **4326**
National Research Council of Philippines Research Bulletin see N R C P Research Bulletin **4325**
National Research Council of Thailand. Journal. (TH ISSN 0028-0011) **4326, 4380**
National Research Insititute of Police Science. Report. Research on Prevention of Crime and Delinquency. see Kagaku Keisatsu Kenkyujo Hokoku Bohan Shonen Hen **1517**
National Research Institute. Division of Educational Research. Occasional Papers. (PP) **1650**
National Research Institute. Division of Educational Research. Research Papers. (PP) **1650**
National Research Institute. Division of Educational Research. Special Report. (PP) **1650**
National Research Institute. Division of Educational Research. Working Papers. (PP) **1650**
National Research Institute Bibliographies see N R I Bibliographies **406**
National Research Institute Discussion Papers see N R I Discussion Papers **4380**
National Research Institute for Mathematical Sciences Current Activities see N R I M S Current Activities **5242**
National Research Institute for Metals. Transactions/Kinzoku Zairyo Gijutsu Kenkyujo Obun Kenkyu Hokoku. (JA ISSN 0453-9222) **3416**
National Research Institute Monographs see N R I Monographs **4380**
National Research Institute of Agricultural Economics. Annual Report. see Nogyo Sogo Kenkyujo Nenpo **110**
National Research Institute of Agriculture. Annual Report see Nogyo Sogo Kenkyujo Nenpo **110**
National Research Institute of Aquaculture. Bulletin/Tansui-ku Suisan Kenkyujo Kenkyu Hokoku. (JA ISSN 0389-5858) **2046**
National Research Institute of Far Seas Fisheries. Bulletin. (JA) **2046, 589, 1492**
National Research Institute of Far Seas Fisheries. S Series. (JA) **2046, 589, 1492**
National Research Institute of Fisheries Science. Report. see Chuo Suisan Kenkyujo Kenkyu Hokoku **2038**
National Research Institute of Police Science. Annual Report. see Kagaku Keisatsu Kenkyujo Nenpo **1517**

NATIONAL SAFE   6475

National Research Institute of Police Science. Data. see Kagaku Keisatsu Kenkyujo Shiryo **5222**
National Research Institute of Police Science. Report see Kagaku Keisatsu Kenkyujo Hokoku Hokagaku Hen **3265**
National Research Institute of Police Science. Report. Research of Forensic Science. see Kagaku Keisatsu Kenkyujo Hokoku Hokagaku Hen **3265**
National Research Institute of Police Science. Report. Research on Traffic Safety and Regulation. see Kagaku Keisatsu Kenkyujo Hokoku Kotsu Ken **4694**
National Research Institute of Tea. Bulletin see National Research Institute of Vegetables, Ornamental Plants and Tea. Bulletin. Series B **108**
National Research Institute of Vegetables, Ornamental Plants and Tea. Bulletin. Series B. (JA) **108, 2078**
National Research Institute Special Publications see N R I Special Publications **4380**
National Research Laboratory of Metrology. Bulletin. (JA ISSN 0451-6109) **3448**
National Retired Teachers Association Bulletin see N R T A Bulletin **1649**
National Review. (US ISSN 0028-0038) **3909**
National Review of Criminal Sciences. (UA ISSN 0028-0054) **1519, 4443**
National Review of Social Sciences. (UA ISSN 0028-0062) **4380, 1519**
†National Reye's Syndrome Foundation.(US ISSN 0276-2293) **5243**
National Rifle Association Journal see N R A Journal **4551**
National Rifle Association of America Action see N R A Action **2656**
National Right to Life News. (US ISSN 0164-7415) **4414**
National Right to Work Newsletter. (US ISSN 0197-7032) **989**
National Risk Retention Association News see N R R A News **2538**
National Rivers Hall of Fame Newsletter. (US) **1492**
National Roofing Contractors Association Membership Directory see N R C A Membership Directory **625**
National Roster of Black Elected Officials see Black Elected Officials **4054**
National Roster of Realtors. (US ISSN 0090-1741) **4153**
National Rugby Post. (CN) **4508**
National Rural Education News. (US ISSN 0036-0023) **1650**
National Rural Electric Cooperative Association. Government Relations Department. Research Division. Research Papers and Circulars. (US ISSN 0077-5657) **1904**
National Rural Electric Cooperative Association. Legislative Research Staff. Research Paper see National Rural Electric Cooperative Association. Government Relations Department. Research Division. Research Papers and Circulars **1904**
National Rural Electric Cooperative Association Legal Reporting Service see N R E C A - A P P A Legal Reporting Service **2656**
National Rural Letter Carrier. (US ISSN 0028-0089) **1353**
National S A M P E Technical Conference Series. N S T C Preprint Series see International S A M P E Technical Conference Series. I S T C Preprint Series **1918**
National Sacred Harp Newsletter. (US) **3570**
National Safe Transit Association Annual Safe Transit Conference. Proceedings see N S T A Annual Safe Transit Conference. Proceedings **3649**

6476 NATIONAL SAFETY

National Safety/Nasionale Veiligheid. (SA ISSN 0028-0097) **4108**
National Sand and Gravel Association Circular see N S G A Circular **1574**
National Sash and Door Jobbers Association. Bulletin. (US) **626**
National Sash and Door Jobbers Association. Newsletter. (US) **626**
▼National Scanning Report. (US) **1357**
National Scholarship Trust Fund Report see N S T F Report **5242**
National School Bus Report. (US ISSN 0889-0749) **4654**
National School Orchestra Association Bulletin see N S O A Bulletin **3569**
National Science Council (Ireland). Progress Report. (IE) **4326**
National Science Council (Ireland). Register of Scientific Research Personnel. (IE ISSN 0085-3836) **4326**
National Science Council of Sri Lanka. Journal. (CE ISSN 0300-9254) **4326**
National Science Council of the Republic of China Review see N S C Review **4325**
National Science Council of the Republic of China Special Publication see N S C Special Publication **4325**
National Science Council of the Republic of China Symposium Series see N S C Symposium Series **4325**
National Science Museum. Bulletin. Series A: Zoology/Kokuritsu Kagaku Hakubutsukan Kenkyu Hokoku. A Rui: Dobutsugaku. (JA ISSN 0385-2423) **589**
National Science Museum. Bulletin. Series B: Botany/Kokuritsu Kagaku Hakubutsukan Kenkyu Hokoku. B Rui: Shokubutsugaku. (JA ISSN 0385-2431) **511**
National Science Museum. Bulletin. Series C: Geology see National Science Museum. Bulletin. Series C: Geology & Paleontology **1574**
National Science Museum. Bulletin. Series C: Geology & Paleontology. (JA ISSN 0385-244X) **1574**
National Science Museum. Bulletin. Series D: Anthropology/Kokuritsu Kagaku Hakubutsukann Kenkyu Hoku. D Rui: Jinruigaku. (JA ISSN 0385-3039) **246**
National Science Museum. Bulletin. Series E: Physical Sciences and Engineering/Kokuritsu Kagaku Hakubutsukan Kenkyu Hokoku. E Rui, Rikogaku. (JA ISSN 0387-8511) **1831**, **3530**
National Science Museum. Memoirs. see Kokuritsu Kagaku Hakubutsukan Senpo **4321**
National Science Supervisors Association Newsletter see N S S A Newsletter **4325**
National Science Teachers Association Reports see N S T A Reports **1649**
National Secular Society. Annual Report.(UK) **3773**
†National Securities and Research Corporation. Annual Forecast. (US ISSN 0077-5703) **5243**
National Security Institute Advisory see N S I Advisory **3466**
National Security Law Report. (US) **2657**
†National Security Record. (US ISSN 0162-3206) **5243**
National Security Review. (PH) **3909**, **1527**, **3466**
National Security Traders Association. Traders' Annual. (US ISSN 0092-4679) **958**
National Senior Citizens Law Center Weekly. (US ISSN 0277-7460) **2657**, **2277**
National Service Newsletter. (US) **4414**, **1241**
National Shellfisheries Association. Proceedings see Journal of Shellfish Research **586**
National Sheriff see Sheriff **1522**
National Shipping Corporation. Report and Accounts. (PK) **4734**
National Shorthand Reporter see Journal of Court Reporting **2638**

National Shorthand Reporters Association. Proceedings of the Annual Convention see National Court Reporters Association. Proceedings of the Annual Convention **2657**
National Singles Directory. (US) **4362**
National Singles Register. (US) **4363**
National Skeet Shooting Association. Records Annual. (US ISSN 0077-5738) **4551**
National Ski Areas Association News see N S A A News **4480**
National Snow and Ice Data Center New Accessions List see World Data Center A for Glaciology (Snow and Ice). New Accessions List **1552**
National Soccer Hall of Fame Newsletter. (US) **4508**
National Social Science Documentation Centre Research Information Series. Social Science News see N A S S D O C Research Information Series. Social Science News **5241**
National Society for Clean Air and Environmental Protection Members Handbook see N.S.C.A. Members Handbook **1963**
National Society for Clean Air and Environmental Protection Pollution Handbook see N.S.C.A. Pollution Handbook **1978**
National Society for Graphology Newsletter. (US) **4036**
National Society for Prevention of Cruelty to Children. Annual Report. (UK ISSN 0077-5754) **4414**
National Society for the Preservation of Covered Bridges Newsletter. (US) **2415**, **1492**
National Society for the Prevention of Blindness. Report see National Society to Prevent Blindness. Report **2295**
National Society for the Study of Education. Yearbook. (US ISSN 0077-5762) **1650**
National Society of Black Engineers Bridge see N S B E Bridge **1831**
National Society of Black Engineers Magazine see N S B E Magazine **1831**
National Society of College Teachers of Education. Occasional Papers see Society of Professors of Education. Occasional Papers **1664**
National Society of College Teachers of Education Monographs see N S C T E Monographs **1649**
National Society of Fund Raising Executives Journal see N S F R E Journal **4413**
National Society of Fund Raising Executives News see N S F R E News **4413**
†National Society of Public Accountants. Annual Report. (US) **5243**
National Society of Public Accountants Washington Reporter see N S P A Washington Reporter **753**
National Society of United States Daughters of 1812. Newsletter. (US) **2415**
National Society to Prevent Blindness. Member News. (US) **2295**, **3302**
National Society to Prevent Blindness. Report. (US ISSN 0270-4234) **2295**
National Soybean Processors Association. Yearbook see National Oilseed Processors Association. Yearbook and Trading Rules **207**
National Spasmodic Torticollis Association Newsletter see N S T A Newsletter **3345**
National Speed Sport News. (US ISSN 0028-0208) **4481**
National Speedway Directory. (US) **4481**
National Speleological Society, Inc. Bulletin see N S S Bulletin **1574**
National Speleological Society, Inc. News see N S S News **1574**
National Spiritualist. (US) **4286**
National Spokesman. (US ISSN 0091-2387) **3346**

National Sporting Goods Association Buying Guide. (US) **4481**, **1048**
National Sporting Goods Association Retail Focus see N S G A Retail Focus **1048**
National Sporting Goods Association Sports Apparel Diary see N S G A Sports Apparel Diary **4498**
†National Sports Daily. (US ISSN 1052-1232) **5243**
National Sports Journal see Sports Journal **4492**
The National Sports Review. (US ISSN 1054-2205) **4481**
National Squares. (US ISSN 0746-3685) **1531**
National Stampagraphic. (US ISSN 0747-5527) **2440**
National Star see Star (Lantana) **2235**
National Statistics Office Monthly Bulletin of Statistics see N S O Monthly Bulletin of Statistics **4580**
National Stock Dog. (US ISSN 0028-0267) **3712**
▼National Stone Association. Buyer's Guide. (US) **3491**
National Storytelling Journal see Storytelling Magazine **2964**
†National Strategy Information Center. Agenda Papers. (US) **5243**
National Strength & Conditioning Association Bulletin. (US) **3806**
National Strength & Conditioning Association Journal. (US ISSN 0744-0049) **3806**
National Stripper Well Survey. (US ISSN 0470-3219) **3693**, **1793**
National Student see N S M **1649**
National Student Medical Association. Journal. (US) **3134**
National Student Speech Language Hearing Association Journal see N S S L H A Journal **3315**
National Supply Distributors Association Bulletin see In Step with N S D A **620**
National Sweet Pea Society. Annual. (UK) **2135**
National Sweet Pea Society. Bulletin. (UK) **2135**
National Symposia on Cryogenics. Proceedings see Indian Journal of Cryogenics **3841**
National Symposium on Mining. Proceedings. (US) **3491**, **1599**
National Symposium on Mining, Hydrology, Sedimentology and Reclamation. Proceedings see National Symposium on Mining. Proceedings **3491**
National Systems Programmers Associations News see N A S P A News **1431**
National Taiwan Normal University. Graduate Institute of Education. Bulletin. (CH) **1650**
National Taiwan University. College of Agriculture. Memoirs. (CH ISSN 0077-5819) **109**
National Taiwan University. College of Law. Journal of Social Science. (CH ISSN 0077-5835) **4380**
National Taiwan University. College of Medicine. Memoirs. (CH ISSN 0028-0275) **3134**
National Taiwan University. Department of Anthropology. Bulletin. (CH) **246**, **279**
National Taiwan University. Department of Archaeology and Anthropology. Bulletin see National Taiwan University. Department of Anthropology. Bulletin **246**
National Taiwan University. Department of Geography. Science Reports. (CH) **2257**
National Taiwan University. Institute of Fishery Biology. Report. (CH) **2046**
National Taiwan University Journal of Sociology. (CH ISSN 0077-5851) **4443**
National Tank Truck Carrier Directory. (US ISSN 0077-586X) **4746**
National Tax Association - Tax Institute of America. Proceedings of the Annual Conference. (US ISSN 0069-8687) **1101**
National Tax Journal. (US ISSN 0028-0283) **1101**

National Teaching and Learning Forum. (US ISSN 1057-2880) **1712**, **1756**
National Technical Association. Journal. (US) **2015**, **4326**
National Technical Report. (JA ISSN 0028-0291) **1904**, **1184**, **3825**
National Telecommunications Conference. Record see Globecom. I E E E Global Telecommunications Conference. Conference Record **1336**
National Telephone Cooperative Association Exchange see N T C A Exchange **1364**
National Telephone Cooperative Association Video Magazine see N T C A Video Magazine **1364**
National Terrazzo and Mosaic Association. Directory. (US) **626**
National Textile Corporation. Annual Report and Accounts. (TZ) **4622**
National Theatre of Japan. (JA ISSN 0388-0648) **4635**
National Thomson's Liquor Guide see National Liquor News **1507**
National Thrift News see National Mortgage News **792**
†National Times. (AT ISSN 0047-911X) **5244**
National Tire Dealers and Retreaders Association, Inc. Dealer News see N T D R A Dealer News **4292**
National Tombstone Epitaph. (US ISSN 0890-068X) **2415**
National Tool, Die and Precision Machining Association. Buyers Guide. see National Tooling and Machining Association. Buyers Guide **3021**
National Tooling and Machining Association. Buyers Guide. (US) **3021**
National Tort Reform see Mealey's Litigation Report: Punitive Damages and Tort Reform **2703**
National Tourist Guide of Nigeria see Nigeria Tourist Guide **4780**
National Towing News see Towing News **1838**
National Trade and Professional Associations of the United States and Labor Unions. (US) **1147**, **2592**
National Trade and Tariff Service. (CN) **1101**, **2657**
National Trade-Index of Southern Africa.(SA ISSN 0077-5894) **838**
National Traffic Law News. (US ISSN 0094-1875) **2657**
National Trails Council. Newsletter. (US) **4551**
National Transportation Safety Board Digest Service. (US) **4676**
National Transportation Safety Board Reporter see N T S B Reporter **4676**
National Travel Survey. (US ISSN 0737-2620) **4779**
National Treasury Employees Union Bulletin see N T E U Bulletin **2587**
National Treatment Resource Issue. (US) **1538**
†National Trend of Business in the Lodging Industry. (US) **5244**
National Trial and Deposition Directory. (US) **2657**
National Trial Lawyer. (US ISSN 1049-684X) **2657**
National Trophy Industry Directory of Manufacturers and Suppliers see Recognition and Identification Blue Book **1151**
National Tropical Botanical Garden. Bulletin. (US) **511**, **2135**
National Trotting Weekly. (AT) **4536**
National Truck Equipment Association. Legislative Report. (US) **4746**, **2657**
National Truck Equipment Association. Regulations Report. (US) **4746**, **2657**
National Trust. (UK ISSN 0266-8068) **1492**
National Trust for Historic Preservation. Information. (US) **303**
National Trust for Scotland Yearbook see Guide to Over 100 Properties **1488**

National Trust of Australia (New South Wales) National Trust Bulletin see National Trust of Australia (New South Wales) National Trust Quarterly **1492**
National Trust of Australia (New South Wales) National Trust Magazine see National Trust of Australia (New South Wales) National Trust Quarterly **1492**
National Trust of Australia (New South Wales) National Trust Quarterly. (AT ISSN 1036-9880) **1492**, 2345
National Trust of Australia (W.A.) Annual Report. (AT) **2345**
National Tuberculosis Institute Newsletter see N T I Newsletter **3366**
National Tuberous Sclerosis Association Newsletter see N T S A Newsletter **3133**
National Turfgrass Council Workshop Report Series see N T C Workshop Report Series **510**
National U F O Investigation Society News see N U F O I S News **59**
National Underwriter. Life & Health Insurance Edition. (US ISSN 0028-033X) **2538**
National Underwriter. Property & Casualty Insurance Edition. (US ISSN 0163-8912) **2538**
National Underwriter Profiles. (US) **2538**
National Union Catalog see National Union Catalog. Books **2795**
National Union Catalog. Audiovisual Materials. (US) **3520**, 2794
National Union Catalog. Books. (US ISSN 0734-7650) **2795**, 4142
National Union Catalog of Manuscript Collections. (US ISSN 0090-0044) **407**
National Union Catalogue of Library Materials for People with Disabilities. (AT ISSN 1032-8149) **2285**, 407
National Union Catalogue of Library Materials for the Handicapped see National Union Catalogue of Library Materials for People with Disabilities **2285**
National Union Catalogue of Monographs on the National Bibliographic Database see N U C O M 5 **406**
▼National Union Catalogue of Non-Book Materials. (AT ISSN 1031-9425) **407**
National Union Catalogue of Serials. (AT ISSN 0812-9258) **407**
National Union for Civil and Public Servants. Journal. (UK) **4068**
National Union of Bank Employees Suara N U B E see Suara N U B E **2589**
National Union of Coal Mine Workers. Journal. (JA) **2587**, 3491
National Union of Insurance Workers. Prudential Section. Gazette. (UK) **2538**
National Union of Journalists Freelance Directory see N U J Freelance Directory **2573**
National Union of Public Employees Journal see N U P E Journal **989**
National Union of Students Action see N U S Action **1649**
National Union of Teachers. Annual Report. (UK ISSN 0077-5940) **1756**
National Union of Teachers Education Review see N U T Education Review **1649**
National Union of the Footwear, Leather and Allied Trades Journal and Report. (UK) **4361**
National Union of the Footwear, Leather and Allied Trades Monthly Journal and Report see National Union of the Footwear, Leather and Allied Trades Journal and Report **4361**
National Unionist. see Al Watani Al Ittihadi **2170**
National United Affiliated Beverage Association. Newsletter. (US) **384**, 1048
National University Continuing Education Association. Directory. (US) **1712**, 1695

National University Continuing Education Association. Handbook and Directory see National University Continuing Education Association. Directory **1712**
National University Continuing Education Association News see N U C E A News **1712**
National University Extension Association. N U E A Newsletter see N U C E A News **1712**
National University of Iran. Dental School. Journal see Shaheed Beheshti University. Faculty of Dentistry. Journal **3242**
National University of Singapore. Economics & Statistics Society. Annual Journal - Suara Ekonomi. (SI) **681**
National University of Singapore. Economics and Statistics Society. Journal see National University of Singapore. Economics & Statistics Society. Annual Journal - Suara Ekonomi **681**
National Urban League Annual Report. (US) **2492**
National Urban League Progress Report see National Urban League Annual Report **2492**
National Utility Contractor. (US ISSN 0192-0359) **1871**
National Voice of Salesmen. (US ISSN 0028-0364) **1048**
National Voter. (US ISSN 0028-0372) **3909**
National Water Safety Congress Journal see Water Safety Journal **4496**
National Water Well Association. Briefings see National Ground Water Association. Briefings **1599**
National Weather Association Newsletter. (US ISSN 0271-1044) **3439**
National Weather Digest. (US ISSN 0271-1052) **3439**
National Westminster Bank Quarterly Review. (UK ISSN 0028-0399) **792**, 875
National Wetlands Newsletter. (US ISSN 0164-0712) **1963**, 2657
National Wheelchair Basketball Association. Directory. (US) **4508**
National Wheelchair Basketball Association. Newsletter. (US) **4509**
National Wholesale Druggists' Association Executive Newsletter see N W D A Executive Newsletter **3735**
National Wildcat Monthly. (US) **3693**
National Wildlife. (US ISSN 0028-0402) **1492**, 4551
National Women's Health Network. (US) **4849**, 4835
National Women's Health Network Newsletter see Network NewsNews **4836**
National Women's Health Report. (US ISSN 0741-9147) **4836**, 4849
National Women's Register National Newsletter see N W R National Newsletter **4849**
National Women's Studies Association Action see N W S Action **4860**
National Women's Studies Association Journal see N W S A Journal **4860**
National Wood Stove and Fireplace Journal see National Energy Journal **642**
National Woodlands Magazine. (US) **2116**
National Wool Grower. (US ISSN 0028-0410) **222**
National Writers Club Market Update see N W C Market Update **2573**
National Writing Project. Center for the Study of Writing Quarterly. (US ISSN 0896-3592) **1756**
National Yellow Book of Funeral Directors see Yellow Book of Funeral Directors **1160**
National Yellow Pages Agency Association. Newsletter. (US) **35**
National Zip Code and Post Office Directory see National Five Digit Zip Code and Post Office Directory **1353**
Nationale Buchhaltung der Schweiz/Comptes Nationaux de la Suisse. (SZ) **754**

†Der Nationale Demokrat. (GW ISSN 0028-0437) **5244**
Nationale Havenraad. Jaarverslag (Year). (NE) **4734**
Nationale Maatschappij van Belgische Spoorwegen. Documentatiebulletin. (BE ISSN 0771-517X) **4712**
Nationale Maatschappij voor de Huisvesting. Jaarverslag see Societe National du Logement. Rapport Annuel **2496**
Nationale-Nederlanden. Annual Report. (NE ISSN 0077-5975) **2538**
Nationale Plantentuin van Belgie. Bulletin. see Jardin Botanique National de Belgique. Bulletin **507**
Nationale Vereniging voor Beveiliging tegen Brand Magazine see N V B B Magazine **2034**
Nationalism Today see Third Way - Beyond Capitalism and Communism **3930**
Nationalist and Munster Advertiser. (IE) **2203**
Nationalities. see Minzu **2014**
Nationalities Papers. (US ISSN 0090-5992) **4380**, 2511
Nationality Education of China. see Zhongguo Minzu Jiaoyu **1673**
Nationality Pictorial. see Minzu Huabao **2014**
Nationalmuseets Arbejdsmark. (DK) **2377**
Nationaloekonomisk Tidsskrift. (DK ISSN 0028-0453) **4380**
Nationalratswahlen (Year)/Elections au Conseil National (Year). (SZ) **4081**
National's Forecast For (Year) see National Securities and Research Corporation. Annual Forecast **5243**
Nationaltheater Mannheim Theaterzeitung. (GW ISSN 0934-9383) **4635**
Nation's Building News. (US) **626**
Nation's Business. (US ISSN 0028-047X) **820**, 681
Nation's Cities Weekly. (US ISSN 0164-5935) **4092**
Nation's Health. (US ISSN 0028-0496) **4108**
Nations Nouvelles. (CX ISSN 0028-050X) **3909**
▼Nations of the World: A Factbook. (US) **407**
Nation's Restaurant News. (US ISSN 0028-0518) **2478**
†Nation's Schools Report. (US ISSN 0194-2263) **5244**
Nations Unies. Assemblee Generale. Index des Actes see United Nations. General Assembly. Index to Proceedings **3939**
Nations Unies. Commission de Droit International. Annuaire see United Nations. International Law Commission Yearbook **2729**
Nations Unies. Conseil de Securite. Documents Officials. Supplement see United Nations. Security Council. Official Records. Supplement **3975**
Nations Unies. Recueil des Traites. Index Cumulatif see United Nations. Treaty Series. Cumulative Index **2701**
Nations Unies. Traites Mulitnationaux Deposes aupres de Secretaire General see United Nations. Multilateral Treaties Deposited with the Secretary-General **2729**
Nations Unies Annuaire de Desarmement see United Nations Disarmament Yearbook **3473**
Nations Unies Annuaire Juridique see United Nations Juridical Yearbook **2730**
Nationwide Anglia Building Society. House Prices. (UK ISSN 0263-3639) **626**, 4153
Nationwide Anglia Building Society. Occasional Bulletin see Nationwide Anglia Building Society. House Prices **626**
Nationwide Directory of Association Meeting Planners & Conference - Convention Directors. (US) **3393**
Nationwide Directory of Corporate Meeting Planners. (US) **3394**

Nationwide Directory of Gift and Housewares Buyers see Nationwide Directory of Gift, Housewares & Home Textile Buyers **2281**
Nationwide Directory of Gift, Housewares & Home Textile Buyers. (US) **2281**, 2448, 2561
Nationwide Directory of Men's and Boys' Wear Buyers (Exclusive of New York Metropolitan Area). (US ISSN 0077-5983) **1287**
Nationwide Directory of Premium, Incentive & Travel Buyers. (US ISSN 0196-8262) **1147**, 958, 1048
Nationwide Directory of Sporting Goods Buyers. (US ISSN 0739-6074) **4481**, 1048
Nationwide Directory of Women's and Children's Wear Buyers (Exclusive of New York Metropolitan Area). (US ISSN 0077-5991) **1287**
▼Nationwide Footwear & Related Accessories Buyers. (US) **1287**, 1048
Nationwide Light Industrial News. see Quanguo Qinggong Xinxi **686**
Nationwide Major Mass Market Merchandisers (Exclusive of New York Metropolitan Area). (US ISSN 0077-6009) **1287**
Nationwide Overnight Stabling Directory see Nationwide Overnight Stabling Directory & Equestrian Vacation Guide **4536**
Nationwide Overnight Stabling Directory & Equestrian Vacation Guide. (US) **4536**, 1147, 4779
Native American Bibliography Series. (US) **2030**
Native American Rights Fund. Catalogue see National Indian Law Library. Catalogue **2030**
Native American Rights Fund Legal Review see N A R F Legal Review **2015**
Native American Studies. (US) **2015**
Native American Texts Series see I J A L Native American Texts Series **5209**
†Native Hawaiian Report. (US) **5244**
Native Issues. (CN) **2015**, 246
Native Nations. (US) **2015**
Native Nevadan. (US ISSN 0028-0534) **2015**
Native Peoples. (US ISSN 0895-7606) **2015**
Native Plant Society of New Mexico. Newsletter. (US) **2135**
Native Press see Press Independent **2020**
†Native Vision. (US) **5244**
Native Voice. (CN ISSN 0028-0542) **2016**
NATS News see Contemporary Times **3626**
Natsionalen Voennoistoricheski Muzei, Sofia. Izvestiya. (BU ISSN 0324-0835) **3466**, 2377
Nattke News see Phi Pi Epsilon B E T A News **2588**
Natturufraedingurinn. (IC ISSN 0028-0550) **4326**
Natuerlich. (GW ISSN 0934-3407) **3806**
Natuerlich und Gesund. (GW ISSN 0721-8982) **3609**
Natun Bangla. (BG) **2174**
Natun Katha. (BG) **2174**
Natun Thikana. (II ISSN 0300-3809) **2875**
Natunkatha see Uthon **2973**
Natur. (GW ISSN 0723-5038) **511**
Natur og Miljoe. (DK) **1963**, 1492
Natur og Miljoe. (NO) **1963**
Natur og Museum. (DK ISSN 0028-0585) **4326**
Natur- und Ganzheitsmedizin, Wissenschaft und Praxis. (GW ISSN 0934-7909) **3134**
Natur und Heilen. (GW ISSN 0932-3503) **3609**
Natur und Heimat. (GW ISSN 0028-0593) **4326**
Natur und Land. (AU ISSN 0028-0607) **4327**
Natur und Landschaft. (GW ISSN 0028-0615) **1493**, 2135
Natur- und Landschaftkunde. (GW ISSN 0722-7795) **4327**

NATUR- UND

Natur- und Landschaftskunde in Westfalen see Natur- und Landschaftkunde 4327
Natur und Mensch: Jahresmitteilungen der Naturhistorischen Gesellschaft Nuernberg. (GW ISSN 0077-6025) 448, 279, 1547, 1574
Natur und Museum. (GW ISSN 0028-1301) 4327
Natur und Recht. (GW ISSN 0172-1631) 109
Natur und Tierschutz Kalender des Deutschen Tierschutzbundes. (GW) 1261, 589
Natura. (BL) 449
Natura. (MX) 3806
Natura. (NE ISSN 0028-0631) 4327
Natura. (VE ISSN 0028-064X) 4327
Natura. (IT ISSN 0369-6243) 4327
Natura & Montagna. (IT) 449, 1547, 1963, 2104
Natura e Societa. (IT ISSN 0393-8875) 1963
Natura Jutlandica. (DK ISSN 0077-6033) 449
Natura Med. (GW ISSN 0931-1513) 3134
Natura Mosana. (BE ISSN 0028-0666) 511, 536
Natura Oggi. (IT) 4551
Natural and Synthetic Gas see Natural Gas Monthly 3693
Natural Areas Journal. (US ISSN 0885-8608) 1963, 1493
Natural Environment Research Council News see N E R C News 1963
Natural Family Planning Council of Victoria. Bulletin. (AT ISSN 0312-7567) 4443, 597
Natural Food & Farming. (US) 3609, 185
Natural Food Trader. (UK) 3609, 2078
Natural Foods Merchandiser. (US) 1048, 3609
Natural Gas. (UK) 3693
Natural Gas. (US) 3693
Natural Gas Annual. (US) 3693, 1793
Natural Gas Industry. see Tianranqi Gongye 3702
Natural Gas Intelligence. (US) 3693
Natural Gas Marketing Pipeline Guide. (US) 3693, 1147
Natural Gas Monthly. (US) 3693, 1793
Natural Gas Monthly Report see Natural Gas Monthly 3693
Natural Gas Policy Act Notices of Determination (F E R C Form 121). (US) 3693, 1793, 2657
Natural Gas Processors Association. Annual Convention. Proceedings see Gas Processors Association. Annual Convention. Proceedings 3687
Natural Gas Vehicle. (US) 4698, 3693
Natural Gas Week. (US) 3693
Natural Gas Yearbook. (US ISSN 1042-1440) 3693
Natural Hazard Research Working Papers. (US ISSN 0082-5166) 4414
Natural Hazards. (NE ISSN 0921-030X) 1547
Natural Hazards Observer. (US ISSN 0193-8355) 4414
Natural Healing & Nutrition Annual. (US) 3806, 3595
Natural Health. (AT ISSN 0816-2751) 3609, 3806
Natural Health and Fitness Bulletin. (US) 3806
†Natural Health Bulletin. (US ISSN 0047-9152) 5244
Natural Health World. (US ISSN 0028-0704) 3806
Natural History. (US ISSN 0028-0712) 4327
Natural History. see Watashitachi no Shizenshi 4351
Natural History Book Reviews. (UK ISSN 0308-180X) 4357
Natural History Contributions. (CN ISSN 0707-3887) 449, 3658
†Natural History Handbook Series. (CN ISSN 0068-1628) 5244
Natural History Miscellanea. (US) 449

▼Natural History Museum and Institute, Chiba. Journal. (JA ISSN 0915-9452) 2340, 3530
Natural History Museum of Los Angeles County. Contributions in Science see Contributions in Science 4306
Natural History Museum of Los Angeles County. Science Series. (US ISSN 0076-0943) 4327
Natural History Report of Kanagawa. see Kanagawa Shizenshi Shiryo 4319
Natural History Research. (JA ISSN 0915-9444) 2340, 3530
Natural History Society of Northumberland Durham and Newcastle Upon Tyne. Transactions see Natural History Society of Northumbria. Transactions 4327
Natural History Society of Northumbria. Transactions. (UK ISSN 0144-221X) 4327
Natural Hygiene Society of New Jersey. Newsletter. (US) 3609
Natural Immunity and Cell Growth Regulation. (SZ ISSN 0254-7600) 556
Natural Language and Linguistic Theory.(NE ISSN 0167-806X) 2831
Natural Physique. (US) 3806, 3399
Natural Product Reports. (UK ISSN 0265-0568) 1220
Natural Product Research and Development. see Tianran Chanwu Yanjiu yu Kaifa 1189
Natural Product Updates. (UK ISSN 0950-1711) 1220
Natural Resources. see Al-Mawarid al-Tabi'iyyah 1491
Natural Resources. see Ziran Ziyuan 1501
Natural Resources & Environment. (US ISSN 0882-3812) 1493, 2657
Natural Resources Defense Council, Inc. Newsline see N R D C Newsline 4108
Natural Resources Forum. (UK ISSN 0165-0203) 2257, 1493, 1793
Natural Resources Journal. (US ISSN 0028-0739) 1493, 2657
Natural Resources Law Newsletter. (US ISSN 0077-6084) 1493, 2657
Natural Resources Lawyer see Natural Resources & Environment 1493
Natural Resources Metabase. (US) 1974, 18, 1501
Natural Resources Research. (UN ISSN 0077-6092) 1547, 1493
Natural Rights. (US) 1963, 1493, 2657
Natural Rights Center Annual Report. (US) 1963, 1493, 2657
Natural Sciences and Engineering Research Council of Canada. List of Scholarships and Grants in Aid of Research/Conseil de Recherches en Sciences Naturelles et en Genie du Canada. Liste des Bourses et Subventions de Recherche. (CN) 1712, 4327
Natural Sciences and Engineering Research Council of Canada. Report of the President/Conseil de Recherches en Sciences Naturelles et en Genie du Canada. Rapport du President. (CN) 1712, 4327
Natural Solutions. (US) 185, 2135
Natural Therapist. (AT ISSN 1031-6965) 3134
▼Natural Toxins. (US ISSN 1056-9014) 1207
Natural World. (UK ISSN 0261-7358) 1493
Naturalia. (BL ISSN 0101-1944) 449
†Naturalia Hispanica. (SP) 5244
Naturalist. (UK ISSN 0028-0771) 449
Naturalist. (SA) 1493
Naturalist see New Crucible 1964
Naturalist. (TR) 4327
Naturaliste Canadien. (CN ISSN 0028-0798) 4327
Naturaliste du N.B. see N.B. Naturalist 4325
†Les Naturalistes. (CN ISSN 0836-0928) 5244
Les Naturalistes Belges. (BE ISSN 0028-0801) 449

Naturalists. (JA) 4327
Naturalists' Directory and Almanac International. (US) 449
Naturalists' Directory International see Naturalists' Directory and Almanac International 449
Naturally. (US) 3806
Der Naturarzt. (GW ISSN 0028-081X) 3806
Nature. see Watakushitachi no Shizen 568
Nature. see Daziran 4306
Nature. (UK ISSN 0028-0836) 4327
Nature. see Shizen 4608
Nature and Environment Series. (FR) 1493
Nature and Health. (AT ISSN 0158-9911) 3609
Nature and Man. see Ziran yu Ren 2327
Nature and Resources. (UN ISSN 0547-9665) 1493, 1574, 1963, 4327
Nature and Science. see Kyodo to Kagaku 4322
Nature and Technology. see Natuur en Techniek 4328
Nature Canada. (CN ISSN 0374-9894) 1493, 1963
Nature Conservancy Council. Annual Report. (UK) 1493
†Nature Conservancy Council. Chief Scientist Directorate Reports. (UK) 5244
Nature Conservancy Council. Chief Scientist Team Reports see Nature Conservancy Council. Chief Scientist Directorate Reports 5244
Nature Conservancy Magazine. (US) 1493, 1963
Nature Conservancy News see Nature Conservancy Magazine 1493
Nature Conservation. see Varstvo Narave 1499
Nature Conservation Council of N.S.W. Bulletin see Nature Conservation News 1493
Nature Conservation Council of N.S.W. Newsletter see Nature Conservation News 1493
Nature Conservation News. (AT) 1493, 1963
Nature Conservation Society of Japan. Reports. see Nihon Shizen Hogo Kyokai Chosa Hokoku 1494
Nature et Mieux-Vivre. (FR) 1963
Nature in Devon. (UK ISSN 0143-9634) 1493
Nature in Hokkaido. see Hokkaido no Shizen 1489
Nature in Okayama. see Okayama no Shizen 1494
Nature Information see Pecheur Romand 4553
Nature Journal. see Ziran Zazhi 4354
Nature Magazine see Natural History 4327
Nature of Enshu. see Enshu no Shizen 4309
Nature of Tohoku. see Tohoku no Shizen 4347
Nature Photography. (UK) 3793
†Nature - Science Annual. (US ISSN 0085-3860) 5244
Nature, Society, and Thought. (US ISSN 0890-6130) 3909, 4380
Nature Society News. (US ISSN 0890-3735) 1493, 565
Nature Study. (US ISSN 0028-0860) 1964, 1493
Nature Study. see Neicha Sutadi 4329
Naturen. (NO ISSN 0028-0887) 4327
Naturens Verden. (DK ISSN 0028-0895) 4327
Natureza em Revista. (BL ISSN 0100-4700) 4327
Naturforschende Gesellschaft in Basel. Verhandlungen/Society for Natural Sciences, Basel. Proceedings. (SZ ISSN 0077-6122) 4327
Naturforschende Gesellschaft in Bern. Mitteilungen. (SZ ISSN 0077-6130) 4328
Naturforschende Gesellschaft in Zuerich. Vierteljahrsschrift. (SZ ISSN 0042-5672) 4328

Naturforschende Gesellschaft zu Freiburg. Berichte. (GW ISSN 0028-0917) 4328
Naturfreund/Ami de la Nature. (SZ ISSN 0028-0925) 4779
Naturfreunde - Kinderpost. (GW) 1261, 231
Naturgas Nyt. (DK ISSN 0108-3422) 3693
Naturgemaesser Land- und Gartenbau see Garten Organisch 2127
Naturheilpraxis. (GW ISSN 0028-0941) 3134
Naturhistorica Chikuhoana. see Chikuho Hakubutsu 4304
Naturhistorische Gesellschaft Hannover. Beihefte zu den Berichten. (GW ISSN 0374-6054) 449, 1547
Naturhistorische Gesellschaft Hannover. Berichte. (GW ISSN 0365-9844) 1547
Naturhistorische Gesellschaft Nuernberg. Abhandlungen. (GW ISSN 0077-6149) 279, 449, 1547, 2016
Naturhistorische Gesellschaft Nuernberg. Mitteilungen und Jahresbericht see Natur und Mensch: Jahresmitteilungen der Naturhistorischen Gesellschaft Nuernberg 448
Naturhistorischer Verein Augsburg. Bericht see Naturwissenschaftlicher Verein fuer Schwaben. Berichte 449
Naturhistorisches Museum Basel. Veroeffentlichungen. (SZ) 4328, 1574, 3658
Naturhistorisches Museum Bern. Jahrbuch. (SZ ISSN 0253-4401) 4328
Naturhistorisches Museum in Wien. Annalen. (AU ISSN 0083-6133) 4328
Naturhistorisches Museum in Wien. Monatsprogramm. (AU ISSN 0028-095X) 3530
Naturhistorisches Museum in Wien. Veroeffentlichungen. Neue Folge. (AU ISSN 0505-5164) 4328
Naturism. (BE) 4779
Naturisme. (NE ISSN 0028-0968) 3806
Naturismo. (IT ISSN 0392-4173) 3806
Naturkundliches Jahrbuch der Stadt Linz. (AU ISSN 0470-3901) 4328
Naturopa. (FR ISSN 0250-7102) 1493
Naturopath. (US ISSN 0028-100X) 3806
Naturschutz und Landschaftsplanung. (GW) 303
Naturstein. (GW ISSN 0028-1026) 626
Die Naturstein-Industrie. (GW ISSN 0028-1034) 626
Naturvaardsverkets Foerfattningssamling. (SW ISSN 0347-5301) 1493
Die Naturwissenschaften. (GW ISSN 0028-1042) 4328
Naturwissenschaften im Unterricht see Naturwissenschaften im Unterricht. Physik-Chemie 1756
Naturwissenschaften im Unterricht see Naturwissenschaften im Unterricht. Biologie 4328
Naturwissenschaften im Unterricht. Biologie. (GW ISSN 0342-5487) 4328, 1756
Naturwissenschaften im Unterricht. Physik-Chemie. (GW) 1756, 1184, 3825
Naturwissenschaften im Unterricht Chemie. (GW) 1184
Naturwissenschaften im Unterricht Physik. (GW) 3825, 1756
Naturwissenschaftliche Rundschau. (GW ISSN 0028-1050) 4328
Naturwissenschaftliche Rundschau. Buecher der Zeitschrift. (GW ISSN 0077-6157) 4328
Naturwissenschaftliche Zeitschrift fuer Niederbayern. (GW) 449, 1547
Naturwissenschaftlicher Verein fuer Schleswig-Holstein. Schriften. (GW ISSN 0077-6165) 4328

Naturwissenschaftlicher Verein fuer Schwaben. Berichte. (GW ISSN 0720-3705) **449**, 1547, 1574, 3658
Naturwissenschaftlicher Verein fuer Steiermark. Mitteilungen. (AU) **4328**
Naturwissenschaftlicher Verein in Hamburg. Abhandlungen. (GW ISSN 0301-2697) **449**
Naturwissenschaftlicher Verein in Hamburg. Abhandlungen und Verhandlungen *see* Naturwissenschaftlicher Verein in Hamburg. Abhandlungen **449**
Naturwissenschaftlicher Verein in Hamburg. Abhandlungen und Verhandlungen *see* Naturwissenschaftlicher Verein in Hamburg. Verhandlungen **449**
Naturwissenschaftlicher Verein in Hamburg. Verhandlungen. (GW ISSN 0173-7481) **449**
Naturwissenschaftlicher Verein Wuppertal. Jahresberichte. (GW ISSN 0547-9789) **511**, 589, 1574
Natuur en Milieu. (NE) **1493**
Natuur en Museum. (NE ISSN 0028-1085) **4328**
Natuur en Techniek/Nature and Technology. (NE ISSN 0028-1093) **4328**, 4604
Natuurbeleving. (NE) **1493**
Natuurhistorisch Genootschap in Limburg. Publicaties. (NE ISSN 0374-955X) **449**, 3658
Natuurhistorisch Maandblad. (NE ISSN 0028-1107) **4328**
Natuurwetenschappelijk Tijdschrift. (BE ISSN 0770-1748) **4328**
Natuurwetenschappelijke Studiekring voor Suriname en de Nederlandse Antillen. Uitgaven. (NE ISSN 0300-5534) **449**, 1547
Natya. (II ISSN 0028-1115) **4635**, 1531
Nauchen Zhivot. (BU ISSN 0028-1123) **4328**
Nauchnaya Apparatura/Scientific Instrumentation. (PL ISSN 0257-3881) **2524**
Nauchno-Issledovatel'skii Institut Kul'tury. Trudy *see* Sotsiologiya Kul'tury **4452**
Nauchno-Issledovatel'skii Institut Prikladnoi Geodezii. Trudy. (RU) **1574**
Nauchno-Tekhnicheskaya Informatsiya *see* Nauchno-Tekhnicheskaya Informatsiya. Seriya 1. Organizatsiya i Metodika Informatsionnoi Raboty **2775**
Nauchno-Tekhnicheskaya Informatsiya. Seriya 1. Organizatsiya i Informatsionnoi Raboty. (RU ISSN 0548-0019) **2775**
Naucna Sveska. (BN ISSN 0351-4471) **109**
Naucni i Strucni Skupovi u Jugoslavii i u Inostranstvu/Scientific and Professional Meetings in Yugoslavia and Foreign Countries. (YU ISSN 0350-011X) **3394**, 4328
Naucni Podmladak: Drustvene Nauke i Filozofija. (YU ISSN 0351-5699) **4381**, 3773
Naucni Podmladak: Medicinske Nauke. (YU ISSN 0352-5856) **3134**
Naucni Podmladak: Tehnicke Nauke. (YU ISSN 0351-1030) **4604**
Naucni Sastanak Slavista u Vukove Dane. Referati i Saopstenja. (YU) **2831**
Naucno-tehnicki Pregled. (YU ISSN 0350-0667) **1857**, 1921, 1924
Naughty Baby. *see* Wanpi Wawa **1270**
Nauka dla Wszystkich/Science for Everyone. (PL ISSN 0077-6181) **4328**
Nauka i Religiya. (RU ISSN 0028-1239) **4191**, 4328
Nauka i Suspil'stvo. (RU ISSN 0028-1247) **4328**
Nauka i Tekhnika/Zinatne un Tekhnika. (LV ISSN 0028-1255) **4328**, 4604
Nauka i Zhizn' (RU ISSN 0028-1263) **4328**, 4604
†Nauka o Zemi. Seria Geographica. (CS) **5244**

Nauka Polska. (PL ISSN 0028-1271) **4329**
†Nauka Segodnya. (UR) **5244**
Nauka u Praksi. (YU ISSN 0350-1388) **109**, 2135, 4813
Nauka v S.S.S.R. (RU ISSN 0203-4425) **4329**
Nauki Ekonomiczne. (PL ISSN 0137-1428) **681**
Nauki Polityczne. (PL ISSN 0137-141X) **3909**
Naukove Tovarystvo Imeni Shevchenka. Biblioteka Ukrainoznavstva/Library of Ukrainian Studies. (US) **2377**
Naukove Tovarystvo Imeni Shevchenka. Proceedings of the Section of Chemistry, Biology and Medicine. (US) **1184**, 449, 3134
Naukove Tovarystvo Imeni Shevchenka. Proceedings of the Section of Mathematics and Physics. (US) **4329**
Naukove Tovarystvo Imeni Shevchenka. Ukrainska Literaturna Biblioteka/Ukrainian Literary Library. (US) **2941**
Naukove Tovarystvo Imeni Shevchenka. Ukrains'kyi Arkhiv/Ukrainian Archives. (US) **2016**
Naukove Tovarystvo Imeni Shevchenka. Zapysky/Shevchenko Scientific Society. Memoirs/Mitteilungen. (US) **2016**
Naukovedenie i Informatika. (KR ISSN 0374-3896) **1442**
Nauncni Skupovi u SFRJ i u Inostranstvu *see* Naucni i Strucni Skupovi u Jugoslavii i u Inostranstvu **3394**
Naunyn-Schmiedeberg's Archives of Pharmacology. (GW ISSN 0028-1298) **3735**
Naut Argus. (FR) **4527**
Nautakarja/Cattle. (FI ISSN 0028-131X) **202**, 222
Nautic Press. (SP) **4527**
Nautica. (IT) **4527**
Nautical Almanac. (UK ISSN 0077-619X) **4734**
Nautical Brass. (US ISSN 0882-4401) **258**
Nautical Brass, Etc. *see* Nautical Brass **258**
Nautical Magazine. (UK ISSN 0028-1336) **4734**
Nautical News *see* Australian Yachting **4522**
†Nautical Quarterly. (US ISSN 0199-0837) **5244**
Nautical Research Journal. (US ISSN 0738-7245) **4734**, 2440, 4527
Nauticus. (GW) **4734**
Nautilus (Independence). (US) **3806**, 3609
Nautilus (Silver Spring). (US ISSN 0028-1344) **589**
Nautique News. (US) **4527**
†Nautisches Jahrbuch. (GW ISSN 0433-681X) **5244**
Nautisches Jahrbuch, oder Ephemeriden und Tafeln. (GW ISSN 0077-6211) **367**
Nautisk Tidskrift. (SW ISSN 0028-1379) **4734**
Nautologia. (PL ISSN 0548-0523) **1608**

Nav-Chitrapat. (II ISSN 0042-2444) **3514**
Nava Sama Samaja Bulletin. (CE) **3909**
Nava Yugaya. (CE) **2941**
Navaho. (US) **2016**
†Navajo Area Newsletter. (US) **5244**
Navajo Times. (US) **2016**
Navajo Times Today *see* Navajo Times **2016**
Naval Affairs. (US ISSN 0028-1409) **3466**
Naval Architect. (UK ISSN 0306-0209) **4734**
Naval Architecture and Ocean Engineering. (JA) **3466**, 1608
Naval Aviation News. (US ISSN 0028-1417) **59**
Naval Base Newspapers. (UK) **3466**
Naval Engineers Journal. (US ISSN 0028-1425) **1831**, 3466
Naval Forces. (UK) **3466**

Naval History. (US) **3466**, 2415
Naval Institute Guide to Combat Fleets of the World. (US) **3466**
Naval Law Review. (US) **2657**, 3466
Naval Research Logistics: An International Journal. (US ISSN 0894-069X) **3477**, 4580
Naval Research Logistics Quarterly *see* Naval Research Logistics: An International Journal **3477**
Naval Reservist News. (US) **3466**
Naval Review. (US ISSN 0077-6238) **3466**
Naval Review. (UK) **3466**
Naval Stores Review. (US) **3654**
Naval Stores Review and Terpene Chemicals *see* Naval Stores Review **3654**
Naval War College Review. (US ISSN 0028-1484) **3466**
†Navalkatha. (II ISSN 0028-1492) **5244**
Navalokaya. (CE) **3909**
Navarra Agraria. (SP) **222**
Navarro Leaves and Branches. (US) **2159**
Navasart Monthly. (US) **2016**
Navbharat Times. (II ISSN 0028-1506) **2200**
Nave Parva. (II) **4779**, 3909
Navicula. (GW) **3755**
Navigation. (AT ISSN 0077-6262) **4654**
Navigation. *see* Kokai **4730**
Navigation. (FR ISSN 0028-1530) **4734**, 59
Navigation (Washington). (US ISSN 0028-1522) **59**
Navigation, Ports and Industries *see* Revue de la Navigation Fluviale Europeenne, Ports et Industries **4737**
Navigationssaellskapets Medlemsblad. (SW) **4527**
Navigatoer. (DK ISSN 0107-4806) **4734**
Navigatoer Nyt *see* Navigatoer **4734**
Navigator. (BL ISSN 0100-1248) **4734**
Navigator (Virginia). (US) **2159**
Navigazione Interna. (IT) **4734**
Navin Weekly. (UK ISSN 0307-0832) **3909**
Navioneers. (US ISSN 0028-1581) **59**
Navires Ports & Chantiers. (FR ISSN 0028-159X) **4734**
Navis *see* Navigationssaellskapets Medlemsblad **4527**
Navis. (FR ISSN 0077-6270) **4734**
Navitecnia y Comercio Maritimo. (AG) **4734**
†Navjiwan Punjabi News. (MY) **5244**
Navnirman. (II ISSN 0028-162X) **1831**
Navorsingsnuus vir die Geesteswetenskaplike. *see* Bulletin - News for the Human Science Researcher **4367**
Navy, Army & Air Force Institutes News *see* N A A F I News **3466**
Navy Chaplains Bulletin. (US ISSN 0028-1654) **3466**, 4191
Navy Civil Engineer. (US ISSN 0096-9419) **3466**, 1871
Navy International. (UK ISSN 0144-3194) **3467**
Navy Journal. *see* Mornaricki Glasnik **3466**
Navy List of Retired Officers. (UK) **3467**
Navy Medicine. (US) **3134**
Navy News. (UK ISSN 0028-1670) **3467**
Navy News. (US ISSN 0028-1662) **3467**
Navy News. Sea Cadet Edition. (UK) **1261**, 1300
Navy News (Virginia Beach). (US) **3467**
Navy News & Undersea Technology. (US ISSN 8756-1700) **3467**, 1608
Navy Supply Corps Newsletter. (US ISSN 0360-716X) **3467**
Navy: the Magazine of Sea Power *see* Sea Power **3471**
Navy Times. (US ISSN 0028-1697) **3467**

NEBRASKA FARMERS 6479

Nawpa Pacha. (US ISSN 0077-6297) **279**
Nayajug. (BG) **2174**
†Nayer Dor/New Generation. (CN ISSN 0705-7822) **5244**
Nayi Talim/Basic Education. (II) **1650**
Naz' al-silah *see* Disarmament **3457**
Nazareth. (IT ISSN 0028-1700) **4191**
Nazionaler Katalog der Heizung und Klimatisierung. *see* Catalogue National du Genie Climatique-Chauffage et Conditionnement d'Air **2298**
Ndertuesi/Constructeur. (AA) **626**
Ne Skenen e Femijeve. (AA) **1261**, 4635
Nea Agrotiki Epitheorissis. (GR ISSN 0028-1727) **109**
Nea Dimossiotis. (GR) **35**, 1048
Nea Epochi/New Epoch. (CY) **2875**
Nea Hestia. (GR ISSN 0028-1735) **2941**, 2875
Nea Paphos. (PL) **279**
Nea Poreia. (GR) **2941**
Neal's Catalog File. (US) **163**
Near and Middle East Monographs. (GW ISSN 0932-2728) **3642**
Near East and North Africa Report *see* Near East - South Asia Report **875**
Near East Archaeological Society Bulletin. (US ISSN 0739-0068) **279**, 2431
Near East Foundation. Annual Report. (US) **933**, 3966
Near East Report. (US ISSN 0028-176X) **3966**
Near East - South Asia Report. (US) **875**, 3909
Near North News. (US ISSN 0028-1778) **2229**
Nebelhorn. (GW) **989**, 1964, 2492, 4414
Nebelspalter. (SZ ISSN 0028-1786) **2875**
Nebo. (US ISSN 0741-1316) **2941**
Nebraska. Accounting Division. Annual Fiscal Report *see* Nebraska. Department of Administrative Services. Annual Fiscal Report **4068**
Nebraska. Department of Administrative Services. Annual Fiscal Report. (US) **4068**
Nebraska. Department of Roads. Nebraska Selected Statistics. (US) **4665**, 4720
Nebraska. Department of Roads. Traffic Analysis Unit. Continuous Traffic Count Data and Traffic Characteristics on Nebraska Streets and Highways. (US ISSN 0091-844X) **4720**
Nebraska. Department of Social Services. Annual Report. (US) **4414**
Nebraska. Fisheries Division. Annual Report. (US ISSN 0092-1696) **2046**
Nebraska. Indian Commission. Report. (US ISSN 0360-683X) **2016**
Nebraska. Natural Resources Commission. State Water Planning and Review Process. (US) **4827**
Nebraska. State Patrol. Annual Report. (US ISSN 0094-1247) **1519**
Nebraska Academy of Sciences. Proceedings. (US ISSN 0077-6343) **4329**
Nebraska Academy of Sciences. Transactions. (US ISSN 0077-6351) **4329**
Nebraska Agriculture *see* Nebraska Farm Bureau News **109**
Nebraska Alumnus. (US ISSN 0028-1794) **1318**
Nebraska Baptist Messenger *see* Messenger (Omaha) **4243**
Nebraska Beverage Analyst. (US ISSN 0028-1808) **384**
The Nebraska Bird Review. (US ISSN 0028-1816) **565**
Nebraska Blue Print. (US) **1831**
Nebraska Cattleman. (US) **222**
Nebraska Economic Developments. (US) **875**
Nebraska Farm Bureau News. (US ISSN 0745-6522) **109**
Nebraska Farmer. (US) **109**
Nebraska Farmers Fastline *see* Farmers Fastline: Nebraska Edition **162**

6480 NEBRASKA FERTILIZER

Nebraska Fertilizer and Ag-Chemical Digest. (US ISSN 0199-672X) **185**, 1857
Nebraska Highway Program. (US) **4720**, 1871
Nebraska History. (US ISSN 0028-1859) **2415**
Nebraska - Iowa Retailer see Heartland Retailer **2299**
Nebraska Journal. (US) **1650**, 3806
Nebraska Law Review. (US ISSN 0047-9209) **2657**
Nebraska Legionnaire. (US ISSN 0028-1875) **1300**
Nebraska Libraries: A Directory. (US) **1147**, 2775
Nebraska Library Association. Newsletter see Nebraska Library Association Quarterly **2776**
Nebraska Library Association Quarterly. (US ISSN 0028-1883) **2776**
Nebraska Library Commission. Library Directory. see Nebraska Libraries: A Directory **1147**
Nebraska Limitations Manual. (US) **2657**
Nebraska Livestock Brand Book. (US) **222**, 2657
Nebraska Medical Journal. (US ISSN 0091-6730) **3134**
Nebraska Mortar and Pestle. (US ISSN 0028-1891) **3736**
Nebraska Municipal Review. (US ISSN 0028-1905) **4092**
Nebraska Music Educator. (US) **3570**, 1650
Nebraska Newspaper. (US ISSN 0028-1913) **2573**
Nebraska Now see Nebraska Economic Developments **875**
Nebraska Nurse. (US ISSN 0028-1921) **3282**
Nebraska Oil Jobber see Nebraska Petroleum Marketer **3693**
Nebraska Petroleum Marketer. (US) **3693**
Nebraska Resources. (US ISSN 0047-9217) **1493**
Nebraska Retailer. (US ISSN 0028-1948) **1048**
Nebraska Review. (US ISSN 8755-514X) **2941**
Nebraska Smoke-Eater. (US) **2034**
Nebraska State Historical Society. Historical Newsletter. (US ISSN 0199-9664) **2415**
†Nebraska State Publications Checklist. (US ISSN 0091-0406) **5244**
Nebraska Statistical Handbook. (US ISSN 0097-9325) **4081**, 4580
Nebraska Statistical Report of Abortions. (US ISSN 0095-3105) **598**
Nebraska Symposium on Motivation (Publication). (US ISSN 0070-2099) **4036**
Nebraska Transcript. (US) **2657**
Nebraska Trucker. (US) **4746**
Nebraska Water Resources Research Institute. University of Nebraska. Annual Report of Activities see University of Nebraska. Water Center. Annual Report of Activities **4830**
Nebraskaland. (US ISSN 0028-1964) **1493**, 4551
Nebula Award Stories see Nebula Winners **2941**
Nebula Winners. (US ISSN 0162-3818) **2941**
NebulousFan. (US) **2986**
Necessary Catalogue see Natural Solutions **185**
Neckarwerke Elektrizitaetsversorgungs AG Aktuell see N W Aktuell **1904**
Neckwear Industry Directory. (US) **1287**
▼Necrofile. (US) **3013**
Nedbank. Guide to the Economy. (SA) **875**
Nedcor Group. Guide to the Economy see Nedbank. Guide to the Economy **875**
Neddy Books and Videos see N E D O Books and Catalogue **730**
Nedeljna Dalmacija. (CI) **2875**
Nedeljne Informativne Novine see N I N **2239**
Nedeljne Novine. (YU ISSN 0028-1980) **2239**

Nedeljne Novosti. (YU ISSN 0028-1999) **2239**
Nederduitse Gereformeerde Kerk van Natal Gemeente Vryheid. Maandbrief.(SA ISSN 0024-8665) **4245**
Nederduitse Gereformeerde Teologiese Tydskrif. (SA ISSN 0028-2006) **4245**
Nederland-Israel. (NE ISSN 0028-2014) **820**
Nederland onder de Loep. (GW) **3755**
Nederland-U S S R Instituut. Maandberichten. (NE ISSN 0028-2022) **918**
Nederland's Adelsboek. (NE) **2159**
Nederlands Archief voor Kerkgeschiedenis. (NE ISSN 0028-2030) **4191**
Nederlands Archievenblad. (NE ISSN 0028-2049) **2377**
Nederlands Bibliotheek en Lektuur Centrum Info Bulletin see N B L C Info Bulletin **2774**
Nederlands Bosbouw Tijdschrift. (NE) **2105**
Nederlands Elektronica- en Radiogenootschap. Tijdschrift. (NE) **1340**
Nederlands Geodetisch Tijdschrift see Geodesia **2248**
Nederlands Historisch Institutute Rome. Mededelingen see Nederlands Instituut te Rome. Mededelingen **2377**
Nederlands Instituut te Rome. Mededelingen. (NE) **2377**, 279
Nederlands Interdisciplinair Demografisch Instituut Literatuur- en Dokumentatieoverzicht N I D I-Biblotheek see Literatuur- en Dokumentatieoverzicht N I D I-Biblotheek **3993**
Nederlands Interdisciplinair Demografisch Instituut Rapport - Report - Bericht - Rapporto see N I D I. Rapport - Report - Bericht - Rapporto **3985**
Nederlands Interuniversitair Demografisch Instituut. Publications. (NE) **3985**
†Nederlands Interuniversitair Demografisch Instituut. Working Papers. (NE) **5244**
Nederlands Korfbalblad. (NE ISSN 0028-2073) **4481**
Nederlands Kunsthistorisch Jaarboek. (NE ISSN 0169-6726) **338**
Nederland's Patriciaat. (NE) **2159**
Nederlands Repertorium van Familienamen. (NE) **2159**
Nederlands Theologisch Tijdschrift. (NE ISSN 0028-212X) **4191**
Nederlands Tijdschrift voor Criminology see Tijdschrift voor Criminologie **1523**
Nederlands Tijdschrift voor E H B O en Reddingwngwezen. (NE) **4108**
Nederlands Tijdschrift voor Geneeskunde. (NE ISSN 0028-2162) **3134**
Nederlands Tijdschrift voor Natuurkunde see Nederlands Tijdschrift voor Natuurkunde A en B **4329**
Nederlands Tijdschrift voor Natuurkunde A en B. (NE) **4329**
Nederlands Tijdschrift voor Opvoeding, Vorming, en Onderwijs. (NE ISSN 0169-1872) **1650**
Nederlands Tijdschrift voor Psychiatrie see Tijdschrift voor Psychiatrie **3355**
Nederlands Tijdschrift voor Tandheelkunde. (NE ISSN 0028-2200) **3238**
Nederlands Tijdschrift voor Vacuumtechniek - Dutch Journal of Vacuum Technology see N E V A C Blad **3825**
Nederlands-Zuidafrikaanse Vereniging. Jaarverslag. (NE ISSN 0077-6416) **2334**
Nederlandsch Kruidkundig Archief see Acta Botanica Neerlandica **492**
De Nederlandsche Bank N.V. Annual Report. (NE ISSN 0167-3998) **792**

De Nederlandsche Bank N.V. Quarterly Bulletin/Dutch Central Bank. Quarterly Bulletin. (NE ISSN 0922-6184) **792**
Nederlandsche Bank N.V. Quarterly Statistics see De Nederlandsche Bank N.V. Quarterly Bulletin **792**
Nederlandsche Internationale Wegvervoer Organisatie Mededelingen see N I W O Mededelingen **4653**
De Nederlandsche Leeuw. (NE ISSN 0028-226X) **2159**
Nederlandse Aannemersvereniging van Afbouw- en Stukadoorswerken see N A V A S **625**
Nederlandse Bibliotheek- en Documenatiegids. (NE) **2776**
Het Nederlandse Boek. (NE ISSN 0166-0586) **2875**, 2941
Nederlandse Bosstatistiek. (NE) **4580**
Nederlandse Centrale Organisatie voor Toegepast-Natuurwetenschappelijk Onderzoek. Technisch-Physische Dienst. Annual Report. (NE) **3825**
Nederlandse Cystic Fibrosis Stichting. Bericht see Nederlandse Cystic Fibrosis Stichting. C F Nieuws **3366**
Nederlandse Cystic Fibrosis Stichting. C F Nieuws. (NE ISSN 0925-1944) **3366**
Nederlandse Entomologische Vereniging. Monographs. (NE ISSN 0548-1163) **536**
†Nederlandse Gedachten. (NE ISSN 0028-2278) **5244**
Nederlandse Gemeente see N G Gemeentelijk Magazine **4092**
Nederlandse Geografische Studies/ Netherlands Geographical Studies. (NE ISSN 0169-4839) **2257**
Nederlandse Hervormde Kerk. Persbureau. Weekbulletin. (NE ISSN 0031-5567) **4245**
Nederlandse Historien. (NE) **2377**
Nederlandse Historische Bronnen. (NE) **2377**
Nederlandse Houtbond. Jaarverslag. (NE) **640**
Nederlandse Investeringsbank voor Ontwikkelingslanden. Verslag. see Netherlands Investment Bank for Developing Countries. Report **793**
Nederlandse Jeugd en Haar Onderwijs/ Netherlands Youth and Its Education.(NE ISSN 0168-4809) **1650**
Nederlandse Kamer van Koophandel voor Belgie en Luxemburg, C.V. Handelsoverzicht. see Chambre de Commerce Neerlandaise pour la Belgique et le Luxembourg, S.C. Revue Commerciale **812**
Nederlandse Kermisbond see N K B **4779**
Nederlandse Krijgsman see P M T - Nieuws **3468**
Nederlandse Malacologische Vereniging. Correspondentieblad. (NE ISSN 0077-6432) **589**
Nederlandse Orde van Accountants - Administratieconsultenten. Leden - Info. (NE) **754**
Nederlandse Organisatie van Welzijnswerkers Nieuws see N O W Nieuws **5242**
Nederlandse Sport Federatie. Technische Mededelingen see Sportaccom **4490**
Nederlandse Vacuumvereniging Blad see N E V A C Blad **3825**
Nederlandse Venture Capital Gids - N V P Jaarboek. (NE) **792**
Nederlandse Vereniging "de Rijwiel- en Automobiel Industrie" Actueel see R A I Actueel **4700**
Nederlandse Vereniging van Legpluimveehouders. Mededelingen. (NE) **222**
Nederlandse Vereniging van Rubber- en Kunststoffabrikanten Informatief see N V R - Informatief **3864**
Nederlandse Vereniging van Vrienden van de Ceramiek. Mededelingenblad. (NE ISSN 0920-1009) **356**
Nederlandse Vereniging van Vrouwen met Academische Opleiding. Mededelingen. (NE ISSN 0028-2332) **1318**

Nederlandse Vereniging voor Klinische Chemie. Almanak. (NE) **3262**
Nederlandse Vereniging voor Klinische Chemie. Tijdschrift/Netherlands Society for Clinical Chemistry. Journal. (NE ISSN 0168-8472) **1184**
Nederlandse Vereniging voor Zeegeschiedenis. Mededelingen see Tijdschrift voor Zeegeschiedenis **4740**
Nederlandse Vliegtuigencyclopedie. (NE) **59**
Nedjma. (FR) **2169**
Need a Lift? (US ISSN 0548-1384) **1650**
Needle and Bobbin Club Bulletin. (US ISSN 0273-0197) **3591**
Needle Arts. (US ISSN 0047-925X) **3592**
Needlepoint Bulletin. (US) **3592**
Needlepoint News see Needlepoint Plus **3592**
Needlepoint Plus. (US ISSN 1040-5518) **3592**
Needle's Eye. (US ISSN 0028-2359) **1287**
Needs. (JA ISSN 0287-3052) **4329**
Neem Mijnou. (NE ISSN 0922-2472) **1650**
Neerlandia. (NE ISSN 0028-2383) **4443**
Neerlands Postduiven Orgaan. (NE ISSN 0028-2391) **4481**, 565
Neetee. (II) **2200**
Neeuropa. (LU) **338**, 2941
Neft', Gaz i Neftekhimiya za Rubezhom/Oil, Gas and Petrochemistry Abroad. (RU) **3693**, 1857
Neftegazonosnye i Perspektivnye Kompleksy Tsentral'nykh i Vostochnykh Oblastei Russkoi Platformy. (RU) **3693**
Neftekhimiya. (RU ISSN 0028-2421) **3693**
Neftena i Vuglistna Geologiia/Petroleum and Coal Geology. (BU ISSN 0204-5109) **1574**, 3693
Neftepererabotka i Neftekhimiya. (KR ISSN 0548-1406) **3693**
Neftyanik (Moscow, 1956). (RU ISSN 0028-243X) **3693**
Neftyanik (Moscow, 1974). (RU) **3706**
Neftyanoe Khozyaistvo. (RU ISSN 0028-2448) **3693**
Negative Capability. (US ISSN 0277-5166) **2875**
Negba. (IS) **1712**
Neged Hazerem see Youth and Nation **3935**
Negentiende Eeuw. (NE) **2377**
Negev. (IS) **2204**
Negin. (IR) **2941**
Negobancos see Negocios y Bancos **792**
Negoce et Agriculture. (FR) **185**
Negocios. (CK) **681**
▼Negocios Al Dia. (UK ISSN 0960-8710) **918**
Negocios y Bancos. (MX ISSN 0028-2456) **792**
Negotiated Working Conditions from Collective Agreements in Nova Scotia.(CN ISSN 0226-3882) **989**
Negotiation Journal. (US ISSN 0748-4526) **3966**
Negotiations Management see Inside Negotiations **983**
Negozio Moderno. (IT) **2554**
Negritud see Presencia Negra **2020**
Negro Airmen International Newsletter. (US) **1300**, 59
Negro Almanac: A Reference Work on the African American. (US) **2016**, 420
Negro Educational Review. (US) **1650**, 2016
Negro History Bulletin. (US ISSN 0028-2529) **2016**, 2318
Negro Traveler and Conventioneer see Traveler & Conventioneer **4794**
Nehag Nyengu see Language Research **2824**
Nei Jing. (CC) **3134**

Nei Menggu Daxue Xuebao (Shehui Kexue Ban)/Inner Mongolian University. Journal (Social Science Edition). (CC ISSN 1000-5218) 4381
Nei Menggu Daxue Xuebao (Ziran Kexue Ban)/Inner Mongolian University. Journal (Natural Science Edition). (CC ISSN 1000-1638) 4329
Nei Menggu Funu/Inner Mongolian Women. (CC) 4849
Nei Menggu Shehui Kexue/Inner Mongolian Social Sciences. (CC) 4381
Nei Menggu Shifan Daxue Xuebao (Ziran Kexue Ban)/Inner Mongolian Normal University. Journal (Natural Science Edition). (CC ISSN 1001-7623) 4329
Nei Ming. (HK) 4215
Neicha Sutadi/Nature Study. (JA ISSN 0466-6089) 4329
†Neige Magazine. (FR ISSN 0247-1906) 5244
Neighbor Magazine. (US) 2229
Neighborhood Works. (US ISSN 0193-791X) 2492, 1793, 1964
Neighboring Property Owners. (US) 2715, 4153
Neighbors. (US ISSN 0162-3974) 109
Neighbors - Interracial Living. (US ISSN 0047-9314) 3945
Neihardt Foundation Newsletter. (US) 2875
Neil Good's San Diego Report see San Diego Political Watch 4094
▼Neil Muscott's Success Newsletter. (CN ISSN 1188-2921) 4036, 1022, 1048, 1685
Neil Sperry's Gardens. (US ISSN 1052-3243) 2135
Neiranji Gongcheng/Chinese Internal Combustion Engine Engineering. (CC) 1921, 3021
Neiranji Xuebao/Chinese Society for Internal Combustion Engines. Transactions. (CC ISSN 1000-0909) 1936
Neirofiziologiya/Neurophysiology. (KR ISSN 0028-2561) 573, 3346
Neisser Heimatblatt fuer den Stadt- und Landkreis Neisse. (GW) 2377
Neki Pokazatelji Tehnickog Razvoja Privrede Jugoslavije. (YU ISSN 0300-2497) 730
Nekotorye Filosofskie Voprosy Sovremennogo Estestvoznaniya. (RU) 3773, 4329
Nekuda. (IS) 2204
Nelen Yubu. (AT ISSN 0726-0458) 4191, 4443
Nelineinye Granichnye Zadachi. (KR) 3048
Nelson-Atkins Museum of Art. Calendar of Events. (US) 3530
Nelson Gallery and Atkins Museum. Gallery Events see Nelson-Atkins Museum of Art. Calendar of Events 3530
†Nelson Notes. (US) 5244
Nelson's Directory of Investment Managers. (US ISSN 0896-0143) 1147, 792, 958
Nelson's Directory of Investment Research. (US ISSN 0896-0135) 1147, 792, 918, 958
▼Nelson's Directory of Plan Sponsors and Tax Exempt Funds. (US ISSN 1053-0312) 1147, 958
Nelson's Directory of Wall Street Research see Nelson's Directory of Investment Research 1147
▼Nelson's Earnings Outlook. (US ISSN 1049-3344) 958
Nelson's Global Research. (US ISSN 1044-0267) 958
†Nelson's Guide to "Neglected" Stocks. (US ISSN 0897-6538) 5244
▼Nelson's Guide to Pension Fund Consultants. (US ISSN 1053-2536) 958
Nelson's Research Monthly see Nelson's Global Research 958
Nemalah/Myren. (DK ISSN 0108-3023) 4191
Neman. (BW ISSN 0130-7517) 2875

Nematologia Mediterranea. (IT ISSN 0391-9749) 185
Nematologica. (NE ISSN 0028-2596) 589, 109
Nematological Abstracts. (UK ISSN 0957-6797) 140, 18, 466
Nemcon. (UK) 2776
Nemity. (PY ISSN 0254-8178) 2511
Nemli' (DK) 4245, 1261
†Nemo: The Classic Comics Library. (US ISSN 0746-9438) 5244
Nemouria: Occasional Papers of the Delaware Museum of Natural History.(US ISSN 0085-3887) 4329
Nemunas. (LI) 1261
Nemuno Krastas. (GW ISSN 0028-260X) 2016
Nemzetor. (GW ISSN 0028-2626) 2875
Nena dhe Femija. (AA) 3806
Neng Yuan/Energy Sources. (CC ISSN 0258-1469) 1793
Nengyuan Gongcheng. (CC) 1793
Nengyuan Yanjiu yu Liyong. (CC ISSN 1001-5523) 1793
†Nenpo Nihon no Roshi Kankei. (JA) 5244
Nentori. (AA ISSN 0548-1600) 2875
Neo-Hellenika. (US ISSN 0077-6521) 1278
Neo Restauration. (FR ISSN 1145-377X) 2478
Neo Restauration Hotellerie Collectives see Neo Restauration 2478
Neodidagmata. (PL ISSN 0077-653X) 1756
Neohelicon. (NE ISSN 0324-4652) 2941
†Neologie en Marche. Serie A. Langue Generale. (CN ISSN 0380-9366) 5244
Neometaphysical Digest. (UK) 3670
†Neon. (US) 5244
Neonatal Intensive Care. (US) 3295, 3323
Neonatal Network. (US ISSN 0730-0832) 3282, 3323
†Neonatal Physiology. (UK ISSN 0263-7359) 5244
Neophilologus. (NE ISSN 0028-2677) 2831, 2941
Neoplasia. (SP) 3200
Neoplasia of the Head and Neck-- Diagnosis, Treatment see I C R D B Cancergram: Neoplasia of the Head and Neck - Diagnosis, Treatment 3175
†Neoplasm Immunology. (UK ISSN 0142-8500) 5244
Neoplasma. (CS ISSN 0028-2685) 3200
Neos Kosmos. (AT ISSN 0028-2693) 2016
Neotestamentica. (SA ISSN 0254-8356) 4191
Nepal. Central Bureau of Statistics. Statistical Pocket Book. (NP) 4580
Nepal. Department of Agricultural Education and Research. Annual Report. (NP) 109, 1650
Nepal. Department of Medicinal Plants. Annual Report. (NP) 511, 3736
Nepal. Rashtriya Pancayata. Arthika Samiti. (NP) 875
Nepal - Antiquary. (NP) 3642, 3909
Nepal - Antiquary. Bibliographical Series. (NP) 3647
Nepal Bank Bulletin. see Nepal Bank Patrika 792
Nepal Bank Limited. Annual Report and Balance Sheet. (NP) 792
Nepal Bank Limited. Tathyank Bibaran. (NP) 730
Nepal Bank Patrika/Nepal Bank Bulletin. (NP) 792
Nepal Chronicle. (NP) 2211
Nepal Documentation. (NP) 730, 18
Nepal Family Planning and Maternal Child Health Board. Annual Report. (NP) 597, 4414
Nepal Foreign Trade Association. Bulletin. (NP) 918
Nepal Gazette Translation Service see Nepal Recorder 2658
Nepal Industrial Development Corporation. Annual Report. (NP ISSN 0077-6548) 1081

Nepal Industrial Development Corporation. Industrial Digest. (NP ISSN 0077-6556) 1081
Nepal Industrial Development Corporation. Statistical Abstracts. (NP ISSN 0077-6564) 730
Nepal Law Review. see Nepala Kanuna Paricarca 2658
Nepal Law Translation Series see Nepal Miscellaneous Series 2658
Nepal Medical Association. Journal. (NP ISSN 0028-2715) 3134
Nepal Miscellaneous Series. (NP) 2658
Nepal Pharmaceutical Association. Journal. (NP) 3736
Nepal Press Digest. (NP ISSN 0028-2723) 2211
Nepal Press Report. (NP ISSN 0028-2731) 2211
Nepal Rastra Bank. Annual Report. (NP) 792
Nepal Rastra Bank. Quarterly Economic Bulletin. (NP ISSN 0028-274X) 875
Nepal Recorder. (NP) 2658
Nepal Research Centre. Journal. (GW ISSN 0720-6615) 3642
Nepala Kanuna Paricarca/Nepal Law Review. (NP) 2658
Nepalese Journal of Political Science. (NP) 3909
Nepali Weekly. see Matribhoomi 2211
Nepegeszeg. (CS) 3806
Nephrologie. (SZ ISSN 0250-4960) 3389
Nephrology, Dialysis and Transplantation. (GW ISSN 0931-0509) 3389
Nephrology News & Issues. (US ISSN 0896-1263) 3389
Nephrology News and Issues, Inc. Product and Service Directory see N N & I - E S R D Product and Service Directory 3389
Nephron. (SZ ISSN 0028-2766) 3389
Nepi Kultura - Nepi Tarsadalom. (HU ISSN 0541-9522) 4443
Nepmuveles. (CS) 2875
Neprajz es Nyelvtudomany. see Acta Universitatis Szegediensis de Attila Jozsef Nominatae. Sectio Ethnographica et Linguistica 2801
Neprajzi Ertesito/Ethnographic Review. (HU ISSN 0077-6599) 246
Neprajzi Kozlemenyek. (HU ISSN 0028-2774) 246, 2057
Neprajzi Tanulmanyok. (HU ISSN 0077-6602) 246
Nepriklausoma Lietuva. (CN ISSN 0047-9357) 2016
Neptun see Delphin 4470
Neptune Nautisme see Neptune Yachting 4527
Neptune Yachting. (FR ISSN 0762-7378) 4527
Neptune's Kingdom. (IE) 2998
Neptunus. (BE ISSN 0028-2790) 4734
†Neraca. (MY) 5244
Nerium News. (US) 2135
Nerve Cell Biology. (UK ISSN 0142-8225) 526
Nerve Chemistry see Shinkei Kagaku 3354
Der Nervenarzt. (GW ISSN 0028-2804) 3346
Nervenheilkunde. (GW ISSN 0722-1541) 3346
Nesselblatt. (GW) 2539
Nessuno see La Voce della U I L 2591
Nestekide. (FI ISSN 0472-8874) 4698, 4520
Nestle Foundation. Annual Report. (SZ) 3609
Nestle Nutrition Series. (US) 3609
Nestor. (US ISSN 0028-2812) 279, 1278, 2831
Net. (GW ISSN 0177-5499) 1340
Net. (UK ISSN 0028-2820) 4191
Net Friend News. (US) 4509
Net Net see Log On 1445
Netback. (US ISSN 0742-4507) 958
Netbacking see Netback 958
Netball. (UK ISSN 0144-0810) 4509

Netherlands. Centraal Bureau voor de Statistiek. Beleggingen van Institutionele Beleggers see Netherlands. Centraal Bureau voor de Statistiek. Institutionele Beleggers 958
Netherlands. Centraal Bureau voor de Statistiek. Civil and Administrative Jurisdiction. Burgerlijke en Administratieve Rechtspraak. (NE) 2658
Netherlands. Centraal Bureau voor de Statistiek. Conjunctuurtest. (NE ISSN 0166-9087) 730
Netherlands. Centraal Bureau voor de Statistiek. Criminaliteit en Strafrechtspleging/Criminal Statistics.(NE) 1525
Netherlands. Centraal Bureau voor de Statistiek. Criminele Statistiek see Netherlands. Centraal Bureau voor de Statistiek. Criminaliteit en Strafrechtspleging 1525
Netherlands. Centraal Bureau voor de Statistiek. Diagnosestatistiek Bedrijfsverenigingen (Omslagleden). (NE ISSN 0168-4108) 2547
Netherlands. Centraal Bureau voor de Statistiek. Faillissementsstatistiek. Bankruptcies. (NE ISSN 0077-6793) 730
Netherlands. Centraal Bureau voor de Statistiek. Gevangenisstatistiek/ Statistics of Prisons. (NE ISSN 0077-6815) 1519
Netherlands. Centraal Bureau voor de Statistiek. Hypotheken. Statistics of Mortgages. (NE ISSN 0168-4590) 730
Netherlands. Centraal Bureau voor de Statistiek. Institutionele Beleggers. (NE) 958
Netherlands. Centraal Bureau voor de Statistiek. Jaaroverzicht Bevolking en Bevolking en Volksgezondheid see Netherlands. Centraal Bureau voor de Statistiek. Jaarstatistiek van de Bevolking 3993
Netherlands. Centraal Bureau voor de Statistiek. Jaarstatistiek van de Bevolking/Population Statistics. (NE ISSN 0168-4000) 3993, 4118
Netherlands. Centraal Bureau voor de Statistiek. Justiciele Kinderbescherming. (NE) 1247, 4580
Netherlands. Centraal Bureau voor de Statistiek. Justitiele Statistiek. Judicial Statistics see Netherlands. Centraal Bureau voor de Statistiek. Civil and Administrative Jurisdiction. Burgerlijke en Administratieve Rechtspraak 2658
Netherlands. Centraal Bureau voor de Statistiek. Kwartaalbericht Rechtsbescherming en Veiligheid/ Quarterly Bulletin on Justice and Security Statistics. (NE) 2658
Netherlands. Centraal Bureau voor de Statistiek. Maandschrift. (NE ISSN 0166-0268) 4580
Netherlands. Centraal Bureau voor de Statistiek. Maandstatistiek Financiewezen. (NE) 730
Netherlands. Centraal Bureau voor de Statistiek. Maandstatistiek Rechtsbescherming en Veiligheid - Monthly Bulletin on Justice and Security Statistics see Netherlands. Centraal Bureau voor de Statistiek. Kwartaalbericht Rechtsbescherming en Veiligheid/Quarterly Bulletin on Justice and Security Statistics 2658
Netherlands. Centraal Bureau voor de Statistiek. Maandstatistiek van de Bevolking. (NE ISSN 0024-8711) 3993, 4580
Netherlands. Centraal Bureau voor de Statistiek. Maandstatistiek van de Binnenlandse Handel see Netherlands. Centraal Bureau voor de Statistiek. Maandstatistiek van de Binnenlandse Handel en Dienstverlening 730
Netherlands. Centraal Bureau voor de Statistiek. Maandstatistiek van de Binnenlandse Handel en Dienstverlening. (NE ISSN 0166-9281) 730

6482 NETHERLANDS. CENTRAAL

Netherlands. Centraal Bureau voor de Statistiek. Maandstatistiek van de Buitenlandse Handel per Goederensoort. (NE ISSN 0024-8738) **730**

Netherlands. Centraal Bureau voor de Statistiek. Maandstatistiek van de Buitenlandse Handel per Land. (NE ISSN 0024-8746) **730**

Netherlands. Centraal Bureau voor de Statistiek. Maandstatistiek van de Industrie. (NE ISSN 0470-6684) **4615**

Netherlands. Centraal Bureau voor de Statistiek. Maandstatistiek van de Landbouw. (NE ISSN 0024-8754) **140,** 4580

Netherlands. Centraal Bureau voor de Statistiek. Maandstatistiek Verkeer en Vervoer. (NE ISSN 0024-8770) **4665**

Netherlands. Centraal Bureau voor de Statistiek. Muziek en Theater. (NE ISSN 0168-3519) **4635**

†Netherlands. Centraal Bureau voor de Statistiek. Naamlijsten voor de Statistiek van de Buitenlandse Handel/List of Goods for the Statistics of Foreign Trade. Supplement. (NE ISSN 0168-4094) **5244**

Netherlands. Centraal Bureau voor de Statistiek. Naamlijsten voor de Statistiek van de Buitenlandse Handel. List of Goods for the Statistics of Foreign Trade. (NE) **730**

Netherlands. Centraal Bureau voor de Statistiek. Nationale Rekeningen/National Accounts. (NE ISSN 0168-3489) **730,** 1101

Netherlands. Centraal Bureau voor de Statistiek. Nederlandse Energiehuishouding. (NE ISSN 0168-5236) **1974**

Netherlands. Centraal Bureau voor de Statistiek. Productie Statistiek van de Zuivelindustrie/Production Statistics of the Dairy Industry. (NE ISSN 0168-518X) **140,** 202

Netherlands. Centraal Bureau voor de Statistiek. Produktiestatistieken: Alcoholfabrieken, Bierbrouwerijen en Mouterijen, Distilleerderijen en Frisdrankenindustrie. (NE ISSN 0168-5767) **730**

Netherlands. Centraal Bureau voor de Statistiek. Produktiestatistieken: Papier- en Kartonindustrie. (NE ISSN 0168-4361) **3668**

Netherlands. Centraal Bureau voor de Statistiek. Produktiestatistieken: Rijwiel- en Motorrijwielindustrie. (NE ISSN 0168-5864) **4498**

Netherlands. Centraal Bureau voor de Statistiek. Produktiestatistieken: Suikerindustrie. (NE ISSN 0168-5287) **2085**

Netherlands. Centraal Bureau voor de Statistiek. Produktiestatistiek Strokartonindustrie *see* Netherlands. Centraal Bureau voor de Statistiek. Produktiestatistieken: Papier- en Kartonindustrie **3668**

Netherlands. Centraal Bureau voor de Statistiek. Produktiestatistieken: Veevoederindustrie. (NE ISSN 0168-5333) **207**

Netherlands. Centraal Bureau voor de Statistiek. Produktiestatistiek van de Papierindustries *see* Netherlands. Centraal Bureau voor de Statistiek. Produktiestatistieken: Papier- en Kartonindustrie **3668**

Netherlands. Centraal Bureau voor de Statistiek. Regionaal Statistisch Zakboek. (NE) **4580**

Netherlands. Centraal Bureau voor de Statistiek. Sociaal-Economische Maandstatistiek. (NE ISSN 0168-549X) **4426**

Netherlands. Centraal Bureau voor de Statistiek. Sociale Maandstatistiek *see* Netherlands. Centraal Bureau voor de Statistiek. Sociaal-Economische Maandstatistiek **4426**

Netherlands. Centraal Bureau voor de Statistiek. Statistical Studies. (NE) **4580**

Netherlands. Centraal Bureau voor de Statistiek. Statistiek der Branden/Fire Statistics. (NE ISSN 0077-6955) **2035**

Netherlands. Centraal Bureau voor de Statistiek. Statistiek der Motorvoertuigen/Statistics of Motor Vehicles. (NE ISSN 0168-4973) **4665**

Netherlands. Centraal Bureau voor de Statistiek. Statistiek der Motorrijtuigen *see* Netherlands. Centraal Bureau voor de Statistiek. Statistiek der Motorvoertuigen **4665**

Netherlands. Centraal Bureau voor de Statistiek. Statistiek der Rijksfinancien/Statistics of the State Finances of the Netherlands. (NE ISSN 0168-373X) **730,** 1101

Netherlands. Centraal Bureau voor de Statistiek. Statistiek der Verkiezingen. Gemeenteraden/Election Statistics. Municipal Councils. (NE ISSN 0168-4884) **3938**

Netherlands. Centraal Bureau voor de Statistiek. Statistiek der Verkiezingen. Provinciale Staten/Netherlands. Central Bureau of Statistics. Election Statistics. Provincial Councils. (NE ISSN 0168-5732) **4081**

Netherlands. Centraal Bureau voor de Statistiek. Statistiek der Verkiezingen. Tweede Kamer der Staten-Generaal/Election Statistics. Second Chamber of the States-General. (NE ISSN 0168-5686) **3938**

Netherlands. Centraal Bureau voor de Statistiek. Statistiek van Aan-, Af- en Doorvoer. Goederenvervoer per Goederensoort van en naar de Zeehavens van Rotterdam en Amsterdam. (NE ISSN 0168-4825) **4665**

†Netherlands. Centraal Bureau voor de Statistiek. Statistiek van de Visserij/Statistics of Fisheries. (NE ISSN 0168-4167) **5244**

Netherlands. Centraal Bureau voor de Statistiek. Statistiek van de Zeevaart/Statistics of Seaborne Shipping. (NE ISSN 0168-5422) **4734**

Netherlands. Centraal Bureau voor de Statistiek. Statistiek van de Aan-, Af- en Doorvoer. Goederenvervoer van en naar Nederland/Statistics of the International Goods Traffic. (NE ISSN 0168-4876) **730**

Netherlands. Centraal Bureau voor de Statistiek. Statistiek van de Algemene Bijstand/Statistics of Public Assistance. (NE ISSN 0168-4086) **4426**

Netherlands. Centraal Bureau voor de Statistiek. Statistiek van de Bejaardenoorden/Homes for the Aged. (NE) **4426**

†Netherlands. Centraal Bureau voor de Statistiek. Statistiek van de Gemeentewege per Leerling Beschikbaar Gestelde Bedragen voor het Lager Onderwijs/Statistics of the Amounts per Pupil Provided for Primary Education. (NE ISSN 0168-5244) **5244**

Netherlands. Centraal Bureau voor de Statistiek. Statistiek van de Internationale Binnenvaart/Statistics of the International Inland Shipping. (NE ISSN 0168-5376) **4734**

Netherlands. Centraal Bureau voor de Statistiek. Statistiek van de Inkomsten en Uitgaven der Overheid voor Cultuur en Recreatie/Statistics of Government Expenditure on Culture and Recreation. (NE ISSN 0168-4248) **4498**

Netherlands. Centraal Bureau voor de Statistiek. Statistiek van de Investeringen in Vaste Activa in de Industrie *see* Netherlands. Centraal Bureau voor de Statistiek. Statistiek van de Investeringen in Vaste Activa in de Nijverheid **730**

Netherlands. Centraal Bureau voor de Statistiek. Statistiek van de Investeringen in Vaste Activa in de Nijverheid/Statistics on Fixed Capital Formation in Industry. (NE ISSN 0168-7956) **730,** 4580

Netherlands. Centraal Bureau voor de Statistiek. Statistiek van de Koopvaardijvloot. Statistics of the Merchant Marine. (NE) **4734**

Netherlands. Centraal Bureau voor de Statistiek. Statistiek van de Luchtvaart/Netherlands. Central Bureau of Statistics. Civil Aviation Statistics. (NE ISSN 0168-552X) **4676**

Netherlands. Centraal Bureau voor de Statistiek. Statistiek van de Land- en Tuinbouw/Statistics of Agriculture. (NE ISSN 0168-3918) **140**

Netherlands. Centraal Bureau voor de Statistiek. Statistiek van de Openbare Bibliotheken. (NE ISSN 0168-3462) **2795**

Netherlands. Centraal Bureau voor de Statistiek. Statistiek van de Spaargelden/Statistics of Savings. (NE ISSN 0168-3330) **730**

Netherlands. Centraal Bureau voor de Statistiek. Statistiek van de Uitgaven der Overheid voor Onderwijs/Statistics of the Expenditure of the State, the Provinces and the Municipalities on Education. (NE ISSN 0168-7905) **1678,** 1730

†Netherlands. Centraal Bureau voor de Statistiek. Statistiek van de Voorlichting Bij Scholen en Beroepskeuze/Statistics of Vocational Guidance. (NE ISSN 0168-423X) **5244**

Netherlands. Centraal Bureau voor de Statistiek. Statistiek van de Verkeersongevallen op de Openbare Weg/Statistics of Road-Traffic Accidents. (NE ISSN 0168-5023) **4665**

Netherlands. Centraal Bureau voor de Statistiek. Statistiek van het Beroepsonderwijs *see* Netherlands. Centraal Bureau voor de Statistiek. Statistiek van het Beroepsonderwijs: Technisch en Nautisch Onderwijs **1678**

Netherlands. Centraal Bureau voor de Statistiek. Statistiek van het Beroepsonderwijs: Beroepsbegeleidend Onderwijs Leerlingwezen. (NE ISSN 0168-5708) **1678**

Netherlands. Centraal Bureau voor de Statistiek. Statistiek van het Beroepsonderwijs: Kunstonderwijs. Art Colleges. (NE ISSN 0168-5503) **1678,** 1695, 1712

Netherlands. Centraal Bureau voor de Statistiek. Statistiek van het Beroepsonderwijs: Landbouwonderwijs *see* Netherlands. Centraal Bureau voor de Statistiek. Statistiek van het Hoger Beroepsonderwijs: Agrarisch Onderwijs **1678**

Netherlands. Centraal Bureau voor de Statistiek. Statistiek van het Beroepsonderwijs: Opleidingsscholen Kleuterleidsters en Pedagogische Academies. (NE) **1678**

Netherlands. Centraal Bureau voor de Statistiek. Statistiek van het Beroepsonderwijs: Sociaal-Pedagogisch Onderwijs/Statistics on Socio-Pedagogic Training. (NE ISSN 0168-5600) **1678**

Netherlands. Centraal Bureau voor de Statistiek. Statistiek van het Beroepsonderwijs: Technisch en Nautisch Onderwijs/Statistics of Vocational Training. (NE ISSN 0168-5457) **1678,** 3632

Netherlands. Centraal Bureau voor de Statistiek. Statistiek van het Erkende Schriftelijk Onderwijs/Statistics on Correspondence Courses. (NE ISSN 0168-4906) **1756**

Netherlands. Centraal Bureau voor de Statistiek. Statistiek van het Gesubsidieerde Toneel *see* Netherlands. Centraal Bureau voor de Statistiek. Muziek en Theater **4635**

Netherlands. Centraal Bureau voor de Statistiek. Statistiek van het Hoger Beroepsonderwijs: Agrarisch Onderwijs. (NE) **1678,** 3632

Netherlands. Centraal Bureau voor de Statistiek. Statistiek van het Internationaal Goederenvervoer *see* Netherlands. Centraal Bureau voor de Statistiek. Statistiek van de Aan-, Af- en Doorvoer. Goederenvervoer van en naar Nederland **730**

Netherlands. Centraal Bureau voor de Statistiek. Statistiek van het Internationaal Zeehavenvervoer *see* Netherlands. Centraal Bureau voor de Statistiek. Statistiek van Aan-, Af- en Doorvoer. Goederenvervoer per Goederensoort van en naar de Zeehavens van Rotterdam en Amsterdam **4665**

Netherlands. Centraal Bureau voor de Statistiek. Statistiek van het Kunstonderwijs. Statistics on Art Colleges *see* Netherlands. Centraal Bureau voor de Statistiek. Statistiek van het Beroepsonderwijs: Kunstonderwijs. Art Colleges **1678**

Netherlands. Centraal Bureau voor de Statistiek. Statistiek van het Kweekschoolonderwijs. Statistics on Teacher Training Colleges *see* Netherlands. Centraal Bureau voor de Statistiek. Statistiek van het Beroepsonderwijs: Opleidingsscholen Kleuterleidsters en Pedagogische Academies **1678**

Netherlands. Centraal Bureau voor de Statistiek. Statistiek van het Personenvervoer/Statistics of Passenger Transport. (NE ISSN 0168-5074) **4654**

Netherlands. Centraal Bureau voor de Statistiek. Statistiek van het Schriftelijk Onderwijs *see* Netherlands. Centraal Bureau voor de Statistiek. Statistiek van het Erkende Schriftelijk Onderwijs **1756**

Netherlands. Centraal Bureau voor de Statistiek. Statistiek van het Sociaal-Pedagogisch Onderwijs *see* Netherlands. Centraal Bureau voor de Statistiek. Statistiek van het Beroepsonderwijs: Sociaal-Pedagogisch Onderwijs **1678**

Netherlands. Centraal Bureau voor de Statistiek van het Binnenlands Goederenvervoer. Statistics of Internal Goods Transport in the Netherlands. (NE ISSN 0168-5325) **4734**

Netherlands. Centraal Bureau voor de Statistiek. Statistiek van Het Wetenschappelijk Onderwijs/Statistics of University Education. (NE ISSN 0168-5058) **1678,** 1712

Netherlands. Centraal Bureau voor de Statistiek. Statistiek van het W V O, H A V O en M A V O: Scholen en Leerlingen. (NE ISSN 0168-5856) **1678,** 1730

Netherlands. Centraal Bureau voor de Statistiek. Statistiek van het W V O, H A V O en M A V O: Instroom, Doorstroom en Uitstroom van Leerlingen *see* Netherlands. Centraal Bureau voor de Statistiek. Statistiek van het W V O, H A V O en M A V O: Scholen en Leerlingen **1678**

Netherlands. Centraal Bureau voor de Statistiek. Statistiek Vreemdelingenverkeer. (NE ISSN 0168-5538) **4800**

Netherlands. Centraal Bureau voor de Statistiek. Statistiek Werkzame Personen. (NE ISSN 0168-3667) **730**

Netherlands. Centraal Bureau voor de Statistiek. Statistisch Bulletin. (NE ISSN 0166-9680) **4580**

Netherlands. Centraal Bureau voor de Statistiek. Statistisch Zakboek/Pocket Yearbook. (NE ISSN 0168-3705) **4580**

Netherlands. Centraal Bureau voor de Statistiek. Statistische en Econometrische Onderzoekingen *see* Netherlands. Centraal Bureau voor de Statistiek. Statistische Onderzoekingen **731**

Netherlands. Centraal Bureau voor de Statistiek. Statistische Onderzoekingen. (NE) **731,** 4580

Title

Netherlands. Centraal Bureau voor de Statistiek. Toepassing der Kinderwetten see Netherlands. Centraal Bureau voor de Statistiek. Justiciele Kinderbescherming **1247**
Netherlands. Centraal Bureau voor de Statistiek. Vakantieonderzoek. (NE ISSN 0168-3411) **4800**
Netherlands. Centraal Bureau voor de Statistiek. Vermogensverdeling. Regionale Gegevens/Distribution of Personal Wealth. Regional Data. (NE ISSN 0168-3888) **731**
Netherlands. Centraal Bureau voor de Statistiek. Voortgezet Onderwijs Regionaal Bezien. (NE ISSN 0168-485X) **1678**
†Netherlands. Centraal Bureau voor de Statistiek. Winststatistiek der Grotere Naamloze Vennootschappen/Profit-Statistics of the Limited Liability Companies. (NE ISSN 0077-751X) **5244**
Netherlands. Centraal Bureau voor de Statistiek. Zuivelstatistiek see Netherlands. Centraal Bureau voor de Statistiek. Productie Statistiek van de Zuivelindustrie **140**
Netherlands. Centraal Planbureau. Centraal Economisch Plan. (NE ISSN 0077-7536) **1081**
Netherlands. Central Bureau of Statistics. Civil Aviation Statistics. see Netherlands. Centraal Bureau voor de Statistiek. Statistiek van de Luchtvaart **4676**
Netherlands. Central Bureau of Statistics. Election Statistics. Provincial Councils. see Netherlands. Centraal Bureau voor de Statistiek. Statistiek der Verkiezingen. Provinciale Staten **4081**
Netherlands. Centrale Commissie voor de Statistiek. Jaarverslag. (NE) **4580**
Netherlands. Commissie voor Geodesie. Publications on Geodesy. New Series.(NE) **2257**, **1871**
Netherlands. Departement van Marine. Catalogus van Nederlandse Zeekaarten en Boekwerken see Catalogus van Nederlandse Zeekaarten en Andere Hydrografische Publikaties **4823**
Netherlands. Ministerie van Onderwijs en Wetenschappen. Documentatieblad see Netherlands. Ministerie van Onderwijs en Wetenschappen. Onderwijsliteratuur **1678**
Netherlands. Ministerie van Onderwijs en Wetenschappen. Onderwijsliteratuur. (NE ISSN 0167-6644) **1678**, **18**
Netherlands. Ministerie van Onderwijs en Wetenschappen. Onderwijsverslag.(NE) **1650**
Netherlands. Ministerie van Onderwijs en Wetenschappen. Pedagogische Bibliografie. (NE ISSN 0028-2987) **1678**
Netherlands. Ministerie van Volksgezondheid en Milieuhygiene. Verslag Levensmiddelen en Keuring van Waren see Netherlands. Ministerie van Welzijn, Volksgezondheid en Cultuur. Verslag Levensmiddelen en Keuring van Waren **2078**
Netherlands. Ministerie van Welzijn, Volksgezondheid en Cultuur. Verslag Levensmiddelen en Keuring van Waren. (NE) **2078**
Netherlands. Provisional National Ports Council. Jaarverslag see Nationale Havenraad. Jaarverslag (Year) **4734**
Netherlands. Rijks Geologische Dienst. Jaarverslag/Netherlands Geological Survey. Annual Report. (NE ISSN 0077-7617) **1574**
Netherlands. Rijkscommissie voor Geodesie. Publications on Geodesy. New Series see Netherlands. Commissie voor Geodesie. Publications on Geodesy. New Series **2257**
Netherlands. Rijksinstituut voor de Volksgezondheid. Mededelingen. (NE) **4109**
Netherlands. Rijksinstituut voor Oorlogsdocumentatie. Documenten. (NE ISSN 0066-1287) **2377**
Netherlands. Rijksinstituut voor Oorlogsdocumentatie. Progress Report. (NE) **2377**
Netherlands. Rijksmuseum Amsterdam. Bulletin. (NE ISSN 0569-9665) **338**, **2318**
Netherlands. Rijksmuseum. Bulletin see Netherlands. Rijksmuseum Amsterdam. Bulletin **338**
Netherlands. Sociaal en Cultureel Planbureau. Cahiers. (NE) **4443**
Netherlands. Sociaal en Cultureel Planbureau. Sociale and Culturele Rapporten/Social and Cultural Reports. (NE) **4443**
Netherlands. Sociaal en Cultureel Planbureau. Studies. (NE) **4443**
Netherlands - American Trade see Holland - U S A (New York) **817**
Netherlands-American Trade Directory. (NE) **820**
Netherlands-British Trade Directory. (UK ISSN 0308-1273) **1147**, **820**
Netherlands Energy Research Foundation. Activities Report. see Energieonderzoek Centrum Nederland. Jaarverslag **1786**
Netherlands Federation of Trade Unions. Information Bulletin see F N V News **2583**
Netherlands Fertilizer Technical Bulletin.(NE ISSN 0169-2313) **185**
Netherlands Geographical Studies. see Nederlandse Geografische Studies **2257**
Netherlands Geological Survey. Annual Report. see Netherlands. Rijks Geologische Dienst. Jaarverslag **1574**
Netherlands Institute of Archaeology and Arabic Studies in Cairo. Publications. (NE ISSN 0169-8923) **280**, **2431**
Netherlands International Law Review. (NE ISSN 0165-070X) **2727**
Netherlands Investment Bank for Developing Countries. Annual Report see Netherlands Investment Bank for Developing Countries. Report **793**
Netherlands Investment Bank for Developing Countries. Report/Nederlandse Investeringsbank voor Ontwikkelingslanden. Verslag. (NE) **793**, **933**
Netherlands Journal of Agricultural Science. (NE ISSN 0028-2928) **109**
Netherlands Journal of Aquatic Ecology.(NE) **449**
Netherlands Journal of Economic and Social Geography. see Tijdschrift voor Economische en Sociale Geografie **2264**
Netherlands Journal of Housing and Environmental Research. (NE ISSN 0920-1580) **2493**, **1964**
Netherlands Journal of Medicine. (NE ISSN 0300-2977) **3134**
Netherlands Journal of Plant Pathology.(NE ISSN 0028-2944) **511**
Netherlands Journal of Sea Research. (NE ISSN 0077-7579) **1608**, **449**
Netherlands Journal of Social Sciences. (NE) **4444**
Netherlands' Journal of Sociology see Netherlands Journal of Social Sciences **4444**
Netherlands Journal of Veterinary Science. see Tijdschrift voor Diergeneeskunde **4816**
Netherlands Journal of Zoology. (NE ISSN 0028-2960) **589**
Netherlands Milk and Dairy Journal. (NE ISSN 0028-209X) **202**
Netherlands Nitrogen Technical Bulletin see Netherlands Fertilizer Technical Bulletin **185**
Netherlands Philately Journal. (US) **3755**
Netherlands Phonetic Archives. (US) **2831**
Netherlands Quarterly of Human Rights. Newsletter. (NE ISSN 0169-3441) **2658**, **3945**
Netherlands Society for Clinical Chemistry. Journal. see Nederlandse Vereniging voor Klinische Chemie. Tijdschrift **1184**
Netherlands Yearbook of International Law. (NE) **2727**
Netherlands Youth and Its Education. see Nederlandse Jeugd en Haar Onderwijs **1650**
Netline. (US ISSN 0892-9467) **1427**, **1471**
NetManager. (US) **1022**, **1447**
Neto. (IS) **681**
Netsu Kanri to Kogai - Heat Management and Pollution Control see Sho Enerugi **1836**
Netsu Shori/Japan Society for Heat Treatment. Journal. (JA ISSN 0288-0490) **3416**, **4604**
Nettai Igaku. see Tropical Medicine **3224**
Nettai Nogaku Kenkyu. see Kyushu University. Institute of Tropical Agriculture. Bulletin **104**
Nettai Nogyo. see Japanese Journal of Tropical Agriculture **101**
Netted Gem see Gem **1312**
Netvaerkstedet. (DK) **1022**
▼Netware Solutions. (US) **1427**
†NetWare Technical Journal. (US ISSN 1040-4503) **5244**
Network see Network for Public Schools **1650**
Network (Arlington). (US) **35**, **1650**
Network (Atlanta). (US) **4191**
Network (Bismarck). (US) **1081**
Network (Calgary). (CN ISSN 0830-1417) **2119**
Network (Chicago) see American Bar Association. Law Practice Management Section. Network **2597**
Network (Denville). (US) **1507**, **3134**
Network (Durham). (US ISSN 0270-3637) **597**, **3295**
Network (East Peoria). (US) **4654**
†Network (London, 1965). (UK ISSN 0261-1708) **5244**
Network (London, 1984) see Community Network **5169**
Network (Melbourne). (AT ISSN 0159-7302) **4712**
Network (New York). (US ISSN 1044-1476) **2573**, **4849**
Network (Salt Lake City). (US) **4849**
†Network (Toronto). (CN ISSN 0831-0254) **5244**
Network (Washington, 1971) see Network Connection **4270**
†Network (Washington, 1986). (US ISSN 1040-3388) **5244**
Network Africa see N A **2511**
Network Bed & Breakfast Directory. (US) **4779**
Network Bed and Breakfast Registry see Network Bed & Breakfast Directory **4779**
▼Network - Computation in Neural Systems. (UK ISSN 0954-898X) **4360**, **1427**
†Network Computing (Cedar Knolls). (US) **5244**
▼Network Computing (Manhasset). (US) **1428**, **1438**
Network Computing News. (US) **1463**, **827**, **1454**, **1479**
Network Connection. (US) **4270**, **3945**
Network Entertainment. (CN) **2178**
Network for Public Schools. (US) **1650**
Network Futures see Network Futures & ProLog **1377**
Network Futures & ProLog. (US) **1377**
Network Management Systems & Strategies. (US ISSN 1043-1217) **1428**
Network Monitor. (UK ISSN 0953-8402) **1428**, **827**
Network Monitor. (US ISSN 0890-4685) **1438**
Network News. (AT ISSN 0158-9539) **1241**, **1685**
Network News (Cleveland). (US) **4036**, **1685**, **3945**
Network News (New York). (US) **3570**
Network News (Sudbury) see A B U I
Network News **1426**
†Network Newsletter. (US) **5244**
Network NewsNews. (US ISSN 8755-867X) **4836**, **3806**, **4849**
Network Planning Paper. (US ISSN 0160-9742) **1428**
Network Press. (GW) **3570**
†Network - Urban Coalition. (US ISSN 0047-9373) **5244**
Network World. (US ISSN 0887-7661) **1351**
Network World Canada. (CN) **1351**
Networker. (US) **1116**, **1793**
Networker: Civil, Human and Voting Rights. (US) **3945**
Networker: Domestic Poverty and Human Needs. (US) **4414**
Networker: Economic Policy and Sustainable Development. (US) **933**
Networker: Environment, Energy and Agriculture. (US) **1964**, **109**, **1793**
Networker: International Peace. (US) **3909**
Networker: Justice for Women and Families. (US) **4849**
Networking Directory. (US) **1428**
Networking Management. (US) **1447**, **1340**
Networking Management Europe. (US) **1447**, **1340**
▼NetWorks. (GW ISSN 0939-6675) **1479**
†Networks. (UK ISSN 0954-9145) **5245**
Networks: An International Journal. (US ISSN 0028-3045) **3066**
Networks Update. (US) **1428**
Netz. (GW) **3966**, **933**
Netz Werk Magazin. (GW) **4720**
▼Netzwerkfuehrer: Lokale Netze. (GW ISSN 0939-0367) **1431**, **1471**
†Neu Leben. (GW ISSN 0863-3045) **5245**
Neucleus. (AT) **1318**
Neudrucke Deutscher Literaturwerke. (GW ISSN 0077-7668) **2941**
Neudrucke Deutscher Literaturwerke. Sonderreihe. (GW ISSN 0077-7676) **2941**
Neudrucke Deutscher Literaturwerke des XVI und XVII Jahrhunderts see Neudrucke Deutscher Literaturwerke **2941**
Neudrucke Deutscher Literaturwerke des XVIII und XIX Jahrhunderts see Neudrucke Deutscher Literaturwerke **2941**
Das Neue. (GW) **2190**, **1293**
†Neue Aerztliche. (GW ISSN 0178-787X) **5245**
Neue Agrarzeitung. (AU) **109**
Neue Alpine Hydrologie. see Nouvelle Hydrologie Alpine **4827**
Neue Arbeiterpresse. (GW) **3909**
Neue Arzneimittel. (GW ISSN 0724-567X) **3736**
Neue Arzneimittel und Spezialitaeten see Neue Arzneimittel **3736**
Neue Ausgrabungen und Forschungen aus Niedersachsens Urgeschichte. (GW ISSN 0548-2682) **280**
Neue B S. (AU) **3619**, **989**
Die Neue Baeckerei. (GW) **2089**
Neue Bahn. (AU) **4712**
Neue Beitraege zur George-Forschung. (GW ISSN 0342-9547) **2998**
▼Neue Beitraege zur Juelicher Geschichte. (GW ISSN 0939-2904) **2377**
Neue Bergbautechnik. (GW ISSN 0047-9403) **3491**, **1547**
Neue Bienenzucht. (GW) **109**
Neue Blaetter des Theaters in der Josefstadt. (AU ISSN 0028-3096) **4635**
Neue Blaetter fuer Taubstummenbildung Hoergeschaedigten-Paedagogik **2287**
Das Neue Blatt. (GW) **2190**
Neue Blumenbindekunst see Gestalten und Verkaufen **94**
Das Neue Buch. (GW ISSN 0028-3118) **4213**, **4142**
Die Neue Buecherei. (GW ISSN 0028-3126) **2776**, **4133**
Das Neue China. (GW ISSN 0172-4878) **2016**
Neue D E L I W A - Zeitschrift. (GW ISSN 0341-0323) **1793**, **4827**

Die Neue D L. (GW) 109
Neue Denkschriften des Naturhistorischen Museums in Wien. (AU) 1547, 449, 589
Neue Deutsche-Amerikanische Studien. see New German-American Studies 2511
Neue Deutsche Bauernzeitung see Bauernzeitung 78
†Neue Deutsche Hefte. (GW ISSN 0028-3142) 5245
Neue Deutsche Literatur. (GW ISSN 0028-3150) 2941
Neue Deutsche Presse. (GW ISSN 0323-4339) 2573
Neue Deutsche Schule. (GW) 1650
†Neue Didaktische Modelle. (GW ISSN 0723-3280) 5245
Neue Entomologische Nachrichten. (GW ISSN 0722-3773) 536
Das Neue Erlangen. (GW ISSN 0028-3169) 4329, 2511
Neue Erziehung im Kindergarten. (GW ISSN 0323-3022) 1756
Neue Feinbaeckerei see Die Neue Baeckerei 2089
Neue Fleischer-Zeitung. (GW) 2078
Neue Formen. see Revue Formes Nouvelles 306
Neue Front: Zeitung der Freiheitlichen see N F Z; Neue Freie Zeitung 3908
Neue Gastronomische Zeitschrift Service Manager see N G Z Service Manager 2478
Die Neue Gesellschaft - Frankfurter Hefte. (GW ISSN 0177-6738) 3909
Neue Gespraeche. (GW ISSN 0930-1143) 4270
Neue Hanauer Zeitung see N H Z 2875
Neue Hefte fuer Philosophie. (GW ISSN 0085-3917) 3774
Neue Heimat. (GW ISSN 0548-2801) 3966
Neue Helvetische Gesellschaft. Mitteilungen. (SZ ISSN 0257-3830) 1300
Die Neue Hochschule. (GW ISSN 0340-448X) 1831, 1756
Neue Huette. (GW ISSN 0028-3207) 3416
Neue Illustrierte Wochenschau. (AU ISSN 0028-3223) 2173
Neue Juristische Wochenschrift. (GW ISSN 0341-1915) 2658
Neue Justiz. (GW ISSN 0028-3231) 2658
Der Neue Kaufmann. (AU ISSN 0028-324X) 838
Neue Keramik. (GW ISSN 0933-2367) 1165
Neue Kommentare. (GW ISSN 0028-3258) 3909
Der Neue Konditor. (AU) 2089
Neue Kronstaedter Zeitung. (GW ISSN 0934-4713) 2190
Neue Kunst in Europa see N I K E 337
Neue Landschaft. (GW ISSN 0548-2836) 2135
▼Neue Landwirtschaft. (GW) 109
Neue Literatur. (RM) 2941
Der Neue Mahnruf. (AU ISSN 0028-3274) 3909
Neue Medien. (GW ISSN 0176-6619) 1377, 4133
Neue Mitte. (GW) 4270, 681, 4068
Neue Mode. (GW) 1293
Neue Muenchner Beitraege zur Geschichte der Medizin und Naturwissenschaften. Medizinhistorische Serie. (GW ISSN 0300-8371) 3134
Neue Muenchner Beitraege zur Geschichte der Medizin und Naturwissenschaften. Naturwissenschaftshistorische Reihe. (GW) 4329
Neue Museumskunde. (GW ISSN 0028-3282) 3530
Neue Musikgeschichtliche Forschungen. (GW ISSN 0077-7714) 3570
Neue Musikzeitung. (GW ISSN 0028-3290) 3570, 1261
Neue Nettelstedter Blaetter. (GW) 2377
Neue Oderzeitung. (GW) 2190
Neue Ordnung. (AU) 2875

Die Neue Ordnung. (GW ISSN 0028-3304) 4444, 4270
Neue Politische Literatur. (GW ISSN 0028-3320) 3909
Neue Politische Literatur. Beihefte. (GW ISSN 0176-604X) 3909
Neue Post. (GW) 4849
Neue Praxis. (GW ISSN 0342-9857) 4414
Neue Produkte. (SZ ISSN 0028-3339) 918
Neue Produkte aus Daenemark see New Products from Denmark 5246
Neue Revue. (GW) 2190
Neue Rundschau. (GW ISSN 0028-3347) 2876
Neue Sammlung. (GW ISSN 0028-3355) 1650, 2876
Neue Schulpraxis. (SZ) 1756
Neue Solidaritaet. (GW) 2876, 2190
Neue Stadt. (GW ISSN 0344-7022) 4191
Neue Stenographische Praxis. (GW ISSN 0028-3371) 1059
Neue Steuerpraxis. (SZ ISSN 0028-338X) 1101
Neue Technik/Nouvelles Techniques/New Techniques. (SZ ISSN 0028-3398) 1398
†Neue Technik im Buero. (GW ISSN 0028-3401) 5245
Das Neue Unternehmen. (GW ISSN 0723-2500) 989, 831, 1022
Neue Verpackung see N V 3650
Neue Volksbildung see Erwachsenenbildung in Oesterreich 1683
Neue Weg. (GW) 793
Der Neue Weg. (GW) 1048
Neue Wege. (AU ISSN 0028-3444) 1261, 1650, 4635
Neue Welt see Illustrierte Neue Welt 2005
Neue Welt. (GW) 2190
Neue Werbung. (GW ISSN 0028-3452) 35
Die Neue Wirtschaft. (AU) 681
Neue Wirtschafts-Briefe. (GW ISSN 0028-3460) 1101, 2658
Neue Wissenschaft see Zeitschrift fuer Parapsychologie und Grenzgebiete der Psychologie 3672
Das Neue Wort. (AU) 3909
Neue Zeit. (GW ISSN 0138-5011) 2876
Neue Zeitschrift fuer Arbeits- und Sozialrecht. (GW ISSN 0176-3814) 2658
Neue Zeitschrift fuer Missionswissenschaft/Nouvelle Revue de Science Missionnaire. (SZ ISSN 0028-3495) 4191
Neue Zeitschrift fuer Strafrecht. (GW ISSN 0720-1753) 2658
Neue Zeitschrift fuer Systematische Theologie und Religionsphilosophie. (GW ISSN 0028-3517) 4191
Neue Zeitschrift fuer Verkehrsrecht. (GW ISSN 0934-1307) 4654, 2658
Neue Zeitschrift fuer Verwaltungsrecht. (GW ISSN 0721-880X) 2658
Neue Zeitschrift fuer Wehrrecht. (GW ISSN 0028-3525) 2658
Neue Zeitung. (HU ISSN 0415-3049) 2198
†Neuer Weg. (GW) 5245
Neuer Zions Freund see Zions Freund 4211
Die Neueren Sprachen. (GW ISSN 0342-3816) 2831, 1650
Neuerer. Ausgaben A-C see Innovation & Management 3675
Neuerwerbung Suedasien. (GW ISSN 0720-2695) 3647
Neuerwerbung Theologie und Allgemeine Religionswissenschaft. (GW ISSN 0720-3772) 4191
Neuerwerbungen Vorderer Orient. (GW ISSN 0720-2741) 3647
Neues Athenaeum. see New Athenaeum 2941
Neues aus Japan. (GW) 2208
Neues Bei Uns see S T E W E A G Rundschau 1907
Neues Forvm see Forvm 2866
Neues Glas/New Glass. (GW ISSN 0723-2454) 356

Neues Jahrbuch fuer Geologie und Palaeontologie. Abhandlungen. (GW ISSN 0077-7749) 1574, 3658
Neues Jahrbuch fuer Geologie und Palaeontologie, Monatshefte. (GW ISSN 0028-3630) 1574, 3658
Neues Jahrbuch fuer Mineralogie. Abhandlungen. (GW ISSN 0077-7757) 3491, 1574
Neues Jahrbuch fuer Mineralogie. Monatshefte. (GW ISSN 0028-3649) 3491, 1575
Neues Jahrbuch fuer Mineralogie, Geologie und Palaeontologie. Abhandlungen. Abt. B see Neues Jahrbuch fuer Mineralogie. Abhandlungen 3491
Neues Jahrbuch fuer Mineralogie, Geologie und Palaeontologie. Abhandlungen see Neues Jahrbuch fuer Geologie und Palaeontologie. Abhandlungen 1574
Neues Land. (AU) 109
Neues Leben see Neu Leben 5245
Neues Leben (Moers). (GW ISSN 0028-3665) 4191
Neues Polizeiarchiv. (GW ISSN 0028-3681) 1519
Neues Schrifttum zur Deutschen Landeskunde. (GW) 4381
Neues Steuerrecht von A bis Z. (GW ISSN 0340-9260) 1102, 2658
Neues Trierisches Jahrbuch fuer Heimatpflege und Heimatgeschichte. (GW) 2377
Neues vom Bau. (AU) 626
Neues von Rohde und Schwarz. (GW ISSN 0548-3093) 59, 1340
Neues von Synanon. (GW) 1538
Neues Wohnen. (GW ISSN 0863-4076) 2554, 2448
Neuf see Nieuw - Neuf 304
Neuheiten. (GW) 1081
Neuigkeidnblaeddle. (GW) 3909, 2190, 2493
Neuindische Studien. (GW ISSN 0340-6385) 2831, 2340
†Neujahrsgabe der Deutschen Buecherei. (GW ISSN 0457-3897) 5245
Neumann - Handbuch fuer den Pressevertrieb. (GW ISSN 0935-7866) 4133, 1147
Neunhofer Land. (GW) 2377
Neuphilologische Mitteilungen. (FI ISSN 0028-3754) 2831
†Neural Circulation and C S F. (UK ISSN 0264-9403) 5245
Neural Computation. (US ISSN 0899-7667) 1409, 3226, 3346
Neural Network Almanac see Cognizer Almanac 1877
Neural Network News see I S R: Intelligent Systems Report 1408
†Neural Network Review. (US ISSN 0896-436X) 5245
Neural Networks. (US ISSN 0893-6080) 1409, 3346, 3346
Neural Networks Today see Cognizer Report 1350
†Neural Organisation. (UK ISSN 0264-9411) 5245
†Neural Tube Defects. (UK ISSN 0261-4804) 5245
Neuro-Chirurgie. (FR ISSN 0028-3770) 3382, 3346
Neuro-Fibroma-Tosis. (US) 546, 3346
Neuro-Fibroma-Tosis Research Newsletter. (US) 546, 3346
Neuro-Ophthalmology. (NE ISSN 0165-8107) 3302
Neuro-Orthopedics. (US ISSN 0177-7955) 3310, 3346, 3382
Neuro-Psychiatry see Korean Neuropsychiatric Association. Journal 3344
Neurobiologia. (BL ISSN 0028-3800) 3346, 3382
Neurobiology of Aging. (US ISSN 0197-4580) 573, 3346
Neurochemical Pathology see Molecular and Chemical Neuropathology 3345
Neurochemical Research. (US ISSN 0364-3190) 3346
Neurochemistry. (UK ISSN 0142-8403) 480, 3346
Neurochemistry. (US ISSN 0749-4300) 480

Neurochemistry International. (US ISSN 0197-0186) 3346, 1184
Neurochirurgia. (GW ISSN 0028-3819) 3346, 3382
Neurocomputers see Sixth Generation Systems 1410
Neurocomputing. (NE ISSN 0925-2312) 1409
Neuroelectric News. (US ISSN 0047-942X) 3346, 1904
Neuroendocrine Perspectives. (US ISSN 0168-0617) 3346, 3255
Neuroendocrinology. (SZ ISSN 0028-3835) 3255, 3346
Neuroendocrinology Letters. (GW ISSN 0172-780X) 3346
Neuroepidemiology. (SZ ISSN 0251-5350) 3346
Neurohypophysial Hormones. (UK ISSN 0143-4276) 3255, 573, 3736
▼NeuroImage. (US ISSN 1053-8119) 3346
†Neuroimmunoendocrinology. (UK ISSN 0950-0553) 5245
†Neurolinguistics. (NE ISSN 0301-6412) 5245
Neurologia. (SP ISSN 0213-4853) 3346
Neurologia Colombia. (CK ISSN 0120-1034) 3346
Neurologia Croatica. (CI ISSN 0353-8842) 3346
†Neurologia i Neurochirurgia Polska. (PL ISSN 0028-3843) 5245
Neurologia Medico-Chirurgica. (JA ISSN 0387-2572) 3346
Neurologic Clinics. (US ISSN 0733-8619) 3346
Neurological Research. (US ISSN 0161-6412) 3347
Neurological Surgery/Shinkei Geka. (JA ISSN 0301-2603) 3347, 3382
Neurologie a Psychiatrie Ceskoslovenska see Ceskoslovenska Neurologie a Neurochirurgie 3333
Neurologija see Neurologia Croatica 3346
Neurology. (US ISSN 0028-3878) 3347
Neurology Alert. (US ISSN 0741-4234) 3347
Neurology and Neurobiology. (US) 3347
Neurology India. (II ISSN 0028-3886) 3347
Neurology - Psychiatry. see Zentralblatt Neurologie - Psychiatrie 3182
Neuromuscular Diseases. (UK) 3347
▼Neuromuscular Disorders. (UK ISSN 0960-8966) 3347
Neuron. (US ISSN 0896-6273) 3347, 449
Neuroorthopaedie. (US) 3310, 3347
Neuropaediatrie see Neuropediatrics 3323
Neuropathology and Applied Neurobiology. (UK ISSN 0305-1846) 3347
Neuropatologia Polska. (PL ISSN 0028-3894) 3347
Neuropediatrics. (GW ISSN 0174-304X) 3323, 3347, 3382
Neuropeptides (Edinburgh). (UK ISSN 0143-4179) 556
Neuropeptides (Sheffield). (UK ISSN 0142-8233) 3736
Neuropharmacology. (US ISSN 0028-3908) 3736, 3347
Neurophysiologie Clinique/Clinical Neurophysiology. (FR ISSN 0987-7053) 3347
Neurophysiology. see Neirofiziologiya 573
Neurophysiology. (UK ISSN 0142-8241) 573, 3347
Neurophysiology. (English translation of: Neirofiziologiya) (US ISSN 0090-2977) 3347
▼NeuroProtocols. (US ISSN 1058-6741) 3347
Neuropsicofarmacologia del Comportamento. (IT ISSN 0394-9540) 3347, 3736
Neuropsychiatrie. (GW) 3347
Neuropsychiatrie de l'Enfance et de l'Adolescence. (FR ISSN 0222-9617) 3323, 3347

Neuropsychiatry, Neuropsychology and Behavioral Neurology. (US ISSN 0894-878X) **3347**
Neuropsychobiology. (SZ ISSN 0302-282X) **3347, 573**
Neuropsychologia. (US ISSN 0028-3932) **3348**
▼Neuropsychological Rehabilitation. (UK ISSN 0960-2011) **3348, 4036**
Neuropsychology. (US ISSN 0894-4105) **3348, 4036**
Neuropsychology Review. (US ISSN 1040-7308) **3348, 4036**
Neuropsychopharmacology. (US ISSN 0893-133X) **3348, 3736**
Neuroptera International. (FR ISSN 0223-5137) **536**
Neuroradiology. (GW ISSN 0028-3940) **3361**
▼NeuroRehabilitation. (US ISSN 1053-8135) **3348**
▼NeuroReport. (UK ISSN 0959-4965) **3348**
Neuroscience. (US ISSN 0306-4522) **3348**
Neuroscience and Behavioral Physiology. (US ISSN 0097-0549) **3348**
Neuroscience and Biobehavioral Reviews. (US ISSN 0149-7634) **3348**
Neuroscience Letters. (IE ISSN 0304-3940) **3348**
Neuroscience Newsletter. (US ISSN 0278-3738) **3348**
Neuroscience Nursing see Journal of Neuroscience Nursing **3280**
Neuroscience Research. (IE ISSN 0168-0102) **3348**
Neuroscience Research Communicatons. (UK ISSN 0893-6609) **3348**
Neurosciences. (JA ISSN 0388-7448) **3348, 480**
Neurospora Newsletter see Fungal Genetics Newsletter **439**
Neurosurgery (Baltimore). (US ISSN 0148-396X) **3349, 3382**
†Neurosurgery (Philadelphia). (US ISSN 0887-9842) **5245**
Neurosurgery Clinics. (US) **3382, 3349**
▼Neurosurgery Quarterly. (US ISSN 1050-6438) **3382**
Neurosurgical Review. (GW ISSN 0344-5607) **3382, 3349**
†Neurotoxicology. (US ISSN 0160-2748) **5245**
Neurotoxicology and Teratology. (US ISSN 0892-0362) **3349, 480, 1983**
Neurotraumatology. see Shinkei Gaisho **3354**
Neurourology and Urodynamics. (US ISSN 0733-2467) **3389**
Neusprachliche Mitteilungen aus Wissenschaft und Praxis. (GW ISSN 0028-3983) **2831, 1650**
Neusser Jahrbuch fuer Kunst, Kulturgeschichte und Heimatkunde. (GW ISSN 0077-7862) **2377**
Neutron Activation Analysis Abstracts. (UK ISSN 0047-9446) **3838, 18**
▼Neutron News. (US ISSN 1044-8632) **3848**
Neuzeit im Aufbau. (GW) **2318**
Neuzulassungen Besitzumschreibungen Loeschungen von Kraftfahrzeugen und Kraftfahrzeugenanhaengern. (GW) **4746**
Neva. (RU ISSN 0028-4009) **2876**
Nevada. (US ISSN 0199-1248) **4779**
Nevada. Bureau of Mines and Geology. Bulletin. (US) **1575, 3491**
Nevada. Bureau of Mines and Geology. Open-File Reports. (US) **1575, 3491**
Nevada. Bureau of Mines and Geology. Report. (US ISSN 0095-5264) **1575, 3491**
Nevada. Bureau of Mines and Geology. Special Publications. (US) **1575, 3491**
Nevada. Office of Fiscal Analyst. Annual Report see Nevada. Office of Legislative Auditor. Biennial Report **4068**

Nevada. Office of Legislative Auditor. Biennial Report. (US) **4068**
Nevada. State Museum, Carson City. Anthropological Papers. (US ISSN 0077-7897) **246, 280**
Nevada. State Museum, Carson City. Natural History Publications. (US ISSN 0077-7900) **4329**
Nevada. State Museum, Carson City. Occasional Papers. (US ISSN 0077-7919) **3531**
Nevada. State Museum, Carson City. Popular Series. (US ISSN 0077-7927) **3531**
Nevada Beverage Analyst. (US) **384**
Nevada Business Journal. (US) **681**
Nevada Business Review see Nevada Review of Business and Economics **681**
Nevada Education Journal. (US ISSN 0028-4033) **1650**
Nevada Events. (US) **4779**
Nevada Farm Bureau's Agriculture & Livestock Journal. (US ISSN 0899-8434) **109**
Nevada Geology. (US) **1575**
†Nevada Government Today. (US ISSN 0360-9731) **5245**
Nevada Historical Society Quarterly. (US ISSN 0047-9462) **2415**
Nevada Industrial Directory. (US) **1147**
Nevada Library Directory and Statistics. (US) **1148, 2776, 4580**
Nevada Mineral Industry (Year). (US) **1575, 3491**
Nevada Official Publications. (US) **4068**
Nevada Public Affairs Review. (US ISSN 0196-7355) **3909**
Nevada R Nformation. (US) **3282**
Nevada Rancher. (US ISSN 0047-9489) **222**
Nevada Review of Business and Economics. (US ISSN 0148-5881) **681**
Nevada State Library. Official Nevada Publications see Nevada Official Publications **4068**
Nevada State Medical Association. Bulletin. (US) **3134**
Nevada State Museum Newsletter. (US) **3531**
Nevada Statewide Wage Survey see Nevada Wage Survey **989**
Nevada Studies in History and Political Science see Wilbur S. Shepperson Series in History and Humanities **2426**
Nevada Wage Survey. (US) **989**
Neve International. (IT ISSN 0028-4114) **4551**
Never Again. (US) **2016**
Nevesole. (IT) **2205**
Nevesport Illustrato. (IT ISSN 0028-4122) **4551**
Neville Coleman's Underwater see Neville Coleman's Underwater Geographic **589**
Neville Coleman's Underwater Geographic. (AT ISSN 1032-5212) **589, 1493**
Nevrologia, Psihiatrija i Nevrohirurgija. (BU ISSN 0548-3794) **3349, 3382**
New. (GW) **1059**
New Abolitionist. (US) **3909**
New Accessions to East Africana see East Africana Accessions Bulletin **2328**
New Accountant. (US ISSN 0882-8067) **754**
New Acquisitions in the U N E C A Library. (UN) **407**
New Acronyms, Initialisms and Abbreviations. (US ISSN 0148-866X) **2831**
The New Advocate. (US ISSN 0895-1381) **2941, 1241, 1756**
New African. (UK ISSN 0142-9345) **933**
New African Yearbook. (UK ISSN 0140-1378) **3909, 681**
New Age. (II ISSN 0047-9500) **3909**
New Age (Washington) see Scottish Rite Journal **1301**
New Age Astrology Guide (Year). (US) **359, 3595**
New Age Digest. (US) **3595**

New Age Exchange. (US) **3595, 3774**
New Age Guide to Events and Resources see Sourcefinder **5279**
New Age Journal. (US ISSN 0746-3618) **3595**
New Age Literary Arts see Heaven Bone **2994**
New Age Retailer. (US ISSN 1042-6566) **3595, 4133**
New Age Teachings. (US) **3595, 4286**
New Al-Hoda. (US ISSN 0300-5453) **2016**
†New Aladdin. (US) **5245**
New Alaska Outdoors. (US) **4551**
New Alaskan. (US ISSN 0300-8959) **2229**
New Albania see Shqiperia e Re **2883**
†New Alchemy Quarterly. (US ISSN 0895-1497) **5245**
New Alpine Hydrology. see Nouvelle Hydrologie Alpine **4827**
New Amberola Graphic. (US ISSN 0028-4181) **3570**
New America: A Review see New Native American Novel **5246**
New American (Appleton). (US) **3910, 897, 2229, 4381**
New American (New York). (US) **2016**
New American Review see American Review **311**
New American Writing. (US ISSN 0893-7842) **2998**
New & Emerging Technology. (US ISSN 0882-6382) **4604, 958**
New and Expanding Industries Report for Alabama. (US) **1081**
†New & Forthcoming Canadian Books. (CN) **5245**
New and Used Foreign and Japanese Car Prices. (US ISSN 1050-5423) **4698, 1049**
New Arab. (II) **2431**
New Arcadian Journal. (UK ISSN 0262-558X) **2998, 303, 338**
New Arizona Pharmacist see Arizona Pharmacist **3718**
New Art Examiner. (US) **338**
New Asian Market Atlas. (US) **918, 1049**
New Associations and Projects see E A Supplement **1780**
New Athenaeum/Neues Athenaeum. (US ISSN 1048-8545) **2941, 3774, 4191**
New Aurora. (US ISSN 0028-4254) **4191**
New Baby. (UK) **1241**
The New Bajan. (BB) **2239**
New Beacon (Braille Edition). (UK) **2295**
New Beacon (Inkprint Edition). (UK ISSN 0028-4270) **2295**
New Bedford Magazine. (US) **2229**
New Beginnings (Franklin Park). (US ISSN 8756-9981) **1241, 3806**
†New Beginnings (Pisgah Forest). (US) **5245**
New Belize see Belize Today **2239**
†The New Biologist. (US ISSN 1043-4674) **5245**
New Bioresources see Canadian Plant Biotech News **489**
†New Biotech. (CN ISSN 0832-6614) **5245**
New Biotech Business. (CN ISSN 0838-5777) **490, 480, 681**
New Blackfriars. (UK ISSN 0028-4289) **4270**
New Blood. (US ISSN 1040-4392) **2876**
New Bodies. (US) **1293, 1287**
New Body. (US) **3806**
New Body Diet and Exercise. (US) **3806**
New Book of Knowledge Annual. (US ISSN 0196-0148) **1781**
New Book of Popular Science Annual. (US ISSN 0742-7514) **4329**
New Bookbinder. (UK ISSN 0261-5363) **4133**
New Books Catalog of P R C. see Quanguo Xin Shumu **410**
New Books on Asia Announced for Publication in the Soviet Union. (US ISSN 0199-9796) **2340, 407**
New Books on Family Planning. (II ISSN 0028-4327) **598**

New Books on Women & Feminism. (US ISSN 0742-7123) **407, 4849**
New Books on World Affairs see Council Spotlight Booknotes **398**
New Books Preview Bulletin see Forecast (Bridgewater) **4128**
New Books Quarterly on Islam & the Muslim World. (UK) **4220, 4133**
New Books Received by the Faculty Library. (IS) **66**
New Botanist. (II ISSN 0377-1741) **511**
New Breed. (CN) **2876**
New Breed. (US ISSN 3467**
New Brewer. (US ISSN 0741-0506) **384**
New Brooklyn. (US ISSN 0160-2217) **2229**
New Brunswick. Beach Resources - Eastern New Brunswick. (CN) **3491**
New Brunswick. Department of Agriculture and Rural Development. Apple Newsletter see New Brunswick. Department of Agriculture. Apple Newsletter **186**
New Brunswick. Department of Agriculture. Apple Newsletter. (CN) **186**
New Brunswick. Department of Fisheries and Aquaculture. Annual Report. (CN) **2046**
New Brunswick. Department of Fisheries. Annual Report see New Brunswick. Department of Fisheries and Aquaculture. Annual Report **2046**
New Brunswick. Department of Health and Community Services. Annual Report. (CN ISSN 0838-3693) **4109**
New Brunswick. Department of Health. Annual Report see New Brunswick. Department of Health and Community Services. Annual Report **4109**
New Brunswick. Department of Labour and Human Resources. Annual Report see New Brunswick. Department of Labour. Annual Report **989**
New Brunswick. Department of Labour. Annual Report. (CN) **989**
New Brunswick. Department of Tourism. Annual Report see New Brunswick. Department of Tourism, Recreation and Heritage. Annual Report **5245**
†New Brunswick. Department of Tourism, Recreation and Heritage. Annual Report. (CN ISSN 0839-6434) **5245**
New Brunswick. Department of Youth and Welfare. Report see New Brunswick. Department of Youth. Report **1261**
New Brunswick. Department of Youth. Report. (CN ISSN 0077-8079) **1261, 1241**
New Brunswick. Field Services Branch. Provincial Park Statistics see New Brunswick. Tourism Recreation & Heritage. Technical Services Branch. Provincial Park Statistics **1501**
New Brunswick. Mineral Resources Branch. Report of Investigations. (CN ISSN 0077-8109) **3491**
New Brunswick. Research and Productivity Council. Annual Report. (CN) **1081**
New Brunswick. Research and Productivity Council. Report see New Brunswick. Research and Productivity Council. Annual Report **1081**
New Brunswick. Tourism Recreation & Heritage. Technical Services Branch. Provincial Park Statistics. (CN) **1501, 4580**
New Brunswick. Wetlands - Peatlands Resources. (CN) **3491**
†New Brunswick Development Corporation. Annual Report. (CN ISSN 0548-4065) **5245**
New Brunswick Institute of Agrologists News see N B I A News **108**
New Brunswick Institute of Chartered Accountants. Newsletter. (CN) **754**
New Brunswick Medical Society. Newsletter. (CN) **3135**

NEW BRUNSWICK

New Brunswick Public Employees Association. News Letter see New Brunswick Public Employees Association. Newsline - Bulletin **4092**

New Brunswick Public Employees Association. Newsline - Bulletin. (CN) **4092**

New Brunswick Reports. (CN) **2658**

New Bruswick Historical Society Newsletter. (CN) **2415**

New Builder. (UK ISSN 0956-9081) **626**

†New Business. (US) **5245**

New Business Books. (UK) **4142, 731**

New Business Incorporations. (US ISSN 0028-4378) **1081**

New Business Opportunities. (US ISSN 1041-3707) **1116**

▼New Business Sourcebook. (US) **1148**

New Caledonia. Institut Territorial de la Statistique et des Etudes Economiques. Bulletin de Conjoncture. (NL ISSN 0757-9888) **731, 4580**

New Caledonia. Institut Territorial de la Statistique et des Etudes Economiques. Indice des Prix a la Consommation. (NL ISSN 0988-3215) **731**

New Caledonia. Institut Territorial de la Statistique et des Etudes Economiques. Indices des Prix la Consommation. (NL ISSN 0758-0339) **731, 4580**

New Caledonia. Institut Territorial de la Statistique et des Etudes Economiques. Indices et Index du B T P. (NL ISSN 0758-0347) **638, 731**

New Caledonia. Institut Territorial de la Statistique et des Etudes Economiques. Indice et Index du B T P. (NL ISSN 0984-2594) **731**

New Caledonia. Institut Territorial de la Statistique et des Etudes Economiques. Informations Statistiques Rapides. (NL ISSN 0336-3945) **4580**

New Caledonia. Institut Territorial de la Statistique et des Etudes Economiques. Tableaux de l'Economie Caledonienne. (NL) **731, 4580**

New Caledonia. Service des Mines et de l'Energy. Rapport Annuel. (NL) **3491, 1575**

New Calliope. (US) **4635**

New Canaan Historical Society Annual. (US ISSN 0734-2802) **2415**

New Canadian. (CN ISSN 0028-4394) **2016**

New Canadian Fandom. (CN ISSN 0229-1932) **3013**

New Canadian Review. (CN ISSN 0832-932X) **2941, 2876, 2998**

New Canadian Stories see Best Canadian Stories **2899**

New Canterbury Literary Society Newsletter. (US) **2941**

New Car Price-List. (SW) **4665**

New Car Prices - Buyer's Guide Reports. (US ISSN 1049-8583) **4698, 1049**

New Catalyst. (CN ISSN 0834-969X) **1964, 1650**

New Catholic Explorer. (US) **4270**

New Catholic Miscellany. (US) **4270**

New Catholic World see The Catholic World **4260**

New Century. see Xin Shiji **700**

New Century. (UG) **4286**

New Ceylon Writing. (AT) **2941, 2831**

New China see U S - China Review **3974**

New Chislehurst Announcer. (UK ISSN 0047-956X) **2194**

New Choices. (US ISSN 1041-6277) **2277, 4414**

New Chronicle. (DQ) **2239**

New Church Life. (US) **4286**

New Church Magazine. (UK) **4286**

New Church Messenger see Messenger (La Porte) **4285**

New Cicada. (JA ISSN 0911-6567) **2998**

New City. (PH) **4191**

New City. (UK ISSN 0140-5845) **4192**

New City Times. (US) **4192**

New Civil Engineer. (UK ISSN 0307-7683) **1872**

New Civil Engineer International see Construction Today **1864**

New Cleveland Woman Journal. (US) **4849, 4836**

New Coin see New Coin Poetry **2998**

New Coin Poetry. (SA) **2998**

New Collage Magazine. (US ISSN 0028-4467) **2941, 338, 4002**

New Collecting Lines see Collectors Mart **2435**

New Comparison. (UK ISSN 0950-5814) **2941**

New Comprehensive Biochemistry. (NE) **480**

New Computer Careers. (UK ISSN 0260-9150) **1426**

New Confucians. see Hsin Ju Chia **3768**

New Connections. (US) **2448**

New Connections: Studies in Interdisciplinarity. (US ISSN 0891-0073) **2941**

New Consciousness Sourcebook. (US) **3595, 3670**

New Consultants. (US ISSN 0192-091X) **1022**

New Contrast. (SA) **2942**

New Conversations. (US ISSN 0360-0181) **4192**

New Country. (AT) **2016**

New Covenant. (US ISSN 0744-8589) **4270**

New Criterion. (US ISSN 0734-0222) **2876**

New Crucible. (US) **1964**

New Culture. (NR) **338, 3570, 4635**

New Cyclist. (UK) **4520**

†New Dance. (UK ISSN 0950-4303) **5245**

New Dance Review. (US ISSN 1040-8908) **1531**

New Dawn. (US) **2455, 4849**

New Dawn see U S D A W Today **2591**

New Dawn. see Fajr al-Jadid **4842**

New Dawn Fades. (UK) **3013**

New Day. (UK) **3222**

The New Day. (US ISSN 0028-453X) **4192**

New Day see New Century **4286**

New Day Herald. (US ISSN 1040-2047) **3595**

New Day International. (AT) **4192**

New Day Publications. (US) **2998**

New Delhi. (II) **2200**

New Delta Review. (US ISSN 1050-415X) **2876**

New Democracy. (II) **3910**

New Democrat (Dublin) see Fine Gael News **3894**

New Democrat (London) see New Democrat International **3910**

New Democrat International. (UK) **3910, 681**

New Departures. (UK) **2942, 338**

New Detroit Annual Report see New Detroit, Inc. Annual Report **4414**

New Detroit, Inc. Annual Report. (US) **4414**

New Detroit Now. (US) **4414**

New Developments in Automobile Materials for the 90's. (JA) **4698**

New Dimensions (Grants Pass). (US) **2230**

New Dimensions (Philadelphia). (US) **2016**

New Dimensions (Reston) see D E C A Dimensions **1037**

†New Dimensions in Glass. (US) **5245**

New Directions see Roanoke Regional Chamber of Commerce. Agenda **822**

New Directions (New York, 1936). (US) **2942, 2998**

New Directions (Washington). (US ISSN 0047-9616) **1713**

New Directions - Action Line see Legal Plan Letter **2648**

New Directions for Adult and Continuing Education. (US) **1685**

New Directions for Child Development. (US ISSN 0195-2269) **4036**

New Directions for Community Colleges.(US ISSN 0194-3081) **1713**

New Directions for Continuing Education see New Directions for Adult and Continuing Education **1685**

New Directions for Higher Education. (US ISSN 0271-0560) **1713**

New Directions for Institutional Research. (US ISSN 0271-0579) **1713**

New Directions for Mental Health Services. (US ISSN 0193-9416) **3349, 4036**

New Directions for Program Evaluation. (US ISSN 0164-7989) **1650, 4414**

New Directions for Student Services. (US ISSN 0164-7970) **1713**

New Directions for Teaching and Learning. (US ISSN 0271-0633) **1650**

New Directions for Women. (US ISSN 0160-1075) **4860**

New Directions in Information Management. (US ISSN 0887-3844) **2776**

New Directions in Librarianship see New Directions in Information Management **2776**

New Directions in Philosophy. (US) **3774**

New Directions in Public Administration Research. (US) **4068, 3910**

†New Disciples. (US) **5245**

New Doctor. (AT ISSN 0313-2153) **3135, 4444**

New Documents Illustrating Early Christianity. (AT) **4192**

New Dog. (US ISSN 0893-8563) **2876, 2998, 4635**

New Dominion. (US) **2230**

New Drug Approval Pipeline see N D A Pipeline **3735**

New Drugs and Clinical Remedies. see Xinyao yu Linchuang **3746**

New Drugs in Japan. see Saikin no Shinyaku **3742**

New Earth. (US) **4270**

New East. see Ha-Mizrah Hehadash **3641**

New East Asia. see Shin Dong-A **2575**

New Edition. (CN) **1318**

New Editions - Directories, Annuals & Reference Books see Armstrong's Monthly Bulletin **5138**

New Education. (AT ISSN 0156-0905) **1650**

New Electric Railway Journal. (US) **4712**

New Electronics. (NZ ISSN 0110-8034) **1776**

New Electronics. (UK ISSN 0047-9624) **1904, 1341**

New England Accounting Research Studies (No.). (AT ISSN 0155-123X) **754, 793, 1022**

New England Advertising Week. (US ISSN 0028-4653) **35**

New England and Regional Allergy Proceedings see Allergy Proceedings **3183**

New England Antiques Journal. (US ISSN 0897-5795) **258**

New England Antiquities Research Association Journal. (US ISSN 0149-2551) **280, 246**

New England Antiquities Research Association Newsletter see New England Antiquities Research Association Journal **280**

New England Antiquities Research Association Transit Newsletter see N E A R A Transit Newsletter **279**

New England Association of Teachers of English Newsletter see N E A T E Newsletter **2830**

New England Beat. (US) **2230**

New England Beauty Journal. (US) **374**

New England Board of Higher Education. New England Regional Student Program: Graduate Level. (US) **1713**

New England Board of Higher Education. New England Regional Student Program: Undergraduate Level. (US) **1713**

New England Board of Higher Education. New England Regional Student Services: Enrollment Report. (US) **1713**

New England Bride. (US ISSN 0744-6861) **3067, 4849**

New England Builder see Journal of Light Construction **622**

†New England Business. (US ISSN 0164-3533) **5245**

New England Classical Newsletter see New England Classical Newsletter & Journal **1278**

New England Classical Newsletter & Journal. (US) **1278**

New England Community Guide for Gay Males and Lesbians. (US) **2456**

New England Economic Indicators. (US ISSN 0548-4448) **875**

†New England Economic Indicators Monthly Update. (US ISSN 0895-5662) **5245**

New England Economic Review. (US ISSN 0028-4726) **875**

New England Engineering Journal. (US) **1831**

New England Farm Bulletin see New England Farm Bulletin and Garden Gazette **109**

New England Farm Bulletin and Garden Gazette. (US) **109**

New England Farmer. (US) **109**

New England Food Service Buyer's Guide see North East Food Service Buyer's Guide **2478**

New England Gardener. (US ISSN 0896-8160) **2135**

New England Getaways. (US ISSN 0893-1089) **4779**

New England Golf Magazine. (US) **4509**

New England Guide see Original New England Guide **4781**

New England Historic Genealogical Society Nexus see N E H G S Nexus **2159**

New England Historical and Genealogical Register. (US ISSN 0028-4785) **2159, 2415**

New England Insurance Times see Insurance Times **2535**

New England Interstate Water Pollution Control Commission Annual Report see N E I W P C C Annual Report **1978**

New England Interstate Water Pollution Control Commission Water Connection see N E I W P C C Water Connection **1978**

New England Journal of Black Studies. (US) **2016**

New England Journal of History. (US) **2415, 1756, 4381**

New England Journal of Human Services. (US ISSN 0277-996X) **4414, 4381**

New England Journal of Medicine. (US ISSN 0028-4793) **3135**

New England Journal of Medicine (International Edition). (US) **3135**

New England Journal of Optometry. (US ISSN 0028-4807) **3302**

New England Journal of Public Policy. (US ISSN 0749-016X) **4092, 875**

New England Journal of Transportation. (US) **4654, 4676, 4720, 4734**

New England Journal on Criminal and Civil Confinement. (US ISSN 0740-8994) **2658, 1519**

New England Law Review. (US ISSN 0028-4823) **2658**

New England Library Association, Inc. Newsletter see N E L A Newsletter **2774**

†New England Living Magazine. (US ISSN 0884-5166) **5245**

New England Monographs in Continuing Education (No.). (AT ISSN 0811-5982) **1650**

†New England Monthly. (US ISSN 8750-216X) **5245**

New England News. (AT ISSN 1031-1718) **1713**

New England Offshore see Offshore (Needham) **4527**

New England Out-of-Doors. (US) **4551**

New England Printer and Publisher. (US ISSN 0162-8771) **4002**

New England Progress. (US) 2301
New England Purchaser. (US) 1049
New England Purchaser - Connecticut Purchaser see New England Purchaser 1049
New England Quarterly. (US ISSN 0028-4866) 2942, 2415, 2876
New England Reading Association. Journal. (US ISSN 0028-4882) 1651
New England Real Estate Directory see New England Real Estate News 4153
New England Real Estate Journal. (US ISSN 0028-4890) 4153
New England Real Estate Journal - Shopping Centers. (US) 4153
New England Real Estate News. (US ISSN 1042-9689) 4153
†New England Real Estate News Directory. (US) 5245
New England Review. (US ISSN 1053-1297) 2942
New England Review and Bread Loaf Quarterly see New England Review 2942
New England Runner. (US) 4551
New England Sailboard Journal. (US) 4527
New England Science Fiction Association Inc. Index to Short Science Fiction see N E S F A Index to Short Science Fiction 2982
†New England Senior Citizen. (US ISSN 0163-2248) 5245
New England Sierran. (US) 1493, 1964, 4551
New England Skiers' Guide. (US) 4551
New England Small Press Review see Stony Hills 2885
▼New England Snowboarder. (US) 4551
New England Social Studies Bulletin see New England Journal of History 2415
New England Sounding Line. (US) 3178, 2776
New England Square Dance Caller see Northeast Square Dancer Magazine 1531
†New England States Limited. (US ISSN 0162-1599) 5245
▼New England Theatre Journal. (US ISSN 1050-9720) 4635
New England Topics. (US) 1364
New England Truck Exchange. (US) 4746
New England War Tax Resistance. Annual Report. (US) 1102
New England War Tax Resistance Newsletter. (US) 1102
New England Water Works Association. Journal. (US ISSN 0028-4939) 4827
New England Wild Flower Society Newsletter. (US) 2135
New England World of Sanyo. (US) 1471, 1463
New English Art Club. (UK) 338
New Environment. (CN) 1964
New Environment Bulletin. (US) 3595, 4444
New Epoch. see Nea Epochi 2875
New Equipment Digest. (US ISSN 0028-4963) 4605
New Equipment News. (CN ISSN 0028-4971) 4605
New Equipment News. (SA ISSN 0028-498X) 4605, 1831
New Equipment Reporter. (US) 1454, 1424
New Era. (GH ISSN 0028-4998) 1651
New Era see New Era in Education 1651
New Era. (CN) 2277
New Era see Nave Parva 4779
New Era (Ely)/Nova Doba. (US ISSN 0028-5021) 1300
New Era (Salt Lake City). (US ISSN 0164-5285) 4286
New Era in Education. (UK) 1651, 2831
New Era Laundry & Cleaning Lines. (US ISSN 0028-5056) 1282
New Era of Telecommunications in Japan. (JA ISSN 0912-0076) 1341

New Ethicals see Current Therapeutics 3722
New Ethicals Catalogue. (NZ ISSN 0110-9510) 3736
New Europe. (LU) 2998
New Europe (London, 1989). (UK ISSN 0958-1537) 918
New European Books. (UK) 4142
New Expression. (US) 1261
New Facts of Life see Canadian A I D S News 3218
New Families see Home Business Advisor 5205
New Family. (US) 2448, 4849
New Farm. (US ISSN 0163-0369) 186
New Federalist. (US) 3910
New Film and Play Scripts. see Yingju Xinzuo 2979
New Films. see Dianying Xinzuo 3507
New Finance. see Xin Jinrong 804
New Fine Art. see Xin Meishu 350
New Flowers. see Shin Kaki 2139
New Food Products in Japan. (UK) 2093
New Forests. (NE ISSN 0169-4286) 2105
New Formations. (UK ISSN 0950-2378) 2876
New Forms. see Revue Formes Nouvelles 306
New Freeman. (CN ISSN 0838-0341) 4271
New French Books see Bulletin Critique du Livre Francais 4140
New from Europe. (US ISSN 0740-3569) 4605
New from Japan. (US ISSN 0740-3550) 4605
New from U S. (US ISSN 0740-3577) 4605
New Frontier. (US ISSN 0886-4616) 3595, 3774
New Fuels Report. (US) 1793
New Future. see Paa Flukt 3968
New Gandy Dancer. (UK ISSN 0260-3330) 3570
New Generation. see Shine Uye 3925
New Generation. see Nayer Dor 5244
New Generation Computing. (GW ISSN 0288-3635) 1463, 1479
New German-American Studies/Neue Deutsche-Amerikanische Studien. (US ISSN 1043-5808) 2511, 4444
New German Critique. (US ISSN 0094-033X) 2512
New German Review. (US ISSN 0889-0145) 2942, 2831
New German Studies. (UK ISSN 0307-2770) 2942
New Ghana. (GH) 2192
New Glass. see Neues Glas 356
New Glass Review. (US ISSN 0275-469X) 356
New Gleanings. (US) 3531, 258, 2159, 2415
New Ground. (UK ISSN 0266-7835) 3910, 989, 1964
New Guard. (US ISSN 0028-5137) 3910
New Gun Week. (US ISSN 0195-1599) 4481, 2440
New Hampshire. Agricultural Experiment Station, Durham. Research Reports. (US ISSN 0077-832X) 109
New Hampshire. Agricultural Experiment Station, Durham. Station Bulletins. (US ISSN 0077-8338) 109
New Hampshire. Fish and Game Department. Biennial Report. (US ISSN 0077-8362) 1493
New Hampshire. Fish and Game Department. Game Management and Research Division. Biological Survey Bulletin. (US ISSN 0077-8397) 449, 2046
New Hampshire. Fish and Game Department. Game Management and Research Division. Biological Survey Series. (US ISSN 0077-8370) 449
New Hampshire. Fish and Game Department. Game Management and Research Division. Technical Circular Series. (US ISSN 0077-8389) 449, 2046
New Hampshire Alumnus see Alumni Companion 1303

New Hampshire Archeological Society Newsletter. (US ISSN 0545-1604) 280
New Hampshire Archeologist. (US ISSN 0077-8346) 280
New Hampshire Arts. (US) 338
New Hampshire Audubon. (US ISSN 0162-5284) 1493, 565
New Hampshire Audubon News see New Hampshire Audubon 1493
New Hampshire Bar News. (US ISSN 1051-4023) 2658
New Hampshire Beverage Journal. (US) 384
New Hampshire Bird Records. (US) 565
New Hampshire Business Education Association. Journal see New Hampshire Business Education Association. Newsletter 681
New Hampshire Business Education Association. Newsletter. (US) 681, 1651
New Hampshire Business Review. (US ISSN 0164-8152) 838
New Hampshire Civil Jury Instructions. (US) 2704
New Hampshire Code of Administrative Rules Annotated. (US) 4068, 2658
New Hampshire Committee for the Promotion of History. Bulletin. (US) 2415
New Hampshire Committee for the Promotion of History. Newsletter see New Hampshire Committee for the Promotion of History. Bulletin 2415
New Hampshire Corporations, Partnerships and Associations. (US) 681, 2711
New Hampshire Court Rules Annotated.(US) 2658
New Hampshire Criminal Code. (US) 2714
New Hampshire Dental Society Newsletter see N H D S Newsletter 3238
New Hampshire Educator. (US ISSN 0028-5234) 1651
New Hampshire Facts. (US ISSN 0895-8114) 1781
New Hampshire Fish and Game Laws. (US) 2658, 4551
New Hampshire Highways. (US ISSN 0028-5242) 4720
New Hampshire Historical Society Newsletter. (US) 2415
New Hampshire Labor Market Areas Planning Guide Fiscal Year. (US) 989
New Hampshire Lambda Newsletter see N H Lambda Newsletter 5242
New Hampshire Land Sales Disclosure and Condominium Laws and Rules. (US) 2715
New Hampshire Landlord and Tenant Law. (US) 2715
New Hampshire Law Weekly see New Hampshire Bar News 2658
New Hampshire Library Association Newsletter see N H L A Newsletter 2774
†New Hampshire Life. (US) 5245
New Hampshire Manufacturing Directory. (US) 1148
New Hampshire Marketing Directory see New Hampshire Manufacturing Directory 1148
New Hampshire Motor Vehicle and Boating Laws. (US) 2658
New Hampshire Municipal Practice Series. Vol. 2: Municipal Finance and Taxation. (US) 4092, 1102
New Hampshire Municipal Practice Series. Vol. 3: Public Health, Safety and Highways. (US) 4092, 3619
New Hampshire Municipal Practice Series. Vols. 1 and 1A: Land Use and Planning. (US) 4092, 2493
New Hampshire Planning and Land Use Regulation. (US) 2715
New Hampshire Polyglot. (US ISSN 0028-5293) 2831, 1756
New Hampshire Practice Series. Vol. 3: Family Law. (US) 2718
New Hampshire Practice Series. Vol. 7: Wills, Trusts and Gifts. (US) 2704

New Hampshire Practice Series. Vols. 1 and 2: Criminal Practice and Procedure. (US) 2714
New Hampshire Practice Series. Vols. 4, 5 and 6: Civil Practice and Procedure. (US) 2704
New Hampshire Practice Series. Vols. 8 and 9: Personal Injury - Tort and Insurance Practice. (US) 2658, 2539
▼New Hampshire Practice Series. Vols. 10, 11 and 12: Probate Law and Procedure. (US) 2658
▼New Hampshire Practice Series. Vols. 13 and 14: Local Government Law. (US) 4092, 2658
New Hampshire Profiles. (US ISSN 0028-5307) 2230
New Hampshire Quarter Notes. (US ISSN 0028-5315) 3570, 1651
New Hampshire Real Estate Guide. (US) 4153, 35
New Hampshire Register: State Yearbook and Legislative Manual. (US) 4092, 4068
New Hampshire Reports. (US) 2658
New Hampshire Revised Statutes Annotated. (US) 2658
New Hampshire Rule of Evidence Manual. (US) 2658
New Hampshire Rules of Evidence. (US) 2659
New Hampshire Statutes Relating to Surveying and Boundaries. (US) 2659
New Hampshire Vital Statistics. (US ISSN 0095-5523) 3993, 4580
New Hampshire Workers' Compensation Manual. (US) 2711, 1068
New Haven Business. (US) 681
New Haven Business Digest. (US) 681
New Haven Colony Historical Society. Journal. (US ISSN 0548-4987) 2415
New Haven County Woman. (US) 4849
New Haven Local News. (US) 2230, 2016
New Haven Studies in International Law and World Public Order. (NE ISSN 0738-2812) 2727, 3966
†New Heaven - New Earth. (US ISSN 0896-3150) 5245
New Hebrides. Condominium Geological Survey. Report see Vanuatu. Geological Survey. Reports 1584
New Hi-Fi Sound see High Fidelity 4460
†New Home. (US) 5245
New Home Design/Atrashi Sumai-No Sekkai. (JA) 2493
New Home Economics. (UK ISSN 0265-6930) 2448, 1651
New Home Magazine. (US) 2448
†New Home Magazine. (CN) 5245
New Homeland. see Novy Domov 2017
New Homeowner. (US) 4153
New Homes and Renovations Magazine see Lifestyles Magazine 4152
New Homes Magazine. (US ISSN 0192-4893) 4153
New Hope International see New Hope International Writing 2998
New Hope International Review. (UK) 2998, 2876
New Hope International Review Supplement see New Hope International Review 2998
New Hope International Writing. (UK) 2998
New Hope International Zine. (UK) 2942
New Horizon. (NR ISSN 0794-439X) 3910
New Horizon - Polish American Review. (US ISSN 0364-8184) 2016
New Horizons (Horsham). (US ISSN 0199-3518) 4245
New Horizons (New York). (US ISSN 0028-5374) 1713, 4245
New Horizons in Education. (AT ISSN 0028-5382) 1651
New Horizons in Therapeutics: Smith, Kline & French Laboratories Research Symposia Series. (US) 3135
New Humanist see P R O U T Press 2231

6488 NEW HUMANIST

New Humanist. (UK ISSN 0306-512X) 3774, 4381
New Humanity Journal. (UK ISSN 0307-0980) 3774
New Hungarian Exporter *see* Hungarian Trade Journal 5207
†New Hungarian Exporter Technical Series. (HU) 5245
New Hungarian News. *see* Uj Magyar Hirek 2198
New Hungarian Quarterly. (HU ISSN 0028-5390) 2876
New Idea. (AT ISSN 0819-9981) 4849
New Ideas in Psychology. (US ISSN 0732-118X) 4036
New in Chess Magazine. (US ISSN 0168-8782) 4481
New in Chess Yearbook. (US ISSN 0168-7697) 4481
New India Bulletin. (CN) 2016
New Indicator. (US) 2876
New Information on Horticulture *see* New Information on Horticulture: Flowers 2135
New Information on Horticulture *see* New Information on Horticulture: Vegetables 2135
New Information on Horticulture: Flowers/Engei Shin Chishiki: Hana no Go. (JA) 2135
New Information on Horticulture: Vegetables/Engei Shin Chishiki: Yasai no Go. (JA) 2135
New Information Systems and Services *see* Information Industry Directory Supplement 1425
New International. (US ISSN 0737-3724) 3910
New International Review. (IS) 3910
New International Review. *see* Nuova Rivista Internazionale 3967
New Internationalist. (UK ISSN 0305-9529) 3966
New Issue Digest. (US) 958
New Issue Investor *see* Emerging & Special Situations 945
New Issue Report *see* World Postal Stationery - New Issue Report 3759
New Issues. (US ISSN 0162-9050) 958
New Issues Alert. (US) 958
New Issues in Neurosciences. (GW ISSN 1012-9871) 3349
New Jersey. Administrative Office of the Courts. Annual Report of the Administrative Director of the Courts *see* New Jersey. Administrative Office of the Courts. Annual Report of the New Jersey Judiciary 2732
New Jersey. Administrative Office of the Courts. Annual Report of the New Jersey Judiciary. (US) 2732
New Jersey. Administrative Office of the Courts. Court Management Report. (US) 2700
New Jersey. Bureau of Fire Safety Newsletter. (US) 2034, 4109
New Jersey. Bureau of Geology and Topography. Bulletin *see* New Jersey. Geological Survey. Bulletin 1575
New Jersey. Bureau of Geology and Topography. Geologic Report Series *see* New Jersey. Geological Survey. Report Series 1575
New Jersey. Casino Control Commission. Annual Report. (US) 4481
New Jersey. Department of Banking. Annual Report. (US) 793
New Jersey. Department of Environmental Protection. Annual Report. (US ISSN 0092-3311) 1964
†New Jersey. Department of Higher Education. Research Report. (US) 5245
New Jersey. Department of Labor. Labor Market Review. Southern N.J. Region. (US) 875
New Jersey. Department of the Treasury. Local Property Branch News. (US) 4154
New Jersey. Department of Transportation. Annual Report. (US) 4654
New Jersey. Developmental Disabilities Council. Annual Report. (US ISSN 0090-077X) 4414

New Jersey. Division of Labor Market and Demographic Research. Population Estimates for New Jersey.(US) 3994
New Jersey. Division of Taxation. Annual Report. (US) 1102
†New Jersey. Economic Policy Council. Annual Report of Economic Policy Council and Office of Economic Policy. (US ISSN 0077-8478) 5245
New Jersey. Environmental News. (US) 1964
New Jersey. Geological Survey. Bulletin. (US) 1575
New Jersey. Geological Survey. Report Series. (US ISSN 0741-7357) 1575
New Jersey. Office of Demographic and Economic Analysis. Population Estimates for New Jersey *see* New Jersey. Division of Labor Market and Demographic Research. Population Estimates for New Jersey 3994
†New Jersey. Office of Economic Policy. Economic Report of the Governor. (US) 5245
†New Jersey. State Law Enforcement Planning Agency. Applicants Guide. (US) 5245
New Jersey Academy of Science. Bulletin. (US ISSN 0028-5455) 4329
New Jersey Academy of Science. Newsletter. (US ISSN 0028-5463) 4329
New Jersey Afro-American. (US) 2016
New Jersey Airport Directory. (US ISSN 0091-6978) 4676
New Jersey Association of Osteopathic Physicians and Surgeons Journal *see* N J A O P S Journal 3215
New Jersey Audubon Society Audubon *see* N J Audubon 565
New Jersey Aviation. (US) 59
New Jersey Aviation News and Views *see* New Jersey Aviation 59
New Jersey Bell Journal. (US) 1364
New Jersey Beverage Journal. (US ISSN 0028-5552) 384
New Jersey Bride. (US) 3067
New Jersey Business. (US ISSN 0028-5560) 1081
New Jersey Casino Journal. (US) 4481
New Jersey Classical Association. Bulletin. (US) 1278
New Jersey Clean Air Council. Report. (US ISSN 0077-8451) 1978
New Jersey Comprehensive Annual Financial Report. (US) 4068
New Jersey Conservation Foundation (Year) Annual Report. (US) 1493
New Jersey Dental Association. Journal. (US ISSN 0093-7347) 3238
New Jersey Directory of Manufacturers. (US) 1148
New Jersey Economic Indicators. (US) 875, 989
New Jersey Education Association Review *see* N J E A Review 1729
†New Jersey Education Bulletin. (US) 5246
New Jersey Education Law Report. (US ISSN 0279-8557) 1651, 2587, 2659
▼New Jersey Environmental Law Letter.(US) 2659
New Jersey Environmental Times *see* New Jersey Outdoors 1964
New Jersey Facts. (US ISSN 0898-5405) 1781
New Jersey Farmer. (US) 109
New Jersey Federation of Planning Officials. Federation Planner. (US ISSN 0028-5714) 2493
New Jersey Federation of Planning Officials. Federation Planning Information Reports. (US ISSN 0028-5722) 2493
New Jersey Folklife. (US ISSN 0887-8048) 2057
New Jersey Folklore *see* New Jersey Folklife 2057
New Jersey Folklore Society Newsletter *see* New Jersey Folklore Society Review 2057
New Jersey Folklore Society Review. (US) 2057
New Jersey Goodlife. (US) 4779

New Jersey Historical Commission Newsletter. (US ISSN 0047-9772) 2416
New Jersey History. (US ISSN 0028-5757) 2416, 2159
New Jersey Home and Garden *see* New Jersey Monthly 2230
New Jersey Home and Garden *see* Garden State Home & Garden 5198
New Jersey Housing and Mortgage Finance Agency Annual Report. (US) 2493
New Jersey Humanities. (US) 2512
New Jersey Journal of Pharmacy. (US ISSN 0028-5773) 3736
New Jersey Journal of School Psychology. (US ISSN 0896-3126) 4036, 1651
New Jersey Lake Survey Fishing Maps Guide. (US ISSN 1054-4623) 4551
New Jersey Lake Survey Map Guide *see* New Jersey Lake Survey Fishing Maps Guide 4551
New Jersey Law Journal. (US ISSN 0028-5803) 2659
New Jersey Lawyer. (US ISSN 0195-0983) 2659
New Jersey Libraries. (US ISSN 0028-5811) 2776
New Jersey Libraries Newsletter. (US) 2776
New Jersey Manufacturers Directory *see* George D. Hall's New Jersey Manufacturers Directory 1136
New Jersey Media Directory *see* Burrelle's New Jersey Media Directory (Year) 29
New Jersey Medicine. (US) 3135
New Jersey Mental Retardation Planning Board. Annual Report *see* New Jersey. Developmental Disabilities Council. Annual Report 4414
New Jersey Messenger. (US ISSN 0028-582X) 2416
New Jersey Monthly. (US ISSN 0273-270X) 2230
New Jersey Mosquito Control Association. Proceedings. (US) 536
New Jersey Mosquito Extermination Association. Proceedings *see* New Jersey Mosquito Control Association. Proceedings 536
New Jersey Motor Truck Association. Bulletin. (US ISSN 0028-5838) 4746
New Jersey Municipalities. (US ISSN 0028-5846) 4092
New Jersey Nature News *see* N J Audubon 565
New Jersey Network Guide *see* N J N Guide 1377
New Jersey Notes. (US) 681
New Jersey Numismatic Journal. (US) 3600
New Jersey Nurse. (US) 3282
New Jersey Office Buildings. (US) 4154
New Jersey Orchard and Vineyard Survey. (US ISSN 0098-9541) 186
New Jersey Outdoors. (US) 1964
New Jersey Parent Teacher. (US ISSN 0028-5897) 1651
New Jersey, Pennsylvania TourBook *see* Tourbook: New Jersey, Pennsylvania 4790
New Jersey Professional Engineer *see* Perspectives in Engineering 1833
New Jersey Public Libraries. Statistics *see* New Jersey Public Library Statistics For (Year) 2795
New Jersey Public Library Statistics For (Year). (US) 2795
New Jersey Queries. (US ISSN 0899-1340) 2159
New Jersey Realtor. (US ISSN 0028-5919) 4154
New Jersey Register. (US ISSN 0300-6069) 4068
New Jersey Reporter. (US ISSN 0195-3192) 2230
New Jersey Savings League News. (US) 793
New Jersey School Boards Association. School Board Notes. (US ISSN 0039-0070) 1730

New Jersey School Boards Association. School Leader. (US) 1730
New Jersey School Development Council Research Bulletin *see* N J S D C Research Bulletin 1712
New Jersey Speech and Hearing Association. Journal. (US ISSN 0028-5935) 3135, 2288
New Jersey State Bar Advocate. (US) 2659
New Jersey State Fire Code. (US) 2034, 4109
New Jersey State Industrial Directory *see* MacRae's State Industrial Directory: New Jersey 1144
New Jersey State Tax News. (US) 1102
†New Jersey Success. (US ISSN 0886-9995) 5246
New Jersey Tax Court. Reports. (US ISSN 0279-6481) 1102
New Jersey Trial Lawyer. (US) 2659
New Jersey Woman Magazine. (US) 4849
New Journal. (US ISSN 0028-6001) 1318
New Journal of Chemistry. (FR ISSN 0398-9836) 1184
New Journal of Statistics and Operational Research. (UK ISSN 0028-601X) 4580
New Journal of Traditional Chinese Medicine. *see* Xinzhongyi 3163
New Kent Quarterly. (US) 2942
New Korea. (US) 2016
New Korea Times. (CN) 2016
New Labor Review. (US) 989
New Laurel Review. (US ISSN 0145-8388) 2942
New Law Books Reviewer. (US ISSN 0890-2941) 2659, 4133
New Law for General Practice Surveyors *see* New Law for Surveyors 4154
New Law for Surveyors. (UK) 4154, 2659
New Law Journal. (UK ISSN 0306-6479) 2659
New Leader. (US ISSN 0028-6044) 2230
New Leader. (II) 4192
New Left Review. (UK ISSN 0028-6060) 2876, 3910
New Letters. (US ISSN 0146-4930) 2942
†New Letters Review of Books. (US) 5246
The New Liberian. (LB) 2169
New Libertarian. (US) 3910
New Libertarian Horizon *see* Libertas Review 2872
New Library Scene. (US ISSN 0735-8571) 2776, 4133
New Library World. (UK ISSN 0307-4803) 2776
New Life. (US) 3595, 3806
New Life. (AT ISSN 1033-7903) 4245
New Life (London, 1965). (UK ISSN 0028-6079) 4271, 4444
New Life (London, 1971). (UK) 4192, 1519
New Life News. (US) 3806
New Life Post. (MY) 2210
New Listings Profiles. (US) 35
New Literary History. (US ISSN 0028-6087) 2942
New Literature and Ideology. (CN ISSN 0702-7532) 2876, 2998
New Literature on Old Age. (UK ISSN 0140-2447) 2280, 407
New Literature on Women: A Bibliography. *see* Ny Litteratur om Kvinnor: En Bibliografi 4861
New Literatures Review. (AT ISSN 0314-7495) 2942
New Living. (US) 3806
†New Local Government Series. (UK) 5246
New Lugano Review *see* Art International 314
New Magazine *see* New Weekly Magazine 2178
†New Magazine Review. (US ISSN 0192-2319) 5246
New Magic Lantern Journal. (UK ISSN 0143-036X) 3793
New Management. (UK ISSN 0548-5924) 1353, 1022
†New Management. (US) 5246

New Maritimes. (CN) **2876**
New Markets Newsletter *see* Italian Voice **2007**
New Materials Developed in Japan (Year). (JA) **3864**
New Materials - Japan. (UK ISSN 0265-3443) **4605**
†New Materials - Korea. (UK ISSN 0952-6196) **5246**
New Media Marketing Newsletter *see* Telecommunications **1344**
New Media Markets. (UK) **1341**
New Media Products. (US) **1341**
New Medical Science. *see* Xin Yixue **3163**
New Medical World Weekly. *see* Shukan Igakkai Shinbun **3153**
New Members Round Table Newsletter *see* N M R T Newsletter **2775**
New Menorah: The P'nai or Journal of Jewish Renewal. (US) **4225**
†New Messenger (Talking Book). (US) **5246**
New Methods. (US ISSN 0277-3015) **4813**
New Mexico. Bureau of Mines and Mineral Resources. Bulletin. (US) **3491**
†New Mexico. Bureau of Mines and Mineral Resources. Circular. (US) **5246**
New Mexico. Bureau of Mines and Mineral Resources. Hydrologic Report. (US) **1599**
New Mexico. Bureau of Mines and Mineral Resources. Memoir. (US ISSN 0548-5975) **3491**
New Mexico. Bureau of Mines and Mineral Resources. Progress Report. (US ISSN 0098-7077) **3491**
New Mexico. Department of Labor. Covered Employment and Wages. Quarterly Report. (US) **989**
New Mexico. Employment Security Department. Covered Employment and Wages. Quarterly Report *see* New Mexico. Department of Labor. Covered Employment and Wages. Quarterly Report **989**
New Mexico. State Records Center & Archives. Annual Publications List. (US) **2329**
New Mexico. State Records Center and Archives. Publications and Rules Filed *see* New Mexico. State Records Center & Archives. Annual Publications List **2329**
New Mexico. Veterans' Service Commission. Report. (US ISSN 0094-7326) **3467**, **4414**
New Mexico Agricultural Statistics. (US ISSN 0077-8540) **140**
New Mexico: An Annotated Directory of Information Sources. (US) **407**
New Mexico Appellate Practice Manual. (US) **2659**
New Mexico Association of Elementary School Principals. Newsletter and Journal *see* Nuevo Mexico Elementary Principal **1730**
New Mexico Beverage Analyst. (US ISSN 0194-813X) **384**
New Mexico Beverage Journal *see* New Mexico Beverage Analyst **384**
New Mexico Blue Book *see* Official New Mexico Blue Book **2417**
New Mexico Business Current Economic Report. (US) **681**
New Mexico Business Journal. (US ISSN 0164-6796) **681**
New Mexico Collections Manual *see* New Mexico Creditor - Debtor Law **2659**
New Mexico Construction Law. (US) **2659**, **626**
New Mexico Creditor - Debtor Law. (US) **2659**
New Mexico Directory of Manufacturers.(US) **1148**, **3491**
New Mexico Engineering. (US) **1831**
New Mexico Farm & Ranch. (US ISSN 0028-6192) **109**
New Mexico Forest Products Directory *see* Wood Industries of New Mexico **2118**
New Mexico Geological Society. Guidebook, Field Conference. (US ISSN 0077-8567) **1575**

New Mexico Geology. (US) **1575**, **1592**, **1599**
New Mexico Historical Review. (US ISSN 0028-6206) **2416**
New Mexico Humanities Review. (US ISSN 0738-9671) **2512**
New Mexico Independent. (US ISSN 0193-5356) **2942**
New Mexico Labor Market Review. (US) **989**
New Mexico Law Review. (US ISSN 0028-6214) **2659**
New Mexico Library Association Newsletter. (US ISSN 0893-2956) **2776**
New Mexico Lobo. (US ISSN 0028-6230) **1318**
New Mexico Local and Federal Rules Handbook. (US) **4068**, **2659**
New Mexico Magazine. (US ISSN 0028-6249) **4779**
New Mexico Manufacturing Directory *see* New Mexico Directory of Manufacturers **1148**
New Mexico Municipal League. Municipal Reporter. (US ISSN 0028-6257) **4092**
New Mexico Musician. (US ISSN 0028-6265) **3570**
New Mexico Probate Manual. (US) **2659**
New Mexico Professional Engineer *see* New Mexico Engineering **1831**
New Mexico Progress. (US ISSN 0896-6478) **2288**, **1739**
New Mexico Real Estate Law Reporter. (US ISSN 0951-547X) **2715**
New Mexico Reports *see* Report of Cases Determined in the Supreme Court and Court of Appeals of the State of New Mexico **2672**
New Mexico Rules of Evidence. (US) **2659**
New Mexico Skiers' Guide. (US) **4551**, **4779**
New Mexico State Bar Bulletin & Advance Opinions *see* State Bar of New Mexico. Bar Bulletin **2682**
New Mexico State University. Agricultural Experiment Station. Bulletin. (US) **155**
New Mexico State University. Agricultural Experiment Station. Research Report. (US ISSN 0548-5967) **109**
New Mexico Statistical Abstract. (US ISSN 0077-8575) **4580**
New Mexico Stockman. (US) **222**
New Mexico Wildlife. (US ISSN 0028-6338) **1494**
New Miami. (US) **838**
New Mitre *see* Mitre **2874**
New Moon. (UK ISSN 0963-0805) **3013**
New Morality. (IT ISSN 0028-6354) **2942**
New Motor Vehicle Sales. (CN ISSN 0705-5595) **4665**
New Muses. (US ISSN 0253-293X) **2998**, **3966**
New Museum News *see* New Museum Newsletter **3531**
New Museum Newsletter. (US) **3531**
New Music Articles *see* N M A **3569**
†New Music Distribution Service Manual. (US) **5246**
New Musical Express. (UK ISSN 0028-6362) **3570**
New Nation. (GY) **2196**
†New Native American Novel. (US) **5246**
New Nigeria Development Company Limited. Annual Report and Accounts.(NR) **1081**
New Nigeria Development Company Ltd. Newsletter *see* N N D C Newsletter **1081**
New Nippon Electric Technical Review. *see* Shin Nippon Denki Giho **5276**
†New North Artscape. (US ISSN 1040-3892) **5246**
New Observations. (US ISSN 0737-5387) **338**
New Official Guide: Japan. (JA ISSN 0077-8591) **4779**
▼New Ohio Journal. (US) **1964**, **3807**
New on the Charts. (US ISSN 0276-7031) **3570**

New Options. (US ISSN 0890-1619) **2876**, **3910**
New Orient. *see* Novy Orient **3642**
New Orleans *see* New Orleans Magazine **4779**
New Orleans Academy of Ophthalmology. Transactions. (US ISSN 0077-8605) **3302**
New Orleans CityBusiness. (US ISSN 0279-4527) **1116**
New Orleans Heath Users Group News *see* N O H U G News **1471**
New Orleans Magazine. (US ISSN 0897-8174) **4779**
New Orleans Menu. (US ISSN 8756-498X) **2078**, **2478**
New Orleans Port Record *see* Port of New Orleans Record **5260**
New Orleans Preservation in Print. (US) **304**
New Orleans Review. (US ISSN 0028-6400) **2942**, **2998**, **3514**, **3793**
New Orleans Times-Picayune Index. (US ISSN 0893-2484) **2578**
New Orleans Tribune. (US) **2016**
New Outlook. (IS ISSN 0028-6427) **3910**
New Outlook *see* New Outlook Tanzania **3910**
New Outlook Tanzania. (TZ) **3910**
New Oxford History of Music. (US) **3570**
New Oxford Review. (US ISSN 0149-4244) **4192**
New Pacific *see* Pacific Magazine **919**
New Packaging *see* Packaging Japan **3650**
New Pages. (US ISSN 0271-8197) **4133**
New Paradigms Newsletter. (UK ISSN 0951-6026) **4329**, **3048**, **3774**
New Parent. (AT ISSN 1030-3987) **3295**, **597**, **4849**
New Party. (US) **3945**
New Pathway *see* Novy Shliakh **2017**
New Pathway Almanac. *see* Kalendar - Al'manakh Novoho Shliakhu **2010**
New Pathways. (US ISSN 0886-2451) **3013**
The New Perspective. (US) **1318**
New Perspectives. (CN) **2016**
†New Perspectives. (FI) **5246**
†New Perspectives. (AT ISSN 1034-4284) **5246**
New Perspectives in History. (US) **2318**
New Perspectives in Philosophical Scholarship: Texts and Issues. (US ISSN 1045-4500) **3774**
New Perspectives in Powder Metallurgy.(US ISSN 0146-9711) **3416**
New Perspectives on the South. (US) **2416**
New Perspectives Quarterly. (US ISSN 0893-7850) **3910**
The New Philosophy. (US ISSN 0028-6443) **3774**
New Physician. (US ISSN 0028-6451) **3135**
New Phytologist. (UK ISSN 0028-646X) **511**
New Pioneer *see* Pioneer **1538**
New Plant Report. (US) **626**, **681**
†New Plays U S A. (US ISSN 0731-4523) **5246**
New Poets Series - Chestnut Hills Press. (US) **2998**
New Polish Publications *see* Soon to Appear **412**
New Political Science. (US ISSN 0739-3148) **3910**
New Polymeric Materials. (NE ISSN 0169-6424) **1220**
New Practice Planning. (US) **3135**
New Press. (US ISSN 0894-6078) **2998**
New Priorities *see* International Interactions **3961**
New Product Card Index *see* New Product Launch Letter **3736**
†New Product Development. (US ISSN 0733-8252) **5246**
New Product Development News. (UK) **1049**

New Product Launch Letter. (UK) **3736**
New Product Newsletter *see* International New Product Newsletter **1079**
New Product Newsletter. (UK) **1081**
New Product Report *see* International New Product Report **2092**
New Product Survey. (US) **3736**
New Products from C R S. (US) **407**
†New Products from Denmark. (DK ISSN 0108-1497) **5246**
New Products of the P.R.C. *see* Quanguo Xinchanpin **1083**
†New Publications for Architecture Libraries. (US ISSN 0271-0994) **5246**
New Publications Received at the Library. (IS) **141**
New Pulpit Digest *see* Pulpit Digest (1978) **4196**
New Quarrying & Mining. (UK) **3492**
New Quest. (II ISSN 0258-0381) **2876**
New Race. (US) **2159**
New Race. (II ISSN 0028-6532) **4444**
†New-Radio Cable Audio & Pay Radio Report. (US ISSN 0738-3371) **5246**
New Rain. (US) **2942**
New Rambler. (UK ISSN 0028-6540) **2942**
†New Realities. (US ISSN 0147-7625) **5246**
New Reference Books. (IS ISSN 0334-5262) **407**
New Registrations. (SW) **4665**
†New Release Magazine. (CN) **5246**
New Releases Publications List. (AT) **2659**, **4133**
New Religions Newsletter. (CN) **4192**
New Religious Movements Series. (US ISSN 1040-0974) **4192**
The New Renaissance. (US ISSN 0028-6575) **2942**, **338**
New Republic. (US ISSN 0028-6583) **2876**
New Research Centers. (US ISSN 0028-6591) **4329**
New Research in Museum Studies: An International Series. (UK) **3531**
New Resources. (US) **407**, **4068**
New Resources for State Government and Agencies *see* New Resources **407**
New Reveille *see* Reveille **2195**
New Review. *see* Novyi Zhurnal **2017**
New Review *see* Church Army. Frontline News **4171**
New Review. (UK) **4444**, **4414**
New River News. (US ISSN 0548-6599) **2416**
New Route. (US) **3570**, **1261**
New St. George Hospital Gazette *see* Saint George's Hospital Gazette **2469**
New Scandinavian Technology. (SW ISSN 1100-956X) **4605**
New Scholarly Books in America. (US) **407**
New Scholasticism *see* American Catholic Philosophical Quarterly **3760**
New School for Social Research. Philosophy Department. Graduate Faculty Philosophy Journal. (US ISSN 0093-4240) **3774**
New School Observer. (US) **1319**, **4444**
New Schools Exchange. Directory and Resource Guide. (US) **1651**
†New Scientific & Technical Books in America. (US) **5246**
New Scientist. (UK ISSN 0028-6664) **4329**
New Sense. (US) **2876**, **2016**
New Sense Bulletin. (US) **3349**, **4036**
New Serial Titles. (US ISSN 0028-6680) **407**
New Settler's Guide for Washington, D.C. and Communities in Nearby Maryland and Virginia. (US ISSN 0097-8213) **4779**, **3629**
New Shetlander. (UI ISSN 0047-987X) **2194**
†New Silver Technology. (US ISSN 0095-9286) **5246**
New Sins. (US) **2999**, **2456**

New Socialist. (UK ISSN 0261-6912) 3910
New Society see New Statesman & Society 2876
▼New Solutions. (US ISSN 1048-2911) 1964, 3619
New South see Southern Changes 3947
New South Carolina State Gazette. (US) 2416
New South Wales. Agriculture and Fisheries. Plant Disease Survey. (AT) 109
New South Wales. Attorney-General Justice Department. Bureau of Crime Statistics and Research. Research Report see New South Wales. Attorney General's Department. Bureau of Crime Statistics and Research. Research Studies 1519
New South Wales. Attorney General's Department. Bureau of Crime Statistics and Research. Research Studies. (AT) 1519
New South Wales. Department of Agriculture. Annual Report. (AT ISSN 0156-255X) 109, 2046, 4068
New South Wales. Department of Agriculture. Commodity Bulletin. (AT ISSN 0310-186X) 155
New South Wales. Department of Agriculture. Fisheries Bulletin see New South Wales. Department of Fisheries. Fisheries Bulletin 2046
New South Wales. Department of Agriculture. Plant Disease Survey see New South Wales. Agriculture and Fisheries. Plant Disease Survey 109
New South Wales. Department of Agriculture. Science Bulletin. (AT ISSN 0369-5867) 109
New South Wales. Department of Agriculture. Soil Survey Bulletin. (AT ISSN 0727-9078) 186
New South Wales. Department of Agriculture. Technical Bulletin. (AT ISSN 0311-8576) 109
New South Wales. Department of Fisheries. Fisheries Bulletin. (AT) 2046
New South Wales. Department of Housing. Annual Report. (AT) 2493
New South Wales. Department of Industrial Relations and Technology. Safety. (AT) 989, 4109
New South Wales. Department of Labour and Industry. Safety see New South Wales. Department of Industrial Relations and Technology. Safety 989
New South Wales. Department of Mineral Resources. Annual Report. (AT) 3492
New South Wales. Department of Minerals and Energy. Annual Report see New South Wales. Department of Mineral Resources. Annual Report 3492
New South Wales. Department of Mines. Memoirs: Palaeontology see New South Wales. Geological Survey. Memoirs: Palaeontology 3658
New South Wales. Forestry Commission. Research Notes. (AT ISSN 0085-3984) 2105
New South Wales. Geological Survey. Bulletin. (AT ISSN 0155-5561) 1575
New South Wales. Geological Survey. Memoirs: Geology. (AT ISSN 0077-8710) 1575
New South Wales. Geological Survey. Memoirs: Palaeontology. (AT) 3658
New South Wales. Geological Survey. Mine Data Sheets and Metallogenic Study see New South Wales. Geological Survey. Mineral Deposit Data Sheets and Metallogenic Study 1575
New South Wales. Geological Survey. Mineral Deposit Data Sheets and Metallogenic Study. (AT) 1575, 3492
New South Wales. Geological Survey. Mineral Industry Series. (AT ISSN 0077-8729) 3492, 1575
New South Wales. Geological Survey. Mineral Resources Series. (AT ISSN 0077-8737) 3492, 1575

New South Wales. Geological Survey. Quarterly Notes. (AT ISSN 0155-3410) 1575
New South Wales. Geological Survey. Records. (AT ISSN 0155-3372) 1575
New South Wales. Housing Commission. Annual Report see New South Wales. Department of Housing. Annual Report 2493
New South Wales. Law Reform Commission. Report. (AT ISSN 0085-400X) 2659
▼New South Wales and A.C.T. Stamp Duties. (AT) 1102
New South Wales & Australian Capital Territory Retail Directory. (AT ISSN 0817-024X) 1148, 1507
New South Wales Association for Mental Health. Newsletter see N S W A M H News 3133
New South Wales Association for Mental Health News see N S W A M H News 3133
New South Wales, Australia, Government Gazette. (AT ISSN 0155-6320) 4068
New South Wales Coal Yearbook (Year). (AT ISSN 1034-2109) 3502, 4580
New South Wales Conveyancing Law and Practice. (AT) 2659, 1102
New South Wales Dairymen's Digest. (AT ISSN 0310-3722) 202
New South Wales Farmers News see N.S.W. Farmers News 221
New South Wales Forest Products Association. Prologue Notes see N S W Forest Products Association. Prologue Notes 2104
New South Wales Golf Association Golf see N.S.W. Golf 4508
New South Wales in Brief. (AT ISSN 0725-5039) 4580
New South Wales Industrial Gazette. (AT ISSN 0028-677X) 989
New South Wales Institute of Technology Calendar see University of Technology. Sydney Calendar 4612
New South Wales Journal of Optometry see Clinical and Experimental Optometry 3299
New South Wales Land Tax. (AT) 1102
New South Wales Law Reports. (AT ISSN 0312-1674) 2659
New South Wales Local Courts Civil Practice. (AT) 2704
New South Wales Mineral Industry Review. (AT) 3492
New South Wales National Herbarium. Contributions see Telopea 519
New South Wales Official Publications Received in the Library of New South Wales see New South Wales Official Publications Received in the State Library of New South Wales 407
New South Wales Official Publications Received in the State Library of New South Wales. (AT ISSN 0729-5464) 407
New South Wales Ports Handbook. (AT ISSN 0266-0652) 1148, 4734
New South Wales Realty Auctioneer see N.S.W. Realty Auctioneer 4153
New South Wales Skindiver see N.S.W. Skindiver 4551
†New South Wales Statutes Annotation and References. (AT ISSN 0729-5987) 5246
New South Wales Statutes Annotations. (AT ISSN 1031-7872) 2659
New South Wales Strata and Community Titles Law. (AT) 2659
New South Wales Strata Title Law see New South Wales Strata and Community Titles Law 2659
New South Wales Weekly Notes see New South Wales Law Reports 2659
New South Wales Year Book. (AT ISSN 0810-9338) 4580
New Sower see Sower 4202
New Special Libraries. (US ISSN 0193-4287) 2776
New Spectator see Church & Nation 4233
New Spirit. (US) 1519
New Spokes. (UK) 2999, 338, 3793

New Sports. see Xin Tiyu 4497
New Statesman see New Statesman & Society 2876
New Statesman & Society. (UK ISSN 0954-2361) 2876
New Student Baker see Student Baker 2089
New Studies in Aesthetics. (US ISSN 0893-6005) 3774
New Studies in Archaeology. (UK) 280
New Studies in Athletics. (UK) 4481
New Studies on the Left. (US) 2876
New Surveys in the Classics. (UK) 1278
New Swedish Technology see New Scandinavian Technology 4605
New Teacher. (PK ISSN 0077-8826) 1651, 1756
New Tech Times. (US) 1319
New Technical Books. (US ISSN 0028-6869) 4357, 4615
New Techniques. see Neue Technik 1398
New Technologies and Innovation Policy see Innovation and Technology Transfer 2763
New Technology in the Human Services.(UK ISSN 0959-0684) 4459, 4414
New Technology Japan. (JA ISSN 0385-6542) 3021, 3825, 3864
New Technology Week. (US ISSN 0894-0789) 4605
New Technology, Work & Employment. (UK ISSN 0268-1072) 989
New Testament Abstracts. (US ISSN 0028-6877) 4213, 18
New Testament Studies. (UK ISSN 0028-6885) 4192
New Testament Tools and Studies. (NE ISSN 0077-8842) 4192
New Texas. (US) 2230
New Theatre Quarterly. (UK ISSN 0266-464X) 4635
New Thought (Mesa). (US ISSN 0146-7832) 4286
New Times. see Nova Doba 2017
New Times. (NR) 2212
New Times see Novoe Vremya 3967
New Times. (AT) 4245
New Times (Phoenix) see New Times Weekly 2876
New Times (Seattle). (US ISSN 1044-2782) 3595, 3774
New Times Weekly. (US ISSN 0273-9836) 2876
New Titles in Bioethics. (US ISSN 0361-6347) 3135, 3774
New Tolkien Newsletter. (UK ISSN 0260-3268) 2942
New Toy see Hominids, Oh 2923
New Trade Names see Brands and Their Companies Supplement 3673
New Trade Names in the Rubber and Plastics Industries see R A P R A New Trade Names in the Rubber and Plastics Industries 4293
New Trader. (SZ) 918
New Trail. (CN ISSN 0028-6907) 1319
New Trend. (US) 4220, 1651
New Trends in Biology Teaching. (UN ISSN 0077-8877) 449
New Trends in Chemistry Teaching. (UN ISSN 0077-8885) 1184
New Trends in Integrated Science Teaching. (UN) 1756
New Trends in Lipid Mediators Research. (SZ ISSN 1011-6672) 3736, 3188
New Trends in Mathematics Teaching. (UN ISSN 0077-8893) 3049
New Trends in Physics Teaching. (UN ISSN 0077-8907) 3825, 1651
New Unionist. (US) 3910, 989
New United Nations Publications. (DK ISSN 0108-1829) 3910
New Venture. (CN) 3013
New Veteran see Star Serviceman 3472
New Vico Studies. (US ISSN 0733-9542) 3774
New Virginia Review. (US) 2942, 3793
The New Voices. (TR ISSN 0254-9549) 2942
New Voices (Clintondale). (US) 2942
New Voices (Methuen). (US) 2999
New Voyager see Space Voyager 3014

New Wave. (Il ISSN 0047-9969) 3910
New Waves (Washington). (US ISSN 1040-8185) 3596, 3774
†New Ways (Evanston). (US ISSN 0882-9659) 5246
New Weekly Magazine. (CN ISSN 0835-9423) 2178
New Welsh Review. (UK ISSN 0954-2116) 2877
New West Indian Guide. see Nieuwe West Indische Gids 254
New West Notes. (US ISSN 0895-8505) 3910, 681
New West Virginia Hillbilly. (US ISSN 0887-4743) 2416
†New Wilderness Letter. (US ISSN 0197-4874) 5246
New Wine see Christian Conquest 4169
▼New Wine. (US) 4192
New Woman. (US ISSN 0028-6974) 4849
New World. (GY ISSN 0028-7008) 3910
New World. (UK ISSN 0028-6990) 3966
The New World. (US) 4271, 3774
New World Archaeological Foundation. Papers. (US) 280
▼New World Journal (New York). (US) 1964
New World News see For a Change 4372
New World Outlook. (US ISSN 0043-8812) 4192, 4245
New World Quarterly of the Inner-City Cultural Center see Neworld 338
New World Review see Update U S S R 3976
New World Times. (US) 2230
New Worldwide Tanker Nominal Freight Scale. (US ISSN 0953-9336) 4734, 3693
New Writer's Magazine. (US ISSN 0895-6510) 2942, 2999
†New Yarn. (JA) 5246
New York (City). Commission on the Status of Women. Status Report. (US ISSN 0149-8452) 4850, 3945
New York (City) Comptrollers Report. (US) 1102
New York (City). Department of Juvenile Justice. Annual Report. (US) 2659, 1261, 1519
New York (City). Health Systems Agency. Quarterly Bulletin. (US) 4109
New York (City). Human Resources Administration. Equal Employment Opportunity Quarterly Report. (US) 989
New York (City). Mayor. Schedules Supporting the Executive Budget. see New York (City). Schedules Supporting the Executive Budget 4092
New York (City). Museum of the City of New York. Annual Report. (US) 3531, 2416
New York (City). Office of Midtown Enforcement. Annual Report. (US) 2659
New York (City). Schedules Supporting the Executive Budget. (US ISSN 0094-7547) 4092
New York (State). Assembly. Standing Committee on Children and Families. Annual Report. (US) 4414, 1241
New York (State). Assembly. Standing Committee on Veterans' Affairs. Annual Report. (US) 3467, 4414
New York (State). Board of Social Welfare. Annual Report see New York (State). Department of Social Services. Annual Report 4414
New York (State). Commission on Quality of Care for the Mentally Disabled. Annual Report. (US) 2468, 3349, 4414
New York (State) Consumer Protection Board. Annual Report. (US ISSN 0095-5590) 1507
New York (State). Crime Victims Board. Report. (US) 1519
†New York (State) Department of Economic Development. Research Bulletin. (US) 5246

New York (State). Department of Environmental Conservation. Annual Report. (US) **1494**
New York (State). Department of Health. Monograph. (US) **4109**
New York (State) Department of Labor. Division of Research and Statistics. Labor Research Report. (US ISSN 0093-5034) **731, 989**
New York (State) Department of Labor. Operations - Employment Service and Unemployment Insurance. (US) **989**
New York (State). Department of Labor. Statistics on Operations. Annual Report. (US ISSN 0550-6638) **731**
New York (State). Department of Social Services. Annual Report. (US ISSN 0363-9835) **4414**
New York (State) Department of Social Services. Bureau of Data Management and Analysis. Program Analysis Report. (US ISSN 0090-4716) **4414**
New York (State) Department of Social Services. Bureau of Data Management and Analysis. Program Brief. (US ISSN 0162-6302) **4414**
New York (State) Department of Social Services. Bureau of Research. Program Analysis Report see New York (State) Department of Social Services. Bureau of Data Management and Analysis. Program Analysis Report **4414**
New York (State) Department of Social Services. Bureau of Research. Program Brief. see New York (State) Department of Social Services. Bureau of Data Management and Analysis. Program Brief **4414**
New York (State) Department of State. Manual for the Use of the Legislature of the State of New York. (US) **4068**
New York (State). Division of Criminal Justice Service. Annual Report. (US ISSN 0095-4047) **1519**
New York (State). Division of Criminal Justice Services. Felony Processing Quarterly Report. (US) **2714, 1519**
New York (State) Division of Criminal Services. Office of Justice Systems Analysis. Bulletin. (US) **1519**
New York (State) Division of Employment. Research and Statistics Office. Research Bulletin see New York (State) Department of Labor. Division of Research and Statistics. Labor Research Report **731**
New York (State). Division of Human Rights. Annual Report. (US) **3945**
New York (State) Division of the Budget. New York State Statistical Yearbook see New York (State). Rockefeller Institute of Government. New York State Statistical Yearbook **4581**
New York (State). Education Department. Employees in Colleges and Universities see College and University Employees, New York State **1703**
New York (State). Energy Office. Annual Report. (US) **1793**
New York (State). Health Planning Commission, Administrative Program for Health Planning and Development. (US) **4109**
New York (State). Information Center on Education. Education Statistics, New York State see Education Statistics, New York State **1676**
New York (State). Insurance Department. Annual Report of the Superintendent of Insurance to the New York Legislature. (US) **2539**
New York (State). Insurance Department. Bulletin. (US) **2539**
New York (State). Insurance Department. Fees and Taxes Charged Insurance Companies Under the Laws of New York Together with Abstracts of Fees, Taxes and Other Requirements of Other States. (US) **2539**

†New York (State). Insurance Department. Loss and Expense Ratios. (US ISSN 0467-6769) **5246**
New York (State) Insurance Department. Statistical Tables from Annual Statements. (US) **2547**
New York (State) Legislative Commission on Expenditure Review. Program Audits. (US) **4068**
New York (State). Medical Care Facilities Finance Agency. Annual Report. (US ISSN 0361-4018) **4109**
New York (State) Office for the Aging. Newsletter see Aging News **2270**
New York (State). Office of Advocate for the Disabled. Annual Report. (US) **4414**
New York (State). Opinions of the Attorney General. (US) **2659**
New York (State). Opinions of the Comptroller. (US) **2659, 4092**
New York (State). Rockefeller Institute of Government. New York State Statistical Yearbook. (US) **4581**
New York (State). Workmen's Compensation Board. Summary of Activities. (US) **2539**
New York (Year). (US) **4779**
New York Academy of Medicine. Annual Report. (US) **3135**
New York Academy of Medicine. Bulletin. (US ISSN 0028-7091) **3135**
†New York Academy of Medicine. News Notes. (US ISSN 0028-7105) **5246**
New York Academy of Sciences. Annals. (US ISSN 0077-8923) **4329**
New York Academy of Sciences. Transactions. (US ISSN 0028-7113) **4329**
▼New York Actions and Remedies. (US) **2659**
New York Agricultural Statistics. (US ISSN 0276-8798) **186**
New York Alive. (US ISSN 0734-0265) **1116**
New York Alliance see National Alliance (New York) **3908**
New York Amsterdam News. (US ISSN 0028-7121) **2016**
New York Antique Almanac. (US) **258**
New York Apartment Law Insider. (US ISSN 0898-2961) **4154, 626, 2659**
New York Apparel News. (US ISSN 0279-7844) **1287**
New York Art Review. (US) **338**
New York Auto Repair News. (US ISSN 0028-713X) **4698**
New York Banking Law. (US) **793, 2659**
▼New York Bodies. (US) **3807, 3596**
New York Botanical Garden. Memoirs. (US ISSN 0077-8931) **511**
New York Building Laws Manual. (US) **626, 2659**
New York Business Speaks. (US) **681**
New York C.S. Lewis Society Bulletin see C S L Bulletin **2901**
New York Casting - Survival Guide. (US) **4636, 1377, 1531**
New York Chamber of Commerce and Industry, Inc. Action see C C I Action **5156**
▼New York Christian Times. (US) **4192**
New York City Association of Life Underwriters. (US) **2539**
New York City Ballet News. (US) **1531**
New York City Charter: Administrative Code. (US) **2659**
New York City Environmental Bulletin. (US) **1964**
New York City Model Agency Directory. (US) **1148, 1695**
New York City Notes on Natural History. (US) **4329**
New York City Opera Spotlight see N Y City Opera Spotlight **5242**
New York City Parents and Friends of Lesbians and Gays Parents - F L A G Newsletter see N.Y.C. Parents - F L A G Newsletter **2455**

New York City Trade Union Handbook see Trade Union Handbook **2590**
New York City Transit Authority Facts & Figures see N Y C T A Facts & Figures **4653**
†New York Co-op & Condo Insider. (US) **5246**
New York Construction News. (US ISSN 0028-7164) **626**
New York Convention & Visitors Bureau. Quarterly Calendar of Events. (US ISSN 0028-7288) **4779**
New York County Medical Society Newsletter see M M News **3123**
New York Dairy Statistics see New York State Dairy Statistics **202**
New York Doctor. (US ISSN 0898-6401) **3135**
New York Economic Review. (US) **875**
New York Education Law Report. (US ISSN 0896-4122) **1651, 2659**
New York Employer's Alert. (US) **989, 2659, 4068**
New York Employer's Guide. (US) **990, 2659, 4068**
New York Entomological Society. Journal. (US ISSN 0028-7199) **536**
New York Estates - Wills - Trusts. (US) **2660**
New York Facts. (US ISSN 0888-4285) **1781**
New York Family. (US ISSN 0896-7199) **1241**
†New York Fish and Game Journal. (US ISSN 0028-7210) **5246**
New York Folklore. (US ISSN 0361-204X) **2057**
New York Folklore Newsletter. (US) **2057**
New York Folklore Quarterly see New York Folklore **2057**
New York Genealogical and Biographical Record. (US ISSN 0028-7237) **2159, 420**
New York Generator. (US ISSN 0028-7245) **2587, 1341**
New York Giants Official Yearbook (Year). (US) **4509**
New York Giants Yearbook (Year) see New York Giants Official Yearbook (Year) **4509**
New York Good News. (US) **2230**
New York Habitat Times. (US) **4414, 2493**
New York History. (US ISSN 0146-437X) **2416**
New York Holstein News. (US ISSN 0279-8611) **202**
New York Image. (US) **2230**
New York International Law Review. (US ISSN 1050-9453) **2727**
New York Issues. (US) **2230**
New York Jets Official Yearbook. (US) **4509**
New York Journal Japan. (US) **4779**
New York Journal of Dentistry. (US ISSN 0028-7296) **3238**
New York Jury Verdict Reporter. (US ISSN 0748-3430) **2732**
New York Knicks Yearbook. (US) **4509**
New York Law Journal. (US) **2660**
New York Law Journal Digest Annotator. (US) **2660**
New York Law School Journal of Human Rights. (US ISSN 8756-8926) **3945**
New York Law School Journal of International and Comparative Law. (US ISSN 0736-4075) **2727**
New York Law School Law Review. (US ISSN 0145-448X) **2660**
New York Law School Reporter. (US) **1319, 2660**
New York League News. (US) **793**
New York League of Savings Institutions. Legislative Bulletin. (US) **793**
New York Letter Carriers' Outlook. (US ISSN 0028-7342) **2587**
New York Library Association Bulletin see N Y L A Bulletin **2775**
New York Life Insurance Co. Review see N Y L I C Review **2538**
†New York Literary Forum. (US ISSN 0149-1040) **5246**
New York Magazine. (US ISSN 0028-7369) **2230, 2877**

NEW YORK 6491

New York Manufacturers Directory see George D. Hall's New York Manufacturers Directory **1136**
†New York Medical Quarterly. (US ISSN 0196-6871) **5246**
New York Mercantile Exchange Guide. (US) **875, 918**
New York Metro Area Postal Union. Union Mail. (US) **1353**
New York Mets Inside Pitch. (US ISSN 0887-5863) **4509**
▼New York Mix. (US) **4415**
New York Motor Express Guide see Official Shippers Guide - New York Motor Express Guide **4747**
New York Motorist. (US ISSN 0028-7385) **4698, 4779**
New York Native. (US ISSN 0744-060X) **2456**
New York Nichibei. (US) **2016**
New York Nightlife. (US) **2230**
New York No-Fault Arbitration Reports. (US) **2660, 2539**
New York Notary Law Primer. (US) **2660**
New York on Stage. (US) **4636, 1531, 3570**
New York Opera Newsletter. (US) **3570**
New York Pediatrician. (US) **3323**
New York - Pennsylvania Collector. (US) **258**
New York Personal Computer Inc. Magazine see N Y P C Magazine **1471**
New York Personnel Management Association Bulletin see N Y P M A Bulletin **1067**
New York Pinewoods Folk Music Club Newsletter. (US ISSN 1041-4150) **3570, 2057**
New York Planning News. (US) **2493**
New York Press. (US) **2230**
New York Professional Engineer. (US) **1831**
New York Psychoanalytic Institute. Kris Study Group. Monographs. (US ISSN 0077-9008) **4037**
New York Public Interest Research Group, Inc. Agenda see N Y P I R G Agenda **1506**
New York Public Library News. (US) **2776**
New York Publicity Outlets. (US ISSN 0077-9024) **35**
New York Purchasing Review see Metropolitan Purchasor **1047**
New York Quarterly. (US ISSN 0028-7482) **2999**
New York Rangers Blue Book see New York Rangers Yearbook **4481**
New York Rangers Yearbook. (US) **4481**
New York Real Estate Journal. (US) **4154**
New York Real Estate Reporter. (US) **2715**
New York Red Book. (US) **4068**
New York Review of Books. (US ISSN 0028-7504) **4133, 2877**
New York Review of Science Fiction. (US ISSN 1052-9438) **3013**
New York Runners Club Newsletter see New York Running News **4481**
New York Running News. (US ISSN 0161-7338) **4481**
New York School Counselor Association News see N Y S C A News **1649**
New York Sea Grant Institute. Annual Report. (US) **4068**
New York Shakespeare Society Bulletin see Shakespeare Bulletin **4638**
New York Skirt and Sportswear Association. Bulletin. (US) **1287**
New York Society of Ethical Hypnosis. Newsletter. (US) **4037**
New York Spectator. (US ISSN 0737-5379) **2016**
New York Sports (Deer Park). (US) **4481**
New York Sportsman. (US) **4551**
New York State. Assembly Subcommittee on Food, Farm and Nutrition Policy. Report. (US) **3609**
New York State. Education Department. College and University Enrollment. (US) **1713**

6492 NEW YORK

New York State. Education Department. College and University Revenues and Expenditures. (US) **1713, 1730**
New York State Archaeological Association. Bulletin. (US ISSN 1046-2368) **280**
New York State Bar Journal. (US ISSN 0028-7547) **2660**
New York State Bulletin see New York State Register **4092**
New York State Business Fact Book. Supplement. (US ISSN 0077-9105) **875,** 1148
New York State Committee on Open Government. Annual Report. (US) **2660**
New York State Criminal Law Review. (US ISSN 0271-6283) **2714**
New York State Dairy Statistics. (US ISSN 0732-9121) **202**
New York State Dental Journal. (US ISSN 0028-7571) **3238**
New York State Directory. (US ISSN 0737-1314) **4092**
†New York State Directory of Business Permits. (US) **5246**
†New York State Environment. (US ISSN 0048-0053) **5246**
New York State Environmental Facilities Corporation. Industrial Materials Recycling Act. Annual Report. (US) **1964**
New York State Fair Magazine. (US) **4779**
New York State FairGround see New York State Fair Magazine **4779**
New York State Journal of Medicine. (US ISSN 0028-7628) **3135**
New York State Library, Albany. Library Development. Excerpts from New York State Education Law, Rules of the Board of Regents, and Regulations of the Commissioner of Education Pertaining to Public and Free Association Libraries, Library Systems, Trustees and Librarians. (US ISSN 0077-930X) **2776**
New York State Library, Albany. Library Development. Institution Libraries Statistics. (US ISSN 0077-9318) **2795**
New York State Library, Albany. Library Development. Public and Association Libraries Statistics. (US ISSN 0077-9326) **2795**
New York State Media Directory see Burrelle's New York State Media Directory (Year) **29**
New York State Medical News. (US) **3135**
New York State Municipal Bulletin. (US) **4092**
New York State Museum. Biennial Report. (US ISSN 0883-1548) **4068**
New York State Museum. Bulletin. (US) **4330**
New York State Museum. Circular. (US) **4330**
New York State Museum. Leaflet. (US) **4330**
New York State Museum. Map and Chart Series. (US) **1575**
New York State Museum. Memoir. (US) **4330**
New York State Museum and Science Service. Circular see New York State Museum. Circular **4330**
New York State Museum and Science Service. Memoir see New York State Museum. Memoir **4330**
New York State Nurse see New York State Nurses Association. Journal **3282**
New York State Nurses Association. Journal. (US ISSN 0028-7644) **3282**
New York State Nurses Association. Report. (US ISSN 0028-7652) **3282**
New York State Pesticides Recommends (Redbook) see N Y S Pesticides Recommends (Redbook) **5242**
New York State Pharmacist see N Y State Pharmacist **3735**
New York State Pharmacist - Century II.(US) **3736**

New York State Planning News see New York Planning News **2493**
New York State Psychologist. (US ISSN 0028-7687) **4037**
New York State Queries. (US ISSN 1041-6560) **2159**
New York State Register. (US) **4092**
New York State School Boards Association. Employee Relations News. (US) **1730,** 1651
New York State School Boards Association. Legislative Bulletin. (US) **1730, 2660**
New York State School Boards Association Journal see N Y School Boards **1730**
New York State School of Industrial and Labor Relations. Bulletin. (US ISSN 0070-0134) **990**
New York State School of Industrial and Labor Relations. Institute of Public Employment. Monograph. (US) **990**
New York State School of Industrial and Labor Relations. Key Issues Series. (US ISSN 0070-0185) **990**
New York State School of Industrial and Labor Relations Paperbacks see I L R Paperbacks **981**
New York State Science Service. Biennial Report see New York State Museum. Biennial Report **4068**
New York State Society of Anesthesiologists, Inc. Sphere see N Y S S A Sphere **3191**
New York State Statistical Yearbook see New York (State). Rockefeller Institute of Government. New York State Statistical Yearbook **4581**
New York State Urban Development Corporation. Annual Report. (US ISSN 0077-9423) **4068**
†New York Stock Exchange. Statistical Highlights. (US ISSN 0275-4479) **5246**
New York Stock Exchange Guide. (US) **958**
New York Stock Exchange Monthly Review see New York Stock Exchange. Statistical Highlights **5246**
New York Stock Exchange Stock Reports. (US) **958**
†New York Style & Design. (US) **5246**
New York Supervisor. (US) **1730**
New York Tax Update. (US) **1102**
New York Teacher. (US) **2587,** 1651
New York Telephone Tickler for Insurance Men and Women. (US) **2539**
New York Theatre Critics' Reviews. (US ISSN 0028-7784) **4636**
New York Times Book Review. (US ISSN 0028-7806) **4133,** 2942
New York Times Book Review (Microform Editions). (US) **4133,** 2942
†New York Times Book Reviews. (US) **5246**
New York Times Current Events Edition.(US ISSN 0190-1990) **2318**
New York Times Film Reviews. (US ISSN 0362-3688) **3514**
New York Times Index. (US ISSN 0147-538X) **2578**
New York Times Index Highlights. (US) **2578,** 3938
New York Times Large Type Weekly. (US ISSN 0028-7814) **2295**
New York Times Magazine (Microfiche Edition). (US) **2230**
New York Times School Microfilm Collection Index. (US) **407**
New York Times School Microfilm Collection Index by Reels see New York Times School Microfilm Collection Index **407**
New York Times Theatre Reviews. (US ISSN 0160-0583) **4636**
New York TourBook see Tourbook: New York **4790**
New York Truck Exchange. (US) **4746**
New York Turtle and Tortoise Society Newsnotes see N Y T T S Newsnotes **231**
New York Typographical Union Number Six. Bulletin. (US ISSN 0049-4968) **2587,** 4002

†New York University. Bulletin of the Tamiment Institute - Ben Josephson Library. (US) **5246**
New York University. Comparative Criminal Law Project. Publications see Wayne State University Law School. Comparative Criminal Law Project. Publications Series **1524**
New York University. Institute of Labor Relations. Annual Conference on Labor at New York University see Annual National Conference on Labor at New York University. Proceedings **971**
New York University. Institute on Federal Taxation. Conference on Charitable Foundations. (US) **1102,** 2660
New York University. Salomon Center. Monograph Series. (US) **793**
New York University. Salomon Center. Newsletter. (US) **793**
New York University. Salomon Center. Occasional Papers. (US) **793**
New York University. Salomon Center. Occasional Papers in Business and Finance. (US) **793**
New York University. Salomon Center. Working Papers Series. (US) **793**
New York University. Studies in Near Eastern Civilization. (US ISSN 0081-8291) **3642,** 2431
New York University Alumni News see N Y U Alumni News **5242**
New York University Biomedical Engineering Series. (US) **3135**
New York University Business Magazine Publishing Series. (US) **4133,** 681
New York University Journal of International Law and Politics. (US ISSN 0028-7873) **2727**
New York University Law Review. (US ISSN 0028-7881) **2660**
†New York University Medical Center News. (US ISSN 0028-789X) **5246**
New York University Medical Center Physician see N Y U Physician **1318**
New York University Medical Quarterly see N Y U Physician **1318**
New York University Report see N Y U Today **1318**
New York University Salomon Brothers Center for the Study of Financial Institutions. Newsletter see New York University. Salomon Center. Newsletter **793**
New York University School of Law. Ingram Documents in American Legal History. (US ISSN 0894-3303) **2660**
New York University School of Law. Linden Studies in Legal History. (US ISSN 0894-329X) **2660**
†New York University Studies in Comparative Literature. (US ISSN 0077-9504) **5246**
New York University Studies in French Culture and Civilization. (US) **2377,** 2942
New York University Today see N Y U Today **1318**
New York Urban League. Annual Report. (US) **4415**
New York Voice. (US) **2230**
†New York Woman. (US) **5246**
†New York Woman's News. (US) **5246**
†New York Writer. (US) **5246**
The New Yorker. (US ISSN 0028-792X) **2877**
New Yorkin Uutiset/Finnish New York News. (US) **2016**
New York's Finest. (US) **1519**
†New York's Food and Life Sciences Bulletin. (US ISSN 0362-0069) **5246**
New York's Food and Life Sciences Quarterly see Cornell Focus **85**
New York's Nightlife. (US) **4780**
New Youth. see Xin Qingnian **1246**
New Youth Connections see N Y C **1261**
New Yugoslav Law see Yugoslav Law **2696**
New Zealand. Audit Office. Report on the Public Accounts. (NZ) **1102**

New Zealand. Central Advisory Committee on the Appointments and Promotion of Primary Teachers. Report to the Minister of Education. (NZ ISSN 0077-958X) **1651**
New Zealand. Customs Department. Customs Bulletin see Contraband **904**
New Zealand. Customs Department. Import Licensing Bulletin see Contraband **904**
New Zealand. Dairy Board. Annual Report and Statement of Accounts. (NZ) **202**
New Zealand. Dairy Production and Marketing Board. Annual Report and Statement of Accounts see New Zealand. Dairy Board. Annual Report and Statement of Accounts **202**
New Zealand. Department of Health. National Radiation Laboratory. Environmental Radioactivity Annual Report. (NZ ISSN 0110-9944) **1964**
†New Zealand. Department of Maori Affairs. Annual Report. (NZ) **5247**
New Zealand. Department of Maori Affairs. Report see New Zealand. Department of Maori Affairs. Annual Report **5247**
New Zealand. Department of Scientific and Industrial Research. Annual Report. (NZ ISSN 0077-9601) **4330**
†New Zealand. Department of Scientific and Industrial Research. Bulletin. (NZ ISSN 0077-961X) **5247**
†New Zealand. Department of Scientific and Industrial Research. Geophysics Division. Research Report. (NZ ISSN 0113-2903) **5247**
†New Zealand. Department of Scientific and Industrial Research. Geophysics Division. Technical Report. (NZ ISSN 0113-3055) **5247**
New Zealand. Department of Scientific and Industrial Research. Geological Survey. Bulletin see New Zealand Geological Survey. Bulletin **1575**
†New Zealand. Department of Scientific and Industrial Research. Information Series. (NZ ISSN 0077-9636) **5247**
New Zealand. Department of Scientific and Industrial Research. Paleontological Bulletin see New Zealand Geological Survey. Paleontological Bulletin **3658**
†New Zealand. Department of Scientific and Industrial Research. Social Science Series. (NZ ISSN 0112-2339) **5247**
New Zealand. Department of Statistics. Agricultural Statistics. (NZ ISSN 0110-4624) **141**
†New Zealand. Department of Statistics. Annual Report of the Government Statistician. (NZ ISSN 0077-9652) **5247**
New Zealand. Department of Statistics. Balance of Payments see New Zealand. Department of Statistics. Overseas Balance of Payments **5247**
†New Zealand. Department of Statistics. Building Statistics. (NZ ISSN 0110-3490) **5247**
†New Zealand. Department of Statistics. Census of Building and Construction. (NZ ISSN 0110-4640) **5247**
†New Zealand. Department of Statistics. Census of Transport, Storage & Communication. (NZ ISSN 0112-3629) **5247**
New Zealand. Department of Statistics. Consumer Expenditure. (NZ ISSN 1170-747X) **731,** 4581
†New Zealand. Department of Statistics. Consumers Price Index. (NZ ISSN 0112-6598) **5247**
New Zealand. Department of Statistics. Demographic Trends. (NZ ISSN 0113-3667) **3994,** 4581
New Zealand. Department of Statistics. Demographic Trends Bulletin see New Zealand. Department of Statistics. Demographic Trends **3994**

NEW ZEALAND 6493

New Zealand. Department of Statistics. Exports *see* New Zealand. Department of Statistics. Overseas Trade **731**

†New Zealand. Department of Statistics. External Migration Statistics. (NZ ISSN 0112-6709) **5247**

New Zealand. Department of Statistics. External Trade Price and Volume Indexes *see* New Zealand. Department of Statistics. Overseas Trade **731**

New Zealand. Department of Statistics. Imports *see* New Zealand. Department of Statistics. Overseas Trade **731**

New Zealand. Department of Statistics. Incomes. (NZ ISSN 1170-8271) **731,** 4581

†New Zealand. Department of Statistics. Insurance Statistics. (NZ ISSN 0110-3474) **5247**

†New Zealand. Department of Statistics. Justice Statistics: Part A. (NZ ISSN 0112-4447) **5247**

†New Zealand. Department of Statistics. Justice Statistics: Part B. (NZ ISSN 0112-4501) **5247**

New Zealand. Department of Statistics. Key Statistics. (NZ ISSN 0114-2119) **4581**

New Zealand. Department of Statistics. Life Annuity Tables *see* New Zealand. Department of Statistics. New Zealand Life Tables **2547**

†New Zealand. Department of Statistics. Local Authority Statistics. (NZ ISSN 0110-3466) **5247**

New Zealand. Department of Statistics. Monthly Abstract of Statistics *see* New Zealand. Department of Statistics. Key Statistics **4581**

New Zealand. Department of Statistics. New Zealand Life Tables. (NZ ISSN 0111-0225) **2547**

†New Zealand. Department of Statistics. Overseas Balance of Payments. (NZ ISSN 0112-5117) **5247**

New Zealand. Department of Statistics. Overseas Trade. (NZ ISSN 0114-2607) **731,** 918

New Zealand. Department of Statistics. Population Census: Ages and Marital Status *see* New Zealand. Department of Statistics. Population Census: Ages, Marital Status and Fertility **3994**

New Zealand. Department of Statistics. Population Census: Ages, Marital Status and Fertility. (NZ) **3994**

New Zealand. Department of Statistics. Population Census: Birthplaces and Ethnic Origin. (NZ) **3994**

New Zealand. Department of Statistics. Population Census: Dwellings. (NZ ISSN 0077-9695) **3994**

New Zealand. Department of Statistics. Population Census: Education *see* New Zealand. Department of Statistics. Population Census: Education and Training **3994**

New Zealand. Department of Statistics. Population Census: Education and Training. (NZ) **3994**

New Zealand. Department of Statistics. Population Census: Families. (NZ) **3994**

New Zealand. Department of Statistics. Population Census: General Information. (NZ ISSN 0110-8700) **3994**

New Zealand. Department of Statistics. Population Census: General Report *see* New Zealand. Department of Statistics. Population Census: General Information **3994**

New Zealand. Department of Statistics. Population Census: Households and Families *see* New Zealand. Department of Statistics. Population Census: Families **3994**

New Zealand. Department of Statistics. Population Census: Incomes and Social Security Benefits *see* New Zealand. Department of Statistics. Population Census: Incomes and Welfare Payments **3994**

New Zealand. Department of Statistics. Population Census: Incomes and Welfare Payments. (NZ) **3994**

New Zealand. Department of Statistics. Population Census. Increase and Location of Population *see* New Zealand. Department of Statistics. Population Census: Total Population Statistics **3994**

New Zealand. Department of Statistics. Population Census: Industries and Occupations *see* New Zealand. Department of Statistics. Population Census: Labour Force **3994**

New Zealand. Department of Statistics. Population Census: Internal Migration. (NZ) **3994,** 4581

New Zealand. Department of Statistics. Population Census: Labour Force. (NZ) **3994**

New Zealand. Department of Statistics. Population Census. Location and Increase of Population. Part A: Population Size and Distribution *see* New Zealand. Department of Statistics. Population Census: Total Population Statistics **3994**

New Zealand. Department of Statistics. Population Census: Maori Population and Dwellings. (NZ) **3994**

New Zealand. Department of Statistics. Population Census: Race *see* New Zealand. Department of Statistics. Population Census: Birthplaces and Ethnic Origin **3994**

New Zealand. Department of Statistics. Population Census: Religious Professions. (NZ ISSN 0077-9784) **3994**

New Zealand. Department of Statistics. Population Census: Total Population Statistics. (NZ) **3994,** 4581

New Zealand. Department of Statistics. Report and Analysis of External Trade *see* New Zealand. Department of Statistics. Overseas Trade **731**

New Zealand. Department of Statistics. Shipping and Cargo *see* New Zealand. Department of Statistics. Overseas Trade **731**

New Zealand. Department of Statistics. Statistical Report of Farm Production *see* New Zealand. Department of Statistics. Agricultural Statistics **141**

†New Zealand. Department of Statistics. Vital Statistics. (NZ ISSN 0110-4586) **5247**

New Zealand. Department of Trade and Industry. Import Licensing Schedule *see* New Zealand. Ministry of Commerce. Import Licensing Schedule **918**

New Zealand. F R I Bulletin. (Forest Research Institute) (NZ ISSN 0111-8129) **2105**

New Zealand. Forest Research Institute. Report. (NZ ISSN 0077-9997) **2105**

New Zealand. Health Statistical Services. Cancer Data: New Registrations and Deaths. (NZ) **3178**

New Zealand. Health Statistical Services. Client Services Newsletter. (NZ) **4109,** 4581

New Zealand. Health Statistical Services. Fetal and Infant Deaths. (NZ) **3178,** 4581

New Zealand. Health Statistical Services. Hospital and Selected Morbidity Data.(NZ ISSN 0548-9938) **2471,** 3985

†New Zealand. Health Statistical Services. Hospital Management Data.(NZ ISSN 0110-1900) **5247**

New Zealand. Health Statistical Services. Mental Health Data. (NZ ISSN 0548-992X) **3178**

New Zealand. Health Statistical Services. Mortality and Demographic Data. (NZ ISSN 0548-9911) **3994**

New Zealand. Lottery Board of Control. Report *see* New Zealand Lottery Board. Report **1102**

New Zealand. Meat and Wool Boards' Economic Service. Annual Review of the New Zealand Sheep & Beef Industry. (NZ) **222**

New Zealand. Meat and Wool Boards' Economic Service. Annual Review of the Sheep Industry *see* New Zealand. Meat and Wool Boards' Economic Service. Annual Review of the New Zealand Sheep & Beef Industry **222**

New Zealand. Ministry of Agriculture and Fisheries. Fisheries Research Division. Bulletin *see* New Zealand Fisheries Research Bulletin **2046**

New Zealand. Ministry of Agriculture and Fisheries. Fisheries Research Division: Information Leaflet *see* New Zealand Fisheries Technical Report **2046**

New Zealand. Ministry of Agriculture and Fisheries. Fisheries Research Division Occasional Publication *see* New Zealand Fisheries Occasional Publication **2046**

New Zealand. Ministry of Commerce. Import Licensing Schedule. (NZ) **918**

†New Zealand. Ministry of Energy. Annual Report. (NZ) **5247**

New Zealand. Ministry of Energy. Annual Returns of Production from Quarries and Mineral Production Statistics *see* New Zealand Annual Mining Review **3502**

New Zealand. Ministry of External Relations and Trade. Annual Report. (NZ) **3966**

New Zealand. Ministry of Foreign Affairs. Development. (NZ ISSN 0110-4802) **3966**

New Zealand. Ministry of Foreign Affairs. Project Profiles. (NZ ISSN 0111-5251) **3966**

New Zealand. Ministry of Foreign Affairs. Report *see* New Zealand. Ministry of External Relations and Trade. Annual Report **3966**

†New Zealand. Ministry of Transport. Traffic Research Circular. (NZ) **5247**

†New Zealand. Ministry of Transport. Traffic Research Report. (NZ ISSN 0110-6872) **5247**

New Zealand. National Health Statistics Centre. Fetal and Infant Deaths *see* New Zealand. Health Statistical Services. Fetal and Infant Deaths **3178**

†New Zealand. Nature Conservation Council. Newsletter. (NZ ISSN 0111-686X) **5247**

New Zealand. Railways Corporation. Annual Report *see* New Zealand Rail Ltd. Annual Report **4712**

†New Zealand. Road Research Unit. Bulletin. (NZ ISSN 0549-0030) **5247**

New Zealand. Road Research Unit. Newsletter *see* New Zealand. Transit New Zealand. Road Research Unit. Newsletter **5247**

†New Zealand. Road Research Unit. Occasional Paper. (NZ ISSN 0111-0756) **5247**

†New Zealand. Transit New Zealand. Road Research Unit. Newsletter. (NZ ISSN 1170-4683) **5247**

New Zealand Accounts Preparation Manual. (NZ) **754**

New Zealand Administrative Reports. (NZ ISSN 0110-1277) **2660**

†New Zealand Agricultural Engineering Institute. Current Publications. (NZ ISSN 0111-0829) **5247**

New Zealand Agriculture *see* AgLink Leaflets **68**

New Zealand Annual Mining Review. (NZ) **3502**

New Zealand Antarctic Record. (NZ ISSN 0110-5124) **2257,** 1547

New Zealand Archaeological Association. Newsletter *see* Archaeology in New Zealand **264**

New Zealand Architect *see* Architecture New Zealand **293**

New Zealand Association of Radio Transmitters, Inc. Amateur Radio Callbook *see* N.Z.A.R.T. Amateur Radio Callbook **1357**

New Zealand Baptist. (NZ ISSN 0027-7177) **4245**

New Zealand Books in Print. (AT ISSN 0157-7662) **407**

New Zealand Business. (NZ ISSN 0113-4957) **1148**

New Zealand Business Bulletin. (NZ) **682,** 2660

New Zealand Business Law Guide. (NZ) **1102,** 2660

New Zealand Business Who's Who. (NZ ISSN 0077-9571) **1148,** 420

New Zealand Car. (NZ ISSN 0113-0196) **4698,** 4481

New Zealand Cartographic Journal *see* New Zealand Cartography and Geographic Information Systems **2257**

New Zealand Cartography and Geographic Information Systems. (NZ) **2257**

†New Zealand Census of Agricultural Contracting Services. (NZ ISSN 0112-3718) **5247**

New Zealand Chess. (NZ) **4481,** 1419

New Zealand Company Law and Practice. (NZ) **2711**

New Zealand Company Law and Practice Manual. (NZ) **2711**

New Zealand Company Law Service *see* New Zealand Company Law and Practice Manual **2711**

New Zealand Company Secretary's Guide. (NZ) **2711,** 754

New Zealand Company Secretary's Practice Manual and Company Law Service *see* New Zealand Company Law and Practice **2711**

▼New Zealand Concise Stamp Catalogue. (UK) **3755**

New Zealand Concrete Construction. (NZ ISSN 0549-0219) **626**

New Zealand Constructor. (NZ) **626**

New Zealand Conveyancing Bulletin *see* Butterworths Conveyancing Bulletin **2607**

New Zealand Conveyancing Law and Practice. (NZ) **2660**

New Zealand Council for Educational Research Newsletter *see* N Z C E R Newsletter **1649**

New Zealand Council of Trade Unions. Official Trade Union Directory. (NZ ISSN 1170-7887) **2587**

New Zealand Current Taxation. (NZ ISSN 0545-7572) **1102**

New Zealand Dairy Exporter. (NZ ISSN 0111-915X) **202**

New Zealand Dairy Research Institute. Biennial Review *see* New Zealand Dairy Research Institute. Report **202**

New Zealand Dairy Research Institute. Report. (NZ) **202**

New Zealand Dental Journal. (NZ ISSN 0028-8047) **3238**

New Zealand Diplomatic Corps and Consular and Other Representatives *see* Diplomatic List - Diplomatic and Consular Representatives in New Zealand **3955**

New Zealand District Court Reports *see* Butterworths District Court Reports **2607**

New Zealand Duties and Sales Tax Guide *see* New Zealand Duties Guide **2660**

New Zealand Duties Guide. (NZ) **2660,** 1102

New Zealand Ecological Society. Proceedings see New Zealand Journal of Ecology **449**

New Zealand Economic Papers. (NZ ISSN 0077-9954) **682**

New Zealand Educational Institute Rourou *see* N Z E I Rourou **1649**

New Zealand Electrician *see* N Z Electrical Focus **1904**

†New Zealand Electronics Review. (NZ) **5247**

▼New Zealand Employers Handbook. (NZ) **1068,** 2660

New Zealand Employment Law Library. (NZ) **1068,** 2660

New Zealand Engineering. (NZ ISSN 0028-808X) **1831**

New Zealand Entomologist. (NZ ISSN 0077-9962) **536**

New Zealand Environment. (NZ ISSN 0110-6287) **1964**

Title

NEW ZEALAND

New Zealand Environmental Health Inspector see New Zealand Journal of Environmental Health **4109**
New Zealand Export-Import Corporation. Report. (NZ) **918**
New Zealand Export Yearbook. (NZ) **1148**, **918**
New Zealand External Relations Review.(NZ ISSN 0114-3999) **3966**
New Zealand Family Law Bulletin see Butterworths Family Law Bulletin **2716**
▼New Zealand Family Law Court Handbook. (NZ) **2660**
New Zealand Family Law Reports see Butterworths Family Law Reports **2716**
New Zealand Farmer. (NZ ISSN 0028-8098) **109**
New Zealand Federation of Labour. Official Trade Union Directory see New Zealand Council of Trade Unions. Official Trade Union Directory **2587**
New Zealand Fisheries Occasional Publication. (NZ ISSN 0113-227X) **2046**
New Zealand Fisheries Research Bulletin. (NZ ISSN 0113-2261) **2046**
New Zealand Fisheries Technical Report. (NZ ISSN 0113-2180) **2046**
New Zealand Fisherman. (NZ ISSN 0113-9606) **4551**, **4527**
New Zealand Flight Safety. (NZ ISSN 0112-8949) **59**
New Zealand Foreign Affairs Review see New Zealand External Relations Review **3966**
New Zealand Forest Industries. (NZ ISSN 0113-3128) **2116**
New Zealand Forestry. (NZ ISSN 0112-9597) **2105**
New Zealand Forms & Precedents. (NZ) **2660**
New Zealand Fuchsia Society. News Letter. (NZ) **2135**
New Zealand Gardener. (NZ ISSN 0028-8136) **2135**
New Zealand Gay News see Out **2456**
New Zealand Genealogist. (NZ ISSN 0110-4012) **2159**
New Zealand General Practice. (NZ ISSN 0114-2550) **3135**
New Zealand General Practice, Business Management. (NZ ISSN 1170-327X) **3135**, **1022**
New Zealand Geographer. (NZ ISSN 0028-8144) **2257**
New Zealand Geographical Society. Miscellaneous Series. (NZ ISSN 0078-0022) **2257**
New Zealand Geographical Society. Record see New Zealand Journal of Geography **2257**
New Zealand Geography Conference Proceedings Series. (NZ ISSN 0078-0030) **2257**
New Zealand Geological Survey. Bulletin. (NZ) **1575**
New Zealand Geological Survey. Paleontological Bulletin. (NZ ISSN 0114-2283) **3658**
New Zealand Geological Survey Basin Studies. (NZ) **1575**, **3693**
New Zealand Goods and Services Tax Guide. (NZ) **1102**, **2660**
New Zealand Gymnast. (NZ ISSN 0110-0297) **4481**
New Zealand Hardware Journal. (NZ ISSN 0028-8160) **642**
New Zealand Health & Hospital. (NZ ISSN 0114-3727) **2468**
†New Zealand Health Statistics Report. (NZ ISSN 0110-5264) **5247**
New Zealand Historic Places. (NZ ISSN 0114-9172) **2345**
New Zealand Home and Building. (NZ ISSN 0110-098X) **626**, **2135**, **2554**
New Zealand Horse & Pony. (NZ ISSN 0028-8209) **4536**
New Zealand Hospital see New Zealand Health & Hospital **2468**
New Zealand Household Expenditure and Income Survey see New Zealand. Department of Statistics. Consumer Expenditure **731**

New Zealand Household Expenditure and Income Survey see New Zealand. Department of Statistics. Incomes **731**
New Zealand Income Tax Guide. (NZ) **1102**
New Zealand Income Tax Law and Practice. (NZ) **1102**
New Zealand Income Tax Legislation. (NZ) **1102**, **2660**
New Zealand Institute of Chemistry. Journal see Chemistry in New Zealand **1174**
New Zealand Institute of Economic Research. Annual Report. (NZ ISSN 0078-0057) **682**
New Zealand Institute of Economic Research. Discussion Paper. (NZ ISSN 0078-0049) **682**
New Zealand Institute of Economic Research. Medium Term Review see Quarterly Predictions of National Income and Expenditure **1000**
New Zealand Institute of Economic Research. Quarterly Survey of Business Opinion. (NZ ISSN 0110-4470) **682**
New Zealand Institute of Economic Research. Research Monographs. (NZ ISSN 0113-1877) **682**
New Zealand Institute of Economic Research. Research Paper see New Zealand Institute of Economic Research. Research Monographs **682**
New Zealand Institute of Science and Technology. Newsletter see Food Technologist **2070**
New Zealand International Review. (NZ ISSN 0110-0262) **3966**
New Zealand Jeweller and Watchmaker see Jewellery Time **2565**
†New Zealand Journal of Adult Learning. (NZ ISSN 0112-224X) **5247**
New Zealand Journal of Agricultural Research. (NZ ISSN 0028-8233) **110**
New Zealand Journal of Archaeology. (NZ ISSN 0110-540X) **280**
New Zealand Journal of Botany. (NZ ISSN 0028-825X) **511**
New Zealand Journal of Crop and Horticultural Science. (NZ ISSN 0114-0671) **110**
†New Zealand Journal of Dairy Science and Technology. (NZ ISSN 0300-1342) **5247**
New Zealand Journal of Ecology. (NZ ISSN 0110-6465) **449**
New Zealand Journal of Educational Studies. (UK ISSN 0028-8276) **1651**
New Zealand Journal of Environmental Health. (NZ ISSN 0112-0212) **4109**
New Zealand Journal of Experimental Agriculture see New Zealand Journal of Crop and Horticultural Science **110**
New Zealand Journal of Forestry see New Zealand Forestry **2105**
New Zealand Journal of Forestry Science. (NZ ISSN 0048-0134) **2105**
New Zealand Journal of French Studies. (NZ ISSN 0110-7380) **2942**, **2999**
New Zealand Journal of Geography. (NZ ISSN 0028-8292) **2257**
New Zealand Journal of Geology and Geophysics. (NZ ISSN 0028-8306) **1575**, **1592**
New Zealand Journal of Health, Physical Education and Recreation. (NZ ISSN 0028-8314) **1756**, **4481**
New Zealand Journal of History. (NZ ISSN 0028-8322) **2345**
New Zealand Journal of Industrial Relations. (NZ ISSN 0110-0637) **990**, **2660**
New Zealand Journal of Marine and Freshwater Research. (NZ ISSN 0028-8330) **1608**, **449**, **1599**
New Zealand Journal of Mathematics. (NZ) **3049**
New Zealand Journal of Medical Laboratory Science. (NZ ISSN 1171-0195) **3262**

New Zealand Journal of Medical Laboratory Technology see New Zealand Journal of Medical Laboratory Science **3262**
New Zealand Journal of Physiotherapy. (NZ ISSN 0303-7193) **3135**
New Zealand Journal of Psychology. (NZ ISSN 0112-109X) **4037**
New Zealand Journal of Public Administration see Public Sector **4071**
New Zealand Journal of Zoology. (NZ ISSN 0301-4223) **589**
New Zealand Kiwifruit. (NZ) **186**
New Zealand Labour Force. (NZ ISSN 0113-1222) **990**
New Zealand Law Journal. (NZ ISSN 0028-8373) **2660**
New Zealand Law Register. (AT ISSN 0078-0081) **2660**
New Zealand Law Reports. (NZ ISSN 0110-148X) **2660**
New Zealand Libraries. (NZ ISSN 0028-8381) **2776**
New Zealand Listener. (NZ ISSN 0110-5787) **1377**
New Zealand Local Government. (NZ) **4092**
New Zealand Local Government Yearbook. (NZ ISSN 0028-8403) **4092**
New Zealand Lottery Board. Report. (NZ) **1102**
New Zealand Manufacturer see Manufacturer **678**
New Zealand Marine News. (NZ ISSN 0549-0502) **4734**
New Zealand Marine Sciences Newsletter see New Zealand Marine Sciences Society Newsletter **449**
New Zealand Marine Sciences Society Newsletter. (NZ ISSN 0112-8396) **449**, **1608**, **2046**
New Zealand Master Tax Guide Manual see New Zealand Income Tax Guide **1102**
New Zealand Meat. (NZ) **2078**
New Zealand Medical Journal. (NZ ISSN 0028-8446) **3135**
New Zealand Mercantile Gazette. (NZ) **838**
New Zealand Monthly Review. (NZ ISSN 0028-8489) **2212**
New Zealand National Bibliography. (NZ ISSN 0028-8497) **407**
New Zealand National Society for Earthquake Engineering. Bulletin. (NZ ISSN 0550-6743) **1872**
New Zealand Natural Sciences. (NZ ISSN 0113-7492) **449**
†New Zealand News Review. (NZ ISSN 0545-7785) **5247**
New Zealand News U.K. (UK ISSN 0028-8500) **2212**
New Zealand Nursing Forum. (NZ ISSN 0110-0890) **3282**
New Zealand Nursing Journal. (NZ ISSN 0028-8535) **3283**
New Zealand Oceanographic Institute. Memoir. (NZ ISSN 0083-7903) **1608**
New Zealand Office Technology & Equipment News. (NZ) **1059**
New Zealand Official Year-Book. (NZ ISSN 0078-0170) **2345**
New Zealand Outlook. (UK ISSN 0962-2918) **2212**
New Zealand Packaging Yearbook. (NZ) **1148**, **3650**
New Zealand Pharmacy. (NZ ISSN 0111-431X) **3736**, **3807**
†New Zealand Planning Council. Monitoring Reports. (NZ ISSN 0112-2061) **5247**
New Zealand Planning Council. Planning Papers see New Zealand Planning Council. Monitoring Reports **5247**
New Zealand Planning Institute. Planning Quarterly. (NZ ISSN 0111-9435) **2493**
New Zealand Plumbing Review. (NZ ISSN 0028-8594) **2301**
New Zealand Powerboat. (NZ ISSN 0112-4412) **4527**, **4551**
New Zealand Printer. (AT) **4002**
New Zealand Property. (NZ ISSN 0113-4620) **4154**

New Zealand Publishing News. (NZ ISSN 0111-834X) **4133**
New Zealand Purchasing Yearbook. (NZ) **1049**
New Zealand R S A Review. (NZ) **4415**, **3467**
New Zealand Rail Ltd. Annual Report. (NZ) **4712**
New Zealand Railway Observer. (NZ ISSN 0028-8624) **4712**
New Zealand Rationalist see New Zealand Rationalist and Humanist **3774**
New Zealand Rationalist and Humanist. (NZ ISSN 0028-8632) **3774**, **4444**
New Zealand Red Cross Society. Report. (NZ ISSN 0080-0392) **4415**
New Zealand Sales, Goods and Service Taxes Guide see New Zealand Goods and Services Tax Guide **1102**
New Zealand School Journal. (NZ ISSN 0111-6355) **1261**
New Zealand Science Review. (NZ ISSN 0028-8667) **4330**
New Zealand Shipping Directory. (NZ ISSN 0545-7866) **4734**
New Zealand Shipping Gazette. (NZ ISSN 0027-724X) **4734**
New Zealand Slavonic Journal. (NZ ISSN 0028-8683) **2512**, **3910**, **4381**
New Zealand Society of Animal Production. Proceedings. (NZ ISSN 0370-2731) **222**
New Zealand Society of Periodontology. Bulletin see New Zealand Society of Periodontology. Journal **3238**
New Zealand Society of Periodontology. Journal. (NZ ISSN 0111-1485) **3238**
New Zealand Soil News. (NZ ISSN 0545-7904) **186**
New Zealand Speech-Language Therapists Journal. (NZ ISSN 0110-571X) **3315**
New Zealand Speech Therapists Journal see New Zealand Speech-Language Therapists Journal **3315**
New Zealand Stamp Collector. (NZ ISSN 0112-5443) **3755**
New Zealand Stamp Monthly. (NZ ISSN 0028-8721) **3755**
New Zealand Statistician. (NZ ISSN 0111-9176) **4581**
New Zealand Superannuation Guide. (NZ) **1102**, **2660**
New Zealand Surveyor. (NZ ISSN 0048-0150) **1872**
New Zealand Tablet. (NZ ISSN 0028-8748) **4271**
New Zealand Tax Cases. (NZ ISSN 0112-3823) **1102**, **2660**
New Zealand Tax Planning Report. (NZ ISSN 0110-4233) **1102**
New Zealand Tax Reports. (NZ ISSN 0110-0246) **754**, **2660**
New Zealand Tenders Gazette. (NZ ISSN 0028-8756) **3021**
New Zealand Times see Dominion Sunday Times **2212**
New Zealand Tourism Department. Catalogue Series. (NZ) **407**
New Zealand Tourism Department. Domestic Research Series. (NZ) **4780**
New Zealand Tourism Department. Economic Research Series. (NZ) **682**, **4780**
New Zealand Tourism Department. Implications of Tourism Growth Series. (NZ) **4780**
New Zealand Tourism Department. International Visitors Research Series.(NZ) **4800**
New Zealand Tourism Department. Marketing Series. (NZ) **1049**
New Zealand Tourism Department. Product Research Series. (NZ) **4800**, **2482**
New Zealand Tourism Department. Regional Research Series. (NZ) **4780**
New Zealand Tourism Department. Social Research Series. (NZ) **4444**, **4780**

New Zealand Tourism Department. Tourism Incentives Series. (NZ) **4780**
New Zealand Tourism Department. Visitor Statistics Research Series. (NZ) **4800**, 4581
New Zealand Town Planning Appeals. (NZ ISSN 0110-1390) **2715**, 4092
New Zealand Tribune. (NZ) **3910**, 3945
New Zealand Turf Digest. (NZ) **2212**
New Zealand Universities Law Review. (NZ ISSN 0549-0618) **2660**
New Zealand Valuers' Journal. (NZ ISSN 0113-0315) **4154**
New Zealand Veterinary Journal. (NZ ISSN 0048-0169) **4813**
†New Zealand Wheat Review. (NZ ISSN 0078-0219) **5247**
New Zealand Wildlife. (NZ ISSN 0028-8802) **4551**
New Zealand Wings. (NZ ISSN 0110-1471) **59**
New Zealand Woman's Weekly. (NZ ISSN 0028-8829) **4850**
New Zealand Wool Board. Statistical Handbook. (NZ ISSN 0110-1242) **141**, 4628
New Zealand Wool Market Review. (NZ ISSN 0113-2792) **155**
New Zealandia. (NZ) **4271**
Newark Churchman see Voice (Newark) **4252**
Newark Historical Society Newsletter. (US) **2318**
Newark Museum. Exhibitions & Events. (US) **3531**
Newark Museum. News Notes see Newark Museum. Exhibitions & Events **3531**
Newark Trader. (UK) **2194**
Newberg on Class Actions, 2-E. (US) **2660**
Newberry County Historical Society. Bulletin. (US) **2416**
Newberry Newsletter. (US) **2776**
Newbuildings. (UK) **4734**
Newcastle History Monographs. (AT ISSN 0078-0243) **2345**
Newcastle Microcomputer Club. Newsletter. (AT) **1471**, 1428, 1463
Newcomen Bulletin. (UK) **4605**
Newcomen Society for the Study of the History of Engineering and Technology. Transactions. (UK ISSN 0372-0187) **1831**, 2318, 4605
Newcomer. (BE) **2175**, 4780
†Newcomer Housing Guide. (US) **5247**
Newes. (US) **2440**, 2573
NeWest Review. (CN ISSN 0380-2817) **4133**, 2877
Newf-Tide. (US ISSN 0194-7206) **3712**
Newfoundland. Department of Social Services. Annual Report. (CN ISSN 0078-0294) **4415**
Newfoundland. Geological Survey Branch. Bulletin. (CN) **1575**
Newfoundland. Geological Survey Branch. Information. (CN) **3492**
Newfoundland. Geological Survey Branch. Information Circular. (CN) **3492**
Newfoundland. Mineral Development Division. Geological Survey. Bulletin. see Newfoundland. Geological Survey Branch. Bulletin **1575**
Newfoundland. Mineral Development Division. Information see Newfoundland. Geological Survey Branch. Information **3492**
Newfoundland. Mineral Development Division. Information Circular see Newfoundland. Geological Survey Branch. Information Circular **3492**
Newfoundland. Mines Branch. Annual Report Series. (CN ISSN 0078-0367) **3492**
Newfoundland. Mines Branch. Geological Survey of Newfoundland. Report Series. (CN ISSN 0078-0383) **1575**
Newfoundland & Labrador Business Journal. (CN) **682**
Newfoundland and Labrador Provincial Libraries. Newsletter see Library Footnotes **2769**

Newfoundland and Labrador Women's Institutes. Newsletter. (CN) **4850**, 1685
Newfoundland & Prince Edward Island Reports. (CN) **2660**
Newfoundland Churchman. (CN) **4245**
Newfoundland Gazette. (CN ISSN 0028-8888) **2178**
Newfoundland Herald. (CN) **1377**
Newfoundland Lifestyle. (CN) **2178**
Newfoundland Medical Directory. (CN ISSN 0078-0316) **3135**
†Newkirk Notes. (US ISSN 0882-6773) **5247**
†Newlywed. (US) **5247**
▼NewMedia Age. (US) **1377**, 1398
NewMonth: The Good Life in Upper Wisconsin. (US) **2230**
Neworld. (US) **338**, 2942, 4415
NewPaper. (US) **2230**
Newport Beach (714). (US) **2230**
Newport Dining Guide. (US) **4780**
Newport History. (US ISSN 0028-8918) **2416**
Newport Navalog. (US) **3467**
Newport Review. (US ISSN 0276-5241) **2942**
News (Marlin) see Wang in the News **1424**
News About Library Services for the Blind and Physically Handicapped. (US ISSN 0883-5845) **2284**, 2776
News About the A - V Scene. (US ISSN 0886-6511) **3514**, 1341, 2776
News Advertiser. (XK ISSN 1010-5735) **2573**
News and Cine India see News India **2017**
News & Clues. (US ISSN 0730-1618) **2776**
News and Farmer. (US ISSN 0048-0215) **110**
News and Food Report. (US) **2078**
News and Ideas. (US) **1353**
News & Letters. (US ISSN 0028-8969) **3910**
News & Notes (Chicago). (US) **3382**
News & Notes (Milwaukee). (US) **3188**
News & Notes (Washington). (US ISSN 1044-9752) **1756**
News and Notes From All Over see S E T Free **1379**
News and Notes from Mee to Mee see Lucky Mee Family Association News & Notes **2157**
†News and Notes on the Social Sciences. (US) **5247**
News and Review. (US) **1463**
News and Views see Australian Rationalist **3762**
News & Views (Belmont). (US) **110**, 2448
News and Views (Bethesda). (US) **3238**
News and Views (Portales) see Cow News & Bull Views **215**
News & Views (Portland). (US) **1049**, 1081, 4002
†News and Views (Santa Monica). (US) **5247**
News and Views from Federally Employed Women see F E W's News and Views **4842**
News & Views of Independent Education. (UK) **1651**
News - Association of Collegiate Schools of Architecture see A C S A News **291**
News Behind the News. (US) **3910**
News - Broadcast Network. (US) **1377**
News Bureau Contacts (Year). (US) **2573**
News C A S T. (US ISSN 0886-814X) **110**
News Canada. (CN) **1049**
News Capsule. (US) **3135**
News Circle. (US ISSN 0193-1814) **2017**
News Computing Journal. (US ISSN 0888-1596) **4143**, 1463, 1691, 2573
News Cuba. (US) **3910**
News Digest - International. (AT ISSN 0159-7345) **3910**
News Extra. (CN) **1293**, 2230, 3670
News, Facts, Actions. (US) **958**

News-Flite. (US) **259**
News for Farmer Cooperatives see Farmer Cooperatives **91**
News for Industry, Commerce and Education. (UK) **4068**
News for Investors. (US) **958**
▼News for Kids. (US) **1261**
News for Naturalists see Habitat (London) **4312**
News for Seniors. (CN) **2277**
News for South Carolina Libraries. (US ISSN 0146-1842) **2776**
†News for the Bread Manufacturers and Pastry Cooks of Queensland. (AT) **5247**
News for You. (US ISSN 0884-3910) **1685**
News from Africa Watch see Africa Watch **3939**
News from Americas Watch see Americas Watch **3939**
News from Aprovecho. (US) **1723**, 933
News from Asia Watch see Asia Watch **3950**
†News from Cally Curtis. (US) **5247**
News from E C N P. (Environmental Coalition on Nuclear Power) (US) **1964**
News from Helsinki Watch see Helsinki Watch **3942**
News from Holt. (US) **4133**
News from Hope College. (US) **1319**
News from I B C A M see I B C A M Journal **4692**
News from I C S I D. (International Centre for Settlement of Investment Disputes) (US) **958**
News from I E S see News from I E S - I A S **1723**
News from I E S - I A S. (Institute of European Studies - Institute of Asian Studies) (US) **1723**
News from Iceland. (IC ISSN 0253-8083) **2198**
News from Kenya. (KE) **2169**
News from Middle East Watch see Middle East Watch **3945**
News from Native California. (US) **2017**, 2416
News from Nisshin Steel. (JA ISSN 0911-8764) **3416**
News from Nowhere. (US) **2230**
News from O E C D. (FR) **875**
News from Pondy. (II ISSN 0028-9094) **2200**
News from Rohde & Schwarz see Neues von Rohde und Schwarz **59**
News from Rumania. (RM ISSN 0028-9116) **2251**
News from the Congregational Christian Historical Society. (US ISSN 0362-1510) **4245**
News from the Gutter. (US ISSN 0028-9159) **3021**
News from the Northwest. (US ISSN 0747-8739) **2159**
News from the Rare Book Room. (CN ISSN 0085-4166) **407**
News from the Ukraine. (KR ISSN 0549-110X) **2220**
News I B M. (US) **1463**
News in Engineering. (US ISSN 0028-9205) **1831**
News in Pharmacology and Medicine. see Novosti Farmatsii i Meditsiny **3736**
News in Physiological Sciences. (US ISSN 0886-1714) **573**
News in Tennessee History. (US) **2416**
News India. (US ISSN 0199-901X) **2017**
†News - Jugoslavija Film. (YU ISSN 0448-021X) **5248**
News Library News. (US ISSN 1047-417X) **2776**
News Media and the Law. (US ISSN 0149-0737) **2573**, 2660
News Media Yellow Book of Washington and New York. (US ISSN 1043-2620) **1148**
News Network International. (US ISSN 1042-606X) **4192**, 3945
News - North. (CN) **2178**
News Notes (Washington). (US) **3910**

News, Notes, and Quotes. (US ISSN 0028-923X) **1319**
News Notes from the Provincial Library see Focus (Regina) **2758**
News Novel. (US) **3670**
News of Graphic Arts. (GR) **4002**
News of Hungarian Philately. (US) **3755**
News of Hymnody. (UK ISSN 0263-2306) **3570**
News of New York. (US ISSN 0028-9264) **3135**
News of Norway. (US ISSN 0028-9272) **2017**
News of Science and Technology of Tomorrow. see Junkan Asu no Kagaku Gijutsu **4602**
News of Shinobazu. see Shinobazu Dayori **1968**
News of the Tohuku Plant Association. see Sennke **517**
News of the Week. see Akhbar al-Usbou **2208**
News of the World. (UK ISSN 0028-9280) **2194**, 3910
News of the World Football Annual. (UK) **4509**
News of the Yivo see Yivo News **2519**
News on Tests. (US ISSN 0271-8472) **1651**
News on Women in Government. (US) **4850**, 3629, 4068
News Photographer. (US ISSN 0199-2422) **3793**
News Plus Church Magazine Outset. (UK) **4245**
News Reel. (US) **3514**
News Review. (JM ISSN 0021-4116) **1081**
News Review on China, Mongolia and the Koreas see News Review on East Asia **3966**
News Review on East Asia. (II) **3966**
News Review on Japan, South East Asia, and Australia see News Review on South East Asia, and Australasia **3966**
News Review on North America & Europe see News Review on U.S.S.R. & Europe **3966**
News Review on South Asia and Indian Ocean. (II) **3966**
News Review on South East Asia, and Australasia. (II) **3966**
News Review on U.S.S.R. & Europe. (II) **3966**
News Review on West Asia. (II) **3642**
News Scan. (US) **1049**
News Special. (UK) **2195**, 4192
News Sweep. (US) **1986**
News Tibet. (US) **2017**
News Today Church Magazine Outset see News Plus Church Magazine Outset **4245**
†News Trade Weekly. (UK ISSN 0028-9353) **5248**
News Weekly. (AT) **2172**
News Weekly. see Tuan Tin Tuc **2238**
News 3X-400. (US ISSN 1040-6093) **1454**
News 34-38 see News 3X-400 **1454**
NewsBank (New Canaan). (US ISSN 0737-3813) **2230**
NewsBank Library see NewsBank (New Canaan) **2230**
NewsBank Review of the Arts: Film and Television. (US ISSN 0737-3988) **3515**, 1377, 4636
NewsBank Review of the Arts: Fine Arts and Architecture. (US ISSN 0737-4003) **338**, 3531
Newsbank Review of the Arts: Literature. (US ISSN 0737-4011) **2942**
NewsBank Review of the Arts: Performing Arts. (US ISSN 0737-3996) **4636**
Newsbeam - NatWest N J. (US) **793**
Newsbeat. (UK) **1519**
Newsbeat. (AT) **4415**
NewsBits. (US) **1398**
Newsboy. (US ISSN 0028-9396) **420**
Newsbreak (New York). (US) **3945**, 2017
Newsbreak (San Francisco. (US ISSN 0891-6063) **1319**
Newsbriefs (Delran). (US) **1452**
NewsBrk see Night Owl **1428**
Newscan. (UK) **4245**

NEWSCAST

NewsCAST see News C A S T 110
Newscheck. (UK ISSN 0307-8477) 3630
Newscope. (US) 4245
Newscope - Current Events Edition see Newscope - Middle-Intermediate-Junior High School Edition 1756
Newscope - Elementary Edition. (US) 1756, 2318, 3910
Newscope - High School-College Edition.(US) 1756, 2318, 3910
Newscope - Middle-Intermediate-Junior High School Edition. (US) 1756, 2318, 3910
Newscope - Science Edition. (US) 1756, 4330
Newscope - Secondary Current Events Edition see Newscope - High School-College Edition 1756
Newscribes. (US ISSN 0194-4118) 2943
Newsdom/Sinwen Tienti. (HK) 2197
Newsette. (PH ISSN 0028-9418) 754
Newsflashes. (AT) 4245
▼NewsFor. (IT) 3570, 4461
Newsfront - Greek Shipping Intelligence.(GR) 4734
NewsGleaner - Bustleton - Somerton Edition. (US) 2230
NewsGleaner - Far Northeast Edition. (US) 2230
NewsGleaner - Frankford - Oxford Circle Edition. (US) 2230
NewsGleaner - Mayfair - Northeast Edition. (US) 2230
Newshunter see Hunter Magazine 1314
News Inc. (US) 4133, 338
Newsletter: A Lesbian Position. (US) 2456, 4850
Newsletter - Avanti Owners Association see Avanti Owners Association Newsletter 4684
Newsletter Called Fred see Visual Media 3519
Newsletter Cowan Clan United see Cowan Clan United. Newsletter 2148
Newsletter Design. (US) 2573, 4143
Newsletter Digest. (US ISSN 0733-432X) 731, 18, 875, 918, 958
Newsletter Directory see Newsletters in Print 4133
Newsletter for Birdwatchers. (II ISSN 0028-9426) 565
†Newsletter for Family-Owned Business. (US ISSN 1040-8193) 5248
†Newsletter for Information Executives. (US ISSN 0896-4912) 5248
Newsletter for Leonardisti. (US ISSN 0741-9597) 338
Newsletter for People with Lactose Intolerance and Milk Allergy. (US) 3807
Newsletter for Photo Educators see Photo Educator 3794
Newsletter for Research in Chinese Studies. (CH ISSN 0253-2875) 3642
Newsletter for Soulmates see Network News (Cleveland) 4036
Newsletter from Rural Arts Services see Arc 5137
Newsletter: Frontier Research Program.(JA) 573
Newsletter Gold, Silver and Uranium from Seas and Oceans Progress Update. (US) 1857, 1214, 1608
Newsletter Inago. (US ISSN 0743-6882) 2999
Newsletter - Music Library Association see Music Library Association. Newsletter 3565
Newsletter of Biomedical Safety & Standards. (US ISSN 0048-0282) 3135
Newsletter of Engineering Analysis Software. (US ISSN 0739-697X) 1880, 1479
Newsletter of Research on Japanese Politics see Japan Political Research 3901
Newsletter of Temporary Culture see Temporary Culture 2886
Newsletter of the Democratic Left see Democratic Left 3890
Newsletter of the Freudian Field. (US ISSN 0894-1750) 4037

†Newsletter on Beekeeping. (US) 5248
†Newsletter on Church and State Abroad. (US) 5248
Newsletter on Contemporary Japanese Prints. (US ISSN 0085-4174) 338
Newsletter on Intellectual Freedom. (US ISSN 0028-9485) 2776, 4133
Newsletter on Newsletters. (US ISSN 0028-9507) 2573
Newsletter on Radionuclides Migration in the Geosphere see Nuclear Waste Bulletin 1986
Newsletter on Serials Pricing Issues. (US ISSN 1046-3410) 2776, 4133
Newsletter on the Common Agricultural Policy see Green Europe 94
Newsletter - Oral History Association see Oral History Association. Newsletter 2319
Newsletter - Society for the Preservation of Long Island Antiquities. see Society for the Preservation of Long Island Antiquities. Newsletter 259
Newsletter - Southeastern Wisconsin Regional Planning Commission see S E W R P C Newsletter 2495
Newsletters in Print. (US) 4133
Newsletters on Stratigraphy. (GW ISSN 0078-0421) 1575
Newsline see Democrat 3890
Newsline (Deerfield). (US) 3515, 1377
Newsline (Evanston). (US) 4654
Newsline (Knoxville). (US) 2416
Newsline (Lawrence). (US) 682, 1341, 1575
Newsliner (Little Rock). (US) 1651
Newslink (Denver). (US) 4037, 3349
Newslink (Westerville). (US) 1471, 1463
Newslitter see Pitch-In News 1965
▼Newsmakers. (US) 420
Newsman. (II ISSN 0028-9531) 2573
Newsmeter. (CN) 36, 2524, 3394
Newsmonth. (AT) 2587, 990, 1723
Newsnames - Current Events. (US) 1756, 3910
Newsnames - Wordsearch see Newsnames - Current Events 1756
NewsNet Action Letter. (US) 1351
Newsounds. (US ISSN 0147-4057) 2288
Newspack. (PH) 3650
Newspacket. (CN ISSN 0384-1642) 2943
†Newspan Minerals. (AT) 5248
†Newspan Petroleum. (AT) 5248
Newspaper Advertising Bureau. Creative Newspaper. (US) 36, 2468
Newspaper Advertising Bureau. Newspaper Advertising Planbook. (US) 36, 2468
Newspaper Advertising Co-op Network. (US) 36, 2468
Newspaper and Broadcasting. (KO) 2573
Newspaper and Mail Deliverers' Union Bulletin. (US) 2587, 1353
Newspaper Circulation Analysis see Circulation 91 29
Newspaper Financial Executives Journal.(US ISSN 0889-4590) 1022, 2573
Newspaper Fund Adviser Update. (US) 2573
Newspaper Fund Newsletter see Newspaper Fund Adviser Update 2573
Newspaper Guild. Annual T.N.G. Convention Officers' Report. (US ISSN 0090-2209) 2573
Newspaper Guild. Proceedings of the Annual Convention. (US ISSN 0741-7950) 2573
Newspaper Investor. (US ISSN 1042-4326) 1341
Newspaper Marketing. (US ISSN 0745-5089) 1049, 2468
Newspaper Newsletter see Ad-Pro 5130
Newspaper of Cardiology. (US) 3210
Newspaper Publishers Handbook. (UK) 2573, 4133
Newspaper Rates and Data see Standard Rate and Data Service. Newspaper Rates and Data 41

Newspaper Research Journal. (US) 2573
Newspaper Sales see Headlines (London) 2570
Newspaper Society News see Headlines (London) 2570
Newspaper Techniques. (GW) 4002
Newspapers & Technology. (US) 2573
▼Newspapers and Voice. (US) 2573
Newspapers Index: Mauritius see Subject Index to Articles in Newspapers in Mauritius 2579
Newspeace see Peacelinks 4195
Newspeak. (US) 1319
Newspot. (TU) 2220
Newspuzzler and Newsquestionnaire see Newspuzzler: Current Events 1756
Newspuzzler and Newsquestionnaire see Newsquestionnaire: Current Events 1756
Newspuzzler: Current Events. (US) 1756, 3910
Newsquestionnaire: Current Events. (US) 1756, 3910
Newstime (London) see Headlines (London) 2570
Newswatch. (NR ISSN 0189-8892) 2212
Newswave. (US) 4527
Newsweek. (US ISSN 0028-9604) 2230
Newsweek Business. (US) 682
Newsweek International. (UK) 2195
Newsweek Nihon Ban. (JA) 2208
Newswire (Manhattan). (US) 2573, 1713
Newswire (Wheaton). (US) 4286
Newth-Nuth Family History Society. Newsletter. (UK ISSN 0260-695X) 2159
Newton/Nyuton. (JA ISSN 0286-0651) 4330, 4605
Next. (JA) 1022
Next Exit. (CN ISSN 0828-8496) 2999
▼Nextworld. (US) 1479
Nexus. (CN ISSN 0711-5342) 246
Nexus (Dayton). (US) 2943, 2999
Nexus: China in Focus. (CC) 2182, 4381
Nezam Pezeshki-Ye Iran. Nashriyeh. see Medical Council of Iran. Publication 3125
▼Nezavisimaya Gazeta. (RU) 3966, 918
Nezelezne Kovy. (CS ISSN 0322-7189) 3416
Ngabu. (ZR) 2539
Ngao. (TZ ISSN 0856-1222) 2539
Nghe Thuat Dien Anh/Cinematography. (VN) 3515
Ngoma News. (ZA) 2240
Nguoi Cong Giao Viet-Nam/Vietnamese Catholic. (VN) 4271
Nguoi Dai Bieu Nhan Dan/People's Deputy. (VN) 3911, 4068
Ngwetaryi Magazine. (BR) 2220
Nharireyomurindi. (SA ISSN 0028-9639) 4286
Niagara Anglican. (CN ISSN 0703-5888) 4192
Niagara Falls Area Chamber of Commerce. Business - Industrial Directory. (US) 820
Niagara Farmers' Monthly. (CN) 222
Niagara Frontier Transportation Authority Annual Report see N F T A Annual Report 4653
Niagara Frontier Transportation Authority On the Move see N F T A On the Move 5242
Niagara Magazine. (US) 2999
Niagara Parks Commission. Annual Report. (CN ISSN 0078-0502) 1494, 4780
Nianbao - Taiwan Sheng Nongye Shiyansuo see Taiwan Agricultural Research Institute. Annual Report 123
Nianqingren/Young People. (CC) 1261
Nibble. (US ISSN 0734-3795) 1471, 1463
Nibble Express. (US) 1471, 1463
Nibble Mac see Macintosh Hands On 5230
Nibble Mac Annual. (US) 1471
†Nicaragua. Archivo Nacional. Boletin. (NQ) 5248

Nicaragua. Corte Suprema de Justicia. Boletin Judicial. (NQ) 2660
Nicaragua. Direccion General de Aduanas. Memoria. (NQ ISSN 0078-0510) 838
Nicaragua. Instituto Nacional de Estadisticas y Censos. Boletin Demografico. (NQ) 3985
Nicaragua. Instituto Nacional de Estadisticas y Censos. Encuesta Anual Industria Manufacturere. (NQ) 731
Nicaragua. Instituto Nacional de Estadisticas y Censos. Estadisticas Vitales. (NQ) 3994
Nicaragua. Oficina Ejecutiva de Encuestos y Censos. Boletin Demografico see Nicaragua. Instituto Nacional de Estadisticas y Censos. Boletin Demografico 3985
Nicaragua. Secretaria de Informacion y Prensa. Carta Informativa. (NQ) 2180
†Nicaragua, Central America: A Country to Discover. (NR) 5248
Nicaragua Heute. (GW) 2180
Nicaragua Update. (US) 3911, 2416
Nicaraguan Perspectives. (US ISSN 0885-5706) 3911
Nicarauac. (NQ) 2512
Nichi-Futsu Igaku. see Bulletin Medical Franco-Japonais 3084
Nichi-Futsu Rikoka Kaishi/Societe Franco-Japonaise des Sciences Pures et Appliquees. Bulletin. (JA ISSN 0285-3922) 4330, 4605
Nichidai Igaku Zasshi/Nihon University. Journal of Medicine. (JA ISSN 0029-0424) 3136
Nichidai Koku Kagaku. see Nihon University. Journal of Oral Science 3238
Nicholls State University Library. Genealogy Series see N S U Library. Genealogy Series 2159
Nichols Alumnus see Nichols News 1319
Nichols News. (US) 1319
Nicht Notierten Deutschen Aktiengesellschaften see N N 1146
Nickel. (CN ISSN 0829-8351) 3416
Nicolaus. (IT) 4271, 4306
Nicosia This Month. (CY) 2184
Nida al-Islam. (UA) 4220
Nie. (PL ISSN 0867-2237) 2214
▼Nie z tej Ziemi/Not from that World. (PL) 3013
Niederbayerische Wirtschaft. (GW) 820
Niederdeutsche Beitraege zur Kunstgeschichte. (GW ISSN 0078-0537) 338
Niederdeutsches Wort. (GW ISSN 0078-0545) 2831
Der Niedergelassene Arzt. (GW ISSN 0468-1746) 3136
Niederoesterreich-Perspektiven. (AU) 2173
Niederoesterreichische Landes-Landwirtschaftskammer. Amtlicher Marktbericht. (AU ISSN 0028-9744) 141
NiederrheinKammer. (GW) 820
Niedersachsenturner. (GW) 4481
Niedersachsisches Jahrbuch. (GW) 2377
Niedersaechsische Evangelische Zeitung. (GW) 4245
Niedersaechsische Archivverwaltung. Veroeffentlichungen. (GW) 2318
Niedersaechsische Gemeinde. (GW ISSN 0028-9779) 4092
Niedersaechsische Staats- und Universitaetsbibliothek, Goettingen. Arbeiten. (GW ISSN 0072-4866) 2776
Niedersaechsische Wirtschaft. (GW ISSN 0341-1982) 875
Niedersaechsischer Jaeger. (GW ISSN 0048-0339) 4551
Niedersaechsischer Staatsanzeiger. (GW ISSN 0028-9787) 2661
Niedersaechsischer Staedtetag. (GW ISSN 0178-4226) 4093
Niedersaechsisches Aerzteblatt. (GW ISSN 0028-9795) 3136
Niedzica Seminars. see Seminaria Niedzickie 2386
Niekas. (US) 3013

Niels Bohr - Collected Works. (NE) **3825**, 1807
Nielsen Focus. (GW) **1049**
Nielsen Newscast. (US ISSN 0468-1835) **36**, 1377
Nielsen Report on Television. (US) **1377**
Nielsen Researcher. (US ISSN 0885-6206) **1049**
Nielsen's International Investment Letter. (US ISSN 0896-3223) **958**
Nielsen's Investment Letter *see* Nielsen's International Investment Letter **958**
Nielsen's New Products Bulletin *see* Preview (Northbrook) **1050**
Nieman Reports. (US ISSN 0028-9817) **2573**
†Niemandsland. (GW ISSN 0933-3282) **5248**
Nienhua Yishu/Art of New Year Picture.(CC) **338**
Niepodleglosc/Independence. (US ISSN 0272-0280) **2377**
Nieren- und Hochdruckkrankheiten. (GW ISSN 0300-5224) **3210**
Nierenpatient. (GW ISSN 0176-5183) **3389**
Niespulver. (GW ISSN 0720-6542) **2877**
Niet Zo Benauwd. (NE ISSN 0166-2767) **2159**
Nietzsche-Studien. (GW ISSN 0342-1422) **3774**
Nieuw Archief voor Wiskunde. (NE ISSN 0028-9825) **3049**
Nieuw Geluid. (NE ISSN 0028-9833) **4225**, 3911
Nieuw Klimaat. (BE) **4068**
Nieuw - Neuf. (BE) **304**
Nieuw Ruimzicht *see* Ruimzicht **4199**
Nieuw Wereld Nieuws. (NE ISSN 0028-9876) **3967**
Nieuw Zicht. (NE) **1651**
Nieuwe Damspel. (NE) **4481**
Nieuwe Drogist *see* Drogist **3723**
Nieuwe Geografenkrant. (NE ISSN 0166-0926) **2257**
Nieuwe Nederlandse Bijdragen Tot de Geschiedenis der Geneeskunde en der Natuurwetenschappen. (NE ISSN 0168-9827) **3136**, 2318
Nieuwe Pockets en Paperbacks. (NE ISSN 0048-0355) **4133**
Nieuwe Revu. (NE) **2211**
Nieuwe Taalgids. (NE ISSN 0028-9922) **2831**, 2943
Nieuwe Theta *see* Theta **4289**
Nieuwe West Indische Gids/New West Indian Guide. (NE ISSN 0028-9930) **254**
Nieuws Berichten Informatie. (NE ISSN 0920-1319) **1398**
Nieuwsblad Transport. (NE) **4654**, 3650
Nieuwsblad voor de Boekhandel *see* Boekblad **4121**
Nieuwsbrief Direkt Marketing en Verkoop. (BE) **1049**
Nieuwsbrief Duoane. (BE) **918**
Nieuwsbrief Sportsecretariaat. (BE) **4481**, 1300
Nieuwsbrief Transport. (BE) **918**
Nieuwsbrief Verkeerspecialist. (BE) **4720**
Niger. (NG ISSN 0550-6891) **2169**
Niger. Direction de la Statistique et des Comptes Nationaux. Bulletin Trimestriel de Statistique. (NG) **4581**
Niger. Ministere du Developpement et de la Cooperation. Direction de la Statistique. Bulletin de Statistique *see* Niger. Direction de la Statistique et des Comptes Nationaux. Bulletin Trimestriel de Statistique **4581**
Niger. Office des Postes et Telecommunications. Annuaire Officiel des Telephones. (NG) **1364**
Niger: Fraternite - Travail - Progres. (NG ISSN 0545-9532) **3911**
Nigerama. (NG) **2169**
Nigeria. Federal Department of Fisheries. Federal Fisheries Occasional Paper. (NR) **2046**
Nigeria. Federal Department of Forest Research. Research Paper. (NR ISSN 0300-2403) **2105**

Nigeria. Federal Department of Petroleum Resources. Monthly Petroleum Information *see* Nigerian National Petroleum Corporation. Monthly Petroleum Information **3693**
Nigeria. Federal Ministry of Employment, Labour and Productivity. Annual Report. (NR) **990**
Nigeria. Federal Ministry of Labour. Quarterly Review *see* Nigeria. Federal Ministry of Employment, Labour and Productivity. Annual Report **990**
Nigeria. Federal Office of Statistics. Annual Abstract of Statistics. (NR ISSN 0078-0626) **4581**
Nigeria. Federal Office of Statistics. Building and Construction Survey. (NR) **638**, 4581
Nigeria. Federal Office of Statistics. Digest of Statistics. (NR ISSN 0029-0017) **4581**
Nigeria. Federal Office of Statistics. Industrial Survey. (NR) **731**, 4581
Nigeria. Federal Office of Statistics. Report on General Consumer Survey Report. (NR) **731**, 4581
Nigeria. Federal Office of Statistics. Report on General Household. (NR) **731**, 4581
Nigeria. Federal Office of Statistics. Report on General Household Survey.(NR ISSN 0794-4055) **2500**, 4581
Nigeria. Federal Office of Statistics. Report on National Consumer Survey. (NR) **731**, 4581
Nigeria. Federal Office of Statistics. Report on Rural Consumer Survey *see* Nigeria. Federal Office of Statistics. Report on National Consumer Survey **731**
Nigeria. Federal Office of Statistics. Report on Rural Economic Survey *see* Nigeria. Federal Office of Statistics. Report on General Household **731**
Nigeria. Federal Office of Statistics. Report on Rural Household Survey *see* Nigeria. Federal Office of Statistics. Report on General Household Survey **2500**
Nigeria. Federal Office of Statistics. Report on Rural Household Survey. *see* Nigeria. Federal Office of Statistics. Report on Urban Household Survey **2500**
Nigeria. Federal Office of Statistics. Report on Urban Consumer Survey *see* Nigeria. Federal Office of Statistics. Report on General Consumer Survey Report **731**
Nigeria. Federal Office of Statistics. Report on Urban Household Survey. (NR) **2500**, 4581
Nigeria. Federal Office of Statistics. Review of External Trade. (NR ISSN 0078-0634) **731**
Nigeria. Federal Office of Statistics. Social Statistics in Nigeria. (NR) **4395**, 4581
Nigeria. Meteorological Service. Agrometeorological Bulletin. (NR ISSN 0545-9923) **3439**, 110
Nigeria. National Animal Production Research Institute. Journal. (NR ISSN 0189-0514) **222**, 4813
Nigeria. National Electric Power Authority. Annual Report and Accounts. (NR) **1802**
Nigeria. National Manpower Board. Manpower Studies. (NR) **990**
Nigeria. National Universities Commission. Annual Report. (NR) **1713**
Nigeria. National Universities Commission. Bulletin *see* Nigeria. National Universities Commission. University System News **1713**
Nigeria. National Universities Commission. University System News. (NR ISSN 0795-9931) **1713**
Nigeria. Work in Progress. (NR) **2877**
Nigeria Bulletin on Foreign Affairs. (NR ISSN 0331-2151) **3967**
Nigeria Business Guide Annual. (NR ISSN 0794-2877) **731**

Nigeria Confidential. (NR ISSN 0048-0363) **2212**
Nigeria Educational Forum. Journal. (NR ISSN 0189-2916) **1651**
Nigeria English Studies Association Journal. (NR ISSN 0029-0009) **2831**, 1756
Nigeria Forum. (NR ISSN 0189-0816) **3967**, 933
Nigeria Industrial Directory. (NR ISSN 1116-1027) **1148**
†Nigeria Magazine. (NR ISSN 0029-0033) **5248**
†Nigeria Newsletter. (UK ISSN 0142-9272) **5248**
Nigeria Periodicals Review. (NR ISSN 0794-3865) **2776**
Nigeria Tourist Guide/Guide du Tourisme Nigerien. (NR) **4780**, 2478
Nigeria Trade Journal. (NR ISSN 0029-0041) **918**
Nigeria Trade Summary. (NR ISSN 0078-0650) **918**
Nigeria Year Book. (NR ISSN 0078-0685) **3967**
Nigerian Accountant. (NR ISSN 0048-0371) **754**
Nigerian Agricultural Journal. (NR ISSN 0300-368X) **110**
Nigerian Business Digest. (NR ISSN 0048-038X) **875**
Nigerian Business Journal. (NR ISSN 0189-5036) **820**
Nigerian Businessman's Magazine. (NR) **875**
Nigerian Christian. (NR ISSN 0029-005X) **4192**
Nigerian Current Law Review. (NR ISSN 0189-207X) **2661**
Nigerian Economic Society. Proceedings of the Annual Conference. (NR ISSN 0331-0361) **682**
Nigerian Engineer. (NR ISSN 0331-5967) **1832**
Nigerian Exporter. (NR) **682**
Nigerian Field. (NR ISSN 0029-0076) **2169**
Nigerian Geographical Journal. (NR ISSN 0029-0084) **2257**
Nigerian Industrial Development Bank. Annual Report and Accounts. (NR ISSN 0549-2734) **793**
Nigerian Institute for Oil Palm Research. Journal *see* Nigerian Journal of Palms and Oil Seeds **511**
Nigerian Institute of International Affairs. Dialogues. (NR ISSN 0189-0840) **918**
Nigerian Institute of International Affairs. Lecture Series. (NR ISSN 0331-6262) **3967**
Nigerian Institute of International Affairs. Monograph Series. (NR ISSN 0331-6254) **3967**
Nigerian Institute of Social and Economic Research. Annual Report. (NR ISSN 0078-074X) **4381**, 682
Nigerian Institute of Social and Economic Research. Library. List of Accessions. (NR ISSN 0078-0766) **4395**
Nigerian Institute of Social and Economic Research. Research for Development. (NR) **4381**
Nigerian Institute of Social and Economic Research Occasional Papers *see* N I S E R Occasional Papers **4380**
Nigerian Insurance Monitor. (NR ISSN 0048-0398) **2539**
Nigerian Journal of Business Management. (NR) **1022**
Nigerian Journal of Contemporary Law. (NR ISSN 0048-0401) **2661**
Nigerian Journal of Economic & Social Studies. (NR ISSN 0029-0092) **682**, 4444
Nigerian Journal of Entomology. (NR ISSN 0331-0094) **589**
Nigerian Journal of Financial Management. (NR ISSN 0189-3319) **682**, 793
Nigerian Journal of Forestry. (NR) **2105**, 2116
Nigerian Journal of International Affairs.(NR ISSN 0331-3646) **3967**

NIHON DAIGAKU 6497

Nigerian Journal of International Studies. (NR) **3967**
Nigerian Journal of Medical Laboratory Technology. (NR) **3262**
Nigerian Journal of Nutritional Sciences.(NR ISSN 0189-0913) **3609**
Nigerian Journal of Paediatrics. (NR) **3323**
Nigerian Journal of Palms and Oil Seeds. (NR) **511**
Nigerian Journal of Political Science. (NR ISSN 0331-8524) **3967**
Nigerian Journal of Science. (NR ISSN 0029-0114) **4330**
Nigerian Journal of Social Science Research Abstracts. (NR) **4395**, 18
Nigerian Libraries. (NR ISSN 0029-0122) **2776**, 4133
Nigerian Library and Information Science Review. (NR ISSN 0189-4412) **2776**
Nigerian Management Review. (NR ISSN 0189-2568) **1022**
Nigerian Medical Journal. (NR ISSN 0300-1652) **3136**
Nigerian Mining and Geosciences Society. Journal. (NR) **3492**, 1575
Nigerian Mining, Geological and Metallurgical Society. Journal *see* Nigerian Mining and Geosciences Society. Journal **3492**
Nigerian Names. (NR) **2159**
Nigerian National Petroleum Corporation. Monthly Petroleum Information. (NR) **3693**
Nigerian Nurse. (NR ISSN 0331-4448) **3283**
Nigerian Office and Residential Directory *see* Nigerian Yellow Pages **1060**
Nigerian Packaging News. (NR ISSN 0794-7054) **3650**
Nigerian Periodicals Index. (NR ISSN 0794-6406) **2795**
Nigerian Ports Authority Annual Report *see* N P A Annual Report **4733**
Nigerian Ports Authority Bulletin *see* N P A Bulletin **4733**
Nigerian Printer. (NR) **4002**
Nigerian Radio - T V Times. (NR) **1357**, 1377
Nigerian Schoolmaster. (NR ISSN 0029-0157) **1651**
Nigerian Society of Physiotherapy. Journal. (NR ISSN 0331-3735) **3136**
Nigerian Stored Products Research Institute. Annual Report. (NR ISSN 0794-6414) **163**, 1207
Nigerian Tobacco Company. Annual Report and Accounts. (NR) **4644**
Nigerian Yellow Pages. (NR ISSN 0331-0973) **1060**
†Night & Day. (US) **5248**
Night Club & Bar Magazine. (US) **2478**
Night Owl. (US) **1428**, 1463, 1471
Nightfall. (UK) **3013**
Nightingale. (US ISSN 0894-5780) **3283**, 4850
Nightsun. (US ISSN 0278-6079) **2943**, 2877, 3774
Nigrizia. (IT ISSN 0029-0173) **4192**
▼Nihilistic Review. (US ISSN 1055-842X) **2943**, 2999
Nihon Boeki Shinkokai. *see* Japan Trade Directory (Year) **1141**
Nihon Boseki Geppo/Japan Spinners' Association. Monthly Report. (JA ISSN 0910-8505) **4622**
Nihon Bungaku/Japanese Literature. (JA ISSN 0386-9903) **2943**
Nihon Butsuri Gakkaishi *see* Butsuri **3815**
Nihon Contact Lens Gakkaishi. (JA ISSN 0374-9851) **3302**
Nihon Daigaku Bunrigakubu Shizen Kagaku Kenkyujo Kenkyu Kiyo/Nihon University. Institute of Natural Sciences. Proceedings. (JA ISSN 0369-3562) **4330**
Nihon Daigaku Igaku Zasshi *see* Nichidai Igaku Zasshi **3136**
Nihon Daigaku Koku Kagaku *see* Nihon University. Journal of Oral Science **3238**

6498 NIHON DAIGAKU

Nihon Daigaku Rikogaku Kenkyujo Shoho/Nihon University. Research Institute of Science and Technology. Journal. (JA ISSN 0369-4313) **4605**, 4330

Nihon Daigaku Rikogakubu Gakujutsu Koenkai Koen Ronbunshu. (JA) **4605**

Nihon Daigaku Shigakubu Obun Zasshi. see Nihon University. School of Dentistry. Journal **3238**

Nihon Eiseigaku Zasshi. see Japanese Journal of Hygiene **3804**

Nihon Fujin Kagakusha no Kai Nyusu. (JA) **4850**, 4330

Nihon Gakujutsu Kaigi Geppo/Science Council of Japan. Monthly Report. (JA ISSN 0029-019X) **4330**

Nihon Ganka Kiyo. see Folia Ophthalmologica Japonica **3300**

Nihon Gasu Kyokaishi/Japan Gas Association. Journal. (JA ISSN 0029-0211) **3693**

Nihon Geirui Kenkyujo Eibun Hokoku. see Scientific Report of Cetacean Research **591**

Nihon Geka Hokan. see Archiv fuer Japanische Chirurgie **3375**

Nihon Genshiryoku Gakkai Obun Ronbunshi. see Journal of Nuclear Science and Technology **3848**

Nihon Genshiryoku Gakkai Shi. see Atomic Energy Society of Japan. Journal **1803**

Nihon Gomu Kyokaishi/Society of Rubber Industry. Journal. (JA ISSN 0029-022X) **4292**

Nihon Hakushiroku. (JA) **407**

Nihon Heikatsukin Gakkai Zasshi - Japanese Journal of Smooth Muscle Research see Journal of Smooth Muscle Research **3118**

Nihon Hifuka Gakkai Zasshi. see Japanese Journal of Dermatology: Series A **3248**

Nihon Hifuka Gakkai Zasshi. see Japanese Journal of Dermatology: Series B **3248**

Nihon Hinyokika Gakkai Zasshi. see Japanese Journal of Urology **3388**

Nihon Insatsu Nenkan/Japan Printing Art Annual. (JA ISSN 0546-0719) **4003**

Nihon Jibi Inkoka Gakkai Kaiho. see Journal of Otolaryngology of Japan **3315**

Nihon Junkankigakushi. see Japanese Circulation Journal **3209**

Nihon Kagaku Gijutsu Kankei Chikuji Kankobutsu Mokuroku see Nihon Kagaku Gijutsu Kankei Chikuji Kankobutsu Soran **4357**

Nihon Kagaku Gijutsu Kankei Chikuji Kankobutsu Soran/Directory of Japanese Scientific Periodicals. (JA ISSN 0916-1198) **4357**

Nihon Kagaku Kogyo Kyokai Nikkakyo Geppo see Nikkakyo Geppo **1857**

Nihon Kagaku Ryoho Gakkai Zasshi/Chemotherapy. (JA ISSN 0009-3165) **3736**

Nihon Kagakushi Gakkai Nenkai Kenkyu Happyo Koen Yoshishu. (JA) **4615**

Nihon Kaihatsu Ginko. Chosabu. Chosa.(JA ISSN 0285-5887) **793**

Nihon Kaiji Shinbun/Japan Maritime Daily. (JA) **2573**

Nihon Kakin Gakkaishi/Japanese Poultry Science. (JA ISSN 0029-0254) **222**

Nihon Kaku Igakkai Kikanshi see Kaku Igaku **3360**

Nihon Kasei Gakkaishi/Journal of Home Economics of Japan. (JA ISSN 0913-5227) **2449**

Nihon Keizai Shihyo/Japanese Economic Indicators. (JA ISSN 0029-0262) **875**

Nihon Keizai Shimbun. (JA) **682**

Nihon Kikai Gakkai Ronbunshu/Japan Society of Mechanical Engineers. Transactions. (JA ISSN 0029-0270) **1936**

Nihon Kikan Shokudoka Gakkai Kaiho/Japan Broncho-Esophagological Society. Journal. (JA ISSN 0029-0645) **3366**, 3269

Nihon Kinzoku Gakkai Kaiho. see Japan Institute of Metals. Bulletin **3410**

Nihon Kodo Keiryo Gakkai Taikai Happyo Ronbun Shorokushu. (JA) **4051**, 3063, 4458

Nihon Kogyokaishi - Mining and Metallurgical Institute of Japan. Journal see Shigen Sozai **3495**

Nihon Kokai Gakkai Ronbunshu. see Japan Institute of Navigation. Journal **4730**

Nihon Koku Uchu Gakkai-shi. see Japan Society for Aeronautical and Space Sciences. Journal **57**

Nihon Kokuka Gakkai Zasshi/Japanese Stomatological Society. Journal. (JA ISSN 0029-0297) **3238**

Nihon Kyoikuho Gakkai Nenpo. (JA) **2661**, 1651

Nihon Kyosei Shika Gakkai Zasshi. see Japan Orthodontic Society. Journal **3235**

Nihon Naibunpi Gakkai. see Endocrinologia Japonica **3253**

Nihon Naika Gakkai Zasshi. see Japanese Society of Internal Medicine. Journal **3113**

Nihon no Kagaku to Gijutsu/Japan Science and Technology. (JA ISSN 0029-0327) **4330**, 4605

Nihon no Kagakusha/Journal of Japanese Scientists. (JA ISSN 0029-0335) **4330**

Nihon Onsen Kiko Butsuri Igakkai Zasshi/Japanese Association of Physical Medicine, Balneology, and Climatology. Journal. (JA ISSN 0029-0343) **3136**

Nihon Opereshonzu Risachi Gakkai Ronbunshi. see Operations Research Society of Japan. Journal **1023**

Nihon Oyo Dobutsu Konchu Gakkaishi. see Japanese Journal of Applied Entomology and Zoology **534**

Nihon Purasuchikkusu Shinpo/Japan Plastics Journal. (JA ISSN 0029-0351) **3864**

Nihon Reito Reibo Shinbun/Japan Refrigeration and Air Conditioning News. (JA ISSN 0029-036X) **2302**

Nihon Rikagaku Kyokai. Kenkyu Kiyo. (JA ISSN 0287-864X) **3825**, 1184, 1756

Nihon Rimoto Senshingu Gakkaishi/Remote Sensing Society of Japan. Journal. (JA ISSN 0289-7911) **2257**

Nihon Ringakkaishi. see Japanese Forestry Society. Journal **2103**

Nihon Rodo Kyokai Zasshi/Japan Institute of Labour. Journal. (JA ISSN 0029-0378) **990**

Nihon Sakumotsu Gakkai Kiji. see Japanese Journal of Crop Science **182**

Nihon Sangyo Gijutsushi Gakkai Nenkai Koen Gaiyoshu/Japan Society for the History of Industrial Technology. Annual Conference. Proceedings. (JA) **4615**

Nihon Seikisho Gakkai Zasshi/Japanese Journal of Biometeorology. (JA ISSN 0389-1313) **3440**, 1832, 1964

Nihon Seikosho Giho/Japan Steel Works Technical Review. (JA ISSN 0546-126X) **3416**

Nihon Seirigaku Zasshi. see Physiological Society of Japan. Journal **574**

Nihon Senten Ijo Gakkai Kaiho see Congenital Anomalies **3090**

Nihon Setchaku Kyokaishi. see Adhesion Society of Japan. Journal **3861**

Nihon Shashin Gakkai Eibungo. see Society of Photographic Science and Technology of Japan. Journal **3797**

Nihon Shashin Sokuryo Gakkai. Gakujutsu Koenkai Happyo Ronbunshu. (JA) **2257**, 3440, 3793

Nihon Shika Ishikai Zasshi. see Japan Dental Association. Journal **3235**

Nihon Shinkei Gaisho Kenkyukai Koenshu see Shinkei Gaisho **3354**

Nihon Shinseiji Gakkai Zasshi/Acta Neonatologica Japonica. (JA ISSN 0029-0386) **3323**

Nihon Shizen Hogo Kyokai Chosa Hokoku/Nature Conservation Society of Japan. Reports. (JA) **1494**

Nihon Shokubutsu Bunrui Gakkai Kaiho. see Japan Society of Plant Taxonomists. Proceedings **506**

Nihon Shokubutsu Byori Gakkaiho. see Phytopathological Society of Japan. Annals **513**

Nihon Shosen Senpuku Tokei. (JA) **4665**, 4734

Nihon Soshiki Saibo Kagakkai Gakkaishi. see Acta Histochemica et Cytochemica **522**

Nihon Soshikigaku Kiroku. see Archives of Histology and Cytology **522**

Nihon Sugakkai Koen Abusutorakuto. Daisu Bunkakai. (JA) **3063**

Nihon Sugakkai Koen Abusutorakuto. Jitsukansuron Bunkakai. (JA) **3063**

Nihon Sugakkai Koen Abusutorakuto. Kansu Hoteishikiron Bunkakai. (JA) **3063**

Nihon Sugakkai Koen Abusutorakuto. Kansu Kaisekigaku Bunkakai. (JA) **3063**

Nihon Sugakkai Koen Abusutorakuto. Kansuron. (JA) **3063**

Nihon Sugakkai Koen Abusutorakuto. Kikagaku Bunkakai. (JA) **3063**

Nihon Sugakkai Koen Abusutorakuto. Oyo Sugaku Bunkakai. (JA) **3063**

Nihon Sugakkai Koen Abusutorakuto. Sugaku Kisoron Bunkakai. (JA) **3063**

Nihon Sugakkai Koen Abusutorakuto. Tokei Sugaku Bunkakai. (JA) **3063**, 4581

Nihon Sugakkai Koen Abusutorakuto. Toporoji Bunkakai. (JA) **3063**

Nihon Taipugurafi Nenkan. see Japan Typography Annual **4002**

Nihon Tenmon Gakkai Koen Yokoshu. (JA) **2268**

Nihon Tenmon Gakkai Obun Kenkyu Hokoku. see Astronomical Society of Japan. Publications **361**

Nihon Tenmon Kenkyukai Kansoku Geppo/Japan Astronomical Study Association. Monthly Bulletin. (JA) **371**

Nihon Tokei Gakkaishi/Japan Statistical Society. Journal. (JA ISSN 0389-5602) **731**

Nihon Tokei Gakkaishi/Horological Institute of Japan. Journal. (JA ISSN 0029-0416) **2565**

Nihon University. Atomic Energy Research Institute. Annual Report. (JA) **1807**, 1832

Nihon University. Institute of Natural Sciences. Proceedings. see Nihon Daigaku Bunrigakubu Shizen Kagaku Kenkyujo Kenkyu Kiyo **4330**

Nihon University. Journal of Medicine. see Nichidai Igaku Zasshi **3136**

Nihon University. Journal of Oral Science/Nichidai Koku Kagaku. (JA ISSN 0385-0145) **3238**

Nihon University. Research Institute of Science and Technology. Journal. see Nihon Daigaku Rikogaku Kenkyujo Shoho **4605**

Nihon University. Research Institute of Science and Technology. Report. (JA ISSN 0549-2998) **4330**, 4605

Nihon University. School of Dentistry. Journal/Nihon Daigaku Shigakubu Obun Zasshi. (JA ISSN 0029-0432) **3238**

Nihon Yakurigaku Zasshi. see Folia Pharmacologica Japonica **3726**

Nihon Zenkoku Shoshi. see Japanese National Bibliography Weekly List **404**

Nihongo Magazine. (JA) **2831**

Nihonkai-ku Suisan Kenkyujo Kenkyu Hokoku. see Japan Sea Regional Fisheries Research Laboratory. Bulletin **2044**

Nihul. (IS) **1022**

Niigata Airglow Observatory. Bulletin. (JA) **3825**

Niigata Daigaku Kogakubu Kenkyu Hokoku/Niigata University. Faculty of Engineering. Research Report. (JA ISSN 0374-4345) **1832**

Niigata Daigaku Kyoikugakubu Kiyo. Shizen Kagaku Hen/Niigata University. Faculty of Education. Memoirs. Natural Sciences. (JA ISSN 0288-3422) **4330**

Niigata Daigaku Nogakubu Kenkyu Hokoku/Niigata University. Faculty of Agriculture. Bulletin. (JA ISSN 0385-8634) **110**

Niigata Daigaku Nogakubu Kiyo/Niigata University. Faculty of Agriculture. Memoirs. (JA ISSN 0549-4826) **110**

Niigata Daigaku Rigakubu Fuzoku Sado Rinkai Jikkenjo Kenkyu Hokoku. see Sado Marine Biological Station. Report **454**

Niigata Daigaku Rigakubu Kenkyu Hokoku. A-rui, Sugaku. see Niigata University. Faculty of Science. Science Reports. Series A: Mathematics **3049**

Niigata Igakkai Zasshi/Niigata Medical Journal. (JA ISSN 0029-0440) **3136**

Niigata Kogyo Tanki Daigaku Kenkyu Kiyo/Niigata Technical Junior College. Journal. (JA ISSN 0913-7912) **4605**

Niigata Medical Journal. see Niigata Igakkai Zasshi **3136**

Niigata Rikagaku/Journal of Physics and Chemistry of Niigata. (JA ISSN 0286-7125) **3825**, 1184

Niigata-shi ni Okeru Kogai/Environmental Pollution in Niigata City. (JA) **1964**

Niigata Technical Junior College. Journal. see Niigata Kogyo Tanki Daigaku Kenkyu Kiyo **4605**

Niigata University. Faculty of Agriculture. Bulletin. see Niigata Daigaku Nogakubu Kenkyu Hokoku **110**

Niigata University. Faculty of Agriculture. Memoirs. see Niigata Daigaku Nogakubu Kiyo **110**

Niigata University. Faculty of Education. Memoirs. Natural Sciences. see Niigata Daigaku Kyoikugakubu Kiyo. Shizen Kagaku Hen **4330**

Niigata University. Faculty of Engineering. Research Report. see Niigata Daigaku Kogakubu Kenkyu Hokoku **1832**

Niigata University. Faculty of Science. Science Reports. Series A: Mathematics/Niigata Daigaku Rigakubu Kenkyu Hokoku. A-rui, Sugaku. (JA ISSN 0369-576X) **3049**

Niigata University. Faculty of Science. Science Reports. Series B: Physics. (JA) **3825**

Niigata University. Faculty of Science. Science Reports. Series C: Chemistry.(JA) **1184**

Niigata University. Faculty of Science. Science Reports. Series D: Biology. (JA ISSN 0371-2672) **449**

Niigata University. Faculty of Science. Science Reports. Series E: Geology and Mineralogy. (JA ISSN 0369-3627) **1575**, 3492

Niihama Kogyo Koto Senmon Gakko Kiyo. Rikogaku Hen/Niihama National College of Technology. Memoirs. Science and Engineering. (JA ISSN 0286-2743) **4605**, 1832, 4330

Niihama National College of Technology. Memoirs. Science and Engineering. see Niihama Kogyo Koto Senmon Gakko Kiyo. Rikogaku Hen **4605**

Nijenrode Studies in Economics. (NE) **875**

Nijgh Catalogus Bouwwereld. (NE) **626**

Nijhoff Information, New Publications from Germany, Austria and Switzerland. (NE) **4142**, 407, 4357

Nijhoff Information, New Publications from the Netherlands. (NE ISSN 0029-0459) **4142**, 407

Nijhoff Information, New Publications from West Germany, Austria and Switzerland see Nijhoff Information, New Publications from Germany, Austria and Switzerland **4142**

Nijhoff International Philosophy Series. (NE) **3774**

Nijhoff Law Specials. (NE) **2661**

Nijverheidsschool see Sint Bernardus **1663**

Nikephoros. (GW ISSN 0934-8913) **2318**, **4481**
Nikhef K Bulletin see N I K H E F. K Bulletin **3825**
Nikkakyo Geppo/Japan Chemical Industry Association Monthly. (Nihon Kagaku Kogyo Kyokai) (JA ISSN 0029-0483) **1857**
Nikkan Kogyo Shinbun/Business & Technology Daily News. (JA) **682**
Nikkei Aerospace. (JA ISSN 0289-9841) **59**
Nikkei Architecture. (JA) **304**
Nikkei Art. (JA) **338**
Nikkei Artificial Intelligence. (JA) **1409**
Nikkei Biotechnology. (JA ISSN 0285-4600) **490**
Nikkei Business. (JA ISSN 0029-0491) **875**
Nikkei Byte. (JA ISSN 0289-6508) **1471**
Nikkei Communications. (JA) **1341**
Nikkei Computer. (JA ISSN 0285-4619) **1398**
Nikkei Computer Graphics. (JA) **1422**
Nikkei Construction. (JA) **1872**
Nikkei Datapro: Data Communication Standards/Nikkei Detapuro: Deta Tsushin Hyojun. (JA) **1447**
Nikkei Datapro: Data Communications. (JA) **1447**
Nikkei Datapro: E D P. (JA) **1452**
Nikkei Datapro: Financial Systems. (JA) **805**
Nikkei Datapro: Marketing Systems. (JA) **827**, **1049**
Nikkei Datapro: Microprocessors. (JA) **1398**
†Nikkei Datapro: Minicomputers. (JA) **5248**
Nikkei Datapro: O A. (JA) **1022**, **1060**
Nikkei Datapro: Personal Computers. (JA) **1471**
Nikkei Datapro: Software. (JA) **1479**
Nikkei Datapro: Telecommunication Services/Nikkei Detapuro: Terekomu Sabisu. (JA) **1447**, **1351**, **1364**
Nikkei Datapro: Workstations/Nikkei Detapuro: Wakusuteshon. (JA) **1060**, **1463**
Nikkei Design. (JA) **338**, **682**
Nikkei Detapuro: Deta Tsushin Hyojun. see Nikkei Datapro: Data Communication Standards **1447**
Nikkei Detapuro: Terekomu Sabisu. see Nikkei Datapro: Telecommunication Services **1447**
Nikkei Detapuro: Wakusuteshon. see Nikkei Datapro: Workstations **1060**
Nikkei Electronics. (JA) **1776**
Nikkei Entertainment. (JA) **1341**, **36**, **3515**, **3570**
Nikkei Events. (JA) **3394**, **4780**
Nikkei Gifts/Nikkei Gifuto. (JA) **2281**
Nikkei Gifuto. see Nikkei Gifts **2281**
Nikkei Health Business. (JA) **2468**, **3136**
Nikkei Healthcare. (JA) **2468**, **3136**
†Nikkei High Tech Report. (UK) **5248**
▼Nikkei Jewellery. (JA) **2565**
▼Nikkei Logistics. (JA) **1068**, **4734**
Nikkei Mechanical. (JA) **1936**
Nikkei Medical/Nikkei Medikaru. (JA ISSN 0385-1699) **3136**
Nikkei Medikaru. see Nikkei Medical **3136**
Nikkei Microdevices. (JA) **1776**, **1398**
Nikkei New Materials. (JA ISSN 0911-1018) **4605**, **1832**
Nikkei New Media. (JA ISSN 0288-5026) **1341**
▼Nikkei Office. (JA) **1068**, **1022**
Nikkei Personal Computing. (JA ISSN 0287-9506) **1471**
Nikkei Real Estate - Tokyo. (JA) **4154**
Nikkei Resort. (JA) **4780**
Nikkei Restaurants. (JA) **2478**, **2078**
Nikkei Superconductors. (JA) **1776**
Nikkei Venture. (JA ISSN 0289-6516) **1116**
Nikkei Watcher on I B M. (JA) **1424**
The Nikkei Weekly. (JA) **682**
Nikkyoso Kyoiku Shinbun. (JA ISSN 0029-0505) **1651**, **2587**
Nikon Hunter's World. (US) **4551**
Nikon's Big Game Hunting see Nikon Hunter's World **4551**

Nile Gazette. (UG ISSN 0048-041X) **4271**
Nile Mirror. (SJ) **2218**
Nilson Report. (US) **793**
Nilzlal. (CN) **2017**
Nimrod. (US ISSN 0029-053X) **2943**, **2999**
†Nine-O-One Network. (US) **5248**
▼Nine to Five. (CN ISSN 1180-5749) **682**
Nine to Five. (UK) **2195**
Nineteen. (UK ISSN 0029-0556) **1261**
†Nineteenth Century (Philadelphia). (US ISSN 0097-5184) **5248**
Nineteenth Century (Westfield). (US) **2416**, **259**
Nineteenth-Century Fiction see Nineteenth-Century Literature (Berkeley) **2943**
Nineteenth Century French Studies. (US ISSN 0146-7891) **2943**
Nineteenth-Century Literary Criticism. (US ISSN 0732-1864) **2943**
Nineteenth-Century Literature (Berkeley). (US ISSN 0891-9356) **2943**
Nineteenth-Century Literature (Rochester). (US) **2943**
Nineteenth-Century Prose. (US) **2943**
Nineteenth-Century Studies. (US ISSN 0893-7931) **2943**, **2318**
Nineteenth Century Theatre. (US ISSN 0893-3766) **4636**
Nineteenth Century Theatre Research see Nineteenth Century Theatre **4636**
The Nineties Monthly/Jiu Shi Nian Dai. (HK) **2197**
Ninety-Nine News. (US) **60**
Ningbo Daxue Xuebao (Shehui Kexue Ban)/Ningbo University. Journal (Social Science Edition). (CC ISSN 1001-5124) **4381**
Ningbo Daxue Xuebao (Ziran Kexue Ban)/Ningbo University. Journal (Natural Science Edition). (CC ISSN 1001-5132) **4330**
Ningbo University. Journal (Natural Science Edition). see Ningbo Daxue Xuebao (Ziran Kexue Ban) **4330**
Ningbo University. Journal (Social Science Edition). see Ningbo Daxue Xuebao (Shehui Kexue Ban) **4381**
Ningen Igaku/Human Medicine. (JA ISSN 0029-0572) **3609**
Ningxia Shehui Kexue/Social Science in Ningxia. (CC) **4381**
Ninnau. (US ISSN 0890-0485) **2017**, **2057**
Nintendo Power. (US) **1419**
†Ninth Decade. (UK ISSN 0264-6773) **5248**
Ninth Street Center Journal. (US ISSN 0895-5239) **2456**, **4037**
Nippon Acta Radiologica/Nippon Igaku Hoshasen Gakkai Zasshi. (JA ISSN 0048-0428) **3361**
Nippon Dental University. Annual Publications. (JA ISSN 0549-5245) **3238**
Nippon Dojo Hiryogaku Zasshi/Japanese Journal of Soil Science and Plant Nutrition. (JA ISSN 0911-9973) **186**
Nippon Eiyo Shokuryo Gakkaishi. see Japanese Society of Nutrition and Food Science. Journal **3607**
Nippon Electric Co. Ltd. Research and Development see N E C Research and Development **1904**
Nippon Electric Company News see N E C News **1340**
Nippon Electric Company This is N E C (Year) see This is N E C (Year) **1344**
Nippon Gakushiin Kiyo A. see Japan Academy. Proceedings. Series A: Mathematical Sciences **3040**
Nippon Gakushiin Kiyo B. see Japan Academy. Proceedings. Series B: Physical and Biological Sciences **4317**
Nippon Ginko. Keizai Toket Nenpo. see Bank of Japan. Economic Statistics Annual **705**
Nippon Ginko Geppo/Bank of Japan Monthly Bulletin. (JA) **793**

Nippon Gyosei Kenkyu Nenpo/Japanese Society for Public Administration. Annals. (JA) **4068**
Nippon Hoigaku Zasshi. see Japanese Journal of Legal Medicine **3265**
Nippon Hoso Kyokai Gijutsu Kenkyu see N H K Gijutsu Kenkyu **5242**
Nippon Hoso Kyokai Giken Geppo see N H K Giken Geppo **5242**
Nippon Hoso Kyokai Laboratories Note see N H K Laboratories Note **5242**
Nippon Hoso Kyokai Technical Monograph see N H K Technical Monograph **5242**
Nippon Ibaraki Chikusan Shikenjo. Chikusan Shikenjo Kenkyu Hokoku. see Japan. Ibaraki National Institute of Animal Industry. Bulletin **219**
Nippon Ibaraki Chikusan Shikenjo Nenpo. see Japan. Ibaraki National Institute of Animal Industry. Annual Report **219**
Nippon Igaku Hoshasen Gakkai Zasshi. see Nippon Acta Radiologica **3361**
Nippon Ika Daigaku Zasshi. see Nippon Medical School. Journal **3136**
Nippon Insatsu Shinbun/Japan Printing News. (JA) **4003**
Nippon Institute for Biological Science. Journal. see Nisseiken Tayori **450**
Nippon Jui Chikusan Daigaku Kenkyu Hokoku/Nippon Veterinary and Animal Science University. Bulletin. (JA ISSN 0373-8361) **4813**
Nippon Jui Chikusan Daigaku Kiyo see Nippon Jui Chikusan Daigaku Kenkyu Hokoku **4813**
Nippon Kagaku Kaishi/Chemical Society of Japan. Chemistry and Industrial Chemistry. Journal. (JA ISSN 0369-4577) **1184**, **1857**
Nippon Kayaku. Annual Report. (JA) **3736**, **1184**
Nippon Kikinzoku Tokei Shinbun/Japan Precious Metals and Watch News. (JA ISSN 0029-0653) **2565**
Nippon Kinzoku Gakkaishi. see Japan Institute of Metals. Journal **3410**
Nippon Medical School. Journal/Nippon Ika Daigaku Zasshi. (JA ISSN 0048-0444) **3136**
Nippon Mishima Kokuritsu Idengaku Kenkyujo. Nenpo. see Japan. National Institute of Genetics, Mishima. Annual Report **544**
Nippon Nogeikaggaku Kaishi/Japan Society for Bioscience, Biotechnology, and Agrochemistry. Journal. (JA) **491**, **186**
†Nippon Nyt. (NO ISSN 0107-752X) **5248**
Nippon Rinsho. see Japanese Journal of Clinical Medicine **3112**
Nippon Sanshigaku Zasshi. see Journal of Sericultural Science of Japan **535**
Nippon Seikei Geka Gakkai Zasshi. see Japanese Orthopaedic Association. Journal **3308**
Nippon Seitai Gakkaishi. see Japanese Journal of Ecology **1959**
Nippon Shokuhin Kogyo Gakkaishi/Journal of Food Science and Technology. (JA ISSN 0029-0394) **2078**
Nippon Sochi Gakkai-shi. see Japanese Society of Grassland Science. Journal **182**
Nippon Steel Forum. (JA) **3416**
Nippon Steel News. (JA ISSN 0048-0452) **3416**
Nippon Steel Report. (JA) **3416**
Nippon Steel Technical Report. (English translation of: Seitetsu Kenkyu) (JA ISSN 0300-306X) **3416**
Nippon Steel Technical Report. Overseas see Nippon Steel Technical Report **3416**
Nippon Suisan Gakkaishi. see Japanese Society of Scientific Fisheries. Bulletin **2044**
Nippon Telegraph & Telephone Company Topics see N T T Topics **1364**
Nippon Telegraph and Telephone Corporation Review see N T T Review **1340**
Nippon Thompson Company. Annual Report. (JA) **3021**

Nippon Tungsten Review. (JA ISSN 0388-0664) **1214**
Nippon Veterinary and Animal Science University. Bulletin. see Nippon Jui Chikusan Daigaku Kenkyu Hokoku **4813**
Nippon Yusen. Annual Report. (JA) **4734**
Nippondenso Technical Disclosure. Journal. (JA ISSN 0285-0303) **1936**, **1904**
Nipun. (BG) **2174**
Niranjan. (II ISSN 0029-0688) **2201**
Nisaba. (NE ISSN 0169-930X) **4192**
Nisaki Mas i Kea. (GR ISSN 0040-8255) **2196**
Nisarg Ane Arogya. (II ISSN 0029-070X) **3807**, **3609**
▼Nisf al-Dunya. (UA) **2185**
Nishi Nihon Hifuka. see Nishi Nihon Journal of Dermatology **3249**
Nishi Nihon Hinyokika. see Nishinihon Journal of Urology **3389**
Nishi Nihon Journal of Dermatology/Nishi Nihon Hifuka. (JA) **3249**
Nishinihon Journal of Urology/Nishi Nihon Hinyokika. (JA ISSN 0029-0726) **3389**
Nishinippon Institute of Technology. Memoirs. Science and Technology. see Nishinippon Kogyo Daigaku Kiyo. Rikogaku Hen **4605**
Nishinippon Kogyo Daigaku Kiyo. Rikogaku Hen/Nishinippon Institute of Technology. Memoirs. Science and Technology. (JA ISSN 0910-6227) **4605**
Nissan Diesel Technical Review. (JA ISSN 0029-0734) **4698**, **4747**
Nissan Graphic/Nissan Gurafu. (JA ISSN 0029-0742) **4698**
Nissan Gurafu. see Nissan Graphic **4698**
Nissan Kagaku Shinko Zaidan Jigyo Hokokusho/Nissan Science Foundation. Annual Report. (JA ISSN 0914-1340) **4330**
Nissan Kagaku Shinko Zaidan Kenkyu Hokokusho/Nissan Science Foundation. Research Projects in Review. (JA ISSN 0911-4572) **4330**
Nissan Life. (GW) **4698**
Nissan Science Foundation. Annual Report. see Nissan Kagaku Shinko Zaidan Jigyo Hokokusho **4330**
Nissan Science Foundation. Research Projects in Review. see Nissan Kagaku Shinko Zaidan Kenkyu Hokokusho **4330**
Nisseiken Tayori/Nippon Institute for Biological Science. Journal. (JA ISSN 0029-0750) **450**
Nisshin. (JA) **3416**
Nisshin Steel. Annual Report. (JA) **3416**
Nisuco Chronicle. (NR) **2078**
Nit & Wit. (US ISSN 0199-3941) **2943**
Niti Vimamsa. (CE) **2661**
Nitividya. (CE) **2661**
Nitrogen. (UK ISSN 0029-0777) **186**
Nityanand Universal Series. (II ISSN 0078-0855) **2340**
Niv Hamidrashia. (IS ISSN 0048-0460) **4225**
Niwatori no Kenkyu/Poultry Researches. (JA ISSN 0029-0785) **222**
Nix Wie Weg. (GW) **4654**, **4780**
Nizam Pezeshki Jomhuriye Islamiye Iran. Majalleh/Medical Council of the Islamic Republic of Iran. Journal. (IR) **3136**
Njanja. (ZR) **4712**
Nkwantabisa. (GH) **2192**
Nnidnid: Surreality. (UK ISSN 0269-9915) **338**, **2943**, **3670**
No. (CS) **4850**, **1241**, **4415**
No. 1. (UK) **3570**
No Circ Newsletter. (US) **3323**
No Deadline. (US) **36**
▼No - Dig International. (UK) **626**
No K K K, No Fascist U S A! (US) **3911**, **3945**
No Kenkyukai Kaishi see Neurosciences **3348**
No-Load Fund Investor. (US ISSN 0736-6256) **958**

6500 NO STONE

No Stone Unturned. (US) **2159**
No-Till Farmer. (US ISSN 0091-9993) **110**
No to Hattatsu. (JA) **3349**
No to Shinkei. see Brain and Nerve **3332**
Noah's Ark. (US ISSN 0892-4945) **1261**, 2017, 4225
Nob Hill Gazette. (US) **2230**
Nobel Hefte. (GW ISSN 0029-0858) **1857**
Nobel Symposium Series. (SW ISSN 0078-0901) **2512**
Nobeyama Newsletter. (JA ISSN 0911-5870) **367**
Nobeyama Uchu Denpa Kansokujo Nyusu. (JA ISSN 0911-5242) **367**
Noble Official Catalog of Canada Precancels. (US ISSN 0078-091X) **3755**
Noble Official Catalog of United States Bureau Precancels. (US ISSN 0078-0928) **3755**
Nocaut. (MX) **4481**
Noctes Romanae. (SZ ISSN 0078-0936) **1278**
Nocturnal Lyric. (US) **2999**
Nocturnal News. (US) **2943**
Noda Institute for Scientific Research. Report/Noda Sangyo Kagaku Kenkyujo Kenkyu Hokoku. (JA ISSN 0078-0944) **4330**
Noda Sangyo Kagaku Kenkyujo Kenkyu Hokoku. see Noda Institute for Scientific Research. Report **4330**
Node. (US ISSN 0882-8075) **3226**, 3774, 4037
Noerre-Alslev Kommune. Lokalhistorisk Arkiv. Aarsskrift. (DK ISSN 0106-6145) **2377**
Noetic Sciences Review. (US ISSN 0897-1005) **4330**
Noetkoett. (SW ISSN 0281-8205) **110**, 2078
Noga. (IS ISSN 0333-6387) **4850**
Nogaku Kenkyu. (JA ISSN 0029-0874) **450**, 186
Nogyo Fumin/Agriculture and Better Farming. (JA ISSN 0029-0882) **186**
Nogyo Kankyo Gijutsu Kenkyujo Hokoku/National Institute of Agro-Environmental Sciences. Bulletin. (JA ISSN 0911-9450) **110**, 450
Nogyo Keizai Kenkyu/Journal of Agricultural Economics. (JA ISSN 0387-3234) **155**
Nogyo Kikai Nenkan/Farm Machinery Yearbook. (JA ISSN 0071-3937) **163**
Nogyo Kisho. see Journal of Agricultural Meteorology **3437**
†Nogyo no Kairyo/Improvement of Agriculture. (JA ISSN 0029-0904) **5248**
Nogyo Sogo Kenkyu. (JA ISSN 0387-3242) **155**
Nogyo Sogo Kenkyujo Nenpo/National Research Institute of Agricultural Economics. Annual Report. (JA) **110**
Nogyo to Keizai/Agriculture and Economy. (JA ISSN 0029-0912) **155**
Noi Donne. (IT ISSN 0029-0920) **4850**
Noi Due. (IT) **2984**
▼Noir. (US) **338**, 2017
▼The Noise. (US) **1261**
Noise & Vibration Bulletin. (UK ISSN 0029-0947) **1974**, 18, 1978
Noise and Vibration Contro - Worldwide see Noise and Vibration Worldwide **1978**
Noise and Vibration for Works Managers see Noise & Vibration in Industry **3860**
Noise & Vibration in Industry. (UK ISSN 0950-8163) **3860**
Noise and Vibration Worldwide. (UK ISSN 0957-4565) **1978**, 1832
Noise Control Engineering Journal. (US ISSN 0736-2501) **1936**
Noise Control Report see Noise Regulation Report **1978**
†Noise Manual. (US) **5248**
Noise - News. (US) **1978**
Noise Regulation Report. (US ISSN 1043-5565) **1978**, 2661

Noise Regulation Reporter. (US ISSN 0148-7957) **2661**, 1964
Noki Shinbun/Agricultural Machinery News. (JA ISSN 0029-0971) **163**
Noko to Engei. see Agriculture and Horticulture **72**
Nolo News. (US ISSN 0890-2208) **2661**
NoLoad Fund X. (US ISSN 0194-0104) **958**
Noma. (NR ISSN 0331-6742) **110**
Nomad. (CN) **1319**
Nomadic Peoples. (CN ISSN 0822-7942) **246**
Nomen Nudum. (AT ISSN 0159-818X) **3658**
Nomenclator Zoologicus. (UK ISSN 0078-0952) **589**
Nomenclature des Entreprises Nationales a Caractere Industriel ou Commercial et des Societies d'Economie Mixte d'Interet National. (FR ISSN 0078-0960) **1081**
Nomiko Vima. (GR) **2661**
Nomina. (UK ISSN 0141-6340) **2831**
Nomina Africana/Names of Africa. (SA ISSN 1012-0254) **2831**
Nomismatika Chronica. (GR) **3600**
Nommo. (US) **2017**
Nomos. (US ISSN 0078-0979) **3911**
Non. (YU) **1241**
Non-Commissioned Officers Association Journal see N C O A Journal **3466**
Non-Credit Learning News. (US ISSN 0886-0165) **1685**
Non-Destructive Testing see Non-Destructive Testing - Australia **1921**
Non-Destructive Testing - Australia. (AT ISSN 0157-6461) **1921**, 3416
Non Destructive Testing International see N D T International **1921**
Non-European Societies see Studies of Developing Countries **4454**
Non-Ferrous Metal Data. (US ISSN 0360-9553) **3416**
Non-Ferrous Metal Works of the World. (US ISSN 0078-0987) **3416**
Non-Foods Merchandising. (US ISSN 0029-103X) **1049**
Non-Life Insurance. (KO) **2539**
Non-Manual Worker in the Free Labour World see International Federation of Commercial Clerical, Professional and Technical Employees. Newsletter **2585**
†Non-Metallic Solids. (US ISSN 0078-0995) **5248**
Non-No. (JA) **1293**
Non-Prescription Products Guide see Prescription Products Guide **3741**
Non-Profit Organization Tax Letter. (US ISSN 0550-8401) **1102**
Non-Store Marketing Report. (US ISSN 0279-2893) **1049**
Non-Wage Provisions in Saskatchewan Collective Agreements. (CN ISSN 0830-0763) **990**
Nondestructive Testing and Evaluation. (US) **1921**
Nondestructive Testing Communications see Nondestructive Testing and Evaluation **1921**
Nondestructive Testing Monograms and Tracts. (US ISSN 0730-7152) **1921**
Nonferrous Alert see Nonferrous Metals Alert **3427**
Nonferrous Castings. (US ISSN 0146-5678) **3427**, 4581
Nonferrous Metals Alert. (US) **3427**, 731
Nong You see Farmers' Friend **91**
Nongame News. (US ISSN 1061-0928) **589**, 565, 1964
Nongcun Caiwu Kuaiji/Rural Finance and Accounting. (CC) **754**
Nongcun Dashijie. (CC) **110**
Nongcun Gongzuo Tongxun/Rural Affairs Bulletin. (CC ISSN 0546-9503) **4381**
Nongcun Jingji/Rural Economy. (CC) **876**
Nongcun Jingji yu Shehui/Rural Economy and Society. (CC) **682**, 110
Nongcun Jixiehua/Mechanization in Rural Areas. (CC) **163**

Nongcun Kexue - Science in Countryside see Kexue Zhifu Yu Shenghuo **4320**
Nongcun Kexue Shiyan/Agricultural Experiment. (CC ISSN 0577-5825) **110**
Nongcun Qingnian/Country Youth. (CC ISSN 0469-2225) **1261**, 110, 1686, 2943
Nongcun Shiyong Gongcheng Jishu/Practical Rural Engineering Technology. (CC) **110**
Nongji Shiyan yu Tuiguang/Agricultural Machinery Experiment and Popularization. (CC) **163**
Nongji Tuiguang/Agricultural Technology Marketing. (CC) **110**
Nongmin Ribao/Chinese Peasants' Gazette. (US) **110**
Nongmin Wenzhai. (CC ISSN 1000-7741) **110**
Nongsa Siheom Yeon'gu Pogo see Korea (Republic). Office of Rural Development. Research Report **103**
Nongyao Kexue yu Guanli/Pesticide Science and Management. (CC) **186**
Nongye Huanjing Baohu/Agro-Environmental Protection. (CC ISSN 1000-0267) **1964**, 110
Nongye Jingji Wenti/Problems of Agricultural Economics. (CC ISSN 1000-6389) **155**
Nongye Jingying Guanli yu Kuaiji Yanjiu/Research in Agricultural Management and Accounting. (CC) **1022**, 754
Nongye Jishu Jingji/Economics for Agricultural Technology. (CC ISSN 1000-6370) **155**
Nongye Jixie/Agricultural Machinery. (CC ISSN 0546-9538) **163**
Nongye Jixie Xuebao/Chinese Society of Agricultural Machinery. Transactions. (CC) **163**
Nongye Jixie Zazhi/Journal of Agricultural Machinery. (CC) **163**
Nongye Kaogu/Agricultural Archaeology.(US) **280**, 110
Nongye Keji Tongxun/Agricultural Science and Technology Bulletin. (CC ISSN 1000-6400) **110**
Nongye Quhua/Agricultural Division. (CC) **110**
Nongye Tushu Qingbao Xuekan/Agricultural Books Information Journal. (CC) **2776**, 4133
Nongye Zhishi/Agricultural Knowledge. (CC) **110**
Nongye Zhoukan - Agri-Week see Xiangjian Xiaolu **130**
Nonlinear Analysis. (US ISSN 0362-546X) **1832**
▼Nonlinear Dynamics. (NE ISSN 0924-090X) **1936**, 1832, 1880
Nonlinear Optics see Molecular Crystals and Liquid Crystals Science and Technology. Section B: Nonlinear Optics **3855**
Nonlinear Science: Theory and Applications. (UK) **3049**
Nonlinearity. (UK ISSN 0951-7715) **3049**, 3826
Nonparametric Statistics. (US ISSN 1048-5252) **4581**
Nonpareil. (US) **1319**
Nonprivate Foundations: A Tax Guide for Charitable Organizations. (US) **1102**
▼Nonprofit and Voluntary Sector Quarterly. (US ISSN 0899-7640) **4415**
NonProfit Insights. (US) **1022**, 1102
Nonprofit Mailers Federation. News Update. (US) **1300**, 1353
▼Nonprofit Management and Leadership. (US ISSN 1048-6682) **1022**
Nonprofit Management Association Bulletin Board see N M A Bulletin Board **1299**
Nonprofit Times. (US ISSN 0896-5048) **1022**
Nonprofit World. (US) **4415**
Nonprofit World Report see Nonprofit World **4415**
Nonpublic School Enrollment and Staff, New York State. (US ISSN 0077-9253) **1651**

▼Nonrenewable Resources. (US ISSN 0961-1444) **3492**, 1575, 3693
Nonviolent Activist. (US ISSN 8755-7428) **3911**
Nonviolent Anarchist Newsletter. (US) **3911**
Nonviolent Sanctions. (US ISSN 1052-0384) **4444**, 3911
Nonwovens Abstracts. (UK ISSN 0956-1234) **3869**, 731
Nonwovens Industry. (US ISSN 0163-4429) **4622**, 3663
Nonwovens Markets and Fiber Structures Report. (US ISSN 1053-9832) **4622**
▼Nonwovens Patent News. (US) **4622**, 3676
Nonwovens Report International. (UK) **4622**
†Nonwovens World. (US ISSN 0888-1979) **5248**
†Nonwovens World Buyers Guide. (US) **5248**
Noor Al-Islam. (LE) **4220**, 3774
Noord-Amsterdammer. (NE ISSN 0029-1137) **2211**
Noord-Brabant. (NE ISSN 0029-1145) **876**
Noord - Nederlands Orkest Magazine see N N O Magazine **3569**
Noord - Zuid Cahier. (BE) **4444**
Noord-Zuid-Hollandse Vervoer Mij Maandblad see N.Z.H. Maandblad **5242**
Noordbrabants Historisch Jaarboek. (NE) **2377**
Noorus. (ER ISSN 0134-2304) **1261**, 2295
Noospapers. (US) **2999**
Nor'-easter see Student Nationalist **2885**
Nor Or. (US ISSN 0029-1161) **2877**
NorAct. (CN ISSN 0706-8921) **1964**
Noray. (SP ISSN 0213-8239) **2046**
NorCal Community Forum. (US) **2288**, 4415
Le Nord. (CN) **2105**, 1964, 4654, 4827
Nord. (IT) **2877**
Nord-Automobile. (FR) **4698**
Nord e Sud. (IT ISSN 0029-1188) **3911**
Nord-Emballage. (SW ISSN 0039-6494) **3650**
Nord Genealogie. (FR ISSN 0755-7469) **2159**
Nord- Midt- og Vestsjaellands Landbrugs-Nyt. (DK) **110**
Nord-Norge Naeringsliv og Oekonomi. (NO ISSN 0078-1029) **682**
Nord Nytt. (DK ISSN 0008-1345) **2057**
Nord Refo. (FI ISSN 0345-8326) **4381**, 2257
Nord - Rhein Westfalen International see N R W - International **989**
†Norda Briefs. (US ISSN 0090-1903) **5248**
Nordbayern. Landesarbeitsamt. Bundesanstalt fuer Arbeit. Beratungs- und Vermittlungsdienste. Informationen. (GW) **682**, 1686
Norddeutsche Einzelhandels Zeitung. (GW) **838**
Norddeutsche Hausbesitzer-Zeitung. (GW) **4154**
Norddeutscher Molkerei und Kaeserei Adresskalender. (GW ISSN 0724-3227) **202**
Norddeutschland von Hinten see Hamburg - Norddeutschland von Hinten **2453**
Nordelbingen. (GW ISSN 0078-1037) **2377**
Nordelbische Stimmen. (GW ISSN 0938-3697) **4245**
Norden. (NO ISSN 0029-1226) **110**
Norden News see Topics in Veterinary Medicine **4816**
Nordens Jaernvaegar. (SW) **4712**
Nordenskiold-Samfundets Tidskrift. (FI ISSN 0356-0910) **450**
Nordeste. (AG ISSN 0029-1242) **2877**
Nordeste: Analise Conjuntural. (BL ISSN 0101-2223) **876**
Nordeste Conjuntura Industrial. (BL) **1081**

Nordeuropa Studien. (GW ISSN 0138-2802) **4381**, 2943
Nordeutsche Familienkunde in Verbindung mit der Zeitschrift fuer Niederdeutsche Familienkunde. (GW) **2159**
Nordfriesisches Jahrbuch. (GW ISSN 0078-1045) **2377**
Nordfriesland (Bredstedt). (GW ISSN 0029-1196) **2877**
†Nordfriesland (Flensburg). (GW) **5248**
Nordic Archaeological Abstracts see N A A **290**
Nordic Contract. (DK) **2554**
Nordic Economic Outlook. (SW ISSN 1100-7559) **682**
Nordic Hydrology. (DK ISSN 0029-1277) **1600**
Nordic Institute of Asian Studies Nytt see N I A S - Nytt **3641**
Nordic Institute of Asian Studies Report see N I A S Report **3641**
Nordic Institute of Folklore. Publications see N I F Publications **2057**
Nordic Institute of Folklore Newsletter see N I F Newsletter **2057**
Nordic Institute of Folklore Publications see N I F Publications **2057**
Nordic Journal of Botany. (DK ISSN 0107-055X) **511**
Nordic Journal of Documentation. see Tidskrift foer Dokumentation **2787**
Nordic Journal of Freshwater Research. (SW ISSN 1100-4096) **2046**
Nordic Journal of L S P and Terminology. see Nordisk Tidsskrift for Fagsprog og Terminologi **5248**
Nordic Journal of Linguistics. (NO ISSN 0332-5865) **2831**
Nordic Journal of Psychiatry. see Nordisk Psykiatrisk Tidsskrift **3349**
Nordic Journal on Latin American Studies. (SW) **2329**, 4395
Nordic Middle East Institute. Bulletin. see Nordisk Mellemoesten Institut. Bulletin **2431**
Nordic Network. (US) **4551**, 1148, 4780
Nordic Pulp & Paper Research Journal.(SW ISSN 0283-2631) **2116**
Nordic Sounds. (DK) **3570**
Nordic Statistical Secretariat. Technical Reports. see Nordisk Statistisk Sekretariat. Tekniske Rapporter **4581**
Nordic Times International see Anglo - Nordic Times **900**
Nordica. (DK ISSN 0109-3967) **2877**
Nordicana. (CN ISSN 0078-1053) **246**, 4330
Nordicom. (DK ISSN 0105-1385) **1349**
Nordicom - Information om Masskommunikationsforskning i Norden. (SW ISSN 0349-5949) **1341**
Nordicom Review of Nordic Mass Communication Research. (SW ISSN 0349-6244) **1341**
Nordinfo-Nytt. (FI ISSN 0356-9624) **2776**
Nordisk Aatervinning. (SW) **3416**
Nordisk Administrativt Tidsskrift. (DK ISSN 0029-1285) **4068**
Nordisk Arkivnyt. (SW ISSN 0546-2851) **2377**
†Nordisk Betong. (SW ISSN 0029-1307) **5248**
Nordisk Domssamling. (NO ISSN 0029-1315) **2661**
†Nordisk Ekumenisk Aarsbok. (SW ISSN 0085-4212) **5248**
Nordisk Exlibris Tidsskrift. (DK ISSN 0029-1323) **4133**
Nordisk Filateli. (SW ISSN 0029-134X) **3755**, 3600
Nordisk Filateli med Mynt - Magazinet. (SW) **3600**, 3755
Nordisk Filatelistisk Tidsskrift. (DK ISSN 0903-3440) **3755**
Nordisk Flaggskrift. (DK) **2159**
Nordisk Foersaekringstidsskrift/ Scandinavian Insurance Quarterly. (SW ISSN 0348-6516) **2539**
Nordisk Hydrologisk Forening Rapport see N H P Rapport **1599**

Nordisk Hygienisk Tidskrift see Scandinavian Journal of Work, Environment & Health **3622**
Nordisk Jaernbane Tidskrift. (SW ISSN 0029-1382) **4712**
Nordisk Jordbruksforskning. (FI ISSN 0048-0495) **110**
Nordisk Julemaerke Katalog. (DK ISSN 0105-9106) **3755**, 3600
Nordisk Komite for Transport Forskning. Publikation. (NO ISSN 0359-7601) **4654**, 682
†Nordisk Kriminalteknisk Tidsskrift. (NO ISSN 0029-1390) **5248**
Nordisk Kvaekartidskrift see Kvaekartidskrift **4284**
Nordisk Matematisk Tidsskrift see Normat: Nordisk Matematisk Tidsskrift **3049**
Nordisk Medicin. (DK ISSN 0029-1420) **3136**
Nordisk Medicinhistorisk Aarsbok. (SW ISSN 0078-1061) **3136**
Nordisk Mejeriindustri - Scandinavian Dairy Industry see N M I - Nordisk Mejeriinformation **202**
Nordisk Mellemoesten Institut. Bulletin/ Nordic Middle East Institute. Bulletin. (DK) **2431**
Nordisk Missions Tidsskrift see Mission **4190**
†Nordisk Numismatisk Aarsskrift/ Scandinavian Numismatic Journal. (NO ISSN 0078-107X) **5248**
Nordisk Numismatisk Union Medlemsblad. (DK ISSN 0025-8539) **3600**
Nordisk Posttidsskrift. (SW ISSN 0345-8539) **1353**
Nordisk Psykiatrisk Tidsskrift/Nordic Journal of Psychiatry. (NO ISSN 0029-1455) **3349**
Nordisk Psykologi. (DK ISSN 0029-1463) **4037**
Nordisk Psykologisk Litteratur. (DK ISSN 0900-8772) **4037**
Nordisk Samkatalog foer Periodica Mikro see N O S P - Mikro **406**
Nordisk Sexologi. (DK ISSN 0108-271X) **3136**
Nordisk Sosialt Arbeid. (NO ISSN 0333-1342) **4415**
Nordisk Statistisk Aarsbok/Yearbook of Nordic Statistics. (DK ISSN 0078-1088) **4581**
Nordisk Statistisk Sekretariat. Tekniske Rapporter/Nordic Statistical Secretariat. Technical Reports. (DK ISSN 0106-9039) **4581**
Nordisk Statistisk Skriftserie/Statistical Reports of the Nordic Countries. (DK ISSN 0078-1096) **4581**
Nordisk Statutsamling. (SW ISSN 0300-3094) **2661**
Nordisk Tidende. see Norway Times **2017**
Nordisk Tidsskrift foer Beteendeterapi. see Scandinavian Journal of Behaviour Therapy **4045**
Nordisk Tidskrift Foer Bok- och Biblioteksvaesen/Scandinavian Journal of Libraries. (SW ISSN 0029-148X) **4133**, 2777
Nordisk Tidsskrift foer Doevundervisning.(SW) **2288**, 1739
Nordisk Tidsskrift foer Hoersel och Doevundervisning see Nordisk Tidskrift foer Doevundervisning **2288**
Nordisk Tidsskrift for Fackspraak och Terminologi. see Nordisk Tidsskrift for Fagsprog og Terminologi **5248**
Nordisk Tidsskrift for Vetenskap, Konst och Industri. (SW ISSN 0029-1501) **2877**, 338, 2318
Nordisk Tidsskrift for Fagspraak og Terminologi. see Nordisk Tidsskrift for Fagsprog og Terminologi **5248**
†Nordisk Tidsskrift for Fagsprog og Terminologi/Norraent Timarit um Fagmaal og Idord/Nordisk Tidsskrift for Fagspraak og Terminologi/ Pohjoismainen Erikoiskielten ja Terminologian Aikakauslehti/Nordisk Tidskrift for Fackspraak och Terminologi/Nordic Journal of L S P and Terminology. (DK ISSN 0108-7789) **5248**

Nordisk Tidsskrift for Rensning og Vask/Scandinavian Magazine for Cleaning and Washing. (DK ISSN 0105-6611) **1282**
Nordisk Tidsskrift for Spesialpedagogikk. (NO ISSN 0048-0509) **1739**, 4037
†Nordisk Veterinaermedicin/ Scandinavian Journal of Veterinary Science. (DK ISSN 0029-1579) **5248**
†Nordiska Afrikainstitutet. Annual Report. (SW ISSN 1100-6749) **5248**
Nordiska Afrikainstitutet. Discussion Papers. (SW ISSN 1100-2131) **933**
Nordiska Samarbetsorgan. (SW) **2587**
Nordiska Samarbetsorganet for Vetenskaplig Information Publikation see N O R D I N F O Publikation **2775**
Nordiske Domme i Sjofartsanliggender. (NO ISSN 0085-4220) **2661**
Nordiskt Lantbruk. (SW ISSN 0349-7038) **111**
Nordistica Gothoburgensia. (SW ISSN 0078-1134) **2831**, 2943
Nordlauenburgische Chronik. (GW) **2378**
Nordost-Archiv. (GW ISSN 0029-1595) **2378**
Nordrhein Verkehr. (GW) **4712**
Nordrhein-Westfaelische Verwaltungblaetter. (GW ISSN 0932-710X) **2661**, 4068
Nordrhein - Westfaelischen Industrie- und Handelskammer. Statistisches Jahrbuch. (GW) **731**, 4581
▼Nordrhein-Westfalen. Finanzministerium. Finanz Report. (GW) **4068**, 793
Nordrhein-Westfalen. Finanzministerium. Mitteilungsblatt. (GW) **876**
Nordrhein-Westfalen. Justizministerialblatt. (GW) **2661**
Nordrhein-Westfalen. Statistisches Jahrbuch. (GW ISSN 0468-656X) **4581**
Nordrhein-Westfalen von Hinten see Koeln - Rheinland von Hinten **2454**
†Nordschleswig. (DK ISSN 0107-2188) **5248**
Nordsee. (IT) **2999**
Nordsee - Cerchio see Nordsee **2999**
Nordslesvigske Museer. (DK ISSN 0107-9336) **2378**
Nordwestdeutsche Gesellschaft fuer Innere Medizin. Kongressbericht. (GW ISSN 0029-1609) **3136**
Nordwestdeutsches Handwerk. (GW ISSN 0029-1617) **1082**
Nordwestliche see Gesund und Sicher **830**
Nor'Easter (Duluth). (US) **2416**, 4734
Nor'easter (Narragansett). (US) **1608**
Nor'easter (Syracuse). (US) **4245**
Norfolk and Western see Norfolk Southern World **4712**
Norfolk Botanical Garden Society Bulletin. (US ISSN 0029-1641) **2135**, 511
Norfolk Farmer. (UK) **111**
Norfolk Farmers' Union Gazette see Norfolk Farmer **111**
Norfolk Record Society. Publications. (UK ISSN 0078-1169) **2378**
Norfolk Southern World. (US) **4712**
Norfolklore. (CN) **2159**
Norge-Amerika Foreningen. Report see Norge-Amerika Foreningen. Yearbook **3967**
Norge-Amerika Foreningen. Yearbook. (NO) **3967**
Norge og Utviklingslandene. (NO) **933**
Norges Apotekerforenings Tidsskrift. (NO ISSN 0802-8400) **3736**
Norges Bank. Annual Report see Norges Bank. Report and Accounts **793**
Norges Bank. Economic Bulletin. (NO ISSN 0029-1676) **876**
Norges Bank. Report and Accounts. (NO ISSN 0078-1185) **793**
Norges Bank. Skriftserie. (NO ISSN 0802-7188) **876**
Norges Bondeblad see Bondebladet **80**

NORIN SUISAN-SHO 6501

Norges Forsvar. (NO ISSN 0029-1692) **3467**
Norges Geologiske Undersoekelse. Aarsmelding. (NO ISSN 0333-4112) **1575**
Norges Geologiske Undersoekelse Bulletin see N G U Bulletin **1574**
Norges Geologiske Undersoekelse Skrifter see N G U Skrifter **1574**
Norges Geologiske Undersoekelser Special Publication see N G U Special Publication **1574**
Norges Geotekniske Institutt. Publikasjon/Norwegian Geotechnical Institute. Publications. (NO ISSN 0078-1193) **1592**
Norges Handels-Kalender/Norwegian Directory of Commerce/Annuaire du Commerce du Norvege/Norwegische Handels-Adressbuch. (NO ISSN 0078-1215) **1148**
Norges Industri. (NO ISSN 0029-1706) **1082**
Norges Kjoebmannsblad. (NO) **2093**
†Norges Landbrukshoegskole. Institutt for Bygningsteknikk. Aarsmelding/ Agricultural University of Norway. Department of Building Technology in Agriculture. Annual Report. (NO ISSN 0065-0226) **5248**
†Norges Landbrukshoegskole. Institutt for Bygningsteknikk, Byggekostnadsindeks for Driftsbygninger i Jordbruket. Prisutviklingen. (NO ISSN 0065-0218) **5248**
†Norges Landbrukshoegskole. Institutt for Bygningsteknikk. Melding. (NO ISSN 0065-0234) **5248**
Norges Landbrukshoegskole. Institutt for Jordskifte og Arealplanlegging. Melding/Agricultural University of Norway. Department of Land Use Planning. Serie. (NO ISSN 0801-2334) **155**
Norges Landbrukshoegskole. Institutt for Jordskifte og Eiendomsutforming. Melding see Norges Landbrukshoegskole. Institutt for Jordskifte og Arealplanlegging. Melding **155**
▼Norges Landbrukshoegskole. Institutt for Tekniske Fag. Proevemeldinger/ Agricultural University of Norway, Department of Agricultural Engineering, Test Reports. (NO ISSN 0802-8524) **111**, 626
▼Norges Landbrukshoegskole. Institutt for Tekniske Fag. Rapporter/ Agricultural University of Norway. Department of Agricultural Engineering. Research Reports. (NO ISSN 0802-8532) **111**, 626
Norges Landbruksoekonomiske Institutt. Driftsgranskinger i Jordbruket see Norsk Institutt for Landbruksoekonomisk Forskning. Driftsgranskinger i Jord- og Skogbruk **155**
Norges Samarbeid med Utviklingslandene see Norge og Utviklingslandene **933**
Norges Teknisk-Naturvitenskapelige Forskningsraad. Aarsberetning/Royal Norwegian Council for Scientific and Industrial Research. Annual Report. (NO ISSN 0078-1231) **4330**, 4605
Norges Teknisk-Naturvitenskapelige Forskningsraad. Transportoekonomisk Institutt. Aarsberetning see Transportoekonomisk Institutt. Aarsberetning **4716**
Norges Utenrikshandel see Eksport Aktuelt **906**
†Norges Veterinaerhoegskole. Aarsmelding/Norwegian College of Veterinary Medicine. Annual Report. (NO) **5248**
Norges Veterinaerhoegskole. Publikasjoner/Norwegian College of Veterinary Medicine. Publications. (NO ISSN 0078-6721) **4813**
Norin Suisan-sho Kachiku Eisei Shikenjo Kenkyu Hokoku. see Japan. National Institute of Animal Health. Bulletin **4811**

6502 NORIN SUISAN

Norin Suisan Tokei Geppo. see Monthly Statistics on Agriculture, Forestry and Fisheries **140**
Norin Tosho Shiryo Geppo. (JA ISSN 0029-1773) **141**, 2112
Norinsho Ringyo Shikenjo Nenpo. see Japan. Forestry and Forest Products Research Institute. Annual Report **2103**
Norkontakt see Utvikling **936**
Normal. (US ISSN 0892-5836) **338**
Normalisatie Magazine. (NE ISSN 0921-8211) **3448**
Normalizace see Magazin C S N **3447**
Normalizacja. (PL ISSN 0029-179X) **1832**, 3448
Norman Ford's Florida. (US ISSN 0546-3432) **4780**
Norman Mackenzie Art Gallery Vista see Vista **3535**
Normandie Industrielle. (FR ISSN 0029-1803) **4605**
Normat: Nordisk Matematisk Tidskrift. (NO ISSN 0801-3500) **3049**
Normenausschuss Bibliotheks- und Dokumentationswesen Mitteilungen see N A B D - Mitteilungen **2774**
Normerede og Besatte Laegestillinger Samt Sengepladser paa Institutioner see Laegestillinger og Sengepladser paa Institutioner **2467**
Normtalsundersoegelse for Sportsbranchen. (DK ISSN 0900-0283) **4481**
Normtalsundersoegelsen for Isenkrambranchen. (DK ISSN 0900-0275) **642**
Norna - Rapporter. (SW ISSN 0346-6728) **2831**
Noroil see Euroil **3685**
Noroil Contacts see Noroil Contacts - Offshore Directory **3693**
Noroil Contacts - Offshore Directory. (NO) **3693**
Noroil Newswire. (NO) **3693**
Norois. (FR ISSN 0029-182X) **2258**
Norraent Timarit um Fagmaal og Idord. see Nordisk Tidsskrift for Fagsprog og Terminologi **5248**
Norrlaendsk Tidskrift. (SW ISSN 0029-1838) **682**
Norseman. (NO ISSN 0029-1846) **2877**
Norsk Artilleri-Tidsskrift. (NO ISSN 0029-1854) **3467**
Norsk Baatindustri. (NO) **4734**, 4527
Norsk Bedriftshelsetjeneste see Norsk Tidsskrift for Arbejdsmedisin **3136**
†Norsk Bibliografisk Bibliotek. (NO ISSN 0029-1862) **5248**
Norsk Bokfortegnelse Aarskatalog. (NO ISSN 0029-1870) **407**
Norsk Dampkjelforening. Meddelelser see Norsk Energi **1832**
Norsk Drosjeeierblad see Taxi **4656**
Norsk Elghund Quarterly. (US) **3712**
Norsk Energi. (NO ISSN 0800-7896) **1832**, 1793
Norsk Farmaceutisk Tidsskrift. (NO ISSN 0029-1935) **3736**
Norsk Filatelistisk Tidsskrift. (NO) **3755**
Norsk Filosofisk Tidsskrift/Norwegian Journal of Philosophy. (NO ISSN 0029-1943) **3774**
Norsk Fiskaralmanakk. (NO) **2046**, 4551
Norsk Fiskeindustri. (NO) **2046**
Norsk Fotografisk Tidsskrift. (NO) **3793**
Norsk Galvano Teknisk Tidsskrift see Overflate Teknikk **1212**
Norsk Geografisk Tidsskrift/Norwegian Journal of Geography. (NO ISSN 0029-1951) **2258**
Norsk Geologisk Tidsskrift/Norwegian Journal of Geology. (NO ISSN 0029-196X) **1575**
Norsk Grafisk Tidsskrift. (NO ISSN 0029-1978) **4003**
Norsk Hagetidend. (NO ISSN 0029-1986) **2135**
Norsk Hotell og Restaurantblad see Hotell og Restaurant **2476**
Norsk Husflid. (NO ISSN 0048-0592) **2449**
Norsk Idrett. (NO ISSN 0029-1994) **4481**

Norsk Institutt for By- og Regionforskning Rapport see N I B R Rapport **2492**
Norsk Institutt for Landbruksoekonomisk Forskning. Driftsgranskinger i Jord- og Skogbruk. (NO ISSN 0333-2500) **155**
Norsk Institutt for Skogforskning. Meddelelser see Skogforsk. Meddelelser **2108**
Norsk Institutt for Skogforskning. Rapport see Skogforsk. Rapport **2108**
Norsk Institutt for Vannforskning. Aarbok see Norsk Institutt for Vannforskning. Aarsberetning **1600**
Norsk Institutt for Vannforskning. Aarsberetning. (NO) **1600**
Norsk Institutt for Vannforskning. Research Reports. (NO) **1600**
Norsk Institutt for Vannforskning. Temarapport see Norsk Institutt for Vannforskning. Research Reports **1600**
Norsk Kommuneforbund. Fagblad. (NO) **4093**
Norsk Landbruk. (NO ISSN 0332-5474) **111**
Norsk Landbruksforsking/Norwegian Agricultural Research. (NO ISSN 0801-5333) **111**
Norsk Litteraer Aarbok. (NO ISSN 0078-1266) **2943**
Norsk Maskin-Tidende/Norwegian Marine Engineers' Magazine. (NO ISSN 0333-0192) **4734**
Norsk Maskin-Tidende Styrmansblad see Norsk Skibsfoerertidende. Maskin-Tidende Styrmansblad **4735**
Norsk Motor Nytt see De Motor Nytt **5240**
Norsk Musikerblad. (NO ISSN 0029-2044) **3570**
Norsk Musikktidsskrift. (NO ISSN 0332-5482) **3570**
Norsk Naturforvalterforbund NaFo - Nytt see NaFo - Nytt **108**
Norsk Pedagogisk Tidsskrift/Norwegian Journal of Education. (NO ISSN 0029-2052) **1651**
Norsk Pelsdyrblad. (NO ISSN 0369-5255) **2737**
Norsk Petroleumsforening. Aarbok/Norwegian Petroleum Society. Yearbook. (NO) **3693**
Norsk Plast. (NO ISSN 0332-6136) **3864**
Norsk Polarinstitutt. Aarbok. (NO ISSN 0085-4271) **1575**, 2258
Norsk Polarinstitutt. Meddelelser. (NO ISSN 0373-5605) **1576**, 2258
Norsk Polarinstitutt. Polarhaandbok. (NO ISSN 0474-8042) **1576**, 2258
Norsk Polarinstitutt. Skrifter. (NO ISSN 0369-5417) **1576**, 2258
Norsk Retstidende. (NO ISSN 0029-2060) **2661**
Norsk Rikskringkastning. Programbladet. (NO ISSN 0033-0353) **1377**
Norsk Sjakkblad. (NO) **4481**
Norsk Sjoefartsmuseum. Aarsberetning.(NO ISSN 0801-423X) **2378**, 280
Norsk Sjoemannsforbund. Medlemsblad.(NO ISSN 0029-2079) **4735**, 2587
Norsk Skattelovsamling. (NO ISSN 0333-1423) **1102**
Norsk Skibsfoerertidende. (NO ISSN 0048-0606) **4735**
Norsk Skibsfoerertidende. Maskin-Tidende Styrmansblad. (NO) **4735**
Norsk Skogbruk. (NO ISSN 0029-2087) **2105**
Norsk Skogbruksmuseum. Aarbok. (NO ISSN 0549-6896) **2378**
Norsk Skoleblad. (NO ISSN 0029-2117) **1651**
Norsk Slektshistorisk Tidsskrift. (NO ISSN 0029-2141) **2159**
Norsk Statsvitenskapelig Tidsskrift/Norwegian Political Science Journal. (NO ISSN 0801-1745) **3911**
Norsk Sykehustidende see Helsetjenesten. Fagtidsskriftet **2463**

Norsk Teknisk Museum. Yearbook see Volund **3535**
Norsk Tekstiltidende. (NO ISSN 0029-2168) **4622**
Norsk Teologisk Tidsskrift/Norwegian Theological Journal. (NO ISSN 0029-2176) **4192**
Norsk Tidende for det Industrielle Rettsvern. Del 1: Patenter. (NO ISSN 0029-2206) **3676**
Norsk Tidende for det Industrielle Rettsvern. Del 2: Varemerker see Norsk Varemerketidende **3676**
Norsk Tidende for det Industrielle Rettsvern. Del 3: Moenstre. (NO ISSN 0029-2184) **3676**
Norsk Tidskrift for Arbejdsmedisin/Norwegian Journal of Occupational Medicine. (NO ISSN 0803-2394) **3136**
Norsk Tidsskrift for Misjon/Norwegian Journal of Mission and Missionary Questions. (NO ISSN 0029-2214) **4192**
Norsk Tidsskrift for Sjovesen. (NO ISSN 0029-2222) **3467**
Norsk Ukeblad. (NO ISSN 0029-2257) **2213**
Norsk Utenrikspolitisk Aarbok. (NO ISSN 0332-7299) **3967**
Norsk Utenrikspolitisk Institutt Notat see N U P I Notat **3966**
Norsk Utenrikspolitisk Institutt Rapport see N U P I Rapport **3966**
Norsk V V S. (NO ISSN 0029-2265) **2302**
Norsk Varemerketidende. (NO) **3676**
Norsk Veitidsskrift see Samferdsel **4721**
Norsk Veterinaertidsskrift. (NO ISSN 0029-2273) **4813**
†Norsk Viltforskning. Meddelelser. (NO) **5248**
Norske Arkitektkonkurranser. (NO ISSN 0332-6578) **304**
Norske Creditbank. (NO) **793**
Norske Creditbank. Annual Report see Norske Creditbank **793**
Norske Creditbank. Report of the Board of Directors see Norske Creditbank **793**
Norske Handelsreisende. (NO) **1049**
Norske Institutt for Kosmisk Fysikk. Magnetic Observations see Auroral Observatory. Magnetic Observations **362**
Norske Laegeforening. Tidsskrift/Norwegian Medical Association. Journal. (NO ISSN 0029-2001) **3136**
Norske Myrselskap. Meddelelser see Jord og Myr **101**
Norske Skogforsoeksvesen. Meddelelser see Skogforsk. Meddelelser **2108**
Norske Tannlegeforenings Tidende. (NO ISSN 0029-2303) **3238**
Norske Videnskaps-Akademi. Historisk-Filosofisk Klasse. Avhandlinger. (NO ISSN 0029-2311) **2318**, 3774
Norske Vitenskapelige og Faglige Biblioteker. (NO) **2777**
Norte. (AG) **2416**
Norte. (MX) **2943**, 3967
†North Africa Monitor. (US) **5248**
North African Historical Review. see Revue d'Histoire Maghrebine **2334**
North American Archaeologist. (US ISSN 0197-6931) **280**
North American Association of Christians in Social Work. Practice Monograph Series. (US ISSN 8756-5013) **4415**, 4271
North American Association of Jewish Homes & Housing for the Aging. Perspectives. (US) **2277**
North American Association of Jewish Homes and Housing for the Aging. Progress Report see North American Association of Jewish Homes & Housing for the Aging. Perspectives **2277**
North American Association of Summer Sessions. Annual Conference. Proceedings. (US) **1730**, 1713
North American Association of Summer Sessions. Newsletter. (US) **1319**

North American Association of Wardens and Superintendents Grapevine Newsletter see N A A W S Grapevine Newsletter **1518**
North American Benefit Association Review see N A B A Review **1299**
North American Bird Bander. (US) **565**
North American Callbook. (US) **1357**
North American Culture. (US ISSN 0882-1968) **2258**, 2416, 4444
North American Die Casting Association International Die Casting Congress. Transactions see N A D C A International Die Casting Congress. Transactions **1921**
North American Directory of Contract Manufacturers in Electronics. (US) **1148**, 1776
North American Electric Reliability Council. Annual Report. (US) **1904**
North American Electric Reliability Council Winter Assessment (Year) see N A E R C Winter Assessment (Year) **1903**
†North American Environment. (CN ISSN 0840-5662) **5248**
North American Farmer. (US) **111**, 3911, 4444
North American Fauna. (US ISSN 0078-1304) **589**
North American Fisherman. (US ISSN 1043-2450) **4551**
North American Flora. (US ISSN 0078-1312) **511**
North American Gladiolus Council Bulletin. (US ISSN 0029-2370) **2135**
North American Gold Mining Stocks. (US) **958**
North American Guide to Nude Recreation. (US) **4780**
North American Horticulture: A Reference Guide. (US) **2135**
North American Hostels Handbook see Hostelling North America **4771**
†North American Human Rights Directory. (US ISSN 0270-2282) **5249**
North American Hunter. (US ISSN 0194-4320) **4551**
North American International Business see International Business **912**
North American Journal of Fisheries Management. (US ISSN 0275-5947) **2047**
North American Lily Society. Quarterly Bulletin. (US) **2135**
North American Lily Society. Yearbook. (US ISSN 0741-9910) **2135**
North American Man-Boy Love Association Bulletin see N A M B L A Bulletin **2455**
North American Manufacturing Research Conference. Proceedings see Transactions of the North American Manufacturing Research Conference. Proceedings **1838**
North American Moravian see Moravian (Bethlehem, 1856) **4285**
North American New Product Report. (UK) **2093**
North American Post/Hokubei Hochi. (US) **2017**, 838
North American Pylon. (US ISSN 1053-4881) **4698**, 4551
North American Review. (US ISSN 0029-2397) **2877**, 2416
▼North American Review of Economics and Finance. (US ISSN 1042-752X) **876**, 793
North American Riding for the Handicapped Association, Inc. News see N A R H A News **4536**
North American Serials Interest Group Newsletter see N A S I G Newsletter **2774**
North American Society for Oceanic History. Newsletter. (US) **2416**, 4735
North American Society for Oceanic History. Proceedings see North American Society for Oceanic History. Newsletter **2416**
North American Society for Sport History. Newsletter. (US) **4481**, 2416
North American Society for Sport History. Proceedings. (US ISSN 0093-6235) **4481**, 2416

North American Society of Adlerian Psychology. Newsletter. (US ISSN 0889-9428) 4037
North American Students of Cooperation Guide to Campus Co-Ops see N A S C O Guide to Campus Co-Ops 1146
North American Studies in Nineteeth-Century German Literature. (US ISSN 0891-4109) 2943
North American Whitetail. (US ISSN 0746-6250) 4551
North American Wildlife and Natural Resources Conference. Transactions. (US ISSN 0078-1355) 1494
North American Youth Sport Institute Resource List see N A Y S I Resource List 4480
North Atlantic Treaty Organization. Directorate of Economic Affairs. Colloquium. Series see N A T O. Annual Economic Colloquia. Proceedings 918
North Atlantic Treaty Organization. Expert Panel on Air Pollution Modeling. Proceedings. (BE ISSN 0377-7669) 1978
North Atlantic Treaty Organization. Facts and Figures/Alliance Atlantique. Structure, Faits et Chiffres. (BE) 3967
North Atlantic Treaty Organization Advanced Science Institutes Series A: Life Sciences see N A T O Advanced Science Institutes Series A: Life Sciences 448
North Atlantic Treaty Organization Advanced Science Institutes Series C: Mathematical and Physical Sciences see N A T O Advanced Science Institutes Series C: Mathematical and Physical Sciences 3048
North Atlantic Treaty Organization Advanced Science Institutes Series D: Behavioural and Social Sciences see N A T O Advanced Science Institutes Series D: Behavioural and Social Sciences 4380
North Atlantic Treaty Organization Advanced Science Institutes Series E: Applied Sciences see N A T O Advanced Science Institutes Series E: Applied Sciences 4604
North Atlantic Treaty Organization Advanced Science Institutes Series F: Computer and Systems Sciences see N A T O Advanced Science Institutes Series F: Computer and Systems Sciences 1438
North Atlantic Treaty Organization Advanced Science Institutes Series G: Ecological Sciences see N A T O Advanced Science Institutes Series G: Ecological Sciences 1963
North Atlantic Treaty Organization Review see N A T O Review 3908
North Atlantic Treaty Organization Sixteen Nations see N A T O's Sixteen Nations 3966
North Cal-Neva Resource Conservation and Development Area. Annual Work Plan. (US) 1494
North Cal-Neva Resource Conservation and Development Project. Annual Work Plan see North Cal-Neva Resource Conservation and Development Area. Annual Work Plan 1494
North Carolina. Council on State Goals and Policy. Annual Report see North Carolina. State Goals and Policy Board. Annual Report 4068
North Carolina. Department of Agriculture. Agricultural Review. (US) 111
North Carolina. Department of Environment, Health, and Natural Resources. Division of Land Resources. Bulletin. (US) 1576
North Carolina. Department of Environment, Health, and Natural Resources. Division of Land Resources. Information Circular. (US) 1576

North Carolina. Department of Environment, Health and Natural Resources. State Center for Health and Environmental Statistics. North Carolina Vital Statistics. (US) 3994, 4118
†North Carolina. Department of Human Resources. Publication. (US) 5249
North Carolina. Department of Natural Resources and Community Development. Division of Land Resources. Bulletin see North Carolina. Department of Environment, Health, and Natural Resources. Division of Land Resources. Bulletin 1576
†North Carolina. Department of Natural Resources and Community Development. Division of Land Resources. Economic Paper. (US) 5249
North Carolina. Department of Natural Resources and Community Development. Division of Land Resources. Information Circular see North Carolina. Department of Environment, Health, and Natural Resources. Division of Land Resources. Information Circular 1576
†North Carolina. Department of Natural Resources and Community Development. Division of Land Resources. Regional Geology Series. (US) 5249
†North Carolina. Department of Natural Resources and Community Development. Division of Land Resources. Special Publication. (US) 5249
North Carolina. Department of Revenue. Franchise Tax and Corporate Income Tax Rules and Regulations. (US) 1102
North Carolina. Division of Health Services. State Center for Health Statistics. North Carolina Vital Statistics see North Carolina. Department of Environment, Health and Natural Resources. State Center for Health and Environmental Statistics. North Carolina Vital Statistics 3994
North Carolina. Secretary of State. Directory of State and County Officials. (US) 4068
North Carolina. State Goals and Policy Board. Annual Report. (US) 4068
North Carolina Agricultural Chemicals Manual. (US ISSN 0065-4418) 186
North Carolina Archeological Society. Newsletter. (US) 280
†North Carolina Architect. (US ISSN 0029-2427) 5249
North Carolina Architecture. (US) 304
North Carolina Association of Educators News Bulletin see N C A E News Bulletin 1648
▼North Carolina Black Journal. (US) 2017
North Carolina Builder. (US) 626
North Carolina Catholic. (US) 4271
North Carolina Christian Advocate. (US ISSN 0029-2435) 4245
North Carolina Communicable Disease Morbidity Statistics. (US ISSN 0085-428X) 4118
North Carolina Dental Review. (US) 3239
North Carolina Directory of Trade and Professional Associations. (US) 1148
North Carolina Education. (US ISSN 0029-2451) 1651
▼North Carolina Employment Law Letter. (US ISSN 1054-6359) 2661, 990
North Carolina English Teacher. (US) 1756
▼North Carolina Environmental Law Letter. (US ISSN 1047-4633) 2661, 1964
North Carolina Facts. (US ISSN 0895-8106) 1782
North Carolina Farm Bureau News. (US ISSN 0744-9593) 111

North Carolina Farmers Fastline see Farmers Fastline: North Carolina Edition 162
North Carolina Folklore Journal. (US ISSN 0090-5844) 2057
North Carolina Game & Fish. (US) 4551
North Carolina Genealogical Society Journal. (US ISSN 0360-1056) 2160
North Carolina Genealogical Society Newsletter. (US) 2160
North Carolina Geological Survey Open-File Report see N C G S Open-File Report 1574
North Carolina Historical Review. (US ISSN 0029-2494) 2416
North Carolina Housing Network. (US) 4154, 626
North Carolina Insight. (US) 3911
North Carolina Journal of International Law and Commercial Regulation. (US ISSN 0743-1759) 2727
North Carolina Law Monitor. (US ISSN 0883-7783) 4069, 2661
North Carolina Law Review. (US ISSN 0029-2524) 2661
North Carolina Lawyers Weekly. (US) 2661
North Carolina Libraries. (US ISSN 0029-2540) 2777
North Carolina Magazine. (US) 838
North Carolina Manual. (US) 4069
North Carolina Manufacturing Firms Directory. (US) 1148
North Carolina Medical Journal. (US ISSN 0029-2559) 3136
North Carolina Metalworking Directory. (US) 1148, 3021, 3416
North Carolina Museum of Art. Bulletin. (US ISSN 0029-2567) 3531
North Carolina Museum of Art. Preview.(US) 3531
North Carolina Plastics Processors and Producers. (US) 3864
North Carolina Plumbing - Heating - Cooling Forum. (US ISSN 0739-3830) 2302
North Carolina Preservation. (US) 2416
North Carolina Propane Gas News. (US) 3693
North Carolina Reported Abortions see North Carolina Reported Pregnancies 598
North Carolina Reported Pregnancies. (US) 598, 4581
North Carolina School Boards Association Bulletin see Voice of North Carolina School Boards Association 1732
North Carolina Seed Law. (US) 111
North Carolina State Bar Quarterly. (US ISSN 0164-6850) 2661
North Carolina State University. Chancellor's Annual Report see North Carolina State University. Chancellor's Report 1713
North Carolina State University. Chancellor's Report. (US) 1713
North Carolina State University. College of Forest Resources. Technical Report. (US) 2105
†North Carolina State University. College of Textiles News. (US) 5249
North Carolina State University. School of Design. (Student Publication Magazine). (US ISSN 0078-1444) 304
North Carolina State University. School of Forest Resources. Technical Report see North Carolina State University. College of Forest Resources. Technical Report 2105
North Carolina State University. School of Textiles News see North Carolina State University. College of Textiles News 5249
North Carolina State University. Water Resources Research Institute. Report see W R R I News 4830
North Carolina State University Libraries Focus see N C S U Libraries Focus 2774
North Carolina Studies in the Romance Languages and Literatures. (US) 2943
†North Carolina Tarheel Coast. (US ISSN 0164-6761) 5249

North Carolina Tobacco Report. (US) 4644
North Carolina Wild Flower Preservation Society. Newsletter. (US) 2135
North Castle History. (US) 2416
North-Caucasus Scientific Center of High School. Natural Sciences. News. see Severo-Kavkazskii Nauchnyi Tsentr Vysshei Shkoly. Estestvennye Nauki. Izvestiya 3055
North-Caucasus Scientific Center of High School. Social Science. News. see Severo-Kavkazskii Nauchnyi Tsentr Vysshei Shkoly. Obshchestvennye Nauki. Izvestiya 2386
North-Caucasus Scientific Center of High School. Technical Science. News. see Severo-Kavkazskii Nauchnyi Tsentr Vysshei Shkoly. Tekhnicheskie Nauki. Izvestiya 4608
North Central Association Quarterly. (US ISSN 0029-2648) 1651
North Central Campbook. (US ISSN 0147-8613) 4780, 4551
North Central-Iowa, Minnesota, Nebraska, North Dakota, South Dakota Tourbook see Tourbook: North Central 4790
North Central Journal of Agricultural Economics. (US ISSN 0191-9016) 155
North Central Kansas Genealogical Society. Newsletter see Waconda Roots and Branches 2167
North Central Name Society. Journal. (US) 2831
North Central Regional Center for Rural Development. Research Report see Rural Development News 157
North-Central State. Ministry of Works. Report see Kaduna State. Ministry of Works. Report 4065
North Central State Statistical Yearbook see Kaduna State Statistical Yearbook 4576
North Cheshire Family Historian. (UK ISSN 0306-9206) 2160
North China Agriculture Journal. see Huabei Nongxue Bao 96
North Circular. (UK) 1319
North Coast Bride and Groom. (US) 3067, 3399, 4850
North Coast Co-Op Newsletter. (US) 2078
North Coast Labor Force Trends. (US) 990
North Communications University. Journal. see Beifang Jiaotong Daxue Xuebao 1332
North Conway Institute, Inc. Catalyst see N C I Catalyst 1538
†North Country Anvil. (US) 5249
North Country Cheviot Sheep Society. Flock Book. (UK) 222
North Country Farm News. (US) 111, 2449
North Country Notes. (US) 2416
North Country Reference and Research Resources Council. Newsletter see Points North 2779
North County Catholic. (US) 4271
North Dakota. Council on Vocational Education. Biennial Evaluation Report. (US) 1756
North Dakota. Department of Agriculture. Annual Report see North Dakota. Department of Agriculture. Biennial Report 111
North Dakota. Department of Agriculture. Biennial Report. (US) 111
North Dakota. Department of Public Instruction. Biennial Report of the Superintendent of Public Instruction. (US) 1678
North Dakota. Employment Security Bureau. Annual Report see Job Service North Dakota. Annual Report 984
North Dakota. Employment Security Bureau. Biennial Report to the Governor see Job Service North Dakota. Biennial Report to the Governor 984
North Dakota. Geological Survey. Bulletin. (US ISSN 0546-5001) 1576

6504 NORTH DAKOTA

North Dakota. Geological Survey. Educational Series. (US ISSN 0091-9004) **1576**
North Dakota. Geological Survey. Miscellaneous Series. (US ISSN 0078-1576) **1576**
North Dakota. Geological Survey. Report of Investigations. (US) **1576**
North Dakota. Judicial Conference. Annual Report see North Dakota. Judicial System. Annual Report **2700**
North Dakota. Judicial System. Annual Report. (US) **2700, 4581**
North Dakota. Milk Stabilization Board. Annual Report of Administrative Activities. (US ISSN 0091-9446) **202**
North Dakota. State Advisory Council for Vocational Education. Annual Evaluation Report see North Dakota. Council on Vocational Education. Biennial Evaluation Report **1756**
North Dakota. State Bar Board. Directory of Lawyers and Judges. (US) **2661**
North Dakota Academic Library Statistics. see North Dakota Library Statistics **2795**
North Dakota Academy of Science. Proceedings. (US) **4330**
North Dakota Agricultural Statistics. (US) **141**
North Dakota Crop and Livestock Statistics see North Dakota Agricultural Statistics **141**
North Dakota Directory of Lawyers and Judges see North Dakota. State Bar Board. Directory of Lawyers and Judges **2661**
North Dakota Economic Data Book. (US) **876**
North Dakota Economic Development Commission News see Network (Bismarck) **1081**
North Dakota Education News. (US ISSN 0048-0681) **1651**
North Dakota Farm Research. (US) **111**
North Dakota Geological Survey Newsletter see N D G S Newsletter **1574**
North Dakota Grain and Oilseed Transportation Statistics. (US) **141**
†North Dakota Growth Indicators. (US ISSN 0549-8368) **5249**
North Dakota History. (US ISSN 0029-2710) **2416**
North Dakota Horizons. (US) **2416**
North Dakota Hospitality & Beverage News. (CN) **2416**
North Dakota Human Services. (US) **4415**
†North Dakota Journal of Education. (US ISSN 0029-2737) **5249**
North Dakota Law Review. (US ISSN 0029-2745) **2661**
North Dakota League of Cities Bulletin. (US) **4093**
North Dakota Library Statistics. (US) **2795**
North Dakota Music Educator. (US ISSN 0029-2753) **3570**
North Dakota Outdoors. (US ISSN 0029-2761) **1494, 4551**
North Dakota Quarterly. (US ISSN 0029-277X) **2512, 4381**
North Dakota R E C Magazine. (US ISSN 0885-2499) **2231**
North Dakota Rural Electric Magazine see North Dakota R E C Magazine **2231**
North Dakota Securities Bulletin. (US ISSN 0549-8333) **958**
North Dakota Society of Medical Technologists. Newsletter. (US ISSN 0048-069X) **3262**
North Dakota State Plan for Rehabilitation Facilities and Workshops. (US ISSN 0093-7843) **1739**
North Dakota State University at Fargo. University Computer Center. Newsletter see NewsBits **1398**
North Dakota's Highway Safety Plan. (US) **4720**
North Dakota's Highway Safety Work Programs see North Dakota's Highway Safety Plan **4720**

North Force. (US ISSN 0895-0024) **876, 838**
North Gardening. see Beifang Yuanyi **2122**
North Georgia Journal. (US ISSN 8756-9256) **4780, 2057, 2416**
North-Holland Linguistic Series. (NE ISSN 0078-1592) **2831**
North-Holland Mathematical Library. (NE) **3049**
North-Holland Mathematics Studies. (NE) **3049**
North-Holland Series in Applied Mathematics and Mechanics. (NE ISSN 0066-5460) **3049**
†North-Holland Series in Crystal Growth.(NE) **5249**
†North-Holland Series in General Systems Research. (NE) **5249**
†North-Holland Series in Probability and Applied Mathematics. (NE) **5249**
North-Holland Series in System Science and Engineering. (NE) **1880**
North-Holland Studies in Telecommunication. (NE) **1341**
North-Holland Systems and Control Series. (NE) **1438**
North India Churchman. (II) **4192**
North Island Televiewer. (CN) **1377**
North Jersey Highlander. (US ISSN 0029-2850) **2416**
North Jersey Regional Industrial Buying Guide. (US) **1148**
North Jersey Regional Industrial Purchasing Guide see North Jersey Regional Industrial Buying Guide **1148**
North Jersey Telephone Tickler for Insurance Men & Women. (US) **2539**
North Korea Directory (Year). (JA) **3967, 420, 4069**
North Korea News. (KO) **3911**
North Korea Quarterly. (GW) **3911**
North Light. (US) **338**
North Loop News. (US ISSN 0029-2877) **2231**
North Louisiana Genealogical Society Journal. (US) **2160**
North Lousiana Historical Association. Journal. (US ISSN 0739-005X) **2416**
North of England Museums Service Annual Report see N E M S Annual Report **3530**
North of England Museums Service News see N E M S News **3530**
†North of Scotland Visitor. (UK ISSN 0260-2415) **5249**
North Queensland Naturalist. (AT ISSN 0078-1630) **450**
North Queensland Register. (AT) **2172**
North Riding and Durham Farmer. Durham Edition see North Riding and Durham Farmer. Whole Edition **111**
North Riding and Durham Farmer. North Riding Edition see North Riding and Durham Farmer. Whole Edition **111**
North Riding and Durham Farmer. Whole Edition. (UK) **111**
North Ryde Cityscope. (AT) **4160**
North Sea Letter. (US) **3694, 793**
†North Sea Observer. (NO ISSN 0332-6144) **5249**
North Sea Oil & Gas Directory. (UK ISSN 0265-5039) **3694**
North Shore see Sandwich Islands Magazine **4785**
North Shore (Winnetka). (US) **2231**
North Shore Business. (SU) **682**
North Shore Life. (US) **2231**
North Shore New Residents' Guide. (US) **2258**
North Shore Newcomers' Guide see North Shore New Residents' Guide **2258**
North Shore Philatelic Society. Bulletin. (US) **3755**
North South Trader's Civil War. (US ISSN 1053-0010) **2416**
North Staffordshire Journal of Field Studies see Staffordshire Studies **2389**
North Staffordshire Polytechnic. Department of Economics. Discussion Papers see Staffordshire Polytechnic. Department of Economics. Discussion Papers **692**

North Staffordshire Polytechnic. Department of Sociology. Occasional Papers see Staffordshire Polytechnic. Department of Sociology. Occasional Papers **4453**
North Stone Review. (US) **2943**
North Suburban Genealogical Society. Newsletter. (US ISSN 0743-1341) **2160**
North Sydney Cityscope. (AT) **4160**
North Texas Golfer. (US) **4509**
North Texas P C News. (US) **1471, 1428, 1463**
North Texas Retailer see Retailer and Marketing News **1052**
North Texas Sanyo Users Group. Newsletter. (US) **1471, 1463**
North Wales Farming News. (UK) **111**
North Wind. (US) **1319**
North Wind. (UK ISSN 0265-7295) **2877**
North Woods Call. (US ISSN 0029-2958) **1494**
North York Business Age. (CN) **682**
North York Poetry see Genera **2993**
Northampton Business Directory. (UK ISSN 0957-106X) **1148**
Northamptoniana. (UK ISSN 0309-8486) **2160**
Northamptonshire and Bedfordshire Life see Bedfordshire Life **5147**
Northamptonshire and Bedfordshire Life see Northamptonshire Life **5249**
Northamptonshire Archaeology. (UK ISSN 0305-4659) **280**
Northamptonshire Federation of Archaeological Societies. Bulletin see Northamptonshire Archaeology **280**
Northamptonshire Image. (UK) **2195**
†Northamptonshire Life. (UK) **5249**
Northamptonshire Natural History Society and Field Club Journal. (UK ISSN 0144-0586) **4330**
Northamptonshire Past and Present. (UK ISSN 0140-9131) **2378**
Northbound. (US) **2105, 1964**
Northcoast View. (US ISSN 0893-7680) **2231, 338**
Northeast (La Crosse). (US) **2943**
Northeast (Portland). (US) **4245**
Northeast African Monograph Series. (US) **2017, 2334**
Northeast African Studies. (US ISSN 0740-9133) **2017, 2334**
Northeast Agriculture. (US) **111**
Northeast Bioengineering Conference. Proceedings. (US) **470, 1832**
Northeast Canine Companion. (US) **3712, 231**
North East Coast Institution of Engineers and Shipbuilders. Transactions. (UK ISSN 0029-280X) **1832, 4735**
Northeast Equine Journal. (US) **4536**
Northeast Folklore. (US ISSN 0078-1681) **2057**
Northeast Folklore Society Newsletter. (US ISSN 0546-5370) **2057**
North East Food Service Buyer's Guide. (US) **2478**
Northeast Forestry College. Journal see Dongbei Linye Daxue Xuebao **2098**
Northeast Forestry University. Journal. see Dongbei Linye Daxue Xuebao **2098**
Northeast Gulf Science. (US ISSN 0148-9836) **1609**
North-East India Council for Social Science Research. Journal. (II ISSN 0970-7913) **3911, 4444**
North East India Geographical Society. Journal see North Eastern Geographer **2258**
Northeast Indian Quarterly see Akwe Kon Journal **1990**
Northeast Institute of Agriculture. see Dongbei Nongxueyuan Xuebao **87**
Northeast Institute of Technology. Journal. see Dongbei Gongxueyuan Xuebao **4596**
Northeast Journal. (US) **2943**
Northeast Journal of Business and Economics see Journal of Business and Economic Studies **673**
North East Labour History Bulletin. (UK) **990**
Northeast Memo. (US) **4551, 1494**

Northeast Mississippi Historical and Genealogical Society Quarterly. (US) **2416, 2160**
North East Modern Language Association. Newsletter see Modern Language Studies **2939**
Northeast Modern Language Association Conference Italian Studies see N E M L A Italian Studies **2940**
Northeast Normal University. Journal (Natural Science Edition). see Dongbei Shida Xuebao (Ziran Kexue Ban) **4308**
Northeast Normal University. Journal (Philosophy, Social Science Edition). see Dongbei Shida Xuebao (Zhexue Shehui Kexue Ban) **4370**
Northeast Ohio Areawide Coordinating Agency News see N O A C A News **2492**
Northeast Ohio Avenues. (US) **2231**
Northeast Oil World. (US ISSN 0884-4771) **3694**
Northeast Outdoor Memo see Northeast Memo **4551**
Northeast Outdoors. (US ISSN 0199-8463) **4551**
Northeast Pacific Pink and Chum Salmon Workshop. Proceedings. (US ISSN 0094-128X) **2047**
Northeast Pennsylvania Business Journal. (US) **682**
Northeast Petroleum Industry. (US) **3694, 1148**
▼Northeast Power Report. (US) **1802**
▼Northeast Real Estate News. (US ISSN 1047-8833) **4154**
Northeast Regional Science Review. (US) **2493, 4069**
Northeast Riding. (US) **4520**
Northeast Square Dancer Magazine. (US) **1531**
Northeast Sun (Greenfield). (US) **1793**
Northeast Sun (Los Angeles). (US) **2017**
▼Northeastarts Magazine. (US) **2999**
North-Eastern Affairs. (II ISSN 0301-6404) **3911**
Northeastern Alumni Magazine see Northeastern University Magazine **1319**
Northeastern Campbook. (US ISSN 0732-7315) **4780**
North Eastern Doctors Calling. (II) **3136**
Northeastern Environmental Science see Northeastern Geology **1576**
North Eastern Farmer. (AT) **163, 186, 222**
North Eastern Geographer. (II) **2258**
Northeastern Geology. (US ISSN 0194-1453) **1576**
Northeastern Journal of Agricultural Economics and Resource Economics.(US) **155**
Northeastern Nevada Historical Society Quarterly. (US ISSN 0160-9602) **2417**
Northeastern News. (US ISSN 0029-3032) **1319**
Northeastern University Magazine. (US) **1319**
Northeastern Weed Science Society. Proceedings. (US ISSN 0078-1703) **511**
Northeastern Wisconsin Business Review. (US) **682**
Northeimer Heimatblaetter see Northeimer Jahrbuch **280**
Northeimer Jahrbuch. (GW ISSN 0936-8345) **280, 2057, 2378**
Northern Adventures Magazine. (US) **2231**
Northern Advertiser/Moanamesi Was Bokone. (BS) **36**
Northern Advocate. (NZ) **36, 2573, 4003**
Northern Air. (CN ISSN 0048-0754) **2777**
Northern Aquaculture. (CN) **2047**
†Northern Arizona Scene. (US) **5249**
Northern Automotive News. (US) **4698**
†Northern Bibliography. (UK ISSN 0144-123X) **5249**
Northern Business Services & Manufacturers' Guide. (CN) **682**
Northern Bytes. (US) **1463**

▼Northern California Business Directory and Buyers Guide. (US ISSN 1052-8822) **1148**
Northern California Golf Association. Blue Book *see* N C G A News **4480**
Northern California Golf Association News *see* N C G A News **4480**
Northern California Home & Garden. (US ISSN 0898-1191) **2554**, 2135
Northern California Jewish Bulletin. (US) **2017**
Northern California Labor. (US) **2587**
Northern California Retailer *see* Retailer News: Northern California Edition **1052**
Northern California Schedule. (US) **4481**
Northern Chess. *see* Beifang Qiyi **4466**
Northern Club Trade News *see* Club Committee & Northern Free Trade News **1297**
Northern Curling Review. (CN ISSN 0011-3115) **4552**
Northern Decisions. (CN ISSN 0715-7983) **1964**
Northern Development *see* Oil & Gas Report **683**
Northern E D C Newsletter *see* E D C Newsletter **2756**
Northern Eastern Education Library Board. Library Bulletin. (UK) **2777**
Northern Economic Review. (UK ISSN 0262-0383) **2493**
Northern Engineer. (US ISSN 0029-3083) **1832**
Northern Engineering Industries plc. News *see* N E I News **5242**
Northern Environment. *see* Beifang Huanjing **1944**
Northern Executive. (UK) **1022**, **1832**
Northern Forum. *see* Beifang Luncong **2503**
Northern Fruit Trees. *see* Beifang Guoshu **170**
Northern Gay *see* Gay Star **2453**
▼Northern Greece - Thessaloniki International Trade Fair (Year). (GR) **918**, **682**
Northern Hardware *see* Hardware Trade **642**
Northern History. (UK ISSN 0078-172X) **2378**
Northern House Pamphlet Poets. (UK ISSN 0078-1738) **2999**
Northern Illinois University. Center for Southeast Asian Studies. Occasional Papers Series. (US) **2340**, **2512**
Northern Illinois University. Center for Southeast Asian Studies. Special Report Series. (US ISSN 0073-4934) **2340**, **2512**
Northern Illinois University Law Review. (US ISSN 0734-1490) **2661**
Northern Iowan. (US) **1319**
Northern Ireland. Commissioner for Complaints. Annual Report. (UK) **4069**
Northern Ireland. Department of Agriculture. Annual Report on Research and Development. (UK) **111**
Northern Ireland. Department of Agriculture. Annual Report on Research, Development and Technical Work *see* Northern Ireland. Department of Agriculture. Annual Report on Research and Development **111**
†Northern Ireland. Department of Agriculture. Record of Agricultural Research. (UK ISSN 0078-1754) **5249**
Northern Ireland. Department of Finance and Personnel. Northern Ireland Estimates (Year). (UK) **1102**
Northern Ireland. Ministry of Education. Education Statistics. (UK ISSN 0048-0770) **1678**
Northern Ireland Bibliography. (UK ISSN 0959-8812) **407**
Northern Ireland Chamber of Commerce and Industry Yearbook. (UK) **820**
Northern Ireland Council for Educational Research Bulletin *see* N I C E R Bulletin **1649**
Northern Ireland Law Reports. (IE) **2661**

Northern Ireland Legal Quarterly. (UK ISSN 0029-3105) **2661**
Northern Ireland Local Studies *see* Northern Ireland Bibliography **407**
Northern Ireland News Service. (US ISSN 1040-8614) **3911**, **2727**, **3467**
Northern Journal. (CN) **2178**
Northern Journal of Applied Forestry. (US ISSN 0742-6348) **2105**
Northern Kentucky Law Review. (US ISSN 0198-8549) **2661**
Northern Librarian. (UK) **2777**
Northern Light. (US) **1300**
Northern Lights. (CN) **2017**
Northern Lights. *see* Beiji Guang **2898**
Northern Lights (Minneapolis). (US ISSN 0029-3148) **4698**
Northern Lights Magazine. (CN) **2178**
Northern Lights Studies in Creativity. (US ISSN 0739-2974) **338**, **2943**
Northern Line. (US) **1964**
Northern Literature. *see* Beifang Wenxue **2898**
Northern Logger and Timber Processer.(US ISSN 0029-3156) **2116**
The Northern Miner. (CN ISSN 0029-3164) **3492**
Northern Miner Magazine. (CN) **3492**
Northern Mosaic. (CN) **2017**
Northern Music. *see* Beifang Yinyue **3541**
†Northern Neighbors. (CN ISSN 0029-3199) **5249**
Northern Nevada Native Plant Society. Newsletter. (US) **2135**
Northern New England Real Estate Journal. (US) **4154**, **958**
Northern New England Review. (US ISSN 0190-3012) **2943**
Northern News *see* North Wind **1319**
Northern Nigeria. Ministry of Economic Planning. Statistical Year Book *see* Kano State Statistical Year Book **4576**
Northern Nigeria Development Corporation. Report *see* New Nigeria Development Company Limited. Annual Report and Accounts **1081**
Northern Nigeria Gazette *see* Kano State of Nigeria Gazette **4065**
Northern Now. (US) **1319**
Northern Nut Growers Association. Annual Report. (US) **2135**
Northern Offshore *see* Offshore Engineer **3694**
Northern Ohio Live. (US ISSN 0271-5147) **2231**
Northern Ontario Business. (CN) **682**
Northern Ontario Directory. (CN ISSN 0714-0541) **3985**
Northern Perspectives. (CN ISSN 0380-5522) **1964**, **4605**
Northern Railway Newsletter. (Il ISSN 0029-3210) **4712**
†Northern Raven. (US ISSN 0277-0997) **5249**
Northern Regional Research Center Publications and Patents *see* National Center for Agricultural Utilization Research Publications and Patents **140**
Northern Review. (US ISSN 0894-3362) **2512**
Northern Rhodesia Journal *see* Zambia Museums Journal **253**
Northern Rockies Action Group, Inc. Papers *see* N R A G Papers **4413**
Northern Scotland. (UK ISSN 0306-5278) **2378**
Northern States Power Company News *see* N S P News **1792**
Northern States Review. (NR) **2212**
Northern Sun News. (US ISSN 0278-4408) **1793**, **3911**
†Northern Teacher. (US ISSN 0048-0797) **5249**
Northern Territory. Conservation Commission. Annual Report. (AT ISSN 0159-8821) **1494**
Northern Territory. Department of Industries and Development. Agnotes *see* Northern Territory. Department of Primary Industry and Fisheries. Agnotes **155**

Northern Territory. Department of Primary Industry and Fisheries. Agnotes. (AT) **155**, **2047**
Northern Territory. Territory Parks and Wildlife Commission. Annual Report *see* Northern Territory. Conservation Commission. Annual Report **1494**
Northern Territory at a Glance. (AT ISSN 0815-3809) **4581**
Northern Titles: K W I C Index. (Key Word in Context) (CN ISSN 0704-6839) **3938**, 18, **2329**
▼Northern Turf Management. (US) **2135**
Northian. (CN ISSN 0029-3253) **1651**, **2017**
Northland Quarterly. (US ISSN 0899-708X) **2877**, **2999**
Northliner Magazine. (US ISSN 0029-327X) **4803**
Northpoint. (CN) **1832**
Northrop University Law Journal of Aerospace, Business and Taxation. (US ISSN 0887-4301) **60**, **1793**, **1964**
Northumberland & Durham Family History Society. Journal. (UK ISSN 0307-8140) **2160**
Northumberland Farmer. (UK) **111**
Northumbrian Pipers' Society Magazine.(UK ISSN 0261-5096) **3570**
Northumbriana. (UK ISSN 0308-4809) **2943**, **280**
Northward Journal. (CN ISSN 0706-0955) **2943**, **2999**
Northwater. (US) **4827**, **1872**
Northwest Airlines Compass Readings *see* Compass Readings **4802**
North West and Hunter Valley Magazine *see* North West Magazine **36**
Northwest Anthropological Research Notes. (US ISSN 0029-3296) **246**
Northwest Architect *see* Architecture Minnesota **293**
Northwest Association of Schools and Colleges. Committee on Research and Service. Newsletter *see* Northwest Association of Schools and Colleges. Newsletter **1651**
Northwest Association of Schools and Colleges. Convention Proceedings. (US ISSN 0892-2489) **1713**, **1651**
Northwest Association of Schools and Colleges. Newsletter. (US) **1651**
Northwest Atlantic Fisheries Organization Annual Report *see* N A F O Annual Report **2046**
Northwest Atlantic Fisheries Organization List of Fishing Vessels *see* N A F O List of Fishing Vessels **2046**
Northwest Atlantic Fisheries Organization Scientific Council Reports *see* N A F O Scientific Council Reports **2046**
Northwest Atlantic Fisheries Organization Scientific Council Studies *see* N A F O Scientific Council Studies **2046**
Northwest Atlantic Fisheries Organization Statistical Bulletin *see* N A F O Statistical Bulletin **2051**
North West Auto Trader. (UK ISSN 0958-4277) **4698**
North West Automart *see* North West Auto Trader **4698**
Northwest Beverage Journal *see* Spirits, Wine & Beer Marketing in Minnesota, North & South Dakota **385**
North West Business. (UK ISSN 0306-5650) **838**
North West Business Monthly *see* North West Business **838**
Northwest Chess. (US ISSN 0146-6941) **4481**
Northwest Community Hospital Medical Bulletin. (US ISSN 0029-3334) **3136**
Northwest Construction News Daily. (US) **626**
Northwest Construction News Weekly *see* Northwest Construction Weekly **626**
Northwest Construction Weekly. (US) **626**
Northwest Dentistry. (US) **3239**

Northwest Discovery. (US ISSN 0272-1570) **2417**
Northwest Electric Utility Directory. (US) **1802**
Northwest Energy News. (US) **1793**, **1964**
North West England Directory of Industry and Commerce. (UK) **820**
North West England Industrial Classified Directory *see* North West England Directory of Industry and Commerce **820**
Northwest Environmental Journal. (US ISSN 0749-7962) **1964**
Northwest Ethnic News. (US) **2017**
Northwest Explorer Magazine. (CN) **4803**
Northwest Farm Equipment Journal. (US ISSN 0029-3350) **163**
Northwest Farmer - Rancher. (CN) **111**
North-West Federation of Folk Clubs Newsletter *see* Folk North-West **3551**
Northwest Folkdancer. (US) **1531**
Northwest Fuchsia Society. Bulletin *see* Fuchsia Flash **2126**
Northwest Gay Guide. (US) **2456**, **1148**
Northwest Geology. (US) **1576**
Northwest Georgia Historical & Genealogical Quarterly. (US ISSN 0887-588X) **2160**, **2417**
Northwest Historical Series. (US ISSN 0078-1789) **2417**
Northwest Indiana Catholic. (US) **4271**, **1261**, **1377**
North West Kent Family History. (UK ISSN 0263-6506) **2160**
Northwest Kitchen & Bath Quarterly. (US) **627**
Northwest Labor Press. (US ISSN 0894-444X) **2587**, **990**
Northwest Living! (US ISSN 0888-5346) **2231**, **2135**, **2258**, **4552**
Northwest Lookout *see* Christmas Tree Lookout **2097**
North West Magazine. (AT) **36**, **111**, **627**, **4481**
†Northwest Magazine (Portland). (US) **5249**
Northwest Mileposts. (US ISSN 1052-6722) **4780**
Northwest Minorities Studies. *see* Xibei Minzu Yanjiu **3645**
Northwest Motor. (US ISSN 0029-3393) **4698**
Northwest Ohio Quarterly. (US ISSN 0029-3407) **2417**
Northwest Orient. (US) **4803**
Northwest Palate. (US ISSN 0892-8363) **4780**, **384**
Northwest Passages. (US) **4676**
Northwest Phoenix. (US) **1319**
Northwest Prospector Miners and Developers Bulletin *see* Prospector Exploration & Investment Bulletin **3494**
Northwest Public Power Bulletin. (US) **4069**, **1793**
Northwest Relocation News. (US) **4154**
Northwest Review. (US ISSN 0029-3423) **2943**, **338**
Northwest Runner. (US) **4481**
Northwest Sailboard. (US) **4527**
Northwest Sanyo Enthusiasts Newsletter. (US) **1471**, **1463**
Northwest Science. (US ISSN 0029-344X) **4330**
Northwest Ski News *see* Northwest Skiing **4552**
Northwest Skier. (US) **4552**
Northwest Skier and Northwest Sports *see* Northwest Skier **4552**
Northwest Skiing. (US) **4552**
North West Societies. Combined Register of Members' Interests. (UK) **2160**
Northwest Stock Guide *see* Western Investor **5304**
Northwest Stylist & Salon. (US) **374**
North West Suburban Association of Commerce and Industry News *see* N S A C I News **680**
Northwest Technocrat. (US ISSN 0029-3474) **4381**
North West Telegraph. (AT) **2172**

6506 NORTHWEST TERRITORIES

Northwest Territories Reports. (CN ISSN 0824-3433) **2661**
▼Northwest Travel. (US) **4780**
Northwest University. Journal. Social Sciences Edition. see Xibei Daxue Xuebao. Shehui Kexue Ban **4392**
Northwest Wine Almanac see Wine & Food Almanac of the Pacific Northwest **387**
Northwestern Alumni News. (US) **1319**
Northwestern Bank Directory: Iowa. (US) **1148, 793**
Northwestern Bank Directory: Nebraska.(US) **1148, 793**
Northwestern Bank Directory: Upper Midwest. (US) **1148, 793**
Northwestern Banker see Northwestern Financial Review **793**
Northwestern Campbook. (US) **4780, 4552**
Northwestern Endicott Lindquist Report see Northwestern Lindquist Endicott Report **3630**
North-Western European Language Evolution see N O W E L E **2830**
North Western European Language Evolution. (DK ISSN 0900-8675) **2831, 2378**
Northwestern Farmer see The Farmer - The Dakota Farmer **91**
Northwestern Financial Review. (US) **793**
Northwestern Illinois Farmer. (US) **111**
Northwestern-Iowa Dealer Reference Manual see Northwestern Lumbermens Association Dealer Reference Manual **2116**
Northwestern Jeweler see Jewelers, Inc **2564**
Northwestern Journal of International Law & Business. (US ISSN 0196-3228) **2727, 918**
Northwestern Lindquist Endicott Report.(US) **3630, 1319**
Northwestern Lumbermens Association Dealer Reference Manual. (US) **2116, 1148**
Northwestern Lutheran. (US ISSN 0029-3512) **4245**
Northwestern Mindanao Research Journal. (PH) **246**
Northwestern Naturalist. (US ISSN 1051-1733) **589**
Northwestern Perspective. (US) **1319**
Northwestern University. Center for American Archeology. Research Series see K A C Research Series **276**
Northwestern University. Dental School Library Acquisitions Lists. (US) **3178**
Northwestern University. Dental School Library. Current Subscriptions List. (US) **3178**
Northwestern University. Materials Research Center. Annual Technical Report. (US) **1921**
Northwestern University. Robert H. Lurie Cancer Center. Journal. (US) **3200**
Northwestern University. Transportation Center. Publications List. (US) **4654**
Northwestern University Cancer Center. Journal see Northwestern University. Robert H. Lurie Cancer Center. Journal **3200**
Northwestern University Law Review. (US ISSN 0029-3571) **2661**
Northwestern University Medical Center Magazine. (US) **3136**
Northwestern University Medical School Magazine see Northwestern University Medical Center Magazine **3136**
Northwestern University Quarter Notes see N U Quarter Notes **3569**
Northwesterner. (US ISSN 0894-0800) **4712, 2318**
NorthwestLetter. (US ISSN 0890-9776) **3911**
Norton Bankruptcy Law Adviser. (US) **2661**
Norton County Tracer. (US) **2160**
Norton Notes. (US ISSN 1049-1821) **2160**
Norveg. (NO ISSN 0029-3601) **2057**
Norvega Esperantisto. (NO ISSN 0029-361X) **2831**

Norway. Arbeidsdirektoratet. Aarsmelding. (NO ISSN 0801-1621) **990**
Norway. Central Bureau of Statistics. External Trade. see Norway. Statistisk Sentralbyraa. Utenrikshandel **732**
Norway. Central Bureau of Statistics. Municipal and County Elections. see Norway. Statistisk Sentralbyraa. Kommune og Fylkestings Valget **4081**
Norway. Central Bureau of Statistics. Parliamentary Elections. see Norway. Statistisk Sentralbyraa. Stortingsvalg **4081**
Norway. Central Bureau of Statistics. Population Projections: Regional Figures. see Norway. Statistisk Sentralbyraa. Framskriving Av Folkemengden: Regionale Tall **5249**
Norway. Central Bureau of Statistics. Population Statistics Vol.2. see Norway. Statistisk Sentralbyraa. Befolknings Statistisk Hefte 2 **3994**
Norway. Central Bureau of Statistics. Transport and Communication Statistics. see Norway. Statistisk Sentralbyraa. Samferdselsstatistikk **4666**
Norway. Direktoratet for Arbeidstilsynet. Forskrifter/Regulations. (NO) **3619, 1713**
Norway. Direktoratet for Brann og Eksplosjonsvern. Aarsberetning. (NO) **1857, 2034**
Norway. Fiskeridirektoratet. Fiskeflaaten.(NO) **2047**
Norway. Fiskeridirektoratet. Skrifter. Serie Ernaering. (NO ISSN 0332-5083) **3610**
Norway. Fiskeridirektoratet. Skrifter. Serie Havundersoekelser. (NO ISSN 0015-3117) **2047**
Norway. Forsvaret Forskningsinstitutt. N D R E Report see N D R E Publications **4325**
Norway. Ministry of Industry. Reports to the Storting. (NO) **838**
Norway. Riksbibliotektjenesten. Aarsmelding. (NO ISSN 0800-4153) **2777**
Norway. Riksbibliotektjenesten. Skrifter.(NO ISSN 0800-4129) **2777**
Norway. Royal Norwegian Ministry of Finance. Final Budget Proposal. (Year). (NO) **1102**
Norway. Royal Norwegian Ministry of Finance. The National Budget. (Year) .(NO) **1102**
Norway. Royal Norwegian Ministry of Finance. The Revised National Budget. (Year). (NO) **1102**
Norway. Statens Arbeidstilsyn Direktoratet. Verneregler see Norway. Direktoratet for Arbeidstilsynet. Forskrifter **3619**
Norway. Statens Institutt for Alkoholforskning. Skrifter. (NO ISSN 0078-673X) **1538**
Norway. Statens Sprengstoffinspeksjon. Aarsberetning see Norway. Direktoratet for Brann og Eksplosjonsvern. Aarsberetning **1857**
Norway. Statistisk Sentralbyraa. Alkohol og Andre Rusmidler/Alcohol and Drugs. (NO ISSN 0332-7965) **5249**
Norway. Statistisk Sentralbyraa. Arbeidsmarkedstatistikk - Labour Market Statistics. (NO ISSN 0078-1878) **731, 4581**
Norway. Statistisk Sentralbyraa. Befolknings Statistisk Hefte 2/ Norway. Central Bureau of Statistics. Population Statistics Vol.2. (NO ISSN 0801-6690) **3994, 4581**
Norway. Statistisk Sentralbyraa. Elektrisitesstatistikk/Electricity Statistics. (NO) **1800, 1802**
†Norway. Statistisk Sentralbyraa. Familie Statistikk/Family Statistics. (NO ISSN 0332-7957) **5249**
Norway. Statistisk Sentralbyraa. Fiskeristatistikk. (NO ISSN 0333-3728) **2051, 4581**

Norway. Statistisk Sentralbyraa. Folkmengde Etter Alder og Ekteskapelig Status - Norway. Central Bureau of Statistics. Population by Age and Marital Status see Norway. Statistisk Sentralbyraa. Befolknings Statistisk Hefte 2 **3994**
†Norway. Statistisk Sentralbyraa. Framskriving Av Folkemengden: Regionale Tall/Norway. Central Bureau of Statistics. Population Projections: Regional Figures. (NO ISSN 0332-8015) **5249**
Norway. Statistisk Sentralbyraa. Helsepersonellstatistikk. (NO ISSN 0800-403X) **3178, 4581**
Norway. Statistisk Sentralbyraa. Helsestatistikk/Health Statistics. (NO ISSN 0332-7906) **4118, 4581**
Norway. Statistisk Sentralbyraa. Industristatistikk. Vol.1/Industrial Statistics. Vol.1. (NO ISSN 0800-580X) **731, 4581**
Norway. Statistisk Sentralbyraa. Industristatistikk. Vol.2/Industrial Statistics. Vol.2. (NO ISSN 0800-5818) **731, 4581**
Norway. Statistisk Sentralbyraa. Jordbruksstatistikk/Agricultural Statistics. (NO ISSN 0078-1894) **141, 4581**
Norway. Statistisk Sentralbyraa. Kommune og Fylkestings Valget/ Norway. Central Bureau of Statistics. Municipal and County Elections. (NO ISSN 0332-8023) **4081, 4581**
Norway. Statistisk Sentralbyraa. Kommunevalget see Norway. Statistisk Sentralbyraa. Kommune og Fylkestings Valget **4081**
Norway. Statistisk Sentralbyraa. Kredittmarked Statistikk/Credit Market Statistics. (NO ISSN 0078-1908) **731, 4581**
Norway. Statistisk Sentralbyraa. Kriminalstatistikk/Criminal Statistics. (NO ISSN 0333-3914) **1525, 4581**
Norway. Statistisk Sentralbyraa. Legestatistikk see Norway. Statistisk Sentralbyraa. Helsepersonellstatistikk **3178**
Norway. Statistisk Sentralbyraa. Loennsstatistikk/Wage Statistics. (NO ISSN 0078-1916) **731, 4582**
Norway. Statistisk Sentralbyraa. Nasjonalregnskap see Norway. Statistisk Sentralbyraa. Nasjonalregnskapsstatistikk **731**
Norway. Statistisk Sentralbyraa. Nasjonalregnskapsstatistikk/National Accounts Statistics. (NO ISSN 0550-0494) **731, 4582**
†Norway. Statistisk Sentralbyraa. Oekonomisk Utsyn/Economic Survey.(NO ISSN 0078-1924) **5249**
Norway. Statistisk Sentralbyraa. Reiselivstatiskk/Statistics on Travel. (NO ISSN 0333-208X) **4800, 4582**
Norway. Statistisk Sentralbyraa. Samferdselsstatistikk/Norway. Central Bureau of Statistics. Transport and Communication Statistics. (NO ISSN 0468-8147) **4666, 1349, 4582**
†Norway. Statistisk Sentralbyraa. Sivilrettsstatistikk/Civil Judicial Statistics. (NO ISSN 0550-0532) **5249**
Norway. Statistisk Sentralbyraa. Skogstatstikk. (NO ISSN 0468-8155) **2112, 4582**
Norway. Statistisk Sentralbyraa. Social and Economic Studies. (NO ISSN 0085-4344) **4458, 732**
Norway. Statistisk Sentralbyraa. Statistisk Aarbok/Statistical Yearbook. (NO ISSN 0377-8908) **4582**
Norway. Statistisk Sentralbyraa. Statistisk Maanedshefte/Monthly Bulletin of Statistics. (NO ISSN 0029-3636) **4582**
Norway. Statistisk Sentralbyraa. Statistik Ukehefte/Weekly Bulletin of Statistics. (NO ISSN 0550-0567) **4582**

Norway. Statistisk Sentralbyraa. Stortingsvalg/Norway. Central Bureau of Statistics. Parliamentary Elections.(NO ISSN 0802-9067) **4081, 4582**
Norway. Statistisk Sentralbyraa. Utdanningsstatistikk. (NO ISSN 0800-2169) **1678, 4582**
Norway. Statistisk Sentralbyraa. Utenrikshandel/Norway. Central Bureau of Statistics. External Trade. (NO ISSN 0078-1940) **732, 4582**
Norway. Statistisk Sentralbyraa. Varehandelsstatistikk/Wholesale and Retail Trade Statistics. (NO ISSN 0078-1959) **732, 4582**
Norway. Statistisk Sentralbyraa. Vejviser i Norsk Statistikk/Guide to Norwegian Statistics. (NO) **4582**
Norway. Televerket. Statistikk. (NO ISSN 0800-2177) **1349**
Norway. Televerket. Statistikk Arbok see Norway. Televerket. Statistikk **1349**
Norway at Your Service. (US) **820**
Norway Times/Nordisk Tidende. (US) **2017**
Norwegian Agricultural Research. see Norsk Landbruksforsking **111**
†Norwegian American Commerce. (US ISSN 0029-3644) **5249**
Norwegian-American Historical Association. Newsletter. (US ISSN 0078-1967) **2417**
Norwegian-American Historical Association. Topical Studies. (US ISSN 0085-4352) **2417**
Norwegian-American Historical Association. Travel and Description Series. (US ISSN 0078-1975) **2417**
Norwegian-American Studies. (US ISSN 0078-1983) **2417**
Norwegian Archaeological Review. (NO ISSN 0029-3652) **280**
Norwegian Chamber of Commerce. Year Book and Directory of Members.(UK ISSN 0305-0998) **820**
Norwegian College of Veterinary Medicine. Annual Report. see Norges Veterinaerhoegskole. Aarsmelding **5248**
Norwegian College of Veterinary Medicine. Publications. see Norges Veterinaerhoegskole. Publikasjoner **4813**
Norwegian Commercial Banks Financial Review see Financial Review **781**
Norwegian Defence Research Establishment Publications see N D R E Publications **4325**
Norwegian Directory of Commerce. see Norges Handels-Kalender **1148**
Norwegian Elkhound News. (US) **3712**
Norwegian Foreign Policy Studies. see Utenrikspolitiske Skrifter **3976**
Norwegian Geotechnical Institute. Publications. see Norges Geotekniske Institutt. Publikasjon **1592**
Norwegian Hydrotechnical Laboratory. Bulletin. (NO) **1924**
Norwegian Journal of Agricultural Sciences. (NO ISSN 0801-5341) **111**
Norwegian Journal of Botany see Nordic Journal of Botany **511**
Norwegian Journal of Education. see Norsk Pedagogisk Tidsskrift **1651**
Norwegian Journal of Geography. see Norsk Geografisk Tidsskrift **2258**
Norwegian Journal of Geology. see Norsk Geologisk Tidsskrift **1575**
Norwegian Journal of Linguistics see Nordic Journal of Linguistics **2831**
Norwegian Journal of Mission and Missionary Questions. see Norsk Tidsskrift for Misjon **4192**
Norwegian Journal of Occupational Medicine. see Norsk Tidsskrift for Arbejdsmedisin **3136**
Norwegian Journal of Philosophy. see Norsk Filosofisk Tidsskrift **3774**
Norwegian Marine Engineers' Magazine. see Norsk Maskin-Tidende **4734**
Norwegian Medical Association. Journal. see Norske Laegeforening. Tidsskrift **3136**

Norwegian Music Information Center. Bulletin. (NO ISSN 0801-1087) **3570**
Norwegian Offshore Index. (NO ISSN 0377-1806) **3706,** 18
Norwegian Petroleum Society. Yearbook. *see* Norsk Petroleumsforening. Aarbok **3693**
Norwegian Political Science Journal. *see* Norsk Statsvitenskapelig Tidsskrift **3911**
Norwegian Pulp and Paper Association. Annual Review/Treforedlingindustriens Landsforening. Aarsoversikt. (NO) **3663**
Norwegian Savings Bank News. *see* Sparebankbladet **800**
Norwegian Theological Journal. *see* Norsk Teologisk Tidsskrift **4192**
Norwegian Tracks. (US) **2160**
Norwegian Trade Bulletin. (US) **820**
Norwegian Yearbook of Maritime History. *see* Sjoefartshistorisk Aarbok **2386**
Norwegica Pharmaceutica Acta *see* Acta Pharmaceutica Nordica **3715**
Norwegische Handels-Adressbuch. *see* Norges Handels-Kalender **1148**
Nor'westing. (US ISSN 0739-747X) **4527**
Norwich and Norfolk Chamber of Commerce and Industry. Directory. (UK ISSN 0953-5470) **820**
Norwich & Norfolk News. (US) **3712**
Norwich Guidon. (US) **1319**
Norwood Commodity Fund Index. *see* Norwood Index Report **958**
Norwood Index Report. (US) **958**
Norwottuck. (US) **2944**
Nos Chasses. (FR ISSN 0048-0835) **4552**
Nos Lettres. (BE) **2944**
Nos Lettres. Informations *see* Nos Lettres **2944**
Nos Maisons Familiales de Vacances. (FR ISSN 0048-0843) **4780**
Nos Monuments d'Art et d'Histoire. *see* Unsere Kunstdenkmaeler **308**
Nos Oiseaux. (SZ ISSN 0029-3725) **565**
Nos Spectacles *see* Theatre et Animation **4641**
Noson to Toshi o Musubu. *see* Journal of Communication between Rural Communities and Towns **153**
Nosotros. (US) **2017**
Nost-Algia. (US) **4482**
Nostalgia. (UK) **4461,** 3570
Nostalgia (Milwaukee). (US ISSN 8750-8923) **2318**
Nostalgia (Orangeburg). (US ISSN 0892-2616) **2944**
Nostalgia World. (US ISSN 0194-5041) **2440,** 3515
Nostalgic Cars *see* Car Collector and Car Classics **4686**
Nostoc. (US) **2999**
La Nostra Domenica. (IT) **2205**
Nostra Voce. (IT ISSN 0029-3768) **2206**
Nostri Bambini. (IT) **1652**
Nostri Cani. (IT ISSN 0029-3784) **3712**
Nostri Ragazzi. (IT ISSN 0029-3792) **1652**
Nostro Tempo. (IT ISSN 0029-3814) **338,** 2944
Not from that World. *see* Nie z tej Ziemi **3013**
Not Guilty. (US ISSN 1049-2356) **2714**
†Not Just the Classifieds. (US) **5249**
Not Man Apart *see* Friends of the Earth. Magazine **1955**
Notable Books. (US) **407**
Notable Children's Trade Books in the Field of Social Studies. (US) **4395,** 407, 1261, 4133
Notarius. (HU ISSN 0238-4043) **2378,** 2057
Notaro. (IT ISSN 0029-3857) **2661**
Notary Public Practices & Glossary. (US) **2662**
Notary Viewpoint. (US) **2662**
Notary's Compendium. (CN) **2662**
Der Notarzt. (GW ISSN 0177-2309) **3136**
Notas. (BO) **682,** 3911

Notas Americanas *see* Notas Mesoamericanas **246**
Notas de Algebra y Analisis. (AG ISSN 0078-2009) **3049**
Notas de Desarrollo. (DR) **1082**
▼Notas de Enfermeria. (SP ISSN 1130-734X) **3283**
Notas de Geometria y Topologia. (AG ISSN 0325-8963) **3049**
Notas de Logica Matematica. (AG ISSN 0078-2017) **3049**
Notas de Matematica Discreta. (AG ISSN 0326-1336) **3049**
Notas e Comunicacoes de Matematica. (BL ISSN 0085-5413) **3049**
Notas e Estudos, Serie Recursos e Ambiente Aquaticos *see* Portugal. Instituto Nacional de Investigacao das Pescas. Boletim **590**
Notas Matematicas. (CL) **3049**
Notas Mesoamericanas. (MX) **246,** 280
Notas Sobre la Economia y el Desarrollo. (UN ISSN 0257-2168) **876**
Notas Sobre la Economia y el Desarrollo de America Latina *see* Notas Sobre la Economia y el Desarrollo **876**
Notas y Noticias Linguisticas. (BO) **2831**
Notatki Ornitologiczne/Ornithological Papers. (PL ISSN 0550-0842) **566**
Notatki Plockie. (PL ISSN 0029-389X) **2378**
Notatky z Mystetstba. *see* Ukrainian Art Digest **347**
Note de Conjoncture de l'I N S E E. (Institut National de la Statistique et des Etudes Economiques) (FR ISSN 0766-6268) **682**
Note de Conjoncture Internationale. (FR ISSN 0990-9435) **683**
Note di Pastorale Giovanile. (IT ISSN 0029-3903) **4271**
Note di Tecnica Cinematografica. (IT) **3515**
Note Economiche. (IT ISSN 0391-8289) **683,** 897
Note sulla Congiuntura. (IT) **820**
Note Us. (US) **18,** 2855, 4458
Notebook (Barstow)/Cuaderno. (US ISSN 0883-6337) **2944,** 2318, 3774
Notebooks for Study and Research. (NE ISSN 0298-7902) **3911,** 990, 4381
Noter Up. (US) **2662**
Notes (Canton) *see* Music Library Association. Notes **2774**
Notes (New York). (US ISSN 0731-2385) **4093,** 1102
Notes a Tempo. (US ISSN 0029-3946) **3570,** 1756
Notes Africaines. (SG ISSN 0029-3954) **3911,** 4444
Notes and Abstracts in American and International Education. (US ISSN 0029-3962) **1678,** 18, 4458
Notes & Comment. (US) **1845,** 18
Notes & Furphies. (AT ISSN 0156-806X) **2944,** 2345
Notes and Queries. (UK ISSN 0029-3970) **2944,** 2777, 4133
Notes and Reports in Computer Science *see* Perspectives in Computing (San Diego) **1399**
Notes and Tracings. (US) **2777**
Notes Bibliographiques Caraibes. (GP ISSN 0180-4103) **407**
Notes d'Informations Communautaires *see* Actualites Communautaires **2594**
Notes de Mathematiques Appliquees. *see* Applied Mathematics Notes **5137**
Notes et Documents Voltaiques. (UV ISSN 0550-0923) **4381**
Notes et Etudes Documentaires. (FR ISSN 0029-4004) **876**
Notes for Medical Catalogers *see* National Library of Medicine. Current Catalog **3178**
Notes from Eastman (1979) *see* Eastman Notes **3550**
†Notes from Europe/Cahiers Europeens/Europaeische Hefte. (GW) **5249**
Notes from S I U S A. (US) **246,** 933

Notes from the Royal Botanic Garden, Edinburgh. (UK ISSN 0080-4274) **511**
Notes from Underground. (US ISSN 0029-4039) **4654**
†Notes on Agriculture. (CN ISSN 0380-5735) **5249**
Notes on Computing. (US ISSN 0887-9206) **2857**
Notes on Contemporary Literature. (US ISSN 0029-4047) **2944**
Notes on Current Politics *see* Politics Today **3918**
Notes on Linguistics. (US ISSN 0736-0673) **2831**
Notes on Literacy. (US ISSN 0737-6707) **2832**
Notes on Mississippi Writers. (US ISSN 0029-4071) **2944**
Notes on Modern American Literature *see* N M A L: Notes on Modern American Literature **2940**
Notes on Pure Mathematics. (AT) **3049**
Notes on Scripture in Use *see* Notes on Scripture in Use and Language Programs **2832**
Notes on Scripture in Use and Language Programs. (US) **2832,** 4192
Notes on Teaching English. (US ISSN 0163-7088) **2832,** 1756
Notes on the Science of Building. (AT ISSN 0300-371X) **627**
Notes on Tin. (UK ISSN 0029-4098) **3416**
Notes on Translation. (US ISSN 0734-0788) **2832**
Notes Plus. (US ISSN 0738-8624) **1756,** 2832
Notfallmedizin. (GW ISSN 0341-2903) **3310**
Notfallvorsorge und Zivile Verteidigung. (GW ISSN 0938-7390) **1273**
†Notgroschen. (GW) **5249**
Nothampton Diocesan Directory. (UK) **4271**
†Noti C R E F A L Internacional. (MX) **5249**
Noti Cuba. (US) **3911**
Noti S A I. (CK) **1832**
Notices to Airmen. (US) **60**
Notices to Mariners. *see* Oglas za Pomorce **4735**
Noticia B A D *see* Associacao Portuguesa de Bibliotecarios Arquivistas e Documentalistas. Noticia **2745**
Noticia Comercial del Oriente. (CK) **820**
Noticia Geomorfologica *see* Geociencias **1544**
Noticiarie a Imprensa Falada e Escrita. (BL ISSN 0029-4136) **111,** 3807
†Noticiario. (US) **5249**
Noticiario Arqueologico Hispanico. (SP ISSN 0211-1748) **280**
Noticiario Arqueologico Hispanico: Arqueologia *see* Noticiario Arqueologico Hispanico **280**
Noticiario C O P P E. (Coordenacao dos Programas de Pos-Graduacao de Engenharia) (BL) **1713,** 1832
†Noticiario de Canada. (CN ISSN 0384-2282) **5249**
Noticiario de Comercio Exterior. (SP) **918**
▼Noticiario de Productos Eletro-Electronicos. (US) **1776**
Noticiario de Produtos da Construcao. (US) **627**
Noticiario de Testes e Laboratorios. (US) **2524,** 3022
†Noticiario - Odontologia Sanitaria nas Americas. (BL ISSN 0029-4144) **5249**
Noticias (New York). (US ISSN 0747-0878) **918**
Noticias. Weekly Digest of Hemisphere Reports *see* Noticias (New York) **918**
Noticias Aliadas *see* Latinamerica Press **4187**
Noticias Aliadas. (PE) **4192**
Noticias COMALFI. (Sociedad Colombiana de Control de Malezas y Fisiologia Vegetal) (CK) **186**
Noticias da Africa do Sul *see* S.A. Panorama **2334**

NOTIZIARIO SULLE 6507

Noticias da O T A N *see* N A T O Review **3908**
Noticias de Cosmetica y de Perfumeria.(SP) **376**
Noticias de Cosmetica y de Perfumeria Documenta *see* N C P Documenta **376**
Noticias de Galapagos. (US ISSN 0550-1067) **4330,** 450, 1494
Noticias de Ingenieria. (AG) **1832**
Noticias de la Semana. (US) **990**
Noticias de Seguridad. (US) **3619**
Noticias del I C O M *see* I C O M News **3525**
Noticias del Puerto de Monterey. (US ISSN 0886-7151) **2417,** 407
Noticias del Seguro. (CK) **2539**
†Noticias do Canada. (CN ISSN 0228-5843) **5249**
Noticias Evangelicas. (NQ) **4192**
Noticias Medicas. (SP ISSN 0029-4225) **3136**

Noticierio Mercantil *see* Noticia Comercial del Oriente **820**
Noticiero Aeronautico y Turismo Caribense. *see* Caribbean Aviation and Tourism News **49**
Noticiero Cientifico. Serie: Biologia. (CU) **450**
Noticiero Cientifico. Serie: Tecnologia. (CU) **4605**
Noticiero de la Fe. (AG ISSN 0029-425X) **4245**
Noticiero del Cafe. (CR ISSN 0550-1105) **2078**
Noticiero del Plastico - Elastomeros. (AG ISSN 0325-0407) **3864,** 4292
Noticiero del Sistema - Internacional de Informacion Cientifico-Tecnica. (CU) **4330**
Noticiero I.D.U.N. (Instituto de Desarrollo Urbano) (CK) **2493**
Noticiero Quimico. (AG ISSN 0048-0908) **1185**
Noticiero Tuberosas. (VE ISSN 0085-4387) **511**
Notisai *see* Noti S A I. **1832**
Notitiae. (VC ISSN 0029-4306) **4271**
Notivest *see* La Bobina - Notivest **1283**
Notizario Bibliografico di Audiologia. (IT ISSN 0392-3711) **3315,** 407
Notizen zur Flora der Steiermark. (AU) **511**
Notiziario (Arezzo). (IT ISSN 0004-5918) **1082**
Notiziario (Rome). (IT) **280,** 338
†Notiziario Aggiornamenti Professionali.(IT) **5249**
Notiziario Assicurativo. (IT) **2539**
Notiziario Chimico e Farmaceutico. (IT ISSN 0550-1156) **3736**
Notiziario Chirurgico. (IT) **3382**
Notiziario Commercio Estero. (IT) **820**
Notiziario Culturale. (IT) **2206**
Notiziario d'Arte. (IT ISSN 0029-4322) **338**
Notiziario dell'Edilizia. (IT) **627**
Notiziario dell'Istituto Storico della Resistenza in Cuneo e Provincia. (IT ISSN 1120-0634) **2378**
Notiziario di Caccia e Pesca-Tiro a Volo.(IT ISSN 0029-4365) **4552**
▼Notiziario di Citologia. (IT) **526**
Notiziario Economico Bresciano *see* Banca Santo Paulo di Brescia. Notiziario Economico **760**
Notiziario Enasarco. (IT) **683**
†Notiziario F.I.P.S. (Federazione Italiana Pesca Sportiva ed Attivita Subacquee) (IT) **5249**
Notiziario Informativo *see* Smalto **1215**
Notiziario Interfederale *see* Servizi Pubblici Locali **4094**
Notiziario Medico Farmaceutico. (IT ISSN 0029-439X) **3736**
Notiziario Motoristico/Motor News/Motor - Nachrichten/Bulletin Motoristique. (IT) **4698,** 918, 4747
Notiziario S I M. (Societa Italiana di Malacologia) (IT) **589**
Notiziario Storico Numismatico Filatelico. (IT) **3600,** 3755
Notiziario sulle Malattie delle Piante. (IT) **511,** 536

6508 NOTIZIARIO

Notiziario U F O. (IT) 60, 367
Notiziario Vinciano. (IT ISSN 0391-3716) 338, 3531
Notizie da Palazzo Albani. (IT) 338
Notizie dall'Albania. (IT ISSN 0048-0916) 3967
Notizie dell'Economia Teramana. (IT) 820
Notizie di Fabbrica see Notizie Olivetti 3022
Notizie Dow. (IT) 1185
Notizie F A I D. (Federazione Associazione Imprese Distribuzione) (IT) 838
Notizie Mese. (IT) 2017, 1377
Notizie N A T O see N A T O Review 3908
Notizie Olivetti. (IT ISSN 0029-4438) 3022
Notizie Statistiche sull'Energia Elettrica. (IT) 1800, 1802
Notnaya Letopis' (RU ISSN 0029-4462) 3570
Notornis. (NZ ISSN 0029-4470) 566
Notre Comte/Ons Graafschap. (BE ISSN 0048-0924) 2378, 280, 2057
Notre Dame Alumnus see Notre Dame Magazine 1319
▼Notre Dame Conferences in Medieval Studies. (US) 2378
Notre Dame Journal. (PH ISSN 0048-0932) 1652, 2512
Notre Dame Journal of Formal Logic. (US ISSN 0029-4527) 3049, 3774
Notre Dame Journal of Law, Ethics & Public Policy. (US ISSN 0883-3648) 4069, 2662, 4192
Notre Dame Law Review. (US) 2662
Notre Dame Magazine. (US ISSN 0161-987X) 1319
Notre Dame Report. (US) 1319
Notre Dame Studies in American Catholicism. (US) 4271
Notre Dame Studies in Law and Contemporary Issues. (US) 2662
Notre Dame Technical Review. (US ISSN 0029-4543) 1832, 4605
Notre Metier - Ons Beroep see Vie Professionnelle 2090
Notre Petit Ami see Our Little Friend 1262
Notre Planete see Our Planet 1965
Notre Revue. (FR) 2295, 2187
Notre Temps. (FR ISSN 0029-456X) 2277
Notre Voix. (FR) 3911, 2017, 4225
Les Notres. (CN ISSN 0029-4578) 4271
†Notschrei der Tiere. (GW) 5249
Nottingham Arrow. (UK) 2195
Nottingham Countryside see Nottingham Topic 2195
Nottingham French Studies. (UK ISSN 0029-4586) 2944, 2378
Nottingham Law Journal. (UK ISSN 0965-0660) 2662
Nottingham Licensed Taxi Owners & Drivers Association. Newsletter. (UK ISSN 0260-8294) 1116, 4654
Nottingham Medieval Studies. (UK ISSN 0078-2122) 2378
Nottingham Topic. (UK ISSN 0048-0940) 2195
Nottinghamshire Farmer. (UK) 111
Nottinghamshire Farmers' Journal see Nottinghamshire Farmer 111
Nottinghamshire Historian. (UK ISSN 0308-6348) 2378
Nottinghamshire Industrial Archaeological Society. Newsletter see Nottinghamshire Industrial Archaeological Society Journal 280
Nottinghamshire Industrial Archaeological Society Journal. (UK ISSN 0143-0297) 280
†Nottola. (IT) 5249
Notulae Entomologicae see Entomologica Fennica 530
Notulae Naturae. (US ISSN 0029-4608) 4331
Notulae Naturae of the Academy of Natural Sciences of Philadelphia see Notulae Naturae 4331
Notulae Odonatologicae. (NE ISSN 0166-6584) 450
†Notus New Writing. (US ISSN 0889-0803) 5249

Noukogude Naine see Eesti Naine 4840
Noul Cinema. (RM) 3515
Noum Lao/Lao Youth. (LS) 1241
Nouncements. (US) 3467, 4850
Nous. (FR) 1507
Nous. (US ISSN 0029-4624) 3774
Nous Deux Presente. (FR ISSN 0029-4632) 2187, 2984
Nous Fiances. (FR) 2178
Nous Letter see Journal for the Study of Consciousness 3770
Nouveau. (NE) 1293
Nouveau Centre de Sante. (FR ISSN 0292-384X) 3136, 2587
Nouveau Chemin. see Novy Shliakh 2017
Nouveau Clarte. (FR) 3911
Nouveau Commerce. (FR ISSN 0550-1326) 2944, 2999
Nouveau Commerce de la Lecture. (FR ISSN 0223-3533) 2944
Nouveau Detective. (FR) 1519
Nouveau F see F Magazine 4842
Nouveau Genie Medical see N G M 3133
Nouveau Glossaire Nautique d'Augustin Jal. (FR) 1609
Nouveau Journal de Charpente-Menuiserie-Parquets. (FR ISSN 0029-4675) 640
Nouveau Magazine Communaute Chretienne see Presence 4195
Nouveau Masculin see Votre Succes 1119
Nouveau Militant. (MF) 3911
Nouveau Photo-Cine-Expert see Photo-Cine-Expert (1979) 3794
Nouveau Pouvoir Judiciaire. (FR ISSN 0338-1552) 2732
Nouveau Quartier Libre. (CN) 1319
Nouveautes de la Bibliotheque Administrative. (CN) 407
A I U Les Nouveaux Cahiers. (Alliance Israelite Universelle en France) (FR ISSN 0029-4705) 2378, 2944
Nouveaux Cahiers du Second Empire. (FR) 2378
Nouvel Absolu see Absous 3395
†Le Nouvel Agriculteur. (FR) 5250
Nouvel Automatisme see Bureaux d'Etudes 3016
Nouvel Economiste. (FR) 876
Nouvel Europe-Magazine see Europe-Magazine 2865
▼Nouvel Horizon. (IV) 3911
Le Nouvel Humanisme. (FR ISSN 0244-7878) 3911, 1964
Nouvel Introspec see Uniscope 1327
Nouvel Observateur. (FR ISSN 0029-4713) 2187
Nouvel Officiel de l'Ameublement. (FR) 2561
Nouvelle Bibliotheque Nervalienne. (FR ISSN 0078-2165) 2944, 420
Nouvelle Ecole. (FR ISSN 0048-0967) 2877
Nouvelle Famille Educatrice. (FR ISSN 0029-4748) 1652
Nouvelle Fipregazette. (SW) 2078, 4780
Nouvelle France. (CN ISSN 0029-4756) 2877
Nouvelle Hydrologie Alpine/New Alpine Hydrology/Neue Alpine Hydrologie/Nuova Idrologia Alpina. (FR) 4827
†La Nouvelle Lettre d'Information. (MQ) 5250
Nouvelle Litterature et Ideologie see New Literature and Ideology 2876
Nouvelle Revue d'Ethnopsychiatrie. (FR ISSN 0762-6819) 3349, 4444
Nouvelle Revue d'Onomastique/Journal of Onomastic Studies. (FR ISSN 0755-7752) 2832
Nouvelle Revue d'Optique. see Journal of Optics 3854
Nouvelle Revue de Psychanalyse. (FR) 4037
Nouvelle Revue de Science Missionnaire. see Neue Zeitschrift fuer Missionswissenschaft 4191
Nouvelle Revue du Son. (FR) 4461
Nouvelle Revue Franc-Comtoise. (FR ISSN 0029-4799) 2378
Nouvelle Revue Francaise. (FR ISSN 0029-4802) 2877
Nouvelle Revue Maritime see Revue Maritime 3470

Nouvelle Revue Neuchateloise. (SZ) 2378, 338
Nouvelle Revue Pedagogique. (FR) 1652
Nouvelle Revue Socialiste see N R S 3908
Nouvelle Revue Theologique. (BE ISSN 0029-4845) 4192
Nouvelle Tour de Feu. (FR ISSN 0294-4030) 2999, 2877
†La Nouvelle Voix de l'Ancai. (CN ISSN 0822-5435) 5250
Nouvelles see L E S Nouvelles 3676
Nouvelles Africaines de Securite Sociale see African News Sheet 2526
Nouvelles C E Q. (Centrale de l'Enseignement du Quebec) (CN ISSN 0710-5568) 1652
Nouvelles de Chretiente. (FR ISSN 0029-487X) 4192
Nouvelles de France. (FR ISSN 0398-9682) 2187
Nouvelles de l'A S T E D see Association pour l'Avancement des Sciences et des Techniques de la Documentation. Nouvelles de l'ASTED 2745
Nouvelles de l'A T C see T A C News 4656
Nouvelles de l'Eau. see Water News 4832
Nouvelles de l'Estampe. (FR ISSN 0029-4888) 4003, 338
Nouvelles de l'I C O M see I C O M News 3525
Nouvelles de l'O I J see I O J Newsletter 2570
Nouvelles de l'Or. see Gold News 3484
Nouvelles de la Boulangerie. (FR) 2089
Nouvelles de la F I P E S O see F I P E S O Newsletter 1633
Nouvelles de la F I T. see F I T Newsletter 2813
Nouvelles de la Republique des Lettres. (IT ISSN 0392-2332) 3774
Nouvelles du Livre Ancien. (FR ISSN 0335-752X) 4133
Nouvelles du Vietnam. (FR ISSN 0754-3786) 3967
Nouvelles Economiques. (AE ISSN 0078-2211) 820
Nouvelles Economiques. (RE) 876
Nouvelles Esthetiques. (FR ISSN 0029-490X) 374
Nouvelles Etudes Marxistes see Tribune Internationale 3930
Nouvelles Fiscales. (FR) 793
Nouvelles Graphiques/Grafisch Nieuws. (BE ISSN 0029-4926) 4003
Nouvelles Industrielles et Commerciales et de Midi-Pyrenees. (FR ISSN 0029-4934) 876
Nouvelles Pratiques Sociales. (CN) 4415, 4444, 4850
Nouvelles Questions. (FR) 3136
Nouvelles Questions Feministes. (FR) 4850
Nouvelles Ricard. (FR) 2187
†Nouvelles Scientifiques Franco-Danoises. (DK ISSN 0108-3333) 5250
Nouvelles Techniques. see Neue Technik 1398
Nouvelles Technologies de l'Information see N T I 4604
Nouvelles Universitaires Africaines see Universites 1719
Nouvelles Universitaires Europeennes see European University News 1633
Nova. (CK ISSN 0029-4993) 338
Nova. (GW ISSN 0029-4993) 4133
Nova see Cosmopolitan Nova 4840
Nova. (BL) 4850
Nova. (IO ISSN 0853-0300) 4850
Nova (El Paso). (US ISSN 0029-4985) 1319
Nova (New Berlin). (US ISSN 1047-2398) 4271
Nova Acta Leopoldina. (GW ISSN 0369-5034) 4331
Nova Angiologicae/Nova Angioroji. (JA) 573
Nova Angioroji. see Nova Angiologicae 573
Nova Doba. see New Era (Ely) 1300
Nova Doba/New Times. (AT) 2017
Nova Ecclesia. (SW ISSN 0029-5019) 4286

Nova et Vetera. (SZ ISSN 0029-5027) 4271
Nova et Vetera see Nova (New Berlin) 4271
Nova Express. (US) 3013
Nova Giulianiad. (GW ISSN 0254-9565) 3570
Nova Hedwiga. (GW ISSN 0029-5035) 511
Nova Hedwiga, Beihefte. (GW ISSN 0078-2238) 511
Nova Hrvatska. (UK ISSN 0143-3563) 3911
Nova Kepleriana. Neue Folge. (GW ISSN 0078-2246) 367
Nova Law Journal see Nova Law Review 2662
Nova Law Review. (US) 2662
Nova Matica. (CI ISSN 0353-8052) 2877
Nova Mysl. (CS) 3911, 3774
Nova Poesia Brasileira. (BL) 2999
Nova Praha see Praha 2184
Nova Proizvodnja. (XV ISSN 0029-5051) 1082
Nova Report on Lung Health and Wellness. (US) 3366
Nova Scotia. Commission on Drug Dependency. Annual Report. (CN ISSN 0707-9834) 1538
Nova Scotia. Department of Economic Development. Annual Report. (CN) 4069
Nova Scotia. Department of Health. Nutrition Division. Annual Report. (CN ISSN 0078-236X) 3610, 4109
Nova Scotia. Department of Industry, Trade and Technology. Annual Report see Nova Scotia. Department of Economic Development, Annual Report 4069
Nova Scotia. Department of Labour and Manpower. Compendium of Grievance Arbitration Decisions see Nova Scotia. Department of Labour. Compendium of Grievance Arbitration Decisions 990
Nova Scotia. Department of Labour. Annual Report. (CN ISSN 0380-5689) 990
Nova Scotia. Department of Labour. Compendium of Grievance Arbitration Decisions. (CN) 990
Nova Scotia. Environmental Control Council. Annual Report. (CN ISSN 0317-3526) 1964
Nova Scotia. Fire Marshal. Annual Report. (CN ISSN 0085-4395) 2034
Nova Scotia. Office of the Ombudsman. Annual Report. (CN) 4069
Nova Scotia Association of Architects. Newsletter. (CN) 304
Nova Scotia Barristers' Society. Annual Report. (CN) 2662
Nova Scotia Birds. (CN) 566
Nova Scotia Business Journal. (CN ISSN 0820-2737) 1116, 1060
Nova Scotia Craft News. (CN ISSN 0834-3136) 356, 1049, 1116, 1652
Nova Scotia Current Law. (CN) 2700, 18
Nova Scotia Dentist. (CN) 3239
Nova Scotia Department of Community Services (Year). (CN) 4415
Nova Scotia Federation of Agriculture. Annual Report. (CN) 111
Nova Scotia Fruit Growers Association. Annual Report and Proceedings. (CN ISSN 0078-2386) 186
Nova Scotia Genealogist. (CN ISSN 0714-3672) 2160
Nova Scotia Historical Review. (CN ISSN 0227-4752) 2417
†Nova Scotia Hosteller. (CN) 5250
Nova Scotia Lands and Forests Conservation see N.S. Conservation 1492
Nova Scotia Law News. (CN ISSN 0316-6325) 2662
Nova Scotia Medical Bulletin see Nova Scotia Medical Journal 3137
Nova Scotia Medical Journal. (CN ISSN 0838-2638) 3137
Nova Scotia Power Corporation. Annual Report. (CN ISSN 0078-2459) 1793, 1904

Nova Scotia Real Property Practice Manual. (CN) **4154**
Nova Scotia Reports. (CN ISSN 0048-0983) **2662**
Nova Scotia Research Foundation Corporation. Annual Report. (CN) **4605**, 4331
Nova Scotia School Boards Association Newsletter. (CN ISSN 0702-9292) **1730**
Nova Scotia Trappers Newsletter. (CN ISSN 0705-4831) **2737**, 1494
Nova Scotian Institute of Science. Proceedings. (CN ISSN 0078-2521) **4331**
Nova Scotian Surveyor. (CN ISSN 0380-9242) **1872**, 2258
Nova Tellus. (MX) **2512**, 1278, 2944
Nova Trgovina. (YU ISSN 0469-0281) **838**
Novaensia. (PL) **280**
Novalis. (SZ) **2877**
Novamaquina 2000. (SP ISSN 0210-0118) **3022**
Novantiqua. (IT) **2832**
Novarien. (IT ISSN 0078-253X) **4271**
Novas de Alegria. (PO ISSN 0029-5116) **4286**
Novascope. (US) **2231**
▼Novaya Gazeta. (RU) **1261**, 2877
Novaya i Noveishaya Istoriya. (RU ISSN 0029-5124) **2318**
Novaya Inostrannaya Literatura po Obshchestvennym Naukam. Ekonomika. (RU ISSN 0134-2835) **732**, 408
Novaya Inostrannaya Literatura po Obshchestvennym Naukam. Filosofiya i Sotsiologiya. (RU ISSN 0134-2851) **3787**, 408, 4458
Novaya Inostrannaya Literatura po Obshchestvennym Naukam. Gosudarstvo i Pravo. (RU ISSN 0134-2843) **2700**, 408
Novaya Inostrannaya Literatura po Obshchestvennym Naukam. Istoriya - Arkheologiya - Etnografiya. (RU ISSN 0134-2827) **2329**, 254, 290, 408
Novaya Inostrannaya Literatura po Obshchestvennym Naukam. Literaturovedenie. (RU ISSN 0134-2797) **2982**, 408
Novaya Inostrannaya Literatura po Obshchestvennym Naukam. Naukovedenie. (RU ISSN 0134-2800) **3938**, 408
Novaya Inostrannaya Literatura po Obshchestvennym Naukam. Yazykoznanie. (RU ISSN 0134-2819) **2855**, 408
Novaya Literatura po Tsenoobrazovaniyu, Opublikovannaya v S.S.S.R. (RU) **732**, 408
Novaya Sovetsakaya i Inostrannaya Literatura po Obshchestvennym Naukam. Sotsialisticheskaya Respublika Rumyniya see Novaya Sovetskaya i Inostrannaya Literatura po Obshchestvennym Naukam. Rumyniya **4395**
Novaya Sovetskaya i Inostrannaya Literatura po Obshchestvennym Naukam. Bolgariya. (RU) **4395**, 408
Novaya Sovetskaya i Inostrannaya Literatura po Obshchestvennym Naukam. Blizhnii i Srednii Vostok - Afrika. (RU ISSN 0134-2916) **4395**, 408
Novaya Sovetskaya i Inostrannaya Literatura po Obshchestvennym Naukam. Chekhoslovakiya. (RU) **4395**, 408
Novaya Sovetskaya i Inostrannaya Literatura po Obshchestvennym Naukam. Chekhoslovatskaya Sotsialisticheskaya Respublika see Novaya Sovetskaya i Inostrannaya Literatura po Obshchestvennym Naukam. Chekhoslovakiya **4395**

Novaya Sovetskaya i Inostrannaya Literatura po Obshchestvennym Naukam. Evropeiskie Sotsialisticheskie Strany. Obshchie Problemy see Novaya Sovetskaya i Inostrannaya Literatura po Obshchestvennym Naukam. Strany Vostochnoi Evropy. Obshchie Problemy **4395**
Novaya Sovetskaya i Inostrannaya Literatura po Obshchestvennym Naukam. Germanskaya Demokraticheskaya Respublika. (RU ISSN 0134-2975) **4395**
Novaya Sovetskaya i Inostrannaya Literatura po Obshchestvennym Naukam. Mezhdunarodnoe Rabochee Dvizhenie. (RU ISSN 0134-2940) **3938**, 408
Novaya Sovetskaya i Inostrannaya Literatura po Obshchestvennym Naukam. Narodnaya Respublika Bolgariya see Novaya Sovetskaya i Inostrannaya Literatura po Obshchestvennym Naukam. Bolgariya **4395**
Novaya Sovetskaya i Inostrannaya Literatura po Obshchestvennym Naukam. Pol'sha. (RU) **4395**, 408
Novaya Sovetskaya i Inostrannaya Literatura po Obshchestvennym Naukam. Problemy Ateizma i Religii. (RU ISSN 0134-2932) **4213**, 408
Novaya Sovetskaya i Inostrannaya Literatura po Obshchestvennym Naukam. Pol'skaya Narodnaya Respublika see Novaya Sovetskaya i Inostrannaya Literatura po Obshchestvennym Naukam. Pol'sha **4395**
Novaya Sovetskaya i Inostrannaya Literatura po Obshchestvennym Naukam. Problemy Slavyanovedeniya i Balkanistiki. (RU ISSN 0134-3041) **4395**, 408
Novaya Sovetskaya i Inostrannaya Literatura po Obshchestvennym Naukam. Rumyniya. (RU) **4395**, 408
Novaya Sovetskaya i Inostrannaya Literatura po Obshchestvennym Naukam. Strany Azii i Afriki. Obshchie Problemy. (RU ISSN 0134-3033) **4395**, 408
Novaya Sovetskaya i Inostrannaya Literatura po Obshchestvennym Naukam. Sotsialisticheskaya Federativnaya Respublika Yugoslaviya see Novaya Sovetskaya i Inostrannaya Literatura po Obshchestvennym Naukam. Yugoslaviya **4395**
Novaya Sovetskaya i Inostrannaya Literatura po Obshchestvennym Naukam. Strany Vostochnoi Evropy. Obshchie Problemy. (RU) **4395**, 408
Novaya Sovetskaya i Inostrannaya Literatura po Obshchestvennym Naukam. Vengriya. (RU) **4395**, 408
Novaya Sovetskaya i Inostrannaya Literatura po Obshchestvennym Naukam. Vengerskaya Narodnaya Respublika see Novaya Sovetskaya i Inostrannaya Literatura po Obshchestvennym Naukam. Vengriya **4395**
Novaya Sovetskaya i Inostrannaya Literatura po Obshchestvennym Naukam. Yugoslaviya. (RU) **4395**, 408
Novaya Sovetskaya i Inostrannaya Literatura po Obshchestvennym Naukam. Yuzhnaya i Yugo-Vostochnaya Aziya - Dal'nii Vostok. (RU ISSN 0134-2959) **4395**, 408
Novaya Sovetskaya Literatura po Gosudarstvu i Pravu. Novaya Yuridicheskaya Literatura v S.S.S.R. (RU) **2700**
Novaya Sovetskaya Literatura po Obshchestvennym Naukam. Ekonomika. (RU ISSN 0134-272X) **732**, 408

Novaya Sovetskaya Literatura po Obshchestvennym Naukam. Filosofskie Nauki. (RU ISSN 0134-2789) **3787**, 408
Novaya Sovetskaya Literatura po Obshchestvennym Naukam. Gosudarstvo i Pravo. (RU ISSN 0134-2738) **2700**, 408
Novaya Sovetskaya Literatura po Obshchestvennym Naukam. Istoriya - Arkheologiya - Etnografiya. (RU ISSN 0134-2746) **2329**, 254, 290, 408
Novaya Sovetskaya Literatura po Obshchestvennym Naukam. Literaturovedenie. (RU ISSN 0134-2770) **2982**, 408
Novaya Sovetskaya Literatura po Obshchestvennym Naukam. Nauchnyi Kommunizm. (RU ISSN 0208-0052) **3938**
Novaya Sovetskaya Literatura po Obshchestvennym Naukam. Naukovedenie. (RU ISSN 0134-2754) **4357**, 408
Novaya Sovetskaya Literatura po Obshchestvennym Naukam. Yazykoznanie. (RU ISSN 0134-2762) **2855**, 408
Nove Obzory. (CS ISSN 0546-8051) **2512**
Nove Slovo. (CS) **2877**
Novedades. (SP) **408**
Novedades Cientificas Alemanas. (GW ISSN 0722-0855) **4331**
Novedades Cientificas Alemanas - Ciencia Aplicada. (GW ISSN 0722-0863) **4331**
Novedades Cientificas Serie Zoologia see Sociedad de Ciencias Naturales la Salle. Memoria **4343**
Novedades Cubanas. (CU) **2184**
Novel: A Forum on Fiction. (US ISSN 0029-5132) **2944**
Novel & Short Story Writer's Market. (US ISSN 0897-9812) **2944**
Novela Musical. (MX) **2984**
Novelas de Amor. (MX) **2984**
Novelette. see Zhongpian Xiaoshuo **2980**
Novelistic Works/Hsiao Shuo Ch'uang Tso. (CH) **2944**
Novelists. see Xiaoshuo Jia **2977**
Novella 2000. (IT) **4850**
†Novelle Magasinet. (DK ISSN 0107-8941) **5250**
Novelleregister. (DK ISSN 0106-035X) **408**
Novenyvedelem/Plant Protection. (HU ISSN 0133-0829) **186**
Novice. (XV) **793**
Novii Vik. (RM) **2215**
†Novinar/Journalist. (CS ISSN 0029-5167) **5250**
Novinarstvo. (YU ISSN 0029-5175) **2573**, 1341
†Novinky Literatury: Ekonomie. (CS ISSN 0139-5203) **5250**
Novinky Literatury: Novinky Knihovnicke Literatury. (CS ISSN 0139-5459) **2795**, 18
Novinky Literatury: Prehled Pedagogicke Literatury see Prehled Pedagogicke Literatury **1679**
Novinky Literatury: Prehledy Informativni Literatury see Prehledy Informativni Literatury **5261**
Novinky Literatury: Zdravotnictvi. (CS ISSN 0029-5205) **3178**
Novita Bibliografiche: Antichita Greca e Romana. (IT ISSN 0392-0925) **2329**
†Novitates Arthropodae. (US ISSN 0278-3274) **5250**
Novo Livros. (BL) **4133**
Novo Mundo. (CN) **2017**
Novoe Vremya. (RU ISSN 0029-5280) **3967**
Novogradiski Zbornik. (CI ISSN 0352-7417) **2512**
▼Novon. (US ISSN 1055-3177) **511**
Novos Estudos C E B R A P. (Centro Brasileiro de Analise e Planejamento) (BL ISSN 0100-7025) **3911**
Novosti. (AT) **2017**
Novosti Farmatsii i Meditsiny/News in Pharmacology and Medicine. (PL ISSN 0209-3928) **3736**, 3137

Novosti Iz Jugoslavije see Yu Novosti **2240**
Novosti Tekhnicheskoi Literatury. Poligraficheskaya Promyshlennost' (RU) **4007**
Novoye Russkoye Slovo. (US ISSN 0730-8949) **2017**
Novum Gebrauchsgraphik/International Journal for Communication Design. (GW ISSN 0302-9794) **36**, 338, 4003
Novum Testamentum. (NE ISSN 0048-1009) **4193**
Novum Testamentum. Supplements. (NE ISSN 0167-9732) **4193**
Novy Domov/New Homeland. (CN) **2017**
Novy Orient/New Orient. (CS ISSN 0029-5302) **3642**
Novy Shliakh/New Pathway/Nouveau Chemin. (CN ISSN 0029-5310) **2017**
Novye Elementy Sistem Avtomatiki, Telemekhaniki i Vychislitelnoi Tekhniki see Avtomatika i Vychislitel'naya Tekhnika (Minsk) **1412**
Novye Issledovaniya v Gornoi Elektromekhanike. (RU) **1776**
Novye Issledovaniya v Khimii, Metallurgii i Obogashchenii. (RU) **3417**, 1857
Novyi Mir. (RU ISSN 0029-5329) **2877**
Novyi Zhurnal/New Review. (US ISSN 0029-5337) **2017**, 2877
Now. (CN ISSN 0712-1326) **2178**
Now. (II ISSN 0029-5345) **2201**
Now (London, 1970). (UK) **4245**
Now and Then. (US ISSN 0896-2693) **2944**, 1494
Now Hiring. (US) **3630**, 2662
Now in Japan. (JA) **918**
Now in Southampton see Southampton City News **4074**
Nowa Szkola. (PL ISSN 0029-537X) **1652**
Nowator. (PL) **1082**, 1832
Nowe Prawo. (PL) **2662**
Nowe Rolnictwo. (PL ISSN 0029-5396) **111**
Nowi Dni. (CN ISSN 0048-1017) **2017**
Nowotwory. (PL ISSN 0029-540X) **3200**
Nowy Dziennik. see Polish Daily News **2574**
Nowy Kurier. see Polish Canadian Courier **2019**
Nowy Medyk see Medyk **3131**
Noyaku Jidai. see Ag-Chem Age **68**
Nozzle. (US ISSN 0029-5434) **4698**, 3694
Nozzle Chatter. (US) **1936**
Nr 1. (GW) **627**
Nsanja Ya Olonda. (SA ISSN 0029-5442) **4286**
Nsukka Library Notes. (NR ISSN 0331-1481) **2777**
Nsukka Studies in African Literature. (NR) **2944**
Nu. (NE ISSN 0165-8220) **2539**
Nu see Magasinet Nu **2572**
Nu Pa Vej. (DK) **4193**, 1261
†NucCompact: European-American Communications in Nuclear Medicine.(GW) **5250**
†Nuclear Active. (SA ISSN 0048-1025) **5250**
Nuclear Almanac. see Genshiryoku Nenkan **1805**
Nuclear and Chemical Waste Management see Waste Management: Nuclear, Chemical, Biological, Municipal **1988**
Nuclear Applications and Technology see Nuclear Technology **3849**
Nuclear Arms. (US ISSN 0748-2876) **3967**, 3467
Nuclear Assurance Corporation Focus see N A C - Focus **1807**
Nuclear Awareness News. (CN) **1807**, 1964
Nuclear Bulletin of Malaysia. see Warta Nuklear Malaysia **1810**
Nuclear Canada/Canada Nucleaire. (CN ISSN 0029-5469) **1807**
Nuclear Canada. Yearbook. (CN ISSN 0383-8536) **1807**

6510 NUCLEAR DATA

Nuclear Data *see* Atomic Data and Nuclear Data Tables **3846**
Nuclear Data Newsletter. (UN) **1807**
Nuclear Data Sheets. (US ISSN 0090-3752) **1807**
Nuclear Data Tables *see* Atomic Data and Nuclear Data Tables **3846**
Nuclear Energy. *see* Iaderna Energiia **1805**
Nuclear Energy. *see* Jaderna Energie **1806**
Nuclear Energy. (UK ISSN 0140-4067) **1807**
Nuclear Energy *see* Peace and the Sciences **3968**
Nuclear Engineer. (UK ISSN 0262-5091) **1832**, **1807**
Nuclear Engineering/Genshiryoku Kogyo. (JA ISSN 0433-4035) **1807**
Nuclear Engineering and Design. (NE ISSN 0029-5493) **1921**, **1807**
Nuclear Engineering International. (UK ISSN 0029-5507) **1807**, **1832**
Nuclear Europe *see* Nuclear Europe Worldscan **1807**
Nuclear Europe Worldscan. (SZ) **1807**
Nuclear Fuel Cycle. (US ISSN 0735-2506) **1807**
Nuclear Fuel Status and Forecast *see* N A C - Focus **1807**
Nuclear Fusion/Fusion Nucleaire. (UN ISSN 0029-5515) **3848**, **3826**
Nuclear Geophysics *see* International Journal of Radiation Applications and Instrumentation. Part E: Nuclear Geophysics **1591**
Nuclear Index. (US ISSN 0271-0706) **1800**, **1807**
Nuclear India. (II ISSN 0029-5523) **1807**
Nuclear Industrial Newspaper. (JA) **1807**, **1832**
Nuclear Industrial Survey. *see* Genshiryoku Chosa Jiho **1805**
Nuclear Industry. (US ISSN 0029-5531) **1807**
Nuclear Industry Status *see* Worldwide Uranium Producer Profiles **1810**
Nuclear Info *see* U.S. Council for Energy Awareness. Info **1810**
Nuclear Instruments & Methods in Physics Research. Section A. Accelerators, Spectrometers, Detectors, and Associated Equipment.(NE ISSN 0168-9002) **3848**
Nuclear Instruments & Methods in Physics Research. Section B. Beam Interactions with Materials and Atoms. (NE ISSN 0168-583X) **3849**
Nuclear Law Bulletin. (FR ISSN 0304-341X) **1808**, **2662**
Nuclear Lemons. (US) **1808**, **1793**, **4109**
Nuclear Magnetic Resonance. (UK ISSN 0305-9804) **1229**
Nuclear Magnetic Resonance *see* N M R **3848**
Nuclear Magnetic Resonance Biomedicine *see* N M R in Biomedicine **3360**
Nuclear Magnetic Resonance Spectrometry Abstracts. (UK ISSN 0048-1033) **3838**, **18**, **1202**
Nuclear Materials Management *see* Journal of Nuclear Materials Management **1806**
Nuclear Medicine. (US ISSN 0896-0607) **3361**
Nuclear Medicine and Biology *see* International Journal of Radiation Applications and Instrumentation. Part B: Nuclear Medicine and Biology **3359**
Nuclear Medicine Annual. (US ISSN 0272-0108) **3361**
Nuclear Medicine Communications. (UK ISSN 0143-3636) **3361**
Nuclear Monitor. (US ISSN 0889-3411) **1808**, **1793**
Nuclear News. (US ISSN 0029-5574) **1808**
Nuclear News Buyers Guide. (US ISSN 0029-5574) **1808**
Nuclear News Industry Report *see* Nuclear News Buyers Guide **1808**

†Nuclear Physics Monographs. (US) **5250**
Nuclear Physics News. (US) **3849**
Nuclear Physics, Section A. (NE ISSN 0375-9474) **3849**
Nuclear Physics, Section B. (NE ISSN 0550-3213) **3849**
Nuclear Physics, Section B, Proceedings Supplements. (NE ISSN 0920-5632) **3849**
Nuclear Plant Journal. (US ISSN 0892-2055) **1808**, **1793**, **4109**
Nuclear Plant Maintenance Newsletter. (US) **1808**, **1832**
Nuclear Plant O & M Cost Data. (US) **1808**
Nuclear Plant Safety *see* Nuclear Plant Journal **1808**
Nuclear Power Plants in the World/Genshiryoku Hatsudensho. (JA) **1808**, **1793**
Nuclear Power Safety Report *see* Nuclear Lemons **1808**
Nuclear Reactor Safety. (US ISSN 0735-2492) **1808**, **4109**
Nuclear Reactors and Technology. (US) **3838**
Nuclear Reactors Built, Being Built, or Planned in the United States. (US ISSN 0364-6866) **1808**, **1793**
Nuclear Regulation Reports. (US ISSN 0360-7690) **2662**, **1808**
Nuclear Regulatory Commission Docket Microfiche *see* N R C Docket Microfiche **3837**
Nuclear Regulatory Commission Guides.(US) **3838**
†Nuclear Report. (US) **5250**
Nuclear Resister. (US ISSN 0883-9875) **3911**, **2318**
Nuclear Safety. (US ISSN 0029-5604) **1808**, **1793**, **1832**
Nuclear Safety Research Association News *see* N S R A News **1807**
Nuclear Science Abstracts of Japan *see* Nuclear Science Information of Japan. Oral Presentation **3849**
Nuclear Science and Engineering. (US ISSN 0029-5639) **1808**, **1832**
Nuclear Science and Techniques. (CC) **3849**
Nuclear Science Applications *see* Nuclear Science Applications - Section A: Short Reviews, Research Papers, and Comments **3849**
Nuclear Science Applications *see* Nuclear Science Applications - Section B: In Depth Reviews **3849**
Nuclear Science Applications - Section A: Short Reviews, Research Papers, and Comments. (US) **3849**
Nuclear Science Applications - Section B: In Depth Reviews. (US) **3849**
Nuclear Science Information of Japan *see* Nuclear Science Information of Japan. Oral Presentation **3849**
Nuclear Science Information of Japan. Oral Presentation. (JA) **3849**
Nuclear Science Journal. (CH ISSN 0029-5647) **3849**
Nuclear Science Research Conference Series. (US ISSN 0250-4375) **3849**
†Nuclear Sector Focus. (CN ISSN 0838-3871) **5250**
†Nuclear Spectrum. (AT ISSN 0815-0249) **5250**
Nuclear Standards News. (US ISSN 0029-5655) **1808**, **3448**
Nuclear Technology. (US ISSN 0029-5450) **3849**, **1832**
Nuclear Times. (US ISSN 0734-5836) **3911**, **3467**
Nuclear Tracks and Radiation Measurements *see* International Journal of Radiation Applications and Instrumentation. Part D: Nuclear Tracks and Radiation Measurements **3847**
Nuclear Unit Performance Data. (US) **1808**
Nuclear Waste Bulletin/Bulletin sur les Dechets Nucleaires. (FR) **1986**
Nuclear Waste News. (US ISSN 0276-2897) **1986**, **1808**
Nuclear Weapons Data File. (UK) **3467**
NuclearFuel. (US ISSN 0149-3574) **1808**, **1793**

Nucleic Acids Research. (UK ISSN 0305-1048) **481**, **1220**
Nucleonics Week. (US ISSN 0048-105X) **1793**, **1808**
Nucleosides & Nucleotides. (US ISSN 0732-8311) **481**
Nucleotecnica. (CL ISSN 0716-0054) **1808**
Nucleus. (II ISSN 0029-568X) **526**, **546**
Nucleus. (PK ISSN 0029-5698) **1808**
Nucleus. (PH) **1808**, **111**, **1185**, **3361**
Nucleus *see* Recherche **4335**
Nucleus (Cambridge). (US ISSN 0888-5729) **3911**, **1793**, **4109**
Nucleus Science Journal. (US) **3137**
Nudist Park Guide *see* North American Guide to Nude Recreation **4780**
Nudos en la Cultura Argentina. (AG ISSN 0325-4453) **2877**
Nuernberg Heute. (GW) **4780**
Nuernberger Forschungen. (GW ISSN 0078-2653) **2378**
Nuernberger Statistik Aktuell. (GW) **4081**
Nuernberger Wirtschafts-und Sozialgeographische Arbeiten. (GW ISSN 0546-9112) **2258**
Nuestra America. (MX ISSN 0185-2248) **2417**
Nuestra Arquitectura. (AG ISSN 0029-5701) **304**, **2554**
Nuestra Cabana. (SP ISSN 0210-5659) **222**
Nuestra Lucha. *see* Our Struggle **3945**
Nuestra Palabra. (AG) **3912**
▼Nuestra Parroquia. (US) **4271**
Nuestra Tarea. (US) **4245**
Nuestra Voz. (US) **2944**, **4850**
Nuestro Amigo. (DR ISSN 0029-5752) **4193**
Nuestro Anhelo. (AG ISSN 0029-5760) **2170**
†Nuestro Encuentro. (US) **5250**
Nuestro Planeta *see* Our Planet **1965**
Nuestro Tiempo. (PY) **2213**
Nuestro Tiempo. (SP ISSN 0029-5795) **2877**
Nuestros Talleres. (SP) **4698**
Nueva. (EC) **3912**
Nueva Antropologia. (MX) **246**
Nueva Caceres Review. (PH) **246**, **4381**
Nueva Ciencia. (VE) **876**
Nueva Cultura *see* Cultura **2863**
Nueva Economia. (AG ISSN 0326-5730) **999**
Nueva Estetica. (SP ISSN 0210-4245) **376**
Nueva Ferreteria. (SP ISSN 0213-0823) **642**
Nueva Frontera. (CK) **2183**
Nueva Gaceta de Cuba. (CU) **2944**
Nueva Historia. (UK ISSN 0261-2909) **2417**
Nueva Horizonte. (PH) **2877**
Nueva Lente. (SP) **3793**, **3515**
Nueva Linea. (CL) **2999**
Nueva Poetica Andaluza. (SP) **2999**
Nueva Pompeya. (AG ISSN 0029-585X) **4271**
Nueva Republica. (UY) **2238**
Nueva Revista de Filologia Hispanica. (MX ISSN 0185-0121) **2832**, **2944**
Nueva Revista del Pacifico. (CL ISSN 0716-6346) **2832**, **2944**
Nueva Sociedad. (VE ISSN 0251-3552) **3912**
▼Nueva Vida/A New Life. (US) **3295**
Nuevas Propuestas. (AG) **4381**
Nuevo Estilo. (SP) **4850**
Nuevo Mexico Elementary Principal. (US) **1730**
Nuevo Mundo. (AG) **4193**
Nuevo Patria. (US) **2018**
Nuevo Tiempo Hispano. (US) **2018**
La Nuez. (US ISSN 0898-1140) **2999**, **338**
Nufusbilim Dergisi. *see* Turkish Journal of Population Studies **3988**
▼The Nugget. (US ISSN 1059-9711) **2160**
Nuggets. (US) **2160**, **2417**
Nuggets. (UK ISSN 0048-1106) **2295**

Nuit Blanche. (CN ISSN 0823-2490) **2944**, **2877**
Nukada Institute for Medical and Biological Research. Reports. (JA ISSN 0469-2071) **3137**, **450**
Nuklearmedizin. (GW ISSN 0029-5566) **3361**
Der Nuklearmediziner. (GW ISSN 0723-7065) **3361**
Nuklearna Tehnologija. (YU ISSN 0351-689X) **1808**
Nukleonika. (PL ISSN 0029-5922) **1808**
Nullzwei *see* Edition Weiss-Blau **4689**
Numaga. (NE ISSN 0029-5949) **2378**
Number One. (US) **2999**, **2944**
Number Six. (UK) **1377**
Number Three St. Jame's Street. (UK ISSN 0029-5965) **384**
Numbers. (UK ISSN 0950-2858) **2999**
Numbers News. (US ISSN 0732-1597) **3985**
Numen. (NE ISSN 0029-5973) **4193**, **2318**
Numen Supplements. (NE ISSN 0169-8834) **4193**
▼Numerical Algorithms. (SZ ISSN 1017-1398) **3049**
Numerical Algorithms Group Ltd. Newsletter *see* N A G Newsletter **3048**
Numerical Control Computer Integrated Manufacturing Guidebook *see* N C - C I M Guidebook **3025**
Numerical Control ShopOwner *see* N C ShopOwner **5242**
Numerical Control Society - AIMTECH Integrated Manufacturing *see* N C S Integrated Manufacturing **1936**
Numerical Engineering. (UK ISSN 0143-8115) **1442**
Numerical Functional Analysis and Optimization. (US ISSN 0163-0563) **3049**
Numerical Heat Transfer *see* Numerical Heat Transfer Part A: Applications **1936**
Numerical Heat Transfer *see* Numerical Heat Transfer Part B: Fundamentals **1936**
Numerical Heat Transfer Part A: Applications. (US ISSN 1040-7782) **1936**, **1880**
Numerical Heat Transfer Part B: Fundamentals. (US ISSN 1040-7790) **1936**, **1880**
Numerical Methods for Partial Differential Equations: An International Journal. (US ISSN 0749-159X) **3049**
Numerische Mathematik. (GW ISSN 0029-599X) **3049**
Numero. (VE) **683**
Numero Quebrado. (CL) **2417**, **338**
Numero Zero. (IT) **2587**, **2573**
Numerus Clausus - Alternativen *see* Numerus Clausus - Finessen **1652**
Numerus Clausus - Finessen. (GW) **1652**
Numis-Post. (SZ) **3600**
Numismaatikko. (FI ISSN 0355-5615) **3600**
Numismatic Association of Southern California Quarterly *see* N A S C Quarterly **3600**
Numismatic Books in Print. (US) **408**, **3602**
Numismatic Bulletin. *see* Biuletyn Numizmatyczny **3598**
Numismatic Chronicle and Journal. (UK ISSN 0078-2696) **3600**
Numismatic Circular. (UK ISSN 0029-6023) **3600**
Numismatic Communications. *see* Numismatiska Meddelanden **3601**
Numismatic Literature. (US ISSN 0029-6031) **3600**
Numismatic News. (US ISSN 0029-604X) **3601**
Numismatic News. *see* Wiadomosci Numizmatyczne **3602**
Numismatic Notes and Monographs. (US ISSN 0078-2718) **3601**
Numismatic Scrapbook *see* Coin World **3599**
Numismatic Society of India. Journal. (II ISSN 0029-6066) **3601**

Numismatic Studies. (US ISSN 0517-404X) **3601**
Numismatica. (IT) **3601**
Numismatica e Antichita Classiche. (SZ) **3601, 280**
Numismatica Lovaniensia. (BE) **3601**
Numismatica Moravica. (CS ISSN 0078-2726) **3601**
Numismaticke Listy. (CS ISSN 0029-6074) **3601**
Numismaticky Sbornik. (CS ISSN 0546-9414) **3601, 2378**
Numismatique & Change. (FR ISSN 0335-1971) **3601**
Numismatische Beitraege. (GW ISSN 0323-8962) **3601**
Numismatisches Nachrichtenblatt. (GW ISSN 0937-6488) **3601**
Numismatiska Meddelanden/Numismatic Communications. (SW ISSN 0078-2734) **3601**
The Numismatist. (US ISSN 0029-6090) **3601**
Numizmatika. (BU) **3601**
Nummer 1 see Nr 1 **627**
Nunatsiag News. (CN ISSN 0702-7915) **2178**
Nunatsiaq News. (CN) **2178**
Nuncius. (IT ISSN 0394-7394) **4331**
Nuncius. Biblioteca. (IT) **4331**
Nungalinya Occasional Bulletin. (AT) **2018**
†Nuntia. (VC) **5250**
Nuntiaturberichte aus Deutschland Nebst Ergaenzenden Aktenstuecken. (GW ISSN 0078-2742) **2318**
Nuorten Sarka. (FI ISSN 0029-6139) **111, 1300**
Nuova Agricoltura. (IT) **111**
Nuova Alimentazione Dolciaria. (IT) **2089**
Nuova Antologia. (IT) **2877**
▼Nuova Citta Oggi. (IT) **2206**
Nuova Civilta delle Macchine. (IT) **3774**
Nuova, Clinica Otorinolaringoiatrica. (IT) **3315**
Nuova Corrente. (IT ISSN 0029-6155) **2944, 3774**
Nuova Ecologia. (IT) **1964**
Nuova Economia. (IT ISSN 0029-6171) **820, 683**
Nuova Elettrauto. (IT) **1904**
Nuova Elettronica. (IT) **1776**
Nuova Finestra. (IT) **642**
Nuova Fotografia. (IT) **3793**
Nuova Gazzetta di Calabria. (IT ISSN 0029-6198) **2206**
Nuova Giurisprudenza Civile Commentata. (IT) **2662**
Nuova Guida Cinematografica. (IT) **3515, 1357, 1377**
Nuova Guida T V. (IT) **1377**
Nuova Idrologia Alpina. see Nouvelle Hydrologie Alpine **4827**
Nuova Linea Grafica see Lineagrafica **4002**
Nuova Polizia e Riforma dello Stato. (IT ISSN 0392-0100) **1519**
Nuova Rassegna. (IT ISSN 0029-6201) **2877, 338, 4636**
Nuova Rassegna di Studi Musicali. (IT) **3570**
Nuova Rassegna: Rivista Trimestrale. (IT) **2999**
Nuova Ristorazione & Catering. (IT) **2478**
Nuova Rivista di Neurologia. (IT) **3349**
Nuova Rivista Europea. (IT) **2877**
Nuova Rivista Internazionale/New International Review. (IT ISSN 0029-621X) **3967, 2877**
Nuova Rivista Musicale Italiana. (IT ISSN 0029-6228) **3570**
Nuova Rivista Pedagogica. (IT ISSN 0469-2454) **1652**
Nuova Rivista Storica. (IT ISSN 0029-6236) **2318**
Nuova Secondaria. (IT) **1652**
Nuova Selezione Tessile. (IT ISSN 0391-6448) **4622**
Nuova Tradotta. (IT ISSN 0048-1122) **3467, 2318**
Nuova Umanita. (IT) **4271**
Nuova Universale Studium. (IT ISSN 0391-8548) **2944, 2318, 3774**
Nuova Venezia. (IT ISSN 0029-6260) **2206**
Nuova Via. (US) **3985**

Nuove Armonie. (IT) **376**
Nuove Leggi Civili Commentate. (IT) **2662**
†Nuove Prospettive. (IT ISSN 0033-1570) **5250**
Nuove Prospettive Letterarie see Prospettive Culturali **2950**
Nuovi Annali di Igiene e Microbiologia. (IT ISSN 0029-6287) **556**
Nuovi Argomenti. (IT ISSN 0029-6295) **2877**
Nuovi Orientamenti. (IT) **2877**
Nuovi Saggi. (IT ISSN 0078-2769) **2512**
Nuovi Studi Politici. (IT) **3912**
Nuovi Tempi see C O M - Nuovi Tempi **4167**
†Nuovo. (IT ISSN 0394-9583) **5250**
Nuovo Agora Omaggio. (IT ISSN 0029-6309) **2877**
Il Nuovo Bagno. (IT) **627**
Nuovo Bollettino Bibliografico Sardo. (IT ISSN 0029-6317) **4142, 408**
Nuovo Borghese. (IT) **2206**
Nuovo Bullettino Archeologico Sardo. (IT) **280, 2378**
Il Nuovo Cantiere. (IT ISSN 0029-6325) **627**
Nuovo Cinema Europeo. (IT) **3515**
Nuovo Commercio. (IT) **820**
Nuovo Corriere della Calzatura see Foto Shoe 15 **4361**
Nuovo Diritto. (IT ISSN 0029-6368) **2662**
Nuovo Governo Locale. (IT ISSN 0393-8212) **1022, 1068**
†Il Nuovo Laboratorio. (IT) **5250**
Nuovo Medioevo. (IT ISSN 0391-6049) **2378**
Nuovo Mezzogiorno. (IT ISSN 0029-6376) **683**
Nuovo Mondo Occulto. (IT) **3670**
Il Nuovo Mundo. (CN) **2018**
Nuovo Osservatore. (IT ISSN 0029-6384) **3912**
Il Nuovo Saggiatore. (IT ISSN 0393-4578) **3826**
Nuovo Totoguida Sport. (IT) **4482**
Nuovo Vai. (IT) **4482**
Le Nurb. (UK ISSN 0307-9244) **1319**
Nurscene. (CN ISSN 0382-8476) **3283**
Nurse. see Meditsinskaya Sestra **3282**
▼Nurse Anesthesia. (US ISSN 0897-7437) **3283**
▼Nurse Author and Editor. (US ISSN 1054-2353) **3283, 2573**
Nurse Education Today. (UK ISSN 0260-6917) **3283**
Nurse Educator. (US ISSN 0363-3624) **3283, 1756**
Nurse in Israel. see Ha-Achote be-Yisrael **3275**
▼Nurse Practitioner Forum. (US ISSN 1045-5485) **3283**
The Nurse Practitioner: The American Journal of Primary Health Care. (US ISSN 0361-1817) **3283**
Nurse Student. see Kango Gakusei **3281**
The Nurse, the Patient and The Law. (US ISSN 0196-6790) **3283, 2662**
Nurse to Nurse. (CN ISSN 0849-3383) **3283**
Nursery Business. (US ISSN 0029-6406) **2135**
Nursery Manager. (US) **2135**
Nursery News. (US) **2135**
Nursery Trader. (UK) **2561, 1241**
Nursery Trades B.C. see Hort West **2130**
Nursery World. (UK ISSN 0029-6422) **1241**
Nurseryman & Garden Centre. (UK ISSN 0029-6430) **2136**
Nurses' Drug Alert. (US ISSN 0191-2291) **3283, 3736**
Nurses in Transition. (US) **3283, 3215**
Nurses News see Caring **3277**
Nurseweek. (US) **3283**
Nursing. see Kango **3281**
Nursing (Year) Career Directory. (US ISSN 0192-2394) **1148, 3283**
Nursing (Year) Drug Handbook. (US ISSN 0273-320X) **3283**

Nursing (Year) (Edicion Espanola). (SP ISSN 0212-5382) **3283**
Nursing (Year) (Springhouse). (US ISSN 0360-4039) **3283**
Nursing Abstracts. (US ISSN 0195-3354) **3178, 18, 3283**
†Nursing Administration & Law Manual.(US) **5250**
Nursing Administration Quarterly. (US ISSN 0363-9568) **3283**
Nursing and Allied Health Index see Cumulative Index to Nursing & Allied Health Literature **3169**
Nursing and Health Care. (US ISSN 0276-5284) **3283**
▼Nursing and Health Science Education. (AT ISSN 1033-6303) **3283, 1739**
Nursing and Healthcare see Nursing and Health Care **3283**
Nursing B C. (CN ISSN 1185-3638) **3283**
Nursing Bibliography. (UK ISSN 0300-9947) **3178**
Nursing Clinics of North America. (US ISSN 0029-6465) **3283**
Nursing Connections. (US ISSN 0895-2809) **3283**
Nursing Diagnosis. (US ISSN 1046-7459) **3284**
Nursing Economics. (US ISSN 0746-1739) **3284**
Nursing Faculty Census. (US) **3284, 1713**
Nursing Focus see Senior Nurse (London) **3287**
†Nursing Forms Manual. (US) **5250**
Nursing Forum. see Minbar al-Tamrid **3282**
Nursing Forum. (US ISSN 0029-6473) **3284**
†Nursing Home Loss Control. (US) **5250**
Nursing Home Yearbook. (UK) **2277**
Nursing Homes and Senior Citizen Care.(US ISSN 0896-6915) **3284, 2277**
Nursing Info (Fredericton). (CN) **3284**
Nursing Job News see Nursingworld Journal **3285**
Nursing Journal. (CE) **3284**
Nursing Journal of India. (II ISSN 0029-6503) **3284**
Nursing Journal of Singapore/Berita Jururawat. (SI ISSN 0067-5814) **3284**
Nursing Magazine. see Kangogaku Zasshi **3281**
Nursing Management. (US ISSN 0744-6314) **3284**
Nursing News see Connecticut Nursing News **3277**
Nursing News/Verpleegnuus. (SA) **3284**
Nursing News (Brooklyn). (US ISSN 0029-6546) **3284**
Nursing News (Concord). (US ISSN 0029-6538) **3284**
Nursing Opportunities. (US) **3284**
Nursing Outlook. (US ISSN 0029-6554) **3284**
Nursing Papers - Perspectives en Nursing see Canadian Journal of Nursing Research **3276**
Nursing Photobook. (US) **3284**
Nursing Pulse of New England. (US) **3284**
Nursing Quebec. (CN ISSN 0381-6419) **3284**
Nursing R S A Verpleging. (SA ISSN 0258-1647) **3284**
Nursing Research. (US ISSN 0029-6562) **3284, 4381**
Nursing Research Abstracts. (UK ISSN 0141-3899) **3178, 3137, 3284**
Nursing Scan in Administration. (US ISSN 0888-6288) **3178, 18, 3284**
Nursing Scan in Research: Application for Clinical Practice. (US) **3178, 18, 3284**
†Nursing Science Quarterly. (US ISSN 0894-3184) **5250**
Nursing Standard. (UK ISSN 0029-6570) **3284**
Nursing Student Census. (US) **3284, 1713**
▼Nursing Technology. (II) **3284**
Nursing the Elderly. (UK) **2277**

NUTRITION REPORTS 6511

Nursing Times. (UK) **3285**
Nursing Yearbook. (US) **3285**
Nursingworld Digest see Nursingworld Journal **3285**
Nursingworld Journal. (US) **3285**
Nursingworld Journal Annual Hospital Directory see Nursingworld Journal Nursing Job Guide **3285**
Nursingworld Journal Nursing Job Guide. (US) **3285**
Nurture. (AT) **1756, 4193**
Nurturing News see Nurturing Today **1241**
Nurturing Today. (US) **1241, 4444**
Nurungi. (AT ISSN 0311-1016) **2345**
Nusa. (IO ISSN 0126-2874) **2832**
Nusleca. (UK) **2302**
Nut Grower. (US ISSN 0745-3469) **186**
Nutan Kahaniyan. (II) **2201**
Nutida Musik/Contemporary Music. (SW ISSN 0029-6597) **3571**
Nutricion Clinica. (SP ISSN 0211-6057) **3610**
Nutricion en Salud Publica. (FR ISSN 1013-8293) **4118, 3614**
Nutrition. (II ISSN 0550-404X) **3610**
Nutrition. (US) **3610**
Nutrition. see Vyziva **3613**
Nutrition Abstracts and Reviews see Nutrition Abstracts and Reviews. Series B: Livestock Feeds and Feeding **141**
Nutrition Abstracts and Reviews see Nutrition Abstracts and Reviews. Series A: Human and Experimental **3614**
Nutrition Abstracts and Reviews. Series A: Human and Experimental. (UK ISSN 0309-1295) **3614, 18**
Nutrition Abstracts and Reviews. Series B: Livestock Feeds and Feeding. (UK ISSN 0309-135X) **141, 18**
Nutrition Action see Nutrition Action Healthletter **3610**
Nutrition Action Healthletter. (US) **3610**
Nutrition and Cancer. (US ISSN 0163-5581) **3200, 3610**
Nutrition & Dietary Consultant. (US) **3610**
Nutrition and Food Science. (UK ISSN 0034-6659) **3610, 2449**
Nutrition and Health. (UK ISSN 0260-1060) **3610, 3807**
Nutrition and Health. see Vyziva a Zdravie **3613**
Nutrition and the Brain. (US) **3610, 450**
Nutrition & the M.D. (US ISSN 0732-0167) **3610, 3137**
Nutrition Clinics. (US ISSN 0888-3483) **3610**
Nutrition Counselor. (US) **3610**
Nutrition de Sante Publique. (FR ISSN 1013-8056) **4118, 3614**
Nutrition for Optimal Health Association News see N O H A News **3609**
Nutrition Forum/Forum de Nutrition. (CN) **3610**
Nutrition Forum. (US ISSN 0748-8165) **3610**
Nutrition Funding Report. (US ISSN 0892-1474) **3610**
Nutrition Health Review. (US ISSN 0164-7202) **3610, 4037**
Nutrition in Clinical Practice. (US ISSN 0884-5336) **3610**
†Nutrition in Health and Disease. (US ISSN 0160-2470) **5250**
Nutrition Intelligence see Food and Drug Letter **1076**
Nutrition Journal. (US) **3610**
Nutrition Legislation News. (US ISSN 8756-6060) **3610, 2078, 2662**
Nutrition News (Riverside). (US ISSN 8756-5919) **3610**
Nutrition News (Rosemont). (US ISSN 0369-6464) **3610**
Nutrition News in Zambia. (ZA ISSN 0078-284X) **2078, 3610**
Nutrition Newsletter see Food and Nutrition **5195**
Nutrition Notes. (US) **3610**
Nutrition Report. (US ISSN 0740-8684) **3610**
Nutrition Reports International see Journal of Nutritional Biochemistry **3608**

6512 NUTRITION RESEARCH

Nutrition Research. (US ISSN 0271-5317) **3610**
Nutrition Research Newsletter. (US ISSN 0736-0037) **3611**
Nutrition Research Reviews. (UK ISSN 0954-4224) **3611**
Nutrition Review. (CN) **3137, 3611**
Nutrition Reviews. (US ISSN 0029-6643) **3611**
Nutrition Society. Proceedings. (UK ISSN 0029-6651) **3611**
Nutrition Society of Australia. Proceedings. (AT ISSN 0314-1004) **3611**
Nutrition Society of India. Proceedings. (II) **3611, 111, 2078**
Nutrition Today. (US ISSN 0029-666X) **3611**
Nutrition Week. (US ISSN 0736-0096) **3611**
Nutritional Consultant see Nutrition & Dietary Consultant **3610**
†Nutritional Support Services. (US) **5250**
Nutshell see Campus Voice **1306**
Nutshell. (US) **2999**
Nutshell. (SA) **3694**
†Nutshell (Knoxville). (US) **5250**
Nutshell (New Carlisle). (US) **2136, 186**
Nutshell News. (US ISSN 0164-3290) **2440**
Nuttall Ornithological Club. Publications.(US ISSN 0550-4082) **566**
Nutzfahrzeug. (GW ISSN 0029-6686) **4747**
Nutzverkehr Magazin T I R. (SZ) **4654**
Nuus Oor Afrika. (SA ISSN 0029-6694) **2018**
Nuwe Afrikaner see Midland News **2216**
Nuwe Protestant. (SA ISSN 0029-6708) **4245**
Nux. (SA ISSN 0029-6716) **1319**
Nuytsia. (AT ISSN 0085-4417) **512**
Nuzi Shijie/Women's World. (CC) **4850**
Nuzi Wenxue/Women's Literature. (CC) **2944**
Nwy News. (UK) **3694**
†Ny Abstraktion. (DK ISSN 0109-5544) **5250**
Ny Carlsberg Glyptotek. Meddelelser. (DK ISSN 0085-3208) **280, 338**
Ny Dag. (NO) **1261, 4193**
†Ny Elektronik. (DK ISSN 0105-4880) **5250**
Ny Fremtid see Paa Flukt **3968**
Ny i Sverige. (SW ISSN 0345-8660) **3985**
†Det Ny Infodont. (DK) **5250**
Ny Jord see Jord og Myr **101**
Ny Korea see Korea Bulletin **3964**
Ny Litteratur om Kvinnor: En Bibliografi/New Literature on Women: A Bibliography. (SW ISSN 0348-7962) **4861, 408**
Ny Mponin'i Madagasikara. (MG) **3985**
Ny Teknik. (SW ISSN 0550-8754) **1832**
Ny Teknik Med Teknisk Tidskrift see Ny Teknik **1832**
Ny Tid. (NO) **3912**
Ny Tid og Vi see Tidsskriftet Ny Tid og Vi **5290**
Ny Torsdag. (DK ISSN 0108-0105) **1049**
Den Ny Verden. (DK ISSN 0029-6775) **933**
Nya Argus. (FI ISSN 0027-7126) **2877**
Nya Byggnormer see Nya Byggregler **638**
Nya Byggregler. (SW ISSN 0281-7276) **638, 18**
Nya Cyklisten. (SW ISSN 0048-1211) **4520**
Nya Kraftsport. (SW) **4482**
Nya Perspektiv. (SW ISSN 0550-4112) **111**
Nya Svenska Pressen. see Swedish Press **2025**
Nyala. (MW ISSN 0251-1924) **1494, 589**
Nyam News. (JM ISSN 0255-8203) **3611**
Nyando Roots. (US) **2160**

Nyankpala Agricultural Research Report. (GW ISSN 0933-4351) **111**
Nyasaland Journal see Society of Malawi Journal **4344**
†Nyctalops. (US) **5250**
Nycticorax (Citrus Heights). (US) **2999**
Nydanske Studier og almen Kommunikationsteori. (DK) **2832**
Det Nye. (NO ISSN 0048-122X) **4850**
Nye Aar. (DK ISSN 0108-8297) **4193**
Det Nye Computer. (DK) **1463, 1471**
Nye Family Newsletter. (US) **2160, 3531**
Nyelv- es Irodalomtudomanyi Kozlemenyek. (RM) **2832, 2944**
Nyelveszeti Tanulmanyok. (HU ISSN 0078-2858) **2832**
Nyelvtudomanyi Ertekezesek. (HU ISSN 0078-2866) **2832**
Nyelvtudomanyi Kozlemenyek/Linguistic Studies. (HU ISSN 0029-6791) **2832**
Nyengu Bogo - Rimmog Nyugjoh Nyenguso see Institute of Forest Genetics, Suwon, Korea. Research Report **2102**
Nyensubrim Nyengu Bogo: Seoul Daihaggyo Nongkwa Daihag. see Seoul National University Forests. Research Bulletin **2107**
Nyere Dansk Faglitteratur. (DK ISSN 0900-1166) **408**
Nyhedsbrev. (Teologiske Fakultet) (DK ISSN 0109-3169) **4193**
†Nyhedsbrev for Social og Sundhedssektor. (DK ISSN 0900-2685) **5250**
Nyhedsinformation for Social-, Sygehus-og Sundhedssektor. (DK) **4118**
Nykyposti. (FI ISSN 0355-9637) **2186**
Nykytekstiili. (FI ISSN 0029-6813) **4622, 1287**
Nylon Filament & Polyester Filament Growth. (US) **4622, 876, 1049**
Nyrenyt. (DK ISSN 0108-2388) **3389**
Nysvenska Studier. (SW ISSN 0345-8768) **2832**
Nyt Aspekt. (DK ISSN 0108-3503) **3596**
Nyt Danmarks Restauranter. (DK) **2478**
Nyt fra Bibelselskabet. (DK ISSN 0108-898X) **4193**
Nyt fra Bornholms Museum see Fra Bornholms Museum **3524**
Nyt fra D U K. (Danmarks Unge Katolikker) (DK ISSN 0109-0518) **4271, 1261**
Nyt fra Danmark. (DK ISSN 0107-4687) **2185, 2018**
Nyt fra Historien. (DK ISSN 0029-6848) **2318**
Nyt fra Nationalmuseet. (DK ISSN 0105-8819) **280, 246**
Nyt fra Nyhavn. (DK ISSN 0903-6342) **2777**
Nyt fra S S F see Samfundsforskning **4448**
Nyt om Flygtninge see Flygtninge Nyt **4405**
†Nyt om Moebler. (DK ISSN 0109-6222) **5250**
†Nytt fraan D F I. (SW ISSN 0349-3210) **5250**
Nytt Lif. (IC ISSN 1017-3595) **1293**
Nytt Norsk Tidsskrift. (NO ISSN 0800-336X) **3912**
Nyuton. see Newton **4330**
O A A News. (Opticians Association of America) (US) **3302**
O A B - R J. Revista. (Ordem dos Advogados do Brasil - Rio de Janeiro) (BL) **2662**
†O A - F A Update. (US ISSN 0737-7592) **5250**
O A G Air Cargo Guide. (Official Airline Guides, Inc.) (US) **4676**
O A G Business Travel Planner. North American Edition. (Official Airline Guides, Inc.) (US ISSN 1053-0002) **4780**
O A G Frequent Flyer. (Official Airline Guides, Inc. (New York)) (US ISSN 0277-2108) **4676**

O A G North American Pocket Flight Guide see O A G Pocket Flight Guide North American Edition **4676**
O A G Pocket Flight Guide Europe and Middle East Edition see O A G Pocket Flight Guide Europe, Middle East, Africa Edition **4676**
O A G Pocket Flight Guide Europe, Middle East, Africa Edition. (Official Airline Guides, Inc.) (US) **4676**
O A G Pocket Flight Guide North American Edition. (Official Airline Guides, Inc.) (US) **4676**
O A G Pocket Flight Guide Pacific Area Edition see O A G Pocket Flight Guide Pacific Asia Edition **4676**
O A G Pocket Flight Guide Pacific Asia Edition. (Official Airline Guides, Inc.) (US) **4676**
O A G Travel Planner and Hotel-Motel Guide. European Edition see O A G Travel Planner Hotel & Motel Redbook. European Edition **4780**
O A G Travel Planner and Hotel-Motel Guide. Pacific Area Edition see O A G Travel Planner Hotel & Motel Redbook. Pacific Asia Edition **4780**
O A G Travel Planner Hotel and Motel Guide Redbook. North American Edition see O A G Business Travel Planner. North American Edition **4780**
O A G Travel Planner Hotel & Motel Redbook. European Edition. (Official Airline Guides, Inc.) (US ISSN 0894-1718) **4780**
O A G Travel Planner Hotel & Motel Redbook. Pacific Asia Edition. (Official Airline Guides, Inc.) (US ISSN 0894-1734) **4780**
O A G Worldwide Cruise & Shipline Guide. (Official Airline Guides, Inc.) (US ISSN 0097-8779) **4780, 4735**
O.A.N. Digger. (Oregon Association of Nurserymen) (US) **2136**
O A P E C Energy Bibliography. (Organization of Arab Petroleum Exporting Countries) (KU) **3706, 18**
O A P E C Energy Resources Monitor. (Organization of Arab Petroleum Exporting Countries) (KU) **3694**
O A P E C Library Index see O A P E C Library Index of Periodical Articles **3706**
O A P E C Library Index of Periodical Articles. (Organization of Arab Petroleum Exporting Countries) (KU) **3706, 18**
O A P E C Monthly Bulletin. (Organization of Arab Petroleum Exporting Countries) (KU) **3694**
O A P E C Monthly Bulletin of Current Awareness see O A P E C Monthly Bulletin **3694**
O A P E C News Bulletin see O A P E C Monthly Bulletin **3694**
O A S. General Secretariat. Annual Report. (Organization of American States) (US ISSN 0078-6403) **2417**
O A U Echo. (Organization of African Unity) (ET) **3967, 2334**
O & A Marketing News. (US) **3694**
O & M. (SA ISSN 0029-6937) **1022**
O & M Intelligence. (Operation & Maintenance) (US) **3467, 60**
O & P Almanac. (American Orthotics and Prosthetics Association) (US) **3310**
O. Ars. (US) **2999**
O B T see Impact (North York) **1314**
O-blek. (US ISSN 0896-3053) **2999**
O C A Image. (Organization of Chinese Americans) (US) **2018**
O C A W Reporter. (Oil, Chemical and Atomic Workers International Union) (US ISSN 8756-1727) **2587**
O C D Diamond. (Organic Chemical Division) (US) **4605**
O C D E. Bibliotheque. Bibliographie Speciale Analytique: Automation. see O E C D. Library. Special Annotated Bibliography: Automation **1405**

O C D E. Bulletin d'Information Relatif a la R & D sur les Techniques d'Extraction de l'Uranium. see O E C D. Newsletter on R & D in Uranium Extraction Technology **5250**
O C D E. Bulletin des Comptes Nationaux Trimestriels. see O E C D. Quarterly National Accounts **1103**
O C D E. Code de la Liberation des Mouvements de Capitaux. see O E C D. Code of Liberalization of Capital Movements **793**
O C D E. Enquete sur l'Equipement Electrique. see O E C D. Survey of Electric Power Equipment **5251**
O C D E..Industrie de l'Electricite. see O E C D. Electricity Supply Industry **5250**
O C D E. Industrie du Ciment. see O E C D. Cement Industry **5250**
O C D E. Principaux Indicateurs de la Science et de la Technologie. see O E C D. Main Science and Technology Indicators **4605**
O C D E. Principaux Indicateurs Economiques. see O E C D. Main Economic Indicators **877**
O C D E. Principaux Indicateurs Economiques. Statistiques Retrospectives. see O E C D. Main Economic Indicators. Historical Statistics **732**
O C D E. Production Industrielle. see O E C D. Industrial Production **5250**
O C D E. Statistiques de la Population Active. see O E C D. Labour Force Statistics **732**
O C D E. Statistiques du Commerce Exterieur. Serie B: Tableaux par Pays Declarants. see O E C D. Statistics of Foreign Trade. Series B: Tables by Reporting Countries **5250**
O C D E. Statistiques Industrielles. see O E C D. Industrial Statistics **5250**
O C D E. Statistiques Mensuel du Commerce Exterieur. see O E C D. Monthly Statistics of Foreign Trade Series A **732**
O C D E. Statistiques Trimestrielles de la Population Active. see O E C D. Quarterly Labour Force Statistics **990**
O C D E - A E N Bulletin. see O E C D - N E A Newsletter **1809**
▼O C D - The Hidden Disorder. (Obsessive Compulsive Disorder Support Groups of New South Wales) (AT) **3349**
O C E A C Bulletin de Liaison et de Documentation. (Organisation de Coordination pour la Lutte Contre les Endemies en Afrique Centrale) (CM ISSN 0255-5352) **3137**
O C International. (US) **4286**
O C L A E Revista. (Organizacion Continental Latino Americana de Estudiantes) (CU ISSN 0029-6961) **2878**
O C L C Annual Report. (Online Computer Library Center, Inc.) (US ISSN 0730-5125) **2777**
O C L C Micro. (Online Computer Library Center, Inc.) (US ISSN 8756-5196) **1463**
O C L C Newsletter. (Online Computer Library Center, Inc.) (US ISSN 0163-898X) **2777, 1713**
O C S Nouvelles. (Office des Communications Sociales) (CN ISSN 0381-8632) **1341, 36**
O D A N see Opus Dei Awareness Network **4271**
O D A Newsletter. (Oregon Dental Association) (US) **3239**
O D I Review see Development Policy Review **928**
O D L Archives. (Department of Libraries) (US) **2777**
O D L Record. (Department of Libraries) (US) **2777**
O D L Source. (Department of Libraries) (US ISSN 0193-3086) **2777**
O D V see Obiettivi e Documenti Veterinari **4813**
O. Dos. (UY) **2878**
O E A Communique see Communique (Columbus, 1967) **1058**
O E A Focus. (Oklahoma Education Association) (US) **1652**

O E and M, Office Equipment and Methods *see* Office Systems & Technology **1060**

O E C D. Activities of the O E C D: Report by the Secretary General. (FR) **933**

O E C D. Agricultural Policies, Markets and Trade. Monitoring Outlook. (FR) **1103**

O E C D. Agricultural Policy Reports *see* O E C D. Agricultural Policies, Markets and Trade. Monitoring Outlook **1103**

O E C D. Annual Oil Market Report. (FR) **3694**

O E C D. Catalogue of Publications. (FR ISSN 0474-5086) **408, 933**

†O E C D. Cement Industry/O C D E. Industrie du Ciment. (FR ISSN 0474-5493) **5250**

O E C D. Coal Information. (FR) **3492**

O E C D. Code of Liberalization of Capital Movements/O C D E. Code de la Liberation des Mouvements de Capitaux. (FR ISSN 0474-5655) **793, 918, 933**

O E C D. Consumer Policy in O E C D Countries. (FR) **838**

†O E C D. Development Centre. Employment Series. (FR) **5250**

O E C D. Development Centre Seminars.(FR) **933**

O E C D. Development Centre Studies. (FR) **933**

O E C D. Development Cooperation. (FR ISSN 0474-5663) **933**

O E C D. Economic Outlook Historical Statistics. (FR) **732, 18**

O E C D. Economic Surveys. (FR ISSN 0376-6438) **876**

O E C D. Economic Surveys: Australia. (FR) **876**

O E C D. Economic Surveys: Austria. (FR ISSN 0474-5124) **876**

O E C D. Economic Surveys: Belgium - Luxembourg. (FR ISSN 0474-5132) **876**

O E C D. Economic Surveys: Canada. (FR ISSN 0474-5140) **876**

O E C D. Economic Surveys: Denmark. (FR ISSN 0474-5159) **876**

O E C D. Economic Surveys: Finland. (FR) **876**

O E C D. Economic Surveys: France. (FR ISSN 0474-5167) **876**

O E C D. Economic Surveys: Germany. (FR ISSN 0474-5175) **876**

O E C D. Economic Surveys: Greece. (FR ISSN 0474-5183) **876**

▼O E C D. Economic Surveys: Hungary.(FR) **877**

O E C D. Economic Surveys: Iceland. (FR ISSN 0474-5191) **877**

O E C D. Economic Surveys: Ireland. (FR ISSN 0474-5205) **877**

O E C D. Economic Surveys: Italy. (FR ISSN 0474-5213) **877**

O E C D. Economic Surveys: Japan. (FR ISSN 0474-5221) **877**

O E C D. Economic Surveys: Netherlands. (FR ISSN 0474-523X) **877**

O E C D. Economic Surveys: New Zealand. (FR) **877**

O E C D. Economic Surveys: Norway. (FR ISSN 0474-5248) **877**

O E C D. Economic Surveys: Portugal. (FR ISSN 0474-5256) **877**

O E C D. Economic Surveys: Spain. (FR ISSN 0474-5272) **877**

O E C D. Economic Surveys: Sweden. (FR ISSN 0474-5280) **877**

O E C D. Economic Surveys: Switzerland. (FR ISSN 0474-5299) **877**

O E C D. Economic Surveys: Turkey. (FR ISSN 0474-5302) **877**

O E C D. Economic Surveys: United Kingdom. (FR ISSN 0474-5310) **877**

O E C D. Economic Surveys: United States. (FR ISSN 0474-5329) **877**

O E C D. Economic Surveys: Yugoslavia.(FR ISSN 0474-5264) **877**

†O E C D. Electricity Supply Industry/O C D E. Industrie de l'Electricite. (FR ISSN 0474-5477) **5250**

O E C D. Employment Outlook. (Organization for Economic Cooperation and Development) (FR) **877**

O E C D. Energy Statistics of O E C D Countries. (FR) **1800**

†O E C D. Engineering Industries in O E C D Countries. (FR ISSN 0474-5876) **5250**

O E C D. Environmental Data Compendium. (FR) **1974**

O E C D. External Debt Statistics. (FR) **732, 1103, 4582**

O E C D. Food Consumption Statistics. (FR) **2085**

O E C D. Foreign Trade by Commodities. Series C. (FR ISSN 0474-540X) **732**

†O E C D. Guide to Legislation on Restrictive Business Practices Supplements. (FR ISSN 0304-3282) **5250**

O E C D. Indicators of Industrial Activity. (Organization for Economic Cooperation and Development) (FR ISSN 0250-4278) **732**

†O E C D. Industrial Production/O C D E. Production Industrielle. (FR ISSN 0474-5450) **5250**

†O E C D. Industrial Statistics/O C D E. Statistiques Industrielles. (FR ISSN 0474-5469) **5250**

O E C D. Industrial Structure Statistics. (FR) **732, 18**

O E C D. International Energy Agency. Energy Prices and Taxes. (FR ISSN 0256-2332) **1793**

O E C D. Iron and Steel Industry. (FR ISSN 0474-5973) **3417**

O E C D. Labour Force Statistics/O C D E. Statistiques de la Population Active. (FR ISSN 0474-5515) **732**

O E C D. Library. Special Annotated Bibliography: Automation/O C D E. Bibliotheque. Bibliographie Speciale Analytique: Automation. (FR ISSN 0474-5868) **1405, 408**

O E C D. Main Economic Indicators/O C D E. Principaux Indicateurs Economiques. (FR ISSN 0474-5523) **877**

O E C D. Main Economic Indicators. Historical Statistics/O C D E. Principaux Indicateurs Economiques. Statistiques Retrospectives. (FR) **732**

O E C D. Main Science and Technology Indicators/O C D E. Principaux Indicateurs de la Science et de la Technologie. (FR ISSN 1011-792X) **4605**

O E C D. Maritime Transport Committee. Maritime Transport. (FR ISSN 0474-5884) **4735**

O E C D. Monthly Statistics of Foreign Trade Series A/O C D E. Statistiques Mensuel du Commerce Exterieur. (FR ISSN 0474-5388) **732**

†O E C D. Newsletter on R & D in Uranium Extraction Technology/O C D E. Bulletin d'Information Relatif a la R & D sur les Techniques d'Extraction de l'Uranium. (FR) **5250**

O E C D. Nuclear Energy Agency. Activity Report *see* O E C D Nuclear Energy Agency Activities in (Year) **1809**

O E C D. Nuclear Energy Agency. Electricity, Nuclear Power and Fuel Cycle in O E C D Countries. Main Data *see* O E C D. Nuclear Energy Agency. Nuclear Energy Data **1808**

O E C D. Nuclear Energy Agency. Nuclear Energy Data. (Organization for Economic Cooperation and Development) (FR ISSN 1017-9402) **1808, 1793, 1832**

O E C D. Oil Statistics. Supply and Disposal. (FR ISSN 0474-6007) **3706**

O E C D. Quarterly Labour Force Statistics/O C D E. Statistiques Trimestrielles de la Population Active.(FR ISSN 0255-3627) **990**

O E C D. Quarterly National Accounts/O C D E. Bulletin des Comptes Nationaux Trimestriels. (FR ISSN 0304-3738) **1103**

O E C D. Quarterly Oil Statistics and Energy Balances. (FR ISSN 1013-9362) **3706**

O E C D. Revenue Statistics of O E C D Member Countries. (FR) **732**

O E C D. Reviews of Manpower and Social Policies. (FR ISSN 0473-6788) **990**

O E C D. Reviews of National Policies for Education. (FR) **1730**

O E C D. Reviews of National Science and Technology Policy. (FR) **4605, 4331**

†O E C D. Social Affairs Division. Developing Job Opportunities. (FR ISSN 0474-5892) **5250**

O E C D. Social Policy Studies Series. (FR) **4069**

†O E C D. Statistics of Foreign Trade. Series B: Tables by Reporting Countries/O C D E. Statistiques du Commerce Exterieur. Serie B: Tableaux par Pays Declarants. (FR ISSN 0474-5396) **5250**

O E C D. Steel Market in (Year) and Outlook for (Year). (Organization for Economic Cooperation and Development) (FR) **732, 3427**

†O E C D. Studies in Resource Allocation. (FR) **5251**

†O E C D. Survey of Electric Power Equipment/O C D E. Enquete sur l'Equipement Electrique. (FR ISSN 0474-5353) **5251**

O E C D. Tourism Committee. Tourism Policy and International Tourism in O E C D Member Countries. (FR) **4780**

O E C D. Uranium Resources, Production and Demand. (FR) **1809, 3492**

†O E C D. Wages and Labour Mobility Supplement. (FR ISSN 0474-5620) **5251**

O E C D. World Energy Statistics. (Organization for Economic Cooperation and Development) (FR) **1800**

O E C D Economic Outlook. (Organization for Economic Cooperation and Development) (FR ISSN 0474-5574) **877, 918**

O E C D Economic Studies. (FR ISSN 0255-0822) **877**

O E C D Financial Statistics/Statistiques Financieres de l'O C D E. (FR ISSN 0304-3371) **732**

O E C D Financial Statistics. Part 1: Monthly Financial Statistics. (FR) **732**

O E C D Financial Statistics. Part 2: Financial Accounts. (FR ISSN 0255-6979) **732**

O E C D Financial Statistics. Part 3: Non-Financial Enterprises Financial Statements. (FR) **732**

O E C D Foreign Trade Statistics. Series A *see* O E C D. Monthly Statistics of Foreign Trade Series A **732**

†O E C D Halden Reactor Project. (FR ISSN 0078-6284) **5251**

O E C D Liaison Bulletin Between Research and Training Institutes. (FR ISSN 0029-7038) **1082**

O E C D - N E A Newsletter/O C D E - A E N Bulletin. (Organization for Economic Cooperation and Development, Nuclear Energy Agency) (FR) **1809**

O E C D Nuclear Energy Agency Activities in (Year). (FR) **1809, 1793, 1832**

O E C D Observer. (Organization for Economic Cooperation and Development) (FR ISSN 0029-7054) **877**

O E C D Oil and Gas Information. (FR) **3706**

O E C S Annual Digest of Statistics. (Organisation of Eastern Caribbean States) (AQ) **4582, 877**

O E C S Current Awareness Bulletin. (Organisation of Eastern Caribbean States) (AQ) **878, 18**

O E C S Energy Bulletin. (AQ) **1800, 4582**

O E C S National Account Digest. (AQ) **4582, 878**

O E C S Select Bibliography. (Organisation of Eastern Caribbean States) (AQ) **878, 408**

O E C S Statistical Pocket Digest. (AQ) **4582, 878**

O E C S Trade Digest. (AQ) **732, 878**

O E C T A Reporter. (Ontario English Catholic Teachers Association) (CN) **1652, 4271**

O E Communique *see* Army Organizational Effectiveness Journal **5138**

O E G A I Journal. (Oesterreichische Gesellschaft fuer Artificial Intelligence) (AU ISSN 0254-4326) **1880, 1409**

O E M Design. (UK ISSN 0306-0381) **1832**

O E M Integrator. (US) **1832**

O E M Newsletter. (UK ISSN 0267-307X) **163**

O E M Off-Highway. (Original Equipment Manufacturers) (US) **164**

O E P *see* Office Equipment and Products **1776**

O E Report. (UK ISSN 0309-2097) **4622**

O E Reports. (Optical Engineering) (US ISSN 1048-6879) **3856, 1832**

O F C E Observations et Diagnostics Economiques. Lettre. (Observatoire Francais des Conjonctures Economiques) (FR) **3912**

O F C E Observations et Diagnostics Economiques. Revue. (Observatoire Francais des Conjonctures Economiques) (FR ISSN 0751-6614) **3912**

O F I Occasional Papers. (Oxford Forestry Institute) (UK ISSN 0269-5790) **2105**

O F S Philatelic Magazine. (Orange Free State Philatelic Society) (SA ISSN 1016-6734) **3755**

O G B - L Aktuell. (LU) **2587**

O G Informazione. (Consiglio Nazionale dell' Ordine dei Giornalisti) (IT) **1341, 1398**

O H A Hockey News. (CN) **4482**

O H A I Bulletin. (US ISSN 0888-9341) **3215**

O H & S Canada. (Occupational Health & Safety) (CN ISSN 0827-4576) **3619**

O H L A Newsletter *see* O H L A Newsline **2777**

O H L A Newsline. (Ontario Hospital Libraries Association) (CN) **2777, 2468**

O H S Bulletin. (Ontario Historical Society) (CN) **2417**

O H S U Views. (Oregon Health Sciences University) (US) **3137**

O.I.E. Bulletin. (Office International des Epizooties) (FR ISSN 0300-9823) **4813, 556**

O I E C Bulletin. (Office International de l'Enseignement Catholique) (BE ISSN 0770-1683) **4193, 1652**

O.I.E. Revue Scientifique et Technique/ O.I.E. Scientific and Technical Review. (Office International des Epizooties) (FR ISSN 0253-1933) **4813, 556**

O.I.E. Scientific and Technical Review. *see* O.I.E. Revue Scientifique et Technique **4813**

O I F Memorandum. (Office for Intellectual Freedom) (US) **2777**

†O.I.G.G. (BL ISSN 0078-2874) **5251**

O I O C Newsletter. (Oriental and India Office Collections) (UK ISSN 0960-7935) **3642, 2777, 3912**

O I O Journal *see* O I O News **2018**

O I O News. (Oklahomans for Indian Opportunity) (US) **2018, 1652**

O I V Bulletin. (Office International de la Vigne et du Vin) (FR ISSN 0029-7127) **384, 186**

O.I.V. Lettre. (Office International de la Vigne et du Vin) (FR) **384**

O I W Communique. (Order of the Indian Wars) (US) **3467, 2417**

O K Age Tendre. (FR) **1261**

O K C Action. (Oklahoma City Chamber of Commerce) (US) **820**

O K Magazine *see* Our Kids Magazine **1242**

O L A Bulletin *see* Ohio Libraries **2777**

O L A C Newsletter. (Online Audiovisual Catalogers, Inc.) (US ISSN 0739-1153) **2777**
O L A Focus see Focus (Toronto) **2758**
O L B G - Info. (GW ISSN 0172-732X) **2799**
O L O G O S. (Orthodox Lore Of the Gospel of Our Savior Mission) (US, ISSN 0029-7143) **4286**
O L S News. (Open Learning Systems) (UK) **1756,** 1691
†O L W. (Oesterreichische Lederwaren) (AU ISSN 0029-7151) **5251**
O Literature dlya Detei. (RU) **2944**
O M B Watcher. (Office of Management and Budget) (US) **4069**
O M C. (Organizacion Medica Colegial de Espana) (SP) **3137**
O M I Mission Magazine see Oblate World and Voice of Hope **4271**
†O.M.I. Missions. (Missionary Oblates of Mary Immaculate) (IT ISSN 0029-7178) **5251**
O M N I. (Optical Media News and Information) (UK) **1385**
O M R - Organic Magnetic Resonance see Magnetic Resonance in Chemistry **1228**
†O M S Annual Report. (Office of Management Services) (US ISSN 0278-7946) **5251**
O M S - Organic Mass Spectrometry. (UK ISSN 0030-493X) **1207**
O M S Outreach. (US ISSN 0274-9459) **4245,** 1261, 1723
O N. (Office Newsletter) (US ISSN 0893-1224) **1060**
O N I I T E M. Boletin see Cuba. Oficina Nacional de Invenciones, Informacion Tecnica y Marcas. Boletin Oficial **3674**
O N I S E P Communique. (Office National d'Information sur les Enseignements et les Professions (ONISEP)) (FR) **3630**
O N S - Mitteilungen. (Obersten Nationalen Sportkommission fuer den Automobil in Deutschland GmbH) (GW) **4698,** 4482
O O A - Saertryk. (Organisationen til Oplysning om Atomkraft) (DK ISSN 0105-4899) **1809**
O P A see Office Products Analyst **1060**
O P A L. (Ontario Puppetry Association Letter) (CN ISSN 0030-3062) **4636**
O P A L Journal. (Oriental Philatelic Association of London) (UK ISSN 0267-8071) **3755**
O P A S T C O Roundtable. (Organization for the Protection and Advancement of Small Telephone Companies) (US ISSN 1043-6073) **1364,** 1117, 2662
O P D Chemical Buyers Directory. (US ISSN 0276-5293X) **1148,** 1185
O P D I N Update. (Ocean Pollution Data and Information Network) (US) **1609**
O P D Restauro. (Opifico delle Pietre Dure) (IT ISSN 1120-2513) **304**
O.P. Doc. (IT) **2018**
O P E C Review. (Organization of the Petroleum Exporting Countries) (UK ISSN 0277-0180) **3694**
O P E R Research Working Paper see Office of Thrift Supervision **794**
O P Journal. (GW ISSN 0178-1715) **3382**
O P M A Overseas Media Guide. (Overseas Press and Media Association) (UK) **1149,** 36
O.P. Market. (Out of Print) (US ISSN 0078-2882) **4134**
O P N see Office Products News **1060**
O P R A Newsletter. (Organization of Psychic Research Associates) (US) **3596**
O P S E U News see Voices **997**
O P T I M A Newsletter/Informateur O P T I M A. (Organization for the Phyto-Taxonomic Investigation of the Mediterranean Area) (GW ISSN 0376-5016) **512**
O P T: One Parent Times. (UK ISSN 0143-0211) **1241,** 4444

O P W Z - Dokumentation see Betriebswirtschaftliche O P W Z - Dokumentation **5147**
O - Posten. (DK ISSN 0107-4202) **4482**
O Q E see Optical and Quantum Electronics **1776**
O R A C L. (Office Regional d'Action Culturelle) (FR ISSN 0294-4480) **2944**
O R C Notes. (Old Roman Catholic Church) (UK ISSN 0144-9117) **4271**
O R Insight. (Operational Research Society) (UK ISSN 0953-5543) **1652**
O R L. (SZ ISSN 0301-1569) **3315**
O.R.L. Dips. (SP ISSN 0210-7309) **3316**
O R L - Head and Neck Nursing. (US) **3316,** 3285
O R - M S Today. (Operations Research - Management Science) (US) **4331**
O R Manager. (Operating Room) (US ISSN 8756-8047) **2468**
O R S A - T I M S Bulletin see T I M S - O R S A Meeting Bulletin **4346**
†O.R.S.T.O.M. Initiations Documentations Techniques. (Office de la Recherche Scientifique et Technique Outre-Mer) (FR ISSN 0071-9021) **5251**
O R S T O M Institut Francais de Recherche pour le Developement en Cooperation. Rapport d'Activite. (FR ISSN 0071-9013) **4331,** 4605
O.R.S.T.O.M. Memoires see Memoires O.R.S.T.O.M **5235**
O.R.S.T.O.M. Recueils des Travaux. Oceanographie see O.R.S.T.O.M. Resumes des Travaux. Oceanographie **1609**
O.R.S.T.O.M. Resumes des Travaux. Oceanographie. (Office de la Recherche Scientifique et Technique Outre-Mer) (NL) **1609,** 1576
O R Spektrum. (Operations Research) (GW ISSN 0171-6468) **1398**
O R T Bulletin. (American Organization for Rehabilitation Through Training Federation) (US) **2018**
O R T Reporter see The Reporter (New York) **4417**
O R T Yearbook see World O R T Union. Yearbook **1742**
O S A Annual Meeting Digest. (Optical Society of America, Inc.) (US) **3856,** 3394, 4605
O S A Annual Meeting Proceedings see O S A Annual Meeting Digest **3856**
O.S.A.H.R.C. Reports see U.S. Occupational Safety and Health Review Commission. Administrative Law Judge and Commission Decisions **3622**
O S C A Reports. (Ontario School Counsellors' Association) (CN ISSN 0383-9931) **1652**
O S C Bulletin. (CN ISSN 0226-9325) **958**
O S E A P Centre Update. (Organisation for Scientific Evaluation of Aerial Phenomena) (UK ISSN 0262-7795) **60**
O S E A P Journal. (Organisation for Scientific Evaluation of Aerial Phenomena) (UK ISSN 0262-5954) **60**
†O S G N Wetenschappelijke Publikatie. (Organisatie van Studenten in de Geschiedenis van Nederland) (NE) **5251**
O S H A Compliance Advisor. (Occupational Safety and Health Administration) (US) **1964**
O S H A Litigation see Industrial Accident Law Bulletin **3617**
O S H A News. (US) **2539**
O S H A Report see Job Safety Consultant **3618**
O S H A Training Bulletin for Supervisors. (Occupational Safety and Health Administration) (US) **1964,** 3619
O S H A Up To Date Newsletter. (US) **3619**
O S H A Week. (Occupational Safety and Health) (US) **3619**
O S I Communication see Open Systems Communication **1447**

O S I Netter Newsletter. (Open Systems Interconnection) (US ISSN 0888-6997) **1428**
O S I S see Open Systems Information Systems **5253**
O S L A Newsletter. (Ontario Association of Speech - Language Pathologists and Audiologists) (CN) **2288,** 1739, 2832, 3316
O S M T Update. (Ontario Society of Medical Technologists) (CN ISSN 0832-5332) **3262**
O S N I E see Ocular Surgery News International Edition **3382**
O S N Z News. (Ornithological Society of New Zealand Inc.) (NZ) **566**
O S S C Bulletin. (Oregon School Study Council) (US ISSN 0095-6694) **1652**
O Sao Paulo see Sao Paulo **2175**
O T A N Communiques Finals. see N A T O Final Communiques **3966**
O T A N Documents Fondamentaux. see N A T O Basic Documents **3966**
O T A News Round-up see Update (Rexdale) **4749**
O T C and Regional Exchange Stock Reports see O T C Stock Reports **958**
O T C Chart Manual see Trendline O T C Chart Manual **966**
O T C Growth Stock Watch. (Over-the-Counter) (US ISSN 0892-2632) **958**
O T C Handbook. (Over-the-Counter) (US ISSN 0733-026X) **958**
O T C Insight see M P T Review **954**
O T C Medication see Community Pharmacy **3721**
O T C Review see Equities **945**
O T C Stock Reports. (US) **958**
O T F - F E O Interaction. (Ontario Teachers' Federation) (CN ISSN 0316-3903) **1713**
O T F Interaction see O T F - F E O Interaction **1713**
O T J R see Occupational Therapy Journal of Research **3137**
O T Kaner. (Oostelike Transvaalse) (SA ISSN 0029-7321) **111**
O U Health Sciences Magazine see Vital Signs (Oklahoma) **3810**
†O U T - Line. (Organization for Use of the Telephone) (US) **5251**
O V Z - Mitteilungen. (AU) **3650**
O W A A Outdoor Writers Directory see Outdoor Writers Association of America. Directory **2574**
O W N. (Office World News) (US ISSN 0164-5951) **1060**
O Z E. (Oesterreichische Zeitschrift fuer Elektrizitaetswirtschaft) (US ISSN 0029-9618) **1904**
†Oahu, a Paradise Guide. (US) **5251**
Oahu Drive Guide. (US) **4781**
†Oahu Update. (US ISSN 1042-8038) **5251**
Oak Lawn Reporter. (US) **2231**
Oak Leaf. (US ISSN 0029-7356) **3467**
Oak Leaves. (US ISSN 0740-8013) **2160**
Oak Ridge Associated Universities. Annual Report. (US) **1713**
Oak Ridge Associated Universities. Medical Sciences Division. Research Report. (US) **3137**
Oak Ridge Institute for Nuclear Studies. Medical Division. Research Report see Oak Ridge Associated Universities. Medical Sciences Division. Research Report **3137**
Oak Ridge Institute for Nuclear Studies. Report see Oak Ridge Associated Universities. Annual Report **1713**
Oak Ridge National Laboratory Review. (US ISSN 0048-1262) **3849,** 4605
Oakhamian. (UK ISSN 0029-7380) **1319**
Oakland Business Monthly. (US) **683**
Oakland Port and Shipping Handbook. (UK ISSN 0268-6481) **1149,** 4735
Oakland University Magazine. (US ISSN 1054-6480) **1319**
†Oakley's Aggressive Stock Alert. (US) **5251**

Oakley's Insiders Money Report. (US) **958**
Die Oase. (GW ISSN 0029-7402) **3467**
Oasis. (IT) **1494,** 1964, 3793
Oasis (Carthage) see Educational Oasis **1748**
Oasis (London). (UK) **2944**
Ob G Management. (US ISSN 1044-307X) **3295,** 1022
Ob-Gyn Clinical Alert. (US ISSN 0743-8354) **3295**
Ob-Gyn Collected Letters see International Correspondence Society of Obstetrics and Gynecology. Collected Letters **3293**
†Ob-Gyn Digest (Year). (US ISSN 0198-9197) **5251**
†Ob-Gyn Litigation Reporter. (US ISSN 0735-9551) **5251**
Ob-Gyn News. (US ISSN 0029-7437) **3295**
▼Ob-Gyn Resident. (US) **3295**
Obaa Sima. see Ideal Woman **4845**
Obafemi Awolowo University. Faculty of Law. Law Report. (NR) **2662**
Obafemi Awolowo University Law Journal. (NR) **2662**
Obaly see Manipulace, Skladovani, Baleni **3649**
Obchod-Prumysl-Hospodarstvi see Revue Obchodu, Prumyslu, Hospodarstvi **821**
†Obedience Competitor Magazine. (UK) **5251**
Obelezja. (YU ISSN 0350-9400) **2378**
Oberflaeche/Surface. (SZ ISSN 0048-1270) **3654**
Oberflaeche und J O T see J O T **3018**
Oberfraenkische Wirtschaft. (GW ISSN 0029-7496) **820**
Oberhessische Gesellschaft fuer Natur- und Heilkunde, Giessen. Berichte. (GW ISSN 0078-2920) **4331**
Oberlin Alumni Magazine. (US ISSN 0029-7518) **1319**
Oberlin Review. (US ISSN 0029-7526) **1319**
Obermenzinger Hefte. (GW) **2190**
Oberoesterreich. (AU ISSN 0253-7435) **338,** 2878
Oberoesterreichische F P O - Nachrichten fuer Freiheit und Recht. (Freiheitliche Partei Oesterreichs) (AU ISSN 0029-7534) **3912**
Oberoesterreichische Gemeindezeitung. (AU ISSN 0029-7542) **2173**
Oberoesterreichische Heimatblaetter. (AU ISSN 0029-7550) **2378,** 2057
Oberoesterreichischer Musealverein. Jahrbuch. (AU) **2378,** 280
†Oberoesterreichisches Landesarchiv. Mitteilungen. (AU ISSN 0572-192X) **5251**
Oberoesterreichisches Volksbildungswerk. Mitteilungen see Bildungsimpuls **1682**
Oberpfalz. (GW) **2378**
†Oberrheinische Geologische Abhandlungen. (GW ISSN 0078-2939) **5251**
Oberrheinischer Geologischer Verein. Jahresberichte und Mitteilungen. (GW ISSN 0078-2947) **1576**
Oberstdorfer Magazin. (GW) **2190**
Obersten Nationalen Sportkommission fuer den Automobil in Deutschland GmbH Mitteilungen see O N S - Mitteilungen **4698**
Oberweis Report: A Monthly Review. (US) **793**
Oberweis Securities Monthly Review see Oberweis Report: A Monthly Review **793**
Obesity & Health. (US ISSN 1044-1522) **3611,** 3210
▼Obesity Surgery. (UK ISSN 0960-8923) **3382**
Obiettivi e Documenti Veterinari. (IT ISSN 0392-1913) **4813**
Obiettivo Diabete. (IT) **3255**
Obiettivo Marca. (IT ISSN 0394-1612) **1149**
Obispado de Tortosa. Boletin Oficial. (SP) **4193**
Obiter. (SA) **2662**

Obiter Dicta. (CN ISSN 0029-7585) 2662
▼Object Magazine. (US) 1398
▼Object Oriented Strategies. (US) 1452
Objectif. (MG) 878, 3912
Objectif et Action Mutualistes. (FR ISSN 0154-8530) 4415
†Objectif, Inter 8000. (FR) 5251
Objectif: Justice see Objective: Justice 3945
Objectif Prevention. (BE ISSN 0771-2634) 3619
Objectif Prevention see Operatie Veiligheid 4109
▼Objections at Trials. (US) 2662
Objective: Justice. (UN ISSN 0029-7593) 3945
Objector. (US ISSN 0279-103X) 3912
Objektiv. (DK ISSN 0107-6329) 3793
Objektivet. (NO) 3793, 3515
Objets et Mondes. (FR ISSN 0029-7615) 246, 2057
Oblastni Muzeum Jihovychodni Moravy. Acta Musealia. (CS) 2378, 3912
Oblastni Muzeum v Gottwaldove. Zpravy see Oblastni Muzeum Jihovychodni Moravy. Acta Musealia 2378
Oblate World and Voice of Hope. (US) 4271
Oblates. (US) 4193
Obnovljeni Zivot/Life Renewed. (CI ISSN 0351-3947) 4193
Oboe - Klarinette - Fagott. (GW ISSN 0179-8170) 3571
Obogashchenie Rud. (RU ISSN 0202-3776) 3492
Obrabotka Simvol'noi Informatsii. (RU) 1398
Obras. (MX) 2493
Obras Publicas. (SP) 4069, 2493
Obraz Literatury Polskiej. (PL ISSN 0078-2963) 2944
Obrazovy Archiv. (CS) 2184
Obrero Ferroviario. (AG ISSN 0029-7658) 4712, 2587
Obrero Revolucionario see Revolutionary Worker 3923
Obrobka Plastyczna see Obrobka Plastyczna Metali 3417
Obrobka Plastyczna Metali/Metal Forming. (PL ISSN 0867-2628) 3417
Obrtnicki Vjesnik see Hrvatski Obrtnik 1115
Obrzedy i Zwyczaje Ludowe. (PL) 3571
Obscenity Law Bulletin. (US ISSN 0195-1696) 2662
Obscura see Frame-Work 3791
Observateur de l'O C D E see O E C D Observer 877
Observateur Diplomatique. see Diplomatic Observer 3955
Observation. (CN ISSN 0826-9947) 683
Observation and Study of Earthquakes and Geomagnetism. see Dizhen Dici Guance yu Yanjiu 1588
The Observation Post/Ch'un Ch'iu. (HK) 338
Observations et Travaux. (FR ISSN 0769-0878) 367
†Observations et Travaux (Special Issues). (FR) 5251
Observatoire Astronomique d'Alger. Annales. (AE ISSN 0065-6232) 367
Observatoire de Geneve. Pre-Publications. Serie C. (SZ) 367
Observatoire de Geneve. Publications. Serie A. (SZ ISSN 0085-0942) 367
Observatoire de Geneve. Publications. Serie B. (SZ ISSN 0435-2939) 367
Observatoire de Strasbourg. Centre de Donnees Stellaires. Information Bulletin. (FR ISSN 0242-6536) 367
Observatoire Francais des Conjonctures Economiques Observations et Diagnostics Economiques. Lettre see O F C E Observations et Diagnostics Economiques. Lettre 3912

Observatoire Francais des Conjonctures Economiques Observations et Diagnostics Economiques. Revue see O F C E Observations et Diagnostics Economiques. Revue 3912
Observator. (NO) 683
Observatorio Astronomico de Madrid. Anuario. (SP ISSN 0373-5125) 367
Observatorio Astronomico Municipal de Rosario. Boletin. (AG ISSN 0302-2277) 367
Observatorio Nacional Rio de Janeiro. Efemerides Astronomicas. (BL) 367
Observatorio Nacional Rio de Janeiro. Publicacoes. (BL) 367, 1592
Observatory. (UK ISSN 0029-7704) 367
Observer. (UK ISSN 0029-7712) 2195
Observer. (AU) 3912
Observer (Aptos). (US) 1060, 1415
Observer (Ellensburg). (US) 1319
The Observer. (US) 3302
Observer (Newark). (US) 1319
Observer (Newton Highlands). (US) 1399
Observer (Philadelphia). (US) 384
Observer (Rock Island). (US) 1319
Observer (Rockford). (US ISSN 0029-7739) 4271
Obserwatorium Krakowskie. Rocznik Astronomiczny. Dodatek Miedzynarodowy. (PL ISSN 0075-7047) 367
Obsessive Compulsive Disorder Support Groups of New South Wales The Hidden Disorder see O C D - The Hidden Disorder 3349
Obshchestvennye Nauki i Sovremennost'(RU) 4381
Obshchestvennye Nauki v S.S.S.R. Ekonomika. (RU ISSN 0202-2044) 732, 18
Obshchestvennye Nauki v S.S.S.R. Filosofskie Nauki. (RU ISSN 0202-2052) 3787, 18
Obshchestvennye Nauki v S.S.S.R. Gosudarstvo i Pravo. (RU ISSN 0202-2060) 2700, 18
Obshchestvennye Nauki v S.S.S.R. Istoriya. (RU ISSN 0202-2079) 2329, 18
Obshchestvennye Nauki v S.S.S.R. Literaturovedenie. (RU ISSN 0202-2095) 2982, 18
Obshchestvennye Nauki v S.S.S.R. Seriya 1: Problemy Nauchnogo Kommunizma. (RU ISSN 0202-2036) 3912
Obshchestvennye Nauki v S.S.S.R. Yazykoznanie. (RU ISSN 0202-2087) 2855, 18
Obshchestvennye Nauki v Tadzhikistane.(TA) 4395
Obshchestvennye Nauki v Uzbekistane. (UZ ISSN 0029-7763) 4381
Obshchestvennye Nauki za Rubezhom. Ekonomika. (RU ISSN 0132-7372) 732, 18
Obshchestvennye Nauki za Rubezhom. Filosofiya. (RU) 3787, 18
Obshchestvennye Nauki za Rubezhom. Filosofiya i Sotsiologiya see Obshchestvennye Nauki za Rubezhom. Filosofiya 3787
Obshchestvennye Nauki za Rubezhom. Filosofiya i Sotsiologiya see Obshchestvennye Nauki za Rubezhom. Sotsiologiya 4458
Obshchestvennye Nauki za Rubezhom. Gosudarstvo i Pravo. (RU ISSN 0202-2109) 2700, 18
Obshchestvennye Nauki za Rubezhom. Istoriya. (RU) 2329, 18
Obshchestvennye Nauki za Rubezhom. Kitavedenie. (RU ISSN 0235-6821) 4395, 18
Obshchestvennye Nauki za Rubezhom. Literaturovedenie. (RU ISSN 0202-2117) 2982, 18
Obshchestvennye Nauki za Rubezhom. Naukovedenie. (RU ISSN 0202-2141) 4357, 18
Obshchestvennye Nauki za Rubezhom. Problemy Nauchnogo Kommunizma. (RU ISSN 0202-2125) 3912

Obshchestvennye Nauki za Rubezhom. Sotsiologiya. (RU ISSN 0868-4448) 4458, 18
Obshchestvennye Nauki za Rubezhom. Vostokovedenie i Afrikanistika. (RU ISSN 0132-7348) 3647, 18
Obshchestvennye Nauki za Rubezhom. Yazykoznanie. (RU ISSN 0202-2133) 2856, 18
Obsidian II: Black Literature in Review. (US ISSN 0888-4412) 2944, 2018
Obst-Gemuese. (AU ISSN 0029-778X) 2078
Obst und Garten. (GW ISSN 0029-7798) 2136
Obst- und Weinbau see Obst - Wein - Garten 2136
Obst - Wein - Garten. (AU) 2136, 186
Obsta i Sravnitelna Patologiia. (BU ISSN 0324-1998) 3137
Obstbau. (GW) 111
Obstbau Aktuell. (AU) 112
Obstetric Anesthesia Digest. (US ISSN 0275-665X) 3192, 3295
Obstetrical & Gynecological Survey. (US ISSN 0029-7828) 3295
Obstetrics and Gynecology. see Akusherstvo i Ginekologiya 3289
Obstetrics and Gynecology. (US ISSN 0029-7844) 3295
Obstetrics and Gynecology Clinics. (US ISSN 0889-8545) 3295
Obstetrics - Gynecology Report. (US) 3295
Obvesila Republiske Maticne Sluzbe see Knjiznicarske Novice 2767
Obvestila. (XV) 338
Obwaldner Geschichtsblaetter. (SZ) 2378
Obzor. (IS) 2204
Obzor. (BU ISSN 0029-7852) 2945, 339
Obzor Vengerskogo Prava see Revue de Droit Hongrois 5270
Obzornik. (XV ISSN 0029-7860) 2878
Ocarina. (II) 2999
Occasional. (CN ISSN 0704-5824) 3531
Occasional Papers and Monographs - Centre of Asian Studies see University of Hong Kong. Centre of Asian Studies. Occasional Papers and Monographs 3645
Occasional Papers in Anthropology. (US ISSN 0078-3005) 246
Occasional Papers in Anthropology see Tempus 250
Occasional Papers in Commerce. (AT ISSN 0818-5166) 838
Occasional Papers in Economic and Social History see Monographs in Economic and Social History 897
Occasional Papers in English Local History. (UK ISSN 0078-303X) 2378
Occasional Papers in Entomology. (US ISSN 0362-2622) 536
Occasional Papers in Environmental Studies. (UK) 1965
Occasional Papers in Estate Management. (UK ISSN 0078-3048) 4154
Occasional Papers in Geography see Monographs in Geography 2256
Occasional Papers in German Studies. (UK ISSN 0307-7497) 2945, 2378, 2832
Occasional Papers in Linguistics and Language Learning. (UK ISSN 0308-2075) 2832
Occasional Papers in Middle Eastern Librarianship. (US ISSN 0278-4882) 2777
Occasional Papers in Modern Dutch Studies see Monographs in Modern Dutch Studies 2376
Occasional Papers in Modern Languages see Monographs in Modern Languages 2830
Occasional Papers in Slavic Languages and Literature. (US ISSN 0739-8972) 2945, 2832
Occasional Papers of the Museum of Zoology, University of Michigan see University of Michigan. Museum of Zoology. Occasional Papers 593

Occasional Papers on Linguistics. (US) 2832
Occasional Papers on Religion in Eastern Europe. (US ISSN 0731-5465) 4193, 2258
Occasional Papers on the Near East. (US ISSN 0732-6475) 2431
Occasional Papers - Reprint Series in Contemporary Asian Studies. (US ISSN 0730-0107) 2662, 2340
Occasional Publications in Northeastern Anthropology. (US ISSN 0276-8607) 246
Occasioni Giudiziarie. (IT) 2662
Occitania Passat e Present. (FR) 3912, 2378, 4444
Occult Publications Directory. (US) 3672, 408
Occultation Newsletter. (US ISSN 0737-6766) 367
†Occultism Update. (US ISSN 0731-7840) 5251
Occupation and Health. see Zhiye yu Jiankang 4116
Occupational Disease in California. (US) 3623, 990, 4582
Occupational Education. (US ISSN 0360-5434) 1713
Occupational Education News see Industrial Education 1708
Occupational Hazards. (US ISSN 0029-7909) 3619, 1965
Occupational Health. (US) 3838, 3623
Occupational Health & Safety. (US ISSN 0362-4064) 3619
▼Occupational Health & Safety Asbestos Control Buyer's Guide. (US) 3619
Occupational Health & Safety Canada see O H & S Canada 3619
Occupational Health and Safety Law. (CN ISSN 0706-5019) 2662, 3619
Occupational Health & Safety Letter. (US ISSN 0196-058X) 3619
Occupational Health & Safety News. (US) 3620, 1149
Occupational Health and Safety Topics/ Sujets se Rapportant a la Sante et la Securite au Travail. (CN ISSN 0706-5043) 3620
Occupational Health in Ontario. (CN ISSN 0705-9388) 3620, 1207, 4109
▼Occupational Health Management. (US) 3620, 3137
Occupational Health Nursing Newsletter.(US) 3620
Occupational Health Review. (UK ISSN 0951-4600) 3620
Occupational Hygiene Monographs. (UK ISSN 0141-7568) 3620
Occupational Injuries & Illnesses in Maine. (US) 990
Occupational Medicine. (UK) 3137, 3620
Occupational Medicine. see Zhiye Yixue 3164
Occupational Medicine. (US ISSN 0885-114X) 3620
Occupational Outlook Quarterly see U.S. Bureau of Labor Statistics. Occupational Outlook Quarterly 996
Occupational Pensions. (UK ISSN 0952-231X) 2539, 990, 4415
Occupational Programs in California Public Community Colleges. (US ISSN 0731-8650) 1695, 3630
Occupational Radiation Exposure, Annual Report see U.S. Nuclear Regulatory Commission. Occupational Radiation at Commercial Nuclear Power Reactors and Other Facilities. Annual Report 3622
Occupational Safety and Health Administration Compliance Advisor see O S H A Compliance Advisor 1964
Occupational Safety and Health Administration Training Bulletin for Supervisors see O S H A Training Bulletin for Supervisors 1964
Occupational Safety and Health Association Cal - O S H A Reporter see Cal - O S H A Reporter 3615
Occupational Safety and Health Decisions. (US ISSN 0092-3435) 3620

6516 OCCUPATIONAL SAFETY

Occupational Safety & Health Reporter. (US ISSN 0095-3237) **3620**
Occupational Safety and Health Series. (UN ISSN 0078-3129) **3620**
Occupational Safety and Health Series (New York). (US) **4109**
Occupational Safety and Health Week see O S H A Week **3619**
Occupational Therapy Forum. (US) **3137**
Occupational Therapy in Health Care. (US ISSN 0738-0577) **3137**
Occupational Therapy in Mental Health. (US ISSN 0164-212X) **3349**, 3137, 4415
Occupational Therapy Index. (UK ISSN 0950-6675) **3178**
Occupational Therapy Journal of Research. (US ISSN 0276-1599) **3137**
Occupational Therapy Newspaper see Occupational Therapy Week **3137**
Occupational Therapy Week. (US) **3137**
Ocean-Air Interactions. (US ISSN 0743-0876) **1609**
Ocean and Coast Exploitation. see Haiyang yu Hai'andai Kaifa **1604**
Ocean and Coastal Law Memo. (US ISSN 1052-6730) **2735**, 1494
Ocean and Coastal Management. (UK) **1609**
Ocean & Cruise News. (US) **4735**, 4781
Ocean and Shoreline Management see Ocean and Coastal Management **1609**
Ocean Challenge. (UK) **1609**
Ocean Construction Locator see Offshore Field Development International **3694**
†Ocean County Business Today. (US) **5251**
Ocean Development and International Law. (US ISSN 0090-8320) **1609**, 2727
†Ocean Dumping Control Act Annual Report. (CN) **5251**
Ocean Energy Program Summary see Conservation and Renewable Energy Technologies for Utility Technologies **1785**
Ocean Engineering. (US ISSN 0029-8018) **1609**, 1832
Ocean Indien Actuel. (MG) **2209**
Ocean Industry. (US ISSN 0029-8026) **3694**
Ocean Law Memo see Ocean and Coastal Law Memo **2735**
Ocean Navigator. (US ISSN 0886-0149) **4527**
Ocean Oil Weekly Report. (US ISSN 0029-8042) **3694**
†Ocean Physics and Engineering. (US ISSN 0890-5460) **5251**
Ocean Pollution Data and Information Network Update see O P D I N Update **1609**
Ocean Science and Engineering see Ocean Physics and Engineering **5251**
Ocean Science News. (US ISSN 0029-8069) **1609**
Ocean Science, Resources and Technology. (US) **1609**, 4827
Ocean Shipping Technology. see Hanghai Jishu **4728**
Ocean Soundings see Marine Technology Society Journal **1608**
Ocean Sports International. (US) **4552**
Ocean State College News. (US) **1319**
Ocean Technology. see Haiyang Jishu **1604**
Ocean Thermal Energy Conversion Workshop. Workshop Proceedings. (US ISSN 0271-2946) **1793**, 4827
Ocean University of Qingdao. Journal/ Qingdao Haiyang Daxue Xuebao. (CC ISSN 1001-1862) **1609**
Ocean Voice. (UK ISSN 0261-6777) **4735**, 1341
Ocean Wave and Tidal Energy Systems. (US) **1800**, 4835
Ocean Yearbook. (US ISSN 0191-8575) **1609**
Oceana Magazine. (US) **4781**
Oceana's Legal Almanacs, Second Series. (US) **2735**
Oceania. (AT ISSN 0029-8077) **246**
Oceanic Abstracts. (US ISSN 0748-1489) **1551**, 18
Oceanic Linguistics. (US ISSN 0029-8115) **2832**, 246
Oceanic Linguistics. Special Publications.(US ISSN 0078-3188) **2832**
Oceanic World. see Haiyang Shijie **1604**
Oceanis. (FR ISSN 0182-0745) **1609**
Oceanite. (Il ISSN 0029-8123) **4735**
Oceanografiska Institutet, Goeteborg. Meddelanden see Goeteborgs Universitet. Oceanografiska Institutionen. Reports **1604**
Oceanographic Monthly Summary see U.S. Department of Commerce. National Oceanic and Atmospheric Administration. Oceanographic Monthly Summary **1611**
Oceanographic Research Institute. Investigational Report. (SA ISSN 0078-320X) **590**, 1609
Oceanographical Magazine/Kisho-cho Obun Kaiyo Hokoku. (JA) **1609**
Oceanographical Society of Japan. Journal see Journal of Oceanography **1607**
Oceanography and Marine Biology: an Annual Review. (UK ISSN 0078-3218) **1609**, 450
Oceanologia. (PL ISSN 0078-3234) **1609**
Oceanologia et Limnologia Sinica see Haiyang yu Huzhao **1605**
Oceanologica Acta. (FR ISSN 0399-1784) **1609**
Oceanological Society of Korea. Journal.(KO ISSN 0374-8049) **1609**, 1576
Oceans. see Haiyang **1604**
Oceans. (FR ISSN 0475-171X) **4482**
†Oceans. (US ISSN 0029-8174) **5251**
Oceans. Conference Record. (US ISSN 0197-7385) **1832**
Oceans Policy News. (US) **2735**, 1965
Oceanus. (US ISSN 0029-8182) **1610**
Ochanomizu Chiri/Ochanomizu Geographical Society. Annals. (JA ISSN 0288-8726) **2258**
Ochanomizu Geographical Society. Annals. see Ochanomizu Chiri **2258**
Ochanomizu Joshi Daigaku Shizen Kagaku Hokoku/Ochanomizu University. Natural Science Report. (JA ISSN 0029-8190) **4331**
Ochanomizu University. Natural Science Report. see Ochanomizu Joshi Daigaku Shizen Kagaku Hokoku **4331**
Ocherki po Istorii Estestvoznaniya i Tekhniki. (KR) **2319**
Ochistka Vodnogo i Vozdushnogo Basseinov na Predpriyatiyakh Chernoi Metallurgii. (RU) **3417**
Ocho X Ocho. (SP) **4482**
Ochrana a Tvorba Zivotniho Prostredi v Zemedelstvi a Lesnictvi/ Environmental Conservation and Management in Agriculture and Forestry. (CS ISSN 0862-0598) **112**, 2105
Ochrana Ovzdusi/Air Conservation. (CS) **1978**
Ochrana Prirody see Pamatky a Priroda **1495**
Ochrana Rostlin/Plant Protection. (CS) **186**
Ochrona Powietrza. (PL) **3417**
Ochrona Pracy. (PL ISSN 0029-8220) **990**
Ochrona przed Korozja. (PL ISSN 0473-7733) **1832**
Ochrona Przyrody. (PL ISSN 0078-3250) **1494**
Ochrona Roslin. (PL ISSN 0029-8239) **112**
Ochrona Zabytkow. (PL ISSN 0029-8247) **339**
Ocrotirea Naturii si a Mediului Inconjurator. (RM ISSN 0029-8263) **4331**, 450
The Octagon. (US ISSN 0029-8271) **1185**
Octane. (CN ISSN 0835-1740) **4698**
Octane Week. (US) **3694**
October. (US ISSN 0162-2870) **339**, 2878, 2945, 3515
October. (UA) **878**
October. see Shi Yue **2959**
October Review/Shih Yueh P'ing Lun. (HK) **3912**
Ocular Fundus. see Yandi Bing **3305**
Ocular Surgery News. (US ISSN 8750-3085) **3382**, 3302
▼Ocular Surgery News International Edition. (US ISSN 1047-9120) **3382**, 3302
Ocular Therapeutics and Pharmacology.(US) **3302**, 3736
Oculi. (US) **339**, 2417
Ocultaciones de Estrellas por la Luna. (SP ISSN 0210-8119) **368**
Oculus. (NE ISSN 0029-8328) **3303**
Ocupacion y Desocupacion en el Gran Santiago. (CL) **990**
Od. (NE ISSN 0923-6600) **2777**, 4093
Od Meida. (IS ISSN 0792-3279) **2662**
O'Day Today. (US) **4527**
Odbrana. (YU ISSN 0029-8336) **3467**
Odbrana i Zastita. (YU ISSN 0029-8344) **1273**, 3467
Odd Fellow. (UK ISSN 0048-1408) **1300**
Oddfellow. (AT) **1300**
Odense Universitet. Arabisk Informationscenter. Nyhedsbrev see Mellemoest Information. Maanedsoversigt **3965**
Odense Universitet. Institut for Virksomhedsledelse. Skrifter. (DK ISSN 0108-8165) **1022**
Odense Universitet. Laboratorium for Folkesproglig Middelalderlitteratur. Mindre Skrifter. (DK ISSN 0106-2212) **2945**
Odense Universitetsbibliotek. Specialer og Prisopgaver. (DK ISSN 0107-1742) **1713**
†Odense University. Department of Commercial Law and Political Science. Publications. (DK ISSN 0903-5079) **5251**
Odense University Classical Studies. (DK ISSN 0107-1378) **1278**, 280
Odense University Slavic Studies. (DK ISSN 0078-3277) **2832**
Odense University Studies in Art History. (DK ISSN 0078-3285) **339**
Odense University Studies in English. (DK ISSN 0078-3293) **2832**
Odense University Studies in History and Social Sciences. (DK ISSN 0078-3307) **2378**
Odense University Studies in Linguistics.(DK ISSN 0078-3315) **2832**
Odense University Studies in Literature. (DK ISSN 0078-3323) **2945**
Odense University Studies in Philosophy. (DK ISSN 0107-7384) **3774**
Odense University Studies in Psychiatry and Medical Psychology. (DK ISSN 0105-0621) **3349**, 4037
Odense University Studies in Scandinavian Languages and Literatures. (DK ISSN 0078-3331) **2832**, 2945
Der Odenwald. (GW ISSN 0029-8360) **2190**
Odessa Poetry Review. (US) **2999**
Odgoj i Samoupravljanje. (CI ISSN 0351-4889) **1652**, 3774, 4037
Odi. (MW) **2945**
Odini/Welcome. (MW ISSN 0300-4651) **4271**
Odinn Magazine see Harvest Moon **3669**
Odjek. (BN ISSN 0029-8387) **2878**
Odlocanje/Decision. (XV) **4093**
Odonatologica. (NE ISSN 0375-0183) **450**
Odonto-Stomatologie Tropicale/Tropical Dental Journal. (FR ISSN 0251-172X) **3239**
Odontoiatria Oggi. (IT ISSN 0393-7631) **3239**
Odontoiatria Pratica. (IT) **3239**
Odontologi. (DK ISSN 0105-0141) **3239**
Odontologia see Revista Odontologia **3241**
Odontologia Chilena. (CL ISSN 0029-8417) **3239**
Odontologia Uruguaya. (UY ISSN 0029-8425) **3239**
Odontological Bulletin see Dental Society of Western Pennsylvania. Bulletin **3232**
Odontologiska Samfundet i Finland. Aarsbok. (FI ISSN 0078-3358) **3239**
Odontologo Moderno. (BL) **3239**
Odontology. see Shigaku **3242**
Odontoprotesi. (IT ISSN 0029-8492) **3239**
Odontostomatologia e Implantoprotesi. (IT ISSN 0391-3783) **3239**
Odontostomatological Progress. (GR ISSN 0029-8506) **3239**
Odra. (PL ISSN 0472-5182) **2945**, 339, 3774
Odrodzenie i Reformacja w Polsce. (PL ISSN 0029-8514) **2378**
▼Odtey Bichig/Special Delivery. (MP) **4654**
Odu. (NR ISSN 0029-8522) **2334**, 2945
†Oduma. (NR) **5251**
O'Dwyer's Directory of Corporate Communications. (US ISSN 0149-1091) **1149**, 1341
O'Dwyer's Directory of Public Relations Executives. (US ISSN 0191-0051) **1149**, 36
O'Dwyer's Directory of Public Relations Firms. (US ISSN 0078-3374) **1149**, 36
▼O'Dwyer's F A R A Report. (US ISSN 1055-3304) **36**, 2662
O'Dwyer's P R Services Report. (US) **36**
Odysseus. (US ISSN 0883-3664) **2456**, 4781
Odyssey. (SA ISSN 0256-0356) **3774**, 3596
Odyssey (Brattleboro). (US) **3967**
Odyssey (Daly City). (US) **4482**
Odyssey (Lexington). (US) **1713**
Odyssey (Peterborough). (US ISSN 0163-0946) **1261**, 368
Odyssey Institute Journal see Spotlight on A I D S **3224**
Odyssey International see Odyssey (Brattleboro) **3967**
Odziez. (PL ISSN 0471-0320) **1287**
Odzivi. (YU ISSN 0350-6584) **2378**
Oe G Z see Oesterreichische Gastgewerbe- und Hotelzeitung **2478**
Oe M V Annual Report (Year). (AU) **3694**
Oe M V - Magazin. (AU) **1220**
Oe M V - Zeitschrift see Oe M V - Magazin **1220**
Oecologia. (GW ISSN 0029-8549) **450**
Oecologia Applicata see Acta Oecologica **426**
Oecologia Generalis see Acta Oecologica **426**
Oecologica Plantarum see Acta Oecologica **426**
†Oeconomica Polona. (PL ISSN 0137-5806) **5251**
Oecumene. (FR) **4213**
Der Oeffentlich Bestellte und Vereidigte Sachverstaendige. (GW ISSN 0341-2016) **831**
Der Oeffentliche Dienst. (GW ISSN 0029-8565) **2662**, 4093
Oeffentliche Finanzen der Schweiz/ Finances Publiques en Suisse. (SZ) **1103**
Oeffentliche Gesundheitsdienst see Das Oeffentliche Gesundheitswesen **4109**
Das Oeffentliche Gesundheitswesen. (GW ISSN 0029-8573) **4109**
Oeffentliche Kunstsammlung. Jahresbericht see Oeffentliche Kunstsammlung. Museum fuer Gegenwart. Jahresbericht **3531**
Oeffentliche Kunstsammlung. Museum fuer Gegenwart. Jahresbericht. (SZ) **3531**
Oeffentliche Verkehr/Transports Publics.(SZ) **4666**

Die Oeffentliche Verwaltung. (GW ISSN 0029-859X) **4069**, 2662, 3912
†Oeffentliche Wirtschaft und Gemeinwirtschaft. (GW) **5251**
Das Oeffentliche Haushaltswesen in Oesterreich. (AU ISSN 0029-8581) **4069**
L'Oeil. (FR ISSN 0029-862X) **339**
Oeil. (SZ ISSN 0472-5263) **339**
Oeil et Lumiere. (FR) **3303**
Oeko.L. (AU) **4331**
Oeko-Mitteilungen. (GW) **1965**
Oeko-Test Magazin. (GW ISSN 0178-7608) **1507**, 1965
Oekologie und Landbau. (GW) **112**
Oekologie und Politik *see* OekologiePolitik **1494**
OekologiePolitik. (GW) **1494**, 3912
Oekonomaen. (DK) **2468**
Oekonomen *see* Juristen og Oekonomen **2641**
Oekonometrie und Unternehmensforschung/Econometrics and Operations Research. (US ISSN 0078-3390) **683**, 1022
Oekonomi og Politik. (DK ISSN 0030-1906) **683**
Oekonomiehistorische Texte. (GW ISSN 0233-0946) **683**
Oekonomische Studientexte *see* Oekonomiehistorische Texte **683**
Oekonomisk Analyse, Sommerregnskaber. (DK ISSN 0109-7725) **683**
Oekonomisk Kronik. (DK ISSN 0029-8646) **878**
Oekonomisk Oversigt for Amtskommunerne *see* Amstkommunernes Oekonomi **4084**
Oekonomisk Rapport. (NO) **1082**
Oekonomisk Revy. (NO ISSN 0030-1914) **878**
Oekonomisk Utsyn *see* Norway. Statistisk Sentralbyraa. Oekonomisk Utsyn **5249**
Oekonomiske Udvikling paa Faeroerne. (DK ISSN 0108-6464) **683**
Oekonomistryring og Informatik. (DK ISSN 0900-8322) **1022**, 1399
Oekoring. (GW) **112**
Oekowerkmagazin. (GW ISSN 0935-7602) **1494**, 450, 1965
†Oekumene am Ort. (GW ISSN 0175-5838) **5251**
Oekumenische Rundschau. (GW ISSN 0029-8654) **4193**
Oekumenische Studien. (NE ISSN 0169-9555) **4193**
Oekumenischer Informationsdienst. (GW ISSN 0179-9959) **4193**
Oel- und Gasfeuerung *see* Waermetechnik **2304**
Oelhydraulik und Pneumatik. (GW ISSN 0029-8697) **1937**, 3022
Oerlikon Schweissmitteilungen. (GW ISSN 0078-3420) **3417**
Oern Bladet. (SW ISSN 0284-4524) **1261**
†Oesterbottniska Posten. (FI) **5251**
Oesterreich Archiv. (AU) **2378**
†Oesterreich Florist. (AU) **5251**
Oesterreich-Nederland. (AU ISSN 0029-8751) **820**
Oesterreich - Polen, Austria - Polska. (AU ISSN 0030-6398) **2018**, 3967
Oesterreich 2000 *see* Grossunternehmen in Oesterreich **1076**

Oesterreichische Aerztezeitung. (AU ISSN 0029-8786) **3137**
Oesterreichische Akademie der Wissenschaften. Almanach. (AU ISSN 0378-8644) **4331**, 2512
Oesterreichische Akademie der Wissenschaften. Archiv fuer Oesterreichische Geschichte. (AU) **2379**
Oesterreichische Akademie der Wissenschaften. Iranische Kommission. Veroeffentlichungen. (AU) **2431**, 2832
Oesterreichische Akademie der Wissenschaften. Kommission fuer die Tabula Imperii Byzantini. Veroeffentlichungen. (AU) **2379**
Oesterreichische Akademie der Wissenschaften. Kommission fuer Linguistik und Kommunikationsforschung. Veroeffentlichungen. (AU) **2832**
Oesterreichische Akademie der Wissenschaften. Kommission fuer Literaturwissenschaft. Veroeffentlichungen. (AU) **2945**
Oesterreichische Akademie der Wissenschaften. Kommission fuer Musikforschung. Mitteilungen. (AU ISSN 0023-3048) **3571**
†Oesterreichische Akademie der Wissenschaften. Kommission fuer Sozial- und Wirtschaftswissenschaften. Veroeffentlichungen. (AU) **5251**
Oesterreichische Akademie der Wissenschaften. Kommission zur Herausgabe des Corpus der Lateinischen Kirchenvaeter. Veroeffentlichungen. (AU) **4271**
Oesterreichische Akademie der Wissenschaften. Numismatische Kommission. Veroeffentlichungen. (AU) **3601**
Oesterreichische Akademie der Wissenschaften. Philosophisch-Historische Klasse. Anzeiger. (AU ISSN 0378-8652) **2379**, 3774
Oesterreichische Akademie der Wissenschaften. Philosophisch-Historische Klasse. Sitzungsberichte. (AU) **2379**, 2945
Oesterreichische Akademie der Wissenschaften. Praehistorische Kommission. Mitteilungen. (AU ISSN 0065-5376) **2379**
Oesterreichische Akademie der Wissenschaften, Vienna. Mathematisch-Naturwissenschaftliche Klasse. Denkschriften. (US ISSN 0379-0207) **3049**, 4331
Oesterreichische Apotheker-Zeitung. (AU ISSN 0029-8859) **3736**
Oesterreichische Arbeitersaenger *see* Chormagazin **3545**
Oesterreichische Arbeitsgemeinschaft fuer Ur- und Fruehgeschichte. Mitteilungen *see* Archaeologie Oesterreichs **263**
Der Oesterreichische Arzt. (AU ISSN 0029-8875) **3137**
Oesterreichische Autorenzeitung. (AU ISSN 0029-8883) **3676**, 2945, 3571
Oesterreichische Baecker Zeitung. (AU) **2089**
Oesterreichische Bankwissenschaftliche Gesellschaft. Bankwissenschaftliche Schriftenreihe. (AU) **793**
Oesterreichische Bau-Wirtschaft. (AU ISSN 0048-1416) **627**
Oesterreichische Bauchronik. (AU) **627**
Oesterreichische Bauerbuendler. (AU) **112**
Oesterreichische Bauernzeitung. (AU ISSN 0029-8905) **112**
Oesterreichische Bauzeitung. (AU ISSN 0029-8891) **627**
Oesterreichische Beitraege zu Meteorologie und Geophysik. (GW) **3440**, 1592
Oesterreichische Blaetter fuer Gewerblichen Rechtsschutz und Urheberrecht. (AU ISSN 0029-8921) **3677**
Oesterreichische Botanische Zeitschrift *see* Plant Systematics and Evolution **515**
Das Oesterreichische Buch. (AU ISSN 0078-3455) **4134**
Oesterreichische Buergermeister Zeitung. (AU ISSN 0048-1424) **4093**
Oesterreichische Byzantinische Gesellschaft Jahrbuch *see* Oesterreichische Byzantinistik. Jahrbuch **2379**
Oesterreichische Byzantinistik. Jahrbuch.(AU ISSN 0378-8660) **2379**
Oesterreichische Caritas Zeitschrift *see* Caritas-Zeitschrift **4400**
Oesterreichische Chemie Zeitschrift. (AU) **1185**
Oesterreichische Dachdecker- und Pflasterer-Zeitung *see* Dach und Wand Abdichtung **615**

Oesterreichische Dentistenzeitschrift *see* Oesterreichische Zahnaerzte - Zeitung **3239**
Die Oesterreichische Feuerwehr. (AU ISSN 0029-9030) **2034**
Oesterreichische Fleischer-Zeitung. (AU) **222**
Oesterreichische Foerster Zeitung. (AU ISSN 0029-9502) **2105**
Oesterreichische Forstzeitung. (AU) **2105**
Oesterreichische Foto-Zeitung. (AU ISSN 0048-1459) **3793**
Der Oesterreichische Friseur. (AU ISSN 0029-9065) **374**
Oesterreichische Fussbodenzeitung. (AU ISSN 0029-9081) **2561**
Oesterreichische Galerie. Mitteilungen. (AU ISSN 0029-909X) **3531**
Oesterreichische Gastgewerbe- und Hotelzeitung. (AU) **2478**, 4781
Oesterreichische Gastgewerbe-Zeitung *see* Oesterreichische Gastgewerbe- und Hotelzeitung **2478**
Oesterreichische Gefluegelwirtschaft. (AU ISSN 0029-9111) **222**
Oesterreichische Gemeinde-Zeitung. (AU ISSN 0029-912x) **4093**
Oesterreichische Geographische Gesellschaft. Mitteilungen. (AU ISSN 0029-9138) **2258**, 1547
Oesterreichische Geologische Gesellschaft. Mitteilungen. (AU ISSN 0251-7493) **1576**, 3658
Oesterreichische Gesellschaft fuer Artificial Intelligence Journal *see* O E G A I Journal **1880**
†Oesterreichische Gesellschaft fuer Chirurgie. Mitteilungen. (AU) **5251**
Oesterreichische Gesellschaft fuer Filmwissenschaft. Mitteilungen *see* Oesterreichische Gesellschaft fuer Filmwissenschaft, Kommunikations- und Medienforschung. Mitteilungen **3515**
Oesterreichische Gesellschaft fuer Filmwissenschaft, Kommunikations- und Medienforschung. Mitteilungen. (AU) **3515**
Oesterreichische Gesellschaft fuer Holzforschung. Schrifttumskarteidienst - Card Index Service. (AU ISSN 0029-9154) **2116**
Oesterreichische Gesellschaft fuer Musik. Beitraege. (GW ISSN 0078-3471) **3571**
Oesterreichische Glaserzeitung *see* Glas - Oesterreichische Glaserzeitung **1163**
Das Oesterreichische Graphische Gewerbe. (AU ISSN 0029-9170) **4003**
Oesterreichische Handelskammer in der Schweiz. Mitteilungen. (SZ) **820**
Oesterreichische Hausbesitz. (AU ISSN 0029-9189) **4154**
Oesterreichische Hochschulstatistik. (AU ISSN 0067-2343) **1679**
Oesterreichische Hochschulzeitung. (AU) **4331**
Die Oesterreichische Hoehere Schule. (AU ISSN 0029-9200) **1713**
Oesterreichische Immobilien-Zeitung. (AU) **4154**
Der Oesterreichische Installateur. (AU ISSN 0029-9227) **2302**
Oesterreichische Installateurzeitung. (AU ISSN 0029-9235) **2302**
Oesterreichische Juristen - Zeitung. (AU ISSN 0029-9251) **2662**
Oesterreichische Komponisten des 20. Jahrhunderts. (AU ISSN 0078-3501) **3571**, 420
Oesterreichische Krankenhaus Zeitung (AU ISSN 0029-876X) **2468**
Oesterreichische Krankenpflegezeitschrift. (AU ISSN 0303-4461) **3285**
Oesterreichische Kunststoff Zeitschrift. (AU) **3864**
Oesterreichische Kunststoff Zeitung *see* Oesterreichische Kunststoff Zeitschrift **3864**
Oesterreichische Landwirtschaft. Monatsberichte. (AU ISSN 0026-9220) **155**
Oesterreichische Lederwaren *see* O L W **5251**

DER OESTERREICHISCHE

Oesterreichische Luftfahrt Presse. (AU) **4676**
Die Oesterreichische Milchwirtschaft. (AU) **202**
Oesterreichische Militaerische Zeitschrift.(AU ISSN 0048-1440) **3467**
Oesterreichische Monatshefte. (AU ISSN 0029-9308) **3912**
Oesterreichische Musikzeitschrift. (AU ISSN 0029-9316) **3571**
Oesterreichische Naehmaschinen- und Fahrrad-Zeitung *see* Oesterreichische Naehmaschinen- und Zweirad-Zeitung **3022**
Oesterreichische Naehmaschinen- und Zweirad-Zeitung. (AU) **3022**
▼Oesterreichische Nationalbank. Berichte und Studien. (AU) **793**
Oesterreichische Nationalbank. Geschaeftsbericht ueber das Geschaeftsjahr mit Jahresabschluss - Annual Report. (AU) **794**
Oesterreichische Nationalbank. Mitteilungen des Direktoriums *see* Oesterreichische Nationalbank. Statistisches Monatsheft **794**
Oesterreichische Nationalbank. Statistisches Monatsheft. (AU) **794**
Oesterreichische Nationalbank, Bericht ueber das Geschaeftsjahr mit Rechnungsabschluss - Annual Report *see* Oesterreichische Nationalbank. Geschaeftsbericht ueber das Geschaeftsjahr mit Jahresabschluss - Annual Report **794**
Oesterreichische Notariats-Zeitung. (AU ISSN 0029-9340) **2662**
Oesterreichische Numismatische Gesellschaft. Mitteilungen. (AU ISSN 0029-9359) **3601**
Oesterreichische Osthefte. (AU ISSN 0029-9375) **3912**, 4444
Oesterreichische Paedagogische Warte *see* K L O E Impulse **1644**
Oesterreichische Papier *see* Papier aus Oesterreich **3665**
Oesterreichische Papier-Zeitung *see* Papier und Druck **3665**
Oesterreichische Raumausstatterzeitung. (AU ISSN 0029-9405) **2561**
Oesterreichische Reiter - Zeitung. (AU) **4536**
Oesterreichische Restaurant & G V - Praxis. (AU) **2478**
Oesterreichische Schriften zur Entwicklungshilfe. (AU ISSN 0078-3536) **933**
Oesterreichische Schuhhaendler *see* Schuh-Revue **4361**
Oesterreichische Sparkassenzeitung. (AU) **794**
Der Oesterreichische Spengler und Kupferschmied. (AU ISSN 0029-9499) **627**
Oesterreichische Staatsfoerster-Zeitung *see* Oesterreichische Foerster Zeitung **2105**
Oesterreichische Steuer und Wirtschaftskarei *see* Steuer und Wirtschaftskartei **740**
Oesterreichische Steuerzeitung. (AU ISSN 0029-9529) **1103**
Oesterreichische Textil-Mitteilungen. (AU ISSN 0029-9545) **4622**
Oesterreichische Textil Zeitung. (AU) **4622**
Oesterreichische Textilreiniger-, Waescher- und Faerberzeitschrift *see* T W F **1282**
Oesterreichische Tieraerztezeitung. (AU ISSN 0048-1475) **4813**
Oesterreichische Tierschutzzeitung. (AU) **1494**
Oesterreichische Touristenzeitung. (AU ISSN 0048-1483) **4781**, 4552
Oesterreichische Trafikanten-Zeitung. (AU ISSN 0029-9561) **4644**
Oesterreichische Verkehrswissenschaftliche Gesellschaft. Mitteilungen. (AU) **4720**
Oesterreichische Volkskundliche Bibliographie. (AU ISSN 0259-0778) **2057**, 246, 339
Der Oesterreichische Volkswirt. (AU ISSN 0029-957X) **878**

6518 OESTERREICHISCHE WASSERWIRTSCHAFT

Oesterreichische Wasserwirtschaft. (US ISSN 0029-9588) **4827**
Oesterreichische Weinzeitung. (AU) **112**
Oesterreichische Zahnaerzte - Zeitung. (AU ISSN 0029-9596) **3239**
Oesterreichische Zahntechniker see Das Oesterreichische Zahntechnikerhandwerk **3239**
Das Oesterreichische Zahntechnikerhandwerk. (AU) **3239**
Oesterreichische Zeitschrift fuer Elektrizitaetswirtschaft see O Z E **1904**
Oesterreichische Zeitschrift fuer Kunst und Denkmalpflege. (AU ISSN 0029-9626) **339, 280**
Oesterreichische Zeitschrift fuer Oeffentliches Recht und Voelkerrecht. Supplement. (US ISSN 0173-1718) **2662**
Oesterreichische Zeitschrift fuer Oeffentliches Recht und Voelkerrecht/Austrian Journal of Public and International Law. (US ISSN 0378-3073) **2663, 2727**
Oesterreichische Zeitschrift fuer Politikwissenschaft. (AU) **3912**
Oesterreichische Zeitschrift fuer Rechnungswesen. (AU ISSN 1018-3779) **754**
Oesterreichische Zeitschrift fuer Soziologie. (AU) **4444**
Oesterreichische Zeitschrift fuer Vermessungswesen see Oesterreichische Zeitschrift fuer Vermessungswesen und Photogrammetrie **2258**
Oesterreichische Zeitschrift fuer Vermessungswesen und Photogrammetrie. (AU) **2258**
Oesterreichische Zeitschrift fuer Volkskunde. (AU ISSN 0029-9669) **2057**
Oesterreichische Zeitschrift fuer Wirtschaftsrecht. (AU ISSN 0379-4407) **1103, 2727**
Der Oesterreichische Zimmermeister. (AU ISSN 0029-9677) **640**
Oesterreichische Zoll und Steuer Nachrichten. (AU ISSN 0029-9685) **1103**
Oesterreichischen Gesellschaft zur Erforschung des 18. Jahrhunderts. Beihefte zum Jahrbuch. (AU) **2379**
Oesterreichischen Karl-Jaspers-Gesellschaft. Jahrbuch. (AU) **3774**
Oesterreichischer Alpenverein. Akademische Sektion Graz. Mitteilungen. (AU ISSN 0029-8840) **4552**
Oesterreichischer Alpenverein. Mitteilungen. (AU ISSN 0029-9715) **4552**
Oesterreichischer Auslandsstudentendienst. Rechenschaftsbericht. (AU) **1723**
Oesterreichischer Blindenverband. Mitteilungen. (AU ISSN 0029-9723) **2295**
Oesterreichischer Buchklub der Jugend. Jahrbuch. (AU ISSN 0078-3560) **1261**
Der Oesterreichische Filmamateur. (AU ISSN 0029-9057) **3515, 2440**
Oesterreichischer Kleintierzuechter. (AU ISSN 0029-9766) **4813**
Oesterreichischer Krankenpflegerverband. Fortbildungsprogramm. (AU) **3285, 1713**
Oesterreichischer Luftfahrt Pressedienst see Oesterreichische Luftfahrt Presse **4676**
Oesterreichischer Markenanzeiger. (AU ISSN 0029-9782) **3677**
Oesterreichischer Musikrat - Bulletin. (AU) **3571**
Oesterreichischer Patentinhaber- und Erfinderverband. (AU) **3571**
Oesterreichischer Personenverkehr. (AU ISSN 0029-9790) **4654**
†Der Oesterreichischer Schuhmarkt. (AU) **5251**
Oesterreichisches Archaeologisches Institut. Jahreshefte. (AU) **280**
Oesterreichisches Archaeologisches Institut. Jahreshefte: Grabungen see Oesterreichisches Archaeologisches Institut. Jahreshefte **280**
Oesterreichisches Archiv fuer Kirchenrecht. (AU ISSN 0029-9820) **2663, 4193**
Oesterreichisches Cafe Journal. (AU ISSN 0029-9847) **2478**
Oesterreichisches Forschungsinstitut fuer Sparkassenwesen. Schriftenreihe.(AU ISSN 0472-5859) **794**
Oesterreichisches Getraenke Institut. Mitteilungen. (AU) **384**
Oesterreichisches Institut fuer Bauforschung Nachrichten see I B Nachrichten **620**
Oesterreichisches Institut fuer Mittelstandspolitik. Schriftenreihe see Oesterreichisches Wirtschaftsinstitut fuer Strukturforschung und Strukturpolitik. Schriftenreihe **5251**
Oesterreichisches Institut fuer Raumplanung. Oe I R - Forum. (AU) **2493**
Oesterreichisches Institut fuer Wirtschaftsforschung. Monatsberichte. (AU ISSN 0029-9898) **683**
Oesterreichisches Jahrbuch fuer Internationale Politik. (AU) **3967**
Oesterreichisches Jahrbuch fuer Politik. (AU ISSN 0170-0847) **3912**
Oesterreichisches Jugendrotkreuz. Arbeitsblaetter. (AU ISSN 0029-9901) **4415, 1261, 3807**
Oesterreichisches Kolpingblatt. (AU ISSN 0029-9928) **1261**
Oesterreichisches Kulturinstitut, Rom. Abteilung fuer Historische Studien. Publikationen I. Abteilung: Abhandlungen. (AU) **2379**
Oesterreichisches Kulturinstitut, Rom. Abteilung fuer Historische Studien. Publikationen II. Abteilung: Quellen. (AU) **2379**
Oesterreichisches Museum fuer Volkskunde. Kataloge. (AU) **3536**
Oesterreichisches Museum fuer Volkskunde: Veroeffentlichungen. (AU) **2057, 246, 339**
Oesterreichisches Ost- und Suedosteuropa Institut. Schriftenreihe. (AU ISSN 0078-3439) **2379**
Oesterreichisches Patentblatt. (AU ISSN 0029-9944) **3677**
Oesterreichisches Produktivitaets- und Wirtschaftlichkeits-Zentrum (OPWZ) Betriebswirtschaftliche O P W Z - Dokumentation see Betriebswirtschaftliche O P W Z - Dokumentation **5147**
Oesterreichisches Raiffeisenblatt. (AU) **112**
Oesterreichisches Recht der Wirtschaft. (AU ISSN 1013-9486) **683, 2663**
Oesterreichisches Staatsarchiv. Mitteilungen. (AU ISSN 0067-2297) **2379**
Oesterreichisches Staatsarchiv. Publikationen. (AU) **2777**
Oesterreichisches Standesamt. (AU ISSN 0029-9952) **2663**
Oesterreichisches Statistisches Zentralamt. Wirtschaftsstatistik der Elektrizitatsversorgungsunternehmen. (AU) **1904**
Oesterreichisches Volksliedwerk. Jahrbuch. (AU ISSN 0473-8624) **3571**
†Oesterreichisches Wirtschaftsinstitut fuer Strukturforschung und Strukturpolitik. Schriftenreihe. (AU ISSN 0078-3595) **5251**
Oesterreichisches Fischerei. (AU ISSN 0029-9987) **2047**
Oesterreichs Kanusport. (AU) **4527**
Oesterreichs Paddelsport see Oesterreichs Kanusport **4527**
Oesterreichs Volkseinkommen. (AU ISSN 0085-4433) **733**
Oesterreichs Weidwerk. (AU ISSN 0030-0012) **4482, 1494**
Oesterreichs Wirtschaft im Ueberblick. see Survey of the Austrian Economy **839**
Oesteuropa Frimaerkekatalog see A F A Oesteuropa Frimaerkekatalog **3748**
†Oestnyt. (DK ISSN 0108-4380) **5251**
L'Oeuf. (CN) **1319**
Oeuvres et Critiques. (GW ISSN 0338-1900) **2945**
Of a Like Mind. (US ISSN 0892-5984) **4193, 4850**
▼Of Cabbages and Kings. (US ISSN 0000-1376) **1261**
Of Counsel. (US ISSN 0730-3815) **2663, 1022, 1060, 1068**
Of Human Rights. (US) **3945**
Of Sea and Shore. (US ISSN 0030-0055) **590**
Ofakim. (IS ISSN 0017-8926) **3912, 4381**
Ofari's Bi-Monthly. (US) **2018, 3912**
Ofenbau Plattenbelage. (SZ) **1165**
La Oferta Review. (US) **2231**
†Off Beat. (US) **5251**
Off-Beat Letters. (US) **3399**
Off Broadway. (US) **4636, 1531**
Off Campus Study Programs: U S and Abroad see Architecture Schools: Special Programs **293**
Off Duty America. (US) **3467**
Off Duty - Europe. (US) **3467**
Off Duty - Pacific. (HK) **3467**
Off-Hollywood Report. (US) **3515**
Off-Lead. (US ISSN 0094-0186) **3712**
Off Licence News. (UK ISSN 0043-5775) **384**
Off-Line see C S O Update **1390**
Off Main Street. (US) **2945**
Off Our Backs. (US ISSN 0030-0071) **4860**
Off-Price News see Value Retail News **1056**
Off Road. (US) **4698**
Off-Road Advertiser. (US ISSN 1042-0819) **4698**
Off Road and 4 Wheel Drive. (UK ISSN 0953-203X) **4698, 3022**
Off-Road Canada see Custom Truck & Trail Canada **4688**
Off Road Vehicles and Adventure see Off Road **4698**
Off-Shore Technology Conference. Record. (US ISSN 0078-3706) **3694, 1904**
Offa-Jahrbuch; Vor- und Fruehgeschichte. (GW ISSN 0078-3714) **2379**
Offenbacher Geschichtsblaetter. (GW ISSN 0471-122X) **2379**
Offenbacher Verein fuer Naturkunde. Abhandlungen. (GW ISSN 0171-7936) **590, 512**
Offenbacher Verein fuer Naturkunde. Bericht. (GW ISSN 0343-2793) **590, 512**
Offene Tor. (GW) **2190**
Offene Tore. (SZ ISSN 0030-0101) **4286**
Offene Tueren. (GW ISSN 0030-011X) **4193**
Offense Newsletter. (US) **3571**
Offer see Rond de Tafel **4199**
Office. (US ISSN 0030-0128) **1060, 1452, 1471**
Office Administration and Automation see Administrative Management (New York) **1001**
Office at Home. (UK ISSN 0951-9718) **1117**
Office Automation Report. (US) **1482**
Office Automation Update. (US) **1415**
Office Central des Transports Internationaux Ferroviaires. Bulletin. (SZ) **4712, 2663**
Office Computing Report. (US ISSN 1057-8889) **1452, 1482**
Office - Data Processing Machines: Latin American Industrial Report. (US) **1424, 838**
Office de la Recherche Scientifique et Technique Outre-Mer de M'Bour. Centre de Geophysique. Bulletin Seismique. (SG) **1592**
Office de la Recherche Scientifique et Technique Outre-Mer Initiations Documentations Techniques see O.R.S.T.O.M. Initiations Documentations Techniques **5251**
Office de la Recherche Scientifique et Technique Outre-Mer Resumes des Travaux. Oceanographie see O.R.S.T.O.M. Resumes des Travaux. Oceanographie **1609**
Office Dealer (Year). (US) **1060, 1149**
Office des Communications Sociales, Montreal. Cahiers d'Etudes et de Recherches. (CN ISSN 0078-3722) **1341, 1377**
Office des Communications Sociales Nouvelles see O C S Nouvelles **1341**
Office Equipment and Methods see Office Systems & Technology **1060**
Office Equipment and Products. (JA ISSN 0387-5245) **1776, 1060**
Office Equipment Exporter. (US ISSN 0471-1424) **1060, 918**
Office Equipment News. (UK ISSN 0030-0187) **1060**
Office for Metropolitan History. Plans Filed. (US) **2417**
Office for Metropolitan History. Research and Remarks on Current Topics see Office for Metropolitan History. Plans Filed **2417**
Office Furniture. (IT ISSN 1120-2386) **2554**
Office General de la Musique Annuaire O.G.M. see Annuaire O.G.M **3538**
Office Guide. (US ISSN 0273-964X) **1060**
Office Guide for Working Women see Office Guide **1060**
Office Guide to Broward & Palm Beach Counties. (US) **1060**
Office Guide to Miami see South Florida Office Guide **1061**
Office Guide to Orlando. (US ISSN 0733-1266) **4154**
Office Guide to Phoenix see Arizona Business & Development **1057**
Office Guide to Tampa Bay. (US) **683**
Office Intercantonal de Controle de Medicaments. Bulletin Mensuel. see Interkantonale Kontrollstelle fuer Heilmittel. Monatsbericht **3109**
Office International de l'Enseignement Catholique Bulletin see O I E C Bulletin **4193**
Office International de la Vigne et du Vin. Reglements. (FR) **384**
Office International de la Vigne et du Vin Bulletin see O I V Bulletin **384**
Office International de la Vigne et du Vin Lettre see O.I.V. Lettre **384**
Office International de la Vigne et du Vin Memento de l'O.I.V. see Memento de l'O.I.V **5235**
Office International des Epizooties Bulletin see O.I.E. Bulletin **4813**
Office International des Epizooties Revue Scientifique et Technique see O.I.E. Revue Scientifique et Technique **4813**
Office Life. (SZ ISSN 0379-248X) **1452, 827**
Office Magazine. (UK ISSN 0269-3046) **1060**
Office Management. (GW ISSN 0343-2319) **828**
Office Management see Officemation Product Reports **828**
Office Management and Automation see Office Systems & Technology **1060**
Office Management Report see Professional Office Manager **5262**
Office National d'Information sur les Enseignements et les Professions (ONISEP) Communique see O N I S E P Communique **3630**
Office National de Recherches Scientifiques du Cameroun. Recherches et Etudes Camerounaises. (CM) **246**
Office News. (AT) **1060**
Office News and Automation see Office News **1060**
Office Newsletter see O N **1060**
Office Number One. (US) **2999**
Office of Management and Budget Watcher see O M B Watcher **4069**

OFFIZIELLES VERZEICHNIS

Office of the Provost at Notre Dame see Notre Dame Report **1319**
Office of Thrift Supervision. (US ISSN 1050-4834) **794, 4154**
†Office Pride. (UK) **5251**
Office Product News. (CN) **1022**
Office Product News Directory. (CN) **1022**
Office Products Analyst. (US) **1060, 1399**
Office Products Dealer Buying Guide and Directory. (US) **1060**
Office Products Industry Report. (US ISSN 0746-5467) **1060**
▼Office Products News. (NZ) **1060**
Office Products S A. (SA) **1060**
Office Professional. (US ISSN 0739-3156) **1060**
Office Regional d'Action Culturelle see O R A C L **2944**
Office Skills Workshop. (US) **1060, 3630**
Office Supervisor's Bulletin see Supervisor's Bulletin: Office Edition **1062**
Office Supplies Business Magazine. (CN) **1060**
Office Systems (Year). (US) **1060**
Office Systems & Technology. (CN) **1060, 828**
Office Systems Dealer (Year) see Office Dealer (Year) **1060**
Office Systems Research Association. Conference Proceedings. (US) **1060, 733**
Office Systems Research Journal. (US ISSN 0737-8998) **1060**
†Office Technology Management. (US) **5251**
Office Trade News. (UK) **1060**
Office Universitaire de Recherche Socialiste. Cahiers. (FR ISSN 0078-3803) **3912**
Office World News see O W N **1060**
Officemation Product Reports. (US ISSN 0161-8768) **828, 1445**
Officemation Reports see Officemation Product Reports **828**
†OfficeNews. (US) **5252**
Officer. (US ISSN 0030-0268) **3467**
Officer Review. (US ISSN 0736-7317) **3467**
Officers Call. (US ISSN 1040-029X) **3467**
Offices de Commercialisation au Canada. see Marketing Boards in Canada **5232**
Official (Los Angeles). (US ISSN 0192-5784) **2302**
Official (Year) Directory of Festivals, Sports & Special Events see I E G Directory of Sponsorship Marketing **1040**
Official Airline Guide. North American Edition. (US ISSN 0191-1619) **4676**
Official Airline Guide. WorldWide Edition.(US ISSN 0364-3875) **4676**
Official Airline Guides, Inc. Air Cargo Guide see O A G Air Cargo Guide **4676**
Official Airline Guides, Inc. Business Travel Planner. North American Edition see O A G Business Travel Planner. North American Edition **4780**
Official Airline Guides, Inc. (New York) Frequent Flyer see O A G Frequent Flyer **4676**
Official Airline Guides, Inc. Pocket Flight Guide Europe, Middle East, Africa Edition see O A G Pocket Flight Guide Europe, Middle East, Africa Edition **4676**
Official Airline Guides, Inc. Pocket Flight Guide North American Edition see O A G Pocket Flight Guide North American Edition **4676**
Official Airline Guides, Inc. Pocket Flight Guide Pacific Asia Edition see O A G Pocket Flight Guide Pacific Asia Edition **4676**
Official Airline Guides, Inc. Travel Planner Hotel & Motel Redbook. European Edition see O A G Travel Planner Hotel & Motel Redbook. European Edition **4780**

Official Airline Guides, Inc. Travel Planner Hotel & Motel Redbook. Pacific Asia Edition see O A G Travel Planner Hotel & Motel Redbook. Pacific Asia Edition **4780**
Official Airline Guides, Inc. Worldwide Cruise & Shipline Guide see O A G Worldwide Cruise & Shipline Guide **4780**
Official Baseball Guide. (US ISSN 0078-3838) **4509**
Official Baseball Record Book see Complete Baseball Record Book **4502**
Official Baseball Register. (US ISSN 0162-542X) **4509**
Official Baseball Rules. (US ISSN 0078-3846) **4509**
Official Board Markets. (US ISSN 0030-0284) **3650, 3663**
Official Bulletin for Industrial Property. see Buletin Oficial de Proprietate Industrial **3673**
Official Bus Guide see Russell's Official National Motor Coach Guide **4785**
Official Catholic Directory. (US ISSN 0078-3854) **4271**
Official Container Directory. (US ISSN 0030-0292) **3650, 3663**
Official Detective Stories. (US ISSN 0030-0306) **2986**
Official Directory of New Jersey Libraries and Media Centers. (US) **1149, 2777**
Official Directory of New Jersey Libraries and Media Centers Including Finding see Official Directory of New Jersey Libraries and Media Centers **1149**
Official Electronic Keyboard Bluebook. (US) **3571**
Official Export Guide. (US) **918**
Official Gazette for the Sunday Democrats. see Episimos Ephimeris tis Kyriakes Demokratias **2184**
Official Gazette of Guyana. (GY ISSN 0030-0314) **4069**
Official Gazette of the United States Patent and Trademark Office. Patents. (US ISSN 0098-1133) **3677**
Official Gazette of the United States Patent and Trademark Office. Trademarks Supplements. (US ISSN 0360-5132) **3677**
Official Guide for G M A T Review. (Graduate Management Admission Test) (US) **1022, 1713**
Official Guide of the Railways and Steam Navigation Lines of the United States, Puerto Rico, Canada, Mexico and Cuba, Airline Schedules see Official Railway Guide. North American Freight Service Edition **4712**
Official Guide to Airline Careers. (US) **3630**
Official Guide to American Historic Bed and Breakfast Inns and Guesthouses see Official Guide to American Historic Inns **4781**
Official Guide to American Historic Inns.(US ISSN 1043-1195) **4781, 2478**
Official Guide to Christian Camps & Conference Centers. (US) **4193**
Official Guide to Flight Attendants Careers. (US) **3630, 4676**
Official Guide to Food Service and Hospitality Management Careers. (US) **3630, 2078**
Official Guide to Hotels and Restaurants in Great Britain, Ireland and Overseas see Hotels and Restaurants of Britain **2476**
Official Guide to M B A Programs. (US) **1022, 1713**
Official Guide to Travel Agent & Travel Careers. (US) **3630, 4676**
Official Guide to U.S. Law Schools. (US ISSN 0886-3342) **1713, 2663**
Official Guide: Tractors and Farm Equipment. (US ISSN 0162-6809) **164, 1049, 3022**
Official Handbook of Ghana. (GH ISSN 0072-9825) **2334**
Official Handbook of the A.A.U. Code see Amateur Athletic Union of the United States. Official Handbook of the A A U Code **4463**

Official Hotel and Resort Guide see Official Hotel Guide **2478**
Official Hotel Guide. (US) **2478, 4781**
▼Official I R S Publications. (US) **1103**
Official Industrial Equipment Guide. (US ISSN 0889-3950) **164, 1049, 3022**
Official Intermodal Equipment Register. (US ISSN 0190-6690) **4654**
Official Intermodal Guide. (US) **1149, 4654**
Official International Business Directory of the Latin American World. (US) **1149**
Official International Business Directory of the Spanish Speaking World see Official International Business Directory of the Latin American World **1149**
Official International Wrestling Insider. (US) **4482**
Official Journal (Patents). (UK ISSN 0030-0330) **3677**
Official Journal of Industrial and Commercial Property. (IE ISSN 0030-0349) **3677**
Official Journal of the European Communities. C Series: Information and Notices. (EI) **3967**
Official Journal of the European Communities. L & C: Legislation and Competition. (EI) **3967**
Official Journal of the European Communities. L Series: Legislation see Official Journal of the European Communities. L & C: Legislation and Competition **3967**
Official Lawn Bowls Almanac. (US) **4509**
Official Meeting Facilities Guide. (US ISSN 0094-5242) **3394**
Official Meeting Facilities Guide - European Edition. (US) **3394**
Official Motor Carrier Directory. (US) **4747**
Official Motor Freight Guide. (US ISSN 0030-0357) **4747**
Official Museum Directory. (US ISSN 0090-6700) **3531**
Official N A S C A R Yearbook and Press Guide. (US) **4698**
Official N B A Guide. (National Basketball Association) (US ISSN 0078-3862) **4509**
Official National Collegiate Athletic Association Football Rules and Interpretations see N C A A Football Rules and Interpretations **4508**
Official National Collegiate Athletic Association Soccer Guide see N C A A Men's and Women's Soccer Rules **4508**
Official National Collegiate Athletic Association Track and Field Guide see N C A A Men's and Women's Cross Country and Track & Field Rules **4550**
Official National Collegiate Athletic Association Wrestling Guide see N C A A Wrestling Rules **4480**
Official National Directory of Service and Product Providers to Nonprofit Organizations. (US) **1149**
Official New Mexico Blue Book. (US ISSN 0732-3093) **2417**
Official Ohio State University Men's Basketball Program. (US) **4509**
Official Port of Detroit World Handbook.(US ISSN 0093-1799) **4735**
Official Railway Equipment Register. (US ISSN 0030-0373) **4712**
Official Railway Guide. North American Freight Service Edition. (US ISSN 0190-6704) **4712**
Official Railway Guide. North American Passenger Travel Edition see Official Railway Guide. North American Travel Edition **4712**
Official Railway Guide. North American Travel Edition. (US ISSN 0273-9658) **4712, 4781**
Official Read-Easy Basketball Rules see N C A A Men's Read-Easy Basketball Rules **4508**
Official Registry of C B Operators. (US) **1357**

Official S S Guide see Official Steamship Guide **4735**
Official Shippers Guide - Chicago Motor Freight Directory. (US) **4654**
Official Shippers Guide - New York Motor Express Guide. (US) **4747**
Official Shippers Guide - St. Louis Motor Freight Directory. (US) **4747, 4735**
Official South African Municipal Yearbook/Amptelike Suid-Afrikaanse Munisipale Jaarboek. (SA) **4093**
Official Southern California Ports Maritime Directory and Guide. (US ISSN 0094-8454) **4735**
Official Steamship Guide. (US ISSN 0030-0381) **4735, 4781**
Official Used Car Trade-In Guide see N A D A Official Wholesale Used Car Trade-In Guide **4697**
Official Video Directory & Buyer's Guide.(US ISSN 0890-782X) **1149, 1385**
Official Visitors Guide to Central Florida.(US) **4781**
Official Wisconsin Pastoral Handbook. (US) **4271**
Official Year Book of New South Wales see New South Wales Year Book **4580**
Official Year Book of Western Australia see Western Australian Yearbook **2346**
Officiel Batiment et Travaux Publics see Saint-Lambert, l'Annuaire Batiment et Travaux Publics **631**
L'Officiel de l'Artisan Rural. (FR) **164**
Officiel de l'Automobile. (FR ISSN 0030-0454) **4698**
Officiel de l'Equipement Menager see Officiel des Cuisinistes, des Bainistes et des Electromenagistes **838**
Officiel de l'Homeopathie et de l'Acupuncture. (FR) **3215**
Officiel de la Couture et de la Mode de Paris. (FR ISSN 0030-0403) **1293**
Officiel de la Droguerie. (FR ISSN 0030-0411) **1049**
Officiel de la Sage-Femme. (FR) **3295, 3285**
Officiel des Activites des Plastiques et du Caoutchouc see Officiel des Plastiques et du Caoutchouc **3864**
Officiel des Comites d'Entreprise et Services Sociaux. (FR ISSN 0010-2458) **4415**
Officiel des Cuisinistes, des Bainistes et des Electromenagistes. (FR ISSN 0399-8290) **838**
Officiel des Galeries. (FR) **3531**
Officiel des Plastiques et du Caoutchouc. (FR ISSN 0030-0462) **3864, 4292**
Officiel des Spectacles. (FR ISSN 0030-0500) **4781**
L'Officiel des Terrains de Camping et de Caravaning. (FR) **4552**
Officiel des Textiles. (BE) **4622**
†Officiel des Textiles (Ameublement). (FR) **5252**
Officiel des Textiles (Habillement). (FR) **4622, 1287**
Officiel des Transporteurs see Officiel des Transports **4747**
Officiel des Transports. (FR) **4747**
Officiel du Batiment et des Travaux Publics de Toulouse et de Midi-Pyrenees. (FR) **627**
Officiel du Bois (Edition Rouge). (FR) **640, 2561**
Officiel du Bois (Edition Verte). (FR) **2105, 2116**
Officiel du Cycle et du Motocycle. (FR ISSN 0751-994X) **4520**
Officiel du Pret a Porter. (FR ISSN 0040-5221) **4622, 1293**
Officiel - Hommes. (FR) **1293**
L'Officiel Jardin-Motoculture. (FR ISSN 0752-4250) **164**
Officier de Reserve see Ares **3451**
Offizieller Salzburger Wochenspiegel. (AU ISSN 0030-0586) **2173**
▼Offizielles Aerzteblatt fuer Sachsen-Anhalt. (GW ISSN 0938-9261) **3137**
▼Offizielles Verzeichnis der Treuhandanstalt. (GW) **1082**

OFFIZIN

Die Offizin. (GW ISSN 0930-2115) 3736
Offrir International. (FR) 2282
Offroad America. (US) 4482
Offset Printer see Offset Printing & Reproduction 4003
Offset Printing & Reproduction. (UK ISSN 0263-4384) 4003
Offset-Technik. (GW) 4003
Offsetpraxis. (GW ISSN 0030-0594) 3793, 4003
Offshoots of Orgonomy. (US ISSN 0730-1502) 2512, 4381
Offshore (Needham). (US) 4527
Offshore (Tulsa) see Offshore Incorporating the Oilman 3694
Offshore Abstracts see International Petroleum Abstracts 3705
Offshore Australian Yachting. (AT) 4527
Offshore Banking News see Worldwide Investment News 804
Offshore Business. (UK) 3694, 1937
Offshore Construction Report see Offshore International Newsletter 3694
Offshore Contractors and Equipment Directory see Offshore Contractors and Equipment Worldwide Directory 3694
Offshore Contractors and Equipment Worldwide Directory. (US) 3694
Offshore Design Guide: Helioports. (US) 4676
Offshore Engineer. (UK ISSN 0305-876X) 3694, 1832
Offshore Engineering. (UK) 1872, 3694
Offshore Engineering Abstracts. (UK ISSN 0268-1374) 1845
Offshore Field Development International. (US ISSN 1058-5869) 3694
Offshore Fleet Economics. (US ISSN 0266-3112) 3694, 4735
Offshore Incorporating the Oilman. (US) 3694
Offshore International Newsletter. (US ISSN 1058-5842) 3694
Offshore Investment. (UK ISSN 0954-0628) 794, 958, 1103
Offshore Mechanics and Arctic Engineering Symposium. Proceedings. (US) 1937, 1610
Offshore Petroleum Industry. (US) 3694
Offshore Resources. (CN ISSN 0820-0858) 3695
Offshore Rig Locator. (US) 3695
Offshore Rig Newsletter. (US ISSN 0147-1481) 3695
Offshore Rig Owners Directory see International Offshore Rig Owners Directory 3690
Offshore Rig Report. (US) 3695
Offshore Service Vessel Register. (UK ISSN 0309-040X) 3695, 4735
Offshore U S Oil Company Operating Personnel Directory. (US ISSN 1058-5877) 3695
▼Offshore Worldwide. (US) 4527
Offshore Yacht Racing and Cruising see Offshore Australian Yachting 4527
Offspring see Offspring - Boing 1262
Offspring - Boing. (US) 1262, 1241, 1652
El Oficial. (CU) 3467
Oficina. (US ISSN 0085-445X) 1061
Oficina Moderna. (SP ISSN 0030-0624) 1061
Oficina Sanitaria Panamericana. Boletin.(UN ISSN 0030-0632) 4109
Oficinas. (SP) 1061
Oftalmolog. (DK ISSN 0108-5344) 3303
Oftal'mologicheskii Zhurnal. (KR ISSN 0030-0675) 3303
Ofthalmologika Chronika see Greek Annals of Ophthalmology 3301
Ogam. (FR ISSN 0030-0691) 2379, 280
Ogasawara Kenkyu/Ogasawara Research. (JA ISSN 0386-8176) 4381

Ogasawara Kenkyu Nenpo/Tokyo Metropolitan University. Annual Report of Research on the Ogasawara (Bonin) Islands. (JA ISSN 0387-9844) 4331
Ogasawara Research. see Ogasawara Kenkyu 4381
Oggi. (IT ISSN 0030-0705) 2206
Oggi Domani Anziani. (IT) 4415, 2277
Oggi e Domani. (IT) 3670, 683, 3912

Oglas za Pomorce/Notices to Mariners. (CI ISSN 0030-0713) 4735
Ogniwo. (CS) 1652
Ogonek. (RU ISSN 0030-0721) 2878
Ogoniok. (CS ISSN 0030-073X) 1262
Ogrodnictwo. (PL ISSN 0030-0756) 2136
Ogsa En Avis. (DK) 2573
Oh Boy Monthly. (UK) 2984
Oh Calcutta. (II) 2201
†Oh Hi Yoh Noh. (US) 5252
Oh! Idaho. (US ISSN 1051-2373) 2231
Oh! Zone. (US) 1965
Ohak Yon'gu. see Language Research 2824
Ohinemuri. (NZ ISSN 0472-6480) 2345
Ohio. Commission on Aging. Annual Report see Ohio Department of Aging. Annual Report 2277
Ohio. Council on Vocational Education. Annual Report. (US ISSN 0098-5139) 1739
Ohio. Department of Human Services. Child Welfare Statistics. (US) 4426, 1248, 4582
Ohio. Division of Geological Survey. Bulletin. (US ISSN 0097-5478) 1576
Ohio. Division of Geological Survey. Educational Leaflet. (US ISSN 0472-6685) 1576
Ohio. Division of Geological Survey. Geological Note. (US) 1576
Ohio. Division of Geological Survey. Guidebook. (US ISSN 0097-9473) 1576
Ohio. Division of Geological Survey. Information Circular. (US) 1576
Ohio. Division of Geological Survey. Miscellaneous Report. (US ISSN 0361-0519) 1576
Ohio. Division of Geological Survey. Report of Investigations. (US) 1576
Ohio. Division of Mines. Report see Report on Ohio Mineral Industries 3494
Ohio. Division of State Personnel. Annual Report. (US ISSN 0078-4001) 1068
Ohio. State Library. Annual Report. (US) 2777
Ohio. State Library. State Library Review see Ohio. State Library. Annual Report 2777
Ohio A F L - C I O News and Views. (US ISSN 0030-0772) 2587
Ohio Academy of Science News. (US ISSN 0030-0764) 4331, 1756
Ohio Agent. (US) 2663
†Ohio Agricultural Research and Development Center, Wooster. List of References: Maize Virus and Mycoplasma Diseases. (US) 5252
Ohio Agricultural Research and Development Center, Wooster. Research Bulletin. (US ISSN 0078-3951) 112
Ohio Agricultural Research and Development Center, Wooster. Research Circular. (US ISSN 0078-396X) 112
Ohio & Northern Kentucky Gasoline Dealers & Garage News. (US) 4699, 683
Ohio Antique Review see Antique Review 255
Ohio Archaeologist. (US ISSN 0048-153X) 280
Ohio Archivist. (US ISSN 1047-5400) 2777

Ohio Arts Council. Annual Report see Ohio Arts Council. Biennial Report 339
Ohio Arts Council. Biennial Report. (US ISSN 0731-3284) 339
Ohio Attorney General Opinions. (US ISSN 0748-6170) 2663
Ohio Banker. (US ISSN 0030-0802) 794
Ohio Beverage Journal. (US) 384, 2478
Ohio Biological Survey. Biological Notes. (US ISSN 0078-3986) 450
Ohio Biological Survey. Bulletin. New Series. (US ISSN 0078-3994) 450
Ohio Biological Survey. Informative Circular. (US ISSN 0270-5443) 450
Ohio Builder. (US) 627
Ohio C P A Journal. (Ohio Society of Certified Public Accountants) (US) 754
Ohio Chess Bulletin. (US ISSN 0885-6583) 4482
▼Ohio Civil Practice Journal. (US ISSN 1047-5419) 2704
Ohio College Library Center. Annual Report see O C L C Annual Report 2777
Ohio Contractor. (US ISSN 0030-0861) 627
Ohio Criminal Law Handbook. (US) 1519, 2663
Ohio Dental Journal. (US ISSN 0030-087X) 3239
Ohio Department of Aging. Annual Report. (US) 2277
Ohio District Court Review. (US ISSN 0274-7294) 2663
Ohio Documents. (US ISSN 0147-2542) 408
Ohio Ecological Food and Farm Association News. (US) 186, 1965
▼Ohio Employment Law Letter. (US ISSN 1046-9206) 2663, 990
Ohio-En Engineering News see Ohio Engineering 1832
Ohio Engineering. (US) 1832
▼Ohio Environmental Law Letter. (US ISSN 1052-4355) 2663, 1965
Ohio Environmental Report. (US) 1965, 1494
Ohio Facts. (US ISSN 1040-4872) 1782
Ohio Family Physician News. (US ISSN 0030-0888) 3137
Ohio Farm Bureau News see Buckeye Farm News 80
Ohio Farmer. (US ISSN 0030-0896) 112
Ohio Farmers Fastline see Farmers Fastline: Ohio Edition 91
Ohio Fish and Wildlife Report. (US ISSN 0085-4468) 1494, 590
Ohio Fisherman. (US) 4552
Ohio Florists Association. Bulletin. (US ISSN 0030-090X) 2142
Ohio Genealogical Society. Report. (US) 2160
Ohio Genealogical Society. Wood County Chapter. Newsletter. (US ISSN 0893-1593) 2160
Ohio Genealogical Society Newsletter. (US ISSN 1052-858X) 2160
†Ohio Geographers: Recent Research Themes. (US ISSN 0094-9043) 5252
▼Ohio Golfer's Travel Guide. (US) 4509, 4781
Ohio Government Directory - Ohio Trucking Times. (US) 4069, 4747
Ohio Granger. (US) 112
Ohio Health Law Insider see Health Law Journal of Ohio 2632
Ohio Higher Education. Basic Data Series. (US ISSN 0094-6109) 1679
Ohio History. (US ISSN 0030-0934) 2417
Ohio Holstein News see Ohio News 202
Ohio Jersey News. (US ISSN 0048-1556) 222
Ohio Journal of Religious Studies see Journal of Religious Studies 4185
Ohio Journal of Science. (US ISSN 0030-0950) 4331
Ohio Labor Market Information: Labor Market Review. (US) 990

Ohio Lawyer. (US) 2663
Ohio Legal Rights Service. Annual Report. (US) 2734
Ohio Legislative Service see Baldwin's Ohio Legislative Service 4054
Ohio Libraries. (US ISSN 1046-4336) 2777
Ohio Libraries Newsletter see Ohio Libraries 2777
Ohio Library Trustee see Ohio Libraries 2777
Ohio Magazine. (US ISSN 0164-7172) 2231
Ohio Manufacturers Directory. (US ISSN 0737-7495) 1149
Ohio Media Spectrum. (US ISSN 0192-6942) 2777, 1652
Ohio Medicine. (US) 3137
Ohio Monitor. (US ISSN 0198-7208) 3620
Ohio Monthly Record. (US ISSN 0163-0008) 4069
Ohio Motorist. (US ISSN 0030-0985) 4781, 4699
Ohio News. (US ISSN 0899-4862) 202, 222
Ohio Northern University Law Review. (US ISSN 0094-534X) 2663
Ohio Nurses Review. (US ISSN 0030-0993) 3285
Ohio P T A News. (US ISSN 0199-0918) 1652
Ohio Pharmacist. (US ISSN 0030-1027) 3736
Ohio Pipeline. (US) 2302
Ohio Postal History Journal. (US) 3755
Ohio Reading Teacher. (US ISSN 0030-1035) 1739
Ohio Records & Pioneer Families. (US) 2160
†Ohio Renaissance Review. (US) 5252
†Ohio Report. (US ISSN 0749-1492) 5252
†Ohio Restaurant Journal. (US) 5252
Ohio Restaurant News see Midwest Food Service 2478
Ohio Review. (US ISSN 0360-1013) 2999, 2945
Ohio Runner. (US ISSN 0279-9634) 4482
Ohio School Boards Association. Journal.(US ISSN 0893-5289) 1730
Ohio Schools. (US ISSN 0030-1086) 1652
Ohio Slavic and East European Newsletter. (US) 1723
Ohio Society of Certified Public Accountants Ohio C P A Journal see Ohio C P A Journal 754
▼Ohio Sourcebook (Year). (US) 4003, 339
Ohio Southland. (US) 2417
Ohio Speech Journal. (US ISSN 0078-4052) 1341
Ohio State Alumni Magazine. (US ISSN 0744-8899) 1319
Ohio State Bar Association Report. (US ISSN 0744-8376) 2663
Ohio State Engineer. (US) 1832
Ohio State Journal on Dispute Resolution. (US) 2663
Ohio State Lantern. (US ISSN 0030-1116) 1320, 2573
Ohio State Law Journal. (US ISSN 0048-1572) 2663
Ohio State Medical Journal see Ohio Medicine 3137
Ohio State University. Agricultural Research and Development Center. Special Circular. (US ISSN 0736-8003) 112, 2105
Ohio State University. Byrd Polar Research Center. Contribution Series.(US) 4331, 1592
Ohio State University. Byrd Polar Research Center. Miscellaneous Series. (US) 4331, 1592
Ohio State University. Byrd Polar Research Center. Report Series. (US ISSN 0896-2472) 4331, 1592
Ohio State University. College of Medicine. Journal. (US ISSN 0030-1132) 3137
Ohio State University. Disaster Research Center. Report Series see University of Delaware. Disaster Research Center. Report Series 4114

Ohio State University. Institute of Polar Studies. Contribution Series see Ohio State University. Byrd Polar Research Center. Contribution Series **4331**
Ohio State University. Institute of Polar Studies. Miscellaneous Series see Ohio State University. Byrd Polar Research Center. Miscellaneous Series **4331**
Ohio State University. Institute of Polar Studies. Report Series see Ohio State University. Byrd Polar Research Center. Report Series **4331**
Ohio State University. School of Public Administration. Working Paper Series. (US) **4069**
Ohio State University. Working Papers in Linguistics. (US ISSN 0473-9604) **2832**
Ohio State University Alumni Magazine see Ohio State Alumni Magazine **1319**
Ohio State University, Columbus. Disaster Research Center. Miscellaneous Reports see University of Delaware. Disaster Research Center. Miscellaneous Reports **4114**
Ohio Tavern News. (US ISSN 0030-1183) **384**, **2663**
Ohio Truck Times see Ohio Government Directory - Ohio Trucking Times **4069**
Ohio Underwriter. (US ISSN 0198-683X) **2539**
Ohio University. Working Papers in Linguistics and Language Teaching. (US) **2832**
Ohio Veterinary Medical Association. Newsletter. (US) **4813**
Ohio Wesleyan Magazine. (US ISSN 0030-1221) **1320**
Ohio Woodlands. (US ISSN 0030-123X) **2105**
Ohio Writer. (US ISSN 0896-5730) **4134**
Ohio 21. (US) **112**
Ohioana see Ohioana Quarterly **2945**
Ohioana Quarterly. (US ISSN 0030-1248) **2945**, **2777**
Ohio's Finest Singles. (US) **4363**
Ohio's Heritage. (US) **2277**
Ohnicek. (CS ISSN 0030-1272) **1262**
Ohnik. (CS) **1262**
†Ohoyo. (US) **5252**
Ohr Hakollel. (US) **4225**
Oi Hwan Eun Haing Wol Bo. (KO) **878**, **794**
Oiga. (PE ISSN 0030-1280) **3912**
Oikogeneia kai Scholeio/Family and School. (CY ISSN 0253-0910) **1241**, **1652**
Oikos. (DK ISSN 0030-1299) **1965**
Oikos. (US) **2999**
Oil Activity Review. (CN) **3695**
Oil and Arab Cooperation. (KU) **3695**, **1793**
Oil and Chemical Pollution see Marine Environmental Research **1977**
Oil & Chemical Worker. (II ISSN 0030-1329) **2587**, **1185**, **3695**
Oil and Colour Chemists' Association. Journal see Surface Coatings International **3655**
Oil and Energy Trends. (UK ISSN 0950-1045) **3695**, **1793**
Oil and Gas. (US) **3695**, **1576**
Oil and Gas Accounting. (US) **754**, **1103**, **3695**
Oil and Gas Compact Bulletin see Interstate Oil Compact Commission. Compact & Committee Bulletin **3690**
Oil and Gas Developments in Pennsylvania. (US) **3695**, **1793**
Oil & Gas Directory. (US ISSN 0471-380X) **3695**, **1149**
Oil and Gas Equipment see Oil, Gas & Petroleum Equipment **3696**
†Oil & Gas Federal Tax Alert. (US) **5252**
Oil and Gas Field Designations. (CN) **1576**, **3695**
Oil & Gas Finance and Accounting. (UK ISSN 0962-3752) **3695**, **754**
Oil and Gas Geology. see Shiyou yu Tianranqi Dizhi **1580**
Oil & Gas Interests Newsletter. (US) **3695**

Oil and Gas Investor. (US ISSN 0744-5881) **3695**
Oil & Gas Journal. (US ISSN 0030-1388) **3695**
Oil & Gas: Law and Taxation Review. (UK ISSN 0263-5070) **3695**
Oil and Gas News. (SI ISSN 0217-6602) **3695**
Oil and Gas Pool Descriptions. (CN) **1576**, **3695**
Oil and Gas Producing Industry in Your State see Oil & Natural Gas Producing Industry in Your State **3706**
Oil and Gas Production Report. (CN) **3695**
Oil & Gas Report. (CN ISSN 0824-4952) **683**, **1833**, **4605**
Oil and Gas Reporter. (US ISSN 0472-7630) **3695**, **1793**, **2663**
Oil and Gas Tax Quarterly. (US ISSN 0030-1396) **1103**, **3695**
Oil and Natural Gas Commission. Bulletin. (II) **3695**
Oil & Natural Gas Producing Industry in Your State. (US) **3706**
†Oil and Oil Field Equipment & Service Companies Worldwide. (US) **5252**
Oil and Petroleum Year Book see Financial Times International Year Books: Oil and Gas **3686**
Oil Buyers' Guide. (US) **3695**
Oil Buyers' Guide International. (US) **3695**
Oil Can. (US) **3695**
Oil Caravan Weekly see Al-Qafilah **3700**
Oil, Chemical and Atomic Workers International Union. Union News see O C A W Reporter **2587**
Oil, Chemical and Atomic Workers International Union Reporter see O C A W Reporter **2587**
Oil Chemical Rubber Workers Trade Union of Turkey. Yearbook. (TU) **2587**, **1857**, **3695**, **4292**
Oil Company Operating Personnel Directory see Offshore U S Oil Company Operating Personnel Directory **3695**
Oil Daily. (US ISSN 0030-1434) **3695**
Oil Daily Weekly Edition. (US) **3696**
Oil Directory of Canada see Canada Petroleum Industry **3684**
Oil Directory of Companies Outside the U.S. and Canada see International Petroleum Industry **3690**
Oil Directory of Houston, Texas see Houston Petroleum Industry **3688**
Oil - Energy Statistics Bulletin. (US) **3706**
Oil Express. (US) **3696**
Oil, Gas & Petrochem Equipment. (US ISSN 0030-1353) **3696**
Oil, Gas & Petrochemicals Abroad. (US) **3696**
Oil, Gas and Petrochemistry Abroad. see Neft', Gaz i Neftekhimiya za Rubezhom **3693**
Oil Gas European Magazine. (GW ISSN 0342-5622) **3696**
Oil Imports into the United States and Puerto Rico (E I A 814). (Energy Information Administration) (US) **733**, **3706**
†Oil in Texas. (US) **5252**
Oil in the Rockies. (US) **3696**
Oil Industry Comparative Appraisals 1. (US) **3696**
Oil Industry Comparative Appraisals 2. (US) **3696**
Oil Industry Comparative Appraisals 3. (US) **3696**
Oil Industry Outlook for the U S A. (US ISSN 0741-3343) **3696**, **878**
Oil Investment Guidelines see Quentin Cameron's Oil & Gas Bulletin **961**
Oil Marketer. (US) **3696**
Oil Marketing and Wholesale Distributors see Oil Marketing Industry **3696**
The Oil Marketing Bulletin. (US) **3696**
Oil Marketing Industry. (US) **3696**
▼Oil Markets of the Pacific Rim - Into the 1990s. (UK) **1576**
Oil Mill Gazetter. (US ISSN 0030-1442) **1857**

Oil News. (IR ISSN 0030-1450) **3696**
Oil News Service Newsletter. (UK) **3696**
Oil Packer International. (UK) **3696**
Oil Palm News see Tropical Agriculture **125**
†Oil Price Databook. (US) **5252**
Oil Price Information Service. (US ISSN 0279-7801) **3696**
Oil Shale Symposium Proceedings. (US ISSN 0271-0315) **3492**, **3696**
Oil Spill Intelligence Report. (US ISSN 0195-3524) **3696**, **1965**
▼Oil Spill U S Law Report. (US ISSN 1055-9175) **2663**, **3696**
Oil Spot. (UK ISSN 0261-3247) **3696**
Oil Technologists' Association of India. Journal. (II ISSN 0970-4094) **1220**, **3696**
Oil Well Supply Industry. (US) **3696**, **1082**, **1149**
Oil World Annual. (GW) **155**
Oil World Statistics see Know More About Oil World Statistics **3691**
Oil World Weekly. (GW ISSN 0029-8700) **155**, **2078**
Oilcan see Oil Can **3695**
Oilfield Review. (NE ISSN 0923-1730) **3696**, **1576**, **1592**
Oilfield Service, Supply, and Manufacturers Worldwide Directory see U S A Oilfield Service, Supply, and Manufacturers Directory **3702**
Oilgas. (SP ISSN 0030-1493) **3696**
Oilman see Offshore Incorporating the Oilman **3694**
Oilpatch Magazine. (CN ISSN 0164-887X) **3696**
Oils & Fats International. (UK ISSN 0267-8853) **1221**
Oils and Fats International Directory. (UK) **1149**, **1221**
†Oilscan. (AT) **5252**
Oilseeds Journal. see Telhan Patrika **1223**
Oilways see Results (Houston) **3700**
Oilweek. (CN ISSN 0030-1515) **3696**
Oink! see New American Writing **2998**
Oise Agricole. (FR ISSN 0030-1523) **112**
Oiseau et la Revue Francaise d'Ornithologie. (FR ISSN 0030-1531) **566**
Oita Daigaku Keizai Kenkyujo Kenkyujoho/Oita University. Research Institute of Economics. Bulletin. (JA ISSN 0287-0916) **683**
Oita Daigaku Keizai Ronshu/Oita University Economic Review. (JA ISSN 0474-0157) **683**
Oita Daigaku Kyoikugakubu Kenkyu Kiyo/Oita University. Faculty of Education. Research Bulletin. (JA ISSN 0914-580X) **4331**
Oita Prefecture Monthly Report of Meteorology. (JA) **3440**
Oita University. Faculty of Education. Research Bulletin. see Oita Daigaku Kyoikugakubu Kenkyu Kiyo **4331**
Oita University. Research Institute of Economics. Bulletin. see Oita Daigaku Keizai Kenkyujo Kenkyujoho **683**
Oita University Economic Review. see Oita Daigaku Keizai Ronshu **683**
El Ojito. (US) **2878**
Ojito Review see El Ojito **2878**
Okajima Foria Anatomika Yaponika. see Okajima's Folia Anatomica Japonica **450**
Okajima's Folia Anatomica Japonica/ Okajima Foria Anatomika Yaponika. (JA ISSN 0030-154X) **450**, **3137**
Okanagan Business Magazine. (CN) **683**
Okanagan History. (CN ISSN 0830-0739) **2417**
Okanagan Life Magazine. (CN ISSN 0840-5492) **2178**
Okanogan Natural News see Columbiana **1485**
Okapi. (FR) **1262**
Okay. (GW) **1262**, **4245**
▼Okay America. (US ISSN 1056-1595) **2231**
Okay Anglers Fishing Directory & Atlas see B.C. Fishing Directory & Atlas **2037**

OKLAHOMA. DEPARTMENT 6521

Okayama Daigaku Rigakubu Kaimen-kagaku Kenkyu Shisetsu Hokoku. see Okayama University. Faculty of Science. Research Laboratory for Surface Science. Reports **1229**
Okayama Igakkai Zasshi/Medical Association of Okayama. Journal. (JA ISSN 0030-1558) **3137**
Okayama no Shizen/Nature in Okayama. (JA ISSN 0912-4071) **1494**
Okayama Prefectural Dairy Experiment Station. Bulletin. (JA ISSN 0388-631X) **202**
Okayama Rika Daigaku. Hiruzen Kenkyujo Kenkyu Hokoku/Okayama University of Science. Hiruzen Research Institute. Bulletin. (JA ISSN 0385-2776) **4331**
Okayama Rika Daigaku Kiyo A. Shizen Kagaku/Okayama University of Science. Bulletin A. Natural Science. (JA ISSN 0285-7685) **4331**
Okayama University. Berichte des Ohara Instituts fuer Landwirtschaftliche Biologie. (JA ISSN 0365-9860) **450**
Okayama University. Faculty of Science. Research Laboratory for Surface Science. Reports/Okayama Daigaku Rigakubu Kaimen-kagaku Kenkyu Shisetsu Hokoku. (JA ISSN 0078-429X) **1229**
†Okayama University. School of Engineering. Memoirs. (JA ISSN 0475-0071) **5252**
Okayama University of Science. Bulletin A. Natural Science. see Okayama Rika Daigaku Kiyo A. Shizen Kagaku **4331**
Okayama University of Science. Hiruzen Research Institute. Bulletin. see Okayama Rika Daigaku. Hiruzen Kenkyujo Kenkyu Hokoku **4331**
Okeanologiia. (BU ISSN 0324-0878) **1610**
Okeanologiya. (RU ISSN 0030-1574) **1610**
Oke's Magisterial Formulist. (UK) **2663**
Okhota i Okhotnich'e Khozyaistvo. (RU ISSN 0131-2596) **4482**
Okhrana Truda i Sotsial'noe Strakhovanie. (RU ISSN 0030-1590) **2539**, **990**
Okike. (NR ISSN 0331-0566) **2945**, **2018**
Okikiolu Scientific and Industrial Organization. Bulletin of Mathematics.(UK ISSN 0261-1023) **3049**
Okinawa-ken Kachiku Eisei Shikenjo Nenpo. (JA ISSN 0911-5137) **4813**
Okinawa-kenritsu Hakubutsukan Kiyo/ Okinawa Prefectural Museum. Bulletin. (JA ISSN 0385-0285) **3531**, **4331**
Okinawa Library Association. Annals. see Okinawa Toshokan Kyokai Shi **2777**
Okinawa Prefectural Museum. Bulletin. see Okinawa-kenritsu Hakubutsukan Kiyo **3531**
Okinawa Prefecture. Annual Report of Fire and Disaster Prevention. (JA) **2034**
Okinawa Today. (US) **3468**
Okinawa Toshokan Kyokai Shi/Okinawa Library Association. Annals. (JA) **2777**
Okki. (NE ISSN 0030-1612) **1262**
Oklahoma see O K C Action **820**
Oklahoma see Midcontinent Petroleum Industry **3692**
Oklahoma. Ad Valorem Tax Division. (Year) Progress Report to the Legislature on Property Revaluation. (US) **1103**
Oklahoma. Attorney General's Office. Opinions of the Attorney General. (US ISSN 0475-0926) **2663**
Oklahoma. Commission on Consumer Affairs. Annual Report. (US) **1507**
Oklahoma. Conservation Commission. Biennial Report. (US ISSN 0095-442X) **1494**
Oklahoma. Department of Health. Monthly Vital Statistics Report. (US) **3985**, **4109**

6522 OKLAHOMA. DEPARTMENT

Oklahoma. Department of Highways. Sufficiency Rating Report and Needs Study: Oklahoma State Highways see Oklahoma. Department of Transportation. Sufficiency Rating Report and Needs Study: Oklahoma State Transportation **4720**
Oklahoma. Department of Human Services. Annual Report. (US ISSN 0277-8289) **4415**
Oklahoma. Department of Institutions, Social and Rehabilitative Services. Annual Report see Oklahoma. Department of Human Services. Annual Report **4415**
Oklahoma. Department of Libraries. Annual Report and Directory of Libraries in Oklahoma see Oklahoma Department of Libraries. Annual Report **2778**
Oklahoma. Department of Mental Health and Substance Abuse Services. Annual Report. (US) **4037**
Oklahoma. Department of Mental Health. Annual Report see Oklahoma. Department of Mental Health and Substance Abuse Services. Annual Report **4037**
Oklahoma. Department of Transportation. Sufficiency Rating Report and Needs Study: Oklahoma State Transportation. (US) **4720**
†Oklahoma. Employment Security Commission. Actuarial Division. Handbook of Employment Security Program Statistics. (US) **5252**
Oklahoma. Employment Security Commission. Research and Planning Division. Annual Report to the Governor see Oklahoma. Employment Security Commission. Research Division. Annual Report to the Governor **990**
Oklahoma. Employment Security Commission. Research and Planning Division. County Employment and Wage Data see Oklahoma. Employment Security Commission. Research Division. County Employment and Wage Data **733**
Oklahoma. Employment Security Commission. Research Division. Annual Report to the Governor. (US) **990**
Oklahoma. Employment Security Commission. Research Division. County Employment and Wage Data. (US) **733**
Oklahoma. Grand River Dam Authority. Annual Report. (US ISSN 0078-4508) **1924**
Oklahoma. Public Employees Retirement System. Annual Report. (US) **1068**
Oklahoma Anthropological Society. Bulletin. (US ISSN 0078-432X) **246**
Oklahoma Anthropological Society. Memoir. (US ISSN 0474-0696) **246**
Oklahoma Anthropological Society. Newsletter. (US ISSN 0078-4338) **246**
Oklahoma Banker. (US ISSN 0030-1647) **794**
Oklahoma Baptist Chronicle. (US ISSN 0889-745X) **4245**, 2417
Oklahoma Bar Journal. (US) **2663**
Oklahoma Beverage News. (US ISSN 0030-1663) **384**
Oklahoma Bluegrass Gazette. (US) **3571**
Oklahoma Business Bulletin. (US ISSN 0030-1671) **733**, 4582
†Oklahoma C.P.A. (US ISSN 0030-168X) **5252**
Oklahoma City Chamber of Commerce Action see O K C Action **820**
Oklahoma City Living Magazine. (US) **2231**
Oklahoma City University Law Review. (US) **2663**
Oklahoma Council on Economic Education Newsletter. (US) **683**, 1756
Oklahoma Cowman. (US ISSN 0030-1698) **222**
Oklahoma Criminal Practice Manual. (US) **2714**

Oklahoma Current Farm Economics. (US ISSN 0030-1701) **155**
Oklahoma Daily. (US ISSN 0030-171X) **1320**
Oklahoma Dental Association Journal. (US ISSN 0164-9442) **3239**
Oklahoma Department of Libraries. Annual Report. (US) **2778**
Oklahoma Directory of Manufacturers and Processors. (US ISSN 1051-919X) **1149**
Oklahoma Directory of Manufacturers & Products. (US ISSN 1059-4523) **1149**
Oklahoma Discovery Practice Manual. (US) **2663**
Oklahoma Economic Development News. (US) **683**
Oklahoma Education Association Focus see O E A Focus **1652**
Oklahoma Electric Co-op News. (US) **1904**
Oklahoma Farm Bureau Farmer see Oklahoma Farm Bureau Journal **112**
Oklahoma Farm Bureau Journal. (US) **112**
Oklahoma Farmer-Stockman. (US ISSN 0145-9392) **186**
Oklahoma Food Journal see Oklahoma Grocers Journal **2093**
Oklahoma Game & Fish. (US ISSN 0746-6013) **4552**
Oklahoma Genealogical Society Quarterly. (US ISSN 0474-0742) **2160**
Oklahoma Geological Survey. Bulletin. (US ISSN 0078-4389) **1576**
Oklahoma Geological Survey. Circular. (US ISSN 0078-4397) **1576**
Oklahoma Geological Survey. Educational Publication. (US ISSN 0160-8746) **1576**
Oklahoma Geological Survey. Guidebook. (US ISSN 0078-4400) **1577**
Oklahoma Geological Survey. Special Publication Series. (US ISSN 0275-0929) **1577**
Oklahoma Geology Notes. (US ISSN 0030-1736) **1577**
Oklahoma Government Documents see Oklahoma Government Publications **4069**
Oklahoma Government Publications. (US) **4069**, 2778
Oklahoma Grocers Journal. (US) **2093**
Oklahoma Health Statistics. (US ISSN 0098-5651) **4118**
†Oklahoma Home and Lifestyle. (US) **5252**
Oklahoma Home - Garden see Oklahoma Home and Lifestyle **5252**
Oklahoma Journal of Forensic Medicine see Medicolegal-Gram **3265**
Oklahoma Journal Record. (US) **683**
†Oklahoma Labor Market. (US ISSN 0030-1744) **5252**
Oklahoma Lake Living. (US) **2258**
Oklahoma Law Review. (US ISSN 0030-1752) **2663**
Oklahoma Librarian. (US ISSN 0030-1760) **2778**
Oklahoma Lien Laws. (US) **2663**
▼Oklahoma Manufacturers Register. (US) **1149**
Oklahoma Mason. (US ISSN 0030-1779) **1300**
Oklahoma Motor Carrier see Truck & Commerce **4748**
Oklahoma Natural Resources Report. (US) **1965**
Oklahoma Nurse. (US ISSN 0030-1787) **3285**
Oklahoma Observer. (US ISSN 0030-1795) **3912**
Oklahoma Odd Fellow. (US ISSN 0030-1809) **1300**
Oklahoma Oil Marketer see Oil Marketer **3696**
Oklahoma Ornithological Society. Bulletin. (US ISSN 0474-0750) **566**
Oklahoma Parent - Teacher. (US ISSN 0030-1817) **1652**
Oklahoma Pontotoc County Quarterly. (US ISSN 0091-1054) **2417**, 2160
Oklahoma Population Estimates. (US) **3994**

Oklahoma Professional Engineer. (US) **1833**
Oklahoma Publisher. (US) **4134**, 36, 2468
Oklahoma Reader. (US ISSN 0030-1833) **1756**
Oklahoma Register (Oklahoma City). (US ISSN 0030-1728) **2663**
Oklahoma Retailer. (US ISSN 0030-1841) **1049**
Oklahoma Rural News. (US ISSN 0048-1610) **1904**, 112
Oklahoma School Board Journal. (US ISSN 0030-185X) **1652**
Oklahoma State Agencies, Boards, Commissions, Courts, Institutions, Legislature and Officers. (US) **4069**
Oklahoma State Medical Association. Journal. (US ISSN 0030-1876) **3137**
Oklahoma State University. College of Business Administration. Working Papers. (US) **683**
Oklahoma Today. (US ISSN 0030-1892) **2231**
Oklahoma Turnpike Authority. Annual Report to the Governor. (US) **4720**
Oklahoma Turnpike Authority. Report to Bondholders. (US) **4720**
Oklahoma Union Farmer see Farm News and Views **90**
Oklahoma Water Resources Research Institute. Annual Report. (US ISSN 0092-2528) **4827**
Oklahoma Wills and Interstate Succession. (US) **2663**
Oklahomans for Indian Opportunity News see O I O News **2018**
Okochi Memorial Foundation. Journal. see Gocho **4311**
Okonomisk Virksomhedsledelse see Lederskab og Loensomhed **1018**
Okresni Archiv v Olomouci. Vyrocni Zprava. (CS ISSN 0862-2833) **2379**, 281
Okresni Muzeum v Blansku. Sbornik. (CS) **2379**, 281
Okresni Vlastivedneho Muzeum v Blansku. Sbornik see Okresni Muzeum v Blansku. Sbornik **2379**
Oktobar. (YU ISSN 0030-1949) **2945**, 339
Oktyabr' (RU ISSN 0030-1957) **2878**
Olam ha-Eisha. (IS) **4850**
Olam Hadash. (US ISSN 0472-8637) **1262**, 2018
Olam Hasusim. (IS) **2440**
Olam Hazeh. (IS ISSN 0017-7555) **2204**
Old Abe's News. (US ISSN 0896-4955) **164**, 2417
Old Age: a Register of Social Research. (UK) **2277**, 4415
Old Allis News. (US ISSN 0897-2540) **164**
Old and Rare Wall Street Book Club. Wall Street Letter see Library of the Economists **677**
Old and Rare Wall Street Books. (US) **733**, 408
Old Athlone Society Journal. (IE ISSN 0475-1388) **2379**
Old Autos. (CN) **4699**, 259
Old Ben News. (UK) **838**
Old Car Value Guide see Classic Old Car Value Guide **5166**
Old Cars see Old Cars Weekly **4699**
Old Cars Price Guide. (US ISSN 0194-6404) **259**
Old Cars Show see Car Shows and Auctions **5162**
Old Cars Weekly. (US) **4699**, 259
Old Cornwall. (UK) **2160**, 2258, 2379
Old Courthouse News. (US) **2417**
Old English Newsletter. (US ISSN 0030-1973) **2945**, 2832
Old English Times. (US) **3712**
Old Farmer's Almanac. (US ISSN 0078-4516) **1782**
Old Fort Genealogical Society. Newsletter see Old Fort Genealogical Society: Quarterly **2160**
Old Fort Genealogical Society: Quarterly.(US) **2160**
Old Fort Log. (US ISSN 0098-4760) **2160**
Old Gold and Black. (US) **1713**

Old Hickory Review. (US) **2999**
Old-House Journal. (US ISSN 0094-0178) **627**, 304, 4154
Old-House Journal Catalog. (US ISSN 0271-7220) **627**, 304, 4154
Old Lady of Threadneedle Street. (UK ISSN 0030-199X) **2195**, 2945
Old Man. (SZ ISSN 0030-2007) **1377**
Old Mill News. (US ISSN 0276-3338) **2417**, 304
Old Motor (Teddington) see Classic & Sportscar **4688**
Old News. (US ISSN 1047-3068) **2231**
Old Northwest. (US ISSN 0360-5531) **2417**
†Old Nun. (CN) **5252**
Old Oregon. (US) **1320**
Old People's World. see Laoren Shijie **2275**
Old Red Kimono. (US) **2945**
Old Roman Catholic Church Notes see O R C Notes **4271**
†Old Salem Gleaner. (US ISSN 0078-4540) **5252**
Old Sturbridge Visitor. (US ISSN 0485-6724) **2417**
Old Testament Abstracts. (US ISSN 0364-8591) **4213**, 18
Old Testament Essays. (SA) **4193**
Old Time Country. (US ISSN 1044-1042) **3571**
Old Time Crochet. (US ISSN 1050-9518) **3592**
Old Time Crochet Patterns and Designs see Old Time Crochet **3592**
Old-Time Herald. (US) **3571**
Old Time Western Film Club Newsletter. (US) **3515**
†Old Timers' Bulletin. (US ISSN 0030-204X) **5252**
Old Times. (CN) **1320**
Old Toy Soldier. (US ISSN 8756-7652) **259**
Old Toy Soldier Newsletter see Old Toy Soldier **259**
Old West. (US ISSN 0030-2058) **2417**
Old Westmoreland. (US) **2160**
Old York Road Historical Society Bulletin. (US) **2417**
Olde Mecklenburg Genealogical Society Quarterly. (US) **2160**
Das Oldenburger Sportpferd. (GW ISSN 0030-2066) **4536**
Oldenburgische Familienkunde. (GW ISSN 0030-2074) **2160**
The Older American. (US ISSN 0738-9639) **2277**
Older Americans Report. (US ISSN 0146-3640) **4415**, 2277
Older Boat Price Guide see Used Boat Price Guide **4530**
Older Car Red Book. (US ISSN 0736-6124) **4747**
†Older Texan. (US) **5252**
Older Women's Network see Visible **2280**
†Older Worker. (US) **5252**
Olderr's Fiction Index for (Year). (US) **2890**
Olderr's Young Adult Fiction Index for (Year). (US) **1248**, 1262, 2890
Oldie - Markt. (GW) **3571**
Oldtimer Adressen Lexikon. (GW ISSN 0932-0075) **4699**
Oldtimer Katalog. (GW) **4699**
Oldtimers' Hockey News. (CN) **4482**
Ole Miss Alumni Review. (US) **1320**
Ole Miss Engineer. (US) **1833**
Oleagineux. (FR ISSN 0030-2082) **1221**
Oleander Games and Pastimes Series. (UK) **4482**
Oleander Travel Books Series. (UK) **4781**
Oleo. (SP ISSN 0472-8807) **1221**
Oleo: Anuario Espanol de Aceites y Grasas e Industrias Auxiliares. (SP) **1221**
Oleodinamica - Pneumatica - Lubrificazione. (IT ISSN 0391-8645) **1937**
Olie see Shell-Venster **3701**
Olieberetning. (DK ISSN 0109-3916) **3696**
Oliebranchens Faellesrepraesentation. Beretning see Olieberetning **3696**

Olifant. (US ISSN 0381-9132) **2999**
Olimpiiskaya Panorama. (RU ISSN 0204-2177) **4482**
Oliphant Washington Service. Energy Summary. (US ISSN 0733-0219) **1793, 1965**
Olivae. (SP ISSN 0255-996X) **186**
Olivetti News. (IT) **3022**
Oljebladet see Bilbransjen - Bilteknisk Fagblad **4685**
Oljyposti see Nestekide **4698**
†Olmstead's Genealogy Recorded. (US ISSN 0162-0800) **5252**
O'Lochlainns Irish Family Journal. (US) **2160, 2018**
Ologies and Isms. (US) **2832**
Olomeinu/Our World. (US ISSN 0030-2139) **4225, 1262**
Olomouc. Vysoke Skoly Pedagogicke. Sbornik. Historie see Sbornik Praci Historickych **2385**
Olschwanger Journal. (US ISSN 0882-1933) **2160**
Olsen's Agribusiness Report. (US ISSN 0197-9361) **112, 2078**
Oltre il Ponte. (IT) **878**
Oltreconfine. (GW) **2018**
Olum-e Kampiuter. see Computer Science **1392**
Olum-e Tarbiati/Education. (IR) **1652**
Olympia Aktuell. (AU) **4482**
Olympia Genealogical Society. Quarterly.(US) **2160**
Olympian (Colorado Springs). (US ISSN 0094-9787) **4482**
Olympian (San Francisco). (US ISSN 0030-2163) **1300, 4482**
Olympic Collectors Newsletter see Bill Nelson Newsletter **2434**
Olympic Message. see Message Olympique **4479**
Olympic Panorama see Olimpiiskaya Panorama **4482**
Olympic Review (Year). (SZ ISSN 0010-2431) **4482**
Olympic Travel Guide see Ferry Travel Guide **4762**
Olympics. (BE) **4482**
Olympische Jugend. (GW ISSN 0343-0235) **4482**
Olympische Sport see Olympia Aktuell **4482**
Olympisches Feuer. (GW) **4482**
Olympisches Panorama see Olimpiiskaya Panorama **4482**
Om Forsoegsarbejdet. (DK ISSN 0900-162X) **1652**
Om Statsregnskabet. (DK ISSN 0900-8187) **683, 794**
Oma. (NR ISSN 0030-218X) **2212**
Omaba see Omabe **2999**
Omabe. (NR) **2999**
†Omaha (Nebraska). (US) **5252**
Omaha (Princeton). (US) **2984**
Omaha - Council Bluffs Metropolitan Area Planning Agency. Population and Housing Unit Estimates. (US) **3994, 2500**
Omaha - Council Bluffs Metropolitan Area Planning Agency Annual Report see M A P A Annual Report **4066**
Omaha District Dental Society. Chronicle. (US ISSN 0030-2201) **3239**
Omaha Profile see Profile (Omaha) **821**
Al-Omal see Al-Ummal **2591**
Omaly sy Anio/Hier et Aujourd'hui. (MG) **2334**
Oman Commerce. see Al-Ghurfah **816**
Oman Today. (MK) **2211**
Al-Omaniyyah. (MK) **4850, 2211**
Omanuyot Halichima. (IS) **4482**
Ombra d'Argo see Allegoria **2893**
Ombres de l'Histoire. (FR ISSN 0078-4591) **2379**
Ombudsman Journal. (CN ISSN 0710-538X) **2664**
Omega (Amityville). (US ISSN 0030-2228) **4037, 4444**
Omega (Tarrytown). (US ISSN 0305-0483) **1023**
Omega New Age Directory. (US) **1149, 3596, 4286**
Omens. (UK ISSN 0308-4752) **2999**
Omhoog. (SR) **4271**
Omkring et Kunstvaerk. (DK ISSN 0108-3511) **339**
Omladinski Pokret. (YU) **1262**

Omni. (US ISSN 0149-8711) **4331**
†Omni Japan/Omuni. (JA ISSN 0286-5300) **5252**
Omni U K. (UK) **1904**
Omnia Medica et Therapeutica. (IT ISSN 0030-2260) **3137**
▼Omnibus. (US) **408, 2778**
Omnibus. (IT) **4654, 36**
†Omnibus (Bracknell). (UK ISSN 0305-5981) **5252**
Omnibus (London). (UK ISSN 0261-507X) **1278**
Omnibus (Piscataway). (US) **2231**
†Omnibus (Pittsburgh). (US) **5252**
Omnibus Magazine. (UK ISSN 0305-9243) **4654**
Omnibus-Revue see Omnibus-Revue und Bus Aktuell **4699**
Omnibus-Revue und Bus Aktuell. (GW) **4699**
Omnibusspiegel. (GW ISSN 0724-7664) **4654**
Omnific. (US) **2999**
Omnigatherum see Scottish Museum News **3532**
Omuni. see Omni Japan **5252**
Omvang der Vakbeweging in Nederland see Statistiek der Vakbeweging in Nederland **2592**
▼On! (US) **1507, 1904**
On Achieving Excellence. (US ISSN 0887-5332) **1023**
†On Air - Off Air. (UK ISSN 0953-9492) **5252**
On Balance. (CN ISSN 0840-612X) **1378**
On Being. (AT ISSN 0156-6296) **4245**
On Board International. (UK ISSN 0269-9575) **4552**
On Board Surf Magazine. (UK ISSN 0956-019X) **4552**
▼On Campus. (AT) **1320**
On Campus with Women. (US ISSN 0734-0141) **1714, 4860**
On Cassette see Words on Cassette (Year) **416**
On Continuing Practice. (CN ISSN 0315-1042) **3736**
On Course. (UK) **1757**
On Course. (US) **3596, 3774, 4037**
On Court. (CN) **4509**
On Cue. (US ISSN 1041-6234) **2288, 1739**
On-Dirt Magazine. (US) **4482**
On Dit. (AT ISSN 0030-2333) **1320**
On Gogol Boulevard. (US) **2999**
On Guard. (US) **3468, 3945**
On Ice. (CN) **4482**
On Line. (US) **3515**
On-Line (Durham). (US ISSN 0731-8367) **1428, 1463**
†On - Line (New York). (US) **5252**
On Line (Sunbury-on-Thames). (UK ISSN 0263-2187) **1457**
On Literary Freedom. see Wenxue Ziyou Tan **2889**
On Location Directory. (US) **3515, 1385**
On Location Magazine. (US ISSN 0149-7014) **3515, 1385**
On One Wheel. (US) **4520**
On Our Backs. (US ISSN 0890-2224) **2456, 4850**
On Premise. (US) **384**
On - Premise Report. (US) **384**
On Priniciple. (US) **3912, 878**
On Production. (US) **3515, 1385**
▼On Production and Post-Production. (US) **3515**
On Sat - America's Weekly Guide to Satellite TV see ONSAT - America's Weekly Satellite Guide **1378**
On Scene. (US ISSN 0093-2124) **4735**
On - Stage Studies. (US) **4636**
On Starting Work. (AT) **3630**
On Target. (UK ISSN 0308-1230) **3912**
On Target. (CN) **3912**
▼On the Air Magazine. (US ISSN 1057-9893) **3571**
On the Beach. (AT ISSN 0810-820X) **2878, 339**
On the Beam. (US ISSN 0740-218X) **2295, 546, 3137**
On the Beat. (US) **1519**
On The Bus see Onthebus **2999**
On the Docket. (US) **1364, 1793**

†On the Edge (Cambridge). (US) **5252**
On the Edge (Madison). (US) **1320**
On the Edge (New York). (US) **4245**
On the Edge (Philadelphia). (US) **1494**
On the Fringe. (US) **2136, 512**
On the Go. (AT) **4781**
On the Green. (US) **1320**
On the Issues. (US ISSN 0895-6014) **4850, 597, 4836**
On the Level. (CN) **627**
On the Level. (US) **3492**
On the Line. (US) **1364, 2664**
On the Line (Cincinnati) see Spaniels in the Field **3714**
On the Line (Laurel). (US ISSN 0190-2571) **1519**
On the Line (New York) see East European News **977**
On the Line (Scottdale). (US ISSN 0043-7999) **1262**
On the Market. (US) **1049**
On the Markets. (US) **958**
On the Move. (CN) **3807, 1757**
On the Move. (AT) **4482**
†On the Move. (UK ISSN 0269-3208) **5252**
†On the Move (Buffalo). (US) **5252**
†On the Move (Melbourne, 1973). (AT ISSN 0310-9348) **5252**
On the Road (Cape Town). (SA ISSN 0030-2368) **1049**
On the Road (Fords). (US) **4134**
On the Road (New York). (US) **4520**
On the Rock. (US ISSN 0196-1446) **3571**
On the Safe Side. (US) **3620**
On the Scene. (US) **4363**
On the Street. (AT) **3571, 1378, 3515, 4636**
On the Town. (US) **2231**
On The Trail. (US) **4552**
On the Wing. (US ISSN 0162-4385) **4245**
On Track. (US ISSN 0279-2737) **4699**
On Watch. (AT ISSN 0030-2392) **1937**
On Watch. (US) **3468**
On Wings. (US) **4850, 3774**
On Wisconsin Magazine. (US) **1320**
On Your Mark. (US) **3611, 186**
Oncodevelopmental Biology and Medicine see Tumor Biology **3202**
Oncogene. (UK ISSN 0950-9232) **3200, 481, 546**
Oncogene Research. (US ISSN 0890-6467) **3201**
Oncogenes. (UK ISSN 0950-0561) **3201, 546**
Oncogenes and Growth Factors Abstracts. (US ISSN 1043-8963) **3178, 18**
Oncologia. (SP ISSN 0378-4835) **3201**
Oncology. (SZ ISSN 0030-2414) **3201**
†Oncology Abstracts. (US) **5252**
†Oncology & Biotechnology News. (US) **5252**
Oncology Issues. (US ISSN 1046-3356) **3201**
Oncology Nursing Forum. (US ISSN 0190-535X) **3285, 3201**
Oncology Research. (US ISSN 0965-0407) **3201**
Oncology Times. (US ISSN 0276-2234) **3201**
Onda Tivu. (IT) **1378**
Ondas. (PE ISSN 0472-948X) **2878**
Onde Electrique. (FR ISSN 0030-2430) **1776, 1378**
Onderneming. (NE ISSN 0165-6643) **1023**
Onderneming. see Entreprise **2299**
Onderstepoort Journal of Veterinary Research. (SA ISSN 0030-2465) **4813**
Onderwatersport. (NE ISSN 0048-1696) **4552**
Onderwaterwereld. (NE) **4482**
Onderwijs en Opvoeding. (NE ISSN 0030-2481) **1652**
Onderwijs & Welzijn - Vakmatig. (NE ISSN 0925-4862) **4415, 1652, 4069**
Onderwys en Kultuur. see Education & Culture **1627**
Ondes Courtes Informations. (FR ISSN 0754-2623) **1378**

One. (UK) **1452**
One. (SP) **4814, 222**
One Church/Yedinaya Tserkov. (US ISSN 0030-2503) **4286**
†One Earth. (UK ISSN 0143-8247) **5252**
One-Eyed Cat. see El Gato Tuerto **2919**
†One Family. (US) **5252**
One in Christ. (UK ISSN 0030-252X) **4271**
One-in-Ten. (US) **3137**
One Letter see ONEletter **2456**
One Parent Families see O P T: One Parent Times **1241**
†One Peaceful World. (US) **3611, 2231**
One-Person Library. (US ISSN 0748-8831) **2778**
One Person's Impact. (US) **1965, 1793**
One Shot. (US) **3571**
One Show. (SZ ISSN 0273-2033) **36**
One to One. (UK ISSN 0268-8786) **4193**
One to One (Fresno). (US) **1357, 1782**
One-Two-Testing. (UK) **3571**
One World. (JA) **2208**
One World. (SZ ISSN 0303-125X) **4193**
†One World. (US) **5252**
O'Neill Clan News. (UK ISSN 0265-5683) **2160**
ONEletter. (US) **2456**
†Oneri Fiscali sulla Motorizzazione. (IT) **5252**
Onfilm. (NZ) **3515**
Ongaku Bunken Yoshi Mokuroku. (JA) **3589**
Ongaku Gaku/Japanese Musicological Society. Journal. (JA ISSN 0030-2597) **3571**
Ongaku Geijutsu/Art of Music. (JA ISSN 0030-2600) **3571**
Ongaku Kenkyu. see Music Research **3565**
Ongaku Kyoiku Kenkyu/Study of Musical Education. (JA ISSN 0289-3657) **3571, 1757**
Ongaku no Tomo/Friends of Music. (JA ISSN 0289-3606) **3571**
Ongoing Current Bibliography of Plastic and Reconstructive Surgery see Current Bibliography of Plastic & Reconstructive Surgery **3169**
Onio Cities and Villages see Cities and Villages **2485**
†Onion. (CN ISSN 0380-285X) **5252**
Onion World. (US ISSN 0892-578X) **186**
Oniota. (US) **2417**
Onkologie. (SZ ISSN 0378-584X) **3201**
Onkologija. (BU ISSN 0369-7649) **3201**
Online. (GW ISSN 0340-1545) **1428**
Online (Weston). (US ISSN 0146-5422) **1428**
Online Access. (US) **1471, 828, 1463**
Online Access Guide see Online Access **1471**
Online Alert. (US ISSN 1050-6667) **1428, 1463, 1471**
Online Audiovisual Catalogers, Inc. Newsletter see O L A C Newsletter **2777**
Online Business Information. (UK ISSN 0267-9515) **828**
Online Business Sourcebook. (UK) **683, 2778**
Online Catalog News see Library Automation News **5227**
Online Computer Library Center, Inc. Annual Report see O C L C Annual Report **2777**
Online Computer Library Center, Inc. Micro see O C L C Micro **1463**
Online Computer Library Center, Inc. Newsletter see O C L C Newsletter **2777**
Online Currents. (AT ISSN 0816-956X) **2795**
Online Digital Music Review. (US) **3571**
Online Hotline News Service. (US ISSN 1040-6646) **1428, 1463, 1471**
Online Info. (GW) **1457**

ONLINE INFO

Online Info see O L B G - Info 2799
Online Informator see Online Kontakt 1399
Online Kontakt. (CS ISSN 0862-7509) 1399
Online Libraries and Microcomputers. (US) 2799
▼Online Manual. (UK) 1453
Online Newsletter. (US) 1428, 1463, 1471
Online Notes. (UK ISSN 0144-025X) 1428
Online - Onward. (CN ISSN 0827-4932) 2799, 1438
Online Product News. (US) 1445
Online Review. (US ISSN 0309-314X) 1428, 1463, 1471
Online Searcher see Information Searcher 1690
Online Today see CompuServe 1468
Online with Adult and Continuing Educators. (US) 1686, 1714
Onlooker. (II ISSN 0030-2619) 2201
Onoma. (BE ISSN 0078-463X) 2833
Onomastica. (PL ISSN 0078-4648) 2833
Onomastica Canadiana. (CN ISSN 0078-4656) 2833
Onomasticky Zpravodaj C S A V see Ceskoslovenska Akademie Ved. Ustav pro Jazyk Cesky. Onomasticky Zpravodaj 2356
Onomastics Research Center. Onomastics Series. (SA) 2833
Onomata/Revue Onomastique. (GR) 2258
Ons Burgerschap. (NE) 3912
Ons Erfdeel. (BE ISSN 0030-2651) 2175
Ons Fruitteeltblad see Boer en de Tuinder 80
Ons Geestelijk Leven see Geest en Leven 4179
Ons Graafschap. see Notre Comte 2378
†Ons Jeug. (SA ISSN 0030-2694) 5252
Ons Leger see Armex 3451
Ons Platteland. (NE ISSN 0030-2732) 112
Ons Politeuma see Ons Burgerschap 3912
Ons Vee. (NE ISSN 0030-2775) 222, 4814
†Ons Volk. (BE) 5252
Ons Wapen. (NE ISSN 0030-2783) 3468
Ons Zeewezen see Zeewezen 4742
ONSAT - America's Weekly Satellite Guide. (US) 1378
Onsei Gengo Igaku/Japan Journal of Logopedics and Phoniatrics. (JA ISSN 0030-2813) 3316
Onsei Kagaku Kenkyu. see Studia Phonologica 2844
Onsen Kagaku. see Science of Hot Springs 1579
Onslow Historian. (NZ ISSN 0110-4896) 2345
Ontario. Advisory Council on Women's Issues. Annual Report on the Status of Women's Issues see Ontario Advisory Council on Women's Issues. Annual Report 4850
Ontario. Agricultural Research Institute. Report see Agricultural Research Institute of Ontario. Annual Report 71
Ontario. Federal Cabinet. Orders-in-Council. (CN ISSN 0227-3268) 4069
Ontario. Human Rights Commission. Annual Report. (CN ISSN 0702-0538) 3945
Ontario. Labour Relations Board. Annual Report. (CN ISSN 0711-849X) 990
Ontario. Labour Relations Board. Decisions see Ontario. Labour Relations Board. Reports. A Monthly Series of Decisions 990
Ontario. Labour Relations Board. Reports. A Monthly Series of Decisions. (CN ISSN 0383-4778) 990
Ontario. Ministere des Affaires Culturelles et des Lois de l'Ontario. Rapport Annuel. (CN ISSN 0702-7842) 4482

Ontario. Ministry of Agriculture and Food. Agri-Food Outlook and Policy Review. (CN ISSN 1180-2936) 112
Ontario. Ministry of Agriculture and Food. Agri-Food Trade Update. (CN ISSN 1183-1588) 112
Ontario. Ministry of Agriculture and Food. Agricultural Statistics for Ontario (Year). (CN) 141
Ontario. Ministry of Agriculture and Food. Agricultural Trade Update. (CN) 112
†Ontario. Ministry of Agriculture and Food. Facts and Figures on the Agri-Food Sector. (CN) 5252
†Ontario. Ministry of Agriculture and Food. Farm Input Review. (CN) 5252
Ontario. Ministry of Agriculture and Food. Fruit Tree Census Part 3: Apples (Year). (CN) 141
Ontario. Ministry of Agriculture and Food. Fruit Tree Census Part 1: Grapes (Year). (CN) 141
Ontario. Ministry of Agriculture and Food. Fruit Tree Census Part 2: Tender Fruit (Year). (CN) 141
Ontario. Ministry of Agriculture and Food. Grain Letter. (CN ISSN 0843-6533) 207
Ontario. Ministry of Agriculture and Food. Monthly Crop and Livestock Report. (CN ISSN 0027-0342) 222, 186
Ontario. Ministry of Agriculture and Food. Monthly Dairy Report. (CN ISSN 0030-2872) 141
Ontario. Ministry of Agriculture and Food. P D R Notes. (Processing, Distribution and Retailing) (CN) 112
Ontario. Ministry of Agriculture and Food. Seasonal Fruit and Vegetable Report. (CN ISSN 0474-1560) 141, 2141
Ontario. Ministry of Community and Social Services. Social Assistance Review Board. Annual Report of the Board. (CN) 4415
Ontario. Ministry of Community and Social Services. Social Assistance Review Board. Annual Report of the Chairman see Ontario. Ministry of Community and Social Services. Social Assistance Review Board. Annual Report of the Board 4415
Ontario. Ministry of Education. Report. (CN ISSN 0317-6436) 1652
Ontario. Ministry of Housing. Annual Report. (CN ISSN 0835-0213) 2493
Ontario. Ministry of Labour. Library. Infolink. (CN ISSN 0836-1525) 733, 4118
Ontario. Ministry of Labour. Library. Library Bulletin see Ontario. Ministry of Labour. Library. Infolink 733
Ontario. Ministry of Municipal Affairs and Housing. Annual Report see Ontario. Ministry of Housing. Annual Report 2493
Ontario. Ministry of Municipal Affairs. Annual Report. (CN ISSN 0833-1731) 4093
Ontario. Ministry of Natural Resources. Forest Research Report. (CN ISSN 0381-3924) 2105
Ontario. Ministry of Natural Resources. Ontario Forest Research Institute. Forest Research Note. (CN) 2105
Ontario. Ministry of Natural Resources. Tree Improvement and Forest Biomass Institute. Forest Research Note see Ontario. Ministry of Natural Resources. Ontario Forest Research Institute. Forest Research Note 2105
†Ontario. Ministry of the Environment. Annual Report. (CN) 5252
Ontario. Ministry of the Environment. Ground Water Bulletin. (CN ISSN 0078-5156) 4827
Ontario. Ministry of the Environment. Industrial Waste Conference. Proceedings. (CN ISSN 0078-4893) 1986

Ontario. Ministry of the Environment. Pollution Control Branch. Research Publication. (CN ISSN 0078-5148) 1978
Ontario. Ministry of the Environment. Water Resources Branch. Water Resources Report. (CN ISSN 0475-0942) 1600
Ontario. Ministry of Transportation and Communications. Ontario Road Safety Annual Report see Ontario. Ministry of Transportation. Ontario Road Safety Annual Report 4699
Ontario. Ministry of Transportation. Ontario Road Safety Annual Report. (CN) 4699
Ontario. Provincial-Municipal Affairs Secretariat. Municipal Directory. (CN ISSN 0318-0743) 4069, 4093
Ontario Advisory Council on Women's Issues. Annual Report. (CN ISSN 0830-9442) 4850
Ontario Annotated Family Law Service. (CN) 2718
Ontario Annual Practice. (CN) 2664
Ontario Appeal Cases. (CN) 2664
Ontario Archaeological Society. Arch Notes. (CN ISSN 0048-1742) 281
Ontario Archaeology. (CN ISSN 0078-4672) 281
Ontario Arts Council. Annual Report. (CN) 339
Ontario Association of Children's Aid Societies. Journal. (CN ISSN 0030-283X) 4415
Ontario Association of Speech - Language Pathologists and Audiologists Newsletter see O S L A Newsletter 2288
▼Ontario Bed & Breakfast Guide. (CN) 2478, 4781
Ontario Churchman see Dialogue (Kingston) 4236
Ontario Colleges of Applied Arts and Technology Tracks see C A A T Tracks 2750
Ontario Conservation News. (CN ISSN 0383-6479) 1494
Ontario Corn Producer. (CN) 112
Ontario Corporations Law Guide. (CN) 2711
Ontario Craft. (CN ISSN 0229-1320) 356
Ontario Dairy Farmer see Dairy Farmer Quarterly Magazine 198
Ontario Decisions - Criminal Conviction and Sentence Cases. (CN) 2714
Ontario Dentist. (CN ISSN 0300-5275) 3239
Ontario Directory of Education. (CN ISSN 0316-8549) 1652
Ontario Economic Council. Research Studies. (CN) 683
Ontario Education Relations Commission. Annual Report. (CN ISSN 0706-0092) 1547, 990
Ontario English Catholic Teachers Association Reporter see O E C T A Reporter 1652
Ontario Family Law Quantum Service. (CN) 2718, 4444
Ontario Family Law Reform Act Manual.(CN) 2718
Ontario Family Law Reporter. (CN ISSN 0835-636X) 2718
Ontario Farmer (Eastern Edition). (CN) 112
Ontario Farmer (Western Edition). (CN) 112
Ontario Field Biologist. (CN ISSN 0078-4834) 450
Ontario Fisherman. (CN) 4552
Ontario Forestry Association. Newsletter.(CN ISSN 0834-2008) 2105
Ontario Gazette. (CN ISSN 0030-2937) 2178
Ontario Genealogical Society. Kingston Branch. Kingston Relations. (CN ISSN 1188-1089) 2161
Ontario Genealogical Society. Kingston Branch. Newsletter see Ontario Genealogical Society. Kingston Branch. Kingston Relations 2161
Ontario Genealogical Society. Ottawa Branch News. (CN) 2161

Ontario Genealogical Society. Ottawa Branch. Publication see Ontario Genealogical Society. Ottawa Branch News 2161
Ontario Genealogy Society. Newsleaf. (CN ISSN 0380-1616) 2161
Ontario Geography. (CN ISSN 0078-4850) 2258
Ontario Geological Survey. Aggregate Resources Inventory Paper. (CN ISSN 0708-2061) 3492
Ontario Geological Survey. Annual Report of the Regional and Resident Geologists. (CN) 3492, 1577
Ontario Geological Survey. Exploration Technology Development Fund Grants see Ontario Geological Survey. Exploration Technology Development Fund, Summary of Research 3492
Ontario Geological Survey. Exploration Technology Development Fund, Summary of Research. (CN) 3492
Ontario Geological Survey. Geological Report see Ontario Geological Survey. Report 3493
Ontario Geological Survey. Geoscience Research Grant Program. Summary of Research. (CN ISSN 0225-5316) 3492
Ontario Geological Survey. Guide Books.(CN) 1577, 3492
Ontario Geological Survey. Mineral Deposits Circular. (CN ISSN 0706-4551) 3492
Ontario Geological Survey. Miscellaneous Paper. (CN ISSN 0704-2752) 3492
Ontario Geological Survey. Northern Ontario Engineering Geology Terrain Study. (CN ISSN 0709-4671) 3492
Ontario Geological Survey. Report. (CN) 3493, 1577
Ontario Geological Survey. Study. (CN ISSN 0704-2590) 3493
Ontario Geological Survey. Summary of Field Work. (CN ISSN 0829-8203) 3493
Ontario Geological Survey. Supplement to M.P.77. (CN) 3493
Ontario Golf News. (CN) 4509
Ontario Government Libraries Council. Exchange. (CN ISSN 0826-7871) 2778
Ontario Government Publications, Monthly Checklist/Publications du Gouvernement de l'Ontario, Liste Mensuelle. (CN ISSN 0316-1617) 408
Ontario Herbalists Association. Journal see Canadian Journal of Herbalism 3720
Ontario Historical Society. Bulletin. (CN ISSN 0714-6736) 2417
Ontario Historical Society Bulletin see O H S Bulletin 2417
Ontario Historical Studies Series. (CN) 2417
Ontario History. (CN ISSN 0030-2953) 2417
Ontario Hog Farmer. (CN) 222
Ontario Home Builder. (CN) 627
Ontario Hospital Libraries Association Newsline see O H L A Newsline 2777
Ontario Hydro Research Review. (CN ISSN 0227-9916) 1904
Ontario Industrial Magazine. (CN) 1082
Ontario Institute of Pedology. Department of Land Resource Science. Progress Report. (CN) 186, 1577
Ontario Insurance Directory. (CN) 2539
†Ontario Labour Relations Board Law and Practice. (CN) 5253
Ontario Land Surveyor. (CN) 1872
Ontario Lawyers Weekly see The Lawyers Weekly 2647
Ontario Legislative Digest Service. (CN) 2664
Ontario Limitation Periods. (CN) 2664
Ontario Living see London Magazine (London) 2178
Ontario Mathematics Gazette. (CN ISSN 0030-3011) 3050
Ontario Medical Review. (CN ISSN 0030-302X) 3138

†Ontario Medical Technologist. (CN ISSN 0228-877X) 5253
Ontario Medicine. (CN) 3138
Ontario Milk Producer. (CN ISSN 0030-3038) 202
Ontario Mineral Score. (CN ISSN 0714-122X) 3493, 3502
Ontario Motor Coach Association Resources. (CN) 4781
Ontario Motor Coach Association Yearbook. (CN) 4781
Ontario Municipal Board Reports. (CN ISSN 0318-7527) 2664
Ontario Museum News see Currently: Ontario Museum News 3523
Ontario New Democrat. (CN ISSN 0028-4564) 3912
Ontario Numismatist. (CN ISSN 0048-1815) 3601
Ontario Nursing Home Journal see Canadian Nursing Home Journal 2460
Ontario Out of Doors. (CN ISSN 0707-3178) 4552
Ontario Plumbing Inspectors Association. Bulletin. (CN ISSN 0048-1823) 2302
Ontario Psychologist. (CN ISSN 0030-3054) 4037
Ontario Public Sector. (CN) 4081, 4582
Ontario Puppetry Association Letter see O P A L 4636
Ontario Real Estate Law Guide. (CN ISSN 0382-5906) 2715
Ontario Recycling Update. (CN ISSN 0823-6143) 1986, 1494, 3650
Ontario Regional Lily Society. Newsletter. (CN) 2136
Ontario Reports. (CN ISSN 0030-3089) 2664
Ontario Research Foundation. Annual Report see ORTECH International. Annual Report 684
Ontario Restaurant Association. Membership Directory & Buyers' Guide. (CN) 2478
Ontario Restaurant News. (CN) 2478
Ontario Review. (US ISSN 0316-4055) 2945
Ontario Ringette Association. Official Rules see Ringette Canada. Official Rules (Years) 4485
Ontario Safety League. News see Safety Update 4112
Ontario School Counsellors' Association Reports see O S C A Reports 1652
Ontario Science Centre. Newscience. (CN ISSN 0228-4642) 4332
Ontario Securities Legislation. (CN) 2664
Ontario Sheep News. (CN ISSN 0844-5303) 222
Ontario Ship-by-Truck Directory. (CN) 1149, 4747
▼Ontario Ski Guide. (CN) 4552
Ontario Snowmobiler. (CN) 4552
Ontario Society of Medical Technologists Update see O S M T Update 3262
†Ontario Statistics. (CN ISSN 0319-7751) 5253
Ontario Statute Citator. (CN ISSN 0030-3127) 2664
Ontario Symposia on Personality and Social Cognition Series. (US) 4037, 4444
Ontario Tax Reports. (CN ISSN 0048-1866) 1103
Ontario Teachers' Federation Interaction see O T F - F E O Interaction 1713
Ontario Technologist. (CN ISSN 0380-1969) 4605
Ontario Tennis. (CN) 4509
Ontario Today see Education Today 1727
Ontario TourBook see Tourbook: Ontario 4790
Ontario Tourism News. (CN ISSN 0707-1442) 4781
Ontario Universities Benefits Survey. (CN ISSN 0711-6896) 1730, 1714
Ontario Veterinary Association. Update. (CN ISSN 0821-6320) 4814
Ontario Water Skier. (CN ISSN 0226-5702) 4552
Ontario Woman. (CN) 4850
Ontario Wrestler Magazine. (CN) 4482, 3399, 3611, 3807

Ontarion. (CN) 1320
Ontario Decisions - Criminal Cases see Ontario Decisions - Criminal Conviction and Sentence Cases 2714
Ontarion Shade Tree Council. Newsletter see Urban Forest 2110
Ontario's Common Ground Magazine. (CN ISSN 0845-471X) 3596
Onthebus. (US ISSN 1043-884X) 2999, 2945
Ontladingen. (NE ISSN 0030-3135) 1904
Ontwaak! (SA ISSN 0030-316X) 4286
Onward-Voorwaarts see Volkstem 3933
Onze Bostons. (NE) 3712
Onze Luchtmacht/Our Air Force. (NE ISSN 0030-3208) 3468, 60
Onze Vogels. (NE ISSN 0030-3224) 566
Onze Wereld. (NE ISSN 0030-3232) 3967
Oomoto. (JA ISSN 0030-3259) 4286, 3774
Oorlogsdocumentatie '40-'45. (NE) 3468
Oorspronkelijk Christendom. (NE ISSN 0030-3267) 4193
Ooru Yomimono/All Reading Matters. (JA) 2945
Oosamala. (Il) 112
Oostelike Transvaalse Kaner see O T Kaner 111
Oostenrijkse Economische Berichten. (NE) 820
Oostenrijkse Handelsdelegatie in Nederland see Oostenrijkse Economische Berichten 820
Op. (US ISSN 0276-8747) 3571
Op Cit. (IT ISSN 0030-3305) 339, 304
Opady Atmosferyczne/Precipitation. (PL) 3440, 1600
Opakowanie. (PL ISSN 0030-3348) 3650
Opbouw. (NE ISSN 0030-3356) 4245
Opcao. (PO) 2214
Opcion. (VE) 4381, 2878
Opciones. (CL ISSN 0716-4513) 3967, 2418
Opdraettervejviseren. (DK ISSN 0106-6714) 3712
Opel Post. (GW) 1068
Opema em Ritmo de Brasil Jovem. (BL) 4605
Open. (NE ISSN 0030-3372) 2778
Open Access. (UK ISSN 0048-1904) 2778
Open-Apple see A2 - Central 1467
Open Book. (AT) 1652
Open Deur. (BE ISSN 0030-3399) 339, 2945
Open Deur. (NE ISSN 0030-3402) 4245
Open Door International for the Emancipation of the Woman Worker. Report of Congress. (BE ISSN 0078-5164) 990, 4850
Open Doors. (US ISSN 0078-5172) 1723
Open Doors News Service see News Network International 4192
▼Open Economies Review. (NE ISSN 0923-7992) 897, 918, 933
Open Exchange. (US) 1652
Open Forum. (US ISSN 0030-3429) 2664, 3945
Open Hands. (US ISSN 0888-8833) 4245, 2456
Open House. (UK) 1241, 4415
Open House. (AT) 2478
Open Learning. (UK) 1714
Open Learning Systems News see O L S News 1756
▼Open Magazine. (HK) 2197
†Open Magazine. (US ISSN 0894-265X) 5253
▼Open Magazine Pamphlet Series. (US) 3967, 3912
Open Market. (UK ISSN 0954-1470) 878
Open Mind. (UK ISSN 0265-511X) 3285, 3349, 4415
Open: O S I Product and Equipment News. (US ISSN 0898-0489) 1479, 1454

Open Road. (AT ISSN 0048-1947) 4699
†Open Road. (CN) 5253
Open Shop Building Construction Cost Data (Year) see Means Open Shop Building Construction Cost Data (Year) 624
Open Spaces. (UK) 4552, 1494
†Open Systems. (US) 5253
Open Systems and Software see Network Monitor 1428
Open Systems Communication. (US ISSN 0741-2851) 1447
†Open Systems Information Systems. (NE ISSN 0921-8327) 5253
Open Systems Interconnection Netter Newsletter see O S I Netter Newsletter 1428
Open Systems Newsletter see Open Systems 5253
▼Open Systems Report. (US ISSN 1052-701X) 1428
Open -to- Buy. (US) 1049, 1149
Open Venster. (NE ISSN 0030-3453) 2277
Open Wheel. (US) 4699
Open Windows. (US ISSN 0162-4296) 4246
†Open Word. (GY) 5253
Openbaar Vervoer (Amsterdam, 1958). (NE) 4654
Opening Price Statistical Data. (US) 959
Oper und Konzert. (GW ISSN 0030-3518) 3571
Opera. (IT ISSN 0030-3542) 3571
Opera. (UK ISSN 0030-3526) 3571
L'Opera (Milan). (IT) 3571
†Opera America. Management Resource Volume. (US) 5253
Opera America. Repertoire Survey. (US) 3571, 4636
Opera America. Survey of Professional Training-Apprentice Programs see Singer's Guide to the Professional Opera Companies 3580
Opera America Newsline. (US) 3572, 1652, 4636
Opera Annual U S (Year). (US) 3572
Opera Australia. (AT ISSN 0155-4980) 3572
Opera Australia Libretto Series. (AT ISSN 0810-8021) 3572
Opera Botanica. (DK ISSN 0078-5237) 512
Opera Botanica. Series B. Flora of Ecuador see Flora of Ecuador 503
Opera - Canada. (CN ISSN 0030-3577) 3572
Opera Digest. (US) 3572
Opera Fanatic. (US) 3572
Opera Journal. (US ISSN 0030-3585) 3572
Opera Lilloana. (AG ISSN 0078-5245) 512, 536, 590, 1577
Opera Monthly. (US ISSN 0897-6554) 3572
Opera News. (US ISSN 0030-3607) 3572
Opera Now. (UK) 3572
Opera Quarterly. (US ISSN 0736-0053) 3572
Opera Slavica see Opera Slavica. Neue Folge 2833
Opera Slavica. Neue Folge. (GW) 2833, 2945
Operabladet Ascolta. (DK ISSN 0900-6354) 3572
Operant Subjectivity. (US ISSN 0193-2713) 4458, 4582
Operatie Veiligheid. (BE ISSN 0771-2588) 4109
†Operating and Programming Systems Series. (NE) 5253
Operating Banks and Branches. Data Book: United States, States, Counties, Other Areas. (US) 794
Operating Banks and Branches. Data Book 1: Connecticut, Maine, Massachusetts, New Hampshire, New Jersey, New York, Pennsylvania, Rhode Island, Vermont, Puerto Rico, Virgin Islands. (US) 794
Operating Banks and Branches. Data Book 2: Delaware, District of Columbia, Florida, Georgia, Maryland, North Carolina, South Carolina, Virginia, West Virginia. (US) 794

Operating Banks and Branches. Data Book 3: Illinois, Indiana, Kentucky, Michigan, Ohio, Wisconsin. (US) 794
Operating Banks and Branches. Data Book 4: Alabama, Arkansas, Louisiana, Mississippi, Oklahoma, Tennessee, Texas. (US) 794
Operating Banks and Branches. Data Book 5: Iowa, Kansas, Minnesota, Missouri, Nebraska, North Dakota, South Dakota. (US) 794
Operating Banks and Branches. Data Book 6: Alaska, Arizona, California, Colorado, Hawaii, Idaho, Montana, Nevada, New Mexico, Oregon, Utah, Washington, Wyoming, Pacific Islands. (US) 794
Operating Results of Independent Supermarkets. (US) 1117, 1023, 2093
Operating Results of Mass Retail Stores - Mass Retailers' Merchandising Report-Cornell Study. (US) 991
Operating Results of Self-Service Discount Department Stores see Operating Results of Mass Retail Stores - Mass Retailers' Merchandising Report-Cornell Study 991
Operating Room Manager see O R Manager 2468
Operating Room Risk Management. (US) 3382
Operating Section Proceedings see American Gas Association. Operating Section. Proceedings 3681
Operating Systems Review. (US ISSN 0163-5980) 1454
Operating Techniques and Products Bulletin. see Journal of Property Management 4151
Operation. see Shujutsu 3384
Operation & Maintenance Intelligence see O & M Intelligence 3467
Operation Enterprise News. (US) 1023, 3630
†Operation Liberte. (CN) 5253
Operational Geographer/Geographie Appliquee. (CN ISSN 0822-4838) 2258, 1399, 1965, 2493
Operational Hydrology Reports. (UN) 1600
Operational Research Society. Journal. (US ISSN 0160-5682) 1399
Operational Research Society Insight see O R Insight 1652
Operations Alert (Chicago). (US) 794
Operations des Transporteurs Aeriens au Canada. see Air Carrier Operations in Canada 66
Operations - Employment Service and Unemployment Insurance see New York (State) Department of Labor. Operations - Employment Service and Unemployment Insurance 989
Operations Exchange. (US) 794, 831
Operations Forestieres et de Scierie. (CN ISSN 0030-3631) 2116
Operations Forum. (US ISSN 0887-2104) 4827
Operations Research. (US ISSN 0030-364X) 1399, 3050
Operations Research. see R A I R O Recherche Operationnelle 1442
Operations Research Letters. (NE ISSN 0167-6377) 4332
Operations Research - Management Science. (US ISSN 0030-3658) 733, 18
Operations Research - Management Science Today see O R - M S Today 4331
Operations Research - Management Science Yearbook. (US ISSN 0473-0496) 733, 18
Operations Research Society of America. Meeting Bulletin see T I M S - O R S A Meeting Bulletin 4346
Operations Research Society of Japan. Journal/Nihon Opereshonzu Risachi Gakkai Ronbunshi. (JA ISSN 0453-4514) 1023
Operations Research Spektrum see O R Spektrum 1398
Operations Research, Statistics and Applied Mathematics. see Universite Libre de Bruxelles. Centre d'Etudes de Recherche Operationnelle. Cahiers 1401

Operations Research - Verfahren/ Methods of Operations Research. (GW ISSN 0078-5318) **1023**
Operations Update (Mountain View). (US) **2778**
Operations Update (New York). (US) **683**, 1023
Operationsmoensteret paa Danske Sygehuse. (DK ISSN 0109-9957) **2468**
Operative Dentistry. (US ISSN 0361-7734) **3239**
Operative Orthopaedie und Traumatologie. (GW ISSN 0934-6694) **3310**
Operative Techniques in Orthopaedics. (US) **3310**
Operative Techniques in Otolaryngology.(US) **3316**
Opereshonzu Risachi/Communications of the Operations Research Society of Japan. (JA ISSN 0030-3674) **1023**
Opernglas. (GW ISSN 0935-6398) **3572**
Opernjournal see Deutsche Oper Berlin Aktuell **3548**
Opernwelt. (SZ ISSN 0030-3690) **3572**
Opettaja/Teacher. (FI ISSN 0355-3965) **1652**
Opettajain Lehti see Opettaja **1652**
OpFlow. (US ISSN 0149-8029) **1833**, 4827
Opgavesaet til Dansk Skr. Fremstilling, Folkeskolens Udvidede Afgangsproeve see Opgavesaet til Dansk Skriftlig Fremstilling, Folkeskolens Afgangsproeve **1652**
Opgavesaet til Dansk Skriftlig Fremstilling, Folkeskolens Afgangsproeve. (DK ISSN 0109-1255) **1652**
Opgavesamling i Skat 1. (DK ISSN 0108-9722) **1103**
Opgavesamling i Skat 2 og Erhvervsjura. (DK ISSN 0108-9730) **1103**
Opgavesamling i Skatteret I see Opgavesamling i Skat 1 **1103**
Opgavesamling i Skatteret II og Erhvervsjura see Opgavesamling i Skat 2 og Erhvervsjura **1103**
Ophelia. (DK ISSN 0078-5326) **450**
Ophtalmologie. (FR ISSN 0989-3105) **3303**
Ophtalmologiste Praticien. (FR) **3303**
Ophthalmic Abstract Journal. (CN ISSN 1180-0984) **3178**
Ophthalmic and Physiological Optics. (UK ISSN 0275-5408) **3303**
Ophthalmic Forum. (US) **3303**
†Ophthalmic Laser Therapy. (US ISSN 8756-0402) **5253**
Ophthalmic Literature. (UK ISSN 0030-3720) **3178**, 18
Ophthalmic Optician see Optometry Today **3304**
Ophthalmic Paediatrics and Genetics. (NE ISSN 0167-6784) **3303**, 3323
Ophthalmic Plastic and Reconstructive Surgery. (US ISSN 0740-9303) **3303**, 3382
Ophthalmic Practice. (CN ISSN 0832-9869) **3303**
Ophthalmic Research. (SZ ISSN 0030-3747) **3303**
Ophthalmic Surgery. (US ISSN 0022-023X) **3382**, 3303
Ophthalmo Chirurgie. (GW ISSN 0936-2517) **3303**
Ophthalmologia. (BU ISSN 0374-2105) **3303**
Ophthalmologica. (SZ ISSN 0030-3755) **3303**
Ophthalmologica Hungarica. see Szemeszet **3305**
Ophthalmological Society of Egypt. Bulletin. (UA ISSN 0078-5342) **3303**
†Ophthalmologists' Exchange. (AT) **5253**
Ophthalmology. see Zentralblatt Ophthalmologie **3182**
Ophthalmology/Ganka. (JA ISSN 0016-4488) **3303**
Ophthalmology. (US ISSN 0161-6420) **3303**, 3316

Ophthalmology Alert see Hospital's Medicare Policy & Payment Report **3106**
†Ophthalmology Management. (US ISSN 0746-1070) **5253**
▼Ophthalmology Report. (US) **3303**
Ophthalmology Times. (US ISSN 0193-032X) **3303**
Opifico delle Pietre Dure Restauro see O P D Restauro **304**
Opinie see Linksaf **3905**
Opinion. (US) **3774**, 4193, 4444
Opinion see National Union for Civil and Public Servants. Journal **4068**
Opinion Agropecuaria. (MX) **222**
Opinion Economica. (CK) **683**
Opinion Manual Letters (Chronological). (US) **2539**
Opinion Manual Updates (Sectional). (US) **2539**
Opinion Popular. (CR) **3912**
Opinione. (IT) **3913**
Opinions/Seiron. (JA) **3913**
Opinions (Year). (US ISSN 1050-0383) **4582**
Opinions of the Utah State Superintendent of Public Instruction see Utah. State Office of Education. Opinions of the Utah State Superintendent of Public Instruction **1732**
The Opisthobranch. (US) **450**, 1610
Oplagsbulletin. (DK ISSN 0107-380X) **4134**
Oplagstal og Markedstal/Circulation Data and Marketing Data. (DK ISSN 0070-2854) **36**
Opleiding & Ontwikkeling. (NE ISSN 0922-0895) **1068**
Opolskie Roczniki Ekonomiczne. (PL ISSN 0474-2893) **683**
Oposicion Obrera. see Working Class Opposition **3935**
Opossum Holler Tarot. (US) **3774**
Oppikoululehti see Opettaja **1652**
Opportunites du Tele-Achat. (FR) **1424**
Opportunites Industrielles Bulletin. (FR ISSN 0249-5163) **820**
Opportunities. (UK ISSN 0030-3852) **4069**
Opportunities Abroad for Teachers see U.S. Department of Education. Opportunities for Teachers Abroad **1724**
▼Opportunities Briefing. (US ISSN 0960-5088) **918**, 3967
Opportunities in Options. (US) **959**
Opportunities in Science and Engineering. (US) **1833**, 420, 3630
Opportunities Unlimited. (CN) **4699**
Opportunity. (CN) **878**
Opportunity in Northern Canada see Opportunity **878**
Opportunity Magazine. (US ISSN 0741-3750) **1049**
†Ops: The Data Center Newsletter. (US ISSN 0886-4659) **5253**
Opsaal. (SA ISSN 0030-3879) **794**
Opsearch. (II ISSN 0030-3887) **1023**
†Opstap. (NE ISSN 0169-7269) **5253**
Opstestveno Politickite Organizacii na SR Makedonija. Bilten. (XN) **3913**
Opstina. (YU ISSN 0030-3895) **3913**, 4069
Optica Acta: International Journal of Optics see Journal of Modern Optics **3854**
Optica Applicata. (PL ISSN 0078-5466) **3856**
Optica Pura y Aplicada. (SP ISSN 0030-3917) **3856**
▼Optical and Acoustical Review. (US) **3856**, 3860
▼Optical & Magnetic Report. (US ISSN 1047-5117) **1454**
Optical and Quantum Electronics. (UK ISSN 0306-8919) **1776**
▼Optical Computing and Processing. (UK ISSN 0954-2264) **1454**, 1418
Optical Data Systems see O M N I **1385**
Optical-Electronic Publishing Directory see Optical Publishing Directory **4143**
Optical Engineering. (US ISSN 0091-3286) **3856**, 1833

Optical Engineering Reports see O E Reports **3856**
†Optical Engineering Reports: European Edition. (GW) **5253**
Optical Engineering Series. (US) **3856**
Optical Fibre and Cable. see Guangxian yu Dianlan **1893**
Optical Information Systems see Document Image Automation **2755**
Optical Information Systems Update see Document Image Automation Update **1372**
Optical Instruments. see Guangxue Yiqi **2522**
†Optical Management. (UK ISSN 0267-4041) **5253**
▼Optical Materials. (NE ISSN 0925-3467) **3856**
▼Optical Materials and Engineering News. (US ISSN 1045-6570) **3856**
Optical Media News and Information see O M N I **1385**
Optical Memory News. (US ISSN 0741-5869) **1418**, 1351, 4360
Optical Memory Report. (US) **3856**, 1341, 1454
Optical Physics and Engineering. (US ISSN 0078-5482) **3856**, 1833
Optical Prism. (CN ISSN 0824-3441) **3303**
Optical Publishing Directory. (US ISSN 0896-9841) **4143**
Optical Receptionist. (UK ISSN 0266-9390) **3303**
Optical Society of America. Journal Part A. (US ISSN 0740-3232) **3856**
Optical Society of America. Journal Part B. (US ISSN 0740-3224) **3856**
Optical Society of America, Inc. Annual Meeting Digest see O S A Annual Meeting Digest **3856**
Optical World. (UK) **3303**
Optician. (UK ISSN 0030-3968) **3303**
Opticians Association of America News see O A A News **3302**
†Opticien Belge/Belgische Opticien. (BE ISSN 0030-3976) **5253**
Opticien-Lunetier. (FR ISSN 0030-3984) **3303**
Optics see Scottish Optometrist **3305**
Optics and Laser Technology. (UK ISSN 0030-3992) **3856**, 1833
Optics and Lasers in Engineering. (UK ISSN 0143-8166) **3856**, 1833
Optics & Photonics News. (US ISSN 1047-6938) **3856**
Optics and Spectroscopy. (English translation of: Optika i Spektroskopiya) (US ISSN 0030-400X) **3856**
Optics and Spectroscopy. Supplement. (US ISSN 0078-5504) **3856**
Optics Communications. (NE ISSN 0030-4018) **3857**
Optics Letters. (US ISSN 0146-9592) **3857**
Optics News see Optics & Photonics News **3856**
Optik. (GW ISSN 0030-4026) **3857**
Optika i Spektroskopiya. (RU ISSN 0030-4034) **3857**
Optikko. (FI ISSN 0048-2021) **3304**
Optima. (SA ISSN 0030-4050) **3493**
Optimal Control Applications and Methods. (UK ISSN 0143-2087) **1415**
†Optimal Health. (US ISSN 0885-4858) **5253**
Optimist. (US ISSN 0030-4069) **1320**
Optimization. (GW) **3063**
Optimizatsiya. (RU) **3050**
Optimum. (CN ISSN 0475-1906) **1023**
▼Optimum Delivery. (US) **1353**
Option. (US) **1686**, 1723
Option Advisor. (US) **959**
Option - Bio. (FR ISSN 0992-5945) **450**
Option Magazine. (US ISSN 0882-178X) **3572**
Option Qualite. (FR) **1082**
Option Serre. (CN ISSN 0838-1674) **2136**
Option Weekly. (US) **959**
†OptionProfits. (CN ISSN 0831-4853) **5253**

Options (Port Chester). (US) **3399**, 2456
†Options (Van Nuys). (US) **5253**
Options (Washington). (US) **3985**, 4415, 4850
Options (Wayne). (US ISSN 0362-2770) **4225**
Options Alert. (US) **959**
Options & Futures Factors - The Futures Portfolio Advisor. (US) **959**
Options: News for Older New Yorkers. (US) **2277**
Options Politiques. see Policy Options **4070**
Opto. (FR ISSN 0988-3525) **3304**
Opto & Laser Products. (UK) **3857**
Opto Electronique. (FR ISSN 0247-4808) **1776**
Opto Elektronik Magazin. (GW) **1776**
Opto Magazine. (BE) **3304**, 3857
Optoelectronics see Electronic Materials and Processing **1768**
Optoelectronics. (JA ISSN 0912-5434) **1776**
Optoelectronics D.A.T.A. Book see Optoelectronics D.A.T.A. Digest **1776**
Optoelectronics D.A.T.A. Digest. (US ISSN 1040-0907) **1776**
Optoelectronics, Instrumentation and Data Processing. (English translation of: Avtometriya) (US ISSN 8756-6990) **1776**, 2524
Optoelektronika i Poluprovodnikovaya Tekhnika. (KR ISSN 1011-6559) **1776**
Optolaser. (IT) **3857**
▼Optometric Economics. (US ISSN 1052-7346) **3304**, 897
Optometric Education. (US) **3304**
Optometric Management. (US ISSN 0030-4085) **3304**
Optometric World. (US ISSN 0030-4107) **3304**
Optometrie see Opto **3304**
▼Optometry. (US) **3178**, 3304
Optometry and Vision Science. (US ISSN 1040-5488) **3304**
▼Optometry Clinics. (US ISSN 1050-6918) **3304**
†Optometry Times. (US) **5253**
Optometry Today. (II ISSN 0048-203X) **3304**
Optometry Today. (UK ISSN 0268-5485) **3304**
Opus. (US ISSN 1047-2355) **4461**, 3572
Opus Building Services Design File. (UK ISSN 0266-1063) **1149**, 627
▼Opus Dei Awareness Network. (US ISSN 1059-3144) **4271**
Opus Musicum. (CS ISSN 0862-8505) **3572**
Opus One. (US ISSN 0162-430X) **4246**
Opus Two. (US ISSN 0147-1597) **4246**
Opuscula Atheniensia. (SW ISSN 0078-5520) **281**, 1278
Opuscula - aus Wissenschaft und Dichtung. (GW ISSN 0078-5539) **2512**
Opuscula Byzantina see Acta Universitatis de Attila Jozsef Nominatae. Acta Antiqua et Archaeologica **1274**
Opuscula Medica. (SW ISSN 0030-414X) **3138**
Opuscula Zoologica. (HU ISSN 0473-1034) **590**
Opuscula Zoologica Fluminensia. (SZ ISSN 1010-5220) **590**, 536
Opusculum. (FI ISSN 0358-5581) **4134**, 2319
Opzij. (NE) **1293**
Or du Rhine. (FR) **2379**
B'Or Ha'Torah. (IS ISSN 0333-6298) **4225**
Or Vert. (FR) **2136**
Ora di Ottawa. (CN) **2018**
Ora et Labora. (IT ISSN 0030-4174) **4271**
Orachot. (IS) **4225**
Oracle. (II) **2201**
Oracle. (US) **3239**
▼Oracle News. (US) **1463**, 1479
Oracle Science Fiction and Fantasy Magazine. (US) **2984**

OREGON PSYCHOLOGY 6527

Orafo Italiano. (IT ISSN 0471-7376) 2565
Orafo Italiano nel Mondo/Italian Goldsmith in the World. (IT ISSN 0473-1174) 2565
Orafo Orologiaio. (IT ISSN 0030-4182) 2565
Orah. (CN) 2018, 4850
Oraita. (IS ISSN 0333-9270) 4225
Oral and Maxillofacial Surgery Clinics. (US ISSN 1042-3680) 3382, 3239
†Oral Biology. (UK ISSN 0261-4820) 5253
Oral Health. (CN ISSN 0030-4204) 3239
Oral History. (PP) 2345
Oral History. (UK ISSN 0143-0955) 2379, 246
Oral History Association. Newsletter. (US ISSN 0474-3253) 2319
Oral History Association of Australia. Journal. (AT ISSN 0158-7366) 2345
Oral History Review. (US ISSN 0094-0798) 2319
Oral History Series. (US) 2418, 2319, 4069
Oral Microbiology and Immunology. (DK ISSN 0902-0055) 556, 3188
Oral Oncology see European Journal of Cancer Part B: Oral Oncology 3197
Oral Surgery, Oral Medicine and Oral Pathology. (US ISSN 0030-4220) 3239
Oral Therapeutics and Pharmacology. see Shika Yakubutsu Ryoho 3743
Oral Tradition. (US ISSN 0883-5365) 2057, 2945
Oralprophylaxe. (GW ISSN 0724-4991) 3239
Oralrama! (US) 3399
Orana. (AT) 2778, 1262
Orang Peladang. (NE ISSN 0030-4239) 112
Orang-Utan (Sokolsky or Polish Opening). (GW) 4482
Orange Coast Magazine. (US) 2231
Orange County Apartment News. (US) 4154, 627
Orange County Business Journal. (US) 878
Orange County California Genealogical Society Quarterly. (US) 2161
Orange County Farm News see Ag Focus 68
Orange County Genealogical Society. Quarterly see Orange County California Genealogical Society Quarterly 2161
Orange County Jewish Heritage. (US ISSN 0030-4298) 2018
Orange County Metropolitan. (US) 878
Orange County Report. (US ISSN 0882-0589) 838, 4154
Orange County Resources. (US) 3596
Orange County Stamp News. (US) 3755
Orange Free State. Director of Hospital Services. Report/Orange Free State. Direkteur van Hospitaldienste. Verslag. (SA ISSN 0078-5547) 2468
Orange Free State. Direkteur van Hospitaldienste. Verslag. see Orange Free State. Director of Hospital Services. Report 2468
†Orange Free State. Nature Conservation Branch. Annual Report. (SA) 5253
†Orange Free State. Nature Conservation Branch. Miscellaneous Publications Series. (SA) 5253
Orange Free State Philatelic Society Philatelic Magazine see O F S Philatelic Magazine 3755
Orange Seed see Orange Seed Technical Bulletin 2778
Orange Seed Technical Bulletin. (US) 2778
†Oranim. (IS) 5253
Oranje-Nassau Museum. Jaarboek. (NE) 3531
Oratoire. (CN ISSN 0030-4344) 4272
Gli Oratori del Giorno. (IT) 2878
Oratoriana. (FR ISSN 0030-4352) 4193
The Oratory. (CN) 4272

Oratory School Magazine. (UK) 1714
Orben's Current Comedy see Current Comedy for Speakers 1334
Orbis. (BE ISSN 0030-4379) 2833
Orbis. (UK ISSN 0030-4425) 2999, 2945
Orbis (Philadelphia). (US ISSN 0030-4387) 3967
Orbis Antiquus. (GW ISSN 0078-5555) 1279
Orbis Geographicus. (GW ISSN 0030-4395) 2258
Orbis Litterarum. (DK ISSN 0105-7510) 2945
Orbis Musicae. (IS ISSN 0303-3937) 3572, 3642
Orbit. (ZA) 1262
Orbit. (CN ISSN 0030-4433) 1652
Orbit. (NE ISSN 0167-6830) 3304, 3316, 3382
†Orbit (New York). (US ISSN 0474-3326) 5253
Orbit Searchlight. (US) 2799
Orbit Video. (US) 1385
Orbiter. (US) 1378
Orcadian. (UK) 2195
Orchadian. (AT ISSN 0474-3342) 2136
Orchardist of New Zealand. (NZ ISSN 0110-6260) 186, 2136
Das Orchester. (GW ISSN 0030-4468) 3572
Orchestra Canada/Orchestres Canada. (CN ISSN 0380-1799) 3572
Orchestres Canada. see Orchestra Canada 3572
Orchid Advocate. (US ISSN 0097-9546) 2136
Orchid Digest. (US) 2136
Orchid Monographs. (NE ISSN 0920-1998) 512
Orchid Review. (UK ISSN 0030-4476) 2136
Die Orchidee. (GW ISSN 0473-1425) 2136
Orchideeen. (NE ISSN 0030-4484) 512, 186, 2136
Ord & Sag. (DK ISSN 0108-8025) 2833, 2878
Ord och Ton see Stim Nytt 3582
Ord og Sed see Norveg 2057
Ordem dos Advogados do Brasil - Rio de Janeiro Revista see O A B - R J. Revista 2662
Ordem dos Medicos. Boletim. (PO ISSN 0030-4506) 3138
Orden pour le Merite fuer Wissenschaften und Kuenste. Reden und Gedenkworte. (GW) 2512, 2945
Ordenador Personal. (SP) 1471
Order. (NE ISSN 0167-8094) 3050
Order of Buddhist Contemplatives. Journal. (US ISSN 0891-1177) 4286
Order of St. John. Bulletin. (MM) 1300
Order of the Indian Wars Communique see O I W Communique 3467
†Order of the Indian Wars Journal. (US) 5253
Orders and Medals Society of America. Official Journal. (US) 2440, 3468
Orders Guam. (GU) 3468
Ordi 5. (FR) 1399
†Ordinariate und Bischoefliche Aemter in der D D R. Kirchliche Amtsblatt. Ausgabe der Apostlichen Administratur Goerlitz. (GW ISSN 0323-7532) 5253
†Ordinariate und Bischoefliche Aemter in der D D R. Kirchliche Amtsblatt. Ausgabe des Bischoeflichen Amtes Erfurt-Meiningen. (GW ISSN 0323-763X) 5253
†Ordinariate und Bischoefliche Aemter in der D D R. Kirchliche Amtsblatt. Ausgabe des Bischoefliche Amtes Schwerin. (GW ISSN 0323-7737) 5253
†Ordinariate und Bischoefliche Aemter in der D D R. Kirchliche Amtsblatt. Ausgabe des Bistums Dresden-Meissen. (GW ISSN 0323-7680) 5253
†Ordinariate und Bischoeflichen Aemter in der D D R. Kirchliche Amtsblatt. Ausgabe des Bischoeflichen Amtes Magdeburg. (GW ISSN 0323-7583) 5253

Ordinary Lives. (UK) 2945
Ordinary People's Health. see Dazhong Jiankang 3800
Ordinateur de Poche/Pocket Computer.(BE) 1399
Ordinateur Individuel. (FR) 1399
Ordinateur Individuel/Individual Computer. (BE) 1399
Ordinateurs see Computers 5170
Ordine dei Giornalisti della Lombardia. (IT) 2574
Ordine dei Medici della Provincia di Venezia. Notiziario. (IT) 3138
Ordine Pubblico. (IT) 1519
Ordnance see National Defense 3466
Ordnance Survey Publication News. (UK) 2258, 1965
Ordnance Survey Publication Report see Ordnance Survey Publication News 2258
Ordo. (GW ISSN 0048-2129) 1023
Ordo et Annuaire de l'Archdiocese de Lyon see Annuaire du Diocese de Lyon 4255
Ordre des Comptables Agrees du Quebec. Bilans. (CN ISSN 0828-6833) 754
Ordre des Geometres-Experts. Annuaire.(FR ISSN 0078-5601) 4332
Ordre des Ingenieurs Forestiers du Quebec. Aubelle Bi-Mestriel. (CN) 2106
Ordre des Ingenieurs Forestiers du Quebec. Congres Annuel. Texte des Conferences. (CN) 2106
Ordre National des Chirurgiens-Dentistes. Conseil National. Bulletin Officiel. (FR) 3239
Ordre National des Medecins. Bulletin. (FR ISSN 0030-4565) 3138
Ordre Souverain Militaire de Malta. Revue International. (IT) 3468
Ore. (UK ISSN 0030-459X) 3000
Ore Geology Reviews. (NE ISSN 0169-1368) 1577
Oread. (US) 3000
Oregon. Department of Geology and Mineral Industries. Bulletin. (US ISSN 0078-5709) 1577, 3493
Oregon. Department of Geology and Mineral Industries. Open File Reports.(US) 1577
Oregon. Department of Geology and Mineral Industries. Special Papers. (US) 1577
Oregon. Department of Revenue. Income, Inheritance and Gift Tax Law Book. (US) 1103
Oregon. Department of Revenue. Property Assessment and Taxation Law Book. (US) 1103
Oregon. Department of Revenue. Sales Ratio Study see Oregon Ratio and Assessment Data Roll 1103
Oregon. Department of Revenue. Summary of Levies and Statistics see Oregon Property Tax Statistics 733
Oregon. Department of Revenue. Summary of Oregon Taxes. (US) 1103
Oregon. Public Utility Commissioner. Oregon Utility Statistics. (US) 4081
Oregon. State Board of Accountancy. Certified Public Accountants, Public Accountants, and Accountants Authorized to Conduct Municipal Audits in Oregon. (US) 754
Oregon. State Board of Accountancy. Certified Public Accountants, Public Accountants, Professional Corporations, and Accountants Authorized to Conduct Municipal Audits in Oregon see Oregon. State Board of Accountancy. Certified Public Accountants, Public Accountants, and Accountants Authorized to Conduct Municipal Audits in Oregon 754
Oregon. State Department of Geology and Mineral Industries. Oil and Gas Investigations. (US ISSN 0078-5741) 3696, 1577
Oregon, a Statistical Profile. (US) 878
Oregon Academy of Science. Proceedings. (US ISSN 0370-1093) 4381
Oregon Appellate Manual. (US) 2664

Oregon Art Institute Newsletter see Portland Art Museum Newsletter 3531
Oregon Association of Nurserymen Digger see O.A.N. Digger 2136
Oregon Beef Producer. (US) 222
†Oregon Beverage Analyst. (US ISSN 0030-462X) 5253
Oregon Blue Book. (US) 4069
Oregon Business Magazine. (US) 683
Oregon Cattleman see Oregon Beef Producer 222
Oregon Coast. (US ISSN 0744-8317) 2231
Oregon Contractor Pipeline. (US) 2302
Oregon Daily Emerald. (US ISSN 0030-4662) 1320
Oregon Debtor - Creditor Law. (US) 2664
Oregon Dental Association. Journal. (US ISSN 0030-4670) 3240
Oregon Dental Association Newsletter see O D A Newsletter 3239
Oregon Department of Revenue. Income and Inheritance Tax Law Abstracts. (US) 733
Oregon Department of Revenue. Property Tax Law Abstracts. (US) 733, 1103
Oregon Distance Runner. (US) 4482, 3807
Oregon Education. (US ISSN 0030-4689) 1653
Oregon Environmental Council Newsletter see Earthwatch Oregon 1947
Oregon Episcopal Church News. (US) 4246
Oregon Episcopal Churchman see Oregon Episcopal Church News 4246
Oregon Evidence. (US) 2664
Oregon Farm Bureau News. (US ISSN 0162-5179) 112
Oregon Farmer-Stockman see Inland Farmer-Stockman 218
Oregon Feed, Seed and Suppliers Association. Commercial Review see Commercial Review 205
Oregon Food Journal. (US) 2078
Oregon Genealogical Society Quarterly. (US ISSN 0738-1891) 2161
Oregon Geology. (US ISSN 0164-3304) 1577
Oregon Grange Bulletin. (US ISSN 0030-4697) 112
Oregon Health Division, Vital Statistics Annual Report see Oregon Public Health Statistics Report 4118
Oregon Health Sciences University News see O H S U Views 3137
Oregon Health Sciences University Views see O H S U Views 3137
Oregon Historical Quarterly. (US ISSN 0030-4727) 2418
Oregon Historical Society. News. (US ISSN 0474-4535) 2418
Oregon International Trade Directory. (US ISSN 0731-9096) 918
Oregon Law Review. (US ISSN 0196-2043) 2664
Oregon Library News. (US ISSN 0030-4735) 2778
Oregon Magazine see Pacific Northwest 2231
Oregon Music Educator. (US ISSN 0030-4743) 3572, 1757
Oregon Notary Law Primer. (US) 2664
Oregon Nurse. (US ISSN 0030-4751) 3285
Oregon Optometrist see Oregon Optometry 3304
Oregon Optometry. (US ISSN 0274-6549) 3304
Oregon Outlook. (US) 2288, 1739
Oregon Personal Income Tax Statistics. (US) 733, 1103
Oregon Plumbing - Heating - Cooling Contractor see Pipeline (Oregon City) 2302
Oregon Postal History Journal. (US ISSN 0892-5208) 3755
Oregon Property Tax Statistics. (US) 733, 1103, 4582
Oregon Psychological Association. Newsletter see Oregon Psychology 4037
Oregon Psychology. (US) 4037

6528 OREGON PUBLIC

Oregon Public Health Statistics Report. (US) **4118**, **4582**
Oregon Public Utility Commissioner. Statistics of Electric, Gas, Steam Heat, Telephone, Telegraph and Water Companies *see* Oregon. Public Utility Commissioner. Oregon Utility Statistics **4081**
Oregon Purchasor. (US ISSN 0030-4786) **1049**
Oregon Ratio and Assessment Data Roll. (US) **1103**
Oregon Revised Statutes Annotated. (US) **2664**
▼Oregon Rules of Civil Procedure Annotated (Year). (US) **2704**
Oregon Rules of Civil Procedure Handbook (Year). (US) **2715**
Oregon School Directory. (US ISSN 0078-5679) **1695**
Oregon School Study Council. Bulletin *see* O S S C Bulletin **1652**
Oregon Science Teacher. (US ISSN 0030-4794) **4332**, **1653**
Oregon State Bar Bulletin. (US ISSN 0030-4816) **2664**
Oregon State Dental Journal *see* Oregon Dental Association. Journal **3240**
Oregon State Monographs. Bibliographic Series. (US ISSN 0078-5768) **408**
Oregon State University. Forest Research Laboratory. Annual Report *see* Oregon State University. Forest Research Laboratory. Biennial Report **2106**
Oregon State University. Forest Research Laboratory. Biennial Report. (US) **2106**
Oregon State University. Forest Research Laboratory. Research Bulletin. (US ISSN 0078-5903) **2106**
Oregon State University. Forest Research Laboratory. Research Note.(US ISSN 0078-5911) **2106**
Oregon State University. Forest Research Laboratory. Research Paper. (US ISSN 0078-592X) **2106**
The Oregon Stater. (US ISSN 0885-3258) **1320**
Oregon Teamster. (US ISSN 0030-4840) **2587**
Oregon Trail Magazine. (US) **2231**
Oregon Uniform Commercial Code. (US) **2664**
Oregon Uniform Trial Court Rules and Supplementary Local Rules. (US) **2732**
Oregon Vital Statistics *see* Oregon Public Health Statistics Report **4118**
Oregon, Washington TourBook *see* Tourbook: Oregon, Washington **4790**
Oregon Wheat. (US) **207**, **186**
Orella. (SZ ISSN 0030-4867) **1287**
Orff Echo. (US ISSN 0095-2613) **3572**
Orff-Schulwerk Association of Queensland. Bulletin. (AT) **3572**
Orgadata. (GW ISSN 0342-0523) **1061**
Orgamatik. (SZ) **1471**, **1454**, **1479**
Organ. (UK ISSN 0030-4883) **3572**
Organ Building Periodical/Zeitschrift fuer Orgelbau. (International Society of Organbuilders) (GW) **3572**
Organ Club Journal. (UK ISSN 0306-0357) **3572**
Organ Historical Society. National Convention (Proceedings) *see* Annual Organ Handbook **3539**
Organ Portfolio. (US) **3573**
Organ Site Carcinogenesis - Gastrointestinal Tract and Pancreas *see* I C R D B Cancergram: Organ Site Carcinogenesis - Gastrointestinal Tract and Pancreas **5209**
Organ Site Carcinogenesis - Kidney and Urinary Tract *see* I C R D B Cancergram: Organ Site Carcinogenesis - Kidney and Urinary Tract **5209**
Organ Site Carcinogenesis - Liver *see* I C R D B Cancergram: Organ Site Carcinogenesis - Liver **5209**

Organ Site Carcinogenesis - Lymphatic and Hematopoietic Tissues *see* I C R D B Cancergram: Organ Site Carcinogenesis - Lymphatic and Hematopoietic Tissues **5209**
Organ Site Carcinogenesis - Mammary Gland *see* I C R D B Cancergram: Organ Site Carcinogenesis - Mammary Gland **5209**
Organ Site Carcinogenesis - Reproductive Tract *see* I C R D B Cancergram: Organ Site Carcinogenesis - Reproductive Tract **5209**
Organ Site Carcinogenesis - Respiratory Tract *see* I C R D B Cancergram: Organ Site Carcinogenesis - Respiratory Tract **5209**
Organ Teacher *see* Keyboard Teacher **3560**
Organ Yearbook. (NE ISSN 0078-6098) **3573**
Organe Permanent pour la Securite dans les Mines de Houille. Rapport. *see* Mines Safety and Health Commission. Report **3489**
Organi di Trasmissione. (IT ISSN 0030-4905) **1833**
Organic and Organometallic Crystal Structures; Bibliography. (NE) **408**, **1221**
Organic Chemistry. (US ISSN 0078-611X) **1221**
Organic Chemistry. *see* Youji Huaxue **1224**
Organic Chemistry and Biochemistry *see* Acta Chemica Scandinavica **1224**
Organic Coatings and Plastics Chemistry Preprints *see* Polymeric Materials Science and Engineering **1222**
Organic Consumer Report. (US) **3611**
Organic Electronic Spectral Data. (US ISSN 0078-6136) **1207**, **1221**
Organic Food Business News. (US) **2078**
Organic Gardening *see* Rodale's Organic Gardening **2138**
Organic Geochemistry. (US ISSN 0146-6380) **1221**, **1577**
Organic Grower. (AT ISSN 0157-2601) **1965**, **1494**
Organic Growing (Ulverstone). (AT ISSN 0816-6668) **2136**, 112
Organic Photochemistry: A Series of Advances. (US ISSN 0078-6152) **1221**, **1229**
Organic Preparations and Procedures International. (US ISSN 0030-4948) **1221**, **1229**
Organic Reaction Mechanisms. Annual Survey. (US ISSN 0078-6160) **1221**, **1229**
Organic Reactions. (US ISSN 0078-6179) **1221**, **1229**
Organic Syntheses. (US ISSN 0078-6209) **1221**, **1229**
Organic Syntheses Collective Volumes. (US ISSN 0078-6217) **1221**, **1229**
Organic Wholesalers Directory & Yearbook: Organic Food & Farm Supplies. (US) **112**, **1149**
Organica. (US ISSN 0897-2648) **2945**, **3775**
Organisatie van Studenten in de Geschiedenis van Nederland Wetenschappelijke Publikatie *see* O S G N Wetenschappelijke Publikatie **5251**
Organisation. (GW ISSN 0323-3049) **4069**, **2664**
Organisation and Management of a Solicitors Practice. (UK) **2664**
Organisation de Coordination pour la Lutte Contre les Endemies en Afrique Centrale Bulletin de Liaison et de Documentation *see* O C E A C Bulletin de Liaison et de Documentation **3137**
Organisation for Scientific Evaluation of Aerial Phenomena Centre Update *see* O S E A P Centre Update **60**
Organisation for Scientific Evaluation of Aerial Phenomena Journal *see* O S E A P Journal **60**
Organisation Gestion des Enterprises. (FR ISSN 0030-4964) **1023**

Organisation Meteorologique Mondiale. Association Regionale I (Afrique). Rapport Final Abrege de la (No.) Session *see* World Meteorological Organization. Regional Association I (Africa). Abridged Final Report of the (No.) Session **3443**
Organisation Meteorologique Mondiale. Association Regionale II (Asie). Rapport Final Abrege de la (No.) Session *see* World Meteorological Organization. Regional Association II (Asia). Abridged Final Report of the (No.) Session **3443**
Organisation Meteorologique Mondiale. Association Regionale V (Pacifique Sud-Ouest). Rapport Final Abrege de la (No.) Session *see* World Meteorological Organization. Regional Association V (South West Pacific). Abridged Final Report of the (No.) Session **3443**
Organisation Meteorologique Mondiale. Association Regionale VI (Europe). Rapport Final Abrege de la (No.) Session *see* World Meteorological Organization. Regional Association VI (Europe). Abridged Final Report of the (No.) Session **3443**
Organisation Meteorologique Mondiale. Commission d'Hydrologie. Rapport Final Abrege de la (No.) Session *see* World Meteorological Organization. Commission for Hydrology. Abridged Final Report of the (No.) Session **3443**
Organisation Meteorologique Mondiale. Commission de Meteorologie Aeronautique. Rapport Final Abrege de la (No.) Session *see* World Meteorological Organization. Commission for Aeronautical Meteorology. Abridged Final Report of the (No.) Session **3442**
Organisation Meteorologique Mondiale. Commission de Meteorologie Agricole. Rapport Final Abrege de la (No.) Session *see* World Meteorological Organization. Commission for Agricultural Meteorology. Abridged Final Report of the (No.) Session **3443**
Organisation Meteorologique Mondiale. Commission de Meteorologie Maritime. Rapport Final Abrege de la (No.) Session *see* World Meteorological Organization. Commission for Marine Meteorology. Abridged Final Report of the (No.) Session **3443**
Organisation Meteorologique Mondiale. Commission des Applications Speciales de la Meteorologie et de la Climatologie. Rapport Final Abrege de la (No.) Session *see* World Meteorological Organization. Commission for Special Applications of Meteorology and Climatology. Abridged Final Report of the (No.) Session **5307**
Organisation Meteorologique Mondiale. Commission des Instruments et des Methodes d'Observation. Rapport Final Abrege de la (No.) Session *see* World Meteorological Organization. Commission for Instruments and Methods of Observation. Abridged Final Report of the (No.) Session **3442**
Organisation Meteorologique Mondiale. Commission des Sciences de l'Atmosphere. Rapport Final Abrege de la (No.) Session *see* World Meteorological Organization. Commission for Atmospheric Sciences. Abridged Final Report of the (No.) Session **3443**
Organisation Meteorologique Mondiale. Commission des Systems de Base. Rapport Final Abrege de la (No.) Session *see* World Meteorological Organization. Commission for Basic Systems. Abridged Final Report of the (No.) Session **3443**
Organisation Meteorologique Mondiale. Congres. Rapport Abrege et Resolutions *see* World Meteorological Organization. Congress. Abridged Report with Resolutions **3443**

Organisation Meteorologique Mondiale. Session du Conseil Executif. Rapport Abrege et Resolutions *see* World Meteorological Organization. Executive Council Session. Abridged Final Reports with Resolutions **3443**
Organisation of Eastern Caribbean States Annual Digest of Statistics *see* O E C S Annual Digest of Statistics **4582**
Organisation of Eastern Caribbean States Current Awareness Bulletin *see* O E C S Current Awareness Bulletin **878**
Organisation of Eastern Caribbean States Select Bibliography *see* O E C S Select Bibliography **878**
Organisationen til Oplysning om Atomkraft Saertryk *see* O O A - Saertryk **1809**
Organisationer og Tal i Gartneriet. (DK ISSN 0109-4262) **2136**
Organisationsentwicklung in der Praxis. (SZ) **683**
Organisatoriske Fragmenter. (DK ISSN 0107-2064) **683**
Organische Chemie in Einzeldarstellungen. (US ISSN 0078-6225) **1221**
Organiser. (Il ISSN 0030-5014) **2201**
Organist. (US) **3573**
Organista *see* Celebriamo **3544**
Organists' Benevolent League. Annual Report. (UK) **3573**
Organists' Review. (UK ISSN 0048-2161) **3573**
Organizacija i Kadrovi/Organization and Personnel. (YU ISSN 0048-217X) **1068**
Organizacija in Kadri. (XV ISSN 0350-1531) **1068**
Organizacija Poslovanja. (YU) **1068**
Organizacija Rada. (YU) **991**
Organizacija Samoupravljanja OUR. (YU) **1023**
Organizacion Continental Latino Americana de Estudiantes Revista *see* O C L A E Revista **2878**
Organizacion Latinoamericana de Energia. Energy Bulletin *see* Revista Energetica **1795**
Organizacion Medica Colegial de Espana *see* O M C **3137**
Organizacion Meteorologica Especiales de la Meteorologia y de la Climatologia. Informe Final Abreviado de la (No.) Reunion *see* World Meteorological Organization. Commission for Special Applications of Meteorology and Climatology. Abridged Final Report of the (No.) Session **5307**
Organizacion Meteorologica Mundial. Asociacion Regional III (America del Sur). Informe Final Abreviado de la (No.) Reunion *see* World Meteorological Organization. Regional Association III (South America). Abridged Final Report of the (No.) Session **3443**
Organizacion Meteorologica Mundial. Asociacion Regional IV (America del Norte y America Central). Informe Final Abreviado de la (No.) Reunion *see* World Meteorological Organization. Regional Association IV (North America and Central America). Abridged Final Report of the (No.) Session **3443**
Organizacion Meteorologica Mundial. Comision de Ciencias Atmosfericas. Informe Final Abreviado de la (No.) Reunion *see* World Meteorological Organization. Commission for Atmospheric Sciences. Abridged Final Report of the (No.) Session **3443**
Organizacion Meteorologica Mundial. Comision de Hidrologia. Informe Final Abreviado de la (No.) Reunion *see* World Meteorological Organization. Commission for Hydrology. Abridged Final Report of the (No.) Session **3443**

Organizacion Meteorologica Mundial. Comision de Instrumentos y Metodos de Observacion. Informe Final Abreviado de la (No.) Reunion *see* World Meteorological Organization. Commission for Instruments and Methods of Observation. Abridged Final Report of the (No.) Session **3442**

Organizacion Meteorologica Mundial. Comision de Meteorologia Aeronautica. Informe Final Abreviado de la (No.) Reunion *see* World Meteorological Organization. Commission for Aeronautical Meteorology. Abridged Final Report of the (No.) Session **3442**

Organizacion Meteorologica Mundial. Comision de Meteorologia Agricola. Informe Final Abreviado de la (No.) Reunion *see* World Meteorological Organization. Commission for Agricultural Meteorology. Abridged Final Report of the (No.) Session **3443**

Organizacion Meteorologica Mundial. Comision de Meteorologia Marina. Informe Final Abreviado de la (No.) Reunion *see* World Meteorological Organization. Commission for Marine Meteorology. Abridged Final Report of the (No.) Session **3443**

Organizacion Meteorologica Mundial. Congreso. Informe Abreviado y Resoluciones *see* World Meteorological Organization. Congress. Abridged Report with Resolutions **3443**

Organizacion Meteorologica Mundial. Reunion del Consejo Ejecutivo. Informe Abreviado y Resoluciones *see* World Meteorological Organization. Executive Council Session. Abridged Final Reports with Resolutions **3443**

Organizacion Regional Interamericana de Trabajadores Inter-American Labor News *see* I C F T U - O R I T Inter-American Labor News **2584**

Organizacion Techint. Boletin Informativo *see* Boletin Informativo Techint **4367**

†Organizacja - Metody - Technika w Administracji Panstwowej. (PL ISSN 0860-4673) **5253**

Organization and Personnel. *see* Organizacija i Kadrovi **1068**

Organization Development Journal. (US ISSN 0889-6402) **1023, 1068**

Organization for Economic Cooperation and Development. Annual Reports on Consumer Policy in O E C D Member Countries *see* O E C D. Consumer Policy in O E C D Countries **838**

Organization for Economic Cooperation and Development. Labour Statistics *see* O E C D. Quarterly Labour Force Statistics **990**

Organization for Economic Cooperation and Development. Quarterly Oil and Gas Statistics *see* O E C D. Quarterly Oil Statistics and Energy Balances **3706**

Organization for Economic Cooperation and Development. Statistics of Energy *see* O E C D. Energy Statistics of O E C D Countries **1800**

Organization for Economic Cooperation and Development. Statistics of Foreign Trade. Series B. Trade by Commodities. Country Summaries *see* O E C D. Statistics of Foreign Trade. Series B: Tables by Reporting Countries **5250**

Organization for Economic Cooperation and Development. Statistics of Foreign Trade. Series C: Tables by Commodities. - Imports and Exports - Statistiques du Commerce Exterieur. Serie C: Tableaux par Produits *see* O E C D. Foreign Trade by Commodities. Series C **732**

Organization for Economic Cooperation and Development Economic Outlook *see* O E C D Economic Outlook **877**

Organization for Economic Cooperation and Development Employment Outlook *see* O E C D. Employment Outlook **877**

Organization for Economic Cooperation and Development Indicators of Industrial Activity *see* O E C D. Indicators of Industrial Activity **732**

Organization for Economic Cooperation and Development Microtables Imports - Exports of O E C D Countries *see* Microtables Imports - Exports of O E C D Countries **917**

Organization for Economic Cooperation and Development Newsletter *see* O E C D - N E A Newsletter **1809**

Organization for Economic Cooperation and Development Nuclear Energy Agency. Nuclear Energy Data *see* O E C D. Nuclear Energy Agency. Nuclear Energy Data **1808**

Organization for Economic Cooperation and Development Observer *see* O E C D Observer **877**

Organization for Economic Cooperation and Development Steel Market in (Year) and Outlook for (Year) *see* O E C D. Steel Market in (Year) and Outlook for (Year) **732**

Organization for Economic Cooperation and Development World Energy Statistics *see* O E C D. World Energy Statistics **1800**

Organization for Obstetric, Gynecologic and Neonatal Nurses Women's Health Nursing Scan *see* N A A C O G's Women's Health Nursing Scan **3178**

Organization for Rehabilitation through Training World O R T Union. Yearbook *see* World O R T Union. Yearbook **1742**

Organization for the Phyto-Taxonomic Investigation of the Mediterranean Area Newsletter *see* O P T I M A Newsletter **512**

Organization for the Protection and Advancement of Small Telephone Companies Roundtable *see* O P A S T C O Roundtable **1364**

Organization for Use of the Telephone Line *see* O U T - Line **5251**

Organization of African Unity. Scientific Technical and Research Commission. Publication. (NR ISSN 0474-6171) **4332, 4605**

Organization of African Unity Echo *see* O A U Echo **3967**

Organization of American Historians Magazine of History. (US ISSN 0882-228X) **2319**

Organization of American Historians Newsletter. (US ISSN 0196-3341) **2418**

Organization of American States. Department of Cultural Affairs. Manuales del Bibliotecario. (US ISSN 0078-6381) **2778**

Organization of American States. Department of Scientific Affairs. Report of Activities. (US) **4332**

Organization of American States. Department of Scientific Affairs. Serie de Biologia: Monografias. (US ISSN 0553-0342) **450**

Organization of American States. Department of Scientific Affairs. Serie de Fisica: Monografias. (US ISSN 0078-6322) **3826**

Organization of American States. Department of Scientific Affairs. Serie de Matematica: Monografias. (US ISSN 0078-6330) **3050**

Organization of American States. Department of Scientific Affairs. Serie de Quimica: Monografias. (US ISSN 0553-0377) **1185**

Organization of American States. Directory. (US ISSN 0250-6211) **1149, 3967**

Organization of American States. General Assembly. Actas y Documentos. (US) **3968**

Organization of American States. General Secretariat. Program of Scientific Monographs. (US) **4332**

Organization of American States. Legal Newsletter. (US) **2664**

Organization of American States. Official Records. Indice y Lista General. (US ISSN 0078-642X) **2418**

Organization of American States. Permanent Council. Decisions Taken at Meetings (Cumulated Edition). (US ISSN 0078-6438) **2418, 2727**

Organization of American States. Statistical Bulletin. (US ISSN 0250-6289) **4582**

Organization of American States General Secretariat. Annual Report *see* O A S. General Secretariat. Annual Report **2417**

Organization of Arab Petroleum Exporting Countries. Current Awareness *see* O A P E C Monthly Bulletin **3694**

Organization of Arab Petroleum Exporting Countries. Secretary General's Annual Report. (KU) **3696**

Organization of Arab Petroleum Exporting Countries Energy Bibliography *see* O A P E C Energy Bibliography **3706**

Organization of Arab Petroleum Exporting Countries Energy Resources Monitor *see* O A P E C Energy Resources Monitor **3694**

Organization of Arab Petroleum Exporting Countries Library Index of Periodical Articles *see* O A P E C Library Index of Periodical Articles **3706**

Organization of Arab Petroleum Exporting Countries Monthly Bulletin *see* O A P E C Monthly Bulletin **3694**

Organization of Black Airline Pilots. Convention Journal. (US) **60, 2018**

Organization of Black Airline Pilots. Newsletter. (US) **60, 2018**

Organization of Chinese Americans Image *see* O C A Image **2018**

Organization of Psychic Research Associates Newsletter *see* O P R A Newsletter **3596**

Organization of Teachers of Oral Diagnosis. News *see* Organization of Teachers of Oral Diagnosis. Newsletter **3138**

Organization of Teachers of Oral Diagnosis. Newsletter. (US) **3138**

†Organization of the Petroleum Exporting Countries. Annual Report. (AU) **5253**

Organization of the Petroleum Exporting Countries. Annual Statistical Bulletin. (AU ISSN 0475-0608) **3706**

Organization of the Petroleum Exporting Countries. Bulletin. (AU ISSN 0474-6279) **3697, 1793**

Organization of the Petroleum Exporting Countries Review *see* O P E C Review **3694**

▼Organization Science. (US ISSN 1047-7039) **1023**

Organization Studies. (GW ISSN 0170-8406) **4381**

Organizational and Occupational Psychology. (US) **4037**

Organizational Behavior and Human Decision Processes. (US ISSN 0749-5978) **4037**

Organizational Directory of the Government of Thailand. (TH ISSN 0475-2015) **4069**

Organizational Dynamics. (US ISSN 0090-2616) **1023**

Organizations and Change. (US) **1068, 1023**

Organizatsiya Ob'edinennykh Natsii. Komissiya Mezhdunarodnogo Prava. Ezhegodnik *see* United Nations. International Law Commission Yearbook **2729**

Organizatsiya Ob'edinennykh Natsii. Sovet Bezopasnosti. Ofitsial'nye Otchety. Dopolnenie *see* United Nations. Security Council. Official Records. Supplement **3975**

Organizatsiya Upravleniya. (RU) **1023**

Organizatsiya Ob'edinennykh Natsii. Yuridicheskiy Ezhegodnik *see* United Nations Juridical Yearbook **2730**

Organize Your Luck! (US ISSN 0734-1776) **3630, 1068**

Organized Crime Digest. (US ISSN 0889-5716) **1519**

Organizing Corporate and Other Business Enterprises. (US) **2711, 683**

Organizzarsi. (IT ISSN 0474-635X) **1023**

Organizzazione Scientifica. (IT) **4332**

Organo. (IT ISSN 0474-6376) **3573**

Organographes du Cymbalum Pataphysicum. (FR) **3775**

Organometallic Chemistry. (UK ISSN 0301-0074) **1221**

Organometallic Chemistry in the U S S R. (English translation of: Metalloorganicheskaya Khimiya) (UK ISSN 0955-8586) **1221**

Organometallic Compounds. (UK ISSN 0030-5138) **1221**

Organometallic Syntheses. (US) **3417**

Organometallics. (US ISSN 0276-7333) **1221**

Organon. (PL ISSN 0078-6500) **4332**

Organophosphorus Chemistry. (UK ISSN 0306-0713) **1221**

†Organorama. (NE ISSN 0030-5162) **5253**

▼Orgonomic Functionalism. (US) **3349, 3826**

Orgue. (FR ISSN 0030-5170) **3573**

†Oriel. (UK) **5253**

Oriens. (NE ISSN 0078-6527) **3642**

Oriens Antiquus. (IT ISSN 0030-5189) **3642**

Oriens Christianus. (GW ISSN 0340-6407) **4193**

Oriens Extremus. (GW ISSN 0030-5197) **3642, 2833**

Orient. (GW ISSN 0030-5227) **3642**

Orient. (CN ISSN 0472-0490) **4272**

▼Orient Express. (UK) **3515**

▼Orient Express. (FR ISSN 1161-0344) **3642, 281**

Orient Express. (US) **3712**

Orientacion. (ES) **4272**

Oriental and India Office Collections Newsletter *see* O I O C Newsletter **3642**

Oriental Archives. *see* Archiv Orientalni **3633**

Oriental Art. (UK ISSN 0030-5278) **3642, 339**

Oriental Ceramic Society of Hong Kong. Bulletin. (HK) **1165, 356**

Oriental Ceramic Society of Hong Kong. Exhibition Catalogue. (HK) **1165, 356**

Oriental College. Magazin. (PK) **2945**

Oriental Dolls. (US) **3399**

Oriental Economist *see* Tokyo Business Today **695**

Oriental Entrepreneurs. *see* Dongfang Qiyejia **659**

Oriental Geographer. (BG ISSN 0030-5308) **2258**

Oriental Healing Arts International Bulletin *see* O H A I Bulletin **3215**

Oriental Insects. (US ISSN 0030-5316) **536**

Oriental Insects Monographs Series. (US) **536**

Oriental Institute. Journal. (II ISSN 0030-5324) **3642**

Oriental Institute Communications. (US ISSN 0146-678X) **2340**

Oriental Library. Research Department. Memoirs/Zaidan Hojin Toyo Bunko. (JA ISSN 0082-562X) **2340**

Oriental Notes and Studies. (IS ISSN 0078-6543) **2341**

Oriental Philatelic Association of London Journal *see* O P A L Journal **3755**

Oriental Qigong. *see* Dongfang Qigong **3801**

Oriental Rug. (US ISSN 0030-5332) **2561**

Oriental Rug Review. (US ISSN 1044-4807) **2561**

Oriental Society of Australia. Journal. (AT ISSN 0030-5340) **3642**

Oriental Studies. (US ISSN 0078-6551) **339**

ORIENTAL STUDIES

Oriental Studies. see Dornodahiny Sudlal **3637**
Oriental Studies. see Keleti Tanulmanyok **3640**
Oriental World. see Dongfang Shijie **2337**
Orientalia. (VC ISSN 0030-5367) **3642**, **2431**
Orientalia Christiana Analecta. (VC) **3642**, **4272**
Orientalia Christiana Periodica. (VC ISSN 0030-5375) **4194**
Orientalia Gothoburgensia. (SW ISSN 0078-656X) **3642**
Orientalia Journal. (US) **259**, **959**
Orientalia Lovaniensia Periodica. (BE ISSN 0085-4522) **3642**
Orientalia Monspeliensia. (NE ISSN 0169-9458) **2431**
Orientalia Rheno-Traiectina. (NE ISSN 0169-9504) **3642**
Orientalia Suecana. (SW ISSN 0078-6578) **3642**
Orientalistische Literaturzeitung. (GW ISSN 0030-5383) **3642**, **2945**
Orientamenti Linguistici. (IT) **2833**
Orientamenti Nuovi per la Piccola e Media Industria. (IT) **3913**, **683**
Orientamenti Pastorali. (IT ISSN 0472-0784) **4194**
Orientamenti Pedagogici. (IT ISSN 0030-5391) **1653**
Orientamento Scolastico Professionale. (IT) **1739**
L'Orientation. (CN ISSN 0833-0530) **3630**
Orientation et Formation Professionnelles. see Berufsberatung und Berufsbildung **1618**
Orientation Professionnelle - Vocational Guidance see L'Orientation **3630**
Orientation Scolaire et Professionnelle. (FR ISSN 0249-6739) **4037**, **1714**
Orientations. (HK ISSN 0030-5448) **339**, **3642**
Orientations. (BE ISSN 0030-543X) **2175**
Oriente e Occidente. (IT) **2512**
Oriente Moderno. (IT ISSN 0030-5472) **3642**
Orienteering North America. (US ISSN 0886-1080) **4552**
Orientering see Ny Tid **3912**
†Orientering. (DK ISSN 0030-5499) **5253**
Orientierung. (SZ ISSN 0030-5502) **4194**, **3775**
Orientierungen zur Gesellschafts- und Wirtschaftspolitik. (GW ISSN 0724-5246) **4381**, **683**
Orienting om Skoleaaret. (DK ISSN 0106-7125) **1653**
Origin Technical Journal/Orijin Giho. (JA ISSN 0474-6767) **1904**
Origin to Destination. (US ISSN 0732-0981) **2106**
The Original Airport News. (CN) **4676**
The Original Art Report. (US ISSN 0030-5529) **339**
Original Donna Kossy's Kooks Magazine see Kooks Magazine **3595**
Original Equipment Manufacturers Off-Highway see O E M Off-Highway **164**
Original Home Plans. (US) **304**
Original New England Guide. (US ISSN 0734-4066) **4781**, **2258**
Original News and Comments from Middle Eastern Newspapers. see Aktueller Informationsdienst Moderner Orient **3633**
†Original Romance Digest. (US) **5253**
Origine des Familles Paquin au Canada see Pasquin **2161**
Origins. (UK) **2161**
Origins (Loma Linda). (US ISSN 0093-7495) **4332**, **3775**
Origins (Washington) see Origins, C N S Documentary Service **4272**
Origins, C N S Documentary Service. (Catholic News Service) (US) **4272**
Origins, N C Documentary Service see Origins, C N S Documentary Service **4272**
Origins of Life and Evolution of the Biosphere. (NE ISSN 0169-6149) **450**, **1185**
Origo. (UK) **4134**

Orijin Giho. see Origin Technical Journal **1904**
Oriole. (US ISSN 0030-5553) **566**
Orion. (SZ ISSN 0030-557X) **368**
Orion. (US) **1320**
▼Orion. (UK) **3013**
Orion. (SA ISSN 0259-191X) **3050**, **1023**
Orion Nature Quarterly. (US ISSN 0732-0876) **1965**, **1494**
Orissa Education. (II ISSN 0030-5588) **1714**
Orissa Family Planning Bulletin. (II) **597**
Orissa Homoeopathic Bulletin. (II ISSN 0048-2242) **3215**
Orissa, India. Finance Department. Annual Financial Statement. (II) **878**
Orissa, India. Finance Department. White Paper on Departmental Activities, Government of Orissa see Orissa, India. Finance Department. White Paper on the Economic Conditions and the Developmental Activities in Orissa **878**
Orissa, India. Finance Department. White Paper on the Economic Conditions and the Developmental Activities in Orissa. (II) **878**
Orissa State Road Transportation Corporation. Annual Administration Report. (II) **4720**
Orita. (NR ISSN 0030-5596) **4194**, **2018**
Oriya-Aurovilian. (II) **3775**
Orizont. (RM ISSN 0030-560X) **2945**
Orizzonti Aperti. (IT ISSN 0030-5618) **3349**
Orizzonti di Chirurgia. (IT ISSN 0394-0756) **3382**
Orizzonti Industriali. (IT) **1117**
Orizzonti Professionali. (IT ISSN 0030-5634) **1353**
Orkester Journalen. (SW ISSN 0030-5642) **3573**
Orlando Business Journal. (US) **684**
Orlando Magazine. (US ISSN 0279-1323) **4781**
Orlando Sun Review. (US) **2231**
Orleans Parish Medical Society. Bulletin. (US ISSN 0030-5669) **3138**
Ornament. (US ISSN 0148-3897) **2565**
Ornamental Crops National Market Trends. (US) **113**
Ornamental Horticulture. (UK ISSN 0305-4934) **2141**, **18**
Ornamental - Miscellaneous Metal Fabricator. (US) **3417**
Ornamental Outlook. (US) **2142**
Ornamental Plants. see Instytut Sadownictwa i Kwiaciarstwa w Skierniewicach. Prace. Seria B: Rosliny Ozdobne **2131**
Ornamentals NorthWest see Ornamentals NorthWest Newsletter **2136**
Ornamentals NorthWest Newsletter. (US) **2136**
Ornis. (SZ) **566**, **1494**
Ornis Fennica. (FI ISSN 0030-5685) **566**
Ornis Scandinavica. (DK ISSN 0030-5693) **566**
Ornithological Monographs. (US ISSN 0078-6594) **566**
Ornithological Newsletter. (US ISSN 0274-564X) **566**
Ornithological Papers. see Notatki Ornitologiczne **566**
Ornithological Society of New Zealand Inc. News see O S N Z News **566**
Ornithological Society of the Middle East Bulletin. (UK ISSN 0959-6739) **566**
Ornithological Society of Turkey Bulletin see Ornithological Society of the Middle East Bulletin **566**
Ornithologische Arbeitsgruppe Mitteilungen see Lanioturdus Ornithologische Arbeitsgruppe Mitteilungen **565**
Der Ornithologische Beobachter. (SZ ISSN 0030-5707) **566**
Ornithologische Gesellschaft in Bayern. Anzeiger see Ornithologischer Anzeiger **566**

Ornithologische Mitteilungen. (GW ISSN 0030-5723) **566**
Ornithologischer Anzeiger. (GW ISSN 0940-3256) **566**
Ornithologischer Verein zu Hildesheim. Mitteilungen. (GW ISSN 0179-5813) **566**, **512**, **1494**, **1547**
Oro Madre. (US ISSN 0730-3475) **2945**, **2778**
Orologi. (IT) **2565**
Orologi da Polso. (IT) **2565**
Orophrys. (SP) **2142**
L'Oroptero. (IT ISSN 0394-0314) **3304**
Orphan Disease Update. (US ISSN 0887-0306) **3138**
Orphan Voyage. Adoption Series. (US) **4415**
Orphan Voyage. Log see Orphan Voyage. Adoption Series **4415**
Orphan's Messenger and Advocate of the Blind see St. Joseph's Messenger and Advocate of the Blind **2295**
Orphee Contact see Famille Nouvelle **4178**
Orphelinat. (FR) **4415**
Orpheus. (IT ISSN 0030-5790) **2945**, **1279**, **3775**
Orpheus. (US ISSN 0162-296X) **3000**
Orpheus. (GW) **3573**
Orphic Lute. (US ISSN 0030-5804) **3000**
Orquidea (Mex). (MX ISSN 0300-3701) **512**
Orszag-Vilag. (HU) **2198**
Orszagos Muemleki Felugyeloseg. Kiadvanyok. (HU ISSN 0073-4063) **304**
Orszagos Szechenyi Konyvtar Evkonyve. (HU ISSN 0524-8868) **2778**
Orszagos Szechenyi Konyvtar Konyvtartudomanyi es Modszertani Kozpont. Gyarapodasi Jegyzek - Accession List see Konyvtari es Informatikai Kozponti Gyarapodasi Jegyzek **5224**
Orte. (SZ) **2945**
ORTECH International. Annual Report. (CN) **684**
Ortenau. (GW ISSN 0342-1503) **2379**
Orthodontie Francaise. (FR ISSN 0078-6608) **3240**
Orthodox America. (US ISSN 0890-099X) **4216**
Orthodox Church. (US ISSN 0048-2269) **4286**
Orthodox Church in America. Yearbook and Church Directory. (US ISSN 0145-7950) **4286**
Orthodox Life. see Pravoslavnaya Zhyzn **4217**
Orthodox Lore Of the Gospel of Our Savior Mission see O L O G O S **4286**
Orthodox Missionary. see Pravslavni Misionar **4287**
Orthodox News. (UK ISSN 0267-8470) **4286**
Orthodox Observer. (US ISSN 0731-2547) **4286**
Orthodox Outlook. (UK ISSN 0950-8376) **4286**
Orthodox Southwest see Desert Voice **4282**
Orthodox Word. (US ISSN 0030-5839) **4286**
Orthodoxes Forum. (GW ISSN 0933-8586) **4216**
Orthodoxy. see Pravoslavlje **4287**
Orthomolecular Review see International Clinical Nutrition Review **3607**
Orthomolekular. (GW ISSN 0178-7624) **3611**, **3349**
Der Orthopaede. (GW ISSN 0085-4530) **3310**
Orthopaedic and Traumatic Surgery/Sekeisai Gaigeka. (JA ISSN 0387-4095) **3310**, **3372**, **3382**
Orthopaedic Nursing Journal. (US ISSN 0744-6020) **3285**, **3310**
Orthopaedic Physical Therapy Practice. (US) **3310**
Orthopaedic Review. (US ISSN 0094-6591) **3310**
Orthopaedic Transactions. (US ISSN 0162-9379) **3310**

Orthopaedie-schuhtechnik. (GW ISSN 0344-6026) **4361**
Orthopaedieschuhmachermeister see Orthopaedie-schuhtechnik **4361**
Orthopaedische Praxis. (GW ISSN 0030-588X) **3310**
Orthopedic and Sports Medicine News. (US) **3372**, **4482**
Orthopedic Clinics of North America. (US ISSN 0030-5898) **3310**
†Orthopedic Products News. (US) **5253**
▼Orthopedic Resident. (US) **3310**
Orthopedic Surgery/Seikei Geka. (JA ISSN 0030-5901) **3310**
Orthopedics (Thorofare). (US ISSN 0147-7447) **3310**
Orthopedics and Traumatology. see Seikei Geka to Saigai Geka **3311**
Orthopedics Today. (US ISSN 0279-5647) **3310**
Orthopedics, Traumatology and Prosthetics. see Ortopediya, Travmatologiya i Protezirovanie **3311**
Orthopedische Schoentechniek. (NE) **3310**, **4361**
Orthopod. (US ISSN 0030-591X) **3215**
Ortnamnssallskapet i Uppsala. Aarsskrift. (SW ISSN 0473-4351) **2833**
Ortodoncia. (AG ISSN 0030-5936) **3240**
Ortodoncia Espanola. (SP) **3240**
Ortodontia. (BL ISSN 0030-5944) **3240**
Orton Society. Bulletin. see Annals of Dyslexia **1733**
Ortopedia e Traumatologia Oggi. (IT ISSN 0392-1417) **3311**
Ortopedia i Traumatologia. (BU ISSN 0473-4378) **3311**
Ortopedici e Sanitari. (IT ISSN 0030-5979) **3311**, **3807**
Ortopediya, Travmatologiya i Protezirovanie/Orthopedics, Traumatology and Prosthetics. (RU ISSN 0030-5987) **3311**
Ortschroniken. (AU) **2379**
Ortskrankenkasse see D O K: Politik - Praxis Recht **2617**
Orvosi es Gyogyszereszeti Szemle. see Revista de Medicina si Farmacie **3148**
Orvosi Hetilap. (HU ISSN 0030-6002) **3138**
Orvosi Konyvtaros/Medical Librarian. (HU ISSN 0030-6010) **2778**
Orvoskepzes. (HU ISSN 0030-6037) **3138**
Orvostorteneti Kozlemenyek/Communications de Historia Artis Medicinae. (HU ISSN 0010-3551) **3138**, **2319**
Oryx. (UK ISSN 0030-6053) **1494**, **590**
Orzecznictwo Sadow Polskich. (PL) **2664**
Orzecznictwo Sadow Polskich i Komisji Arbitrazowych see Orzecznictwo Sadow Polskich **2664**
Osaka (Prefecture). Radiation Research Institute. Annual Report see University of Osaka Prefecture. Research Institute for Advanced Science and Technology. Annual Report **1971**
Osaka City Medical Journal. (JA ISSN 0386-4103) **3138**
Osaka City University. Faculty of Engineering. Memoirs/Osaka-shiritsu Daigaku Kogakubu Obun Kiyo. (JA ISSN 0078-6659) **1833**
Osaka City University Economic Review. (JA ISSN 0078-6640) **684**
Osaka Daigaku Iryo Gijutsu Tanki Daigakubu Kenkyu Kiyo. Shizen Kagaku Iryo Kagaku Hen/Osaka University. College of Bio-Medical Technology and Nursing. Studies in Natural Science and Health Technology. (JA ISSN 0387-446X) **3138**
Osaka Daigaku Keizaigaku/Osaka Economic Papers. (JA ISSN 0473-4548) **684**
Osaka Daigaku Kyojiba see Handai Kyojiba **3819**

Osaka Daigaku Obun Igaku Zasshi. see Osaka University. Medical Journal **3138**
Osaka Daigaku Sangyo Kagaku Kenkyujo Kiyo. see Osaka University. Institute of Scientific and Industrial Research. Memoirs **4606**
Osaka Daigaku Shigaku Zasshi/Osaka University Dental Society. Journal. (JA ISSN 0473-4629) **3240**
Osaka Daigaku Tanpakushitsu Kenkyujo Kiyo. see Osaka University. Institute for Protein Research. Memoirs **481**
Osaka Daigaku Yakugakubu Kiyo. see Osaka University. Faculty of Pharmaceutical Sciences. Memoirs **3736**
Osaka Denki Tsushin Daigaku Kenkyu Ronshu. Shizen Kagaku Hen/Osaka Electro-Communication University. Memoirs. Natural Science. (JA ISSN 0386-4987) **1341**, 1904, 4332
Osaka Dental University. Journal. (JA ISSN 0475-2058) **3240**
Osaka District Meteorological Observatory. Monthly Report/Osaka-fu Kisho Geppo. (JA ISSN 0030-6088) **3440**
Osaka Economic Papers. see Osaka Daigaku Keizaigaku **684**
Osaka Electro-Communication University. Memoirs. Natural Science. see Osaka Denki Tsushin Daigaku Kenkyu Ronshu. Shizen Kagaku Hen **1341**
Osaka-fu Ikkyu Suijun Sokuryo Seikahyo. (JA) **1845**, 2268
Osaka-fu Kisho Geppo. see Osaka District Meteorological Observatory. Monthly Report **3440**
Osaka-furitsu-Daigaku Fuzokukenkyusho Nenpo. see University of Osaka Prefecture. Research Institute for Advanced Science and Technology. Annual Report **1971**
Osaka-furitsu Daigaku Kiyo, A. Kogaku, Shizen Kagaku. see University of Osaka Prefecture. Bulletin. Series A: Engineering and Natural Sciences **1839**
Osaka-furitsu Daigaku Kiyo, B. Nogaku, Seibutsugaku. see University of Osaka Prefecture. Bulletin. Series B: Agriculture and Biology **127**
Osaka-furitsu Daigaku Kiyo, D. Keizaigaku, Keieigaku, Hogaku. see University of Osaka Prefecture. Bulletin. Series D: Economics, Business Administration and Law **697**
Osaka Ika Daigaku Zasshi. see Osaka Medical College. Journal **3138**
Osaka Industrial University. Journal. Natural Sciences. see Osaka Sangyo Daigaku Ronshu. Shizen Kagaku Hen **4332**
Osaka Institute of Technology. Memoirs. Series A. Science and Technology. see Osaka Kogyo Daigaku Kiyo. Riko Hen **4605**
Osaka Institute of Technology. Memoirs. Series B: Liberal Arts. see Osaka Kogyo Daigaku Kiyo. Jinbun Hen **2512**
Osaka Joshi Daigaku Kiyo. Kiso Rigaku Hen, Taiikugaku Hen/Osaka Women's University. Bulletin. Series of Natural Science, Physical Education. (JA ISSN 0289-8888) **4332**, 3807
Osaka Journal of Mathematics. (JA ISSN 0030-6126) **3050**
Osaka-ko. see Port of Osaka **4736**
Osaka Kogyo Daigaku Kiyo. Jinbun Hen/Osaka Institute of Technology. Memoirs. Series B: Liberal Arts. (JA ISSN 0030-6134) **2512**
Osaka Kogyo Daigaku Kiyo. Riko Hen/Osaka Institute of Technology. Memoirs. Series A. Science and Technology. (JA ISSN 0375-0191) **4605**, 4332
Osaka Kyoiku Daigaku Kiyo. Dai-3-Bumon. Shizen Kagaku/Osaka Kyoiku University. Memoirs. Series 3: Natural Science and Applied Science. (JA ISSN 0373-7411) **4332**, 4606

Osaka Kyoiku University. Memoirs. Series 3: Natural Science and Applied Science. see Osaka Kyoiku Daigaku Kiyo. Dai-3-Bumon. Shizen Kagaku **4332**
Osaka Medical College. Bulletin. (JA ISSN 0030-6142) **3138**
Osaka Medical College. Journal/Osaka Ika Daigaku Zasshi. (JA ISSN 0030-6118) **3138**
Osaka Municipal Water Works Bureau. Water Examination Laboratory. Annual Report. (JA) **4827**
Osaka Museum of Natural History. Annual Report. see Osaka-shiritsu Shizenshi Hakubutsukan Kanpo **3531**
Osaka Museum of Natural History. Bulletin. see Osaka-shiritsu Shizenshi Hakubutsukan Kenkyu Hokoku **4332**
Osaka Museum of Natural History. Occasional Papers. see Shizenshi Kenkyu **4343**
Osaka Museum of Natural History. Special Publications. see Osaka-shiritsu Shizenshi Hakubutsukan Shuzo Shiryo Mokuroku **450**
Osaka no Kagakusha. (JA ISSN 0911-209X) **4332**
Osaka Odontological Society. Journal/Shika Igaku. (JA ISSN 0030-6150) **3240**
Osaka Sangyo Daigaku Ronshu. Shizen Kagaku Hen/Osaka Industrial University. Journal. Natural Sciences. (JA ISSN 0287-1394) **4332**
Osaka-shiritsu Daigaku Kogakubu Obun Kiyo. see Osaka City University. Faculty of Engineering. Memoirs **1833**
Osaka-shiritsu Daigaku Rigakubu Chigaku Kiyo. see Journal of Geosciences **1546**
Osaka-shiritsu Shizenshi Hakubutsukan Kanpo/Osaka Museum of Natural History. Annual Report. (JA ISSN 0389-8105) **3531**
Osaka-shiritsu Shizenshi Hakubutsukan Kenkyu Hokoku/Osaka Museum of Natural History. Bulletin. (JA ISSN 0078-6675) **4332**
Osaka-shiritsu Shizenshi Hakubutsukan Shuzo Shiryo Mokuroku/Osaka Museum of Natural History. Special Publications. (JA ISSN 0389-9047) **450**, 512, 536
Osaka University. College of Bio-Medical Technology and Nursing. Studies in Natural Science and Health Technology. see Osaka Daigaku Iryo Gijutsu Tanki Daigakubu Kenkyu Kiyo. Shizen Kagaku Iryo Kagaku Hen **3138**
Osaka University. College of General Education. Science Reports. (JA ISSN 0474-781X) **4332**, 1757
Osaka University. Economic Review see Osaka Daigaku Keizaigaku **684**
Osaka University. Faculty of Pharmaceutical Sciences. Memoirs/Osaka Daigaku Yakugakubu Kiyo. (JA ISSN 0387-480X) **3736**
Osaka University. Faculty of Science. Report on Research and Development in High Magnetic Field Laboratory. see Handai Kyojiba **3819**
Osaka University. Institute for Cancer Research. Annual Report. (JA) **3201**
Osaka University. Institute for Protein Research. Memoirs/Osaka Daigaku Tanpakushitsu Kenkyujo Kiyo. (JA ISSN 0078-6705) **481**, 1229
Osaka University. Institute of Scientific and Industrial Research. Memoirs/Osaka Daigaku Sangyo Kagaku Kenkyujo Kiyo. (JA ISSN 0369-0369) **4606**
Osaka University. Laboratory of Nuclear Studies. Annual Report. (JA ISSN 0473-4580) **3849**
Osaka University. Medical Journal/Osaka Daigaku Obun Igaku Zasshi. (JA ISSN 0030-6169) **3138**
Osaka University. Research Institute for Microbial Diseases. Annual Reports. (JA ISSN 0913-4751) **3178**

Osaka University Dental Society. Journal. see Osaka Daigaku Shigaku Zasshi **3240**
Osaka Women's University. Bulletin. Series of Natural Science, Physical Education. see Osaka Joshi Daigaku Kiyo. Kiso Rigaku Hen, Taiikugaku Hen **4332**
Oscar Israelowitz's Guide to Jewish New York City. (US) **4781**, 2018
Oseanologi di Indonesia. (IO ISSN 0125-9830) **1610**, 2047
Osgoode Hall Law Journal. (CN ISSN 0030-6185) **2664**
Oshawa - Whitby Business News. (CN) **684**
Oshima-Hiyama Chiho Nogyo Kisho Sokuho/Monthly Report of Agricultural Meteorology. (JA) **3440**
▼Oshkaabewis Native Journal. (US) **2018**
Oshkosh Advance-Titan. (US ISSN 0300-676X) **1320**
Osho Times International. (II) **4217**, 3775
Osiguranje i Privreda. (CI ISSN 0030-6193) **2539**
Osim Inyan. (IS) **4415**, 2587
Osiris (Chicago). (US ISSN 0369-7827) **4332**, 2319
Osiris (Deerfield). (US ISSN 0095-019X) **2945**
Osler Library Newsletter. (CN ISSN 0085-4557) **2778**, 3138
Oslo Boers. Beretning/Oslo Stock Exchange. Annual Report. (NO ISSN 0085-4565) **959**
Oslo City Guide. (NO) **4781**
Oslo Stock Exchange. Annual Report. see Oslo Boers. Beretning **959**
Osmania Papers in Linguistics. (II ISSN 0970-0277) **2833**
Osmania University. Department of Psychology. Research Bulletin. (II) **4037**
Osmeh. (YU) **2878**
Osnabruecker Mitteilungen. (GW ISSN 0474-8158) **2379**
Osnabruecker Naturwissenschaftliche Mitteilungen. (GW ISSN 0340-4781) **4332**
Osnovac. (BN) **339**, 2945, 3793
Osnovaniya, Fundamenty i Mekhanika Gruntov. (RU ISSN 0030-6223) **1872**, 1577
Osogovski Glas. (XN ISSN 0352-1362) **2945**
Ospedale. (IT ISSN 0030-6231) **2468**
Ospedale al Mare. Archivio. (IT ISSN 0030-624X) **2468**, 3138
Ospedali d'Italia. (IT ISSN 0030-6258) **2468**
Ospedali d'Italia-Chirurgia. (IT ISSN 0030-6266) **3382**
Ospedali Italiani-Pediatria. (IT ISSN 0030-6274) **3323**
†Osprey's Seafood Newsletter. (US) **5253**
Oss Verter Imellom. (NO) **2478**
Osservatore Filatelico. (IT) **3755**
Osservatore Legale. (IT ISSN 0030-6290) **2664**
Osservatore Politico Letterario. (IT ISSN 0030-6304) **2878**, 3913
Osservatore Romano. (VC) **4272**
Osservatorio Economico. (IT) **820**
Ossia. (AT) **3573**
Ost-Dienst. (GW ISSN 0179-3071) **2018**
Ost-Dokumentation see Ost-Dokumentation - Wirtschaft **878**
Ost-Dokumentation Bildungs- und Wissenschaftspolitik. (AU) **1714**
Ost-Dokumentation Bildungswesen see Ost-Dokumentation Bildungs- und Wissenschaftspolitik **1714**
Ost-Dokumentation - Wirtschaft. (AU) **878**
Ost-Wirtschaftsreport. (GW ISSN 0344-7030) **878**
Ostaro's Market Newsletter. (US ISSN 0197-3592) **684**
Ostava. (CS) **2379**
Ostbairische Grenzmarken. (GW ISSN 0078-6845) **2379**
Ostdeutsche Familienkunde. (GW ISSN 0472-190X) **2161**
Ostehandleren see Maelk & Ost **201**

Osten. (XN ISSN 0030-6363) **2878**
Ostentatious Mind. (US) **2878**, 3399
Osteopathic Annals. (US ISSN 0092-9336) **3215**
Osteopathic Hospital Leadership see A O H A Today **2458**
Osteopathic Medical Education: A Handbook for Minority Applicants. (US) **1714**, 2018, 3215
Osteopathic Medical News. (US) **3215**
Osteoporosis International. (UK ISSN 0937-941X) **3138**
Osteoporosis Report. (US) **3138**
Osterbotten. (FI ISSN 0473-8063) **2379**
Osteroder Zeitung. (GW ISSN 0030-638X) **2379**, 2258
Osteuropa. (GW ISSN 0030-6428) **3913**
†Osteuropa-Forum. (GW) **5253**
Osteuropa Institut, Munich. Veroeffentlichungen. Reihe Geschichte. (GW ISSN 0078-687X) **2379**
Osteuropa-Recht. (GW ISSN 0030-6444) **2664**

Osteuropa-Wirtschaft. (GW ISSN 0030-6460) **684**
†Ostfriesland. (GW ISSN 0030-6479) **5253**
Ostkirchliche Studien. (GW ISSN 0030-6487) **4286**
†Osto. (FI ISSN 0356-7931) **5253**
Ostomy Management see Ostomy - Wound Management **3285**
Ostomy Quarterly. (US ISSN 0030-6517) **3138**
Ostomy - Wound Management. (US ISSN 0889-5899) **3285**, 3382
Ostpanorama. (AU ISSN 0078-6896) **2379**
Ostrich. (SA ISSN 0030-6525) **566**
Ostrich. (UK ISSN 0307-0786) **3000**
Ostschwaebische Wirtschaft see Wirtschaft in Ostwuerttemberg **824**
Ostseejahrbuch. (GW ISSN 0720-4868) **820**
Ostwestfalische Wirtschaft. (GW) **820**
Osuuskauppalehti see Assa **829**
Osuustoimintalehti. (FI ISSN 0039-5609) **878**
Osveta. (CS) **1686**
Osvetova Praca. (CS) **1686**
Oswald Outlines. (US ISSN 0890-2631) **2161**
The Oswegonian. (US) **1320**
†Oswiata Doroslych. (PL ISSN 0472-2191) **5253**
Otago Geographer. (NZ ISSN 0078-690X) **2258**
Otago Law Review. (NZ ISSN 0078-6918) **2664**
†Otago Museum Bulletin: Zoology. Spiders of N.Z. (NZ) **5254**
Otago Southland Farmer. (NZ) **113**
Otazky Miru a Socialismu. (CS ISSN 0030-655X) **3913**
Otazky Zurnalistiky. (CS) **2574**
Otbor i Obrabotka Informatsii. (KR ISSN 0135-3071) **1442**
Otbor i Peredacha Informatsii see Otbor i Obrabotka Informatsii **1442**
Otechestvo. (BU ISSN 0204-4056) **2379**, 3913
Other Black Woman. (US) **2018**, 2456, 4850
The Other Israel. (IS ISSN 0792-4615) **3913**
Other Networks. (US) **1341**
†Other Poetry. (UK ISSN 0144-5847) **5254**
Other Press. (CN) **1320**
Other Realities. (US ISSN 0742-1184) **246**
The Other Side (Philadelphia). (US ISSN 0145-7675) **4194**, 3945
Other Side (Washington) see Balance Report **3979**
▼Other Side of the Boat. (CN) **4194**
Other Voices. (US ISSN 8756-4696) **2945**
Other Worlds. (US) **3013**
Otica. (BE ISSN 0773-4409) **3316**
Otisian Directory. (US) **2982**, 408
Otium see Aeldre Sagen **2269**
Otkrytiya, Izobreteniya. (RU ISSN 0208-287X) **3677**

Otkrytiya, Izobreteniya, Promyshlennye Obraztsy, Tovarnye Znaki see Promyshlennye Obraztsy. Tovarnye Znaki 3678
Oto Review. (US) 3316
Oto-Rhino-Laryngology, Plastic Surgery of Head and Neck. see Zentralblatt Hals-, Nasen- und Ohrenheilkunde, Plastische Chirurgie an Kopf und Hals 3182
Oto-Rino Laringologie. (RM ISSN 0030-6649) 3316
Otolaryngologia Polska. (PL ISSN 0030-6657) 3316
Otolaryngologic Clinics of North America. (US ISSN 0030-6665) 3316
Otolaryngology see Otolaryngology - Head and Neck Surgery 3316
Otolaryngology - Head and Neck Surgery. see Jibi Inkoka, Tokeibu Geka 3315
Otolaryngology - Head and Neck Surgery. (US ISSN 0194-5998) 3316, 3382
Otologia Fukuoka - Jibi to Rinsho. (JA) 3316
Otomaquia. (VE) 4381
Otorinolaringologia Pediatrica. (IT ISSN 1120-3455) 3316, 3323
Otorinolaringologica. (IT) 3316
Otorinolaringologija. (BU ISSN 0473-5609) 3316
El Otro. (CK) 2456
Otrok in Druzina. (XV ISSN 0030-6681) 1653
Otsuka Pharmaceutical Factory. Journal/Otsuka Yakuho. (JA ISSN 0030-669X) 3736
Otsuka Yakuho. see Otsuka Pharmaceutical Factory. Journal 3736
Ottagono. (IT ISSN 0391-7487) 2554
Ottar. (NO ISSN 0030-6703) 3531
Ottawa Archaeologist. (CN) 281
Ottawa Business Magazine see Ottawa Business Quarterly 684
Ottawa Business News. (CN ISSN 0832-2546) 684
Ottawa Business Quarterly. (CN) 684, 794, 1023, 1117
Ottawa Campus. (US) 1320
Ottawa Construction News. (CN) 627
Ottawa Ethnic Groups Directory. (CN ISSN 0315-0771) 2018
Ottawa Jewish Bulletin and Review. (CN) 2018
Ottawa Law Review. (CN ISSN 0048-2331) 2664
Ottawa Letter. (CN ISSN 0702-8210) 878
Ottawa Magazine. (CN ISSN 0824-9075) 2178
†Ottawa Newcomer. (CN ISSN 0826-0265) 5254
Ottawa R & D Report. (CN ISSN 0380-6251) 1833, 3826, 4606
Ottawa Real Estate News. (CN) 4154
Ottawa's Senior Executives Guide see Canadian Federal Government Handbook 417
Otter. (UK) 3000
Otterbein Miscellany. (US) 2878
Otterwise. (US) 1262
Otto-Novecento. (IT ISSN 0391-2639) 2946
Otto - Novecento Ritrovato. (IT) 2946
Ottot. (IS ISSN 0334-0104) 36, 1049, 1341
Ou Monter a Cheval see Guide du Cheval Arabe en France 4534
Oud-Holland. (NE ISSN 0030-672X) 339
Oud Utrecht. Maandblad. (NE ISSN 0030-6738) 2379
Oude Paden. (NE ISSN 0030-6746) 4194
Oudtestamentische Studien. (NE ISSN 0169-7226) 4194
Ouest Horticole et Maraicher. (FR) 2136
Ouest Industriel, Maritime, Agricole et Commercial. (FR ISSN 0030-6754) 878
Oui. (US ISSN 0090-2047) 3399
Our Afghans. (US) 3712
Our Aim. see Nasha Meta 2015

Our Air Force. see Onze Luchtmacht 3468
Our Animals. (US ISSN 0030-6789) 231
Our Apostolate see Word in Life 4279
†Our Boys. (IE ISSN 0030-6797) 5254
Our Country. see Batkivshchyna 1993
Our Dogs. (UK) 3712
Our Dumb Animals see Animals 230
Our Dwelling. see Vaar Bostad 2498
Our Economy: Review of Current Problems in Economics. see Nase Gospodarstvo 681
Our Effort. see Perpjekja e Jone 340
Our Faith. see Vor Tru 4290
Our Family. (CN ISSN 0030-6843) 4272
Our Family. (GW) 4286
Our Fourfooted Friends. (US ISSN 0030-6851) 231
Our Furred Animals. see Vaara Paelsdjur 2738
Our Gang. (US) 4636, 1378
Our Generation. (CN ISSN 0030-686X) 4444, 3913
▼Our Gifted Children. (US) 1242, 4037
Our Haven. see Musu Pastoge 2015
Our Heritage. (US ISSN 0733-4559) 2161
Our Heritage. (II ISSN 0474-9030) 3642, 2833
Our History. (UK) 3913
†Our Home. (SI) 5254
Our Islam. (US) 4220
Our Kids Houston. (US) 1242
Our Kids Magazine. (US) 1242, 2288
Our Kids San Antonio. (US) 1242
Our Lady of Holy Cross College. Journal.(US) 1320
Our Lady of the Sacred Heart see Annals Magazine 4255
Our Lady's Digest. (US ISSN 0030-6886) 4272
Our Land. (US) 1494
Our Language. see Nase Rec 2830
Our Life. see Meie Elu 2013
Our Life. (US ISSN 0740-0225) 2018
Our Link. (II) 4194
Our Little Friend. (US ISSN 0030-6894) 1262, 4194
Our Local Sixty Six. (US ISSN 0048-2390) 2587, 1287
†Our Mag. (UK) 5254
Our Missing Links. (US) 2161
Our Movement. see Meidan Liike 5235
Our News see D V R News 4403
Our Northland Diocese. (US ISSN 0030-6924) 4272
Our Own. (US) 2456
Our Paper. (US ISSN 0030-6932) 2539
Our Planet. (UN ISSN 1013-7394) 1965, 1494
Our Platform. see Manay Inder 3906
†Our Port - Port of Yokohama. (JA) 5254
Our Review/Mabat Shelanv. (IS ISSN 0792-0814) 2288, 1653, 4416
†Our Right to Know. (US) 5254
Our Schools. (CN ISSN 0384-6636) 1653
Our Special. (US ISSN 0030-6959) 2295, 4836, 4850
Our Stake in the Urban Condition see American Jewish Committee. Domestic Affairs Department. Pertinent Papers 5134
Our Stories. (US ISSN 1053-296X) 2456, 2418
Our Struggle/Nuestra Lucha. (US) 3945
Our Sunday Visitor. (US ISSN 0030-6967) 4272
Our Times Magazine. (CN ISSN 0822-6377) 2587
Our Voice. (US) 2539
Our Way. (US) 4225, 1242, 2288
Our Work see C S C Newsletter 4232
Our World. (US ISSN 1044-6699) 2456, 4781
Our World. see Olomeinu 4225
Ouroboros. (US) 2946, 339, 3000
Ours (Minneapolis). (US ISSN 0899-9333) 1242
Al-Ourubah see Al-Urubah 2211

Ousbou' al-Arabi. (LE ISSN 0002-3965) 2209
Out ! (NZ ISSN 0110-4454) 2456
▼Out. (US) 2456, 3399, 4850
Out and About Smith Mountain Lake. (US) 4781, 4552
Out - Look. (US ISSN 0896-7733) 2456
Out of Jerusalem. (IS ISSN 0333-6271) 2878, 281, 304
Out of Print Market see O.P. Market 4134
Out-of-Print Scientific, Medical and Technical Books. (US) 4357, 3178
Out West. (US ISSN 0899-1413) 4781, 4552
Outbound. (CN ISSN 0843-1566) 60, 2418
Outcry see Animal Liberation Magazine 230
Outdoor. (GW ISSN 0935-3356) 4552, 4781
Outdoor Action. (UK) 4552, 4781
Outdoor Advertising Expenditure Report.(US) 36
Outdoor America. (US ISSN 0021-3314) 1494, 1965
Outdoor & Travel Photography. (US) 3793, 4781
Outdoor California. (US ISSN 0030-7025) 4482, 1494
Outdoor Canada. (CN ISSN 0315-0542) 4552, 1494, 4781
Outdoor Crest. (CN ISSN 0700-9909) 4552
†Outdoor Digest. (US) 5254
Outdoor Indiana. (US ISSN 0030-7068) 1494, 2231, 2418
Outdoor Life. (US ISSN 0030-7076) 4552
Outdoor Life Guides. (US) 4552
Outdoor Life's Guide to Fishing the South see Bass and Freshwater Fishing 4541
Outdoor Living and Sports Goods (Year). (SA ISSN 1015-1451) 4553
Outdoor News. (US ISSN 0279-9065) 1494, 4553
Outdoor News Bulletin. (US ISSN 0030-7092) 1494, 4553
Outdoor Oklahoma. (US ISSN 0030-7106) 1495, 4553
Outdoor Photographer. (US) 3793
Outdoor Power Equipment. (US ISSN 0192-7558) 2136
Outdoor Power Equipment News. (UK) 164
Outdoor Power Equipment Official Guide. (US ISSN 0735-6676) 164, 1049, 3022
Outdoor Press. (US) 4553
Outdoor Retailer. (US) 4553
†Outdoor Review. (US) 5254
Outdoor Showman. (AT) 4553
Outdoor Singles Network. (US) 4363, 4553
Outdoor Sports and Recreation. (US) 4553
Outdoor West Virginia see Wonderful West Virginia 1501
†Outdoor Woman. (US) 5254
Outdoor Writers Association of America. Directory. (US ISSN 0195-6124) 2574
Outdoors see British Journal of Physical Education 1745
Outdoors see Chevy Outdoors 4543
Outdoors Illustrated. (US) 4553
Outdoors Magazine see Australian Outdoors 4541
Outdoors, Recreation & Leisure. (US ISSN 0893-195X) 4553, 2739
Outdoors Unlimited. (US ISSN 0030-7181) 1495, 2574, 4553
Outdoors West. (US) 1495
Outer Continental Shelf Resource Development News. (US) 1610, 1577
Outerbridge. (US ISSN 0739-4969) 2946
▼Outerwear. (US) 1287
Outilite see Circuit Industriel 5166
Outlaw Biker. (US ISSN 0885-2030) 4520
Outlet Report. (US) 1149, 1287
Outline of Communication Industry. (JA) 1341
Outline of Japanese Tax. (JA ISSN 0078-7094) 1103

Outlines. (US) 2456, 3945
Outlook. (CN ISSN 0834-0242) 2018, 4225
Outlook. see Liaowang 2182
Outlook. (TU ISSN 0030-7254) 2220
Outlook see Newscan 4245
Outlook see Reform 4247
Outlook see Mission Outlook 4269
†Outlook. (CN) 5254
Outlook (Alexandria, 1953). (US) 627
†Outlook (Alexandria, 1974). (US ISSN 0161-2131) 5254
Outlook (Ames). (US) 2449
Outlook (Logan). (US) 1320
Outlook (Palo Alto). (US ISSN 0273-835X) 754
Outlook (San Jose). (US) 919
Outlook (Seattle). (US ISSN 0737-3732) 4109, 597, 3395, 4850
Outlook (Wake Forest). (US ISSN 0030-7238) 4246
Outlook (Year) Proceedings. (US) 156
Outlook for Travel and Tourism. (US) 4781
Outlook for U.S. Agricultural Exports. (US ISSN 0148-9526) 156, 919
Outlook in Alcohol & Drug Abuse. (US) 1538
Outlook in Education. (US) 1653
Outlook on Agriculture. (UK ISSN 0030-7270) 113
†Outlook on I B M. (US ISSN 0742-9916) 5254
Outlook on Research Libraries see Information Management Report 2797
Outlook on Science Policy. (UK ISSN 0165-0262) 4332
Outlook on the North. see Kijk op het Noorden 871
Outpost. (RH ISSN 0030-7289) 1519
Outpost. (US) 3968
Outpost Exchange. (US ISSN 0748-8394) 3611, 2078
Outposts see Outposts Poetry Quarterly 3000
Outposts Poetry Quarterly. (UK ISSN 0950-7264) 3000
Output. (SZ ISSN 0379-2501) 1023
†Output (Cleveland). (US) 5254
Output Oesterreich. (AU ISSN 0254-5306) 1082
Outrage. (AT ISSN 0811-2169) 2456
Outrageous Letters. (US) 3399, 4850
Outre. (US) 3000
Outreach. (US) 4093
Outreach (Chicago). (US ISSN 0270-207X) 2468, 3311
Outreach (Nashville) see Sunday School Leadership 4250
Outreach (New York). (US) 2018, 4286
†Outreach Newsletter. (US) 5254
Outrider. (US ISSN 0030-7319) 2778
Outrider. (AT ISSN 0813-5886) 2946, 3000
Outside (Chicago, 1980). (US ISSN 0278-1433) 4553
†Outside Business Magazine. (US) 5254
Outside Magazine see Outside Business Magazine 5254
Outside Plant Magazine. (US) 1364
Outsider. (UK ISSN 0260-6402) 3945
Outstanding Science Trade Books for Children. (US) 1248, 408, 4357
†Outten Quarterly Stock Evaluation. (US) 5254
†OutWeek. (US ISSN 1047-8442) 5254
Outwrite Women's Newspaper. (UK ISSN 0265-8429) 4850
Ouvrages au Crochet. (FR) 3592
Ovation see N A C Calendar of Events 1531
†Ovation. (US ISSN 0196-433X) 5254
Over Broen. (DK ISSN 0904-3853) 2778
Over-the-Counter and Regional Exchange Stock Reports see O T C Stock Reports 958
Over-the-Counter Growth Stock Watch see O T C Growth Stock Watch 958
Over-the-Counter Handbook see O T C Handbook 958

Over-the-Counter Trendline O T C Chart Manual see Trendline O T C Chart Manual **966**
Over-the-Counter 1000 see N A S D Q Yellow Book **1021**
Over-the-Counter 1000 Yellow Book see N A S D Q Yellow Book **1021**
Over the Garden Fence. (US) **2136, 2079, 3611**
Over the Rainbow. (US) **1739, 1723, 4781**
Over the Road. (US) **4747**
Over 2 U. (AT) **2587**
Over 21. (UK) **4850**
Over 40. (US) **3399, 4850**
Over 50. (US) **3399**
Overbacher Bruecke. (GW) **1262, 1695**
Overbrook Adviser. (US ISSN 0030-7386) **2231**
Overflate Teknikk. (NO ISSN 0801-9606) **1212, 1857**
Overheidsdocumentatie see Od **2777**
Overholser Family Association. Bulletin. (US ISSN 0742-8472) **2161**
Overland. (AT ISSN 0030-7416) **2878**
Overland Journal. (US ISSN 0738-1093) **2418**
Overseas! (US) **3468**
Overseas. (UK ISSN 0030-7424) **4781**
Overseas Advertising. (UK ISSN 0048-251X) **36**
Overseas Books. (UK ISSN 0048-2528) **4134**
Overseas Building Notes. (UK ISSN 0030-7432) **627**
▼Overseas Business. (US) **919, 959**
Overseas Development see British Overseas Development **926**
Overseas Development Council. Annual Report. (US ISSN 0092-7643) **933**
Overseas Development Council. Policy Focus. (US) **933**
Overseas Development Council. Working Papers. (US) **933**
†Overseas Digest Semimonthly/Hai Wai Wen Chai Pan Yueh K'an. (CH) **5254**
Overseas Directories, Who's Who, Press Guides, Year Books and Overseas Periodical Subscriptions. (UK ISSN 0078-7124) **408**
Overseas Economic Cooperation Fund. Annual Report/Kaigai Keizai Kyoryoku Kikin Nenpo. (JA) **933**
Overseas Food Legislation Manual. (UK) **2727, 2079**
Overseas Living. (US ISSN 0882-8938) **4781, 933, 3968**
Overseas Media Guide see O P M A Overseas Media Guide **1149**
Overseas Newspapers and Periodicals. (UK ISSN 0078-7159) **4134**
Overseas Outlook (Large Print Edition). (US ISSN 0161-1828) **2778**
Overseas-Post Trade Journal. see Uebersee-Post - Europa-Post **923**
Overseas Press and Media Association Overseas Media Guide see O P M A Overseas Media Guide **1149**
Overseas Press Club Bulletin. (US) **2574**
Overseas Private Investment Corporation. Annual Report. (US ISSN 0196-1276) **959**
Overseas Representatives in New Zealand and New Zealand Representatives Overseas see Diplomatic List - Diplomatic and Consular Representatives in New Zealand **3955**
Overseas Review see Politics Today **3918**
Overseas Trade Directories. (UK) **1149**
Overseas Trade Statistics of the United Kingdom. (UK) **733**
Overseas Trading. (AT ISSN 0030-7513) **919**
Oversight. (US) **2878**
†Oversigt over By- og Regionforskning. (DK ISSN 0108-4151) **5254**
Oversigt Over de Danske Statsskoves Udbytte af Ved og Penge for Finansaaret see Skov og Natur **2108**

†Oversigt over de Meteorologiske Forhold paa Forsoegsstationerne. (DK ISSN 0107-8801) **5254**
Oversigt over Forsoeg og Undersoegelser i Landsbo- og Husmandsforeninger see Planteavlsarbejdet i de Landoekonomiske Foreninger **189**
Oversigt over Landsforsoegene. (DK ISSN 0900-5293) **186**
†Oversigt over Rapporter m.m. Vedroerende Vandkraftundersoegelser i Groenland.(DK ISSN 0107-4997) **5254**
Overspill. (UK) **3000**
Overstreet Comic Book Price Guide. (US ISSN 0891-8872) **2440**
Overthrow. (US) **2878**
Overtone Series. (US) **2878**
Overtones. (US ISSN 0149-5011) **2778**
Overtones from the Underground see Overtones **2778**
Overture (Baltimore). (US) **3573**
Overture (Los Angeles). (US ISSN 0030-7556) **3573**
Overture (New York). (US) **4636, 2018**
Overtures. (UK) **4636, 3573**
†Overtures (Toronto). (CN) **5254**
Overview. (CN ISSN 0700-3617) **878, 3913**
Overview (Chicago). (US ISSN 0030-7564) **4272**
Overview (Olympia). (US) **4416, 4109**
▼Overview (Woodridge). (US) **3000**
Overview of the F A A Engineering & Development Programs. (U.S. Federal Aviation Administration) (US ISSN 0092-3591) **60**
†Overzicht Boeken. (NE) **5254**
Overzicht Onderwijs, Onderzoek en Ontwikkeling see Overzicht Onderwijs, Onderzoek en Ontwikkelingssamenwerking **1714**
Overzicht Onderwijs, Onderzoek en Ontwikkelingssamenwerking. (NE) **1714**
†Overzicht Tijdschriftartikelen. (NE) **5254**
Ovni-Presence. (FR ISSN 0223-0976) **60**
Ovtsevodstvo. (RU ISSN 0030-7572) **222**
Ovulation Method Teachers Association (Publication). (US) **597, 4836, 4850**
Owen Wister Review. (US) **2946**
Owen's Africa Business Company see Owen's Africa Business Directory **919**
Owen's Africa Business Directory. (UK) **919, 1149, 4781**
Owl. (CN ISSN 0382-6627) **1262, 4332**
Owl see C A B News **2607**
Owl Hooter's Gazette see Owlhooters **3493**
Owl of Minerva. (US ISSN 0030-7580) **3775**
Owlflight. (US) **3013**
Owlhooters. (US ISSN 1042-7902) **3493**
Owner. (US) **959**
Owner and Operator Directory. (US) **4747**
Owner Builder. (US) **627, 2501**
Owner Builder Magazine. (AT ISSN 0728-7275) **627, 2501**
Owner Built Home Plans. (US) **304**
Owner Occupied Housing Statistics from Homestead Rebate and Income Tax Data Match. (US) **2500, 1103, 3985**
Owner Operator. (US ISSN 0475-2112) **4747**
Owner - Operator News. (US) **4747**
Owners see Owners Trainers & Breeders **4536**
Owners Trainers & Breeders. (UK) **4536**
Oxalis. (US) **2946**
Oxbridge Careers Handbook. (UK) **3630**
Oxbridge Directory of Newsletters. (US ISSN 0163-7010) **408**
Oxcart. (US ISSN 0737-0954) **3755**

Oxfam News. (UK ISSN 0262-3803) **933**
Oxfam Research Paper. (UK) **933**
Oxford. (UK ISSN 0030-7645) **2878, 1653**
Oxford Agrarian Studies. (UK ISSN 0264-5491) **156**
Oxford and Berkshire Farmer see Berks, Bucks and Oxon Farmer **79**
Oxford Area Arts Council. Newsletter see Tuition, Entertainment, News, Views **347**
Oxford Art Journal. (UK ISSN 0142-6540) **339**
Oxford Bibliographical Society. Occasional Publications. (UK ISSN 0078-7175) **409**
Oxford Bibliographical Society. Publications. New Series. (UK ISSN 0078-7183) **409**
Oxford Bulletin of Economics and Statistics. (UK ISSN 0305-9049) **684, 733, 4582**
Oxford Classical and Philosophical Monographs. (US) **1279, 3775**
Oxford Diocesan Magazine see The Door **4236**
Oxford Diocesan Year Book. (UK) **4246**
Oxford Economic Papers. (UK ISSN 0030-7653) **684**
Oxford English Monographs. (US) **2946**
Oxford Forestry Institute Occasional Papers see O F I Occasional Papers **2105**
Oxford German Studies. (UK ISSN 0078-7191) **2946, 2833**
Oxford Historical Monographs. (US) **2379**
Oxford Institute of Retail Management. Research Papers. (UK) **1023**
Oxford Journal of Archaeology. (UK ISSN 0262-5253) **281**
Oxford Journal of Legal Studies. (UK ISSN 0143-6503) **2664**
Oxford Literary Review. (UK) **2946, 3775**
Oxford Literary Review: A Post-Structuralist Journal see Oxford Literary Review **2946**
Oxford Magazine. (UK ISSN 0268-1137) **1320**
Oxford Magazine. (US) **2946, 2878**
Oxford Mathematical Monographs. (US) **3050**
Oxford Medical School Gazette. (UK ISSN 0030-7661) **3138**
Oxford Mission. (UK ISSN 0048-2579) **4194**
Oxford Mission Quarterly Paper see Oxford Mission **4194**
Oxford Modern Language and Literature Monographs. (US) **2946**
Oxford Monographs on Biogeography. (US) **450**
Oxford Monographs on Classical Archaeology. (US) **281, 1279**
Oxford Monographs on Medical Genetics. (US) **3138, 546**
Oxford Monographs on Meteorology see Oxford Monographs on Meteorology and Physical Oceanography **3440**
Oxford Monographs on Meteorology and Physical Oceanography. (US) **3440**
Oxford Monographs on Music. (US) **3573**
Oxford Monographs on Social Anthropology. (US) **246**
Oxford Neurological Monographs. (US) **3349**
Oxford Papers on Contemporary Society see Southwell and Oxford Papers on Contemporary Society **4202**
Oxford Poetry. (UK) **3000**
Oxford Review of Economic Policy. (UK ISSN 0266-903X) **684**
Oxford Review of Education. (UK ISSN 0305-4985) **1653**
Oxford Reviews of Reproductive Biology.(US ISSN 0260-0854) **590**
Oxford Slavonic Papers. (UK ISSN 0078-7256) **2379, 2946**
▼Oxford Studies in Comparative Education. (UK ISSN 0961-2149) **1653**
Oxford Studies of Composers. (US ISSN 0078-7264) **3573**

Oxford Survey in Information Technology. (UK ISSN 0265-0711) **1457**
Oxford Surveys in Evolutionary Biology. (UK ISSN 0265-072X) **546**
Oxford Surveys of Plant Molecular and Cell Biology. (UK ISSN 0264-861X) **512**
Oxford Surveys on Eukaryotic Genes. (UK ISSN 0265-0738) **546**
Oxford Theatre Texts. (UK ISSN 0141-1152) **4636, 2946**
Oxford Theological Monographs. (US ISSN 0078-7272) **4194**
Oxford Today. (UK) **1320**
Oxford Tracer. (CN) **2161**
Oxford University. Institute of Statistics. Bulletin see Oxford Bulletin of Economics and Statistics **684**
Oxford University Almanack. (US) **1714**
Oxford University Calendar. (US) **1714**
Oxford University List of Resident Members. (UK) **1714**
Oxfordshire Family Historian. (UK ISSN 0309-2275) **2161**
Oxfordshire Family History Society. Newsletter see Oxfordshire Family Historian **2161**
Oxfordshire Local History. (UK ISSN 0260-7565) **2379**
Oxfordshire Record Society. (UK) **2379**
Oxidation Communications. (BU ISSN 0861-0568) **1221, 481**
Oxidation of Metals. (US ISSN 0030-770X) **1229, 3417**
Oxoniensia. (UK ISSN 0308-5562) **281, 304, 2379**
Oxy-Fuel News. (US) **1793, 2664**
OxyChem Newsbriefs. (US) **3864**
Oxygen Radicals. (UK ISSN 0950-057X) **481**
Oyez. (CN ISSN 0475-1671) **2664**
Oyez Review. (US) **2946**
Oyo Igaku. see Journal of Applied Medicine **3114**
Oyo Kikai Kogaku/Mechanical Engineering Applications. (JA ISSN 0474-9847) **3022, 1937**
Oyo Rikigaku Kenkyujo Obun Hokoku. see Kyushu University. Research Institute for Applied Mechanics. Reports **1919**
Oyo State. Estimates Including Budget Speech and Memorandum. (NR) **4069**
Oyo State. Ministry of Economic Planning and Community Development. Annual Report. (NR) **1082**
Oyo State of Nigeria Estimates see Oyo State. Estimates Including Budget Speech and Memorandum **4069**
Oyo State of Nigeria Gazette. (NR) **4069**
Oyo Tokeigaku/Japanese Journal of Applied Statistics. (JA ISSN 0285-0370) **4582, 3050**
Oyo Yakuri/Pharmacometrics. (JA ISSN 0300-8533) **3736**
OZ. (DK) **1357**
Oz Trading Post. (US) **2440, 2946**
Ozarker. (US ISSN 0030-7750) **2418**
Ozarks Mountaineer. (US ISSN 0030-7769) **4781**
Ozarts. (AT ISSN 0157-9169) **339**
Ozbike. (AT ISSN 0155-4360) **4520**
Oziana. (US) **1300, 2946**
L'Ozio. (IT) **2946, 3000**
Ozone. (US ISSN 0191-9512) **1857, 1965, 4827**
Ozone Layer Bulletin. (UN) **1978, 3440**
Ozone News. (US) **1978, 1857, 3440**
Ozone Science and Engineering see Ozone **1857**
†P A. (Physician Assistant) (US ISSN 0747-5551) **5254**
P A A Affairs. (Population Association of America) (US ISSN 0300-6816) **3985**
P A C E. (Process & Control Engineering) (AT ISSN 0728-3636) **1857**
P A C E. (Pacing and Clinical Electrophysiology) (US ISSN 0147-8389) **3211**

P A C E see Professional Approaches for Christian Educators **4196**

P A C Newsletter. (Polish American Congress Charitable Foundation, Inc.) (US) **2018**

P A C O F S News/S U K O V S Nuus. (Performing Arts Council, Orange Free State) (SA) **4636**

P A C: Paper and Advertising Collector. (US) **259**

P A Cs & Lobbies. (Political Action Committees) (US) **3913**, 794

†P A C World. (Pan Africanist Congress of Azania) (TZ) **5254**

P A Cer. (Pharmaceutical Advertising Council) (US) **36**, 3736

P A D F News. (Pan American Development Foundation) (US) **933**

P A D S see American Dialect Society. Publications **2802**

P.A. Drug Update see P.A. Update **5254**

P A E - Mitteilungen. (Paedagogische Arbeitsstelle fuer Erwachsenenbildung in Baden-Wuerttemberg) (GW ISSN 0720-910X) **1686**

P A F Magazine. (Pan African Festival) (KE) **2334**

P A H A Bulletin see P A H A Newsletter **2018**

P A H A Newsletter. (Polish American Historical Association) (US ISSN 0739-9766) **2018**

P A I D Reports. see I P D Cahier **931**

P A I S Bulletin see P A I S International in Print **733**

P A I S Foreign Language Index see P A I S International in Print **733**

P A I S International in Print. (Public Affairs Information Service, Inc.) (US ISSN 1051-4015) **733**, 18, 4395

P A - Kontakte. (AU) **1653**

P A L I N E T News see PaLiNet News **2799**

P A M A News. (Professional Aviation Maintenance Association) (US ISSN 0896-8926) **60**

P A M I see I E E E Transactions on Pattern Analysis and Machine Intelligence **1421**

P A N E S A Newsletter. (Pasture Network for Eastern and Southern Africa) (UN) **222**

P A N Magazine see Paedo Alert News Magazine **4037**

P A R see Pseudo-Allergic Reactions **5263**

P A R Analysis. (Public Affairs Research Council of Louisiana, Inc.) (US) **3913**, 4093

P A R D Bulletin. (US ISSN 0030-7815) **3736**

P A R Legislative Bulletin. (Public Affairs Research Council of Louisiana, Inc.) (US) **4093**

P.A.R. News Analysis see P A R Analysis **3913**

P A S A A Journal. (TH ISSN 0125-2488) **1757**, 2833

P A S C A L. E 27: Methodes de Formation et Traitement des Images. (FR ISSN 1146-5360) **3838**, 18

P A S C A L. T 295: Batiment. Travaux Publics. (FR ISSN 1146-5093) **1845**, 18

P A S C A L Explore. E 11: Physique Atomique et Moleculaire. Plasmas. (FR ISSN 0761-1951) **3838**, 18

P A S C A L Explore. E 12: Etat Condense. (FR ISSN 0761-196X) **3838**, 18

P A S C A L Explore. E 13: Structure des Liquides et des Solides. Cristallographie. (FR ISSN 0761-1978) **1202**, 18

P A S C A L Explore. E 20: Electronique et Telecommunications. (FR ISSN 0246-1161) **1776**, 1341

P A S C A L Explore. E 30: Microscopie Electronique et Diffraction Electronique. (FR ISSN 0761-2028) **466**, 19

P A S C A L Explore. E 32: Metrologie et Appareillage en Physique et Physicochimie. (FR ISSN 0761-2044) **3449**, 19, 3838

P A S C A L Explore. E 33. Informatique. (FR ISSN 0761-2052) **1405**, 19

P A S C A L Explore. E 34: Robotique. Automatique et Automatisation des Processus Industriels. (FR ISSN 0761-2060) **1405**, 19

P A S C A L Explore. E 36: Pollution de l'Eau, de l'Air et du Sol, Dechets, Bruit. (FR ISSN 0246-117X) **1974**, 19, 1978

P A S C A L Explore. E 48: Environnement Cosmique Terrestre, Astronomie et Geologie Extraterrestre. (FR ISSN 0761-2109) **1551**, 19, 371

P A S C A L Explore. E 49: Meteorologie. (FR ISSN 0761-2117) **3444**, 19

P A S C A L Explore. E 58: Genetique. (FR ISSN 0246-1447) **466**, 19

P A S C A L Explore. E 61: Microbiologie: Bacteriologie, Virologie, Mycologie, Protozoaires Pathogenes. (FR ISSN 0761-2133) **466**, 19

P A S C A L Explore. E 62: Immunologie. (FR ISSN 0761-2141) **466**, 19

P A S C A L Explore. E 63: Toxicologie. (FR ISSN 0761-215X) **3748**, 19, 1983

P A S C A L Explore. E 64: Endocrinologie Humaine et Experimentale. Endocrinopathies. (FR ISSN 0761-2168) **3179**, 19

P A S C A L Explore. E 65: Psychologie, Psychopathologie, Psychiatrie. (FR ISSN 0761-2176) **3179**, 19, 4051

P A S C A L Explore. E 71: Ophtalmologie. (FR ISSN 0761-2184) **3179**, 19

P A S C A L Explore. E 72: Otorhinolaryngologie. Stomatologie. Pathologie Cervicofaciale. (FR ISSN 0761-2192) **3179**, 19

P A S C A L Explore. E 73: Dermatologie. Maladies Sexuellement Transmissibles. (FR ISSN 0761-2206) **3179**, 19

P A S C A L Explore. E 74: Pneumologie. (FR ISSN 0761-2214) **3179**, 19

P A S C A L Explore. E 75: Cardiologie et Appareil Circulatoire. (FR ISSN 0761-2222) **3179**, 19

P A S C A L Explore. E 76: Gastroenterologie, Foie, Pancreas, Abdomen. (FR ISSN 0761-2230) **3179**, 19

P A S C A L Explore. E 77: Nephrologie. Voies Urinaires. (FR ISSN 0761-2249) **3179**, 19

P A S C A L Explore. E 78: Neurologie. (FR ISSN 0761-2257) **3179**, 19

P A S C A L Explore. E 79: Pathologie et Physiologie Osteoarticulaires. (FR ISSN 0761-2265) **3179**, 19

P A S C A L Explore. E 80: Hematologie. (FR ISSN 0761-2273) **3179**, 19

P A S C A L Explore. E 81: Maladies Metaboliques. (FR ISSN 0761-2281) **3179**, 19

P A S C A L Explore. E 82: Gynecologie. Obstetrique. Andrologie. (FR ISSN 0761-229X) **3179**, 19

P A S C A L Explore. E 83: Anesthesie et Reanimation. (FR ISSN 0761-2303) **3179**, 19

P A S C A L Explore. E 84: Genie Biomedical. Informatique Biomedicale.(FR ISSN 0761-2311) **3179**, 19, 466

P A S C A L Explore. Part 20: Electronique et Telecommunications see P A S C A L Explore. E 20: Electronique et Telecommunications **1776**

P A S C A L Explore. Part 27: Methodes de Formation et Traitement des Images see P A S C A L. E 27: Methodes de Formation et Traitement des Images **3838**

P A S C A L Explore. Part 30: Microscopie Electronique et Diffraction Electronique see P A S C A L Explore. E 30: Microscopie Electronique et Diffraction Electronique **466**

P A S C A L Explore. Part 33: Informatique see P A S C A L Explore. E 33. Informatique **1405**

P A S C A L Explore. Part 34: Robotique. Automatique et Automatisation des Processus Industriels see P A S C A L Explore. E 34: Robotique. Automatique et Automatisation des Processus Industriels **1405**

P A S C A L Explore. Part 36: Pollution de l'Eau, de l'Air et du Sol see P A S C A L Explore. E 36: Pollution de l'Eau, de l'Air et du Sol, Dechets, Bruit **1974**

P A S C A L Explore. Part 49: Meteorologie see P A S C A L Explore. E 49: Meteorologie **3444**

P A S C A L Explore. Part 60: Genetique see P A S C A L Explore. E 58: Genetique **466**

P A S C A L Explore. Part 61: Microbiologie: Bacteriologie, Virologie, Mycologie, Protozoaires Pathogenes see P A S C A L Explore. E 61: Microbiologie: Bacteriologie, Virologie, Mycologie, Protozoaires Pathogenes **466**

P A S C A L Explore. Part 62: Immunologie see P A S C A L Explore. E 62: Immunologie **466**

P A S C A L Explore. Part 64: Endocrinologie Humaine et Experimentale. Endocrinopathies see P A S C A L Explore. E 64: Endocrinologie Humaine et Experimentale. Endocrinopathies **3179**

P A S C A L Folio. F 10: Mecanique et Acoustique see P A S C A L Folio. F 10: Mecanique et Acoustique et Transfert de Chaleur **3025**

P A S C A L Folio. F 10: Mecanique et Acoustique et Transfert de Chaleur. (FR) **3025**

P A S C A L Folio. F 16: Chimie Analytique Minerale et Organique. (FR ISSN 0761-1749) **1202**

P A S C A L Folio. F 17: Chimie Generale, Minerale et Organique. (FR ISSN 0761-1757) **1202**, 19

P A S C A L Folio. F 21: Electrotechnique. (FR ISSN 0761-1773) **1776**, 19

P A S C A L Folio. F 23: Genie Chimique. Industries Chimique et Parachimique. (FR ISSN 0761-1781) **1202**, 19, 1974

P A S C A L Folio. F 24: Polymeres. Peintures. Bois. (FR ISSN 0761-179X) **1202**, 19, 3869

P A S C A L Folio. F 25: Transports Terrestres et Maritimes. (FR ISSN 0761-1803) **4666**, 19

P A S C A L Folio. F 40: Mineralogie. Geochimie. Geologie Extraterrestre. (FR ISSN 0761-1811) **1551**, 19

P A S C A L Folio. F 41: Gisements Metalliques et Non-Metalliques. Economie Miniere. (FR ISSN 0761-182X) **3502**, 19

P A S C A L Folio. F 42: Roches Cristallines. (FR ISSN 0761-1838) **1551**, 19

P A S C A L Folio. F 43: Roches Sedimentaires. Geologie Marine. (FR ISSN 0761-1846) **1551**, 19

P A S C A L Folio. F 44: Stratigraphie. Geologie Regionale. Geologie Generale. (FR ISSN 0761-1854) **1551**, 19

P A S C A L Folio. F 45: Tectonique. Geophysique Interne. (FR ISSN 0761-1862) **1552**, 19

P A S C A L Folio. F 46: Hydrologie. Geologie de l'Ingenieur. Formations Superficielles. (FR ISSN 0761-1870) **1552**, 19

P A S C A L Folio. F 47: Paleontologie. (FR ISSN 0761-1889) **3661**, 19

P A S C A L Folio. F 52: Biochimie. Biophysique Moleculaire. Biologie Moleculaire et Cellulaire. (FR ISSN 0761-1897) **466**, 486

P A S C A L Folio. F 53: Anatomie et Physiologie des Vertebres. (FR ISSN 0761-1900) **466**, 19

P A S C A L Folio. F 54: Reproduction des Vertebres. Embryologie des Vertebres et des Invertebres. (FR ISSN 0761-1919) **3179**, 19

P A S C A L Folio. F 55: Biologie Vegetale. (FR ISSN 0761-1927) **466**, 19

P A S C A L Folio. F 56: Ecologie Animale et Vegetale. (FR ISSN 0246-1153) **467**, 19

P A S C A L Folio. F 70: Pharmacologie. Traitements Medicamenteux. (FR ISSN 0761-1943) **3748**, 19, 1983

P A S C A L Folio. Part 16: Chimie Analytique Minerale et Organique see P A S C A L Folio. F 16: Chimie Analytique Minerale et Organique **1202**

P A S C A L Folio. Part 23: Genie Chimique. Industries Chimique et Parachimique see P A S C A L Folio. F 23: Genie Chimique. Industries Chimique et Parachimique **1202**

P A S C A L Folio. Part 24: Polymeres. Peintures. Bois see P A S C A L Folio. F 24: Polymeres. Peintures. Bois **1202**

P A S C A L Folio. Part 25: Transports Terrestres et Maritimes see P A S C A L Folio. F 25: Transports Terrestres et Maritimes **4666**

P A S C A L Folio. Part 41: Gisements Metalliques et Non-Metalliques. Economie Miniere see P A S C A L Folio. F 41: Gisements Metalliques et Non-Metalliques. Economie Miniere **3502**

P A S C A L Folio. Part 47: Paleontologie see P A S C A L Folio. F 47: Paleontologie **3661**

P A S C A L Folio. Part 52: Biochimie. Biophysique Moleculaire. Biologie Moleculaire et Cellulaire see P A S C A L Folio. F 52: Biochimie. Biophysique Moleculaire. Biologie Moleculaire et Cellulaire **466**

P A S C A L Folio. Part 55: Biologie Vegetale see P A S C A L Folio. F 55: Biologie Vegetale **466**

P A S C A L Folio. Part 56: Ecologie Animale et Vegetale see P A S C A L Folio. F 56: Ecologie Animale et Vegetale **467**

P A S C A L Folio. Part 64: Anatomie et Physiologie des Vertebres see P A S C A L Folio. F 53: Anatomie et Physiologie des Vertebres **466**

P A S C A L Thema. Part 240: Metaux. Metallurgie see P A S C A L Thema. T 240: Metaux. Metallurgie **3427**

P A S C A L Thema. Part 260: Zoologie Fondamentale et Appliquee des Invertebres (Milieu Terrestre, Eaux Douces) see P A S C A L Thema. T 260: Zoologie Fondamentale et Appliquee des Invertebres (Milieu Terrestre, Eaux Douces) **467**

†P A S C A L Thema. T 210: Industries Agroalimentaires. (FR) **5254**

P A S C A L Thema. T 215: Biotechnologies (Editions Francaise). (FR ISSN 0761-165X) **3179**, 450

P A S C A L Thema. T 230: Energie. (FR ISSN 0761-1668) **3838**, 19

P A S C A L Thema. T 235: Medecine Tropicale. (FR ISSN 0761-1676) **3180**

P A S C A L Thema. T 240: Metaux. Metallurgie. (FR ISSN 0761-1684) **3427**, 19

P A S C A L Thema. T 260: Zoologie Fondamentale et Appliquee des Invertebres (Milieu Terrestre, Eaux Douces). (FR ISSN 0761-1714) **467**, 19

P A S C A L Thema. T 295: Batiment. Travaux Publics see P A S C A L. T 295: Batiment. Travaux Publics **1845**

P A S Memo. (Planning Advisory Service) (US) **2493**

†P A S Reporter. (Professional Activity Study) (US ISSN 0078-7353) **5254**
P A S S. (Professional Accountancy Student Service) (UK) **754**, **1320**
P.A.S.T. see Pioneer America Society Transactions **2419**
P A S T I C Translations. (Pakistan Scientific and Technological Information Centre) (PK) **4606**
P A T A Indonesia. (Pacific Area Travel Association) (IO ISSN 0048-2625) **4781**
P A T A Research. Annual Statistical Report. (Pacific Asia Travel Association) (US) **4800**
P A T E F A News Bulletin. (Printing & Allied Trades Employers Federation of Australia) (AT ISSN 0158-6319) **4003**, **3650**, **3663**, **4134**
†P A T E F A Printing Industry Quarterly. (Printing & Allied Trades Employers Federation of Australia) (AT) **5254**
†P.A. Update. (US) **5254**
P A X. (UK ISSN 0266-6014) **4272**
P & A. (Preiswert & Attraktiv) (GW) **3913**, **1653**
P & A: Paysage et Amenagment. (FR) **1495**, **1547**
P & D Magazine. (Pickup & Delivery) (US) **4747**
P & I International. (Protection & Indemnity) (UK ISSN 0950-4044) **2539**, **4735**
P and I M Review see Production & Inventory Management **5262**
P & M. (Politics & Money) (UK ISSN 0032-3284) **794**, **3913**
P & S A News. (Performance & Specialty Automotive) (US) **4699**
P & S Journal. (Physicians and Surgeons) (US) **3138**
P & T. (Produtos e Tecnicas) (BL) **627**, **304**
P & T. (Pharmacy & Therapeutic) (US ISSN 1052-1372) **3737**
P B A Tour Official Program (Year). (Professional Bowlers Association of America) (US) **4483**
P B E Spectrum. (Paint, Body, & Equipment) (US) **4699**
▼P B L Business Leader. (Phi Beta Lambda) (US) **3630**, **1023**
P B S Aktuell. (Papierwaren, Buerobedarf, Schreibwaren) (AU ISSN 0030-784X) **3663**, **1061**
P B S Bulletin. (Philippine Biochemical Society) (PH ISSN 0115-6403) **481**, **113**, **3138**
P B S Report. (GW ISSN 0344-726X) **1061**
P B X Systems Guide. (US ISSN 0092-8828) **1364**
P C see Personal Computer **1464**
P C A I Magazine. (Personal Computer Artificial Intelligence) (US ISSN 0894-0711) **1410**
P C A Messenger. (Presbyterian Church in America) (US) **4246**
P C A S Newsletter. (Pacific Coast Archaeological Society, Inc.) (US ISSN 0270-6776) **281**
†P C Accounting. (US) **5254**
P C Accounting Trends see C P A Micro Report **805**
P.C. Action (Year) see P.C. Talk **3913**
P C Actual. (SP) **1471**
†P C Advisor. (US ISSN 1054-867X) **5254**
P C & Office Technology. (SA) **1463**
P C Business Products. (US) **805**
P C - Business Software. (UK ISSN 0954-2833) **1479**, **1463**, **1466**
P C C Alumni News. (Palmer College of Chiropractic) (US) **1320**
P C C I Trade and Industry Directory see Philippine Trade and Industry Directory **821**
P C C Sound Consumer. (Puget Consumers Co-Op) (US) **1507**, **4416**
P C Chronicles. (US) **1471**, **1463**
†P C Clones. (Personal Computer) (US) **5254**
P C Computing. (US) **1471**
P C Digest. (US ISSN 0891-575X) **1454**
P C Direct see P C Direkt **1471**

▼P C Direkt. (GW) **1471**
P C Disc. (SP) **1472**
P C Disk Quarterly. (US ISSN 0897-8913) **1472**
▼P C Distributor. (CK) **1472**
P C E (Photochemical Etching) see P C M - P C E **5254**
P C E A Annual Engineering & Operating Conference (Proceedings). (Pacific Coast Electrical Association, Inc.) (US) **1904**
P C Games. (US ISSN 0897-893X) **1419**
P C Hands On. (US) **1472**
▼P C Home Journal. (US) **1472**
P C I Journal. (Precast - Prestressed Concrete Institute) (US ISSN 0887-9672) **627**
P C Insider's Newsletter see P L C Insider's Newsletter **1454**
P C LapTop Computers. (US ISSN 1043-1314) **1472**
P C Letter. (US ISSN 8756-7822) **1433**, **1424**, **1463**, **1472**
P C Life. (US ISSN 0890-4863) **1472**
P C M. (US ISSN 0747-0460) **1472**, **1463**
†P C M - P C E. (Photochemical Machining Photochemical Etching) (US ISSN 0030-7866) **5254**
P C Magazin. (GW) **1472**
P C Magazin Plus. (GW ISSN 0934-8468) **1472**, **1431**, **1454**
P C Magazine see P C Magazine: The Independent Guide to I B M - Standard Personal Computing **1472**
P C Magazine (Italy). (IT) **1472**, **1454**, **1463**, **1479**
P C Magazine: The Independent Guide to I B M - Standard Personal Computing. (US ISSN 0888-8507) **1472**, **1463**
P.C. Management. (Personal Computer) (UK ISSN 0269-0640) **1472**, **828**
▼P C Market Monitor. (US) **1472**, **1049**
P C Master. (GR) **1472**
P C Monthly. (IS) **1472**
P C Mundo. (US) **1472**
▼P C N News. (Personal Communications Network) (US ISSN 1051-3833) **1364**
P C N Y State Report. (Police Conference of New York, Inc.) (US) **1519**
P C Netline see Netline **1427**
P C Netter Newsletter. (US ISSN 0893-8075) **1472**
P C News Watch see Hyatt's P C News Report **5207**
▼P C Novice. (US ISSN 1052-1186) **1472**
P C O - Magazine. (Protestants Christelijke Onderwijsvakorganisatie) (NE) **1653**
P C O T Bulletin see Press Council of the Republic of China **2574**
P C Opportunities. (US) **1472**
P C P C I Membership Directory and Product Listing. (Power Conversion Products Council International) (US) **1904**, **1149**
P C P C I Newsletter. (Power Conversion Products Council International) (US) **1904**
P C Plus/Anashim Vemachshevim. (IS) **1472**
P C Plus. (NE) **1472**, **1454**, **1479**
P C Praxis. (GW ISSN 0934-7178) **1472**
†P C Products. (US) **5254**
▼P C Professionell. (GW) **1472**
P C Publishing see P C Publishing and Presentations **4143**
P C Publishing and Presentations. (US ISSN 0896-8209) **4143**, **1464**, **1472**
P C R see Psychological Cinema Register **4051**
P C R see Personal Composition Report **4144**
P C R Information. (Programme to Combat Racism) (SZ) **3945**, **4194**
▼P C R Methods and Applications. (Polymerase Chain Reaction) (US ISSN 1054-9803) **556**
▼P C Regional. (CK) **1472**

P C Report see Buero und Computer Report **825**
P C Report. (US) **1472**, **1464**
P C Retailing. (Personal Computer) (US ISSN 0736-0894) **1433**, **1464**, **1472**
P.C. Review. (US) **1479**, **1464**, **1472**
P C S Advisor. (Progressive Computer Software) (US) **1472**
P C - S I G Magazine see Shareware Magazine (Sunnyvale) **1474**
P C S W Annual Report. (Permanent Commission on the Status of Women) (US) **4850**
P C Software Communications. (US) **1472**
▼P C Sources. (US) **1424**
P C Special Monthly. (HK) **1472**
P C T E Newsletter. (FR) **1479**
P C T Gazette. (Patent Cooperation Treaty) (UN ISSN 0250-7757) **3680**
P.C. Talk. (CN) **3913**
†P C Tech Journal. (US ISSN 0738-0194) **5254**
P C Tech Journal Directory. (Personal Computer) (US) **1472**
▼P C Techniques. (US ISSN 1053-6205) **1473**
P C: The Independent Guide to I B M Personal Computers see P C Magazine: The Independent Guide to I B M - Standard Personal Computing **1472**
P C Today. (US ISSN 1040-6484) **1473**
P C Today. (UK) **1473**
P C Upgrade. (US) **4144**, **1149**
P C User. (UK ISSN 0263-5720) **1464**
P C Videolog. (US) **1351**, **1385**
P C Week. (US ISSN 0740-1604) **1473**
P C Welt. (GW) **1473**, **1464**
P C World. (US ISSN 0737-8939) **1473**
P C World. (DK ISSN 0904-4191) **1473**, **1464**
P C World Benelux. (NE) **1473**
P C World Espana. (SP) **1473**
P C World France see Info P C **1396**
P C World Magazine see P C Magazine (Italy) **1472**
P C Year Book. (UK) **1464**
P D A Letter. (Parenteral Drug Association, Inc.) (US) **3737**
P D C A Magazine see Painting and Wallcovering Contractor **3655**
P.D. Cue see N A T P E Programmer **1377**
P.D. Gune Memorial Lecture Series. (II) **2833**
P D M see Physicians' Drug Manual **3740**
P - D News. (US ISSN 0478-9997) **4606**
P D S. (Perspektiven des Demokratishen Sozialismus) (GW ISSN 0176-0750) **3913**, **3968**, **4444**
P E & R S see Photogrammetric Engineering and Remote Sensing **2259**
P E D. (Production & Industrial Equipment Digest) (UK ISSN 0030-7904) **1833**, **4606**
P E D Forum. (Public Employee Department) (US) **2587**
P E D Industrial Selector. (UK) **36**
P E G G. (Professional Engineer, Geologist, Geophysicist) (CN ISSN 0823-1745) **1833**, **1577**
P.E.I. Community Studies. (Prince Edward Island) (CN) **4444**, **246**
P E L: Panorama Economico Latinoamericano. (CU ISSN 0030-7920) **878**
P E M: Plant Engineering & Maintenance. (CN ISSN 0710-362X) **1023**
P E M: Plant Engineering and Maintenance Sourcebook. (CN ISSN 0710-362X) **1023**, **1149**
P.E.N. Hongrois. see Hungarian P.E.N. **2923**
P E N International. (UK) **2982**, **4142**

P E News see Professional Engineer **1834**
P E Newsletter. (US) **2946**
P E P see P S I: Report Series **3913**
P E P S Y. (Pedagogisk och Psykologisk Litteratur i Norden) (FI ISSN 0781-2477) **1653**, **4037**
P E P Talk - Group Marriage News see Loving More **4442**
P E R A Bulletin see P E R A News **4606**
P E R A News. (Production Engineering Research Association International) (UK) **4606**
P E R B News. (Public Employment Relations Board) (US) **4069**, **991**
P E S see Pediatric Exercise Science **3324**
P E S C Record see I E E E Power Electronics Specialists Conference. Record **55**
P E T A News. (People for the Ethical Treatment of Animals, Inc.) (US ISSN 0899-9708) **231**
P E X: Australia's Petroleum Exploration Newsletter. (AT ISSN 0310-4184) **3697**
P F. (Papierhandelsfachblatt) (AU) **3663**
P F A Revista see Mundo Policial **1518**
†P F M. (Professional Furniture Merchant) (US ISSN 0030-7963) **5254**
†P F N A News. (Pentecostal Fellowship of North America) (US) **5254**
P - Form. (US) **339**, **2946**, **3000**
P G A Magazine. (Professional Golfers' Association of America) (US ISSN 0161-1259) **4509**
P G - C A T M. (Federation Nationale des Combattants Prisonniers de Guerre Combattants d'Algerie, Tunise et Maroc) (FR ISSN 0154-7313) **3468**
P G M S Newsletter. (Professional Grounds Management Society) (US) **2136**
P G R Bulletin see P G R S A Quarterly **512**
P G R S A Quarterly. (Plant Growth Regulator Society of America) (US) **512**
P G S Country. (Plains Genealogical Society) (US) **2161**
P G W News see P G W Newsline **3697**
P G W Newsline. (Philadelphia Gas Works) (US) **3697**
P H see Panorama Harinero **208**
P H - F R. (Paedagogische Hochschule Freiburg) (GW) **1757**, **1686**
P H L Bulletin. (Packaging, Handling, Logistics) (US) **3650**
P H L S H I V Bulletin. (Public Health Laboratory Service) (UK ISSN 0958-1316) **3222**
P H L S Library Bulletin. (Public Health Laboratory Service Board) (UK ISSN 0267-6850) **3222**, **556**, **3180**, **4109**
P H L S Microbiology Digest. (Public Health Laboratory Service Board) (UK ISSN 0265-3400) **3222**, **556**, **4109**
P H M, Revue Horticole. (FR ISSN 0758-1688) **2136**
P H P see P H P Intersect **2574**
P H P Intersect. (Peace, Happiness and Prosperity) (JA ISSN 0910-4607) **2574**
P H S C Journal. (CN ISSN 0714-8305) **3755**
P H S News. (Pennsylvania Horticultural Society) (US ISSN 0479-947X) **2136**
P-H'atom. (IS ISSN 0333-6948) **1262**, **3826**
P I B C News. (Planning Institute of British Columbia) (CN ISSN 0048-4326) **2493**
P I B Monthly see Publishers Information Bureau Report **37**
P I B Monthly Service-Leading National Advertisers Monthly Service see Publishers Information Bureau Report **37**

6536 P I

P I C I C. Annual Report. (Pakistan Industrial Credit and Investment Corporation Ltd.) (PK ISSN 0078-8198) **959**

P I C I C News. (Pakistan Industrial Credit and Investment Corporation Ltd.) (PK ISSN 0030-8005) **959**

†P I C K and U N I X Guide. (US) **5254**

P I C News. (Productivity Improvement Circles Association of the Philippines) (PH ISSN 0116-4864) **1117**

P I C Newsletter. (Pacific Information Centre) (FJ ISSN 1011-5080) **2778**

†P I C O Laptops & Portables Magazine. (US ISSN 0890-6246) **5254**

P I D C Journal see Civil Aviation in Pakistan: Half-Yearly Newsletter **50**

P I D E Tidings. (PK) **684**

P I D S Monograph Series. (Philippine Institute for Development Studies) (PH ISSN 0115-9194) **933**, 113, 1793

P I D S Special Publications. (Philippine Institute for Development Studies) (PH) **933**

P I D S Staff Paper Series see P I D S Working Paper Series **933**

P I D S Working Paper Series. (Philippine Institute for Development Studies) (PH) **933**

P I E. (Publications Indexed for Engineering) (US ISSN 0085-4581) **1845**, 409

†P I - L T; Occasional Papers on Programmed Instruction and Language Teaching. (US ISSN 0078-7388) **5254**

P I M A Magazine. (Paper Industry Management Association) (US ISSN 1046-4352) **3663**

P I M E World. (Pontifical Institute for Foreign Missionaries (PIME)) (US) **4272**

†P.I.M.R. Informator Patentowy. (PL ISSN 0020-0670) **5254**

P I M S Advisor see A M S Advisor **2705**

P I Magazine. (Private Investigator) (US) **2986**

P I N. (US) **4483**, 1495

P I N Magazine see Alberta Parent Magazine **5133**

P I News see Pantera International News **4699**

P.I.O.L. see Universite Catholique de Louvain. Institut Orientaliste. Publications **2342**

P I P see Psychiatry in Practice **3351**

P I P College "H E L P S" Newsletter. (Partners in Publishing) (US ISSN 0732-5258) **1739**, 1262

P I P E R. (Pensions & Investments Performance Evaluation Reports) (US ISSN 0164-176X) **959**, 2539

P I P S' - Investment Advisory Monthly Newsletter. (Personal Investment Portfolio Service) (US) **959**

P I P S' - Monthly Newsletter see P I P S' - Investment Advisory Monthly Newsletter **959**

▼P I Quality. (Process Industry) (US) **1833**

P I R A Annual Review of Research & Services. (Paper, Printing & Packaging Industries Research Association) (UK ISSN 0262-8600) **3664**, 4003

P I S A L see Periodicals in Southern African Libraries **409**

P I T C O M see Information Technology and Public Policy **2763**

P J G. (Parrot Jungle and Gardens) (US ISSN 1043-0083) **566**, 512

P K L Kemikalier. (Plast- och Kemikalieleverantoerers Foerening) (SW) **1185**

P K L Plaster. (Plast- och Kemikalieleverantoerers Foerening) (SW) **3864**

P K V Informationdienst. (Private Krankenversicherung) (GW ISSN 0343-9321) **2539**

P K V Publik. (GW ISSN 0176-3261) **2539**

P L A Bulletin see Pennsylvania Library Association. Bulletin **2779**

P L A Monthly see Port of London **4736**

P L A N S see I E E E Position Location and Navigation Symposium. Record **1895**

P L A Newsletter. (Pakistan Library Association) (PK ISSN 0048-2714) **2778**

P L A Pictorial. see Jiefangjun Huabao **3462**

†P L A Report. (Post Library Association) (US ISSN 0146-2237) **5255**

P L C Insider's Newsletter. (Programmable Logic Controller) (US ISSN 1040-9718) **1454**

P L D Reporter see Public Library Reporters **5264**

P L E R U S. (Planning: Economic, Regional, Urban, Social) (PR ISSN 0048-4466) **2493**

P L G C Newsletter. (Poets' League of Greater Cleveland) (US) **3000**

P L G P P U R. (Plein la Gueule pour pas un Rond) (FR ISSN 0223-0844) **339**

P L I A N News. (Public Legal Information Association of Newfoundland) (CN) **2665**

P L M. (Production Laitiere Moderne) (FR) **222**, 202

P.M. (GW) **1262**

P M A. (Professional Medical Assistant) (US) **3285**

P M A C News. (Purchasing Management Association of Canada) (CN) **1049**

P M A Directory. (Property Management Association) (US) **4154**, 1023

P M A Newsletter see Freshline **2071**

P M A Newsletter. (Pharmaceutical Manufacturers Association) (US ISSN 0030-8099) **3737**

P M A Statistical Factbook. (Pharmaceutical Manufacturers Association) (US) **3748**, 4582

P M & R see Physical Medicine & Rehabilitation **3141**

P M C C Bulletin. (Post Mark Collectors Club) (US ISSN 1041-4894) **3755**

P M C C Membership Roster. (Post Mark Collectors Club) (US) **3755**, 1300

P M C of N Y Newsletter. (Premium Merchandising Club of New York, Inc.) (US) **1049**, 36

P M D - Praxis Medizinischer Dokumentation. (GW ISSN 0722-477X) **3138**

P M E A Bulletin of Research see Bulletin of Research in Music Education **5154**

P M E A News. (Pennsylvania Music Educators Association, Inc.) (US ISSN 0030-8102) **3573**, 1653

P M E Madagascar. (MG) **878**

P M Environment see Environment Business **1950**

P M I - Powder Metallurgy International.(GW ISSN 0048-5012) **3417**

P M L A. (US ISSN 0030-8129) **2946**, 2833

P M M see Journal of Applied Mathematics and Mechanics **1918**

P M N see Polish Maritime News **5259**

P M Network. (Project Management) (US ISSN 1040-8754) **1023**

P M News. (Purchasing Management Association of Philadelphia) (US) **1049**

P.M. News. (US) **3349**

P M Newsletter (Blackburn) see Global Tapestry Journal **2994**

P.M.O. Notes. (Purdue University Musical Organizations) (US ISSN 0030-8153) **3573**

P M P : Patient of the Month Program.(CN) **3316**

P.M. Perspektive. (GW ISSN 0935-9400) **4332**

▼P M Plus. (Personnel Management) (UK) **1068**

P M S Access Newsletter. (Premenstrual Syndrome) (US) **3295**, 4836, 4850

P M S Today. (Policy Management Systems Corp.) (US) **828**, 1453, 1479

P M T - Nieuws. (NE) **3468**

P - M Technology Newsletter. (Powder Metallurgy) (US) **3417**

P N B International. (Philippine National Bank) (PH) **794**, 878

P N C Review. (Power Reactor and Nuclear Fuel Development Corporation) (JA) **1809**, 1857

P N G Business. (Papua New Guinea) (PP) **2213**

P N G L A Nius. (Papua New Guinea Library Association) (PP) **2778**

P N G Post-Courier Index. (PP) **2578**

P N G Times Index. (PP) **2578**

P N I. (Pharmaceutical News Index) (US ISSN 0362-4439) **3748**, 19

P N L A Quarterly. (Pacific Northwest Library Association) (US ISSN 0030-8188) **2778**

P N P A Press. (Pennsylvania Newspaper Publishers Association) (US ISSN 0030-8196) **2574**

P N P M see International Workshop on Petri Nets and Performance Models **1418**

P N Review. (UK ISSN 0144-7076) **3000**, 2878

P O A. (US) **4536**

P O B - Point of Beginning. (US ISSN 0739-3865) **1872**

P O M P I. (Popular Music Periodicals Index) (UK ISSN 0951-1318) **3589**, 2578

P O P A I News. (Point of Purchase Advertising Institute) (US) **1049**

P O P S I. (Popular Song Index) (UK ISSN 0958-5702) **409**

P-O-P Times. (Point-of-Purchase) (US ISSN 1040-8169) **878**, 1049

P O S I S. (Point-of-Sale Information Service) (US) **1049**

P O S News. (Point of Sale) (US) **794**

P P A G Newsletter. (Planned Parenthood Association of Ghana) (GH) **597**

†P.P.A. North West Region Newsletter. (Pre-School Playgroups Association) (UK ISSN 0260-7751) **5255**

P P C. (Petits Propos Culinaires) (UK) **2449**, 2079

P P C C Bulletin. (Planetary Professional Citizens Committee) (US) **60**

P P F Bulletin. (Public Policy Forum) (US) **4093**, 1653

P P F Survey. (Personnel Policies Forum) (US ISSN 0361-7467) **1068**

P P M M A Newsletter see A P M A Newsletter **3015**

P P M P see Psychotherapie - Psychosomatik - Medizinische Psychologie **3352**

†P - P M Technology. (US ISSN 0747-2722) **5255**

▼P P O Letter. (Preferred Provider Organization) (US ISSN 1054-2396) **684**, 2539

P P O Update. (Principles and Practices of Oncology) (US) **3201**, 3222

P P P see Stamme-Bladet **1741**

P P S Report. (Produktion-Plannung-Steuerung) (GW ISSN 0930-8490) **1023**

P R see Presse Report **4134**

P R Activity Report. (US ISSN 0892-9343) **36**, 2778

P R A's Party Line see PartyLine **36**

P R Bulletin. (UK) **36**

P R C News. (Pre Recorded Cassette) (US ISSN 0898-302X) **1385**, 1117

P R C Newsletter and Calendar. (Poetry Resource Center of Michigan) (US) **3000**

P R - Chicago. (US) **36**

P R D see Publizistikwissenschaftlicher Referatedienst **5264**

P R E A L C Investigaciones sobre Empleo. (Programa Regional del Empleo para America Latina y el Caribe) (UN) **878**, 897

P R E A L C Newsletter. (Programa Regional del Empleo para America Latina y el Caribe) (UN) **3630**, 878

P R en Voorlichting. (NE) **36**

P R I D E Quarterly Newsletter. (National Parents' Resource Institute for Drug Education, Inc.) (US) **1538**

P R - Magazin. (GW) **36**

P R News see Public Relations News **37**

P R O M T. Predicasts Overview of Markets and Technologies see Predicasts Overview of Markets and Technology **1846**

P R O S I. (Public Relations Office of the Sugar Industry) (MF ISSN 0254-5047) **2079**

P R O U T Press. (Progressive Utilization Theory) (US ISSN 1045-7585) **2231**, 3775

P R Planner - Europe. (UK) **1149**, 36

P R Planner - U.K. (UK) **1149**, 36

P R R C: Emerging Trends. (Princeton Religion Research Center, Inc.) (US ISSN 0889-8936) **4194**, 1653

P R Reporter. (US ISSN 0048-2609) **36**

P R Revue. (Schweizerische Public Relations Gesellschaft) (SZ ISSN 0033-3727) **36**

†P R S Journal. (Philosophical Research Society Inc.) (US ISSN 0030-8250) **5255**

▼P R S Members Handbook. (Performing Right Society Ltd.) (UK ISSN 0964-9875) **3573**

P R S News. (Performing Right Society Ltd.) (UK) **3573**

P R Week. (Public Relations) (UK) **36**

P R Week Marketing and Public Relations Guide. (UK) **919**

P R Week Marketing and Public Relations Handbook see P R Week Marketing and Public Relations Guide **919**

P S. (DK ISSN 0109-1549) **1023**

P S. (DK ISSN 0109-4831) **2878**

P S. (Postscript) (AT ISSN 0156-0433) **3737**

P S. (SP) **4194**

P S (Wynantskill). (US ISSN 0885-9256) **1353**, 2418, 3755

P S A. (Public Service Advertising) (US) **36**

P S A. (Pirandello Society of America) (US ISSN 1042-4822) **2946**

P S A C Union Update. (CN) **2587**, 4850

P S A Industrial Bulletin. (Public Service Association of New South Wales) (AT) **2587**

P S A Journal. (Photographic Society of America, Inc.) (US ISSN 0030-8277) **3793**

P S A Journal see Public Service Association Journal **4072**

P S A News. (Political Studies Association of the United Kingdom) (UK ISSN 0955-6281) **3913**

P S A Reporter. (Public Service Association of New South Wales) (AT ISSN 0812-7573) **2587**, 4069

P S A Specifications. (Property Services Agency) (UK) **2493**

P S B A Bulletin. (Pennsylvania School Boards Association) (US ISSN 0162-3559) **1730**

P S B Bulletin see Australia. Public Service Board. Bulletin **4054**

P S C Clarion. (Professional Staff Congress) (US) **1714**, 2587

P S C P Times. (Philadelphia Society of Clinical Psychologists) (US) **4037**

P S Die Motorrad-Zeitung. (GW) **4699**

P.S. for Professional Secretaries see Professional Secretary - Administrative Support Letter **5262**

P S I. Jahresbericht. (Paul Scherrer Institut) (SZ) **1809**

P S I Abstracts. (Payment Systems Incorporated) (US) **733**

P S I Discussion Papers. (Policy Studies Institute) (UK) **4381**, 684

P S I Monitor. (Payment Systems, Inc.) (US ISSN 0731-4396) **805**

P S I Net Connection. (US) **1428**

P S I: Report Series. (Policy Studies Institute) (UK) **3913**, 684, 4381

P S L G. (Public Service & Local Government) (UK ISSN 0144-4212) **4069**
P S L S. (Publication of the Society for Literature and Science) (US ISSN 0886-1102) **2946, 4332**
P S O Aktuellt. (SW ISSN 0345-9616) **3249**
P S P Pflanzenschutz-Praxis. (GW) **113**
P S: Political Science & Politics. (US ISSN 1049-0965) **3913**
P S Postscript on Information Technology see Paradigm Shift **1399**
P.S.: Postscript to Education see Alumnews **1303**
P S R Monitor. (Physicians for Social Responsibility) (US) **4109, 3968**
P S R Newsletter see P S R Reports **4109**
▼P S R Quarterly. (Physicians for Social Responsibility) (US ISSN 1051-2438) **4109, 3968**
P S R Reports. (Physicians for Social Responsibility) (US ISSN 0894-6264) **4109, 3968**
P S S C Social Science Information. (Philippine Social Science Council) (PH ISSN 0115-1169) **4381**
P S S R U Bulletin. (Personal Social Services Research Unit) (UK) **4416**
P S Y E T A Bulletin see Society and Animals **231**
P T A Communicator. (US) **1730**
P T A Heute. (GW ISSN 0302-167X) **3737**
P T A in der Apotheke. (GW ISSN 0722-1029) **3737**
P T A in der Praktischen Pharmazie see P T A in der Apotheke **3737**
†P T A in Focus. (National Parent - Teacher Association) (US) **5255**
P T A in a Pennsylvania Bulletin. (US) **1653**
P T A Today. (US ISSN 0195-2781) **1653**
P T B Berichte. (Physikalisch Technische Bundesanstalt) (GW ISSN 0936-0492) **4606, 4332**
P T B Mitteilungen see P T B - Mitteilungen Forschen und Pruefen **3448**
P T B - Mitteilungen Forschen und Pruefen. (Physikalisch-Technische Bundesanstalt) (GW) **3448, 1833**
P T C Newsletter. (Patent, Trademark and Copyright Law Section) (US ISSN 0736-8232) **3677**
P T C Quarterly see Pacific Telecommunications **1365**
P T - Civiele Techniek/Civil Engineering. (Polytechnisch Tijdschrift) (NE) **1872**
P T Distributor. (Power Transmission) (US ISSN 1045-3962) **1937, 684**
P T - Elektrotechniek - Elektronica/ Electronics - Electrical Engineering. (Polytechnisch Tijdschrift) (NE ISSN 0032-4086) **1904**
P T I C Bulletin. (Patent and Trademark Institute of Canada) (CN ISSN 0849-3154) **3677**
P T I C Newsletter see P T I C Bulletin **3677**
P T J see Passenger Train Journal **4712**
P T M see Police Technology and Management **1520**
P T N Americas see Pata Travel News Americas **4782**
P T N Asia - Pacific see Pata Travel News Asia - Pacific **4782**
P T N Europe see Pata Travel News Europe **4782**
P T N Master Buying Guide & Directory. (Photographic Trade News) (US) **3794, 1149**
P T - Procestechniek/Process Engineering. (Polytechnisch Tijdschrift) (NE ISSN 0032-4094) **1833**
P T S Journal see P T S News **3755**
P T S News. (UK) **3755**
▼P T - Sports Science. (II) **4483**
†P T T Bedrijf. (Staatsbedrijf der Posterijen Telegrafie en Telefonie) (NE ISSN 0030-8366) **5255**

P T T I Studies. (Postal Telegraph and Telephone International) (SZ) **1353, 1364**
P T T Info. (FR) **1353**
P T T Informations see P T T Info **1353**
P T T Novice. (XV) **1365, 1353**
P T T Revue. (CS) **1341**
P T T Technische Mitteilungen. (Postes, Telephones et Telegraphes Suisses) (SZ ISSN 0040-1471) **1365**
P T U Nyt. (DK) **3349**
P U E S D B see Public Use Energy Statistical Data Base **4118**
†P.U.-Kaner. (Potchefstroom University for Christian Higher Education) (SA ISSN 0030-8412) **5255**
P U M R L see Purdue University Monographs in Romance Language **2836**
P.U.R. Executive Information Service see P.U.R. Letter **1793**
P.U.R. Letter. (Public Utilities Reports, Inc.) (US) **1793, 1904**
P.U.S.H. see People United to Save Humanity. P.U.S.H.-Operation Push **2879**
P V - Report. (Personal-Verpflegung) (GW ISSN 0343-7507) **2478**
P W see Praxis der Werbung **37**
P W see P W Personeelsmanagement - Magazine **1068**
P.W.A.C. National Newsletter see P.W.A.Contact **2574**
P.W.A.C. Newsletter see P.W.A.Contact **2574**
P W A Coalition Newsline. (People with AIDS) (US) **3222**
P.W.A.Contact. (Periodical Writers Association of Canada) (CN ISSN 0845-8499) **2574**
P W Nieuws en Actualiteit see P W Personeelsmanagement - Nieuws & Actualiteit **1068**
P W P Newsletter. (Professional Women Photographers) (US) **3794, 4850**
P W P Times see P W P Newsletter **3794**
P W Personeelsmanagement - Magazine. (NE) **1068**
P W Personeelsmanagement - Nieuws & Actualiteit. (NE) **1068**
P z L - Papiere zur Linguistik. (GW ISSN 0343-4133) **2833**
P-75 Posten see Skole og Fremtid **5277**
Pa Mi Erh ZaZhi. see Pamir Magazine **2018**
Paa Flukt/New Future. (NO) **3968, 4416**
Paa Fritid see Kommun-Aktuelt **4089**
Paa Hjul. (NO ISSN 0801-0986) **4520**
†Paa Jobbet. (DK ISSN 0107-6949) **5255**
Paa Kryss see Paa Kryss och till Rors **4527**
Paa Kryss och till Rors. (SW) **4527**
Paa Vej see Nu Pa Vej **4193**
Paardesport in Ren en Draf. (NE ISSN 0039-1387) **4536**
Paarl Post. (SA ISSN 0030-8447) **2216**
Paarlse Padwyser see Strooidak **4250**
Paasikivi - Society. Mimeograph Series. (FI ISSN 0355-1849) **3968**
Pablo. (CU) **3913**
Pablo Lennis. (US) **3013, 4332**
Pac-Rim Defense Marketing see Defense Marketing International **3456**
Pace (Mt. Kisco) see P A C E **3211**
Pace Environmental Law Review. (US ISSN 0738-6206) **2665, 1965**
Pace Law Review. (US ISSN 0272-2410) **2665**
Pace Press. (US) **1320**
Pacer. (US) **1320**
Pacer Times. (US) **1320**
Pacesetter. (US) **3468**
Pachim Bangla. (II) **2201**
Pacific see Monterey Bay Magazine **2229**
Pacific see Aloha **4751**
Pacific Affairs. (CN ISSN 0030-851X) **3913, 2341**
Pacific Affairs Current Awareness Bulletin. (AT ISSN 0158-5789) **4458, 19**

Pacific Alert see California Chamber of Commerce Alert **809**
Pacific and Asian Journal of Energy. (II ISSN 0970-3888) **1793**
Pacific Anthropological Records. (US ISSN 0078-740X) **247**
Pacific Area Travel Association Indonesia see P A T A Indonesia **4781**
Pacific Arts. (US ISSN 1018-4252) **339**
Pacific Arts Newsletter see Pacific Arts **339**
Pacific Asia Travel Association Research. Annual Statistical Report see P A T A Research. Annual Statistical Report **4800**
Pacific Automotive News. (US ISSN 0744-8155) **4699**
†Pacific Aviation Yearbook. (AT ISSN 0156-3726) **5255**
Pacific Bakers News. (US ISSN 0030-8528) **2089**
Pacific Banker. (US ISSN 8750-6718) **794**
Pacific Banker and Business see Pacific Banker **794**
Pacific Boating Almanac. Northern California & Nevada. (US ISSN 0193-3515) **4527, 4781**
Pacific Boating Almanac. Oregon, Washington, British Columbia & Southeastern Alaska. (US ISSN 0276-8771) **4527, 4781**
Pacific Boating Almanac. Southern California, Arizona, Baja. (US ISSN 0193-3507) **4527, 4781**
Pacific Builder and Engineer. (US ISSN 0030-8544) **627**
†Pacific Business Guide. (UK) **5255**
Pacific Business News. (US ISSN 0030-8552) **684**
Pacific Christian College Bulletin. (US) **4194**
Pacific Citizen. (US ISSN 0030-8579) **2018**
Pacific Coast Archaeological Society, Inc. Newsletter see P C A S Newsletter **281**
Pacific Coast Archaeological Society Quarterly. (US ISSN 0552-7252) **281**
Pacific Coast Builder see Sun Coast Architect - Builder **633**
Pacific Coast Council on Latin American Studies. Proceedings see Review of Latin American Studies **2420**
Pacific Coast Electrical Association, Inc. Annual Engineering & Operating Conference (Proceedings) see P C E A Annual Engineering & Operating Conference (Proceedings) **1904**
Pacific Coast Journal. (US) **4536**
Pacific Coast Nurseryman and Garden Supply Dealer. (US ISSN 0192-7159) **2136**
Pacific Coast Obstetrical and Gynecological Society. Transactions. (US ISSN 0078-7442) **3295**
Pacific Coast Oil Directory. (US) **3697**
Pacific Coast Philology. (US ISSN 0078-7469) **2946, 2833**
Pacific Coast Society of Obstetrics and Gynecology. Transactions see Pacific Coast Obstetrical and Gynecological Society. Transactions **3295**
Pacific Companion. (US) **4781**
Pacific Computer Weekly. (AT) **1399**
Pacific Defence Reporter. (AT) **3468**
Pacific Discovery. (US ISSN 0030-8641) **4332**
Pacific Diver. (US) **4553**
Pacific Farmer-Stockman. (US ISSN 1041-2727) **113**
Pacific Fishing. (US ISSN 0195-6515) **2047**
†Pacific Foods. (NL) **5255**
Pacific Forest Research Centre. Pest Leaflet. (CN) **2106**
Pacific Forest Research Centre. Pest Report. (CN) **2106**
Pacific Forests. (US) **2106**
Pacific Fruit News. (US ISSN 0030-8668) **2079**
Pacific Geology. (JA ISSN 0552-7333) **1577**
Pacific Historical Review. (US ISSN 0030-8684) **2418**

Pacific Horticulture. (US ISSN 0163-7843) **2136**
Pacific Hosteller. (CN ISSN 0030-8692) **4781, 1262**
Pacific Impact. (NL ISSN 1016-9970) **684**
Pacific Information Centre Newsletter see P I C Newsletter **2778**
Pacific Islands Books News Letters. (II) **409**
Pacific Islands Monograph Series. (US) **2418**
Pacific Islands Monthly. (AT) **878, 3913**
Pacific Islands Monthly. (FJ ISSN 0030-8722) **4781**
Pacific Islands Studies and Notes. (US ISSN 0085-459X) **2329, 409**
Pacific Islands Year Book. (AT ISSN 0078-7523) **2345**
Pacific Islands Year Book and Who's Who see Pacific Islands Year Book **2345**
Pacific Journal of Mathematics. (US ISSN 0030-8730) **3050**
Pacific Law Journal. (US ISSN 0030-8757) **2665**
Pacific Linguistics. Series A: Occasional Papers. (AT ISSN 0078-7531) **2833**
Pacific Linguistics. Series B: Monographs. (AT ISSN 0078-754X) **2833**
Pacific Linguistics. Series C: Books. (AT ISSN 0078-7558) **2833**
Pacific Linguistics. Series D: Special Publications. (AT ISSN 0078-7566) **2833**
Pacific Logging Journal see Pacific Forests **2106**
Pacific Magazine. (US) **919, 933**
Pacific Marine Fisheries Commision. Newsletter see Pacific States Marine Fisheries Commission. Newsletter **2047**
Pacific Marine Fisheries Commission. Annual Report see Pacific States Marine Fisheries Commission. Annual Report **2047**
Pacific Maritime Magazine. (US ISSN 0741-7586) **4735**
Pacific Maritime Studies Series. (CN ISSN 0847-0529) **2418**
Pacific Marketer. (US ISSN 0048-2633) **2561**
Pacific - Mountain Oil Directory. (US) **1149, 3697**
Pacific Northwest. (US ISSN 0199-6363) **2231, 4781**
Pacific Northwest Council on Foreign Languages. Proceedings see Selecta (Corvallis) **2840**
Pacific Northwest Executive. (US) **1024**
Pacific Northwest Forum. (US) **2418**
Pacific Northwest Library Association Quarterly see P N L A Quarterly **2778**
Pacific Northwest Lily Society. Bulletin. (US) **2136**
Pacific Northwest Quarterly. (US ISSN 0030-8803) **2418**
Pacific Northwesterner. (US ISSN 0030-882X) **2418**
Pacific Oil World. (US ISSN 0008-1329) **3697**
†Pacific Perspective. (FJ ISSN 0379-525X) **5255**
Pacific Philosophical Quarterly. (UK ISSN 0279-0750) **3775**
Pacific Plant Areas. (NE) **512**
†Pacific Property. (UK) **5255**
†Pacific Purchasor. (US ISSN 0030-8846) **5255**
Pacific Quarterly Moana see Crosscurrent **5175**
Pacific Rail News. (US) **4712, 2319**
Pacific Research. (AT ISSN 1031-9379) **3968, 3468**
Pacific Research Monograph. (AT ISSN 0155-9060) **4381**
Pacific Review. see Pazifische Rundschau **2019**
Pacific Review. (US) **2878, 3000**
Pacific Review. (UK ISSN 0951-2748) **3968, 2213**
†Pacific Rim Intelligence Report. (US ISSN 0738-9035) **5255**

PACIFIC RIM

Pacific Rim Research Series. (US) 1610
Pacific Science. (US ISSN 0030-8870) 4332
Pacific Science Association. Congress and Inter-Congress Proceedings. (US) 4332
Pacific Science Association. Information Bulletin. (US ISSN 0030-8889) 4332
Pacific Shipper. (US ISSN 0030-8900) 4735
Pacific Society. Journal/Taiheiyo Gakkai Shi. (JA ISSN 0387-4745) 247, 1610, 2345
Pacific Southwest Directory. (US ISSN 0555-8581) 1149
Pacific Sport. (US) 4483
Pacific States Marine Fisheries Commission. Annual Report. (US) 2047
Pacific States Marine Fisheries Commission. Newsletter. (US) 2047
Pacific Stock Exchange. Annual Report. (US) 959
Pacific Stock Exchange Guide. (US) 959
Pacific Stock Exchange Highlights see Coastlines 942
Pacific Strategic Papers. (SI ISSN 0218-1924) 3968
Pacific Studies. (US ISSN 0275-3596) 4381, 247, 2018, 2319
Pacific Summary Report - Index. (US) 3697
Pacific Sun. (US ISSN 0048-2641) 2231
Pacific Telecommunications. (US ISSN 0899-434X) 1365, 1351
Pacific Theological Review. (US ISSN 0360-1897) 4246, 4194
Pacific Ties. (US) 2018
†Pacific Traffic. (US ISSN 0030-8943) 5255
Pacific Travel Directory. (AT ISSN 0311-0826) 1149, 4781
†Pacific Travel News. (CN ISSN 0030-8951) 5255
Pacific Traveller. (HK) 4782
Pacific Tropical Botanical Garden. Bulletin see National Tropical Botanical Garden. Bulletin 511
Pacific Viewpoint. (NZ ISSN 0030-8978) 2258, 3985
Pacific World. (US ISSN 0897-3962) 4215
Pacific Yachting. (CN ISSN 0030-8986) 4527
Pacifica. (UK ISSN 0306-0896) 3755
Pacifica. (AT ISSN 1030-570X) 4194, 3775
†Pacifica. (US ISSN 1043-8130) 5255
Pacifique Action see Pacific Impact 684
Pacifist. (UK ISSN 0048-265X) 3968
Pacing and Clinical Electrophysiology see P A C E 3211
Pack-o-Fun. (US ISSN 0030-901X) 356
Pack-Peck-Peek Pioneers. (US) 2161
Pack Report. (GW) 1049
Package Printing & Converting. (US) 4003, 3022
Packaged Software Reports. (US ISSN 0747-9573) 1479, 828, 1464, 1466
Packaging. (UK ISSN 0030-9060) 3650
Packaging. (US ISSN 0746-3820) 3650
Packaging see Retail Packaging 3651
Packaging (Year). (SA ISSN 1011-8519) 3650
Packaging and Converting Technology Series. (US) 3650
Packaging Bulletin see Current Packaging Abstracts 3652
Packaging Casebook Directory. (US) 3650, 1149
Packaging Digest. (US ISSN 0030-9117) 3650
Packaging Digest see Packaging India 3650
Packaging Encyclopedia see Packaging Line Planning Guide 5255
Packaging, Handling, Logistics Bulletin see P H L Bulletin 3650

Packaging India. (II ISSN 0030-9125) 3650
Packaging Industry Directory. (UK ISSN 0269-9834) 3650
Packaging Institute see Packaging India 3650
Packaging Japan. (JA ISSN 0288-3864) 3650
Packaging Letter see Techpak 3652
†Packaging Line Planning Guide. (US) 5255
Packaging Machinery Directory see Packaging Machinery Manufacturers Institute. Official Packaging Machinery Directory 3650
Packaging Machinery Manufacturers Institute. Official Packaging Machinery Directory. (US ISSN 0078-7698) 3650
Packaging Marketplace. (US) 3650
Packaging News. (AT ISSN 0048-2676) 3650
Packaging News. (UK ISSN 0030-9133) 3651
Packaging News Product Information Cards. (US) 3651
Packaging Product Sources Guide see Packaging Casebook Directory 3650
Packaging Production International. (GW ISSN 0933-4165) 3651
Packaging Review see Packaging Week 3651
Packaging Review Directory see Packaging Industry Directory 3650
Packaging Review South Africa. (SA) 3651
Packaging Science and Technology Abstracts/Referatedienst Verpackung. (GW ISSN 0722-3218) 3652, 19
Packaging Strategies. (US ISSN 8755-6189) 3651
Packaging, Technology and Science. (UK ISSN 0894-3214) 3651, 1185
Packaging Technology Series see Packaging and Converting Technology Series 3650
Packaging Today. (AT) 3651
Packaging Update. (II) 3651
Packaging Week. (UK) 3651
Packard Cormorant. (US ISSN 0362-9368) 259, 4699
Packer. (US ISSN 0030-9168) 2079
Packer Report. (US) 4509
Packer's Produce Availability and Merchandising Guide. (US) 2079
Packet. (US ISSN 0195-9646) 2778
Packmarknaden Scandinavia. (SW) 3651
Packung und Transport. (GW ISSN 0343-7183) 3651, 1857, 4654
Packung und Transport in der Chemischen Industrie see Packung und Transport 3651
†Paco. (GW) 5255
Pact. (BE) 281, 4333
Padania. (IT ISSN 0394-5359) 2379
Paddle Wheels. (UK) 4735
Paddler. (US) 4527
Paddling Magazine. (US) 4527
Paderborn nu Tag. (GW) 4782
Paderborner Almanach. (GW ISSN 0343-4184) 2190
Paderborner Universitaets Zeitschrift. (GW) 1320
Padova. (IT ISSN 0479-1290) 2206
Padova Economica. (IT ISSN 0030-9206) 821
Padre Santo. (IT ISSN 0030-9214) 4194
Padres' Trail. (US ISSN 0030-9222) 4272
Padres y Hijos. (MX) 1242
†Paedagogica Belgica Academica. (BE ISSN 0079-0370) 5255
Paedagogica Historica. (BE ISSN 0030-9230) 1653
Paedagogik. (GW ISSN 0030-9249) 1653
Paedagogik Heute see Paedagogik Heute - Paedagogische Beitraege 1653
Paedagogik Heute - Paedagogische Beitraege. (GW) 1653
Paedagogische Arbeitsstelle fuer Erwachsenenbildung. Schriften. (GW ISSN 0723-7197) 1686

Paedagogische Arbeitsstelle fuer Erwachsenenbildung in Baden-Wuerttemberg Mitteilungen see P A E - Mitteilungen 1686
Paedagogische Hochschule Freiburg see P H - F R 1757
Paedagogische Hochschule Karl Friedrich Wilhelm Wander. Wissenschaftliche Zeitschrift. Gesellschaftswissenschaftliche Reihe.(GW) 4381
Paedagogische Hochschule Karl Friedrich Wilhelm Wander. Wissenschaftliche Zeitschrift. Mathematisch-naturwissenschaftliche Reihe. (GW) 3050, 4333
Paedagogische Hochschule Karl Friedrich Wilhelm Wander. Wissenschaftliche Zeitschrift. Paedogogische Reihe. (GW) 1714
Paedagogische Hochschule "Karl Liebknecht" Potsdam. Wissenschaftliche Zeitschrift see Brandenburgischen Landeshochschule Potsdam. Wissenschaftliche Zeitschrift 5152
†Paedagogische Hochschule Liselotte Herrmann Guestrow. Paedagogische Fakultaet. Wissenschaftliche Zeitschrift. (GW ISSN 0138-1768) 5255
Paedagogische Hochschule Liselotte Herrmann Guestrow. Philosophische Fakultaet. Wissenschaftliche Zeitschrift. (GW ISSN 0138-1377) 1714
Paedagogische Hochschule Weingarten. Personen- und Vorlesungsverzeichnis.(GW) 1320
Paedagogische Institute. Mitteilungen. (AU) 1653
Paedagogische Korrespondenz. (GW ISSN 0933-6389) 1653
Paedagogische Rundschau. (GW ISSN 0030-9273) 1653
Paedagogische Umschau. see Rassegna di Pedagogia 1657
Paedagogische Welt. (GW ISSN 0342-8257) 1757
Paedagogisches Institut der Stadt Wien. Mitteilungen see Paedagogische Institute. Mitteilungen 1653
Paediatric & Perinatal Epidemiology. (UK ISSN 0269-5022) 3323
Paediatric Nursing. (UK ISSN 0269-9079) 3285
Paediatrica Indonesiana. (IO ISSN 0030-9311) 3323
Paediatrie und Grenzgebiete/Pediatrics and Related Topics. (GW ISSN 0030-932X) 3323
Paediatrie und Paedologie. (US ISSN 0030-9338) 3323
Paediatrie und Paedologie. Supplement.(US ISSN 0300-9556) 3323
Paediatrie: Weiter- und Fortbildung. (US) 3323
†Paediatrische Fortbildungskurse fuer die Praxis. (SZ ISSN 0078-7795) 5255
Paediatrische Praxis. (GW ISSN 0030-9346) 3323
Paedo Alert News Magazine. (NE ISSN 0167-4749) 4037
Paedonoson. (US ISSN 0737-5158) 1242
Paedoperisse. (US ISSN 0737-514X) 1739
Paedovita. (US ISSN 0737-5131) 4416, 1242
▼Paeleoanthropology Annuals. (US ISSN 1059-4124) 247
Paepste und Papsttum. (GW ISSN 0340-7993) 2380, 4272
▼Paesaggio Urbano. (IT) 2493
Paethiki Hara/Children's Joy. (CY) 1653
Pagana. (US) 4286
Page. (UK ISSN 0030-9362) 352, 1426
Page. (GW ISSN 0935-6274) 1473
The Page (Chicago). (US) 1422, 1473
The Page (Seattle). (US) 1653, 1262
▼Pageantry Ontario. (CN) 3573
Pages. (US ISSN 0883-6752) 2574
Pages Juridiques de la Vie Ouvriere. (FR) 2587

Paginas. (VE) 4850, 1293
Paginas de Contenido. Economia Agricola y Desarrollo Rural. (CK ISSN 0120-4467) 141, 19
Paginas de Contenido. Fisiologia Vegetal. (CK ISSN 0120-4416) 141, 19
Paginas de Contenido. Pastos, Nutricion y Produccion Animal see Paginas de Contenido. Pastos, Produccion Animal y Nutricion 141
Paginas de Contenido. Pastos, Produccion Animal y Nutricion. (CK ISSN 0120-4440) 141, 19
Paginas de Contenido. Proteccion de Plantas. (CK ISSN 0120-4424) 141, 19
Paginas de Contenido. Suelos y Nutricion de Plantas. (CK) 141, 19
Paginas de Contenido: Ciencias de la Informacion. (CR ISSN 0257-0114) 2778, 113
Pagine. (PL ISSN 0137-3935) 3573
Pagine Aperte. (IT) 409
Pagine del Vino. (IT) 384
Pagine della Dante. (IT) 2878
Pagine di Storia della Medicina see Medicina nei Secoli: Arte e Scienza 3129
Pagine Giovani. (IT) 4134, 1262
Paging Handbook see R C R Paging Handbook 1358
Pahal. (II) 2946
Pahlavi University. Asian Institute. Bulletin see Shiraz University. Asian Institute. Bulletin 2431
Pai Shing Semi-Monthly. (HK) 2878
Paideia. (PL ISSN 0137-3943) 1653
Paideia. (US) 3775, 1653
Paideia. (IT ISSN 0030-9435) 4134, 2878
Paideuma. (GW ISSN 0078-7809) 247
Paideuma. (US ISSN 0090-5674) 2946
Paideusis. (CN ISSN 0838-4517) 3775, 1653
Paidika. (NE ISSN 0167-5907) 2456, 4037
Paikallislehdisto. (FI ISSN 0030-9443) 2574
Pain. (NE ISSN 0304-3959) 3349
Pain and Headache. (SZ ISSN 0255-3910) 3349
The Pain Clinic. (NE ISSN 0169-1112) 3192, 3201, 3349
Pain Control in Dentistry. (US ISSN 0164-1700) 3192, 3240
▼Pain Digest. (GW ISSN 0938-9016) 3138
Pain Management. (US ISSN 0896-9132) 3138, 573
Pain Series. (US) 3138
Pain Society of Great Britain and Ireland. Journal. (UK) 3138
Paint & Coatings Industry. (US ISSN 0884-3848) 3654
Paint and Ink International. (UK) 3654, 4003
Paint and Resin. (UK ISSN 0261-5746) 3654
Paint and Varnish Production see Modern Paint and Coatings 3654
Paint, Body, & Equipment Spectrum see P B E Spectrum 4699
Paint Check. (US) 4483
▼Paint Dealer. (US) 3654, 1024
Paint Horse Journal. (US ISSN 0164-5706) 4536
Paint Manufacture and Resin News see Paint and Resin 3654
Paint, Oil Colour Year Book see Polymers Paint and Colour Year Book 3655
Paint Rag. (US) 339
Paint Technology see Pigment and Resin Technology 3655
Paint Titles. (UK ISSN 0144-4425) 3656, 19
Paintball. (US) 4483
Paintball Games Magazine. (UK) 4483
Paintbrush. (US ISSN 0094-1964) 2946
Painted Bride Quarterly. (US ISSN 0362-7969) 3000, 2946
▼Painted Hills Review. (US) 3000
Painter & Allied Trades Journal. (US ISSN 0030-9532) 2587, 2554

Painter and Decorator see Painter & Allied Trades Journal **2587**
Paintindia. (II ISSN 0030-9540) **3654**
Painting & Decorating. (UK) **2554**
Painting and Decorating Craftsman Manual and Textbook. (US) **3655**
Painting and Wallcovering Contractor. (US ISSN 0735-9713) **3655**, 627, 2554
†Paiperlek. (LU ISSN 0257-7046) **5255**
El Pais. (SP) **2217**
Pais see Mela **4848**
Pais e Filhos. (BL ISSN 0030-9567) **2175**
El Paisano. (US) **1965**
Paix et Securite. see Peace & Security **3968**
Pajtas. (HU ISSN 0030-9583) **1262**, 1242
Pak Jamhuriat. (PK ISSN 0030-9591) **2213**
Pak-Scout. (PK ISSN 0030-9605) **1242**, 1300
Pakeeza International. (CN) **2018**
Pakenham Gazette and Berwick City News see Pakenham Gazette Berwick Gazette **113**
Pakenham Gazette Berwick Gazette. (AT) **113**, 1242, 4416
Pakha Sanjam. (II) **2833**
Pakin. (LE ISSN 0030-9613) **2946**, 2319
Pakistan. Central Bureau of Education. Educational Statistics Bulletin Series. (PK ISSN 0078-7914) **1679**, 4582
Pakistan. Central Bureau of Education. Yearbook see Pakistan. Ministry of Education. Yearbook **1653**
Pakistan. Directorate of Livestock Farms. Report. (PK ISSN 0083-8292) **222**
Pakistan. Finance Division. Annual Budget Statement (Final). (PK ISSN 0304-6478) **1103**
Pakistan. Finance Division. Budget in Brief. (PK) **1103**
Pakistan. Finance Division. Economic Analysis of the Budget. (PK) **1103**
Pakistan. Finance Division. Estimates of Foreign Assistance. (PK) **1103**
Pakistan. Finance Division. Public Finance Statistics. (PK) **733**
Pakistan. Finance Division. Supplementary Demands for Grants and Appropriations. (PK) **1103**
Pakistan. Food and Agricultural Division. Yearbook of Agricultural Statistics see Pakistan. Food and Agriculture Division. Agricultural Statistics of Pakistan **141**
Pakistan. Food and Agriculture Division. Agricultural Statistics of Pakistan. (PK) **141**
Pakistan. Geological Survey. Memoirs; Paleontologia Pakistanica. (PK ISSN 0078-8155) **3659**
Pakistan. Geological Survey. Records. (PK ISSN 0078-8163) **1577**
Pakistan. Ministry of Education. Yearbook. (PK ISSN 0078-8287) **1653**
Pakistan. Ministry of Finance. Basic Facts About the Budget see Pakistan Basic Facts **1103**
Pakistan. Ministry of Finance. Budget in Brief see Pakistan. Finance Division. Budget in Brief **1103**
Pakistan. Ministry of Finance. Budget of the Central Government see Budget of the Government of Pakistan. Demands for Grants and Appropriations **1088**
Pakistan. Ministry of Finance. Economic Analysis of the Central Government see Pakistan. Finance Division. Economic Analysis of the Budget **1103**
Pakistan. Ministry of Finance. Estimates of Foreign Assistance see Pakistan. Finance Division. Estimates of Foreign Assistance **1103**
Pakistan. National Assembly. Debates. Official Report. (PK ISSN 0078-8333) **4069**, 2665, 3913

Pakistan. Office of the Economic Adviser. Government Sponsored Corporations and Other Institutions. (PK ISSN 0078-8392) **1082**
Pakistan. Planning and Development Division. Development Programme. (PK ISSN 0078-8414) **1082**
Pakistan. Survey of Pakistan. General Report. (PK ISSN 0078-8481) **2341**
Pakistan. Water and Power Development Authority. Report. (PK ISSN 0083-8349) **1924**
Pakistan Academy of Sciences. Proceedings. (PK ISSN 0377-2969) **4333**
Pakistan Affairs. (US ISSN 0030-963X) **2213**
Pakistan and Gulf Economist. (PK ISSN 0253-1941) **684**
Pakistan Annual Law Digest. (PK ISSN 0078-785X) **2665**
Pakistan Archaeology. (PK ISSN 0078-7868) **281**
Pakistan Army Journal. (PK ISSN 0030-9656) **3468**
Pakistan Association for the Advancement of Science. Annual Report. (PK) **4333**
Pakistan Basic Facts. (PK ISSN 0078-7892) **1103**
Pakistan Book of Cricket. (PK) **4509**
Pakistan Central Cotton Committee. Agricultural Survey Report. (PK ISSN 0078-7930) **186**, 4622
Pakistan Central Cotton Committee. Monthly Cotton Review. (PK ISSN 0027-0334) **186**
Pakistan Central Cotton Committee. Technological Bulletin. Series A. (PK ISSN 0078-7949) **187**, 4622
Pakistan Central Cotton Committee. Technological Bulletin. Series B. (PK ISSN 0078-7957) **187**, 4622
Pakistan Chess Magazine. (PK) **4483**
Pakistan Cooperative Review see Punjab Cooperative Union. Review **831**
Pakistan Cottons. (PK ISSN 0030-9699) **113**
Pakistan Council of Scientific and Industrial Research Directory of the Scientists, Technologists, and Engineers of the P C S I R see Directory of the Scientists, Technologists, and Engineers of the P C S I R **4307**
Pakistan Criminal Law Journal. (PK) **1520**, 2665
Pakistan Customs Tariff. (PK ISSN 0078-8058) **919**, 1103
Pakistan Dental Review. (PK ISSN 0030-9710) **3240**
Pakistan Development Review. (PK ISSN 0030-9729) **684**, 933
Pakistan Digest. (PK) **2213**
Pakistan Directory of Trade and Industry. (PK) **821**
Pakistan Economic and Social Review. (PK) **934**, 684
Pakistan Economic Journal. (PK) **684**
Pakistan Economic Survey. (PK ISSN 0078-8082) **878**
Pakistan Economist see Pakistan and Gulf Economist **684**
Pakistan Engineer see Institution of Engineers, Bangladesh. Journal **1826**
Pakistan Exports. (PK ISSN 0030-977X) **919**
Pakistan Forest Institute, Peshawar. Annual Progress Report. (PK ISSN 0078-8147) **2106**
Pakistan Forum see Middle East Report **2431**
Pakistan Heart Journal. (PK ISSN 0048-2706) **3211**
Pakistan Historical Society. Journal. (PK ISSN 0030-9796) **2319**
Pakistan Historical Society. Memoir. (PK ISSN 0078-8171) **2341**
Pakistan Historical Society. Proceedings of the Pakistan History Conference. (PK ISSN 0078-818X) **2341**
Pakistan Horizon. (PK ISSN 0030-980X) **3968**
Pakistan Hotel and Restaurant Guide. (PK ISSN 0250-4340) **2478**

Pakistan Hotel and Travel Review. (PK ISSN 0250-3662) **4782**, 2479
Pakistan Hotel Guide. (PK ISSN 0250-3654) **2479**
Pakistan Hotels & Tourism. (PK) **4782**
Pakistan Industrial Credit and Investment Corporation Ltd. Annual Report see P I C I C. Annual Report **959**
Pakistan Industrial Credit and Investment Corporation Ltd. News see P I C I C News **959**
Pakistan Industrial Development Corporation. Report. (PK ISSN 0078-8201) **1082**
Pakistan Institute of Development Economics. Report. (PK ISSN 0078-821X) **684**, 934
Pakistan Institute of Development Economics. Research Reports. (PK ISSN 0078-8228) **684**, 934
Pakistan Institute of Development Economics. Statistical Papers Series. (PK) **733**, 4582
Pakistan Journal of Agricultural Research. (PK ISSN 0251-0480) **113**
Pakistan Journal of Agricultural Sciences. (PK ISSN 0552-9034) **113**
Pakistan Journal of Agriculture, Agricultural Engineering and Veterinary Sciences. (PK ISSN 1015-3055) **113**, 4814
Pakistan Journal of Animal Sciences. (PK) **222**, 4814
Pakistan Journal of Applied Economics. (PK ISSN 0254-9204) **878**
Pakistan Journal of Botany. (PK ISSN 0556-3321) **512**
Pakistan Journal of Forestry. (PK ISSN 0030-9818) **2106**
Pakistan Journal of Health. (PK ISSN 0030-9834) **4109**
Pakistan Journal of Medical Research. (PK ISSN 0030-9842) **3139**
Pakistan Journal of Otolaryngology. (PK ISSN 0257-4985) **3316**
Pakistan Journal of Pharmaceutical Sciences. (PK ISSN 1011-601X) **3737**, 481
Pakistan Journal of Pharmacology. (PK) **3737**
Pakistan Journal of Pharmacy. (PK ISSN 0030-9850) **3737**
Pakistan Journal of Science. (PK ISSN 0030-9877) **4333**
Pakistan Journal of Scientific and Industrial Research. (PK ISSN 0030-9885) **4333**, 4606
Pakistan Journal of Scientific Research.(PK ISSN 0552-9050) **4333**
Pakistan Journal of Social Science. (PK) **3968**
Pakistan Journal of Soil Science see Bangladesh Journal of Soil Science **170**
Pakistan Journal of Veterinary Science see Bangladesh Veterinary Journal **4807**
Pakistan Journal of Zoology. (PK ISSN 0030-9923) **590**
Pakistan Jute Association. Monthly Summary of Jute Goods Statistics see Quarterly Summary of Jute Goods Statistics **4622**
Pakistan Labour Cases. (PK ISSN 0030-994X) **2665**, 991
Pakistan Law Journal. (PK) **2665**
Pakistan Leather Trade Journal. (PK) **2737**
Pakistan Library Association Newsletter see P L A Newsletter **2778**
Pakistan Library Bulletin. (PK ISSN 0030-9966) **2778**
Pakistan Management Review. (PK ISSN 0969-8027) **1024**
Pakistan Medical Association. Journal. (PK ISSN 0030-9982) **3139**
Pakistan Nursing and Health Review. (PK ISSN 0078-8376) **3285**
Pakistan Pediatric Journal. (PK ISSN 0048-2722) **3323**
Pakistan Petroleum Limited. Annual Report. (PK ISSN 0552-9115) **3697**

Pakistan Philosophical Congress. Proceedings. (PK ISSN 0078-8406) **3775**
Pakistan Philosophical Journal. (PK) **3775**
Pakistan Pictorial. (PK ISSN 0377-2586) **2213**
Pakistan Postage Stamps. (PK ISSN 0078-8422) **3755**
Pakistan Science Abstracts. (PK ISSN 0031-0085) **4357**, 19
Pakistan Science Conference. Proceedings. (PK ISSN 0078-8430) **4333**
Pakistan Scientific and Technological Information Centre Lists of P A S T I C Bibliographies see Lists of P A S T I C Bibliographies **4614**
Pakistan Scientific and Technological Information Centre Translations see P A S T I C Translations **4606**
Pakistan Seafood Digest. (PK ISSN 1010-3562) **2047**, 2079
Pakistan Statistical Association. Proceedings. (PK ISSN 0078-8473) **4582**
Pakistan Studies. (UK) **2341**
Pakistan Supreme Court Cases. (PK) **2665**
Pakistan Tax Decisions. (PK ISSN 0031-0115) **1103**
Pakistan Textile. (PK) **4622**
Pakistan Textile Journal. (PK ISSN 0048-2757) **4622**
Pakistan Times Overseas Weekly. (PK) **2213**
†Pakistan Tourism Review. (II) **5255**
Pakistan Trade Directory - Exporters and Manufacturers. (PK) **1149**
Pakistan University of Engineering and Technology. Research Bulletin. (PK) **1833**
Pakistan Veterinarian. (PK) **4814**
Pakistan Veterinary Index. (PK) **4814**
Pakistan Veterinary Journal. (PK ISSN 0253-8318) **4814**
Pakistan Year Book. (PK) **2213**
Pakistan's Balance of Payments. (PK ISSN 0078-852X) **1103**, 919
Pakistan's Balance of Payments (Quarterly). (PK) **1103**, 919
Pakistan's Books & Libraries. (PK) **4134**, 409, 2778
Pakkaus. (FI ISSN 0031-0131) **3651**
Pakshika Pratirodha see Monthly Pratirodha **4067**
La Palabra. (US ISSN 0277-1535) **2946**, 2018
La Palabra Diaria. (US ISSN 0475-4816) **4194**
La Palabra Entre Nosotros. (US ISSN 0896-1727) **4272**
Palabra y el Hombre. (MX ISSN 0185-0431) **2512**
Las Palabras. (US) **3531**
Palace Museum. Journal. see Gugong Bowuyuan Yuankan **273**
Palace Peeper. (US) **4636**, 3573
El Palacio. (US ISSN 0031-0158) **2418**
Paladin. (US) **1320**
Palaentology and Stratigraphy see Geological Abstracts **1551**
Palaeo Ichthyologica. (GW ISSN 0724-6331) **3659**, 590
Palaeobotanist. (II ISSN 0031-0174) **512**
Palaeobulgarica. (BU ISSN 0204-4021) **2380**
Palaeogeography, Palaeoclimatology, Palaeoecology. (NE ISSN 0031-0182) **3659**, 1547
Palaeontographica. Abt. A: Palaeozoologie - Stratigraphie. (GW ISSN 0375-0442) **3659**
Palaeontographica. Abt. B: Palaeophytologie. (GW ISSN 0375-0299) **3659**
Palaeontographica. Supplementbaende. (GW ISSN 0085-4611) **3659**
Palaeontographica Americana. (US ISSN 0078-8546) **3659**
Palaeontographica Italica. (IT) **3659**
Palaeontographical Society. Monographs (London). (UK) **1577**, 3659
Palaeontologia Africana. (SA ISSN 0078-8554) **3659**
Palaeontologia Cathayana/Huaxia Gushengwu. (CC) **3659**

Palaeontologia Jugoslavica. (CI ISSN 0552-9352) **3659**
Palaeontologia Polonica. (PL ISSN 0078-8562) **3659**
Palaeontological Society of Japan. Transactions and Proceedings. (JA ISSN 0031-0204) **3659**
Palaeontologische Zeitschrift. (GW ISSN 0031-0220) **3659**
Palaeontology. (UK ISSN 0031-0239) **3659**
Palaeontology, Geology, Physics, and Chemistry. Proceedings see Royal Netherlands Academy of Sciences. Proceedings **4336**
Palaeovertebrata. (FR ISSN 0031-0247) **3659**
Palaestra. (US ISSN 8756-5811) **2284**, 1739, 3807, 4483
Palaestra. (IT ISSN 0031-0255) **2946**, 339
Palaios. (US ISSN 0883-1351) **3659**
Palais de la Decouverte. Revue. (FR ISSN 0180-3344) **4333**
Palante. (CU ISSN 0552-9395) **2878**
Palatin y Patatan. (UY) **1262**
Palatinate. (UK) **2946**, 3794
Palatine Leaves. (US) **2161**
Paleobiology. (US ISSN 0094-8373) **3659**
PaleoBios. (US ISSN 0031-0298) **3659**, 1577
Paleoceanography. (US ISSN 0883-8305) **4333**, 4606
▼Paleoclimate Data Record. (US) **3659**, 3440
Paleoclimate Publications Series Report see National Oceanic and Atmospheric Administration. National Geophysical Data Center. Paleoclimate Publications Series **3658**
Paleoecology of Africa. (NE ISSN 0168-6208) **3659**
Paleoecology of Africa and the Surrounding Islands see Paleoecology of Africa **3659**
Paleontological Bulletins see New Zealand Geological Survey. Paleontological Bulletin **3658**
Paleontological Journal. (English translation of: Paleontologicheskii Zhurnal) (US ISSN 0031-0301) **3660**
Paleontological Society. Memoir. (US ISSN 0078-8597) **3660**
Paleontologicheskii Zhurnal. (RU ISSN 0031-031X) **3660**
Paleontologiia, Stratigrafiia i Litologiia. (BU) **3660**
Paleorient. (FR) **3660**
La Palestine. (SZ) **3913**
Palestine Documents see Institute for Palestine Studies. Arabic Annual Documentary Series **5214**
Palestine Exploration Quarterly. (UK ISSN 0031-0328) **281**, 2431
Palestine Focus. (US ISSN 0883-8577) **3968**
Palestine Human Rights Campaign Newsletter. (US) **3945**
Palestine Refugees Today. (UN ISSN 0031-0336) **4416**, 3968
Palestine Yearbook of International Law.(CY) **2727**
Palestinian Documents. see Al-Watha'iq al-Filastiniyyah **2432**
Palestra/Bar. (PL ISSN 0031-0344) **2665**
Palette. (AU) **113**
Palette. (GW ISSN 0179-9711) **3000**
Palimpsest. (US ISSN 0031-0360) **2418**
PaLiNet News. (US ISSN 0278-9469) **2799**
Palingenesia. (GW ISSN 0552-9638) **1279**
Palladio. (IT ISSN 0031-0379) **304**
Pallas. (FR ISSN 0031-0387) **1279**
†Pallas. (BE) **5255**
†Pallavolo. (IT) **5255**
Pallet Digest. (US) **640**
Pallet Enterprise. (US) **2106**
Palliative Care Index. (UK ISSN 0961-4591) **3180**
Palliative Medicine. (UK ISSN 0269-2163) **3139**

Pallottis Werk. (GW ISSN 0031-0395) **4194**
Palm. (LB) **2169**
Palm Beach Illustrated. (US) **2231**
Palm Beach Jewish World. (US) **2018**, 4225
Palm Beach Life. (US ISSN 0031-0417) **2231**
Palm Beach Review. (US) **684**
Palm Beach Social Pictorial see Palm Beach Society **2231**
Palm Beach Society. (US ISSN 1045-7259) **2231**
Palm Springs Life. (US ISSN 0031-0425) **4782**
Palm Springs Life Desert Guide. (US) **4782**
Palmer College of Chiropractic Alumni News see P C C Alumni News **1320**
Palmer Video Magazine. (US) **1386**, 3515
Palmer Video News see Palmer Video Magazine **1386**
Palmetto. (US ISSN 0276-4164) **2136**
Palmetto Economics. (US) **156**
Palmetto Pharmacist. (US) **3737**
Palmetto Piper. (US ISSN 0048-2781) **2302**
The Palmtop Paper. (US) **1454**, 1479
Palomino Horses. (US ISSN 0031-045X) **4536**
Palontorjunta/Brandvaern. (FI ISSN 0031-0468) **2034**
Palontorjuntatekniika. (FI ISSN 0031-0476) **2034**
Palstek. (GW ISSN 0936-5877) **4527**
Palynology. (US ISSN 0191-6122) **3660**, 1577
Pamatkova Pece see Pamatky a Priroda **1495**
Pamatky a Priroda. (CS) **1495**
Pamatky Archeologicke/Archaeological Monuments. (CS ISSN 0031-0506) **281**
Pamatky Archeologicke. Bibliographical Register. (CS) **281**
Pamietnik Literacki. (PL ISSN 0031-0514) **2946**
Pamietnik Slowianski. (PL ISSN 0078-866X) **2833**
Pamietnik Teatralny. (PL ISSN 0031-0522) **4636**
Pamietnikarstwo Polskie. (PL ISSN 0137-3234) **2380**, 3913
Pamir Magazine/Pa Mi Erh ZaZhi. (US) **2018**
Pamir Monthly see Pamir Magazine **2018**
Pam'iyatky Ukrainy. (KR) **2380**, 281
Pam'iyatnyky Ukrainy see Pam'iyatky Ukrainy **2380**
Pammatone see San Martino **3151**
Pamphlet for Biology Teachers. (IS ISSN 0333-9815) **451**
Pamyatniki Kul'tury. Novye Otkrytiya/ Monuments of Culture. New Discoveries. (RU) **339**, 281
Pan. (MX ISSN 0187-8492) **2089**
PAN. (IT) **2833**
Pan. (GW) **3531**, 339
Pan African Festival Magazine see P A F Magazine **2334**
Pan Africanist Congress of Azania World see P A C World **5254**
†Pan Am Clipper. (US) **5255**
Pan Am World Guide. (US ISSN 0553-0601) **4782**
The Pan - American. (US) **1320**
Pan American Development Foundation. Annual Report. (US ISSN 0552-9913) **934**
Pan American Development Foundation News see P A D F News **933**
Pan American Federation of Engineering Societies. Bulletin. (AG ISSN 0078-8791) **1833**
Pan American Health Organization. Bulletin. (UN ISSN 0085-4638) **4109**
Pan-American Indian Association News. (US) **2019**
Pan American Institute of Geography and History. Commission on Geophysics. Boletin. (BO) **1592**
Pan American Review. (US ISSN 0031-059X) **2946**

†Pan-American Trader. (US ISSN 0300-6514) **5255**
Pan American Union. Department of Scientific Affairs. Report of Activities. see Organization of American States. Department of Scientific Affairs. Report of Activities **4332**
Pan Bladet. (DK ISSN 0902-347X) **2456**
Pan Directorio de Proveedores/Bread Caterers' Directory. (MX ISSN 0187-8506) **2089**
▼Pan-Erotic Review. (US ISSN 0896-2898) **339**, 2946, 3794
Pan-European Associations. (UK) **1150**, 3968
Pan-Pacific Entomologist. (US ISSN 0031-0603) **537**
Pan Pipes see Sigma Alpha Iota Quarterly: Pan Pipes **3580**
Pan Player Plus see Poker Player **5259**
Pan T'ai Hsueh Pao/Majallah Pantai/ University of Malaya. Chinese Language Society. Journal. (MY ISSN 0553-0644) **2833**
Panache (Elmhurst). (US) **1320**
▼Panache (Phoenix). (US) **2231**
Panaderia Noticias. (SP ISSN 0214-3984) **2089**
Panama. Contraloria General. Boletin de Contabilidad see Panama. Contraloria General. Informe Trimestral de Rentas y Gastos **1103**
Panama. Contraloria General. Informe Trimestral de Rentas y Gastos. (PN) **1103**
Panama. Direccion de Estadistica y Censo. Estadistica Panamena. Serie F. Industrias-Encuestas see Estadistica Panamena. Situacion Economica. Seccion 314, 321, 323, 324, 325. Industria **714**
Panama. Direccion Nacional de Planeamiento y Reforma Educativa. Departamento de Estadistica. Serie: Analisis Estadistico. (PN) **1679**
Panama. Instituto de Investigacion Agropecuaria. Informe Anual. (PN) **113**
Panama. Instituto de Investigacion Agropecuaria. Memoria. Foro Nacional de Informacion Documental.(PN) **113**
Panama. Instituto de Investigacion Agropecuaria. Memoria. Reunion Panamena de Informacion Agricola see Panama. Instituto de Investigacion Agropecuaria. Memoria. Foro Nacional de Informacion Documental **113**
Panama. Ministerio de Planificacion y Politica Economica. Informe Economico. (PN) **878**
Panama. Ministerio de Vivienda. Memoria. (PN) **2493**
Panama. Tribunal Electoral. Memoria. (PN) **4069**
Panama en Cifras. (PN ISSN 0078-8996) **4582**
Panama Handbook 1983. (UK ISSN 0263-4260) **4735**, 1150
Panama Hoy see Panama Now **838**
Panama Now. (PN) **838**, 4782
Pananaw see Sambahayan **2495**
Pancevac. (YU ISSN 0031-0662) **2239**
Panchajanya. (II) **2201**
Panchayati Raj (Calcutta). (II) **2201**
Pancreas. (US ISSN 0885-3177) **3255**, 3269
Pancreatic and Salivary Secretion. (UK ISSN 0142-825X) **573**, 3255
Panda. (IT) **1495**
Panda Junior. (IT) **1495**
Panda-Nyt see Levende Natur **446**
Pandora. (US ISSN 0275-519X) **3013**
Pandulipi. (II) **2878**, 339
Panel World. (US) **2116**
Paneuropa Deutschland. (GW) **3968**, 878, 2878
Paneuropa-Jugend in Paneuropa Deutschland see Paneuropa Deutschland **3968**
†Pangloss Papers. (US ISSN 0897-7941) **5255**
Panhandle Magazine. (US ISSN 0031-076X) **3697**

Panhandle-Plains Historical Review. (US ISSN 0148-7795) **2418**
Panhandler. (US ISSN 0738-8705) **2946**
Paniere. (IT) **1507**
Panificazione e Pasticceria. (IT) **2079**
Panim Lekan Velekan. (IS) **1653**
Panjab Past and Present. (II ISSN 0031-0786) **2341**
Panjab University Law Review. (II) **2665**
Panjab University News. (II) **1714**
Panjab University Research Bulletin (Arts). (II) **2512**, 4381
Panjab University Research Bulletin (Sciences). (II ISSN 0555-7631) **4382**
Panjandrum Poetry Journal. (US ISSN 0092-5535) **3000**
Pankey-Gram. (US) **1320**, 3240
Panminerva Medica see Panminerva Medica - Europa Medica **3139**
Panminerva Medica - Europa Medica. (IT) **3139**
Panning Gold see Locating Gold, Gems, & Minerals **3487**
Pannonia. (AU) **2380**
Panorama see Panorama - De Post **2175**
Panorama. (GT) **2180**
Panorama. (IT) **2206**
Panorama. (NE ISSN 0031-0867) **2211**
Panorama. (PL) **2214**
Panorama. (UK) **2380**, 2161
Panorama. (FR ISSN 0299-6898) **4194**
†Panorama. (UN) **5255**
Panorama (Bhilai) see Steel Bulletin **3420**
Panorama (Boston). (US ISSN 0048-282X) **4782**
Panorama (Melbourne). (AT ISSN 0814-9089) **4735**
Panorama (Sydney). (AT) **4803**
†Panorama A P E C of the Brazilian Economy. (BL) **5255**
Panorama Aujourd'hui see Panorama **4194**
Panorama Cheshskoi Literatury see Panorama of Czech Literature **2946**
†Panorama de Agricultura en (Year). (SP) **5255**
Panorama de Fils et Cables see Draht und Kabel Panorama **3405**
Panorama de l'Economie de la Reunion see Tableau Economique de la Reunion **886**
Panorama de la Literatura Checa see Panorama of Czech Literature **2946**
Panorama de la Litterature Tcheque see Panorama of Czech Literature **2946**
Panorama de la Teologia Latinoamericana. (CL) **4272**
Panorama - De Post. (BE) **2175**, 1293
Panorama der Tschechischen Literatur see Panorama of Czech Literature **2946**
Panorama Difesa. (IT ISSN 0394-3429) **3468**
Panorama Economico. (MX ISSN 0479-4346) **878**
Panorama Estatistico de Setor Bancaria.(BL) **794**
Panorama Farmaceutico. (IT) **3737**
Panorama Harinero. (SP ISSN 0210-5535) **208**
Panorama Magazine/Ta Ch'eng. (HK) **2878**
Panorama Medico. (MX) **3139**
Panorama Minero. (SP) **3493**
Panorama Moda & Abbigliamento. (IT) **1293**
Panorama of Czech Fine Arts. (CS) **340**
Panorama of Czech Literature. (CS) **2946**, 3000
Panorama of Events (Haliyyat). (LE) **2878**
Panorama Olimpico see Olimpiiskaya Panorama **4482**
Panorama Olympique see Olimpiiskaya Panorama **4482**
Panorama Plastico. (MX) **3864**, 4292
Panorama Polnocy. (PL ISSN 0031-0964) **2214**

Panorama Polska (Nasza Ojczyzna). (PL ISSN 0137-2955) **2214**
Panorama Tierce. (FR) **4536**
Panorama Veterinario. (SP ISSN 0210-1017) **4814**
†Panoramas Bibliograficos de Espana. (SP) **5255**
Panpere. (FR ISSN 0031-0972) **4286**
Panstwo i Prawo. (PL ISSN 0031-0980) **2665, 3913**
Panstwowa Wyzsza Szkola Muzyczna. Prace Specjalne see Akademia Muzyczna. Prace Specjalne **3537**
Panstwowa Wyzsza Szkola Muzyczna. Skrypty see Akademia Muzyczna. Skrypty **3537**
Panstwowa Wyzsza Szkola Muzyczna. Sprawozdania see Akademia Muzyczna. Sprawozdania **3537**
Panstwowa Wyzsza Szkola Muzyczna. Wydawnictwa Okolicznosciowe see Akademia Muzyczna. Wydawnictwa Okolicznosciowe **3537**
Panstwowy Instytut Geologiczny. Prace.(PL ISSN 0208-645X) **1577, 3660**
Panstwowy Zaklad Higieny. Roczniki. (PL ISSN 0035-7715) **3807**
Panta. (GW) **3139**
Panta-Rhei. (IO) **2665**
Pantagruel. (IT) **3913**
Pantera International News. (US ISSN 0887-9613) **4699**
Pantheon. (GR) **2196**
Panther see Advocate (Johnstown) **1302**
Pantograph. (NZ) **4712**
Pantograph of Postal Stationery. (US) **3755**
Panurge. (UK ISSN 0951-4546) **2946, 2878, 4134**
Panzerfaust and Campaign see Campaign **2434**
†Pap Talk. (US) **5255**
Papa Joe's Kunst und Bierblatt. (GW) **2190**
Papeis Avulsos de Zoologia. (BL ISSN 0031-1049) **590**
Papel. (BL ISSN 0031-1057) **3664**
Papel Impreso. (CR ISSN 0048-2854) **2946**
Papeles de Economia Espanola. (SP ISSN 0210-9107) **878**
The Paper. (CN) **1320**
Paper. (US) **1320**
Paper. (UK ISSN 0306-8234) **3664**
Paper Age. (US ISSN 0031-1081) **3664**
†Paper Air. (US ISSN 0890-4359) **5255**
Paper and Allied Products Industries see Canada. Statistics Canada. Paper and Allied Products Industries **3667**
Paper and Board Abstracts. (UK ISSN 0307-0778) **3668, 19**
Paper and Packaging Analyst. (UK) **3651**
Paper and Packaging Bulletin see Paper and Packaging Analyst **3651**
Paper and Paper Manufacturing. see Zhi he Zaozhi **3667**
Paper & Pulp Statistical Monthly. see Kami Parupu Tokei Geppo **3663**
Paper and Timber. see Paperi ja Puu **3664**
Paper Asia. (SI) **3664**
Paper Bag. (US) **2947**
Paper Book. (US ISSN 0011-8060) **2665**
Paper Clip. (NZ) **2587**
Paper Collector's Marketplace. (US ISSN 0741-4927) **259, 2440**
†Paper Curtain. (US) **5255**
▼Paper Distribution Data Source. (US) **3668**
Paper European Data Book. (UK ISSN 0950-4478) **3664**
Paper Facts and Figures. (UK ISSN 0031-112X) **3664**
Paper, Film and Foil Converter. (US ISSN 0031-1138) **3651, 3664, 3864**
Paper Industry & Printing Abstracts. see Papiripari es Nyomdaipari Szakirodalmi Tajekoztato **3668**
Paper Industry Equipment see Paper Industry Magazine **3664**
Paper Industry Magazine. (US) **3664**

Paper Industry Management Association Magazine see P I M A Magazine **3663**
Paper Industry Technical Association. Fundamental Research International Symposia. (UK) **3664**
Paper Manufacturing in Foreign Countries. see Guowai Zaozhi **3663**
Paper Merchant Performance. (US) **3664**
Paper Merchant Sales Report. (US) **3664**
Paper News. (US) **2878**
Paper, Printing & Packaging Industries Research Association Annual Review of Research & Services see P I R A Annual Review of Research & Services **3664**
Paper Radio. (US) **3000**
▼Paper Recycler. (US) **3664**
Paper Review of the Year. (UK ISSN 0302-4180) **3664**
Paper Sales. (US ISSN 0031-1170) **3664**
Paper Sales Convention News. (US) **3664, 684**
Paper Southern Africa. (SA ISSN 0254-3494) **3664**
▼Paper Stock Report. (US) **3664**
Paper Technology. (UK) **3664**
Paper Technology and Industry see Paper Technology **3664**
Paper Toadstool. (US) **3000**
†Paper Trade Journal. (US ISSN 0031-1197) **5255**
Paper Tree Letter. (US) **2116, 3664**
Paper Year Book. (US) **1150, 3664**
Paperback Inferno. (UK ISSN 0260-0595) **3013, 2947, 4134**
Paperback Parade. (US) **4134, 2986, 3013**
Paperback Previews. (US) **2947, 3013**
†Paperback Quarterly. (US) **5255**
Paperboard Packaging. (US ISSN 0031-1227) **3651**
Paperbound Books in Print. (US ISSN 0031-1235) **409**
Paperi ja Puu/Paper and Timber. (FI ISSN 0031-1243) **3664, 2116**
Papermakers' and Merchants' Directory of All Nations see Phillips' International Paper Directory (Paper) **3665**
Paperprintpack India. (II ISSN 0048-2862) **3664, 3651**
Papers and Recordings in Education. (US) **1757**
Papers and Reports on Child Language Development. (US) **2833, 1242**
Papers and Studies in Contrastive Linguistics. (PL ISSN 0137-2459) **2833**
Papers: Explorations into Children's Literature. (AT ISSN 1034-9243) **2947, 1262**
Papers in Anthropology (Springfield) see Illinois. State Museum. Research Series. Papers in Anthropology **241**
Papers in Australian Linguistics. (AT ISSN 0078-9062) **2833**
†Papers in Borneo Linguistics. (AT ISSN 0078-9070) **5255**
Papers in Comparative Studies. (US ISSN 0736-9123) **2947**
Papers in Japanese Linguistics. (JA) **2833, 1757**
†Papers in Linguistics of Melanesia. (AT ISSN 0078-9127) **5255**
Papers in Mediaeval Studies. (CN ISSN 0228-8605) **2380**
Papers in Meteorology and Geophysics. (JA ISSN 0031-126X) **3440, 1592**
†Papers in New Guinea Linguistics. (AT ISSN 0078-9135) **5255**
†Papers in Philippine Linguistics. (AT ISSN 0078-9143) **5255**
Papers in Pidgin and Creole Linguistics.(AT ISSN 0811-0026) **2833**
Papers in Public Administration. (US ISSN 0078-9151) **4069**
†Papers in Public Administration (Ann Arbor). (US ISSN 0078-916X) **5255**
Papers in Regional Science. (US ISSN 1056-8190) **4382**

†Papers in Slavonic Linguistics. (UK ISSN 0263-5798) **5255**
Papers in Social Sciences. (CH) **4382**
†Papers in Sociology. (IS) **5256**
Papers in South East Asian Linguistics. (AT ISSN 0078-9178) **2833**
Papers in Text Linguistics. see Papiere zur Textlinguistik **2833**
Papers in the Administration of Development. (UK ISSN 0268-4020) **934**
Papers of Robert Morris, 1781-1784. (US) **2418**
Papers of Woodrow Wilson. (US ISSN 0031-1286) **420, 2319**
†Papers on European and Mediterranean Societies. (NE ISSN 0317-8382) **5256**
Papers on Far Eastern History. (AT ISSN 0048-2870) **2341, 3642**
Papers on Language and Literature. (US ISSN 0031-1294) **2947**
Papers on the History of Bourke. (AT ISSN 0085-4670) **2345**
Paperworker. (US ISSN 0363-6437) **2588, 3664**
▼Paperworld. (US) **3664**
Papeterie. (FR ISSN 0031-1308) **3664**
Papeterist/Papetier/Cartolaio. (SZ ISSN 0031-1316) **3664, 1061**
Papetier. (CN ISSN 0048-2889) **3664**
Papetier. see Papeterist **3664**
Papetier see Script **3666**
Papetier de France. (FR ISSN 0031-1324) **1061**
Papetier Libraire. (FR ISSN 0031-1332) **1061**
▼Papetieres du Quebec. (CN ISSN 0847-2645) **3664**
Das Papier. (GW ISSN 0031-1340) **3664**
Papier aus Oesterreich. (AU) **3665**
Papier Carton et Cellulose. (FR ISSN 0031-1367) **3665**
Papier, Carton et Cellulose. Annuaire. (FR) **3665**
Papier, Carton et Cellulose. Annuaire Financier. (FR) **3665**
Papier, Carton et Cellulose. Catalogue des Materiels et Equipements. (FR) **3665**
Papier, Carton et Cellulose. Guide du Papier. (FR) **3665, 1049**
Papier- und Buchgewerbe-rundschau see Papier und Druck **3665**
Papier und Druck. (AU ISSN 0259-7454) **3665**
Papier und Druck. (GW ISSN 0031-1375) **3665, 4003**
Papier und Kunststoff Verarbeiter. (GW ISSN 0048-2897) **3665**
Papier Verarbeiter see Papier und Kunststoff Verarbeiter **3665**
Papiere zur Textlinguistik/Papers in Text Linguistics. (GW ISSN 0341-3195) **2833**
Papierhandel. see Script **3666**
Papierhandelsfachblatt see P F **3663**
Der Papiermacher. (GW ISSN 0031-1405) **3665**
Papiershandels-Fachblatt see Boss - Oesterreich **5152**
Papierwaren, Buerobedarf, Schreibwaren Aktuell see P B S Aktuell **3663**
▼Papillomavirus Report. (UK ISSN 0957-4190) **3180, 467**
Papir a Celuloza. (CS ISSN 0031-1421) **3665**
Papirhandleren. (DK ISSN 0031-143X) **1061**
Papirhandleren. (NO) **3665**
Papirindustriens Sentralforbund. Annual Review see Norwegian Pulp and Paper Association. Annual Review **3663**
Papiripar. (HU ISSN 0031-1448) **3665**
Papiripari es Nyomdaipari Szakirodalmi Tajekoztato/Paper Industry & Printing Abstracts. (HU ISSN 0231-0740) **3668, 19, 2116, 3665**
Papiro. (DR) **2778**
Papper & Kontor Data. (SW) **1061**
Papper och Kontor see Papper & Kontor Data **1061**

Pappershandlaren see Papper & Kontor Data **1061**
Pappus. (CN ISSN 0710-0469) **2136**
Papua and New Guinea Education Gazette. (PP ISSN 0048-2919) **1653**
Papua and New Guinea Law Reports. (AT ISSN 0085-4689) **2665**
Papua New Guinea. Bureau of Statistics. Consolidated National Economic Accounts see Papua New Guinea. National Statistical Office. Gross Domestic Product and Expenditure **733**
Papua New Guinea. Bureau of Statistics. Gross Domestic Product and Domestic Factor Incomes by Kind of Economic Activity see Papua New Guinea. National Statistical Office. Gross Domestic Product and Expenditure **733**
Papua New Guinea. Bureau of Statistics. Gross Domestic Product at Constant Prices see Papua New Guinea. National Statistical Office. Gross Domestic Product and Expenditure **733**
Papua New Guinea. Bureau of Statistics. Industrial Accidents see Papua New Guinea. Department of Labour and Employment. Worker's Compensation Claims **2547**
Papua New Guinea. Bureau of Statistics. Statistical Bulletin: Survey of Retail Sales and Selected Services see Papua New Guinea. National Statistical Office. Statistical Bulletin: Census of Retail Sales and Selected Services **734**
Papua New Guinea. Department of Labour and Employment. Worker's Compensation Claims. (PP) **2547**
Papua New Guinea. National Statistical Office. Abstract of Statistics. (PP ISSN 0310-5377) **4582, 19**
Papua New Guinea. National Statistical Office. Building Statistics. (PP ISSN 0479-4826) **638**
Papua New Guinea. National Statistical Office. Census of Employment. (PP) **733, 991, 4582**
Papua New Guinea. National Statistical Office. Consumer Price Index. (PP ISSN 1017-6500) **4582, 19**
Papua New Guinea. National Statistical Office. Domestic Factor Incomes, by Region and Province. (PP ISSN 1017-6403) **733, 4582**
Papua New Guinea. National Statistical Office. Economic Indicators. (PP) **733, 4582**
Papua New Guinea. National Statistical Office. Export Price Indexes. (PP ISSN 1017-6527) **733, 919**
Papua New Guinea. National Statistical Office. Government Finance Statistics.(PP ISSN 1017-6411) **733, 4582**
Papua New Guinea. National Statistical Office. Gross Domestic Product and Expenditure. (PP ISSN 1017-639X) **733, 4582**
Papua New Guinea. National Statistical Office. Household Expenditure Survey. Preliminary Bulletin. (PP) **2450**
Papua New Guinea. National Statistical Office. Import Price Indexes. (PP ISSN 1017-6543) **733, 919, 4582**
Papua New Guinea. National Statistical Office. International Trade - Exports. (PP ISSN 1017-6519) **733, 919, 4582**
Papua New Guinea. National Statistical Office. International Trade - Imports. (PP ISSN 1017-6535) **733, 919, 4582**
Papua New Guinea. National Statistical Office. Production Statistics. (PP ISSN 1017-6497) **733, 1082, 4582**
Papua New Guinea. National Statistical Office. Rural Industries. (PP ISSN 0078-7701) **734**
Papua New Guinea. National Statistical Office. Rural Industries. Agriculture Largeholdings (Preliminary). (PP) **734**

Papua New Guinea. National Statistical Office. Rural Industries. Preliminary Statement see Papua New Guinea. National Statistical Office. Rural Industries. Agriculture Largeholdings (Preliminary) **734**

Papua New Guinea. National Statistical Office. Secondary Industries (Factories and Works). Preliminary Statement see Papua New Guinea. National Statistical Office. Secondary Industries (Preliminary Statement) **734**

Papua New Guinea. National Statistical Office. Secondary Industries (Preliminary Statement). (PP) **734**

Papua New Guinea. National Statistical Office. Secondary Industries. (PP ISSN 0078-933X) **734**

Papua New Guinea. National Statistical Office. Statistical Bulletin: Capital Expenditure by Private Businesses. (PP ISSN 0078-9259) **734**

Papua New Guinea. National Statistical Office. Statistical Bulletin: Census of Retail Sales and Selected Services. (PP ISSN 1017-6470) **734, 4583**

Papua New Guinea. National Statistical Office. Statistical Bulletin: Registered Motor Vehicles. (PP) **4666**

†Papua New Guinea. National Statistical Office. Summary of Statistics. (PP) **5256**

Papua New Guinea. National Statistical Office. Taxation Statistics. Preliminary Bulletin. (PP ISSN 0078-9372) **734**

Papua New Guinea. National Statistical Office. Worker's Compensation Claims see Papua New Guinea. Department of Labour and Employment. Worker's Compensation Claims **2547**

Papua New Guinea. Public Service Board. Report see Papua New Guinea. Public Service Commission. Report **4069**

Papua New Guinea. Public Service Commission. Report. (PP) **4069**

Papua New Guinea Agricultural Journal see Papua New Guinea Journal of Agriculture, Forestry and Fisheries **113**

Papua New Guinea Business see P N G Business **2213**

Papua New Guinea Companies Legislation. (AT) **2711**

Papua New Guinea Handbook. (AT) **4782**

Papua New Guinea Income Tax Legislation. (AT) **1103**

Papua New Guinea Institute of Medical Research. Monograph Series. (PP ISSN 0256-2901) **3139**

Papua New Guinea International Arrivals and Departures. (PP ISSN 1017-6551) **3994, 4583**

Papua New Guinea International Migration see Papua New Guinea International Arrivals and Departures **3994**

Papua New Guinea Journal of Agriculture, Forestry and Fisheries. (PP) **113, 2047**

Papua New Guinea Journal of Education. (PP ISSN 0031-1472) **1653**

Papua New Guinea Labour Law. (AT) **2665**

Papua New Guinea Library Association Nius see P N G L A Nius **2778**

Papua New Guinea Medical Journal. (PP ISSN 0031-1480) **3139**

Papua New Guinea National Bibliography. (PP ISSN 0252-8347) **409, 19, 247, 4134**

†Papua New Guinea University of Technology. Mathematics Education Centre. Reports. (PP) **5256**

Papua New Guinea University of Technology. Reporter. (PP) **1320, 4606**

Papua New Guinea Writing see Bikmaus **2899**

Papurau Gwaith leithyddol Cymraeg Caerdydd. see Cardiff Working Papers in Welsh Linguistics **2808**

Papyri aus den Staatlichen Museen zu Berlin. (GW ISSN 0232-3257) **3643**

Papyrologica Bruxellensia. (BE ISSN 0078-9402) **281**

Papyrologica Coloniensia. (GW ISSN 0078-9410) **2380**

Papyrologica Florentina. (IT) **2319**

Papyrologica Lugduno-Batava. (NE ISSN 0169-9652) **2947**

Papyrologische Texte und Abhandlungen. (GW) **2319**

Papyrus. (CN) **1300**

†Par Excellence. (US) **5256**

Par Golf. (JA) **4509**

Para Ti. (AG) **4850**

Para Usted desde Checoslovaquia see For You from Czechoslovakia **815**

Parabas. (II ISSN 0031-1553) **2878**

Parabola. (US ISSN 0362-1596) **2057, 4194**

Paraboles. (FR ISSN 0031-1561) **4272**

Parachute (Montreal). (CN ISSN 0318-7020) **340**

Parachutist. (US ISSN 0031-1588) **4483, 60**

Paraclete. (US ISSN 0190-4639) **4246**

Paracletic Counselor see Professional Christian Counselor **4039**

Parade. (UK ISSN 0031-160X) **2195**

Parade. (II) **2201**

Parade and Foto-Action see Parade Magazine **2240**

Parade Magazine. (RH) **2240**

Parades & Pageantry. (CN) **3573**

Paradigm Shift. (US) **1399**

Paradise. (PP) **4782**

▼Paradox Developer's Journal. (US) **1410**

Paradox User's Journal. (US ISSN 0889-2911) **1410**

▼The Paradoxist Movement. (US ISSN 1055-761X) **2947**

Parag. (II ISSN 0031-1642) **1262**

Paragone. (IT ISSN 0031-1650) **2947, 340**

Paragraph. (CN ISSN 0838-9624) **2178**

Paragraph. (UK ISSN 0264-8334) **2947**

Paragraph. (US ISSN 0891-7248) **2947**

Paragraphic. (CN ISSN 0048-2935) **1739, 3349**

Paraguay. (PY ISSN 0257-7070) **409**

Paraguay. Centro de Promocion de las Exportaciones. Directorio de Exportadores - Export Directory. (PY) **919**

Paraguay. Direccion General de Estadistica y Censos. Boletin Estadistico. (PY ISSN 0031-1677) **4583**

Paraguay. Ministerio de Industria y Comercio. Division de Registro y Estadistica Industrial. Encuesta Industrial. (PY ISSN 0085-4743) **734**

Paraguay. Ministry of Industry and Trade. Investment Guide. (PY) **959**

Paraguay Noticias. (PY) **3945**

Paralegal. (US ISSN 0739-3601) **2665**

Paralegal School Directory. (US) **2665, 1695**

Paralegal Update. (US) **2665**

Parallel Computing. (NE ISSN 0167-8191) **1438**

▼Parallel Processing Letters. (SI ISSN 0129-6264) **1399**

Parallelogram International. (UK ISSN 0953-7252) **1455, 1431, 1479**

Parallelogramme. (CN) **340**

Paralogue. (FR ISSN 0078-9429) **2947**

Paramagnitnyi Rezonans. (RU) **3826**

Parameters (Carlisle Barracks). (US ISSN 0031-1723) **3468, 3913**

Parameters (Portland). (US) **2878**

Parametric World. (US) **754, 3050**

Parametro. (IT ISSN 0031-1731) **304, 2493**

Paramillo. (VE ISSN 0798-278X) **2512**

Parana, Brazil. Secretaria de Estado para os Negocios da Fazenda. (BL) **734**

Parana em Paginas. (BL ISSN 0031-174X) **879**

Parana Informacoes see Information on Parana **869**

Parapara see Parapara Revista de Literatura Infantil **4134**

Parapara see Parapara Boletin Informativo **4134**

Parapara see Parapara Seleccion de Libros para Ninos y Jovenes **4134**

Parapara Boletin Informativo. (VE) **4134, 1262**

Parapara Revista de Literatura Infantil. (VE) **4134, 1262**

Parapara Seleccion de Libros para Ninos y Jovenes. (VE) **4134, 1248**

Parapet. (CN ISSN 0384-0417) **3468**

Parapharmex. (FR) **3737, 3249**

Paraphernalia. (AT) **2778**

Paraplegia News. (US ISSN 0031-1766) **1739, 3349**

Paraplegiker. (GW ISSN 0723-5070) **3139**

Parapsychological Journal of South Africa. (SA) **3670**

Parapsychological Monographs. (US ISSN 0078-9437) **3670**

Parapsychology Abstracts International see Exceptional Human Experience **3672**

Parapsychology Foundation. Newsletter see Parapsychology Review **5256**

Parapsychology Foundation. Proceedings of International Conferences. (US) **3670**

Parapsychology-Psychic Science Journal see Parapsychology-Psychic Science Reports **3670**

Parapsychology-Psychic Science Reports. (US) **3670**

†Parapsychology Review. (US ISSN 0031-1804) **5256**

Parascope. (US ISSN 0738-1247) **2665**

Parasession: Non-Declarative Sentences see Chicago Linguistic Society. Papers from the Regional Meetings **2809**

Parasite Immunology. (UK ISSN 0141-9838) **3222, 451, 3188**

Parasitica. (BE ISSN 0031-1812) **451**

Parasitologia al Dia. (CL ISSN 0716-0720) **556**

Parasitology. see Parazitologiya **3222**

Parasitology (Cambridge). (UK ISSN 0031-1820) **3222**

▼Parasitology (Sheffield). (UK ISSN 0964-7570) **590**

Parasitology Research. (GW ISSN 0932-0113) **3222, 556**

Parasitology Today. (UK ISSN 0169-4758) **3139, 451, 4814**

Paraskino/Behind the Scenes. (CY) **2184**

Parassitologia. (IT ISSN 0048-2951) **3222**

†Parathyroid Hormones. (UK ISSN 0261-4847) **5256**

Paratus. (SA ISSN 0031-1839) **3468**

Parazitologiya/Parasitology. (RU ISSN 0031-1847) **3222, 556**

Parazity, Parazitozy ta Shliakhyikh Likvidatsii. (KR) **537**

Parc National de La Vanoise. Travaux Scientifiques. (FR ISSN 0180-961X) **4333**

Parc Naturel Regional et des Reserves Naturelles de Corse. Travaux Scientifiques. (FR ISSN 0246-1579) **1965**

Le Parchemin. (BE) **2161**

Le Parchemin. Recueil Genealogique et Heraldique. (BE) **2161**

Parcs see Parks **1495**

Parcs Industriels Municipaux. (CN ISSN 0831-1161) **684**

Pardes. (FR ISSN 0295-5652) **4225, 2319**

Pardon. (GW ISSN 0031-1855) **2878**

Parent and Citizen. (AT ISSN 0726-7126) **1654**

Parent and Preschooler Newsletter. (US ISSN 0887-0365) **1242**

†Parent Care. (US ISSN 0888-2843) **5256**

Parent Compound Handbook see Ring Systems Handbook **1223**

Parent Connection see Pierce County Parent **1242**

Parent Cooperative Preschools International. Directory. (US) **1654**

Parent News. (US) **2284**

Parent - Teacher see Home and School **1637**

Parent - to - Parent. (CN) **1242**

Parenteral Drug Association. Journal see Journal of Parenteral Science and Technology **3732**

Parenteral Drug Association. Technical Information Bulletin. (US) **3737**

Parenteral Drug Association. Technical Methods Bulletin. (US) **3737**

Parenteral Drug Association. Technical Reports. (US) **3737**

Parenteral Drug Association, Inc. Letter see P D A Letter **3737**

Parentguide News. (US ISSN 0896-1468) **1242**

Parenting. (US ISSN 0890-247X) **1242, 2449**

Parenting Magazine of Orange County. (US) **1242, 2449, 4850**

Parenting Studies. (US ISSN 0737-5123) **4037, 4444**

Parents. (US ISSN 0195-0967) **1242, 2449**

Parents. (FR ISSN 0553-2159) **1242**

Parents. (UK) **1242**

Parents and Children Magazine see Australia's Parents **1232**

Parents and Friends of Lesbian and Gays Newsletter. (US) **2456**

Parents and Kids Directory. (US) **1242**

Parents Baby Care. (US) **1242**

Parents' Choice. (US) **1242**

Parents d'Eleves. (FR) **1654**

Parents' Guide to Accredited Camps see Guide to Accredited Camps (Year) **4547**

▼Parent's Guide to Children's Video. (US) **1386, 1262**

†Parents' Guide to Highly-Rated Educational Software. (US) **5256**

Parent's Health Adviser. (US) **3139, 1242**

Parents Monthly. see Fumu Bidu **1237**

Parents' Press. (US) **1242**

Parents Shopping Guide. (AT ISSN 1030-1968) **1507**

Parents Voice see Mencap News **2284**

Parerga. (SP) **2512**

Parergon. (AT ISSN 0313-6221) **2947, 2319**

Parfuemerie Aktuell. (GW) **376**

Parfuemerie und Kosmetik. (GW ISSN 0031-1952) **376**

Parfums-Beaute. (FR) **376**

Parfums, Cosmetiques, Aromes. (FR) **376**

Parfyme og Portefoelje. (NO) **376, 2737**

Parinfo. (US) **3670**

Paris (Year). (US) **4782**

Paris-Anglophone. (FR) **1150**

Paris-Chamonix. (FR) **4553**

Paris - Cote d'Azur. (FR) **2187**

Paris - Cote d'Azur International. (FR) **2187**

Paris le Journal. (FR ISSN 1153-026X) **627**

Paris Match. (FR ISSN 0031-2029) **2187**

Paris Match (Switzerland). (SZ) **2219**

Paris Post-Intelligencer. (US ISSN 0893-3669) **2232**

Paris Projet. (FR) **2493, 304**

Paris Review. (US ISSN 0031-2037) **2947**

Paris-Sud. (FR ISSN 0031-2045) **2187**

Paris Voices. (FR ISSN 0181-5210) **2947**

Pariscop see Une Semaine de Paris-Pariscope **4795**

†Pariser Kurier. (FR ISSN 0031-2053) **5256**

Parish and Community Libraries News. (US) **2778**

Parish and Lending Library News see Parish and Community Libraries News **2778**

Parish Communication. (US ISSN 0279-7828) **4272**, 4246
Parish Coordinator of Religious Education *see* Parish Coordinators - Directors of Religious Education **1654**
Parish Coordinators - Directors of Religious Education. (US) **1654**, 4272
Parish Councils Review *see* Local Council Review **4090**
Parish Family Digest. (US) **4272**
Parish Teacher. (US ISSN 0738-7962) **4246**
Parish Visitor. (US) **4272**
Parishioner. (SA ISSN 0031-2088) **4246**
Pariyal Kalyan. (II ISSN 0031-2096) **4416**, 1242
Park. (UK ISSN 0031-210X) **2947**
Park Administration. (SA ISSN 0031-2118) **1495**
Park & Grounds Management. (US ISSN 1057-204X) **1495**
Park and Recreation Opportunities Job Bulletin. (US) **3630**, 1495
Park Avenue Social Review. (US) **2232**
Park East. (US ISSN 0031-2126) **2232**
Park Maintenance and Grounds Management *see* Park & Grounds Management **1495**
Park News *see* Borealis **1484**
Park-Nicollet Medical Foundation Bulletin. (US) **3139**
Park Watch. (AT) **1495**, 1654, 1965
Park World. (UK) **1049**
Parke Society News Letter. (US ISSN 0148-3994) **2161**
Parker Directory of Attorneys *see* Parker Directory of California Attorneys **2665**
Parker Directory of California Attorneys.(US ISSN 0196-6138) **2665**
Parker Papers. (US ISSN 0898-5456) **2161**
Parkers Car Price Guide. (UK) **4699**
Parkett. (SZ ISSN 0256-0917) **340**
Parkett Magazin. (GW ISSN 0934-9014) **2561**
Parkh. (II) **2833**, 2947
Parking. (US ISSN 0031-2193) **4699**
Parking Professional. (US) **4699**
Parking Security Report. (US ISSN 1052-9985) **1527**
▼Parking Technology. (US) **4654**, 627, 1024
Parking World *see* Parking **4699**
Parkinson Report. (US) **3349**
Parks. (US ISSN 0363-0617) **1495**
▼Parks. (UK ISSN 0960-233X) **1965**
Parks and Grounds. (SA) **2136**, 1495
Parks and Grounds Buyer's Guide. (SA) **2136**
Parks and Recreation. (US ISSN 0031-2215) **1495**, 4069, 4553
Parks and Sports Grounds *see* Parks, Golf Courses and Sports Grounds **4553**
Parks, Golf Courses and Sports Grounds. (UK) **4553**, 304, 627
Das Parlament. (GW ISSN 0031-2258) **3913**
Parlaments- und Parteistiftungsarchivare Berichten. (GW ISSN 0933-6958) **3913**
Parlanghe. (FR ISSN 1151-941X) **2947**, 2833, 3000
Parlements et Francophonie. (FR ISSN 0223-5765) **2878**
Parlements, Etats & Representation. *see* Parliaments, Estates & Representation **2319**
Parley Papers. (UK ISSN 0142-9388) **2161**
PARlez *see* P A R Analysis **3913**
Parliament House Book. (UK ISSN 0079-0095) **2665**
Parliamentarian. (UK ISSN 0031-2282) **3913**
Parliamentary Affairs. (UK ISSN 0031-2290) **3913**

Parliamentary and Common Market News Bulletin. (UK) **879**
Parliamentary Bulletin for Local Government Executives. (UK) **4069**
Parliamentary Handbook of the Commonwealth of Australia. (AT) **3913**
Parliamentary History. (UK ISSN 0264-2824) **2319**
Parliamentary Housing News. (UK) **2665**, 2493
Parliamentary Journal. (US ISSN 0048-2994) **3913**, 1341
Parliamentary News *see* Parliamentary Housing News **2665**
Parliamentary Studies *see* Democratic World **3890**
Parliamentary Year Book. (UK) **4070**, 4081
Parliaments, Estates & Representation/ Parlements, Etats & Representation. (UK ISSN 0260-6755) **2319**
Parliamo di Golf. (IT) **4509**
Parlons Affaires au Saguenay - Lac-St-Jean. (CN) **684**
Parlons Affairs en Beauce. (CN) **684**
▼Parlons Plein Air Chasse & Peche. (CN) **4553**
Parma nell'Arte. (IT) **2380**, 281
Parma per l'Arte *see* Parma nell'Arte **2380**
Parma Realta *see* Dal Comune-Notizie **1946**
Parmamedica. (IT ISSN 0031-2312) **3139**
Parmarth. (II) **3775**, 4194
Parmigiano-Reggiano. (IT) **203**
Parnasso. (FI ISSN 0031-2320) **2947**
Parnassos. (GR ISSN 0048-301X) **2512**, 2380, 2833
Parnassus Literary Journal. (US ISSN 0748-8785) **3000**
Parnassus: Poetry in Review. (US ISSN 0048-3028) **3000**
Parodontologia e Stomatologia Nuova. (IT) **3240**
Parodontologie. (GW) **3240**
Paroi Anterielle. (FR) **3211**
Paroisses et Communes de France. (FR) **3913**
Parola e il Libro. (IT ISSN 0031-2371) **2779**, 4134
Parole de l'Orient. (LE) **4194**
Parole di Vita. (IT ISSN 0031-2398) **4272**
Parole in the United States *see* Probation and Parole in the United States **1521**
Parole Ukrainienne. (FR) **2019**
Paroles et Musique. (FR ISSN 0247-0357) **3573**
Parques *see* Parks **1495**
Parramatta Cityscope. (AT) **4160**
Parrocchia. (IT ISSN 0031-2428) **4272**
Parrot Jungle and Gardens *see* P J G **566**
Parrott Talk. (US ISSN 0093-9811) **2161**
Parsiana. (II ISSN 0048-3036) **4217**
Parson and Parish. (UK ISSN 0031-2436) **4194**
Part B News. (US) **2539**, 3139
Part-Time Professional. (US) **3630**
Parta *see* Amerikan Uutiset **1991**
Partelet. (CS) **2878**
The Parthenon. (US) **1320**
Participation. (FR ISSN 0338-4284) **991**
Participation. (NO ISSN 0709-6941) **3914**
Particle Accelerator Conference *see* I E E E Particle Accelerator Conference. Proceedings **1895**
Particle Accelerators. (US ISSN 0031-2460) **3849**
Particle & Particle Systems Characterization. (GW ISSN 0934-0866) **3826**
Particle Characterization *see* Particle & Particle Systems Characterization **3826**
▼Particle World. (US ISSN 1043-6790) **3826**
Particulate Information *see* Current Awareness in Particle Technology **1842**

Particulate Science and Technology. (US ISSN 0272-6351) **1857**, 1937, 3417, 3737
Partido Socialista Popular. Congreso. (Actas). (SP) **3914**
Partido Socialista Revolucionario. Informes. (PE) **3914**
Partiinaya Zhizn' (RU ISSN 0031-2509) **3914**
Parting Gifts. (US ISSN 1043-3325) **3000**
Partio. (FI ISSN 0556-3488) **1262**
Partiojohtaja/Scoutledaren. (FI ISSN 0085-4794) **1242**
Partisan Review. (US ISSN 0031-2525) **2879**
Partner Report *see* D V R Report **4718**
Partners. (UK ISSN 0308-745X) **3222**
Partners. (US ISSN 0031-2568) **3968**
Partners in Education. (US ISSN 1041-1542) **1654**
Partners in Learning. (UK ISSN 0079-0117) **4246**
Partners in Publishing College "H E L P S" Newsletter *see* P I P College "H E L P S" Newsletter **1739**
Partners in Transition: Hungary *see* O E C D. Economic Surveys: Hungary **877**
Partners-in-Travel. (US) **4782**
Partners Newsletter for Gay & Lesbian Couples. (US) **2456**
Partner's Report, a Monthly Brief for Law Firm Owners. (US ISSN 0892-4805) **2711**
Partner's Report, The Monthly Update for CPA Firm Owners. (US ISSN 1043-7428) **754**
Partnerschaft mit der Arabischen Welt. (GW) **3968**, 934
Partnership *see* Marriage Partnership **3067**
Partnership and S Corporation Coordinator. (US) **959**, 1103
Partnership Christian Brethren Review. (UK) **4246**
Partnership Management. (UK ISSN 0263-7928) **794**, 1103
Partnership News. (US) **4416**, 4194
Partnership Tax Reporter. (US) **1103**
Partnership Taxation, 3-E. (US) **1103**
Partnerships in Education Journal. (US ISSN 1042-6590) **1654**, 684
Parts. (IT ISSN 1120-1789) **4699**
Parts & People. (US) **4699**
†Parttorteneti Kozlemenyek. (HU ISSN 0464-476X) **5256**
Party & Paper Retailer. (US ISSN 0899-6008) **3665**, 1049
Party Construction. *see* Dang Jian **3890**
Party Life. (II) **3914**
▼Party Source. (US) **2282**
PartyLine. (US) **36**
Pas-de-Calais. Commission Departemental des Monuments Historiques. Bulletin *see* Commission Departemental d'Histoire et d'Archeologie. Bulletin **269**
Pas Tant. (FR ISSN 0769-4679) **4037**
†Pasadena Journal of Business. (US ISSN 0743-6610) **5256**
Pascal International *see* Toolbox **1432**
†Pascal Newsletter. (US) **5256**
Paschim Banga. (II) **2201**
Paschim Bongal. (II) **2201**
Paseo del Rio Showboat *see* Reflexiones **821**
Pashosh. (IS ISSN 0334-3022) **1262**
Pashto *see* Pushto **2836**
Pashto Academy. Monthly Journal. (AF) **2947**, 3775
Pashtu Quarterly. (AF) **2833**, 2947
Pashupalan *see* Kheti **103**
Pasicrisie Belge. (BE ISSN 0031-2614) **2665**
Pasinomie. (BE ISSN 0031-2630) **2665**
†El Paso Magazine. (US) **5256**
Pasque Petals. (US ISSN 0031-2649) **3000**
Pasquin. (CN ISSN 0710-5185) **2161**
Pasquino. (US ISSN 0031-2657) **1320**

PASTORALIST 6543

Pass. (UK) **754**
Passage. (DK ISSN 0901-8883) **2947**
Passagen. (GW ISSN 0933-7253) **2947**, 340
Passages. (FR) **2019**, 2879, 4225
Passages North. (US ISSN 0278-0828) **2947**
Passaic County Dental Society Newsletter. (US) **3240**
Passaic Review. (US ISSN 0731-4663) **2879**
Passaic River Restoration Newsletter *see* Passaic River Review **1495**
Passaic River Review. (US) **1495**, 4827
†Passatempi Marvel. (IT) **5256**
Passauer Bistumsblatt. (GW ISSN 0031-2681) **4194**
Passauer Pegasus. (GW ISSN 0724-0708) **2947**
Passeggiate nel Lazio. (IT) **4782**
Passenger Pigeon. (US ISSN 0031-2703) **566**
Passenger Train Journal. (US ISSN 0160-6913) **4712**
Passenger Transport. (US ISSN 0364-345X) **4654**
Passenger Transport Year Book *see* Little Red Book, Classified to All Public Transport Fleet Owners and Operators and Vehicle Manufacturers **4652**
†Passerelle. (FR ISSN 0031-2711) **5256**
Passion Magazine. (CN ISSN 0835-4162) **4782**
Passionist Youth. *see* Gioventu Passionista **4179**
Passport. (US ISSN 0031-272X) **4782**
Passport. (JA) **4782**
Passport to Legal Understanding. (US ISSN 0737-7630) **2734**
Passport to World Band Radio. (US ISSN 0897-0157) **1358**
Password. (AT) **754**
Password. (GW ISSN 0930-3693) **1445**
Password. (US ISSN 0031-2738) **2418**
Past and Present *see* Family Historian **2150**
†Past & Present. (CN) **5256**
Past and Present: a Journal of Historical Studies. (UK ISSN 0031-2746) **2319**
Past, Present, and Future. (US ISSN 0895-0857) **2418**
▼Past Times: The Nostalgia Entertainment Newsletter. (US ISSN 1050-5504) **1378**, 3515, 3573
Pasta Journal. (US ISSN 8750-9393) **2079**
Paste-up. (US) **3755**
Pasticceria Internazionale. (IT ISSN 0392-4718) **2089**
Pastizales. (MX ISSN 0304-2502) **222**
Pastoral Andina. (PE) **4272**
Pastoral Care and Counseling Abstracts *see* Abstracts of Research in Pastoral Care and Counseling **4212**
Pastoral Care in Education. (UK ISSN 0264-3944) **1654**
Pastoral Life. (US ISSN 0031-2762) **4194**
Pastoral Misionera. (SP ISSN 0210-3559) **4194**
Pastoral Music. (US ISSN 0363-6569) **3573**
Pastoral Music Notebook. (US ISSN 0145-6636) **3573**
Pastoral Newsletter *see* New Covenant **4270**
Pastoral Popular *see* Vida Pastoral **4208**
Pastoral Psychology. (US ISSN 0031-2789) **4037**, 4194
Pastoral Renewal *see* Faith & Renewal **4177**
Pastoralblaetter. (GW ISSN 0031-2800) **4194**
Pastoralblatt. (GW) **4272**
Pastoralia. (CR) **4194**
Pastoralist and Grazier *see* Rural Update **225**

PASTORALTHEOLOGIE

Pastoraltheologie - Monatsschrift fuer Wissenschaft und Praxis in Kirche und Gesellschaft. (GW ISSN 0720-6259) **4194**
Pastos Tropicales. Boletin Informativo see Pasturas Tropicales **113**
Pastrycooks & Bakers News Monthly. (AT) **2079**
Pastrycooks' Review see Baking Industry Review **2062**
Pasturas Tropicales. (CK ISSN 1012-7410) **113**
Pasturas Tropicales. Boletin see Pasturas Tropicales **113**
Pasture Network for Eastern and Southern Africa Newsletter see P A N E S A Newsletter **222**
▼Pata Travel News Americas. (HK) **4782**
Pata Travel News Asia - Pacific. (HK) **4782**
▼Pata Travel News Europe. (HK) **4782**
Patalogo. (IT) **4636**
Pate Pioneers. (US ISSN 0887-1280) **2161**
Paten. (GW ISSN 0176-2982) **4444, 4416**
Patent Abridgements see Australian Official Journal of Patents **3672**
Patent Abstracts Supplement to the Australian Official Journal of Patents. (AT) **3680**
Patent Abstracts Supplement to the Australian Official Journal of Patents, Trade Marks and Designs see Patent Abstracts Supplement to the Australian Official Journal of Patents **3680**
Patent and Trade Mark Review. see Szabadalmi Kozlony es Vedjegyertesito **3678**
Patent and Trademark Institute of Canada. Annual Proceedings. (CN ISSN 0079-015X) **3677**
Patent and Trademark Institute of Canada. Bulletin see Canadian Intellectual Property Review **3673**
Patent and Trademark Institute of Canada Bulletin see P T I C Bulletin **3677**
Patent and Trademark Office Notices. (US) **3677**
Patent Cooperation Treaty Gazette see P C T Gazette **3680**
Patent Digest. (US) **3677, 1082**
Patent Journal Including Trademarks and Models. (SA ISSN 0031-286X) **3677**
Patent Law Handbook. (US ISSN 0192-8198) **3677**
Patent Law Review see Intellectual Property Law Review **3675**
Patent Licensing Gazette see World Technology **4613**
Patent Office Record (Canada)/Gazette du Bureau des Brevets. (CN ISSN 0008-4670) **3677**
Patent Office Technical Society. Journal.(II) **3677**
Patent Review of China. see Zhongguo Zhuanli Bao **3679**
Patent, Trademark & Copyright Journal see B N A's Patent, Trademark & Copyright Journal **3673**
Patent World. (UK ISSN 0950-2513) **3677**
Patentblatt. (GW ISSN 0031-2894) **3677**
Patentdirektoratet Orienterer. (DK ISSN 0904-275X) **3677**
Patentni Glasnik. (YU ISSN 0031-2908) **3677**
Patents Abstracts. (American Petroleum Institute) (US) **3706, 19**
Patents and Engineering see Patents and Licensing **3677**
Patents and Licensing. (JA ISSN 0388-7081) **3677**
Patents and the Federal Circuit. (US) **3677, 2665**
Patents and the Federal Circuit. Supplement. (US) **3677, 2665**
†Patentspiegel Metallbau. (GW) **5256**
Pater Newsletter. (UK ISSN 0264-8342) **2947**
Paterson's Licensing Acts. (UK ISSN 0269-3658) **2665**
Path see Crime & Society **2712**

Path of Truth. (SA ISSN 0031-2932) **4286**
Pathfinder see Traveller **4794**
†Pathfinder (Washington). (US) **5256**
†Pathfinders. Biennial Report. (US) **5256**
Pathobiology. (SZ ISSN 1015-2008) **3139, 526, 556**
†Pathobiology Annual. (US ISSN 0362-3025) **5256**
Der Pathologe. (GW ISSN 0172-8113) **3139**
Pathologia Veterinaria see Veterinary Pathology **4818**
Pathologica. (IT ISSN 0031-2983) **3139**
Pathological Physiology and Experimental Therapy. see Patologicheskaya Fiziologiya i Eksperimental'naya Terapiya **3140**
Pathologie see Berichte Pathologie **3166**
Pathologie Biologie. (FR ISSN 0031-3009) **3139, 451**
Pathology. (AT ISSN 0031-3025) **3139, 451**
Pathology. (US ISSN 1041-3480) **3139**
Pathology and Immunopathology Research see Pathobiology **3139**
Pathology and Practice see Pathology, Research and Practice **3140**
Pathology Annual. (US ISSN 0079-0184) **3139, 451**
Pathology Patterns. (US) **3139, 451**
Pathology, Research and Practice. (GW ISSN 0344-0338) **3140**
Pathukavalan. (CE) **4272**
Pathway to God. (II) **4194, 3775**
▼Pathways. (CN) **3807**
Pathways (Garden Grove). (US) **4246, 4272**
Pathways (Maynardville). (US ISSN 8755-4747) **2418**
Pathways (Takoma Park). (US) **4037**
Pathways (Watsonville). (US) **4215**
Pathways to Health. (US) **3775, 3807**
Pathways to Profitability. (US) **2554, 684**
Patient Accounts. (US) **754, 2468**
Patient Care. (US ISSN 0031-305X) **3140**
Patient Care Law. (US) **2665, 2468**
Patient Education and Counseling. (IE ISSN 0738-3991) **4109**
▼Patient Hospital Relations. (II) **2468**
Patient Management (Australia). (AT ISSN 0314-660X) **3140**
†Patient Pleasers! Dental Edition. (US ISSN 0882-6471) **5256**
†Patient Pleasers! Health Care Edition. (US ISSN 0882-6471) **5256**
Patient Update. (CN) **3140**
Patientenpost. (GW) **1262, 1538, 2468, 4416**
Patient's Digest. (US) **3807**
Patients' Rights in California see Patients' Rights Reporter **5256**
†Patients' Rights Reporter. (US) **5256**
Patissier Moderne. (FR) **2089**
Patma-Banasirakan Handes. (AI ISSN 0135-0536) **2380, 281**
Patna Journal of Medicine. (II ISSN 0031-3084) **3140**
Pato Donald. (BL) **1262**
Patologia. (MX) **451, 3140**
Patologia e Clinica Ostetrica e Ginecologica. (IT ISSN 0304-0313) **3295**
Patologia Polska. (PL ISSN 0031-3114) **3140, 451**
Patologicheskaya Fiziologiya i Eksperimental'naya Terapiya/ Pathological Physiology and Experimental Therapy. (RU ISSN 0031-2991) **3140, 451**
Patranu. (II ISSN 0031-3122) **2947**
Patre. (FR ISSN 0475-9141) **222**
Patria. (CU) **3914**
Patria Indipendente. (IT ISSN 0031-3130) **3946**
Patria y Pueblo. (AG) **3914**
Patriarchal Institute for Patristic Studies. Theological Studies. (GR) **4286**
Patricia Seybold's Network Monitor see Network Monitor **1438**

Patricia Seybold's Office Computing Report see Office Computing Report **1452**
Patrikapanjee. (II) **409**
Patrimonium see Bouw en Beheer **604**
Patriot. (US ISSN 0749-6761) **3000**
Patriote. (GO) **2879**
Patriote Guadeloupeen. (FR) **2879**
Patristic and Byzantine Review. (US ISSN 0737-738X) **2380, 4194**
Patristica et Mediaevalia. (AG ISSN 0325-2280) **2319**
Patristics. (US ISSN 0360-652X) **4194, 2833**
Patrol Log see A S W Log **42**
Patrologia Syriaca et Orientalis. (BE) **4272**
Patronat Francais see C N P R Revue des Entreprises **1073**
Patronato Municipal de la Vivienda de Barcelona. Memoria. (SP ISSN 0067-4168) **2493**
Patrones. (SP) **4850**
Patrys. (SA ISSN 0031-3181) **1262**
Patt. (GW) **4483**
Pattern Makers & Allied Crafts Journal. (US) **2588, 1287**
Pattern Makers' Journal see Pattern Makers & Allied Crafts Journal **2588**
Pattern Recognition. (US ISSN 0031-3203) **4333, 1833**
▼Pattern Recognition and Image Analysis. (US ISSN 1054-6618) **3050**
Pattern Recognition Letters. (NE ISSN 0167-8655) **1422**
Patterns see Stone Country **5283**
Patterns Galore. (UK ISSN 0957-381X) **3592**
Patterns of Prejudice. (UK ISSN 0031-322X) **4444, 3946**
▼Patterson People. (US ISSN 1057-3445) **2161**
Patterson Post. (US ISSN 0885-5749) **2161**
Patterson's American Education. (US ISSN 0079-0230) **1696**
Patterson's Beverage Journal. (US ISSN 0895-3872) **384**
Patterson's California Beverage Gazetteer see Patterson's Beverage Journal **384**
Patterson's Elementary Education. (US ISSN 1044-1417) **1696**
Patterson's Schools Classified. (US ISSN 0553-4054) **1696**
†Patuxent Business Digest. (US) **5256**
†Paukenslag. (NE ISSN 0031-3246) **5256**
Paul Anthony Brick Lectures. (US ISSN 0079-0249) **3775**
Paul Carus Lectures. (US ISSN 0079-0257) **3775**
▼Paul Edwards' Travel Confidential. (US) **4782**
Paul Raymond's Model Directory. (UK) **3399**
Paul Scherrer Institut Jahresbericht see P S I. Jahresbericht **1809**
Paula. (CL) **4850**
Paulo-Coutiana. (BL ISSN 0102-6887) **590**
Paul's Police Offences. (AT ISSN 0728-3210) **2665**
Paul's Record Magazine. (US ISSN 0360-2109) **3573, 4461**
Paunch. (US ISSN 0031-3262) **2879**
Pause. (UK) **3000**
Pavement Maintenance. (US) **1872, 4720**
Pavia Economica. (IT) **821**
Paving and Transportation Conference. Proceedings. (US) **1872**
Paving Conference. Proceedings. see Paving and Transportation Conference. Proceedings **1872**
Pavliha. (XV ISSN 0031-3289) **2879**
Pavlovian Journal of Biological Science see Integrative Physiological and Behavioral Science **4024**
Pavo. (II ISSN 0031-3297) **566**
Pax. (US) **2947**
Pax. (SW ISSN 0048-3087) **3914**
Pax Bulletin see JustPeace **4186**
Pax Christi U S A. (US ISSN 0897-9545) **4272**
Pax et Libertas. (SZ ISSN 0031-3327) **3968**

Pax Regis. (CN ISSN 0031-3335) **4194**
†Pax Romana. (SZ ISSN 0079-0281) **5256**
Pay and Benefits Bulletin. (UK ISSN 0143-8328) **991, 2665**
Pay Dirt. Rocky Mountain Edition. (US ISSN 0886-0912) **3493**
Pay Dirt. Southwestern Edition. (US ISSN 0886-0920) **3493**
Pay-Per-View Update. (US) **1378**
†Pay Phone News. (US ISSN 0886-5396) **5256**
Pay T V Newsletter. (US ISSN 0146-0072) **1378**
Pay T V Sports see Media Sports Business **1376**
Pay TV Movie Log. (US) **1378**
Payment Systems, Inc. Monitor see P S I Monitor **805**
Payment Systems Incorporated Abstracts see P S I Abstracts **733**
Payment Systems Worldwide. (US) **795**
Payphone Exchange. (US) **1049, 1365**
▼Payroll Administration Guide. (US) **991, 2665**
Payroll Exchange. (US ISSN 0194-6196) **991**
Payroll Guide. (US) **754, 1068**
Payroll Management Guide. (US) **795**
Payroll Practitioner's Compliance Handbook. (US) **754, 1103**
Pays-Bas Francais. see De Franse Nederlanden **2175**
Pays Bas-Normand. (FR ISSN 0031-3386) **2380, 281**
Le Pays Breton. (FR) **2019**
Pays Lorrain. (FR ISSN 0031-3394) **2380, 281**
La Paz. (US) **1321**
Paz e Alegria. (PO) **4272**
Paz y Justicia. (AG) **3914**
Paz y Justicia: Sumario de Derechos Humanos. (UY) **3946**
Paz y Soberania. (CU) **3968**
Pazifische Rundschau/Pacific Review. (CN ISSN 0048-3095) **2019**
PBX Systems Guide see P B X Systems Guide **1364**
Pcela. (CI ISSN 0031-3416) **113**
Pchelovodstvo. (RU ISSN 0369-8629) **113**
Pea River Trails. (US) **2418**
Peabody Journal of Education. (US ISSN 0031-3432) **1654**
Peabody Museum Bulletins. (US) **281**
Peabody Museum of Archaeology and Ethnology. Memoirs. (US ISSN 0079-029X) **281**
Peabody Museum of Archaeology and Ethnology. Monographs. (US) **281**
Peabody Museum of Archaeology and Ethnology. Papers. (US ISSN 0079-0303) **281**
Peabody Museum of Natural History. Bulletin. (US ISSN 0079-032X) **4333**
Peabody Museum of Natural History. Special Publication. (US ISSN 0079-0338) **4333**
Peabody News. (US) **1321, 3573**
Peabody Notes see Peabody News **1321**
Peabody Reflector. (US ISSN 0031-3459) **1321**
Peace. (II ISSN 0031-3467) **4217**
Peace & Change. (US ISSN 0149-0508) **3968, 4444**
Peace & Democracy News. (US ISSN 0749-5900) **3946, 3968**
Peace and Freedom. (US ISSN 0015-9093) **3968, 4850**
Peace and Freedom. (UK ISSN 0031-3491) **3968**
Peace & Justice News. (US) **3914**
Peace and Justice Series. (US) **4194, 1520**
Peace & Security/Paix et Securite. (CN ISSN 0831-1846) **3968**
Peace and the Sciences. (AU ISSN 0031-3513) **3968**
Peace Chronicle. (US) **3914**
Peace Conversion Times. (US) **3968**
Peace Corps Times. (US ISSN 0884-9196) **934, 3968**
Peace Courier. (FI ISSN 0031-594X) **3968**

Peace Currents. (US) 3914
Peace Developments. (US) 2512, 3914
Peace Education Center Monthly of Peace and Justice Action. (US) 3914
Peace Education Center Newsletter see Peace Education Center Monthly of Peace and Justice Action 3914
Peace Gazette. (US) 3914, 1300, 1686, 3969
Peace, Happiness and Prosperity Intersect see P H P Intersect 2574
Peace Institute Reporter see Peace Reporter 3969
Peace Law Docket. (US) 3946
Peace Magazine. (CN ISSN 0826-9521) 3969, 1809, 1965, 3468
Peace News. (UK ISSN 0031-3548) 3914
Peace Newsletter. (US ISSN 0735-4134) 3914
Peace Office Newsletter. (US) 4246
Peace Officer see Police Officers Journal 1520
Peace Plans. (AT ISSN 0031-3564) 3969
Peace Pledge Union Newsletter see Pacifist 3968
Peace Press. (US) 2879
Peace Progress. (US ISSN 0857-0760) 1723, 1696, 1757
Peace Reporter. (US ISSN 1049-0779) 3969
Peace Research. (CN ISSN 0008-4697) 3969
Peace Research Abstracts Journal. (CN ISSN 0031-3599) 3938, 19, 4458
Peace Research Centre Newsletter see Pacific Research 3968
Peace Research Reviews. (CN ISSN 0553-4283) 3914
Peace Review. (US ISSN 1040-2659) 3914
Peace Studies. see Jeiwa Kenkyu 3901
Peace Tax Fund Newsletter. (US) 3946, 1104
Peaceful Pieces. (US) 3592
Peaceletter. (US) 3914
Peacelines. (US) 3914, 3969, 4850
Peacelinks. (UK) 4195
Peacemaker. (UK) 2879
Peacemaker. (NZ) 3914, 4287
Peacemaker. (US ISSN 0031-3602) 3969
Peacework. (US ISSN 0748-0725) 3914
Peach-Times. (US ISSN 0031-3610) 187, 2079
Peachtree Magazine. (US) 2232
Peak. (CN ISSN 0031-3629) 1321
Peak and Prairie. (US) 1495, 1965, 4553
Peak District Mines Historical Society. Bulletin. (UK ISSN 0031-3637) 3493
Peak Performance Selling. (US ISSN 1043-4364) 1049
Peak to Peak. (US) 2232
Peake Studies. (SZ ISSN 1013-1191) 2879
Pe'amim. (IS ISSN 0334-4088) 2431
Peanut Butter. (US) 1262
Peanut Farmer. (US ISSN 0031-3653) 187
Peanut Grower. (US ISSN 1042-9379) 187
Peanut Industry Guide. (US) 156, 187
Peanut Journal and Nut World. (US ISSN 0031-3661) 2079
Peanut Market News. (US ISSN 0093-4429) 156, 187
Peanut News. (US) 156, 187
Peanut Research. (US) 187
Peanut Science. (US ISSN 0095-3679) 187
Pearce-Sellards Series. (US ISSN 0079-0354) 3531
Pearl. (US) 3000
Pearl Harbor Shipyard Log see Shipyard Log 3471
Pearls of Wisdom. (US) 3775
Pears Cyclopaedia. (UK ISSN 0079-0362) 1782

Pears Junior Encyclopaedia. (UK) 1782, 1262
Pearson Investment Letter. (US) 959
Peasant Studies. (US ISSN 0149-1547) 2380
Peasants in History and Literature. (AT) 2512
Peat Abstracts. (IE ISSN 0031-367X) 3502, 19
Pebble. (US ISSN 0031-3696) 3000
Pecan Press. (US ISSN 0892-2942) 187
Pecan South see Pecan South Including Pecan Quarterly 187
Pecan South Including Pecan Quarterly. (US ISSN 8750-5797) 187
Pechat Belorusskoi S.S.R./Byelorussian Publications. (BW) 409
Peche et les Poissons. (FR ISSN 0031-3718) 2047
Peche Maritime. (FR ISSN 0031-3726) 2047
Pecheur Belge. (BE) 2047
Pecheur Romand. (SZ) 4553
Peckerwood. (CN) 3000
Pecsi Muszaki Szemle. (HU ISSN 0031-3750) 4606
Pedagogia e Vita. (IT ISSN 0031-3777) 1654
Pedagogia Medica. (IT) 3350
Pedagogia para el Adiestramiento. (MX) 1686
Pedagogiai Szemle/Pedagogical Review. (HU ISSN 0031-3785) 1654
Pedagogic Reporter. (US ISSN 0031-3793) 1654
Pedagogical Review. see Pedagogiai Szemle 1654
Pedagogicka Fakulta v Ostrave. Matematika, Fyzika. (CS) 3050, 3826
Pedagogicka Fakulta v Ostrave. Sbornik Praci. Radi C: Dejepis-Zemepis. (CS ISSN 0139-6595) 2380
Pedagogicka Fakulta v Plzni. Sbornik. Dejepis. (CS ISSN 0139-7346) 2380
Pedagogicka Fakulta v Usti nad Labem. Sbornik: Rada Bohemisticka. (CS) 2834
Pedagogicka Fakulta v Usti nad Labem. Sbornik: Rada Chemicka. (CS) 1185
Pedagogiekjoernaal/Journal of Pedagogics. (SA ISSN 0256-520X) 1654
Pedagogija. (YU ISSN 0031-3807) 1654
Pedagogika/Pedagogy. (CS ISSN 0031-3815) 1654
Pedagogisch Forum see Pedagogisch Tijdschrift 1654
Pedagogisch Tijdschrift. (BE ISSN 0166-5855) 1654
Pedagogisch Tijdschrift-Forum voor Opvoedkunde see Pedagogisch Tijdschrift 1654
Pedagogische Studien. (NE ISSN 0552-7775) 1654
Pedagogisk Dokumentation. (SW ISSN 0346-5039) 4051
Pedagogisk Forskning see Scandinavian Journal of Educational Research 1661
Pedagogisk och Psykologisk Litteratur i Norden see P E P S Y 1653
Pedagogisk-Psykologiska Problem. (SW ISSN 0346-5004) 4037
Pedagogiska Hjaelpmedel. (SW ISSN 0346-5047) 1654
Pedagogiska Rapporter/Educational Reports. (SW ISSN 0281-6776) 1654
Pedagogiska Rapporter Umeaa see Pedagogiska Rapporter 1654
Pedagogusok Lapja. (HU) 2588, 1654
Pedagogy. see Pedagogika 1654
Pedagoski Rad. (CI ISSN 0031-384X) 1654
Pedagoski Zivot. (YU ISSN 0031-3858) 1654
Pedal Power see Canberra Cyclist 4516
Pedal Steel Newsletter. (US) 3573
Pedale d'Oro. (IT ISSN 0031-3866) 4520

Pedalpoint. (US ISSN 0272-9199) 3573, 4246
Peddler. (US) 1507, 838
Pedersore. (FI) 2380
Pedestrian Research. (US) 4720, 1965
Pedi kai Nei Gonis. (GR) 3323, 3295
Pediatre (Paris). (FR ISSN 0397-9180) 3323
Pediatria. (IT ISSN 0031-3890) 3323
Pediatria. (BU ISSN 0479-7876) 3323
Pediatria. Boletin. (SP) 3323
Pediatria e Puericultura. (BL ISSN 0031-3912) 3323
Pediatria Moderna. (BL ISSN 0031-3920) 3323
Pediatria Oggi Medica e Chirurgica. (IT ISSN 0391-898X) 3324, 3382
†Pediatria Polska. (PL ISSN 0031-3939) 5256
Pediatria Pratica. (BL ISSN 0031-3947) 3324
▼Pediatric A I D S and H I V Infection: Fetus to Adolescent. (US ISSN 1045-5418) 3222, 3324
Pediatric Alert. (US ISSN 0160-0184) 3324
Pediatric and Adolescent Endocrinology. (SZ ISSN 0304-4254) 3255
Pediatric and Adolescent Medicine. (SZ ISSN 1017-5989) 3324
Pediatric Annals. (US ISSN 0090-4481) 3324
Pediatric Asthma, Allergy & Immunology. (US ISSN 0883-1874) 3324, 3188
Pediatric Cardiology. (US ISSN 0172-0643) 3211, 3324, 3382
Pediatric Clinics of India. (II ISSN 0048-3133) 3324, 2468
Pediatric Clinics of North America. (US ISSN 0031-3955) 3324
Pediatric Dentistry. (US ISSN 0164-1263) 3240
Pediatric Dermatology. (US ISSN 0736-8046) 3249, 3324
Pediatric Emergency & Critical Care. (US ISSN 1059-0870) 3180, 3324
Pediatric Emergency Care. (US ISSN 0749-5161) 3324
Pediatric Exercise Science. (US ISSN 0899-8493) 3324, 3372
Pediatric Habilitation Series. (US) 3324
Pediatric Hematology & Oncology. (US ISSN 0888-0018) 3324, 3201, 3273
Pediatric Hematology - Oncology Series. (US) 3324, 3201, 3273
The Pediatric Infectious Disease Journal. (US ISSN 0891-3668) 3324, 3222
Pediatric Length of Stay by Diagnosis and Operation, United States. (US ISSN 0891-1223) 2471, 4583
▼Pediatric Management. (US) 3324, 1024
Pediatric Mental Health. (US ISSN 0278-4998) 4037, 3324
Pediatric Nephrology. (GW ISSN 0931-041X) 3389
Pediatric Neuroscience see Pediatric Neurosurgery 3350
Pediatric Neurosurgery. (SZ ISSN 1016-2291) 3350
Pediatric News. (US ISSN 0031-398X) 3324
Pediatric Nurse Practitioner. (US) 3285
Pediatric Nursing. (US ISSN 0097-9805) 3285
Pediatric Nutrition Handbook. (US) 3324
Pediatric Oncology see I C R D B Cancergram: Pediatric Oncology 3175
Pediatric Pathology. (US ISSN 0277-0938) 3324, 3201, 3222
Pediatric Physical Therapy. (US ISSN 0898-5669) 3324, 3140
Pediatric Pulmonology. (US ISSN 8755-6863) 3324, 3366
Pediatric Radiology. (GW ISSN 0301-0449) 3325, 3361

Pediatric Research. (US ISSN 0031-3998) 3325
Pediatric Review. see Shoni Igaku 3326
Pediatric Reviews and Communications. (US ISSN 0882-9225) 3325
Pediatric Social Work. (US ISSN 0195-5926) 4416
Pediatric Surgery International. (US ISSN 0179-0358) 3382, 3325
Pediatric Therapeutics & Toxicology. (US ISSN 0893-6218) 3180, 1983, 3325
Pediatric Trauma and Acute Care see Pediatric Emergency & Critical Care 3180
Pediatrician. (US) 3325
†Pediatrician. (SZ ISSN 0300-1245) 5256
Pediatricke Listy see Ceskoslovenska Pediatrie 3319
Pediatrics. see Zentralblatt Kinderheilkunde 3182
Pediatrics. see Pediatriya 3325
Pediatrics. (US ISSN 0031-4005) 3325
Pediatrics (Edicion Espanola). (SP ISSN 0210-5721) 3325
Pediatrics and Related Topics. see Paediatrie und Grenzgebiete 3323
Pediatrics for Parents. (US ISSN 0730-6725) 3325, 1242
Pediatrics in Review. (US ISSN 0191-9601) 3325
Pediatrie. (FR ISSN 0031-4021) 3325
Pediatrika see Ciencia Pediatrika 3319
Pediatriya/Pediatrics. (RU ISSN 0031-403X) 3325
Pediatriya, Akusherstvo ta Ginekologiya. (KR ISSN 0031-4048) 3325, 3295
Pedmed see South African Paediatrics Magazine 3326
Pedobiologia. (GW ISSN 0031-4056) 187, 451
Pedofauna. (BE ISSN 0378-181X) 187
Pedologist/Pedorojisuto. (JA ISSN 0031-4064) 187
Pedology. see Turang 1548
Pedoman Masyarakat. (MY) 2210
Pedoman Rakyat. (MY) 2210
Pedorojisuto. see Pedologist 187
▼Pedosphere/Turang Quan. (CC ISSN 1002-0160) 1547
Peek at Pike. (US) 2161
Peek 65. (US ISSN 0739-0653) 1455, 1464, 1479
Peelings (Washington). (US ISSN 0895-786X) 2418, 2136
Peeping Tom. (US) 3013
Peerage. (UK) 2195
Pegasus. (IE) 4814
Pegasus (Nevada). (US ISSN 0888-322X) 3000
Pegasus Journal. (UK ISSN 0031-4080) 3468, 60
The Pegasus Review. (US) 3000
Peiling. (NE ISSN 0031-4099) 4735
Peinture/Cahiers Theoriques. (FR) 340
Peinture, Sculpture et Arts Decoratifs Europeen et Americains, Volume 1: 1300-1800 see European and American Painting, Sculpture and Decorative Arts, Volume 1: 1300-1800 325
Pekin Shuho see Beijing Review 2181
Peking Informers. (HK ISSN 0031-4110) 2879
Pekingese Club of America. Bulletin. (US) 3712
Pekingese News. (US) 3712
Pelagos. (AE ISSN 0031-4137) 1610, 451
Pelangi. (AT ISSN 0815-6816) 1757, 2019, 2258, 2341
Pelangi Rainbow see Pelangi 1757
Pelargonium News. (UK ISSN 0267-1891) 2137
Pelerin. (FR ISSN 0399-5755) 4195
Pelerin du Vingtieme Siecle see Pelerin 4195
Pelican Farm News. (US) 113, 2665
Pelita Brunei. (BX) 4070
Pelita Methodist. (MY) 4246
Pellennorath. (US) 2947

Pellervo. (FI ISSN 0031-4188) 113
Pellissippian. (US) 2161
Peluquerias de Gran Seleccion. (SP) 374
†Pelz International. (GW) 5256
Pelz und Leder. (AU) 2737
Pelzspiegel see L P T Journal 2737
Pelzwirtschaft see L P T Journal 2737
Pembrita. (MY) 2210
Pembroke Magazine. (US ISSN 0097-496X) 2879
Pembroke Welsh Corgi Club of America. Newsletter. (US) 3712
Pembrokeshire Historical Society. Journal. (UK) 2380
Pemex. Boletin Bibliografico. (Petroleos Mexicanos) (MX ISSN 0186-3401) 3706
Pemungut Setem Malaysia/Malaysian Philatelist. (MY) 3755
Pen. see Aqlam Journal 2895
Pen and Quill. (US) 2440
Pen-Based Computing. (US) 1464
Pen en Toets. (NE ISSN 0165-8867) 1061, 1739
Pen Fancier's Magazine. (US) 2440
Pen in Hand. (US ISSN 0895-0180) 2574, 2879, 3394, 4134
Pen: Umbra. (UK) 3000
The Pen Woman. (US ISSN 0031-4242) 2947, 2512, 4850
Pen World. (US ISSN 1045-1188) 2440, 340
Penang Port Handbook. (AT ISSN 0267-7369) 1150, 4735
Pendle Hill Pamphlets. (US ISSN 0031-4250) 4287
Pendragon. (US) 2947
Pendulum. (US) 1321
Pendulum. (SA) 4195
Penerbit Universiti Kebangsaan Malaysia Jurnal Perubatan U K M see Jurnal Perubatan U K M 3119
PENewsletter see P E Newsletter 2946
PenFinder. (US) 2440, 340
Penfriend & Ethnic Linkup Index. (AT) 1300
Pengasoh. (MY) 2210
Penge og Privatoekonomi. (DK) 684
Penger og Kreditt. (NO ISSN 0332-5598) 795
Pengtiao Zhishi/Cook Knowledge. (CC) 2449
Penguin News. (FK) 2217
Penguin Pipeline. (US) 2079
▼Peninhand. (US) 3000
Peninsula. (IT) 2206
Peninsula. (US ISSN 0888-4846) 2232
Peninsula Group Magazine. (HK) 4782, 2197, 2479
†Peninsula Living. (US ISSN 0031-4293) 5256
Peninsula Poets. (US ISSN 0031-4307) 3000
Peninsula Prime. (CN) 2277
Peninsulaguest. (US) 2232, 4782
Peninsular Philatelist. (US) 3755
Penitentiaire Informatie see Sancties 1522
Penmen's News Letter. (CN ISSN 0031-4315) 1654
Penn Dental Journal. (US ISSN 0031-4331) 3240
Penn Lines. (US) 2232
†Penn State Update. (US) 5256
Penn Stater. (US) 1321, 36
The Pennant. (UK ISSN 0048-3192) 3468
Pennine Magazine. (UK ISSN 0261-2836) 4782
Pennine Platform. (UK ISSN 0306-140X) 3000
Pennsylvania. Administration on Aging. State Plan on Aging. (US) 4416, 2277
Pennsylvania. Agricultural Statistics Service. Crop and Livestock Annual Summary. (US ISSN 0079-046X) 187
Pennsylvania. Board of Probation and Parole. Monthly Statistical Report. (US ISSN 0031-4366) 1525, 4583
Pennsylvania. Citizens Advisory Council to the Department of Environmental Resources. Annual Report. (US ISSN 0092-7937) 1965

Pennsylvania. Crime Commission. Report. (US ISSN 0091-4118) 1520
Pennsylvania. Department of Agriculture. Seed Report. (US) 208
Pennsylvania. Department of Environmental Resources. Annual Report on Mining Activities. (US) 3493
Pennsylvania. Developmental Disabilities Planning Council. Pennsylvania State Plan. (US) 4416
Pennsylvania. Historical and Museum Commission. Anthropological Series. (US) 247, 2418
Pennsylvania. Labor Relations Board. Annual Report. (US) 991
Pennsylvania. Labor Relations Board. Report see Pennsylvania. Labor Relations Board. Annual Report 991
Pennsylvania. Office of Mines and Land Protection. Annual Report. see Pennsylvania. Department of Environmental Resources. Annual Report on Mining Activities 3493
Pennsylvania. State Tax Equalization Board. Annual Certification. (US) 1104
Pennsylvania Academy of Science. Journal. (US ISSN 1044-6753) 451
Pennsylvania Academy of Science. Proceedings see Pennsylvania Academy of Science. Journal 451
Pennsylvania Agriculture News. (US ISSN 1043-6235) 156
Pennsylvania Angler. (US ISSN 0031-434X) 4553, 4527
Pennsylvania Anthracite Weekly see Weekly Coal Production 1797
Pennsylvania Architect. (US) 304
Pennsylvania Baker. (US) 2089
†Pennsylvania Ballet. (US) 5256
Pennsylvania Business Survey. (US ISSN 0031-4382) 685
Pennsylvania C P A Journal. (US ISSN 0746-1062) 755
Pennsylvania Chamber of Business and Industry. Checklist. (US) 4109, 2665
Pennsylvania Chamber of Business and Industry. Legislative Directory. (US) 4070
Pennsylvania Chamber of Business and Industry. Legislative Reporter. (US) 2665, 4070
Pennsylvania Chamber of Business and Industry. State & Regional Directory. (US) 821
Pennsylvania Chamber of Business and Industry. Tax Bulletin. (US) 1104, 2665
Pennsylvania Chamber of Commerce. State and Regional Directory see Pennsylvania Chamber of Business and Industry. State & Regional Directory 821
Pennsylvania Chiefs of Police Association Bulletin. (US ISSN 0031-4404) 1520
Pennsylvania Commission for Women News see WomeNews 4857
Pennsylvania Conference of Economists. Proceedings of the Annual Meeting. (US) 685
Pennsylvania Contractor. (US ISSN 0031-4412) 2302
Pennsylvania Crop Reporting Service. C.R.S. see Pennsylvania. Agricultural Statistics Service. Crop and Livestock Annual Summary 187
Pennsylvania Dental Journal. (US ISSN 0031-4439) 3240
Pennsylvania Directory of Manufacturers. (US ISSN 0733-5237) 1150
Pennsylvania Dutch News and Views. (US) 2057
Pennsylvania Education. (US ISSN 0031-4455) 1654
Pennsylvania Education Law Report. (US) 1654, 2588, 2665
▼Pennsylvania Employment Law Letter.(US ISSN 1052-4363) 2665, 991
Pennsylvania Environmental Law Letter.(US ISSN 1046-6568) 2665, 1965

Pennsylvania Ethnic Studies Newsletter.(US) 2019, 247
Pennsylvania Facts. (US ISSN 0894-3850) 1782
Pennsylvania Farmer. (US ISSN 0031-4471) 113
Pennsylvania Flower Growers. Bulletin. (US ISSN 0031-448X) 2137
Pennsylvania Folklife. (US ISSN 0031-4498) 2418, 2057
Pennsylvania Forests. (US ISSN 0031-4501) 2106
Pennsylvania Game & Fish. (US) 4553
Pennsylvania Game News. (US ISSN 0031-451X) 4553
Pennsylvania Gazette. (US) 1321
Pennsylvania Genealogical Magazine. (US) 2161
Pennsylvania Geographer. (US) 2258
Pennsylvania Geology. (US ISSN 0048-3214) 1577
▼Pennsylvania Good Times Magazine. (US) 2232
Pennsylvania Heritage. (US ISSN 0270-7500) 2418, 3531
Pennsylvania History. (US ISSN 0031-4528) 2418
Pennsylvania Horticultural Society News see P H S News 2136
Pennsylvania Journal of Health, Physical Education and Recreation see Pennsylvania Journal of Health, Physical Education, Recreation and Dance 1757
Pennsylvania Journal of Health, Physical Education, Recreation and Dance. (US) 1757, 4483
Pennsylvania Law Journal Reporter. (US) 2666
Pennsylvania Lawyer. (US) 2666
Pennsylvania Library Association. Bulletin. (US ISSN 0197-9299) 2779
Pennsylvania Magazine. (US ISSN 0744-4230) 2232, 4782
Pennsylvania Magazine of History and Biography. (US ISSN 0031-4587) 2419, 420
Pennsylvania Manufacturers Register. (US ISSN 0887-3682) 1150
Pennsylvania Marketing Bulletin. (US) 2116, 1049
▼Pennsylvania Mechanics' Liens. (US) 2666
Pennsylvania Medicine. (US ISSN 0031-4595) 3140
Pennsylvania Mennonite Heritage. (US ISSN 0148-4036) 2161, 2419, 4287
Pennsylvania Message. (US ISSN 0031-4609) 1739, 3350
Pennsylvania Music Educators Association, Inc. News see P M E A News 3573
Pennsylvania Natality and Mortality Statistics see Pennsylvania Vital Statistics 3994
†Pennsylvania Naturalist. (US ISSN 0164-7822) 5256
Pennsylvania Newspaper Publishers Association Press see P N P A Press 2574
Pennsylvania Nurse. (US ISSN 0031-4617) 3285
Pennsylvania Osteopathic Medical Association. Journal. (US ISSN 0479-9534) 3215
Pennsylvania Outdoors see Pennsylvania Game & Fish 4553
Pennsylvania Parent Teacher Bulletin see P T A in Pennsylvania Bulletin 1653
Pennsylvania Pharmacist. (US ISSN 0031-4633) 3737
Pennsylvania Police Criminal Law Bulletin. (US ISSN 0098-7174) 1520
Pennsylvania Portfolio. (US ISSN 0890-1465) 420, 2947
Pennsylvania Review. (US ISSN 8756-5668) 2947
Pennsylvania School Boards Association Bulletin see P S B A Bulletin 1730
Pennsylvania School Study Council. Reports. (US ISSN 0079-0508) 1654
Pennsylvania Schoolmaster. (US) 1654
Pennsylvania Sportsman. (US) 4553

Pennsylvania State Industrial Directory see MacRae's State Industrial Directory: Pennsylvania 1144
Pennsylvania State University. Environmental Resources Research Institute. Newsletter. (US) 1495, 4827
Pennsylvania State University. Institute for Research on Land and Water Resources. Newsletter see Pennsylvania State University. Environmental Resources Research Institute. Newsletter 1495
Pennsylvania State University. Libraries. Bibliographical Series. (US ISSN 0079-0656) 2779
†Pennsylvania Statistical Abstract. (US ISSN 0476-1103) 5256
Pennsylvania Taxation. (US) 1104
▼Pennsylvania Technology. (US) 4606, 1479
Pennsylvania Township News. (US ISSN 0162-5160) 4093
Pennsylvania Triangle. (US) 1833
Pennsylvania Vital Statistics. (US) 3994, 3985
Pennsylvanian. (US ISSN 0031-4714) 4093
Pennsylvania's Machinery Custom Rates see Pennsylvania. Agricultural Statistics Service. Crop and Livestock Annual Summary 187
Penntrux. (US) 4747
Penny Mining Stock Report see Gold Mining Stock Report 947
Penny Power see Zillions 1272
Penny Resistance. (US) 2666
Penny Speculator see Speculator 964
Penny Stock Journal see Individual Investor 949
Penny Stock Magazine. (US) 959
Penny Stock Preview see Penny Stock Magazine 959
Penny Stocks Newsletter. (US) 959
Penpals. (BG ISSN 0379-0649) 2440
Pensacola History Illustrated. (US) 2419
Pensamiento. (SP ISSN 0031-4749) 3775
Pensamiento Costarricense. (CR) 2180
Pensamiento Critico. (PR) 879
Pensamiento Economico. (HO) 685
Pensamiento Economico. (AG) 821
Pensamiento Iberoamericano. (SP ISSN 0212-0208) 879
Pensamiento Propio. (NQ) 4382
Pensamiento y Accion. (CK ISSN 0031-4765) 4333, 4382
Pensamiento y Nacion. (AG) 3914
Pensare Faenza/Thinking about Faenza.(IT) 2879
Pensee (Paris). (FR) 3914
Pensee Catholique. (FR ISSN 0031-4781) 4272
†La Pensee Francaise. (FR ISSN 0031-479X) 5256
Pensee Russe. (FR) 2019
Pensez Plastiques. (FR ISSN 0031-4803) 3865
Pensiero ed Arte. (IT) 2879, 2947
Pensiero Mazziniano. (IT ISSN 0031-482X) 3914
Pensiero Politico. (IT ISSN 0031-4846) 3914, 2319, 4444
Pensiero Politico. Biblioteca. (IT) 3914, 4444
Pensioen Bulletin. (NE ISSN 0031-4854) 991
Pension and Profit Sharing. (US) 1068
Pension and Profit Sharing Guide. (US) 1068
Pension and Profit-Sharing Plans Compliance Guide. (US) 2711, 991
Pension and Profit-Sharing Plans: Forms and Practice with Tax Analysis. (US) 2711, 991
Pension and Welfare News see Pension World 795
Pension Boards see United Church of Christ. Pension Boards (Annual Report) 4289
†Pension Briefings. (US) 5256
Pension Coordinator. (US) 1068, 755
†Pension Facts. (US) 5256
▼Pension Fund Litigation Reporter. (US ISSN 1052-9640) 2711

PERIODICAL WRITERS 6547

Pension Fund News *see* Employee Benefit News **977**
Pension Funds & Their Advisers. (UK ISSN 0140-6647) **2540**, 4416
Pension Plan Guide. (US) **2540**, 991
Pension Plan Guide Summary *see* Pension Plan Guide **2540**
Pension Reporter *see* B N A Pension Reporter **973**
Pension World. (US ISSN 0098-1753) **795**, 2540, 4416
Pensionaeren *see* Pro - Pensionaeren **4416**
Pensioners Voice. (UK ISSN 0048-3281) **4416**
Pensioners Voice. (AT ISSN 1035-3615) **4416**, 1507
Pensions *see* Pensions & Employee Benefits Magazine **959**
Pensions & Employee Benefits Magazine. (UK) **959**, 795
Pensions and Investment Age *see* Pensions & Investments **959**
Pensions & Investments. (US ISSN 1050-4974) **959**
Pensions & Investments Performance Evaluation Reports *see* P I P E R **959**
Pensions Intelligence. (UK ISSN 0267-9035) **685**
Pensions Management. (UK) **1068**
Pensions Today. (UK) **2540**
Pensions World. (UK ISSN 0307-191X) **2540**, 959, 4416
Pentagon. (US ISSN 0031-4870) **3050**
Pentagramma *see* Primi Piani **3575**
Pentatette. (US) **3000**
Pentax Life. (US) **3794**
Pentecostal Evangel. (US ISSN 0031-4897) **4287**
Pentecostal Fellowship of North America News *see* P F N A News **5254**
Pentecostal Messenger. (US ISSN 0031-4919) **4246**
Pentecostal Testimony. (CN ISSN 0031-4927) **4246**
Pentecostes *see* Moralia **4270**
Penthouse. (HK) **3399**
Penthouse. (US ISSN 0090-2020) **3399**
Penthouse. (UK). (UK) **3399**
Penthouse Forum *see* Forum (New York, 1976) **3397**
Penthouse Letters. (US ISSN 0883-8798) **3399**
Penton Executive Network. (US) **4782**
Pentru Patrie. (RM) **2215**
Penzinger Museumsblaetter. (AU) **2380**
Penzugyi Szemle. (HU ISSN 0031-496X) **795**
Peony. *see* Mudan **2940**
People. *see* Renmin **420**
People. (UK ISSN 0301-5645) **597**, 4444
People. (AT) **2172**
People. (IE) **2203**
People. (KE) **2208**
People. (NR ISSN 0048-329X) **2212**
People. *see* Achaab **2857**
People. *see* Moun **3908**
†People. (RH) **5256**
People (Kansas City). (US ISSN 0031-501X) **1723**, 3969
People (Palo Alto). (US ISSN 0199-350X) **3914**
People and Communication. (US) **1341**
People and Computers Magazine *see* P C Plus **1472**
People & Computers Weekly. (IS) **1399**
People and Countries. *see* Lide a Zeme **2255**
People and Products. (US) **1082**
People and Programs. (US ISSN 1041-1941) **2666**, 4416
People and Progress *see* Vital Signs (Oklahoma) **3810**
People, Animals, Environment *see* People, Animals, Nature **3712**
People, Animals, Nature. (US) **3712**
†People, Communication Organization. (US) **5256**
People, Food & Land. (US) **187**
People for the Ethical Treatment of Animals, Inc. News *see* P E T A News **231**

People from the Past Series. (UK ISSN 0079-0729) **420**
People in Power. (UK) **3938**, 424
People Like That. (UK) **2947**
People Searching News. (US ISSN 1047-6598) **2161**, 4444
People Soup *see* Synapse (Boston) **2885**
People-to-People Newsletter *see* People (Kansas City) **1723**
People United to Save Humanity. P.U.S.H.-Operation Push. (US ISSN 0048-332X) **2879**
People Weekly. (US) **2232**
People with AIDS Coalition Newsline *see* P W A Coalition Newsline **3222**
People with Special Needs - Down Syndrome Report. (US ISSN 0731-566X) **1739**
Peoplenet. (US) **1739**, 4416
People's Army. *see* Ardyn Armi **2858**
People's China. *see* Jinmin Chugoku **2182**
People's Daily. *see* Renmin Ribao **2182**
People's Daily. Index. *see* Renmin Ribao Suoyin **2578**
People's Deputy. *see* Nguoi Dai Bieu Nhan Dan **3911**
People's Doctor *see* Doctor's People **3214**
People's Education. *see* Renmin Jiaoyu **1658**
People's Friend. (UK) **4850**
Peoples in Atoms. (JA) **1809**
People's Korea. (JA ISSN 0031-5036) **3914**
People's Literature. *see* Renmin Wenxue **2953**
†People's Local Government Journal/Al-Hukm al-Shabi al-Mahalli. (SJ) **5256**
People's Medical Society Newsletter. (US ISSN 0736-4873) **1507**, 3140, 4416
People's Music. *see* Renmin Yinyue **3577**
Peoples of East Africa. (TZ) **2334**, 247
People's Police. *see* Renmin Jingcha **1521**
People's Power. (II ISSN 0377-2713) **3914**
People's Pulse. (BH) **3914**
People's Railway. *see* Renmin Tiedao **4714**
People's Republic of China Year Book. (HK ISSN 1000-9396) **1782**, 2182, 3914
People's Songletter. (US) **3573**
People's State. *see* Ardyn Tor **3873**
People's Theatre. *see* Giao Vien Nhan Dan **4633**
People's Tribune. (US) **3914**
People's Voice. *see* Dwon Lwak **2220**
People's Voice. (SJ) **3914**
People's Yangtze River. *see* Renmin Chang Jiang **2260**
People's Yellow River. *see* Renmin Huang He **2260**
Peopling of the British Peripheries in the Eighteenth Century. Series: Esso Lecture: No.2. (AT) **2512**
Peoria Area Manufacturers' Directory. (US) **821**, 1150
Peoria Labor News *see* Labor Paper **986**
Peoria Today. (US) **4782**
Pep Talk. (UK ISSN 0268-2419) **3914**, 1757
Peparimi. (YU ISSN 0553-6979) **2380**
Peperomia and Exotic Plant Society. Gazette. (US) **2137**
Peperomia Society International. Gazette *see* Peperomia and Exotic Plant Society. Gazette **2137**
Pepper 'n Salt. (US) **3712**
Pepperdine Law Review. (US ISSN 0092-430X) **2666**
Peptide Hormone Receptors. (UK ISSN 0268-1552) **3255**, 526
Peptide Research. (US ISSN 1040-5704) **481**
Peptides. (US ISSN 0196-9781) **481**
Pequena Diana. (MX) **356**
Pequeno Universo. (DR) **2512**
Pequod. (US ISSN 0149-0516) **2948**
Per Jacobsson Foundation. Lectures. (US) **795**

Per Jacobsson Foundation. Proceedings *see* Per Jacobsson Foundation. Lectures **795**
Per Jacobsson Memorial Lecture *see* Per Jacobsson Foundation. Lectures **795**
Per Lui. (IT) **2206**
Peraba. (IO) **4272**
Peradarstvo. (YU ISSN 0031-6792) **223**
Perbadanan Perpustakaan Awam Selangor. Lapuran Tahunan. *see* Selangor Public Library Corporation. Annual Report **2784**
Perbadanan Produktiviti Negara. Lapuran Tahunan. *see* National Productivity Corporation, Malaysia. Annual Report **1022**
Perception. (UK ISSN 0301-0066) **4038**, 3304
Perception. (CN ISSN 0704-5263) **4416**
Perception & Psychophysics. (US ISSN 0031-5117) **4038**
Perceptions (Duluth). (US) **795**
Perceptions (Indianapolis). (US ISSN 0730-5435) **3531**
Perceptions (Missoula). (US) **3000**
Perceptual and Motor Skills. (US ISSN 0031-5125) **4038**
PerChance. (UK) **3013**, 4483
Percheron Progress Newsletter. (CN) **223**
Percussion News. (US) **3573**
Percussionist *see* Percussive Notes **3573**
Percussive Notes. (US ISSN 0553-6502) **3573**
Pere Marquette Theology Lecture Series. (US) **4195**
Peregrine. (US ISSN 0890-622X) **3000**
Perekrestki *see* Vstrechi **3008**
Perennial Plant Association. Newsletter.(US) **2137**
Perets. (KR ISSN 0031-5176) **2879**
▼The Perfect Lawyer. (US) **2666**
Perfect Vision. (US ISSN 0895-4143) **1378**, 1358
Perfil. (CR) **4850**
Perfil da Administracao Federal. (BL) **4070**
Perfiles Contemporaneos. (AG) **420**
Perfiles Educativos. (MX ISSN 0185-2698) **1714**
Perfins Bulletin. (US ISSN 8750-1627) **3755**
Perfis Parlamentares. (BL) **4070**, 420
†Performance. (CN ISSN 0832-8196) **5256**
Performance (Bensalem). (US) **4699**
Performance Aftermarket Magazine *see* P & S A News **4699**
Performance & Instruction. (US ISSN 0884-1985) **1757**
Performance & Specialty Automotive News *see* P & S A News **4699**
Performance Car. (UK ISSN 0265-6183) **4699**
Performance Chemicals. (UK ISSN 0950-3870) **1185**, 685
Performance Evaluation. (NE ISSN 0166-5316) **1399**
Performance Evaluation Review *see* S I G M E T R I C S Performance Evaluation Review **1418**
Performance Guide. (US) **1378**
†Performance Guide Publications. Mutual Funds and Timing. (US ISSN 0300-7693) **5256**
Performance Horseman *see* Horse & Rider **4535**
Performance Improvement Quarterly. (US ISSN 0898-8952) **1757**
Performance Management Magazine. (US) **1024**
Performance Materials. (US ISSN 0888-3467) **60**
Performance Practice Review. (US ISSN 1044-1638) **3573**
Performance Racing News. (CN ISSN 0834-809X) **4527**
Performance Sailing. (US) **4483**
Performance Sailing. (AT) **4528**
†Performances. (FR) **5256**
Performer. (CN) **1531**

Performing Arts. (US ISSN 0031-5222) **4636**, 3573
Performing Arts Biography Master Index. (US) **4643**, 1349, 3520
Performing Arts Buyers Guide: Footnotes. (US) **1531**, 4636
Performing Arts Council, Orange Free State News *see* P A C O F S News **4636**
Performing Arts Forum *see* International Society of Performing Arts Administrators. Forum **3557**
Performing Arts in Canada. (CN ISSN 0031-5230) **4636**, 1531, 3573
Performing Arts Journal. (US ISSN 0735-8393) **4636**
†Performing Arts Magazine (San Francisco Edition). (US ISSN 0480-0257) **5256**
Performing Arts Resources. (US ISSN 0360-3814) **4636**
Performing Right News *see* P R S News **3573**
Performing Right Society Ltd. Members Handbook *see* P R S Members Handbook **3573**
Performing Right Society Ltd. News *see* P R S News **3573**
Performing Right Year Book. (UK ISSN 0309-0884) **3574**
Performing Woman. (US ISSN 0191-1554) **3574**, 4850
Perfumer & Flavorist. (US ISSN 0272-2666) **376**, 1185
Perfumeria Moderna/Modern Perfuming. (MX ISSN 0185-6588) **376**
Perfusion. (UK ISSN 0267-6591) **3211**
Perfusion Life. (US ISSN 0747-3079) **3140**
Pergamon Chess *see* Chess **4468**
Pergamon Chess Books *see* Maxwell Macmillan Chess Books **4479**
Pergamon Journals Bulletin. (UK) **2779**
Pergolesi Studies/Studi Pergolesiani. (US) **3574**
Perigord Magazine. (FR) **2187**, 4782
Perinatal Press. (US ISSN 0160-7219) **3295**
PerinatalMedizin. (GW ISSN 0936-7160) **3295**
Period Building Restoration Trades & Suppliers Directory. (AT ISSN 0158-7374) **304**, 1150
Period Piece and Paperback *see* Vigil **4138**
Periodica. Indice de Revistas Latinoamericanas en Ciencias. (MX ISSN 0185-1004) **4357**, 19
Periodica de Re Morali Canonica Liturgica. (VC ISSN 0031-529X) **4272**
Periodica Mathematica Hungarica. (NE ISSN 0031-5303) **3050**
Periodica Polytechnica. Architecture. (HU ISSN 0031-5346) **304**
Periodica Polytechnica. Chemical Engineering. (HU ISSN 0031-5311) **1857**
Periodica Polytechnica. Civil Engineering. (HU ISSN 0553-6626) **1872**
Periodica Polytechnica. Electrical Engineering. (HU ISSN 0031-532X) **1905**
Periodica Polytechnica. Engineering, Maschinen- und Bauwesen *see* Periodica Polytechnica. Mechanical Engineering **1937**
Periodica Polytechnica. Mechanical Engineering. (HU ISSN 0324-6051) **1937**
Periodica Polytechnica. Transportation. (HU) **4654**
Periodical. *see* Periodiko **2184**
Periodical Source Index. (US) **2329**, 19, 2168
Periodical Title Abbreviations. (US ISSN 0737-7843) **4134**
Periodical Writers Association of Canada. Directory *see* Periodical Writers Association of Canada. Directory of Members **2574**
Periodical Writers Association of Canada. Directory of Members. (CN ISSN 0829-0857) **2574**

PERIODICAL WRITERS

Periodical Writers Association of Canada. Fees Survey *see* Periodical Writers Association of Canada. Magazine Markets and Fees **2574**
Periodical Writers Association of Canada. Magazine Markets and Fees.(CN ISSN 0829-0865) **2574**
Periodical Writers Association of Canada Contact *see* P.W.A.Contact **2574**
Periodicals in Print in Japan. *see* Zasshi Shinbun Sokatarogu **416**
Periodicals in Southern African Libraries. (SA ISSN 0379-4482) **409**
Periodicals of Asia and Oceania *see* Periodicals of Asia and the Pacific **2268**
Periodicals of Asia and the Pacific. (UN) **2268**
Periodicum Biologorum. (CI ISSN 0031-5362) **451**, **3140**
Periodiko/Periodical. (CY) **2184**
Periodista. (VE ISSN 0048-3370) **2574**
▼Periodoncia. (SP) **3240**
Periodontal Abstracts *see* Western Society of Periodontology. Journal. Periodontal Abstracts **3182**
Periodontology. (AT ISSN 0726-5247) **3240**
Peripherals (Internatioal). (US) **1455**
Peripherie. (GW ISSN 0173-184X) **934**, **247**, **3914**, **4444**
Periplo. (SP) **2106**
Periscope. (FR) **1654**
Periscope. (UK ISSN 0048-3400) **4735**, **3468**
Periscope (Great Neck). (US) **384**
Periscope (McLean). (US) **1527**
Peristil. (CI ISSN 0553-6707) **304**, **340**, **356**
Peritia. (IE ISSN 0332-1592) **2380**, **281**, **2834**
Peritoneal Dialysis Bulletin *see* Peritoneal Dialysis International **3140**
Peritoneal Dialysis International. (CN ISSN 0896-8608) **3140**, **3262**, **3389**
Perkin Transactions 1 *see* Royal Society of Chemistry. Journal: Perkin Transactions 1 **1223**
Perkin Transactions 2 *see* Royal Society of Chemistry. Journal: Perkin Transactions 2 **1230**
Perkins Family Newsletter. (US ISSN 0895-4488) **2161**
Perkins Press. (US ISSN 0898-1574) **2161**
Perkumpulan Kontrasepsi Mantap Indonesia (PKMI) Mantap: Majalah Ilmaih P K M I *see* Mantap: Majalah Ilmaih P K M I **3294**
Perlin *see* Perlin et Pinpin **1242**
Perlin et Pinpin. (FR) **1242**, **4272**
Permaculture Activist. (US) **113**
Permaculture with Native Plants. (US) **2137**
Permafrost. (US ISSN 0740-7890) **2948**
▼Permafrost and Periglacial Processes.(UK ISSN 1045-6740) **1577**
†Permail Hospital Book. (AT) **5256**
Permanences. (FR ISSN 0031-5478) **3914**
Permanencia. (BL ISSN 0031-5486) **4195**, **3775**
†Permanency Report. (US) **5256**
Permanent Commission on the Status of Women Annual Report *see* P C S W Annual Report **4850**
Permanent International Altaistic Conference (PIAC). Newsletter. (US ISSN 0031-5508) **3643**
Permanent International Association of Navigation Congresses. Bulletin. (BE ISSN 0480-0516) **4735**
†Permanent International Committee of Linguists. Committee on Linguistic Statistics. Publication. (NE ISSN 0553-6812) **5256**
Permanent Missions to the United Nations/Missions Permanentes Aupres des Nations Unies a Geneve et Orga Principaux des Nations Unies. (UN) **3969**

Permanent Way Institution. Journal and Report of Proceedings. (UK ISSN 0031-5524) **4712**
Permit Patter. (US) **3755**
Pernambuco. Secretaria do Saneamento, Habitacao e Obras. Boletim Tecnico. (BL ISSN 0006-9469) **4070**
Pernambuco, Brazil. Secretaria da Agricultura. Plano Anual de Trabalho.(BL) **156**
Peronista. (AG) **3914**
Perpjekja e Jone/Our Effort. (US) **340**, **2948**
Perrin & Treggett's Review. (US) **1538**, **1242**
†Perry Rhodan Science Fiction Paperback Magazine. (US) **5257**
Pers. *see* Presse **2574**
Persian Quarterly. (US) **3712**
Persian Study Circle Bulletin *see* Iran Philatelic Study Circle Bulletin **3753**
Persica. (BE ISSN 0079-0893) **2341**, **281**
Persimmon Hill. (US ISSN 0093-707X) **2419**
Persistence of Vision. (US) **3515**, **3775**
Persistence of Vision. (CN) **3515**, **1386**
PersoCom World. (GW) **1473**, **1464**
†Person-Centered Review. (US ISSN 0883-2293) **5257**
Persona. (US) **2232**
Persona y Derecho. (SP ISSN 0211-4526) **2666**
Persona y Sociedad. (CL ISSN 0716-730X) **4382**, **3775**, **4195**
Personal. (GW ISSN 0031-5605) **991**, **1068**
Personal. (SW ISSN 0348-5242) **1068**
Das Personal A B C. (GW ISSN 0724-360X) **2666**
▼Personal and Departmental Computing Corporate Planner. (US) **1473**
Personal-Buero in Recht und Praxis. (GW ISSN 0341-2792) **2666**
Personal Communications Network News *see* P C N News **1364**
Personal Composition Report. (US ISSN 0196-4127) **4144**
Personal Computer. (GW ISSN 0724-469X) **1464**
Personal Computer. (BE) **1473**, **828**
Personal Computer. (IT) **1473**
Personal Computer - An Industry Source Book *see* Microleads Vendor Directory **1425**
Personal Computer Artificial Intelligence Magazine *see* P C A I Magazine **1410**
Personal Computer Clones *see* P C Clones **5254**
†Personal Computer Koopgids. (NE) **5257**
Personal Computer Local Networks Report. (US) **1473**, **1428**
Personal Computer Magazine. (NE) **1473**, **1464**, **1479**
Personal Computer Management *see* P.C. Management **1472**
Personal Computer Markets. (UK) **1050**, **1399**
Personal Computer Retailing *see* P C Retailing **1433**
Personal Computer Tech Journal Directory *see* P C Tech Journal Directory **1472**
Personal Computer World. (UK ISSN 0142-0232) **1473**
†Personal Computing. (US) **5257**
†Personal Computing Series. (US ISSN 0888-3262) **5257**
Personal Computing with the I B M - P C and Compatibles *see* P C Today **1473**
Personal Engineering & Instrumentation News. (US ISSN 0748-0016) **1473**
Personal Finance. (SA) **795**
Personal Finance. (US) **959**
Personal Finance Intelligence. (UK) **795**
Personal Finance Planning Quarterly. (US) **755**
Personal Finance: The Inflation Survival Letter *see* Personal Finance **959**

Personal Financial Planning. (US ISSN 1044-4343) **959**
Personal Fitness. (US ISSN 0738-7857) **3807**, **3372**, **3611**
▼Personal Fitness and Weight Loss. (US) **3807**
Personal Income in Areas and Counties of New York State. (US) **999**
Personal Income in Counties of New York State *see* Personal Income in Areas and Counties of New York State **999**
Personal Injury Damage Assessments in Alberta. (CN) **2666**, **991**
Personal Injury Damage Assessments in British Columbia. (CN) **2666**, **991**
Personal Injury Newsletter. (US) **2666**, **2540**
Personal Injury Review (Year). (US) **2666**, **3140**
Personal Injury Valuation Handbooks. (US ISSN 0031-5591) **2666**, **2540**
Personal Injury Verdict Reviews. (US) **2540**, **2666**
Personal Injury Verdict Survey. (US) **2540**
Personal Investing News. (US) **959**
Personal Investment. (AT ISSN 0813-2992) **959**
Personal Investment Portfolio Service Investment Advisory Monthly Newsletter *see* P I P S' - Investment Advisory Monthly Newsletter **959**
Personal Investor. (UK ISSN 0268-0599) **959**
Personal Investor *see* Worth **969**
†Personal Lines Letter. (US) **5257**
Personal M T M - Report (Year). (GW) **1068**
Personal Pensions (Year). (UK) **2540**
Personal Property Section News. (US ISSN 0737-6839) **2540**
Personal Publishing *see* Business Publishing **1468**
†Personal Report for the Executive. (US ISSN 0048-3443) **5257**
Personal Report for the Professional Secretary. (US) **1061**
Personal Romances. (US ISSN 0031-5613) **2984**
Personal Selling Power. (US) **1050**, **1024**
Personal Social Services Research Unit Bulletin *see* P S S R U Bulletin **4416**
†Personal Software. (UK) **5257**
Personal- und Vorlesungsverzeichnis. (GW) **1714**
Personal- und Vorlesungsverzeichnis der Universitaet Wuerzburg. (GW) **1696**
Personal-Verpflegung Report *see* P V - Report **2478**
Personal Watercraft Illustrated. (US) **4528**
Personal Wealth Reporter *see* Investment Reporter **951**
†Personal Workstation. (US ISSN 1047-4013) **5257**
Personale- og Oekonomiatistik for Sygehusvaesenet. (DK ISSN 0107-1173) **2471**, **4583**
Personale og Sengepladser ved de Sygedomsbehandlende Institutioner *see* Personale- og Oekonomiatistik for Sygehusvaesenet **2471**
Personalfuehrung. (GW ISSN 0723-3868) **1068**
Personalhistorisk Tidsskrift. (DK ISSN 0300-3655) **2161**
Personalist Forum. (US ISSN 0889-065X) **3775**
Personalities. Events. Times. (RU) **3574**
Personality. (SA) **2216**
Personality and Individual Differences. (US ISSN 0191-8869) **4038**
Personality and Psychopathology *see* Personality, Psychopathology and Psychotherapy **4038**
Personality and Social Psychology Bulletin. (US ISSN 0146-1672) **4038**
Personality, Psychopathology and Psychotherapy. (US ISSN 0079-0931) **4038**
Personality Study and Group Behaviour.(II ISSN 0970-8111) **4038**

Personals. (US) **36**
Die Personalvertretung. (GW ISSN 0476-3475) **1068**
Personalwirtschaft. (GW ISSN 0341-4698) **1068**
Personeel. (BE) **1069**
▼Personeel en Organisatie - Vakmatig. (NE ISSN 0924-9834) **1069**, **4093**
Personeelbeleid. (NE ISSN 0031-5656) **1069**
Personen-Compass. (AU) **795**
Personenvervoer. (NE ISSN 0376-6772) **4654**
Personhistorisk Tidskrift. (SW ISSN 0031-5699) **420**
Personnel *see* H R Focus **1065**
Personnel Administrator *see* H R Magazine **1065**
Personnel Advisory Bulletin *see* Personnel Manager's Letter **1069**
Personnel & Training Abstracts. (UK ISSN 0305-067X) **734**, **19**
Personnel Consultant. (US ISSN 0161-2425) **3630**
Personnel d'Enseignement des Colleges Communautaires. *see* Canada. Statistics Canada. Educational Staff in Community Colleges **5159**
Personnel de la Sante au Canada. *see* Health Personnel in Canada **3103**
Personnel des Nations Unies et des Agences Specialisees en Republique de Rwanda. (UN) **934**
Personnel Development. *see* Rencai Kaifa **1070**
Personnel Forms and Employment Checklists. (US) **1069**, **2666**
Personnel Guide to Canada's Travel Industry. (CN ISSN 0048-3451) **4782**
Personnel - Industrial Relations Report, Parts 1 and 2 *see* Salaries & Bonuses in Personnel - Industrial Relations Functions **993**
Personnel Journal. (US ISSN 0031-5745) **1069**, **991**
Personnel Literature. (US ISSN 0031-5753) **734**, **4081**
Personnel Management. (UK ISSN 0031-5761) **1069**
Personnel Management Abstracts. (US ISSN 0031-577X) **734**, **19**
Personnel Management Guide. (US) **1069**, **1117**
Personnel Management Plus *see* P M Plus **1068**
Personnel Manager's Legal Reporter *see* Human Resource Manager's Legal Reporter **981**
Personnel Manager's Letter. (US) **1069**
Personnel News. (US) **1069**
Personnel News for School Systems *see* Wages and Benefits **1732**
Personnel Policies and Benefits for the Apparel Industry. (US) **1069**
Personnel Policies Forum Survey *see* P F Survey **1068**
Personnel Policy Briefs *see* Management Policies & Personnel Law **1019**
Personnel Practice Ideas. (US) **1069**
Personnel Psychology. (US ISSN 0031-5826) **4038**, **1069**
Personnel Review. (UK ISSN 0048-3486) **1069**
Personnel Today. (II ISSN 0970-8405) **1069**, **991**
Personnel Today. (UK) **1069**
Personnel, Training and Education. (UK) **2779**
Personnel Update *see* Human Resources Update **1066**
Personnel Yearbook *see* Human Resource Management Yearbook **1066**
Persons to Contact for Visiting School Library Media Programs. (US) **1723**, **2779**
Persoonia. (NE ISSN 0031-5850) **512**
Persoverzicht. (NE ISSN 0031-5869) **113**
Perspecta. (US ISSN 0079-0958) **304**
Perspectiva. (GT) **4333**, **4382**
Perspectiva Economica. (BL ISSN 0100-039X) **685**

Perspectiva Escolar. (SP ISSN 0210-2331) **1654**
Perspectiva Mundial. (US ISSN 0164-3169) **3915**
Perspectiva Social. (SP ISSN 0210-0436) **2512**
Perspectivas. (BL ISSN 0101-3459) **4382**
Perspectivas en Psicologia. (CK ISSN 0120-3878) **4038**
Perspectivas en Salud Publica. (SP ISSN 0188-0012) **4109**
Perspectivas Internacionales en Planificacion Familiar. (US) **598, 3295**
Perspective. (SZ ISSN 0031-5923) **642, 1165**
The Perspective/Nan Pei Chi. (HK) **2197**
Perspective. (PK) **2948, 340**
Perspective. (SA ISSN 0012-8473) **3794**
Perspective (Cleveland). (US) **4416, 4109**
Perspective (Indiana). (US) **2258**
Perspective (Indianapolis). (US) **4154, 627**
Perspective (Madison). (US) **2666, 1654**
Perspective (New York, 1970). (US) **1723, 1757**
†Perspective (Newton). (US) **5257**
Perspective (Washington) see Perspectives on Political Science **3915**
Perspective (Wheaton). (US) **4195, 1686**
Perspective of Physics (New York). (US ISSN 0260-4280) **3826**
†Perspective on A T & T and Boc Products and Marketing. (US ISSN 0740-5324) **5257**
Perspective on Aging. (US ISSN 0096-2740) **2277**
Perspective on Consciousness & Psi Research. (US) **3596, 3775**
Perspective on Current Affairs. (II) **3915**
Perspectives. (SA ISSN 1017-141X) **879, 1024**
Perspectives. (UN) **1654**
Perspectives see New Perspectives **5246**
Perspectives (Alexandria) see G C A Review **4007**
†Perspectives (Baltimore). (US) **5257**
Perspectives (Bloomington). (US ISSN 0745-3027) **1024, 1300**
Perspectives (Columbus). (US ISSN 0890-9792) **1655**
†Perspectives (Des Moines). (US) **5257**
Perspectives (Grand Rapids). (US ISSN 0888-5281) **4195**
†Perspectives (Hampton). (US) **5257**
Perspectives (Liberty). (US) **1024, 4003**
▼Perspectives (Madison). (US) **795, 934**
Perspectives (New York). (US) **2019**
†Perspectives (Norwood). (US ISSN 0883-6086) **5257**
Perspectives (Pittsburgh) see Managing (Pittsburgh) **1020**
Perspectives (Providence). (US) **1321**
Perspectives (Saskatoon). (CN ISSN 0316-3334) **1757**
Perspectives (Toronto). (CN ISSN 0831-7445) **2277, 3285**
Perspectives (Washington). (US) **2319**
Perspectives (Washington, 1971). (US ISSN 0048-3508) **2019**
Perspectives and Plans for Graduate Studies. (CN ISSN 0317-7025) **1714**
Perspectives C I L see I C I Spectrum **1077**
Perspectives de l'Economique. Serie 1. Fondateurs de l'Economie. (FR ISSN 0079-0982) **897**
Perspectives de l'Economique. Serie 2. Economie Contemporaine. (FR) **685**
Perspectives de l'Economique. Serie 3. Critique. (FR) **685**
Perspectives de l'Education see Perspectives **1654**
Perspectives Economiques de l'O E C D.(FR ISSN 0304-3274) **685**

Perspectives Feministes. see Feminist Perspectives **4842**
Perspectives for Teachers of the Hearing Impaired see Perspectives in Education and Deafness **1739**
Perspectives Immobilieres. (FR) **4154**
Perspectives in Artificial Intelligence. (US) **1410**
Perspectives in Biology and Medicine. (US ISSN 0031-5982) **3140, 451**
Perspectives in Biomechanics. (US ISSN 0272-6327) **451**
▼Perspectives in California Archaeology. (US) **281**
Perspectives in Cardiology. (CN) **3211**
Perspectives in Cardiovascular Research. (US ISSN 0361-0527) **3211**
Perspectives in Clinical Pharmacology see Perspectives in Clinical Pharmacy **3737**
Perspectives in Clinical Pharmacy. (US) **3737**
†Perspectives in Computing (Armonk). (US ISSN 0273-4621) **5257**
Perspectives in Computing (San Diego) .(US) **1399**
†Perspectives in Criminal Justice. (US) **5257**
Perspectives in E.N.T. - Immunology. (IT) **3188**
Perspectives in Economic History see South African Journal of Economic History **898**
Perspectives in Education and Deafness.(US ISSN 1051-6204) **1739**
Perspectives in Emergency Medicine. (CN) **3140**
▼Perspectives in Energy. (UK) **1793**
Perspectives in Engineering. (US) **1833**
Perspectives in Ethology. (US) **4814**
Perspectives in Geriatrics. (CN) **2277**
Perspectives in Healthcare Risk Management. (US ISSN 0899-1073) **2468, 2540**
Perspectives in Hospital Risk Management see Perspectives in Healthcare Risk Management **2468**
Perspectives in Hypertension Series. (US) **3140**
Perspectives in Immunology. (US) **3188**
Perspectives in Jewish Learning see Solomon Goldman Lectures **4226**
Perspectives in Law and Psychology. (US) **2666, 4038**
Perspectives in Mathematical Logic. (US ISSN 0172-6641) **3050**
Perspectives in Mathematics. (US) **3050**
Perspectives in Neurolinguistics, Neuropsychology, and Psycholinguistics. (US) **3350, 2834**
Perspectives in Pediatric Pathology. (SZ ISSN 0091-2921) **3325, 3140**
Perspectives in Physics (San Diego). (US) **3826**
Perspectives in Powder Metallurgy see New Perspectives in Powder Metallurgy **3416**
Perspectives in Primate Biology. (II) **590**
Perspectives in Psychiatric Care. (US ISSN 0031-5990) **3285, 3350**
Perspectives in Psychological Researches. (II ISSN 0971-1562) **4038, 1655**
Perspectives in Psychotherapy. (US ISSN 0735-4037) **4038**
Perspectives in Religious Studies. (US ISSN 0093-531X) **4246**
†Perspectives in Structural Science. (UK) **5257**
Perspectives in Total Compensation. (US) **1069**
†Perspectives in Toxicology. (US) **5257**
Perspectives in Urban Geography. (II) **2258, 4444**
Perspectives Internationales Sur le Planning Familial. (US) **598, 3295**
Perspectives Mediterraneennes. (FR ISSN 0240-8430) **879**
Perspectives of New Music. (US ISSN 0031-6016) **3574**

Perspectives on Labour and Income. (CN ISSN 0840-8750) **734**
Perspectives on Local Public Finance and Public Policy. (US ISSN 0740-0624) **1104**
Perspectives on Political Science. (US ISSN 1045-7097) **3915, 4070, 4134**
Perspectives on Science and Christian Faith. (US ISSN 0892-2675) **4195, 4333**
Perspectives on Southern Africa. (US) **3915, 2334**
Perspectives on the American South. (US ISSN 0275-584X) **2419, 4444**
Perspectives Polonaises see Polish Perspectives **2879**
Perspectives Psychiatriques. (FR ISSN 0031-6032) **3350**
Perspectives Quebecoises. (CN) **1050**
Perspectives Spatiales see Space Markets **5281**
Perspectives Universitaires. (CN ISSN 0820-005X) **1714, 2834**
Perspektief. (NE ISSN 0167-9104) **3794**
†Perspektiven. (GW ISSN 0171-3183) **5257**
Perspektiven der Philosophie. Neues Jahrbuch. (NE) **3775**
Perspektiven des Demokratishen Sozialismus see P D S **3913**
Perspektivy. (RU) **3915**
Perspektywy. (PL ISSN 0031-6059) **2214**
Persuasion. (US) **3399**
Persuasion at Work see Family in America **4435**
Persuasions. (CN ISSN 0821-0314) **2948**
Persuasions, Occasional Papers. (CN ISSN 0835-9628) **2948**
Pertani P T. (IO) **113**
Pertanika. (MY ISSN 0126-6128) **114**
Pertes Causee par l'Incendie au Canada. Rapport Annuel. see Fire Losses in Canada. Annual Report **2035**
Pertes Dues a l'Incendie de Biens Immobiliers de l'Administration Federale. see Fire Losses in Government of Canada Properties. Report **2035**
Perth Hungarian News. see Perthi Magyar Hirek **2019**
Perth Observatory. Communications. (AT ISSN 0079-1067) **368**
Perthi Magyar Hirek/Perth Hungarian News. (AT) **2019**
Peru. (BO) **3969**
†Peru. Biblioteca Nacional. Bibliografia Nacional. (PE) **5257**
Peru. Direccion de Sanidad. Revista de la Sanidad see Peru. Policia Nacional. Revista de la Sanidad **3140**
Peru. Fuerzas Policiales. Revista de la Sanidad see Peru. Policia Nacional. Revista de la Sanidad **3140**
Peru. Instituto Nacional de Estadistica. Boletin Anual. (PE) **734, 999**
Peru. Ministerio de Educacion Publica. Oficina Sectorial de Planificacion. Plan Bienal. (PE) **1655**
Peru. Ministerio de Relaciones Exteriores. Boletin Trimestral. (PE) **3969**
Peru. Policia Nacional. Revista de la Sanidad. (PE) **3140, 4109**
†Peru: Compendio Estadistico. (PE) **5257**
Peru Economico. (PE) **879**
Peru Exporta. (PE) **919**
Peru Indigena. (PE) **247**
Peru - Problema. (PE ISSN 0079-1075) **4444**
Perugia Quadrennial International Conferences on Cancer. Proceedings.(IT ISSN 0069-8520) **3201**
Perutusan Ratu Darul Ehsan. (MY) **2779**
Pesca al Dia see Ciencia y Tecnologia Pesquera **2038**
Pesca In. (IT) **4553, 1965**
Pesca in Mare. (IT) **4553**

PESTICIDES BULLETIN 6549

Pesca y Marina. (US ISSN 0258-5812) **2047**
Pescare. (IT ISSN 0031-6091) **4483, 2051**
Pescare Mare. (IT) **4553**
Pescatur. (BL) **4553**
Pesefas. (IS) **2948**
Peshitta Institute, Leiden. Monographs. (NE ISSN 0169-9008) **4225, 4195**
Pesquisa Agropecuaria Brasileira/Brazilian Journal of Agricultural Research. (BL ISSN 0100-204X) **114**
Pesquisa Agropecuaria Pernambucana. (BL ISSN 0100-8501) **114**
Pesquisa e Debate - Economia. (BL) **685**
Pesquisa e Planejamento see Pesquisa e Planejamento Economico **1082**
Pesquisa e Planejamento Economico. (BL ISSN 0100-0551) **1082**
Pesquisa em Andamento. (BL ISSN 0100-8161) **114**
Pesquisa Medica. (BL ISSN 0048-3567) **3140**
Pesquisas: Publicacoes de Antropologia.(BL ISSN 0553-8467) **247**
Pesquisas: Publicacoes de Botanica. (BL ISSN 0553-8475) **512**
Pesquisas: Publicacoes de Historia. (BL ISSN 0553-8491) **2319**
Pesquisas: Publicacoes de Zoologia. (BL ISSN 0553-8505) **590**
Pest Advisory Leaflet. (NL ISSN 1017-6276) **187**
Pest Control. (US ISSN 0031-6121) **187**
Pest Control for the Home Garden see Gardener's Guide to Pest Prevention and Control in the Home and Garden **2127**
Pest Control Technology. (US ISSN 0730-7608) **1857, 187**
Pest Management. (US ISSN 0744-6357) **537**
Pest Management for Livestock and Poultry (Year). (US) **223**
Pest Management for Public Health. (US) **1857, 4109**
Pest Management Recommendations for Commercial Tree-Fruit Production.(US) **187, 512**
Pest Management Recommendations for Commercial Vegetable and Potato Production. (US) **187**
Pest Management Recommendations for Control of Vertebrates (Year). (US) **187**
Pest Management Recommendations for Small Fruit Crops. (US) **187**
Pest Megyei Konyvtaros. (HU ISSN 0209-6145) **2779**
Pest Resistance Management see Resistant Pest Management **116**
Pesticide Analytical Manual. (US) **4110, 1857**
Pesticide & Toxic Chemical News. (US ISSN 0146-0501) **2079**
Pesticide Biochemistry and Physiology. (US ISSN 0048-3575) **187, 481**
Pesticide Chemical News see Pesticide & Toxic Chemical News **2079**
Pesticide Chemical News Guide. (US) **2079**
▼Pesticide Outlook. (UK ISSN 0956-1250) **187**
Pesticide Progress. (US) **2137**
Pesticide Residues in Danish Food. see Pesticidrester i Danske Levnedsmidler **188**
Pesticide Residues in Food. (UN ISSN 0587-5943) **4110**
Pesticide Resistance Management see Resistant Pest Management **116**
Pesticide Science. (UK ISSN 0031-613X) **188**
Pesticide Science and Management. see Nongyao Kexue yu Guanli **186**
†Pesticides. (II ISSN 0031-6148) **5257**
Pesticides (Sacramento). (US ISSN 0092-6752) **188**
Pesticides Abstracts. (US ISSN 0093-3295) **1974, 19, 141, 1983**
Pesticides and You. (US ISSN 0896-7253) **188, 1857, 1965**
Pesticides Bulletin. (PK) **188**

6550 PESTICIDES DISC

†Pesticides Disc. (UK ISSN 0956-0602) **5257**
Pesticides News. (UK) **1857**
Pesticides Research and Monitoring Annual Report. (CN) **188, 1965**
Pesticidi. (YU ISSN 0352-9029) **188**
Pesticidrester i Danske Levnedsmidler/ Pesticide Residues in Danish Food. (DK ISSN 0108-2086) **188, 2079**
Pesum Padam. (II ISSN 0031-6164) **3515**
Pet Age. (US ISSN 0098-5406) **3712**
Pet Business. (US ISSN 0191-4766) **3712, 1050**
Pet Business World. (UK) **1117, 3712**
Pet Care Report. (US) **3712**
Pet Dealer. (US ISSN 0553-8572) **3712**
Pet Focus. (US ISSN 1046-2112) **3712, 4814**
†Pet Health News. (US) **5257**
Pet Product Marketing. (UK ISSN 0262-5849) **3712**
Pet Product Marketing and Garden Supplies - The Pet Trade Journal see Pet Product Marketing **3712**
Pet Product News. (US) **3713**
Pet Store Trader see Pet Business World **1117**
Pet Stuff. (US) **3713**
Pet Veterinarian. (US ISSN 1043-7533) **4814, 3713**
Petalon. (GR) **2319**
Petanque News. (US) **4509**
Peter Dag Investment Letter. (US ISSN 0196-9323) **795**
Peter Warlock Society Newsletter. (UK ISSN 0266-366X) **3574**
Peterborough & District Family History Society Journal. (UK ISSN 0262-4427) **2161**
Peterborough Business Directory. (UK ISSN 0957-1078) **1150**
Peterborough Historical Society Bulletin.(CN ISSN 0380-6642) **2419**
Petermanns Geographische Mitteilungen. (GW ISSN 0031-6229) **2258**
▼Petersen's College Basketball. (US) **4509**
Petersen's College Football. (US ISSN 0276-2129) **4509**
Petersen's Complete Guide to Hunting see Big Game Hunting **4542**
†Petersen's Fishing. (US ISSN 1041-4703) **5257**
Petersen's Handguns. (US ISSN 1040-1865) **4553**
Petersen's Hunting. (US ISSN 0146-4671) **4553**
Petersen's Photographic. (US ISSN 0199-4913) **3794**
Petersen's Pro Baseball. (US) **4509**
Petersen's Pro Basketball. (US ISSN 0192-2238) **4509**
Petersen's Super Motocross see Super-Moto Cross **5285**
Petersen's 4 Wheel & Off-Road. (US ISSN 0162-3214) **4520, 4699**
Peterson's Annual Guides to Graduate Study. Graduate Programs in the Physical Science and Mathematics. see Peterson's Guide to Graduate Programs in the Physical Sciences and Mathematics (Year) (Book 4) **1696**
†Peterson's Applying to Colleges and Universities in the United States: A Handbook for International Students. (US ISSN 0890-3085) **5257**
Peterson's Business and Management Jobs (Year) see Peterson's Job Opportunities for Business and Liberal Arts Graduates (Year) **3630**
Peterson's College Money Handbook (Year). (US ISSN 0894-9395) **1696**
Peterson's Competitive Colleges (Year). (US ISSN 0887-0152) **1696**
Peterson's Engineering, Science, and Computer Jobs (Year) see Peterson's Job Opportunities For Engineering, Science, and Computer Graduates (Year) **3630**

Peterson's Grants for Graduate Students (Year). (US ISSN 1040-1091) **1714**
Peterson's Guide to Colleges in New England (Year). (US ISSN 0742-4973) **1696**
Peterson's Guide to Colleges in New York (Year). (US ISSN 0742-4965) **1696**
Peterson's Guide to Colleges in the Middle Atlantic States (Year). (US ISSN 0742-4957) **1696**
Peterson's Guide to Colleges in the Midwest (Year). (US ISSN 0742-4949) **1696**
Peterson's Guide to Colleges in the Southeast (Year). (US ISSN 0882-309X) **1696**
Peterson's Guide to Colleges in the Southwest (Year). (US ISSN 0882-3103) **1696**
Peterson's Guide to Colleges in the West (Year). (US ISSN 0888-8159) **1696**
Peterson's Guide to Four-Year Colleges (Year). (US ISSN 0894-9336) **1696**
Peterson's Guide to Graduate and Professional Programs: An Overview (Year) (Book 1). (US ISSN 0894-9344) **1696**
Peterson's Guide to Graduate Programs in Business, Education, Health, and Law (Year) (Book 6). (US ISSN 0897-6023) **1696**
Peterson's Guide to Graduate Programs in Engineering and Applied Sciences (Year) (Book 5). (US ISSN 0894-9387) **1696, 1833**
Peterson's Guide to Graduate Programs in the Biological and Agricultural Sciences (Year) (Book 3). (US ISSN 0894-9360) **1696, 451**
Peterson's Guide to Graduate Programs in the Humanities and Social Sciences (Year) (Book 2). (US ISSN 0894-9352) **1696**
Peterson's Guide to Graduate Programs in the Physical Sciences and Mathematics (Year) (Book 4). (US ISSN 0894-9379) **1696, 4333**
Peterson's Guide to Independent Secondary Schools (Year). (US ISSN 0894-9409) **1697**
Peterson's Guide to Two-Year Colleges (Year). (US ISSN 0894-9328) **1697**
Peterson's Guides. Annual Guides to Graduate Study. Book 2: Humanities and Social Sciences. see Peterson's Guide to Graduate Programs in the Humanities and Social Sciences (Year) (Book 2) **1696**
Peterson's Guides. Annual Guides to Graduate Study. Book 5: Engineering and Applied Sciences see Peterson's Guide to Graduate Programs in Engineering and Applied Sciences (Year) (Book 5) **1696**
Peterson's Higher Education Directory (Year) see Peterson's Register of Higher Education (Year) **1697**
Peterson's Job Opportunities for Business and Liberal Arts Graduates (Year). (US ISSN 1048-3411) **3630, 1024**
Peterson's Job Opportunities For Engineering, Science, and Computer Graduates (Year). (US ISSN 1048-342X) **3630, 1833**
Peterson's Register of Higher Education (Year). (US ISSN 1046-2406) **1697**
Peterson's Summer Opportunities for Kids and Teenagers (Year). (US ISSN 0894-9417) **4782**
Petfood Industry. (US ISSN 0031-6245) **2079, 3713**
†Le Petit Baton. (US) **5257**
Le Petit Journal du Brasseur. (BE ISSN 0031-6253) **384**
Le Petit Mensuel. (CN) **1321**
Petit Meunier. (FR ISSN 0031-6261) **208**
Petit Moniteur des Assurances see Le Moniteur des Assurances **2538**
Petit Samedi Soir. (HT) **2197**
▼Petite. (US ISSN 0886-5302) **1293, 4850**

Petite Caisse. (CN) **1321**
Petits Propos Culinaires see P P C **2449**
Petnaest Dana/Fifteen Days. (CI ISSN 0031-6296) **340**
Petofi Irodalmi Muzeum Evkonyve/ Yearbook of the Literary Museum. (HU ISSN 0524-8906) **2948**
Petra. (GW ISSN 0031-630X) **4851, 2449**
Petri-Heil. (SZ ISSN 0031-6318) **4553**
The Petro-Philatelist. (US ISSN 0279-3709) **3755**
Petro Quimica see Guia de la Industria Quimica: Productos Quimicos **1853**
Petrobras. Consolidated Report. (BL) **3697**
Petrobras News. (BL) **3697**
Petrochemical Equipment. (CC ISSN 1000-7466) **1857, 3697, 3841**
▼Petrochemical Industry. (US) **3697, 1150**
PetroChemical News. (US ISSN 0031-6342) **1857**
Petrochemical Technology. see Shiyou Huagong **3701**
Petrochemical Units in the O P E C and O A P E C Countries. see Unites Petrochimiques dans les Pays de l'O P E C et de l'O P A E P **5296**
Petrochemicals and Plastics News see Chemicals & Polymers News **3684**
Petrofax. (US) **3697**
Petroflash. (US) **3697**
Petrol si Gaze see Mine, Petrol si Gaze **3692**
Petrole et Gaz. (FR ISSN 0761-2095) **3697**
Petrole et Gaz Arabes see Arab Oil & Gas **3682**
Petrole et le Gaz en Afrique. (FR) **3697**
Petrole et Techniques. (FR ISSN 0152-5425) **3697**
Petrole Informations (International Edition) see Petrole Informations International (English Edition) **3697**
Petrole Informations International (Edition Bilingue). (FR ISSN 0755-561X) **3697**
Petrole Informations International (English Edition). (FR ISSN 0762-0357) **3697**
Petroleo. (SP ISSN 0213-8360) **3697**
Petroleo Internacional. (US ISSN 0093-7851) **3697**
Petroleo y Petroquimica Internacional see Petroleo Internacional **3697**
Petroleos Mexicanos. Boletin Bibliografico see Pemex. Boletin Bibliografico **3706**
Petroleos Mexicanos Pemex. Boletin Bibliografico see Pemex. Boletin Bibliografico **3706**
Petroleum. (VE) **3697**
Petroleum Abstracts. (US ISSN 0031-6423) **3707, 19**
Petroleum and Chemical Industry Conference. Record of Conference Papers. (US ISSN 0090-3507) **1857, 3697**
Petroleum and Chemical Transporter see Modern Bulk Transporter **4746**
Petroleum and Coal Geology. see Neftena i Vuglistna Geologiia **1574**
Petroleum and Industry in Abu Dhabi. see Al-Butrul wal-Sina'a fi Abu Dhabi **3705**
Petroleum and Industry News. see Akhbar al-Butrul wal-Sina'a **3681**
Petroleum and Natural Gas Production Tape. (CN) **3707**
Petroleum Asia Journal. (II) **3697**
Petroleum - C-Store Products. (US ISSN 0899-6369) **3697**
Petroleum Chemistry U.S.S.R. (English translation of: Neftekhimiya) (US ISSN 0031-6458) **3697, 1857**
Petroleum Community - Mujtama' al-Bitrul see A D N O C News **3680**
Petroleum Concession Handbook. (US) **2727, 3697**
Petroleum Economist. (UK ISSN 0306-395X) **3697**
Petroleum-Energy Business News Index.(US) **3707, 19**

Petroleum Engineer International. (US ISSN 0031-6466) **3698**
Petroleum Engineering Construction. see Shiyou Gongcheng Jianshe **3701**
Petroleum Equipment see Petroleum - C-Store Products **3697**
Petroleum Equipment Directory. (US) **3698**
Petroleum Exploration and Development. see Shiyou Kantan yu Kaifa **3701**
Petroleum Facts and Figures see Basic Petroleum Data Book **3705**
Petroleum Frontiers. (US) **3698**
Petroleum Gazette. (AT ISSN 0048-3591) **3698**
Petroleum Geology: a Digest of Russian Literature on Petroleum Geology. (US) **3698, 1577**
Petroleum Geology of Taiwan/T'aiwan Shih-yu Ti-chih. (CH) **3698, 1577**
▼Petroleum Geology Special Paper Series. (CN) **3698, 1577**
Petroleum Independent. (US ISSN 0747-2528) **3698**
Petroleum Industry Conference. Record see Petroleum and Chemical Industry Conference. Record of Conference Papers **1857**
Petroleum Industry in Illinois. (US) **3698**
Petroleum Industry in Japan. (JA) **3698**
Petroleum Intelligence Weekly. (US ISSN 0480-2160) **3698**
Petroleum: Latin American Industrial Report. (US) **3698, 838**
Petroleum Legislation. (US) **2728, 3698**
†Petroleum Management. (US ISSN 0884-4550) **5257**
Petroleum Market Intelligence. (US) **3707, 4583**
Petroleum Marketer. (US ISSN 0362-7799) **3698**
Petroleum Marketer's Handbook. (US) **3698**
Petroleum Marketing Monthly. (US ISSN 0741-9643) **3698**
Petroleum News. (HK ISSN 0250-7765) **3698, 1793**
Petroleum Newsletter. (US) **3620, 3698**
Petroleum Newsletter see Iran Oil News **3690**
Petroleum Newsletter. (AT ISSN 0312-9837) **3698**
Petroleum Outlook. (US ISSN 0031-6490) **3698**
Petroleum Press Service see Petroleum Economist **3697**
Petroleum Review. (UK ISSN 0020-3076) **3698**
Petroleum Services. Annual Petroleum Review. (UK) **3698**
Petroleum Services. Weekly Service. (UK) **3698**
Petroleum Services. Weekly Service (Offshore). (UK) **3698**
Petroleum Services. Weekly Service. Offshore Report see Petroleum Services. Weekly Service (Offshore) **3698**
Petroleum Services. Weekly Service (Onshore). (UK) **3698**
Petroleum Services. Weekly Service. Onshore Report see Petroleum Services. Weekly Service (Onshore) **3698**
†Petroleum Situation. (US) **5257**
Petroleum Software Directory. (US ISSN 0743-6750) **1479, 3698**
Petroleum Supply Annual. (US) **3698**
Petroleum Supply Monthly. (US ISSN 0733-0553) **3699**
Petroleum Taxation & Legislation Report. (US) **3699**
Petroleum Taxation Report see Petroleum Taxation & Legislation Report **3699**
Petroleum Times Price Report. (UK ISSN 0261-3883) **3699**
Petroleum Titles Data Tape. (CN) **3707**
†Petroleum Wholesaler. (US) **5257**
Petrolieri d'Italia. (IT ISSN 0031-6563) **3699**
Petrolieri International. (IT) **3699**

Petrolio. (IT ISSN 0031-6571) **3699**
Petrotecnica. (AG ISSN 0031-6598) **3699**
Pets Europe. (NE) **3713**
Pets Magazine. (CN ISSN 0715-8947) **3713**
Pets, Supplies, Marketing. (US ISSN 0162-8666) **1050**, 3713
Pets Welcome. (UK ISSN 0079-130X) **4782**, 3713
Pettaquamscutt Reporter. (US) **2419**
Pettine. (IT) **2206**
Pettpouri. (US) **3713**
Petts Wood Post. (UK ISSN 0048-3605) **2195**
Petty Sessions Review. (AT ISSN 0158-2720) **2666**, 1520
†Petzold on Stocks. (US) **5257**
Petzold on the Market. (US) **959**
Peuple. (FR ISSN 0031-661X) **2588**
Peuple see Nouveau Militant **3911**
Peuples see People **597**
Peuples du Monde. (FR) **4272**
Peuples Mediterraneens - Mediterranean Peoples. (FR ISSN 0399-1253) **4382**
Peuples Noirs, Peuples Africains. (FR ISSN 0181-4087) **2879**, 2019
Pewter Collectors' Club of America. Bulletin. (US ISSN 0031-6644) **259**
El Pez y la Serpiente. (NQ ISSN 0031-6652) **2948**
Pfaelzer Bauer. (GW ISSN 0031-6660) **188**
Pfaelzer Heimat. (GW ISSN 0031-6679) **2380**
Pfaelzer Saenger. (GW ISSN 0031-6687) **3574**
Pfaelzer Turner. (GW) **4483**
Pfaff Information. (GW) **1287**
Die Pfalz am Rhein. (GW ISSN 0031-6695) **2058**, 2380
Pfarrago. (NE) **4195**
Pfarrbrief. (AU ISSN 0031-6709) **4195**
Pfeiffer & Company. Annual. (US ISSN 1046-333X) **1024**
†Pferd und Sport. (GW ISSN 0138-1342) **5257**
Pferde. (GW) **4536**
Pferde Heute. (GW ISSN 0176-490X) **4536**
Pferdeheilkunde. (GW ISSN 0177-7726) **4814**
†Pferdemarkt. (GW) **5257**
▼Pferderevue. (AU) **4536**
▼Pfinztal an Wochenende. (GW) **2190**
Pflanzenarzt. (AU ISSN 0031-6733) **512**
Pflanzenschutz Kurier. (GW ISSN 0405-0738) **188**
Pflanzenschutz-Nachrichten Bayer. (GW ISSN 0340-1723) **188**
Pflanzenschutzberichte. (AU ISSN 0031-675X) **512**
Pflasterstrand see Journal Frankfurt **2189**
Pfluegers Archiv. (GW ISSN 0031-6768) **3140**, 573
Pfluegers Archiv fuer die Gesamte Physiologie des Menschen und der Tiere see Pfluegers Archiv **3140**
†Die Pforte. (GW ISSN 0031-6784) **5257**
Phaenomen Farbe. (GW) **3655**
Phaenomenologica. (NE ISSN 0079-1350) **3775**
Phaenomenologische Forschungen/ Phenomenological Studies. (GW) **3775**
▼Phafoga. (SA) **4287**
†Phagocytes. (UK ISSN 0142-8519) **5257**
Phalanx. (US ISSN 0195-1920) **3468**, 1921
Phanerogamarum Monographiae. (GW ISSN 0079-1369) **512**
Phantastische Zeiten. (GW) **3013**
Phaphama! (SA ISSN 0031-6806) **4287**
Le Phare. (GW) **2834**, 1757
Pharetra. (NE ISSN 0031-6822) **1321**
Pharma Brief. (GW) **934**
Pharma-Flash. (SZ ISSN 0378-7958) **3737**
Pharma Japan. (JA ISSN 0285-4937) **3737**

Pharma Japan Yearbook. (JA) **3737**
Pharma-Marketing Journal. (GW ISSN 0721-5665) **1050**, 36, 3737
Pharma Times. (II ISSN 0031-6849) **3737**
Pharma und Wir. (GW) **3737**
Pharmabulletin. (AT) **3737**
Pharmaca. (CI ISSN 0031-6857) **3737**
Pharmaceutica Acta Helvetiae. (SZ ISSN 0031-6865) **3737**
Pharmaceutical Activities Index - Directory. (US) **3748**
Pharmaceutical Advertising Council Cer see P A Cer **36**
Pharmaceutical and Cosmetic Equipment see Pharmaceutical Processing **3738**
Pharmaceutical & Cosmetic Review. (SA ISSN 0257-2028) **3737**, 376
Pharmaceutical Business News. (UK) **3737**, 685
Pharmaceutical Chemistry Journal. (English translation of: Khimiko-farmatsevticheskii Zhurnal) (US ISSN 0091-150X) **3738**, 1185
Pharmaceutical Codex. (UK) **3738**
▼Pharmaceutical Digest. (US) **3738**
Pharmaceutical Engineering. (US ISSN 0273-8139) **1833**, 3738
Pharmaceutical Executive. (US ISSN 0279-6570) **3738**
Pharmaceutical Historian. (UK ISSN 0079-1393) **3738**
Pharmaceutical Journal. (UK ISSN 0031-6873) **3738**
Pharmaceutical: Latin American Industrial Report. (US) **3738**, 838
Pharmaceutical Library Bulletin/ Yakugaku Toshokan. (JA ISSN 0386-2062) **2779**, 3738
Pharmaceutical Litigation Reporter. (US ISSN 0887-7815) **2666**, 3738
Pharmaceutical Manufacturers Association Newsletter see P M A Newsletter **3737**
Pharmaceutical Manufacturers Association Statistical Factbook see P M A Statistical Factbook **3748**
Pharmaceutical Manufacturers of Japan. (JA) **1150**, 3738
Pharmaceutical Manufacturing Review. (UK) **3738**, 1082
Pharmaceutical Marketers Directory. (US) **3738**, 1050
Pharmaceutical Marketing and Media see Medical Marketing & Media **3734**
Pharmaceutical Medicine (Houndmills). (UK ISSN 0265-0673) **3738**, 3140
Pharmaceutical Medicine (Worthing). (UK ISSN 0142-1581) **3140**, 3738
Pharmaceutical News Index see P N I **3748**
Pharmaceutical Processing. (US) **3738**
Pharmaceutical Representative. (US ISSN 0161-8415) **3738**
Pharmaceutical Research. (US ISSN 0724-8741) **3738**
Pharmaceutical Society of Japan. Journal/Yakugaku Zasshi. (JA ISSN 0031-6903) **3738**
Pharmaceutical Society of Korea. Journal/Yakhak Hoeji. (KO ISSN 0513-4242) **3738**
Pharmaceutical Technology. (US ISSN 0147-8087) **3738**
Pharmaceutical Technology International. (US ISSN 0164-6826) **3738**
Pharmaceuticals Monthly/Gekkan Yakuji. (JA ISSN 0016-5980) **3738**
Pharmaceutisch Tijdschrift. (BE) **3738**
Le Pharmacien. (CN ISSN 0031-692X) **3738**
Pharmacien Biologiste see Eurobiologiste **476**
Pharmacien de France. (FR ISSN 0031-6938) **3738**
Pharmacien Hospitalier. (FR ISSN 0768-9179) **3738**, 2468
†Pharmacist's Assets. (US) **5257**
Pharmacochemistry Library. (NE ISSN 0165-7208) **1185**

▼Pharmacoepidemiology and Drug Safety. (UK ISSN 1053-8569) **3738**
▼Pharmacogenetics. (UK ISSN 0960-314X) **546**, 3739
Pharmacognosy see International Journal of Pharmacognosy **3730**
Pharmacological Research. (UK ISSN 1043-6618) **3739**
Pharmacological Research Communications see Pharmacological Research **3739**
Pharmacological Reviews. (US ISSN 0031-6997) **3739**
Pharmacologist. (US ISSN 0031-7004) **3739**
Pharmacology. (SZ ISSN 0031-7012) **3739**
Pharmacology and Clinics of Chinese Materia Medica. see Zhongyao Yaoli yu Linchuang **3746**
Pharmacology and the Skin. (SZ ISSN 1011-291X) **3249**, 3739
Pharmacology and Therapeutics. (US ISSN 0163-7258) **3739**, 1983
Pharmacology and Toxicology. see Farmakologiya i Toksikologiya **3726**
Pharmacology & Toxicology. (DK ISSN 0901-9928) **3739**, 1983
Pharmacology & Toxicology. Supplementum. (DK ISSN 0901-9936) **1983**, 3739
Pharmacology, Biochemistry and Behavior. (US ISSN 0091-3057) **590**
Pharmacometrics. see Oyo Yakuri **3736**
Pharmacopeial Forum. (US ISSN 0363-4655) **3739**
Pharmacopoeia of the People's Republic of China. (CC) **3739**
Pharmacopsychiatry. (GW ISSN 0176-3679) **3350**, 3739
Pharmacotherapy. (US ISSN 0277-0008) **3739**
Pharmactuel. (CN) **3739**
Pharmacy. see Farumashia **3726**
Pharmacy. see Farmacia **3726**
Pharmacy. see Farmatsiya **3726**
Pharmacy & Therapeutic see P & T **3737**
Pharmacy Bulletin see Encapsulator **3725**
Pharmacy Companion/Yakkyoku No Tomo. (JA ISSN 0044-0043) **3739**
Pharmacy Counselor. (US) **3739**
Pharmacy Guild of Australia. Annual Report. (AT) **3739**
Pharmacy Guild of Australia. National Newsletter. (AT) **3739**
Pharmacy Health-Line. (US) **3739**, 3285, 4110
Pharmacy in History. (US ISSN 0031-7047) **3739**
Pharmacy Law Digest. (US ISSN 0149-1717) **3739**, 2666
Pharmacy Management. (SA) **3739**
Pharmacy News. (II ISSN 0031-7063) **3739**
Pharmacy Practice see A P P M Update **3715**
Pharmacy Practice. (CN) **3739**
Pharmacy Practice News. (US) **3739**
Pharmacy Review. (AT ISSN 0314-6316) **3739**
Pharmacy Student. (US ISSN 0279-5272) **3739**, 1714
Pharmacy Times. (US ISSN 0003-0627) **3740**
Pharmacy Today. (US ISSN 1042-0991) **3740**
Pharmacy Trade. (AT ISSN 0031-7071) **3740**
▼Pharmacy Update. (US ISSN 1055-9744) **3740**
Pharmacy Weekly see Pharmacy Today **3740**
Pharmacy West. (US ISSN 0191-6394) **3740**
Pharmaklinik see Ciencia Pharmaceutica **3721**
Pharmakopsychiatrie - Neuro-Psychopharmakologie see Pharmacopsychiatry **3350**
†Pharmakotherapie. (GW ISSN 0344-7154) **5257**
PharmAlert. (US ISSN 0278-6850) **1538**, 3740

Pharmascope. (US ISSN 0048-3648) **3740**
Pharmtherapeutica. (UK ISSN 0308-051X) **3140**
Die Pharmazeutische Industrie. (GW ISSN 0031-711X) **3740**
Pharmazeutische Rundschau. (GW ISSN 0031-7128) **3740**
Pharmazeutische Zeitung. (GW ISSN 0031-7136) **3740**
Pharmazie Heute. (GW ISSN 0369-979X) **3740**
Pharmazie in Unserer Zeit. (GW ISSN 0048-3664) **3740**
PharmChem Newsletter. (US ISSN 0146-3128) **1538**
Pharmindex. (US ISSN 0031-7152) **3748**, 20
Pharmstudent. (II ISSN 0379-556X) **3740**
Pharos. (CN) **1321**
Pharos see Pharos International **2120**
Pharos (Menlo Park). (US ISSN 0031-7179) **3140**
Pharos (Northville). (US) **3755**
Pharos (St. Petersburg). (US ISSN 0031-7160) **3531**
Pharos International. (UK) **2120**
Pharr Quarterly. (US) **2162**
Phase and Cycle. (US) **3001**
Phase Transitions. Sections A & B. (US ISSN 0141-1594) **3826**
Pheasants Forever. (US) **4553**
Phelps County Genealogical Society Quarterly. (US) **2162**
▼Phenomena. (FR ISSN 1157-4704) **60**
Phenomena. (US) **3775**
PhenomeNews. (US) **3596**, 3775
Phenomenological Inquiry. (US ISSN 0885-3886) **3775**
Phenomenological Studies. see Phaenomenologische Forschungen **3775**
Phenomenological Theology. (US) **3775**, 4195
Phenomenology and Buddhist Thought. (US) **3775**, 4215
Phenomenology & Pedagogy. (CN ISSN 0820-9189) **3775**
Phenomenology Information Bulletin see Phenomenological Inquiry **3775**
Phi Delta Kappa Fastbacks. (US) **1655**
Phi Delta Kappan. (US ISSN 0031-7217) **1655**
Phi Eta Sigma. Forum. (US) **1321**
Phi Kappa Phi Newsletter. (US ISSN 0093-5328) **1321**, 1655
Phi Lambda Upsilon. Register. (US) **1185**
Phi Pi Epsilon B E T A News. (UK) **2588**, 1378
Phi Rho Sigma Journal. (US ISSN 0022-3581) **1321**
Phi Sigma Iota Forum. (US) **2834**, 2512, 2948
†Phi Theta Papers. (US) **5257**
Phila City Paper. (US ISSN 0733-6349) **2232**
Phila-Lupe. (GW) **3755**
Phila-Report. (GW ISSN 0720-2245) **3755**, 3601
Philabook International see Philatelic Literature News **3756**
Philadelphia Bar Association. Legal Directory. (US) **2666**, 2734
Philadelphia Business Journal. (US ISSN 0744-3587) **879**
Philadelphia College of Pharmacy and Science Bulletin. (US ISSN 0031-725X) **3740**
Philadelphia College of Textiles & Science. Portfolio. (US) **1321**, 4622
Philadelphia County Dental Society. Bulletin. (US ISSN 0031-7268) **3240**
Philadelphia Folksong Society Newsletter. (US) **3574**
Philadelphia Gas Works Newsline see P G W Newsline **3697**
Philadelphia Gay News. (US) **2456**
Philadelphia Golf Magazine. (US) **4509**
Philadelphia Magazine. (US ISSN 0031-7233) **2232**
Philadelphia Medicine. (US ISSN 0031-7306) **3140**

PHILADELPHIA MUSEUM

Philadelphia Museum of Art. Bulletin. (US ISSN 0031-7314) **3531**
†Philadelphia Papers. (US) **5257**
Philadelphia Photo Review see Photo Review **3795**
Philadelphia Photo Review Newsletter see Photo Review Newsletter **3795**
Philadelphia Small Business Chronicle see Small Business Chronicle **1118**
Philadelphia Society of Clinical Psychologists Times see P S C P Times **4037**
▼Philadelphia Sports Focus. (US) **4483**, 3372
Philadelphia Stock Exchange Guide. (US) **1150**
Philadelphia Tribune. (US ISSN 0048-3702) **2232**
Philamath. (US) **3756**
Philanthropic Digest. (US ISSN 0480-2853) **4416**, 340, 2468
▼Philanthropic Studies Index. (US) **4426**, 20
Philanthropic Trends Digest. (US) **4416**
The Philanthropist. (CN) **2666**
Philas News. (AT ISSN 0725-2323) **3756**
Philastannumy see Tin Canner **3758**
Philateli-Graphics. (US ISSN 0739-6198) **3756**
Philatelia Chimica see Philatelia Chimica et Physica **3756**
Philatelia Chimica et Physica. (US ISSN 1041-2999) **3756**
Philatelia Fennica see Filatelisti **3752**
Philatelic Bulletin see Australian Stamp Bulletin **3749**
Philatelic Bulletin. (KE) **3756**
Philatelic Communicator. (US) **3756**
Philatelic Exhibitor. (US ISSN 0892-032X) **3756**, 1300, 3394
The Philatelic Exporter. (UK ISSN 0031-7381) **3756**, 3601
Philatelic Foundation Bulletin see Philatelic Foundation Quartely **3756**
Philatelic Foundation Quartely. (US ISSN 0196-5034) **3756**
Philatelic Guild's Investment Newsletter.(US) **3756**
Philatelic Literature News. (NE) **3756**
Philatelic Literature Review. (US ISSN 0270-1707) **3756**
Philatelic Observer. (US ISSN 0273-5598) **3756**
Philatelic Prospector. (US) **3756**
Philatelic Quill. (UK ISSN 0265-2641) **3756**
Philatelic Society of T & T Bulletin. (TR) **3756**
Philatelie. (NE ISSN 0166-3437) **3756**
Philatelie. (GW) **3756**
Philatelie Francaise. (FR ISSN 0183-3634) **3756**
Philatelie Quebec. (CN) **3756**
PhilateLion. (US) **3756**, 2419
Philatelist and Philatelic Journal of Great Britain. (UK ISSN 0260-6739) **3756**
Philatelistic Catalogue Key. see Filatelistisk Katalog-Noegle **3752**
Philatelistischer Katalog-Schluessel. see Filatelistisk Katalog-Noegle **3752**
Philately from Australia. (AT ISSN 0031-7403) **3756**
Philately in Japan. (JA) **3756**
Philately Research. see Jiyou Yanjiu **3753**
Philately Vision. see Jiyou Bolan **3753**
Philatex. (US) **3756**
†Philatopic Magazine. (CN ISSN 0048-3737) **5257**
Philemat. (FR) **3756**, 4483
Philharmonische Blaetter (Berlin). (GW) **3574**
Philharmonische Blaetter (Munich). (GW) **3574**
Philip Journal fuer Restaurative Zahnmedizin see Phillip Journal **3240**
†Philip K. Dick Society Newsletter. (US) **5257**
Philip Morris Magazine. (US) **4644**, 1050
Philippe de Monte Opera. Series A, Motets. (BE) **3574**
Philippe de Monte Opera. Series B, Masses. (BE) **3574**
Philippe de Monte Opera. Series D, Madrigals. (BE) **3574**
Philippia. (GW ISSN 0343-7620) **3531**, 451
Philippine Agricultural Meteorology Bulletin. (PH) **3440**, 114
†Philippine Agricultural Situation. (PH ISSN 0031-7446) **5257**
Philippine Agriculturist. (PH ISSN 0031-7454) **114**
Philippine-American Studies Journal. (PH ISSN 0116-7081) **4382**
Philippine Astronomical Handbook. (PH ISSN 0115-1207) **371**
Philippine Atomic Energy Commission. Annual Report see Philippine Nuclear Research Institute. Annual Report **1809**
Philippine Biochemical Society Bulletin see P B S Bulletin **481**
Philippine Business and Industry Index. (PH ISSN 0115-4192) **734**, 20, 141
Philippine Business Index see Philippine Economics and Business Index **734**
Philippine Coconut Authority. Agricultural Research Department. Annual Report. (PH) **188**
Philippine Commercial and Industrial Bank. Investment Information Folio. (PH) **959**
Philippine Council for Agriculture, Forestry, and Natural Resources Research & Development. Monitor. (PH ISSN 0115-0529) **114**
Philippine Dental Association. Journal. (PH ISSN 0031-7497) **3240**
Philippine Economic Indicators see Economic Indicators **714**
Philippine Economic Journal. (PH ISSN 0031-7500) **685**
Philippine Economics and Business Index. (PH) **734**, 20
Philippine Education Quarterly. (PH) **1655**
Philippine Educational Forum. (PH ISSN 0031-7527) **1655**
The Philippine Entomologist. (PH ISSN 0048-3753) **537**
Philippine Fishing Journal. (PH ISSN 0031-7543) **2047**
Philippine Food Balance Sheet. (PH) **156**
Philippine Geographical Journal. (PH ISSN 0031-7551) **2258**
Philippine Geology, Mining and Mineral Resources see Bibliography on Philippine Geology, Mining and Mineral Resources **3479**
Philippine Institute for Development Studies Monograph Series see P I D S Monograph Series **933**
Philippine Institute for Development Studies Special Publications see P I D S Special Publications **933**
Philippine Institute for Development Studies Working Paper Series see P I D S Working Paper Series **933**
Philippine Insurance Commission Annual Report. (PH) **2540**
†Philippine Journal of Animal Industry. (PH ISSN 0048-3761) **5257**
Philippine Journal of Animal Science see Philippine Journal of Veterinary and Animal Sciences **4814**
Philippine Journal of Cancer. (PH ISSN 0031-7608) **3201**
Philippine Journal of Child-Youth Development. (PH ISSN 0031-7616). **1242**
Philippine Journal of Counseling Psychology. (PH) **4038**
Philippine Journal of Dermatology and Leprosy. (PH) **3222**
Philippine Journal of Education. (PH ISSN 0031-7624) **1655**
Philippine Journal of Fisheries. (PH ISSN 0048-377X) **2047**
Philippine Journal of Industrial Relations see Philippine Journal of Labor and Industrial Relations **991**
Philippine Journal of Labor and Industrial Relations. (PH) **991**
Philippine Journal of Leprosy see Philippine Journal of Dermatology and Leprosy **3222**
Philippine Journal of Linguistics. (PH ISSN 0048-3796) **2834**
Philippine Journal of Mental Health. (PH ISSN 0048-380X) **4110**
Philippine Journal of Nursing. (PH ISSN 0048-3818) **3285**
Philippine Journal of Nutrition. (PH ISSN 0031-7640) **3611**
Philippine Journal of Ophthalmology. (PH ISSN 0031-7659) **3304**
Philippine Journal of Pediatrics. (PH ISSN 0031-7667) **3325**
Philippine Journal of Psychology. (PH) **4038**
Philippine Journal of Public Administration. (PH ISSN 0031-7675) **4070**
Philippine Journal of Science. (PH ISSN 0031-7683) **4333**
Philippine Journal of Soils. (PH ISSN 0048-3834) **188**
Philippine Journal of Surgery and Surgery Specialties see Philippine Journal of Surgical Specialties **3382**
Philippine Journal of Surgical Specialties. (PH ISSN 0031-7691) **3382**
Philippine Journal of Veterinary and Animal Sciences. (PH ISSN 0115-2173) **4814**
Philippine Journal of Veterinary Medicine. (PH ISSN 0031-7705) **4814**
†Philippine Journal of Volcanology. (PH ISSN 0116-0109) **5257**
†Philippine Junior Red Cross Magazine.(PH ISSN 0031-7713) **5257**
Philippine Labor Review. (PH) **991**
Philippine Law Journal. (PH ISSN 0031-7721) **2666**
Philippine Law Report. (PH ISSN 0115-7205) **2666**
Philippine Letter. (HK ISSN 0379-2870) **879**
Philippine Library Association. Bulletin. (PH) **2779**
Philippine Medical Association. Journal. (PH ISSN 0031-7748) **3141**
Philippine Mining & Engineering Journal. (PH ISSN 0048-3842) **3493**
Philippine Mining and Engineering Journal. Mining Annual and Directory.(PH ISSN 0085-4875) **3493**
Philippine National Bank. Economic Brief. (PH) **795**
Philippine National Bank International see P N B International **794**
Philippine National Bibliography. (PH ISSN 0303-190X) **409**
Philippine Normal College Research Series. (PH) **1714**
Philippine Nuclear Research Institute. Annual Report. (PH) **1809**
Philippine Phytopathology. (PH ISSN 0115-0804) **512**
Philippine Planning Journal. (PH ISSN 0048-3850) **2493**
Philippine Political Science Journal. (PH) **3915**
Philippine Quarterly of Culture and Society. (PH ISSN 0115-0243) **2512**
Philippine Revenue Journal. (PH ISSN 0116-3426) **1104**
Philippine Review of Economics and Business. (PH ISSN 0031-7780) **685**
Philippine Science and Technology Abstracts. (PH) **4357**, 20
Philippine Science and Technology Abstracts Bibliography see Philippine Science and Technology Abstracts **4357**
Philippine Scientific Journal. (PH ISSN 0031-7799) **4333**
Philippine Scientist. (PH ISSN 0079-1466) **4333**
Philippine Social Science Council Social Science Information see P S S C Social Science Information **4381**
Philippine Sociological Review. (PH ISSN 0031-7810) **4444**, 247
Philippine Standard Commodity Classification. (PH) **960**
Philippine Statistical Yearbook. (PH) **734**, 4583
Philippine Statistician. (PH ISSN 0031-7829) **4583**
Philippine Studies. (PH ISSN 0031-7837) **2512**, 4195, 4416
Philippine Tax Journal. (PH ISSN 0031-7845) **1104**
Philippine Technology Journal. (PH ISSN 0116-7294) **4606**
†Philippine Textile Digest. (PH ISSN 0115-2351) **5257**
Philippine Trade and Industry Directory.(PH) **821**, 1150
Philippine Witness. (US) **3946**, 4195
Philippine Women's University Administrative News. (PH ISSN 0031-7853) **1321**
Philippine Yearbook. (PH ISSN 0116-1520) **3994**
Philippine Yearbook of International Law. (PH) **2728**
Philippines. (CN) **4272**
Philippines. Board of Investments. Annual Report. (PH ISSN 0079-1504) **960**
†Philippines. Bureau of Agricultural Economics. Crop and Livestock Statistics. (PH) **5258**
†Philippines. Bureau of Agricultural Economics. Report. (PH ISSN 0079-1520) **5258**
Philippines. Bureau of Labor and Employment Statistics. Current Labor Statistics. (PH) **734**, 991
Philippines. Bureau of Labor and Employment Statistics. Labor and Employment Statistical Report. (PH) **734**, 991
▼Philippines. Bureau of Labor and Employment Statistics. Occupational Wages Survey. (PH) **734**, 991, 4583
†Philippines. Bureau of Labor and Employment Statistics. Selected Labor Indicators. (PH) **5258**
Philippines. Bureau of Labor and Employment Statistics. Yearbook of Labor Statistics. (PH) **734**
Philippines. Department of Agrarian Reform. Planning Service. Annual Report. (PH) **156**
†Philippines. Department of Agriculture. Bureau of Agricultural Statistics. Crop Statistics Bulletin. (PH) **5258**
Philippines. Department of Agriculture. Bureau of Agricultural Statistics. Development Indicators in Philippine Agriculture. (PH) **141**
Philippines. Department of Agriculture. Bureau of Agricultural Statistics. Livestock, Poultry and Fishery Statistics Bulletin. (PH) **141**
†Philippines. Department of Agriculture. Bureau of Agricultural Statistics. Rice and Corn Inventory. (PH) **5258**
Philippines. Department of Agriculture. Bureau of Agricultural Statistics. Rice and Corn Outlook. (PH) **142**
Philippines. Department of Agriculture. Bureau of Agricultural Statistics. Retail Market Price Bulletin. (PH) **142**
Philippines. Department of Agriculture. Bureau of Agricultural Statistics. Selected Statistics in Agriculture. (PH) **142**
Philippines. Department of Agriculture. Bureau of Agricultural Statistics. Weekly Agricultural Situation Report see AGRIDEV Weekly Bulletin **132**
Philippines. Department of Agriculture. Bureau of Agricultural Statistics. Wholesale Price Bulletin. (PH) **142**
Philippines. Department of Public Information. Policy Statements. (PH) **4070**
Philippines. Department of Science and Technology. Annual Report. (PH) **4333**
Philippines. Department of Trade and Industry. Annual Report. (PH) **919**, 838
Philippines. Food and Nutrition Research Center. Annual Report see Philippines. Food and Nutrition Research Institute. Annual Report **3611**
Philippines. Food and Nutrition Research Institute. Annual Report. (PH) **3611**

Philippines. Labor Statistics Service. Yearbook of Labor Statistics see Philippines. Bureau of Labor and Employment Statistics. Yearbook of Labor Statistics **734**
Philippines. Ministry of Agriculture. Bureau of Soils. Soils Farmers Bulletin. (PH) **188**
Philippines. Ministry of Agriculture. Bureau of Soils. Soils Technical Bulletin. (PH) **188**
Philippines. Ministry of Natural Resources. Annual Report. (PH) **1965, 1495**
Philippines. Ministry of Natural Resources. Plans and Programs. (PH) **1495, 1965**
Philippines. Ministry of Trade. Annual Report see Philippines. Department of Trade and Industry. Annual Report **919**
†Philippines. Ministry of Trade. Trend Analysis of the Twenty Leading Exports and Prospects in the Year Ahead. (PH) **5258**
†Philippines. Ministry of Trade. Twenty Leading Imports. (PH) **5258**
Philippines. National Census and Statistics Office. Annual Survey of Establishments see Philippines. National Statistics Office. Annual Survey of Establishments **734**
†Philippines. National Census and Statistics Office. Annual Survey of Wholesale and Retail Establishments.(PH) **5258**
†Philippines. National Census and Statistics Office. Coastwise Trade Report. (PH) **5258**
†Philippines. National Census and Statistics Office. Listing of Cities, Municipalities and Municipal Districts by Province. (PH) **5258**
Philippines. National Census and Statistics Office. Sample Survey of Households Bulletin. see Philippines. National Statistics Office. Integrated Survey of Households Bulletin **4583**
†Philippines. National Census and Statistics Office. Social Indicator. (PH) **5258**
†Philippines. National Census and Statistics Office. Special Report. (PH) **5258**
Philippines. National Census and Statistics Office. Vital Statistical Report see Philippines. National Statistics Office. Vital Statistics Report **3994**
Philippines. National Economic and Development Authority. Food Balance Series see Philippine Food Balance Sheet **156**
Philippines. National Economic and Development Authority. National Income Series see National Income Accounts of the Philippines **999**
†Philippines. National Food Authority. Grains Journal. (PH) **5258**
Philippines. National Grain Authority. Grains Journal see Philippines. National Food Authority. Grains Journal **5258**
Philippines. National Library. T N L News. (PH ISSN 0115-7167) **2779**
Philippines. National Library. T N L Research Guide Series. (PH ISSN 0115-7213) **409**
Philippines. National Printing Office. Itemization of Personal Services and Organizational Charts. (PH) **4070, 2779**
Philippines. National Science and Technology Authority. Annual Report see Philippines. Department of Science and Technology. Annual Report **4333**
Philippines. National Statistics Office. Annual Survey of Establishments. (PH ISSN 0116-2659) **734, 4583**
Philippines. National Statistics Office. Directory of Large Establishments. (PH) **734, 685, 4583**
Philippines. National Statistics Office. Integrated Survey of Households Bulletin. (PH ISSN 0116-2624) **4583**

Philippines. National Statistics Office. Vital Statistics Report. (PH ISSN 0116-2675) **3994, 4583**
†Philippines. National Tax Research Center. Tax Monthly. (PH ISSN 0040-0068) **5258**
Philippines. Public Information Office. Official Gazette. (PH) **4070**
▼Philippines. Republic. National Museum Papers. (PH ISSN 0117-0686) **3531**
Philippines Business Directory. (PH) **1150**
Philippines Chinese Historical Association. Annals. (PH) **2341, 3969**
Philippines Footwear Leathergoods & Accesories Journal. (PH ISSN 0115-6608) **2738**
Philippines Labor Relations Journal. (PH ISSN 0031-787X) **991**
Philippines Mail. (US) **2019**
Philippines Nuclear Journal. (PH ISSN 0079-1490) **3849**
Philippines Transportation. (PH ISSN 0031-7888) **4654, 4782**
Philips Cronache see Cronache **1885**
Philips Exeter Bulletin see Exeter **1311**
Philips Journal of Research. (UK ISSN 0165-5817) **3050, 1229, 1905**
Philips Research Reports see Philips Journal of Research **3050**
†Philips Technical Review. (NE ISSN 0031-7926) **5258**
Phillies Report. (US ISSN 8750-4278) **4509**
Phillip Edwards Million Dollar Record Review. (US) **3574**
Phillip Journal. (GW ISSN 0174-5980) **3240**
Phillips County Historical Quarterly see Phillips County Historical Review **2419**
Phillips County Historical Review. (US ISSN 1046-4204) **2419**
Phillips' International Paper Directory (Paper). (UK ISSN 0954-8521) **3665**
Phillips' Paper Trade Directory - Europe-Mills of the World see Phillips' International Paper Directory (Paper) **3665**
Philnews. (US) **3699**
Philobiblon. (GW ISSN 0031-7969) **4134**
Philologen-Jahrbuch. (GW ISSN 0079-1598) **2834**
Philologia Frisica. (NE) **2834**
Philologica Pragensia see Linguistica Pragensia **2826**
Philologica Pragensia see Litteraria Pragensia **2935**
Philological Monographs. (US ISSN 0079-1628) **2834, 1279**
Philological Quarterly. (US ISSN 0031-7977) **2834, 1279**
Philological Review. see Filologiai Kozlony **2814**
Philological Society Transactions. (UK ISSN 0079-1636) **2834**
Philologische Studien und Quellen. (GW) **2948**
Philologos. (GR) **1279, 3775**
Philologus. (GW ISSN 0031-7985) **1279, 2319**
Philosopher. (UK) **3775**
Philosopher of Creativity Monograph Series. (US) **3775**
Philosopher's Index. (US ISSN 0031-7993) **3787, 20**
Philosophes Contemporains. (BE ISSN 0079-1660) **3776**
Philosophes Medievaux. (BE ISSN 0079-1679) **3776**
Philosophia. (AG ISSN 0031-8000) **3776**
Philosophia. (IS ISSN 0048-3893) **3776**
Philosophia. (GR) **3776**
Philosophia. (DK ISSN 0108-1632) **3776**
Philosophia Aarhusiensis see Philosophia **3776**
Philosophia Antiqua. (NE ISSN 0079-1687) **3776, 1279**
Philosophia Mathematica. (US ISSN 0031-8019) **3050, 1279**
Philosophia Naturalis. (GW ISSN 0031-8027) **3776**

Philosophia Patrum. (NE ISSN 0166-5030) **2948**
Philosophia Reformata. (NE ISSN 0031-8035) **3776**
Philosophia Spinozae Perennis. (NE) **3776**
Philosophic Research and Analysis see Contemporary Philosophy **3764**
Philosophic Studies in the Unity of Religions. (US) **3776, 4195**
Philosophica. (Il) **3776**
Philosophica. (BE ISSN 0379-8402) **3776**
Philosophica see Revista Philosophica **3779**
Philosophical Books. (UK ISSN 0031-8051) **3776, 4134**
Philosophical Forum. (US ISSN 0031-806X) **3776**
Philosophical Investigations. (UK ISSN 0190-0536) **3776**
Philosophical Journal. see Filosoficky Casopis **3766**
Philosophical Magazine. (UK ISSN 0031-8086) **3826**
Philosophical Magazine Letters. (UK ISSN 0950-0839) **3826**
Philosophical Papers see Rhodes University. Department of Philosophy. Philosophical Papers **3780**
Philosophical Perspectives on Society and Science. see Wijsgerig Perspectief op Maatschappij en Wetenschap **3786**
Philosophical Psychology. (UK ISSN 0951-5089) **4038, 3776**
Philosophical Quarterly. (UK ISSN 0031-8094) **3776**
Philosophical Research. (CH) **3776**
Philosophical Research Society Inc. Journal see P R S Journal **5255**
Philosophical Review. (US ISSN 0031-8108) **3776**
Philosophical Studies. (NE ISSN 0031-8116) **3776**
Philosophical Studies in Education. (US ISSN 0160-7561) **1655**
Philosophical Studies Series in Philosophy. (NE) **3776**
Philosophical Texts and Studies. see Wijsgerige Teksten en Studies **3786**
Philosophical Topics. (US ISSN 0276-2080) **3776**
Philosophie (Paris). (FR ISSN 0294-1805) **3776**
Philosophie (Toulouse) see Kairos **3771**
Philosophie Imaginaire. (FR ISSN 0760-9620) **3776**
Philosophiehistorische Texte. (GW ISSN 0233-089X) **3776**
▼Die Philosophin. (GW ISSN 0936-7586) **3776, 4851**
Philosophiques. (CN ISSN 0316-2923) **3776**
Philosophische Abhandlungen. (GW ISSN 0175-6508) **3776**
Philosophische Rundschau. (GW ISSN 0031-8159) **3777**
Philosophische Studientexte see Philosophiehistorische Texte **3776**
Philosophische und Soziologische Veroeffentlichungen see Freie Universitaet Berlin. Osteuropa-Institut. Philosophische und Soziologische Veroeffentlichungen **3767**
Philosophischer Literaturanzeiger. (GW ISSN 0031-8175) **3777**
Philosophisches Jahrbuch. (GW ISSN 0031-8183) **3777**
Philosophus see P S **2878**
Philosophy. see Filozofia **3767**
Philosophy. (UK ISSN 0031-8191) **3777**
▼Philosophy and Artificial Intelligence. (GW ISSN 0937-3225) **1410, 3777**
†Philosophy and History. (GW ISSN 0016-884X) **5258**
Philosophy and Literature. (US ISSN 0190-0013) **3777, 2948**
Philosophy and Medicine. (NE) **3777, 3141**
Philosophy and Phenomenological Research. (US ISSN 0031-8205) **3777**
Philosophy and Public Affairs. (US ISSN 0048-3915) **3915**

Philosophy and Religion: A Comparative Yearbook. (NE) **3777, 4195**
Philosophy and Rhetoric. (US ISSN 0031-8213) **3777, 2834**
Philosophy & Social Action. (Il ISSN 0377-2772) **4382**
Philosophy and Social Criticism. (US ISSN 0191-4537) **2513, 4195**
†Philosophy and the Arts. (US ISSN 0739-1218) **5258**
Philosophy East and West. (US ISSN 0031-8221) **3777**
Philosophy for Children Newsletter. (US) **3777, 1242**
Philosophy in Context. (US ISSN 0742-2733) **3777**
Philosophy in Science. (US ISSN 0277-2434) **3777**
Philosophy of Education. (US ISSN 8756-6575) **1655**
Philosophy of Education Society. Proceedings of the Annual Meetings see Philosophy of Education **1655**
Philosophy of History and Culture. (NE ISSN 0922-6001) **3777, 4444**
Philosophy of Science. see Kagaku Tetsugaku **4319**
Philosophy of Science. (US ISSN 0031-8248) **4333, 3777**
Philosophy of Science Association Newsletter. (US ISSN 0163-0881) **3777**
Philosophy of the Social Sciences. (US ISSN 0048-3931) **4382, 3777**
Philosophy Studies. see Zhexue Yanjiu **3787**
Philosophy Today. (US ISSN 0031-8256) **3777**
Philotelia. (GR ISSN 0031-8264) **3756**
Philwomenian. (PH ISSN 0031-8272) **1321**
Phlebologie. (GW ISSN 0939-978X) **3141**
Phlebologie und Proktologie see Phlebologie **3141**
Phlebology. (UK ISSN 0268-3555) **3211**
†Phobia Practice and Research Journal.(US ISSN 0894-9565) **5258**
Phoebe. (US ISSN 0270-868X) **2948, 2879**
Phoebus (Tempe). (US ISSN 0193-8061) **340**
Phoenix. (NE ISSN 0031-8329) **281, 3643**
Phoenix see I S T C Phoenix **3408**
†Phoenix. (UK) **5258**
†Phoenix (Dumont). (US) **5258**
Phoenix (Phoenix). (US ISSN 1045-1773) **2232**
Phoenix. Supplementary Volumes. (CN ISSN 0079-1784) **1279**
Phoenix (Toronto, 1946). (CN ISSN 0031-8299) **1279**
Phoenix (Toronto, 1980). (CN) **2019**
Phoenix Broadsheet. (UK) **2948**
Phoenix Conference on Computers and Communications. Conference Proceedings. (US) **1351**
Phoenix Home & Garden. (US ISSN 0270-9341) **2554, 2137**
Phoenix International. (SZ) **1965**
▼Phoenix Liberator. (US) **2232**
Phoenix Literature. (US) **2948**
Phoenix Living see Living (Phoenix Edition) **5228**
Phoenix Metro see Phoenix (Phoenix) **2232**
Phoenix Poets. (US) **3001**
Phoenix Quarterly see Phoenix: Voice of the Scrap Recycling Industries **1495**
Phoenix: Voice of the Scrap Recycling Industries. (US) **1495, 3417**
Phone Plus. (US) **1365**
Phonefacts. (US) **1365**
Phonetic Society of Japan. Bulletin. (JA ISSN 0911-0402) **2834**
Phonetica. (SZ ISSN 0031-8388) **2834**
Phonetician. (US ISSN 0741-6164) **2834, 1341**
Phonetics and Phonology. (US) **2834**
Phoni Tou Evangeliou/Voice of the Gospel. (GR ISSN 0031-8396) **4195**
Phono Press. (GW) **3574**

Phonographic Bulletin. (SZ ISSN 0253-004X) 4461
Phonolog Reporter. (US) 3574
Phonology. (UK ISSN 0952-6757) 2834
Phonology Yearbook see Phonology 2834
Phorologike Epitheoresis. (GR) 1104
Phos. (UA) 2019
Phosphating News see European Paint and Resin News 3653
Phospholipids. (UK ISSN 0264-9624) 481
Phosphore. (FR) 1262
Phosphorous and Sulfur and the Related Elements see Phosphorus, Sulphur and Silicon and the Related Elements 1214
Phosphorus and Potassium. (UK ISSN 0031-8426) 1857, 3493
▼Phosphorus in Agriculture. (UK ISSN 0960-2976) 142, 20
Phosphorus, Sulphur and Silicon and the Related Elements. (US ISSN 1042-6507) 1214
Phot 'argus (Edition Professionnelle). (FR ISSN 0151-783X) 3794
Photo. (FR) 3794
Photo and Electronics Marketing. (UK) 3794
Photo & Video Retailer. (AT) 3794, 1386
†Photo & Video Trader. (UK) 5258
Photo Answers. (UK) 3794
Photo Business. (UK) 3794
Photo Chemical Machining Institute. Journal. (US) 4003, 3794
Photo-Cine-Expert (1979). (SZ) 3794, 3515
†Photo, Cine, Video Buyer's Guide. (GR) 5258
†Photo Communique. (CN ISSN 0708-5435) 5258
Photo Design. (US ISSN 0888-5680) 3794
Photo Design und Technik. (GW) 3794
▼Photo Digest. (CN) 3794
Photo District News. (US) 3794
Photo Educator. (US) 3794, 1757, 4003
Photo Electronic Imaging. (US ISSN 1060-4936) 3794
Photo Forum. (AT) 3794
Photo Gallery see Coiffure Gallery 372
†Photo Information Almanac. (US ISSN 0093-1365) 5258
Photo Interpretation. (FR ISSN 0031-8523) 2259, 3794
Photo Italia. (IT) 3794
Photo-Lab Index. (US) 3794
Photo Lab Management. (US ISSN 0164-4769) 3794, 1024
Photo Letter. (US) 3794
Photo Life. (CN) 3794
Photo Love Monthly see Oh Boy Monthly 2984
Photo Made in Italy. (IT) 3794
Photo Marketing Magazine. (US) 3794
Photo Marketing Newsline. (US ISSN 0031-8531) 3794
Photo Merchandising. (US) 3794
Photo News see Florida Photo News 3790
Photo Pro. (UK ISSN 0956-2745) 3795
Photo Retailer see Photo & Video Retailer 3794
Photo Review. (US) 3795
Photo Review Newsletter. (US) 3795
Photo Screen. (US ISSN 0031-8566) 3515
Photo Selection. (CN ISSN 0226-9708) 3795
Photo Society of Dayton Beach Community College Photographic Society. Newsletter see D B C C Photographic Society. Newsletter 3789
Photo Star. (US ISSN 0191-7935) 114, 1300
Photo Technik International. (GW) 3795
Photo Trader see Photo & Video Trader 5258
†Photo Traveller. (AT) 5258
Photobiology Bulletin. (UK) 486
Photoblaetter. (GW ISSN 0342-8613) 3795

Photobulletin. (US ISSN 0885-4270) 3795
Photochemical & Photobiological Reviews. (US) 1185, 451
Photochemical Machining Photochemical Etching see P C M - P C E 5254
Photochemistry (Cambridge). (UK ISSN 0556-3860) 1185
Photochemistry (Oxford). (UK ISSN 0079-1806) 1229
Photochemistry and Photobiology. (US ISSN 0031-8655) 1185, 451
†Photochemotherapy. (UK ISSN 0952-0368) 5258
Photocinema see Photomagazine 3515
Photocopy Authorizations Report see Copyright Clearance Center. Report 4126
Photodermatology see Photodermatology, Photoimmunology & Photomedicine 3249
Photodermatology, Photoimmunology & Photomedicine. (DK ISSN 0905-4383) 3249
Photoelectron - Laser. see Guangdianzi - Jiguang 3852
Photofile. (AT ISSN 0811-0859) 3795
Photofinishing News Letter. (US ISSN 0889-2393) 3795
Photofolio. (US) 3795
Photogrammetria see I S P R S Journal of Photogrammetry and Remote Sensing 2252
Photogrammetric Coyote. (US) 2259
Photogrammetric Engineering and Remote Sensing. (US ISSN 0099-1112) 2259, 3795
Photogrammetric Record. (UK ISSN 0031-868X) 2259, 3795
Photogrammetric Reports. see Fotogrammetriska Meddelanden 2248
Photogrammetry and Remote Sensing. see Shashin Sokuryo to Rimoto Senshingu 2262
Photograph Collector. (US ISSN 0271-0838) 2440, 960
Photograph Collector's Resource Directory. (US) 3795
Photographe. (FR ISSN 0369-9560) 3795
Photographer. (CN) 3795
Photographer's Almanac of the Sun & Moon (Year). (US) 368
▼Photographer's Dispatch. (US) 3795
Photographer's Forum. (US ISSN 0194-5467) 3795
Photographer's Market. (US ISSN 0147-247X) 3795
†Photographer's Market Newsletter. (US ISSN 0278-2790) 5258
Photographia. (GR ISSN 0259-7349) 3795
Photographic Abstracts see Imaging Abstracts 3798
Photographic Applications in Science, Technology and Medicine see Functional Photography (Woodbury) 3791
Photographic Art Market Auction Price Results and Analysis see Photographic Art Market: Auction Prices (Year) 3795
Photographic Art Market: Auction Prices (Year). (US ISSN 1053-7031) 3795
Photographic Business and Product News see Studio Photography 3797
Photographic Canadiana. (CN ISSN 0704-0024) 3795, 2319
Photographic Journal. (UK ISSN 0031-8736) 3795
Photographic Processing. (US ISSN 0031-8744) 3795
Photographic Resource Center. Newsletter. (US) 3795
Photographic Science and Photochemistry. see Ganguang Kexue yu Guanghuaxue 3791
Photographic Society of America, Inc. Journal see P S A Journal 3793
Photographic Trade News. (US ISSN 0031-8779) 3795

Photographic Trade News Master Buying Guide & Directory see P T N Master Buying Guide & Directory 3794
Photographic World see Photoworld 3796
Photographica. (US) 3795
Photographica Journal see Photographica 3795
Photographis see Graphis Photo 3791
Photography. see Fotografie 3791
Photography. (UK ISSN 0265-7198) 3795
Photography at Open Space Monographs. (CN) 3795
Photography Fans. see Sheying zhi You 3797
Photography in Japan. (JA) 3795
Photography in New York. (US ISSN 1040-0346) 3795
†Photography Magazine Index. (US) 5258
Photography Monograph Series. (CN) 3795
†Photography Report. (UK) 5258
Photography World. see Sheying Shijie 3797
Photography Year Book. (UK ISSN 0079-1865) 3795
Photojournalist (Newark). (US ISSN 0893-5610) 3795, 2574
Photoletter. (US ISSN 0190-1400) 3796
Photomagazine. (FR) 3515, 3796
Photomarket. (US ISSN 0885-4262) 3796
Photomed. (GW) 3141
Photomethods see Photo Electronic Imaging 3794
Photon. (US ISSN 0031-8833) 3515
Photonics Directory. (US ISSN 1044-1425) 3857
Photonics Industry and Systems Purchasing Directory see Photonics Directory 3857
Photonics Spectra. (US ISSN 0731-1230) 3857, 1207
†Photonics: Technology and Applications. (US ISSN 1049-5290) 5258
†Photoplay. (UK ISSN 0269-8293) 5258
Photoplay Movies and Video see Photoplay 5258
▼Photopro. (US) 3796
Photorin see Lichtenberg-Jahrbuch 419
PhotoRock & Records. (IT) 3574
Photoromance Darling. (US) 2984
†PhotoStatic Magazine. (US ISSN 0893-4835) 5258
Photosynthesis Bibliography. (NE) 467
Photosynthesis Research. (NE ISSN 0166-8595) 574
Photosynthetica. (CS ISSN 0300-3604) 512
Photovaltaic Energy. (US) 1800, 1811
Photovoltaic Energy Progam Summary see Conservation and Renewable Energy Technologies for Utility Technologies 1785
Photoworld. (AT ISSN 0727-3959) 3796
Photoworld Annual see Focus on Photography 5193
Photoworld Buyer's Directory. (AT ISSN 0813-4545) 3796
Phreno - Cosmian. (US) 1321
Phronesis. (NE ISSN 0031-8868) 3777
Phu Nu Viet-Nam/Vietnamese Women. (VN) 4851
Phuket Marine Biological Center. Research Bulletin. (TH ISSN 0858-1088) 451
Phulwadi. (II) 2201
Phulwari. (CN) 2019
Phycologia. (UK ISSN 0031-8884) 513
Phycological Newsletter. (US ISSN 0045-3072) 513
Phykos. (II ISSN 0031-8892) 513
Phyllis Schlafly Report. (US ISSN 0556-0152) 4851, 879, 1655, 3468
Phylon. (US ISSN 0031-8906) 4444
Phys 13 News. (CN) 3826

Physica A - Statistical and Theoretical Physics. (NE ISSN 0378-4371) 3826
Physica B en C see Physica C - Superconductivity 3826
Physica B en C see Physica B - Physics of Condensed Matter 3826
Physica B - Physics of Condensed Matter. (NE ISSN 0921-4526) 3826, 1905, 3841
Physica C - Superconductivity. (NE ISSN 0921-4534) 3826, 1905
Physica D - Nonlinear Phenomena. (NE ISSN 0167-2789) 3826, 1905
Physica Didactica. (GW ISSN 0340-2134) 3826, 1757
Physica Fennica see Physica Scripta 3826
Physica Medica. (IT ISSN 1120-1797) 3141, 3826
Physica Norvegica see Physica Scripta 3826
Physica Scripta. (SW ISSN 0031-8949) 3826
Physica Scripta Topical Issues. (SW ISSN 0281-1847) 3827
Physica Status Solidi (A). Applied Research. (GW ISSN 0031-8965) 3827
Physica Status Solidi (B). Basic Research. (GW ISSN 0370-1972) 3827
Physical Acoustics: Principles and Methods. (US ISSN 0079-1873) 3860
Physical & Occupational Therapy in Geriatrics. (US ISSN 0270-3181) 2277
Physical & Occupational Therapy in Pediatrics. (US ISSN 0194-2638) 3325
Physical Education and Sport. (IS ISSN 0333-5259) 1655
Physical Education Around the World. Monograph. (US ISSN 0079-189X) 1757
Physical Education Association of Great Britian and Northern Ireland. Research Supplement. (UK) 3807
Physical Education Digest. (CN ISSN 0843-2635) 4483, 3807
Physical Education Index. (US ISSN 0191-9202) 3811, 20, 1757
Physical Educator. (US ISSN 0031-8981) 1655
Physical Fitness - Sports Medicine. (US ISSN 0163-2582) 3180, 3372, 3811, 4498
Physical Geography. (US ISSN 0272-3646) 1547, 3440
Physical Medicine & Rehabilitation. (US ISSN 0888-7357) 3141
Physical Research Laboratory, Ahmedabad: Annual Report. (II) 3827
Physical Review A (General Physics). (US ISSN 0556-2791) 3827
Physical Review B (Condensed Matter). (US ISSN 0163-1829) 3827
Physical Review C (Nuclear Physics). (US ISSN 0556-2813) 3849
Physical Review D (Particles and Fields). (US ISSN 0556-2821) 3850
Physical Review Abstracts. (US ISSN 0048-4024) 3838, 20
Physical Review - Index. (US ISSN 0094-0003) 3838, 20
Physical Review Letters. (US ISSN 0031-9007) 3827
Physical Sciences Data. (NE) 1229
Physical Society of Japan. Journal. (JA ISSN 0031-9015) 3827
Physical Society of Japan. Journal. Supplement. (JA) 3827
Physical Surveillance Training Manual. (US) 1520
Physical Therapy. (US ISSN 0031-9023) 3141
Physical Therapy in Health Care. (US ISSN 0742-9711) 3141
▼Physical Therapy Practice. (US ISSN 1054-8513) 3215
Physical Therapy Products. (US ISSN 1059-096X) 3141
Physical Therapy Today. (US ISSN 1042-2579) 3141
Physician. see Medyk 3131
Physician & Patient. (US) 3141, 1024

Physician and Sportsmedicine. (US ISSN 0091-3847) **3372**
Physician Assistant. (US) **3141**
Physician Assistant see P A **5254**
Physician Assistant Programs, A National Directory see Physician Assistant Programs Directory **3141**
Physician Assistant Programs Directory.(US ISSN 1051-600X) **3141**
Physician Characteristics & Distribution in the U S. (US ISSN 0731-0315) **3180**
†Physician Computer Monthly. (US) **5258**
Physician Executive Review. (US) **1024**, 3141
Physician Manager. (US) **3141**
Physicians & Computers. (US) **3226**
Physicians and Surgeons Journal see P & S Journal **3138**
Physician's Coding Strategist. (US) **3141**
Physicians' Current Procedural Terminology see C P T **3085**
Physicians' Desk Reference. (US ISSN 0093-4461) **3141**
Physicians' Desk Reference for Nonprescription Drugs. (US ISSN 1044-1395) **3141**, 3740
Physicians' Desk Reference for Ophthalmology. (US) **3304**
Physicians' Drug Alert. (US) **3740**
Physicians' Drug Manual. (US ISSN 0031-9058) **3740**
Physicians Financial News. (US ISSN 8750-9407) **795**, 3141
▼Physicians Food Advisor. (US) **2079**, 3611
Physicians for Social Responsibility Monitor see P S R Monitor **4109**
Physicians for Social Responsibility Quarterly see P S R Quarterly **4109**
Physicians for Social Responsibility Reports see P S R Reports **4109**
Physician's Handbook. (US ISSN 0079-192X) **3141**
Physicians Lifestyle Magazine. (US) **2232**, 3141
Physician's Management. (US ISSN 0031-9066) **3141**
Physician's Management Manuals. (CN ISSN 0705-6311) **3141**, 1024
Physician's Marketing see Physicians Marketing & Management **3141**
Physicians Marketing & Management. (US ISSN 1042-2625) **3141**
Physician's Payment Advisory see Hospital's Medicare Policy & Payment Report **3106**
Physician's Payment Update see Hospital's Medicare Policy & Payment Report **3106**
Physician's Resource Manual on Osteoporosis. (US) **3141**
Physicians' Travel & Meeting Guide. (US ISSN 0745-4554) **4782**
Physician's Weekly. (US) **3141**
Physico-Chemical Mechanics. see Fiziko-Khimicheska Mekhanika **1226**
Physicochemical Hydrodynamics see International Journal of Multiphase Flow **1932**
Physics. see Wuli **3835**
Physics: A Series of Monographs & Tracts. (US) **3827**
Physics Abstracts. (UK ISSN 0036-8091) **3838**, 20, 368
Physics and Applications. (CS) **3827**
Physics and Chemistry in Space. (US ISSN 0079-1938) **1185**, 368, 3827
Physics and Chemistry of Glasses. (UK ISSN 0031-9090) **1167**, 20
Physics and Chemistry of Liquids. (US ISSN 0031-9104) **3844**, 1229
Physics and Chemistry of Materials Treatment. (English translation of: Fizika i Khimiya Obrabotki Materialov) (UK ISSN 0264-729X) **1921**, 1185, 3827
Physics and Chemistry of Materials with Low Dimensional Structures. Series A. Layered Structures. (NE) **1229**
Physics and Chemistry of Materials with Low Dimensional Structures. Series B. Quasi-One-Dimensional Structures. (NE) **1229**

Physics and Chemistry of Materials with Low Dimensional Structures. Series C. Molecular Structures. (NE) **1229**
Physics and Chemistry of Materials with Low-Dimensional Structures. (NE) **3844**, 1185
Physics and Chemistry of Minerals. (GW ISSN 0342-1791) **3493**
Physics and Chemistry of the Earth. (US ISSN 0079-1946) **1548**
Physics and Evolution of the Earth's Interior. (NE) **1577**, 1592
Physics and Society. (US) **3827**, 4444
Physics Briefs - Physikalische Berichte. (GW ISSN 0170-7434) **3838**, 20
Physics Bulletin see Physics World **3828**
Physics Bulletin. see Wuli Tongbao **3835**
Physics, Chemistry and Mechanics of Surfaces. (US ISSN 0734-1520) **1937**, 1185, 3827
Physics Education. (UK ISSN 0031-9120) **3827**, 1757
Physics Education. (II ISSN 0970-5953) **3827**, 1714
Physics Essays. (CN ISSN 0836-1398) **3827**
Physics Experiments. see Wuli Shiyan **3835**
Physics for Middle School Students. see Zhongxuesheng Wuli Yuandi **3836**
Physics in Canada/Physique au Canada. (CN ISSN 0031-9147) **3827**
Physics in Medicine and Biology. (UK ISSN 0031-9155) **3141**, 486
Physics in Technology see Physics World **3828**
Physics Letters. Section A: General, Atomic and Solid State Physics. (NE ISSN 0375-9601) **3850**, 1809
Physics Letters. Section B: Nuclear, Elementary Particle and High-Energy Physics. (NE ISSN 0370-2693) **3850**
†Physics Manpower - Education and Employment Statistics. (US ISSN 0569-5716) **5258**
Physics - Mathematics Information Review. (US) **3827**, 1833, 3050
Physics News. (US) **3827**
Physics News. (II ISSN 0253-7583) **3827**
Physics of Electronic and Atomic Collisions see International Conference on the Physics of Electronic and Atomic Collisions. Abstracts of Contributed Papers and Invited Papers **3847**
Physics of Fluids see Physics of Fluids B: Plasma Physics **3828**
Physics of Fluids see Physics of Fluids A: Fluid Dynamics **3828**
Physics of Fluids A: Fluid Dynamics. (US ISSN 0899-8213) **3828**
Physics of Fluids B: Plasma Physics. (US ISSN 0899-8221) **3828**
Physics of Metals. (English translation of: Metallofizika) (US ISSN 0275-9144) **3417**, 3828
Physics of Metals and Metallography. (English translation of: Fizika Metallov i Metallovedenie) (US ISSN 0031-918X) **3417**, 1921
Physics of Sintering see Science of Sintering **3419**
Physics of the Earth and Planetary Interiors. (NE ISSN 0031-9201) **1593**
Physics of Thin Films; Advances in Research and Development. (US ISSN 0079-1970) **3828**
Physics Reports. (NE ISSN 0370-1573) **3828**
Physics Reports Reprints Book Series. (NE) **3828**
▼Physics Review. (UK ISSN 0959-8472) **3828**
Physics Teacher. (II) **3828**, 1757
Physics Teacher (College Park). (US ISSN 0031-921X) **3828**, 1757
Physics Teaching. see Wuli Jiaoxue **3835**
Physics Today. (US ISSN 0031-9228) **3828**
Physics World. (UK ISSN 0953-8585) **3828**

Physik in der Schule. (GW ISSN 0031-9244) **3828**
Physik in Unserer Zeit. (GW ISSN 0031-9252) **3828**
Physik und Didaktik. (GW ISSN 0340-8515) **1757**, 3828
Physikalisch-Chemische Trenn- und Messmethoden. (GW ISSN 0079-1997) **3828**
Physikalisch Technische Bundesanstalt Berichte see P T B Berichte **4606**
Physikalisch-Technische Bundesanstalt Mitteilungen Forschen und Pruefen see P T B - Mitteilungen Forschen und Pruefen **3448**
Physikalisch-Technischen Bundesanstalt Braunschweig und Berlin. Jahresbericht. (GW ISSN 0340-4366) **4606**, 4333
Physikalische Blaetter. (GW ISSN 0031-9279) **3828**
Physikalische Medizin Rehabilitationsmedizin Kurortmedizin.(GW ISSN 0940-6689) **3142**
Physikunterricht see Naturwissenschaften im Unterricht Physik **3825**
Physio-Quebec. (CN ISSN 0706-4284) **3142**
Physiognomy. (DK) **2879**
Physiologia Bohemoslovaca see Physiological Research **574**
Physiologia Plantarum. (DK ISSN 0031-9317) **513**
Physiological and Molecular Plant Pathology. (UK ISSN 0885-5765) **513**
Physiological Chemistry and Physics see Physiological Chemistry and Physics and Medical N M R **486**
Physiological Chemistry and Physics and Medical N M R. (US ISSN 0748-6642) **486**, 481
Physiological Entomology. (UK ISSN 0307-6962) **537**
Physiological Plant Pathology see Physiological and Molecular Plant Pathology **513**
Physiological Psychology see Psychobiology **4040**
Physiological Research. (UK) **574**, 3142
Physiological Reviews. (US ISSN 0031-9333) **574**, 3142
Physiological Society, London. Monographs. (US ISSN 0079-2020) **574**
Physiological Society of Japan. Journal/ Nihon Seirigaku Zasshi. (JA ISSN 0031-9341) **574**, 3142
†Physiological Society of Philadelphia. Monographs. (US ISSN 0148-4427) **5258**
Physiological Zoology. (US ISSN 0031-935X) **590**
Physiologie Vegetale see Plant Physiology and Biochemistry **515**
Physiologist. (US ISSN 0031-9376) **574**, 3142
Physiology and Behavior. (US ISSN 0031-9384) **574**
Physiology and Biochemistry of Cultivated Plants. see Fiziologiya i Biokhimiya Kul'turnykh Rastenii **571**
Physiology and Ecology Japan. (JA ISSN 0370-9612) **1965**
Physiology Canada. (CN ISSN 0822-9058) **3142**, 574
Physiotherapeut/Physiotherapeute. (SZ) **3142**
Physiotherapeute. see Physiotherapeut **3142**
Physiotherapie. (GW ISSN 0031-9392) **3807**
Physiotherapists' Quarterly. (UK ISSN 0048-4083) **2295**, 3304
Physiotherapy. (UK ISSN 0031-9406) **3142**
Physiotherapy Canada. (CN ISSN 0300-0508) **3142**
Physiotherapy Index. (UK ISSN 0950-6659) **3180**
†Physiotherapy Practice. (UK ISSN 0266-6154) **5258**
Physiotherapy Theory and Practice. (UK ISSN 0959-3985) **3142**, 3807
Physiotherapy Today. (CN) **3142**

Physique au Canada. see Physics in Canada **3827**
Physis. (AG ISSN 0325-0342) **590**, 513
Physis. (GW ISSN 0931-9069) **3142**
Physis. (IT ISSN 0031-9414) **4333**
Physis Computer see Physis Medizin Computer **3226**
Physis Medizin Computer. (GW) **3226**
Phytiatrie-Phytopharmacie. (FR ISSN 0031-8876) **3740**
▼Phytochemical Analysis. (UK ISSN 0958-0344) **481**, 513
Phytochemical Society. Proceedings. (US) **513**
Phytochemical Society of Europe. Annual Proceedings. (UK ISSN 0197-8969) **481**
Phytochemical Society Symposia Series. Proceedings see Phytochemical Society. Proceedings **513**
Phytochemistry. (US ISSN 0031-9422) **513**
Phytocoenologia. (GW ISSN 0340-269X) **513**
Phytologia. (US ISSN 0031-9430) **513**
Phytoma. (FR ISSN 0048-4091) **188**
Phytomorphology. (II ISSN 0031-9449) **513**
Phyton. (AG ISSN 0031-9457) **513**
Phyton. Annales Rei Botanicae. (AU ISSN 0079-2047) **513**
Phytoparasitica: Israel Journal of Plant Protection Sciences. (IS ISSN 0334-2123) **188**
Phytopathological Papers see C.A.B. International. Mycological Institute. Phytopathological Papers **498**
Phytopathological Society of Japan. Annals/Nihon Shokubutsu Byori Gakkaiho. (JA ISSN 0031-9473) **513**
Phytopathologische Zeitschrift. see Journal of Phytopathology **507**
Phytopathology. (US ISSN 0031-949X) **513**
Phytopathology News. (US ISSN 0031-9503) **513**
Phytophaga. (IT ISSN 0393-8131) **188**
Phytophylactica. (SA ISSN 0302-7120) **188**
Phytoprotection. (CN ISSN 0031-9511) **188**, 513
Phytotherapy see Revue de Phytotherapy Pratique **3149**
Phytotherapy Research. (UK ISSN 0951-418X) **514**, 3142
Pi. (UK ISSN 0263-2128) **1321**
Pi Mu Epsilon Journal. (US ISSN 0031-952X) **3050**
Pia-Shaver/Poultry. (PK) **223**
Il Piacere. (IT) **2206**
Piada. see Pie **2058**
Piano. (FR ISSN 0999-5404) **3574**
Piano Guild Notes. (US ISSN 0031-9546) **3574**
Piano-Jahrbuch. (GW ISSN 0173-8607) **3574**
Piano Journal. (UK ISSN 0267-7253) **3574**, 1757
Piano Quarterly. (US ISSN 0031-9554) **3574**
Piano Technicians Journal. (US ISSN 0031-9562) **3574**
Piano Time. (IT) **3574**
Piano-Tuners Quarterly. (UK ISSN 0048-4105) **2295**, 3574
La Pianura. (IT ISSN 0031-9570) **821**
Piazza Grande. (IT) **2206**, 2019
Picabia. (JA) **340**, 1422
Piccolo Missionario see Piemme **4195**
Piccolo Teatro di Milano. (IT) **4636**
Picentino. (IT) **114**, 879
Picenum Seraphicum. (IT) **4272**
Pichi. (JA) **3592**
Pick of the Year. (UK) **1262**, 2948
Pick Resources Guide - International. (UK) **1399**, 1455, 1479
▼Pick Resources Quarterly. (UK) **1424**
The Pick User Digest. (US) **1473**
Pickaway Quarterly. (US) **2419**
Picket Post see Valley Forge Journal **2425**
Pick's Currency Yearbook see World Currency Yearbook **804**

6556 PICKUP

Pickup & Delivery Magazine see P & D Magazine 4747
Pickup in Progress. (UK ISSN 0263-936X) 1686
Pickworld. (US) 1464
Picky Profits. (US) 960
Picsou. (FR ISSN 0767-807X) 1262
Pictorial Directory - Washington State Legislature see Washington (State) Legislature. Pictorial Directory 4077
Pictorial Education see Junior Education 1644
Pictorial News Review. (PK ISSN 0031-9651) 3915
Pictorialist. (US) 3796
Picture Framing Magazine. (US) 2440
Picture House. (UK ISSN 0263-7553) 2554, 304
▼Picture Perfect. (US) 3796, 1294
Picture Postcard Monthly. (UK) 2440
Picture Stories. see Lianhuan Huabao 2572
Picture Stories for Children. see Wawa Huabao 1270
Picture Talk. see Kantu Shuohua 1258
Picturpost. (II) 3515
Piddiddle. (US) 3001
Pie/Piada. (IT ISSN 0031-9708) 2058, 2948
Pie de Pagina. (AG) 2948
The Pied Cow. (US ISSN 0741-0360) 2162
Piedmont Literary Review. (US ISSN 0275-357X) 3001, 2948
Piegan Storyteller. (US) 2948, 420
Piel. (SP ISSN 0213-9251) 3249
Pielegniarka i Polozna. (PL ISSN 0048-4148) 3285, 3295
Pielegniarka Polska see Pielegniarka i Polozna 3285
Piemme. (IT) 4195, 247
Piemonte Medico. (IT) 3142
Pientalo. (FI) 4154, 627
Pierce-Arrow Service Bulletin. (US) 4699
Pierce County Parent. (US) 1242
▼Piero. (IT) 821
Pierre et Marbre/Steen en Marmer. (BE) 1577
Pietismus und Neuzeit. (GW) 4246
Pig. see Sika 226
Pig Farmer. (AT ISSN 0031-9740) 223
Pig Farming. (UK ISSN 0031-9759) 223
Pig Farming. see Svinskoetsel 227
Pig in a Pamphlet. (US) 3001
Pig International. Europe, Africa and Asia - Pacific see Pig International. Europe, Africa and Asia - Pacific and Latin America 223
Pig International. Europe, Africa and Asia - Pacific and Latin America. (US) 223
Pig Iron. (US ISSN 0362-5214) 2948, 3796
Pig News & Information. (UK ISSN 0143-9014) 223
Pig Paper. (CN ISSN 0710-3034) 2879
Pig Tail Times. (US ISSN 1054-5123) 3713
Pig Veterinary Journal. (UK ISSN 0956-0939) 4814
Pigeon Racing Gazette. (UK) 4483, 566
Pigeon Racing News and Gazette see Pigeon Racing Gazette 4483
Piggin String. (US ISSN 0031-9791) 4536
Pigment and Resin Technology. (UK ISSN 0369-9420) 3655
Pigment Cell. (SZ ISSN 0301-0139) 546
Pigment Cell Research. (DK ISSN 0893-5785) 526
Pigs. (NE ISSN 0168-9533) 223
Pikes Peak Area Council of Governments. Quarterly Economic Indicators. (US) 2493
Pikestaff Forum. (US ISSN 0192-8716) 2948
Pikeville Review. (US) 3001
Pilbladet. (DK ISSN 0901-2508) 642
Pilgrim Journal. (US ISSN 0885-4947) 2419
Pilgrim State News. (US) 4246
Pilgrim State Newsletter see Pilgrim State News 4246

Pilgrimage: The Journal of Pastoral Psychotherapy see Pilgrimage: The Journal of Psychotherapy and Personal Exploration 3350
Pilgrimage: The Journal of Psychotherapy and Personal Exploration. (US) 3350, 4195
Pilgrim's Guide to Planet Earth. (US) 4782
Pilipinas. (US ISSN 0889-5244) 2341, 247, 2019, 2259
Pillow Talk. (US) 3399, 4851
▼Pillsbury Fast and Healthy Magazine. (US) 3807
Pilon. (IS) 1262
Pilot. (US ISSN 0744-933X) 4272
Pilot (Clapham). (UK ISSN 0300-1695) 60
Pilot (Nairobi). (UN) 1495
Pilot (Westminster). (UK) 4735
Pilot Dogs. (US) 3713, 2295
The Pilot Log. (US ISSN 1045-179X) 1300
†Pilot News. (US ISSN 0193-211X) 5258
†Pilot Studies Approved for State Aid in Public School Systems in Virginia. (US ISSN 0079-2071) 5258
Pilot und Flugzeug. (GW ISSN 0175-0143) 4676, 3468
†Pilote. (FR) 5258
Piloting Careers see Career Pilot 49
Pilots International. (UK) 60
Pima see P I M A Magazine 3663
†Pimienta. (US ISSN 0146-2075) 5258
Pims Business, Investor and Government Relations Directory. (UK) 795, 1150, 4134
Pims European Consumer Directory. (UK ISSN 0957-6916) 409, 2574
Pims European Directory see Pims European Trade & Technical Directory 1150
Pims European Newspapers Directory. (UK ISSN 0955-1581) 409, 2574
Pims European Trade & Technical Directory. (UK ISSN 0953-7597) 1150, 4134
Pims Financial Directory see Pims Business, Investor and Government Relations Directory 795
Pims Media Directory see Pims U K Media Directory 4134
Pims Media Townslist. (UK) 4134, 1150, 2574
Pims U K Media Directory. (UK) 4134, 1150, 2574
Pims U S A Consumer Directory. (UK ISSN 0957-6908) 409, 2574
Pims U S A Newspaper Directory. (UK) 409, 2574
Pims U S A Trade & Technical Directory. (UK) 409, 2574
Pimsleur's Checklist of Basic American Legal Publications. (US) 2700
Pinal Pioneer. (US) 2232
†Pinchpenny. (US) 5258
Pine Cone. (US ISSN 0031-9856) 3350, 1739
Pine Log. (US) 1321
Pine News International. (UK ISSN 0964-0959) 2561
Pine, the Plow and the Pioneer. (US) 2162, 2259
†Pineal Gland. (UK ISSN 0268-1501) 5258
Pinellas C.R.A.P. Report see What's News in Florida Politics 3934
Pinellas County Review. (US ISSN 0746-746X) 685
†Pinery. (US) 5258
Pingouin Knitting. (US) 3592
Pingpang Shijie/Table Tennis World. (CC ISSN 1000-3452) 4509
Pingrin. (YU ISSN 0031-9880) 4782
†Pink! (US) 5258
Pink Pages. (UK) 2479, 4782
Pinker Moda. (SP) 4622, 1294
Pinkerton Eye on Travel. (US) 4782, 1473
Pinkerton World Status Map. (US) 4782
Pinkes Fun der Kehile in Buenos Ayres see Anales de la Comunidad Israelita de Buenos Aires 5135

Pinkster Protestant. (SA ISSN 0031-9902) 4246
Pinnacle. (US) 4782
Pinpointer. (AT ISSN 0031-9910) 1509, 20, 4498
Pinter Review: Annual Essays. (US ISSN 0895-9706) 4636, 2948
Pinto Horse. (US ISSN 0031-9937) 4536
Pinto Horse International see Pinto Horse 4536
Pintores. (SP ISSN 0031-9945) 3655
Pinturas y Acabados Industriales. (SP ISSN 0031-9953) 3655
†Pinwheel Pink Pages. (US) 5258
Pioneer see Backwoods 78
Pioneer. (IE) 1538
Pioneer. see Raivaaja 2020
Pioneer. (SI ISSN 0048-4199) 3468
Pioneer. (CN) 4246
The Pioneer. (AT ISSN 1035-1035) 4246
Pioneer (Memphis). (US) 4246, 1262
Pioneer (San Francisco). (US) 2419
Pioneer America Society. Newsletter. (US) 2419, 2058
Pioneer America Society Transactions. (US ISSN 0884-3309) 2419, 2058
Pioneer Branches. (US) 2162
Pioneer Christian Monthly. (CN) 2019, 4195
Pioneer Clubs Perspective see Perspective (Wheaton) 4195
Pioneer Times. (US) 2162
Pioneer Wagon. (US ISSN 0735-309X) 2162
Pioneer Woman see Na'Amat Woman 4225
Pioneers of British Columbia. (CN ISSN 0847-0537) 2419
Pioner. (RU ISSN 0032-003X) 1262
Pioneriya. (KR ISSN 0032-0102) 1262
Pionerskaya Pravda. (RU ISSN 0032-0048) 1262
Pionier see Domino 1253
Pionier. (SZ) 3468
Pionier. (NE ISSN 0032-0056) 4195
Pionieri. (AA) 1262
†Pionierleiter. (GW ISSN 0476-8612) 5258
Pionir-Kekec. (YU ISSN 0032-0099) 1263
Pionnier. (FR ISSN 0751-5723) 1263, 1300
Pionyr. (CS ISSN 0042-4919) 1263
Pionyrska Stafeta. (CS) 1242
Pionyrska Stezka. (CS) 1263, 4483, 4553
Pipe Club. (GW) 4644, 1538
Pipe Line & Pipe Line Contractors see Pipeline Industry (Tulsa) 3699
Pipe Line Annual Directory of Pipelines see Pipeline & Gas Journal Annual Directory of Pipelines and Equipment 3699
Pipe Line Industry. (US ISSN 0032-0145) 3699
Pipe Smoker and Tobacciana Trader see Smokers Pipeline 4644
Pipe Smoker's Ephemeris. (US ISSN 0032-0161) 4644
†Pipeline. (CN) 5259
Pipeline (Houston) see Pipeline & Gas Journal 3699
Pipeline (Oregon City). (US) 2302
Pipeline (Roy). (US) 3713
Pipeline & Gas Journal. (US ISSN 0032-0188) 3699
Pipeline & Gas Journal Annual Directory of Pipelines and Equipment. (US) 3699
Pipeline and Underground Utilities Construction see Pipeline & Utilities Construction 3699
Pipeline and Underground Utilities Construction. Annual Directory. (US) 1150
Pipeline & Utilities Construction. (US) 3699
Pipeline and Utility Contractors Directory. (US) 3699
Pipeline Contractors Directory see Pipeline and Utility Contractors Directory 3699
Pipeline Digest. (US ISSN 0197-1506) 3699, 1793

Pipeline Industries Guild Journal see Pipes and Pipelines International 3699
Pipeline Industry (Houston). (US) 3699
Pipeline Industry (Tulsa). (US) 3699
Pipelines Abstracts. (UK ISSN 0265-3990) 3707, 20, 4835
Piper's Magazine. (US) 4676
Pipes and Pipelines International. (UK ISSN 0032-020X) 3699, 4827
Pipestone County Historical Society News. (US) 2419
Piraiki-Patraiki. (GR ISSN 0032-0234) 4622
Pirandello Society Newsletter see P S A 2946
Pirandello Society of America see P S A 2946
Piranesi. (DK ISSN 0108-9935) 2834, 2879
Pirineos. (SP ISSN 0373-2568) 2259, 451
Pirkka. (FI ISSN 0032-0242) 1050
Pirmasens Zahlen und Fakten: Statistische Jahrbuch Stadt Pirmasens. (GW) 4583, 4081
Pirogue. (FR ISSN 0048-4229) 3946
Die Pirsch. (GW ISSN 0340-7829) 4553
Pirsig on Minnesota Pleading. (US) 2666
Pisarze Slascy 19 i 20 Wieku. (PL ISSN 0079-211X) 2948
Piscator. (SA ISSN 0032-0277) 2047
Pisciculture Francaise. (FR ISSN 0048-4237) 2047
Piscinas. (SP ISSN 0210-6868) 627
Piscine Oggi. (IT) 4483
Piscines see Piscines - Spas Magazine 627
Piscines - Spas Magazine. (FR ISSN 0295-5725) 627
Piscines, Terrasses et Patios. (CN) 2554
Pis'ma v Astronomicheskii Zhurnal. (RU ISSN 0320-0108) 368
Pistas de Auditoria. (US) 755
Pit & Quarry. (US ISSN 0032-0293) 3493
Pit & Quarry Handbook and Buyers Guide. (US) 3493
Pit Inn. (JA) 4699
Pit Stop see Pit Inn 4699
Pitanja. (CI) 2948, 340, 3515
Pitcairn Log. (US) 3756
Pitch. (US) 3574
Pitch-In News. (CN ISSN 0383-9168) 1965
Pitcher and Team Report (Year). (US) 4509
Pitcher Performance Handbook. (US ISSN 0731-8138) 4509
Pitt Latin American Series. (US) 4382, 3969
Pitt Magazine. (US) 1321, 1714
Pitt Poetry Series. (US) 3001
†Pitt Series in English as a Second Language. (US) 5259
†Pitts Choice. (US ISSN 0882-3189) 5259
Pittsburgh. (US ISSN 0194-8431) 2232
Pittsburgh Business Times. (US) 685
Pittsburgh Business Times and Journal see Pittsburgh Business Times 685
Pittsburgh Catholic. (US ISSN 0032-0323) 4272
Pittsburgh Engineer. (US) 1833
Pittsburgh History. (US) 2419
Pittsburgh Jewish Chronicle. (US) 2574, 2019, 4134
Pittsburgh Legal Journal. (US ISSN 0032-0331) 2666
Pittsburgh Magazine see Pittsburgh 2232
Pittsburgh Musician. (US ISSN 0032-034X) 3574
▼Pittsburgh Quarterly. (US) 2948, 3001
Pittsburgh Regional Library Center. Newsletter. (US ISSN 0196-6707) 2779
Pittsburgh Series in Bibliography. (US) 2982
Pittsburgh Series in Labor and Social History. (US) 991

Pittsburgh Series in Labor History see Pittsburgh Series in Labor and Social History **991**
Pittsburgh Series in Policy & Institutional Studies. (US) **3915**
Pittsburgh Series in Russian & East European Studies. (US) **2380**
Pittsburgh Singles' Lifestyles. (US ISSN 1048-5554) **4363**
Pittsburgh Singles Lifestyles. (US) **4363**
Pittsburgh Studies in Theatre and Culture. (US) **4636, 4444**
Pittsburgh Symphony Orchestra Program. (US ISSN 0032-0358) **3574**
Pitture e Vernici. (IT ISSN 0048-4245) **3655**
Pivarstvo. (YU ISSN 0554-2308) **384, 481**
Pivot (New York). (US) **3001**
Pix see People **2172**
Pixel. (GR) **1464**
Pixel. (US) **1464**
Pizhuhish/Research. (IR) **2513**
Pizza & Pasta. (US) **2079**
Pizza Today. (US ISSN 0743-3115) **2079**
Pjichk. (LE ISSN 0032-0404) **3142**
Plaaslike Regering in Suidelike Afrika. see Local Government in Southern Africa **4090**
Placar. (BL) **4483**
Place (Detroit). (US) **304, 2493**
Place Names. see Diming Zhishi **2246**
Place of Graduation for Selected Health Occupations. (CN) **3142**
Placement Age see Personnel Consultant **3630**
†Placement Bulletin. (US) **5259**
Placenta. (UK ISSN 0143-4004) **526, 556**
Places (New York). (US ISSN 0731-0455) **304, 2493**
Places: A Directory of Public Places for Private Events and Private Places for Public Functions. (US ISSN 0895-4682) **1150**
Places for Men (Year). (US) **2456, 4782**
Places of Interest (Year). (US) **2456, 4782**
Places of Interest to Women: USA and Canada see Places of Interest to Women: USA and Worldwide **2456**
Places of Interest to Women: USA and Worldwide. (US) **2456, 4782, 4851**
Pladeanmeldelser, Rytmisk Musik. (DK ISSN 0109-534X) **3574**
Plaedoyer. (SZ) **2666, 3946**
Plague Watch. (US) **2879**
Plain Truth. (US ISSN 0032-0420) **4287, 3969**
Plain Turkey. (AT ISSN 0311-0753) **2948**
Plains Anthropologist. (US ISSN 0032-0447) **247, 281**
Plains Genealogical Society. Newsletter see P G S Country **2161**
Plains Genealogical Society Country see P G S Country **2161**
Plains Poetry Journal. (US ISSN 0730-6172) **3001**
Plains Talk. (US) **2419**
Plainsong. (US) **3001, 2879**
Plainsong & Mediaeval Music Society. Journal. (UK ISSN 0143-4918) **3574**
†Plainswoman. (US ISSN 0148-902X) **5259**
Plaisance Mer et Peche. (FR) **2047**
Plaisanciers. (CN) **4528**
Plaisirs. (FR) **2479, 4783**
Plaisirs de la Chasse. (FR ISSN 0048-427X) **4553**
Plaisirs de la Peche. (FR ISSN 0032-0501) **4553**
Plaisirs de la Table. (CN) **2079, 384**
Plaisirs du Cinema see Video Pratique **1387**
†Plaisirs Equestre. (FR ISSN 0032-051X) **5259**
Plamuk. (BU ISSN 0032-0528) **2879**
Plan. (IE) **304**
Plan. (CN ISSN 0032-0536) **1833**
Plan. (SW ISSN 0032-0560) **2493**
Plan Administrator's Compliance Manual. (US) **1024**

Plan Ahead. (US ISSN 0032-0587) **1050**
Plan and Action. (NE ISSN 0167-6172) **4416, 934**
Plan & Print. (US ISSN 0032-0595) **4003**
Plan Canada. (CN) **2493**
Plan de Classement P A S C A L. (Programme Applique a la Selection et la Compilation Automatique de la Literature) (FR ISSN 0992-5996) **2799, 2779**
Plan News Review see Space **2496**
Plan og Arbeid. (NO ISSN 0032-0609) **991**
†Plan Review Process for Consolidated Program Schools. (US) **5259**
Planahome Book of Home Plans see Planahome Home Improvement Guide **627**
Planahome Home Improvement Guide. (UK) **627, 2554**
Planche a Voile. (FR) **4553**
Planche Magazine. (FR) **4553**
Plane and Pilot. (US ISSN 0032-0617) **60**
Plane Talk. (US) **60**
Planeamento. (PO ISSN 0870-3043) **879**
Planedenn. (FR ISSN 0750-9189) **2948**
†Planejamento. (BL) **5259**
Planen und Bauen. (SZ) **304**
Planen und Bauen see B B A Planen und Bauen **601**
Planet. (UK ISSN 0048-4288) **2948, 340, 2834**
Planet Drum see Planet Drum Bundles **2948**
Planet Drum Bundles. (US) **2948**
†Planet Earth. (US) **5259**
The Planet Today. (CN) **2178**
Planet Walk. (US) **2948, 4195**
Planet Walker see Planet Walk **2948**
Planetarian. (US ISSN 0090-3213) **368, 1655**
Planetary and Space Science. (US ISSN 0032-0633) **368, 1548**
Planetary Association for Clean Energy. Newsletter. (CN ISSN 0708-918X) **1793, 1965**
Planetary Geodesy. (PL ISSN 0208-841X) **60**
Planetary Professional Citizens Committee Bulletin see P P C C Bulletin **60**
Planetary Report. (US ISSN 0736-3680) **368, 60**
Planete Survie. (FR) **2187**
Planeur see Aeronovum **43**
Planiranje i Analiza Poslovanja. (YU ISSN 0554-2537) **685**
Plankton Society of Japan. Bulletin. (JA ISSN 0387-8961) **451**
Planned Economy. see Planovane Hospodarstvi **1082**
Planned Parenthood. (II) **598**
Planned Parenthood Association of Ghana Newsletter see P P A G Newsletter **597**
Planned Parenthood in Europe. (UK ISSN 0309-0736) **598**
Planned Parenthood - World Population. Washington Memo see Alan Guttmacher Institute. Washington Memo **3289**
Planned Savings. (UK ISSN 0032-0668) **795**
Planner. (UK ISSN 0309-1384) **2493**
Planner see Queensland Planner **2494**
†Planner Magazine. (AT) **5259**
Planners Network Newsletter. (US) **2493**
Planning. (SA ISSN 0377-2780) **304, 627**
Planning. (US ISSN 0001-2610) **2494**
Planning. (NE ISSN 0167-3572) **2494**
Planning Advisory Service Memo see P A S Memo **2493**
Planning and Action Newsletter. (US) **4416**
Planning & Changing. (US ISSN 0032-0684) **1730**
†Planning and Development Digest. (UK) **5259**

Planning and Development Service (New South Wales). (AT ISSN 0727-792X) **2666, 627**
Planning & Environment Law Service - Victoria. (AT) **1965, 2666**
Planning and Public Policy. (US) **2494**
Planning and Transport Research and Computation. Summer Annual Meeting. Proceedings. (UK) **4707**
Planning & Zoning News. (US ISSN 0738-114X) **2494, 4093**
Planning Appeal Decisions. (UK) **2666**
▼Planning Commissioners Journal. (US ISSN 1058-5605) **2494, 4093**
Planning Consumer Markets. (UK ISSN 0308-7751) **795**
Planning: Economic, Regional, Urban, Social see P L E R U S **2493**
Planning for Higher Education. (US ISSN 0736-0983) **1714**
Planning for Living/Kurashi no Sekkei. (JA) **2449**
Planning for Social Change. (UK ISSN 0141-2779) **4444, 685**
Planning Guide X-1. (US) **1365**
Planning Guide 1. Inter-L A T A Telecommunications Rates and Services. (US) **1365**
Planning Guide 2. Intra-L A T A Telecommunications Rates and Services. (US) **1365**
Planning Guide 3. Value-Added Networks and Data Private Line. Telecommunications Rates and Services. (US) **1365**
Planning History Present. (US) **2494**
Planning in Northeastern Illinois. (US ISSN 0048-4318) **2494**
Planning Information Digest see Planning and Development Digest **5259**
Planning Institute of British Columbia News see P I B C News **2493**
Planning News see New York Planning News **2493**
Planning Outlook see Journal of Environmental Planning and Management **2490**
Planning Perspectives. (UK ISSN 0266-5433) **2319**
Planning Practice and Research. (UK ISSN 0269-7459) **2494**
Planning Reporter see Issue Brief **2489**
Planning Review (Oxford). (US ISSN 0094-064X) **1024**
Planning Tax-Exempt Organizations. (US) **1104**
Plano da Safra Acucar e Alcool. (BL) **188, 384, 2666**
Planovane Hospodarstvi/Planned Economy. (CS ISSN 0032-0749) **1082**
Planovoe Khozyaistvo. (RU ISSN 0032-0757) **1082**
Plans de Developpement des Pays d'Afrique Noire. (FR) **879**
Plans de Maisons du Quebec. (CN ISSN 0826-4392) **2554, 4154**
Plant. (SA) **1082**
The Plant (Westmount). (CN) **1321**
Plant and Cell Physiology. (JA ISSN 0032-0781) **514, 526**
Plant and Equipment Guide see Spon's Plant and Equipment Price Guide **3023**
Plant and Soil. (NE ISSN 0032-079X) **514**
Plant & Works Engineering. (UK ISSN 0262-0227) **1926**
Plant Biochemical Journal. (II ISSN 0379-5578) **481, 514**
Plant Biotechnology. (UK ISSN 0260-5902) **514, 491**
Plant Breeding/Zeitschrift fuer Pflanzenzuechtung. (GW ISSN 0179-9541) **514, 188**
Plant Breeding Abstracts. (UK ISSN 0032-0803) **2141, 20, 467**
Plant Breeding Reviews. (US ISSN 0730-2207) **188**
Plant - Canada's Industrial Newsletter. (CN ISSN 0845-4213) **1024, 1833**
Plant Cell. (US ISSN 1040-4651) **514**
Plant, Cell and Environment. (UK ISSN 0140-7791) **451**

PLANT PROTECTION 6557

Plant Cell Reports. (GW ISSN 0721-7714) **514**
†Plant Cell, Tissue and Organ Culture. (NE ISSN 0167-6857) **5259**
Plant Computerization. (CN) **1422**
Plant Disease. (US ISSN 0191-2917) **188**
Plant Disease and Insect Forecast. see Bingchong Cebao **170**
Plant Disease Research. (II ISSN 0970-4914) **514**
Plant Diseases and Pests in Denmark see Plant Diseases, Pests and Weeds in Denmark **514**
Plant Diseases, Pests and Weeds in Denmark. (DK) **514**
Plant Engineer. (UK) **1833**
Plant Engineer. (JA) **1937**
Plant Engineering. (US ISSN 0032-082X) **1833**
Plant Engineering & Maintenance. (UK) **3620, 1833**
Plant Engineering Directory and Yearbook see Plant Engineering Product Supplier Guide **1833**
Plant Engineering Product Supplier Guide. (US) **1833**
The Plant Finder. (UK ISSN 0961-2599) **2143**
Plant Foods for Human Nutrition. (NE ISSN 0921-9668) **3611**
Plant Genetic Resources Newsletter. (UN ISSN 0048-4334) **1495, 514**
Plant Growth Regulation. (NE ISSN 0167-6903) **514**
Plant Growth Regulator Abstracts. (UK ISSN 0305-9154) **142, 20**
Plant Growth Regulator Society of America Quarterly see P G R S A Quarterly **512**
Plant Hire Review. (UK ISSN 0958-6571) **627**
Plant Industry News. (US) **114**
Plant Introduction Newsletter see Plant Genetic Resources Newsletter **1495**
▼Plant Journal for Cell and Molecular Biology. (UK ISSN 0960-7412) **514**
†Plant Lore. (US) **5259**
Plant Management and Engineering see Plant - Canada's Industrial Newsletter **1024**
Plant Manager's Directory. (UK ISSN 0267-2049) **1024, 627, 1150**
Plant Managers Journal. (UK) **1024, 628**
†Plant Managers Survey. (US) **5259**
Plant Molecular Biology. (NE ISSN 0167-4412) **451**
Plant Molecular Biology Reporter. (US ISSN 0735-9640) **514, 546**
Plant - Operations Progress. (US ISSN 0278-4513) **1857**
Plant Pathology. (UK ISSN 0032-0862) **514**
Plant Pathology Bulletins see Florida. Department of Agriculture and Consumer Services. Division of Plant Industry. Bulletin Series **503**
Plant Physiology. (US ISSN 0032-0889) **514**
Plant Physiology. Supplement Abstracts of Annual Meeting. (US ISSN 0079-2241) **515**
Plant Physiology and Biochemistry. (FR ISSN 0981-9428) **515**
Plant Physiology Communications. see Zhiwu Shenglixue Tongxun **521**
Plant Press. (US) **2137, 515**
Plant Production. see Rostlinna Vyroba **117**
Plant Production. (HU ISSN 0546-8191) **189**
Plant Protection. see Ochrana Rostlin **186**
Plant Protection. see Novenyvedelem **186**
Plant Protection. see Shokubutsu Boeki **192**
Plant Protection. see Zhiwu Baohu **521**
†Plant Protection Abstracts. (IS ISSN 0032-0897) **5259**
Plant Protection Bulletin/Bitki Koruma Bulteni. (TU ISSN 0406-3597) **189**
Plant Protection Bulletin (Taiwan). (CH ISSN 0577-750X) **189**

6558 PLANT PROTECTION

Plant Protection News. (PH) **189,** 1965
Plant Protection News. (NL ISSN 1017-4214) **189**
Plant Protection Quarterly. (AT ISSN 0815-2195) **189**
Plant Protection Research Institute. Annual Report. (RH) **189,** 537
Plant Science. (IE ISSN 0168-9452) **515**
Plant Science Bulletin. (US ISSN 0032-0919) **515**
Plant Security. (CN) **1527,** 3620
Plant Services. (US ISSN 0199-8013) **1937,** 3022
Plant Shutdowns Monitor see Corporate Responsibility Monitor **1006**
Plant Sites & Locations. (CN) **628**
Plant Systematics and Evolution/ Entwicklungsgeschichte und Systematik der Pflanzen. (US ISSN 0378-2697) **515**
Plant Tissue Culture Letters. (JA ISSN 0289-5773) **515**
Plant Varieties and Seeds. (UK ISSN 0952-3863) **189**
Plant Varieties and Seeds Gazette. (UK ISSN 0048-4342) **189**
Plant Variety Protection. (UN) **189,** 515
Plant World. (UK) **628**
Planta. (GW ISSN 0032-0935) **515**
Planta Medica. (GW ISSN 0032-0943) **3740**
Plantagenet Productions. (UK) **2948,** 420
Plantation Monthly. (US) **2232**
Plantation Society in the Americas. (US ISSN 0192-5059) **4382**
Planteavlsarbejdet i de Landoekonomiske Foreninger. (DK ISSN 0106-8113) **189**
Plantebeskyttelsemidler. (DK ISSN 0108-4887) **189**
Planter. (MY ISSN 0126-575X) **114**
Planters Bulletin. (MY ISSN 0032-096X) **4292,** 114
Planters' Chronicle. (II ISSN 0032-0978) **2079**
Planters Journal and Agriculturist. (II ISSN 0032-0986) **114**
Plantes Medicinales et Phytotherapie. (FR ISSN 0032-0994) **515,** 3740
Plantevaern i Landbruget. (DK ISSN 0109-3312) **189**
Planting to Harvest. (US) **142**
Plantline. (AT) **1937**
Plants. see Zhiwu Zazhi **521**
Plants & Gardens: Brooklyn Botanic Garden Record. (US ISSN 0362-5850) **2137**
Plants & Gardens News. (US) **2137**
Plants, Sites & Parks. (US ISSN 0191-2933) **1082**
†Plants Today. (UK ISSN 0952-3855) **5259**
The Plantsman. (UK ISSN 0143-0106) **2137**
Planung und Analyse. (GW) **1050**
Planung und Kontrolle in der Unternehmung. (SZ ISSN 0079-2276) **1024**
Planungsstudien. (GW ISSN 0079-2284) **1082**
Plasma Chemistry & Plasma Processing. (US ISSN 0272-4324) **1857,** 1185, 3828
▼Plasma Devices and Operations. (US ISSN 1051-9998) **3828**
Plasma Physics and Controlled Fusion. (US ISSN 0741-3335) **3828**
▼Plasma Sources Science and Technology. (US ISSN 0963-0252) **3828**
Plasma Therapy and Transfusion Technology see Transfusion Science **3274**
Plasmid. (US ISSN 0147-619X) **451**
Plast. (IT ISSN 0391-7401) **3865**
Plast Emballage Scandinavia. (DK ISSN 0106-1720) **3865**
Plast- och Kemikalieleverantoerers Foerening Kemikalier see P K L Kemikalier **1185**
Plast- och Kemikalieleverantoerers Foerening Plaster see P K L Plaster **3864**

Plast Panorama Scandinavia. (DK) **3865**
Plaste und Kautschuk. (GW ISSN 0048-4350) **3865**
Plastforum see Plastforum Scandinavia **3865**
Plastforum Scandinavia. (SW ISSN 0347-8262) **3865,** 4292
Plasti-Noticias. (MX) **3865**
Plastic and Reconstructive Surgery. (US ISSN 0032-1052) **3382**
The Plastic Bottle Reporter. (US) **3865**
Plastic Business News. (US) **3865**
Plastic Canvas! Magazine. (US ISSN 1045-1854) **3592,** 356
Plastic Canvas World. (US) **3592,** 356
Plastic Industry Directory. (UK) **3865**
Plastic Surgery News. (US) **3382**
▼Plastic Surgery Products. (US) **3382**
Plastic Surgical Nursing. (US ISSN 0741-5206) **3285,** 3382
Plastic Tower. (US) **3001**
Plastic Waste Strategies. (US ISSN 1046-3046) **4110,** 2666, 3865
Plastichem. (SI) **1857,** 1229, 3865
Plasticke Hmoty a Kaucuk see Plasty a Kaucuk **3867**
Plastico Moderno. (BL ISSN 0102-1931) **3865**
Plasticos. (AG) **3865**
Plasticos em Revista. (BL ISSN 0032-1133) **3865**
Plasticos Universales. (GW ISSN 0303-4011) **3865**
Plasticos y Resinas (Annual) see Guia de la Industria: Hule, Plasticos y Resinas **3862**
Plastics. (US) **3865**
Plastics. see Suoliao **3868**
Plastics Age/Purasuchikkusu Eji. (JA ISSN 0551-0503) **3865**
Plastics & Environment. (US ISSN 1051-0567) **3865,** 1965
Plastics and Rubber. see Muanyag es Gumi **3864**
Plastics and Rubber. see Plasty a Kaucuk **3867**
Plastics and Rubber International. (UK ISSN 0032-1303) **3865,** 4292
Plastics and Rubber Processing and Applications see Plastics, Rubber and Composites Processing and Applications **3866**
Plastics and Rubber Weekly. (UK ISSN 0032-1168) **3865,** 4292
▼Plastics and Rubbers Materials Disc. (UK ISSN 0961-9305) **4295,** 20, 3869
Plastics Business. (CN) **3865**
Plastics Business News. (US ISSN 0734-1784) **3865**
▼Plastics - Composites Molding Digest.(US) **3865,** 1833
Plastics Compounding. (US ISSN 0148-9119) **3865**
Plastics Compounding Redbook. (US) **3865**
Plastics Conference Proceedings (Year). (US) **3865**
Plastics D.A.T.A. Digest. (US ISSN 1045-0769) **3865**
Plastics Design Forum. (US ISSN 0362-9376) **3866**
Plastics Distributor. (US) **3866**
Plastics Engineering. (US ISSN 0091-9578) **3866**
Plastics Engineering Series. (US ISSN 0032-1303) **3866**
Plastics Euro-Guide see I A L Plastics Yearbook **3862**
Plastics Focus (Amherst). (US ISSN 0554-2952) **3866**
Plastics in Building Construction. (US ISSN 0147-2429) **628,** 3866
Plastics Industry see Plastics World **3866**
Plastics Industry News. (US) **3866**
Plastics Industry News, Japan. (JA ISSN 0032-1206) **3866**
Plastics: Latin American Industrial Report. (US ISSN 0032-1303) **3866,** 1082
Plastics Machinery and Equipment. (US ISSN 0149-4899) **3866,** 3022
Plastics News see Plastics News International **3866**
Plastics News. (II) **3866**
Plastics News. (US) **3866,** 4292
Plastics News International. (AT) **3866**
†Plastics Packaging. (US) **5259**

Plastics Processing. (UK) **3866**
Plastics Recycling Update. (US ISSN 1052-4908) **1986,** 3651, 3866
Plastics, Rubber and Composites Processing and Applications. (UK ISSN 0959-8111) **3866,** 4292
Plastics, Rubber and Leather Industries Journal. (II ISSN 0032-1249) **3866,** 2738, 4292
Plastics Southern Africa. (SA ISSN 0048-4385) **3866**
Plastics Technology. (US ISSN 0032-1257) **3866**
Plastics Technology. Plastics Manufacturing Handbook and Buyers' Guide. (US) **3866**
†Plastics Today. (US) **5259**
Plastics World. (US ISSN 0032-1273) **3866**
▼Plastics World Machinery and Equipment Yellow Pages. (US) **3866**
Plastics World Yellow Pages. (US) **1150,** 3866
PlasticsBrief: Design & Materials Edition. (US) **3866**
PlasticsBrief: Extrusion & Blow Molding Edition. (US) **3866**
PlasticsBrief: Injection Molding Edition. (US) **3866**
PlasticsBrief: Marketing Edition see PlasticsBrief: Thermoplastics Marketing Edition **3866**
PlasticsBrief: Reinforced Plastic Edition.(US ISSN 0744-5296) **3866**
PlasticsBrief: Thermoplastics Marketing Edition. (US) **3866,** 1050
PlasticsWeek. (US ISSN 1044-9663) **3867**
†Plastictrends. (US) **5259**
Plastika i Guma. (YU) **3867,** 4292
Plastindustrien. (NO) **3867,** 4292
Plastiques Flash. (FR ISSN 0180-9237) **3867**
Plastiques Informations see Plastiques Modernes et Elastomeres **3867**
Plastiques Modernes et Elastomeres. (FR ISSN 0032-1303) **3867**
Plastnytt see Plastindustrien **3867**
Plastverarbeiter. (GW ISSN 0032-1338) **3867**
Plasty a Kaucuk/Plastics and Rubber. (CS ISSN 0322-7340) **3867,** 4292
Plastyka i Wychowanie w Szkole. (PL) **1655,** 340
Plastyka w Wychowanie w Szkole see Plastyka i Wychowanie w Szkole **1655**
Plate World. (US ISSN 0195-5780) **340,** 2440
▼Plateau. (GW) **340,** 3574, 4636
Plateau. (US ISSN 0032-1346) **3531**
▼Platelets (Edinburgh). (UK ISSN 0953-7104) **481,** 3273
Platelets (Sheffield). (UK ISSN 0142-8268) **3273**
Platform. see Uthon **2973**
Platform (Luddendenfoot) see Pennine Platform **3000**
Platform (Manchester). (UK ISSN 0032-1370) **3915**
Platform (Sutton-on-Craven). (UK ISSN 0143-8875) **4712**
Platform Tennis News. (US) **4510**
Platformance see Dive **4470**
Plating and Finishing. see Diandu yu Jingshi **1212**
Plating and Surface Finishing. (US ISSN 0360-3164) **3417**
Platinum (Year). (UK ISSN 0268-7305) **3493,** 2565
Platinum Metals Review. (UK ISSN 0032-1400) **3417,** 1185
Platon. (GR) **1279,** 281
Platou Report. (NO) **4735**
Der Platow Brief. (GW) **879,** 755
Platow Prognose. (GW) **879**
Platt Saco Lowell Replacement Parts News. (US) **4622**
Plattdeutsche Bibliographie. (GW ISSN 0930-021X) **2856,** 2982
Plattduetsch Land un Waterkant. (GW ISSN 0931-3931) **2948**
Platte County Historical and Genealogical Society Bulletin. (US) **2162,** 2419
Platte Valley Review. (US ISSN 0092-4318) **1321**

Platt's Asia - Pacific - Arab Gulf Marketscan. (US) **3699,** 1793
Platt's Crude Oil Market Wire. (US) **3699,** 1793
Platt's Crude Tankerwire. (US) **3699,** 1793
Platt's European Petrochemicalscan. (US) **3699,** 1793
Platt's Export - Import Report. (US) **919**
Platt's Far Eastern Petrochemical Scan. (US) **3699,** 1793
Platt's Feedstock Reports. (US) **208**
Platt's International Petrochemical Report. (US) **3699**
Platt's L P Gaswire. (US) **1794,** 3699
Platt's Oil Marketing Bulletin. (US ISSN 0277-0415) **3699**
Platt's Oil Price Handbook. (US) **3699,** 960
Platt's Oilgram Bunkerwire. (US) **1794,** 3699
Platt's Oilgram Marketscan. European Edition. (US) **1794,** 3699
Platt's Oilgram Marketscan. U S Edition.(US) **1794,** 3699
Platt's Oilgram News. (US ISSN 0163-1284) **3699**
Platt's Oilgram News Service see Platt's Oilgram News **3699**
Platt's Oilgram News - Wire. (US) **1794,** 3699
Platt's Oilgram Price Report. (US) **3699**
Platts Oilgram Price Service see Platt's Oilgram Price Report **3699**
Platt's Olefinscan. (US) **3699,** 1794
Platt's Petrochemicalscan. (US) **1794,** 3700
Platt's Polymerscan. (US) **1794,** 1858
Platt's Price Report. (US) **960**
Platt's Product Tankerwire. (US) **3700,** 1794
Platt's Solventwire. (US) **3700,** 1794
Play & Culture. (US ISSN 0894-4253) **4444,** 247, 4483
Play and Parenting Connections. (CN ISSN 0835-4014) **1242,** 4416
Play Index. (US ISSN 0554-3037) **2982,** 20
Play It Safe. (US ISSN 0882-8768) **4110**
Play Meter. (US ISSN 0162-1343) **4483,** 3574
Play Schools Newsletter. (US ISSN 0032-1443) **1655,** 1242
Play Scripts. see Juben **4634**
Play Source. (US) **4636**
Playamar. (SP) **4735**
Playback. (CN) **1378,** 36, 3515
Playback. (IE) **1378,** 1358
Playback Strategy. (CN) **1050**
Playbill. (US ISSN 0032-146X) **4636**
Playboard. (CN ISSN 0048-4415) **4636**
Playboy. (SZ) **2219**
Playboy. (US ISSN 0032-1478) **3399**
Playboy. (BL) **3399**
Playboy. (UK) **3399**
Playboy. (FR) **3399**
Playboy. (NE) **3399**
Playboy. (GW) **3399**
Playboy Enterprises. Annual Report. (US) **734,** 3399
Player. (US ISSN 1047-5303) **4483**
Player Piano Group Bulletin. (UK) **3574**
Players. (US ISSN 0149-466X) **2019**
†Player's Sports for Kids. (US) **5259**
Playfair Cricket Annual. (UK ISSN 0079-2314) **4510**
Playfair Football Annual. (UK ISSN 0079-2322) **4510**
†Playfair S.A. Rugby Yearbook. (SA) **5259**
Playgirl. (US) **4851**
Playgroup see Playtimes **1243**
Playgroup. (UK) **1263**
Playguy. (US ISSN 0733-5695) **3400,** 2456
Playhour. (UK ISSN 0032-1508) **1263**
†Playhour Annual. (UK) **5259**
Playmen. (IT ISSN 0032-1532) **3400**
PlayRights. (US) **1243**

Plays. (US ISSN 0032-1540) **4637**, 1757
Plays. A Classified Guide to Play Selection. (UK ISSN 0554-3045) **4637**
Plays & Playwrights. (US) **4637**, 2948
Plays in Process. (US ISSN 0736-0711) **4637**
Playthings. (US ISSN 0032-1567) **2282**, 2440
Playthings Directory. (US ISSN 0079-2349) **1150**, 2282
Playtimes. (AT) **1243**
Playwright. *see* Juzuojia **4634**
Plaza. (US) **2948**
Pleamar. (AG) **2170**
†Pleasant Hawaii. (US) **5259**
Pleasure Boating *see* Caribbean Sports & Travel **4468**
Pleasure Hunt Magazine *see* Delaware Valley **4759**
Pleasure Quest. (US) **3807**
Pleaters, Stitchers and Embroiderers Association. Newsletter. (US) **1287**
Pleiades/Subaru. (JA) **2948**
Pleiades Magazine. (US) **2879**
Pleiadi. (IT) **2948**
Plein Chant. (FR) **2948**
Plein la Gueule pour pas un Rond *see* P L G P P U R **339**
†Plein Nord. (FR) **5259**
Plein Soleil. (CN ISSN 0384-7810) **3255**
Pleine Marge. (BE ISSN 0295-1630) **2948**, 340
Plejehjemshaandbogen *see* Haandbog for Social og Sundhedssektor **4407**
Plenty Bulletin. (US) **156**, 3611, 3807
Plenty News *see* Plenty Bulletin **156**
Plexus: Annual Medical Specialty Updates. (US) **3180**, 20
Ploegvoor. (US) **114**
Plomberie Chauffage et Climatisation. (CN ISSN 0032-1591) **2302**
Plomje *see* Plomjo **1263**
Plomjo. (GW ISSN 0032-1605) **1263**
La Plongee. (CN ISSN 0228-3530) **4553**
Plough. (UK) **4287**
The Plough (Farmington). (US ISSN 0740-9125) **4195**, 4382
†Plough (Huron). (US) **5259**
Ploughshares. (US ISSN 0048-4474) **2948**
Ploughshares Monitor. (CN ISSN 0703-1866) **3915**
Ploutarkhos. (US ISSN 0258-655X) **1279**
†Plover/Chidori. (JA) **5259**
Plowman. (CN ISSN 0840-707X) **3001**
Plowshare News. (US) **3915**
Plowshare Press *see* Positive Alternatives **3919**
Plug. (NE ISSN 0032-1621) **4637**, 340, 2948, 3515
Plug-In. (CN ISSN 0704-0628) **2779**
Plugs 'n Points *see* Classic Trucks **4743**
Pluimvee. (BE) **223**
Pluimvee Documentatie. (NE ISSN 0168-1168) **142**, 20, 2738
Pluimveehouderij. (NE) **223**
Plum Creek Almanac. (US ISSN 0898-5197) **2419**, 2162
▼Plum Review. (US) **3001**
Pluma. (CK) **2879**
Pluma y Pincel. (AG) **2879**
Plumb. (US) **2302**
Plumb and Heat. (UK) **2302**
Plumb Line. (US ISSN 0032-163X) **1300**
Plumbers Friend. (US ISSN 0085-4905) **2302**
Plumbers' News. (AT) **2302**
Plumbers Pot. (CN) **1321**
Plumbing. (UK ISSN 0032-1656) **2302**
Plumbing and Heating *see* Plumb and Heat **2302**
Plumbing and Heating Equipment News *see* Plumbing and Heating News **2302**
Plumbing and Heating News. (UK) **2302**
Plumbing & Mechanical. (US ISSN 8750-6041) **2302**

▼Plumbing Business. (US) **2302**
†Plumbing Engineer. (US ISSN 0192-1711) **5259**
Plumbing, Heating, Piping. (US) **2302**
Plume Limousine. (FR ISSN 0220-5157) **2574**
Plumeria Society of America. Newsletter. (US) **2137**
Plunkett Development Series. (UK ISSN 0143-8484) **831**, 156
Plunkett Foundation for Co-Operative Studies. Study Series. (UK ISSN 0142-5005) **831**
Plural. (MX ISSN 0185-4925) **2949**
Plural. (AG ISSN 0326-677X) **4444**, 3915
Plural Societies. (NE ISSN 0048-4482) **4445**, 3915
Plurial. (FR ISSN 0765-1112) **2949**
Pluriel. (FR ISSN 0336-1721) **4382**
Plurilingua. (BE) **2834**
Plus. (UK) **1263**
Plus. (FR ISSN 1011-4955) **2431**, 3946
Plus. (US ISSN 0000-1341) **4144**, 1464, 1473, 2799
▼Plus Fifty. (CN) **2277**
Plus: Magazine of Positive Thinking. (US) **4287**
Plus-Minus-Zero. (BE) **340**
Plus One. *see* Futari no Heya **2207**
Plus Proces. (DK ISSN 0902-5057) **2079**
Plus: The Total Computer Magazine. (II ISSN 0970-5392) **1399**, 1479
Pluteus. (IT) **2380**
Ply - Svenska Schackdatorfoerderingen *see* Ply: Svenska Schackdatorfoeringen **1419**
Ply: Svenska Schackdatorfoeringen. (SW) **1419**, 4483
Plymothian. (UK ISSN 0048-4490) **1321**
Plymouth Bulletin. (US ISSN 0032-1737) **259**, 4699
Plymouth County Business Review. (US) **838**, 821
Plymouth Diocesan Year Book. (UK) **4272**
Plyn/Gas. (CS ISSN 0032-1761) **3700**
Plywood and Panel World *see* Panel World **2116**
Pneuma. (US ISSN 0272-0965) **4246**
Pneumatic Packaging. (US) **1937**, 3651
Pneumatiki Kypros/Cultural Cyprus. (CY) **2879**
Pneumatique. (FR) **4292**, 4699
Pneumogram. (US) **3366**
Pneumonia i Ftiziatria. (BU ISSN 0324-1491) **3366**
Pneumologie. (GW ISSN 0934-8387) **3366**
Pneumonologia Hungarica. (HU) **3366**
Pneumonologia i Alergologia Polska. (PL) **3366**
Pneumonologia Polska *see* Pneumonologia i Alergologia Polska **3366**
Pneumonologie - Pneumonology *see* Lung **3365**
Po & Sie. (FR ISSN 0152-0032) **3001**
Po Leninskomu Puti *see* Leninyan Ugiov **3904**
Po Prostu. (PL) **3915**
Po Svete. *see* Po Svetu **2834**
Po Svetu/Po Swiecie/Po Svete. (GW) **2834**, 1757
Po Swiecie. *see* Po Svetu **2834**
Pobeda. (YU ISSN 0032-1796) **2239**
Pochvovedenie. (RU ISSN 0032-180X) **189**
Pochvoznanie, Agrokhimiia i Rastitelna Zashtita. (BU) **189**
Pocitace a Umela Inteligencia. *see* Computers and Artificial Intelligence **1407**
Pocket & Laptop Computer. (GW ISSN 0934-8654) **1464**, 1479
Pocket Australian Stamp Catalogue. (AT ISSN 0155-6215) **3756**
Pocket Book of Transport Statistics of India. (II ISSN 0079-2381) **4666**, 4654
Pocket Computer. *see* Ordinateur de Poche **1399**

†Pocket Data Book, USA. (US ISSN 0079-2403) **5259**
Pocket Digest of New Zealand Statistics. (NZ ISSN 0079-2411) **2329**
Pocket Guide to the Bahamas. (BF) **4783**
Pocket Library of Studies in Art. (IT ISSN 0079-242X) **340**
Pocket List of Railroad Officials. (US ISSN 0032-1826) **4713**
Pocket List of Railroad Officials International Edition. (US) **4713**
Pocket Poets Series. (US ISSN 0079-2438) **3001**
Pocket Pro Golf Magazine. (CN) **4510**
Pocket Year Book, Australia. (AT ISSN 0727-145X) **4583**
Pocket Year Book of South Australia. (AT ISSN 0079-2446) **4583**
Pocket Yearbook. *see* Netherlands. Centraal Bureau voor de Statistiek. Statistisch Zakboek **4580**
Pocket Yearbook of New South Wales. (AT ISSN 0159-9321) **4583**
Pockets. (US ISSN 0278-565X) **4246**, 1263
Pocono Mt. News. (US) **3756**
Pod'emno-Transportnaya Tekhnika i Sklady. (RU ISSN 0235-5116) **4654**
Poder y Libertad. (SP) **4851**
Podiatric Medicine and Surgery *see* American Podiatric Medical Association. Journal **3375**
Podiatric Products. (US ISSN 0890-3972) **3311**
Podiatry Management Magazine. (US) **3142**
Podiatry Today. (US) **3311**
Podiatry Tracts. (US ISSN 0894-6116) **3311**
Podium. (FR) **2187**
Podnikova Organizace/Enterprise Organization. (CS ISSN 0032-1869) **1024**
Podravka. (CI ISSN 0352-1753) **114**, 384, 2079, 3740
Podstawy Sterowania *see* Archiwum Informatyki Teoretycznej i Stosowanej **1389**
Poduzece Banka. (CI) **795**
The Poe Messenger. (US ISSN 0276-3737) **3001**, 2949
Poe Studies Association Newsletter. (US) **3013**
Poe Studies - Dark Romanticism. (US ISSN 0090-5224) **3013**
Poem. (US ISSN 0032-1885) **3001**
Poems Deity. *see* Shi Shen **3005**
Poesia. (UY ISSN 0079-2462) **3001**
Poesia de Venezuela. (VE ISSN 0032-1893) **3001**
Poesia en la Calle. (AG ISSN 0032-1907) **3001**
Poesia Panamena Actual. (PN) **3001**
Poesie (Year). (FR) **3001**
Poesie Presente. (FR ISSN 0048-4563) **3001**
Poesie - U.S.A. (US ISSN 0364-4022) **3001**
Poesie und Wissenschaft. Sammlung. (GW) **3001**, 2949
Poesie 1. (FR) **3001**
Poet. (II ISSN 0032-194X) **3001**
Poet. (US) **3001**
Poet *see* Realities **3004**
Poet. *see* Shiren **3005**
Poet and Critic. (US ISSN 0032-1958) **3001**
Poet Lore. (US ISSN 0032-1966) **3001**
Poet News. (US) **3001**, 2879
Poetas. (PY) **3001**
Poetas Brasileiros de Hoje (Year). (BL) **3001**
Poetes et Leurs Amis: Cahiers de Literature et de Poesie *see* Cahiers de Litterature et de Poesie: Poetes et Leurs Amis **5158**
Poetes et Prosateurs du Portugal. (FR ISSN 0079-2470) **3001**, 2949
†Poetessa. (US) **5259**
Poeti della Nuova Italia *see* Nuova Rassegna: Rivista Trimestrale **2999**
Poeti e Prosatori Tedeschi. (IT ISSN 0079-2500) **3001**, 2949
Poetic Drama and Poetic Theory. (AU) **3001**, 2949

Poetic Justice. (US) **3001**
Poetic Page. (US) **3001**
Poetic Space. (US) **3001**
Poetica. (JA) **2834**, 3001
Poetica. (GW ISSN 0303-4178) **2949**, 2834
Poetica. (IT) **3001**
Poetica et Analytica. (DK ISSN 0109-2820) **2834**
Poetics. (NE ISSN 0304-422X) **2949**
Poetics. (US ISSN 1043-0814) **3001**
Poetics Journal. (US ISSN 0731-5236) **2879**, 2949
Poetics Today. (US ISSN 0333-5372) **2879**
Poetidings. (US) **3001**
Poetique. (FR ISSN 0032-2024) **2879**
Poetpourri. (US) **3001**
Poetry. (II ISSN 0970-7182) **3002**
Poetry. *see* Shikan **3005**
Poetry (Chicago). (US ISSN 0032-2032) **3002**
Poetry and Little Press Information. (UK ISSN 0260-9339) **3002**
Poetry Anthology. (UK) **3002**
Poetry Australia. (AT ISSN 0032-2059) **3002**
Poetry Book Society Bulletin. (UK) **3002**
Poetry Canada. (CN) **3002**
Poetry Canada Review *see* Poetry Canada **3002**
Poetry Comics. (US) **3002**
The Poetry Connection. (US) **3002**
▼Poetry Criticism. (US) **3002**
Poetry Durham. (UK) **3002**
Poetry East. (US ISSN 0197-4009) **3002**
Poetry Flash. (US ISSN 0737-4747) **3002**
Poetry Halifax Dartmouth. (CN ISSN 0838-200X) **3002**
Poetry Index Annual. (US ISSN 0736-3966) **2983**
Poetry Information *see* Poetry and Little Press Information **3002**
Poetry Ireland Review. (IE) **3002**, 2949
Poetry Kanto. (JA) **3002**
Poetry - L A. (US ISSN 0275-1739) **3002**
Poetry Magic *see* Writer's Voice **3009**
Poetry Miscellany. (US ISSN 0048-4601) **3002**
Poetry Nation *see* P N Review **3000**
Poetry New York. (US) **3002**
Poetry Nippon. (JA ISSN 0032-2105) **3002**
Poetry Northwest. (US ISSN 0032-2113) **3002**
Poetry Nottingham. (UK ISSN 0143-3199) **3002**
Poetry Now. (UK) **3002**
†Poetry Now. (US) **5259**
Poetry of the Circle in the Square *see* Circle in the Square Broadsheet **2990**
Poetry of the People. (US) **3002**
Poetry Peddler. (US) **3002**
Poetry Pilot. (US ISSN 0554-3983) **3002**
Poetry Post. (UK ISSN 0306-0195) **3002**
Poetry Project Newsletter. (US) **3002**
Poetry Quarterly. (UK) **3002**
Poetry Resource Center of Michigan Newsletter and Calendar *see* P R C Newsletter and Calendar **3000**
Poetry Review. (UK ISSN 0032-2156) **3002**
Poetry: San Francisco Quarterly *see* Poetry: U S A Quarterly **3002**
Poetry Society of America Newsletter. (US) **3002**
Poetry Supplement *see* Poetry Anthology **3002**
†Poetry Texas. (US) **5259**
Poetry Time. (II) **3002**
Poetry: U S A Quarterly. (US) **3002**
Poetry Wales. (UK ISSN 0032-2202) **3003**
†Poetry World. (UK ISSN 0268-1390) **5259**
Poets & Writers Magazine. (US ISSN 0891-6136) **3003**, 2949
Poets at Work. (US) **3003**
Poet's Handbook. (US ISSN 1055-1670) **409**, 3003

POETS

†Poets in the South. (US ISSN 0197-6338) **5259**
Poets International. (II) **3003**
Poets' League of Greater Cleveland Newsletter see P L G C Newsletter **3000**
Poet's Market. (US ISSN 0883-5470) **3003**
Poet's Newsletter. (US) **3003**
Poets On: (US ISSN 0146-3136) **3003**
Poets, Painters, Composers. (US) **2949**, **340**
Poets' Roundtable. (US) **3003**
Poetyka. Zarys Encyklopedyczny. (PL ISSN 0079-2527) **3003**
Poeziya (Kiev) see Boyan **2989**
Poeziya (Moscow). (RU) **3003**
Poezja. (PL ISSN 0032-2237) **3003**
Pofam. (MY ISSN 0127-9068) **3985**
Pogledi (Kragujevac)/Views. (YU ISSN 0353-3832) **2879**
Pogledi (Skopje). (XN ISSN 0032-2245) **2879**
Pogrom. (GW) **3946**, **2019**
Pohjoismaiden Kouluoloista see Skolen i Norden **1663**
Pohjoismainen Erikoiskielten ja Terminologian Aikakauslehti. see Nordisk Tidsskrift for Fagsprog og Terminologi **5248**
Pohyb a My. (CS) **4483**
†Poids Lourd. (FR ISSN 0032-227X) **5259**
Le Poing et la Rose. (FR) **3915**
Le Poingt. (CN) **1321**
Point see Commerce. Le Point **834**
Point see Revue Commerce **839**
Le Point. (FR) **2187**
Point Blank. (US) **3946**
Le Point d'Appui. (CN) **1321**
Point de Repere. (CN) **20**
Point de Vue. see Point of View **1294**
Point Economique. (FR ISSN 0758-573X) **821**
Point Economique. (SZ) **821**
Point of Purchase Advertising Institute. Buyer's Guide. (US) **36**, **1050**
Point of Purchase Advertising Institute. Industry Magazine. (US) **1050**, **36**
Point of Purchase Advertising Institute News see P O P A I News **1049**
Point-of-Purchase Times see P-O-P Times **878**
Point-of-Sale Information Service see P O S I S **1049**
Point of Sale News see P O S News **794**
Point of View/Point de Vue. (CN) **1294**, **374**
Point of View. (US ISSN 0032-2318) **3946**
Point Series. (PP ISSN 0253-2913) **3643**, **247**
Point Veterinaire. (FR) **4814**
Point 3. (UK ISSN 0032-2326) **2513**
Pointe see Dance News **1530**
Pointer. (AT) **2565**, **2440**
Pointer (Washington) see Preventing School Failure **1740**
Pointer (West Point). (US) **1321**
Pointer Points. (US) **3713**
Points. Films. (FR ISSN 0079-2535) **3515**
Points Chauds see France des Points Chauds **3895**
Points de Repere. (FR) **4195**
Points de Vente. (FR) **1050**
Points et Contrepoints. (FR ISSN 0032-2369) **3003**
Points for Emphasis; International Sunday School Lessons in Pocket Size. (US ISSN 0079-2543) **4195**
Points North. (US) **2779**
Points Northwest. (US) **2779**
Points West see Horizon (Salt Lake City) **1314**
Poirieria. (NZ ISSN 0032-2377) **590**
Poison Management Manual. (CN) **3740**
Poison Pen Writers News. (US) **2949**
Poisoned Pen. (US) **2879**
Pojistny Obzor. (CS ISSN 0032-2393) **2540**
†Poker Player. (US) **5259**
Poker Tips. (US) **4483**
Pokolenia. (PL ISSN 0551-2050) **2380**, **1243**
Pokret. (YU ISSN 0032-2407) **1243**
Pokrof. (NE ISSN 0032-2415) **4216**
Pokroky Matematiky, Fyziky a Astronomie/Progress in Mathematics, Physics and Astronomy. (CS ISSN 0032-2423) **4334**
Pol-Am Journal. (US) **2540**, **2019**
Pol-Dok see Politische Dokumentation **3938**
Pola. (IO) **304**
Pola Esperantisto/Esperantist's Magazine. (PL ISSN 0032-2431) **2834**
Poland. (PL ISSN 0032-244X) **2214**
Poland. Central Statistics Office. Accidents at Work. see Poland. Glowny Urzad Statystyczny. Wypadki przy Pracy **4118**
Poland. Central Statistics Office. Concise Statistical Yearbook. see Poland. Glowny Urzad Statystyczny. Maly Rocznik Statystyczny **4583**
Poland. Central Statistics Office. Property and Personal Insurance. see Poland. Glowny Urzad Statystyczny. Ubezpieczenia Majatkowe i Osobowe **2547**
Poland. Central Statistics Office. State Budget. see Poland. Glowny Urzad Statystyczny. Budzet Panstwa **734**
Poland. Central Statistics Office. Statistical Yearbook. see Poland. Glowny Urzad Statystyczny. Rocznik Statystyczny **4583**
Poland. Central Statistics Office. Statistical Yearbook of Culture. see Poland. Glowny Urzad Statystyczny. Rocznik Statystyczny Kultury **2520**
Poland. Central Statistics Office. Yearbook of Construction Statistics. see Poland. Glowny Urzad Statystyczny. Rocznik Statystyczny Budownictwa **638**
Poland. Central Statistics Office. Yearbook of Education Statistics. see Poland. Glowny Urzad Statystyczny. Rocznik Statystyczny Szkolnictwa **1679**
Poland. Central Statistics Office. Yearbook of Finance Statistics. see Poland. Glowny Urzad Statystyczny. Rocznik Statystyczny Finansow **734**
Poland. Central Statistics Office. Yearbook of Industry Statistics. see Poland. Glowny Urzad Statystyczny. Rocznik Statystyczny Przemyslu **735**
Poland. Central Statistics Office. Yearbook of International Statistics. see Poland. Glowny Urzad Statystyczny. Rocznik Statystyki Miedzynarodowej **4583**
Poland. Central Statistics Office. Yearbook of Investment and Fixed Assets Statistics. see Poland. Glowny Urzad Statystyczny. Rocznik Statystyczny Inwestycji i Srodkow Trwalych **735**
Poland. Central Statistics Office. Yearbook of Labour Statistics. see Poland. Glowny Urzad Statystyczny. Rocznik Statystyczny Pracy **735**
Poland. Central Statistics Office. Yearbook of Public Health Statistics. see Poland. Glowny Urzad Statystyczny. Rocznik Statystyczny Ochrony Zdrowia **4118**
Poland. Central Statistics Office. Yearbook of Sea Economy Statistics. see Poland. Glowny Urzad Statystyczny. Rocznik Statystyczny Gospodarki Morskiej **4666**
Poland. Central Statistics Office. Yearbook of Transport Statistics. see Poland. Glowny Urzad Statystyczny. Rocznik Statystyczny Transportu **4666**
Poland. Glowny Urzad Statystyczny. Biuletyn Statystyczny. (PL ISSN 0006-4025) **4583**
Poland. Glowny Urzad Statystyczny. Budzet Panstwa/Poland. Central Statistics Office. State Budget. (PL ISSN 0079-2594) **734**, **1104**, **4583**
Poland. Glowny Urzad Statystyczny. Kultura see Poland. Glowny Urzad Statystyczny. Rocznik Statystyczny Kultury **2520**
Poland. Glowny Urzad Statystyczny. Maly Rocznik Statystyczny/Poland. Central Statistics Office. Concise Statistical Yearbook. (PL ISSN 0079-2608) **4583**
Poland. Glowny Urzad Statystyczny. Maly Rocznik Statystyki Miedzynarodowej. (PL) **4583**
Poland. Glowny Urzad Statystyczny. Rocznik Demograficzny. (PL ISSN 0079-2616) **3994**
Poland. Glowny Urzad Statystyczny. Rocznik Statystyczny/Poland. Central Statistics Office. Statistical Yearbook. (PL ISSN 0079-2780) **4583**
Poland. Glowny Urzad Statystyczny. Rocznik Statystyczny Budownictwa/Poland. Central Statistics Office. Yearbook of Construction Statistics. (PL ISSN 0079-2632) **638**
Poland. Glowny Urzad Statystyczny. Rocznik Statystyczny Finansow/Poland. Central Statistics Office. Yearbook of Finance Statistics. (PL ISSN 0079-2640) **734**
Poland. Glowny Urzad Statystyczny. Rocznik Statystyczny Gospodarki Morskiej/Poland. Central Statistics Office. Yearbook of Sea Economy Statistics. (PL ISSN 0079-2667) **4666**
Poland. Glowny Urzad Statystyczny. Rocznik Statystyczny Gospodarki Mieszkaniowej i Komunalnej. (PL ISSN 0079-2659) **2500**
Poland. Glowny Urzad Statystyczny. Rocznik Statystyczny Inwestycji i Srodkow Trwalych/Poland. Central Statistics Office. Yearbook of Investment and Fixed Assets Statistics. (PL ISSN 0079-2705) **735**
Poland. Glowny Urzad Statystyczny. Rocznik Statystyczny Kultury/Poland. Central Statistics Office. Statistical Yearbook of Culture. (PL) **2520**
Poland. Glowny Urzad Statystyczny. Rocznik Statystyczny Lesnictwa see Poland. Glowny Urzad Statystyczny. Rocznik Statystyczny Lesnictwa i Gospodarki Drewnem **2112**
Poland. Glowny Urzad Statystyczny. Rocznik Statystyczny Lesnictwa i Gospodarki Drewnem. (PL) **2112**
Poland. Glowny Urzad Statystyczny. Rocznik Statystyczny Ochrony Zdrowia/Poland. Central Statistics Office. Yearbook of Public Health Statistics. (PL ISSN 0079-2748) **4118**
Poland. Glowny Urzad Statystyczny. Rocznik Statystyczny Pracy/Poland. Central Statistics Office. Yearbook of Labour Statistics. (PL ISSN 0079-2772) **735**
Poland. Glowny Urzad Statystyczny. Rocznik Statystyczny Przemyslu/Poland. Central Statistics Office. Yearbook of Industry Statistics. (PL ISSN 0079-2764) **735**
Poland. Glowny Urzad Statystyczny. Rocznik Statystyczny Rolnictwa i Gospodarki Zywnosciowej. (PL) **142**
Poland. Glowny Urzad Statystyczny. Rocznik Statystyczny Szkolnictwa/Poland. Central Statistics Office. Yearbook of Education Statistics. (PL ISSN 0079-2799) **1679**
Poland. Glowny Urzad Statystyczny. Rocznik Statystyczny Transportu/Poland. Central Statistics Office. Yearbook of Transport Statistics. (PL ISSN 0079-2802) **4666**
Poland. Glowny Urzad Statystyczny. Rocznik Statystyki. Handel Zagraniczny (Year) (PL ISSN 0079-2691) **735**
Poland. Glowny Urzad Statystyczny. Rocznik Statystyki Miedzynarodowej/Poland. Central Statistics Office. Yearbook of International Statistics. (PL ISSN 0079-273X) **4583**
Poland. Glowny Urzad Statystyczny. Rolniczy Rocznik Statystyczny - Poland. Central Statistics Office. Yearbook of Agricultural Statistics see Poland. Glowny Urzad Statystyczny. Rocznik Statystyczny Rolnictwa i Gospodarki Zywnosciowej **142**
Poland. Glowny Urzad Statystyczny. Statystyka Polski. Seria: Materialy Statystyczne. Ceny Detaliczne. (PL ISSN 0860-6730) **735**
Poland. Glowny Urzad Statystyczny. Statystyka Polski. Seria: Materialy Statystyczne. Warunki Mieszkaniowe Gospodarstw Domowych oraz Wydadki na Mieszkanie (Year). (PL) **735**
Poland. Glowny Urzad Statystyczny. Statystyka Polski. Studia i Prace Statystyczne. (PL) **4583**
Poland. Glowny Urzad Statystyczny. Statystyka Zeglugi Srodladowej i Drog Wodnych Srodladowych. (PL ISSN 0079-2837) **4666**
Studia i Prace Statystyczne see Poland. Glowny Urzad Statystyczny. Statystyka Polski. Studia i Prace Statystyczne **4583**
Poland. Glowny Urzad Statystyczny. Turystyka. (PL) **4800**
Poland. Glowny Urzad Statystyczny. Ubezpieczenia Majatkowe i Osobowe/Poland. Central Statistics Office. Property and Personal Insurance. (PL ISSN 0079-2853) **2547**
Poland. Glowny Urzad Statystyczny. Wiadomosci Statystyczne. (PL ISSN 0043-518X) **4583**
Poland. Glowny Urzad Statystyczny. Wyniki Spisu Rolniczego. Uzytkowanie Gruntow i Powierzchnia Zasiewow, oraz Zwierzeta Gospodarskie. (PL) **142**
Poland. Glowny Urzad Statystyczny. Wypadki Drogowe. (PL ISSN 0079-287X) **4118**
Poland. Glowny Urzad Statystyczny. Wypadki przy Pracy/Poland. Central Statistics Office. Accidents at Work. (PL ISSN 0079-2888) **4118**
Poland. Glowny Urzad Statystyczny. Zatrudnienie w Gospodarce Narodowej. (PL ISSN 0079-2896) **735**
Poland. Glowny Urzad Statystyczny. Zeszyty Metodyczne. (PL ISSN 0079-2829) **4583**
Poland. Patent Office. Bulletin. see Poland. Urzad Patentowy. Biuletyn **3677**
Poland. Patent Office. News. see Poland. Urzad Patentowy. Wiadomosci **3677**
Poland. Urzad Patentowy. Biuletyn/Poland. Patent Office. Bulletin. (PL ISSN 0137-8015) **3677**
Poland. Urzad Patentowy. Wiadomosci/Poland. Patent Office. News. (PL ISSN 0043-5201) **3677**
Poland China World see Purebred Picture **224**
Poland News. see Polen-Nyt **5259**
Poland of Tomorrow. see Jutro Polski **2010**
Poland Today. (US) **2019**
†Poland - Tourism. (PL) **5259**
†Poland Watch Reports. (US ISSN 0892-2519) **5259**
Polar and Glaciological Abstracts. (UK ISSN 0957-5073) **1552**
Polar Biology. (GW ISSN 0722-4060) **451**
Polar Geography and Geology. (US ISSN 0273-8457) **2259**, **1577**
Polar Information. (GW) **3022**
Polar News. see Kyokuchi **4322**
Polar Record. (UK ISSN 0032-2474) **2259**
Polar Research. (NO ISSN 0800-0395) **4334**, **2259**
Polar Times. (US ISSN 0032-2482) **2259**
Polarforschung. (GW ISSN 0032-2490) **1548**, **2259**
Polarhaandbok see Norsk Polarinstitutt. Polarhaandbok **1576**

Polaris Almanac for Azimuth Determination. *see* Hokkyokusei Hoikakuhyo **4664**
Pole et Tropiques. (FR ISSN 0032-2504) **4273**
Polemica. (CR) **3915**
Polemical Documents Series. (CN) **2019**, **3969**
†Polen-Nyt/Poland News. (DK ISSN 0108-7371) **5259**
Polen - Touristik *see* Poland - Tourism **5259**
Polen und Wir. (GW ISSN 0930-4584) **3969**, **2380**
Polens Gegenwart *see* Contemporary Poland **3882**
Polestar. (UK) **1655**
†Polet. (YU ISSN 0032-2520) **5259**
Poletarac. (YU ISSN 0032-2547) **1263**
Police. (UK ISSN 0032-2555) **1520**
Police. (US ISSN 0893-8989) **1520**
Police & Constabulary Almanac. (UK ISSN 0477-2008) **1520**
Police and Law Enforcement. (US ISSN 0092-8933) **1520**
†Police and Security Bulletin. (US ISSN 0271-7565) **5259**
Police and Security News. (US) **1520**
Police Chief. (US) **1520**
Police Conference of New York, Inc. State Report *see* P C N Y State Report **1519**
Police Journal. (UK ISSN 0032-258X) **1520**
Police Life. (AT ISSN 0032-2598) **1520**
Police Misconduct and Civil Rights Law Report. (US ISSN 0738-0623) **1520**, **2667**
Police Mutualite. (FR) **1520**
Police Nationale. (FR ISSN 0048-4695) **1520**
Police News. (GH) **1520**
Police Officers Journal. (US) **1520**
Police Plaintiff. (US) **2667**, **1520**
Police Product News *see* Police **1520**
Police Studies. (US ISSN 0141-2949) **1520**
▼Police Technology and Management. (US ISSN 1051-385X) **1520**
Police Times. (US) **1520**
Police Times and Police Command *see* Police Times **1520**
†Police Yearbook. (US ISSN 0079-2950) **5259**
Policeman. *see* Al-Shurti **1522**
Policia. (SP ISSN 0213-4012) **1520**
Policia Espanola *see* Policia **1520**
Policies and Practices. (US) **1069**
Policies for World Farming. (FR) **114**
Policies Review. (US) **2540**
▼Policing and Society. (US ISSN 1043-9463) **1520**, **4445**
Policlinico. Sezione Chirurgica. (IT ISSN 0032-2636) **3382**
Policlinico. Sezione Medica. (IT ISSN 0048-4717) **3142**
Policlinico. Sezione Pratica. (IT ISSN 0032-2644) **3142**
Policordo. (IT) **2513**, **340**, **2949**
Policy. (AT ISSN 1032-6634) **685**
Policy *see* Policy Market **2540**
Policy and Politics. (UK ISSN 0305-5736) **1714**, **4070**
Policy Bites. (US) **685**, **4382**
Policy Forum. (US) **4070**
Policy Grants Directory. (US ISSN 0160-2675) **3915**
Policy Management Systems Corp. Today *see* P M S Today **828**
Policy Market. (UK ISSN 0263-6700) **2540**
†Policy Notes. (US ISSN 8755-9412) **5259**
Policy Options/Options Politiques. (CN ISSN 0226-5893) **4070**, **3915**
Policy Papers in International Affairs *see* University of California, Berkeley. Institute of International Studies. Policy Papers in International Affairs **3976**
Policy Publishers and Associations Directory. (US ISSN 0272-0671) **3915**, **4134**
Policy Report *see* Cato Policy Report **829**
Policy Research Centers Directory. (US ISSN 0270-1200) **3915**

Policy Review. (US ISSN 0146-5945) **3915**
Policy Sciences. (NE ISSN 0032-2687) **3915**, **685**, **4445**
Policy Studies. (UK ISSN 0144-2872) **3915**, **685**, **4382**
Policy Studies Directory. (US ISSN 0362-6016) **3915**
Policy Studies in Employment and Welfare. (US) **4416**
Policy Studies Institute Discussion Papers *see* P S I Discussion Papers **4381**
Policy Studies Institute Report Series *see* P S I: Report Series **3913**
Policy Studies Journal. (US ISSN 0190-292X) **3916**
Policy Studies Personnel Directory. (US ISSN 0275-4002) **3916**
Policy Studies Review. (US ISSN 0278-4416) **3916**
Policy Studies Review Annual. (US ISSN 0163-108X) **4070**
Policy Study. (CN ISSN 0832-7912) **685**
Poliedro. (IT) **340**
Poligrafico Italiano. (IT ISSN 0032-2709) **4003**
Poligrafika. (PL ISSN 0373-9864) **4003**
Poligrafiya. (RU ISSN 0032-2717) **4003**, **4134**
Poliisimies. (FI ISSN 0048-4725) **1520**
Polimeri. (CI ISSN 0351-1871) **3867**, **4292**
Polimery/Polymers. (PL ISSN 0032-2725) **1221**
Polimery v Melioratsii i Vodnom Khozyaistve. (LV) **1925**, **4827**
†Polimitas. (CU) **5259**
Polimlje. (YU ISSN 0032-2733) **2240**
Polin. (UK ISSN 0268-1056) **2019**
Polio-France. (FR ISSN 0032-2741) **3350**
Polio Network News. (US) **3142**
Polio-Nyt *see* P T U Nyt **3349**
Poliorama. (IT) **2206**
Poliplasti. (IT) **3867**
Polis. (IT ISSN 1120-9488) **3916**, **4445**
Polish Academy of Sciences. Bulletin. Biological Sciences. (PL ISSN 0239-751X) **451**
Polish Academy of Sciences. Bulletin. Chemical Sciences. (PL ISSN 0239-7285) **1185**
Polish Academy of Sciences. Bulletin. Earth Sciences. (PL ISSN 0239-7277) **1577**, **2259**
Polish Academy of Sciences. Bulletin. Mathematical Sciences. (PL ISSN 0239-7269) **3050**, **368**, **3828**
Polish Academy of Sciences. Bulletin. Technical Sciences. (PL ISSN 0239-7528) **4606**
Polish Academy of Sciences. Institute of Computer Science. Reports. (PL) **1399**
Polish Academy of Sciences. Institute of Fluid-Flow Machinery. Transactions. *see* Polska Akademia Nauk. Instytut Maszyn Przeplywowych. Prace **1937**
Polish Academy of Sciences. Institute of Geography and Spatial Organization. Geographical Studies. Special Issue. (PL ISSN 0209-1577) **2259**
Polish Academy of Sciences. Institute of Geophysics. Publications. Series A: Physics of the Earth's Interior. (PL ISSN 0137-2440) **1593**
Polish Academy of Sciences. Institute of Geophysics. Publications. Series B: Seismology. (PL ISSN 0138-0109) **1593**
Polish Academy of Sciences. Institute of Geophysics. Publications. Series C: Geomagnetism. (PL ISSN 0138-0117) **1593**
Polish Academy of Sciences. Institute of Geophysics. Publications. Series D: Physics of the Atmosphere. (PL ISSN 0138-0125) **1593**
Polish Academy of Sciences. Institute of Geophysics. Publications. Series F: Planetary Geodesy. (PL ISSN 0138-0141) **1593**

†Polish Academy of Sciences. Institute of Geophysics. Publications. Series G. Numerical Methods in Geophysics. (PL ISSN 0208-8061) **5259**
Polish Academy of Sciences. Institute of Geophysics. Publications. Series M: Miscellanea. (PL ISSN 0138-015X) **1593**
Polish Academy of Sciences. Mathematical Institute. Banach Center Publications. (PL ISSN 0137-6934) **3050**
Polish Affairs. (UK ISSN 0032-2784) **3916**
Polish Agriculture. (FR) **156**
Polish American Congress Charitable Foundation, Inc. Newsletter *see* P A C Newsletter **2018**
Polish American Historical Association Newsletter *see* P A H A Newsletter **2018**
Polish American Journal. (US ISSN 0032-2792) **2019**
Polish American Studies. (US ISSN 0032-2806) **2019**
Polish American World. (US) **2019**
Polish-AngloSaxon Studies. (PL ISSN 0860-5882) **2319**, **3969**
Polish Archaeological Abstracts. (PL ISSN 0137-4885) **290**, **20**
Polish Archives of Hydrobiology. *see* Polskie Archiwum Hydrobiologii **451**
Polish Archives of Internal Medicine. *see* Polskie Archiwum Medycyny Wewnetrznej **3142**
Polish Art Studies. (PL) **340**
▼Polish Building Market. (PL ISSN 0867-5880) **628**, **685**
Polish Canadian Courier/Nowy Kurier. (CN ISSN 0319-5147) **2019**
Polish Cartographical Review. *see* Polski Przeglad Kartograficzny **2259**
Polish Co-Operative Review. (PL ISSN 0032-2822) **831**
Polish Daily. *see* Dziennik Zwiazkowy **1999**
Polish Daily and the Soldiers Daily. *see* Dziennik Polski i Dziennik Zolnierza **1999**
Polish Daily News/Nowy Dziennik. (US) **2574**
Polish Ecological Studies. (PL ISSN 0324-8763) **1965**
Polish Engineering. (PL ISSN 0209-0260) **1833**, **919**
Polish Fair Magazine *see* Polish Trade Magazine **919**
Polish Falcon. *see* Sokol Polski **1301**
†Polish Film. (PL) **5259**
Polish Folk Culture. *see* Polska Sztuka Ludowa **340**
Polish Foreign Trade. (PL ISSN 0032-2881) **919**
Polish Genealogical Society Newsletter. (US ISSN 0735-9349) **2162**
Polish Heritage. (US ISSN 0735-9209) **2019**
Polish Historical Library. Anthologies. Monographs. Opera Minora. (PL ISSN 0208-7359) **2380**, **4445**
Polish Journal of Applied Chemistry. (PL) **1185**
Polish Journal of Chemistry. (PL ISSN 0137-5083) **1185**
Polish Journal of Ecology. *see* Ekologia Polska **437**
Polish Journal of Occupational Medicine *see* Polish Journal of Occupational Medicine and Environmental Health **3620**
Polish Journal of Occupational Medicine and Environmental Health. (PL) **3620**, **4110**
Polish Journal of Pharmacology and Pharmacy. (PL ISSN 0301-0244) **3740**
Polish Journal of Soil Science. (PL ISSN 0079-2985) **189**
Polish Machine Industry Offers *see* Polish Engineering **1833**
†Polish Maritime News. (PL ISSN 0032-2911) **5259**
Polish Music/Polnische Musik. (PL ISSN 0032-2946) **3574**
Polish Music History Series. (US ISSN 0741-9945) **3574**
Polish News/Wiadomosci Polskie. (AT ISSN 0032-2954) **2019**

Polish Paper Review. *see* Przeglad Papierniczy **3668**
Polish Perspectives. (PL ISSN 0032-2962) **2879**, **3916**
Polish Political Science. (PL ISSN 0208-7375) **3916**
Polish Psychological Bulletin. (PL ISSN 0079-2993) **4038**
Polish Publishing in Figures. *see* Ruch Wydawniczy w Liczbach **4142**
Polish Review. (US ISSN 0032-2970) **2214**
Polish Round Table *see* Polish Political Science **3916**
Polish Scientific Abstracts on Mechanics. *see* Polska Bibliografia Analityczna Mechaniki **3025**
Polish Sociological Bulletin. (PL ISSN 0032-2997) **4445**
Polish Studies Newsletter. (US) **2019**
Polish Technical and Economic Abstracts. (PL ISSN 0032-3004) **4615**, **20**, **735**
Polish Technical Review. (PL ISSN 0032-3012) **1834**, **4606**
Polish Thought. *see* Mysl Polska **2875**
Polish Times. *see* Czas **1998**
Polish Trade Magazine. (PL ISSN 0239-989X) **919**
Polish Western Affairs. (PL ISSN 0032-3039) **3969**
Polish Western Association of America. Quarterly. (US ISSN 0032-3047) **3916**, **2019**
Polish Womens' Voice. *see* Glos Polek **2003**
Polish Yearbook of International Law/Annuaire Polonais de Droit International. (PL ISSN 0554-498X) **2728**
Polit. (US) **2949**, **3916**
Politechnico di Torino. Istituto de Scienza dei Sistemi Architettonici e Territoriali della Facolta de Architettura. Studi e Recherche. (IT) **304**
Politechnika Czestochowska. Zeszyty Naukowe. Budownictwo. (PL ISSN 0860-7214) **628**
Politechnika Czestochowska. Zeszyty Naukowe. Nauki Spoleczno-Ekonomiczne. (PL ISSN 0574-9077) **4382**, **897**, **3916**
Politechnika Czestochowska. Zeszyty Naukowe. Nauki Techniczne. Elektrotechnika. (PL ISSN 0137-6977) **1905**
Politechnika Czestochowska. Zeszyty Naukowe. Nauki Techniczne. Hutnictwo. (PL ISSN 0372-9699) **3417**
Politechnika Czestochowska. Zeszyty Naukowe. Nauki Techniczne. Mechanika. (PL ISSN 0137-6969) **1937**
†Politechnika Gdanska. Instytut Organizacji i Projektowania. Raport. (PL) **5259**
Politechnika Gdanska. Zeszyty Naukowe. Architektura. (PL ISSN 0518-3138) **304**
Politechnika Gdanska. Zeszyty Naukowe. Budownictwo Ladowe. (PL ISSN 0373-8671) **1872**, **628**
Politechnika Gdanska. Zeszyty Naukowe. Budownictwo Okretowe. (PL ISSN 0373-868X) **4735**
Politechnika Gdanska. Zeszyty Naukowe. Budownictwo Wodne. (PL ISSN 0373-8663) **1925**
Politechnika Gdanska. Zeszyty Naukowe. Chemia. (PL ISSN 0416-7341) **1185**
Politechnika Gdanska. Zeszyty Naukowe. Ekonomia. (PL ISSN 0208-5666) **685**
Politechnika Gdanska. Zeszyty Naukowe. Elektronika. (PL ISSN 0373-8698) **1442**, **1365**, **1415**, **1905**
Politechnika Gdanska. Zeszyty Naukowe. Elektryka. (PL ISSN 0373-8647) **1905**
Politechnika Gdanska. Zeszyty Naukowe. Fizyka. (PL ISSN 0072-0364) **3828**
Politechnika Gdanska. Zeszyty Naukowe. Matematyka. (PL ISSN 0072-0372) **3050**

Politechnika Gdanska. Zeszyty Naukowe. Mechanika. (PL ISSN 0072-0380) **1937**
Politechnika Gdanska. Zeszyty Naukowe. Architektura. (PL ISSN 0137-1371) **304**
Politechnika Krakowska. Zeszyty Naukowe. Budownictwo Ladowe see Politechnika Krakowska. Zeszyty Naukowe. Inzynieria Ladowa **1872**
Politechnika Krakowska. Zeszyty Naukowe. Budownictwo Wodne i Inzynieria Sanitarna see Politechnika Krakowska. Zeszyty Naukowe. Inzynieria Sanitarna i Wodna **4827**
Politechnika Krakowska. Zeszyty Naukowe. Chemia see Politechnika Krakowska. Zeszyty Naukowe. Inzynieria i Technologia Chemiczna **1185**
Politechnika Krakowska. Zeszyty Naukowe. Inzynieria i Technologia Chemiczna. (PL) **1185**
Politechnika Krakowska. Zeszyty Naukowe. Inzynieria Ladowa. (PL) **1872**
Politechnika Krakowska. Zeszyty Naukowe. Inzynieria Sanitarna i Wodna. (PL) **4827**
Politechnika Krakowska. Zeszyty Naukowe. Inzynieria Transportowa i Elektryczna. (PL) **4654**
Politechnika Krakowska. Zeszyty Naukowe. Mechanika. (PL ISSN 0372-9486) **3845**
Politechnika Krakowska. Zeszyty Naukowe. Nauki Ekonomiczne. (PL ISSN 0548-0442) **685**
Politechnika Krakowska. Zeszyty Naukowe. Podstawowe Nauki Techniczne. (PL ISSN 0137-138X) **4606**
Politechnika Krakowska. Zeszyty Naukowe. Transport see Politechnika Krakowska. Zeszyty Naukowe. Inzynieria Transportowa i Elektryczna **4654**
Politechnika Lodzka. Zeszyty Naukowe. Budownictwo. (PL ISSN 0076-0323) **1872**, **628**
Politechnika Lodzka. Zeszyty Naukowe. Chemia. (PL ISSN 0458-1555) **1185**
Politechnika Lodzka. Zeszyty Naukowe. Cieplne Maszyny Przeplywowe. (PL ISSN 0137-2661) **1937**
Politechnika Lodzka. Zeszyty Naukowe. Elektryka. (PL ISSN 0459-682X) **1905**
Politechnika Lodzka. Zeszyty Naukowe. Fizyka. (PL ISSN 0137-2564) **3828**
▼Politechnika Lodzka. Zeszyty Naukowe. Informatyka. (PL ISSN 0860-0082) **1457**
Politechnika Lodzka. Zeszyty Naukowe. Inzynieria Chemiczna. (PL ISSN 0137-2602) **1858**
Politechnika Lodzka. Zeszyty Naukowe. Matematyka. (PL ISSN 0137-2572) **3051**
Politechnika Lodzka. Zeszyty Naukowe. Mechanika. (PL ISSN 0458-1563) **1937**
Politechnika Lodzka. Zeszyty Naukowe. Organizacja i Zarzadzanie. (PL ISSN 0137-2599) **4382**, **685**
Politechnika Lodzka. Zeszyty Naukowe. Technologia I. Chemia Spozywcza. (PL ISSN 0528-9254) **2079**
Politechnika Lodzka. Zeszyty Naukowe. Wlokiennictwo. (PL ISSN 0076-0331) **4622**
Politechnika Poznanska. Instytut Nauk Ekonomicznych i Spolecznych. Prace Naukowe see Politechnika Poznanska. Instytut Nauk Ekonomicznych i Spolecznych. Zeszyty Naukowe **897**
Politechnika Poznanska. Instytut Nauk Ekonomicznych i Spolecznych. Zeszyty Naukowe. (PL ISSN 0239-9423) **897**
Politechnika Poznanska. Materialy Historyczno-Metodyczne. Studia Filozoficzne see Materialy Historyczno-Metodyczne **2317**

†Politechnika Poznanska. Zeszyty Naukowe. Bibliografia. (PL ISSN 0551-651X) **5259**
Politechnika Poznanska. Zeszyty Naukowe. Budownictwo see Politechnika Poznanska. Zeszyty Naukowe. Budownictwo Ladowe **1872**
Politechnika Poznanska. Zeszyty Naukowe. Budownictwo Ladowe. (PL) **1872**
Politechnika Poznanska. Zeszyty Naukowe. Ekonomika i Organizacja Przemyslu see Politechnika Poznanska. Zeszyty Naukowe. Organizacja i Zarzadzanie **1082**
Politechnika Poznanska. Zeszyty Naukowe. Elektryka. (PL ISSN 0079-4503) **1905**
Politechnika Poznanska. Zeszyty Naukowe. Geometria. (PL ISSN 0239-488X) **3051**
Politechnika Poznanska. Zeszyty Naukowe. Geometria Wykreslna see Politechnika Poznanska. Zeszyty Naukowe. Geometria **3051**
Politechnika Poznanska. Zeszyty Naukowe. Maszyny Robocze i Pojazdy. (PL ISSN 0137-6918) **1937**
Politechnika Poznanska. Zeszyty Naukowe. Matematyka see Fasciculi Mathematici **3035**
Politechnika Poznanska. Zeszyty Naukowe. Mechanika. (PL ISSN 0079-4538) **3845**, **1937**
Politechnika Poznanska. Zeszyty Naukowe. Mechanizacja i Elektryfikacja Rolnictwa see Politechnika Poznanska. Zeszyty Naukowe. Maszyny Robocze i Pojazdy **1937**
Politechnika Poznanska. Zeszyty Naukowe. Organizacja i Zarzadzanie. (PL ISSN 0239-9415) **1082**
Politechnika Slaska. Zeszyty Naukowe. Architektura. (PL ISSN 0860-0074) **305**
Politechnika Slaska. Zeszyty Naukowe. Automatyka. (PL ISSN 0434-0760) **1415**
Politechnika Slaska. Zeszyty Naukowe. Budownictwo. (PL ISSN 0434-0779) **1872**
Politechnika Slaska. Zeszyty Naukowe. Chemia. (PL ISSN 0372-9494) **1185**, **1858**
Politechnika Slaska. Zeszyty Naukowe. Elektryka. (PL ISSN 0072-4688) **1905**
Politechnika Slaska. Zeszyty Naukowe. Energetyka. (PL ISSN 0372-9796) **1794**
Politechnika Slaska. Zeszyty Naukowe. Gornictwo. (PL ISSN 0372-9508) **3493**
Politechnika Slaska. Zeszyty Naukowe. Hutnictwo. (PL ISSN 0324-802X) **3417**
Politechnika Slaska. Zeszyty Naukowe. Informatyka. (PL ISSN 0208-7286) **1457**
Politechnika Slaska. Zeszyty Naukowe. Inzynieria Srodowiska. (PL ISSN 0867-6038) **1965**
Politechnika Slaska. Zeszyty Naukowe. Matematyka - Fizyka. (PL ISSN 0072-470X) **3051**, **3829**
Politechnika Slaska. Zeszyty Naukowe. Mechanika. (PL ISSN 0434-0817) **1937**
Politechnika Slaska. Zeszyty Naukowe. Nauki Spoleczne. (PL ISSN 0072-4718) **4382**
Politechnika Slaska. Zeszyty Naukowe. Transport. (PL ISSN 0209-3324) **4655**
Politechnika Warszawska. Instytut Fizyki. Prace. (PL) **3829**
Politechnika Warszawska. Instytut Technologii i Organizacji Produkcji Budowlanej. Prace. (PL) **628**
†Politechnika Wroclawska. Biblioteka Glowna i Osrodek Informacji Naukowo-Technicznej. Prace Naukowe. Prace Bibliograficzne. (PL) **5259**

Politechnika Wroclawska. Biblioteka Glowna i Osrodek Informacji Naukowo-Technicznej. Prace Naukowe. Studia i Materialy. (PL ISSN 0137-6225) **4334**
Politechnika Wroclawska. Centrum Obliczeniowe. Prace Naukowe. Konferencje. (PL ISSN 0860-1615) **1399**
Politechnika Wroclawska. Centrum Obliczeniowe. Prace Naukowe. Monografie. (PL ISSN 0860-7311) **1399**
Politechnika Wroclawska. Centrum Obliczeniowe. Prace Naukowe. Studia i Materialy. (PL ISSN 0860-1623) **1399**
Politechnika Wroclawska. Instytut Architektury i Urbanistyki. Prace Naukowe. Konferencje. (PL ISSN 0137-6233) **305**, **340**
Politechnika Wroclawska. Instytut Architektury i Urbanistyki. Prace Naukowe. Monografie. (PL ISSN 0324-9905) **305**, **340**
Politechnika Wroclawska. Instytut Architektury i Urbanistyki. Prace Naukowe. Studia i Materialy. (PL ISSN 0324-9891) **305**, **340**
Politechnika Wroclawska. Instytut Budownictwa. Prace Naukowe. Konferencje. (PL ISSN 0324-9883) **628**
Politechnika Wroclawska. Instytut Budownictwa. Prace Naukowe. Monografie. (PL ISSN 0324-9875) **628**
Politechnika Wroclawska. Instytut Budownictwa. Prace Naukowe. Studia i Materialy. (PL ISSN 0137-6241) **628**
Politechnika Wroclawska. Instytut Chemii i Technologii Nafty i Wegla. Prace Naukowe. Konferencje. (PL ISSN 0324-9867) **1858**
Politechnika Wroclawska. Instytut Chemii i Technologii Nafty i Wegla. Prace Naukowe. Monografie. (PL ISSN 0324-9859) **1858**
Politechnika Wroclawska. Instytut Chemii i Technologii Nafty i Wegla. Prace Naukowe. Studia i Materialy. (PL ISSN 0084-2818) **1858**
Politechnika Wroclawska. Instytut Chemii Nieorganicznej i Metalurgii Pierwiastkow Rzadkich. Prace Naukowe. Konferencje. (PL ISSN 0324-9832) **1214**
Politechnika Wroclawska. Instytut Chemii Nieorganicznej i Metalurgii Pierwiastkow Rzadkich. Prace Naukowe. Monografie. (PL ISSN 0324-9840) **1214**
Politechnika Wroclawska. Instytut Chemii Nieorganicznej i Metalurgii Pierwiastkow Rzadkich. Prace Naukowe. Studia i Materialy. (PL ISSN 0370-0755) **1214**
Politechnika Wroclawska. Instytut Chemii Organicznej i Fizycznej. Prace Naukowe. Konferencje. (PL ISSN 0324-9824) **1221**, **1229**
Politechnika Wroclawska. Instytut Chemii Organicznej i Fizycznej. Prace Naukowe. Monografie. (PL ISSN 0324-9816) **1221**, **1229**
Politechnika Wroclawska. Instytut Chemii Organicznej i Fizycznej. Prace Naukowe. Studia i Materialy. (PL ISSN 0370-081X) **1221**, **1229**
Politechnika Wroclawska. Instytut Cybernetyki Technicznej. Prace Naukowe. Konferencje. (PL ISSN 0324-9794) **1442**
Politechnika Wroclawska. Instytut Cybernetyki Technicznej. Prace Naukowe. Monografie. (PL ISSN 0324-9786) **1442**
Politechnika Wroclawska. Instytut Cybernetyki Technicznej. Prace Naukowe. Studia i Materialy. (PL ISSN 0324-9808) **1442**
Politechnika Wroclawska. Instytut Energoelektryki. Prace Naukowe. Konferencje. (PL ISSN 0324-9778) **1905**

Politechnika Wroclawska. Instytut Energoelektryki. Prace Naukowe. Monografie. (PL ISSN 0324-976X) **1905**
Politechnika Wroclawska. Instytut Energoelektryki. Prace Naukowe. Studia i Materialy. (PL ISSN 0084-2826) **1905**
Politechnika Wroclawska. Instytut Fizyki. Prace Naukowe. Konferencje. (PL ISSN 0137-625X) **3829**
Politechnika Wroclawska. Instytut Fizyki. Prace Naukowe. Monografie. (PL ISSN 0370-0828) **3829**
Politechnika Wroclawska. Instytut Fizyki. Prace Naukowe. Studia i Materialy. (PL ISSN 0324-9697) **3829**
Politechnika Wroclawska. Instytut Geotechniki i Hydrotechniki. Prace Naukowe. Konferencje. (PL) **1548**
Politechnika Wroclawska. Instytut Geotechniki i Hydrotechniki. Prace Naukowe. Monografie. (PL) **1548**
Politechnika Wroclawska. Instytut Geotechniki. Prace Naukowe. Konferencje see Politechnika Wroclawska. Instytut Geotechniki i Hydrotechniki. Prace Naukowe. Konferencje **1548**
Politechnika Wroclawska. Instytut Geotechniki. Prace Naukowe. Monografie see Politechnika Wroclawska. Instytut Geotechniki i Hydrotechniki. Prace Naukowe. Monografie **1548**
Politechnika Wroclawska. Instytut Geotechniki. Prace Naukowe. Studia i Materialy. (PL ISSN 0084-2842) **1548**
Politechnika Wroclawska. Instytut Gornictwa. Prace Naukowe. Konferencje. (PL ISSN 0324-9670) **3493**
Politechnika Wroclawska. Instytut Gornictwa. Prace Naukowe. Monografie. (PL ISSN 0324-9689) **3493**
Politechnika Wroclawska. Instytut Gornictwa. Prace Naukowe. Studia i Materialy. (PL ISSN 0370-0798) **3493**
Politechnika Wroclawska. Instytut Historii Architektury, Sztuki i Techniki. Prace Naukowe. Konferencje. (PL ISSN 0860-1194) **340**, **305**
Politechnika Wroclawska. Instytut Historii Architektury, Sztuki i Techniki. Prace Naukowe. Monografie. (PL ISSN 0324-9662) **340**, **305**
Politechnika Wroclawska. Instytut Historii Architektury, Sztuki i Techniki. Prace Naukowe. Studia i Materialy. (PL ISSN 0324-9654) **340**, **305**
Politechnika Wroclawska. Instytut Inzynierii Chemicznej i Urzadzen Cieplnych. Prace Naukowe. Konferencje. (PL ISSN 0324-9743) **1858**
Politechnika Wroclawska. Instytut Inzynierii Chemicznej i Urzadzen Cieplnych. Prace Naukowe. Monografie. (PL ISSN 0084-2850) **1858**
Politechnika Wroclawska. Instytut Inzynierii Chemicznej i Urzadzen Cieplnych. Prace Naukowe. Studia i Materialy. (PL ISSN 0324-9751) **1858**, **628**
Politechnika Wroclawska. Instytut Inzynierii Ladowej. Prace Naukowe. Konferencje. (PL ISSN 0324-9735) **1872**
Politechnika Wroclawska. Instytut Inzynierii Ladowej. Prace Naukowe. Monografie. (PL ISSN 0324-9727) **1872**
Politechnika Wroclawska. Instytut Inzynierii Ladowej. Prace Naukowe. Studia i Materialy. (PL ISSN 0370-0844) **1872**
Politechnika Wroclawska. Instytut Inzynierii Ochrony Srodowiska. Prace Naukowe. Konferencje. (PL ISSN 0324-9719) **1834**

POLITICAL RISK 6563

Politechnika Wroclawska. Instytut Inzynierii Ochrony Srodowiska. Prace Naukowe. Studia i Materialy. (PL ISSN 0084-2877) **1834**
Politechnika Wroclawska. Instytut Inzynierii Ochrony Srodowska. Prace Naukowe. Monografie. (PL ISSN 0084-2869) **1965**, 4110
Politechnika Wroclawska. Instytut Konstrukcji i Eksploatacji Maszyn. Prace Naukowe. Konferencje. (PL ISSN 0324-9646) **3022**
Politechnika Wroclawska. Instytut Konstrukcji i Eksploatacji Maszyn. Prace Naukowe. Monografie. (PL ISSN 0324-962X) **3022**
Politechnika Wroclawska. Instytut Konstrukcji i Eksploatacji Maszyn. Prace Naukowe. Studia i Materialy. (PL ISSN 0324-9638) **3022**
Politechnika Wroclawska. Instytut Konstrukcji i Eksploatacji Maszyn. Prace Naukowe. Wspolpraca. (PL ISSN 0239-3182) **3022**
Politechnika Wroclawska. Instytut Matematyki. Prace Naukowe. Konferencje. (PL ISSN 0137-6268) **3051**
Politechnika Wroclawska. Instytut Matematyki. Prace Naukowe. Monografie. (PL ISSN 0324-9603) **3051**
Politechnika Wroclawska. Instytut Matematyki. Prace Naukowe. Studia i Materialy. (PL ISSN 0324-9611) **3051**, 3829
Politechnika Wroclawska. Instytut Materialoznawstwa i Mechaniki Technicznej. Prace Naukowe. Konferencje. (PL ISSN 0324-9573) **1937**, 3845
Politechnika Wroclawska. Instytut Materialoznawstwa i Mechaniki Technicznej. Prace Naukowe. Monografie. (PL ISSN 0324-9565) **3845**
Politechnika Wroclawska. Instytut Materialoznawstwa i Mechaniki Technicznej. Prace Naukowe. Studia i Materialy. (PL ISSN 0370-0917) **3845**
Politechnika Wroclawska. Instytut Metrologii Elektrycznej. Prace Naukowe. Konferencje. (PL ISSN 0324-9557) **1905**, 3448
Politechnika Wroclawska. Instytut Metrologii Elektrycznej. Prace Naukowe. Monografie. (PL ISSN 0324-9549) **1905**, 3448
Politechnika Wroclawska. Instytut Metrologii Elektrycznej. Prace Naukowe. Studia i Materialy. (PL ISSN 0084-2958) **1905**, 3448
Politechnika Wroclawska. Instytut Nauk Ekonomiczno-Spolecznych. Prace Naukowe. Konferencje. (PL ISSN 0860-3200) **4382**
Politechnika Wroclawska. Instytut Nauk Ekonomiczno-Spolecznych. Prace Naukowe. Monografie. (PL ISSN 0239-3204) **4382**
Politechnika Wroclawska. Instytut Nauk Ekonomiczno-Spolecznych. Prace Naukowe. Studia i Materialy. (PL ISSN 0239-3212) **4382**
Politechnika Wroclawska. Instytut Nauk Spolecznych. Prace Naukowe. Monografie see Politechnika Wroclawska. Instytut Nauk Ekonomiczno-Spolecznych. Prace Naukowe. Monografie **4382**
Politechnika Wroclawska. Instytut Nauk Spolecznych. Prace Naukowe. Studia i Materialy see Politechnika Wroclawska. Instytut Nauk Ekonomiczno-Spolecznych. Prace Naukowe. Studia i Materialy **4382**
Politechnika Wroclawska. Instytut Organizacji i Zarzadzania. Prace Naukowe. Konferencje. (PL ISSN 0324-9484) **1024**
Politechnika Wroclawska. Instytut Organizacji i Zarzadzania. Prace Naukowe. Monografie. (PL ISSN 0324-9492) **1024**
Politechnika Wroclawska. Instytut Organizacji i Zarzadzania. Prace Naukowe. Studia i Materialy. (PL ISSN 0324-9468) **1024**

Politechnika Wroclawska. Instytut Podstaw Elektrotechniki i Elektrotechnologii. Prace Naukowe. Konferencje. (PL ISSN 0324-9441) **1905**
Politechnika Wroclawska. Instytut Podstaw Elektrotechniki i Elektrotechnologii. Prace Naukowe. Monografie. (PL ISSN 0324-945X) **1905**
Politechnika Wroclawska. Instytut Podstaw Elektrotechniki i Elektrotechnologii. Prace Naukowe. Studia i Materialy. (PL ISSN 0370-0852) **1905**
Politechnika Wroclawska. Instytut Podstaw Elektrotechniki i Elektrotechnologii. Prace Naukowe. Wspolpraca. (PL ISSN 0137-6276) **1905**
Politechnika Wroclawska. Instytut Sterowania i Techniki Systemow. Prace Naukowe. Konferencje. (PL ISSN 0239-3433) **1834**
Politechnika Wroclawska. Instytut Sterowania i Techniki Systemow. Prace Naukowe. Monografie. (PL ISSN 0209-2573) **1834**
Politechnika Wroclawska. Instytut Techniki Cieplnej i Mechaniki Plynow. Prace Naukowe. Konferencje. (PL ISSN 0324-9395) **3845**
Politechnika Wroclawska. Instytut Techniki Cieplnej i Mechaniki Plynow. Prace Naukowe. Monografie. (PL ISSN 0324-9387) **3845**
Politechnika Wroclawska. Instytut Techniki Cieplnej i Mechaniki Plynow. Prace Naukowe. Studia i Materialy. (PL ISSN 0324-9409) **3845**
Politechnika Wroclawska. Instytut Technologii Budowy Maszyn. Prace Naukowe. Konferencje see Politechnika Wroclawska. Instytut Technologii Maszyn i Automatyzacji. Prace Naukowe. Konferencje **1937**
Politechnika Wroclawska. Instytut Technologii Budowy Maszyn. Prace Naukowe. Monografie see Politechnika Wroclawska. Instytut Technologii Maszyn i Automatyzacji. Prace Naukowe. Monografie **1937**
Politechnika Wroclawska. Instytut Technologii Budowy Maszyn. Prace Naukowe. Studia i Materialy see Politechnika Wroclawska. Instytut Technologii Maszyn i Automatyzacji. Prace Naukowe. Studia i Materialy **1937**
Politechnika Wroclawska. Instytut Technologii Elektronowej. Prace Naukowe. Konferencje. (PL ISSN 0370-0887) **1905**
Politechnika Wroclawska. Instytut Technologii Elektronowej. Prace Naukowe. Monografie. (PL ISSN 0084-280X) **1905**
Politechnika Wroclawska. Instytut Technologii Elektronowej. Prace Naukowe. Studia i Materialy. (PL ISSN 0084-2885) **1905**
Politechnika Wroclawska. Instytut Technologii Maszyn i Automatyzacji. Prace Naukowe. Konferencje. (PL) **1937**
Politechnika Wroclawska. Instytut Technologii Maszyn i Automatyzacji. Prace Naukowe. Monografie. (PL) **1937**
Politechnika Wroclawska. Instytut Technologii Maszyn i Automatyzacji. Prace Naukowe. Studia i Materialy. (PL) **1937**
Politechnika Wroclawska. Instytut Technologii Nieorganicznej i Nawozow Mineralnych. Prace Naukowe. Konferencje. (PL ISSN 0084-2893) **1858**
Politechnika Wroclawska. Instytut Technologii Nieorganicznej i Nawozow Mineralnych. Prace Naukowe. Monografie. (PL ISSN 0084-2907) **1858**
Politechnika Wroclawska. Instytut Technologii Nieorganicznej i Nawozow Mineralnych. Prace Naukowe. Studia i Materialy. (PL ISSN 0084-2915) **1858**

Politechnika Wroclawska. Instytut Technologii Organicznej i Tworzyw Sztucznych. Prace Naukowe. Konferencje. (PL ISSN 0137-1398) **1858**
Politechnika Wroclawska. Instytut Technologii Organicznej i Tworzyw Sztucznych. Prace Naukowe. Monografie. (PL ISSN 0239-5495) **1858**
Politechnika Wroclawska. Instytut Technologiii Organicznej i Tworzyw Sztucznych. Prace Naukowe. Studia i Materialy. (PL ISSN 0370-0879) **3867**
Politechnika Wroclawska. Instytut Telekomunikacji i Akustyki. Prace Naukowe. Konferencje. (PL ISSN 0324-9344) **1365**, 1905, 3860
Politechnika Wroclawska. Instytut Telekomunikacji i Akustyki. Prace Naukowe. Monografie. (PL ISSN 0324-9328) **1365**, 1905, 3860
Politechnika Wroclawska. Instytut Telekomunikacji i Akustyki. Prace Naukowe. Studia i Materialy. (PL ISSN 0324-9336) **1365**, 1905, 3860
Politechnika Wroclawska. Instytut Ukladow Elektromaszynowych. Prace Naukowe. Konferencje. (PL ISSN 0324-931X) **1905**
Politechnika Wroclawska. Instytut Ukladow Elektromaszynowych. Prace Naukowe. Monografie. (PL ISSN 0137-6284) **1905**
Politechnika Wroclawska. Instytut Ukladow Elektromaszynowych. Prace Naukowe. Studia i Materialy. (PL ISSN 0084-294X) **1905**
†Politechnika Wroclawska. Osrodek Badan Prognostycznych. Prace Naukowe. Konferencje. (PL ISSN 0137-6306) **5260**
†Politechnika Wroclawska. Osrodek Badan Prognostycznych. Prace Naukowe. Monografie. (PL ISSN 0137-6314) **5260**
†Politechnika Wroclawska. Osrodek Badan Prognostycznych. Prace Naukowe. Studia i Materialy. (PL ISSN 0137-6322) **5260**
†Politechnika Wroclawska. Osrodek Badan Prognostycznych. Prace Naukowe. Wspolpraca/Sotrudnichestvo. (PL ISSN 0137-6330) **5260**
Politechnika Wroclawska. Prace Naukoznawcze i Prognostyczne. (PL ISSN 0137-1215) **4334**
Politechnika Wroclawska. Studium Nauki Jezykow Obcych. Prace Naukowe. Monografie. (PL) **2834**
Politechnika Wroclawska. Studium Praktycznej Nauki Jezykow Obcych. Prace Naukowe. Monografie see Politechnika Wroclawska. Studium Nauki Jezykow Obcych. Prace Naukowe. Monografie **2834**
Politechnika Wroclawska. Studium Praktycznej Nauki Jezykow Obcych. Prace Naukowe. Studia i Materialy. (PL ISSN 0137-6349) **2834**
Politecnica. (EC ISSN 0032-3055) **1834**, 4334
Politecnico. (IT) **4606**
Politeia. (VE) **3916**
Politeia. (SI ISSN 0217-7587) **3916**
Politeia. (SA) **3916**
Politekhnichnyi Instytut Kiev. Vestnik. Seriya Mashinostroeniya. (KR ISSN 0372-6053) **3022**
Politi- og Lensmannsetaten. (NO ISSN 0803-4087) **1520**
Politibladet see Politi- og Lensmannsetaten **1520**
Politica. (IS) **2879**
Politica. (BE) **3916**
Politica. (BL) **3916**
Politica. (UY ISSN 0079-3027) **3916**
Politica. (CL) **3916**
Politica del Diritto. (IT ISSN 0032-3063) **2667**
Politica del Turismo. (IT) **4783**
Politica della Scuola. (IT) **1655**
Politica e Estrategia. (BL) **3969**, 3468
Politica e Societa. (IT) **3916**

Politica Economica. (IT ISSN 1120-9496) **3916**, 897
Politica ed Economia/Politics and Economics. (IT) **3916**, 685, 2879
Politica Exterior. (SP ISSN 0213-6856) **3916**
Politica Hermetica. (FR) **3916**
Politica in Italia. (IT ISSN 1120-950X) **3916**
Politica International. (VE) **3916**
Politica International see Review of International Affairs **3970**
Politica Internazionale (Florence). (IT ISSN 0032-3101) **3969**, 3916
Politica Meridionalista. (IT ISSN 0393-7844) **879**, 1730, 3394
Politica Obrera. (AG) **3916**
Politica Popolare. (IT) **2879**
Politica Social. (SP) **3916**
Politica y Economia. (AG) **3916**, 685
Politica y Sociedad. (EC) **2879**
Political Action Committees Lobbies see P A Cs & Lobbies **3913**
Political Advisor. (US) **4003**
Political Affairs. (US ISSN 0032-3128) **3916**
▼Political and Economic Spectrum of Russia. (US ISSN 1057-2295) **3916**, 879
Political and Economic Spectrum of the Soviet Union see Political and Economic Spectrum of Russia **3916**
Political and Legal Anthropology. (US ISSN 0732-1228) **4445**, 3916
Political Animal see Joe Scott's the Political Animal **3901**
▼Political Archives of the Soviet Union. (US) **3969**, 2380
Political Behavior. (US ISSN 0190-9320) **3916**
†Political Behavior Annual. (US) **5260**
Political Climate for International Business see Country Forecasts **3883**
Political Communication and Persuasion. (US ISSN 0195-7473) **3916**
Political Digest Series. (CN) **2019**, 3969
Political Economy. (IT ISSN 0393-5744) **879**
Political Economy and Public Policy. (US) **897**
Political Education. see Zhengzhi Jiaoyu **1673**
Political Finance - Lobby Reporter see P A Cs & Lobbies **3913**
Political Geography Quarterly. (UK ISSN 0260-9827) **2259**
Political Handbook of the World. (US ISSN 0193-175X) **3917**, 2259
Political Life in Sweden see Viewpoint Sweden **2218**
Political Parties of the World. (UK) **3917**
Political Portraits. (UK) **420**
Political Power and Social Theory. (US ISSN 0198-8719) **3917**, 4445
Political Profiles see Profiles (Arlington) **3920**
Political Psychology. (US ISSN 0162-895X) **3917**, 4038
Political Pulse. (US ISSN 8756-9248) **4070**
Political Quarterly. (UK ISSN 0032-3179) **3917**
Political Report. (US ISSN 1051-4287) **3917**, 4070
Political Resource Director. (US ISSN 0898-4271) **3917**
Political Risk Database see Country Forecasts **3883**
Political Risk Letter. (US ISSN 0887-7629) **919**, 795, 960, 3917
Political Risk Review see Risk Management Review **920**
Political Risk Yearbook. (US) **795**, 919, 960, 1024
Political Risk Yearbook. Volume 1: North & Central America. (US ISSN 0897-8557) **795**, 919, 960, 1024
Political Risk Yearbook. Volume 2: Middle East & North Africa. (US ISSN 0897-8530) **795**, 919, 960, 1024
Political Risk Yearbook. Volume 3: South America. (US ISSN 0897-8549) **795**, 919, 960, 1024

POLITICAL RISK

Political Risk Yearbook. Volume 4: Sub-Saharan Africa. (US ISSN 0889-2725) **795**, 919, 960, 1024
Political Risk Yearbook. Volume 5: Asia & the Pacific. (US ISSN 0897-8565) **795**, 919, 960, 1024
Political Risk Yearbook. Volume 6: Europe - Countries of the E C. (US) **795**, 919, 960, 1024
Political Risk Yearbook. Volume 6: Western Europe *see* Political Risk Yearbook. Volume 6: Europe - Countries of the E C **795**
Political Risk Yearbook. Volume 7: Eastern Europe *see* Political Risk Yearbook. Volume 7: Europe - Outside the E C **795**
Political Risk Yearbook. Volume 7: Europe - Outside the E C. (US) **795**, 919, 960, 1024
Political Science. (NZ ISSN 0032-3187) **3917**
Political Science Abstracts. (US) **3938**
Political Science and Jurisprudence. *see* Allam- es Jogtudomany **2597**
Political Science & Law Tribune. *see* Zhengfa Luntan **2697**
Political Science Quarterly. (US ISSN 0032-3195) **3917**
Political Science Research. *see* Zhengzhixue Yanjiu **3936**
Political Science Review. (II ISSN 0554-5196) **3917**
Political Science Reviewer. (US ISSN 0091-3715) **3917**
Political Science Teacher *see* P S: Political Science & Politics **3913**
Political Science Utilization Directory. (US ISSN 0362-4765) **4070**
Political Scientist. (II ISSN 0032-3209) **3917**, 3969
Political Social Economic Review. (UK ISSN 0306-6061) **3917**
Political Studies. (UK ISSN 0032-3217) **3917**
Political Studies Association of the United Kingdom. Newsletter *see* P S A News **3913**
Political Studies Association of the United Kingdom News *see* P S A News **3913**
Political Theory. (US ISSN 0090-5917) **3917**
Political Thought. *see* Politicka Misao **3917**
Political Trends and Perspectives *see* Politics and Public Affairs **3917**
†Political Woman. (US ISSN 0896-7202) **5260**
Politiche del Lavoro. (IT) **991**, 3917
Politiche del Territorio. (IT) **3917**
Politicheskoe Samoobrazovanie. (RU ISSN 0032-3225) **3917**, 1655
Politicien. (SG ISSN 0850-1807) **2879**
Politicka Ekonomie/Journal of Political Economy. (CS ISSN 0032-3233) **685**
Politicka Misao/Political Thought. (CI ISSN 0032-3241) **3917**
Politico. (IT ISSN 0032-325X) **3917**
Politicon. (AG) **2880**
Politics *see* Australian Journal of Political Science **3874**
Politics. (US ISSN 0032-3276) **3917**
Politics. (UK ISSN 0263-3957) **3917**
Politics and Economics. *see* Politica ed Economia **3916**
Politics and Law. *see* Zhengzhi yu Falu **2697**
Politics & Money *see* P & M **794**
Politics and Public Affairs. (US) **3917**
Politics and Society. (US ISSN 0032-3292) **3917**, 4445
Politics and Strategy. *see* Siyassa was Strategia **3925**
▼Politics and the Individual. (GW ISSN 0939-6071) **3917**, 4445
Politics and the Life Sciences. (UK ISSN 0730-9384) **3142**, 3969, 4070
Politics in America. (US) **3918**
Politics in Latin America. (US) **3918**
Politics in Minnesota. (US) **3918**
Politics of Liberation Series. (US) 2380, 3468, 3969
▼Politics Review. (UK ISSN 0959-8480) **3918**

Politics Today. (UK ISSN 0307-7039) **3918**
†Politicum. (GW) **5260**
Politie, Dier en Milieu. (NE) **3713**
Politie Magazine. (NE) **1520**
Politieke Dokumentatie. (BE ISSN 0048-475X) **3918**
Politiembetsmennenes Blad. (NO ISSN 0332-883X) **1520**
Politiets Aarsberetning. (DK ISSN 0108-3376) **1520**
Politihistorisk Selskab. Aarsskrift. (DK ISSN 0107-3893) **1520**
Politiidrett. (NO ISSN 0032-3357) **4483**
Politiikka. (FI ISSN 0032-3365) **3918**
Politik - Aktuell fuer den Unterricht. (GW ISSN 0342-5746) **3918**
Politik Betrifft Uns. (GW ISSN 0176-9448) **1757**
†Politik und Kultur. (GW ISSN 0340-5869) **5260**
Politik und Unterricht. (GW ISSN 0344-3531) **1757**, 1697
Politik und Wirtschaft. (GW) **879**
Politika-Ekspres. (YU ISSN 0032-3381) **2880**
Politika Themata. (GR) **3918**
Politikai Gazdasagtan. *see* Acta Universitatis Szegediensis de Attila Jozsef Nominatae. Sectio Oeconomico-Politica **644**
Politiken Weekly. (DK) **2880**
Politikin Zabavnik. (YU ISSN 0032-339X) **2880**
Politikon. (SA ISSN 0258-9346) **3918**
Politinformator i Agitator. (BW) **3918**
Politique Africaine. (FR ISSN 0244-7827) **3918**
Politique de la Sante: Informations. *see* Gesundheitspolitische Informationen **4101**
Politique de la Science. (SZ ISSN 0085-4980) **4334**
Politique et Strategie. *see* Siyassa was Strategia **3925**
Politique Etrangere. (FR) **3918**, 3969
Politique Etrangere de la France. (FR) **3918**
Politique Interieure *see* Flash Actualite **3894**
Politique Internationale. (FR ISSN 0221-2781) **3918**
Politique Sociale au Canada. *see* Issues in Canadian Social Policy **5219**
Politiques Culturelles *see* Cultural Policy **3954**
Politische Bildung. (AU) **3918**, 1757
Politische Dokumentation. (GW ISSN 0032-3438) **3938**, 2795
Die Politische Meinung. (GW ISSN 0032-3446) **3918**
Politische Perspektiven. (AU ISSN 0032-3454) **3918**
Politische Rundschau/Revue Politique. (SZ) **3918**
Politische Vierteljahresschrift. (GW ISSN 0032-3470) **3918**
Politix. (FR ISSN 0295-2319) **3918**
Polity. (US ISSN 0032-3497) **3918**
Polityka. (PL ISSN 0032-3500) **3918**
Polityka Polska. (PL) **3918**
Die Polizei. (GW ISSN 0032-3519) **1520**
Die Polizei im Lande Berlin. (GW ISSN 0032-3527) **1520**
Polizei Info Polizeiforum. (GW ISSN 0177-4573) **1521**
Polizei Technik Verkehr *see* Polizeiverkehr und Technik **1521**
Polizeiliche Kriminalstatistik N - W. (GW ISSN 0171-2802) **1525**
Polizeiliche Kriminalstatistik Niedersachsen mit Informationen aus dem Landeskriminalamt. (GW) **1525**
Polizeimagazin *see* Magazin fuer die Polizei **1518**
Polizeiverkehr und Technik. (GW) **1521**
Polizia Moderna. (IT ISSN 0032-356X) **1521**
Polja. (YU ISSN 0032-3578) **2880**
Poljoprivredna Znanstvena Smotra/Agriculturae Conspectus Scientificus. (CI ISSN 0370-0291) **114**

Polk Bank Directory. International Edition. (US ISSN 1058-0603) **1150**, 795
Polk Bank Directory. North American Edition. (US ISSN 1058-0611) **1150**, 795
Polka. (US ISSN 0032-3594) **4851**, 2019, 4195
▼Polk's Financial Institutions Buyers Guide and Services Directory. (US) **1150**, 795
Polk's World Bank Directory. International Edition *see* Polk Bank Directory. International Edition **1150**
Polk's World Bank Directory. North American Edition *see* Polk Bank Directory. North American Edition **1150**
Poll Hereford Annual *see* Australian Poll Hereford Magazine **211**
Polled Hereford World. (US ISSN 0032-3608) **223**
Pollen et Spores. (FR ISSN 0032-3616) **515**
Pollen Science. (JA ISSN 0386-6688) **189**, 515
Pollichia. Mitteilungen. (GW ISSN 0341-9665) **1548**, 451
†Polling. (US) **5260**
Polling Report. (US ISSN 0887-171X) **3938**, 4583
▼Pollock Potpourri. (US) **2162**
Pollstar. (US) **3574**
Pollution. (UK ISSN 0048-4784) **1978**
Pollution Abstracts. (US ISSN 0032-3624) **1974**, 20, 1978
Pollution Atmospherique. (FR ISSN 0032-3632) **1978**
Pollution Control Review *see* Pollution Technology Review **4110**
Pollution Engineering. (US ISSN 0032-3640) **1978**
Pollution Engineering Locator *see* Pollution Engineering Product - Service Locator **1986**
Pollution Engineering Product - Service Locator. (US) **1986**, 1150, 1978
Pollution Equipment News. (US ISSN 0032-3659) **1979**
Pollution Law Reporting Service. (CN ISSN 0827-2123) **2667**, 1979
▼Pollution Prevention Review. (US ISSN 1052-1550) **1986**, 1979, 2667
Pollution Research. (II) **1979**
Pollution Technology Review. (US ISSN 0090-516X) **4110**, 1979
Polnische Musik. *see* Polish Music **3574**
Polnische Perspektiven *see* Polish Perspectives **2879**
Polnischer Aussenhandel *see* Polish Foreign Trade **919**
Polnisches Engineering *see* Polish Engineering **1833**
Polnisches Handelsmagazin *see* Polish Trade Magazine **919**
Polnohospodarstvo/Agriculture. (CS) **114**
Il Polo. (IT ISSN 0032-3667) **2259**
Polo. (US ISSN 0146-4574) **4510**, 4536
Pologne Contemporaine *see* Contemporary Poland **3882**
†Pologne et les Affaires Occidentales. (PL ISSN 0032-3675) **5260**
Pologne - Tourisme *see* Poland - Tourism **5259**
Polonia Library. *see* Biblioteka Polonijna **3875**
Polonia Typographica Saeculi Sedecimi. (PL ISSN 0079-3132) **340**, 4003
▼Polonia Voice. (CN ISSN 1183-8000) **2019**
Polonian. (US) **2232**, 2513
Polonia's Voice *see* Polish American Journal **2019**
Polonica. (PL ISSN 0137-9712) **2834**
Polonistyka. (PL ISSN 0551-3707) **2949**, 2834
Pol'ovnictvo a Rybarstvo/Hunting and Fishing. (CS) **4553**
Polozna *see* Pielegniarka i Polozna **3285**
Polska Akademia Nauk. Biblioteka, Krakow. Rocznik. (PL ISSN 0079-3140) **2779**

Polska Akademia Nauk. Centrum Badan Naukowych w Wojewodztwie Katowickim. Prace i Studia *see* Polska Akademia Nauk. Instytut Podstaw Inzynierii Srodowiska. Prace i Studia **1966**
Polska Akademia Nauk. Centrum Obliczeniowe. Prace *see* Polish Academy of Sciences. Institute of Computer Science. Reports **1399**
Polska Akademia Nauk. Instytut Geografii i Przestrzennego Zagospodarowania. Prace Geograficzne. (PL ISSN 0373-6547) **2259**
Polska Akademia Nauk. Instytut Geografii. Prace Geograficzne *see* Polska Akademia Nauk. Instytut Geografii i Przestrzennego Zagospodarowania. Prace Geograficzne **2259**
Polska Akademia Nauk. Instytut Krajow Socjalistycznych. Biuletyn Informacyjny. (PL ISSN 0137-3544) **2380**
Polska Akademia Nauk. Instytut Maszyn Przeplywowych. Prace/Polish Academy of Sciences. Institute of Fluid-Flow Machinery. Transactions. (PL ISSN 0079-3205) **1937**
Polska Akademia Nauk. Instytut Podstaw Inzynierii Srodowiska. Prace i Studia. (PL) **1966**, 1834
Polska Akademia Nauk. Instytut Slawistiki. Prace Slawistyczne. (PL ISSN 0208-4058) **2834**, 2380, 2949
Polska Akademia Nauk. Komisja Metalurgii i Odlewnictwa. Metalurgia *see* Polska Akademia Nauk. Oddzial w Krakowie. Komisja Metalurgiczno-Odlewnicza. Prace: Metalurgia **3417**
Polska Akademia Nauk. Komitet Gospodarki Wodnej. Prace i Studia. (PL ISSN 0079-3477) **4827**, 4110
Polska Akademia Nauk. Komitet Nauk Orientalistycznych. Prace Orientalistyczne. (PL ISSN 0079-4783) **3643**
Polska Akademia Nauk. Komitet Przestrzennego Zagospodarowania Kraju. Biuletyn. (PL ISSN 0079-3493) **2494**
Polska Akademia Nauk. Komitet Przestrzennego Zagospodarowania Kraju. Studia. (PL ISSN 0079-3507) **2494**
Polska Akademia Nauk. Oddzial w Krakowie. Komisja Archeologiczna. Prace. (PL ISSN 0079-3256) **281**
Polska Akademia Nauk. Oddzial w Krakowie. Komisja Ceramiczna. Prace: Ceramika. (PL ISSN 0079-3264) **1165**
Polska Akademia Nauk. Oddzial w Krakowie. Komisja Filologii Klasycznej. Prace. (PL ISSN 0079-3272) **2834**
Polska Akademia Nauk. Oddzial w Krakowie. Komisja Gorniczo-Geodezyjna. Prace: Geodezja. (PL ISSN 0079-3299) **2259**
Polska Akademia Nauk. Oddzial w Krakowie. Komisja Gorniczo-Geodezyjna. Prace: Gornictwo. (PL ISSN 0079-3280) **3493**
Polska Akademia Nauk. Oddzial w Krakowie. Komisja Historycznoliteracka. Prace. (PL ISSN 0554-579X) **2949**
Polska Akademia Nauk. Oddzial w Krakowie. Komisja Historycznoliteracka. Rocznik. (PL ISSN 0079-337X) **2319**, 2949
Polska Akademia Nauk. Oddzial w Krakowie. Komisja Jezykoznawstwa. Prace. (PL ISSN 0079-3310) **2835**
Polska Akademia Nauk. Oddzial w Krakowie. Komisja Jezykoznawstwa. Wydawnictwa Zrodlowe. (PL ISSN 0079-3329) **2835**
Polska Akademia Nauk. Oddzial w Krakowie. Komisja Mechaniki Stosowanej. Prace: Mechanika. (PL ISSN 0079-3337) **3845**

Polska Akademia Nauk. Oddzial w Krakowie. Komisja Metalurgiczno-Odlewnicza. Prace: Metalurgia. (PL ISSN 0079-3345) **3417**
Polska Akademia Nauk. Oddzial w Krakowie. Komisja Nauk Ekonomicznych. Prace. (PL ISSN 0079-3353) **685**
Polska Akademia Nauk. Oddzial w Krakowie. Komisja Nauk Historycznych. Prace. (PL ISSN 0079-3388) **2330,** 409
Polska Akademia Nauk. Oddzial w Krakowie. Komisja Nauk Historycznych. Materialy. (PL) **2319**
Polska Akademia Nauk. Oddzial w Krakowie. Komisja Nauk Mineralogicznych. Prace Mineralogiczne. (PL ISSN 0079-3396) **1577**
Polska Akademia Nauk. Oddzial w Krakowie. Komisja Nauk Pedagogicznych. Rocznik. (PL ISSN 0079-3418) **1655**
Polska Akademia Nauk. Oddzial w Krakowie. Komisja Nauk Pedagogicznych. Prace. (PL ISSN 0079-340X) **1655**
Polska Akademia Nauk. Oddzial w Krakowie. Komisja Orientalistyczna. Prace. (PL ISSN 0079-3426) **3643**
Polska Akademia Nauk. Oddzial w Krakowie. Komisja Slowianoznawstwa. Prace. (PL ISSN 0079-3434) **2949**
Polska Akademia Nauk. Oddzial w Krakowie. Komisja Socjologiczna. Prace. (PL ISSN 0079-3442) **4445**
Polska Akademia Nauk. Oddzial w Krakowie. Komisja Urbanistyki i Architektury. Teka. (PL ISSN 0079-3450) **305,** 2494
Polska Akademia Nauk. Oddzial w Krakowie. Komisje Naukowe. Sprawozdania z Posiedzen. (PL ISSN 0079-354X) **4334,** 4382
Polska Akademia Nauk. Oddzial w Krakowie. Osrodek Dokumentacji Fizjograficznej. Studia. (PL ISSN 0137-2939) **2259**
Polska Akademia Nauk. Oddzial w Krakowie. Rocznik. (PL ISSN 0079-3531) **2513**
Polska Akademia Nauk. Wydzial Nauk Medycznych. Rozprawy. (PL ISSN 0079-3558) **3142**
Polska Bibliografia Analityczna Mechaniki/Polish Scientific Abstracts on Mechanics. (PL ISSN 0032-3713) **3025,** 20
Polska Bibliografia Literacka. (PL ISSN 0079-3590) **2983**
Polska Mysl Polityczna XIX i XX Wieku. (PL ISSN 0208-4090) **2380,** 3918
Polska Piesn i Muzyka Ludowa. Zrodla i Materialy. (PL ISSN 0079-3612) **3574,** 2058
Polska Sztuka Ludowa/Polish Folk Culture. (PL ISSN 0032-3721) **340**
Polska 2000. (PL ISSN 0079-3620) **4445,** 2380
Pol'skaya Vneshnyaya Torgovlya see Polish Foreign Trade **919**
Polski Instytut Spraw Miedzynarodowych International Relations: Studies of the P I S M see International Relations: Studies of the P I S M **3961**
Polski Klub Ekologiczny Okregu Malopolska. Prace Naukowe. (PL ISSN 0860-4045) **451**
†Polski Przeglad Chirurgiczny. (PL ISSN 0032-373X) **5260**
Polski Przeglad Kartograficzny/Polish Cartographical Review. (PL) **2259**
Polski Tygodnik Lekarski. (PL ISSN 0032-3756) **3142**
Polski Zwiazek Krotkofalowcow. Biuletyn see Krotkofalowiec Polski **1357**
Polskie Archiwum Hydrobiologii/Polish Archives of Hydrobiology. (PL ISSN 0032-3764) **451**

Polskie Archiwum Medycyny Wewnetrznej/Polish Archives of Internal Medicine. (PL ISSN 0032-3772) **3142**
Polskie Archiwum Weterynaryjne/Archiwum Veterinarium Polonicum. (PL ISSN 0079-3647) **4814**
Polskie Pismo Entomologiczne/Bulletin Entomologique de Pologne. (PL ISSN 0032-3780) **537**
Polskie Towarzystwo Cybernetyczne. Biuletyn see Postepy Cybernetyki **1442**
Polskie Towarzystwo Geologiczne. Rocznik/Societatis Geologorum Poloniae. Annales. (PL ISSN 0079-3663) **1577**
Polskie Towarzystwo Jezykoznawcze. Biuletyn. (PL ISSN 0032-3802) **2835**
Polskie Towarzystwo Matematyczne. Prace. Matematyczne see Annales Societatis Mathematicae Polonae. Seria 1: Commentationes Mathematicae **3029**
Polskie Towarzystwo Matematyczne. Roczniki. Seria 1: Commentationes Mathematicae. Prace Matematyczne. (PL ISSN 0373-8299) **3051**
Polskie Towarzystwo Matematyczne. Roczniki. Seria 2: Wiadomosci Matematyczne. (PL ISSN 0079-3698) **3051**
Polskie Towarzystwo Matematyczne. Roczniki. Seria 3: Matematyka Stosowana see Annales Societatis Mathematicae Polonae. Seria 3: Matematyka Stosowana **3029**
Polskie Towarzystwo Naukowe na Obczyznie. Rocznik. (UK ISSN 0079-371X) **4334,** 2513
Polskij Torgowyj Zhurnal see Polish Trade Magazine **919**
Polsky Injiniring see Polish Engineering **1833**
Il Polso. (IT) **3142**
Polutehniline Instituut Tallinn. Statisticheskie Metody Analiza Effektivnosti Proizvodstva see Tallinna Tehnikaulikool. Statisticheskie Metody Analiza Effektivnosti Proizvodstva **1085**
Poly. (US) **3596**
Poly Topics. (US) **4292**
Polyaisthesis. (AU ISSN 0259-0824) **340**
†Polyamines. (UK ISSN 0263-7367) **5260**
Polybios-Lexicon. (GW) **2835**
▼Polycyclic Aromatic Compounds. (US ISSN 1040-6638) **1222**
Der Polygraph. (GW ISSN 0032-3845) **4003**
Polygraph (Severna Park). (US ISSN 0197-7024) **1521,** 4038
Polygraph International. (GW ISSN 0343-5199) **4003**
Polyhedron. (US ISSN 0277-5387) **1214**
Polyhedron Newszine. (US) **4554**
▼Polylingua. (US) **2835,** 2949
Polymer. (UK ISSN 0032-3861) **1222,** 1858
Polymer Age see British Plastics and Rubber Magazine **3861**
Polymer Application/Kobunshi Kako. (JA ISSN 0023-2564) **1858**
Polymer Blends, Alloys and Interpenetrating Polymer Networks Abstracts. (US ISSN 0893-6684) **1202,** 20
Polymer Bulletin. (GW ISSN 0170-0839) **1185**
Polymer Composites. (US ISSN 0272-8397) **3867**
Polymer Contents. (UK ISSN 0883-153X) **1845,** 20, 1202
Polymer Degradation and Stability. (UK ISSN 0141-3910) **1222,** 3867
Polymer Engineering. Journal see Journal of Polymer Engineering **1855**
Polymer Engineering and Science. (US ISSN 0032-3888) **1858,** 1222
Polymer Friends for Rubber, Plastics and Fiber/Porima no Tomo. (JA ISSN 0032-4779) **4292,** 3867
Polymer International. (UK ISSN 0959-8103) **3867**

Polymer Journal. (JA ISSN 0032-3896) **1222,** 1858
Polymer Journal see Plastichem **1857**
Polymer Mechanics - Mekhanika Polimerov see Mechanics of Composite Materials **1856**
Polymer Monographs. (US ISSN 0275-5777) **1222**
Polymer News. (US ISSN 0032-3918) **1222,** 1858
Polymer Photochemistry see Polymer Degradation and Stability **1222**
Polymer-Plastics Manufacturing Journal see Polymer-Plastics Technology and Engineering **1222**
Polymer-Plastics Technology and Engineering. (US ISSN 0360-2559) **1222,** 1858
Polymer Preprints. (US ISSN 0032-3934) **1222**
Polymer Science and Technology. (US) **1222**
Polymer Science Library. (NE) **1186**
Polymer Science U.S.S.R. (English translation of: Vysokomolekulyarnye Soedineniya) (US ISSN 0032-3950) **1222**
Polymer Science Yearbook. (US ISSN 0738-1743) **1186**
Polymer Testing. (UK ISSN 0142-9418) **1857,** 1222
Polymerase Chain Reaction Methods and Applications see P C R Methods and Applications **556**
Polymeric Materials Science and Engineering. (US) **1222,** 3867
Polymers. see Kobunshi **1220**
Polymers. see Polimery **1221**
Polymers and Rubber Asia. (UK ISSN 0268-9812) **3867,** 4292
Polymers, Ceramics, Composite Alert. (US) **3869,** 735
▼Polymers for Advanced Technologies. (UK ISSN 1042-7147) **3867,** 1186
Polymers Paint and Colour Journal. (UK ISSN 0370-1158) **3655**
Polymers Paint and Colour Year Book. (UK ISSN 0078-7817) **3655,** 340
Polymers - Properties and Applications. (US ISSN 0171-709X) **3867**
Polymya. (BW ISSN 0130-8068) **2949**
Polypeptides. (UK ISSN 0143-4225) **481**
Polyphonies. (FR ISSN 0766-1924) **3003**
Polyphony. (CN ISSN 0704-7002) **2019,** 2419
Polysar Progress. (CN) **4293,** 3867
Le Polyscope. (CN) **1321**
Polyscope. (SZ) **1415,** 1399
Polytechnic see Rensselaer Polytechnic **1322**
Polytechnic Cable see Polytechnicable **1321**
†Polytechnic Engineer. (US ISSN 0032-406X) **5260**
Polytechnicable. (US) **1321**
Polytechnical Institute of Bucharest. Scientific Bulletin. see Institutul Politehnic Bucuresti. Buletin Stiintific **4601**
PolyTechnical Weekly. see PolyTechnisch Weekblad **1834**
Polytechnisch Tijdschrift: Bouwtechniek see Architectuur - Bouwen **1861**
Polytechnisch Tijdschrift Civiele Techniek see P T - Civiele Techniek **1872**
Polytechnisch Tijdschrift Elektrotechniek - Elektronica see P T - Elektrotechniek - Elektronica **1904**
Polytechnisch Tijdschrift Procestechniek see P T - Procestechniek **1833**
Polytechnisch Tijdschrift: Werktuigbouw/Mechanical Engineering. (NE ISSN 0032-4108) **1937,** 3417
PolyTechnisch Weekblad/PolyTechnical Weekly. (NE) **1834**
Polytechnische Bildung und Erziehung. (GW ISSN 0032-4116) **628**
Polyteknikeren. (DK ISSN 0032-4124) **1834**
Polytekniske Laereanstalt, Danmarks Tekniske Hoejskole. Electronics Institute. Annual Report. (DK) **1905**

Polytekniske Laereanstalt, Danmarks Tekniske Hoejskole. Laboratoriet for Elektronik. Beretning see Polytekniske Laereanstalt, Danmarks Tekniske Hoejskole. Electronics Institute. Annual Report **1905**
Pome News. (US) **2137**
Pomeranian Review. (US) **3713**
Pomiary - Automatyka - Kontrola. (PL ISSN 0032-4140) **1415**
Pomme d'Api. (FR) **4445**
Pomme de Terre Francaise. (FR ISSN 0032-4159) **189**
Pommern. (GW ISSN 0032-4167) **340,** 2058, 2319
Die Pommerschen Leute. (US ISSN 0747-6558) **2020,** 2162, 2380
Pomniki Histor'ii Kul'tury Belarusi. (BW ISSN 0131-2669) **2380**
Pomona. (US ISSN 0748-6510) **2137,** 189
Pomona College Today. (US) **1321**
Pomona Today see Pomona College Today **1321**
Pomorania Antiqua. (PL ISSN 0556-0691) **2380**
Pomoranisches Woerterbuch. (GW) **2835**
Pomorskie Monografie Toponomastyczne. (PL ISSN 0208-4082) **2259**
Pompadour Notariat 2000. (FR) **2667**
Pompebleden. (NE ISSN 0032-4205) **2835,** 2949
Pompes, Pompes a Vide, Compresseurs. (GW) **1921**
Pom's/Apple. (FR) **1473,** 1464
Pondicherry Industrial Promotion, Development and Investment Corporation. Annual Reports and Accounts. (II) **838,** 960
Ponente. (IT) **4783**
Le Pont. (CN ISSN 1183-0824) **2779**
Pont. see Most **2940**
Pont Flash see Flash Alternative **3894**
Ponte. (IT ISSN 0032-423X) **2880**
Ponte d'Oro. (VC) **4195**
Pontiac - Oakland and County Legal News. (US ISSN 0739-0203) **2667**
Pontiake Hestia. (GR) **2381**
Pontifical Institute for Foreign Missionaries (PIME) World see P I M E World **4272**
Pontifical Institute of Mediaeval Studies. Studies and Texts. (CN ISSN 0082-5328) **2381**
Pontificia Academia Scientiarum. Commentarii. (VC) **4334**
Pontificia Academia Scientiarum. Documenta. (VC) **4334**
Pontificia Academia Scientiarum. Scripta Varia. (VC) **4334**
Pontificia Universidad Catolica. Revista. (PE) **4382**
Pontificia Universidad Catolica. Taller de Estudios Urbano Industriales. Serie: Estudios Sindicales. (PE) **2588**
Pontificia Universidad Catolica Argentina. Facultad de Ciencias Sociales y Economicas. Cuadernos. (AG) **4382**
Pontificia Universidad Catolica de Chile. Instituto de Estudios Urbanos. Documentos de Trabajo. (CL) **2494**
Pontificia Universidad Catolica del Ecuador. Instituto de Investigaciones Economicas. Documentos. (EC) **879**
Pontificia Universidad Catolica del Peru. Anthropologica see Anthropologica (Lima) **234**
Pontificia Universidad Catolica del Peru. Departamento de Ciencias Sociales. Serie: Ediciones Previas. (PE) **4382**
Pontificia Universidad Catolica del Peru. Derecho see Derecho **2618**
Pontificia Universidad Catolica del Peru. Revista de Psicologia see Revista de Psicologia **4044**
†Pontificia Universidade Catolica de Sao Paulo. Revista. (BL) **5260**
Pontificia Universidade Catolica do Rio Grande do Sul. Anais see Veritas **2175**
Pontificia Universidade Catolica do Rio Grande do Sul. Educacao. (BL ISSN 0101-465X) **1655**

PONTIFICIA UNIVERSIDADE

Pontificia Universidade Catolica do Rio Grande do Sul. Odontociencia. Revista. (BL ISSN 0102-9460) **3240**
Pontificia Universita Gregoriana. Documenta Missionalia. (VC) **4273**
Pontificia Universita Gregoriana. Istituto di Scienze Sociali Studia Socialia. (VC ISSN 0080-3960) **4382**
Pontificia Universita Gregoriana. Miscellanea Historiae Pontificiae. (VC ISSN 0080-3979) **4273**
Pontificia Universita Gregoriana. Studia Missionalia. (VC ISSN 0080-3987) **4273**
Pontificio Istituto Missioni Estere Missionari del P.I.M.E. *see* Missionari del P.I.M.E **4269**
†Pontifico Museo Missionario Etnologico. Annali. (VC) **5260**
Pontius Family Association. Newsletter. (US) **2162**
Pontotoc County Quarterly *see* Oklahoma Pontotoc County Quarterly **2417**
Pony. (UK ISSN 0032-4256) **4536**
†Pony. (GW ISSN 0930-1186) **5260**
Pony Baseball. Blue Book. (US) **4510**
Pony Baseball Express *see* Pony Baseball - Softball Express **4510**
Pony Baseball Rules and Regulations. (US) **4510**
Pony Baseball - Softball Express. (US) **4510**, **1243**
Pony Club Magazine *see* Pony Club Monthly **4537**
Pony Club Monthly. (UK ISSN 0958-1812) **4537**
Pony Express Mail. (US) **3531**
Pony Journal. (US) **4537**
Poodle Review. (US ISSN 0477-5449) **3713**
Poodle Variety. (US ISSN 0882-2816) **3713**
Pool & Billiard Magazine. (US) **4510**
Pool and Spa Industry Review *see* Pool & Spa Review **1082**
Pool & Spa News. (US ISSN 0194-5351) **1150**
Pool and Spa News Directory *see* Pool & Spa News Source Book **1150**
Pool & Spa News Source Book. (US) **1150**
Pool & Spa Review. (AT) **1082**
Pool News *see* Pool & Spa News **1150**
Poole - Commercial Users Handbook *see* Poole Handbook **4735**
Poole Handbook. (UK) **4735**, **1150**
Poolife. (US) **4483**
▼PoolWays. (US) **4483**, **2440**, **3807**, **4554**
Poona Agricultural College Magazine. (II ISSN 0032-4299) **114**
Poor's Register of Corporations, Directors and Executives *see* Standard & Poor's Register of Corporations, Directors and Executives **1028**
Pootaardappelwereld *see* Aardappelwereld **833**
Pop. (IT) **2206**
Pop-Foto-Tuney Tunes *see* Popfoto **3574**
Pop Rock. (CN) **3574**
Pop Thriller Magazine. (AT) **1263**
Popayan. (CK ISSN 0032-4388) **2419**
Pope John Paul II Center Newsletter *see* Centrum Jana Pawla II Biuletyn **418**
Pope Speaks. (US ISSN 0032-4353) **4273**
Pope Teaches. (UK ISSN 0143-0149) **4273**
Popeye. (JA) **1294**
Popfoto. (NE) **3574**, **1263**
Popindex Africa. (ET) **3985**
Popline. (US) **3985**
Popoli. (IT ISSN 0394-4247) **2206**
Popoli e Missioni *see* Popoli **2206**
Popoli e Persone. (IT) **420**
Popolo. (IT) **4195**, **4416**
Popolo del Friuli-Venezia Giulia. (IT ISSN 0032-437X) **3918**
Popolo e Liberta. (IT) **3918**
Il Popolo Italiano. (US) **2020**
Popster. (IT) **3574**
†Populacni Zpravy. (CS) **5260**

Populaer Filateli. (DK ISSN 0032-4418) **3756**
Populaer Radio *see* Ny Elektronik **5250**
Populaire Literatuur. (NE) **2949**
Popular/Spanish Daily News. (CN) **2020**
Popular. (CS) **3575**
Popular Archaeology. (US) **281**
Popular Archaeology *see* Archaeology Today **5137**
Popular Astronomy. (UK ISSN 0261-0892) **368**
Popular Bridge Monthly *see* International Popular Bridge Monthly **4476**
†Popular Caravan. (UK ISSN 0262-4001) **5260**
Popular Cars. (US) **4699**
Popular Ceramics. (US ISSN 0032-4477) **1165**, **2440**
Popular Cinema. *see* Dazhong Dianying **3507**
Popular Communications. (US ISSN 0733-3315) **1358**
Popular Crafts. (UK ISSN 0144-2937) **356**
Popular Culture Association. Newsletter and Popular Culture Methods. (US) **4445**
Popular Culture Association Newsletter *see* Popular Culture Association. Newsletter and Popular Culture Methods **4445**
Popular Culture Bio-Bibliographies. (US ISSN 0193-6891) **2419**
▼Popular Culture in Libraries. (US ISSN 1053-8747) **2779**
Popular Electronics. (US ISSN 1042-170X) **1776**
Popular Electronics. (II ISSN 0970-9223) **1776**
Popular Electronics Hobbyists Handbook. (US) **2440**, **1906**
Popular Essays from the Late Republic.(NE) **2949**
Popular Flying. (UK ISSN 0032-4493) **60**
Popular Foodservice *see* Restaurateur **2480**
Popular Government. (US ISSN 0032-4515) **3918**, **2667**
Popular Hot Rodding. (US ISSN 0032-4523) **4699**, **4483**
†Popular Lures. (US ISSN 0889-4752) **5260**
Popular Magazine Review *see* Magazine Article Summaries **16**
Popular Mechanics. (US ISSN 0032-4558) **4606**
Popular Mechanics Do-It-Yourself Yearbook. (US ISSN 0360-2273) **4606**
Popular Medicine. *see* Dazhong Yixue **3093**
Popular Motoring. (UK ISSN 0032-4574) **4699**
Popular Music. (UK ISSN 0261-1430) **3575**
Popular Music & Society. (US ISSN 0300-7766) **3575**, **4445**
Popular Music Periodicals Index *see* P O M P I **3589**
Popular Periodical Index. (US ISSN 0092-9727) **20**
Popular Photography. *see* Dazhong Sheying **3790**
Popular Photography. (US ISSN 0032-4582) **3796**
Popular Plastics. (II ISSN 0253-7303) **3867**
Popular Plastics and Rubber *see* Popular Plastics **3867**
Popular Psychology. *see* Dazhong Xinlixue **4018**
Popular Rotorcraft Flying *see* Rotorcraft **61**
Popular Science. (US ISSN 0161-7370) **4606**
Popular Science and Technology. (II ISSN 0032-4639) **4334**, **3468**, **4606**
Popular Science Series *see* Illinois. State Museum. Popular Science Series **4314**
Popular Short Stories. *see* Dazhong Xiaoshuo **2910**
Popular Song Index *see* P O P S I **409**

Popular Songs. *see* Tongsu Gequ **3584**
Popular Sports. (US) **4483**
Popular Statistics Series. (US) **4583**
Popular Tribune. *see* Qun Yan **2881**
Popular Woodworking. (US ISSN 0884-8823) **640**
Population. (UN) **3985**
Population. (FR ISSN 0032-4663) **3985**
Population (Washington). (US) **3985**
Population and Development. *see* Renkou yu Fazhan **3987**
Population and Development Review. (US ISSN 0098-7921) **3985**
Population & Economics. *see* Renkou yu Jingji **3987**
Population and Environment. (US ISSN 0199-0039) **4038**
Population and Environmental Psychology Newsletter. (US) **4038**, **3985**
Population and Family in the Low Countries. (NE ISSN 0169-1422) **3985**
†Population and Family Planning Programs. (US ISSN 0161-0902) **5260**
Population and Family Study Centre. Progress Report. (BE) **3986**
Population Association of America Affairs *see* P A A Affairs **3985**
Population Bulletin. (US ISSN 0032-468X) **3986**
Population Bulletin of the United Nations. (UN ISSN 0251-7604) **3986**
Population Census of Papua New Guinea. Population Characteristics Bulletin Series. (PP ISSN 0079-3868) **3986**
Population Council Annual Report. (US ISSN 0361-7858) **3986**
Population de la Grece au Recensement. (GR) **3994**
Population Education Accessions List. (UN) **1679**
Population Education in Asia and the Pacific Newsletter *see* Population Education in Asia and the Pacific Newsletter and Forum **3986**
Population Education in Asia and the Pacific Newsletter and Forum. (UN) **3986**, **1655**
†Population Education Interchange. (US) **5260**
Population Estimates of Arizona *see* Demographic Guide to Arizona (Year) **3981**
Population et Societes. (FR ISSN 0184-7783) **3986**, **4382**
Population Front. *see* Renkou Zhanxian **3987**
†Population Growth of Iran. (IR) **5260**
Population Headliners. (UN ISSN 0252-3639) **3986**
Population in Tochigi Prefecture. *see* Tochigi-ken no Jinko **3988**
Population Index. (US ISSN 0032-4701) **3994**, **20**
Population Mobility in Hawaii *see* Population Reports **3995**
Population Newsletter *see* Population **3985**
Population Newsletter. (TH ISSN 0125-6440) **3986**
Population of the Municipalities of the Netherlands. (NE ISSN 0168-3853) **3994**, **3986**
Population Reports. (US ISSN 0145-9643) **3995**, **3986**
Population Research and Policy Review.(NE ISSN 0167-5923) **3986**, **879**
Population Research Center Newsletter.(US) **3986**
Population Research Center Papers. (US ISSN 0191-913X) **3986**
Population Research Laboratory. Discussion Paper Series *see* Population Research Laboratory. Research Discussion Paper Series **3986**
Population Research Laboratory. Population Reprint Series. (CN ISSN 0317-3100) **3986**
Population Research Laboratory. Research Discussion Paper Series. (CN) **3986**, **4445**

Population Statistics. *see* Netherlands. Centraal Bureau voor de Statistiek. Jaarstatistiek van de Bevolking **3993**
Population Studies. (UK ISSN 0032-4728) **3986**
Population Studies. (UN ISSN 0082-805X) **3986**
Population Studies. *see* Renkou Yanjiu **3987**
Population Studies Centre. Highlights. (CN ISSN 0712-5828) **3986**
Population Today. (US ISSN 0749-2448) **3986**, **4445**
Population Trends. (UK ISSN 0307-4463) **3986**
Population Trends and Public Policy. (US ISSN 0736-7716) **3986**, **4070**
Populations of Municipalities. *see* Befolkningen i Kommunerne **3991**
Populi. (UN ISSN 0251-6861) **3986**
Populist. (NO) **2880**
Poradnik Bibliotekarza. (PL ISSN 0032-4752) **2779**
Poradnik Gospodarski. (PL ISSN 0137-6780) **114**
Porarografi. *see* Review of Polarography **1208**
Porc. (FR) **223**
Porc Magazine. (FR) **223**, **2079**
Poreditsa Balkani. (BU ISSN 0554-7040) **2381**
Porentief. (GW ISSN 0935-7149) **36**
Porima no Tomo. *see* Polymer Friends for Rubber, Plastics and Fiber **4292**
Pork (Year). (US ISSN 0745-3787) **223**
Pork (Year) Disease Control Guide *see* Pork (Year) Guide to Health and Nutrition **223**
Pork (Year) Guide to Health and Nutrition. (US) **223**
Pork Journal. (AT ISSN 1032-3759) **223**
Pork Producer News. (US) **223**
Pork Report. (CN) **223**
Pork Roundup *see* Pork Producer News **223**
Porodica i Dijete. (BN ISSN 0032-4787) **1243**
Poroshkovaya Metallurgiya. (KR ISSN 0032-4795) **3417**
Porphyre. (FR) **3740**
Porsche Panorama. (US ISSN 0147-3565) **4699**, **4483**
Porsche ueber Alles. (US ISSN 0192-8481) **4699**
Port. (UK ISSN 0032-4809) **4735**
Port and Harbour Research Institute. Guide. *see* Kowan Gijutsu Kenkyujo. Gaido **4730**
Port and Harbour Technical Research Institute. Guide *see* Kowan Gijutsu Kenkyujo. Gaido **4730**
Port Authority of New York and New Jersey. Aviation Department. Airport Statistics. (US) **4676**
Port Authority of New York and New Jersey. Aviation Department. Aviation Annual Report. (US) **4676**
Port Autonome du Havre. Bulletin Analytique de Documentation Generale. (FR ISSN 0396-4388) **4735**
Port Autonome du Havre. Bulletin Analytique de Documentation Technique. (FR ISSN 0396-4396) **4735**
Port Bustamante Handbook. (JM) **4735**
Port Development International. (UK ISSN 0267-4823) **4735**
Port Folio, Port of Chittagong *see* Chittagong Port Authority. Port Folio, Port of Chittagong **4725**
Port Hole. (CN) **4528**
Port Kelang Shipping Handbook. (AT ISSN 0266-3856) **4736**, **1150**
Port Lincoln Times. (AT) **2172**
†Port of Baltimore Bulletin. (US ISSN 0032-4817) **5260**
Port of Baltimore Handbook *see* Port of Baltimore Magazine **4736**
Port of Baltimore Magazine. (US) **4736**
Port of Bristol Authority *see* The Bristol Port Company **4725**

Port of Copenhagen Review. see Koebenhavns Havneblad **4730**
Port of Detroit Log. (US) **4655**
Port of Fremantle see Fremantle Port News **4727**
Port of Houston Magazine. (US ISSN 0032-4825) **4736**
Port of Kingston Handbook see Port Bustamante Handbook **4735**
Port of le Havre Flashes. (FR) **4736**
Port of London. (UK ISSN 0030-8064) **4736**
Port of Melbourne Quarterly see Panorama (Melbourne) **4735**
Port of New Orleans Annual Directory. (US ISSN 0085-5030) **4655**
†Port of New Orleans Record. (US) **5260**
Port of Osaka/Osaka-ko. (JA) **4736**
Port of Piraeus Authority. Annual Report. (GR) **4736**
Port of Piraeus Authority. Quarterly Report. (GR) **4736**
Port of Piraeus Authority. Statistical Bulletin see Port of Piraeus Authority. Statistical Report **4736**
Port of Piraeus Authority. Statistical Report. (GR) **4736**
Port of Rotterdam Magazine. (NE ISSN 0922-7148) **4736**
Port of Tokyo. (JA) **4736**
Port of Toledo News see Connections (Toledo, 1956) **4726**
Port of Yokohama. Annual Report. (JA) **4736**
Port of Yokohama. Annual Statistics. (JA) **4666**
Port of Yokohama. Monthly Statistics. see Port of Yokohama. Annual Statistics **4666**
†Port of Yokohama. Plans for Future. (JA) **5260**
Port Panorama see Panorama (Melbourne) **4735**
Port Rashid: Dubai Shipping Handbook.(UK ISSN 0266-3848) **4736**, 1150
Port Stephens Examiner. (AT) **2880**
Port Transport Statistics of India see Basic Port Statistics of India **4662**
Porta Linguarum Orientalium. (GW ISSN 0554-7342) **2835**, 3643
Portable Companion. (US ISSN 0732-7501) **1464**, 1473
Portable Computer Review see Portable Office **1473**
Portable Computing. (US) **1464**
Portable Computing see Portable Office **1473**
▼The Portable Computing Letter. (US) **1473**, 1464
Portable Lower East Side. (US ISSN 8756-5978) **2949**
Portable Office. (US) **1473**, 1464
Portable Paper see The Palmtop Paper **1454**
Portable 100. (US ISSN 0888-0131) **1473**, 1464
Portable 100-200-600 see Portable 100 **1473**
†Portage. (US ISSN 0197-1085) **5260**
Portal. (US) **3670**, 4287
Portals of Prayer. (US ISSN 0032-4884) **4246**
Portcullis. (SA ISSN 0032-4892) **4736**
Portefeuille. (ZR) **879**
Portents. (US) **2984**
Portfolio Letter. (US) **960**
†Portfolio of Sales and Marketing Plans.(US) **5260**
Porti Mare Territorio see Trasporti Mare Territorio **5292**
Portico see A S I Journal **291**
Portico. (IT) **2949**
Porticus. (US ISSN 8755-2035) **3531**
Portique Saint-Denis see Presence Orthodoxe **4287**
Portland Alliance. (US) **2588**, 879, 1966, 2020
Portland and the Pacific Northwest. (US) **4803**
Portland Art Museum Newsletter. (US) **3531**
Portland Life and Business. (US) **2232**
Portland Metropolitan Labor Trends. (US) **991**

Portland Observer. (US) **2020**
Portland Parent. (US) **1243**
Portland Review Magazine. (US) **2949**
Portland Review of the Arts see The Review (Portland) **3004**
Portland Souvenir Magazine. (UK) **4783**
Il Porto di Savona. (IT ISSN 0032-4957) **4736**
†Porto di Venezia. (IT ISSN 0032-4965) **5260**
Portos e Navios. (BL ISSN 0032-4973) **4736**, 2047
Portrait Photography. see Renxiang Sheying **3796**
Portraits Poetry Magazine. (US) **3003**
Ports and Dredging. (NE ISSN 0166-5766) **1925**, 1872
Ports and Harbors. (JA ISSN 0554-7555) **1872**
Ports Annual. (CN) **4736**
Ports Magazine. (NE) **4736**
†Ports O'Call. (US ISSN 0032-5015) **5260**
Ports of South Africa. (SA) **4736**
Ports of Virginia see Virginia Maritimer **4741**
Ports - Routes - Trafics. (FR ISSN 0079-4074) **897**
Portsea Boomer. (AT) **4483**, 1300
Portside. (US ISSN 0048-489X) **4736**
Portsmouth Chamber of Commerce. Newsletter see Portsmouth Chamber of Commerce. Report **5260**
†Portsmouth Chamber of Commerce. Report. (US) **5260**
Portsmouth Papers. (UK ISSN 0554-7598) **2381**
Portu-Info. (US ISSN 0892-5178) **3756**
Portugal. Administracao Geral dos Correios e Telegrafos. Boletim Oficial dos C.T.T. see Correios e Telecomunicacoes de Portugal. Boletim Oficial **1362**
Portugal. Comissao da Condicao Feminina. Coleccao Informar as Mulheres see Portugal. Comissao para a Igualdade e Direitos das Mulheres. Coleccao Informar as Mulheres **4851**
Portugal. Comissao da Condicao Feminina. Informacao Bibliografica see Portugal. Comissao para a Igualdade e Direitos das Mulheres. Informacao Bibliografica **4851**
Portugal. Comissao da Condicao Feminina. Noticias see Portugal. Comissao para a Igualdade e Direitos das Mulheres. Noticias **4851**
Portugal. Comissao para a Igualdade e Direitos das Mulheres. Coleccao Informar as Mulheres. (PO) **4851**
Portugal. Comissao para a Igualdade e Direitos das Mulheres. Informacao Bibliografica. (PO ISSN 0871-9799) **4851**
Portugal. Comissao para a Igualdade e Direitos das Mulheres. Noticias. (PO ISSN 0871-3316) **4851**
Portugal. Direccao Geral de Marinha do Comercio. Boletim. (PO) **4736**
†Portugal. Estatisticas da Energia: Continente, Acores e Madeira. (PO ISSN 0377-2233) **5260**
Portugal. Estatisticas Industriais: Continente, Acores e Madeira. Volume 1: Industrias Extractivas, Electricidade, Gas, Agua/Portugal. Statistiques Industrielles: Continent, Acores et Madere. Volume 1: Industries Extractives, Electricite, Gaz, Eau. (PO ISSN 0377-2314) **735**
Portugal. Estatisticas Industriais: Continente, Acores e Madeira. Volume 2: Industrias Transformadoras/Portugal. Statistiques Industrielles: Continent, Acores et Madere. Volume 2: Industries Manufacturieres. (PO ISSN 0079-418X) **735**
Portugal. Instituto Nacional de Estatistica. Anuario Estatistico. Continente, Acores e Madeira. (PO ISSN 0871-8741) **4583**

Portugal. Instituto Nacional de Estatistica. Boletim Mensal de Estatistica: Continente, Acores e Madeira. (PO) **4583**
Portugal. Instituto Nacional de Estatistica. Centro de Estudos Demograficos. Caderno. (PO ISSN 0379-7007) **3995**
Portugal. Instituto Nacional de Estatistica. Centro de Estudos Demograficos. Revista see Portugal. Instituto Nacional de Estatistica. Gabinete de Estudos Demograficos. Estudos Demograficos **3995**
Portugal. Instituto Nacional de Estatistica. Estatisticas Agricolas. Continente, Acores e Madeira. (PO ISSN 0079-4139) **142**
Portugal. Instituto Nacional de Estatistica. Estatisticas Agricolas see Portugal. Instituto Nacional de Estatistica. Estatisticas Agricolas. Continente, Acores e Madeira **142**
Portugal. Instituto Nacional de Estatistica. Estatisticas da Educacao. Continente, Acores e Madeira. (PO) **1655**
Portugal. Instituto Nacional de Estatistica. Estatisticas da Pesca - Statistiques de la Peche see Portugal. Instituto Nacional de Estatistica. Estatisticas da Pesca - Statistiques de la Peche. Continente, Acores e Madeira **2051**
Portugal. Instituto Nacional de Estatistica. Estatisticas da Pesca - Statistiques de la Peche. Continente, Acores e Madeira. (PO) **2051**
Portugal. Instituto Nacional de Estatistica. Estatisticas Contribuicoes e Impostos see Portugal. Instituto Nacional de Estatistica. Estatisticas das Contribuicoes e Impostos. Continente, Acores e Madiera **735**
Portugal. Instituto Nacional de Estatistica. Estatisticas das Contribuicoes e Impostos. Continente, Acores e Madeira. (PO) **735**
Portugal. Instituto Nacional de Estatistica. Estatisticas das Financas Publicas. Continente, Acores e Madeira. (PO) **735**
†Portugal. Instituto Nacional de Estatistica. Estatisticas das Sociedades: Continente, Acores e Madeira. (PO) **5260**
Portugal. Instituto Nacional de Estatistica. Estatisticas das Sociedades. Continente e Ilhas Adjacentes see Portugal. Instituto Nacional de Estatistica. Estatisticas das Sociedades: Continente, Acores e Madeira **5260**
Portugal. Instituto Nacional de Estatistica. Estatisticas de Proteccao Social, Associacoes Sindicais e Patronais. (PO ISSN 0870-4406) **4445**
Portugal. Instituto Nacional de Estatistica. Estatisticas Demograficas. Continente, Acores e Madeira. (PO) **3995**
Portugal. Instituto Nacional de Estatistica. Estatisticas Demograficas Continente e Ilhas Adjacentes see Portugal. Instituto Nacional de Estatistica. Estatisticas Demograficas. Continente, Acores e Madeira **3995**
Portugal. Instituto Nacional de Estatistica. Estatisticas do Comercio Externo. Continente, Acores e Madeira. (PO) **735**
Portugal. Instituto Nacional de Estatistica. Estatisticas do Turismo. Continente, Acores e Madeira. (PO ISSN 0377-2306) **4800**
Portugal. Instituto Nacional de Estatistica. Estatisticas do Turismo see Portugal. Instituto Nacional de Estatistica. Estatisticas do Turismo. Continente, Acores e Madeira **4800**
Portugal. Instituto Nacional de Estatistica. Estatisticas dos Transportes e Communicacoes: Continente, Acores e Madeira. (PO ISSN 0377-2292) **4666**, 1349, 4583

Portugal. Instituto Nacional de Estatistica. Gabinete de Estudos Demograficos. Estudos Demograficos.(PO ISSN 0871-875X) **3995**
Portugal. Instituto Nacional de Estatistica. Serie Estatisticas Regionais. (PO ISSN 0378-3227) **4583**
Portugal. Instituto Nacional de Investigacao das Pescas. Boletim. (PO ISSN 0870-1245) **590**, 2047
Portugal. Ministerio da Habitacao e Obras Publicas. Comissao Nacional do Ambiente. Relatorio de Actividades see Portugal. Ministerio da Qualidade de Vida. Comissao Nacional do Ambiente. Boletim **1966**
Portugal. Ministerio da Justicia. Boletim.(PO) **2667**
Portugal. Ministerio da Qualidade de Vida. Comissao Nacional do Ambiente. Boletim. (PO) **1966**
Portugal. Ministerio das Corporacoes e Previdencia Social. Gabinete de Planeamento. Inguerito Emprego. (PO) **1069**
Portugal. Ministerio das Financas e do Plano. Departamento Central de Planeamento. Plano see Economic Situation in the Year **5184**
Portugal. Ministerio das Financas. Relatorio do Orcamento Geral do Estado. (PO ISSN 0079-4201) **1104**
Portugal. Ministerio do Trabalho. Servico de Estatisticas. Estatisticas do Trabalho. (PO) **735**
Portugal. Ministerio do Trabalho. Servico de Informacao Cientifica e Tecnica. Boletim do Trabalho e Emprego. (PO) **991**
Portugal. Servico de Administracao Militar. Revista Bimestral. (PO) **3468**
Portugal. Servico de Administracao Militar. Revista Mensal see Portugal. Servico de Administracao Militar. Revista Bimestral **3468**
Portugal. Servicos Geologicos. Comunicacoes. (PO ISSN 0037-2730) **1577**, 3493
Portugal. Statistiques Industrielles: Continent, Acores et Madere. Volume 1: Industries Extractives, Electricite, Gaz, Eau. see Portugal. Estatisticas Industriais: Continente, Acores e Madeira. Volume 1: Industrias Extractivas, Electricidade, Gas, Agua **735**
Portugal. Statistiques Industrielles: Continent, Acores et Madere. Volume 2: Industries Manufacturieres. see Portugal. Estatisticas Industriais: Continente, Acores e Madeira. Volume 2: Industrias Transformadoras **735**
Portugal (Year) see Portugal em Numeros **4583**
Portugal (Year). (US) **4783**
Portugal & Spain Stamp Catalogue. (UK ISSN 0142-9833) **3756**
Portugal; Economic and Social Indicators see Portugal em Numeros; Situacao Socio-Economica **4583**
Portugal em Numeros. (PO ISSN 0871-8725) **4583**
Portugal em Numeros; Situacao Socio-Economica. (PO ISSN 0871-4614) **4583**
Portugal Evangelico. (PO ISSN 0032-5066) **4246**
Portugal Illustrado. (CN) **2020**
Portugal - Magazin. (GW ISSN 0932-2272) **3918**, 934, 2259, 2319
Portugal - Nachrichten see Portugal - Magazin **3918**
Portugal Socialista. (PO) **3918**
Portugal Turismo Actualidade. (PO) **4783**
Portugaliae Acta Biologica see Portugaliae Acta Biologica. Serie A. Morfologia, Fisiologia, Genetica e Biologia Geral **451**

Portugaliae Acta Biologica see Portugaliae Acta Biologica. Serie B. Sistematica, Ecologia, Biogeografia e Paleontologia 452

Portugaliae Acta Biologica. Serie A. Morfologia, Fisiologia, Genetica e Biologia Geral. (PO) 451

Portugaliae Acta Biologica. Serie B. Sistematica, Ecologia, Biogeografia e Paleontologia. (PO ISSN 0375-0280) 452

Portugaliae Historica. (PO) 2381

Portugaliae Mathematica. (PO ISSN 0032-5155) 3051

Portugaliae Physica. (PO ISSN 0048-4903) 3829

Portugiesische Forschungen der Goerresgesellschaft. Reihe 1: Aufsaetze zur Portugiesischen Kulturgeschichte. (GW ISSN 0079-421X) 2381

Portugiesische Forschungen der Goerresgesellschaft. Reihe 2: Monographien. (GW ISSN 0079-4228) 2381

O Portugues na Australia. (AT) 2020

Portuguese Journal/Jornal Portugues. (US ISSN 0032-5163) 2020

Portuguese Studies. (UK ISSN 0267-5315) 2949

Portuguese Times. (US ISSN 0746-3928) 2020, 3918

Portuguese Water Dog Club of America. Newsletter. (US) 3713

Poruka Borca. (CI ISSN 0032-5171) 2319

†Poruncna Vremii. (US) 5260

Pos- en Telegraafherald. see Postal and Telegraph Herald 1353

Poseidon. (GW ISSN 0032-5198) 4483

Posener Stimmen. (GW) 4246

Posible. (PE) 2880

Posicion Socialista. (DR) 3918

Positif. (FR ISSN 0048-4911) 3515

Position. (GW) 838

Positionen. (GW) 879

Positions Lutheriennes. (FR ISSN 0032-5228) 4246

Positive Alternatives. (US) 3919, 4606

A Positive Approach. (US ISSN 0891-8791) 2290, 1739

Positive Review. (NR ISSN 0331-9911) 3919

▼Positive Teaching. (UK ISSN 0959-6828) 4038

Posjoernaal. see Postal Journal 1353

Possessions. (US ISSN 0164-6184) 3756

Possev. (GW ISSN 0032-5201) 3919

Possibilities. (US) 4246

Possibles. (CN ISSN 0703-7139) 2880

Possum County News. (US) 2880

The Post. (GH) 2193

Post. (UK ISSN 0032-5236) 2588

Post. (KE) 4334, 4606

Post (Athens). (US) 1321

The Post (Blissfield). (US) 628

Post (Port Washington). (US ISSN 0891-5628) 1341, 4461

Post-Amerikan. (US) 3919

Post Eagle. (US ISSN 0300-6786) 2020

Post Gutenberg. (US ISSN 1040-6301) 4003

Post Library Association Report see P L A Report 5255

Post Magazine Almanack. Insurance Directory see Insurance Directory and Year Book 2534

Post Magazine and Insurance Monitor. (UK ISSN 0032-5252) 2540

Post Mark Collectors Club Bulletin see P M C C Bulletin 3755

Post Mark Collectors Club Membership Roster see P M C C Membership Roster 3755

Post Marketing Surveillance. (NE ISSN 0269-2333) 3740, 1050, 3142

Post-Medieval Archaeology. (UK ISSN 0079-4236) 281

Post Mortem. (US ISSN 0032-5279) 4483

Post Mortem Tax Planning. (US) 1104

Post Office Electrical Engineers' Journal see British Telecommunications Engineering 1361

Post Office Engineering Union Journal see National Communications Union Journal 1364

Post Office Savings Bank. Annual Report. (MF) 795

Post Office Xpress. (SA) 1353

Post-Polio Directory. (US) 3142

Post Script see P S (Wynantskill) 1353

Post Script (Columbia). (US) 1321

Post Script (Commerce). (US ISSN 0277-9897) 2513, 3515

Post-Season Football Handbook. (US) 4510

Post, Telefon und Telegrafen. Amtsblatt.(SZ) 1353

La Posta. (US ISSN 0885-7385) 1353, 3756

Posta de Arte y Literatura see Nudos en la Cultura Argentina 2877

Posta, Telegraf, Telefon see P T T Revue 1341

Postage Stamps of New Zealand. (NZ) 3756

Postal and Telecommunications Journal see Communications Worker 2581

Postal and Telegraph Herald/Pos- en Telegraafherald. (SA ISSN 0032-5317) 1353, 1365

†Postal Bell/Ekirei. (US ISSN 0032-5325) 5260

Postal Bulletin. (US ISSN 0364-863X) 1353

Postal Christian Witness see TransAction 4251

†Postal Employees' Newsletter. (US ISSN 0888-0794) 5260

Postal History Journal. (US ISSN 0032-5341) 1353

Postal History Society of Canada. Journal see P H S C Journal 3755

†Postal History U.S.A. (US ISSN 0146-9983) 5260

Postal Journal/Posjoernaal. (SA ISSN 0032-535X) 1353

Postal Life. (US ISSN 0032-5368) 1353

Postal Record. (US ISSN 0032-5376) 2588, 1354

Postal Service Guide to U S Stamps. (US) 3757

Postal Service Today/Chin Jih Yu Cheng. (CH) 1354

Postal Stationery. (US) 1354

Postal Stationery Notes. (CN) 3757

Postal Stationery Study Group. (US) 3757

Postal Supervisor. (US ISSN 0032-5384) 1354

Postal Telegraph and Telephone International Studies see P T T I Studies 1353

▼Postal Watch. (US ISSN 1052-3944) 1354

Postal World. (US) 1354

Postales de Bolivia. (BO) 3757

Postbuechl. (AU) 1354, 1104

Postcard Art - Postcard Fiction. (US) 340, 259, 2949

Postcard Classics. (US ISSN 0897-4020) 2440

Postcard Collector. (US ISSN 0746-6102) 2440

Postcard History Society. Newsletter. (US) 2440

Postcard Journal see Image File 2410

Postcontemporary Interventions. (US) 3919

Postcript. (US) 1354

Poste de Varsovie see Warsaw Post 5302

Poste e Telecomunicazioni. (IT ISSN 0032-5406) 1365

Postel see Post Office Xpress 1353

Postepy Astronautyki/Progress in Astronautics. (PL ISSN 0373-5982) 60

Postepy Astronomii. (PL ISSN 0032-5414) 368

Postepy Biochemii. (PL ISSN 0032-5422) 481, 486

Postepy Biologii Komorki. (PL ISSN 0324-833X) 526

Postepy Cybernetyki/Progress in Cybernetics. (PL ISSN 0137-3595) 1442

Postepy Fizyki. (PL ISSN 0032-5430) 3829

Postepy Fizyki Medycznej. (PL ISSN 0137-8465) 3142, 3829

Postepy Higieny i Medycyny Doswiadczalnej. (PL ISSN 0032-5449) 3143

Postepy Mikrobiologii. (PL ISSN 0079-4252) 556

Postepy Napedu Elektrycznego. (PL ISSN 0079-4260) 1906

Postepy Nauk Rolniczych. (PL ISSN 0032-5457) 114

Postepy Pediatrii. (PL ISSN 0079-4279) 3325

Postes, Telephones et Telegraphes Suisses Technische Mitteilungen see P T T Technische Mitteilungen 1365

Postgraduate Courses in United Kingdom Universities see British Universities' Guide to Graduate Study 1692

Postgraduate Doctor: Africa. (UK ISSN 0142-7946) 3143

Postgraduate Doctor: Caribbean. (UK ISSN 0267-0275) 3143

Postgraduate Doctor: Middle East. (UK ISSN 0140-7724) 3143

▼Postgraduate Education for General Practice. (UK ISSN 0959-4299) 3143, 1714

Postgraduate Institute of Medical Education and Research, Chandigarh. Bulletin. (II ISSN 0302-2404) 3143, 1757

Postgraduate Medical Journal. (UK ISSN 0032-5473) 3143

Postgraduate Medicine. (US ISSN 0032-5481) 3143

Postgraduate Radiology. (US ISSN 0273-0278) 3361

Postgraduate Study at the University of Liverpool see University of Liverpool Post Graduate Prospectus 1719

▼Postharvest Biology and Technology. (NE ISSN 0925-5214) 491, 114

▼Postharvest News and Information. (UK ISSN 0957-7505) 142, 189

Posthorn. (US) 3757

Postiljon see Koerier 3754

Postilla. (US ISSN 0079-4295) 4334

Postillon. (GW) 3757

Postmaennens Tidning. (SW ISSN 0032-5503) 1354

Postman Pat Picture Paper. (UK) 1263

Postmasters Advocate. (US ISSN 0032-5511) 1354

Postmasters Gazette. (US ISSN 0032-552X) 1354

▼Postmodern Culture. (US) 2949

Posto. see L'Emploi 3627

Postscript. (US) 2949

Postscript see P S 3737

Postscript Language Journal - International Edition see Postscript Review 1431

Postscript Review. (UK) 1431

Postsjakk. (NO) 4483

Postup. see Progress 4273

Pot a Lait. (FR) 203

▼Pot-Bellied Pigs. (US) 3713

Potash Review. (SZ ISSN 0032-5546) 189

Potato Abstracts. (UK ISSN 0308-7344) 142, 20

Potato Chipper see Snack World 2081

Potato Councillor see Maine Potato News 184

Potato Country. (US ISSN 0886-4780) 189, 1050

Potato Eyes. (US ISSN 1041-9926) 3003, 2880

†Potato Grower News. (AT ISSN 0032-5589) 5260

Potato Grower of Idaho. (US) 189

Potato Marketing Board, London. Annual Report and Accounts. (UK ISSN 0079-4309) 156, 189

Potato Markets. (US ISSN 0141-2221) 114, 2079

Potato News. (UK) 189, 156

Potato Newsletter. (CN) 189

Potato Quarterly see Potato World 5260

Potato Research. (NE ISSN 0014-3065) 189

Potato Statistics in Great Britain. (UK) 142

†Potato World. (UK ISSN 0265-7015) 5260

Potboiler Magazine. (CN ISSN 0228-3344) 2880

Potchefstroom University for Christian Higher Education. Wetenskaplike Bydraes. Reeks A: Geesteswetenskappe. (SA ISSN 0079-4333) 2513

Potchefstroom University for Christian Higher Education. Wetenskaplike Bydraes. Reeks B: Natuurwetenskappe. Series. (SA ISSN 0079-4341) 1686, 1714, 4195

Potchefstroom University for Christian Higher Education. Wetenskaplike Bydraes. Reeks H: Inougurele Redes.(SA) 1714

Potchefstroom University for Christian Higher Education Kaner see P.U.-Kaner 5255

Potencia. (SP ISSN 0032-5600) 628

Potentials in Marketing. (US ISSN 0032-5619) 1050

Potentials Mart. (US) 1050

Potere Locale. (IT) 4070

Potomac Appalachian. (US ISSN 0092-2226) 4554, 1495

Potomac Basin Reporter. (US) 4827, 1966

Potomac Issues. (US) 4827

▼Potomac Life. (US) 2232

Potomac River Basin Water Quality Reports. (US) 4827, 1966

Potomac View on Lung Health see Nova Report on Lung Health and Wellness 3366

Potopoto. (EG) 2169

Potpourii Party-Line see Flora-Line 2125

Potpourri from Herbal Acres. (US ISSN 0197-4084) 2137, 2079

Potravinar. (CS ISSN 0032-566X) 3611, 2588

Potravinarske Vedy/Food Sciences. (CS) 2079

Potsdamer Kirche see Berlin - Brandenburgisches Sonntagsblatt 4230

Potter (Auckland). (NZ ISSN 0113-583X) 356

Potter County Historical Society. Quarterly Bulletin. (US ISSN 0895-0865) 2419

Potters' Society of Australia. Newsletter.(AT) 356

The Pottersfield Portfolio. (CN ISSN 0226-0840) 2949, 3003

Pottery in Australia. (AT ISSN 0048-4954) 356

Pottery Quarterly see Real Pottery 356

Pottery Southwest. (US ISSN 0738-8020) 281, 1165

Poty Cuntu. (IT ISSN 0032-5686) 3003

Poudre Noire see Gazette des Armes 2436

Poultry see Misset World Poultry 221

Poultry. see Pia-Shaver 223

Poultry. see Ptitsevodstvo 224

Poultry. (US) 2880

Poultry Abstracts. (UK ISSN 0306-1582) 142, 20

Poultry Adviser. (II ISSN 0970-1958) 223, 4814

Poultry and Egg Marketing. (US ISSN 0032-5716) 223, 203

Poultry and Eggs Weekly see Poultry and Egg Marketing 223

Poultry Digest. (US ISSN 0032-5724) 223

Poultry Digest. (AT ISSN 1032-3767) 223

Poultry Guide. (II ISSN 0032-5740) 223

Poultry Husbandry Research Foundation Symposium see Australian Poultry Science Symposium 211

Poultry Industry. see Drobiarstwo 215

Poultry International. (US ISSN 0032-5767) 223

Poultry Market News Report. (US) 223, 1050

Poultry Market Report. (CN) 223, 156

Poultry Market Review. (CN ISSN 0032-5775) 223

Poultry Market Statistics. (US ISSN 0565-1980) **142**, **223**, **4583**
Poultry Press. (US ISSN 0032-5783) **224**
Poultry Processing. (US) **224**
Poultry Reporter. (II) **224**
Poultry Researches. see Niwatori no Kenkyu **222**
Poultry Review. see Revista Avicultura **224**
Poultry Roundup. (US) **224**
Poultry Science. (US ISSN 0032-5791) **224**
Poultry Science Reviews. (UK ISSN 0964-6604) **224**, **590**
Poultry Times. (US ISSN 0885-3371) **224**
Poultry Tribune see Egg Industry **216**
Poultry World. (UK ISSN 0032-5813) **224**
†Poumons. (CN ISSN 0318-9236) **5260**
Pour la Danse. (FR ISSN 0183-3189) **1531**
Pour la Science. (French translation of: Scientific American) (FR ISSN 0153-4092) **4334**, **4606**
Pour la Verite. (FR ISSN 0751-5987) **4246**
Pour la Vie. (FR ISSN 0032-583X) **3986**, **4445**
Pour Nos Jardins. (FR) **2137**
Pour Vous/Voor U. (BE) **1906**
Pour Vous de Tchecoslovaquie see For You from Czechoslovakia **815**
Pourquoi. (FR ISSN 0048-5004) **2187**
Pourquoi, Comment. (FR) **1655**
Pourquoi Pas? (BE) **2175**
Pouvoirs. (FR ISSN 0152-0768) **3919**
Poverty. (UK ISSN 0032-5856) **4416**
Poverty and Human Resources Abstracts see Human Resources Abstracts **4457**
Poverty in South Dakota. (US) **4416**
Poverty Pamphlets see Poverty Publications Series **4416**
Poverty Publications Series. (UK) **4416**
Poverty Watch. (AT ISSN 0810-5537) **4416**
Povijesni Prilozi/Historical Contributions. (CI) **2319**
Povijest Sporta. (CI ISSN 0350-9419) **4483**
Povo Libre. (PO) **3919**
Povratak u Zivot. (YU ISSN 0032-5880) **2540**
Powder. (US ISSN 0145-4471) **4554**
Powder and Bulk Engineering. (US ISSN 0897-6627) **1834**
Powder - Bulk Solids. (US) **1858**
Powder - Bulk Solids' Catalog Review. (US) **1858**
Powder - Bulk Solids' Directalog see Powder - Bulk Solids' Guide & Directory **1858**
Powder - Bulk Solids' Guide & Directory.(US) **1858**
▼Powder Coating. (US ISSN 1055-0259) **1834**
Powder Diffraction. (US ISSN 0885-7156) **1834**
Powder Diffraction File Search Manual. Alphabetical Listing. Inorganic. (US ISSN 0092-0509) **1207**, **1214**
†Powder Diffraction File Search Manual. Fink Method. Inorganic. (US ISSN 0092-1300) **5260**
Powder Diffraction File Search Manual. Hanawalt Method. Inorganic. (US ISSN 0092-1319) **1208**, **1214**
Powder Diffraction File Search Manual. Organic. (US ISSN 0092-0576) **1222**
Powder Handling & Processing. (GW ISSN 0934-7348) **4606**, **3022**, **4655**
Powder Metallurgy. (UK ISSN 0032-5899) **3417**
†Powder Metallurgy in Defense Technology. (US ISSN 0149-3922) **5260**
Powder Metallurgy Technology Newsletter see P - M Technology Newsletter **3417**

Powder River Breaks. (US) **1966**, **1495**
Powder Technology. (SZ ISSN 0032-5910) **1858**
Powell Gold Industry Guide & International Mining Analyst. (US ISSN 0146-7204) **3494**
Powell Monetary Analyst. (US ISSN 0146-7190) **960**
Power. (SA) **991**, **1906**, **2588**
Power. (SW) **4483**
Power (New York). (US ISSN 0032-5929) **1938**
Power (Niagara Falls). (US) **3919**
Power and Motoryacht. (US ISSN 0886-4411) **4528**
Power and Ski see Power Boat and Ski **4554**
Power Authority of the State of New York. Annual Report. (US) **1794**
Power Boat and Ski. (SA ISSN 1018-1385) **4554**
†Power Boat and Waterskiing. (UK) **5260**
Power Boating Canada. (CN) **4528**
Power Conditioning Specialists Conference. Record see I E E E Power Electronics Specialists Conference. Record **55**
Power Conversion International see Powerconversion & Intelligent Motion **1794**
Power Conversion Products Council International Membership Directory and Product Listing see P C P C I Membership Directory and Product Listing **1904**
Power Conversion Products Council International Newsletter see P C P C I Newsletter **1904**
▼Power Delivery Product News. (US) **1906**
Power Design. (JA) **1834**
†Power Energy Ecology. (US ISSN 1044-5137) **5260**
Power Engineering. see Energetika **1801**
Power Engineering (Tulsa). (US ISSN 0032-5961) **1906**, **1794**, **1834**, **3829**
Power Engineering (U S S R Academy of Sciences). (English translation of: Akademiya Nauk S.S.S.R. Izvestiya. Energetika i Transport) (US ISSN 0160-5216) **1938**
Power Engineering Abstracts. see Energiaipari es Energiagazdalkodasi Tajekoztato **1798**
Power Engineering Journal. (UK ISSN 0950-3366) **1906**
Power Equipment Australasia. (AT) **164**, **2106**
Power Equipment Trade. (US) **685**, **1906**
Power Europe see Power in Europe **1906**
Power Farming. (AT ISSN 0311-1911) **164**
Power Farming. (UK ISSN 0032-5988) **164**
Power Farming and Better Farming Digest see Power Farming **164**
Power Farming Annual. (AT) **164**
Power Farming Technical Annual see Power Farming Annual **164**
Power for Living. (US ISSN 0032-6003) **4195**
Power for Today. (US ISSN 0032-6011) **4195**
Power Generation Industrial see European Power News **1892**
Power Hotline. (US) **4483**
Power in Asia. (UK) **1906**
Power in Europe. (UK) **1906**
†Power International. (UK ISSN 0950-1487) **5260**
Power Letter. (US) **1794**, **1938**, **4655**
Power Line. (US ISSN 0738-5676) **1794**, **1495**, **1507**, **1906**
Power Machinery Abstracts. see Dongli Jixue Wenzhai **1843**
Power Machinery Construction. see Energomashinostroenie **1786**
†Power Metal. (US) **5260**
Power Modulator Symposium. I E E E Conference Record. (US) **1906**
Power Places of California. (US) **1593**, **281**, **3670**

Power Plant Report (E I A 759). (Energy Information Administration) (US) **1794**, **2667**
Power - Play Magazine see Commodore Magazine **5168**
Power Press and Forging Newsletter. (US) **3620**
Power Reactor and Nuclear Fuel Development Corporation Review see P N C Review **1809**
Power Reactor Events see U.S. Nuclear Regulatory Commission. Power Reactor Events **1810**
Power Reactors. (US) **3838**
Power Semiconductors D.A.T.A. Digest. (US ISSN 1040-0214) **1776**
†Power Sources Symposium. Proceedings. (US ISSN 0079-4457) **5260**
Power Sport. (GW) **4484**, **3807**
Power Statistics Journal of Nepal. (NP) **1800**, **1802**
Power Stroke. (CN) **4528**, **1300**, **4554**
Power System Technology. see Dianwang Jishu **1885**
Power Systems Computation Conference. P S C C Proceedings. (SW) **1834**
Power Technology International. (UK ISSN 0951-9653) **1906**
Power Technology News. (US) **1794**, **1906**
Power Transmission and Bearing Handbook see Power Transmission Design Handbook **1938**
Power Transmission Design. (US ISSN 0032-6070) **1938**
Power Transmission Design Handbook. (US) **1938**
Power Transmission Distributor see P T Distributor **1937**
Powerboat. (US ISSN 0032-6089) **4528**
Powerboat Reports. (US ISSN 1040-3663) **4528**
Powerconversion & Intelligent Motion. (US ISSN 0885-0259) **1794**, **1906**
Poweredge Magazine. (US) **4484**
Powerlifting U S A. (US ISSN 0199-8536) **4484**
Power's Electric Utility Generation Planbook see Electric Utility Generation Planbook **5185**
Powertechnics Magazine. (US ISSN 0882-7419) **1906**
Poweshiek County, Iowa Searcher. (US) **2419**, **2162**
Powhatan Newsletter see Powhatan Newspaper **2020**
Powhatan Newspaper. (US) **2020**
Powloki Ochronne. (PL) **1834**
Powstanie Styczniowe. Materialy i Dokumenty. (PL ISSN 0079-4465) **2381**
Powys Chronicle. see Cronicl Powys **2148**
Powys Notes. (US ISSN 1058-7691) **2949**
Powys Review. (UK ISSN 0309-1619) **2949**
Poynter Center Newsletter. (US) **2667**
Poynton Local History Society Newsletter. (UK ISSN 0261-8818) **2381**
Poyyamozhi. (II) **359**
Pozadina. (YU ISSN 0351-3912) **3468**, **2381**
Pozar Eksplozija Preventiva. (BN ISSN 0351-4714) **2034**
†Pozemni Stavby/Construction Engineering. (CS ISSN 0477-8685) **5260**
Pozirnik. (CS) **2034**
▼Pozitsiya. (RU) **3919**
Poznaj Swoj Kraj. (PL ISSN 0032-6151) **4783**
Poznan Fair Magazine. (PL ISSN 0860-0023) **919**
Poznan Messemagazin see Poznan Fair Magazine **919**
Poznan Studies in the Philosophy of the Sciences and the Humanities. (NE ISSN 0303-8157) **3919**, **3777**
Poznanskie Towarzystwo Przyjaciol Nauk. Komisja Archeologiczna. Prace.(PL ISSN 0137-3250) **282**

Poznanskie Towarzystwo Przyjaciol Nauk. Komisja Automatyki. Prace see Studia z Automatyki **1416**
Poznanskie Towarzystwo Przyjaciol Nauk. Komisja Biologiczna. Prace. (PL ISSN 0079-4619) **452**
Poznanskie Towarzystwo Przyjaciol Nauk. Komisja Filozoficzna. Prace. (PL ISSN 0079-4635) **3777**
Poznanskie Towarzystwo Przyjaciol Nauk. Komisja Geograficzno-Geologiczna. Prace. (PL ISSN 0137-9771) **1578**, **2259**
Poznanskie Towarzystwo Przyjaciol Nauk. Komisja Historii Sztuki. Prace. (PL ISSN 0079-466X) **340**
Poznanskie Towarzystwo Przyjaciol Nauk. Komisja Historyczna. Prace. (PL ISSN 0079-4651) **2381**
Poznanskie Towarzystwo Przyjaciol Nauk. Komisja Jezykoznawcza. Prace. (PL ISSN 0079-4678) **2835**
Poznanskie Towarzystwo Przyjaciol Nauk. Komisja Matematyczno-Przyrodnicza. Prace. (PL ISSN 0137-8996) **3829**, **3051**
Poznanskie Towarzystwo Przyjaciol Nauk. Komisja Nauk Rolniczych i Komisja Nauk Lesnych. Prace. (PL ISSN 0079-4708) **114**, **2106**
Poznanskie Towarzystwo Przyjaciol Nauk. Komisja Nauk Spolecznych. Prace. (PL ISSN 0079-4716) **4383**
Poznanskie Towarzystwo Przyjaciol Nauk. Komisja Technologii Drewna. Prace. (PL ISSN 0079-4724) **2117**
Pozoriste. (BN ISSN 0032-616X) **4637**
Prabuddha Bharata/Awakened India. (II ISSN 0032-6178) **3777**
Praca i Zabezpieczenia Spoleczne. (PL ISSN 0032-6186) **3919**
Praca Szkolna see Ogniwo **1652**
Praca a Mzda. (CS ISSN 0032-6208) **991**
Prace Archeologiczne see Towarzystwo Naukowe w Toruniu. Prace Archeologiczne **287**
Prace Archivum Slaskiej Kultury Muzycznej. (PL) **3575**
Prace Astronomickeho Observatoria na Skalnatom Plese/Contributions of the Astronomical Observatory on Skalnate Pleso. (CS) **368**
Prace COBiRTK see Centralny Osrodek Badan i Rozwoju Techniki Kolejnictwa. Prace **5163**
Prace Geologiczne. (PL ISSN 0079-3361) **1578**
Prace Instytutu Gornictwa Naftowego i Gazownictwa see Instytut Gornictwa Naftowego i Gazownictwa. Prace **3689**
Prace Instytutu Techniki Budowlanej. Kwartalnik. (PL) **1872**, **628**
Prace Jezykoznawcze. (PL ISSN 0079-3485) **2835**
Prace Onomastyczne. (PL ISSN 0079-4775) **2835**
Prace Polonistyczne. (PL ISSN 0079-4791) **2949**
Prace Popularnonaukowe. Biblioteczka Prawnicza. (PL ISSN 0138-0508) **2667**
†Prace Popularnonaukowe. Ekonomia i Organizacja. (PL) **5261**
Prace Popularnonaukowe. Zabytki Polski Polnocnej. (PL ISSN 0138-0516) **340**
Prace Wydzialu Filologiczno-Filozoficznego see Wydzial Filologiczno-Filozoficzny. Prace **3786**
Prace z Dejin Prirodnich Ved. (CS) **2381**
Prachya Pratibha. (II) **3643**
Pracovni Lekarstvi. (CS ISSN 0032-6291) **3143**, **3620**
Practica Otologica Kyoto/Jibi Inkoka Rinsho. (JA ISSN 0032-6313) **3316**
Practical Accountant. (US ISSN 0032-6321) **755**
Practical Accountant Alert. (US) **755**
Practical Accounting see Practical Accountant **755**

Practical Allergy & Immunology. (CN ISSN 0831-0998) 3188
Practical Alternatives. (UK ISSN 0262-4540) 1966
Practical Boat Owner. (UK ISSN 0032-6348) 4528
Practical Caravan. (UK) 4554
Practical Cardiology. (US ISSN 0361-3372) 3211
Practical Caring. (UK) 4416
Practical Cash Management. (US) 795, 755
Practical Christianity see Contact (Aldershot) 4172
Practical Civil Defence see Journal of Practical Civil Defence 1273
Practical Classics. (UK ISSN 0260-2911) 4699
Practical Computing. (UK ISSN 0141-5433) 1399
Practical Conveyancing Precedents. (UK) 2667
Practical Diabetes. (UK ISSN 0266-447X) 3255
Practical Diabetes Digest. (UK ISSN 0960-8893) 3255
Practical Diabetology. (US ISSN 0730-3491) 3255
Practical Education for the Handicapped/Jissen Shogaiji Kyoiku. (JA) 1739
Practical Electronics. (UK ISSN 0032-6372) 1776
Practical English Teaching. (UK ISSN 0260-4752) 1757, 2835
Practical Farmer. (IE) 115
Practical Financial Planning. (US) 795, 960
Practical Fishkeeping. (UK) 2047
Practical Forms and Precedents. (AT ISSN 0048-508X) 2667
Practical Gardening. (UK ISSN 0032-6399) 2137
Practical Gastroenterology. (US ISSN 0277-4208) 3269, 3369
†Practical Guide to Countertrade. (US) 5261
Practical Guide to Individual Income Tax Return Preparation see 1040 Preparation 1112
Practical Guide to Preventing Legal Malpractice. (US) 2667, 3143
Practical Guide to the Use of the European Communities' Scheme of Generalized Tariff Preferences. (EI) 919
The Practical Homeowner. (US ISSN 1042-4601) 2501, 628
Practical Homeowner's Do-It-Yourself Annual. 2449, 628
Practical Homes. (CN ISSN 0226-9597) 628
Practical Horseman. (US ISSN 0090-8762) 4537
Practical Householder. (UK) 628, 2554
†Practical Knowledge. (US ISSN 0032-6410) 5261
†Practical Law Books Review. (US ISSN 0160-8177) 5261
The Practical Lawyer. (US ISSN 0032-6429) 2667
▼The Practical Litigator. (US) 2667
Practical Lubrication and Maintenance see P - P M Technology 5255
Practical Marketing for Printers. (US) 4003, 1050
Practical Methods in Electron Microscopy. (NE) 561
Practical Motorist see Motorist 4697
†Practical Nursing Career. (US) 5261
Practical Optometry. (CN ISSN 1181-6058) 3304
Practical Papers for the Bible Translator. (US ISSN 0260-0943) 2835, 4195
Practical Periodontics and Aesthetic Dentistry. (US) 3240
Practical Pharmacy/Yakkyoku. (JA ISSN 0044-0035) 3740
Practical Photography. (UK ISSN 0032-6445) 3796
The Practical Real Estate Lawyer. (US) 2715
Practical Rural Engineering Technology. see Nongcun Shiyong Gongcheng Jishu 110
Practical Sailor. (US ISSN 0161-8059) 4528

Practical Spectroscopy Series. (US) 1208
Practical Supervision. (US ISSN 0742-7859) 1069
▼Practical Survival. (US) 4554
The Practical Tax Lawyer. (US) 2667, 1104
Practical Television see Television (London, 1934) 1382
Practical Wargamer. (UK ISSN 0953-0592) 4484
Practical Winemaking and Brewing. (UK) 385
Practical Winery see Practical Winery & Vineyard 385
Practical Winery & Vineyard. (US ISSN 0739-8077) 385
Practical Wireless. (UK ISSN 0141-0857) 1378, 1906
Practical Woodworking. (UK ISSN 0032-6488) 640
▼Practice. (UK) 3143, 1024
Practice. (UK ISSN 0950-3153) 4416
Practice (New York). (US) 3919, 685, 4038, 4445
†Practice Applications. (US) 5261
Practice in Prosthodontics/Hotetsu Rinsho. (JA ISSN 0018-6341) 3240
†Practice Marketing & Management. Health Care Edition. (US) 5261
Practice Marketing and Management. Veterinary Edition see Veterinary Management Update 5300
Practice Nurse. (UK ISSN 0953-6612) 3285
Practice Personel Bulletin see Physicians Marketing & Management 3141
Practice, the journal of politics, economics, psychology, sociology and culture see Practice (New York) 3919
Practice Under the California Corporate Securities Laws. (US) 2711, 960
Practiciens et 3eme Age. (FR) 2277
Practicing Anthropology. (US ISSN 0888-4552) 247
Practicing Architect. (US) 305
Practicing C P A. (US) 755
Practicing Manager. (AT ISSN 0159-1193) 1024
Practicus. (DK ISSN 0109-2235) 3143
Practitioners' Child Law Bulletin. (UK ISSN 0954-6421) 2667, 1243
Practising Administrator. (AT ISSN 0157-3357) 1730
Practitioner see N A S S P Practitioner 1729
Practitioner. (UK ISSN 0032-6518) 3143
Practitioners' Child Law Journal see Practioners' Child Law Bulletin 2667
▼Practitioner's Guide to the Oklahoma Uniform Consumer Credit Code. (US) 2667
Praedicta see Israel Customs Import Duty Tariff Rates and Purchase Tax. English Translation and Amendments 870
▼Praeger Series in Political Communications. (US) 3919, 1341
Praeger Series in Political Economy. (US) 3919, 685
▼Praeger Series in Presidential Studies. (US ISSN 1062-0931) 3919
▼Praeger Series in Transformational Politics and Political Science. (US) 3919
Praehistorische Zeitschrift. (GW ISSN 0079-4848) 282
Der Praeparator. (GW ISSN 0032-6542) 1495, 452, 3143
Praesteforeningens Blad. (DK ISSN 0106-6218) 4195
Praevention und Rehabilitation. (GW) 3143
Pragati. (II ISSN 0032-6550) 2949
Prager Nachrichten. (GW ISSN 0344-7006) 2020
Prager Volkszeitung. (CS ISSN 0032-6569) 2020
Pragma's Product Profiles. (US) 1455, 1438

Pragmatics and Beyond see Pragmatics and Beyond New Series 2835
Pragmatics and Beyond Companion Series see Pragmatics and Beyond New Series 2835
Pragmatics and Beyond New Series. (US ISSN 0922-842X) 2835
▼Pragmatics & Cognition. (NE) 2857, 2835
Pragmatics and Discourse Analysis. (US) 2835, 3777, 4038
Pragmatist. (US ISSN 0885-6699) 897
Prague Bulletin of Mathematical Linguistics. (CS ISSN 0032-6585) 2857
Praha. (CS) 2184
Praha - Moskva. (CS ISSN 0032-6593) 3969
Praire. (US) 1321
Prairie. see Caoyuan 2903
Prairie Club Bulletin. (US ISSN 0032-6607) 1495, 4484
Prairie Farmer. (US ISSN 0032-6615) 115
Prairie Farmers Catalogue. (CN ISSN 0831-2338) 164
Prairie Fire. (CN ISSN 0821-1124) 2950
Prairie Forum. (CN ISSN 0317-6282) 1966, 4334
Prairie Gleaner. (US ISSN 0032-6623) 2162
Prairie Gold Rush. (US ISSN 0896-5617) 164, 259
Prairie Harvester. (CN ISSN 0383-7653) 1321
Prairie Hotelier. (CN) 2479
Prairie Hotelman see Prairie Hotelier 2479
Prairie Journal. (CN ISSN 0827-2921) 2950, 3003
Prairie Landscape Magazine. (CN ISSN 0820-6848) 305
Prairie Messenger. (CN ISSN 0032-664X) 4273
Prairie Naturalist. (US ISSN 0091-0376) 4334
Prairie News. (US) 2079, 2093, 2449
Prairie of Flowers. see Hua de Yuanye 2923
Prairie Pedaler. (CN) 4520
Prairie Pioneer. (US) 2162
Prairie Profile. (US) 4783
Prairie Provinces Water Board Annual Report. (CN) 4827
Prairie Rose. (US ISSN 0032-6666) 3285
Prairie Schooner. (US ISSN 0032-6682) 2950
Prairie Scout. (US ISSN 0092-8313) 2419
Prairie Sounds. (CN ISSN 0822-7500) 3575
Prairie Wind. (US) 1966, 1495
Prairie Wool Companion see Weavers 3593
Praise & Prayer Calendar. (AT) 4195
Prajamata Illustrated Weekly. (II) 2201
Prajna. (II ISSN 0554-9884) 1714
†Prajnan. (II ISSN 0032-6690) 5261
Prakalpana Literature. see Prakalpana Sahitya 2950
Prakalpana Sahitya/Prakalpana Literature. (II) 2950
Prakit Jain Institute Research Publication Series. (II ISSN 0554-9906) 4215
†Prakla Seismos Report. (GW ISSN 0933-7660) 5261
Praklit. (IS ISSN 0017-7571) 2667
Prakrit Text Society. Publications. (II) 2950, 2835
Prakriti see Prakriti Vani 3215
Prakriti Vani. (II ISSN 0303-7967) 3215, 2468, 3143
Praksa. (YU ISSN 0032-6704) 4445
Prakseologia. (PL ISSN 0079-4872) 3777
Prakticka Zena. (CS ISSN 0231-6471) 1294
Prakticke Zubni Lekarstvi. (CS ISSN 0032-6720) 3240
Prakticky Lekar. (CS ISSN 0032-6739) 3143
Prakticna Zena. (YU ISSN 0032-6747) 4851

Praktijk Register Accountants (Year). (NE) 755
Praktijkgids. (NE ISSN 0165-0025) 2667
Praktika. (GW ISSN 0179-7298) 2835, 1655
Der Praktiker. (GW) 3429
Praktikus see Urob - Udelej si Sam 4612
Der Praktische Arzt. (AU ISSN 0048-5128) 3143
Praktische Betriebswirtschaft. (SZ ISSN 0079-4880) 1024
Praktische Chirurgie. (GW ISSN 0079-4899) 3382
Praktische Kieferorthopaedie. (GW ISSN 0931-6965) 3240
Praktische Landtechnik. (AU) 115
Praktische Metallographie. (GW ISSN 0032-678X) 3417
Der Praktische Schaedlingsbekaempfer. (GW ISSN 0032-6801) 190
Der Praktische Tierarzt. (GW ISSN 0032-681X) 4814
Praktisk Oekonomi see Praktisk Oekonomi & Ledelse 685
Praktisk Oekonomi & Ledelse. (NO) 685
Praktiskt Butiksarbete. (SW ISSN 0347-3899) 2093
†Praktisyn. (SA) 5261
Praline. (GW ISSN 0032-6828) 2190
Pram and Nursery Trader Year Book see Toy Directory 2282
Pramana. (II ISSN 0304-4289) 3829
Prameny a Studie. (CS) 115
Prameny Ceske a Slovenske Lingvistiky. Rada Ceska. (CS ISSN 0079-4902) 2835
Pramo. (GW ISSN 0032-6852) 1294
Prampra. (II) 2058, 2950
Prana. (NE ISSN 0165-4373) 2513
Prana Yoga Life. (US ISSN 0149-953X) 3777
Prapor see Berezil 2859
†Prasa Techniczna. (PL) 5261
Prasar. (II) 1686
Prashasnika. (II) 4070
Prather Bulletin. (US) 2162
Pratibha India. (II ISSN 0970-2849) 2950, 340
Pratica Aziendale. (IT) 755, 1024
Pratica Odontoiatrica. (IT) 3240
Praticien du Sud Ouest. (FR) 3143
Pratique. (FR) 2561, 2501
Pratique. (UK ISSN 0269-1396) 3757
Pratique Medicale et Chirurgicale de l'Animal de Compagnie. (FR) 4814, 3713
Prato Pagano. (IT) 2950
Prato - Storia ed Arte. (IT ISSN 0032-6925) 2381, 341
Pratt Journal of Architecture. (US ISSN 0883-7279) 305
Prattfolio. (US) 1321
Pratt's Guide to Venture Capital Sources. (US ISSN 0884-1616) 960
Prausis. (NO) 2588
Pravasi. (II) 2201
Pravna Misal. (BU ISSN 0032-6968) 2667
Pravnehistoricke Studie. (CS ISSN 0079-4929) 2667
Pravnicke Studie. (CS ISSN 0551-9039) 2667
Pravnik/Lawyer. (CS ISSN 0324-7007) 2667
Pravny Obzor/Law Review. (CS ISSN 0032-6984) 2667
Pravo a Zakonnost. (CS) 2667
Pravoslavlje/Orthodoxy. (YU) 4287
Pravoslavnaya Rus' (US ISSN 0032-7018) 4216
Pravoslavnaya Zhyzn/Orthodox Life. (US ISSN 0032-6992) 4217
Pravoslavno Misao. (YU ISSN 0032-700X) 4217
Pravoslavny Theologicky Sbornik. (CS ISSN 0079-4937) 4217
Pravslavni Misionar/Orthodox Missionary. (YU) 4287, 4195
Prawo. (PL) 2667
Prawo i Zycie. (PL ISSN 0551-9101) 2667
Praxis. (US) 341, 3515, 4637
Praxis. (CR) 3777
Praxis. (IT) 3919

Praxis. (PH ISSN 0116-709X) **3919**
Die Praxis. (GW) **4416,** 1739
Praxis Computer. (GW ISSN 0179-1133) **1399**
Praxis - Depesche. (GW) **3143**
Praxis der Anaesthesiologie und Intensivmedizin. (GW ISSN 0932-9196) **3192**
Praxis der Chirurgie. (US) **3383**
Praxis der Kinderpsychologie und Kinderpsychiatrie. (GW ISSN 0032-7034) **3350, 4038**
Praxis der Kinderpsychologie und Kinderpsychiatrie. Beihefte. (GW ISSN 0085-5073) **4038,** 3350
Praxis der Klinischen Verhaltensmedizin und Rehabilitation. (GW ISSN 0933-842X) **1739,** 3143
Praxis der Mathematik. (GW ISSN 0032-7042) **3051,** 1757
Praxis der Naturwissenschaften. Biologie. (GW ISSN 0341-8510) **452,** 1757
Praxis der Naturwissenschaften. Chemie. (GW ISSN 0342-8745) **1186,** 1757
Praxis der Naturwissenschaften. Physik.(GW ISSN 0177-8374) **3829,** 1757
Praxis der Psychomotorik. (GW ISSN 0170-060X) **1740, 2290**
Praxis der Psychotherapie und Psychosomatik. (GW ISSN 0171-791X) **3350, 4039**
Praxis der Verkuendigung. (GW) **1686**
Praxis der Werbung. (GW) **37**
Praxis des Bundesgerichts. (SZ ISSN 0254-9441) **4070,** 2667
Praxis des Neusprachlichen Unterrichts.(GW ISSN 0032-7085) **2835,** 1757
Praxis des Rechnungswesens. (GW ISSN 0341-7948) **685**
Praxis Deutsch. (GW ISSN 0721-8400) **2835,** 1757
Praxis Ergotherapie. (GW ISSN 0932-9692) **1740**
Praxis Geographie. (GW ISSN 0171-5178) **2259,** 1757
Praxis Geschichte. (GW ISSN 0933-5374) **1757,** 2319
Praxis Grundschule. (GW ISSN 0170-3722) **1757**
▼Praxis Handbuch Personal. (GW ISSN 0940-8428) **685**
Praxis in der Gemeinde. (GW ISSN 0172-7478) **4273**
Praxis International. (UK ISSN 0260-8448) **3919,** 3777
Praxis Juridique et Religion. (FR ISSN 0758-802X) **2667,** 4195
Praxis-Kurier see Selecta **3152**
▼Praxis Schule 5-10. (GW ISSN 0936-6970) **1757**
Praxis Spiel und Gruppe. (GW ISSN 0934-5256) **1655,** 1243, 4039
Praxis und Klinik der Pneumologie see Pneumologie **3366**
Praxis Verkehrserziehung. (GW) **1655**
Prayaasa. (II ISSN 0303-2906) **2950**
Prayer Book Society Newsletter. (UK) **4195**
Prayerline. (US) **4246**
Prayers for Worship. (US ISSN 0274-600X) **4273,** 4246
Praying. (US) **4273**
Prazsky Sbornik Historicky. (CS) **2381,** 282
Pre-. (US ISSN 1042-0304) **4007**
Pre- and Peri-Natal Psychology Journal.(US ISSN 0883-3095) **3295,** 598
Pre-Columbian Research Resources Review see Caribe Magazine **321**
Pre-K Today. (US ISSN 0888-3009) **1655,** 1464, 1479, 1691
Pre Law Journal. (US ISSN 0741-1162) **2668**
†Pre-Parent Adviser. (US) **5261**
Pre Recorded Cassette News see P R C News **1385**
Pre-Retirement Choice see Choice **2271**
†Pre-School & Kindergarten Market-Center. (US) **5261**
Pre-School Playgroups Association North West Region Newsletter see P.P.A. North West Region Newsletter **5255**

Pre-Text. (US ISSN 0731-0714) **2835**
Preacher's Quarterly see Worship and Preaching **4253**
Preaching. (US ISSN 0882-7036) **4195**
Precambrian Research. (NE ISSN 0301-9268) **1578**
Precancel Forum. (US ISSN 0273-5415) **3757**
Precancel Stamp Collector. (US) **3757**
Precast - Prestressed Concrete Institute Journal see P C I Journal **627**
Precios del Mercado Mundial: Pulpa, Papel y Carton. (CU) **821**
Precious Metals Data Base. (US) **960**
Precipitation. see Opady Atmosferyczne **3440**
Precis. (US ISSN 0887-8781) **305**
Precisely. (US ISSN 0163-4631) **2950**
Precision. (SZ ISSN 0255-6944) **2524**
Precision and Intelligence. (JA) **1938**
Precision Engineering. (US ISSN 0141-6359) **1834**
Precision Guided Munitions. (US) **3468**
Precision Machinery. (US ISSN 1045-4160) **1410,** 1415
Precision Machinery and Robotics see Precision Machinery **1410**
†Precision Metal. (US ISSN 0032-714X) **5261**
Precision Shooting. (US ISSN 0048-5144) **4484**
Precision Toolmaker. (UK ISSN 0264-4703) **3417**
†Precos Medios do Boi Gordo e La. (BL ISSN 0100-5162) **5261**
Precos Pagos Pelos Agricultores. (BL ISSN 0302-5195) **156**
Precos Recebidos Pelos Agricultores. (BL ISSN 0100-5219) **156**
Predi-Briefs. (US ISSN 0551-9276) **735,** 20
Predicament. (US) **4484**
Predicasts Basebook. (US ISSN 0738-9906) **735,** 20
Predicasts Company Thesaurus. (US ISSN 0739-1862) **735,** 20
Predicasts Electronic Trends see Electronics Trends (Cleveland) **5185**
Predicasts F & S Index Europe. (US ISSN 0270-4536) **735,** 20
Predicasts F & S Index International. (US ISSN 0270-4528) **735,** 20
Predicasts F & S Index of Corporate Change. (US ISSN 0744-2785) **735,** 20
Predicasts F & S Index United States. (US ISSN 0270-4544) **735,** 20
Predicasts Forecasts. (US ISSN 0278-0135) **736,** 20
Predicasts Overview of Markets and Technology. (US ISSN 0161-8032) **1846,** 20, 1202
Predicasts Source Directory. (US ISSN 0092-7767) **736,** 20
Prediction. (UK ISSN 0032-7182) **3670**
Prediction Annual. (UK ISSN 0079-4953) **3670**
Der Prediger und Katechet. (GW ISSN 0032-7212) **4273**
Predigtstudien. (GW ISSN 0079-4961) **4195**
Predskolska Vychova. (CS ISSN 0032-7220) **1655**
Preet Lari. (II ISSN 0032-7239) **2201**
Prefabbricare. (IT ISSN 0032-7247) **628**
†Preface. (UK ISSN 0032-7263) **5261**
Prefectural Economic Statistics. (JA) **736**
Preferred Provider Organization Letter see P P O Letter **684**
▼Preferred Stock Journal. (US) **960**
†Preferred Traveller. (US) **5261**
Pregled (Sarajevo, 1910). (BN ISSN 0032-7271) **4383**
Pregled (Sarajevo, 1964). (BN ISSN 0350-1256) **2117**
†Pregled Prava Zemalja u Razvoju. (YU) **5261**

Pregled Problema Mentalno Retardiranih Osoba. (CI ISSN 0032-7298) **3350**
Pregled Sudske Prakse. (CI) **2668**
Pregled Svetske Privrede/World Economy Survey. (YU) **879**
†Pregled Zakonodavstva u Stranim Drzavama. (YU ISSN 0032-731X) **5261**
Pregnancy. see Embarazo **3291**
Pregnancy. (AT ISSN 1035-5448) **3296**
†Pregnancy. (UK ISSN 0261-4898) **5261**
Pregnancy, Birth and the Next 6 Months see Pregnancy **3296**
Pregon. (SP) **2880**
†Pregon de la T F P. (Sociedad Argentina de Defensa de la Tradicion, Familia y Propiedad) (AG) **5261**
Pregonero Hispano. (CN) **2020**
Prehistoria see Noticiario Arqueologico Hispanico **280**
Prehistoric Archaeology and Ecology. (US) **282,** 452
Prehistoric Society, London. Proceedings. (UK ISSN 0079-497X) **282**
†Prehled Lesnicke a Myslivecke Literatury/Review of Literature on Forestry and Game Management. (CS ISSN 0032-7336) **5261**
Prehled Pedagogicke Literatury. (CS ISSN 0139-9489) **1679,** 409
†Prehledy Informativni Literatury. (CS ISSN 0862-1187) **5261**
Prehledy Potravinarske Literatury/Survey of Food Literature. (CS ISSN 0032-7379) **2085,** 20
Prehospital and Disaster Medicine. (US ISSN 1049-023X) **3143,** 2468, 3311, 4110
▼Prehospital Care Reports. (US) **3144**
Prehrambeno-Tehnoloska i Biotehnoloska Revija/Food Technology and Biotechnology Review. (CI ISSN 0352-9193) **491,** 2079
▼Preisliste der Wiener Wertpapierboerse - Handel mit Optionen und Finanzterminkontrakten. (AU) **960**
▼Preisliste der Wiener Wertpapierboerse - Sonstiger Wertpapierhandel. (AU) **960**
Preiswert & Attraktiv see P & A **3913**
Prelaw Handbook. Official Law School Guide see Official Guide to U.S. Law Schools **1713**
Preliminary Determination of Epicenters see U.S. National Earthquake Information Service. Preliminary Determination of Epicenters, Monthly Listing **1596**
Preliminary Statement of Canadian International Trade. (CN ISSN 0828-1998) **736**
Prelo. (PO) **2214**
Premenstrual Syndrome Access Newsletter see P M S Access Newsletter **3295**
Premiere. (CN) **3515,** 1378
Premiere (New York). (US) **3515**
Premio Grandes Educadores Brasileiros.(BL) **1655**
Premium - Incentive Business see Business and Incentive Strategies **29**
Premium Merchandising Club of New York, Inc. Newsletter see P M C of N Y Newsletter **1049**
Prenatal Diagnosis. (UK ISSN 0197-3851) **3296**
Prenatal Educator. (US) **3325**
Prensa Confidencial. (AG ISSN 0032-7433) **879**
Prensa Medica. (BO) **3144**
Prensa Medica (Caracas). (VE) **3144**
Prensa Medica Argentina. (AG ISSN 0032-745X) **3144**
Prensa Obrera. (AG) **3919**
La Prensa San Diego. (US ISSN 0738-9183) **2020**
Prent 190. (NE ISSN 0032-7476) **4003,** 341
Prep School. (UK ISSN 0963-8601) **1656**
Preparative Biochemistry. (US ISSN 0032-7484) **481**

Preparative Chromatography. (US ISSN 0890-9075) **1208**
Preparatory Schools Review see Prep School **1656**
Prepared Foods. (US ISSN 0747-2536) **2079**
Prepared Foods Buyers' Guide see Prepared Foods Food Industry Sourcebook **2079**
Prepared Foods Food Industry Sourcebook. (US) **2079,** 1150
Preparing for the Future: E S A Technology Quarterly. (NE) **60**
Prepodavanie Istorii v Shkole. (RU ISSN 0132-0696) **2319,** 1757
Prepravni a Tarifni Vestnik/Transportation and Tariff News. (CS ISSN 0032-7514) **4655**
Prepress Bulletin. (US ISSN 8750-2224) **4003**
Preprints of Papers Presented at National Meeting - American Chemical Society. Division of Environmental Chemistry see American Chemical Society. Division of Environmental Chemistry.
Preprints of Papers **1169**
Prepublications. (DK ISSN 0900-9507) **2835,** 2319, 2950
Presa Diretta. (IT) **4699**
Presa Noastra. (RM) **4134**
Presbyterian. (US) **4247**
Presbyterian Banner. (AT ISSN 0729-3542) **4247**
Presbyterian Church in America Messenger see P C A Messenger **4246**
Presbyterian Church in Canada. General Assembly. Acts and Proceedings. (CN ISSN 0079-4996) **4195**
Presbyterian Herald. (UK ISSN 0032-7530) **4247**
Presbyterian Newsletter. (CM) **4247**
Presbyterian Outlook. (US ISSN 0032-7565) **4247**
Presbyterian Record. (CN ISSN 0032-7573) **4247**
Presbyterian Survey. (US ISSN 0032-759X) **4247**
Presbyterion. (US) **4247**
Preschool Bible Teacher A. (US) **4247**
Preschool Bible Teacher B. (US ISSN 0732-944X) **4247**
Preschool Bible Teacher C. (US ISSN 0732-9458) **4247**
Preschool Education. see Xueqian Jiaoyu **1672**
Preschool Leadership. (US ISSN 0162-4393) **4247**
†Preschool Patterns. (US) **5261**
†Preschool Perspectives. (US ISSN 0748-4054) **5261**
Prescribers' Journal. (UK ISSN 0032-7611) **3740**
Prescription and O T C Pharmaceuticals: The Pink Sheet. (US) **3741**
Prescription Drug Industry Fact Book see P M A Statistical Factbook **3748**
Prescription Products Guide. (AT ISSN 0818-4445) **3741**
Prescription Proprietaries Guide for Health Professionals see Prescription Products Guide **3741**
Presek. (XV ISSN 0351-6652) **4334**
Presenca Filosofica. (BL) **3777**
Presence. (CN ISSN 1188-5580) **4195**
Presence Africaine. (FR ISSN 0032-7638) **2880**
Presence Croix-Rouge. (FR ISSN 0301-0260) **4416**
Presence de Gabriel Marcel. (FR) **3777**
Presence de Gabriel Marcel. Cahier. (FR) **3778**
Presence de l'Enseignement Agricole Prive. (FR ISSN 0339-0055) **115,** 1656
Presence des Lettres et des Arts. (FR ISSN 0336-321X) **2950**
Presence du Cinema Francais. (FR) **3515**
Presence Francophone. (CN ISSN 0048-5195) **2950**
Presence Orthodoxe. (FR ISSN 0032-4922) **4287**

▼Presence: Teleoperators and Virtual Environments. (US ISSN 1054-7460) **1457**
Presences. (BE) **879**, 1024
Presencia. (SP ISSN 0032-7689) **2218**
Presencia. (CK) **4196**
Presencia Negra. (CK) **2020**
Presencia Universitaria. (HO) **1714**
Present. (GW ISSN 0032-7697) **356**, 341, 2282
†Present Tense. (US ISSN 0092-4091) **5261**
Present Truth and Herald of Christ's Epiphany. (US ISSN 0032-7700) **4287**
†Presentation Business News. (US) **5261**
Presentation Products Magazine. (US ISSN 1041-9780) **37**, 1050
Presente. (GW) **2180**
Presenter's Handbook/Guide du Diffuseur. (CN) **4783**
Presenza. (IT ISSN 0478-1376) **1714**
Presenza Economica. (VE) **821**
Presenza Pastorale. (IT ISSN 0032-7727) **4273**
Presenza Tecnica. (IT) **1834**, 305
Preservation Forum. (US ISSN 0893-9403) **305**, 2494
Preservation in Action. (UK ISSN 0267-4343) **305**
Preservation Law Reporter. (US ISSN 0882-715X) **1966**, 2668
Preservation New Mexico. (US) **2419**
Preservation News. (US ISSN 0032-7735) **305**
Preservation Perspective. (US) **305**, 2419
Preservation Press see New Orleans Preservation in Print **304**
Preservation Progress (Charleston). (US ISSN 0478-1392) **305**
Preservation Progress (Crownsville, MD). (US ISSN 1051-0192) **2419**
Preserved Milk. (UK ISSN 0141-223X) **203**
▼Preserving Lands: Legal Issues. (US) **2715**
PreShipment Testing. (US ISSN 1043-2841) **3651**, 4655
President. (JA ISSN 0032-7751) **1024**
President. (NR) **2880**
President Transport World. (US) **4713**, 2440
Presidential - Air Destinations. (US) **4803**
Presidential Museum. News and Views. (US) **3532**, 341, 2419, 3919
Presidential Studies Quarterly. (US ISSN 0360-4918) **3919**
President's Council of Physical Fitness & Sports. Newsletter. (US) **3807**
▼President's Fiscal Year (Year) Budget and Its Impact on the American Family. (US) **1104**
Presidents' Journal. (US ISSN 8755-8939) **2419**, 2440, 4783
President's Letter see Canadian Manufacturers Association. President's Letter **1073**
President's Letter see Arkansas Hospital Association. President's Letter **2459**
President's Log. (US) **755**, 1024, 2479
President's National Urban Policy Report. (US ISSN 0163-8602) **2494**
President's Report. (US) **796**, 1507
†The President's Team. (US) **5261**
Preslia. (CS ISSN 0032-7786) **515**
Press. (CN) **1321**
†Press and the People. (UK) **5261**
Press Braille, Adult see Braille Books (Large Print Edition) **2285**
†Press Briefing. (UK ISSN 0269-1752) **5261**
Press Circles. see Xinwenjie **2577**
Press Council of India Review. (II) **2574**
Press Council of the Republic of China. (National Press Council of the Republic of China) (CH) **2574**
Press Digest. (UK) **1540**, 3748
Press in India. (II ISSN 0445-6653) **409**
Press Independent. (CN) **2020**

▼Press-kur'er. (RU) **2215**
Press Magazine. (US ISSN 0744-3161) **1287**, 4484
Press Press Magazine. (AT ISSN 0819-1565) **4637**, 1531, 3575
Press Review. (CN) **2574**
Press, The Law and Beyond. Series: Esso Lecture: No.1. (AT) **2513**
Press Woman. (US ISSN 0032-7824) **2574**
Press Working/Puresu Gijutsu. (JA ISSN 0387-3544) **3022**
Presse/Pers. (BE ISSN 0478-1546) **2574**
Presse Actualite see Medias Pouvoirs **2572**
†Presse der Sowjetunion. (GW ISSN 0032-7840) **5261**
Presse du Vin-Vinetec. (FR ISSN 0221-301X) **385**
Presse-Inter. (BE) **3596**, 3778
La Presse Medicale. (FR ISSN 0755-4982) **3144**
La Presse Medicale: Edizione Italiana. (IT ISSN 0393-0653) **3144**
Presse-Portraets. (GW ISSN 0176-5248) **409**, 4134
Presse Report. (GW ISSN 0341-8073) **4134**, 2574
Presse Specialisee Suisse. see Schweizer Fachpresse **2575**
Presse Thermale et Climatique. (FR ISSN 0032-7875) **3144**
Presse und Sprache. (GW) **2574**
Presse Voyages. (CN) **4783**
Pressehandbuch (Year). (AU) **4134**, 2574
Pressens Aarbog. (DK ISSN 0106-6579) **2381**, 1341
Pressens Tidning. (SW ISSN 0032-7883) **2574**
Presseschau Ostwirtschaft. (AU ISSN 0032-7891) **879**
Pressespiegel aus Zeitungen und Zeitschriften der DDR. (GW) **2190**, 20
Pressespiegel Blicknach Drueben see Pressespiegel aus Zeitungen und Zeitschriften der DDR **2190**
Pressespiegel zur Rechtsentwicklung. (GW) **3946**
PressNews. (US) **2574**
Presstime. (US ISSN 0194-3243) **2574**, 4003
Pressure (Bethesda). (US ISSN 0889-0242) **3144**
Pressure Sensitive Tape Council. Technical Seminar. Proceedings. (US) **4293**, 3665, 3867
Prestige. (IT) **2206**
Prestige. (UK) **2479**
Presto. (SZ) **3575**
Presupuesto y Gasto Publico. (SP ISSN 0210-5977) **1104**
Preto & Branco/Brazilian Chess Magazine. (BL) **4484**
Pretres Diocesains. (FR ISSN 0032-7956) **4196**
Pretrial Reporter. (US ISSN 0193-4015) **1521**
Preussenland. (GW ISSN 0032-7972) **2381**
Prevenir les Risques du Metier. (FR) **3620**
†Prevenire. (Italian translation of: Prevention) (IT) **5261**
Prevent. (UK ISSN 0300-2659) **4110**
Preventing School Failure. (US ISSN 1045-988X) **1740**, 2284
Preventing Sexual Abuse. (US ISSN 0886-6694) **4039**, 1656
Prevention. (US ISSN 0032-8006) **3807**
Prevention au Canada see Safety Canada **4112**
Prevention des Incendies Canada. Rapport Public. see Fire Prevention Canada. Public Report **2032**
Prevention in Human Services. (US ISSN 0270-3114) **4051**, 20, 4118
Prevention of Food Adulteration Cases. (II) **2668**, 2080, 3741
Prevention Pipeline. (US) **1540**, 1538, 1740
Prevention Routiere. (FR ISSN 0032-8022) **4110**, 4700

Prevention's Medical Care Yearbook. (US) **3144**
Preventique. (FR) **3620**
Preventive Medicine. (US ISSN 0091-7435) **3144**, 4110
†Preventive Medicine Quarterly. (US) **5261**
Preventive Pediatrics. (IS ISSN 0334-7524) **3325**
Preventive Veterinary Medicine. (NE ISSN 0167-5877) **4814**
Prevenzione e Assistenza Dentale. (IT) **3240**
Prevenzione e Salute. (IT) **3807**
Prevenzione Stomatologica see Prevenzione e Assistenza Dentale **3240**
Previdenza Agricola. (IT ISSN 0032-8057) **115**
Previdenza Sociale. (IT ISSN 0032-8065) **2540**
Previdenza Sociale nell'Agricoltura. (IT ISSN 0478-1805) **156**
Previdenza Sociale nell'Artigianato. (IT ISSN 0032-809X) **2540**
Preview (Ann Arbor). (US ISSN 0899-9821) **2779**, 2950
Preview (Northbrook). (US ISSN 0738-0690) **1050**
Preview (Tempe). (US) **1538**
Preview Bermuda. (BM ISSN 0048-5268) **4783**, 2479
Preview of United States Supreme Court Cases. (US ISSN 0363-0048) **2668**
Preview Theater Brochure. (US) **3515**
Previews of Heat and Mass Transfer. (US ISSN 0094-9477) **1846**, 20, 1858
Previsioni a Breve Termine. (IT) **879**
Previsions Glissantes Detaillees. (FR) **879**
Previsions Glissantes Detaillees en Perspectives a Moyen Terme. (FR) **879**
Previsions Glissantes Detaillees en Perspectives Macroeconomiques a Court et Moyen Terme (Year). (FR) **879**
Previsions Glissantes Detaillees en Perspectives Sectorielles (Vol.35): Sante. (FR) **879**, 3144
Previsions Glissantes Detaillees en Perspectives Sectorielles (Vol.1): Agriculture. (FR) **880**
Previsions Glissantes Detaillees en Perspectives Sectorielles (Vol.2): Industries Agro-Alimentaires. (FR) **880**
Previsions Glissantes Detaillees en Perspectives Sectorielles (Vol.3): Textile - Habillement - Cuir. (FR) **880**, 1294, 2738
Previsions Glissantes Detaillees en Perspectives Sectorielles (Vol.4): Industries du Bois et de l'Ameublement. (FR) **880**, 2117, 2561
Previsions Glissantes Detaillees en Perspectives Sectorielles (Vol.5): Construction de Machines. (FR) **880**, 628, 3022
Previsions Glissantes Detaillees en Perspectives Sectorielles (Vol.6): Equipement Industriel. (FR) **880**, 3022
Previsions Glissantes Detaillees en Perspectives Sectorielles (Vol.7): Mecanique de Precision. (FR) **880**, 3022
Previsions Glissantes Detaillees en Perspectives Sectorielles (Vol.8): Fonderie et Transformation des Metaux. (FR) **880**, 3418
Previsions Glissantes Detaillees en Perspectives Sectorielles (Vol.9): Construction Electrique et Electronique Grand-Public. (FR) **880**, 1906
Previsions Glissantes Detaillees en Perspectives Sectorielles (Vol.10): Construction Electrique Professionnelle. (FR) **880**, 1906
Previsions Glissantes Detaillees en Perspectives Sectorielles (Vol.11): Construction Electronique Professionnelle. (FR) **880**, 1906

Previsions Glissantes Detaillees en Perspectives Sectorielles (Vol.12): Construction Automobile. (FR) **880**, 4700
Previsions Glissantes Detaillees en Perspectives Sectorielles (Vol.13): Construction Aerospatiale. (FR) **880**, 60
Previsions Glissantes Detaillees en Perspectives Sectorielles (Vol.14): Energie. (FR) **880**, 1794
Previsions Glissantes Detaillees en Perspectives Sectorielles (Vol.15): Siderurgie et Premiere Transformation de l'Acier. (FR) **880**, 3418
Previsions Glissantes Detaillees en Perspectives Sectorielles (Vol.16): Industrie des Non-Ferreux. (FR) **880**, 3418
Previsions Glissantes Detaillees en Perspectives Sectorielles (Vol.17): Chimie Minerale. (FR) **880**, 1214
Previsions Glissantes Detaillees en Perspectives Sectorielles (Vol.18): Chimie Organique. (FR) **880**, 1222
Previsions Glissantes Detaillees en Perspectives Sectorielles (Vol.19): Parachimie et Pharmacie. (FR) **881**, 3741
Previsions Glissantes Detaillees en Perspectives Sectorielles (Vol.20): Transformation du Caoutchouc et des Matieres Plastiques. (FR) **881**, 3867, 4293
Previsions Glissantes Detaillees en Perspectives Sectorielles (Vol.21): Industrie du Verre. (FR) **881**, 1165
Previsions Glissantes Detaillees en Perspectives Sectorielles (Vol.22): Industrie des Pates, Papiers et Cartons. (FR) **881**, 3665
Previsions Glissantes Detaillees en Perspectives Sectorielles (Vol.23): Emballages. (FR) **881**, 3651
Previsions Glissantes Detaillees en Perspectives Sectorielles (Vol.24): Logement. (FR) **881**, 2494
Previsions Glissantes Detaillees en Perspectives Sectorielles (Vol.25): Batiments d'Activite. (FR) **881**, 628
Previsions Glissantes Detaillees en Perspectives Sectorielles (Vol.26): Travaux Publics. (FR) **881**, 1872
Previsions Glissantes Detaillees en Perspectives Sectorielles (Vol.27): Materiaux de Construction I. (FR) **881**, 628
Previsions Glissantes Detaillees en Perspectives Sectorielles (Vol.28): Materiaux et Composants de Construction II. (FR) **881**, 628
Previsions Glissantes Detaillees en Perspectives Sectorielles (Vol.29): Industries de la Communication. (FR) **881**, 1341
Previsions Glissantes Detaillees en Perspectives Sectorielles (Vol.30): Banques. (FR) **881**, 796
Previsions Glissantes Detaillees en Perspectives Sectorielles (Vol.31): Assurances. (FR) **881**, 2540
Previsions Glissantes Detaillees en Perspectives Sectorielles (Vol.32): Commerce. (FR) **881**
Previsions Glissantes Detaillees en Perspectives Sectorielles (Vol.33): Transports. (FR) **881**, 4655
Previsions Glissantes Detaillees en Perspectives Sectorielles (Vol.34): Tourisme, Hotellerie, Restauration, Loisirs. (FR) **881**, 4783
Previsions Glissantes Detaillees en Perspectives Sectorielles (Vol.36): Services Publics. (FR) **881**, 4070
Previsions Glissantes Detaillees en Perspectives Sectorielles (Vol.37): Services aux Entreprises. (FR) **881**
Previsions Glissantes Detaillees Horizon 1990 see France dans l'Europe de 1993 **666**
Previsoes Ionosfericas M U F. (BL ISSN 0032-812X) **1378**
Prevodilac. (YU ISSN 0351-8892) **2835**
Prevoyance. (HT) **3620**, 4110
Prevue. (US ISSN 0199-9257) **3516**, 341, 3575

Prezentacje. (PL ISSN 0137-3609) **4445**, 3919
Prezzi dei Materiali e delle Opere Edili in Ferrara. (IT ISSN 1120-3919) **821**
Priamur'e Moe. (RU) **2950**
Priatel' (CS) **2835**
Pribory i Sistemy Upravleniya. (RU ISSN 0032-8154) **1438**
Pribory i Tekhnika Eksperimenta. (RU ISSN 0032-8162) **2524**
Price Guide (Dubuque). (US) **259**
Price Guide Presents. (US ISSN 1044-4629) **4700**, 4747
Price Guide to Baseball Collectibles *see* The Sport Americana Price Guide to Baseball Collectibles **2442**
Price Guide to Wallace Nutting Pictures.(US) **3796**, 259
Price Index for the Manufacturing Sector *see* Cyprus. Department of Statistics and Research. Industrial Statistics **712**
Price Indexes Monthly. (JA ISSN 0386-6297) **736**, 796
Price Trends of Food Ingredients Newsletter. (US ISSN 0194-2972) **2080**
Price Waterhouse Review. (US ISSN 0032-8170) **755**
Prices and Earnings Around the Globe. (SZ) **999**
Prices of Agricultural Products and Selected Inputs in Europe and North America. (UN) **156**, 881
Pricing Advisor. (US ISSN 0748-4755) **1507**, 1050
Pride. (US) **1287**
Pride (Collingwood). (AT ISSN 1032-0229) **3222**
Pride Institute Journal of Long Term Health Care *see* Pride Institute Journal of Long Term Home Health Care **2468**
Pride Institute Journal of Long Term Home Health Care. (US) **2468**, 2277
Prier. (FR) **4196**
Priest. (US ISSN 0032-8200) **4273**
Priesterjahrheft. (GW ISSN 0172-0929) **4273**
Priests and People. (UK) **4273**
Prikazi in Studije. (XV ISSN 0032-8227) **4583**
Prikladnaya Biokhimiya i Mikrobiologiya.(RU ISSN 0555-1099) **481**, 556
Prikladnaya Geofizika. (RU) **1593**
Prikladnaya Matematika i Mekhanika. (RU ISSN 0032-8235) **3051**
Prikladnaya Mekhanika. (KR ISSN 0032-8243) **1938**
Prikladnaya Mekhanika i Priborostroenie. (RU) **3845**
Prilozi/Contributions. (BN ISSN 0350-1159) **282**, 897, 2381
Prilozi za Istrazivanje Hrvatske Filozofske Bastine. (CI ISSN 0350-2791) **3778**
Prilozi za Knjizevnost, Jezik, Istoriju i Folklor. (YU ISSN 0350-6673) **2835**, 2058, 2381, 2950
La Prim Holstein. (FR) **203**
Prima. (FR ISSN 0293-2407) **1294**
†Prima. (FI ISSN 0359-6079) **5261**
†Prima Ballerina. (US) **5261**
Prima Comunicazione. (IT) **1341**, 37, 2574
Prima Liv. (SW) **4484**, 1069
Prima Pagina. (IT) **685**
Prima Pagina International *see* Prima Pagina **685**
Prima Vita. (GW ISSN 0179-7360) **3807**
Primal Institute Newsletter. (US ISSN 0164-5056) **4039**
Primary & Middle School Equipment. (UK) **1656**
Primary Cardiology. (US ISSN 0363-5104) **3211**
Primary Care. (JA ISSN 0914-8426) **3144**
Primary Care & Cancer. (US ISSN 0743-8176) **3201**
Primary Care: Clinics in Office Practice. (US ISSN 0095-4543) **3144**
Primary Care Physician's Guide to Practical Gastroenterology *see* Practical Gastroenterology **3269**

†Primary Care Records. (US) **5261**
Primary Care Reports. (US ISSN 0893-9837) **3325**
Primary Care Rheumatology. (US) **3369**
▼Primary D A T A. (Design and Technology Association) (UK ISSN 0964-8941) **1757**, 4606
Primary Days. (US ISSN 0032-8278) **4196**
Primary Education. (AT ISSN 0048-5284) **1656**
Primary Education Directory. (UK ISSN 0950-4508) **1697**
Primary Education Review *see* N U T Education Review **1649**
Primary Geographer. (UK ISSN 0956-277X) **2259**
▼Primary Health Care Management. (UK ISSN 0960-250X) **3144**
Primary Industry Newsletter. (AT ISSN 0155-9222) **156**
†Primary Journal K-7. (AT) **5261**
▼Primary Life. (UK ISSN 0962-8789) **1656**
Primary Point. (US) **4215**, 3596
Primary Producers' Guide. (AT) **831**
The Primary Source. (US ISSN 0741-6563) **2779**, 1495, 2419
Primary Sources *see* Tax Management Primary Sources **1109**
Primary Sources & Original Works. (US ISSN 1042-8216) **2779**
Primary Treasure. (US ISSN 0032-8316) **1243**
Primary Trend. (US) **960**
Primate News. (US ISSN 0032-8324) **590**
Primate Report. (GW ISSN 0343-3528) **247**, 590
Primates. (JA ISSN 0032-8332) **590**, 247, 4039, 4814
Primavera. (IT ISSN 0032-8340) **1263**
Primavera (Chicago). (US ISSN 0364-7609) **4851**, 2950, 3400
Prime. (PP) **3051**
Prime Areas. (CN ISSN 0032-8359) **1656**
Prime Beef. (AT ISSN 1030-1992) **224**
Prime of Life. (US) **4445**, 4416
Prime Real Estate. (US) **4154**
Prime Time. (AT ISSN 0729-5545) **2277**, 2172
Prime Times. (US) **4416**
Primer of Labor Relations. (US) **991**, 2668
Primer on Employee Retirement Income Security Act. (US) **991**, 2711
Primera Luz. (SP) **4196**, 1263
Primera Plana. (AG ISSN 0032-8375) **2170**
Primerjalna Knjizevnost. (XV ISSN 0351-1189) **2950**
PrimeTime. (CN) **1378**
▼PrimeTime Living. (US) **2277**
Primeval Sculpture. (IT) **247**, 341, 2319
Primi Piani. (IT) **3575**, 341, 4334, 4783
Primicia. (BO ISSN 0032-8383) **2175**
Primitiae. (AT ISSN 0726-4399) **1279**
Primo *see* Real Times **2233**
Primo Maggio. (IT) **3919**, 4445
Primorska Srecanja. (YU ISSN 0350-5723) **2880**
Primroses. (US ISSN 0162-6671) **2137**
▼Primus. (US ISSN 1051-1970) **3051**
†Prince Edward Island. Agricultural Development Corporation. Annual Report. (CN) **5261**
Prince Edward Island. Civil Service Commission. Annual Report. (CN) **3919**
Prince Edward Island. Department of Agriculture. Agricultural Statistics. (CN) **142**
Prince Edward Island. Department of Community and Cultural Affairs. Annual Report. (CN) **1966**, 4070
Prince Edward Island. Department of Fisheries and Aquaculture. Annual Report. (CN) **2047**

Prince Edward Island. Department of Fisheries. Annual Report *see* Prince Edward Island. Department of Fisheries and Aquaculture. Annual Report **2047**
Prince Edward Island. Department of Health and Social Services. Annual Report. (CN) **4110**
Prince Edward Island. Department of Health. Annual Report *see* Prince Edward Island. Department of Health and Social Services. Annual Report **4110**
Prince Edward Island. Department of Industry. Annual Report. (CN) **4070**
Prince Edward Island. Department of Labour. Annual Report. (CN ISSN 0085-512X) **991**
Prince Edward Island. Public Utilities Commission. Annual Report. (CN ISSN 0079-5151) **4070**
Prince Edward Island Community Studies *see* P.E.I. Community Studies **4444**
Prince Edward Island Development Agency. Annual Report. (CN) **1082**
Prince George's County Genealogical Society. Bulletin. (US ISSN 1052-1380) **2162**
Princess Grace Irish Library. (UK ISSN 0269-2619) **2950**
Princess Grace Irish Library Lectures. (UK ISSN 0950-5121) **2950**
Princess Style. (US) **2232**
Princeton Alumni Weekly. (US ISSN 0149-9270) **1322**
Princeton Conference on Cerebrovascular Diseases *see* Princeton Research Conferences on Cerebrovascular Diseases **3211**
Princeton Engineer. (US ISSN 0032-8405) **1834**
Princeton Essays in Literature. (US ISSN 0079-5186) **2950**
Princeton Essays on the Arts. (US) **2513**, 341
Princeton History. (US) **2419**
Princeton Journal: Studies in Thematic Architecture. (US) **305**
Princeton Library of Asian Translations. (US) **3643**, 2950
Princeton Mathematical Series. (US ISSN 0079-5194) **3051**
Princeton Modern Greek Studies. (US) **2381**
Princeton Monographs in Art and Archaeology. (US ISSN 0079-5208) **341**, 282
Princeton Parents. (US) **1322**
Princeton Recollection *see* Princeton Recollector **2419**
Princeton Recollector. (US) **2419**
Princeton Religion Research Center, Inc. Emerging Trends *see* P R R C: Emerging Trends **4194**
Princeton Research Conferences on Cerebrovascular Diseases. (US) **3211**
Princeton Series in Computer Science. (US) **1482**, 1399
Princeton Series in Culture - Power - History. (US) **2513**, 2319
Princeton Series in Opera. (US) **3575**
Princeton Series in Physics. (US ISSN 0079-5216) **3829**
Princeton Series of Contemporary Poets. (US) **3003**
Princeton Studies in International History and Politics. (US) **3919**, 2319
†Princeton Studies in Mathematical Economics. (US ISSN 0079-5240) **5261**
†Princeton Studies in Music. (US ISSN 0079-5259) **5261**
Princeton Studies on the Near East. (US) **2431**, 3643
Princeton University. Art Museum. Record. (US ISSN 0032-843X) **3532**, 282
Princeton University. Center of International Studies. Monograph Series. (US) **3969**, 2728
†Princeton University. Center of International Studies. Policy Memorandum Series. (US ISSN 0079-5267) **5261**

Princeton University. Center of International Studies. Program on U S - Japan Relations. Monograph Series. (US) **3969**, 2728
†Princeton University. Center of International Studies. Research Monograph Series. (US ISSN 0555-1501) **5261**
Princeton University. Center of International Studies. World Order Studies Program: Occasional Paper. (US) **3969**
Princeton University. Department of Computer Science. Technical Report Librarian *see* Princeton University. Department of Computer Science. Technical Reports **1399**
Princeton University. Department of Computer Science. Technical Reports. (US) **1399**
Princeton University. Econometric Research Program. Research Memorandum. (US ISSN 0079-5291) **686**
Princeton University. Industrial Relations Section. Research Report. (US ISSN 0079-5305) **991**
Princeton University. Industrial Relations Sections Selected References. (US ISSN 0037-1351) **736**
Princeton University Cutaneous Research Project Reports. (US ISSN 0032-8448) **4039**
Princeton University Library Chronicle. (US ISSN 0032-8456) **2513**, 4334, 4383
Princeton Weekly Bulletin. (US) **1322**
Principal (Alexandria). (US ISSN 0271-6062) **1730**
†Principal (New York). (US) **5261**
Principal International Businesses *see* Million Dollar Directory Series **1048**
Principal International Businesses. (US ISSN 0097-6288) **1050**, 919
Principal Legislative Staff Offices *see* State Legislative Leadership, Committees and Staff **4074**
Principales Industries Installees en Cote d'Ivoire. (IV) **1082**
Principales Industries Ivoiriennes *see* Principales Industries Installees en Cote d'Ivoire **1082**
Principales Procedures de Financement des Besoins des Entreprises et des Menages. (FR) **796**
†Principality of Liechtenstein - A Documentary Handbook. (LH ISSN 0048-5306) **5261**
Principal's Report. (US ISSN 1044-4998) **1025**, 2540
Principaux Mecanismes de Distribution de Credit *see* Principales Procedures de Financement des Besoins des Entreprises et des Menages **796**
Principe de Viana. (SP ISSN 0032-8472) **2381**
Principes. (US ISSN 0032-8480) **515**
Principles and Practices of Oncology Update *see* P P O Update **3201**
Principles of Computer Science Series. (US ISSN 0888-2096) **1880**, 3066
Principles of Pediatric Neurosurgery. (US) **3325**, 3383
Pring Market Review. (US ISSN 0892-189X) **1050**
Prinosi za Poredbeno Proucavanje Prava i Medunarodno Pravo. *see* Institute of International Law and International Relations. Contributions to the Study of Comparative and International Law **2724**
†Prinsejagt. (NE ISSN 0032-8499) **5261**
Print. (US ISSN 0032-8510) **1422**, 341, 4003
Print. (DK ISSN 0108-1608) **1464**
Print. (UK ISSN 0032-8529) **4003**
Print. (SZ) **4134**, 4003
Print & Converting Monthly. (UK) **4003**
Print & Graphics. (US ISSN 0273-9550) **4003**
Print and Production Manual. (UK) **4004**, 4134
Print Business Register. (US) **4004**
Print Buyer *see* Print Buying **4004**
Print Buyers Review. (US) **4004**

6574 PRINT BUYING

Print Buying. (UK) **4004**
Print Collector's Newsletter. (US ISSN 0032-8537) **341**
Print-Equip News. (US ISSN 0048-5314) **4004**
Print Media Production Data *see* Standard Rate and Data Service. Print Media Production Data **41**
Print Monthly *see* Print & Converting Monthly **4003**
Print Quarterly. (UK ISSN 0265-8305) **341**
Print World. *see* Banhua Shijie **318**
Print World. Journal. (US ISSN 0737-7436) **4134**
PrintAction. (CN) **4004**
Printed Circuit Assembly *see* Circuits Assembly **1765**
Printed Circuit Design. (US) **1777**
Printed Circuit Fabrication. (US ISSN 0274-8096) **1777**, 1212
Printed Circuit Network. (US) **1777**
Printed Circuits and Electronics Coatings Abstracts. (UK ISSN 0953-0509) **1777**, 20
Printed in Tanzania *see* Tanzania National Bibliography **413**
Printed Matter. (JA) **3003**
Printers Buyer's Guide and Handbook. (US) **4007**, 1507
Printer's Devil. (US) **4004**, 4134
Printers Hot Line. (US ISSN 0192-6314) **4004**
Printer's Ink. (US) **4004**
Printers News. (NZ ISSN 0048-5330) **4004**
†Printers News. (AT ISSN 0048-5322) **5261**
†Printer's News. (US) **5261**
Printers Yearbook. (UK) **4004**
Printing Abstracts. (UK ISSN 0031-109X) **4007**, 20
Printing & Allied Trades Employers Federation of Australia News Bulletin *see* P A T E F A News Bulletin **4003**
Printing & Allied Trades Employers Federation of Australia Printing Industry Quarterly *see* P A T E F A Printing Industry Quarterly **5254**
Printing and Bookbinding Trade Review.(UK) **4004**, 4134
Printing and Dyeing. *see* Yin Ran **4627**
Printing & Packaging. (GW) **3651**, 4004
Printing & Publishing: Latin American Industrial Report. (US) **4134**, 838, 4004
Printing and Publishing Newsletter. (US) **3620**, 4004
Printing Equipment and Materials *see* Printing World **4005**
Printing Historical Society. Journal. (UK ISSN 0079-5321) **4004**
Printing Historical Society Bulletin. (UK ISSN 0144-7505) **4004**
Printing Historical Society Newsletter *see* Printing Historical Society Bulletin **4004**
Printing History. (US ISSN 0192-9275) **4004**, 4134
Printing Impressions. (US ISSN 0032-860X) **4004**
Printing Industries. (UK ISSN 0307-7195) **4004**
Printing Industries Annual *see* Printers Yearbook **4004**
Printing Journal. (US ISSN 0191-8273) **4004**
Printing Magazine. *see* Yinshua Zazhi **4006**
Printing Manager. (US) **4004**, 1025
Printing News *see* Printing News - East **4004**
Printing News - East. (US ISSN 1046-8595) **4004**
Printing News - Midwest. (US) **4004**
†Printing Product Guide. (CN) **5261**
Printing Product Information Cards. (UK ISSN 0032-8642) **4004**
Printing Product International. (US) **4004**, 3651
Printing Sales Index. (US) **4004**, 1117
Printing Technology *see* Professional Printer **4005**
Printing Times. (II ISSN 0401-3956) **4004**

Printing Today *see* Printing World **4005**
Printing Trades Blue Book. Southeastern Edition *see* Graphic Arts Blue Book. Southeastern Edition **4000**
Printing Trades Directory. (UK ISSN 0079-5372) **4004**
Printing Trades Journal. (AT ISSN 1030-9160) **4005**, 992
Printing Views *see* Printing News - Midwest **4004**
Printing World. *see* Insatsukai **4001**
Printing World. (UK ISSN 0032-8715) **4005**
▼Printmaking Today. (UK ISSN 0960-9253) **4005**
Printout *see* Update Newsletter **802**
Printout. (US ISSN 0887-7556) **4007**
Prints. (AT ISSN 0816-3065) **3003**, 341, 3796
Prints (Alton). (US ISSN 0274-5097) **341**
Printshop. (UK) **4005**, 3796
Printwear Magazine. (US) **1294**, 4484
Printworld Directory of Contemporary Prints (Year). (US) **341**, 1150
Prions en Eglise - Edition Complete *see* Living with Christ - Complete Edition **4268**
Prions en Eglise - Edition Dominicale. (CN ISSN 0383-8277) **4273**
Prior Park Magazine. (UK) **1714**
Priority Parenting. (US) **1243**
Prirastky Ekonomickej Literatury *see* Eko-Index **714**
Prirastky Zahranicnych Knih. Seria B: Ekonomia, Ekonomika. (CS) **736**
Priroda. (CI) **452**
Priroda. (BU ISSN 0032-8731) **4334**
Priroda. (RU ISSN 0032-874X) **4334**
Priroda a Spolocnost. (CS) **4334**, 4383
Prirodni Vedy a Matematika *see* Pedagogicka Fakulta v Ostrave. Matematika, Fyzika **3050**
Prirodni Vedy ve Skole. (CS ISSN 0032-8766) **1656**, 4334
Prirodnjacki Muzej u Beogradu. Glasnik. Serija A: Mineralogija, Geologija, Paleontologija. (YU ISSN 0367-4983) **1578**, 3660
Prirodnjacki Muzej u Beogradu. Glasnik. Serija B: Bioloske Nauke. (YU ISSN 0373-2134) **452**
Prirodnyi Gaz Sibiri. (RU) **3700**
Prirodoslovna Istrazivanja: Acta Biologica. (CI ISSN 0448-0147) **452**
Prirodoslovna Istrazivanja: Acta Geologica. (CI ISSN 0448-0155) **1578**, 1600
Prirodovedne Prace Ustavu C S A V v Brne *see* Ceskoslovenska Acedemie Ved. Ustav v Brne. Prirodovedne Prace **4304**
Prism. (CN) **1656**
Prism. (UA) **2185**, 4383, 4783
Prism. (AT) **4196**
Prism (Fort Lauderdale). (US ISSN 0742-0013) **1263**
Prism (New Brighton). (US ISSN 0887-5049) **4196**
Prism International. (CN ISSN 0032-8790) **2950**
Prism: The Magazine of Japanese Industry and Lifestyles. (JA) **686**
Prisma. (IO ISSN 0126-270X) **2202**, 4383
Prisma. (CN ISSN 0380-8815) **2835**, 1757
Prisma. (SA) **3946**
Prisma (Hamburg). (GW ISSN 0937-0927) **2191**
Prisma (Kassel). (GW ISSN 0171-3604) **4334**, 341, 1656, 4606
Prisma Latinoamericano. (CU) **2184**
Prisma: Majalah Pemikiran Sosial Ekonomi. (IO) **2202**, 4383
†Prismal-Cabral. (US) **5262**
Prismet. (NO ISSN 0032-8847) **1656**, 4196
Prison Action Group. Newsletter. (US) **1521**
Prison - Ashram Project Newsletter *see* Human Kindness Foundation Newsletter **4181**

Prison Decisions. (US ISSN 0270-2703) **1521**
Prison Information Bulletin. (FR ISSN 0254-5233) **1521**
Prison Journal. (US ISSN 0032-8855) **1521**
Prison Officers Magazine *see* Gatelodge **1514**
Prison Service Journal. (UK ISSN 0300-3558) **1521**
Prisoners Assistance Directory. (US) **1521**, 3946
Prisons *see* South Africa. Prisons Department. Report of the Commissioner of Prisons **5279**
Prispevki za Novejso Zgodovino. (XV ISSN 0353-0329) **2381**
▼Priusadebnoe Khozyaistvo. (RU) **190**
Privacy Journal. (US ISSN 0145-7659) **3946**, 1434
Privacy Law and Practice. (US) **2668**, 3946
Privacy Times. (US) **3946**, 2668
Privata Affaerer. (SW) **1507**, 686
Private Banker International. (IE) **796**
Private Banking Report. (US) **796**
Private Cable *see* Private Cable Plus Wireless Cable **1378**
Private Cable Plus Wireless Cable. (US) **1378**
Private Carrier. (US ISSN 0032-8871) **4747**
Private Clubs. (US) **1300**
Private Country Club Guest Policy Directory. (US) **4510**
Private Development Corporation of the Philippines. Annual P D C P Survey on Business Performance. (PH) **960**
Private Development Corporation of the Philippines. Economic Performance and Prospects. (PH) **686**
Private Development Corporation of the Philippines. Executive Update. (PH) **919**, 934
Private Development Corporation of the Philippines. Industry Digest. (PH ISSN 0115-4419) **1082**
Private Development Corporation of the Philippines. Policy Analysis. (PH) **934**, 999
Private Eye. (UK ISSN 0032-888X) **2880**
Private Foundations Reports *see* Exempt Organizations Reports **1093**
Private Independent Schools (Year). (US ISSN 0079-5399) **1697**
Private Investigator Magazine *see* P I Magazine **2986**
Private Investigator's Connection. (US) **1521**
Private Investments Abroad. (US ISSN 0090-9742) **960**, 2728
Private Investor's Ledger. (UK) **960**
Private Krankenversicherung *see* P K V Publik **2539**
Private Krankenversicherung Informationdienst *see* P K V Informationdienst **2539**
Private Label. (US ISSN 0190-9851) **1082**, 2093
Private Label Directory. (US) **1150**
Private Label Executive Edition *see* Private Label **1082**
Private Label International. (US ISSN 0886-5582) **1082**, 2093
Private Label Product News. (US) **686**
Private Letter Rulings. (US) **1104**, 2668
Private Library. (UK ISSN 0032-8898) **2779**, 4134
Private Line. (US) **4747**
Private Moments. (US) **3400**
▼Private Multifamily Manager. (US ISSN 1057-1426) **2494**
Private Pilot. (US ISSN 0032-8901) **4676**
†Private Placement Advisory. (US) **5262**
▼Private Placement Alert. (US) **960**
Private Placement Letter. (US) **796**
Private Placements *see* Private Placement Letter **796**
Private Post. (UK ISSN 0140-8003) **3757**
Private Practice. (US ISSN 0032-891X) **3144**
Private Practice News. (US ISSN 0895-3228) **1025**

Private Press Books. (UK ISSN 0079-5402) **409**
†Private School Law Digest. (US) **5262**
Private School Quarterly. (US) **1656**
†Private Schools of the United States. (US ISSN 0885-1603) **5262**
Private Sector Conference. (US) **3144**
Private Security Case Law Reporter. (US ISSN 0738-6958) **1527**, 2668
De Private Skoler i de Enkelte Kommuner. (DK ISSN 0905-1449) **1697**
Private Varnish. (US) **4713**
Private Woodlands Survey. (UK) **2106**
Privates Bausparwesen. (GW ISSN 0085-5154) **628**
Privates Eigentum. (GW) **4154**
Privatization. (US ISSN 0888-7446) **4093**, 686
Privatization Watch. (US) **3919**, 4093
Prive. (NE) **1294**
Privilege. (CN) **4655**
Privileged Information. (US) **2232**
†Privileged Traveler. (US) **5262**
Privlacica. (CI) **2880**
Privreda (Osijek). (CI ISSN 0350-9427) **821**
Privreda Dalmacije. (CI) **821**
Privreda i Rukovodjenje. (YU) **1025**
Privredna Izgradnja. (YU ISSN 0032-8979) **686**
Privredne Novine. (BN) **1082**
Privredni Vjesnik/Economic Herald. (CI ISSN 0032-8995) **686**
Privredno Pravni Prirucnik. (YU ISSN 0032-9002) **2668**, 1061, 1069
Priya. (II) **3516**
Priyavi. (CE) **1243**
Prize! - Africa and Radio Post *see* Prize Beat **1378**
Prize Beat. (RH) **1378**
Pro. (US ISSN 1041-5610) **2137**
Pro. (IT ISSN 1120-4079) **3796**
Pro and Amateur Hockey Guide *see* Hockey Guide **4474**
Pro Austria Romana. (AU ISSN 0478-3166) **282**, 2381
Pro Basketball Guide *see* Basketball Guide **4500**
Pro Basketball Illustrated (Year). (US) **4510**
(Year) Pro Bike Directory. (US) **4520**
Pro Bike News. (US) **4520**
Pro - Choice News. (CN ISSN 0836-7221) **598**, 4836, 4851
Pro-Development Letter. (US) **4655**
Pro Driver *see* Pro Trucker **4747**
Pro Ecclesia *see* Pro Ecclesia Magazine **4273**
Pro Ecclesia Magazine. (US) **4273**
†Pro-Farm. (CN) **5262**
Pro Football (Los Angeles). (US ISSN 0079-5526) **4510**
Pro Football Illustrated (Year). (US ISSN 1054-0156) **4510**
Pro Football Weekly. (US ISSN 0032-9053) **4510**
Pro Justitia. (BE) **2668**
Pro-Life Reporter. (US) **3946**
Pro Motion. (US ISSN 0886-6104) **1341**, 2232
Pro Motion. (CN ISSN 0048-5381) **1757**
Pro Mundi Vita Bulletin *see* Pro Mundi Vita Studies **5262**
†Pro Mundi Vita Studies. (BE ISSN 1012-4543) **5262**
Pro Natura Genova. (IT) **1966**
Pro Patria. (NO ISSN 0032-910X) **3468**
Pro - Pensionaeren. (SW ISSN 0345-9225) **4416**
Pro Re Nata. (Utah Nurses Association) (US) **3285**
Pro Rege. (US ISSN 0276-4830) **1322**
Pro Sound. (JA) **4461**
Pro Sound News. (US ISSN 0164-6338) **4461**
Pro Sound News (Europe). (UK ISSN 0269-4735) **4461**
†Pro-Sports. (US ISSN 0032-9126) **5262**
Pro Tem. (CN ISSN 0032-9134) **1322**
Pro Trucker. (US) **4747**
Pro und Kontra. (SZ) **3919**

Pro Wrestling Illustrated. (US) **4484**
Proa. (CK ISSN 0032-9150) **305, 2494**
Proa y Puerto *see* Transportes **4659**
Probabilistic Engineering Mechanics. (UK ISSN 0266-8920) **1938**
Probability and Mathematical Statistics. (US ISSN 0079-5607) **3051**
Probability and Mathematical Statistics. (PL ISSN 0208-4147) **3063, 4583**
Probability in the Engineering and Informational Sciences. (UK ISSN 0269-9648) **1846, 1457**
Probability: Pure and Applied. (US) **3051**
Probability Theory and Related Fields. (GW ISSN 0178-8051) **3051**
Probable Levels of R & D Expenditures: Forecast and Analysis. (US) **4606, 4334**
Probate & Property. (US ISSN 0164-0372) **2668, 4154**
Probate and Property Newsletter *see* Probate & Property **2668**
Probate Law Journal. (US ISSN 0737-3112) **2668**
▼Probate Law Journal of Ohio. (US ISSN 1050-5342) **2668**
Probate Practice Reporter. (US) **2668**
Probation *see* Probation Journal **1521**
Probation and Parole Directory. (US ISSN 0732-0965) **1521**
Probation and Parole in the United States. (US) **1521**
Probation and Parole Law Reports. (US ISSN 0276-6965) **2668, 1521**
Probation and Parole Law Summaries *see* Probation and Parole Law Reports **2668**
Probation Journal. (UK ISSN 0264-5505) **1521**
Probation Officer. (AT) **1521**
Probatum Est. (GW) **3144, 3741**
Probatum Est Therapeutica Nova *see* Probatum Est **3144**
Probe. (SA) **3013**
Probe. (UK ISSN 0032-9185) **3240**
Probe. (AT ISSN 0079-5631) **3240**
Probe *see* Le Milieu **3562**
Probe (Chicago). (US) **4273, 4851**
Probe (Memphis) *see* Pioneer (Memphis) **4246**
Probe (New York). (US) **3919**
Probe (Rockville Centre) *see* Life Association News **2536**
Probe (Santa Barbara). (US ISSN 0032-9177) **3946**
Probe Directory of Foreign Direct Investment in the United States. (US ISSN 0094-3134) **1150, 960**
Probe India. (II) **2201**
†Probe Post. (CN ISSN 0707-1922) **5262**
Probe Report. (UK ISSN 0260-8189) **3670, 60**
Probitas. (II) **2950**
Problem Behavior Management. (US) **4039**
Problem Books in Mathematics. (US) **3051**
Problem-Solving News. (UK ISSN 0260-5554) **1757**
Problemas. (SP ISSN 0032-9223) **4484**
Problemas de Organizacion de la Ciencia. (CU ISSN 0138-7170) **4334**
Problemas del Desarrollo. (MX ISSN 0301-7036) **686**
Problemas del Mundo Contemporaneo. *see* Problems of the Contemporary World **4383**
Problemata. (GW) **3778, 2513**
Probleme de Antropologie *see* Studii si Cercetari de Antropologie **250**
Probleme de Automatizare. (RM) **1834, 4606**
Probleme de Documentare si Informare *see* Probleme de Informare si Documentare **2779**
Probleme de Geografie *see* Studii si Cercetari de Geografie **2263**
Probleme de Informare si Documentare.(RM ISSN 0018-9111) **2779**
Probleme de Logica. (RM) **3778**
Probleme de Pedagogie Contemporana.(RM) **1656**

Probleme der Aegyptologie. (NE ISSN 0169-9601) **3643**
Probleme der Kuestenforschung im Suedlichen Nordseegebiet. (GW) **4334**
†Probleme des Friedens und des Sozialismus. (GW ISSN 0032-9258) **5262**
Probleme Ekonomike. (AA) **686**
Problemes d'Amerique Latine. (FR) **2419**
Problemes d'Histoire des Religions. (BE) **4273**
Problemes d'Histoire du CHristianisme *see* Problemes d'Histoire des Religions **4273**
Problemes des Genres Litteraires. *see* Zagadnienia Rodzajow Literackich **2979**
Problemes du Monde Contemporain. *see* Problems of the Contemporary World **4383**
Problemes Economiques. (FR ISSN 0032-9304) **686**
Problemes Politiques et Sociaux. (FR ISSN 0015-9743) **3969**
Problemes Sociaux Zairois. (ZR) **4445**
Problemi. (IT ISSN 0032-9339) **2880**
Problemi dell'Informazione. (IT ISSN 0390-5195) **1341, 4445**
Problemi della Pedagogia. (IT ISSN 0032-9347) **1656**
Problemi della Transizione *see* Transizione **3930**
Problemi di Amministrazione Pubblica. (IT ISSN 0391-2655) **4070**
Problemi di Civilta. (IT) **4383**
Problemi di Gestione. (IT ISSN 0032-9363) **1025**
Problemi e Ricerche di Storia Antica. (IT ISSN 0079-5682) **1279**
Problemi na Izkustvoto/Problems of Art. (BU ISSN 0032-9371) **341**
Problemi na Tekhnicheskata Kibernetika i Robotika/Problems of Engineering Cybernetics and Robotics. (BU ISSN 0204-9848) **1442**
Problemi Sjevernog Jadrana. (CI) **247, 2381**
†Problemi Spoljne Trgovine i Konjunkture/Foreign Trade & Business Cycles Problems. (YU ISSN 0032-938X) **5262**
Problemist. (UK ISSN 0032-9398) **4484**
Problems in Anesthesia. (US ISSN 0889-4698) **3192**
Problems in Contemporary Philosophy. (US) **3778**
Problems in Critical Care. (US ISSN 0889-4701) **3144**
Problems in Economic Transition. (US) **686**
Problems in Economics *see* Problems in Economic Transition **686**
Problems in General Surgery. (US ISSN 0739-8328) **3383**
Problems in Oncology. *see* Voprosy Onkologii **3203**
▼Problems in Plastic and Reconstructive Surgery. (US ISSN 1050-0197) **3383**
Problems in Private International Law. (NE) **2728**
Problems in Respiratory Care. (US ISSN 0897-9677) **3366**
Problems in Urology. (US ISSN 0889-471X) **3389**
Problems in Veterinary Medicine. (US ISSN 1041-0228) **4814**
Problems of Agricultural Economics. *see* Nongye Jingji Wenti **155**
Problems of Art. *see* Problemi na Izkustvoto **341**
Problems of Building Growth. *see* Problemy Rozwoju Budownictwa **628**
Problems of Communism. (US ISSN 0032-941X) **3919**
Problems of Communism. (UK) **3919**
Problems of Control and Information Theory/Problemy Upravleniya i Teorii Informatsii. (HU ISSN 0370-2529) **1457**
Problems of Desert Development. (English translation of: Problemy Osvoeniya Pustyn') (US ISSN 0278-4750) **1966**

Problems of Diffraction and Spreading of Waves. *see* Problemy Difraktsii i Rasprostraneniya Voln **3860**
Problems of Endocrinology. *see* Problemy Endokrinologii **3255**
Problems of Engineering Cybernetics and Robotics. *see* Problemi na Tekhnicheskata Kibernetika i Robotika **1442**
Problems of Health Resorts, Physiotherapy and Exercise Therapy. *see* Voprosy Kurortologii, Fizioterapii i Lechebnoi Fizicheskoi Kul'tury **3161**
Problems of Industrial Psychiatric Medicine Series. (US ISSN 0277-4178) **4039, 3350**
Problems of Information Transmission. (English translation of: Problemy Peredachi Informatsii) (US ISSN 0032-9460) **1447**
Problems of Large Metropolitan Areas. *see* Problemy Bol'shikh Gorodov **1966**
Problems of Lithuanian Linguistics. *see* Lietuviu Kalbotyros Klausimai **2825**
Problems of Medical Chemistry. *see* Voprosy Meditsinskoi Khimii **483**
Problems of Motherhood and Childhood Protection. *see* Voprosy Okhrany Materinstva i Detstva **3288**
Problems of National Liberation. (II) **3919**
Problems of Nutrition. *see* Voprosy Pitaniya **3613**
Problems of the Contemporary World/ Problemes du Monde Contemporain/ Problemas del Mundo Contemporaneo. (RU ISSN 0079-5763) **4383, 2319**
Problems of the Far East *see* U S S R Report: Problems of the Far East **3974**
Problems of the Science of Science *see* Science of Science **3781**
Problems of Tuberculosis. *see* Problemy Tuberkuleza **3366**
Problems of Virology. *see* Voprosy Virusologii **558**
Problemy. (PL ISSN 0032-9487) **4334**
Problemy Agrofizyki. (PL ISSN 0137-6586) **115**
Problemy Alkoholizmu. (PL ISSN 0032-9495) **1538**
Problemy Arkheologii i Etnografii. (RU) **282**
†Problemy Biologie Krajiny/Questiones Geobiologicae. (CS) **5262**
Problemy Bioniki. (KR ISSN 0555-2656) **452**
Problemy Bol'shikh Gorodov/Problems of Large Metropolitan Areas. (RU ISSN 0233-5816) **1966, 1872, 2494**
Problemy Dal'nego Vostoka *see* Far Eastern Affairs **2361**
Problemy Difraktsii i Rasprostraneniya Voln/Problems of Diffraction and Spreading of Waves. (RU) **3860**
Problemy Ekonomiczne. (PL ISSN 0079-578X) **686**
Problemy Endokrinologii/Problems of Endocrinology. (RU ISSN 0375-9660) **3255**
Problemy Endokrinologii i Gormonoterapii *see* Problemy Endokrinologii **3255**
Problemy Fiziki Atmosfery. (RU) **3829, 3440**
Problemy Istorii Matematiki i Mekhaniki.(RU) **3051, 3845**
Problemy Jakosci. (PL ISSN 0137-8651) **3448**
Problemy Kontrolya i Zashchita Atmosfery ot Zagryazneniya. (KR ISSN 0135-2253) **1966**
Problemy Mashinostroeniya. (KR ISSN 0131-2928) **3022**
Problemy Opiekunczo-Wychowawcze. (PL ISSN 0552-2188) **1656**
Problemy Osvoeniya Pustyn' (TK ISSN 0032-9428) **115, 4827**
†Problemy Oswiaty na Wsi. (PL) **5262**
Problemy Poles'ya. (BW ISSN 0131-3010) **4828**
Problemy Polonii Zagranicznej *see* Biblioteka Polonijna **3875**
Problemy Prochnosti. (KR ISSN 0556-171X) **1921**

Problemy Projektowe *see* Problemy Projektowe Przemyslu i Budownictwa **3418**
Problemy Projektowe Przemyslu i Budownictwa. (PL) **3418, 1214, 1222**
Problemy Rad Narodowych. Studia i Materialy. (PL ISSN 0079-5801) **4070**
Problemy Rodziny. (PL ISSN 0552-2234) **3986**
Problemy Rozwoju Budownictwa/ Problems of Building Growth. (PL) **628**
Problemy Severa. (RU) **409**
Problemy Slov'iyanoznavstva. (KR ISSN 0203-9494) **2381**
†Problemy Szkolnictwa i Nauk Medycznych. (PL ISSN 0137-7183) **5262**
Problemy Tuberkuleza/Problems of Tuberculosis. (RU ISSN 0032-9533) **3366**
Problemy Upravleniya i Teorii Informatsii. *see* Problems of Control and Information Theory **1457**
Probus. (US ISSN 0921-4771) **2835**
†Procedural Aspects of International Law. (US) **5262**
Proceedings. Annual A A Z P A Conference *see* American Association of Zoological Parks and Aquariums. Proceedings. A A Z P A Annual Conference **577**
Proceedings. Annual Symposium. Incremental Motion Control Systems and Devices *see* Symposium on Incremental Motion Control Systems and Devices. Proceedings **3023**
Proceedings, A W W A Annual Conference *see* American Water Works Association. Proceedings, A W W A Annual Conference **4821**
Proceedings - Committee on Computer Technology *see* American Association of State Highway and Transportation Officials. Sub-Committee on Computer Technology. National Conference. Proceedings **4706**
Proceedings - Conference on Ground Water *see* Conference on Ground Water. Proceedings **1597**
Proceedings in Life Sciences. (US ISSN 0172-6625) **452**
Proceedings in Print. (US ISSN 0032-9568) **3395, 409**
Proceedings of Annual Meeting - American Association of Veterinary Laboratory Diagnosticians *see* American Association of Veterinary Laboratory Diagnosticians. Proceedings of Annual Meeting **5134**
Proceedings of Fishing Port Engineering. *see* Gyoko Kensetsu Gijutsu Kenkyu Happyokai Koenshu **1866**
Proceedings of S S O R. *see* S S O R Yokoshu **1405**
Proceedings of Speech Tech Conferences. (US) **1341**
Proceedings of Sugar Beet Research *see* Bulletin of Sugar Beet Research. Supplement **171**
Proceedings of the A A J R *see* American Academy for Jewish Research. Proceedings of the A A J R **4221**
Proceedings of the A C S A Annual Meeting *see* Association of Collegiate Schools of Architecture. Proceedings of the Annual Meeting **295**
Proceedings of the Annual Meeting of the Western Society for French History *see* Western Society for French History. Proceedings of the Annual Meeting **2395**
Proceedings of the Annual Southeastern Symposium on System Theory *see* Southeastern Symposium on System Theory. Proceedings **1439**
Proceedings of the Arizona Section, American Water Resources Association and the Hydrology Section, Arizona-Nevada Academy of Science. (US) **1600**
Proceedings of the I E E E *see* Institute of Electrical and Electronics Engineers. Proceedings **1899**

PROCEEDINGS

Proceedings of the Institute of Statistical Mathematics. see Tokei Suri **3063**
Proceedings of the Japanese Conference on Coastal Engineering. see Kaigan Kogaku Koenkai Ronbunshu **1870**
Proceedings of the Marine Safety Council see U.S. Coast Guard Marine Safety Council. Proceedings **4741**
Proceedings of the National - International Sculpture Conference see International Sculpture Conference. Proceedings **331**
Proceedings of the Northeast Pacific Pink Salmon Workshop see Northeast Pacific Pink and Chum Salmon Workshop. Proceedings **2047**
Proceedings of the Ocean Development Symposium. see Kaiyo Kaihatsu Ronbunshu **1870**
Proceedings of the South Carolina Historical Association see South Carolina Historical Association. Proceedings **2422**
Proceedings of the Special Convention of the National Collegiate Athletic Association see National Collegiate Athletic Association. Proceedings of the Special Convention **4480**
Proceedings of the Straub Pacific Health Foundation. (US) **3144**
Proceedings of the Symposium of Computer Research. see Densanki Riyo Ni Kansuru Shinpojumu Koengaiyo **1864**
Proceedings of the Symposium on Rock Mechanics. see Ganban Rikigaku Ni Kansuri Shinpojumu Ronbunshu **1865**
Proceedings on Nondestructive Evaluation see Symposium on Nondestructive Evaluation **63**
Proceedings - Ultrasonics Symposium see Ultrasonics Symposium. Proceedings **3860**
Proceedings - United States Naval Institute see U S Naval Institute. Proceedings **3473**
Procellaria. (IT) **2880**
Proces. (NE ISSN 0165-0076) **1521**
Proceso. (ES ISSN 0259-9864) **3920, 686**
Process see Process Magazine **203**
Process & Control Engineering see P A C E **1857**
Process Biochemistry. (UK ISSN 0032-9592) **491, 481**
▼Process Control and Quality. (NE ISSN 0924-3089) **3448**
Process Engineering. see P T - Procestechniek **1833**
Process Engineering. (UK ISSN 0370-1859) **1858**
Process Engineering. (AT) **1858**
Process Engineering Directory. (UK ISSN 0143-1455) **1858, 1150**
Process Engineering Index. (UK) **1846**
Process Engineering News see Process Engineering **1858**
Process Engineering, Plant and Control see Process Engineering **1858**
Process Equipment News. (UK ISSN 0261-7412) **1834, 828**
Process Equipment Series. (US) **1859**
Process Industries Canada. (CN) **1859**
†Process Industry International. (UK ISSN 0954-4917) **5262**
Process Industry Quality see P I Quality **1833**
Process Industry Selector. (UK) **1834**
Process Instrumentation Review. (UK) **4606**
Process Journal see Print **4003**
Process Magazine. (FR) **203**
Process Metallurgy. (NE) **3418**
Process Plant Layout and Piping Design. (US) **2302, 1834**
▼Process Safety and Environmental Protection. (UK ISSN 0957-5820) **1186, 1966**
Process Studies. (US ISSN 0360-6503) **3778**
Process Technology Proceedings. (NE) **1400**
†Processed Poultry. (US) **5262**
Processed World. (US ISSN 0735-9381) **1400, 2588**
Processing. (UK ISSN 0305-439X) **1859**
Processing Ad - Lits. (US) **1859**
Processing, Distribution and Retailing Ontario. Ministry of Agriculture and Food. P D R Notes see Ontario. Ministry of Agriculture and Food. P D R Notes **112**
▼Processing of Advanced Materials. (UK ISSN 0960-3158) **1922**
Processing Snapshots. (US) **1859**
Processo Legislativo nel Parlamento Italiano. (IT) **2668**
Processor. (US) **1453**
Proche-Orient Chretien. (IS ISSN 0032-9622) **4196**
†Proche-Orient Etudes Economiques. (LE ISSN 0254-9379) **5262**
Proche-Orient Etudes Juridiques. (LE ISSN 0032-9649) **2668**
Proclaim (Nashville). (US ISSN 0162-4326) **4247**
Proclaim (Petaluma). (US) **4247**
Procomm Enterprises Magazine. (US ISSN 0896-7229) **1365**
Procordia. Aarsredovisning/Procordia. Annual Report. (SW) **1082**
Procordia. Annual Report. see Procordia. Aarsredovisning **1082**
Proctology see Colo-Proctology **3090**
Proctor. (AT) **2668**
Procurement Weekly. (UK ISSN 0306-1922) **1050**
Prodei. (SP ISSN 0079-5836) **1150**
Prodent. (GW ISSN 0932-4488) **3241**
▼ProDirect. (US) **1150**
Prodoc-Kunststoff-Magazin see Kunststoff-Magazin-Prodoc **1182**
Prodoc-Kunststoff-Technik see Kunststoff-Magazin-Prodoc **1182**
Prodotti di Marca. (IT ISSN 0032-9665) **1050**
†Produccion. (VE ISSN 0032-9681) **5262**
Produccion Agricola - Periodo de Invierno. (VE) **142**
Produccion Agricola - Periodo de Verano. (VE) **142, 4583**
Produccion Alimentaria - Nutricion see Nutricion en Salud Publica **4118**
Produccion Quimica Mexicana. (MX) **1859**
†Produccion Rural Argentina. (AG ISSN 0079-5852) **5262**
Produccion y Exportaciones Chilenas de Cobre. (CL) **1083, 3494**
Produce Availability and Merchandising Guide. (US) **2093**
Produce Business. (US ISSN 0886-5663) **2093, 2143**
Produce Marketing Almanac - Membership Directory see Produce Marketing Association Membership Directory & Buyer's Guide **2080**
Produce Marketing Association Membership Directory & Buyer's Guide. (US) **2080, 3651**
Produce Merchandiser. (US) **2093**
Produce Merchandising. (US) **2080**
Produce News. (US ISSN 0032-969X) **2080**
Produce Packaging and Materials Handling Digest see Produce Packaging Handling Digest **3651**
Produce Packaging Handling Digest. (US) **3651**
Producenter og Importoerer af Goedninger og Jordforbedringsmidler.(DK) **190**
Producer News. (US) **2540**
Producer Price Indexes. (US) **736, 1083**
Producer's MasterGuide. (US ISSN 0732-6653) **1151, 1341, 3516**
▼Producers Quarterly. (US) **3516, 1378**
†Product Acceptance News. (US) **5262**
Product Alert. (US) **2080, 1507**
▼Product & Process Innovation. (US) **1453, 4606**
Product Design and Development see Chilton's Product Design and Development **1816**
†Product Directory & Buyers'Guide. (US ISSN 0882-2700) **5262**
Product Directory of the Refractories Industry of the United States see Directory of the Refractories Industry (Year) **1132**
Product File for Agricultural Machinery and Related Material. (JA) **164**
Product Finder: Swift-Sasco Buyers Guide. (UK ISSN 0261-4073) **1507**
Product Finishing. (UK ISSN 0032-9762) **4606**
Product Liability & Safety Encyclopedia.(UK) **2668, 1507**
Product Liability International. (UK ISSN 0143-1587) **1025, 1050**
Product Liability Law and Strategy. (US) **1083, 1507, 2668**
Product Liability Law in Oklahoma. (US) **2668**
Product Liability Newsletter see Product Liability Law and Strategy **1083**
Product Liability Trends. (US ISSN 0164-9574) **2668, 4110**
▼Product Management Today. (US) **1050, 3741**
Product Productivity Review see Public Productivity and Management Review **4071**
Product Safety & Liability Reporter. (US ISSN 0092-7732) **4110**
Product Safety Letter. (US ISSN 0098-7530) **4110, 1083**
Product Safety News. (US ISSN 0009-1162) **4110**
Product Safety Up To Date. (US ISSN 0091-8954) **4110**
Producteur Agricole. (CN ISSN 0706-5264) **115**
Producteur d'Amiante. see Asbestos Producer **600**
Producteur de Lait. (SZ ISSN 0019-9125) **203**
Producteur de Lait Quebecois. (CN ISSN 0228-1686) **203**
Producteur de Porc Quebecois. (CN ISSN 0229-7876) **224**
†Le Producteur Horticole. (CN) **5262**
Le Producteur Laitier. (CN ISSN 0829-1411) **203**
Production. (US ISSN 0032-9819) **1083**
Production. (CN) **3144**
Production Alimentaire - Nutrition see Nutrition de Sante Publique **4118**
Production and Casting Report. (UK) **3516, 4637**
Production & Industrial Equipment Digest see P E D **1833**
Production and Inventory Management. (US ISSN 0032-9843) **1025**
†Production & Inventory Management. (US ISSN 1057-2341) **5262**
Production and Marketing California Grapes, Raisins and Wine see California. Agricultural Statistics Service. Fruit and Nut Acreage **135**
Production Costs: Operating Steam Electric Plants. (US) **1800, 1802**
Production Costs - U S Gas Turbine and Combined Cycle Power Plants. (US) **1906, 1794**
Production Engineer see Manufacturing Engineer **1830**
Production Engineering Research Association International News see P E R A News **4606**
Production Journal. (UK ISSN 0032-9878) **4005, 2574**
Production Laitiere Moderne see P L M **222**
Production Machinery. (AT) **3022, 1834**
Production of Canada's Leading Minerals. (CN) **3502, 4583**
▼Production Planning & Control. (UK ISSN 0953-7287) **1880, 1083**
Production, Prices, Employment and Trade in Northwest Forest Industries. (US) **2106**
Production Research. see Seisan Kenkyu **4608**
Production Statistics of the Dairy Industry. see Netherlands. Centraal Bureau voor de Statistiek. Productie Statistiek van de Zuivelindustrie **140**
Production Supervisor's Bulletin. (US) **1083, 1025**
Productions Animales. (FR ISSN 0990-0632) **590**
Productions Nouvelles du Danemark see New Products from Denmark **5246**
Productive Farming. see Effektivt Landbrug **88**
Productive Farming. (ZA) **156, 190**
Productive Management see Retail Opportunity Letter **1026**
Productividad. (PE ISSN 0032-9908) **1083**
Productivity. (US) **1025, 1083**
Productivity. (II ISSN 0032-9924) **1083**
Productivity and Management in Construction see Contractor Profit News **614**
Productivity and Performance see High Standards in Productivity and Performance **5204**
Productivity Brief see Brief (Houston) **1004**
Productivity Digest see American Productivity & Quality Center. Digest (Year) **5135**
Productivity Improvement Circles Association of the Philippines News see P I C News **1117**
Productivity Letter see American Productivity & Quality Center. Letter **1002**
Productivity News. (Management Development Centre) (TR) **1025**
Productivity News. (II) **1083**
Productivity Perspectives see American Productivity & Quality Center. Perspectives (Year) **1002**
Productivity S A. (SA) **1025**
Productivity Software. (US) **1479**
Productiv's Handbuch fuer Musiker. (GW) **4461, 3575**
Productiv's Solo. (GW) **4461, 3575**
Productos Nuevos de Dinamarca see New Products from Denmark **5246**
Productronic. (GW ISSN 0722-6012) **1777**
Productronica. (SP ISSN 0213-571X) **1083**
Products. (US) **3838**
Products Finishing. (US ISSN 0032-9940) **3655, 4606**
Products Finishing Directory. (US ISSN 0478-4251) **3655, 4606**
Products Liability. (US) **2668, 1083**
Products Liability: Design and Manufacturing Defects. (US) **2668, 1083**
Products Liability Law Journal. (US) **2668, 1507**
Products Liability Reporter. (US ISSN 0162-122X) **2668, 686**
Products of Uruguay. (UY) **1083**
Produits Alimentaires & Boissons. see Danmark Export: Food & Beverages **905**
Produits pour l'Industrie Quebecoise. (CN ISSN 0701-1687) **4607**
Produkt Atlas: Industrielle Elektronik see Grosse Elektronik Atlas **1771**
Produkthaftpflicht International. (GW ISSN 0723-3604) **2540**
Produktion. (GW ISSN 0032-9967) **1083**
Produktion. (DK ISSN 0108-5883) **1083**
Produktion-Plannung-Steuerung Report see P P S Report **1023**
Produktions Nyt. (DK ISSN 0106-0104) **3022**
Produktions Nyts Leverandoerregister. (DK) **3022, 3418**
Produktionshaandbogen. (DK) **4005, 37**
Produktionsmenge und Produktionswert der Verpackungsindustrie in der Bundesrepublik. (GW ISSN 0724-5661) **3651**
Produktivnost. (YU ISSN 0032-9975) **1083**
Produktnieuws voor Kantoor en Bedrijf see Kantoor Revue **1059**
Produktnoeglen for Transportemballageindkoebere see Transport (Aarlig) **5291**
Produktschap voor Siergewassen. Jaarverslag see Produktschap voor Siergewassen. Jaarverslag - Statistiek **2137**
Produktschap voor Siergewassen. Jaarverslag - Statistiek. (NE) **2137**

Produktschap voor Siergewassen. Statistiek see Produktschap voor Siergewassen. Jaarverslag - Statistiek **2137**
Produktwijzer - Elektres. (NE ISSN 0922-615X) **1906**
Produsenten see Bondebladet **80**
Produtos e Tecnicas see P & T **627**
Produzione Animale. (IT ISSN 0033-0000) **224**
Produzione e Consumo di Energia Elettrica in Italia. (IT) **1800, 1802**
Proem Pamphlets. (UK) **3003**
Profesional. (EC) **2880**
Profesiones y Empresas. (SP) **1714**
Profession. (US ISSN 0740-6959) **2835, 2950**
Profession Architecte. (FR) **305**
Profession Negoce et Bricolage see Profession Negociant - Bricolage **2501**
Profession Negociant - Bricolage. (FR) **2501**
Profession Textile. (FR ISSN 0299-3678) **1294**
Professional. (US) **1834, 2020**
Professional. (IT) **3655, 640, 642**
Professional see Jolly **4361**
Professional A D P A Newsletter see A D P A Professional **1532**
Professional Accountancy Student Service see P A S S **754**
Professional Activity Study Reporter see P A S Reporter **5254**
Professional Administration see Administrator **4083**
Professional Administrator see Corporate Management **1006**
Professional Advisers to New Issues. (UK) **796**
Professional Agent. (US ISSN 0148-8899) **2540**
†Professional and Industrial Photographic Equipment. (AT) **5262**
Professional and Trade Organisations in India. (II ISSN 0079-5925) **1151**
Professional Apartment Management. (US ISSN 0891-2599) **4154, 2668**
Professional Approaches for Christian Educators. (US) **4196, 1656**
Professional Approaches for Christian Educators see P A C E **5254**
Professional Aviation Maintenance Association News see P A M A News **60**
Professional Boatbuilder. (US) **4528**
Professional Bowlers Association of America Tour Official Program (Year) see P B A Tour Official Program (Year) **4483**
Professional Broker. (US) **4655**
Professional Builder see Professional Builder & Remodeler **628**
Professional Builder. (SA) **628**
Professional Builder. (UK) **640, 2302**
Professional Builder and House Remodeller see Professional Builder **640**
Professional Builder & Remodeler. (US) **628**
Professional Builder & Remodeler Consumer Study Annual. (US) **628, 1507**
Professional Builder & Remodeler Custom - Luxury Trends. (US) **628, 305, 2554**
Professional Builder & Remodeler House Plans Annual. (US) **628**
Professional Builder & Remodeler Product Technology Annual. (US) **629**
Professional Car Washing see Professional Car Washing & Detailing **4700**
Professional Car Washing & Detailing. (US) **4700**
†Professional Careers Magazine. (US) **5262**
Professional Christian Counselor. (US) **4039, 4196**
Professional Circle see Circle **4469**
Professional Communicator. (US ISSN 0891-1207) **1342**
Professional Computing. (AT) **1424**
Professional Consultant. (US) **37, 1025, 1050**

Professional Consultant and Information Marketing Report see Professional Consultant **37**
Professional Corporation of Physicians of Quebec. Bulletin. (CN) **3144**
Professional Corporations Handbook. (US) **686**
Professional Counselor Magazine. (US ISSN 1042-7570) **1538**
Professional Development Journal see Prism **1656**
Professional Document Retrieval. (US ISSN 8755-0253) **2779**
Professional Edge. (CN) **1834**
Professional Educator. (US ISSN 0196-786X) **1758**
Professional Electrician and Installer. (UK) **1906**
Professional Electronics. (US) **1906**
Professional Electronics Yearbook. (US) **1777**
Professional Engineer see Engineer **1819**
Professional Engineer. (AT) **1834**
Professional Engineer. (II ISSN 0033-0078) **1834**
The Professional Engineer (Raleigh). (US) **1834**
Professional Engineer, Geologist, Geophysicist see P E G G **1833**
Professional Engineer in Nova Scotia see Engineer **1819**
Professional Engineering. (UK ISSN 0953-6639) **1938**
Professional Farm Management Guidebook. (AT ISSN 0312-889X) **156**
Professional Fisherman. (AT ISSN 0156-403X) **2047**
Professional Floral Designer. (US) **2143**
Professional Forester. (CN) **2106**
Professional Freelance Writers Directory.(US) **2574**
Professional Furniture Merchant see P F M **5254**
Professional Geographer. (US ISSN 0033-0124) **2260**
Professional Golfers' Association of America Magazine see P G A Magazine **4509**
Professional Grounds Management Society Newsletter see P G M S Newsletter **2136**
Professional Group on Circuit Theory Transactions see I E E E Transactions on Circuits and Systems Part 2: Analog and Digital Signal Processing **1772**
Professional Horticulture. (UK ISSN 0950-0928) **2137**
Professional Hotel and Restaurant Interiors. (UK) **2554, 2479**
Professional Institute of the Public Service of Canada. Communications. (CN ISSN 0318-0646) **4070**
Professional Insurance Agents of New York - New Jersey - Connecticut. (US) **2540**
Professional Interiors see Professional Hotel and Restaurant Interiors **2554**
Professional Investor. (US ISSN 0889-0897) **960**
Professional Landscaper. (UK) **2137, 305**
Professional Lawyer. (US ISSN 1042-5675) **2668**
▼Professional Liability Litigation Reporter. (US) **2668**
Professional Liability Reporter. (US ISSN 0145-3505) **2668, 992**
Professional Liability Today. (UK ISSN 0268-9669) **2540, 686, 2668**
Professional Licensing Report. (US ISSN 1043-2051) **2668**
Professional Locksmithing see Safe & Vault Technology **643**
†Professional Marketing Report. (US ISSN 0160-0362) **5262**
Professional Medical Assistant. (US ISSN 0033-0140) **3144**
Professional Medical Assistant see P M A **3285**
Professional Model Newsletter. (US) **4851, 1294**
†Professional Monitor. (US) **5262**
Professional Negligence. (UK ISSN 0267-078X) **2669**
Professional Nurse. (UK) **3285**

Professional Office Design see Designer Specifier **5179**
†Professional Office Manager. (US) **5262**
Professional Officer. (AT ISSN 0048-5454) **2588**
Professional Officer. (UK) **4070**
Professional Photographer. (UK) **3796**
Professional Photographer. (US ISSN 0033-0167) **3796**
Professional Photographer Directory and Buyer's Guide. (UK) **1151, 3796**
Professional Photographic Equipment Directory and Buying Guide. (US) **3796**
Professional Photography. (IT) **3796**
Professional Photography. see Tzeilum Miktzoei **3797**
Professional Photography in Australia. (AT ISSN 0159-8880) **3796**
Professional Pilot see Combat Crew **3454**
Professional Pilot Magazine. (US ISSN 0555-3407) **4676**
Professional Placement Newsnotes. (US) **3630**
†Professional Practice Development. (UK) **5262**
Professional Printer. (UK ISSN 0308-4205) **4005**
Professional Production. (GW ISSN 0932-0393) **3516**
†Professional Promotion Media Directory. (UK ISSN 0267-5528) **5262**
Professional Psychology: Research and Practice. (US ISSN 0735-7028) **4039**
†Professional Publishing Media Directory. (UK) **5262**
Professional Quilter. (US ISSN 0891-5237) **1117, 3592**
Professional Register of Artists see Register of Performers & Composers **3577**
Professional Register of Private Teachers of Music see Register of Professional Private Music Teachers **3577**
▼Professional Renovation Magazine. (CN) **629**
▼Professional Report of Industrial and Office Real Estate. (US) **4155**
Professional Responsibility see B A R - B R I Bar Review. Professional Responsibility **2603**
Professional Roofing. (US ISSN 0199-7742) **629**
Professional Safety. (US ISSN 0099-0027) **3620**
Professional Sanitarian. (US) **4110**
Professional Sanitation Management see Environmental Management **4100**
Professional School Psychology see School Psychology Quarterly **4046**
†Professional Secretary. (UK ISSN 0957-5936) **5262**
†Professional Secretary - Administrative Support Letter. (US) **5262**
Professional Selling. (US) **1050**
†Professional Selling: Financial Services Edition. (US) **5262**
▼Professional Sound. (CN ISSN 1186-1797) **3575**
Professional Spraying. (US) **3655**
Professional Staff Congress Clarion see P S C Clarion **1714**
Professional Stained Glass. (US ISSN 0885-1808) **356, 1165**
Professional Surveyor. (US ISSN 0278-1425) **1872, 2260**
†Professional T V & Radio Media Directory. (UK) **5262**
Professional Tape Reader. (US) **960**
Professional Teacher. (UK ISSN 0269-0411) **1656**
Professional Telephone Selling. (US) **1050**
Professional Theatre for Young Audiences. (US) **4637, 1263, 1758**
Professional Timing Service. (US) **960**
▼Professional Tool and Equipment News. (US) **4700**
†Professional Trainer. (US) **5262**
Professional Translator and Interpreter. (UK ISSN 0955-615X) **2835**

†Professional Upholsterer. (US) **5262**
Professional Women and Minorities. (US ISSN 0190-1796) **3630, 4851**
Professional Women Photographers Newsletter see P W P Newsletter **3794**
Professional Wrestling/Shu-Kan. (JA) **4484**
Professionalita. (IT ISSN 0392-2790) **1714**
Professional's Guide to Patient Drug Facts. (US) **3741**
Professional's Guide to Public Relations Services. (US) **37**
Professioneallevatore. (IT) **224, 3611**
Professionele Fotografie. (NE) **3796**
Professions and Projects Register. (SA) **629, 305**
Professions et Entreprises. (FR ISSN 0033-0213) **1025**
Professor see Professor an A H S & B H S **1656**
Professor an A H S & B H S. (AU) **1656**
Profi am Steuer. (GW) **4700**
Profifoto. (GW) **3796, 1378, 3516**
Profil. (GW) **1322**
Profil. (AU) **2173**
Profil. (GW ISSN 0344-7065) **2191**
Profile see E S O P Report **1008**
Profile see Canadian Ski Pro Canadien **4543**
Profile (Los Angeles). (US) **821**
Profile (Norfolk). (US ISSN 0145-112X) **3468**
Profile (Omaha). (US ISSN 0162-5241) **821**
ProFile (Topeka). (US ISSN 0190-8766) **305**
Profile (Washington). (US) **3575, 4637**
Profile (Wheaton). (US) **1686, 1758**
Profile of Electoral Districts. (CN) **4081**
Profile of Jewish Dissidents Series. (CN) **2020, 3969**
†Profile of the Sao Paulo Stock Exchange. (BL) **5262**
Profile of the Worldwide Semiconductor Industry. (UK ISSN 0951-5631) **1777**
Profiles see Montanan **1318**
Profiles. (NE) **3778**
Profiles (Arlington). (US) **3920**
†Profiles (Solana Beach). (US ISSN 8755-464X) **5262**
Profiles in Healthcare Marketing. (US ISSN 0275-9632) **1050, 4110**
Profiles of Earnings in Cyprus: by Education, Occupation, Experience, Age, Sex and Sector. (CY) **736, 4584**
†Profiles of Ohio Lawyers. (US) **5262**
Profils Economiques. (FR ISSN 0247-5421) **881**
Profils I F P. (FR) **3700**
Profils Medico-Sociaux. (FR ISSN 0339-3666) **3144**
Profit. (CN) **686**
Profit see Handelspartner **816**
†Profit (Studio City). (US) **5262**
Profit Center. (US ISSN 0894-2641) **305**
Profit Sharing. (US ISSN 0033-0280) **960, 992**
Profit-Statistics of the Limited Liability Companies. see Netherlands. Centraal Bureau voor de Statistiek. Winststatistiek der Grotere Naamloze Vennootschappen **5244**
Profit Strategy Letter. (US) **960**
Profitability by Line by State. (US) **2547, 2669**
Profitability of Citrus Growing in Israel/ Ha-Rivhiyut shel Gidul ha-Darim. (IS) **156**
Profitability of Cotton Growing in Israel/ Ha-Rivhiyut shel Gidul ha-Kutnah. (IS ISSN 0079-595X) **156**
Profitability of Dairy in Israel/Ha-Rivhiyut shel 'anaf ha-Refet. (IS) **156, 203**
Profitability of Poultry Farming in Israel/Ha-Rivhiyut shel-Anaf ha-Lul. (IS ISSN 0079-5968) **156, 224**
Profitable Craft Merchandising. (US) **2440, 1050, 1117**
Profitable Gifts. (UK ISSN 0958-5133) **2282**

Profitable Greetings. (UK ISSN 0266-7703) **2282**
Profitable Hobby Merchandising see Profitable Craft Merchandising **2440**
Profitable Machine Knitting. (UK ISSN 0954-5468) **1117**, **1287**
Profitips fuer Selbermacher. (GW ISSN 0930-7133) **2501**
†Profitmaker. (US) **5262**
▼Profitravel. (GW ISSN 0932-4631) **4783**
Profits. (US) **1117**
Profodcil Bulletin. (Il ISSN 0030-8242) **2080**
Profsoyuzy i Vremya see Vremya **2591**
Progenitor. (AT) **2162**
Progettare. (IT) **3022**
Progettare & Costruire. (IT) **629**
Progettista Industriale. (IT ISSN 0392-4823) **3022**
Progetto (Milan). (IT ISSN 0391-741X) **1938**
Progetto (Rome). (IT) **2206**
Progetto (Turin). (IT ISSN 0391-5514) **2206**
Progetto: Rivista di Progettazione di Macchine. (IT) **3022**
Prognostico. (BL ISSN 0100-526X) **190**
Prognostico da Agricultura Paulista see Prognostico **190**
†Prognostico Regiao Centro-Sul. (BL ISSN 0100-5316) **5262**
Program. (UK ISSN 0033-0337) **2799**
Program Manager. (US ISSN 0199-7114) **1438**, **3468**
†Program News. (US) **5263**
Program on Central and Eastern Europe Working Paper Series. (US) **2381**
Program Plans: Nursing Basic Series. (US ISSN 0734-1431) **3286**
Program Statistics - Michigan Department of Social Services see Michigan. Department of Social Services. Program Statistics **4426**
Program Trends for Business & Industry. (US) **1730**, **1714**
Program Trends in Museum Education. (US) **1656**
Programa. (UY) **341**
Programa. (PO) **4637**
Programa de Estudios Conjuntos para la Integracion Economica Latinoamericano Ensayos E C I E L see Ensayos E C I E L **863**
Programa Regional del Empleo para America Latina y el Caribe Investigaciones sobre Empleo see P R E A L C Investigaciones sobre Empleo **878**
Programa Regional del Empleo para America Latina y el Carige Newsletter see P R E A L C Newsletter **3630**
Programaids. (US) **4247**
Ihr Programm. (GW) **2381**, **3969**
Programm Wien. (AU) **4783**
Programmable Logic Controller Insider's Newsletter see P L C Insider's Newsletter **1454**
Programmazione in Sardegna. (IT) **1083**
Programme Applique a la Selection et la Compilation Automatique de la Literature Plan de Classement P A S C A L see Plan de Classement P A S C A L **2799**
Programmed Learning and Educational Technology see Educational and Training Technology International **1748**
Programmed Learning and Individually Paced Instruction - Bibliography see Individually Paced or Self Teaching Instruction Source Book **403**
†Programmer's Journal. (US) **5263**
Programming and Computer Software. (English translation of: Programmirovanie) (US ISSN 0361-7688) **1431**, **1479**
Programming Trends in Therapeutic Recreation. (US) **1740**, **2739**, **4484**
Programs-in-Progress Encyclopedia see E A Supplement **1780**

Programs in Public Affairs and Administration see Graduate Programs in Public Affairs and Public Administration **4062**
Programs of the Woman's Building. Newsletter see Woman's Building. Calendar **350**
Progres Agricole et Viticole. (FR) **190**
Progres Contre le Cancer. see Progress Against Cancer **3201**
Progres des Recherches Pharmaceutiques. see Fortschritte der Arzneimittelforschung **3727**
Le Progres Egyptien. (UA) **2186**
Progres Social. (GP) **4445**
Progres Technique. (FR ISSN 0397-8060) **4607**, **4334**
Progreso. (MX ISSN 0033-0485) **882**
Progreso. (US) **1025**
Progreso. (BE ISSN 0048-5489) **2835**
Progreso Economico y Social en America Latina. Informe see Economic and Social Progress in Latin America; Annual Report **861**
Progreso en Puerto Rico. see Progress in Puerto Rico **796**
Progresos de Obstetricia y Ginecologia. (SP ISSN 0304-5013) **3296**
Progresos en Diagnostico Prenatal. (SP ISSN 1130-0523) **3296**
Progress see Dealer Progress **175**
Progress. (AT ISSN 1035-1396) **882**
Progress. (UK ISSN 0033-0566) **2295**
Progress. (PK ISSN 0033-0574) **3700**
Progress see Democrat **3890**
Progress/Postup. (CN ISSN 0033-054X) **4273**
Progress. see Jinzhan **4317**
Progress (Columbus). (US) **4110**
Progress (Medford). (US) **4196**, **3778**
†Progress (Muscle Shoals). (US ISSN 0730-7322) **5263**
Progress (Springfield) see Environmental Progress (Springfield) **1953**
Progress Against Cancer/Progres Contre le Cancer. (CN ISSN 0033-0604) **3201**
Progress & Care. (US ISSN 0033-0612) **2468**, **3144**
Progress and Topics in Cytogenetics. (US ISSN 0733-9003) **546**
Progress in Aerospace Sciences. (US ISSN 0376-0421) **60**
Progress in Agriculture. see Unnatkrishi **127**
†Progress in Agriculture. (CN) **5263**
Progress in Allergy see Chemical Immunology **3184**
Progress in Analytical Spectroscopy see Spectrochimica Acta Reviews **1208**
Progress in Anesthesiology. (US ISSN 0099-1546) **3192**
Progress in Applied Microcirculation. (SZ ISSN 0254-5195) **3211**
Progress in Astronautics. see Postepy Astronautyki **60**
Progress in Astronautics and Aeronautics Series. (US ISSN 0079-6050) **60**
Progress in Astronomy. see Tianwenxue Jinzhan **370**
Progress in Basic and Clinical Pharmacology. (SZ ISSN 1011-0267) **3741**
Progress in Behavior Modification. (US ISSN 0099-037X) **4039**
Progress in Biochemical Pharmacology. (SZ ISSN 0079-6085) **3741**
Progress in Biochemistry and Biophysics. see Shengwu Huaxue yu Shengwu Wuli Jinzhan **482**
Progress in Biometeorology. (NE) **3440**
Progress in Biophysics & Molecular Biology. (US ISSN 0079-6107) **486**
Progress in Botany. (US ISSN 0340-4773) **515**
Progress in Brain Research. (NE ISSN 0079-6123) **3350**
Progress in Cancer Research and Therapy. (US ISSN 0145-3726) **3201**

Progress in Cardiology. (US ISSN 0097-109X) **3211**
Progress in Cardiovascular Diseases. (US ISSN 0033-0620) **3211**, **3273**
Progress in Cardiovascular Nursing. (US ISSN 0889-7204) **3211**, **3286**
†Progress in Chemical Fibrinolysis and Thrombolysis. (US ISSN 0361-0233) **5263**
†Progress in Chemical Toxicology. (US ISSN 0079-6158) **5263**
Progress in Chemistry and Chemical Industry. (KO) **1186**, **1859**
Progress in Clinical and Biological Research. (US ISSN 0361-7742) **3144**, **452**
Progress in Clinical Biochemistry and Medicine. (US) **481**
†Progress in Clinical Neurophysiology. (SZ ISSN 0378-4045) **5263**
Progress in Colloid and Polymer Science. (US ISSN 0340-255X) **1229**, **1222**
Progress in Communication Sciences. (US ISSN 0163-5689) **1342**, **2779**
†Progress in Computer-Aided V L S I Design. (US ISSN 1052-6692) **5263**
Progress in Coronary Sinus Interventions. (US) **3211**
†Progress in Critical Care Medicine. (SZ ISSN 0254-623X) **5263**
Progress in Crystal Growth and Characterization see Progress in Crystal Growth and Characterization of Materials **1211**
Progress in Crystal Growth and Characterization of Materials. (US ISSN 0960-8974) **1211**
Progress in Cybernetics. see Postepy Cybernetyki **1442**
†Progress in Cybernetics and Systems Research. (US ISSN 0275-8717) **5263**
Progress in Dermatology. (US ISSN 0033-0639) **3249**
Progress in Drug Research. see Fortschritte der Arzneimittelforschung **3727**
Progress in Ecology see Recent Researches in Ecology, Environment and Pollution **453**
Progress in Endocrine Research and Therapy. (US) **3255**
Progress in Energy and Combustion Science. (US ISSN 0360-1285) **1859**, **1794**
Progress in Environmental Science & Technology. (Il) **1966**, **4828**
Progress in Experimental Tumor Research. (SZ ISSN 0079-6263) **3201**
Progress in Filtration and Separation. (NE) **1186**
Progress in Food & Nutrition Science. (US ISSN 0306-0632) **3611**
Progress in Geotechnical Engineering. (Il) **1578**, **1593**, **1872**
Progress in Growth Factor Research. (US ISSN 0955-2235) **561**, **3255**
Progress in Hematology. (US ISSN 0079-6301) **3273**
Progress in Hemostasis see Progress in Hemostasis and Thrombosis **3211**
Progress in Hemostasis and Thrombosis. (US) **3211**
Progress in High Temperature Superconductivity. (SI) **3829**
Progress in Histochemistry and Cytochemistry. (GW ISSN 0079-6336) **481**, **526**
Progress in Human Geography. (UK ISSN 0309-1325) **2260**
Progress in Industrial Microbiology. (NE ISSN 0555-3989) **556**
Progress in Inorganic Chemistry. (US ISSN 0079-6379) **1214**
Progress in Lipid Research. (US ISSN 0163-7827) **1222**
Progress in Low Temperature Physics. (NE ISSN 0079-6417) **3841**
†Progress in Marketing. (UK ISSN 0952-4452) **5263**
Progress in Materials Handling and Logistics. (US) **3022**

Progress in Materials Science. (US ISSN 0079-6425) **1922**
Progress in Mathematics, Physics and Astronomy. see Pokroky Matematiky, Fyziky a Astronomie **4334**
Progress in Medical Microbiology. see Fortschritte der Medizinischen Mikrobiologie **552**
Progress in Medical Virology. (SZ ISSN 0079-645X) **3223**, **556**
Progress in Medicinal Chemistry. (NE ISSN 0079-6468) **1186**, **3144**
Progress in Molecular and Subcellular Biology. (US ISSN 0079-6484) **526**
Progress in Mutation Research. (NE) **546**
▼Progress in Natural Science. (CC ISSN 1002-0071) **4334**
▼Progress in Neural Networks. (US ISSN 1055-713X) **1410**, **3350**
Progress in Neuro-Psychopharmacology and Biological Psychiatry. (UK ISSN 0278-5846) **3741**
Progress in Neurobiology. (US ISSN 0301-0082) **452**
Progress in Neuroendocrin Immunology.(US ISSN 1045-2001) **3188**
Progress in Neurological Surgery. (SZ ISSN 0079-6492) **3350**, **3383**
Progress in Neuropathology. (US) **3350**
Progress in Nuclear Energy. (US ISSN 0149-1970) **1208**, **1186**, **1809**
Progress in Nuclear Magnetic Resonance Spectroscopy. (US ISSN 0079-6565) **3850**, **1809**, **3857**
Progress in Nuclear Medicine see Recent Advances in Nuclear Medicine **3362**
Progress in Nucleic Acid Research and Molecular Biology. (US ISSN 0079-6603) **452**
†Progress in Obstetrics and Gynaecology. (UK ISSN 0261-0140) **5263**
Progress in Oceanography. (US ISSN 0079-6611) **1610**
Progress in Optics. (NE ISSN 0079-6638) **3857**
Progress in Organic Coatings. (SZ ISSN 0033-0655) **3655**, **1222**
Progress in Particle and Nuclear Physics. (US ISSN 0146-6410) **3850**
Progress in Passive Solar Energy Systems see American Solar Energy Society. Passive Conference. Annual Meeting **1810**
▼Progress in Pediatric Cardiology. (US ISSN 1058-9813) **3211**, **3325**
Progress in Pediatric Surgery. (US ISSN 0079-6654) **3325**, **3383**
Progress in Pesticide Biochemistry see Progress in Pesticide Biochemistry and Toxicology **190**
Progress in Pesticide Biochemistry and Toxicology. (UK ISSN 0730-1898) **190**, **1983**
Progress in Phycological Research. (NE) **515**
Progress in Physical Geography. (UK ISSN 0309-1333) **2260**
Progress in Physical Organic Chemistry.(US ISSN 0079-6662) **1229**, **1222**
†Progress in Physics. (US) **5263**
Progress in Physiological Sciences. see Shengli Kexue Jinzhan **574**
Progress in Planning. (US ISSN 0305-9006) **2494**
Progress in Polymer Science. (US ISSN 0079-6700) **1222**, **1859**
†Progress in Powder Metallurgy. (US ISSN 0079-6719) **5263**
Progress in Protozoology. (US) **590**
Progress in Psychobiology and Physiological Psychology. (US) **4039**
Progress in Puerto Rico/Progreso en Puerto Rico. (PR) **796**
Progress in Quantum Electronics. (US ISSN 0079-6727) **1777**
Progress in Reaction Kinetics. (US ISSN 0079-6743) **1229**
Progress in Reproductive Biology and Medicine. (SZ ISSN 0254-105X) **3286**, **574**

Progress in Respiration Research. (SZ ISSN 0079-6751) **3366**
Progress in Retinal Research. (US ISSN 0278-4327) **3304**
▼Progress in Robotics and Intelligent Systems. (US) **1410**
Progress in Rubber and Plastics Technology. (UK ISSN 0266-7320) **4293**, 3867
Progress in Self Psychology. (US ISSN 0893-5483) **4039**
Progress in Sensory Physiology. (US ISSN 0721-9156) **3144**
▼Progress in Simulation. (US) **1435**
Progress in Solar Energy see American Solar Energy Society. Annual Meeting **1810**
Progress in Solid State Chemistry. (US ISSN 0079-6786) **1229**
Progress in Surface and Membrane Science. (US) **1229**
Progress in Surface Science. (US ISSN 0079-6816) **3829**
Progress in Surgery. (SZ ISSN 0079-6824) **3383**
Progress in the Chemistry of Organic Natural Products. see Fortschritte der Chemie Organischer Naturstoffe **1218**
Progress in Theoretical Organic Chemistry. (NE) **1222**
Progress in Tourism, Recreation and Hospitality Management. (UK ISSN 0952-5424) **4783**, 2479
†Progress in Underwater Science. (UK ISSN 0959-2822) **5263**
▼Progress in Veterinary & Comparative Ophthalmology. (US) **4814**, 3304
†Progress in Veterinary Microbiology and Immunology. (SZ ISSN 0255-3686) **5263**
▼Progress in Veterinary Neurology. (US) **4814**
Progress in Zoology. see Fortschritte der Zoologie **583**
Progress: International Exchange in Trade, Science and Technology. see Jinzhan: Guoji Maoyi yu Keji Jiaoliu **914**
Progress Notes. (US) **4039**
Progress of Digestive Endoscopy. see Shokaki Naishikyo no Shinpo **3270**
Progress of Education. (II ISSN 0033-0663) **1656**
Progress of Education in Saudi Arabia. (SU) **1679**, 1723
†Progress of Education in the United States of America. (US) **5263**
Progress of Physics. see Fortschritte der Physik **3818**
Progress of Public Education in the United States see Progress of Education in the United States of America **5263**
Progress of Rubber Technology see Progress in Rubber and Plastics Technology **4293**
Progress of Theoretical Physics/Riron Butsurigaku no Shinpo. (JA ISSN 0033-068X) **3829**
Progress Polimernoi Khimii. (RU ISSN 0079-6883) **1222**
Progress Report. (US) **3144**
Progress Report - New Mexico Bureau of Mines & Mineral Resources see New Mexico. Bureau of Mines and Mineral Resources. Progress Report **3491**
Progress Towards European Integration see Work of the European Parliament **5306**
Progress Wales. (UK ISSN 0019-8854) **821**
Progressi Clinici: Chirurgia. (IT ISSN 0393-764X) **3383**
Progressi Clinici: Medicina. (IT ISSN 0393-7658) **3144**
Progressi in Patologia Cardiovascolare. (Italian translation of: Progress in Cardiovascular Disease) (IT ISSN 0033-0701) **3211**
Progressio. (SA ISSN 0256-8853) **1758**
Progressio. (IT ISSN 0033-0728) **4287**
Progression. (CN) **1300**
Progressiste. (MQ) **3920**
Progressive (Madison). (US ISSN 0033-0736) **3920**

Progressive Architecture. (US ISSN 0033-0752) **305**
Progressive Builder see Custom Builder **615**
Progressive Computer Software Advisor see P C S Advisor **1472**
Progressive Farmer. (US ISSN 0033-0760) **115**
Progressive Farming. (PK) **115**
Progressive Fish-Culturist. (US ISSN 0033-0779) **2047**
Progressive Grocer. (US ISSN 0033-0787) **2093**
Progressive Grocer's Annual Report of the Grocery Industry. (US) **2093**
Progressive Grocer's Annual Report of the Grocery Trade see Progressive Grocer's Annual Report of the Grocery Industry **2093**
Progressive Grocer's Directory of Convenience Stores. (US) **2080**
Progressive Grocer's Directory of Mass Merchandisers. (US ISSN 0890-7986) **1151**, 2080
Progressive Grocer's Market Scope. (US ISSN 0146-9223) **2080**, 1151
Progressive Grocer's Marketing Guidebook. (US ISSN 0079-6921) **2080**
Progressive Mail Trade see Mail Trade **1045**
Progressive Media see C M J New Music Report **3543**
Progressive Periodicals Directory. (US) **4142**, 2578
Progressive Periodicals Directory Update. (US) **409**
Progressive Platter Music Review. (US ISSN 0738-8861) **3575**
Progressive Railroading. (US ISSN 0033-0817) **4713**
Progressive Rentals. (US ISSN 8750-6106) **1025**
Progressive Review. (US ISSN 0889-2202) **2880**
Progressive Teacher. (US ISSN 0033-0825) **1656**
Progressive Utilization Theory Press see P R O U T Press **2231**
Progressive Young Farmer. (UK) **115**
Progresso Fotografico. (IT ISSN 0033-0868) **3796**
Il Progresso Medico. (IT ISSN 0370-1514) **3145**
Project. (US) **3920**, 2320
▼Project Analyse. (NE) **2494**
Project Appraisal. (UK ISSN 0268-8867) **960**, 4607
Project Concern News see Concern News **4402**
†Project Defnyddiau ac Adnoddau y Swyddfa Gymreig. (UK) **5263**
Project Magazine. (CN) **1834**
Project Management Journal. (US ISSN 8756-9728) **1025**
Project Management Network see P M Network **1023**
†Project Personeelsvoorziening Kwartaire Sector. Bulletin. (NE) **5263**
Project Planning and Control for Construction. (US) **2494**, 629
Project Scotland. (UK) **629**
†Project Skywater. Annual Report. (US ISSN 0079-6956) **5263**
†Project Update. (US) **5263**
Projected Capital Costs: U S Electric Utility Plants. (US) **1802**
Projection (Montreal). (CN) **2020**
Projection (Toronto). (CN ISSN 0229-2947) **1538**
Projections of Education Statistics. (US) **1656**
Projecto Historia. (BL) **2320**
Projecto I2 do PIDDAC. Boletim. (PO ISSN 0870-4724) **3440**
Projekt. (CS) **305**
Projekt. (PL ISSN 0033-0957) **341**
Projekt Umwelt und Gesundheit. (GW) **1966**
Projektio. (FI ISSN 0356-4096) **3516**
Projektowanie i Systemy. (PL ISSN 0239-3174) **4607**
Projektresumeer see Denmark. Statens Byggeforskningsinstitut.
Projektresumeer **5178**
Projet. (FR ISSN 0033-0884) **4383**
Projeto. (BL) **1083**

Prokla. (GW) **686**
Prolactin. (UK ISSN 0142-8276) **3255**, 481
Proletarian Path. (II) **3920**
Proletarian Revolution. (US ISSN 0894-0754) **3920**
Prolife News. (CN ISSN 0715-4356) **4110**, 546, 598, 3296
Prolix. (GW) **3575**
Prologue (Medford). (US ISSN 0033-1007) **4637**, 1656
Prologue (Milwaukee). (US) **4637**
Prologue (Washington). (US ISSN 0033-1031) **2419**, 2381
Promacasa. (MX) **629**
Promat News. (SA) **3022**
†Promecanica. (SP ISSN 0214-3135) **5263**
Promenade. (US) **2232**, 4783
Promet. (GW ISSN 0340-4552) **3440**
Prometeo. (MX) **3778**
†Prometeo (Messina). (IT) **5263**
Prometeo (Milan). (IT) **2320**
Promethean. (US) **1322**
Promethee. (FR ISSN 0181-0146) **2950**
Promethee. (BE ISSN 0033-1082) **4334**
Prometheus. (AT ISSN 0810-9028) **1342**
Prometheus (Florence). (IT) **1279**
Prometheus (Milan). (IT) **3920**
Promien. (US ISSN 0033-1090) **2020**, 1263
Promin. (CN ISSN 0380-2140) **2020**, 4851
Promise. (US) **3003**, 2950
Promissory Note Survey. (AT ISSN 0729-2910) **796**
Promo. (US ISSN 1047-1707) **1050**
Promobil. (GW) **4700**, 4783
▼Promobile. (CN) **4700**
Promofluid. (FR) **1925**
Promosafe. (BE ISSN 0771-2782) **3620**
Promoteur Zairois. (ZR) **919**
Promotieservice. (NE) **1050**
Promoting Church Music see Church Music Quarterly **3545**
▼Promoting Store Traffic. (US) **1050**, 37
Promotion de la Sante see Health Promotion **4103**
†Promotion Digest. (US ISSN 0891-1681) **5263**
Promotion Exchange see Ad-Pro **5130**
Promotion Immobiliere. (FR) **4155**
Promotion Newsletter. (US) **1050**, 1378
Promotion Power. (US) **1050**
Promotions that Work see Promotion Newsletter **1050**
Promotor de Educacion Cristiana. (US ISSN 0033-1139) **4247**
Prompt. (JA) **1479**
Prompt. (US ISSN 0033-1147) **4637**
†Prompt Report of the Scientific Survey of the South Pacific. (JA) **5263**
PROMT see Predicasts Overview of Markets and Technology **1846**
Promyshlennaya Energetika. (RU ISSN 0033-1155) **1794**, 1906
Promyshlennaya Teplotekhnika. (KR ISSN 0204-3602) **1938**
Promyshlennoe Stroitel'stvo. (RU ISSN 0033-118X) **629**
Promyshlennost' Armenii. (RU ISSN 0033-1163) **1083**
Promyshlennost' Belorussii. (RU ISSN 0033-1171) **1083**
Promyshlennye Obraztsy. Tovarnye Znaki. (RU ISSN 0208-2888) **3678**
Promyshlennyi Transport see Pod'emno-Transportnaya Tekhnika i Sklady **4654**
Pronab. (II ISSN 0033-1201) **2880**
Pronic. (GW) **1906**
Pronto. (US) **882**
Pronto. (SP) **2218**
Prontuario Agroquimico. (MX) **190**
Prontuario de Especialidades Veterinarias. (MX) **4814**
Prontuario Tecnico de la Construccion. (VE) **629**
Proof. (US) **1050**
†Proof. (UK ISSN 0305-7992) **5263**
Proof Collectors Corner. (US) **3601**

PROPOSED APPROVED 6579

Proof Rock. (US) **2880**
Proof Sheet see S A L S in Brief **2782**
Prooficinas. (VE) **1061**
Proofs. (US ISSN 0033-1236) **3241**
Prooftexts. (US ISSN 0272-9601) **4226**, 2950
Propaganda see Markedsfoering **1045**
Propaganda Handbook. see Xuanchuan Shouce **3935**
Propaganda Review. (US) **3920**
Propaganda Rural. (UY) **115**
Propagation & Distribution of Fishes from National Fish Hatcheries for the Fiscal Year. (US ISSN 0197-4106) **2047**
Propane - Canada. (CN ISSN 0033-1260) **3700**
Propane Industry Profile. (US) **3707**, 4584
Propel. (DK ISSN 0033-1279) **60**, 3468
Propellants and Explosives see Propellants, Explosives, Pyrotechnics **1859**
Propellants, Explosives, Pyrotechnics. (GW ISSN 0721-3115) **1859**
Propeller. (US ISSN 0194-6218) **4528**
Propeller Club Quarterly. (US ISSN 0048-5551) **4736**
Proper Dharma Seal. (US) **4287**
Properties. (US ISSN 0033-1287) **4155**, 629
Properties de France. (FR) **4155**
Property and Investment see Lifestyle and London Living **4151**
Property Confidential. (UK) **4155**
†Property Data Update. (US ISSN 0888-6903) **5263**
Property Fortnightly see Property Guide **4155**
Property Guide. (UK) **4155**
Property Journal. (UK ISSN 0033-1309) **4155**
Property Law and Practice in Queensland. (AT ISSN 0727-6346) **2669**, 4155
Property Law Bulletin. (UK ISSN 0144-6517) **2669**
Property Management. (UK ISSN 0263-7472) **4155**
Property Management Association. Bulletin. (UK) **4155**, 1025
Property Management Association Directory see P M A Directory **4154**
Property Management Monthly. (US ISSN 1049-2372) **4155**
Property Market Review see Estates Gazette **4148**
†Property Monthly Review. (UK ISSN 0267-4173) **5263**
Property, Planning and Compensation Reports. (UK) **2669**
Property Register. (UK) **4155**
Property Review. (HK) **4155**
Property Services Agency Specifications see P S A Specifications **2493**
Property Studies in the U.K. and Overseas. (UK ISSN 0305-5752) **4155**
Property Tax Journal. (US ISSN 0731-0285) **4155**
Prophetic Expositor. (CN ISSN 0048-5578) **4196**
Prophetic News and Israel's Watchman see Your Tomorrow **4290**
Prophetic Newsletter. (US ISSN 0033-1341) **4287**
Prophetic Voices. (US ISSN 0734-3027) **2950**, 3778
Prophetic Witness see Your Tomorrow **4290**
Prophygram. (US) **3241**, 3807
Prophylaxe (Heidelberg) see Zentralblatt fuer Arbeitsmedizin, Arbeitsschutz und Prophylaxe **3623**
Prophyta. (NE ISSN 0921-5506) **2137**, 115
†Prophyways. (US) **5263**
Propos de Cuisine. (CN) **629**
Propos de Vol. see Flight Comment **52**
Propos en l'Air see A P a la Une **4669**
Propos Utiles aux Medecins. (FR ISSN 0033-1392) **3145**
Proposed Approved Accounting Standard and Proposed Australian Accounting Standard see Exposure Draft (Accounting Standards) **750**

6580 PROPOSED AUSTRALIAN

Proposed Australian Accounting Standard see Exposure Draft (Accounting Standards) **750**
Proposed Statement of Accounting Concepts. (AT ISSN 1030-5890) **755**
Proposed Statement of Accounting Standards see Exposure Draft (Accounting Standards) **750**
Proposed Statement of Auditing Practice see Exposure Draft (Auditing Practice) **750**
Proposed Statement on Applicability see Exposure Draft (Auditing Practice) **750**
Proprieta Edilizia Lombarda. (IT ISSN 0033-1422) **4155**
Proprieta Fondiaria. (IT) **156**
Proprietary Articles Trade Association. Publication. (UK ISSN 0268-8654) **3741**, 1151
Propriete Agricole. (FR ISSN 0985-1976) **115**
Propriete Industrielle. (UN ISSN 0033-1430) **3678**
Propriete Industrielle Bulletin Documentaire. (FR ISSN 0338-6473) **3678**
Propriete Industrielle, Statistiques B. Partie 1 - Brevets. see Industrial Property, Statistics B. Part 1 - Patents **3679**
Propriete Industrielle, Statistiques B. Partie 2 - Marques de Produits et des Services, Modeles d'Utilit. see Industrial Property, Statistics B. Part 2 - Trademarks and Service Marks, Utility Models, Industrial Designs, Varieties of Plants, Microorganisms **3680**
Propuesta. (UY) **2238**
Propuestas para el Desarrollo. (PE) **2494**
Propulsor. (PO) **4736**
Prorodeo Sports News. (US ISSN 0161-5815) **4484**
ProSales. (US) **629**
Proscopos. (GR ISSN 0033-1465) **1263**, 1300
Prose Monthly. see Sanwen **2957**
Prose Studies. (UK ISSN 0144-0357) **2950**
Prosecution of Felony Arrests (Year). (US) **1525**
Prosecutor. (US ISSN 0027-6383) **2669**
Proserpine Guardian. (AT) **2880**
Prosessori. (FI ISSN 0357-4121) **1415**
Prosit. (US ISSN 0016-6316) **259**
Prospeccion Siglo 21. Venezuela Ano 2000. (VE) **1083**
Prospect. (AT ISSN 0814-7094) **1686**, 2836
Prospect. (SA ISSN 0033-1481) **1859**, 3867
Prospect. (NE) **2494**, 4383
Prospect see Swansea Review **2967**
Prospect (Edinburgh). (UK ISSN 0143-8883) **305**, 629
Prospect (London). (UK) **2540**
Prospect Review. (US) **3003**
Prospect: Western Australia. (AT) **960**
Prospecting in Areas of Glaciated Terrain. (UK ISSN 0141-3376) **1578**
Prospective Payment Survival. (US ISSN 0746-4703) **2468**, 3145
†Prospectives. (CN ISSN 0033-1511) **5263**
Prospector. (US) **1322**
Prospector Exploration & Investment Bulletin. (CN ISSN 1181-6414) **3494**
Prospectors, Diggers & Doers. (US) **2162**
Prospects. (BE) **686**
Prospects see Economic and Financial Prospects **861**
Prospects. (UN) **1656**
Prospects. (UK ISSN 0361-2333) **2420**, 2020
Prospects in Education see Prospects **1656**
Prospectus. (CN) **3920**
Prosperity. (NR ISSN 0048-5608) **882**
Prosperous Times. (US) **2232**

Prospettiva. (IT ISSN 0394-0802) **341**, 282
Prospettiva Sindacale. (IT ISSN 0391-7797) **2588**
Prospettive Culturali. (IT) **2950**
Prospettive Culturali Calabresi. (IT) **3003**, 2880
Prospettive Giovanili see Nuove Prospettive **5250**
Prospettive nel Mondo. (IT) **3920**
Prospettive Psicoanalitiche nel Lavoro Istituzionale. (IT) **3350**
Prospettive Settanta. (IT ISSN 0391-836X) **2513**
†Prospice. (UK ISSN 0308-2776) **5263**
To Prossopo/Face. (CY) **2184**
Prostaglandins. (US ISSN 0090-6980) **3255**
Prostaglandins and Medicine see Prostaglandins, Leukotrienes and Medicine **3256**
Prostaglandins - Biology. (UK ISSN 0142-8284) **3256**, 481
Prostaglandins, Leukotrienes and Medicine. (UK ISSN 0952-3278) **3256**
The Prostate. (US ISSN 0270-4137) **3145**, 3201
Prosthetics and Orthotics International. (DK ISSN 0309-3646) **3145**
Prostor. (KZ ISSN 0131-5587) **2880**
Prosveta. (US) **2020**
Prosvetni Delavec. (XV ISSN 0033-1643) **1656**
Prosvetni Pregled. (YU ISSN 0033-1651) **1656**
Prosvetni Rabotnik. (XN ISSN 0033-1635) **1656**
Prosvjetni List. (BN ISSN 0033-1678) **1656**
Prosvjetni Rad. (YU ISSN 0033-1686) **1656**
Protagora. (IT) **2880**
Proteases and Inhibitors. (UK ISSN 0950-0588) **481**, 3741
Protec. (IT ISSN 1120-1681) **1966**
Protect. (US) **1966**
Protect and Survive Monthly and British Civil Defence News see Journal of Practical Civil Defence **1273**
†Protect Yourself. (CN ISSN 0701-8525) **5263**
Protecting Australian Agriculture. Directory. (AT) **190**
Protecting Children. (US ISSN 0893-4231) **4417**, 1243, 1521
Protecting Consumer Rights. (US) **2669**, 1507
Protection & Indemnity International see P & I International **2539**
Protection de la Nature. see Schweizer Naturschutz **4338**
Protection des Animaux. (FR) **231**
Protection of Assets Bulletin. (US 0740-137X) **1527**
Protection of Atmosphere Against Pollution. (LI ISSN 0203-7483) **1979**, 1214, 1222, 3448
Protection of Metals. (English translation of: Zashchita Metallov) (US ISSN 0033-1732) **3418**
Protection Officer. (US ISSN 0823-9304) **1527**
Protection, Securite, Hygiene du Travail see Revue de la Securite **3621**
Protector. (SZ ISSN 0256-4319) **1521**
Protee. (CN ISSN 0300-3523) **2513**
Protegez-Vous. (CN ISSN 0701-8517) **1507**
†Protein Abnormalities. (US ISSN 0736-4547) **5263**
Protein-Calorie Advisory Group of the United Nations System. P A G Bulletin see Food and Nutrition Bulletin **3605**
Protein Engineering. (UK ISSN 0269-2139) **482**
▼Protein Expression and Purification. (US ISSN 1046-5928) **482**
Protein Identification Resource Newsletter. (US) **452**
Protein, Nucleic Acid, Enzyme. see Tanpakushitsu Kakusan Koso **483**
Protein Phosphorylation see Proteins: Post-Translational Processing **482**
▼Protein Science. (US ISSN 0961-8368) **482**

†Protein Secretion. (UK ISSN 0950-0596) **5263**
†Protein Separation. (UK ISSN 0261-4901) **5263**
Protein Sequences & Data Analysis. (GW ISSN 0931-9506) **452**
†Protein Synthesis. (UK ISSN 0142-8306) **5263**
Proteins: Post-Translational Processing.(UK ISSN 0952-0406) **482**
Proteins: Structure, Function, and Genetics. (US ISSN 0887-3585) **452**
Protestant. (RU) **4196**
Protestant Beacon see Gospel Magazine **4239**
Protestantesimo. (IT ISSN 0033-1767) **4247**
Protestants Christelijke Onderwijsvakorganisatie Magazine see P C O - Magazine **1653**
Protestantse Gezondheidszorg see Intramurale Gezondheidszorg **2466**
Protetyka Stomatologiczna. (PL ISSN 0033-1783) **3241**
Proteus. (US ISSN 0889-6348) **2232**
Proteus. (IT ISSN 0033-1791) **3778**
Proteus. (XV ISSN 0033-1805) **4334**
Protialkoholicky Obzor. (CS) **1538**
Protides of the Biological Fluids. (US ISSN 0079-7065) **452**
Protirodh. (BG) **2174**
Protistologica see European Journal of Protistology **3657**
Protokoll der Sitzung der Gruppe Berliner Mondbeobachter see Gruppe Berliner Mondbeobachter. Protokoll der Sitzung **364**
Protokolle. (AU ISSN 0555-5027) **2950**, 341, 3575
Protokolle zur Fischereitechnik. (GW ISSN 0438-4555) **2047**
Protoplasma. (US ISSN 0033-183X) **526**
Protostar see J C M T - U K I R T Newsletter **366**
Protozoological Abstracts. (UK ISSN 0309-1287) **467**, 20
Proud. (US ISSN 0048-5632) **2020**
Proust Research Association Newsletter. (US ISSN 0048-5659) **2950**
†Prove di Letteratura. (IT ISSN 0033-1848) **5263**
Provenance. (US ISSN 0739-4241) **2420**, 2779
Provence Genealogie. (FR) **2162**
Provence Historique. (FR ISSN 0033-1856) **2381**
Providence Business News. (US ISSN 0887-8226) **686**
Provident Book Finder. (US) **4247**, 2020, 4135, 4213
Province du Maine. (FR ISSN 0033-1880) **2381**
Provincetown Arts. (US ISSN 1053-5012) **341**, 2950
Provincia. (SP) **3003**
Provincia. (AG) **3003**
Provincia di Forli in Cifre. (IT ISSN 0033-1902) **882**
†Provincia di Padova in Cifre. (IT ISSN 0033-1910) **5263**
Provincia Iblea. (IT) **3920**
Provincia Nuova. (IT) **4070**, 2494
Provincia Social. (MX ISSN 0033-1929) **2210**
Provincial Building Trades Yearbook. (CN) **629**
Provincial Drug Benefit Programs. (CN) **3741**
Provincial Farmer. (IE) **115**
Provincial Geologists Journal (Regina). (CN) **1578**
Provincial Geologists Journal (Victoria). (CN) **1578**
Provincial Legislative Record. (CN) **4070**, 686
Provincial Newsletter. (CN) **3575**
Provincial Outlook. (CN ISSN 0827-5785) **882**
Provincial Pulse Newsletter see Provincial Legislative Record **4070**
Provincial Results in Canada of Fire and Casualty Companies see The Brown Chart. Provincial Results **2528**

Provincial Results in Canada of General Insurance Companies see The Brown Chart. Provincial Results **2528**
Provinzialinstitut fuer Westfaelische Landes- und Volkforschung. Veroeffentlichungen see Provinzialinstitut fuer Westfaelische Landes- und Volksforschung des Landschaftsverbandes Westfalen-Lippe. Veroeffentlichungen **2381**
Provinzialinstitut fuer Westfaelische Landes- und Volksforschung des Landschaftsverbandes Westfalen-Lippe. Veroeffentlichungen. (GW) **2381**
†Provisions of California Collective Bargaining Agreements. (US) **5263**
Provo Radicale. (IT) **3920**
Provost Parade. (UK ISSN 0033-1945) **3468**
Prowoman. (US) **4851**, 3630
Proxima. (FR ISSN 0758-7686) **2880**
Proyeccion. (SP ISSN 0478-6378) **4196**
Proyecciones. (CL ISSN 0716-0917) **3051**
Proyecto 2000. (SP ISSN 0213-6171) **1922**, 1834
Proyectos Quimicos. (SP) **1186**
Proza. (IS ISSN 0334-4975) **2950**, 341
Prozessrechtliche Abhandlungen. (GW) **2669**
Prudent Speculator. (US ISSN 0743-0809) **960**
Prudentia. (NZ ISSN 0110-487X) **2320**, 2950
Prudential Insurance Company of America. Economic Forecast. (US) **882**
Prudential Staff Gazette see National Union of Insurance Workers. Prudential Section. Gazette **2538**
Pruef mit. (SZ) **1507**
Pruefen und Entscheiden. (SZ ISSN 0079-7111) **1025**
Prumysl Potravin/Food Industry. (CS ISSN 0033-1988) **2080**
Prumyslove Oblasti. (CS) **992**, 2381
Prumyslovy Design. (CS) **1834**
Pryor Report. (US ISSN 0742-9770) **3630**
Przedsiebiorstwo i Rynek. (PL) **838**
Przeglad Antropologiczny. (PL ISSN 0033-2003) **247**
Przeglad Archeologiczny. (PL ISSN 0079-7138) **282**
Przeglad Artystyczny see Sztuka **346**
†Przeglad Bibliograficzny Pismiennictwa Ekonomicznego. (PL ISSN 0032-8138) **5263**
Przeglad Biblioteczny. (PL ISSN 0033-202X) **2780**
Przeglad Budowlany/Building Review. (PL ISSN 0033-2038) **629**
Przeglad Dermatologiczny. (PL ISSN 0033-2526) **3249**
Przeglad Dokumentacyjny Elektrotechniki. (PL ISSN 0033-2062) **1777**, 20
Przeglad Dokumentacyjny Informacji Naukowej. (PL) **2795**
Przeglad Dokumentacyjny Maszyn Rolniczych. (PL ISSN 0033-2054) **115**
Przeglad Dokumentacyjny Materialow Ogniotrwalych. (PL ISSN 0033-2046) **1165**
Przeglad Dokumentacyjny Obrobki Plastycznej. (PL ISSN 0209-3413) **3418**
Przeglad Dokumentacyjny z Zakresu Handlu Wewnetrznego i Uslug. (PL ISSN 0239-541X) **838**
Przeglad Elektrotechniczny. (PL ISSN 0033-2097) **1906**
Przeglad Epidemiologiczny. (PL ISSN 0033-2100) **4110**
Przeglad Gastronomiczny. (PL ISSN 0033-2119) **2449**
Przeglad Geodezyjny. (PL ISSN 0033-2127) **1593**
Przeglad Geofizyczny/Review of Geophysics. (PL ISSN 0033-2135) **1593**
Przeglad Geograficzny/Geographical Review. (PL ISSN 0033-2143) **2260**

PSYCHOLOGICAL SCIENCE

Przeglad Geologiczny/Geological Review. (PL ISSN 0033-2151) **1578**, 1593
Przeglad Glottodydaktyczny. (PL ISSN 0137-544X) **2836**
Przeglad Gorniczy. (PL ISSN 0033-216X) **3494**
†Przeglad Gospodarczy. (PL) **5263**
Przeglad Historyczny. (PL ISSN 0033-2186) **2320**
Przeglad Kolejowy Przewozowy see Eksploatacja Kolei **5185**
Przeglad Komunikacyjny. (PL ISSN 0033-2232) **4655**
Przeglad Lekarski. (PL ISSN 0033-2240) **3145**
Przeglad Lubuski. (PL ISSN 0137-4761) **2381**, 3920
Przeglad Mechaniczny. (PL ISSN 0033-2259) **1938**
Przeglad Naukowej Literatury Rolniczej i Lesnej. (PL ISSN 0079-7154) **190**
Przeglad Naukowej Literatury z Zakresu Genetyki i Hodowli Roslin see Przeglad Zagranicznej Literatury Naukowej z Zakresu Genetyki i Hodowli Roslin **467**
Przeglad Odlewnictwa. (PL ISSN 0033-2275) **3418**
Przeglad Papierniczy/Polish Paper Review. (PL ISSN 0033-2291) **3668**, 20
Przeglad Piekarski i Cukierniczy. (PL ISSN 0033-2313) **2089**
Przeglad Pismiennictwa o Ksiazce see Bibliografia Analityczna Bibliotekoznawstwa i Informacji Naukowej **2792**
Przeglad Pismiennictwa Zagadnien Informacji see Przeglad Dokumentacyjny Informacji Naukowej **2795**
Przeglad Polonijny. (PL ISSN 0137-303X) **2381**
Przeglad Psychologiczny/Psychological Review. (PL ISSN 0048-5675) **4039**
Przeglad Skorzany. (PL ISSN 0370-1743) **2738**
Przeglad Socjologiczny. (PL ISSN 0033-2356) **4445**
Przeglad Spawalnictwa. (PL ISSN 0033-2364) **3430**
Przeglad Statystyczny. (PL ISSN 0033-2372) **4584**
Przeglad Techniczny, Innowacje. (PL ISSN 0137-8783) **4607**
Przeglad Telekomunikacyjny. (PL ISSN 0033-2399) **1365**
Przeglad Tygodnia. (GW ISSN 0179-2636) **2020**, 2191
Przeglad Tygodniowy. (PL) **2214**
Przeglad Ustawodawstwa Gospodarczego/Economic Legislation Review. (PL) **882**
Przeglad Wlokienniczy see Przeglad Wlokienniczy plus Technik Wlokienniczy **4622**
Przeglad Wlokienniczy plus Technik Wlokienniczy. (PL) **4622**
Przeglad Zachodni. (PL ISSN 0033-2437) **3969**, 2381
Przeglad Zachodniopomorski. (PL ISSN 0552-4245) **2513**
Przeglad Zagranicznej Literatury Geograficznej/Review of Foreign Geographical Literature. (PL ISSN 0079-7170) **2260**
Przeglad Zagranicznej Literatury Naukowej z Zakresu Genetyki i Hodowli Roslin. (PL ISSN 0033-2453) **467**, 20
Przeglad Zbozowo - Mlynarski. (PL ISSN 0033-2461) **208**
Przeglad Zoologiczny. (PL ISSN 0033-247X) **591**
Przekazy i Opinie. (PL ISSN 0137-8708) **1378**, 1358, 2574
Przekroj. (PL ISSN 0033-2488) **2214**
Przemysl Chemiczny. (PL ISSN 0033-2496) **1186**
Przemysl Drobny i Uslugi see Firma **1076**
Przemysl Drzewny. (PL ISSN 0478-6726) **2117**

Przemysl Fermentacyjny i Owocowo Warzywny. (PL ISSN 0137-2645) **2080**
Przemysl Fermentacyjny i Rolny see Przemysl Fermentacyjny i Owocowo Warzywny **2080**
Przemysl Gastronomiczny see Przeglad Gastronomiczny **2449**
Przemysl Spozywczy. (PL ISSN 0033-250X) **2080**
Przemyslowy Instytut Elektroniki. Prace/Industrial Institute of Electronics. Proceedings. (PL ISSN 0509-7053) **1777**
†Przemyslowy Instytut Maszyn Rolniczych. Prace. (PL ISSN 0324-8739) **5263**
Przemyslowy Instytut Telekomunikacji. Prace. (PL ISSN 0032-6283) **1365**, 1906
Przestepczosc na Swiecie. (PL ISSN 0137-5415) **1521**
Przeszlosc Demograficzna Polski. (PL ISSN 0079-7189) **3986**
Przewodnik Bibliograficzny. (PL ISSN 0033-2518) **409**
Przyjaciolka. (PL ISSN 0033-2534) **4851**, 2214
Przysposobienie Obronne w Szkole. (PL ISSN 0867-0420) **1656**, 3468
Pseudepigrapha Veteris Testamenti Graece. (NE ISSN 0079-7197) **4196**
†Pseudo-Allergic Reactions. (SZ ISSN 0250-8087) **5263**
Psi Chi Newsletter. (US ISSN 0033-2569) **4039**
Psi - M. (US ISSN 0197-2138) **3670**
Psichiatria dell'Infanzia e dell'Adolescenza. (IT ISSN 0393-361X) **3350**
Psichiatria e Psicoterapia Analitica/Analytic Psychotherapy and Psychopathology. (IT ISSN 0393-9774) **3350**, 4039
Psichiatria Generale e dell'Eta Evolutiva.(IT ISSN 0555-5299) **3350**
Psicodeia. (SP ISSN 0377-8320) **4039**
Psicologia. (PO) **4039**
Psicologia Contemporanea. (IT ISSN 0390-346X) **4039**
Psicologia e Lavoro. (IT ISSN 0048-5691) **4039**, 992
Psicologia Medica. (AG ISSN 0325-0695) **3350**, 4039
Psicologia: Teoria e Pesquisa/Psychology: Theory and Research. (BL ISSN 0102-3772) **4039**
Psicopatologia. (SP ISSN 0211-5549) **4039**
Psicoterapia e Scienze Umane. (IT) **3350**, 2513
Psihijatrija Danas/Psychiatry Today. (YU ISSN 0350-2538) **3350**, 4039
▼Psihologia. (RM) **4039**
Psikhologicheskie Issledovaniya. (RU) **4039**
Psikhologiia. (BU) **4039**
Psionic Medicine. (UK ISSN 0033-2585) **3145**
Psiquis. (SP ISSN 0210-8348) **3350**, 4039
Pso Magazin. (GW ISSN 0931-1521) **3249**
Psoriasis Magazin see Pso Magazin **3249**
Psoriasis Newsletter. (US) **3249**
PsycBOOKS. (US ISSN 1044-1514) **4039**, 409
Psych Discourse. (US) **4039**, 1656
Psych It. (US ISSN 0893-8148) **3596**, 4039
Psychanalyse a l'Universite. (FR ISSN 0338-2397) **4039**
Psyche. (US ISSN 0033-2615) **537**
Psyche. (GW ISSN 0033-2623) **4040**
Psyche und Soma. (GW ISSN 0721-0949) **3350**
Psychiatria et Neurologia Japonica (Tokyo, 1899)/Seishin Shinkeigaku Zasshi. (JA ISSN 0033-2658) **3351**
Psychiatria Fennica. (FI ISSN 0079-7227) **3351**

Psychiatria Fennica. Julkaisusarja see Psychiatria Fennica. Reports **3351**
Psychiatria Fennica. Monografiasarja/Psychiatria Fennica. Monographs. (FI ISSN 0355-7707) **3351**
Psychiatria Fennica. Monographs. see Psychiatria Fennica. Monografiasarja **3351**
Psychiatria Fennica. Reports. (FI) **3351**
†Psychiatria Polska. (PL ISSN 0033-2674) **5263**
†Psychiatric Abstract and Comment. (US ISSN 1042-041X) **5263**
Psychiatric & Psychological Evidence. (US) **2669**, 4040
Psychiatric Annals. (US ISSN 0048-5713) **3351**
Psychiatric Aspects of Mental Retardation Reviews see Habilitative Mental Healthcare Newsletter **3337**
Psychiatric Bulletin. (UK) **3351**
Psychiatric Clinics of North America. (US ISSN 0193-953X) **3351**
†Psychiatric Developments. (UK ISSN 0262-9283) **5263**
Psychiatric Forum. (US ISSN 0033-2690) **3351**
▼Psychiatric Genetics. (UK ISSN 0955-8829) **546**, 3351
Psychiatric Hospital. (US) **3351**, 2468
Psychiatric Journal of the University of Ottawa see Journal of Psychiatry and Neuroscience **3343**
Psychiatric Length of Stay Series. (US) **3351**
Psychiatric Medicine. (US ISSN 0732-0868) **3351**
Psychiatric News. see Bollettino di Psichiatria Biologica **3332**
Psychiatric News. (US ISSN 0033-2704) **3351**
Psychiatric Quarterly. (US ISSN 0033-2720) **3351**
▼Psychiatric Resident. (US) **3351**
Psychiatric Times. (US ISSN 0893-2905) **3351**
Psychiatrie de l'Enfant. (FR ISSN 0079-726X) **3325**, 3351
†Psychiatrie, Neurologie und Medizinische Psychologie. (GW ISSN 0033-2739) **5263**
Psychiatrie Sociale. see Social Psychiatry and Psychiatric Epidemiology **3354**
Psychiatrische Praxis. (GW ISSN 0303-4259) **3351**
Psychiatry. (US ISSN 0033-2747) **3351**
Psychiatry. (CN) **3351**
Psychiatry and Psychobiology see European Psychiatry **3336**
Psychiatry in Practice. (UK ISSN 0262-5377) **3351**
Psychiatry Journal/Majallat al-Sihhah al-Nafsiyyah. (JO) **3351**
Psychiatry Research. (IE ISSN 0165-1781) **3351**
▼Psychiatry Research: Neuroimaging Section. (IE ISSN 0925-4927) **3351**
Psychiatry Today. see Psihijatrija Danas **3350**
Psychic Connections see Catalyst (Marietta) **3594**
Psychic Guide see Body, Mind & Spirit Magazine **3593**
Psychic Life see Psychic Reader **3670**
Psychic Messenger. (US) **3670**
Psychic News. (UK ISSN 0033-2801) **3670**
Psychic Reader. (US) **3670**, 3596
Psychic Studies. (US ISSN 0276-1610) **3670**
Psychical Studies. (UK) **3670**, 3596, 4196
Psycho. (GW ISSN 0340-7845) **3351**
Psycho Geriatrie. (FR) **2277**, 4040
Psycho-Lingua. (II ISSN 0377-3132) **2836**, 1342, 4040
▼Psycho-Oncology. (UK ISSN 1057-9249) **3201**
Psychoanalysis and Contemporary Thought. (US) **3352**
Psychoanalysis and Psychotherapy. (US) **3352**, 4040

▼Psychoanalytic Books. (US ISSN 1044-2103) **3352**
Psychoanalytic Crosscurrents. (US) **4040**
▼Psychoanalytic Dialogues. (US ISSN 1048-1885) **4040**
Psychoanalytic Inquiry. (US ISSN 0735-1690) **4040**
†Psychoanalytic Perspectives on Art. (US) **5264**
Psychoanalytic Psychology. (US ISSN 0736-9735) **4040**, 3352
Psychoanalytic Quarterly. (US ISSN 0033-2828) **4040**
Psychoanalytic Review. (US ISSN 0033-2836) **4040**
Psychoanalytic Study of Society. (US ISSN 0079-7294) **4040**
Psychoanalytic Study of the Child. (US ISSN 0079-7308) **4040**
Psychobiologie. (GW ISSN 0478-6866) **3352**
Psychobiology. (US ISSN 0889-6313) **4040**
Psychobiology and Physiological Psychology see Progress in Psychobiology and Physiological Psychology **4039**
Psychoenergetics see Theoretical Parapsychology **4048**
Psychohistory Review. (US ISSN 0363-891X) **4040**
Psychologen Adresboek. (NE ISSN 0079-7324) **4040**
Psychologia/Pushikorogia. (JA ISSN 0033-2852) **4040**
Psychologia a Patopsychologia Dietata. (CS) **4040**, 1758, 3145
Psychologia a Skola. (CS) **4040**, 1656
Psychologia-Pedagogika. (PL) **4040**
Psychologia Universalis Forschungsergebnisse aus dem Gesamtgebiet der Psychologie. (GW) **4040**
Psychologia Wychowawcza/Educational Psychology. (PL ISSN 0033-2860) **1656**, 4040
†Psychologica. (AG ISSN 0325-6502) **5264**
Psychologica Belgica. (BE ISSN 0033-2879) **4040**
Psychological Abstracts. (US ISSN 0033-2887) **4051**, 20
Psychological Assessment: A Journal of Consulting and Clinical Psychology. (US ISSN 1040-3590) **4040**
Psychological Association of South Africa. Newsletter. (SA) **4040**
Psychological Association of South Africa. Proceedings. (SA) **4040**
Psychological Bulletin. (US ISSN 0033-2909) **4041**
Psychological Cinema Register. (US ISSN 0272-0582) **4051**, 3520
▼Psychological Inquiry. (US ISSN 1047-840X) **4041**
Psychological Institute of the Republic of South Africa. Newsletter see Psychological Association of South Africa. Newsletter **4040**
Psychological Institute of the Republic of South Africa. Proceedings see Psychological Association of South Africa. Proceedings **4040**
Psychological Issues. (US ISSN 0048-5748) **4041**
Psychological Issues. Monograph see Psychological Issues **4041**
Psychological Medicine. (UK ISSN 0033-2917) **3352**
Psychological Perspectives. (US ISSN 0033-2925) **4041**
Psychological Record. (US ISSN 0033-2933) **4041**
Psychological Reports. (US ISSN 0033-2941) **4041**
Psychological Research. (GW ISSN 0340-0727) **4041**
Psychological Research Bulletin. (SW ISSN 0555-5620) **4041**
Psychological Research Journal. (II ISSN 0970-6097) **4041**
Psychological Review see Przeglad Psychologiczny **4039**
Psychological Review. (US ISSN 0033-295X) **4041**
▼Psychological Science. (UK ISSN 0956-7976) **4041**

Psychological Studies. (II ISSN 0033-2968) **4041**
Psychological Test Bulletin. (AT) **4041**
Psychologie see Psychologies **4041**
†Psychologie-Almanach. (GW) **5264**
Psychologie et Education. (FR ISSN 0151-2137) **1656**, 4041
Psychologie et Psychometrie. (FR ISSN 0296-8770) **4041**
Psychologie Francaise. (FR ISSN 0033-2984) **4041**
Psychologie Heute. (GW ISSN 0340-1677) **4041**
†Psychologie im Gespraech. (SZ) **5264**
Psychologie in Erziehung und Unterricht. (GW ISSN 0342-183X) **1657**
Psychologie Medicale. (FR ISSN 0048-5756) **3352**
Psychologie Scolaire see Psychologie et Education **1656**
†Psychologie und Geschichte. (GW ISSN 0935-0179) **5264**
Psychologie und Gesellschaftskritik. (GW ISSN 0170-0537) **4041**, 4851
Psychologie und Person. (GW ISSN 0079-7405) **4041**
Psychologie und Praxis see Zeitschrift fuer Arbeits- und Organisationspsychologie **4050**
Psychologie v Ekonomicke Praxi/Applied Industrial Psychology. (CS ISSN 0033-300X) **4041**
Psychologies. (FR) **4041**
Psychologische Beitraege. (GW ISSN 0033-3018) **4042**
Psychologische Forschung see Psychological Research **4041**
Psychologische Menschenkenntnis see Psychologie im Gespraech **5264**
Psychologische Rundschau. (GW ISSN 0033-3042) **4042**
Psychologischer Index. (GW ISSN 0722-1533) **4051**
The Psychologist. (UK ISSN 0952-8229) **4042**
Psychology. (US ISSN 0033-3077) **4042**
Psychology and Aging. (US ISSN 0882-7974) **2277**, 4042
Psychology and Developing Societies. (US) **4042**
Psychology & Health. (US ISSN 0887-0446) **4042**
Psychology and Human Development see Social Behavior and Personality **4047**
Psychology & Marketing. (US ISSN 0742-6046) **4042**, 1051
Psychology and Sociology of Sport: Current Selected Research. (US ISSN 0885-7423) **4042**, 3372, 3807, 4445, 4554
Psychology Book Guide see Bibliographic Guide to Psychology **4051**
Psychology in the Schools. (US ISSN 0033-3085) **4042**, 1758
Psychology of Addictive Behaviors. (US ISSN 0893-164X) **1538**
Psychology of Learning and Motivation: Advances in Research and Theory. (US ISSN 0079-7421) **4042**
Psychology of Music. (UK ISSN 0305-7356) **3575**, 4042
Psychology of Women Quarterly. (UK ISSN 0361-6843) **4042**, 4860
Psychology Quarterly. (PK ISSN 0033-3093) **4042**
Psychology: Theory and Research. see Psicologia: Teoria e Pesquisa **4039**
Psychology Today. (US ISSN 0033-3107) **4042**, 4383
De Psycholoog. (NE ISSN 0033-3115) **4042**
Psychomed. (GW) **4042**
Psychometrika. (US ISSN 0033-3123) **4042**
Psychomusicology. (US ISSN 0275-3987) **3575**, 4042
Psychoneuroendocrinology. (US ISSN 0306-4530) **3352**, 3256
Psychonomic Society. Bulletin. (US ISSN 0090-5054) **4042**
Psychopathologie Africaine. (SG ISSN 0033-314X) **3352**

Psychopathology. (SZ ISSN 0254-4962) **3352**
Psychopharmacology. (GW ISSN 0033-3158) **3741**
Psychopharmacology. (NE) **3741**
†Psychopharmacology. (UK ISSN 0142-8411) **5264**
Psychopharmacology Bulletin. (US ISSN 0048-5764) **3741**, 3352
Psychopharmacology Supplementa. (US) **3741**
Psychophysiology. (US ISSN 0048-5772) **3145**, 574, 4042
Psychophysiology Newsletter see Psychophysiology **3145**
Psychopoetica. (UK) **3003**
Psychoscope. (SZ ISSN 1013-5987) **4042**
Psychosocial Epidemiology Series. (US) **3223**, 4042
Psychosocial News. (US) **3273**, 4042
Psychosocial Rehabilitation Journal. (US ISSN 0147-5622) **4043**, 4445
Psychosomatic Medicine. (US ISSN 0033-3174) **3352**
Psychosomatics. (US ISSN 0033-3182) **3352**
Psychosozial. (GW ISSN 0171-3434) **4043**
Psychosoziale Umschau. (GW ISSN 0930-4177) **3352**, 4417
Psychotheque. (FR ISSN 0079-7448) **4383**
Psychotherapie Medizinische Psychologie see Psychotherapie - Psychosomatik - Medizinische Psychologie **3352**
Psychotherapie - Psychosomatik - Medizinische Psychologie. (GW ISSN 0173-7937) **3352**
Psychotherapies. (SZ ISSN 0251-737X) **4043**
Psychotherapy. (US) **4043**
†Psychotherapy. (UK ISSN 0143-7593) **5264**
Psychotherapy and Psychosomatics. (SZ ISSN 0033-3190) **3352**
Psychotherapy Bulletin. (US) **4043**
Psychotherapy Digest. (US ISSN 0164-078X) **4043**
Psychotherapy Finances. (US ISSN 0163-1543) **4043**
Psychotherapy in Private Practice. (US ISSN 0731-7158) **4043**
Psychotherapy Letter. (US ISSN 1047-9848) **4043**
Psychotherapy Marketing and Practice Development Reports see Journal of Nonprofit & Public Sector Marketing **1043**
†Psychotherapy Newsletter. (US ISSN 0737-0938) **5264**
Psychotherapy Patient. (US ISSN 0738-6176) **4043**
▼Psychotherapy Research. (US ISSN 1050-3307) **4043**
Psychotherapy Today see Psychotherapy Letter **4043**
Psychotronic Video. (US) **1386**, 3013, 3829
Psychotropes. (FR ISSN 0715-9684) **3741**, 3352
Psychotropic Guidelines. (AT) **3352**
PsycInfo News. (US) **4051**, 2795
PsycScan: Applied Experimental and Engineering Psychology. (US ISSN 0891-0685) **4051**, 20
Psyscan: Applied Psychology. (US ISSN 0271-7506) **4051**, 20
Psyscan: Clinical Psychology. (US ISSN 0197-1484) **4051**, 20
Psyscan: Developmental Psychology. (US ISSN 0197-1492) **4051**, 20
Psyscan: Learning and Communication Disorders and Mental Retardation. (US) **4052**, 20, 1740
Psyscan: Learning Disabilities - Mental Retardation see PsycScan: Learning and Communication Disorders and Mental Retardation **4052**
PsycScan: Psychoanalysis. (US ISSN 0889-5236) **4052**, 20
Psyke & Logos. (DK ISSN 0107-1211) **4043**
Psykisk Forum see Nyt Aspekt **3596**
Psykisk Haelsa/Mental Health. (SW ISSN 0033-3212) **4043**, 3352
Psykolog Nyt. (DK) **4043**
Psykologi see Psykologisk Set **4043**

Psykologisk Laboratorium. Forskningsrapport. (DK ISSN 0107-3060) **4043**
Psykologisk Paedagogisk Raadgivning/Journal of School Psychology. (DK ISSN 0906-219X) **4043**, 1657
Psykologisk Set. (DK ISSN 0906-2483) **4043**
Pszichologia a Gyakorlatban. (HU ISSN 0079-7456) **4043**
Pszichologiai Tanulmanyok. (HU ISSN 0079-7464) **4043**
Pteridines. (GW ISSN 0933-4807) **482**, 1208
Pteridologia. (US) **515**
Pteridologist. (UK ISSN 0266-1640) **515**
Ptisi/Flight. (GR ISSN 1105-1310) **4676**
P'tit Loup. (FR) **1263**
Ptitsevodstvo/Poultry. (RU ISSN 0033-3239) **224**
Ptolemy. (US) **3003**
P'u Men. see Universal Door **4216**
Pub. (US) **2950**
Pub Magazine. (BE) **4135**
Pub Monitor see Publican Monitor **5264**
Pub Newsletter. (BE) **4135**
Pubblica Amministrazione Oggi. (IT) **4070**
Pubblicazioni di Verifiche. (IT) **3778**, 2381
Pubblicita Domani. (IT) **37**
Pubblico. (IT) **2880**
Pubblico Esercizio. (IT ISSN 0393-9413) **4070**
Pubcaterer. (UK ISSN 0264-827X) **2479**
Pubdisco News. (UK ISSN 0033-3263) **4135**
Publi and Consult News. (IT) **60**, 3468
Publi - P E Q. (CN) **1322**
Publi 10. (FR ISSN 0751-5464) **37**
Public Accounting Report. (US ISSN 0160-3094) **755**
Public Accounts of British Columbia. (CN) **882**
Public Administration. (US) **1025**, 992
Public Administration see Australian Journal of Public Administration **4054**
Public Administration. (UK ISSN 0033-3298) **4071**
Public Administration Abstracts and Index of Articles see Documentation in Public Administration **4080**
Public Administration and Development.(UK ISSN 0271-2075) **934**, 3920
Public Administration and Public Policy.(US) **4071**
▼Public Administration Briefing. (US) **4071**
Public Administration Quarterly. (US ISSN 0734-9149) **4071**
Public Administration Review. (PK ISSN 0033-3344) **4071**
Public Administration Review. (US ISSN 0033-3352) **4071**
†Public Administration Series: Bibliography. (US ISSN 0193-970X) **5264**
Public Administration Survey. (US ISSN 0033-3360) **4071**, 3920
Public Administration Times. (US ISSN 0149-8797) **4071**
†Public Administrator and the Courts. (US ISSN 0735-4703) **5264**
Public Affairs. (US ISSN 0555-5914) **3920**
†Public Affairs Bulletin. (US) **5264**
Public Affairs Comment. (US ISSN 0033-3395) **4383**, 3920, 4071
Public Affairs Information Service, Inc. International in Print see P A I S International in Print **733**
Public Affairs Quarterly. (US ISSN 0887-0373) **3778**
Public Affairs Report. (US ISSN 0033-3417) **3920**
Public Affairs Research Council of Louisiana, Inc. Analysis see P A R Analysis **3913**
Public Affairs Research Council of Louisiana, Inc. Legislative Bulletin see P A R Legislative Bulletin **4093**

Public and Local Acts of the Legislature of the State of Michigan. (US ISSN 0893-2573) **4093**, 2669
Public Art Fund Newsletter see In Process **330**
Public Art Review. (US ISSN 1040-211X) **341**
Public Assistance Report. (US) **4417**, 2669
Public Assistance Success see Public Assistance Report **4417**
Public Authorities Directory. (UK) **4093**, 4417
Public Broadcasting Report. (US ISSN 0193-3663) **1378**
Public Budgeting and Finance. (US ISSN 0275-1100) **686**
Public Budgeting and Financial Management. (US ISSN 1042-4741) **796**, 1025
Public Choice. (NE ISSN 0048-5829) **686**
Public Citizen. (US ISSN 0738-5927) **1507**
Public Cleansing Service in Tokyo see Public Cleansing Services in Tokyo **4110**
Public Cleansing Services in Tokyo/Seiso Jigyo Gaiyo. (JA) **4110**
Public Communications Magazine. (US) **1351**
Public Contract Law Journal. (US ISSN 0033-3441) **2669**
Public Contract Newsletter. (US ISSN 0569-3314) **2669**
Public Culture. (US ISSN 0899-2363) **2880**, 2513
†Public Documents Highlights for Texas.(US) **5264**
Public Domain. (UK ISSN 0952-7095) **4071**, 1104
▼Public Domain Software for Earth Scientists. (US) **4360**, 1548
Public Education Alert. (US) **1657**
†Public Education in Virginia. (US) **5264**
Public Employee (Boston). (US ISSN 0739-9294) **992**
Public Employee (Washington). (US ISSN 0161-7494) **2588**
†Public Employee Bargaining. (US) **5264**
Public Employee Benefit Plans (Year). (US) **992**, 1069
Public Employee Newsletter. (US) **3620**, 4071
Public Employee Press. (US ISSN 0033-345X) **2588**, 4071
Public Employment Relations Board News see P E R B News **4069**
Public Eye. (UK ISSN 0268-0149) **2780**, 37
Public Eye (Boston). (US ISSN 0275-9322) **3920**
Public Eye (Madison). (US) **1507**, 2669
Public Finance/Finances Publiques. (GW ISSN 0033-3476) **4071**
Public Finance and Accountancy. (UK ISSN 0305-9014) **4093**
Public Finance in Hungary. (HU ISSN 0230-9718) **1104**
Public Finance Quarterly. (US ISSN 0048-5853) **1104**
Public Finance - Washington Watch. (US) **796**
Public Fire Education Digest. (US) **2034**
Public Gaming. (US) **4484**
Public Garden. (US ISSN 0885-3894) **2137**
Public General Acts & General Synod Measures. (UK) **4071**
Public Health. (UK ISSN 0033-3506) **3145**, 4110
Public Health and Hygiene. (UG) **4110**
Public Health Conference on Records and Statistics. Proceedings. (US ISSN 0079-7588) **4118**
Public Health Dentistry see Journal of Public Health Dentistry **3237**
Public Health Economics and Medical Care Abstracts see Medical Care Review **4118**
Public Health Education. see Kenko Kyoiku **4106**
†Public Health in Europe. (UN ISSN 0300-4880) **5264**

PUBLICATIONS 6583

Public Health Laboratory Service Board. Biennial Report. (UK ISSN 0142-3517) **3223**, 4110
Public Health Laboratory Service Board. Year Book *see* Public Health Laboratory Service Board. Biennial Report **3223**
Public Health Laboratory Service Board Library Bulletin *see* P H L S Library Bulletin **3222**
Public Health Laboratory Service Board Microbiology Digest *see* P H L S Microbiology Digest **3222**
Public Health Laboratory Service Bulletin *see* P H L S H I V Bulletin **3222**
Public Health Monograph. (US ISSN 0079-7596) **4110**
Public Health News. (UK ISSN 0959-2946) **3223**
Public Health Nursing. (US ISSN 0737-1209) **3286**
Public Health Nutrition. (FR ISSN 1013-8285) **4118**, 3614
Public Health of Mexico. *see* Salud Publica de Mexico **4112**
Public Health of the Russian Federation. *see* Zdravookhranenie Rossiiskoi Federatsii **4116**
Public Health Papers. (UN ISSN 0555-6015) **4110**
Public Health Reports. (US ISSN 0090-2918) **4110**
Public Health Reviews. (IS ISSN 0301-0422) **4110**, 1538, 3201
Public Health Technical Monograph *see* Public Health Monograph **4110**
The Public Historian. (US ISSN 0272-3433) **2320**
Public History News. (US ISSN 0891-2610) **2420**
Public Innovation Abroad. (US ISSN 0887-4468) **2494**
Public Interest. (US ISSN 0033-3557) **4383**, 686, 3920
Public Interest Alert *see* Columbia Journalism Review **2568**
Public Interest Briefs. (US) **2734**, 1966, 4071
Public Interest Clearinghouse Directory *see* Directory of Bay Area Public Interest Organizations **2619**
Public International Law. (GW ISSN 0340-7349) **2700**, 2728
Public Investor. (US) **960**
Public Justice Report. (US ISSN 0742-5325) **2669**
Public Land & Resources Law Digest. (US ISSN 0148-6489) **2669**, 3494
Public Land Statistics *see* U.S. Bureau of Land Management. Public Land Statistics **4082**
Public Lands News. (US) **1495**, 1966, 2106
Public Lands Use *see* Public Lands News **1495**
Public Law. (UK ISSN 0033-3565) **2669**, 2712
Public Law Review/Koho Kenkyu. (JA) **2669**
Public Law Review. (AT ISSN 1034-3024) **2669**
Public Ledger. (UK ISSN 0048-5888) **1051**
Public Ledger and Commodity Week. (UK) **1104**
Public Ledger Commodity Year Book *see* Public Ledger and Commodity Week **1104**
Public Legal Information Association of Newfoundland News *see* P L I A N News **2665**
Public Libraries. (US ISSN 0163-5506) **2780**
Public Libraries Board. Newsletter. (UG) **2780**
Public Libraries in Western Australia. Statistical Bulletin. (AT ISSN 0729-199X) **2795**
Public Libraries of Victoria. Annual Statistical Bulletin *see* Victorian Public Libraries. Annual Survey **2796**
Public Library Catalog. (US) **2795**
Public Library Journal. (UK ISSN 0268-893X) **2780**
Public Library Quarterly. (US ISSN 0161-6846) **2780**

†Public Library Reporters. (US ISSN 0555-6031) **5264**
Public Library Statistics. (UK ISSN 0951-8983) **2795**
Public Management. (US ISSN 0033-3611) **4093**
The Public Manager. (US ISSN 1061-7639) **4071**
Public Money and Management. (UK ISSN 0954-0962) **4071**
Public Officials Liability Litigation Reporter *see* Municipal Liability Litigation Reporter **5240**
Public Opinion (Washington) *see* American Enterprise **3872**
▼Public Opinion in the Soviet Union: Statistics and Analysis. (US ISSN 1054-6626) **3920**, 882
Public Opinion Quarterly. (US ISSN 0033-362X) **3920**, 4383
Public Opinion Report. (US) **3920**, 2574
Public Papers of the Presidents of the United States. (US ISSN 0079-7626) **4071**
Public Personnel Management. (US ISSN 0091-0260) **1069**
▼Public Perspective. (US ISSN 1050-5067) **4445**
Public Policy Forum Bulletin *see* P P F Bulletin **4093**
Public Policy Issues in Resource Management. (US ISSN 0079-7634) **1083**
Public Policy Studies in the South. (US) **4383**
Public Post. (US) **2020**
Public Power. (US ISSN 0033-3654) **1802**
Public Power Weekly. (US) **1802**
Public Productivity and Management Review. (US ISSN 1044-8039) **4071**, 1025
Public Pulse. (US ISSN 1053-9751) **4445**
Public Radio Legal Handbook. (US) **1358**, 2669
†Public Relations. (UK ISSN 0263-6166) **5264**
†Public Relations Cues & Coups. (US) **5264**
Public Relations Handbook for Managers and Executives. (AT) **992**
Public Relations Journal of India. (II ISSN 0033-3689) **37**
Public Relations News. (US ISSN 0033-3697) **37**
Public Relations Office of the Sugar Industry *see* P R O S I **2079**
Public Relations Quarterly. (US ISSN 0033-3700) **37**
Public Relations Review. (US ISSN 0363-8111) **37**
Public Relations Week *see* P R Week **36**
Public Relations Yearbook. (UK) **37**
Public Risk. (US ISSN 0891-7183) **4093**, 2540, 4110
Public Roads. (US ISSN 0033-3735) **1873**, 4071
Public School Directory of the State of Texas *see* Texas School Directory **1697**
Public School Enrollment and Staff, New York State. (US) **1657**
Public School Professional Personnel Report, New York State. (US ISSN 0077-9229) **1657**
Public Scrutiny *see* Health Freedom News **4103**
Public Sector. (NZ ISSN 0110-5191) **4071**
Public Sector. (CN ISSN 0700-2092) **4071**
Public Sector. (US) **4071**, 1104
Public Sector Arbitration Awards. (US ISSN 0093-9161) **992**
Public Sector - Health Care Risk Management *see* Health Insurance Medical Records Risk Management Report **5203**
Public Sector Management/Management et Secteur Public. (CN ISSN 0380-3988) **4071**
Public Sector Research Papers. (NZ) **4071**
Public Security Study. *see* Gong'an Yanjiu **1526**

Public Servant/Staatsamptenaar. (SA ISSN 0033-376X) **4071**
Public Servant. (GY) **4071**
Public Service Advertising *see* P S A **36**
Public Service Advertising Bulletin. (US) **37**
Public Service Alliance of Canada. Weekly Newsletter *see* P S A C Union Update **2587**
Public Service & Local Government *see* P S L G **4069**
Public Service Association Journal. (NZ ISSN 0110-6945) **4072**, 2588, 3620
Public Service Association of New South Wales Industrial Bulletin *see* P S A Industrial Bulletin **2587**
Public Service Association of New South Wales Reporter *see* P S A Reporter **2587**
Public Service Notices. (AT) **2669**
Public Service Review. (AT ISSN 0033-3786) **4072**
†Public Technology. (US ISSN 0882-1445) **5264**
Public Technology News *see* Public Technology **5264**
Public Television Transcripts Index. (US ISSN 0897-9642) **1349**, 20, 1378
Public Transit Report *see* Urban Transport News **4660**
Public Transport International. (BE) **4655**
Public Use Energy Statistical Data Base.(US) **4118**, 1800
Public Use of the National Park System (Washington) *see* U.S. National Park Service. Public Use of the National Park System: Fiscal Year Report **1499**
Public Utilities. *see* Chengshi Gongyong Shiye **4056**
Public Utilities Communicators Association. Newsletter. (US) **37**, 1794
Public Utilities Fortnightly. (US ISSN 0033-3808) **1906**, 1365, 3700, 4072
Public Utilities Law Anthology. (US ISSN 0095-5086) **2669**, 4072
Public Utilities Newsletter. (US) **3621**, 4072
Public Utilities Reports, Inc. Letter *see* P.U.R. Letter **1793**
Public Welfare. (US ISSN 0033-3816) **4417**
Public Welfare Directory. (US ISSN 0163-8297) **4417**
Public Welfare in Oregon *see* Adult and Family Services in Oregon **4397**
Public Works. (US ISSN 0033-3840) **4093**
Public Works Historical Society Newsletter. (US) **2420**, 4072
Public Works Manual. (US ISSN 0163-9730) **4093**
Public Works News. (US ISSN 0146-5473) **4072**
Public Works Review *see* Construction Weekly **1864**
Publicacoes Culturais da Companhia. (AO) **4335**, 4383
Publican. (UK ISSN 0142-0755) **385**
†Publican Monitor. (US) **5264**
Publicat Index to Canadian Federal Publications *see* Microlog: Canadian Research Index **17**
Publication - Brome County Historical Society *see* Brome County Historical Society. Publication **2400**
Publication Design Annual. (US ISSN 0885-6370) **341**, 4135
Publication of the Society for Literature and Science *see* P S L S **2946**
Publication Profiles. (CN) **37**, 4135
Publication Speciale Canadienne des Sciences Halieutiques et Aquatiques *see* Canadian Special Publication of Fisheries and Aquatic Sciences **2038**
Publications-Bureau of Business Research, the University of Texas at Austin *see* University of Texas, Austin. Bureau of Business Research. Publications **697**

Publications Catalog of the U.S. Department of Commerce *see* U.S. Department of Commerce. Publications Catalog **5295**
Publications de l'Institut Mathematique. (YU ISSN 0350-1302) **3051**
Publications de l'Institute Orientaliste de Louvain *see* Universite Catholique de Louvain. Institut Orientaliste. Publications **2342**
Publications du Gouvernement de l'Ontario, Liste Mensuelle. *see* Ontario Government Publications, Monthly Checklist **408**
Publications for the Advancement of Theory and History in Psychology. (US) **4043**
Publications from the Sado Museum. *see* Sado Hakubutsukan Kenkyu Hokoku **4337**
Publications in African Languages and Linguistics. (US) **2836**
Publications in Archaeology. (US ISSN 0270-1308) **1495**
Publications in Climatology. (US) **3440**
Publications in Language Series. (NE) **2836**
Publications in Medieval Science. (US ISSN 0079-7685) **4335**
Publications in Medieval Studies. (US ISSN 0079-7677) **2381**, 3778
Publications in Psychology. (NZ ISSN 0079-7731) **4043**
Publications in Seismology. (FI ISSN 0079-774X) **1593**
Publications in the American West. (US ISSN 0085-5227) **2420**
Publications in Tropical Geography Savanna Research Series *see* McGill University Savanna Research Project - Savanna Research Series **2255**
Publications Indexed for Engineering *see* P I E **1845**
Publications of the Faculty - Research Council, Florida State University *see* Florida State University. Publications of the Faculty **1706**
Publications of the Henri Frankfort Foundation *see* Henri Frankfort Foundation. Publications **1277**
Publications of the I R S. (US) **1104**
Publications of the Institute of Geophisics. A: Physics of the Earth's Interior *see* Polish Academy of Sciences. Institute of Geophysics. Publications. Series A: Physics of the Earth's Interior **1593**
Publications of the Institute of Geophysics. B: Seismology *see* Polish Academy of Sciences. Institute of Geophysics. Publications. Series B: Seismology **1593**
Publications of the Institute of Geophysics. C: Geomagnetism *see* Polish Academy of Sciences. Institute of Geophysics. Publications. Series C: Geomagnetism **1593**
Publications of the Institute of Geophysics. D: Physics of the Atmosphere *see* Polish Academy of Sciences. Institute of Geophysics. Publications. Series D: Physics of the Atmosphere **1593**
Publications of the Institute of Geophysics. F: Planetary Geodesy *see* Polish Academy of Sciences. Institute of Geophysics. Publications. Series F: Planetary Geodesy **1593**
Publications of the Institute of Geophysics. M: Miscellanea *see* Polish Academy of Sciences. Institute of Geophysics. Publications. Series M: Miscellanea **1593**
Publications of the New Society of Letters at Lund. (SW) **341**, 2320, 2836
Publications of the Technical University for Heavy Industry. Series A, Mining. (HU ISSN 0324-4628) **3494**
Publications of the Technical University for Heavy Industry. Series B, Metallurgy. (HU ISSN 0324-4679) **3418**
Publications of the Technical University for Heavy Industry. Series C, Mechanical Engineering. (HU ISSN 0133-297X) **1938**

6584 PUBLICATIONS

Publications of the Technical University for Heavy Industry. Series D: Natural Sciences. (HU ISSN 0133-2929) **4335**
Publications on Asia *see* School of International Studies. Publications on Asia **2341**
†Publications on Ethnicity and Nationality. (US) **5264**
Publications on Ocean Development. (NE) **1610**
Publications Romanes et Francaises. (SZ ISSN 0079-7812) **2950**, 2836
Publications Yearbook, Republic of China. (CH) **4135**
Publicidad y Mercadeo. (VE) **37**, 1051
†Publicist. (US) **5264**
Publicite. *see* Werbung **39**
Publicite Club de Montreal Au P C *see* Au P C **28**
Publicity Break *see* Publicist **5264**
Publicity Guide *see* Media Guide (Cleveland) **1376**
Publicity Herald. *see* Dzar Bichig **1372**
†Publicity Opportunities. (US) **5264**
Publicity Record *see* Media News Keys **35**
Publico. (SP) **4637**
Publicum. (AU ISSN 0020-1642) **4637**, 3575
Publicus. (SZ ISSN 0080-7249) **4072**
Publieke Werken *see* Gemeentewerken **1866**
Publik-Forum. (GW ISSN 0343-1401) **4196**, 4445
Publikationen zu Wissenschaftlichen Filmen. Sektion Ethnologie. (GW ISSN 0341-5910) **3516**, 247
Publikationen zu Wissenschaftlichen Filmen. Sektion Geschichte, Paedagogik *see* Publikationen zu Wissenschaftlichen Filmen. Sektion Geschichte, Publizistik **3516**
Publikationen zu Wissenschaftlichen Filmen. Sektion Geschichte, Publizistik. (GW ISSN 0341-5937) **3516**, 1657, 2320
Publikationen zu Wissenschaftlichen Filmen. Sektion Medizin. (GW ISSN 0341-5929) **3516**, 3145
Publikationen zu Wissenschaftlichen Filmen. Sektion Psychologie, Paedagogik. (GW ISSN 0344-9300) **3516**
Publikationen zu Wissenschaftlichen Filmen. Sektion Technische Wissenschaften, Naturwissenschaften.(GW ISSN 0073-8433) **3516**, 4607
Publikationen zu Wissenschftlichen Filmen. Sektion Biologie *see* Institut fuer den Wissenschaftlichen Film. Publikationen zu Wissenschaftlichen Filmen. Sektion Biologie **3512**
Publiquip - Roucam. (CN) **629**
Publish! (US ISSN 0897-6007) **1464**, 4144
†Published Data on European Industrial Markets. (UK) **5264**
†Published Data on Middle & Far East Industrial Markets. (UK) **5264**
Published Searches. (US) **4357**
Publisher. (CN ISSN 0380-8025) **4135**
Publisher. (NR) **4135**
Publisher's Ad Club. Newsletter. (US) **37**
Publishers and Distributors of the United States *see* Publishers, Distributors & Wholesalers of the United States **1151**
Publishers' Auxiliary. (US ISSN 0048-5942) **2574**
Publishers' Catalogs Annual. (US ISSN 0735-665X) **409**, 2780, 4135
Publishers' Circle. (US) **409**
Publishers Directory. (US ISSN 0742-0501) **4135**
Publishers, Distributors & Wholesalers of the United States. (US ISSN 0000-0671) **1151**, 4135
Publishers Handbook. (UK) **4135**
Publishers in the United Kingdom and Their Addresses. (UK ISSN 0079-7839) **4135**

Publishers' Information Bureau Inc. Publishers Information Bureau Report *see* Publishers Information Bureau Report **37**
Publishers Information Bureau Report. (Publishers' Information Bureau Inc.) (US) **37**, 4135
Publishers' International I S B N Directory. (GW) **4142**
Publishers' Monthly. (II) **4135**
Publishers' Photocopy Fee Catalog *see* Catalog of Publisher Information **4125**
Publisher's Report. (US ISSN 0884-3090) **4135**
Publishers Reports. (UK ISSN 0953-7899) **4135**
Publishers' Trade List Annual. (US ISSN 0079-7855) **410**
Publishers Weekly. (US ISSN 0000-0019) **4135**
Publishing Affairs. *see* Chuban Gongzuo **4125**
Publishing and Distributing Research. *see* Chuban Faxing Yanjiu **4125**
†Publishing and New Media Technology Newsletter. (US ISSN 0885-6214) **5264**
Publishing & Production Executive. (US ISSN 1048-3055) **4135**, 4005
Publishing History. (UK ISSN 0309-2445) **4135**
Publishing Markets. (US) **4135**, 1051
Publishing News. (UK) **4135**
Publishing Poynters. (US) **1051**, 4135
Publishing Research Quarterly. (US ISSN 1053-8801) **4135**
Publishing Systems. (US) **4135**
Publishing Technology *see* Publishing & Production Executive **4135**
Publishing Trade *see* Magazine Issues **4132**
Publishing Trends and Trendsetters. (US) **4135**, 1025
Publitransport. (IT ISSN 0033-3999) **37**
Publituris. (PO) **4783**
Publius. (US ISSN 0048-5950) **3920**, 4072
Publizistik. (GW ISSN 0033-4006) **1342**, 2574
†Publizistik-Historische Beitraege. (GW) **5264**
Publizistik und Kunst. (GW) **2574**
†Publizistikwissenschaftlicher Referatedienst. (GW ISSN 0552-6981) **5264**
La Puce a l'Oreille. (CN) **1243**
Puckerbrush Review. (US ISSN 0890-3433) **2951**
Pudding Magazine. (US ISSN 0196-5913) **3003**, 4043
Puddler. (US) **1263**, 1495
Der Pudel Spiegel. (GW) **3713**
†Pueblo Indio. (PE) **5264**
Pueblo Oriental. (UY) **2238**
Pueblo Unido. (US) **3920**
Puente. *see* Most **2940**
▼La Puerta. (PY ISSN 1017-2815) **4851**
†Puerta del Sol. (US ISSN 1041-2026) **5264**
Puerto del Sol. (US ISSN 0738-517X) **2951**
Puerto Rico. Bureau of Labor Statistics. Census of Manufacturing Industries of Puerto Rico *see* Census of Manufacturing Industries of Puerto Rico **1073**
Puerto Rico. Bureau of Labor Statistics. Salarios, Horas Semanales Trabajadas y Otras Condiciones de Trabajo *see* Puerto Rico. Department of Labor. Empleo, Horas y Salarios en las Industrias Manufactureras/Employment, Hours and Earnings in the Manufacturing Industries **736**
Puerto Rico. Departamento de la Vivienda. Secretaria Auxiliar de Planificacion y Programacion. Informe Anual. (PR) **2494**
Puerto Rico. Department of Agriculture. Agricultural and Fisheries Contributions *see* Puerto Rico. Fisheries Research Laboratory. Contributions **2048**

Puerto Rico. Department of Health. Annual Health Services Report. (PR) **4118**, 4584
Puerto Rico. Department of Health. Boletin Estadistico. (PR) **4119**, 3807, 4417
Puerto Rico. Department of Health. Informe Anual de Facilidades de Salud. (PR) **2468**, 3807, 4417
Puerto Rico. Department of Health. Informe del Registro de Profesionales de la Salud. (PR) **3145**, 3807, 4417
Puerto Rico. Department of Health. Office of Planning, Evaluation and Reports. Division of Statistics and Reports. Annual Vital Statistics Report. (PR) **3995**, 4584
Puerto Rico. Department of Labor. Bureau of Labor Statistics. Employment Hours and Earnings in the Manufacturing Establishments Promoted by the Economic Development Administration of the Puerto Rican Industrial Development Company. (PR ISSN 0091-9233) **736**
Puerto Rico. Department of Labor. Directorio de Organizaciones del Trabajo. (PR) **2588**
Puerto Rico. Department of Labor. Empleo, Horas y Salarios en las Industrias Manufactureras/Employment, Hours and Earnings in the Manufacturing Industries. (PR) **736**
Puerto Rico. Division of Demographic Registry and Vital Statistics. Annual Vital Statistics Report *see* Puerto Rico. Department of Health. Office of Planning, Evaluation and Reports. Division of Statistics and Reports. Annual Vital Statistics Report **3995**
Puerto Rico. Division of Health Facilities. Plan for Hospital and Medical Facilities. (PR) **2468**
Puerto Rico. Fisheries Research Laboratory. Contributions. (PR) **2048**
Puerto Rico. Oficina de Estadisticas Agricolas. Boletin Semestral de Estadisticas Agricolas. (PR) **142**
Puerto Rico. Oficina de Presupuesto y Gerencia. Resoluciones Conjuntas del Presupuesto General y de Presupuestos Especiales. (PR) **1104**
†Puerto Rico. Oficina de Presupuesto y Gerencia. Revista. (PR) **5264**
Puerto Rico. Ports Authority. Office of Economic Research. Statistical Report. (PR) **4676**, 4736
Puerto Rico. Statistics, Analysis and Control of Information. Annual Vital Statistics Report *see* Puerto Rico. Department of Health. Annual Health Services Report **4118**
Puerto Rico Business Review. (PR) **796**
Puerto Rico Economic Indicators. (PR) **882**
Puerto Rico Health Sciences Journal. (PR ISSN 0738-0658) **3145**, 452
Puerto Rico Living. (PR ISSN 0033-4049) **2215**, 4783
Puerto Rico Official Industrial Directory. (PR ISSN 0090-3612) **1151**
Puerto Rico Taxes. (US) **1104**
Puertos: Toward World Commerce. (MX) **919**
Pug Dog Club of America. Bulletin. (US) **3713**
Puget Consumers Co-op Newsletter *see* P C C Sound Consumer **1507**
Puget Consumers Co-Op Sound Consumer *see* P C C Sound Consumer **1507**
Puget Sound Business Journal. (US) **686**, 882
Puget Sound Computer User. (US ISSN 0886-8174) **1473**
Puget Sound Dahlia Association. Bulletin *see* Dahlias of Today **2124**
†Puget Sound Small System Users Group Newsletter. (US) **5264**
Puhelin/Telephone. (FI ISSN 0048-5977) **1365**
Pui Bella. (IT) **4851**, 374

Pula. (BS) **3969**, 2334
Pulheimer Beitraege zur Geschichte und Heimatkunde. (GW ISSN 0171-3426) **2381**
Puli News. (US) **3713**
Pulizia Industriale e Sanificazione. (IT) **4110**
Pull. (US) **4484**
†Pull. (IT) **5264**
Puller. (US ISSN 8750-4219) **4484**
†Pulling Power. (US) **5264**
Pulmonary and Critical Care Medicine. (US) **3211**
†Pulmonary Disease Reviews. (US ISSN 0272-7900) **5264**
Pulmonary Pharmacology (Sheffield). (UK ISSN 0954-3333) **3741**
Pulp and Paper. (US ISSN 0033-4081) **3665**
Pulp & Paper Buyers Guide. (US) **3665**, 1151
Pulp & Paper Canada. (CN ISSN 0316-4004) **3665**
Pulp and Paper Canada Business Directory *see* Pulp & Paper Canada Directory **3665**
Pulp & Paper Canada Directory. (CN ISSN 0708-501X) **3665**
▼Pulp & Paper Canada Grade Directory. (CN ISSN 1181-6562) **3665**
Pulp & Paper Canada's Annual & Directory. (CN ISSN 0709-2563) **3665**
Pulp and Paper Canada's Reference Manual and Buyers' Guide *see* Pulp & Paper Canada's Annual & Directory **3665**
Pulp & Paper Forecaster. (US) **3666**
Pulp and Paper Industry in O E C D Member Countries/Industrie des Pates et Papiers dans les Pays Membres de l'O C D E. (FR) **3666**
Pulp and Paper Industry in O E C D Member Countries and Finland - Industrie des Pates et Papiers dans les Pays Membres de l'O C D E et la Finlande *see* Pulp and Paper Industry in O E C D Member Countries **3666**
Pulp and Paper Industry Technical Conference. Conference Record. (US ISSN 0190-2172) **3666**
Pulp & Paper International. (US ISSN 0033-409X) **3666**
Pulp & Paper International Fact & Price Book. (US) **3666**
Pulp and Paper International Factbook *see* Pulp & Paper International Fact & Price Book **3666**
Pulp & Paper Journal. (CN ISSN 0713-5807) **3666**
Pulp & Paper North American Industry Factbook. (US) **3666**
Pulp & Paper Project Report. (US) **3666**
Pulp and Paper Research Institute of Canada. Annual Report. (CN ISSN 0079-7960) **3666**
Pulp & Paper Week. (US) **3666**
†Pulp & Paper Week Price - Export-Import Databook. (US ISSN 0277-0156) **5264**
Pulp and Paper Worker *see* Paperworker **2588**
Pulp Vault. (US) **3013**
▼Pulphouse - A Fiction Magazine. (US) **3013**, 2951
Pulphouse - A Weekly Fiction Magazine *see* Pulphouse - A Fiction Magazine **3013**
▼Pulphouse Fiction Spotlight. (US) **3013**, 2951
†Pulphouse: The Hardback Magazine. (US) **5264**
Pulpit Digest (1978). (US ISSN 0160-838X) **4196**
Pulpit Helps. (US ISSN 0193-3914) **4196**
Pulpit Resource. (US ISSN 0195-1548) **4196**
†Pulpsmith (Year). (US ISSN 0276-0436) **5264**
Pulsar. (FR ISSN 0154-4101) **368**
Pulse. (SA ISSN 0555-6945) **1834**
Pulse. (UK ISSN 0048-6000) **3145**
Pulse. (JM) **3575**, 1531, 4637
Pulse (Orlando). (US) **598**, 4836
Pulse (Wheaton). (US ISSN 0747-8631) **4196**

Pulse Buyers Guide. (SA) **1906**
Pulse Electronics in South Africa. (SA) **1777**
Pulse of Radio. (US) **1358**
Pulse of the Planet. (US ISSN 1041-6773) **1966**, 1794, 4043
Pulse of Youth. (II ISSN 0033-4227) **1263**
Pulse Power Modulator Symposium. I E E E Conference Record *see* Power Modulator Symposium. I E E E Conference Record **1906**
Pulse Survey of Victorian Manufacturing *see* Survey of Victorian Manufacturing **823**
▼Pulso. (US ISSN 0105-8126) **2574**
Pulso Bursatil. (SP) **960**
Pulteney St. Survey. (US ISSN 0883-6590) **1322**
Pump News. (US ISSN 0887-5081) **3022**, 1859, 1938, 2302
Pumps and Other Fluids Machinery Abstracts. (UK ISSN 0302-2870) **3025**, 20
Pun American Newsletter. (US) **2951**
Puna/Travail. (AA) **2588**
†Punch. (US ISSN 0033-4278) **5264**
Punch Bowl. (US) **1714**, 2880
▼Punch Digest for Canadian Doctors. (CN ISSN 1182-5405) **3145**
†Punch Digest for Doctors. (UK) **5264**
Punch in International Travel and Entertainment Magazine. (US ISSN 1053-3842) **4783**
The Punch List. (US) **992**, 2669
Puncture. (US ISSN 1047-4528) **3575**, 341
Pundit. (CN ISSN 0712-1318) **2951**
Pungolo del Sud. (IT ISSN 0033-4286) **2206**, 4783
Pungolo Verde. (IT ISSN 0033-4294) **2880**, 341
Punjab Agricultural University. Journal of Research. (II ISSN 0048-6019) **115**
Punjab Cooperative Union. Review. (PK) **831**
Punjab Fruit Journal. (PK ISSN 0033-4316) **2137**, 115
Punjab Horticultural Journal. (II ISSN 0033-4324) **2137**, 115
Punjab Law Reporter. (II ISSN 0033-4332) **2669**
Punjab Medical Journal. (II ISSN 0033-4340) **3145**, 3807
Punjab National Bank. Annual Report. (II ISSN 0304-8101) **796**
Punjab Punch. (PK ISSN 0048-6027) **2880**
Punjab State Industrial Development Corporation. Annual Report. (II) **1083**
Punjab University Economist *see* Pakistan Economic and Social Review **934**
Punjab University Indological Series. (II) **3643**, 2341
Punjab University Journal of Mathematics. (PK) **3051**
Punjab University Journal of Zoology. (PK) **591**
Punjabi Digest. (II) **2201**
Punjabi Sahitya. (UK) **2880**
Punkt. (PL ISSN 0208-8363) **2951**, 341, 4637
†Der Punkt. (GW ISSN 0178-9953) **5264**
†Punkt 95. (DK ISSN 0901-5469) **5264**
Punsok Hwahak. (KN) **4335**
Punters' Way - Singapore Edition. (SI) **4537**
Punto. (IT) **882**
Punto d'Incontro. (IT) **2513**
Punto de Partida. (MX ISSN 0033-4367) **2951**
Punto de Vista. (AG) **2170**
Punto Final Internacional. (MX) **3920**
Punto Omega. (AG ISSN 0033-4391) **3003**
Punto - Tecnica y Moda *see* Wirkerei - und Strickerei - Technik **4627**
Punto 21. (UY) **1657**
Puntos de Vista. (BO) **3920**
Pupa. (IT) **1263**
Pupil. *see* Koululainen **1259**
Pupil Exchange News *see* Schools Unit News **1723**

Pupila: Libros de Nuestro Tiempo. (UY ISSN 0079-8061) **2320**
Pupille. (GW) **1263**
Puppen und Spielzeug. (GW ISSN 0722-2408) **2282**, 2440
Puppenspiel und Puppenspieler/Marionnettes et Marionnettistes. (SZ ISSN 0033-4405) **4637**
Puppetry Journal. (US ISSN 0033-443X) **4637**
Pupukahi/Harmoniously United. (US) **3468**
Pura Verdad. (US) **4287**, 3969
Pura Verita *see* Plain Truth **4287**
Purabhilekh - Puratatva/Archives - Archaeology. (II ISSN 0970-1923) **2341**, 282
Purana Research Publications, Tuebingen. (GW ISSN 0931-9158) **3643**
Purasuchikkusu Eji. *see* Plastics Age **3865**
Purbani. (BG) **3516**
Purchase Guide of Japan. (JA) **919**
Purchaser's Guide to the Music Industries. (US) **3575**
Purchasing. (II ISSN 0014-6544) **1051**
Purchasing (Newton). (US ISSN 0033-4448) **1051**
Purchasing Administration *see* Hospital Purchasing News **2465**
Purchasing and Supply *see* Purchasing and Supply Management **1051**
Purchasing and Supply Management. (UK ISSN 0265-2072) **1051**
Purchasing Bulletin *see* Procurement Weekly **1050**
Purchasing Executive's Bulletin. (US) **1051**, 1025
Purchasing Magazine's Buying Strategy Forecast *see* Buying Strategy Forecast **1035**
Purchasing Management. (US) **1051**
Purchasing Management. (CN) **1051**
Purchasing Management Association of Canada News *see* P M A C News **1049**
Purchasing Management Association of Philadelphia News *see* P M News **1049**
Purchasing Management Digest *see* Purchasing Management **1051**
†PurchasingWorld. (US) **5264**
Purdue Alumnus. (US ISSN 0033-4502) **1322**
Purdue Engineer. (US ISSN 0033-4510) **1835**
Purdue Exponent. (US) **1322**
Purdue Pharmacist. (US ISSN 0033-4529) **3741**
Purdue University. Office of Manpower Studies. Manpower & Technical Education Requirements Reports. (US) **992**
Purdue University. Office of Manpower Studies. Manpower Report *see* Purdue University. Office of Manpower Studies. Manpower & Technical Education Requirements Reports **992**
Purdue University. Road School. Proceedings of Annual Road School. (US ISSN 0079-8142) **4720**
Purdue University. School of Electrical Engineering. Annual Research Summary. (US ISSN 0033-4537) **1906**
Purdue University. Water Resources Research Center. Annual Report. (US) **4828**
Purdue University Agricultural Economics *see* North Central Journal of Agricultural Economics **155**
Purdue University Monographs in Romance Language. (US ISSN 0165-8743) **2836**, 2951
Purdue University Musical Organizations Notes *see* P.M.O. Notes **3573**
Pure and Applied Chemistry. (UK ISSN 0033-4545) **1186**, 1859
Pure and Applied Geophysics. (SZ ISSN 0033-4553) **1593**
Pure and Applied Mathematics. (US ISSN 0079-8169) **3051**
Pure and Applied Mathematics: A Wiley Interscience Series of Texts, Monographs and Tracts. (US) **3051**

Pure and Applied Mathematics Series. (US ISSN 0079-8177) **3051**
Pure and Applied Mathematika Sciences. (II ISSN 0379-3168) **3051**, 1400
†Pure and Applied Physics. (US ISSN 0079-8193) **5264**
Pure-Bred Dogs, American Kennel Gazette. (US ISSN 0033-4561) **3713**, 4484
Pure Facts. (US) **3352**, 1740, 2080
Pure Life Society. Annual Report. (MY ISSN 0552-6426) **4417**, 3778
Pure Verite. (US ISSN 0033-4588) **4287**, 3969
Purebred Picture. (US ISSN 8750-1880) **224**
Puresu Gijutsu. *see* Press Working **3022**
Purificacion. (UY) **3920**
†Purines. (UK ISSN 0260-1141) **5264**
Purjehtija/Seglaren. (FI ISSN 0355-6980) **4528**
†Purna Yoga. (US ISSN 0930-8857) **5264**
†Purnama Raya. (MY) **5265**
Purnasa. (BG) **2951**
Purometeusu. (JA ISSN 0386-2828) **4335**, 4607
Purpa Lines. (US) **1794**
Purple Cow *see* Purple Cow - The Newspaper for Young Adults and Teens **1263**
Purple Cow - The Newspaper for Young Adults and Teens. (US) **1263**
Purple Heart Magazine. (US) **3469**
Purple Heather Publications. (UK) **3003**
Purple Martin News *see* Nature Society News **1493**
Purple Patch. (UK) **3003**
Purple Report. (CN) **686**
Purpose. (US ISSN 0163-7274) **4287**
†Purrrrr! (US ISSN 0731-0366) **5265**
Pursuit. (AT ISSN 0156-4919) **1263**
Pursuit. *see* Zhuiqiu **2183**
Pursuit *see* Pursuit - S I T U **3671**
Pursuit - S I T U. (US) **3671**, 4335
Purushartha. (FR ISSN 0339-1744) **4383**, 247, 2341
Pusan Economic Survey. (KO) **821**
Pusat Meteorologi dan Geofisika. Laporan Evaluasi Hujan dan Perkiraan Hujan *see* Badan Meteorologi dan Geofisika. Laporan Evaluasi Hujan dan Perkiraan Hujan **3433**
Pusat Penelitian Atma Jaya. Laporan Penelitian Keagamaan. *see* Atma Jaya Research Centre. Socio-Religious Research Report **4213**
Pusat Penelitian Atma Jaya. Penelitian Tentang Kebutuhan Kesehatan Masyarakat dan Sistem Peleyanan Kesehatan di Kecamatan Penjaringan. *see* Atma Jaya Research Centre. Socio-Medical Research Report **3079**
Pusat Penelitian Atma Jaya. Studi Tentang Pengembangan Pendidikan. *see* Atma Jaya Research Centre. Education Development Research Report **1617**
Pusat Penelitian Perkebunan Gula Indonesia. Annual Report/Indonesian Sugar Research Center. Annual Report. (IO ISSN 0216-9967) **190**
Pusat Penelitian Perkebunan Gula Indonesia. Berita/Indonesian Sugar Research Center. News. (IO ISSN 0852-0321) **190**
Pusat Penelitian Perkebunan Gula Indonesia. Bulletin/Indonesian Sugar Research Center. Bulletin. (IO ISSN 0125-9997) **190**
Pusat Penelitian Perkebunan Gula Indonesia. Prosiding/Indonesian Sugar Research Center. Prosiding. (IO ISSN 0216-0021) **190**
The Push: A Journal of Early Australian Social History. (AT) **2345**
Push from the Bush *see* The Push: A Journal of Early Australian Social History **2345**
Push On *see* Australian Cyclist **4515**

Pushcart Prize: Best of the Small Presses. (US ISSN 0149-7863) **2951**
Pushikorogia. *see* Psychologia **4040**
Pushto. (PK ISSN 0555-8158) **2836**, 2951
Puspaniaga. (MY) **686**
Pustakala Pravrtti. (CE) **2780**
Pustakalaya. (II ISSN 0033-4693) **2780**
Put' i Putevoe Khozyaistvo. (RU ISSN 0033-4715) **4713**
Puteoli. (IT) **2381**, 282
Puthiya Ulaham. (CE) **4196**
Putishta/Roads. (BU ISSN 0204-6350) **4720**
Putt-Putt World. (US ISSN 1041-5785) **4510**
Putting Your Amstrad to Work. (UK ISSN 0950-3188) **1400**
Puumies. (FI ISSN 0355-953X) **640**, 2106, 2117
Puzzle Monthly. (UK) **4484**
†Puzzles for Pleasure. (UK) **5265**
Pyinnya Lawka Journal. (BR) **1025**
Pymatuning Symposia in Ecology. (US) **1966**, 515
Pynchon Notes. (US ISSN 0278-1891) **2951**
The Pyongyang Times. (KN) **3920**
Pyramid *see* Truxpress **4749**
Pyramid Film and Video Catalog. (US) **3516**, 1386
Pyramida. (CS) **2951**
Pyrenae: Cronica Arqueologica. (SP ISSN 0079-8215) **282**
Pyrenees. (FR ISSN 0033-474X) **2381**
Pyrethrum Post. (KE ISSN 0048-6043) **482**
Pyrotechnica. (US ISSN 0272-6521) **1186**, 1859
Pytannia Istorii Narodiv S R S R *see* Pytannya Istorii S R S R **2381**
Pytannya Istorii S R S R. (KR) **2381**
Pythian International. (US ISSN 0199-0144) **1300**
Pythian Record. (CN) **1300**
Pyttersen's Nederlandse Almanak. (NE ISSN 0079-8223) **1782**
▼P3: Planet Three. (US ISSN 1050-3536) **1263**, 1966
Q A. (Questione Agraria) (IT) **156**
Q A C C Motor Trader *see* Motor Trader **4696**
Q A News *see* Quality News **3448**
Q A Quest. (Quality Assurance Institute) (US) **3448**
Q A Section Connection. (Quality Assurance Section) (US ISSN 1040-2950) **3145**
Q - Avisen. (DK ISSN 0109-887X) **3920**
Q B Beam. (Quiet Birdmen) (US ISSN 0033-4774) **60**
Q C Circle. (Quality Control) (JA) **1025**
Q C Review. (US) **4417**
Q C W A Journal. (Quarter Century Wireless Association, Inc.) (US) **1378**
Q C W A News *see* Q C W A Journal **1378**
Q D T. (US ISSN 1060-1341) **3241**
Q D T Yearbook *see* Q D T **3241**
Q E X A R R L Experimenters' Exchange. (American Radio Relay League, Inc.) (US) **1378**
Q I E R Journal *see* Queensland Researcher **1715**
Q I M A. (Institute of Municipal Administration) (AT ISSN 0048-6078) **4093**
Q I M P Quarterly. (Quick Index of Medical Preparations) (PK ISSN 0033-4790) **3741**
▼Q I - T Q M. (Quality Improvement - Total Quality Management) (US) **2468**
Q J A *see* Quarterly Journal of Administration **4072**
Q J B E *see* Quarterly Journal of Business and Economics **687**
†Q J I. (Quarterly Journal of Ideology) (US ISSN 0738-9752) **5265**
Q L A Bulletin/Bulletin A B Q. (Quebec Library Association) (CN ISSN 0380-7150) **2780**

Q M A A News. (Queensland Motel & Accommodation Association Inc.) (AT ISSN 0818-9889) **2479**
Q.P.A. News. (Queensland Potters Association) (AT ISSN 0728-0858) **1165**, 356
†Q P S Reporter. (Quaker Peace and Service) (UK ISSN 0265-7848) **5265**
Q R C Advisor. (Quality, Risk and Cost) (US) **2468**, 2540
Q R F V see Quarterly Review of Film and Video **3516**
Q R L Poetry Series see Quarterly Review of Literature Poetry Series **3003**
Q S T. (US ISSN 0033-4812) **1358**
Q S T Canada. (CN) **1358**
Q T C. (SW ISSN 0033-4820) **1378**
Q T Directory. (Quality Travel) (IT) **1151**, 4783
Q T - Quarterly Two-Way Transmissions.(US) **1358**, 1365
Q U A. (RH) **1358**
▼Q W. (Queer World) (US) **2456**, 3400, 4851
†Q X. (Questioning Exchange) (US ISSN 0950-0332) **5265**
Q 38 Technical Journal see Midrange **5237**
Qadmoniot see Kadmoniot **276**
Al-Qafilah/Caravan. (TS) **2058**
Al-Qafilah/Caravan. (SU) **3700**
Qanoun Wal Iqtisad/Droit et Economie Politique. (UA) **2669**, 686
Al Qantara. (SP ISSN 0211-3589) **2836**
Qantas Airways. Report. (AT) **4676**
Qarch. (UK ISSN 0260-0781) **3051**
Qatar National Bank (S.A.Q.). Report of the Directors and Balance Sheet. (QA) **796**
Qatar News. (US) **3920**
Qatar Yearbook. (QA) **4081**, 4584
Qazaq S.S.R. Ghylym Akademiasynyng Khabarlary. see Akademiya Nauk Kazakhskoi S.S.R. Izvestiya **2347**
Qedem. (IS ISSN 0333-5844) **282**
Qesher/Connection. (IS) **2575**
Qi Meng. (CC) **1657**
Qiangjiguang yu Lizisu. (CC) **1809**
Qiao see Nexus: China in Focus **2182**
Qiaopai/Bridge. (CC ISSN 1000-3479) **4484**
Qiche Gongcheng/Automotive Engineering. (CC ISSN 1000-680X) **4700**
Qiche Gongyi/Automotive Technology. (CC) **4700**
Qiche Jishu/Automobile Technology. (CC ISSN 1000-3703) **4700**
Qiche zhi You/Friends of Automobile. (CC ISSN 1000-6796) **4700**
Qidong Shiyan yu Celiang Kongzhi. (CC ISSN 1001-1641) **3845**
Qigong. (CC ISSN 1000-825X) **3807**, 4484
Qigong and Science. see Qigong yu Kexue **3807**
Qigong yu Kexue/Qigong and Science. (CC ISSN 1000-0895) **3807**
Qilu Xiangqing. (CC) **2182**
Qilu Xuekan. (CC) **4383**
Qilunji Jishu/Steam Turbine Technology.(CC ISSN 1001-5884) **1938**
Qing Ming. (CC) **2951**
Qing Shi Wen Ti see Late Imperial China **2339**
Qing Yinyue/Light Music. (CC) **3575**
Qingbao Kexue/Information Science. (CC ISSN 1000-8489) **1457**, 2780, 3051
Qingbao Lilun yu Shijian/Information Science: Theory and Application. (CC ISSN 1000-7490) **2780**
Qingbao Xuebao/Chinese Society for Scientific and Technical Information. Journal. (CC ISSN 1000-0135) **2780**
Qingbao Xuekan. (CC) **2780**
Qingbao Ziliao Gongzuo. (CC) **2780**
Qingchun/Youth. (CC) **2951**
Qingchun Suiyue/Youthful Years. (CC) **1263**
Qingchun yu Jiankang/Youth and Health. (CC) **3807**

Qingdao Haiyang Daxue Xuebao. see Ocean University of Qingdao. Journal **1609**
Qingdao Medical Institute. Journal. see Qingdao Yixueyuan Xuebao **3145**
Qingdao Yixueyuan Xuebao/Qingdao Medical Institute. Journal. (CC ISSN 1001-4047) **3145**
Qinghai Hu/Qinghai Lake. (CC ISSN 0257-5795) **2951**
Qinghai Institute of Nationalities. Journal. see Qinghai Minzu Xueyuan Xuebao **3643**
Qinghai Lake. see Qinghai Hu **2951**
Qinghai Minzu Xueyuan Xuebao/Qinghai Institute of Nationalities. Journal. (CC) **3643**, 247, 2058, 4383
Qinghai Normal University. Journal (Social Science Edition). see Qinghai Shifan Daxue Xuebao (Shehui Kexue Ban) **4383**
Qinghai Shifan Daxue Xuebao (Shehui Kexue Ban)/Qinghai Normal University. Journal (Social Science Edition). (CC ISSN 1000-5102) **4383**
Qingnian Bolan/Well-read Youth. (CC) **1263**
Qingnian Shejiao/Social Affairs for Youth. (CC) **1263**
Qingnian Tansuo/Youth Exploration. (CC) **1243**
Qingnian Wenxue/Youth Literature. (CC) **2951**, 3003
Qingnian Wenxuejia/Young Writers. (CC) **2951**
Qingnian Wenzhai. (CC) **1263**
Qingnian Yidai/Young Generation. (CC ISSN 1000-4807) **1263**
Qingnian Yuekan/Youth Monthly. (CC) **1263**
Qingnian Zuojia/Young Writers. (CC ISSN 1003-1669) **2951**, 1263, 2575, 3003
Qingshi Yanjiu Tongxun/Studies on History - Qing Dynasty. (US) **2341**
Al-Qistas/Scales. (TS) **2669**, 4220
Qitan/Strange Tales. (CC) **2182**
Qiu Shi/Seeking Truth. (CC ISSN 0529-3766) **4383**
Qiu Shi Wenxuan/Seeking Truth - Select Articles. (Select translation of: Qiu Shi) (CC ISSN 1000-7504) **4383**
Qiu Zhi/Seek Knowledge. (CC) **3920**, 3778
Qixiang/Meteorological Monthly. (CC ISSN 1000-0526) **3440**
Qixiang Xuebao. (CC ISSN 0577-6619) **3440**
Qiye Guanli/Enterprise Management. (CC) **1025**, 1117
Qiye Jishu Jinbu. (CC ISSN 1000-968X) **686**
Qiye Wenhua/Enterprise Culture. (CC) **2951**
Qiye Yanjiu/Enterprise Studies. (CC) **1117**
Qizhong Yunshu Jixie/Mechanical Handling Equipment. (CC ISSN 1000-2073) **1938**
Qu Yi/Variety Show. (CC ISSN 0578-0608) **4637**, 1378, 3575
Quad. (CN) **1322**
Quaderni Bianchi. (IT) **2880**
Quaderni Ce D R E S. (IT ISSN 0065-6151) **882**
Quaderni Costituzionali. (IT ISSN 0392-6664) **2706**
Quaderni d'Informatica. (IT) **1457**
Quaderni d'Italianistica. (CN ISSN 0226-8043) **2951**
Quaderni de il Gallo. (IT) **4196**
Quaderni de "la Terra Santa". (IS) **4196**, 2431, 4783
▼Quaderni del Cardello. (IT) **2381**
Quaderni dell'Atlante Lessicale Toscano. (IT) **2382**
Quaderni dell'Emilceramica. (IT) **356**
Quaderni di Anatomia Pratica. (IT ISSN 0390-7139) **452**, 3145
Quaderni di Archeologia della Libia. (IT ISSN 0079-8258) **282**
Quaderni di Azione Sociale. (IT) **3920**
Quaderni di Cinema. (IT ISSN 0393-8379) **3516**
Quaderni di Clinica Ostetrica e Ginecologica. (IT ISSN 0033-491X) **3296**

Quaderni di Cultura Materiale. (IT) **2382**
Quaderni di Disegni come Scrittura - Lettura. (IT) **305**
Quaderni di Economia del Lavoro. (IT) **992**, 1025
Quaderni di Filosofia. (IT) **3778**
Quaderni di Lingue e Letterature. (IT ISSN 1120-9178) **2951**, 2836, 3003
Quaderni di Parapsicologia. (IT) **3671**
Quaderni di Poesia Neogreca. (IT ISSN 0079-8274) **3003**
†Quaderni di Retorica e Poetica. (IT ISSN 0393-7496) **5265**
Quaderni di Scienza. (IT) **4335**
Quaderni di Semantica. (IT ISSN 0393-1226) **2836**
Quaderni di Sociologia. (IT ISSN 0033-4952) **4445**
Quaderni di Storia. (IT ISSN 0390-1068) **1279**
Quaderni di Storia dell'Arte. (IT) **341**
Quaderni di Storia dell'Economia Politica. (IT) **897**
†Quaderni di Studi Storici Toscani. (IT) **5265**
Quaderni di Topografia Antica. (IT) **2260**
Quaderni di Verifiche. (IT) **3778**
Quaderni Fiorentini per la Storia del Pensiero Giuridico Moderno. (IT) **2669**, 2320, 3920
Quaderni Gnosis. (IT) **3671**
Quaderni Ibero-Americani. (IT ISSN 0033-4960) **2836**, 2951
Quaderni Internazionali di Storia Economica e Sociale/International Journal of Economic and Social History/Cahiers Internationaux d'Histoire Economique et Sociale. (IT ISSN 0066-2283) **2382**
Quaderni Isril. (IT) **992**
Quaderni Italiani di Psichiatria. (IT ISSN 0393-0645) **3352**
†Quaderni Latinoamericani. (IT) **5265**
Quaderni Medievali. (IT ISSN 0392-1875) **2382**
Quaderni Patavini di Linguistica. (IT) **2836**
Quaderni Portoghesi. (IT) **2836**
Quaderni Pucciniani. (IT) **3575**
Quaderni Regionali. (IT) **2669**
Quaderni Rossiniani. (IT) **3575**
Quaderni Sardi di Economia. (IT ISSN 0391-8394) **882**
Quaderni Sardi di Filosofia e Scienze Umane. (IT) **3778**, 2513, 4383
Quaderni Sardi di Storia. (IT) **2382**
†Quaderni Sclavo di Diagnostica Clinica e di Laboratorio. (IT ISSN 0033-4979) **5265**
Quaderni Storici. (IT ISSN 0301-6307) **2320**, 4445
Quaderni Terzo Mondo. (IT ISSN 0391-7312) **247**
Quaderni Urbinati di Cultura Classica. (IT ISSN 0033-4987) **1279**
Quaderni Veneti. (IT ISSN 0394-2694) **2951**
Quaderns Agraris. (SP) **156**
Quaderns d'Arquitectura i Urbanisme. (SP) **305**
Quaderns d'Historia Tarraconense. (SP ISSN 0211-142X) **282**, 2382
†Quaderns de Treball. (SP ISSN 0210-8291) **5265**
Quadrangolo. (IT) **4043**
Quadrant. (AT ISSN 0033-5002) **2880**
Quadrant. (FR) **2951**, 2836
Quadrant. (US ISSN 0033-5010) **4043**, 3352
Quadrante. (IT) **3469**
Quadrimestre - Rivista di Diritto Privato.(IT) **2669**
Quads. (NE) **2836**
Quaerendo. (NE ISSN 0014-9527) **4135**, 4005
†Quaestiones Entomologicae. (CN ISSN 0033-5037) **5265**
Quaestiones Geographicae. (PL ISSN 0137-477X) **2260**
Quagga see Endangered Wildlife **1487**
Quagmire. (US) **2880**
Quaker Action see Quaker Life **4287**
Quaker Campus. (US ISSN 0033-5045) **1322**

Quaker Concern. (CN ISSN 0229-1916) **3946**, 4287
Quaker Encounters. (UK) **4287**, 3778
Quaker History. (US ISSN 0033-5053) **4287**
†Quaker Information Network. (UK) **5265**
Quaker Life. (US ISSN 0033-5061) **4287**
Quaker Monthly. (UK ISSN 0033-507X) **4287**
Quaker Peace and Service see Q P S Reporter **5265**
Quaker Peace & Service. Annual Report. (UK ISSN 0260-9584) **4417**, 4287
Quaker Peace and Service Reporter see Q P S Reporter **5265**
Quaker Queries. (US ISSN 0899-1332) **2162**
Quaker Religious Thought. (US ISSN 0033-5088) **4287**
Quaker Service Bulletin. (US ISSN 0033-5096) **4196**, 3946, 3969
†Quaker Social Responsibility & Education Journal. (UK) **5265**
Quaker Yeomen. (US ISSN 0737-8246) **2162**, 4287
Quale Impresa. (IT ISSN 0391-6146) **1083**
Qualesocieta. (IT) **3920**, 4445
Qualified Contractor see Electrical Contractor **1887**
Qualified Remodeler. (US ISSN 0098-9207) **629**
Qualita. (IT) **3448**
Qualita della Vita. (IT ISSN 0391-8521) **4445**
Qualitaet und Zuverlaessigkeit (1980). (GW) **3448**
Qualitas Plantarum see Plant Foods for Human Nutrition **3611**
▼Qualitative Health Research. (US ISSN 1049-7323) **3145**
Qualitative Sociology. (US ISSN 0162-0436) **4445**
Qualite en Mouvement. (FR) **3448**
Qualite Magazine see Qualite en Mouvement **3448**
Quality. (US ISSN 0360-9936) **1025**, 1835
Quality. (SZ ISSN 0033-5169) **4607**, 1835
Quality and Quantity. (NE ISSN 0033-5177) **4445**
Quality and Reliability. (US) **1835**
Quality and Reliability Engineering International. (UK ISSN 0748-8017) **1906**, 1938
▼Quality & Risk Management in Health Care. (US ISSN 2468, 2669, 3145
Quality and Standards. see Chanar Standart **1005**
▼Quality Assurance. (US ISSN 1052-9411) **1025**, 2669
Quality Assurance see Quality Forum **3448**
†Quality Assurance Abstracts. (UK) **5265**
Quality Assurance and Utilization Review. (US ISSN 0885-713X) **1026**, 2540
Quality Assurance Bulletin. (US ISSN 1040-0664) **1026**
Quality Assurance in Health Care. (US ISSN 1040-6166) **3145**
Quality Assurance Institute Quest see Q A Quest **3448**
Quality Assurance New Zealand see Quality New Zealand **1026**
Quality Assurance Procedures. (US) **1083**, 1835
Quality Care Advocate. (US ISSN 0892-6174) **2468**, 2277
Quality Circle Digest see Quality Digest **992**
Quality Circles Journal see Journal for Quality and Participation **1067**
Quality Cities. (US ISSN 0892-4171) **4093**
Quality Client Service. (US) **755**
Quality Control. see Zhiliang Guanli **1087**
Quality Control and Applied Statistics. (US ISSN 0033-5207) **1679**, 20
Quality Control Circle see Q C Circle **1025**
Quality Control for the Foreman see Q C Circle **1025**

Quality Control Reports: The Gold Sheet. (US ISSN 0163-2418) 3741
Quality Control Scanner. (US ISSN 0739-6732) 4005
Quality Digest. (US) 992
Quality Engineering. (US ISSN 0898-2112) 1835
Quality Forum. (UK ISSN 0959-3268) 3448
Quality Improvement - Total Quality Management see Q I - T Q M 2468
▼Quality in Manufacturing. (US) 3022
Quality New Zealand. (NZ) 1026, 1083, 1835
Quality News. (UK ISSN 0959-3756) 3448
▼Quality Observer. (US) 686
Quality of Care. (US) 3352, 1740, 3286
†Quality of Life and Cardiovascular Care. (US ISSN 0748-6901) 5265
Quality of Life in Loisaida. (US) 2232
▼Quality of Life Research. (UK ISSN 0962-9343) 3145
Quality of Markets Quarterly. (UK) 961
Quality Paperback Book Club Review. (US) 4135
Quality Progress. (US ISSN 0033-524X) 1835, 1026
†Quality Review. (US ISSN 0892-0087) 5265
Quality Review Program Manual. (US) 828
Quality, Risk and Cost Advisor see Q R C Advisor 2468
▼Quality Source. (US) 3145
Quality Today. (UK) 3448
Quality Travel Directory see Q T Directory 1151
QualityTravel Magazine. (IT) 4783
Qualm. (AT ISSN 0813-6440) 231
Quandong. (AT ISSN 0312-8989) 190, 2080
Quanguo Qinggong Xinxi/Nationwide Light Industrial News. (CC) 686
Quanguo Xin Shumu/New Books Catalog of P R C. (CC) 410, 4142
Quanguo Xinchanpin/New Products of the P.R.C. (US) 1083
Quanguo Zhongxue Youxiu Zuowen Xuan/Selected Excellent Compositions from Nation-wide Middle Schools. (CC) 2836, 1263
Quantitative Applications in the Social Sciences. (US ISSN 0149-192X) 4383
Quantitative Geology and Geostatistics. (NE) 1578
Quantitative Methoden der Unternehmnsplanung. (GW) 1026
Quantitative Structure-Activity Relationships. (GW ISSN 0722-3676) 3741
Quantity and Quality in Economic Research. (US) 4584, 882
Quantity Surveyor see Building Economist 606
Quantity Surveyor. (NZ) 2260
Quantity Surveyors Inquiry. (IE ISSN 0791-4857) 736
†Quantum (Cincinnati). (US) 5265
Quantum (Gaithersburg). (US) 3013
▼Quantum (Washington). (US ISSN 1048-8820) 4335, 1263, 3051
Quantum Mechanics and Nonlinear Waves see Physics: A Series of Monographs & Tracts 3827
Quantum Optics see Quantum Optics: Journal of European Optical Society, Part B 3857
Quantum Optics: Journal of European Optical Society, Part B. (UK) 3857
Quanzhou Literature. see Quanzhou Wenxue 2951
Quanzhou Wenxue/Quanzhou Literature.(CC) 2951
Quapaw Quarter Chronicle. (US) 305, 2420
†Quarante. (US ISSN 8756-520X) 5265
Quarantine Advisory Leaflet. (NL ISSN 1017-6268) 190
Quark. see Kuoku 4321
▼QuarkXPress In-Depth. (US) 4144, 1464
Quarry see Quarry West 2880
Quarry. (CN ISSN 0033-5266) 2951
Quarry. (AT) 3494

Quarry and Construction. (IT) 629
Quarry and Mining News see New Quarrying & Mining 3492
Quarry Farm Papers. (US ISSN 1055-1492) 2951
Quarry Management. (UK) 3494
Quarry Management and Products see Quarry Management 3494
Quarry Managers' Journal see Quarry Management 3494
Quarry West. (US ISSN 0736-4628) 2880
Quartaer. (GW ISSN 0375-7471) 282
Quartaerpalaeontologie. (GW ISSN 0138-3116) 1548, 3660
Quarter Century Wireless Association, Inc. Journal see Q C W A Journal 1378
Quarter Horse Journal. (US ISSN 0164-6656) 4537
Quarter Horse News. (US) 4537
Quarter Horse Track. (US) 4537
The Quarter Racing Journal. (US ISSN 0899-3130) 4537
Quarter Racing Record. (US ISSN 0091-7516) 4537
Quarterdeck. (US ISSN 0891-2661) 3532, 2420, 4736
Quarterdeck Review see Quarterdeck 3532
The Quarterly (New York). (US ISSN 0893-3103) 2951
Quarterly and Annual Industrial Production Indexes. (TH) 687
Quarterly Banking Review. see Riveon Lebankaut 798
Quarterly Blue Book on Joint Stock Companies in India. (II ISSN 0033-5312) 961
Quarterly Bulletin of Economics and Statistics see Maharashtra Quarterly Bulletin of Economics and Statistics 728
Quarterly Bulletin of Statistics for Asia and the Far East see Quarterly Bulletin of Statistics for Asia and the Pacific 5265
†Quarterly Bulletin of Statistics for Asia and the Pacific. (UN ISSN 0125-0019) 5265
Quarterly Bulletin of Statistics Relating to the Mining Industry of Malaysia. (MY ISSN 0025-1313) 3502
Quarterly Bulletin on Solar Activity. (JA ISSN 0048-6167) 371
Quarterly Business Failures. (US) 882, 796, 1083
Quarterly Business Failures Report see Quarterly Business Failures 882
†Quarterly Business Starts. (US) 5265
Quarterly Byte. (US ISSN 1052-5521) 4155, 1400
Quarterly Coal Report. (US) 1794, 3494
Quarterly Completion Report see American Petroleum Institute. Quarterly Completion Report 3704
Quarterly Construction Statistics. (KO ISSN 0033-5452) 638
Quarterly Countdown. (SA ISSN 1011-5536) 3946
Quarterly Cumulated Index Medicus see Cumulated Index Medicus 3169
Quarterly Domestic & Global Forecasts of Key Economic Indicators. (US ISSN 0888-787X) 687
Quarterly Drilling Completions see American Petroleum Institute. Quarterly Completion Report 3704
Quarterly Economic Review of Algeria see Country Report. Algeria 853
Quarterly Economic Review of Angola, Sao Tome & Principe see Country Report. Angola, Sao Tome & Principe 853
Quarterly Economic Review of Argentina see Country Report. Argentina 853
Quarterly Economic Review of Australia see Country Report. Australia 853
Quarterly Economic Review of Austria see Country Report. Austria 853
Quarterly Economic Review of Bahrain, Qatar, Oman, Yemen see Country Report. Bahrain, Qatar 853
Quarterly Economic Review of Bangladesh see Country Report. Bangladesh 854

Quarterly Economic Review of Belgium, Luxembourg see Country Report. Belgium, Luxembourg 854
Quarterly Economic Review of Brazil see Country Report. Brazil 854
Quarterly Economic Review of Cameroon, Central African Republic, Chad see Country Report. Cameroon, Central African Republic, Chad 854
Quarterly Economic Review of Canada see Country Report. Canada 854
Quarterly Economic Review of Chile see Country Report. Chile 854
Quarterly Economic Review of China, North Korea see Country Report. China, North Korea 854
Quarterly Economic Review of Colombia see Country Report. Colombia 854
Quarterly Economic Review of Congo, Gabon, Equatorial Guinea see Country Report. Congo, Gabon, Equatorial Guinea 854
Quarterly Economic Review of Cote d'Ivoire see Country Report. Cote d'Ivoire 854
Quarterly Economic Review of Cuba, Dominican Republic, Haiti, Puerto Rico see Country Report. Cuba, Dominican Republic, Haiti, Puerto Rico 854
Quarterly Economic Review of Czechoslovakia see Country Report. Czechoslovakia 854
Quarterly Economic Review of Denmark, Iceland see Country Report. Denmark, Iceland 854
Quarterly Economic Review of Ecuador see Country Report. Ecuador 854
Quarterly Economic Review of Egypt see Country Report. Egypt 854
Quarterly Economic Review of Finland see Country Report. Finland 854
Quarterly Economic Review of France see Country Report. France 854
Quarterly Economic Review of Germany see Country Report. Germany 854
Quarterly Economic Review of Ghana, Sierra Leone, Liberia see Country Report. Ghana, Sierra Leone, Liberia 855
Quarterly Economic Review of Greece see Country Report. Greece 855
Quarterly Economic Review of Guatemala, El Salvador, Honduras see Country Report. Guatemala, El Salvador, Honduras 855
Quarterly Economic Review of Guinea, Mali, Mauritania see Country Report. Guinea, Mali, Mauritania 855
Quarterly Economic Review of Hong Kong, Macau see Country Report. Hong Kong, Macau 855
Quarterly Economic Review of Hungary see Country Report. Hungary 855
Quarterly Economic Review of India, Nepal see Country Report. India, Nepal 855
Quarterly Economic Review of Indochina - Vietnam, Laos, Cambodia see Country Report. Indochina: Vietnam, Laos, Cambodia 855
Quarterly Economic Review of Indonesia see Country Report. Indonesia 855
Quarterly Economic Review of Iran see Country Report. Iran 855
Quarterly Economic Review of Iraq see Country Report. Iraq 855
Quarterly Economic Review of Ireland see Country Report. Ireland 855
Quarterly Economic Review of Israel see Country Report. Israel 855
Quarterly Economic Review of Italy see Country Report. Italy 855
Quarterly Economic Review of Jamaica, Belize, Bahamas, Bermuda see Country Report. Jamaica, Belize, Bahamas, Bermuda 855
Quarterly Economic Review of Japan see Country Report. Japan 855
Quarterly Economic Review of Jordan see Country Report. Jordan 855
Quarterly Economic Review of Kenya see Country Report. Kenya 855
Quarterly Economic Review of Kuwait see Country Report. Kuwait 855
Quarterly Economic Review of Lebanon, Cyprus see Country Report. Lebanon, Cyprus 855

Quarterly Economic Review of Libya see Country Report. Libya 856
Quarterly Economic Review of Madagascar, Mauritius, Seychelles, Comoros see Country Report. Madagascar, Mauritius, Seychelles, Comoros 856
Quarterly Economic Review of Malaysia, Brunei see Country Report. Malaysia, Brunei 856
Quarterly Economic Review of Mexico see Country Report. Mexico 856
Quarterly Economic Review of Morocco see Country Report. Morocco 856
Quarterly Economic Review of Namibia, Botswana, Lesotho, Swaziland see Country Report. Namibia, Botswana, Lesotho, Swaziland 856
Quarterly Economic Review of Netherlands see Country Report. Netherlands 856
Quarterly Economic Review of New Zealand see Country Report. New Zealand 856
Quarterly Economic Review of Nicaragua, Costa Rica, Panama see Country Report. Nicaragua, Costa Rica, Panama 856
Quarterly Economic Review of Nigeria see Country Report. Nigeria 856
Quarterly Economic Review of Norway see Country Report. Norway 856
Quarterly Economic Review of Oman, Yemen see Country Report. Oman, Yemen 856
Quarterly Economic Review of Pacific Islands - Papua New Guinea, Fiji, Solomon Islands, Western Samoa, Vanuatu, Tonga see Country Report. Pacific Islands: Papua New Guinea, Fiji, Solomon Islands, Western Samoa, Vanuatu, Tonga 856
Quarterly Economic Review of Pakistan, Afghanistan see Country Report. Pakistan, Afghanistan 856
Quarterly Economic Review of Peru, Bolivia see Country Report. Peru, Bolivia 856
Quarterly Economic Review of Philippines see Country Report. Philippines 856
Quarterly Economic Review of Poland see Country Report. Poland 856
Quarterly Economic Review of Portugal see Country Report. Portugal 856
Quarterly Economic Review of Romania, Bulgaria, Albania see Country Report. Romania, Bulgaria, Albania 857
Quarterly Economic Review of Saudia Arabia see Country Report. Saudi Arabia 857
Quarterly Economic Review of Senegal, The Gambia, Guinea-Bissau, Cape Verde see Country Report. Senegal, The Gambia, Guinea-Bissau, Cape Verde 857
Quarterly Economic Review of Singapore see Country Report. Singapore 857
Quarterly Economic Review of South Africa see Country Report. South Africa 857
Quarterly Economic Review of South Korea see Country Report. South Korea 857
Quarterly Economic Review of Spain see Country Report. Spain 857
Quarterly Economic Review of Sri Lanka see Country Report. Sri Lanka 857
Quarterly Economic Review of Sudan see Country Report. Sudan 857
Quarterly Economic Review of Sweden see Country Report. Sweden 857
Quarterly Economic Review of Switzerland see Country Report. Switzerland 857
Quarterly Economic Review of Syria see Country Report. Syria 857
Quarterly Economic Review of Taiwan see Country Report. Taiwan 857
Quarterly Economic Review of Tanzania, Mozambique see Country Report. Tanzania, Mozambique 857
Quarterly Economic Review of Thailand, Burma see Country Report. Thailand, Burma 857

Quarterly Economic Review of Togo, Niger, Benin, Burkina Faso see Country Report. Togo, Niger, Benin, Burkina Faso **857**

Quarterly Economic Review of Trinidad and Tobago, Guyana, Barbados, Windward and Leeward Islands see Country Report. Trinidad & Tobago, Guyana, Barbados, Windward & Leeward Islands **857**

Quarterly Economic Review of Tunisia, Malta see Country Report. Tunisia, Malta **857**

Quarterly Economic Review of Turkey see Country Report. Turkey **857**

Quarterly Economic Review of U S A see Country Report. U S A **858**

Quarterly Economic Review of Uganda, Ethiopia, Somalia, Djibouti see Country Report. Uganda, Ethiopia, Somalia, Djibouti **858**

Quarterly Economic Review of United Arab Emirates see Country Report. United Arab Emirates **858**

Quarterly Economic Review of United Kingdom see Country Report. United Kingdom **858**

Quarterly Economic Review of Uruguay, Paraguay see Country Report. Uruguay, Paraguay **858**

Quarterly Economic Review of Venezuela, Suriname, Netherland Antilles see Country Report. Venezuela, Suriname, Netherlands Antilles **858**

Quarterly Economic Review of Yugoslavia see Country Report. Yugoslavia **858**

Quarterly Economic Review of Zaire, Rwanda, Burundi see Country Report. Zaire, Rwanda, Burundi **858**

Quarterly Economic Review of Zambia see Country Report. Zambia **858**

Quarterly Economic Review of Zimbabwe, Malawi see Country Report. Zimbabwe, Malawi **858**

Quarterly Economic Reviews see Country Reports **858**

Quarterly Farm Guide see Farm Guide **90**

Quarterly Financial Report for Manufacturing, Mining and Trade Corporations see U.S. Federal Trade Commission. Quarterly Financial Report for Manufacturing, Mining and Trade Corporations **5295**

Quarterly Forecast of Japanese Economy. (JA) **1083**

Quarterly Forecast of Japan's Economy by the S.A. Method see Quarterly Forecast of Japanese Economy **1083**

Quarterly Geological Notes. (AT ISSN 0584-3219) **1578**

†Quarterly Index: Information Access for the Small Animal Practitioner. (US ISSN 0740-2430) **5265**

Quarterly Index Islamicus. (UK ISSN 0308-7395) **2330, 2431, 3643**

†Quarterly Index to Current Contents - Life Sciences. (US ISSN 0196-5530) **5265**

Quarterly Information of Sugar Industry. see Kikan Togyo Shiho **2076**

Quarterly Journal of Administration. (NR ISSN 0001-8333) **4072**

Quarterly Journal of Agricultural Economy see Nogyo Sogo Kenkyu **155**

Quarterly Journal of Business and Economics. (US ISSN 0747-5535) **687**

Quarterly Journal of Economics. (US ISSN 0033-5533) **897**

Quarterly Journal of Engineering Geology. (UK ISSN 0481-2085) **1873, 1578**

Quarterly Journal of Experimental Physiology see Experimental Physiology **571**

Quarterly Journal of Experimental Psychology. Section A: Human Experimental Psychology. (UK ISSN 0272-4987) **4043**

Quarterly Journal of Experimental Psychology. Section B: Comparative and Physiological Psychology. (UK ISSN 0272-4995) **4044**

Quarterly Journal of Forestry. (UK ISSN 0033-5568) **2106**

Quarterly Journal of Ideology see Q J I **5265**

Quarterly Journal of Indian Studies in Social Sciences see Asian Economic and Social Review **4366**

Quarterly Journal of International Agriculture. see Zeitschrift fuer Auslaendische Landwirtschaft **130**

Quarterly Journal of Mathematics. (UK ISSN 0033-5606) **3052**

Quarterly Journal of Mechanics and Applied Mathematics. (UK ISSN 0033-5614) **3052, 1922**

Quarterly Journal of Medicine. (UK ISSN 0033-5622) **3145**

Quarterly Journal of Seismology. (JA) **1593**

Quarterly Journal of Speech. (US ISSN 0033-5630) **1657**

Quarterly Journal of Surgical Sciences. (II ISSN 0033-5657) **3383**

Quarterly Journal of Taiwan Land Credit.(CH ISSN 0033-5665) **156**

Quarterly Journal of the History of Science and Technology. see Kwartalnik Historii Nauki i Techniki **4322**

Quarterly Listing of Alien Insurers. (US) **2540, 2669**

Quarterly Medical Review. (II ISSN 0481-2158) **3145**

Quarterly of Applied Mathematics. (US ISSN 0033-569X) **3052**

Quarterly of the Virginia Genealogy Society see Magazine of Virginia Genealogy **2158**

Quarterly Pension Investment Report. (US ISSN 0889-4396) **961**

Quarterly Performance Report. (US) **882, 961**

Quarterly Predictions of National Income and Expenditure. (NZ ISSN 0033-5711) **1000**

Quarterly Printing Industry Business Indicator Report see Business Indicator Report **3998**

†Quarterly Public Assistance Statistics. (US) **5265**

†Quarterly Report. (US ISSN 0882-8679) **5265**

Quarterly Report on Money Fund Expense Ratios see I B C's Quarterly Report on Money Fund Performance **949**

Quarterly Report on the Guam Consumer Price Index. (GU) **736, 1000**

Quarterly Report to the Congress and the East-West Foreign Trade Board on Trade Between the United States and the Nonmarket Economy Countries see U.S. International Trade Commission. Quarterly Report to the Congress and the East-West Foreign Trade Board on Trade Between the United States and the Nonmarket Economy Countries **923**

Quarterly Review - Federal Reserve Bank of New York see Federal Reserve Bank of New York. Quarterly Review **865**

Quarterly Review of Afghan Statistics/ Shmayr Siranah-yi Ihsa'iyah. (AF) **4584**

Quarterly Review of Archaeology see Review of Archaeology **282**

Quarterly Review of Australian Education. see Australian Education Review **1617**

Quarterly Review of Biology. (US ISSN 0033-5770) **452**

Quarterly Review of Commission Proceedings see National Capital Planning Commission. Quarterly Review of Commission Proceedings **2492**

Quarterly Review of Doublespeak. (US ISSN 0735-5920) **2836**

Quarterly Review of Economics and Business see Quarterly Review of Economics and Finance **687**

Quarterly Review of Economics and Finance. (US) **687**

Quarterly Review of Film and Video. (US ISSN 1050-9208) **3516, 1386, 4044**

Quarterly Review of Film Studies see Quarterly Review of Film and Video **3516**

Quarterly Review of Historical Studies. (II ISSN 0033-5800) **2320**

▼Quarterly Review of Indian Economy. (II) **882**

Quarterly Review of Literature Contemporary Poetry Series see Quarterly Review of Literature Poetry Series **3003**

Quarterly Review of Literature Poetry Series. (US ISSN 0748-0873) **3003**

†Quarterly Review of Marketing. (UK ISSN 0307-7667) **5265**

Quarterly Review of Wines. (US ISSN 0740-1248) **385**

Quarterly Reviews of Biophysics. (UK ISSN 0033-5835) **486**

Quarterly Salary Review. (AT) **1069**

†Quarterly Serial Bulletin. (UK ISSN 0265-5837) **5265**

Quarterly Statement see Financial Managers' Statement **5192**

Quarterly Statistics of the Working of Capital Issues Control. (II ISSN 0536-8014) **796**

Quarterly Strategic Bibliography see Current World Affairs **1274**

Quarterly Summary of Business Statistics, New York State. (US ISSN 0033-5851) **736**

Quarterly Summary of Jute Goods Statistics. (BG) **4622**

Quarterly Survey of Agricultural Credit Conditions. (US) **156**

Quarterly Survey of General Freight Carrier Operating Results. (US) **4666**

Quarterly Survey of Japanese Finance and Industry see Japanese Finance and Industry: Quarterly Survey **787**

Quarterly Timber Statistics. (AT) **2112, 4584**

Quarterly Transportation Activity Report.(US) **4720**

Quarterly Welfare Statistical Bulletin see Idaho. Department of Health and Welfare. Research and Statistics Section. Quarterly Welfare Statistical Bulletin **4426**

Quarterly West. (US ISSN 0194-4231) **2951**

Quarternote. (UK) **3575**

Quarternote. (US) **3575, 2588**

Quarto Mondo. (IT ISSN 0048-6205) **4851**

Quarto Potere. (IT ISSN 0302-5063) **2575**

Quash see M S N Newsletter **2651**

Quasi. (IT ISSN 0048-6213) **3003**

Quatember. (GW ISSN 0341-9495) **4247**

Quaternaire. (FR ISSN 1142-2904) **1578**

Quaternaria Sinica. see Disiji Yanjiu **1559**

Quaternary International. (US ISSN 1040-6182) **1578**

Quaternary Research. (US ISSN 0033-5894) **3660**

Quaternary Research. (JA ISSN 0418-2642) **3660**

Quaternary Science Reviews. (US ISSN 0277-3791) **4335**

Quaternary Studies. (UK ISSN 0261-9784) **1578**

Quatra see Solo Flyer **3006**

Quatre Verites. (FR ISSN 0033-5878) **2880**

Quatro Rodas. (BL ISSN 0033-5908) **4783, 4700**

Quattro see Inside Quattro Pro **1477**

Quattro Zampe. (IT) **3713**

Quattroruote. (IT ISSN 0033-5916) **4700**

Quattroruotine. (IT) **2440**

Quaver see M U C G - Raker **1571**

▼Quayle Quarterly. (US ISSN 1049-5452) **2881, 420**

Que Automovil Compro? (SP) **1507, 4700**

Que Faire de l'Economie. (FR) **3778, 3920**

Que Ordenador Compro. (SP) **1433**

Que Pasa? (CL) **2180**

Que Pasa? (VE) **2238**

Que Pasa. (PR) **4783**

Que Savoir. (CM) **687, 4783**

Que Tal. (UK ISSN 0033-5940) **2836, 1657**

Que Vous en Semble? (BD) **247**

Quebec (Province). Bureau de Statistique. Statistiques de l'Agriculture, des Peches et de l'Alimentation, Edition (Year). (CN) **142, 2051**

Quebec (Province) Bureau of Statistics. Statistiques. (CN ISSN 0227-0668) **4584**

Quebec (Province). Centrale des Bibliotheques. Choix: Documentation Audiovisuelle see Quebec (Province). Services Documentaires Multimedia. Choix: Documentation Audiovisuelle **410**

Quebec (Province). Centrale des Bibliotheques. Choix: Documentation Imprimee see Quebec (Province). Services Documentaires Multimedia. Choix: Documentation Imprimee **410**

Quebec (Province) Centrale des Bibliotheques. Choix Jeunesse: Documentation Imprimee see Quebec (Province) Services Documentation Multimedia. Choix Jeunesse: Documentation Imprimee **2780**

Quebec (Province). Commission de Protection du Territoire Agricole. Decisions. (CN) **2669**

Quebec (Province). Commission des Services Juridiques. Rapport Annuel. (CN ISSN 0703-0762) **2669**

Quebec (Province). Commission des Transports du Quebec. Rapport Annuel. (CN ISSN 0702-0996) **4655**

Quebec (Province). Commission des Transports. Rapports des Activites de la Commission des Transports du Quebec see Quebec (Province). Commission des Transports du Quebec. Rapport Annuel **4655**

Quebec (Province). Commission des Valeurs Mobilieres du Quebec. Bulletin Hebdomadaire. (CN) **961**

Quebec (Province). Conseil Consultatif de l'Environnement et de la Conservation. Rapport Annuel. (CN) **1966**

Quebec (Province). Conseil Consultatif de l'Environnement. Rapport Annuel see Quebec (Province). Conseil Consultatif de l'Environnement et de la Conservation. Rapport Annuel **1966**

Quebec (Province). Conseil Consultatif sur les Reserves Ecologiques. Rapport Annuel see Quebec (Province). Conseil de la Conservation et de l'Environnement. Rapport Annuel **1495**

Quebec (Province). Conseil de la Conservation et de l'Environnement. Rapport Annuel. (CN) **1495, 2106**

Quebec (Province). Conseil de la Protection du Consommateur. Rapport Annuel see Quebec (Province). Office de la Protection du Consommateur. Rapport Annuel **1507**

Quebec (Province). Conseil des Affaires Sociales et de la Famille. Rapport Annuel. (CN) **4446**

Quebec (Province). Departement d'Energie et Resources. Rapport des Representants Regionaux. (CN) **1578**

†Quebec (Province). Departement d'Energie et Resources. Repertoire des Publications. (CN) **5265**

Quebec (Province) Department of Energy and Resources. Geological Reports. (CN) **1578**

Quebec (Province). Department of Energy and Resources. Report. (CN) **1794, 3494**

Quebec (Province). Department of Natural Resources. Geological Reports see Quebec (Province) Department of Energy and Resources. Geological Reports **1578**

Quebec (Province) Department of Natural Resources. Geological Services. Field Work *see* Quebec (Province). Departement d'Energie et Resources. Rapport des Representants Regionaux **1578**
Quebec (Province). Department of Natural Resources. Report *see* Quebec (Province). Department of Energy and Resources. Report **1794**
Quebec (Province) Department of Recreation, Fish and Game. Annual Report/Ministere du Loisir de la Chasse et de la Peche. Rapport Annuel. (CN ISSN 0229-3811) **4554**
Quebec (Province) Direction de la Recherche Scientifique et Technique. Activites (Year). (CN) **452**
Quebec (Province). Direction de la Recherche Scientifique et Technique Cahier d'Information. (CN) **452**
Quebec (Province). Direction Generale des Peches Maritimes. Cahier d'Information *see* Quebec (Province). Direction de la Recherche Scientifique et Technique Cahier d'Information **452**
Quebec (Province) Direction Generale des Peches Maritimes. Direction de la Recherche. Rapport Annuel *see* Quebec (Province) Direction de la Recherche Scientifique et Technique. Activites (Year) **452**
Quebec (Province). Direction Generale des Ressources Materielles et Financieres. Regles Budgetaires des Commission Scolaires et des Commissions Regionales *see* Quebec (Province). Ministere de l'Education. Direction Generale du Financement. Regles Budgetaires des Commission Scolaires **1730**
Quebec (Province). Family and Social Affairs Council. Annual Report *see* Quebec (Province). Conseil des Affaires Sociales et de la Famille. Rapport Annuel **4446**
Quebec (Province). Manufacturing and Trade Sectors. Outlook for (Year). *see* Quebec (Province). Ministere de l'Industrie, du Commerce et de la Technologie. Direction de l'Analyse et de la Conjoncture Industrielle **1083**
†Quebec (Province). Ministere de l'Agriculture, des Pecheries et de l'Alimentation. Direction Generale des Peches Maritimes. Travaux sur les Pecheries. (CN) **5265**
Quebec (Province) Ministere de l'Agriculture. Rapport Annuel: Merite Agricole. (CN ISSN 0701-6557) **115**
Quebec (Province). Ministere de l'Education. Direction Generale du Financement. Regles Budgetaires des Commission Scolaires. (CN) **1730**
Quebec (Province). Ministere de l'Education. Regles Budgetaires des Commissions Scolaires et des Commissions Regionales *see* Quebec (Province). Ministere de l'Education. Direction Generale du Financement. Regles Budgetaires des Commission Scolaires **1730**
Quebec (Province) Ministere de l'Energie et des Ressources. Direction de la Recherche et du Developpement. Guide *see* Quebec (Province) Ministere de l'Energie et des Ressources. Direction de la Recherche. Guide **1794**
Quebec (Province) Ministere de l'Energie et des Ressources. Direction de la Recherche et du Developpement. Memoire *see* Quebec (Province) Ministere de l'Energie et des Ressources. Direction de la Recherche. Memoire **1794**
Quebec (Province) Ministere de l'Energie et des Ressources. Direction de la Recherche et du Developpement. Note de Recherche Forestiere *see* Quebec (Province) Ministere de l'Energie et des Ressources. Direction de la Recherche. Note de Recherche Forestiere **2106**
Quebec (Province) Ministere de l'Energie et des Ressources. Direction de la Recherche. Guide. (CN) **1794**, 1495
Quebec (Province) Ministere de l'Energie et des Ressources. Direction de la Recherche. Memoire. (CN) **1794**, 1495
Quebec (Province) Ministere de l'Energie et des Ressources. Direction de la Recherche. Note de Recherche Forestiere. (CN) **2106**
Quebec (Province). Ministere de l'Industrie, du Commerce et de la Technologie. Direction de l'Analyse et de la Conjoncture Industrielle/Quebec (Province). Manufacturing and Trade Sectors. Outlook for (Year). (CN) **1083**, 687
Quebec (Province). Ministere de l'Industrie, du Commerce et de la Technologie. Direction de l'Analyse et de la Prevision Economique *see* Quebec (Province). Ministere de l'Industrie, du Commerce et de la Technologie. Direction de l'Analyse et de la Conjoncture Industrielle **1083**
Quebec (Province). Ministere des Communications. Rapport Annuel. (CN) **1342**
Quebec (Province) Ministere des Communications. Rapport des Activites *see* Quebec (Province). Ministere des Communications. Rapport Annuel **1342**
Quebec (Province). Ministere des Richesses Naturelles. Repertoire des Publications *see* Quebec (Province). Departement d'Energie et Resources. Repertoire des Publications **5265**
†Quebec (Province) Ministere du Travail et de la Main d'Oeuvre. Jurisprudence en Droit du Travail: Tribunal du Travail. (CN ISSN 0700-1681) **5265**
Quebec (Province) Office de la Langue Francaise. Cahiers *see* Vocabulaire des Imprimes Administratifs **5301**
Quebec (Province). Office de la Langue Francaise. Rapport d'Activites. (CN) **2836**
Quebec (Province). Office de la Protection du Consommateur. Rapport Annuel. (CN) **1507**
Quebec (Province) Regie de l'Assurance-Depots du Quebec. Rapport Annuel. (CN ISSN 0701-5666) **2540**
Quebec (Province) Regie de l'Assurance-Maladie. Statistiques Annuelles. (CN ISSN 0226-5346) **2547**
Quebec (Province). Regie des Rentes du Quebec. Perspectives Statistiques *see* Quebec (Province). Regie des Rentes du Quebec. Statistical Outlook **5265**
†Quebec (Province). Regie des Rentes du Quebec. Statistical Outlook. (CN ISSN 0712-8231) **5265**
Quebec (Province). Services Documentaires Multimedia. Choix: Documentation Audiovisuelle. (CN) **410**
Quebec (Province). Services Documentaires Multimedia. Choix: Documentation Imprimee. (CN) **410**
Quebec (Province) Services Documentation Multimedia. Choix Jeunesse: Documentation Imprimee. (CN) **2780**
Quebec Astronomique *see* Astronomie Quebec **361**
Quebec Chasse et Peche *see* Sentier Chasse - Peche **4555**
Quebec Corporation and Income Tax Legislation. (CN) **1104**, 2669
Quebec Economique International. (CN ISSN 0823-2229) **882**
Quebec Farmers Advocate. (CN ISSN 0714-9158) **115**
Quebec Habitation. (CN) **629**
Quebec Home & School News. (CN ISSN 0033-5967) **1657**
†Quebec Industriel. (CN ISSN 0033-5975) **5265**
Quebec Library Association Bulletin *see* Q L A Bulletin **2780**
Quebec Official Gazette. (CN ISSN 0033-5983) **4072**
Quebec Science. (CN ISSN 0021-6127) **4335**, 4607
Quebec Soccer. (CN) **4510**
Quebec Studies. (US ISSN 0737-3759) **2951**, 2420
Quebec Tax Reports. (CN ISSN 0048-6299) **1104**
Quebec Vert. (CN ISSN 0705-6923) **2137**
Quebec Yachting et Voile *see* Quebec Yachting, Voile et Moteur **4528**
Quebec Yachting, Voile et Moteur. (CN ISSN 0833-918X) **4528**
Quebecensia. (CN ISSN 0226-210X) **2320**, 2260
Quechee Times. (US) **2232**
Queen *see* Harpers & Queen **4844**
Queen Alexandra Hospital for Children. Annual Report *see* Arbutus Society for Children. Annual Report **2459**
Queen City Heritage. (US ISSN 0746-3472) **2420**
Queen Mary and Westfield College. Department of Geography. Research Papers in Geography. (UK) **2260**
Queen Mary College. Department of Geography. Research Papers in Geography *see* Queen Mary and Westfield College. Department of Geography. Research Papers in Geography **2260**
Queen Mary College Students Union Handbook. (UK) **1715**
Queen of All Hearts. (US ISSN 0033-6017) **4196**
Queen Victoria Museum and Art Gallery. Annual Report. (AT) **3532**
Queen Victoria Museum and Art Gallery. Launceston, Tasmania. Records. (AT ISSN 0085-5278) **3532**, 4335
Queen's Alumni Review. (CN ISSN 0843-8048) **1322**
Queen's Award Magazine. (UK ISSN 0141-1780) **919**
Queens Bar Bulletin. (US ISSN 0048-6302) **2669**
†Queens College Publications in Anthropology. (US) **5265**
†Queens College Studies in Librarianship. (US ISSN 0146-8677) **5265**
Queens County Dental Society. Bulletin. (US) **3241**
Queen's File. (UK) **4484**
Queen's Journal. (CN) **1322**
Queen's Law Journal. (CN ISSN 0316-778X) **2669**
Queens Medical Magazine. (UK ISSN 0033-6033) **3145**
Queen's Medical Review. (CN ISSN 0079-8789) **3145**
Queen's Papers in Pure and Applied Mathematics. (CN ISSN 0079-8797) **3052**
Queen's Quarterly. (CN ISSN 0033-6041) **2178**
Queen's Regulations for the Army Amendments. (UK) **3469**
Queen's Regulations for the R.A.F. Amendments. (UK) **3469**
Queen's University. Industrial Relations Centre. Queen's Papers in Industrial Relations Series. (CN) **992**
†Queen's University. Industrial Relations Centre. Research and Current Issues Series. (CN ISSN 0317-2546) **5265**
Queen's University. Industrial Relations Centre. School of Industrial Relations Research Essay Series. (CN) **992**
Queen's University. Institute for Economic Research. Discussion Paper. (CN ISSN 0316-5078) **687**
†Queen's University at Kingston. Annual Report on the Libraries. (CN) **5265**
Queen's University at Kingston. Department of Electrical Engineering. Research Report. (CN ISSN 0075-6091) **1906**
Queen's University at Kingston. Douglas Library. Occasional Papers. (CN ISSN 0075-6113) **2795**
Queen's University at Kingston. Industrial Relations Centre. Bibliography Series. (CN ISSN 0075-613X) **736**
†Queen's University at Kingston. Industrial Relations Centre. Reprint Series. (CN ISSN 0075-6156) **5265**
Queensborough. (US ISSN 0033-6068) **821**
Queensland. Air Pollution Council. Annual Report. (AT) **1979**
Queensland. Department of Business, Industry and Regional Development. Annual Report. (AT) **1083**
Queensland. Department of Business, Industry and Regional Development. Client Update. (AT) **687**
Queensland. Department of Business, Industry and Regional Development. Industry. (AT) **1083**
▼Queensland. Department of Business, Industry and Regional Development. Research and Development Directory.(AT) **410**
Queensland. Department of Education. Curriculum Development Services. Curriculum Paper. (AT) **1657**
†Queensland. Department of Education. Information and Publications Branch. Document. (AT) **5265**
†Queensland. Department of Education. Information and Publications Branch. Information Statement. (AT) **5265**
Queensland. Department of Education. Research and Curriculum Branch. Curriculum Paper *see* Queensland. Department of Education. Curriculum Development Services. Curriculum Paper **1657**
Queensland. Department of Education. Research and Curriculum Branch. Document *see* Queensland. Department of Education. Information and Publications Branch. Document **5265**
†Queensland. Department of Education. Research Branch. Reporting Research. (AT) **5265**
Queensland. Department of Education. Research Branch. Research Series *see* Queensland. Department of Education. Research Services. Research Series **1657**
Queensland. Department of Education. Research Services. Research Series. (AT) **1657**
Queensland. Department of Forestry. Annual Report *see* Queensland Forest Service. Department of Primary Industries. Annual Report **2106**
Queensland. Department of Forestry. Research Note *see* Queensland Forest Service. Research Note **2106**
Queensland. Department of Forestry. Research Paper *see* Queensland Forest Service. Research Paper **2106**
Queensland. Department of Forestry. Technical Paper *see* Queensland Forest Service. Technical Paper **2107**
Queensland. Department of Industry Development. Annual Report *see* Queensland. Department of Business, Industry and Regional Development. Annual Report **1083**
Queensland. Department of Industry Development. Industry *see* Queensland. Department of Business, Industry and Regional Development. Industry **1083**
Queensland. Department of Manufacturing and Commerce. Industry *see* Queensland. Department of Business, Industry and Regional Development. Industry **1083**
Queensland. Land Administration Commission. Annual Report. (AT) **4072**, 115
Queensland. Qeensland Department of Manufacturing and Commerce. Annual Report *see* Queensland. Department of Business, Industry and Regional Development. Annual Report **1083**
Queensland. Registrar of Co-Operative and Other Societies. Report. (AT ISSN 0481-3375) **832**
†Queensland Agricultural Journal. (AT ISSN 0157-7786) **5265**
Queensland at a Glance. (AT ISSN 0157-3713) **4584**

6590 QUEENSLAND BOOKBINDERS'

Queensland Bookbinders' Guild. Newsletter. (AT ISSN 0725-0711) **4135**, 356
Queensland Chess. (AT) **4484**
Queensland Conservation Council Newsletter. (AT) **1496**
Queensland Conveyancing Law and Practice. (AT) **2669**
Queensland Country Life. (AT ISSN 0033-6084) **115**
Queensland Country Woman. (AT ISSN 0033-6092) **4851**
Queensland Dairyfarmer. (AT ISSN 0033-6106) **203**
Queensland District Courts Practice. (AT) **2670**
Queensland Electrical Contractor. (AT ISSN 0033-6114) **1906**
Queensland Family Historian. (AT ISSN 0811-3394) **2162**
Queensland Farmer & Grazier. (AT) **115**
Queensland Forest Service. Advisory Leaflet. (AT ISSN 1035-977X) **2106**
Queensland Forest Service. Department of Primary Industries. Annual Report.(AT) **2106**
Queensland Forest Service. Research Note. (AT ISSN 1035-9788) **2106**
Queensland Forest Service. Research Paper. (AT ISSN 1035-9796) **2106**
Queensland Forest Service. Research Report. (AT) **2106**
Queensland Forest Service. Technical Note. (AT ISSN 1035-9818) **2106**
Queensland Forest Service. Technical Paper. (AT ISSN 1035-9826) **2107**
Queensland Fruit and Vegetable News. (AT ISSN 0033-6122) **2137**
Queensland Gardener see Australian Gardener **2122**
Queensland Government Mining Journal.(AT ISSN 0033-6149) **3494**
Queensland Government Publications. (AT ISSN 0313-7813) **410**
Queensland Graingrower. (AT) **208**
Queensland Hosteller see On the Go **4781**
†Queensland in Relation to Australia. (AT ISSN 1031-279X) **5265**
Queensland Institute for Educational Research Queensland Researcher see Queensland Researcher **1715**
Queensland Institute of Technology Law Journal see Queensland University of Technology Law Journal **2670**
Queensland Law Reporter. (AT ISSN 0726-0784) **2670**
Queensland Law Society Journal. (AT ISSN 0313-4253) **2670**
Queensland Lawyer. (AT ISSN 0312-1658) **2670**
Queensland Magistrates Courts. (AT ISSN 0727-8063) **2732**
†Queensland Manufacturers Directory. (AT) **5266**
Queensland Master Plumber. (AT ISSN 0048-637X) **2302**
Queensland Motel & Accommodation Association Inc. News see Q M A A News **2479**
Queensland Museum, Brisbane. Memoirs. (AT ISSN 0079-8835) **3532**, 247, 1593
Queensland Naturalist. (AT ISSN 0079-8843) **452**
Queensland Planner. (AT) **2494**
Queensland Pocket Year Book. (AT ISSN 0085-5316) **4584**
Queensland Potters Association News see Q.P.A. News **1165**
†Queensland Profile. (AT) **5266**
Queensland Reports. (AT ISSN 0726-3759) **2732**
Queensland Researcher. (Queensland Institute for Educational Research) (AT ISSN 0818-545X) **1715**
†Queensland Roads. (AT ISSN 0048-6388) **5266**
Queensland Shopkeeper see Retailer of Queensland **2093**
Queensland Society of Sugar Cane Technologists. Proceedings see Australian Society of Sugar Cane Technologists. Proceedings **2062**

▼Queensland Stamp Duties. (AT) **1104**
Queensland Statutes Annotations. (AT) **2670**
Queensland Supreme Court Practice. (AT) **2732**
Queensland Teachers' Journal. (AT ISSN 0033-6238) **1657**
Queensland - the Manufacturing Environment. (AT) **838**
Queensland Tourist and Travel Corporation. Annual Report. (AT) **4783**
Queensland Transport News. (AT) **4747**, 1026
Queensland Unit & Group Titles Law and Practice. (AT) **2670**
Queensland University of Technology Law Journal. (AT ISSN 1032-6693) **2670**
Queensland Worker see Australian Worker **2580**
Queer World see Q W **2456**
QueHacer. (PE ISSN 0250-9806) **3920**
Quehacer Nacional. (AG) **3921**
Die Quelle. (GW ISSN 0033-6246) **2588**
Quellen und Forschungen aus Italienischen Archiven und Bibliotheken. (GW ISSN 0079-9068) **2320**
Quellen und Forschungen zur Basler Geschichte. (SZ ISSN 0079-9076) **2382**
Quellen und Forschungen zur Geschichte des Ersten Weltkrieges see Quellen und Studien zu den Friedensversuchen des Ersten Weltkrieges **2382**
Quellen und Forschungen zur Wuerttembergischen Kirchengeschichte. (GW ISSN 0079-9084) **4196**
Quellen und Studien zu den Friedensversuchen des Ersten Weltkrieges. (GW) **2382**
Quellen und Studien zur Geschichte des Oestlichen Europa. (GW ISSN 0170-3595) **2382**
Quellen und Studien zur Geschichte Osteuropas. (GW ISSN 0079-9114) **2382**
Quellen und Untersuchungen zur Lateinischen Philologie des Mittelalters. (GW ISSN 0721-6203) **1279**, 2836
Quellen zur Geschichte des Islamischen Aegyptens. (GW ISSN 0481-0023) **2334**, 4220
Quellen zur Geschichte des 19. und 20. Jahrhunderts. (AU) **2382**
Quellen zur Theatergeschichte. (AU ISSN 0259-0786) **4637**
Quellenkataloge zur Musikgeschichte. (GW ISSN 0079-905X) **3575**
Quellenschriften zur Westdeutschen Vor- und Fruehgeschichte. (GW ISSN 0079-9149) **282**
Quellenwerke zur Alten Geschichte Amerikas. (GW ISSN 0079-9157) **2420**, 2058
Quem e Quem na Economia Brasileira. (BL) **1151**
Quem e Quem na Industria Quimica Brasileira. (BL) **1859**, 1186
Quentin Cameron's Oil & Gas Bulletin. (AT) **961**, 3700
Querce. (IT ISSN 0033-6262) **1263**
†Quercus. (US) **5266**
Query Magazine. (FR) **2187**, 4783
Quercy Recherche. (FR ISSN 0335-3958) **2382**
Query. (CN ISSN 0380-240X) **1657**
Query. (US ISSN 0033-6270) **2540**
Quest. see T'an So **2886**
Quest. (NE ISSN 1011-226X) **3778**
Quest (Champaign). (US ISSN 0033-6297) **1758**, 3372
Quest (Dallas) see Cancer Review **3195**
The Quest (Wheaton). (US ISSN 1040-533X) **3596**, 3778, 4196
Quest in Education. (II ISSN 0048-6434) **1657**
Quest Magazine. (US) **341**, 2456
Quest: Manhattan Properties & Country Estates. (US) **4155**, 2554, 2881

Questa Sicilia. (IT ISSN 0033-6335) **2206**
Queste Istituzioni. (IT) **3921**, 687, 3969, 4072
Question de. (FR) **3671**, 2951, 4196
Question de Racines, Pensees, Sciences Eclairees see Question de **3671**
Question Mark. (US) **1521**
Questione Agraria see Q A **156**
Questione Giustizia. (IT) **2670**
Questiones Geobiologicae. see Problemy Biologie Krajiny **5262**
Questiones Informaticae see South African Computer Journal **1400**
Questiones Medii Aevi. (PL) **2382**
Questioni Attuali del Socialismo see Aktuelna Pitanja Socijalizma **3871**
Questioning Exchange see Q X **5265**
Questioning Techniques and Tactics. (US) **2670**
Questions Actuelles du Socialisme. (YU ISSN 0033-6351) **3921**
Questions & Reponses Canadiennes. see Canadian Notes & Queries **2504**
Questions Clefs. (FR) **2881**
Questions de Vida Cristiana. (SP) **4196**
Questitalia. (IT ISSN 0033-6378) **3921**
Questor Strategic Real Estate Letter see Roulac's Strategic Real Estate **4157**
Quetico-Superior Wilderness Research Center, Ely, Minnesota. Annual Report. (US ISSN 0079-9211) **1496**, 452
Quetico-Superior Wilderness Research Center, Ely, Minnesota. Technical Notes. (US ISSN 0079-922X) **1496**
Quetta Times. (PK ISSN 0033-6386) **2213**
El Quetzal. (US ISSN 0162-7902) **3757**
Queueing Systems. (SZ ISSN 0257-0130) **1880**, 1906
Queyras. (FR ISSN 0048-6450) **4783**
Qufo. (SW ISSN 0348-7377) **1578**
Qufu Normal University. Journal. see Qufu Shifan Daxue Xuebao **4383**
Qufu Shifan Daxue Xuebao/Qufu Normal University. Journal. (CC) **4383**
Qui Construit des Machines et des Installations see Wer Baut Maschinen und Anlagen **1941**
Qui Est Qui en France. see Who's Who in France **422**
Qui Fabrique et Fournit Quoi. (FR) **3655**
†Qui-Light. (US) **5266**
Qui Parle. (US ISSN 1041-8385) **2951**, 341
Qui Represente Qui. (FR ISSN 0079-9262) **1151**
Qui Touring. (IT ISSN 0042-546X) **4783**, 2206
Qui Vend et Achete Quoi? (FR ISSN 0079-9270) **1151**
Quick. (GW) **2191**
Quick & Easy Crafts. (US ISSN 1048-3659) **3592**
Quick and Easy Crochet. (US) **3592**
Quick & Easy Plastic Canvas. (US ISSN 1048-5341) **3592**, 356
Quick & Easy Quilting. (US ISSN 1045-5965) **3592**
Quick Caller: Boston Area Air Cargo Directory. (US) **4676**, 4747
Quick Caller: Chicago Area Air Cargo Directory. (US) **4677**, 4747
Quick Caller: Detroit Area Air Cargo Directory. (US) **4677**, 4747
Quick Caller: Los Angeles Area Air Cargo Directory. (US) **4677**, 4747
Quick Caller: Miami Area Air Cargo Directory. (US) **4677**, 4747
Quick Caller: New York Metro Area Air Cargo Directory. (US) **4677**, 4747
Quick Caller: San Francisco Bay Area Air Cargo Directory. (US) **4677**, 4747
†Quick Frozen Foods. (US ISSN 0033-6408) **5266**
†Quick Frozen Foods Directory of Frozen Food Processors. (US ISSN 0079-9289) **5266**

Quick Frozen Foods International. (US ISSN 0033-6416) **2080**, 115, 2048, 2093
Quick Guide to the New Telecom Lingo. (US) **1365**, 1151
Quick Index of Medical Preparations Quarterly see Q I M P Quarterly **3741**
Quick 'n Easy Cookin' see Country Quick 'n Easy Cookin **2445**
Quick Printing. (US ISSN 0191-4588) **4005**
Quick Release to the Mineral Statistics of India. (II) **3502**, 3494
Quick Response News. (US ISSN 1045-6643) **805**
Quick Strokes see Dvorak Developments **5182**
Quick Topics Newsletter. (US) **2089**
Quickborn. (GW ISSN 0170-7558) **2836**, 2951
Quickborn Buecher. (GW) **2951**, 2836
Quickening. (US) **3286**
Quickenings in Trillum Land. (US) **3003**
Quickoats see Quixote **3921**
Quiddity. (UK ISSN 0952-7532) **1051**, 4607
Quien Construye Maquinas e Instalaciones see Wer Baut Maschinen und Anlagen **1941**
Quien Vende en Espana los Productos Extranjeros/Who Sells Foreign Products in Spain. (SP) **1151**
Quiet Birdmen Beam see Q B Beam **60**
The Quill. (CN) **1322**
Quill. (II) **2881**
Quill (Greencastle). (US ISSN 0480-7898) **2575**
Quill (Wood Ridge). (US ISSN 0033-6483) **4093**
Quill and Quire. (CN ISSN 0033-6491) **4135**
Quill and Scroll. (US ISSN 0033-6505) **2575**, 1657
Quilt. (US) **3592**
Quilt see Ismael Reed and Al Young's Quilt **5219**
▼Quilt Craft. (US) **3592**
Quilt Digest. (US ISSN 0740-4093) **3592**
Quilt World. (US ISSN 0149-8045) **3592**
Quilt World Omnibook see Quick & Easy Quilting **3592**
The Quilter. (UK) **3592**
Quilters Guild. Newsletter see The Quilter **3592**
Quilter's Newsletter Magazine. (US ISSN 0274-712X) **3592**
Quilting International. (US) **3592**
Quilting Today. (US ISSN 1040-4457) **3592**
Quilting U S A see Quilting International **3592**
Quiltmaker. (US ISSN 1047-1634) **3592**
Quiltmakers Time. (US) **356**
†Quimby. (US) **5266**
Quimera. (SP ISSN 0211-3325) **2951**
Quimica e Derivados. (BL ISSN 0481-4118) **1186**
Quimica e Industria. (SP ISSN 0033-6521) **1859**
Quinault Natural Resources. (US) **1496**, 2020, 2048, 2107
Quincaillerie Materiaux. (CN ISSN 0318-8531) **642**, 1051
†Quincaillerie Moderne. (FR) **5266**
Quincaillier Belge see Mars-Magazine **642**
Quincy Business News. (US) **687**
Quincy College Bulletin. (US ISSN 0033-6556) **1322**
Quinnehtukqut. (US) **1496**, 1966, 4554
Quinn's Uniform Commercial Code Law Journal. (US) **2700**, 20, 736
Quinquereme. (UK ISSN 0140-3397) **2836**, 2881, 2951
Quinta Generazione: Rivista di Poesia. (IT) **3003**
Quintessence. (US) **3145**, 3643
Quintessence (Edicion Espanola). (SP ISSN 0214-0985) **3241**
Quintessence International. (US ISSN 0033-6572) **3241**

Quintessence of Dental Technology see Q D T 3241
▼Quintessenz Tecnica (Edicion Espanola). (Spanish translation of: Quintessenz der Zahntechnik) (SP) 3241
Quintessenz. (GW) 2191
Die Quintessenz. (GW) 3241
Quintessenz der Zahntechnik. (GW) 3241
Quintessenz Journal. (GW ISSN 0033-6599) 3241
Quintessenza. (IT ISSN 0390-6841) 3241
▼Quintile. (US) 3596
Quinto Lingo. (US ISSN 0033-6602) 2836
Quinzaine Africaine. (FR) 3969, 882
Quinzaine Litteraire. (FR ISSN 0048-6493) 2952
Quinzaine Universitaire. (FR) 1657
Quinze Ans. (FR) 1263
Quipu. (MX ISSN 0185-5093) 4335, 2420, 4607
Quirk's Marketing Research Review. (US ISSN 0893-7451) 1051
Quiron. (AG ISSN 0325-2345) 3146
Quitumbe. (EC) 2420
Quixote. (US ISSN 0033-6629) 3921
Quixote, Quixotl. (US) 2881
†Quiz Trivia. (UK ISSN 0952-8148) 5266
Qun Yan/Popular Tribune. (CC) 2881, 2182
Qunzhong Wenhua/Mass Culture. (CC) 2182, 2881
Quo Vadis. (SA ISSN 0033-6637) 4247
Quodlibet. (US) 3575
Quondam Magazine. (SA ISSN 0033-6661) 1300, 4484
Quorum. (CI ISSN 0352-7654) 2952, 2513
Quorum. (AT ISSN 0811-594X) 3394
Quorum Quotes. (US) 3516
Quorum Report. (US ISSN 0882-3456) 3921, 4072
Quotasport. (IT) 4484
Quote. (US ISSN 0273-6705) 1657
Quote...Unquote. (US) 4273, 2420
Quote American. (US) 961
Quote Magazine see Quote 1657
Quote New York. (US) 961
Quote O-T-C. (US) 961
Quranulhuda. (PK) 4220
Quser News. (US ISSN 1052-0775) 1464
Al-Quwwa. (BA) 3469
Al-Quwwat al-Jawwiyyah/U A E Air Force Magazine. (TS) 3469
"R" (Rhumatologie). (FR) 3369
R A B Instant Background. (Radio Advertising Bureau) (US) 37
R A B S. (Religionspaedagogik an Berufsbildenden Schulen) (GW) 4247
R A C A R. (Revue d'Art Canadienne / Canadian Art Review) (CN ISSN 0315-9906) 341
R A C B Royal Auto. (Koninklijke Automobiel Club van Belgie) (BE ISSN 0022-7242) 4700, 4783
R A C Continental Hotel Guide see R A C European Hotel Guide 4783
R A C Digest. (Retail Advertising Conference) (US) 37
R A C European Hotel Guide. (Royal Automobile Club) (UK) 4783, 4700
R A C Hotel Guide see R A C Hotel Guide Great Britain & Ireland 4783
R A C Hotel Guide Great Britain & Ireland. (Royal Automobile Club) (UK) 4783, 4700
R A C Motor Sport Year Book. (UK) 4484, 4700, 4783
†R.A.C.S. Newsletter. (Royal Australasian College of Surgeons) (NZ ISSN 0033-6696) 5266
R A C V's Out and About see Attractions Australia 4752
R A D see Revista Amazonense de Desenvolvimento 1659
R-A-D-A-R. (US ISSN 0162-5217) 1263, 4196
R A D A R Bulletin. (Royal Association for Disability and Rehabilitation) (UK ISSN 0954-237X) 3146

R A D A R Contact. (Royal Association for Disability and Rehabilitation) (UK) 2284
R A D I A L S Bulletin see Current Research in Library & Information Science 2753
R A E C Gazette see Torch (London) 3473
†R A E News. (Royal Aerospace Establishment) (UK ISSN 0033-6718) 5266
R A I A Memo. (Royal Australian Institute of Architects) (AT ISSN 0818-1233) 305
R A I A News see R A I A Memo 305
R A I Actueel. (Nederlandse Vereniging "de Rijwiel- en Automobiel Industrie") (NE ISSN 0166-1922) 4700
R A I Orgaan see R A I Actueel 4700
R A I R O APII Automatique - Productique Informatique Industrielle. (Revue Francaise d'Automatique d'Informatique et de Recherche Operationelle) (FR ISSN 0296-1598) 1442
R A I R O Automatique - Systems Analysis and Control see R A I R O APII Automatique - Productique Informatique Industrielle 1442
R A I R O Informatique - Computer Science see R A I R O - T S I Technique et Sciences Informatiques 1442
R A I R O Informatique Theorique et Appliquee - Theoretical Informatics and Applications. (FR ISSN 0988-3754) 1442
R A I R O Informatique Theorique - Theoretical Informatics see R A I R O Informatique Theorique et Appliquee - Theoretical Informatics and Applications 1442
R A I R O - M 2 A N Mathematical Modelling and Numerical Analysis. (FR ISSN 0764-583X) 3052
R A I R O Recherche Operationnelle/ Operations Research. (FR ISSN 0399-0559) 1442
R A I R O - T S I Technique et Sciences Informatiques. (FR ISSN 0752-4072) 1442
†R A L Report. (US ISSN 0884-3740) 5266
R A M see Revista Agropecuario de Manfredi y Marcos Juarez 190
R A M Research Bank Card Barometer.(US ISSN 1040-6905) 796, 1507
R A M Research Bank Card Update. (US ISSN 1040-8959) 796, 1507
R A M Research Bank Credit Card Issuers Yearbook see R A M Research Bank Card Barometer 796
R A M Research Card Search. (US ISSN 1040-6662) 796, 1507
▼R A M Research Cardtrak. (US ISSN 1053-9719) 796, 1507
R A M Research Consumer Credit Card Yearbook see R A M Research Card Search 796
R A News. (Recreation Association of the Public Service of Canada) (CN ISSN 0033-6734) 1300, 4072
R A - Nytt. (SW ISSN 0347-4585) 2330
R A O U Monographs. (Royal Australasian Ornithologists Union) (AT) 566
R A O U Newsletter. (Royal Australasian Ornithologists Union) (AT ISSN 0812-8014) 566
R A O U Report. (Royal Australasian Ornithologists Union) (AT) 566
R A P. (Radicals Against Poverty) (US ISSN 0033-6742) 4446
R A P R A Abstracts. (Rubber and Plastics Research Association of Great Britain) (UK ISSN 0033-6750) 4295, 20, 3869
R A P R A New Trade Names in the Rubber and Plastics Industries. (Rubber and Plastics Research Association of Great Britain) (UK ISSN 0747-4954) 4293, 3867
R A P R A News. (Rubber and Plastics Research Association of Great Britain) (UK ISSN 0140-041X) 3867, 1835, 4293

R A P R A Review Reports. (Rubber and Plastics Research Association of Great Britain) (US ISSN 0889-3144) 3869, 4295
†R A R Challenge. (Interfaith Center to Reverse the Arms Race) (US) 5266
R A S. (Rohr-Armatur-Sanitaer-Heizung) (GW ISSN 0033-6769) 2302
R A S D Update. (Reference and Adult Services Division) (US ISSN 0198-8344) 2780, 1686
R A S E. (Remedial and Special Education) (US ISSN 0741-9325) 1740
R A S E News. (National Agricultural Centre) (UK) 115
R A S Kennel Control Journal see Victorian Canine Association Journal 3714
R A U - Rapport. (Rand Afrikaans University) (SA ISSN 0033-6785) 1715, 1322
▼R & B Music & Entertainment Monthly. (Rhythm and Blues) (US) 3575
▼R & D Activities of Major Japanese Chemical Companies. (JA) 687
R & D Contracts Monthly. (Research & Development) (US ISSN 0033-6793) 4335, 60, 1835, 3469
R & D Digest. (Research & Development) (UK ISSN 0268-330X) 1794, 1208
R & D Focus. (US) 3430, 1966
R & D Magazine. (US) 4335
R & D Management. (UK ISSN 0033-6807) 1026
†R & D Management Digest. (US ISSN 0361-753X) 5266
R & D Outlook. (CN) 687
R & D Preview. (US) 1758
▼R & D Strategist. (US) 4607
R & D Survey. (SI ISSN 0217-6440) 4335
R & R Entertainment Digest see R & R Shoppers News 1378
R & R Entertainment Digest. (Rest & Relaxation) (US) 3469
†R & R Pacific. (GU) 5266
R & R Shoppers News. (Rest & Relaxation) (GW) 1378, 3469, 4484
R & S Report (Honolulu) see Hawaii. Department of Health. Research and Statistics Office. R & S Report 3992
R B A Fresh Baked see Fresh Baked 2088
R B C Newsletter see P I C Newsletter 2778
R B Congress Marketing. (GW) 1051
R B Elektronica Magazine. (NE) 1777
R B Hotel Marketing. (GW) 4783
R.B.I. Annual Report see Reserve Bank of India. Annual Report 797
R B Luftfahrt Marketing. (GW) 4783
R B M see Revista Brasileira de Medicina 3147
R B M A Bulletin. (Radiology Business Management Association) (US) 3361
R B Marketing. (GW) 4783
R B O C, A T & T, and I B M Newsletter see Telecom Outlook 1055
†R B R O T A L. (Resource-Based Resource-Oriented Teaching and Learning) (AT) 5266
R.B.R.R. Kale Memorial Lectures. (II) 3921, 687
R B Weekender. (Robinson-Blackmore Ltd.) (CN) 1378
R C D A. (Religion in Communist Dominated Areas) (US) 4196, 3969
R C D A - Religion in Communist Dominated Areas see R C D A 4196
R C - Freizeit. (GW) 2440
R C Fundgrube see R C - Freizeit 2440
R C H A Newsletter. (Regional Council of Historical Agencies) (US) 3532
R C H A Technical Information Sheet. (Regional Council of Historical Agencies) (US) 3532
R C I. (Riscaldamento Climatizzazione Idronica) (IT ISSN 0392-6087) 1835

R.C.I.A. Resource. (AT ISSN 1033-1050) 4273
R C M A Journal. (Radio Communications Monitoring Association) (US) 1358
R C M A Newsletter see R C M A Journal 1358
R C M Magazine. (Royal College of Music) (UK ISSN 0033-684X) 3575
R C M P Quarterly/G R C. Revue Trimestrielle. (Royal Canadian Mounted Police) (CN ISSN 0033-6858) 1521
R-C Modeler. (US ISSN 0033-6866) 2440, 60
R C N P Annual Report. (Research Center for Nuclear Physics) (JA) 3850
R C News. (Radio Control) (US) 2440
R C R A see Resource Conservation Recovery Act Notification Data File 1502
R C R Cellular Handbook. (Radio Communications Report) (US) 1358
R C R Paging Handbook. (Radio Communications Report) (US) 1358
R, D & A. (Research, Development and Acquisition) (US ISSN 0162-7082) 3469
R D B M Computing. (US) 1479, 1455
R D H. (US) 3241
R D I P see Respiratory Disease in Practice 3366
R D P. (Rural Development Perspectives) (US ISSN 0271-2172) 115, 687, 4446
R D V see Recht der Datenverarbeitung 1434
R E. (Review of Ethnology) (AU ISSN 0048-6507) 247
R E A L see Re: Arts and Letters 2513
R E A L. Yearbook. (Research in English and American Literature) (GW ISSN 0723-0338) 2952
†R E A P. (Research Exchange and Practice in Mental Retardation) (NE) 5266
R E C see Recreational & Educational Computing 1473
R E C Mission Bulletin. (Reformed Ecumenical Council) (US) 4247
R E C News Exchange. (US) 4247
R E C Newsletter see Recreational & Educational Computing 1473
R E C O E X. (Recopilacion Tecnica de Comercio Exterior) (SP) 919
R E C S A M Annual Report. (Regional Centre for Education in Science and Mathematics) (MY ISSN 0377-3450) 1657, 1758
R E C S A M News. (Regional Centre for Education in Science and Mathematics) (MY ISSN 0126-7612) 1758, 3052, 4335
R E C S A M Newsletter see R E C S A M News 1758
R E C Theological Forum. (US) 4247
R E E Action. (Real Estate Educators Association) (US) 4155
R E F A see Revue Economique et Financiere Ivoirienne 883
R E F A Nachrichten. (GW ISSN 0033-6874) 992
R E I D Quarterly. (Real Estate Investment Quarterly) (US) 2540
R E I S Report: Industrial Market Service. (US) 4155
R E I S Report: Residential Market Service. (US) 4155
R E I S Reports: Office Market Service. (Real Estate Information Service) (US) 4155
R E I S Reports: Retail Market Service. (Real Estate Information Service) (US) 4155
R.E.I.T. Fact Book. (US ISSN 0095-1374) 4155, 961
R.E.I.T. Report. (National Association of Real Estate Investment Trusts, Inc.) (US) 4155, 961
R.E.L. see Recherches Economiques de Louvain 687
R E L C Annual Report. (Regional Language Centre) (SI ISSN 0129-7716) 2836

R E L C Guidelines. (Regional Language Centre) (SI ISSN 0129-7767) **2836**

R E L C Journal. (Regional Language Centre) (SI ISSN 0033-6882) **2836**, 1657

R E L C Newsletter. (Regional Language Centre) (SI ISSN 0217-3077) **2836**

R E L C Occasional Papers. (Regional Language Centre) (SI ISSN 0129-8844) **2836**

R E L C Seminar Report. (Regional Language Centre) (SI) **2836**

▼R E M. (UK) **3013**

R E M E Journal. (Royal Electrical & Mechanical Engineers) (UK ISSN 0432-2924) **1938**, 60

R E Magazine. (Rural Electrification) (US) **1907**

R E N Illinois Rural Electric News see Illinois Rural Electric News **1898**

R E News see R E View **1794**

R E News see Focus on Technology **4598**

R.E. Olds Transportation Museum Newsletter. (US) **4655**, 3532

R E P see Recording Engineering Production **4461**

R E R see Rental Equipment Register **1051**

R E R I C International Energy Journal. (Regional Energy Resources Information Center) (TH ISSN 0857-6173) **1794**

R E R I C News. (Regional Energy Resources Information Center) (TH ISSN 0125-1775) **1794**, 1811, 1812

R E S. (Relacion de Empresas Suspensas en Pagos, Embargos y Subastas) (SP) **796**

R E S Mission Bulletin see R E C Mission Bulletin **4247**

R E S N A News. (US) **1740**, 2288, 2295

R E S News Exchange see R E C News Exchange **4247**

R E S S see Cahiers Vilfredo Pareto **4368**

R E S Theological Forum see R E C Theological Forum **4247**

†R E T S Digest. (Research Engineering Technical Services) (US ISSN 0885-9809) **5266**

R E View. (Renewable Energy) (UK ISSN 0955-5188) **1794**

R F Avisen. (Reklamefotograf Foreningen) (DK ISSN 0109-5196) **37**

R F D. (US ISSN 0149-709X) **2456**, 2881

R F D News. (US ISSN 0481-5084) **115**, 37

R F Design. (US ISSN 0163-321X) **1777**

▼R F E - R L Daily Report. (Radio Free Europe - Radio Liberty Inc.) (GW) **3969**

R F F S A. Anuario Estatistico. (Rede Ferroviaria Federal, S.A.) (BL ISSN 0102-4930) **4666**, 4713

R F L - Rundschau Fleischhyiene und Lebensmittelueberwachung. (GW ISSN 0178-2010) **4814**

R F M. (Revue Francaise des Metallurgistes) (FR) **3418**

R F - Magazin. (Deutscher Radio- und Fernseh-Fachverband e.V.) (GW) **1358**, 1378

R F Medlemsblad. (Romansk Filmklub) (DK ISSN 0109-0631) **3516**

†R F Z. Technische Mitteilungen. (Rundfunk- und Fernsehtechnisches Zentralamt) (GW ISSN 0040-1455) **5266**

R G. (CN) **2456**

R G D A News. (Retail Gasoline and Garage Dealers Association) (US) **3700**

†R G H Reflexe. (Rationalisierungs-Gemeinschaft des Handels beim R K M) (GW) **5266**

R G L in (Year) see Research Libraries Group News **2781**

R G S. (Revue Generale de Securite) (FR ISSN 0242-6277) **1527**

R G U Aarbog see Danmarks Geologiske Undersoegelse. Aarbog **5177**

R G W in Zahlen see Comecon Data (Year) **927**

R H G H Vital Signs. (Richmond Heights General Hospital) (US ISSN 0300-6654) **2468**

R.H.M. Convertible Survey. (US) **961**

R.H.M. Survey of Warrants, Options & Low-Price Stocks. (US) **961**

R.H.S. Gardener's Diary. (Royal Horticultural Society) (UK ISSN 0080-441X) **2137**

R.H.S.V. History News. (Royal Historical Society of Victoria, Inc.) (AT ISSN 0157-5740) **2345**

R I A. (FR) **2080**

▼R I A Analysis of Federal Taxes: Estate and Gift. (Research Institute of America, Inc.) (US) **1104**

▼R I A Analysis of Federal Taxes: Excise. (Research Institute of America, Inc.) (US) **1104**

▼R I A Analysis of Federal Taxes: Income. (Research Institute of America, Inc.) (US) **1104**

▼R I A Complete Federal Tax Forms. (Research Institute of America, Inc.) (US) **1104**

R I A I Architects Yearbook. (Royal Institute of the Architects of Ireland) (IE) **305**

R I A I Bulletin see Irish Architect **301**

▼R I A Internal Revenue Code and Regulations. (Research Institute of America, Inc.) (US) **1104**

R I A L News. (Religion in American Life) (US) **4196**

R I A Quarterly Statistics Report - Robotics. (Robotic Industries Association) (US) **1415**, 4584

†R I A S-Funkuniversitaet, Berlin. Schriftenreihe. Forschung und Information. (GW) **5266**

R I B A Directory of Practices. (Royal Institute of British Architects) (UK ISSN 0269-0810) **306**

R I B A Interior Design Product Selector see R I B A Interior Design Selector **2554**

R I B A Interior Design Selector. (Royal Institute of British Architects) (UK) **2554**, 306

R I B A Journal. (Royal Institute of British Architects) (UK ISSN 0953-6973) **306**

R I B A Library Bulletin see Architectural Periodicals Index **309**

R I B A Product Selector. (Royal Institute of British Architects) (UK ISSN 0265-8739) **306**

R I B L A see Revista de Interpretacion Biblica Latinoamericana **4198**

R I C. (Repertoire Bibliographique des Institutions Chretiennes.) (FR ISSN 0079-9300) **4213**

R I C Insight. (Rare-earth Information Center) (US) **3418**, 3494

R I C News. (Rare-earth Information Center) (US) **3418**, 3494

R I C O Business Disputes Guide. (Racketeer Influenced and the Corrupt Organizations) (US) **687**

R I C O Law Reporter. (Racketeer Influenced and Corrupt Organizations) (US) **1400**, 2670

R I C S Library Information Service. Weekly Briefing. (Royal Institution of Chartered Surveyors) (UK) **1873**, 2780

R I C S Library Information Service Abstracts and Reviews. (Royal Institution of Chartered Surveyors) (UK) **1846**, 20, 638

R I C S Technical Information Service. Weekly Briefing see R I C S Library Information Service. Weekly Briefing **1873**

R I D see Rivista Italiana di Dialettologia **2838**

R.I.D.E. see Revue Internationale de Droit Economique **2674**

R I D I M - R C M I Inventory of Music Iconography. (Repertoire Internationale d'Iconographie Musicale. Research Center for Music Iconography) (US ISSN 0889-6607) **3575**

R I D I M - R C M I Newsletter. (Repertoire Internationale d'Iconographie Musicale. Research Center for Music Iconography) (US ISSN 0360-8727) **3575**

R I E see Resources in Education **1679**

R I E V see Revista Internacional de los Estudios Vascos **248**

R I F Newsletter. (Reading Is Fundamental, Inc.) (US ISSN 0364-8389) **1657**, 2952

R I L. (CU) **1083**

R I L A (Repertoire International de la Litterature de l'Art) see B H A **351**

†R I L A News. (Repertoire International de la Litterature de l'Art/International Repertory of the Literature of Art) (US) **5266**

R I L I S A R Bulletin. (Ranganathan Institute of Library and Information Science for Applied Research) (II) **2780**

R I L M Abstracts of Music Literature. (Repertoire International de Litterature Musicale) (US ISSN 0033-6955) **3589**, 20

R I M see Research in Ministry **4213**

R I M A: Review of Indonesian and Malaysian Affairs. (AT) **3969**, 2341

R I O see Religion Index One: Periodicals **4213**

R I P A Report. (Royal Institute of Public Administration) (UK ISSN 0144-6525) **4072**

R I: Revista dos Recursos Humanos na Empresa. (BL) **1069**

R I S C Management. (Reduced Instruction Set Computer) (US) **1400**

R I S C User. (Reduced Instruction Set Computer) (UK) **1464**, 1473

R I S C World. (Reduced Instruction Set Computer) (US) **1464**

▼R I S C 6000 News. (Reduced Instruction Set Computer) (US) **1464**, 1479

R I S D Press see R I S D Voice **341**

R I S D Voice. (Rhode Island School of Design) (US) **341**, 2952, 3796

R I S News. (US) **828**, 1051

R I S S: Regional Information Support Service. (UN ISSN 0252-354X) **142**, 920

R I T see Religion Index Two: Multi-Author Works **4213**

†R K M Publishing Tape & Book Club Bulletin. (US) **5266**

R K W Kontakt. (Rationalisierungs-Kuratorium der Deutschen Wirtschaft e.V.) (GW) **4044**

R L A. (CL ISSN 0033-698X) **2836**

R.L.C.'s Museum Gazette. (CN ISSN 0035-7154) **3532**

R L E Currents. (Research Laboratory of Electronics) (US ISSN 1040-2012) **1777**

R L J: Roskill's Letter from Japan. (UK ISSN 0143-4861) **3418**

R L; Revista Literaria see Universidade Federal de Minas Gerais. Corpo Discente. Revista Literaria **2971**

R L S: Regional Language Studies - Newfoundland see Regional Language Studies - Newfoundland **2837**

R M. (UK) **3575**

R M A Annual Statement Studies. (Robert /Morris Associates) (US ISSN 0080-3340) **796**

R M A Highlights. (Retail Merchants Association of Alberta) (CN) **1051**

†R.M. Bucke Memorial Society for the Study of Religious Experience. Proceedings of the Conference. (CN ISSN 0079-9351) **5266**

R M F. (Rail Miniature Flash) (FR ISSN 0033-8737) **2440**, 4655

R M S News. (CN ISSN 0824-5665) **2780**, 2020

R M 1 Italian Knitwear. see R M 1 Maglieria in Italia **1287**

R M 1 Maglieria in Italia/R M 1 Italian Knitwear. (IT) **1287**

R N. (US ISSN 0033-7021) **3286**

†R N A. (UK ISSN 0142-8799) **5266**

R N A B C News see Nursing B C **3283**

R N A N S Bulletin see Nurse to Nurse **3283**

R N A Newsletter. (Religion Newswriters Association) (US ISSN 0034-4109) **2575**, 4196

†R N A O News. (Registered Nurses Association of Ontario) (CN ISSN 0048-7112) **5266**

R N A Viruses Associated with Cancer see I C R D B Cancergram: R N A Viruses Associated with Cancer **5209**

R N Advocate see Rural Network Advocate **2233**

R N & W P L Encyclopedia. (Registered Number & Wool Products Label) (US) **1051**, 1083

R N D. (Revue Notre-Dame) (CN ISSN 0035-3795) **4273**, 4446

R N I D Research Report. (Royal National Institute for the Deaf) (UK) **2289**

R N I S. (Reseau Numerique a Integration de Services) (FR ISSN 0990-5243) **1428**

R.N. Idaho. (US ISSN 0192-298X) **3286**

†R O C. (Reseau d'Organisme Culturels) (FR ISSN 0033-703X) **5266**

R - O - C - K. (NO ISSN 0800-0549) **3576**

R O D News see Acquisition, Bibliography, Cataloguing News **2792**

R O G - Bond and Money Market Letter see Washington Bond & Money Market Report **969**

R O M see R O M Magazine **1966**

R O M Magazine. (Ruimtelijke Ordening en Milieubeheer) (NE ISSN 0923-7674) **1966**, 2494

R O S Bulletin see Reed Organ Society Bulletin **3577**

R O S C see Review of Scottish Culture **2021**

R O: The Magazine of River Oaks. (US) **2233**

R O V Review (Year). (Remotely Operated Vehicles) (US) **1610**

R P A Bulletin. (Mededelingen over Rijkspersoneelsaangelegenheden) (NE ISSN 0033-7056) **4072**

R P A News see Regional Plan News **5268**

R p B see Religionspaedagogische Beitraege **4274**

R P C Data File. (Regional Planning Commission of Cuyahoga County) (US) **2494**

R P C Voice see WorldView Magazine **937**

R P F. (FR) **2302**

R P M Weekly. (Records - Promotion - Music) (CN ISSN 0033-7064) **3576**

R P P see Religionspaedagogische Praxis **4198**

R P R C Counselor. (Religious Public Relations Council) (US) **37**, 4196

R P R C Media Kit. (Religious Public Relations Council) (US) **37**, 4196

R Q. (Reference Quarterly) (US ISSN 0033-7072) **2780**

R R I S L Bulletin. (Rubber Research Institute of Sri Lanka) (CE) **4293**

R R T: the Canadian Journal of Respiratory Therapy. (CN ISSN 0831-2478) **3366**

R R V Monthly. (Institute of Revenues, Rating and Valuation) (UK) **4155**

R S see Cuadernos de Realidades Sociales **4433**

R S A: Dialogue with the Future see R S A 2000: Dialogue with the Future **5266**

R S A Journal. (UK ISSN 0958-0433) **341**, 1657

†R S A 2000: Dialogue with the Future/R S A 2000: Gesprek met die Toekoms. (SA) **5266**

R S A 2000: Gesprek met die Toekoms. see R S A 2000: Dialogue with the Future **5266**

R.S.C. see Refrigeration Service and Contracting (Troy) **2303**

†R S C Paperback Series. Monographs for Teachers. (Royal Society of Chemistry) (UK) **5266**

R S F Newsletter. (Rhododendron Species Foundation) (US) 2137
R S G B Amateur Radio Call Book. (Radio Society of Great Britain) (UK) 1358
R S G B Inform Newsletter. (Reform Synagogues of Great Britain) (UK) 4226
R S G Richting - Sport-Gericht. (NE) 4484, 1758, 3807
R S I. (Roofing, Siding, Insulation) (US ISSN 0033-7129) 629
R S I C Newsletter. (Radiation Shielding Information Center) (US) 1809, 1835
R S I Extra. (Roofing, Siding, Insulation) (US) 629
R S - Magazine. (US) 1464
R S P A Bulletin. (Royal Society for the Prevention of Accidents) (UK) 4111
R S P B Annual Report and Accounts see Birds 562
R S P C A Today see Animal Life 230
R S R. (Reference Services Review) (US ISSN 0090-7324) 4142
R S Rifiuti Solidi. (IT ISSN 0394-5391) 4111
R S S I. (Recherches Semiotiques - Semiotic Inquiry) (CN ISSN 0229-8651) 2836
R S T S Professional see V A X Professional 1402
R S U. (Rivista di Studi Ungheresi) (IT) 2513
R S V P: The Directory of Creative Talent see R S V P: The Directory of Illustration and Design 1151
R S V P: The Directory of Illustration and Design. (US) 1151, 4005
▼R S Wavelength. (Radiologic Science) (US) 3361
R T A C News see T A C News 4656
R T C A Digest. (Radio Technical Commission for Aeronautics) (US ISSN 0193-4422) 1358, 60
R T C Report. (Resolution Trust Corporation) (US) 4155
R T D E see Research and Teaching in Developmental Education 1658
R.T.D.F. see Revue Trimestrielle de Droit Familial 2718
R T E. (SZ) 1358, 1378, 1777
R T E C S see Registry of Toxic Effects of Chemical Substances 3621
R T E C S Regulatory Subfile. Regulations, Recommendations and Assessments. (Registry of Toxic Effects of Chemical Substances) (US) 4111, 1859
R T E Guide. (Radio Telefis Eireann) (IE ISSN 0033-7145) 1358, 1378, 1777
R T F. (Revista Tecnica de los Ferrocarriles) (GW) 4713
R T I A see R I A 2080
R T Image. (Radiologic Technology) (US ISSN 1041-2182) 3361
R T - Incola. (Editora /Revista dos Tribunais) (BL) 2670, 796
R T: Journal of Respiratory Care Professionals. (US) 3366
R T Magazine. (Respiratory Therapy) (US) 3366
R T N D A Communicator. (Radio-Television News Directors Association) (US ISSN 0033-7153) 1358, 1378, 2575
R T S Music Gazette. (US) 3576
R T S Video Gazette. (US) 1386, 3516
R T T Y Journal. (US ISSN 0033-7161) 1358, 1365
†R T T Y Journal. Beginners Handbook. (US) 5266
R T und G T. (Rangiertechnik und Gleisanschlusstechnik) (GW) 4713
R T - Uutiset see Rakennustieto 629
R T V. (GW) 1378, 1358
R T W Review. (US) 1294
R U S I and Brassey's Defence Yearbook. (Royal United Services Institute for Defence Studies) (UK ISSN 0305-6155) 3469
R U S I Journal. (Royal United Services Institute for Defence Studies) (UK ISSN 0307-1847) 3469

R U S I Newsbrief. (Royal United Services Institute for Defence Studies) (UK ISSN 0268-2656) 3469, 3969
R und V Gruppenbild. (GW) 2540
R und V Report. (GW) 2541, 796, 832
R V A Monthly see R R V Monthly 4155
R V and Tent Sites in Alabama, Florida, Georgia, Kentucky, Louisiana, Mississippi, North Carolina, South Carolina, Tennessee see Southeastern Campbook 4787
R V and Tent Sites in Alberta, British Columbia, Manitoba, Northwest Territories, Saskatchewan, Yukon Territory and Alaska see Western Canada Alaska Campbook 4797
R V and Tent Sites in Arizona, Colorado, New Mexico, Utah see Southwestern Campbook 4787
R V and Tent Sites in Arkansas, Kansas, Missouri, Oklahoma, Texas see South Central Campbook 4787
R V and Tent Sites in California, Nevada see California - Nevada Campbook 4756
R V and Tent Sites in Connecticut, Maine, Massachusetts, New Hampshire, New York, Rhode Island, Vermont see Northeastern Campbook 4780
R V and Tent Sites in Delaware, District of Columbia, Maryland, New Jersey, Pennsylvania, Virginia, West Virginia see Mideastern Campbook 4778
R V and Tent Sites in Idaho, Montana, Oregon, Washington, Wyoming see Northwestern Campbook 4780
R V and Tent Sites in Iowa, Minnesota, Nebraska, North Dakota, South Dakota see North Central Campbook 4780
R V and Tent Sites in New Brunswick, Newfoundland, Nova Scotia, Ontario, Prince Edward Island, Quebec see Eastern Canada Campbook 4760
R V Business. (Recreational Vehicle) (US) 4498, 4584
R V Buyers Guide. (Recreational Vehicle) (US) 4655
R V Campground & Services Guide see Trailer Life's Recreational Vehicle Campground and Services Directory 1156
†R V Guide. (Recreational Vehicle) (CN) 5266
R V News. (Recreational Vehicle) (US) 4655, 4484
R V S Fee Schedule. (Relative Value Scale) (US) 2541, 3146
R V Times. (Recreational Vehicle) (CN) 4783
R V Trade Digest. (Recreational Vehicle) (US ISSN 0745-0389) 4747
R V West. (US) 4783, 4700
R W D S U Record. (Retail Wholesale and Department Store Union) (US ISSN 0033-7196) 2670
R W I Handwerksberichte. (Rheinisch-Westfaelisches Institut fuer Wirtschaftsforschung, Essen) (GW ISSN 0931-0622) 1117
R W I - Konjunkturberichte. (Rheinisch-Westfaelisches Institut fuer Wirtschaftsforschung, Essen) (GW ISSN 0023-3447) 1083
R W I Konjunkturbrief. (Rheinisch-Westfaelisches Institut fuer Wirtschaftsforschung, Essen) (GW ISSN 0939-2335) 1084
R W Mansfield Stock Chart Service. (US) 961
R W P. (Rechts- und Wirtschafts-Praxis) (GW ISSN 0723-0095) 2670
R W P S Steuerrecht. Ausgabe A und B see R W P 2670
R Y A News. (Royal Yachting Association) (UK ISSN 0557-661X) 4484
R Z - Illustrierte Romanzeitung. (AU ISSN 0033-7218) 2984, 2173
R - 12 see M A C S Service Reports 4694
Raabe-Gesellschaft. Jahrbuch. (GW ISSN 0075-2371) 2952
Raabser Maerchen-Reihe. (AU) 2058

Raabta. (SU) 3516, 1378
Raad och Roen/Advice and Results. (SW ISSN 0035-7235) 2216, 2449
Raad vir Geesteswetenskaplike Navorsing. Bulletin. Nuus vir die Geesteswetenskappe. see Human Sciences Research Council. Bulletin. News for the Human Sciences 4374
Raadgevend Ingenieur see Bouwadviseur 604
Raadgiveren. (DK) 4247, 1263
Raadsnyt. (DK) 156
Raakpunt. (NE ISSN 0166-4298) 3146, 4417
Raastofproduktionen, Havemraadet. (DK ISSN 0109-7466) 1578
Raastofproduktionen, Landomraadet. Handelsvarer og Anvendelse, Gravforhold, Arealforhold. (DK ISSN 0109-7474) 1578
Raastofproduktionen, Landomraadet. Produktionsmaengden af Geologiske Raastoffer Fordelt paa Amtskommuner og Kommuner. (DK ISSN 0109-7458) 1578
Raastofproduktionsopgoerelse see Raastofproduktionen, Landomraadet. Handelsvarer og Anvendelse, Gravforhold, Arealforhold 1578
Raastofproduktionsopgoerelse fra Havbunden see Raastofproduktionen, Havomraadet 1578
Raastofproduktionsopgoerelse fra Landomraadet see Raastofproduktionen, Landomraadet. Produktionsmaengden af Geologiske Raastoffer Fordelt paa Amtskommuner og Kommuner 1578
Rabbinical Assembly, New York. Proceedings. (US ISSN 0079-936X) 4226
Rabbit Gazette. (US) 224, 3713
Rabbit Tracks. (US) 2162
Rabbits see Rabbit Gazette 224
Rabbits in Canada. (CN ISSN 0033-7242) 224
Rabelais. (AT) 1322
Rabels Zeitschrift fuer auslaendisches und internationales Privatrecht. (GW ISSN 0033-7250) 2728
†Rabies Magazine. (UK ISSN 0140-9069) 5266
Rabindra Bharati Journal. (II) 3004
Rabitat al-Alam al-Islami. Majallah. see Muslim World League. Journal 4220
Rabobank. (NE) 796, 156
▼Rabochaya Solidarnost'. (KR) 3921
Rabotnichka. (BU) 4851
Raccoon. (US ISSN 0148-0162) 3004
Race Across America Program. (US) 4520, 3611
Race and Class. (UK ISSN 0306-3968) 4446
Race and Immigration: Runnymede Trust Bulletin see Runnymede Bulletin 3947
Race & Rally. (US) 4554
Race Relations News. (SA ISSN 0033-734X) 3946
Race Relations Survey. (SA ISSN 0258-7246) 3946
Race Today. (UK ISSN 0033-7358) 4446
Race Walking Record. (UK) 4554
Raceform Flat Annual. (UK) 4484
Raceform Handicap Book. (UK) 4537
Raceform "Horses in Training". (UK ISSN 0081-3761) 4537
Raceform Up-to-Date see Raceform Weekly 4484
Raceform Up-to-Date Form Book Annual see Raceform Flat Annual 4484
Raceform Weekly. (UK) 4484
Racehorse see Raceform Handicap Book 4537
Racehorses. (UK ISSN 0079-9408) 4537
RaceTime. (US) 4554
Rachel's Hazardous Waste News. (US) 1966, 1986, 2670
Rachna. (UK) 2881, 2020
Rachunkowosc. (PL ISSN 0481-5475) 755

Racial - Ethnic Distribution of Public School Students and Staff, New York State. (US ISSN 0085-4093) 1657
Racine Labor. (US) 2588
Racing. (NO ISSN 0802-7293) 4484
Racing. (FR) 4537
Racing Action. (US) 4537
Racing & Football Outlook. (UK ISSN 0033-7366) 4484
Racing and Football Outlook: Football Annual. (UK) 4484, 4510
Racing and Football Outlook: Jumping Annual. (UK) 4484, 4510
Racing and Football Outlook: Racing Annual. (UK ISSN 0079-9424) 4484, 4510
Racing and Football Racing Annual see Racing and Football Outlook: Racing Annual 4484
Racing Car News. (AT ISSN 0033-7374) 4484, 4700
Racing Guide. (SI) 4484
Racing Pictorial Magazine. (US) 4484
Racing Pigeon/Wedvlugduif. (SA) 4484
Racing Pigeon. (UK ISSN 0033-7390) 4484
Racing Pigeon Bulletin. (US ISSN 0146-8383) 4485
Racing Pigeon Pictorial. (UK ISSN 0033-7404) 3713, 566
Racing Report see Speedhorse - Racing Report 4538
Racing - Revyen see Racing 4484
Racing South see Running Journal 4554
Racing Specialist. (UK ISSN 0033-7420) 4537
Racing Star Weekly. (US ISSN 0033-7439) 4537
Racing Times. (US) 4485
Racing Update. (US) 4537
Racing Wheels. (US) 4485, 4700
Racketeer Influenced and Corrupt Organizations Law Reporter see R I C O Law Reporter 1400
Racketeer Influenced and the Corrupt Organizations Business Disputes Guide see R I C O Business Disputes Guide 687
Racketeering Litigation Reporter see Civil R I C O Litigation Reporter 2701
Rackham Journal of the Arts and Humanities. (US ISSN 0731-4817) 2952
Rackham Literary Studies see Rackham Journal of the Arts and Humanities 2952
Racking Review. (US) 4537
Racquet (La Crosse). (US ISSN 0033-930X) 1322
Racquet (New York). (US ISSN 0273-9194) 4510
Racquetball Around Ohio. (US) 4510
▼Racquetball Magazine. (US ISSN 1060-877X) 4510
Racquette. (US ISSN 0033-7447) 1322
Rad. (YU ISSN 0033-7463) 2588
Das Rad. (UK ISSN 0033-7455) 2836, 1657
Rad for Radiographers, Radiologists and Radiotherapists. (UK ISSN 0264-6412) 3361
Rad und Sparren. (GW ISSN 0342-2860) 2382
Rada Narodowa see Rada Narodowa, Gospodarka, Administracja 882
Rada Narodowa, Gospodarka, Administracja. (PL) 882
Radar. (PL ISSN 0033-7501) 341, 2952, 3576
Radar fuer Trends. (GW) 1026
Radar - sei. (IT) 341, 2952, 3004
Radar Systems International. (UK) 1342
Radcliffe College Newsletter see L A R C Newsletter 2454
Radcliffe News. (US) 1322
Radcliffe Quarterly. (US ISSN 0033-7528) 1322, 4851
Raddle Moon. (CN ISSN 0826-5909) 2952
†Rader Relatives Newsletter. (US) 5266
Radfahren. (GW ISSN 0720-8545) 4520

RADFORD

Radford. (US) **1322**
Radiaesthesie. (SZ) **3671**
Radiaesthesie - Geopathie - Strahlenbiologie see Radiaesthesie **3671**
Radiance. (US ISSN 0889-9495) **4851**, 3807, 4836
The Radiance Technique Journal. (US ISSN 1040-5836) **3596**
Radiation & Alternatives Bulletin. (US) **1966**, 1795, 1809
Radiation and Environmental Biophysics. (GW ISSN 0301-634X) **486**
Radiation Carcinogenesis see I C R D B Cancergram: Radiation Carcinogenesis **5209**
Radiation Chemistry. (JA ISSN 0286-6722) **1186**, 3829
Radiation Curing see Radiation Curing - Journal of Radiation Curing **1186**
†Radiation Curing Buyer's Guide. (US ISSN 0197-8039) **5266**
Radiation Curing - Journal of Radiation Curing. (US ISSN 1057-5715) **1186**
Radiation Dosimetry Data: Catalogue. (UN) **3361**
Radiation Effects. (UK ISSN 0033-7579) **3850**
Radiation Effects and Defects in Solids. (US ISSN 1042-0150) **3850**
Radiation Effects and Defects in Solids Bulletin. (US ISSN 1042-6493) **3850**
Radiation Effects and Defects in Solids Express. (UK ISSN 1042-6485) **3850**
Radiation Effects Bulletin. (UK ISSN 0888-448X) **3850**
Radiation Effects Express. (UK ISSN 0888-7322) **3850**
Radiation Effects Letters see Radiation Effects Bulletin **3850**
Radiation Events Monitor. (US) **1966**, 1809
Radiation Medicine. (JA ISSN 0288-2043) **3361**, 3201
Radiation Observations in Bergen. (NO) **3440**
Radiation Oncology News. (US) **3361**
Radiation Physics and Chemistry see International Journal of Radiation Applications and Instrumentation. Part C: Radiation Physics and Chemistry **3847**
Radiation Protection Dosimetry. (UK ISSN 0144-8420) **3850**, 1966, 4111
Radiation Protection Management. (US ISSN 0740-0640) **4111**
Radiation Research. (US ISSN 0033-7587) **3850**, 486, 1809
Radiation Shielding Information Center Newsletter see R S I C Newsletter **1809**
Radiator Reporter. (US ISSN 0739-2060) **4700**
Radical America. (US ISSN 0033-7617) **3921**
Radical Bookseller. (UK ISSN 0144-1779) **4136**, 2881, 4142
Radical Education. (UK ISSN 0305-6147) **1657**
Radical Historians Newsletter. (US) **2420**
Radical History Review. (US ISSN 0163-6545) **2320**
†Radical Option. (US) **5266**
Radical Philosophy. (UK ISSN 0300-211X) **3778**
†Radical Religion. (US ISSN 0360-8212) **5266**
Radical Science Series see Science as Culture **4339**
†Radical Scotland. (UK ISSN 0262-6993) **5266**
Radical Statistics. (UK ISSN 0268-6376) **4584**
Radical Teacher. (US ISSN 0191-4847) **1657**
Radicals Against Poverty see R A P **4446**
▼Radikal. (RU) **2215**
Radikal Politik. (DK) **3921**
Radio. (RU ISSN 0033-765X) **1358**
Radio. see Wuxiandian **1360**
Radio (Year). (AT ISSN 1034-2516) **1358**

Radio Advertisers' Guide. (UK ISSN 0260-2423) **1358**, 37
Radio Advertising Bureau. Radio Facts. (US) **41**, 1358
Radio Advertising Bureau. Retail Marketing Kit. (US) **37**, 1358
Radio Advertising Bureau Instant Background see R A B Instant Background **37**
Radio Aids to Marine Navigation. (CN ISSN 0033-7692) **1378**, 4736
Radio-Amater. (YU ISSN 0033-8168) **1358**
Radio Amateur's Handbook. (US ISSN 0079-9440) **1358**
Radio and Electrical Retailing. (UK) **1051**, 1358, 1777
Radio and Electronics Constructor see Radio & Electronics World **5266**
†Radio & Electronics World. (UK ISSN 0262-2572) **5266**
Radio & Records. (US) **1358**, 3576
Radio & T V Times. (SI) **1358**, 1378
Radio & Television. (SW ISSN 0033-7749) **1358**, 1378
Radio and Television. see Al-Izaa wal-Television **1375**
Radio and Television. see Wuxiandian yu Dianshi **1384**
Radio Broadcaster see Ad-Pro **5130**
Radio Bulletin Elektronica Computers see R B Elektronica Magazine **1777**
Radio Business Report. (US) **1358**
Radio Chassis Television. (AG ISSN 0033-7781) **1378**, 1358, 1907
Radio - Chicago. (US ISSN 1044-9647) **1358**
Radio Club of America. Proceedings. (US ISSN 0033-779X) **1358**
Radio Co-op Sources. (US) **1358**, 37, 1151
Radio Communication. (UK ISSN 0033-7803) **1359**
Radio Communication Technology. see Wuxiandian Tongxin Jishu **1360**
Radio Communications Monitoring Association Journal see R C M A Journal **1358**
Radio Communications Report. (US) **1365**
Radio Communications Report Cellular Handbook see R C R Cellular Handbook **1358**
Radio Communications Report Paging Handbook see R C R Paging Handbook **1358**
Radio Contacts (Year). (US) **1359**, 1151
Radio Control Action Series. (US) **2441**
Radio Control Boat Modeler. (US ISSN 0890-0078) **2441**, 4528
Radio Control Boat Modeller. (UK ISSN 0268-5248) **2441**, 4528
Radio Control Car Action. (US ISSN 0886-1609) **2441**
Radio Control Model Cars. (US ISSN 0269-8315) **4700**
Radio Control Models & Electronics. (UK ISSN 0033-7838) **2441**
Radio Control News see R C News **2440**
Radio Control Scale Aircraft Quarterly. (UK ISSN 0267-8101) **2441**
Radio Database International see Passport to World Band Radio **1358**
Radio Denmark see Baereboelgen **5146**
Radio-Diffusion. see Radio Perhapja **1379**
Radio Directory see Professional T V & Radio Media Directory **5262**
Radio Electronica Practica. (AG) **1359**, 1777
Radio-Electronics. (US ISSN 0033-7862) **1777**, 1359
Radio Electronics and Communications Systems see Radioelectronics and Communications Systems **1777**
Radio - Electronics Annual see Radio - Electronics Electronics Experimenters Handbook (Year) **1777**
Radio - Electronics Electronics Experimenters Handbook (Year). (US) **1777**, 1359
Radio Elektronik Schau see Elektronikschau **1373**

Radio Elettronica and Computer. (IT) **1359**, 1400, 1777
Radio Engineering. see Wuxiandian Gongcheng **1360**
Radio es Televizioujsag. (HU) **1359**, 1378
Radio Fernsehen Elektronik. (GW ISSN 0033-7900) **1777**, 1359, 1378
Radio Free Europe - Radio Liberty Inc. Daily Report see R F E - R L Daily Report **3969**
Radio Free Europe Research Reports on Eastern Europe see Report on Eastern Europe **3970**
Radio Free Jazz see JazzTimes **3558**
Radio Free Rock. (US) **3576**
Radio Frequenza. (IT) **1359**
Radio Fun. (US) **2441**, 1359
Radio Guide see National Radio Guide **1357**
Radio Handbook. (US ISSN 0079-9467) **1359**
Radio Japan News. (JA ISSN 0033-7927) **1359**
Radio Kit Elettronica. (IT ISSN 0391-383X) **2441**, 4607
Radio Liberty Research Bulletins on the Soviet Union see Report on the U S S R **3970**
Radio Magazine. (US) **1359**, 1026
Radio Modeller. (UK ISSN 0144-0713) **2441**
Radio Nederland see Radio Nederland Programme Schedule **1359**
Radio Nederland Programme Schedule.(NE) **1359**
Radio Observer. (US) **368**
Radio Only see Radio Magazine **1359**
Radio Perhapja/Radio-Diffusion. (AA) **1379**
Radio - Plans. (FR ISSN 0033-7668) **1359**
Radio Programme. (CY) **1359**, 1379
Radio Propagation Predictions for Southern Africa. (SA ISSN 0033-7986) **1359**
Radio Research Laboratory. Journal see Communications Research Laboratory. Journal **1371**
Radio Science. (US ISSN 0048-6604) **1593**, 3840
Radio Society of Great Britain Amateur Radio Call Book see R S G B Amateur Radio Call Book **1358**
Radio T V Tecnico. (BL) **1359**, 1379
Radio Technical Commission for Aeronautics. Proceedings of the Annual Assembly Meeting. (US) **1359**, 60
Radio Technical Commission for Aeronautics Digest see R T C A Digest **1358**
Radio Tecnica. (AG ISSN 0033-8052) **1359**
Radio Telefis Eireann Guide see R T E Guide **1358**
†Radio - Television. (CS ISSN 0033-7676) **5266**
Radio-Television News Directors Association Communicator see R T N D A Communicator **1358**
Radio Times. (UK ISSN 0033-8060) **1359**
Radio - TV - Electronic Service see R T E **1358**
Radio und Television see R T V **1378**
Radio-Vision Times. (NR) **1359**, 1379
†Radio Week. (US) **5266**
Radio World. (US ISSN 0274-8541) **1359**
▼Radio World International. (US ISSN 0279-151X) **1359**
Radio y Television Practica see Radio Electronica Practica **1359**
Radio Z S. (SA ISSN 0033-815X) **1359**
Radioactive see Radio Week **5266**
Radioactive Waste Management (Oak Ridge). (US ISSN 0275-3707) **1986**
Radioactive Waste Management and the Nuclear Fuel Cycle. (US ISSN 0739-5876) **1986**, 1809
Radioactive Waste Management Handbook. (US ISSN 0898-8161) **1986**, 1809

Radioactive Waste Management Series. (US ISSN 0275-7273) **1986**, 1809
La Radioactivite des Principales Sources d'Eau Minerale en Belgique. Etude. (BE) **4828**, 4111
Radioactivity & Radiochemistry. (US) **1229**
Radioactivity Survey Data in Japan. (JA ISSN 0441-2516) **1229**
†Radiobiologia - Radiotherapia. (GW ISSN 0033-8184) **5266**
Radiobiologiya. (RU ISSN 0033-8192) **3361**, 486
Radiobote. (AU ISSN 0033-8214) **1359**
Radiobranchen. (DK ISSN 0108-6626) **1359**
Radiobransjen see Elektronikk Bransjen **1770**
Radiocarbon. (US ISSN 0033-8222) **4335**
Radiocomm in Canada. (CN ISSN 0845-4531) **1359**
Radiocorriere - T V. (IT ISSN 0033-8257) **1359**, 1379
Radioelectronics and Communications Systems. (English translation of: Izvestiya Vysshikh Uchebnykh Zavedenii. Seriya Radioelektronika) (US ISSN 0033-7870) **1777**, 1359
Radiographer. (AT ISSN 0033-8273) **3361**
Radiographics. (US ISSN 0271-5333) **3361**
Radiography. (UK ISSN 0033-8281) **3361**
Radioisotopes. (JA ISSN 0033-8303) **482**, 1186, 3146, 3829
Radiokauppias see Kodintekniikka **1357**
Radiokhimiya. (RU ISSN 0033-8311) **3361**
▼RadioLit. (GW) **3361**
Der Radiologe. (US ISSN 0033-832X) **3361**
Radiologia. (SP ISSN 0033-8338) **3361**
Radiologia Brasileira. (BL ISSN 0100-3984) **3361**
Radiologia Iugoslavica. (XV ISSN 0485-893X) **3362**
Radiologia Medica. (IT ISSN 0033-8362) **3362**
Radiologic Clinics of North America. (US ISSN 0033-8389) **3362**
Radiologic Science Wavelength see R S Wavelength **3361**
Radiologic Technology Image see R T Image **3361**
Radiological Protection Bulletin. (UK ISSN 0308-4272) **1809**, 1966
Radiological Respiratory Protection Newsletter see Respiratory Protection Newsletter **3621**
Radiologie. (GW ISSN 0720-3322) **3362**
Radiologische Klinik. (US) **3362**
Radiology. see Zentralblatt Radiologie **3182**
Radiology. (US ISSN 0033-8419) **3362**
Radiology and Imaging Letter. (US ISSN 0741-160X) **3362**
Radiology Business Management Association Bulletin see R B M A Bulletin **3361**
Radiology Management. (US ISSN 0198-7097) **2469**, 3362
†Radiology - Nuclear Medicine International. (US ISSN 0161-7516) **5266**
Radiology of Iatrogenic Disorders. (US) **3362**
Radiology Today (New York). (US) **3362**
Radiology Today (Thorofare). (US ISSN 0893-1054) **3362**
▼Radiolyubitel'. (BW ISSN 0236-4964) **1359**, 1379
Radionic Quarterly. (UK ISSN 0481-6722) **3146**
Radiopharmacy and Radiopharmacology Yearbook Series.(UK ISSN 0748-6111) **3741**

Radiophysics and Quantum Electronics. (English translation of: Izvestiya Vysshikh Uchebnykh Zavedenii. Seriya Radiofizika) (US ISSN 0033-8443) **1777**
Radioprotection. (FR ISSN 0033-8451) **1809**
Radioschau *see* Elektronikschau **1373**
Radiotechnika. (HU ISSN 0033-8478) **1359**
Radiotekhnika (Kharkov). (KR ISSN 0485-8972) **3860**
Radiotekhnika (Moscow). (RU ISSN 0033-8486) **1359**
Radiotekhnika i Elektronika. (RU ISSN 0033-8494) **1359**, **1777**
Radiotenica TV - Elettronik' Consumo *see* Apparecchi Elettrodomestici Nella Casa Moderna **1882**
Radiotherapy & Oncology. (NE ISSN 0167-8140) **3362**
†Radisen. (DK ISSN 0108-8491) **5266**
Radius. (US ISSN 0886-7771) **341**
†Radius. (GW ISSN 0033-8532) **5266**
Radix. (US ISSN 0275-0147) **4196**, **4446**
Radmarkt. (GW ISSN 0033-8540) **4520**
Radna Jedinica *see* Organizacija Samoupravljanja OUR **1023**
Radner Lectures. (US ISSN 0079-9491) **3921**, **3969**
Radnor Historical Society. Bulletin. (US) **2420**
Radnorshire Society. Transactions. (UK ISSN 0306-848X) **2382**
Radosna Vijest. (BN) **4196**
Radovi Medicinskog Fakulteta u Zagrebu *see* Sveuciliste u Zagrebu. Medicinski Fakultet. Radovi **3155**
Radovi Poljporivrednog Fakulteta Univerziteta u Sarajevu *see* Univerzitet u Sarajevu. Poljoprivredni Fakultet. Radovi **127**
Radsportler. (GW ISSN 0138-1393) **4520**
RadTech Report. (US ISSN 1056-0793) **1859**
Raduga. (KR ISSN 0131-8136) **2952**
Radyans'ka Osvita. (KR ISSN 0033-8605) **1657**
Radyans'ke Literaturoznavstvo. (KR ISSN 0131-0194) **2952**
Radyans'ke Pravo. (KR ISSN 0132-1331) **2670**
Raethinge-Posten. (DK ISSN 0106-9616) **2382**
Raetsel in Grosser Schrift. (GW) **4485**
Raetsel Krone. (AU) **4485**
Raetsel Schule. (GW) **4485**
Raetselfreund. (GW) **4485**
Raetselfreund Doppelband. (GW) **4485**
Rafale. (US) **3004**
Rafidain Development. *see* Tanmiat al-Rafidain **4075**
Rafinerijski List. (CI) **3700**
Raft. (US ISSN 0891-0545) **3004**, **2020**
Rag Mag. (US ISSN 0742-2768) **2881**
Rag Times. (US ISSN 0090-4570) **3576**
Ragan Report. (US ISSN 0197-6060) **1342**, **687**
Ragazza In. (IT) **2984**
Ragguaglio Librario. (IT ISSN 0033-8648) **4136**
Ragioni Critiche. (IT ISSN 0047-4401) **2837**, **2952**
Ragtime *see* A A C A News **1282**
Ragtimer. (CN ISSN 0033-8672) **3576**
Ragtrader (Chippendale). (AT) **1287**
Rahavard *see* Rahavard Persian Journal **2952**
Rahavard Persian Journal. (US) **2952**
Rahnamay-i Majallah-ha-y Iran. *see* Directory of Iranian Periodicals **399**
Al - Raida. (LE) **4851**
Raiffeisen. (SZ) **796**
Raiffeisen: Informationen des Deutschen Raiffeisenverbandes. (GW) **115**
†Raiffeisenbote. (GW ISSN 0033-8710) **5266**
Raiffeisenzeitung. (AU) **832**

Raiken/Lichen. (JA ISSN 0285-0850) **515**
Le Rail. (FR) **4713**
Rail. (UK) **4713**
Rail and Wire. (US) **4713**
Rail Canadien. *see* Canadian Rail **4708**
Rail Carrier Service. (US) **4713**
Rail Classics. (US) **4713**
Rail Engineering International. (UK ISSN 0048-6612) **4713**
Rail Enthusiast *see* Rail **4713**
Rail International/Schienen der Welt. (BE ISSN 0020-8442) **4713**
Rail Mazdoor. (II) **4713**
Rail Miniature Flash *see* R M F **2440**
Rail Syndicaliste. (FR) **2588**, **4713**
Rail Travel News. (US ISSN 0896-4440) **4713**
▼Rail Whispers. (US) **2233**
Railfan & Railroad. (US ISSN 0163-7266) **4713**
Railnews. (UK ISSN 0033-8745) **4713**
Railpace Newsmagazine. (US) **4713**
Railpower. (UK ISSN 0262-8805) **4713**
Railroad Enthusiasts. New York Division. Bulletin. (US) **4713**
Railroad Evangelist. (US) **4287**
Railroad History. (US ISSN 0090-7847) **4713**, **2320**
Railroad Model Craftsman. (US ISSN 0033-877X) **2441**, **4713**
Railroad Newsletter. (US) **3621**, **4713**
Railroad Station Historical Society. Bulletin. (US) **4713**
Railroad Station Historical Society. Railroad Station Monograph. (US) **4713**
Rails. (NZ ISSN 0110-6155) **4713**
Railwatch. (UK ISSN 0267-5943) **4713**
Railway Accounting Rules. (US) **4713**, **755**
Railway Advocate. (AT ISSN 0033-8818) **4713**
Railway Age. (US ISSN 0033-8826) **4713**
Railway and Canal Historical Society Journal. (UK ISSN 0033-8834) **4713**, **4736**
Railway and Locomotive Historical Society. Bulletin *see* Railroad History **4713**
Railway & Locomotive Historical Society Newsletter. (US) **4713**
†Railway Carmen's Journal. (US ISSN 0033-8850) **5266**
Railway Clerk - Interchange *see* Interchange (Rockville) **2584**
Railway Construction. *see* Tiedao Jianzhu **4715**
Railway Development News *see* Railwatch **4713**
Railway Digest. (AT ISSN 0157-2431) **4714**, **2320**
Railway Digest International. (UK ISSN 0048-6647) **4714**
Railway Directory and Yearbook. (UK ISSN 0079-9513) **4714**
†Railway Engineer. (UK) **5267**
Railway Fuel and Operating Officers Association. Proceedings. (US ISSN 0079-9521) **4714**
Railway Gazette International. (UK ISSN 0373-5346) **4714**
Railway History Monograph. (US ISSN 0093-8505) **4714**
Railway Knowledge. *see* Tiedao Zhishi **4716**
Railway Line Clearances. (US) **4714**
Railway Magazine. (UK ISSN 0033-8923) **4714**
Railway Modeller. (UK ISSN 0033-8931) **2441**
Railway Passenger Car Annual. (US ISSN 0094-2278) **4714**
Railway Philately. (UK ISSN 0951-886X) **3757**
Railway Pictorial. *see* Tetsudo Pikutoriaru **4715**
Railway Review *see* Transport Review **4716**
Railway Technical Research Institute. Quarterly Report. (JA ISSN 0033-9008) **4714**

Railway Technical Review. (GW ISSN 0079-9548) **4714**
Railway Track & Structures. (US ISSN 0033-9016) **4714**
Railway Transportation Abstracts. *see* Vasuti Kozlekedesi Szakirodalmi Tajekoztato **4668**
Railway Transportation and Economics. *see* Tiedao Yunshu yu Jingji **4715**
Railway World. (UK ISSN 0033-9032) **4714**
Railway World Annual *see* Railway World Yearbook **4714**
Railway World Yearbook. (UK) **4714**
Railways *see* Railways in Southern Africa **4714**
Railways. (US) **4784**, **4714**
Railways in Southern Africa. (SA) **4714**
Railways Institute Magazine. (AT ISSN 0033-9040) **4714**
Railways of Sweden. *see* Sveriges Jaernvaegar **4715**
Railways Restored. (UK) **4714**
Railways Today. (UK ISSN 0265-0231) **4714**
Rain. (US ISSN 0739-621X) **1967**, **3921**
Rain Flower. *see* Yuhua **2979**
Rainbow. *see* Mavrica **1260**
Rainbow. *see* Der Reggeboge **2020**
Rainbow. *see* Keste Damena **2186**
Rainbow. (UK) **2295**
Rainbow (Jersey City)/Veselka. (US ISSN 0300-6379) **1263**
Rainbow (Prospect). (US ISSN 0746-4797) **1473**, **1422**
Rainbow Ray Focus. (US) **3596**, **3778**
Rainer Foundation. Annual Report. (UK) **1521**, **1243**
Rainey Times. (US ISSN 0734-2055) **2162**
†Raionnye Biblioteki Belorussii. (UR) **5267**
Raise the Stakes. (US ISSN 0278-7016) **2881**
Raised Dot Computing Newsletter. (US) **2295**, **1417**
Raison Presente. (FR ISSN 0033-9075) **3778**
▼Raisons Pratiques. (FR ISSN 1150-1367) **4383**
Raivaaja/Pioneer. (US ISSN 1059-4779) **2020**
Raizes. (CV) **341**
†Raizes. (BL) **5267**
Rajasthan Agriculturalist. (II) **156**
Rajasthan Board Journal of Education. (II ISSN 0033-9083) **1657**
Rajasthan Forest Statistics. (II ISSN 0377-3302) **2112**
Rajasthan, India. Directorate of Economics and Statistics. Basic Statistics. (II ISSN 0079-9564) **736**, **4584**
Rajasthan, India. Directorate of Economics and Statistics. Budget Study. (II ISSN 0079-9556) **1104**
Rajasthan Journal of Agricultural Sciences. (II) **115**
Rajasthan Medical Journal. (II ISSN 0485-9561) **3146**
Rajasthan State Tanneries Limited. Annual Report. (II ISSN 0302-4881) **2738**
Rajasthan State Warehousing Corporation. Annual Report and Accounts. (II) **1084**
Rajasthan University Studies in English.(II ISSN 0448-1690) **2952**, **2837**
Rajasthan Year Book and Who's Who. (II ISSN 0079-9572) **2341**
Rajawali. (IO) **4784**
Rajneesh Times International *see* Osho Times International **4217**
Rakam. (IT ISSN 0033-9113) **4851**, **2554**, **3592**
Rakennusextra. (FI) **629**, **1873**
Rakennuslehti. (FI ISSN 0033-9121) **629**, **1873**, **2494**
Rakennusplussa. (FI) **629**, **1873**
Rakennustaito. (FI ISSN 0048-6663) **629**, **306**
Rakennustekniikka. (FI ISSN 0033-913X) **1873**
Rakennustieto. (FI ISSN 0781-8904) **629**

RAND MCNALLY   6595

Rakennustuotanto *see* Rakennuslehti **629**
Rakennusviesti *see* Meidan Talo **624**
Rakentaja. (FI ISSN 0355-8614) **629**
Rakentajain Kalenteri/Builder's Calendar. (FI ISSN 0355-550X) **629**
Rakuno Gakuen Daigaku Kiyo. Jinbun Shakai Kagaku Hen/College of Dairying. Journal: Cultural and Social Sciences. (JA ISSN 0388-0028) **115**, **2513**
Rakuno Gakuen Daigaku Kiyo. Shizen Kagaku Hen/College of Diarying. Journal: Natural Science. (JA ISSN 0388-001X) **203**, **4335**
Rally. (II ISSN 0048-668X) **4273**
Rally Sport. (UK ISSN 0140-542X) **4485**, **4700**
Rallye Racing. (GW ISSN 0033-9148) **4700**
Ralph H. Blanchard Memorial Endowment Series. (US) **2541**, **4417**
Ram Page. (US) **1322**
Ram Report. (US) **1117**, **1287**
Ram - The Letter Box. (US) **3004**
Ramakrishna Mission Institute of Culture. Bulletin. (II ISSN 0033-9156) **2513**
Rambler *see* Rambling Today **1496**
Rambling Today. (UK) **1496**, **4554**
Rambukken. (DK ISSN 0109-1700) **3921**
Rambunctious Review. (US) **2952**
Ramjham. (NP) **882**
Rampart Individualist. (US) **2881**
Die Rampe (Linz). (AU) **2952**
Rampenlicht. (SZ ISSN 0079-9599) **341**
Rampike Magazine. (CN) **342**, **2952**, **3576**
Rampura Sahitya Parishada Patrika. (BG) **2952**
Ram's Horn. (US ISSN 0272-2747) **2837**, **2952**
Ramsay Society of Chemical Engineers. Journal. (UK ISSN 0456-4804) **1859**
Ramuri. (RM) **2215**
Ramus. (AT ISSN 0048-671X) **1279**
Ran. (GW ISSN 0004-7899) **3921**, **1263**, **2191**
Ranch & Coast. (US ISSN 0164-8780) **2233**
Ranch Dog Trainer. (US ISSN 0899-1111) **3713**, **224**
Ranch Magazine. (US ISSN 0145-8515) **224**
Rancher. *see* Ganadero **216**
†Rancher. (CN) **5267**
Ranchero Courier. (US) **2441**, **4700**
Ranchi University Mathematical Journal.(II ISSN 0079-9602) **3052**
Ranching Review. *see* Revista Pecuaria **224**
Rand Afrikaans University Rapport *see* R A U - Rapport **1715**
The Rand Corporation's Research Publications. (US) **4335**, **4607**
Rand Journal of Economics. (US ISSN 0741-6261) **687**
Rand McNally Bankers Directory. (US ISSN 0895-4623) **796**
Rand McNally Business Traveler's Road Atlas. (US) **4784**, **687**
Rand McNally Campground and Trailer Park Guide *see* Rand McNally Campground and Trailer Park Guide. Eastern **4554**
Rand McNally Campground and Trailer Park Guide. Eastern. (US ISSN 0733-8309) **4554**
Rand McNally Commercial Atlas and Marketing Guide. (US) **1051**, **2260**
Rand McNally Fishing Hotspots: Midwest. (US) **4554**, **4784**
Rand McNally Goode's World Atlas. (US) **2260**
Rand McNally International Bankers Directory *see* Rand McNally Bankers Directory **796**
†Rand McNally Interstate Road Atlas. (US) **5267**
Rand McNally Motor Carriers' Road Atlas. (US) **4747**
Rand McNally Places Rated Almanac. (US) **2494**, **4155**

RAND MCNALLY

Rand McNally Places Rated Retirement Guide see Rand McNally Retirement Places Rated **2494**
Rand McNally Retirement Places Rated. (US) **2494**
Rand McNally Road Atlas. (US) **4784**
Rand McNally Road Atlas & City Guide of Europe. (US) **4784**
Rand McNally Road Atlas & Vacation Guide. (US) **4784**
Rand McNally Road Atlas of Britain. (US) **4784**
Rand McNally Road Atlas of Europe. (US) **4784**
Rand McNally Vacation Places Rated. (US) **4784**
Rand - Pretoria Directory. (SA) **1151**
Rand Report Series see The Rand Corporation's Research Publications **4335**
Rand Research Review. (US) **3921**
Randax Education Guide. (US ISSN 0097-5206) **1697**
Randgebieden. (NE) **2857**
Randolph-Macon Alumni Bulletin see Randolph-Macon College. Bulletin **1322**
Randolph-Macon College. Bulletin. (US) **1322**
Random Lengths. (US ISSN 0483-9420) **2117**
Random Lengths Export. (US ISSN 8756-288X) **2117**, **920**
▼Random Lengths Yardstick. (US ISSN 1055-0895) **2112**
Random Lengths Yearbook. (US ISSN 0485-9960) **2112**
Random Notes. see Suibi **2967**
▼Random Operators and Stochastic Equations. (NE ISSN 0926-6364) **3052**
▼Random Structures & Algorithms. (US ISSN 1042-9832) **3052**
Random Thoughts. (CN ISSN 0380-8114) **2441**
Randschriften; a Newsletter for the Guild of Carillonneurs see Carillon News **3544**
Randse Afrikaanse Universiteit. Jaarboek. (SA) **1715**, **1657**
†Randse Afrikaanse Universiteit. Prospektus. (SA) **5267**
Randspringer. (GW) **4485**
Ranganathan Institute of Library and Information Science for Applied Research Bulletin see R I L I S A R Bulletin **2780**
Rangbhumi. (II) **3516**
Range Management Newsletter. (AT ISSN 0812-4930) **115**, **1026**
Rangefinder. (US ISSN 0033-9202) **3796**
Rangelands. (US ISSN 0190-0528) **224**
Rangel's Reports. (US) **3969**
Rangeman's Journal see Rangelands **224**
Ranger. (US) **1322**
Ranger Rick. (US ISSN 0738-6656) **1263**, **1496**
Ranger Rick's Naturescope. (US) **1758**, **4335**
Rangiertechnik und Gleisanschlusstechnik see R T und G T **4713**
Rani Muthu. (II) **2201**
Ranliao Huaxue Xuebao/Journal of Fuel Chemistry and Technology. (CC ISSN 0253-2409) **1859**, **1229**, **3700**
Ranliao yu Huagong. (CC ISSN 1001-3709) **1859**
Rannsoknastofnun Fiskidnadarins. Arsskyrsla. (IC) **2048**
Ransomer. (UK ISSN 0033-9245) **4273**
Rap Express. (US) **3576**
Rap Master. (US) **3576**, **1263**
Rapa Nui Journal. (US ISSN 1040-1385) **247**
Rapa Nui Notes see Rapa Nui Journal **247**
Raphael's Astrological Almanac. (UK) **359**
Rapid Communications in Mass Spectrometry. (UK ISSN 0951-4198) **3857**, **1342**
Rapid Notice News Service. (US) **3757**, **61**

▼Rappages. (US) **3576**
†Rappin' (US) **5267**
Rapport. (UK) **4417**
Rapport. (US) **4446**
Rapport Annuel see European Free Trade Association. Annual Report **906**
Rapport Annuel du Conseil des Arts du Canada et son Supplement. see Canada Council Annual Report and Supplement **320**
Rapport Annuel et Compte-Rendu Financier. see Cameroon Development Corporation. Annual Report and Accounts **1073**
Rapport Annuel sur l'Assistance au Developpement: Burundi see Rapport Annuel sur la Cooperation au Developpement - Burundi **934**
Rapport Annuel sur l'Assistance au Developpement: Rwanda. (UN) **934**
Rapport Annuel sur l'Economie Syrienne. (SY ISSN 0079-9696) **882**
Rapport Annuel sur la Cooperation au Developpement - Burundi. (UN) **934**
Rapport Canadien a l'Industrie sur les Sciences Halieutiques et Aquatiques see Canadian Industry Report of Fisheries and Aquatic Sciences **2038**
Rapport d'Activites des Entreprises du Secteur Moderne. (CF) **736**
Rapport des Recherches Collectives. see I C E S Cooperative Research Report **1605**
Rapport fra S T I K K. (Samarbejdsgruppen for Trafiksikkerhed i Kommuneerne i Koebenhavns-Omraadet) (DK ISSN 0105-6956) **4720**
Rapport General sur la Securite Sociale au Grand-Duche du Luxembourg see Luxembourg. Inspection Generale de la Securite Sociale. Rapport General sur la Securite Sociale au Grand-Duche de Luxembourg **2547**
Rapport Hebdomadaire des Maladies au Canada. see Canada Diseases Weekly Report **4099**
Rapport I V V O. (NE ISSN 0922-3282) **224**
Rapport om Kontrollen med Konsummaelkprodukter. (DK ISSN 0107-8666) **1084**
Rapport sur l'Application de la Loi sur les Prestations d'Adaptation pour les Travailleurs. see Report on the Administration of the Labour Adjustment Benefits Act **992**
Rapport sur la Situation Demographique de la France. (FR) **3987**
Rapport sur le Commerce et le Developpement see Trade and Development Report **922**
Rapport Technique Canadien des Sciences Halieutiques et Aquatiques see Canadian Technical Report of Fisheries and Aquatic Sciences **2038**
Rapport Trimestriel de Sanitares Mondiales. see World Health Statistics Quarterly **4119**
Rapporto sull'Economia del Mezzogiorno. (IT ISSN 1120-9518) **687**
Rapporto sulla Industria Cotoniera Italiana. (IT) **4622**
Rapports de Pratique de Quebec see Revue de Droit Judiciaire **2674**
Raps. (GW ISSN 0724-4606) **190**
The Raptor Report. (US ISSN 1048-8030) **566**, **1496**
Rare Books and Manuscripts Librarianship. (US ISSN 0884-450X) **2780**
Rare Books Newsletter. (UK ISSN 0959-1656) **2780**
Rare Coin Review. (US ISSN 0095-263X) **3601**
Rare Earth Bulletin. (UK ISSN 0307-8531) **3418**
Rare-earth Information Center Insight see R I C Insight **3418**
Rare-earth Information Center News see R I C News **3418**
Rare Fruit Council International. Newsletter. (US) **2137**

Rare Fruit Council International. Yearbook. (US) **2137**
Rare Metal News. (JA) **3418**
Rare Metals. (CC ISSN 1001-0521) **3418**
Raritan. (US ISSN 0275-1607) **2952**
Ras al-Khaimah. (TS) **2211**
Ras al-Khaimah Municipality. see Baladiah Ras al-Khaimah **4084**
Rasant. (GW ISSN 0936-871X) **1263**, **2588**
Rasen - Turf - Gazon. (GW ISSN 0341-9789) **2138**
Rashut Nayerot Haerech. Annual Report. (IS) **796**
Rasilimali. (TZ ISSN 0856-0382) **961**
Rasmi Jaridah. see Afghanistan. Ministry of Justice. Official Gazette **2595**
Rasp. (DK ISSN 0107-8747) **4072**
Raspberry Press. (US) **2881**
Rasprave Zavoda za Hrvatski Jezik see Zavod za Hrvatski Jezik. Rasprave **2853**
Rasprostranenie Pechati. (RU ISSN 0033-9318) **2575**
Rassegna. (IT ISSN 0393-0203) **2449**
Rassegna Amministrativa della Scuola. (IT ISSN 0393-4586) **1657**
Rassegna Bagno Cucina. (IT) **2554**
Rassegna Centro di Cultura e Storia Amalfitana. (IT) **342**, **410**, **2320**
Rassegna Chimica. (IT ISSN 0033-9334) **1208**
Rassegna d'Arte. (IT) **342**
Rassegna degli Archivi di Stato. (IT ISSN 0037-2781) **2382**
Rassegna dei Beni Culturali. (IT) **2206**
Rassegna dei Lavori Pubblici. (IT ISSN 0033-9377) **1873**
Rassegna del Bagno see Rassegna Bagno Cucina **2554**
†Rassegna del Lavoro. (IT ISSN 0033-9385) **5267**
Rassegna del Mondo Arabo. (IT) **3969**
Rassegna dell'Arbitrato. (IT ISSN 0033-9415) **992**
Rassegna dell'Imballaggio. (IT ISSN 1120-6136) **3651**
Rassegna della Letteratura Italiana. (IT ISSN 0033-9423) **2952**
Rassegna della Letteratura Sui Cicli Economici. (IT ISSN 0033-944X) **1084**
Rassegna della Stampa. (IT ISSN 0033-9458) **1104**
Rassegna di Cultura e Vita Scolastica. (IT ISSN 0033-9482) **2881**, **1657**
Rassegna di Dermatologia e Sifilografia.(IT ISSN 0033-9490) **3249**
Rassegna di Diritto Civile. (IT) **2670**
Rassegna di Diritto e Tecnica dell'Alimentazione. (IT) **2080**
Rassegna di Diritto, Legislazione e Medicina Legale Veterinaria. (IT ISSN 0300-3485) **2670**, **4814**
Rassegna di Diritto Pubblico. (IT ISSN 0033-9512) **2670**
Rassegna di Informazioni. (IT) **796**
Rassegna di Letteratura Tomistica. (IT) **3778**, **4196**
Rassegna di Meccanica. (IT) **4607**, **3022**
†Rassegna di Medicina d'Urgenza. (IT) **5267**
Rassegna di Medicina Sperimentale. (IT ISSN 0033-9555) **3262**
Rassegna di Patologia dell'Apparato Respiratorio. (IT ISSN 0033-9563) **3366**
Rassegna di Pedagogia/Paedagogische Umschau. (IT ISSN 0033-9571) **1657**
Rassegna di Psicologia. (IT) **4044**
†Rassegna di Psicoterapie - Ipnosi. (IT) **5267**
Rassegna di Servizio Sociale. (IT ISSN 0033-9601) **4417**
Rassegna di Studi Etiopici. (IT) **2334**
Rassegna di Teologia (IT ISSN 0033-9644) **4197**
Rassegna di Urologia e Nefrologia. (IT ISSN 0033-992X) **3146**
Rassegna Economica (Naples). (IT) **882**

Rassegna Economica della Provincia di Sondrio. (IT) **821**
Rassegna Forense. (IT) **2670**
Rassegna Geriatrica. (IT ISSN 0486-0306) **2277**
Rassegna Giuridica dell'Energia Elettrica. (IT) **1907**, **2670**
Rassegna Grafica. (IT ISSN 0033-9687) **4005**
Rassegna Internazionale di Clinica e Terapia. (IT ISSN 0033-9695) **3146**
Rassegna Internazionale di Logica/International Logic Review. (IT ISSN 0048-6779) **3778**
▼Rassegna Italiana di Criminologia. (IT) **1521**
Rassegna Italiana di Linguistica Applicata. (IT ISSN 0033-9725) **2837**
Rassegna Italiana di Sociologia. (IT ISSN 0486-0349) **4446**
†Rassegna Lucchese. (IT ISSN 0033-975X) **5267**
†Rassegna Medica. English Edition. (IT) **5267**
Rassegna Medica Sarda. (IT ISSN 0033-9776) **3383**
Rassegna: Medical and Cultural Review see Rassegna Medica. English Edition **5267**
Rassegna Melodrammatica. (IT ISSN 0033-9784) **3576**
Rassegna Mensile della Imposte Dirette.(IT) **1104**
Rassegna Mensile di Israel. (IT ISSN 0033-9792) **4226**, **2952**
Rassegna Modi di Abitare Oggi see Rassegna **2449**
Rassegna Musicale Curci. (IT ISSN 0033-9806) **3576**
Rassegna Odontotecnica. (IT ISSN 0048-6787) **3241**
Rassegna Parlamentare. (IT) **2670**
Rassegna Penitenziaria e Criminologica.(IT) **1521**
Rassegna Petrolifera. (UK ISSN 0033-9822) **3700**
Rassegna Quindicinale dell'Agricoltura see Ecomese **88**
Rassegna Sindacale. (IT ISSN 0033-9849) **2588**
Rassegna Sovietica. (IT ISSN 0033-9857) **342**, **2952**, **3576**
Rassegna Stampa. (IT ISSN 1120-3927) **821**
Rassegna Storica del Risorgimento. (IT ISSN 0033-9873) **2382**
Rassegna Storica Toscana. (IT ISSN 0033-9881) **2382**
Rassegna sulla Sperimentazione Organizzativa e Didattica nelle Universita. (IT) **3262**
Rassegna Tecnica di Problemi dell'Energia Elettrica. (IT) **1907**
Rassegna Tecnica Enel see Rassegna Tecnica di Problemi dell'Energia Elettrica **1907**
Rassegna Tributaria. (IT) **1104**
Rassegna Trimestrale di Odontoiatria. (IT ISSN 0033-9911) **3241**
Rassemblement pour la Republique. (RE) **4383**
Rassembler see Celebrate **4260**
Rassenbericht. (NE) **190**
Rassenlijst voor Fruitgewassen. (NE ISSN 0169-6750) **190**
Rassenlijst voor Groentegewassen: Glasgroenten. (NE) **190**
Rassenlijst voor Groentegewassen: Vollegrondsgroenten. (NE) **190**
Rasskaz. (RU ISSN 0235-4241) **2952**
Rastenievadni Nauki. (BU ISSN 0568-465X) **190**
Raster. (NE) **2952**
Rastitelna Zashtita. (BU) **190**
Rastitel'nye Resursy/Vegetative Resources. (RU ISSN 0033-9946) **516**
Rastitel'nye Resursy Sibiri i Dal'nego Vostoka see Rastitel'nyi Mir Sibiri i Dal'nego Vostoka **467**
Rastitel'nyi Mir Sibiri i Dal'nego Vostoka.(RU) **467**
Rat and Mouse Tales. (US) **3713**
Rat fuer Formgebung. Literaturhinweise.(GW ISSN 0024-4805) **4615**, **20**

REAL ESTATE 6597

†Rat News Letter. (US ISSN 0309-1848) **5267**
Rat Race Record. (US) **3004**
Rataplan. *see* Maky **1259**
Ratcliffian. (UK ISSN 0048-6809) **1322**
Rate Watch. (US) **796, 961**
RateGram. (US ISSN 0887-7408) **796, 961**
Rateko. (SW ISSN 0033-9962) **1359**
Rateksa *see* Radiobranchen **1359**
Der Ratgeber. (GW ISSN 0033-9989) **2541**
Ratgeber aus der Apotheke. (GW) **3807**
Ratgeber Forschung und Technologie. (GW) **4607**
Ratgeber fuer Fernunterricht. (GW) **1686**
Ratgeber fuer Kranke und Gesunde *see* Ratgeber aus der Apotheke **3807**
Ratgeber fuer Schwangere und Junge Muetter. (GW) **3296**
Rathaus. (GW) **4093**
Ratherby. (CN) **4554**
Rating and Valuation *see* R R V Monthly **4155**
Rating and Valuation Reporter. (UK ISSN 0048-6817) **2670, 4072**
Ratio. (UK ISSN 0034-0006) **3778**
Ratio Juris. (UK ISSN 0952-1917) **2670, 3778**
†Rational Drug Therapy. (US ISSN 0031-7020) **5267**
Rational Individualist *see* Individualist **3769**
Rational Use of Energy *see* Energy Saving and Alternative Energy Sources Newsletter **5186**
Rationalisierungs - Gemeinschaft des Handels beim R K M Reflexe *see* R G H Reflexe **5266**
Rationalisierungs-Kuratorium der Deutschen Wirtschaft e.V. Kontakt *see* R K W Kontakt **4044**
The Rationalist News. (AT ISSN 0156-7594) **3778, 4197**
Rationality and Society. (US ISSN 1043-4631) **4383**
Rationell Reinigen. (GW) **629**
Rationelle Buero *see* B T S **1057**
Rationelle Hauswirtschaft. (GW ISSN 0341-5295) **2449**
Ratulanka. (CE) **3921**
▼Raum. (AU) **2494**
Raum und Siedlung *see* Structur **2496**
Raum und Zeit. (GW ISSN 0722-7949) **3596, 1967, 3146, 3829**
Raumfahrt Wirtschaft. (GW ISSN 0179-5627) **61, 687**
Raumforschung und Raumordnung. (GW ISSN 0034-0111) **2500, 4584**
Raumplanung und Umweltschutz im Kanton Zurich. (SZ) **2494, 4111**
Rautatieliikenne. (FI ISSN 0048-6833) **4714**
Rautaviesti *see* Asu Hyvin **641**
Raute. (GW) **4417**
Rautulaisten Lehti. (FI) **2382**
Rave. (US) **4637**
Rave Reviews *see* Romantic Times **2984**
Raven. (UK ISSN 0951-4066) **3921**
Raven (Lynchburg). (US ISSN 0034-0146) **566**
Raven Press Series in Physiology. (US) **574, 3262**
Raven Press Series on Molecular and Cellular Biology. (US) **452**
Raven Review. (US) **1322**
Ravi. (UK ISSN 0962-225X) **2881, 2020**
Ravi. (PK) **2952**
Ravinia Festival. (US) **3576**
Raw. (US ISSN 0742-4434) **342, 2881**
†Raw Materials for the Pulp and Paper Industry. (US) **5267**
Raw Materials for the Refactories Industry. (US ISSN 0950-8198) **3418, 1151**
Raw Materials Report. (SW ISSN 0349-6287) **934, 3494**
Rawal Medical Journal. (PK) **3146**
Rawhide Press. (US ISSN 0300-6328) **2020**

Rawlinsons Australian Construction Handbook (Year). (AT ISSN 0810-8064) **629**
Rawlinsons New Zealand Construction Handbook. (NZ ISSN 0813-5207) **1151, 629**
Rawls Museum Arts Bulletin. (US) **3532**
Ray. (JA) **4851**
Al-Rayah. (QA) **2211**
Raydan. (BE ISSN 1015-4523) **2431, 282**
Rayden & Jackson on Divorce & Family Matters. (UK) **2718**
Raymond Dart Lectures. (SA ISSN 0079-9815) **247**
Rayons. (FR ISSN 0034-0197) **4273, 1263**
Rays. (IT ISSN 0390-7740) **3362**
Ray's Adlet. (US) **37**
Rays from the Rose Cross. (US) **3778**
▼Raystown Review. (US) **3004**
†La Raza Habla Magazine. (US) **5267**
La Raza Law Journal. (US ISSN 8755-8815) **2670, 4446**
Razem. (PL) **1264**
Razgledi. (XN ISSN 0034-0227) **2952**
†Razon Espanola. (SP ISSN 0212-5978) **5267**
Razon y Fe. (SP ISSN 0034-0235) **2513**
Razonoda Miliona. (YU ISSN 0034-0243) **4485**
Razoruzhenie *see* Disarmament **3457**
Razprave in Gradivo/Treatises and Documents. (XV) **2020**
Razvedka i Okhrana Nedr. (RU ISSN 0034-026X) **3494**
Razvitok. (XN ISSN 0351-3769) **2952, 342, 2513**
Razvoj/Development. (CI ISSN 0352-4728) **934, 3970**
Razvoj: Development - International. (CI ISSN 0352-8553) **934, 897**
Razza Bovina Piemontese. (IT ISSN 0300-3477) **224**
Re-actions. (US) **1758, 1809**
Re: Arts and Letters. (US ISSN 1054-5212) **2513**
Re: View. (US ISSN 0891-5326) **3796**
†Re-View. (US ISSN 0161-5114) **5267**
Reach *see* Between Times **5148**
Reaching for the Skies. (NE) **61**
Reaching Out. (US) **2284, 3146**
Reaching the Manitoba Market. (CN ISSN 0706-8085) **37**
Reaction Kinetics and Catalysis Letters. (HU ISSN 0133-1736) **1229**
ReActions. (UK ISSN 0953-5640) **2541**
Reactions. (NZ ISSN 0157-7271) **3741**
†Reactive Personal Distress. (UK ISSN 0143-7585) **5267**
Reactive Polymers. (NE ISSN 0923-1137) **1859, 3418**
Reactive Polymers, Ion Exchangers, Sorbents *see* Reactive Polymers **1859**
Reactivity and Structure: Concepts of Organic Chemistry. (US ISSN 0341-2377) **1223**
Reactivity of Solids *see* Solid State Ionics **3831**
Read. *see* Iqra **1256**
Read. *see* Baca **2746**
Read, America! (US ISSN 0891-4214) **1758, 2780**
Read Magazine. (US ISSN 0034-0359) **1264, 1657**
†Read Me. (US ISSN 0899-5044) **5267**
Read More About It - Book of Days. (US) **2420**
Read, See and Hear. (US) **2780, 1657**
Readaptation. (FR ISSN 0484-0305) **1740, 1657**
Reader. (UK ISSN 0300-3469) **4247**
Reader (Houghton). (US ISSN 0742-9681) **2881**
Reader (San Diego). (US) **2881**
Reader (Syracuse). (US) **1686**
The Reader's Adviser. (US) **2952**
Readers Advisory Service. (US) **2795**
Reader's Aid. *see* Yad Lakore **2791**

Reader's Digest. *see* Duzhe Wenzhai **2181**
Reader's Digest. (US ISSN 0034-0375) **2233**
Reader's Digest (Asia Edition). (HK ISSN 0034-0383) **2197**
Reader's Digest (Australian Edition). (AT ISSN 0034-0391) **2172**
Reader's Digest (British Edition). (UK ISSN 0034-0405) **2195**
Reader's Digest (Canadian-English Edition). (CN ISSN 0034-0413) **2178**
Reader's Digest (Finnish edition). *see* Valitut Palat **2186**
†Reader's Digest (Greek Edition). (GR) **5267**
Reader's Digest (Indian Edition). (II ISSN 0034-0421) **2201**
†Reader's Digest (Japanese Edition). (JA ISSN 0034-043X) **5267**
Reader's Digest (New Zealand Edition). (AT ISSN 0034-0448) **2212**
Reader's Digest (South African Edition) .(SA ISSN 0034-0456) **2216**
Reader's Digest (South Korea). (KO) **2209**
Reader's Digest - Das Beste (German Braille Edition). (GW) **2295, 2191**
Reader's Digest - Das Beste (German Edition). (GW) **2191**
Reader's Digest - Det Baesta. (SW ISSN 1100-4843) **2218**
Readers' Guide Abstracts. Microfiche Edition. (US ISSN 0886-0092) **4142, 20**
Reader's Guide Abstracts. Print Edition.(US ISSN 0899-1553) **4142**
Readers' Guide to Periodical Literature. (US ISSN 0034-0464) **20**
Reading. (UK ISSN 0034-0472) **1657**
Reading *see* Reading Today **1658**
Reading. *see* Du Shu **2912**
Reading Abstracts *see* Linguistics and Language Behavior Abstracts **2855**
Reading and Writing. (NE ISSN 0922-4777) **2837, 1658, 3352, 4044**
Reading and Writing. *see* Yuedu yu Xiezuo **2979**
Reading Around. (AT) **1758, 2837**
Reading - Berks Auto Club Magazine. (US) **4784**
Reading Business Directory. (UK ISSN 0957-1086) **1151**
Reading Center. (US) **4136**
†Reading Clinic. (US ISSN 0146-1176) **5267**
Reading Horizons. (US ISSN 0034-0502) **1740**
Reading Improvement. (US ISSN 0034-0510) **1740**
Reading in a Foreign Language. (UK ISSN 0264-2425) **2837, 1758**
Reading in Indianapolis. (US) **2780**
Reading in Political Economy. (UK ISSN 0305-814X) **687**
Reading in Virginia. (US) **1740**
Reading Informer *see* Sounds of Reading **1664**
Reading Intercom. (US) **1758**
Reading Is Fundamental, Inc. Newsletter *see* R I F Newsletter **1657**
Reading Journal. (II ISSN 0377-3426) **1758**
Reading Plus. (US ISSN 0882-6196) **3778**
Reading Psychology. (US ISSN 0270-2711) **1758, 1740, 4044**
Reading Research and Instruction. (US ISSN 0886-0246) **1758**
Reading Research Quarterly. (US ISSN 0034-0553) **1658**
Reading Teacher. (US ISSN 0034-0561) **1758**
Reading Time. (AT ISSN 0155-218X) **2952**
Reading Today. (US ISSN 0737-4208) **1658**
Reading World *see* Reading Research and Instruction **1758**
Readings. (US ISSN 0886-3784) **3353, 4044, 4136**
▼Readings from Criminal Justice History. (US) **1521**
Readings in Glass History. (IS ISSN 0792-4224) **282, 2431**

Readings in Linguistics. *see* Lingvisticke Citanky **2827**
Readings in Long Island Archaeology and Ethnohistory. (US) **282**
Readings in Political Economy *see* Reading in Political Economy **687**
Readings in Social and Political Theory. (US) **3921, 4446**
Readings in Spanish-English Contrastive Linguistics. (PR) **2837**
Readings in Western Civilization. (US) **2320**
Readings on Equal Education. (US ISSN 0270-1448) **1740**
Readmore Newsletter. (US) **410**
Ready. (UK) **3469, 4247**
▼Ready Mix. (US) **629**
▼Ready, Set, Go! In-Depth. (US) **1473**
Readywear. (UM) **1287**
Reagent Chemicals. (US) **1208**
†Reaktorn. (SW ISSN 0034-057X) **5267**
Real Academia de Ciencias Exactas, Fisicas y Naturales. Revista. (SP ISSN 0034-0596) **4335**
Real Academia de Cordoba de Ciencias, Bellas Letras y Nobles Artes. Boletin. (SP ISSN 0034-060X) **2952**
Real Academia de Farmacia. Anales. (SP ISSN 0034-0618) **3741**
Real Academia de la Historia. Boletin. (SP ISSN 0034-0626) **2320**
Real Academia Espanola. Boletin. (SP ISSN 0210-4822) **2837**
Real Academia Nacional de Medicina. Anales. (SP ISSN 0034-0634) **3146**
Real Academia Sevillana de Buenas Letras. Boletin. (SP) **2952**
Real Analysis Exchange. (US ISSN 0147-1937) **3052**
The Real Calvin Coolidge. (US ISSN 0898-9745) **420**
Real Estate Accounting and Taxation. (US) **755, 4155**
Real Estate Analysis and Planning Service. (US) **4155, 882**
Real Estate and Business Atlanta *see* Business Atlanta **649**
Real Estate Appraisal Newsletter *see* N A R E A Real Estate Appraisal Newsletter **4153**
Real Estate Appraiser. (US) **4155**
Real Estate Appraiser and Analyst *see* Real Estate Appraiser **4155**
†Real Estate Bulletin. (US) **5267**
Real Estate Business. (US ISSN 0744-642X) **4155**
Real Estate Center Journal. (US ISSN 0164-5781) **4155**
Real Estate Center Law Letter. (US) **4155**
Real Estate Computer Review. (US) **4156, 1464**
Real Estate Coordinator. (US) **4156**
Real Estate Development Annual *see* Canadian Building **608**
Real Estate Directory of Manhattan. (US ISSN 0098-8936) **4156**
Real Estate Educators Association. Journal. (US) **4156**
Real Estate Educators Association. Proceedings. (US) **4156**
Real Estate Educators Association Action *see* R E E Action **4155**
Real Estate - Environmental Liability News. (US ISSN 1046-9966) **2715**
Real Estate Finance. (US ISSN 0748-318X) **4156**
Real Estate Finance Journal. (US ISSN 0898-0209) **4156, 796**
Real Estate Finance Today. (US ISSN 0742-0021) **4156**
Real Estate Financing Update. (US ISSN 0891-9852) **4156, 796**
Real Estate for Professional Practitioners: a Wiley Series. (US) **4156**
Real Estate Forum. (US ISSN 0034-0707) **4156**
Real Estate Information Service Reports: Office Market Service *see* R E I S Reports: Office Market Service **4155**
Real Estate Information Service Reports: Retail Market Service *see* R E I S Reports: Retail Market Service **4155**

REAL ESTATE

Real Estate Insider. (US ISSN 0034-0715) **4156**
Real Estate Institute of Queensland. Annual Report. (AT) **4156**
†Real Estate Intelligence Report. (US ISSN 0194-6900) **5267**
Real Estate Investing Letter. (US ISSN 0145-1022) **4156**, 961
Real Estate Investment Ideas. (US ISSN 0034-0723) **4156**
Real Estate Investment Planning. (US ISSN 0034-0731) **4156**
Real Estate Investment Planning Checklist and Forms. (US ISSN 0034-0693) **4156**
Real Estate Investment Quarterly Quarterly see R E I D Quarterly **2540**
Real Estate Investment Situations. (US) **4156**
Real Estate Investor Letter see Real Estate Investing Letter **4156**
Real Estate Issues. (US ISSN 0146-0595) **4156**
Real Estate Jamaica. (JM) **4156**
Real Estate Journal (Brisbane). (AT ISSN 0048-685X) **4156**
Real Estate Journal (Sydney South). (AT ISSN 0034-074X) **4156**
Real Estate Law Digest (Supplement). (US) **2715**
Real Estate Law Journal. (US ISSN 0048-6868) **2716**
†Real Estate Law Locator. (US) **5267**
Real Estate Law Report. (US ISSN 0162-752X) **2716**
Real Estate Leasing Report. (US ISSN 0748-3163) **4156**
Real Estate Magazine see Metro Chicago Real Estate **4152**
Real Estate News. (US) **4156**
Real Estate News. (CN) **4156**
Real Estate News and Buyers Guide. (CN) **4156**, 629, 2495
Real Estate Newsletter. (US) **4156**
Real Estate Opportunity Report see R T C Report **4155**
†Real Estate Outlook. (US) **5267**
The Real Estate Price Guide. (AT ISSN 1033-3363) **4156**
†Real Estate Quarterly. (US ISSN 0742-2644) **5267**
Real Estate Record and Builder's Guide.(US ISSN 0034-0774) **4156**, 629
Real Estate Reports. (US ISSN 0079-9890) **4156**
Real Estate Research/Fudosan Kenkyu.(JA ISSN 0532-7776) **4156**
Real Estate Review. (US ISSN 0034-0790) **4156**
Real Estate Securities & Capital Markets. (US) **2716**
Real Estate Sourcebook. (US) **4156**
†Real Estate Syndication Alert. (US) **5267**
Real Estate Syndication News. (US) **4157**
Real Estate Syndicator Newsletter see Real Estate Securities & Capital Markets **2716**
Real Estate Tax Ideas. (US ISSN 0162-7538) **4157**, 1104
Real Estate Times see Commercial Property News **4147**
Real Estate Times/Fangdichan Dao Bao.(HK ISSN 1012-3253) **4157**
Real Estate Today. (US ISSN 0034-0804) **4157**
Real Estate U S A. (US) **4157**
Real Estate Victoria. (CN) **4157**
Real Estate Week. (US) **4157**
Real Estate Weekly. (US) **4157**
Real Estate West. (US) **4157**, 1051
Real Fiction. (US) **2952**
†Real Fun Mag. (US) **5267**
The Real Ghostbusters Magazine. (US) **1264**
Real Instituto y Observatorio de la Armada. Almanaque Nautico. (SP) **368**
Real Instituto y Observatorio de la Armada. Boletin Astronomico. (SP) **368**
Real Instituto y Observatorio de la Armada. Efemerides Astronomicas. (SP) **368**

Real Instituto y Observatorio de la Armada. Observaciones Meteorologicas, Magneticas y Sismicas. Anales. (SP) **1593**
Real Life Magazine. (US ISSN 0739-196X) 342, 2952
Real Living. (CN ISSN 0034-0847) **4247**
Real People. (US) **420**
Real Pottery. (UK) **356**
Real Property see B A R - B R I Bar Review. Real Property **2603**
Real Property Institute. (US) **2716**
Real Property Law Communicator. (US) **2716**
Real Property Law Reporter. (US ISSN 0898-1698) **2716**
Real Property, Probate and Trust Journal. (US ISSN 0034-0855) **2716**
Real Property Reports. (CN ISSN 0703-4687) **4157**
Real Sociedad Arqueologica. Boletin Arqueologico. (SP ISSN 0034-0863) **282**, 2320
Real Sociedad Espanola de Fisica. Anales de Fisica. (SP) **3829**
Real Sociedad Espanola de Fisica y Quimica. Anales de Fisica see Real Sociedad Espanola de Fisica. Anales de Fisica **3829**
Real Sociedad Espanola de Fisica y Quimica. Anales de Quimica see Real Sociedad Espanola de Quimica. Anales de Quimica **1186**
Real Sociedad Espanola de Historia Natural. Boletin de Geologia y Biologia see Real Sociedad Espanola de Historia Natural. Seccion Biologica y Seccion Geologica. Boletin **452**
Real Sociedad Espanola de Historia Natural. Seccion Biologica y Seccion Geologica. Boletin. (SP) **452**, 1578
Real Sociedad Espanola de Quimica. Anales de Quimica. (SP) **1186**
Real Talk. (US) **1264**, 1538, 1697, 3630
Real-Time Interface. (US) **1464**
Real-Time Systems. (NE ISSN 0922-6443) **1438**
Real-Time Systems Symposium. Proceedings. (US ISSN 1052-8725) **1438**
Real Times. (US ISSN 0275-4770) **2233**
†Real West. (US ISSN 0034-0898) **5267**
Real World see Career World **3625**
Realidad Economica. (AG) **882**
Realidad Peruana. (PE) **882**
Realidades. (MX) **4655**
Realisations Recentes a Petawawa/Recent Achievements at Petawawa. (CN ISSN 0824-8818) **2107**
The Realist. (US ISSN 0034-091X) **2881**
Realist Flyer. (US) **4157**
Realites Danoises see Denmark Review **859**
Realites Familiales. (FR ISSN 0220-9926) **4417**
Realites Gabonaises. (GO ISSN 0486-106X) **3921**
Realites Industrielles. (FR) **3494**, 1026
Realities. (US) **3004**
Realities Franc-Comtoises. (FR ISSN 0223-5793) **821**
Reality. (SA ISSN 0034-0979) **2881**
Reality. (US ISSN 0034-0987) **4197**
Reality. (IE ISSN 0034-0960) **4273**
Reality Change. (US ISSN 0886-036X) 3596, 3671, 4044
Reality Now. (CN) **2881**, 1967
Reality Theory Newsletter see Fed Tracker - Reality Theory Newsletter **665**
Die Realschule. (GW ISSN 0342-829X) **1658**
Realta. (IT ISSN 0034-0995) **1026**
Realta Economica. (IT) **821**
Realta Nuova. (IT) **2206**
Realta Regionale. Fonti e Studi. (IT) **282**, 306
Realta Sociale d'Oggi. (IT) **4383**
†Realta Sudafricana. (IT) **5267**
†Realtor. (US) **5267**
Realtor News. (US ISSN 0279-6309) **4157**

Realtor Voice. (US) **4157**
Realtors Land Institute. (US ISSN 0888-5427) **4157**
†Realtors Review. (US) **5267**
Realty. (US) **4157**
Realty. (IT) **4157**
Realty and Building. (US ISSN 0034-1045) **4157**, 629
Realty Bluebook. (US ISSN 0090-399X) **4157**
†Realty Roundup. (US) **5267**
Realty Stock Digest. (US) **961**
Realty Stock Review. (US) **961**
Reanimation et Medecine d'Urgence see Reanimation, Soins Intensifs, Medecine d'Urgence **3146**
Reanimation, Soins Intensifs, Medecine d'Urgence. (FR ISSN 0765-5290) **3146**
Reaper. (NZ ISSN 0034-107X) **4247**
†Reaper. (US ISSN 0882-6757) **5267**
Reappraisals. (CN) **2952**
Rear Guard. (CN) **1322**
RearGarde. (US) **3576**
Reason. (US ISSN 0048-6906) **2233**
Reasons for Choosing. (AT) **3630**
Reassurance see L'Argus International **5138**
Rebe und Wein. (GW ISSN 0034-1118) **385**, 190
Rebel Youth. (CN) **3921**
Rebirth of Artemis. (US) **3004**, 4851
Rebis Chapbook Series. (US ISSN 0147-0396) **3004**
Reborn see Churchyard **5166**
Rebound Reporter. (US) **1521**, 1243
Rebuild see Focus **618**
De Rebus. (SA ISSN 0250-0329) **2670**
Rec Naroda. (YU ISSN 0034-1142) **2240**
Recall Clearinghouse. (US) **1507**
Recall Clearinghouse Service see Recall Clearinghouse **1507**
Recambios y Accesorios see Tienda de Recambios y Accesorios **4703**
Recap of Milk Receipts and Utilization in Montana. (US) **203**
Recensement Suisse de la Circulation Routiere. see Schweizerische Strassenverkehrszaehlung **4666**
Recent Achievements at Petawawa. see Realisations Recentes a Petawawa **2107**
Recent Achievements in Restorative Neurology. (SZ ISSN 1013-7467) **3353**
Recent Advances in Animal Nutrition in Australia (Year). (AT ISSN 0819-4823) **453**
Recent Advances in Biological Psychiatry see Biological Psychiatry **3332**
Recent Advances in Crosslinking & Curing. (UK ISSN 0144-6266) **3867**, 1859, 4293
Recent Advances in Epilepsy. (UK) **3353**
†Recent Advances in Infection. (UK ISSN 0144-1078) **5267**
Recent Advances in Nuclear Medicine. (US ISSN 0163-6170) **3362**
†Recent Advances in Nursing. (UK ISSN 0144-6592) **5267**
Recent Advances in Obesity Research. (US ISSN 0306-7548) **3146**, 3807
†Recent Advances in Occupational Health. (UK) **5267**
Recent Advances in Tobacco Science. (US ISSN 0363-8480) **4644**
Recent American History. (US ISSN 0899-2371) **2420**
Recent Awards in Engineering. (US) **1835**
Recent Developments in Alcoholism. (US) **1538**
Recent Developments in the Chemistry of Natural Carbon Compounds. (HU ISSN 0079-9947) **1223**
Recent Developments of Neurobiology in Hungary. (HU ISSN 0079-9955) **453**
Recent Developments of World Seismology. see Guoji Dizhen Dongtai **1590**
Recent Ethics Opinions. (US) **2670**
Recent Indian Books. (II) **410**

Recent Literature on Medicinal Plants. (AT) **3180**, 2141
Recent Polar and Glaciological Literature see Polar and Glaciological Abstracts **1552**
Recent Polar Literature see Polar and Glaciological Abstracts **1552**
Recent Progress in Hormone Research. Proceedings of the Laurentian Hormone Conference. (US ISSN 0079-9963) **3256**
Recent Progress in Surface Membrane Science. (US) **1230**
Recent Progress in Surface Science see Recent Progress in Surface Membrane Science **1230**
Recent Publications in Natural History. (US ISSN 0738-0925) **4335**, 4136
Recent Publications on Governmental Problems. (US ISSN 0034-1185) **4072**
Recent Research Funded by C M H C. (Canada Mortgage and Housing Corporation) (CN) **2495**
Recent Researches in American Music. (US ISSN 0147-0078) **3576**
Recent Researches in Ecology, Environment and Pollution. (II ISSN 0971-1708) **453**
Recent Researches in Geology. (II) **1578**
Recent Researches in the Music of the Baroque Era. (US ISSN 0484-0828) **3576**
Recent Researches in the Music of the Classical and Early Romantic Era see Recent Researches in the Music of the Classical Era **3576**
Recent Researches in the Music of the Classical Era. (US ISSN 0147-0086) **3576**
Recent Researches in the Music of the Middle Ages and Early Renaissance. (US ISSN 0362-3572) **3576**
Recent Researches in the Music of the Nineteenth and Early Twentieth Centuries. (US ISSN 0193-5364) **3576**
Recent Researches in the Music of the Renaissance. (US ISSN 0486-123X) **3576**
Recent Results in Cancer Research/Fortschritte der Krebsforschung. (US ISSN 0080-0015) **3201**
†Recent Transportation Literature for Planning and Engineering Librarians. (US ISSN 0737-772X) **5267**
Recent Trends in Social Sciences. (II) **4383**
Recenti Progressi in Medicina. (IT ISSN 0034-1193) **3146**
†Recently Published Articles. (US ISSN 0145-5311) **5267**
Receptarius. (NE ISSN 0048-6914) **3741**
Receptionist's Update. (CN) **1069**
▼Receptor. (US) **482**, 574, 3146
†Receptors (Sensory). (UK ISSN 0142-8802) **5267**
Receptors and Ligands in Intercellular Communication Series. (US ISSN 0742-4108) **526**
Recercare. (IT ISSN 1120-5741) **3576**
Rechabite. (UK ISSN 0034-1215) **2541**
Rechentechnik - Datenverarbeitung. (GW ISSN 0300-3450) **1400**
Rechentechnik-Datenverarbeitung. Beiheft see E D V - Aspekte **1450**
Recherche. (FR ISSN 0029-5671) **4335**, 4607
Recherche Aerospatiale. (FR ISSN 0034-1223) **61**
Recherche Agronomique en Suisse. see Schweizerische Landwirtschaftliche Forschung **119**
Recherche en Dance. (FR ISSN 0752-5729) **1531**
▼Recherche en Education. (BE ISSN 0777-0820) **1658**
Recherche en Matiere d'Economie des Transports/Research on Transport Economics. (FR ISSN 0304-3320) **4655**
Recherche et Applications en Marketing.(FR ISSN 0767-3701) **1051**

Recherche et Culture. (MG) **4383**
Recherche Sociale. (FR ISSN 0034-124X) **4383**
Recherche sur le XVIIe Siecle. (FR) **2382**
Recherche Urbaine. (FR) **2495**
Recherches Amerindiennes au Quebec. (CN ISSN 0318-4137) **247, 282**
Recherches Anglaises et Americaines. (FR ISSN 0557-6989) **4383**
Recherches Archeologiques en Hainaut Occidental. Bilan. (BE) **282**
Recherches d'Histoire et de Sciences Sociales/Studies in History and the Social Sciences. (FR ISSN 0249-5619) **2320, 4383**
Recherches de Science Religieuse. (FR ISSN 0034-1258) **4197**
Recherches de Theologie Ancienne et Medievale. (BE ISSN 0034-1266) **4197**
Recherches Economiques de Louvain. (BE ISSN 0770-4518) **687**
Recherches en Didactique des Mathematiques. (FR ISSN 0246-9367) **3052**
Recherches en Linguistique Etrangere. (FR) **2837**
Recherches en Securite Sociale. see Current Research in Social Security **2530**
Recherches Feministes. (CN ISSN 0838-4479) **4851**
Recherches Geographiques a Strasbourg. (FR ISSN 0396-9657) **2260**
Recherches Germaniques. (FR ISSN 0399-1989) **2952, 2837**
Recherches Iberiques et Cinematographiques. (FR) **2952, 3516**
Recherches Iberiques Strasbourg II see Recherches Iberiques et Cinematographiques **2952**
Recherches Institutionnelles. (FR) **4197**
Recherches Internationales a la Lumiere du Marxisme see Institut des Recherches Marxistes. Recherches Internationales **3960**
Recherches Linguistiques. (FR) **2837**
Recherches Philosophiques Africaines. (ZR) **3778, 247**
Recherches Pyreneennes. (FR ISSN 0293-311X) **410, 2260**
Recherches Regionales (Cote d'Azur et Contree Limitrophe). (FR) **2495**
Recherches Semiotiques - Semiotic Inquiry see R S S I **2836**
Recherches Sociographiques. (CN ISSN 0034-1282) **4446**
Recherches Sociologiques. (BE ISSN 0771-677X) **4446**
Recherches sur Diderot et sur l'Encyclopedie. (FR ISSN 0769-0886) **2952**
Recherches sur la Renaissance (Paris). (FR) **2382**
Recherches Universitaires see Mutu **1711**
Recherches Universitaires sur l'Integration Europeenne. (LU) **1715**
Rechnoi Transport. (RU ISSN 0034-1290) **4736**
Recht. (SZ ISSN 0253-9810) **2670**
Recht & Psychiatrie. (GW ISSN 0724-2247) **4044, 2670, 3265, 3353**
Recht der Arbeit. (GW ISSN 0342-1945) **2670**
Recht der Datenverarbeitung. (GW ISSN 0178-8930) **1434, 1400, 2670**
Recht der Elektrizitaetswirtschaft. (GW ISSN 0171-712X) **1907**
Recht der Internationalen Wirtschaft. (GW ISSN 0340-7926) **2728**
Recht der Jugend und des Bildungswesens. (GW ISSN 0034-1312) **1243, 1658**
Recht der Landwirtschaft. (GW ISSN 0486-1469) **116**
Recht der Schiffahrt/Maritime Law Review. (GW ISSN 0034-1320) **4736, 2670**
Das Recht der Wirtschaft. (GW) **2670, 687**
Recht en Kritiek. (NE ISSN 0165-7607) **2670**

Recht im Amt. (GW ISSN 0034-1339) **2670**
Recht in Ost und West. (GW) **2728**
Recht und Geschichte. (GW ISSN 0486-1493) **2320**
Recht und Politik. (GW ISSN 0344-7871) **2671**
Recht und Schaden. (GW ISSN 0343-9771) **2728, 920**
Recht-Wirtschaft-Aussenhandel Schriftenreihe. (AU) **2671, 920**
Rechte Lijn. (BE ISSN 0048-6949) **2588, 4714**
Rechts- und Staatswissenschaften. (US ISSN 0080-0163) **2671, 3921**
Rechts- und Wirtschafts-Praxis see R W P **2670**
Rechtsbibliographie/Bibliographie Juridique/Law Bibliography. (SZ ISSN 0250-5940) **2700, 410**
Rechtshistorisch Instituut Leiden. Series 1. (NE ISSN 0169-9032) **2671, 2320**
†Rechtshistorische Studies. (NE ISSN 0169-9806) **5267**
▼Rechtsmedizin. (GW ISSN 0937-9819) **3146, 2671**
Rechtspflege Jahrbuch. (GW ISSN 0080-018X) **2671**
Rechtspfleger - Studienhefte. (GW ISSN 0174-0156) **2671, 4157**
Rechtspflegerblatt. (GW ISSN 0034-1363) **2671**
Rechtsprechung. (GW ISSN 0931-6183) **2671**
Rechtsprechung in Strafsachen. (SZ ISSN 0034-138X) **1521**
Rechtsprechung Zum Privaten Baurecht. (GW) **630**
Rechtsrheinisches Koeln. (GW ISSN 0179-2938) **2382**
Rechtsstaat in der Bewaehrung. (GW) **2728, 2671**
Rechtstheorie. (GW ISSN 0034-1398) **2671**
Rechtswissenschaft und Sozialpolitik. (AU) **2671, 3921**
Recien Nacido. (SP) **1243**
Recife, Brazil. Secretaria de Educacao e Cultura. Arquivos. (BL) **2420**
Recipe Annual. (US) **2449, 2080**
Recipe Yearbook (Year). (US) **2449, 2080**
Recipes For Sale. (US ISSN 0738-3932) **2080, 2449, 4851**
Recipientundersoegelser ved Marmorilik see Miljoeundersoegelser ved Marmorilik **1963**
Reciprocal Meat Conference. Proceedings see American Meat Science Association. Reciprocal Meat Conference. Proceedings **2061**
†Reciprocating Pump Specifications. (US) **5267**
Reckless Ralph's Dime Novel Round-Up see Dime Novel Round-Up **4126**
▼Reclaim. (CN) **4828**
Reclamation and Revegetation Research see Landscape and Urban Planning **1491**
Reclamation Newsletter. (CN ISSN 0826-7049) **1967, 3494**
Reclamation Safety News see Safety News (Denver) **4828**
Recognition and Identification Blue Book. (US) **1151, 2162**
Recognition & Promotions Business. (US) **2162, 4485**
Recognition Technologies Today see Remittance and Document Processing Today **1423**
Recollections of the Pioneers of British Columbia see Pioneers of British Columbia **2419**
Recombinant D N A. (UK ISSN 0261-4979) **546, 3146**
Recombinant D N A Technical Bulletin. (US ISSN 0196-0229) **470, 491, 546**
Recommend: Florida see Recommend: Magazine **4784**
Recommend: Magazine. (US) **4784**
Recommendation for Accountants and Auditors. (UK) **755**
Recommendation for Survival in Business. (UK) **687**
Recommended Country Hotels of Britain. (UK ISSN 0267-3428) **4784**

Recommended Lending Stance. (US) **961**
Recommended Recordings. (UK ISSN 0309-0574) **3576**
Recommended Reference Books for Small & Medium-Sized Libraries and Media Centers. (US ISSN 0277-5948) **2780**
Recommended Short Break Holidays. (UK) **4784**
Recommended Wayside Inns of Britain. (UK ISSN 0080-0252) **4784**
Recon. (US ISSN 0093-5336) **3469**
Reconciliation International. (NE) **4197, 3946**
Reconciliation Quarterly. (UK ISSN 0034-1479) **4247**
Reconstruction. see Aufbau **1992**
Reconstruction. (NE ISSN 0034-1487) **4226**
Reconstruction Surgery and Traumatology. (SZ ISSN 0080-0260) **3383, 3311**
Reconstructionist. (US ISSN 0034-1495) **4226, 3778**
Recontres see Etudes Rwandaises **2332**
Recopilacion Tecnica de Comercio Exterior see R E C O E X **919**
The Record. (CN ISSN 0712-8290) **3576**
The Record. (AT) **4273**
Record. (MX) **4485**
Record. (PO) **4485**
Record (Nashville). (US ISSN 0360-4608) **4417**
Record (New York, 1940). (US ISSN 0034-1541) **2588**
Record (New York, 1967). (US ISSN 0745-2594) **3576**
Record (New York, 1976). (US) **2456, 4197**
Record Collector. (UK ISSN 0261-250X) **3576**
Record Collector (Broomfield). (UK ISSN 0034-1568) **3576**
Record Collector (Leicester). (UK ISSN 0034-155X) **4461, 3576**
Record Collector's Monthly. (US ISSN 8755-6154) **3576**
Record - Dossier see Phosphore **1262**
Record Exchanger. (US ISSN 0557-9147) **3576, 4461**
Record-Farm and Ranch. (US) **116**
Record Geijutsu/Art of Records, Discography Review. (JA ISSN 0289-3614) **3576**
Record Horseman see Horse Sheets **4535**
Record Mart. (UK) **3576**
Record Mirror see R M **3575**
Record Research. (US ISSN 0034-1592) **3576**
▼Record Retailing Directory. (US) **1151, 3576**
†Record Review (Los Angeles). (US) **5267**
Record-Serie. (GW) **3576**
Record Stockman. (US ISSN 0034-1614) **224**
Record Sun. (US) **3004**
Record - Vehicular Technology Conference see I E E E Vehicular Technology Conference. Record **4692**
Recorder (New York). (US ISSN 0885-7741) **2020**
Recorder (Searcy). (US ISSN 0893-889X) **1715, 2952**
Recorder and Music Magazine see Recorder Magazine **3576**
Recorder Magazine. (UK ISSN 0961-3544) **3576**
Recording & Publishing News. (US) **2881**
Recording Engineer Producer see Recording Engineering Production **4461**
Recording Engineering Production. (US) **4461**
Recording for the Blind. Catalog of Recorded Books. (US ISSN 0484-1506) **2285, 2295**
Recording for the Blind Annual Report. (US) **2295**
Recording for the Blind News. (US) **2295**
Recording Locator see Christian Music Directories: Recorded Music **3545**

RECREATIONAL VEHICLE 6599

Records & Retrieval Report. (US) **1061, 2780**
Records Management Bulletin. (UK) **1457**
Records Management Journal. (UK ISSN 0956-5698) **1026**
Records Management Quarterly. (US ISSN 1050-2343) **2781**
Records of Civilization. Sources and Studies. (US ISSN 0080-0287) **2320, 3643**
Records of Early English Drama Newsletter. (CN ISSN 0700-9283) **4637, 2953**
Records of Geological Survey and Mines. (UG) **1578**
Records of Huntingdonshire. (UK ISSN 0034-1738) **2382**
Records of the Ancient Near East. (GW ISSN 0340-8450) **3643**
Records - Promotion - Music Weekly see R P M Weekly **3576**
▼Recover. (CN ISSN 1180-5722) **1496, 1967**
Recovering Literature. (US ISSN 0300-6425) **2953**
†Recovery Now. (US) **5267**
Recreatie en Toerisme. (NE) **4554**
Recreatievoorzieningen see Recreatie en Toerisme **4554**
Recreation. (UK) **4485**
▼Recreation - Access in the '90's. (US) **2284, 4485**
Recreation Advisor. (US) **4784, 4485**
Recreation and Outdoor Life Directory. (US) **1151, 4554**
Recreation and Parks Law Reporter. (US ISSN 0743-5649) **2671, 1496**
†Recreation and Sport in the Holidays. (AT ISSN 1030-763X) **5267**
†Recreation and Tourism Research Unit. Occasional Paper. (AT ISSN 0156-6962) **5267**
Recreation Association of the Public Service of Canada News see R A News **1300**
Recreation Canada. (CN ISSN 0031-2231) **2739, 3807, 4111, 4485**
Recreation: Current Selected Research. (US ISSN 0894-4830) **4446, 4485**
Recreation Executive Report. (US ISSN 0890-2194) **2739, 4554**
†Recreation Management Handbook. (UK ISSN 0144-624X) **5267**
Recreation Managers' Association of Great Britain Year Book see Leisure and Fitness **2738**
Recreation News. (US) **4554**
Recreation Research Review see Journal of Applied Recreation Research **4773**
Recreation Resources. (US) **2739**
Recreation, Sports and Leisure see Recreation Resources **2739**
Recreation Vehicle Appraisal Guide see N A D A Recreation Vehicle Appraisal Guide **4697**
Recreational & Educational Computing. (US ISSN 0899-014X) **1473**
Recreational Ice Skating. (US) **4485**
†Recreational Safety Newsletter. (US) **5268**
Recreational Skier. (US ISSN 0746-4541) **4554**
Recreational Sports Directory. (US) **1697**
Recreational Vehicle Blue Book. (US ISSN 0733-4745) **4700, 2441**
Recreational Vehicle Business see R V Business **4498**
Recreational Vehicle Buyers Guide see R V Buyers Guide **4655**
Recreational Vehicle Campground and Services Directory see Trailer Life's Recreational Vehicle Campground and Services Directory **1156**
Recreational Vehicle Dealer see R V Business **4498**
Recreational Vehicle Guide see R V Guide **5266**
Recreational Vehicle News see R V News **4655**
Recreational Vehicle Times see R V Times **4783**
Recreational Vehicle Trade Digest see R V Trade Digest **4747**

6600 RECREATIONAL VEHICLES

Recreational Vehicles Trade see Lawn & Garden Trade **1044**
Recruiter Journal. (US) **3469**
Recruiting and Search Report. (US) **1069**, 1151
Recruiting Engineers and Computer Professionals see Recruiting Trends **1069**
Recruiting Highlights see Federal Staffing Digest **4060**
Recruiting Trends. (US ISSN 0034-1827) **1069**
▼Recruitment and Development Report. (UK ISSN 0959-146X) **1070**
Recruitment and Retention in Higher Education. (US) **1715**
Recruitment & Retention Report. (US ISSN 1044-0666) **3286**, 1051
Recruitment Directions. (US) **3630**, 3807
▼Recruitment Solution. (US) **1070**, 1151
†Recruitment Today. (US ISSN 1040-6271) **5268**
Recueil Annuel de Jurisprudence Belge. (BE) **2671**
Recueil Annuel de Windsor d'Acces a la Justice. see Windsor Yearbook of Access to Justice **2695**
Recueil Complet des Budgets de la Syrie. (SY ISSN 0080-0309) **1104**
Recueil Dalloz-Sirey. (FR ISSN 0034-1835) **2671**
Recueil de Documents. see Zbior Dokumentow **3978**
Recueil de Medecine Veterinaire d'Alfort.(FR ISSN 0034-1843) **4815**
Recueil des Brevets d'Invention. (BE ISSN 0034-1851) **3678**
Recueil des Corrections de Cartes (Year). (FR ISSN 0180-9970) **2260**
Recueil des Decisions du Conseil d'Etat.(FR ISSN 0249-7271) **2671**
Recueil des Films. (CN ISSN 0085-543X) **3516**
Recueil des Instructions Donnees aux Ambassadeurs et Ministres de France. (FR ISSN 0080-0333) **3970**
Recueil des Sentences de l'Education. (CN) **1730**
Recueil des Travaux Botaniques Neerlandais see Acta Botanica Neerlandica **492**
Recueil des Travaux Chimiques des Pays-Bas. (NE ISSN 0165-0513) **1186**, 1859
Recueil des Travaux de l'Histoire de la Litterature. see Zbornik Istorije Knjizevnosti **2979**
Recueil des Travaux sur la Protection des Monuments Historiques. see Zbornik Zastite Spomenika Kulture **350**
Recueil International de Statistiques des Transports Publics Urbains. see International Statistical Handbook of Urban Public Transport **4664**
Recueil Juridique de l'Est Securite Sociale. (FR ISSN 0034-1878) **2671**, 2541
Recueil Periodique des Juris-Classeurs: Droit Civil. (FR) **2671**
Recuperare: Progetti Cantieri Tecnologie Prodotti. (IT) **630**
Recuperation see Recyclage Recuperation **1026**
†Recurring Bibliography of Hypertension. (US ISSN 0090-1326) **5268**
Recursos Hidricos. (AG ISSN 0048-6981) **4828**, 1938
Recusant History. (UK ISSN 0034-1932) **2382**, 4273
Recyclage Recuperation. (FR ISSN 1156-962X) **1026**
▼Recycle & Save. (US) **1117**, 1967, 1986
Recyclegram see Commpost **1984**
Recycling. (GW ISSN 0174-1446) **1986**
▼Recycling - Reclamation Digest. (US) **1986**, 1496, 1835
▼Recycling Related Newsletter, Publications, Periodicals. (US ISSN 1053-0525) **1967**, 1496

Recycling Technology. (US) **1986**, 687
Recycling Times. (US ISSN 1042-0614) **1986**
▼Recycling Today (Municipal Market Edition). (US ISSN 1051-0109) **1986**, 4093
Recycling Today (Scrap Market Edition) .(US ISSN 1051-1091) **1986**, 3418
Recycling Update. (US ISSN 0736-1890) **1986**
Recycling World. (US) **1986**
▼Red. (SA) **1294**, 4851
Red and Black (Baltimore). (US) **1322**
Red & Black (Middletown). (US ISSN 8750-9989) **1322**
Red and Black (Washington). (US ISSN 0034-1940) **1322**
Red and Green. (US ISSN 0034-1959) **1322**
Red Bass. (US ISSN 0883-0126) **2881**, 342, 2953
Red Book of Eye, Ear, Nose and Throat Specialists see Red Book of Ophthalmology **3304**
Red Book of Housing Manufacturers. (US ISSN 0149-7642) **630**
Red Book of Ophthalmology. (US ISSN 0146-4582) **3304**
Red Book Used Car Guide. (US ISSN 0736-7953) **4700**
Red Cedar Review. (US ISSN 0034-1967) **2953**, 3004
Red Contable Agraria Nacional. (SP) **156**
Red Cross News. (NZ) **4417**
Red Cross News. (UK) **4417**
Red Cross Quarterly/Reda Krasa Traimasika. (NP ISSN 0048-7023) **4417**
▼Red Dancefloor. (US) **3004**
Red de Recursos de Comunicacion Alternativa. (BO) **1342**
Red Deer Advocate Plus. (CN) **116**
Red Deer Commerce. (CN) **838**
▼Red Dirt. (US) **3004**
Red Double-Barred Cross/Fukujuji. (JA ISSN 0016-2531) **3366**
Red Dwarf. see Czerwony Karzel **3010**
†Red Herring. (US) **5268**
Red Hill Press see Invisible City **2995**
Red Letter. (UK) **2984**
Red Letters. (UK ISSN 0308-6852) **2881**, 3921
Red Light see Satyachar **3924**
†Red Line. (US) **5268**
Red Machinery Guide. (UK) **164**
Red Men Magazine. (US) **1300**
Red Menace. (CN) **2881**, 3921
Red Pagoda. (US) **3004**
Red Poll Herd Book. (UK) **224**
Red Poll News. (US ISSN 0034-2033) **224**
Red Poll Newsletter. (AT) **224**
Red Power. (CE) **3921**
Red River Valley Heritage Press. (US) **2420**
Red Shield see Red Shield News **2541**
Red Shield News. (US) **2541**
Red Star Weekly. (UK ISSN 0034-2068) **2984**
Red Tape. (AT ISSN 1030-0740) **2588**, 4072
Red Tape. (UK ISSN 0034-2076) **4072**
La Red - The Net. (US) **1715**, 2020
La Red - The Net Hotline. (US) **1715**, 2020
Red Weather. (US) **2953**
Reda Krasa Traimasika. see Red Cross Quarterly **4417**
Redaccion. (AG) **4136**
Redactuel. (BE) **2575**, 4136
Redai Dili/Tropical Geography. (CC ISSN 1001-5221) **2260**
Redai Haiyang/Tropic Oceanology. (CC ISSN 1000-3053) **1610**
Redai Qixiang/Tropical Atmosphere. (CC ISSN 1000-4068) **3440**
Redai Zuowu Xuebao/Journal of Tropical Plants. (CC ISSN 1000-2561) **516**
Redaktions Adress. (GW ISSN 0173-959X) **1151**, 37, 4136
Redaktions-Archiv. (GW ISSN 0034-2092) **3921**, 882
Redbook. (US ISSN 0034-2106) **2233**, 4851

▼Redbook (North Burnaby). (CN) **4093**
†Redbook's Young Mother. (US) **5268**
Redcoat. (UK) **4677**
Redding Museum. Occasional Papers. (US) **3532**
Reddingwezen see Nederlands Tijdschrift voor E H B O en Reddingwngwezen **4108**
Redditch Business Directory. (UK ISSN 0957-1094) **1151**
†Rede Ferroviaria Federal. Lista de Artigos Selecionados. (BL ISSN 0100-3941) **5268**
Rede Ferroviaria Federal, S.A. Anuario Estatistico see R F F S A. Anuario Estatistico **4666**
Rede Ferroviaria Federal, S.A. Sistema Ferroviario R F F S A see Sistema Ferroviario R F F S A **4715**
Reden-Berater. (GW ISSN 0932-1543) **37**
Redes de Telecomunicaciones. (SP) **1351**
Rediscovery. (US) **282**
Redlands Bulldog see Bulldog Weekly **1305**
Redneck Review. (US ISSN 0887-5715) **2953**
Redneck Review of Literature see Redneck Review **2953**
Redningshistorisk Forening. Information see Redningshistorisk Forenings Information **4111**
Redningshistorisk Forenings Information. (DK ISSN 0108-254X) **4111**
Reds Report. (US) **4510**
Redstart. (US ISSN 0034-2165) **566**, 4335
Reduced Instruction Set Computer Management see R I S C Management **1400**
Reduced Instruction Set Computer User see R I S C User **1464**
Reduced Instruction Set Computer World see R I S C World **1464**
Reduced Instruction Set Computer 6000 News see R I S C 6000 News **1464**
Reduced Size Asahi Shimbun. see Asahi Shimbun Shukusatuban **2207**
Reducing Benefits Costs see I O M A's Report on Reducing Benefits Costs **751**
Redwood News. (US) **306**, 640
Redwood Researcher. (US ISSN 0890-2968) **2162**
Reed Organ Society Bulletin. (US ISSN 0736-9549) **3577**
Reed Organ Society Newsletter see Reed Organ Society Bulletin **3577**
Reed's Commercial Salvage Practice. (UK) **4736**
Reed's Mediterranean Navigator. (UK ISSN 0263-3620) **4736**
Reed's Nautical Almanac. (UK ISSN 0080-0422) **4655**
Reed's Ocean Navigator. (UK) **4736**
Reeducation Orthophonique. (FR ISSN 0034-222X) **3146**, 2289
The Reef. (SA) **3494**
Reeflections (Townsville). (AT ISSN 0314-6510) **1967**, 1496, 1548
Reel. (US ISSN 0034-2238) **3516**, 2588
Re'em. (IS ISSN 0334-1461) **591**
▼Reenactor's Journal. (US) **3469**
Reeves Journal. (US ISSN 0048-7066) **2302**
Refer. (US ISSN 0144-2384) **2781**
†Referatblatt Soziologie. (GW ISSN 0138-5836) **5268**
Referate: Schweissen und Verwandte Verfahren/Bulletin of Abstracts: Welding and Allied Processes. (GW ISSN 0340-4749) **3428**, 21
†Referateblatt Philosophie. Reihe E. Aktuelle Probleme und Kritik der Buergerlichen Philosophie. (GW ISSN 0138-2721) **5268**
Referateblatt zur Raumentwicklung. (GW ISSN 0341-2512) **4081**, 21, 2500
Referateblatt zur Raumordnung see Referateblatt zur Raumentwicklung **4081**
†Referatedienst Jugendforschung. (GW ISSN 0138-3655) **5268**

†Referatedienst Rehabilitationspaedagogik. (GW ISSN 0232-7503) **5268**
Referatedienst Verpackung. see Packaging Science and Technology Abstracts **3652**
Referatedienst zur Literaturwissenschaft. (GW ISSN 0138-340X) **2953**
Referatekartei Philosophie mit Bibliographischem Anhag see Bibliographie Philosophie **5148**
Referateorgan: Messen Mechanischer Groessen/Bulletin of Abstracts: Measurement of Mechanical Quantities. (GW ISSN 0722-0057) **1846**, 21
Referateorgan: Zerstoerungsfreie Pruefung/Abstract Journal: Non-Destructive Testing. (GW ISSN 0341-0544) **1846**
Referativnyi Zhurnal. Astronomiya. (RU ISSN 0486-2236) **371**, 21
Referativnyi Zhurnal. Aviatsionnye i Raketnye Dvigateli. (RU ISSN 0373-6407) **66**, 21
Referativnyi Zhurnal. Avtomatika i Vychislitel'naya Tekhnika. (RU) **1846**, 21, 1405
Referativnyi Zhurnal. Avtomatika, Telemekhanika i Vychislitel'naya Tekhnika see Referativnyi Zhurnal. Avtomatika i Vychislitel'naya Tekhnika **1846**
Referativnyi Zhurnal. Avtomobil'nye Dorogi. (RU ISSN 0486-2252) **4666**, 21
Referativnyi Zhurnal. Avtomobil'nyi i Gorodskoi Transport. (RU ISSN 0034-2297) **4666**, 21
Referativnyi Zhurnal. Biologicheskaya Khimiya see Referativnyi Zhurnal. Biologiya **467**
Referativnyi Zhurnal. Biologiya. (RU ISSN 0034-2300) **467**, 21
Referativnyi Zhurnal. Biologiya Sel'skokhozyaistvennykh Zhivotnykh. (RU) **142**, 21, 467
Referativnyi Zhurnal. Bionika - Biokibernetika - Bioinzheneriya. (RU ISSN 0202-912X) **467**, 21
Referativnyi Zhurnal. Dvigateli Vnutrennego Sgoraniya. (RU ISSN 0486-2279) **4666**, 21
Referativnyi Zhurnal. Ekologiya Cheloveka. (RU ISSN 0202-5140) **467**
Referativnyi Zhurnal. Ekonimika, Organizatsiya, Teknnologiya i Oborudovanie Poligraficheskogo Proizvodstva see Referativnyi Zhurnal. Izdatel'skoe Delo i Poligrafiya **4007**
Referativnyi Zhurnal. Ekonomika Promyshlennosti. (RU ISSN 0203-6223) **736**, 21
Referativnyi Zhurnal. Elektronika. (RU ISSN 0206-5452) **1777**, 21
Referativnyi Zhurnal. Elektronika i ee Primenenie see Referativnyi Zhurnal. Elektronika **1777**
Referativnyi Zhurnal. Elektrotekhnika. (RU ISSN 0203-5316) **1778**, 21
Referativnyi Zhurnal. Elektrotekhnika i Elektroenergetika see Referativnyi Zhurnal. Elektrotekhnika **1778**
Referativnyi Zhurnal. Energetika. (RU ISSN 0203-5308) **1800**
Referativnyi Zhurnal. Environment Management Abstracts. (RU ISSN 0234-7059) **1974**
Referativnyi Zhurnal. Farmakologiya Effektornykh Sistem. Khimioterapevticheskie Sredstva. (RU ISSN 0202-5132) **3748**
Referativnyi Zhurnal. Farmakologiya. Obshchaya Farmakologiya Nervnoi Sistemy. (RU ISSN 0134-580X) **3748**, 21
Referativnyi Zhurnal. Fitopatologiya. (RU ISSN 0202-9235) **467**, 21
Referativnyi Zhurnal. Fizika. (RU ISSN 0034-2343) **3838**, 21
Referativnyi Zhurnal. Fiziologiya i Morfologiya Cheloveka i Zhivotnykh. (RU ISSN 0207-141X) **467**, 21
Referativnyi Zhurnal. Fotokinotekhnika. (RU ISSN 0370-8063) **3798**, 21, 3520

Referativnyi Zhurnal. Genetika Cheloveka. (RU ISSN 0202-9146) **467**, 21
Referativnyi Zhurnal. Genetika i Selektsiya Vozdelyvaemykh Rastenii. (RU ISSN 0202-9138) **467**, 21
Referativnyi Zhurnal. Geodeziya i Aeros'emka **1552**
Referativnyi Zhurnal. Geodeziya i Aeros'emka. (RU ISSN 0375-9717) **1552**, 21
Referativnyi Zhurnal. Geofizika. (RU ISSN 0034-236X) **1552**, 21
Referativnyi Zhurnal. Geografiya. (RU ISSN 0034-2378) **2268**, 21
Referativnyi Zhurnal. Geologiya. (RU ISSN 0486-2309) **1552**, 21
Referativnyi Zhurnal. Gornoe Delo. (RU ISSN 0034-2386) **3502**, 21
Referativnyi Zhurnal. Gornoe i Neftepromyslovoe Mashinostroenie. (RU ISSN 0373-6415) **3502**, 21, 3025
Referativnyi Zhurnal. Immunologiya - Allergologiya. (RU ISSN 0202-9154) **3180**, 21
Referativnyi Zhurnal. Informatika. (RU ISSN 0486-235X) **2795**, 21
Referativnyi Zhurnal. Issledovanie Kosmicheskogo Prostranstva. (RU ISSN 0034-2408) **371**, 21, 66
Referativnyi Zhurnal. Izdatel'skoe Delo i Poligrafiya. (RU ISSN 0235-2222) **4007**, 21
Referativnyi Zhurnal. Khimicheskoe i Kholodil'noe Mashinostroenie see Referativnyi Zhurnal. Khimicheskoe, Neftepererabatyvayuschchee i Polimernoe Mashinostroenie **2305**
Referativnyi Zhurnal. Khimicheskoe, Neftepererabatyvayuschchee i Polimernoe Mashinostroenie (RU ISSN 0370-8098) **2305**, 21
Referativnyi Zhurnal. Khimiya. (RU ISSN 0486-2325) **1202**, 21
Referativnyi Zhurnal. Kibernetika see Referativnyi Zhurnal. Tekhnicheskaya Kibernetika **1405**
Referativnyi Zhurnal. Klinicheskaya Farmakologiya. (RU ISSN 0202-9162) **3748**, 21
Referativnyi Zhurnal. Kommunal'noe, Bytovoe i Torgovoe Oborudovanie. (RU ISSN 0484-2286) **2556**, 21
Referativnyi Zhurnal. Korroziya i Zashchita ot Korrozii. (RU ISSN 0131-3533) **3428**, 21, 3656
Referativnyi Zhurnal. Kotlostroenie. (RU ISSN 0034-2424) **1846**, 21, 1800
Referativnyi Zhurnal. Legkaya Promyshlennost' (RU ISSN 0034-2432) **736**, 21
Referativnyi Zhurnal. Lesovedenie i Lesovodstvo. (RU ISSN 0034-2440) **2113**, 21
Referativnyi Zhurnal. Mashinostroitel'nye Materialy, Konstruktsii i Raschet Detali Mashin. Gidroprivod. (RU ISSN 0034-2459) **1846**, 21, 3025
Referativnyi Zhurnal. Matematika. (RU ISSN 0034-2467) **3063**, 21
Referativnyi Zhurnal. Meditsinskaya Geografiya. (RU ISSN 0034-2475) **3180**, 21
Referativnyi Zhurnal. Mekhanika. (RU ISSN 0034-2483) **1846**, 21
Referativnyi Zhurnal. Metallurgiya. (RU ISSN 0034-2491) **3428**, 21
Referativnyi Zhurnal. Metrologiya i Izmeritel'naya Tekhnika. (RU ISSN 0034-2505) **3449**, 21
Referativnyi Zhurnal. Nasosostroenie i Kompressorostroenie. Kholodil'noe Mashinostroenie. (RU) **1846**, 21, 3025
Referativnyi Zhurnal. Nasosostroenie i Kompressorstroenie see Referativnyi Zhurnal. Nasosostroenie i Kompressorostroenie. Kholodil'noe Mashinostroenie **1846**
Referativnyi Zhurnal. Oborudovanie Pishchevoi Promyshlennosti. (RU ISSN 0034-2521) **2085**, 21
Referativnyi Zhurnal. Obshchie Voprosy Patologicheskoi Anatomii. (RU) **467**, 21, 3180

Referativnyi Zhurnal. Obshchie Voprosy Patologii see Referativnyi Zhurnal. Obshchie Voprosy Patologicheskoi Anatomii **467**
Referativnyi Zhurnal. Okhrana i Uluchshenie Gorodskoi Sredy. (RU ISSN 0206-6157) **1974**, 21
Referativnyi Zhurnal. Okhrana Prirody i Vosproizvodstvo Prirodnykh Resursov. (RU ISSN 0202-9332) **1974**, 21, 1501
Referativnyi Zhurnal. Onkologiya. (RU ISSN 0202-9197) **3180**, 21
Referativnyi Zhurnal. Organizatsiya i Bezopasnost' Dorozhnogo Dvizheniya.(RU ISSN 0202-9952) **4666**, 21, 4119
Referativnyi Zhurnal. Organizatsiya Upravleniya. (RU ISSN 0132-5639) **736**, 21
Referativnyi Zhurnal. Organizatsiya Upravleniya Promyshlennost'yu see Referativnyi Zhurnal. Organizatsiya Upravleniya **736**
Referativnyi Zhurnal. Pochvovedenie i Agrokhimiya. (RU ISSN 0034-2548) **142**, 21
Referativnyi Zhurnal. Pozharnaya Okhrana. (RU ISSN 0202-9898) **4119**, 21
Referativnyi Zhurnal. Promyshlennyi Transport. (RU ISSN 0034-2556) **3025**, 21
Referativnyi Zhurnal. Radiatsionnaya Biologiya. (RU ISSN 0131-355X) **3180**, 21, 467
Referativnyi Zhurnal. Radiotekhnika. (RU ISSN 0034-267X) **1349**, 1359
Referativnyi Zhurnal. Raketostroenie see Referativnyi Zhurnal. Raketostroenie i Kosmicheskaya Tekhnika **66**
Referativnyi Zhurnal. Raketostroenie i Kosmicheskaya Tekhnika. (RU) **66**, 21
Referativnyi Zhurnal. Rastenievodstvo (Biologicheskie Osnovy). (RU ISSN 0202-9200) **142**, 21, 467
Referativnyi Zhurnal. Sistemy, Pribory i Metody Kontrolya Kachestva Okruzhayushchei Sredy. (RU ISSN 0206-6149) **1974**, 21
Referativnyi Zhurnal. Stroitel'nye i Dorozhnye Mashiny. (RU ISSN 0484-2480) **1846**, 21
Referativnyi Zhurnal. Svarka. (RU ISSN 0131-3525) **3428**, 21
Referativnyi Zhurnal. Tekhnicheskaya Estetika i Ergonomika. (RU) **4615**
Referativnyi Zhurnal. Tekhnicheskaya Kibernetika. (RU) **1405**, 21
Referativnyi Zhurnal. Tekhnologicheskie Aspekty Okhrany Okruzhayushchei Sredy. (RU ISSN 0206-6130) **1975**, 21
Referativnyi Zhurnal. Tekhnologiya Mashinostroeniya. (RU ISSN 0034-2599) **3025**, 21
Referativnyi Zhurnal. Teplo i Massobmen. (RU ISSN 0203-6436) **1800**, 21
Referativnyi Zhurnal. Toksikologiya. (RU ISSN 0202-9219) **3748**, 21
Referativnyi Zhurnal. Traktory i Sel'skokhozyaistvennye Mashiny i Orudiya. (RU ISSN 0034-2602) **142**, 21, 3025
Referativnyi Zhurnal. Truboprovodnyi Transport. (RU ISSN 0034-2610) **1846**, 22, 4666
Referativnyi Zhurnal. Turbostroenie. (RU ISSN 0034-2629) **1846**, 22
Referativnyi Zhurnal. Vodnyi Transport. (RU ISSN 0484-2545) **4666**, 22
Referativnyi Zhurnal. Volokonno-opticheskie Systemy. (RU ISSN 0234-9647) **3838**, 3857
Referativnyi Zhurnal. Voprosy Tekhnicheskogo Progressa i Organizatsii Proizvodstva v Mashinostroenii. (RU ISSN 0034-2637) **1846**, 22
Referativnyi Zhurnal. Vozdushnyi Transport. (RU ISSN 0484-2561) **4666**, 22

Referativnyi Zhurnal. Vzaimodeistvie Raznykh Vidov Transporta i Konteinernye Perevozki. (RU ISSN 0034-2645) **4666**, 22
Referativnyi Zhurnal. Yadernye Reaktory. (RU ISSN 0034-2653) **3838**, 22
Referativnyi Zhurnal. Zheleznodorozhnyi Transport. (RU ISSN 0484-2596) **4666**, 22
Referativnyi Zhurnal. Zhivotnovodstvo see Referativnyi Zhurnal. Biologiya Sel'skokhozyaistvennykh Zhivotnykh **142**
Referativnyj Bjulleten Rumynskoj Nauchno-Tehnicheskoj Literatury. (RM) **4357**, 4615
Referatovy Vyber z Anestesiologie a Resuscitace/Abstracts of Anesthesiology and Resuscitation. (CS ISSN 0034-2688) **3180**, 22
Referatovy Vyber z Chirurgie/Abstracts of Surgery. (CS ISSN 0034-2696) **3180**, 22
Referatovy Vyber z Chorob Infekcnich/ Abstracts of Infectious Diseases. (CS ISSN 0034-270X) **3180**, 22
Referatovy Vyber z Dermatovenerologie/Abstracts of Dermatology and Venerology. (CS ISSN 0034-2718) **3180**, 22
†Referatovy Vyber z Endokrinologie/ Abstracts of Endocrinology. (CS ISSN 0034-2726) **5268**
†Referatovy Vyber z Fysiologie/ Abstracts of Physiology. (CS ISSN 0034-2734) **5268**
Referatovy Vyber z Gastroenterologie/ Abstracts of Gastroenterology. (CS ISSN 0034-2742) **3180**, 22
Referatovy Vyber z Geriatrie see Referatovy Vyber z Gerontologie a Geriatrie **5268**
†Referatovy Vyber z Gerontologie a Geriatrie/Abstracts of Gerontology and Geriatrics. (CS ISSN 0034-2750) **5268**
Referatovy Vyber z Kardiologie, Fysiologie a Patologie Obehoveho Ustroji/Abstracts of Cardiology and Physiology and Pathology of the Circulation System. (CS ISSN 0034-2769) **3180**, 22
Referatovy Vyber z Lekarenstvi/ Abstracts of Pharmacy. (CS ISSN 0034-2777) **3748**, 22
Referatovy Vyber z Lekarenstvi. Abstracts of Farmaci see Referatovy Vyber z Lekarenstvi **3748**
Referatovy Vyber z Neurologie/ Abstracts of Neurology. (CS ISSN 0034-2793) **3180**, 22
Referatovy Vyber z Oftalmologie/ Abstracts of Ophthalmology. (CS ISSN 0034-2807) **3180**, 22
†Referatovy Vyber z Onkologie/ Abstracts of Oncology. (CS ISSN 0034-2815) **5268**
Referatovy Vyber z Ortopedie, Traumatologie a Pribuznych Oboru/ Abstracts of Orthopedics, Traumatology and Related Subjects. (CS ISSN 0034-2823) **3180**, 22
†Referatovy Vyber z Otorhinolaryngologie a Foniatrie/ Abstracts of Otorhinolaryngology and Phoniatrics. (CS ISSN 0034-2831) **5268**
†Referatovy Vyber z Patologicke Anatomie/Abstracts of Pathology. (CS ISSN 0034-284X) **5268**
Referatovy Vyber z Pediatrie/Abstracts of Pediatrics. (CS ISSN 0034-2858) **3180**, 22
Referatovy Vyber z Pneumologie a Tuberkulosy/Abstracts of Pneumology and Tuberculosis. (CS ISSN 0034-2890) **3180**, 22
Referatovy Vyber z Porodnictvi a Gynekologie/Abstracts of Obstetrics and Gynecology. (CS ISSN 0034-2866) **3180**, 22
Referatovy Vyber z Rentgenologie/ Abstracts of Radiology. (CS ISSN 0034-2874) **3180**, 22
Referatovy Vyber z Revmatologie/ Abstracts of Rheumatology. (CS ISSN 0034-2882) **3180**, 22

Referatovy Vyber z Urologie/Abstracts of Urology. (CS ISSN 0139-9322) **3181**, 22
Referatovy Vyber ze Sportovni Mediciny a Lecebne Rehabilitace/Abstracts of Sports Medicine and Rehabilitation. (CS) **3181**, 3372, 4498
Referatovy Vyber ze Sportovni Mediciny - Abstracts of Sports Medicine see Referatovy Vyber ze Sportovni Mediciny a Lecebne Rehabilitace **3181**
Referee. (US ISSN 0733-1436) **4485**
Reference and Research Book News. (US ISSN 0887-3763) **410**, 2781
Reference Book - Argentina. (US ISSN 0080-0449) **882**
Reference Book for World Traders. (US) **1151**
Reference Book of Corporate Managements. (US) **1026**
Reference Book of Highway Personnel see A A S H T O Reference Book of Member Department Personnel and Committees **4646**
Reference Book - Republic of South Africa. (US ISSN 0080-0457) **882**
Reference Book Review. (US ISSN 0272-1988) **410**
Reference Books Bulletin see Booklist **4140**
Reference Data for Engineers. (US) **1342**, 1400, 1778
Reference Data for Radio Engineers see Reference Data for Engineers **1342**
Reference Encyclopedia of the American Indian. (US) **2020**, 1782
†Reference Guide for N A S D A Q Companies. (US) **5268**
▼Reference Guides to Archival and Manuscript Sources in World History. (US ISSN 1054-9110) **2320**
Reference Guides to Archives and Manuscript Collections on Immigrant Culture. (US ISSN 0885-7555) **2330**
Reference Guides to State History and Research. (US) **2320**
▼Reference Guides to the State Constitutions of the United States. (US) **4072**
Reference Librarian. (US ISSN 0276-3877) **2781**
Reference Point: Food Industry Abstracts. (US) **2085**, 22
Reference Quarterly see R Q **2780**
Reference Report. (US) **4136**
Reference Reviews. (UK ISSN 0950-4125) **2781**
Reference Services Review see R S R **4142**
Reference Source (Year). (US) **2080**
Reference Sources for the Social Sciences and Humanities. (US ISSN 0730-3335) **4395**, 2520, 2520, 2520
References see References de la Poste **1354**
References de la Poste. (FR ISSN 0983-1924) **1354**
Referencias Medicas de Informacion Actualizada see Remedia **410**
Referente. (AG) **2953**
Refining & Gas Processisng. (US) **3700**
Refining and Petrochemical Technology Yearbook see Worldwide Petrochemical Directory **3704**
Refining and Petrochemical Technology Yearbook see Worldwide Refining and Gas Processing Directory **3704**
Refining, Construction, Petrochemical & Natural Gas Processing Plants of the World see Refining & Gas Processisng **3700**
Refinisher. (AT) **4700**
Reflect. (US) **2953**, 259
Reflection (Spokane). (US ISSN 0484-2650) **2953**
Reflections. (AT ISSN 0156-7799) **1758**
Reflections. (UK ISSN 0260-8499) **2195**
▼Reflections. (HK) **4136**
Reflections (Duncan Falls). (US) **3004**, 1264
Reflections (Glendale). (US) **2233**

6602 REFLECTIONS

Reflections (New Haven). (US) **4197**
Reflections (North Battleford). (CN ISSN 0384-0697) **2781**
Reflections Quarterly Resource Directory. (US ISSN 0893-5009) **1151, 3596**
Reflector. (CN) **1322**
Reflector. (NE ISSN 0034-2947) **2541**
Reflector Newsletter. (US ISSN 0034-2963) **368**
Reflets de l'Economie. *see* Wirtschaftsspiegel **743**
†Reflets Economiques et Commerciaux.(FR) **5268**
Reflets et Nuances. (FR) **630**
Reflets et Perspectives de la Vie Economique. (BE ISSN 0034-2971) **687**
Reflex. (IT) **3796**
†Reflex Foto. (IT) **5268**
Reflex Magazine. (US ISSN 1054-3465) **342**
Reflexionen. (GW) **3418**
Reflexiones. (US) **821**
Reflexiones del Batallismo. (UY) **4383**
Reflexions Historiques. *see* Historical Reflections **2312**
Reform. (HU) **2198**
Reform. (AT ISSN 0313-153X) **2671**
Reform. *see* Al-Islah **4218**
Reform. (UK ISSN 0306-7262) **4247**
Reform. *see* Gaige **4373**
Reform in Northern Ireland. (UK) **2671**
Reform Judaism. (US ISSN 0482-0819) **4226**
Reform Synagogues of Great Britain Inform Newsletter *see* R S G B Inform Newsletter **4226**
Reforma Agraria, Colonizacion y Cooperativas. *see* Land Reform, Land Settlement and Cooperatives **153**
Reforma Newsletter. (US ISSN 0891-8880) **2781, 2020**
Reformatio *see* ZeitSchrift fuer Kultur Politik Kirche **4211**
Reformation of Economic System. *see* Jingji Tizhi Gaige **999**
Reformation Review. (US ISSN 0034-303X) **4197**
Reformation Today. (UK ISSN 0034-3048) **4247**
Reformationsgeschichtliche Studien und Texte. (GW ISSN 0171-3469) **4247**
Reformatus Egyhaz. (HU) **4247**
Reformatusok Lapja. (HU) **4247**
Reforme. (FR ISSN 0223-5749) **4247**
Reforme Agraire, Colonisation et Cooperatives Agricoles. *see* Land Reform, Land Settlement and Cooperatives **153**
Reformed Church of America. Historical Series. (US ISSN 0080-0481) **4247**
Reformed Ecumenical Council Mission Bulletin *see* R E C Mission Bulletin **4247**
Reformed Journal *see* Perspectives (Grand Rapids) **4195**
Reformed Review. (US ISSN 0034-3064) **4248, 3778**
Reformed Scope. (US) **4197**
Reformed Theological Review. (AT ISSN 0034-3072) **4197**
Reformed World. (SZ ISSN 0034-3056) **4248**
Reformed Worship. (US ISSN 0890-8583) **4248**
Reformer. (UK ISSN 0034-3080) **4248**
Refractive & Corneal Surgery. (US ISSN 0883-0444) **3383**
Refractories. (English translation of: Ognepuory) (US ISSN 0034-3102) **1165**
Refractories. *see* Taikabutsu **3421**
Refractories Journal *see* World Ceramics & Refractories **1167**
Refractories Overseas. *see* Taikabutsu Overseas **3421**
Refractory News. (US) **1859**
Refrattari e Laterizi *see* L'Industria dei Laterizi **620**
Refrigerated Transporter. (US ISSN 0034-3129) **4747**

Refrigeration/Reito. (JA ISSN 0034-3714) **2302**
Refrigeration Air Conditioning and Heat Recovery *see* Refrigeration and Air Conditioning **2303**
Refrigeration and Air Conditioning. (UK ISSN 0263-5739) **2303**
Refrigeration and Air Conditioning Directory *see* Refrigeration and Air Conditioning Year Book **2303**
Refrigeration and Air Conditioning Year Book. (UK ISSN 0305-0777) **2303**
Refrigeration News. (US) **2303**
Refrigeration Service and Contracting. (US) **2303**
Refrigeration Service and Contracting (Troy). (US ISSN 0148-382X) **2303**
Ha-Refuah. (IS ISSN 0017-7768) **3146**
Refuge. (CN ISSN 0229-5113) **3987**
Refugee Abstracts. (UN ISSN 0253-1445) **3995, 22, 2700, 4426**
Refugee and Immigrant Resource Directory (Year). (US) **3970, 3987**
Refugee Reports. (US ISSN 0884-3554) **3987**
Refugees. (SZ) **3946, 3970, 4197**
Refugees. (UN ISSN 0252-791X) **3970**
Refugees Magazine. (UN ISSN 1014-1235) **3970**
Refunding Update. (US ISSN 0736-1688) **2449**
Refundle Bundle. (US ISSN 0194-0139) **1507**
Refurbishment Products. (UK) **630, 306**
Refusal of Treatment Legislation (Year) .(US) **2671**
Regan Report on Hospital Law. (US ISSN 0034-317X) **2671, 2469**
Regan Report on Medical Law. (US ISSN 0034-3188) **2671, 3146**
Regan Report on Nursing Law. (US ISSN 0034-3196) **2671, 3286**
†Regard de Foi. (CN ISSN 0025-3065) **5268**
Regardie's. (US) **687**
Regards *see* Foresight **2532**
Regards la Revue de l'Assurance. (CN) **2541**
Regards sur Israel. (CN ISSN 0384-9120) **3921**
Regards sur l'Actualite. (FR ISSN 0337-7091) **4072**
Regards sur l'Ile-de-France. (FR ISSN 0990-2562) **4584**
Regards sur le Comite d'Etablissement d'Orly Sud. (FR ISSN 0034-320X) **61**
Regatta. (UK) **4528**
Regel & Recht Nieuws. (NE ISSN 0920-8720) **2671**
Regelrecht. (NE ISSN 0034-3218) **37**
Regelungstechnik *see* Automatisierungstechnik **1448**
RegelVisie. (NE) **2303**
Regenbogen. (AU) **4197, 1264**
Regency International Directory. (UK ISSN 0080-0538) **1151, 1521**
†Regeneration Newsletter. (US ISSN 8756-3002) **5268**
Regensbergs Muensterischer Almanach.(GW) **1782**
Regensburger Beitraege zur Betriebswirtschaftlichen Forschung. (SZ) **687**
Regensburger Beitraege zur Deutschen Sprach- und Literaturwissenschaft. Reihe A: Quellen. (GW) **2953, 2837**
Regensburger Beitraege zur Deutschen Sprach- und Literaturwissencahft. Reihe B: Untersuchungen. (GW) **2953, 2837**
Regensburger Bistumsblatt. (GW ISSN 0034-3250) **4197**
Regensburger Universitaetszeitung. (GW ISSN 0557-6377) **1322, 2513, 4335**
Regenwaelder Report. (GW) **2107, 1496**
Regenwaelder Zeitung *see* Regenwaelder Report **2107**
Reger-Studien. (GW) **3577**
†Reggae. (CN ISSN 0714-4369) **5268**

Reggae and African Beat *see* The Beat (Los Angeles) **3540**
Reggae Quarterly *see* Reggae **5268**
Der Reggeboge/Rainbow. (US ISSN 0034-3269) **2020, 2953**
Reggio Storia. (IT ISSN 0393-8034) **2382**
Regi Magyar Dallamok Tara/Corpus Musicae Popularis Hungaricae. (HU ISSN 0080-0562) **886**
Regi Magyar Prozai Emlekek. (HU ISSN 0080-0570) **2953**
Regie Autonome des Transports Parisiens. Bulletin d'Information et de Documentation Generale *see* Regie Autonome des Transports Parisiens. Bulletin de Documentation et d'Information **4655**
Regie Autonome des Transports Parisiens. Bulletin de Documentation et d'Information. (FR) **4655, 4093**
†Regie de l'Assurance Maladie du Quebec. Bulletin. (CN) **5268**
Regimen Legal Tributario. (CK) **1104, 2671**
Regina. (FI ISSN 0355-841X) **4851**
†Regina. (CN) **5268**
†Regina Chamber of Commerce Exchange. (CN) **5268**
Regina Geographical Studies. (CN ISSN 0228-5851) **2260**
Regio Basiliensis. (SZ ISSN 0034-3293) **2260**
Region Six Sentinel. (US ISSN 0034-3315) **1658**
Regional Advisory Council for Technological Education. Science Education in the Region *see* Science Education in the Region **1716**
Regional Airline Association. Annual Report. (US) **4677**
Regional and Community Planning *see* Geographical Abstracts: Human Geography **2268**
†Regional & Dinner Theater Guide. (US) **5268**
Regional and Industrial Research Series. (UK) **687, 4072**
†Regional and Local Affairs News. (FR ISSN 0253-1968) **5268**
Regional and Urban Economics - Operational Methods *see* Regional Science & Urban Economics **2495**
Regional Anesthesia. (US ISSN 0146-521X) **3192**
Regional Aviation Weekly. (US) **4677**
Regional Bibliography Series. (AT) **1552, 1578**
Regional Cancer Treatment. (GW ISSN 0935-0411) **3021**
Regional Centre for Book Promotion in Africa. Bulletin of Information/Centre Regional de Promotion du Livre en Afrique. Bulletin d'Information. (CM) **4136**
Regional Council of Historical Agencies Newsletter *see* R C H A Newsletter **3532**
Regional Council of Historical Agencies Technical Information Sheet *see* R C H A Technical Information Sheet **3532**
Regional Cultural Institute. Journal. (IR ISSN 0034-3358) **934, 2431**
Regional Development *see* Regional Development International **688**
Regional Development Communicator. (PH) **882**
Regional Development Corporation. Annual Report/Societe d'Amenagement Regional. Rapport Annuel. (CN) **882**
Regional Development Dialogue. (UN ISSN 0250-6505) **934**
Regional Development International. (UK) **688**
▼Regional Development - The Regions of Greece. (GR) **934, 688**
Regional Directory of Key Business Prospects - South West. (UK) **1151, 838**
Regional District Legislation. (CN) **4094**
Regional Economic Digest. (US ISSN 1049-5339) **796**
Regional Economies and Markets. (US ISSN 0896-2537) **882, 1051**

Regional Educational Building Institute for Africa. Letter/Institut Regional pour les Constructions Scolaires en Afrique. Lettre. (SJ) **1658**
Le Regional Gens d'Affaires. (CN) **839**
Regional Information Series *see* See Australia Regional Information Series **4786**
Regional Information Service Review *see* U S Markets Review **886**
Regional Journal of Energy, Heat and Mass Transfer. (II) **1795, 3841**
Regional Journal of Social Issues. (AT ISSN 0158-7102) **4384**
Regional Language Studies - Newfoundland. (CN) **2837**
Regional Levies Service. (SA) **2671, 1105**
Regional Plan Association Library Acquisitions *see* Regional Plan Association Selected Library Acquisitions **2781**
Regional Plan Association Selected Library Acquisitions. (US) **2781**
†Regional Plan News. (US) **5268**
Regional Planning Commission of Cuyahoga County Data File *see* R P C Data File **2494**
▼Regional Politics and Policy. (UK ISSN 0959-230X) **3921**
Regional Population Estimates and Projections. (CN) **3995**
Regional Science & Urban Economics. (NE ISSN 0166-0462) **2495, 688**
Regional Science Association. Papers *see* Papers in Regional Science **4382**
Regional Science Perspectives. (US ISSN 0097-1197) **688**
Regional Science Review *see* Northeast Regional Science Review **2493**
Regional Spotlight. (US ISSN 0034-3390) **1715**
Regional Studies. (UK ISSN 0034-3404) **2495**
Regional Tuna Bulletin. (NL ISSN 1018-094X) **2048**
The Regionalist Seminar. (UK ISSN 0264-522X) **3921**
Regional'naya i Geneticheskaya Mineralogiya i Konstitutsiya i Svoystva Mineralov *see* Mineralogicheskii Zhurnal **3489**
Regional'naya Nauka o Razmeshchenii Proizvoditel'nykh Sil. (RU) **1084**
Regionalni Muzeum v Teplicich. Zpravy a Studie. (CS) **2382**
Regionalplanung in Kanton Zurich *see* Raumplanung und Umweltschutz im Kanton Zurich **2494**
Regione Abruzzo. (IT) **4417, 882, 4072**
Regione e Potere Locale. (IT ISSN 0034-3412) **2495**
Regioni. (IT ISSN 0391-7576) **2671**
Region's Agenda. (US ISSN 0034-3420) **2495**
Regis Today. (US) **1322**
Register *see* North Queensland Register **2172**
Register *see* Central California Register **4260**
Register Development Research Projects Africa. (SG ISSN 0850-4008) **934**
Register of Architects. (UK) **306**
Register of Authorized Laboratories. *see* Register over Autoriserede Laboratorier **3263**
Register of Indexers. (US ISSN 0149-4694) **2781, 22**
Register of Laws of the Arabian Gulf. (UK) **2728**
Register of Medical Practitioners, Interns and Dentists for the Republic of South Africa. (SA) **3146**
Register of Musicians in Education. (UK ISSN 0953-5330) **3577, 1658**
Register of Non-Thoroughbred Mares. (UK) **4537**
Register of Offshore Units, Submersibles and Diving Systems *see* Register of Offshore Units, Submersibles and Underwater Systems **4736**
Register of Offshore Units, Submersibles and Underwater Systems. (UK) **4736**

Register of Patent Agents. (UK) 3678
Register of Performers & Composers. (UK) 3577
Register of Professional Private Music Teachers. (UK ISSN 0951-6239) 3577, 1658
Register of Registrars see Annual Registrars Service 4562
Register over Autoriserede Laboratorier/Register of Authorized Laboratories. (DK ISSN 0105-9173) 3263
Register over Danske Patenter Udstedt.(DK ISSN 0107-590X) 3678
Register over Gaellande S F S-Foerfattningar. (SW) 4072
Registered Names of Horses. (UK) 4537
Registered Number & Wool Products Label Encyclopedia see R N & W P L Encyclopedia 1051
Registered Nurse. (CN) 3286
Registered Nurses Association of Ontario News see R N A O News 5266
Registered Plumbers Association. Journal see Plumbing 2302
Registered Representative. (US ISSN 0193-1865) 961
Registered Writer's Communique - Contacts and Assignments. (US) 2575
Registered Writer's Forum - Assignments see Registered Writer's Communique - Contacts and Assignments 2575
Registers & Directory of Veterinary Surgeons. (UK) 4815
Registre Aeronautique International. (FR ISSN 0080-066X) 4677
Registre International de Classification de Navires et d'Aeronefs see Registre Maritime 4736
Registre Maritime. (FR) 4736
Registreringstidning foer Varumaerken. Part A (Publications for Opposition) see Svensk Varumaerkestidning - Swedish Trademark Journal. Part A (Publications for Opposition) 3678
Registreringstidning foer Varumaerken. Part B (Publications of Registrations) see Svensk Varumaerkestidning - Swedish Trademark Journal. Part B (Publications of Registrations) 3678
Registreringstidning foer Varumaerken. Part C (Renewals, Changes of Ownership) see Svensk Varumaerkestidning - Swedish Trademark Journal. Part C (Renewals, Changes of Ownership) 3678
Registro de Organismos de Salud. (CK) 4111
Registro Industrial Brasileiro. (BL) 1151
Registro Industrial Mexicano. (MX) 1151
Registry News. (US) 4537, 1026
Registry of Interpreters for the Deaf. National Convention Proceedings. (US) 2289
Registry of Toxic Effects of Chemical Substances. (US ISSN 0361-2546) 3621
Registry of Toxic Effects of Chemical Substances Regulatory Subfile. Regulations, Recommendations and Assessments see R T E C S Regulatory Subfile. Regulations, Recommendations and Assessments 4111
Registry Review. (US) 4157
Regmaker. (SA ISSN 0034-3471) 1538
Regmi Research Series. (NP ISSN 0034-348X) 2341
Regnkabsresultater see Denmark. Statens Jordbrugsoekonomiske Institut. Serie B: Oekonomien i Landbrugets Driftsgrene 5178
Il Regno. (IT) 4273
Regno - Attualita. (IT ISSN 0034-3498) 4273
Regno - Documenti. (IT ISSN 0009-000X) 4197
Regnskabsstatistik-Landbrug. (DK) 157

Regnskabsundersoegelsen for Isenkrambranchen see Normtalsundersoegelsen for Isenkrambranchen 642
Regnum. (GW ISSN 0341-3322) 4273
Regnum Vegetabile. (NE ISSN 0080-0694) 516
Regroupement des Chercheurs-res en Histoire des Travailleurs et Travailleuses du Quebec. Bulletin. (CN ISSN 1187-6484) 2420
Regulae Benedicti Studia. Annuarium Internationale. (GW) 4197
Regular. (US) 992, 3469
Regulated Rivers: Research and Management. (UK ISSN 0886-9375) 1967
†Regulation (Washington, 1977). (US ISSN 0147-0590) 5268
Regulation News. (US) 1365
Regulation of Building Standards N S W. (AT) 2716, 630
Regulation of Building Standards Queensland. (AT) 2716, 630
▼Regulation of Foreign Banks. (US) 2728, 796
Regulation of the Commodities Futures and Options Markets. (US) 2671, 961
Regulations. see Norway. Direktoratet for Arbeidstilsynet. Forskrifter 3619
Regulations for Electrical Installations. (UK) 1907, 630
Regulations for the Electrical Equipment of Buildings see Regulations for Electrical Installations 1907
Regulatory Compliance Watch. (US) 797
Regulatory Peptides. (NE ISSN 0167-0115) 1223, 482
Regulatory Toxicology and Pharmacology. (US ISSN 0273-2300) 3265, 1983, 3741
Regulatory Watchdog Service. (US ISSN 0275-0902) 4111
Rehab Management. (US) 3146
†Rehab-Report. (GW ISSN 0931-8224) 5268
†Rehabfilm Newsletter. (US ISSN 0740-5294) 5268
Rehabilitacia/Rehabilitation. (CS ISSN 0033-8680) 3146
Rehabilitacion. (SP ISSN 0048-7120) 3146, 1740
Rehabilitacion Fisica XXI. (SP) 3146
Rehabilitacion: Prevencion y Integracion. (US) 3146, 2284
Rehabilitasie in Suid-Afrika. see Rehabilitation in South Africa 2284
Rehabilitation. see Ryoiku 1741
Rehabilitation. see Kang Fu 3119
Die Rehabilitation. (GW ISSN 0034-3536) 3146
Rehabilitation. see Rehabilitacia 3146
Rehabilitation (Tokyo, 1953). see Rihabiriteshon 4418
Rehabilitation and Supportive Care see I C R D B Cancergram: Rehabilitation and Supportive Care 3175
Rehabilitation Counseling Bulletin. (US ISSN 0034-3552) 2284, 3353, 3630
Rehabilitation der Entwicklungsgehemmten. (GW ISSN 0080-0708) 1740, 3146
Rehabilitation Digest. (CN ISSN 0048-7139) 1740, 3146
Rehabilitation Education. (US ISSN 0889-7018) 1740
Rehabilitation Gazette. (US ISSN 0361-4166) 1740, 2284
Rehabilitation in South Africa/Rehabilitasie in Suid-Afrika. (SA ISSN 0034-3501) 2284
Rehabilitation Index. (UK ISSN 0955-0984) 3181, 1679, 1740
Rehabilitation Industries Corporation. Annual Report. (II ISSN 0080-0724) 1740, 1084
Rehabilitation Institute of Montreal. Bulletin see Institut de Readaptation de Montreal. Bulletin 3109
Rehabilitation International. World Congress. Proceedings. (US) 1740
Rehabilitation Nursing. (US ISSN 0278-4807) 3286, 1740
Rehabilitation Psychology. (US ISSN 0090-5550) 4044, 1740

†Rehabilitation Report. (US ISSN 0885-1123) 5268
Rehabilitation Technology Review see R E S N A News 1740
Rehabilitation Today. (US) 3311
Rehabilitation und Praevention. (US ISSN 0172-6412) 3146
†Rehabilitation - World. (US ISSN 0360-0726) 5268
RehabINFO. (CN) 1740
Rehovot. (IS ISSN 0034-3609) 4335, 1758
Reichenbachia. (GW ISSN 0070-7279) 537
Reign of the Sacred Heart. (US ISSN 0048-7155) 4273
Reihe der Villa Vigoni. (GW ISSN 0936-8965) 3970
Reihe Strafrecht. (SZ) 2671
Reiki Journal see The Radiance Technique Journal 3596
Reil. (CK) 4714
Reimbursement Advisor. (US) 2469, 797, 2541
Reimpression. (UK ISSN 0757-8237) 2953
Reinardus. (NE ISSN 0925-4757) 2953
Reine und Angewandte Metallkunde. see Materials Research and Engineering 3413
Reinforced Concrete Research Council. Bulletins. (US ISSN 0569-8057) 630
Reinforced Plastics. (UK ISSN 0034-3617) 3867
Reinforced Plastics. Composite Papers. (UK) 3868
Reinforced Plastics Congress see Reinforced Plastics. Composite Papers 3868
Reiniger und Waescher. (GW ISSN 0034-3625) 1282
Reinigung & Service. (GW ISSN 0724-603X) 1282
Reino. (BL ISSN 0034-3633) 4197, 4446
Reino dos Sagrados Coracoes see Reino 4197
Reinraumtechnik. (GW ISSN 0931-9190) 1835
Reinsurance. (UK ISSN 0048-7171) 2541
Reinsurance Directory. (US ISSN 0747-5276) 2541
Reinsurance Market Report. (UK ISSN 0266-8653) 2541
Reinsurance Reporter. (US ISSN 0034-3641) 2541
Reinwardtia. (IO ISSN 0034-365X) 516
Reinwater. (NE) 1979
▼Reise Motorrad. (GW) 4520
Reise und Camping. (AU) 4784
Reise und Preise. (GW ISSN 0932-4186) 4784
Reisebuero Bulletin. (GW) 4784
Reisefieber. (GW ISSN 0177-4050) 4784
Reisefuhrer - Wohin in Berlin. (GW) 4784
Reiseland Oesterreich see Euro-City 4761
Reiseliv. (NO) 4784
Reiseliv i Norge see Reiseliv 4784
Reiselivstatiskk see Norway. Statistisk Sentralbyraa. Reiselivstatiskk 4800
Reisen in Deutschland: Reisefuehrer. (GW ISSN 0177-2953) 4784
Reisen in Deutschland: Zimmerkatalog. (GW) 4784
Reisen mit dem Auto. (GW) 4784, 4700
Reisen mit dem Auto durch Europa see Reisen mit dem Auto 4784
Reisen und Leben. (GW ISSN 0936-627X) 4784, 2320
Reiseverkehr der Schweizer im Ausland/Touristes Suisses a l'Etranger. (SZ) 4800
Reisewege nach Skandinavien. (GW) 4784
Reiseziele. (GW) 4784
Reisiesduif see Racing Pigeon 4484
Reiten - St. Georg. (GW) 4537
Reiten und Fahren. (GW ISSN 0720-5104) 4537
Reiter Revue International. (GW ISSN 0034-3692) 4537

Reiter und Pferde in Westfalen. (GW) 4537
Reiterjournal. (GW ISSN 0173-2404) 4537
Reito. see Refrigeration 2302
Reitsport in Weser - Ems. (GW) 4537
Reizen. (NE) 4784
Rejisumeito. (JA ISSN 0914-2045) 2781
Rejoice! (US) 3577, 4197
Rejsebogen (Year). (DK ISSN 0108-6812) 4784
Rejuvenation. (BE) 2278
Rekenschap. (NE ISSN 0034-3749) 2881, 3778
Rekexue Xuebao. see Journal of Thermal Science 3841
†Rekishi to Bungaku/History and Literature. (JA) 5268
Rekishi to Jinbutsu/History and Personalities. (JA) 2320
Rekishi to Tabi/History and Travel. (JA) 4784
Rekisho Nenpyo. (JA) 3444
Reklamefotograf Foreningen Avisen see R F Avisen 37
Relacion de Empresas Suspensas en Pagos, Embargos y Subastas see R E S 796
Relacion de Ingenieros de Caminos, Canales y Puertos. (SP) 1873
Relaciones. (MX ISSN 0185-3929) 2420, 4446
Relaciones. (UY ISSN 0797-9754) 4044
Relaciones Internacionales. (MX ISSN 0185-0814) 3970
Relaciones Publicas see Revista Internacional de Comunicacion y Relaciones Publicas 38
Relais. (NE ISSN 0034-3773) 797
Relais Routiers. (FR) 4784
Relais - Statistiques de l'Economie Picarde. (FR ISSN 0396-3128) 736, 882, 4584
Relations. (CN ISSN 0034-3781) 4417, 4273
Relations Industrielles/Industrial Relations. (CN ISSN 0034-379X) 992
Relations Industrielles au Canada. see Industrial Relations Legislation in Canada 983
Relations Internationales. (FR ISSN 0335-2013) 3970
Relations Publiques Informations. (FR ISSN 0034-3811) 37
Relationship & Family Communications.(US ISSN 0887-5480) 4446
Relationships Today. (US) 4851, 3400
Relative Value Scale Fee Schedule see R V S Fee Schedule 2541
Relative Values: Determining Attorneys' Fees. (US) 2671
Relatively Speaking. (CN ISSN 0701-8878) 2162
Relatoria D N O C S see Brazil. Departamento Nacional de Obras Contra as Secas. Relatorio 4055
Relax. (US) 4784, 3146
Relazioni Clinico Scientifiche. (IT ISSN 0048-7198) 3146, 482
Relazioni Industriali. (IT) 992, 2671
Relazioni Internazionali. (IT ISSN 0034-3846) 3970
Release. (AT ISSN 0157-3470) 1521
Release. (US) 2021, 3921, 4417
Release Print. (US) 3516
Release to the Membership. (US) 961
Release 1.0. (US) 1479
Releasing Hormones. (UK ISSN 0142-8314) 3256
Releve. (RW) 3921, 4784
Reliability and Maintainability Symposium. Proceedings. (US ISSN 0149-144X) 1907
Reliability Assessment. (US) 1802
Reliability Engineering and System Safety. (UK ISSN 0951-8320) 1835, 4607
Reliability Physics. (US ISSN 0735-0791) 3838
Reliability Review see Reliability Assessment 1802
Relics. (US ISSN 0034-3897) 2420
Relics and Museology see Wen Bo 3535

RELICS

Relics of Central China. *see* Zhongyuan Wenwu **290**
Relics of North China. *see* Beifang Wenwu **266**
Relics of Sichuan. *see* Sichuan Wenwu **284**
Relief, Boden, Palaeoklima. (GW) **1578**
Religieuses d'Action Hospitaliere et Social *see* Religieuses dans les Professions de Sante **2469**
Religieuses dans les Professions de Sante. (FR) **2469**, **4197**
Religieuses Enseignantes. (FR) **1658**
Religion. (UK ISSN 0048-721X) **4197**
▼Religion and American Culture. (US ISSN 1052-1151) **4197**, **4446**
Religion and Intellectual Life *see* Cross Currents: Religion and Intellectual Life **4173**
Religion and Life Letters. (US ISSN 0730-2363) **4197**
Religion and Literature. (US) **2953**, **4197**
Religion and Society. (II ISSN 0034-3951) **4197**, **4384**
Religion and Society *see* St. Croix Review **4448**
Religion & Society Report. (US ISSN 0742-6984) **4197**
Religion en Afrique. *see* Journal of Religion in Africa **4185**
Religion et Sciences de l'Homme. (FR ISSN 0080-0864) **4197**
Religion for Peace. (SZ) **4197**, **1723**
Religion Heute. (GW) **4197**
Religion Heute: Supplement. (GW) **1658**, **4197**
Religion in America. (US) **4197**, **1658**
Religion in American Life News *see* R I A L News **4196**
Religion in Communist Dominated Areas *see* R C D A **4196**
Religion in Communist Lands *see* Religion, State and Society **4197**
Religion in Education *see* British Journal of Religious Education **4166**
Religion in Southern Africa *see* Journal for the Study of Religion **4184**
Religion Index One: Periodicals. (US ISSN 0149-8428) **4213**, **22**
Religion Index Two: Multi-Author Works.(US ISSN 0149-8436) **4213**, **22**
Religion Indexes: Thesaurus. (US) **4197**
Religion Newswriters Association Newsletter *see* R N A Newsletter **2575**
Religion Research. *see* Zongjiaoxue Yanjiu **4211**
Religion, State and Society. (UK ISSN 0963-7494) **4197**
Religion Teacher's Journal. (US ISSN 0034-401X) **4197**
Religion Today. (UK ISSN 0267-1700) **4198**
Religione e Scuola. (IT) **4274**, **1658**
Religione e Societa. (IT ISSN 0391-853X) **4198**, **4446**
Religioni e Societa. (IT ISSN 0394-9397) **4198**, **4446**
Religionspaedagogik an Berufsbildenden Schulen *see* R A B S **4247**
Religionspaedagogische Beitraege. (GW ISSN 0173-0339) **4274**
Religionspaedagogische Praxis. (GW) **4198**
Religionsunterricht an hoeheren Schulen. (GW ISSN 0341-8960) **1658**, **4198**
Religionsunterricht und Konfirmandenunterricht fuer Gehoerlose und Schwerhoerige. (GW) **2289**, **4248**
Religionsvidenskabeligt Tidsskrift. (DK ISSN 0108-1993) **4198**
Religionswissenschaftliche Reihe. (GW ISSN 0934-2192) **4198**
Religious and Inspirational Books and Serials in Print. (US ISSN 0000-0868) **410**, **4198**
Religious & Theological Abstracts. (US ISSN 0034-4044) **4213**, **22**
Religious Book Review Index. (II ISSN 0034-4060) **4213**

Religious Books in Print. (UK ISSN 0305-960X) **410**
Religious Broadcasting. (US ISSN 0034-4079) **1379**, **4198**
Religious Conference Manager. (US ISSN 1050-2742) **4784**, **4198**
Religious Consultancy. (II) **4198**
Religious Education. (US ISSN 0034-4087) **4198**, **1658**
Religious Freedom Reporter. (US ISSN 0275-3529) **3946**, **2671**, **3671**
Religious Humanism. (US ISSN 0034-4095) **4287**, **3778**
▼Religious Leaders of America. (US) **4198**, **420**
Religious Life Review. (IE) **4274**
Religious Public Relations Council Counselor *see* R P R C Counselor **37**
Religious Public Relations Council Media Kit *see* R P R C Media Kit **37**
Religious Round Table *see* Roundtable Report **4199**
Religious Studies. (UK ISSN 0034-4125) **4198**
Religious Studies Journal. (PH ISSN 0115-6349) **4198**
Religious Studies Review. (US ISSN 0319-485X) **4198**
Reliure. *see* Bindetechnik **4121**
Relix. (US ISSN 0146-3489) **3577**
The Relocation Report. (US ISSN 0275-7613) **1070**, **4157**
Remag. (BL ISSN 0034-4168) **4005**
Remainders' Book Italiano. (IT ISSN 0034-4176) **4136**
Remanso. (SP ISSN 0034-4184) **797**
▼Remark (New York). (US ISSN 1053-7201) **2953**, **2881**
REMark (St. Joseph). (US) **1474**, **1464**
Remarques Africaines *see* Remarques Arabo-Africaines **2334**
Remarques Arabo-Africaines. (BE) **2334**, **2431**
Remedia. (MX) **410**, **3146**
Remedial and Special Education *see* R A S E **1740**
▼Remediation. (US ISSN 1051-5658) **1986**, **2671**
Remediation Review. (US) **1987**, **1496**
Remedies *see* B A R - B R I Bar Review. Remedies **2603**
Remeny. (IS) **2204**
Reminder List of Eligible Releases. (US) **3516**
Reminder Plus. (US) **38**, **3022**
Remineralize the Earth. (US) **190**, **1967**
†Remington Hunting & Shooting Guide. (US) **5268**
▼Reminisce. (US ISSN 1057-2368) **2058**, **2320**
Reminiscing *see* Rockin' 50's **3578**
Remittance and Document Processing Today. (US) **1423**
Remnant of Israel. (US) **4226**, **4274**
Remodeled Homes. (US) **2554**, **630**
Remodeling. (US ISSN 0885-8039) **630**, **2561**
Remodeling Contractor (Washington) *see* Remodeling **630**
Remodeling Made Easy *see* Decorating Remodeling **2550**
Remodeling News. (US) **630**
Remodeling World *see* Remodeling **630**
Remote Sensing Information. *see* Yaogan Xinxi **2267**
Remote Sensing of Earth Resources: A Quarterly Bibliography. (US ISSN 1055-9922) **1552**, **22**, **3502**
Remote Sensing of Environment. *see* Huanjing Yaogan **2252**
Remote Sensing of Environment. (US ISSN 0034-4257) **2260**, **1967**, **2524**
Remote Sensing of Natural Resources: A Quarterly Literature Review *see* Remote Sensing of Earth Resources: A Quarterly Bibliography **1552**
Remote Sensing Photogrammetry and Cartography *see* Geographical Abstracts: Physical Geography **2268**

Remote Sensing Reviews. (US ISSN 0275-7257) **1835**
Remote Sensing Society of Japan. Journal. *see* Nihon Rimoto Senshingu Gakkaishi **2257**
†Remote Sensing Yearbook. (UK ISSN 0267-6133) **5268**
Remote Systems Technology Proceedings *see* Conference on Remote Systems Technology. Proceedings **1804**
Remotely Operated Vehicles Review (Year) *see* R O V Review (Year) **1610**
Removals and Storage. (UK ISSN 0034-4265) **4655**
An Rems und Murr. (GW ISSN 0170-6802) **2191**
Ren Sheng. (CC) **598**
Renacimiento. (US) **2021**, **2233**
Renaissance (Salem). (US) **2233**
Renaissance and Baroque: Studies and Texts. (US ISSN 0897-7836) **2382**
Renaissance and Modern Studies. (UK ISSN 0486-3720) **2513**
Renaissance and Reformation/ Renaissance et Reforme. (CN ISSN 0034-429X) **2953**, **2382**
Renaissance Deux-Mille *see* Tribune Gaulliste **3930**
Renaissance Drama. (US ISSN 0486-3739) **4637**, **2953**
Renaissance et Reforme. *see* Renaissance and Reformation **2953**
Renaissance Manuscript Studies. (GW ISSN 0196-7037) **3577**
Renaissance Papers. (US) **2953**
Renaissance Quarterly. (US ISSN 0034-4338) **2953**, **342**, **2320**
Renaissance Studies. (UK ISSN 0269-1213) **2320**
Renaissance Two. (US ISSN 0360-7410) **2021**
Renaissance 2 *see* Renaissance Two **2021**
Renaitre 2000. (FR ISSN 0151-4016) **3671**
Renal Failure. (US ISSN 0886-022X) **3389**
Renal Family. (CN) **3146**
Renal Physiology. (UK ISSN 0300-3434) **3389**, **574**
Renal Physiology *see* Renal Physiology and Biochemistry **3389**
Renal Physiology and Biochemistry. (SZ ISSN 1011-6524) **3389**
Renal Transplantation and Dialysis. (UK ISSN 0142-8357) **3389**
Renascence. (US ISSN 0034-4346) **2953**
Renault Contact. (UK) **4700**
Rencai Kaifa/Personnel Development. (CC ISSN 1000-7628) **1070**
Rencontre. (CN ISSN 0709-9487) **2021**
Rencontres *see* Etudes Rwandaises. Sciences Naturelles et Appliquees **1632**
Rencontres Gaies *see* R G **2456**
Rencontres Internationales de Geneve. (SZ) **4384**, **3778**
Render. (US ISSN 0090-8932) **116**
Rendez-Vous Canada. (CN) **4784**
Rendezvous. (US ISSN 0034-4400) **2513**
Rendezvous Wien. (AU) **2173**
†Rendiconti. (IT ISSN 0034-4419) **5268**
Rendiconti della Societa Italiana di Mineralogie e Petrologia *see* European Journal of Mineralogy **3483**
Rendiconti di Gastroenterologia *see* Italian Journal of Gastroenterology **3269**
Rendiconti di Matematica. (IT ISSN 0034-4427) **3052**
Renditions. (HK ISSN 0377-3515) **3643**
Rendon Report. (US) **3921**
Rendsburger Jahrbuch. (GW) **2382**
Rene Dubos Center for Human Environments. Newsletter. (US) **1967**
Renegade (Bloomfield Hills). (US) **3004**
Renel. (IT) **1294**

Reneng Dongli Gongcheng/Heat Dynamics Engineering. (CC ISSN 1001-2060) **1938**, **4736**
Renew. (CN ISSN 0845-5341) **2495**, **630**
Renew America Report. (US) **1967**
Renew Newsletter. (UK) **1795**, **1811**, **1812**
Renewable Energy *see* Renewable Energy News Digest **1797**
Renewable Energy *see* Abstracts on Science and Technology in Japan: Energy Technology **1797**
Renewable Energy (Tarrytown). (US ISSN 0960-1481) **1795**
Renewable Energy Bulletin. (UK ISSN 0306-364X) **1795**, **1967**, **1987**
Renewable Energy Manufacturers Lists: Biomass Fuels. (US) **1795**
Renewable Energy Manufacturers Lists: Heat Conservation. (US) **1795**
Renewable Energy Manufacturers Lists: Solar Energy. (US) **1811**
Renewable Energy Manufacturers Lists: Wind and Hydro Power. (US) **1812**, **1803**
Renewable Energy News Digest. (US) **1795**, **1579**
Renewable Energy Review Journal *see* R E R I C International Energy Journal **1794**
Renewable Energy View *see* R E View **1794**
†Renewable Materials Institute Series. (US) **5268**
Renewable Resources Journal. (US ISSN 0738-6532) **1987**, **453**, **1548**, **2048**
Renewal. (US) **3921**
Renewal News. (US ISSN 1043-125X) **4248**
†Renews. (US ISSN 0192-3153) **5268**
Renfro Valley Bugle. (US ISSN 0034-4451) **2233**, **3577**
Renglon. (MX) **3921**
Renhold Vedligehold *see* Rent i Danmark **1026**
Renholdsnytt. (NO ISSN 0802-2100) **1061**
Renin, Angiotensin & Kinins. (UK ISSN 0143-4284) **574**, **3256**, **3741**
Renkou Dongtai. (CC) **3987**
Renkou Yanjiu/Population Studies. (CC ISSN 1000-6087) **3987**
Renkou yu Fazhan/Population and Development. (CC) **3987**
Renkou yu Jingji/Population & Economics. (CC ISSN 1000-4149) **3987**, **882**, **1000**
Renkou yu Yousheng. (CC) **3987**
Renkou Zhanxian/Population Front. (CC) **3987**
Renleixue Xuebao/Acta Anthropologica Sinica. (CC ISSN 1000-3193) **247**, **3660**
Renmin/People. (CC) **420**, **2341**
Renmin Chang Jiang/People's Yangtze River. (US ISSN 1001-4179) **2260**
Renmin Huabao. (CC ISSN 0448-9373) **2182**
Renmin Huang He/People's Yellow River. (CC ISSN 1000-1379) **2260**, **1925**
Renmin Jiancha. (CC) **2671**
Renmin Jiaoyu/People's Education. (CC ISSN 0448-9365) **1658**
Renmin Jingcha/People's Police. (CC) **1521**
Renmin Ribao/People's Daily. (CC) **2182**
Renmin Ribao Suoyin/People's Daily. Index. (CC) **2578**
Renmin Tiedao/People's Railway. (US) **4714**
Renmin Wenxue/People's Literature. (CC ISSN 0258-8218) **2953**, **3004**
Renmin Yinyue/People's Music. (CC ISSN 0447-6573) **3577**
Renmin Zhengxie Bao/Journal of the C P P C C. (Zhongguo Renmin Zhengzhi Xieshang Huiyi) (US) **4072**, **3921**
Renmin Zhongguo. *see* Jinmin Chugoku **2182**
Renninger's Antique Guide. (US) **259**
Reno. (GW ISSN 0721-4588) **688**

†Reno. (US) **5268**
Renovacion. (DR ISSN 0034-446X) **3921, 4384**
Renovatec. (SP ISSN 0214-3127) **630**
Renovateur. (SG) **3921**
Renovatie en Onderhoud. (NE ISSN 0922-4114) **630**
Renovatio. (IT ISSN 0034-4486) **4198**
Renovatio. (GW ISSN 0340-8280) **4274**
Renovation *see* U.I.A.M.S. Informations **3930**
Renovation Bricolage. (CN ISSN 0381-0992) **2501**
Renovator's Supply. (US) **2554, 640**
Renover. (CN) **4157**
Renseignements Techniques *see* Het Kleine Brouwersblad **383**
Renshen Yanjiu/Ginseng Studies. (CC) **116**
Rensheng yu Banlu/Life and Companions. (CC) **4384**
Rensheng Zixun/Life Consultation. (CC) **1264**
Rensselaer Engineer. (US ISSN 0034-4508) **4335**
Rensselaer Polytechnic. (US) **1322**
Rent. (SW) **1282**
Rent Cases. (II) **2671**
Rent i Danmark. (DK) **1026, 4111**
Rent Review and Lease Renewal. (UK ISSN 0263-7499) **4157, 2495**
Renta Nacional de Espana. (SP) **4072**
Rental. (US ISSN 0898-7106) **1084**
Rental Age *see* Rental Management **1051**
Rental Dealer News. (US) **1051, 1507**
Rental Equipment Register. (US ISSN 0034-4524) **1051**
Rental Management. (US) **1051, 38, 1070**
Rental Product News *see* Rental **1084**
Rental Rates Compilation *see* Associated Equipment Distributors. Rental Rates Compilation **600**
Der Rentenfuehrer. (GW) **961**
Die Rentenversicherung. (GW ISSN 0340-5753) **2541**
Renters News. (CN) **4157**
Rentgenologija i Radiologija. (BU ISSN 0486-400X) **3362**
Renton Historical Society Newsletter. (US) **2420**
Renwen Zazhi/Journal of Humanities. (CC ISSN 0447-662X) **2513**
Renwu. (CC ISSN 1001-6635) **420**
Renxiang Sheying/Portrait Photography. (CC) **3796**
Rep Talk. (US ISSN 0272-7323) **1026, 1051, 1117**
Rep World. (US) **1051**
Repair and Remodeling Cost Data *see* Means Repair and Remodeling Cost Data (Year) **624**
Repair & Remodelling Quarterly. (US) **630**
Repap (Year) Media Guide. (US) **38**
Repeat. (NE) **3796**
Reperes. (FR ISSN 0761-4241) **342**
Repertoire. (FR ISSN 0987-6030) **2513**
†Repertoire Administratif. (CN) **5268**
Repertoire Bibliographique de la Philosophie/International Philosophical Bibliography/ Bibliografisch Repertorium van de Wijsbegeerte. (BE ISSN 0034-4567) **3788, 410**
Repertoire Bibliographique des Institutions Chretiennes. *see* R I C **4213**
Repertoire Bibliographique des Livres Imprimes en France. (GW ISSN 0085-5499) **410**
Repertoire Canadien des Bourses d'Etudes Superieures (Year). *see* Canadian Directory of Awards for Graduate Study (Year) **5161**
Repertoire Canadien sur l'Education. *see* Canadian Education Index **1675**
Repertoire Complementaire Alphabetique des Valeurs Mobilieres Francaises et Etrangeres Non Cotees en France. (FR ISSN 0080-0945) **1105**

Repertoire d'Annuaires Francais. (FR) **821**
Repertoire de l'Ethnologie de la France. (FR) **247**
Repertoire de la Recherche dans les Universites Subventionnee Par le Gouvernement Federal. *see* Directory of Federally Supported Research in Universities **5180**
Repertoire de la Vie Francaise en Amerique. (CN ISSN 0708-1510) **2021**
†Repertoire de Materiaux et Elements Controles du Batiment. (FR ISSN 0335-3559) **5268**
Repertoire des Annuaires. (FR) **410**
Repertoire des Banques de Donnees Teletel Pour l'Entreprise. (FR ISSN 0987-7401) **1351, 828**
Repertoire des Bibliotheques Specialisees de la Region de Montreal. *see* Directory of Special Libraries in the Montreal Area **2755**
Repertoire des Centres de Soins de Longue Duree au Canada. *see* Directory of Long-Term Care Centres in Canada **2272**
†Repertoire des Cooperatives du Quebec. (CN ISSN 0080-097X) **5268**
Repertoire des Geographes Francais. (FR) **2260**
†Repertoire des Groupes d'Entreprises. (BE) **5268**
Repertoire des Manuscripts Medievaux (Corbin). (FR) **3577**
Repertoire des Organisations de Travailleurs et Travailleuses au Canada. *see* Directory of Labour Organizations in Canada **2582**
Repertoire des Produits Disponibles au Quebec. (CN) **1152**
Repertoire des Produits Fabriques au Quebec *see* Repertoire des Produits Disponibles au Quebec **1152**
Repertoire des Publications Seriees Canadiennes. *see* Canadian Serials Directory **2792**
Repertoire des Salles de Spectacle. *see* Facilities Directory **1530**
Repertoire des Services aux Victimes d'Actes Criminels. *see* Directory of Services for Victims of Crime **1514**
Repertoire des Services Communautaires du Grand Montreal. *see* Directory of Community Services of Greater Montreal **4404**
Repertoire des Societes de Commerce Exterieur Francaises. (FR ISSN 0080-1070) **920**
Repertoire des Textes Legislatifs et Reglementaires et des Reponses aux Questions Ecrites Concernant la Reunion. (RE) **4072**
†Repertoire des Theses Africanistes Francaises. (FR) **5268**
Repertoire des Universites Canadiennes (year). *see* Directory of Canadian Universities (Year) **1693**
Repertoire des Voyages/Travel Trade Repertory. (FR ISSN 0034-4575) **4784**
Repertoire Dictionnaire Industriel. (FR ISSN 0080-1089) **1084**
Repertoire du Notariat Defrenois. (FR) **2671**
Repertoire Fiscal *see* Journal de Droit Fiscal **2638**
Repertoire General Alphabetique des Valeurs Cotees en France et des Valeurs Non Cotees. (FR ISSN 0080-1127) **1105**
Repertoire General de la Production Francaise *see* La France de l'Industrie et ses Services **1135**
Repertoire Geographique du Canada. *see* Gazetteer of Canada **2248**
Repertoire International de la Litterature de l'Art/International Repertory of the Literature of Art News *see* R I L A News **5266**
Repertoire International de la Presse Musicale. (US) **3589, 22**
Repertoire International de Litterature Musicale Abstracts of Music Literature *see* R I L M Abstracts of Music Literature **3589**

▼Repertoire International des Banques de Donnees Biomedicales. (FR) **3226, 410**
Repertoire International des Banques de Donnees Juridique. (FR) **2705, 410**
Repertoire International des Dix-Huitiemistes. *see* International Directory of Eighteenth-Century Studies **2508**
Repertoire International des Editeurs et Diffuseurs de Langue Francaise. (FR) **4136**
Repertoire International des Medievistes. (FR ISSN 0080-1151) **2382, 2513**
Repertoire Internationale d'Iconographie Musicale. Research Center for Music Iconography Inventory of Music Iconography *see* R I D I M - R C M I Inventory of Music Iconography **3575**
Repertoire Internationale d'Iconographie Musicale. Research Center for Music Iconography Newsletter *see* R I D I M - R C M I Newsletter **3575**
Repertoire Permanent de l'Administration Francaise. (FR) **4072**
Repertoire Permanent des Groupes Financiers et Industriels *see* Repertoire des Groupes d'Entreprises **5268**
†Repertoire Theatral du Quebec (Year). (CN ISSN 0226-1804) **5269**
Repertoria Heidelbergensia. (GW) **2953, 3778**
Repertorien zur Erforschung der Freuhen Neuzeit. (GW ISSN 0724-9578) **2382**
Repertoriex. *see* French Periodical Index **400**
Repertorio Americano. (CR ISSN 0252-8479) **2953**
Repertorio Aranzadi del Tribunal Constitucional. (SP) **2671**
†Repertorio Chimico Italiano. (IT) **5269**
Repertorio Cronologico de Legislacion. (SP) **2671**
Repertorio de Exportadores. (SP) **821**
Repertorio de Importadores. (SP) **821**
Repertorio de Jurisprudencia. (SP) **2672**
Repertorio de Servicios de Documentacion e Informacion Educativa IberoAmericanos *see* Repertorio de Servicios IberoAmericanos de Documentacion e Informacion Educativa **2781**
Repertorio de Servicios IberoAmericanos de Documentacion e Informacion Educativa/Repertorio de Servicos IberoAmericanos de Documentacao e Informacao Educativas. (SP ISSN 1010-2973) **2781, 1658**
Repertorio de Servicos IberoAmericanos de Documentacao e Informacao Educativas. *see* Repertorio de Servicios IberoAmericanos de Documentacion e Informacion Educativa **2781**
Repertorio del Foro Italiano. (IT) **2672**
Repertorio delle Decisioni della Corte Costituzionale. (IT) **2672**
†Repertorio delle Industrie Siderurgiche Italiane. (IT ISSN 0080-1216) **5269**
Repertorio di Giurisprudenza del Lavoro. (IT) **2672**
Repertorio General: La Ley. (AG) **2672**
Repertorio Latino Americano. (AG) **2881**
†Repertorio Terapeutico. (IT) **5269**
Repertorium. (NE) **3147**
Repertorium Farmaceutische Specialites Periodiek Overzicht voor Artsen *see* Repertorium **3147**
Repertorium Plantarum Succulentarum.(SZ ISSN 0486-4271) **516**
Repertorium van Boeken en Tijdschriftartikelen Betreffende de Geschiedenis van Nederland. (NE) **2330, 2382**
Repertuar Khudozhestvennoi Samodeyatel'nosti. (RU ISSN 0034-4648) **3516**
Replay. (US ISSN 0360-7348) **3577**

RePlay Magazine *see* Replay **3577**
Replica. (US) **2021**
Replica in Scale *see* Aerophile **2433**
La Replique. (CN) **1323**
Reply Coupon Collector. (US) **3757**
The Report (Eugene). (US) **3013, 2953**
Report and Studies in the History of Art *see* Studies in the History of Art **345**
Report by the Auditor General on the Accounts of Lesotho. (LO ISSN 0085-2740) **1105**
Report - C.O.D.A.S.Y.L. Data Base Task Group *see* Conference on Data Systems Languages. Data Base Task Group. Report **1430**
Report from the Capital. (US) **4248, 3921**
Report from the Hill. (US ISSN 0893-0708) **2672, 1273, 1967, 3921**
Report from Your Vestal Schools *see* V C S Newsletter **1670**
Report fuer die Mitarbeiter in Deutschland. (GW) **164**
Report - Hastings Center *see* Hastings Center Report **3102**
Report - Judicial Inquiry Board (Chicago) *see* Illinois. Judicial Inquiry Board. Report **3943**
Report - Maryland Division of Correction *see* Maryland. Division of Correction. Report **1518**
Report - Nevada Bureau of Mines and Geology *see* Nevada. Bureau of Mines and Geology. Report **1575**
Report of a Vantage Conference. (US ISSN 0748-0571) **3970**
Report of Cases Argued and Determined in the Supreme Court of the State of Arizona *see* Arizona Appeal Reports **2600**
Report of Cases Determined in the Supreme Court and Court of Appeals of the State of New Mexico. (US ISSN 0094-7148) **2672**
Report of Educational Statistics *see* Delaware. State Board of Education. Report of Educational Statistics **1624**
Report of Environmental Pollution in Meguro Ward. *see* Kogai Chosa Hokokusho **1962**
Report of Milk Utilization in Montana *see* Recap of Milk Receipts and Utilization in Montana **203**
Report of Overseas Mining Investigation: India, Pakistan, Bangladesh/Kaigai Kogyo Jijo Chosa Hokokusho: Indo, Pakisutan, Banguradesshu. (JA) **3494**
Report of Overseas Mining Investigation: Madagascar, Swaziland/Kaigai Kogyo Jijo Chosa Hokokusho: Madagasukaru, Suwajirando. (JA) **3494**
Report of Secretary of Defense to the Congress *see* U.S. Department of Defense. Report of Secretary of Defense to the Congress **3474**
Report of the Auditor General on the Public Accounts of the Republic of Trinidad and Tobago. (TR) **1105**
Report of the Council for Tobacco Research - U.S.A., Inc. *see* Council for Tobacco Research, U.S.A. Report **3091**
Report of the Federal Home Loan Mortgage Corporation *see* Federal Home Loan Mortgage Corporation. Report **779**
Report of the Judicial Department, State of Connecticut *see* Connecticut. Judicial Department. Report **2615**
Report of the Nebraska Indian Commission *see* Nebraska. Indian Commission. Report **2016**
Report of the New Mexico Veteran's Service Commission *see* New Mexico. Veterans' Service Commission. Report **3467**
Report of the Proceedings. Annual Meeting and Technical Forum *see* Foundation of Flexographic Technical Association. Report of the Proceedings: Annual Meeting and Technical Forum **3999**

6606 REPORT

Report of the State Board of Independent Colleges and Universities (Tallahassee) see Florida. State Board of Independent Colleges and Universities. Report **1706**
Report on A T & T. (US ISSN 0741-8361) **1351, 1365, 1464, 1474**
Report on Applications for Orders Authorizing or Approving the Interception of Wire or Oral Communications see U.S. Administrative Office of the United States Courts. Report on Applications for Orders Authorizing or Approving the Interception of Wire or Oral Communications **2733**
Report on British Palaeobotany & Palynology. (UK ISSN 0266-4755) **3660**
Report on Business Canada Company Handbook. (CN ISSN 0847-2831) **961**
Report on Business Magazine. (CN) **688**
†Report on Canada. (CN) **5269**
Report on Credit Unions. (US ISSN 0482-2803) **797, 832**
Report on Development Assistance to Ethiopia. (UN) **934**
Report on Development Cooperation to the Democratic Republic of the Sudan. (UN) **934**
Report on Disability Programs. (US ISSN 1043-1209) **4417, 4111**
Report on Eastern Europe. (GW ISSN 0937-7441) **3970**
Report on Education of the Disadvantaged. (US ISSN 0034-4680) **1740, 4417**
Report on Education Research. (US ISSN 0034-4699) **1658**
Report on Foreign Currencies Held by the U.S. Government see U.S. Treasury Department. Bureau of Government Financial Operations. Report on Foreign Currencies Held by the U.S. Government **5296**
†Report on Geoscience and Mineral Resources. (KO) **5269**
Report on Guatemala. (US ISSN 1043-3856) **3970, 882**
Report on I B M. (US ISSN 0742-5341) **1455, 1424**
†Report on I B M in Communications. (US) **5269**
Report on Institutional Foodservice. (US) **2080, 2479, 3611**
Report on Ohio Mineral Industries. (US) **3494**
Report on Passenger Road Transport in Zambia. (ZA) **4666, 4584**
▼The Report of Pediatric Infectious Diseases. (US ISSN 1050-964X) **3326**
Report on Performance Materials see Performance Materials **60**
Report on Preschool Programs. (US) **1658**
Report on School-Aged Child Care. (US ISSN 1041-5246) **1243, 1658**
Report on Science and Human Rights. (US ISSN 0895-5999) **4335, 3946, 3970**
Report on Telco Marketing see B O C Week **1361**
Report on the Administration of the Labour Adjustment Benefits Act/Rapport sur l'Application de la Loi sur les Prestations d'Adaptation pour les Travailleurs. (CN) **992**
Report on the Americas. (US ISSN 1058-5397) **3970, 920**
Report on the Background, Current Programmes and Planned Development of the Bangladesh Institute of Development Studies see Bangladesh Institute of Development Studies. Annual Report **845**
Report on the Marketing of Tobacco in Andhra Pradesh. (II) **157**
Report on the Situation on Human Rights in the Republic of Guatemala.(US) **3970**

Report on the Survey of Personal Income Distribution in Taiwan Area see China, Republic. Executive Yuan. Directorate-General of Budget, Accounting & Statistics. Report on the Survey of Personal Income Distribution in Taiwan Area **998**
Report on the Survey of Research and Development. see Kagaku Gijutsu Kenkyu Chosa Hokoku **4602**
Report on the Treatment of Offenders in Mauritius; Part 1: Prisons Service. (MF) **1521**
Report on the Treatment of Offenders in Mauritius; Part 2: Probation Service. (MF) **1521**
Report on the U S S R. (GW) **3970**
Report on the World Health Situation. (UN ISSN 0085-5529) **4111**
Report on Tourism Statistics in Tanzania. (TZ ISSN 0564-836X) **4800**
Report on Urban Research. see Toshi Kenkyu Hokoku **2497**
Report on Virginia's Industry of Agriculture. (US) **116**
Report on Vital Statistics. (IE ISSN 0790-7710) **3995, 4584**
Report on World Affairs. (UK ISSN 0034-4737) **3921**
Report Psychologie. (GW ISSN 0344-9602) **4044**
Report to Business. (US) **1507**
Report to Business and Consumer Information see Report to Business **1507**
Report to Congress on Abnormal Occurrences see U.S. Nuclear Regulatory Commission. Report to Congress on Abnormal Occurrences **1810**
Report to S C A R on South African Antarctic Research Activities. (Scientific Committee for Antarctic Research) (SA ISSN 0081-2412) **4335, 4607**
Report to the American People. (US) **38**
Report to the Congress on Ocean Pollution, Overfishing, and Offshore Development see U.S. National Oceanic and Atmospheric Administration. Report to the Congress on Ocean Pollution, Overfishing, and Offshore Development **1979**
Report to the Governor - Arizona Commission on the Arts see Arizona Commission on the Arts. Report to the Governor **312**
Reportage. (IT ISSN 0034-4745) **2881**
Reportage Canada. (CN) **2178**
Reportage Literature. see Baogao Wenxue **2567**
Reportaje Canada see Canada Reports **2176**
Reportaje Canada see Reportage Canada **2178**
Reportajes: Documentos para la Historia. (BO) **2420**
Reporte Laboral. (MX) **821**
Reporter. (CN ISSN 0580-8537) **1323**
Reporter. (BG) **2174**
Reporter. (BH) **2180**
Reporter. (PL) **2214**
▼Reporter. (RU) **2575**
†Reporter (Clinton). (US) **5269**
The Reporter (New York). (US) **4417, 4226**
Reporter (St. Louis). (US ISSN 0360-7119) **4248**
Reporter (Washington). (US) **3469**
Reporter of Construction Equipment see Equipment Today **617**
Reportero Industrial. (US ISSN 0034-4818) **3022, 688, 4607**
Reportero Industrial see World Industrial Reporter **3024**
Reportero Industrial Mexicano. (MX) **1152**
Reportero Medico. (AG) **3147**
Reporting Classroom Research/Compte-Rendu de Recherches Pedagogiques. (CN ISSN 0315-369X) **1658**

Reporting from the Russell Sage Foundation. (US ISSN 0736-217X) **4384**
Reporting to Governments. (US ISSN 0034-4834) **961, 882**
Reports. see Denmark. Jordbrugsoekonomiske Institut. Rapport **149**
Reports and Papers in the Social Sciences. (UN ISSN 0080-1348) **4384**
Reports in Applied Measurement. (GW ISSN 0930-7923) **1938, 1880**
Reports in Emergency Nursing see Emergency Department Management **3096**
Reports in Mackinac History and Archaeology. (US) **2420, 282**
†Reports in Molecular Theory. (US ISSN 1048-2008) **5269**
Reports in the Fields of Science and Technology. see Forschungsberichte aus Technik und Naturwissenschaften **4614**
Reports Magazine. (US) **1658**
Reports Magazine see World Education Reports **5306**
Reports of Cases Before the Court of Justice of the European Communities. (EI ISSN 0378-7591) **2672**
Reports of D L O - The Winand Staring Centre see Agricultural Research Department. Winand Staring Centre for Integrated Land, Soil and Water Research. Reports **166**
Reports of Family Law (3rd Series). (CN ISSN 0317-4859) **2718**
†Reports of Interest to Lawyers. (US ISSN 0890-3271) **5269**
Reports of Investigations - Illinois State Museum see Illinois. State Museum. Reports of Investigations **4314**
Reports of Patent, Design, Trade Mark and Other Cases. (UK ISSN 0080-1364) **3678**
Reports on Astronomy see International Astronomical Union. Transactions **365**
Reports on Higher Education see W I C H E Reports **1720**
Reports on Historiographical Studies of Taiwan. see T'ai-wan Wen Hsien **2342**
Reports on International Compensation. Argentina see Executive Compensation Service. Reports on International Compensation. Argentina **5189**
Reports on International Compensation. Puerto Rico see Executive Compensation Service. Reports on International Compensation. Puerto Rico **5189**
Reports on Marine Research. see Meeresforschung **1608**
Reports on Mathematical Logic. (PL ISSN 0137-2904) **3778, 3052**
Reports on Mathematical Physics. (US ISSN 0034-4877) **3829**
Reports on Progress in Physics. (UK ISSN 0034-4885) **3829**
Reports on Research Assisted by the Petroleum Research Fund. (US ISSN 0190-8715) **3700**
Reports on Rheumatic Diseases. (UK ISSN 0048-7279) **3369**
Reports on Statistical Co-ordination. see Sweden. Statistiska Centralbyraan. Meddelanden i Samordningsfraagor **4590**
▼Reports to the Nation on Our Changing Planet. (US) **1967, 1264**
Representation. (UK ISSN 0034-4893) **3921**
Representations. (US ISSN 0734-6018) **2513**
Representative. (US) **164, 1084, 3022**
Representative Research in Social Psychology. (US ISSN 0034-4907) **4044, 4446**
Reprint Bulletin Book Reviews. (US ISSN 0275-682X) **4142**
Reprints from the Soviet Press. (US ISSN 0034-4931) **3970**
Reprints in International Finance. (US ISSN 0080-1380) **797**

Repro Bulletin. (SZ) **4005, 3796**
Repro en Druk see Grafisch Nederland **4000**
Reproduction. (UK ISSN 0034-4958) **4005**
Reproduction Bulletin. (US) **4005, 3666**
Reproduction, Fertility and Development. (AT ISSN 1031-3613) **453**
Reproduction in Domestic Animals. (GW ISSN 0936-6768) **4815**
Reproduction, Nutrition, Development. (FR ISSN 0181-1916) **453, 482, 486**
Reproductions. (PH) **453, 3987**
Reproductive and Genetic Engineering see Issues in Reproductive and Genetic Engineering **544**
Reproductive Endocrinology see Seminars in Reproductive Endrocrinology **3256**
Reproductive Freedom. (US) **3946, 2672**
†Reproductive Immunology. (UK ISSN 0266-660X) **5269**
Reproductive Rights Update. (US) **3946, 2672**
Reproductive Technology Update see Contraceptive Technology Update **596**
Reproductive Toxicology. (US ISSN 0890-6238) **1983, 482, 574, 3296**
Reproduire. (FR) **3796**
Reproduktie see Repeat **3796**
Der Reprograf. (GW) **3796**
Reprographics Quarterly see Information Media & Technology **1337**
Repsol Pamphlets. (IE) **3921**
Reptile Review see Chicago Herpetological Society. Bulletin **580**
Republic. see Al-Gomhouria **2185**
Republic Forge Company. Annual Report. (II) **1084**
Republic of Botswana. Department of Broadcasting. Annual Report. (BS) **1379**
Republic of China. Chamber of Commerce Bulletin. (CH) **821**
Republic of China. National Science Council. Annual Report. (CH) **4335**
Republic of China. National Science Council Monthly. (CH ISSN 0250-1651) **4335**
Republic of China. National Science Council. Proceedings. Part A: Physical Science and Engineering. (CH ISSN 0255-6588) **1835, 3829**
Republic of China. National Science Council. Proceedings. Part B: Life Sciences. (CH ISSN 0255-6596) **3147, 453**
▼Republic of China. National Science Council. Proceedings. Part C: Humanities and Social Sciences. (CH ISSN 1018-4473) **4384**
▼Republic of China. National Science Council. Proceedings. Part D: Mathematics, Science, and Technology Education. (CH ISSN 1017-7124) **4336, 4607**
Republic of China: A Reference Guide see Republic of China Yearbook (Year) **1782**
Republic of China Yearbook (Year). (CH ISSN 1013-0942) **1782, 2219**
Republic of Seychelles Official Gazette. (SE) **4072**
Republic of Singapore Government Gazette. (SI) **4072**
Republica Croata. see Republika Hrvatska **2021**
Republican Almanac. (US ISSN 0363-9290) **3921**
Republican China. (US) **2341, 3921**
Republican Englishman. (UK ISSN 0144-7548) **3921**
Republican Journal. (US ISSN 0034-5075) **2233**
Republican Woman. (US) **3922**
Republicii Socialiste Romania. Bibliografia. (RM) **2953**
Republicki Zavod za Unapredjivanje Vaspitanja i Obrazovanja. Bibliografija. (YU) **1679**
Republika Hrvatska/Republica Croata. (AG) **2021**

Republique. (SG) **2170**
Republique Centrafricaine. Journal Officiel. (CX) **688**
Republique de Congo en Quelques Chiffres. (CF) **3995**
Repulesi Szakirodalmi Tajekoztato/Aviation and Air Transport Abstracts. (HU ISSN 0231-3928) **4666**
Request. (US) **3577**
Requirements for Certification of Teachers, Counselors, Librarians, Administrators for Elementary Schools, Secondary Schools, Junior Colleges. (US ISSN 0080-1429) **1731**
Requirements for Teaching Certificates in Canada. (CN ISSN 0080-1437) **1658**
Res. (US ISSN 0277-1322) **282, 247**
Res et Jura Immobilia. (BE) **2672**
Res Facta. (PL ISSN 0486-4689) **3577**
Res Ipsa Loquitur. (US) **2672**
Res Mechanica see Reliability Engineering and System Safety **1835**
Res Medicae. (IT ISSN 0014-8784) **3147, 4198**
Res Publica. (PL ISSN 0860-4592) **2214**
Res Publica. (BE ISSN 0486-4700) **3922**
Resale Weekly. (UK ISSN 0034-5105) **630, 116, 1835, 4655**
Rescue (Carlsbad). (US ISSN 1041-0651) **3147**
Rescue (Kansas City). (US ISSN 1049-586X) **4198**
▼Rescue (Woodstock). (US) **231**
Rescue - E M S News. (US) **3621**
Rescue News. (UK ISSN 0950-5830) **282**
Reseach Report. see Denmark. Kgl. Veterinaer- og Landbohoejskole. Forskningsrapport **175**
Research. (US) **961**
Research see Research - Penn State **1715**
Research. see Pizhuhish **2513**
†Research. (GW ISSN 0722-6349) **5269**
Research Abstracts in Scientific Research Council. (IQ ISSN 1012-3458) **4357**
Research Advances in Alcohol & Drug Problems. (US ISSN 0093-9714) **1538**
Research Alert (New York). (US ISSN 0739-358X) **1507, 1051**
Research Alert (Philadelphia). (US) **22**
Research and Bibliographical Guides in Criminal Justice. (US ISSN 1042-4636) **1521**
Research and Clinical Center for Child Development. Annual Report. (JA ISSN 0386-8435) **1243, 3147**
Research and Clinical Forums. (UK ISSN 0143-3083) **3147**
Research & Development. (GW ISSN 0935-7238) **1548, 1795, 1835**
Research & Development. (US ISSN 0746-9179) **4607**
Research and Development Activities in the Netherlands. see Speur- en Ontwikkelingswerk in Nederland **4609**
Research & Development Associates for Military Food and Packaging Systems. Activities Report. (US ISSN 0099-6335) **3469, 3651**
Research & Development Contracts Monthly see R & D Contracts Monthly **4335**
Research & Development Digest see R & D Digest **1794**
Research and Development Directory. (US ISSN 0080-1461) **4336**
†Research and Development in Agriculture. (UK ISSN 0264-5467) **5269**
Research & Development in Industry. (II) **4607**
Research and Development in Ireland. (IE ISSN 0085-5545) **4335**
Research and Development in Japan Awarded the Okochi Memorial Prize. (JA) **4607, 4336**

Research and Development in the Canadian Corporate Sector see R & D Outlook **687**
Research and Development News see Water Newsletter **4832**
Research and Development Newsletter. (US) **3621**
Research & Development Product Source Telephone Directory. (US) **4607, 1152**
Research and Development Reporter. (II ISSN 0257-3245) **190**
Research and Development Telephone Directory see Research & Development Product Source Telephone Directory **4607**
▼Research & Education Networking. (US ISSN 1051-4791) **1715, 1428**
Research and Farming see Research Perspectives **116**
Research and Industry. (II ISSN 0034-513X) **4607**
Research and Practice in Forensic Medicine. see Hoigaku no Jissai to Kenkyu **3264**
Research and Studies. (CN) **1679, 2520, 2520, 2520, 4357, 4584**
Research and Teaching in Developmental Education. (US ISSN 1046-3364) **1658, 4044**
Research and Test Reactors. (US) **3838**
Research at Los Banos. (PH) **116**
Research Bulletin see New York State School of Industrial and Labor Relations. Bulletin **990**
Research Bulletin: Journal for the S A P R H S see Bulletin - News for the Human Science Researcher **4367**
Research Bulletin of the Seoul National University Forests see Seoul National University Forests. Research Bulletin **2107**
Research Center for Nuclear Physics Annual Report see R C N P Annual Report **3850**
Research Centers Directory. (US ISSN 0080-1518) **4336**
Research Committee of Essential Amino Acids. Reports/Hissu Aminosan Kenkyu. (JA ISSN 0387-4141) **482**
Research Communications in Chemical Pathology and Pharmacology. (US ISSN 0034-5164) **3147, 3741**
Research Communications in Psychology, Psychiatry and Behavior.(US ISSN 0362-2428) **4044, 3353, 4417**
Research Communications in Substances of Abuse. (US ISSN 0193-0818) **3742, 1538**
Research, Development and Acquisition see R, D & A **3469**
Research Development in Higher Education. Publications. (AT ISSN 0155-6223) **1658, 1715**
Research Disclosure. (UK ISSN 0374-4353) **3678, 1084**
†Research Discussion Papers. (AT ISSN 0158-9830) **5269**
Research Engineering Manufacturing. (GW) **1835, 4607**
Research Engineering Technical Services Digest see R E T S Digest **5266**
▼Research Evaluation. (UK ISSN 0958-2029) **4336**
Research Exchange and Practice in Mental Retardation see R E A P **5266**
Research Fields in Physics at United Kingdom Universities and Polytechnics. (UK ISSN 0308-9290) **3829, 1715**
†Research for Marketing. (SA) **5269**
Research for Religion & Parapsychology. (JA) **3671**
Research Group for European Migration Problems. Publications. (NE ISSN 0080-1623) **3987**
Research Guides in Military Studies. (US ISSN 0899-0166) **3469**
†▼Research Highlights in Animal Nutrition. (UK ISSN 0958-823X) **5269**

Research in African Literatures. (US ISSN 0034-5210) **2953, 2021**
Research in Agricultural Management and Accounting. see Nongye Jingying Guanli yu Kuaiji Yanjiu **1022**
Research in British Universities Polytechnics and Colleges. Vol.2: Biological Sciences see Current Research in Britain. Biological Sciences **465**
Research in British Universities Polytechnics and Colleges. Vol.1: Physical Sciences see Current Research in Britain. Physical Sciences **4355**
Research in British Universities Polytechnics and Colleges. Vol.3: Social Sciences see Current Research in Britain. Social Sciences **4394**
Research in Clinic and Laboratory. (IT) **3147, 3263**
Research in Community and Mental Health. (US ISSN 0192-0812) **4111, 4044**
Research in Consumer Behavior. (US ISSN 0885-2111) **1051**
Research in Contemporary and Applied Geography. (US) **2260**
Research in Corporate Social Performance and Policy. (US ISSN 0191-1937) **688**
Research in Criminology. (US) **1522**
Research in Developmental Disabilities. (US ISSN 0891-4222) **3147**
Research in Developmental Education see Review of Research in Developmental Education **1715**
Research in Domestic and International Agribusiness Management. (US ISSN 0276-1653) **157, 1026**
Research in Economic Anthropology. (US ISSN 0190-1281) **247**
Research in Economic History. (US ISSN 0363-3268) **897**
Research in Education. (UK ISSN 0034-5237) **1658**
Research in English and American Literature Yearbook see R E A L. Yearbook **2952**
Research in Experimental Economics. (US ISSN 0193-2306) **897**
Research in Experimental Medicine. (GW ISSN 0300-9130) **3263**
Research in Finance. (US ISSN 0196-3821) **797**
Research in Fisheries. (US ISSN 0083-7555) **2048**
Research in Governmental and Non-Profit Accounting. (US) **755**
Research in Health Economics see Advances in Health Economics and Health Services Research **3799**
Research in Higher Education. (US ISSN 0361-0365) **1731, 1715**
Research in Human Capital and Development. (US ISSN 0194-3960) **1000**
Research in Immunology. (FR ISSN 0923-2494) **3188**
Research in Informatics. (GW ISSN 0863-4300) **1457**
Research in International Business and Finance. (US ISSN 0275-5319) **920**
Research in Labor Economics. (US ISSN 0194-3057) **992**
Research in Law and Economics. (US ISSN 0193-5895) **688, 2672**
Research in Law, Deviance and Social Control see Studies in Law, Politics, and Society **2683**
†Research in Librarianship. (AT ISSN 0034-5245) **5269**
Research in Marketing. (US ISSN 0191-3026) **1051**
Research in Mathematics Education in Australia see Mathematics Education Research Journal **1754**
Research in Melanesia. (PP ISSN 0254-0665) **247, 4446**
Research in Microbiology. (FR ISSN 0923-2508) **557**
Research in Ministry. (US) **4213**
Research in Molecular Biology. (GW ISSN 0340-5400) **526**
Research in National Minority Literature. see Minzu Wenxue Yanjiu **2939**

RESEARCH INSTITUTE 6607

Research in Nursing & Health. (US ISSN 0160-6891) **3286**
Research in Organizational Behavior. (US ISSN 0191-3085) **4044**
Research in Parapsychology. (US ISSN 0094-7172) **3671**
Research in Personnel and Human Resources Management. (US) **1070**
Research in Phenomenology. (US ISSN 0085-5553) **3779**
Research in Philosophy and Technology. (US ISSN 0161-7249) **3779, 4607**
Research in Political Economy. (US ISSN 0161-7230) **897, 3922**
Research in Population Economics. (US ISSN 0163-7878) **3987**
Research in Public Policy Analysis and Management. (US ISSN 0732-1317) **4446, 1026, 4072**
Research in Race and Ethnic Relations.(US ISSN 0195-7449) **4446**
Research in Real Estate. (US ISSN 0731-7999) **4157**
Research in Religion and Family: Black Perspectives. (US ISSN 1055-1158) **4198, 2021, 4446**
†Research in Reproduction. (UK ISSN 0034-5253) **5269**
Research in Rural Sociology and Development. (US) **4446**
Research in Science & Technological Education. (UK ISSN 0263-5143) **1658**
Research in Social Movements, Conflicts and Change. (US ISSN 0163-786X) **4446**
Research in Social Problems and Public Policy. (US ISSN 0196-1152) **4446, 3922**
Research in Social Stratification and Mobility. (US ISSN 0276-5624) **4446**
Research in Sociology of Education and Socialization. (US ISSN 0197-5080) **1658**
Research in Sociology of Knowledge, Science and Art see Knowledge and Society **4441**
Research in the History of Economic Thought and Methodology. (US ISSN 0743-4154) **897**
Research in the History of Education: A List of Theses for Higher Degrees in the Universities of England and Wales. (UK ISSN 0080-1674) **1679**
Research in the History of the International Communist Movement. see Guoji Gongyunshi Yanjiu **3959**
Research in the Interweave of Social Roles. (US ISSN 0272-2801) **4446**
Research in the Social Scientific Study of Religion. (US) **4198, 4384**
Research in the Sociology of Health Care. (US ISSN 0275-4959) **3147, 4111, 4446**
Research in the Sociology of Organizations. (US ISSN 0733-558X) **4446**
Research in the Sociology of Work. (US ISSN 0277-2833) **4446, 992**
Research in the Teaching of English. (US ISSN 0034-527X) **1758**
▼Research in Third World Accounting. (UK) **755**
Research in Tourism. (II ISSN 0378-7478) **4784**
Research in Transportation Economics. (US) **4655**
Research in Urban Economics. (US) **4094, 2495**
Research in Urban Policy. (US) **2495**
Research in Veterinary Science. (UK ISSN 0034-5288) **4815**
Research in Virology. (FR ISSN 0923-2516) **3223**
Research in Word Processing Newsletter. (US ISSN 0748-5484) **1482, 1415, 1464**
Research Institute for Agricultural Economics. Bulletin. (HU ISSN 0541-9417) **157**
Research Institute for Mathematical Sciences. Publications/Kyoto Daigaku Suri Kaiseki Kenkyujo Kiyo. (JA ISSN 0034-5318) **3052, 3829**

RESEARCH INSTITUTE

Research Institute for Plant Protection. Annals. see Institutul de Cercetari pentru Protectia Plantelor. Analele 98
Research Institute for Plant Protection. Annual Report. see Instituut voor Plantenziektenkundig Onderzoek. Jaarverslag 181
†Research Institute Lawyers Tax Alert. (US ISSN 0163-9994) 5269
Research Institute Master Federal Tax Manual see Master Federal Tax Manual 1101
Research Institute Nedri-As. Bulletin. (IC) 516, 1548
Research Institute of America. Estate Planners Alert see Estate and Financial Planners Alert 945
Research Institute of America. Special Studies. (US) 755, 1105
Research Institute of America, Inc. Analysis of Federal Taxes: Estate and Gift see R I A Analysis of Federal Taxes: Estate and Gift 1104
Research Institute of America, Inc. Analysis of Federal Taxes: Excise see R I A Analysis of Federal Taxes: Excise 1104
Research Institute of America, Inc. Analysis of Federal Taxes: Income see R I A Analysis of Federal Taxes: Income 1104
Research Institute of America, Inc. Complete Federal Tax Forms see R I A Complete Federal Tax Forms 1104
Research Institute of America, Inc. Internal Revenue Code and Regulations see R I A Internal Revenue Code and Regulations 1104
Research Institute of Animal Production at Nitra. Scientific Works. see Vyskumny Ustav Zivocisnej Vyroby v Nitre. Vedecke Prace 129
Research Institute of Brewing. Report. (JA ISSN 0389-9136) 385
Research Institute of Industrial Safety. Annual Report. (JA) 3621
Research Institute of Industrial Safety. Research Report. see Sangyo Anzen Kenkyujo Kenkyu Hokoku 3621
Research Institute of Industrial Safety. Technical Recommendation. see Sangyo Anzen Kenkyujo Gijutsu Shishin 3621
Research Institute of Scripps Clinic. Scientific Report see Scripps Research Institute. Scientific Report 3152
Research Intelligence see British Educational Research Journal 1619
Research into Higher Education Abstracts. (UK ISSN 0034-5326) 1679, 22
Research Journal: Humanities and Social Sciences. (II) 2513, 4384
Research Journal of Educational Methods. (JA ISSN 0385-9746) 1758
Research Journal of Philosophy. (II ISSN 0048-7325) 3779
Research Journal of Philosophy and Social Sciences. (II) 3779, 4384
Research Journal: Science. (II ISSN 0253-9306) 4336
Research Journal Water Pollution Control Federation see Water Pollution Control Federation. Research Journal 1979
Research Laboratories Review of Activities. (SA ISSN 0314-1357) 1342, 1379
Research Laboratory of Electronics Currents see R L E Currents 1777
Research Libraries Group News. (US ISSN 0196-173X) 2781
Research Libraries in O C L C: A Quarterly. (US ISSN 0273-2351) 2799
Research Management see Research Technology Management 1026
Research Methods in Neurochemistry. (US) 482, 3353
Research Money. (CN ISSN 0833-1677) 797
Research Monographs in Cell and Tissue Physiology. (NE) 3147

Research Monographs in Immunology. (NE) 3188
Research Monographs on Human Population. (US) 3987
Research Note N C see U.S. Forest Service. Research Note N C 2109
Research Notes and Memoranda of Applied Geometry for Prevenient Natural Philosophy. (JA) 3052, 3779
Research Notes in Mathematics. (US) 3052
Research on Aging. (US ISSN 0164-0275) 2278
Research on Chemical Intermediates. (NE ISSN 0922-6168) 1186
Research on Drug Actions and Interactions. see Iyakuhin Sogo Sayo Kenkyu 3730
Research on Economics and Management. see Jingji yu Guanli Yanjiu 1015
Research on Environmental Disruption/ Kogai Kenkyu. (JA) 1967
Research on Latin America in the Humanities and Social Sciences in the Universities and Polytechnics of the United Kingdom. (UK) 410, 2420
Research on Latin American Studies in the Humanities and Social Sciences see Research on Latin America in the Humanities and Social Sciences in the Universities and Polytechnics of the United Kingdom 410
Research on Negotiation in Organizations. (US) 1026
▼Research on Social Work Practice. (US ISSN 1049-7315) 4446, 4417
Research on Technological Innovation, Management and Policy. (US ISSN 0737-1071) 4607
Research on Transport Economics. see Recherche en Matiere d'Economie des Transports 4655
Research Opportunities in Renaissance Drama. (US ISSN 0098-647X) 4637
Research Papers in Education. (UK ISSN 0267-1522) 1658
Research Papers in Geography. (AT) 2260
Research - Penn State. (US) 1715
Research Perspectives. (US ISSN 0732-4766) 116
Research Policy. (NE ISSN 0048-7333) 1026
Research, Policy and Planning. (UK ISSN 0264-519X) 4417
†Research Publications. Report. (US ISSN 0737-0083) 5269
Research Quarterly for Exercise and Sport. (US ISSN 0270-1367) 3808, 1758, 4485
Research Recommendations. (US) 1117, 2672
Research Relating to Children. Bulletins.(US ISSN 0080-1704) 1264
Research Report of Foreign Wood. (JA) 2117
Research Report - Texas Department of Corrections; Treatment Directorate, Research and Development Division see Texas. Department of Corrections. Research and Development Division. Research Report 1523
†Research Reports Digest. (UK ISSN 0143-0386) 5269
Research Reports Esprit - Project 322: CAD Interfaces. (US) 1400
Research Reports from the Rockefeller Archive Center see Rockefeller University. Rockefeller Archive Center. Research Reports 2321
Research Reports on Information Sciences. Series A, Mathematical Science. (JA ISSN 0912-2370) 1457, 3052
Research Reports on Information Sciences. Series B, Operations Research. (JA ISSN 0912-2389) 1457
Research Reports on Information Sciences. Series C, Computer Sciences. (JA ISSN 0912-2397) 1457

Research Resources Reporter. (US ISSN 0160-807X) 3147, 453
†Research Reviews in Animal and Plant Sciences. (US) 5269
†Research Reviews in Biochemistry. (US) 5269
†Research Reviews in Medicine. (US) 5269
†Research Reviews in Neuroscience. (US) 5269
Research Services Directory. (US ISSN 0278-1743) 1152
Research Society of Pakistan. Journal. (PK ISSN 0034-5431) 2341
Research Strategies. (US ISSN 0734-3310) 2781
Research Symposium on the Psychology and Acoustics of Music. Proceedings. (US) 3577, 4044
Research Technology Management. (US ISSN 0895-6308) 1026
Research: the Bayer Scientific Magazine. (GW) 3742, 1186
Research Update. (US) 2781
Research: Virginia Tech. (US ISSN 0731-9649) 1715
Researcher. (PH ISSN 0048-7341) 116
Researcher (Albany) see Albany 1303
Researches on Anatolian Art. see Anadolu Sanati Arastirmalari 311
Researches on Population Ecology/ Kotaigun Seitaigaku no Kenkyu. (JA ISSN 0034-5466) 3987, 1967
Researchin' Ouachita - Calhoun Counties, Ar. (US) 2162
Reseau. (CN ISSN 0700-6004) 1715
Reseau Automatique Belge de la Pollution Atmospherique. (BE ISSN 0773-7777) 4111
Reseau d'Organisme Culturels see R O C 5266
Reseau Femmes. see Women's Network 5305
Reseau Numerique a Integration de Services see R N I S 1428
Reseaux. (BE ISSN 0773-1213) 3779, 3922
Reseller Management. (US) 1433
▼Reseller Quarterly. (US) 1433
Resena de Literatura, Arte y Espectaculos. (SP ISSN 0080-1763) 342, 2953
Resenha de Livros para a Infancia e Juventude. (BL) 1264
Resenha Estatistica do Rio Grande do Sul. (BL) 4584
Resenha Judaica. (BL) 2021
Reserve. (US) 1323
Reserve Bank Bulletin. (NZ ISSN 0112-871X) 797, 882
Reserve Bank of Australia. Annual Report. (AT ISSN 0080-1771) 797
Reserve Bank of Australia. Bulletin. (AT ISSN 0725-0320) 736
Reserve Bank of Australia. Occasional Papers. (AT ISSN 0080-178X) 797, 883
Reserve Bank of Australia. Statistical Bulletin see Reserve Bank of Australia. Bulletin 736
Reserve Bank of India. Annual Report. (II ISSN 0080-1801) 797
Reserve Bank of India. Bulletin. (II ISSN 0034-5512) 797
Reserve Bank of India. Bulletin. Weekly Statistical Supplement. (II) 797
Reserve Bank of India. Occasional Papers. (II) 797
Reserve Bank of India. Report on Currency and Finance. (II) 797
Reserve Bank of Malawi. Annual Report and Statement of Account see Reserve Bank of Malawi. Report and Accounts 797
Reserve Bank of Malawi. Economic and Financial Review see Reserve Bank of Malawi. Financial and Economic Review 883
Reserve Bank of Malawi. Financial and Economic Review. (MW ISSN 0376-5725) 883, 797
Reserve Bank of Malawi. Report and Accounts. (MW ISSN 0486-5383) 797
Reserve Bank of New Zealand. Annual Report. (NZ) 797

Reserve Bank of New Zealand. Research Papers. (NZ ISSN 0110-523X) 883
Reserve Forces Almanac. (US ISSN 0363-860X) 3469
Reserves of Coal, Province of Alberta. (CN ISSN 0380-4275) 1795, 3494
Reservist. (US) 3469
Reservist. (SI) 3469
Reshimat Ma'amarim be-Mada'e ha-Yahadut. see Index of Articles on Jewish Studies 2030
▼Residences. (CN) 2554, 306, 630
†Residencia Medica. (BL) 5269
Resident Abroad. (UK) 3987
Resident and Staff Physician. (US ISSN 0034-5555) 2469, 3147
Residential Accommodation - Scotland. (UK) 4417, 2495
▼Residential and Commercial Sunspaces. (US) 630
Residential Construction Costs. (US) 630
Residential - Light Commercial Cost Data see Means Residential Cost Data 624
Residential Social Work see Social Work Today 4420
Residential Treatment for Children & Youth. (US ISSN 0886-571X) 1243
▼Residual Value Forecasts for D E C Systems and Peripherals. (US) 1474, 1051
Residual Value Forecasts for I B M Systems and Peripherals. (US) 1474, 1051
Residue Reviews. (US ISSN 0080-181X) 1186
Resilog. (CN ISSN 0225-5804) 1987
Resin Review. (US ISSN 0034-5571) 1859
Resist Newsletter. (US) 3946, 3970, 4851
Resistance News. (US) 3946, 1243, 1264, 3469
Resistant Pest Management. (US) 116, 1026
Resolution. (US) 1400
Resolution Trust Corporation Report see R T C Report 4155
Resolution Trust Reporter. (US) 4157, 2672
Resolutions, Beliefs & Policies, Constitution and Bylaws. (US) 1731, 2672
Resolutions of the Seminar on the Acquisition of Latin American Library Materials and List of Committees see Seminar on the Acquisition of Latin American Library Materials. Resolutions and Lists of Committees 5275
Resolve. (US) 1496
Resonance. see Tehuda 3833
Resonance (New York). (US) 3596, 3004
Resonance (Sumterville). (US) 486, 1907
Resonanz. (GW) 2953
Resort Development & Operation. (US) 4157
Resorts and Great Hotels. (US) 4784
†Resorts & Incentives. (US) 5269
Resorts & Parks Purchasing Guide. (US) 2479
Resorts and R V Parks Purchasing Guide see Resorts & Parks Purchasing Guide 2479
Resound. (US ISSN 0749-2472) 3577
Resource. (CN ISSN 0832-9354) 4248
Resource (New York). (US) 1715
Resource-Based Resource-Oriented Teaching and Learning see R B R O T A L 5266
†Resource Book/Ressources. (CN) 5269
Resource Book of Educational Suppliers.(AT) 1659
Resource Center for Non Violence. Newsletter. (US) 3922
Resource Center Index. (US) 1061
Resource Conservation Recovery Act Notification Data File. (US) 1502

Resource Development and Conservation. see Ziyuan yu Kaifa **1501**
†Resource Directory of National Alcohol-Related Associations, Agencies and Organizations. (US) **5269**
Resource Directory of Scientists and Engineers with Disabilities. (US) **410, 420**
Resource Guide to Influencing State Legislatures. (US) **4082**
Resource-Mag. (CN ISSN 0712-7243) **4136**, 2575
Resource Magazine (Bridgeport). (US) **2469**
Resource Management and Optimization. (US ISSN 0142-2391) **1496**
Resource Recovery Report. (US ISSN 0735-3081) **1987, 1496**
Resource Recovery Yearbook. (US ISSN 0893-4673) **1987, 1795**
Resource Recycling. (US ISSN 0744-4710) **1987, 1496**
Resource Sharing & Information Networks. (US ISSN 0737-7797) **2781**
Resource Technology see Oil & Gas Report **683**
Resources. (CN ISSN 0714-5918) **2672**, 1795
Resources (Cambridge) see Alternative America **1296**
Resources (Fort Worth). (US) **3700**
Resources (Lake Oswego). (US ISSN 1042-217X) **1342**, 1026
Resources (Nashville). (US) **961**
Resources (Washington, 1959). (US ISSN 0048-7376) **1496, 157, 1967**
Resources and Energy. (NE ISSN 0165-0572) **1795**
†Resources and Industry of Central Queensland. (AT) **5269**
†Resources and Industry of Far North Queensland. (AT) **5269**
Resources, Conservation and Recycling.(NE ISSN 0921-3449) **1987, 1496, 1967**
Resources for Comparative Biomedical Research. (US) **3181, 3263**
Resources for Educators of Adults. (US) **1686**
Resources for Feminist Research/ Documentation sur la Recherche Feministe. (CN ISSN 0707-8412) **4860, 4384**
Resources for the Study of Anthropology. (US) **248**
Resources for Youth Ministry see Youth Ministry Quarterly (St. Louis) **1272**
Resources in Aging. (US ISSN 0892-0818) **2278, 1686, 3394, 4136**
Resources in Education. (US ISSN 0098-0897) **1679, 22**
Resources in Education Annual Cumulation. (US ISSN 0197-9973) **1679, 22, 1659**
Resources Industry - Quarry Mine and Construction Equipment see Resources - Quarry Mine & Construction News **3494**
Resources: News You Can Use. (US) **1070**
Resources of Music Series. (UK) **3577**
†ReSources Pharmaceutical and Healthcare Information News. (UK ISSN 0954-5271) **5269**
Resources Policy. (UK ISSN 0301-4207) **1795, 1967, 3494**
Resources - Quarry Mine & Construction News. (AT ISSN 1032-0776) **3494**, 630
Respiration. (SZ ISSN 0025-7931) **3366, 3383**
Respiration Physiology. (NE ISSN 0034-5687) **574, 3147**
Respiratory Care. (US ISSN 0730-8418) **3366**
Respiratory Disease in Practice. (UK ISSN 0262-7043) **3366**
Respiratory Diseases Digest. (NE) **3366**
Respiratory Diseases Research Centre. Annual Report. (KE) **3367**
Respiratory Management. (US ISSN 0892-9289) **3367**

Respiratory Medicine. (UK ISSN 0954-6111) **3367**
Respiratory Practitioner. (US) **3367**
Respiratory Protection Newsletter. (US) **3621, 1809**
Respiratory System. (UK ISSN 0142-8780) **574, 3367**
Respiratory Technology see R R T: the Canadian Journal of Respiratory Therapy **3366**
Respiratory Therapy see Respiratory Management **3367**
Respiratory Therapy Magazine see R T Magazine **3366**
Responding to H I V - A I D S in Canada. (CN) **3223**
Responsabilita Civile e Previdenza. (IT) **2672**
Responsabilita del Sapere. (IT) **2953, 2881**
Responsables. (FR) **1835**
Response. (AT) **1051, 1117, 4005**
Response (Fairfax). (US) **3621**
Response (Lebanon). (US ISSN 1040-3957) **3286**
Response (Los Angeles). (US) **2021**
Response (New York, 1967). (US ISSN 0034-5709) **2021, 2953**
Response (New York, 1969). (US ISSN 0034-5725) **4248**
Response (Seattle). (US) **1323**
Response (Solana Beach) see Rescue (Carlsbad) **3147**
Response to the Victimization of Women and Children. (US ISSN 0894-7597) **4851**
Response to Violence in the Family and Sexual Assault see Response to the Victimization of Women and Children **4851**
Responsibilities of Insurance Agents and Brokers. (US) **2541, 2672**
▼Responsive Community. (US ISSN 1053-0754) **3922**
Responsive Philanthropy. (US) **4417, 4851**
†Respuesta. (US) **5269**
Ressources. see Resource Book **5269**
Rest & Relaxation Entertainment Digest see R & R Entertainment Digest **3469**
Rest & Relaxation Shoppers News see R & R Shoppers News **1378**
Restatement in the Courts. Pocket Parts. (US) **2672**
Restauranger & Storkoek. (SW ISSN 0282-0390) **2080**
Restaurant and Hotel Design see Restaurant - Hotel Design International **2554**
Restaurant and Hotel Management. (GW ISSN 0344-4422) **2479**
Restaurant Business. (US ISSN 0097-8043) **2479**
Restaurant Buyers Guide see H R I - Buyers Guide **2072**
Restaurant Digest. (US) **2479**
Restaurant Exchange News. (US) **2479**, 2080
Restaurant Hospitality. (US ISSN 0147-9989) **2479**
Restaurant Hotel Club & Caterer. (AT) **2479**
Restaurant - Hotel Design International. (US ISSN 0745-4929) **2554, 2479**
Restaurant Management Insider. (US) **2479**
Restaurant Management Today see Restaurant Management Insider **2479**
Restaurant Merchandising News. (US) **2479**
Restaurant News. (US ISSN 0048-7406) **2479**
Restaurant News of the Rockies. (US) **2479**
Restaurant Row Magazine. (US) **2479**
Restaurant Show Daily. (US) **2479**
†Restaurant South. (US) **5269**
▼Restaurant Trends. (US) **2479, 2080**
Restaurant Wine. (US) **2479**, 385
Restaurants and Institutions. (US ISSN 0273-5520) **2479**
Restaurants & Institutions Marketplace.(US) **2479, 1051**
Restaurants U S A. (US ISSN 0890-5584) **2479**

Restaurateur. (US) **2480**
Restaurateur. (UK ISSN 0955-2979) **2480**
Restauratoeren. (SW ISSN 0034-5814) **2480**
Restaurator. (DK ISSN 0034-5806) **2781**
Restaurierung und Museumstechnik. (GW ISSN 0232-2609) **282**
Restauro. (GW) **342**
Restauro. (IT) **2495**
Restauro & Citta. (IT) **306**
Resto-Flash. (FR) **2480**
Reston Series in Construction Technology. (US) **630**
Restoration. (CN ISSN 0708-2177) **4198**
Restoration. (UK ISSN 0950-1568) **4198**
Restoration & Eighteenth Century Theatre Research. (US ISSN 0034-5822) **4637, 2382**
Restoration and Management Notes. (US ISSN 0733-0707) **1496**
Restoration Herald. (US ISSN 0034-5830) **4198**
Restoration Quarterly. (US ISSN 0486-5642) **4198**
Restoration: Studies in English Literary Culture, 1660-1700. (US ISSN 0162-9905) **2953**
Restoration Witness. (US ISSN 0191-0167) **4287**
Restorative Dentistry. (UK) **3241**
Restorative Neurology and Neuroscience. (NE ISSN 0922-6028) **3353, 3742**
Restored Cars. (AT ISSN 0311-4163) **4700**
Restorica. (SA) **306**
Restoring Classic Cars see Your Classic **4706**
Restricted - Commercial Operator History File. (US) **1349**
Restrictive Practices Reports see Industrial Cases Reports **2710**
Restructuring. (BU) **883**
▼Restyling and Accessories Marketing. (US) **4700**
Resultados das Observacoes Meteorologicas de Macau. (MH ISSN 0460-3060) **3440**
Resultate der Mathematik. see Results in Mathematics **3052**
Resultats Comptables des Entreprises Suisse. see Buchhaltungsergebnisse Schweizerische Unternehmungen **707**
Resultats du Recensement de la Population et des Habitations. (GR) **3995**
Results (Houston). (US) **3700**
Results and Problems in Cell Differentiation. (US ISSN 0080-1844) **526**
Results in Mathematics/Resultate der Mathematik. (SZ ISSN 0378-6218) **3052**
Results of Geomagnetic Observations at the Hurbanovo Geomagnetic Observatory. (CS ISSN 0231-7737) **1593**
Results of Investigations of the Polish Scientific Spitsbergen Expeditions. (PL ISSN 0137-1142) **2260**
Results of Researches on the International Geophysical Projects. Glaciologicla Researches. see Rezul'taty Issledovanii po Mezhdunarodnym Geofizicheskim Proektam. Glyatsiologicheskie Issledovaniya **1594**
Results of the Business Survey Carried out Among Heads of Enterprises in the Community see Results of the Business Survey Carried out Among Management in the Community **1084**
Results of the Business Survey Carried out Among Management in the Community. (EI) **1084**
Results of the National Operations & Automation Survey see American Bankers Association. Operations and Automation Division. Results of the National Operations & Automation Survey **804**
Resume. (SW) **38**

RETAIL LABOR 6609

Resume. (US ISSN 0270-7527) **3700**
†Resumen. (VE) **5269**
Resumen de Actividades I N I (Year) see Grupo I N I (Resumen de Actividades) **1077**
Resumen Semanal. (Centro de Estudios y Promocion del Desarrollo (DESCO)) (PE ISSN 0250-9792) **3922**
Resumenes Analiticos C I N T E R F O R see Resumenes de Formacion Profesional C I N T E R F O R **1659**
Resumenes Analiticos en Educacion. (CL ISSN 0716-0151) **1679, 22**
Resumenes Analiticos sobre Pastos Tropicales. (CK ISSN 0120-2944) **143, 22**
Resumenes de Formacion Profesional C I N T E R F O R. (UY) **1659**
Resumenes de Informacion sobre el Desarrollo. see Development Information Abstracts **713**
Resumenes sobre Poblacion Dominicana. (DR) **3987, 598**
Resumes for Employment in the U S and Overseas. (US) **3630**
Resumos Analiticos em Educacao. (BL) **1659**
Resurgence. (UK ISSN 0034-5970) **3922, 3779**
Resuscitation. (IE ISSN 0300-9572) **3367, 3192**
Retablos de Papel. (MX) **1686**
Retail see Retail Market **1052**
Retail Advertising Conference Digest see R A C Digest **37**
Retail Advertising Week. (US ISSN 0034-5997) **38**
Retail Attraction. (UK) **1051, 38**
Retail Bakers of America. Government Bulletin. (US) **2089, 1051**
Retail Bakers of America. Research & Merchandising Bulletin. (US) **2089, 1051**
Retail Bank Credit Report. (US) **797**
Retail Banker International. (IE ISSN 0261-1740) **797, 1026**
Retail Banker's Yearbook. (IE) **797**
Retail Banking Products Survey: At Call Deposits. (AT ISSN 1032-870X) **797**
Retail Banking Products Survey: Continuing Credit. (AT ISSN 1032-8726) **797**
Retail Banking Products Survey: Credit Cards. (AT ISSN 1032-8742) **797**
Retail Banking Products Survey: Term Deposits. (AT ISSN 1032-8718) **797**
Retail Banking Products Survey: Term Loans. (AT ISSN 1032-8734) **797**
Retail Broadcaster see Ad-Pro **5130**
Retail Business. (UK ISSN 0034-6012) **1051**
Retail Chemist see Chemist & Druggist **3720**
Retail Control. (US ISSN 0034-6047) **1052**
Retail Council of Canada. Operating Survey of Canadian Retailing. (CN) **1052**
Retail Council of Canada. Shrinkage Survey. (CN) **1052**
Retail Credit Federation Membership Directory see Consumer Credit Association of the United Kingdom. Membership Directory **773**
Retail Deposit Services Report. (US ISSN 0270-2762) **797**
Retail Directions. (CN) **1052**
Retail Directions see Department Store Economist **5179**
Retail Directory. (UK) **1052, 1152**
Retail Distribution in Japan. (JA) **839**
Retail Food Price Report. (CN) **2080**
Retail Fruit Trade Review. (UK) **2138**
Retail Gasoline and Garage Dealers Association News see R G D A News **3700**
Retail Info Systems News. (US) **828**
Retail Info Systems News Directory. (US) **1052, 828**
▼Retail Ink. (US) **1117**
Retail Intelligence. (UK) **1052**
Retail Jeweller. (UK ISSN 0034-6063) **2565**
Retail Labor Report see Labor Relations Week **986**

6610 RETAIL LEASING

Retail Leasing Reporter see The Deal Makers 4147
▼Retail Market. (UK) 1052
Retail Marketing & Management. (UK) 832
Retail Marketing and Management see Retail Marketing & Management 832
†Retail Merchandising. (CN) 5269
Retail Merchants Association of Alberta Highlights see R M A Highlights 1051
Retail News see Merchant 1047
Retail News. (IE) 1052
Retail News Reporter. (US) 1052
Retail Newsagent Tobacconist Confectioner. (UK ISSN 0961-5202) 4644, 2089, 4136
▼Retail Observer. (US) 2561
Retail Opportunity Letter. (US) 1026
Retail Packaging. (UK) 3651
Retail Price Index for Addis Ababa (Excluding Rent). (ET) 1000
Retail Reporter see Retail News Reporter 1052
Retail Review. (UK ISSN 0144-6835) 1052
Retail - Services Labor Report see Labor Relations Week 986
▼Retail Store Image. (US ISSN 1047-8841) 2554, 1052
Retail Tenant Directory see Monitor's Retail Tenant Directory 4152
Retail Tobacconist. (US) 4644
Retail Trade Europe see Retail Trade International 1052
Retail Trade International. (UK) 1052
Retail Wholesale and Department Store Union Record see R W D S U Record 2588
Retail World. (AT ISSN 0034-6136) 2093
Retailer. (MM) 1052
Retailer and Marketing News. (US) 1052
Retailer News: Northern California Edition. (US) 1052
Retailer News: Northwest Edition. (US) 1052
Retailer News: Southern California - Western States Edition. (US) 1052
Retailer of Queensland. (AT ISSN 0034-6144) 2093
Retailing Age/Shoten Kai. (JA) 1052
Retailing Today. (US ISSN 0360-506X) 1052
†RetailNews. (US) 5269
Retfaerd. (DK ISSN 0105-1121) 2672
Retford and Bawlry Trader. (UK) 2195
Rethinking Marxism. (US ISSN 0893-5696) 897, 3922
Reti - Pratiche e Saperi di Donne. (IT) 3922, 2881, 4851
Retina. (US ISSN 0275-004X) 3304
Retire Right: The Practical Guide to RRIF's, Annuities and Pensions. (CN) 961
Retired Military Almanac. (US ISSN 0149-7197) 3469
The Retired Officer. (US ISSN 0034-6160) 3469
▼Retirement and Benefit Planning. (US) 1070, 1105, 2672
▼Retirement Community Business. (US) 4157, 2278
†Retirement Housing Industry. (US) 5269
Retirement Housing Report. (US ISSN 0890-7757) 2278, 4157
Retirement Letter. (US ISSN 0093-5352) 797, 2278
Retirement Life (Portland). (US) 2278
Retirement Life (Washington). (US ISSN 0034-6179) 2278
Retirement Lifestyle Publication. (CN ISSN 0844-5982) 2278, 1507, 2178
†Retirement Money. (US) 5269
Retirement Paradises of the World. (US) 4784
Retirement Plan Success Letter see All Weather Fund Investor 938
Retirement Real Estate Report. (US) 4157, 2278
Retirement World. (UK) 2278
Retorik. (DK ISSN 0900-3339) 2837
Retorno del Pueblo. (AG) 2170, 3922

Retreader's Journal see Retreading - Repair Journal 4293
Retreading - Repair Journal. (US ISSN 1046-7157) 4293
Retrieval. (AT ISSN 0310-9143) 3922
Retriever Field Trial News. (US ISSN 0279-9693) 3713
Retrospect. (UK ISSN 0261-5061) 2382
Retrospectiva da Agropecuaria. (BL) 157
Retrovirus. (FR ISSN 0996-5637) 557, 3223
Rettens Gang. (NO ISSN 0034-6187) 2672
Rettung. (GW ISSN 0048-7430) 1538
Rettungsdienst. (GW ISSN 0178-2525) 3147
Return of Outstanding Debt see Chartered Institute of Public Finance and Accountancy. Capital Expenditure and Debt Financing Statistics. Actuals 710
Return to Paradise see One Peaceful World 3611
Reuma. (SW ISSN 0034-6209) 3369
Reuma Bulletin. (NE ISSN 0034-6217) 3369
Reumatismo. (IT ISSN 0048-7449) 3369
Reumatizam. (CI ISSN 0374-1338) 3369
Reumatologia. (PL ISSN 0034-6233) 3369
Reumatologo. (IT ISSN 0391-8963) 3369
Reuniao Geral de Cultura do Arroz. Anais. (BL ISSN 0101-9708) 208
Reunion. Direction de l'Agriculture et de la Foret. Agreste. Donnees, Annuaire de Statistique Agricole Reunion. (RE ISSN 1150-1456) 143
Reunion. Direction de l'Agriculture et de la Foret. Agreste. Donnees, Bulletin de Statistique Agricole Reunion. (RE ISSN 1150-1448) 116
Reunion. Institut National de la Statistique et des Etudes Economiques. Collection: Documents.(RE) 736
Reunion. Institut National de la Statistique et des Etudes Economiques. Fiches Bibliographiques. (RE) 883
†Reunion. Institut National de la Statistique et des Etudes Economiques. Indicateurs Conjoncturels. (RE ISSN 0750-0750) 5269
Reunion. Service de Statistique Agricole. Bulletin de Statistique Agricole see Reunion. Direction de l'Agriculture et de la Foret. Agreste. Donnees, Bulletin de Statistique Agricole Reunion 116
Reunion Agricole. (RE) 116
Reunion Annuelle des Sciences de la Terre see Reunion des Sciences de la Terre 1548
Reunion des Sciences de la Terre. (FR) 1548
Reunion Nacional Sobre Problemas de Contaminacion Ambiental. Memoria. (MX) 1979
Reunion Talks on Risleys. (US ISSN 1050-7914) 2162
Reunions Jointes des Membres de l'Assemblee Consultative du Conseil de l'Europe et des Membres du Parlement Europeen. Compte Rendu in Extenso des Debats see Joint Meeting of the Members of the Consultative Assembly of the Council of Europe and of the Members of the European Parliamentary Assembly. Official Report of Debates 5221
▼Reunions - The Magazine. (US) 4417, 2162
Reus. (SP) 2218
Reuse - Recycle. (US ISSN 0048-7457) 1987
Reuss Jahrbuch der Luft- und Raumfahrt. (GW) 61
Reutlinger Alpinist. (GW) 4554
Reveil Missionnaire. (CN ISSN 0034-6284) 4198

Reveil Socialiste de Lannemezan. (FR ISSN 0034-6292) 3922
Reveille. (UK) 2195
Reveille. (AT ISSN 0034-6306) 3469, 61
Revelation. (LB) 2881, 342, 4446
†Revelation. (UK ISSN 0143-0181) 5269
Revelations of Awareness. (US) 3596, 3779
†Revenar. (CR) 5269
Revenews. (US ISSN 8756-7903) 934, 805
Revenu Francais. (FR) 961
Reverse Acronyms, Initialisms and Abbreviations Dictionary. (US ISSN 0270-4390) 2837
Revier und Werk. (GW) 3494
Review. (YU ISSN 0034-6357) 2240
Review (Alexandria) see Intermission (Alexandria) 4634
Review (Charlottesville). (US ISSN 0190-3233) 2954, 2837
Review (New York). (US) 2457, 4198
The Review (Portland). (US) 3004
The Review (Uppercó). (US) 2138
Review (Washington). (US ISSN 0899-1510) 2295, 1659
Review and Expositor. (US ISSN 0034-6373) 4248
The Review: Ewing Township Edition. (US) 2233
Review for Religious. (US ISSN 0034-639X) 4274
Review for the Study of Enlightenment and Free-Thinking. see Tijdschrift voor de Studie van de Verlichting en van het Vrije Denken 2969
Review Journal of Philosophy and Social Science. (II ISSN 0258-1701) 3779, 4384
Review la Booche. (US) 3004
Review: Latin American Literature and Arts. (US ISSN 0890-5762) 2954
Review of Accidents on Indian Government Railways see Indian Railways Safety Performance - A Review 4710
Review of African Political Economy. (UK ISSN 0305-6244) 3970
Review of Agricultural Entomology. (UK ISSN 0957-6762) 143, 22
Review of Applied Entomology. Series A: Agricultural see Review of Agricultural Entomology 143
Review of Applied Entomology. Series B: Medical and Veterinary see Review of Medical and Veterinary Entomology 4820
Review of Applied Mycology see Review of Plant Pathology 467
Review of Archaeology. (US) 282
†Review of Architecture and Landscape Architecture. (CN ISSN 0705-1913) 5269
†Review of Australia's Demographic Trends. (AT ISSN 0727-6982) 5269
Review of Austrian Economics. (US ISSN 0889-3047) 897
Review of Bank Performance. (US) 797
Review of Banking & Financial Services.(US) 797
Review of Behavior Therapy: Theory & Practice. (US) 4044
Review of Black Political Economy. (US ISSN 0034-6446) 688
Review of Books and Religion see Books and Religion 4123
Review of Books on the Book of Mormon. (US ISSN 1050-7930) 4287
Review of Business. (US ISSN 0034-6454) 688
Review of Business and Economics Research see Review of Financial Economics 688
Review of Child Development Research. (US ISSN 0091-3065) 1243, 1659
Review of Commerce Studies. (II) 688
Review of Contemporary Fiction. (US ISSN 0276-0045) 2954
Review of Currency Law and International Economics. see Rivista di Diritto Valutario e di Economia Internazionale 2729

Review of Czechoslovak Medicine see Czechoslovak Medicine 3092
Review of Econometrics. see Ekonomicko-Matematicky Obzor 663
Review of Economic Situation of Air Transport see Economic Situation of Air Transport. Review and Outlook (Years) 4672
Review of Economic Studies. (UK ISSN 0034-6527) 688
Review of Economics and Business. (JA ISSN 0302-6574) 688
Review of Economics and Statistics. (NE ISSN 0034-6535) 736, 4584
Review of Education. (US ISSN 0098-5597) 1679, 410, 1659
Review of Education in India. (II) 1659
Review of Educational Research. (US ISSN 0034-6543) 1659
Review of Employment in Madras State see Review of Employment in Tamil Nadu 992
Review of Employment in Tamil Nadu. (II) 992
Review of English Studies. (UK ISSN 0034-6551) 2954, 2837
Review of Ethnology see R E 247
▼Review of European Community and International Environmental Law. (UK ISSN 0962-8797) 1026, 2728
Review of Existential Psychology and Psychiatry. (US ISSN 0361-1531) 4044
Review of Financial Economics. (US ISSN 1058-3300) 688
Review of Financial Studies. (US ISSN 0893-9454) 797
Review of Fisheries in O E C D Member Countries. (FR ISSN 0078-6241) 2048
Review of Foreign Geographical Literature. see Przeglad Zagranicznej Literatury Geograficznej 2260
Review of Forestry Culture. see Shinrin Bunka Kenkyu 2107
Review of Futures Markets. (US ISSN 0898-011X) 688, 116
Review of Geophysics. see Przeglad Geofizyczny 1593
Review of Ghana Law. (GH ISSN 0034-6578) 2672
Review of Higher Education. (US ISSN 0162-5748) 1715
Review of Historical Demography. see Historisch-Demographische Mitteilungen 3982
Review of Income and Wealth. (US ISSN 0034-6586) 1000
Review of Indian Spiritualism. (II) 3671, 4215
Review of International Affairs. (YU ISSN 0486-6096) 3970
Review of International Broadcasting. (US ISSN 0149-9971) 1379
Review of International Business Law see Canada - U S Business Law Review 2708
Review of International Cooperation. (SZ ISSN 0034-6608) 3970
Review of International Studies. (UK ISSN 0260-2105) 3970
Review of Latin American Studies. (US) 2420, 920, 2954
Review of Law & Social Change. (US ISSN 0048-7481) 2672
Review of Literature on Forestry and Game Management. see Prehled Lesnicke a Myslivecke Literatury 5261
Review of Litigation. (US ISSN 0734-4015) 2672
Review of Maritime Transport. (UN ISSN 0085-560X) 4736
Review of Marketing and Agricultural Economics. (AT ISSN 0034-6616) 157
Review of Medical and Veterinary Entomology. (UK ISSN 0957-6770) 4820, 22
Review of Medical and Veterinary Mycology. (UK ISSN 0034-6624) 467, 22, 4820
Review of Medical Microbiology see Jawetz, Melnick & Adelberg's Medical Microbiology 553
Review of Metaphysics. (US ISSN 0034-6632) 3779

Review of Military History see Revista de Istorie Militara 3469
Review of National Literatures. (US ISSN 0034-6640) 2954
Review of Optometry see Chilton's Review of Optometry 3299
Review of Palaeobotany and Palynology. (NE ISSN 0034-6667) 3660
Review of Personality and Social Psychology. (US ISSN 0270-1987) 4044
Review of Plant Pathology. (UK ISSN 0034-6438) 467, 22
Review of Polarography/Porarogurafi. (JA ISSN 0034-6691) 1208, 1212, 1230
Review of Political Economy. (UK ISSN 0953-8259) 3922, 883
Review of Politics. (US ISSN 0034-6705) 3922
Review of Population Reviews. (FR ISSN 0377-8967) 3987
Review of Progress in Coloration and Related Topics. (UK ISSN 0557-9325) 4607
Review of Public Personnel Administration see Public Administration 1025
▼Review of Quantitative Finance and Accounting. (NE ISSN 0924-865X) 755, 797, 897
Review of Radical Political Economics. (US ISSN 0486-6134) 897
Review of Regional Studies. (US ISSN 0048-749X) 2495
Review of Religions. (UK) 4198, 4220
Review of Religions. (PK ISSN 0034-6721) 4220
Review of Religious Research. (US ISSN 0034-673X) 4198, 4446
Review of Research in Developmental Education. (US ISSN 0894-3907) 1715
Review of Research in Education. (US ISSN 0091-732X) 1758
Review of Research in Future Markets see Review of Futures Markets 688
Review of Scientific Instruments. (US ISSN 0034-6748) 2524
Review of Scottish Culture. (UK) 2021, 282
Review of Slavic Studies. see Zbornik za Slavistiku 2853
Review of Social Economy. (US ISSN 0034-6764) 688, 4446
Review of Socialist Law. (NE ISSN 0165-0300) 2672, 3922
Review of Surgery see Current Surgery 3378
Review of Taxation of Individuals. (US) 1105
Review of the Agricultural Situation in Europe at the End of (Year) see Agricultural Review for Europe 146
Review of the Economic Situation of Mexico see Examen de la Situacion Economica de Mexico 864
Review of the Economy and Employment. (UK ISSN 0265-9387) 883, 3630
Review of the Mineral Industry in Tanzania. (TZ ISSN 0082-1659) 3494
Review of the Mosaic Creed. see Revista Cultului Mozaic 2954
Review of the River Plate. (AG ISSN 0034-6810) 883
Review of the World Wheat Situtation see International Wheat Council. Report for Crop Year 99
Review of Tropical Plant Pathology. (II ISSN 0254-1300) 516
Review of Tuberculosis for Public Health Nurse. see Hokenfu no Kekkaku Tenbo 3278
Review of World Economics. see Weltwirtschaftliches Archiv 699
Review on Commodity. see Shangpin Pingjie 1508
Review on Liberal Arts/Kyoyo Ronshu. (JA) 2514
Review on the Working of the Trade Unions Act, 1926 see Trade Unions in India 2590
Review - S W A P. (Sharing with a Purpose) (US) 4082, 22

Review: Worldwide Reinsurance. (UK ISSN 0034-6349) 2541
Reviewing Librarian see Teaching Librarian 2786
Reviewing Sociology. (UK ISSN 0261-0272) 4446
Reviews in American History. (US ISSN 0048-7511) 2420
Reviews in Analytical Chemistry. (UK ISSN 0048-752X) 1208
Reviews in Anthropology. (US ISSN 0093-8157) 248
Reviews in Aquatic Sciences. (US ISSN 0891-4117) 1610
Reviews in Biochemical Toxicology. (US ISSN 0163-7673) 482, 1983
Reviews in Cancer Epidemiology. (NE) 3201
Reviews in Chemical Engineering. (NE ISSN 0167-8299) 1859, 1186
Reviews in Clinical and Basic Pharmacology see Journal of Basic and Clinical Physiology and Pharmacology 3731
▼Reviews in Clinical Gerontology. (UK ISSN 0959-2598) 2278
Reviews in Clinical Nutrition see Nutrition Abstracts and Reviews. Series A: Human and Experimental 3614
Reviews in Engineering Geology. (US ISSN 0080-2018) 1873
Reviews in Fish Biology and Fisheries. (UK ISSN 0960-3166) 591, 2048
Reviews in Inorganic Chemistry. (UK ISSN 0193-4929) 1214
Reviews in Mathematical Physics. (SI ISSN 0129-055X) 3829, 3052
▼Reviews in Medical Microbiology. (UK ISSN 0954-139X) 557, 3147
▼Reviews in Medical Virology. (UK ISSN 1052-9276) 557, 3188
Reviews in Perinatal Medicine. (US ISSN 0362-5699) 3296
Reviews in the Neurosciences. (UK ISSN 0334-1763) 3353
Reviews of Chemical Intermediates see Research on Chemical Intermediates 1186
Reviews of Geophysics. (US ISSN 8755-1209) 1593, 368, 3829
Reviews of Hematology. (US) 3273, 482
Reviews of Infectious Diseases see Clinical Infectious Diseases 3218
Reviews of Magnetic Resonance in Medicine. (US ISSN 0883-8291) 3362
Reviews of Modern Physics. (US ISSN 0034-6861) 3830
†Reviews of Neuroscience. (US ISSN 0095-7550) 5269
Reviews of Physiology, Biochemistry and Experimental Pharmacology. (US ISSN 0303-4240) 574, 482, 3742
Reviews of Plasma Physics. (US ISSN 0080-2050) 3830
Reviews of Solid State Science. (SI ISSN 0218-1029) 3830
Reviews on Coatings and Corrosion see Corrosion Reviews 3404
Reviews on Deformation Behaviour of Materials see Journal of the Mechanical Behavior of Materials 3411
Reviews on Drug Interactions see Drug Metabolism and Drug Interactions 3723
Reviews on Drug Metabolism and Drug Interactions see Drug Metabolism and Drug Interactions 3723
Reviews on Environmental Health. (UK ISSN 0048-7554) 1967, 4111
Reviews on Powder Metallurgy & Physical Ceramics. (UK ISSN 0379-0002) 3418
Reviews on Silicon, Germanium, Tin and Lead Compounds see Main Group Metal Chemistry 3412
Revija (Belgrade). (YU ISSN 0027-8076) 2289
Revija (Osijek). (CI ISSN 0034-6888) 2881
Revija Obrazovanja. (YU ISSN 0351-0697) 1659

Revija Skolstva i Prosvetna Dokumentacija see Revija Obrazovanja 1659
Revija za Kriminalistiko in Kriminologijo.(XV ISSN 0034-690X) 1522
Revija za Psihologiju. (CI ISSN 0352-1605) 4044
Revija za Razvoj. (XV) 688
Revija za Sociologiju/Sociological Review. (CI ISSN 0350-154X) 4446
Revision. (US ISSN 0275-6935) 3596
Revision de Programas see C I M M Y T Review 5157
Revision & Regnskabsvaesen. (DK ISSN 0034-6918) 755
Revisioning Philosophy. (US ISSN 0899-9937) 3779
Revisionist History. (SW ISSN 0348-9078) 2382
Revisions (Notre Dame). (US) 3779
Revisions: Papers in Architectural Theory. (US) 306
Revisjon og Regnskap. (NO ISSN 0332-7795) 755
Revisor. (NE ISSN 0302-8852) 2881
Revisor Posten. (DK ISSN 0108-9196) 755
Revisorbladet. (DK) 755
Revisorhaandbogen. (DK) 755
Revisorn Informerar. (SW) 755
Revista A B B see A B B Review 1880
Revista A B P - A P A L see Associacao Brasileira de Psiquiatria e Asociacion Psiquiatrica de la America Latina. Revista 3331
Revista A C O M A C. (Asociacion de Comerciantes en Materiales para Construccion y Afines) (AG) 630
Revista A C O R. (Azucarera Cooperativa "Onesimo Redondo") (SP) 190
Revista A C P. (Automovel Club de Portugal) (PO ISSN 0870-273X) 4700
Revista A I B D A. (Asociacion Interamericana de Bibliotecarios y Documentalistas Agricolas) (CR ISSN 0250-3190) 2781, 116
Revista A M R I G S. (BL) 3147
Revista A P H. (Asociacion de Prensa Hondurena) (HO ISSN 0034-6926) 2180
Revista A T E M C O P. (Asociacion Espanola de Tecnicos de Maquinaria para la Construccion, Obras Publicas y Mineria) (SP) 1873
Revista Acento. (AG) 3004
Revista Acodal. (CK ISSN 0120-0798) 1925, 1873
Revista Aerea. (US ISSN 0279-4519) 61
Revista Aerea Latinoamericana see Revista Aerea 61
Revista Aeronautica. (CK ISSN 0034-6942) 61
Revista Agronomica de Manfredi see Revista Agropecuario de Manfredi y Marcos Juarez 190
Revista Agronomica del Noroeste Argentino. (AG ISSN 0080-2069) 116
Revista Agropecuaria. (CR ISSN 0048-7597) 116
Revista Agropecuario de Manfredi y Marcos Juarez. (AG ISSN 0327-151X) 190
Revista Alentejana. (PO ISSN 0034-6977) 2881
Revista Amazonense de Desenvolvimento. (BL) 1659
Revista Americana de Estudios Semioticos y Culturales/American Journal of Semiotic and Cultural Studies. (US) 2837, 2954
Revista Andina. (PE) 4384
Revista Argentina de Angiologia. (AG ISSN 0034-6993) 3211
Revista Argentina de Ciencia Politica. (AG ISSN 0034-7019) 3922
Revista Argentina de Ciencias Penales. (AG) 1522
Revista Argentina de Estudios Estrategicos. (AG ISSN 0326-6427) 3922
Revista Argentina de Estudios Politicos.(AG) 3922

Revista Argentina de Linguistica. (AG ISSN 0326-6400) 2837
Revista Argentina de Microbiologia. (AG ISSN 0325-7541) 557, 3188
Revista Argentina de Politica. (AG) 3922
Revista Argentina de Psicopedagogia. (AG) 4044
Revista Argentina de Relaciones Internacionales see Ceinar 3952
Revista Arhivelor. (RM ISSN 0034-7043) 2382, 2781
†Revista Artes de la Comunicacion. (CL) 5269
Revista Astronomica. (AG ISSN 0044-9253) 368
Revista Ateneo Dominicano. (DR) 3922
Revista Aunarte see Aunarte 2859
Revista Avicultura/Poultry Review. (CU ISSN 0138-6409) 224
Revista Awraq. (SP ISSN 0214-834X) 2383, 2954
Revista Baiana de Saude Publica. (BL ISSN 0100-0233) 4111
Revista Banca Central. (GT) 797
Revista Bancaria Brasileira. (BL ISSN 0034-706X) 797
Revista Bancos y Bancarios de Colombia see Bancos y Bancarios de Colombia 762
Revista Biblica. (AG ISSN 0034-7078) 4198
Revista Bilingue. see Bilingual Review 2806
Revista Boliviana de Investigacion. (BO) 4384
▼Revista Boliviana de Nefrologia. (BO ISSN 1018-5321) 3389
Revista Brasileira de Anestesiologia. (BL ISSN 0034-7094) 3192
▼Revista Brasileira de Anestesiologia - International Issue. (BL) 3192
Revista Brasileira de Bebidas e Alimentos. (BL) 385, 2080
Revista Brasileira de Biblioteconomia e Documentacao. (BL) 2781
Revista Brasileira de Biologia. (BL ISSN 0034-7108) 453
Revista Brasileira de Botanica/Brazilian Journal of Botany. (BL ISSN 0100-8404) 516
Revista Brasileira de Cancerologia. (BL ISSN 0034-7116) 3201
Revista Brasileira de Ciencias do Esporte. (BL ISSN 0101-3289) 4485
Revista Brasileira de Cirurgia. (BL ISSN 0034-7124) 3383
Revista Brasileira de Clinica e Terapeutica. (BL ISSN 0100-3232) 3147
Revista Brasileira de Economia. (BL ISSN 0034-7140) 688
Revista Brasileira de Enfermagem. (BL ISSN 0034-7167) 3286
Revista Brasileira de Entomologia. (BL ISSN 0085-5626) 537
Revista Brasileira de Estatistica/ Brazilian Statistical Journal. (BL ISSN 0034-7175) 4584
Revista Brasileira de Estudos Pedagogicos. (BL ISSN 0034-7183) 1659
Revista Brasileira de Estudos Politicos. (BL ISSN 0034-7191) 3922
Revista Brasileira de Farmacia. (BL ISSN 0370-372X) 3742
Revista Brasileira de Fisica. (BL ISSN 0374-4922) 3830
Revista Brasileira de Fisiologia Vegetal/ Brazilian Journal of Plant Physiology.(BL ISSN 0103-3131) 516
Revista Brasileira de Genetica. see Brazilian Journal of Genetics 540
Revista Brasileira de Geociencias. (BL) 1548
Revista Brasileira de Geografia/Brazilian Geographic Journal. (BL ISSN 0034-723X) 2261
Revista Brasileira de Historia. (BL) 2420, 1715
Revista Brasileira de Leprologia see Hansenologia Internationalis 3219
†Revista Brasileira de Lingua e Literatura. (BL ISSN 0101-8248) 5269

6612 REVISTA BRASILEIRA

Revista Brasileira de Malariologia e Doencas Tropicais. (BL ISSN 0034-7256) **3223**
Revista Brasileira de Medicina. (BL ISSN 0034-7264) **3147**
Revista Brasileira de Mercado de Capitais. (BL) **688**, 961
Revista Brasileira de Musica. (BL) **3577**
Revista Brasileira de Odontologia. (BL ISSN 0034-7272) **3241**
Revista Brasileira de Oftalmologia. (BL ISSN 0034-7280) **3304**
Revista Brasileira de Patologia Clinica. (BL ISSN 0034-7302) **3147**
Revista Brasileira de Pesquisas Medicas e Biologicas/Brazilian Journal of Medical and Biological Research. (BL ISSN 0100-879X) **3147**, 453
Revista Brasileira de Politica Internacional. (BL ISSN 0034-7329) **3970**
Revista Brasileira de Psiquiatria *see* Associacao Brasileira de Psiquiatria e Asociacion Psiquiatrica de la America Latina. Revista **3331**
Revista Brasileira de Tecnologia. (BL ISSN 0048-7643) **4607**, 4336
Revista Brasileira de Xadrez Postal. (BL) **4485**
Revista Brasileiro de Neurologia. (BL ISSN 0101-8469) **3353**
Revista Brasileira de Mandioca/Brazilian Journal of Cassava. (BL ISSN 0101-563X) **190**
Revista Brasileira de Sementes. *see* Brazilian Seed Journal 171
Revista C & I *see* C & I **2521**
Revista C E N I P E C. (Centro de Investigaciones Penales y Criminologicas) (VE) **1522**
Revista C I A F *see* Centro Interamericano de Fotointerpretacion. Revista **2245**
Revista Cafetalera/Coffee Review. (GT) **2080**
Revista Cafetera de Colombia. (CK ISSN 0120-2278) **2080**
Revista Camoniana. (BL ISSN 0486-6460) **2954**
Revista Campinense de Cultura. (BL ISSN 0034-7353) **2954**, 342
Revista Canaria de Estudios Ingleses. (SP ISSN 0211-5913) **2837**, 1479, 2954
Revista Canaria de Filosofia y Ciencia Social. (SP ISSN 0212-8780) **3779**, 4384
Revista Cartografica. (MX ISSN 0080-2085) **2261**
Revista Castilla. (SP ISSN 0378-200X) **2954**
Revista Catalana de Geografia. (SP ISSN 0210-6000) **2261**, 4784
Revista Catolica. (CL ISSN 0716-033X) **4274**
Revista Caucho. (AG ISSN 0528-3280) **4293**
Revista Cenic Ciencias Biologicas *see* Revista de Ciencias Biologicas **453**
†Revista Centaurus. (BL) **5269**
Revista Centroamericana de Administracion Publica. (CR) **4072**
Revista Centroamericana de Economia. (HO) **883**, 1000
Revista Ceres. (BL) **116**, 4815
Revista Chicano - Riquena *see* The America's Review **2894**
Revista Chilena de Antropologia. (CL ISSN 0716-3312) **248**
Revista Chilena de Derecho. (CL) **2672**
Revista Chilena de Entomologia. (CL ISSN 0034-740X) **537**
Revista Chilena de Historia y Geografia.(CL ISSN 0080-2093) **2420**
Revista Chilena de Literatura. (CL ISSN 0048-7651) **2954**
Revista Chilena de Neuropsiquiatria. (CL ISSN 0034-7388) **3353**
Revista Chilena de Obstetricia y Ginecologia. (CL ISSN 0048-766X) **3296**
Revista Chilena en Venta. (CL) **410**
Revista Ciencias Farmaceuticas. (CR) **3742**
Revista Ciencias Sociales. (EC) **4384**

Revista Ciencias Tecnicas Agropecuarias. (CU ISSN 1010-2760) **116**
Revista Citobiologica. *see* Cytobiologische Revue **5176**
Revista Clinica Espanola. (SP ISSN 0014-2565) **3147**
Revista Colombiana de Anestesiologia. (CK ISSN 0120-3347) **3192**
Revista Colombiana de Antropologia. (CK ISSN 0486-6525) **248**
Revista Colombiana de Ciencias Quimico Farmaceuticas. (CK ISSN 0034-7418) **3742**, 1186
Revista Colombiana de Investigacion Musical. (CK) **3577**
Revista Colombiana de Matematicas. (CK ISSN 0034-7426) **3052**
Revista Colombiana de Obstetricia y Ginecologia. (CK ISSN 0034-7434) **3296**
Revista Colombiana de Pediatria y Puericultura. (CK ISSN 0034-7442) **3326**
Revista Colombiana de Psiquiatria. (CK ISSN 0034-7450) **3353**
Revista COMALFI. (Sociedad Colombiana de Control de Malezas y Fisiologia Vegetal) (CK ISSN 0120-0682) **191**
Revista Comercio Exterior de Colombia.(CK ISSN 0120-324X) **920**
Revista Contactor. (CL) **1907**
Revista Contribuciones Cientificas y Tecnologicas. (CL) **4336**
Revista Costarricense de Ciencias Medicas. (CR ISSN 0253-2948) **3147**
Revista Critica de Ciencias Siciais. (PO ISSN 0254-1106) **4384**
Revista Cubana Cardiologia y Cirugia Cardiovascular. (CU) **3211**
Revista Cubana de Ciencia Agricola. (CU ISSN 0034-7485) **116**, 591
Revista Cubana de Ciencia Avicola. (CU ISSN 0138-6352) **224**
Revista Cubana de Ciencias Matematicas. (CU ISSN 0256-5374) **3052**
Revista Cubana de Ciencias Sociales. (CU) **4384**
Revista Cubana de Ciencias Veterinarias. (CU ISSN 0048-7678) **4815**
Revista Cubana de Cirugia. (CU ISSN 0034-7493) **3383**
Revista Cubana de Educacion Superior. (CU) **1715**
Revista Cubana de Enfermeria. (CU ISSN 0864-0319) **3286**
Revista Cubana de Estomatologia. (CU ISSN 0034-7507) **3241**
Revista Cubana de Farmacia. (CU ISSN 0034-7515) **3742**
Revista Cubana de Fisica. (CU ISSN 0253-9268) **3830**
Revista Cubana de Hematologia, Inmunologia y Hematerapia. (CU ISSN 0864-0289) **3273**
Revista Cubana de Higiene y Epidemiologia. (CU ISSN 0864-0319) **4111**, 3808
Revista Cubana de Investigaciones Biomedicas. (CU ISSN 0864-0300) **453**, 3147
Revista Cubana de Investigaciones Pesqueras *see* Revista Cubana de Investigaciones Pesqueras. Boletines Bibliograficos **2048**
Revista Cubana de Investigaciones Pesqueras. Boletines Bibliograficos. (CU) **2048**
Revista Cubana de Medicina. (CU ISSN 0034-7523) **3148**
Revista Cubana de Medicina General Integral. (CU ISSN 0864-2125) **3148**
Revista Cubana de Medicina Tropical. (CU) **3223**
Revista Cubana de Obstetricia y Ginecologia. (CU ISSN 0138-600X) **3296**
Revista Cubana de Oncologia. (CU ISSN 0864-0297) **3201**
Revista Cubana de Ortopedia y Traumatologia. (CU ISSN 0864-215X) **3311**
Revista Cubana de Pediatria. (CU ISSN 0034-7531) **3326**

Revista Cubana de Psicologia. (CU ISSN 0257-4322) **4044**
Revista Cubana de Quimica. (CU) **1186**
Revista Cubana de Reproduccion Animal. (CU ISSN 0138-6700) **453**
Revista Cubana de Salud Publica. (CU ISSN 0864-3466) **4111**
Revista Cubano de Derecho. (CU ISSN 0864-165X) **2672**
Revista Cuestiones Economicas *see* Cuestiones Economicas **775**
Revista Cultului Mozaic/Review of the Mosaic Creed. (RM ISSN 0034-754X) **2954**, 342, 4226
Revista Cultural Loteria *see* Loteria **2213**
Revista da Construcao Civil. (BL ISSN 0034-7566) **630**, 1873, 2495
Revista da Madeira. (BL ISSN 0034-7582) **2117**
Revista Danesa *see* Denmark Review **859**
Revista de Actualidad Odonto Estomatologica Espanola. (SP ISSN 1130-0094) **3241**
Revista de Actualidades de Estomatologica Espanola *see* Revista de Actualidad Odonto Estomatologica Espanola **3241**
Revista de Acustica. (SP ISSN 0210-3680) **3860**
Revista de Administracao. (BL ISSN 0080-2107) **1026**
Revista de Administracao de Empresas.(BL ISSN 0034-7590) **1026**
Revista de Administracao Municipal. (BL ISSN 0034-7604) **4094**, 1105, 2495, 3987
Revista de Administracao Publica. (BL ISSN 0034-7612) **4072**
Revista de Administracion Publica. (PR ISSN 0034-7620) **4072**
Revista de Administracion Publica. (SP ISSN 0034-7639) **4072**
Revista de Agricultura. (BL ISSN 0034-7655) **116**
Revista de Agroquimica y Tecnologia de Alimentos *see* Revista Espanola de Ciencia y Tecnologia de Alimentos **2080**
Revista de Analisis Economico. (CL ISSN 0716-5927) **883**
Revista de Antropologia. (EC) **248**
Revista de Antropologia. (BL ISSN 0034-7701) **248**
Revista de Antropologia *see* Revista de Antropologia y Arqueologia **248**
Revista de Antropologia y Arqueologia. (CK) **248**
Revista de Arqueologia. (BL) **282**
▼Revista de Arqueologia Americana. (MX) **282**
▼Revista de Arqueologia Mexicana. (MX ISSN 0188-3631) **282**
Revista de Arquitectura. (AG ISSN 0327-330X) **306**
Revista de Ascolbi. (CK ISSN 0121-0203) **2781**
Revista de Biblioteconomia de Brasilia. (BL ISSN 0100-7157) **2781**
Revista de Biologia. (PO ISSN 0034-7736) **453**
Revista de Biologia del Uruguay. (UY ISSN 0304-971X) **453**
Revista de Biologia Marina. (CL ISSN 0080-2115) **453**, 2048
Revista de Biologia Tropical. (CR ISSN 0034-7744) **453**
Revista de Chimie. (RM ISSN 0034-7752) **1187**
Revista de Chirurgie, Oncologie, Radiologie, O.R.L., Oftalmologie, Stomatologie. Chirurgia. (RM) **3383**
Revista de Chirurgie, Oncologie, Radiologie, O.R.L., Oftalmologie, Stomatologie. Oncologie. (RM) **3202**, 3148
Revista de Chirurgie, Oncologie, Radiologie, O.R.L., Oftalmologie, Stomatologie. Oftalmologie. (RM) **3304**
Revista de Chirurgie, Oncologie, Radiologie, O.R.L., Oftalmologie, Stomatologie. Radiologie. (RM ISSN 0481-6684) **3362**

Revista de Chirurgie, Oncologie, Radiologie, O.R.L., Oftalmologie, Stomatologie. Stomatologie. (RM) **3241**
†Revista de Ciencia Politica. (BL ISSN 0716-1417) **5270**
Revista de Ciencias Agricolas *see* Agronomia Costarricense **74**
Revista de Ciencias Biologicas. (CU ISSN 0258-6002) **453**
Revista de Ciencias Biomedicas. (BL ISSN 0101-322X) **3148**
Revista de Ciencias Economicas. Temas de Administracion *see* Administracion **1001**
Revista de Ciencias Economicas. Temas de Economia *see* Economia **660**
Revista de Ciencias Economicas: Economia, Financas, Administracao, Estatistica *see* Ciencias Economicas **655**
Revista de Ciencias Economicas y Sociales. (DR) **4384**
Revista de Ciencias Farmaceuticas. (BL ISSN 0101-3793) **3742**
Revista de Ciencias Juridicas Sociales. (AG ISSN 0325-0601) **2672**
Revista de Ciencias Penales. (CL) **1522**
Revista de Ciencias Quimicas. (CU ISSN 0254-0525) **1187**
Revista de Ciencias Sociais. (BL ISSN 0303-9862) **4384**
Revista de Ciencias Sociales. (PR ISSN 0034-7817) **4384**
Revista de Ciencias Sociales. (CR ISSN 0482-5276) **4384**
Revista de Ciencias Sociales. (VE) **4384**
Revista de Ciencias Sociales. (UY) **4446**
Revista de Citologia. (SP ISSN 0210-1130) **526**
Revista de Compendios de Articulos de Economia. (AG ISSN 0034-7825) **736**, 22
Revista de Comunicacao e Linguagens. (PO) **1342**, 2837
Revista de Construccion de Maquinarias. (CU) **3023**
Revista de Critica Literaria Latinoamericana. (US ISSN 0252-8843) **2954**
Revista de Cultura Vozes. (BL ISSN 0100-7076) **4384**
Revista de Debates: Debates en Antropologia *see* Anthropologica (Lima) **234**
Revista de Debates: Debates en Sociologia. (PE) **4446**
Revista de Derecho. (BO ISSN 0034-7868) **2672**
Revista de Derecho. (HO) **2672**
Revista de Derecho (Concepcion). (CL ISSN 0303-9986) **2672**, 4384
Revista de Derecho (Valparaiso). (CL) **2672**
Revista de Derecho Comercial *see* Revista de Derecho Comercial y de la Empresa **2672**
Revista de Derecho Comercial y de la Empresa. (UY) **2672**
Revista de Derecho Deportivo. (AG ISSN 0034-7884) **1659**, 4485
Revista de Derecho Internacional y Ciencias Diplomaticas. (AG ISSN 0034-7892) **2728**, 3970
Revista de Derecho, Jurisprudencia y Administracion. (UY ISSN 0034-7906) **2672**
Revista de Derecho Laboral. (AG) **2672**, 992
Revista de Derecho Penal. (UY) **2673**
Revista de Derecho Privado. (SP ISSN 0034-7922) **2673**
Revista de Derecho Procesal. (CL) **2673**
Revista de Derecho Publico. (SP ISSN 0210-2897) **2673**
Revista de Derecho Publico. (AG) **2673**
Revista de Derecho Publico. (VE) **2673**
Revista de Derecho Puertorriqueno. (PR ISSN 0034-7930) **2673**
Revista de Derecho Social Ecuatoriano. (EC ISSN 0484-6923) **2673**

Revista de Derecho y Ciencias Politicas.(PE ISSN 0034-7949) **2673**, 3922
Revista de Derecho y Reforma Agraria. (VE) **2673**, 116
Revista de Diagnostico Biologico. (SP ISSN 0034-7973) **3148**
Revista de Dialectologia y Tradiciones Populares. (SP ISSN 0034-7981) **2837**, 2058
†Revista de Direito Administrativo. (BL ISSN 0034-8007) **5270**
Revista de Direito Agrario. (BL) **2673**, 116
Revista de Direito Civil. (BL) **2673**
Revista de Direito do Trabalho (Petropolis). (BL) **2673**
Revista de Direito do Trabalho (Sao Paulo). (BL) **2673**, 992
Revista de Direito Mercantil, Industrial, Economico, e Financeiro. (BL) **2673**
Revista de Direito Publico. (BL ISSN 0034-8015) **2673**
Revista de Direito Tributario. (BL) **2673**
Revista de Economia. (PO) **688**
Revista de Economia de El Salvador *see* El Salvador: Coyuntura Economica **663**
Revista de Economia Latinoamericana *see* Banco Central de Venezuela. Revista **761**
Revista de Economia y Estadistica. (AG ISSN 0034-8066) **688**, 736, 4584
Revista de Edificacion. (SP ISSN 0213-8948) **306**
Revista de Educacao A E C. (BL) **1659**
Revista de Educacao e Cultura. (BL ISSN 0482-5527) **1659**
Revista de Educacion. (AG ISSN 0034-8074) **1659**
Revista de Educacion. (CR ISSN 0379-7082) **1659**
Revista de Educacion (Granada). (SP) **1659**
Revista de Educacion (Madrid). (SP ISSN 0034-8082) **1659**
Revista de Egresados. (CK ISSN 0120-1557) **1323**, 4607
Revista de Engenharia Mackenzie. (BL ISSN 0034-8112) **1835**
Revista de Ensino de Engenharia. (BL) **1835**
Revista de Espiritualidad. (SP ISSN 0034-8147) **4198**
Revista de Estetica/Aesthetics Magazine. (AG) **342**
Revista de Estudios Agro-Sociales. (SP ISSN 0034-8155) **116**
Revista de Estudios Andaluces. (SP ISSN 0212-8594) **2261**
Revista de Estudios Colombianos. (US) **2420**, 2954
Revista de Estudios Cooperativos. (SP ISSN 0425-3485) **4447**
Revista de Estudios de Administracion Local y Autonomica. (SP ISSN 0213-4675) **4094**
Revista de Estudios de Juventud. (SP ISSN 0211-4364) **4417**
Revista de Estudios Economicos. (DR) **688**
Revista de Estudios Extremenos. (SP ISSN 0210-2854) **2218**
Revista de Estudios Hispanicos. (PR ISSN 0378-7974) **2514**
Revista de Estudios Hispanicos. (US ISSN 0034-818X) **2954**, 2837
Revista de Estudios Historico Juridico. (CL) **2732**
Revista de Estudios Penitenciarios. (SP ISSN 0210-6035) **1522**
Revista de Estudios Politicos. (SP ISSN 0048-7694) **3922**
Revista de Estudios Procesales. (AG) **2673**
Revista de Estudios Sociales. (SP ISSN 0303-9889) **4447**
Revista de Estudos Ibero-Americanos. (BL) **2021**
Revista de Etnografia. (PO) **248**
Revista de Etnografie si Folclor. (RM ISSN 0034-8198) **248**, 2058
Revista de Extension Agraria. (SP ISSN 0210-1742) **116**
Revista de Farmacia e Odontologia *see* Especialidades Odontologicas **3233**

Revista de Farmacologia Clinica y Experimental. (SP ISSN 0213-0157) **3742**
Revista de Ferreteria. (SP ISSN 0210-7988) **643**
Revista de Filologia. (SP ISSN 0212-4130) **2837**, 2954
Revista de Filologia Espanola. (SP ISSN 0210-9174) **2837**
Revista de Filologia y Linguistica. (CR ISSN 0377-628X) **2837**
Revista de Filosofia. (CL ISSN 0034-8236) **3779**
Revista de Filosofia. (CR ISSN 0034-8252) **3779**
Revista de Filosofia. (VE) **3779**
Revista de Filosofia. (MX ISSN 0185-3481) **3779**
Revista de Filosofie/Revue de Philosophie. (RM ISSN 0034-8260) **3779**
Revista de Financas Publicas *see* Financas Publicas **1094**
Revista de Fizica si Chimie. (RM) **3830**, 1187
Revista de Fomento Social. (SP ISSN 0015-6043) **4447**
Revista de Gastronomia y Enologia. (SP) **2480**, 385
Revista de Geofisica. (SP ISSN 0034-8279) **1593**
Revista de Geografia. (SP ISSN 0048-7708) **2261**
Revista de Geografia. (BL ISSN 0101-9457) **2261**
Revista de Geografia. (MX ISSN 0186-2715) **2261**
Revista de Geografia Canaria. (SP ISSN 0213-9480) **2261**, 1548
Revista de Geografia e Ensino. (BL) **2261**
Revista de Guimaraes. (PO ISSN 0034-8295) **2383**
Revista de Hacienda. (VE) **883**
Revista de Historia. (CK) **2320**
Revista de Historia. (CU ISSN 0138-8207) **2320**, 248, 282, 1758
Revista de Historia. (BL ISSN 0034-8309) **2420**
Revista de Historia. (CR ISSN 1012-9790) **2420**
Revista de Historia Contemporanea. (SP ISSN 0212-4416) **2383**
Revista de Historia de America. (MX ISSN 0034-8325) **2421**
Revista de Historia de Canarias. (SP ISSN 0213-9480) **2383**
Revista de Historia de Derecho. (AG) **2673**
Revista de Historia de las Ideas. (EC ISSN 0556-5987) **2421**
Revista de Historia de Rosario. (AG ISSN 0556-5995) **2421**
Revista de Historia Economica e Social. (PO) **2320**, 897
Revista de Historia Economica e Social. Cadernos. (PO) **2320**, 897
Revista de Historia Jeronimo Zurita. (SP ISSN 0044-5517) **2383**
Revista de Humanidades, Ciencias Sociales y Relaciones Internacionales.(BO) **4384**
Revista de Igiena, Bacteriologie, Virusologie, Parazitologie, Pneumoftiziologie. Bacteriologie, Virusologie, Parazitologie, Epidemiologie. (RM ISSN 0301-7338) **557**, 3223, 4111
Revista de Igiena, Bacteriologie, Virusologie, Parazitologie, Pneumoftiziologie. Igiena. (RM ISSN 0019-1620) **3808**, 3148
Revista de Igiena, Bacteriologie, Virusologie, Parazitologie, Pneumoftiziologie. (RM) **3367**, 3223
Revista de Imprensa. (PO) **4005**
Revista de Indias. (SP ISSN 0034-8341) **2421**, 4384
Revista de Informacao Legislativa. (BL ISSN 0034-835X) **2673**
Revista de Informacion Cientifica y Tecnica Cubana. (CU ISSN 0138-6107) **4336**
Revista de Ingenieria. (AG ISSN 0482-5772) **1835**
Revista de Ingenieria/Engineering Review. (UY) **1835**

Revista de Ingenieria Mecanica. (CL) **1922**
Revista de Interpretacion Biblica Latinoamericana. (CR) **4198**
Revista de Investigacion Clinica. (MX ISSN 0034-8376) **3148**, 3612
Revista de Investigacion Contable (Teuken). (AG ISSN 0327-022X) **755**
Revista de Investigaciones Marinas. (CU ISSN 0252-1962) **453**
Revista de Investigaciones Pecuarias. (PE) **4815**
Revista de Istorie *see* Revista Istorica **2383**
Revista de Istorie a Moldovei/Moldavskii Istoricheskii Zhurnal. (MV ISSN 0236-3100) **2383**
Revista de Istorie Militara. (RM ISSN 1220-5710) **3469**
Revista de la C E P A L *see* C E P A L Review **849**
Revista de la Educacion Superior. (MX) **1715**
Revista de la Facultad de Derecho. (SP) **2673**
Revista de la Fuerza Aerea *see* Fuerza Aerea **3459**
Revista de la Integracion *see* Integracion Latinoamericana **931**
Revista de la Integracion Centroamericana *see* Revista de la Integracion y el Desarrollo de Centroamerica **934**
Revista de la Integracion y el Desarrollo de Centroamerica. (HO) **934**
Revista de la Lengua Inglesa. *see* English Language Journal **2812**
▼Revista de la Medicina Tradicional China. (SP ISSN 1130-4405) **3148**, 3215
Revista de la O T A N *see* N A T O Review **3908**
Revista de la Promocion Tecnica de la Industria de Generos de Punto *see* Revista Tecnica de la Industria de Generos de Punto **1287**
Revista de la Salud. (SP) **3808**
Revista de la Secretaria de Estado de Trabajo, Economia y Comercio (1953-1954) *see* Dominican Republic. Secretaria de Estado de Industria y Comercio. Revista **835**
Revista de las Fuerzas Armadas. (CK ISSN 0120-0631) **3469**
Revista de las Fuerzas Armadas. (VE ISSN 0034-8473) **3469**
Revista de Legislacao e de Jurisprudencia. (PO ISSN 0870-8487) **2673**
Revista de Legislacion Argentina. (AG ISSN 0034-8481) **2673**
Revista de Legislacion y Documentacion en Derecho y Ciencias Sociales. (CL) **2673**, 4384
Revista de Letras. (BL ISSN 0101-3505) **2954**
Revista de Libreria Antiquaria. (SP ISSN 0211-3945) **2383**, 2781
Revista de Literatura. (SP) **2954**, 3779
Revista de Literatura Cubana. (CU ISSN 0138-6948) **2954**
Revista de Literatura Hispanoamericana. (VE) **2954**
Revista de Marina. (CL ISSN 0034-8511) **3469**
Revista de Marina. (EC ISSN 0034-852X) **3469**
Revista de Marina del Peru. (PE ISSN 0034-8538) **3469**
Revista de Marinha. (PO ISSN 0034-8546) **2048**
Revista de Matematica e Estatistica. (BL ISSN 0102-0811) **3052**
Revista de Matematica y Fisica Teorica. Serie A. (AG ISSN 0080-2360) **3830**
Revista de Medicina. (BL ISSN 0034-8554) **3148**
Revista de Medicina. (SP ISSN 0556-6177) **3148**
Revista de Medicina Interna, Neurologie, Psichiatrie, Neuro-Chirurgie, Dermato-Venerologie. Medicina Interna. (RM ISSN 0025-7869) **3148**

REVISTA 6613

Revista de Medicina Interna, Neurologie, Psihiatrie, Neuro-Chirurgie, Dermato-Venerologie. (RM ISSN 0028-386X) **3353**, 3249
Revista de Medicina Militar. (CU) **3148**
Revista de Medicina Militara. (RM) **3148**, 3469
Revista de Medicina si Farmacie/Orvosi es Gyogyszereszeti Szemle. (RM) **3148**
Revista de Medicina Veterinaria y Parasitologia *see* Universidad Central de Venezuela. Facultad de Ciencias Veterinarias. Revista **4816**
Revista de Menorca. (SP) **2881**
Revista de Metalurgia. (SP ISSN 0034-8570) **3418**
Revista de Microbiologia. (BL ISSN 0001-3714) **557**
Revista de Minas. (SP ISSN 0210-8356) **3494**
Revista de Mineria y Geologia. (CU) **3494**
Revista de Musica Latino Americana. *see* Latin American Music Review **3561**
Revista de Musicologia. (SP ISSN 0210-1459) **3577**
Revista de Neuro-Psiquiatria. (PE ISSN 0034-8597) **3353**
Revista de Normalizacion. (CU ISSN 0138-8118) **4336**, 3448
Revista de Nutricion y Aterosclerosis. (AG ISSN 0034-8600) **3612**, 3211
Revista de Obras Publicas. (SP ISSN 0034-8619) **1873**
Revista de Obras Sanitarias de la Nacion. (AG ISSN 0034-8627) **1873**
Revista de Obstetricia y Ginecologia de Venezuela. (VE ISSN 0048-7732) **3296**
Revista de Occidente. (SP ISSN 0034-8635) **2881**
Revista de Ortopedia y Traumatologia. (SP ISSN 0482-5985) **3311**
Revista de Otorrinolaringologia y Cirugia de Cabeza y Cuello. (CL ISSN 0716-4084) **3316**
Revista de Pedagogia *see* Universidade de Sao Paulo. Faculdade de Educacao. Revista **1669**
Revista de Pediatrie, Obstetrica, Ginecologie. Obstetrica si Ginecologie.(RM ISSN 0029-781X) **3296**
Revista de Pediatrie, Obstetrica, Ginecologie. Pediatrie. (RM ISSN 0031-3904) **3326**
Revista de Plasticos Modernos. (SP ISSN 0034-8708) **3868**
Revista de Poesia Centroamericana. (CR) **3004**
Revista de Precos para Construcao de Predios. (BL) **630**
Revista de Precos para Instalacoes Eletricas e Hidraulicas. (BL) **3023**
Revista de Prevencion. (SP ISSN 0034-8732) **4111**
Revista de Processo. (BL) **2673**
Revista de Produccion Animal. (CU) **224**
Revista de Proteccion Vegetal. (CU) **191**
Revista de Psicanalise Integral. (BL) **4044**
Revista de Psicoanalisis. (AG ISSN 0034-8740) **4044**
Revista de Psicologia. (PE ISSN 0254-9247) **4044**
Revista de Psicologia Normal e Patologica. (BL ISSN 0048-7740) **4044**
Revista de Psihologie. (RM ISSN 0034-8759) **4044**
†Revista de Psiquiatria Dinamica. (BL ISSN 0034-8767) **5270**
Revista de Publicaciones Navales. (AG ISSN 0034-8775) **3477**
Revista de Quimica Textil. (SP ISSN 0300-9718) **4623**
Revista de Referate in Bibliologie *see* Biblioteconomie. Culegere de Traduceri Prelucrate **2792**
Revista de Relaciones Internacionales *see* Relaciones Internacionales **3970**

6614 REVISTA

Revista de Revistas. (MX) **410**
Revista de Robotica *see* Automatizacion Integrada y Revista de Robotica **1877**
Revista de Salud Animal. (CU) **4815**
Revista de Sanidad e Higiene Publica. (SP ISSN 0034-8899) **4111**
Revista de Saude Publica. (BL ISSN 0034-8910) **4111**
Revista de Seguridad Social. (SP ISSN 0210-4792) **4417**
Revista de Senologia y Patologia Mamaria. (SP ISSN 0214-1582) **3296**
Revista de Servicio Social. (PR ISSN 0034-8937) **4418**
Revista de Sociologia. (CK) **4447**
Revista de Soldadura. (SP ISSN 0048-7759) **3430**
Revista de Statistica. (RM ISSN 0035-8037) **4584**
Revista de Teatro. (BL ISSN 0102-7336) **4637**
Revista de Tecnologia Educativa. (PE ISSN 0034-866X) **1442, 1400**
Revista de Tecnologia Educativa. (CL) **1659**
†Revista de Temas Militares. (AG) **5270**
Revista de Trabajo. (SP ISSN 0034-897X) **992**
Revista de Trabajo. (VE ISSN 0034-8988) **992**
Revista de Tuberculosis del Uruguay *see* Torax **3367**
Revista del Caucho. (SP ISSN 0212-2138) **4293**
Revista del Comercio. (CU) **839**
Revista del Derecho Industrial. (AG) **2673, 688**
Revista del Ejercito. (MX ISSN 0034-9046) **3469**
Revista del Ejercito y Armada. (PY ISSN 0034-9054) **3470**
Revista del Hogar. (AG ISSN 0034-9070) **4274**
Revista del Museo Americanista. (AG) **3532**
Revista del Pensamiento Centroamericano. (CR ISSN 0378-3340) **3922, 2881**
Revista del Suboficial. (AG ISSN 0034-9119) **3470**
Revista Desarrollo y Sociedad *see* Desarrollo y Sociedad **859**
Revista Diners. (CK) **2183**
Revista Diners. (EC) **4785**
Revista Diners - Mundo. (CL) **2480**
Revista Diplomatica e Internacional. (BO ISSN 0034-9194) **3971**
Revista do Ar. (PO ISSN 0034-9208) **61**
Revista do B I N D E. (Banco Nacional do Desenvolvimento Economico) (BL) **798**
Revista do Comercio de Cafe. (BL ISSN 0034-9224) **2080**
Revista do Exercito Brasileiro. (BL ISSN 0101-7284) **3470**
Revista do Gas. (BL) **3700**
†Revista do Livro (Rio de Janeiro). (BL ISSN 0035-0605) **5270**
Revista do Livro (Sao Paulo). (BL) **4136**
Revista do Produtor de Leite. (BL) **203**
Revista do Seite. (BL) **4584**
Revista do Servico Publico. (BL ISSN 0034-9240) **4072**
Revista do Setor de Ciencias Agrarias. (BL ISSN 0100-607X) **116**
Revista DocPop. (BL ISSN 0101-7217) **3987, 2261**
Revista Documentos de Ciencia y Tecnica. (CU) **4336**
Revista Dominicana de Antropologia e Historia. (DR) **248, 2421**
Revista dos Criadores. (BL ISSN 0034-9259) **224**
Revista dos Tribunais. (BL ISSN 0034-9275) **2673**
Revista Doyma de Inmunologia *see* Inmunologia **3186**
†Revista E A C. (CL ISSN 0302-8003) **5270**
Revista E A F I T - Temas Administrativos *see* Revista Universidad E A F I T **1026**
Revista Eclesiastica Brasileira. (BL) **4198**

Revista Economia *see* Economia **660**
Revista Economia. (VE) **688, 4584**
Revista Economia. (PN) **883**
Revista Economia Politica. (BL ISSN 0101-3157) **3922, 883**
Revista Economica *see* I I E. Revista **669**
Revista Economica. (AG ISSN 0013-0419) **688**
Revista Economica *see* Revista Economica do Nordeste **883**
Revista Economica *see* Tribuna Economica **886**
Revista Economica do Nordeste. (BL ISSN 0100-4956) **883**
Revista Economica y Financiera *see* Universidad Nacional Mayor de San Marcos. Facultad de Ciencias Economicas y Comerciales. Revista **696**
Revista Economica Y Politica. (AG) **897**
Revista Ecuatoriana de Higiene y Medicina Tropical. (EC ISSN 0048-7775) **3223**
Revista Ecuatoriana de Historia Economica. (EC) **688, 798**
Revista Ecuatoriana de Medicina y Ciencias Biologicas. (EC ISSN 0034-9313) **3148, 453**
Revista Electrotecnica. (AG ISSN 0370-7857) **1907**
Revista Embalagem Vende. (BL) **1052**
Revista Encuentro *see* Encuentro **2506**
Revista Energetica. (EC) **1795**
Revista Espanola de Anestesiologia y Reanimacion. (SP ISSN 0034-9356) **3192**
Revista Espanola de Cardiologia. (SP ISSN 0300-8932) **3211**
Revista Espanola de Ciencia y Tecnologia de Alimentos/Spanish Journal of Food Science and Technology. (SP ISSN 1131-799X) **2080**
Revista Espanola de Cirugia Oral y Maxilofacial. (SP ISSN 1130-0558) **3383, 3241**
Revista Espanola de Derecho Canonico. (SP ISSN 0034-9372) **4199**
Revista Espanola de Derecho Constitucional. (SP) **2706**
Revista Espanola de Derecho Internacional. (SP ISSN 0034-9380) **2728**
Revista Espanola de Derecho Militar. (SP ISSN 0034-9399) **2673, 3470**
Revista Espanola de Documentacion Cientifica. (SP ISSN 0210-0614) **2782, 4336**
Revista Espanola de Economia. (SP ISSN 0210-1025) **688**
Revista Espanola de Electronica. (SP) **1907**
Revista Espanola de Endodoncia. (SP ISSN 0212-4688) **3241**
Revista Espanola de Entomologia. (SP) **537**
Revista Espanola de Fisiologia. (SP ISSN 0034-9402) **574, 3148**
Revista Espanola de Geriatria y Gerontologia. (SP ISSN 0211-139X) **2278**
Revista Espanola de Investigaciones Sociologicas. (SP ISSN 0210-5233) **4447**
Revista Espanola de las Enfermedades del Aparato Digestivo *see* Revista Espanola de las Enfermedades Digestivas **3269**
Revista Espanola de las Enfermedades Digestivas. (SP ISSN 1130-4588) **3269**
Revista Espanola de Lecheria. (SP ISSN 0300-5550) **203**
Revista Espanola de Linguistica. (SP ISSN 0210-1874) **2837**
Revista Espanola de Medicina Legal. (SP) **3265**
Revista Espanola de Medicina Nuclear. (SP ISSN 0212-6982) **3362**
Revista Espanola de Micropaleontologia.(SP ISSN 0556-655X) **3660**
Revista Espanola de Ortodoncia. (SP ISSN 0210-0576) **3241**

Revista Espanola de Pedagogia. (SP ISSN 0034-9461) **1659**
Revista Espanola de Pediatria. (SP ISSN 0034-947X) **3326**
Revista Espanola de Quimioterapia/ Spanish Journal of Chemotherapy. (SP ISSN 0214-3429) **3263**
Revista Espanola de Reumatismo y Enfermedades Osteoarticulares. (SP ISSN 0048-7791) **3369**
Revista Espanola de Reumatologia. (SP ISSN 0304-4815) **3369**
Revista Espanola de Teologia. (SP ISSN 0210-7112) **4199**
Revista Estadistica. (CU) **883**
Revista Estudios Dominicanos. (DR) **3922**
Revista Estudos Economicos. (BL ISSN 0101-4161) **689, 897**
Revista Europea de Estudios Latinoamericanos y del Caribe. *see* European Review of Latin American and Caribbean Studies **4371**
Revista F A. (Facultad de Arquitectura) (MX) **306**
Revista Farmaceutica. (AG ISSN 0034-9496) **3742**
Revista Fasecolda. (CK ISSN 0120-1972) **2541**
Revista FeLaBan. (CK) **798**
Revista Ferroviaria. (BL ISSN 0034-950X) **4714**
Revista Filologia Moderna *see* Filologia Moderna **2814**
Revista Forestal Baracoa. (CU ISSN 0138-6441) **2117, 3666**
Revista Forestal Latinoamericana. (VE ISSN 0798-2437) **2107**
Revista Foro. (CK) **4384**
†Revista Fotoptica. (BL) **5270**
Revista Gaucha de Odontologia. (BL ISSN 0034-9542) **3241**
Revista General de Marina. (SP ISSN 0034-9569) **3470**
Revista Geofisica. (MX ISSN 0252-9769) **1594**
Revista Geografica. (MX ISSN 0556-6630) **2261**
Revista Geografica de America Central. (CR) **2261**
Revista Geografica de Valparaiso. (CL ISSN 0034-9577) **2261**
Revista Geografica Venezolana. (VE) **2261**
Revista Geologica de Chile. (CL ISSN 0716-0208) **1579**
Revista Goiana de Medicina. (BL ISSN 0034-9585) **3148**
Revista Habis. (SP ISSN 0210-7694) **1279**
Revista Hispanica Moderna. (US ISSN 0034-9593) **2954**
Revista Historia, Instituciones, Documentos. (SP ISSN 0210-7716) **3922**
Revista Historia Natural de Costa Rica *see* Brenesia **4302**
Revista Historica *see* Historica **2409**
Revista Historica. (UY) **2421**
†Revista Historica. (AG) **5270**
Revista Historica Hungara. *see* Magyar Tortenelmi Szemle **2374**
†Revista Historico: Critica de Literatura Centroamericana. (CR) **5270**
Revista I C A I T I. (Instituto Centroamericano de Investigacion y Tecnologia Industrial) (GT) **4607**
Revista I M C Y C *see* Construccion y Tecnologia **611**
Revista Iberica de Micologia *see* Revista Iberoamericana de Micologia **516**
Revista Iberica de Parasitologia. (SP ISSN 0034-9623) **3223, 557**
Revista Iberoamericana. (US ISSN 0034-9631) **2954**
Revista Iberoamericana de Corrosion y Proteccion. (SP ISSN 0210-6604) **3418**
Revista Iberoamericana de Micologia. (SP) **516, 557, 3148**
Revista Iberoamericana de Trombosis y Hemostasia. (SP ISSN 0214-3941) **3211, 3273**
Revista Idea. (AG) **1026**
Revista Ideas y Valores. (CK) **3779**
Revista Interamericana *see* Revista - Review Interamericana **2215**
Revista Interamericana de Bibliografia. (US ISSN 0250-6262) **410**

Revista Interamericana de Bibliografia. *see* Inter-American Review of Bibliography **2520**
Revista Interamericana de Bibliotecologia. (CK ISSN 0120-0976) **2782**
Revista Interamericana de Educacion de Adultos. (MX) **1686**
Revista Interamericana de Planificacion. Correo Informativo. (GT) **934**
†Revista Interamericana de Radiologia. (US ISSN 0034-9704) **5270**
Revista Interamericana de Sociologia. (MX ISSN 0557-8558) **4447**
Revista Internacional de Ajedrez. (SP ISSN 0214-8900) **4485**
Revista Internacional de Ciencias Sociales. (SP ISSN 0379-0762) **4384**
Revista Internacional de Comunicacion y Relaciones Publicas. (SP ISSN 0211-3333) **38**
Revista Internacional de Entidades Fiscalizadoras Superiores. *see* International Journal of Government Auditing **4064**
Revista Internacional de Estudos Africanos. (PO ISSN 0871-2344) **2334, 2021**
Revista Internacional de la Cruz Roja *see* International Review of the Red Cross **2725**
Revista Internacional de los Estudios Vascos. (SP ISSN 0212-7016) **248**
Revista Internacional de Luminotecnia *see* International Lighting Review **621**
Revista Internacional de Musica Sagrada. *see* Rivista Internazionale di Musica Sacra **3578**
Revista Internacional de Pediatria. (CK ISSN 0120-6311) **3326**
Revista Internacional de Politica Criminal *see* International Review of Criminal Policy **1516**
Revista Internacional de Proteccion Civil. *see* International Civil Defence Journal **1273**
Revista Internacional de Seguridad Social *see* International Social Security Review **2535**
Revista Internacional de Sociologia. (SP ISSN 0034-9712) **4447**
▼Revista Internacional de Sociologia sobre Agricultura y Alimentos/ International Journal of Sociology of Agriculture and Food. (VE ISSN 0798-1759) **4447, 116, 2081**
†Revista Internacional de Vivienda Rural/International Rural Housing Journal. (VE) **5270**
Revista Internacional del Trabajo. (UN ISSN 0378-5548) **992, 4111, 4447**
Revista Internacional la Ensenanza Comercial. *see* International Review for Business Education **672**
Revista Investigaciones Marinas. (CL ISSN 0716-1069) **1610, 591**
Revista Ion. (CK ISSN 0120-100X) **1859**
Revista Istorica. (RM ISSN 0567-6304) **2383**
Revista Juridica. (BL ISSN 0034-9739) **2673**
Revista Juridica. (BO) **2673**
Revista Juridica. (CU) **2673**
Revista Juridica Argentina: La Ley *see* Ley **2649**
Revista Juridica de Cataluna. (SP ISSN 0210-4296) **2673**
Revista Juridica del Peru. (PE) **2673**
Revista Juridica del Trabajo. (CL) **2673, 992**
Revista Juridica Dominicana. (DR) **2673**
Revista la Nacion. (AG) **2170**
Revista Lagascalia. (SP ISSN 0210-7708) **516**
Revista Latinoamericana de Estudios Educativos. (MX ISSN 0185-1284) **1659, 4384**
Revista Latinoamericana de Estudios Etnolinguisticos. (PE) **2837**
Revista Latinoamericana de Estudios Urbano Regionales. (CL ISSN 0250-7161) **2495**

Revista Latinoamericana de Filosofia. (AG ISSN 0325-0725) **3779**
Revista Latinoamericana de Geotechnica. (VE) **1873**
†Revista Latinoamericana de Ingenieria Quimica y Quimica Aplicada/Latin American Journal of Chemical Engineering and Applied Chemistry. (AG ISSN 0325-0474) **5270**
Revista Latinoamericana de Microbiologia. (MX ISSN 0034-9771) **557**
Revista Latinoamericana de Psicologia. (CK ISSN 0120-0534) **4044**
Revista Latinoamericana de Quimica. (MX ISSN 0370-5943) **1187**
Revista Letras. (BL ISSN 0100-0888) **2954**, 2837
Revista Libros Elegidos. (AG) **4136**
Revista Lusitana. (PO) **248**
Revista Manizales. (CK ISSN 0034-9852) **2881**
Revista Mar - Vela e Motor. (BL) **4700**, 4528
Revista Maritima Brasileira. (BL ISSN 0034-9860) **3470**
Revista Matematica Iberoamericana. (SP ISSN 0213-2230) **3052**
Revista Materiale Plastice see Materiale Plastice **3864**
Revista Mea. (IS) **2204**
Revista Medica (La Paz). (BO) **3148**
Revista Medica da Aeronautica do Brasil. (BL ISSN 0370-6141) **3148**, 3470
Revista Medica de Chile. (CL ISSN 0034-9887) **3148**
Revista Medica de Costa Rica. (CR ISSN 0034-9909) **3148**
Revista Medica de Mocambique. (MZ) **3148**
Revista Medica de Valparaiso. (CL ISSN 0034-9917) **3148**
Revista Medica del Hospital General de Mexico S.S.A. (MX ISSN 0034-9925) **3148**
Revista Medica del Paraguay. (PY ISSN 0034-9933) **3148**
Revista Medica do Estado da Guanabara see Revista Medica do Estado do Rio de Janeiro **3148**
Revista Medica do Estado do Rio de Janeiro. (BL ISSN 0100-0195) **3148**
Revista Medicala - Medical Review see Revista de Medicina si Farmacie **3148**
Revista Medico-Chirurgicala. (RM ISSN 0048-7848) **3148**, 3383
Revista Mensajero. (EC) **4199**
Revista Mensal de Exportacao/ Exportation Monthly Review. (BL ISSN 0014-5203) **920**
Revista Mexicana de Analisis de la Conducta/Mexican Journal of Behavior Analysis. (MX ISSN 0185-4534) **4045**
Revista Mexicana de Astronomia y Astrofisica. (MX ISSN 0185-1101) **368**, 3830
Revista Mexicana de Ciencias Politicas y Sociales. (MX ISSN 0185-1918) **3922**
Revista Mexicana de Fianzas. (MX ISSN 0556-6835) **798**
Revista Mexicana de Fisica. (MX ISSN 0035-001X) **3830**
Revista Mexicana de Fitopatologia. (MX ISSN 0185-3309) **191**
Revista Mexicana de la Propiedad Industrial y Artistica. (MX ISSN 0035-0044) **3678**
Revista Mexicana de Micologia. (MX ISSN 0187-3180) **516**, 557, 3148
Revista Mexicana de Oftalmologia. (MX ISSN 0187-4519) **3304**
Revista Mexicana de Seguros Fianzas y Finanzas. (MX) **798**
Revista Mexicana de Sociologia. (MX ISSN 0188-2503) **4447**
Revista Mexicana del Petroleo. (MX) **3700**
Revista Militar. (DR ISSN 0035-0117) **3470**
Revista Militar Brasileira see Revista do Exercito Brasileiro **3470**
Revista Militar del Peru. (PE ISSN 0035-0141) **3470**

Revista Minelor see Mine, Petrol si Gaze **3692**
Revista Minera Bamin. (BO) **3494**
Revista Mjekesore. (AA ISSN 0255-6790) **3148**
Revista Monitor de Radio e Televisao. (BL) **1359**, 1379
▼Revista Musica. (BL ISSN 0103-5525) **3577**
Revista Musical Chilena. (CL ISSN 0716-2790) **3577**
Revista Muzeelor. (RM) **3532**
Revista Muzeelor si Monumentelor. Monumente Istorice si de Arta see Monumente Istorice si de Arta **3527**
Revista Muzeelor si Monumentelor. Muzee see Revista Muzeelor **3532**
Revista Nacional de Aeronautica see Aeroespacio **43**
Revista Nacional de Agricultura. (CK ISSN 0035-0222) **117**
Revista Nacional de Cultura. (CR) **2421**, 342
Revista Nacional de Cultura. (PN) **2514**
Revista Nacional de Cultura. (AG) **2514**
Revista Nacional de Cultura. (VE) **2514**
†Revista Nacional de Oncologia. (SP ISSN 0482-640X) **5270**
Revista Natura. (SP) **2107**
Revista Negocios. (PO) **689**
Revista O C L A E see O C L A E Revista **2878**
Revista o Carreteiro. (BL) **4655**
Revista o Produtor Rural. (BL) **117**
Revista Obra - Planejamento e Construcao. (BL) **630**
Revista Odontologica. (CK ISSN 0120-2855) **3241**
Revista Odontologica see Universidad Nacional de Cordoba. Facultad de Odontologica. Revista **3243**
Revista Odontologica de Merida see Universidad de Los Andes. Facultad de Odontologica. Revista **3243**
Revista Olimpica see Olympic Review (Year) **4482**
Revista Otorrinolaringologica. (VE) **3316**
Revista Pacifico Sur. (CL) **453**
Revista Padurilor. (RM) **2107**
Revista Padurilor-Industria Lemnului-Celuloza si Hirtie see Celuloza si Hirtie **3662**
Revista Padurilor-Industria Lemnului, Celuloza si Hirtie, Silvicultura si Exploatarea Padurilor see Revista Padurilor **2107**
Revista Panamena de la Construccion. (PN) **630**
Revista para Jubilados y Pensionados. (AG) **2278**, 2541
▼Revista para Novias. (US) **3067**
Revista Paraguaya de Microbiologia. (PY ISSN 0556-6908) **557**, 591
Revista Paraguaya de Sociologia. (PY ISSN 0035-0354) **4447**
Revista Pasos. (CR) **4199**, 4384
Revista Pastos y Forrajes. (CU) **203**
Revista Patagonica. (AG ISSN 0326-0658) **2261**
Revista Paulista de Medicina. (BL ISSN 0035-0362) **3149**
Revista Paulista de Odontologia. (BL ISSN 0100-705X) **3241**
Revista Pecuaria/Ranching Review. (VE) **224**
Revista Pedagogjike. (AA ISSN 0304-3509) **1659**
Revista Pernambucana de Folclore. (BL) **2058**
Revista Perspectiva Educacional. (CL) **1715**
Revista Peruana de Ciencias Sociales. (PE ISSN 1011-0410) **4384**
Revista Peruana de Derecho de la Empresa. (PE) **2673**
Revista Peruana de Derecho Internacional. (PE ISSN 0035-0370) **2728**
Revista Peruana de Entomologia. (PE ISSN 0080-2425) **537**
Revista Philosophica. (CL) **3779**
Revista Plantas Medicinales. (CU ISSN 0138-6492) **117**
Revista Politica Comparada. (SP ISSN 0211-5581) **3922**, 2673

Revista Portuguesa de Ciencias Veterinarias. (PO ISSN 0035-0389) **4815**
Revista Portuguesa de Estomatologia e Cirurgia Maxilo-Facial. (PO ISSN 0035-0397) **3241**, 3383
Revista Portuguesa de Farmacia. (PO) **3742**
Revista Portuguesa de Filologia. (PO ISSN 0080-2433) **2837**
Revista Portuguesa de Filosofia. (PO ISSN 0870-5283) **3779**
Revista Portuguesa de Medicina Militar.(PO ISSN 0482-7171) **3149**
Revista Portuguesa de Pediatria e Puericultura. (PO ISSN 0048-7880) **3326**
Revista Portuguesa de Psicanalise. (PO) **4045**
Revista Presencia see Presencia **4196**
Revista Profesional del Gremio de Estaciones de Servicio. (SP) **2588**, 3700
Revista Quirurgica Espanola see British Journal of Surgery (Edicion Espanola) **3376**
Revista Realidad e Rural/Rural Realty. (BL) **117**
†Revista Referativa. Organizacion de la Direccion. (CU ISSN 0138-6921) **5270**
Revista Referativa de Educacion. (CU) **1659**
Revista Referativo de la Construccion see Servicio Referativo de la Construccion **638**
Revista Relaciones de Trabajo. (VE) **992**
Revista - Review Interamericana. (PR ISSN 0360-7917) **2215**
Revista Rodoviaria. (BL) **4720**
Revista Romana de Drept. (RM ISSN 0035-0435) **2673**
▼Revista Romana de Proprietate Industriala/Romanian Review for Industrial Property. (RM ISSN 1220-3009) **3678**
Revista Romana de Sah. (RM) **4485**
Revista Romana de Studii Internationale/Romanian Journal of International Studies. (RM) **920**, 934
Revista Romana de Studii Internationale see Revue Roumaine d'Etudes Internationales **3971**
†Revista Rotaria. (US ISSN 0035-0443) **5270**
Revista S A I. (Sociedad Antioquena de Ingenieros y Arquitectos) (CK ISSN 0120-5862) **1835**, 306
Revista Sanitara Militara see Revista de Medicina Militara **3148**
Revista Sao Paulo em Perspectiva. (BL ISSN 0102-8839) **4384**
Revista Scriitorilor Romani. (IT ISSN 0080-2441) **2954**
Revista Signos see Revista Signos de Valparaiso **2954**
Revista Signos de Valparaiso. (CL ISSN 0035-0451) **2954**, 2837
Revista Svizzera di Medicina dello Sport. see Schweizerische Zeitschrift fuer Sportmedizin **3373**
Revista Tamaulipas. (MX ISSN 0035-0486) **2210**
Revista Tecnica de la Industria de Generos de Punto. (SP) **1287**
Revista Tecnica de los Ferrocarriles see R T F **4713**
Revista Tecnica Militar. (CU) **3470**
Revista Tecnologia: Electroenergetica. (CU) **1907**
Revista Tecnologia: Geologia. (CU) **1579**
Revista Tecnologia: Mineria y Metalurgia. (CU) **3418**
Revista Tecnologia: Quimica. (CU) **1187**
Revista Telebras. (BL) **1379**
Revista Telegrafica Electronica. (AG ISSN 0035-0516) **1365**
Revista Temas Economicos y Sociales. (BO) **4384**
Revista Teologica Limense. (PE) **4274**
Revista Textil. (BL ISSN 0035-0524) **4623**
Revista Theobroma. (BL ISSN 0370-7962) **117**, 4447, 4815

REVUE AFRICAINE 6615

Revista Tienda. (AG) **1052**
Revista Trabajo Social. (CL ISSN 0716-2642) **4418**
Revista Transporturilor si Telecomunicatiilor. (RM) **4655**, 1342
Revista Tricontinental. (CU ISSN 0049-4682) **3971**
Revista Trimestral de Jurisprudencia. (BL) **2673**
Revista UniMar. (BL ISSN 0100-9354) **1715**
Revista Universidad E A F I T. (Escuela de Administracion y Finanzas y Tecnologias) (CK ISSN 0120-341X) **1026**
Revista Universidad Tecnologica. (CK ISSN 0120-1603) **4607**, 1715
Revista Universitaria. (CL ISSN 0250-3670) **1715**
Revista Uruguaya de Derecho Procesal.(UY) **2673**
Revista Uruguaya de Estudios Internacionales. (UY) **1659**
Revista Uruguaya de Psicologia. (UY) **4045**
Revista Varona. (CU) **1659**
Revista Venezolana de Filosofia. (VE) **3779**
Revista Venezolana de Sanidad y Asistencia Social. (VE ISSN 0035-0583) **4111**, 4418
Revista Veterinaria Venezolana. (VE) **4815**
Revista Veterinaria y Zootecnica de Caldas. (CK ISSN 0120-4114) **4815**, 591
Revista Viet-Nam. (CU) **2238**
Revista W I Z O. (IS) **2204**
Revista 13 Grafico. (GT) **2196**, 2421
Revistas Espanolas con I S S N. (SP ISSN 0211-1993) **410**
Revistero. (US ISSN 0085-5642) **410**
Revitec. (SP) **1282**
Reviver. (AT) **1539**
Revmatikeren. (NO) **3369**
Revmatologiya/Rheumatology. (RU ISSN 0233-7029) **3370**
▼Revocable Trusts, 2-E. (US) **2674**
Revoltes Logiques. (FR ISSN 0339-6886) **3779**
Revolucion see Revolution **3922**
Revolucion y Cultura. (CU ISSN 0864-1315) **2954**
Revolution. (FR ISSN 0246-9405) **2187**
Revolution. (US ISSN 0193-3612) **3922**
Revolution. see An Reabhloid **3940**
Revolution Africaine. (AE ISSN 0035-0621) **3922**, 2334
Revolution et Travail. (AE ISSN 0484-8365) **3922**
Revolution Malagasy. (MG) **3922**
Revolution Socialiste. (MQ) **992**
▼Revolution: The Journal of Nurse Empowerment. (US) **3286**
Revolutionary Communist Bulletin see Australasian Spartacist **3874**
Revolutionary Russia. (UK ISSN 0954-6545) **2383**
Revolutionary Worker. (US ISSN 0193-3485) **3923**
Revolutionary Zimbabwe. (UK) **3946**
Revon Lebankaut - Banking Quarterly see Riveon Lebankaut **798**
Revs Motorcycle News (Revs). (AT ISSN 0027-2175) **4520**
Revue. (LU ISSN 0035-0729) **4785**
Revue A B B see A B B Review **1880**
Revue A C C S see C H A C Review **2459**
Revue Abolitionniste. (FR) **3946**
Revue Administrative. (FR ISSN 0035-0672) **4072**, 1026
Revue Administrative et Juridique du Burundi. (BD) **2674**
Revue Aerospatiale. (FR ISSN 0065-3780) **61**
Revue Africaine de la Protection des Vegetaux. see African Journal of Plant Protection **166**
Revue Africaine de Theologie. (ZR) **4274**
Revue Africaine des Sciences de l'Education/African Review of Educational Sciences. (ZR) **1659**

REVUE AFRICAINE

Revue Africaine et Malgache de Psychologie. (SG) 4045
Revue Agricole et Sucriere de Maurice/ Agricultural and Sugar Review of Mauritius. (MF) 191
Revue Algerienne des Sciences Juridiques. (AE) 2674, 689, 3923
Revue Algerienne des Sciences Juridiques, Economiques et Politiques see Revue Algerienne des Sciences Juridiques 2674
Revue Algerienne du Travail. (AE ISSN 0568-9848) 4447
Revue Alpine. (FR) 4554
Revue Andre Malraux Review. (CN ISSN 0839-458X) 2954
Revue Annuelle d'Histoire du Quatorzieme Arrondissement de Paris. (FR ISSN 0556-7335) 2383
Revue Annuelle de l'Industrie Chimique see Annual Review of the Chemical Industry 1071
Revue Annuelle des Industries Mecaniques et Electriques et de l'Automatisation see Annual Review of Engineering Industries and Automation 1915
Revue Arachnologique. (FR ISSN 0398-4346) 453
Revue Archeologique. (FR ISSN 0035-0737) 282
Revue Archeologique de l'Est et du Centre-Est. (FR ISSN 0035-0745) 283
Revue Archeologique de l'Est et du Centre-Est. Supplement. (FR) 283
Revue Archeologique de l'Ouest. (FR ISSN 0767-709X) 283
Revue Archeologique du Centre de la France. (FR ISSN 0220-6617) 283
Revue Archeologique Narbonnaise. (FR ISSN 0557-7705) 283
Revue Automobile. (SZ ISSN 0005-1314) 4655, 4700
Revue Avicole. (FR ISSN 0048-7902) 225
Revue Belge d'Archeologie et d'Histoire de l'Art. (BE ISSN 0035-077X) 283, 342
Revue Belge d'Histoire Contemporaine/ Belgisch Tijdschrift voor Nieuwste Geschiedenis. (BE ISSN 0035-0869) 2320
Revue Belge d'Histoire Militaire/Belgisch Tijdschrift voor Militaire Geschiedenis.(BE ISSN 0035-0877) 3470
Revue Belge d'Homoeopathie. (BE ISSN 0035-0885) 3215
Revue Belge de Droit International/ Belgian Review of International Law. (BE ISSN 0035-0788) 2728
Revue Belge de Geographie. (BE ISSN 0770-0717) 2261
Revue Belge de Medecine Dentaire. (BE) 3242
Revue Belge de Musicologie/Belgisch Tijdschrift voor Muziekwetenschap. (BE) 3577
Revue Belge de Numismatique et de Sigillographie. (BE) 3601, 283, 2383
Revue Belge de Philologie et d'Histoire. (BE ISSN 0035-0818) 2320, 2837
Revue Belge de Psychologie et de Pedagogie. (BE ISSN 0035-0826) 4045, 1659
Revue Belge de Securite Sociale. (BE ISSN 0035-0834) 4418, 4072
Revue Belge du Cinema. (BE ISSN 0774-0115) 3516
Revue Belge du Feu see A N P I Magazine - Protection Incendie et Vol 2030
Revue Benedictine. (BE ISSN 0035-0893) 4274
Revue Bibliographique de Sinologie. (FR ISSN 0080-2484) 2330, 410
Revue Biblique. (FR ISSN 0035-0907) 4199
Revue Bulgare d'Histoire. see Bulgarian Historical Review 2354
Revue C E L F A N - C E L F A N Review. (US ISSN 0890-6998) 2955, 2334, 2431
Revue Camerounaise de Pedagogie see Syllabus 1666

Revue Canadienne d'Economie. see Canadian Journal of Economics 654
Revue Canadienne d'Enseignement Superieur. see Canadian Journal of Higher Education 1702
Revue Canadienne d'Ergotherapie. see Canadian Journal of Occupational Therapy 3086
Revue Canadienne d'Etudes du Developpement. see Canadian Journal of Development Studies 4368
Revue Canadienne d'Etudes Neerlandaises. see Canadian Journal of Netherlandic Studies 2903
Revue Canadienne d'Evaluation de Programme. see Canadian Journal of Program Evaluation 1005
Revue Canadienne d'Optometrie. see Canadian Journal of Optometry 3299
Revue Canadienne de Biologie et Biologie Experimentale see Experimental Biology 5189
Revue Canadienne de Comptes Rendus en Philosophie. see Canadian Philosophical Reviews 3763
Revue Canadienne de Criminologie. see Canadian Journal of Criminology 1511
Revue Canadienne de Defense. see Canadian Defence Quarterly 3453
Revue Canadienne de Droit et Societe. see Canadian Journal of Law and Society 2611
Revue Canadienne de Genie Civil. see Canadian Journal of Civil Engineering 1863
Revue Canadienne de Geotechnique. see Canadian Geotechnical Journal 1542
Revue Canadienne de l'Education. see Canadian Journal of Education 1620
Revue Canadienne de l'Histoire des Sports. see Canadian Journal of History of Sport 4468
Revue Canadienne de Linguistique. see Canadian Journal of Linguistics 2808
Revue Canadienne de Litterature Comparee. see Canadian Review of Comparative Literature 2903
Revue Canadienne de Nursing Oncologique. see Canadian Oncology Nursing Journal 3276
Revue Canadienne de Philosophie. see Dialogue: Canadian Philosophical Review 3765
Revue Canadienne de Psychiatrie. see Canadian Journal of Psychiatry 3333
Revue Canadienne de Psycho-Education. (CN ISSN 0080-2492) 4045, 1740, 4447
Revue Canadienne de Psychologie. see Canadian Journal of Psychology 4015
Revue Canadienne de Recherche en Sciences Infirmieres. see Canadian Journal of Nursing Research 3276
Revue Canadienne de Recherche Veterinaire. see Canadian Journal of Veterinary Research 4807
Revue Canadienne de Sante Mentale Communautaire. see Canadian Journal of Community Mental Health 4015
Revue Canadienne de Science Politique. see Canadian Journal of Political Science 3878
Revue Canadienne de Service Social. see Canadian Social Work Review 4400
Revue Canadienne de Sociologie et d'Anthropologie. see Canadian Review of Sociology and Anthropology 4430
Revue Canadienne de Statistique. see Canadian Journal of Statistics 4567
Revue Canadienne de Theorie Politique et Sociale. see Canadian Journal of Political & Social Theory 3878
Revue Canadienne de Voile. see Canadian Sailing Review 4523
Revue Canadienne des Etudes Africaines. see Canadian Journal of African Studies 4368

Revue Canadienne des Resources en Eau. see Canadian Water Resources Journal 4823
Revue Canadienne des Sciences du Comportement. see Canadian Journal of Behavioural Science 4015
Revue Canadienne des Sciences du Sport. see Canadian Journal of Sport Sciences 4468
Revue Canadienne des Sciences Regionales. see Canadian Journal of Regional Science 889
Revue Canadienne des Slavistes. see Canadian Slavonic Papers 2504
Revue Canadienne du Vieillissement. see Canadian Journal on Aging 2271
Revue Clivages see Clivages 2990
Revue Co-Textes. (FR ISSN 0249-6356) 2955
Revue Commerce. (CN ISSN 0380-9811) 839
Revue Critique de Droit International Prive. (FR ISSN 0035-0958) 2728
Revue Critique de Jurisprudence Belge. (BE ISSN 0035-0966) 2674
Revue Cytobiologique. see Cytobiologische Revue 5176
†Revue d'Acoustique. (FR ISSN 0557-7713) 5270
Revue d'Allemagne et des Pays de Langue Allemande. (FR ISSN 0035-0868) 3971
Revue d'Architecture de Paysage. see Landscape Architectural Review 302
Revue d'Art Canadienne /Canadian Art Review see R A C A R 341
Revue d'Assyriologie et d'Archeologie Orientale. (FR) 3643
Revue d'Auvergne. (FR ISSN 0035-1008) 2383, 1548, 2261
Revue d'Ecologie Alpine. (FR) 516, 2261
Revue d'Ecologie et de Biologie du Sol see European Journal of Soil Biology 438
Revue d'Ecologie: La Terre et la Vie. (FR ISSN 0249-7395) 1967
Revue d'Economie d'Enterprise. see Coop Fachblatt fuer Unternehmungsfuehrung 5172
Revue d'Economie Financiere. (FR) 798, 883
Revue d'Economie Industrielle. (FR) 883, 1084
Revue d'Economie Politique. (FR ISSN 0373-2630) 689
Revue d'Economie Regionale et Urbaine. (FR ISSN 0180-7307) 883
Revue d'Egyptologie. (BE ISSN 0035-1849) 283, 2320, 3643
Revue d'Electroencephalographie et de Neurophysiologie Clinique see Neurophysiologie Clinique 3347
Revue d'Elevage et de Medecine Veterinaire des Pays Tropicaux. (FR ISSN 0035-1865) 4815, 225
Revue d'Entomologie du Quebec. (CN ISSN 0825-1215) 537
Revue d'Epidemiologie et de Sante Publique. (FR ISSN 0398-7620) 4111
Revue d'Esthetique. (FR ISSN 0035-2292) 3779, 342
Revue d'Ethnolinguistique see Cahiers du L A C I T O - Revue d'Ethnolinguistique 2808
Revue d'Ethnologie. see Etnoloski Pregled 239
Revue d'Etudes Canadiennes. see Journal of Canadian Studies 2509
Revue d'Etudes Comparatives Est-Ouest. (FR) 897
Revue d'Etudes Ligures. see Rivista di Studi Liguri 2384
Revue d'Etudes Militaires, Aeriennes et Navales. (FR ISSN 0035-2306) 3470
Revue d'Etudes Palestiniennes. (FR ISSN 0252-8290) 2021
Revue d'Etudes sur le Conte Populaire. see Fabula 2054
Revue d'Histoire de l'Amerique Francaise. (CN ISSN 0035-2357) 2421
Revue d'Histoire de l'Eglise de France. (FR ISSN 0300-9505) 4199

Revue d'Histoire de la Medecine Hebraique. (FR ISSN 0035-2330) 3149
Revue d'Histoire de la Pharmacie. (FR ISSN 0035-2349) 3742
Revue d'Histoire des Sciences et de leurs Applications. (FR ISSN 0048-7996) 4336, 4607
Revue d'Histoire des Textes. (FR) 2955, 2383
Revue d'Histoire Diplomatique. (FR ISSN 0035-2365) 2321
Revue d'Histoire du Bas-Saint-Laurent. (CN ISSN 0381-8454) 2321
Revue d'Histoire du Droit. see Tijdschrift voor Rechtsgeschiedenis 2686
Revue d'Histoire du Theatre. (FR ISSN 0035-2373) 4637
Revue d'Histoire Ecclesiastique. (BE ISSN 0035-2381) 4274, 2421
Revue d'Histoire Ecclesiastique Suisse. see Zeitschrift fuer Schweizerische Kirchengeschichte 4211
Revue d'Histoire et de Civilisation du Maghreb. (AE ISSN 0556-7343) 2334
Revue d'Histoire et de Philosophie Religieuses. (FR ISSN 0035-2403) 4199, 2321
Revue d'Histoire Litteraire de la France. (FR ISSN 0035-2411) 2955, 2321
Revue d'Histoire Maghrebine/North African Historical Review. (TI ISSN 0330-8987) 2334
Revue d'Histoire Moderne et Contemporaine. (FR ISSN 0048-8003) 2321
Revue d'Histoire Urbaine. see Urban History Review 2425
Revue d'Hydrobiologie Tropicale. (FR ISSN 0240-8783) 453
Revue d'Information des Techniques Viticoles. (FR) 191
Revue d'Informations et d'Etudes Economique et Financieres. (CM) 883
Revue d'Integration Europeenne/Journal of European Integration. (CN ISSN 0703-6337) 3971, 883
Revue d'Odonto-Stomatologie. (FR ISSN 0300-9815) 3242
Revue d'Odonto-Stomatologie du Midi de la France. (FR ISSN 0035-2470) 3242
Revue d'Orthopedie Dento-Faciale. (FR ISSN 0337-9736) 3311
Revue d'Orthophonie et d'Audiologie. see Journal of Speech Language Pathology and Audiology 1737
Revue Danoise see Danish Journal 2185
La Revue de Belles-Lettres. (SZ ISSN 0035-1016) 2881, 342
Revue de Bibliologie. (FR ISSN 0982-6548) 2955, 2837
Revue de Bio-Mathematique/ Biomathematics Review. (FR ISSN 0035-1024) 3052
Revue de Chimie Minerale - Inorganic Chemistry Review - Revue fuer Anorganische Chemie see European Journal of Solid State and Inorganic Chemistry 1213
Revue de Chirurgie Orthopedique et Reparatrice de l'Appareil Moteur. (FR ISSN 0035-1040) 3311
Revue de Comminges. (FR ISSN 0035-1059) 2383, 283
Revue de Coree. (UN) 3643, 4384
Revue de Cytologie et de Biologie Vegetales see Revue de Cytologie et de Biologie Vegetales - Le Botaniste 516
Revue de Cytologie et de Biologie Vegetales - Le Botaniste. (FR ISSN 0181-7582) 516
Revue de Deux Mondes: Litterature, Histoire, Arts et Sciences. (FR ISSN 0750-9278) 2881
Revue de Droit Commercial Belge/ Tijdschrift voor Belgisch Handelsrecht. (BE ISSN 0772-8050) 2674
Revue de Droit de l'U L B see Universite Libre de Bruxelles. Revue de Droit 2689
Revue de Droit de McGill. see McGill Law Journal 2651

Revue de Droit Francais Commercial Maritime et Fiscal. (FR ISSN 0768-9659) **2674**, 2728
†Revue de Droit Hongrois. (HU ISSN 0139-2026) **5270**
Revue de Droit Immobilier. (FR ISSN 0180-9849) **2674**
Revue de Droit Intellectuel l'Ingenieur-Conseil. (BE ISSN 0035-1083) **2674**
Revue de Droit International de Sciences Diplomatiques et Politiques.(SZ ISSN 0035-1091) **3923**, 2674, 2728
Revue de Droit International et de Droit Compare. (BE ISSN 0035-1105) **2728**, 2674
Revue de Droit Judiciaire. (CN) **2674**
Revue de Droit Penal et de Criminologie. (BE ISSN 0035-4384) **2714**, 1522
Revue de Droit Rural. (FR) **2674**
Revue de Droit Sanitaire et Social. (FR) **4072**
Revue de Droit Social/Tijdschrift voor Sociaal Recht. (BE ISSN 0035-1113) **2674**
Revue de Droit Suisse. *see* Zeitschrift fuer Schweizerisches Recht **2697**
Revue de Geographie Alpine. (FR ISSN 0035-1121) **2261**
Revue de Geographie de Lyon. (FR ISSN 0035-113X) **2261**
Revue de Geographie du Maroc. (MR ISSN 0035-1156) **2261**
Revue de Geriatrie. (FR) **2278**
Revue de Hongrie *see* Hungarian Digest **2198**
Revue de Jurisprudence Commerciale. (FR ISSN 0048-7937) **2674**
Revue de Jurisprudence Fiscale. (FR ISSN 0337-7393) **4072**, 2674
Revue de l'Action Populaire *see* Projet **4383**
Revue de l'Agenais. (FR ISSN 0035-1288) **2383**
Revue de l'Agriculture - Landbouwtijdschrift. (BE ISSN 0776-2143) **117**
Revue de l'Aide-Soignante. (FR ISSN 0987-8947) **3286**
†Revue de l'Alcoolisme. (FR ISSN 0035-130X) **5270**
Revue de l'Alimentation Animale. (FR) **208**, 225
Revue de l'Ameublement. (FR ISSN 0242-8903) **2561**
Revue de l'Arpenteur-Geometre. (CN) **1873**, 2261
Revue de l'Art. (FR ISSN 0035-1326) **342**, 2321
Revue de l'Avranchin et du Pays de Granville. (FR ISSN 0035-1342) **283**
Revue de l'Economie du Centre-Est. (FR ISSN 0035-1350) **689**
Revue de l'Education Physique. (BE ISSN 0035-1377) **1758**
†Revue de l'Embouteillages et des Industries Connexes. (FR) **5270**
Revue de l'Energie. (FR ISSN 0303-240X) **1795**
Revue de l'Enseignement Philosophique *see* L'Enseignement Philosophique **1632**
Revue de l'Enseignement Superieur *see* Revue de l'Enseignement Superieur et de la Recherche Scientifique **1659**
Revue de l'Enseignement Superieur et de la Recherche Scientifique. (AE) **1659**
Revue de l'Est *see* Revue d'Etudes Comparatives Est-Ouest **897**
Revue de l'Habitat Francais. (FR ISSN 0048-7953) **4157**
Revue de l'Histoire des Religions. (FR ISSN 0035-1423) **4199**, 2321
†Revue de l'Histoire du Quebec et du Canada Francais. (CN ISSN 0713-7958) **5270**
Revue de l'Imperiale. *see* Imperial Oil Review **3688**
Revue de l'Industrie Alimentaire. (FR) **2081**, 3612
Revue de l'Infirmiere. (FR ISSN 0397-7900) **3286**
Revue de l'Infirmiere Luxembourgeoise. (LU) **3286**

Revue de l'Ingenieur Industriel *see* Ingenieur et Industrie **1825**
Revue de l'Ocean Indien. (MG) **2170**
Revue de l'Ocean Indien. Economie. (MG) **839**
Revue de l'OTAN *see* N A T O Review **3908**
Revue de l'Universite de Moncton *see* Universite de Moncton. Revue **2179**
Revue de la Bonte Singe *see* Monkey Kindness Magazine **231**
Revue de la Brasserie et des Boissons. *see* Brauerei und Getraenke-Rundschau **379**
Revue de la Cinematheque. (CN ISSN 0843-6827) **3516**
Revue de la Concurrence et de la Consommation. (FR ISSN 0220-9896) **839**
Revue de la Fonction Publique. (AE) **4073**
Revue de la France Libre. (FR ISSN 0035-1210) **3470**
Revue de la Main d'Oeuvre: Region du Quebec. *see* Manpower and Immigration Review: Quebec Region **988**
Revue de la Mercerie, Nouveautes, Bonneterie, Lingerie, Confections. (FR) **1287**
Revue de la Navigation Fluviale Europeenne, Ports et Industries. (FR ISSN 0767-094X) **4737**
Revue de la Negotiation Collective *see* Collective Bargaining Review **975**
Revue de la Pensee Educative. *see* J E T: Journal of Educational Thought **1641**
Revue de la Police Nationale. (FR ISSN 0035-1237) **1522**
Revue de la Presse Arabe. (SY ISSN 0035-1245) **3923**
Revue de la Presse de l'Ocean Indien. (MG) **2575**
Revue de la Presse Egyptienne *see* C E D E J Egypte - Monde Arabe **2608**
Revue de la Protection *see* R G S **1527**
Revue de La Saintonge et de l'Aunis. (FR) **2383**
Revue de la Securite. (FR ISSN 0035-1261) **3621**
Revue de la Soudure/Lastijdschrift. (BE ISSN 0035-127X) **3430**
Revue de la Technique Europeenne *see* Indicateur Industriel **5212**
Revue de Laryngologie - Otologie - Rhinologie. (FR ISSN 0035-1334) **3316**, 3149
Revue de Linguistique *see* Revue Roumaine de Linguistique **2838**
Revue de Linguistique Romane. (FR ISSN 0035-1458) **2837**
Revue de Litterature Comparee. (FR ISSN 0035-1466) **2955**
Revue de Mathematiques Elementaires. *see* Elemente der Mathematik **3035**
Revue de Mathematiques Speciales. (FR ISSN 0035-1504) **3052**
Revue de Medecine de Tours. (FR) **3149**
Revue de Medecine du Travail. (FR ISSN 0300-0559) **3621**
Revue de Medecine Interne. (FR ISSN 0248-8663) **3149**
Revue de Medecine Psychosomatique. (FR ISSN 0035-1547) **3353**
Revue de Medecine Veterinaire. (FR ISSN 0035-1555) **4815**
Revue de Metallurgie *see* Revue de Metallurgie. Cahiers d'Information Techniques **3418**
Revue de Metallurgie. Cahiers d'Information Techniques. (FR) **3418**
Revue de Metallurgie. Memoires et Etudes Scientifiques. (FR ISSN 0245-8292) **3418**
Revue de Metallurgie. Memoires Scientifiques *see* Revue de Metallurgie. Memoires et Etudes Scientifiques **3418**
Revue de Metaphysique et de Morale. (FR ISSN 0035-1571) **3779**
Revue de Metrologie Pratique et Legale.(FR ISSN 1161-4951) **3448**
Revue de Micropaleontologie. (FR ISSN 0035-1598) **3660**

Revue de Modification du Comportement *see* Science et Comportement **4046**
Revue de Musicologie. (FR ISSN 0035-1601) **3579**
Revue de Musique des Universites Canadiennes. *see* Canadian University Music Review **3544**
Revue de Nematologie *see* Fundamental and Applied Nematology **583**
Revue de Neuropsychiatrie de l'Ouest. (FR ISSN 0035-161X) **3353**
Revue de Paleobiologie. (SZ ISSN 0253-6730) **1579**, 3660
Revue de Parapsychologie. (FR ISSN 0294-2623) **3671**
Revue de Pau et du Bearn. (FR) **2514**
Revue de Pediatrie. (FR ISSN 0035-1644) **3326**
Revue de Philologie, de Litterature et d'Histoire Anciennes. (FR ISSN 0035-1652) **1279**, 2837
Revue de Philosophie. *see* Revista de Filosofie **3779**
Revue de Philosophie. (RM) **3779**
Revue de Phonetique Appliquee. (FR ISSN 0035-1660) **2837**
Revue de Physique Appliquee *see* Journal de Physique III **3821**
Revue de Phytotherapy Pratique. (FR) **3149**
Revue de Planification de l'Education dans les Pays Arabes. *see* Sahifat al-Takhtit al-Tarbawi fi al-Bilad al-Arabiyah **1660**
Revue de Pneumologie Clinique. (FR ISSN 0761-8417) **3367**, 3211
Revue de Podologie. (FR ISSN 0484-8594) **3149**
Revue de Politique Internationale *see* Review of International Affairs **3970**
Revue de Press. (FR) **821**
Revue de Presse et de Documentation Allemande. (FR) **821**
Revue de Psychologie Appliquee *see* Revue Europeene de Psychologie Appliquee **4045**
Revue de Qumran. (FR ISSN 0035-1725) **3643**, 4199
Revue de Science Criminelle et de Droit Penal Compare. (FR ISSN 0035-1733) **1522**, 2674
Revue de Statistique Appliquee. (FR ISSN 0035-175X) **4584**
Revue de Stomatologie et de Chirurgie Maxillo-Faciale. (FR ISSN 0035-1768) **3242**, 3383
Revue de Synthese. (FR ISSN 0035-1776) **3779**
Revue de Theologie et de Philosophie. (SZ ISSN 0035-1784) **4199**, 3779
Revue de Theologie et de Philosophie. Cahiers. (SZ ISSN 0250-6971) **4199**, 3779
Revue de Tourisme. *see* Zeitschrift fuer Fremdenverkehr **4798**
Revue des Affaires Europeennes. (FR ISSN 1152-9172) **2728**
Revue des Archeologues et Historiens d'Art de Louvain. (BE ISSN 0080-2530) **342**, 283, 3577
Revue des Cahiers du Barreau de Paris.(FR) **2674**
Revue des Caisses d'Epargne. (FR ISSN 0035-1938) **798**
Revue des Comites d'Entreprise. (FR) **992**
Revue des Communes et des Etablissements Publics. (FR) **4073**
Revue des Douanes. *see* Zoll - Rundschau **1112**
Revue des Ecoles. (BE ISSN 0035-1997) **1659**
Revue des Etudes Anciennes. (FR ISSN 0035-2004) **1279**
Revue des Etudes Armeniennes Nouvelle Serie. (FR ISSN 0080-2549) **2431**, 3643
Revue des Etudes Augustiniennes. (FR ISSN 0035-2012) **4199**, 2955
Revue des Etudes Byzantines. (FR ISSN 0766-5598) **2431**
Revue des Etudes Cooperatives *see* Revue des Etudes Cooperatives, Mutualistes et Associatives **832**
Revue des Etudes Cooperatives, Mutualistes et Associatives. (FR) **832**

REVUE DROMOISE 6617

Revue des Etudes Georgiennes et Caucasiennes. (BE ISSN 0991-8086) **2383**
Revue des Etudes Grecques. (FR ISSN 0035-2039) **1279**, 283
Revue des Etudes Islamiques. (FR ISSN 0336-156X) **3643**, 4220
Revue des Etudes Italiennes. (FR ISSN 0035-2047) **2838**
Revue des Etudes Juives. (BE ISSN 0035-2055) **2021**, 2321, 4226
Revue des Etudes Latines. (FR) **1279**, 2838
Revue des Etudes Slaves. (FR ISSN 0080-2557) **2955**, 2838
Revue des Etudes Sud-Est Europeennes.(RM ISSN 0035-2063) **2514**
Revue des Fermieres *see* Revue Fermieres Aujourd'hui **4851**
Revue des Finances Communales *see* Vie Communale et Departementale **4077**
Revue des Industries d'Art - Offrir *see* Offrir International **2282**
Revue des Ingenieurs. (FR ISSN 0150-7516) **3494**
Revue des Ingenieurs et Techniciens Europeens. (FR) **1835**, 4607
Revue des Langues Romanes. (FR) **2838**, 1279
Revue des Lettres *see* Journal des Lettres et de l'Audiovisuel **2928**
Revue des Lettres Modernes. (FR ISSN 0035-2136) **2955**
Revue des Lettres Modernes. Etudes Bernanosiennes. (FR ISSN 0425-4791) **2955**
Revue des Livres pour Enfants. (FR ISSN 0398-8384) **4136**, 2782
Revue des Loyers et des Fermages. (FR) **2495**, 4157
Revue des Maladies Respiratoires. (FR ISSN 0761-8425) **3367**
Revue des Peintures Belges. (BE) **2555**
Revue des Postes Belges/Tijdschrift der Belgische Posterijen. (BE) **1354**
Revue des Produits Chimiques *see* Chimie Actualites **1852**
Revue des Questions Scientifiques. (BE ISSN 0035-2160) **4336**
La Revue des Revues. (NE ISSN 0980-2797) **410**, 2955
Revue des Revues Demographiques *see* Review of Population Reviews **3987**
Revue des Roulements *see* Kullagertidningen **1934**
Revue des S A M U *see* Services d'Aide Medicale Urgente. Revue **3311**
Revue des Sciences Morales et Politiques. (FR ISSN 0751-5804) **3779**
Revue des Sciences Naturelles d'Auvergne. (FR) **453**
Revue des Sciences Philosophiques et Theologiques. (FR ISSN 0035-2209) **3780**
Revue des Sciences Religieuses. (FR ISSN 0035-2217) **4274**, 2321
Revue des Sciences Sociales de la France de l'Est. (FR ISSN 0336-1578) **4384**
Revue des Services d'Arbitrage. *see* Arbitration Services Reporter **972**
Revue des Societes. (FR) **2674**
Revue des Societes - Journal des Societes *see* Revue des Societes **2674**
Revue des Societes Savantes de Haute Normandie. (FR ISSN 0035-2241) **4336**, 2514
Revue des Tabacs. (FR ISSN 0035-225X) **4644**
Revue des Transmissions *see* Federation Nationale des Anciens Combattants et Coalets des Transmissions. Liaison des Transmissions **3458**
Revue des Travaux de l'Institut des Peches Maritimes *see* Aquatic Living Resources **2037**
Revue Desjardins. (CN ISSN 0035-2284) **798**
Revue Diplomatique de l'Ocean Indien. (MG) **3971**
Revue Dromoise. (FR ISSN 0398-0022) **283**, 4584

6618 REVUE

Revue du Barreau. (CN ISSN 0383-669X) **2674**
Revue du Bois et de ses Applications. (FR ISSN 0035-2519) **2117**
Revue du Cardiologue Praticien. (FR ISSN 1146-6537) **3211**
Revue du Courtage. (FR) **2541**
Revue du Droit Public et de la Science Politique en France et a l'Etranger. (FR ISSN 0035-2578) **2674, 3923**
Revue du Gynecologue Obstetricien. (FR ISSN 1141-5886) **3296**
†Revue du Jeune Medecin. (FR) **5270**
Revue du Jouet. (FR ISSN 0035-2594) **2282**
Revue du Liban. (LE) **2209**
Revue du Louvre et des Musees de France. (FR ISSN 0035-2608) **3532**
Revue du M A U S S. (Mouvement Anti-Utilitariste dans les Science Sociales) (FR) **4447, 3780**
Revue du Magnetisme-Etude du Psychisme Experimental. (FR ISSN 0338-2079) **3671**
Revue du Marche Commun. (FR ISSN 0035-2616) **920**
Revue du Monde Arabe. see Canadian Arab World Review **1995**
Revue du Monde Musulman de la Mediterranee. (FR ISSN 0997-1327) **2514**
Revue du Moteur Tchecoslovaque see Czechoslovak Motor Review **5176**
Revue du Nord. (FR ISSN 0035-2624) **2383, 283**
Revue du Notariat. (CN ISSN 0035-2632) **2674**
Revue du Notariat Belge. (BE) **2674**
Revue du Pediatre. (FR ISSN 0995-1180) **3326**
Revue du Praticien. (FR ISSN 0035-2640) **3149**
Revue du Rhumatisme et des Maladies Osteoarticulaires. (FR ISSN 0035-2659) **3370**
Revue du Rosaire. (FR) **4274**
Revue du Secretariat et de la Comptabilite. (FR) **1061**
Revue du Son see Nouvelle Revue du Son **4461**
Revue du Travail. (BE ISSN 0035-2705) **992**
Revue du Travail. (HT ISSN 0482-8062) **992, 4418**
Revue du Tresor. (FR ISSN 0035-2713) **755**
Revue du Verre see Glass Review **1164**
Revue du Vieux Geneve. (SZ) **2383**
Revue du Vin de France. (FR ISSN 0035-273X) **385**
Revue Economique. (FR ISSN 0035-2764) **689**
Revue Economique du Sud-Ouest. (FR) **689**
Revue Economique et Financiere Ivoirienne. (IV) **883**
Revue Economique et Sociale. (SZ ISSN 0035-2772) **689, 4447**
Revue Economique et Technique de l'Industrie Alimentaire Europeenne. (FR) **2081**
Revue Economique Francaise. (FR ISSN 0035-2780) **689**
Revue Economique Franco Suisse. (FR ISSN 0035-2799) **821**
Revue Egyptienne de Droit International. see Egyptian Review of International Law **2722**
Revue Europeene de Psychologie Appliquee/European Review of Applied Psychology. (FR) **4045, 3353**
Revue Europeenne de Demographie. see European Journal of Population **3992**
Revue Europeenne de Droit de la Consommation. (FR) **2674, 689**
Revue F H see Federation de l'Industrie Horlogere Suisse. Revue **2564**
Revue Femmes et Droit. see Canadian Journal of Women and the Law **2611**
Revue Fermieres Aujourd'hui. (CN) **4851**
Revue Fiduciaire. (FR ISSN 0223-4718) **961**

Revue Fiduciaire Comptable. (FR ISSN 0396-3640) **961**
Revue Fiscale. see Steuer Revue **1106**
Revue Forestiere Francaise. (FR ISSN 0035-2829) **2107**
Revue Formes Nouvelles/Neue Formen/New Forms. (LU) **306**
†Revue Fotografie. (CS ISSN 0232-0576) **5270**
Revue Francaise d'Administration Publique. (FR ISSN 0152-7401) **4073**
Revue Francaise d'Allergologie et Immunologie see Revue Francaise d'Allergologie et Immunologie Clinique **3188**
Revue Francaise d'Allergologie et Immunologie Clinique. (FR ISSN 0335-7457) **3188**
Revue Francaise d'Automatique d'Informatique et de Recherche Operationelle APII Automatique - Productique Informatique Industrielle see R A I R O APII Automatique - Productique Informatique Industrielle **1442**
Revue Francaise d'Endocrinologie Clinique, Nutrition et Metabolisme. (FR ISSN 0048-8062) **3256**
Revue Francaise d'Esperanto. (FR ISSN 0988-6729) **2838**
Revue Francaise d'Etudes Americaines. (FR ISSN 0397-7870) **4447**
Revue Francaise d'Etudes Politiques Africaines. (SG ISSN 0035-3027) **3923**
Revue Francaise d'Etudes Politiques Mediterraneennes. (SG ISSN 0338-2060) **3923**
Revue Francaise d'Histoire d'Outre-Mer see Revue Francaise d'Histoire d'Outre-Mer, Explorations, Colonisations, Independences **2321**
Revue Francaise d'Histoire d'Outre-Mer, Explorations, Colonisations, Independences. (FR) **2321**
Revue Francaise d'Histoire du Livre. (FR ISSN 0037-9212) **2782, 2321, 4136**
Revue Francaise de Comptabilite. (FR ISSN 0484-8764) **755**
Revue Francaise de Cooperation Economique Avec Israel. (FR ISSN 0080-2506) **821**
Revue Francaise de Dietetique. (FR ISSN 0556-7793) **3612**
Revue Francaise de Droit Administratif. (FR) **2674**
Revue Francaise de Droit Aerien. (FR ISSN 0035-287X) **61, 2674**
▼Revue Francaise de Droit Constitutionnel. (FR) **2706**
Revue Francaise de Finances Publiques.(FR) **1105**
Revue Francaise de Gastro Enterologie. (FR ISSN 0035-2888) **3269**
Revue Francaise de Genealogie. (FR ISSN 0222-6782) **2162**
Revue Francaise de Gerontologie see Revue de Geriatrie **2278**
Revue Francaise de Gestion. (FR) **1027**
Revue Francaise de Gestion Industrielle.(FR ISSN 0242-9780) **1027**
Revue Francaise de Gynecologie et d'Obstetrique. (FR ISSN 0035-290X) **3296**
Revue Francaise de Pedagogie. (FR ISSN 0556-7807) **1758**
Revue Francaise de Psychanalyse. (FR ISSN 0035-2942) **4045**
Revue Francaise de Science Politique. (FR ISSN 0035-2950) **3923**
Revue Francaise de Service Social. (FR ISSN 0121-4977) **4418**
Revue Francaise de Sociologie. (FR ISSN 0035-2969) **4447**
Revue Francaise de Transfusion see Revue Francaise de Transfusion et Immuno-Hematologie **3273**
Revue Francaise de Transfusion et Immuno-Hematologie. (FR ISSN 0338-4535) **3273**
Revue Francaise des Affaires Sociales. (FR ISSN 0035-2985) **4447, 992**
Revue Francaise des Laboratoires. (FR ISSN 0338-9898) **453**

Revue Francaise des Metallurgistes see R F M **3418**
Revue Francaise des Telecommunications see France Telecom **1336**
Revue Francaise du Dommage Corporel.(FR) **3265**
Revue Franco-Ukrainienne Echanges. (FR) **3971**
Revue Francophone de Louisiane. (US ISSN 0890-9555) **2021**
Revue Genealogique Normande. (FR ISSN 0294-7382) **2162**
Revue Generale. (BE ISSN 0770-8602) **2514**
Revue Generale de Droit International Public. (FR ISSN 0035-3094) **2728**
Revue Generale de Fiscalite. (BE) **755, 1105**
Revue Generale de l'Electricite. (FR ISSN 0035-3116) **1907**
†Revue Generale de l'Enseignement des Deficients Auditifs. (FR ISSN 0035-3124) **5270**
Revue Generale de l'Etancheite et de l'Isolation. (FR ISSN 0035-3132) **630**
Revue Generale de Securite see R G S **1527**
Revue Generale des Assurances Terrestres. (FR ISSN 0035-3167) **2541**
Revue Generale des Chemins de Fer. (FR ISSN 0035-3183) **4714**
Revue Generale des Routes et des Aerodromes. (FR ISSN 0035-3191) **4720, 61**
Revue Generale des Transmissions see Entrainements **1929**
Revue Generale des Transmissions Mecaniques, Hydrauliques, Pneumatiques, Commandes et Assertissements see Entrainements **1929**
Revue Generale du Froid. (FR ISSN 0035-3205) **1835**
Revue Generale Nucleaire. (FR) **1809, 1835**
Revue Generale Nucleaire: International Edition. (FR ISSN 0298-7783) **1809, 1835**
Revue Geographique de l'Est. (FR ISSN 0035-3213) **2261**
Revue Geographique des Pyrenees et du Sud-Ouest. (FR ISSN 0035-3221) **2261**
Revue Hellenique de Droit International.(GR ISSN 0035-3256) **2728**
Revue Historique. (FR ISSN 0035-3264) **2321**
Revue Historique Ardennaise. (FR ISSN 0035-3272) **283, 2321**
Revue Historique de Bordeaux et du Departement de la Gironde. (FR) **2383**
Revue Historique de Droit Francais et Etranger. (FR ISSN 0035-3280) **2674, 2321**
Revue Historique des Armees. (FR ISSN 0035-3299) **3470, 2321**
Revue Historique et Archeologique du Maine. (FR) **283, 2383**
Revue Historique Vaudoise. (SZ) **283, 2383**
Revue Hospitaliere de France. (FR) **2469**
Revue Imprevue. (FR ISSN 0242-5149) **4447, 4336**
Revue Independante. (FR ISSN 0035-3310) **2882**
Revue Independante de Philosophie. see Independent Journal of Philosophy **3769**
Revue Independantiste. (CN ISSN 0702-8571) **3923**
Revue Interdisciplinaire d'Etudes Juridiques. (BE) **2674**
Revue Internationale d'Action Communautaire. (CN ISSN 0707-9699) **4447, 4418**
†Revue Internationale d'Histoire de la Banque. (SZ ISSN 0080-2611) **5270**
Revue Internationale d'Histoire de la Psychanalyse. (FR) **4045**

Revue Internationale d'Histoire Militaire.(BE ISSN 0254-8186) **3470**
Revue Internationale d'Oceanographie Medicale. (FR ISSN 0035-3493) **3149, 1610**
Revue Internationale de Droit Compare. (FR ISSN 0035-3337) **2728**
Revue Internationale de Droit Contemporain see International Review of Contemporary Law **2636**
Revue Internationale de Droit Economique. (BE) **2674, 689**
Revue Internationale de l'Eclairage see International Lighting Review **621**
Revue Internationale de la Croix Rouge see International Review of the Red Cross **2725**
Revue Internationale de la Propriete Industrielle et Artistique. (FR ISSN 0035-337X) **3678**
Revue Internationale de la Verification des Comptes Publics. see International Journal of Government Auditing **4064**
Revue Internationale de Musique Sacree. see Rivista Internazionale di Musica Sacra **3578**
Revue Internationale de Pedagogie. see International Review of Education **1640**
Revue Internationale de Pediatrie. (FR) **3326**
Revue Internationale de Philosophie. (BE ISSN 0048-8143) **3780**
Revue Internationale de Police Criminelle. (FR ISSN 0035-3396) **1522**
Revue Internationale de Politique Criminelle see International Review of Criminal Policy **1516**
Revue Internationale de Protection Civile. see International Civil Defence Journal **1273**
▼Revue Internationale de Pyschopathologie. (FR) **3353, 4045**
Revue Internationale de Science Politique. see International Political Science Review **3961**
Revue Internationale de Securite Sociale see International Social Security Review **2535**
Revue Internationale de Systemique. (FR ISSN 0980-1472) **897**
Revue Internationale des Droits de l'Antiquite. (BE ISSN 0556-7939) **2674, 2383**
Revue Internationale des Enseignants see Educadores del Mundo **1627**
Revue Internationale des Hautes Temperatures et des Refractaires. (FR ISSN 0035-3434) **1230, 3841**
Revue Internationale des Jeux et Jouets/International Tijdschrift voor Spel en Speelgoed. (BE ISSN 0021-6232) **2282**
Revue Internationale des Sciences Administratives see International Review of Administrative Sciences **4064**
Revue Internationale des Sciences Sociales. (UN) **4384**
Revue Internationale du Droit d'Auteur. (FR ISSN 0035-3515) **3678, 2674**
Revue Internationale du Mouvement Communiste. (FR) **3923**
Revue Internationale du Trachome et de Pathologie Tropicale et Subtropicale. (FR ISSN 0301-5017) **3305**
Revue Internationale du Travail. (UN ISSN 0378-5599) **992, 4111, 4447**
Revue Internationale P M E. (CN) **1117**
Revue Internationale pour l'Enseignement Commercial. see International Review for Business Education **672**
Revue Ita. (MG) **4384**
Revue Ivoirienne de Droit. (IV ISSN 0048-816X) **2674**
Revue Jonathan see Information Proche-Orient **2869**
Revue Juive. see Israelitisches Wochenblatt fuer die Schweiz **2007**

REVUE TUNISIENNE   6619

Revue Juridique de l'Environnement. (FR) **1967**, 2674
Revue Juridique du Burundi. (BD) **2674**
Revue Juridique du Rwanda. (RW ISSN 1010-8238) **2732**, 2674
Revue Juridique du Zaire. (ZR) **2732**, 2674
Revue Juridique et Economique du Sud-Ouest *see* Revue Economique du Sud-Ouest **689**
Revue Juridique Themis. (CN ISSN 0556-7963) **2732**, 2674
Revue l'Assureur Conseil *see* Revue du Courtage **2541**
Revue l'Educateur. (HT) **1659**
Revue Laitiere Francaise. (FR ISSN 0035-3590) **203**
Revue Landis et Gyr *see* Landis und Gyr Mitteilungen **5226**
†Revue Languedocienne de Sociologie Ethnologie. (FR ISSN 0986-6426) **5270**
Revue Legale. (CN ISSN 0035-3604) **2674**
†Revue Libanaise des Sciences Politiques. (LE ISSN 0557-9414) **5270**
Revue Litteraire et Culturelle de l'Ocean Indien. (MG) **4785**
Revue "M" Mecanique *see* European Journal of Mechanical Engineering **1929**
Revue Mabillon. (BE ISSN 0035-3620) **4274**, 4199
Revue Maritime. (FR) **3470**
Revue Matricule. (CN) **1323**
Revue Medicale de Bruxelles. (BE ISSN 0035-3639) **3149**
Revue Medicale de la Suisse Romande. (SZ ISSN 0035-3655) **3149**
Revue Medicale de Liege. (BE ISSN 0035-3663) **3149**
Revue Medicale Rwandaise. (RW) **3149**, 4111
Revue Metapsychique. (FR ISSN 0484-8934) **3671**
Revue Militaire Suisse. (SZ ISSN 0035-368X) **3470**
Revue Moto Technique. (FR ISSN 0150-7214) **4520**
Revue Municipale. (CN ISSN 0035-3728) **2495**
Revue Musicale. (FR ISSN 0035-3736) **3577**
Revue Musicale de Suisse Romande. (SZ ISSN 0035-3744) **3577**
Revue Nationale de la Chasse. (FR ISSN 0035-3752) **4554**
Revue Neuchateloise *see* Nouvelle Revue Neuchateloise **2378**
Revue Neurologique. (FR ISSN 0035-3787) **3353**
Revue Notre-Dame *see* R N D **4273**
Revue Notre Dame du Cap. (CN ISSN 0700-6500) **4199**
Revue Numismatique. (FR ISSN 0484-8942) **3601**
Revue Obchodu, Prumyslu, Hospodarstvi. (CS) **821**
Revue of International Affairs. (US) **3971**
Revue Olympique *see* Olympic Review (Year) **4482**
Revue Onomastique. *see* Onomata **2258**
Revue Ouest Africaine des Langues Vivantes. *see* West African Journal of Modern Languages **2851**
Revue Pedagogique et Litteraire *see* Ecoles des Lettres **1626**
Revue Penale Suisse. *see* Schweizerische Zeitschrift fuer Strafrecht **1522**
Revue Penitentiaire et de Droit Penal. (FR ISSN 0035-3825) **2674**, 1522
Revue Pharmaceutique Canadienne. *see* Canadian Pharmaceutical Journal **3720**
Revue Philosophique de Kinshasa. (ZR) **3780**
Revue Philosophique de la France et de l'Etranger. (FR ISSN 0035-3833) **3780**
Revue Philosophique de Louvain. (BE ISSN 0035-3841) **3780**
Revue Politique. *see* Politische Rundschau **3918**

Revue Politique et Parlementaire. (FR ISSN 0035-385X) **3923**
Revue Polytechnique. (SZ ISSN 0374-4256) **4607**, 1835, 3023
Revue Pratique de Controle Industriel. (FR ISSN 0766-5210) **3448**
Revue Pratique de Droit Social. (FR ISSN 0399-1148) **2674**
Revue Pratique des Societes Civiles et Commerciales. (BE) **2674**
Revue Pratique du Froid *see* R P F **2302**
Revue Pratique du Froid et du Conditionnement d'Air *see* R P F **2302**
Revue Pratique du Froid et du Conditionnement de l'Air. (FR) **2303**
Revue Protection Civile. *see* Emergency Preparedness Digest **1273**
Revue Prumyslu a Obchodu. (CS) **1084**, 4607
Revue Quart Monde. (FR) **4418**
Revue Quebecois de Droit International. (CN ISSN 0828-9999) **2728**
Revue Quebecoise de Linguistique. (CN ISSN 0710-0167) **2838**
Revue Radiodiffusion et Television. (FR) **1379**, 1359
Revue Romaine de Geologie, Geophysique et Geographie. Geophysique *see* Revue Roumaine de Geophysique **1594**
Revue Romaine des Sciences Sociales. Serie de Psychologie *see* Revue Roumaine de Psychologie **4045**
Revue Romane. (DK ISSN 0035-3906) **2838**, 2955
Revue Roumaine d'Endocrinologie/ Romanian Journal of Endocrinology. (RM) **3256**
Revue Roumaine d'Etudes Internationales. (RM ISSN 0048-8178) **3971**, 2728
Revue Roumaine d'Histoire. (RM) **2383**
Revue Roumaine d'Histoire de l'Art. Serie Beaux-Arts. (RM ISSN 0080-262X) **342**
Revue Roumaine d'Histoire de l'Art. Serie Theatre, Musique, Cinematographie. (RM ISSN 0080-2638) **342**
Revue Roumaine de Biochimie. (RM ISSN 0001-4214) **482**
Revue Roumaine de Biologie. Serie Biologie Animale. (RM) **591**
Revue Roumaine de Biologie. Serie Biologie Vegetale. (RM) **516**
Revue Roumaine de Biologie. Serie Botanique *see* Revue Roumaine de Biologie. Serie Biologie Vegetale **516**
Revue Roumaine de Chimie. (RM ISSN 0035-3930) **1187**
Revue Roumaine de Geographie. (RM) **2261**
Revue Roumaine de Geologie. (RM) **1579**
Revue Roumaine de Geologie, Geophysique et Geographie *see* Revue Roumaine de Geologie **1579**
Revue Roumaine de Geologie, Geophysique et Geographie. Geographie *see* Revue Roumaine de Geographie **2261**
Revue Roumaine de Geophysique. (RM) **1594**
Revue Roumaine de l'Histoire de l'Art. Serie Arts Plastiques *see* Revue Roumaine d'Histoire de l'Art. Serie Beaux-Arts **342**
Revue Roumaine de Linguistique. (RM ISSN 0035-3957) **2838**
Revue Roumaine de Mathematiques Pures et Appliquees. (RM ISSN 0035-3965) **3052**
Revue Roumaine de Medecine. Serie Endocrinologie *see* Revue Roumaine d'Endocrinologie **3256**
Revue Roumaine de Medecine. Serie Medecine Interne *see* Revue Roumaine de Medecine Interne **3149**
Revue Roumaine de Medecine. Serie Neurologie et Psychiatrie *see* Revue Roumaine de Neurologie et Psychiatrie **3353**
Revue Roumaine de Medecine. Serie Virologie *see* Revue Roumaine de Virologie **3223**

Revue Roumaine de Medecine Interne/ Romanian Journal of Internal Medicine. (RM) **3149**
Revue Roumaine de Morphologie, d'Embryologie et de Physiologie. Serie Morphologie et Embryologie *see* Revue Roumaine de Morphologie et d'Embryologie **454**
Revue Roumaine de Morphologie, d'Embryologie et de Physiologie. Serie Physiologie *see* Revue Roumaine de Physiologie **574**
Revue Roumaine de Morphologie et d'Embryologie/Romanian Journal of Morphology and Embryology. (RM) **454**, 3149
Revue Roumaine de Neurologie *see* Revue Roumaine de Neurologie et Psychiatrie **3353**
Revue Roumaine de Neurologie et Psychiatrie/Romanian Journal of Neurology and Psychiatry. (RM) **3353**
Revue Roumaine de Physiologie/ Rumanian Journal of Physiology. (RM) **574**, 3149
Revue Roumaine de Physique. (RM ISSN 0035-4090) **3830**
Revue Roumaine de Psychologie. (RM) **4045**
Revue Roumaine de Sciences Economiques. (RM) **689**
Revue Roumaine de Sciences Juridiques. (RM) **2732**
Revue Roumaine de Virologie/ Rumanian Journal of Virology. (RM) **3223**, 557
Revue Roumaine des Sciences Sociales. Serie de Philosophie et Logique *see* Revue de Philosophie **3779**
Revue Roumaine des Sciences Sociales. Serie de Sciences Economiques *see* Revue Roumaine de Sciences Economiques **689**
Revue Roumaine des Sciences Sociales. Serie de Sciences Juridiques *see* Revue Roumaine de Sciences Juridiques **2732**
Revue Roumaine des Sciences Sociales. Serie de Sociologie *see* Roumanian Journal of Sociology **4447**
Revue Roumaine des Sciences Techniques. Serie de Mecanique Appliquee. (RM ISSN 0035-4074) **1938**, 61
Revue Roumaine des Sciences Techniques. Serie Electrotechnique et Energetique. (RM ISSN 0035-4066) **1907**, 1835
Revue Sainte Anne *see* Annals of Good St. Anne **4255**
Revue Schweiz Suisse Svizzera. (SZ) **2219**
Revue Slowakei. (GW) **2882**
Revue Socialiste. (FR ISSN 0035-4139) **3923**
Revue Stomato-Odontologique du Nord de la France. (FR ISSN 0035-4147) **3242**
Revue Suisse d'Agriculture. (SZ) **117**
Revue Suisse d'Art et d'Archeologie. *see* Zeitschrift fuer Schweizerische Archaeologie und Kunstgeschichte **290**
Revue Suisse d'Assurances. *see* Schweizerische Versicherungszeitschrift **2542**
Revue Suisse d'Economie Politique et de Statistique. *see* Schweizerische Zeitschrift fuer Volkswirtschaft und Statistik **737**
Revue Suisse d'Histoire. *see* Schweizerische Zeitschrift fuer Geschichte **2322**
Revue Suisse de Jurisprudence. *see* Schweizerische Juristen-Zeitung **2677**
Revue Suisse de l'Aluminium. *see* Schweizer Aluminium Rundschau **5274**
Revue Suisse de Medecine. *see* Schweizerische Rundschau fuer Medizin Praxis **3152**
Revue Suisse de Medecine des Sports. *see* Schweizerische Zeitschrift fuer Sportmedizin **3373**

Revue Suisse de Medecine Militaire et de Catastrophes. *see* Schweizerische Zeitschrift fuer Militaer- und Katastrophenmedizin **3152**
Revue Suisse de Numismatique/ Schweizerische Numismatische Rundschau. (SZ ISSN 0035-4163) **3601**
Revue Suisse de Psychologie. *see* Schweizerische Zeitschrift fuer Psychologie **4046**
Revue Suisse de Sociologie. *see* Schweizerische Zeitschrift fuer Soziologie **4448**
Revue Suisse de Viticulture, Arboriculture et Horticulture. (SZ) **2138**, 191
Revue Suisse de Viticulture et Arboriculture *see* Revue Suisse de Viticulture, Arboriculture et Horticulture **2138**
Revue Suisse de Zoologie. (SZ ISSN 0035-418X) **591**
Revue Suisse des Chorales. *see* Schweizerische Chorzeitung **3579**
Revue Suisse des Marches Agricoles *see* Schweizerischer Bauernverband. Information **203**
Revue Svetovej Literatury. (CS) **2882**
Revue Syndicale Suisse. (SZ ISSN 0035-421X) **2588**
Revue Technique Automobile. (FR ISSN 0017-307X) **4700**
Revue Technique Carrosserie. (FR ISSN 0150-7206) **4700**
Revue Technique de la Viande et des Abattoirs *see* Revue Technique Veterinaire de l'Alimentation **2081**
Revue Technique de Radio-Canada. *see* C B C Engineering Review **1355**
Revue Technique des Hotels, Restaurants, Bars, Brasseries, Limonadiers, Tabacs, Habitats Collectifs. (FR ISSN 0035-4228) **2480**
Revue Technique des Industries du Cuir *see* Industrie du Cuir **2736**
Revue Technique Diesel. (FR ISSN 0037-2579) **4700**
Revue Technique du Batiment et des Constructions Industrielles. (FR ISSN 0048-8186) **630**
Revue Technique du Feu *see* R G S **1527**
Revue Technique et Economique de l'Industrie Alimentaire *see* Revue Economique et Technique de l'Industrie Alimentaire Europeenne **2081**
Revue Technique Luxembourgeoise. (LU ISSN 0035-4260) **4608**
Revue Technique Machinisme Agricole. (FR ISSN 0223-0135) **164**
Revue Technique Maritime. *see* Marine Engineering Digest **1830**
Revue Technique Thomson - C S F. (FR ISSN 0035-4279) **1400**, 1907
Revue Technique Thomson - C S F. Electronique. (FR ISSN 0040-6341) **1907**, 1400
Revue Technique Veterinaire de l'Alimentation. (FR) **2081**
Revue Tele-Africa. *see* Tele-Africa Revue **2335**
Revue Theologique de Louvain. (BE ISSN 0080-2654) **4274**
Revue Theologique de Louvain. Cahiers.(BE) **4274**
Revue Thomiste. (FR ISSN 0035-4295) **4199**, 3780
Revue Tricontinental *see* Revista Tricontinental **3971**
Revue Trimestrielle de Droit Civil. (FR ISSN 0397-9873) **2704**
Revue Trimestrielle de Droit Commercial et du Droit Economique. (FR ISSN 0244-9358) **2675**
Revue Trimestrielle de Droit Europeen. (FR ISSN 0035-4317) **2675**
Revue Trimestrielle de Droit Familial. (BE) **2718**
Revue Trimestrielle de Droit Sanitaire et Social *see* Revue de Droit Sanitaire et Social **4072**
Revue Tunisienne de Communication. (TI ISSN 0330-8480) **1342**, 2575
Revue Tunisienne de l'Energie. (TU) **1795**

Revue Tunisienne de l'Equipement. (TI) 1873, 1925
Revue Tunisienne des Sciences Medicales see La Tunisie Medicale 3158
Revue Tunisienne des Sciences Sociales. (TI ISSN 0035-4333) 4384
Revue Vervietoise d'Histoire Naturelle. (BE) 454
Revue Veterinaire Canadienne. see Canadian Veterinary Journal 4807
Revue Voir. (CN) 1507
Revue Zairoise de Droit. (ZR) 2675
Revue Zairoise de la Comptabilite see Conseiller Comptable 1091
Revue Zairoise de Psychologie et de Pedagogie. (ZR) 1659, 4045
Revues d'Histoire de la Deuxieme Guerre Mondiale see Guerres Mondiales et Conflits Contemporains 2311
La Revuo Orienta. (JA ISSN 0035-4406) 2838
Revuser. (US) 1466, 1428
Rewriting Indian and World History. (II) 2341, 2321
El Rey. (AG ISSN 0326-0011) 4485
▼Reynolds Records. (US ISSN 1057-6010) 2162
Reynolds Review. (US ISSN 0192-9569) 3418
The Rez. (CN) 1264
Rezanie i Instrument. (KR ISSN 0370-808X) 3845
Rezepte mit Pfiff. (GW) 4851, 2449
Rezul'taty Issledovanii po Mezhdunarodnym Geofizicheskim Proektam. Glyatsiologicheskie Issledovaniya/Results of Researches on the International Geophysical Projects. Glaciologicla Researches. (RU ISSN 0568-6245) 1594
Rheinhessische Wirtschaft. (GW ISSN 0035-4449) 822
Rheinisch-Bergischer Kalender. (GW ISSN 0722-7671) 2058
Rheinisch-Pfaelzische Hotels and Gaststaetten. (GW) 2480
Rheinisch-Westfaelische Akademie der Wissenschaften. Jahrbuch. (GW) 1323
Rheinisch-Westfaelische Akademie der Wissenschaften. Vortraege Natur-Ingenieur-und Wirtschaftswissenschaften. (GW) 4336, 4608
Rheinisch-Westfaelische Boerse zu Duesseldorf. Amtliches Kursblatt. (GW ISSN 0035-4457) 961
Rheinisch-Westfaelische Zeitschrift fuer Volkskunde. (GW ISSN 0556-8218) 2383, 248
Rheinisch-Westfaelisches Institut fuer Wirtschaftsforschung. Mitteilungen. (GW ISSN 0035-4465) 689
Rheinisch-Westfaelisches Institut fuer Wirtschaftsforschung, Essen Handwerksberichte see R W I Handwerksberichte 1117
Rheinisch-Westfaelisches Institut fuer Wirtschaftsforschung, Essen Konjunkturberichte see R W I - Konjunkturberichte 1083
Rheinisch-Westfaelisches Institut fuer Wirtschaftsforschung, Essen Konjunkturbrief see R W I Konjunkturbrief 1084
Rheinische Ausgrabungen. (GW ISSN 0557-7853) 283
Rheinische Heimatpflege. (GW ISSN 0342-1805) 2383, 2058
Rheinische Lebensbilder. (GW ISSN 0080-2670) 420
Rheinische Monatsschrift fuer Gemuese Obst Zierpflanzen. (GW) 191
†Rheinische Schriften. (GW ISSN 0080-2689) 5270
Rheinische Vierteljahrsblaetter. (GW ISSN 0035-4473) 2383
Rheinisch-Westfaelischer Jaeger. (GW ISSN 0171-0796) 4554
Rheinische Merkur. (GW ISSN 0173-3028) 2191, 4199
Rheinisches Aerzteblatt. (GW ISSN 0035-4481) 3149
Rheinisches Genossenschaftsblatt. (GW) 117

Rheinisches Jahrbuch fuer Volkskunde. (GW ISSN 0080-2697) 2058
Rheinisches Landesmuseum, Bonn. Schriften. (GW ISSN 0067-9968) 283
Rheinisches Museum fuer Philologie. (GW ISSN 0035-449X) 2838, 1279
Rheinland Aktuell. (GW) 143, 157
Rheinland Pfalz. Kultusministerium. Amtsblatt. (GW) 1731, 1758
Rheinland-Pfalz. Statistisches Landesamt Rheinland-Pfalz. Statistische Monatshefte. (GW ISSN 0174-2914) 4082, 4094
Rheinland - Pfalz Heute. (GW ISSN 0174-2876) 4082
Rhema Life. (AT) 4199
Rheologica Acta. (GW ISSN 0035-4511) 3845
▼Rheology (Year). (GW ISSN 0939-5059) 3845
Rheology Abstracts. (US ISSN 0035-452X) 3839, 22
Rheology Bulletin. (US ISSN 0035-4538) 3845
Rhetoric Review. (US ISSN 0735-0198) 1715, 2838
Rhetoric Society Newsletter see Rhetoric Society Quarterly 3780
Rhetoric Society Quarterly. (US ISSN 0277-3945) 3780
Rhetoric Study. see Xiuci Xuexi 2978
Rhetorica. (US ISSN 0734-8584) 2838
Rhetorik. (GW ISSN 0720-5775) 1758
Rheuma. (GW ISSN 0720-390X) 3149
†Rheuma Praxis-Aktuell. (GW ISSN 0930-5580) 5270
Rheuma Schmerz und Entzuendung. (GW ISSN 0721-8222) 3370
Rheumatic Diseases Clinics see Bailliere's Clinical Rheumatology 3368
Rheumatism. (II ISSN 0035-4546) 3370
Rheumatologia, Balneologia, Allergologia. (HU ISSN 0035-4554) 3370, 3188
Rheumatology. see Revmatologiya 3370
Rheumatology. (SZ ISSN 0080-2727) 3370
Rheumatology and Rehabilitation see British Journal of Rheumatology 3084
Rheumatology International. (GW ISSN 0172-8172) 3370
▼Rheumatology Review. (UK ISSN 0958-2584) 3370
Rhine Ships Register. (NE) 4737
Rhino. (US) 3004
Rhinology. (NE ISSN 0300-0729) 3316
Rhode Island. Department of Education. (Year) Statistical Tables. (US) 1679, 4584
Rhode Island. Department of Employment and Training. Employment Bulletin. (US) 993
Rhode Island. Department of Employment Security. Employment Bulletin see Rhode Island. Department of Employment and Training. Employment Bulletin 993
Rhode Island. Department of Health. Vital Statistics. (US) 3995
Rhode Island. Department of State Library Services. Newsletter. (US ISSN 0035-4597) 2782, 4136
Rhode Island Appellate Practice. (US) 2732
Rhode Island Audubon Report see Audubon Society of Rhode Island. Report 1483
Rhode Island Bar Journal. (US ISSN 0556-8595) 2675
Rhode Island Beverage Journal. (US ISSN 0035-4562) 385
Rhode Island Builder see The Rhode Island Builder Report 630
The Rhode Island Builder Report. (US) 630
Rhode Island College Alumni Association. Alumni Review see Perspectives (Providence) 1321

Rhode Island Criminal Procedure. (US) 2714
Rhode Island Dental Association. Journal. (US) 3242
Rhode Island Dental Association. Newsletter. (US) 3242
Rhode Island Directory of Manufacturers. (US) 1152
Rhode Island Directory of Manufacturers and List of Commercial Establishments see Rhode Island Directory of Manufacturers 1152
Rhode Island Division of Planning Monthly Progress Report. (US) 2495
Rhode Island Genealogical Register. (US ISSN 0190-3055) 2162
Rhode Island Herald. (US) 2021
Rhode Island History. (US ISSN 0035-4619) 2421, 2162
Rhode Island Jewish Historical Notes. (US ISSN 0556-8609) 2021, 2321
Rhode Island Lawyers Weekly. (US ISSN 0279-0882) 2675, 4157
Rhode Island Library Association. Bulletin. (US ISSN 0146-8685) 2782
Rhode Island Medical Journal. (US ISSN 0363-7913) 3149
Rhode Island Monthly. (US) 2233
Rhode Island Parents' Paper. (US) 1243
†Rhode Island Queries. (US ISSN 0893-181X) 5270
Rhode Island Review. (US) 2233
▼Rhode Island Rules of Evidence. (US) 2675
Rhode Island School of Design. Bulletin see Museum Notes (Providence) 3529
Rhode Island School of Design Voice see R I S D Voice 341
Rhode Island Statewide Planning Program Monthly Progress Report see Rhode Island Division of Planning Monthly Progress Report 2495
Rhode Island Supreme Court and the Law of Crimes. (US) 2714
Rhodeo. (SA ISSN 0035-466X) 1323
Rhodes Directory of Black Dentists Registered in the United States see Who's Who in Black Dentistry in America 3244
†Rhodes Directory of Black Physicians in the United States. (US) 5270
Rhodes-Livingstone Journal see African Social Research 4427
Rhodes-Livingstone Papers see Zambian Papers 2335
Rhodes Newsletter see Rhodes Review 1323
Rhodes Real Estate Review. (US) 4157
Rhodes Review. (SA) 1323
Rhodes University. Department of Philosophy. Philosophical Papers. (SA ISSN 0556-8641) 3780
Rhodesia and World Report. (RH ISSN 0035-4694) 3923
Rhodesia Stamp Catalogue. (RH) 3757
Rhodesian Journal of Economics. (RH ISSN 0035-4821) 689
Rhodesian Ridgeback Quarterly. (US) 3713
The Rhododendron. (AT) 2138
Rhododendron. (US ISSN 1047-2207) 2955
Rhododendron Society of Canada. Bulletin. (CN) 2138
Rhododendron Species Foundation Newsletter see R S F Newsletter 2137
Rhododendron und Immergruene Laubgehoelze. (GW ISSN 0482-9905) 2138
Rhododendrons, with Camellias and Magnolias. (UK ISSN 0080-2891) 2138
Rhodora. (US ISSN 0035-4902) 516
Rhoenbrief. (GW) 4248
Rhombus see Cross Section 3033
Rhumatologie. (FR) 3370
†Rhyme Time Poetry Newsletter. (US) 5270
Rhythm. (UK) 3577

Rhythm and Blues Music & Entertainment Monthly see R & B Music & Entertainment Monthly 3575
Rhythm & News. (US) 3577
Rhythm Rag. (UK) 3577
Rhythmus. (BL) 2955
Riabilitazione. (IT ISSN 0557-9430) 3149
Riabilitazione e Apprendimento. (IT) 3149, 1740
Riabita. (IT ISSN 0393-4411) 630
Riada. (SY) 4485
Rialto. (UK ISSN 0268-5981) 3004
Ribarski List. (BN ISSN 0035-4953) 4554
Ribe Stiftsbog. (DK ISSN 0108-0806) 2383
Riben Wenti/Japanese Problems. (US) 883
Riben Wenti Yanjiu/Journal of Japanese Studies. (CC) 3643
Ribno Stopanstvo. (BU) 2048
Ribolov. (CI ISSN 0350-6789) 4554
Ribosomes see Ribosomes and Translation 526
Ribosomes and Translation. (UK ISSN 0952-0414) 526, 482
Ricardian. (UK ISSN 0048-8267) 2383
Ricardian Register. (US) 2383
Rice. (US ISSN 0899-7357) 2021
Rice Abstracts. (UK ISSN 0141-0164) 143, 22
Rice Council Review. (US) 191
Rice Farming. (US) 191
Rice Farming and Rice Industry News. (US ISSN 0194-0929) 208
Rice Journal. (US ISSN 0035-4961) 191
Rice Lake Vacation Guide. (CN) 4785
Rice Market Circular. (UK) 191
Rice Thresher. (US) 1323
Rice World & Soybean News. (US ISSN 0738-5943) 191
Ricerca & Practica. (IT) 3149, 3742
Ricerca in Clinica e in Laboratorio see Research in Clinic and Laboratory 3147
Ricerca Operativa. (IT) 828
Ricerca Sociale. (IT) 4384
Ricerche di Biologia della Selvaggina. (IT ISSN 0375-0736) 591
Ricerche di Biologia della Selvaggina. Supplemento. (IT) 591, 566
Ricerche di Matematica. (IT ISSN 0035-5038) 3053
Ricerche di Psicologia. (IT ISSN 0391-996X) 4045
Ricerche di Sociologia dell'Educazione e Pedagogia Comparata. (IT) 1659
Ricerche di Storia della Lingua Latina. (IT ISSN 0080-293X) 2838
†Ricerche di Storia Moderna. (IT) 5270
Ricerche di Storia Politica. (IT ISSN 1120-9526) 2321
Ricerche di Storia Sociale e Religiosa. (IT) 4447, 4199
Ricerche di Zoologia Applicata alla Caccia. Supplemento see Ricerche di Biologia della Selvaggina. Supplemento 591
Ricerche Didattiche. (IT ISSN 0035-5046) 1659
Ricerche Economiche. (IT ISSN 0035-5054) 689
Ricerche Pedagogiche. (IT) 1758
Ricerche per la Storia Religiosa di Roma. (IT) 4199, 2383
Ricerche Storiche (Naples). (IT ISSN 0392-162X) 2321
Ricerche Storiche (Reggio Emilia). (IT ISSN 0035-5070) 2383
Ricerche Storiche Salesiane. (IT ISSN 0393-3849) 4274, 3780
Ricerche Sul '600 Napoletano. (IT) 342
Ricerche Sulle Dimore Rurali in Italia. (IT ISSN 0080-2964) 306
Richard B. Russell Lecture Series. (US) 2321
Richard C. Young's Intelligence Report. (US ISSN 0884-3031) 961
Richard C. Young's International Gold Report. (US ISSN 0895-1306) 961
▼Richard E. Band's Profitable Investing. (US ISSN 1048-3667) 961

Richard Strauss-Blaetter. (GW) **3577**, 420
Richard Wagner Blaetter. (GW) **3577**, 420
Richardson Family Researcher and Historical News. (US ISSN 0147-2488) **2162**
Richelieu Agricole *see* Le Richelieu Dimanche **117**
Le Richelieu Dimanche. (CN) **117**, 2138
Richesses de France. (FR ISSN 0035-5097) **4785**
Richland Report. (US) **961**
Richmond Afro-American. (US) **2021**
†Richmond Collage. (UK ISSN 0261-6505) **5270**
Richmond Flyer Magazine. (US) **2233**
Richmond Heights General Hospital Vital Signs *see* R H G H Vital Signs **2468**
Richmond Hill Month. (CN) **1507**
Richmond Lesbian Feminist Flyer. (US) **2457**, 4851
Richmond Magazine. (CN ISSN 0845-9762) **1508**
Richmond Quarterly. (US ISSN 0276-6515) **2421**, 2955
Richmond Surroundings. (US) **2233**
Richmond Times *see* College Voice (Staten Island) **1308**
†Richmond Times. (AT) **5270**
Richting *see* R S G Richting - Sport-Gericht **4484**
Rickia *see* Hoehnea **505**
Ricklinger Monatspost. (GW) **38**
Ricky McMountain Buyer's Guide. (CN) **2555**
Ridecab. (PE) **1660**
Rider. (US ISSN 0095-1625) **4520**, 4785
Rider College Magazine. (US) **1323**
Ridge Detail in Nature. (UK ISSN 0951-645X) **248**
Ridge Review. (US ISSN 0891-1231) **2882**
Ridgeback. (US) **3713**
Riding. (UK ISSN 0035-516X) **4537**
Ridings *see* Yorkshire Ridings Magazine **2196**
Ridotto. (IT ISSN 0035-5186) **4637**
Riebeling - Nachrichten der Familie Riebeling auf der Schwalm. (GW) **2162**
Riegos y Drenajes. (SP) **191**
†Riesgo. (SP) **5270**
Rieti. (IT) **2383**
Rieti-Sport. (IT) **4485**
Rifle. (US ISSN 0162-3583) **4485**
Rifleman. (UK ISSN 0035-5224) **4485**
Riforma Amministrativa. (IT) **1027**
Riforma della Scuola/School Reform. (IT ISSN 0035-5210) **1660**, 2882
La Riforma Medica. (IT ISSN 0035-5259) **3149**
Rig. (SW ISSN 0035-5267) **248**
Rig Market Forecast. (UK) **3700**
Rigaku Ryoho Janaru/Japanese Journal of Physical Therapy. (JA) **3216**, 3742
Rigaku Ryoho to Sagyo Ryoho - Japanese Journal of Physical Therapy and Occupational Therapy *see* Rigaku Ryoho Janaru **3216**
†Rigaku Senkoka Zasshi. (JA ISSN 0286-4487) **5270**
Right Choices. (US) **2021**, 1264
†Right Here. (US ISSN 0895-3139) **5270**
The Right of Aesthetic Realism to Be Known. (US ISSN 0882-3731) **2514**, 1264
Right of Way. (US ISSN 0035-5275) **4157**
Right On! (US ISSN 0048-8305) **2021**, 1264
Right On *see* Radix **4196**
Right Start. (UK ISSN 0957-3704) **1264**, 1243
Right to Choose. (AT ISSN 0311-8754) **4852**
Right to Housing Report. (US) **2495**, 4199
Right to Know and the Freedom to Act. (US) **3946**, 3923
Right to Know Compliance Advisor *see* O S H A Compliance Advisor **1964**

Right-to-Know Planning Guide (Series). (US) **4418**, 1508
Right-to-Know Planning Report. (US) **4418**
Righting Words. (US ISSN 0892-581X) **2838**, 2575
Rights. (SZ ISSN 1011-0240) **3678**
Rights. (US ISSN 0035-5283) **3946**
Rights and Freedoms. (CN) **3947**
Rights and Liabilities of Publishers, Broadcasters, and Reporters. (US) **2704**, 1379, 4136
Rights and Liberties. (CN ISSN 1187-3272) **3947**
†Rights Canada. (CN) **5270**
Rights of Man *see* Human Rights Bulletin (New York) **3943**
Rights of Physically Handicapped Persons. (US) **2704**, 3947
Rights of Prisoners. (US) **2714**
Rigsbibliotekarembedet. Retningslinier *see* Denmark. Statens Bibliotekstjeneste. Retningslinier **2754**
Rigsbibliotekaren. Meddelelser *see* Kongelige Bibliotek. Magasin **2767**
Rihabiriteshon/Rehabilitation (Tokyo, 1953). (JA ISSN 0035-5305) **4418**
Rihabiriteshon Igaku/Japanese Journal of Rehabilitation Medicine. (JA ISSN 0034-351X) **3149**, 3311
†Riista- ja Kalatalouden Tutkimuslaitos. Kalantutkimusosasto. Tiedonantoja. (FI ISSN 0355-0648) **5270**
Het Rijk der Vrouw. (BE ISSN 0035-5313) **4852**
Rijks Geologische Dienst. Mededelingen. Nieuwe Serie. (NE ISSN 0165-1951) **1579**
Rijks Geschiedkundige Publicatien. Grote Serie. (NE) **2383**
Rijks Geschiedkundige Publicatien. Kleine Serie. (NE) **2383**
Rijksdienst voor het Oudheidkundig Bodemonderzoek te Amersfoort. Berichten. (NE ISSN 0467-006X) **283**
Rijksinstituut voor het Rassenonderzoek van Cultuurgewassen. *see* Centrum voor Rassenonderzoek en Zaadtechnologie. Mededelingen **172**
Rijksinstituut voor het Rassenonderzoek van Cultuurgewassen. Jaaverslag *see* Centrum voor Rassenonderzoek en Zaadtechnologie. Jaarsverslag **172**
Rijksinstituut voor Oorlogsdocumentatie. Monografieen. (NE ISSN 0066-1295) **2383**
Rijksmuseum van Natuurlijke Historie. Zoologische Bijdragen *see* Nationaal Natuurhistorisch Museum. Zoologische Bijdragen **589**
Rijksmuseum van Natuurlijke Historie. Zoologische Mededelingen *see* Nationaal Natuurhistorisch Museum. Zoologische Mededelingen **589**
Rijksmuseum van Natuurlijke Historie. Zoologische Verhandelingen *see* Nationaal Natuurhistorisch Museum. Zoologische Verhandelingen **589**
Rijksmuseum van Oudheden, Leiden. Oudheidkundige Mededelingen. (NE ISSN 0920-4776) **283**
Rijkspolitie Magazine *see* Politie Magazine **1520**
Rijksuniversiteit te Gent. Centrum voor Onkruidonderzoek. Mededeling. (BE ISSN 0435-950X) **191**
Rijksuniversiteit te Gent. Faculteit Landbouwwetenschappen. Mededelingen. (BE ISSN 0035-533X) **117**
Rijksuniversiteit te Gent. Faculteit van de Economische Wetenschappen. Werken. (BE) **689**
†Rijksuniversiteit te Gent. Laboratorium voor Experimentele, Differentiele en Genetische Psychologie. Mededelingen en Werkdocumenten. (BE ISSN 0085-1078) **5270**
Rijksuniversiteit te Gent. Sterrenkundig Observatorium. Mededelingen. (BE ISSN 0072-4432) **368**
Rijksuniversiteit te Gent. Sterrenkundig Observatorium. Mededelingen: Meteorologie en Geofysica. (BE ISSN 0072-4440) **3440**, 1594

Rijksuniversiteit te Groningen. Nedersaksisch Instituut. Driemaandelijkse Bladen. (NE ISSN 0012-6209) **2955**, 2058, 2838
Rijksuniversiteit te Groningen. Universiteitskrant *see* Universiteitskrant Groningen **1328**
Rijksuniversiteit te Leiden. Instituut voor Culturele Antropologie en Sociologie der Niet-Westerse Samenlevingen. Publicatie. (NE) **248**, 4447
Rijksuniversiteit te Leiden. Instituut voor Culturele Antropologie en Sociologie der Niet-Westerse Volken. Publicatie *see* Rijksuniversiteit te Leiden. Instituut voor Culturele Antropologie en Sociologie der Niet-Westerse Samenlevingen. Publicatie **248**
Rijksuniversiteit te Utrecht. Department of Stratigraphy and Paleontology. Special Publications. (NE) **3660**
Rijksuniversiteit Utrecht. De Universiteit Media Bulletin. (NE) **1715**
Rijksuniversiteit Utrecht. Jaarvslag *see* Rijksuniversiteit Utrecht. Wetenschappelijk Jaaverslag **1715**
Rijksuniversiteit Utrecht. Wetenschappelijk Jaaverslag. (NE) **1715**, 4336
Rika Nenpyo. (JA) **4357**
Rikagakkaishi/Journal of Physics, Chemistry and Earth Science. (JA ISSN 0287-718X) **4336**, 1187, 1548, 3830
Rikagaku Kenkyujo Hokoku/Institute of Physical and Chemical Research. Reports. (JA ISSN 0020-3084) **3830**, 1187
Rikagaku Kenkyujo Kenkyu Happyo Ronbun Mokuroku/Institute of Physical and Chemical Research. List of Papers. (JA) **3839**, 1202
Rikagaku Kenkyujo Kenkyu Nenpo/I P C R. Annual Reports of Research Activities. (JA ISSN 0557-0220) **3839**, 1202
Rikagaku Kenkyujo Nyusu/Riken News.(JA ISSN 0916-619X) **3839**, 1202
Rikagaku Kenkyujo Riken. Accelerator Progress Report *see* Riken. Accelerator Progress Report **3850**
Riken. Accelerator Progress Report. (Rikagaku Kenkyujo) (JA ISSN 0289-842X) **3850**
Riken. Cyclotron Report *see* Riken - A F - N P **3850**
Riken - A F - N P. (JA) **3850**
Riken News. *see* Rikagaku Kenkyujo Nyusu **3839**
Rikka. (CN) **2882**
Rikkyo Daigaku Kenkyu Hokoku. Shizen Kagaku/St. Paul's Review of Science.(JA ISSN 0387-6837) **4336**
Rikkyo Daigaku Sugaku Zasshi. *see* Commentarii Mathematici Universitatis Sancti Pauli **3033**
Rikkyo Keizaigaku Kenkyu. *see* St. Paul's Economic Review **690**
Rikkyo University. Institute for Atomic Energy. Report. (JA) **1809**, 1835
Riksarkivets Rapporter. (SW ISSN 0280-3046) **2782**
Riksfoereningen foer Laerarna i Moderna Spraak Lingua *see* L M S - Lingua **2822**
Riksgaeldkontoret. Statistisk Aarsbok. (SW ISSN 0280-4182) **798**
Riksgaeldskontoret. Aarsbok *see* Riksgaeldkontoret. Statistisk Aarsbok **798**
Rikujo Kyogi. (JA) **4485**
Rikujo-Kyogi Magazine. *see* Athletic Sports Magazine **4464**
Rikusui Gaku Zasshi. *see* Japanese Journal of Limnology **1599**
Rilancio. (IT ISSN 0016-5700) **4815**
Rilce. (SP) **2838**
Rimba Indonesia. (IO ISSN 0035-5372) **2107**
Rimbaud Vivant. (FR) **2882**
Rimonim. (IS) **342**
Rimu *see* Crosscurrent **5175**
Rinascimento. (IT ISSN 0080-3073) **2514**, 2383
Rinascimento. Quaderni. (IT) **2383**
Rinascita. (IT ISSN 0035-5380) **3923**

Rinboku no Ikushu/Forest Tree Breeding. (JA ISSN 0387-9119) **2107**, 526, 546
Rincontro. (CN ISSN 0380-8416) **2021**
Rind und Schlegel. (GW ISSN 0720-0463) **3004**
Ring. (PL ISSN 0035-5429) **566**
Ring. (US ISSN 0035-5410) **4485**
Ring des Wortes. (GW) **4274**, 2278, 2289
Ring Junger Buende. Mitteilungen. (GW) **1243**, 4554
Ring-Post. (SZ) **2882**
Ring Rhetoric. (US) **4485**
Ring Systems Handbook. (US ISSN 0742-5996) **1223**
Ringette Canada. Official Rules (Years). (CN) **4485**
Ringette Review. (CN) **4485**
Ringing and Migration. (UK ISSN 0307-8698) **567**
Ringing, Migration, Monitoring - Methods and Information *see* Ring **566**
Ringing World. (UK ISSN 0035-5453) **3578**
Ringkoebing Aarbog. (DK) **2384**
Ringling Museums *see* John & Mable Ringling Museum of Art **3525**
Ringside. (US) **4485**
Ringsport. (UK ISSN 0037-6310) **4485**
Ringyo Shiken Kenkyu Hokoku. *see* Tokyo Metropolitan Agricultural Experiment Station, Itsukaichi Office. Forestry Experimental Bulletin **2109**
Ringyo Shikenjo Kyushu Shijo Nenpo. *see* Japan. Government Forest Experiment Station. Kyushu Branch. Annual Report **2103**
Ringyo to Kakuzai. (JA) **2107**, 2117
Rink Digest. (US) **4485**
Rinksider. (US) **1027**, 4485
Rinnovamento della Scuola. (IT) **1660**
Rinsho Eiyo. *see* Japanese Journal of Clinical Nutrition **3607**
Rinsho Fujinka Sanka/Clinical Obstetrics and Gynecology. (JA ISSN 0386-9865) **3296**
Rinsho Hifuka. *see* Japanese Journal of Clinical Dermatology **3248**
Rinsho Hinyokika/Japanese Journal of Clinical Urology. (JA ISSN 0385-2393) **3389**
Rinsho Hoshasen. *see* Japanese Journal of Clinical Radiology **3359**
Rinsho Kensa/Journal of Medical Technology. (JA ISSN 0485-1420) **3263**
Rinsho Kensagaku Zasshi/Medical Technology. (JA ISSN 0389-1887) **3149**
Rinsho Seikei Geka/Clinical Orthopaedic Surgery. (JA) **3311**
Rinsho Shika/Folia Odontologica Practica. (JA ISSN 0035-5488) **3242**
Rinsho Shinkeigaku/Clinical Neurology. (JA ISSN 0009-918X) **3353**
Rinsho Shoni Igaku. *see* Journal of Clinical Pediatrics **3321**
Rinsho to Kenkyu. *see* Japanese Journal of Clinical and Experimental Medicine **3260**
Rio de Janeiro, Brazil (City). Arquivo Geral da Cidade do Rio de Janeiro. Boletim Informativo. (BL) **2782**
Rio de Janeiro, Brazil (State). Instituto Estadual do Livro. Divisao de Bibliotecas. Boletim Bibliografico. (BL) **410**
Rio Grande do Sul, Brazil. Fundacao de Economia e Estatistica. Boletim Estatistico do Seite *see* Revista do Seite **4584**
Rio Grande do Sul, Brazil. Fundacao de Economia e Estatistica. Indicadores Economicos RS. (BL) **883**
Rio Grande do Sul, Brazil. Procuradoria Geral do Estado. Revista. (BL ISSN 0101-1480) **2675**
Rio Grande Educational Association Newsletter. (US) **1660**
†Rio Grande History. (US ISSN 0146-1869) **5270**
Rio Grande Sun. (US) **2233**

Rio Grande Valley Horticultural Society. Journal see Subtropical Plant Science 2139
Rip. (US ISSN 0889-5791) 3578
†Rip Off Comix. (US) 5270
Rip Photo Specials. (US) 3578
Rip Presents. (US) 3578
Ripartizione Cultura e Spettacolo. Rassegna di Studi e di Notizie. (IT) 342
Ripley P. Bullen Monographs in Anthropology and History. (US ISSN 0271-6925) 283, 2421
Ripley's Believe It or Not. (US ISSN 0035-5518) 3013
Ripon College Magazine. (US ISSN 0300-7928) 1323
Ripon Forum. (US ISSN 0035-5526) 3923
Ripon Society Newsletter see Ripon Forum 3923
Ripples. (US) 2955
Riron Butsurigaku no Shinpo. see Progress of Theoretical Physics 3829
Al-Risalah. (TS) 4220
Al-Risalah al Islamiah. (LE) 4220
Al-Risalah al-Islamiyyah. (LE) 4220
Risalat al-Maktaba. see Message of the Library 2773
Risalat al-Masjid. (MK) 4220
Risalat al-Mu'allim. see Message of the Teacher 1711
Risalat al Sina'a/Amman Chamber of Industry. Bimonthly Industrial Bulletin.(JO) 822
Risalat al-Talib. see Student's Message 1665
Risc Management see R I S C Management 1400
Risc World see R I S C World 1464
Risc 6000 News see R I S C 6000 News 1464
Riscaldamento Climatizzazione Idronica see R C I 1835
Risco. (PO ISSN 0870-9912) 3923
Rise Hvezd. (CS ISSN 0035-5550) 368
Risicoltore. (IT) 117
Rising Star. (US) 3013
Rising Sun. (II) 3923
Risk. (UK ISSN 0952-8776) 798
Risk Abstracts. (US ISSN 0824-3336) 1975, 22, 1983
Risk Analysis. (US ISSN 0272-4332) 3053
▼Risk and Benefits Journal. (US) 2541
Risk & Benefits Management. (US ISSN 0893-2654) 2541, 1027
▼Risk & Insurance. (US) 2541
Risk Factor Method of Investing. (US) 961
Risk Management. (US ISSN 0035-5593) 2541, 961
Risk Management for Executive Women. (US ISSN 0732-2666) 2541, 1117, 2675
Risk Management News. (US ISSN 0194-1038) 798
Risk Management Newsletter. (US) 2541
Risk Management Review. (US) 920, 3971
Risk Measurement Service. (UK ISSN 0261-3344) 798
Risk Report. (US) 2541
Riskienhallinta see Sampovisio 1027
RiskWatch. (US) 2541, 4073
Risley Record. (US ISSN 1050-7922) 2162
Risoe Annual Report. see Forskningscenter Risoe. Aarsberetning 1790
Risoe International Symposium on Metallurgy and Materials Science. Proceedings. (DK ISSN 0108-8599) 3419
Risoe-M. (DK ISSN 0418-6435) 3830
Risorgimento. (IT ISSN 0035-5607) 2384
Risparmio. (IT ISSN 0035-5615) 798
Risques du Metier see Prevenir les Risques du Metier 3620
Rissalat al-Jihad. (LY) 4220
Rissener Jahrbuch. (GW) 3923
Rissener Rundbrief. (GW) 3923
Ristorazione Piu. (IT) 2480

Risveglio. (IT) 2206
Risveglio Bandistico see Risveglio Musicale 3578
Risveglio del Molise e del Mezzogiorno. (IT ISSN 0035-5623) 4384
Risveglio Musicale. (IT) 3578
Risveglio Ostetrico. (IT) 3296
Rit Fiskideildar/Marine Research Institute. Journal. (IC ISSN 0484-9019) 2048
Ritchie County Historical Society Newsletter. (US) 2163, 2421
Ritenour News. (US) 1660
Ritenour Reporter. (US) 1660
Rites. (CN ISSN 0828-5802) 2457, 3947
†Ritmo. (MX) 5270
Ritsumeikan Daigaku Rikogaku Kenkyujo Kiyo/Ritsumeikan University. Research Institute of Science and Engineering. Memoirs. (JA ISSN 0370-4254) 1835
Ritsumeikan Economic Review. see Ritsumeikan Keizaigaku 689
Ritsumeikan Keizaigaku/Ritsumeikan Economic Review. (JA) 689
Ritsumeikan University. Research Institute of Science and Engineering. Memoirs. see Ritsumeikan Daigaku Rikogaku Kenkyujo Kiyo 1835
Ritz Newspaper. (UK ISSN 0144-7416) 1294
Riv Lib File see Australian Library Review 2746
Rivacha Veavada. (IS) 993
Rivages. (FR) 4737
Rivaon ha-Yisraeli l'Misim/Israeli Tax Review. (IS ISSN 0334-3065) 1105
Rivarol see Rivarol and Political 4384
Rivarol and Political. (FR) 4384
Riveon Lebankaut/Quarterly Banking Review. (IS) 798
River Behaviour and Control. (II ISSN 0970-9258) 4828
River Bend Library System. Report of the Director. (US ISSN 0080-3227) 2782
River City Library Times. (US) 2782
River Currents. (US ISSN 0145-0689) 4737, 3470
River Rat Review. (US ISSN 0893-9721) 3004
River Runner see Paddler 4527
River Styx. (US ISSN 0149-8851) 2882, 342
River Yarns see National Rivers Hall of Fame Newsletter 1492
Riverfront. (US) 2882
Riverina Library Review see Australian Library Review 2746
Riverlander see Riverlander Notes 1496
Riverlander Notes. (AT) 1496, 883
Riverrun. (US) 3004
▼Rivers. (US ISSN 0898-8048) 4828, 1967, 2675
River's Edge. (US) 2233
Rivers State. Ministry of Information. Quarterly Journal. (NR) 2212
Riverside County Agriculture. (US) 117
Riverside County Farm and Agricultural Business News see Riverside County Agriculture 117
Riverside Quarterly. (US ISSN 0889-2326) 3013
Riverwind. (US) 3004
Ha-Rivhiyut shel-Anaf ha-Lul. see Profitability of Poultry Farming in Israel 156
Ha-Rivhiyut shel 'anaf ha-Refet. see Profitability of Dairy in Israel 156
Ha-Rivhiyut shel Gidul ha-Darim. see Profitability of Citrus Growing in Israel 156
Ha-Rivhiyut Shel Gidul ha-Kutnah. see Profitability of Cotton Growing in Israel 156
Riviera Eco. (IT) 4785
Riviere. (FR ISSN 0035-5720) 4528
Rivista. (UK) 3971
Rivista Abruzzese. (IT ISSN 0035-5739) 2514
Rivista Aeronautica. (IT ISSN 0391-6162) 61
Rivista Amministrativa della Repubblica Italiana. (IT ISSN 0035-5763) 2675, 3923

Rivista Araldica. (IT ISSN 0035-5771) 2163
Rivista Archeologica dell'Antica Provincia e Diocesi di Como. (IT ISSN 0080-3235) 283
Rivista Archeologica della Provincia di Como see Rivista Archeologica dell'Antica Provincia e Diocesi di Como 283
Rivista Arredos. (IT) 2561
Rivista Critica di Storia della Filosofia see Rivista di Storia della Filosofia 3780
Rivista d'Arte. (IT) 342
Rivista d'Europa. (IT) 3923
Rivista Dalmatica. (IT ISSN 0393-4624) 2384, 342, 420, 2882
†Rivista de Chimica. (IT) 5270
Rivista degli Infortuni e delle Malattie Professionali. (IT ISSN 0035-5836) 3621
Rivista degli Scambi Italo-Svizzeri. (SZ) 822
Rivista degli Studi Orientali. (IT ISSN 0392-4866) 3643
La Rivista dei Combustibili. (IT ISSN 0035-5852) 3700, 1967
Rivista dei Dottori Commercialisti. (IT) 689
Rivista dei Fonti Comuni d'Investimento.(IT) 962
Rivista del Catasto e dei Servizi Tecnici Erariali. (IT ISSN 0035-5860) 1105
Rivista del Clero Italiano. (IT ISSN 0042-7586) 4274
Rivista del Colore. (IT ISSN 0048-8348) 3655
Rivista del Consiglio. (IT) 2675
Rivista del Consulente Tecnico. (IT) 2675, 4608
Rivista del Diritto Commerciale e del Diritto Generale delle Obbligazioni. (IT ISSN 0035-5887) 2675
Rivista del Latte. (IT) 203
Rivista del Lavoro. (IT ISSN 0483-142X) 993
Rivista del Medico Pratico. (IT ISSN 0392-4858) 3149
Rivista del Notariato. (IT) 2675
Rivista del Personale dell'Ente Locale. (IT) 4094
Rivista del Porto di Napoli. (IT ISSN 0035-5925) 4737
▼Rivista dell'Arbitrato. (IT) 2675
Rivista dell'Infermiere. (IT) 3286
Rivista dell'Instruzione. (IT) 1660
Rivista della Borsa. (IT) 962
Rivista della Citta di Trieste. (IT ISSN 0035-6972) 4094
Rivista della Donna. (IT) 4852
Rivista della Guardia di Finanza see Testata: Rivista della Guardia di Finanza 1111
Rivista della Ortoflorofrutticoltura Italiana see Advances in Horticultural Science 2120
Rivista della Scuola. (IT) 1731
Rivista delle Birrerie e delle Bevande. see Brauerei and Getraenke-Rundschau 379
Rivista delle Cancelliere. (IT ISSN 0394-9028) 2675
Rivista delle Dogane. see Zoll - Rundschau 1112
Rivista delle Societa. (IT ISSN 0035-6018) 2675, 1084
Rivista di Agricoltura Subtropicale e Tropicale. (IT ISSN 0035-6026) 117
Rivista di Agronomia. (IT ISSN 0035-6034) 191
Rivista di Anatomia Patologica e di Oncologia. (IT ISSN 0048-8364) 3149, 454, 3202
Rivista di Antropologia. (IT ISSN 0085-5723) 248
Rivista di Archeologia. (IT ISSN 0392-0895) 283
Rivista di Archeologia Cristiana. (VC ISSN 0035-6042) 283
Rivista di Archeologia, Storia e Costume. (IT) 2384
Rivista di Ascetica e Mistica. (IT) 4274
Rivista di Avicoltura. (IT ISSN 0005-2213) 225
Rivista di Bellinzona. (SZ) 2384
Rivista di Biologia/Biology Forum. (IT ISSN 0035-6050) 454

Rivista di Biologia Normale e Patologica. (IT ISSN 0391-1551) 454
Rivista di Chirurgia del Piede see Chirurgia del Piede 3377
Rivista di Chirurgia della Mano. (IT ISSN 0080-3243) 3383
Rivista di Coniglicoltura. (IT ISSN 0010-5929) 225
Rivista di Cultura Classica e Medioevale. (IT ISSN 0035-6085) 1279, 1660
Rivista di Cultura Classica e Medioevale. Quaderni. (IT ISSN 0080-3251) 1279
Rivista di Diritto Agrario. (IT) 117
Rivista di Diritto Civile. (IT ISSN 0035-6093) 2704
Rivista di Diritto del Lavoro see Rivista Italiana di Diritto del Lavoro 2675
Rivista di Diritto dell'Impresa. (IT) 2675
Rivista di Diritto Economia e Tecnica della Pesca. (IT ISSN 0035-6115) 2048
Rivista di Diritto ed Economia Valutaria see Rivista di Diritto Valutario e di Economia Internazionale 2729
Rivista di Diritto Europeo. (IT ISSN 0035-6123) 2675
Rivista di Diritto Finanziario e Scienza delle Finanze. (IT ISSN 0035-6131) 798, 2675
Rivista di Diritto Industriale. (IT ISSN 0035-614X) 2675, 689
Rivista di Diritto Internazionale. (IT ISSN 0035-6158) 2728
Rivista di Diritto Internazionale e Comparato del Lavoro. (IT ISSN 0035-6166) 2728, 993
Rivista di Diritto Internazionale Privato e Processuale. (IT ISSN 0035-6174) 2729
Rivista di Diritto Processuale. (IT ISSN 0035-6182) 2704
Rivista di Diritto Processuale Penale see Rivista Italiana di Diritto e Procedura Penale 2675
Rivista di Diritto Sportivo. (IT ISSN 0048-8372) 4485, 2675
▼Rivista di Diritto Tributario. (IT) 2675
Rivista di Diritto Valutario e di Economia Internazionale/Review of Currency Law and International Economics. (IT ISSN 0392-8748) 2729, 920
Rivista di Economia Agraria. (IT ISSN 0035-6190) 157
Rivista di Economia e Politica Industriale see Industria: Rivista di Economia Politica Industriale 1077
Rivista di Estetica. (IT ISSN 0035-6212) 3780
Rivista di Etnografia. (IT ISSN 0085-5731) 4447
Rivista di Filologia Classica. (IT ISSN 0035-6220) 2838, 1279
Rivista di Filosofia. (IT ISSN 0035-6239) 3780
Rivista di Filosofia Neoscolastica. (IT ISSN 0035-6247) 3780
Rivista di Gastroenterologia. (IT ISSN 0035-6255) 3270
Rivista di Grammatica Generativa. (IT) 2838
Rivista di Idrobiologia. (IT ISSN 0048-8399) 454, 1967
Rivista di Informatica. (IT ISSN 0390-668X) 1457
Rivista di Ingegneria Agraria. (IT ISSN 0304-0593) 191
Rivista di Letterature Moderne e Comparate. (IT) 2955
Rivista di Linguistica. (IT ISSN 1120-2726) 2838
Rivista di Lugano. (SZ ISSN 0035-628X) 2219
Rivista di Matematica Elementare. see Elemente der Mathematik 3035
Rivista di Matematica per le Scienze Economiche e Sociali. (IT) 3053
Rivista di Meccanica. (IT ISSN 0035-6301) 3023
Rivista di Meccanica International Edition. (IT ISSN 0391-4631) 3419

Rivista di Medicina Aeronautica e Spaziale. (IT ISSN 0035-631X) **3149**
Rivista di Medicina del Lavoro ed Igiene Industriale. (IT ISSN 0391-2825) **3621, 3808**
Rivista di Medicina e Chirurgia. (IT) **3150, 3383**
Rivista di Meteorologia Aeronautica. (IT ISSN 0035-6328) **3440,** 61
Rivista di Micologia. (IT ISSN 0394-9486) **516**
Rivista di Microchirurgia. (IT) **3383**
Rivista di Neurobiologia. (IT ISSN 0035-6336) **3353,** 454
Rivista di Neurologia *see* Nuova Rivista di Neurologia **3349**
Rivista di Neuropsichiatria e Scienze Affini. (IT ISSN 0035-6352) **3353**
Rivista di Neuroradiologia. (IT) **3362, 3353**
Rivista di Oftalmologia Sociale. (IT) **2295**
†Rivista di Ostetricia, Ginecologia Pratica e Medicina Perinatale. (IT) **5270**
Rivista di Parassitologia. (IT ISSN 0035-6387) **3223,** 557
Rivista di Pastorale Liturgica. (IT ISSN 0035-6395) **4199**
Rivista di Patologia Clinica e Sperimentale *see* Rivista di Patologia e Sperimentazione Clinica **3150**
Rivista di Patologia dell'Apparato Locomotore. (IT ISSN 0394-0772) **3150**
Rivista di Patologia e Clinica. (IT ISSN 0035-6417) **3150**
Rivista di Patologia e Clinica della Tubercolosi *see* Rivista di Patologia e Clinica della Tubercolosi e di Pneumologia **3367**
Rivista di Patologia e Clinica della Tubercolosi e di Pneumologia. (IT ISSN 0302-4717) **3367**
Rivista di Patologia e Sperimentazione Clinica. (IT ISSN 0394-4549) **3150**
Rivista di Patologia Vegetale. (IT ISSN 0035-6441) **516**
Rivista di Pediatria Preventiva e Sociale-Nipiologia. (IT ISSN 0392-4416) **3326**
Rivista di Politica Agraria. (IT ISSN 0035-645X) **117**
Rivista di Politica Economica. (IT ISSN 0035-6468) **689**
Rivista di Polizia. (IT ISSN 0035-6476) **1522**
Rivista di Psichiatria. (IT ISSN 0035-6484) **3353**
Rivista di Psicoanalisi/Journal of the Italian Psychoanalytical Society. (IT ISSN 0035-6492) **4045**
Rivista di Psicologia. (IT ISSN 0035-6506) **4045**
Rivista di Psicologia Analitica. (IT) **4045**
Rivista di Psicologia dell'Arte. (IT ISSN 0393-9898) **342, 3780, 4045**
Rivista di Radiologia. (IT) **3362**
Rivista di Riabilitazione Psichiatrica e Psicosociale. (IT) **3353**
Rivista di Scienze dell'Educazione. (IT) **1715**
Rivista di Scienze Preistoriche. (IT ISSN 0035-6514) **283**
Rivista di Servizio Sociale. (IT ISSN 0035-6522) **4418**
†Rivista di Sessuologia. (IT) **5270**
Rivista di Storia Contemporanea. (IT) **2321**
Rivista di Storia della Chiesa in Italia. (IT ISSN 0035-6557) **4199, 2384**
Rivista di Storia della Filosofia. (IT) **3780**
Rivista di Storia della Storiografia Moderna. (IT) **2384**
Rivista di Storia delle Scienze Mediche e Naturali. Biblioteca *see* Biblioteca di Storia della Scienza **4302**
Rivista di Storia e Letteratura Religiosa.(IT ISSN 0035-6573) **4199, 2321**
▼Rivista di Storia e Letteratura Religiosa. Biblioteca. Studi. (IT) **4199**

Rivista di Storia e Letteratura Religiosa. Biblioteca. Testi e Documenti. (IT) **4199, 2321**
Rivista di Storia Economica. (IT ISSN 0393-3415) **898**
Rivista di Studi Bizantini e Slavi. (IT) **2384,** 2431
Rivista di Studi Classici. (IT ISSN 0035-6581) **1279**
Rivista di Studi Crociani. (IT ISSN 0035-659X) **3780,** 342
Rivista di Studi Fenici. (IT) **283**
Rivista di Studi Liguri/Revue d'Etudes Ligures. (IT ISSN 0035-6603) **2384,** 306
Rivista di Studi Politici Internazionali. (IT ISSN 0035-6611) **3971**
Rivista di Studi Pompeiani. (IT) **283**
Rivista di Studi Ungheresi *see* R S U **2513**
Rivista di Suinicoltura. (IT ISSN 0035-662X) **225**
Rivista di Teologia Morale. (IT) **4274**
Rivista di Tossicologia Sperimentale e Clinica. (IT) **3742**
Rivista di Vita Spirituale. (IT ISSN 0035-6638) **4274**
Rivista di Zootecnia *see* Rivista di Zootecnia e Veterinaria **225**
Rivista di Zootecnia e Veterinaria. (IT) **225, 4815**
Rivista Diocesana del Patriarcato di Venezia. (IT ISSN 0035-6654) **4274**
Rivista Economica del Mezzogiorno. (IT ISSN 1120-9534) **689**
Rivista Generale Italiana di Chirurgia. (IT ISSN 0035-6689) **3383**
Rivista Geografica Italiana. (IT ISSN 0035-6697) **2261**
Rivista Giuridica del Lavoro e della Previdenza Sociale. Dottrina. (IT ISSN 0392-7229) **2588,** 2675
Rivista Giuridica del Mezzogiorno. (IT ISSN 1120-9542) **2675**
▼Rivista Giuridica del Molise e del Sannio. (IT) **2675**
Rivista Giuridica dell'Ambiente. (IT) **306, 2675**
Rivista Giuridica dell'Edilizia. (IT ISSN 0485-2435) **630, 2675**
Rivista Giuridica della Circolazione e dei Trasporti. (IT ISSN 0035-6700) **2675, 4655**
Rivista Giuridica di Polizia Locale. (IT) **1522**
Rivista Giuridica di Urbanistica. (IT) **4094,** 2495
Rivista Giuridica Sarda. (IT) **2675**
Rivista Internazionale dei Diritti dell' Uomo. (IT ISSN 0394-6495) **2675,** 3947
Rivista Internazionale di Chirurgia Vertebrale e dei Nervi Periferici. (IT ISSN 0393-9715) **3150**
Rivista Internazionale di Economica dei Trasporti. *see* International Journal of Transport Economics **4651**
Rivista Internazionale di Filosofia del Diritto. (IT ISSN 0035-6727) **2675,** 3780
Rivista Internazionale di Musica Sacra/ International Church Music Review/ Internationale Zeitschrift fuer Kirchenmusik/Revue Internationale de Musique Sacree/Revista Internacional de Musica Sagrada. (IT ISSN 0394-6282) **3578**
†Rivista Internazionale di Psicologia e Ipnosi. (IT ISSN 0035-6743) **5271**
Rivista Internazionale di Scienze Economiche e Commerciali. (IT ISSN 0035-6751) **689**
Rivista Internazionale di Scienze Sociali.(IT ISSN 0035-676X) **4385,** 689
Rivista Internazionale per la Cultura Commerciale. *see* International Review for Business Education **672**
Rivista Italiana d'Igiene. (IT ISSN 0035-6921) **3808**
Rivista Italiana degli Odontotecnici. (IT) **3242**
Rivista Italiana del Leasing *see* Rivista Italiana del Leasing e dell'Intermediazione Finanziaria **689**
Rivista Italiana del Leasing e dell'Intermediazione Finanziaria. (IT) **689**

Rivista Italiana dell'Intermediazione Finanziaria *see* Rivista Italiana del Leasing e dell'Intermediazione Finanziaria **689**
Rivista Italiana della Saldatura. (IT ISSN 0035-6794) **3430**
Rivista Italiana delle Sostanze Grasse. (IT ISSN 0035-6808) **1223**
Rivista Italiana di Agopuntura. (IT) **3150**
Rivista Italiana di Biologia e Medicina. (IT) **3150,** 454
Rivista Italiana di Chirurgia Plastica. (IT ISSN 0391-2221) **3383**
Rivista Italiana di Colon-Proctologia. (IT ISSN 0394-9109) **3150**
Rivista Italiana di Dialettologia. (IT) **2838**
Rivista Italiana di Diritto del Lavoro. (IT ISSN 0393-2494) **2675,** 993
Rivista Italiana di Diritto e Procedura Penale. (IT ISSN 0557-1391) **2675**
Rivista Italiana di Diritto Penale *see* Rivista Italiana di Diritto e Procedura Penale **2675**
▼Rivista Italiana di Diritto Pubblico Comunitario. (IT) **2675**
Rivista Italiana di Economia Demografia e Statistica. (IT ISSN 0035-6832) **3995,** 737
Rivista Italiana di Geotecnica. (IT) **1579**
Rivista Italiana di Medicina Legale. (IT) **3265**
Rivista Italiana di Medicina Sociale. (IT ISSN 0025-7915) **3150**
Rivista Italiana di Musicologia. (IT ISSN 0035-6867) **3578**
Rivista Italiana di Musicologia. Quaderni.(IT) **3578**
Rivista Italiana di Nutrizione Clinica e Preventiva. (IT) **3612**
Rivista Italiana di Nutrizione Parenterale ed Enterale. (IT ISSN 0393-5582) **3612**
▼Rivista Italiana di Odontoiatria Infantile. (IT) **3242,** 3326
Rivista Italiana di Ornitologia. (IT ISSN 0035-6875) **567**
Rivista Italiana di Ortopedia e Traumatologia. (IT) **3311**
Rivista Italiana di Ortopedia e Traumatologia Pediatrica. (IT ISSN 0393-5221) **3311**
Rivista Italiana di Otorinolaringologia, Audiologia e Foniatria. (IT ISSN 0392-1360) **3316**
Rivista Italiana di Paleontologia e Stratigrafia. (IT ISSN 0035-6883) **3660**
Rivista Italiana di Pediatria. (IT) **3326**
Rivista Italiana di Previdenza Sociale. (IT) **4111**
Rivista Italiana di Scienza Politica. (IT ISSN 0048-8402) **3923**
Rivista Italiana di Stomatologia. (IT ISSN 0035-6905) **3242**
Rivista Italiana di Studi Napoleonici. (IT ISSN 0035-6913) **2384**
Rivista Italiana Difesa. (IT) **3470**
Rivista Letteraria. (IT) **2955,** 3004
Rivista Liturgica. (IT ISSN 0035-6956) **4274**
Rivista Marittima. (IT ISSN 0035-6964) **3470**
Rivista Militare. (IT ISSN 0035-6980) **3470**
Rivista Militare della Svizzera Italiana. (SZ ISSN 0035-6999) **3470**
Rivista Oto-Neuro-Oftalmologica. (IT ISSN 0048-8410) **3305**
▼Rivista P S - 1. (IT) **1474**
Rivista Penale. (IT ISSN 0035-7022) **2675,** 1522
Rivista Penale dell'Economia. (IT) **689,** 2675
Rivista Rosminiana di Filosofia e di Cultura. (IT ISSN 0035-7030) **3780,** 2955
†Rivista Siciliana della Tubercolosi e delle Malattie Respiratorie. (IT ISSN 0035-7049) **5271**
Rivista Sperimentale di Freniatria. (IT ISSN 0035-7057) **3353**
Rivista Storica Calabrese. (IT ISSN 0393-022X) **2384,** 2882
Rivista Storica del Mezzogiorno. (IT ISSN 0035-7065) **2321**

Rivista Storica dell'Antichita. (IT ISSN 0300-340X) **2321,** 283
Rivista Storica Italiana. (IT ISSN 0035-7073) **2384**
Rivista Storica Svizzera. *see* Schweizerische Zeitschrift fuer Geschichte **2322**
Rivista Tecnica di Cinematografia. (IT ISSN 0035-7081) **3516**
Rivista Telettra *see* Rivista Telettra Review (Italian Edition) **1379**
Rivista Telettra Review (English Edition). (IT ISSN 0392-8268) **1379,** 1365
Rivista Telettra Review (Italian Edition). (IT ISSN 0392-8276) **1379,** 1365
Rivista Tributaria. (IT ISSN 0035-709X) **1105**
†Rivista Tributaria Ticinese. (SZ ISSN 0048-8429) **5271**
Rivista Trimestrale degli Appalti. (IT ISSN 0394-8374) **630, 689,** 2716
Rivista Trimestrale di Diritto e Procedura Civile. (IT) **2704**
Rivista Trimestrale di Diritto Penale dell'Economia. (IT) **2675,** 689
Rivista Trimestrale di Diritto Pubblico. (IT ISSN 0557-1464) **2675**
Rivista Trimestrale di Scienza dell'Amministrazione. (IT) **4073**
La Rivolta. (IT) **248**
Rivon Cheshev. (IS) **1052,** 798, 839
Rivon Kutna. (IS) **157**
Riv'on l'Inyanei Misim - Quarterly Tax Journal *see* Rivaon ha-Yisraeli I'Misim **1105**
Riv'on Le-Mehkar Hevrati. *see* Social Research Review **4387**
Riwayat al-Hilal. (UA) **2186**
Al-Riyadah wal-Shabab. (TS) **4486,** 1264
Al-Riyadiyyah. (UK) **4486**
Riyu Xuexi/Learning Japanese. (US) **2838**
Riyu Xuexi yu Yanjiu/Studies of Japanese Language. (CC) **2838**
Riyu Zhishi/Japanese Language. (CC) **2838**
Riza Psicosomatica. (IT) **3150**
Riza Scienza. (IT) **4336**
†Rizeni Ekonomiky. (CS) **5271**
Rjettur. (IC ISSN 0034-6195) **3923**
Road Accidents in Great Britain. (UK ISSN 0307-6822) **4720**
Road Ahead. (AT ISSN 0035-7170) **4700, 4785**
Road and Concrete. *see* Doro to Konkurito **616**
Road & Track. (US ISSN 0035-7189) **4701**
Road & Track Sports & G T Cars. (US) **4701**
Road and Transport Research. (AT) **1873**
Road Builder's Clinic. Proceedings. (US ISSN 0080-3278) **1873**
Road Construction News *see* Transportation Topics **4722**
Road Documentation for Developing Countries. (UK) **4655,** 4720
Road Engineering. *see* Vaare Veger **1876**
Road Engineering Intelligence and Research. (UK ISSN 0267-050X) **1873**
Road Home. (JA ISSN 0917-0863) **4655**
Road-House. (US ISSN 0148-3730) **3004**
Road King. (US) **4747**
Road Law. (UK) **2675,** 4720
Road Maps of Industry *see* Economic Road Maps **5184**
Road Notes *see* Transport and Road Research Laboratory. Research Reports **4722**
Road of National Culture. *see* Undesniy Soyolyn Dzam **347**
Road of the Party. (CN ISSN 0047-6110) **3923**
Road Race Management Newsletter. (US ISSN 0739-3784) **4554**
Road Rider. (US ISSN 0035-7243) **4520,** 4785
▼Road Service News. (US) **4701**
Road Traffic Reports. (UK ISSN 0306-5286) **4720**

6624 ROAD TRANSPORT

Road Transport Abstracts. see Kozuti Kozlekedesi Szakirodalmi Tajekoztato **4665**
†Road Transporter of Australia. (AT) **5271**
Road Way. (UK ISSN 0035-7316) **4747**
Roadracing World & Motorcycle Technology. (US) **4486, 4520**
Roads see Roads & Bridges **1873**
Roads. see Gong Lu **4718**
Roads. see Putishta **4720**
Roads and Bridges. see Ceste i Mostovi **1863**
Roads & Bridges. (US ISSN 8750-9229) **1873**
Roadshow. (JA) **3516**
Roadside Business Association. Newsletter. (US) **689**
Roadwise. (US) **4747**
Roan Antelope see Mining Mirror **3490**
Roanoke Regional Chamber of Commerce. Agenda. (US) **822**
Roanoke Regional Chamber of Commerce. Industrial Directory. (US) **822, 1152**
Roanoke Review. (US ISSN 0035-7367) **2955, 3004**
Roanoke Tribune. (US) **2021**
Roanoke Valley Chamber of Commerce. Industrial Directory see Roanoke Regional Chamber of Commerce. Industrial Directory **822**
Roanoke Valley Historical Society Journal. (US ISSN 0278-2936) **2421**
Roanoker. (US) **2233**
Roar. (US) **2882, 3578**
Robabara. (BG) **3004**
Robb Report. (US ISSN 0279-1447) **2233**
Robbins Report. (US) **962**
Robert Burns Chronicle. (UK ISSN 0307-8957) **2955**
Robert E. Howard's Fight Magazine. (US) **2984, 2955**
Robert Frost Newsletter. (US) **3004**
Robert Morris Associates Annual Statement Studies see R M A Annual Statement Studies **796**
Robert Morris Associates Bulletin see Journal of Commercial Bank Lending **788**
Robert Noah's Paris en Cuisine Newsletter. (FR) **2081, 1723, 2480, 4785**
Robert Wood Johnson Foundation. Annual Report. (US ISSN 0091-3472) **3150, 3808**
Roberts Register. (US ISSN 8756-7741) **2163**
Robertson Report. (US ISSN 0898-5448) **2163**
Robes Couture. (SZ) **1294**
Robes Manteaux. (SZ) **1294**
Robeson County Register. (US ISSN 0888-3807) **2163, 2421**
Robin. (US ISSN 1041-5955) **1967, 2058**
Robin Right Fan Club. Newsletter. (US) **1300**
Robinson-Blackmore Ltd. Weekender see R B Weekender **1378**
Robinson Jeffers Newsletter. (US ISSN 0300-7936) **3004**
Robinson, Roberson, Robison, Robertson of Virginia Letter. (US) **2163**
Robomatix Reporter see Robotics Abstracts **1405**
Robot. see Jiqiren **1414**
Robot. (SA ISSN 0035-7391) **4701**
Robot Times. (US) **1415**
Roboter. (GW ISSN 0724-1712) **1415, 1880**
Robotersysteme. (GW ISSN 0178-0026) **1415, 1410**
Robotic Age. (AT) **1415**
Robotic Industries Association Quarterly Statistics Report - Robotics see R I A Quarterly Statistics Report - Robotics **1415**
Robotica. (UK ISSN 0263-5747) **1410**

Robotics see Robotics and Autonomous Systems **1410**
Robotics Abstracts. (US ISSN 0000-1139) **1405**
Robotics and Autonomous Systems. (NE ISSN 0921-8890) **1410, 1415**
Robotics and Computer-Integrated Manufacturing. (US ISSN 0736-5845) **1410, 1415**
Robotics and Expert Systems. (US ISSN 0891-4621) **1410**
Robotics - C A D - C A M Directory see Robotics Technical Directory (Year) **5271**
†Robotics Technical Directory (Year). (US) **5271**
Robotics Today. (US ISSN 0193-6913) **1415, 3023**
Robotics World. (US ISSN 0737-7908) **1410**
Robotics World Directory. (US ISSN 0737-7908) **1152, 1410**
Robotnik. (UK ISSN 0483-2027) **3923**
Robotronics Age Newsletter. (CN) **1410**
Robots. (FR ISSN 0752-4978) **1410**
Roc Science Fiction Advance. (US) **3013, 2955**
Rocas y Minerales. (SP ISSN 0378-3316) **3494**
Rocca. (IT ISSN 0391-108X) **4199**
Rocenka Odborara. (CS ISSN 0557-1693) **2588**
Rochade see Europa-Rochade **4471**
Rochester Business. (US) **689**
Rochester Business Journal. (US) **883**
Rochester Chemunications. (US) **1187**
Rochester Engineer. (US ISSN 0035-7405) **1835**
Rochester Golf Week & Sports Ledger. (US) **4510**
Rochester History. (US ISSN 0035-7413) **2421**
Rochford St. Press see Meuse **2938**
†Rock. (US) **5271**
The Rock (Epping). (AT) **4248, 4274**
Rock (Prahran). (AT ISSN 0816-2425) **4554**
Rock and Dirt. (US) **630**
Rock & Folk. (FR ISSN 0048-8445) **3578**
Rock & Gem. (US ISSN 0048-8453) **2441**
Rock & Ice. (US ISSN 0885-5722) **4554**
Rock & Pop L P - Preiskatalog. (GW ISSN 0930-6994) **3578**
Rock & Pop Stars. (UK) **3578**
Rock & Roll Confidential. (US) **3578**
Rock & Roll Disc. (US) **3578**
Rock and Snow. see Iwa-To-Yuki **4549**
Rock and Soil Mechanics. see Yantu Lixue **3846**
Rock Art. (US ISSN 0278-2871) **248, 283**
Rock Art Research. (AT ISSN 0813-0426) **248, 283, 342**
†Rock Beat. (US ISSN 1058-9848) **5271**
Rock Drill. (UK ISSN 0144-7262) **3004**
Rock Express see Music Express **3564**
Rock Fever. (US) **3578**
Rock Garden. (UK ISSN 0265-5500) **2138**
Rock Magnetism and Paleogeophysics. (JA ISSN 0385-2520) **1594**
Rock Mechanics see Rock Mechanics and Rock Engineering **1579**
Rock Mechanics and Rock Engineering.(US ISSN 0723-2632) **1579, 1873, 3494**
Rock Mechanics - Felsmechanik - Mechanique des Roches. Supplement. (US ISSN 0080-3375) **3494**
Rock Products. (US ISSN 0035-7464) **3495**
Rock Scene. (US ISSN 0090-3353) **3578**
†Rock Shot. (US) **5271**
Rock Show. (JA) **3578**
Rockbill. (US) **3578**

Rockbridge Historical Society, Lexington, Virginia. Proceedings. (US ISSN 0080-3383) **2421**
Rockefeller Archive Center. Newsletter. (US) **2321**
Rockefeller College. School of Information Science and Policy. Bulletin. (US) **2782**
▼Rockefeller University. Rockefeller Archive Center. Research Reports. (US) **2321**
Rockefeller University, New York. Scientific and Educational Programs. (US) **3150**
Rockers. (JM) **3578**
Rocket. (US) **3578**
Rocket. (MY ISSN 0048-8461) **3923**
Rocket News. (JA ISSN 0485-2877) **61**
Rockford Magazine. (US) **2233**
Rockford Review. (US ISSN 1046-0985) **2955, 342, 3796**
RockHead. (US) **3578, 342, 3780**
Rockhurst Hawk. (US ISSN 0035-7510) **1323**
Rockin' Records. (US) **3578, 259, 2441**
Rockin' 50's. (US ISSN 0738-7717) **3578**
Rockingchair: The Review Newsletter for Librarians and Popular Music Fans Who Buy Records see Voice of Youth Advocates **1245**
Rockingham Recorder. (US) **2163**
Rockland - Bergland Spotlight. (US) **2233**
Rocks and Minerals. (US ISSN 0035-7529) **3495, 1579**
Rockwell Lecture Series. (US ISSN 1052-2204) **4199**
Rockwell Water Journal see Sensus Water Journal **4828**
Rocky Mountain Construction (South Edition). (US ISSN 0192-3951) **630**
Rocky Mountain Council on Latin American Studies. Proceedings. (US ISSN 0886-9154) **4385**
▼Rocky Mountain E M S. (US) **3150**
Rocky Mountain Food Dealer. (US ISSN 0035-7588) **2093**
Rocky Mountain Food Dealer Association. Bulletin. (US) **2093**
Rocky Mountain High Technology Directory. (US ISSN 0883-8046) **4608, 1152**
Rocky Mountain Jewish Historical Notes. (US) **2021, 4226**
Rocky Mountain Journal of Mathematics. (US ISSN 0035-7596) **3053**
Rocky Mountain Medical Journal see Colorado Medicine **3090**
Rocky Mountain Medieval and Renaissance Association. Journal. (US ISSN 0195-8453) **2384, 2955**
Rocky Mountain Mineral Law Foundation. Newsletter. (US) **2676, 3495**
Rocky Mountain Mineral Law Institute. Proceedings. (US ISSN 0886-747X) **3495, 2676, 3700, 4157**
Rocky Mountain Mineral Law Newsletter see Rocky Mountain Mineral Law Foundation. Newsletter **2676**
Rocky Mountain Motorist. (US) **4785, 4701**
Rocky Mountain Petroleum Industry. (US) **3700, 1152**
Rocky Mountain Quarter Horse Magazine. (US ISSN 0738-8381) **4537**
Rocky Mountain Review of Language and Literature. (US ISSN 0361-1299) **2955, 2838, 2882**
Rocky Mountain Southwest African Studies Association. Newsletter see Western Association of Africanists. Newsletter **5303**
Rocky Mountain Sports & Fitness. (US) **4486**
Rocky Mountain Union Farmer. (US ISSN 0035-7650) **117**
Rocky Mountain Visitor see Where Rocky Mountains **4797**
Rockyssimo. (IT) **3578**
Rocznik Bialostocki. (PL ISSN 0080-3421) **2384**

Rocznik Biblioteki Narodowej/National Library Year-Book. (PL ISSN 0083-7261) **2782**
Rocznik Chopinowski. (PL ISSN 0208-5992) **3578**
Rocznik Ekonomiczny. (PL ISSN 0080-343X) **689**
†Rocznik Elektrycznosci Atmosferycznej i Meteorologii. (PL ISSN 0080-3448) **5271**
Rocznik Gdanski. (PL ISSN 0080-3456) **2384**
Rocznik Grudziadzki. (PL ISSN 0080-3464) **2384**
Rocznik Historii Czasopismiennictwa Polskiego see Kwartalnik Historii Prasy Polskiej **2572**
Rocznik Historii Sztuki. (PL ISSN 0080-3472) **342**
Rocznik Hydrograficzny. Dorzecze Odry see Rocznik Hydrologiczny Wod Powirzchniowych. Dorzecze Odry i Rzeki Przymorza Miedzy Odra i Wisla **1600**
Rocznik Hydrograficzny. Wisla i Rzeki Przymorza na Wschod od Wisly see Rocznik Hydrologiczny Wod Powierzchniowych. Dorzecze Wisly i Rzeki Przymorza na Wschod od Wisly **1600**
Rocznik Hydrologiczny Wod Podziemnych/Ground Waters Hydrological Yearbook. (PL) **1600**
Rocznik Hydrologiczny Wod Powierzchniowych. Dorzecze Wisly i Rzeki Przymorza na Wschod od Wisly/Hydrological Yearbook of Surface Waters. The Vistula Basin and the Rivers of the Coast Region East of the Vistula River. (PL) **1600**
Rocznik Hydrologiczny Wod Powirzchniowych. Dorzecze Odry i Rzeki Przymorza Miedzy Odra i Wisla/Hydrological Yearbook of Surface Waters. The Oder Basin and the Rivers of the Coast Region Between the Oder and the Vistula. (PL) **1600**
Rocznik Hydrometryczny/Hydrometric Yearbook. (PL) **1600**
Rocznik Jeleniogorski. (PL ISSN 0080-3480) **2384**
Rocznik Kaliski. (PL ISSN 0137-3501) **2384**
Rocznik Krakowski. (PL ISSN 0080-3499) **2384**
Rocznik Kulturalny Ziemi Gdanskiej see Gdanski Rocznik Kulturalny **2363**
Rocznik Lubelski. (PL ISSN 0080-3510) **2384**
†Rocznik Magnetyczny/Annuaire Magnetique. (PL ISSN 0082-0458) **5271**
Rocznik Meteorologiczny/Meteorological Yearbook. (PL) **3440**
Rocznik Meteorologiczny Stacji Hornsundu see Stacja Hornsund. Rocznik Meteorologiczny **3441**
Rocznik Olsztynski. (PL ISSN 0080-3537) **2384**
Rocznik Orientalistyczny. (PL ISSN 0080-3545) **3643**
Rocznik Pedagogiczny. (PL ISSN 0137-9585) **1660**
Rocznik Sadecki. (PL ISSN 0080-3561) **2058, 2384**
Rocznik Slawistyczny. (PL ISSN 0080-3588) **2838, 2856**
Rocznik Ziemi Klodzkiej. (PL) **2384**
Roczniki Akademii Medycznej w Bialymstoku see Akademia Medyczna w Bialymstoku. Roczniki **3073**
Roczniki Biblioteczne. (PL ISSN 0080-3626) **2782**
Roczniki Dziejow Spolecznych i Gospodarczych/Annales d'Histoire Sociale et Economiques. (PL ISSN 0080-3634) **2384**
Roczniki Filozoficzne. (PL ISSN 0035-7685) **3780**
Roczniki Gleboznawcze. (PL ISSN 0080-3642) **191**
Roczniki Humanistyczne. (PL) **2514**
Roczniki Nauk Rolniczych. Seria A. Produkcja Roslinna. (PL ISSN 0080-3650) **191**
Roczniki Nauk Rolniczych. Seria B. Zootechniczna. (PL ISSN 0080-3669) **225**

Roczniki Nauk Rolniczych. Seria C. Technika Rolnicza. (PL ISSN 0080-3677) **164**
Roczniki Nauk Rolniczych. Seria D. Monografie. (PL ISSN 0080-3685) **117**
Roczniki Nauk Rolniczych. Seria E. Ochrona Roslin. (PL ISSN 0080-3693) **191**
Roczniki Nauk Rolniczych. Seria F. Melioracji i Uzytkow Zielonych. (PL ISSN 0080-3707) **191**
Roczniki Nauk Rolniczych. Seria G. Ekonomika Rolnictwa. (PL ISSN 0080-3715) **157**
Roczniki Nauk Rolniczych. Seria H. Rybactwo. (PL ISSN 0080-3723) **2048**, 117
Roczniki Nauk Spolecznych. (PL) **4385**
Roczniki Pomorskiej Akademii Medycznej w Szczecinie. see Annales Academiae Medicae Stetinensis **3076**
Roczniki Sociologii Morskiej. (PL ISSN 0239-5568) **4447**
Roczniki Socjologii Wsi. Studia i Materialy. (PL ISSN 0080-3731) **4447**
Roczniki Teologiczno-Kanoniczne. (PL ISSN 0035-7723) **4274**
Roczniki Towarzystwa Naukowego w Toruniu see Towarzystwo Naukowe w Toruniu. Roczniki **2324**
Rod Action. (US) **4701**
Rod & Custom Magazine. (US) **4701**
Rod and Reel see Fly Rod & Reel **4546**
The Rodale Report. (US) **3808**
Rodale's Food & Nutrition Letter. (US) **3612**
Rodale's Organic Gardening. (US ISSN 0884-3252) **2138**
Rodale's Practical Homeowner see The Practical Homeowner **2501**
▼Rodale's Scuba Diving. (US) **4554**
▼Rodale's Straight Talk. (US) **1264**, 1539
Rodder's Digest. (US) **4486**
Rodd's Chemistry of Carbon Compounds. (NE ISSN 0080-3758) **1223**
Rodeo News. (US ISSN 0149-6425) **4537**
Rodina. (CS) **2882**
Rodina a Skola. (CS ISSN 0035-7766) **1660**
Rodna Gruda. (XV ISSN 0557-2282) **2021**
Rodo Ho/Labour Law. (JA) **993**, 2676
Rodo Kagaku (Kawasaki, 1924)/Journal of Science of Labour. (JA ISSN 0022-443X) **3621**
Rodo no Kagaku (Kawasaki, 1946)/Digest of Science of Labour. (JA ISSN 0035-7774) **3621**
Rodoliubie. (BU ISSN 0205-194X) **2384**, 689
Rodopi Perspectives on Modern Literature. (NE) **2955**
Rodriguesia. (BL ISSN 0370-6583) **454**
Rodzina i Szkola. (PL ISSN 0485-3504) **1660**
Roeda Korsets Tiding. (SW ISSN 1101-413X) **4418**
†Roedderne. (DK ISSN 0109-2952) **5271**
Roede Kors. (NO ISSN 0333-2985) **4418**
RoeFo. Fortschritte auf dem Gebiete der Roentgenstrahlen und der Nuklearmedizin see RoeFo. Fortschritte auf dem Gebiete der Roentgenstrahlen und der Neuen Bildgebenden Verfahren **3362**
RoeFo. Fortschritte auf dem Gebiete der Roentgenstrahlen und der Neuen Bildgebenden Verfahren. (GW ISSN 0936-6652) **3362**
Roeh Hacheshbon. (IS ISSN 0035-7790) **756**
Roeien. (NE ISSN 0048-8518) **4528**
†Roemer Pelizaeus Museum. Zeitschrift des Museums zu Hildesheim. (GW) **5271**

Roemisch-Germanisches Zentralmuseum, Mainz. Jahrbuch. (GW ISSN 0076-2741) **2384**
Roemisch-Germanisches Zentralmuseum, Mainz. Kataloge Vor- und Fruehgeschichtlicher Altertuemer.(GW ISSN 0076-275X) **2321**
Roemische Bronzen aus Deutschland. (GW ISSN 0080-3782) **283**, 342
Roemische Historische Mitteilungen. (AU ISSN 0080-3790) **2384**, 1279, 4199
Roemische Quartalschrift fuer Christliche Altertumskunde und Kirchengeschichte. (GW ISSN 0035-7812) **4199**
Roemisches Jahrbuch fuer Kunstgeschichte see Bibliotheca Hertziana. Roemisches Jahrbuch **319**
Roentgen Blaetter see Aktuelle Radiologie **3357**
Roentgen Technology. (II ISSN 0303-2590) **3362**
Roentgenpraxis. (GW ISSN 0035-7820) **3362**
Roerfag. (NO ISSN 0048-8526) **2303**
Roesch Market Memo. (US) **962**
Roessleria. (BL ISSN 0101-7616) **1496**
Roester i Radio-TV. (SW ISSN 0035-7839) **1359**, 1379
Rofei ha-Mishpacha/Family Physician. (IS ISSN 0374-776X) **3150**
Rogue Digger. (US ISSN 0048-8534) **2163**, 2321
Rogues Gallery. (US) **3578**
Rohac. (CS) **2882**
Rohini. (II) **2955**
Rohm and Haas Reporter. (US ISSN 0035-7847) **1859**
Rohmer Review. (US ISSN 0145-5753) **2955**
Rohr-Armatur-Sanitaer-Heizung see R A S **2302**
Rohre-Rohrleitungsbau-Rohrleitungstransport see 3 R - International **3704**
Rohstoff Rundschau. (GW ISSN 0035-7863) **4608**, 4111
Rohwedder. (US ISSN 0892-6956) **2955**
Ha-Rokeach ha-Ivri. see Israel Pharmaceutical Journal **3730**
Rola Boza/God's Field. (US ISSN 1046-5030) **4274**
Role of State Legislatures in the Freedom Struggle. (II) **3923**, 4073
†Roll Back the Years. (NZ ISSN 0111-2805) **5271**
Roll of Arms. (US) **2163**
Roll on Roll off in Europe. (GW ISSN 0170-5253) **920**, 4737
Roll Sign. (US ISSN 0035-7898) **4714**
Rolladen & Sonnenschutz. (GW) **1152**, 883
Rollcall. (CN ISSN 0707-3542) **3150**
Roller Coaster! (US ISSN 0896-7261) **4785**, 2441
Rolling Along. (US ISSN 0048-8542) **4655**
Rolling Stock. (US ISSN 0886-2249) **2882**
Rolling Stone. (US ISSN 0035-791X) **3578**
Rolling Stone. (AT) **3578**, 1300, 3516
Rollins Sandspur. (US ISSN 0035-7936) **1323**
Rolls of Ancilliary Dental Workers see Rolls of Dental Auxiliaries **3242**
Rolls of Dental Auxiliaries. (UK) **3242**
Rolls-Royce Magazine. (UK ISSN 0142-9469) **1938**
Rolls Royce Owner. (UK ISSN 0035-7952) **4701**
Rolls-Royce Worldwide. (UK) **1835**
Rollsport. (UK) **4486**
Rollstuhlsport. (GW) **4486**, 1740
Roma. (II) **2021**
†Roma Aeterna. (NE ISSN 0169-975X) **5271**
Roma e Provincia Attraverso la Statistica. (IT ISSN 0035-7960) **4584**
Romach. (IS ISSN 0334-8466) **3470**

La Romagna Agricola e Zootecnica. (IT) 117
Romagna Arte e Storia. (IT) **2514**
Romagna Punto Sport. (IT) **4486**
Romagna Sera. (IT) **2206**
†Roman. (FR ISSN 0754-2275) **5271**
Roman Catholic Studies. (US) **4274**
Roman Coins and Culture see The Celator **3598**
†Roman Reports. (US) **5271**
†Roman-Zeitung. (GW ISSN 0035-7979) **5271**
Romance Bibliography. see Romanische Bibliographie **2856**
†Romance Group. (US) **5271**
Romance Notes. (US ISSN 0035-7995) **2955**
Romance of Life. (NR) **342**, 2955
Romance Philology. (US ISSN 0035-8002) **2838**, 2955
Romance Quarterly. (US ISSN 0883-1157) **2984**
Romance Studies. (UK ISSN 0263-9904) **2955**
Romances see Mujeres y Muchacha **3399**
Romanfuehrer. (GW ISSN 0557-2614) **2955**
Romania. (RM) **2215**
Romania. (FR ISSN 0035-8029) **2838**, 2384
Romania Apicola. (RM) **117**
Romania: Articles-Features-Information. (RM) **2215**
Romania: Documents-Events. (RM ISSN 0048-8658) **2215**
Romania Literara. (RM ISSN 0048-8550) **2955**, 342
Romania, Pages of History. (RM) **2384**
Romania Pitoreasca. (RM) **4785**
Romania Today see Romanian Panorama **2215**
Romanian Books. (RM ISSN 0035-8045) **4136**
Romanian Engineering. (RM ISSN 0035-8061) **1835**, 822
Romanian Film. (RM) **3516**
Romanian Foreign Trade. (RM ISSN 0035-807X) **822**
Romanian Journal of Endocrinology. see Revue Roumaine d'Endocrinologie **3256**
Romanian Journal of Gerontology and Geriatrics. (RM ISSN 0254-2307) **2278**
Romanian Journal of Internal Medicine. see Revue Roumaine de Medecine Interne **3149**
Romanian Journal of International Studies. see Revista Romana de Studii Internationale **920**
Romanian Journal of Morphology and Embryology. see Revue Roumaine de Morphologie et d'Embryologie **454**
Romanian Journal of Neurology and Psychiatry. see Revue Roumaine de Neurologie et Psychiatrie **3353**
Romanian Language. see Limba Romana **2825**
Romanian Orthodox Church News. (RM) **4287**
Romanian Panorama. (RM ISSN 1220-5028) **2215**
Romanian Review. (RM ISSN 0035-8088) **2882**
Romanian Review for Industrial Property. see Revista Romana de Proprietate Industriala **3678**
Romanian Sources. (US ISSN 0098-6054) **2384**
Romanic Review. (US ISSN 0035-8118) **2984**, 2955
Romanica Gandensia. (BE ISSN 0080-3855) **2838**
Romanica Gothoburgensia. (SW ISSN 0080-3863) **2838**, 2955
Romanica Helvetica. (SZ ISSN 0080-3871) **2838**, 2955
Romanica Neapolitana. (IT ISSN 0391-1950) **2838**
Romanische Bibliographie/Bibliographie Romane/Romance Bibliography. (GW ISSN 0080-388X) **2856**
Romanische Forschungen. (GW ISSN 0035-8126) **2956**
†Romanische Philologie. Beitraege. (GW ISSN 0005-8181) **5271**

Romanistik in Geschichte und Gegenwart. (GW ISSN 0341-3209) **1279**
Romanistische Arbeitshefte. (GW ISSN 0344-676X) **2839**
†Romanistische Versuche und Vorarbeiten. (GW) **5271**
Romanistisches Jahrbuch. (GW ISSN 0080-3898) **2839**
Romanobarbarica. (IT) **1279**
Romanserier og Selvbiografiske Serier. (DK ISSN 0106-8253) **2956**, 420
Romansk Filmklub Medlemsblad see R F Medlemsblad **3516**
Romanske Stenarbejder. (DK ISSN 0107-2366) **283**, 342
†Romantic Reassessment. (AU) **5271**
Romantic Shelters. (US) **1873**
Romantic Times. (US) **2984**
Romantic Traveling. (US ISSN 1053-0177) **4785**, 4136
Romanticismo e Dintorni. (IT) **342**
†Romantik. (GW) **5271**
Romantikk. (NO ISSN 0035-8142) **2984**
Romantisme. (FR ISSN 0048-8593) **2956**
The Romantist. (US ISSN 0161-682X) **2984**, 3013
Romantizm v Russkoi i Sovetskoi Literature. (RU) **2956**, 2384
Romantzo. (GR) **2196**
Rombo. (IT) **4486**, 4701
Romboid. (CS) **2882**
Rome (Year). (US) **4785**
Romford Record. (UK ISSN 0306-1140) **2384**
Romisch-Germanischen Kommission. Berichte. (GW ISSN 0341-9312) **283**
Romney Sheep Breeders' Society. Flock Book see Romney Sheep Breeders' Society. Handbook **225**
Romney Sheep Breeders' Society. Handbook. (UK) **225**
Romu. (Roskilde Museums Forlag) (DK ISSN 0107-928X) **3532**
Rond de Tafel. (NE ISSN 0035-8169) **4199**
Ronda Iberia. (SP) **4803**
Rondell Programm. (GW) **3516**, 2441, 4637
Rondo see Australian Esperantist **2804**
Ronduit Magazine. (NE) **4248**
Ronen Igaku. see Geriatric Medicine **2272**
Ronzatore. (IT ISSN 0035-8185) **1365**
Roof. (UK ISSN 0307-6911) **2495**
Roof Design. (US) **630**
Roofer and Waterproofer. (US) **630**
Roofer Magazine. (US ISSN 0279-4616) **631**, 306
Roofing, Cladding and Insulation. (UK) **631**
Roofing Contractor. (UK ISSN 0035-8193) **631**
Roofing, Siding, Insulation see R S I **629**
Roofing, Siding, Insulation Extra see R S I Extra **629**
Roofing Spec see Professional Roofing **629**
Rooi Rose. (SA ISSN 0035-8207) **4852**
Room for Two see Futari no Heya **2207**
Room of One's Own. (CN ISSN 0316-1609) **2956**, 4860
Roopa-Lekha. (II ISSN 0035-8215) **356**
Roope-Seta. (FI ISSN 0357-8755) **1264**
Roopvati. (II) **2956**
Root. (US) **1464**
Root. (UK ISSN 0267-3460) **2195**
Root Cellar Preserves. (US) **2163**
Root Directory. (US) **1474**, 1464
Rooting Around. (US) **2163**
Roots. (US ISSN 0148-6659) **2421**, 1758
Roots and Branches. (US ISSN 0737-9242) **2163**
Roots & Leaves. (US ISSN 0748-2485) **2163**
Roots View. (JM) **2021**

Ropa a Uhlie. (CS ISSN 0035-8231) **3700,** 1187
Rope Links. (US) **3742**
Rope Newsletter *see* Rope Links **3742**
Rosa Flieder. (GW ISSN 0930-0716) **2457**
Rosacruz. (US ISSN 0035-8266) **3780**
Rosarian. (CN) **2138**
Rosario de Maria. (PO ISSN 0035-8274) **4274**
Il Rosario e la Nuova Pompei. (IT ISSN 0035-8282) **4274**
Rosdorfer Mitteilungen. (GW) **4094**
The Rose. (UK) **2138**
Rose al-Yusuf. (UA) **2882**
Rose Arranger's Bulletin. (US) **2138**
Rose Exhibitors Forum. (US) **2138**
Rose Hybridizers Association Newsletter. (US) **2138**
Rosenberry Newsletter. (US) **2163**
Der Rosenthaler. (GW) **1165,** 689
Rosicrucian Digest. (US ISSN 0035-8339) **3780,** 1660, 4287
Roskilde Museums Forlag Romu *see* Romu **3532**
Roskilde Universitetsbibliotek. Skriftserie. (DK ISSN 0105-564X) **2782**
Roskilde Universitetscenter. Department of Geography, Social Economics and Computer Science. Kompendium. (DK ISSN 0106-3545) **2261**
Roskilde Universitetscenter. Department of Geography, Social Economics and Computer Science. Meddelelser. (DK ISSN 0106-2778) **2261**
Roskilde Universitetscenter. Department of Geography, Social Economics and Computer Science. Research Reports. (DK ISSN 0106-3537) **2262**
Roskilde Universitetscenter. Department of Geography, Social Economics and Computer Science. Working Papers. (DK ISSN 0106-5920) **2262**
Roskilde Universitetscenter. Institut for Samfundsoekonomi og Planlaegning. Arbejdspapir. (DK ISSN 0108-2205) **4447**
Roskilde Universitetscenter. Institut for Samfundsoekonomi og Planlaegning. Research Report. (DK ISSN 0105-8827) **689**
Roskilde Universitetscenter. Lingvistgruppen. Rolig-Papir. (DK ISSN 0106-0821) **2839**
Il Rosone. (IT) **2882**
Ross Reports Television. (US ISSN 0035-8355) **1379**
Rossica Olomucensia. (CS) **2839,** 2956
Rossica Society of Russian Philately Journal. (US ISSN 0035-8363) **3757**
Rossing Magazine. (SX ISSN 0257-2001) **1496,** 2217, 3495
Roster - California State, County, City and Township Officials State Officials of the United States. (US) **4073**
Roster of Africa Social Scientists. (SG) **935,** 4418
Roster of Black Elected Officials in the South. (US ISSN 0093-9951) **2021**
Rostlinna Vyroba/Plant Production. (CS ISSN 0370-663X) **117**
Rostock Universitaet. Wissenschaftliche Zeitschrift. Gesellschafts- und Sprachwissenschaftliche Reihe *see* Rostock Universitaet. Wissenschaftliche Zeitschrift. Gesellschafts-Wissenschaftliche Reihe **4336**
Rostock Universitaet. Wissenschaftliche Zeitschrift. Gesellschafts-Wissenschaftliche Reihe. (GW ISSN 0323-4630) **4336**
Rostock Universitaet. Wissenschaftliche Zeitschrift. Naturwissenschaftliche Reihe. (GW ISSN 0323-4681) **4336**
Rosy Outlook. (US) **2138**
Rota Gene. (US ISSN 0730-5168) **2163**
Rota Trade and Industrial Directory. North Central State. (NR) **1152**
Rotacion. (SP ISSN 0211-2892) **4737**

Rotacion de la Tierra. (SP ISSN 0210-6485) **368**
The Rotarian. (US ISSN 0035-838X) **1300**
Rotary. (UK ISSN 0035-8401) **1300**
Rotary. (IT) **1300**
Rotary Down Under. (AT ISSN 0048-8631) **1301**
Rotary in Africa. (SA) **1301**
Rotary Norden. (FI ISSN 0780-4288) **689**
Rote Bausteine. (GW) **1264,** 3923
Rote Fahne. (GW ISSN 0936-1421) **3923**
Das Rote Kreuz. (AU) **4418**
Rote Liste. (GW) **3742**
Die Rote Mappe. (GW) **1496**
Rote Revue. (SZ) **3923**
Rote Revue - Profil *see* Rote Revue **3923**
Rotem. (IS ISSN 0333-9904) **516**
Rotenburger Schriften. (GW) **2384,** 516, 2262
Roter Morgen. (GW ISSN 0939-2947) **3923**
Rothamsted Experimental Station Report *see* A F R C Institute of Arable Crops Research. Report **165**
Rothmans Football Yearbook. (UK ISSN 0080-4088) **4510**
†Rothmans Grand Prix Motorcycle Yearbook. (UK) **5271**
Rothmans Rugby League Yearbook. (UK ISSN 0262-4745) **4510**
Rothmans Snooker Yearbook. (UK) **4486**
Rothmill Quarterly. (UK) **2195**
Roth's American Poetry Annual. (US ISSN 1040-5461) **2983**
Rothwell Advertiser. (UK ISSN 0035-8444) **38**
Rotkin Review. (US ISSN 0883-735X) **3796,** 342
Rotlicht. (GW) **1359**
Roto Information. (GW) **631**
Rotonde *see* Fulcrum **1312**
Rotonde. (CN) **1323**
Rotor and Wing *see* Rotor and Wing International **61**
Rotor and Wing International. (US ISSN 0191-6408) **61**
Rotor: By the Industry - For the Industry. (US ISSN 0897-831X) **61,** 4111
Rotor Magazine. (US) **61**
Rotor Roster. (US) **4677,** 61
Rotorcraft. (US) **61,** 2441
Rotorgram *see* Rotor Magazine **61**
†Rotornews. (US) **5271**
Rotpunkt. (GW ISSN 0935-3372) **4554**
Rottenburger Blaettle. (GW) **2191**
Rottenburger Jahrbuch fuer Kirchengeschichte. (GW ISSN 0722-7531) **2384,** 4199
Rotterdam Europoort Delta *see* Port of Rotterdam Magazine **4736**
Rottweiler Quarterly. (US ISSN 1040-8037) **3713**
Rotunda. (CN ISSN 0035-8495) **342,** 283, 1548
Rotunda. (US) **1323**
Rotweissrot. (AU) **2173**
Roudao yu Shuaijiao/Judo & Wrestling. (CC) **4486**
Rouen Port and Shipping Handbook. (UK ISSN 0268-702X) **1152,** 4737
Rouergue Magazine. (FR) **2187,** 4785
Rouge. (FR) **3923**
Rough Notes. (US ISSN 0035-8525) **2541**
Rough Rock News. (US) **1660,** 2021
Roughneck. (CN) **3700**
Rougsoe Lokalhistoriske Forening. Aarsskrift. (DK ISSN 0106-5327) **2385**
Roulac's Strategic Real Estate. (US) **4157**
Roulez Sans Vous Faire Roulez *see* Lemon Aid Magazine **4694**
Roumanian Archives of Microbiology and Immunology. (RM) **3188,** 557
Roumanian Journal of Sociology. (RM) **4447**
Round Bobbin. (US) **3592,** 1287

The Round Table. (UK ISSN 0035-8533) **3971**
Round Table (Anderson). (US) **4136**
Round Table (Beloit). (US ISSN 1053-5020) **1323**
Round Table (Rochester). (US) **3004,** 2956
Round Table: A Journal of Poetry & Fiction. (US) **2956**
Round the Table. (US) **2541**
Round Up. (US) **1323**
Roundabout. (UK ISSN 0048-8666) **2295,** 1264
Roundalab Journal. (US) **1531,** 1758
▼Roundsmanship (Year). (US ISSN 1040-8487) **3150**
The Roundtable (Southfield). (US) **4418**
Roundtable Report. (US) **4199**
Roundup (Clarksville). (US) **4361**
Roundup (Dallas) *see* Southwest Economy **800**
Roundup (El Paso). (US ISSN 0035-855X) **2575,** 2421
Roustabout. (UK) **3700**
Route. (FR ISSN 0035-8568) **4701,** 4111
Route Libre. *see* Freie Fahrt **4101**
Routes. (UK) **4655,** 1152
†Routes du Monde. (SZ ISSN 1017-0448) **5271**
Routes et Transports. (CN ISSN 0319-3780) **4720**
Routes - Roads. (FR) **1873,** 4720
Les Routiers. (FR) **4747,** 4720
Roux's Archives of Developmental Biology. (GW ISSN 0930-035X) **454**
Rover Blatt. (GW) **4486**
Rovesnik. (RU ISSN 0131-5994) **1264**
Rovid Uton. (HU ISSN 0230-4430) **1660**
Roving Commissions. (UK ISSN 0485-5175) **4528**
Row. (UK) **4528**
▼Rowboat. (US) **3004**
Rowe Register. (US) **2163**
Rowett Research Institute Report. (UK ISSN 0952-7222) **4815**
Rowing Magazine *see* Rowing Magazine Monthly **4486**
Rowing Magazine Monthly. (UK) **4486,** 4528
Rowing U S A *see* American Rowing **4521**
Roy Morgan Magazine & Newspaper Survey. (AT) **2575**
Roy of the Rovers. (UK) **1264**
Royal Academy of Letters, History and Antiquities. Proceedings. Antiquarian Series. *see* Kungliga Vitterhets Historie och Antikvitets Akademien. Handlingar. Antikvariska Serien **2372**
Royal Academy of Letters, History and Antiquities. Proceedings. Historical Series. *see* Kungliga Vitterhets Historie och Antikvitets Akademien. Handlingar. Historiska Serien **2372**
Royal Academy of Letters, History and Antiquities. Proceedings. Philological-Philosophical Series. *see* Kungliga Vitterhets Historie och Antikvitets Akademien. Handlingar. Filologisk-Filosofiska Serien **2822**
Royal Aerospace Establishment News *see* R A E News **5266**
Royal Agricultural Society of England. Journal. (UK ISSN 0080-4134) **117**
Royal Agricultural Society of England Reference Book and Buyers' Guide. (UK ISSN 0266-7924) **1152,** 157, 191
Royal Agricultural Society of Natal. Royal Show Catalogue. (SA) **117**
Royal Air Force College Journal. (UK ISSN 0035-8606) **3470**
Royal Air Force Education Bulletin. (UK) **3470**
Royal Air Force News. (UK ISSN 0035-8614) **3470**
Royal Air Force Yearbook. (UK ISSN 0954-092X) **3470**

Royal Anthropological Institute of Great Britain and Ireland. Library. Anthropological Index *see* Anthropological Index to Current Periodicals in the Library of the Museum of Mankind Library **253**
Royal Arch Mason. (US ISSN 0035-8649) **1301**
Royal Architectural Institute of Canada. Directory. (CN) **306**
†Royal Army Pay Corps Journal. (UK ISSN 0035-8673) **5271**
Royal Asiatic Society. Hong Kong Branch. Journal. (HK ISSN 0085-5774) **3643**
Royal Asiatic Society. Malaysian Branch. Journal. (MY ISSN 0304-2251) **2341,** 2262
Royal Asiatic Society of Great Britain and Ireland. Journal. (UK ISSN 0035-869X) **3643**
Royal Association for Disability and Rehabilitation Bulletin *see* R A D A R Bulletin **3146**
Royal Association for Disability and Rehabilitation Contact *see* R A D A R Contact **2284**
Royal Astronomical Society. Monthly Notices. (UK ISSN 0035-8711) **368,** 3440
Royal Astronomical Society. Quarterly Journal. (UK ISSN 0035-8738) **368**
Royal Astronomical Society Geophysical Journal *see* Geophysical Journal International **1589**
Royal Astronomical Society of Canada. Journal. (CN ISSN 0035-872X) **368**
Royal Astronomical Society of Canada. Observer's Handbook. (CN ISSN 0080-4193) **368**
Royal Australasian College of Dental Surgeons. Annals. (AT ISSN 0158-1570) **3242**
Royal Australasian College of Surgeons Newsletter *see* R.A.C.S. Newsletter **5266**
Royal Australasian Ornithologists Union Monographs *see* R A O U Monographs **566**
Royal Australasian Ornithologists Union Newsletter *see* R A O U Newsletter **566**
Royal Australasian Ornithologists Union Report *see* R A O U Report **566**
Royal Australian College of General Practitioners Family Medicine Programme. R.A.C.G.P. Victoria Newsletter *see* Family Medicine Programme. R.A.C.G.P. Victoria Newsletter **3097**
Royal Australian Historical Society. History Magazine. (AT) **2345**
Royal Australian Historical Society. Journal. (AT ISSN 0035-8762) **2345**
Royal Australian Historical Society. Newsletter *see* Royal Australian Historical Society. History Magazine **2345**
Royal Australian Historical Society. Technical Information Service. (AT) **2345,** 306, 2163, 3532
Royal Australian Institute of Architects Memo *see* R A I A Memo **305**
Royal Automobile Association of South Australia. Accommodation Guide *see* Australian Accommodation Guide **4752**
Royal Automobile Club European Hotel Guide *see* R A C European Hotel Guide **4783**
Royal Automobile Club Hotel Guide Great Britain & Ireland *see* R A C Hotel Guide Great Britain & Ireland **4783**
Royal Bank Letter. (CN ISSN 0229-0243) **798,** 883
Royal Bank of Scotland Review. (UK ISSN 0267-1190) **798,** 883
Royal Bank of Trinidad and Tobago. Annual Report. (TR) **798**
Royal Bath & West Show Catalogue. (UK) **117**
Royal Botanical Gardens, Hamilton, Ont. Gardens' Bulletin. (CN ISSN 0046-6751) **2138,** 516

ROYAL SOCIETY 6627

Royal Botanical Gardens, Hamilton, Ont. Special Bulletin. (CN ISSN 0072-9647) **2138**, 516
Royal Botanical Gardens, Hamilton, Ont. Technical Bulletin. (CN ISSN 0072-9655) 516, **2138**
†Royal British Columbia Museum. Occasional Papers Series. (CN ISSN 0068-1636) **5271**
Royal British Columbia Museum. Special Publications. (CN ISSN 0840-7681) **3532**
Royal British Columbia Museum Memoirs. (CN ISSN 0843-5383) **3532**, 4336
Royal British Legion Annual Report and Accounts. (UK) **3470**
Royal Caledonian Curling Club. Annual. (UK ISSN 0080-4282) **4486**
Royal Canadian Mounted Police Quarterly see R C M P Quarterly **1521**
Royal College of General Practitioners. Journal. see British Journal of General Practice **3084**
Royal College of General Practitioners. Occasional Papers. (UK) **3150**
Royal College of General Practitioners. Official Reference Book. (UK ISSN 0262-9275) **1323**, 3150
Royal College of Midwives. Current Awareness Service. (UK ISSN 0260-5848) **3181**, 3296
Royal College of Music Magazine see R C M Magazine **3575**
Royal College of Organists. Year Book. (UK ISSN 0080-4320) **3578**
Royal College of Pathologists of Australasia. Broadsheets. (AT) **3150**, 454
Royal College of Pathologists of Australia. Broadsheets see Royal College of Pathologists of Australasia. Broadsheets **3150**
Royal College of Physicians and Surgeons of Canada. Annals/College Royal des Medecins et Chirurgiens du Canada. Annales. (CN ISSN 0035-8800) **3150**
Royal College of Physicians of Edinburgh. Directory. (UK) **3150**
Royal College of Physicians of Edinburgh. Yearbook and Calendar see Royal College of Physicians of Edinburgh. Directory **3150**
Royal College of Psychiatrists. Bulletin see Psychiatric Bulletin **3351**
Royal College of Surgeons of Edinburgh. Journal. (UK ISSN 0035-8835) **3383**
Royal College of Surgeons of England. Annals. (UK ISSN 0035-8843) **3383**
Royal College of Surgeons of England. Faculty of Anaesthetists. Dean's Newsletter see College of Anaesthetists. Newsletter **3191**
†Royal College of Surgeons of England. Handbook. (UK) **5271**
†Royal Commonwealth Society Library Notes. (UK ISSN 0035-8851) **5271**
Royal Electrical & Mechanical Engineers Journal see R E M E Journal **1938**
Royal Engineers Journal. (UK ISSN 0035-8878) **3470**, 1835
Royal Entomological Society of London. Proceedings see Antenna **528**
Royal Entomological Society of London. Symposia. (UK ISSN 0080-4363) **537**
Royal Gazette. (CN ISSN 0035-8908) **2179**
Royal Geographical Society of Australasia. South Australian Branch. Proceedings see South Australian Geographical Journal **2263**
Royal Highland and Agricultural Society of Scotland. Review. (UK) **117**
Royal Highland and Agricultural Society of Scotland. Show Guide and Review see Royal Highland and Agricultural Society of Scotland. Review **117**
Royal Historical Society. Annual Bibliography of British and Irish History. (UK ISSN 0308-4558) **2330**

Royal Historical Society. Guides and Handbooks. (UK ISSN 0080-4398) **2385**
Royal Historical Society. Transactions. Sixth Series. (UK ISSN 0080-4401) **2385**
Royal Historical Society of Queensland. Journal. (AT ISSN 0085-5804) **2321**
Royal Historical Society of Queensland Bulletin. (AT ISSN 0035-8916) **2321**
Royal Historical Society of Victoria. Journal see Victorian Historical Journal **2326**
Royal Historical Society of Victoria, Inc. History News see R.H.S.V. History News **2345**
Royal Horticultural Society. Garden Journal see The Garden **2126**
Royal Horticultural Society Gardener's Diary see R.H.S. Gardener's Diary **2137**
Royal Humane Society. Annual Report. (UK) **4418**
Royal Institute of British Architects Directory of Practices see R I B A Directory of Practices **306**
Royal Institute of British Architects Interior Design Selector see R I B A Interior Design Selector **2554**
Royal Institute of British Architects Journal see R I B A Journal **306**
Royal Institute of British Architects Product Selector see R I B A Product Selector **306**
Royal Institute of Oil Painters. Exhibition Catalogue. (UK) **342**
Royal Institute of Public Administration Report see R I P A Report **4072**
Royal Institute of the Architects of Ireland. Yearbook see R I A I Architects Yearbook **305**
Royal Institute of the Architects of Ireland Architects Yearbook see R I A I Architects Yearbook **305**
Royal Institution of Chartered Surveyors Library Information Service. Weekly Briefing see R I C S Library Information Service. Weekly Briefing **1873**
Royal Institution of Chartered Surveyors Library Information Service Abstracts and Reviews see R I C S Library Information Service Abstracts and Reviews **1846**
Royal Institution of Great Britain. Annual Report see Royal Institution of Great Britain. Record **4336**
Royal Institution of Great Britain. Proceedings. (UK) **4336**
Royal Institution of Great Britain. Record. (UK) **4336**
Royal Institution of Great Britain. Royal Institution Lectures. (UK) **4336**
Royal Institution of Naval Architects. Soft Back Transactions. Parts A & B. (UK) **4737**
Royal Institution of Naval Architects. Supplementary Papers see Royal Institution of Naval Architects. Soft Back Transactions. Parts A & B **4737**
Royal Institution of Naval Architects. Transactions. (UK ISSN 0035-8967) **4737**
Royal Insurance Newsletter. (UK) **2541**
Royal Irish Academy. Proceedings. Section A: Mathematical and Physical Sciences. (IE) **3053**, 368, 3830
Royal Irish Academy. Proceedings. Section B: Biological, Geological and Chemical Sciences. (IE ISSN 0035-8983) **1187**, 454, 1579
Royal Irish Academy. Proceedings. Section C: Archaeology, Celtic Studies, History, Linguistics and Literature. (IE ISSN 0035-8991) **283**, 2385, 2956
Royal Irish Academy of Music. Prospectus. (IE) **3578**
The Royal Life Saving Society. Lifesaver U.K. (UK) **4111**
Royal Life Saving Society - U.K. Quarterly Journal see The Royal Life Saving Society. Lifesaver U.K **4111**

Royal Meteorological Society. Quarterly Journal. (UK ISSN 0035-9009) **3440**
Royal Microscopical Society. Proceedings. (UK ISSN 0035-9017) **561**
Royal Military Police Journal. (UK ISSN 0035-9025) **3470**
Royal Musical Association. Journal. (UK ISSN 0269-0403) **3578**
Royal Musical Association. R.M.A. Research Chronicle. (UK ISSN 0080-4460) **3578**
Royal Musical Association, London. Proceedings see Royal Musical Association. Journal **3578**
Royal National Institute for the Blind. Law Notes. Extracts. (UK ISSN 0023-9291) **2295**, 2676
Royal National Institute for the Blind. School Magazine see Fizz **2292**
Royal National Institute for the Deaf Research Report see R N I D Research Report **2289**
Royal Naval Medical Service. Journal. (UK ISSN 0035-9033) **3150**
Royal Naval Sailing Association Journal.(UK ISSN 0035-9041) **4528**
Royal Neighbor. (US ISSN 0035-905X) **1301**
Royal Netherlands Academy of Sciences. Proceedings. (NE ISSN 0924-8323) **4336**, 454, 3150, 3830
Royal New Zealand Institute of Horticulture. Annual Journal see Horticulture in New Zealand (Lincoln) **2130**
Royal New Zealand Institute of Horticulture. Journal see Horticulture in New Zealand (Lincoln) **2130**
Royal New Zealand Institute of Horticulture. Newsletter. (NZ ISSN 0114-1481) **2138**
Royal Norwegian Council for Scientific and Industrial Research. Annual Report. see Norges Teknisk-Naturvitenskapelige Forskningsraad. Aarsberetning **4330**
Royal Norwegian Society of Sciences. Publications. see Kongelige Norske Videnskabers Selskab. Skrifter **4321**
Royal Numismatic Society. Special Publications. (UK ISSN 0080-4487) **3601**
Royal Observatory. Occasional Reports. (UK ISSN 0309-099X) **369**
Royal Observatory. Research and Facilities. (UK ISSN 0267-6281) **369**
Royal Ontario Museum. Annual Report. (CN ISSN 0082-5115) **3532**
Royal Ontario Museum. Archaeology Monographs. (CN ISSN 0316-1285) **283**
†Royal Ontario Museum. Archaeology Occasional Papers. (CN) **5271**
†Royal Ontario Museum. Ethnography Monograph. (CN ISSN 0316-1277) **5271**
Royal Ontario Museum. History, Technology and Art Monographs. (CN ISSN 0316-1269) **3532**
Royal Ontario Museum. Life Sciences. Contributions. (CN ISSN 0384-8159) **454**, 591
Royal Ontario Museum. Life Sciences. Miscellaneous Publications. (CN ISSN 0082-5093) **454**
Royal Ontario Museum. Life Sciences. Occasional Papers. (CN ISSN 0082-5107) **454**
Royal Philatelic Society of New Zealand. Annual Report. (NZ) **3757**
Royal Philatelic Society of New Zealand. Monograph Series. (NZ) **3757**
Royal Pioneer. (US ISSN 0035-9076) **3470**
Royal Purple. (US) **1323**
Royal School of Mines, London. Journal.(UK ISSN 0080-4495) **3495**
Royal Scottish Automobile Club Official Handbook. (UK) **4486**, 1301
Royal Scottish Country Dance Society Bulletin. (UK) **1531**
Royal Service. (US ISSN 0035-9084) **4248**

Royal Shakespeare Company. Publication. (UK) **2956**
Royal Society for the Prevention of Accidents Bulletin see R S P A Bulletin **4111**
Royal Society News. (UK ISSN 0260-2725) **4336**, 4608
Royal Society of Antiquaries of Ireland. Journal. (IE ISSN 0035-9106) **284**, 2163, 2385
Royal Society of Arts. Journal see R S A Journal **341**
Royal Society of British Artists. Publication. (UK) **342**
Royal Society of Canada. Proceedings. (CN ISSN 0080-4517) **4336**
Royal Society of Canada. Proceedings and Transactions see Royal Society of Canada. Proceedings **4336**
Royal Society of Canada. Proceedings and Transactions see Royal Society of Canada. Transactions **4337**
Royal Society of Canada. Transactions. (CN ISSN 0035-9122) **4337**
Royal Society of Chemistry. Analytical Division. Analytical Proceedings see Analytical Proceedings **1204**
Royal Society of Chemistry. Annual Reports on the Progress of Chemistry. Section A: Inorganic Chemistry. (UK ISSN 0260-1818) **1214**
Royal Society of Chemistry. Annual Reports on the Progress of Chemistry. Section A: Physical and Inorganic Chemistry see Royal Society of Chemistry. Annual Reports on the Progress of Chemistry. Section C: Physical Chemistry **1230**
Royal Society of Chemistry. Annual Reports on the Progress of Chemistry. Section B: Organic Chemistry. (UK ISSN 0069-3030) **1223**
Royal Society of Chemistry. Annual Reports on the Progress of Chemistry. Section C: Physical Chemistry. (UK ISSN 0260-1826) **1230**
†Royal Society of Chemistry. Database Newsletter. (UK) **5271**
Royal Society of Chemistry. Information Services. Newsletter see Royal Society of Chemistry. Database Newsletter **5271**
Royal Society of Chemistry. Journal: Dalton Transactions. (UK ISSN 0300-9246) **1214**
Royal Society of Chemistry. Journal: Faraday Transactions. (UK ISSN 0956-5000) **1230**
Royal Society of Chemistry. Journal: Faraday Transactions 1 see Royal Society of Chemistry. Journal: Faraday Transactions **1230**
Royal Society of Chemistry. Journal: Perkin Transactions 1. (UK ISSN 0300-922X) **1223**, 482
Royal Society of Chemistry. Journal: Perkin Transactions 2. (UK ISSN 0300-9580) **1230**
Royal Society of Chemistry. Reviews. (UK ISSN 0306-0012) **1187**
Royal Society of Chemistry Paperback Series. Monographs for Teachers see R S C Paperback Series. Monographs for Teachers **5266**
Royal Society of Edinburgh. Proceedings. (Natural Environment) see Royal Society of Edinburgh. Proceedings. Section B (Biological Sciences) **454**
Royal Society of Edinburgh. Proceedings. Section A. Mathematical and Physical Sciences see Royal Society of Edinburgh. Proceedings. Section A (Mathematics) **3053**
Royal Society of Edinburgh. Proceedings. Section A (Mathematics). (UK ISSN 0308-2105) **3053**, 4337
Royal Society of Edinburgh. Proceedings. Section B (Biological Sciences). (UK) **454**
Royal Society of Edinburgh. Transactions. (Earth Sciences). (UK ISSN 0263-5933) **1548**, 4337
Royal Society of Edinburgh. Year Book. (UK ISSN 0080-4576) **4337**

ROYAL SOCIETY

Royal Society of Health Journal. (UK ISSN 0264-0325) **4418**, 3808, 4111

Royal Society of London. Biographical Memoirs of Fellows of the Royal Society. (UK ISSN 0080-4606) **420**

Royal Society of London. Notes and Records. (UK ISSN 0035-9149) **4337**

Royal Society of London. Philosophical Transactions. Series A. Mathematical and Physical Sciences *see* Royal Society of London. Philosophical Transactions. Series A. Physical Sciences and Engineering **3830**

Royal Society of London. Philosophical Transactions. Series A. Physical Sciences and Engineering. (UK ISSN 0962-8428) **3830**, 1835, 3053

Royal Society of London. Philosophical Transactions. Series B. Biological Sciences. (UK ISSN 0080-4622) **454**

Royal Society of London. Proceedings. Series A. Mathematical and Physical Sciences. (UK ISSN 0080-4630) **3053**, 4337

Royal Society of London. Proceedings. Series B. Biological Sciences. (UK ISSN 0080-4649) **454**

Royal Society of London. Year Book. (UK ISSN 0080-4673) **4337**

Royal Society of Marine Artists. Exhibition Catalogue. (UK) **343**

Royal Society of Medicine. Annual Report of the Council. (UK ISSN 0144-8676) **3150**

Royal Society of Medicine. Forum Series *see* Royal Society of Medicine. Round Table Series **3150**

Royal Society of Medicine. International Congress and Symposium Series. (UK ISSN 0142-2367) **3150**

Royal Society of Medicine. Journal. (UK ISSN 0141-0768) **3150**

Royal Society of Medicine. Proceedings *see* Royal Society of Medicine. Journal **3150**

Royal Society of Medicine. Round Table Series. (UK ISSN 0268-3091) **3150**

Royal Society of Miniature Painters, Sculptors and Gravers. Publication. (UK) **343**

Royal Society of New South Wales. Journal and Proceedings. (AT ISSN 0035-9173) **4337**

Royal Society of New Zealand. Bulletin *see* Royal Society of New Zealand. Bulletin Series **4337**

Royal Society of New Zealand. Bulletin Series. (NZ ISSN 0370-6559) **4337**

Royal Society of New Zealand. Journal. (NZ ISSN 0303-6758) **4337**

Royal Society of New Zealand. Journal. Collected Papers *see* Collected Papers from the Journal of the Royal Society of New Zealand **4305**

Royal Society of New Zealand. Miscellaneous Series. (NZ ISSN 0111-3895) **4337**

Royal Society of New Zealand. Proceedings. (NZ ISSN 0557-4161) **421**, 1027

Royal Society of New Zealand. Transactions *see* Royal Society of New Zealand. Journal **4337**

Royal Society of Portrait Painters. Publication. (UK) **343**

Royal Society of Queensland, St. Lucia. Proceedings. (AT ISSN 0080-469X) **4337**

Royal Society of South Africa. Transactions. (SA ISSN 0035-919X) **4337**

Royal Society of South Australia. Transactions. (AT ISSN 0085-5812) **4337**

Royal Society of Tasmania, Hobart. Papers and Proceedings. (AT ISSN 0080-4703) **4337**, 2321

Royal Society of Tropical Medicine and Hygiene, London. Yearbook. (UK ISSN 0080-4711) **3223**

Royal Society of Tropical Medicine and Hygiene Transactions. (UK ISSN 0035-9203) **3223**

Royal Society of Ulster Architects. Year Book. (UK ISSN 0080-472X) **306**

Royal Society of Victoria. Proceedings. (AT ISSN 0035-9211) **4337**

Royal Society of Western Australia. Journal. (AT ISSN 0035-922X) **4337**

Royal Statistical Society. Journal. Series A: General *see* Royal Statistical Society. Journal. Series A: Statistics in Society **4584**

Royal Statistical Society. Journal. Series A: Statistics in Society. (UK) **4584**

Royal Statistical Society. Journal. Series B: Methodological. (UK ISSN 0035-9246) **4584**

Royal Statistical Society. Journal. Series C: Applied Statistics. (UK ISSN 0035-9254) **4584**

Royal Swedish Academy of Agriculture and Forestry. Journal. *see* Kungliga Skogs- och Lantbruksakademiens Tidskrift **103**

Royal Tehran Hilton. (IR ISSN 0035-9262) **2480**, 4785

Royal Television Society. Journal *see* Television (London, 1927) **1382**

Royal Television Society Bulletin *see* Royal Television Society Talkback **5271**

†Royal Television Society Talkback. (UK) **5271**

Royal Town Planning Institute Journal *see* Planner **2493**

Royal Tropical Institute. Bulletin. (NE ISSN 0922-7911) **118**, 935, 2495

Royal United Service Institution. Journal *see* R U S I Journal **3469**

Royal United Services Institute for Defence Studies Brassey's Defence Yearbook *see* R U S I and Brassey's Defence Yearbook **3469**

Royal United Services Institute for Defence Studies Journal *see* R U S I Journal **3469**

Royal United Services Institute for Defence Studies Newsbrief *see* R U S I Newsbrief **3469**

Royal United Services Institute of Australia. Journal. (AT ISSN 0728-1188) **3470**, 3971

Royal Western Australian Historical Society. Journal and Proceedings *see* Early Days **2344**

Royal Western Australian Historical Society. Newsletter. (AT ISSN 0557-4242) **2345**

Royal Yachting Association News *see* R Y A News **4484**

Royal Zoological Society of Scotland. Zoo Guide. (UK) **591**

Royalauto. (AT ISSN 0035-9300) **4701**, 4785

Royale Federation Colombophile Belge. Bulletin Federal *see* Royale Federation Colombophile Belge. Bulletin National **567**

Royale Federation Colombophile Belge. Bulletin National. (BE) **567**

Royaliste. (FR ISSN 0151-5772) **3923**

Royalton Review. (US) **3923**

Royalty. (UK ISSN 0950-3439) **2163**

▼Royalty Collector's Edition. (UK) **2163**

Roze Maryi. (US ISSN 0745-3299) **4274**

Rozhlad. (GW ISSN 0557-4250) **2021**

Rozhlas *see* Tydenik Rozhlas **1360**

Rozhlasova Prace. (CS ISSN 0035-9335) **1379**

Rozhledy Matematicko-Fyzikalni. (CS ISSN 0035-9343) **1660**, 369, 3053, 3830

Rozhledy v Chirurgii. (CS ISSN 0035-9351) **3383**

Rozhledy v Tuberkuloze a Nemocech Plicnich *see* Studia Pneumologica et Phtiseologica Cechoslovaca **3367**

Rozprawy Elektroniki i Telekomunikacji. Kwartalnik. (PL) **1778**

Rozprawy Elektrotechniczne *see* Rozprawy Elektroniki i Telekomunikacji. Kwartalnik **1778**

Rozprawy Hydrotechniczne/ Hydrotechnical Transactions. (PL ISSN 0035-9394) **4828**, 1835

Rozprawy i Szkice Filozoficzno-Estetyczne o Muzyce. (PL) **3578**

Rozprawy Matematyczne. *see* Dissertationes Mathematicae **3034**

Rozprawy z Dziejow Oswiaty. (PL ISSN 0080-4754) **1660**

Rozvoj Mistniho Hospodarstvi. (CS ISSN 0035-9416) **1084**, 832

Rruga e Partise. (AA) **3923**

Rtam. (Il ISSN 0035-9424) **2839**, 3643

Ruan Kexue. (CC ISSN 1001-8409) **4337**

Ruanjian/Software. (CC) **1479**

Ruanjian Xuebao/Journal of Software. (CC) **1479**

Il Rubastino. (IT) **2206**

Rubber and Plastics Digest. (Il) **4293**, 3868

Rubber and Plastics Fire and Flammability Bulletin *see* Fire & Flammability Bulletin **2032**

Rubber & Plastics News. (US ISSN 0300-6123) **4293**, 3868

Rubber & Plastics News II. (US ISSN 0197-2219) **4293**, 3868

Rubber and Plastics Newsletter. (US) **3621**, 4293

Rubber and Plastics Research Association of Great Britain Abstracts *see* R A P R A Abstracts **4295**

Rubber and Plastics Research Association of Great Britain New Trade Names in the Rubber and Plastics Industries *see* R A P R A New Trade Names in the Rubber and Plastics Industries **4293**

Rubber and Plastics Research Association of Great Britain News *see* R A P R A News **3867**

Rubber and Plastics Research Association of Great Britain Review Reports *see* R A P R A Review Reports **3869**

Rubber and Polyurethane Directory B.R.M.A. (British Rubber Manufacturers' Association Ltd.) (UK ISSN 0955-8772) **4293**

Rubber Board Bulletin. (Il) **4293**

Rubber Chemistry and Technology. (US ISSN 0035-9475) **4293**

Rubber Developments. (UK) **4293**

Rubber Directory and Buyers Guide (Year). (US) **4293**

Rubber India. (Il ISSN 0035-9491) **4293**

Rubber: Latin American Industrial Report. (US) **4293**

Rubber Manufacturers Association. Natural and Synthetic Rubber Import and Export Report. (US) **4295**

†Rubber Manufacturers Association. Statistical Report. Industry Rubber Report. (US) **5271**

Rubber Manufacturers Association. Statistical Report. Monthly Tire Report. (US) **4295**

Rubber Manufacturers Association. Tire and Tube Import and Export Report. (US) **4295**

Rubber News. (Il ISSN 0035-9513) **4293**

Rubber Progress *see* Polysar Progress **4293**

Rubber Reporter. (Il ISSN 0257-859X) **4293**

Rubber Research Institute of Malaysia. Annual Report. (MY ISSN 0126-8279) **4293**

Rubber Research Institute of Malaysia. Rubber Growers' Conference - Proceedings. (MY ISSN 0127-9785) **4293**

Rubber Research Institute of Malaysia. Technology Bulletin. (MY ISSN 0126-9410) **4293**

Rubber Research Institute of Sri Lanka. Annual Review. (CE) **4293**

Rubber Research Institute of Sri Lanka. Journal. (CE ISSN 0379-1130) **4294**, 3868

Rubber Research Institute of Sri Lanka Bulletin *see* R R I S L Bulletin **4293**

Rubber Southern Africa. (SA ISSN 0258-9737) **4294**, 3868

Rubber Statistical Bulletin. (UK ISSN 0035-9548) **4293**

Rubber Trends. (UK ISSN 0035-9564) **4294**

Rubber World. (US ISSN 0035-9572) **4294**

Rubber World Blue Book. (US) **4294**

Rubberstampmadness. (US ISSN 0746-7672) **356**, 2441

Rubbicana (Year) *see* Rubber Directory and Buyers Guide (Year) **4293**

Rubbicana-Europe (Year). (UK) **4294**, 3868

†Rubicon. (CN ISSN 0715-8610) **5271**

Ruby Focus *see* Rainbow Ray Focus **3596**

Ruby Magazine. (Il ISSN 0035-9580) **2441**

Ruch Filozoficzny. (PL ISSN 0035-9599) **3780**

Ruch Literacki. (PL ISSN 0035-9602) **2956**

Ruch Muzyczny. (PL ISSN 0035-9610) **3578**, 4637

Ruch Prawniczy, Ekonomiczny i Socjologiczny. (PL ISSN 0035-9629) **2676**, 689, 4447

Ruch Wydawniczy w Liczbach/Polish Publishing in Figures. (PL ISSN 0511-1196) **4142**

Ruchi. (Il) **4637**

Rucuperare: Edilizia, Design, Impianti *see* Recuperare: Progetti Cantieri Tecnologie Prodotti **630**

Rudarski Glasnik/Bulletin of Mines. (YU ISSN 0035-9637) **3495**

Rudarsko-Metalurski Zbornik/Mining and Metallurgy Quarterly. (XV ISSN 0035-9645) **3495**, 3419

Rudarstvo - Geologija - Metalurgija. (YU ISSN 0350-2627) **3419**, 3495

Rudersport. (GW ISSN 0342-8281) **4528**

Rudnyckiana. (CN ISSN 0827-6307) **424**

Rudolf Steiner Publications. (FR ISSN 0080-4789) **3788**, 410

Rudoobrazuvatelni Protsesi i Mineralni Nakhodishta. (BU ISSN 0204-5311) **1579**

Rudy. (CS ISSN 0035-9688) **3495**

Rudy i Metale Niezelazne. (PL ISSN 0035-9696) **3419**, 3495

La Rue. (FR ISSN 0035-970X) **2882**, 3923

Rue Morgue. (IT) **4448**

Rue-Revue. (DK ISSN 0109-0984) **1660**, 689

Rueckert Studien. (GW ISSN 0557-4404) **2956**

Rueckert zu Ehren. (GW ISSN 0933-9094) **2956**

Ruff Times. (US) **962**

Ruff's Guide to the Turf and the Sporting Life Annual. (UK ISSN 0080-4819) **4537**

Rug Hooking. (US ISSN 1045-4373) **2441**

Rugama *see* Molaetsa-Molaetsa **4244**

Rugby. (US ISSN 0162-1297) **4510**

Rugby Annual for Wales. (UK) **4510**

Rugby Football League Official Guide. (UK ISSN 0080-4827) **4510**

Rugby League News *see* Big League **4501**

Rugby League News. (PP) **4510**

Rugby League Week. (AT ISSN 0035-9742) **4510**

Rugby Magazine. (JA) **4510**

Rugby Nieuws. (NE) **4510**

†Rugby Nyt. (DK ISSN 0108-1233) **5271**

Rugby Post *see* Rugby World and Post **4510**

Rugby Wales *see* Rugby World and Post **4510**

Rugby World *see* Rugby World and Post **4510**

Rugby World and Post. (UK) **4510**

Rugging Room Bulletin. (US ISSN 1043-2701) **357**

Ruh al-Qawanin. (UA) **2676**

Ruhr-Universitaet Bochum. Ostasien Institut. Veroeffentlichungen. (GW ISSN 0340-6687) **2341**

Ruimtelijke Ordening en Milieubeheer Magazine *see* R O M Magazine **1966**

Ruimzicht. (NE ISSN 0166-4069) **4199**, 1660

Ruizia. (SP ISSN 0212-9108) **516**

Rukovet. (YU ISSN 0035-9793) **2882**
Rules and Regulations - Board of Cosmetology (Sacramento) *see* California. State Board of Cosmetology. Rules and Regulations **372**
Rules of Court and Related Enactments. (CN) **2732**
Rules of the Game of Field Hockey. (US) **4486**
Rumanian Communion. *see* Comuniunea Romaneasca **2215**
Rumanian Journal of Chemistry. (RM ISSN 0048-8577) **1859**, 822, 920
Rumanian Journal of Physiology. *see* Revue Roumaine de Physiologie **574**
Rumanian Journal of Virology. *see* Revue Roumaine de Virologie **3223**
Rumanian Scientific Abstracts. (RM ISSN 0035-8096) **4357**, 22
Rumanian Studies. (NE ISSN 0304-3495) **2385**
Rumbo. (CR) **2180**
Rumbo Centroamericano *see* Rumbo **2180**
†Rumors. (CN ISSN 0829-0067) **5271**
Rumunia. (RM) **2215**
Run. (GW) **1400**
Run. (US ISSN 0741-4285) **1474**
†Run. (DK) **5271**
Runa. (PE) **2882**
Runaway. (US) **4785**
Rund um den Alheimer. (GW) **2385**
Rund um den Pelz International *see* Pelz International **5256**
Rund Um die Boerse. (GW) **883**
†Rundbrief. (US) **5271**
†Rundbrief der Dobrudscha-Deutschen. (GW) **5271**
Rundbrief Ehemaliger Schueler und Freunde der Schulbrueder. (AU ISSN 0013-2489) **1323**, 4199
Rundbrief Heimatkreis Friedeberg (Neumark). (GW) **2191**
Runde Tisch. (GW) **2541**
Rundfunk und Fernsehen. (GW ISSN 0035-9874) **1360**, 1379
Rundfunk- und Fernsehprogramm. (GW ISSN 0323-5998) **1360**, 1379
Rundfunk- und Fernsehtechnisches Zentralamt Technische Mitteilungen *see* R F Z. Technische Mitteilungen **5266**
†Rundfunkjournalistik in Theorie und Praxis. (GW ISSN 0035-9882) **5271**
Rundfunkrecht. (AU ISSN 0379-4423) **2704**
Rundfunktechnische Mitteilungen. (GW ISSN 0035-9890) **1360**
Rundschau fuer den Deutschen Einzelhaendler. (GW ISSN 0035-9904) **2093**
Rundschau fuer die Deutsche Damenschneiderei *see* Rundschau fuer Internationale Damenmode **1294**
Rundschau fuer Internationale Damenmode. (GW ISSN 0035-9912) **1294**
Rundschau fuer Internationale Herrenmode. (GW) **1287**
Rundschreiben. (GW) **2782**
Rundt's New York Intelligence Briefs *see* Rundt's World Business Intelligence **920**
Rundt's Weekly Intelligence *see* Rundt's World Business Intelligence **920**
Rundt's World Business Intelligence. (US) **920**, 1527
Rundy's Journal and Confederation Courier. (US ISSN 0882-018X) **3004**
†Runestone (Breckenridge). (US) **5271**
Runner's World. (US ISSN 0897-1706) **4486**
Runner's World (1987) *see* Runner's World **4486**
Running. (UK ISSN 0144-8560) **3808**, 4486
Running and Fitness *see* Running & FitNews **3808**
Running & FitNews. (US ISSN 0898-5162) **3808**, 3612, 4486

Running Board. (CN ISSN 0048-8771) **4701**
Running Journal. (US ISSN 0892-5038) **4554**
†Running Review. (UK) **5271**
Running Times. (US ISSN 0147-2968) **4486**
Runnymede Bulletin. (UK) **3947**, 4448
†Runways. (US) **5271**
Runzheimer on Cars & Living Costs. (US ISSN 0730-8647) **4701**, 883, 4785
Runzheimer Reports on Fleet Maintenance & Safety. (US ISSN 0894-492X) **4701**
Runzheimer Reports on Fleet Management. (US) **4701**, 1027
Runzheimer Reports on Relocation. (US ISSN 0731-9150) **993**, 4785
Runzheimer Reports on Transportation *see* Runzheimer Reports on Fleet Management **4701**
Runzheimer Reports on Travel Management. (US ISSN 0730-8663) **4785**, 1027
Ruotaspring. (IT ISSN 0393-7526) **4294**
Ruote in Pista International. (IT) **4520**
Ruoteclassiche. (IT) **259**, 4701
Rupambara. (II ISSN 0035-9963) **2956**
Ruperto-Carola. (GW ISSN 0035-998X) **1323**, 2191
Ruppin Institute Library. Library's Accession List. (IS) **411**
Ruprecht Karls Universitaet Heidelberg. Personal- und Informationsverzeichnis. (GW ISSN 0178-5338) **1323**
Rural Adjustment and Finance Corporation of Western Australia. Annual Report. (AT) **2495**
Rural Adjustment of Western Australia. Annual Report *see* Rural Adjustment and Finance Corporation of Western Australia. Annual Report **2495**
Rural Affairs Bulletin. *see* Nongcun Gongzuo Tongxun **4381**
Rural Africana. (US ISSN 0085-5839) **4385**
Rural Arkansas. (US ISSN 0048-878X) **2233**
Rural Builder. (US) **631**, 118
Rural Business. (AT) **157**
†Rural Construction. (CN ISSN 0838-9357) **5272**
Rural Councillor. (CN ISSN 0036-0007) **118**
Rural Delivery. (CN) **2179**, 2138
Rural Demography. (BG ISSN 1010-3783) **3987**
†Rural Development. (US) **5272**
Rural Development Abstracts. (UK ISSN 0140-4768) **4082**, 22
Rural Development News. (US ISSN 0886-8611) **157**
Rural Development Perspectives *see* R D P **115**
Rural Development Research Paper. (UG ISSN 0080-4851) **157**
Rural Development Series *see* Scandinavian Institute of African Studies. Rural Development **248**
†Rural Development Working Papers. (AT ISSN 0816-5173) **5272**
Rural Economy. *see* Nongcun Jingji **876**
Rural Economy and Society. *see* Nongcun Jingji yu Shehui **682**
Rural Educator. (US ISSN 0273-446X) **1660**
Rural Electric Missourian *see* Rural Missouri **832**
Rural Electric Nebraskan. (US) **1907**, 2233
Rural Electric Power Conference. Papers Presented. (US) **1907**
Rural Electrification Magazine *see* R E Magazine **1907**
Rural Enterprise. (US) **157**
†Rural Extension, Education and Training Abstracts. (UK ISSN 0140-4776) **5272**
Rural Finance and Accounting. *see* Nongcun Caiwu Kuaiji **754**
†Rural Folio. (US) **5272**
Rural Georgia *see* Georgia Magazine (Atlanta, 1945) **2226**

Rural Heritage. (US ISSN 0889-2970) **4537**
▼Rural History: Economy, Society, Culture. (UK ISSN 0956-7933) **2385**
Rural India. (II ISSN 0036-0058) **157**, 839
Rural Industry Directory. (AT ISSN 0812-1729) **118**, 2048, 2107
Rural Kentuckian *see* Kentucky Living **2227**
Rural Life *see* Heartland Journal (Mason City) **95**
Rural Life. *see* Vida Rural **128**
Rural Living. (US ISSN 1054-4801) **2233**, 1907
Rural Medicine. *see* Medycyna Wiejska **3131**
Rural Merchant Magazine *see* Rural Business **157**
Rural Missouri. (US ISSN 0164-8578) **832**, 1907
Rural Montana. (US) **2233**
Rural Network Advocate. (US) **2233**
†Rural Newsletter. (AT) **5272**
Rural Progress. (UN) **935**, 118
Rural Property Bulletin. (US) **4158**
Rural Quarterly. (AT ISSN 0729-8757) **118**
Rural Realty. *see* Revista Realidad e Rural **117**
Rural Reconstruction Review. (US ISSN 1011-873X) **935**
Rural Roundup. (US ISSN 0036-0104) **225**
Rural Sociologist. (US ISSN 0279-5957) **4448**, 118
Rural Sociology. (US ISSN 0036-0112) **4448**, 118
Rural Southern Voice for Peace. (US ISSN 1055-3908) **3923**
Rural Special Education Quarterly. (US ISSN 8756-8705) **1740**
Rural Technology Guide. (UK ISSN 0141-898X) **118**
Rural Telecommunications. (US ISSN 0744-2548) **1365**
Rural Transportation Reporter *see* Community Transportation Reporter **4648**
Rural Update. (AT) **225**, 208
Rural Viewpoint. (UK ISSN 0264-4002) **4448**
Rural Virginia Voice. (US) **118**, 2262
Rural Voice. (CN) **118**
Rural Wales *see* Rural Wales - Cymru Wledig **1496**
Rural Wales - Cymru Wledig. (UK) **1496**, 1967
RuraLink. (US) **1740**
Ruralite. (US) **2233**
Ruralter. (PE) **157**
Ruritan. (US ISSN 0036-0147) **1301**, 118
Rusayl Magazine. (MK) **1084**
Rushing Past. (US) **2163**
Rusistika. (UK ISSN 0957-1760) **2839**, 1660, 2956
Ruske Slovo. (YU ISSN 0350-4603) **2240**
Ruskin College, Oxford. Library. Occasional Publication. (UK ISSN 0261-5649) **993**, 2321
Rusky Jazyk a Literatura *see* Universita Palackeho. Pedagogicka Fakulta. Sbornik Praci: Rusky Jazyk a Literatura **2849**
Rusky Jazyk ve Skole. (CS) **1660**, 2839, 2956
Russ Cochran Newsletter. (US) **343**, 4136
Russ Reports. (US) **962**
Russell Register. (US) **2163**
Russell Review. (NZ ISSN 0111-7343) **2345**, 1496
Russell: The Journal of the Bertrand Russell Archives. (CN ISSN 0036-0163) **3780**, 2782
Russell's Official National Motor Coach Guide. (US ISSN 0036-0171) **4785**
▼Russia and Commonwealth Business Law Report. (US) **2676**
Russia Mediaevalis. (GW ISSN 0721-9431) **2385**
Russia Stamp Catalogue. (UK ISSN 0142-9841) **3757**
Russian Abroad. *see* Russkii Yazyk za Rubezhom **2839**

▼Russian Affairs. (UK ISSN 0964-4024) **2385**
Russian and East European Finance and Trade. (US) **920**
†Russian and Soviet Composers. (UR) **5272**
Russian Archival Series. (US) **2021**, 2385
Russian Buyers' Guide. (UK) **920**
Russian Chemical Reviews. (English translation of: Uspekhi Khimii) (UK ISSN 0036-021X) **1187**
Russian Classical Musical Critics. (RU) **3578**
Russian Education and Society. (US) **1660**
Russian Engineering Journal *see* Soviet Engineering Research **3023**
▼Russian Journal of Engineering Thermophysics. (US ISSN 1051-8053) **3830**, 1938
Russian Journal of Inorganic Chemistry. (English translation of: Zhurnal Neorganicheskoi Khimii) (UK ISSN 0036-0236) **1215**
Russian Journal of Physical Chemistry. (English translation of: Zhurnal Fizicheskoi Khimii) (UK ISSN 0036-0244) **1230**
▼Russian Journal of Theoretical and Applied Mechanics. (US ISSN 1051-8045) **3830**, 1938
Russian Language Journal. (US ISSN 0036-0252) **2839**, 1660
Russian Life Daily. (US) **2021**
Russian Linguistics. (NE ISSN 0304-3487) **2839**
Russian Literature. (NE ISSN 0304-3479) **2956**
Russian Literature. *see* Sulian Wenxue (Liankan) **2967**
†Russian Literature Triquarterly. (US ISSN 0048-881X) **5272**
Russian Mathematical Surveys. (English translation of: Uspekhi Matematicheskikh Nauk) (UK ISSN 0036-0279) **3053**
Russian Messenger - Russkij Vistnik *see* U R O B A Messenger **4289**
Russian Metallurgy. (English translation of: Akademiya Nauk S.S.S.R. Metally) (US ISSN 0036-0295) **3419**
Russian Metallurgy and Fuels *see* Russian Metallurgy **3419**
Russian Music Studies. (US) **3579**
Russian Orthodox Journal. (US ISSN 0036-0317) **4287**
Russian Petroleum Press Review. (SZ) **3700**
Russian Piano Music. (RU) **3579**
Russian Poetics in Translation. (UK) **2956**, 343, 2839
Russian Politics. (US) **2676**, 3923
Russian Review. (US ISSN 0036-0341) **2385**
Russian Series on Social History. (NE ISSN 0080-4916) **2385**
Russian Social Science Review. (US) **3923**, 4385
Russian Studies in History. (US) **2321**
Russian Studies in Literature. (US) **2956**
Russian Studies in Philosophy. (US) **3780**
Russian Symphonic Music. (RU) **3579**
Russian Ultrasonics. (UK ISSN 0048-8828) **3860**, 1835
Russian Voice. *see* Russky Golos **2021**
Russischer Samisdat *see* Samisdat **2385**
Russisklaererforeningen. Meddelelser. (DK ISSN 0108-2442) **2839**
Russkaja Mysl *see* Pensee Russe **2019**
Russkaya Pravoslavnaya Tserkov'. Moskovskaya Patriarkhiya. Zhurnal/ Journal of the Moscow Patriarchate. (RU ISSN 0044-4553) **4217**
Russkaya Rech'. (RU ISSN 0036-0368) **2839**
Russkii Yazyk v Natsional'noi Shkole *see* Russkii Yazyk v S.S.S.R **2839**
Russkii Yazyk v S.S.S.R. (RU) **2839**
Russkii Yazyk v Shkole. (RU ISSN 0131-6141) **2839**, 1758
Russkii Yazyk za Rubezhom/Russian Abroad. (RU ISSN 0036-0384) **2839**

6630 RUSSKOE VOZROZHDENIE

Russkoe Vozrozhdenie. (US ISSN 0222-1543) **4288**, 2385
Russky Golos/Russian Voice. (US ISSN 0036-0406) **2021**
Russland und Wir. (GW ISSN 0036-0414) **3971**, 2385
Rustica. (FR) **2555**
Rustinar. (CS) **2839**, 1758
Rutas de Pasion. (MX ISSN 0036-0430) **2984**
Rute und Rolle. (GW) **4554**
Rutebil-Bladet see Turist- og Rutebilbladet **4704**
Rutebiltidende see Transportforum-Kollektivtrafikk **4659**
Rutgers Alumni Magazine see Rutgers Magazine **1323**
Rutgers American Women Writers Series. (US) **2956**
Rutgers - Camden Gleaner. (US) **1323**
Rutgers Center of Alcohol Studies. Monograph. (US) **1539**
Rutgers Class and Culture Series. (US) **2421**
Rutgers Computer & Technology Law Journal. (US ISSN 0735-8938) **2705**, 828
Rutgers Films in Print Series. (US) **3516**
Rutgers Gleaner see Rutgers - Camden Gleaner **1323**
Rutgers Law Journal. (US ISSN 0277-318X) **2676**
Rutgers Law Review. (US ISSN 0036-0465) **2676**
Rutgers Magazine. (US) **1323**
Rutgers Mind and Medicine Series. (US) **3150**
†Rutgers Symposia in Applied Psychology. (US) **5272**
Rutgers University. Bureau of Engineering Research. Annual Report. (US ISSN 0557-5486) **1836**
Rutgers University. Libraries. Journal. (US ISSN 0036-0473) **2782**
Rutgers University Studies in Classical Humanities. (US ISSN 0732-9814) **1279**
Rutherglen, Australia. Research Station. Digest of Recent Research see Rutherglen Research Institute. Research Report **118**
Rutherglen Research Institute. Research Report. (AT ISSN 0814-4990) **118**
Rutland Area Shopper. (US) **38**
Rutland Historical Society Newsletter see Rutland Historical Society Quarterly **2421**
Rutland Historical Society Quarterly. (US ISSN 0748-2493) **2421**
Rutland Record. (UK ISSN 0260-3322) **2385**
Ruvigny's Titled Nobility of Europe. (UK) **2163**
Ruvue d'Histoire de la Culture Materielle. see Material History Review **2317**
Al-Ruwalah. (TS) **4637**
Ruxton Report. (US) **1105**
Rwanda. Direction Generale de la Documentation et de la Statistique Generale. Bulletin de Statistique see Rwanda. Direction Generale de la Statistique. Bulletin de Statistique **4584**
Rwanda. Direction Generale de la Documentation et de la Statistique Generale. Situation Economique de la Republique Rwandaise au 31 Decembre see Rwanda. Direction Generale de la Statistique. Situation Economique de la Republique Rwandaise au 31 Decembre **883**
Rwanda. Direction Generale de la Documentation et de la Statistique. Rapport Annuel see Rwanda. Direction Generale de la Statistique. Rapport Annuel **4073**
Rwanda. Direction Generale de la Statistique. Bulletin de Statistique. (RW) **4584**
Rwanda. Direction Generale de la Statistique. Rapport Annuel. (RW) **4073**

Rwanda. Direction Generale de la Statistique. Situation Economique de la Republique Rwandaise au 31 Decembre. (RW) **883**
Rwanda. Ministere de l'Agriculture et de l'Elevage. Rapport Annuel. (RW) **118**, 225
Rwanda. Ministere de l'Education Nationale. Direction de la Planification, Statistique et Information. Statistique de l'Enseignement see Rwanda. Ministere de l'Enseignement Primaire et Secondaire. Direction de la Planification. Statistique de l'Enseignement **1679**
Rwanda. Ministere de l'Enseigneemnt Primaire et Secondaire. Direction de la Planification. Statistique de l'Enseignement. (RW) **1679**
Rwanda. Ministere de la Defense Nationale. Forces de Securite au Service de la Nation. (RW) **3470**
Rwanda. Ministere de la Sante Publique. Rapport Annuel. (RW) **4111**
Rwanda. Office National de la Population. Famille, Sante, Developpement. (RW) **3987**
Rwanda. Projet Pilote Forestier. Programme d'Appui au Service Forestier Prefectoral de Kibuye. (RW) **2107**
Rwanda. Projet Pilote Forestier. Rapport Annuel see Rwanda. Projet Pilote Forestier. Programme d'Appui au Service Forestier Prefectoral de Kibuye **2107**
Rwanda Agricultural Bulletin. see Bulletin Agricole du Rwanda **80**
Rwanda-Carrefour d'Afrique see Releve **3921**
†Rx Being Well. (US) **5272**
†Rx Home Care. (US ISSN 0191-961X) **5272**
†Rx Home Care Directory. (US) **5272**
Rx Weight Control. (US) **3612**
▼Ryan Ramblings. (US ISSN 1049-1848) **2163**
▼Ryan's Review. (US) **3004**
Rybarstvi. (CS ISSN 0009-0670) **2048**, 4554
Rybnoe Khozyaistvo. (RU ISSN 049X) **2048**
Rybovodstvo i Rybolovstvo. (RU ISSN 0131-6672) **2048**
Ryde Recorder. (AT ISSN 0048-8879) **2345**
Ryder. (US) **2882**
†Rydge's C C E M - Construction, Civil Engineering and Mining. (AT) **5272**
Ryerson Rambler. (CN ISSN 0705-9191) **1323**
Ryland's Directory. (UK ISSN 0080-505X) **3419**
Rynki Zagraniczne/Foreign Markets. (PL ISSN 0036-052X) **920**
Rynok Produktsii Chernoi Metallurgii see Steel Market **3421**
Ryoiku/Rehabilitation. (JA ISSN 0036-0538) **1741**, 2284
Ryoksagwahak/Historical Science. (KN) **2321**
Rytme. (DK ISSN 0107-6280) **3579**, 4637
Rytmus. (CS) **1532**
Ryugin Keizai Report. (JA ISSN 0916-3158) **883**
Ryukyu Daigaku Nogakubu Gakujutsu Hokoku. see University of the Ryukyus. College of Agriculture. Science Bulletin **127**
Ryukyu Daigaku Rigakubu Kiyo. see University of the Ryukyus. College of Science. Bulletin **3061**
Ryuseijin Kaiho/Circular of Meteoric Dust. (JA ISSN 0385-0994) **371**
S see Secretaresse Magazine: S **1061**
S A. (Sociological Analysis) (US ISSN 0038-0210) **4448**, 4274
S A A Age see Strategic Systems **1465**
S A A D Digest. (Society for the Advancement of Anaesthesia in Dentistry) (UK ISSN 0049-1160) **3242**
S A A O Newsletter. (South Africa Astronomical Observatory) (SA) **369**

▼S A A R C Journal of Education. (II) **1660**
S A A T News see Atrium **295**
S.A. Advisory. (SA) **962**
S A Athlete/S A Atleet. (SA ISSN 0049-1381) **4486**
S A Atleet. see S A Athlete **4486**
S A B Choir. (Soprano, Alto, Bass) (US) **3579**
S A B R Bulletin. (Society for American Baseball Research, Inc.) (US) **4510**
†S A B R Review of Books. (Society for American Baseball Research, Inc.) (US ISSN 0888-8124) **5272**
S A B S Catalogue/S A B S Katalogus. (South African Bureau of Standards) (SA ISSN 1018-4295) **3448**
S A B S Katalogus. see S A B S Catalogue **3448**
S A B W O News. (SA) **2295**
S.A. Bakery and Confectionary Review see South African Bakery and Confectionery Review **2089**
S A Barometer. (SA ISSN 1018-3493) **3947**, 993, 4418
S A Besproeiing. see S A Irrigation **191**
S.A. Builder - Bouer see South African Builder **632**
S.A. Building and Decorating Materials see Building Products News **606**
S.A. Building Products News see Building Products News **606**
S A C see Symposuim on Applied Computing **1401**
S A C E Bulletin. (Saskatchewan Association for Computers in Education) (CN) **1417**, 1691
S A C I Slants. (Sales Association of the Chemical Industry, Inc.) (US) **1187**, 1052
S A C O - S R-Tidningen. (SW ISSN 0347-0342) **2588**
S A C S O S Newsletter. (South Australian Coloured Sheep Owners' Society Inc. (SACSOS)) (AT) **225**
S A Cleaning Review. (SA) **1282**
S A Co-op. (AT) **118**
S.A. Crafts. (AT ISSN 0819-2936) **357**
S.A. Crafts News see S.A. Crafts **357**
S A D C C Energy Bulletin. (Southern African Development Coordination Conference) (AO) **1795**
S A Draughtsman see South African Draughtsman **4609**
S A E. (Sammlung Arbeitsrechtlicher Entscheidungen) (GW ISSN 0048-9069) **993**, 2676
S A E - Australasia. (Society of Automotive Engineers) (AT ISSN 0036-0651) **4701**
S A E Handbook. (Society of Automotive Engineers) (US ISSN 0362-8205) **4701**
S A E Technical Literature Abstracts. (Society of Automotive Engineers) (US ISSN 0741-2029) **4666**, 22
S A E Technical Papers. (Society of Automotive Engineers) (US ISSN 0148-7191) **4701**
S A E Transactions. (Society of Automotive Engineers) (US ISSN 0096-736X) **4701**
S A E Update. (Society of Automotive Engineers) (US ISSN 0742-972X) **1938**
S A F. (Society of American Florists) (US) **2143**
S A F C E C Bulletin. (South African Federation of Civil Engineering Contractors) (SA) **1873**
S A F E - Nachrichten. (Salzburger Aktiengesellschaft fuer Elektrizitaetswirtschaft) (AU ISSN 0036-0708) **1907**
S A F E Symposium Proceedings. (US ISSN 0743-846X) **61**
S A F Position Paper. (South African Forum) (SA) **3947**
S A F R A see Soviet Armed Forces Review Annual **3472**
S A F T O Annual Report/Suid-Afrikaanse Buitelandse Handelsorganisasie Jaarverslag. (South African Foreign Trade Organisation) (SA ISSN 0081-2552) **920**

S A F T O Exporter. (South African Foreign Trade Organisation) (SA ISSN 0036-0716) **920**
S A F T T A Newsletter. (South African Film and Television Technicians Association) (SA) **3517**, 1379
S A F - Tidningen. (Svenska Arbetsgivarefoereningen) (SW ISSN 0349-6740) **1027**
S A Family Safety/Gesinsveiligheid. (SA) **4112**
S A G A News. (Smocking Arts Guild) (US) **357**, 3592
S.A. Geographer Bulletin see South Australian Geographer **2263**
S A Golf Journal. (SA ISSN 1013-3356) **4510**
S.A. Hairdressing and Beauty Culture. (SA ISSN 0036-0759) **374**
S.A. Hotel Review see Hotelier & Caterer (Cape Town) **2476**
S A I B I Nuusbrief. see S A I L I S Newsletter **2782**
S A I L I S Newsletter/S A I B I Nuusbrief. (South African Institute for Librarianship and Information Science) (SA ISSN 0256-6710) **2782**
†S A I N T. (Special and Individual Needs Technology) (US) **5272**
S A I P A. (South African Institute of Public Administration) (SA ISSN 0036-0767) **4073**, 3923
S A I S Review. (Paul H. Nitze School of Advanced International Studies) (US ISSN 0036-0775) **3971**, 920, 1323
S A I S Studies on Africa. (US) **2334**
S A I T Journal. (South Australian Institute of Teachers) (AT) **1731**
S A Irrigation/S A Besproeiing. (SA ISSN 0258-5081) **191**
S A Joint Catalogue of Monographs of Microfiche, Series 2, Author Index see Second Supplement to the S A Joint Catalogue of Monographs on Microfiche. Author Index **411**
S A Joint Catalogue of Monographs on Microfiche, Series 1, Title Index see Second Supplement to the S A Joint Catalogue of Monographs on Microfiche. Title Index **411**
S A Joint Catalogue of Monographs on Microfiche, Series 3, UNICAT. (SA) **2795**
S A L A L M Bibliography and Reference Series. (Seminar on the Acquisition of Latin American Library Materials) (US) **2795**, 411
S A L A L M Bibliography Series see S A L A L M Bibliography and Reference Series **2795**
S A L A L M Newsletter. (Seminar on the Acquisition of Latin American Library Materials) (US ISSN 0098-6275) **411**, 2782
S A L A Newsletter - S A B V Nuusbrief see S A I L I S Newsletter **2782**
S A L G Newsletter. (South Asia Library Group) (UK ISSN 0307-1456) **2795**, 411
S A L I S Directory. (Substance Abuse Librarians and Information Specialists) (US) **2782**, 1539
S A L I S News. (Substance Abuse Librarians and Information Specialists) (US) **2782**, 1539
S A L S in Brief. (Southern Adirondack Library System) (US) **2782**
S A L T Equalizer. (Society of American Law Teachers) (US) **2676**, 1715
S A L Z. (GW) **993**
S A M see Adweek: Midwest **27**
S A M Advanced Management Journal see Advanced Management Journal **1002**
S A M Focus on Management. (Society for Advancement of Management) (US) **1027**
S A M I K S A. (II) **4045**, 3353
S A M Management Journal. (Society for Advancement of Management) (US) **1027**
S A M News International see S A M Management Journal **1027**
S A M P E Journal. (Society for the Advancement of Material and Process Engineering) (US ISSN 0091-1062) **1922**

S A M P E Quarterly. (Society for the Advancement of Material and Process Engineering) (US ISSN 0036-0821) **1922**, 1836
S.A. Marksman/S.A. Skerpskutter. (SA) **4486**
S.A. Mining and Engineering Yearbook *see* South African Mining and Engineering Yearbook **5279**
S A Mining World. (SA) **3495**
S A Motor Sport Bulletin. (South Africa Motor Sport Control) (SA) **4520**
S A Motorscene *see* Chequered Flag **4687**
S A N B *see* South African National Bibliography **412**
S A N C B News. (South African National Council for the Blind) (SA) **2295**
S A N R B Nuus *see* S A N C B News **2295**
S A N T A. T B News/S A N T A. T B Nuus. (South African National Tuberculosis Association) (SA ISSN 0036-0872) **3367**
S A N T A. T B Nuus. *see* S A N T A. T B News **3367**
S A N T A Annual Report/S A N T A Jaarlikse Verslag. (South African National Tuberculosis Association) (SA ISSN 0081-2501) **3367**
S A N T A Bantu *see* S A N T A Health Magazine **3367**
S A N T A Health Magazine. (South African National Tuberculosis Association) (SA) **3367**
S A N T A Jaarlikse Verslag. *see* S A N T A Annual Report **3367**
S A P Magazine *see* Servamus **1522**
S.A. Panorama. (South African Embassy) (PO) **2334**
S A Public Law. *see* S A Publiekreg **2676**
S A Publiekreg/S A Public Law. (SA ISSN 0258-6568) **2676**
S A Q: The South Atlantic Quarterly. (US ISSN 0038-2876) **2882**
S A R A D. (South African Rates and Data) (SA) **38**
S.A.R. and H. Employees' Review *see* Emplo Review/Tydskrif **2582**
S A R E C Annual Report. (Swedish Agency for Research Cooperation with Developing Countries) (SW ISSN 0349-0874) **935**
S A R E C Report. (Swedish Agency for Research Cooperation with Developing Countries) (SW ISSN 0348-2626) **3971**
S A R F Newsletter. (Southern Africa Road Federation) (SA) **4721**
S A R Magazine *see* Sons of the American Revolution Magazine **2422**
S A R Statistics. (Search and Rescue) (US ISSN 0163-2833) **4666**, **4737**
S A Refrigeration and Airconditioning. (SA) **2303**
S A S B O News/S A S B O Nuus. (South African Society of Bank Officials) (SA) **798**
S A S B O Nuus. *see* S A S B O News **798**
S A S Bulletin. (Society for Archaeological Sciences) (US ISSN 0899-8922) **284**
S A S C A Journal - Newsletter. (Saskatchewan Association of Student Council Advisors) (CN) **1731**, **1758**
S A S C H Newsletter. (Saskatchewan Association of Special Care Homes) (CN) **3150**, **4418**
S A S Newsletter *see* S A S Bulletin **284**
S.A. Shoemaker and Leather Review *see* South African Shoemaker and Leather Review **4362**
S.A. Skerpskutter. *see* S.A. Marksman **4486**
S A Sports Trader. (SA) **1052**, **4486**
S A Swimmer. (SA) **4486**
†S A T R A: Agricultural Sciences. (Science and Technology Research Abstracts) (US) **5272**
S A Tekenaar. *see* South African Draughtsman **4609**

S A Transport Services Annual Report (Year) *see* Transnet Annual Report (Year) **4657**
S A UNICAT *see* S A Joint Catalogue of Monographs on Microfiche, Series 3, UNICAT **2795**
S A V S News *see* Animal Concern **230**
S A W E Newsletter. (Society of Allied Weight Engineers) (US) **61**
S A W T R I Technical Report *see* TexReport **4624**
S.A. Werker. *see* S.A. Worker **2588**
S.A. Worker/S.A. Werker. (SA ISSN 0036-1011) **2588**
S A Y N. (Slovak-American Youth News) (US) **2022**
S A Z. (Sport Artikel Zeitung Verlag) (GW) **1052**, **4486**
†S - Agrar-Aktuell. (GW) **5272**
The S & B Report. (Sales and Bargains) (US) **1287**
S & L Quarterly. (US) **798**
S & L - Savings Bank Financial Quarterly. (Savings and Loan) (US) **689**
S and M M Sales and Marketing Management *see* Sales & Marketing Management **1053**
S & V *see* Sound and Vibration **1939**
S B. (Sportstaettenbau und Baederanlagen - Sports Facilities and Swimming Pools) (GW ISSN 0036-102X) **631**, **3739**, **4486**
S B A C News. (Society of British Aerospace Companies Ltd.) (UK) **61**
S B A N E Enterprise. (Smaller Business Association of New England) (US) **1117**
S B A R M O Bulletin. (Scientific Ballooning and Radiations Monitoring Organization) (FR) **3440**
S B Artikel. (Selbstbedienung) (GW) **1052**
S B B Tax News *see* Small Business **1117**
†S B C A Weekly. (Satellite Broadcasting & Communications Association) (US) **5272**
S B C Booklet. (Schweizerischer Bankverein) (SZ) **798**
S B C Newsletter. (Society of Biological Chemists) (II) **482**
S B I Aarsberetning. (Statens Byggeforskningsinstitut) (DK ISSN 0107-900X) **631**
S B I C Directory and Handbook of Small Business Finance. (US) **1117**, **798**
S B I C Industry Review *see* U.S. Small Business Administration. S B I C Digest **1119**
S B K Julkaisuja *see* Suomen Betoniteollisuuden Keskusjarejesto. Julkaisuja **633**
S B Warenhaus *see* Checkout **1035**
S B Z-monteur. (GW ISSN 0342-8206) **2303**
S B Z - Sanitaer, Heizungs- und Klimatechnik. (GW ISSN 0342-8184) **2303**, **4112**
S B Z - Sanitaer-Technik, Heizungs-, und Lueftungsbau *see* S B Z - Sanitaer, Heizungs- und Klimatechnik **2303**
S-Bilten *see* Komisija za Ispitivanje S-Uredjaja. Bilten **1901**
S C *see* Semiotic Crossroads **2840**
S C A D Bulletin. (Systeme Communautaire d'Acces a la Documentation) (EI ISSN 0256-3096) **411**, **2676**
S C A E Network. (Society for Computer-Aided Engineering) (US) **1880**
S C A Free Speech Yearbook. (Speech Communication Association) (US) **3924**
S C A L A C S. (American Chemical Society) (US ISSN 0044-7595) **1187**, **3394**
S C A N. (Selected Current Aerospace Notices) (US) **61**
†S C A N. (Superior California Administration Newsletter) (US) **5272**
S C A N (Singles Connection and Network) *see* National Singles Directory **4362**

S C A N Newsletter. (Scanning, Coding & Automation Newsletter Ltd.) (US ISSN 0273-3080) **1415**
S C A N Newsletter *see* Santa Cruz Action Network. Newsletter **2495**
S C A R Boletin. (Scientific Committee on Antartic Research) (AG ISSN 0325-6146) **4337**
S C A R Bulletin *see* S C A R Boletin **4337**
S C A Radio Subcarrier Report *see* Data Broadcasting Report **1334**
S C A Report. (Synagogue Council of America) (US) **2022**, **4226**
S C A - Tidningen *see* Concern **2114**
S C A U L Newsletter *see* African Journal of Academic Librarianship **2741**
S C & O: Specialty & Custom Dealer. (US) **4701**
S C & R A Newsletter. (Specialized Carriers & Rigging Association) (US) **4747**, **4655**
S C - D L O Rapporten *see* Dienst Landbouwkundig Onderzoek. Staring Centrum, Instituut voor Onderzoek van het Landelijk Gebied. Rapporten **176**
S C E A Emphasis. (South Carolina Education Association) (US) **1660**
S C E H Newsletter. (Society for Clinical and Experimental Hypnosis) (US ISSN 0583-8975) **3274**
S C E R T Journal. (State Council of Educational Research and Training) (II) **1758**
S C I *see* Science Citation Index **4357**
S C I Grants News *see* Federal Grants & Contracts Weekly **4060**
S C I - J C R *see* Science Citation Index Journal Citation Report **4339**
S C I Journal of Music Scores. (Society of Composers International) (US) **3579**
S C I M A. (Society of Management Science and Applied Cybernetics) (II ISSN 0376-4087) **1442**, **828**
S C I M A Special Series. (Society of Management Science and Applied Cybernetics) (II) **1443**
S C I M P. (Selective Cooperative Index of Management Periodicals) (FI ISSN 0782-2979) **737**, **22**
S C I O S. (AT) **1759**
S C J. (Sydney Cinema Journal) (AT ISSN 0036-1135) **3517**
S C L A Newsletter. (Southern Comparative Literature Association) (US) **2956**
S C Musician. (South Carolina Music Educators Association) (US) **3579**
†S C O C L I S News. (Standing Conference of Co-Operative Library and Information Services) (UK ISSN 0307-6903) **5272**
S C O L A G. (Scottish Legal Action Group) (UK ISSN 0264-8717) **2676**, **4418**
†S C O P E. (Scholarly Communication: Online Publishing and Education) (US ISSN 0735-8296) **5272**
S C P Journal. (Spiritual Counterfeits Project, Inc.) (US ISSN 0883-1300) **4199**
S C P Newsletter. (Spiritual Counterfeits Project, Inc.) (US ISSN 0883-1319) **4200**
S C P S Yearbook on P L A Affairs *see* China's Military: P L A in (Year) **2337**
S C R A M Journal *see* S C R A M Safe Energy Journal **1795**
S C R A M Safe Energy Journal. (Scottish Campaign to Resist the Atomic Menace) (UK) **1795**, **1809**
S C R L C Reports *see* South Central Research Library Council. Reports **2785**
S C T A Hi-Lights. (South Carolina Trucking Association, Inc.) (US) **4747**
S C U P News. (Society for College and University Planning) (US) **1715**
S C U P News and Journal *see* Planning for Higher Education **1714**
S C W E A Newsletter. (Saskatchewan Career - Work Education Association) (CN) **3630**, **1759**

S Corporations (Englewood Cliffs). (US) **1105**
†S Corporations (New York). (US ISSN 0897-800X) **5272**
S Corporations Guide. (US) **1105**
S D A C C County Comment. (Association of County Commissioners) (US ISSN 1049-7838) **4073**
S D A C C County Government *see* S D A C C County Comment **4073**
S D A Journal - Newsletter. (Saskatchewan Drama Association) (CN) **4637**, **1759**
S D A Newsletter. (Southern Demographic Association) (US) **3987**
S D C Bulletin. (Scientific Documentation Centre Ltd.) (UK ISSN 0036-1178) **3839**, **22**
S D C E International Die Casting Congress. Transactions *see* N A D C A International Die Casting Congress. Transactions **1921**
S D E A Catalogue of Shopfittings and Display *see* S D E A Directory of Shopfittings and Display Equipment **38**
S D E A Directory of Shopfittings and Display Equipment. (Shop and Display Equipment Association) (UK) **38**
S D I Intelligence Report. (US) **3470**
S D I Monitor. (Strategic Defense Initiative) (US ISSN 0886-7607) **3470**
S D I - Scandinavian Dairy Information. (SW) **203**
S D S - Rivista di Cultura Sportiva. (Scuola Dello Sport) (IT) **4486**
S D S U Alumnus. (South Dakota State University) (US) **1323**
S E *see* Sementi Elette **192**
S E A C Assessment Matters. (School Examinations and Assessment Council) (UK) **1759**
S E A G Boletin del Algodon *see* E A G Publicaciones **87**
S E A G Boletin del Maiz *see* E A G Publicaciones **87**
S E A G Boletin del Trigo *see* E A G Publicaciones **87**
S E A I S I Quarterly Journal. (South East Asia Iron and Steel Institute) (PH ISSN 0129-5721) **3419**
S E A M E O Quarterly. (Southeast Asian Ministers of Education Organization) (TH ISSN 0857-0361) **1731**
S E A M E O Regional Language Centre. Anthology Series. (Southeast Asian Ministers of Education Organization) (SI ISSN 0129-8895) **2839**
S E A M O Digest *see* S E A M E O Quarterly **1731**
S E A N *see* Scientific Event Alert Network **1552**
S E A R *see* South East Asian Review **2342**
†S E A R M G Newsletter. (AT ISSN 0158-1953) **5272**
▼S E B E S. (SZ ISSN 1016-8397) **1967**, **1795**
S e C. (Serramenti e Componenti) (IT ISSN 1120-7876) **1527**
S E C A C Review *see* Southeastern College Art Conference Review **344**
S E C A C Review and Newsletter *see* Southeastern College Art Conference Review **344**
S E C Accounting and Reporting Update Service. (Securities and Exchange Commission) (US) **756**
S E C Accounting Report. (Securities and Exchange Commission) (US ISSN 0146-485X) **756**
S E C Accounting Rules. (Securities and Exchange Commission) (US) **962**, **756**
S E C Annual Reports. Banking Supplement *see* Shareholders, Form 10-K. Banking Supplement **799**
S E C Compliance: Financial Reporting and Forms. (US) **962**, **2676**
S E C Docket. (U.S. Securities and Exchange Commission) (US ISSN 0091-4061) **962**

6632 S E

S E C Financial Reporting: Annual Reports to Shareholders, Form 10-K, Quarterly Financial Reporting. (US) **962**, 756

S E C Guidelines (Year). (Security, Exchange and Commission) (US) **962**, 2676

S E C I N Abstracts *see* S E C I N Abstracts. Journal **4458**

S E C I N Abstracts. Journal. (Socio-Economic Information Network) (JM) **4458**, 22, 737

S E C News Digest. (U.S. Securities and Exchange Commission) (US ISSN 0364-6718) **962**

S E C O L A S Annals. (Southeastern Council on Latin American Studies) (US ISSN 0081-2951) **2421**

S E D M E. (Small Enterprises Development, Management and Extension) (II) **1117**

S E D O C. (Servicio de Documentacao) (BL ISSN 0036-1267) **4200**

S E E *see* Journal for Studies in Economics and Econometrics **896**

S E E J *see* Slavic and East European Journal **2841**

S E E Journal. (Society for Environmental Education) (UK ISSN 0307-2614) **1967**

S E E L *see* Bulletin on Soviet and East European Law **2720**

S E I *see* Structural Engineering International **1874**

S E I News. (Sumitomo Electric Industries Ltd.) (JA) **1907**

S E I U Leadership News Update *see* S E I U Update **2588**

S E I U Update. (Service Employees International Union) (US) **2588**

S E K - Lesbisch en Homoblad. (NE ISSN 0166-1973) **2457**

▼S E M A. (Semiotic Abstracts) (NE) **2856**, 22, 2839

S E M A News. (Specialty Equipment Market Association) (US ISSN 0279-5051) **4701**

S E M Proceedings. (Society for Experimental Mechanics) (US) **1922**

S E N G A. (Sensitive to the Educational Needs of Growing Americans) (US ISSN 1044-0275) **1243**, 1741, 1759, 2022

S E N Incorporating Oil and Gas Pipeline News *see* Subsea Engineering News **3702**

S E News *see* Southeastern Newsline **2785**

S E P I R M Issues *see* Institut des Recherches Marxistes. Issues **671**

S E R America. (Service, Employment, Redevelopment) (US) **993**

S E R B Official Reporter. (State Employment Relations Board) (US ISSN 0894-3486) **2676**, 3263

S E R Bulletin. (Sociaal-Economisches Raad) (NE ISSN 0920-4849) **883**

S E R C Bulletin. (Science and Engineering Research Council) (UK ISSN 0262-7671) **4337**, 4608

S E R I. Ethanol Annual Report. (Solar Energy Research Institute) (US) **1795**, 557, 1860

S E R I Science and Technology in Review. (Solar Energy Research Institute) (US) **1811**

S E R in Action Newsletter. (Society for Educational Reconstruction) (US) **1660**, 3780

S E R O M D A Scene. (South Eastern Regional Office Machine Dealers Association) (US) **1061**

S.E.R.T. Journal *see* Electronic Technology **5185**

S E R Tidningen *see* Maskinentreprenoeren **623**

S E S I Journal. (Solar Energy Society of India) (II ISSN 0970-2466) **1811**

S E S Newsletter. (Saskatchewan Environmental Society) (CN) **1967**

S E T Free. (Society for the Eradication of Television) (US) **1379**, 4418

S E T: Research Information for Teachers. (NZ ISSN 0110-6376) **1660**

S E V Bulletin *see* Bulletin S E V - V S E **1883**

S E W R P C Newsletter. (Southeastern Wisconsin Regional Planning Commission) (US ISSN 0584-4266) **2495**

S en V *see* Stedebouw en Volkshuisvesting **2496**

†S F (San Francisco). (US) **5272**

S F. Status. (Socialistiske Perspektiver Forlag) (DK ISSN 0902-1612) **3924**

S F (Woburn). (Square Foot) (US) **4158**

S F Camerawork Quarterly. (San Francisco) (US) **3796**, 343

S F Commentary. (Science Fiction) (AT) **3014**

S F E. (Santa Fe East) (US) **343**, 3532, 4785

S F Eye *see* Science Fiction Eye **3014**

S F I Bulletin. (Sport Fishing Institute) (US ISSN 0085-6592) **4554**

S F M *see* C S F M Journal **2031**

S F N O W Times. (National Organization for Women) (US) **4852**

S F Newsletter. (Southern Forest Products Association) (US) **2117**

S F S Catalogue. (Suomen Standardisoimisliitto) (FI) **3448**, 1836

S F W A Bulletin. (Science Fiction Writers of America) (US ISSN 0036-1364) **3014**, 2956

S F Weekly. (US ISSN 1060-2526) **2233**

S G *see* Sport Giovane **4489**

S G A Journal *see* Gastroenterology Nursing **3268**

S G I. (Soka Gakkai International) (JA ISSN 0288-2930) **3971**, 1967

S G I - Auto Fund. Annual Report. (Saskatchewan Government Insurance) (CN) **4721**

S G M A Comprehensive Quarterly Sales Trends Report. (Sporting Goods Manufacturers Association) (US) **1052**, 4486

S G M A Today - Action Update. (Sporting Goods Manufacturers Association) (US) **4486**

S G M News. (Scripture Gift Mission) (UK) **4200**

S G M News Digest *see* S G M News **4200**

S G P B Alert. (Southern Growth Policies Board) (US ISSN 8755-7282) **883**

S G V Group Journal. (SyCip, Gorres, Velayo & Co.) (PH) **1084**

S Gaugian. (US ISSN 0273-6241) **2441**

S-Gravenhage *see* Den Haag **4088**

†S H A R E. (Sisters Have Resources Everywhere) (US ISSN 0273-2343) **5272**

S H E. (Subject Headings for Engineering) (US) **2782**, 1836

S H H H Journal. (Self Help for Hard of Hearing People, Inc.) (US ISSN 0883-1688) **2289**

S H O T Newsletter. (Society for the History of Technology) (US) **4608**

S H P E National Newsletter. (Society of Hispanic Professional Engineers) (US) **1836**, 2022

S H S B. Bulletin. (Societe Historique de Saint-Boniface) (CN ISSN 0384-0158) **2421**, 2163, 3532

†S H - Technik. (Sanitaeinstallation und Heizungsbau) (GW ISSN 0931-7775) **5272**

S I. (Snackfood International) (UK) **2089**

S I A Directory & Guide. (Securities Industry Association) (US) **1152**, 962

S I A M - A M S Proceedings. (Society for Industrial and Applied Mathematics) (US ISSN 0080-5084) **3053**

S I A M Journal on Algebraic and Discrete Methods *see* S I A M Journal on Discrete Mathematics **3053**

S I A M Journal on Algebraic and Discrete Methods *see* S I A M Journal on Matrix Analysis and Applications **3053**

S I A M Journal on Applied Mathematics. (Society for Industrial and Applied Mathematics) (US ISSN 0036-1399) **3053**

S I A M Journal on Computing. (Society for Industrial and Applied Mathematics) (US ISSN 0097-5397) **3066**

S I A M Journal on Control *see* S I A M Journal on Control and Optimization **3053**

S I A M Journal on Control and Optimization. (Society for Industrial and Applied Mathematics) (US ISSN 0363-0129) **3053**, 4608

S I A M Journal on Discrete Mathematics. (Society for Industrial and Applied Mathematics) (US ISSN 0895-4801) **3053**, 3066

S I A M Journal on Mathematical Analysis. (Society for Industrial and Applied Mathematics) (US ISSN 0036-1410) **3053**

S I A M Journal on Matrix Analysis and Applications. (Society for Industrial and Applied Mathematics) (US ISSN 0895-4798) **3053**

S I A M Journal on Numerical Analysis. (US ISSN 0036-1429) **3053**, 4608

▼S I A M Journal on Optimization. (US ISSN 1052-6234) **3054**, 4608

S I A M Journal on Scientific and Statistical Computing. (US ISSN 0196-5204) **4585**, 3054

S I A M News. (Society for Industrial and Applied Mathematics) (US) **3054**, 4608

S I A M Review. (Society for Industrial and Applied Mathematics) (US ISSN 0036-1445) **3054**, 4608

S I A Semiconductor Industry Association. Yearbook and Directory (Year) *see* Semiconductor Industry Association. Yearbook and Directory (Year) **1778**

S I A - Surface and Interface Analysis. (UK ISSN 0142-2421) **1208**

S I A Washington Report. (Securities Industry Association (Washington)) (US) **962**, 2676

▼S I Business. (Systems Integrator) (CN) **1438**, 1453

S I C C Dolphin *see* College Voice (Staten Island) **1308**

S I D *see* Serie de Investigaciones y Desarrollo **119**

S I D A Development Studies *see* S A R E C Report **3971**

S I D A: Realites. *see* Canadian A I D S News **3218**

S I D I C. (Service International de Documentation Judeo-Chretienne) (IT) **4200**

S I D International Symposium. Digest of Technical Papers. (Society for Information Display) (US ISSN 0097-966X) **1836**, 4608

S I D Journal *see* Information Display **2797**

S.I.D. Proceedings. (Society for Information Display) (US ISSN 0036-1496) **1423**

S I E (Year) Guide to Investment Services. (Select Information Exchange) (US) **962**

S I E C A. Cuadernos. (Secretaria Permanente del Tratado General de Integracion Economica Centroamericana) (GT) **920**

S I E C C A N Journal. (Sex Information and Education Council of Canada) (CN ISSN 0844-3718) **4045**

S I E C C A N Newsletter. (Sex Information and Education Council of Canada) (CN ISSN 0381-873X) **4045**

S I E C U S Newsletter *see* S I E C U S Report **3808**

S I E C U S Report. (Sex Information and Education Council of the U S) (US ISSN 0091-3995) **3808**, 1759

S I E Sophisticated Investor *see* S I E (Year) Guide to Investment Services **962**

S I E T Studies *see* S E D M E **1117**

S I G A C T News. (Special Interest Group on Automata and Computability Theory) (US ISSN 0163-5700) **1415**, 1418

S I G A R C H Computer Architecture News. (Special Interest Group on Architecture of Computer Systems) (US ISSN 0163-5964) **1416**

S I G A R T Newsletter. (Special Interest Group on Artificial Intelligence) (US ISSN 0163-5719) **1410**

S I G B D P Database *see* Database (New York) **1444**

S I G B I O Newsletter. (Special Interest Group on Biomedical Computing) (US) **3226**

S I G C A P H Newsletter. (Special Interest Group on Computers and the Physically Handicapped) (US ISSN 0163-5727) **1417**

S I G C A S Newsletter *see* Computers & Society **4458**

S I G C H I Bulletin. (Special Interest Group on Computer and Human Interaction) (US ISSN 0736-6906) **4459**

S I G C O M M Computer Communications Review *see* Computer Communications Review **1446**

†S I G C O S I M Newsletter. (Special Interest Group on Computer Systems Installation Management) (US) **5272**

S I G C P R Newsletter. (Special Interest Group on Computer Personnel Research) (US ISSN 0160-2497) **1424**

S I G C S E Bulletin. (Special Interest Group on Computer Science Education) (US ISSN 0097-8418) **1691**

S I G C S Newsletter. (Special Interest Groups for Computer Science) (US ISSN 1040-7553) **1400**

S I G D O C Newsletter. (Special Interest Group on Systems Documentation) (US) **1438**

S I G F I D E T Record *see* S I G M O D Record **1445**

S I G G R A P H Computer Graphics *see* Computer Graphics (New York) **1421**

S I G I R Forum. (Special Interest Group on Information Retrieval) (US ISSN 0163-5840) **1457**

†S I G L A S H Newsletter. (Special Interest Group on Language Analysis and Studies in the Humanities) (US) **5272**

▼S I G L I N K Review. (Special Interest Group for Hypertext - Hypermedia) (US) **1438**

S I G M A P Newsletter. (Special Interest Group on Mathematical Programming) (US) **1431**

S I G M A Update *see* Independent Gasoline Marketing **3688**

S I G M E T R I C S Performance Evaluation Review. (Special Interest Group on Measurement and Evaluation) (US ISSN 0163-5999) **1418**

S I G M O D Record. (Special Interest Group on Management of Data) (US ISSN 0163-5808) **1445**

S I G N U M Newsletter. (Special Interest Group on Numerical Mathematics) (US ISSN 0163-5778) **3066**

S I G O I S Newsletter. (Special Interest Group for Office Information Systems) (US) **1438**, 1061

S I G P C Newsletter *see* S I G P C Notes **1474**

S I G P C Notes. (Special Interest Group on Personal Computing) (US) **1474**

S I G P L A N Notices *see* A C M S I G P L A N Notices **1429**

S I G P L A N - S T A P L Quote Quad *see* A P L Quote Quad **1429**

S I G S A C Review. (Special Interest Group for Security Audit Control) (US) **1435**, 1527

S I G S A C Review. (Special Interest Group for Security and Audit) (US) **1435**, 805

S I G S A M Bulletin. (Special Interest Group on Symbolic and Algebraic Manipulation) (US ISSN 0163-5824) **3066**

S I G S I M Simuletter. (Special Interest Group on Simulation) (US ISSN 0163-6103) **1435**

S I G S O C Bulletin *see* S I G C H I Bulletin **4459**

S I G S O F T Software Engineering Notes *see* Software Engineering Notes **1480**

S I G Small Newsletter. (Special Interest Group on Small Computing Systems and Applications) (US ISSN 0272-720X) **1464**

S I G T C Connections. (US) **1691**

S I G U C C S Newsletter. (Special Interest Group on University Computing Centers) (US ISSN 0736-6892) **1400**

S I H Bulletin *see* S I H Magazin **2449**

S I H Magazin. (Schweizerisches Institut fuer Hauswirtschaft) (SZ) **2449**

S I H O L S *see* Amsterdam Studies in the Theory and History of Linguistic Science. Series 3: Studies in the History of the Language Sciences **2802**

S I I - Socialist International Information *see* Socialist Affairs **3926**

S I Informationen. (GW ISSN 0344-8789) **2303**

S I K Annual Report. (Svenska Livsmedelsinstitutet (SIK)) (SW) **2081**

S I K Information. (Svenska Livsmedelsinstitutet (SIK)) (SW) **2081**

S I L - A A B Bibliography *see* S I L - A A I B Bibliography **2856**

S I L - A A I B Bibliography. (Summer Institute of Linguistics, Australian Aborigines and Islanders Branch) (AT ISSN 1031-5020) **2856**, 411

S I L - A A I B Occasional Papers. (Summer Institute of Linguistics, Australian Aborigines and Islanders Branch) (AT ISSN 1036-1243) **2839**, 248, 1686, 1759

S I L News *see* Individual Liberty **3898**

S I L Publications in Linguistics *see* Summer Institute of Linguistics and The University of Texas at Arlington Publications in Linguistics **2846**

S I M. (Small Industries Magazine) (II) **1117**

S I M Boletin de Informacion *see* Informacion Iberoamericana **4089**

†S I M - I M Exchange. (Society for Information Management) (US) **5272**

S I M Network. (Society for Information Management) (US) **1457**

S I M Now. (Sudan Interior Mission) (CN ISSN 0711-6683) **4200**

S I M Spectrum *see* Executive Brief **1456**

S I N. (Studies in Nonviolence) (UK) **3971**

S I N E T. (US ISSN 0885-6729) **4448**

S I N Information *see* S I N - Staedtebauinstitut. Information **2495**

S I N Jahresberichte *see* S I N - Staedtebauinstitut. Jahresberichte **2495**

†S I N Medical Newsletter. (Schweizerisches Institut fuer Nuklearforschung) (SZ) **5272**

†S I N Newsletter. (Schweizerisches Institut fuer Nuklearforschung) (SZ) **5272**

S I N - Staedtebauinstitut. Information. (GW) **2495**

S I N - Staedtebauinstitut. Jahresberichte. (GW) **2495**

S I N - Staedtebauinstitut. Schriftenreihe. (GW ISSN 0078-2807) **2495**

S I N - Staedtebauinstitut. Studienhefte. (GW ISSN 0078-2815) **2495**

S I N - Staedtebauinstitut. Werkberichte.(GW ISSN 0078-2823) **2495**

†S I O R Reports. (Society of Industrial and Office Realtors) (US ISSN 0894-5594) **5272**

S I P E. (Servizio Stampa Educazione e Sviluppo) (IT ISSN 0391-8599) **1715**

S I P R I Chemical & Biological Warfare Studies. (Stockholm International Peace Research Institute) (UK ISSN 0267-2537) **3971**

S I P R I Yearbook: World Armaments and Disarmament. (Stockholm International Peace Research Institute) (UK) **3971**

S I P - Siebdruck Infopost. (GW) **4005**

S I R *see* School Intervention Report **1244**

S I R O W Newsletter. (Southwest Institute for Research on Women) (US) **4852**

S.I.S. Chronology & Catastrophism Workshop. (Society for Interdisciplinary Studies) (UK ISSN 0951-5984) **1579**, 369, 3660

S.I.S.F. Documenti. (Societa Italiana di Scienze Farmaceutiche) (IT ISSN 0081-0703) **3742**

S I S Review *see* Chronology & Catastrophism Review **1557**

S.I.S. Workshop *see* S.I.S. Chronology & Catastrophism Workshop **1579**

S I T R A M Results Generaux: Trafic Interieur - Trafic International *see* Systeme d'Information sur les Transports de Marchandises: Resultats Generaux, Trafic Interieur et International **921**

S I T R A M Traffic International Resultats Trimestriels. (FR) **4666**

S I U S A News *see* Notes from S I U S A **246**

S.J. Hall Lectureship in Industrial Forestry. (US ISSN 0080-5092) **2107**

S J-Nytt. (Statens Jaernvaegars Huvudkontor) (SW ISSN 0037-5985) **4714**, 4785

S J R *see* Jazznytt **3558**

S K A V - Fachblatt. (SZ) **4418**

S K M. (Schweizer Kontakt) (SZ) **4448**, 2956

S. Klein Newsletter on Computer Graphics. (US ISSN 0731-9207) **1423**

S L. (Studentski List) (CI ISSN 0039-288X) **1660**

S L *see* Soviet Literature **2962**

S L A D E Journal *see* Print **4003**

S L A News *see* Scottish Libraries **2783**

S L A T E Newsletter. (Support for the Learning and Teaching of English) (US) **1759**

S L A Triennial Salary Survey. (Special Libraries Association) (US) **2782**

S L B Kurier. (Saechsische Landesbibliothek) (GW ISSN 0863-0682) **2782**

S L C S *see* Studies in Language Companion Series **2845**

S L F Information. (Seminarielaererforeningen) (DK ISSN 0108-3856) **1660**

S L J, School Library Journal *see* School Library Journal **2783**

S L U - E I S S I F Newsletter. (Saint Louis University, Extension Institute for Small-Scale Industries Foundation) (PH ISSN 0115-8341) **1716**, 689

S L U Journal of Medicine. (Saint Louis University) (PH) **3150**

S M A C N A Convention Daily. (Sheet Metal & Air Conditioning Contractors of North America) (US) **631**, 2303

S M A R C Monitor *see* U S M A R C Monitor **125**

S M A T V News. (Satellite Master Antenna TV) (US ISSN 0734-5399) **1379**

S M A - the African Missionary. (IE) **4274**

S M A Weighlog. (Scale Manufacturers Association) (US) **3448**

S M Archives *see* Solid Mechanics Archives **4344**

†S.M.B.A. Collected Reprints. (Scottish Marine Biological Association) (UK ISSN 0080-8121) **5272**

S M E A *see* Maskin - Aktuelt **3412**

S M E A. Journal *see* Cadenza **3543**

S M E A. Newsletter *see* Cadenza **3543**

S M F A. (Stores, Menuiseries, Fermetures et Protections Solaires, Amenagements) (FR ISSN 0761-9634) **631**, 640

S M I L Quarterly Journal of Linguistic Calculus *see* Linguistic Calculation **2826**

S M M *see* S I **2089**

S.M.M.B. Bulletin *see* Milk Bulletin **201**

S M M T Buyers Guide. (Society of Motor Manufacturers and Traders Ltd.) (UK) **4701**

S M N *see* Software Maintenance News **1480**

S M P T E Journal. (Society of Motion Picture and Television Engineers) (US ISSN 0036-1682) **3517**, 1379

S M R *see* Sociological Methods & Research **4451**

S M R C Newsletter. (Southwestern Mission Research Center, Inc.) (US ISSN 0584-5025) **2421**

S M R Commodity Service. (Security Market Research) (US) **962**

S M R Stock Service. (Security Market Research) (US) **962**

S M S G Newsletter. (School Management Study Group) (US ISSN 0048-9441) **1731**

S M - Successful Meetings *see* Successful Meetings **1054**

S M T S Journal - Newsletter. (Saskatchewan Mathematics Teachers' Society) (CN ISSN 0316-5779) **3054**, 1759

S M T T *see* Surface Mount Technology Today **1922**

S M T Trends. (Surface Mount Technology) (US ISSN 0890-7900) **3651**, 1052, 2524

S M U V Zeitung. (Schweizerischer Metall- und Uhrenarbeitnehmer-Verband) (SZ) **3419**

S M Y A L News. (Sexual Minority Youth Assistance League, Inc.) (US ISSN 0895-3120) **2457**, 1243

S N *see* Rivista di Suinicoltura **225**

S N A A Newsletter *see* Hand in Hand **3278**

S N A Boletin de Mercado. (Sociedad Nacional de Agricultura) (CL) **118**

S N A Boletino Economico. (Sociedad Nacional de Agricultura) (CL) **118**, 689

†S N A Communications Report. (Systems Network Architecture) (US ISSN 1040-1393) **5272**

S N A P. Bulletin. (Society of National Association Publishers) (US) **4136**, 1301

S N A P. Buyers' Guide. (Society of National Association Publishers) (US) **4136**, 1301

S N A P Shot. (Society of National Association Publishers) (US) **4136**

S N A Perspective. (Systems Network Architecture) (US ISSN 0270-7284) **1438**

S N A Vocero Agricola. (Sociedad Nacional de Agricultura) (CL) **118**

S N Distribution Study of Grocery Store Sales. (US) **2081**, 1052, 2094

S N E A Impact: The Student Voice of the United Teaching Profession. (Student National Education Association) (US ISSN 0195-153X) **1660**

S N E C M A *see* S N E C M A Informations **61**

S N E C M A Informations. (Societe Nationale d'Etude et de Construction de Moteurs d'Aviation) (FR ISSN 0750-7569) **61**

S N E S U P Bulletin. (Syndicat National de l'Enseignement Superieur) (FR) **1716**

S N G A N S *see* Sylloge Nummorum Graecorum **3602**

S N I C Bulletin. (Singapore National Institute of Chemistry) (SI) **1187**

S N I: Selective Notification of Information *see* N I J Reports **1518**

S N M Newsline *see* Journal of Nuclear Medicine **3359**

S O A P. (Selly Oak Alternative Paper) (UK ISSN 0261-1953) **2882**

S O C M A Newsletter. (Synthetic Organic Chemical Manufacturers Association) (US) **1187**

S O C M Sentinel. (Save Our Cumberland Mountains) (US) **1967**

S O D I P A. (Sociaal Dienstbetoon Voor Het Personeel der Stad Antwerpen) (BE) **4073**

†S O E - Bois. (Service d'Observation Economique) (FR) **5272**

S O I-Bilanz. (Schweizerisches Ost-Institut) (SZ) **3924**

S O L Etter. (Society of Logistics Engineers) (US ISSN 0747-623X) **4608**, 61

S O L I N E W S. (Southeastern Library Network, Inc.) (US ISSN 0193-273X) **2799**

▼S O L O. (Surviving Our Leukemia on Our Own) (US) **3202**, 4045

S O P A Newsletter. (US ISSN 0888-9570) **284**

S O R T Bulletin. (Staff Organizations Round Table) (US) **2782**

S O S Amitie France. Bulletin National. (FR ISSN 0003-1887) **4418**

†S.O.S. Directory. (US ISSN 0276-6701) **5272**

S O S Kinderdorf International. (AU) **4418**, 1243

S O S Kinderdorfbote. (AU ISSN 0023-1509) **4418**, 1243

S O S Messenger *see* S O S Kinderdorf International **4418**

S O S Newsletter *see* Singles Outreach Services Newsletter **4363**

S O S P Noticias *see* Sindicato dos Odontologistas do Estado de Sao Paulo. Noticias **3242**

S O S Press *see* S T O P Press **1979**

S O S S I Journal. (Scouts on Stamps Society International) (US) **3757**, 1243

S O V A News *see* Inside Out **5214**

S O W. (Save Our World) (US ISSN 0279-6716) **4200**

S P A C E S. (Saving and Preserving Art and Cultural Environments) (US ISSN 0748-8378) **357**

S P A F A S W A P *see* Spafaswap **5281**

S P A I D News. (Society for the Prevention of Asbestosis and Industrial Diseases) (UK ISSN 0144-4301) **3621**

†S.P.A.N. (State Planning Authority News) (AT) **5272**

S P A News. (Screen Printing Association (UK) Ltd.) (UK) **4005**

S P A R C Jimu-kyokuho. (Space Research Co-Operative Association) (JA) **369**, 61

S P A Water Landing Directory. (Seaplane Pilots Association) (US ISSN 0894-5667) **61**, 4677

S P C - I L O Reports on Migration, Employment and Development in the South Pacific. (South Pacific Commission) (NL) **3987**

S P C N I Almanac. (Society for Pacific Coast Native Iris) (US) **2138**

S P Computer Magazine. (IT) **1907**, 1379, 1400

S P E *see* Scientia Paedagogica Experimentalis **1662**

S P E C Kit. (Systems and Procedures Exchange Center) (US ISSN 0160-3582) **2782**

S P E Drilling Engineering. (Society of Petroleum Engineers, Inc.) (US ISSN 0885-9744) **3700**

S P E E A Spotlite. (Seattle Professional Engineering Employees Association) (US) **1836**, 2588

S P E Formation Evaluation. (Society of Petroleum Engineers, Inc.) (US ISSN 0885-923X) **3700**

†S P E L. (Selected Publications in European Languages) (UK ISSN 0307-5354) **5272**

S P E L D Bulletin. (Specific Learning Difficulties Association of Victoria) (AT) **1741**

S P E L D Information. (Societe de Promotion a l'Etranger du Livre de Droit (S.P.E.L.D.)) (FR ISSN 0038-7282) **4395**

S P

S P E L D News. (Specific Learning Difficulties Association of New South Wales) (AT) **1741**

S P E Monograph Series. (Society of Professors of Education) (US ISSN 0882-1100) **1660**

S P E Production Engineering. (Society of Petroleum Engineers, Inc.) (US ISSN 0885-9221) **3700**

S P E R Annuaire. (Syndicat des Industries de Materiel Professionnel Electronique et Radioelectrique) (FR) **1778**, 1360

S P E Reservoir Engineering. (Society of Petroleum Engineers, Inc.) (US ISSN 0885-9248) **3700**

S P E X. (Self-Publishers Exchange) (US ISSN 0730-2223) **4136**

S P F E Newsletter. (Society of Photo Finishing Engineers) (US) **3796**

S P I C. (SP ISSN 0036-1852) **4785**, 4677

S P I E Optical Engineering Reports see O E Reports **3856**

S P I Membership Directory and Buyer's Guide. (Society of the Plastics Industry, Inc.) (US) **3868**

S P N E A News. (Society for the Preservation of N E Antiquities) (US) **2321**, 343

S P N E A's Historic Houses in New England. (Society for the Preservation of New England Antiquities) (US) **306**, 2421

S P O R T S. (Science Periodical on Research and Technology in Sport) (CN) **4486**

S P R C Newsletter. (Social Policy Research Centre) (AT) **4418**, 4448

S P R C Reports and Proceedings. (Social Policy Research Centre) (AT) **4418**, 4448

S P R E P Environmental Case Studies. (South Pacific Regional Environment Programme) (WS) **1967**, 1496

S P R E P Fact Sheet. (South Pacific Regional Environment Programme) (WS) **1967**, 1496

S P R E P Meeting Reports. (South Pacific Regional Environment Programme) (WS) **1967**, 1496

S P R E P Occasional Papers. (WS) **1967**, 1496

S P R E P Topic Review. (WS) **1967**, 1496

S P R E P Training Reports. (WS) **1967**, 1496

S P R I Informerar see Sweden. Sjukvaardens och Socialvaardens Planerings- och Rationaliseringsinstitut. S P R I Informerar **4113**

S P R I Litteraturtjaenst see Sweden. Sjukvaardens och Socialvaardens Planerings- och Rationaliseringsinstitut. S P R I Litteraturtjaenst **4119**

S P R I Raad 7. see Sweden. Sjukvaardens och Socialvaardens Planerings- och Rationaliseringsinstitut. S P R I Raad 7 **5286**

S P R I Rapport see Sweden. Sjukvaardens och Socialvaardens Planerings- och Rationaliseringsinstitut. S P R I Rapport **4113**

S P R Newsletter. (Society for Psychical Research) (UK) **3671**

S P S Bulletin. (Separation Processes Service) (UK) **1860**

S P S C Letter. (Saharan Peoples Support Committee) (US ISSN 0891-608X) **3947**

S P S E. Annual Conference. Paper Summaries (Year). (Society for Imaging Science and Technology (SPSE)) (US) **3796**, 1423, 1836, 3857

S P S M & H. (Shakespeare, Petrarch, Sidney, Milton & Hopkins) (US ISSN 0891-2378) **3004**

S P: Sociological Practice see Sociological Practice **4451**

S P U M S Journal. (South Pacific Underwater Medicine Society Incorporated) (AT ISSN 0813-1988) **3151**

S P W. (Sozialistische Politik und Wirtschaft) (GW ISSN 0170-4613) **3924**, 4448

S P W A O Showcase. (Small Press Writers and Artists Organization) (US) **2956**

†S Q. (Syntax Quarterly) (US ISSN 0734-0133) **5272**

S R A Directory see State and Regional Associations of the United States **1154**

S R A Journal see Society of Research Administrators. Journal **1028**

S R A Newsletter. (Society of Research Administrators, Inc.) (US) **1027**

S R C Blue Book of 5-Trend Cycli-Graphs. (Securities Research Company) (US ISSN 8750-2356) **962**

S R C Brown Book of 5-Trend O-T-C Charts. (Securities Research Company) (US ISSN 1042-1610) **962**

S R C Green Book of 5-Trend 35-Year Charts. (Securities Research Company) (US ISSN 0884-8475) **962**

S R C Red Book of 5-Trend Security Charts. (Securities Research Company) (US ISSN 8750-2461) **962**

S R Construccion see Servicio Referativo de la Construccion **638**

S R D G Newsletter see S D A Newsletter **3987**

▼S R D S: Bullet. (Standard Rate and Data Service, Inc.) (US) **1052**

S R D S Media and Market Planner. (Standard Rate and Data Service) (US) **38**, 1052

S R D S Report. (Standard Rate and Data Service, Inc.) (US) **38**, 1052

▼S R D S Tradeshow Catalog. (US) **1052**, 3394

S R Dallas see S R Texas **2278**

S R E A Briefs see Briefs **5153**

S R F Resume see Resume **38**

S R H E Bulletin see S R H E News **1716**

S R H E News. (Society for Research into Higher Education) (UK) **1716**

S R I M see Selected Research in Microfiche **4342**

S R I S Newsletter. (Science Reference and Information Service) (UK ISSN 0951-4635) **2782**, 4136

S R Info. (Saarlaendischer Rundfunk) (GW) **1360**

S R L News see S R I S Newsletter **2782**

S R O A Newsletter see Radiation Oncology News **3361**

S R R T Newsletter. (Social Responsibilities Round Table) (US ISSN 0749-1670) **2882**, 2782

S R Texas. (Senior Residents) (US) **2278**

S S A M. (Soldier, Sailor, Airman, Marine) (US) **3470**

S S C Booknews. (Spiritual Studies Center) (US ISSN 0730-2371) **4213**

S S C I see Social Sciences Citation Index **4396**

S S C I - J C R see Social Sciences Citation Index Journal Citation Reports **4396**

S S D A Newsletter. (Social Science Data Archives) (IS) **4385**

S S E U News see Unionist **2591**

S S I. (Small Scale Industries) (II) **1117**

S S I see Short Story International **2959**

S S I A and S S P H M Newsletter see Scottish Industrial History **4608**

S S I D Liaison Bulletin. (Social Science Information and Documentation) (FI ISSN 0358-7088) **4385**

S S J see Sociology of Sport Journal **4452**

S S M Arrt. (School Science & Mathematics Association, Inc.) (US) **1759**, 3054, 4337

S S O R Yokoshu/Proceedings of S S O R. (Summer Symposium of Operation Research) (JA) **1405**, 3063

S S P see Studies in Slavic Literature and Poetics **2966**

S S P C Bulletin. (Steel Structures Painting Council) (US) **3655**

S S P I Update. (Society of Satellite Professionals International) (US) **1379**

S S R see Sport Science Review **3373**

S S R C Data Archive Bulletin see E S R C Data Archive Bulletin **4370**

S S R - Tidningen. (SW ISSN 0283-1910) **4418**

S S R - Tidningen Socionomen see S S R - Tidningen **4418**

S S S A Special Publication Series. (Soil Science Society of America) (US ISSN 0081-1904) **191**

S S S L see Society for the Study of Southern Literature. Newsletter **2961**

S S S Newsletter (Simulation in the Service of Society) see Simulation (San Diego) **1436**

S Select see Infocus (Philadelphia) **1430**

S.Sh.A. (RU ISSN 0321-2068) **2421**

S T A: Its Roles and Activities. (Science and Technology Agency) (JA) **4608**, 4337

S T A L. (Sciences et Techniques de l'Animal de Laboratoire) (FR ISSN 0339-722X) **3263**

S T A News see Catalyst (Vancouver) **1746**

S T A R. (Scientific and Technical Aerospace Reports) (US ISSN 0036-8741) **66**, 22

†S T D Fact Sheet. (Sexually Transmitted Diseases) (US) **5272**

S T D: Japanese Journal of the Sexually Transmitted Diseases. (JA) **3249**

S T E W E A G Rundschau. (Steirische Wasserkraft- und Elektrizitaets-AG) (AU) **1907**

S T F I Meddelande. Series A. (Svenska Traeforskningsinstitutet (STFI)) (SW ISSN 0348-2650) **3666**

S T F M Messenger. (Society of Teachers of Family Medicine) (US) **3151**, 1759

S T F M Newsletter see S T F M Messenger **3151**

S T I Review. (Science Technology Industry) (FR ISSN 1010-5247) **4608**

S T I Revue see S T I Review **4608**

S T L E Tribology Transactions. (Society of Tribologists and Lubrication Engineers) (US) **1860**

S T L: The Art of Living in St. Louis. (US ISSN 8750-877X) **2233**

†S T - Log. (US) **5272**

S T - Magazin. (GW ISSN 0934-3237) **1419**

S T O P Press. (Society to Overcome Pollution, Inc.) (CN ISSN 0705-1212) **1979**

S T P Pharma see S T P Pharma Sciences **3742**

S T P Pharma see S T P Pharma Techniques Pratiques Reglementations **3742**

S T P Pharma Sciences. (Sciences Techniques Pratiques) (FR ISSN 1157-1489) **3742**

S T P Pharma Techniques Pratiques Reglementations. (Sciences Techniques Pratiques) (FR ISSN 1157-1497) **3742**

†S T V Guide. (Satellite Television) (US ISSN 0885-6745) **5272**

S T World. (US ISSN 0888-1057) **1455**, 1479

S U C Bulletin. (Society of Cartographers) (UK ISSN 0036-1984) **2262**

S U D E N E Plano de Acao see Brazil. Superintendencia do Desenvolvimento do Nordeste. S U D E N E Plano de Acao **2484**

S U F O I. News. (Skandinavisk U F O Information) (DK) **61**

S U G I A see Sprache und Geschichte in Afrika **2843**

S U K O V S Nuus. see P A C O F S News **4636**

S U M A. (UY ISSN 0797-0064) **883**, 898, 993

S.U.N. (Solar Utilization News) (US) **1811**

S U N A. (Sudan News Agency) (SJ) **2218**

S U N A Daily Bulletin see S U N A **2218**

S U N Y L A Newsletter. (State University of New York Librarians Association) (US ISSN 0731-7883) **2782**

S U N Y Research (Year) see State University of New York. Research **1665**

S.U. News. (Scripture Union (A.C.T.)) (AT ISSN 0725-6140) **4248**

S U S S. (Sydney University Speleological Society) (AT) **1579**

S U T Bulletin. (Science University of Tokyo) (JA ISSN 0289-7016) **4608**, 1759, 4337

S U T Journal of Mathematics. (Science University of Tokyo) (JA) **3054**

S und F see Sicherheit und Frieden **3972**

S und H Report see Sanitaer und Heizungs Report **2303**

S V see Schoen - Visie **4361**

†S V Leveringsbetingelser og Proevningsmetoder. (Statens Vejlaboratorium) (DK ISSN 0106-3111) **5272**

S V M Mac. (Science et Vie Micro) (FR) **1474**, 1464

S V M Macintosh see S V M Mac **1474**

S.V.M. Science et Vie Micro. (FR ISSN 0760-6516) **1464**, 1474

S V Zeitung. (Sondenhaeuser Verband) (GW) **1323**, 3579

S W A P see Review - S W A P **4082**

S.W.A.T. Magazine. (Special Weapons and Tactics) (US) **1522**

S W B - Information. (Schweizerischer Werkbund) (SZ) **306**

S W E B News. (South Western Electricity) (UK) **1907**

S W F Journal see Suedwestfunk Journal **1360**

S W I B see Social Work Information Bulletin **4388**

S W I E E C O Record of Technical Papers see I E E E Region 5 Conference. Record **1895**

S W L. (Shortwave Listener) (US ISSN 0162-5934) **1360**, 1301

†S W L Swapper. (US) **5272**

S W R C Newsletter see S P R C Newsletter **4418**

S W R C Reports and Proceedings see S P R C Reports and Proceedings **4418**

S W S - Rundschau. (Sozialwissenschaftliche Studiengesellschaft) (AU) **4385**, 4448

S Y L F Nytt see Tidskrift foer Yngre Laekare **995**

S Z. (Sozialwirtschaftliche Korrespondenz) (AU ISSN 0036-1585) **3924**, 883

S Z F-Bulletin see Zukunftsforschung **4393**

Saab-Scania Technical Notes see Saab Technical Notes **61**

Saab Technical Notes. (SW ISSN 0080-5149) **61**

Saagrevyn see Skog & Saag **2117**

Saagverken/Sawmills. (SW ISSN 0036-259X) **2117**

Saagverken - Traevarunindustrin see Saagverken **2117**

Saarberg. (GW) **3495**, 1795

Saarbruecker Beitraege zur Altertumskunde. (GW ISSN 0080-5181) **2321**

Saarbruecker Bergmannskalender. (GW) **3495**

Saarbruecker Hefte. (GW ISSN 0036-2115) **2882**

†Saarbruecker Studien zur Musikwissenschaft. (GW ISSN 0080-519X) **5272**

Saarlaendischer Arbeitnehmer see Arbeitnehmer **2580**

Saarlaendischer Rundfunk Info see S R Info **1360**

Saarlaendisches Aerzteblatt. (GW ISSN 0340-644X) **3151**, 3242

Saarlaendisches Bauernblatt. (GW) **118**

Saastopankki. (FI ISSN 0036-2123) **798**

†Saat- und Pflanzgut. (GW ISSN 0323-4436) 5273
Sabado. (PO) 2214
Al-Sabah. (UA) 2186
Al-Sabah/Morning. (JO) 2208
Sabah. Forest Department. Annual Report. (MY ISSN 0080-5211) 2107
Sabah. Marine Department. Annual Report. (MY ISSN 0080-522X) 4737
Sabah al-Khair. (UA) 2882
Sabah Society. Journal. (MY ISSN 0036-2131) 4337
Sabato Sera. (IT) 2022
Sabazia. (IT) 2385, 284, 343
Sabbath Recorder. (US ISSN 0036-214X) 4248
Sabbath Sentinel. (US) 4288
Sabbath Watchman. (US ISSN 0098-9517) 4248
Sabena Revue. (BE ISSN 0036-2158) 4803
Sabena Sphere. (BE) 4803
Saber Leer. (SP ISSN 0213-6449) 2956
†Sabermetric Review. (US ISSN 0889-2997) 5273
Sabouraudia: Journal of Medical and Veterinary Mycology see Journal of Medical & Veterinary Mycology 3221
Sabretache. (AT ISSN 0048-8933) 3470, 2321
†Sabrina. (IT) 5273
Sacerdozio Regale. (IT) 4200
Sachguetererzeugung Schnellbericht. (AU) 1167, 2525, 4628
Sachitra Sandhani. (BG) 2882
Sachunterricht und Mathematik in der Grundschule. (GW ISSN 0170-0944) 1759, 3054
Sackville Tribune-Post. (CN ISSN 0049-4658) 2179
Sacra Doctrina. (IT ISSN 0036-2190) 4200
†Sacramento Business. (US ISSN 0036-2204) 5273
Sacramento Magazine. (US ISSN 0191-8796) 2233
Sacramento Newsletter. (US ISSN 0486-8161) 3924, 2676
Sacramento Observer. (US ISSN 0036-2212) 2022
†Sacramento Sanyo User's Group Newsletter. (US) 5273
Sacramento Valley Union Labor Bulletin.(US ISSN 0036-2247) 2589
Sacred Art Journal. (US ISSN 0741-9163) 343, 4200
▼Sacred Fire. (CN) 3004
Sacred Heart Messenger. (IE) 4275
Sacred Music. (US ISSN 0036-2255) 3579
Sacred Name Broadcaster. (US) 4288
Sacred Octagon. (US) 259, 4701
Sacred Organ Journal. (US ISSN 0036-2263) 3579
Sada-a-tarbiya. (IS) 1660
Sada al-Usbou' (BA) 2173
Saddle and Bridle. (US ISSN 0036-2271) 4537
Saddle and Striker. (CN ISSN 0048-895X) 2441
Saddle Horse Report. (US) 4537
Sadelmager-og Tapetserer Tidende. (DK ISSN 0036-228X) 2561, 2555
Sadhana. (II ISSN 0256-2499) 4337
Sadie's Chatter. (US) 2956, 2449
Sadler's Wells Theatre Programme. (UK) 4637, 3579
Sado Hakubutsukan Kenkyu Hokoku/ Publications from the Sado Museum.(JA) 4337, 3532
Sado Marine Biological Station. Annual Report see Sado Marine Biological Station. Report 454
Sado Marine Biological Station. Report/ Niigata Daigaku Rigakubu Fuzoku Sado Rinkai Jikkenjo Kenkyu Hokoku. (JA ISSN 0289-6389) 454
▼Sadovod K.M.K. (RU) 118
Sadovodstvo see Sadovodstvo i Vinogradarstvo 2138
Sadovodstvo i Vinogradarstvo. (RU) 2138

Saechsische Akademie der Wissenschaften, Leipzig. Jahrbuch. (GW ISSN 0080-5262) 4338
Saechsische Akademie der Wissenschaften, Leipzig. Mathematisch-Naturwissenschaftliche Klasse. Abhandlungen. (GW ISSN 0365-6470) 4338, 3054
Saechsische Akademie der Wissenschaften, Leipzig. Mathematisch-Naturwissenschaftliche Klasse. Sitzungsberichte. (GW ISSN 0371-327X) 4338, 3054
Saechsische Akademie der Wissenschaften, Leipzig. Philologisch-Historische Klasse. Abhandlungen. (GW ISSN 0080-5297) 2839, 2321
Saechsische Akademie der Wissenschaften, Leipzig. Philologisch-Historische Klasse. Sitzungsberichte. (GW ISSN 0138-3957) 2839, 2321
Saechsische Bibliographie. (GW ISSN 0419-7305) 411
Saechsische Heimatblaetter. (GW ISSN 0486-8234) 2385
Saechsische Landesbibliothek. Bibliographie Illustrierte Buecher der Deutschen Demokratischen Republik.(GW ISSN 0232-5616) 4142
Saechsische Landesbibliothek. Neuerwerbungen. (GW) 2782
Saechsische Landesbibliothek Kurier see S L B Kurier 2782
Saecula Spiritalia. (GW ISSN 0343-2009) 2321, 2514
Saeculum. (GW ISSN 0080-5319) 2321
Saelgeren. (DK) 1052
Saen Sanuk. (TH) 2220
Saenger-Taschenkalender. (GW) 3579
Saenger- und Musikantenzeitung. (GW ISSN 0036-2328) 3579
Saenger-Zeitung. (US ISSN 0036-2336) 3579
Saengmulhak/Biology. (KN) 454
Saerrakke. (DK) 3517
Saeugetierkundliche Mitteilungen. (GW ISSN 0036-2344) 591
Safari. (US) 4555
Safari. (KE ISSN 0036-2352) 4785
Safarir. (CN ISSN 0835-7919) 2179
Safe & Vault Technology. (US) 643
Safe Cycling. (US ISSN 1051-0613) 4520
Safe Deposit Bulletin. (US ISSN 0036-2379) 798
Safe Driver. (US ISSN 0486-8323) 4656
Safe Driver. (UK ISSN 0036-2387) 4701
Safe Journal. (US) 4112
Safe Worker. (US) 3621
SAFECO Agent. (US ISSN 0036-2409) 2542
Safeguard. (AT) 1243
Safer (Volkswagen) Motoring see V W Motoring 4704
Safety see New South Wales. Department of Industrial Relations and Technology. Safety 989
Safety. see Sigurnost 4112
Safety & Health. (US ISSN 0891-1797) 4112
Safety and Health at Work. (UN ISSN 1010-7053) 3623, 22
The Safety & Health Practitioner. (UK ISSN 0265-4792) 4112
Safety and Hygiene of Work. see Bezpecnost a Hygiena Prace 2580
Safety & Industry Law Service N S W. (AT) 2676, 3621
Safety and Rescue. (UK) 4112
Safety and Security. see Skydd & Saekerhet 2034
Safety & Security for Supervisors. (US ISSN 1040-4236) 3621, 1527
Safety at Sea. (UK ISSN 0142-0666) 4737
Safety Briefs. (US ISSN 0036-245X) 4112
Safety Canada. (CN ISSN 0048-8968) 4112
Safety Compliance Letter. (US) 3621
Safety Concepts see Health and Safety at Work 4102
Safety Education. (UK) 4112

†Safety Evaluation and Regulation of Chemicals. (SZ ISSN 0256-730X) 5273
†Safety Forum. (US) 5273
Safety in Australia see Health and Safety at Work 4102
Safety in Industry see Safety Management 3621
Safety, Industrial Relations, and Government Affairs Special Report. (US) 4747, 4656
Safety Management/Veiligheidsbestuur. (SA ISSN 0377-8592) 3621
Safety Management. (US) 3621, 1027
†Safety Management Newsletter. (US) 5273
Safety News (Denver). (US ISSN 0270-4447) 4828, 191, 1925, 3621
Safety Newsletter: Aerospace Section see Aerospace Newsletter 44
Safety Newsletter: Automotive, Tooling, Metalworking and Associated Industries see Automotive, Tooling, Metalworking, and Associated Industries. Newsletter 3615
Safety Newsletter: Cement, Quarry and Mineral Aggregates Section see Cement, Quarry and Mineral Aggregates Newsletter 3615
Safety Newsletter: Chemical Section see Chemical Newsletter 3615
Safety Newsletter: Coal Mining Section see Coal Mining Newsletter 3616
Safety Newsletter: Construction Section see Construction Newsletter 3616
Safety Newsletter: Fertilizer and Agricultural Chemical Section see Fertilizer and Agricultural Chemical Newsletter 3616
Safety Newsletter: Food and Beverage Section see Food & Beverage Newsletter 3616
Safety Newsletter: Forest Industries Section see Forest Industries Newsletter (Chicago) 3616
Safety Newsletter: Glass and Ceramics Section see Glass and Ceramics Newsletter 5200
Safety Newsletter: Health Care Section see Health Care Newsletter 3617
Safety Newsletter: Marine Section see Marine Newsletter 3619
Safety Newsletter: Metals Section see Metals Newsletter 3619
Safety Newsletter: Mining Section see Mining Newsletter 3619
Safety Newsletter: Occupational Health Nursing Section see Occupational Health Nursing Newsletter 3620
Safety Newsletter: Petroleum Section see Petroleum Newsletter 3620
Safety Newsletter: Power Press and Forging Section see Power Press and Forging Newsletter 3620
Safety Newsletter: Printing and Publishing Section see Printing and Publishing Newsletter 3620
Safety Newsletter: Public Employee Section see Public Employee Newsletter 3620
Safety Newsletter: Public Utilities Section see Public Utilities Newsletter 3621
Safety Newsletter: Railroad Section see Railroad Newsletter 3621
Safety Newsletter: Research and Development see Research and Development Newsletter 3621
Safety Newsletter: Rubber and Plastics Section see Rubber and Plastics Newsletter 3621
Safety Newsletter: Textile Section see Textile Newsletter 3622
Safety Newsletter: Trades and Services Section see Trades and Services Newsletter 3622
Safety Practitioner see The Safety & Health Practitioner 4112
Safety Representative see W R A P 3623
Safety Research News see Lettre d'Information sur la Recherche Hygiene et Securite 3619
Safety Resources. (US) 3621
Safety Science. (NE ISSN 0925-7535) 3621

Safety Science Abstracts Journal see Health and Safety Science Abstracts 4117
Safety Surveyor and Protection see The Safety & Health Practitioner 4112
Safety Update. (CN) 4112
Safety W A. (AT) 3621
Safetymate. (UK) 1967
Safn til Soegu Islands og Islenzkra Bokmennta. (IC ISSN 0558-1257) 2956, 2385
Saga Daigaku Nogakubu Iho/Saga University. Faculty of Agriculture. Bulletin. (JA ISSN 0581-2801) 118
Saga Daigaku Rikogakubu Koho. see Scien Tech 1836
Saga Daigaku Rikogakubu Shuho/Saga University. Faculty of Science and Engineering. Reports. (JA ISSN 0385-6186) 1836, 3054, 3830
Saga-ken Kisho Geppo/Saga Prefecture. Monthly Report of Meteorology. (JA) 3440
Saga och Sed. (SW ISSN 0586-5360) 2058, 284, 2385, 2839
Saga of the Sanpitch. (US) 2421, 2058
Saga Prefecture. Monthly Report of Meteorology. see Saga-ken Kisho Geppo 3440
Saga University. Faculty of Agriculture. Bulletin. see Saga Daigaku Nogakubu Iho 118
Saga University. Faculty of Science and Engineering. Reports. see Saga Daigaku Rikogakubu Shuho 1836
Le Sagamien. (CN ISSN 0226-2169) 2262
Sagamore. (US) 1323
Sagamore Army Materials Research Conference. Proceedings. (US ISSN 0080-5335) 3470
Sagan-Sprottauer Heimatbriefe. (GW ISSN 0036-2573) 2385
▼The Sagarin Review. (US ISSN 1056-2591) 2956
Sage (Cork) see The Gazette (Cork) 1312
Sage: A Scholarly Journal on Black Women. (US ISSN 0741-8639) 4860, 2022, 3947
Sage Annual Reviews of Communication Research. (US ISSN 0099-1414) 1342
Sage Criminal Justice Systems Annual. (US) 1522, 4418
Sage Family Studies Abstracts. (US ISSN 0164-0283) 4458, 22
Sage Library of Social Research. (US) 4385
Sage Notes. (US) 2138
Sage Public Administration Abstracts. (US ISSN 0094-6958) 4082, 22
Sage Race Relations Abstracts. (UK ISSN 0307-9201) 3938, 22, 4458
Sage Series in Cross Cultural Research and Methodology. (US) 4045, 248
Sage Series in Interpersonal Communication. (US) 1342
Sage Studies in International Sociology. (US) 4448
Sage Urban Studies Abstracts. (US ISSN 0090-5747) 2500, 22
Sage Woman. (US) 4852
Sage Yearbooks in Politics and Public Policy. (US) 3924
Sage Yearbooks in Women's Policy Studies. (US) 4852, 421
Sageret: Annuaire General du Batiment et des Travaux Publics see Sageret: Annuaire National du Batiment et des Travaux Publics 631
Sageret: Annuaire National du Batiment et des Travaux Publics. (FR) 631
Sagetrieb. (US ISSN 0735-4665) 3004
Saggi. (IT ISSN 0390-5179) 3353, 1741
▼Saggi di Storia Antica. (IT) 2321
Saggi e Memorie di Storia dell'Arte. (IT ISSN 0080-5394) 343
†Saggi Filosofici. (IT) 5273
Saginaw County Historian. (US) 2421
Sagittarius. see Streletz 2515
Sagittarius see Schuetz-Jahrbuch 3579
Sagners Slavistische Sammlung. (GW) 2839

SAGRADA BIBLIA

Sagrada Biblia. (SP) **4200**
Sagtevrugteboer. see Deciduous Fruit Grower **2125**
Saguaro. (US ISSN 0885-5013) **3004**
Saguaroland Bulletin see Sonoran Quarterly **517**
Saguenayensia. (CN ISSN 0581-295X) **2421**
Sahakar Path. (II) **832**
†Sahamies. (FI ISSN 0036-262X) **5273**
Sahara. (FR ISSN 0036-2638) **3924**
Sahara Info. (GW ISSN 0177-0969) **2334**
Saharan People's Support Committee. Monograph Series. (US) **3947**
Saharan Peoples Support Committee Letter see S P S C Letter **3947**
Saharien. (FR ISSN 0036-2646) **2170**
Sahifat al Makta-Bah. see Egyptian Library Journal **2756**
Sahifat al-Takhtit al-Tarbawi fi al-Bilad al-Arabiyah/Revue de Planification de l'Education dans les Pays Arabes. (LE ISSN 0581-2984) **1660**
Sahifat Al-Tarbiya. (UA ISSN 0036-2654) **1660**
Sahitya Akademi, New Delhi. Report. (II ISSN 0080-5416) **2514**
Sahitya Chinta. (II) **2956**
Sahko-Electricity and Electronics see Sahko - Tele **1907**
Sahko - Tele. (FI) **1907**
Sahkoala. (FI) **1907**
Sahkourakoitsija see Sahkoala **1907**
Sahmatnyj Informator. see Sahovski Informator **4486**
Sahoekwahak/Social Sciences. (KN) **4385**
Sahovki Glasnik. (CI ISSN 0350-2570) **4486**
Sahovska Kompozicija. (YU ISSN 0352-115X) **4486**
Sahovski Informator/Chess Informant/ Sahmatnyj Informator. (YU ISSN 0351-1375) **4486**
Sahs see Sahs Baltija **4486**
Sahs Baltija. (LV) **4486**
Sahy. (MG) **3924**
Sai Suddha. (II) **4215**
Saibokaku Byorigaku Zasshi/Journal of Karyopathology. (JA ISSN 0022-2119) **3202**
Saiensu. (Japanese translation of: Scientific American) (JA ISSN 0386-4324) **4338, 4608**
Saiensupedia. see Sciencepedia **4341**
Saigai no Jittai to Shobo no Genkyo/ Annual Report of Fire and Disaster Prevention. (JA) **2034, 4073**
Saigon Thoi Bao see Lang Van **2011**
Saihhyag Haghoi Ji (Sehur) see Korean Journal of Pharmacognosy **479**
Saikin no Shinyaku/New Drugs in Japan. (JA) **3742**
Sail. (US ISSN 0036-2700) **4528**
†Sailboard News. (US) **5273**
Sailboard Retailer. (US) **4528, 1052**
Sailboat & Equipment Directory. (US ISSN 0148-8732) **4528**
Sailing. (US ISSN 0036-2719) **4528**
Sailing Beat. (CN) **4528**
Sailing Canada. (CN) **4528**
Sailing Scene. (US) **4528**
Sailing World. (US ISSN 0889-4094) **4529**
Sailorman Star Magazine. (US ISSN 1051-063X) **4529, 2676**
Sailplane and Gliding. (UK ISSN 0036-2735) **61**
Sainik Samachar. (II ISSN 0036-2743) **3471**
Sains Malaysiana: Jernal Sains Alam Semula. (MY ISSN 0126-6039) **4338, 3054**
Sa'insu. (PK) **4338**
St. Agnes News. (US) **2469**
St. Andrews Citizen. (UK) **2195**
St. Andrews Review. (US ISSN 0036-2751) **2956, 3005**
St. Ansgar's Bulletin. (US) **4275**
St. Anthony Messenger. (US ISSN 0036-276X) **4275**
St. Augustine's Magazine. (UK) **1716**
St. Bartholomew's Hospital Journal see Barts Journal **2459**

Saint Bonaventure University. Franciscan Institute. Philosophy Series. (US ISSN 0080-5432) **4275**
Saint Bonaventure University. Franciscan Institute. Text Series. (US ISSN 0080-5440) **4275**
St. Camillusbode see Camillusbode **4258**
St. Clair County Genealogical Society. Newsletter. (US) **2163**
St. Clair County Genealogical Society Quarterly. (US ISSN 0882-6528) **2163**
St. Cloud State Chronicle. (US) **1323**
St. Croix Review. (US ISSN 0093-2582) **4448**
St. Croix This Week. (VI) **4785**
†St. David's Day Bilingual Series. (UK) **5273**
St. Dunstan's Annual Report. (UK) **2295**
St. Dunstan's Review. (UK ISSN 0036-2808) **2295**
St. Edward's College Review see Image (Liverpool) **330**
St. Edwards School Chronicle. (UK) **1323**
Saint Fancier. (US) **3713**
St. Francis Xavier University Alumni News. (CN) **1323**
St. Gallen. (SZ ISSN 0036-2832) **4785**
St. Galler Studien zum Privat-, Handels- und Wirtschaftsrecht. (SZ) **2676, 689**
Saint George's Hospital Gazette. (UK ISSN 0036-2840) **2469, 3151**
St. Hallvard. (NO ISSN 0036-2859) **2385**
†St. Hedwigsblatt. (GW ISSN 0487-2088) **5273**
St. Helena and Dependencies Philatelic Society Newsletter. (US) **3757**
Saint Hubert. (FR ISSN 0036-2867) **4555**
Saint Hubert d'Ardenne. (BE) **2321**
Saint John Business Today. (CN ISSN 1184-731X) **839**
St. John Review see St. John World **4112**
Saint John Today see Saint John Business Today **839**
St. John World. (UK) **4112**
Saint John's. (US) **1323, 1716**
St. John's Journal of Medicine. (II ISSN 0970-4221) **3151**
St. John's Law Review. (US ISSN 0036-2905) **2676**
St. John's Reporter. (US) **1716, 1323**
St. John's Review. (US ISSN 0277-4720) **1716, 1323**
St. Joseph's Messenger and Advocate of the Blind. (US) **2295, 4200**
St. Kilda Road Cityscope. (AT) **4160**
St. Kitts Nevis Anguilla National Bank Limited and its Subsidiaries. Annual Report and Accounts. (XI) **798**
Saint-Lambert, l'Annuaire Batiment et Travaux Publics. (FR) **631, 1873**
St. Lawrence. (US) **1716**
St. Lawrence County Historical Association. Quarterly. (US ISSN 0558-1931) **2421**
Saint Lawrence Seaway Authority. Annual Report. (CN ISSN 0581-3298) **4737**
St. Louis. (US ISSN 0272-1279) **2234**
St. Louis Art Museum. Bulletin. (US) **3532**
St. Louis Bar Journal. (US) **2676**
St. Louis Bowling Review. (US ISSN 0193-5321) **4510**
St. Louis Business Journal. (US) **690**
Saint Louis Chronicle. (PH ISSN 0048-8992) **1716**
St. Louis Commerce. (US ISSN 0036-293X) **822**
St. Louis Computing. (US) **1474**
St. Louis Construction News & Review. (US) **631**
St. Louis Countian. (US ISSN 0036-2948) **2575, 2676**
St. Louis Daily Record. (US) **2676**
St. Louis Genealogical Society. News and Notes. (US) **2163**

St. Louis Genealogical Society Quarterly.(US ISSN 0036-2956) **2163**
St. Louis Jewish Light. (US ISSN 0036-2964) **2022, 4226**
St. Louis Journalism Review. (US ISSN 0036-2972) **2575**
St. Louis Labor Tribune see St. Louis - Southern Illinois Labor Tribune **2589**
St. Louis Law Review see Washington University Law Quarterly **2694**
St. Louis Lawyer. (US) **2676**
St. Louis Metropolitan Medicine. (US ISSN 0892-1334) **3242**
St. Louis Nine see S T L: The Art of Living in St. Louis **2233**
St. Louis Post-Dispatch Index. (US ISSN 0893-2417) **2579, 22**
St. Louis Purchaser. (US ISSN 0036-3006) **1052**
St. Louis Review. (US ISSN 0036-3022) **4275, 2882**
St. Louis - Southern Illinois Labor Tribune. (US) **2589**
Saint Louis University Journal of Medicine see S L U Journal of Medicine **3150**
Saint Louis University Law Journal. (US ISSN 0036-3030) **2676**
Saint Louis University Newsletter see S L U - E I S S I F Newsletter **1716**
Saint Louis University Public Law Review. (US ISSN 0898-8404) **2676**
Saint Louis University Research Journal.(PH ISSN 0036-3014) **2514, 4338**
St. Lucia. Statistical Department. Annual Bulletin on C A R I C O M Trade. (XK) **883**
St. Lucia. Statistical Department. Annual Migration and Tourism Statistics. (XK) **3995, 4800**
†St. Lucia. Statistical Department. Annual Overseas Trade Report: Part 1. (XK) **5273**
St. Lucia. Statistical Department. Annual Overseas Trade Report: Part 2. (XK) **737, 920**
St. Lucia. Statistical Department. Annual Statistical Digest. (XK) **4585**
St. Lucia. Statistical Department. Monthly Consumer Price Index. (XK) **883**
St. Lucia. Statistical Department. Quarterly Bulletin on C A R I C O M Trade. (XK) **883**
St. Lucia. Statistical Department. Quarterly Migration & Tourism Statistics. (XK) **3995, 4800**
St. Lucia. Statistical Department. Quarterly Overseas Trade Reports. (XK) **737, 920**
St. Lucia. Statistical Department. Statistical Pocket Digest. (XK) **4585**
St. Lucia. Statistical Department. Vital Statistics Report. (XK) **3995**
St. Luke's Journal of Theology. (US) **4200**
St. Maarten Business Journal. (NE) **690**
St. Maarten Journal see St. Maarten Business Journal **690**
St. Marianna University School of Medicine. Bulletin (General Education). see Sei Marianna Ika Daigaku Kiyo. Ippan Kyoiku **1697**
St. Mark's Review. (AT ISSN 0036-3103) **4200**
St. Martin's Review. (UK ISSN 0036-3111) **4248**
St. Mary Armenian Church. Bulletin. (US) **4288**
St. Mary's Hospital Gazette. (UK ISSN 0036-312X) **3151**
St. Mary's Law Journal. (US ISSN 0581-3441) **2676**
Saint Mary's University. Atlantic Region Geographical Studies. (CN ISSN 0831-8093) **2262, 118**
Saint Mary's University. Occasional Papers in Geography. (CN ISSN 0831-8107) **2262, 1548**
Saint Mary's University. Studies in Marine and Coastal Geography. (CN ISSN 0832-6266) **2262, 2048**
Saint Mary's University Journal. (CN ISSN 0036-3138) **1323**

St. Mawr. (US) **3005**
St. Paul Legal Ledger. (US) **2676**
St. Paul, Minnesota. Metropolitan Transit Commission. Annual Report see St. Paul, Minnesota. Twin Cities Area Metropolitan Transit Commission. Annual Report **4701**
St. Paul, Minnesota. Twin Cities Area Metropolitan Transit Commission. Annual Report. (US) **4701**
St. Paul Urban League. Annual Report. (US) **4418**
St. Paul's Economic Review/Rikkyo Keizaigaku Kenkyu. (JA ISSN 0035-5356) **690**
St. Paul's Printer. (US ISSN 0038-8815) **4200**
St. Paul's Review of Science. see Rikkyo Daigaku Kenkyu Hokoku. Shizen Kagaku **4336**
St. Peter the Aleut Orthodox Educational Series. (US ISSN 0897-7690) **4288**
Saint Peter's. (US) **1323, 4275**
▼St. Petersburg News. (US) **4785**
†St. Pierre Park Hotel Magazine. (UK) **5273**
St. Poeltner Dioezesanblatt. (AU ISSN 0036-3162) **4200**
St. Raphael's Better Health. (US) **3808**
St. Regis News. (US) **3666, 3651**
St. Regis News, Southern Edition see St. Regis News **3666**
St. Stefaner Gemeindenachrichten. (AU) **4094**
†St. Thomas More Lectures. (US ISSN 0082-4208) **5273**
St. Thomas More Society. Journal. (AT ISSN 0310-6861) **2676**
St. Thomas This Week. (VI) **4785**
St. Thomas's Gazette see St. Thomas's Hospital Gazette **2469**
St. Thomas's Hospital Gazette. (UK) **2469**
Saint Vincent de Paul Record. (AT ISSN 0036-3219) **4275**
St. Vincent Government Information Service News Bulletin. (XM) **4073, 3924**
St. Vladimir's Seminary Quarterly see St. Vladimir's Theological Quarterly **4288**
St. Vladimir's Theological Quarterly. (US ISSN 0036-3227) **4288**
▼St. Willibrord Studies in Philosophy and Religion. (US ISSN 1059-8375) **3780, 4200**
Sainte Therese de Lisieux. Annales. (FR ISSN 0036-3243) **4275**
Saints' Herald. (US ISSN 0036-3251) **4288**
Sairaala. (FI ISSN 0036-326X) **2469**
Saishu to Shiku. see Collecting and Breeding **540**
†Saison. (GW ISSN 0036-3294) **5273**
Saison Cyclonique a Madagascar. (MG) **3440**
Saisons d'Alsace. (FR ISSN 0048-9018) **2187**
Saitama Daigaku Kiyo. Kyoikugakubu. Sugaku, Shizen Kagaku/Saitama University. Journal: Mathematics and Natural Sciences. (JA ISSN 0387-9313) **3054, 4338**
Saitama Daigaku Kiyo. Shizen Kagaku Hen/Saitama University. Journal. Natural Science. (JA ISSN 0581-3662) **4338**
Saitama-ken Eisei Tokei Nenpo/Annual Report of Public Health, Saitama Prefecture. (JA) **4112**
Saitama-kenritsu Shizenshi Hakubutsukan Kenkyu Hokoku/ Saitama Museum of Natural History. Bulletin. (JA ISSN 0288-5611) **4338, 3532**
Saitama Mathematical Journal. (JA ISSN 0289-0739) **3054, 1187, 3830**
Saitama Museum of Natural History. Bulletin. see Saitama-kenritsu Shizenshi Hakubutsukan Kenkyu Hokoku **4338**
Saitama University. College of Liberal Arts. Journal. (JA) **2882**

Saitama University. Journal: Mathematics and Natural Sciences. see Saitama Daigaku Kiyo. Kyoikugakubu. Sugaku, Shizen Kagaku **3054**
Saitama University. Journal. Natural Science. see Saitama Daigaku Kiyo. Shizen Kagaku Hen **4338**
Saitama University. Science Reports. Series A: Mathematics see Saitama Mathematical Journal **3054**
Saitenspiel. (GW) **3579**
Saito Ho-on Kai Museum of Natural History. News. see Hakubutsukan Dayori **4312**
Saito Ho-on Kai Museum of Natural History. Research Bulletin. (JA ISSN 0375-1821) **4338**, 3532
Saiva Siddhanta. (II ISSN 0036-3316) **3780**
Saiwa. (NR ISSN 0795-2864) **2956**
Sajit Monthly. (II) **2882**
Sak'art'velos S.S.R. Mec'nierebat'a Akademiis Mac'ne. Istoriis Ark'eologiis, Et'nograp'iisa da Xelovnebis Istoriis Seria. (GS ISSN 0132-6058) **2385**, 284
Sake-Brief see Business Brief **848**
▼Sake Connection. (US) **385**
†Sakharnaya Promyshlennost' (UR ISSN 0036-3340) **5273**
Sakharnaya Svekla Proizvodstvo i Pererabotka. (RU ISSN 0036-3359) **191**
Sakhi. (II) **2201**
Sakkelet. (HU) **4486**, 1419
Sal Terrae. (SP ISSN 0211-4569) **4200**
Sala Bano. (SP) **2561**
▼Salad. (US) **3005**
Salam. (BX) **3701**
Salam Ual Kheir. (IS) **4275**
Salamandra. (GW ISSN 0036-3375) **591**
Salamandra. (MX ISSN 0300-3388) **2882**
Salar. (CN) **2048**, 1496, 4555
Salar Jung Museum. Annual Report. (II ISSN 0304-8152) **3532**
Salar Jung Museum Bi-Annual Research Journal. (II) **3532**
Salaries & Bonuses in Personnel - Industrial Relations Functions. (US) **993**, 1070
Salaries and Fringe Benefits: Benchmark Employee Compensation Report. (US) **4094**
Salaries and Fringe Benefits in Colorado Cities and Towns Under 3,000 Population. (US) **4094**
Salaries and Fringe Benefits: Management Compensation Report for Colorado Cities. (US) **4094**
Salaries & Related Matters in the Service Department. (US) **993**
Salaries and Wages for Michigan Municipalities over 1,000 Population.(US) **4094**
Salaries and Wages for Michigan Municipalities over 4,000 Population see Salaries and Wages for Michigan Municipalities over 1,000 Population **4094**
Salaries and Wages for Michigan Municipalities under 4,000 Population see Salaries and Wages for Michigan Municipalities over 1,000 Population **4094**
Salaries of Salaried Employees (Year). (SW ISSN 1100-6722) **3995**
Salaries of Scientists, Engineers and Technicians. (US ISSN 0146-5015) **3630**
Salary and Fringe Benefits Survey of Tennessee Municipalities. (US) **4073**
Salary and Merit see Wages and Benefits **1732**
Salary Budget Survey. (US) **1070**, 993
Salary Characteristics see Salary Survey (Cleveland) **884**
Salary Survey (Cleveland). (US) **884**, 1027
Salary Survey (St. Louis). (US) **993**, 1716
Sale e Pepe. (IT) **2449**

Salem County Historical Society Newsletter. (US ISSN 0036-3383) **2421**
Salemba. (IO) **1323**
Salers Stockman - Salers Source. (US ISSN 0897-2273) **225**
Sales. (JA) **1052**
Sales and Bargains Report see The S & B Report **1287**
Sales & Marketing Digest. (US) **1052**
†Sales & Marketing Digest (Boca Raton). (US ISSN 0741-6601) **5273**
Sales & Marketing Digest (New York). (US) **1052**
Sales and Marketing Executive Report. (US) **1052**, 1027
Sales & Marketing Management. (US) **1053**
Sales and Marketing Management. (UK ISSN 0264-3200) **1053**
Sales and Marketing Management in Canada see Sales & Marketing Manager Canada **1053**
Sales & Marketing Management Survey of Buying Power (Part I). (US) **737**
Sales & Marketing Management Survey of Buying Power (Part II). (US) **737**
Sales and Marketing Management Survey of Industrial and Commercial Buying Power see Survey of Industrial Purchasing Power **5285**
Sales & Marketing Management Survey of Selling Costs. (US) **737**
Sales & Marketing Manager Canada. (CN) **1053**
Sales and Marketing Newsletter. (US) **1053**
▼Sales and Marketing Strategies & News. (US) **1053**
Sales and Marketing Training. (US ISSN 0890-6912) **1053**
Sales and Operations Comparison see Pathways to Profitability **2554**
▼Sales & Use Tax Alert. (US ISSN 1054-6812) **1105**
Sales Association of the Chemical Industry, Inc. Slants see S A C I Slants **1187**
Sales Counter. (US) **3797**, 690
Sales Direction. (UK) **1053**, 1027
Sales Executive. (US ISSN 0036-3405) **1053**
Sales Guide to Germany. (GW) **4785**
Sales Management see Sales and Marketing Management **1053**
Sales Management Survey of Buying Power (Part I) see Sales & Marketing Management Survey of Buying Power (Part I) **737**
Sales Management Survey of Buying Power (Part II) see Sales & Marketing Management Survey of Buying Power (Part II) **737**
Sales Management Survey of Selling Costs see Sales & Marketing Management Survey of Selling Costs **737**
Sales Manager. (JA) **1053**
Sales Manager's Bulletin. (US ISSN 0036-3421) **1053**
▼Sales of a Business in Minnesota. (US) **2676**, 1105
Sales of Vine Products see Cyprus. Department of Statistics and Research. Industrial Statistics **712**
Sales Pro. (US) **1053**, 38
Sales Promotion. (CN) **1053**
†Sales Promotion Monitor. (US ISSN 0891-1622) **5273**
Sales Promotion News. (CN) **1053**
Sales Prospector. (US ISSN 0036-3456) **1084**, 631
Sales Rep's Advisor. (US ISSN 0278-5048) **1117**
Sales Tax Advices. (II ISSN 0036-3472) **1105**
Sales Tax Newsletter. (US) **1105**
Sales Ways. (US) **1053**, 2022
Salesian. (US ISSN 0036-3480) **4200**
Salesian Bulletin. (IE ISSN 0790-1216) **4275**
Salesianum. (VC ISSN 0036-3502) **4275**, 3780
Salesmanship. (US) **1053**
Salezijanski Vestnik. (XV ISSN 0353-0477) **4275**, 1660
Saline. (US ISSN 0893-3057) **2163**

Saling Aktienfuehrer. (GW ISSN 0080-5572) **962**
Salisbury. (UK) **4785**, 2385
Salisbury Review. (UK ISSN 0265-4881) **2882**
Salit. (IS ISSN 0334-4479) **1264**, 1967, 2262
Sally Ann. (CN) **4852**, 4288
Salmagundi. (US ISSN 0036-3529) **2514**, 4385
Salmanticensis. (SP ISSN 0036-3537) **4275**
Salmo Salar. (CN) **4555**
Salmon. (IE ISSN 0790-1631) **3005**
Salmon and Trout Magazine. (UK ISSN 0036-3545) **4555**
Salmon Arm Observer. (CN) **2179**
Salmon Farming. (UK ISSN 0951-9882) **2051**
Salmon International Literary Journal. (IE) **2956**
Salmon Market Newsletter. (US ISSN 1048-9495) **2048**
Salmon - Trout Steelheader. (US ISSN 0029-3431) **4555**, 2048
Salome. (IO) **343**
Salomon Brothers Center for the Study of Financial Institutions. Monograph Series see New York University. Salomon Center. Monograph Series **793**
Salomon Brothers Center for the Study of Financial Institutions. Occasional Papers see New York University. Salomon Center. Occasional Papers **793**
Salomon Brothers Center for the Study of Financial Institutions. Occasional Papers in Business and Finance see New York University. Salomon Center. Occasional Papers in Business and Finance **793**
Salomon Brothers Center for the Study of Financial Institutions. Working Paper Series see New York University. Salomon Center. Working Papers Series **793**
†Salon Biz. (US) **5273**
Salon Report. (US) **374**
Salon Today. (US) **374**
Salpisma. (GR ISSN 0036-357X) **4288**
Salt. (US ISSN 0883-2587) **4200**
Salt. (AT ISSN 0816-0031) **4200**
Salt and Trace Minerals Report. (US) **225**
Salt Lake City. (US) **2234**
Salt Lake City Messenger. (US ISSN 0586-7282) **4288**
Salt 'n' Pepper see Culpepper Letter **1476**
Salt Water Fishing. (US) **4555**
Salt Water Sportsman. (US ISSN 0036-3618) **4555**
†Salthouse. (US ISSN 0737-5506) **5273**
Saltzman's Eurail Guide Annual see Eurail Guide **4761**
Salud Fronteriza. see Border Health **4098**
Salud Mental. (MX ISSN 0185-3325) **3353**
Salud para Todos. (CR) **1264**, 3808
Salud Publica de Mexico/Public Health of Mexico. (MX ISSN 0036-3634) **4112**
▼Salud y Familia. (CR ISSN 1018-4430) **3151**, 4045
Saludos Hispanos. (US) **2022**
Saluki Club of America. Newsletter. (US) **3713**
Saluki Quarterly. (US ISSN 0194-5297) **3713**
Salus Militiae. (VE ISSN 0036-3642) **3151**
Salut. (FR) **1264**
Salut les Copains see Salut **1264**
Salute. (US) **2234**
Salute e Territorio. (IT ISSN 0392-4505) **4418**
Der Salutist. (GW) **4200**
Salvacion. (CU) **4418**
Salvage Bids. (US ISSN 0036-3669) **2542**
Salvage Locator see Locator (Whiting) **4694**
Salvation Army Year Book. (UK ISSN 0080-567X) **4248**
Salvationist. (UK) **4248**, 4418

Salve. (IT) **3808**
Salvo. (US) **2421**, 3471
Salvo Imprevisti. (IT) **2882**
Salz. (AU) **3005**
Salzburger Aktiengesellschaft fuer Elektrizitaetswirtschaft Nachrichten see S A F E - Nachrichten **1907**
Salzburger Beitraege zur Paracelsusforschung. (AU ISSN 0259-0794) **3780**, 2321
Salzburger Exkursionsberichte see Salzburger Geographische Materialien **2262**
Salzburger Geographische Arbeiten. (AU) **2262**
Salzburger Geographische Materialien. (AU) **2262**
Salzburger Jahrbuch fuer Philosophie. (AU ISSN 0080-5696) **3780**
Salzburger Studien zur Philosophie. (AU ISSN 0080-5726) **3780**
Salzburger Wirtschaft. (AU ISSN 0036-3677) **822**
Sam. (SP) **225**, 203
Sam. (CI ISSN 0350-7483) **2441**
Sam Houston Literary Review see Texas Review **2968**
Sam Nyied Sam see San Yue San **2956**
Samaj Kalyan. (II ISSN 0036-3693) **4418**
Samaj Nirikkhon. (BG) **4385**
Samajawadhaya. (CE) **3924**
Samar. (LE) **1264**
Samarbejdsgruppen for Trafiksikkerhed i Kommuneerne i Koebenhavns-Omraadet Rapport fra S T I K K see Rapport fra S T I K K **4720**
Samarbete. (FI ISSN 0036-3715) **832**, 1294, 1508
Samaritano see La San Vincenzo in Italia **4275**
Samaru Agricultural Newsletter see Noma **110**
Samaru Journal of Agricultural Research. (NR ISSN 0331-7285) **118**
Samaru Miscellaneous Papers. (NR ISSN 0080-5769) **118**
Samaru Research Bulletin. (NR ISSN 0080-5777) **118**
Sambahayan. (PH ISSN 0116-7979) **2495**
Sambalpur University. Post-Graduate Department of Oriya. Journal. (II) **2956**
Sambodhana. (II) **2956**
Sambodhi. (II) **3643**
Sambre et Heure. (BE) **2321**, 2956
Same-Day Surgery. (US ISSN 0190-5066) **3383**
Samelblatt fuer Rechtsvorschriften des Bundes und der Laender. (GW) **2676**
Samenwijs. (NE) **1741**
Samferdsel. (NO ISSN 0332-8988) **4721**, 4656
Samford Crimson. (US) **1323**
Samfundet til Udgivelse af Dansk Musik. Bulletin. (DK ISSN 0109-8438) **3579**
Samfundsforskning. (DK ISSN 0903-7543) **4448**
Samhaellsgemenskap see Kristdemokraten **3903**
Samir. (UA) **2186**
Samisdat. (SZ ISSN 0254-1521) **2385**, 3924
†Samisdat. (US ISSN 0226-840X) **5273**
Samiske Samlinger. (NO ISSN 0581-4480) **248**, 4448
Samizdat. (UK ISSN 0954-6499) **3005**
†Samizdat Bulletin. (US ISSN 0361-1302) **5273**
Samizdat Review see Protestant **4196**
Samkaleen Kala Aur Kavita. (II ISSN 0970-0986) **3005**
Samlaren. (SW ISSN 0348-6133) **2983**
Samlernyt. (DK ISSN 0109-3460) **385**
Samling af Bekendtgoerelser see Love og Bekendtgoerelser m.v **2651**
Sammler Express. (GW ISSN 0036-3820) **3757**
Sammler Journal. (GW ISSN 0342-7684) **259**

Sammlung Arbeitsrechtlicher Entscheidungen see S A E **993**
Sammlung Arbeitsrechtlicher Entscheidungen der Gerichte und Einigungsaemter. (AU) **2676**
Sammlung Denkwuerdiger Reisen. (GW) **4785,** 2385
Sammlung der Entscheidungen des Bundesfinanzhofs. (GW ISSN 0342-197X) **1105**
Sammlung Geltender Staatsangehoerigkeitsgesetze. (GW ISSN 0080-5823) **2676**
Sammlung Groos. (GW ISSN 0344-0591) **1716,** 2839
Sammlung Kurzer Grammatiken Germanischer Dialekte. (GW) **2839**
Sammlung Lebensmittelrechtlicher Entscheidungen. (GW ISSN 0080-5831) **2676,** 2081
Sammlung Musikwissenschaftlicher Abhandlungen/Collection d'Etudes Musicologiques. (GW ISSN 0085-588X) **3579**
Samnium. (IT ISSN 0391-8718) **2385,** 343
Samoa Bulletin see Samoa Times **2213**
Samoa Times. (WS ISSN 0036-3839) **2213**
Samolyot/Aircraft. (US) **61**
Samos. (GW ISSN 0080-5866) **284**
Samoupravna Organizacija see Organizacija i Kadrovi **1068**
Samoyed Quarterly. (US) **3713**
Sampada. (II ISSN 0036-3871) **884**
Sampan. (US) **2022**
Sample Case. (US ISSN 0036-3898) **1301**
Sample Surveys in the ESCAP Region. (UN ISSN 0125-0027) **737**
Sampovisio. (FI) **1027**
Samra'a see Hiya **4844**
Samruddhi. (II) **822**
Samskriti Vibhaga Ki Anudanom Ki Mangem. see India. Department of Culture. Demands for Grants **1728**
Samson Personal Computer. (BE) **1474,** 828
Samspil. (DK ISSN 0109-0429) **2185**
Samtiden. (NO ISSN 0036-3928) **2882**
Samuel. (IC) **2198**
Samuel H. Kress Foundation. Annual Report. (US ISSN 0581-4766) **343**
Samuel Neaman Institute for Advanced Studies in Science and Technology. Annual Report. (IS) **4338,** 4608
Samupakara Vigrahaya. (CE) **832**
Samurai - Bushido e Super Banzi - Pugilato. (IT) **4486**
Samvadadhvam. (II ISSN 0581-4790) **4585**
Samvardhana. (CE) **884**
Samvirke. (DK ISSN 0036-3944) **1508**
San Antonio Business Journal. (US) **690**
San Antonio District Dental Society. Journal see San Antonio District Dental Society Newsletter **3242**
San Antonio District Dental Society Newsletter. (US) **3242**
San Antonio Focus. (US) **2234**
†San Antonio Homes & Gardens. (US ISSN 0893-2697) **5273**
San Antonio Living. (US ISSN 0741-3432) **4158,** 2495
San Antonio M.D. (US) **3151**
San Antonio Monthly. (US ISSN 0036-3960) **2234**
†San - B U G. (US) **5273**
San Bernardino County Library. Newsletter. (US) **2782**
San Bernardino County Studies see West Coast Studies **2426**
San Bernardino - Riverside Business Chronicle. (US) **690**
San Carlos Publications. Series A: Humanities. (PH) **2514**
San Diegan. (US) **4785**
San Diego. (US ISSN 0036-4045) **2234**
San Diego Applause Magazine see Applause **5137**
San Diego Business. (US) **690**

San Diego Business Journal. (US) **690,** 884
San Diego County. Department of Planning and Land Use. County Data Base see San Diego County. Info Bulletin. Population & Housing Estimates **2500**
San Diego County. Info Bulletin. Population & Housing Estimates. (US) **2500**
▼San Diego County Business Directory.(US ISSN 1047-9619) **1152**
San Diego County Dental Society. News see Facets (San Diego) **3233**
San Diego Daily Transcript. (US) **690**
San Diego Executive. (US) **690**
San Diego Executive Magazine. (US) **690**
San Diego Family Press. (US) **1243**
San Diego Home-Garden. (US) **2555,** 2138
San Diego Jewish Press Heritage. (US) **2022,** 4226
San Diego Law Review. (US ISSN 0036-4037) **2677**
San Diego Libertarian. (US) **3924**
San Diego Log see The Log and San Diego Log **4525**
San Diego Museum of Man. Ethnic Technology Notes. (US ISSN 0080-5890) **248,** 284
San Diego Museum of Man. Papers. (US ISSN 0080-5904) **248,** 284
San Diego Numismatic Society. Bulletin.(US ISSN 0036-4053) **3601**
San Diego Parent. (US) **1243,** 2449, 4852
San Diego Physician. (US ISSN 0036-4061) **3151**
San Diego Political Watch. (US) **4094,** 3924
†San Diego Population and Land Use Bulletin. (US) **5273**
▼San Diego Resources. (US) **3596**
†San Diego Society of Natural History. Memoirs. (US ISSN 0080-5920) **5273**
San Diego Society of Natural History. Occasional Papers see San Diego Society of Natural History. Transactions **5273**
▼San Diego Society of Natural History. Proceedings. (US) **4338**
†San Diego Society of Natural History. Transactions. (US ISSN 0080-5947) **5273**
San Diego State University. Bureau of Business and Economic Research. Monographs. (US ISSN 0068-5836) **690**
San Diego State University. Bureau of Business and Economic Research. Research Studies and Position Papers. (US ISSN 0068-5844) **690**
San Diego Voice & Viewpoint. (US) **2234**
San Fernando Poetry Journal. (US ISSN 0196-2884) **3005**
San Francisco (Year). (US) **4785**
San Francisco Attorney Magazine. (US) **2677**
San Francisco Bay Area Gay and Lesbian Historical Society. Newsletter see Our Stories **2456**
San Francisco Bay Area Rapid Transit District. Annual Report. (US ISSN 0362-2800) **4656**
San Francisco Bay Area Register of Experts and Consultants. (US) **2677**
San Francisco Bay Area Sanyo Group Newsletter. (US) **1474,** 1464
▼San Francisco Bay Area's 680 Magazine. (US) **2234**
San Francisco Bay Conservation and Development Commission. Annual Report. (US ISSN 0085-5898) **1496**
San Francisco Bay Guardian. (US ISSN 0036-4096) **2234**
San Francisco Bay Times. (US) **2457**
San Francisco Book. (US) **4785**
San Francisco Business. (US ISSN 0036-410X) **822**
San Francisco Business Computers. (US) **1464**

San Francisco Business Times. (US ISSN 0890-0337) **839**
San Francisco Camerawork Quarterly see S F Camerawork Quarterly **3796**
San Francisco Catholic. (US) **4275**
San Francisco Chronicle Index. (US ISSN 0893-2425) **2579,** 22
San Francisco Daily Journal. (US) **2677**
San Francisco Focus. (US ISSN 0274-5933) **2234**
San Francisco Fresh Fruit and Vegetable Wholesale Market Prices. (US) **157,** 191
San Francisco Giftcenter and JewelryMart Buyer's Guide. (US) **2282,** 2566
San Francisco Jewish Bulletin see Northern California Jewish Bulletin **2017**
San Francisco Labor see Northern California Labor **2587**
San Francisco Maritime Museum. Sea Letter see Sea Letter **4738**
San Francisco Medical Society. Bulletin see San Francisco Medicine **3151**
San Francisco Medicine. (US) **3151**
San Francisco Peninsula Parent. (US) **1243**
San Francisco Review of Books. (US) **4136**
San Francisco Sentinel. (US) **2457**
San Francisco Sports Review see Bay Sports Review **4466**
San Francisco Wholesale Fruit and Vegetable Report. (US) **157,** 191
San Francisco Wholesale Ornamental Crops Report. (US) **118**
San Gabriel Valley Magazine. (US) **2234**
San Joaquin N O W Newsletter. (US) **4852**
San Joaquin Valley Business Perspectives see Valley Business Perspectives **887**
San Jose Film & Video Commission Directory. (US) **3517,** 1386
San Jose Metro. (US) **2234**
San Jose Post-Record. (US ISSN 0036-4185) **2677,** 798, 4158
San Jose Studies. (US ISSN 0097-8051) **2514,** 4338, 4385
San Juan Review see Caribbean Review **2861**
San Juans Beckon. (US) **4785**
San Khau/Theatre. (VN) **4637**
San Luis Valley Historian. (US ISSN 0036-4215) **2421**
San Marcos. (PE) **343,** 2514
San Marino (Repubblica) Bollettino Ufficiale. (SM ISSN 0036-4223) **4073**
San Marino (Repubblica). Dipartimento Affari Esteri. Notizia. (SM) **4073,** 3971
San Marino (Repubblica). Segreteria di Stato per gli Affari Esteri. Notizia see San Marino (Repubblica). Dipartimento Affari Esteri. Notizia **4073**
San Martino. (IT ISSN 0393-6414) **3151**
San Mateo County Dental Society. Bulletin see Mouthpiece (San Mateo) **3238**
▼San Miguel Quarterly. (US) **3005**
San Miguel Review. (US) **3005**
San Salvatore da Horta. (IT ISSN 0036-424X) **4200**
San Sun. (JA) **1294**
La San Vincenzo in Italia. (IT) **4275**
San Yue San. (CC) **2956,** 248, 2022, 2058
Sanaet El-Nassig/Industrie Textile. (UA) **4623**
Sananda. (II) **2201**
Sananjalka. (FI) **2839**
Sanatatea. (RM) **4112**
Sanatorio Sao Lucas. Boletim. (BL ISSN 0036-4258) **3383**
Una Sancta. (GW ISSN 0342-1465) **4200**
Sancta Crux. (AU) **2385**
Sancties. (NE) **1522**
▼Sanctions in Federal Litigation. (US) **2677**
Sanctuary. (US ISSN 0272-8966) **1496**

Sanctuary Circles. (US) **4288**
Sanctuary News. (US) **231**
Sandalion. (IT) **1279**
Sandara/League. (US ISSN 8750-2348) **2022**
Sandeviften. (DK ISSN 0108-9315) **567**
Sandgrouse. (UK ISSN 0260-4736) **567**
Sandip. (BG) **2174**
Sandlapper. (US ISSN 1046-3267) **2234**
Sandmutopia Guardian & Dungeon Journal. (US) **3400,** 4852
Sandpiper. (US) **567**
Sandra. (GW) **3592**
Sandringham-Brighton Advertiser see Advertiser **2171**
Sandscript. (US) **2956**
Sanduq Abu Dhabi lil-Inma' al-Iqtisadi al-Arabi. Al-Taqrir al-Sanawi/Abu Dhabi Fund for Arab Economic Development. Annual Report. (TS) **935**
Sandvigske Samlinger. Aarbok see Maihaugen **2374**
Sandwich Islands Magazine. (US) **4785**
SANE see Sources from the Ancient Near East **2432**
SANE - Freeze News. (US) **3971,** 3471
SANE World - Freeze Focus see SANE - Freeze News **3971**
Saneamento. (BL ISSN 0036-4312) **4112**
Sanford Evans Gold Book of Motorcycle Data & Used Prices. (CN ISSN 0705-1840) **4520**
Sanford Evans Gold Book of Snowmobile Data and Used Prices. (CN ISSN 0318-9422) **4498,** 4555, 4585
Sanford Evans Gold Book of Used Car Prices. (CN ISSN 0381-8179) **4701**
Sang Tao/Creativity. (VN) **690,** 4608
Sang Thrombose Vaisseaux. (FR ISSN 0999-7385) **3273**
Sangaku Shashin Nenkan. (JA) **3797**
Sangamon County Genealogical Society of Illinois. Quarterly see Circuit Rider (Springfield) **2147**
Sangbad Bichitra. (US) **2022**
Sangeet Natak. (II ISSN 0036-4339) **3579,** 1532, 4638
Sanger-Hilsen/Singers Greetings. (US) **2022,** 3579
Sangkakala Peradilan. (IO ISSN 0303-321X) **2677**
Sangre. (SP ISSN 0036-4355) **3273**
Sangyo Anzen Kenkyujo Gijutsu Shishin/Research Institute of Industrial Safety. Technical Recommendation. (JA ISSN 0911-8063) **3621,** 1836, 1907
Sangyo Anzen Kenkyujo Hokoku see Sangyo Anzen Kenkyujo Kenkyu Hokoku **3621**
Sangyo Anzen Kenkyujo Kenkyu Hokoku/Research Institute of Industrial Safety. Research Report. (JA ISSN 0911-6923) **3621**
Sangyo Gijutsu Joho Yokkaichi/Industrial and Technological Information of Yokkaichi City. (JA ISSN 0036-4371) **4608**
Sangyo Gijutsu no Rekishiteki Tenkai Chosa Kenkyu. (JA) **4608**
Sangyo Igaku. see Japanese Journal of Industrial Health **3618**
Sangyo Keiei Kenkyujoho/Journal of Industry and Management. (JA) **1027**
Sangyo Kunren. see Industrial Training **1013**
Sangyo Sharyo/Industrial Vehicles. (JA ISSN 0036-4398) **4701**
Sanita Pubblica. (IT) **4112**
Sanitaeinstallation und Heizungsbau Technik see S H - Technik **5272**
Sanitaer-Installateur see Installateur **2300**
Sanitaer und Heizungs Report. (GW ISSN 0344-9122) **2303,** 4112
Sanitaer- und Heizungstechnik. (GW ISSN 0344-4401) **2303**
Sanitair - Dakwerk. see Sanitaire - Couverture **2303**

Sanitaire - Couverture/Sanitair - Dakwerk. (BE) **2303**
Sanitary and Air Technics. *see* Zdravotni Technika a Vzduchotechnika **2304**
Sanitary Engineering and Hydraulics. *see* Santechnika ir Hidraulika **1925**
Sanitary Maintenance. (US ISSN 0036-4436) **4112**
Sanitation Canada. (CN) **631**
†Sanity. (UK ISSN 0036-4444) **5273**
Sanjiao Zhou. (CC) **2956**
Sankhya. Series A. (II ISSN 0581-572X) **4585**
Sankhya. Series B. (II ISSN 0581-5738) **4585**
St. Galler Studien zum Wettbewerbs und Immaterialgueterrecht. (SZ) **2677**
Sankt Galler Beitraege zum Fremdenverkehr und zur Verkehrswirtschaft: Reihe Verkehrswirtschaft. (SZ ISSN 0080-6048) **4656**
St. Galler Studien zur Politikwissenschaft. (SZ) **3924**
Sankt Gallische Naturwissenschaftliche Gesellschaft. Bericht ueber die Taetigkeit *see* Sankt Gallische Naturwissenschaftliche Gesellschaft. Berichte **4338**
Sankt Gallische Naturwissenschaftliche Gesellschaft. Berichte. (SZ) **4338**
Sankyo Kenkyujo Nenpo *see* Sankyo Kenkyusho Nempo **3742**
Sankyo Kenkyusho Nempo/Sankyo Research Laboratories. Annual Report. (JA ISSN 0080-6064) **3742**
Sankyo Research Laboratories. Annual Report. *see* Sankyo Kenkyusho Nempo **3742**
Sannio Elegante. (IT ISSN 0036-4460) **1287**
Sannivedana. (CE) **1342**
Sanomalehtimies/Journalisten. (FI ISSN 0036-4479) **2575**
Sanop Kwa Kyongyong/Yonsei Business Review. (KO ISSN 0036-4487) **690**
Sans Frontieres - Les Forces Psychologiques. (CN ISSN 0833-0247) **4045**
Sans Tache. (US) **2163**
Sanshi. Konchunogyo Gijutsu Kenkyu Shiryo/National Institute of Sericultural and Entomological Science. Miscellaneous Publication. (JA ISSN 0915-2679) **537**
†Sanshi Kenkyu/Acta Sericologica. (JA ISSN 0036-4495) **5273**
▼Sanshi Konchu Nogyo Gijutsu Kenkyujo Hokoku/National Institute of Sericultural and Entomological Science. Bulletin. (JA ISSN 0915-2652) **537**
Sanshi Shikenjo Nenpo. *see* Sericultural Experiment Station. Annual Report **5276**
Sanskriti. (II ISSN 0581-4758) **2514**
Sant Sipahi. (II) **3924**
Santa Ana Mountain Series. (US) **2421**, **3517**
Santa Barbara Magazine. (US) **2234**
Santa Barbara Museum of Natural History. Museum Bulletin. (US) **3532**, **4338**
Santa Barbara Museum of Natural History. Occasional Papers. (US) **248**, **1579**
Santa Barbara Stock Market Report *see* Takeover Target Weekly Forecast **5287**
Santa Casa di Loreto. Messaggio. (IT ISSN 0036-116X) **4275**
Santa Clara Computer and High-Technology Law Journal. (US) **2677**, **2705**, **4608**
Santa Clara County Business Magazine.(US ISSN 0162-8763) **690**
Santa Clara County Connections. (US ISSN 0895-6103) **2163**, **2421**
Santa Clara County Historical and Genealogical Quarterly *see* Santa Clara County Connections **2163**
Santa Clara Law Review. (US ISSN 0146-0315) **2677**
Santa Cruz Action Network. Newsletter. (US) **2495**, **4418**

†Santa Cruz Island Preserve News. (US) **5273**
Santa Fe East *see* S F E **343**
The Santa Fean Magazine. (US ISSN 1046-2708) **2234**
Santa Gertrudis Journal. (US ISSN 0036-455X) **225**
Santa Monica Review. (US ISSN 0899-9848) **2957**
Santa Rosa News. (US ISSN 0894-783X) **2022**
▼Santag. (GW ISSN 0940-0265) **3643**
Santakuti Vedic Research Series. (II ISSN 0080-6137) **2341**
Santana. (US) **4529**
Sante. (CN ISSN 0832-6770) **3808**, **3612**
Sante. (AE) **4112**
La Sante de l'Abeille. (FR ISSN 0036-4568) **118**
Sante du Monde. *see* World Health **4115**
Sante Mentale au Canada *see* Canada's Mental Health **3085**
Sante Mentale au Quebec. (CN ISSN 0383-6320) **4045**
Sante Publique. (RM ISSN 0048-9107) **4112**
Santechnika ir Hidraulika/Sanitary Engineering and Hydraulics. (LI ISSN 0208-2438) **1925**, **2303**
Santi. (II) **4217**
Santiago. (CU ISSN 0048-9115) **2882**
Santiago del Estero. Direccion General de Investigaciones Estadistica y Censos. Estadistica Agricola-Ganadera. (AG) **143**
Santiago del Estero. Direccion General de Investigaciones Estadistica y Censos. Estadisticas Sociales. (AG) **4585**
Santo. (IT ISSN 0391-7819) **2385**, **343**, **352**, **4275**
Santo dei Voli. (IT ISSN 0036-4606) **4275**
Santo Tomas Journal of Medicine. (PH ISSN 0115-1126) **3151**
Santo Tomas Nursing Journal. (PH ISSN 0048-9123) **3286**
Santuario de Aparecida. (BL ISSN 0036-4614) **4200**, **1660**
Santuario della Madonna delle Rocche. (IT ISSN 0036-4622) **4275**
Santuario di N.S.D. Grazie e di S. Maria Goretti *see* La Stella del Mare **4202**
Sanwa Bank. Corporate Communications Department. Annual Report. (JA) **798**
Sanwen/Prose Monthly. (CC ISSN 0257-5809) **2957**
Sanwen Baijia. (CC) **2957**
Sanwen Xuankan. (CC) **2957**
Sanyo Kasei News. (JA ISSN 0036-4649) **1187**
Sanyo P C Hackers Newsletter. (US ISSN 1054-4232) **1474**, **1464**
Sanyo Source. (US) **1474**, **1464**
Sanyo Users Group of Los Angeles Newsletter. (US) **1474**, **1464**
Sanyuefeng/Spring Breezes. (CC) **2284**, **2957**
Sanz. (IS) **4226**
Sao Paulo. (BL ISSN 0036-4657) **2175**
Sao Paulo. Biblioteca Mario de Andrade. Boletim Bibliografico *see* Sao Paulo. Biblioteca Mario de Andrade. Revista **411**
Sao Paulo. Biblioteca Mario de Andrade. Revista. (BL) **411**
Sao Paulo (City) Arquivo Municipal. Revista. (BL ISSN 0034-9216) **2421**
Sao Paulo. Coordenadoria de Saude Mental. Arquivos *see* Arquivos de Saude Mental do Estado de Sao Paulo **3331**
Sao Paulo, Brazil (State). Observatorio. Anuario Astronomico *see* Universidade de Sao Paulo. Instituto Astronomico e Geofisico. Anuario Astronomico **370**
Sao Paulo, Brazil (State). Secretaria da Educacao. Atividades Desenvolvidas. (BL) **1660**, **2677**

Sao Paulo, Brazil (State). Superintendencia de Saneamento Ambiental. Relatorio Anual de Atividades. (BL) **1967**
Sao Paulo Yearbook. (BL) **822**
Sao Tome e Principe. Reparticao Provincial dos Servicos de Estatistica. Boletim Trimestral de Estatistica. (SF) **4585**
Saobracaj. (YU ISSN 0558-6208) **4721**
Saopstenja. (YU ISSN 0408-9936) **4828**
Saotharlann Staire Eireann. *see* Irish History Workshop **2369**
Sapanut. (IS ISSN 0334-2751) **4737**
Hasapanut Hayisraelit. (IS) **4737**
Sapere. (IT ISSN 0036-4681) **4338**
Sapeur-Pompier. (FR ISSN 0036-469X) **2034**
Sapiens. (US) **2882**
Sapientia. (AG ISSN 0036-4703) **3780**
Sapienza. (IT ISSN 0036-4711) **3781**, **4200**
Sapphic Touch. (US ISSN 0275-6757) **4852**, **2457**, **2957**
Sappho's Isle. (US) **2883**
Sapporo Igaku Zasshi/Sapporo Medical Journal. (JA ISSN 0036-472X) **3151**
Sapporo Ika Daigaku Jinbun Shizen Kagaku Kiyo/Sapporo Medical College. Journal of Liberal Arts and Sciences. (JA ISSN 0389-3944) **2514**, **4338**
Sapporo Medical College. Journal of Liberal Arts and Sciences. *see* Sapporo Ika Daigaku Jinbun Shizen Kagaku Kiyo **2514**
Sapporo Medical Journal. *see* Sapporo Igaku Zasshi **3151**
Sapporo-shi Seishonen Kagakukan Kiyo.(JA ISSN 0914-2401) **4338**, **1264**
Saptahik Hindustan. (II) **2201**
Saptahika Bicitra. (BG) **2883**
Saptahika Thikana. (BG) **3924**, **2341**
Saptimina Culturala a Capitalei *see* Viata Capitalei **348**
Saqer - Falcon *see* Al-Saqr al-Riyadi **4510**
Al-Saqr al-Riyadi. (QA) **4510**
Sarah Lawrence Literary Review *see* Sarah Lawrence Review **2883**
Sarah Lawrence Review. (US) **2883**
Sarance. (EC) **248**
Sarasaviya. (CE) **3517**
Sarasota Magazine. (US ISSN 0192-4265) **2234**
Sarasvat. (II ISSN 0036-4754) **2201**
Sarathi Gujarati Weekly. (II) **2201**
The Saratoga. (US ISSN 0740-9702) **2163**
Sarawak. Department of Agriculture. Research Branch. Annual Report. (MY ISSN 0080-6420) **118**
Sarawak. Department of Statistics. Annual Statistical Bulletin *see* Malaysia. Department of Statistics. Annual Statistical Bulletin Sarawak **4579**
Sarawak Electricity Supply Corporation. Annual Report. (MY ISSN 0127-144X) **1907**
Sarawak External Trade Statistics *see* Malaysia. Department of Statistics. Statistics of External Trade Sarawak **728**
Sarawak Gazette. (MY ISSN 0036-4762) **2210**
Sarawak Journal. (UK ISSN 0261-7226) **3757**
Sarcastics Anonymous and Laugh Lovers News. (US) **2883**
Sarcomas and Related Tumors - Diagnosis, Treatment *see* I C R D B Cancergram: Sarcomas and Related Tumors - Diagnosis, Treatment **3175**
Sarcophagus *see* Westerfield's Review **3008**
Sardegna - Agricoltura (Cagliari). (IT) **118**
Sardegna Economica. (IT ISSN 0036-4770) **822**
Sargasso. (PR) **2883**, **2839**, **3005**
Sari. (MY ISSN 0127-2721) **2839**, **2957**

SASKATCHEWAN BUILDING 6639

Sari Karangan Indonesia. (IO ISSN 0216-4167) **4357**, **22**
Sarie. (SA) **4852**
Sarika. (II ISSN 0036-4797) **2957**
Sarita. (II) **2957**
Sarkiyat Mecmuasi. (TU ISSN 0578-9761) **2431**
Sarmatian Review. (US) **2022**, **2883**
Sarsia. (NO ISSN 0036-4827) **454**
Sarvadanand Universal Series. (II ISSN 0080-6471) **2957**
Sarvekshana. (II) **4585**
Sarvodaya. (II ISSN 0036-4835) **4418**, **3971**
Sarvotkrushta Marathi Katha. (II ISSN 0303-3074) **2957**
Sasco Catalogue *see* Product Finder: Swift-Sasco Buyers Guide **1507**
Sash. (SA ISSN 0036-4843) **3947**
Sask Report Magazine. (CN) **2179**
Sask Report Newsmagazine *see* Sask Report Magazine **2179**
Saskatchewan. Agriculture and Food. Annual Report. (CN ISSN 0713-1844) **118**
Saskatchewan. Alcohol and Drug Abuse Commission. Annual Report. (CN) **1539**
Saskatchewan. Alcoholism Commission. Annual Report *see* Saskatchewan. Alcohol and Drug Abuse Commission. Annual Report **1539**
Saskatchewan. Department of Culture and Recreation. Annual Report. (CN) **343**, **284**, **306**
Saskatchewan. Department of Culture and Youth. Annual Report *see* Saskatchewan. Department of Culture and Recreation. Annual Report **343**
†Saskatchewan. Department of Highways and Transportation. Technical Report. (CN) **5273**
Saskatchewan. Department of Industry and Commerce. Industrial Benefits from Resource Development. (CN) **690**, **884**
Saskatchewan. Department of Industry and Commerce. Report for the Fiscal Year. (CN ISSN 0080-6498) **4073**
Saskatchewan. Department of Labour. Wages and Working Conditions by Occupation. (CN ISSN 0706-4926) **993**
Saskatchewan. Department of Social Services. Annual Report. (CN) **4418**
Saskatchewan. Department of the Environment and Public Safety. Annual Report. (CN) **1967**
Saskatchewan. Department of the Environment. Annual Report *see* Saskatchewan. Department of the Environment and Public Safety. Annual Report **1967**
Saskatchewan. Medical Care Insurance Commission. Annual Report *see* Saskatchewan Health. Annual Report **2542**
Saskatchewan. Prescription Drug Plan. Annual Report. (CN ISSN 0707-0152) **3742**, **2542**
Saskatchewan Administrator *see* Saskatchewan Educational Administrator **1731**
Saskatchewan, Alberta, Yukon Trapper. (CN) **2738**
Saskatchewan Archaeological Society Newsletter. (CN ISSN 0227-7514) **284**
Saskatchewan Archaeology. (CN) **284**
Saskatchewan Archaeology Newsletter *see* Saskatchewan Archaeological Society Newsletter **284**
Saskatchewan Association for Computers in Education Bulletin *see* S A C E Bulletin **1417**
Saskatchewan Association of Architects. Newsletter. (CN) **306**
Saskatchewan Association of Special Care Homes Newsletter *see* S A S C H Newsletter **3150**
Saskatchewan Association of Student Council Advisors Journal - Newsletter *see* S A S C A Journal - Newsletter **1731**
Saskatchewan Association of Teachers of French. Bulletin de Service. (CN) **2839**, **1759**
†Saskatchewan Building Trades Yearbook. (CN) **5273**

Saskatchewan Bulletin. (CN ISSN 0036-4886) 1661
Saskatchewan Business. (CN ISSN 0709-0854) 690
Saskatchewan Care see S A S C H Newsletter 3150
Saskatchewan Career - Work Education Association Newsletter see S C W E A Newsletter 3630
Saskatchewan Centre of the Arts. Annual Report. (CN) 343
Saskatchewan Conce R N. (CN) 3286
Saskatchewan Decisions Citator. (CN) 2677
Saskatchewan Decisions, Civil and Criminal Cases. (CN ISSN 0319-7999) 2677
Saskatchewan Decisions - Rules and Statute Citator see Saskatchewan Decisions Citator 2677
Saskatchewan Drama Association Journal - Newsletter see S D A Journal - Newsletter 4637
Saskatchewan Economic and Finance Position see Economic and Fiscal Policy 861
Saskatchewan Economic Review. (CN ISSN 0558-6976) 884
Saskatchewan Educational Administrator. (CN ISSN 0709-8146) 1731
Saskatchewan Energy & Mines. Annual Report. (CN) 3495, 3701
Saskatchewan Energy & Mines. Mineral Statistics Yearbook. (CN) 3495, 3701
Saskatchewan Energy & Mines. Petroleum and Natural Gas Reservoir Annual. (CN) 3701
Saskatchewan Environmental Society Newsletter see S E S Newsletter 1967
Saskatchewan Farm Life. (CN) 118
Saskatchewan Farm Science see Agricultural Science Bulletin 5132
Saskatchewan FarmStart Corporation. Annual Report see Agricultural Credit Corporation of Saskatchewan. Annual Report 146
Saskatchewan Gazette. (CN ISSN 0036-4894) 2677
Saskatchewan Genealogical Society. Bulletin. (CN ISSN 0048-9182) 2163
Saskatchewan Guidance and Counseling Association. Guidelines. (CN ISSN 0048-9190) 1661
Saskatchewan Health. Annual Report. (CN) 2542
Saskatchewan Health. Medical Care Insurance Branch. Annual Report see Saskatchewan Health. Annual Report 2542
Saskatchewan History. (CN ISSN 0036-4908) 2421
Saskatchewan Housing Corporation. Annual Report. (CN) 2495
Saskatchewan Indian. (CN ISSN 0048-9204) 2022
Saskatchewan Indian Federated College Journal. (CN ISSN 0828-3907) 2022
Saskatchewan Labour Report. (CN ISSN 0317-7335) 993
Saskatchewan Law Review. (CN ISSN 0036-4916) 2677
Saskatchewan Library Association. Forum. (CN ISSN 0831-3016) 2782
Saskatchewan Manufacturers Guide. (CN ISSN 0080-6536) 1152
Saskatchewan Mathematics Teachers' Society Journal - Newsletter see S M T S Journal - Newsletter 3054
Saskatchewan Medical Journal. (CN) 3151
Saskatchewan Monthly Statistical Review. (CN) 737
Saskatchewan Motor Transport Guide see Saskatchewan Trucking - Ship by Truck Directory 4747
Saskatchewan Motorist see Westworld Saskatchewan 4706
Saskatchewan Municipal Directory. (CN ISSN 0581-8435) 4094
Saskatchewan Music Festival Association Official Syllabus. (CN) 3579

Saskatchewan Natural History Society. Special Publications. (CN ISSN 0080-6552) 567
Saskatchewan Oil and Gas Corporation. Annual Report. (CN) 3701
Saskatchewan Orchid Society. Newsletter. (CN) 2138
Saskatchewan Planning News. (CN) 2495
Saskatchewan Poetry Book. (CN ISSN 0080-6560) 3005
Saskatchewan Professional Engineer see Professional Edge 1834
Saskatchewan Psychiatric Nurses' Association. Newsletter. (CN) 3286
Saskatchewan Rail Committee. News Bulletin see Transport 2000 Canada. News Bulletin 4716
Saskatchewan Reports. (CN) 2677
Saskatchewan Research Council. Annual Report. (CN ISSN 0080-6587) 4338, 4608
Saskatchewan Research Council. Climatological Reference Station. Annual Summary. (CN) 3440
Saskatchewan Ski Journal see Western Skier 4560
Saskatchewan Skier see Western Skier 4560
Saskatchewan Software Directory. (CN) 1479
Saskatchewan Stockgrower. (CN) 225
Saskatchewan Telecommunications. Annual Report. (CN ISSN 0080-6633) 1365
Saskatchewan Telecommunications SaskTel News see SaskTel News 1365
Saskatchewan Trapper see Saskatchewan, Alberta, Yukon Trapper 2738
Saskatchewan Trucking. (CN) 4747
Saskatchewan Trucking - Ship by Truck Directory. (CN) 4747
†Saskatoon Parent. (CN) 5273
Saskatoon S.R.C. Climatological Reference Station. Annual Summary see Saskatchewan Research Council. Climatological Reference Station. Annual Summary 3440
SaskAuto Annual Report see S G I - Auto Fund. Annual Report 4721
▼Sasktech Directory. (CN) 4615
SaskTel News. (Saskatchewan Telecommunications) (CN ISSN 0036-4851) 1365
†Sasmira Technical Digest. (II) 5273
†Sasmira's Bulletin. (II ISSN 0970-6739) 5273
Sassafras. (US) 3579
Sassy (New York, 1988). (US ISSN 0899-9953) 1243, 4852
Sat SanDesh. (US) 3781, 4200
Satapitaka. Indo-Asian Literatures. (II ISSN 0581-8532) 2957
Satawa Liang. (TH) 2220
Satchell's Writer's Club Newsletter. (US) 2957
†Satellite Age. (US) 5273
†Satellite Audio Report. (US ISSN 0739-1935) 5273
Satellite Broadcasting & Communications Association Weekly see S B C A Weekly 5272
†Satellite Business. (US ISSN 0743-0361) 5273
Satellite College Network. (US) 1323
Satellite Communications. (US ISSN 0147-7439) 1342, 61
Satellite Directory see World Satellite Directory 1160
Satellite Master Antenna TV News see S M A T V News 1379
Satellite News. (US ISSN 0161-3448) 1342, 1027, 1053
Satellite Orbit. (US ISSN 0732-7668) 1379
Satellite Retailer. (US) 1379
Satellite T V Pre Vue. (US) 1379
Satellite T V Week. (US ISSN 0744-7841) 1379
Satellite Telecommunications Newsletter see Satellite Age 5273
Satellite Television Guide see S T V Guide 5272
Satellite Week. (US ISSN 0193-2861) 1379
Satellites de Saturne I to VIII. (FR ISSN 0769-1025) 369

Satellites Galileens de Jupiter. (FR ISSN 0769-1033) 369
Sather Classical Lectures. (US ISSN 0080-6684) 1279
Satin News. (US) 3713
Satira. (IT) 2883
Satire & Humor. see Fengci yu Youmo 2866
†Satori. (US) 5273
Satri Sarn. (TH) 4852
Satsang. (US ISSN 0735-1321) 118, 1967, 3808
Sattar Dashak. (II) 2957
Satul Romanesc. (RM) 118
Saturday Evening Post. (US ISSN 0048-9239) 2234, 2957
Saturday Night. (CN ISSN 0036-4975) 2179
Saturn Five's Market Update. (US) 962, 3495
SatVision Magazine. (US) 1379
Satya Prakash. (II ISSN 0036-4991) 2201
Satyachar. (II) 3924
Satyagraha. (US) 3924
Satyakatha. (II) 2201
Sau og Geit. (NO ISSN 0036-5009) 225
Sauces and Spreads. (UK) 2081
Saude! (BL) 3808
Saudi Arabia. Central Department of Statistics. Foreign Trade Statistics. (SU) 737
Saudi Arabia. Central Department of Statistics. Quarterly Digest of Foreign Trade Statistics. (SU) 737, 920
Saudi Arabia. Central Department of Statistics. Statistical Indicator. (SU) 737
Saudi Arabia. Central Department of Statistics. Statistical Yearbook. (SU) 4585
Saudi Arabia. Ministry of Education. Annual Statistical Report. (SU) 1679, 1723
Saudi Arabia. Ministry of Education. Educational Abstracts. (SU) 1679
Saudi Arabia. Ministry of Education. Educational Documentation. (SU) 1723
Saudi Arabia. Ministry of Education. Educational Statistics. (SU) 1679, 4585
Saudi Arabia Business Week. (SU) 690
†Saudi Arabia Market Conditions. (US) 5273
Saudi Arabia Monitor. (US) 920, 798
Saudi Arabian Monetary Agency. Annual Report. (SU ISSN 0558-7220) 1105
Saudi Arabian Monetary Agency. Statistical Summary. (SU ISSN 0581-8672) 798, 737
Saudi-Arabian Saso Standards Microfile.(UK) 1836, 4608
Saudi Economic Survey. (SU ISSN 0252-967X) 690
Saudi Gazette. (SU) 690
Saudi Medical Journal. (SU ISSN 0379-5284) 3151
Saul Bellow Journal. (US ISSN 0735-1550) 2957
Saul Bellow Newsletter see Saul Bellow Journal 2957
Saul Bellow Society Newsletter. (US) 2957
Saumons. (FR) 591, 1496
Sauna Nachrichten mit Sauna Archiv see Internationales Sauna - Archiv 3804
Sauria. (GW ISSN 0176-9391) 591
Saussurea. (SZ ISSN 0373-2525) 517
Sauti Nykani. (KE) 2170
Sauti Ya Vita. (KE) 4288
Sauvagine et Sa Chasse. (FR ISSN 0751-9907) 4555
Sauvegarde. see Heimatschutz 1489
Sauvegarde de l'Enfance. (FR ISSN 0036-5041) 1243
Sauvegarde des Chantiers. (FR ISSN 0036-505X) 631
Sauver. (FR) 2034
Le Sauveur. (CN ISSN 0315-7970) 4200, 4448
Savacou. (JM ISSN 0036-5068) 343, 2957
Savage Family Depository Newsletter. (US) 2163

Savanna. (NR ISSN 0331-0523) 4385, 1967
▼Savannah Business Journal. (US) 690
Savannah Jewish Law see Savannah Jewish News 2022
Savannah Jewish News. (US) 2022
Savant see Voice 1329
Save Energy. (US) 1795, 1496
Save Our Cumberland Mountains Sentinel see S O C M Sentinel 1967
Save Our World see S O W 4200
Save the Children. Annual Report. (US) 4418, 1243
Save the Harbor - Save the Bay Newsletter. (US) 1967, 1600
†Savez Omladine. (YU ISSN 0036-5092) 5273
Savez Organizacija Kompozitora Jugoslavije. Bilten. (YU) 2589, 3579
Savez Organizacija Kompozitora Jugoslavije. Bilten. (YU) 3579
Savez Sindikata Jugoslavije. Centralni Vec. Bilten see Savez Sindikata Jugoslavije. Veca S S J. Bilten 2589
Savez Sindikata Jugoslavije. Veca S S J. Bilten. (YU) 2589
Savia Argentina. (AG) 2170, 2058
Savigny-Stiftung fuer Rechtsgeschichte. Zeitschrift. Germanistische Abteilung. (GW ISSN 0323-4045) 2677
Savigny-Stiftung fuer Rechtsgeschichte. Zeitschrift. Kanonistische Abteilung. (GW ISSN 0323-4142) 2677
Savigny-Stiftung fuer Rechtsgeschichte. Zeitschrift. Romanistische Abteilung. (GW ISSN 0323-4096) 2677
Saving and Preserving Art and Cultural Environments see S P A C E S 357
Saving Energy. (US ISSN 0279-2338) 1795
Saving Health. (UK ISSN 0036-5106) 4200
Saving Social Security. (US) 2542
Savings and Development. (IT ISSN 0393-4551) 798
Savings and Loan Fact Book see Savings Institutions Sourcebook 798
Savings and Loan Investor. (US) 962
Savings and Loan Monthly see Mortgage Finance Monthly 4153
Savings and Loan News see Savings Institutions 798
Savings and Loan Reporter see Banking Reporter 766
Savings and Loan Savings Bank Financial Quarterly see S & L - Savings Bank Financial Quarterly 689
Savings and Loan Sourcebook see Savings Institutions Sourcebook 798
Savings Association League of New York State. Legislative Bulletin see New York League of Savings Institutions. Legislative Bulletin 793
Savings Association News see New York League News 793
Savings Bank International. (SZ) 798
Savings Institutions. (US ISSN 0746-1321) 798
Savings Institutions Sourcebook. (US) 798
Savings Market. (UK ISSN 0308-1729) 2542
Savings Weekly see Bank Worker 765
Savoia. (IT ISSN 0036-5157) 3924, 2385
Savoir Education Formation. (FR) 1661
Savon Luonto. (FI ISSN 0356-276X) 454, 1496
Savona A C L I. (Associazioni Cristiane Lavoratori Italy) (IT) 3947
Savonia. (FI ISSN 0356-3189) 455, 1496
Savremena Poljoprivreda/Contemporary Agriculture. (YU ISSN 0581-8850) 118
Savremena Poljoprivredna Tehnika/Advanced Agricultural Engineering. (YU ISSN 0350-2953) 118
Savremena Praksa. (YU ISSN 0036-5173) 2677
Savremeni Vozac. (YU) 4701, 4721, 4747
Savremenik. (YU ISSN 0036-519X) 2957

Savremenna Medicina. (BU ISSN 0562-7192) **3151**
Savremenna Zhurnalistika/Modern Journalism. (BU ISSN 0205-1656) **2575**
Savremeno Domacinstvo. (BN ISSN 0036-5203) **2449**
Savunma ve Havacilik. (TU) **3471**, 61
Savvy. (II) **2201**
Savvy *see* Savvy Woman **5273**
†Savvy Woman. (US) **5273**
Sawasdee. (HK) **4803**
Sawmills. *see* Saagverken **2117**
Sawt al-Mar'ah/Woman's Voice. (TS) **4852**
Sawt Al Sudan/Voice of Sudan. (SJ) **2170**
Sawt Al Ummah/Voice of the Nation. (SJ) **2170**
Sawt Al Ummal/Worker's Voice. (SJ) **2589**
Sawt el-Ard el-Mukaddash. *see* Voice of the Holy Land **4278**
Sawt ul-Ta'wun. *see* Voice of Cooperation **833**
Sawt Ummal al-Urdon. *see* Voice of Jordanian Labourers **2591**
Sawtooth News. (US) **1464**
Sawyer's Gas Turbine International *see* Turbomachinery International **1940**
Saxophone Journal. (US ISSN 0276-4768) **3579**
Saxophone Sheet *see* Saxophone Journal **3579**
Saybrook Review. (US ISSN 0740-0853) **4045**
Sayidati/My Lady. (UK) **1294**
Al-Sayyarah al-Arabiyyah. (TS) **4701**
Sbirka Rozhodnuti a Sdeleni Soudu C S S R *see* Sbirka Soudnich Rozhodnuti a Stanovisek **2677**
Sbirka Soudnich Rozhodnuti a Stanovisek. (CS ISSN 0036-522X) **2677**
Sbornik Archivnich Praci. (CS ISSN 0036-5246) **2783**, 2321
Sbornik Geologickych Ved: Antropozoikum/Journal of Geological Sciences: Anthropozoic. (CS ISSN 0036-5270) **1579**
Sbornik Geologickych Ved: Geologie/Journal of Geological Sciences: Geology. (CS ISSN 0581-9172) **1579**
Sbornik Geologickych Ved: Hydrogeologie, Inzenyrska Geologie/Journal of Geological Sciences: Hydrogeology, Engineering Geology. (CS ISSN 0036-5289) **1600**
Sbornik Geologickych Ved: Loziskova Geologie, Mineralogie/Journal of Geological Sciences: Economic Geology, Mineralogy. (CS ISSN 0581-9180) **1579**
Sbornik Geologickych Ved: Paleontologie/Journal of Geological Sciences: Paleontology. (CS ISSN 0036-5297) **3660**
Sbornik Geologickych Ved: Technologie, Geochemie/Journal of Geological Sciences: Technology, Geochemistry. (CS ISSN 0036-5300) **1579**
Sbornik Geologickych Ved: Uzita Geofyzika/Journal of Geological Sciences: Applied Geophysics. (CS ISSN 0036-5319) **1594**
Sbornik Historicky. (CS ISSN 0577-3725) **2385**
Sbornik k Dejinam 19 a 20 Stoleti. (CS ISSN 0231-6153) **2385**
Sbornik k Problematice Dejin Imperialismu. (CS ISSN 0231-620X) **2385**
Sbornik Lekarsky. (CS ISSN 0036-5327) **3151**
Sbornik Praci Historickych. (CS) **2385**
Sbornik Praci Vychodoceskych Archivu. (CS) **2385**
Sbornik Statei po Frantsuzskoi Lingvistike i Metodike Prepodavaniya Inostrannogo Yazika v V V U Ze. (RU) **2839**, 1759
Sbornik Statniho Oblastniho Archivu v Opave *see* Statni Oblastni Archiv v Opave. Sbornik **2389**
Sbornik U V T I Z - Genetika a Slechteni *see* Genetika a Slechteni **543**
Sbornik U V T I Z - Meliorace *see* Meliorace **107**

Sbornik U V T I Z - Ochrana Rostlin *see* Ochrana Rostlin **186**
Sbornik U V T I Z - Potravinarske Vedy *see* Potravinarske Vedy **2079**
Sbornik U V T I Z - Sociologie Zemedelstvi *see* Sociologie Venkova a Zemedelstvi **120**
Sbornik U V T I Z - Zahradnictvi *see* Zahradnictvi **2141**
Sbornik Vlastivednych Praci z Podblannicka. (CS) **2385**
Scabbard and Blade Journal. (US ISSN 0036-5408) **3471**
Scacco. (IT) **4486**
Scaffold Industry Association. Newsletter. (US) **631**, 3655
Scala. (GW ISSN 0340-0441) **2191**, 2385, 3924
Scala International. (GW ISSN 0036-5416) **2191**
Scala International *see* Scala **2191**
Scale *see* Spielzeug-Markt **2282**
Scale. (GW) **2441**
Scale Auto Enthusiast. (US) **2441**
Scale Cabinetmaker. (US ISSN 0145-8213) **2441**
†Scale Coupler. (US) **5273**
Scale Journal *see* Weighing & Measurement **3449**
Scale Manufacturers Association Weighlog *see* S M A Weighlog **3448**
Scale Model Trains. (UK) **2441**
Scale Modeler. (US ISSN 0036-5424) **2441**
Scale Models *see* Scale Models International **2441**
Scale Models International. (UK ISSN 0269-834X) **2441**, 4701
Scale R - C Modeler. (US ISSN 0199-7327) **2441**
Scales. *see* Al-Qistas **2669**
Scales of Cost Queensland. (AT ISSN 0727-7903) **2677**
Scales of Costs, Charges and Fees N.S.W. (AT ISSN 0727-7881) **2677**
Scalpel. (US) **1323**
Scalpel and Tongs. (US ISSN 0048-9255) **3757**
SCAN *see* S C A N **61**
▼Scan. (NE ISSN 0925-1413) **191**, 1967, 4828
Scan. (AT ISSN 0811-9929) **1360**
Scan. (UK ISSN 0141-4100) **1686**, 4418
Scan (New York). (US ISSN 0036-5467) **2022**, 1661
Scan Magazine *see* Popular Communications **1358**
Scan Ref. (DK ISSN 0284-0758) **2303**
Scandal Sheet. (US) **2441**
Scandanavian and European Shipping Review. (UK ISSN 0955-4408) **4737**
Scandanavian Journal of the Old Testament. (DK ISSN 0901-8328) **4200**
Scandia. (SW ISSN 0036-5483) **2385**
†Scandica Magazin. (GW ISSN 0721-2089) **5273**
Scandinavia Stamp Catalogue. (UK ISSN 0142-985X) **3757**
Scandinavian Actuarial Journal. (SW ISSN 0346-1238) **2542**
Scandinavian - American Bulletin. (US ISSN 0048-9263) **2022**
Scandinavian Atlas of Historic Towns. (DK) **2385**, 4094
Scandinavian Audiology. (SW ISSN 0048-9271) **2289**, 3151
Scandinavian Economic History Review. (SW ISSN 0036-5491) **898**
Scandinavian Forum. (CN) **2022**
Scandinavian Heritage. (CN) **2022**, 2422
Scandinavian Housing and Planning Research. (SW ISSN 0281-5737) **2496**
Scandinavian Institute of African Studies. Annual Seminar Proceedings *see* Scandinavian Institute of African Studies. Seminar Proceedings **2334**
Scandinavian Institute of African Studies. Research Report. (SW ISSN 0080-6714) **2334**

Scandinavian Institute of African Studies. Rural Development. (SW) **248**, 157
Scandinavian Institute of African Studies. Seminar Proceedings. (SW ISSN 0281-0018) **2334**
Scandinavian Institute of Asian Studies. Annual Newsletter *see* N I A S Report **3641**
Scandinavian Institute of Asian Studies. Monograph Series. (UK ISSN 0069-1712) **3643**
Scandinavian Institute of Asian Studies. Occasional Papers. (UK ISSN 0266-206X) **3643**
Scandinavian Insurance Quarterly. *see* Nordisk Foersaekringstidskrift **2539**
Scandinavian Journal of Behaviour Therapy/Nordisk Tidskrift foer Beteendeterapi. (SW ISSN 0345-1402) **4045**
Scandinavian Journal of Caring Sciences. (SW) **3151**
Scandinavian Journal of Clinical & Laboratory Investigation. (UK ISSN 0036-5513) **3263**, 3151
Scandinavian Journal of Clinical and Laboratory Investigation. Supplement.(UK ISSN 0085-591X) **3263**, 3151
Scandinavian Journal of Dental Research. (DK ISSN 0029-845X) **3242**
Scandinavian Journal of Developing Countries *see* Scandinavian Journal of Development Alternatives **4385**
Scandinavian Journal of Development Alternatives. (SW ISSN 0280-2791) **4385**
Scandinavian Journal of Economics. (UK ISSN 0347-0520) **690**
Scandinavian Journal of Educational Research. (UK ISSN 0031-3831) **1661**
Scandinavian Journal of Forest Research. (SW ISSN 0282-7581) **2107**
Scandinavian Journal of Gastroenterology. (NO ISSN 0036-5521) **3270**
Scandinavian Journal of Gastroenterology. Supplement. (NO ISSN 0085-5928) **3270**
Scandinavian Journal of Haematology *see* European Journal of Haematology **3271**
Scandinavian Journal of Haematology. Supplementum *see* European Journal of Haematology. Supplementum **3272**
Scandinavian Journal of History. (SW ISSN 0346-8755) **2322**
Scandinavian Journal of Immunology. (UK ISSN 0300-9475) **3188**
Scandinavian Journal of Infectious Diseases. (SW ISSN 0036-5548) **3223**
Scandinavian Journal of Libraries. *see* Nordisk Tidskrift Foer Bok- och Biblioteksvaesen **4133**
Scandinavian Journal of Management. (US ISSN 0281-7527) **1027**
Scandinavian Journal of Medicine & Science in Sports. (DK ISSN 0905-7188) **3373**, 3151
Scandinavian Journal of Metallurgy. (DK ISSN 0371-0459) **3419**
Scandinavian Journal of Photography and Film *see* Fotonyheterna **3791**
Scandinavian Journal of Plastic and Reconstructive Surgery. (SW ISSN 0036-5556) **3384**
Scandinavian Journal of Primary Health Care. (SW ISSN 0107-833X) **3151**
Scandinavian Journal of Psychology. (SW ISSN 0036-5564) **4045**
Scandinavian Journal of Rehabilitation Medicine. (SW ISSN 0036-5505) **3151**
Scandinavian Journal of Rheumatology. (SW ISSN 0300-9742) **3370**
Scandinavian Journal of Social Medicine.(SW ISSN 0300-8037) **3151**, 4385
Scandinavian Journal of Sports Sciences *see* Scandinavian Journal of Medicine & Science in Sports **3373**
Scandinavian Journal of Statistics. (UK ISSN 0303-6898) **4585**

Scandinavian Journal of Thoracic and Cardiovascular Surgery. (SW ISSN 0036-5580) **3384**
Scandinavian Journal of Urology and Nephrology. (SW ISSN 0036-5599) **3389**
Scandinavian Journal of Veterinary Science. *see* Nordisk Veterinaermedicin **5248**
Scandinavian Journal of Work, Environment & Health. (FI ISSN 0355-3140) **3622**
Scandinavian Magazine for Cleaning and Washing. *see* Nordisk Tidskrift for Rensning og Vask **1282**
Scandinavian Numismatic Journal. *see* Nordisk Numismatisk Aarsskrift **5248**
Scandinavian Oil - Gas Magazine. (NO ISSN 0332-5334) **3701**
Scandinavian Periodicals Index in Economics and Business *see* Scanp **737**
Scandinavian Political Studies. (NO ISSN 0080-6757) **3924**
Scandinavian Political Studies Yearbook *see* Scandinavian Political Studies **3924**
Scandinavian Psychoanalytic Review. (DK ISSN 0106-2301) **3354**
Scandinavian Public Library Quarterly. (SW ISSN 0036-5602) **2783**, 4136
Scandinavian Review. (US ISSN 0098-857X) **2022**, 2216
Scandinavian Saga. (US) **2163**
Scandinavian Shipping Gazette. (DK ISSN 0036-5629) **4737**
Scandinavian Shipping Gazette. *see* Svensk Sjoefarts Tidning **4740**
Scandinavian Studies (Eugene). (US ISSN 0036-5637) **2840**, 2957
Scandinavian Studies (Lewiston). (US) **2022**
Scandinavian Studies in Criminology. (NO ISSN 0085-5936) **1522**
Scandinavian Studies in Law. (SW ISSN 0085-5944) **2677**
Scandinavica. (UK ISSN 0036-5653) **2957**, 4638
Scando-Slavica. (DK ISSN 0080-6765) **2840**, 2957
Scanner. (CN) **1907**
Scanning. (US ISSN 0161-0457) **561**
Scanning, Coding & Automation Newsletter Ltd. Newsletter *see* S C A N Newsletter **1415**
Scanning Electron Microscopy *see* Scanning Microscopy **561**
Scanning Microscopy. (US ISSN 0891-7035) **561**, 3263, 3857
Scanning Microscopy Supplement. (US ISSN 0892-953X) **561**
Scanorama. (SW) **4803**
Scanp. (FI ISSN 0358-0520) **737**, 22
Scapulier *see* Tegenwoordig **4205**
Scarboro Missions. (CN ISSN 0700-6802) **4200**
Scarborough Business Leader *see* Scarborough Business Magazine **1117**
Scarborough Business Magazine. (CN) **1117**, 822
Scarcity. (UG) **690**
Scarecrow Author Bibliographies. (US) **411**
Scarecrow Library Administration Series.(US) **2783**
Scarlet & Gold. (CN) **1522**
Scarlet Letter. (AT ISSN 0311-7057) **4852**, 4363, 4419, 4836
Scarlet Woman. (AT ISSN 0313-4423) **4852**, 3924
Scarlett. (US) **1465**, 1474
Scarlett Letter *see* Scarlett **1465**
Scarp. (AT) **3005**
Scat! (CN) **2957**, 343
Scautismo. (IT ISSN 0036-5696) **1243**, 1301
Scavenger's Newsletter. (US ISSN 0894-2617) **2575**, 2957
Sceala Scoil an Leinn Cheiltigh. *see* School of Celtic Studies. Newsletter **2840**
†Scen och Salong. (SW ISSN 0036-5718) **5273**
Scena. (GW ISSN 0036-5726) **4638**, 306

6642 SCENA

Scena. (YU ISSN 0036-5734) **4638**
Scena Illustrata. (IT ISSN 0036-5742) **2883**
Scena Svizzera. *see* Szene Schweiz **4639**
Scenaria. (SA ISSN 0256-002X) **4638**, 3579
Scene. (CN) **2179**
▼Scene. (US) **3517**
†Scene. (AT) **5273**
Scene (New York) *see* W **1295**
Scene (Northridge). (US ISSN 0048-931X) **2883**, 1324
Scene Musicale *see* Music Scene **5241**
Scene Out. (UK ISSN 0960-5754) **2457**, 3947
Scene Suisse. *see* Szene Schweiz **4639**
Scenery, Costumes, and Musical Materials Directory. (US) **3579**, 4638
Scenes et Pistes. (FR ISSN 0036-5793) **4785**
Scenes Magazine. (SZ) **343**, 3579, 4638
Scenic Spots and Historical Sites. *see* Fengjing Mingsheng **4762**
Scepter. (US) **1324**
Schaak. (NE) **4487**
Schaaknieuws. (NE) **4487**
Schaakschakeringen. (NE) **4487**
Het Schaap. (NE) **225**
†Schabacker Investment Management. Weekly Advisory Bulletin. (US ISSN 0882-2190) **5274**
Schabacker's Switch Fund Advisory *see* Jay Schabacker's Mutual Fund Investing **952**
Schach. (GW ISSN 0048-9328) **4487**
Schach Aktiv. (AU) **4487**
Schach-Archiv. (GW) **4487**
Schach-Echo *see* Schachmagazin 64 - Schach-Echo **4487**
Schach in Baden. (GW) **4487**
Schach Informationen. (GW) **4487**
Schachklub Hietzing Memphis Nachrichtenblatt. (AU) **4487**
Schachmagazin 64 *see* Schachmagazin 64 - Schach-Echo **4487**
Schachmagazin 64 - Schach-Echo. (GW) **4487**
Die Schachwoche. (SZ ISSN 0176-2257) **4487**
Schacklub Hietzing Nachrichtenblatt *see* Schachklub Hietzing Memphis Nachrichtenblatt **4487**
Schacknytt. (SW ISSN 0346-0770) **4487**
Schadenprisma. (GW ISSN 0343-3560) **2034**
Schakend Nederland. (NE ISSN 0036-5890) **4487**
Scharnhorst Auslese. (GW ISSN 0036-5920) **3477**, 2330
Schartzer - Schertzer Connection. (US ISSN 0882-5890) **2163**
Schatzkammer. (US ISSN 0740-1965) **2840**, 1759
Schau ins Land. (US ISSN 1041-2018) **2191**
Die Schaubuehne. (GW ISSN 0176-1188) **4638**
Schaufenster *see* Schaufenster & Shop Design **38**
Schaufenster & Shop Design. (GW ISSN 0933-016X) **38**
Die Schaulade. (GW ISSN 0036-5947) **1166**, 357
Schauspielfuehrer. (GW ISSN 0342-4553) **4638**
Scheben News. (GW) **38**
Scheckheft Studium. (GW) **1661**
Schedario. (IT ISSN 0036-5955) **1661**, 4136
Schede Medievali. (IT ISSN 0392-5404) **2385**
Schede Perforate e Calcolo Elettronico *see* Sistemi e Impresa **1439**
†Schedule of Wells Drilled for Oil and Gas in Alberta. (CN ISSN 0380-4305) **5274**
▼Scheherezade. (UK) **3014**
Schema de Classification de la Statistique Scolaire. *see* Klassifikationsschema der Schulstatistik **1729**
Schema et Schematisation *see* Revue de Bibliologie **2955**
Scherma. *see* Fechten **4472**

Scherma. (IT ISSN 0036-6005) **4487**
Schermer's Motorrad Katalog. (GW) **4520**
Scherzo *see* Scherzo - Guide Musical **3579**
Scherzo. (US ISSN 1048-2180) **3579**, 1264
Scherzo - Guide Musical. (FR) **3579**
Schiedsmanns Zeitung. (GW ISSN 0342-7471) **2677**, 3947, 4045, 4073
Schienen der Welt. *see* Rail International **4713**
Schienenfahrzeuge *see* Der Eisenbahningenieur **4709**
Schietsport. (NE ISSN 0048-9344) **4487**
Schiff und Hafen *see* Schiff und Hafen - Kommandobruecke **4737**
Schiff und Hafen. (GW ISSN 0938-1643) **4737**
Schiff und Hafen - Kommandobruecke. (GW) **4737**, 1873
Schiff und Zeit. (GW) **4737**
Schiffahrt International. (GW ISSN 0342-491X) **4737**, 2048
Schiffahrt International mit Seekiste und Nautilus *see* Schiffahrt International **4737**
Schiffahrt und Strom. (AU) **4737**
Schiffahrtmedizinisches Institut der Marine, Kiel. Veroeffentlichungen. (GW ISSN 0080-679X) **3151**
Schiffbauforschung. (GW ISSN 0036-6056) **4737**
Schiffbautechnik *see* Seewirtschaft **4738**
Schiffbautechnischen Gesellschaft. Jahrbuch. (US ISSN 0374-1222) **4737**
Schiffli Digest and Directory *see* Embroidery Directory **4618**
Schiffs-Ingenieur Journal. (GW) **4737**
Schiffs Modell. (GW ISSN 0722-7108) **2441**
Schiffsbetriebstechnik Flensburg. (GW ISSN 0177-1116) **4737**, 1938, 3023
Schiffsliste. (GW) **4737**
Schiffspropeller. (GW) **2441**
Schiffstechnik. (GW ISSN 0036-6064) **4737**
Die Schilddruese. (GW ISSN 0720-065X) **3256**
Schip en Werf. (NE ISSN 0036-6099) **4737**
Schipperke Club of America. Bulletin. (US) **3713**
Schirmer - News. (US) **3579**
Schizophrenia Bulletin. (US ISSN 0586-7614) **3354**
Schizophrenia Research. (NE ISSN 0920-9964) **3354**
Schizophrenics Anonymous International. Bulletin *see* Health and Nutrition Update **3338**
Schlach Peremohy/Way to Victory. (GW) **2022**
Schlager fuer Dich. (GW ISSN 0036-6137) **3579**
Schlegel Translations. (US) **3005**
Schleiermacher Studies and Translation.(US) **4200**
Schlern. (IT ISSN 0036-6145) **343**, 2058, 2262, 2322
Schlesien. (GW ISSN 0036-6153) **4338**, 2514
Schlesierbund Nuernberg. Rundbrief. (GW) **2022**
Schlesierbundes Nuernberg. Rundbrief. (GW) **2385**
Schlesischer Kulturspiegel. (GW) **2191**
Schleswig-Holstein. (GW ISSN 0937-7247) **2386**
Schleswig-Holstein. Jahrbuch - Heimatkalender. (GW ISSN 0937-2644) **2957**
Schleswig-Holstein. Kulturminister. Nachrichtenblatt *see* Schleswig-Holstein. Ministerin fuer Bildung, Wissenschaft, Jugend und Kultur. Nachrichtenblatt **1661**
Schleswig-Holstein. Ministerin fuer Bildung, Wissenschaft, Jugend und Kultur. Nachrichtenblatt. (GW ISSN 0937-0005) **1661**
Schleswig-Holstein-Kalender. (GW) **2386**

Schleswig-Holsteinischen Landesmuseum. Jahrbuch. (GW) **3532**
Schleswig-Holsteinischer Heimatkalender *see* Schleswig-Holstein. Jahrbuch - Heimatkalender **2957**
Schleswig-Holsteinisches Aerzteblatt. (GW ISSN 0341-8707) **3151**
Schlittenpost. (GW) **4487**
Schloss & Beschlag & Markt. (GW ISSN 0179-1591) **643**
Schluessel fuer Berufsausbildung/Code de la Formation Professionelle. (SZ) **1686**
Schlumberger Limited. Technical Review *see* Oilfield Review **3696**
Schmalenbachs Zeitschrift fuer Betriebswirtschaftliche Forschung *see* ZFBF **1031**
Schmalfilm. (GW) **3517**
†Schmankerl. (GW ISSN 0085-5952) **5274**
Der Schmerz. (GW ISSN 0932-433X) **3151**
Schmerz (Heidelberg) *see* European Journal of Pain **3097**
Schmerzdiagnostik und Therapie. (GW ISSN 0178-692X) **3192**, 3311, 3354
Schmerzensgeld-Betraege *see* A D A C Handbuch: Schmerzensgeld-Betraege **2719**
Schmiede Journal. (GW ISSN 0933-8330) **3419**
†Schmierungstechnik. (GW ISSN 0036-6226) **5274**
Schmollers Jahrbuch fuer Wirtschafts- und Sozialwissenschaften *see* Zeitschrift fuer Wirtschafts- und Sozialwissenschaften **701**
Schmuck und Uhren. (GW ISSN 0341-9002) **2566**
Schneider Connections. (US ISSN 0882-5904) **2163**
Schneller Bote *see* Schneller-Magazin **4248**
Schneller-Magazin. (GW) **4248**, 1243
Schnellertsbericht. (GW) **2386**
Schnellreport *see* Wella Aktiengesellschaft. Report **699**
Scho Wida. (GW) **1661**
Schoeffe. (GW ISSN 0036-6250) **3924**
Schoen - Visie. (NE ISSN 0036-6269) **4361**
Schoenberger Hefte. (GW ISSN 0170-6128) **4248**, 1661
Das Schoene Allgaeu. (GW) **2191**
Schoener Bayerischer Wald. (GW) **2191**
Schoener Wohnen. (GW) **2555**, 2449
Schoenere Heimat. (GW ISSN 0177-4492) **2386**
Schoenhengster Heimat. (GW ISSN 0937-6356) **2191**
Schoenhengster Jahrbuch. (GW ISSN 0487-6598) **2191**
Schoenste Schweizer Buecher. (SZ ISSN 0080-6838) **4136**
†Die Schoensten Buecher der Deutschen Demokratischen Republik. (GW) **5274**
Schoenwereld. (NE ISSN 0036-6307) **4361**, 2738
Schoharie County Historical Review. (US ISSN 0361-8528) **2422**
Schoharie Museum of the Iroquois Indian. Museum Notes *see* Iroquois Indian Museum. Museum Notes **3525**
Scholar *see* Views **1269**
Scholarly Communication: Online Publishing and Education *see* S C O P E **5272**
Scholarly Inquiry for Nursing Practice: An International Journal. (US ISSN 0889-7182) **3286**
Scholarly Publishing. (CN ISSN 0036-634X) **4136**
Scholarly Research and Review. (US ISSN 1047-6377) **2514**
Scholars' Choice. (US ISSN 0036-6358) **4213**
Scholars' Facsimiles & Reprints. (US ISSN 0161-7729) **2514**

Scholarships, Fellowships and Loan News Service and Counselors Information Services *see* Student Aid Newsletter: Fellowships, Grants, Loans, Awards and Scholarships **1717**
Scholarships Guide for Commonwealth Postgraduate Students *see* Awards for Postgraduate Study at Commonwealth Universities **1701**
Scholastic Action. (US ISSN 0163-3570) **1759**
Scholastic Coach. (US ISSN 0036-6382) **3808**, 1759
Scholastic Editor *see* Trends in College Media **2576**
Scholastic Editor's Trends in Publications *see* Trends in College Media **2576**
Scholastic Editor's Trends in Publications *see* Trends in High School Media **2576**
Scholastic Magazine. (US) **1324**
Scholastic Math. (US ISSN 0198-8379) **3054**, 1759
Scholastic News: Citizen. (US) **1264**
Scholastic News: News Citizen *see* Scholastic News: Citizen **1264**
Scholastic News: News Explorer. (US ISSN 0736-0592) **1264**, 1661
Scholastic News: News Pilot. (US ISSN 0744-916X) **1264**, 1661
Scholastic News: News Ranger. (US ISSN 0736-055X) **1264**, 1661
Scholastic News: Newstime. (US ISSN 0736-0622) **1264**, 1661
Scholastic News Trails. (US ISSN 0736-0576) **1264**, 1661
Scholastic Scope. (US ISSN 0036-6412) **1661**
Scholastic Search *see* Scholastic Update **1264**
Scholastic Sprint. (US ISSN 0163-3589) **1264**
Scholastic Update. (US ISSN 0745-7065) **1264**, 1661
Scholastic Voice. (US ISSN 0032-6380) **1264**, 1661
Scholastic Wrestling News *see* Wrestling U.S.A. Magazine **4497**
Scholastik *see* Theologie und Philosophie **4206**
School. (NE ISSN 0377-5054) **1661**
School Administrator. (US ISSN 0036-6439) **1731**
School Age Notes. (US ISSN 0278-3126) **1243**, 1759
School and College. (US ISSN 1045-3970) **1661**
School and College. (IE) **1697**
School and Community. (US ISSN 0036-6447) **1661**
School Arts. (US ISSN 0036-6463) **1759**, 357
School Bell. (AT ISSN 0048-9387) **1731**
School Board News. (US ISSN 1045-8115) **1731**
School Board Notes *see* New Jersey School Boards Association. School Board Notes **1730**
School Boards *see* American School Board Journal **1725**
School Bookshop News *see* Books for Keeps **4123**
School Bus Briefs. (US) **4656**, 1731
School Bus Fleet. (US ISSN 0036-6501) **4656**
School Business Affairs. (US ISSN 0036-651X) **1731**
†School - Business Partnerships Report.(US) **5274**
School Calendar/Calendrier Scolaire. (CN ISSN 0382-7879) **1661**
School Child Care Report *see* Report on School-Aged Child Care **1243**
School Counselor. (US ISSN 0036-6536) **1661**
†School Curriculum Development Committee. Annual Report (Year). (UK) **5274**
▼School Effectiveness and School Improvement. (NE ISSN 0924-3453) **1661**
School en Besturen. (NE) **1731**
School en Godsdienst. (NE ISSN 0036-6544) **1759**, 4275

School Examinations and Assessment Council Assessment Matters see S E A C Assessment Matters **1759**
School Food Service Journal. (US ISSN 0160-6271) **2081**, 1731
School Food Service News. (US) **2480**, 1731
School Foodservice Who's Who. (US) **1152**, 2081, 3612
School Governor. (UK) **1661**
School Guide. (US) **1697**
School Health: A Guide for Health Professionals. (US) **3326**
School Health Bulletin see H E A P Journal **4102**
School House Alert. (US ISSN 1048-3896) **3286**
†School Improvement Exchange. (US) **5274**
School Intervention Report. (US ISSN 0894-5152) **1244**, 1539
School Law Bulletin (Boston). (US ISSN 8755-8297) **2677**
School Law Bulletin (Chapel Hill). (US ISSN 0886-2508) **2677**, 1661
School Law News. (US ISSN 0194-2271) **1731**
School Leader see New Jersey School Boards Association. School Leader **1730**
School Leaver. (UG) **1661**, 4419
School Leaver. (UK) **1716**
School Librarian. (UK ISSN 0036-6595) **2783**, 1731
School Librarian's Workshop. (US ISSN 0271-3667) **2783**
School Libraries Bulletin. (NR ISSN 0331-8109) **2783**
School Libraries Group News. (UK ISSN 0261-1678) **2783**
†School Libraries in Australia. (AT ISSN 0158-9172) **5274**
School Libraries in Canada. (CN ISSN 0227-3780) **2783**, 1661
School Library Journal. (US ISSN 0362-8930) **2783**, 1661, 4136
School Library Media Activities Monthly.(US ISSN 0889-9371) **2783**, 1759
School Library Media Annual. (US ISSN 0739-7712) **2783**
School Library Media Quarterly. (US ISSN 0278-4823) **2783**, 1661
†School Library Newsletter. (CN ISSN 0706-2915) **5274**
School Magazine. (AT ISSN 0155-1108) **1264**, 2957
School Management Study Group Newsletter see S M S G Newsletter **1731**
School Marketing Newsletter. (US) **1731**, 1053
School Mates. (US ISSN 1040-7707) **4487**, 1264
†School Mathematics Journal. (AT ISSN 0158-6289) **5274**
School Media Centre see Media Focus **2773**
School Music News. (US ISSN 0036-6668) **3579**, 1759
School News see EdNews **1626**
School of Business Update. (US) **690**, 1324
School of Celtic Studies. Newsletter/ Sceala Scoil an Leinn Cheiltigh. (IE ISSN 0790-9853) **2840**, 1759
School of International Studies. Publications on Asia. (US) **2341**
School of International Studies. Publications on Russia and Eastern Europe. (US) **3924**
School of Library and Information Science. Occasional Papers Series. (US ISSN 1050-8147) **2783**
School of Ocean and Earth Science and Technology. Reports and Special Publications. (US) **1594**
School of Ocean and Earth Science and Technology. Yearbook. (US) **1594**
School Organisation. (UK ISSN 0260-1362) **1731**
School Organisation & Management Abstracts. (UK ISSN 0261-2755) **1679**, 22
School Photographer. (US) **3797**, 1731
School Practitioner Series. (US) **4045**, 1244

School Press Review. (US ISSN 0036-6730) **2575**
School Psychology Digest see School Psychology Review **4046**
School Psychology Emergency Centre. Newsletter see Community Stress Prevention **4017**
School Psychology International. (UK ISSN 0143-0343) **1759**, 4045
School Psychology Quarterly. (US ISSN 1045-3830) **4046**, 1244
School Psychology Review. (US ISSN 0279-6015) **4046**
School Reform. see Riforma della Scuola **1660**
School Safety see School Safety World **1731**
School Safety World. (US) **1731**
School Scene. (US) **1661**, 4608
School Science. (II ISSN 0036-679X) **4338**, 1661
School Science and Mathematics. (US ISSN 0036-6803) **1661**, 3054, 4338
School Science & Mathematics Association, Inc. Arrt see S S M Arrt **1759**
School Science Review. (UK ISSN 0036-6811) **4338**, 1759
School Security Report. (US) **1527**, 1661
School Shop see School Shop - Tech Directions **1759**
School Shop - Tech Directions. (US ISSN 1050-3749) **1759**
School Social Work Journal. (US ISSN 0161-5653) **1741**, 1244, 4419
School Tech News. (US) **1661**
†School Technology. (UK ISSN 0140-7732) **5274**
▼School Transportation News. (US) **4656**, 1661
School Trustee. (CN ISSN 0036-6854) **1731**
School Volunteering. (US) **1661**, 4419
School Yarn Magazine. (UK ISSN 0036-6862) **1264**
Schoolblad. (NE ISSN 0036-6889) **1661**
Schooldays. (US ISSN 0746-2018) **1662**
Schoolgirl Story Magazine. (UK ISSN 0036-6897) **1264**
Schoolmaster and Career Teacher see N A S U W T Career Teacher Journal **1648**
Schools see Which School **1697**
Schools. (UK) **1697**, 2840
Schools Abroad. (US ISSN 0080-6900) **1723**
Schools Abroad of Interest to Americans see Schools Abroad **1723**
†Schools and Colleges Welcome. (UK) **5274**
Schools and the Courts. (US ISSN 0164-3851) **2677**, 1662
Schools in the Middle. (US ISSN 0276-4482) **1662**
Schools in the United States and Canada Offering Graduate Education in Pharmacology. (US) **3742**, 1697
Schools of Prayer. (UK ISSN 0261-5703) **4200**
Schools of the United Kingdom see Independent Schools of the United Kingdom **1695**
Schools Unit News. (UK) **1723**
Schooltime see Top (Benningen) **1268**
†Schoolword. (US) **5274**
De Schoonheidsspecialist. (NE ISSN 0168-9630) **374**
Schopenhauer-Jahrbuch. (GW ISSN 0080-6935) **3781**
Schornsteinfegerhandwerk. (GW) **631**, 2561
Schott Aktuell. (GW) **3579**
Schott Intern. (GW ISSN 0343-9445) **1166**
Schott-Kurier see Schott Aktuell **3579**
Schottische Terrier Gazette. (GW ISSN 0178-2177) **3713**
Schreibheft. (GW ISSN 0174-2132) **2957**, 3005
†Schreisse. (GW ISSN 0179-6429) **5274**
Schrift. (NE) **4275**

Schriften aus dem Finnland-Institut Koeln. (GW ISSN 0430-5809) **2957**, 2322
Schriften des Oesterreichischen Kulturinstituts Kairo. Archaeologisch-Historische Abteilung. (GW ISSN 0342-4839) **2431**, 284
Schriften des Werksarchivs. (GW ISSN 0724-2557) **1084**
Schriften und Quellen der Alten Welt. (GW ISSN 0080-696X) **284**, 2322
Schriften zum Staats- und Voelkerrecht.(GW) **2729**
Schriften zur Friedens- und Konfliktforschung. (AU) **4385**
Schriften zur Geistesgeschichte des Oestlichen Europa. (GW ISSN 0340-6490) **2386**
Schriften zur Geschichte und Kultur der Antike. (GW ISSN 0138-595X) **1279**
Schriften zur Geschichte und Kultur des Alten Orients. (GW ISSN 0080-6994) **2341**, 3643
Schriften zur Handelsforschung. (GW ISSN 0080-7001) **839**
Schriften zur Kooperationsforschung. Berichte. (GW ISSN 0080-7028) **832**
Schriften zur Kooperationsforschung. Studien. (GW ISSN 0080-7036) **832**
Schriften zur Kooperationsforschung. Vortraege. (GW ISSN 0080-7044) **832**
Schriften zur Oeffentlichen Verwaltung und Oeffentlichen Wirtschaft. (GW) **4073**
Schriften zur Philosophie und ihrer Geschichte. (GW ISSN 0138-3418) **3781**, 2386
Schriften zur Phonetik, Sprachwissenschaft und Kommunikationsforschung. (GW ISSN 0558-9274) **2840**
Schriften zur Ur- und Fruehgeschichte. (GW ISSN 0138-3361) **2322**
Schriftenreihe Aktuelle Fragen der Energiewirtschaft. (GW) **1795**
†Schriftenreihe das Andere Deutschland.(GW) **5274**
†Schriftenreihe der Hochschule der Kuenste Berlin. (GW ISSN 0723-0788) **5274**
Schriftenreihe des Bayerisches Landesamtes fuer Wasserwirtschaft. (GW ISSN 0172-665X) **4828**, 1600
Schriftenreihe des Managementzentrums. (SZ) **690**
Schriftenreihe Finanzwirtschaft und Finanzrecht. (SZ) **798**, 2677
†Schriftenreihe fuer Agrarwirtschaft. (AU) **5274**
Schriftenreihe fuer die Evangelische Frau. (GW ISSN 0036-696X) **4852**, 4248
Schriftenreihe fuer Geologische Wissenschaften/Serials in Geological Sciences. (GW ISSN 0323-8946) **1579**
Schriftenreihe fuer Laendliche Sozialfragen. (GW ISSN 0080-7133) **4419**
†Schriftenreihe fuer Raumforschung und Raumplanung. (AU ISSN 0558-9746) **5274**
Schriftenreihe fuer Sportwissenschaft und Sportpraxis see Sportwissenschaft und Sportpraxis **4492**
Schriftenreihe fuer Vegetationskunde. (GW ISSN 0085-5960) **517**
Schriftenreihe: Gesellschaft und Betrieb.(AU) **2677**
Schriftenreihe Neurologie - Neurology Series. (US ISSN 0080-715X) **3354**
Schriftenreihe zur Orts-, Regional- und Landesplanung. (SZ) **2496**
▼Schriftenreihe zur Philosophie Karl L. Poppers und des Kritischen Rationalismus. (NE ISSN 0925-2657) **3781**
Das Schrifttum der Agrarwirtschaft. (AU ISSN 0036-6986) **157**
Schrifttum fur Deutschen Kunst. (GW ISSN 0080-7176) **343**

SCHWARZWALD 6643

Schrifttums fuer den Bereich Haushalt und Verbauch. Bibliographie. (GW ISSN 0170-5768) **2449**, 1508
†Schrifttumsspiegel. (AU) **5274**
Schrottbetrieb see Recycling **1986**
▼Schubert Durch Die Brille. (GW) **421**, 3579
Schuetz-Jahrbuch. (GW ISSN 0174-2345) **3579**
Der Schuetze. (GW) **4487**, 4555
Schuetzen und Helfen. (GW ISSN 0138-4414) **1274**
Schuh-Kurier. (GW ISSN 0036-7044) **4361**
Schuh-Revue. (AU) **4361**
Schuh-Zeitung. (AU ISSN 0036-7060) **4361**, 2738
Der Schuhmacher. (GW ISSN 0936-6121) **4361**
Schuhmacher Fachreport. (GW) **4361**
Schuhmarkt. (GW ISSN 0036-7079) **4361**, 2738
Schuhtechnik A B C see Schuhtechnik International **4361**
Schuhtechnik International. (GW ISSN 0933-808X) **4361**
Schul-Management. (GW ISSN 0341-8235) **1731**
Schul- und Sportstaettenbau see Schule- und Sportstaette **631**
Schulbibliothek Aktuell. (GW ISSN 0341-471X) **2783**
Schuldrucker. (GW) **1686**
Schule Heute. (GW) **1686**
Schule in der Europaeischen Gemeinschaft see E G Informationen fuer die Schule **1626**
Schule und Mission. (GW) **4275**
Schule und Psychologie see Psychologie in Erziehung und Unterricht **1657**
Schule- und Sportstaette. (AU) **631**, 1662
Schuler im Museum see M P Z - Kooperationsprojekt **3527**
Schuler Lectures in History and Political Science. (US) **2322**, 3924
Schulfernsehen. (GW) **1759**
Schulfernsehen (Munich). (GW ISSN 0036-7125) **1662**, 1379
Der Schulgeograph. (GW ISSN 0172-5408) **1759**, 2262
Schulleiter Handbuch. (GW ISSN 0170-7922) **1731**
SchulPraxis. (GW ISSN 0720-8634) **1759**, 1731
Schulreport. (GW ISSN 0586-965X) **1662**
†Schultz Medicinalbibliotek. Publikation.(DK ISSN 0109-260X) **5274**
Schulverkehrswacht see Zeitschrift fuer Verkehrserziehung **4723**
Schulverwaltungsblatt fuer Niedersachsen. (GW ISSN 0048-9484) **1731**
Schuss. (UK ISSN 0048-9492) **2840**, 1759
Schutz Aktuell. (GW ISSN 0937-2555) **2034**, 1527
Schutz Society Reports see Seventeenth - Century Music **3580**
Schuyler County Historical Society. Journal. (US) **2422**
Schuylerite. (US) **2422**
Schwachamer Du Ford Genealogical Society. Bulletin. (US) **2163**
Schwaebischer Heimatkalender. (GW) **2386**
Schwaedds. (GW ISSN 0933-7024) **2840**
Schwaelmer Jahrbuch. (GW) **2386**, 2058
Schwalbacher Blaetter see Praxis Spiel und Gruppe **1655**
Schwamm. (GW) **1265**, 1662
†Schwann. (US ISSN 0893-0449) **5274**
†Schwann C D. (US ISSN 0893-0430) **5274**
Schwann-1 Record and Tape Guide see Opus **4461**
Schwann-2 Record and Tape Guide see Spectrum (Boston) **3589**
Schwarte. (GW) **1244**, 1265
Schwartzsche Vakanzen-Zeitung. (GW ISSN 0342-7722) **4073**
Schwarzer Faden. (GW ISSN 0722-8988) **3924**, 2957, 4638
Der Schwarzwald. (GW) **2386**

Schwebstaubmessungen in Hessen. Bericht im Messjahr. (GW ISSN 0724-4770) **1979**
Schweden Heute *see* Sweden Now **2218**
Schweinezucht und Schweinemast. (GW ISSN 0036-7176) **225**
Schweissen und Schneiden. (GW ISSN 0036-7184) **3430**
Schweisstechnik *see* Schweissen und Schneiden **3430**
Schweisstechnik/Soudure. (SZ ISSN 0036-7206) **3430**
Schweitzer's Vademecum Recht. (GW) **2700**
Schweitzer's Vademecum Steuerrecht, Jahresabschleiss und Wirtschaftspruefung. (GW) **2700**
Schweitzer's Vademecum Steuerrecht und Wirtschaftspruefung *see* Schweitzer's Vademecum Steuerrecht, Jahresabschleiss und Wirtschaftspruefung **2700**
Schweiz Arbeitslehrerinnen-Zeitung *see* Schweizerische Arbeitslehrerinnen-Zeitung **1662**
Schweiz, Suisse, Svizzera, Svizra, Switzerland *see* Revue Schweiz Suisse Svizzera **2219**
†Schweizer Aluminium Rundschau/Revue Suisse de l'Aluminium. (SZ ISSN 0036-7257) **5274**
Schweizer Anglistische Arbeiten/Swiss Studies in English. (GW ISSN 0080-7214) **2840**
Schweizer Archiv fuer Neurologie, Neurochirurgie und Psychiatrie. (SZ ISSN 0036-7273) **3354**, **3384**
Schweizer Archiv fuer Tierheilkunde. (SZ ISSN 0036-7281) **4815**
Schweizer Artillerist *see* Artillerie, Armee & Technik **3452**
Schweizer Bank. (SZ ISSN 1010-5808) **799**
Schweizer Baublatt. (SZ ISSN 0036-7303) **631**
Schweizer Baumarkt. (SZ ISSN 0255-6898) **631**
Schweizer Bauwirtschaft/Journal Suisse des Entrepreneurs/Giornale Svizzero degli Impresari Costruttori. (SZ) **631**
Schweizer Beitraege zur Kulturgeschichte und Archaeologie des Mittelalters. (SZ) **284**
Schweizer Beitrage zur Musikwissenschaft. (SZ) **3579**
Schweizer Brauerei-Rundschau *see* Brauerei und Getraenke-Rundschau **379**
Schweizer Briefmarken-Zeitung. (SZ) **3757**
Schweizer Buch. (SZ ISSN 0036-732X) **4136**
Schweizer Buchhandel/Librairie Suisse/Libreria Svizzera. (SZ ISSN 0036-7338) **4136**
Schweizer Buchhandels-Adressbuch. (SZ ISSN 0080-7230) **4136**
Schweizer Cafetiers *see* Cafetier **2472**
Schweizer Fachpresse/Presse Specialisee Suisse/Stampa Specializata Svizzera. (SZ) **2575**
Schweizer Foerster. (SZ ISSN 0378-6919) **2107**
Schweizer Frauenblatt. (SZ ISSN 0036-7346) **4852**, **1294**
Schweizer Gastronomie. (SZ) **2480**
Schweizer Handels - Boerse. (SZ) **208**
Schweizer Heimatbuecher. (SZ) **2386**
Schweizer Heimatwerk: Handwerk - Volkskunst - Kunsthandwerk. (SZ) **357**
Schweizer Holz-Boerse. (SZ) **2107**, **640**, **2117**
Schweizer Hotel Journal. (SZ ISSN 0048-9514) **2480**
Schweizer Hundesport *see* Hunde Haltung Zucht Sport **3711**
Schweizer Industrie. (SZ) **1084**
Schweizer Ingenieur und Architekt/Ingenieurs et Architectes Suisses/Ingegneri e Architetti Svizzeri. (SZ) **306**, **1836**
Schweizer Jaeger/Chasseur Suisse/Cacciatore Svizzero. (SZ ISSN 0036-8016) **4555**
Schweizer Journal. (SZ ISSN 0036-7370) **306**, **631**

Schweizer Journal. *see* Swiss Journal **2219**
Schweizer Kavallerist. (SZ ISSN 0036-7389) **4537**, **3471**
Schweizer Kontakt *see* S K M **4448**
Schweizer Landtechnik. (SZ) **118**, **157**
Schweizer Maschinenmarkt. (SZ ISSN 0036-7397) **3023**, **1907**
Schweizer Monatshefte. (SZ ISSN 0036-7400) **2883**
Schweizer Monatsschrift fuer Zahnmedizin. (SZ ISSN 1011-4203) **3242**
Schweizer Muenzblaetter. *see* Gazette Numismatique Suisse **3599**
Schweizer Musiker-Revue. (SZ ISSN 0036-7419) **3579**
Schweizer Musikerblatt - Bulletin Musical Suisse *see* Presto **3575**
Schweizer Naturschutz/Protection de la Nature. (SZ ISSN 0036-7427) **4338**
Schweizer Pferde. (SZ) **4537**
Schweizer Psychologen. Bulletin *see* Psychoscope **4042**
Schweizer Reklame-Publicite en Suisse *see* Werbung **39**
Schweizer Schach-Magazin/Magazine Suisse d'Echecs. (SZ) **4487**, **1419**
Schweizer Schule. (SZ ISSN 0036-7443) **1662**
Schweizer Soldat und M F D. (SZ) **3471**
Schweizer Spital-Veska. (SZ) **2469**
Schweizer Sport & Mode. (SZ) **4487**
Schweizer Textil-Zeitung *see* Textil-Revue **4625**
Schweizer Tierschutz. (SZ) **231**
Schweizer Tourismus in Zahlen/Tourisme Suisse en Chiffres. (SZ) **4800**
Schweizer Touristik. (SZ) **4785**
Der Schweizer Treuhaender/Expert-Comptable Suisse. (SZ ISSN 0036-746X) **756**
Schweizer Verpackungskatalog. (SZ) **3651**
Schweizer Versicherung. (SZ) **2542**
Schweizer Volkskunde. (SZ ISSN 0048-9522) **2058**
Schweizer Volksport/Sport Populaire Suisse. (SZ) **4487**
Schweizer Waffen-Magazin *see* Internationales Waffen-Magazin **4476**
Schweizer Zeitschrift fuer die Junge Familie *see* Wir Eltern **1246**
Schweizeteische Aerztezeitung/Bulletin des Medecins Suisses/Bollettino dei Medici Svizzeri. (SZ ISSN 0036-7486) **3151**
Schweizerische Amerikanisten-Gesellschaft. Bulletin. *see* Societe Suisse des Americanistes. Bulletin **2422**
Schweizerische Apotheker-Zeitung/Journal Suisse de Pharmacie/Swiss Journal of Pharmacy. (SZ ISSN 0036-7508) **3742**
Schweizerische Arbeitgeber-Zeitung/Journal des Associations Patronales. (SZ ISSN 0036-7516) **993**
Schweizerische Arbeitsgemeinschaft fuer Qualitaetsfoerderung. Bulletin. (SZ) **3448**
Schweizerische Arbeitslehrerinnen-Zeitung. (SZ ISSN 0036-7214) **1662**
Schweizerische Bankwesen. (SZ) **799**
Schweizerische Beitraege zur Altertumswissenschaft. (SZ ISSN 0080-7273) **2386**
Schweizerische Beobachter. (SZ ISSN 0036-7532) **2219**
Schweizerische Bibliotheken/Bibliotheques Suisses. (SZ) **2783**
Schweizerische Bienen-Zeitung. (SZ ISSN 0036-7540) **119**
Schweizerische Blaetter fuer Beruflichen Unterricht Blaetter. (SZ) **1759**, **1301**
Schweizerische Blasmusikzeitung. (SZ) **3579**
Schweizerische Blatter fuer Heizung und Lueftung - Revue Suisse du Chauffage et de la Ventilation *see* Heizung und Lueftung **2300**

Schweizerische Buchdrucker-Zeitung *see* Print **4134**
Schweizerische Chorzeitung/Revue Suisse des Chorales. (SZ) **3579**
Schweizerische Drogistenzeitung. (SZ ISSN 0036-7567) **3742**
Schweizerische Entomologische Gesellschaft. Mitteilungen/Societe Entomologique Suisse. Bulletin. (SZ ISSN 0036-7575) **537**
Schweizerische Fachschrift fuer Buchbindereien *see* Bindetechnik **4121**
Schweizerische Feuerwehr-Zeitung. (SZ) **2034**
Schweizerische Gefluegelzeitung. (SZ) **225**
Schweizerische Gesellschaft fuer Aussenpolitik. Schriftenreihe. (SZ) **3971**
Schweizerische Gesellschaft fuer Klinische Chemie. Bulletin. (SZ ISSN 0253-035X) **482**, **3263**
Schweizerische Gesellschaft fuer Marktforschung. Geschaeftsbericht. (SZ ISSN 0302-2048) **1053**
Schweizerische Gesellschaft fuer Theaterkultur. Jahrbuecher. (SZ) **4638**
Schweizerische Gesellschaft fuer Theaterkultur. Schriften. (SZ) **4638**
Schweizerische Gesellschaft fuer Ur- und Fruehgeschichte. Jahrbuch. (SZ ISSN 0252-1881) **2386**
Schweizerische Gesellschaft fuer Volkskunde. Schriften. (GW ISSN 0080-732X) **2058**
Schweizerische Hauseigentuemer. (SZ) **4158**
Schweizerische Hochschulkonferenz. Jahresbericht *see* Conference Universitaire Suisse. Rapport Annuel **1704**
Schweizerische Juristen-Zeitung/Revue Suisse de Jurisprudence. (SZ ISSN 0036-7613) **2677**
Schweizerische Kaufmaennische Zeitung/Journal Suisse des Employes de Commerce. (SZ) **1053**
Schweizerische Konditor Confiseurmeister Zeitung. (SZ) **2089**
Schweizerische Konjunktur und ihre Aussichten *see* Schweizerische Konjunktur und Vorausschau **884**
Schweizerische Konjunktur und Vorausschau. (SZ) **884**
Schweizerische Landwirtschaftliche Forschung/Recherche Agronomique en Suisse. (SZ ISSN 0036-763X) **119**
Schweizerische Lehrerzeitung. (SZ ISSN 0036-7656) **1662**
Schweizerische Luftverkehrsstatistik - Statistique du Trafic Aerien Suisse *see* Die Schweizerische Zivilluftfahrt **4677**
Schweizerische Medizinische Wochenschrift. (SZ ISSN 0036-7672) **3151**
Schweizerische Medizinische Wochenschrift (Supplementum). (SZ) **3152**
Schweizerische Metzger-Zeitung/Journal Suisse des Bouchers-Charcutiers/Giornale Svizzero dei Macellai. (SZ ISSN 0036-7680) **2081**
Schweizerische Milchzeitung. (SZ) **203**
Schweizerische Mineralogische und Petrographische Mitteilungen/Bulletin Suisse de Mineralogie et Petrographie/Bolletino Svizzero di Mineralogia e Petrografia. (SZ ISSN 0036-7699) **3495**, **1579**
Schweizerische Monatsschrift fuer Zahnheilkunde *see* Schweizer Monatsschrift fuer Zahnmedizin **3242**
Schweizerische Musikforschende Gesellschaft. Publikationen. Serie 2. (SZ ISSN 0080-7354) **3579**
Schweizerische Nationalbank. Monatsbericht. (SZ ISSN 0036-7729) **799**
Schweizerische Naturforschende Gesellschaft. Denkschriften. (SZ) **4338**

Schweizerische Numismatische Rundschau. *see* Revue Suisse de Numismatique **3601**
Schweizerische Palaeontologische Abhandlungen/Memoires Suisse de Paleontologie. (SZ ISSN 0080-7389) **3660**
Schweizerische Photorundschau. (SZ ISSN 0036-7737) **3797**
Schweizerische Politik. *see* Annee Politique Suisse **3873**
Schweizerische Public Relations Gesellschaft Revue *see* P R Revue **36**
Schweizerische Radio- und Fernsehgesellschaft. Jahrbuch. (SZ) **1360**, **1379**
Schweizerische Rundschau fuer Medizin Praxis/Revue Suisse de Medecine. (SZ) **3152**
Schweizerische Schachzeitung. (SZ ISSN 0036-7745) **4487**, **1419**
Schweizerische Schreinerzeitung. (SZ ISSN 0036-7753) **640**, **2561**
Schweizerische Spenglermeister- und Installateur-Zeitung. (SZ) **2303**
Schweizerische Strassenverkehrszaehlung/Recensement Suisse de la Circulation Routiere. (SZ) **4666**
Schweizerische Technische Zeitschrift. (SZ ISSN 0040-151X) **1836**
Schweizerische Textildetaillisten-Zeitung *see* Textil-Revue **4625**
Schweizerische Uhrmacher- und Goldschmiede-Zeitung/Journal Suisse des Horlogers et des Bijoutiers-Orfevres. (SZ) **2566**
Schweizerische Vereinigung der Versicherungsmathematiker. Mitteilungen. (SZ ISSN 0042-3815) **2542**
Schweizerische Vereinigung fuer Atomenergie. Bulletin. (SZ ISSN 0036-777X) **1809**, **1836**
Schweizerische Verkehrsstatistik/Statistique Suisse des Transports. (SZ) **4666**
Schweizerische Versicherungszeitschrift/Revue Suisse d'Assurances. (SZ) **2542**
Schweizerische Weinzeitung/Journal Vinicole Suisse. (SZ ISSN 0036-7796) **385**
Schweizerische Wirte-Zeitung *see* Schweizer Gastronomie **2480**
Schweizerische Zeitschrift fuer Forstwesen/Journal Forestier Suisse. (SZ ISSN 0036-7818) **2107**
Schweizerische Zeitschrift fuer Gemeinnuetzigkeit. (SZ ISSN 0036-7826) **4448**
Schweizerische Zeitschrift fuer Geschichte/Revue Suisse d'Histoire/Rivista Storica Svizzera. (SZ ISSN 0036-7834) **2322**
Schweizerische Zeitschrift fuer Militaer- und Katastrophenmedizin/Revue Suisse de Medecine Militaire et de Catastrophes. (SZ ISSN 0377-8347) **3152**
Schweizerische Zeitschrift fuer Obst und Weinbau. (SZ) **385**, **119**, **1968**
Schweizerische Zeitschrift fuer Pilzkunde. (SZ) **517**, **557**, **561**
Schweizerische Zeitschrift fuer Psychologie/Revue Suisse de Psychologie. (SZ) **4046**
Schweizerische Zeitschrift fuer Psychologie *see* Schweizerische Zeitschrift fuer Psychologie **4046**
Schweizerische Zeitschrift fuer Sozialversicherung *see* Schweizerische Zeitschrift fuer Sozialversicherung und Berufliche Vorsorge **4448**
Schweizerische Zeitschrift fuer Sozialversicherung und Berufliche Vorsorge. (SZ) **4448**
Schweizerische Zeitschrift fuer Soziologie/Revue Suisse de Sociologie. (SZ ISSN 0379-3664) **4448**
Schweizerische Zeitschrift fuer Sportmedizin/Revue Suisse de Medecine des Sports/Revista Svizzera di Medicina dello Sport. (SZ ISSN 0036-7885) **3373**

Schweizerische Zeitschrift fuer
  Strafrecht/Revue Penale Suisse. (SZ
  ISSN 0036-7893) **1522**
Schweizerische Zeitschrift fuer
  Volkswirtschaft und Statistik/Revue
  Suisse d'Economie Politique et de
  Statistique. (SZ ISSN 0303-9692)
  737
Die Schweizerische Zivilluftfahrt. (SZ)
  4677
Schweizerischen Wald- und
  Holzwirtschaft. Jahrbuch/Annuaire
  Suisse de l'Economie Forestiere et de
  l'Industrie du Bois. (SZ) **2113**
†Schweizerischer Arbeitgeberverband
  fuer das Schneidergewerbe.
  Newsletter. (SZ) **5274**
Schweizerischer Bankverein Booklet see
  S B C Booklet **798**
Schweizerischer Bauernverband.
  Information. (SZ) **203**
Schweizerischer Bund fuer
  Jugendliteratur. Jahresbericht/Ligue
  Suisse de Litterature pour la
  Jeunesse. Rapport Annuel. (SZ)
  1265
Schweizerischer Bund fuer
  Jugendliteratur. Nachrichten see
  Jugendliteratur **1240**
Schweizerischer Burgenverein. (SZ)
  4158
Schweizerischer Elektrotechnischer
  Verein Bulletin S E V - V S E see
  Bulletin S E V - V S E **1883**
Schweizerischer Forstverein Zeitschrift.
  Beihefte. (SZ) **2107**
Schweizerischer Medizinalkalender see
  Schweizerischer Medizinalkalender
  und Arzneimitteluebersicht **3152**
Schweizerischer Medizinalkalender und
  Arzneimitteluebersicht. (SZ) **3152**
Schweizerischer Metall- und
  Uhrenarbeitnehmer-Verband Zeitung
  see S M U V Zeitung **3419**
Schweizerischer Muehlen - Anzeiger.
  (SZ) **208**
†Schweizerischer Verband der Zeitungs-
  und Zeitschriftenverleger. Bulletin.
  (SZ) **5274**
Schweizerischer Verband fuer
  Beruflichen Unterricht. Blaetter see
  Schweizerische Blaetter fuer
  Beruflichen Unterricht Blaetter **1759**
Schweizerischer Werkbund Information
  see S W B - Information **306**
Schweizerischer Wissenschaftsrat.
  Jahresbericht/Conseil Suisse de la
  Science. Rapport Annuel. (SZ) **4338**
Schweizerischer Zeitungsverleger-
  Verband. Bulletin see Schweizerischer
  Verband der Zeitungs- und
  Zeitschriftenverleger. Bulletin **5274**
Schweizerisches Archiv fuer
  Volkskunde.(SZ ISSN 0036-794X)
  2058
Schweizerisches Handelsamtsblatt. (SZ)
  839
Schweizerisches Institut fuer
  Hauswirtschaft Magazin see S I H
  Magazin **2449**
Schweizerisches Institut fuer
  Nuklearforschung. Jahresbericht see
  P S I. Jahresbericht **1809**
Schweizerisches Institut fuer
  Nuklearforschung Medical Newsletter
  see S I N Medical Newsletter **5272**
Schweizerisches Institut fuer
  Nuklearforschung Newsletter see S I
  N Newsletter **5272**
Schweizerisches Jahrbuch fuer
  Politische Wissenschaft. see Annuaire
  Suisse de Science Politique **3873**
Schweizerisches Kaufmaennisches
  Zentralblatt see Schweizerische
  Kaufmaennische Zeitung **1053**
Schweizerisches Medizinisches
  Jahrbuch. (SZ ISSN 0080-7400)
  3152
Schweizerisches Ost-Institut. Etudes
  Politiques see Etudes Politiques
  3893
Schweizerisches Ost-Institut Bilanz see S
  O I-Bilanz **3924**
Schweizerisches Patent-, Muster- und
  Markenblatt/Feuille Suisse des
  Brevets, Dessins et Marques/Foglio
  Svizzero dei Brevetti, Disegni e
  Marchi. (SZ ISSN 0036-7974)
  3678

Schweizerisches Zentralblatt fuer Staats-
  und Gemeindeverwaltung. (SZ ISSN
  0036-7990) **4073**
Schwenkfeldian. (US ISSN 0036-
  8032) **4288**
†Schwerpunkt-Medizin. (GW) **5274**
Die Schwester - Der Pfleger. (GW ISSN
  0340-5303) **3286**
Schwestern Revue. (GW ISSN 0048-
  9549) **3286**
Schwimmbad und Sauna. (GW) **631**
Schwimmsportverein Esslingen.
  Vereinsnachrichten. (GW) **4487**
Schwule Maenner. (GW ISSN 0932-
  4925) **2457**
Sci. (IT ISSN 0036-8040) **4555,
  4785**
Sci Fondo. (IT) **4555**
Sci Svizzero. see Ski - Schweizer
  Skisport **4555**
Sci-Tech News. (US ISSN 0036-8059)
  4357, 4615
Sciare. (IT) **4555**
Sciare Moda. (IT) **1294**
†Sciarts. (US) **5274**
Scien Tech/Saga Daigaku Rikogakubu
  Koho. (JA) **1836, 3054, 3830**
Science. see Kagaku **4318**
Science. see Kexue **4320**
Science. see Kexue **4320**
Science. (US ISSN 0036-8075) **4338**
Science Abstracts. Section A see
  Physics Abstracts **3838**
Science Abstracts. Section B see
  Electrical & Electronics Abstracts
  1843
Science Abstracts. Section C see
  Computer & Control Abstracts **1403**
Science Activities. (US ISSN 0036-
  8121) **1662**
Science and Archaeology. (UK ISSN
  0586-9668) **4360, 290**
Science and Arts - Research Studies/
  Ulum wa Funun - Dirasat wa Buhuth.
  (UA) **4338, 2514**
†Science & Business. (UK) **5274**
Science and Business Link-Up see
  Science & Business **5274**
Science and Children. (US ISSN 0036-
  8148) **4339, 1662**
Science and Christian Belief. (UK ISSN
  0954-4194) **4200, 3781**
Science and Computer Literacy
  Audiovisuals. (US) **1457**
Science & Culture. see Kexue yu
  Wenhua **4320**
Science and Culture. (II ISSN 0036-
  8156) **4339**
Science and Engineering. (II ISSN
  0036-8164) **1836**
Science and Engineering of Composite
  Materials. (UK) **1187**
Science and Engineering Research
  Council. Report. (UK ISSN 0261-
  7005) **4339, 4608**
Science and Engineering Research
  Council Bulletin see S E R C Bulletin
  4337
Science and Environment. (II) **1968**
Science and Faith see Science and
  Christian Belief **4200**
Science and Global Security. (US ISSN
  0892-9882) **4339, 1527**
Science and Global Security Monograph
  Series. (US ISSN 1048-7042)
  3971, 4339
Science and Government Report. (US
  ISSN 0048-9581) **3924, 4073**
Science and Industry. see Kagaku to
  Kogyo (Osaka) **4602**
Science and its Conceptual
  Foundations.(US) **4339**
Science and Life. see Khoa Hoc va Doi
  Song **4320**
Science and Life. see Kexue yu
  Shenghuo **4320**
Science and Life. see Shinjleh Uhaan
  Am'dral **4342**
†Science and Nature. (US ISSN 0193-
  3396) **5274**
Science and Practice of Surgery Series.
  (US) **3384**
Science and Public Affairs. (UK ISSN
  0268-490X) **4339**
Science and Public Policy. (UK ISSN
  0302-3427) **4339, 4608**
Science and Society. (US ISSN 0036-
  8237) **3924**

Science and Technology. (KO) **4339,
  4608**
†Science and Technology (New York).
  (US ISSN 0036-8245) **5274**
Science and Technology (Pittsburgh).
  (US ISSN 0080-746X) **4339,
  737**
Science and Technology (San Diego)
  see Science and Technology Series
  61
Science and Technology (San Diego,
  1987). (US ISSN 0894-539X)
  455, 4360, 4608
Science and Technology Agency Its
  Roles and Activities see S T A: Its
  Roles and Activities **4608**
†Science & Technology Annual
  Reference Review. (US ISSN 1041-
  2557) **5274**
Science & Technology Daily. see Ke-Ji
  Ribao **4319**
Science and Technology Development
  and Reform. see Keji Fazhan yu
  Gaige **4378**
†Science and Technology Dimensions.
  (CN) **5274**
Science and Technology Exploration
  Trend. see Keji Kaifa Dongtai **4319**
Science and Technology Herald. see Keji
  Daobao **4319**
Science and Technology in China. (UK)
  4339, 4608
Science and Technology in Japan. (JA
  ISSN 0286-0406) **4339, 4608**
Science and Technology in Japan. (UK)
  4339, 4608
Science and Technology in Latin
  America. (UK) **4339, 4608**
Science and Technology in the Middle
  East. (UK) **4339, 4608**
Science and Technology Information.
  see Keji Qingbao Gongzuo **2766**
Science and Technology Information on
  Aquatic Products. see Shuichan Keji
  Qingbao **2049**
Science and Technology Information
  Service. see Kagaku Gijutsu Bunken
  Sabisu **4318**
Science and Technology Libraries. (US
  ISSN 0194-262X) **2783**
Science and Technology of Nuclear
  Energy. see Yuanzineng Kexue Jishu
  1810
Science and Technology of Prospecting.
  see Kancha Kexue Jishu **3486**
Science and Technology Policy. (UK
  ISSN 0952-9616) **4339**
Science and Technology Publishing. see
  Keji Chuban **4130**
Science and Technology Research
  Abstracts Agricultural Sciences see S
  A T R A: Agricultural Sciences **5272**
Science and Technology Serial Reports:
  China: Energy. (US) **1795**
Science and Technology Serial Reports:
  U S S R: Computers. (US) **1400**
Science and Technology Series. (US
  ISSN 0278-4017) **61**
Science and Technology Today. see Jinri
  Keji **4317**
†Science & Technology Update. (US)
  5274
†Science & Technology Video
  Magazine.(US) **5274**
Science as Culture. (UK ISSN 0950-
  5431) **4339, 3924**
Science Books & Films. (US ISSN
  0098-342X) **4357, 4615**
Science Bulletin. (CH) **4339**
Science Challenge see Biology Bulletin
  Monthly **432**
Science Chelsea. (UK ISSN 0300-
  3361) **4339**
Science - Ciencia. (PR ISSN 0164-
  7741) **4339**
Science Citation Index. (US ISSN
  0036-827X) **4357, 22**
Science Citation Index Journal Citation
  Report. (US ISSN 0161-3170)
  4339
Science Council of Japan. Monthly
  Report. see Nihon Gakujutsu Kaigi
  Geppo **4330**
Science Digest see Breakthroughs in
  Health & Science **5152**
Science Diliman. (PH ISSN 0115-
  7809) **4339, 4385**
Science Education. (US ISSN 0036-
  8326) **4339, 1662**

Science Education in the Region. (UK)
  1716
Science Education in Zambia. (ZA)
  1662, 4339
Science Education News. (AT ISSN
  0048-9603) **1759, 4339**
Science et Changement Planetaires,
  Secheresse. (FR) **1968**
Science et Comportement. (CN) **4046**
Science et Culture. (BE ISSN 0773-
  3429) **4339**
Science et Esprit. (CN ISSN 0316-
  5345) **3781, 4200**
Science et Nature. (FR ISSN 0036-
  8342) **4339**
Science et Peche see Equinoxe **2039**
Science et Sports. (FR ISSN 0765-
  1597) **3373**
Science et Technologie Alimentaire. see
  Food Science and Technology **2070**
Science et Technologie de la
  Conservation et de la Restoration des
  Oeuvres d'Art et du Patrimoine. (FR)
  343
Science et Vie. (FR ISSN 0036-8369)
  4339
Science et Vie. see Shkenca dhe Jeta
  4343
Science et Vie Economie. (FR ISSN
  0765-0027) **690**
Science et Vie Junior. (FR ISSN 0992-
  5899) **4339, 1265**
Science et Vie Micro Mac see S V M
  Mac **1474**
Science - Fantasy Correspondent. (US)
  3014
Science Fiction. (AT ISSN 0314-6677)
  3014
Science Fiction and Fantasy Book
  Review Annual. (US) **3014**
Science Fiction and Fantasy Research
  Index. (US) **2983, 22, 3014**
Science Fiction and Fantasy Workshop.
  (US) **3014**
Science Fiction Australian S F News see
  Australian S F News **3010**
Science Fiction Chronicle. (US ISSN
  0195-5365) **3014, 4136**
Science Fiction Commentary see S F
  Commentary **3014**
Science Fiction Convention Register.
  (US) **3394, 3014**
▼Science Fiction Eye. (US) **3014**
Science Fiction, Fantasy, & Horror. (US)
  2983, 411, 3014
Science Fiction Media. (GW ISSN
  0930-2492) **3014, 3517**
Science Fiction Media News see Matrix
  3012
†Science Fiction News. (AT ISSN 0156-
  6342) **5274**
Science Fiction Research Association
  Newsletter. (US ISSN 0048-9646)
  3014
Science-Fiction Studies. (US ISSN
  0091-7729) **3014**
Science Fiction Times. (GW ISSN
  0048-9654) **3014**
Science Fiction Voices. (US ISSN 0164-
  1093) **3014**
Science Fiction Writers of America
  Bulletin see S F W A Bulletin **3014**
Science for Conservation. see Hozon
  Kagaku **1489**
Science for Everyone. see Nauka dla
  Wszystkich **4328**
†Science for People. (UK ISSN 0144-
  8447) **5274**
Science for the People. (US ISSN
  0048-9662) **4340**
Science Frontiers. (US) **4340**
Science - Health Abstracts. (US) **3811,
  22**
Science Illustrated. (US ISSN 0897-
  8581) **4340**
Science Impact on Society. see Kexue
  Dui Shehui de Yingxiang **4378**
Science in China. Series A:
  Mathematics, Physics, Astronomy &
  Technological Sciences. (CC ISSN
  1001-6511) **4340**
Science in China. Series B: Chemistry,
  Life Sciences & Earth Sciences. (CC
  ISSN 1001-652X) **4340**
Science in Context. (UK ISSN 0269-
  8897) **4340**
Science in New Guinea. (PP ISSN
  0310-4303) **4340**

Science in Parliament. (II ISSN 0036-8407) **4340**
Science in the U.S.S.R. *see* Nauka v S.S.S.R **4329**
Science Indicators. (US ISSN 0092-315X) **4357**
Science Land - Kagaku Land *see* Kagaku Land **1257**
▼Science Leadership Trend Notes. (US) **4340**, **1759**
Science Museum News. (US) **3532**, **284**
Science Museum of Minnesota. Monograph. (US) **4340**
Science Museum of Minnesota. Scientific Bulletin *see* Science Museum of Minnesota. Scientific Publications, New Series **4340**
Science Museum of Minnesota. Scientific Publications *see* Science Museum of Minnesota. Scientific Publications, New Series **4340**
Science Museum of Minnesota. Scientific Publications, New Series. (US ISSN 0161-4452) **4340**
Science Networks Historical Studies. (SZ) **4340**
Science News. *see* Kagaku Shinbun **4319**
Science News. (US ISSN 0036-8423) **4340**
Science Notes and News. (JM) **4340**, **1759**
Science Nouvelle. (FR ISSN 0080-7540) **4340**
Science of Advanced Material and Process Engineering Series. (US ISSN 0080-7559) **1922**
Science of Computer Programming. (NE ISSN 0167-6423) **1431**
Science of Education. *see* Jiaoyu Kexue **1641**
Science of Food and Agriculture. (US ISSN 0738-9310) **2081**, **191**, **208**
Science of Hot Springs/Onsen Kagaku. (JA ISSN 0030-2821) **1579**
Science of Law. *see* Faxue **2625**
Science of Mind Magazine. (US ISSN 0036-8458) **4288**, **3781**
Science of Religion. (NE ISSN 0165-8794) **4213**, **4200**
Science of Religion Bulletin *see* Science of Religion **4213**
Science of Science. (PL ISSN 0138-0532) **3781**, **4340**
Science of Sintering. (YU ISSN 0350-820X) **3419**, **1166**
Science of Tea. *see* Chaye Kexue **2063**
Science of the Soul. (SA ISSN 0036-8466) **4288**
Science of the Total Environment. (NE ISSN 0048-9697) **1968**, **482**, **1979**, **1983**
Science of Thought Review. (UK) **4200**
Science Panorama. *see* Kexue Bolan **5223**
Science Periodical on Research and Technology in Sport *see* S P O R T S **4486**
Science Pictorial. *see* Kexue Huabao **4320**
Science Policy *see* Science and Public Policy **4339**
Science Policy News *see* Science and Public Policy **4339**
Science Policy Studies and Documents. (UN ISSN 0080-7591) **4340**
▼Science Probe! (US ISSN 1049-7730) **4340**
Science Progress. (UK ISSN 0036-8504) **4340**
Science Prosperity and Life. *see* Kexue Zhifu Yu Shenghuo **4320**
Science Reference and Information Service Newsletter *see* S R I S Newsletter **2782**
Science Research Management. *see* Keyan Guanli **4320**
Science Scope. (US ISSN 0887-2376) **4340**, **1759**
Science Society of Thailand. Journal. (TH ISSN 0303-8122) **4340**
Science Studies. (FI ISSN 0786-3012) **4340**, **4608**
Science Supply News. (US) **3263**
The Science Teacher. (US ISSN 0036-8555) **4340**, **1662**

Science Teacher/Vigyan Shikshak. (II ISSN 0378-8717) **4340**, **1759**
Science Teachers Association of Queensland. Newsletter. (AT) **4341**
Science Teachers Association of the Australian Capital Territory Science Teacher *see* A.C.T. Science Teacher **1743**
Science, Technology & Development. (UK ISSN 0950-0707) **935**, **3924**
Science, Technology and Development. *see* Keji yu Fazhan **4320**
Science, Technology, and Dialectics. *see* Kexue Jishu yu Bianzhengfa **4320**
Science, Technology & Human Values. (US ISSN 0162-2439) **4341**, **2514**
Science, Technology and We. *see* Veda, Technika a My **1269**
Science Technology Industry Review *see* S T I Review **4608**
†Science Technology: Information. (US) **5274**
Science Today. (II ISSN 0036-858X) **4341**
†Science Tools. (SW ISSN 0036-8598) **5274**
Science Trends. (US ISSN 0043-0749) **4341**
Science University of Tokyo. Collected Papers. *see* Tokyo Rika Daigaku Kenkyu Ronbunshu **4348**
Science University of Tokyo Bulletin *see* S U T Bulletin **4608**
Science University of Tokyo Journal of Mathematics *see* S U T Journal of Mathematics **3054**
▼Science Watch. (US ISSN 1047-8043) **4341**
Science Weekly. (US) **1265**, **4341**
Science World. (US ISSN 0036-8601) **4341**, **1265**, **1759**
Science Year. (US ISSN 0080-7621) **1782**, **4341**
ScienceCope *see* Newscope - Science Edition **1756**
Scienceland. (US ISSN 0147-3654) **1265**, **1759**, **4341**
Sciencepedia/Saiensupedia. (JA) **4341**
Sciences. (US ISSN 0036-861X) **4341**
Sciences & Nature. (FR ISSN 0987-0717) **4341**, **1265**
Sciences de l'Eau. (FR ISSN 0298-6663) **1600**, **4828**
Sciences de l'Information. (FR) **1457**
Sciences de l'Information. Lexique. (FR) **2783**
Sciences de la Terre: Informatique Geologique *see* Sciences de la Terre: Serie Informatique Geologique **1579**
Sciences de la Terre: Serie Informatique Geologique. (FR ISSN 0335-9255) **1579**, **1548**
Sciences de la Terre: Serie Memoires. (FR) **1579**
Sciences des Aliments. (FR ISSN 0240-8813) **2081**
Sciences et Avenir. (FR ISSN 0036-8636) **4341**
Sciences et Techniques de l'Animal de Laboratoire *see* S T A L **3263**
Sciences et Techniques de l'Eau. (CN ISSN 0823-0269) **4828**
Sciences Exactes et Technologie. Sciences de la Vie. Lexique/Exact Science and Technology. Life Sciences. Lexicon. (FR) **455**
Sciences Geologiques. Bulletin. (FR ISSN 0302-2692) **1579**
Sciences Geologiques - Memoires. (FR ISSN 0302-2684) **1579**
Sciences Medicales. (FR ISSN 0048-9727) **3152**
Sciences Monthly Magazine. *see* El-Elm **4308**
Sciences Orgonomiques. (FR ISSN 0767-6891) **455**, **3152**
Sciences Religieuses. *see* Studies in Religion **4204**
Sciences Sociales et Sante. (FR ISSN 0294-0337) **4112**
Sciences, Techniques, Informations C R I A C. (ZR ISSN 0377-5135) **1084**
Sciences Techniques Pratiques Pharma Sciences *see* S T P Pharma Sciences **3742**

Sciences Techniques Pratiques Pharma Techniques Pratiques Reglementations *see* S T P Pharma Techniques Pratiques Reglementations **3742**
Sciences Veterinaires - Medecine Comparee. Bulletin. (FR) **4815**
Scientia. (CL ISSN 0036-8679) **4341**
Scientia Agriculturae Bohemoslovaca. (CS ISSN 0582-2343) **119**, **2107**, **4815**
Scientia Atmospherica Sinica. *see* Daqi Kexue **3434**
†Scientia Electrica. (SZ ISSN 0036-8695) **5274**
Scientia et Praxis. (PE ISSN 0559-1414) **4385**
Scientia Geographica Sinica. *see* Dili Kexue **2246**
Scientia Geologica Sinica. *see* Dizhi Kexue **1559**
Scientia Horticulturae. (NE ISSN 0304-4238) **2138**
Scientia Juridica. (PO ISSN 0559-1422) **2678**
Scientia Paedagogica Experimentalis. (BE ISSN 0582-2351) **1662**
Scientia Pharmaceutica. (AU ISSN 0036-8709) **3742**
Scientia Silvae Sinica. *see* Linye Kexue **2104**
Scientia Sinica. Series A: Mathematics, Physics, Astronomy and Technological Sciences *see* Science in China. Series A: Mathematics, Physics, Astronomy & Technological Sciences **4340**
Scientia Sinica. Series B: Chemistry, Life Sciences and Earth Sciences *see* Science in China. Series B: Chemistry, Life Sciences & Earth Sciences **4340**
Scientiae *see* Technobrief **4347**
Scientific Agricultural Society of Finland. Journal *see* Journal of Agricultural Science in Finland **101**
Scientific American. (US ISSN 0036-8733) **4341**
Scientific and Applied Photography and Cinematography. (English translation of: Zhurnal Nauchoni i Prikladnoi Fotografii i Kinematografii) (US ISSN 0734-1504) **3797**
Scientific and Professional Meetings in Yugoslavia and Foreign Countries. *see* Naucni i Strucni Skupovi u Jugoslavii i u Inostranstvu **3394**
Scientific and Technical Aerospace Reports *see* S T A R **66**
Scientific and Technical Books and Serials in Print. (US ISSN 0000-054X) **4358**, **4615**
Scientific and Technical Information. *see* Tudomanyos es Muszaki Tajekoztatas **2796**
Scientific and Technical Information in Foreign Countries/Kaigaki Kagaku Gijutsu Joho Shiryo. (JA) **4341**, **4608**
Scientific and Technical Information Processing. (English translation of: Nauchno-Tekhnicheskaya Informatsiya. Seriya 1) (US ISSN 0147-6882) **2783**
Scientific and Technical Societies of Canada/Societes Scientifiques et Techniques du Canada. (CN ISSN 0586-7746) **4341**, **4608**
Scientific and Technological Management in Geological Exploration. *see* Dizhi Keji Guanli **1008**
Scientific Asahi. *see* Kagaku Asahi **4318**
Scientific Ballooning and Radiations Monitoring Organization Bulletin *see* S B A R M O Bulletin **3440**
Scientific Bulletin. (LY) **4341**
Scientific Bulletin of Tea. *see* Chaye Kexue Jianbao **172**
Scientific Committee for Antarctic Research Report to S C A R on South African Antarctic Research Activities *see* Report to S C A R on South African Antarctic Research Activities **4335**
Scientific Committee on Antarctic Research Boletin *see* S C A R Boletin **4337**

Scientific Computing & Automation. (US) **4360**
†Scientific Directory of Hong Kong. (HK ISSN 0586-5751) **5274**
Scientific Documentation Centre Ltd. Bulletin *see* S D C Bulletin **3839**
Scientific Documentation Centre Ltd. Current Awareness. S D I Service *see* Current Awareness. S D I Service **3092**
Scientific Drilling. (GW ISSN 0934-4365) **1594**
Scientific, Engineering, Technical Manpower Comments. (US ISSN 0036-8768) **3631**
Scientific Event Alert Network. (US) **1552**
Scientific Experiments. *see* Kexue Shiyan **4320**
Scientific Exploration Society. Newsletter. (UK) **2262**
†Scientific Films and Videocassettes. (HU ISSN 0236-9702) **5274**
Scientific Horticulture *see* Professional Horticulture **2137**
Scientific Information Bulletin. (SJ) **4341**
Scientific Instrumentation. *see* Nauchnaya Apparatura **2524**
Scientific Instruments: Latin American Industrial Report. (US) **2524**
†Scientific Integrity. (US) **5274**
Scientific Journal of the South African Veterinary Association *see* South African Veterinary Association. Scientific Journal **4816**
Scientific Lubrication *see* Industrial Lubrication & Tribology **1930**
Scientific Meetings. (US ISSN 0487-8965) **3394**, **2783**, **4341**
Scientific Opinion. (II) **4341**, **4608**
Scientific Papers on Japanese Antiques and Art Crafts. *see* Kobunkazai no Kagaku **258**
▼Scientific Programming. (US ISSN 1058-9244) **1479**, **1880**
Scientific Progress - Wetenskaplike Vordering *see* South African Journal of Science **4345**
Scientific Publications of the Science Museum of Minnesota *see* Science Museum of Minnesota. Scientific Publications, New Series **4340**
Scientific Report of Cetacean Research/Nihon Geirui Kenkyujo Eibun Hokoku.(JA ISSN 0917-0537) **591**
Scientific Research Council of Jamaica. Journal *see* Jamaican Journal of Science and Technology **4317**
Scientific Results of Marine Biological Research. *see* Hvalraadets Skrifter **5207**
Scientific Serials in Thai Libraries. (TH ISSN 0125-4529) **4358**, **411**, **4615**
Scientific Sleuthing Newsletter *see* Scientific Sleuthing Review **2714**
Scientific Sleuthing Review. (US) **2714**, **3265**
Scientific Socialism. *see* Kexue Shehui Zhuyi **4378**
Scientific Society of the Silicate Industry. Conference on Silicate Industry and Silicate Science. (HU) **1166**
Scientific Symposium on the Cultivated Mushroom. Proceedings *see* Mushroom Science **510**
Scientific World. *see* Kexue Shijie **4320**
Scientific World. (UK ISSN 0036-8857) **4341**, **1662**
The Scientist. (US ISSN 0890-3670) **4342**
Scientists Center for Animal Welfare. Newsletter. (US ISSN 0742-5260) **231**
Scientometrics. (NE ISSN 0138-9130) **4342**
Scienza Duemila. (IT) **4342**
Scienza e Dossier. (IT) **4342**
Scienza e Tecnica. (IT) **4342**
Scienza e Tecnica Agraria. (IT ISSN 0036-8881) **119**
Scienza e Tecnica Lattiero-Casearia. (IT ISSN 0036-889X) **203**
Scienza e Vita Natura. (IT) **2206**
Scienza Veterinaria e Biologia Animale. (IT ISSN 0392-9639) **4815**, **455**
†Scienza 82. (IT) **5274**

Scienze ed il Loro Insegnamento see Scienze, la Matematica e Il Loro Insegnamento **4342**
Scienze, la Matematica e Il Loro Insegnamento. (IT) **4342**
Scifant. (US ISSN 0882-1348) **3014**
The Scillonian. (UK) **2883**
Scinautico. (IT) **4555**
Scintillation see Cinemonkey **3506**
Scissortail. (US ISSN 0582-2637) **567**
Scitech. (AT ISSN 0725-900X) **4608**
SciTech Book News. (US ISSN 0196-6006) **411**, **4395**, **4615**
SciTech Reference Plus. (US) **4358**, **4615**
Scitech Technology Directory. (AT) **4615**
Scoop. (NE ISSN 0924-9370) **1975**, **22**, **191**, **4828**
Scoop Sport Annual. (UK ISSN 0262-4206) **1265**
▼Scooter Magazine. (IT) **4521**
Scope. (GW ISSN 0048-9735) **1084**
Scope. (AT) **1496**
The Scope. (GH) **2193**
Scope. (PP) **2957**
Scope. (SA ISSN 0036-9012) **3400**
Scope see Lutheran Woman Today **4243**
Scope (Belfast). (UK ISSN 0144-0462) **4419**
Scope (Year). (UK) **756**, **631**
Scope (York). (UK) **3830**, **2469**
Scope Camping News. (CN) **4555**
Scope - Journal see Scope **1084**
Scopus. (KE ISSN 0250-4162) **567**
Scopus. (IS ISSN 0036-9020) **1662**
Score. (CN ISSN 0711-3226) **4511**
▼Score (Brooklyn). (US) **3580**, **4200**
Score (Oakland). (US) **3005**
†Scoreboard. (US) **5275**
Scoreboard Alert. (US) **3924**, **4248**
Scorpion. (GW ISSN 0265-5543) **2883**
†Scotch Game Call Hunting Annual. (US) **5275**
Scotia. (US ISSN 0273-0693) **2022**
Scotiabanker. (CN) **799**
Scotian. (CN) **2163**
Scotland. (UK) **4785**
Scotland. Red Deer Commission. Annual Report. (UK ISSN 0080-7850) **1496**
Scotland. Registrar General. Annual Report. (UK ISSN 0080-7869) **3995**, **4585**
Scotland: Bed and Breakfast. (UK) **4786**
Scotland: Camping and Caravan Parks. (UK) **4786**
Scotland: Camping and Caravan Sites see Scotland: Camping and Caravan Parks **4786**
Scotland Chambers of Commerce. National Directory. (UK) **822**
Scotland: Conference and Incentive Brochure. (UK) **3394**
Scotland: Conferences, Meetings, Seminars see Scotland: Conference and Incentive Brochure **3394**
Scotland for Fishing. (UK) **4555**
▼Scotland for Outdoor Activities. (UK) **4786**
Scotland for the Motorist. (UK) **4786**
Scotland Home of Golf. (UK) **4511**
Scotland: Hotels and Guest Houses. (UK) **4786**
Scotland: Self-Catering Accommodation.(UK) **4786**
Scotland Tomorrow see Scotlink **822**
Scotland: Where to Stay, Bed and Breakfast see Scotland: Bed and Breakfast **4786**
Scotland: Where to Stay, Hotels and Guest Houses see Scotland: Hotels and Guest Houses **4786**
Scotland: 1001 Things to See. (UK) **4786**
Scotland: 600 Things to See see Scotland: 1001 Things to See **4786**
†Scotland's Best Holidays. (UK ISSN 0267-338X) **5275**
Scotland's for Me see Scotland **4785**
Scotland's Regions. (UK ISSN 0305-6552) **4073**
Scotlands Top 1000 Companies see Scotlands Top 2000 Companies (Year) **1152**

Scotlands Top 2000 Companies (Year) .(UK) **1152**, **839**
Scotland's What's On. (UK ISSN 0961-6608) **4786**
Scotlink. (UK ISSN 0266-5441) **822**
Scotlit. (UK) **2957**
Scots Independent. (UK ISSN 0036-9071) **3924**
Scots Law Times. (UK ISSN 0036-908X) **2678**
Scots Law Times Christmas Charity. Supplement. (UK) **2678**
Scots Link. (AT) **2163**
Scots Magazine. (UK ISSN 0048-9751) **2195**
Scots Newse. (US) **1324**
Scott Report on Computer Law see International Computer Law Adviser **1397**
†Scott Scanner. (US ISSN 0730-4986) **5275**
Scott Stamp Monthly. (US) **3757**
Scottish Abstract of Statistics. (UK) **4585**, **22**
Scottish Academic Libraries Newsletter. (UK) **2783**
†Scottish Ambassador. (UK ISSN 0268-053X) **5275**
Scottish American see Scottish Banner **2022**
Scottish Anti-Vivisection Society. Annual Report see Animal Concern (Scotland). Annual Report **230**
Scottish Archaeological Review. (UK ISSN 0262-4389) **284**
Scottish Art Review. (UK ISSN 0036-911X) **343**
Scottish Bakers' Year Book. (UK ISSN 0080-7974) **2089**
Scottish Banker. (UK) **799**
Scottish Bankers Magazine see Scottish Banker **799**
Scottish Banner. (CN) **2022**
Scottish Baptist Magazine. (UK ISSN 0036-9136) **4248**
Scottish Birds. (UK ISSN 0036-9144) **567**
Scottish Book Collector. (UK ISSN 0954-8769) **4136**, **2783**
Scottish Building & Civil Engineering Year Book. (UK ISSN 0085-6002) **631**, **1873**
Scottish Bulletin of Evangelical Theology. (UK ISSN 0265-4547) **4248**
Scottish Business Insider. (UK) **799**, **962**, **1027**
Scottish Business Survey see Scottish Chambers Business Survey **690**
Scottish Campaign to Resist the Atomic Menace Safe Energy Journal see S C R A M Safe Energy Journal **1795**
Scottish Chambers Business Survey. (UK) **690**
Scottish Chambers of Commerce National Directory. (UK) **822**
Scottish Chess. (UK) **4487**
Scottish Church History Society. Records. (UK ISSN 0264-5572) **4200**, **2386**
Scottish Civil Law Reports. (UK ISSN 0951-0443) **2704**
Scottish Commercial Travellers' Association. Newscall. (UK) **4786**, **839**
Scottish Criminal Case Reports. (UK ISSN 0263-2381) **2714**
Scottish Curler. (UK ISSN 0036-9160) **4487**
Scottish Current Law Year Book. (UK ISSN 0265-6159) **2678**
Scottish Decorators' Review see Scottish Decorators' Year Book and Review **4005**
Scottish Decorators' Year Book and Review. (UK) **4005**
Scottish Diver. (UK ISSN 0308-7379) **4487**
Scottish Economic and Social History. (UK ISSN 0269-5030) **4385**, **690**
Scottish Economic Bulletin. (UK) **884**
Scottish Educational Journal. (UK) **1662**
Scottish Educational Review. (UK ISSN 0141-9072) **1662**
Scottish Environment Statistics. (UK) **1975**

Scottish Episcopal Church Yearbook. (UK ISSN 0260-0617) **4248**
Scottish Evangelical Theology Society Bulletin see Scottish Bulletin of Evangelical Theology **4248**
Scottish Farmer. (UK ISSN 0036-9195) **119**
†Scottish Farming Leader. (UK) **5275**
Scottish Field. (UK ISSN 0036-9209) **2195**
Scottish Fisheries Bulletin. (UK ISSN 0559-1791) **2048**
Scottish Fisheries Information Pamphlets. (UK ISSN 0309-9105) **2048**
Scottish Fisheries Research Reports. (UK ISSN 0308-8022) **2048**
Scottish Fishing Fleet at December 31 (Year). (UK) **2048**
Scottish Folk Arts Directory. (UK) **3580**
Scottish Folk Directory see Scottish Folk Arts Directory **3580**
Scottish Forestry. (UK ISSN 0036-9217) **2107**
Scottish Genealogist. (UK ISSN 0300-337X) **2164**
Scottish Geographical Magazine. (UK ISSN 0036-9225) **2262**
Scottish Georgian Society. Annual Report see Architectural Heritage I **292**
Scottish Government Yearbook. (UK) **3924**
Scottish Grocer. (UK ISSN 0036-9233) **2094**
Scottish Handbook of Adult and Continuing Education. (UK) **1686**
Scottish Health Services. (UK) **4112**
Scottish Historical Review. (UK ISSN 0036-9241) **2322**
Scottish Home and Country. (UK ISSN 0036-925X) **4852**
Scottish Hosteller. (UK) **4521**
Scottish Industrial History. (UK ISSN 0266-7428) **4608**, **2322**, **3023**
Scottish Institute of Missionary Studies Bulletin. (UK ISSN 0048-9778) **4200**
Scottish Journal of Adult Education. (UK ISSN 0305-795X) **1686**
Scottish Journal of Political Economy. (UK ISSN 0036-9292) **690**
Scottish Journal of Religious Studies. (UK ISSN 0143-8301) **4200**
Scottish Labour History Society. Journal.(UK) **993**, **2386**
Scottish Law Directory. (UK ISSN 0080-8083) **2678**
Scottish Law Gazette. (UK ISSN 0036-9314) **2678**
Scottish Legal Action Group see S C O L A G **2676**
Scottish Legion News. (UK) **3471**
Scottish Libraries. (UK ISSN 0950-0189) **2783**
Scottish Library and Information Resources. (UK ISSN 0267-1425) **2783**
Scottish Licensed Trade Guardian. (UK) **385**
Scottish Licensed Trade News. (UK ISSN 0036-9322) **385**
Scottish Literary Journal. (UK ISSN 0305-0785) **2957**
Scottish Marine Biological Association. Annual Report see Dunstaffnage Marine Laboratory and Scottish Marine Biological Association. Annual Reports **437**
Scottish Marine Biological Association Collected Reprints see S.M.B.A. Collected Reprints **5272**
Scottish Medicine. (UK ISSN 0261-3921) **3152**
Scottish Mountaineering Club. Journal. (UK ISSN 0080-813X) **4555**
Scottish Museum News. (UK ISSN 0266-6898) **3532**
Scottish National Register of Classified Trades see Sell's Scottish Directory **1152**
Scottish Opera Magazine see Scottish Opera News **5275**
†Scottish Opera News. (UK ISSN 0309-7323) **5275**
Scottish Ophthalmic Practitioner see Scottish Optometrist **3305**
Scottish Optometrist. (UK) **3305**

SCOTTSDALE SCENE 6647

Scottish Petroleum Annual. (UK) **3701**
Scottish Photography Bulletin. (UK ISSN 0269-1787) **3797**
Scottish Planning Appeal Decisions. (UK ISSN 0143-8972) **2496**
Scottish Planning Law & Practice. (UK ISSN 0144-8196) **2716**, **2496**
Scottish Postmark Group. Handbook. (UK ISSN 0080-8164) **3757**, **1354**
Scottish Pottery Historical Review. (UK ISSN 0144-1302) **357**
Scottish Pottery Studies. (UK ISSN 0260-7972) **1166**
Scottish Rite Journal. (US) **1301**
Scottish Rock Garden Club Journal see Rock Garden **2138**
Scottish Scout News. (UK) **1244**
Scottish Sea Fisheries Statistical Tables.(UK ISSN 0080-8202) **2048**
Scottish Slavonic Review. (UK ISSN 0265-3273) **2957**, **2386**
Scottish Social Work Statistics see Home Care Services, Day Care Establishments, Day Services - Scotland **4407**
†Scottish Society for Conservation and Restoration. Bulletin. (UK ISSN 0264-9039) **5275**
Scottish Society for Prevention of Vivisection. Annual Pictorial Review see Advocates for Animals. Annual Pictorial Review **230**
Scottish Society for Prevention of Vivisection. Annual Report see Advocates for Animals. Annual Report **576**
Scottish Society for the Conservation and Restoration of Historic and Artistic Works. Newsletter see Scottish Society for Conservation and Restoration. Bulletin **5275**
Scottish Sports Council. Bulletin see Arena (Edinburgh) **4464**
Scottish Stamp News. (UK) **3757**
Scottish Studies. (UK ISSN 0036-9411) **2386**, **248**, **2058**
Scottish Trades and Shops Holidays. (UK) **1053**
Scottish Tradition. (CN) **2386**
Scottish Tramlines see Scottish Transport **4656**
Scottish Transport. (UK ISSN 0048-9808) **4656**
Scottish Vocational Education Council. Journal see On Course **1757**
Scottish Wildlife. (UK ISSN 0143-1234) **1496**
Scottish Wildlife Trust. Newsletter see Scottish Wildlife **1496**
Scottish Women's Temperance News. (UK ISSN 0036-9446) **1539**, **4448**
Scottish Youth Hostels Association Handbook. (UK) **2480**, **1265**
Scott's Directories - Atlantic Manufacturing. (CN) **1152**
Scott's Directories - Ontario Manufacturers. (CN) **1152**
Scott's Directories - Quebec Manufacturers/Scott's Repertoires - Fabricants du Quebec. (CN) **1152**
Scott's Directories - Western Manufacturers. (CN ISSN 0317-879X) **1152**
Scott's Industrial Directories - Atlantic see Scott's Directories - Atlantic Manufacturing **1152**
Scott's Industrial Directories - Ontario see Scott's Directories - Ontario Manufacturers **1152**
Scott's Industrial Directories - Quebec see Scott's Directories - Quebec Manufacturers **1152**
Scott's Industrial Directories - Westerm see Scott's Directories - Western Manufacturers **1152**
Scott's Repertoires - Fabricants du Quebec. see Scott's Directories - Quebec Manufacturers **1152**
Scott's Specialized Catalogue of U.S. Stamps. (US) **3757**
Scott's Standard Postage Stamp Catalogue. (US) **3757**
Scott's Trade Directory of Metropolitan Toronto. (CN) **1152**
Scottsdale Scene Magazine. (US) **2234**

SCOUT

Scout. (SW ISSN 0346-0827) **1244**, 1265
Scout. (FR ISSN 0751-5731) **1265**, 1301
Scout Annual. (UK) **1265**
Scout Association of Australia. Annual Report. (AT) **1301**
Scout Association of Australia. Review of Progress *see* Scout Association of Australia. Annual Report **1301**
Scout - Avenir. (FR ISSN 0249-2644) **1265**
Scout Executive. (CN) **1244**
Scout Leader *see* The Leader **1240**
Scout Magazine. (AT ISSN 0815-4627) **1244**
Scout Memorabilia. (US) **2441**, 1265, 1301
Scouter's Digest. (US ISSN 0890-8206) **1244**, 1301
Scouting. (UK ISSN 0036-9489) **1265**
Scouting. (GW ISSN 0176-4624) **4555**
Scouting Magazine. (US ISSN 0036-9500) **1244**, 1301
Scouting News. (CN) **1244**
Scoutledaren. *see* Partiojohtaja **1242**
Scoutposten. (FI) **1265**
Scouts on Stamps Society International Journal *see* S O S S I Journal **3757**
Scrap Age *see* Scrap Processing and Recycling **1497**
Scrap Processing and Recycling. (US ISSN 0898-0756) **1497**, 3419
Scrapie. (UK) **1324**
Scratch. (UK) **3005**
Scream Factory. (US) **3014**
Scream Magazine. (US ISSN 0890-4596) **2957**, 343
Scream of the Buddha. (US) **3005**
Screaming Eagle. (US) **3471**, 61
Scree. (US ISSN 0360-2672) **2883**, 3005
Screed *see* On the Edge (Madison) **1320**
Screen. (US ISSN 0276-153X) **1379**, 3517
Screen. (UK ISSN 0036-9543) **1759**, 1379, 3517
Screen. (II) **2201**
Screen. (II ISSN 0036-9551) **3517**
Screen. (JA) **3517**
Screen Actor. (US ISSN 0036-956X) **2589**, 3517
Screen Actor Hollywood. (US) **3517**
Screen Actor News *see* Screen Actor **2589**
Screen Digest. (UK) **1379**, 3797
Screen International. (UK ISSN 0307-4617) **3517**, 1379
Screen International and Cinema T V Today *see* Screen International **3517**
Screen International Film and T.V. Yearbook. (UK) **3517**, 1379
Screen Printing. (US ISSN 0036-9594) **4005**
Screen Printing Association (UK) Ltd. News *see* S P A News **4005**
Screen Printing Association, International. Tabloid. (US) **4005**
Screen Printing Network. (US) **4005**
Screen Process. (UK) **4005**
Screen World. (US ISSN 0080-8288) **3517**
Screening. (NE ISSN 0925-6164) **3326**
Screening Industry. (US) **631**
Screening News *see* Screening Industry **631**
Screenings. (US ISSN 0048-9832) **284**
Screenplay. (US) **4005**
Screw. (US ISSN 0036-9624) **2883**, 3400
Scribbler. (US) **2957**
Scribeco. (FR ISSN 0769-0509) **411**
Scribhinni Gaeilgena na Brathar Mionur.(IE ISSN 0332-4249) **2957**, 4275
Scriblerian *see* Scriblerian and the Kit-Cats **2957**
Scriblerian and the Kit-Cats. (US ISSN 0190-731X) **2957**
Scrinium. (AU) **2783**
Scrip - World Pharmaceutical News. (UK ISSN 0143-7690) **3743**

Scripps Clinic and Research Foundation. Annual Report. (US ISSN 0080-830X) **4608**
▼Scripps Clinic Personal Health Letter. (US ISSN 1049-5614) **3152**, 3808
Scripps Institution of Oceanography. Annual Report. (US ISSN 1046-9443) **1610**
Scripps Institution of Oceanography. Bulletin. (US ISSN 0080-8318) **1610**
Scripps Institution of Oceanography. Contributions. New Series. (US) **1610**
Scripps Institution of Oceanography. Deep Sea Drilling Project. Initial Reports. (US ISSN 0080-8334) **1610**
Scripps Research Institute. Scientific Report. (US) **3152**
Scripsi. (AT ISSN 0725-0096) **2957**
Script. (FR) **3517**
Script/Papierhandel. (BE) **3666**
Scripta Academica. (SW ISSN 0348-1093) **411**
Scripta Artis Monographia. (NE ISSN 0080-8350) **343**
Scripta Facultatis Scientiarum Naturalium Univeritatis Masaykianae Brunensis. Geologia *see* Masaryk University. Faculty of Sciences. Scripta Geologia **1572**
Scripta Facultatis Scientiarum Naturalium Universitatis Masarukianae Brunensis. Chemia *see* Masaryk University. Faculty of Sciences. Scripta Chemia **1183**
Scripta Facultatis Scientiarum Naturalium Universitatis Masarykianae Brunensis: Geographia *see* Masaryk University. Faculty of Sciences. Scripta Geographia **4323**
Scripta Facultatis Scientiarum Naturalium Universitatis Masarykianae Brunensis: Mathematica *see* Masaryk University. Faculty of Sciences. Scripta Mathematica **3044**
Scripta Facultatis Scientiarum Naturalium Universitatis Masarykianae Brunensis: Physica *see* Masaryk University. Faculty of Sciences. Scripta Physica **3824**
Scripta Facultatis Scientirarum Naturalium Universitatis Masarykianae Brunensis: Biologia *see* Masaryk University. Faculty of Sciences. Scripta Biologia **447**
Scripta Geobotanica. (GW ISSN 0341-3772) **517**
Scripta Geologica. (NE ISSN 0375-7587) **1579**
Scripta Hierosolymitana. (IS ISSN 0080-8369) **2514**, 4385
Scripta Historica. (FI ISSN 0358-710X) **2386**
Scripta Instituti Donneriani Aboensis. (FI ISSN 0582-3226) **4201**
Scripta Islandica. (SW ISSN 0582-3234) **2840**, 2957
Scripta Medica. (CS ISSN 0036-9721) **3152**
Scripta Mediterranea. (CN) **2431**, 248, 284, 3643
Scripta Mercaturae. (GW ISSN 0036-973X) **898**
Scripta Metallurgica *see* Scripta Metallurgica et Materialia **3419**
Scripta Metallurgica et Materialia. (US ISSN 0956-716X) **3419**
Scripta Minore. Regiae Societatis Humaniorum Litterarum Lundensis. (SW) **284**
Scripta Scientifica Medica. (BU ISSN 0582-3250) **3202**, 3211, 3263
Scripta Theologica. (SP ISSN 0036-9764) **4201**
Scriptores Latini. (IT ISSN 0080-8393) **1280**
Scriptores Latini Hiberniae. (IE ISSN 0332-4214) **2957**
Scriptorium. (BE ISSN 0036-9772) **4136**
Scriptorum Romanorum Quae Extant Omnia. (IT) **1280**
Scriptura. (DR) **2957**
Scriptura. (SA ISSN 0254-1807) **4248**

Scripture Bulletin. (UK ISSN 0036-9780) **4275**
Scripture Gift Mission News *see* S G M News **4200**
Scripture in Church. (IE ISSN 0332-1150) **4275**
Scripture Union (A.C.T.) News *see* S.U. News **4248**
Scriptwriters Market. (US ISSN 0734-8592) **2957**, 1379, 3517
Scrittura e Civilta. (IT) **1280**
Scrittura Scenica. (IT) **2957**
Scrivener. (CN ISSN 0227-5090) **2957**
Scroll of Phi Delta Theta. (US ISSN 0036-9799) **1324**
Scrutiny. (CN ISSN 0838-4525) **1662**
Scrutiny *see* Pakistan Journal of Social Science **3968**
Scuba Diver. (AT ISSN 0729-5529) **4487**
Scuba Times. (US) **4487**
Scubapro Diving and Snorkeling. (US) **4487**
Scugnizzo. (IT ISSN 0036-9802) **1244**, 4419
Sculptors International *see* Sculpture **343**
Sculpture *see* Sculpture Review **343**
Sculpture. (US ISSN 0889-728X) **343**
Sculpture Review. (US ISSN 0747-5284) **343**
Scuola Archeologica di Atene e delle Missioni Italiane in Oriente. Annuario. (IT) **284**
Scuola Archeologica di Atene e delle Missioni Italiane in Oriente. Monografie. (IT ISSN 0067-009X) **284**
Scuola Cattolica. (IT ISSN 0036-9810) **4275**
Scuola del Fardase. (IT) **2441**
Scuola della Salute. (IT) **3612**
Scuola Dello Sport Rivista di Cultura Sportiva *see* S D S - Rivista di Cultura Sportiva **4486**
Scuola di Astrologia. (IT) **359**
Scuola di Cucina. (IT) **2449**
Scuola di Fotografia. (IT) **3797**
Scuola di Taglio e Cucito. (IT) **1294**
Scuola Domenicale. (IT) **1662**
Scuola e Citta. (IT ISSN 0036-9853) **1662**
Scuola e Didattica. (IT ISSN 0036-9861) **1662**
Scuola e l'Uomo. (IT ISSN 0036-987X) **1662**
Scuola Italiana Moderna. (IT ISSN 0036-9888) **1662**
Scuola Materna. (IT) **1731**
Scuola Normale Superiore di Pisa. Annali. Classe di Lettere e Filosofia. (IT) **2514**, 3781
Scuola Normale Superiore di Pisa. Annali. Classe di Scienze. (IT) **3054**, 3830
Scuola Normale Superiore di Pisa. Annali. Scienze, Fisiche e Matematiche *see* Scuola Normale Superiore di Pisa. Annali. Classe di Scienze **3054**
Scuola Nostra. (IT) **1662**
Scuola Primaria. (IT) **1662**
Scuola Speciale per Archivisti e Bibliotecari. Nuova Annali. (IT) **2783**
Scuola Viva. (IT ISSN 0036-9926) **1662**
Sdelovaci Technika/Telecommunications Engineering. (CS ISSN 0036-9942) **1365**, 1907
Se la Vie Poetry Newsletter *see* Se la Vie Writer's Journal **3005**
Se la Vie Writer's Journal. (US) **3005**, 2575
Se og Hoer. (DK) **2185**
Se Pu/Chromatogram. (CC ISSN 1000-8713) **3857**
Se Vuoi. (IT ISSN 0036-9950) **4201**
Sea. *see* Aegir **2050**
Sea. *see* Umi **2971**
Sea. (US ISSN 0746-8601) **4529**
Sea. (UK) **4738**
Sea & Yachting. (GR) **4529**
Sea Angler. (UK ISSN 0306-6568) **4555**

Sea Boating Almanac. Northern California and Nevada *see* Pacific Boating Almanac. Northern California & Nevada **4527**
Sea Breeze. (US) **4786**
Sea Breezes. (UK ISSN 0036-9977) **4738**
Sea Cadet *see* Navy News. Sea Cadet Edition **1261**
Sea Chest. (US ISSN 0582-3471) **4738**, 2422
Sea Fishing Today. (UK ISSN 0265-024X) **4555**
Sea Frontiers. (US ISSN 0897-2249) **1610**
Sea Frontiers - Sea Secrets *see* Sea Frontiers **1610**
Sea Grant Abstracts. (US ISSN 0887-4220) **1552**, 23, 467
Sea Gull Literature. *see* Hai Ou **2921**
Sea Heritage News. (US ISSN 0270-5524) **4529**, 2322
Sea History. (US ISSN 0146-9312) **4738**
Sea History Gazette. (US ISSN 0896-1646) **4738**
▼Sea History's Guide to American & Canadian Maritime Museums. (US) **3532**, 4738
Sea Kayaker. (US ISSN 0829-3279) **4529**
Sea Letter. (US ISSN 0732-6882) **4738**
Sea Magazine *see* Sea **4529**
Sea Pen. (CN ISSN 0700-9275) **2048**
Sea Power. (US ISSN 0199-1337) **3471**, 3971, 4738
Sea Rescue. (SA ISSN 1015-6488) **4738**, 4529
Sea Shelters. (US) **4158**
Sea Spray. (NZ ISSN 0037-0037) **4529**
Sea Technology. (US ISSN 0093-3651) **1836**, 1610
Sea Technology Buyers Guide - Directory. (US) **1836**, 1610
Sea Technology Handbook and Directory *see* Sea Technology Buyers Guide - Directory **1836**
Sea-Tilth *see* Seattle Tilth **2138**
Seabird. (UK ISSN 0267-9310) **567**
Seabird Report *see* Seabird **567**
Seaborne Trade and Transport *see* Seaborne Trade and Transport Reports **4738**
Seaborne Trade and Transport Reports.(UK) **4738**
Seaby's Coin and Medal Bulletin *see* Classical Numismatic Review **3598**
Seaby's Standard Catalogue of British Coins. (UK) **3601**
Seacoast Life *see* New Hampshire Life **5245**
Seacraft *see* Australian Seacraft **4522**
Seafarer. (UK ISSN 0037-007X) **4738**
Seafarers Log. (US) **2589**, 4738
Seafood Business. (US ISSN 0889-3217) **2048**, 2081
Seafood Business Report *see* Seafood Business **2048**
Seafood Export Journal. (II ISSN 0037-010X) **2048**
Seafood Leader. (US ISSN 0744-4664) **2081**
Seafood Price-Current. (US ISSN 0270-417X) **2081**
Seahorse. (UK) **4529**
Seal News. (US) **3757**
Sealandair. (CN ISSN 0048-9883) **3471**
Sealants. (US) **4294**, 3868
Seales Cayman Letter. (CJ) **962**, 4158
Seaman. (UK ISSN 0037-0142) **2589**, 4738
Seamen's Journal. (AT) **4738**
Seaplane Landing Directory *see* S P A Water Landing Directory **61**
Seaplane Pilots Association Water Landing Directory *see* S P A Water Landing Directory **61**
Seaport Magazine *see* Seaport: New York's History Magazine **4738**
Seaport: New York's History Magazine. (US ISSN 0743-6246) **4738**, 2322

Seaports and the Shipping World. (CN ISSN 0037-0150) **4738**
Seaports and the Shipping World. Annual Issue. (CN ISSN 0080-8423) **4738**
Seaposter. (US ISSN 0048-9891) **3757**
Sear. (UK ISSN 0048-9905) **2883**
Seara Nova (Lisbon Codex). (PO ISSN 0870-5291) **2214**, 2022
Seara Nova (Lisbon, 1921). (PO ISSN 0037-0177) **2958**
Search. (IE ISSN 0332-0618) **4248**
Search. (AT ISSN 0004-9549) **4342**
Search (Brattleboro). (US ISSN 0272-5827) **3971**
Search (Devon). (US ISSN 1043-0946) **309**, 2500
Search (London, 1924). (UK) **1265**
Search (London, 1957). (UK) **3152**
Search (Nashville). (US ISSN 0048-9913) **4248**
Search (York). (UK ISSN 0958-3467) **4419**, 2278, 2496
Search and Rescue Statistics see S A R Statistics **4666**
Search and Seizure Bulletin. (US ISSN 0037-0193) **2678**, 2678
Search and Seizure Law Report. (US ISSN 0095-1005) **2678**
†Search - Flying Saucers. (US) **5275**
Search for Health. (US) **3808**
Search Group. Technical Memorandum. (US) **1522**
Search Group. Technical Report. (US) **1522**
Search Inform see Search Tools: The Guide to U M I - Data Courier Online **2784**
Search Light. (US) **2164**
Search Tools: The Guide to U M I - Data Courier Online. (US) **2784**
Searchable Physics Information Notices.(US) **3839**, 23
Searcher. (US ISSN 0037-0401) **2164**
Searcher. (CN ISSN 0037-041X) **2589**, 3419
Searching Dialog: The Complete Guide. (US) **2784**
Searching for Scruggs. (US) **2164**
†Searching Illinois Ancestors - Travel Illinois. (US) **5275**
Searching Together. (US ISSN 0739-2281) **4249**
Searchlight. (US) **1522**
Searchlight. (UK ISSN 0262-4591) **3924**
Searchlight on the City Council. (US) **4094**
Searchlines. (US) **4112**
Sears Foundation for Marine Research. Memoirs. (US) **455**, 1610
▼Sea's Industry West. (US) **4529**
Seashore Trolley Museum Dispatch. (US) **3532**, 4714
▼Seasons. (US) **2234**
†Seatrade Arab Shipping Guide. (UK) **5275**
Seatrade Business Review see Seatrade Review **920**
Seatrade Review. (UK) **920**, 4738
†Seatrade Turkish Shipping Guide. (UK) **5275**
†Seatrade U.S. Shipping Guide. (UK) **5275**
Seatrade U.S. Yearbook see Seatrade U.S. Shipping Guide **5275**
Seatrade Week. (UK) **4738**, 920
▼Seattle Airport Business Directory. (CN) **4677**
Seattle and King County Arts Commission. Newsletter see Seattle Arts **343**
Seattle Arts. (US) **343**
†Seattle Business. (US ISSN 0037-0444) **5275**
Seattle Business Journal see Puget Sound Business Journal **686**
Seattle District Dental Society. Journal see Seattle - King County Dental Society. Journal **3242**
Seattle Folklore Society Newsletter. (US ISSN 0037-0460) **2058**, 3580
Seattle Gay News. (US) **2457**
Seattle Genealogical Society Bulletin. (US) **2164**
Seattle Home and Garden see Greater Seattle **2226**

Seattle - King County Dental Society. Journal. (US ISSN 0037-0452) **3242**
Seattle Professional Engineering Employees Association Spotlite see S P E E A Spotlite **1836**
Seattle Review. (US ISSN 0147-6629) **2958**
Seattle Tilth. (US) **2138**
Seattle University Spectator see Spectator (Seattle) **1325**
Seattle Weekly. (US) **2234**
Seattle's Child. (US) **1244**
Seawater and Desalting. (US ISSN 0720-0773) **4828**
Seaway Review. (US ISSN 0037-0487) **4738**
Seaways. (UK ISSN 0144-1019) **4738**
Sebring Family Newsletter. (US) **2164**
Sechaba. (ZA ISSN 0037-0509) **3947**
Sechzig - Na und? (GW) **2278**, 2191
Secoiul 20. (RM ISSN 0037-0517) **2958**
Secom Annual Report (Year). (JA) **1527**, 1084, 1379, 1435
Second Boat. (US ISSN 0274-6441) **2164**
Second Century. (US ISSN 0276-7899) **4288**
Second Century Radcliffe News see Radcliffe News **1322**
†Second Coming. (US ISSN 0048-9956) **5275**
Second Decade see Wisconsin Environmental Decade **1501**
Second Home. (US) **4158**
Second Impressions. (CN) **4005**
▼Second Language Learning. (US) **2840**
Second Language Research. (UK ISSN 0267-6583) **2840**
Second Line. (US ISSN 0037-0576) **3580**
Second Messengers and Phosphoproteins. (US ISSN 0895-7479) **455**
Second Opinion (Chicago). (US ISSN 0890-1570) **3152**, 3781
†Second Opinion (San Francisco). (US ISSN 0748-9528) **5275**
Second Order. (NR ISSN 0048-9964) **3781**
Second Republic Newsletter see Rangel's Reports **3969**
Second Section Firms see Japan Company Handbook. Second Section **1141**
Second Source Biomedical. (US) **2524**
Second Source Imaging. (US) **3152**
The Second Stone. (US ISSN 1047-3971) **2457**, 4201
Second Supplement to the S A Joint Catalogue of Monographs on Microfiche. Author Index. (SA ISSN 1018-9599) **411**
Second Supplement to the S A Joint Catalogue of Monographs on Microfiche. Title Index. (SA ISSN 1018-9602) **411**
Second 1,500 Companies see Trinet Directory of Leading U S Companies: Second 1,500 **695**
Secondamano. (IT) **38**
Secondary Aluminium. (GW) **3495**
Secondary Education Journal see N U T Education Review **1649**
Secondary Education Today. (US) **1662**
†Secondary Heads Association Review. (UK) **5275**
†Secondary Journal (Sydney). (AT ISSN 0728-9006) **5275**
Secondary Marketing Executive. (US ISSN 0891-2947) **799**
Secondary Markets Handbook. (UK) **962**
†Secondary Mortgage Market Analysis. (US) **5275**
Secondary Mortgage Market Guide. (US) **799**, 4158
Secondary Mortgage Markets. (US ISSN 0740-4271) **799**, 4158
Secondary School Admission Test Board. Annual Report. (US) **1662**
Secondary School Education. see Zhongxue Jiaoyu **1673**

†Secondary Wood Products Manufacturers Directory. (US) **5275**
Secret Place. (US ISSN 0037-0606) **4249**
Secretaresse Magazine: S. (BE) **1061**, 4852
Secretaria de Estado de Agricultura y Ganaderia Publicaciones see E A G Publicaciones **87**
Secretariat a la Jeunesse et aux Sport. Bulletin Officiel see Ministere de la Jeunesse et des Sport. Bulletin Officiel **4479**
Secretariat Permanent des Organisations Non Gouvernementales. Rapport d'Activities. (UV) **1782**
Secretaries and Managers Journal of Australia. (AT) **1027**, 1301
Secretaries Year Book. (TH ISSN 0857-1163) **993**
The Secretary. (US ISSN 0037-0622) **1061**
Secretary of Energy Annual Report to Congress. (US) **4701**
Secretary's Update. (CN) **1070**
Secrets. (US ISSN 0037-0649) **2984**
Secrets. (UK) **2984**
Secrets of Winners. (US) **962**
Sectante. (HO) **2180**
Sector Alimentario en Mexico (Year). (MX) **3612**
Sector Electrico en Mexico. (MX ISSN 0186-050X) **1907**
Sector Energia e Industria. (VE) **1836**, 1795, 1907
Sector Fund Newsletter. (US) **962**
Sectorfund Advisor see Callahan's Fund Advisor **941**
Secularist. (II ISSN 0049-0008) **3781**
Secure Magazine. (US) **962**
Secure Signals. (US) **1379**, 1522
Secured Lender. (US ISSN 0888-255X) **799**
Secured Lending Alert. (US) **799**
Secured Transaction Guide. (US) **962**
Securitas. (IT ISSN 0037-0657) **4112**
Securite au Travail. (BE) **993**
Securite Civile et Industrielle. (FR ISSN 0222-559X) **1274**
Securite et Medecine du Travail. (FR) **3622**
Securite et Sante au Travail. (UN ISSN 1010-7061) **3623**, 23
Securitech see Securitech Europe **1522**
Securitech Europe. (UK) **1522**
Securities and Corporate Regulation Review. (CN ISSN 0831-3482) **2712**
Securities and Exchange Commission Accounting and Reporting Update Service see S E C Accounting and Reporting Update Service **756**
Securities and Exchange Commission Accounting Report see S E C Accounting Report **756**
Securities and Exchange Commission Accounting Rules see S E C Accounting Rules **962**
Securities and Federal Corporate Law Report. (US ISSN 0273-0685) **2712**
Securities & Syndication Review. (US ISSN 0739-8689) **962**
▼Securities Arbitration Procedure Manual. (US) **2678**
Securities Exchange of Thailand. Handbook. (TH) **962**
Securities Fraud and Commodities Fraud. (US) **2678**, 962
Securities Industry Association (Washington) Washington Report see S I A Washington Report **962**
Securities Industry Association Directory & Guide see S I A Directory & Guide **1152**
Securities Industry Trends. (US) **963**
Securities Industry Yearbook. (US) **963**
Securities Insider Trading Litigation Reporter. (US) **2678**
Securities Institute. (US) **2678**, 799, 963
Securities Journal. (HK) **799**
†Securities Law Anthology. (US) **5275**
Securities Law Review. (US ISSN 0080-8474) **799**, 2678

▼Securities Litigation Reporter. (US ISSN 1053-0266) **2678**, 963
Securities Market in Japan. (JA) **963**
Securities Market in Korea see Introduction to the Korean Securities Market **950**
▼Securities Product News. (US) **963**
Securities Regulation. (US) **963**, 2678
Securities Regulation & Law Report. (US ISSN 0037-0665) **2678**
Securities Regulation Law Journal. (US ISSN 0097-9554) **963**, 2678
Securities Traders' Monthly. (US ISSN 0738-4351) **963**
Securities Week. (US ISSN 0149-3582) **963**
Security. see Al-Amn **1525**
Security. (US) **1527**, 1435
Security. see Seguridad **1528**
†Security and Intelligence Foundation. Nightwatch. (US) **5275**
†Security and Intelligence Foundation. Situation Report. (US) **5275**
Security and Intelligence Foundation. Special Report see Journal of Intelligence Studies **3963**
Security and Protection see Security and Protection Equipment **1527**
Security and Protection Equipment. (UK) **1527**
Security and Special Police Legal Update. (US ISSN 0741-482X) **1527**, 2714
Security Australia. (AT) **1527**, 2034
Security Dealer. (US ISSN 0164-3320) **1061**, 1527
Security Dealer Product Directory and Reference Guide. (US) **1152**, 1527
Security Distributing & Marketing. (US ISSN 0049-0016) **1053**, 1527
Security, Exchange and Commission Guidelines (Year) see S E C Guidelines (Year) **962**
Security Gazette. (UK ISSN 0049-0024) **1527**
Security Industry Yearbook see Securities Industry Yearbook **963**
Security Intelligence Report. (US) **3924**, 1522, 3471
Security Journal. (US ISSN 0955-1662) **1527**, 1027
Security Law Newsletter. (US ISSN 0889-0625) **1527**, 2714
Security Letter. (US ISSN 0363-4922) **1527**
Security Letter Source Book. (US ISSN 0736-0401) **1527**
Security Management. (US ISSN 0145-9406) **1027**, 1527
Security Management - Plant and Property Protection see Security Management - Protecting Property, People & Assets **1527**
Security Management - Protecting Property, People & Assets. (US ISSN 0745-6093) **1527**
Security Market Research Commodity Service see S M R Commodity Service **962**
Security Market Research Stock Service see S M R Stock Service **962**
Security News (Los Angeles). (US) **799**
▼Security News (Salamanca). (US ISSN 1059-8294) **1528**
Security Outlook. see Afaq Amniya **1525**
Security Report see Compensation in the Security - Loss Prevention Field **975**
Security Sales. (US) **643**, 1528
Security Specifier. (UK) **1528**, 4112
▼Security Studies. (UK ISSN 0963-6412) **3471**
Security Surveyor. (UK ISSN 0306-6118) **1528**
†Security Systems. (US) **5275**
Security Systems Administratio see Security Systems **5275**
Sedar. (SI ISSN 0559-2674) **4220**
Sedibeng. (SA) **2295**
Sediment Data for Selected Canadian Rivers. (CN ISSN 0080-8482) **1579**
Sedimentary Geology see Geological Abstracts **1551**
Sedimentary Geology. (NE ISSN 0037-0738) **1580**

SEDIMENTOLOGY

Sedimentology. (UK ISSN 0037-0746) **1580**
Sedimentology *see* Geographical Abstracts: Physical Geography **2268**
Sedmicka Pionyru. (CS) **1265**
Sedum Society Newsletter. (UK) **517**
See. (AT ISSN 0037-0754) **4249**
See & Listen. *see* Sehen - Hoeren - Bilden **1759**
See Australia *see* See Australia Regional Information Series **4786**
See Australia Regional Information Series. (AT) **4786**
See Daytona Beach. (US) **4786**
See India. (II ISSN 0037-0762) **4786**
Seed Abstracts. (UK ISSN 0141-0180) **143, 23**
Seed and Nursery Trader *see* Australian Horticulture **2122**
Seed - Business. (FR) **192**
Seed in Canada *see* Agri-Book Magazine. Top Crop Manager **69**
Seed Industry Journal. (US ISSN 1041-0678) **208**
Seed News. (US) **192**
▼Seed Pathology and Microbiology. (UK ISSN 0959-9592) **143, 23**
The Seed Pod. (US ISSN 0745-3590) **2138**
†Seed Potato. (UK) **5275**
Seed Research. (II ISSN 0379-5594) **192**
Seed Savers Exchange. (US) **2138**
Seed Science and Technology. (SZ ISSN 0251-0952) **517, 119**
▼Seed Science Research. (UK ISSN 0960-2585) **517**
Seed Scoop. (CN ISSN 0049-0040) **192**
Seed Trade Buyer's Guide. (US ISSN 0080-8504) **192**
Seed Trade News. (US ISSN 0037-0789) **2138**
Seed World. (US ISSN 0037-0797) **192**
Seedling News. (US) **1497, 2107**
Seedmen's Digest *see* Seed Industry Journal **208**
†Seedpeople Network. Newsletter. (US) **5275**
Seeds. (US ISSN 0194-4495) **4419, 119, 935**
Seeing Clearly. (US) **2296**
Seeing Eye Annual Report. (US) **2296**
Seeing Eye Guide. (US ISSN 0037-0819) **2296**
Seek. (US) **4201**
†Seek. (SA ISSN 0037-0827) **5275**
Seek Knowledge. *see* Qiu Zhi **3920**
Seeker (Pittsburg). (US ISSN 0363-4590) **2164**
Seeker's Guide. (US ISSN 0080-8512) **1152**
Seeking 'n Searching Ancestors. (US) **2164**
Seeking Truth. *see* Qiu Shi **4383**
Seeking Truth - Select Articles. *see* Qiu Shi Wenxuan **4383**
Seems. (US ISSN 0095-1730) **2958, 3005**
Seevoegel. (GW ISSN 0722-2947) **567, 1968**
Seewirtschaft. (GW ISSN 0037-0886) **4738**
Sefarad. (SP ISSN 0037-0894) **2431, 2022, 2840**
Sefunim. (IS ISSN 0077-5193) **284, 3532, 4738**
Segeln. (GW) **4529**
Segelsport. (GW ISSN 0175-1344) **4529, 4555**
Seglarbladet. (SW ISSN 0037-0916) **4529**
Seglaren. *see* Purjehtija **4528**
Segler Zeitung. (GW) **4529**
Segnalazioni Cinematografiche. (IT ISSN 0037-0932) **3517**
Segnalazioni Stradali *see* H P Trasporti **4719**
Segni dei Tempi. (IT ISSN 0394-364X) **4201**
Segni e Comprensione. (IT) **3781**
SegnoCinema. (IT ISSN 0393-3865) **3517**
Sego Lily. (US) **2138, 517**
Segretissimo. (IT) **2984**
Seguranca. (PO ISSN 0049-0059) **4112**

Seguridad/Security. (BL) **1528**
Seguridad Social. (CK) **2542**
Seguridad Social. (BO) **2542**
Seguridad Social. (MX ISSN 0582-4001) **4419, 4112**
Seguridad y Defensa. (VE) **3471**
Segurinotas. (MX) **1027**
Seguros. (UY) **2542**
Sehar Huts Shel Yisrael. *see* Israel. Central Bureau of Statistics. Israel's Foreign Trade **724**
Sehen - Hoeren - Bilden/See & Listen. (AU) **1759**
Sehen und Hoeren *see* Sehen - Hoeren - Bilden **1759**
Sehur Ruidaihagsurji *see* Seoul Journal of Medicine **3152**
Sei Marianna Ika Daigaku Kiyo. Ippan Kyoiku/St. Marianna University School of Medicine. Bulletin (General Education). (JA ISSN 0286-4932) **1697**
Seibt Export Directory of German Industries. (GW) **1152**
Seibt Industriekatalog. (GW) **1084**
Seibt Medizinische Technik. (GW) **3152**
Seibt Oberflaechentechnik. (GW) **3845**
Seibt Pharma-Technik. (GW) **3743**
Seibutsu Kagaku. *see* Biological Science **431**
Seiche. (US ISSN 8755-4682) **4828, 2048**
Seicho/Journal of Growth. (JA ISSN 0287-7775) **248, 517**
Seifen, Oele, Fette, Wachse. (GW ISSN 0173-5500) **376, 1282**
Seihon Shikokai *see* Seihonkai **4137**
Seihonkai/Bookbinding Industry. (JA ISSN 0037-1009) **4137**
Seijo Daigaku Keizai Kenkyu. *see* Seijo University Economic Papers **690**
Seijo University Economic Papers/Seijo Daigaku Keizai Kenkyu. (JA ISSN 0387-4753) **690**
Seika Seipan. (JA) **2089**
Seikagaku/Japanese Biochemical Society. Journal. (JA ISSN 0037-1017) **482**
Seikatsu Hogo Dotai Chosa Hokoku *see* Japan. Ministry of Health and Welfare. Statistics and Information Department. Report on Survey of Public Assistance **4426**
Seikatsu to Kankyo/Life and Environment. (JA ISSN 0037-1025) **1968, 4112**
Seikei Geka. *see* Orthopedic Surgery **3310**
Seikei Geka to Saigai Geka/Orthopedics and Traumatology. (JA ISSN 0037-1033) **3311**
Seikei Kisho Kansokujo Hokoku. (JA ISSN 0388-3515) **3444**
Seikei Ronso - Faculty of Politics, Law and Economics. Journal *see* Kokugakuin University Economic Review **676**
Seiken N S T Shinpojumu Koen Kogaishu. (JA) **1405, 1435, 3063**
Seiken N S T Shinpojumu Koen Ronbunshu. (JA) **1435, 3054**
Seikyo Times. (US) **4215, 3781**
Seilsport. (NO) **4529**
Seimitsu Chosa Hokokusho: Jozankei Chiiki. *see* Close Examination Report: Jozankei Valley Region **3481**
Sein. (FR ISSN 1163-1961) **3296**
Seipone. (SA) **2217, 2022**
Seiron. *see* Opinions **3913**
Seisan Kenkyu/Production Research. (JA ISSN 0037-105X) **4608**
Seisanzai/Industrial Marketing. (JA) **1053, 1922**
†Seishin Bunseki/Tokyo Journal of Psychoanalysis. (JA ISSN 0037-1076) **5275**
Seishin Igaku/Clinical Psychiatry. (JA ISSN 0488-1281) **3354**
Seishin Igaku Institute of Psychiatry, Tokyo. Bulletin. *see* Seishin Igaku Kenkyujo, Tokyo. Gyosekishu **3354**
Seishin Igaku Kenkyujo, Tokyo. Gyosekishu/Seishin Igaku Institute of Psychiatry, Tokyo. Bulletin. (JA ISSN 0080-8547) **3354**

Seishin Shinkeigaku Zasshi. *see* Psychiatria et Neurologia Japonica (Tokyo, 1899) **3351**
Seishin Studies. (JA ISSN 0037-1084) **2515**
Seishonen Sekijuji/Japanese Junior Red Cross. (JA ISSN 0037-1092) **4112**
Seismic Instruments. (US ISSN 0747-9239) **1594**
Seismological Research Letters. (US ISSN 0895-0695) **1594**
Seismological Society of America. Bulletin. (US ISSN 0037-1106) **1594**
Seismological Society of Japan. Journal/Zisin. (JA ISSN 0037-1114) **1594**
Seismology Abstracts. *see* Dizhen Wenzhai **1550**
Seismology and Exploration Geophysics.(NE) **1594**
Seismology and Geology. *see* Dizhen Dizhi **1588**
Seiso Jigyo Gaiyo. *see* Public Cleansing Services in Tokyo **4110**
†Seitai Kagaku/Aquatic Ecological Chemistry. (JA ISSN 0386-8141) **5275**
Seitai no Kagaku/Life Science. (JA ISSN 0370-9531) **455, 482, 486**
Seitenwechsel. (GW ISSN 0930-3308) **4487**
Seiva. (BL ISSN 0037-1122) **119, 2107, 2449**
Seiyo Kotengaku Kenkyu/Journal of Classical Studies. (JA ISSN 0582-4524) **1280**
Seiyoshigaku/Studies in Western History. (JA) **2386, 2422**
▼Seizure. (UK ISSN 1059-1311) **3354**
Sejahtera. (MY) **2958**
Sekai/World. (JA ISSN 0582-4532) **3924, 2322**
Sekai no Chikusan/World Livestock Industry. (JA ISSN 0386-8362) **225**
Sekai no Norinsuisan/World Agriculture, Forestry and Fisheries. (JA) **119**
Sekeisai Gaigeka. *see* Orthopaedic and Traumatic Surgery **3310**
Sekoh. *see* Architectural Engineering **600**
Sekretariat. (GW ISSN 0171-4937) **1061**
Sekretarska Praxe. (CS ISSN 0037-1149) **1061**
Sekstant. (NE ISSN 0037-3087) **4448**
Seksuaalinen Tasavertaisuus ry SETA *see* SETA **2457**
Sekundaer-Rohstoffe. (GW ISSN 0176-2656) **3023, 3666**
Sekvens. (DK ISSN 0106-2484) **3517**
Selangor Public Library. Annual Report *see* Selangor Public Library Corporation. Annual Report **2784**
Selangor Public Library Corporation. Annual Report/Perbadanan Perpustakaan Awam Selangor. Lapuran Tahunan. (MY) **2784**
Selbermachen. (GW) **2441**
†Selbst-Verwirklichung: Jahresheft. (US) **5275**
Selbstaendig in der Wirtschaft. (AU) **884, 1117**
Der Selbstaendige. (GW ISSN 0939-0081) **1117, 1105**
Der Selbstaendige in der Binnenschiffahrt. (GW ISSN 0939-0073) **1117, 1105**
Selbstbedienung Artikel *see* S B Artikel **1052**
Selbstbedienung-Dynamik im Handel *see* Dynamik im Handel **2091**
Selbsthilfe. (GW ISSN 0724-5572) **4419**
Selbsthilfe Spektrum Rhein - Main. (GW) **4419**
Selbstverwaltung und Selbstverantwortung. (GW ISSN 0342-2186) **2542**
Selbyana. (US ISSN 0361-185X) **517**
Selden Society, London. Handbook: Publications, List of Members and Rules. (UK) **2678, 2322**
Selden Society, London. Lectures. (UK) **2678, 2322**

Selden Society, London. Main (Annual) Series. (UK) **2678, 2322**
Selden Society, London. Supplementary Series. (UK ISSN 0582-4788) **2678, 2322**
Selecciones Avicolas. (SP ISSN 0210-0541) **225**
Selecciones de Teologia. (SP ISSN 0037-119X) **4201**
Selecciones del Reader's Digest (Chilean Edition). (CL ISSN 0037-1203) **2180**
Selecciones del Reader's Digest (Mexican Edition). (MX) **2210**
Seleccos do Reader's Digest. (PO) **2214**
Selecoes do Readers Digest (Brazil Edition). (PO) **2175**
Selecoes Economicas/Jitsugyo no Burajiru. (BL) **935**
Select. (US) **4448**
Select Bibliography of Danish Works on the History of Towns Published. (DK ISSN 0105-9475) **2330**
Select Home Designs. (CN ISSN 0833-1103) **631, 2449**
Select Home Designs: Home Design and Decor *see* Select Homes **306**
Select Homes. (CN ISSN 0713-8075) **306**
Select Homes & Food. (CN) **2555**
Select Homes Renovation Ideas. (CN) **2496**
Select Information Exchange Year) Guide to Investment Services *see* S I E (Year) Guide to Investment Services **962**
Select: National Bibliographic Service Newsletter. (UK) **2784**
Selecta. (IO) **2202**
Selecta. (GW ISSN 0582-4877) **3152**
Selecta (Corvallis). (US ISSN 0277-0598) **2840, 2958**
Selecta Mathematica Sovietica. (SZ ISSN 0272-9903) **3054, 3830**
Selected Abstracts on Occupational Diseases. (UK) **3623, 3181**
Selected Agri-Figures of the E.E.C. *see* E E G Vademecum **5183**
Selected Annotated Bibliography of Population Studies in the Netherlands. (NE ISSN 0167-4757) **3995**
Selected Bibliographies on Ageing. (UK ISSN 0267-0348) **2278**
Selected Bibliography of Homosexuality.(US) **2458**
Selected Bibliography of Middle East Geology *see* Israel. Geological Survey. Current Bibliography of Middle East Geology **1569**
†Selected Bibliography of Museological Literature. (CS) **5275**
Selected Bibliography of Recent Economic Development Publications. (US) **737**
Selected Current Aerospace Notices *see* S C A N **61**
Selected Current Awareness Bulletin. (UK) **1540, 3748**
†Selected Documents of the International Petroleum Industry. (AU ISSN 0080-858X) **5275**
Selected Energy Statistics: South Africa.(SA) **1800**
Selected Excellent Compositions from Nation-wide Middle Schools. *see* Quanguo Zhongxue Youxiu Zuowen Xuan **2836**
Selected Information on Insured U.S. Commercial Banks Ranked by Assets. (US) **884**
Selected Legendary Literature. *see* Chuanqi Wenxue Xuankan **2905**
Selected List of Federal Laws and Treaties Relating to Sport Fish and Wildlife *see* U.S. Fish and Wildlife Service. Selected List of Federal Laws and Treaties Relating to Sport Fish and Wildlife **2688**
Selected Novelle. *see* Zhongpian Xiaoshuo Xuankan **2980**
Selected Periodicals for the Medical Library. (US) **3181**
Selected Publications in European Languages *see* S P E L **5272**
Selected Rand Abstracts. (US ISSN 0037-1343) **4358, 23, 4615**

Selected Readings in General Surgery. (US) **3384**
Selected Readings in Oral and Maxillofacial Surgery. (US ISSN 1044-7032) **3384**, 3242
Selected Readings in Plastic Surgery. (US ISSN 0739-5523) **3384**
Selected Reports in Ethnomusicology. (US ISSN 0361-6622) **3580**
Selected Research in Microfiche. (US) **4342**
Selected Short Stories. *see* Xiaoshuo Xuankan **2978**
Selected Sites for Caravanning and Camping in Europe *see* Good Camps Guide Europe (Year) **4768**
Selected Sources of Financial Aid for Osteopathic Medical Students. (US) **1716**, 3216
Selected Streamflow Data for Ontario. (CN) **1600**
Selected Tables in Mathematical Statistics. (US ISSN 0094-8837) **3054**
Selected Taiwan and Hong Kong Literary Works. *see* Taigang Wenxue Xuankan **2967**
Selected Topics in Solid State Physics. (NE ISSN 0080-8636) **3830**
Selected Trade and Professional Associations in Texas *see* Texas Trade and Professional Associations and Other Selected Organizations **1155**
Selected Translations in Mathernatical Statistics and Probability. (US ISSN 0065-9274) **3054**
Selected Vital Statistics and Health Statistics Indicators. Annual Report. (CN ISSN 1188-3642) **3995**, 4585
Selected Water Resources Abstracts. (US ISSN 0037-136X) **1552**, 23, 1600
Selected Works of Juan Luis Vives. (NE ISSN 0921-0717) **2386**, 2958
Selected Writings - Children's Literature. *see* Ertong Wenxue Xuankan **1254**
Selection. (It) **4137**
Selection and Development Review. (UK ISSN 0963-2638) **1027**, 4046
Selection du Reader's Digest (Belgian - French Edition). (BE ISSN 0037-1408) **2175**
Selection du Reader's Digest (Canadian-French Edition). (CN ISSN 0037-1378) **2179**
Selection du Reader's Digest (French Edition). (FR ISSN 0037-1386) **2188**
Selection du Reader's Digest (Swiss-French Edition). (SZ ISSN 0037-1394) **2219**
†Selection Guide Series. (US) **5275**
Selections (Los Angeles). (US ISSN 0882-0228) **1027**, 1716
Selections Avicoles. (FR) **225**
Selections from Educational Records of the Government of India. (II) **1662**
Selective Abstracting Service: Welding and Allied Processes *see* Referate: Schweissen und Verwandte Verfahren **3428**
Selective Cancer Therapeutics. (US ISSN 1043-0733) **3202**, 3743
Selective Cooperative Index of Management Periodicals *see* S C I M P **737**
Selective Electrode Reviews. (US ISSN 0894-3923) **3830**, 1907
Selective Inventory of Social Science Information and Documentation Services. (UN) **4385**
Selektsiya i Semenovodstvo. (RU ISSN 0037-1459) **192**
Selenium - Tellurium Development Association. Bulletin. (BE) **3419**, 1907
Selenology. (US) **369**
Selezionando S I P. (Societa Italiana per l'Esercizio delle Telecomunicazioni P.A.) (IT) **1366**
Selezione Chimica Tintoria. (IT ISSN 0393-652X) **4623**
Selezione Dal Reader's Digest (Italian Edition). (IT ISSN 0037-1483) **2206**
Selezione di Tecnica Radio TV. (IT) **1379**, 1360

Selezione di Tecniche Elettroniche. (IT) **1908**
Selezione Odontoiatrica. (IT) **3242**
Selezione Sicurezze *see* Essecome **1526**
Selezione Tessile *see* Nuova Selezione Tessile **4622**
Selezione Veterinaria. (IT ISSN 0037-1521) **4815**
Self. (FR ISSN 0037-153X) **3808**
Self. (US ISSN 0149-0699) **4852**, 4836
Self & Society. (UK ISSN 0306-0497) **4046**, 3596, 3781
Self-Catering and Furnished Holidays. (UK ISSN 0267-4599) **4786**, 4529
Self-Catering Holiday Homes, Caravans & Boats *see* Self-Catering and Furnished Holidays **4786**
Self Catering Holidays. (UK) **4786**
Self-Employed Pensions *see* Personal Pensions (Year) **2540**
Self-Employment Update. (US ISSN 0736-1912) **1117**
▼Self-Governance. (US) **3925**
Self Health *see* Which? Way to Health **3810**
Self Help for Hard of Hearing People, Inc. Journal *see* S H H H Journal **2289**
Self-Help Group Directory *see* Self-Help Sourcebook **4419**
Self Help Reporter Newsletter. (US) **4046**, 4419
Self-Help Sourcebook. (US ISSN 8756-1425) **4419**, 4046
Self-Help Update *see* Master of Life **3595**
Self-Knowledge. (UK ISSN 0037-1556) **3781**
Self Magazine. (IT) **2081**
Self-Management *see* Workplace Democracy **997**
Self-Medication. (CN) **3743**
Self-Publishers Exchange *see* S P E X **4136**
Self-Realization. (US ISSN 0037-1564) **4201**, 3596, 3781, 4288
Self Storage Journal. (US) **1117**
Self-Teaching. *see* Zi Xue **1688**
Seller - Servicer Update. (US) **963**
Selling *see* Marketing Intelligence & Planning **1046**
Selling. (US) **4137**, 38, 1053
Selling Knacks. (US) **1053**
†Selling Red. (US ISSN 1040-9742) **5275**
Selling Scuba. (US) **4555**
Selling Space's Client Magazine *see* Selling **4137**
Selling to Seniors. (US ISSN 1050-382X) **1053**
▼Selling to the Other Educational Markets. (US ISSN 1054-4593) **1662**, 38, 1053
Selling Today. (UK ISSN 0037-1629) **1053**
Sellowia. (BL ISSN 0375-1651) **517**
Sell's British Aviation *see* Aerospace Europe **44**
Sell's British Exporters. (UK) **920**
Sell's Building Index. (UK ISSN 0080-8717) **631**
Sell's Directory. (UK ISSN 0261-5584) **1152**
Sell's Directory of Products and Services *see* Sell's Directory **1152**
Sell's Government and Municipal Contractors Register *see* Government and Municipal Contractors **4061**
Sell's Health Service Buyers Guide *see* Health Service Buyers Guide **2462**
Sell's Hotel, Restaurant and Canteen Supplies *see* Hotel, Restaurant and Catering Supplies **2072**
Sell's Marine Market. (UK ISSN 0143-1153) **4529**
Sell's Scottish Directory. (UK) **1152**
Selly Oak Alternative Paper *see* S O A P **2882**
▼Selly Oak Colleges. Occasional Papers. (UK) **4201**
†Selly Oak Journal. (UK ISSN 0266-3392) **5275**
Selskab for Nordisk Filologi. Aarsberetning. (DK ISSN 0108-822X) **2840**, 2958

Selskabet for Dansk Fotografi. Kontaktblad *see* Dansk Fotografi **3790**
Sel'skaya Molodezh. (RU ISSN 0203-3569) **1265**
Sel'skaya Nov' (RU ISSN 0582-5164) **192**
Sel'skii Mekhanizator. (RU ISSN 0131-7393) **164**, 3023
Sel'skoe Khozyaistvo v Belorussii *see* Khozyain (Minsk) **103**
Sel'skoe Khozyaistvo za Rubezhom. (RU ISSN 0340-9120) **143**, 23
Sel'skoe Rastenievodstvo i Zhivotnovodstvo *see* Sel'skoe Khozyaistvo za Rubezhom **143**
Sel'skokhozyaistvennaya Biologiya. (RU ISSN 0131-6397) **455**, 119
Sel'skokhozyaistvennaya Literatura S.S.S.R. (RU ISSN 0037-1688) **143**
Selskostopanska Tekhnika. (BU ISSN 0037-1718) **164**, 4608
Selysia. (US ISSN 0080-875X) **537**
Semaine a Berne. *see* Berner Wochen Bulletin **4754**
Semaine Africaine. (CF) **4275**
Semaine Ameublement Informations. (FR) **2561**
Semaine des Hopitaux. (FR) **3152**
Semaine Immobiliere. (FR) **4158**
Semaine Juridique. (FR ISSN 0049-0156) **2678**
Semaine Religieuse du Diocese de Bourges *see* Vie Catholique du Berry **4278**
Semaine Sociale Lamy. (FR ISSN 0223-4637) **2678**
Semaine Veterinaire. (FR ISSN 0396-5015) **4815**
Semajna Bulteno. (DK ISSN 0108-3759) **2840**
Semana. (CK) **2183**
Semana. (SP ISSN 0037-1793) **2218**
Semana. (VE) **2238**
Semana. (IS ISSN 0334-889X) **3925**
Semana Economica. (PE) **690**
▼Semana em Acao. (BL) **4487**
Semana Internacional de Antropologia Vasca. Actas. (SP) **248**, 2022
Semana Israelita *see* Semanario Israelita **2022**
Semana Medica. (AG) **3152**
Semana Politica. (MX) **2883**
Semana Vitivinicola. (SP ISSN 0037-184X) **192**
Semanario Economico. (PO) **691**
Semanario Infantil Pionero. (CU) **3925**, 1265
Semanario Israelita. (AG ISSN 0037-1858) **2022**, 4226
Semanario Libertad. (CR) **3925**
Semanario Universidad. (CR) **1324**
Semaphore Signal. (US) **1438**, 1453
Sembrador. (AG ISSN 0037-1866) **2170**
Seme Lokoi. (SL) **2170**
Semeador Baptista. (PO ISSN 0037-1874) **4249**
Semeia. (US ISSN 0095-571X) **4201**, 2840
Sementi Elette. (IT ISSN 0037-1890) **192**
Semi-Custom I C Yearbook *see* Microelectronics Journal **1775**
Semi-Monthly Tribune. *see* Ban Yue Tan **2859**
Semi-Therm *see* I E E E Semiconductor Thermal and Temperature Measurement Symposium. Proceedings **1895**
†Semiconductor Economics Report. (US) **5275**
Semiconductor Industry & Business Survey Newsletter. (US ISSN 0730-1014) **1778**
Semiconductor Industry Association. Yearbook and Directory (Year). (S I A) (US) **1778**
Semiconductor Industry Plant Site Database Service. (US) **1778**, 1880
Semiconductor International. (US ISSN 0163-3767) **1778**
Semiconductor International Telephone - FAX & Source Guide (year). (US) **1778**

SEMINARS 6651

Semiconductor Products and Solid State Technology *see* Solid State Technology **1778**
Semiconductor Reliability News. (US) **1778**
Semiconductor Science and Technology. (UK ISSN 0268-1242) **1778**
Semiconductors and Insulators. (US ISSN 0309-5991) **1778**
Semigroup Forum. (US ISSN 0037-1912) **3054**
Semillas. (CK ISSN 0120-422X) **192**
Semillas de Progreso. (GT) **119**
Semina. (FI ISSN 0049-0164) **3743**
Seminar. (CN ISSN 0037-1939) **2958**, 2840
Seminar Arghiriade. (RM) **3054**
Seminar for Arabian Studies. Proceedings. (UK) **3971**, 2431
Seminar on Applied Functional Analysis. (JA) **3054**
Seminar on Dravidian Linguistics. Proceedings. (II) **2840**
Seminar on Mathematical Sciences. (JA) **3054**
Seminar on the Acquisition of Latin American Library Materials. Final Report and Working Papers *see* Seminar on the Acquisition of Latin American Library Materials. Papers **2784**
Seminar on the Acquisition of Latin American Library Materials. Microfilming Projects Newsletter. (US ISSN 0080-8857) **2784**
Seminar on the Acquisition of Latin American Library Materials. Papers. (US) **2784**, 2422
†Seminar on the Acquisition of Latin American Library Materials. Resolutions and Lists of Committees. (US ISSN 0361-9966) **5275**
Seminar on the Acquisition of Latin American Library Materials. Report on Bibliographic Activities *see* S A L A L M Bibliography and Reference Series **2795**
Seminar on the Acquisition of Latin American Library Materials Bibliography and Reference Series *see* S A L A L M Bibliography and Reference Series **2795**
Seminar on the Acquisition of Latin American Library Materials Newsletter *see* S A L A L M Newsletter **411**
Seminar Reporteur. (It) **4342**, 4608
Seminaria Niedzickie / Niedzica Seminars. (PL) **2386**, 343
Seminaria Pa'lante. (CU) **2883**, 3925
Seminarielaererforeningen Information *see* S L F information **1660**
Seminario Brasileiro sobre Tecnicas Exploratorias em Geologia. Anais. (BL) **1580**
Seminario de Estudios de Arte y Arqueologia. Boletin. (SP) **343**, 306
Seminario de Filologia Vasca Julio de Urquijo. Anuario. (SP ISSN 0582-6152) **2840**
Seminario de Filologia Vasca Julio de Urquijo. Anuario. Suplemento. (SP) **2840**
Seminario di Scienze Antropologiche. (IT ISSN 0392-9094) **248**
Seminario di Studi e Ricerche Sul Linguaggio Musicale. Atti. (IT) **3580**
Seminarium. (VC ISSN 0582-6314) **4275**
Seminars. (US ISSN 0161-4282) **1716**
Seminars Directory. (US) **1152**, 4094
†Seminars in Adolescent Medicine. (US ISSN 0748-6480) **5275**
Seminars in Anesthesia. (US ISSN 0277-0326) **3192**, 3274, 3384
Seminars in Arthritis & Rheumatism. (US ISSN 0049-0172) **3370**, 482, 2278, 3311
▼Seminars in Arthroplasty. (US ISSN 1045-4527) **3311**
▼Seminars in Avian and Exotic Pet Medicine. (US) **4815**
Seminars in Cancer Biology Series. (UK ISSN 1044-579X) **482**, 3202

6652 SEMINARS

Seminars in Cell Biology Series. (UK) **526**
Seminars in Colon and Rectal Surgery. (US ISSN 1043-1489) **3384**
Seminars in Dermatology. (US ISSN 0278-145X) **3249**
Seminars in Developmental Biology. (UK ISSN 1044-5781) **455**
Seminars in Diagnostic Pathology. (US ISSN 0740-2570) **3152**, 3188, 3223
Seminars in Dialysis. (US) **3389**
Seminars in Facial Plastic Surgery see Facial Plastic Surgery **3378**
Seminars in Hearing. (US ISSN 0734-0451) **3317**
Seminars in Hematology. (US ISSN 0037-1963) **3273**, 526, 3211, 3743
Seminars in Immunology Series. (UK ISSN 1044-5323) **455**
Seminars in Interventional Radiology. (US ISSN 0739-9529) **3362**
Seminars in Liver Diseases. (US ISSN 0272-8087) **3270**
Seminars in Nephrology. (US ISSN 0270-9295) **3389**, 574, 3273, 3384
Seminars in Neurological Surgery. (US ISSN 0160-2489) **3384**, 3354
Seminars in Neurology. (US ISSN 0271-8235) **3354**
Seminars in Neurosciences Series. (UK ISSN 1044-5765) **3354**
Seminars in Nuclear Medicine. (US ISSN 0001-2998) **3363**, 574, 3263
†Seminars in Occupational Medicine. (US) **5275**
Seminars in Oncology. (US ISSN 0093-7754) **3202**, 526, 546, 3743
Seminars in Oncology Nursing. (US ISSN 0749-2081) **3286**, 3202, 3363, 3743
Seminars in Ophthalmology. (US ISSN 0882-0538) **3305**, 561, 3384
Seminars in Orthopaedics. (US ISSN 0882-052X) **3311**, 2278, 3326, 3384
Seminars in Pediatric Gastroenterology and Nutrition. (CN) **3270**, 3612
Seminars in Perinatology. (US ISSN 0146-0005) **3326**, 3296, 3384
▼Seminars in Perioperative Nursing. (US) **3286**
▼Seminars in Radiation Oncology. (US) **3202**
Seminars in Reproductive Endocrinology. (US ISSN 0882-5815) **3256**
Seminars in Respiratory Infections. (US ISSN 0882-0546) **3367**, 526, 3256, 3363
Seminars in Respiratory Medicine. (US ISSN 0192-9755) **3367**
Seminars in Roentgenology. (US ISSN 0037-198X) **3363**, 3311
Seminars in Speech and Language. (US ISSN 0734-0478) **3317**
Seminars in Surgical Oncology. (US) **3202**, 3384
Seminars in Thoracic and Cardiovascular Surgery. (US) **3384**, 3211
Seminars in Thrombosis and Hemostasis. (US ISSN 0094-6176) **3273**
Seminars in Ultrasound see Seminars in Ultrasound, C T and M R **3363**
Seminars in Ultrasound, C T and M R. (US ISSN 0887-2171) **3363**, 3311
Seminars in Urology. (US ISSN 0730-9147) **3389**, 3326, 3384
Seminars in Vascular Surgery. (US ISSN 0895-7967) **3384**, 3212
Seminars in Veterinary Medicine and Surgery: Small Animal. (US ISSN 0882-0511) **4815**, 455
Seminars in Virology Series. (UK) **557**
Seminars, Workshops & Classes. (US ISSN 0740-2791) **1686**, 1117
Seminole Tribune. (US ISSN 0891-8252) **2022**
Semiosis. (GW ISSN 0170-219X) **3781**
Semiotext(e). (US ISSN 0093-9579) **2515**, 2840, 3781

Semiotexte (New York) see Semiotext(e) **2515**
Semiotic Abstracts see S E M A **2856**
Semiotic Crossroads. (US ISSN 0922-5072) **2840**
▼Semiotic Review of Books. (CN ISSN 0847-1622) **2515**, 3781, 4385
Semiotica. (GW ISSN 0037-1998) **2840**
Semiotics and the Human Sciences. (US ISSN 1054-8386) **2840**
Semiotique et Bible. (FR ISSN 0154-6902) **4201**, 2840
Semitic Study Series. (NE ISSN 0169-9911) **3644**, 2022, 4226
Semitica. (FR ISSN 0085-6037) **2515**
Semitica Viva. (GW ISSN 0931-2811) **2840**
Semitica Viva - Series Didactica. (GW) **2840**
†Semitics. (SA ISSN 0256-6044) **5275**
Semper. (AT) **1324**
Semper Floreat see Semper **1324**
Sempervivum Fanciers Association Newsletter. (US) **2138**
Sempervivum Society. International Newsletter see Sempervivum Society. Newsletter **2139**
Sempervivum Society. Newsletter. (UK) **2139**
Sempex. (FR) **3743**
Sempex Pharmaceutique see Sempex **3743**
Sempre Pronto. (PO ISSN 0037-203X) **1662**, 3757
Sem'ya i Shkola. (RU ISSN 0131-7377) **1662**
Sen-i Kogyo Zasshi/Textile Review. (JA ISSN 0037-2064) **4623**
Sen-i Kougyo Yoran/Japan Textile Industry. Directory. (JA) **4628**
Senales. (AG ISSN 0037-2099) **4142**, 23, 2983
Senate History. (US) **2422**, 4073
†Senate Issues Yearbook. (US) **5275**
Senate Report. (US) **3925**
The Senator. (US) **1324**
Senckenbergiana Biologica. (GW ISSN 0037-2102) **591**, 517
Senckenbergiana Lethaea. (GW ISSN 0037-2110) **3660**, 1580
Senckenbergiana Maritima. Zeitschrift fuer Meeresgeologie und Meeresbiologie. (GW ISSN 0080-889X) **1610**, 455
Sendai Astronomiaj Reportoj. (JA) **369**
Sendbote des Herzens Jesu. (AU ISSN 0037-2129) **4201**
Sendero. (PY) **4275**
SENDOC Bulletin. Part 1: Industry and Technology. (II) **4608**
SENDOC Bulletin. Part 2: Economics and Development. (II) **1117**
SENDOC Bulletin. Part 3: Management and Behavioral Sciences. (II) **1070**
Seneca Review. (US ISSN 0037-2145) **3005**
Seneca Searchers. (US ISSN 1046-5545) **2164**
Senegal. Archives du Senegal. Rapport Annuel. (SG ISSN 0850-010X) **2784**
Senegal. Centre de Recherche Oceanographique. Document Scientifique. (SG ISSN 0850-1602) **1610**, 455
Senegal. Liste du Corps Diplomatique. (SG) **3971**
Senegal. Ministere de l'Economie et des Finances. Analyse du Commerce Exterieur. (SG) **920**
Senegal. Ministere de l'Economie et des Finances. Banque de Donnees Economiques et Financieres. (SG) **737**
Senegal. Ministere de l'Economie et des Finances. Bulletin Economique Statistique. (SG) **737**
Senegal. Ministere de l'Economie et des Finances. Bulletin Statistiques et Economique. (SG) **737**
Senegal. Ministere de l'Economie et des Finances. Bulletin Statistique Mensuel see Senegal. Ministere de l'Economie et des Finances. Bulletin Statistiques et Economique **737**

Senegal. Ministere de l'Economie et des Finances. Comptes Economiques du Senegal. (SG) **884**
Senegal. Ministere de l'Economie et des Finances. Dossiers Documentaires. (SG) **737**
Senegal. Ministere de l'Economie et des Finances. Evolution Conjoncturelle. (SG) **737**
Senegal. Ministere de l'Economie et des Finances. Indice des Prix. (SG) **1084**, 737
Senegal. Ministere de l'Economie et des Finances. Indice et la Production Industrielle. (SG) **1084**, 737
Senegal. Service du Protocole. Liste Diplomatique et Consulaire see Senegal. Liste du Corps Diplomatique **3971**
Senegal d'Aujourd'hui. (SG) **4073**
Senegal en Chiffres. (SG) **2334**
Sen'i Gakkaishi. see Society of Fiber Science and Technology, Japan. Journal **4623**
Sen'i Kikai Gakkaishi. (JA ISSN 0371-0580) **4623**, 3023
Sen'i Seihin Shohi Kagaku/Japan Research Association for Textile End-Uses. Journal. (JA ISSN 0037-2072) **4623**
Senior. (NE) **2278**
Senior Adult Bible Study. (US ISSN 0162-4733) **4249**
Senior Advocate. (US) **2278**
Senior American. (US) **2278**
†Senior American News. (US) **5275**
Senior Beacon. (US) **2278**, 2234
▼Senior Cape Cod Forum. (US) **2234**
Senior Care Professional. (US ISSN 1051-6913) **2278**, 2496
Senior Center Report see N C O A Networks **2276**
Senior Citizen. (CN) **2278**
Senior Citizen Sentinel. (US ISSN 0199-7947) **4419**, 2278
Senior Citizens Advocate see Action Memo & Senior Citizens Advocate **5130**
Senior Citizen's Guide to Budget Travel in the United States and Canada. (US) **4786**
Senior Citizens News (Washington). (US) **2278**
Senior Citizens News & Views. (US) **2278**
Senior Citizens Post. (US) **2278**
Senior Edition see Senior Edition U S A **2278**
Senior Edition. (US) **2278**
Senior Edition U S A. (US ISSN 1046-0020) **2278**, 2234
▼Senior Golf World. (US) **4511**
The Senior Golfer. (US ISSN 0037-2218) **4511**, 2279
Senior Health Digest see Senior Care Professional **2278**
Senior High School Library Catalog. (US) **2784**
Senior Highlights. (US) **2279**
Senior Law Report. (US ISSN 1050-3250) **2678**
Senior Lawyer see Experience **2624**
Senior Magazine. (US) **2279**
Senior Media Directory. (US) **1342**
The Senior Messenger. (US) **2279**
Senior News/Senior Nuus. (SA ISSN 0037-2234) **2279**, 4419
Senior Nurse (London). (UK) **3287**
Senior Nurse (W. Sussex). (UK ISSN 0265-9999) **3287**
Senior Nuus. see Senior News **2279**
†Senior Patient. (US) **5275**
Senior Residents Texas see S R Texas **2278**
Senior Scholastic see Scholastic Update **1264**
Senior Science and Science World see Science World **4341**
Senior Spectrum Newspaper. (US) **2279**
Senior Sports News. (US ISSN 0196-6243) **4487**, 2279, 3808
Senior Spotlite. (US) **2279**
Senior Sun. (US) **1795**, 1508
Senior Times. (US) **2234**
Senior Times. (CN) **2279**
Senior Topics. (AT) **1662**
Senior Tribune. (US) **2279**

Senior Voice. (US ISSN 0741-2894) **2279**
Senior World see Senior World of Los Angeles County **2279**
Senior World. (CN) **2279**, 2179
Senior World of Los Angeles County. (US) **2279**
Senior World of Orange County. (US) **2279**
Senior World of San Diego. (US) **2279**
†Senior World of the Central Coast. (US) **5275**
Senioren Echo. (GW) **2279**
Senioren-Zeitschrift. (GW) **2191**
Seniority Travel Directory see Sophisticated Leisure Travel Directory **4787**
Senior's Action Alert. (US) **1522**
Seniors' Advocate see Independent Senior **2274**
Seniors Choice. (CN) **1301**, 2279
Seniors in Sacramento. (US) **2279**
†Seniors' Money Alert. (US) **5275**
▼Seniors on the Move. (US) **2279**
Seniors Today. (CN) **2279**
Senlin Caiyun Kexue/Lumbering Science. (CC ISSN 1001-005X) **2117**
Senlin Fanghuo/Fire Prevention in Forests. (CC) **2107**
Senlin yu Renlei/Forest and Human Kind. (CC) **2107**
Senmon Toshokan/Special Libraries Association, Japan. Bulletin. (JA ISSN 0385-0188) **2784**
Sennachie. (AT) **2322**, 3925
Sennacieca Revuo. (FR ISSN 0080-8903) **3971**
Sennaciulo. (FR) **3971**
Sennke/News of the Tohoku Plant Association. (JA ISSN 0385-3985) **517**
Senpaku - Kaiyo Kogaku Gijutsu Bunken Sokuho. see Marine Technology Research Abstracts & Index (MATRAX) **4665**
Sens des Affaires see Business Insights **651**
Sensations. (US ISSN 1053-9115) **2958**, 2234, 3400, 4852
Senshu Shizen Kagaku Kiyo/Senshu University. Association of Natural Science. Bulletin. (JA ISSN 0386-5827) **4342**
Senshu University. Association of Natural Science. Bulletin. see Senshu Shizen Kagaku Kiyo **4342**
†Sensible Agriculture. (US) **5275**
Sensible Sound. (US ISSN 0199-4654) **4461**, 3580
Sensitive Materials. see Ganguang Cailiao **1177**
Sensitive to the Educational Needs of Growing Americans see S E N G A **1243**
Sensor. (US) **2883**
Sensor Business Digest. (US ISSN 1060-1902) **1053**, 4608
Sensor Report. (GW ISSN 0179-9592) **2525**, 1415
Sensor Review. (UK ISSN 0260-2288) **3023**, 1415
Sensor Technology. (US ISSN 8756-4017) **1443**, 1415, 3830
Sensors. (US ISSN 0746-9462) **2525**, 1410, 1443
Sensors and Actuators see Sensors and Actuators: B Chemical **1212**
Sensors and Actuators see Sensors and Actuators: A Physical **3840**
Sensors and Actuators: A Physical. (SZ ISSN 0924-4247) **3840**
Sensors and Actuators: B Chemical. (SZ ISSN 0925-4005) **1212**
Sensor's Buyers Guide. (US) **2525**, 1443
Sensory Integration. (US) **3152**, 1741
Sensory Perception and Information Processing. (UK ISSN 0143-7526) **4046**
Sensory Systems. (English translation of: Sensornye Sistemy) (US ISSN 0894-4520) **4046**, 455
Sensuous Letters. (US) **3400**, 4852
Sensus Water Journal. (US) **4828**
†Sentai Chii Zappo/Miscellanea Bryologica et Lichenologica. (JA ISSN 0037-2277) **5276**

Sentei Tosho Somokuroku. *see* Catalogue of Books Recommended for Libraries **397**
Senten Ijo *see* Congenital Anomalies **3090**
Sentences Arbitrales de la Fonction Publique. (CN) **2678**
Sentencias en Apelacion de las Audiencias Provinciales. (SP ISSN 0210-3427) **2678**
Sentencing in Washington. (US) **2678**
Sentier Chasse - Peche. (CN ISSN 0711-7957) **4555**
Sentinel (Chicago). (US) **2234**
Sentinel (Franklin). (US) **2422**
Sentinel (Ottawa). (CN ISSN 0037-2315) **3471**
Sentinel (Sacramento) *see* Senior's Action Alert **1522**
Sentinel (San Francisco). (US) **2457**
Sentinel (Willowdale). (CN ISSN 0049-0202) **1301**
Sentinel: Bulletin - N C A I News. (US) **2023**
Sentinel Investment Letter. (US) **963**, **799**, **839**, **884**
Sentinel U S A *see* San Francisco Sentinel **2457**
Sentinella Agricola. (IT ISSN 0037-234X) **119**
Sentinelle *see* Sentinel (Ottawa) **3471**
Seoul. (KO) **2209**
Seoul Journal of Economics. (KO) **691**
Seoul Journal of Medicine/Seoul Uidae Haksulji. (KO ISSN 0582-6802) **3152**
Seoul National University. Agricultural Research *see* Seoul National University Journal of Agricultural Sciences **119**
†Seoul National University. Economic Review. (KO) **5276**
Seoul National University. Engineering Report *see* Journal of Engineering Research **1828**
Seoul National University. Faculty Papers. (KO) **3152**
Seoul National University. Faculty Papers. Biology and Agriculture Series. (KO) **455**, **119**
Seoul National University. Population and Development Studies Center. Bulletin. (KO) **3987**
Seoul National University Forests. Research Bulletin/Nyensubrim Nyengu Bogo: Seoul Daihaggyo Nongkwa Daihag. (KO ISSN 1010-8289) **2107**, **2117**
Seoul National University Journal of Agricultural Sciences. (KO) **119**
Seoul Uidae Haksulji. *see* Seoul Journal of Medicine **3152**
†Separate Doors. (US) **5276**
Separation. (UK ISSN 0950-7140) **3263**, **2525**
Separation and Purification Methods. (US ISSN 0360-2540) **1208**
Separation Processes Service Bulletin *see* S P S Bulletin **1860**
Separation Science and Technology. (US ISSN 0149-6395) **1208**
▼Separations Technology. (US ISSN 0956-9618) **1860**, **1208**
Sephardi Heritage *see* Merkaz Haribaz **2430**
Sephardic Scholar. (US) **2023**
Sepia. (UK ISSN 0140-1165) **3005**
Septentrion. (HT) **2197**
Septentrion. (BE) **2211**, **2175**
Septieme Artifice. (FR ISSN 0996-7109) **3517**
Sequels. (CN) **2179**
Sequences. (CN ISSN 0037-2412) **3517**, **1662**
Sequential Analysis. (US ISSN 0747-4946) **4585**
Sequoia (San Francisco). (US) **4201**, **3925**
Sequoia (Stanford). (US ISSN 0037-2420) **2883**
Sequoia Genealogical Society. Newsletter. (US) **2164**
▼Ser Padres/Being Parents. (US) **4852**, **1244**, **3400**
Ser Padres Hoy. (SP) **1244**
Serafico Vessillo. (IT ISSN 0037-2439) **4275**
Serai. (JA) **2208**
Seramiasht. (AF) **4419**

Seramikkusu/Ceramics Japan. (JA ISSN 0009-031X) **1166**
Seramikkusu Kyokai Shi/Ceramic Society of Japan. Journal. (JA ISSN 0914-5400) **1166**
Serb World *see* Serb World U.S.A **2023**
Serb World U.S.A. (US ISSN 8756-5579) **2023**
Serbia. (CN) **2023**
Serbian Archives of Entire Medicine. *see* Srpski Arhiv za Celokupno Lekarstvo **3155**
Serbian Archives of General Medicine. (YU ISSN 0370-8179) **3152**
†Serbian Bulletin. (AT ISSN 0310-740X) **5276**
Serbian Chemical Society. Journal. (YU ISSN 0352-5139) **1187**
Serbian Struggle/Srpska Borba. (US ISSN 0279-1293) **2023**
Serbian Struggle. (AT) **2023**
Serbische Rechtsquellen. *see* Izvori Srpskog Prava **2637**
Serdica; Bulgaricae Mathematicae Publicationes. *see* Serdika; Bulgarsko Matematichesko Spisanie **3054**
Serdika; Bulgarsko Matematichesko Spisanie/Serdica; Bulgaricae Mathematicae Publicationes. (BU ISSN 0204-4110) **3054**
Y Seren. (UK) **2883**
Serendib. (HK) **4803**
†Serengeti Research Institute. Annual Report. (TZ) **5276**
Serengeti Wildlife Research Centre. Report. (TZ) **455**
Serenity Sentinel *see* The Living Light Philosophy **4188**
Serenity's New Life *see* New Life **3595**
Sereno Symposia Review. (IT) **3152**
Sergent-Major. *see* Feldwebel **3458**
Sergente Maggiore. *see* Feldwebel **3458**
Serial Sources for the BIOSIS Database *see* Serial Sources for the BIOSIS Previews Database **467**
Serial Sources for the BIOSIS Previews Database. (US ISSN 0162-2048) **467**, **23**
Serials. (UK ISSN 0953-0460) **2784**
Serials Directory. (US ISSN 0886-4179) **411**
Serials Holdings in Newfoundland Libraries. (CN ISSN 0709-0536) **411**
†Serials in C L W Library. (College of Librarianship Wales) (UK) **5276**
Serials in Geological Sciences. *see* Schriftenreihe fuer Geologische Wissenschaften **1579**
Serials in the British Library. (UK ISSN 0260-0005) **411**, **2784**
Serials Librarian. (US ISSN 0361-526X) **2784**
Serials Perspective. (US ISSN 0747-5411) **2784**
Serials Review. (US ISSN 0098-7913) **2784**
Serica. (UK ISSN 0266-0822) **4623**
†Sericultural Experiment Station. Annual Report/Sanshi Shikenjo Nenpo. (JA ISSN 0581-5908) **5276**
Sericulture Bulletin. *see* Cansang Tongbao **82**
Serie Afrique Noire. (FR ISSN 0080-8938) **3925**
†Serie Botanica. (SP) **5276**
Serie Capistrano de Abreu. (BL) **3971**
Serie d'Ecriture. (UK) **3005**
Serie de Ciencias Humanas *see* Centro de Estudos de Cabo Verde. Revista: Serie de Ciencias Humanas **4368**
Serie de Cocina por Luis Ripoli. (SP) **2081**
†Serie de Ingenieria de la Calidad. (SP) **5276**
Serie de Investigaciones y Desarrollo. (US) **119**
Serie de Rapportes Techniques A F R O *see* A F R O Technical Report Series **4096**
Serie de Vocabularios y Diccionarios Indigenas "Mariano Silva y Aceves". (US) **2840**, **248**, **2023**, **2058**
Serie di Matematica e Fisica *see* Serie di Matematica e Fisica. Testi **3054**
Serie di Matematica e Fisica. Problemi. (IT) **3054**, **3830**

Serie di Matematica e Fisica. Problemi Risolti *see* Serie di Matematica e Fisica. Problemi **3054**
Serie di Matematica e Fisica. Testi. (IT) **3054**, **3830**
Serie Estudios Literarios. (CR) **2958**
Serie Estudos Penitenciaros. (BL) **1522**
Serie Guias de los Estudios Universitarios. (SP) **1697**
Serie Inmigracion al Cono Sur de America. (US) **3987**
Serie Investigacion Pesquera. (CL) **2048**
Serie Kureren. (DK ISSN 0109-3797) **343**
†Serie Legislacion Educativa Argentina. (AG) **5276**
Serie Legislacion Laboral. (CU) **993**
Serie Linguistica Peruana. (PE) **2840**
†Serie Magasinet. (DK) **5276**
▼Serie Memoria Viva da Educacao Brasileira. (BL) **1662**
Serie Monografias y Estudios de la Educacion. (US) **1662**
Serie Mujer. (PE) **4852**
Serie Novas Perspectivas. (BL) **2422**, **3925**
Serie om Fremmedsprog *see* Aalborg Universitetscenter. Institut for Sprog og Internationale Kulturstudier. Arbeijdspapirer **2800**
Serie Praxis. (PE ISSN 0250-9814) **993**, **1084**
Serie Vie Locale. (FR ISSN 0586-9889) **3925**
Series Desenvolvimento Brasileiro. *see* Brazil Development Series **1073**
Series Entomologica. (NE ISSN 0080-8954) **537**
Series Estadisticas Seleccionadas de Centroamerica y Panama. (GT) **737**
Series: Graph-Agri. (FR ISSN 0242-2085) **157**
Series: Graph-Agri (Regions). (FR ISSN 0755-1908) **143**
Series in Automation. (SI) **1415**
Series in Computer Science. (SI) **1400**
Series in Death Education, Aging, and Health Care. (US ISSN 0275-3510) **4046**
Series in English Language and Literature. (II ISSN 0254-0193) **2958**, **2841**
Series in Geotechnical Engineering *see* Wiley Series in Geotechnical Engineering **196**
Series in Indian Languages and Linguistics. (II) **2841**
▼Series in Indian Studies in Theoretical and Applied Linguistics. (II) **2841**
▼Series in Modern Condensed Matter Physics. (SI) **3831**
Series in Philosophy of Science *see* University of Western Ontario Series in Philosophy of Science **3785**
Series in Pure Mathematics. (SI) **3054**
Series in Real Analysis. (SI) **3054**
▼Series in Robotics and Automated Systems. (SI) **1415**
Series in Semiotics and Linguistics. (II) **2841**
Series in Sikh History and Culture. (II ISSN 0254-0215) **2341**, **2958**
Series in Theoretical & Applied Mechanics. (SI) **3845**
▼Series on Advances in Mathematics for Applied Sciences. (SI) **3055**
Series on Advances in Statistical Mechanics. (SI) **3845**
Series on Bulk Materials Engineering *see* Series on Bulk Materials Handling **1836**
Series on Bulk Materials Handling. (SZ) **1836**
Series on Directions in Condensed Matter Physics. (SI) **3831**
Series on International Taxation. (NE) **1105**
▼Series on Knots and Everything. (SI) **3055**
Series on Machine Perception and Artificial Intelligence. (SI) **1410**
Series on Optics and Photonics. (SI) **3857**
Series on Rock and Soil Mechanics. (SZ ISSN 0080-9004) **1548**, **1873**

SERVICE QUARTERLY   6653

Series on Software Engineering & Knowledge Engineering. (SI) **1479**, **1836**
▼Series on Soviet and East European Mathematics. (SI) **3055**
Series Optimization *see* Optimization **3063**
Series Slavica *see* Universita Palackeho. Filosoficka Fakulta. Slavica **2971**
Series Statistics *see* Statistics **1405**
Series Statistiques de Bruxelles *see* Cahiers Economiques de Bruxelles **653**
Serigrafen. (DK ISSN 0108-0458) **4623**
Serigrafia. (IT ISSN 0394-5901) **4005**
Serigrafia (Rio de Janeiro). (BL) **343**, **4005**
Serious Hip Hop. (US) **3580**
Serlin Report on Parallel Processing. (US ISSN 0894-2226) **1431**
Sermon Builder. (US ISSN 0037-248X) **4201**
Sernaval. (Servicio Informacion Naval) (SP ISSN 0211-304X) **4738**
Serodiagnosis and Immunotherapy. (UK ISSN 0888-0786) **3223**
Serono Clinical Colloquia on Reproduction Series. (US) **3152**
Serono Foundation Symposia. (US) **3152**
Serono Symposia Series: Advances in Experimental Medicine. (US) **3263**
Serpe. (IT ISSN 0037-2498) **2958**
Serpent a Plumes. (FR ISSN 0992-2660) **2958**
Serpentine Muse. (US) **2986**
Serra d'Or. (SP ISSN 0037-2501) **2883**
Serramenti e Componenti *see* S e C **1527**
Serramenti e Falegnameria. (IT) **640**
Servamus. (SA) **1522**
Servant Magazine. (CN ISSN 0848-1741) **4249**
Server - Pennsylvania. (US) **2480**
Servex. (SP ISSN 0488-3721) **920**
Service. (CN ISSN 0227-034X) **4419**
Service Business *see* Cleaning Business **1114**
Service Canadien de la Faune. Cahiers de Biologie. *see* Canadian Wildlife Service. Progress Notes **1485**
†Service Compris. (UK ISSN 0267-7571) **5276**
†Service Corporation Directory. (US) **5276**
Service de Centralisation des Etudes Genealogiques et Demographiques de Belgique. Nouvelles Breves. (BE) **2164**, **3987**
Service Dealer's Newsletter. (US ISSN 0739-6236) **1027**
Service Diesel *see* Revue Technique Diesel **4700**
Service Economique & Financier "Secofi". (FR ISSN 0037-2595) **799**
Service Economique Fonctionnaire. (FR) **4073**
Service Edge. (US) **1027**
Service Employees *see* Service Employees Union **2589**
Service Employees International Union. International Convention Official Proceedings. (US) **2589**
Service Employees International Union Update *see* S E I U Update **2588**
Service Employees Union. (US) **2589**
Service, Employment, Redevelopment America *see* S E R America **993**
Service Industries Journal. (UK ISSN 0264-2069) **691**
Service Industry Newsletter. (US) **1400**
Service International de Documentation Judeo-Chretienne *see* S I D I C **4200**
Service - Jahrbuch. (GW) **4294**
Service News (Yarmouth). (US ISSN 1046-1965) **1400**
†Service- og Varevogne. (DK ISSN 0109-7334) **5276**
Service Point. (UK ISSN 0306-0942) **2784**
Service Quality. (US ISSN 1049-5967) **1027**
Service Quarterly. (US ISSN 1043-7053) **4701**, **1117**

6654 SERVICE REPORTER

Service Reporter. (US ISSN 0193-2128) **2303**
Service Savvy see Service Quality **1027**
Service Side see Motor Industry News **4696**
Service Social. (CN ISSN 0037-2633) **4419**
Service Social dans le Monde. (BE ISSN 0037-2641) **4419**
Service Station. (AT ISSN 0818-2884) **4701**
Service Station & Garage Management. (CN ISSN 0037-2668) **4701**
Service Station Dealers News see Service Quarterly **4701**
Service Station Management. (US ISSN 0488-3896) **4702**
Service to Business and Industry - B P L. (Brooklyn Public Library) (US ISSN 0049-0229) **737**
Service 2000. (FR ISSN 0398-8716) **1282**
Services. (US ISSN 0279-0548) **631**
Services d'Aide Medicale Urgente. Revue. (FR ISSN 0399-0265) **3311**
Services Documentaires Multimedia, Inc. Actualites S D M see Actualites S D M **2741**
Services Law Cases. (II ISSN 0304-100X) **2678**
Services-Marche Commun Europeen. (FR) **1084**
Services Watch see U.S. Chamber Watch on Small Business Legislation & Regulation **2688**
Servicing Dealer. (US) **3023**, 164
Servicing Management. (US) **799**
Servicio de Documentacao see S E D O C **4200**
Servicio Informacion Naval Sernaval see Sernaval **4738**
Servicio Referativo de la Construccion. (CU) **638**, 23, 1846
Servicios Electricos del Gran Buenos Aires S.A. Boletin Bibliografico. (AG) **4615**
Serving Australian Agriculture see Protecting Australian Agriculture. Directory **190**
Servir. (TI ISSN 0035-4120) **4073**
Servir Mieux. (FR ISSN 0037-2757) **2449**
Servire. (IT ISSN 0037-2765) **1265**
Serviteur. (CM) **4249**
Servizi Demografici. (IT) **3987**
Servizi Pubblici Locali. (IT) **4094**
Servizio della Parola. (IT ISSN 0037-2773) **4201**
Servizio Informazioni Avio. (IT ISSN 0037-279X) **1663**
Servizio Migranti. (IT ISSN 0037-2803) **3925**, 4201, 4448
Servizio Stampa Educazione e Sviluppo see S I P E **1715**
Servo. (CN) **3287**
Sesame. (UK ISSN 0267-033X) **1324**
†Sesame. (SA) **5276**
Sesame Street. (US ISSN 0049-0253) **1265**
Sesami. (JA) **1294**
Session Cases. (UK ISSN 0037-282X) **2678**
Sestrinski List. (YU) **4249**
SETA. (Seksuaalinen Tasavertaisuus ry) (FI ISSN 0355-1407) **2457**
La Seta. (IT) **4623**
Setchaku. see Adhesion and Adhesives **3861**
Sete. (PO) **2214**
Setguulch/Journalist. (MP) **2575**
Setimo Ceu. (BL ISSN 0037-2862) **2984**
Seto Marine Biological Laboratory. Publications/Seto Rinkai Jikkenjo Kiyo. (JA ISSN 0037-2870) **455**
Seto Marine Biological Laboratory. Special Publication Series. (JA ISSN 0389-6609) **455**
Seto Marine Biological Laboratory. Special Publications see Seto Marine Biological Laboratory. Special Publication Series **455**
Seto Rinkai Jikkenjo Kiyo. see Seto Marine Biological Laboratory. Publications **455**
Seton Hall Legislative Journal. (US) **2678**

Setsudai Gakujutsu. Shizen Kagaku Hen. see Setsunan University. Scientific Review. Series A, Natural Sciences **4342**
Setsunan University. Scientific Review. Series A, Natural Sciences/Setsudai Gakujutsu. Shizen Kagaku Hen. (JA ISSN 0287-4466) **4342**
†Setter Quarterly. (US ISSN 0199-6738) **5276**
Setters see Setters, Incorporated **3713**
Setters, Incorporated. (US) **3713**
Settestrade. (IT) **4702**
Settimana del Sordo. (IT) **2289**, 4419
Settimana del Sordomuto see Settimana del Sordo **2289**
Settimana Giuridica. (IT) **2678**
Settimana T V. (IT) **1379**
Setting Municipal Priorities. (US ISSN 0272-8362) **1105**
Setting up in Denmark. (DK ISSN 0901-800X) **884**
The Settler. (US) **2422**
Seura (1979). (FI) **2186**
Seva Vani see Caritas India Bulletin **2337**
Sevagram/Farm Weekly. (II) **119**
Sevartham. (II ISSN 0970-8324) **2201**
Seve Eglise Aujourd'hui. (FR ISSN 0985-5734) **4201**
†Seven (Lakewood). (US ISSN 0271-3012) **5276**
†Seven (Oklahoma City). (US) **5276**
Seven County Farm and Home News. (US ISSN 0192-4184) **119**
Seven - Eleven Japan. (Year) Annual Report. (JA) **1084**
Seven Gates. (IS) **2958**
Seventeen. (US ISSN 0037-301X) **4852**
The Seventeenth Century. (UK ISSN 0268-117X) **2958**, 2322
Seventeenth Century French Studies. (UK ISSN 0265-1068) **2958**, 2386, 3580
Seventeenth - Century Music. (US ISSN 1054-6022) **3580**, 421
Seventeenth - Century News. (US ISSN 0037-3028) **2958**
Seventeenth - Century Texts and Studies. (US ISSN 0893-6900) **2958**
Seventy Six. (US) **3701**
Severni Morava. (CS ISSN 0324-6817) **2386**, 3925
Severo-Kavkazskii Nauchnyi Tsentr Vysshei Shkoly. Estestvennye Nauki. Izvestiya/North-Caucasus Scientific Center of High School. Natural Sciences. News. (RU ISSN 0321-3005) **3055**, 1187, 1548, 3831
Severo-Kavkazskii Nauchnyi Tsentr Vysshei Shkoly. Obshchestvennye Nauki. Izvestiya/North-Caucasus Scientific Center of High School. Social Science. News. (RU ISSN 0321-3056) **2386**
Severo-Kavkazskii Nauchnyi Tsentr Vysshei Shkoly. Tekhnicheskie Nauki. Izviestiya/North-Caucasus Scientific Center of High School. Technical Science. News. (RU ISSN 0321-2653) **4608**
Severoceskou Prirodou. (CS) **517**
Sevgi Dunyasi. (TU) **3781**
Sew Beautiful. (US) **3592**, 1294
†Sew Business. (US ISSN 0029-4292) **5276**
Sew It Seams. (US) **3592**, 1294, 2449
Sew News. (US) **1294**, 3592
†Sewage Treatment Construction Grants Manual. (US ISSN 0149-5879) **5276**
Sewanee Mediaeval Studies. (BE ISSN 0896-1638) **2386**
The Sewanee News. (US ISSN 0037-3044) **1324**
The Sewanee Purple. (US) **1324**
Sewanee Review. (US ISSN 0037-3052) **2958**, 2883
Sewerage News see Water News **4832**
Sewing Machine Times see Knitting and Sewing Machine Times **3019**
SewTrade. (AT ISSN 1035-1264) **1287**

†SewTrade C F I Yearbook. (AT) **5276**
Sex and Health. see Sex og Sundhed **4112**
Sex Equity in Education Update. (US) **3947**, 1663
Sex Information and Education Council of Canada Journal see S I E C C A N Journal **4045**
Sex Information and Education Council of Canada Newsletter see S I E C C A N Newsletter **4045**
Sex Information and Education Council of the U S Report see S I E C U S Report **3808**
Sex og Sundhed/Sex and Health. (DK ISSN 0901-9685) **4112**
Sex over Forty. (US ISSN 0740-3593) **4046**
Sex Roles. (US ISSN 0360-0025) **4046**, 4448
Sextant. (SZ) **4738**
†Sextant. (US ISSN 0731-2180) **5276**
Sexual and Marital Therapy. (UK ISSN 0267-4653) **4046**, 3152
Sexual Health Reports see National Coalition of Gay S.T.D. Services. Official Newsletter **5242**
Sexual Minority Youth Assistance League, Inc. News see S M Y A L News **2457**
Sexuality and Disability. (US ISSN 0146-1044) **3152**
Sexuality and Literature. (US ISSN 0893-6889) **2958**
Sexuality Today see Behavior Today **4013**
Sexually Transmitted Diseases. (US ISSN 0148-5717) **3249**
Sexually Transmitted Diseases. Abstracts and Bibliography see Survey of Research for Sexually Transmitted Diseases **5285**
Sexually Transmitted Diseases Fact Sheet see S T D Fact Sheet **5272**
Sexually Transmitted Diseases in Canada. (CN) **3249**
Sexualmedizin. (GW) **3152**
Seybold Outlook on Professional Computing. (US) **1424**, 1465, 1479
Seybold Report on Desktop Publishing. (US ISSN 0889-9762) **1465**
Seybold Report on Professional Computing see Seybold Outlook on Professional Computing **1424**
Seybold Report on Publishing Systems. (US ISSN 0736-7260) **4144**
Seychelles. Department of Finance. Economic Indicators. (SE) **737**, 4585
Seychelles. Department of Finance. National Accounts. (SE) **4082**, 4585
Seychelles. Department of Finance. Statistical Bulletin. (SE) **4585**
Seychelles. Department of Finance. Statistics Division. Statistical Abstract.(SE) **4585**
Seychelles. Department of Finance. Visitor Survey. (SE) **4800**, 737, 4585
Seychelles. Ministry of Finance. Budget Address. (SE) **1105**, 4073
Seychelles. Office of the President. Budget Address see Seychelles. Ministry of Finance. Budget Address **1105**
Seychelles. President's Office. Statistics Division. Agriculture Survey. (SE) **143**
Seychelles. President's Office. Statistics Division. Census. (SE) **3995**, 4585
Seychelles. President's Office. Statistics Division. Employment & Earnings. (SE) **737**, 4585
Seychelles. President's Office. Statistics Division. External Trade. (SE) **737**, 4585
Seychelles. President's Office. Statistics Division. Household Expenditure Survey. (SE) **737**
Seychelles. President's Office. Statistics Division. Migration and Tourism Statistics. (SE) **4800**, 4585
Seychelles. President's Office. Statistics Division. Population and Vital Statistics. (SE) **3995**, 4585

Seychelles. President's Office. Statistics Division. Production Indicators. (SE) **737**, 4585
Seychelles. President's Office. Statistics Division. Retail Prices. (SE) **737**, 4585
Seychelles. President's Office. Statistics Division. Statistical Abstract. (SE) **737**, 4585
Seychelles. President's Office. Statistics Division. Tourism. (SE) **4800**, 4585
Seychelles. President's Office. Statistics Division. Tourism and Migration Report see Seychelles. President's Office. Statistics Division. Migration and Tourism Statistics **4800**
Seychelles Government Gazetta see Republic of Seychelles Official Gazette **4072**
Seychelles Trade Report. (SE) **920**
Seychellois. (SE) **119**
Seyd's Commercial Lists see Dun & Bradstreet Standard Register **1133**
Seymour Britchky's Restaurant Letter. (US ISSN 0196-5220) **2480**
Sez. (US ISSN 0190-3640) **2023**, 2958
Seznam Platnych Ceskoslovenskych Statnich a Oborovych Norem. (CS) **3448**
Sfinge. (IT) **4487**
Sfinx. (DK ISSN 0105-7618) **2431**
Sgraffiti see National Ceramics Quarterly **356**
Shaanxi Huabao/Shaanxi Pictorial. (CC ISSN 1001-0440) **2182**
Shaanxi Institute of Traditional Chinese Medicine. Journal. see Shaanxi Zhongyi Xueyuan Xuebao **3152**
Shaanxi Jiaoyu/Shaanxi Journal of Education. (CC) **1663**
Shaanxi Journal of Education. see Shaanxi Jiaoyu **1663**
Shaanxi Pictorial. see Shaanxi Huabao **2182**
Shaanxi Zhongyi Xueyuan Xuebao/ Shaanxi Institute of Traditional Chinese Medicine. Journal. (CC) **3152**, 3743
Shaarim. (IS) **2204**
Al-Shabab. (TS) **1301**
Shabistan Urdu Digest. (II ISSN 0037-3125) **2201**
†Shachar. (IS) **5276**
†Shackelford Newsletter. (US ISSN 1055-4653) **5276**
Shade Tree. (US ISSN 0037-3133) **2139**
Shadow. (UK ISSN 0266-8599) **3596**, 4201
Shadows. (NZ ISSN 1170-9758) **3363**
Shaftesbury Newsletter see Shaftesbury Review **4419**
Shaftesbury Review. (UK ISSN 0037-3168) **4419**, 3152
Shaheed Beheshti University. Faculty of Dentistry. Journal. (IR) **3242**
Al-Shahid. (LY) **2431**, 2334
Shahid Chamran University Educational Journal. (IR) **1663**
Shakai Fukushi Gyosei Gyomu Hokoku see Japan. Ministry of Health and Welfare. Statistics and Information Department. Statistical Report on Social Welfare Administration and Services **4426**
Shakai Fukushi no Doko. (JA) **4419**
Shakai Fukushi Shisetsu Chosa Hokoku see Japan. Ministry of Health and Welfare. Statistics and Information Department. Report on Survey of Social Welfare Institutions **4426**
Shakai Iryo Shinryo Koibetsu Chosa Hokoku see Japan. Ministry of Health and Welfare. Statistics and Information Department. Report on Survey of National Medical Care Insurance Services **2547**
Shakai Jinruigaku Nenpo. (JA) **248**
Shakai Kagaku Kenkyu. see Social Sciences Journal **4388**
Shakai Keizai Shigaku. see Socio-Economic History **898**
Shakai Kyoiku Gyosei Kihon Shiryo Shu.(JA) **1686**
Shakai Shinpo. (JA) **3925**

Shakaigaku Hyoron. *see* Japanese Sociological Review **4439**
Shakaigaku Nenshi. (JA) **4448**
Shaker Messenger. (US ISSN 0270-9368) **2023**
Shaker Quarterly. (US ISSN 0582-9348) **4288**
†Shaker Spirit. (US ISSN 1041-0198) **5276**
Shakespeare Bulletin. (US ISSN 0748-2558) **4638**
Shakespeare - Jahrbuch. (GW ISSN 0080-9128) **2958**
Shakespeare Newsletter. (US ISSN 0037-3214) **2958, 4638**
Shakespeare Oxford Society. Newsletter.(US) **2958, 4638**
Shakespeare, Petrarch, Sidney, Milton & Hopkins *see* S P S M & H **3004**
Shakespeare Quarterly. (US ISSN 0037-3222) **2958, 4638**
Shakespeare Studies. (JA ISSN 0582-9402) **2958**
Shakespeare Studies. (US ISSN 0582-9399) **2958**
Shakespeare Survey. (UK ISSN 0080-9152) **2958**
Shakespeare Worldwide. (US) **2958, 4638**
Shakespeare Yearbook. (US ISSN 1045-9456) **2958**
Shakespearean Authorship Review *see* Bard **2898**
Shakespearean Criticism. (US ISSN 0883-9123) **2958**
Shakhmatna Misl. (BU) **4487**
Shakhmatnyi Byulleten' *see* Express - Shakhmaty **4471**
Shakhmaty *see* Baltiiskie Shakhmaty **4466**
Shakhmaty v S.S.S.R. (RU ISSN 0037-3249) **4487**
Shakhs/Shakmaty. (LV ISSN 0558-1613) **4487**
Shakmaty. *see* Shakhs **4487**
Shakti. (UK ISSN 0262-9860) **3925**
Shale Shaker. (US ISSN 0037-3257) **1580**
Shalom. (IS) **935, 1686**
Shalom. (IT ISSN 0037-3265) **2023, 4226**
Shalom. (BL) **2023, 3971**
Shalom. (US ISSN 0080-9160) **3947, 2023**
Shalom. (UK) **4226, 4201**
Shalom Infantil. (BL) **2023, 1265**
Shalom Magazine. (CN ISSN 0827-4916) **2023**
Shalom Network Newsletter *see* Agenda in Brief **1989**
Shalshelet: the Chain. (US) **3580**
Shama. (CN) **2023**
Shama. (Il ISSN 0037-3273) **2201**
Shaman's Drum. (US ISSN 0887-8897) **249, 2023**
Shamativ. (IS ISSN 0582-9836) **4226**
Shambhala Sun. (CN) **4215**
Shan Cha/Camellia. (CC) **2959, 2058**
Shan Hai Jing/Folklore. (CC) **2058**
Shandi Yanjiu/Mountain Research. (CC ISSN 1000-002X) **1580, 1968**
Shandong Auditing. *see* Shandong Shenji **756**
Shandong Baoxian/Shandong Insurance.(CC) **2542**
Shandong College of Oceanology. Journal *see* Ocean University of Qingdao. Journal **1609**
Shandong Daxue Xuebao (Shehui Kexue Ban)/Shandong University. Journal (Social Science Edition). (CC) **4385**
Shandong Daxue Xuebao (Ziran Kexue Ban)/Shandong University. Journal (Natural Science Edition). (CC) **4342**
Shandong Economics. *see* Shandong Jingji **691**
Shandong Gongye Daxue Xuebao (Shehui Kexue Ban)/Shandong Industrial University. Journal (Social Science Edition). (CC ISSN 1000-5323) **4385**
Shandong Huabao/Shandong Pictorial. (CC) **2182**

Shandong Industrial University. Journal (Social Science Edition). *see* Shandong Gongye Daxue Xuebao (Shehui Kexue Ban) **4385**
Shandong Insurance. *see* Shandong Baoxian **2542**
Shandong Jingji/Shandong Economics. (CC ISSN 1000-971X) **691**
Shandong Jingji Zhanlue Yanjiu/ Strategic Study of Shandong Economics. (CC) **1000**
Shandong Lawyers. *see* Shandong Lushi **2678**
Shandong Literature. *see* Shandong Wenxue **2959**
Shandong Lushi/Shandong Lawyers. (CC) **2678**
Shandong Luyou/Travel in Shandong. (CC) **4786**
Shandong Medicine. *see* Shandong Yiyao **3153**
Shandong Normal University. Journal (Social Science Edition). *see* Shandong Shida Xuebao (Shehui Kexue Ban) **4385**
Shandong Pictorial. *see* Shandong Huabao **2182**
Shandong Qingnian/Shandong Youth. (CC) **1244**
Shandong Shehui Kexue/Shandong Social Sciences. (CC) **4385**
Shandong Shenji/Shandong Auditing. (CC) **756**
Shandong Shida Xuebao (Shehui Kexue Ban)/Shandong Normal University. Journal (Social Science Edition). (CC) **4385**
Shandong Social Sciences. *see* Shandong Shehui Kexue **4385**
Shandong University. Journal (Natural Science Edition). *see* Shandong Daxue Xuebao (Ziran Kexue Ban) **4342**
Shandong University. Journal (Social Science Edition). *see* Shandong Daxue Xuebao (Shehui Kexue Ban) **4385**
Shandong University of Medical Sciences. Journal. *see* Shandong Yike Daxue Xuebao **3153**
Shandong University of Medical Sciences. Journal (Social Science Edition). *see* Shandong Yike Daxue Xuebao (Shehui Kexue Ban) **4385**
Shandong Wenxue/Shandong Literature.(CC ISSN 0257-5817) **2959**
Shandong Yike Daxue Xuebao/ Shandong University of Medical Sciences. Journal. (CC ISSN 1000-0496) **3153**
Shandong Yike Daxue Xuebao (Shehui Kexue Ban)/Shandong University of Medical Sciences. Journal (Social Science Edition). (CC ISSN 1000-5595) **4385**
Shandong Yiyao/Shandong Medicine. (CC) **3153, 3743**
Shandong Youth. *see* Shandong Qingnian **1244**
Shang Yeh Chou K'an. *see* Business Weekly **652**
Shanghai Academy of Social Sciences. Quarterly Journal. *see* Shanghai Shehui Kexueyuan Xueshu Jikan **4385**
Shanghai Accounting. *see* Shanghai Kuaiji **756**
Shanghai Agricultural Institute. Journal. *see* Shanghai Nongxueyuan Xuebao **119**
Shanghai Artist. *see* Shanghai Yishujia **4638**
Shanghai Baoxian/Shanghai Insurance. (CC) **2542**
Shanghai Baozhuang/Shanghai Packaging. (CC) **3651**
Shanghai Bulletin of Veterinary Science. *see* Shanghai Xumu Shouyi Tongxun **4816**
Shanghai Caishui/Shanghai Financial Taxation. (CC) **1105**
Shanghai Chess. *see* Shanghai Xiangqi **4488**
Shanghai Construction Science and Technology. *see* Shanghai Jianshe Keji **631**

Shanghai Dianqi Jishu/Shanghai Electronic Technology. (CC ISSN 1001-1374) **1778**
Shanghai Dianshi/Shanghai Television. (CC) **1379**
Shanghai Economic Research. *see* Shanghai Jingji Yanjiu **691**
Shanghai Economics. *see* Shanghai Jingji **691**
Shanghai Education (Adult Education Edition). *see* Shanghai Jiaoyu (Chengren Jiaoyu Ban) **1686**
Shanghai Education (Elementary School Edition). *see* Shanghai Jiaoyu (Xiaoxue Ban) **1663**
Shanghai Education (Middle School Edition). *see* Shanghai Jiaoyu (Zhongxue Ban) **1663**
Shanghai Education Research. *see* Shanghai Jiaoyu Keyan **1663**
Shanghai Electronic Technology. *see* Shanghai Dianqi Jishu **1778**
Shanghai Enterprises. *see* Shanghai Qiye **839**
Shanghai Environmental Sciences. *see* Shanghai Huanjing Kexue **1968**
Shanghai Fangzhi Keji/Shanghai Textile Science and Technology. (CC ISSN 1001-2044) **4623**
Shanghai Fayuan/Shanghai Legal World.(CC) **2678**
Shanghai Film Studio Pictorial. *see* Shangying Huabao **3517**
Shanghai Finance. *see* Shanghai Jinrong **799**
Shanghai Financial Taxation. *see* Shanghai Caishui **1105**
Shanghai Fushi. (CC ISSN 1000-8888) **1294**
Shanghai Gaojiao Yanjiu/Shanghai Higher Education Research. (CC ISSN 1000-4394) **1716**
Shanghai Gongshang/Shanghai Industries and Commerce. (CC) **839**
Shanghai Gushi/Shanghai Stories. (CC ISSN 1000-4831) **2959**
Shanghai Haiyun Xueyuan Xuebao. (CC) **4738**
Shanghai Harbor Economy. *see* Hugang Jingji **669**
Shanghai Higher Education Research. *see* Shanghai Gaojiao Yanjiu **1716**
Shanghai Huabao *see* Shanghai Pictorial **2182**
Shanghai Huagong Xueyuan Xuebao/ Shanghai Institute of Chemical Industry. Journal. (CC ISSN 0253-9683) **1187**
Shanghai Huanjing Kexue/Shanghai Environmental Sciences. (CC ISSN 1000-3975) **1968**
Shanghai Industries and Commerce. *see* Shanghai Gongshang **839**
Shanghai Institute of Chemical Industry. Journal. *see* Shanghai Huagong Xueyuan Xuebao **1187**
Shanghai Insurance. *see* Shanghai Baoxian **2542**
Shanghai Investment. *see* Shanghai Touzi **963**
Shanghai Jianshe Keji/Shanghai Construction Science and Technology.(CC) **631**
Shanghai Jiaotong Daxue Xuebao/ Shanghai Jiaotong University. Bulletin. (CC ISSN 0253-9942) **4608, 1324, 4342**
Shanghai Jiaotong University. Bulletin. *see* Shanghai Jiaotong Daxue Xuebao **4608**
Shanghai Jiaoyu (Chengren Jiaoyu Ban) /Shanghai Education (Adult Education Edition). (CC ISSN 0488-5406) **1686**
Shanghai Jiaoyu (Xiaoxue Ban)/ Shanghai Education (Elementary School Edition). (CC) **1663**
Shanghai Jiaoyu (Zhongxue Ban)/ Shanghai Education (Middle School Edition). (CC) **1663**
Shanghai Jiaoyu Keyan/Shanghai Education Research. (CC) **1663**
Shanghai Jichuang/Shanghai Machine Tool. (CC) **3023**
Shanghai Jingji/Shanghai Economics. (CC ISSN 1000-4211) **691**
Shanghai Jingji Yanjiu/Shanghai Economic Research. (CC) **691**

Shanghai Jingshen Yixue/Shanghai Psychiatry. (CC) **3354**
Shanghai Jinrong/Shanghai Finance. (CC) **799**
Shanghai Jinshu. (CC ISSN 0253-2344) **3419**
Shanghai Jinshu (Youse Fence). (CC ISSN 1001-2125) **3419**
Shanghai Jiyou/Shanghai Philately. (CC) **3757**
Shanghai Journal of Mechanics. *see* Shanghai Lixue **3845**
Shanghai Journal of Medical Science. *see* Shanghai Yixue **3153**
Shanghai Journal of Traditional Chinese Medicine. *see* Shanghai Zhongyiyao Zazhi **3153**
Shanghai Kuaiji/Shanghai Accounting. (CC) **756**
Shanghai Legal World. *see* Shanghai Fayuan **2678**
Shanghai Literature. *see* Shanghai Wenxue **2959**
Shanghai Lixue/Shanghai Journal of Mechanics. (CC ISSN 0254-0053) **3845**
Shanghai Machine Tool. *see* Shanghai Jichuang **3023**
Shanghai Nongxueyuan Xuebao / Shanghai Agricultural Institute. Journal. (CC ISSN 1000-193X) **119**
Shanghai Normal University. Journal (Social Science Edition). *see* Shanghai Shifan Daxue Xuebao (Shehui Kexue Ban) **4385**
Shanghai Packaging. *see* Shanghai Baozhuang **3651**
Shanghai Philately. *see* Shanghai Jiyou **3757**
Shanghai Pictorial. (CC) **2182, 3797**
Shanghai Psychiatry. *see* Shanghai Jingshen Yixue **3354**
Shanghai Qiye/Shanghai Enterprises. (CC) **839**
Shanghai Quality. *see* Shanghai Zhiliang **1084**
Shanghai Railroad Institute. Journal. *see* Shanghai Tiedao Xueyuan Xuebao **4714**
Shanghai Secondary School Mathematics. *see* Shanghai Zhongxue Shuxue **3055**
Shanghai Shehui Kexueyuan Xueshu Jikan/Shanghai Academy of Social Sciences. Quarterly Journal. (CC) **4385**
Shanghai Shifan Daxue Xuebao (Shehui Kexue Ban)/Shanghai Normal University. Journal (Social Science Edition). (CC) **4385**
▼Shanghai Statistical Yearbook (Year). (HK) **4585**
Shanghai Statistics. *see* Shanghai Tongji **4585**
Shanghai Stories. *see* Shanghai Gushi **2959**
Shanghai Television. *see* Shanghai Dianshi **1379**
Shanghai Textile Science and Technology. *see* Shanghai Fangzhi Keji **4623**
Shanghai Theater. *see* Shanghai Xiju **4638**
Shanghai Tiedao Xueyuan Xuebao/ Shanghai Railroad Institute. Journal. (CC ISSN 1000-1913) **4714**
Shanghai Tongji/Shanghai Statistics. (CC) **4585**
Shanghai Touzi/Shanghai Investment. (CC) **963**
Shanghai University of Medical Sciences. Journal. *see* Shanghai Yike Daxue Xuebao **3153**
Shanghai Wenxue/Shanghai Literature. (CC ISSN 0582-9542) **2959**
Shanghai Xiangqi/Shanghai Chess. (CC) **4488**
Shanghai Xiju/Shanghai Theater. (CC ISSN 0559-7277) **4638**
Shanghai Xumu Shouyi Tongxun/ Shanghai Bulletin of Veterinary Science. (CC ISSN 1000-7725) **4816**
Shanghai Yike Daxue Xuebao/Shanghai University of Medical Sciences. Journal. (CC ISSN 0257-8131) **3153**

SHANGHAI YISHUJIA

Shanghai Yishujia/Shanghai Artist. (CC) **4638, 343, 3517**
Shanghai Yixue/Shanghai Journal of Medical Science. (CC ISSN 0253-9934) **3153**
Shanghai Zhiliang/Shanghai Quality. (CC) **1084**
Shanghai Zhongxue Shuxue/Shanghai Secondary School Mathematics. (CC) **3055, 1663**
Shanghai Zhongyiyao Zazhi/Shanghai Journal of Traditional Chinese Medicine. (CC) **3153, 3743**
Shangpin Jiage Yuebao see Commodity Price Monthly **851**
Shangpin Pingjie/Review on Commodity. (CC) **1508**
Shangye Jingji yu Guanli/Commercial Economics and Management. (CC ISSN 1000-2154) **1027**
Shangying Huabao/Shanghai Film Studio Pictorial. (CC) **3517**
Shanhua/Mountain Blossoms (Guizhou). (CC ISSN 0559-7218) **2959**
Shankpainter. (US) **2959, 343**
▼Shans. (RU) **2883**
Shanti see Santi **4217**
Shanti Nilaya Newsletter see Elisabeth Kubler Ross Center Newsletter **4020**
†Shantih. (US ISSN 0037-329X) **5276**
Shantou Wenyi see Chao Sheng **2904**
Shanxi Agriculture. see Shanxi Nongye **119**
Shanxi Daxue Xuebao (Shehui Kexue Ban)/Shanxi University. Journal (Social Science Edition). (CC ISSN 1000-5935) **4385, 3701**
Shanxi Daxue Xuebao (Ziran Kexue Ban)/Shanxi University. Journal (Natural Science Edition). (CC) **4342**
Shanxi Difang Zhi. (CC) **2341**
Shanxi Dizhen/Earthquake Research in Shanxi. (CC ISSN 1000-6265) **1594**
Shanxi Folk Literature. see Shanxi Minjian Wenxue **2959**
Shanxi Fruit Trees. see Shanxi Guoshu **119**
Shanxi Guoshu/Shanxi Fruit Trees. (CC) **119**
Shanxi Huabao/Shanxi Pictorial. (CC ISSN 0559-717X) **2182**
Shanxi Institute of Mining Industry. Journal. see Shanxi Kuangye Xueyuan Xuebao **3495**
Shanxi Journal of Medicine. see Shanxi Yiyao Zazhi **3743**
Shanxi Kuangye Xueyuan Xuebao/Shanxi Institute of Mining Industry. Journal. (CC ISSN 1000-1603) **3495**
Shanxi Literature. see Shanxi Wenxue **2959**
Shanxi Meteorology. see Shanxi Qixiang **3440**
Shanxi Minjian Wenxue/Shanxi Folk Literature. (CC) **2959**
Shanxi Nongye/Shanxi Agriculture. (CC ISSN 0488-5368) **119**
Shanxi Nongye Daxue Xuebao/Shanxi University of Agriculture. Journal. (CC ISSN 1000-162X) **119**
Shanxi Pictorial. see Shanxi Huabao **2182**
Shanxi Qixiang/Shanxi Meteorology. (CC) **3440**
Shanxi Traditional Medicine. see Shanxi Zhongyi **3153**
Shanxi University. Journal (Natural Science Edition). see Shanxi Daxue Xuebao (Ziran Kexue Ban) **4342**
Shanxi University. Journal (Social Science Edition). see Shanxi Daxue Xuebao (Shehui Kexue Ban) **4385**
Shanxi University of Agriculture. Journal. see Shanxi Nongye Daxue Xuebao **119**
Shanxi Wenxue/Shanxi Literature. (CC ISSN 0257-5906) **2959**
Shanxi Yiyao Zazhi/Shanxi Journal of Medicine. (CC ISSN 0253-9926) **3743**
Shanxi Zhongyi/Shanxi Traditional Medicine. (CC ISSN 1000-7156) **3153**

Shao Nu/Young Girl. (CC ISSN 1001-5590) **1265**
Shaolin yu Taiji. (CC) **4488, 3808**
Shaonan Shaonu/Boys and Girls. (CC) **2959**
Shaonian Bao/Juvenile Press. (CC) **1265**
Shaonian Ertong Yanjiu/Adolescent Studies. (CC) **1244**
Shaonian Jiyou/Juvenile Philately. (CC) **3757, 1265**
Shaonian Kexue/Juvenile Science. (CC) **1265, 4342**
Shaonian Kexue Huabao/Juvenile Scientific Pictorial. (CC ISSN 1000-7776) **1265, 4342**
Shaonian Wenyi/Literature & Art for Juveniles. (CC ISSN 0559-7412) **1265, 343, 2959**
Shape. (US ISSN 0744-5121) **3808, 4852**
▼Sharapat/Compassion. (MP) **4220**
Shards of Babel. (NE) **3014**
Share. (CN) **2457, 2279**
Share. (UK) **4201**
Share see S H A R E **5272**
Share It. (UK ISSN 0262-9356) **3596, 3781, 4288**
Share Newsletter. (US ISSN 4046, 3296**
Share the Earth Newsletter. (US) **1968**
Shared Housing Quarterly. (US) **4419, 2496**
▼ShareDebate International. (US ISSN 1054-0695) **4385, 4448**
Shareholder. see Aktiespararen **758**
†Shareholder. (AT ISSN 0037-3311) **5276**
Shareholder Remedies in Canada. (CN) **963, 2678**
Shareholders, Form 10-K. Banking Supplement. (US) **799**
Shareware Magazine (Sunnyvale). (US ISSN 1042-0681) **1474**
Sharia. see Theology **4220**
Shari'ah. (JO) **4220**
Sharing. (UK) **1539**
Sharing. (US) **3005**
Sharing Ideas. (US ISSN 0886-1501) **1342**
Sharing of Expertise and Experience. (American Society of Association Executives) (US) **1027**
Sharing the Practice. (US ISSN 0193-8274) **4201**
Sharing the Victory. (US) **4201, 4488**
Sharing with a Purpose Review - S W A P see Review - S W A P **4082**
Sharjah Commercial Directory. (TS) **822**
Sharjah Ports Handbook. (UK ISSN 0267-2316) **1153, 4738**
Sharkara. (II ISSN 0037-332X) **2081**
Sharon News. (IS) **2204**
Al-Sharq. (SU) **343, 2883**
Al-Sharq. (QA) **2211**
Al-Sharq. (IS) **2959**
Al-Sharq al-Awsat see Asharq Al-Awsat **843**
Al-Sharqiyyah Elle. (SU) **4852**
Shashin Sokuryo to Rimoto Senshingu/Photogrammetry and Remote Sensing. (JA ISSN 0285-5844) **2262**
Shatranj Samarat. (II) **4488**
Shattered Wig Review. (US) **3005**
Shaun's Love Letter see Friends Focus **1298**
Shaver Focus. (CN ISSN 0315-6915) **225**
Shaverton. (US) **2984**
Shavian. (UK ISSN 0037-3346) **2959, 4638**
Shavings. (US ISSN 0734-0680) **4529**
Shavings from the Chronicle of the Early American Industries Association. (US) **1084**
Ha-Shavua. (IS) **832, 3925**
Shaw Annual. (US ISSN 0741-5842) **2959, 3781**
Shaw Historical Library. Journal. (US ISSN 0889-0277) **2422**
Shaw Newsletter see Shaw Society Newsletter **2959**
Shaw Society Newsletter. (UK) **2959**
Shaw: the annual of Bernard Shaw Studies see Shaw Annual **2959**
Shawcross & Beaumont: Air Law. (UK) **4677**

Shaw's Directory of Courts in the United Kingdom. (UK ISSN 0264-312X) **2732**
†Shaw's Wine Guide. (UK ISSN 0307-1170) **5276**
Shdemot. (IS) **4448**
She. (UK ISSN 0037-3370) **4852**
Sheaf. (CN) **1324**
Sheep and Goats in Humid West Africa. (UN) **225**
Sheep Breeder and Sheepman. (US ISSN 0037-3400) **225**
Sheep Canada. (CN ISSN 0702-8881) **225**
The Sheep Farmer. (UK) **225**
Sheep! Magazine. (US ISSN 0279-9200) **225, 4623**
Sheeps Clothing. (US) **1716**
Sheet Metal & Air Conditioning Contractors of North America Convention Daily see S M A C N A Convention Daily **631**
Sheet Metal Australia. (AT ISSN 0818-1764) **3419**
Sheet Metal Industries. (UK ISSN 0037-3435) **3430**
Sheet Metal Industries Year Book. (UK ISSN 0305-7798) **3419, 3430**
†Sheet Metal Tubes Sections. (GW ISSN 0178-6849) **5276**
Sheet Music see Sheet Music. Standard Organ Edition **5276**
†Sheet Music. Standard Organ Edition. (US ISSN 0197-3495) **5276**
Sheet Music Exchange. (US ISSN 0741-7780) **3580**
Sheet Music Magazine. Standard Edition see Sheet Music. Standard Organ Edition **5276**
Sheet Music Magazine. Standard Piano-Guitar Edition. (US ISSN 0273-6462) **3580**
Sheffield & South Yorkshire Chambers of Commerce Directory. (UK ISSN 0950-8945) **822**
Sheffield and South Yorkshire Topic see South Yorkshire Topic **2195**
Sheffield City Press. (UK) **2195**
Sheffield University Annual Report. (UK) **1716**
Sheffield University Calendar. (UK ISSN 0307-6202) **1716**
Sheffield University General Prospectus see Sheffield University Undergraduate Prospectus **1716**
Sheffield University Postgraduate Prospectus. (UK) **1716**
Sheffield University Undergraduate Prospectus. (UK) **1716**
Shehui/Society. (CC) **4385**
Shehui Gongzuo Yanjiu/Social Affairs Study. (CC) **4385**
Shehui - Jianting/Society - Family. (CC) **2183**
Shehui Kexue (Lanzhou)/Social Science.(CC) **4386**
Shehui Kexue (Shanghai)/Social Sciences. (CC ISSN 0257-5833) **4386**
Shehui Kexue Jikan/Social Science Journal. (CC ISSN 1001-6198) **4386**
Shehui Kexue Yanjiu/Social Science Research. (CC ISSN 1000-4769) **4386**
Shehui Kexue Zhanxian/Social Science Front. (CC ISSN 0257-0246) **4386**
Shehuixue Yanjiu/Sociological Studies. (US) **4448**
Shekel. (US) **3601, 2023**
Shelburne Securities Forecast. (US) **963**
Shelby County Urban Development Report. (US) **2496**
Shelby Exchange. (US) **2164**
Shelby Report of the Southeast. (US ISSN 0194-1968) **2094**
Shelby Report of the Southwest. (US) **2094**
Shelby's Southwest Foodservice see Sunbelt Foodservice **2082**
Shelf Action. (US) **2081**
Shelfmark. (RH ISSN 0037-3494) **411**
Shell. see La Conchiglia **580**
Shell Bitumen Review. (UK ISSN 0037-3516) **1836, 3701**
Shell Chronicle see Nutshell **3694**

Shell Hausnachrichten see Hausnachrichten **980**
Shell-Post. (NE) **3701**
Shell Tourist Guide to South Africa. (SA) **4786**
Shell-Venster. (NE) **3701**
Shellac Export Promotion Council. Annual Report. (II ISSN 0304-8179) **3655**
Sheller's Directory of Clubs, Books, Periodicals and Dealers. (US ISSN 0085-607X) **591**
Shellfish Farming. (UK ISSN 0958-4684) **2051**
Shells and Sea Life see The Opisthobranch **450**
Shelter. (US ISSN 0164-6559) **631**
Shelter Advertising Association. Buyers' Guide. (US) **38**
Shelter Sense. (US ISSN 0734-3078) **231**
Shelterforce. (US ISSN 0885-9612) **2496**
Sheltie International. (US) **3713**
Sheltie Pacesetter. (US ISSN 0744-6608) **3713**
Sheltie Pacesetter Trade Secrets Book. (US) **3713**
Shem Tov. (CN ISSN 0843-6924) **2164**
Shenandoah: The Washington and Lee University Review. (US ISSN 0037-3583) **2883**
Shenaton Hidrologi Le-Yisrael. see Hydrological Yearbook of Israel **1598**
Shenaton Statisti: Le Nemlei Israel. see Yearbook of Israel Ports Statistics **744**
Shenaton Statisti le-Yisrael. see Israel. Central Bureau of Statistics. Statistical Abstract of Israel **4575**
Shendetesia Popullore. (AA) **4112**
Shendeti. (AA) **4112**
Shenghuo Baishi Tong. (CC) **343**
Shenghuo - Chuangzao/Life - Creation. (CC) **2183**
Shengli Kexue Jinzhan/Progress in Physiological Sciences. (CC ISSN 0559-7765) **574, 3153**
Shengli Xuebao/Acta Physiologica Sinica. (CC ISSN 0371-0874) **574**
Shengli zhi Guang see Victorious **3932**
Shengtai Xuebao/Acta Ecologica Sinica. (CC ISSN 1000-0933) **1968**
Shengtaixue Zazhi/Journal of Ecology. (CC ISSN 1000-4890) **1968**
Shengwu Fangzhi Tongbao/Bulletin of Biological Control. (CC ISSN 1000-1034) **455**
Shengwu Gongcheng Xuebao/Biotechnology. (English translation: Chinese Journal of Biotechnology) (CC ISSN 1000-3061) **491**
Shengwu Huaxue yu Shengwu Wuli Jinzhan/Progress in Biochemistry and Biophysics. (CC ISSN 1000-3282) **482, 486**
Shengwu Huaxue yu Shengwu Wuli Xuebao/Acta Biochemica et Biophysica Sinica. (CC ISSN 0582-9879) **482, 486**
Shengwu Huaxue Zazhi/Chinese Biochemical Journal. (CC ISSN 1000-8543) **483**
Shengwu Shuxue Xuebao. (CC) **455**
Shengwu Yixue Gongchengxue Zazhi/Journal for Biomedical Engineering. (CC ISSN 1001-5515) **3153**
Shengwuxue Jiaoxue/Biology Teaching. (CC ISSN 0488-6054) **455, 1663**
Shengwuxue Tongbao. see Biological Bulletin **431**
Shengxue Jishu/Technical Acoustics. (CC ISSN 1000-3630) **3860**
Shengxue Xuebao. (CC) **3860**
Shenji Lilun yu Shijian/Auditing Theory and Practice. (CC) **756**
Shenji Yanjiu/Auditing Studies. (CC) **756**
Shenyang Pharmaceutical Institute. Journal. see Shenyang Yaoxueyuan Xuebao **3743**
Shenyang Shifan Xueyuan Xuebao. Shehui Kexue Ban/Shenyang Teachers College. Journal. Social Science Edition. (CC ISSN 1000-5226) **4386**

Shenyang Teachers College. Journal. Social Science Edition. see Shenyang Shifan Xueyuan Xuebao. Shehui Kexue Ban **4386**
Shenyang Yaoxueyuan Xuebao/Shenyang Pharmaceutical Institute. Journal. (CC) **3743**
Shenyang Yinyue Xueyuan Xuebao see Yuefu Xin Sheng **3587**
Shenzhen Daxue Xuebao (Ligong Ban)/Shenzhen University. Journal (Science, Engineering Edition). (CC) **4342, 1836**
Shenzhen Daxue Xuebao (Renwen Sheke Ban)/Shenzhen University. Journal (Humanities, Social Sciences Edition). (CC ISSN 1000-2618) **2515, 1663**
Shenzhen Fengcai. (CC) **2183**
▼Shenzhen Today. (HK) **884**
Shenzhen University. Journal (Humanities, Social Sciences Edition). see Shenzhen Daxue Xuebao (Renwen Sheke Ban) **2515**
Shenzhen University. Journal (Science, Engineering Edition). see Shenzhen Daxue Xuebao (Ligong Ban) **4342**
Shenzhou Chuanqi. (CC) **2959**
Shenzhou Xueren/China's Scholars Abroad. (CC) **1716**
Shepard's Bankruptcy Citations. (US ISSN 0730-1936) **799**
Shepard's Code of Federal Regulations Citations. (US ISSN 0730-465X) **2679**
Shepard's Corporation Law Citations. (US ISSN 8750-1104) **2712**
Shepard's Criminal Justice Citations. (US ISSN 0363-0978) **2714**
Shepard's Federal Circuit Table. (US ISSN 0730-7039) **2679**
Shepard's Federal Citations. (US ISSN 0730-4633) **2679**
Shepard's Federal Energy Law Citations.(US ISSN 0746-312X) **2679**
Shepard's Federal Labor Law Citations. (US ISSN 0730-4684) **2679**
Shepard's Federal Law Citations in Selected Law Reviews. (US ISSN 0094-9531) **2679**
Shepard's Federal Occupational Safety and Health Citations. (US ISSN 0732-7722) **993, 2679**
▼Shepard's Federal Securities Law Citations. (US) **963, 2679**
Shepard's Federal Tax Citations. (US ISSN 0732-7714) **1105**
Shepard's Immigration and Naturalization Citations. (US ISSN 0746-3138) **2679**
Shepard's Insurance Law Citations. (US) **2679, 2542**
Shepard's Law Review Citations. (US ISSN 0582-9887) **2679**
Shepard's Medical Malpractice Citations.(US) **2704, 3153**
Shepard's Military Justice Citations. (US ISSN 0163-1101) **2735**
Shepard's Partnership Law Citations. (US ISSN 8750-1112) **2679**
Shepard's Products Liability Citations. (US ISSN 8750-1139) **2679**
Shepard's Professional and Judicial Conduct Citations. (US ISSN 0730-6229) **2733**
Shepard's Texas Briefcase. (US ISSN 0270-529X) **2679**
Shepard's Uniform Commercial Code Citations. (US ISSN 0745-5925) **2679**
Shepard's United States Administrative Citations. (US ISSN 0582-9909) **2679**
Shepard's United States Patents and Trademarks Citations. (US ISSN 0582-9917) **2679**
†Shepard's United States Supreme Court Case Commentaries. (US) **5276**
Shepherd. (US ISSN 8750-7897) **225**
The Shepherd. (UK ISSN 0260-0382) **4288**
Shepherd and Sheep Raiser see Shepherd **225**
The Shepherd College Picket. (US) **1324**
Shepherd Express. (US) **2234, 2883**

†Shepherd's Call. (US ISSN 0037-3605) **5276**
Sheppard's Book Dealers in British Isles.(UK ISSN 0950-0715) **4137**
Sheppard's Book Dealers in India and the Orient. (UK) **4137**
▼Sheppard's Bookdealers in Australia and New Zealand. (UK ISSN 0962-2764) **4137**
Sheppard's Bookdealers in Europe. (UK ISSN 0963-0171) **4137**
Sheppard's Bookdealers in North America. (UK ISSN 0269-1469) **4137**
Sher-i-Punjab. (II) **2201**
Sheraton London Magazine. (UK) **2480**
Sherbondy Beacon. (US ISSN 8755-0547) **2164**
Sherborn Fund Facsimiles. (UK ISSN 0080-9241) **4342**
Sheriff. (US) **1522**
Sheriff & Police Reporter. (US) **1522**
Sheriff Services Selected Operating Procedures. (CN) **2679**
†Sherkin Island. Journal. (IE ISSN 0332-2629) **5276**
Sherlock Holmes Journal. (UK ISSN 0037-3621) **2986**
†Sherlock Holmes Mystery Book. (UK) **5276**
Sherlockian Tidbits. (US ISSN 1040-4937) **2986**
Sherut Maeda Eiskei. (IS) **1153**
Shetho/Forward. (BR) **2220**
Shetkari. (II ISSN 0037-3648) **119**
Shetland Fishing News. (UK) **2048**
Shetland Life. (UK ISSN 0260-5732) **2195**
Shetland Pony Stud-Book Society Magazine. (UK) **4537**
Shetland Times. (UK) **2195**
†SheTotem. (US) **5276**
Shetu-Bondha. (CC) **2959**
Shevchenko Scientific Society. Memoirs. see Naukove Tovarystvo Imeni Shevchenka. Zapysky **2016**
Sheying Shijie/Photography World. (CC) **3797**
Sheying zhi You/Photography Fans. (CC) **3797**
Shi Shen/Poems Deity. (CC) **3005**
Shi Yue/October. (CC ISSN 0257-5841) **2959**
Shia World. (UK) **4220**
Shiah. (PK) **4220**
Shiborudia. see Sieboldia Acta Biologica **455**
Shichang/Market Journal. (US) **1053**
Shichang Zhoubao/Market Weekly. (CC) **839, 963**
Shichokaku Kyoiku/Audio-Visual Education. (JA ISSN 0037-3664) **1663, 1379**
Shidai. (CC) **2183**
Shidai Jianzhu/Modern Architecture. (CC) **1873**
Shidai Jiemei. (CC) **4852**
Shidai Wenxue. (CC) **2959**
Shield. (UK) **3701**
Shield. (US ISSN 0037-3672) **4073**
Shield & Diamond. (US ISSN 8750-7536) **1324**
Shiga Daigaku Kyoikugakubu Kiyo. Shizen Kagaku/Shiga University. Faculty of Education. Memoirs. Natural Science. (JA ISSN 0488-6291) **4342**
Shiga-kenritsu Tanki Daigaku Gakujutsu Zasshi/Shiga Prefectural Junior College. Scientific Reports. (JA ISSN 0371-3385) **164**
Shiga Prefectural Junior College. Scientific Reports. see Shiga-kenritsu Tanki Daigaku Gakujutsu Zasshi **164**
Shiga Shizen Kyoiku Kenkyu Shisetsu Kenkyu Gyoseki/Institute of Nature Education in Shiga Heights. Bulletin. (JA ISSN 0389-9128) **1548**
Shiga University. Faculty of Education. Memoirs. Natural Science. see Shiga Daigaku Kyoikugakubu Kiyo. Shizen Kagaku **4342**
Shigaku/Odontology. (JA ISSN 0029-8484) **3242**
Shigaku Zasshi. see Historical Journal of Japan **2338**

Shigen Kagaku Kenkyujo. see Tokyo Institute of Technology. Research Laboratory of Resources Utilization. Report **4612**
Shigen Sozai/Mining and Materials Processing Institute of Japan. Journal. (JA ISSN 0916-1740) **3495, 3419**
Shigong Qiye Guanli/Building Industry Management. (CC) **1027, 631**
Shih Nu Tsa Chih. see Ladies Magazine **1292**
Shih Tai Chi Yeh/Times Enterprise. (CH) **1084**
Shih Tzu Bulletin. (US) **3713**
Shih Tzu Reporter. (US) **3713**
Shih Yen Sheng Wu Hsueh Pao see Shiyan Shengwu Xuebao **455**
Shih Yueh P'ing Lun. see October Review **3912**
Shijie Bolan/World Vision. (CC ISSN 1003-0271) **2183**
Shijie Daodan yu Hangtian see Zhongguo Hangtian **66**
Shijie Dianxin/World Telecommunications. (CC ISSN 1001-4802) **1342**
Shijie Dianying/World Films. (CC) **3517**
Shijie Dizhen Yicong. (CC) **1594**
Shijie Ertong/World Children. (CC) **1244**
Shijie Faming/World Inventions. (CC) **4342, 4608**
Shijie Hanyu Jiaoxue/Chinese Teaching in the World. (CC) **2841, 1759**
Shijie Jianzhu Daobao/World Architecture Herald. (CC ISSN 1000-8373) **306**
Shijie Jingji/World Economy Monthly. (CC ISSN 1001-3377) **1000, 884**
†Shijie Jingji Daobao/World Economic Herald. (CC) **5276**
Shijie Jingji Yanjiu/World Economy Research. (US) **1000, 884**
Shijie Jingji Yicong/World Economics Translations. (CC) **691**
Shijie Kexue Jishu/World Science and Technology. (CC) **4342, 4608**
Shijie Laodong Anquan Weisheng Dongtai/World Industrial Safety and Hygiene Development. (CC) **3622**
Shijie Lishi/World History. (CC) **2322**
Shijie Meishu/World Art. (CC ISSN 1000-8683) **343**
Shijie Nongye/World Agriculture. (CC) **119**
Shijie Tushu/World Books. (CC ISSN 1000-0097) **4137, 2784**
Shijie Wenxue/World Literature. (CC ISSN 0583-0206) **2959**
Shijie Yanjiu Dongtai. (CC) **2322, 1663**
Shijie zhi Chuang/Window on the World.(CC) **2183**
Shijie Zhishi/World Affairs. (CC ISSN 0583-0176) **3972**
Shijie Zhishi Huabao/World Affairs Pictorial. (CC ISSN 1003-028X) **2183**
Shijie Zongjiao Yanjiu/Studies on World Religion. (CC ISSN 1000-4289) **4201**
Shijie Zongjiao Ziliao. (CC ISSN 1000-4505) **4201**
Shika Gakuho/Tokyo Dental College Society Journal. (JA ISSN 0037-3710) **3242**
Shika Giko/Journal of Dental Technics. (JA ISSN 0389-1895) **3242**
Shika Igaku. see Osaka Odontological Society. Journal **3240**
Shika Yakubutsu Ryoho/Oral Therapeutics and Pharmacology. (JA ISSN 0288-1012) **3743**
Shikai Tenbo. see Dental Outlook **3231**
Shikan/Poetry. (CC ISSN 0583-0230) **3005**
Shiki no Aji/Cooking for Four Seasons. (JA) **2449**
Shikoku Acta Medica. see Shikoku Igaku Zasshi **3153**
Shikoku Electric Power Co. Annual Report. (JA) **1908**
Shikoku Entomological Society. Transactions/Shikoku Konchu Gakkai Kaiho. (JA ISSN 0037-3680) **537**

Shikoku Igaku Zasshi/Shikoku Acta Medica. (JA ISSN 0037-3699) **3153**
Shikoku Konchu Gakkai Kaiho. see Shikoku Entomological Society. Transactions **537**
Shikoku National Agricultural Experiment Station. Bulletin. (JA ISSN 0037-3702) **119**
Shilin. (CC) **3005**
Shilo Stag. (CN ISSN 0037-3729) **3471**
Shiloh Museum. Newsletter. (US) **3532, 2422**
Shima Marineland. Science Report. (JA ISSN 0385-1109) **455, 591, 1610, 2049**
Shimane Daigaku Hobungakubu Kiyo. Bungakuka Hen/Shimane University. Faculty of Law and Literature. Memoirs. (JA) **4386**
Shimane Daigaku Kyoikugakubu Kiyo. Shizen Kagaku/Shimane University. Faculty of Education. Memoirs. Natural Science. (JA ISSN 0586-9943) **4342**
Shimane Daigaku Rigakubu Kiyo/Shimane University. Faculty of Science. Memoirs. (JA ISSN 0387-9925) **4342**
Shimane Ika Daigaku Kiyo/Shimane Medical University. Bulletin. (JA ISSN 0387-9097) **3153, 4342**
Shimane Journal of Medical Science. (JA ISSN 0386-5959) **3153**
Shimane Law Review. (JA ISSN 0583-0362) **2679, 3925**
Shimane Medical University. Bulletin. see Shimane Ika Daigaku Kiyo **3153**
Shimane no Shizen. (JA) **4342**
Shimane University. Faculty of Education. Memoirs. Natural Science. see Shimane Daigaku Kyoikugakubu Kiyo. Shizen Kagaku **4342**
Shimane University. Faculty of Law and Literature. Memoirs. see Shimane Daigaku Hobungakubu Kiyo. Bungakuka Hen **4386**
Shimane University. Faculty of Science. Memoirs. see Shimane Daigaku Rigakubu Kiyo **4342**
Shimano Sport Fishing. (US) **4555**
Shimizu Bulletin. (JA) **632**
Shin Boei Ronshu/Journal of National Defense. (JA ISSN 0286-9241) **3471**
Shin Dong-A/New East Asia. (KO) **2575**
Shin Kaki/New Flowers. (JA ISSN 0037-3737) **2139**
†Shin Nippon Denki Giho/New Nippon Electric Technical Review. (JA ISSN 0037-3745) **5276**
Shinagaku Kenkyu. see Journal of Sinological Studies **3640**
Shinanggye/World of Faith. (KO) **4201**
Shine Uye/New Generation. (MP) **3925**
Shinei Sheji/Interior Design. (CC) **2555**
Shing Wah Daily News see Shing Wah News **2023**
Shing Wah News. (CN) **2023**
Shining Star Magazine. (US) **1265, 4249**
Shinjleh Uhaan Am'dral/Science and Life. (MP) **4342**
Shinjleh Uhaany Akademiyn Medee/Academy of Sciences News. (MP) **4342**
Shinkan News for Readers/Shinkan Nyusu. (JA ISSN 0037-3788) **4137**
Shinkan Nyusu. see Shinkan News for Readers **4137**
Shinkei Gaisho/Neurotraumatology. (JA ISSN 0389-5610) **3354, 3311**
Shinkei Geka. see Neurological Surgery **3347**
Shinkei Geka. (JA ISSN 0470-8105) **3354, 3384**
Shinkei Kagaku/Japanese Neurochemical Society. Bulletin. (JA ISSN 0037-3796) **3354**
Shinkei Kenkyu no Shinpo/Advances in Neurological Sciences. (JA ISSN 0001-8724) **3354**
Shinkenchiku. (JA) **306**

SHINKU TANKU

Shinku Tanku Nenpo/Abstracts of Think Tank Reports. (JA ISSN 0917-7574) **4358**, 4615
Shinobazu Dayori/News of Shinobazu. (JA) **1968**
Shinrigaku Hyoron/Japanese Psychological Review. (JA ISSN 0386-1058) **4046**
Shinrigaku Kenkyu/Japanese Journal of Psychology. (JA ISSN 0021-5236) **4046**
Shinrin Boeki. see Forest Pests **2099**
Shinrin Bunka Kenkyu/Review of Forestry Culture. (JA ISSN 0389-2166) **2107**
Shinseikatsu Tokushin see Jumin Katsudo **1961**
Shinshin-Igaku/Japanese Journal of Psychosomatic Medicine. (JA ISSN 0385-0307) **3354**
Shinshu Daigaku Kogakubu Kiyo. see Shinshu University. Faculty of Engineering. Journal **1836**
Shinshu Daigaku Rigakubu Kiyo. see Shinshu University. Faculty of Science. Journal **4342**
Shinshu Igaku Zasshi. see Shinshu Medical Journal **3153**
Shinshu Medical Journal/Shinshu Igaku Zasshi. (JA ISSN 0037-3826) **3153**
Shinshu University. Faculty of Engineering. Journal/Shinshu Daigaku Kogakubu Kiyo. (JA ISSN 0037-3818) **1836**
Shinshu University. Faculty of Science. Journal/Shinshu Daigaku Rigakubu Kiyo. (JA ISSN 0583-063X) **4342**
Shinshu University. Faculty of Textile Science and Technology. Journal. Series A: Biology. (JA ISSN 0583-0648) **455**, 119, 4623
Shinshu University. Faculty of Textile Science and Technology. Journal. Series B: Engineering. (JA) **1836**
Shinshu University. Faculty of Textile Science and Technology. Journal. Series C: Chemistry. (JA ISSN 0559-8621) **1860**, 4623
Shinshu University. Faculty of Textile Science and Technology. Journal. Series D: Arts. (JA ISSN 0583-0664) **4623**
Shinshu University. Faculty of Textile Science and Technology. Journal. Series E: Agriculture and Sericulture. (JA) **119**
Shinshu University. Faculty of Textile Science and Technology. Journal. Series F: Physics and Mathematics. (JA ISSN 0368-4571) **3831**, 3055
Shinshu University. School of Allied Medical Sciences. Treatises and Studies. (JA ISSN 0385-1982) **3153**
Ship and Boat Builders National. Federation Handbook see British Marine Industries Federation Handbook **4725**
Ship Engineering. see Chuanbo Gongcheng **4726**
Ship of Christ the King. see Kristaus Karaliaus Laivas **5224**
Ship Repair and Maintenance see Shipcare & Maritime Management **4738**
Ship World. see Chuanbo Shijie **4726**
†Shipbuilders Council of America. Statistical Quarterly. (US) **5276**
Shipbuilding and Marine Engineering International see Lloyd's Ship Manager **4731**
Shipbuilding and Shipping. see Korabostroene i Koraboplavane **4730**
Shipbuilding News. (UK) **4738**
Shipcare & Maritime Management. (UK) **4738**
Shipcare International see Shipcare & Maritime Management **4738**
Shipin Ke-Ji/Food Science. (CC) **3612**, 2081
Shipmate. (US ISSN 0488-6720) **1324**, 3471
Shippers' Digest. (PK) **822**
Shippers Today. (HK) **4738**
Shipping. see Kaiun **4730**
Shipping. (GR) **4738**

Shipping Abstracts. see Hajozasi Szakirodalmi Tajekoztato **4664**
Shipping and Aviation Statistics of the Maltese Islands. (MM ISSN 0080-9268) **4666**, 4677, 4738
Shipping and Marine Industries Journal. (Il ISSN 0970-0285) **4738**, 1610, 2049
▼Shipping and Tourism. (GR) **4738**, 691, 4786
Shipping and Trade News. (JA) **4738**, 920
Shipping and Transport News see Shipping & Transport News International **4739**
Shipping & Transport News International. (BA) **4739**
Shipping-Bladet. (DK ISSN 0108-8912) **4739**
Shipping Digest. (US ISSN 0037-3893) **4739**
Shipping Digest Shipping Lines and Agents Directory Issue. (US) **4739**
Shipping Digest's Handbook for International Trade. (US) **4739**
Shipping Gazette. (JA ISSN 0037-3915) **4739**
Shipping Information Services. (Il) **4739**
Shipping News International see Lloyd's Ship Manager. Shipping News International **4731**
Shipping News International see Lloyd's Ship Manager **4731**
Shipping Register and Shipbuilder. (CN ISSN 0037-3923) **4739**
Shipping Statistics and Economics. (UK) **4666**, 691
Shipping World & Shipbuilder. (UK ISSN 0037-3931) **4739**
Ships and Aircraft of the United States Fleet. (US ISSN 0080-9292) **3471**
Ships & Ports. (AT ISSN 1032-3449) **4739**
Ships Monthly. (UK ISSN 0037-394X) **4739**
Shipyard Bulletin. (US) **4739**
Shipyard Chronicle. (US) **4739**
Shipyard Log. (US) **3471**, 4739
Shipyard Orders. Weekly Report. (UK ISSN 0265-8291) **4739**
Shipyard Review. (Il ISSN 0037-3958) **4739**
Shipyard Weekly see Shipyard Chronicle **4739**
Al-Shirah. (TS) **4488**
Shiraz University. Asian Institute. Bulletin. (IR) **2431**
Shiraza. (Il) **2959**
†Shire & Municipal Record. (AT ISSN 0037-3966) **5276**
Shire Horse Show Catalogue. (UK) **4537**
Shire Horse Stud Book. (UK) **4537**
Shiren/Poet. (CC) **3005**
Shiretoko Hakubutsukan Kenkyu Hokoku/Shiretoko Museum. Bulletin. (JA ISSN 0387-8716) **4342**, 3533
Shiretoko Museum. Bulletin. see Shiretoko Hakubutsukan Kenkyu Hokoku **4342**
Shirim. (US) **3005**, 4226
Shiritsu Nagoya Kagakukan Nyusu. (JA) **3533**, 4342
†Shirley Publications. S: Series. (UK) **5276**
Shiseido Annual Report. (JA) **376**
Shiseido Semi-Annual Report. (JA) **376**
Shishu. (BG) **1265**
Shiso/Thought. (JA ISSN 0386-2755) **2515**, 4386
Shitai Fujiyu Kyoiku/Japanese Journal of Education of the Handicapped. (JA ISSN 0037-3990) **1741**
Shituf/Cooperation. (IS ISSN 0037-4008) **832**
Shivaji University, Kolhapur, India. Journal. Humanities and Sciences. (Il ISSN 0080-9314) **2515**, 4342
Shixue Jikan/Collection of Historical Materials. (US) **2322**, 2784
Shixue Lilun/Theory of History. (US) **2322**
Shixue Yanjiu/History Studies. (CC) **2322**
Shixue Yuekan/Journal of Historical Science. (CC ISSN 0583-0214) **2322**

Shixueshi Yanjiu/Journal of Historiography. (US) **2322**
Shiyan Lixue/Experimental Mechanics. (CC ISSN 1001-4888) **3845**
Shiyan Shengwu Xuebao/Acta Biologicae Experimentalis Sinica. (CC ISSN 0001-5334) **455**
Shiyong Erke Zazhi/Journal of Practical Pediatrics. (CC ISSN 1001-0866) **3326**
Shiyong Fuke yu Chanke Zazhi/Journal of Practical Gynecology and Obstetrics. (CC ISSN 1001-0858) **3296**
Shiyong Meishu/Applied Fine Art. (CC ISSN 1000-4483) **343**
Shiyong Neike Zazhi/Journal of Practical Internal Medicine. (CC ISSN 1001-084X) **3153**
Shiyong Waike Zazhi/Journal of Practical Surgery. (CC ISSN 1001-0831) **3384**
Shiyong Zhongliu Zazhi/Journal of Applied Oncology. (CC ISSN 1001-1692) **3202**
Shiyong Zhongliuxue Zazhi/Journal of Applied Oncology. (CC) **3202**
Shiyong Zhongxiyi Jiehe Zazhi. (CC) **3153**
Shiyou Daxue Xuebao (Ziran Kexue Ban)/University of Petroleum, China. Journal (Natural Science Edition). (CC ISSN 1000-5870) **3701**, 4342
Shiyou Dili Wuli Kantan. (CC ISSN 1000-7210) **1580**, 3701
Shiyou Gongcheng Jianshe/Petroleum Engineering Construction. (CC ISSN 1001-2206) **3701**
Shiyou Huagong/Petrochemical Technology. (CC ISSN 1000-8144) **3701**, 1187
Shiyou Kantan yu Kaifa/Petroleum Exploration and Development. (CC) **3701**
Shiyou Shiyan Dizhi. (CC ISSN 1001-6112) **3701**
Shiyou Wutan. (CC ISSN 1000-1441) **3701**
Shiyou Xuebao/Acta Petrolei Sinica. (CC) **3701**
Shiyou yu Tianranqi Dizhi/Oil and Gas Geology. (CC) **1580**
Shizen/Nature. (JA) **4608**
†Shizen Hakubutsuen Kiyo. (JA ISSN 0910-5190) **5276**
Shizen Hogo/Conservation of Nature. (JA ISSN 0386-4138) **1497**
Shizen Kagaku Kenkyu (Tokushima)/University of Tokushima. Faculty of Integrated Arts and Sciences. Natural Science Research. (JA ISSN 0914-6385) **4343**
Shizen Kagaku Kenkyu (Tokyo)/Hitotsubashi University Research Series. Sciences. (JA ISSN 0441-0017) **4343**
Shizen Kagaku Ronso. (JA ISSN 0285-8150) **4343**
Shizen Kansatsukai Kaiho. (JA) **1968**, 4343
Shizen Kyoikuen Hokoku/Ministry of Education. National Science Museum. Institute for Nature Study. Miscellaneous Reports. (JA ISSN 0385-759X) **4343**, 3533
Shizenshi Dayori. (JA) **3533**
Shizenshi Kenkyu/Osaka Museum of Natural History. Occasional Papers. (JA ISSN 0078-6683) **4343**
Shizhi Wencui/History Studies Collection. (CC) **2322**
Shizhuang/Fashion. (CC) **1294**
Shizuoka Daigaku Kyoikugakubu Kenkyu Hokoku. Shizen Kagaku Hen/Shizuoka University. Faculty of Education. Bulletin. Natural Sciences Series. (JA ISSN 0286-7311) **4343**
Shizuoka Daigaku Kyoyobu Kenkyu Hokoku. Shizen Kagaku Hen/Shizuoka University. Faculty of Liberal Arts. Reports: Sciences. (JA ISSN 0285-0435) **4343**
Shizuoka Daigaku Rigakubu Kenkyu Hokoku. see Shizuoka University. Faculty of Science. Reports **4343**

Shizuoka University. Faculty of Education. Bulletin. Natural Sciences Series. see Shizuoka Daigaku Kyoikugakubu Kenkyu Hokoku. Shizen Kagaku Hen **4343**
Shizuoka University. Faculty of Liberal Arts. Reports: Sciences. see Shizuoka Daigaku Kyoyobu Kenkyu Hokoku. Shizen Kagaku Hen **4343**
Shizuoka University. Faculty of Science. Reports/Shizuoka Daigaku Rigakubu Kenkyu Hokoku. (JA ISSN 0583-0923) **4343**
Shizuoka University. Research Institute of Electronics. Bulletin. (JA) **1778**
Shkenca dhe Jeta. (AA) **1663**
Shkenca dhe Jeta/Science et Vie. (AA) **4343**
Shkola i Proizvodstvo. (RU ISSN 0037-4024) **1663**
Shlach see Way - Ukrainian Catholic Bi-Weekly **4278**
Sh'ma. (US ISSN 0049-0385) **2023**
Shma Yisrael. (IS) **2023**
†Der Shmaiser/Spanker. (CN ISSN 0824-7870) **5276**
†Shmate. (US ISSN 0885-8659) **5276**
Shmayr Siranah-yi Ihsa'iyah. see Quarterly Review of Afghan Statistics **4584**
Shmuessen mit Kinder Un Yugent. (US ISSN 0300-7960) **4226**
†Shnaton Hamishpat Haivri. (IS) **5276**
Sho Enerugi/Energy Conservation. (JA ISSN 0387-1819) **1836**
†Shoah. (US) **5276**
Shobo Kenkyujo Hokoku/Fire Research Institute of Japan. Report. (JA ISSN 0426-2700) **2034**, 1938
Shobo Kenshu. (JA) **2034**
The Shock and Vibration Digest. (US ISSN 0583-1024) **1922**
†Shock Suspenstories. (US) **5276**
▼Shock Waves. (US ISSN 0938-1287) **3845**
Shoe and Leather News. (UK ISSN 0037-4040) **4361**, 2738
Shoe Factory Buyers Guide. (US) **4361**, 1153
Shoe Retailers Manual see Shoe Trades Directory **4361**
Shoe Retailing Today. (US ISSN 0886-0963) **4361**
Shoe Trades Directory. (UK ISSN 0080-9349) **4361**
Shoe Tree. (US ISSN 0883-2668) **1265**, 2959
Shoes on Parade. (US ISSN 0037-4083) **4361**
Shofar. (US ISSN 0748-9706) **1265**, 2023
Shofar. (US) **1301**
Shogeki Kogaku Shinpojumu. (JA) **61**, 1836
Shoho No Rajio. see Junior Electronics **1257**
Shokaki Naishikyo no Shinpo/Progress of Digestive Endoscopy. (JA ISSN 0389-9403) **3270**
Shokubutsu Boeki/Plant Protection. (JA ISSN 0037-4091) **192**
Shokubutsu Bunrui Chiri. see Acta Phytotaxonomica et Geobotanica **493**
Shokubutsu Kenkyu Zasshi. see Journal of Japanese Botany **507**
Shokuchu Shokubutsu Kenkyukai Kaishi/Insectivorous Plant Society. Journal. (JA ISSN 0286-6102) **517**, 1497
Shokuchudoku Tokei see Japan. Ministry of Health and Welfare. Statistics and Information Department. Statistical Report on Food Poisonings **3176**
Shokugyo, Sangyobetsu Jinko Dotai Tokei see Japan. Ministry of Health and Welfare. Statistics and Information Department. Report on Survey of Occupational Statistics on Vital Events **3632**
Shokuhin Eiseigaku Zasshi. see Food Hygienic Society of Japan. Journal **4101**
Shokuhin Kogyo/Food Industry. (JA) **2081**
Shokuhin To Kagaku. (JA ISSN 0037-4105) **2081**

Shokun. (JA) 2883
Shokuryo Keizai Nenkan/Food Economics Yearbook. (JA) 1153
Shomei Gakkai Shi. see Illuminating Engineering Institute of Japan. Journal 1898
Shomernik. (AU) 1663, 4226
Shoni Igaku/Pediatric Review. (JA ISSN 0583-1180) 3326
Shoni Naika/Japanese Journal of Pediatric Medicine. (JA ISSN 0385-6305) 3326
Shoni no Hoken/Health for Children. (JA ISSN 0385-2792) 1244, 3153, 4112
Shonika/Clinical Pediatrics. (JA ISSN 0037-4121) 3326
Shonika Kiyo. see Annales Paediatrici Japonici 3318
Shoot! (UK) 4488
Shoot Commercial Production Directory.(US) 3517, 1153
Shooter's Bible. (US ISSN 0080-9365) 4488
†Shooting & Conservation. (UK) 5276
Shooting Commercials (Melville). (US ISSN 0273-2246) 38, 1379
Shooting Commercials and Industrials see Shooting Commercials (Melville) 38
Shooting Industry. (US ISSN 0037-4148) 4488
Shooting Lines. (AT) 4488
Shooting Magazine. (US) 4488
Shooting News and Country Weekly. (UK) 4555, 4488
Shooting News and Weekly see Shooting News and Country Weekly 4555
Shooting Sport-Tir Sportif-Tiro Deportivo-Schiess-Sport see U I T Journal 4495
Shooting Sports Retailer. (US ISSN 0887-9397) 4488, 1053
Shooting Star Review. (US ISSN 0892-1407) 2023, 2959
Shooting Times see Shooting Times and Country Magazine 4488
Shooting Times. (US ISSN 0038-8084) 4488
Shooting Times and Country Magazine. (UK ISSN 0037-4164) 4488
▼Shop. (SZ) 374
Shop. (CN) 3023
Shop and Display Equipment Association Directory of Shopfittings and Display Equipment see S D E A Directory of Shopfittings and Display Equipment 38
Shop-at-Home Directory. (US) 1053
Shop by Mail. (US) 1153, 1287
†Shop by Mail Directory for Personal Computer Users. (US) 5276
Shop Equipment and Materials Guide see Shop Equipment Display & Shopfitting Directory 1153
Shop Equipment & Shopfitting News. (UK ISSN 0037-4172) 643
Shop Equipment Display & Shopfitting Directory. (UK ISSN 0143-0971) 1153, 643
Shop Management Handbook. (US) 1027, 993, 4702
†Shop Property. (UK ISSN 0037-4199) 5276
Shop Talk see Collision 4688
Shop Talk. (US) 4702
Shopper Report. (US) 1053, 2081
Shoppers Bi-Weekly News. (GW) 3471
Shopping Center Developer Directory. (US) 632, 1153
Shopping Center Digest. (US) 1053
Shopping Center Directory. (US ISSN 0037-4210) 1153
Shopping Center Newsletter. (US ISSN 0559-9091) 1054
Shopping Center World. (US ISSN 0049-0393) 4158
Shopping Center World Product and Service Directory see Shopping Center World 4158
▼Shopping Centre. (UK ISSN 0964-1793) 1054
†Shopping Centre Canada. (CN ISSN 0226-7551) 5276
Shopping Centre News. (CN) 839
Shopping for a Better World. (US) 1508
Shopping in Edinburgh. (UK) 4786

Shopping in Glasgow. (UK) 4786
Shoptalk (Chicago). (US) 376
Shoptalk (Englewood). (US) 231
Shoptalk - Abu Dhabi Duty Free Guide. see Matar Abu Dhabi al-Dawli 4775
Shore and Beach. (US ISSN 0037-4237) 1873
Short Alert. (US) 963
Short Book Reviews. (NE ISSN 0254-7694) 4585
Short Courses and Seminars. (CN ISSN 0318-6237) 1027, 1759
▼Short Fiction by Women. (US) 2959, 4852
The Short Line. (US ISSN 0199-4050) 4714
Short Play Series. (US ISSN 0080-9403) 2959
Short Stories. see Duanpian Xiaoshuo 2912
Short Stories. see Xiaoshuo 2977
Short Stories for Children. see Ertong Xiaoshuo 1254
Short Stories Monthly. see Xiaoshuo Yuebao 2978
Short Story. (US ISSN 1052-648X) 2883
Short Story Criticism. (US) 2959
Short Story Index. (US ISSN 0360-9774) 2983, 23
Short Story International. (US ISSN 0147-7706) 2959
Short Story Reviews. see Xiaoshuo Pinglun 2978
Short Takes. (US) 2234
Short-Term Economic Survey of Enterprises in Japan. (JA ISSN 0387-0642) 1084
Short-Term Economic Survey of Principal Enterprises in Japan see Short-Term Economic Survey of Enterprises in Japan 1084
Short-Term Test Systems for Carcinogenicity and Mutagenicity see I C R D B Cancergram: Short-Term Test Systems for Carcinogenicity and Mutagenicity 5209
Short-Timer's Journal. (US ISSN 0276-8135) 3471
Shortcut. (US) 2542
The Shorthorn. (US) 1324, 1716
Shorthorn Country. (US ISSN 0149-9319) 226
Shorthorn Journal. (UK) 226
Shorthorn News. (CN ISSN 0037-427X) 226
Shortliner. (US) 164, 1153
Short's Quarterly Review see Short's Story 62
Short's Story. (UK ISSN 0037-4245) 62
Shortwave Directory. (US) 1360
Shortwave Listener see S W L 1360
Shosetsu Gendai. (JA) 2959
Shosetsu Shincho. (JA) 2959
Shosetsu Suiri. see Mystery Stories 2986
Shoten Kai. see Retailing Age 1052
Shotgun News. (US ISSN 0049-0415) 4488
Shotgun Sports. (US ISSN 0744-3773) 4555
Shots. (US) 3005
Shou Huo/Harvest: A Literary Magazine.(CC ISSN 0583-1288) 2959
Shoudu Yixueyuan Xuebao/Capital Institute of Medical Sciences. Journal.(CC ISSN 1000-0305) 3153
Shoulei Xuebao/Acta Theriologica Sinica. (CC ISSN 1000-1050) 591
Shout. (UK ISSN 0583-1296) 3580
Shout Magazine. (US) 1324
Show. (GW) 3580
▼The Show. (US ISSN 1054-2183) 4511
†Show & Sell. (US) 5276
†Show-Business. (FR ISSN 0037-430X) 5277
Show Guide. (CN) 643
Show-Me Libraries. (US ISSN 0037-4326) 2784
Show-Me Missouri Legionnaire. (US ISSN 0037-4334) 1301
"Show Me" State Genealogical News. (US) 2164
Show Meeting. (IT) 1342, 3394, 4461

Show Music. (US ISSN 8755-9560) 3580, 4638
Show Reporter. (US) 4361, 2738
Showbiz Magazine. (US) 1379
Showboat Centennials Newsletter. (US ISSN 0749-9361) 4529
Showboats International. (US) 4529
Showcall. (UK) 3580, 4638
Showcase. (SI) 822
Showcase. (IT) 2561
Showcase U S A. (US ISSN 0164-3215) 920
Showcast Casting Directory. (AT ISSN 1032-6448) 4638
Showcast Directory see Showcast Casting Directory 4638
Showdates. (UK) 1153
Showman's Directory. (UK) 1153
Shoyakugaku Zasshi/Japanese Journal of Pharmacognosy. (JA ISSN 0037-4377) 3743
Shqiperia e Re. (AA) 2883
Shqiperia Sot/Albanie Aujourd'hui. (AA) 2883
Shqiptarja e Re. (AA) 4852
Shram Patrika. (II) 993
Shramjivi. (II) 993
Shree. (II) 2201
Shree Gurudev Ashram Newsletter. (II) 4217
Shree Hari Katha/Gospel of God. (II ISSN 0251-1746) 3781, 4217
Shreewarsha. (II) 2201
Shreveport Sun. (US) 2234
Shreye. (II) 3644, 2341
Shri Chhatrapati Shivaji University. Report. (II ISSN 0080-9322) 1716
Shrieking Violet. (UK) 1324
Shrine Bulletin. (US) 4275
Shrine of the Holy House. Loreto see Santa Casa di Loreto. Messaggio 4275
Shropshire Family History Journal. (UK ISSN 0261-135X) 2164
Shropshire Farmer. (UK) 119
Shropshire N F U Journal see Shropshire Farmer 119
Shu-Kan. see Professional Wrestling 4484
Shu Lin/Book Forest. (CC ISSN 1000-4793) 4137, 2959
Shu Ma Wa Magazine. (BR) 2959
Shu Mo Chi Kan/Bibliography Quarterly.(CH ISSN 0006-1581) 2795
Shu Pin. (CC) 2784
Shu yu Hua/Calligraphy and Painting. (CC ISSN 1000-6214) 343
Shubyo to Engei. (JA ISSN 0037-4407) 2139
Shucai/Vegetables. (CC) 192
Shufa/Calligraphy. (CC ISSN 1000-6036) 344
Shufa Bao/Calligraphy Weekly. (US) 344
Shufa Shangping/Calligraphy Appreciation and Review. (CC) 344
Shufa Yanjiu/Studies in Calligraphy. (CC ISSN 1000-6044) 344
Shufu no Tomo/Friend of Housewives. (JA) 4852
Shufu-To-Seikatsu. (JA) 4852
Shugoofa. (II) 2959
Shui Chuli see Water Treatment 4833
Shuichan Keji Qingbao/Science and Technology Information on Aquatic Products. (CC ISSN 1001-1994) 2049
Shuichan Kexue. (CC) 2049
Shuichan Wenzhai. (CC ISSN 1000-6257) 2049
Shuichan Xuebao/Journal of Aquatic Products. (CC ISSN 1000-0615) 2049
Shuichan Yangzhi see Aquaculture 2036
Shuidao Wenzhai. (CC ISSN 1001-7224) 208
Shuidong Lixue Yanjiu yu Jinzhan see Journal of Hydrodynamics 3822
Shuili Fadian/Hydro-electric Power. (CC ISSN 0559-9342) 4828, 1548
Shuili Shuidian Jishu/Water Resources and Hydropower Engineering. (CC ISSN 1000-0860) 1925
Shuili Shuiyun Kexue Yanjiu. (CC ISSN 1001-3962) 4739
Shuili Xuebao/Journal of Hydraulic Engineering. (CC) 1925

SIAM SOCIETY 6659

Shuini Jishu/Cement Technology. (CC ISSN 1001-6171) 632
Shuisheng Shengwu Xuebao/Acta Hydrobiologica Sinica. (CC ISSN 1000-3207) 455, 1600, 1610
Shuiwen Dizhi Gongcheng Dizhi/Hydrogeology and Engineering Geology. (CC) 1600
Shuiwu Yanjiu/Taxation Research. (CC) 1105
Shuiyun Guanli/Water Transportation Management. (CC ISSN 1000-8799) 4739, 1027
Shujutsu/Operation. (JA ISSN 0037-4423) 3384
Shukan Asahi/Weekly Asahi. (JA) 2208
Shukan Asahi Hyakka/Weekly Asahi Encyclopedia. (JA) 591
Shukan Bunshun. (JA) 2208
Shukan Computer. (JA) 1400
Shukan Daiyamondo/Weekly Diamond. (JA) 691
Shukan Gendai. (JA) 1027
Shukan Igakkai Shinbun/New Medical World Weekly. (JA) 3153
Shukan Josei. (JA) 4852
Shukan Post/Weekly Post. (JA) 2208
Shukan Shincho. (JA) 2208
Shukan Shojo Friend see Ekubo 1254
Shukan Shosetsu. see Weekly Novels 2985
Shukan Spa! (JA) 2208
Shukan Taishu. see Weekly for the Masses 2208
Shukan Toyo Keizai. (JA) 691
Shukan Yomiuri. (JA) 2208
Shuli Kexue yu Huaxue. (CC ISSN 0253-2743) 4343
Shumen. Pedagogicheski Institut. Godishnik. (BU) 2175
Shuofang/Shuofang Literature. (US ISSN 0257-585X) 2959
Shuofang Literature. see Shuofang 2959
Shuoxie Yuekan/Speaking and Writing Monthly. (CC) 2841
Shupihui. (PE) 4201, 2023
Shuppan News. (JA) 2208
Shurote. (IS ISSN 0037-413X) 2589
Al-Shurta. (TS) 1522
Al-Shurtah. (MK) 1522
Al-Shurti/Policeman. (TS) 1522
Shutdown News see Natural Rights 1963
Shutterbug. (US) 3797
Shuttle Craft Guild. Monographs. (US ISSN 0080-9446) 3592, 357, 4623
Shuttle Quarterly. (US) 4803
Shuttle, Spindle & Dyepot. (US ISSN 0049-0423) 4623, 1282
Shu'un Adabiyyah/Literary Affairs. (TS) 2959
Shu'un al-Sina'ah. (TS) 691
Shuxue de Shijian yu Renshi/Mathematics in Practice and Cognition. (CC ISSN 1000-0984) 3055
Shuxue Jiaoxue/Mathematics Teaching. (CC ISSN 0488-7387) 1759, 3055
Shuxue Jiaoxue Tongxun/Mathematics Teaching Bulletin. (CC) 3055
Shuxue Tongxun/Mathematics Bulletin. (CC ISSN 0488-7395) 3055
Shuxue Wuli Xuebao. (CC) 3055, 3831
Shuxue Xuebao. (CC ISSN 0583-1431) 3055
Shuxue Yilin. (CC) 3055
Shuzan Kenkyu Ronbun Shiryo Mokurokushu. (JA) 3063
Shuzhi Jisuan yu Jisuanji Yingyong/Journal on Numerical Methods and Computer Applications. (CC ISSN 1000-3266) 4360, 3055, 3066
Shveinaya Promyshlennost' (RU ISSN 0037-4431) 1287
Shvut. (IS) 2023, 3925, 4226
Shwe Thwe. (BR) 1265
Si De Ka Magazine. (US ISSN 0037-444X) 2679, 1663
Si yu Yan see Ssu yu Yen 2515
Siah Mesharim. (IS ISSN 0334-7559) 4226, 4201
Siam Rath Weekly Review. (TH) 2220
Siam Society. Journal. (TH ISSN 0304-226X) 4386, 2515

6660 SIAM SOCIETY

Siam Society. Natural History Bulletin. (TH) **4343**
Siamese News Quarterly. (US) **3714**
Siang Khong Gnaovason Song Thanva/ Voice of the 2nd December Youths. (LS) **1265**
Siaran Pekebun. (MY ISSN 0126-5806) **4294**
Siaran Perangkaan Bulanan Semenanjung Malaysia. see Malaysia. Department of Statistics. Monthly Statistical Bulletin, Malaysia **4579**
Al-Siassa al-Dawlya. (UA ISSN 0583-4597) **3972**
▼Siberian Advances in Mathematics. (US ISSN 1055-1344) **3055**
Siberian Husky Club of America Newsletter. (US ISSN 0583-1776) **3714**
Siberian Mathematical Journal. (English translation of: Sibirskii Matematicheskii Zhurnal) (US ISSN 0037-4466) **3055**
Siberian Quarterly. (US ISSN 0274-7286) **3714**
Sibirskii Matematicheskii Zhurnal. (RU ISSN 0037-4474) **3055**
▼Sibirskii Variant. (RU) **2457**
Sibling Information Network Newsletter. (US) **1244**, **2296**
Siboga Expedition. (NE ISSN 0165-2656) **455**
Sibylle. (GW ISSN 0037-4482) **4852**, **1294**
Sic. (VE) **4386**
Sichat Hashavua. (IS) **4226**
Sicher ist Sicher. (GW ISSN 0037-4504) **3622**
Sicher Leben (Hannover). (GW) **119**
Sicher Leben (Speyer). (GW) **119**
Sichere Arbeit. (AU ISSN 0037-4512) **3622**
Sichere Chemiearbeit. (GW) **1860**
Sicherheit am Arbeitsplatz. (GW) **832**
†Sicherheit Bergbau, Energiewirtschaft, Geologie, Metallurgie. (GW) **5277**
Sicherheit Bergbau, Energiewirtschaft, Metallurgie see Sicherheit Bergbau, Energiewirtschaft, Geologie, Metallurgie **5277**
Sicherheit fuer Haus und Hof. (GW) **832**
Sicherheit im Bergland. (AU) **4555**
Sicherheit in Chemie und Umwelt. (US) **1187**, **1968**
Sicherheit und Frieden. (GW ISSN 0175-274X) **3972**
Sicherheit Zuerst. (AU ISSN 0037-4539) **4714**, **4112**
Sicherheits-Berater. (GW ISSN 0344-8746) **1027**
Sicherheitsbeauftragter. (GW ISSN 0300-3337) **993**, **3808**
Sicherheitsingenieur. (GW ISSN 0300-3329) **993**, **3808**
Sicherheitstechnik see Wirtschaftsschutz und Sicherheitstechnik **1524**
Sichou/Silk. (CC ISSN 1001-7003) **4623**
Sichuan Accountants. see Sichuan Kuaiji **756**
Sichuan Architecture. see Sichuan Jianzhu **306**
Sichuan Archives. see Sichuan Dang'an **2341**
Sichuan Baoxian/Sichuan Insurance. (CC) **2542**
Sichuan Caizheng Yanjiu/Sichuan Finance Research. (CC) **799**
Sichuan Commercial Economics. see Sichuan Shangye Jingji **839**
Sichuan Cuisine. see Sichuan Pengren **2449**
Sichuan Dang'an/Sichuan Archives. (CC ISSN 1001-5264) **2341**, **2784**
Sichuan Daxue Xuebao (Shehui Kexue Ban)/Sichuan University. Journal (Social Sciences Edition). (CC ISSN 0490-6748) **4386**, **2515**
Sichuan Daxue Xuebao (Ziran Kexue Ban)/Sichuan University. Journal (Natural Science Edition). (CC ISSN 0490-6756) **4343**
Sichuan Education. see Sichuan Jiaoyu **1663**
Sichuan Environment. see Sichuan Huanjing **1968**
Sichuan Finance. see Sichuan Jinrong **799**

Sichuan Finance Research. see Sichuan Caizheng Yanjiu **799**
Sichuan Ganzhe/Sichuan Sugar Cane. (CC) **2081**
Sichuan Huabao. (CC) **2183**
Sichuan Huanjing/Sichuan Environment.(CC ISSN 1001-3644) **1968**
Sichuan Insurance. see Sichuan Baoxian **2542**
Sichuan Jianzhu/Sichuan Architecture. (CC) **306**, **1873**
Sichuan Jiaoyu/Sichuan Education. (CC) **1663**
Sichuan Jinrong/Sichuan Finance. (CC) **799**
Sichuan Journal of Library Science. see Sichuan Tushuguan Xuebao **2784**
Sichuan Journal of Traditional Chinese Medicine. see Sichuan Zhongyi **3153**
Sichuan Kuaiji/Sichuan Accountants. (CC ISSN 1003-2452) **756**
Sichuan Literature. see Sichuan Wenxue **2960**
Sichuan News Photo see Sichuan Xinwen Tupian **2575**
Sichuan News Photo Press. see Sichuan Xinwen Tupian **2575**
Sichuan Normal College. Journal (Natural Science Edition). see Sichuan Shifan Xueyuan Xuebao (Ziran Kexue Ban) **4343**
Sichuan Normal College. Journal. (Social Science Edition). see Sichuan Shifan Xueyuan Xuebao (Zhexue Shehui Kexue Ban) **4386**
Sichuan Normal University. Journal. (Social Science Edition). see Sichuan Shifan Daxue Xuebao (Shehui Kexue Ban) **4386**
Sichuan Pengren/Sichuan Cuisine. (CC ISSN 1004-2083) **2449**
Sichuan Shangye Jingji/Sichuan Commercial Economics. (CC) **839**
Sichuan Shifan Daxue Xuebao (Shehui Kexue Ban)/Sichuan Normal University. Journal. (Social Science Edition). (CC ISSN 1000-5315) **4386**
Sichuan Shifan Xueyuan Xuebao (Zhexue Shehui Kexue Ban)/Sichuan Normal College. Journal. (Social Science Edition). (CC) **4386**
Sichuan Shifan Xueyuan Xuebao (Ziran Kexue Ban)/Sichuan Normal College. Journal (Natural Science Edition). (CC ISSN 1001-8220) **4343**
Sichuan Sichou/Sichuan Silk. (CC ISSN 1004-1265) **4623**
Sichuan Silk. see Sichuan Sichou **4623**
Sichuan Sugar Cane. see Sichuan Ganzhe **2081**
Sichuan Theatre. see Sichuan Xiju **344**
Sichuan Tushuguan Xuebao/Sichuan Journal of Library Science. (CC) **2784**
Sichuan University. Journal (Natural Science Edition). see Sichuan Daxue Xuebao (Ziran Kexue Ban) **4343**
Sichuan University. Journal (Social Sciences Edition). see Sichuan Daxue Xuebao (Shehui Kexue Ban) **4386**
Sichuan Wenwu/Relics of Sichuan. (CC) **284**
Sichuan Wenxue/Sichuan Literature. (CC) **2960**, **3005**
Sichuan Xiju/Sichuan Theatre. (CC) **344**
Sichuan Xinwen Tupian/Sichuan News Photo Press. (CC) **2575**
Sichuan Yinyue Xueyuan Xuebao see Yinyue Tansuo **3587**
Sichuan Zhongyi/Sichuan Journal of Traditional Chinese Medicine. (CC ISSN 1000-3649) **3153**
Sicilia. (IT ISSN 0037-4563) **2058**, **2386**
Sicilia Archeologica. (IT ISSN 0037-4571) **284**
Sicilia Motori. (IT) **4702**
Sickness and Wellness Publications. (US ISSN 1041-2832) **3181**, **23**
Siculorum Gymnasium. (IT ISSN 0037-458X) **2515**
†Sicurezza Sociale. (IT ISSN 0037-4598) **5277**
Sicurta. (IT) **2542**

Sida: Botanical Miscellany. (US ISSN 0883-1475) **517**
Sida; Contributions to Botany. (US ISSN 0036-1488) **517**
Siddha Vani. (II) **4217**
Side Effects of Drugs Annual. (NE ISSN 0583-1881) **3743**, **3153**
Side Lines. (US) **1324**
Side-Saddle News. (US ISSN 0744-3056) **4538**, **2441**
†Sideline Business Newsletter. (US) **5277**
Sidemount Reporter. (CN ISSN 0037-4601) **2441**
Siderealist. (US) **359**
Siderurgia Brasileira. Relatorio de Diretoria. (BL) **3419**
Siderurgia Latinoamericana. (CL) **3419**
†Sidesporet. (DK ISSN 0900-470X) **5277**
▼Sidewalks. (US ISSN 1059-2210) **2883**
Sidewinder Studies in History & Sociology. (US ISSN 8756-5382) **2322**, **4448**
Sidmouth Herald. (UK) **2195**
Sidra. (IS ISSN 0334-6986) **4226**
Siebdruck. (GW ISSN 0178-2835) **4005**
Siebenbuergische Familienforschung. (GW ISSN 0175-761X) **2164**
Siebenbuergische Semesterblaetter. (GW ISSN 0933-3983) **1324**
Siebenstern. (GW) **1497**, **2262**
Sieboldia Acta Biologica/Shiborudia. (JA ISSN 0559-9822) **455**
Siecle Eclate: Dada, Surrealisme et les Avant-Gardes. (FR) **2960**
Sieg Tech. (GW ISSN 0934-9391) **4609**
Siegel Report see Selected Information on Insured U.S. Commercial Banks Ranked by Assets **884**
Siegener Hochschul Zeitung. (GW) **1716**
Siegrunen. (US ISSN 0733-0367) **3471**
Sieg's Moentkatalog. Danmark (Year). (DK ISSN 0586-4496) **3601**
Sieg's Moentkatalog - Norden (year). (DK ISSN 0900-9310) **3601**
Siehste! (GW ISSN 0939-4044) **1265**
Siemens Components. (GW ISSN 0173-1726) **1778**
Siemens Electromedica see Electromedica **3095**
Siemens Energie und Automation see Engineering und Automation **1789**
†Siemens Energy and Automation with Product News. (GW) **5277**
†Siemens-Magazin COM. (GW) **5277**
Siemens Power Engineering and Automation Product News see Siemens Energy and Automation with Product News **5277**
Siemens Review see Siemens Zeitschrift **1880**
Siemens Zeitschrift. (GW ISSN 0302-2528) **1880**, **1908**
Siempre! (MX) **2883**
Siempre Alerta. (CU) **3471**
Sierra. (US ISSN 0161-7362) **1497**, **1968**
Sierra Atlantic. (US ISSN 0164-825X) **1497**, **1968**, **4555**
Sierra Club. National News Report. (US ISSN 0049-044X) **1497**, **1968**
Sierra Leone. Central Statistics Office. Annual Statistical Digest. (SL) **4585**
Sierra Leone. Library Board. Report. (SL ISSN 0583-2268) **2784**
Sierra Leone. Ministry of Education. Monthly Newsletter. (SL) **1663**
Sierra Leone. Ministry of Education. Report. (SL ISSN 0080-9551) **1663**
Sierra Leone. Ministry of Finance. Budget Speech. (SL) **1105**
Sierra Leone Agricultural Journal. (SL) **119**
Sierra Leone Chamber of Commerce. Journal see Chamber of Commerce of Sierra Leone. Journal **811**
Sierra Leone Geographical Association. Bulletin see Sierra Leone Geographical Journal **2262**
Sierra Leone Geographical Journal. (SL ISSN 0583-239X) **2262**

Sierra Leone in Figures. (SL ISSN 0080-9535) **4585**
Sierra Leone Journal of Education. (SL ISSN 0022-0582) **1663**
Sierra Leone Library Journal. (SL) **2784**
Sierra Leone Medical and Dental Association. Bulletin see Sierra Leone Medical and Dental Association. Journal **3153**
Sierra Leone Medical and Dental Association. Journal. (SL ISSN 0253-8482) **3153**, **3242**
Sierra Leone Newsletter. (SL) **2170**
Sierra Leone Outlook. (SL) **884**
Sierra Leone Publications. (SL) **2795**
Sierra Leone Trade Fairs and Exhibitions. (SL) **1054**
Sierra Leone Trade Journal. (SL ISSN 0037-4768) **839**
Sierra Report. (CN) **1497**, **1968**, **4555**
Siete Dias Ilustrados. (AG ISSN 0037-4784) **2170**
Sifriya Laam. (IS ISSN 0037-4792) **2960**
Ha-Sifrut/Literature. (IS ISSN 0017-8284) **2960**
Sifrut Yeladim Vanoar. (IS ISSN 0334-276X) **1265**
†Sift. (CN ISSN 0380-6693) **5277**
†Sight. (US) **5277**
Sight and Sound. (UK ISSN 0037-4806) **3517**
Sight and Sound News. (AT) **2469**, **3305**, **3317**
Sight Lecture. (US) **4677**
Sighthound Review. (US) **3714**
Sightline. (UK ISSN 0265-9808) **4638**
Sightlines (New York). (US) **4638**
Sightlines (Niles). (US ISSN 0037-4830) **3517**
Sights and Sounds. (US) **2289**, **1741**, **2296**
Siglario Italiano/Italian Trade-Marks. (IT) **3678**
Siglo XX/20th Century. (US ISSN 0740-946X) **2960**
†Siglo 19. (MX) **5277**
Siglo 20 y la Paz see Twentieth Century and Peace **3974**
▼Siglo XXI Ciencia and Tecnologia. (CL ISSN 0716-8136) **4343**, **1265**
Sigma. (SZ ISSN 0037-4857) **2542**
Sigma see Cross Section **3033**
Sigma (Aix-en-Provence). (FR ISSN 0223-0100) **2841**
Sigma (Montpellier). (FR) **2841**
Sigma Alpha Iota Quarterly: Pan Pipes. (US ISSN 0889-7581) **3580**
Sigma Phi Epsilon Journal. (US ISSN 0097-6563) **1324**
Sigma Pi Sigma Radiations. (US) **3831**
Sigma Update see Independent Gasoline Marketing **3688**
Sigma Zetan. (US ISSN 0080-9578) **4343**
Sigmund Freud House Bulletin. (AU ISSN 1015-1184) **4046**
Sign Business. (US ISSN 0893-9888) **38**, **4005**
Sign Control News. (US) **1968**, **2679**
Sign Language Studies. (US ISSN 0302-1475) **2841**, **249**
Sign Makers and Suppliers Year Book and Directory. (UK) **1153**
Sign of the Times. (US ISSN 0891-6926) **2883**
Sign World. (UK ISSN 0049-0466) **38**
Signal. (UK ISSN 0037-4954) **1244**, **1663**, **2960**
Signal see Semaphore Signal **1438**
Signal. (CN) **2179**
Signal. (GW ISSN 0721-6831) **3202**
Signal. (CS ISSN 0037-492X) **3471**
The Signal (Emmett). (US ISSN 1040-4724) **2883**
Signal (Fairfax). (US ISSN 0037-4938) **1342**, **1908**
Signal (Olympia). (US) **1731**
Signal (Streamwood). (US ISSN 0893-0880) **1244**, **1759**, **4249**
Signal A. (BU ISSN 0861-7333) **3471**
Signal International. (FI ISSN 0037-4970) **2441**

Signal Processing. (NE ISSN 0165-1684) **1431**, 1447
Signal Processing: Image Communication. (NE ISSN 0923-5965) **1380**, 1778
†Signal Selection of Children's Books. (UK) **5277**
Signal Transduction *see* Signal Transduction & Cyclic Nucleotides **483**
Signal Transduction & Cyclic Nucleotides. (UK ISSN 0964-7589) **483**, 3153
Signal und Draht. (GW ISSN 0037-4997) **4715**
Signal und Schiene *see* Signal und Draht **4715**
Signal 8-2. (US ISSN 0037-5012) **1522**
Signalman's Journal. (US ISSN 0037-5020) **2589**
Signal'naya Informatsiya. Akustika. (RU ISSN 0320-3123) **3839**, 23
Signal'naya Informatsiya. Analiticheskaya Khimiya. (RU ISSN 0234-9744) **1202**, 23
Signal'naya Informatsiya. Analiticheskaya Khimiya-Oborudovanie Laboratorii *see* Signal'naya Informatsiya. Analiticheskaya Khimiya **1202**
Signal'naya Informatsiya. Atomnoe Yadro. (RU ISSN 0203-5545) **3839**, 23
Signal'naya Informatsiya. Atomy i Molekuly. (RU ISSN 0135-0870) **3839**, 23
Signal'naya Informatsiya. Chastitsy i Polya. (RU ISSN 0320-3182) **3839**, 23
Signal'naya Informatsiya. Elektricheskie Svoistva Tverdykh Tel. (RU ISSN 0320-3166) **3839**, 23
Signal'naya Informatsiya. Enzimologiya. (RU ISSN 0202-8980) **467**, 23
Signal'naya Informatsiya. Fizika Yadernykh Reaktorov. (RU ISSN 0320-314X) **3839**, 23
Signal'naya Informatsiya. Fiziologiya Cheloveka i Zhivotnykh: Krov' i Limfa *see* Signal'naya Informatsiya. Fiziologiya i Morfologiya Cheloveka i Zhivotnykh: Krov' i Limfa **467**
Signal'naya Informatsiya. Fiziologiya i Morfologiya Cheloveka i Zhivotnykh: Krov' i Limfa. (RU ISSN 0233-6618) **467**, 23
Signal'naya Informatsiya. Gazy i Zhidkosti. Termodinamika i Statisticheskaya Fizika. (RU ISSN 0135-0889) **3839**, 23
Signal'naya Informatsiya. Ishemicheskaya Bolezn' Serdtsa. (RU ISSN 0234-9760) **3181**, 3212
Signal'naya Informatsiya. Kataliz i Katalizatory. (RU ISSN 0234-9736) **1202**
Signal'naya Informatsiya. Khimiya Vody.(RU ISSN 0202-8948) **1202**, 23
Signal'naya Informatsiya. Khimiya Vysokikh Energii. (RU ISSN 0234-968X) **1202**
Signal'naya Informatsiya. Kompozitsionnye Materialy. (RU ISSN 0135-0935) **3428**, 23
Signal'naya Informatsiya. Korroziya i Zashchita ot Korrozii. (RU ISSN 0202-8670) **3428**, 23
Signal'naya Informatsiya. Laki - Kraski - Organicheskie Pokrytiya. (RU ISSN 0202-8697) **3656**, 23
Signal'naya Informatsiya. Magnitnye Svoistva Tverdykh Tel. (RU ISSN 0136-0612) **3839**, 23
Signal'naya Informatsiya. Napolnennye i Armirovannye Plastiki. (RU ISSN 0234-971X) **1202**
Signal'naya Informatsiya. Neiropeptidy. (RU ISSN 0234-9752) **3181**, 3354
Signal'naya Informatsiya. Nelineinaya Optika i Kvantovaya Elektronika. (RU ISSN 0203-5553) **3839**, 23
Signal'naya Informatsiya. Ochistka i Utilizatsiya Otkhodov Khimicheskikh Proizvodstv. (RU ISSN 0234-9701) **1202**

Signal'naya Informatsiya. Optika. (RU ISSN 0135-0897) **3839**, 23
Signal'naya Informatsiya. Poverkhnost' (RU ISSN 0208-0656) **3839**, 23
Signal'naya Informatsiya. Radiofizika i Fizicheskie Osnovy Elektroniki. (RU ISSN 0135-0633) **1349**, 23, 1360, 1778
Signal'naya Informatsiya. Sorbenty. Poverkhnostno-Aktivnye Veshchestva.(RU ISSN 0234-9698) **1202**
Signal'naya Informatsiya. Struktura i Dinamika Reshetki Tverdykh Tel. (RU ISSN 0203-5561) **3839**, 23
Signal'naya Informatsiya. Tekhnika Bezopasnosti. Sanitarnaya Tekhnika. (RU ISSN 0202-8905) **3623**, 23
Signal'naya Informatsiya. Toksikologiya *see* Signal'naya Informatsiya. Toksikologiya Lekarstvennaya **3748**
Signal'naya Informatsiya. Toksikologiya Lekarstvennaya. (RU ISSN 0233-6588) **3748**, 23
Signals. (AT ISSN 1033-4688) **3533**, 4739
Signature. (US) **4137**
Signature. (SA) **4786**
Signature. (II) **4786**
Signature. (JA) **4786**
Signature. (SI) **4786**
Signature. (BE) **4786**
Signature *see* Signature Exclusive **4786**
Signature. (KE) **4786**
Signature (Exeter) *see* Third Degree (Exeter) **1326**
Signature Exclusive. (GR) **4786**
Signatures. (US) **1324**
Signcraft. (US ISSN 0270-4757) **38**
Signes des Ameriques. (CN) **2023**
Signes du Present. (MR) **691**, 4386
Signet S F Advance *see* Roc Science Fiction Advance **3013**
†Significant Decisions of the Supreme Court. (US ISSN 0162-0444) **5277**
Significant Issues Facing Directors. (US ISSN 0193-4201) **1028**
Signos Universitarios. (AG) **1716**
Signpost (New York) *see* A E A Newsletter **1613**
Signpost for Northwest Hikers *see* Signpost for Northwest Trails **4555**
Signpost for Northwest Trails. (US ISSN 8750-1600) **4555**, 4786
Signs: Journal of Women in Culture and Society. (US ISSN 0097-9740) **4852**
Signs Magazine. (UK) **839**
Signs of the Times. (JA ISSN 0037-5055) **4288**
†Signs of the Times/Tekens van Die Tye. (SA ISSN 0037-5071) **5277**
Signs of the Times (Cincinnati). (US ISSN 0037-5063) **38**
Signs of the Times (Nampa). (US) **4249**
Signum. (FI ISSN 0355-0036) **2784**
Sigurnost/Safety. (CI ISSN 0350-6886) **4112**
Sihai. (CC ISSN 1001-0165) **2960**
Sihhah. *see* Health **4102**
Sihot/Dialogue. (IS ISSN 0334-9330) **4046**
Siipikarja. (FI ISSN 0037-5098) **226**
Siirtolaisuus/Migration. (FI ISSN 0355-3779) **3987**
Al-Sijil al-Shahri li-Ahdath al-Alam/Monthly Record of World Events. (TS) **3972**
Al-Sijil al-Shahri li-Ahdath Dawlat al-Imarat al-Arabiyyah al-Muttahidah/Monthly Record for the Events of the United Arab Emirates. (TS) **4073**
Sika/Pig. (FI ISSN 0037-5101) **226**
Sikelika. Serie Archeologica. (IT ISSN 0392-0909) **284**, 2322
Sikelika. Serie Storica. (IT ISSN 0392-0917) **2322**, 284
Sikh Courier *see* Sikh Courier International **4215**
Sikh Courier International. (UK) **4215**
Sikh Messenger. (UK ISSN 0266-9153) **4215**
Sikh Religious Studies Information *see* Asian Religious Studies Information **5139**

Sikh Review. (II ISSN 0037-5128) **4215**
Sikio *see* Kenrail **4652**
Sikio *see* Tanzania Railways Corporation. Habari za Reli **4715**
Sikkerhed. (DK ISSN 0108-6650) **4112**
Sikkerhedsmaessig Vurdering og Prioritering af Mindre Anlaegsarbejder paa Hovedlandeveje.(DK ISSN 0107-5179) **4721**
Sikorsky News. (US ISSN 0037-5152) **62**
Siksha. (II) **1663**
Siksha - O - Sahitya. (II ISSN 0037-5160) **1663**
Silarus. (IT ISSN 0037-5179) **2883**
Silence Courier. (GW) **2191**, 2480, 4786
Silent Advocate. (US ISSN 0037-5187) **2289**, 1741
Silent Messenger/Stille Boodskapper. (SA ISSN 0037-5195) **2289**
Silent News. (US ISSN 0049-0490) **2289**
Silent Sports. (US ISSN 0882-9640) **4488**, 3808
Silesia Antiqua. (PL ISSN 0080-9594) **284**
Silesian Studies. *see* Studia Slaskie **2214**
Silhouette. (CN ISSN 0037-5217) **2883**, 1324
Silhouette. (GW ISSN 0173-6310) **2960**
Siliao Bolan/Feed Production. (CC ISSN 1001-0084) **208**
Silicates. *see* Silikaty **1230**
Silicates Industriels. (BE ISSN 0037-5225) **1166**
Silicon Design *see* E D A **1766**
†Silicon Gulch Gazette. (US ISSN 0149-7898) **5277**
Silikattechnik. (GW ISSN 0037-5233) **1166**
Silikaty/Silicates. (CS ISSN 0037-5241) **1230**, 1166, 1208
Silk. *see* Sichou **4623**
Silk Export Bulletin. (II) **4623**, 920
Silk in India. (II) **4628**
Silk Road. *see* Silu **2960**
Silk Screen. (NE ISSN 0037-5268) **4005**
▼Silkroad. (HK) **4803**
Silky Terrier Club of America Newsletter. (US) **3714**
Silky Terrier Quarterly. (US) **3714**
Sillages. (FR) **2841**, 2960
Silliman Journal. (PH ISSN 0037-5284) **4343**, 2515
Sillon. (US) **119**
Sillon Belge. (BE) **119**
Silnicni Doprava *see* Silnicni Obzor **4702**
Silnicni Obzor. (CS ISSN 0322-7154) **4702**, 4721
Silpakon. (TH ISSN 0037-5314) **344**
Sil's'ke Budivnytstvo. (RU ISSN 0037-5322) **120**, 632
Silsoe College News *see* C R I News **5157**
Silu/Silk Road. (US ISSN 1000-7792) **2960**
Silumine Fizika/Thermophysics/Teplofizika. (LI ISSN 0082-4089) **3841**
Silva Belgica. (BE) **2107**
Silva Fennica. (FI ISSN 0037-5330) **2107**
Silvae Genetica. (GW ISSN 0037-5349) **547**, 2107
Silver. (US ISSN 0899-6105) **259**
Silver & Blue. (US ISSN 1054-3031) **1324**
Silver and Gold Report. (US ISSN 0195-8054) **963**
The Silver Baron - Stocks U S A. (US) **963**
Silver Circle. (US ISSN 0745-3353) **2234**, 1301
Silver Flower/Ginka. (JA) **2441**
Silver Institute Letter. (US ISSN 0730-8132) **3495**, 3419
Silver Kris. (SI ISSN 0129-606X) **4803**
Silver Lining *see* Write in There **1271**

SIMULATION SERIES 6661

Silver Market. (US ISSN 0066-4332) **3419**
Silver Screen. (CN) **963**, 1380, 3517
Silver Wings. (US ISSN 0889-9118) **3005**, 4249
Silver Years News. (US) **2234**
Silverfish Review. (US ISSN 0164-1085) **2960**
SilverPlatter Exchange. (US ISSN 0896-4068) **1447**
†Silvicultura Em Sao Paulo. (BL ISSN 0583-3132) **5277**
Silviculture. (CN) **2107**
Sim & Cain: Practice & Procedure of the High Court of Appeal of New Zealand. (NZ) **2733**
Simfraemjaren-Livraeddaren. (SW) **4488**
Simian. (US ISSN 0037-539X) **3714**, 591
Simiente. (CL ISSN 0037-5403) **120**
Simientes. (CU) **1663**
Simiolus. (NE ISSN 0037-5411) **344**, 2322
Simmental Annual. (AT ISSN 0814-561X) **226**
Simmental Country. (CN) **120**
Simmental News. (AT ISSN 0815-6077) **226**
Simmental Shield. (US ISSN 0192-3072) **226**
Simmentaler Journal. (SA) **226**
Simmeringer Museumsblaetter. (AU) **2386**
Simmons Librarian. (US) **2784**, 1324
Simmons Political Report. (US) **4073**, 3925
Simmons Review. (US ISSN 0049-0512) **1324**
Simon Stevin. (BE ISSN 0037-5454) **3055**
Simon van der Stel Foundation. Bulletin *see* Restorica **306**
Simon Wiesenthal Center Annual. (US ISSN 0741-8450) **2023**
Simon's Directory of Theatrical Materials, Services and Information. (US) **4638**
Simon's Tax Cases. (UK ISSN 0308-8030) **1105**
Simon's Tax Intelligence. (UK ISSN 0308-8049) **1105**
Simon's Town Historical Society Bulletin.(SA ISSN 0037-5470) **2334**
Simon's Weekly Tax Service: Cases Only. (UK) **1105**
Simon's Weekly Tax Service: Intelligence & Cases. (UK) **1105**
Simon's Weekly Tax Service: Intelligence Only. (UK) **1105**
Simonson Miscellaneous Research Data.(US ISSN 0899-1618) **2164**
Simpliciana. (SZ ISSN 0259-6415) **2960**
†Simplicity Knitting. (US) **5277**
†Simplicity Magazine. (US) **5277**
Simplified Bible Study *see* Bible Study Special Ministries **4231**
Simplified Spelling Society. Journal. (UK ISSN 0950-9585) **2841**, 1663
▼Simply Cross Stitch. (US) **3592**, 357
Simply Living. (AT ISSN 0314-3155) **1968**
▼Simply Seafood. (US) **2449**, 2049
†Simply You. (US) **5277**
Simposio sobre Mercado de Capitales. (CK) **799**
Simpsons Illustrated. (US) **1265**
Sims Seeker. (US ISSN 1045-9987) **2164**
Simula Newsletter *see* A S U Newsletter **1429**
Simulation (San Diego). (US ISSN 0037-5497) **1436**
Simulation and Games *see* Simulation & Gaming **4448**
Simulation & Gaming. (US ISSN 1046-8781) **4448**, 4046
Simulation Councils Proceedings *see* Simulation Series **1436**
Simulation - Games for Learning. (UK ISSN 0142-9361) **1759**
Simulation Monographs. (NE) **165**
Simulation Series. (US ISSN 0735-9276) **1436**

SIMULATION SYMPOSIUM

Simulation Symposium. Record of Proceedings. (US ISSN 0272-4715) **1436**
Simuletter *see* S I G S I M Simuletter **1435**
Simunhak. (KO) **2960**
▼Simurgh. (IR) **2883**, 4220
Al-Sina'ah/Industry. (TS) **691**
†Sinag-Agham. (PH) **5277**
Sinai. (IS) **4226**
Sinai. *see* Industrialist **5212**
Sinai Hospital of Detroit. Bulletin. (US ISSN 0037-5535) **2469**
Sinamina. (FI ISSN 0359-0267) **4853**
Sinar Jaya. (IO) **120**
Sinatra International. (AT ISSN 0810-5200) **421**, 1380, 3580
Sincere Singles. (US) **4363**
Sinclair Q L World. (UK ISSN 0268-067X) **1400**
Sinclair User. (UK ISSN 0262-5458) **1465**, 1474
Sind Journal of Political Science and Modern History. (PK) **3925**, 2341
Sind University Journal of Education. (PK ISSN 0560-0871) **1663**
Sindacato Moderno. (IT ISSN 0037-5543) **2589**, 3419
Sindbad. (IS) **1265**
Sindh Quarterly. (PK) **4386**, 2341
Sindicalismo en Espana/Trade Unionism in Spain. (SP) **2589**
Sindicato dos Odontologistas do Estado de Sao Paulo. Noticias. (BL) **3242**
Sindicato Nacional de la Pesca Boletin de Informacion. (SP ISSN 0037-556X) **2049**
Sindicato Nacional dos Editores de Livros. Informativo Bibliografico. (BL ISSN 0103-8834) **411**, 4137
Sindicato Unitario Nazionale Inquilini Assegnatari Informazioni S U N I A *see* Informazioni S U N I A **2489**
Sindikalistika Nea *see* Trade Union News **2590**
Sindikalne Novosti. (SW ISSN 0280-9060) **2589**
Sineast/Film Maker. (BN ISSN 0587-0054) **3517**
Sinet. (ET ISSN 0379-2897) **4343**
Sinet Newsletter. (ET) **4343**
Sinet: Proceedings of Annual Programmes Review Conference. (ET) **4343**
Sinfonie Scacchistiche. (IT ISSN 0037-5608) **4488**
Sinformation. (US ISSN 0037-5616) **3601**
Sing Heavenly Muse! (US ISSN 0198-9855) **2960**, 4853
Sing Out! (US ISSN 0037-5624) **3580**, 2058
Sing Tao Jih Pao. (CN) **2023**
Singabout; Journal of Australian Folksong *see* Mulga Wire **3563**
Singapore. (SI ISSN 0129-766X) **2216**
Singapore. Board of Commissioners of Currency. Annual Report *see* Singapore. Board of Commissioners of Currency. Annual Report and Accounts **799**
Singapore. Board of Commissioners of Currency. Annual Report and Accounts. (SI) **799**
Singapore. Catalogue of Government Publications *see* Singapore National Printers. Publications Catalogue **3938**
Singapore. Department of Statistics. Monthly Digest of Statistics. (SI ISSN 0037-5640) **737**
Singapore. Department of Statistics. Report on the Census of Wholesale, Retail Trades, Restaurants and Hotels *see* Singapore. Department of Statistics. Report on the Survey of Wholesale Trade, Retail Trade, Restaurants & Hotels (Year) **2482**
Singapore. Department of Statistics. Report on the Household Expenditure Survey. (SI ISSN 0217-9563) **2450**
Singapore. Department of Statistics. Report on the Survey of Services (Year). (SI ISSN 0129-9786) **4082**, 4585

Singapore. Department of Statistics. Report on the Survey of Wholesale Trade, Retail Trade, Restaurants & Hotels (Year). (SI) **2482**, 4585
Singapore. Department of Statistics. Shipping and Cargo Statistics *see* Singapore Shipping & Cargo Statistics **4666**
Singapore. Economic Development Board. Annual Report. (SI ISSN 0080-9683) **1084**
Singapore. Economic Development Board. Report on the Census of Industrial Production. (SI ISSN 0080-9675) **737**
Singapore. Housing and Development Board. Annual Report. (SI) **2496**
Singapore. Ministry of Labour. Annual Report. (SI ISSN 0129-6310) **993**
Singapore. Ministry of National Development. Annual Report. (SI) **884**, 2496
Singapore. Ministry of the Environment. Annual Report. (SI ISSN 0217-5487) **1968**
Singapore. National Library. Annual Report. (SI ISSN 0217-1546) **2784**
Singapore. National Maritime Board. Report. (SI) **4739**
Singapore. National Science and Technology Board. Annual Reports. (SI) **4343**
Singapore. Science Council. Annual Reports *see* Singapore. National Science and Technology Board. Annual Reports **4343**
Singapore Accountant. (SI ISSN 0217-4456) **756**
Singapore Annual Report on Tourism Statistics. (SI) **4800**
†Singapore Banking, Finance & Insurance. (SI) **5277**
Singapore Book World. (SI ISSN 0080-9659) **4137**
Singapore Bulletin. (SI ISSN 0303-7169) **2216**
Singapore Business. (SI ISSN 0129-2951) **884**
Singapore Changi Airport Timetable. (SI) **4677**
Singapore Chinese Chamber of Commerce and Industry. Economic Quarterly. (SI ISSN 0129-5780) **822**
Singapore Computer Society. Bulletin. (SI ISSN 0217-4936) **1400**
▼Singapore Contractors' Equipment Catalogue. (SI ISSN 0218-2831) **1153**
Singapore Economic Review. (SI ISSN 0217-5908) **691**
Singapore Eve. (HK) **2197**
Singapore Facts and Pictures. (SI ISSN 0217-7773) **2341**
Singapore Government Directory. (SI ISSN 0129-3109) **4073**
Singapore Indian Chamber of Commerce. Annual Report & Directory. (SI) **1153**
Singapore Indian Chamber of Commerce. Directory *see* Singapore Indian Chamber of Commerce. Annual Report & Directory **1153**
Singapore International Chamber of Commerce. Economic Bulletin. (SI ISSN 0037-5659) **822**
Singapore International Chamber of Commerce. Expatriate Living Costs in Singapore. (SI) **822**
Singapore International Chamber of Commerce. Report. (SI ISSN 0377-449X) **822**
Singapore Journal of Education. (SI ISSN 0129-4776) **1663**
Singapore Journal of Legal Studies. (SI ISSN 0218-2173) **2679**
Singapore Journal of Obstetrics & Gynaecology. (SI ISSN 0129-3273) **3296**, 598, 2469
Singapore Journal of Primary Industries.(SI ISSN 0129-6485) **120**, 2049, 4816
Singapore Journal of Tropical Geography. (SI ISSN 0129-7619) **2262**
Singapore Law Reports. (SI ISSN 0218-3161) **2679**

Singapore Law Review. (SI ISSN 0080-9691) **2679**
Singapore Libraries. (SI ISSN 0085-6118) **2784**
Singapore Literature. (SI ISSN 0129-3117) **2960**
Singapore Manufacturers' Association Directory *see* Tradelink - S M A Annual Directory (Year) **1156**
Singapore Medical Journal. (SI ISSN 0037-5675) **3153**
Singapore Mirror *see* Mirror **2216**
Singapore Monthly Report on Tourism Statistics. (SI) **4800**
Singapore Monthly Trade Statistics: Imports & Exports. (SI ISSN 0129-7414) **738**, 4585
†Singapore Motoring Guide. (SI) **5277**
Singapore National Academy of Science. Journal. (SI) **517**
Singapore National Bibliography. (SI ISSN 0129-315X) **2330**
Singapore National Institute of Chemistry Bulletin *see* S N I C Bulletin **1187**
Singapore National Printers. Publications Catalogue. (SI) **3938**
Singapore Periodicals Index. (SI ISSN 0377-7928) **23**
Singapore Polytechnic Engineering Society. Journal. (SI) **1836**
▼Singapore Report on the Growth Triangle. (US) **963**
Singapore Shipping & Cargo Statistics. (SI) **4666**, 4739
Singapore Source Book Architects & Designers. (SI ISSN 0218-3153) **1153**
Singapore Standards Catalogue. (SI ISSN 0129-6256) **1084**
Singapore Stock Exchange Journal. (SI ISSN 0217-3476) **963**
Singapore Tatler. (HK) **2216**
Singapore Tourist Promotion Board. Annual Statistical Report on Visitor Arrivals *see* Singapore Annual Report on Tourism Statistics **4800**
Singapore Tourist Promotion Board. Monthly Statistical Report on Visitor Arrivals *see* Singapore Monthly Report on Tourism Statistics **4800**
Singapore Trade News. (SI ISSN 0217-7528) **691**
Singapore Travel. (SI ISSN 0129-5020) **4786**
Singapore Undergrad. (SI ISSN 0049-0547) **1324**
Singapore Visitor. (SI) **4786**
Singapore Yearbook of Statistics. (SI ISSN 0583-3655) **4585**
Singende Kirche. (AU ISSN 0037-5721) **3580**, 4275
Singers Greetings. *see* Sanger-Hilsen **2022**
Singer's Guide to the Professional Opera Companies. (US) **3580**, 4638
Singing News. (US) **3580**
Single Adult Bible Study. (US ISSN 0731-1478) **4249**, 4363
Single Adult Ministries Journal. (US) **4363**, 4201
Single Adult Ministry Information. (US ISSN 0887-1167) **4363**
Single Again. (US) **4363**, 3067
Single Connections (Fullerton). (US) **4363**
Single Crystal Properties *see* Crystal Properties and Preparation **3816**
Single Family Home Plans. (US) **2555**
Single File Magazine. (US) **4363**
▼Single Gentlemen & Women. (US) **4363**
The Single Hound. (US) **3005**
Single i *see* Single Adult Ministry Information **4363**
†Single Impact. (US ISSN 0888-3335) **5277**
Single Life (Lincoln). (US) **4363**
Single Life (Milwaukee). (US) **4363**
Single Living Magazine. (US) **4363**
Single Magazine and Entertainment Guide. (US) **4363**
▼Single Market Mobile and Satellite Review. (UK ISSN 0958-9155) **1342**
Single Parent. (US ISSN 0037-5748) **4419**, 4363

Single Parent News. (US) **1244**, 4363
Single Pet Lovers. (US) **4363**, 3714
The Single Scene (Gahanna). (US ISSN 0885-6648) **4363**, 3005
†Single Scene (Salem). (US) **5277**
Single Scene (Scottsdale). (US) **4363**
†Single Source. (US) **5277**
Single Source Newsletter. (US ISSN 0738-8578) **4363**, 3400
Single Today. (US) **2960**, 4363
SingleLife Magazine. (US ISSN 8756-0380) **4363**
Singles *see* Dateline Magazine **4362**
Singles. (AT) **4363**
Singles Almanac (Boston). (US ISSN 1044-6184) **4363**
Singles Almanac of New York. (US ISSN 1045-5108) **4363**
Singles Choice. (US) **4363**
Singles Critique *see* Lifestyle Southern California **4362**
Singles Journal. (US) **4363**
Single's Life. (US) **4363**, 3400
Singles Lifeline. (US) **4363**
Singles Magazine *see* Pittsburgh Singles Lifestyles **4363**
Singles Master *see* Music Master Catalogue **3565**
Singles Monthly (Fort Worth). (US) **4363**
Singles News Magazine (Sacramento). (US) **4363**
Singles Outreach Services Newsletter. (US) **4363**
Singles' Paper. (US) **4363**
Singles Scene (Allardt). (US ISSN 0746-7982) **4363**, 4249
Singles' Serendipity. (US) **4363**
Singles Times. (US) **4363**
Singles Today. (US) **4363**
Singles Trumpet. (US) **4364**
Singlesline. (US) **4364**
Singmul Hakhoe Chi *see* Korean Journal of Botany **508**
Singuladuras. (SP) **4739**
Sinica Leidensia. (NE ISSN 0169-9563) **2341**
Sinister Wisdom. (US ISSN 0196-1853) **4853**, 2457, 2960
Sinistra Europea. (IT) **3972**
Sinistralian. (US) **1301**, 4046
Sinn und Form. (GW ISSN 0037-5756) **2960**
Sinnets Helse. (NO ISSN 0049-0563) **4046**, 4112
Sino-American Relations. (CH) **3972**
Sino Azul. (BL ISSN 0037-5764) **1366**
Sino-British Trade Review *see* China - Britain Trade Review **903**
Sino-Japanese Friendship Hospital. Journal. *see* Zhongri Youhao Yiyuan Xuebao **3165**
Sino-Platonic Papers. (US) **2341**, 1342, 2841, 2960
Sinologica Coloniensia. (GW ISSN 0170-3706) **3644**, 2342
Sinological Pioneer. *see* Zhongguoxue Daobao **3646**
Sinological Studies. (CH) **3644**
Sinopse de Ginecologia e Obstetricia. (BL) **3296**
Sinopsis Dun - Brazil. (US ISSN 0080-9756) **884**
Sinorama. (CH ISSN 0256-9043) **2219**
Sinsemilla Tips. (US ISSN 0884-8858) **2139**, 3925
Sint Bernardus. (NE ISSN 0005-9390) **1663**
Sintese. (BL ISSN 0103-4332) **3781**, 3925, 4386
Sintese Ferroviaria Brasileira. (BL ISSN 0102-5694) **4715**
†Sintesi Economica. (IT ISSN 0037-5780) **5277**
Sintesis. (PY ISSN 0049-0598) **2213**
†Sintesis - A L A D I. (Asociacion Latinoamericana de Integracion) (UY) **5277**
Sintesis-Avicola. (MX) **226**
Sintesis Bibliografica. (AG ISSN 0080-9772) **738**
Sintesis Economica. (CK) **691**
Sintesis Estadistica de Chile. (CL ISSN 0716-2456) **691**

Sintesis Informativa Economica y Financiera. (AG ISSN 0037-5799) 884
Sintesis Informativa Iberoamericana see Documentacion Iberoamericana 3955
Sintesis-Porcina. (MX) 226
Sinteticheskie Almazy see Sverkhtverdye Materialy 1215
Sinteza. (XV ISSN 0049-0601) 344, 306
Sinwen Tienti. see Newsdom 2197
Sion. (IS ISSN 0037-5810) 4288
Sipapu. (US ISSN 0037-5837) 2784
Sipario. (IT) 3517
Sipiscope. (US ISSN 0737-0350) 2575, 4343
Sir Frederic Hooper Award Essay. (UK) 691, 1028
Sir George Earle Memorial Lecture on Industry and Government. (UK ISSN 0080-9780) 691, 3925
Sir Robert Madgwick Lecture Series (No.). (AT ISSN 0816-2735) 2515, 4386
Sir Thomas Browne Institute. Publications. General Series see Sir Thomas Browne Institute. Publications. New Series 2386
Sir Thomas Browne Institute. Publications. New Series. (NE) 2386
Sira Limited. Annual Report see Sira Spotlight 2525
Sira Review see Sira Review Annual Brochure 2525
Sira Review Annual Brochure. (UK) 2525
Sira Spotlight. (UK) 2525
Siratim. (IS ISSN 0334-6943) 3517, 1380
Siren. (UN ISSN 0379-2463) 1611
▼Siren Magazine. (US) 2883
Sirena see Siren 1611
Sirene see Siren 1611
Sirene. (NE) 2960
Sires and Dams see U S T A Sires and Dams 4539
Siri Lak-Indo Studies see Kurukshetra 5225
Sirio. (IT) 359
Sirjana. (NP ISSN 0049-0628) 3925
Siskiyou Pioneer and Yearbook. (US ISSN 0583-4449) 2422
Sistema. (SP ISSN 0210-0223) 4386
Sistema de Indicadores Socio-Economicos y Educativos de la O E I. (SP) 4386, 1663
Sistema Ferroviario R F F S A. (Rede Ferroviaria Federal, S.A.) (BL) 4715
Sistema Nacional de Archivos. Inventarios. (MX) 4137
Sistema Nacional de Informacion Cientifica y Tecnologia Boletin S I N I C Y T see Boletin S I N I C Y T 4302
Sistemas de Calidad. (MX) 3448
Sistematica. (IT ISSN 0037-5888) 3781
Sistematica de Plantas Invasoras. (BL) 517
Sistemi e Automazione see Sistemi e Impresa 1439
Sistemi e Impresa. (IT) 1439, 1415
Sistemi Intelligenti. (IT ISSN 1120-9550) 4046, 1410, 2841, 3781
Sistemi Urbani. (IT ISSN 0393-5493) 2496
Sister City News. (US) 4094
Sisterlife Journal. (US) 3947, 4853
Sisters Have Resources Everywhere see S H A R E 5272
Sisters Today. (US ISSN 0037-590X) 4275
Sisters United. (US) 2457, 4853
▼Sistersong. (US) 2960, 4860
Sistra. (GW) 3471
▼Sisyphus. (US) 3005
†Site Development News. (US) 5277
Site San Diego. (US ISSN 0895-6332) 4529
Site Selection and Industrial Development. (US ISSN 1041-3073) 1085
Site Sound. (CN ISSN 0843-8838) 344

Sites. (US ISSN 0747-9409) 306, 2960
▼Siteworld. (US) 935, 1085
Situacion. (SP) 920
Situacion. Suplemento de Coyuntura. (SP ISSN 0213-2273) 921
†Situacion Coyuntural del Sector Agropecuario. (AG ISSN 0325-9161) 5277
Situacion de los Edulcorantes. (CU) 921
Situation de la Viticulture dans le Monde. (FR) 385, 192
Situation du Marche Vinicole. (FR ISSN 0223-4580) 120
Situation Economique a l'Etranger. (FR) 884, 921
Situation Economique de Cote d'Ivoire. (IV ISSN 0080-9829) 884
Situation Economique de la Republique Rwandaise au 31 Decembre see Rwanda. Direction Generale de la Statistique. Situation Economique de la Republique Rwandaise au 31 Decembre 883
Situation Economique du Senegal. (SG ISSN 0080-9853) 884
Situation Economique et Perspectives d'Avenir. (FR) 884
Sivam. (II ISSN 0037-5950) 4217
Siviele Ingenieur in Suid-Afrika. see Civil Engineer in South Africa 1863
Siviele Ingenieurswese-Adviesraad. Jaarverslag. see Civil Engineering Advisory Council. Annual Report 1863
Sivilforsvarsbladet. (NO ISSN 0332-9038) 1274
Sivilrettsstatistikk see Norway. Statistisk Sentralbyraa. Sivilrettsstatistikk 5249
Six Nations New Credit Reporter. (CN) 799
Sixiang Zhanxian/Ideology Front. (CC ISSN 0561-7650) 4386
Sixiang Zhengzhi Gongzuo Yanjiu/Study in Ideology and Politics. (CC) 3925
Sixiang Zhengzhike Jiaoxue. (CC) 1663
Sixteen see 16 Magazine 1273
Sixteen Mm Films Available in the Public Libraries of Metropolitan Toronto. (CN ISSN 0315-7326) 3520
Sixteenth Century Bibliography. (US) 2330
Sixteenth Century Essays and Studies see Sixteenth Century Journal 2386
Sixteenth Century Journal. (US ISSN 0361-0160) 2386
Sixth District Focus. (US) 799
Sixth Generation Systems. (US) 1410
Siyassa was Strategia/Politics and Strategy/Politique et Strategie. (LE) 3925
Al-Siyassah al-Dawliyyah see Al-Siassa al-Dawlya 3972
Sjaelvbetjaening see Supermarket 1054
Sjavarfrettir. (IC ISSN 1017-3609) 2049
Sjoefartshistorisk Aarbok/Norwegian Yearbook of Maritime History. (NO ISSN 0080-9888) 2386
Sjoesport. (NO ISSN 0037-6000) 4529
Sjonvarpsvisir. (IC) 1380
Sjukgymnasten. (SW ISSN 0037-6019) 3153
Sjukhuset. (SW) 2469
Sjukvaardens och Socialvaardens Planerings- och Rationaliseringsinstitut Sweden. Sjukvaardens och Socialvaardens Planerings- och Rationaliseringsinstitut. S P R I Litteraturtjaenst see Sweden. Sjukvaardens och Socialvaardens Planerings- och Rationaliseringsinstitut. S P R I Litteraturtjaenst 4119
Skaeppen. (DK ISSN 0108-397X) 2386
Skagit Farmer. (US) 120
Skak. (IC) 4488
Skakbladet. (DK ISSN 0037-6043) 4488
Skakelblad see University of Pretoria. Annual Report 1328

Skalk. (DK ISSN 0560-1894) 2386, 284
Skanderborg Museum. Aarbog. (DK ISSN 0903-3424) 2386
Skanderborg Museum. Aarsskrift see Skanderborg Museum. Aarbog 2386
Skandinavisk Skipsfarts Tekniske Aarshefte. (DK) 4739
Skandinavisk U F O Information. Newsletter see S U F O I. News 61
Skandinavisk U F O Information News see S U F O I. News 61
Skandinaviska Enskilda Banken Quarterly Review. (SW ISSN 0347-3139) 799, 884
Skandinaviska Mynt Magasinet see Nordisk Filateli med Mynt - Magazinet 3600
Skandinaviska Mynt Magasinet see Nordisk Filateli 3755
Skandinaviska Skipsrederier/Yearbook of Scandinavian Shipowners. (NO ISSN 0800-1235) 4739, 1153
Skandinavistik. (GW) 2960
†Skate. (US ISSN 0037-6124) 5277
Skating. (US ISSN 0037-6132) 4488
Skatt og Budsjett see Skattebetaleren 1085
Skattebetaleren. (NO ISSN 0333-3868) 1085
†Skattebrev. (DK) 5277
Skattelove see F S R's Skattelove med Noter 1093
Skatten. (DK ISSN 0106-8024) 1105
Skatten. Erhverv. (DK ISSN 0107-3885) 1106, 691
Skattepolitisk Oversigt. (DK ISSN 0108-6049) 1106
Skatterett. (NO ISSN 0333-2810) 1106, 2679
Skeet Shooting Review. (US ISSN 0037-6140) 4488
Skeletal Radiology. (GW ISSN 0364-2348) 3363
▼Skeleton Crew. (UK ISSN 0959-8006) 3014
Skema. (IT) 2206
The Skeptic. (AT) 3671
▼Skeptical Briefs. (US ISSN 1060-216X) 3671
Skeptical Inquirer. (US ISSN 0194-6730) 3671
Skermer. see Fencer 4472
Sketch. (US) 2884
Sketch Board Bulletin. (US) 344
Sketch Book. (US) 344
Ski. (US ISSN 0037-6159) 4555
Le Ski (Toronto, 1987). (CN) 4555
Le Ski (Toronto, 1988). (CN) 4488
Ski America. (US) 4555
Ski Area Management. (US ISSN 0037-6175) 4555
Ski Canada. (CN ISSN 0702-701X) 4555, 1265
Ski Directory. (US) 4488, 4786
Ski-Flash Magazine. (FR) 4555
Ski Holidays Scotland see Ski Scotland 4556
Ski Industry Letter. (US ISSN 0197-3479) 4555, 1054
Ski International. (UK) 4555
Ski Journal. (JA) 4555
†Ski Magasinet Danmark. (DK) 5277
†Ski Magazine. (FR) 5277
Ski Patrol Magazine. (US ISSN 0890-6076) 4488
Ski Racing. (US ISSN 0037-6213) 4488
Ski Runner. (CN ISSN 0037-6221) 4555
Ski-Scene Including South African Fishing. (SA) 4555
Ski - Schweizer Skisport/Ski Suisse/Sci Svizzero. (SZ ISSN 0037-623X) 4555
Ski Scotland. (UK) 4556, 4786
Ski Special. (UK ISSN 0954-9765) 4556
Ski Suisse. see Ski - Schweizer Skisport 4555
Ski Survey. (UK ISSN 0955-8225) 4556
Ski Tech. (US) 4556
Ski the West. (CN) 4556
Ski Travel. (US) 4556, 4786
Ski Writers Bulletin. (US) 2575, 4556
Ski X - C. (US ISSN 0161-1054) 4556
Skibs og Baadebygning. (DK) 4739

Skier. (US) 4556
Skier. (UK ISSN 0951-5941) 4556
Skiers Advocate see American Skier 4540
Skier's Pocket Guide. (US) 4556
Skiing. (US ISSN 0037-6264) 4556
Skiing Trade Monthly News see Skiing Trade News 4556
Skiing Trade News. (US ISSN 0037-6299) 4556
†Skiing Utah. (US) 5277
Skilehrer Magazin. (GW) 4556
Skill. (US) 2589
Skill see Ringsport 4485
Skillings' Mining Review. (US ISSN 0037-6329) 3495
Skimbaaja. (FI) 4556
Skin & Allergy News. (US ISSN 0037-6337) 3249
Skin and Psoriasis Newsletter. (AT ISSN 1030-7257) 3249, 3188
Skin Diver Magazine. (US ISSN 0037-6345) 4488
Skin Diving News from New South Wales see N.S.W. Skindiver 4551
Skin Inc. (US ISSN 0898-6525) 3249, 376
Skin Pharmacology. (SZ ISSN 1011-0283) 3743, 3249
Skin Research/Hifu. (JA ISSN 0018-1390) 3249
Skindiving in Australia and the South Pacific see Sportdiving in Australia and the South Pacific 4557
Skinned Knuckles. (UI ISSN 0164-3509) 2442
Skinner Kinsmen Update. (US ISSN 0895-0202) 2164
Skip. (NO ISSN 0300-3310) 4739
Skip Magazine. (US) 1759, 1265, 3400, 4853
Skipjack Survey and Assessment Programme Technical Report see Tuna and Billfish Assessment Programme Technical Report 2050
Skipper. (SA ISSN 0258-8951) 2217
Skipperen. (DK) 4739
Skipper's Mates see Skipper's Mates Friendship Club 2457
Skipper's Mates Friendship Club. (US) 2457
Skipping Stones. (US ISSN 0899-529X) 1265
†Skira Magazine. (SZ) 5277
Skirnir. (IC ISSN 0256-8446) 2960, 2386
Skitrax. (CN) 4556
Skive-egnens Jul. (DK ISSN 0106-2697) 2386
Sklar a Keramik/Glass and Ceramics Maker. (CS ISSN 0037-637X) 1166
SKO. (NO) 4362, 2738
Sko-Magasinet see Sko og Laedervarer 4362
Sko og Laedervarer. (DK ISSN 0901-0114) 4362
Skoena Hem. (SW) 2555, 344
Skog & Saag. (SW) 2117
†Skogbrukets og Skogindustriens Forskningsraad. Aarbok. (NO) 5277
Skogeieren. (NO ISSN 0037-6396) 2108
Skogen. (SW ISSN 0037-640X) 2108
Skogforsk. Meddelelser. (NO ISSN 0803-2866) 2108
Skogforsk. Rapport. (NO ISSN 0803-2858) 2108
Skogsindustriarbetaren. (SW ISSN 0346-1033) 640, 2108
Skogsvaardsfoereningens Tidskrift see Sveriges Skogsvaardsfoerbunds Tidskrift 2108
Skohandlaren. (SW ISSN 0346-1300) 4362
Skol Vreizh- l'Ecole Bretonne see Skol Vreizh- l'Ecole Bretonne. Nouvelle Serie 1663
Skol Vreizh- l'Ecole Bretonne. Nouvelle Serie. (FR ISSN 0755-8848) 1663
Skola Danas. (BN ISSN 0037-6450) 1663
Skolans Artikelservice. (SW ISSN 0037-6469) 411
Skole. (US) 1663
Skole and Landbrug. (DK ISSN 0108-2671) 120, 1663
Skole-Bladet. (DK ISSN 0108-4593) 1663

6664 SKOLE

†Skole og Edb. (DK ISSN 0900-2006) 5277
†Skole og Fremtid. (DK ISSN 0108-3872) 5277
Skolebiblioteket. (DK ISSN 0105-9556) 2784, 1663
Skoleforum. (NO ISSN 0332-7167) 1716
†Skolemusikhaandbogen. (DK ISSN 0108-4402) 5277
Skolen i Norden. (DK ISSN 0109-8985) 1663
†Skolens Aarbok. (NO ISSN 0080-9950) 5277
Skolepsychologi see Psykologisk Paedagogisk Raadgivning 4043
Skolernes Kunstforening Alssund-Kredsen. Katalog see Vore Kunstnere 5302
Skolestart. (DK ISSN 0107-3028) 1663
Skolhistoriskt Arkiv. (FI) 2386
Skolledaren. (SW ISSN 0037-6515) 1663
Skolnytt see Laeraren 1645
Skolska Televizija. (CI ISSN 0037-6523) 1380, 1663
Skolske Novine. (CI ISSN 0037-6531) 1663
Skolski Vjesnik. (CI ISSN 0037-654X) 1663
Skolvaerlden. (SW ISSN 0037-6566) 1663
Skolvux-soe see Soedok 5278
Skoop. (NE) 3517
Skorstensfejarmaestaren. (SW ISSN 0346-1351) 2034
Skotoey see SKO 4362
Skov og Natur/Forest and Nature. (DK) 2108
Skovbrugstidende. (DK) 2108
Skoven. (DK ISSN 0106-8539) 2108
Skozi T A M. (Towarne Avtomobilov in Motorjev) (XV) 1939, 4702
Skozi Ziv T A M see Skozi T A M 1939
Skraeddarmaestaren see Skraedderi 1287
Skraedderi. (SW ISSN 0346-1386) 1287
Skrien. (NE) 3517, 1380, 3797
Skrif en Kerk. (SA ISSN 0257-8891) 4201
Skrifter fra Landslaget for Bygde- og Byhistorie see Skrifter - Landslaget for Lokalhistorie 2386
Skrifter i Fysisk Geografi see Aarhus Universitet. Geologisk Institut. Geoskrifter 1553
Skrifter - Landslaget for Lokalhistorie. (NO ISSN 0802-0434) 2386
Skrifter Utgivna av Svenska Riksarkivet.(SW ISSN 0346-8488) 2784
Skuespilregister. (DK ISSN 0106-665X) 4638
Skul Thai. (TH) 2220
▼Skull Base Surgery. (US ISSN 1052-1453) 3384, 3305
Skulptur Veksoelund. (DK ISSN 0107-4911) 344
Skupnost. (IT) 2023, 3925, 3947
Sky and Telescope. (US ISSN 0037-6604) 369
Sky Magazine. (US) 4803
Sky Outside Sky. see Tian Wai Tian 3518
Sky Watcher. (JA ISSN 0911-7652) 369
Skybox. (US) 4488
Skydd & Saekerhet/Safety and Security.(SW ISSN 0283-5452) 2034
Skydiving. (US ISSN 0192-7361) 4488
Skye Terrier Club of America. Bulletin. (US) 3714
†Skylander Magazine. (US) 5277
Skylark. (US) 2960, 1324
Skylark (Beauport). (CN) 2960
Skylark (Saskatoon). (CN) 2841, 1760
Skyline. (GW) 2191
Skyline (Brooklyn). (US) 2262, 2422
Skyliner. (US) 4702
Skylines (Washington). (US ISSN 0892-7847) 632, 1028
Skylite see Butler Aviation's Echelon 2222
Skylon. (UK) 3652, 3868

Skylook see M U F O N - U F O Journal 58
▼Skypix. (US) 1380
Skyport. (UK) 62
Skytte-bladet. (DK ISSN 0037-6663) 4488
Skywatchers Almanac (Year). (US ISSN 0889-9614) 369
SkyWaves. (AT) 4201, 1380
Skyways. (II) 62
Skyways. (US ISSN 1051-6956) 62
Skywritings. (JM) 4803
Slaboproudy Obzor/Electronics and Telecommunications Review. (CS ISSN 0037-668X) 1342, 1908
Slaegt og Stavn. (DK ISSN 0107-539X) 2164
Slaegten Fisker. (DK ISSN 0108-3880) 2164
Slaekt och Bygd. (FI ISSN 0780-8763) 2164
Slaekthistoriskt Forum. (SW ISSN 0280-3984) 2164, 2387
De Slager. (NE ISSN 0037-6698) 2081
Slagersambacht see Ambacht & Industrie 2061
Slakt och Havd (Terjarv). (FI) 2387
Slant. (US) 1324
Slant: A Journal of Poetry. (US ISSN 0893-7095) 3005
Slapstick. (GW) 2884
Slasher. (UK) 2108, 1497
Slaski Kwartalnik Historyczny "Sobotka".(PL ISSN 0037-7511) 2322
Slate. (CN) 344, 3533
Slate & Style. (US) 2296, 3005
Slatki Grozdovi Vinograda Gospodnjeg. (YU ISSN 0353-1805) 4288
Slave River Journal. (CN) 2179
Slavery & Abolition. (UK ISSN 0144-039X) 4448, 3947
Slavia. (CS ISSN 0037-6736) 2841
Slavia Antiqua. (PL ISSN 0080-9993) 284
Slavia Occidentalis. (PL ISSN 0081-0002) 2841
Slavia Orientalis. (PL ISSN 0037-6744) 2841
Slavic and East European Arts. (US) 2960
Slavic and East European Journal. (US ISSN 0037-6752) 2841, 1760
Slavic and European Arts. (US ISSN 0737-7002) 2960, 2841
Slavic and European Education Review see East-West Education 1626
Slavic Gospel News. (AT) 4217
Slavic Gospel News see Breakthrough (Wheaton) 4280
Slavic Review. (US ISSN 0037-6779) 4386, 2322, 2960
Slavic Studies. (US) 2387
Slavic Western Literary Relations. (US) 2960
Slavica see Universitatis Debreceniensis de Ludovico Kossuth Nominatae. Instituti Philologiae Slavicae. Annales. Slavica 2849
Slavica Gothoburgensia. (SW ISSN 0081-0010) 2841
Slavica Hierosolymitana. (IS ISSN 0334-3405) 2023
Slavica Lundensia. (SW ISSN 0346-8712) 2841, 2960
Slavica Othiniensia. (DK ISSN 0106-1313) 2841
Slavica Slovaca. (CS ISSN 0037-6787) 2841, 2960
Slavisticna Revija. (XV ISSN 0350-6894) 2841, 2960
Slavistische Beitraege. (GW ISSN 0583-5429) 2960, 2841
Slavistische Studienbuecher. Neue Folge. (GW ISSN 0583-5445) 2841
Slavna Nadeje/Glorious Hope. (US ISSN 0700-5202) 4249
Slavonic and East European Review. (UK ISSN 0037-6795) 2960, 2387
Slavonic Review. see Slovansky Prehled 3925
†Slavonski Povijesni Zbornik. (CI ISSN 0352-8650) 5277
Slavyanskaya Filologiya. (RU) 2841
Sleep. (US ISSN 0161-8105) 3354

†Sleep (Substances). (UK ISSN 0268-1498) 5277
Sleep-Learning Association. Journal. (UK ISSN 0037-6817) 1663
Sleep Research. (US ISSN 0093-0407) 3354
Sleepwalker's Journal. (US) 3005
Slesvigland. (GW) 2387
Sleuth Journal. (US) 2960
Slevarenstvi/Foundry Industry. (CS ISSN 0037-6825) 3419
Slezske Muzeum. Casopis. Serie B. Vedy Historicke. (CS ISSN 0323-0678) 2387, 3925
Slezsky Sbornik/Acta Silesiaca. (CS ISSN 0037-6833) 4448, 2322
Slide Atlas of Current Optomology (Year). (US) 3181, 3305
Slide Atlas of Current Orthopaedics (Year). (US) 3181, 23, 3311
Slide Atlas of Current Radiology (Year). (US) 3181, 3363
Slide Atlas of Gastrointestinal Endoscopy (Year). (US) 3181, 3270
Slig Buyers' Guide. (US) 1908
Slightly Soiled. (UK) 2884
Slijtersvakblad. see Drinks 380
Slim Fast Magazine. (US) 3808
Slimming. (UK ISSN 0144-8129) 3612, 3808
Slimming and Nutrition see Slimming 3612
Slingervel. (SA ISSN 0037-685X) 4249, 1265
Slipstream (Niagara Falls). (US ISSN 0749-0771) 3005, 344, 3797
Slo-Pitch News. (US) 4511
Sloan-Kettering Institute for Cancer Research. Progress Report see Sloan-Kettering Institute: Research and Educational Programs 3202
Sloan-Kettering Institute: Research and Educational Programs. 3202
Sloan Management Review. (US ISSN 0019-848X) 1028
Sloane Report. (US ISSN 0882-5939) 1474, 1508
Sloboda. (CS) 2884
Slobodna Rec. (YU ISSN 0037-6884) 2240
Slobodne Slovensko/Free Slovakia. (GW) 2884
Sloejd. (DK ISSN 0106-9608) 357
Slovaci v Zahranici. (CS ISSN 0081-0061) 2387, 249, 2841
Slovak Academy of Sciences. Geophysical Institute. Contributions. (CS ISSN 0586-4607) 1594
Slovak Academy of Sciences. Geophysical Institute. Contributions. Series of Meteorology. (CS ISSN 0231-9004) 3441
Slovak Academy of Sciences. Treatises on Biology. see Slovenska Akademia Vied. Biologicke Prace 456
Slovak American. see Slovak v Amerike 2023
Slovak-American Youth News see S A Y N 2022
Slovak Archeology. see Slovenska Archeologia 284
Slovak Catholic Falcon. (US) 2023, 4275
Slovak Ethnography. see Slovensky Narodopis 2024
Slovak Language. see Slovenska Rec 2841
Slovak Life in Argentina. see Slovensky Zivot 2024
Slovak Literature. see Slovenska Literatura 2960
Slovak Music. (CS) 3580
Slovak Press Digest. (US ISSN 0037-6914) 2023, 3925
Slovak Seismographic Stations: Bratislava, Srobarova, Hurbanovo and Skalnate Pleso. Bulletin. (CS) 1594
Slovak Seismological Stations: Bratislava, Srobarova, Hurbanovo and Skalnate Pleso for the Year. Bulletin. (CS ISSN 0139-9349) 1594
Slovak Shield. (AT) 2023
Slovak Studies Association. Newsletter. (US) 2387, 2262
Slovak Theater. see Slovenske Divadlo 4638
Slovak v Amerike/Slovak American. (US) 2023

Slovak Voice. see Slovensky Hlas 5277
Slovakia. (US ISSN 0583-5623) 2023
Slovakia. see Slowakei 2884
Slovanske Historicke Studie. (CS ISSN 0081-007X) 2387
Slovanske Studie. (CS ISSN 0583-564X) 2387, 2023, 3925, 4448
Slovansky Prehled/Slavonic Review. (CS ISSN 0037-6922) 3925, 2322, 4448
Slovene Studies. (US ISSN 0193-1075) 2387, 2841
Sloveni in Italia. (IT) 2023
Slovenian Chemical Society. Bulletin. see Slovensko Kemijsko Drustvo. Vestnik 1187
Slovenian Journal of Forestry. see Gozdarski Vestnik 2101
Slovenija. (XV ISSN 0353-118X) 2023
Slovenijales. (XV ISSN 0353-1007) 691, 640, 2555, 2561
Slovenska Akademia Vied. Biologicke Prace/Slovak Academy of Sciences. Treatises on Biology. (CS ISSN 0037-6930) 456
†Slovenska Akademia Vied. Geologicky Ustav D. Stura: Zbornik: Zapadne Karpaty. (CS ISSN 0036-1372) 5277
Slovenska Akademija Znanosti in Umetnosti. Filozofski Vestnik. (XV ISSN 0353-4510) 3781, 3925, 4448
Slovenska Archeologia/Slovak Archeology. (CS ISSN 0037-6949) 284
Slovenska Archivistika. (CS) 2387, 3925
Slovenska Bibliografija. Knjige. (XV ISSN 0353-1716) 411
Slovenska Chemicka Spolocnost. Chemicke Zvesti/Chemical Papers. (CS ISSN 0037-6906) 1187
Slovenska Drzava. (CN ISSN 0037-6957) 3925, 2023
†Slovenska Hudba. (CS ISSN 0037-6965) 5277
Slovenska Literatura/Slovak Literature. (CS ISSN 0037-6973) 2960
Slovenska Narodna Bibliografia. Rozpisovy Rad Clanky. (CS) 411
Slovenska Narodna Bibliografia Seria A: Knihy. (CS) 411
Slovenska Narodna Bibliografia Seria B: Periodika. (CS) 411
Slovenska Narodna Bibliografia Seria C: Clanky see Slovenska Narodna Bibliografia. Rozpisovy Rad Clanky 411
Slovenska Narodna Bibliografia Seria C: Mapy. (CS) 411
Slovenska Narodna Bibliografia Seria D: Dizertacne Prace. (CS) 411
Slovenska Narodna Bibliografia Seria E: Specialne Tlace. (CS) 411
Slovenska Narodna Bibliografia Seria F: Firemna Literatura. (CS) 411
Slovenska Narodna Bibliografia Seria G: Grafika. (CS) 352
Slovenska Narodna Bibliografia Seria H: Hudobniny. (CS) 3589, 3580
Slovenska Narodna Bibliografia Seria I: Oficialne Dokumenty. (CS) 412
Slovenska Narodna Bibliografia Seria J: Audiovizualne Dokumenty. (CS) 412
Slovenska Narodna Bibliografia: Serie B-J. (CS) 412
Slovenska Numizmatika. (CS ISSN 0081-0088) 3601
Slovenska Rec/Slovak Language. (CS ISSN 0037-6981) 2841, 2960
Slovenske Banske Muzeum. Zbornik. (CS) 3495, 2387
Slovenske Divadlo/Slovak Theater. (CS ISSN 0037-699X) 4638
Slovenske Kupele. (CS) 2884
Slovenske Ludove Piesne pre Akordeon.(CS) 3580
Slovenske Narodne Muzeum. Annotationes Zoologicae et Botanicae.(CS) 517, 537
Slovenske Narodne Muzeum. Archeologicke Ustav. Fontes Archeologickeho. (CS) 284
Slovenske Narodne Muzeum. Fontes Etnografickeho. (CS) 249

Slovenske Narodne Muzeum. Fontes Historickeho. (CS) **2322**
Slovenske Narodne Muzeum. Zbornik. (CS) **2387**, 284, 3601
Slovenske Narodne Muzeum. Zbornik Etnografia. (CS ISSN 0139-5378) **2387**
▼Slovenske Narodne Noviny. (CS ISSN 0862-8823) **2185**
Slovenske Pohlady na Literaturu a Umenie. (CS ISSN 0037-7007) **2960**, 344
Slovenski Cebelar. (XV ISSN 0350-4697) **2884**
Slovenski Etnograf. (XV ISSN 0350-0330) **249**
†Slovensko. (CS) **5277**
Slovensko Etnolosko Drustvo. Glasnik. (XV ISSN 0351-2908) **2387**, 249, 2058
Slovensko Kemijsko Drustvo. Vestnik/Slovenian Chemical Society. Bulletin. (XV ISSN 0560-3110) **1187**
†Slovensko Morje in Zaledje. (YU) **5277**
†Slovensky Hlas/Slovak Voice. (CN ISSN 0037-7015) **5277**
Slovensky Jazyk a Literatura v Skole. (CS) **2841**, 1760
Slovensky Narodopis/Slovak Ethnography. (CS ISSN 0037-7023) **2024**, 249, 2058
Slovensky Stenograf. (CS) **1061**
Slovensky Zivot/Slovak Life in Argentina. (AG ISSN 0326-3193) **2024**
Slovo. (FR) **3644**
▼Slovo. (RU) **3925**
Slovo a Slovesnost/Word and Writing. (CS ISSN 0037-7031) **2841**
Slovo na Storozhi/Word on Guard. (CN ISSN 0583-6263) **2842**
Slow Dancer. (UK ISSN 0143-1412) **3005**, 2960
Slow Learning Child *see* International Journal of Disability, Development and Education **1736**
Slow Motion Magazine. (US) **3005**
Slowakei/Slovakia. (GW ISSN 0037-7058) **2884**
Slowo i Liturgia. (US ISSN 0892-5100) **4275**
Sludge Newsletter. (US ISSN 0148-4125) **1987**
Slunicko. (CS) **1266**
Sluota. (LI) **2209**
Slur. (CN) **3580**, 1760
Sluzba Bozja. (CI ISSN 0037-7074) **4201**
Sluzba Lidu. (CS ISSN 0037-7082) **1028**, 2589
Sluzben Vesnik na Socijalisticka Republika Makodonija. (YU ISSN 0037-7147) **4073**
Sluzbene Novine Opcine Karlovac. (CI ISSN 0037-7104) **4094**
Sluzbeni Glasnik Opcine Rovinj. (CI ISSN 0037-7120) **4094**
Sluzbeni Vjesnik Opcine Buje, Novigrad i Umag. (CI ISSN 0037-7155) **4094**
Sluzbeni Vjesnik Opcine Krizevci. (CI ISSN 0037-7163) **4094**
Smaafoeretagartidningen *see* Tidningen Foeretagarna **1119**
Smackwarm *see* Nebraska Review **2941**
Smalfilm. (DK) **3517**
Smalfilm og Video. (DK ISSN 0107-8119) **3518**, 1386
Small and Medium Industry Bank, Seoul. Annual Report *see* Industrial Bank of Korea, Seoul. Annual Report (Year) **784**
Small Animal Abstracts *see* Small Animals **4820**
Small Animal Practice. (US) **4816**, 231
Small Animals. (UK ISSN 0961-3501) **4820**, 23, 143
Small Area Summary, Queensland *see* Australia. Bureau of Statistics. Queensland Office. Demography, Queensland **3990**
Small Business *see* Profit **686**
Small Business. (UK ISSN 0262-3102) **1117**
Small Business Advocate (Brooklyn). (US) **1117**

The Small Business Advocate (Mesa). (US) **1117**
Small Business Advocate (Washington). (US ISSN 1045-7658) **1118**
Small Business Bulletin (Worcester). (US ISSN 0893-8326) **1118**
Small Business Chronicle. (US) **1118**, 1028
†Small Business Computer News. (US ISSN 0736-6957) **5277**
Small Business Confidential. (UK ISSN 0265-8399) **1118**
Small Business Controller. (US) **756**
Small Business Economics. (NE ISSN 0921-898X) **1118**
Small Business Magazine. (US) **1118**
▼Small Business, Marketing and Society. (AT ISSN 1035-3097) **1118**
Small Business News. (SA ISSN 0250-2410) **1118**
Small Business News - Akron. (US) **1118**
Small Business News - Cleveland. (US) **1118**
Small Business Opportunities. (US) **1118**
Small Business Preferential Subcontracts Opportunities Monthly. (US ISSN 0887-4050) **1153**
Small Business Report *see* Small Business Bulletin (Worcester) **1118**
Small Business Report. (US) **1118**
Small Business Reporter. (US) **1118**
Small Business Reports (New York). (US ISSN 0164-5382) **1118**
†Small Business Review. (AT ISSN 0811-5680) **5278**
Small Business Sourcebook. (US) **1118**
▼Small Business Start-Up Index. (US) **738**, 1118
Small Business Tax Control. (US ISSN 0162-8658) **1118**
Small Business Tax Planner. (US) **1106**, 1118
Small Business Tax Review. (US ISSN 0276-5322) **1106**, 1118
†Small Business Taxation. (US) **5278**
Small Business Today. (UK) **1118**
Small Business U S A. (US) **1118**
Small Business World Magazine. (CN ISSN 0835-4251) **1118**, 963
†Small Businessman's Clinic. (US ISSN 0094-2464) **5278**
Small Claim Manual. (CN) **2679**
Small College Creativity. (US ISSN 1047-6229) **1716**, 1760
Small Computers in Libraries *see* Computers in Libraries **1459**
Small Computers in Libraries: Buyers Guide and Consultant Directory *see* Computers in Libraries: Buyers Guide & Consultant Directory **1468**
†Small Craft. (UK) **5278**
▼Small Enterprise Development. (UK ISSN 0957-1329) **1118**
Small Enterprises Development, Management and Extension *see* S E D M E **1117**
Small Farm Advocate. (US ISSN 0738-1859) **120**
Small Farm News. (US) **120**
Small Farm Today. (US ISSN 0892-6301) **120**
Small Farmer's Journal. (US ISSN 0743-9989) **120**
Small Fruit Pest Control and Culture Guide *see* Pest Management Recommendations for Small Fruit Crops **187**
Small Group Behavior *see* Small Group Research **4046**
Small Group Letter *see* Discipleship Journal **4236**
Small Group Research. (US ISSN 1046-4964) **4046**, 4449
Small Industries Development Organization. Annual Report. (TZ) **1118**
Small Industries Guide. (II) **1118**
Small Industries Magazine *see* S I M **1117**
Small Industry Bulletin for Asia and the Far East *see* Small Industry Bulletin for Asia and the Pacific **1028**
Small Industry Bulletin for Asia and the Pacific. (UN ISSN 0252-3426) **1028**

Small Offset Australia *see* Australian Small Offset Inplant Printer **5144**
Small or Rural Hospital Report *see* Small or Rural Hospitals Update **2469**
Small or Rural Hospitals Update. (US) **2469**
Small Pond *see* Small Pond Magazine of Literature **2960**
Small Pond Magazine of Literature. (US ISSN 0037-721X) **2960**, 3005
Small Press. (US ISSN 0000-0485) **4137**
Small Press Book Review. (US ISSN 8756-7202) **4137**
†Small Press Book Review Annual. (US ISSN 1052-2697) **5278**
Small Press News. (US) **4137**
Small Press Record of Books in Print. (US) **412**, 4142
Small Press Review. (US ISSN 0037-7228) **4137**, 2575
Small Press Writers and Artists Organization Showcase *see* S P W A O Showcase **2956**
Small Ruminant and Camel Group Document. (UN) **226**
Small Ruminant and Camel Group Newsletter *see* Small Ruminant Research Network Newsletter **226**
Small Ruminant Research. (NE ISSN 0921-4488) **226**, 4816
Small Ruminant Research Network Newsletter. (UN) **226**
Small Scale Industries *see* S S I **1117**
Small Scale Industries Envoy. (II) **1118**
Small-Scale Industries: South Eastern and Benue Plateau States of Nigeria. (NR) **1118**
Small Ships. (UK) **4739**
Small Side Team Games and Potted Sports. (UK) **4488**
Small Talk (North Carolina). (US) **1324**
†Small Talk (Washington). (US) **5278**
Small Time Operator. (US) **1118**
Small Town. (US ISSN 0196-1683) **2496**, 4419
Small Trader and Wholesaler *see* Trader **1055**
†Small Trail. (US) **5278**
▼Small Wars and Insurgencies. (UK ISSN 0959-2318) **3925**, 3471
Small World. (US ISSN 0037-7260) **2561**, 2282
Smaller Business Association of New England Enterprise *see* S B A N E Enterprise **1117**
Smaller Manufacturer *see* Dynamic Business **1114**
Smallholder. (CN ISSN 0383-6312) **120**, 1968
Smallholder. (UK ISSN 0265-7473) **120**, 203
Smallholder Tea Authority. Annual Report. (MW) **192**
▼Smalltalk Report. (US) **1400**
Smalto. (IT) **1215**
▼Smarandache Function Journal. (US ISSN 1053-4792) **3055**
Smar's Industrial Directory of Pakistan. (PK) **1153**
Smart Card Monthly. (US ISSN 0893-9462) **1474**, 1061
Smart Investing. (US) **963**
▼Smart Kids. (US) **1266**, 1244
Smart Money. (US) **963**
Smart Start. (AT ISSN 1035-1116) **3631**
Smart Times. (US) **1465**
▼SmartMoney. (US) **799**
Smarts Insurance Bulletin. (US ISSN 0736-8348) **2542**
Smash. (CN) **4511**
Smash Hits *see* Hot **3555**
Smash Hits. (UK ISSN 0260-3004) **3580**
Smash Hits Magazine. (AT) **3580**, 3518
Smash Hits Yearbook. (AT ISSN 0815-4740) **3580**
Smash Magazine. (CN) **3580**, 3518
Smash-Tennis-Magazin. (SZ) **4511**
Smena. (RU ISSN 0131-6656) **1266**
Smena. (CN) **1266**
Smiles in Dental Health. (US) **3242**
Smit-las *see* Smitweld Reportage **3430**
Smith Alumnae Quarterly. (US) **1324**

†Smith College Museum of Art. Journal.(US) **5278**
Smith College Studies in History. (US ISSN 0081-0193) **2322**
Smith College Studies in Social Work. (US ISSN 0037-7317) **4419**
Smith Funding Report. (US ISSN 0739-2184) **1716**, 23, 3153
Smith - Kettlewell Technical File. (US) **2296**, 1723, 1741, 1908
Smith Papers. (US ISSN 0278-3134) **2164**
Smithersia *see* Syntarsus **592**
Smithsonian. (US ISSN 0037-7333) **4386**, 3533, 4343, 4609
Smithsonian Contributions to Anthropology. (US ISSN 0081-0223) **249**
Smithsonian Contributions to Botany. (US ISSN 0081-024X) **517**
Smithsonian Contributions to Paleobiology. (US ISSN 0081-0266) **3661**
Smithsonian Contributions to the Earth Sciences. (US ISSN 0081-0274) **1548**
Smithsonian Contributions to the Marine Sciences. (US ISSN 0196-0768) **1611**
Smithsonian Contributions to Zoology. (US ISSN 0081-0282) **591**
Smithsonian Folklife Studies. (US) **2058**
†Smithsonian Institution. Archives of American Art. Newsletter. (US) **5278**
†Smithsonian Institution. Astrophysical Observatory. S A O Special Report. (US ISSN 0081-0320) **5278**
Smithsonian Institution Opportunities for Research and Advanced Study *see* Smithsonian Opportunities for Research and Study in History Art Science **4343**
Smithsonian Institution Research Reports. (US ISSN 0364-0175) **4343**
Smithsonian Opportunities for Research and Study in History Art Science. (US ISSN 0081-0339) **4343**
Smithsonian Research Opportunities *see* Smithsonian Opportunities for Research and Study in History Art Science **4343**
Smithsonian Research Reports *see* Smithsonian Institution Research Reports **4343**
Smithsonian Studies in Air and Space. (US) **62**
Smithsonian Studies in American Art *see* American Art **311**
Smithsonian Studies in History and Technology. (US ISSN 0081-0258) **2322**
Smitweld Reportage. (NE) **3430**
Smocking Arts *see* S A G A News **357**
Smocking Arts Guild News *see* S A G A News **357**
Smoke. (UK ISSN 0262-852X) **3005**
Smoke and Cinders. (US) **4715**
Smokebox *see* Pantograph **4712**
Smokeless Air *see* Clean Air **1976**
Smokers Pipeline. (US) **4644**
Smokeshop. (US) **4644**
Smoking and Health Bulletin. (US ISSN 0081-0363) **1540**, 1539
Smoking and Health Newsletter. (US) **3808**, 1539
Smoking Habits of Australians. (AT) **4644**
Smoky Mountain Historical Society. Newsletter. (US) **2164**
Smol. (IS ISSN 0334-7621) **3925**
†Smoloskyp. (US ISSN 0193-5755) **5278**
Smooth Muscle. (UK ISSN 0261-4928) **575**, 3212, 3270
Smurf Collectors Club International Newsletter. (US) **2442**
Smurf Collectors Club Newsletter *see* Smurf Collectors Club International Newsletter **2442**
Snack Food. (US ISSN 0037-7406) **2089**
Snack World. (US ISSN 0896-1670) **2081**

Snackfood International *see* S I **2089**
▼Snail's Pace Review. (US) **3005**
Snake. (JA ISSN 0386-3425) **591**

6666   SNAKE NATION

Snake Nation Review. (US) **3005**
Snake River Echoes. (US) **2422**
Snapdragon see Idaho: The University Magazine **1708**
Snapshot see S N A P Shot **4136**
Snarf. (US) **2884**
Sneak Preview see Media Digest **1754**
SNECS see Studies in Near Eastern Culture and Society **2432**
Sneng Khasi. (II) **249, 2024**
Snews. (US ISSN 0737-2205) **2303**
Snippers. (BE) **1266**
Snips. (US ISSN 0037-7457) **2303**
Sno Times. (US) **4488**
Sno West. (US) **4556**
†SNOBOL4 Information Bulletin. (US) **5278**
Snoeck's Almanach. (BE ISSN 0085-6169) **2515**
Snoeck's: Literatuur Kunst Film Toneel Mode Reizen. (BE ISSN 0085-6177) **2515, 2884**
Snooker Scene. (UK ISSN 0269-0756) **4488**
†Snoopy Magazine. (US) **5278**
Snopje z Domacih in Tujih Njiv Krscanske Misli. (XV) **4249**
Snow Action. (US) **4556**
Snow Brand Milk Products Company. Research Laboratory. Reports/ Yukijirushi Nyugyo Kenkyujo Hokoku.(JA ISSN 0082-4763) **203**
Snow Country. (US ISSN 0896-758X) **4556**
Snow Goer. (CN ISSN 0711-6454) **4556**
▼Snow Goer. (US) **4556**
Snow Surveys and Water Supply Outlook for Alaska see Alaska Snow Surveys - Basin Outlook Reports **4821**
Snowboarder. (US) **4556**
Snowest see Snowmobile West Magazine **4556**
Snowmobile. (US ISSN 0274-8363) **4556**
†Snowmobile Accidents, Manitoba. (CN ISSN 0707-9184) **5278**
Snowmobile Business. (US ISSN 0883-8259) **4556**
Snowmobile Canada. (CN) **4556**
Snowmobile West Magazine. (US ISSN 0164-6540) **4556**
Snowmobiler's Race and Rally see Race & Rally **4554**
Snowshoe. (US) **4556**
Snowy Egret. (US ISSN 0037-7473) **2961**
Snowy Mountains Engineering Corporation. Annual Report. (AT) **1836, 1611**
Snug. (US) **3006**
Snyder-Snider-Schneider Data Letter. (US) **2164**
Sn3 Modeler. (US) **2442**
So-En. (JA) **1294, 2449**
So Planen und Bauen see Deutsches Volksheimstaettenwerk. Informationsdienst **4148**
Soap and Chemical Specialties see Soap, Cosmetics, Chemical Specialties **376**
Soap, Cosmetics, Chemical Specialties. (US ISSN 0091-1372) **376**
Soap Opera Digest. (US) **1380**
Soap Opera Digest Presents. (US) **1380**
Soap Opera Magazine. (US ISSN 1057-9192) **1380**
Soap Opera Stars. (US) **1380**
Soap Opera Update. (US ISSN 0898-1485) **1380**
Soap Opera Weekly. (US) **1380**
Soap, Perfumery and Cosmetics. (UK ISSN 0037-749X) **376**
Soaps, Detergents & Toiletries Review. (II ISSN 0379-5608) **376**
Soaring. (US ISSN 0037-7503) **62, 4488**
†Soaring in the A.C.T. (AT ISSN 0310-9399) **5278**
Sobek. (US) **4556**
Sobek's Adventure Annual see Sobek's Exceptional Adventures **4786**
Sobek's Adventure Vacation see Sobek's Exceptional Adventures **4786**
Sobek's Exceptional Adventures. (US) **4786**
Sober Times. (US) **1539**
Sobering Thoughts. (US) **1539, 4836, 4853**
Sobornost. (UK ISSN 0144-8722) **4249**
Sobre los Derivados de la Cana de Azucar. (CU ISSN 0049-0849) **192**
Soccer America. (US ISSN 0163-4070) **4511**
Soccer and Playgrounds. see Al-Kora wal-Malaeb **4478**
Soccer California. (US) **4511**
Soccer Digest. (US ISSN 0149-2365) **4511**
Soccer Journal. (US ISSN 0560-3617) **4511**
Soccer Magazine. (JA) **4511**
Soccer News. (CN) **4511, 3808**
Soccer Products & Services. (UK) **4511**
Soccer Rulebook. (US ISSN 0731-9541) **4511**
Soccer Year Book for Northern Ireland. (UK ISSN 0081-038X) **4511**
Soccorso Perpetuo di Maria. (IT ISSN 0037-7562) **4201**
Sociaai Dienstbetoon Voor Het Personeel der Stad Antwerpen see S O D I P A **4073**
Sociaal-Economische Raad. Annual Report. see Sociaal-Economische Raad. Jaarverslag **691**
Sociaal-Economische Raad. Jaarverslag/ Sociaal-Economische Raad. Annual Report. (NE ISSN 0560-3641) **691**
Sociaal-Economische Raad Bulletin see S E R Bulletin **883**
Sociaal-Historische Studien. (NE ISSN 0081-0401) **4386, 2334**
Sociaal Maandblad Arbeid. (NE ISSN 0037-7600) **993**
Sociaal Overleg. (BE) **1070**
Social Accounting Monitor. (AT ISSN 0729-0446) **756, 921**
Social Action. (II ISSN 0037-7627) **4386**
Social Action and the Law. (US ISSN 0272-765X) **4047, 2679**
Social Administration. (DK ISSN 0900-1980) **4112**
Social Affairs for Youth. see Qingnian Shejiao **1263**
Social Affairs Statistics of Taiwan/ Chung Hua Min Kuo T'ai-wan Sheng She Hui Shih Yeh T'ung Chi. (CH) **4426**
Social Affairs Study. see Shehui Gongzuo Yanjiu **4385**
Social Alternatives. (AT ISSN 0155-0306) **4449, 3925**
Social Analysis. (AT ISSN 0155-977X) **249, 4449**
Social Anarchism. (US ISSN 0196-4801) **2884, 4853**
†Social and Behavioral Sciences Documents. (US) **5278**
Social and Cultural Reports. see Netherlands. Sociaal en Cultureel Planbureau. Sociale and Culturele Rapporten **4443**
Social and Economic Administration see Social Policy and Administration **4449**
†Social and Economic Impact of New Technology. (UK ISSN 0267-6230) **5278**
Social and Economic Studies. (JM ISSN 0037-7651) **4386, 691**
Social and Economic Update see South African Institute of Race Relations. Update **3947**
Social and Historical Geography see Geographical Abstracts: Human Geography **2268**
Social and Labour Bulletin. (UN ISSN 0377-5380) **993**
▼Social and Legal Studies. (UK ISSN 0964-6639) **4449, 2679**
Social and Liberal Democrats News see Liberal Democrat News **3904**
▼Social and Policy Issues in Education.(US) **1663, 4449**
Social Behavior and Personality. (NZ ISSN 0301-2212) **4047**
Social Behaviour see Journal of Community and Applied Social Psychology **4028**
Social Biology. (US ISSN 0037-766X) **547, 3987**
Social Care Education. (UK ISSN 0955-0801) **4419**
Social Casework see Families in Society **4405**
Social Change. (II ISSN 0049-0857) **4449, 4386**
Social Change and Information Systems.(AT) **2784**
Social Change in Sweden see Viewpoint Sweden **2218**
Social Choice and Welfare. (GW ISSN 0176-1714) **4419**
Social Club Buyers Guide. (UK) **839**
Social Cognition. (US ISSN 0278-016X) **4047**
Social Compass. (UK ISSN 0037-7686) **4449, 4201**
Social Concept. (US ISSN 0737-7762) **691**
Social Debatt. (SW ISSN 0349-9375) **3925, 4449**
Social Defence. (II ISSN 0037-7716) **1522**
Social Democrat. (US) **3925**
▼Social Development. (UK ISSN 0961-205X) **4419**
Social Development see Social Development Overview **5278**
Social Development Issues. (US) **4419**
†Social Development News. (PH ISSN 0115-2661) **5278**
Social Development Newsletter. (UN) **4449**
†Social Development Overview. (CN) **5278**
Social Dynamics. (SA ISSN 0253-3952) **4387**
Social, Economic and Political Studies of the Middle East. (NE ISSN 0085-6193) **2432**
Social Education. (US ISSN 0037-7724) **4387, 1663**
Social Education Yearly. (CH) **1664**
Social Epistemology. (UK ISSN 0269-1728) **3781, 2515, 4387**
Social Europe. (EI ISSN 0255-0776) **4419, 1664**
Social Forces. (US ISSN 0037-7732) **4449**
Social Foundations of the Policy Process see Studies in Political Economy **898**
Social History. see Histoire Sociale **2312**
Social History. (UK ISSN 0307-1022) **4387**
Social History of Alcohol Review. (US ISSN 0887-2783) **385, 2422**
Social History of Canada. (CN ISSN 0085-6207) **2422**
Social History of Medicine. (UK ISSN 0951-631X) **3153**
Social History Project Newsletter. (JM) **2422**
Social Housing. (UK) **2496**
Social Indicators. (US) **4449**
Social Indicators By Prefecture (Year). (JA) **4426, 4586**
Social Indicators of the Philippines see Philippines. National Census and Statistics Office. Social Indicator **5258**
Social Indicators Research. (NE ISSN 0303-8300) **4449**
Social Insects. see Insectes Sociaux **533**
▼Social Intelligence. (UK ISSN 0961-2882) **4387**
Social Inventions. (UK ISSN 0954-206X) **4449**
Social Issues in Southeast Asia. (SI) **4449**
Social Justice. (US) **1523, 2729**
Social Justice Research. (US ISSN 0885-7466) **4449**
Social Justice Review. (US ISSN 0037-7767) **4387, 4275, 4449**
Social Life. (II) **4449**
Social Networks. (NE ISSN 0378-8733) **4387**
†Social Order Series. (US) **5278**
Social Orders Series. (US ISSN 0275-7524) **4449**
Social Perspectives. (KE) **4449**
†Social Perspectives. (US) **5278**
Social Philosophy and Policy. (US ISSN 0265-0525) **3781**
Social Planning - Policy & Development Abstracts. (US ISSN 0195-7988) **4426, 23**
Social Policy. (US ISSN 0037-7783) **4449**
Social Policy and Administration. (UK ISSN 0144-5596) **4449, 1028**
Social Policy Research Centre Newsletter see S P R C Newsletter **4418**
Social Policy Research Centre Reports and Proceedings see S P R C Reports and Proceedings **4418**
Social Policy Review. (UK) **4387**
Social Practice. (US) **4387**
Social Pratique. (FR) **691**
Social Problems. (US ISSN 0037-7791) **4449**
Social Psychiatry see Social Psychiatry and Psychiatric Epidemiology **3354**
Social Psychiatry and Psychiatric Epidemiology/Sozialpsychiatrie/ Psychiatrie Sociale. (GW ISSN 0933-7954) **3354**
Social Psychological Applications to Social Issues. (US) **4047, 4449**
Social Psychology Quarterly. (US ISSN 0190-2725) **4450**
Social Questions Bulletin. (US ISSN 0731-0234) **4249, 4450**
Social Research. (US ISSN 0037-783X) **4387, 3925**
Social Research Review/Riv'on Le-Mehkar Hevrati. (IS ISSN 0334-4762) **4387**
Social Responsibility. (UK) **4419**
Social Responsibility: Business, Journalism, Law, Medicine. (US ISSN 0732-9938) **3781, 2575, 2679, 3153**
Social Review. see Sosiaalinen Aikakauskirja **4421**
Social Science. see Shehui Kexue (Lanzhou) **4386**
†Social Science (Chapel Hill). (US ISSN 0886-280X) **5278**
Social Science Abroad. see Guowai Shehui Kexue **4373**
Social Science & Medicine. (US ISSN 0277-9536) **3153, 4450**
Social Science Computer Review. (US ISSN 0894-4393) **1691, 4083, 4387**
Social Science Data Archives Newsletter see S S D A Newsletter **4385**
Social Science Federation of Canada. Annual Report. (CN) **4387**
Social Science Front. see Shehui Kexue Zhanxian **4386**
Social Science History. (US ISSN 0145-5532) **4387**
Social Science in Ningxia. see Ningxia Shehui Kexue **4381**
Social Science in Xinjiang. see Xinjiang Shehui Kexue **4392**
Social Science in Yunnan. see Yunnan Shehui Kexue **4393**
Social Science Information. (UK ISSN 0539-0184) **4387, 249, 4450**
Social Science Information and Documentation Liaison Bulletin see S S I D Liaison Bulletin **4385**
Social Science Journal see Korean Social Science Journal **4378**
Social Science Journal. see Shehui Kexue Jikan **4386**
Social Science Journal. (US) **4387**
Social Science Microcomputer Review see Social Science Computer Review **1691**
†Social Science Monitor. (US ISSN 0195-7791) **5278**
Social Science Monographs. (UK ISSN 0307-0042) **4387**
†Social Science Probings. (II) **5278**
†Social Science Quarterly. (US ISSN 0038-4941) **4387**
Social Science Research. see Shehui Kexue Yanjiu **4386**
Social Science Research. (US ISSN 0049-089X) **4387**
Social Science Review. (CE) **4387**
Social Sciences. see Sahoekwahak **4385**
Social Sciences. see Shehui Kexue (Shanghai) **4386**
Social Sciences. (RU ISSN 0049-0911) **4387**

SOCIEDAD

Social Sciences and Humanities Index see Humanities Index **2520**
Social Sciences and Humanities Index see Social Sciences Index **4396**
Social Sciences Citation Index. (US ISSN 0091-3707) **4396, 23**
Social Sciences Citation Index Journal Citation Reports. (US ISSN 0161-3162) **4396**
†Social Sciences in Canada. (CN ISSN 0049-092X) **5278**
Social Sciences in China. (CC ISSN 0252-9203) **4388**
†Social Sciences in Forestry. (US) **5278**
Social Sciences in Guizhou (Economics Edition). see Guizhou Shehui Kexue (Jingji Ban) **867**
Social Sciences in Guizhou (Literature, History, Philosophy Edition). see Guizhou Shehui Kexue (Wen-Shi-Zhe Ban) **4373**
Social Sciences in Higher Education. see Gaoxiao Shehui Kexue **4373**
Social Sciences in North Dakota see North Dakota Human Services **4415**
Social Sciences Index. (US ISSN 0094-4920) **4396, 23**
Social Sciences Information - Information sur les Sciences Sociales see Social Science Information **4387**
Social Sciences Journal/Shakai Kagaku Kenkyu. (JA) **4388**
Social Sciences Research Journal. (II ISSN 0251-348X) **4388**
Social Sciences Research Series. (II) **4388**
Social Scientist. (II ISSN 0970-0293) **4388**
Social Scientist. (NR ISSN 0081-0487) **4388**
Social Security. (IS) **2542**
Social Security Bulletin. (US ISSN 0037-7910) **2542, 4419**
Social Security Documentation: African Series. (SZ ISSN 0379-704X) **2542**
Social Security Documentation: Asian Series. (SZ ISSN 0250-4057) **2542**
Social Security Documentation: European Series. (SZ) **2542**
Social Security Library Bulletin. (UK) **2542**
Social Security Manual. (US) **2542**
Social Security Practice Guide. (US) **2543, 4419**
Social Security Reporter. (AT ISSN 0817-3524) **2543, 4419**
Social Security Rulings, Acquiesence Rulings on Federal Old-Age, Survivors, Disability, Supplemental Security Income and Black Lung Benefits. (US) **2543, 4419**
Social Security Rulings on Federal Old-Age, Survivors, Disability, Supplemental Security Income and Black Lung Benefits see Social Security Rulings, Acquiescence Rulings on Federal Old-Age, Survivors, Disability, Supplemental Security Income and Black Lung Benefits **2543**
Social Security Series for Asia and Oceania see Asian News Sheet **2527**
Social Service Abstracts. (UK ISSN 0309-4693) **4427, 23**
Social Service Jobs. (US) **3631, 4047, 4420**
Social Service Organizations and Agencies Directory. (US ISSN 0737-3627) **4420**
Social Service Review. (US ISSN 0037-7961) **4420**
Social Services for Nova Scotians see Nova Scotia Department of Community Services (Year) **4415**
Social Services in Nova Scotia see Nova Scotia Department of Community Services (Year) **4415**
Social Services Research. (UK ISSN 0265-6957) **4420, 1244**
Social Services Research Group. Journal see Research, Policy and Planning **4417**
Social Services Yearbook. (UK ISSN 0307-093X) **4420**

†Social Sikring. (DK ISSN 0900-2030) **5278**
Social Strategies. (SZ) **4450**
Social Studies. (US ISSN 0037-7996) **1664**
Social Studies. (IE) **4450, 4201**
Social Studies Materials and Resources Data Book. Annual see Data Book of Social Studies Materials and Resources **5177**
Social Studies of Science. (UK ISSN 0306-3127) **4343, 4388, 4450**
Social Studies Professional. (US ISSN 0586-6235) **4388, 1760**
Social Studies Review. (US) **4388**
Social Studies Review. (UK ISSN 0267-0712) **4388**
Social Survey. (AT ISSN 0037-8011) **4420**
Social Text. (US ISSN 0164-2472) **4450**
Social Theory: A Bibliographic Series. (US ISSN 0887-3577) **4458, 412**
Social Theory and Practice. (US ISSN 0037-802X) **4450, 3781, 3925**
Social Thought. (US ISSN 0099-183X) **4420**
Social Tidsskrift. (DK) **4450**
Social Trends see Personeel **1069**
Social Trends in New Zealand. (NZ) **4458, 4586**
Social Welfare. (II ISSN 0037-8038) **4420**
Social Welfare Law. (UK) **2679, 4420**
Social Welfare Services in Japan. (JA) **4420**
Social Welfare, Social Planning, Policy and Social Development see Social Planning - Policy & Development Abstracts **4426**
Social Work/Maatskaplike Werk. (SA ISSN 0037-8054) **4420**
Social Work. (US ISSN 0037-8046) **4420**
Social Work. see Socijalni Rad **4421**
Social Work and Christianity. (US ISSN 0737-5778) **4420, 4275**
Social Work and Social Issues. (US ISSN 0081-055X) **4420**
Social Work Education. (UK ISSN 0261-5479) **4420**
Social Work Education Reporter. (US ISSN 0037-8062) **1664, 4420**
Social Work Forum. (II ISSN 0583-7065) **4420**
Social Work in Education. (US ISSN 0162-7961) **4420**
Social Work in Health Care. (US ISSN 0098-1389) **4420, 4113**
Social Work Information Bulletin. (UK ISSN 0144-0969) **4388, 4420**
Social Work Papers of the School of Social Work, University of Southern California see University of Southern California. School of Social Work. Social Work Papers **5298**
Social Work Practice/Maatskaplikewerk-Praktyk. (SA) **4420**
Social Work Research and Abstracts. (US ISSN 0148-0847) **4427, 23**
Social Work Today. (UK ISSN 0037-8070) **4420**
Social Work with Groups. (US ISSN 0160-9513) **4420**
Social Work Year Book see Encyclopedia of Social Work **4404**
Social Worker/Travailleur Social. (CN ISSN 0037-8089) **4420**
Sociale Wetenschappen. (NE ISSN 0037-8097) **4388**
Sociale Ydelser, Hvem, Hvad, og Hvornaar. (DK ISSN 0107-5047) **2543**
Socialfoerfattningar. (SW ISSN 0037-8100) **4420, 2679**
Socialism and Democracy. (US ISSN 0885-4300) **3925**
Socialism: Theory and Practice. (RU) **3925**
Socialisme. (BE ISSN 0037-8127) **3925**
Socialismo & Democracia. (BL) **3925**
Socialismo & Politica. (PO) **3925**
Socialismo Democratico see Umanita **3931**
Socialismo y Participacion. (PE) **3926**
Socialist see Labour & Trade Union Review **2586**

Socialist see Guardian **3897**
Socialist. (US ISSN 0884-6154) **3926**
†Socialist Action. (NZ ISSN 0037-816X) **5278**
Socialist Affairs. (UK ISSN 0049-0946) **3926**
Socialist Challenge. (CN) **3926, 2589, 4853**
Socialist Forum. (US ISSN 0037-8194) **3926**
Socialist India. (II ISSN 0037-8208) **3926**
Socialist Nation. (CE) **3926**
Socialist Perspective. (II ISSN 0970-8863) **3926, 4388**
Socialist Politics. (NZ) **3926**
Socialist Register. (UK ISSN 0081-0606) **3926**
Socialist Republic. (US) **2884**
Socialist Republic see An Reabhloid **3940**
Socialist Review (San Francisco). (US ISSN 0161-1801) **3926**
Socialist Revolution see Socialist Review (San Francisco) **3926**
Socialist Standard. (UK ISSN 0037-8259) **3926**
Socialist Thought and Practice see Aktuelna Pitanja Socijalizma **3871**
Socialist Tribune see Socialist **3926**
Socialist Voice see Proletarian Revolution **3920**
Socialist Worker. (CN ISSN 0836-7094) **3926**
Socialist Worker Review see International Socialism **2869**
Socialist World. (II) **3926**
Socialist Youth see Left **3904**
Socialist Youth see Labour Student **3904**
Socialista see Pensare Faenza **2879**
Socialiste Chretien see L'Espoir du Monde **3892**
Socialisticka Skola. (CS ISSN 0037-8291) **1664**
Socialisticka Zakonnost see Pravo a Zakonnost **2667**
Socialisticke Zemedelstvi. (CS ISSN 0037-8313) **120**
Socialisticky Obchod. (CS ISSN 0037-8321) **839**
Socialisticky Zemedelec. (CS) **120, 2108, 2589**
Socialisticno Kmetijstvo see Sodobno Kmetijstvo **120**
Socialistiske Perspektiver Forlag Status see S F. Status **3924**
Socialmedicinsk Tidskrift. (SW ISSN 0037-833X) **3154**
Socialna Politika. (CS) **4388, 2543**
Socialni Politika. (CS ISSN 0049-0962) **3926, 4420, 4450**
Socialnytt see Vael & Ve **4114**
Socialpaedagogen. (DK ISSN 0105-5399) **4421**
Socialpaedagogernes Landsforbund. T R Information. (Tillidsrepraesentant Information) (DK ISSN 0108-2132) **1664**
Socialraadgiveren. (DK ISSN 0108-6103) **4421**
Socialt Forum see Kommun-Aktuelt **4089**
Sociedad Americana de Oftalmologia y Optometria. Archivos/American Society for Ophthalmology and Optometry. Archives. (CK ISSN 0037-8364) **3305**
Sociedad Andaluza de Ortopedia y Traumatologia. Revista. (SP ISSN 0212-0771) **3311**
Sociedad Antioquena de Ingenieros. Informador see Noti S A I **1832**
Sociedad Antioquena de Ingenieros y Arquitectos Revista S A I see Revista S A I **1835**
Sociedad Argentina de Botanica. Boletin.(AG ISSN 0373-580X) **517**
Sociedad Argentina de Defensa de la Tradicion, Familia y Propiedad Pregon de la T F P see Pregon de la T F P **5261**
Sociedad Argentina de Escritores. Boletin. (AG) **2961**
Sociedad Argentina de Estudios Geograficos. Contribuciones Cientificas. (AG) **2262**

Sociedad Argentina de Estudios Geograficos Boletin. (AG ISSN 0325-2698) **2262**
Sociedad Bolivariana de Venezuela. Revista. (VE ISSN 0037-8402) **2422**
Sociedad Boliviana de Historia Natural. Revista. (BO) **456**
Sociedad Botanica de Mexico. Boletin. (MX ISSN 0185-3619) **517**
Sociedad Castellano-Astur-Leonosa de Pediatria. Boletin see Pediatria. Boletin **3323**
Sociedad Castellonense de Cultura. Boletin. (SP ISSN 0210-1475) **2387**
Sociedad Chihuahuense de Estudios Historicos. Boletin. (MX) **2422**
Sociedad Chilena de Quimica. Boletin/Chilean Chemical Society. Bulletin. (CL ISSN 0366-1644) **1188**
Sociedad Cientifica Argentina. Anales. (AG ISSN 0037-8437) **4343**
Sociedad Cientifica Argentina. Ciclo de Conferencias. (AG) **4343**
Sociedad Colombiana de Control de Malezas y Fisiologia Vegetal Noticias COMALFI see Noticias COMALFI **186**
Sociedad Colombiana de Control de Malezas y Fisiologia Vegetal Revista COMALFI see Revista COMALFI **191**
Sociedad Colombiana de Economistas. Boletin Informativo see Criterio Economico **658**
Sociedad Colombiana de Economistas. Revista see Criterio Economico **658**
Sociedad Colombiana de Endocrinologia. Revista. (CK ISSN 0120-1182) **3256**
Sociedad Colombiana de Ortodoncia. Revista. (CK ISSN 0037-8453) **3242**
Sociedad Colombiana de Quimicos Farmaceuticos. Boletin. (CK ISSN 0037-8461) **3743, 1188**
Sociedad de Biologia de Concepcion. Boletin. (CL ISSN 0037-850X) **456**
Sociedad de Ciencias Naturales la Salle. Memoria. (VE ISSN 0037-8518) **4343**
Sociedad de Estudios Vascos. Boletin. (SP) **249**
Sociedad de Estudios Vascos. Cuadernos de Seccion. Antropologia y Etnografia. (SP ISSN 0213-0297) **249, 2024**
Sociedad de Estudios Vascos. Cuadernos de Seccion. Artes Plasticas y Monumentales. (SP ISSN 0212-3215) **344**
Sociedad de Estudios Vascos. Cuadernos de Seccion. Ciencias Medicas. (SP ISSN 0213-3601) **3154**
Sociedad de Estudios Vascos. Cuadernos de Seccion. Ciencias Naturales. (SP ISSN 0212-4173) **456**
Sociedad de Estudios Vascos. Cuadernos de Seccion. Ciencias Sociales y Economicas. (SP) **691**
Sociedad de Estudios Vascos. Cuadernos de Seccion. Cinematografia. (SP) **3518**
Sociedad de Estudios Vascos. Cuadernos de Seccion. Derecho. (SP ISSN 0213-0483) **2679**
Sociedad de Estudios Vascos. Cuadernos de Seccion. Educacion. (SP ISSN 0213-3636) **1664**
Sociedad de Estudios Vascos. Cuadernos de Seccion. Folklore. (SP ISSN 0212-7547) **2058**
Sociedad de Estudios Vascos. Cuadernos de Seccion. Historia y Geografia. (SP ISSN 0212-6397) **2322, 2262**
Sociedad de Estudios Vascos. Cuadernos de Seccion. Lengua y Literatura. (SP ISSN 0212-3223) **2961, 2842**
Sociedad de Estudios Vascos. Cuadernos de Seccion. Medios de Comunicacion. (SP ISSN 0213-0289) **1342**
Sociedad de Estudios Vascos. Cuadernos de Seccion. Musica. (SP ISSN 0213-0815) **3580**

6668 SOCIEDAD

Sociedad de Estudios Vascos. Cuadernos de Seccion. Prehistoria y Arqueologia. (SP ISSN 0213-3024) **284**

Sociedad de Estudios Vascos. Memoria. (SP) **249**

Sociedad de Eusko Folklore. Anuario. (SP ISSN 0210-7732) **249, 2058**

Sociedad de Ingenieros. Informaciones y Memorias. (PE) **1836**

Sociedad Espanola de Automoviles de Turismo. Memoria y Balance. (SP) **4786, 4702**

Sociedad Espanola de Ceramica y Vidrio. Boletin. (SP) **1166**

Sociedad Espanola de Historia de la Medicina. Boletin. (SP ISSN 0583-7480) **3154**

Sociedad Espanola de Horticultura. Revista. (SP) **2139**

Sociedad Espanola de Quimica Clinica. Revista. (SP ISSN 0213-8514) **1188**

Sociedad Espanola de Socorros Mutuos y Beneficencia. Boletin. (AG ISSN 0037-8569) **4421**

Sociedad Geografica de Colombia. Boletin. (CK ISSN 0037-8577) **2262**

Sociedad Geografica de Lima, Peru. Boletin. (PE ISSN 0037-8585) **2262**

Sociedad Geologica del Peru. Boletin. (PE ISSN 0079-1091) **1580, 2422**

Sociedad Interamericana de Planificacion. Correo Informativo see Revista Interamericana de Planificacion. Correo Informativo **934**

Sociedad Interamericana de Planificacion. Ediciones S I A P. (AG) **2496**

Sociedad Interamericana de Planificacion. Revista. (CK) **691**

Sociedad Latinoamericana de Historia de las Ciencias y la Tecnologia. Boletin Informativo. (BL ISSN 0185-5107) **4343, 2422, 4609**

Sociedad Matematica Mexicana. Boletin.(MX ISSN 0037-8615) **3055**

Sociedad Mexicana de Geografia y Estadistica. Boletin. (MX ISSN 0049-1004) **2268**

†Sociedad Mexicana de Historia de la Ciencia y de la Tecnologia. Actas. (MX) **5278**

Sociedad Mexicana de Historia Natural. Revista. (MX) **1548**

Sociedad Mexicana de Mecanica de Suelos. Boletin. (MX ISSN 0185-4003) **1873**

Sociedad Mexicana de Micologia. Boletin see Revista Mexicana de Micologia **516**

Sociedad Nacional de Agricultura Boletin de Mercado see S N A Boletin de Mercado **118**

Sociedad Nacional de Agricultura Boletino Economico see S N A Boletino Economico **118**

Sociedad Nacional de Agricultura Vocero Agricola see S N A Vocero Agricola **118**

Sociedad Peruana de Historia. Serie: Actos Academicos. (PE) **2422**

Sociedad Quimica de Mexico. Revista. (MX ISSN 0583-7693) **1188**

Sociedad Quimica del Peru. Boletin. (PE ISSN 0037-8623) **1188**

Sociedad Rural Argentina. Anales. (AG ISSN 0037-8631) **226**

Sociedad Rural Argentina. Boletin. (AG ISSN 0037-864X) **120**

Sociedad Rural Argentina. Memoria. (AG ISSN 0081-0630) **226**

Sociedad Uruguaya. (UY ISSN 0081-0649) **4450**

Sociedad Vasco-Navarra de Pediatria. Boletin. (SP ISSN 0037-8658) **3326**

Sociedad Venezolana de Cirugia Boletin.(VE) **3384**

Sociedad Venezolana de Espeleologia. Boletin. (VE ISSN 0583-7731) **1580**

Sociedad Venezolana de Geologos. Boletin. (VE) **1580**

Sociedad y Derecho. (PE) **2679**

Sociedade Brasileira. (BL) **421**

Sociedade Brasileira de Direito Internacional. Boletim. (BL) **2729**

Sociedade Brasileira de Economistas Rurais. Anais da Reuniao see Congresso Brasileiro de Economia e Sociologia Rural. Anais **149**

Sociedade Brasileira de Estudos sobre Discos Voadores. Boletim. (BL ISSN 0037-8666) **62**

Sociedade Brasileira de Geografia. Boletim. (BL ISSN 0037-8674) **2262**

Sociedade Brasileira de Medicina Tropical. Revista. (BL ISSN 0037-8682) **3223**

Sociedade Brasileira de Zootecnia. Revista. (BL ISSN 0100-4859) **4816, 203**

Sociedade Broteriana. Anuario. (PO ISSN 0373-4641) **517**

Sociedade Broteriana. Boletim. (PO ISSN 0081-0657) **517**

Sociedade Broteriana. Memorias. (PO ISSN 0081-0665) **456**

Sociedade das Ciencias Medicas. Jornal see Jornal das Ciencias Medicas **3113**

Sociedade de Lingua Portuguesa. Boletim. (PO ISSN 0049-1039) **2842**

Sociedade de Medicina e Cirurgia de Sao Jose do Rio Preto. Revista. (BL) **3384**

Sociedade e Estado. (BL ISSN 0102-6992) **4450, 4421**

Sociedade e Territorio. (PO) **4450, 2262**

Sociedade Entomologica do Brasil. Anais. (BL ISSN 0301-8059) **537**

Sociedade Paranaense de Matematica. Boletim. (BL ISSN 0037-8712) **3055**

Sociedade Paranaense de Matematica. Monografias. (BL ISSN 0102-3292) **3055**

Sociedade Portuguesa de Antropologia e Etnologia. Trabalhos see Trabalhos de Antropologia e Etnologia **251**

Sociedade Portuguesa de Reumatologia. Boletim Informativo. (PO) **3370**

Sociedades Cotizadas en Bolsa. (SP) **963**

Sociedades por Acoes. (BL) **691, 2679**

Le Societa. (IT) **4450**

Societa Astronomica Italiana. Memorie. (IT ISSN 0037-8720) **369**

Societa degli Ingegneri e degli Architetti in Torino. Atti e Rassegna Tecnica. (IT ISSN 0004-7287) **1874, 306**

Societa dei Naturalisti in Napoli. Bulletin. (IT ISSN 0366-2047) **456**

Societa di Ortopedia e Traumatologia dell' Italia Meridionale ed Insulare. Atti e Memorie. (IT ISSN 0394-0713) **3311**

Societa di Studi Romagnoli. Guide. (IT ISSN 0081-0681) **2387**

Societa di Studi Valdesi. Bollettino. (IT ISSN 0037-8739) **2387**

▼Societa e Ambiente. (IT) **4450**

Societa e la Scienza. (IT ISSN 0391-609X) **4344**

Societa e Storia. (IT) **2322**

Societa Emiliana Romagnola Triveneta di Ortopedia e Traumatologia. Atti. (IT) **3311**

Societa Entomologica Italiana. Bollettino.(IT ISSN 0373-3491) **537**

Societa Entomologica Italiana. Bollettino e Memorie see Societa Entomologica Italiana. Bollettino **537**

Societa Entomologica Italiana. Memorie.(IT) **537**

Societa Geografica Italiana. Bollettino. (IT ISSN 0037-8755) **2262**

Societa Geologica Italiana. Bollettino e Memorie see Societa Geologica Italiana. Bollettino, Memorie e Rendiconti **1580**

Societa Geologica Italiana. Bollettino, Memorie e Rendiconti. (IT) **1580**

Societa Italiana di Biologia Sperimentale. Bollettino. (IT ISSN 0037-8771) **456**

Societa Italiana di Cardiologia. Bollettino see Cardiologia **3205**

Societa Italiana di Fisica. Congresso Nazionale. (IT) **3831**

Societa Italiana di Fisica. Nuovo Cimento A. (IT ISSN 0369-3546) **3831, 1809**

Societa Italiana di Fisica. Nuovo Cimento B. (IT ISSN 0369-3554) **3831, 369**

Societa Italiana di Fisica. Nuovo Cimento C. (IT ISSN 0390-5551) **3831, 1594**

Societa Italiana di Fisica. Nuovo Cimento D. (IT ISSN 0392-6737) **3831**

Societa Italiana di Fisica. Rivista del Nuovo Cimento. (IT ISSN 0393-697X) **3831**

Societa Italiana di Fitosociologia. Notiziario see Fitosociologia **502**

Societa Italiana di Fotogrammetria e Topografia. Bollettino. (IT ISSN 0392-4424) **2262**

Societa Italiana di Malacologia Notiziario S I M see Notiziario S I M **589**

Societa Italiana di Scienza dell'Alimentazione. Rivista. (IT ISSN 0391-4887) **2081**

Societa Italiana di Scienze Farmaceutiche Documenti see S.I.S.F. Documenti **3742**

Societa Italiana di Scienze Naturali e del Museo Civico di Storia Naturale. Atti. (IT ISSN 0037-8844) **4344**

Societa Italiana di Scienze Naturali e del Museo Civico di Storia Naturale. Memorie. (IT ISSN 0376-2726) **4344**

Societa Italiana per il Progresso delle Scienze. Atti della Riunione. (IT) **4344**

Societa Italiana per l'Esercizio delle Telecomunicazioni P.A. Selezionando S I P see Selezionando S I P **1366**

Societa Lombarda di Medicina Legale e delle Assicurazioni. Archivio. (IT) **3265, 2543**

Societa Medica Chirurgica, Cremona. Bollettino. (IT ISSN 0037-8852) **3384**

Societa Medico Chirurgica de Pavia. Bollettino. (IT ISSN 0390-8283) **3263**

Societa Medico-Chirurgica di Modena. Bollettino. (IT) **3384**

Societa Paleontologica Italiana. Bollettino. (IT ISSN 0375-7633) **3661**

Societa per gli Studi Storici, Archeologici ed Artistici della Provincia di Cuneo. Bollettino. (IT) **284, 344**

Societa Sarda di Scienze Naturali. Bollettino. (IT ISSN 0392-6710) **456, 567, 591, 1548**

Societa Savonese di Storia Patria. Atti e Memorie. (IT ISSN 0392-033X) **2387, 284**

Societa Storica Valtellinese. Bollettino. (IT ISSN 0085-6231) **2322**

Societa Tiburtina di Storia e d'Arte. Atti e Memorie. (IT) **284**

Societa Toscana di Scienza Naturali. Atti. Serie A. (IT) **4344**

Societa Toscana di Scienza Naturali. Atti. Serie B. (IT) **4344**

Societas Gaius Julius Caesar Octavianus. Newsletter see Journal of Ancient and Medieval Studies **2315**

Societas Internationalis Odonatologica. Rapid Communications. (NE) **456**

Societas pro Fauna et Flora Fennica. Memoranda. (FI ISSN 0373-6873) **456**

Societas Qualitatis. (JA) **1836**

Societas Scientiarum Fennica. Arsbok Vuosikirja Series A. (FI ISSN 0783-5876) **2387**

Societas Scientiarum Fennica. Arsbok Vuosikirja Series B. Sphinx. (FI ISSN 0783-5892) **2387**

Societas Uralo-Altaica. Veroeffentlichungen. (GW ISSN 0340-6423) **2842**

Societat d'Historia Natural de Balears. Bolleti. (SP ISSN 0583-7405) **456, 1580**

Societat d'Onomastica. Butlleti Interior. (SP ISSN 0213-4098) **2842**

Societatis Geologorum Poloniae. Annales. see Polskie Towarzystwo Geologiczne. Rocznik **1577**

Societe. (US) **4288**

Societe. see Society **4450**

Societe Academique des Arts Liberaux de Paris. Collection. (FR) **2961**

Societe Archeologique de Tarn et Garonne. Bulletin Archeologique, Historique et Artistique. (FR) **284**

Societe Archeologique de Touraine. Bulletin. (FR) **284**

Societe Archeologique de Touraine. Memoires. (FR) **284, 2387**

Societe Archeologique, Historique, Litteraire & Scientifique du Gers. Bulletin. (FR ISSN 0037-8895) **284, 2387**

Societe Astronomique de Bordeaux. Bulletin. (FR ISSN 0081-0738) **369**

Societe Belge d'Etudes Geographiques. Bulletin/Belgische Vereniging voor Aardrijkskundige Studies. Tijdschrift. (BE ISSN 0037-8925) **2262**

Societe Belge d'Ophtalmologie. Bulletin. (BE ISSN 0081-0746) **3305**

Societe Belge de Geologie. Bulletin/ Belgische Vereniging voor Geologie. Bulletin. (BE ISSN 0772-9464) **1580, 3661**

Societe Belge de Medecine Tropicale. Annales/Belgische Vereniging voor Tropische Geneeskunde. Annalen. (BE ISSN 0365-6527) **3223**

Societe Belge de Photogrammetrie - Teledetection et Cartographie. Bulletin Trimestriel. (BE ISSN 0771-7873) **2262**

Societe Botanique de Geneve. Travaux see Saussurea **517**

Societe Calviniste de France. Revue Reformee. (FR ISSN 0035-3884) **4249**

Societe Canadienne d'Etudes Ethniques. Bulletin. see Canadian Ethnic Studies Association. Bulletin **1996**

Societe Canadienne de Genie Biomedical. Bulletin. see Canadian Medical and Biological Engineering Society. Newsletter **3086**

Societe Canadienne de la Biologie Cellulaire et Moleculaire Bulletin. see Canadian Society for Cell and Molecular Biology Bulletin **523**

Societe Canadienne de Physiologie Vegetale. Bulletin. see Canadian Society of Plant Physiologists. Bulletin **499**

Societe Canadienne des Etudes Bibliques. Bulletin. see Canadian Society of Biblical Studies. Bulletin **4168**

Societe Canadienne des Sciences Judiciaires Journal. see Canadian Society of Forensic Science Journal **2611**

Societe Chateaubriand. Bulletin. Nouvelle Serie. (FR ISSN 0081-0754) **2961**

Societe Chimique de France. Bulletin. (FR ISSN 0037-8968) **1188**

Societe d'Amenagement Regional. Rapport Annuel. see Regional Development Corporation. Annual Report **882**

Societe d'Anthropologie de Paris. Bulletins & Memoires. (FR ISSN 0037-8984) **249**

Societe d'Archeologie Copte. Bibliotheque de Manuscrits. (UA ISSN 0068-5283) **285**

Societe d'Archeologie Copte. Bulletin. (UA ISSN 0068-5291) **285**

Societe d'Archeologie Copte. Textes et Documents. (UA ISSN 0068-5305) **285**

Societe d'Archeologie, d'Histoire et de Folklore de Nivelles et du Brabant Wallon. Annales. (BE) **285, 2387**

Societe d'Archeologie et d'Histoire de la Charente Maritime. Bulletin de Liaison. (FR) **285**

SOCIETE LINNEENNE 6669

Societe d'Archeologie et d'Histoire de la Manche. Departement de la Manche. Revue. (FR ISSN 0583-8193) **285**
Societe d'Art et d'Histoire du Diocese de Liege. Bulletin. (BE) **344**, 2387
Societe d'Astronomie Populaire de Toulouse. Bulletin Mensuel *see* Pulsar **368**
Societe d'Edition de Periodiques Sportifs. (FR ISSN 0015-9557) **4488**
Societe d'Emulation de Montbeliard. Bulletin et Memoires. (FR) **2387**
Societe d'Emulation du Bourbonnais. Bulletin. (FR ISSN 0037-9158) **285**, 2322
Societe d'Emulation Historique et Litteraire d'Abbeville. Bulletin. (FR ISSN 0081-0819) **2387**
Societe d'Ergonomie de Langue Francaise. Actes du Congres. (BE ISSN 0081-0835) **1836**
Societe d'Etudes. Revue d'Etudes. (FR ISSN 0049-1063) **1687**
Societe d'Etudes et de Documentation Economiques, Industrielles et Sociales Analyses de la S.E.D.E.I.S. *see* Analyses de la S.E.D.E.I.S **843**
Societe d'Etudes et de Documentation Economiques, Industrielles et Sociales Chroniques d'Actualite de la S.E.D.E.I.S *see* Chroniques d'Actualite de la S.E.D.E.I.S **851**
Societe d'Etudes Historiques de la Nouvelle-Caledonie. Bulletin. (NL) **2345**
Societe d'Etudes Linguistiques et Anthropologiques de France. Numeros Speciaux. (FR ISSN 0249-7069) **2842**, 249
Societe d'Etudes Linguistiques et Anthropologiques de France (SELAF) Bibliotheque de la S E L A F *see* Bibliotheque de la S E L A F **2806**
Societe d'Histoire de France. Annuaire. (FR ISSN 0081-0940) **2387**
Societe d'Histoire de la Guadeloupe. Bulletin. (GP ISSN 0583-8266) **2422**
Societe d'Histoire et d'Archaeologie de Geneve. Bulletin. (SZ ISSN 0081-0959) **285**, 2322
Societe d'Histoire et d'Archeologie. Memoires et Documents. Serie in 4. (SZ) **285**, 2387
Societe d'Histoire et d'Archeologie. Memoires et Documents. Serie in 8. (SZ) **285**, 2387
Societe d'Histoire et d'Archeologie de la Goele. Bulletin d'Information. (FR ISSN 0081-0967) **285**, 2387
Societe d'Histoire et d'Archeologie de Vichy et des Environs. Bulletin. (FR ISSN 1153-3277) **285**, 2387
Societe d'Histoire Moderne. Annuaire. (FR ISSN 0081-0975) **2322**
Societe d'Histoire Moderne. Bulletin. (FR) **2322**
Societe d'Histoire Naturelle du Doubs. Bulletin. (FR ISSN 0753-4655) **4344**
Societe de Bibliologie et de Schematisation. Almanach. (FR ISSN 0982-6548) **2961**, 2842
Societe de Biogeographie. Compte Rendu des Seances. (FR) **456**
Societe de Biologie et de ses Filiales. Comptes Rendus des Seances. (FR ISSN 0037-9026) **456**
Societe de Botanique du Nord de la France. Bulletin. (FR ISSN 0037-9034) **517**
Societe de Chimie Biologique. Bulletin *see* Biochimie **473**
Societe de Developpement du Nouveau-Brunswick. Rapport Annuel *see* New Brunswick Development Corporation. Annual Report **5245**
Societe de l'Ecole des Chartes. Memoires et Documents. (SZ ISSN 0078-9518) **2322**
Societe de l'Histoire du Protestantisme Francais. Bulletin. (FR ISSN 0037-9050) **4249**
Societe de l'Industrie Minerale Guide des Mines et Carrieres. (FR) **3495**

Societe de l'Industrie Minerale Mines et Carrieres. Annuaire *see* Societe de l'Industrie Minerale Guide des Mines et Carrieres **3495**
Societe de la Bourse de Luxembourg. Faits et Chiffres. (LU) **738**, 963
Societe de la Bourse de Luxembourg. Listed Luxembourg Undertakings for Collective Investment. (LU) **738**, 963
Societe de la Bourse de Luxembourg. Rapport Annuel/Luxembourg Stock Exchange. Annual Report. (LU) **963**
Societe de la Bourse de Luxembourg. Statistiques Boursieres/Luxembourg Stock Exchange. Stock Exchange Statistics. (LU) **738**, 963
Societe de Linguistique de Paris. Bulletin. (FR ISSN 0037-9069) **2842**
Societe de Mythologie Francaise Bulletin. (FR ISSN 0037-9077) **2058**
Societe de Pathologie Exotique et de ses Filiales. Bulletin. (FR ISSN 0037-9085) **3154**
Societe de Pharmacie de Bordeaux. Bulletin. (FR ISSN 0037-9093) **3743**
Societe de Pharmacie de Lille. Bulletin. (FR) **3743**
Societe de Pharmacie de Lyon. Bulletin des Travaux. (FR ISSN 0037-9107) **3743**
Societe de Pharmacie de Strasbourg. Bulletin. (FR ISSN 0037-9131) **3743**
Societe de Philosophie du Quebec. Bulletin. (CN) **3781**
Societe de Promotion a l'Etranger du Livre de Droit (S.P.E.L.D.) Information *see* S P E L D Information **4395**
Societe de Statistique de Paris. Journal.(FR) **4586**
Societe de Statistique de Paris et de France. Journal *see* Societe de Statistique de Paris. Journal **4586**
Societe des Alcools du Quebec. Rapport Annuel. (CN) **1539**
Societe des Americanistes. Journal. (FR ISSN 0037-9174) **249**, 2842
Societe des Amis de Marcel Proust et des Amis de Combray. Bulletin. (FR ISSN 0583-8452) **2961**
Societe des Amis des Sciences et des Lettres de Poznan. Bulletin. Serie D: Sciences Biologiques. (PL ISSN 0079-4570) **456**
Societe des Antiquaires de l'Ouest. Bulletin. (FR ISSN 0037-9190) **2387**, 285, 344
Societe des Antiquaires de l'Ouest. Memoires. (FR) **2387**
Societe des Antiquaires de Picardie. Memoires. (FR) **285**, 2387
Societe des Antiquaires de Picardie. Quarterly Bulletin. (FR ISSN 0037-9204) **285**, 2387
Societe des Auteurs, Compositeurs, Editeurs pour la Gerance des Droits de Reproduction Mecanique. Bulletin.(FR ISSN 0081-0843) **2679**
†Societe des Ecrivains Canadiens. Bulletin. (CN ISSN 0049-1055) **5278**
Societe des Explorateurs et des Voyageurs Francais. Annuaire General. (FR ISSN 0081-086X) **2262**, 249
Societe des Francs-Bibliophiles. Annuaire. (FR ISSN 0081-0878) **4137**
Societe des Ingenieurs-Conseils de France, en Genie Civil. Bulletin d'Information. (FR) **1874**
Societe des Naturalistes Luxembourgeois. Bulletin. (LU ISSN 0304-9620) **456**, 1548
Societe des Oceanistes. Journal. (FR ISSN 0300-953X) **4388**, 285
Societe des Oceanistes. Publications. (FR ISSN 0081-0894) **4388**
Societe des Poetes Francais. Annuaire. (FR ISSN 0081-0908) **3006**
Societe des Poetes Francais. Bulletin Trimestriel. (FR ISSN 0296-6867) **3006**

Societe des Professeurs Francais en Amerique. Bulletin Annuel. (US ISSN 0081-0916) **1664**
Societe des Sciences et des Lettres de Lodz. Bulletin. (PL ISSN 0459-6854) **4344**, 2961
Societe des Sciences Historiques et Naturelles de Semur en Auxois et des Fouilles d'Alesia. Bulletin. (FR ISSN 0989-9200) **2387**
Societe des Sciences, Lettres et Arts de Bayonne. Bulletin. (FR) **2961**, 344
Societe des Sciences Medicales du Grand-Duche de Luxembourg. Bulletin. (LU ISSN 0037-9247) **3154**
Societe des Sciences Naturelles. Bulletin *see* Societe Sciences Nat. Bulletin **538**
Societe des Sciences Naturelles et Physiques du Maroc. Bulletin. (MR ISSN 0037-9255) **4344**
Societe des Sciences Veterinaires et de Medecine Comparee de Lyon. Bulletin *see* Sciences Veterinaires - Medecine Comparee. Bulletin **4815**
Societe du Corps Medical Malagache. Bulletin. (MG) **3154**
Societe Entomologique d'Egypte. Bulletin/Entomological Society of Egypt. Bulletin. (UA ISSN 0081-0983) **537**
Societe Entomologique d'Egypte. Bulletin. Economic Series. (UA ISSN 0081-0991) **538**
Societe Entomologique de France. Annales. (FR ISSN 0037-9271) **538**
Societe Entomologique de France. Bulletin. (FR ISSN 0151-0517) **538**
Societe Entomologique de Mulhouse. Bulletin. (FR ISSN 0373-4544) **538**
Societe Entomologique du Quebec. Annales *see* Revue d'Entomologie du Quebec **537**
Societe Entomologique du Quebec. Memoires. (CN ISSN 0071-0784) **538**
Societe Entomologique Suisse. Bulletin. *see* Schweizerische Entomologische Gesellschaft. Mitteilungen **537**
Societe Finno-Ougrienne. Journal. *see* Suomalais-Ugrilaisen Seuran. Aikakauskirja **250**
Societe Finno-Ougrienne. Memoires/Suomalais-Ugrilaisen Seuran. Toimituksia. (FI) **249**, 2842
Societe Francaise. (FR) **4450**, 3926
Societe Francaise d'Egyptologie. Bulletin.(FR ISSN 0037-9379) **285**, 3644
Societe Francaise d'Etude du Dix-Huitieme Siecle. Bulletin. (FR) **2387**
Societe Francaise de Cardiologie. Bulletin d'Informations. (FR ISSN 0395-403X) **3212**
Societe Francaise de Chimie. Annuaire. (FR) **1188**
Societe Francaise de Chirurgie Orthopedique et Traumatologique. Conferences d'Enseignement. (FR ISSN 0081-1033) **3311**
Societe Francaise de Microbiologie. Annuaire. (FR ISSN 0081-1068) **557**
Societe Francaise de Mycologie Medicale. Bulletin. (FR ISSN 0037-9336) **517**, 3154
Societe Francaise de Numismatique. Bulletin. (FR ISSN 0037-9344) **3601**
Societe Francaise de Philosophie. Bulletin. (FR ISSN 0037-9352) **3781**
Societe Francaise de Phlebologie. Bulletin. (FR) **3212**
Societe Francaise de Photogrammetrie et de Teledetection. Bulletin. (FR ISSN 0244-6014) **2263**
Societe Francaise de Physiologie Vegetale. Bulletin *see* Plant Physiology and Biochemistry **515**
Societe Francaise de Physique. Annuaire. (FR ISSN 0081-1076) **3831**
Societe Francaise de Physique. Bulletin. (FR ISSN 0037-9360) **3831**

Societe Francaise de Psycho-Prophylaxie Obstetricale. Bulletin Officiel. (FR) **3296**
Societe Francaise du Vide. Comptes Rendus des Travaux des Congres et Colloques. (FR ISSN 0223-4335) **3831**
Societe Francaise Shakespeare. Actes du Congres. (FR) **2961**
Societe Franco-Japonaise de Geographie. Bulletin. (JA) **2263**
Societe Franco-Japonaise des Sciences Pures et Appliquees. Bulletin. *see* Nichi-Futsu Rikoka Kaishi **4330**
Societe Genealogique Canadienne-Francaise. Memoires. (CN ISSN 0037-9387) **2164**
Societe Generale de Banque. Bulletin *see* Generale Bank. Bulletin **783**
Societe Generale de Banque. Rapport *see* Generale Bank. Report **783**
†Societe Generale de Belgique. Information Bulletin. (BE) **5278**
Societe Generale de Belgique. Rapport - Report. (BE ISSN 0081-1114) **799**
Societe Generale de Presse et d'Editions. Index. (FR) **2575**
†Societe Geographique de Liege. Bulletin. (FR ISSN 0770-7576) **5278**
Societe Geologique de Belgique. Annales. (BE ISSN 0037-9395) **1580**
Societe Geologique de France. Bulletin. (FR ISSN 0037-9409) **1580**
Societe Geologique de France. Memoires. (FR ISSN 0249-7549) **1580**
Societe Geologique de Normandie et des Amis du Museum du Havre. Bulletin Trimestriel. (FR ISSN 0336-9994) **1580**
Societe Geologique du Nord. Annales. (FR) **1580**
Societe Geologique et Mineralogique de Bretagne. Bulletin, Serie C *see* Hercynica **1567**
Societe Guernesiaise. Report and Transactions. (UI ISSN 0144-1973) **2387**, 285
Societe Historique Acadienne. Cahiers. (CN ISSN 0049-1098) **2422**
Societe Historique de Saint-Boniface Bulletin *see* S H S B. Bulletin **2421**
Societe Historique de Villiers sur Marne et de la Brie Francaise. Revue. (FR) **2387**
Societe Historique du Madawaska. Revue. (CN) **2422**
Societe Historique et Archeologique dans le Limbourg. Publications. (NE ISSN 0085-6266) **2388**
Societe Historique et Archeologique de Pontoise, du Val d'Oise et du Vexin. Memoires. (FR) **2388**
Societe Historique et Archeologique du Perigord. Bulletin. (FR ISSN 0037-9425) **2388**, 285
Societe Historique Nicolas Denys. Revue d'Histoire. (CN ISSN 0381-9388) **2422**
Societe Industrielle de Mulhouse. Bulletin. (FR ISSN 0037-9441) **4609**
Societe Internationale Arthurienne. Bulletin Bibliographique. *see* International Arthurian Society. Bibliographical Bulletin **2982**
Societe Internationale de Chirurgie. Bulletin *see* World Journal of Surgery **3386**
Societe Internationale de Psycho-Prophylaxie Obstetricale. Bulletin Officiel *see* Societe Francaise de Psycho-Prophylaxie Obstetricale. Bulletin Officiel **3296**
Societe J.K. Huysmans. Bulletin. (FR) **2884**
Societe Languedocienne de Geographie. Bulletin. (FR ISSN 0373-3297) **2263**
Societe Linneenne de Bordeaux. Bulletin.(FR ISSN 0750-6848) **538**, 591, 1580
Societe Linneenne de Lyon. Bulletin Mensuel. (FR ISSN 0366-1326) **456**

Societe Linneenne de Provence. Bulletin.(FR ISSN 0373-0875) **456**, 1580

Societe Litteraire des P.T.T. Bulletin. (FR) **2884**

Societe Mathematique de Belgique. Bulletin. (BE ISSN 0037-9476) **3055**

Societe Mathematique de France. Bulletin et Memoires. (FR) **3055**

Societe Mathematique de France. Supplements. (FR) **3055**

Societe Medico-Chirurgicale des Hopitaux et Formations Sanitaires des Armees. Bulletin. (FR ISSN 0037-9492) **3384**

Societe National du Logement. Rapport Annuel. (BE ISSN 0067-5652) **2496**

Societe Nationale d'Etude et de Construction de Moteurs d'Aviation Informations *see* S N E C M A Informations **61**

Societe Nationale d'Etude et de Promotion Industrielle. Bulletin d'Information Industrielle. (SG) **1085**

Societe Nationale des Antiquaires de France. Bulletin. (FR ISSN 0081-1181) **285**

Societe Nationale des Chemins de Fer Belges. Bulletin de Documentation *see* Nationale Maatschappij van Belgische Spoorwegen. Documentatiebulletin **4712**

Societe Nationale des Chemins de Fer Belges. Documentaire *see* Nationale Maatschappij van Belgische Spoorwegen. Documentatiebulletin **4712**

Societe Nationale des Chemins de Fer Belges. Rapport Annuel. (BE ISSN 0081-119X) **4715**

Societe Nationale E L F Aquitaine. Rapport Annuel. (FR) **3701**

Societe Neophilologique de Helsinki. Memoires. (FI ISSN 0355-0192) **2842**

Societe Nucleaire Canadienne. Sommaires du Congres *see* Canadian Nuclear Society. Annual Conference Summaries **1804**

Societe Philomatique Vosgienne. Bulletin. (FR) **2388**

Societe pour l'Etude des Langues Africaines. Bulletin *see* Bibliotheque de la S E L A F **2806**

Societe pour le Developpement Minier de la Cote d'Ivoire. Rapport Annuel. (IV ISSN 0250-3697) **3495**

Societe pour Vaincre la Pollution. Bulletin de Liaison *see* Environnement **1954**

Societe Prehistorique Francaise. Bulletin.(FR ISSN 0037-9514) **285**

Societe Royale Belge d'Anthropologie et de Prehistoire. Bulletin. (BE ISSN 0304-1425) **249**

Societe Royale Belge de Gynecologie et d'Obstetrique. Bulletin. (BE ISSN 0037-9522) **3296**

Societe Royale Belge des Electriciens. Bulletin. (BE ISSN 0037-9530) **1908**

Societe Royale d'Economie Politique de Belgique. Comptes Rendus des Travaux *see* Societe Royale d'Economie Politique de Belgique. Seances **691**

Societe Royale d'Economie Politique de Belgique. Seances. (BE) **691**

Societe Royale de Lettres de Lund. Bulletin/Kungliga Humanistiska Vetenskapssamfundet i Lund. Aarsberattelse. (SW) **2961**

Societe Royale de Zoologie d'Anvers. Bulletin *see* Acta Zoologica et Pathologica Antverpiensia **576**

Societe Royale des Sciences de Liege. Bulletin. (BE ISSN 0037-9565) **4344**

Societe Royale Forestiere de Belgique. Bulletin - Koninklijke Belgische Bosbouwmaatschappij. Tydschrift *see* Silva Belgica **2107**

Societe Royale Zoologique de Belgique. Annales *see* Belgian Journal of Zoology **579**

Societe Saint-Jean-Baptiste de Montreal. Information Nationale. (CN ISSN 0537-6211) **4450**, 3926

Societe Saint-Jean-Baptiste de Montreal Bulletin *see* Societe Saint-Jean-Baptiste de Montreal. Information Nationale **4450**

Societe Sciences Nat. Bulletin. (FR ISSN 0249-5805) **538**

Societe Scientifique de Bretagne. Bulletin. (FR ISSN 0037-9581) **4344**

†Societe Scientifique de Bruxelles. Annales. Sciences Mathematiques, Astronomiques et Physiques. (BE ISSN 0037-959X) **5278**

Societe Speleologique de Grece. Bulletin Trimestriel. *see* Greek Speleological Society. Deltion **1567**

Societe Speleologique et Prehistorique de Bordeaux. Memoire. (FR ISSN 0294-5495) **2322**

Societe Suisse des Americanistes. Bulletin/Schweizerische Amerikanisten-Gesellschaft. Bulletin. (SZ ISSN 0582-1592) **2422**, 249, 285

Societe Theophile Gautier. Bulletin. (FR ISSN 0221-7945) **2961**

Societe Vaudoise des Sciences Naturelles. Bulletin. (SZ ISSN 0037-9603) **4344**

Societe Vaudoise des Sciences Naturelles. Memoires. (SZ ISSN 0037-9611) **4344**

Societe Versaillaise des Sciences Naturelles. Bulletin. (FR ISSN 0336-8300) **4344**

Societe Zoologique de France. Bulletin. (FR ISSN 0037-962X) **591**

Societe Zoologique de France. Memoires. (FR ISSN 0750-747X) **591**

Societes. (FR ISSN 0765-3697) **4450**

Societes Anonymes en Suisse. *see* Aktiengesellschaften in der Schweiz **829**

†Societes de Service et de Conseil en Informatique. (FR) **5278**

Societes et Fournisseurs d'Afrique Noire *see* France Afrique **866**

Societes Scientifiques et Techniques du Canada. *see* Scientific and Technical Societies of Canada **4341**

Society. (MC) **2188**

Society. *see* Shehui **4385**

Society. (US ISSN 0147-2011) **4388**

Society/Societe. (CN ISSN 0381-1794) **4450**, 249

Society and Animals. (US) **231**, 1968, 4047

Society and Change. (II) **4388**

Society and Commerce. (II ISSN 0300-4546) **839**

Society and Culture. (II ISSN 0037-9662) **4388**

Society and Leisure. *see* Loisir et Societe **2739**

Society and Natural Resources. (UK ISSN 0894-1920) **1968**, 1497, 4388, 4828

Society and Welfare/Hevra u-Revaha. (IS ISSN 0334-4029) **4421**

Society - Family. *see* Shehui - Jianting **2183**

Society Farsarotul Newsletter. (US ISSN 1042-3230) **2024**

Society for Advancement of Electrochemical Science and Technology Transactions S A E S T *see* Transactions S A E S T **1213**

Society for Advancement of Management Focus on Management *see* S A M Focus on Management **1027**

Society for Advancement of Management Management Journal *see* S A M Management Journal **1027**

Society for American Archaeology. Bulletin. (US ISSN 0741-5672) **285**

†Society for American Archaeology. Memoir Series. (US) **5278**

Society for American Archaeology. Special Publications Series. (US) **285**

Society for American Baseball Research, Inc. Bulletin *see* S A B R Bulletin **4510**

Society for American Baseball Research, Inc. Review of Books *see* S A B R Review of Books **5272**

Society for Applied Bacteriology. Symposium Series. (US) **557**

Society for Applied Bacteriology. Technical Series. (US) **557**

Society for Applied Learning Technology. Newsletter. (US) **1691**, 1417

Society for Archaeological Sciences Bulletin *see* S A S Bulletin **284**

Society for Armenian Studies. Journal. (US ISSN 0747-9301) **2024**, 344, 2961

Society for Army Historical Research. Journal. (UK ISSN 0037-9700) **3471**, 2322

Society for Clinical and Experimental Hypnosis Newsletter *see* C E H Newsletter **3274**

Society for College and University Planning News *see* S C U P News **1715**

Society for College and University Planning Quarterly *see* Planning for Higher Education **1714**

Society for Commercial Archeology. News Journal. (US ISSN 0735-1399) **285**

Society for Common Insights. Journal. (US) **4201**, 4344

Society for Computer-Aided Engineering Network *see* S C A E Network **1880**

Society for Computer Simulation. Transactions. (US ISSN 0740-6797) **1436**

Society for Cryobiology. News Notes. (US) **486**, 3263

Society for Developmental Biology. Symposium. (US ISSN 0583-9009) **456**

Society for Educational Reconstruction Action Newsletter *see* S E R in Action Newsletter **1660**

Society for Environmental Education Journal *see* S E E Journal **1967**

Society for Environmental Therapy. Newsletter. (UK ISSN 0264-5807) **3612**, 3154

Society for Ethnomusicology Newsletter *see* Ethnomusicology Newsletter **3550**

Society for Experimental Biology. Seminar Series. (UK) **456**

Society for Experimental Biology and Medicine. Proceedings. (US ISSN 0037-9727) **456**, 3263

Society for Experimental Mechanics Proceedings *see* S E M Proceedings **1922**

†Society for Folk Arts Preservation. Newsletter. (US) **5278**

Society for General Microbiology. Special Publications. (US) **557**

Society for General Microbiology. Symposium. (UK ISSN 0081-1394) **557**

Society for General Microbiology Proceedings *see* Society for General Microbiology Quarterly **557**

Society for General Microbiology Quarterly. (UK ISSN 0142-7547) **557**

Society for General Systems Research. Proceedings. (US) **4344**

Society for German - American Studies. Newsletter. (US ISSN 0741-5753) **2961**

Society for Health Systems. Journal. (US) **3622**

Society for Historians of American Foreign Relations. Newsletter. (US ISSN 0740-6169) **3972**

Society for Historical Archaeology. Special Publication Series. (US ISSN 0898-0004) **285**

Society for Historical Archaeology Conference. Underwater Proceedings.(US) **285**

Society for Historical Archaeology Newsletter. (US ISSN 0037-9735) **285**, 2322

Society for Imaging Science and Technology (SPSE) Annual Conference. Paper Summaries (Year) *see* S P S E. Annual Conference. Paper Summaries (Year) **3796**

Society for Industrial and Applied Mathematics Journal on Applied Mathematics *see* S I A M Journal on Applied Mathematics **3053**

Society for Industrial and Applied Mathematics Journal on Computing *see* S I A M Journal on Computing **3066**

Society for Industrial and Applied Mathematics Journal on Control and Optimization *see* S I A M Journal on Control and Optimization **3053**

Society for Industrial and Applied Mathematics Journal on Discrete Mathematics *see* S I A M Journal on Discrete Mathematics **3053**

Society for Industrial and Applied Mathematics Journal on Mathematical Analysis *see* S I A M Journal on Mathematical Analysis **3053**

Society for Industrial and Applied Mathematics Journal on Matrix Analysis and Applications *see* S I A M Journal on Matrix Analysis and Applications **3053**

Society for Industrial and Applied Mathematics News *see* S I A M News **3054**

Society for Industrial and Applied Mathematics Proceedings *see* S I A M - A M S Proceedings **3053**

Society for Industrial and Applied Mathematics Regional Conference Series in Applied Mathematics *see* C B M S. N S F. Regional Conference Series in Applied Mathematics **3062**

Society for Industrial and Applied Mathematics Review *see* S I A M Review **3054**

Society for Industrial Archeology Newsletter. (US ISSN 0160-1067) **4609**

Society for Industrial Microbiology. Proceedings of the Annual Meeting *see* Developments in Industrial Microbiology **551**

Society for Information Display. Seminar Lecture Notes. (US) **2799**, 2785

Society for Information Display International Symposium. Digest of Technical Papers *see* S I D International Symposium. Digest of Technical Papers **1836**

Society for Information Display Proceedings *see* S.I.D. Proceedings **1423**

Society for Information Management Exchange *see* S I M - I M Exchange **5272**

Society for Information Management Network *see* S I M Network **1457**

Society for Interdisciplinary Studies Chronology & Catastrophism Workshop *see* S.I.S. Chronology & Catastrophism Workshop **1579**

Society for Italian Historical Studies. Newsletter. (US ISSN 0081-1424) **2388**

Society for Italic Handwriting. Bulletin *see* Society for Italic Handwriting. Newsletter **344**

Society for Italic Handwriting. Journal. (UK ISSN 0037-9743) **344**, 1664

Society for Italic Handwriting. Newsletter. (UK) **344**, 1664

Society for Lincolnshire History and Archaeology. Annual Report and Statement of Accounts. (UK ISSN 0306-4859) **285**, 2388

Society for Lincolnshire History and Archaeology. Newsletter *see* Lincolnshire Past and Present **277**

†Society for Louisiana Irises. Special Publications. (US) **5278**

Society for Louisiana Irises Newsletter. (US) **2139**

Society for Natural Sciences, Basel. Proceedings. *see* Naturforschende Gesellschaft in Basel. Verhandlungen **4327**

SOCIETY 6671

Society for New Testament Studies. Monograph Series. (UK ISSN 0081-1432) **4201**

Society for Old Testament Studies. Monographs. (UK) **4201**

Society for Old Testament Study. Book List. (UK ISSN 0081-1440) **4213**

Society for Pacific Coast Native Iris Almanac see S P C N I Almanac **2138**

Society for Pentecostal Studies. Newsletter. (US) **4249**

Society for Pirandello Studies. Yearbook. (UK) **2961**

Society for Promoting Training of Women. Annual Report. (UK) **4853**

Society for Psychical Research. Journal.(UK ISSN 0037-9751) **3671**

Society for Psychical Research. Proceedings. (UK ISSN 0081-1475) **3671**

Society for Psychical Research Newsletter see S P R Newsletter **3671**

Society for Radiological Protection. Journal see Journal of Radiological Protection **1806**

Society for Renaissance Studies. Bulletin. (UK ISSN 0264-8571) **2961, 344, 2388**

Society for Renaissance Studies. Occasional Papers. (UK) **2961, 344, 3781**

Society for Research in Child Development. Monographs. (US ISSN 0037-976X) **1244**

Society for Research into Higher Education News see S R H E News **1716**

Society for Scholarly Publishing. Proceedings of Annual Meetings. (Society for Scholarly Publishing) (US ISSN 0734-8509) **4137**

Society for Scholarly Publishing Newsletter. (US) **4137**

Society for Scholarly Publishing Society for Scholarly Publishing. Proceedings of Annual Meetings see Society for Scholarly Publishing. Proceedings of Annual Meetings **4137**

Society for Slovene Studies. Documentation Series. (US) **2388, 2842**

Society for South India Studies. Newsletter see South Asia News **2342**

Society for Spanish and Portuguese Historical Studies. Bulletin. (US ISSN 0739-182X) **2388**

Society for Technical Communication. Annual Conference Proceedings. (US) **1342**

Society for Technical Communication Anthology Series. (US) **1342**

Society for the Advancement of Anaesthesia in Dentistry Digest see S A A D Digest **3242**

Society for the Advancement of Food Service Research. Proceedings. (US ISSN 0081-1483) **2081**

Society for the Advancement of Material and Process Engineering International S A M P E Technical Conference Series. I S T C Preprint Series see International S A M P E Technical Conference Series. I S T C Preprint Series **1918**

Society for the Advancement of Material and Process Engineering Journal see S A M P E Journal **1922**

Society for the Advancement of Material and Process Engineering Quarterly see S A M P E Quarterly **1922**

Society for the Eradication of Television Free see S E T Free **1379**

†Society for the History of Technology. Monograph Series. (US ISSN 0081-1491) **5278**

Society for the History of Technology Newsletter see S H O T Newsletter **4608**

Society for the Preservation of Long Island Antiquities. Newsletter. (US ISSN 0583-9181) **259, 344**

Society for the Preservation of N E Antiquities News see S P N E A News **2321**

Society for the Preservation of New England Antiquities Historic Houses in New England see S P N E A's Historic Houses in New England **306**

Society for the Prevention of Asbestosis and Industrial Diseases News see S P A I D News **3621**

Society for the Protection of Unborn Children. Bulletin see Human Concern Newspaper **3293**

Society for the Scientific Study of Religion. Monograph Series. (US) **4201, 4450**

Society for the Social History of Medicine. Bulletin see Social History of Medicine **3153**

Society for the Study of Inborn Errors of Metabolism. Symposia see Journal of Inherited Metabolic Disease **573**

Society for the Study of Labour History. Bulletin see Labour History Review **986**

Society for the Study of Midwestern Literature. Newsletter. (US ISSN 0085-6304) **2961**

Society for the Study of Southern Literature. Newsletter. (US ISSN 0197-8071) **2961**

Society for the Study of State Governments. Journal. (II ISSN 0037-9786) **4073, 2342**

Society for the Study of the Multi-Ethnic Literature of the United States see M E L U S **2936**

Society for Vector Ecology. Bulletin. (US) **538**

Society for Visual Anthropology Newsletter. (US) **249**

Society Newsletter. (US) **4047, 3154, 4450**

Society of Actuaries. Record. (US) **2543**

Society of Actuaries. Transactions (General). (US ISSN 0037-9794) **2543**

Society of Actuaries. Transactions: Reports of Mortality and Morbidity Experience. (US) **2543**

Society of Actuaries. Yearbook. (US) **2543**

Society of Allied Weight Engineers Newsletter see S A W E Newsletter **61**

Society of American Florists see S A F **2143**

Society of American Law Teachers Equalizer see S A L T Equalizer **2676**

Society of Animal Artists Newsletter. (US) **344**

Society of Antiquaries of Newcastle Upon Tyne. Monograph Series. (UK ISSN 0265-1785) **2388**

Society of Antiquaries of Newcastle Upon Tyne. Record Series. (UK) **2388**

Society of Antiquaries of Scotland. Monograph Series. (UK ISSN 0263-3191) **2388, 285**

Society of Antiquaries of Scotland. Proceedings. (UK ISSN 0081-1564) **2388, 285**

Society of Archer-Antiquaries. Journal. (UK ISSN 0560-6152) **4488**

Society of Architectural Administrators. News Journal. (US) **307, 1061**

Society of Architectural Administrators. News Update. (US) **307, 1061**

Society of Architectural Historians. Journal. (US ISSN 0037-9808) **307, 2322**

Society of Architectural Historians. Newsletter. (US ISSN 0049-1195) **307, 2323**

Society of Architectural Historians of Great Britain Newsletter. (UK) **307, 2388**

Society of Archivists. Journal. (UK ISSN 0037-9816) **2785, 2323**

Society of Automotive Engineers Australasia see S A E - Australasia **4701**

Society of Automotive Engineers Handbook see S A E Handbook **4701**

Society of Automotive Engineers of Japan. Journal. see Jidosha Gijutsu **4693**

Society of Automotive Engineers of Japan. Transactions. see Jidosha Gijutsukai Ronbunshu **4693**

Society of Automotive Engineers of Japan, Inc. Review see J S A E Review **4693**

Society of Automotive Engineers Technical Literature Abstracts see S A E Technical Literature Abstracts **4666**

Society of Automotive Engineers Technical Papers see S A E Technical Papers **4701**

Society of Automotive Engineers Transactions see S A E Transactions **4701**

Society of Automotive Engineers Update see S A E Update **1938**

Society of Biblical Literature. Seminar Papers (Year). (US ISSN 0145-2711) **4202**

Society of Biological Chemists. Proceedings. (II ISSN 0300-0486) **483**

Society of Biological Chemists Newsletter see S B C Newsletter **482**

Society of British Aerospace Companies Ltd. News see S B A C News **61**

Society of Cartographers Bulletin see S U C Bulletin **2262**

Society of Chartered Property and Casualty Underwriters. Journal. (US ISSN 0162-2706) **2543**

Society of Chartered Property & Casualty Underwriters News see C P C U News **2529**

Society of Chartered Property & Casualty Underwriters Public Affairs Forum see C P C U Public Affairs Forum **2529**

Society of Chartered Property & Casualty Underwriters Update see C P C U Update **2529**

Society of Chemical Industry. Bulletin. (UK ISSN 0300-5232) **1188, 1860**

Society of Christian Ethics. Annual. (US ISSN 0732-4928) **4202**

Society of Cinematologists. Journal see Cinema Journal **3506**

Society of Colonial Wars. Bulletin. (US) **2422, 3471**

Society of Composers International Journal of Music Scores see S C I Journal of Music Scores **3579**

Society of Composers Newsletter. (US) **3580**

Society of Cosmetic Chemists. Journal. (US ISSN 0037-9832) **376**

Society of Cypriot Studies. Bulletin/ Kypriakai Spoudai. (CY ISSN 0081-1580) **2388**

Society of Dairy Technology. Journal. (UK ISSN 0037-9840) **203**

Society of Dyers and Colourists. Journal.(UK ISSN 0037-9859) **4609**

Society of Engineers. Journal and Transactions see Engineering World **1821**

Society of Environmental Engineers. Journal see Environmental Engineering **1821**

Society of Exploration Geophysicists. Special Publications (Symposia) Series. (US) **1594**

Society of Explosives Engineers. Conference on Explosives and Blasting Technique. Proceedings. (US) **1860, 3495**

Society of Explosives Engineers. Membership Directory and Desk Reference. (US) **1860, 3495**

Society of Explosives Engineers. Symposium on Explosives and Blasting Research. Proceedings. (US) **1860, 3495**

Society of Federal Linguists. Newsletter.(US) **2842**

Society of Fiber Science and Technology, Japan. Journal/Sen'i Gakkaishi. (JA ISSN 0037-9875) **4623**

Society of Flight Test Engineers. Annual Symposium Proceedings. (US) **62**

Society of Flight Test Engineers. Newsletter. (US) **62**

†Society of General Physiologists. Distinguished Lecture Series. (US) **5278**

†Society of General Physiologists Series.(US ISSN 0094-7733) **5278**

Society of Geriatric Ophthalmology. Newsletter. (US) **3305**

Society of Glass and Ceramic Decorators. Seminar Proceeding. (US) **1166**

Society of Glass Decorators. Seminar Proceedings see Society of Glass and Ceramic Decorators. Seminar Proceeding **1166**

Society of Graphic Artists. Publication. (UK) **4005**

Society of Health of Nigeria. Journal. (NR ISSN 0037-9905) **4113**

Society of Hispanic Professional Engineers National Newsletter see S H P E National Newsletter **1836**

Society of Incentive Travel Executives In - S I T E Magazine see In - S I T E Magazine **4772**

Society of Independent Professional Earth Scientists. Newsletter. (US ISSN 0037-9913) **1548**

Society of Industrial and Office Realtors Reports see S I O R Reports **5272**

Society of Instrument Technology. Transactions see Measurement and Control **2524**

Society of Leather Technologists and Chemists. Journal. (UK ISSN 0144-0322) **2738, 1188**

Society of Licensed Aircraft Engineers and Technologists. Journal see Aerospace **43**

Society of Logistics Engineers. Annals. (US ISSN 0885-3916) **4609, 62**

Society of Logistics Engineers. Proceedings. (US ISSN 0893-3499) **4609**

Society of Logistics Engineers Etter see S O L Etter **4608**

Society of Malawi Journal. (MW ISSN 0037-993X) **4344**

Society of Management Science and Applied Cybernetics see S C I M A **1442**

Society of Management Science and Applied Cybernetics Special Series see S C I M A Special Series **1443**

Society of Manufacturing Engineers. Technical Digest. (US ISSN 0049-1209) **4615, 23**

Society of Manufacturing Engineers. Technical Papers. (US ISSN 0081-1653) **1922**

Society of Maritime Arbitrators. Award Service. (US) **4739, 2679**

Society of Medical Friends of Wine. Bulletin. (US ISSN 0037-9956) **385**

Society of Motion Picture and Television Engineers Journal see S M P T E Journal **3517**

Society of Motor Manufacturers and Traders. Monthly Statistical Review. (UK) **4666**

Society of Motor Manufacturers and Traders Ltd. Buyers Guide see S M M T Buyers Guide **4701**

Society of National Association Publishers Bulletin see S N A P. Bulletin **4136**

Society of National Association Publishers Buyers' Guide see S N A P. Buyers' Guide **4136**

Society of National Association Publishers Shot see S N A P Shot **4136**

Society of National Association Publishers Who's Who in S N A P see Who's Who in S N A P **4138**

Society of Naval Architects and Marine Engineers. Transactions. (US ISSN 0081-1661) **4739**

Society of Naval Architects, Japan. Journal. (JA) **4739**

Society of Nippon Dental College. Annual Publications see Nippon Dental University. Annual Publications **3238**

Society of Non-Traditional Technology. Journal. see Mito Kagaku Gijutsu **4604**

6672 SOCIETY

Society of Obstetricians and Gynecologists of Canada Journal S O G C see Journal S O G C **3294**
Society of Occupational Medicine. Journal see Occupational Medicine **3137**
Society of Pediatric Psychology. Newsletter see Progress Notes **4039**
Society of Petroleum Engineers. Reprint Series. (US) **3701**
Society of Petroleum Engineers. Transactions. (US ISSN 0081-1696) **3701**
Society of Petroleum Engineers, Inc. Drilling Engineering see S P E Drilling Engineering **3700**
Society of Petroleum Engineers, Inc. Formation Evaluation see S P E Formation Evaluation **3700**
Society of Petroleum Engineers, Inc. Production Engineering see S P E Production Engineering **3700**
Society of Petroleum Engineers, Inc. Reservoir Engineering see S P E Reservoir Engineering **3700**
Society of Petroleum Engineers of American Institute of Mining, Metallurgical and Petroleum Engineers. Petroleum Transactions Reprint Series see Society of Petroleum Engineers. Reprint Series **3701**
Society of Petroleum Engineers of American Institute of Mining, Metallurgical and Petroleum Engineers. Transactions see Society of Petroleum Engineers. Transactions **3701**
Society of Photo Finishing Engineers Newsletter see S P F E Newsletter **3796**
Society of Photographers and Artist Representatives. Buyers Guide. (US) **3797, 344, 1028**
Society of Photographers and Artist Representatives. Newsletter. (US) **3797, 344, 1028**
Society of Photographers and Artist Representatives. Statements on Photography - Art. (US) **3797, 344, 1028**
Society of Photographic Science and Technology of Japan. Bulletin see Society of Photographic Science and Technology of Japan. Journal **3797**
Society of Photographic Science and Technology of Japan. Journal/Nihon Shashin Gakkai Eibungo. (JA) **3797**
Society of Plant Protection of North Japan. Annual Report. see Kita Nihon Byogaichu Kenkyu Kaiho **184**
Society of Plastics Engineers. Annual Technical Conference (Antec). Proceedings. (US) **3868**
Society of Plastics Engineers Monographs. (US) **3868**
Society of Portrait Sculptors. Publication. (UK) **344**
Society of Powder Technology, Japan. Journal. (JA ISSN 0386-6157) **1836**
Society of Professional Archeologists Newsletter see S O P A Newsletter **284**
Society of Professional Investigators. Bulletin. (US ISSN 0038-0008) **1523**
Society of Professional Well Log Analysts. S P W L A Annual Logging Symposium Transactions. (US ISSN 0081-1718) **3701**
Society of Professors of Education. Occasional Papers. (US ISSN 0882-7141) **1664**
Society of Professors of Education Monograph Series see S P E Monograph Series **1660**
Society of Psychologists in Addictive Behaviors. Bulletin see Psychology of Addictive Behaviors **1538**
Society of Research Administrators. Journal. (US ISSN 0038-0024) **1028**
Society of Research Administrators, Inc. Newsletter see S R A Newsletter **1027**
Society of Rheology. Transactions see Journal of Rheology **3844**

Society of Rubber Industry. Journal. see Nihon Gomu Kyokaishi **4292**
Society of Satellite Professionals International Update see S S P I Update **1379**
Society of Teachers of Family Medicine Messenger see S T F M Messenger **3151**
Society of the Plastics Industry. Reinforced Plastics Composites Institute. Annual Technical Conference. Preprint. (US) **3868**
Society of the Plastics Industry. Urethane Division. Conference Proceedings. (US) **3868**
Society of the Plastics Industry, Inc. Membership Directory and Buyer's Guide see S P I Membership Directory and Buyer's Guide **3868**
Society of the Science of Soil and Manure of Japan. Journal see Nippon Dojo Hiryogaku Zasshi **186**
Society of the Seven Sages Newsletter. (CN ISSN 0701-9890) **2961**
Society of Tribologists and Lubrication Engineers Tribology Transactions see S T L E Tribology Transactions **1860**
Society of Vector Ecologists. Bulletin see Society for Vector Ecology. Bulletin **538**
Society of Vertebrate Paleontology. News Bulletin. (US ISSN 0096-9117) **3661**
Society of Wildlife Artists. Publication. (UK) **344, 456**
Society of Women Engineers. Newsletter see U S Woman Engineer **1839**
Society Page. (US ISSN 0038-0075) **2543**
Society to Overcome Pollution, Inc. Press see S T O P Press **1979**
Socijalisticka Poljoprivreda. (YU) **120**
Socijalizam. (YU ISSN 0489-5967) **3926**
Socijalni Rad/Social Work. (CI ISSN 0038-0105) **4421**
Socio-Economic Differential Mortality in Industrialized Societies. (FR) **3987**
Socio-Economic History/Shakai Keizai Shigaku. (JA ISSN 0038-0113) **898**
Socio-Economic Information Network Abstracts. Journal see S E C I N Abstracts. Journal **4458**
Socio-Economic Planning Sciences. (US ISSN 0038-0121) **4073, 4450**
Socio-Economic Progress in Latin America; Annual Report see Economic and Social Progress in Latin America; Annual Report **861**
Socio-Economic Review of Punjab. (II) **884, 4450**
Sociobiology. (US ISSN 0361-6525) **456**
Sociocriticism. (FR ISSN 0985-5939) **2961**
Sociocriticism: Literature, Society, and History. (US ISSN 1043-5727) **2961, 4450**
Sociodrome. (NE ISSN 0165-1676) **4450**
Socioeconomic Newsletter. (US) **4450**
Sociolinguistica. (GW ISSN 0933-1883) **2856**
†Sociolinguistics. (NE ISSN 0049-1217) **5278**
Sociolinguistique. (FR) **2842, 249**
Sociologia/Sociology. (CS ISSN 0049-1225) **4450**
Sociologia (Naples). (IT) **4450**
Sociologia (Rome). (IT ISSN 0038-0156) **4450, 4388**
Sociologia dei Media. (IT) **4450**
Sociologia dei Progressi Culturali. (IT) **4450**
Sociologia del Diritto. (IT) **2679**
Sociologia del Lavoro. (IT) **4388**
Sociologia della Comunicazione. (IT) **1343**
Sociologia e Ricerca Sociale. (IT) **4450**
Sociologia Indica. (II) **4450**
Sociologia Internationalis. (GW ISSN 0038-0164) **4421**
Sociologia Ruralis. (NE ISSN 0038-0199) **120, 4450**
Sociologia Urbana e Rurale. (IT) **4450**
Sociological Abstracts. (US ISSN 0038-0202) **4458, 23**

Sociological Analysis see S A **4448**
Sociological Bulletin. (II ISSN 0038-0229) **4450**
Sociological Focus. (US ISSN 0038-0237) **4450**
Sociological Forum see Sociological Spectrum **4451**
Sociological Forum. (US ISSN 0884-8971) **4451**
Sociological Information. see Szociologiai Informacio **4458**
Sociological Inquiry. (US ISSN 0038-0245) **4451**
Sociological Methodology. (UK ISSN 0081-1750) **4451**
Sociological Methods & Research. (US ISSN 0049-1241) **4451**
Sociological Microjournal. (DK) **4451**
Sociological Observations. (US) **4451, 249**
Sociological Perspectives. (US ISSN 0731-1214) **4451**
Sociological Practice. (US ISSN 0163-8505) **4451**
▼Sociological Practice Review. (US ISSN 1050-6306) **4451**
Sociological Quarterly. (US ISSN 0038-0253) **4451**
Sociological Record. (US) **4451**
Sociological Review. see Revija za Sociologiju **4446**
Sociological Review. see Sociologicky Casopis **4451**
Sociological Review. (UK ISSN 0038-0261) **4451**
Sociological Spectrum. (US ISSN 0273-2173) **4451**
Sociological Studies. see Shehuixue Yanjiu **4448**
Sociological Symposium see Sociological Spectrum **4451**
Sociological Theory. (UK ISSN 0735-2751) **4451**
Sociological Viewpoints. (US ISSN 1060-0876) **4451**
Sociologiceski Problemi. (BU ISSN 0324-1572) **4451**
Sociologicky Casopis/Sociological Review. (CS ISSN 0038-0288) **4451**
Sociologie Contemporaine. see Current Sociology **4433**
Sociologie du Travail. (FR ISSN 0038-0296) **994, 4451**
Sociologie et Societes. (CN ISSN 0038-030X) **4451, 3926**
Sociologie Permanente. (FR) **4451**
Sociologie Romaneasca. (RM) **4452**
Sociologie Venkova a Zemedelstvi/Sociology of Country and Agriculture.(CS) **120**
Sociologija. (YU ISSN 0038-0318) **4452**
Sociologija Sela. (CI ISSN 0038-0326) **4452**
Sociologisch Tijdschrift. (NE) **4452**
Sociologische Gids. (NE ISSN 0038-0334) **4452**
Sociologische Verkenningen. (BE) **4452**
Sociologisk Forskning. (SW ISSN 0038-0342) **4451**
Sociologiske Meddelelser see Micro Publications. Social Science Series **4443**
Sociologist. (NR ISSN 0081-1807) **4452**
Sociologus. (GW ISSN 0038-0377) **4452**
Sociology. see Sociologia **4450**
Sociology. (UK ISSN 0038-0385) **4452**
Sociology and Social Research. (US ISSN 0038-0393) **4452**
Sociology Occasional Publications. (AT ISSN 0156-4943) **4452**
Sociology of Country and Agriculture. see Sociologie Venkova a Zemedelstvi **120**
Sociology of Education. (US ISSN 0038-0407) **4452, 1664**
Sociology of Education Abstracts. (UK ISSN 0038-0415) **1679, 23, 4458**
Sociology of Health and Illness. (UK ISSN 0141-9889) **4452, 3354**
Sociology of Leisure and Sport Abstracts see Sport & Leisure **5282**

Sociology of Music Series. (US) **4452, 3580**
Sociology of Sport Journal. (US ISSN 0741-1235) **4452, 3373, 4488**
Sociology of the Sciences see Sociology of the Sciences. Yearbook **4344**
Sociology of the Sciences. Yearbook. (NE) **4344, 4452**
Sociology of the Sciences Monographs. (NE) **4452, 4344**
Sociology of Work and Occupations see Work and Occupations **4456**
Sociology Research Monographs. (AT) **4452**
▼Sociology Review. (UK ISSN 0959-8499) **4452**
Sociology Working Papers. (SI) **4452, 249**
Socioscoop see De Bijstaander **4399**
Sociotechnology see Technology in Society **4454**
Socjolingwistyka. (PL ISSN 0208-6808) **2842**
Socjologia Morska see Roczniki Sociologii Morskiej **4447**
Sodobna Pedagogika. (XV ISSN 0038-0474) **1664**
Sodobno Kmetijstvo. (XV ISSN 0350-1655) **120, 2081, 4816**
Sodobnost. (XV ISSN 0038-0482) **2884**
†Soedok. (SW ISSN 1100-5491) **5278**
Soedra see Soedra Skog **2108**
Soedra Skog. (SW) **2108**
Soefart. (DK ISSN 0038-0520) **4739**
Soekaren. (SW ISSN 0038-0504) **3671, 3781**
Soelleroedbogen. (DK ISSN 0085-6339) **2388**
Soendags - B.T. see Ugemagasinet Soendag **2185**
Soendagskolekontakt. (DK ISSN 0109-2375) **4249, 1266**
Soenderjyllands Erhvervsorientering: Produktion, Handel, Kontakt. (DK ISSN 0109-2863) **691**
Soenderjysk Maanedsskrift. (DK ISSN 0049-125X) **2388**
Soenderjyske Aarboeger. (DK ISSN 0106-4452) **2388**
Soer Nord Utvikling see Utvikling **936**
†Soeren Spaette. (DK) **5278**
Soermlandsbygden. (SW ISSN 0349-0297) **2388**
Soester Beitraege. (GW) **2388**
Soester Zeitschrift. (GW ISSN 0176-3946) **2388**
Sofia. Universitet. Bogoslovski Fakultet. Godishnik see Dukhovna Akademiya SV. Kliment Okhridski. Godishnik **4175**
Sofia News. (BU) **3926, 4786**
Sofiiski Universitet. Biologicheski Fakultet. Godishnik. (BU ISSN 0081-1823) **456**
Sofiiski Universitet. Fakultet po Klasiceski i Novi Filologii. Godisnik/Universite de Sofia. Faculte des Lettres Classiques et Modernes. Annuaire. (BU) **2842**
Sofiiski Universitet. Fakultet po Matematika i Mekhanika. Godishnik/Universite de Sofia. Faculte des Mathematiques et de Mecanique. Annuaire. (BU ISSN 0081-1858) **3055**
Sofiiski Universitet. Fakultet po Slavianska Filologiia. Godishnik. (BU ISSN 0081-1831) **2842**
Sofiiski Universitet. Fakultet po Zapadni Filologii. Godisnik see Sofiiski Universitet. Fakultet po Klasiceski i Novi Filologii. Godisnik **2842**
Sofiiski Universitet. Filosofski Fakultet. Godisnik/Universite de Sofia. Faculte de Philosophie. Annuaire. (BU ISSN 0081-184X) **2388**
Sofiiski Universitet. Filosofski-Istoriceski Fakultet. Godisnik see Sofiiski Universitet. Filosofski Fakultet. Godisnik **2388**
Sofiiski Universitet. Geologo-Geografski Fakultet. Geografiia. Godisnik. (BU ISSN 0324-0525) **2263**
Sofiiski Universitet. Geologo-Geografski Fakultet. Geologiia. Godishnik. (BU) **1580**

Sofiiski Universitet. Ideologicheski Katedri. Godishnik *see* Sofiiski Universitet. Katedra po Nauchen Komunizm. Godishnik **3926**
Sofiiski Universitet. Istoricheski Fakultet. Godishnik/Universite de Sofia. Faculte d'Histoire. Annuaire. (BU ISSN 0204-4005) **2323**
Sofiiski Universitet. Juridiheski Fakultet. Godishnik. (BU ISSN 0081-1866) **2679**
Sofiiski Universitet. Katedra po Nauchen Komunizm. Godishnik. (BU ISSN 0204-9619) **3926**
Sofiiski Universitet. Katedra po Politiceska Ikonomiya. Godishnik. (BU ISSN 0204-9627) **898**
Sofiiski Universitet. Khimicheski Fakultet. Godishnik. (BU) **1188**
Sofiya. (BU ISSN 0324-0037) **2388, 3926**
†Soft. (DK ISSN 0109-9531) **5278**
Soft Ad. (Software Advertiser) (US) **1479, 1433**
Soft & Micro. (FR ISSN 0755-3579) **1474, 1465**
Soft Drink Recycler. (US) **691,** 1968
Soft Drinks *see* Beverage World (English Edition) **378**
Soft Drinks *see* Soft Drinks Managment International **385**
Soft Drinks Managment International. (UK) **385**
Soft Drinks Trade Journal *see* Soft Drinks Managment International **385**
Soft.letter. (US ISSN 0882-3499) **1480, 1433, 1465, 1474, 4144**
Soft Technology. (AT) **1497,** 1968, 4609
Softball B.C. Magazine. (CN) **4511**
Softball Illustrated. (US) **4511**
Softball Rule Book. (US ISSN 0732-2844) **4511**
Softball World. (US) **4511**
Softdisk. (US ISSN 0886-4152) **1480, 1474**
Softsell Reseller *see* Frequent Buyer **1433**
Software. *see* Ruanjian **1479**
Software A B C. (GW) **1480**
Software Abstracts for Engineers. (IE ISSN 0790-150X) **1480, 1880**
Software Advertiser Soft Ad *see* Soft Ad **1479**
Software and Microsystems *see* Software Engineering Journal **1480**
†Software Canada. (CN) **5278**
Software Catalog: Microcomputers. (US) **1465**
Software Catalog: Minicomputers. (US) **1466**
Software Developer's Monthly. (US ISSN 0882-8415) **1431, 1433, 1480, 1691**
▼Software Development Monitor. (UK ISSN 0964-6841) **1480**
Software Digest (Annandale) *see* Software Industry Report **1480**
Software Digest Ratings Newsletter *see* Software Digest Ratings Report **1480**
Software Digest Ratings Report. (US ISSN 0893-6455) **1480,** 1465, 1474
Software Encyclopedia. (US) **1480,** 412
▼Software Engineering. (US) **1480**
Software Engineering Journal. (UK ISSN 0268-6961) **1480,** 1465
Software Engineering Notes. (US ISSN 0163-5948) **1480**
Software for Engineering Workstations *see* Advances in Engineering Software **1877**
Software Industry Bulletin. (US) **1480**
Software Industry Business Practice Survey. (US) **1480**
Software Industry Report. (US) **1480**
Software Kurier. (GW ISSN 0934-5841) **3226**
Software Law Bulletin. (US ISSN 0897-2680) **1480, 2679**
Software Law Journal. (US) **1480,** 1445, 2679
Software Magazine. (US ISSN 0897-8085) **1480,** 1433

Software Maintenance News. (US ISSN 0741-4501) **1480**
Software Management. (UK ISSN 0960-0906) **828,** 1480
Software Markets. (UK) **1480**
Software News (Hudson) *see* Software Magazine **1480**
Software: Practice & Experience. (UK ISSN 0038-0644) **1480**
Software Protection. (US ISSN 0733-1274) **1480, 1435, 2679**
†Software Publishers' Catalogs Annual. (US ISSN 0740-5022) **5279**
▼Software Quality Journal. (UK ISSN 0963-9314) **1480**
†Software Reports: Guide to Evaluated Educational Software. (US) **5279**
Software Review (Westport) *see* Library Software Review **1478**
Software Reviews on File. (US ISSN 8755-7169) **1481**
Software Success. (US ISSN 0896-4386) **1481**
Software Systems and Techniques *see* Software Systems and Techniques Abstracts **1405**
Software Systems and Techniques Abstracts. (UK ISSN 0958-465X) **1405**
Software Times. (US) **1481**
Software Users' Year Book. (UK) **1481**
Software World. (UK ISSN 0038-0652) **1481, 1431**
Softwarefuehrer Atari ST-TT. (GW) **1431, 1474**
Softwarefuehrer fuer Personal-Computer. (GW ISSN 0178-1766) **1432, 1474**
Softwarefuehrer UNIX. (GW ISSN 0939-0367) **1432,** 1474
†SoftwareNews. (US) **5279**
Soglasie. (LI) **2884,** 2024
Sogno. (IT) **2984**
Sogo Gakujutsu Kenkyu Shukai. (JA) **4344,** 4609
Sogo Kango. (JA ISSN 0038-0660) **3287**
Sogo Kenkyujo Hokoku. (JA ISSN 0289-5560) **4609,** 4344
Sogo Rehabilitation. (JA ISSN 0386-9822) **3154,** 1741
Soil and Crop Science Society of Florida. Annual Proceedings. (US) **192**
Soil & Health Journal. (NZ ISSN 0038-0687) **2139,** 192
Soil and Tillage Research. (NE ISSN 0167-1987) **120**
Soil and Water *see* Agricultural Engineer **71**
Soil and Water Conservation News. (US ISSN 0199-9060) **192**
Soil Association. Journal *see* Living Earth **184**
Soil Association. Quarterly Review *see* Living Earth **184**
Soil Biology & Biochemistry. (US ISSN 0038-0717) **457, 483**
Soil Conservation *see* Soil and Water Conservation News **192**
Soil Conservation Digest *see* Indian Journal of Soil Conservation **180**
Soil Dynamics and Earthquake Engineering. (UK ISSN 0261-7277) **1594,** 1874
Soil Fertilizer. *see* Turang Feiliao **195**
Soil Mechanics and Foundation Engineering/Tsuchi to Kiso. (JA ISSN 0041-3798) **1874**
Soil Mechanics and Foundation Engineering. (English translation of: Osnovaniya Fundamenty i Mekhanika Gruntov) (US ISSN 0038-0741) **1874**
Soil Remineralization Newsletter *see* Remineralize the Earth **190**
Soil Science. (US ISSN 0038-075X) **192**
Soil Science and Plant Nutrition. (JA ISSN 0038-0768) **192**
Soil Science Library *see* Books in Soils and the Environment Series **171**
Soil Science Society of America. Journal.(US ISSN 0361-5995) **192**
Soil Science Society of America Special Publication Series *see* S S S A Special Publication Series **191**
Soil Science Society of Ceylon. Journal *see* Soil Science Society of Sri Lanka. Journal **193**

Soil Science Society of Sri Lanka. Journal. (CE ISSN 1015-0803) **193**
†Soil Survey and Land Evaluation. (UK ISSN 0260-9088) **5279**
Soil Survey Horizons. (US) **193,** 1497
Soil Technology. (GW ISSN 0933-3630) **193**
Soil Technology Series. (GW ISSN 0936-2568) **193**
Soil Use and Management. (UK ISSN 0266-0032) **193**
Soilless Culture. (NE ISSN 0256-9701) **2139,** 120
Soilless Grower. (US) **2139**
▼Soils. (US) **1987,** 193
Soils and Fertilizers. (UK ISSN 0038-0792) **143,** 23
Soils & Foundations. (JA ISSN 0038-0806) **1874**
Soils and Land Use Series. (AT ISSN 0081-1912) **193**
Soils and Rocks. *see* Solos e Rochas **1836**
Soils News. (AT ISSN 0812-017X) **193**
Soils Newsletter. (UN) **193**
Soins. (FR ISSN 0038-0814) **3287**
Soins Infirmiers. *see* Krankenpflege **3281**
Le Soir Illustre. (BE) **2175**
Sojourn. (SI ISSN 0217-9520) **4452,** 249
Sojourner. (US ISSN 0191-8699) **4853**
Sojourners. (US ISSN 0364-2097) **4288**
Sojourns. (US) **4786**
Soka Gakkai International *see* S G I **3971**
Soka Gakkai News. (JA ISSN 0385-6321) **4215, 3781**
Sokai. (JA) **3808**
Sokol Polski/Polish Falcon. (US ISSN 0038-0822) **1301, 3808**
Sokol Times. (US) **1301**
Sokoni: Official Newsletter of the Marketing Society of Kenya. (KE) **1054**
Sokuchi Gakkaishi/Geodetic Society of Japan. Journal. (JA ISSN 0038-0830) **2263**
Sokuryo/Monthly Surveyor Magazine. (JA ISSN 0285-7790) **2263**
El Sol. (PR ISSN 0034-933X) **1664**
El Sol. (US) **2024, 2575**
Sol. (HO ISSN 0049-1276) **2515, 2422**
El Sol. (UK ISSN 0038-0849) **2842,** 1664
Sol de Cuba. (CU) **4786**
Sol de Texas. (US) **2024**
Sol de Uruapan. (MX ISSN 0038-0857) **3926**
Sol et Murs Magazine. (FR ISSN 0339-1507) **4609,** 2555
Sol Magazine. (CN) **1811**
†Solanaceae Quarterly. (US) **5279**
Solano Historian. (US) **2422**
Solanus. (US ISSN 0038-0903) **2785,** 4137
Solar and Wind Technology *see* Renewable Energy (Tarrytown) **1795**
Solar Beat. (US) **1811**
†Solar Bibliography. (US) **5279**
Solar Buildings Program Summary *see* Conservation and Renewable Energy Technologies for Building Technologies **1810**
Solar Buildings Technology. (US) **1800,** 1811
Solar Cells *see* Solar Energy Materials and Solar Cells **1811**
Solar Collector Manufacturing Activity. (US ISSN 0197-2030) **1811**
Solar Energy. (US ISSN 0038-092X) **1811**
Solar Energy. *see* Taiyangneng **1812**
Solar Energy. *see* Sunceva Energija **1812**
Solar Energy Index. (US) **1800, 1811**
Solar Energy Industries Association. (Year) Industry Journal *see* Solar Industry Journal **1812**
Solar Energy Industries Association. (Year) Solar Source Book *see* Solar Industry Journal **1812**

SOLDADO ARGENTINO 6673

Solar Energy Materials *see* Solar Energy Materials and Solar Cells **1811**
Solar Energy Materials and Solar Cells. (NE ISSN 0927-0248) **1811**
Solar Energy Research and Development in the European Community. Series. A. Solar Energy Applications to Dwellings. (NE) **1811**
Solar Energy Research and Development in the European Community. Series B: Thermo-Mechanical Solar Power Plants. (NE) **1811**
Solar Energy Research and Development in the European Community. Series C. Photovoltaic Power Generation. (NE) **1811**
Solar Energy Research and Development in the European Community. Series D. Photochemical, Photoelectrochemical and Photobiological Processes. (NE) **1812**
Solar Energy Research and Development in the European Community. Series E. Energy from Biomass. (NE) **1812**
Solar Energy Research and Development in the European Community. Series F. Solar Radiation Data. (NE) **1812**
Solar Energy Research and Development in the European Community. Series G. Wind Energy. (NE) **1812**
Solar Energy Research and Development in the European Community. Series H. Solar Energy in Agriculture and Industry. (NE) **1812,** 120
Solar Energy Research and Development Reports. (US) **1795**
Solar Energy Research Institute Ethanol Annual Report *see* S E R I. Ethanol Annual Report **1795**
Solar Energy Research Institute Science and Technology in Review *see* S E R I Science and Technology in Review **1811**
Solar Energy Society of India Journal *see* S E S I Journal **1811**
†Solar Energy Update. (US ISSN 0364-6998) **5279**
Solar Energy Washington Letter *see* International Solar Energy Intelligence Report **1811**
Solar Engineering. (US) **1812**
Solar-Geophysical Data. Part 1 - Prompt Reports. (US) **369, 1594, 3831**
Solar-Geophysical Data: Part 2 - Comprehensive Reports. (US) **369, 1594, 3831**
Solar Indices Bulletin. (US) **1594**
Solar Industry Journal. (US) **1812**
Solar Law. (US) **1812, 2679**
Solar Mind. (US) **4609,** 1968
Solar Physics. (NE ISSN 0038-0938) **369, 3831**
Solar Progress. (AT ISSN 0729-6436) **1812,** 1497
Solar Radiation and Radiation Balance Data. The World Network. *see* Solnechnaya Radiatsiya i Radiatsionnyi Balans. Mirovaya Set **3441**
Solar Space Letter. (US) **62**
Solar System Research. (English translation of: Astronomicheskii Vestnik) (US ISSN 0038-0946) **369, 3831**
Solar System Today. (UK ISSN 0144-4492) **369**
Solar Terrestrial Activity Chart. (JA) **371, 3444**
Solar Terrestrial Environmental Research in Japan. (JA ISSN 0386-5444) **1594, 3831**
Solar Thermal Energy Technology. (US ISSN 0741-5249) **1812**
Solar Thermal Report. (US) **1812**
Solar Times. (US) **1812**
Solar Today. (US) **1812**
Solar Utilization News *see* S.U.N **1811**
Solaria. (SZ) **1812**
Soldado Argentino. (AG ISSN 0038-0954) **3471**

6674 SOLDADURA

Soldadura & Construcao Metalica. (PO) **3430**
Der Soldat. (AU ISSN 0038-0962) **3471**
Soldat und Technik. (GW ISSN 0038-0989) **3471**
Soldering & Surface Mount Technology. (UK) **3430**
Soldi Numismatica. (IT) **3602**
Soldier. (UK) **3471**
Soldier in National Service. (Il) **3471**
Soldier of Fortune. (US ISSN 0145-6784) **3471**
Soldier, Sailor, Airman, Marine see S S A M **3470**
Soldier Shop Annual. (US) **2442, 3471**
Soldier Shop Quarterly see Soldier Shop Annual **2442**
†Soldier Support Advocate. (US) **5279**
Soldiers. (US ISSN 0093-8440) **3472**
Soleil. (FR ISSN 0038-1012) **3926**
Solent Yearbook. (UK) **4529**
Solia. (US ISSN 0038-1039) **4288**
Solicitors' and Barristers' Directory. (UK) **2679**
Solicitors' and Barristers' Directory and Diary see Solicitors' and Barristers' Directory **2679**
Solicitors' Journal. (UK ISSN 0038-1047) **2679**
Solicitor's Journal. (CN) **2679**
Solid Fuel. (UK ISSN 0038-1055) **2303**
Solid Fuel Chemistry. (English translation of: Khimiya Tverdogo Topliva) (US ISSN 0361-5219) **1860**, 1188
Solid Ground: A New World Journal. (US) **2884**
Solid-Liquid Flow Abstracts. (UK ISSN 0038-1063) **1846**, 23, 3839
Solid Mechanics Archives. (UK ISSN 0952-4762) **4344**
Solid State Abstracts Journal see Solid State and Superconductivity Abstracts **3839**
Solid State and Superconductivity Abstracts. (US ISSN 0896-5900) **3839**, 23
Solid State Communications. (US ISSN 0038-1098) **3831**, 1230
Solid-State Electronics. (US ISSN 0038-1101) **1778**
Solid State Ionics. (NE ISSN 0167-2738) **3831**
▼Solid State Nuclear Magnetic Resonance. (NE ISSN 0926-2040) **1208**, 2525, 3363
Solid State Physics see Journal of Physics: Condensed Matter **3822**
Solid State Physics. see Kotai Butsuri **3844**
Solid State Physics: Advances in Research and Applications. (US ISSN 0081-1947) **3831**
†Solid State Processing and Production Buyers Guide and Directory. (US) **5279**
Solid State Technology. (US ISSN 0038-111X) **1778**
Solid Value. (US ISSN 1053-5845) **963**
Solid Waste & Power. (US) **1796, 4073**
Solid Waste Report. (US ISSN 0038-1128) **1968**
Solidaires see Solidaires - Lumiere du Monde **4202**
Solidaires (Paris). (FR ISSN 0338-1757) **4421**, 4853
Solidaires - Lumiere du Monde. (FR) **4202**
Il Solidale. (IT ISSN 0392-9043) **3926**
Solidaridad. (EC) **4276**
Solidaritaet. (AU) **994**
Solidarite. (FR) **2024**
Solidarite Atlantique. (FR ISSN 0296-4333) **3972**
†Solidarite Sante. (FR) **5279**
Solidarite Sante Etudes Statistiques. (FR ISSN 0764-4493) **4427**
Solidaritet. see Dayanisma **3954**
Solidarity. (PH ISSN 0038-1160) **2214**
Solidarity. (UK) **3926**

Solidarity (Detroit). (US ISSN 0164-856X) **2589**
Solidarity (Hicksville). (US ISSN 0038-1152) **2543**, 2589
Solidarity Weekly. see Tygodnik Solidarnosc **886**
Solidarity's Focus see Focus (Tallahassee) **1634**
Solids Handling. (UK ISSN 0143-8557) **3023**
Solinet. Annual Report. (Southeastern Library Network, Inc.) (US) **2785**
Solinews see S O L I N E W S **2799**
Solnechnaya Radiatsiya i Radiatsionnyi Balans. Mirovaya Set/Solar Radiation and Radiation Balance Data. The World Network. (RU ISSN 0235-4519) **3441**
O Solo. (BL ISSN 0584-0821) **120**
Solo. (AT ISSN 0813-4650) **4421**
Solo Flyer. (US) **3006**
†Soloing. (US) **5279**
Solointimo International. (IT) **1287**
Solomon Goldman Lectures. (US ISSN 0196-2183) **4226**
Solomon Islands Museum Association. Journal. (BP) **3533**, 249
Solomon Mahlangu Freedom College Voice of S O M A F C O see Voice of S O M A F C O **2240**
Solos e Rochas/Soils and Rocks. (BL ISSN 0103-7021) **1836**, 1580
Solothurnische Handelskammer. Jahresbericht. (SZ) **822**
Solothurnische Handelskammer. Mitteilungen. (SZ) **822**
▼Solstice: An Electronic Journal of Geography and Mathematics. (US ISSN 1059-5325) **3056**, 2263
Solubility Data Series. (US ISSN 0191-5622) **1188**
Solutions. (US ISSN 0199-9869) **193**
Solvent Extraction and Ion Exchange. (US ISSN 0736-6299) **1208**
Solvent News see Cleaning Technology News **1225**
Soma. (US) **2884**
Soma. (Il) **4786**, 2480
†Soma: Engineering for the Human Body. (US ISSN 0886-8034) **5279**
Somali Institute of Public Administration Newsletter. (SO) **4073**
Somali National Bank. Annual Report and Statement of Accounts see Central Bank of Somalia. Annual Report and Statement of Accounts **771**
Somali National Bank. Bulletin see Central Bank of Somalia. Bulletin **710**
Somalia in Figures. (SO) **4586**
Somatic Cell and Molecular Genetics. (US) **547**, 526
Somatic Cell Genetics see Somatic Cell and Molecular Genetics **547**
Somatics. (US ISSN 0147-5231) **3808**, 3373
Somatosensory and Motor Research. (US ISSN 0899-0220) **575, 3743**, 4047
Somatosensory Research see Somatosensory and Motor Research **575**
Somborske Novine. (YU ISSN 0038-1276) **2240**
Some. (US) **2961**
Some Friends. (US) **2961**
Some Other Magazine. (US) **2961**
Somerset and Dorset Notes and Queries. (UK ISSN 0049-1306) **2388**
Somerset Archaeology and Natural History. (UK ISSN 0081-2056) **285**, 4344
Somerset Birds. (UK ISSN 0081-2048) **567**
Somerset Farmer. (UK ISSN 0038-1314) **120**
▼Somerset Magazine. (UK ISSN 0961-9364) **2195**
Somerset Past. (US) **2164**
Somersetshire Archaeological and Natural History Society. Proceedings see Somerset Archaeology and Natural History **285**
†The (something). (US ISSN 1044-6710) **5279**
Something about the Author. (US ISSN 0276-816X) **1266**, 421, 2961

Something about the Author. Autobiography Series. (US ISSN 0885-6842) **421**
Something on Paper. (AT ISSN 0310-4389) **3666**
Sommerfeltia. (NO ISSN 0800-6865) **517**
Sommers Letter. (US) **884**
Sommets. (CN ISSN 0838-4401) **1324**
Somos. (AG) **2170**
Somos. (NQ) **4853**
Somos Jovenes. (CU) **1244**
Somu-cho. Tokei-kyoku Kenkyu Iho/ Management and Coordination Agency. Statistics Bureau. Research Memoir. (JA ISSN 0446-5849) **4586**
Son! (FR) **344**, 3580
Son Hi-Fi Magazine see Son Hi-Fi Video **1360**
Son Hi-Fi Video. (CN ISSN 0831-0785) **1360**, 1386, 4461
Son - Magazine. (FR) **1360**
Sonda. (SP) **3580**
Sondagem Conjuntural na Industria de Tranformacao do Nordeste see Nordeste Conjuntura Industrial **1081**
Sondenhaeuser Verband Zeitung see S V Zeitung **1323**
Sonderbaende zur Theologischen Zeitschrift. (SZ ISSN 0067-4907) **4202**
Sonderdienst. (GW) **2191**
Sonderschule. (GW ISSN 0038-1357) **1664**, 2289, 2296
Sonderschulmagazin see Lehrermagazin Sonderschulmagazin **1754**
Song Hits see Song Hits' Heartbreakers **5279**
†Song Hits' Heartbreakers. (US) **5279**
Song of Zion. (US ISSN 0273-2920) **3581**
Songhua Jiang/Songhua River. (CC) **2961**
Songhua River. see Songhua Jiang **2961**
Songs. see Gequ **3552**
†Songs from Radio, TV and Film Productions. (UR) **5279**
Songs of New South Wales. Series. (AT ISSN 0726-1306) **3581**
▼Songs of New Zealand. (AT ISSN 1035-6355) **3581**
Songs of Northern Territory. Series. (AT ISSN 0726-1365) **3581**
Songs of Queensland. Series. (AT ISSN 0726-1330) **3581**
Songs of South Australia. Series. (AT ISSN 0726-1322) **3581**
Songs of Tasmania. Series. (AT ISSN 0726-1357) **3581**
Songs of Tianjin. see Tianjin Gesheng **3584**
Songs of Victoria. Series. (AT ISSN 0726-1314) **3581**
Songs of Western Australia. Series. (AT ISSN 0726-1349) **3581**
SongTalk. (US) **3581**
Songwriter's Contacts. (US) **3581**
Songwriter's Guild News see B A S C A News **3540**
Songwriter's Market. (US ISSN 0161-5971) **3581**
Songwriters Musepaper see Los Angeles Songwriters Showcase Musepaper **3561**
Sonics. (AT ISSN 0729-9389) **3581**
Sonics Yearbook. (AT) **4461**
Sonido. (MX) **3581**
Sonne. (GW ISSN 0721-0094) **369**
Sonneck Society Bulletin. (US) **3581**
Sonneck Society Newsletter see Sonneck Society Bulletin **3581**
Sonnenenergie und Waermepumpe. (GW ISSN 0172-5912) **1812**
Sonntag. (GW ISSN 0038-1411) **2884**
Sonntags Schulhelfer see Sonntagsschulmitarbeiter **1664**
Der Sonntagsbrief. (GW ISSN 0174-0350) **2279**, 2191, 4202
Sonntagsschulmitarbeiter. (GW ISSN 0012-2580) **1664**, 4202
Sonntagsdienste. (GW ISSN 0176-862X) **4276**
Sonntagsgruss. (GW) **4249**
Sonntagspost. (US) **2024**, 2234

Sonntagspost. (AU ISSN 0038-139X) **2173**
Sono. (FR) **4461**
Sonoma Business. (US) **691**
Sonoma Mandala. (US) **2961**
†Sonoma Marin Farmer. (US) **5279**
†Sonoma Reader. (US) **5279**
Sonora Review. (US ISSN 0275-5203) **2961**
Sonoran Quarterly. (US) **517**, 2139
Sonorensis. (US) **4344**
Sonorensis. Annual Report. (US) **3533**
Sonovision. (FR) **1343**
Sons and Daughters of the Soddies. Reports. (US) **2164**, 2422
Sons of Italy Magazine see Sons of Italy News **1301**
Sons of Italy News. (US ISSN 0038-1446) **1301**
Sons of Italy Times. (US ISSN 0038-1454) **1301**
Sons of Norway Viking. (US ISSN 0038-1462) **2024**
Sons of the American Revolution Magazine. (US ISSN 0161-0511) **2422**, 2164
Sonus. (US ISSN 0739-229X) **3581**
Sonyon Dong-A. (KO) **1266**
Soochow Journal of Economics and Business. (CH ISSN 0259-3769) **691**, 898, 1000
Soochow Journal of Foreign Languages and Literatures. (CH ISSN 0259-3777) **2842**, 2961
Soochow Journal of Humanities. (CH ISSN 1010-0733) **2515**
Soochow Journal of Mathematical and Natural Sciences see Soochow Journal of Mathematics **3056**
Soochow Journal of Mathematics. (CH ISSN 0250-3255) **3056**, 4344
Soochow Journal of Political Science & Sociology. (CH ISSN 0259-3785) **4388**, 3926
Soochow Journal of Social and Political Sciences see Soochow Journal of Political Science & Sociology **4388**
Soochow Law Review. (CH ISSN 0259-3750) **2680**
†Soochow University Journal of Chinese Art History. (CH ISSN 0259-3742) **5279**
Sooke Mirror. (CN ISSN 0026-5837) **2179**
Soon to Appear... (PL ISSN 0239-0345) **412**
Sooner L P G Times. (US ISSN 0038-1500) **3701**
Sooners Illustrated. (US) **4488**
Sophia. (PH ISSN 0115-8988) **3781**
Sophia. (AT ISSN 0038-1527) **4202, 3781**
Sophia. (US ISSN 0194-7958) **4288**
Sophia (Tokyo, 1952). (JA ISSN 0489-6432) **2515**
Sophia (Tokyo, 1984). (JA) **4853**
Sophia Circle. (US) **4853**
Sophia Kokyuroku in Mathematics. see Jochi Daigaku Sugaku Kokyuroku **3040**
†Sophia Perennis. (IR) **5279**
Sophia University. Institute of Comparative Culture. Business Series. (JA ISSN 0913-1620) **1028**, 1054
Sophisticated Leisure Travel Directory. (US) **4787**, 2480, 2739
Sophisticate's Black Hair. (US) **374, 2024**
Sophisticate's Hairstyle Guide. (US) **374**
Sopi. (SG) **3926**
SOPODA see Social Planning - Policy & Development Abstracts **4426**
Soprano, Alto, Bass Choir see S A B Choir **3579**
Soprintendenza Archeologica di Pompei. Cataloghi. (IT) **285**
Soprintendenza Archeologica di Pompei. Monografie. (IT) **285**
Soprintendenza per i Beni Culturali della Valle d'Aosta. Quaderni. (IT) **344, 307**
SoProDen. (SP ISSN 0213-831X) **3242**
Soproni Szemle. (HU ISSN 0133-0748) **2388**

SOUTH AFRICA 6675

Sorby Natural History Society Newsletter. (UK ISSN 0038-1551) 4344
Sorby Record. (UK ISSN 0260-2245) 4344
Sorenson Health and Fitness Bulletin. (US) 3808
Sorghum and Millets Abstracts. (UK ISSN 0308-2970) 143, 23
Soroptimist. (US ISSN 0097-9562) 4421
Soroush (Monthly). (IR) 2202
Soroush (Weekly). (IR) 2202
Sorrisi e Canzoni T V (Milan). (IT ISSN 0038-156X) 1380
†Sorrow's Reward. (US ISSN 1043-4186) 5279
Sortenversuchsergebnisse. (AU) 120
Sorting Code Numbers. (UK) 799
Sosei to Kako. see Japan Society for Technology of Plasticity. Journal 4601
Sosiaalinen Aikakauskirja/Social Review.(FI ISSN 0038-1594) 4421
Sosial Forum - Sosial Arbeid see Helse og Sosial Forum 4436
Sosial Trygd. (NO ISSN 0038-1608) 4421, 2543
Sosialisma Mpiasa. (MG) 2589
Sosialistinen Aikakauslehti. (FI ISSN 0038-1616) 3926
Sosialistisk Perspektiv see Aktuelt Perspektiv 3871
Sosialoekonomen. (NO ISSN 0038-1624) 691
Sosionomen. (NO) 4421
Il Sospiro del Tifoso. (IT) 2884
Sot la Nape. (IT ISSN 0038-1659) 2884
Sotahistoriallinen Aikakauskirja. (FI ISSN 0357-816X) 3472, 2388
Sotainvalidi. (FI ISSN 0049-1349) 4421
†Sotheby's International Price Guide: Antiques and Collectibles. (US) 5279
Sotheby's Newsletter. (US ISSN 1056-7143) 344, 259
Sotilasaikakauslehti. (FI ISSN 0038-1675) 3472
Sotrudnichestvo. see Politechnika Wroclawska. Osrodek Badan Prognostycznych. Prace Naukowe. Wspolpraca 5260
Sotsialisticheskaya Mysl' i Praktika see Aktualna Pitanja Socijalizma 3871
Sotsialisticheskaya Zakonnost' (RU ISSN 0038-1691) 2680
Sotsialisticheskii Trud. (RU ISSN 0037-8216) 994
Sotsialistychna Kul'tura. (KR ISSN 0038-1705) 2884
▼Sotsial'no-politicheskie Nauki. (RU) 4388
Sotsial'noe Obespechenie. (RU ISSN 0038-1713) 2543
Sotsiologiya Kul'tury. (RU) 4452
▼Sotsium. (RU ISSN 0868-8230) 2884
Soudage dans le Monde. see Welding in the World 3431
Soudage et Techniques Connexes. (FR ISSN 0038-173X) 3430
Soudure. see Schweisstechnik 3430
Soul. (US ISSN 0038-1756) 4276
Soul Bag. (FR ISSN 0398-9089) 3581
Soul Music see Shout 3580
Soul of Martial Arts. see Wuhun 4497
Sound see British Journal of Audiology 2286
Sound. (SZ) 3860
Sound & Communications. (US ISSN 0038-1845) 4461, 1343
Sound & Hi Fi/Ihos. (GR ISSN 1105-1302) 3581, 4461
Sound & Image. (AT) 1380
▼Sound & Image. (US) 4461, 3581
Sound and Meaning. (US) 2842
Sound and Vibration. (US ISSN 0038-1810) 1939
Sound & Video Contractor. (US ISSN 0741-1715) 4461, 1386
Sound & Vision. (CN) 1343, 1778
Sound Boy see Hivi 4460
Sound Buys see Hot Picks 4129
Sound Canada see Sound & Vision 1343
Sound Challenge. (US) 4702, 1908

Sound Check. (GW ISSN 0936-0689) 3581
Sound Choice. (US ISSN 8756-6176) 3581, 4461
Sound Engineer and Producer. (UK ISSN 0957-9508) 4461
Sound International see Studio Sound & Broadcast Engineering 4462
†Sound Management. (US ISSN 8755-0555) 5279
Sound Money Investor. (US) 963, 2884
Sound of Business. (US) 884
Sound of Malaysian's Musician/Ta Ma Ko Yu Chih Sheng. (MY) 3581
Sound of the Economy. (US) 884
Sound-off. (US) 1664
Sound on Sound. (UK ISSN 0951-6816) 3581, 4461
Sound Post. (US ISSN 0749-0755) 3581
Sound Telegraph. (AT) 2172
Sound und R T E (Radio T V Electronics) see Sound 3860
Sound Words. (US) 4202
Soundbarrier. (UK) 2289, 1741, 4421
Soundboard. (US) 3581
Sounding Board. (CN) 691
Soundings. (UK) 2296
Soundings see Wavelength (Newport Beach) 2545
Soundings. (US) 4739
Soundings (Boston) see M P A D Today 2288
Soundings (Deerfield). (US) 632, 2555
Soundings (Essex). (US) 4529
Soundings (Fairfield) see Leadership (Fairfield) 1017
Soundings (Knoxville). (US ISSN 0038-1861) 2515, 4388
Soundings (Milwaukee). (US) 2422, 4739
Soundings (Notre Dame). (US) 3782, 691
Soundings (Santa Barbara). (US ISSN 0038-1853) 2785, 2961
Soundings East. (US) 2961
Soundings from Around the World. (US) 3972
Soundings Trade Only. (US ISSN 0194-8369) 4529
Soundless Sound. see Anahata Nada 4162
Sounds. (UK ISSN 0144-5774) 3581
Sounds Australian Journal. (AT ISSN 0811-3149) 3581
Sounds Australian Update. (AT ISSN 1030-4916) 3581
Sounds of Lexington. (US) 2289
Sounds of Poetry. (US) 3006
Sounds of Reading. (US) 1664
Sounds of Truth and Tradition. (US ISSN 0038-187X) 4276
Soundtrack. (US ISSN 1042-0649) 3581, 4461
Soundtrack! Incorporating CinemaScore.(BE ISSN 0771-6303) 3581, 3518
Soundtrack! The Collector's Quarterly see Soundtrack! Incorporating CinemaScore 3581
Soundview Executive Book Summaries. (US ISSN 0195-1718) 1028, 898, 1070
Soundview Summaries see Soundview Executive Book Summaries 1028
The Source (Abington). (US) 2094, 1118
Source (Casselberry). (US) 691
†Source (Jamaica). (US ISSN 0273-0324) 5279
Source (Menomonee Falls). (US) 1741
†Source (New York). (US) 5279
Source (New York, 1989). (UN) 3972
▼The Source (New York). (US) 3581
Source (Seattle). (US) 4202, 4452
Source (Washington) see Identified Sources of Supply 3446
Source Book of American State Legislation. (US) 4074
Source Book of Franchise Opportunities.(US) 963
Source Book of Health Insurance Data. (US ISSN 0073-148X) 2543
Source Book Profiles see Foundation Center Source Book Profiles 4425

Source Book: Social and Health Services in the Greater New York Area. (US ISSN 0740-4549) 4421
Source Books on Curricula and Methods see Unesco Source Books on Curricula and Methods 1762
Source Directory of Predicasts, Inc. see Predicasts Source Directory 736
Source I. (US ISSN 0278-4378) 4787
Source II. (US ISSN 0278-4386) 4787
Source Journals in Metals and Materials. (US) 3419, 3428
Source Material of Finnish History. see Suomen Historian Laehteitae 2391
Source Materials on the History of Science in India. (II) 4344
Source: Notes in the History of Art. (US ISSN 0737-4453) 344
†Source Tab: A Directory of Program Resources for Public Radio. (US) 5279
Sourcebook of Criminal Justice Statistics. (US ISSN 0360-3431) 1525, 4586
Sourcebook on Asbestos Diseases. (US) 2680, 3154
Sourcebook on Asbestos Diseases Case Law Quarterly. (US) 2680, 3154
†Sourcefinder. (US ISSN 0732-6696) 5279
SourceMex. (US ISSN 1054-8890) 884
Sources. (FR) 38
Sources (Montclair). (US) 4488
Sources (Richmond Heights). (US) 3419
Sources d'Histoire Medievale. (FR) 2388
Sources de Droit Serbe. see Izvori Srpskog Prava 2637
Sources Directory. (CN ISSN 0700-480X) 1349
Sources et Travaux d'Histoire Haut-Pyreneenne. (FR ISSN 0248-5516) 2388
†Sources File. (US) 5279
Sources for Stamping see Sources (Richmond Heights) 3419
Sources for the Study of Religion in Malawi. (MW) 4202, 2785
Sources from the Ancient Near East. (US ISSN 0732-6424) 2432
Sources in the History of Mathematics and Physical Sciences. (US ISSN 0172-6315) 3056
Sources of Connecticut Law. (US) 2680
Sources of Contemporary Jewish Thought/Mekevot. (IS ISSN 0082-4585) 2884, 4226
Sources of Music and Their Interpretation, Duke Studies in Music.(US) 3581, 2422
Sources of State Information on Corporations see How to Find Company Intelligence in State Documents 669
Sources of Supply - Buyers Guide. (US ISSN 0081-2129) 3666
Sourceview see Sourceview Journal of Software Evaluations, Reviews & Ratings 1481
Sourceview Journal of Software Evaluations, Reviews & Ratings. (US) 1481, 1465, 1474
Sourdough. (US ISSN 0002-4570) 2785
Sourozh. (UK ISSN 0950-2742) 4288
Sous un Meme Soleil. see Under the Same Sun 936
South. (UK ISSN 0260-6976) 3926, 884
South Africa. Central Service. Road Traffic Accidents see South Africa. Central Statistical Service. Road Traffic Collisions 4667
South Africa. Central Statistical Service and Government Printing Works see South Africa. Department of Home Affairs. Annual Report 4586
South Africa. Central Statistical Service. Annual Report see South Africa. Department of Home Affairs. Annual Report 4586

South Africa. Central Statistical Service. Births - Whites, Coloureds and Asians. (SA) 3995, 4586
South Africa. Central Statistical Service. Building Plans Passed and Buildings Completed. (SA) 638, 4586
South Africa. Central Statistical Service. Bulletin of Statistics. (SA) 4586
South Africa. Central Statistical Service. Census of Electricity, Gas and Steam.(SA) 1800, 4586
South Africa. Central Statistical Service. Census of Mining. (SA) 3502, 4586
South Africa. Central Statistical Service. Census of Township Development. (SA) 2500
South Africa. Central Statistical Service. Deaths of Blacks. (SA) 3995, 4586
†South Africa. Central Statistical Service. Education: Asian. (SA) 5279
†South Africa. Central Statistical Service. Education: Whites. (SA) 5279
†South Africa. Central Statistical Service. Labour Statistics: Wage Rates, Earnings and Average Hours Worked in the Printing and Newspaper Industry, Engineering Industry, Building Industry and Commerce. (SA) 5279
South Africa. Central Statistical Service. Local Government Statistics. (SA) 4082, 4586
South Africa. Central Statistical Service. Mining: Financial Statistics see South Africa. Central Statistical Service. Census of Mining 3502
South Africa. Central Statistical Service. New Vehicles Registered. (SA) 4667, 4586
South Africa. Central Statistical Service. Registered Vehicles as at 30 June. (SA) 4667, 4586
South Africa. Central Statistical Service. Report on Births: White, Coloured and Asian see South Africa. Central Statistical Service. Births - Whites, Coloureds and Asians 3995
South Africa. Central Statistical Service. Report on Marriages and Divorces: South Africa. (SA) 3995
South Africa. Central Statistical Service. Road Traffic Collisions. (SA) 4667
South Africa. Central Statistical Service. Selected Economic Indicators/South Africa. Sentrale Statistiekdiens. Uitgesoekte Ekonomiese Aanwysers. (SA) 738
South Africa. Central Statistical Service. Statistical News Releases. (SA) 4586
South Africa. Central Statistical Service. Statistical News Release. Retail Prices - All Items. (SA) 738, 4586
South Africa. Central Statistical Service. Statistical News Release. Survey of Houses, Sectional Title Units and Domestic Workers. (SA) 2500, 4586
South Africa. Central Statistical Service. Statistical News Release. Transfers of Rural Immovable Property. (SA) 4160, 4586
South Africa. Central Statistical Service. Statistics of Development Boards. (SA) 4082, 4586
South Africa. Central Statistical Service. Statistics of Houses and Domestic Servants and of Flats see South Africa. Central Statistical Service. Statistical News Release. Survey of Houses, Sectional Title Units and Domestic Workers 2500
South Africa. Central Statistical Service. Statistics of Motor and Other Vehicles see South Africa. Central Statistical Service. Registered Vehicles as at 30 June 4667
South Africa. Central Statistical Service. Statistics of New Vehicles Registered see South Africa. Central Statistical Service. New Vehicles Registered 4667
South Africa. Central Statistical Service. Survey of the Accounts of Companies. (SA) 738, 4586

6676 SOUTH AFRICA

South Africa. Central Statistical Service. Tourism and Migration. (SA) **3995**, 4586, 4800
South Africa. Central Statistical Service. Township Developers *see* South Africa. Central Statistical Service. Census of Township Development **2500**
South Africa. Central Statistical Service. Transfers of Rural Immovable Property *see* South Africa. Central Statistical Service. Statistical News Release. Transfers of Rural Immovable Property **4160**
South Africa. Commissioner for Customs and Excise. Foreign Trade Statistics. (SA) **738**
South Africa. Commissioner For Customs and Excise. Monthly Abstract of Trade Statistics. (SA) **738**, 921
South Africa. Dairy Board. Annual Report. (SA) **203**
South Africa. Dairy Control Board. Annual Report *see* South Africa. Dairy Board. Annual Report **203**
South Africa. Department of Agricultural Development. Annual Report of the Chief for Agricultural Development. (SA) **120**
South Africa. Department of Agricultural Economics and Marketing. Division of Agricultural Marketing and Research. Trends in the Agricultural Sector *see* South Africa. Department of Agriculture and Fisheries. Division of Economic Services. Trends in the Agricultural Sector **157**
South Africa. Department of Agricultural Economics and Marketing. Division of Agricultural Marketing Research. Abstract of Agricultural Statistics *see* South Africa. Department of Agriculture and Fisheries. Division of Economic Services. Abstract of Agricultural Statistics **143**
South Africa. Department of Agriculture. Agricultural Bulletins. (SA) **121**
South Africa. Department of Agriculture. Agricultural Research. (SA) **121**
South Africa. Department of Agriculture and Fisheries. Agricultural Bulletins *see* South Africa. Department of Agriculture. Agricultural Bulletins **121**
South Africa. Department of Agriculture and Fisheries. Agricultural Research *see* South Africa. Department of Agriculture. Agricultural Research **121**
South Africa. Department of Agriculture and Fisheries. Division of Economic Services. Abstract of Agricultural Statistics/Kortbegrip van Landboustatistieke. (SA) **143**, 4586
South Africa. Department of Agriculture and Fisheries. Division of Economic Services. Trends in the Agricultural Sector. (SA) **157**
South Africa. Department of Agriculture and Fisheries. Entomology Memoirs *see* South Africa. Department of Agriculture. Entomology Memoirs **538**
South Africa. Department of Agriculture and Fisheries. Official List of Professional Research Workers, Lecturing Staff and Extension Workers in the Agricultural Field *see* South Africa. Department of Agriculture. Official List of Professional Research Workers, Lecturing Staff and Extension Workers in the Agricultural Field **121**
South Africa. Department of Agriculture and Fisheries. Science Bulletins *see* South Africa. Department of Agriculture. Science Bulletins **121**
South Africa. Department of Agriculture and Fisheries. Special Publications *see* South Africa. Department of Agriculture. Special Publications **121**
South Africa. Department of Agriculture and Fisheries. Technical Communication *see* South Africa. Department of Agriculture. Technical Communication **121**
South Africa. Department of Agriculture and Water Supply. Annual Report of the Chief for Agricultural Development *see* South Africa. Department of Agricultural Development. Annual Report of the Chief for Agricultural Development **120**
South Africa. Department of Agriculture. Entomology Memoirs. (SA) **538**
South Africa. Department of Agriculture. Official List of Professional Research Workers, Lecturing Staff and Extension Workers in the Agricultural Field. (SA) **121**
South Africa. Department of Agriculture. Science Bulletins. (SA) **121**
South Africa. Department of Agriculture. Special Publications. (SA) **121**
South Africa. Department of Agriculture. Technical Communication. (SA) **121**
South Africa. Department of Bantu Education. Annual Report *see* South Africa. Department of Education and Training. Annual Report **1664**
South Africa. Department of Customs and Excise. Foreign Trade Statistics *see* South Africa. Commissioner for Customs and Excise. Foreign Trade Statistics **738**
South Africa. Department of Defense. White Paper on Defense and Armament Production. (SA) **3472**
South Africa. Department of Education and Training. Annual Report. (SA) **1664**
†South Africa. Department of Higher Education. Annual Report. (SA ISSN 0081-220X) **5279**
South Africa. Department of Home Affairs. Annual Report. (SA) **4586**
South Africa. Department of Mineral and Energy Affairs. Annual Report. (SA) **3496**, 1580
South Africa. Department of Mines. Annual Report *see* South Africa. Department of Mineral and Energy Affairs. Annual Report **3496**
†South Africa. Department of National Education. Annual Report. (SA) **5279**
South Africa. Department of Public Work and Land Affairs. Directorate of Surveys and Mapping. Annual Report of the Chief Director *see* South Africa. Department of Regional and Land Affairs. Directorate of Surveys and Land Information. Annual Report of the Chief Surveyor-General **1874**
South Africa. Department of Regional and Land Affairs. Directorate of Surveys and Land Information. Annual Report of the Chief Surveyor-General. (SA) **1874**
South Africa. Department of Statistics. Annual Report of the Statistics Advisory Council and of the Secretary of Statistics *see* South Africa. Department of Home Affairs. Annual Report **4586**
South Africa. Department of Statistics. Building Plans and Buildings Completed *see* South Africa. Central Statistical Service. Building Plans Passed and Buildings Completed **638**
South Africa. Department of Statistics. Bulletin of Statistics *see* South Africa. Central Statistical Service. Bulletin of Statistics **4586**
South Africa. Department of Statistics. Census of Electricity, Gas and Steam *see* South Africa. Central Statistical Service. Census of Electricity, Gas and Steam **1800**
South Africa. Department of Statistics. Local Government Statistics *see* South Africa. Central Statistical Service. Local Government Statistics **4082**
South Africa. Department of Statistics. Report on Bantu Deaths in Selected Magisterial Districts - Verslag oor Bantoesterfgevalle in Uitgesoekte Landdrosdistrikte *see* South Africa. Central Statistical Service. Deaths of Blacks **3995**
South Africa. Department of Statistics. Report on Marriages and Divorces: South Africa *see* South Africa. Central Statistical Service. Report on Marriages and Divorces: South Africa **3995**
South Africa. Department of Statistics. Statistical News Releases *see* South Africa. Central Statistical Service. Statistical News Releases **4586**
South Africa. Department of Statistics. Statistics of Administration Boards *see* South Africa. Central Statistical Service. Statistics of Development Boards **4082**
South Africa. Department of Statistics. Tourism and Migration *see* South Africa. Central Statistical Service. Tourism and Migration **3995**
South Africa. Department of Transport. Technical Methods for Highways. (SA) **4721**
South Africa. Department of Transport. Technical Recommendations for Highways. (SA) **4721**
South Africa. Division of Road and Transport Technology. Technical Methods for Highways *see* South Africa. Department of Transport. Technical Methods for Highways **4721**
†South Africa. Division of Roads and Transport Technology. Annual Report/Divisie vir Pad- en Vertoertegnologie. (SA) **5279**
South Africa. Division of Roads and Transport Technology. Bulletins. (SA) **4721**
South Africa. Division of Roads and Transport Technology. P A D Series. (SA) **4721**
South Africa. Division of Roads and Transport Technology. Technical Recommendations for Highways *see* South Africa. Department of Transport. Technical Recommendations for Highways **4721**
South Africa. Division of Roads and Transport Technology. Transport Statistics/Divisie vir Pad- en Vervoertegnologie. (SA) **4667**
South Africa. Division of Roads and Transport Technology. User Manuals and Computer Programs/Divisie vir Pad- en Vervoertegnologie. Gebruikershandboeke en Rekenaarprogramme. (SA) **4707**
South Africa. Division of Textile Technology. Annual Report. (SA) **4623**
South Africa. Geological Survey. Annals *see* South Africa. Geological Survey. Annual Technical Report **1580**
South Africa. Geological Survey. Annual Technical Report. (SA) **1580**
South Africa. Geological Survey. Bulletin.(SA) **1580**
South Africa. Geological Survey. Contributions to Engineering Geology.(SA) **1580**
South Africa. Geological Survey. Geological Maps. (SA) **1580**
South Africa. Geological Survey. Geological Maps. Explanations. (SA) **1581**
South Africa. Geological Survey. Handbook. (SA ISSN 0560-9208) **1581**
South Africa. Geological Survey. Memoirs. (SA) **1581**
South Africa. Geological Survey. Open File Reports. (SA) **1581**
†South Africa. Geological Survey. Research Digest. (SA) **5279**
South Africa. Geological Survey. Seismologic Series. (SA) **1595**
South Africa. Geological Survey. South African Committee for Stratigraphy. Circular. (SA) **1581**
South Africa. Geological Survey. South African Committee for Stratigraphy. Catalogue of South African Lithostratigraphic Units. (SA) **1581**
South Africa. Geological Survey. South African Committee for Stratigraphy. Chronostratigraphic Series. (SA) **1581**
South Africa. Geological Survey. South African Committee for Stratigraphy. Lithostratigraphic Series. (SA) **1581**
South Africa. Geological Survey. Special Publications *see* South Africa. Geological Survey. Geological Maps **1580**
South Africa. Government Gazette Index *see* Juta - State Library Index to the Government Gazette **4081**
South Africa. Kantoor van die Direkteur van Argiewe en die Staatsheraldikus. Jaarverslag. *see* South Africa. Office of the Director of Archives and the State Herald. Annual Report **2330**
South Africa. Maize Board. Report on Maize for the Financial Year. (SA) **208**
South Africa. National Parks Board. Annual Report. (SA) **1497**
South Africa. Office of the Director of Archives and the State Herald. Annual Report/South Africa. Kantoor van die Direkteur van Argiewe en die Staatsheraldikus. Jaarverslag. (SA) **2330**
South Africa. Office of the Director of Archives. Annual Report of the Director of Archives - South Africa. Kantoor van die Direkteur van Argiewe. Jaarverslag van die Direkteur van Argiewe *see* South Africa. Office of the Director of Archives and the State Herald. Annual Report **2330**
South Africa. Official Yearbook of the Republic of South Africa. (SA ISSN 0302-0681) **2330**, 4586
South Africa. Philatelic Services and Intersapa. Philatelic Bulletin. (SA) **3757**
South Africa. Philatelic Services. Philatelic Bulletin *see* South Africa. Philatelic Services and Intersapa. Philatelic Bulletin **3757**
†South Africa. Prisons Department. Annual Statistics by the Commissioner of Prisons. (SA) **5279**
†South Africa. Prisons Department. Report of the Commissioner of Prisons. (SA ISSN 0300-1555) **5279**
South Africa. Sea Fisheries Branch. Investigational Report *see* South Africa. Sea Fisheries Research Institute. Investigational Report **2049**
South Africa. Sea Fisheries Research Institute. Chief Directorate Sea Fisheries. Annual Report. (SA) **2049**
South Africa. Sea Fisheries Research Institute. Investigational Report. (SA) **2049**
South Africa. Sea Fisheries Research Institute. Marine Development Branch. Annual Report *see* South Africa. Sea Fisheries Research Institute. Chief Directorate Sea Fisheries. Annual Report **2049**
South Africa. Sea Fisheries Research Institute. Special Report. (SA) **2049**
South Africa. Sentrale Statistiekdiens. Uitgesoekte Ekonomiese Aanwysers. *see* South Africa. Central Statistical Service. Selected Economic Indicators **738**
South Africa. State Library Council. Annual Report. (SA) **2785**
South Africa. Tobacco Board. Annual Report. (SA) **4644**
South Africa. Unemployment Insurance Fund. Report/South Africa. Werkloosheidversekeringsfonds. Verslag. (SA) **2543**, 994
South Africa. Water Research Commission. Annual Report. (SA) **4828**
†South Africa. Water Research Commission. Research Projects. (SA) **5279**

Title

SOUTH AFRICAN 6677

South Africa. Weather Bureau. Daily Weather Bulletin. (SA ISSN 0011-5517) **3441**
South Africa. Weather Bureau. Monthly Weather Report. (SA ISSN 0038-1942) **3441**
South Africa. Weather Bureau. Newsletter. (SA ISSN 0032-7948) **3441**
South Africa. Weather Bureau. Technical Paper. (SA ISSN 0379-6736) **3441**
South Africa. Weather Bureau. Ten Daily Rainfall Report. (SA) **3441**
South Africa. Weather Bureau. W.B. Series. (SA ISSN 0081-2331) **3441**
South Africa. Werkloosheidversekeringsfonds. Verslag. see South Africa. Unemployment Insurance Fund. Report **2543**
South Africa. Wheat Board. Annual Report. (SA) **208**
South Africa: A Guide to Foreign Investors. (SA) **963**
South Africa Alert - Issues Monitors. (US) **921, 1085**
South Africa Astronomical Observatory Newsletter see S A A O Newsletter **369**
South Africa Foundation. Information Digest (Year). (SA) **884**
South Africa Foundation News see South Africa Foundation Review **884**
South Africa Foundation Review. (SA) **884, 3926**
South Africa International. (SA ISSN 0015-5055) **3926**
South Africa Motor Sport Control Motor Sport Bulletin see S A Motor Sport Bulletin **4520**
South Africa Reporter. (US) **921, 963**
South African Aeronews. (SA) **62, 4488**
South African Archaeological Bulletin. (SA ISSN 0038-1969) **285**
South African Archives Journal. see Suid-Afrikaanse Argiefblad **2786**
South African Athlete see S A Athlete **4486**
South African Bakery and Confectionery Review. (SA ISSN 0038-1993) **2089**
†South African Banking. (SA ISSN 0036-0570) **5279**
South African Baptist Handbook. (SA) **4249**
South African Bee Journal. (SA ISSN 0038-2019) **121**
South African Biographical and Historical Studies. (SA ISSN 0085-6363) **421, 2334**
South African Boxing World. (SA) **4488**
South African Bride to Be: First Home. (SA) **3067, 2449, 4853**
South African Bridge Bulletin see Bridge S A **4467**
South African Broadcasting Corporation. Annual Report. (SA) **1380**
South African Builder/Suid Afrikaanse Bouer. (SA ISSN 0038-2027) **632**
South African Bureau of Standards. Bulletin. (SA ISSN 0038-2698) **3448**
South African Bureau of Standards Catalogue see S A B S Catalogue **3448**
South African Cerebral Palsy Journal/Suid-Afrikaanse Tydskrif vir Serebraalverlamming. (SA ISSN 0036-0600) **3354**
South African Chartered Accountant - Suid-Afrikaanse Geoktrooieerde Rekenmeester see Accountancy S A **745**
†South African Chemicals. (SA) **5279**
South African Chemicals Manufactured & Imported. (SA) **1860**
†South African Chessplayer. (SA ISSN 0038-2094) **5279**
South African Citrus and Sub-Tropical Fruit Journal. (UK ISSN 0257-2095) **193**
South African Citrus Journal see South African Citrus and Sub-Tropical Fruit Journal **193**

South African Computer Journal/Suid Afrikaanse Rekenaartydskrif. (SA ISSN 1015-7999) **1400**
South African Computer Users Handbook see Computer Users Handbook **1453**
South African Construction News see South African Construction World **632**
South African Construction World. (SA) **632, 1874**
South African Cultural History Museum. Annals. see Suid-Afrikaanse Kultuurhistoriese Museum. Annale **2335**
South African Cultural History Museum. Bulletin. see Suid-Afrikaanse Kultuurhistoriese Museum. Bulletin **2335**
†South African Digest. (SA ISSN 0038-2132) **5279**
South African Draughtsman/S A Tekenaar. (SA ISSN 0036-0643) **4609**
South African Embassy Panorama see S.A. Panorama **2334**
South African Exporters/Exportateurs Sud-Africains/Suedafrikanische Exporteure/Exportadores de Sud Africa. (SA ISSN 0259-1855) **921**
South African Exporters Directory see South African Exporters **921**
South African Federation of Civil Engineering Contractors Bulletin see S A F C E C Bulletin **1873**
South African Film and Television Technicians Association Newsletter see S A F T T A Newsletter **3517**
South African Financial Gazette. (SA ISSN 0049-1403) **799**
South African Fire Services Institute. Quarterly/Suid-Afrikaanse Brandweerinstitut Kwartaalblad. (SA ISSN 0038-2159) **2034**
South African Fishing see Ski-Scene Including South African Fishing **4555**
South African Food Review. (SA ISSN 0257-8867) **2081, 3652**
South African Foreign Trade Organisation Annual Report see S A F T O Annual Report **920**
South African Foreign Trade Organisation Exporter see S A F T O Exporter **920**
South African Forestry Journal/Suid-Afrikaanse Bosboutydskrif. (SA ISSN 0038-2167) **2108**
South African Forum Botanicum see Forum Botanicum **5196**
South African Forum Position Paper see S A F Position Paper **3947**
South African Freedom Review see Terra Nova **3973**
South African Friesland Journal/Suid-Afrikaanse Friesland Joernaal. (SA ISSN 0036-0724) **226**
South African Fuchsia Fanfare see Fuchsia Fanfare **2126**
South African Garden & Home. (SA ISSN 0038-2139) **2139, 2555**
South African Geographer/Suid-Afrikaanse Geograaf. (SA ISSN 0378-5327) **2263, 1968**
South African Geographical Journal. (SA ISSN 0373-6245) **2263**
South African Golf see S A Golf Journal **4510**
South African Hairdressing and Beauty Culture see S.A. Hairdressing and Beauty Culture **374**
South African Historical Journal/Suid-Afrikaanse Historiese Joernaal. (SA ISSN 0258-2473) **2335**
▼South African Home Owner. (SA) **307, 632, 4158**
South African Institute for Librarianship and Information Science Newsletter see S A I L I S Newsletter **2782**
South African Institute for Medical Research. Publication. (SA) **3154, 457**
South African Institute of Assayers and Analysts. Journal. (SA ISSN 0038-2213) **3496, 3419**
South African Institute of Electrical Engineers. Transactions. (SA ISSN 0038-2221) **1908**

South African Institute of International Affairs. Bibliographical Series/Suid-Afrikaanse Instituut van Internasionale Aangeleenthede. Bibliografiese Reeks. (SA) **3938, 412**
South African Institute of International Affairs. Biennial Report of the National Chairman. (SA) **3972**
South African Institute of International Affairs. Occasional Papers. (SA) **3972**
South African Institute of International Affairs. Special Studies. (SA) **3972**
South African Institute of Mining and Metallurgy. Journal. (SA ISSN 0038-223X) **3420, 3496**
South African Institute of Mining and Metallurgy. Monograph Series. (SA) **3420, 3496**
South African Institute of Public Administration see S A I P A **4073**
South African Institute of Race Relations. Special Reports. (SA) **3947**
South African Institute of Race Relations. Topical Briefings. (SA) **3926**
South African Institute of Race Relations. Update. (SA ISSN 1011-5544) **3947**
South African Irrigation see S A Irrigation **191**
South African Jewish News see Herald Times **2004**
South African Journal for Librarianship and Information Science see South African Journal of Library and Information Science **2785**
South African Journal for Research in Sport, Physical Education and Recreation. see Suid-Afrikaanse Tydskrif vir Navorsing in Sport, Liggaamlike Opvoedkunde en Ontspanning **3809**
South African Journal of African Languages. (SA ISSN 0257-2117) **2842, 2961**
South African Journal of Agricultural Extension/Suid-Afrikaanse Tydskrif vir Landbouvoorligting. (SA) **121, 1687, 4609**
South African Journal of Animal Science. (SA ISSN 0375-1589) **226**
South African Journal of Antarctic Research. (SA ISSN 0081-2455) **4344, 4609**
▼South African Journal of Art and Architectural History. (SA) **344, 307**
South African Journal of Botany/Suid-Afrikaanse Tydskrif vir Plantkunde. (SA ISSN 0254-6299) **518**
South African Journal of Business Management/Suid-Afrikaanse Tydskrif vir Bedryfsleiding. (SA ISSN 0378-9098) **1028**
South African Journal of Chemistry/Suid-Afrikaanse Tydskrif vir Chemie. (SA ISSN 0379-4350) **1188**
South African Journal of Communication Disorders/Suid-Afrikaanse Tydskrif vir Kommunikasieafwykings. (SA) **3317**
South African Journal of Cultural and Art History see South African Journal of Cultural History **2335**
South African Journal of Cultural History. (SA) **2335, 249, 344**
South African Journal of Dairy Science. (SA ISSN 0258-3321) **203**
South African Journal of Dairy Technology see South African Journal of Dairy Science **203**
South African Journal of Economic History. (SA) **898**
South African Journal of Economics/Suid-Afrikaanse Tydskrif vir Ekonomie. (SA ISSN 0038-2280) **692**
South African Journal of Education/Suid-Afrikaanse Tydskrif vir Opvoedkunde. (SA ISSN 0256-0100) **1664**
South African Journal of Ethnology. (SA ISSN 0379-8860) **249, 2024**
South African Journal of Geology. (SA ISSN 0371-7208) **1581**

South African Journal of Labour Relations. (SA ISSN 0379-8410) **994, 2589, 2680**
South African Journal of Library and Information Science. (SA ISSN 0256-8861) **2785**
South African Journal of Linguistics/Suid-Afrikannse Tydskrif vir Taalkunde. (SA ISSN 1011-8063) **2842**
South African Journal of Marine Science/Suid-Afrikaanse Tydskrif vir Seewetenskap. (SA) **2049**
South African Journal of Musicology/Suid-Afrikaanse Tydskrif vir Musiekwetenskap. (SA ISSN 0258-509X) **3582**
South African Journal of Occupational Therapy. (SA ISSN 0038-2337) **3154**
South African Journal of Philosophy. (SA ISSN 0258-0136) **3782**
South African Journal of Photogrammetry, Remote Sensing and Cartography. (SA) **1836**
South African Journal of Physics/Suid-Afrikaanse Tydskrif vir Fisika. (SA ISSN 0379-4377) **3831**
South African Journal of Physiotherapy. (SA ISSN 0379-6175) **3154**
South African Journal of Plant and Soil. (SA ISSN 0257-1862) **193**
South African Journal of Psychology/Suid-Afrikaanse Tydskrif vir Sielkunde. (SA ISSN 0081-2463) **4047**
South African Journal of Science/Suid-Afrikaanse Tydskrif vir Wetenskap. (SA ISSN 0038-2353) **4345**
South African Journal of Sociology. (SA ISSN 0258-0144) **4452**
South African Journal of Surgery/Suid-Afrikaanse Tydskrif vir Chirurgie. (SA ISSN 0038-2361) **3384**
South African Journal of Surveying and Mapping/Suid-Afrikaanse Tydskrif vir Landmeetkunde en Kartering. (SA) **1874**
South African Journal of Wildlife Management see South African Journal of Wildlife Research **1497**
South African Journal of Wildlife Research/Suid-Afrikaanse Tydskrif vir Natuurnavorsing. (SA ISSN 0379-4369) **1497**
South African Journal of Zoology/Suid-Afrikaanse Tydskrif vir Dierkunde. (SA ISSN 0254-1858) **592**
South African Journal on Human Rights. (SA ISSN 0258-7203) **3947, 2680**
South African Labour Bulletin. (SA) **994**
South African Lapidary Magazine/Suid-Afrikaanse Lapidere Tydskrif. (SA ISSN 0038-237X) **3496, 2442**
South African Laundry and Cleaning Review see S A Cleaning Review **1282**
South African Law Commission. Annual Report. see Suid-Afrikaanse Regskommissie. Jaarverslag **5285**
South African Law Journal. (SA ISSN 0038-2388) **2680**
South African Law Reports. (SA ISSN 0038-2396) **2680**
South African Law Reports, Index & Noter-Up. (SA) **2680**
South African Library. Quarterly Bulletin/Suid-Afrikaanse Biblioteek. Kwartaalblad. (SA ISSN 0038-2418) **2785**
South African Licensee's Guardian. (SA ISSN 0489-8567) **2480**
South African Machine Tool Review. (SA ISSN 0036-0848) **3023**
South African Mechanical Engineer. (SA ISSN 0038-2442) **1939**
South African Mechanics Handbook. (SA) **3023**
South African Medical and Dental Council. Register of Supplementary Health Services Professions. (SA) **3154, 4421**
South African Medical Journal/Suid-Afrikaanse Mediese Tydskrif. (SA ISSN 0038-2469) **3154**
†South African Medical Post. (SA) **5279**

6678 SOUTH AFRICAN

South African Medical Research Council. Annual Report. (SA ISSN 0375-1880) **3154**

†South African Medical Research Council. Biennial Research Report. (SA ISSN 1015-2377) **5279**

South African Medical Research Council. Research Report see South African Medical Research Council. Annual Report **3154**

South African Medical Research Council. Research Report see South African Medical Research Council. Biennial Research Report **5279**

South African Mercantile Law Journal/Suid-Afrikaanse Tydskrif vir Handelsreg. (SA ISSN 1015-0099) **2680, 692**

South African Mining and Engineering Journal see South African Mining, Coal, Gold and Base Minerals **3496**

†South African Mining and Engineering Yearbook. (SA ISSN 0081-2498) **5279**

South African Mining, Coal, Gold and Base Minerals. (SA) **3496, 1836**

South African Museum. Annals/Suid-Afrikaanse Museum. Annale. (SA ISSN 0303-2515) **457, 249, 285, 3661**

South African Music Teacher/Suid-Afrikaanse Musiekonderwyser. (SA ISSN 0038-2493) **3582, 1664**

South African National Bibliography. (SA ISSN 0036-0864) **412**

South African National Council for the Blind. Biennial Report. (SA) **2296**

South African National Council for the Blind News see S A N C B News **2295**

South African National Council for the Deaf. Annual Diary. (SA) **2289**

South African National Museum of Military History. Review see Military History Journal **3464**

South African National Tuberculosis Association Annual Report see S A N T A Annual Report **3367**

South African National Tuberculosis Association Health Magazine see S A N T A Health Magazine **3367**

South African National Tuberculosis Association News see S A N T A. T B News **3367**

South African Nurseryman/Suid-Afrikaanse Kweker. (SA) **121**

South African Observer. (SA ISSN 0038-2523) **3926**

South African Outlook. (SA) **4202, 4452**

South African Paediatrics Magazine. (SA ISSN 1017-1711) **3326**

†South African Panorama (Chinese Edition)/Nanfi Jingguan. (SA ISSN 1016-1384) **5280**

†South African Panorama (Dutch Edition). (SA ISSN 0167-9767) **5280**

South African Panorama (English Edition). (SA ISSN 0038-254X) **2217**

†South African Panorama (French Edition). (SA ISSN 0259-9198) **5280**

†South African Panorama (German Edition). (SA ISSN 0259-9236) **5280**

†South African Panorama (Italian Edition). (SA ISSN 0259-9201) **5280**

†South African Panorama (Portuguese Edition). (SA ISSN 0259-9228) **5280**

†South African Panorama (Spanish Edition). (SA ISSN 0259-921X) **5280**

South African Pharmaceutical & Cosmetic Review. (SA) **376, 3743**

South African Pharmaceutical Journal/Suid-Afrikaanse Tydskrif vir Apteekwese. (SA ISSN 0038-2558) **3743**

South African Philatelist. (SA ISSN 0038-2566) **3757**

South African Poultry Bulletin. (SA ISSN 0257-201X) **226**

South African Product Digest. (SA) **921, 38**

South African Racehorse. (SA) **4538**

South African Rates and Data see S A R A D **38**

South African Refractionist/Suid-Afrikaanse Gesigkundige. (SA ISSN 0038-2612) **3305**

South African Reserve Bank. Annual Economic Report/Suid-Afrikaanse Reserwebank. Jaarlikse Ekonomiese Verslag. (SA ISSN 0081-2528) **884**

South African Reserve Bank. Monthly Release of Money and Banking Statistics/Suid-Afrikaanse Reserwebank. Maandelikse Vrystelling van Geld- en Bankwesestatistiek. (SA ISSN 0584-3073) **738**

South African Reserve Bank. Quarterly Bulletin/Suid-Afrikaanse Reserwebank. Kwartaalblad. (SA ISSN 0038-2620) **799, 738**

South African Reserve Bank. Quarterly Bulletin of Statistics see South African Reserve Bank. Quarterly Bulletin **799**

South African Reserve Bank. Report of the Ordinary General Meeting/Suid-Afrikaanse Reserwebank. Verslag van die Gewone Algemene Vergadering. (SA) **799**

South African Retail Chemist. (SA ISSN 0038-2639) **3743**

South African Rider. (SA ISSN 0038-2655) **4538**

South African Shoemaker and Leather Review. (SA ISSN 0250-1333) **4362, 2738**

South African Society for Agricultural Extension. Journal see South African Journal of Agricultural Extension **121**

South African Society of Bank Officials News see S A S B O News **798**

South African Society of Pathologists. Congress Brochure. (SA) **3394, 3154**

South African Sociological Review. (SA ISSN 1015-1370) **4453**

South African Speech and Hearing Association. Journal see South African Journal of Communication Disorders **3317**

South African Stationery Trades Journal see Office Products S A **1060**

South African Statistical Journal/Suid-Afrikaanse Statistiese Tydskrif. (SA ISSN 0038-271X) **4586, 3056**

South African Statistics. (SA ISSN 0081-2544) **4586**

South African Sugar Association Experiment Station. Annual Report. (SA ISSN 0375-2682) **193**

South African Sugar Association Experiment Station. Bulletin. (SA) **193**

* South African Sugar Journal. (SA ISSN 0038-2728) **2082, 193**

South African Survey Journal - Suid-Afrikaanse Opmetings Tydskrif see South African Journal of Surveying and Mapping **1874**

South African Table Tennis News. (SA ISSN 0038-2744) **4489**

South African Transport. (SA ISSN 0038-2760) **4656**

South African Treasurer/Suid-Afrikaanse Tesourier. (SA ISSN 0038-2779) **4094, 756**

South African Typographical Journal/Suid-Afrikaanse Tipografiese Joernaal. (SA ISSN 0038-2787) **2589, 4005**

South African Union Lantern see Maranatha **4285**

South African Veterinary Association. Journal see South African Veterinary Association. Scientific Journal **4816**

South African Veterinary Association. Scientific Journal. (SA) **4816**

South African Wool and Textile Research Institute. Annual Report see South Africa. Division of Textile Technology. Annual Report **4623**

South African Wool and Textile Research Institute. Bulletin see Texnews **4624**

South African Yachting. (SA) **4529, 4489**

South African Yachting, Sail, Power and Waterski see South African Yachting **4529**

South African Yearbook of International Law/Suid-Afrikaanse Jaarboek vir Volkereg. (SA ISSN 0379-8895) **2729**

South African Zionist Federation. News and Views. (SA) **2024**

South America (New York). (US ISSN 0193-7944) **4787**

South America, Central America and the Caribbean (Year). (UK ISSN 0268-0661) **3926, 884**

South America Stamp Catalogue. (UK ISSN 0142-9922) **3758**

South American Explorer. (US ISSN 0889-7891) **4787**

South American Ports Handbook. (AG) **4739**

South and East Asia Report see Southeast Asia Report **885**

South and Meso-American Indian Information Center (SIIC) Newsletter. (US ISSN 1056-5876) **2024, 2422**

South & North of the Yangtse River. see Dajiang Nanbei **2337**

South Asia Bulletin. (US ISSN 0732-3867) **2342, 4453**

South Asia in Review. (US) **2342, 3782, 4202**

South Asia Journal. (II ISSN 0970-4868) **3927**

South Asia: Journal of South Asian Studies. (AT ISSN 0085-6401) **2342, 249, 4453**

South Asia Library Group Newsletter see S A L G Newsletter **2795**

South Asia News. (US) **2342**

South Asia Research. (UK ISSN 0262-7280) **3644**

South Asian Anthropologist. (II ISSN 0257-7348) **249**

South Asian Digest of Regional Writing. (GW ISSN 0170-7787) **3644**

South Asian Review. (US ISSN 0275-9527) **2961, 2842**

South Asian Social Scientist. (II ISSN 0970-3764) **3644, 4388**

South Asian Studies. (UK ISSN 0266-6030) **2342**

South Asian Studies. (PK) **2342, 3927**

South Asian Studies. (II ISSN 0038-285X) **3644, 4388**

South Asian Studies. (GW ISSN 0584-3170) **3644, 2342**

South Asian Studies Quarterly. see Nanya Yanjiu Jikan **3641**

South Atlantic Bulletin see South Atlantic Review **2842**

South Atlantic Modern Language Association Awards. (US) **2961**

South Atlantic Review. (US ISSN 0277-335X) **2842, 2961**

†South Atlantic Urban Studies. (US) **5280**

South Australia. Department of Agriculture. Technical Paper. (AT ISSN 0727-6001) **121**

South Australia. Department of Education. Education Gazette. (AT ISSN 0049-1438) **1664**

South Australia. Department of Environment and Planning. Adelaide Statistical Division. Land Monitoring Report. Land Sales, Prices, Land Division and Land Stocks Statistics. (AT ISSN 0726-1926) **1968**

South Australia. Department of Environment and Planning. Forecast Production and Usage of Residential Allotments for Private Purposes. (AT ISSN 1030-4320) **1968**

South Australia. Department of Environment and Planning. Land Monitoring Report. see South Australia. Department of Environment and Planning. Adelaide Statistical Division. Land Monitoring Report. Land Sales, Prices, Land Division and Land Stocks Statistics **1968**

South Australia. Department of Environment and Planning. Metropolitan Adelaide Development Program. (AT) **1968**

South Australia. Department of Environment and Planning. Population Projection for the Adelaide Statistical Division. (AT) **3987**

South Australia. Department of Environment and Planning. State and Regional Projections. Bulletin. (AT ISSN 1032-8793) **3987**

South Australia. Department of Evironment and Planning. Population Projection for South Australia. (AT) **3987**

South Australia. Department of Mines and Energy. Annual Report. (AT ISSN 0159-7043) **1581**

South Australia. Department of Mines and Energy. Special Publications. (AT ISSN 0726-1527) **1548, 3496**

South Australia. Libraries Board. Annual Report. (AT ISSN 0081-2633) **2785**

†South Australia. Woods and Forests Department. Bulletin. (AT) **5280**

▼South Australia and Northern Territory Stamp Duties. (AT) **1106**

South Australia in Business. (AT ISSN 0818-4674) **822**

South Australian Baker and Pastrycook.(AT) **2089**

South Australian Builder. (AT) **632**

South Australian Coloured Sheep Owners' Society Inc. (SACSOS) Newsletter see S A C S O S Newsletter **225**

South Australian Dairyfarmer's Journal. (AT ISSN 0818-7169) **204**

South Australian Dairymen's Journal see South Australian Dairyfarmer's Journal **204**

South Australian Electrical Contractor. (AT ISSN 0038-2892) **1908**

South Australian Football Budget. (AT) **4511**

South Australian Genealogist. (AT ISSN 0311-2756) **2164**

South Australian Geographer. (AT) **2263, 1760**

South Australian Geographical Journal. (AT ISSN 1030-0481) **2263**

South Australian Geographical Papers. (AT ISSN 0811-6504) **2263**

South Australian Government Gazette. (AT ISSN 0038-2906) **4074**

South Australian Institute of Teachers Journal see S A I T Journal **1731**

South Australian Mixed Association Journal see Independent Food Retailer **2072**

South Australian Motor. (AT ISSN 0038-2957) **4702, 4787**

South Australian Museum, Adelaide. Records. (AT ISSN 0081-2676) **249, 592, 1581, 3661**

South Australian Naturalist. (AT ISSN 0038-2965) **4345**

South Australian Racing Calendar. (AT ISSN 0038-2981) **4489**

South Australian State Reports. (AT ISSN 0049-1470) **2680**

South Australian Teachers Journal see S A I T Journal **1731**

South Australian Tennis News. (AT) **4511**

South Australian Volunteering. (AT ISSN 0816-9594) **4421**

South Australian Yearbook. (AT ISSN 0085-6428) **4586**

South Bucks and East Berks Chamber of Commerce and Industry Directory see Thames-Chiltern Chamber of Commerce & Industry Directory **1155**

South Carolina. Department of Archives and History. Annual Report. (US) **2422**

South Carolina. Department of Labor. Annual Report. (US) **994**

South Carolina. State Board of Engineering Examiners. Directory of Engineers and Land Surveyors Registered in South Carolina see Directory of Engineers and Land Surveyors Registered in South Carolina **1818**

South Carolina. State Data Center. Newsletter. (US) **3987**

South Carolina Academy of Science. Bulletin. (US ISSN 0096-414X) 4345
South Carolina Appellate Digest. (US ISSN 0743-2453) 2680
South Carolina Arts Commission. Annual Report. (US ISSN 0081-2684) 344
South Carolina Baptist Historical Society Journal. (US ISSN 0146-0196) 4249
South Carolina Builder. (US) 632, 1153
South Carolina Business Journal. (US) 692
South Carolina Economic Indicators. (US ISSN 0038-304X) 884
South Carolina Economic Report. (US) 884
South Carolina Education Association Emphasis see S C E A Emphasis 1660
▼South Carolina Facts. (US ISSN 1056-960X) 1782
South Carolina Food Journal. (US) 2094
▼South Carolina Forum. (US) 4074, 3927
South Carolina Game & Fish. (US) 4556
South Carolina Geology. (US ISSN 0272-9873) 1581
South Carolina Historical Association. Proceedings. (US ISSN 0361-6207) 2422
South Carolina Historical Magazine. (US ISSN 0038-3082) 2422, 2164
South Carolina Industrial Directory. (US) 1153
South Carolina Law Review. (US ISSN 0038-3104) 2680
South Carolina Lawyer. (US ISSN 1044-4238) 2680
South Carolina Magazine of Ancestral Research. (US) 2164
South Carolina Medical Association. Journal. (US ISSN 0038-3139) 3154
South Carolina Monthly Revenue Letter.(US) 1106
South Carolina Music Educators Association Musician see S C Musician 3579
South Carolina Out-of-Doors. (US ISSN 0887-9249) 1497, 1968, 4556
South Carolina Port News. (US ISSN 0896-2278) 4739, 921
South Carolina Review. (US ISSN 0038-3163) 2961
▼South Carolina Rules and Regulations for Hunting and Fishing Licenses. (US) 4556, 2680
South Carolina Schools. (US ISSN 0038-3171) 1664
South Carolina State Library. Annual Report. (US ISSN 0361-6479) 2785
South Carolina Statistical Abstract. (US) 4586
South Carolina Trucking Association, Inc. Hi-Lights see S C T A Hi-Lights 4747
South Carolina United Methodist Advocate. (US) 4249
South Carolina Vital and Morbidity Statistics. (US ISSN 0094-6338) 3995
South Carolina Wildlife. (US ISSN 0038-3198) 1497, 4556
South Carolina Young Farmer and Future Farmer. (US ISSN 0038-3201) 121, 1266
South Central Bulletin see South Central Review 1280
South Central Campbook. (US) 4787, 4556
South-Central College for Nationalities. Journal (Social Science Edition). see Zhongnan Minzu Xueyuan Xuebao (Shehui Kexue Ban) 4393
South Central Research Library Council. Reports. (US ISSN 0361-7122) 2785
South Central Review. (US ISSN 0743-6831) 1280
South-China Architecture. see Nanfang Jianzhu 303

South-China Normal University. Journal (Natural Science Edition). see Huanan Shifan Daxue Xuebao (Ziran Kexue Ban) 4313
South-China Normal University. Journal (Social Science Edition). see Huanan Shifan Daxue Xuebao (Shehui Kexue Ban) 4374
South-China Seismology. see Huanan Dizhen 1590
South-China University of Science and Engineering. Journal (Natural Science Edition). see Huanan Ligong Daxue Xuebao (Ziran Kexue Ban) 4313
South Coast Herald. (SA ISSN 0038-3228) 2217
South Coast Poetry Journal. (US ISSN 0887-2074) 3006
South Coast Sportfishing. (US) 4556
South Coast Sun. (SA ISSN 0049-1519) 2217
South Dakota. Department of Labor. Labor Bulletin. (US) 994
South Dakota. Department of Labor. Manpower Bulletin see South Dakota. Department of Labor. Labor Bulletin 994
South Dakota. Department of Revenue. Annual Statistical Report. (US ISSN 0085-6460) 738
South Dakota. State Department of Public Welfare. Research and Statistical Annual Report see South Dakota. State Department of Social Services. Annual Statistical Report 4427
South Dakota. State Department of Social Services. Annual Statistical Report. (US) 4427, 4586
South Dakota Academy of Science. Proceedings. (US ISSN 0096-378X) 4345
†South Dakota Authors' Catalog. (US ISSN 0742-8936) 5280
South Dakota Bird Notes. (US ISSN 0038-3252) 567
South Dakota Business Review. (US ISSN 0038-3260) 692
South Dakota Conservation Digest. (US ISSN 0038-3279) 1497
South Dakota Dental Association. Newsletter. (US ISSN 0038-3287) 3242
South Dakota Department of Revenue. Annual Report see South Dakota. Department of Revenue. Annual Statistical Report 738
South Dakota Farm and Home Research see Farm and Home Research 90
South Dakota Genealogical Society Quarterly. (US) 2164
South Dakota Geological Survey. Bulletin. (US ISSN 0085-6479) 1581
South Dakota Geological Survey. Circular. (US ISSN 0085-6487) 1581
South Dakota Geological Survey. Reports of Investigation. (US ISSN 0085-6495) 1581
South Dakota Heritage. (US) 2422
South Dakota High Liner. (US ISSN 0038-3309) 2234
†South Dakota Historical Collections. (US) 5280
South Dakota History. (US ISSN 0361-8676) 2423
South Dakota Journal of County Government see S D A C C County Comment 4073
South Dakota Journal of Medicine. (US ISSN 0038-3317) 3154
South Dakota Law Review. (US ISSN 0038-3325) 2680
South Dakota Legion News. (US ISSN 0745-5801) 1301
South Dakota Manufacturers & Processors Directory. (US ISSN 0094-2758) 1153
South Dakota Municipalities. (US ISSN 0300-6182) 4094
South Dakota Musician. (US ISSN 0038-3341) 1664, 3582
South Dakota Petroleum Marketer. (US) 3701
South Dakota Review. (US ISSN 0038-3368) 2962

South Dakota State Historical Society. Collections see South Dakota Historical Collections 5280
South Dakota State University Alumnus see S D S U Alumnus 1323
South Dakota Stockgrower. (US ISSN 0038-3384) 226
South Dakota Trucking News. (US) 4747
South Dakota Union Farmer. (US) 121
South Dakotan. (US) 1324
The South End. (US ISSN 0038-3430) 2884
South England Conference Communicator. (UK) 4288
South Essex Chamber of Commerce, Trade & Industry. Southend. Monthly Journal. (UK) 822
South Florida. (US ISSN 0895-5352) 2234
South Florida Business Journal. (US ISSN 0746-2271) 692, 884
South Florida Focus. (US) 4202
South Florida History Magazine. (US) 2423
South Florida Home and Garden see Florida Home & Garden 2551
South Florida Home Buyer's Guide. (US) 4158, 2496
South Florida Living (North Edition) see South Florida Home Buyer's Guide 4158
South Florida Office Guide. (US) 1061
▼South Florida Parenting. (US) 1244
South Florida Poetry Institute Presents the Review. (US) 3006
South Florida Poetry Review see South Florida Poetry Institute Presents the Review 3006
South Florida Single Living. (US) 4364
South Florida's Angler's Guide. (US) 4556
South Hamilton Record News. (US) 121
South India Churchman. (II ISSN 0038-3465) 4288
South Indian Horticulture. (II ISSN 0038-3473) 2139
South Indian Teacher. (II ISSN 0038-3481) 1664, 2589
South Jersey. (US ISSN 0164-1433) 2234
South Jersey Jewish Community Voice. (US ISSN 1042-2986) 2024
†South Lincolnshire Farmer. (UK) 5280
South London Press (Friday). (UK) 2195
South London Press (Tuesday). (UK) 2195
South Louisiana Drilling Report. (US) 3701
South Louisiana Land Report see South Louisiana Drilling Report 3701
South Midlands Business and Commerce Digest see Executive on Sunday 5189
South-North Dialogue in Korea. (KO) 3972
South of the Moon. (US) 2986, 3014
South of the Mountains. (US ISSN 0489-9563) 2423
South Pacific Bibliography. (FJ ISSN 0257-9146) 412
†South Pacific Commission. Annual Report. (NL) 5280
South Pacific Commission. Handbook. (NL ISSN 0081-2811) 935
South Pacific Commission. Information Circular. (NL ISSN 1013-9915) 885
South Pacific Commission. Information Document. (NL ISSN 0081-2838) 935, 157
†South Pacific Commission. Monthly News of Activities. (NL) 5280
†South Pacific Commission. Occasional Paper. (NL) 5280
South Pacific Commission. Report of Meetings. (NL ISSN 0377-452X) 885
South Pacific Commission. Statistical Bulletin. (NL ISSN 0377-2039) 4586
South Pacific Commission. Technical Paper. (NL ISSN 0081-2862) 4609

SOUTHEAST ASIA 6679

South Pacific Commission Reports on Migration, Employment and Development in the South Pacific see S P C - I L O Reports on Migration, Employment and Development in the South Pacific 3987
South Pacific Conference. Report. (NL ISSN 1017-9267) 3972
South Pacific Economies: Statistical Summary. (NL ISSN 1018-0958) 738, 4586
South Pacific Epidemiological and Health Information Service Annual Report. (NL ISSN 1018-0893) 4119, 4586
South Pacific Foods Leaflet. (NL ISSN 1018-0966) 2082, 3612
South Pacific Journal of Teacher Education. (UK ISSN 0311-2136) 1760
South Pacific Periodicals Index. (FJ ISSN 1011-5110) 412
South Pacific Regional Environment Programme Environmental Case Studies see S P R E P Environmental Case Studies 1967
South Pacific Regional Environment Programme Fact Sheet see S P R E P Fact Sheet 1967
South Pacific Regional Environment Programme Meeting Reports see S P R E P Meeting Reports 1967
South Pacific Research Register. (FJ ISSN 1011-5145) 412
South Pacific Smallholder Project. Occasional Papers. (AT ISSN 0814-7973) 157, 1118
South Pacific Smallholder Project. Research Notes. (AT ISSN 0814-7965) 157, 1118
South Pacific Underwater Medicine Society Incorporated Journal see S P U M S Journal 3151
The South Sea Digest. (AT) 692
South Seas Society. Journal. (SI ISSN 0081-2889) 2342
South Seas Society. Monograph. (SI ISSN 0081-2897) 2342
South Shore Business. (US) 692
South Shore Record. (US ISSN 0038-352X) 2235
South Staffordshire Archaeological and Historical Society. Transactions. (UK ISSN 0457-7817) 286, 2323
South Suburban Genealogical & Historical Society. Newsletter. (US ISSN 0896-4408) 2164, 2423
South Swedish Placename Society. Journal. see Sydsvenska Ortnamnssaellskapet. Aarsskrift 2846
South Texas AgriNews. (US) 121
South Texas Business Journal. (US ISSN 0746-8482) 692, 2235
South Texas Catholic. (US) 4276
South Texas Journal of Research and the Humanities see Borderlands Journal 2504
South Texas Law Review. (US) 2680
South Wales Ports Tides Tables. (UK) 1611
South Wind see Solar Progress 1812
South Wind. see Nanfeng 2940
South Wood County Historical Corporation. Newsletter. (US) 2423
South Yorkshire Topic. (UK) 2195
Southam Building Guide see Building Homes & Renovation 606
Southam Mining Group's Mining Sourcebook. (CN) 3496
Southampton (Port of), Tide Tables. (UK) 1611
Southampton Chamber of Commerce Regional Directory see Confederation of Chambers of Commerce Central Southern England Directory 813
Southampton City News. (UK) 4074
Southampton Port Handbook. (UK ISSN 0268-6511) 1153, 4739
▼Southbank Cityscope. (AT) 4160
Southeast Asia Building. (SI) 632
Southeast Asia Building Magazine. (SI) 632
Southeast Asia Building Materials and Equipment see Southeast Asia Building Magazine 632
Southeast Asia Business see Journal of Southeast Asia Business 871

SOUTHEAST ASIA

Southeast Asia Development Corporation Berhad. Reports and Accounts. (MY) **935**
†South East Asia Digest. (UK ISSN 0956-0955) **5280**
Southeast Asia High Tech Review see East Asia High Tech Review **4597**
South East Asia Iron and Steel Institute Quarterly Journal see S E A I S I Quarterly Journal **3419**
South East Asia Library Group Newsletter. (UK ISSN 0308-4035) **2785**, 3644
Southeast Asia Microfilms Newsletter. (MY ISSN 0129-511X) **2342**, 3797
South East Asia Monitor. (UK ISSN 0959-2601) **692**
Southeast Asia Papers. (US) **3644**
Southeast Asia Program Series. (US) **3644**
Southeast Asia Report. (US) **885**, 3927
South-East Asia Stamp Catalogue. (UK ISSN 0142-9930) **3758**
South East Asia Traveller. (SI ISSN 0218-0553) **4787**
Southeast Asian Affairs. (UK) **2342**
Southeast Asian Affairs. (SI ISSN 0377-5437) **3927**
Southeast Asian Archives. (MY ISSN 0085-6509) **2342**
Southeast Asian Building Annual see Southeast Asia Building **632**
Southeast Asian Bulletin of Mathematics. (SI ISSN 0218-0006) **3056**
Southeast Asian Institutions of Higher Learning see Association of Southeast Asian Institutions of Higher Learning. Handbook: Southeast Asian Institutions of Higher Learning **1700**
Southeast Asian Journal of Social Sciences. (SI ISSN 0303-8246) **4388**, 4453
Southeast Asian Journal of Tropical Medicine and Public Health. (TH ISSN 0038-3619) **3223**, 4113
Southeast Asian-Ministers of Education Organisation. Regional Centre for Education in Science and Mathematics. Governing Board Meeting. Final Report. (MY ISSN 0126-8155) **1760**
Southeast Asian Ministers of Education Organisation. Regional Centre for Education in Science and Mathematics. Library Accession List. (MY ISSN 0126-7590) **412**, 1760
Southeast Asian Ministers of Education Organization Quarterly see S E A M E O Quarterly **1731**
Southeast Asian Ministers of Education Organization Regional Language Centre. Anthology Series see S E A M E O Regional Language Centre. Anthology Series **2839**
South East Asian Monograph Series. (AT ISSN 0158-6041) **3927**, 2323
Southeast Asian Perspective Series. (SI) **2342**
Southeast Asian Perspectives see Asian Affairs: An American Review **3950**
South East Asian Printer Magazine. (AT ISSN 0129-1262) **4005**
Southeast Asian Research Materials Group. Newsletter see S E A R M G Newsletter **5272**
South East Asian Review. (II ISSN 0257-7364) **2342**
Southeast Asian Studies. see Dongnan Ya Yanjiu **3637**
Southeast Asian Studies. see Nanyang Wenti Yanjiu **3641**
Southeast Asian Studies Working Paper Series see Southeast Asia Papers **3644**
Southeast Conference Lindy's S E C Football Annual see Lindy's S E C Football Annual **4507**
Southeast Dairy Outlook. (US) **204**
Southeast Dragster. (US) **4702**
Southeast - East Asian English Publications in Print. (JA) **4142**, 23
Southeast Farm Press. (US ISSN 0194-0937) **121**

Southeast Food Service News. (US ISSN 0199-2805) **2082**, 2480
Southeast Georgian. (US) **2235**
South East Hampshire Genealogical Society. Journal see Hampshire Family Historian **2153**
Southeast Homebuilder & Remodeler. (US) **632**
Southeast Litigation Guide. (US) **2680**
South East London & Kentish Mercury. (UK ISSN 0038-3422) **2195**
South East Magazine. (AT) **2884**, 38
Southeast Michigan Council of Governments. Annual Report. (US ISSN 0362-3475) **4074**
Southeast Petroleum Industry. (US) **3701**, 1153
Southeast Real Estate News. (US ISSN 0192-1630) **4158**
Southeast Regional Economic Report. (US) **885**
†Southeast Regional Library (Saskatchewan) Library Directory. (CN ISSN 0707-6894) **5280**
Southeast Singles Association Monthly Publication. (US) **4364**
Southeast Transaction Guide. (US) **2680**
Southeast Travel Professional. (US) **4787**
Southeast University. Journal. see Dongnan Daxue Xuebao **4370**
Southeastern Archaeology. (US ISSN 0734-578X) **286**
Southeastern Association of Fish and Wildlife Agencies. Proceedings. (US) **4556**
Southeastern Association of Game and Fish Commissioners. Proceedings of the Annual Conference see Southeastern Association of Fish and Wildlife Agencies. Proceedings **4556**
Southeastern Campbook. (US ISSN 0731-5112) **4787**, 4556
Southeastern College Art Conference Review. (US) **344**
Southeastern Council on Latin American Studies Annals see S E C O L A S Annals **2421**
Southeastern Dairy Review. (US ISSN 0038-3643) **204**
Southeastern Drug - Southern Pharmaceutical Journal see Southern Pharmacy Journal **3743**
Southeastern Economic Insight see Federal Reserve Bank of Atlanta. Economics Update **865**
Southeastern Front. (US ISSN 0886-067X) **344**, 2962
Southeastern Geographer. (US ISSN 0038-366X) **2263**
Southeastern Geology. (US ISSN 0038-3678) **1581**
South Eastern Latin Americanist. (US ISSN 0049-1527) **2423**
Southeastern Librarian. (US ISSN 0038-3686) **2785**
Southeastern Library Network, Inc. see S O L I N E W S **2799**
Southeastern Library Network, Inc. Solinet. Annual Report see Solinet. Annual Report **2785**
†Southeastern Log. (US) **5280**
Southeastern New York Library Resources Council Southeastern Newsline see Southeastern Newsline **2785**
Southeastern Newsline. (Southeastern New York Library Resources Council) (US) **2785**
Southeastern Oil Review. (US) **3701**
Southeastern Peanut Farmer. (US ISSN 0038-3694) **193**
Southeastern Political Review. (US ISSN 0730-2177) **3927**
South Eastern Regional Office Machine Dealers Association Scene see S E R O M D A Scene **1061**
South-Eastern State. Ministry of Economic Development and Reconstruction. State Development Plan see Cross River State. Ministry of Economic Development and Reconstruction. State Development Plan **1091**
Southeastern Symposium on System Theory. Proceedings. (US ISSN 0094-2898) **1439**

Southeastern Wisconsin Regional Planning Commission Newsletter see S E W R P C Newsletter **2495**
Southeastern Writing Center Association. Selected Papers. (US) **1760**, 2962
Southeasterner. (US ISSN 0038-3716) **2575**, 1324
Southend-on-Sea and District Chamber of Commerce, Trade and Industry. Monthly Journal see South Essex Chamber of Commerce, Trade & Industry. Southend. Monthly Journal **822**
Southerly. (AT ISSN 0038-3732) **2962**
Southern. (US) **1324**, 1716
Southern Accents. (US ISSN 0149-516X) **2555**, 2735
Southern Adirondack Library System Brief see S A L S in Brief **2782**
Southern Africa and the Indian Ocean Islands Travel Trade Directory. (SA) **4787**
†Southern Africa Development News. (US) **5280**
Southern Africa Freedom Bulletin. (US ISSN 1011-1980) **3972**
Southern Africa Journal of Aquatic Sciences. (SA) **1600**
Southern Africa Passport. see Nana No Pasuporto **4779**
Southern Africa Record. (SA ISSN 0377-5445) **3972**
Southern Africa Report. (SA) **2217**
Southern Africa Report. (CN ISSN 0820-5582) **3947**, 2024
Southern Africa Road Federation Newsletter see S A R F Newsletter **4721**
Southern Africa Squash Scene. (SA) **4511**
Southern African Development Coordination Conference Energy Bulletin see S A D C C Energy Bulletin **1795**
Southern African Journal of Epidemiology and Infection. (SA) **3250**
Southern African Journal of Sexually Transmitted Diseases see Southern African Journal of Epidemiology and Infection **3250**
†Southern African Metals & Minerals Conference. Proceedings. (US) **5280**
Southern African Museums Association. Bulletin. (SA ISSN 0370-8314) **3533**
Southern African Museums Association. Publication see Southern African Museums Association. Bulletin **3533**
Southern Africa's Travel News see Southern Africa's Travel News Weekly **4787**
Southern Africa's Travel News Weekly. (SA) **4787**
Southern and Southwestern Railway Club. Proceedings. (US ISSN 0038-3805) **4715**
†Southern Angler's and Hunter's Guide. (US ISSN 0081-2986) **5280**
Southern Anthropological Society. Proceedings. (US ISSN 0081-2994) **249**
Southern Arts Association. Publication see The Arts Business **5139**
Southern Arts Bulletin see The Arts Business **5139**
Southern Association for Women Historians. Newsletter. (US) **2323**, 4853
Southern Association of Colleges and Schools. Proceedings. (US ISSN 0038-3813) **1664**
†Southern Banker. (US ISSN 0038-383X) **5280**
Southern Bankers Directory. (US) **800**
Southern Baptist Convention. Annual. (US ISSN 0081-3001) **4249**
Southern Baptist Convention. Historical Commission. Microfilm Catalogue. (US ISSN 0081-301X) **4249**
Southern Baptist Convention. Sunday School Board. Quarterly Review. (US ISSN 0162-4334) **4249**
Southern Baptist Educator. (US ISSN 0038-3848) **4249**
Southern Beef Producer. (US) **226**

Southern Bell Views. (US ISSN 0038-3856) **1366**
Southern Beverage Journal. (US ISSN 0193-0613) **385**
Southern Birds. (SA) **567**, 1497
Southern Boating. (US) **4529**
Southern Bride see Elegant Bride **3066**
Southern Building. (US ISSN 0038-3864) **632**
Southern Business & Economic Journal.(US) **692**, 828
▼Southern Business Review and Forecast. (US) **885**
Southern California Academy of Sciences. Bulletin. (US ISSN 0038-3872) **4345**
Southern California Anthology. (US) **2962**
Southern California Business. (US) **822**
Southern California Business Directory and Buyers Guide. (US ISSN 0093-3090) **1153**, 822
Southern California Dental Laboratory Association. Bulletin. (US ISSN 0038-3945) **3243**, 3263
Southern California Family Living see Family Living **2225**
Southern California Guide. (US ISSN 0038-3902) **4787**, 2480
†Southern California Home & Garden. (US ISSN 1041-5696) **5280**
Southern California Horticultural Institute. Monthly Bulletin. (US) **2139**
Southern California Law Review. (US ISSN 0038-3910) **2680**
▼Southern California Magazine. (US) **2235**
Southern California Property Guide. (US) **4158**
Southern California Psychiatric Society. Newsletter see Southern California Psychiatrist **3354**
Southern California Psychiatrist. (US ISSN 1047-6334) **3354**
Southern California Quarterly. (US ISSN 0038-3929) **2423**
Southern California Rapid Transit District. Annual Report. (US ISSN 0362-2843) **4656**
Southern California Retailer and Western Retailer News see Retailer News: Southern California - Western States Edition **1052**
Southern California Senior Life. (US) **2279**
Southern California State Dental Laboratory Association Bulletin see Southern California Dental Laboratory Association. Bulletin **3243**
Southern California Teamster. (US ISSN 0038-3953) **2589**
Southern California Update. (US) **2457**
Southern California Women Strike for Peace see L.A. W I S P **5225**
Southern Caver. (AT ISSN 0157-8464) **1581**
Southern Changes. (US ISSN 0193-2446) **3947**
Southern City. (US) **4094**
Southern Coalition Report on Jails and Prisons. (US) **1523**
Southern College Personnel Association Journal see College Student Affairs Journal **1308**
▼Southern Commercial Real Estate Review and Forecast. (US) **4158**
Southern Communication Journal. (US) **2842**, 1343
Southern Communities. (US) **2496**, 994, 3947
Southern Comparative Literature Association Newsletter see S C L A Newsletter **2956**
Southern Cooperator. (US ISSN 0038-4003) **832**
Southern Courier. (AT ISSN 0729-5154) **2172**
Southern Cross. (AT ISSN 0313-5861) **4249**
Southern Cross. (SA ISSN 0038-4011) **4276**
Southern Cross. (US ISSN 0745-0257) **4276**
†Southern Dairy Products Journal. (US ISSN 0038-402X) **5280**
Southern Dancer see Middle Eastern Dancer Magazine **1531**

Southern Demographic Association Newsletter see S D A Newsletter 3987
Southern Digest. (US) 1324
Southern Echoes. (US ISSN 0735-6870) 2165
Southern Economic Journal. (US ISSN 0038-4038) 692
Southern Economic Review. (II) 692
Southern Economist. (II ISSN 0038-4046) 692
Southern Engineer. (US ISSN 0038-4054) 1837
Southern Exposure (Carbondale). (US) 2785
Southern Exposure (Durham). (US ISSN 0146-809X) 2884
Southern Exposure (Talladega). (US ISSN 0038-4070) 3797
Southern Exposure Library Staff Bulletin see Southern Exposure (Carbondale) 2785
Southern Farm Equipment Manufacturers. Newsletter. (US) 164, 1085, 3023
Southern Fishing by Outdoor Life see Bass and Freshwater Fishing 4541
Southern Folklore. (US ISSN 0899-594X) 2058
Southern Folklore Quarterly see Southern Folklore 2058
Southern Forest Products Association Newsletter see S F Newsletter 2117
Southern Friend. (US ISSN 0743-7439) 2423, 4288
Southern Gameplan. (US) 4489, 1324
Southern Garden History Association. Newsletter see Magnolia (Winston-Salem) 2134
Southern Gardener. (UK) 2139
Southern Gardens. (US ISSN 0038-4143) 2139
Southern Genealogical Index. (US ISSN 8755-1748) 2165
Southern Genealogy and Heraldry see Southern Genealogical Index 2165
Southern Golf - Landscape & Resort Management. (US) 2139, 307
Southern Golf - Landscape and Turf Industry see Southern Golf - Landscape & Resort Management 2139
Southern Graphics. (US ISSN 0274-774X) 4006
Southern Growth. (US) 885
Southern Growth Policies Board Alert see S G P B Alert 883
Southern Growth Problems and Promises see Southern Growth 885
†Southern Herbs. (US) 5280
Southern History. (UK ISSN 0142-4688) 2388
Southern Hog Producer. (US) 226
Southern Home Counties Chamber of Commerce Directory see Croydon Chamber of Commerce Directory 814
Southern Homes see Atlanta Homes and Lifestyles 2548
Southern Horseman. (US ISSN 0093-3929) 4538
Southern Humanities Review. (US ISSN 0038-4186) 2515
Southern Illinois Labor Tribune see St. Louis - Southern Illinois Labor Tribune 2589
Southern Illinois University. University Museum Studies. (US ISSN 0073-4985) 3533
Southern Illinois University at Carbondale. Library. Bibliographic Contributions. (US) 412
Southern Illinois University at Carbondale. Library. Library Progress. (US) 2785
Southern Illinois University, Carbondale. Center for Archaeological Investigations. Occasional Paper. (US) 286
Southern Illinois University, Carbondale. Center for Archaeological Investigations. Research Paper. (US) 286
Southern Illinois University, Carbondale. Department of Geography. Discussion Paper. (US ISSN 0073-4950) 2263

Southern Illinois University, Carbondale. Occasional Paper Series in Geography. (US ISSN 0073-4969) 2263
Southern Illinois University, Carbondale. University Libraries. Bibliographic Contributions see Southern Illinois University at Carbondale. Library. Bibliographic Contributions 412
Southern Illinois University, Carbondale. University Libraries. Library Progress see Southern Illinois University at Carbondale. Library. Library Progress 2785
Southern Illinois University, Edwardsville. Center For Urban and Environmental Research and Services. C U E R S Report see Southern Illinois University, Edwardsville. Regional Research and Development Services. Report: Private Sector Investments 2496
Southern Illinois University, Edwardsville. Regional Research and Development Services. Report see Southern Illinois University, Edwardsville. Regional Research and Development Services. Report: Private Sector Investments 2496
Southern Illinois University, Edwardsville. Regional Research and Development Services. Report: Private Sector Investments. (US) 2496, 963
Southern Illinois University Law Journal. (US ISSN 0145-3432) 2680
Southern Indian Studies. (US ISSN 0085-6525) 286
Southern Industrial Supplier. (US ISSN 0038-4208) 1028
Southern Insurance. (US) 2543
Southern Israelite see Atlanta Jewish Times 1992
Southern Jeweler see Goldsmith 5200
Southern Jewish Weekly. (US ISSN 0038-4240) 2024
Southern Journal of Agricultural Economics. (US ISSN 0081-3052) 157
Southern Journal of Applied Forestry. (US ISSN 0148-4419) 2108
Southern Journal of Education Research see Education and Psychological Research 1627
Southern Journal of Optometry. (US ISSN 0038-4275) 3305
Southern Journal of Philosophy. (US ISSN 0038-4283) 3782
Southern Libertarian Messenger. (US) 3927
Southern Links. (US ISSN 1043-6375) 4511, 4787
Southern Literary Journal. (US ISSN 0038-4291) 2962
Southern Literature. see Nanfang Wenxue 2940
Southern Living. (US ISSN 0038-4305) 2235
Southern Living Travel South. (US ISSN 1041-3642) 4787, 2235
Southern Loggin' Times. (US) 2117
Southern Lumberman. (US ISSN 0038-4313) 2117
†Southern Magazine. (US ISSN 0889-9304) 5280
Southern Medical Journal. (US ISSN 0038-4348) 3154
Southern Methodist University School of Law. Brief. (US ISSN 0006-9965) 2680
Southern Motor Cargo. (US ISSN 0038-4372) 4747
Southern MotoRacing. (US ISSN 0049-1616) 4489, 4702
Southern Neighborhoods see Southern Communities 2496
Southern News and Views. (US ISSN 0038-4380) 1324
Southern Office Dealer. (US) 1061
Southern Office Outfitter see Southern Office Dealer 1061
Southern Organic Apprenticeship Program. (US) 121
Southern Outdoors. (US ISSN 0199-3372) 4557
Southern Pacific Bulletin. (US) 4715
Southern Partisan. (US ISSN 0739-1714) 2235, 3927
Southern Pharmacy Journal. (US ISSN 0192-5792) 3743

Southern Plumbing, Heating, Cooling. (US ISSN 0038-4461) 2303
Southern Poetry Review. (US ISSN 0038-447X) 3006
Southern Political Report. (US ISSN 0739-3938) 3927
Southern Printer and Lithographer see Southern Graphics 4006
Southern Pulp & Paper. (US ISSN 0270-5222) 3666
Southern Pulp and Paper Manufacturer see Southern Pulp & Paper 3666
Southern Purchasor. (US ISSN 0049-1624) 1054
Southern Quarterly. (US ISSN 0038-4496) 2515, 344
Southern Rag see Folk Roots 3551
Southern Railway System see Norfolk Southern World 4712
Southern Railways. (II ISSN 0038-450X) 4715
Southern Reader. (US ISSN 1042-6604) 2962
Southern Regional Education Board. Annual Report. (US ISSN 0081-3060) 1664
Southern Research Institute. Annual Report. (US) 4345
Southern Review. (AT ISSN 0038-4526) 2962
Southern Review. (US ISSN 0038-4534) 2962
Southern Roots & Shoots. (US ISSN 0895-2876) 2165
Southern Runner. (US) 4489
Southern Rural Development Center. Capsules. (US) 157
Southern Saltwater. (US) 4557
Southern School Law Digest. (US ISSN 0361-0861) 2680
Southern Shipper. (US) 4740
Southern Sierran. (US) 1497, 1968, 4557
Southern Social Studies Journal. (US) 4388, 1760
Southern Social Studies Quarterly see Southern Social Studies Journal 4388
Southern Sociologist. (US ISSN 0038-4577) 4453
Southern Stars. (NZ ISSN 0049-1640) 369
Southern States Communication Journal see Southern Communication Journal 2842
Southern Studies: an Interdisciplinary Journal of the South. (US ISSN 0735-8342) 4388, 2515
Southern Style see American Style 5135
Southern Sun. (AT) 4787
Southern Supermarketing. (US) 2094
▼Southern Surgical Association. Transactions. (US) 3384
Southern Textile News. (US ISSN 0038-4607) 4623
Southern Theatre. (US ISSN 0584-4738) 4638
Southern Tier Town and Country Living. (US ISSN 0192-4168) 121
†Southern Tobacco Journal. (US ISSN 0300-6239) 5280
Southern Traffic Light. (US) 4715, 4748
Southern Travel see Southern Living Travel South 4787
▼Southern Turf Management. (US) 2139
Southern University Law Review. (US ISSN 0099-1465) 2680
Southern Utah News. (US ISSN 0049-1659) 2235
Southern Weed Science Society. Proceedings. (US ISSN 0362-4463) 193
Southern Weekly Magazine. (AT) 2172
Southern Wholesalers Association. Newsletter. (US) 1054
†Southpoint. (US) 5280
Southscan. (UK ISSN 0952-7524) 3927
Southside Virginian. (US) 2423
Southsubkin see South Suburban Genealogical & Historical Society. Newsletter 2164
Southwell and Oxford Papers on Contemporary Society. (UK) 4202

†South West Africa Administration: White Paper on the Activities of the Different Branches. (SX) 5280
South West Africa Scientific Society. Journal see Namibia Scientific Society. Journal 4380
South West Africa Scientific Society. Newsletter - S W A Wetenskaplike Vereniging. Nuusbrief - S W A Wissenschaftliche Gesellschaft. Mitteilungen see Namibia Scientific Society. Newsletter 4326
Southwest Airlines Spirit see SouthWest Spirit 4803
†Southwest & Texas Water Works Journal. (US ISSN 0196-0717) 5280
Southwest Art. (US ISSN 0192-4214) 344
Southwest Art Magazine see Southwest Art 344
Southwest Baptist University Omnibus. (US) 1324
Southwest Book Review. (US) 2884, 2785
Southwest Builder see Southwest Contractor 632
Southwest Builders and Contractors Directory. (US) 1153, 632
Southwest Business and Economic Review see Southwest Journal of Business and Economics 692
Southwest China Nationalities College. Journal. (Social Science Edition). see Xinan Minzu Xueyuan Xuebao (Zhexue Shehui Kexue Ban) 4392
Southwest Computer and Business Equipment Review. (US) 1474, 1061
Southwest Contractor. (US) 632
▼Southwest Crafts. (US) 357
Southwest Cycling. (US) 4521
Southwest Economy. (US) 800
Southwest Farm Press. (US) 121
South West Farmer. (UK) 121
Southwest Institute for Research on Women Newsletter see S I R O W Newsletter 4852
Southwest Institute of Nationalities. Journal (Philosophy, Social Science Edition). see Xinan Minzu Xueyuan Xuebao (Zhexue Shehui Kexue Ban) 4392
Southwest International Wine. (US) 385, 2449
Southwest Jewish Chronicle. (US ISSN 0038-4674) 2024, 4226
Southwest Journal of Business and Economics. (US ISSN 8750-4294) 692
Southwest Journal of Linguistics. (US ISSN 0737-4143) 2842
Southwest Kansas Register. (US ISSN 0038-4690) 4276
Southwest News-Herald. (US ISSN 0038-4704) 2235
Southwest Normal University. Journal (Natural Science Edition). see Xinan Shifan Daxue Xuebao (Ziran Kexue Ban) 4352
Southwest Normal University. Journal (Social Science Edition). see Xinan Shifan Daxue Xuebao (Shehui Kexue Ban) 4392
Southwest Oil World. (US ISSN 0884-6219) 3701
Southwest Philosophy Review. Journal. (US) 3782
Southwest Profile. (US ISSN 0895-6049) 2235
Southwest Real Estate News. (US ISSN 0192-9194) 4158
Southwest Review. (US ISSN 0038-4712) 2884
Southwest Sampler. (US) 2235
Southwest Senior. (US) 2279
Southwest Skier see Skier 4556
SouthWest Spirit. (US) 4803
Southwest Stockman. (US) 226
Southwest Technology Report. (US ISSN 1041-2379) 1778
Southwest Tourism. see Xinan Luyou 4798
Southwestern (Denton). (US ISSN 1053-4911) 2279
Southwestern (Georgetown). (US ISSN 0038-4852) 1324, 2962
Southwestern Anthropological Association Newsletter. (US) 249

Southwestern Bell Corporation. Update. (US) **1366**
Southwestern Business. (CN) **692**
Southwestern Campbook. (US ISSN 0731-8103) **4787**, **4557**
South Western Catholic History. (UK ISSN 0269-8390) **4276**
Southwestern Discoveries. (US) **3006**
South Western Electricity News see S W E B News **1907**
Southwestern Entomologist. (US ISSN 0147-1724) **538**
Southwestern Historical Quarterly. (US ISSN 0038-478X) **2423**
Southwestern Journal of Anthropology see Journal of Anthropological Research **243**
†Southwestern Journal of Social Education. (US ISSN 0049-1683) **5280**
Southwestern Journal of Theology. (US ISSN 0038-4828) **4202**, **3782**
Southwestern Law Journal. (US ISSN 0038-4836) **2680**
Southwestern Legal Foundation. Annual Report. (US ISSN 0561-1784) **2680**, **2729**
†Southwestern Legal Foundation. Patent Law Annual. (US ISSN 0553-3864) **5280**
Southwestern Lore. (US ISSN 0038-4844) **286**, **249**, **2423**
Southwestern Miller see Milling & Baking News **2089**
Southwestern Mission Research Center, Inc. Newsletter see S M R C Newsletter **2421**
Southwestern Musician see Southwestern Musician Combined with The Texas Music Educator **3582**
Southwestern Musician Combined with The Texas Music Educator. (US ISSN 0162-380X) **3582**, **1760**
Southwestern Naturalist. (US ISSN 0038-4909) **4345**
Southwestern News. (US ISSN 0038-4917) **4249**
Southwestern Philosophical Society. Newsletter see Southwest Philosophy Review. Journal **3782**
Southwestern Review. (US ISSN 0276-7155) **2962**
Southwestern Sportsman Magazine. (US) **4557**
Southwestern Studies. Monographs. (US ISSN 0081-315X) **2423**
Southwestern Union Record. (US) **4249**
Souvenir. (US) **2282**, **1118**, **4787**
Souvenir & Geschenk. (GW ISSN 0723-6174) **4489**
Souvenir Card Journal. (US) **2442**
Souvenir Francais. (FR) **2323**
Souvenir Vendeer. (FR) **2388**
Souvenirs and Novelties. (US ISSN 0038-4968) **2282**
Sou'wester. (CN ISSN 0049-1705) **2049**
Sou'wester (Edwardsville). (US ISSN 0098-499X) **2962**, **3006**
Sou'wester (South Bend). (US ISSN 0038-4984) **2423**
Sovet Woman see Sovetskaya Zhenshchina **4853**
Sovetakan Arvest. (AI ISSN 0038-500X) **2515**
Sovetakan Grakanutiun. (AI ISSN 0038-5018) **2962**
Sovetakan Mankavarzh. (AI ISSN 0038-5026) **1664**
Sovetskaya Arkheologiya. (RU ISSN 0038-5034) **286**
Sovetskaya Arkhitektura see Zodchestvo **309**
Sovetskaya Bibliografiya. (RU ISSN 0131-6265) **412**
Sovetskaya Etnografiya. (RU ISSN 0038-5050) **249**
Sovetskaya Geologiya. (RU ISSN 0038-5069) **1581**
Sovetskaya Literatura see Soviet Literature **2962**
Sovetskaya Literatura, Traditsii i Novatorstvo. (RU) **2962**
Sovetskaya Meditsina/Soviet Medicine. (RU ISSN 0038-5077) **3154**
Sovetskaya Militsiya. (RU ISSN 0320-2259) **3472**, **4074**

Sovetskaya Muzyka. (RU ISSN 0038-5085) **3582**
Sovetskaya Pechat' see Zhurnalist **2577**
Sovetskaya Pedagogika. (RU ISSN 0038-5093) **1664**
Sovetskaya Rodina. see Sovietish Heimland **2884**
†Sovetskaya Skul'ptura. (RU) **5280**
Sovetskaya Torgovlya see Torgovaya Gazeta **839**
Sovetskaya Yustitsiya. (RU ISSN 0038-5115) **2680**
Sovetskaya Zhenshchina. (RU ISSN 0038-5913) **4853**
Sovetskie Arkhivy. (RU ISSN 0038-5166) **2388**
Sovetskie Ljudi Segodnja/Vie Quotidienne en U.R.S.S. Prise sur le Vif. (FR ISSN 0303-111X) **2962**
Sovetskie Profsoyuzy. (RU ISSN 0038-5174) **2589**
Sovetskii Ekran see Ekran **4632**
Sovetskii Fil'm. see Soviet Film **3518**
Sovetskii Krasnyi Krest/Soviet Red Cross. (RU ISSN 0132-1226) **4421**
Sovetskii Shakhter. (RU ISSN 0038-5158) **3496**
Sovetskii Shkolnik. (RU) **1266**, **1664**
Sovetskii Soyuz see Soviet Union **2215**
Sovetskoe Finnougrovedenie see Linguistica Uralica **2826**
Sovetskoe Foto. (RU ISSN 0038-5190) **3797**
Sovetskoe Gosudarstvo i Pravo. (RU ISSN 0038-5204) **2681**
Sovetskoe Slavianovedenie. (RU) **2388**
Sovetskoe Voennoe Obozrenie. see Soviet Military Review **3472**
Sovetskoe Zdravookhranenie/Soviet Public Health. (RU ISSN 0038-5239) **4113**
Sovety Narodnykh Deputatov. (RU) **3927**
Soviet Aeronautics - Iz. V U Z. (English translation of: Izvestiya Vysshikh Uchebnykh Zavedenii. Aviatsionnaya Tekhnika) (US ISSN 0364-8117) **62**
Soviet Aerospace see Soviet Aerospace & Technology **62**
Soviet Aerospace & Technology. (US) **62**
†Soviet Agricultural Biology. Part 1: Plant Biology. (English translation (in part) of: Sel'skokhozyaistvennaya Biologiya) (US ISSN 0892-6999) **5280**
†Soviet Agricultural Biology. Part 2: Animal Biology. (English translation (in part) of: Sel'skokhozyaistvennaya Biologiya) (US ISSN 0892-7006) **5280**
Soviet Agricultural Sciences. (English translation of: Vsesoyuznaya Akademiya Sel'skokhozyaistvennykh Nauk im. V.I. Lenina. Doklady) (US ISSN 0735-2700) **121**
Soviet-American Debate. (US ISSN 0883-1270) **921**, **2423**, **3972**
Soviet Analyst. (UK ISSN 0049-1713) **3927**
Soviet and East European Studies in Aesthetics and the Philosophy of Culture. (US) **3782**
Soviet and Eastern European Foreign Trade see Russian and East European Finance and Trade **920**
Soviet & Eastern European Report. (UK) **935**, **2729**
Soviet Anthropology and Archeology see Anthropology and Archeology of Eurasia **234**
Soviet Applied Mechanics. (English translation of: Prikladnaya Mekhanika) (US ISSN 0038-5298) **1922**
▼Soviet Archives of Internal Medicine. (US ISSN 1054-6596) **3154**
Soviet Armed Forces Review Annual. (US) **3472**, **4586**
†Soviet Army. (IS) **5280**
Soviet Astronomy. (English translation of: Astronomicheskii Zhurnal) (US) **369**

Soviet Astronomy Letters. (English translation of: Pis'ma v Astronomicheskii Zhurnal) (US ISSN 0360-0327) **369**
Soviet Atomic Energy. (English translation of: Atomnaya Energiya) (US ISSN 0038-531X) **1809**, **1837**
Soviet Biographical Service. (US) **421**, **2024**
▼Soviet Biological Research Abstracts. (US ISSN 0885-5951) **467**, **23**
Soviet Biotechnology. (English translation of: Biotekhnologiya) (US ISSN 0890-734X) **491**
Soviet Business and Trade. (US ISSN 0731-7727) **885**
▼Soviet Business Law. (US) **2681**, **692**
Soviet Business Law Report see Russia and Commonwealth Business Law Report **2676**
Soviet Castings Technology. (English translation of: Liteinoe Proizvodstvo) (US ISSN 0891-0316) **3420**, **1939**
Soviet Chemical Industry. (English translation of: Khimicheskaya Promyshlennost') (US ISSN 0038-5344) **1188**, **1860**
Soviet Christian Prisoner List see Christian Prisoners in the U.S.S.R **4170**
Soviet, East European and Slavonic Studies in Western Europe see European Bibliography of Soviet, East European and Slavonic Studies **2328**
†Soviet - East European Survey. (US ISSN 0887-0500) **5280**
Soviet Economy. (US ISSN 0882-6994) **885**
Soviet Education see Russian Education and Society **1660**
Soviet Electrical Engineering. (English translation of: Elektrotekhnika) (US ISSN 0038-5379) **1908**
Soviet Electrochemistry. (English translation of: Elektrokhimiya) (US ISSN 0038-5387) **1213**
Soviet Energy Technology see Soviet Journal of Heavy Machinery **1796**
Soviet Engineering Geology. (English translation of: Akademiya Nauk S.S.S.R.: Inzhenernaya Geologiya) (US ISSN 0895-6324) **1581**
Soviet Engineering Research. (English translation of: Stanki i Instrumenty; Vestnik Mashinostroeniya) (US ISSN 0144-6622) **3023**, **1939**
Soviet Export see Business Contact **902**
Soviet Film/Sovetskii Fil'm. (RU ISSN 0038-5395) **3518**
Soviet Foreign Policy Today. (US) **3972**
Soviet Forest Sciences. (English translation of: Akademiya Nauk S.S.S.R.: Lesovedenie) (US ISSN 0891-0324) **2108**, **121**
†Soviet Forging and Sheet Metal Stamping Technology. (English translation of: Kuznechno-Shtampovochnoe Proizvodstvo) (US ISSN 0891-334X) **5280**
Soviet Genetics. (English translation of: Genetika) (US ISSN 0038-5409) **547**, **526**
Soviet Geography. (US) **2263**
Soviet Geology see Soviet Geology and Geophysics **1581**
Soviet Geology and Geophysics. (English translation of: Geologiya i Geofizika) (US ISSN 0361-7149) **1581**, **1595**
Soviet Geophysics see Soviet Geology and Geophysics **1581**
†Soviet Hydrology: Selected Papers. (US ISSN 0038-5425) **5280**
†Soviet Immunology. (English translation of: Immunologiya) (US ISSN 0739-8433) **5280**
Soviet Jewish Affairs. (UK ISSN 0038-545X) **3927**, **4226**
†Soviet Jewry Action Newsletter. (US ISSN 0038-5468) **5280**
Soviet Journal of Automation & Information Sciences. (US ISSN 0882-570X) **1415**

Soviet Journal of Bioorganic Chemistry. (English translation of: Bioorganicheskaya Khimiya) (US ISSN 0360-4497) **1223**, **483**
Soviet Journal of Chemical Physics. (English translation of: Khimicheskaya Fizika) (US ISSN 0733-2831) **3831**, **1230**
Soviet Journal of Communications Technology and Electronics. (English translation of: Radiotekhnika i Elektronika) (US ISSN 8756-6648) **1343**, **1778**
Soviet Journal of Computer & Systems Sciences. (English translation of: Tekhnicheskaya Kibernetika) (US) **1443**, **1880**
Soviet Journal of Contemporary Engineering Mechanics. (English translation of: Akademiya Nauk Armyanskoi S.S.R. Izvestiya. Seriya Mekhanika) (US ISSN 0890-7358) **3845**
Soviet Journal of Contemporary Mathematical Analysis. (English translation of: Akademiya Nauk Armyanskoi S.S.R. Izvestiya. Seriya Matematika) (US ISSN 0735-2719) **3056**
Soviet Journal of Contemporary Physics. (English translation of: Akademiya Nauk Armyanskoi S.S.R. Izvestiya. Seriya Fizika) (US ISSN 8755-4585) **3831**
Soviet Journal of Coordination Chemistry. (English translation of: Koordinatsionnaya Khimiya) (US ISSN 0364-4626) **1188**
Soviet Journal of Developmental Biology. (English translation of: Ontogenez) (US ISSN 0049-173X) **547**
Soviet Journal of Ecology. (English translation of: Ekologiya) (US ISSN 0096-7807) **1969**
Soviet Journal of Friction and Wear. (English translation of: Trenie i Iznos) (US ISSN 0733-1924) **1837**
Soviet Journal of Glass Physics and Chemistry. (English translation of: Fizika i Khimiya Stekla) (US ISSN 0360-5043) **1166**
Soviet Journal of Heavy Machinery. (English translation of: Energomashinostroenie) (US ISSN 1052-6196) **1796**
Soviet Journal of Low Temperature Physics. (English translation of: Fizika Nizkikh Temperatur) (US ISSN 0360-0335) **3842**
Soviet Journal of Marine Biology. (English translation of: Biologiya Morya) (US ISSN 0145-1456) **457**
Soviet Journal of Non-Ferrous Metals. (English translation of: Tsvetnye Metally) (US ISSN 0038-5484) **3420**
Soviet Journal of Nondestructive Testing. (English translation of: Defektoskopiya) (US ISSN 0038-5492) **1188**
Soviet Journal of Nuclear Physics. (English translation of: Yadernaya Fizika) (US ISSN 0038-5506) **3850**
Soviet Journal of Numerical Analysis and Mathematical Modelling. (NE ISSN 0169-2895) **3056**
Soviet Journal of Optical Technology. (English translation of: Optiko-Mekhanicheskaya Promyshlennost') (US ISSN 0038-5514) **3857**, **2525**
Soviet Journal of Particles and Nuclei. (English translation of: Fizika Elementarnykh Chastits i Atomnogo Yadra) (US ISSN 0090-4759) **3850**
Soviet Journal of Physical Oceanography. (NE ISSN 0920-5047) **1611**
Soviet Journal of Plasma Physics. (English translation of: Fizika Plazmy) (US ISSN 0360-0343) **3832**
Soviet Journal of Psychology. (English translation of: Psikhologicheskii Zhurnal) (US) **4047**

Soviet Journal of Quantum Electronics. (English translation of: Kvantovaya Elektronika) (US ISSN 0049-1748) **1908, 3832**

Soviet Journal of Remote Sensing. (English translation of: Issledovanie Zemli iz Kosmosa) (US ISSN 0275-911X) **1837**

Soviet Journal of Superhard Materials. (English translation of: Sverkhtverdye Materialy) (US ISSN 0739-8425) **3832, 1211**

Soviet Journal of Water Chemistry and Technology. (English translation of: Khimiya i Tekhnologiya Vody) (US ISSN 0734-1679) **4828, 1874**

Soviet Journal on Concrete and Reinforced Concrete. (English translation of: Beton i Zhelezobeton) (NE ISSN 0970-244X) **632**

Soviet Journal on Structural Mechanics and Design of Structures. (English translation of: Stroitel'naya Mekhanika i Raschet Sooruzhenii) (NE) **1922, 632**

Soviet Land. (II ISSN 0038-5522) **3927**

Soviet Law. (US) **2681**

Soviet Law and Government see Russian Politics **2676**

†Soviet Life. (US ISSN 0038-5549) **5280**

▼Soviet Lightwave Communications. (UK ISSN 0960-0884) **3832**

Soviet Literature. (RU ISSN 0202-1870) **2962**

Soviet Machine Science see Journal of Machinery Manufacture and Reliability **1414**

Soviet Materials Science. (English translation of: Fiziko-Khimicheskaya Mekhanika Materialov) (US ISSN 0038-5565) **1922**

†Soviet Materials Science Reviews. (US ISSN 0888-689X) **5280**

Soviet Mathematics - Doklady. (English translation of: Akademii Nauk S.S.S.R. Doklady) (US ISSN 0197-6788) **3056**

Soviet Mathematics - Iz. V U Z. (English translation of: Izvestiya Vysshikh Uchebnykh Zavedenii. Seriya Matematika) (US ISSN 0197-7156) **3056**

Soviet Medical Reviews. Section A: Cardiology Reviews. (US ISSN 0888-0697) **3212**

Soviet Medical Reviews. Section B: Physicochemical Aspects of Medicine Reviews. (US ISSN 0887-2392) **575, 483**

Soviet Medical Reviews. Section C: Hematology Reviews. (US ISSN 0888-3920) **3274**

Soviet Medical Reviews. Section D: Immunology Reviews. (US ISSN 0887-3488) **3188**

Soviet Medical Reviews. Section E: Virology Reviews. (US ISSN 0887-3496) **557**

Soviet Medical Reviews. Section F: Oncology Reviews. (US ISSN 0888-0700) **3202**

Soviet Medical Reviews. Section G: Neuropharmacology Reviews. (US ISSN 0896-8306) **3743, 3354**

Soviet Medical Reviews Supplement Series. Section A: Cardiology. (US ISSN 0888-0727) **3212**

Soviet Medical Reviews Supplement Series. Section B: Immunology. (US ISSN 0896-601X) **3188, 575**

Soviet Medicine. see Sovetskaya Meditsina **3154**

Soviet Merchant Ships. (UK) **4740**

Soviet Meteorology and Hydrology. (English translation of: Meteorologiya i Gidrologiya) (US ISSN 0146-4108) **3441, 1600**

Soviet Microelectronics. (English translation of: Mikroelektronika) (US ISSN 0363-8529) **1778**

Soviet Military Review/Sovetskoe Voennoe Obozrenie. (RU ISSN 0038-5220) **3472**

†Soviet Mining Journal. (English translation of: Gornyi Zhurnal) (NE ISSN 0970-2458) **5280**

Soviet Mining Science. (English translation of: Fiziko-tekhnicheskie Problemy Razrabotki Poleznykh Iskopaemykh) (US ISSN 0038-5581) **3496, 1581**

Soviet Neurology and Psychiatry see Journal of Russian and East European Psychiatry **3343**

†Soviet News. (UK ISSN 0038-5603) **5280**

▼Soviet Perspectives. (US ISSN 1055-1042) **921, 935, 3972**

Soviet Physics - Acoustics. (English translation of: Akusticheskii Zhurnal) (US ISSN 0038-562X) **3860**

Soviet Physics - Collection see Lithuanian Physics Journal **3824**

Soviet Physics - Crystallography. (English translation of: Kristallografiya) (US ISSN 0038-5638) **1211**

Soviet Physics - Doklady. (English translation of: Akademii Nauk S.S.S.R. Doklady) (US ISSN 0038-5689) **3832**

Soviet Physics - J E T P. (English translation of: Zhurnal Eksperimental'noi i Teoreticheskoi Fiziki) (US ISSN 0038-5646) **3832**

Soviet Physics Journal. (English translation of: Izvestiya Vysshikh Uchebnykh Zavedenii. Seriya Fizika) (US ISSN 0038-5697) **3832**

Soviet Physics - Lebedev Institute Reports. (English translation of: Kratkie Soobshcheniya po Fizike) (US ISSN 0364-2321) **3832**

Soviet Physics - Semiconductors. (English translation of: Fizika i Tekhnika Poluprovodnikov) (US ISSN 0038-5700) **3832**

Soviet Physics - Solid State. (English translation of: Fizika Tverdogo Tela) (US ISSN 0038-5654) **3832**

Soviet Physics - Technical Physics. (English translation of: Zhurnal Tekhnicheskoi Fiziki) (US ISSN 0038-5662) **3832**

Soviet Physics - Uspekhi. (English translation of: Uspekhi Fizicheskikh Nauk) (US) **3832**

Soviet Plant Physiology. (English translation of: Fiziologiya Rastenii) (US ISSN 0038-5719) **518**

Soviet Powder Metallurgy and Metal Ceramics. (English translation of: Poroshkovaya Metallurgiya) (US ISSN 0038-5735) **3420**

Soviet Progress in Biochemistry see Ukrainian Biochemistry **1190**

Soviet Progress in Chemistry. (English translation of: Ukrainskii Khimicheskii Zhurnal) (US ISSN 0038-5743) **1188**

Soviet Progress in Virology. (English translation of: Voprosy Virusologii) (US ISSN 0734-0311) **557**

Soviet Psychiatry and Psychology Today see Soviet Journal of Psychology **4047**

Soviet Psychology see Journal of Russian and East European Psychology **4033**

Soviet Public Health. see Sovetskoe Zdravookhranenie **4113**

Soviet Radiochemistry. (English translation of: Radiokhimiya) (US ISSN 0038-576X) **1230**

Soviet Red Cross. see Sovetskii Krasnyi Krest **4421**

Soviet Review. (II ISSN 0038-5786) **2215**

Soviet Review see Russian Social Science Review **3923**

Soviet Review see Soviet Society **3972**

Soviet Scientific Reviews. Section A: Physics Reviews. (US ISSN 0143-0394) **3832**

Soviet Scientific Reviews. Section B: Chemistry Reviews. (US ISSN 0143-0408) **1188**

Soviet Scientific Reviews. Section C: Mathematical Physics Reviews. (US ISSN 0143-0416) **3832, 3056**

Soviet Scientific Reviews. Section D: Biological Reviews see Soviet Scientific Reviews. Section D: Physiochemical Biology Reviews **483**

Soviet Scientific Reviews. Section D: Physiochemical Biology Reviews. (US ISSN 0734-9351) **483, 575**

Soviet Scientific Reviews. Section E: Astrophysics & Space Physics Reviews. (US ISSN 0143-0432) **369**

Soviet Scientific Reviews. Section F: Physiology and General Biology Reviews. (US ISSN 0888-4803) **575**

Soviet Scientific Reviews. Section G: Geology Reviews. (US ISSN 0896-7571) **1581**

Soviet Scientific Reviews Supplement Series. Section A: Physics. (US ISSN 0275-7796) **3832**

Soviet Scientific Reviews Supplement Series. Section B: Chemistry. (US ISSN 0275-780X) **1188**

Soviet Scientific Reviews Supplement Series. Section C: Physicochemical Biology. (US) **483**

Soviet Shipping. (RU ISSN 0203-3933) **4740**

▼Soviet Society. (AT ISSN 1034-7437) **3972, 4453**

Soviet Sociology see Sociological Record **4451**

Soviet Soil Science. (English translation of: Referativnyi Zhurnal. Pochvovedenie i Agrokhimiya) (US ISSN 0038-5832) **193**

†Soviet Spaceflight Report. (US ISSN 0889-020X) **5280**

Soviet Sports Review. (US ISSN 0275-598X) **3373, 4489**

Soviet Statutes and Decisions see Statutes and Decisions **2682**

Soviet Studies. (UK ISSN 0038-5859) **692, 3927, 4453**

Soviet Studies. (US ISSN 1046-1809) **4453, 3927**

Soviet Studies in History see Russian Studies in History **2321**

Soviet Studies in Literature see Russian Studies in Literature **2956**

Soviet Studies in Philosophy see Russian Studies in Philosophy **3780**

Soviet Surface Engineering and Applied Electrochemistry. (English translation of: Elektronnaya Obrabotka Materialov) (US ISSN 8756-7008) **1939, 1213, 3023**

Soviet Technical Physics Letters. (English translation of: Pis'ma v Zhurnal Tekhnicheskoi Fiziki) (US ISSN 0360-120X) **3832**

†Soviet Technology Alert. (UK) **5280**

Soviet Technology Reviews. Section A: Energy Reviews. (US ISSN 0275-7893) **1796**

Soviet Technology Reviews. Section B: Thermal Physics Reviews. (US ISSN 0892-6808) **3842**

Soviet Technology Reviews. Section C: Welding and Surfacing Reviews. (US) **3430**

Soviet Technology Reviews. Section C: Welding Reviews see Soviet Technology Reviews. Section C: Welding and Surfacing Reviews **3430**

Soviet Union. (RU ISSN 0206-510X) **2215**

Soviet Union and Eastern Europe see World Today Series: Soviet Union and Eastern Europe **2396**

Soviet Union and the Middle East. (IS ISSN 0334-4142) **3972**

†Soviet Weekly. (UK ISSN 0038-5905) **5280**

Sovietica. Monographs see Sovietica. Publications and Monographs **2388**

Sovietica. Publication see Sovietica. Publications and Monographs **2388**

Sovietica. Publications and Monographs.(NE) **2388, 3782**

Sovietish Heimland/Sovetskaya Rodina. (RU) **2884**

▼Sovmestnye Predpriyatiya. (RU) **692**

Sovremennaya Khudozhestvennaya Literatura za Rubezhom see Diapason **2911**

Sovremennoe Polskoe Pravo. (PL ISSN 0038-5956) **2681**

Sovremeno Pretprijatie. (XN ISSN 0038-5964) **756, 1028**

Sower. (US) **1741**

The Sower. (SA ISSN 0038-5980) **4202**

Sower. (UK) **4202**

Sower. (AT ISSN 0158-1090) **4202, 4421**

†Sowjetwissenschaft. (GW ISSN 0038-6006) **5280**

Sow's Ear. (UK) **2884, 2962, 3006**

Sow's Ear Poetry Journal. (US) **3006**

Soya Bluebook. (US ISSN 0275-4509) **193**

Soya International. (US ISSN 0894-072X) **3612**

Soyabean Abstracts. (UK ISSN 0141-0172) **143, 23**

Soybean Digest. (US ISSN 0038-6014) **193**

Soybean Digest Blue Book see Soya Bluebook **193**

Soyez les Bienvenus en Tchecoslovaquie see Welcome to Czechoslovakia **4796**

Soyfoods see Soya International **3612**

Sozial Info. (GW) **1325**

Sozial Paediatrie. (GW ISSN 0171-9327) **3326**

Sozial Report. (GW ISSN 0171-8738) **4388**

Sozial- und Praeventivmedizin/Medecine Sociale et Preventive. (SZ) **3154**

Sozial- und Wirtschaftshistorische Studien. (AU) **898, 4388**

Sozialarbeit in Oesterreich. (AU) **4421**

Der Sozialdemokrat. (GW ISSN 0038-6030) **3927**

Soziale Arbeit. (GW ISSN 0490-1606) **4421**

Soziale Fortschrett. (LU) **2589**

Soziale Selbstverwaltung. (GW ISSN 0038-6057) **2543**

Soziale Sicherheit. (AU ISSN 0038-6065) **2543**

Soziale Welt. (GW ISSN 0038-6073) **4453**

Sozialer Fortschritt. (GW ISSN 0038-609X) **4388**

Sozialgerichtsbarkeit. (GW ISSN 0490-1657) **4388**

†Sozialisation und Kommunikation. (GW ISSN 0340-9201) **5281**

Sozialist. (GW ISSN 0722-7353) **3927**

†Sozialistische Arbeitswissenschaft. (GW ISSN 0038-6111) **5281**

Sozialistische Erziehung. (AU ISSN 0038-6146) **1664, 3927**

Sozialistische Finanzwirtschaft see Betrieb und Wirtschaft **847**

Sozialistische Forstwirtschaft see Der Wald **2110**

Sozialistische Politik und Wirtschaft see S P W **3924**

Sozialistische Praxis. (GW ISSN 0176-0947) **3927, 3947**

Sozialistische Theorie und Praxis see Aktuelna Pitanja Socijalizma **3871**

Sozialistisches Musikschaffen der Deutschen Demokratischen Republik see Zeitgenoessisches Musikschaffen in der Deutschen Demokratischen Republik. Urauffuehrungen **3587**

Sozialmagazin. (GW ISSN 0340-8469) **4421**

Sozialmedizin. (GW ISSN 0932-5034) **3181, 3811**

Sozialpaedagogik. (GW ISSN 0038-6189) **1664**

Sozialpolitik und Arbeitsrecht. (AU ISSN 0038-6197) **994**

Sozialpolitische Informationen. (GW ISSN 0341-1117) **3927, 4388**

Sozialpsychiatrie. see Social Psychiatry and Psychiatric Epidemiology **3354**

Sozialpsychiatrische Informationen. (GW ISSN 0171-4538) **4047, 3354, 4421**

Sozialrecht & Praxis. (GW) **4421, 3472**

Sozialversicherungs-Berater. (GW ISSN 0936-9198) **1028**

Sozialversicherungs-Beamte und -Angestellte BSBA see G D S - Zeitung **2583**

Sozialversicherungsrechtliche Entscheidungen. (AU) **2681**
Sozialwirtschaftliche Korrespondenz *see* S Z **3924**
Sozialwissenschaften und Berufspraxis. (GW ISSN 0724-3464) **4453**, 4421
Sozialwissenschaftliche Informationen fuer Unterricht und Studium. (GW ISSN 0340-2304) **1664**
Sozialwissenschaftliche Literatur Rundschau. (GW ISSN 0175-6559) **4388**, 4421
Sozialwissenschaftliche Studiengesellschaft Rundschau *see* S W S - Rundschau **4385**
Soziologie. (GW ISSN 0340-918X) **4453**
Soziologische Gegenwartsfragen. Neue Folge. (GW ISSN 0081-3265) **4453**
Soziologische Revue. (GW ISSN 0343-4109) **4453**
Soziooekonomische Forschungen. (SZ) **4389**
Sozo no Sekai/World of the Creation. (JA) **1969**
Spa Destinations/Destinations Spa. (CN) **4787**
Spa Finder. (US) **3808**, **4787**
▼Spa Management. (CN) **1153**
Spa Vacations. (US) **3808**, **4787**
De Spaarbank. (NE ISSN 0169-5401) **800**
Space. *see* Konggan **302**
Space. (AT ISSN 0310-0189) **2496**
Space (Burnham). (UK ISSN 0267-954X) **62**
▼Space Abstracts on Microfiche. (US) **66**, **371**, **3839**
Space Activity in Norway *see* Space Research in Norway **63**
Space Age Times. (US ISSN 0738-0968) **62**
Space and Time. (US ISSN 0271-2512) **3014**
Space Association News. (AT ISSN 1030-2166) **62**
†Space Benefits: Secondary Application of Aerospace Technology in Other Sectors of the Economy. (US) **5281**
Space Biology and Aerospace Medicine. *see* Kosmicheskaya Biologiya i Aviakosmicheskaya Meditsina **3120**
Space Biology and Aerospace Medicine *see* U S S R Report: Space Biology and Aerospace Medicine **3159**
Space Business News. (US ISSN 0738-9884) **62**, **692**
Space Calendar. (US ISSN 0741-1731) **62**
▼Space Commerce. (US ISSN 1043-934X) **62**, **692**
Space Commerce Bulletin *see* Space Commerce Week **62**
Space Commerce News. (US) **62**
Space Commerce Week. (US) **62**
Space Communication. (NE ISSN 0924-8625) **1343**
Space Communication and Broadcasting *see* Space Communication **1343**
Space Daily *see* Space Fax Daily **62**
Space Education *see* Spaceflight **63**
†Space Enterprise. (US) **5281**
†Space Entrepreneurs Directory. (US) **5281**
▼Space Exploration Technology. (US ISSN 1052-3383) **62**
Space Fax Daily. (US ISSN 1048-2652) **62**
†Space for All People. (US) **5281**
Space in Japan. (JA) **62**
Space Information Review. (US) **62**
Space Journal *see* Space R & D Alert **63**
Space Letter. (US ISSN 0038-6278) **62**
†Space Markets. (UK ISSN 0258-4212) **5281**
Space News (Springfield). (US ISSN 1046-6940) **62**, **921**, **3972**
†Space Ornithology Newsletter. (US) **5281**
Space Physics. (PL ISSN 0208-8428) **3832**
Space Policy. (UK ISSN 0265-9646) **62**
Space Power. (US ISSN 0883-6272) **1796**, **62**

Space Power Review *see* Space Power **1796**
Space Press. (US ISSN 0733-8678) **63**
Space R & D Alert. (US) **63**, **839**
Space Research Co-Operative Association Jimu-kyokuho *see* S P A R C Jimu-kyokuho **369**
Space Research in Japan. (JA) **369**, **63**
Space Research in Norway. (NO) **63**
Space Science Reviews. (NE ISSN 0038-6308) **369**, **63**
Space Station Directory & Program Guide. (US) **63**
Space Station News. (US ISSN 0895-8947) **63**
Space Technology. (US ISSN 0892-9270) **4609**, **63**
Space Times. (US) **63**
Space Today. (US ISSN 0889-6054) **63**
Space Ventures Report *see* Space Enterprise **5281**
Space Voyager. (UK) **3014**
†Space World (Amherst). (US ISSN 0038-6332) **5281**
Spaceflight. (UK ISSN 0038-6340) **63**
†Spaceflight News. (UK ISSN 0268-4713) **5281**
†Spaceline. (US) **5281**
Spaciology. (JA) **307**, **2555**
Spaf-Horisont *see* Flyghorisont **52**
†Spafaswap. (US ISSN 0038-6367) **5281**
Spain. Boletin Oficial del Estado. (SP) **4074**
Spain. Direccion General de Aduanas. Informe Mensual sobre el Comercio Exterior. (SP ISSN 0584-6544) **921**
Spain. Direccion General de Bellas Artes. Semana de Musica en la Navidad. (SP) **3582**
Spain. Direccion General de Cooperacion y Relaciones Economicas Internacionales. Sintesis de Informacion Sobre Organismos Internacionales *see* Spain. Ministerio Asintos Exteriores. Direccion General de Cooperacion Tecnica Internacional. Sintesis de Informacion Sobre Organismos Internacionales **1723**
Spain. Direccion General de Correos y Telecomunicacion. Boletin Oficial de Correos y Telecomunicacion. (SP) **1354**, **1366**
Spain. Direccion General de Correos y Telecomunicacion. Boletin Oficial. Telecomunicacion *see* Spain. Direccion General de Correos y Telecomunicacion. Boletin Oficial de Correos y Telecomunicacion **1354**
Spain. Direccion General de la Produccion Agraria. Campana Algodonera. (SP) **193**
Spain. Direccion General de Pesca Maritima. Anuario de Pesca Maritima. (SP) **2051**
Spain. Direccion General de Pesca Maritima. Publicaciones Tecnicas. (SP) **2049**
Spain. Instituto de Credito Oficial. Memoria del Credito Oficial *see* Memoria del Grupo I C O **1101**
Spain. Instituto de Relaciones Agrarias. Boletin de Informacion Extranjera. (SP ISSN 0213-0602) **121**
Spain. Instituto Espanol de Oceanografia. Informes Tecnicos. (SP ISSN 0212-1565) **1611**
Spain. Instituto Geologico y Minero. Coleccion Memorias *see* Spain. Instituto Tecnologico Geominero de Espana. Coleccion Memorias **1581**
Spain. Instituto Geologico y Minero. Coleccion Temas Geologicos - Mineros *see* Spain. Instituto Tecnologico Geominero de Espana. Coleccion Temas Geologicos - Mineros **1548**
Spain. Instituto Geologico y Minero. Informes *see* Spain. Instituto Tecnologico Geominero de Espana. Informes **1581**
Spain. Instituto Nacional de Estadistica. Anuario Estadistico: Edicion Extensa. (SP ISSN 0066-5177) **4586**

†Spain. Instituto Nacional de Estadistica. Anuario Estadistico: Edicion Manual. (SP) **5281**
Spain. Instituto Nacional de Estadistica. Boletin de Estadistica *see* Spain. Instituto Nacional de Estadistica. Boletin Mensual de Estadistica **4586**
Spain. Instituto Nacional de Estadistica. Boletin Mensual de Estadistica. (SP) **4586**
Spain. Instituto Nacional de Estadistica. Encuesta de la Poblacion Activa *see* Spain. Instituto Nacional de Estadistica. Encuesta de Poblacion Activa. Principales Resultados **738**
Spain. Instituto Nacional de Estadistica. Encuesta de Poblacion Activa. Principales Resultados. (SP ISSN 0212-6532) **738**
Spain. Instituto Nacional de Estadistica. Encuesta de Poblacion Activa. Resultados Detallados. (SP ISSN 0212-6990) **738**
Spain. Instituto Nacional de Estadistica. Encuesta Industrial. (SP) **738**
Spain. Instituto Nacional de Estadistica. Estadistica Espanola. (SP ISSN 0014-1151) **4586**
Spain. Instituto Nacional de Estadistica. Indice del Coste de la Vida *see* Spain. Instituto Nacional de Estadistica. Indices de Precios de Consumo. Boletin Informativo **4586**
Spain. Instituto Nacional de Estadistica. Indices de Precios de Consumo. Boletin Informativo. (SP ISSN 0213-7410) **4586**
Spain. Instituto Nacional de Industria. Informe Anual. (SP) **692**
Spain. Instituto Nacional de Industria. Memoria I N I (Year) *see* Spain. Instituto Nacional de Industria. Informe Anual **692**
†Spain. Instituto Nacional de Industria. Programa de Investigaciones Economicas: Serie E. (SP) **5281**
Spain. Instituto Nacional de Investigaciones Agrarias. Anales. Series: Ganaderia *see* Investigacion Agraria. Produccion y Sanidad Animales **219**
Spain. Instituto Nacional de Investigaciones Agrarias. Comunicaciones. Serie: Economia. (SP ISSN 0214-0357) **158**
Spain. Instituto Nacional de Investigaciones Agrarias. Comunicaciones. Serie: General. (SP ISSN 0210-3311) **121**, **518**
Spain. Instituto Nacional de Investigaciones Agrarias. Comunicaciones. Serie: Higiene y Sanidad. (SP ISSN 0211-1314) **226**, **4816**
Spain. Instituto Nacional de Investigaciones Agrarias. Comunicaciones. Serie: Produccion Animal. (SP ISSN 0210-3303) **226**
Spain. Instituto Nacional de Investigaciones Agrarias. Comunicaciones. Serie: Produccion Vegetal. (SP ISSN 0210-329X) **121**
Spain. Instituto Nacional de Investigaciones Agrarias. Comunicaciones. Serie: Proteccion Vegetal. (SP) **193**, **2108**
Spain. Instituto Nacional de Investigaciones Agrarias. Comunicaciones. Serie: Recursos Naturales. (SP ISSN 0210-3338) **1497**, **1969**
Spain. Instituto Nacional de Investigaciones Agrarias. Comunicaciones. Serie: Tecnologia Agraria. (SP ISSN 0210-2560) **121**
Spain. Instituto Nacional de Investigaciones Agrarias. Serie: Produccion y Proteccion Vegetales. (SP ISSN 0302-8755) **193**, **2108**
Spain. Instituto Nacional para la Conservacion de la Naturaleza. Monografias. (SP) **1969**
Spain. Instituto Tecnologico Geominero de Espana. Coleccion Memorias. (SP) **1581**, **3496**

Spain. Instituto Tecnologico Geominero de Espana. Coleccion Temas Geologicos - Mineros. (SP) **1548**, **3496**
Spain. Instituto Tecnologico Geominero de Espana. Informes. (SP) **1581**, **3496**
Spain. Ministerio Asintos Exteriores. Direccion General de Cooperacion Tecnica Internacional. Sintesis de Informacion Sobre Organismos Internacionales. (SP) **1723**
Spain. Ministerio de Agricultura, Pesca y Alimentacion. Boletin de Sanidad Vegetal: Plagas. (SP ISSN 0213-6910) **193**, **518**, **3224**
Spain. Ministerio de Agricultura, Pesca y Alimentacion. Boletin Mensual de Estadistica Agraria. (SP ISSN 0211-9897) **143**
Spain. Ministerio de Agricultura, Pesca y Alimentacion. Boletin Mensual de Precios. (SP) **158**, **4586**
Spain. Ministerio de Agricultura, Pesca y Alimentacion. Boletin Semanal de Precios Agrarios *see* Spain. Ministerio de Agricultura, Pesca y Alimentacion. Boletin Mensual de Precios **158**
†Spain. Ministerio de Agricultura, Pesca y Alimentacion. Informacion Agraria. (SP) **5281**
Spain. Ministerio de Agricultura, Pesca y Alimentacion. Instituto de Reforma y Desarrollo Agrario. Hojas Divulgadoras. (SP) **122**
†Spain. Ministerio de Agricultura, Pesca y Alimentacion. Registro de Variedades Protegidas. Boletin. (SP) **5281**
Spain. Ministerio de Agricultura, Pesca y Alimentacion. Secretaria General Tecnica. Anuario de Estadistica Agraria. (SP) **143**
Spain. Ministerio de Agricultura, Pesca y Alimentacion. Servicio de Extension Agraria. Hojas Divulgadoras *see* Spain. Ministerio de Agricultura, Pesca y Alimentacion. Instituto de Reforma y Desarrollo Agrario. Hojas Divulgadoras **122**
Spain. Ministerio de Comercio y Turismo. Estadisticas de Turismo *see* Spain. Ministerio de Transportes, Turismo y Comunicaciones. Secretaria General de Turismo. Anuario de Estadisticas de Turismo **4800**
Spain. Ministerio de Economia y Hacienda, Delegacion del Gobierno en Campsa. El Petrolero en la C E E.(SP) **3701**
Spain. Ministerio de Economia y Hacienda. Delegacion del Gobierno en Campsa. Memoria. (SP) **3702**
Spain. Ministerio de Economia y Hacienda. Direccion General de Seguros. Balances y Cuentas. (SP) **1106**
Spain. Ministerio de Economia y Hacienda. Estadisticas Presupuestarias y Fiscales. (SP) **738**
Spain. Ministerio de Economia y Hacienda. Informacion Estadistica *see* Spain. Ministerio de Economia y Hacienda. Estadisticas Presupuestarias y Fiscales **738**
Spain. Ministerio de Economia y Hacienda. Informacion Trimestral. Boletin. (SP) **885**
Spain. Ministerio de Economia y Hacienda. Memoria Estadistica. Seguros Privados. (SP) **4586**
†Spain. Ministerio de Economia y Hacienda. Subdireccion General de Organizacion e Informacion. Estadistica de la Informacion al Publico. (SP) **5281**
Spain. Ministerio de Educacion y Ciencia. Boletin Oficial: Actos Administrativos. (SP) **1731**
Spain. Ministerio de Educacion y Ciencia. Boletin Oficial: Coleccion Legislativa. (SP) **2681**, **1664**
Spain. Ministerio de Hacienda. Informacion Estadistica *see* Spain. Ministerio de Economia y Hacienda. Estadisticas Presupuestarias y Fiscales **738**

Spain. Ministerio de Industria. Resultados de la Encuesta de Coyuntura Industrial: Sector Industrial. (SP) **1085**
Spain. Ministerio de Justicia. Boletin de Informacion. (SP) **2681**
Spain. Ministerio de Justicia. Diccionarios Indice de Jurisprudencia Civil. (SP ISSN 0210-1165) **2681**
Spain. Ministerio de Justicia. Diccionarios Indice de Jurisprudencia Penal. (SP ISSN 0210-1157) **2681**, 1523
Spain. Ministerio de Justicia. Secretaria General Tecnica. Documentacion Juridica. (SP ISSN 0210-3419) **2681**
Spain. Ministerio de Justicia. Secretaria General Tecnica. Informacion Juridica *see* Spain. Ministerio de Justicia. Secretaria General Tecnica. Documentacion Juridica **2681**
Spain. Ministerio de la Vivienda. Boletin Oficial. (SP ISSN 0490-3323) **2496**
Spain. Ministerio de la Vivienda. Estadistica de la Industria de la Construccion. (SP ISSN 0561-4902) **638**
Spain. Ministerio de la Vivienda. Serie 3: Vivienda. (SP) **4074**
Spain. Ministerio de Obras Publicas. Boletin de Informacion *see* Obras Publicas **4069**
†Spain. Ministerio de Relaciones con las Cortes y de la Secretaria de Estado. Coleccion Informe. (SP) **5281**
Spain. Ministerio de Relaciones con las Cortes y de la Secretaria del Gobierno. Boletin Official del Estado *see* Spain. Boletin Oficial del Estado **4074**
Spain. Ministerio de Transportes, Turismo y Comunicaciones. Secretaria General de Turismo. Anuario de Estadisticas de Turismo. (SP ISSN 0212-5773) **4800**
Spain. Ministerio del Interior. Direccion General de Trafico. Boletin Informativo. (SP ISSN 0210-9220) **4656**
Spain. Ministerio del Interior. Direccion General de Trafico. Boletin Informativo: Accidentes. (SP ISSN 0085-655X) **4667**
Spain. Ministerio del Interior. Direccion General de Trafico. Boletin Informativo: Anuario Estadistico General. (SP ISSN 0304-9191) **4667**
Spain. Ministero de Educacion y Ciencia. Guia. (SP) **1664**
Spain. Observatorio Astronomico Nacional. Boletin Astronomico. (SP ISSN 0373-7101) **369**
▼Spain. Registro Mercantil. Boletin Oficial. (SP ISSN 0214-9958) **692**
†Spain. Tribunal Central de Trabajo. Repertorio de Sentencias. (SP) **5281**
Spain (Year). (US) **4787**
Spain - U.S. Trade Bulletin *see* The Business Link **902**
Spak-Forum. (GW ISSN 0171-3159) **4389**, 3927
Span *see* M I N Fax **2491**
Span. (AT ISSN 0313-1459) **2962**
Span. (US ISSN 0584-8016) **3702**
Span (London). (UK) **4202**
Spang Robinson Report. (US ISSN 0885-9957) **1410**
Spaniels in the Field. (US) **3714**
Spanische Forschungen der Goerresgesellschaft. Reihe 1: Gesammelte Aufsaetze zur Kulturgeschichte Spaniens. (GW ISSN 0342-1058) **2388**
Spanische Forschungen der Goerresgesellschaft. Reihe 2: Monographien. (GW ISSN 0081-3494) **2388**
Spanish and Spanish-American Poetry. (US) **3006**
Spanish Chemical Industry. Directory. *see* Industria Quimica Espanola. Repertorio **1139**
Spanish Cultural Index. (SP ISSN 0038-6456) **2890**, 23
Spanish Daily News. *see* Popular **2020**

Spanish Journal of Chemotherapy. *see* Revista Espanola de Quimioterapia **3263**
Spanish Journal of Food Science and Technology. *see* Revista Espanola de Ciencia y Tecnologia de Alimentos **2080**
Spanish Official Chamber of Commerce in Australia. Spanish - Australian Trade. (AT) **822**
Spanish River Papers. (US) **2423**
Spanish Studies. (US) **2024**
Spanish Studies. (UK) **2962**, 2842
Spanish Texts *see* Hispanic Texts **2817**
Spanish Today. (US ISSN 0049-1802) **2842**, 345, 2962
Spanish Yellow Pages. (US) **1153**
Spanker. *see* Der Shmaiser **5276**
Spanner (London, 1974). (UK ISSN 0584-8067) **2884**, 345
Spanner N Y C. (US) **345**
Spansk Skandinavisk Forening. Medlemsinformation. (DK ISSN 0107-2072) **2185**
Spansklaererforeningen. Informationer. (DK ISSN 0109-307X) **2842**
†Sparbankerna. (SW ISSN 0346-1602) **5281**
SPARCO. (SP) **2094**
Spare Rib. (UK ISSN 0306-7971) **4853**
Spare Time. (US ISSN 0038-6499) **963**
Sparebankbladet/Norwegian Savings Bank News. (NO ISSN 0038-6502) **800**
Der Sparefroh. (AU ISSN 0038-6510) **1266**, 800
Sparekassestanden. (DK) **800**
Spares and Strikes. (US) **4511**
Sparfraemjaren *see* Sparbankerna **5281**
Spark. (UK) **2296**, 4249
Spark. (LO) **2884**
Spark. *see* Tsog **2970**
Spark. *see* Xing Huo **2978**
Spark. (II) **3006**
▼Spark! (Cincinnati). (US) **1266**
Spark (New York). (US ISSN 0024-0591) **4288**
Sparkle Magazine. (KE) **1266**
†Sparks (Santa Rosa). (US) **5281**
Sparks (Wheaton) *see* Newswire (Wheaton) **4286**
†Sparks Journal. (US) **5281**
Sparks Journal Quarterly *see* Sparks Journal **5281**
Sparrow (Santa Rosa). (US) **2962**
Sparrow (West Lafayette). (US) **3006**
Sparrow Poverty Pamphlets *see* Sparrow (West Lafayette) **3006**
Spartacist. (US ISSN 0038-6596) **3927**
Spartacist Canada. (CN ISSN 0229-5415) **3972**, 994, 3947, 4853
Spartaco. (IT) **3927**, 994
Spartacus International Gay Guide. (GW) **2457**, 3947, 4787
Spatial Vision. (NE ISSN 0169-1015) **3066**
Spawning the Medicine River. (US) **2962**, 2024
Spazio Abitato. (IT) **2496**
Spazio Casa. (IT) **2561**, 2139
Speak. (AT) **4453**, 1497
Speak Up. (IT) **2206**
Speakeasy. (FR) **2884**
Speaker Builder. (US ISSN 0199-7920) **4462**
Speakers' Papers: Speeches from the Gold and Silver Institutes' (Year) Annual Meeting. (US) **3496**
Speakers, Tours and Films. (US ISSN 0193-1725) **3832**
Speaking and Writing Monthly. *see* Shuoxie Yuekan **2841**
Speaking of "Columbias". (US ISSN 0038-6626) **226**
Speaking of Fire. (US) **2035**
†Speaking of Japan. (JA ISSN 0389-3510) **5281**
Speaking Out. (JA ISSN 0915-6690) **1969**
Speaking Relatively. (US) **2165**
Speakout. (US) **2842**, 1760
Spear. (NR ISSN 0038-6634) **2212**
Spear Shaker Review. (US ISSN 0894-8852) **2962**

Spearhead. (KE) **4202**
Spearhead (Mayfield). (US) **4529**
Spearhead (Oakton). (US) **3472**
Spec-Com Journal. (US) **1380**
Spec-Data Manu-Spec System *see* Spec-Data Program **639**
Spec-Data Program. (US) **639**
Spec-Data Program Index. (US) **639**
Specchio. (CN) **2024**
Specchio Economico. (IT) **885**
Special Analysis: Budget of the United States Government *see* U.S. Office of Management and Budget. Special Analysis: Budget of the United States Government **1111**
Special and Individual Needs Technology *see* S A I N T **5272**
Special Aspects of Education. (US ISSN 0731-8413) **1664**
Special Bricolage. (FR ISSN 0151-3648) **2501**
Special Care in Dentistry. (US ISSN 0275-1879) **3243**
Special Collections *see* Primary Sources & Original Works **2779**
Special Court News. (US) **2681**
Special Delivery. (US) **3296**, 4836
Special Delivery. *see* Odtey Bichig **4654**
Special Edition. (US) **3400**
Special Education and Rehabilitation. (IS ISSN 0334-7613) **1741**
Special Education Bulletin and Review. (US) **1741**
†Special Education Journal. (AT ISSN 0813-2402) **5281**
Special Education Leadership. (US ISSN 0896-7784) **4249**
†Special Education Newsletter. (US ISSN 0049-1837) **5281**
Special Educational Needs Abstracts. (UK ISSN 0954-0822) **1679**
Special Effects & Stunts Guide. (US) **1153**, 3518
Special Events. (US) **2480**, 1054
Special Events Report *see* I E G Sponsorship Report **1040**
Special Glass. *see* Tezhong Boli **1215**
Special Interest Autos. (US ISSN 0049-1845) **4702**, 259
Special Interest Groups for Computer Science Newsletter *see* S I G C S Newsletter **1400**
Special Investment Situations. (US) **964**
Special Issues for Chinese Export Commodities Fair/Zhongguo Chukou Shangpin Jiaoyihui Tekan. (HK) **1054**
Special Libraries. (US ISSN 0038-6723) **2785**
Special Libraries Association. Eastern Canada Chapter. Bulletin. (CN ISSN 0824-7749) **2785**
Special Libraries Association. Geography and Map Division. Bulletin. (US ISSN 0036-1607) **2785**, 2263
Special Libraries Association. Montreal Chapter. Bulletin *see* Special Libraries Association. Eastern Canada Chapter. Bulletin **2785**
Special Libraries Association. Social Science Division. Bulletin. (US) **2785**
Special Libraries Association. Upstate New York Chapter. Bulletin. (US) **2785**
Special Libraries Association. Washington D.C. Chapter. Chapter Notes. (US ISSN 0739-7097) **2785**
Special Libraries Association, Japan. Bulletin. *see* Senmon Toshokan **2784**
Special Libraries Association Triennial Salary Survey *see* S L A Triennial Salary Survey **2782**
Special Libraries Association, Virginia Chapter *see* V A S L A **5299**
†Special News for Special People. (US) **5281**
Special Papers in International Economics. (US ISSN 0081-3559) **692**, 800
Special Report: Health. (US) **3808**
Special Report: Living. (US) **2235**

SPECIFIC LEARNING 6685

Special Report on Financial and Economic Data for the Men's and Boy's Clothing Industry *see* Annual Statistical Report on Profit, Sales & Marketing Trends for the Men's & Boy's Tailored Clothing Industry **1288**
Special Report: Sports. (US) **4489**
Special Report to the Office Products Industry *see* N O P A Office Market Update **1059**
Special Scies a Moteur et Techniques Forestieres *see* Motoculture Magazine **2134**
Special Services in the Schools. (US ISSN 0739-9820) **1741**, 4047
Special Situation Report. (US) **964**
Special Situations Newsletter. (US) **964**
†Special Situations Under Five Dollars. (US) **5281**
Special Sports. (NE) **4489**
Special Subject Resources in Maine *see* Maine. State Library. Special Subject Resources in Maine **2772**
Special Teacher. (US) **1741**
†Special United Nations Services. (UN ISSN 0257-7860) **5281**
Special Warfare. (US) **3472**
Special Weapons and Tactics Magazine *see* S.W.A.T. Magazine **1522**
Special Zone Economy. *see* Tequ Jingji **694**
Specialarbejderkurser. (DK ISSN 0107-4733) **1687**
Specialarbejderkurser paa Specialarbejderskolerne *see* Specialarbejderkurser **1687**
Specialarbejderskolen. (DK ISSN 0108-3430) **1687**
SpeciaList. (US ISSN 0273-9399) **2799**
Specialist Building Finishes. (UK) **632**
Specialisten. (DK ISSN 0905-975X) **1665**
SpeciaLists' MarketPlus Newsletter. (US) **1054**
Speciality Chemicals. (UK) **1860**
Specialization Update. (US) **2681**
Specialized Carriers & Rigging Association Newsletter *see* S C & R A Newsletter **4747**
†Specialized Transportation Planning and Practice. (US ISSN 0276-8631) **5281**
†Specialized Transportation Services, Services Guide. (US) **5281**
Specializzata. (IT) **632**
Specializzazione. (IT ISSN 0038-6863) **1061**
Specialny Advertising Business. (US ISSN 0195-0495) **38**
Specialty Advertising Journal. (US) **38**
Specialty Automotive Magazine. (US ISSN 0894-7414) **4702**
Specialty Automotive Parts & Accessories *see* Specialty Automotive Magazine **4702**
Specialty Baker's Voice. (US ISSN 0038-688X) **2089**
†Specialty Booksellers Directory. (US ISSN 0895-254X) **5281**
Specialty Chemicals Handbook. (JA) **1188**
Specialty Cooking. (US) **3612**, 2082
Specialty Equipment Market Association News *see* S E M A News **4701**
Specialty Food Merchandising. (US ISSN 0194-1429) **2094**
Specialty Lab Update. (US) **3797**, 1118
Specialty Law Digest: Health Care. (US ISSN 0198-8778) **2681**
Specialty Petrochemicals. *see* Jingxi Shiyou Huagong **3690**
†Specialty Retailer. (US) **5281**
Specialty Store Service Bulletin *see* Fashion Newsletter **1291**
Specialty Travel Index. (US ISSN 0889-7085) **1153**, 4800
†SpecialWare Directory. (US) **5281**
Species. (SZ ISSN 1016-927X) **1497**
Specific Learning Difficulties Association of New South Wales News *see* S P E L D News **1741**
Specific Learning Difficulties Association of Victoria Bulletin *see* S P E L D Bulletin **1741**

SPECIFICATION

Specification. (UK ISSN 0081-3567) 632
Specifications & Applications of Industrial Robots In Japan: Manufacturing Fields (Year). (JA) 1410
Specifications & Applications of Industrial Robots in Japan: Non-Manufacturing Fields (Year). (JA) 1410
Specifications of Mineral Concessions and Licenses in Greenland. (DK ISSN 0107-430X) 3496
Specifications of Mineral Licenses and Concessions in Greenland see Specifications of Mineral Concessions and Licenses in Greenland 3496
Specifier's Guide to Contract Floor Coverings. (US) 2561
The Specifier's Guide to Heating, Ventilating, Air Conditioning, and Refrigeration. (UK) 2303
Specifile Building Compendium. (SA) 632
Specifile News and Product Update. (SA) 632
Specify. (UK) 632
Specijalna Skola. (YU ISSN 0038-6936) 1665
Specimina Philologiae Slavicae. (GW ISSN 0170-1320) 2842, 2962
Spectacle du Monde - Realites - Perspectives. (FR) 2884
Spectacle du Monde - Spectacle - Perspectives see Spectacle du Monde - Realites - Perspectives 2884
Spectacular Salads see Fresh Produce Workshop 2071
Spectator see U C Davis Magazine 1327
Spectator see Trial Style 2236
Spectator. (UK ISSN 0038-6952) 2885
Spectator (Los Angeles). (US) 3518, 1380
Spectator (Raleigh). (US) 345, 3518, 3582
Spectator (Seattle). (US) 1325
Spectext. (US) 632
Spectra. (US) 1665
Spectra: C I W Newsletter. (Carnegie Institution of Washington) (US) 4345, 370, 547, 1548
Spectra Index and S D C Bulletin see S D C Bulletin 3839
Spectra of Anthropological Progress. (II) 249
Spectrochimica Acta. Part A: Molecular Spectroscopy. (US ISSN 0584-8539) 1208, 3857
Spectrochimica Acta. Part B: Atomic Spectroscopy. (US ISSN 0584-8547) 1208, 3857
Spectrochimica Acta Reviews. (US ISSN 0958-319X) 1208, 3857
Spectroscopic Properties of Inorganic & Organometallic Compounds. (UK ISSN 0584-8555) 1188, 3857
Spectroscopical Society of Japan. Journal/Bunko Kenkyu. (JA ISSN 0038-7002) 3857
Spectroscopy. (US ISSN 0887-6703) 3857, 1208
Spectroscopy: an International Journal. (NE ISSN 0712-4813) 1188
Spectroscopy and Spectral Analysis. see Guangpuxue yu Guangpu Fenxi 3852
Spectroscopy International. (US ISSN 1040-7669) 1188
Spectroscopy Letters. (US ISSN 0038-7010) 3857
Spectroscopy World. (UK ISSN 0956-9820) 3857
Spectrum. (UK) 1380
Spectrum. (AT ISSN 1037-2040) 1665
▼Spectrum. (IS) 3857, 2525
Spectrum. (UK ISSN 0305-7917) 4202
Spectrum. (SA) 4345, 3056
Spectrum. (BL) 4609, 4345
Spectrum (Amherst). (US ISSN 0038-7061) 345, 2962
Spectrum (Boston). (US ISSN 1047-2371) 3589, 4462
Spectrum (Des Moines). (US) 2289
Spectrum (New York) see Wooden Bell 4424

Spectrum (Olathe). (US ISSN 0883-282X) 2785, 2235, 2575
Spectrum (Paxton). (US ISSN 0895-8270) 2962, 1325
Spectrum (St. Paul). (US) 3988, 2423
Spectrum (Takoma Park). (US) 4288
The Spectrum (Topeka). (US ISSN 0012-4427) 3947, 2681
Spectrum (Washington). (US) 756, 2024
Spectrum Convertibles. (US) 964
Spectrum der Herrenmode see Mannenmode 1292
Spectrum Independent. (US) 2235
▼Spectrum International. (US) 964
Spectrum Magazine (Bloomsburg). (US ISSN 0892-9459) 2235
Spectrum Magazine (Los Angeles). (US) 3596
Spectrum Newsletter. (US) 1266
†Spectrum Pharmaceuticum. (HU ISSN 0138-9238) 5281
▼Spectrum Report. (US ISSN 1053-993X) 1343, 1366
†Spectrum Review. (US ISSN 0895-7517) 5281
Spectrum Stories see Wonder 3015
Spectrum Tech Magazine. (US) 1445
Spectrum 1: U S and European Investment Company Stock Holdings Survey. (US) 964
Spectrum 2: U S and European Investment Company Portfolios. (US) 964
Spectrum 3: 13(F) Institutional Stock Holdings Survey. (US) 964
Spectrum 4: 13(F) Institutional Portfolios. (US) 964
Spectrum 5: Five Percent Ownership Based on 13D, 13G, & 14D-1 Filings. (US) 964
Spectrum 6: Insider Ownership. (US) 964
Specula. (GW) 3782
Speculations in Science and Technology.(UK ISSN 0155-7785) 4345
†Speculative Investor. (US) 5281
Speculator. (US) 964
Speculum. (US ISSN 0038-7134) 2388, 345, 2962
Speculum Anniversary Monographs. (US) 2389, 345, 2962
Speculum Artium. (IT) 2962
Speculum Juris. (SA ISSN 0584-8652) 2681
Der Spediteur. (GW ISSN 0342-7749) 4656
†Speech. (UK ISSN 0268-148X) 5281
Speech and Drama. (UK ISSN 0038-7142) 4638, 1665
Speech and Hearing Association of Virginia. Journal. (US ISSN 0038-7150) 2289, 1741, 3317
Speech Communication. (NE ISSN 0167-6393) 2857
Speech Communication Association Free Speech Yearbook see S C A Free Speech Yearbook 3924
Speech Communication Directory. (US ISSN 0190-2075) 1680, 412, 1741
Speech Communication Directory of S C A and the Regional Speech Communication Organizations see Speech Communication Directory 1680
Speech Index. (US ISSN 0081-3656) 2856, 23
Speech Monographs see Communication Monographs 1622
Speech Pathology and Therapy see European Journal of Disorders of Communication 1735
Speech Teacher see Communication Education 1622
Speech Technology. (US ISSN 0744-1355) 1343
Speechwriter's Newsletter. (US ISSN 0272-8079) 2575, 1343
Speed and Custom Dealer see S C & O: Specialty & Custom Dealer 4701
Speedhorse see Speedhorse - Racing Report 4538
Speedhorse - Racing Report. (US) 4538
Speedlines. (US) 4715

Speednews. (US) 4677
Speedtype. (II) 1061
Speedway Scene. (US ISSN 0747-5403) 4489
Speedway Star. (UK ISSN 0038-724X) 4489, 4521
Speedwriter. (II) 1061
Speedx. (US ISSN 0882-8091) 1360, 2442
Speedy Bee. (US ISSN 0190-6798) 122
Speel see D O E 4632
Speelgoed & Hobby. (NE) 2282, 2442
†Spegeln. (SW) 5281
Speideren. (NO ISSN 0800-0646) 1266
Speiding. (NO) 1266
Spejd. (DK) 1266
Spejlet. (DK ISSN 0038-7266) 374
Spektator. (NE ISSN 0165-084X) 2962, 1665
Spektrum. (SZ ISSN 0038-7274) 345, 2962, 3006
Spektrum. (Czech translation of: Dialogue (Washington)) (CS) 3972
Spektrum see Spektrum der Wissenschaft 4345
Spektrum (Gelnhausen). (GW) 1266, 1665
Spektrum (Mainz). (GW) 4094
Spektrum der Augenheilkunde. (US ISSN 0930-4282) 3305
Spektrum der Psychiatrie und Nervenheilkunde. (GW ISSN 0341-9738) 3355
Spektrum der Wissenschaft. (GW ISSN 0170-2971) 4345
Spektrum des Geistes. (GW ISSN 0177-6185) 2962
†Spektrum Film. (GW ISSN 0176-4594) 5281
Spel en Speelgoed see Revue Internationale des Jeux et Jouets 2282
Speleo. (IT ISSN 0394-5057) 1548, 2058, 2263, 4787
Speleo Nederland. (NE ISSN 0167-224X) 1595, 1581
Speleologia Emiliana. (IT ISSN 0038-7290) 1581
Speleological Abstracts/Bulletin Bibliographique Speleologique. (SZ ISSN 0253-8296) 1552, 23
Speleological Society of Japan. Journal. (JA ISSN 0386-233X) 1548, 2263, 3661
Speleonews. (US ISSN 0734-5895) 4557
Speling. (NE ISSN 0038-7320) 4202, 3782
†Spelling Action. (AT) 5281
†Spelmanews. (US) 5281
Spencer Gulf Pictorial. (AT) 2172
Spencer Museum of Art. Register. (US ISSN 0733-866X) 345
Spencer's Research Reports on Employee Benefits. (US) 994
Spenser Newsletter. (US ISSN 0038-7347) 2962
Spenser Studies. (US ISSN 0195-9468) 3006
Spent Fuel Management Seminar Proceedings. (US) 1809
Spent Fuel Storage Seminar (Proceedings) see Spent Fuel Management Seminar Proceedings 1809
Sperimentale. (IT ISSN 0038-7355) 457
Sperimentare see S P Computer Magazine 1907
Sperry New Holland News see Ford New Holland News 92
Spettacolo. (IT ISSN 0038-738X) 4638, 3518
Lo Spettacolo in Italia. (IT) 4498
Spettacolo Viaggiante. (IT) 4638
Spettatore Musicale. (IT ISSN 0038-7401) 3582
Speur- en Ontwikkelingswerk in Nederland/Research and Development Activities in the Netherlands. (NE ISSN 0168-468X) 4609
SPEX see S P E X 4136
Spex Speaker. (US ISSN 0490-4176) 3858

Speyer. Dioezese. Direktorium Spirense - Offizium und Messfeier. (GW) 4276
Spezia Oggi. (IT ISSN 0391-7983) 822
Spezialbibliographien zu Fragen des Staates und des Rechts. (GW ISSN 0081-3680) 2700
Spezielle Pathologische Anatomie. (US ISSN 0081-3699) 3154, 457
†Sphere. (CN ISSN 0700-7426) 5281
Sphincter. (UK ISSN 0038-741X) 3154
Sphinx. (GW) 1266, 1665
Sphinx. (UK ISSN 0038-7428) 2885, 1266, 1325
Sphinx. (CN ISSN 0319-0188) 2962
Sphinx (Winnisquam). (US) 3671
Sphinx Women's International Literary Art Review. (FR ISSN 0755-964X) 345, 2962
Spicae. (FR) 2842
†Spice (Fort Lauderdale). (US) 5281
Spice (New York). (US) 2024, 1266
Spice India. (II) 122
†Spices Newsletter. (II ISSN 0377-547X) 5281
Spicy Isle. (CE) 4787
Spiderweb. (US) 2962
Der Spiegel. (GW ISSN 0038-7452) 2191
Spiegel der Forschung. (GW ISSN 0176-3008) 4345
Spiegel der Lateinamerikanischen Presse/Boletin de Prensa Latinoamericana. (GW ISSN 0342-0388) 3972, 885, 935
Spiegel der Letteren. (BE ISSN 0038-7479) 2963
Spiegel der Zeilvaart. (NE) 4529
Spiegel Historiael. (NE ISSN 0038-7487) 2323, 286
Spiegel Lectures in European Jewish History. (IS) 2389, 2024
Spiel. (GW ISSN 0722-7833) 2963
Spiel-Ebene. (GW) 1419, 1665
Spiel-Sport-Freizeit-Mode. (AU) 4489
Spiel & Buehne. (GW) 4638
Spiel und Theater. (GW ISSN 0038-7509) 4638
Spielcasino. (GW) 4489
Spielfilmliste. (GW ISSN 0071-4933) 3518
Der Spielplan. (GW ISSN 0038-7517) 4638
Das Spielzeug. (GW ISSN 0038-7525) 2282
Spielzeug-Markt. (GW) 2282, 1054
Spielzeug Markt-Scale see Spielzeug-Markt 2282
Spike. (UK) 1325
Spildevandsteknisk Tidsskrift. (DK ISSN 0108-0466) 4828
Spill Reporting Procedures Guide. (US) 1987, 2681
Spill Technology Newsletter. (CN ISSN 0381-4459) 4345, 1497
Spin. (US ISSN 0886-3032) 3582, 4462
Spin Magazine see Table Tennis Topics 4513
Spin-Off. (US ISSN 0198-8239) 357
Spina Bifida Therapy. (US ISSN 0160-9475) 3154
Spinal Connection. (US) 3311, 3326
Spinal Cord Injury Life. (US) 2290
Spindrift (Philadelphia). (US) 3533, 4740
Spine (Philadelphia, 1976). (US ISSN 0362-2436) 3311
Spine (Philadelphia, 1986). (US ISSN 0887-9869) 3311
Spinoff. (US ISSN 0148-2203) 4609
Spiral. (NZ ISSN 0110-1145) 4853, 2963, 3006
Spirale. (CN ISSN 0225-9044) 2515
Spirali. (IT) 2885
†Spiridon. (SZ) 5281
Spiridon Laufmagazin. (GW ISSN 0171-6298) 3808
Spirit. (UK) 2024
Spirit. (CN ISSN 0847-3390) 4421
†Spirit (Princeton). (US ISSN 0886-7267) 5282
Spirit (South Orange). (US ISSN 0038-7584) 3006
Spirit & Life. (US ISSN 0038-7592) 4276

Spirit of Aloha. (US) **4803**
†Spirit of Massachusetts Guidebook. (US) **5282**
Spirit of Service. (US) **2296**
Spirit Speaks. (US) **3671**
The Spirit That Moves Us. (US ISSN 0364-4014) **2963**
†Spirit Wings. (US) **5282**
Spirita. (GW ISSN 0933-8985) **4202**
†SpiritQuest. (US) **5282**
Spirits, Wine and Beer Marketing in Iowa *see* Beverage Alcohol Business Scene **378**
Spirits, Wine & Beer Marketing in Minnesota, North & South Dakota. (US ISSN 0747-3206) **385**
Spirits, Wine & Beer Marketing in Missouri. (US ISSN 0747-3192) **385**
Spiritual Book News. (US ISSN 0038-7606) **4137**
†Spiritual Community Guide. (US ISSN 0160-0354) **5282**
Spiritual Counterfeits Project, Inc. Journal *see* S C P Journal **4199**
Spiritual Counterfeits Project, Inc. Newsletter *see* S C P Newsletter **4200**
Spiritual Emergence Network Newsletter. (US) **3596**, **3671**
†Spiritual Fitness in Business. (US ISSN 0745-6352) **5282**
The Spiritual Healer. (UK ISSN 0038-7622) **3596**, **3782**, **4288**
Spiritual Healing Bulletin *see* Journal of Spiritual and Natural Healing **5222**
Spiritual India *see* Kundalini **4187**
Spiritual Life. (US ISSN 0038-7630) **4276**
Spiritual Light. (US) **2296**, **4249**
Spiritual Mothering Journal. (US ISSN 0886-3156) **4202**, **1244**
Spiritual Mothering Newsletter *see* Spiritual Mothering Journal **4202**
Spiritual Studies Center Booknews *see* S C Booknews **4213**
Spiritual Women's Times *see* New Times (Seattle) **3595**
†Spiritualist Gazette. (UK) **5282**
Spiritualita. (IT ISSN 0038-7649) **3782**
Spiritualita Cristiana. (IT) **4202**
†Spirituality Today. (US ISSN 0162-6760) **5282**
Spirituosen-Jahrbuch. (GW ISSN 0081-3729) **385**
Spirituosen- und Weinhandel. (GW ISSN 0038-7657) **385**
Spiritus. (FR ISSN 0038-7665) **4202**
▼Spit. (US) **3006**
Spitball. (US ISSN 8755-741X) **2963**, **4511**
Spixiana. (GW ISSN 0341-8391) **592**
Splash (Anaheim). (US) **4529**
Splice. (US) **1266**
Splinter. (NE) **1266**, **2589**
Spokane Affairs. (US ISSN 0038-7681) **822**
Spokane Journal of Business *see* Journal of Business (Spokane) **787**
Spokane, Washington. Official Gazette. (US ISSN 0038-7711) **4094**
Spokane Woman. (US) **4853**, **3808**
Spoke 'n Word *see* Boston Cyclist **4516**
Spoken English. (UK ISSN 0038-772X) **2842**, **1760**
Spokes *see* New Spokes **2999**
Spokesman. (US ISSN 0049-1888) **4609**, **1665**
Spokesman Journal *see* Spokesman **4609**
Spolecenske Vedy ve Skole. (CS ISSN 0324-7961) **2389**, **3927**
Spoleczenstwo Otwarte. (PL) **4389**
Spolem. (PL ISSN 0038-7746) **1106**
Spoletium. (IT ISSN 0490-4788) **2515**
Spolia Zeylanica/Bulletin of the National Museums of Sri Lanka. (CE ISSN 0081-3745) **4345**
Spone. (YU ISSN 0350-4778) **2389**
Spon's Architects' & Builders' Price Book. (UK ISSN 0306-3046) **632**, **307**
Spon's Civil Engineering and Highway Works Price Book. (UK ISSN 0957-171X) **1874**

Spon's Civil Engineering Price Book *see* Spon's Civil Engineering and Highway Works Price Book **1874**
Spon's Landscape & External Works Pricebook. (UK ISSN 0267-4181) **632**
Spon's Landscape Pricebook *see* Spon's Landscape & External Works Pricebook **632**
Spon's Mechanical & Electrical Services Price Book. (UK ISSN 0305-4543) **632**, **1908**
Spon's Plant and Equipment Price Guide. (UK ISSN 0263-5038) **3023**
Sponsa Regis *see* Sisters Today **4275**
Sponsor Quest *see* Center for Sports Sponsorship's Sponsor Quest **4468**
†Sponsorbulletin. (NE ISSN 0167-319X) **5282**
Sponsored Research in the History of Art. (US ISSN 0742-0242) **345**
Sponsors' Handbook for the 80's - Guide du Commanditaire *see* Presenter's Handbook **4783**
Sponsorship News. (UK ISSN 0263-3809) **4489**, **38**
▼Spontaneous Combustion. (US) **2963**, **3006**
Spoofing. (US) **2058**, **1244**
Spoon River Quarterly. (US ISSN 0738-8993) **3006**
Het Spoor. (BE ISSN 0773-5901) **4715**
Spor Hekimligi Dergisi/Turkish Journal of Sports Medicine. (TU) **3384**
Spordiilm. (ER) **4489**, **3808**
Sport. (BE ISSN 0038-7770) **4489**
Sport. (NO) **4489**
Sport. (US ISSN 0038-7797) **4489**
Sport. (IT) **4489**
Sport. (PL) **4489**
Sport Africain. (ZR) **4489**
The Sport Americana Baseball Address List. (US) **2442**, **4511**
The Sport Americana Baseball Card Price Guide. (US) **2442**, **4511**
▼The Sport Americana Basketball Card Price Guide and Alphabetical Checklist. (US) **2442**, **4511**
The Sport Americana Football Card Price Guide. (US) **2442**, **4511**
▼The Sport Americana Hockey Card Price Guide. (US) **2442**, **4489**
The Sport Americana Price Guide to Baseball Collectibles. (US) **2442**, **4511**
The Sport Americana Team Baseball Card Checklist. (US) **2442**, **4511**
▼The Sport Americana Team Football and Basketball Card Checklist. (US) **2442**, **4511**
Sport & Fitness. (UK ISSN 0266-8963) **3809**, **4489**
†Sport & Leisure. (CN ISSN 0838-4061) **5282**
Sport & Leisure (Cardiff). (UK) **4489**, **2739**
Sport and Leisure (London). (UK ISSN 0144-7181) **4489**, **2739**
Sport and Recreation Information Group Bulletin. (UK ISSN 0267-3304) **4489**, **2785**, **3809**
Sport Artikel Zeitung Verlag *see* S A Z **1052**
Sport-Auto. (FR ISSN 0038-7827) **4489**, **4702**
Sport Auto. (GW) **4702**
Sport Auto Magazine. (LE) **4702**
Sport Aviation. (US ISSN 0038-7835) **63**, **4557**
Sport- Baeder- Freizeitbauten. (GW ISSN 0344-6492) **4489**, **632**
Sport Bowling. (FR ISSN 0398-8341) **4511**
†Sport Capital. (IT) **5282**
Sport Clothing Expenditures in (Year). (US) **4499**, **738**
Sport Club. (IT) **4489**
Sport Compact Car. (US) **4702**
Sport Construction Buyer's Guide. (US) **4489**, **1054**
Sport de l'Esprit *see* Bouquet **5152**
Sport del Mezzogiorno. (IT) **4489**
Sport dla Kazdego. (PL) **4489**
Sport e Citta. (IT) **4489**
Sport & Medicina. (IT ISSN 0392-9647) **3373**, **3809**, **4489**

†Sport en Roumanie/Sport in Romania.(RM ISSN 0007-5191) **5282**
Sport Equestri. (IT) **4538**
Sport et Plein Air. (FR) **4557**
Sport et Vie. (FR) **4489**
Sport Fishery and Wildlife Research *see* Fisheries and Wildlife Research **2040**
Sport Fishing. (US) **4557**
Sport Fishing Institute Bulletin *see* S F I Bulletin **4554**
Sport-Gericht *see* R S G Richting - Sport-Gericht **4484**
Sport Giovane. (IT) **4489**
Sport Handbuch Wuerttemberg. (GW) **4489**
Sport-Handicap. *see* Behindertensport **3370**
Sport Health. (AT ISSN 1032-5662) **3373**
Sport in Niedersachsen. (GW) **4490**
Sport in Romania. *see* Sport en Roumanie **5282**
Sport Inform. (GW ISSN 0178-1014) **4490**
Sport Intermedium *see* Nationaal Sport Magazine **4480**
Sport International. (BE) **4490**
Sport International Yearbook *see* Sport International **4490**
Sport Italia. (IT ISSN 0038-7916) **4490**
Sport Media Buyer's Guide. (US) **4490**, **38**
Sport Motorrad Katalog. (GW) **4521**
Sport - Overseas Military Edition. (GW) **4490**, **3472**
Sport Parachutist. (UK ISSN 0584-9217) **4557**
Sport Pilot. (US) **63**, **4490**
Sport Pilot Hot Kits Homebuilts. (US) **2442**, **63**
Sport Place International. (US ISSN 0888-9589) **4490**
Sport Plus. (CN) **4490**
Sport Populaire Suisse. *see* Schweizer Volksport **4487**
The Sport Psychologist. (US ISSN 0888-4781) **4047**, **4490**
Sport Scene. (US ISSN 0270-1812) **4490**, **1244**, **1665**, **3809**
Sport Science Forum/Forum Sciences des Sports. (CN) **4490**
▼Sport Science Review. (US ISSN 1056-6724) **3373**
Sport Scolaire. (FR ISSN 0221-0142) **4490**, **1325**
Sport Shop News. (US) **4490**
Sport-Spiel-Freizeit *see* Spiel-Sport-Freizeit-Mode **4489**
Sport Sud. (IT) **4490**
Sport - Talk. (CN) **4490**
Sport Truck. (US ISSN 1044-7903) **4748**, **4490**
Sport- und Baederbauten *see* Sport-Baeder- Freizeitbauten **4489**
Sport und Freizeit *see* World of Sport **4497**
Sport und Mode. (GW ISSN 0049-1926) **4490**, **1054**
Sport und Technik. (GW ISSN 0038-7932) **4490**
Sport Universitario. (IT ISSN 0490-5113) **4490**
Sport ve Rechev. (IS) **4490**, **4702**
Sport Vela. (IT) **4529**
Sport-Vorschau/Sports Preview. (GW ISSN 0342-1724) **4490**
Sport Wales *see* Sport & Leisure (Cardiff) **4489**
†Sport World. (US ISSN 0038-7940) **5282**
Sportaccom. (NE ISSN 0922-4270) **4490**, **4787**
Sportaccommodatie in Nederland/Sports: Public Accommodation. (NE ISSN 0077-6777) **4490**
Sportamo. (MF) **4490**
Sportartikel Wirtschaft. (GW ISSN 0720-1516) **4490**, **1054**
Sportas. (LI) **4490**
Sportaube. (GW ISSN 0490-5687) **3714**
Sportbikes. (US) **4521**
Sportbil. (US) **4490**
SportCare & Fitness. (US ISSN 0899-3815) **3373**, **4490**

SPORTING TRADE 6687

Sportdiving in Australia and the South Pacific. (AT) **4557**
Sportdykaren. (SW ISSN 0038-7967) **4490**
Sportfahrer. (GW) **4702**
Sportfiskaren. (SW) **4557**, **2049**
Sportfiskaren (Year). (SW) **4557**, **2049**
Sporthandbuch Niedersachsen. (GW ISSN 0174-1152) **4490**, **1301**
Sporthandbuch Nordrhein-Westfalen. (GW ISSN 0174-1144) **4490**
Sporti Popullor. (AA) **4490**
Sportimes. (PK ISSN 0038-7991) **4490**
†Sportimpianti. (IT) **5282**
Sporting Classics. (US ISSN 0279-0998) **259**
Sporting Cyclist *see* International Cycle Sport **4518**
Sporting Globe. (AT) **4490**
Sporting Goods Agents Association. Newsletter. (US) **4490**, **1085**
Sporting Goods and Toy Industries *see* Canada. Statistics Canada. Other Manufacturing Industries **709**
Sporting Goods Business. (US ISSN 0146-0889) **4490**, **1054**
Sporting Goods Dealer. (US ISSN 0038-8017) **4490**
Sporting Goods Manufacturers Association. Executive Compensation Study. (US) **994**, **4490**
Sporting Goods Manufacturers Association. Financial Performance Study. (US) **994**, **4490**
Sporting Goods Manufacturers Association Comprehensive Quarterly Sales Trends Report *see* S G M A Comprehensive Quarterly Sales Trends Report **1052**
Sporting Goods Manufacturers Association Today - Action Update *see* S G M A Today - Action Update **4486**
Sporting Goods Market. (US ISSN 0193-8401) **4499**, **738**
Sporting Goods Wholesaler. (US) **4490**, **1054**
Sporting Gun. (UK) **4557**
Sporting News. (US ISSN 0038-805X) **4491**
Sporting News Baseball Yearbook. (US ISSN 0275-0732) **4511**
Sporting News College Basketball. (US) **4511**
Sporting News College Football Yearbook. (US ISSN 0733-2823) **4511**
▼Sporting News Fantasy Baseball Yearbook. (US) **4511**
Sporting News Hockey Directory. (US) **4491**
Sporting News Hockey Guide *see* Hockey Guide **4474**
Sporting News National Basketball Association Register *see* Sporting News Official N B A Register **4512**
Sporting News' National Football Guide *see* Sporting News Pro Football Guide **4512**
Sporting News Official Baseball Record Book *see* Complete Baseball Record Book **4502**
Sporting News Official N B A Register. (US ISSN 0739-3067) **4512**
Sporting News Pro Basketball Yearbook.(US ISSN 0895-0601) **4512**
Sporting News Pro College Basketball Yearbook *see* Sporting News Pro Basketball Yearbook **4512**
Sporting News Pro Football Guide. (US ISSN 0732-1902) **4512**
Sporting News Pro Football Yearbook. (US ISSN 0276-2307) **4512**
Sporting News Sports. (US) **4491**
Sporting News Super Bowl Book. (US ISSN 0275-4487) **4512**
Sporting Press. (IE ISSN 0049-1942) **4491**
Sporting Record. (GH) **4491**
Sporting Records. (NR) **4491**
Sporting Scene. (CN) **4491**
†Sporting Times. (CN) **5282**
Sporting Times (Calgary). (CN ISSN 1181-8808) **4491**
Sporting Trade Canada *see* Sports Business **4491**

Sportivnaya Zhizn' Rossii. (RU ISSN 0038-8092) **4491**
Sportivnye Igry. (RU ISSN 0038-8106) **4491**
Der Sportjournalist. (GW ISSN 0014-6145) **4491**
†Sportkegler. (GW ISSN 0138-144X) **5282**
Sportmanagement. (GW) **1028**, **4491**
Sportmedizinische Schriftenreihe. (GW ISSN 0075-8655) **3373**
†Sportovni a Moderni Gymnastika. (CS) **5282**
Sportowiec. (PL ISSN 0038-8122) **4491**
Sportpaedagogik. (GW) **1760**, **4491**
Sportparachutist. (NE ISSN 0921-8017) **4557**, **63**
Sportparade. (NE ISSN 0038-8130) **1741**, **3809**
Sportpraxis. (GW ISSN 0173-2528) **4491**, **1760**
†Sportrad. (GW) **5282**
†SporTreks. (US) **5282**
Sports. (SI) **4491**
Sports Address Bible. (US) **4491**
▼Sports Advantage. (US) **4491**, **1054**
Sports Afield. (US ISSN 0038-8149) **4491**
†Sports Afield Bass & Panfish. (US) **5282**
†Sports Afield Deer. (US ISSN 0160-1830) **5282**
†Sports Afield Fishing. (US) **5282**
†Sports Afield Fishing Secrets. (US ISSN 0742-0595) **5282**
†Sports Afield Hunting. (US ISSN 0276-8895) **5282**
†Sports Afield Know Your Fish. (US) **5282**
†Sports Afield Special Publications. (US) **5282**
Sports and Culture. see The Thao Van Hoa **4494**
Sports and Leisure Equipment News see Sports & Leisure News **4491**
Sports & Leisure News. (UK ISSN 0961-5822) **4491**, **1054**, **2739**
Sports & Leisure Retailer. (AT ISSN 1035-915X) **4491**, **2282**, **2442**
▼Sports & Lifestyle Marketing. (US) **1054**, **4491**
Sports and Recreation see Outdoor Sports and Recreation **4553**
Sports and Recreational Injuries. (US) **2681**, **3373**
Sports and Recreational Programs of the Nation's Universities and Colleges. (US) **4491**
Sports and the Courts. (US) **4491**, **2681**
Sports Aviation. (US) **4491**, **63**
Sports Business. (CN ISSN 0829-3716) **4491**
Sports Business. (US) **4491**, **692**
Sports Car Illustrated see Sports Car International **4702**
Sports Car International. (US ISSN 1042-9662) **4702**
▼Sports Card Trader. (US) **4512**
Sports Coach. (AT ISSN 0314-5468) **4491**
Sports Collectors Digest. (US ISSN 0278-2693) **2442**, **4512**
Sports Collectors Digest - Baseball Card Price Guide. (US) **4512**, **259**
Sports dans la Cite. (FR) **4491**
Sports Documentation Centre. List of Periodical and Abstracting and Indexing Journal Holdings see Sports Documentation Centre. Serial Holdings **1680**
Sports Documentation Centre. Serial Holdings. (UK) **1680**, **23**, **4499**
Sports Documentation Monthly Bulletin. (UK ISSN 0142-1794) **1680**, **23**, **4499**
Sports Dong-A. (KO) **4491**
Sports Eye. (US) **4491**
Sports Fishing. (US) **4557**
Sports Fitness see Men's Fitness **3806**
▼Sports Focus. (JM) **4491**
Sports Graphic Number. see Nanba **4480**
†Sports History. (US) **5282**
Sports Illustrated. (US ISSN 0038-822X) **4491**
▼Sports Illustrated Classic. (US) **4491**

Sports Illustrated for Kids. (US) **4491**, **1266**
Sports Inc. (US) **4491**
Sports Industry. (UK ISSN 0261-5665) **4492**
Sports Industry News. (US) **4492**, **692**
Sports Information Monthly Bulletin see Sports Documentation Monthly Bulletin **1680**
Sports Journal. (CN) **4492**
Sports Lovers. see Tiyu Aihaozhe **4495**
Sports Magazine. (JA) **4492**
Sports Market Place. (US) **4492**, **1054**
†Sports Marketing News. (US) **5282**
Sports Marketing Profiles. (US) **1054**, **4492**
Sports Media News. (US) **4492**, **692**
Sports Medicine. (US ISSN 0112-1642) **3373**
Sports Medicine Bulletin. (US ISSN 0746-9306) **3373**, **3809**
Sports Medicine Digest. (US ISSN 0731-9770) **3373**, **4492**
Sports Medicine: Health Care for Young Athletes. (US) **3326**, **3373**
Sports Medicine News see Orthopedic and Sports Medicine News **3372**
†Sports Medicine Research Today. (US ISSN 0897-9340) **5282**
Sports Medicine Standards & Malpractice Reporter. (US ISSN 1041-696X) **2681**, **3373**
Sports Medicine, Training and Rehabilitation. (US ISSN 1057-8315) **3373**
Sports Mediscope. (US) **3373**
Sports Merchandiser see Sports Trend **4492**
Sports 'n Spokes. (US ISSN 0161-6706) **4492**
Sports - Nutrition News. (US ISSN 0741-3696) **3612**, **3373**, **4492**
Sport's Official Baseball Yearbook see Street & Smith's Baseball **4512**
Sport's Official College Football Yearbook see Street & Smith's College Football **4512**
Sport's Official Pro Basketball Yearbook see Street & Smith's Pro Basketball **4512**
Sport's Official Pro Football Yearbook see Street & Smith's Pro Football **4512**
Sports Page. (CN) **4492**
Sports, Parks and Recreation Law Reporter. (US ISSN 0893-8210) **2681**, **4492**
Sports Participation in (Year): Lifecycle Demographics. (US) **4499**, **738**
Sports Participation in (Year): Series 1. (US ISSN 0882-8210) **4499**
Sports Participation in (Year): Series 2. (US) **4499**, **738**
Sports Participation in (Year): State by State. (US) **4499**, **738**
Sports Periodicals Index. (US ISSN 0883-1580) **4499**, **23**
Sports Pictorial. see Tiyu Huabao **4495**
Sports Preview. see Sport-Vorschau **4490**
Sports: Public Accommodation. see Sportaccommodatie in Nederland **4490**
▼Sports Pulse. (US) **4492**
†Sports Quarterly - Football Pros. (US) **5282**
Sports Reporter. (US) **4512**
Sports Retailing. (UK) **4492**
Sports Review Series. (US) **4492**
Sports Review Wrestling. (US) **4492**
Sports Science. see Tiyu Kexue **4495**
Sports Science and Medicine Quarterly see Excel **3371**
Sports South. (US) **4492**
Sports Sponsor. (US) **4492**, **692**
Sports Sponsorship Manual Series. (US) **4492**, **692**
Sports Trade Canada see Sports Business **4491**
Sports Trader see Sports Retailing **4492**
Sports Trainers Digest. (AT) **4492**
Sports Training, Medicine and Rehabilitation see Sports Medicine, Training and Rehabilitation **3373**
Sports Travel. (US) **5282**

Sports Trend. (US ISSN 0890-8745) **4492**, **1054**
Sports Turf Bulletin. (UK ISSN 0490-5474) **193**, **1969**
Sports Turf Research Institute. Journal. (UK ISSN 0561-6832) **193**, **1969**
▼Sports View College Basketball Preview. (US) **4512**
Sports View College Football Preview. (US) **4512**
†Sports Week. (II) **5282**
Sports Weekly Newsletter. Football Analyst. (US) **4512**
Sports Weekly Newsletter - Baseball. (US) **4512**
Sports Weekly Newsletter - Basketball. (US) **4512**
†Sportscape. (US) **5282**
Sportscars of the World. (US) **4702**
Sportsdykkeren. (DK) **4492**
SportSearch. (CN ISSN 0882-553X) **4499**, **23**, **1680**
Sportsfiskeren. (DK ISSN 0038-8211) **2049**
Sportsguide see Sports Market Place **4492**
Sportshandleren see Sport **4489**
Sportshop. (GW ISSN 0931-5381) **4492**, **1287**, **1294**
Sportsman. (AT) **4538**
Sportsman Pilot. (US ISSN 0279-1749) **63**
SportsScoop see U S A B A Agenda **4495**
Sportstaetten und Schwimmbaeder. (GW ISSN 0937-9053) **632**, **4492**
Sportstaettenbau und Baederanlagen - Sports Facilities and Swimming Pools see S B **631**
Sportstar. (II) **4492**
Sportsturf. (US) **4512**, **193**
SportStyle. (US ISSN 0162-2242) **4492**, **1287**
▼SportsVision Quarterly. (US) **3305**, **3373**
Sportswatch. (XK ISSN 1010-5743) **4492**
Sportswear International. (US) **1287**
Sportswear Jeans International see Sportswear International **1287**
Sportsworld. (II) **4492**
Sporttaucher. (GW) **4492**
†Sportti. (FI ISSN 0785-6695) **5282**
Sportul Ilustrat. (RM) **4492**
Sportunterricht. (GW ISSN 0342-2402) **1760**
Sportverletzung - Sportschaden. (GW ISSN 0932-0555) **3155**, **4492**
Sportwetenschappelijke Onderzoekingen.(NE) **4492**
Sportwissenschaft. (GW ISSN 0342-2380) **4492**, **1426**
Sportwissenschaft und Sportpraxis. (GW ISSN 0342-457X) **4492**
†Sportwissenschaftliche Dissertationen. (GW ISSN 0340-0956) **5282**
Sportyvna Gazeta. (KR ISSN 0038-8300) **4492**
Sporvejsmuseet Skjoldenaesholm. Aarsberetning. (DK ISSN 0106-6927) **4715**, **3533**
Sposa. (IT ISSN 0038-8319) **3067**, **1294**
Sposa 2000. (CN) **3067**, **3400**
Sposabella. (IT ISSN 0394-3682) **3067**, **1294**
S'postavitelno Ezikoznanie/Contrastive Linguistics. (BU ISSN 0204-8701) **2843**
Spot. (CI) **3797**
Spot. (US) **3797**, **1665**
Spot Radio Rates and Data see Standard Rate and Data Service. Spot Radio Rates and Data **41**
Spot Television Rates and Data see Standard Rate and Data Service. Spot Television Rates and Data **41**
Spotkania (Krakow). (PL) **3582**
▼Spotkania (Warsaw). (PL) **2214**
Spotlight. (BF) **1665**
Spotlight. (GR) **3927**
Spotlight. (NZ) **4137**, **2282**
Spotlight (Bath). (UK ISSN 0049-2000) **3472**, **4740**
Spotlight (Bethlehem). (US ISSN 0162-1068) **3631**
Spotlight (Denver) see Tater News **194**

†Spotlight (Edinburgh). (UK) **5282**
Spotlight (Emporia). (US) **1325**
Spotlight (Mamaroneck). (US ISSN 0745-4937) **2235**
Spotlight (Oak Brook). (US) **800**
Spotlight (Robbinsville). (US ISSN 0887-3453) **4702**, **4787**
Spotlight (Washington). (US) **3927**
Spotlight Bhilai. (II) **3420**
Spotlight on A I D S. (US ISSN 0895-755X) **3224**
Spotlight on Affirmative Employment Programs see Federal Staffing Digest **4060**
Spotlight on Africa. (US ISSN 0584-9365) **3927**
Spotlight on Open Learning. (UK) **1070**
Spotlight on Your Library. (US) **2786**
Spotlight on Youth Sports. (US ISSN 0740-0802) **4492**, **1244**
Spotlight on Zimbabwe. (RH) **2240**
Spotlighting Nebraska see Interchange Customer Newsletter **2227**
Spotlight's Wine Country Guide. (US) **385**
Spotted News. (US ISSN 0038-8432) **226**
Spotter. (US) **3714**
Spraaknytt. (NO ISSN 0333-3825) **2843**
Spraakvaard. (SW ISSN 0038-8440) **2843**
Sprachdienst. (GW ISSN 0038-8459) **2843**
Die Sprache. (GW ISSN 0038-8467) **2843**
Sprache & Kognition. (SZ ISSN 0253-4533) **4047**
Sprache im Technischen Zeitalter. (GW ISSN 0038-8475) **2963**
Sprache - Stimme - Gehoer. (GW ISSN 0342-0477) **3317**, **1741**
Sprache und Datenverarbeitung. (GW ISSN 0343-5202) **1453**
Sprache und Dichtung. Neue Folge. (SZ ISSN 0081-3826) **2843**
Sprache und Geschichte in Afrika. (GW ISSN 0170-5946) **2843**
Sprache und Gesellschaft. (GW ISSN 0138-5852) **2843**
Sprache und Literatur in Wissenschaft. (GW ISSN 0047-472X) **2843**
Sprache und Literatur in Wissenschaft und Unterricht. (GW) **2843**, **2963**
Sprachkunst. (AU ISSN 0038-8483) **2963**
Der Sprachmittler. (GW ISSN 0038-8505) **2843**
Sprachpflege see Sprachpflege and Sprachkultur **5282**
†Sprachpflege and Sprachkultur. (GW) **5282**
Sprachpraxis. (GW ISSN 0323-3715) **1687**, **2843**, **2963**
Sprachreport. (GW ISSN 0178-644X) **2843**
Sprachspiegel. (SZ ISSN 0038-8513) **2843**
Sprachwissenschaft. (GW) **2843**
Sprachwissenschaft - Computerlinguistik. (GW ISSN 0724-3103) **2857**
Sprawozdania Archeologiczne. (PL ISSN 0081-3834) **286**
Sprawozdania Towarzystwa Naukowego w Toruniu see Towarzystwo Naukowe w Toruniu. Sprawozdania **4348**
Sprawy Miedzynarodowe. (PL ISSN 0038-853X) **3972**
Spray Technology & Marketing. (US ISSN 1055-2340) **3652**
Spray's Water Ski Magazine see Water Ski **4559**
Spread Trader. (US) **964**
Spreadsheet. (US) **1465**, **1474**, **1481**
Sprechende Steine. (AU) **286**
Sprechsaal. (GW ISSN 0341-0676) **357**
Sprechsaal fuer Keramik, Glas, Baustoffe see Sprechsaal **357**
Spremost Croatian Weekly. (AT) **2024**
Sprenger Institute. Annual Report. see Sprenger Instituut. Jaarverslag **5282**
†Sprenger Instituut. Communications. (NE) **5282**

†Sprenger Instituut. Jaarverslag/ Sprenger Institute. Annual Report. (NE ISSN 0081-3850) **5282**
†Sprenger Instituut. Rapporten. (NE) **5282**
Spring (Dallas). (US ISSN 0362-0522) **4047**
Spring Arbor College Journal. (US) **1325**
Spring Arbor College Update *see* Spring Arbor College Journal **1325**
Spring Breeze. *see* Chun Feng **2905**
Spring Breezes. *see* Sanyuefeng **2284**
▼Spring Hill Cityscope. (AT) **4160**
Spring Rain. (US) **3006**
Spring Training. (US) **4512**
Spring Wind *see* Buddhism at the Crossroads **4214**
Springbok. (SA) **3472**
Springer Advanced Texts in Chemistry. (US ISSN 0172-6323) **1188**
Springer Advanced Texts in Life Sciences. (US ISSN 0172-6226) **457**
Springer Books on Professional Computing. (US) **1400**, 412
Springer Proceedings in Physics. (US) **3832**
Springer Seminars in Immunopathology.(GW ISSN 0344-4325) **3188**
Springer Series in Biophysics. (US ISSN 0932-2353) **486**
Springer Series in Chemical Physics. (US ISSN 0172-6218) **3832**, 1230
Springer Series in Cognitive Development. (US) **4047**
Springer Series in Computational Mathematics. (US) **3056**
Springer Series in Computational Physics. (US ISSN 0172-5726) **3840**
Springer Series in Electrophysics. (US ISSN 0172-5734) **3840**
Springer Series in Experimental Entomology. (US ISSN 0172-6188) **538**
Springer Series in Information Sciences.(US ISSN 0720-678X) **2786**
Springer Series in Language and Communication. (US ISSN 0172-620X) **2843**
Springer Series in Materials Sciences. (US) **3832**
Springer Series in Microbiology. (US ISSN 0172-6331) **557**
Springer Series in Molecular Biology. (US) **457**
Springer Series in Optical Sciences. (US ISSN 0342-4111) **3858**
Springer Series in Social Psychology. (US) **4017**
Springer Series in Solid State Sciences. (US ISSN 0171-1873) **3832**
Springer Series in Soviet Mathematics. (US) **3056**
Springer Series in Statistics. (US ISSN 0172-7397) **4586**
Springer Series in Surface Sciences. (US) **3832**
Springer Series in Synergetics. (US ISSN 0172-7389) **4345**
Springer Series in Wood Science. (US) **2108**
Springer Series on Environmental Management. (US ISSN 0172-6161) **1969**
Springer Series on Social Work. (US) **4421**
Springer Texts in Electrical Engineering. (US) **1908**
Springer Tracts in Modern Physics. (US ISSN 0081-3869) **3832**
Springer Tracts in Natural Philosophy. (US ISSN 0081-3877) **3832**
Springers on the Line *see* Spaniels in the Field **3714**
†Springfield. Massachusetts. City Library Bulletin. (US ISSN 0038-8599) **5282**
Springfield Business Journal. (US) **692**
Springfield! Magazine. (US ISSN 0195-0894) **2235**
Springfield Magazine. (US) **2235**
Springfield Public Schools. News and Views. (US ISSN 0038-8602) **1665**

Springhillian. (US) **1325**
Springs. (US ISSN 0584-9667) **1939**
Springs & Brakpan Advertiser. (SA ISSN 0038-8629) **2217**
Springs - Chains - Formed Parts *see* Federn - Ketten - Biegeteile **3406**
Sprinkler Age. (US ISSN 0896-2685) **2035**
Sprinkler Bulletin. (UK ISSN 0038-8637) **2543**
Sprint *see* Scholastic Sprint **1264**
Sprint Car. (US) **4492**
Sprocket. (AT) **3518**
Sprog og Erhverv. (DK) **2843**
Sprog og Samfund. (DK ISSN 0108-433X) **2843**
Sprogforeningens Almanak. (DK) **2843**
Sprout/Me. (JA ISSN 0388-4953) **1665**, 1760
Sproutletter. (US ISSN 0744-9860) **3612**, 2082
SPSE's Annual Conference. Paper Summaries *see* S P S E. Annual Conference. Paper Summaries (Year) **3796**
Spudletter. (US) **194**
Spudman. (US ISSN 0038-8661) **194**, 164
Spur. (UK ISSN 0306-5367) **935**
Spur. (US ISSN 0098-5422) **4538**
Spur of Virginia *see* Spur **4538**
Spuren Suchen. (GW ISSN 0933-8799) **2389**
Spuren und Motive. (GW ISSN 0936-7578) **1523**, 2681, 3472
Spurk. (LE ISSN 0038-8696) **2515**
Der Spurkranz. (AU ISSN 0038-870X) **4715**
Sputnik. (RU ISSN 0131-8748) **2215**
Sputnik Junior. (II ISSN 0038-8726) **1266**, 2024
Spy. (US ISSN 0890-1759) **2235**
Square Dance *see* American SquareDance **1528**
Square Foot Woburn) *see* S F (Woburn) **4158**
Square One. (US ISSN 0884-1934) **2963**
Square Peg. (UK) **2457**
Squash etc. (GW) **4492**
Squash Life. (CN) **4512**
Squash News. (UK) **4512**
Squash News. (US ISSN 0164-7148) **4512**
Squash Player International. (UK ISSN 0262-4338) **4512**
Squash Rackets Association. Annual. (UK) **4512**
Squash Rackets Association. Handbook *see* Squash Rackets Association. Annual **4512**
Squash World. (UK ISSN 0952-8512) **4512**
†Squatchberry Journal. (CN ISSN 0383-283X) **5282**
Squilla. (IT ISSN 0038-8750) **4202**
Squilla di S. Gerardo. (IT ISSN 0038-8769) **4202**
Squills International Pigeon Racing Year Book. (UK ISSN 0952-4541) **4492**
The Squire. (US) **2235**
Squires *see* Squires Newsletter **1301**
Squires Newsletter. (US) **1301**, 1266
Srecanja. (XV ISSN 0038-8777) **2885**
Srednee Spetsial'noe Obrazovanie. (RU ISSN 0038-8785) **1665**
Sri. (CE) **4853**
Sri Aurobindo. Archives and Research. (II) **4217**, 3782
Sri Aurobindo International Center of Education. Bulletin. (II) **1665**
Sri Lanka. (CE ISSN 0490-6381) **2218**
Sri Lanka. Census of Population and Housing. (CE) **2500**
Sri Lanka. Irrigation Department. Hydrology Division. Hydrological Annual. (CE) **1600**
†Sri Lanka. Ministry of Plan Implementation. Performance. (CE) **5282**
Sri Lanka. Ministry of Planning and Economic Affairs. Division of External Resources. Economic Indicators. (CE) **885**
Sri Lanka Accommodation Guide. (CE) **4787**

Sri Lanka Architect. (CE) **307**
Sri Lanka Association for the Advancement of Science. Proceedings. (CE) **4345**
Sri Lanka Economic Journal. (CE) **885**
Sri Lanka Export Directory. (CE ISSN 0069-2360) **921**
Sri Lanka Film Annual. (CE) **3518**
Sri Lanka Forester. (CE) **2108**
Sri Lanka Foundation Institute. News. (CE) **1687**
Sri Lanka Government Gazette. (CE) **4074**
Sri Lanka in Brief. (CE) **822**
Sri Lanka Institute of Architects. Journal *see* Sri Lanka Architect **307**
Sri Lanka Journal of Historical and Social Studies. (CE ISSN 0009-0832) **2323**, 4389
Sri Lanka Journal of Tea Science. (CE ISSN 1010-4208) **2082**
Sri Lanka Journal of the Humanities. (CE) **2515**
Sri Lanka Labour Gazette. (CE) **994**
Sri Lanka Library Review. (CE) **2786**
Sri Lanka Meteorological Society. Journal. (CE) **3441**
Sri Lanka National Bibliography. (CE) **4142**
The Sri Lanka News. (CE) **2218**
Sri Lanka Official Tourist Handbook. (CE) **4787**
Sri Lanka Periodicals Index. (CE) **23**
Sri Lanka Pharmaceutical Association. Quarterly Newsletter. (CE) **3743**
Sri Lanka Science Index. (CE) **4358**, 23
Sri Lanka Today. (CE) **4787**
Sri Lanka Tourist Information *see* Sri Lanka Official Tourist Handbook **4787**
Sri Lanka Veterinary Journal. (CE) **4816**
Sri Lanka Yearbook. (CE) **738**
Sri Venkateswara University. Department of Sanskrit. Symposium. (II ISSN 0081-3915) **2843**
Sri Venkateswara University. Oriental Journal. (II ISSN 0081-3907) **2342**, 2843
Sridim. (IS) **4226**
Srinagar Law Journal. (II) **2681**
Srpska Akademija Nauka i Umetnosti. Etnografski Institut. Glasnik. (YU) **249**
Srpska Akademija Nauka i Umetnosti. Etnografski Institut. Zbornik Radova. (YU) **249**
Srpska Akademija Nauka i Umetnosti. Odeljenje Drustvenih Nauka. Glas. (YU ISSN 0081-394X) **4389**
Srpska Akademija Nauka i Umetnosti. Odeljenje Drustvenih Nauka. Posebna Izdanja. (YU ISSN 0081-3982) **4389**
Srpska Akademija Nauka i Umetnosti. Odeljenje Drustvenih Nauka. Spomenik. (YU ISSN 0081-4059) **4389**, 286, 307
Srpska Akademija Nauka i Umetnosti. Odeljenje Jezika i Knjizevnosti. Glas. (YU ISSN 0081-3958) **2843**
Srpska Akademija Nauka i Umetnosti. Odeljenje Jezika i Knjizevnosti. Posebna Izdanja. (YU ISSN 0081-3990) **2963**, 2843
Srpska Akademija Nauka i Umetnosti. Odeljenje Likovne i Muzicke Umetnosti. Muzicka Izdanja. (YU ISSN 0490-6659) **3582**
Srpska Akademija Nauka i Umetnosti. Odeljenje Likovne i Muzicke Umetnosti. Posebna Izdanja. (YU ISSN 0081-4008) **345**, 3582
Srpska Akademija Nauka i Umetnosti. Odeljenje Medicinskih Nauka. Glas. (YU ISSN 0081-3966) **3155**
Srpska Akademija Nauka i Umetnosti. Odeljenje Medicinskih Nauka. Posebna Izdanja. (YU ISSN 0081-4016) **3155**
Srpska Akademija Nauka i Umetnosti. Odeljenje Prirodno-Matematickih Nauka. Posebna Izdanja. (YU ISSN 0081-4024) **4345**
Srpska Akademija Nauka i Umetnosti. Odeljenje Tehnickih Nauka. Glas. (YU ISSN 0081-3974) **4609**

Srpska Akademija Nauka i Umetnosti. Odeljenje Tehnickih Nauka. Posebna Izdanja. (YU ISSN 0081-4040) **4609**
Srpska Akademija Nauka i Umetnosti. Povremena Izdanja. (YU) **4345**
Srpska Akademija Nauka i Umetnosti. Spomenica. (YU ISSN 0081-4032) **2515**, 4345, 4389
Srpska Borba. *see* Serbian Struggle **2023**
Srpski Arhiv za Celokupno Lekarstvo/ Serbian Archives of Entire Medicine. (YU ISSN 0049-0210) **3155**
Srpski Dijalektoloski Zbornik. (YU ISSN 0350-1906) **2843**
Srpski Etnografski Zbornik. Naselja i Poreklo Stanovnistva. (YU ISSN 0081-4067) **249**, 2389
Srpski Etnografski Zbornik. Rasprave i Gradja. (YU ISSN 0081-4075) **249**, 2389
Srpski Etnografski Zbornik. Srpske Narodne Umotvorine. (YU ISSN 0081-4083) **250**, 2389
Srpski Etnografski Zbornik. Zivot i Obicaji Narodni. (YU ISSN 0081-4091) **250**, 2389
Sskk Bulletinen. (SW ISSN 0347-5867) **4492**
Ssu yu Yen/Thought and Words. (CH ISSN 0258-8412) **2515**, 3782, 4389
Staalet. (DK) **3420**
Der Staat. (GW ISSN 0038-884X) **3927**, 2323, 2681
Staat und Politik. (SZ ISSN 0081-4105) **3927**
Staat und Recht. (GW ISSN 0038-8858) **3927**
Staat und Wirtschaft in Hessen. (GW ISSN 0344-5550) **4587**
Staatliche Kunsthalle Karlsruhe. Bildhefte. (GW ISSN 0075-5133) **3533**
Staatliche Kunstsammlungen in Baden-Wuerttemberg. Jahrbuch. (GW ISSN 0067-284X) **3533**
Staatliche Mathematisch-Physikalische Salons, Dresden. Veroeffentlichungen.(GW ISSN 0081-4113) **3056**, 3832
Staatliche Museen zu Berlin. Jahrbuch. Forschungen und Berichte. (GW ISSN 0067-6004) **345**, 3533
Staatliche Zentralstelle fuer Fernunterricht. Amtliches Mitteilungsblatt. (GW) **1687**
Staatliche Denkmalpflege im Saarland. Bericht. (GW) **2389**
Staatliches Museum fuer Tierkunde Dresden. Entomologische Abhandlungen. (GW ISSN 0373-8981) **538**
Staatliches Museum fuer Tierkunde Dresden. Faunistische Abhandlungen.(GW ISSN 0375-2135) **592**
Staatliches Museum fuer Tierkunde Dresden. Malakologische Abhandlungen. (GW ISSN 0070-7260) **592**
Staatliches Museum fuer Tierkunde Dresden. Zoologische Abhandlungen. (GW ISSN 0375-5231) **592**
Staatliches Museum fuer Voelkerkunde Dresden. Abhandlungen und Berichte.(GW ISSN 0070-7295) **3533**, 250
Staats- und Rechtstheoretische Studien.(GW ISSN 0138-5208) **2681**
Staatsamptenaar. *see* Public Servant **4071**
Staatsanzeiger fuer das Land Hessen. (GW ISSN 0724-7885) **2681**
Staatsbedrijf der Posterijen Telegrafie en Telefonie Bedrijf *see* P T T Bedrijf **5255**
Staatsbibliothek Preussischer Kulturbesitz. Ausstellungskataloge. (GW ISSN 0340-0700) **2786**
Staatsbibliothek Preussischer Kulturbesitz. Jahresbericht. (GW ISSN 0340-2274) **2786**
Staatsbibliothek Preussischer Kulturbesitz. Mitteilungen. (GW ISSN 0038-8866) **2786**

STAATSBUERGER

Der Staatsbuerger. (SZ ISSN 0038-8874) 3927
Staatstheater Stuttgart. Monatsvorschau. (GW) 4638
Stabroek News. (GY) 692
Stachelbaer. (GW) 1266, 2191
Stachlige Argumente. (GW) 3927, 1497
Stacja Arctowskiego. Rocznik Meteorologiczny. (PL) 3441
Stacja Hornsund. Rocznik Meteorologiczny. (PL) 3441
Stack. (US) 1474, 1465
Stad Antwerpen. Cultureel Jaarboek. (BE ISSN 0773-9559) 3533, 4638
Stad Gods. (NE ISSN 0038-8904) 4276
Stade. (CF) 4492
Stader Jahrbuch. (GW ISSN 0930-8946) 2389
Stadion. (CS ISSN 0038-8920) 4493
Stadion. (GW ISSN 0172-4029) 4493, 1760
Stadium. (IT) 4493
Stadler Genetics Symposium. Proceedings. (US ISSN 0081-4148) 547
Stadlinger Post. (AU ISSN 0038-8939) 4094
Stads og Havneingenioeren/Municipal Engineer. (DK ISSN 0038-8947) 1837
Stadsbyggnad. (SW ISSN 0038-8963) 1874, 4094
Die Stadt. (GW) 2496
Stadt Bamberg. Mitteilungsblatt. (GW) 4094
Stadt Duisburg. Materialen zur Stadtforschung. (GW) 4094
Stadt Duisburg. Statistisches Jahrbuch. (GW ISSN 0172-4533) 4082
Stadt Duisburg. Verwaltungsbericht. (GW ISSN 0932-8955) 4074
Stadt Freiburg im Breisgau. Amt fuer Statistik und Einwohnerwesen. Jahresheft. (GW) 4082
Stadt Gottes. (GW) 4202
Stadt Linz see Amtsblatt der Landeshauptstadt Linz 4084
Stadt Mannheim. Vierteljahresbericht. (GW) 4082
Stadt Remscheid Statistisches Jahrbuch. (GW ISSN 0930-2034) 4587
Stadt- und Gebaeudetechnik. (GW ISSN 0038-898X) 2303
Stadt und Gemeinde. (GW) 4074
Stadtarchiv Krems. Mitteilungen. (AU) 2389
Stadtbau-Informationen. (GW ISSN 0038-8998) 632, 2496
Stadtbau-Mitteilungen see Stadtbau-Informationen 632
Stadtbauwelt. (GW) 307
Stadtbibliothek Nuernberg. Ausstellungskatalog. (GW ISSN 0078-2777) 3533
Stadtblatt. (GW) 2191
Stadtfuher Kopenhagen. (DK) 4787
Stadthandbuch Nordbaden. (GW) 4493
Stadtverkehr. (GW ISSN 0038-9013) 4656
Stadtzeitung Braunschweig. (GW) 2191
Staeckbrief. (GW) 2191
Staedel Jahrbuch. (GW) 345
Staedte- und Gemeindebund see Stadt und Gemeinde 4074
Staedte- und Kreisstatistik Ruhrgebiet. (GW) 738
Der Staedtetag. (GW ISSN 0038-9048) 4094
Staerke. see Starch 1223
Stafette. (GW ISSN 0174-5832) 1266
Staff. (US) 1028
Staff of Scottish Work Departments. (UK) 4421
Staff Working Papers Series see United Nations Childrens Fund. Programme Division. Staff Working Papers Series 4422
Staffel Aktuell. (GW) 3927
Staffeta Quotidiana Petrolifera. (IT) 3702
Stafford Data. (US ISSN 0899-1596) 2165

Staffordshire Bull Terrier Club of America. Newsletter. (US) 3714
Staffordshire Farmer. (UK) 122
Staffordshire Polytechnic. Department of Economics. Discussion Papers. (UK) 692
Staffordshire Polytechnic. Department of Sociology. Occasional Papers. (UK ISSN 0955-0690) 4453
Staffordshire Studies. (UK ISSN 0950-1630) 2389, 2263
Staffrider. (SA ISSN 0258-7211) 3006
Staffroom Journal. (UK) 1697
Stafo-Nytt. (NO ISSN 0800-658X) 4074
Stage. (ZA) 4638
Stage and Television Today. (UK ISSN 0038-9099) 4638, 1380
Stage Directions. (US) 4638
Stage Managers' Association Directory see Stage Managers Directory 5282
†Stage Managers Directory. (US) 5282
Stagecast-Irish Stage and Screen Directory. (IE) 4638, 3518
†Stagecoach. (US ISSN 1042-2080) 5282
Stages. (US) 4638
Stages. (AT ISSN 1033-3975) 4639
Stahl und Eisen. (GW ISSN 0340-4803) 3420
Stahlbau. (GW ISSN 0038-9145) 1874
Stahlbau - Nachrichten. (GW) 632, 3420
Stahlbau - Rundschau. (AU ISSN 0561-7855) 643
Stahlbau - Rundschau - Mitteilungen. (AU) 632, 3420
Stahlberatung. (GW) 3420
Stahleisen Kalender see Jahrbuch Stahl 3410
Stahlmarkt. (GW) 3420
Stain Technology see Biotechnic and Histochemistry 559
Stained Finger. (US) 2442
Stained Glass. (US ISSN 0895-7002) 357
Stainless Steel. (SA ISSN 0038-917X) 3420
Stainless Steel: An International Directory see Stainless Steel Databook 3420
Stainless Steel: An International Survey and Directory see Stainless Steel Databook 3420
Stainless Steel Buyer's Guide (Year). (SA) 3420
Stainless Steel Databook. (US ISSN 0953-7228) 3420
Stainless Steel Directory. (UK) 3420
Stainless Steel Industry. (UK ISSN 0306-2988) 3420
Stainless Steel Scope. (AT) 3420
Stainless Steels Digest. (US) 3420
Stal' (RU ISSN 0038-920X) 3420
Stall. (US ISSN 0888-7411) 1325
Stallion. (US ISSN 0745-3639) 3400, 2457
Stambog. (DK ISSN 0107-3818) 4538
Stambog og Elitestambog over Tyre af Roed Dansk Malkerace see Stambog over Kvaeg af Roed Dansk Malkerace 5282
†Stambog over Koeer af Roed Dansk Malkerace. (DK ISSN 0108-0903) 5282
†Stambog over Kvaeg af Roed Dansk Malkerace. (DK ISSN 0105-0281) 5282
Stambog over Shetland Ponyer. (DK ISSN 0900-5846) 4538
Stamford Annual Planning Information see Annual Planning Information: Bridgeport - Norwalk - Stamford - Valley Service Delivery Area 843
Stamford Genealogical Society. Bulletin see Connecticut Ancestry 2148
Stamford Journal. (SI) 1325
Stamm Leitfaden Durch Presse und Werbung/Annual Directory through Press and Advertising. (GW ISSN 0075-8728) 412
Stamme-Bladet. (DK) 1741
Stamp and Coin Digest. (US) 3758
Stamp & Coin Mart International. (UK) 3758, 3602
Stamp Auction News. (US) 3758

Stamp Auction Reports. (US) 3758
Stamp Collector. (US ISSN 0277-3899) 3758
†Stamp Dealer. (US ISSN 0273-978X) 5282
Stamp Digest. (II ISSN 0014-5467) 3758
Stamp Duties N.S.W. & A.C.T. (AT ISSN 0727-7970) 1106, 2681
Stamp Exchangers Annual Directory. (US) 3758
Stamp Lover. (UK ISSN 0038-9277) 3758
Stamp Magazine. (UK ISSN 0307-6679) 3758
Stamp Mail. (UK ISSN 0953-5241) 3758
Stamp News. (AT) 3758
Stamp News see Stamp Mail 3758
Stamp News Australasia see Stamp News 3758
Stamp Wholesaler. (US ISSN 0038-9315) 3758
Stampa Italiana see Numero Zero 2587
Stampa Medica. (IT ISSN 0038-9323) 3155
Stampa Specializata Svizzera. see Schweizer Fachpresse 2575
Stampa Sud. (IT ISSN 0049-2051) 2885
Stampi. (IT ISSN 1121-063X) 4609
Stamping Quarterly. (US ISSN 1043-5093) 3420, 1939
Stamps. (US ISSN 0038-9358) 3758
Stamps see Stamps and Foreign Stamps 5282
†Stamps and Foreign Stamps. (UK) 5282
▼Stamps, Coins, Postcards & Related Materials. (US) 3602, 23, 3759
Stamps World. (II ISSN 0255-8254) 3758
Stand Magazine. (UK ISSN 0038-9366) 2963, 2885
Stand To! (UK ISSN 0261-6548) 2389, 3472
Standard. (IE) 2203
The Standard. (KE) 2208
Standard. (GH ISSN 0038-9374) 4276
Standard (Arlington Heights). (US ISSN 0038-9382) 4249
Standard (New York). (US ISSN 0160-6158) 2235
Standard (Quincy). (US ISSN 0038-9390) 2543
Standard & Poor's Bond Guide. (US ISSN 0277-3988) 964
Standard & Poor's Called Bond Record.(US) 964
Standard & Poor's Commercial Paper Ratings Guide. (US) 964
Standard and Poor's Commercial Paper Reports Service see Standard & Poor's Commercial Paper Ratings Guide 964
Standard & Poor's Corporate Registered Bond Interest Record. (US) 964
Standard & Poor's Corporation Records. (US) 964
Standard & Poor's Daily Stock Price Record. American Exchange. (US) 964
Standard & Poor's Daily Stock Price Record. New York Stock Exchange. (US) 964
Standard & Poor's Daily Stock Price Record. Over the Counter Exchange. (US) 964
Standard and Poor's Directory of Bond Agents. (US) 964
Standard & Poor's Dividend Record (Annual). (US) 800
Standard & Poor's Dividend Record (Daily). (US) 964
Standard & Poor's Dividend Record (Quarterly). (US) 964
Standard & Poor's Dividend Record (Weekly). (US) 964
Standard and Poor's I S L Daily Stock Price Index. American Stock Exchange. see Standard & Poor's Daily Stock Price Record. American Exchange 964

Standard and Poor's I S L Daily Stock Price Index. New York Stock Exchange see Standard & Poor's Daily Stock Price Record. New York Stock Exchange 964
Standard and Poor's Industry Surveys. (US) 964
Standard & Poor's Outlook. (US ISSN 0030-7246) 964
Standard and Poor's Over-The-Counter see Standard & Poor's Daily Stock Price Record. Over the Counter Exchange 964
Standard & Poor's Register of Corporations, Directors and Executives. (US) 1028, 1085
Standard & Poor's Review of Securities, Commodities Regulation. (US) 964, 2681
Standard and Poor's Review of Securities Regulation see Standard & Poor's Review of Securities, Commodities Regulation 964
Standard and Poor's Security Owner's Stock Guide see Standard & Poor's Stock Guide 964
Standard & Poor's Statistical Service. (US) 964
Standard & Poor's Stock Guide. (US ISSN 0737-4135) 964
Standard & Poor's Stock Market Encyclopedia. (US) 965
Standard and Poor's Stock Market Encyclopedia of the S and P "500" see Standard & Poor's Stock Market Encyclopedia 965
Standard & Poor's Stock Summary. (US ISSN 0038-9420) 965
Standard & Poor's Trendline Current Market Perspectives see Trendline Current Market Perspectives 966
Standard Bank International Business Report see International Business Report 912
Standard Bearer (Sacramento). (US ISSN 0038-9447) 4288
Standard Catalog for Public Libraries see Public Library Catalog 2795
Standard Corporation Records Current News Edition. (US) 692
Standard Directory of Advertisers. (US ISSN 0081-4229) 1153, 38
Standard Directory of Advertising Agencies. (US ISSN 0085-6614) 1153, 38
Standard Directory of International Advertisers and Agencies. (US) 1154, 38
Standard Federal Tax Reports. (US ISSN 0162-3494) 1106
Standard for Auditing Computer Applications. (US) 828
Standard for Testing Application Software. (US) 1481
Standard Frequency and Time Service Bulletin. (JA ISSN 0387-5857) 1908
Standard Lesson Commentary. (US ISSN 0081-4245) 4202
Standard Periodical Directory. (US ISSN 0085-6630) 412
Standard Rate and Data Service. Business Publication Rates and Data.(US ISSN 0038-948X) 41, 412
Standard Rate and Data Service. Canadian Advertising Rates and Data see Canadian Advertising Rates and Data 40
Standard Rate and Data Service. Community Publication Rates and Data. (US ISSN 0162-8887) 41, 38, 412
Standard Rate and Data Service. Consumer Magazine and Agri-Media Rates and Data. (US) 41, 412
Standard Rate and Data Service. Consumer Magazine and Farm Publication Rates and Data see Standard Rate and Data Service. Consumer Magazine and Agri-Media Rates and Data 41
Standard Rate and Data Service. Direct Mail List Rates and Data. (US ISSN 0419-182X) 41, 412
Standard Rate and Data Service. Newspaper Rates and Data. (US ISSN 0038-9544) 41, 412

Standard Rate and Data Service. Print Media Production Data. (US ISSN 0038-9455) 41, 412
Standard Rate and Data Service. Spot Radio Rates and Data. (US ISSN 0038-9560) 41, 412
Standard Rate and Data Service. Spot Radio Small Markets Edition. (US) 38, 1360
Standard Rate and Data Service. Spot Television Rates and Data. (US ISSN 0038-9552) 41, 412
Standard Rate and Data Service. Weekly Newspaper and Shopping Guide Rates and Data see Standard Rate and Data Service. Community Publication Rates and Data 41
Standard Rate and Data Service, Inc. Bullet see S R D S: Bullet 1052
Standard Rate and Data Service, Inc. Report see S R D S Report 38
Standard Rate and Data Service Media and Market Planner see S R D S Media and Market Planner 38
Standard-Serie see Record-Serie 3576
Standard Specifications for Highway Bridges. (US) 1874
Standard Specifications for Transportation Materials and Methods of Sampling and Testing. (US) 3448, 1922
Standard Trade Index of Japan. (JA ISSN 0585-0444) 1154, 823
Standard Trust Income Tax Guide. (SA) 2681
Standardbred see Standardbred News 4538
Standardbred News. (CN ISSN 0834-0110) 4538
Standardisering. (NO ISSN 0038-9625) 3449
†Standardisierung und Qualitaet. (GW) 5282
Standardization News see A S T M Standardization News 3444
Standardnyt. (DK ISSN 0107-2870) 3449
Standards Action. (US ISSN 0038-9633) 3449, 4615
Standards Activities of Organizations in the U S. (US) 3449
Standards and Practices for Instrumentation. (US ISSN 0074-0527) 2525
Standards and Recommended Practices for Small Craft. (US) 4530
Standards and Specifications Information Bulletin. (US ISSN 0038-9641) 3449
Standards and Technology Bulletin. (UK) 2786, 1085
Standards - Canada see Focus 3446
Standards Engineering. (US ISSN 0038-9668) 3449
Standards Engineering Society. Proceedings of Annual Meeting. (US ISSN 0081-430X) 1922
Standards India. (II ISSN 0970-2628) 3449
Standards: Monthly Additions. (II ISSN 0038-9684) 3449
Standards News. (CE) 3449
Standard's Summary Life Report and Ratio Analysis. (US) 2543
Standard's Summary Reproductions. (US) 2543
Standarty i Kachestvo. (RU ISSN 0038-9692) 3449
Standby. (NE) 3243
Stander. (GW ISSN 0038-9706) 4530
Das Standesamt. (GW) 2681
Standesbeamte see Das Standesamt 2681
Standing Conference of Co-Operative Library and Information Services News see S C O C L I S News 5272
Standing Conference of Local and Regional Authorities of Europe. Official Reports of Debates. (FR) 4074
Standing Conference of Local and Regional Authorities of Europe. Texts Adopted. (FR) 4074
Standing Conference of Rectors, Presidents and Vice-Chancellors of the European Universities Action see C R E - Action 1701

Standpoints. (FR ISSN 0987-7622) 1760
Standpunkt (Berlin). (GW ISSN 0323-4304) 4250
Der Standpunkt (Hamburg). (GW ISSN 0172-9527) 2589
Stanford Art Books. (US) 3533
Stanford Business School Magazine. (US ISSN 0883-265X) 1325
Stanford Chaparral. (US ISSN 0038-9757) 1325, 2885
Stanford Environmental Law Journal. (US ISSN 0892-7138) 2681, 1969
Stanford French & Italian Studies. (US) 2963
Stanford French Review. (US ISSN 0163-657X) 2963, 2389
Stanford G S B see Stanford Business School Magazine 1325
Stanford Gay and Lesbian Awareness Week Program. (US) 2457, 1716, 3947, 4853
Stanford Humanities Review. (US) 2515
Stanford Italian Review. (US ISSN 0730-6857) 2963, 2885
Stanford Journal of International Law. (US ISSN 0731-5082) 2729
Stanford Law and Policy Review. (US ISSN 1044-4386) 2681
Stanford Law Review. (US ISSN 0038-9765) 2681
Stanford Lawyer. (US ISSN 0585-0576) 2682, 3927
Stanford Literature Review. (US ISSN 0886-666X) 2963
Stanford Literature Studies. (US) 2963
Stanford Magazine. (US ISSN 0745-3981) 1325
Stanford Museum. (US ISSN 0085-6665) 3533
†Stanford University. Publications. Geological Sciences. (US ISSN 0081-4350) 5283
Stanford University Campus Report. (US ISSN 0049-2108) 1716
Stanford University Libraries. Library Bulletin. (US) 2786
Stanger Register see Stanger's Investment Advisor 965
Stanger Report. (US) 965
Stanger's Investment Advisor. (US) 965
Stanislaus Connections. (US) 3927
Stanislaw Staszic University of Mining and Metallurgy. Scientific Bulletins. Drillign Oil Gas. see Akademia Gorniczo-Hutnicza im. Stanislawa Staszica. Zeszyty Naukowe. Wiertnictwo Nafta Gas 3681
Stanislaw Staszic University of Mining and Metallurgy. Scientific Bulletins. Electrotechnics. see Akademia Gorniczo-Hutnicza im. Stanislawa Staszica. Zeszyty Naukowe. Elektrotechnika 1881
Stanislaw Staszic University of Mining and Metallurgy. Scientific Bulletins. Mechanics. see Akademia Gorniczo-Hutnicza im. Stanislawa Staszica. Zeszyty Naukowe. Mechanika 1927
Stanki i Instrumenty. (RU ISSN 0038-9811) 2525
▼Stanley Gibbons Catalogue of Telephone Cards. (UK) 2442
Stanley Gibbons Postcard Catalogue. (UK ISSN 0144-249X) 3758
Stanley Gibbons Simplified Catalogue. Stamps of the World. (UK ISSN 0081-4210) 3758
Stanley Gibbons Stamp Catalogue. Part 1: British Commonwealth. (UK ISSN 0142-9752) 3758
Stanly County Genealogical Society. Journal. (US ISSN 0893-3359) 2165
Stanovnistvo. (YU ISSN 0038-982X) 3988
Stanstead Historical Society. Journal. (CN) 2423
Stanza. (US ISSN 0196-2337) 3582
Staple. (IS) 3006
Staple Cotton Review see StaplReview 194
Staples' Guide to New Zealand Income Tax Practice. (AT ISSN 0111-9370) 1106
StaplReview. (US) 194

Stapp Car Crash Conference Proceedings. (US ISSN 0585-086X) 4702
STAR see S T A R 66
Star. (JO) 2208
†Star. (DK ISSN 0109-2588) 5283
Star (Lantana). (US ISSN 1052-875X) 2235
Star (New York, 1945). (US ISSN 0745-8509) 2024, 2235
Star (Tarrytown). (US) 2235
Star Almanac for Land Surveyors. (UK ISSN 0081-4377) 2263
Star and Garter Magazine. (UK ISSN 0038-9846) 2469, 3472, 4421
Star & Style. (II ISSN 0038-9862) 3518, 1294
Star Beacon. (US) 3596, 359
Star Bene. (IT) 3809
Star Carrier. (US) 1354
Star Date. (US ISSN 0889-3098) 370
Star Guide. (US) 3518, 3582, 4493
Star Hairdo. (US) 374
Star in the East. (UK) 4250
Star International. (US) 4493, 4787
†Star News (San Rafael). (US) 5283
Star of Zion. (US ISSN 0038-9870) 4250
Star Poetry Journal. see Xingxing Shikan 3009
Star Route Journal. (US) 3006
Star Serviceman. (CN ISSN 0038-9889) 3472
Star T V Weekly. (HK) 1380
Star Tech. (US ISSN 0893-4614) 370, 3596
Star Tech Journal. (US ISSN 0739-1048) 1419
Star-Telegram Chaser. (US) 2235
▼Star Track. (US) 2786, 1665, 4137
Star Trek: The Official Fan Club Magazine. (US ISSN 0883-3125) 1380, 1301, 3014, 3518
Star War Collection Trading Post. (US) 2442, 2984
Starburst. (UK ISSN 0955-114X) 3014
Starch/Staerke. (GW ISSN 0038-9056) 1223
†Stardance. (UK) 5283
Stardust. (II) 2201
Starinar. (YU ISSN 0350-0241) 286
Het Staring Instituut. Werken. (NE) 2389
Stark Jewish News. (US) 2024
StarLight. (US ISSN 0896-6095) 4250, 3006
Starlights. (US ISSN 0038-9927) 4530
Starlite Times. (US) 3596, 3782
Starlog. (US ISSN 0191-4626) 1380, 3014, 3518
Starmont Contemporary Writers Series see Milford Series 2938
Starmont Popular Culture Studies. (US ISSN 0890-6270) 2963
Starmont Pulp & Paper Dime Novel Studies. (US ISSN 0885-0658) 2963
Starmont Reader's Guides. (US ISSN 0272-7730) 3014
Starmont Reference Guides. (US ISSN 0738-0127) 3014
Starmont Studies in Literary Criticism. (US ISSN 0737-1306) 2963
Stars. (BE ISSN 0776-0698) 3518, 421
▼Stars. (GW) 3518
Stars and Stripes - The National Tribune. (US ISSN 0894-8542) 3472
Stars of Music World. (RU) 3582
Stars of World Variety. (RU) 3582
†Starshore. (US) 5283
Start. (CI ISSN 0352-2873) 2885
Start. (CS) 3809, 4493
Start. (KR ISSN 0038-9935) 4493
Start (Birmingham). (US ISSN 0162-6841) 4250
†Start (San Francisco). (US ISSN 0889-6216) 5283
†Start & Speed. (SW ISSN 0038-9943) 5283
Start Magazine of Literature and the Arts. (UK) 2963, 3006
Start und Aufstieg. (AU ISSN 0038-9951) 3631

Starter. (IT) 4702
Starting from Paumanok. (US) 2963
Starting Line. see Exormisi 2184
Starting Line. (US) 4493
Starting Right in Your New Business. (US) 965
Starting Smart. (US) 1054
Startling Detective. (US ISSN 0038-996X) 2986
Stasinos. (CY) 2389
Stat. (CN ISSN 0844-3955) 122, 921
Stat (Madison). (US ISSN 0038-9986) 3287
Stat a Pravo. (CS ISSN 0585-0967) 2682, 994, 3927
State. (CE) 3927
The State. (US ISSN 0038-9994) 2235
State (Washington). (US ISSN 0278-1859) 3972
State A D M Reports. (US) 4113, 1539
State Administrative Officials: Classified by Function. (US ISSN 0561-8630) 4074
State and Economic Life Series. (CN) 2323
State and Local see Excelsior 4059
State and Local Government Review. (US ISSN 0160-323X) 4095
▼State and Local Statistics Sources. (US ISSN 1047-3394) 4074, 4587
State and Local Taxes. (US) 1106
State and Local Taxes: All States Tax Guide. (US) 1106
State and Local Taxes: Income Taxes. (US) 1106
State and Local Taxes: Property Taxes. (US) 1106
State and Local Taxes: Sales and Use Taxes. (US) 1106
State and National Registers of Historic Places. (US) 4787, 2423
State and Regional Associations of the United States. (US) 1154
State-Approved Schools of Nursing - L.P.N. - L.V.N. (US ISSN 0081-4423) 3287, 1697
State-Approved Schools of Nursing - R.N. (US ISSN 0081-4431) 3287, 1697
State Archives of Assyria Bulletin. (IT) 286
State Arts Agency Directory. (US) 1154, 345, 4074
State Bank of Ethiopia. Report on Economic Conditions and Market Trends see National Bank of Ethiopia. Quarterly Bulletin 791
State Bank of India. Annual Report. (II) 800
State Bank of India. Economic Newsletter. (II) 885
State Bank of India. Economic Research Department. Studies. (II) 885
State Bank of India. Indian Economic Newsletter. (II) 885
State Bank of India. Monthly Review. (II ISSN 0039-0003) 885
State Bank of India. Report of the Central Board of Directors see State Bank of India. Annual Report 800
State Bank of Pakistan. Annual Report. (PK ISSN 0081-444X) 800
State Bank of Pakistan. Bulletin. (PK ISSN 0039-0011) 800
State Bank of Pakistan. Equity Yields on Ordinary Shares. (PK) 738, 965
State Bank of Pakistan. Export Receipts. (PK ISSN 0585-1009) 921
State Bank of Pakistan. Index Numbers of Stock Exchange Securities. (PK ISSN 0081-4466) 738, 23, 965
State Bank of Pakistan. State Bank News. (PK ISSN 0561-8738) 800
State Bank of Pakistan. Statistics on Co-Operative Banks. (PK ISSN 0039-0569) 738
State Bank of Pakistan. Statistics on Scheduled Banks. (PK ISSN 0039-0577) 738
State Bar of New Mexico. Bar Bulletin. (US) 2682
State Bar of New Mexico. Bulletin and Advance Opinions see State Bar of New Mexico. Bar Bulletin 2682

STATE BIOLOGICAL

State Biological Survey of Kansas. Technical Bulletin. (US) **518, 538, 592**
State Blue Books, Legislative Manuals and Reference Publications *see* State Reference Publications **2700**
State Budget and Tax News. (US ISSN 0742-0498) **1106, 4074**
State Chamber News. (US) **693**
†State Child Care Fact Book (Year). (US ISSN 0899-1944) **5283**
State Council of Educational Research and Training Journal *see* S C E R T Journal **1758**
†State Court Caseload Statistics. (US) **5283**
State Court Journal. (US ISSN 0145-3076) **2682**
State Data and Database Finder. (US) **2799**
State Directory of Kentucky. (US ISSN 0585-1173) **4074**
State Domestic Product of Himachal Pradesh. (II) **738**
State - E P A Agreements. Annual Report. (US ISSN 0275-2271) **1969**
State Education Journal Index. (US ISSN 0039-0046) **1680, 23**
State Education Leader. (US ISSN 0736-7511) **1665**
State Elective Officials and the Legislatures. (US) **4074**
State Employment Relations Board Official Reporter *see* S E R B Official Reporter **2676**
State Engineers. (CE) **1837**
State Executive Directory. (US ISSN 0276-7163) **4095, 1154**
State Executive Directory Annual. (US ISSN 1056-7011) **4095, 1154**
State Farming. *see* Allami Gazdasag **75**
State-Federal Issue Briefs. (US) **4074**
State Geologists Journal. (US ISSN 0039-0089) **1581**
State Government (Washington). (US ISSN 0888-8590) **4074, 3927**
State, Government and International Relations. (IS ISSN 0334-2514) **3972, 4453**
State Government Finances *see* Current Governments Reports: State Government Finances **712**
State Government News. (US ISSN 0039-0119) **3927, 4074**
State Government Research Checklist. (US ISSN 0190-6623) **4074, 3928**
▼State Hazardous Waste Regulation. (US) **1987, 2682**
State Health Notes. (US) **4113, 2682, 3155**
State Health Reports *see* State A D M Reports **4113**
State Historical Society of Iowa. Iowa Historian. (US) **2423**
State House Watch. (US) **4421, 4074**
State Housing Development Authority Review *see* M S H D A Review **2491**
State Income of Himachal Pradesh *see* State Domestic Product of Himachal Pradesh **738**
State Index to Non-Government Master Frequency Data Base. (US) **1349**
State Industrial Directory: Connecticut - Rhode Island *see* MacRae's State Industrial Directory: Connecticut - Rhode Island **1144**
State Industrial Directory: Maine - New Hampshire - Vermont *see* MacRae's State Industrial Directory: Maine - New Hampshire - Vermont **1144**
State Industrial Directory: Maryland - District of Columbia - Delaware *see* MacRae's State Industrial Directory: Maryland - District of Columbia - Delaware **1144**
State Industrial Directory: Massachusetts - Rhode Island *see* MacRae's State Industrial Directory: Massachusetts - Rhode Island **1144**
State Industrial Directory: New Jersey *see* MacRae's State Industrial Directory: New Jersey **1144**
State Industrial Directory: New York State *see* MacRae's State Industrial Directory: New York State **1144**

State Industrial Directory: North Carolina - South Carolina - Virginia *see* MacRae's State Industrial Directory: North Carolina - South Carolina - Virginia **1144**
State Information. *see* Toriyn Medeelel **4075**
State Information Book *see* State Yellow Book **4074**
State Inheritance Taxes. (US) **1106**
State Institute of Education, Rajasthan. Annual Report. (II) **1665**
State Investment Portfolio. (Juneau) *see* Alaska. Department of Revenue. State Investment Portfolio **938**
The State Journal. (US) **693**
State Laws and Published Ordinances, Firearms. (US ISSN 0276-7651) **2682**
▼State Legal Issues Quarterly. (US) **4074, 1106**
State Legislative Leadership, Committees and Staff. (US ISSN 0195-6639) **4074**
State Legislative Report. (US) **4074**
State Legislative Sourcebook. (US ISSN 0898-7297) **2682, 4074**
State Legislatures. (US ISSN 0147-6041) **3928, 4074**
State Librarian. (UK ISSN 0305-9189) **2786**
State Library of New South Wales. Library Deposit List. (AT ISSN 0729-5472) **412, 2890**
State Motor Carrier Guide. (US) **4748**
State Municipal League Directory. (US) **4095**
State of Alaska F Y (Year) Report of Performance *see* Alaska. Office of the Governor. Performance Report **5133**
State of America's Children (Year). (US ISSN 1055-9213) **4421**
State of Black America. (US ISSN 0148-6985) **3947**
State of Florida Comprehensive Manpower Plan. (US ISSN 0095-6430) **994**
State of Food and Agriculture. (UN ISSN 0081-4539) **122**
State of Greek Industry in (Year). (GR ISSN 0072-7458) **1085**
State of Hawaii Data Book. (US ISSN 0073-1080) **739**
State of Human Rights in New York *see* New York (State). Division of Human Rights. Annual Report **3945**
State of Louisiana Public Documents. (US) **4074**
State of Montana Investment Program. Report on Audit *see* Montana. Office of the Legislative Auditor. State of Montana Board of Investments. Report on Examination of Financial Statements **956**
State of Nebraska Annual Fiscal Report *see* Nebraska. Department of Administrative Services. Annual Fiscal Report **4068**
State of Nebraska Uniform Crime Report. (US ISSN 0090-3221) **1523**
State of Nevada Wage Report *see* Nevada Wage Survey **989**
State of New Jersey Annual Financial Report *see* New Jersey Comprehensive Annual Financial Report **4068**
State of New York City's Municipal Hospital System. (US ISSN 0895-688X) **2469**
State of New York's Environment *see* New York (State). Department of Environmental Conservation. Annual Report **1494**
State of the Air Transport Industry *see* I A T A Annual Report **4674**
State of the C D - R O M Industry: Applications, Players, Products. (US) **1424**
State of the States. (US) **1969**
State of the Union. (US) **1301**
State of the World. (US) **921**
State of Virginia's Environment: Biennial Report. (US) **1969**
State Peace Officers Journal. (US) **1523**
State Planning Authority News *see* S.P.A.N **5272**

State Policy Reports. (US ISSN 8750-6637) **1106, 4074**
State Rankings. (US ISSN 1057-3623) **2500**
▼State Reference Publications. (US ISSN 1057-0586) **2700, 412**
State Regulation Report. (US ISSN 0276-2870) **1987, 2682**
State Reports W.A. (AT ISSN 0158-1996) **2682**
State Revenue Newsletter. (US ISSN 0883-6760) **3758**
State Service. (AT) **2589**
State Tax Action Coordinator. (US) **756, 1106**
State Tax Cases Reports. (US) **1106**
State Tax Guide. (US) **1106**
State Tax Handbook. (US ISSN 0081-4598) **1106**
State Tax Reports. (US) **1106**
State Tax Review. (US) **1106**
State Telephone Regulation Report. (US ISSN 0741-8388) **1366**
†State University College of Arts & Science at Geneseo. School of Library and Information Science. Newsletter. (US) **5283**
State University of New York. College at Buffalo. Record *see* Buffalo State Record **1305**
State University of New York. Research.(US ISSN 1041-9764) **1665**
State University of New York at Albany. Institute for Mesoamerican Studies. Publication. (US) **250**
State University of New York at Albany. School of Library and Information Science. Bulletin *see* Rockefeller College. School of Information Science and Policy. Bulletin **2782**
State University of New York at Binghamton. Center for Medieval and Early Renaissance Studies. Acta. (US ISSN 0361-7491) **2323**
State University of New York Librarians Association Newsletter *see* S U N Y L A Newsletter **2782**
State Yellow Book. (US ISSN 0899-2207) **4074**
Stateco. (FR ISSN 0224-098X) **739, 3995**
Statehouse Observer. (US ISSN 0091-1402) **4075**
Stateline. (US) **800, 832**
Statement (Fort Collins). (US) **1760**
Statement (Fredonia). (US) **1325**
▼Statement of Accounting Concepts. (AT ISSN 1035-3631) **756**
▼Statement of Auditing Practice. (AT ISSN 1034-859X) **756**
▼Statement of Auditing Standards. (AT ISSN 1034-8603) **756**
Statement of Secretary of Defense Before the House Armed Services Committee on the Defense Budget and Program *see* U.S. Department of Defense. Defense Department Report **4076**
Staten Island Historian. (US ISSN 0039-0232) **2423**
Staten Island Institute of Arts & Sciences. Proceedings. (US ISSN 0039-0240) **4345**
Statens Byggeforskningsinstitut Aarsberetning *see* S B I Aarsberetning **631**
Statens Geotekniska Institut. Rapport/Swedish Geotechnical Institute. Report. (SW ISSN 0348-0755) **1595**
Statens Husdyrbrugsforsoeg. Meddelelse. (DK ISSN 0106-8857) **122**
Statens Informationstjeneste. Status. (DK) **693**
Statens Jaernvaegars Huvudkontor Nytt *see* S J-Nytt **4714**
Statens Laantagning og Gaeld. (DK ISSN 0902-6681) **4075**
Statens og Kommunernes Budgetter. (DK ISSN 0106-2905) **1106**
Statens Planteavlsforsoeg. Meddelelse *see* Groen Viden **179**
Statens Vaeg- och Trafikinstitut Annual Report *see* V T I Annual Report **4722**

Statens Vaeg- och Trafikinstitut Meddelande *see* V T I Meddelande **4722**
Statens Vaeg- och Trafikinstitut Rapport *see* V T I Rapport **4722**
†Statens Vejlaboratorium. Nye Publikationer. (DK ISSN 0901-0963) **5283**
Statens Vejlaboratorium Leveringsbetingelser og Proevningsmetoder *see* S V Leveringsbetingelser og Proevningsmetoder **5272**
States and Cities *see* U.S. Centers for Disease Control. Tuberculosis Statistics in the United States **3368**
The States and Small Business: A Directory of Programs and Activities. (US ISSN 0742-843X) **1118**
States and Small Business: Programs and Activities *see* The States and Small Business: A Directory of Programs and Activities **1118**
States of Malaya Chamber of Mines. Council Report *see* Malaysian Chamber of Mines. Council Report **3487**
States of Malaya Chamber of Mines. Yearbook *see* Malaysian Chamber of Mines. Yearbook **3487**
Stateside Family *see* Family (New York) **3458**
Statesman. (PK ISSN 0039-0313) **2213, 3928**
The Statesman. (US) **3533**
Statesman. (NR) **3928**
Statesman Weekly. (II ISSN 0039-0321) **3928, 2201**
The Statesman's Year - Book. (US ISSN 0081-4601) **3928**
Statewatch. (US) **1969**
Stateways. (US) **385**
Statewide Space Survey *see* Illinois. Board of Higher Education. Statewide Space Survey **5210**
Stati Uniti d'Europa. (IT ISSN 0039-0348) **2206**
Station Biologique de Besse en Chandesse. Annales. (FR) **467, 538, 557**
Station Break. (US) **4677**
Station Log. (US) **3533, 4530**
Station Relay. (US ISSN 0887-8935) **250, 2024, 4453**
Station Seismographique de Lisboa. Bulletin Seismique. (PO ISSN 0039-0356) **1595**
Station to Station. (GW ISSN 0177-4913) **2191, 1266**
Stationary Engine. (UK) **1837**
Stationery *see* Office Products S A **1060**
Stationery and Office Supplies. (CH) **1061**
Stationery Products *see* Office Magazine **1060**
Stationery Trade News. (UK) **1061**
Stationery Trade Reference Book and Buyers Guide. (UK ISSN 0081-461X) **1061**
Stationery Trade Review. (UK ISSN 0039-0372) **1062**
Statistica. (IT ISSN 0039-0380) **4587**
Statistica degli Incidenti Stradali. (IT ISSN 0075-188X) **4119, 4667**
Statistica Neerlandica. (NE ISSN 0039-0402) **4587**
Statistical Abstract of Higher Education in North Carolina. (US ISSN 0081-4644) **1680, 1716**
Statistical Abstract of Iceland. (IC ISSN 1017-6683) **4587**
Statistical Abstract of Latin America. (US ISSN 0081-4687) **2330**
Statistical Abstract of Louisiana. (US ISSN 0081-4695) **739**
Statistical Abstract of Maharashtra State. (II ISSN 0081-4709) **4587**
Statistical Abstract of Oklahoma. (US ISSN 0191-0310) **739**
Statistical Abstract of Rajasthan. (II ISSN 0081-4717) **4587**
Statistical Abstract of the Cayman Islands. (CJ) **4587**
Statistical Abstract of the Democratic Socialist Republic of Sri Lanka. (CE) **4587**

STATISTICAL YEARBOOK 6693

Statistical Abstract of the Government of the Cayman Islands *see* Statistical Abstract of the Cayman Islands **4587**
Statistical Abstract of the Maltese Islands *see* Malta. Central Office of Statistics. Annual Abstract of Statistics **4579**
Statistical Abstract of the United States.(US ISSN 0081-4741) **4587**
Statistical Analysis of New Zealand Wool Production and Disposal *see* New Zealand Wool Board. Statistical Handbook **141**
Statistical and Social Inquiry Society of Ireland. Journal. (IE ISSN 0081-4776) **4587**
Statistical Budget and Activities in Thailand. (TH ISSN 0858-1886) **4587**
†Statistical Compendium of the Americas. (US ISSN 0585-1432) **5283**
Statistical Data on Commercial Banks in Thailand. (TH) **739**
Statistical Data on Libraries in Bulgaria. *see* Statisticeski Danni za Bibliotekite v Bulgaria **2795**
Statistical Handbook of Egypt *see* Egypt. Central Agency for Public Mobilisation and Statistics. Statistical Yearbook **4570**
Statistical Handbook of Tamil Nadu. (II) **4587**
Statistical Handbook of Thailand. (TH ISSN 0857-9466) **4587**
Statistical Handbook of the Philippines. (PH) **4587**
Statistical Handbook of the Republic of Ghana. (GH) **4587**
Statistical Indicator Reports. (US) **739**, 965, 4587
Statistical Indicators for Asia and the Pacific. (UN ISSN 0252-4457) **4587**
Statistical Indicators in E S C A P Countries *see* Statistical Indicators for Asia and the Pacific **4587**
Statistical Indicators of Short Term Economic Changes in E.C.E. Countries. (UN ISSN 0251-0073) **885**
Statistical Information Bulletin for Africa/Bulletin d'Information Statistique pour l'Afrique. (UN) **739**
Statistical Information of Afghanistan/ Ma'lumat-i Ihsa'ivi-i Afghanistan. (AF) **4587**
Statistical Institute of Jamaica. Consumer Price Indices *see* Statistical Institute of Jamaica. Consumer Price Indices Bulletin **739**
Statistical Institute of Jamaica. Consumer Price Indices Bulletin. (JM) **739**
Statistical Institute of Jamaica. Demographic Statistics. (JM) **3995**, 4587
Statistical Institute of Jamaica. External Trade. (JM) **739**
Statistical Institute of Jamaica. External Trade Annual Review. (JM) **739**
Statistical Institute of Jamaica. External Trade Monthly Bulletin. (JM) **739**
Statistical Institute of Jamaica. External Trade Summary Tables *see* Statistical Institute of Jamaica. External Trade Monthly Bulletin **739**
Statistical Institute of Jamaica. Monetary Statistics Report. (JM) **739**, 4587
Statistical Institute of Jamaica. National Income and Product. (JM) **739**, 4587
Statistical Institute of Jamaica. Pocketbook of Statistics. (JM) **4587**
Statistical Institute of Jamaica. Statistical Abstract. (JM) **4587**
Statistical Institute of Jamaica. Statistical Review. (JM) **4587**
Statistical Journal of the United Nations Economic Commission for Europe *see* United Nations. Economic Commission for Europe. Statistical Journal **1030**
Statistical Monthly of Israel. (IS) **4587**
Statistical Notes of Japan. (JA ISSN 0561-922X) **4587**
Statistical Office of the European Communities. Agricultural Prices. (EI) **143**, 226
Statistical Office of the European Communities. Animal Production *see* Agricultural Statistics Series No.2: Animal Production **132**
Statistical Office of the European Communities. Balance of Payments *see* Balance of Payments Statistical Yearbook **704**
Statistical Office of the European Communities. Basic Statistics *see* Basic Statistics of the European Community **706**
Statistical Office of the European Communities. Bulletin of Energy Prices. (EI) **1800**
Statistical Office of the European Communities. Commerce Exterieur: Products C E C A. (EI ISSN 0081-4881) **739**
Statistical Office of the European Communities. Comparison in Real Terms of E S A Aggregates *see* National Accounts E S A - Aggregates (Years) **681**
Statistical Office of the European Communities. Crop Production *see* Agricultural Statistics Series No.1: Crop Production **132**
Statistical Office of the European Communities. Energy *see* Statistical Office of the European Communities. Energy Statistics Monthly Bulletin **1800**
Statistical Office of the European Communities. Energy Statistics. Yearbook. (EI ISSN 0081-489X) **1800**
Statistical Office of the European Communities. Energy Statistics Monthly Bulletin. (EI) **1800**
Statistical Office of the European Communities. Eurostat. Money and Finance. (EI ISSN 0255-6510) **800**
Statistical Office of the European Communities. External Trade. Analytical Tables: Import - Export. (EI) **739**
Statistical Office of the European Communities. External Trade - Monthly Statistics *see* Statistical Office of the European Communities. Monthly External Trade Bulletin **739**
Statistical Office of the European Communities. Foreign Trade: Analytical Tables *see* Statistical Office of the European Communities. External Trade. Analytical Tables: Import - Export **739**
Statistical Office of the European Communities. Foreign Trade - Monthly Statistics *see* Statistical Office of the European Communities. Monthly External Trade Bulletin **739**
Statistical Office of the European Communities. Foreign Trade: Standard Country Classification. (EI ISSN 0081-4903) **739**
Statistical Office of the European Communities. Gas Prices. (EI) **1800**, 739
Statistical Office of the European Communities. Industrial Production. (EI ISSN 0254-0649) **4587**
Statistical Office of the European Communities. Iron and Steel *see* Statistical Office of the European Communities. Monthly Statistics Iron and Steel **3428**
Statistical Office of the European Communities. Iron and Steel. Yearbook *see* Iron and Steel Statistical Yearbook **3427**
Statistical Office of the European Communities. Monthly External Trade Bulletin. (EI) **739**
Statistical Office of the European Communities. Monthly Statistics Iron and Steel. (EI ISSN 0378-7559) **3428**
Statistical Office of the European Communities. Monthly Statistics. Eggs *see* Agricultural Statistics Series No.2: Animal Production **132**
Statistical Office of the European Communities. Monthly Statistics. Meat *see* Agricultural Statistics Series No.2: Animal Production **132**
Statistical Office of the European Communities. Monthly Statistics. Milk *see* Agricultural Statistics Series No.2: Animal Production **132**
Statistical Office of the European Communities. National Accounts Yearbook. (EI ISSN 0081-4911) **739**
Statistical Office of the European Communities. Quarterly Bulletin of Energy Statistics. *see* Statistical Office of the European Communities. Energy Statistics Monthly Bulletin **1800**
Statistical Office of the European Communities. Quarterly National Accounts. (EI ISSN 1010-1764) **739**
Statistical Office of the European Communities. Selling Prices of Animal Products *see* Statistical Office of the European Communities. Agricultural Prices **143**
Statistical Office of the European Communities. Selling Prices of Vegetables Products *see* Statistical Office of the European Communities. Agricultural Prices **143**
†Statistical Office of the European Communities. Siderurgie Annuaire. (EI ISSN 0081-4954) **5283**
†Statistical Office of the European Communities. Social Statistics. (EI ISSN 0039-0488) **5283**
Statistical Office of the European Communities. Statistical Studies and Surveys. (EI) **739**
Statistical Office of the European Communities. Statistical Yearbook. Agriculture. (EI) **143**
Statistical Office of the European Communities. Statistique Agricole *see* Statistical Office of the European Communities. Statistical Yearbook. Agriculture **143**
Statistical Office of the European Communities. Statistiques des Tranports. Annuaire *see* Statistical Office of the European Communities. Transport, Communications, Tourisme - Annuaire Statistique **4667**
†Statistical Office of the European Communities. Statistiques Industrielles Annuaire. (EI ISSN 0081-4970) **5283**
Statistical Office of the European Communities. Transport, Communications, Tourisme - Annuaire Statistique. (EI) **4667**, 4800
Statistical Office of the European Communities. Yearbook of Regional Statistics. (EI ISSN 0081-4997) **739**
Statistical Papers/Statistische Hefte. (GW ISSN 0932-5026) **4587**
Statistical Pocket Book: India. (II ISSN 0081-5012) **4587**
Statistical Pocket-Book of Afghanistan. (AF) **4587**
Statistical Pocket Book of Hungary *see* Magyar Statisztikai Zsebkonyv **4578**
Statistical Pocket Book of Sri Lanka *see* Statistical Pocket Book of the Democratic Socialist Republic of Sri Lanka **4587**
Statistical Pocket Book of the Democratic Socialist Republic of Sri Lanka. (CE) **4587**
Statistical Pocket Book of the Indian Union *see* Statistical Pocket Book: India **4587**
Statistical Pocket Book of Turkey/ Turkiye Istatistik Cep Yilligi. (TU) **4587**
Statistical Pocket-Book of Yugoslavia. (YU ISSN 0585-1815) **4588**
Statistical Pocketbook of Bangladesh. (BG) **4588**
Statistical Pocketbook of Indonesia/ Buku Saku Statistik Indonesia. (IO ISSN 0126-3595) **4588**
Statistical Profile of Iowa. (US) **4588**
Statistical Profile of the Soft Drink Industry. (US) **385**
Statistical Proof of Discrimination. (US) **3947**, 2682
Statistical Record. (UK) **4499**
▼Statistical Record of Black America. (US) **424**, 388
Statistical Reference Index. (US ISSN 0278-694X) **4588**, 23
Statistical Reflection of the Islamic Republic of Iran. (IR ISSN 1010-9617) **4588**
Statistical Report of Hospitals (Tallahassee) *see* Florida. Mental Health Program Office. Statistical Report of Hospitals **5193**
Statistical Report on Tourism in Fiji *see* Fiji. Bureau of Statistics. Tourism and Migration Statistics **4799**
Statistical Report on Visitor Arrivals to Indonesia. (IO) **4800**, 4588
Statistical Report Series (Cheyenne) *see* Wyoming. Division of Planning, Evaluation and Information Services. Statistical Report Series **4592**
†Statistical Reports of Changwat. (TH) **5283**
Statistical Reports of the Nordic Countries. *see* Nordisk Statistisk Skriftserie **4581**
Statistical Review of Coal in Canada. (CN) **3496**
Statistical Review of Government in Utah. (US) **4082**, 4588
Statistical Review of Tourism in Hong Kong. (HK) **4800**
Statistical Science. (US ISSN 0883-4237) **4588**
Statistical Service *see* Standard & Poor's Statistical Service **964**
†Statistical Services Directory. (US ISSN 0732-6971) **5283**
Statistical Society of Australia. Newsletter. (AT ISSN 0314-6820) **4588**
Statistical Software Newsletter *see* Computational Statistics and Data Analysis **1403**
Statistical Supplement to Facts *see* Western Wood Products Association. Statistical Yearbook **2113**
Statistical Survey of the East African Community Institutions. (KE) **739**
Statistical Synthesis of Chile. (CL ISSN 0716-2464) **739**
Statistical Tables of Public Nuisance, Tokyo. (JA) **1969**
Statistical Ten-Year Review of the Municipality of Copenhagen *see* Statistisk Tiaars-Oversigt for Koebenhavns Kommune **4082**
Statistical Theory and Method Abstracts. (NE ISSN 0039-0518) **4588**, 23, 3063
Statistical Trends in Transport. (FR) **4667**
Statistical Year Book of Indonesia. (IO ISSN 0126-2912) **3996**, 122
Statistical Yearbook. *see* Norway. Statistisk Sentralbyraa. Statistisk Aarbok **4582**
Statistical Yearbook for Asia and the Far East *see* Statistical Yearbook for Asia and the Pacific **4588**
Statistical Yearbook for Asia and the Pacific/Annuaire Statistique pour l'Asie et le Pacifique. (UN ISSN 0252-3655) **4588**
Statistical Yearbook for Latin America and the Caribbean. *see* Anuario Estadistico de America Latina y el Caribe **4562**
Statistical Yearbook for the Copenhagen Region. *see* Statistik for Hovedstadsregionen **4589**
Statistical Yearbook of Bangladesh. (BG ISSN 0302-2374) **4588**
Statistical Yearbook of Brazil. *see* Anuario Estatistico do Brasil **4562**
Statistical Yearbook of China *see* China Statistical Yearbook **4568**
Statistical Yearbook of Finland. *see* Suomen Tilastollinen Vuosikirja **4589**
Statistical Yearbook of Greece. (GR ISSN 0081-5071) **4588**
Statistical Yearbook of Iran. (IR) **4588**
Statistical Yearbook of Jamaica. (JM) **4588**

Title

6694 STATISTICAL YEARBOOK

Statistical Yearbook of Liechtenstein/ Statistisches Jahrbuch Fuerstentum Liechtenstein. (LH) 4588
Statistical Yearbook of Thailand. (TH ISSN 0857-9067) 4588
Statistical Yearbook of the Church. see Annuarium Statisticum Ecclesiae 4212
Statistical Yearbook of the Netherlands. (NE ISSN 0303-6448) 1782, 2211
Statistical Yearbook of the Republic of China. (CH) 739, 4588
Statistical Yearbook of the U.S. Department of Housing and Urban Development see U.S. Department of Housing and Urban Development. Statistical Yearbook 5295
Statistical Yearbook of Turkey. see Turkiye Istatistik Yilligi 4590
Statisticeski Danni za Bibliotekite v Bulgaria/Statistical Data on Libraries in Bulgaria. (BU ISSN 0204-4684) 2795
Statistiche dei Bilanci delle Amministrazioni Regionali, Provinciali e Comunali. (IT ISSN 0075-1820) 4082
Statistiche per la Prevenzione. (IT) 2547
Statistiche sulla Pubblica Amministrazione. (IT) 4082
Statisticheski Godishnik na Narodna Republika Bulgaria. (BU) 4588
The Statistician. (UK ISSN 0039-0526) 4588
Statisticki Godisnjak Jugoslavije. (YU ISSN 0585-1920) 4588
Statisticki Kalendar Jugoslavije. (YU ISSN 0352-3349) 4588
Statisticki Pregled Socijalisticke Republike Bosne i Hercegovine. (BN ISSN 0039-0542) 4588
Statistics. (GW) 1405, 3063
†Statistics - Africa. (UK ISSN 0081-5098) 5283
Statistics and Computing. (UK ISSN 0960-3174) 4588, 1400
Statistics and Decisions. (GW ISSN 0721-2631) 3056
Statistics & Probability Letters. (NE ISSN 0167-7152) 4588, 3056
Statistics Annual see Industry Statistics (Year) 4664
†Statistics - Asia & Australasia: Sources for Market Research. (UK ISSN 0309-5371) 5283
Statistics - Europe. (UK ISSN 0081-5101) 739
†Statistics for Electric Utilities in Pennsylvania. (US) 5283
†Statistics for Gas Utilities in Pennsylvania. (US) 5283
Statistics for Iron and Steel Industry in India. (II ISSN 0081-511X) 3428, 4588
†Statistics for Water Utilities Including Water Authorities in Pennsylvania. (US ISSN 0094-4335) 5283
Statistics in Litigation: Practice Applications for Lawyers. (US) 2700
Statistics in Medicine. (UK ISSN 0277-6715) 3181, 4588
Statistics of Education in Cyprus see Cyprus. Department of Statistics and Research. Education Statistics 1675
Statistics of Education in Somalia. (SO) 1665
Statistics of Education in Wales see Statistics of Education in Wales: Schools 1680
Statistics of Education in Wales see Statistics of Education in Wales: Higher & Further Education 1680
Statistics of Education in Wales: Higher & Further Education. (UK ISSN 0951-1245) 1680
Statistics of Education in Wales: Schools. (UK ISSN 0951-1237) 1680
Statistics of Farmer Cooperatives. (US ISSN 0081-5128) 143
Statistics of Fisheries. see Netherlands. Centraal Bureau voor de Statistiek. Statistiek van de Visserij 5244
Statistics of Foreign Trade of Syria. (SY ISSN 0081-5136) 739
Statistics of Government Expenditure on Culture and Recreation. see Netherlands. Centraal Bureau voor de Statistiek. Statistiek van de Inkomsten en Uitgaven der Overheid voor Cultuur en Recreatie 4498
Statistics of Iceland. see Hagskyrslur Islands 4573
Statistics of Indiana Libraries. (US ISSN 0081-5152) 2795
Statistics of Japanese Non-Life Insurance Business. (JA ISSN 0910-5727) 2547, 4588
Statistics of Life Insurance Business in Japan. (JA ISSN 0910-5719) 2547, 4588
Statistics of Marine Products Exports. (II) 739, 921
Statistics of Motor Vehicles. see Netherlands. Centraal Bureau voor de Statistiek. Statistiek der Motorvoertuigen 4665
Statistics of Paper and Paperboard see American Paper Institute. Statistics of Paper, Paperboard and Wood Pulp 3667
Statistics of Passenger Transport. see Netherlands. Centraal Bureau voor de Statistiek. Statistiek van het Personenvervoer 4654
Statistics of Prisons. see Netherlands. Centraal Bureau voor de Statistiek. Gevangenisstatistiek 1519
Statistics of Public Assistance. see Netherlands. Centraal Bureau voor de Statistiek. Statistiek van de Algemene Bijstand 4426
Statistics of Road-Traffic Accidents. see Netherlands. Centraal Bureau voor de Statistiek. Statistiek van de Verkeersongevallen op de Openbare Weg 4665
Statistics of Road Traffic Accidents in Europe. (UN ISSN 0081-5160) 4667
Statistics of Road Traffic Accidents in Japan. (JA) 4667, 4588
Statistics of Savings. see Netherlands. Centraal Bureau voor de Statistiek. Statistiek van de Spaargelden 730
Statistics of Seaborne Shipping. see Netherlands. Centraal Bureau voor de Statistiek. Statistiek van de Zeevaart 4734
Statistics of Southern College and University Libraries. (US) 2795, 4588
Statistics of the Amounts per Pupil Provided for Primary Education. see Netherlands. Centraal Bureau voor de Statistiek. Statistiek van de Gemeentewege per Leerling Beschikbaar Gestelde Bedragen voor het Lager Onderwijs 5244
Statistics of the Communications Industry in the United States. (US ISSN 0081-5179) 1343
Statistics of the Expenditure of the State, the Provinces and the Municipalities on Education. see Netherlands. Centraal Bureau voor de Statistiek. Statistiek van de Uitgaven der Overheid voor Onderwijs 1678
Statistics of the International Goods Traffic. see Netherlands. Centraal Bureau voor de Statistiek. Statistiek van de Aan-, Af- en Doorvoer. Goederenvervoer van en naar Nederland 730
Statistics of the International Inland Shipping. see Netherlands. Centraal Bureau voor de Statistiek. Statistiek van de Internationale Binnenvaart 4734
Statistics of the Misuse of Drugs in the United Kingdom: Seizures and Offenders Dealt With. (UK) 3181, 4588
Statistics of the State Finances of the Netherlands. see Netherlands. Centraal Bureau voor de Statistiek. Statistiek der Rijksfinancien 730
Statistics of the Trade Unions in the Netherlands. see Statistiek der Vakbeweging in Nederland 2592
Statistics of Travel and Tourism/Tayarut v'Sherutei ha-Araha. (IS ISSN 0334-2476) 4800
Statistics of University Education. see Netherlands. Centraal Bureau voor de Statistiek. Statistiek van Het Wetenschappelijk Onderwijs 1678
Statistics of Virginia Public Libraries see Statistics of Virginia Public Libraries and Institutional Libraries 2795
Statistics of Virginia Public Libraries and Institutional Libraries. (US ISSN 0731-8464) 2795
Statistics of Vocational Guidance. see Netherlands. Centraal Bureau voor de Statistiek. Statistiek van de Voorlichting Bij Scholen en Beroepskeuze 5244
Statistics of Vocational Training. see Netherlands. Centraal Bureau voor de Statistiek. Statistiek van het Beroepsonderwijs: Technisch en Nautisch Onderwijs 1678
Statistics of World Trade in Steel. (UN ISSN 0501-3062) 3428, 4588
†Statistics on Alcohol and Drug Use in Canada and Other Countries. (CN ISSN 0715-7657) 5283
Statistics on Correspondence Courses. see Netherlands. Centraal Bureau voor de Statistiek. Statistiek van het Erkende Schriftelijk Onderwijs 1756
Statistics on Fixed Capital Formation in Industry. see Netherlands. Centraal Bureau voor de Statistiek. Statistiek van de Investeringen in Vaste Activa in de Nijverheid 730
Statistics on Insurance. (FR) 2547
Statistics on Japanese Industries. (JA ISSN 0081-5209) 739
Statistics on Social Work Education see Statistics on Social Work Education in the United States 1680
Statistics on Social Work Education in the United States. (US ISSN 0091-7192) 1680, 1716, 4421
Statistics on Socio-Pedagogic Training. see Netherlands. Centraal Bureau voor de Statistiek. Statistiek van het Beroepsonderwijs: Sociaal-Pedagogisch Onderwijs 1678
Statistics on the Mexican Economy. (MX) 739
Statistics on Travel. see Norway. Statistisk Sentralbyraa. Reiselivstatiskk 4800
Statistics on World Trade in Engineering Products. Bulletin. (UN ISSN 0084-8174) 3428, 4588
Statistics Relating to Regional and Municipal Governments in British Columbia. (CN ISSN 0702-0988) 4082, 4095, 4588
Statistics Research. see Tongji Yanjiu 4590
Statistics Sources. (US ISSN 0585-198X) 4589
Statistics Sweden. Quarterly Foreign Trade Statistics S I T C. (SW ISSN 1100-9381) 4589
Statistics: Textbooks and Monographs Series. (US) 4589
Statistiek der Vakbeweging in Nederland/Statistics of the Trade Unions in the Netherlands. (NE ISSN 0168-4035) 2592
Statistiek van de Gasvoorziening in Nederland. (NE ISSN 0081-5225) 3707
Statistiek van de Scheepvaartbeweging in Nederland/Census of Inland Shipping in the Netherlands at Locks and Bridges. (NE) 4667
Statistieken over de Buitenlandse Handel see Belgium. Institut National de Statistique. Statistiques du Commerce Exter 4662
Statistik des Aussenhandels Oesterreichs see Austria. Statistisches Zentralamt. Aussenhandel Oesterreichs 704
Statistik des Hamburgischen Staates. (GW ISSN 0073-0203) 4667
Statistik Ekonomi-Keuangan Indonesia/ Indonesian Financial Statistics. (IO) 739
Statistik for Hovedstadsregionen/ Statistical Yearbook for the Copenhagen Region. (DK ISSN 0106-2344) 4589
Statistik Indonesia see Statistical Pocketbook of Indonesia 4588
Statistik Kehutanan Indonesia. (IO) 2108
Statistik om Hjemmessygeplejerkevirksomheden. (DK ISSN 0109-3002) 2471
Statistik om Legale Aborter see Statistik om Praevention og Aborter 598
Statistik om Praevention og Aborter. (DK ISSN 0106-7729) 598
Statistik om Sundhedsplejerskernes Virksomhed. (DK ISSN 0108-9714) 3181
Statistik over Afregning af Ydelser Inden for den Offentlige Sygesikring see Sygesikringsstatistik 2547
Statistik over Registrering af Nye Automobiler i Danmark. (DK ISSN 0901-6139) 4702
Statistik Perminyakan Indonesia. see Indonesia Oil Statistics 3705
Statistika. (CS ISSN 0039-0593) 740
Statistika a Demografie see Statistika 740
Statistika a Demografie see Demografie 3991
Statistika Spoljne Trgovine S F R Jugoslavije. (YU ISSN 0084-4373) 740
Statistique Annuelle du Commerce Exterieur. see Turkey. Devlet Istatistik Enstitusu. Dis Ticaret Yillik Istatistik 741
Statistique Criminelle de la Belgique see Belgium. Institut National de Statistique. Statistiques Judiciaires 2697
Statistique de l'Eglise. see Annuarium Statisticum Ecclesiae 4212
Statistique de l'Emploi et de la Population Active Occupee. see Beschaeftigungs- und Erwerbstaetigenstatistik 847
Statistique des Prix des Bois. see Holzpreisstatistik 2112
Statistique Judiciaire de la Belgique see Belgium. Institut National de Statistique. Statistiques Judiciaires 2697
Statistique Suisse des Transports. see Schweizerische Verkehrsstatistik 4666
Statistiques Africaines du Commerce Exterieur. Serie C: Tableaux Recapitulatifs. see Foreign Trade Statistics of Africa. Series C: Summary Tables 717
Statistiques de l'Enseignement au Gabon see Gabon. Ministere de l'Education Nationale. Annuaire Statistique de l'Enseignement 1677
Statistiques de l'Industrie Francaise des Pates. Papiers et Cartons. (FR) 3668
Statistiques de l'Industrie Gaziere en France. (FR) 3707
Statistiques du Commerce Exterieur de Cote d'Ivoire. (IV ISSN 0081-5276) 740
Statistiques du Commerce Exterieur de l'Algerie. (AE) 740
Statistiques du Commerce Exterieur de la Tunisie. (TI ISSN 0081-5292) 740
Statistiques du Commerce International et du Development. Manuel. see International Trade and Development Statistics. Handbook 723
Statistiques Financieres de l'O C D E. see O E C D Financial Statistics 732
Statistiques Financieres des Institutions de Depot. (CN) 740, 4589
Statistiques Maritime. see Canada. Statistics Canada. Shipping Statistics 5160
Statistiques Mondiales de Transport. see World Transport Data 4669
Statistiques Relatives aux Science et a la Technologie. see Unesco. Statistics on Science and Technology 4358
Statistisch Jaarboek van Volksgezondheid. see Annuaire Statistique de la Sante Publique 4116
Statistisch Jaaroverzicht Hilversum see Statistisch Overzicht Hilversum 4589
Statistisch Overzicht Hilversum. (NE) 4589

Title

Statistische Hefte. see Statistical Papers 4587
Statistische Mitteilungen der Bergbehoerden der Bundesrepublik see Bergbau in der Bundesrepublik Deutschland 3499
Statistische Monatshefte Schleswig-Holstein. (GW) 4082, 4095, 4589
Statistische Nachrichten Bildungs- und Sozialeinrichtungen fuer Hoergeschaedigte in der Bundesrepublik Deutschland. (GW) 2289
Statistische Nachrichten der Stadt Nuernberg. (GW) 4082
Statistische Nachrichten ueber Bildungs- und Sozialeinrichtungen fuer Hoergeschaedigte im Deutschsprachigen Raum see Statistische Nachrichten Bildungs- und Sozialeinrichtungen fuer Hoergeschaedigte in der Bundesrepublik Deutschland 2289
Statistische Rundschau Nordrhein-Westfalen. (GW) 4589
Statistische Studien. (GW ISSN 0531-9323) 740, 4589
Statistischer Bericht der Stadt Frankenthal. (GW) 4082, 4095, 4589
Statistischer Jahresbericht der Stadt Muenster. (GW) 3996
Statistischer Monatsbericht. (GW) 4082
Statistischer Vierteljahresbericht Hannover. (GW ISSN 0930-3782) 4082, 4095, 4589
Statistisches Handbuch der Oesterreichischen Sozialversicherung see Handbuch der Oesterreichischen Sozialversicherung 2546
Statistisches Handbuch fuer die Republik Oesterreich. (AU ISSN 0081-5314) 4589
Statistisches Jahrbuch Berlin. (GW ISSN 0081-5322) 4589
Statistisches Jahrbuch der D D R. (GW) 4589
Statistisches Jahrbuch der Eisen- und Stahlindustrie. (GW ISSN 0081-5365) 3428
Statistisches Jahrbuch der Schweiz/ Annuaire Statistique de la Suisse. (SZ ISSN 0081-5330) 4589
Statistisches Jahrbuch der Stadt Augsburg. (GW) 4589
Statistisches Jahrbuch der Stadt Koeln. (GW) 4082, 4095, 4589
Statistisches Jahrbuch der Stadt Nuernberg. (GW) 4082
Statistisches Jahrbuch der Stadt Wien. (AU) 4589
Statistisches Jahrbuch Deutscher Gemeinden. (GW) 4082, 4095, 4589
Statistisches Jahrbuch Fuerstentum Liechtenstein. see Statistical Yearbook of Liechtenstein 4588
Statistisches Jahrbuch Muenchen. (GW ISSN 0077-2062) 4589
Statistisches Jahrbuch ueber Ernaehrung, Landwirtschaft und Forsten der Bundesrepublik Deutschland. (GW ISSN 0072-1581) 143
Statistisches Landesamt Hamburg. Daten und Informationen Faltblatt. (GW) 4589
Statistisches Taschenbuch der D D R. (GW ISSN 0433-6844) 4589
Statistisches Taschenbuch der Stadt Wien. (AU) 4589
Statistisches Taschenbuch Ungarns see Magyar Statisztikai Zsebkonyv 4578
Statistisk Aarsbok foer Finland. see Suomen Tilastollinen Vuosikirja 4589
Statistisk Aarsbok foer Sverige/Abstract of Swedish Statistics. (SW ISSN 0081-5381) 4589
Statistisk Tiaars-Oversigt for Koebenhavns Kommune. (DK ISSN 0107-6744) 4082, 4589
Statni Banka Ceskoslovenska. Bulletin. (CS ISSN 0081-539X) 800
Statni Knihovna C S R. Zpravodaj see Narodni Knihovna 2775

Statni Oblastni Archiv v Opave. Sbornik. (CS) 2389
Statni Statky. (CS ISSN 0039-0704) 122
Statni Vedecka Knihovna. Vyber Novinek. Serie A: Prirodni Vedy, Zemedelstvi. (CS) 144, 4358
Statni Vedecka Knihovna. Vyber Novinek. Serie B: Lekarstvi. (CS) 3181
Statni Vedecka Knihovna. Vyber Novinek. Serie C: Clovek a Spolecnost. (CS) 412, 4389
Statni Vedecka Knihovna. Vyber Novinek. Serie D: Ekonomika. (CS) 412, 693
Statni Vedecka Knihovna. Vyber Novinek. Serie E: Kultura. (CS) 2520
Statni Vedecka Knihovna. Vyber Novinek. Serie F: Pedagogika, Psychologie. (CS) 1680, 4052
Statni Vedecka Knihovna. Vyber Novinek. Serie G: Technika. (CS) 4615
Stato e Mercato. (IT ISSN 0392-9701) 3928, 898, 4453
Staton's Money Advisory. (US ISSN 0886-5078) 965
Staton's Stock Market Advisory see Staton's Money Advisory 965
Stats - Monthly Statistical and Marketing Digest. (SA ISSN 0379-8836) 740, 4589
Statsanstaelld. (SW ISSN 0039-0712) 4095
Statsfoeretag. Aarsredovising see Procordia. Aarsredovisning 1082
Statsfroekontrollen. Beretning. (DK ISSN 0106-8598) 194
Statsoekonomisk Tidsskrift. (NO ISSN 0039-0720) 693
Statstjaenstemannen. (SW) 994
Statstjenestemannen see Stafo-Nytt 4074
Statsvetenskaplig Tidsskrift. (SW ISSN 0039-0747) 3928
Status see Statens Informationstjeneste. Status 693
Status. (SW ISSN 0085-6738) 4113
†Status of Black New York Report. (US) 5283
Status Report (New York) see New York (City). Commission on the Status of Women. Status Report 4850
Status Report (Washington) see Insurance Institute for Highway Safety. Status Report 4105
Statute Law Review. (UK ISSN 0144-3593) 2682
Statutes and Decisions. (US) 2682
Statutes and Notifications. (II ISSN 0039-0763) 2682
Statutes of Alberta - Judicially Considered. (CN) 2682
Statutes of New Zealand. (NZ) 2682
Statutes of Newfoundland. (CN) 2682
Statutory Time Limitations: Colorado. (US) 2682
Statutory Time Limitations: Washington State. (US) 2682, 4075
Der Staudengarten. (GW ISSN 0178-837X) 2139
Stavanger Museum. Aarbok. (NO ISSN 0333-0656) 3533
Stavanger Museum. Skrifter. (NO ISSN 0333-0664) 3533
Stavebnicky Casopis. (CS ISSN 0039-078X) 632, 307, 1874, 1939
Stavebnik. (CS ISSN 0039-0798) 633, 2589
Stavivo/Building Materials. (CS ISSN 0039-0801) 633
Stazione Sperimentale del Vetro. Rivista. (IT ISSN 0391-4259) 1166
Stazione Zoologica di Napoli. Pubblicazioni see History and Philosophy of the Life Sciences 440
Steam & Fuel Users' Journal. (II ISSN 0039-0828) 1796
Steam and Heating Engineer see Heating and Air Conditioning Journal 2299
Steam and Stone. (CN) 2423, 1969
Steam Automobile. (US) 4702, 1939
Steam Days. (UK) 4715

Steam Electric Fuels see Steam - Electric Plant Factors (1978) 3496
Steam - Electric Plant Factors (1978). (US) 3496, 3702
Steam Heritage Yearbook, Preserved Transport & Industrial Archaeology Guide. (UK) 4656
Steam Passenger Service Directory. (US ISSN 0081-542X) 4715
Steam Power. (UK) 1939
Steam Railway. (UK) 4715
Steam Train see Steam Days 4715
Steam Turbine Technology. see Qilunji Jishu 1938
Steam Year Book, Preserved Transport and Industrial Archaeology Guide see Steam Heritage Yearbook, Preserved Transport & Industrial Archaeology Guide 4656
Steamboat Bill. (US ISSN 0039-0844) 4740
Steamboat News see Steamboating 4530
Steamboating. (US) 4530, 3023, 4740
Stearns Newsletter. (US ISSN 1046-4387) 3582, 3533
Steaua. (RM ISSN 0039-0852) 2963, 2885
†Steckenpferd. (GW ISSN 0138-5666) 5283
Stedebouw en Volkshuisvesting. (NE ISSN 0039-0879) 2496
Steed. see Jun Ma 2929
Steel Bulletin. (II) 3420
†Steel Can Recycling Newsletter. (US) 5283
†Steel Comments. (US) 5283
Steel Construction. (AT ISSN 0049-2205) 633, 3420
Steel Construction. (SA) 633, 3420
Steel Construction Today. (UK ISSN 0950-9216) 633, 307
Steel Design/Construction Metallique. (CN) 307, 633
Steel Digest. (US) 3420
†Steel Founders' Research Journal. (US) 5283
Steel in the U S S R. (UK ISSN 0038-9218) 3420
Steel India. (II ISSN 0970-1311) 3420, 4609
Steel Industry see I E News: Process Industries 5209
Steel Industry Safety and Health Commission. Information Bulletin. (EI) 3420, 3622
Steel Labor see Steelabor 2589
Steel Market. (UN ISSN 0497-9478) 3421
Steel Research - Archiv fuer das Eisenhuettenwesen. (GW ISSN 0177-4832) 3421
Steel Spiel. (AT ISSN 0310-7582) 3421
Steel Statistical Yearbook (Year). (BE) 3428
Steel Structures Painting Bulletin see S S P C Bulletin 3655
Steel Structures Painting Council Bulletin see S S P C Bulletin 3655
Steel Technology International. (UK ISSN 0953-2412) 3421
Steel Times. (UK ISSN 0039-095X) 3421
Steel Times International. (UK ISSN 0143-7798) 3421
Steel Today and Tomorrow. (JA) 3421
Steel Traders of the World. (US ISSN 0308-8006) 3421
Steel West. (CN) 3421
Steelabor. (US) 2589, 3421
Steelmaking Conference: Proceedings. (US) 3421, 3496, 3702
Steelmaking Proceedings see Steelmaking Conference: Proceedings 3421
Steels Alert. (US) 3428, 740
Steen en Marmer. see Pierre et Marbre 1577
Steentrupia. (DK ISSN 0375-2909) 592
Steering Wheel see Cab Driver 4685
Steering Wheel. (US ISSN 0039-1298) 4748
Stefanus. (GW) 4202
Steffel Chronicle. (US) 2165

Steiermaerkisches Landesarchiv. Mitteilungen. (AU ISSN 0434-38) 2389
Steig Ein. (GW) 4715
Steigenberger Journal. (GW) 2480
Steilacoom Historical Museum Quarterly.(US) 2423
Stein. (GW) 633
Stein on Probate. (US) 2682
Steinbeck Bibliography Series. (US) 2963
Steinbeck Essay Series. (US) 2963, 412
Steinbeck Monograph Series. (US ISSN 0085-6746) 2963
Steinbeck Quarterly. (US ISSN 0039-100X) 2963
Steinbruch und Sandgrube. (GW ISSN 0039-1018) 3496
Steine Sprechen. (AU ISSN 0039-1026) 1497, 4075
Steinmetz und Bildhauer see Stein 633
Steinway News. (US) 3582
Steirische Beitraege zur Hydrogeologie. (US ISSN 0376-4826) 1600
Steirische Gemeinde-Nachrichten. (AU ISSN 0039-1050) 4075
Steirische Kriegsopfer Zeitung. (AU ISSN 0039-1085) 3472, 3972
Steirische Statistiken. (AU ISSN 0039-1093) 4589
Steirische Wasserkraft- und Elektrizitaets-AG Rundschau see S T E W E A G Rundschau 1907
Steirische Wirtschaft. (AU ISSN 0039-1107) 885
Steirischer Burgenverein. Mitteilungen. (AU ISSN 0490-9348) 2389
Steirischer Wirtschaftsbund see Steirische Wirtschaft 885
Steirisches Bauernbuendler see Neues Land 109
Steklo i Keramika. (RU ISSN 0039-1115) 357
Steklov Institute of Mathematics. Proceedings. (US ISSN 0081-5438) 3056
La Stella del Mare. (IT) 4202
Stella Polaris. (UK ISSN 0308-4531) 4288
Stelle. see L'Emploi 3627
Stelle Filanti. (IT) 421, 3518
Stellium Quarterly. (US) 359
Stelutis Alpinis. (IT ISSN 0039-1131) 4787, 4493
Stem van St. John. see Call of St. John 4099
Stemmer fra Oldtiden. (DK ISSN 0108-2833) 345
Sten. (SW) 633
Stendek. (SP) 63
Stenografisk Tidsskrift. (DK ISSN 0039-1166) 1062
Step. (KE) 4202, 2208
Step-by-Step Graphics. (US ISSN 0886-7682) 4006, 1343
Step-by-Step Precedents and Procedures - Companies, Trusts, Superannuation Funds. (AT) 1106
Stepfamilies. (US) 4453
Stepfamilies & Beyond. (US) 1244, 3400, 4853
Stepfamily Bulletin see Stepfamilies 4453
†Stephen F. Austin State University. School of Forestry. Bulletin. (US ISSN 0082-318X) 5283
Stephen Wright's Mystery Notebook see Mystery Notebook 2986
Stephens Life. (US) 1325
Stephenson County Swoghen. (US) 2165
Stephenson Locomotive Society Journal.(UK ISSN 0039-1190) 4715
Stepparent News see Stepfamilies & Beyond 1244
Stepping Stones. (US ISSN 0562-0031) 2423
†Steppingstones. (US ISSN 0735-4789) 5283
▼Steppke. (GW ISSN 0938-0914) 1244
Stereo. (GW ISSN 0340-0778) 4462
Stereo. (JA ISSN 0289-3622) 4462, 3582

6696 STEREO BUYER'S

Stereo Buyer's Guide. Amplifiers, FM Tuners and Receivers see Stereo Buyer's Guide. Loudspeakers, Amplifiers and Tuners **4462**
Stereo Buyer's Guide. Audio Yearbook. (AT ISSN 0819-0216) **4462**
Stereo Buyer's Guide. C D Players, Turntables and Cassettes Decks. (AT ISSN 0819-0208) **4462**
Stereo Buyer's Guide. Loudspeakers, Amplifiers and Tuners. (AT ISSN 0819-0194) **4462**
Stereo Buyer's Guide. Manual see Stereo Buyer's Guide. Audio Yearbook **4462**
Stereo Buyer's Guide. Turntables and Compact Disc Players see Stereo Buyer's Guide. C D Players, Turntables and Cassettes Decks **4462**
Stereo Directory and Buying Guide see Stereo Review's Stereo Buyers' Guide **4462**
Stereo Guide see Stereo - Video Guide **4462**
Stereo Headphones. (UK ISSN 0039-1212) **3006**
Stereo Review. (US ISSN 0039-1220) **4462, 3582**
Stereo Review Compact Disc Buyers' Guide. (US) **4462**
Stereo Review's Stereo Buyers' Guide. (US) **4462**
Stereo Review's Video Buyers' Guide. (US) **1386, 4462**
Stereo Sound. (JA) **4462**
Stereo Technic/Musen to Jikken. (JA) **4462**
Stereo - Video Guide. (CN ISSN 0833-9570) **4462, 1386**
Stereo World. (US ISSN 0191-4030) **3797**
Stereoguida. (IT) **4462**
Stereophile. (US ISSN 0585-2544) **3582, 4462**
Stereophony and Music. (GR ISSN 1105-1345) **3582, 4462**
Stereoplay. (GW ISSN 0172-388X) **3582**
Stereoplay. (IT) **4462**
Stereotactic and Functional Neurosurgery. (SZ ISSN 1011-6125) **3355**
Stern see Stern Magazin **2191**
▼Stern Business Report. (US) **693, 1325**
Stern Magazin. (GW) **2191**
†Sterna. (NO ISSN 0039-1247) **5283**
Sterne. (GW ISSN 0039-1255) **370**
Sterne und Weltraum. (GW ISSN 0039-1263) **370**
Der Sternenbote. (AU ISSN 0039-1271) **370**
Stern's Performing Arts Directory. (US ISSN 0896-3193) **1532**
Sternsinger. (GW) **4202**
Steroid Receptors. (UK ISSN 0142-8330) **526, 3256**
†Steroidogenesis. (UK ISSN 0142-8527) **5283**
Steroids: Structure, Function and Regulation. (US ISSN 0039-128X) **483, 3155**
Sterz. (AU) **2963, 345, 4639**
Stethoscope. (US) **2469**
Stetson Law Journal. (US) **2682**
Stetson Law Review. (US) **2682**
Das Steuer A B C. (GW ISSN 0172-7214) **1106**
Steuer Aktuell. (GW ISSN 0179-0161) **1106**
Steuer-Auslanddienst. (AU) **1106**
Steuer-Eildienst. (GW) **1106**
Steuer-Lexikon Teil II. (GW ISSN 0177-9664) **1106**
Steuer Revue/Revue Fiscale. (SZ) **1106**
Steuer Seminar. (GW ISSN 0177-9656) **1107**
Steuer Telex. (GW ISSN 0170-7620) **1107**
Steuer Telex International. (GW ISSN 0930-7656) **1107**
Steuer Training. (GW ISSN 0170-6845) **2682**
Steuer und Studium. (GW) **2682, 1107**
Steuer und Wirtschaft. (GW ISSN 0341-2954) **1107**

Steuer und Wirtschaft International. (AU) **740, 23**
Steuer und Wirtschaftskartei. (AU) **740, 23**
†Steuer- und Zollblatt fuer Berlin. (GW) **5283**
Steuerbelastung in der Schweiz see Steuerbelastung in der Schweiz - Kantonshauptorte, Kantonsziffern **1107**
Steuerbelastung in der Schweiz - Kantonshauptorte, Kantonsziffern/ Charge Fiscale en Suisse - Chefs-lieux Cantonaux, Chiffres Cantonaux. (SZ) **1107**
Steuerbelastung in der Schweiz - Natuerliche Personen nach Gemeinden/Charge Fiscale en Suisse - Personnes Physiques par Communes. (SZ) **740**
Der Steuerberater. (GW ISSN 0049-223X) **1107**
Steuerberater-Jahrbuch. (GW ISSN 0081-5519) **1107**
Steuerentscheid. (SZ ISSN 0254-8992) **2682, 693**
Die Steuerliche Betriebspruefung. (GW ISSN 0340-9503) **1107**
Steuern in der Elektrizitaetswirtschaft. (GW ISSN 0172-0686) **1908**
Steve. (IT ISSN 0393-9480) **3006**
Steve Canyon Magazine see Milton Caniff's Steve Canyon Magazine **2984**
Stevens Indicator. (US ISSN 0039-1328) **1325, 1837, 4345**
Stevenson Classical Compact Disc Guide see Classical **3546**
Steward. (UK) **2480**
Steward Anthropological Society. Journal. (US ISSN 0039-1344) **250, 286**
Steyler Missionschronik. (GW ISSN 0722-6942) **4202**
Sti og Varde. (NO ISSN 0049-2248) **4557, 4787**
Stichting Ideele Import. Informatiekrant see Ideele Import Informatie **911**
Stichting Nederlands Filmmuseum Programma see N F M - Programma **3514**
Stichting tot Uitgaaf der Bronnen van het oud-Vaderlaandse Recht. 2 Series: Werken, and Verslagen en Mededelingen. (NE) **2389, 2682**
Stichtse Historische Reeks. (NE) **2389**
Stichwort: Bayer. (GW) **994**
Stickers & Stuff. (US) **2442**
Stierenboek see Boerderij Stierenboek **212**
Stifterverband fuer die Deutsche Wissenschaft. Jahrbuch see Stifterverband fuer die Deutsche Wissenschaft. Taetigkeitsbericht **4345**
Stifterverband fuer die Deutsche Wissenschaft. Taetigkeitsbericht. (GW) **4345**
Stiftskirche. (GW) **4250**
Stiftung Lesen. Buchempfehlungen see Stiftung Lesen. Lese-Empfehlungen **1266**
Stiftung Lesen. Lese-Empfehlungen. (GW) **1266, 412**
Stiftung Preussische Kulturbesitz. Jahrbuch. (GW ISSN 0342-0124) **2389**
Stiftung Volkswagenwerk. Schriftenreihe.(GW) **693**
Stigsnaes. (DK ISSN 0109-274X) **567**
Stiinta si Tehnica. (RM ISSN 0039-1417) **4345**
Stikhi. (RU) **3006**
Stil Novo. (IT ISSN 0039-1433) **1665**
Stil und Etikette see Handbuch Stil und Etikette **2189**
Stil- und Etiketteberater see Handbuch Stil und Etikette **2189**
Stile. (US) **3006**
Stile Casa see Casa Stile **2549**
Stiletto. (US ISSN 1043-9501) **3006, 2963**
Stiletto Magazine. (AT ISSN 0814-043X) **2172**
Still Waters Newsletter. (US) **3782**
Still Waters Presents see Still Waters Newsletter **3782**

Still: Yale Photography Annual. (US ISSN 0081-5586) **3797**
La Stilla. (IT) **4421, 3274**
Stille Boodskapper. see Silent Messenger **2289**
Stille Schar. (AU ISSN 0081-5594) **4276, 2389**
Stim Nytt. (SW ISSN 0283-3190) **3582**
Die Stimme. (IS) **2885**
Stimme der Maertyrer. (GW) **4203**
Stimmen der Zeit. (GW ISSN 0039-1492) **4203**
Stimulator; et Fagblad for Socialoekonomer see Observator **683**
Sting. (US) **4493**
Stipendien fuer Sprachkurse. (GW) **1266, 2843**
Stires Family Newsletter. (US) **2165**
†Stirling Technical Reports in Education.(UK ISSN 0144-0764) **5283**
Stirpes. (US ISSN 0039-1522) **2165**
†Stitch. (US) **5283**
Stitch & Sew Crafts. (US) **3592, 357**
Stitch 'n Sew Quilts. (US ISSN 0744-1649) **3592**
Stitches. (US ISSN 0899-5893) **1288, 3592**
Stochastic Analysis and Applications. (US ISSN 0736-2994) **3056**
Stochastic Hydrology and Hydraulics. (GW ISSN 0931-1955) **1925**
Stochastic Processes and Their Applications. (NE ISSN 0304-4149) **4346, 1837, 3056**
Stochastics see Stochastics and Stochastics Reports **3056**
Stochastics and Stochastics Reports. (US ISSN 1045-1129) **3056**
Stochastics Monographs. (US ISSN 0275-5785) **3056**
Stochastik in der Schule. (GW) **4589, 1760**
Stock and Land. (AT ISSN 0039-1565) **122**
Stock & Option Trading Form. (US) **965**
Stock Car. (UK ISSN 0049-2272) **4493, 4702**
Stock Car & Motorsports. (US) **4702**
Stock Car Racing. (US) **4493**
Stock Exchange Fact Sheet Monthly see International Stock Exchange Fact Sheet Monthly **950**
Stock Exchange, London. Members and Firms of the Stock Exchange see I S E Firms and Members **949**
Stock Exchange of Hong Kong. Fact Book (Year). (HK) **800**
Stock Exchange of Hong Kong. Fact Sheet. (HK) **800**
Stock Exchange of Hong Kong. Member List. (HK) **800**
Stock Exchange of Hong Kong. Weekly Report. (HK) **800**
Stock Exchange of Singapore. Handbook. (SI) **965**
Stock Exchange Official Directory. (II) **1154, 965**
Stock Exchange Official Year Book. (UK ISSN 0076-0684) **965**
Stock Haul. (AT) **4748, 1028**
Stock Journal. (AT ISSN 0039-162X) **226**
Stock Market Magazine. (US ISSN 0039-1638) **965**
Stock Price and Ratio Indexes. (US) **740, 23, 965**
Stock Price and Ratio Indexes for Industry Groups see Stock Price and Ratio Indexes **740**
Stock Selector. (US) **965**
Stock Service Digest. (US ISSN 0194-7613) **965**
Stock Trader's Almanac. (US) **965**
Stock Transfer Guide see Corporate Secretary's Guide **1058**
Stock Values and Dividends for Tax Purposes. (US ISSN 0081-5624) **965, 1107**
Stockade. (NZ) **2345**
Stockholders and Creditors News Service Concerning Eastern Airlines, Inc. see Stockholders and Creditors News Service Concerning Eastern - Continental Airlines, Inc **965**

Stockholders and Creditors News Service Concerning Eastern - Continental Airlines, Inc. (US ISSN 1043-9714) **965**
Stockholders and Creditors News Service Concerning L T V Corporation, et al. (US ISSN 1042-5772) **965**
Stockholders and Creditors News Service Concerning the Johns-Manville Corporation, et al. (US ISSN 1042-5780) **2682**
†Stockholders and Creditors News Service Concerning the Public Service Company of New Hampshire. (US ISSN 1042-5799) **5283**
▼Stockholders & Creditors News Service Re: Federated Department Stores, Inc. (US ISSN 1053-0223) **2682, 965**
▼Stockholders & Creditors News Service Re: Hillsborough Holding Corp. (US ISSN 1053-0215) **2682, 965**
Stockholm International Peace Research Institute Chemical & Biological Warfare Studies see S I P R I Chemical & Biological Warfare Studies **3971**
Stockholm International Peace Research Institute Yearbook: World Armaments and Disarmament see S I P R I Yearbook: World Armaments and Disarmament **3971**
Stockholm Stock Exchange. Annual Report. (SW) **965**
Stockholm Stock Exchange and the Stock Market. (Year) see Stockholm Stock Exchange. Annual Report **965**
Stockholm Studies in English. (SW) **2843**
Stockholm Studies in History of Literature. (SW ISSN 0491-0869) **2963**
Stockholm Studies in Modern Philology. see Studier i Modern Spraakvetenskap **2845**
Stockholm Studies in Philosophy. (SW ISSN 0491-0877) **3782**
Stockholm Studies in Politics. (SW ISSN 0346-6620) **3928**
Stockholm Studies in Russian Literature. (SW) **2963**
Stockholm Studies in Social Work. (SW ISSN 0281-2851) **4421**
Stockholms-Foeretagaren. (SW) **345**
Stockholms Universitet. Psykologiska Institutionen. Report Series. (SW ISSN 0345-0139) **4047**
†Stockholms Universitet. Psykologiska Institutionen. Reports. Supplement Series. (SW ISSN 0345-021X) **5283**
The Stocklists. (UK ISSN 0950-5024) **4623**
Stocklists Colour Magazine. (UK ISSN 0950-5032) **2561, 4623**
Stockman Farmer see Stockman - Grass Farmer **226**
Stockman - Grass Farmer. (US) **226, 122**
Stockmarket Confidential. (UK) **965**
Stockmarket Cycles. (US) **965**
†Stockowners' News. (US ISSN 0749-9779) **5283**
Stocks, Bonds, Bills and Inflation (Year) Yearbook. (US ISSN 1047-2436) **965**
Stocks de Viandes Congelees. see Canada. Statistics Canada. Stocks of Frozen Meat Products **5160**
Stodghill's Animal Research Foundation Cowdog Magazine. (US) **3714**
Stoffmisbruk. (NO ISSN 0333-144X) **1539**
Stofskifte see Tidsskriftet Antropologi **251**
†Stokes Report. (US) **5283**
Stokvis Studies in Historical Chronology & Thought. (US ISSN 0270-5338) **2323, 3928**
Stolen Art Alert see I F A R Reports **329**
Stolica. (PL ISSN 0039-1689) **2214**
▼Stolitsa. (RU. ISSN 0868-698X) **2885**
Stomach and Intestine. see I to Cho **3268**

Stomatologia Mediterranea. (IT ISSN 1120-9402) **3243**
Stomatologija. (BU ISSN 0491-0982) **3243**
Stomatologiya/Stomatology. (RU ISSN 0039-1735) **3243**
Stomatology. *see* Estomodeo **3233**
Stomatology. *see* Stomatologiya **3243**
Stomatoloski Glasnik Srbije. (YU ISSN 0039-1743) **3243**
†The Stone. (US) **5283**
Stone and Cox General Insurance Register. (CN ISSN 0380-223X) **2543**
Stone and Cox Life Insurance Tables. (CN ISSN 0835-2933) **2543**
Stone and Cox Ordinary Branch Life Assurance Handbook (and Up-Dates) .(UK) **2543**
Stone and Cox Ordinary Branch Life Assurance Tables *see* Stone and Cox Ordinary Branch Life Assurance Handbook (and Up-Dates) **2543**
Stone and Cox Unit Linked Assurance and Annuity Tables *see* Stone and Cox Unit Linked Life Assurance Handbook (and Up-Dates) **2543**
Stone and Cox Unit Linked Life Assurance Handbook (and Up-Dates) .(UK) **2543**
†Stone Country. (US ISSN 0146-1397) **5283**
Stone County Historical Society Newsletter. (US) **2423**
Stone in America. (US ISSN 0160-7243) **633**, 307
Stone Industries. (UK ISSN 0039-1778) **633**
†Stone Lion Review. (US) **5283**
Stone Review. (US ISSN 8750-9210) **3496**
Stone Soup. (US ISSN 0094-579X) **1266**
†Stone Through the Ages. (US ISSN 1045-4519) **5283**
Stone World. (US) **1166**
Stonehenge Viewpoint. (US ISSN 0140-654X) **286**
Stones and Bones Newsletter. (US) **286**
Stone's Journal. (US) **2885**
Stone's Justices' Manual. (UK ISSN 0269-3682) **2682**
Stono. (US) **3928**
Stony Hills. (US ISSN 0146-2067) **2885**
Stony Thursday Book. (IE) **3006**, 2963
Stoomtractie. (NE) **4715**
†De Stoomtram. (NE) **5283**
Stop. (IT) **2206**
Stop. (CS) **4702**
Stopanski Pregled/Economic Review. (XN ISSN 0039-1816) **693**
Stoperitidende. (NO ISSN 0039-1824) **3421**
Stopinterviewanalyse. (DK ISSN 0106-7540) **4721**
Stopout: Working Ways to Learn. (US) **1665**
Stopp Weekend *see* Maanadens Stopp **2218**
Storage Battery. *see* Chikudenchi **1884**
†Storage, Handling & Distribution. (SA) **5283**
Storage Handling Distribution. (UK ISSN 0039-1832) **4609**
Store Planning Service. (US ISSN 0039-1859) **2555**
Stores. (US ISSN 0039-1867) **1054**
Stores et Fermetures. (FR ISSN 0183-455X) **633**
Stores, Menuiseries, Fermetures et Protections Solaires, Amenagements *see* S M F A **631**
Stores of the Year. (US ISSN 0192-8732) **2555**
Stores, Shops, Hypermarkets Retail Directory *see* Retail Directory **1052**
†Storetalk. (UK) **5283**
Storia. (UK) **2963**, 4853
Storia, Antropologia e Scienze del Linguaggio. (IT) **250**
Storia Architettura. (IT) **307**
Storia Contemporanea. (IT ISSN 0039-1875) **2323**
†Storia, Costumi e Tradizioni. (IT ISSN 0081-5837) **5283**

Storia dell'Arte. (IT ISSN 0587-1131) **345**
▼Storia dell'Arte e della Critica d'Arte. (IT) **345**
Storia dell'Ebraismo in Italia. (IT) **4226**
Storia della Citta. (IT) **2496**
Storia della Miniatura. Studi e Documenti. (IT ISSN 0081-5845) **345**
Storia della Storiografia/History of Historiography. (IT ISSN 0392-8926) **2389**
Storia delle Relazioni Internazionali. (IT ISSN 1120-0677) **3972**
Storia delle Religioni. (IT) **4203**
Storia di Roma. (IT) **2389**, 1280
Storia e Civilta. (IT) **2389**
Storia e Societa. (IT) **2389**
Storia Illustrata. (IT ISSN 0039-1913) **2323**
Storia in Lombardia. (IT) **2389**
Storia, Letteratura e Arte nel Mezzogiorno. (IT) **2389**
Storia Modellismo. (IT) **2442**
Storia Nordamericana. (IT ISSN 0393-3385) **2423**
Storia Urbana. (IT) **2496**
Storiadentro. (IT) **2389**
Storico della Basilicata. Bollettino. (IT) **4203**, 4276
Stories. (US ISSN 0742-2113) **2963**
Stories: a List of Stories to Tell and to Read Aloud. (US) **1248**, 412
Stories from the Hills. (US ISSN 0081-5861) **2963**, 2423
†Stork. (US) **5283**
Storkjoekken. (NO ISSN 0039-1956) **2480**
Storkoek *see* Restauranger & Storkoek **2080**
Storm. (US) **2885**
Storm Data. (US ISSN 0039-1972) **3441**
Stormarnspiegel. (GW) **4203**
Storrs Agricultural Experiment Station. Bulletin. (US) **122**
Storrs Agricultural Experiment Station. Research Report. (US ISSN 0069-8997) **122**
Storstroems Amts Landbrugs-Nyt. (DK) **122**
Story. (US ISSN 1045-0831) **2964**
Story *see* T V Story **4853**
Story Art. (US ISSN 0039-1999) **2964**
Story Friends. (US ISSN 0039-2006) **1266**, 4288
Story of Illinois Series *see* Illinois. State Museum. Story of Illinois Series **4314**
Story Quarterly *see* StoryQuarterly **2964**
▼Story Rhyme Greeting Letters Update. (US) **2964**
▼Story Rhyme Newsletter for Schools. (US) **1266**
†Story So Far. (CN) **5284**
Story Teller. *see* Gushi Jia **2921**
▼Story Time Stories That Rhyme Newsletter. (US ISSN 1045-5515) **1266**
Storyette. (US) **2964**
†Storylines. (AT ISSN 0811-191X) **5284**
StoryQuarterly. (US) **2964**
Storyteller. *see* Gushihui **2921**
Storytelling Magazine. (US ISSN 1048-1354) **2964**
Storyville. (UK ISSN 0039-2030) **3582**
Stosunki Miedzynarodowe. (PL ISSN 0209-0961) **3972**
Stoutonia. (US) **1325**
Stove Parts Needed. (US) **259**, 2303
Stowage and Segregation to I M D G Code. (GW) **4740**, 1154
Strad. (UK ISSN 0039-2049) **3582**
Strada Maestra. (IT) **412**, 2323
Le Strade. (IT ISSN 0373-2916) **1874**
Strade Aperte. (IT ISSN 0039-2057) **1687**
Lo Stradone. (IT) **2885**
Strafverteidiger. (GW ISSN 0720-1605) **2683**, 1523
Strafvollzug in der Schweiz. (SZ ISSN 0491-1245) **1523**, 4421

Strahlenkommission. Veroeffentlichungen. (GW ISSN 1809, 1969
Strahlentherapie und Onkologie. (GW ISSN 0179-7158) **3363**
Strahlentherapie; Zeitschrift fuer Radiologie und Onkologie *see* Strahlentherapie und Onkologie **3363**
Strahovska Knihovna. (CS ISSN 0081-5896) **2964**
Straight. (US) **4203**
†Straight Ahead. (US ISSN 1047-2622) **5284**
Straight Furrow. (NZ) **2212**
Straight Talk (Emmaus) *see* Rodale's Straight Talk **1264**
Straight Talk (Jupiter). (US) **2235**
Strain. (UK ISSN 0039-2103) **1922**
Strain Forward *see* Inner Horizons **4266**
Strait. *see* Haixia **2921**
Straits. (US) **2964**
Straits Times Directory of Singapore *see* Times Business Directory of Singapore **1155**
Stralignano. (IT) **4787**
The Strand. (CN) **1325**
Strandlight. (UK ISSN 0950-0634) **4639**, 1380
▼Strange Attractor. (UK) **3014**
Strange Lime Fruit Stone *see* Sow's Ear **2884**
Strange Plasma. (US) **3014**
Strange Tales. *see* Qitan **2182**
Strani Jezici. (CI) **2843**
Strani Pravni Zivot. Serija D: Teorija, Zakonodavstvo, Praksa. (YU ISSN 0039-2138) **2683**
†Die Strasse. (GW ISSN 0039-2146) **5284**
Strasse und Autobahn. (GW ISSN 0039-2162) **1874**
Strasse und Nuechternheit *see* Freie Fahrt **4101**
Strasse und Verkehr. (SZ ISSN 0039-2189) **1874**
Strassen. (GW) **4787**, 4702
Strassen- und Tiefbau *see* Strassen- und Tiefbau Vereinigt mit Strasse-Bruecke-Tunnel, Bitumen-Teere-Asphalts-Peche **1874**
Strassen- und Tiefbau Vereinigt mit Strasse-Bruecke-Tunnel, Bitumen-Teere-Asphalts-Peche. (GW) **1874**
Strassenbahn Magazin. (GW ISSN 0340-7071) **4715**
Der Strassengueterverkehr. (AU ISSN 0029-9073) **4656**
Strassentransport. (SZ) **4715**
Strassenverkehrstechnik. (GW ISSN 0039-2219) **4721**
Strassenwaerter. (GW) **4721**
Strata Titles (NSW). (AT) **2683**
Strategia. (IT) **38**
Strategia Globale. (IT) **3472**
Strategic and Defence Studies Centre Newsletter. (AT) **3928**, 3472
Strategic Defense Initiative Monitor *see* S D I Monitor **3470**
Strategic Europe. (FR) **921**
Strategic Health Care Marketing. (US ISSN 0749-5153) **1054**, 2469
Strategic Information on U S Air Travel. (US) **4677**, 4787
Strategic Investment. (US) **965**
Strategic Management Journal. (UK ISSN 0143-2095) **1028**
Strategic Planning and Energy Management *see* Strategic Planning for Energy and the Environment **1796**
Strategic Planning for Energy and the Environment. (US ISSN 1048-5236) **1796**, 1969
Strategic Planning for Magazine Executives. (US) **4137**
†Strategic Planning Management. (US ISSN 0748-4895) **5284**
Strategic Review. (US ISSN 0091-6846) **3472**, 3972
Strategic Review for Southern Africa. (SA ISSN 1013-1108) **1274**, 3472, 3928
Strategic Studies. (PK) **3472**
Strategic Study of Shandong Economics. *see* Shandong Jingji Zhanlue Yanjiu **1000**

STREET TALK

Strategic Survey. (UK ISSN 04 7230) **3973**
Strategic Systems. (US) **1465**
Strategic V A S - V A N S Report Telecommunications Strategies **1382**
Strategies. (FR) **38**
Strategies (Los Angeles). (US ISSN 1040-2136) **3973**, 2515, 3782
Strategies (Reston). (US ISSN 0892-4562) **1760**, 3373
Strategies Alimentaires. (FR ISSN 1140-7131) **158**, 2082
Strategies for Healthcare Excellence. (US ISSN 1058-7829) **2469**
Strategique. (FR ISSN 0224-0424) **3472**, 3928
Strategy. (SA) **1028**, 839
Strategy and Executive Action. (US ISSN 0743-2542) **1028**, 756, 1054
Strategy and Tactics. (US ISSN 0736-6531) **3472**, 2323
Strategy for Peace Conference. Report *see* Strategy for Peace U.S. Foreign Policy Conference. Report **3973**
Strategy for Peace U.S. Foreign Policy Conference. Report. (US ISSN 0748-9641) **3973**
Stratford Festival. (CN ISSN 0085-6770) **4639**
Stratford-Upon-Avon Hilton Magazine *see* Hilton International (U.K.) Magazine **2475**
Strathclyde Guardian. (UK) **1523**
Strathclyde Modern Language Studies. (UK ISSN 0261-099X) **2843**, 2964
Strathclyde Regional Council. Annual Report & Financial Statement. (UK) **4075**
Strathclyde Report. (UK) **4095**
Strathclyde Telegraph. (UK ISSN 0039-2243) **1325**
Strathclyde's Budget *see* Strathclyde Regional Council. Annual Report & Financial Statement **4075**
Stratiotiki Epitheorisis/Military Revue. (GR) **3472**
Stratton-Bromley Magazine *see* Stratton Magazine **2235**
Stratton Magazine. (US) **2235**
†Stratton Notes. (US) **5284**
Straub Foundation Proceedings *see* Proceedings of the Straub Pacific Health Foundation **3144**
Strays. (UK ISSN 0143-8859) **2165**
Straz/Guard. (US) **2024**
Stream. (UK ISSN 0307-9074) **4828**
Stream Improvement Technical Bulletin *see* National Council of the Paper Industry for Air and Stream Improvement. Technical Bulletin **1978**
Stream of History. (US) **2423**
Stree. (II) **2201**
Street & Race. (FI) **4702**
Street & Smith's Baseball. (US ISSN 0161-2018) **4512**
Street and Smith's Baseball Yearbook *see* Street & Smith's Baseball **4512**
Street and Smith's College and Pro Official Basketball Yearbook *see* Street & Smith's Pro Basketball **4512**
Street & Smith's College Football. (US ISSN 0091-9977) **4512**
Street & Smith's College - Prep Basketball. (US) **4512**
Street & Smith's Pro Basketball. (US ISSN 0149-7103) **4512**
Street & Smith's Pro Football. (US ISSN 0092-3214) **4512**
Street Artists' Newsletter. (US) **345**, 3582, 3631
Street Machine. (AT) **4656**
Street Machine. (UK ISSN 0143-5949) **4702**
†Street Magazine. (US ISSN 0190-1737) **5284**
Street Pharmacologist. (US ISSN 0735-6544) **1539**, 3743
Street Rod Actions. (US) **4702**
Street Rodder. (US) **4493**, 4702
Street Rodding Illustrated. (US) **4702**
Street Scenes. (US) **1760**
Street Singer *see* Nostalgia **4461**
Street Smart Investing. (US) **965**
†Street Talk. (US) **5284**

Streetlife. (UK) **2885**
Streetsound. (CN ISSN 0841-2650) **3582**
Streetwise. (UK ISSN 0957-6517) **1969, 1760**
Streetwize Comics. (AT ISSN 0815-0486) **1266, 1539, 2683, 4422**
Streiflichter. (GW) **4203**
Streit. (GW) **3947**
Streletz/Sagittarius. (US ISSN 0747-7287) **2515**
Stremez. (XN ISSN 0039-2294) **2885**
Strength & Beauty. *see* Jian yu Mei **3804**
▼Strength and Fracture. (US ISSN 1044-5145) **1837, 1939**
Strength for the Day. (US) **4250, 2296**
Strength in Unity *see* Unity **2027**
Strength of Materials. (English translation of: Problemy Prochnosti) (US ISSN 0039-2316) **1922**
Stress and Anxiety *see* Stress and Emotion **4047**
Stress and Emotion. (US ISSN 1053-2161) **4047**
Stress in Modern Society. (US ISSN 0884-870X) **4453**
Stress Master. (US) **3597, 3809, 4047**
Stress Medicine. (UK ISSN 0748-8386) **3355**
Stressforskningsrapporter. (SW ISSN 0280-2783) **4047, 3355**
Streudaten der Schweizer Presse *see* Verbreitungsdaten der Schweizer Presse **39**
Striae. (SW ISSN 0345-0074) **1581**
Strick und Haekelmode. (GW) **4853**
Strictly Business *see* Central Penn Business Journal **655**
Strictly Nothing But. (US) **3582**
Stride. (II ISSN 0039-2340) **2201**
†Stride. (UK ISSN 0262-9267) **5284**
Strindbergiana. (SW ISSN 0282-8006) **4639, 2964**
Stringer's Assistant. (US) **4512**
Strings. (US ISSN 0888-3106) **3582**
Strings and Squares. (DK ISSN 0906-1061) **3582**
Striolae. (SW ISSN 0348-4386) **1582**
Stripspiegel. (GW ISSN 0936-7802) **2442**
Stritch M.D. (US ISSN 1054-7649) **1325, 3155**
Stroiizdat: The Best-Designed Books. (RU) **412**
Stroitel' (RU ISSN 0039-2375) **633**
Stroitel'naya Mekhanika i Raschet Sooruzhenii. (RU ISSN 0039-2383) **1922, 633**
Stroitelni Materiali i Silikatna Promishlenost. (BU) **633**
Stroitel'nye i Dorozhnye Mashiny. (RU ISSN 0039-2391) **3023**
Stroitel'nye Materialy i Konstruktsii. (KR) **633**
Stroitelstvo. (BU) **633**
Stroitel'stvo i Arkhitektura. (KR ISSN 0039-2405) **633, 307**
Stroitel'stvo i Arkhitektura Leningrada *see* Leningradskaya Panorama **622**
Stroitel'stvo i Arkhitektura Moskvy. (RU ISSN 0039-2421) **633, 307**
Stroitel'stvo i Arkhitektura Uzbekistana. (RU ISSN 0039-243X) **633, 307**
Stroitel'stvo Truboprovodov. (RU ISSN 0039-2448) **3702**
Strojarstvo. (CI ISSN 0562-1887) **1939**
Strojirenska Vyroba/Engineering Production. (CS ISSN 0039-2456) **3023**
Strojirenstvi. (CS ISSN 0039-2464) **3023**
Strojnicky Casopis/Mechanical Engineering Magazine. (CS ISSN 0039-2472) **1939, 3023**
Strojniski Vestnik/Mechanical Engineering Journal. (XV ISSN 0039-2480) **1939, 3430**
Stroke. (US ISSN 0039-2499) **3212**
Stroker. (US) **3006**
Strokesaver. (GW) **4512**
Strolic. (IT) **2059**

Strolling Astronomer *see* Association of Lunar and Planetary Observers. Journal **360**
Strom. (SZ) **1908**
Zeitschrift fuer Unsere Stromkunden. (GW) **1908**
Strom & See. (SZ ISSN 0039-2510) **4740**
Strom und Welle. (GW) **1380**
Stromata. (AG ISSN 0049-2353) **3782, 4203**
Strompraxis. (GW ISSN 0340-7519) **1908**
Strong-Motion Earthquake Records in Japan/Kyoshin Kiroku. (JA ISSN 0563-7902) **1595**
Strongest Funds *see* Mutual Fund Trends **957**
Strooidak. (SA) **4250**
Strophes. (SA) **3006**
Strout World. (US ISSN 0039-2545) **4158**
Strucni Casopis Duro Dakovic. (CI ISSN 0351-627X) **1939, 693, 1908**
Structur. (GW) **2496**
Structural and Functional Aspects of Cell Membranes *see* I C R D B Cancergram: Structural and Functional Aspects of Cell Membranes **5209**
Structural Change and Economic Dynamics. (UK ISSN 0954-349X) **898**
▼Structural Chemistry. (GW ISSN 1040-0400) **1189**
Structural Engineer. (UK) **1874**
Structural Engineer. Part A *see* Structural Engineer **1874**
Structural Engineer. Part B *see* Structural Engineer **1874**
Structural Engineering Documents. (SZ) **1874**
Structural Engineering International. (SZ ISSN 0377-7243) **1874**
Structural Engineering Review. (UK ISSN 0952-5807) **1874, 307, 633**
Structural Foam Conference. Proceedings. (US) **3868**
†Structural Mechanics Software Series. (US ISSN 0146-2059) **5284**
Structural Safety. (NE ISSN 0167-4730) **1874**
Structural Survey. (UK ISSN 0263-080X) **633, 1837**
Structure and Bonding. (US ISSN 0081-5993) **1189**
Structure Engineers. *see* Jiegou Gongchengshi **1869**
Structure in Complexity Theory Conference. Proceedings. (US) **1432**
Structure of the Japanese Auto Parts Industry. (JA) **885, 4702**
Structure of the Japanese Electronics Industry. (JA) **1778**
Structure Reports. Section A. (NE ISSN 0166-6983) **1211**
Structure Reports. Section B. (NE ISSN 0166-7033) **1211**
Structured Language World *see* Structured Programming **1432**
Structured Programming. (US ISSN 0935-1183) **1432**
Structuring Foreign Investment in U.S. Real Estate. (NE) **2683, 4158**
Structurist. (CN ISSN 0081-6027) **345**
Struggle. *see* Fen Tou **2866**
Struggle. *see* Fendou **3894**
Struggle *see* Practice (New York) **3919**
Struggle. (US) **3928, 2964**
Struktura i Rol' Vody v Zhivom Organizme *see* Molekulyarnaya Fizika i Biofizika Vodnykh Sistem **486**
Strumenti & Musica. (IT ISSN 0039-260X) **3582**
Strumenti Bibliografici. (IT) **2786**
Strumenti Critici. (IT ISSN 0039-2618) **2964**
Strumenti di Lessicografia Letteraria Italiana. (IT) **3006**
Strumenti Linguistici. (IT ISSN 0391-1942) **2843**
Strumenti Musicali. (IT ISSN 0392-890X) **3582**
Strutture. (IT) **1874**
Strydkreet. *see* War Cry **4290**

Stubs (Metro NY). (US ISSN 0081-6051) **4639**
Stuckgewerbe *see* Das Stukkateur **633**
Stud and Stable. (AT ISSN 0311-8215) **4538**
Stud. Med. (DK ISSN 0039-2634) **3155**
Studebaker Story. (US ISSN 0300-8703) **2165**
Studencheskii Meridian. (RU ISSN 0321-3803) **1266**
Student. (UK) **1325**
Student. (YU ISSN 0039-2693) **1665**
Student. (SA) **1716**
Student. (NE ISSN 0165-6759) **2885, 1325**
Student (Lincoln). (US ISSN 0039-2677) **2296**
The Student (Nashville). (US ISSN 0039-2685) **4250**
Student Acceleration in Florida Public Education. (US) **1760**
Student Action. (II) **1325**
Student Action. (US) **1325, 3973**
Student Action in Engineering. (US ISSN 0899-5427) **1939, 1723**
Student Activities *see* Leadership (Reston) **1645**
Student Activities Programming *see* Campus Activities Programming **1701**
Student Advocate *see* Advocate (Prattsville) **2892**
Student Aid News. (US ISSN 0194-2212) **1716, 2683**
Student Aid Newsletter: Fellowships, Grants, Loans, Awards and Scholarships. (US) **1717**
Student Assistance Journal. (US ISSN 1042-6388) **1539, 1244, 1741**
Student Baker. (UK) **2089**
†Student Choir Director's Library. (UR) **5284**
Student Echo. (US) **1325**
Student Forum *see* Photographer's Forum **3795**
Student Guide to Graduate Law Study Programs. (US) **1697, 2683**
Student Guide to Summer Law Study Programs. (US ISSN 0197-6656) **2683**
Student Guide to the S A T. (US ISSN 1043-8378) **1697, 1266, 1325, 1717**
Student Lawyer (Chicago). (US ISSN 0039-274X) **2683**
Student Lawyer Journal *see* Student Lawyer (Chicago) **2683**
Student Leadership Journal. (US) **1665, 1325, 4250**
†Student Life. (US) **5284**
Student Life (St. Louis). (US ISSN 0039-2758) **1325**
Student Magazine. (US) **1325**
Student Mathematics. (CN ISSN 0085-6800) **3056**
Student Movement. (US) **1325**
Student National Education Association Impact: The Student Voice of the United Teaching Profession *see* S N E A Impact: The Student Voice of the United Teaching Profession **1660**
Student Nationalist. (US ISSN 0260-2563) **2885**
Student Press Law Center Report. (US ISSN 0160-3825) **2683**
†Student Press Service. (US ISSN 0274-9777) **5284**
Student Success Tutor Directory - Sarasota and Manatee County. (US) **1760**
Student Successs Tutor Directory - Sarasota County *see* Student Success Tutor Directory - Sarasota and Manatee County **1760**
Student Times. (JA) **1244**
Student Times International. (PK ISSN 0039-2790) **1325**
†Student Travel Catalog. (US) **5284**
†Student Traveler. (US ISSN 1043-0709) **5284**
▼Student Travels. (US) **1723, 4787**
Student und Praktikant. (GW ISSN 0721-8672) **3743, 1760**
Student Voice *see* College Voice (Staten Island) **1308**
Student Voice. (US ISSN 0039-2804) **1325**
Student Welfare Manual. (UK) **4422**

Studenten Nachrichten *see* World Student News **1672**
Studenterhaandbogen. (DK ISSN 0108-1020) **1717**
Students Life. (CS) **1325**
Student's Message/Risalat al-Talib. (JO) **1665, 1266**
Students Quarterly Journal *see* I E E Review **1898**
Students Representative Council. Handbook *see* Glasgow University Students' Handbook **1635**
†Students United for Peace Newsletter. (US) **5284**
Students World. (GH) **1665**
Studentski List *see* S L **1660**
Studi Albanesi. Studi e Testi. (IT ISSN 0081-6116) **2843, 2964**
Studi Arabi. Quaderni. (IT) **3644**
Studi Biblici. (IT ISSN 0039-2898) **4203**
Studi Cattolici. (IT ISSN 0039-2901) **4276**
Studi Classici e Orientali. (IT ISSN 0081-6124) **1280, 2342, 2432**
Studi d'Architettura Antica. (IT ISSN 0081-6140) **307**
Studi Danteschi (Florence). (IT) **2964**
Studi di Filologia Italiana. (IT) **2843**
Studi di Grammatica Italiana. (IT) **2843**
Studi di Lessicografia Italiana. (IT) **2843**
Studi di Letteratura Francese. (IT ISSN 0585-4768) **2964**
Studi di Metrica Classica. (IT ISSN 0081-6159) **1280**
Studi di Musica Veneta. (IT) **3582**
Studi di Musica Veneta. Quaderni Vivaldiani. (IT) **3582**
Studi di Psicologia dell'Educazione. (IT ISSN 0393-6163) **4047, 1665**
Studi di Sociologia. (IT ISSN 0039-291X) **4453**
Studi di Storia dell'Educazione. (IT ISSN 0392-1948) **1665**
Studi di Storia delle Arti. (IT) **345**
Studi e Documenti di Architettura. (IT) **307**
Studi e Materiali di Archeologia Greca. (IT) **286**
Studi e Problemi di Critica Testuale. (IT ISSN 0049-2361) **2844, 2964**
Studi e Ricerche Francescane. (IT) **4276**
Studi e Ricerche sui Giacimenti Terziari di Bolca. (IT) **3661**
Studi e Ricerche sull'Oriente Cristiano. (IT ISSN 0394-0616) **4203, 2389**
Studi e Saggi Linguistici. (IT ISSN 0085-6827) **2844**
Studi e Testi dell'Antichita. (IT) **2964**
Studi e Testi di Letteratura Italiana. (IT) **2964**
Studi e Testi di Storia e Critica dell'Arte.(IT) **345**
Studi e Testi per la Storia della Musica. (IT) **3582**
Studi e Testi per la Storia Religiosa del Cinquecento. (IT) **4203**
Studi Eblaiti. (IT) **286, 2432**
Studi Economici. (IT ISSN 0039-2928) **693**
Studi Economici e Sociali. (IT) **693**
Studi Ecumenici. (IT ISSN 0393-3687) **4203**
Studi Emigrazione/Etudes Migrations. (IT ISSN 0039-2936) **3988, 4453**
Studi Etno-Antropologici e Sociologici. (IT) **250**
Studi Etruschi. (IT) **2389**
†Studi Filosofici. (IT) **5284**
Studi Francesi. (IT ISSN 0039-2944) **2844, 2964**
Studi Genuensi. (IT ISSN 0585-4911) **286, 2323**
Studi Germanici. (IT ISSN 0039-2952) **2964**
Studi Goriziani. (IT) **4389**
Studi Grafici. (IT ISSN 0039-2960) **1062**
Studi Internazionali di Filosofia *see* International Studies in Philosophy **3769**
Studi Ispanici. (IT ISSN 0585-492X) **2964**

Studi Italiani di Filologia Classica. (IT ISSN 0039-2987) **2844**, 1280
Studi Italiani di Linguistica Teorica ed Applicata. (IT ISSN 0390-6809) **2844**
Studi Latini e Italiani. (IT) **2844**
Studi Linguistici Salentini. (IT) **2844**
Studi Lunigianesi. (IT) **2024**, 2389
Studi Magrebini. (IT) **2335**
Studi Marittimi. (IT ISSN 0392-5021) **4740**
Studi Medievali. (IT) **2389**
Studi Mediolatini e Volgari. (IT) **2844**
Studi Musicali. (IT ISSN 0391-7789) **3582**
Studi Novecenteschi. (IT) **2964**
Studi Organizzativi. (IT) **1028**
Studi Orientali. (IT) **3644**
Studi Parlamentari e di Politica. (IT ISSN 0303-9714) **1969**, 2729, 3928
Studi per l'Ecologia del Quaternario. (IT ISSN 0392-6788) **250**, 3661
Studi Pergolesiani. *see* Pergolesi Studies **3574**
Studi Piemontesi. (IT) **2964**, 2515, 3006, 3582
Studi Ricerche Documentazione. (IT) **921**
Studi Romagnoli. (IT ISSN 0081-6205) **2389**
Studi Romagnoli. Estratti di Sezione. (IT ISSN 0081-6213) **2389**
Studi Romagnoli. Quaderni. (IT ISSN 0081-6221) **2389**
Studi Romani. (IT ISSN 0039-2995) **2323**
Studi Salentini. (IT ISSN 0039-3002) **2389**
Studi Sassaresi. (IT ISSN 0371-3172) **3155**
Studi Sciacchiani. (IT ISSN 0393-9944) **2515**
Studi Secenteschi. (IT ISSN 0081-6248) **2964**
Studi Senesi. (IT ISSN 0039-3010) **2683**, 2389
Studi Settecenteschi. (IT ISSN 0392-7326) **2323**
Studi Storici/Historical Studies. (IT ISSN 0039-3037) **2323**, 2885
Studi Storici dell'Ordine dei Servi di Maria. (IT ISSN 0039-3045) **4276**
Studi Storici Meridionali. (IT) **2389**
Studi sull'Educazione. (IT ISSN 0392-2146) **1665**
Studi sulla Culture dell'Italia Meridionale e Italo-Americana. *see* Studies in Southern Italian and Italian-American Culture **4454**
Studi sulla Modernizzazione e lo Sviluppo. (IT) **4453**
Studi Tassiani. (IT ISSN 0081-6256) **2964**
Studi Urbinati. Serie A: Diritto. (IT ISSN 0039-307X) **2683**
Studi Urbinati. Serie B: Letteratura, Storia, Filsofia *see* Studi Urbinati. Serie B: Scienze Umane e Sociali **2964**
Studi Urbinati. Serie B: Scienze Umane e Sociali. (IT) **2964**, 2323, 3782
†Studi Veneziani. (IT ISSN 0081-6264) **5284**
Studi Verdiani. (IT ISSN 0393-2532) **3583**
Studia Ad Corpus Hellenisticum Novi Testamenti. (NE ISSN 0169-801X) **4203**
Studia Africana. (GH ISSN 0163-2965) **2024**, 2335
Studia Algoligica Lovaniensia. (BE) **4346**
Studia and Sztuka Renesansu i Baroku/Studies in Art of Renaissance and Baroque. (PL) **345**
Studia Anglica Posnaniensia. (PL ISSN 0081-6272) **2844**, 2964
Studia Anglistica Upsalienses. (SW ISSN 0562-2719) **2844**
Studia Anthroponymica Scandinavica. (SW ISSN 0280-8633) **2844**, 2165, 4453
Studia Archaeologica. (HU ISSN 0081-6280) **286**
Studia Archeologica. (IT ISSN 0081-6299) **286**
Studia Archeologiczne. (PL ISSN 0081-6302) **286**

Studia Aristotelica. (IT ISSN 0081-6310) **3782**
Studia Balcanica. (BU) **2389**
Studia Biblica. (NE ISSN 0169-9954) **4203**
Studia Biologica Academiae Scientiarum Hungaricae. (HU ISSN 0076-244X) **457**
Studia Biophysica. (GW ISSN 0081-6337) **487**
Studia Botanica. (SP ISSN 0211-9714) **518**
Studia Canonica. (CN ISSN 0039-310X) **4203**
Studia Cartesiana. (NE) **3782**
Studia Caucasica. (BE ISSN 0081-6345) **2844**, 2389
Studia Celtica. (UK ISSN 0081-6353) **2844**, 2389
Studia Classica. (US ISSN 0899-9929) **2964**
Studia Comeniana et Historica. (CS ISSN 0323-2220) **2389**
Studia Comitatensia. (HU ISSN 0133-3046) **3533**
Studia Copernicana. (PL ISSN 0081-6701) **370**
Studia Copernicana - Brill Series. (NE ISSN 0925-6806) **370**, 2323
Studia Croatica. (AG ISSN 0326-7997) **2024**
Studia Cywilistyczne. (PL ISSN 0039-3126) **2683**
†Studia Delitzschiana. Neue Folge. (GW) **5284**
Studia Demograficzne. (PL ISSN 0039-3134) **3988**
Studia Diplomatica. (BE) **3973**
Studia do Dziejow Dawnego Uzbrojenia i Ubioru Wojskowego. (PL ISSN 0137-5733) **3472**, 3533
Studia Ekonomiczne. (PL) **885**
Studia Ephemeridis Augustinianum. (IT) **4203**
Studia Estetyczne. (PL ISSN 0081-637X) **3782**
Studia et Documenta Historiae et Iuris. (VC) **2323**, 2683
Studia Ethnographica Upsaliensia. (SW ISSN 0491-2705) **250**
Studia Ethnologica Upsaliensis. (SW) **250**
Studia Fennica. (FI ISSN 0085-6835) **2844**, 250
Studia Filozoficzne. (PL ISSN 0039-3142) **3782**
Studia Forestalia Suecica. (SW ISSN 0039-3150) **2108**
Studia Francisci Scholten Memoriae Dicata. (NE ISSN 0081-6396) **286**
†Studia Gaiana. (NE ISSN 0169-8311) **5284**
Studia Geograficzne. (PL ISSN 0081-640X) **2263**
Studia Geologica Polonica. (PL ISSN 0081-6426) **1582**
Studia Geomorphologica Carpatho-Balcanica. (PL ISSN 0081-6434) **1595**
Studia Geophysica et Geodaetica. (US ISSN 0039-3169) **1595**, 3441
Studia Geotechnica *see* Studia Geotechnica et Mechanica **1837**
Studia Geotechnica et Mechanica. (PL ISSN 0137-6365) **1837**, 1595
Studia Germanica Gandensia. (BE ISSN 0081-6442) **2844**
Studia Germanica Posnaniensia. (PL ISSN 0137-2467) **2964**
Studia Graeca et Latina Gothoburgensia. (SW ISSN 0081-6450) **1280**
Studia Grammatica. (GW ISSN 0081-6469) **2844**
Studia Hellenistica. (BE) **1280**
Studia Hibernica. (IE ISSN 0081-6477) **2964**, 2389
Studia Historiae Oeconomicae. (PL ISSN 0081-6485) **898**
Studia Historica. (FI ISSN 0081-6493) **2389**
Studia Historica. (IT ISSN 0081-6507) **2389**
Studia Historica Academiae Scientiarum Hungaricae. (HU ISSN 0076-2458) **2323**
Studia Historica et Philgia: Sectio Romanica. (IT) **2844**

Studia Historica et Philogica: Sectio Slavica. (IT) **2844**
Studia Historica et Philogica: Sectio Slavo-Romanica. (IT) **2844**
Studia Historica Jyvaskylaensia. (FI ISSN 0081-6523) **2389**
Studia Historica Septentrionalia. (FI ISSN 0356-8199) **2389**
Studia Historica Slavo-Germanica. (PL ISSN 0301-6420) **2390**
Studia Historica Slovaca. (CS) **2390**
Studia Historica Upsaliensia. (SW ISSN 0081-6531) **2390**
Studia Historyczne. (PL ISSN 0025-1429) **2390**
Studia i Materialy do Dziejow Muzyki Polskiej. (PL) **3583**
Studia i Materialy do Dziejow Teatru Polskiego. (PL ISSN 0208-404X) **4639**
Studia i Materialy do Dziejow Wielkopolski i Pomorza. (PL ISSN 0081-654X) **2390**
Studia i Materialy do Dziejow Zup Solnych w Polsce. (PL ISSN 0137-530X) **286**, 1582
Studia i Materialy do Historii Wojskowosci. (PL ISSN 0562-2786) **3472**, 2390
Studia i Materialy do Teorii i Historii Architektury i Urbanistyki. (PL ISSN 0081-6566) **307**, 2496
Studia i Materialy Oceanologiczne. (PL ISSN 0208-421X) **1611**
Studia i Materialy z Dziejow Nauki Polskiej. Seria A. Historia Nauk Spolecznych. (PL ISSN 0081-6574) **4389**, 2390
Studia i Materialy z Dziejow Nauki Polskiej. Seria B. Historia Nauk Biologicznych i Medycznych. (PL ISSN 0081-6582) **457**, 3155
Studia i Materialy z Dziejow Nauki Polskiej. Seria C. Historia Nauk Matematycznych, Fizyko-Chemicznych i Geologiczno-Geograficznych. (PL ISSN 0081-6590) **4346**
Studia i Materialy z Dziejow Nauki Polskiej. Seria D. Historia Techniki i Nauk Technicznych. (PL ISSN 0081-6604) **4609**
Studia i Materialy z Dziejow Nauki Polskiej. Seria E. Zagadnienia Ogolne. (PL ISSN 0081-6612) **4346**, 4609
Studia i Materialy z Dziejow Teatru Polskiego *see* Studia i Materialy do Dziejow Teatru Polskiego **4639**
Studia in Veteris Testamenti Pseudepigrapha. (NE ISSN 0169-8125) **4203**
Studia Instituti Anthropos. (SZ) **250**
Studia Iranica. (BE ISSN 0772-7852) **3644**
Studia Irenica. (GW ISSN 0081-6663) **4203**
Studia Iuridica. (PL ISSN 0081-6671) **2683**
Studia Iuridica Auctoriatate Universitatis Pecs Publicata. (HU ISSN 0324-5934) **2683**
Studia Jezykoznawcze. (PL ISSN 0208-8665) **2844**
Studia Juridica. (IT ISSN 0081-6698) **2683**
Studia Kieleckie. (PL ISSN 0137-4354) **2390**
Studia Latino-Americana *see* Acta Universitatis Szegediensis de Attila Jozsef Nominatae. Acta Historica **2347**
Studia Leibnitiana. (GW ISSN 0039-3185) **3782**, 4346
Studia Leibnitiana. Sonderhefte. (GW ISSN 0341-0765) **3782**
Studia Leibnitiana. Supplementa. (GW ISSN 0303-5980) **3782**
Studia Linguistica. (SW ISSN 0039-3193) **2844**
Studia Linguistica et Philologica. (US) **2844**
Studia Liturgica. (US ISSN 0039-3207) **4203**
Studia Logica. (PL ISSN 0039-3215) **3782**
Studia Lulliana. (SP) **2390**
Studia Maritima. (PL ISSN 0137-3587) **921**

STUDIA ROMANICA

Studia Mathematica. (PL ISSN 3223) **3056**
Studia Mediewistyczne. (PL ISSN 0039-3231) **3782**
Studia Metodologiczne. Dissertatione Methodologicae. (PL ISSN 0039-324X) **3782**
Studia Monastica. (SP ISSN 0039-3258) **4203**, 2323
Studia Moralia. (IT ISSN 0081-6736) **4203**
Studia Musicologica Academiae Scientiarum Hungaricae. (HU ISSN 0039-3266) **3583**
Studia Musicologica Norvegica. (NO ISSN 0332-5024) **3583**
Studia Musicologica Upsaliensia. Nova Series. (SW ISSN 0081-6744) **3583**
Studia Mystica. (US ISSN 0161-7222) **2986**
Studia nad Zagadnieniami Gospodarczymi i Spolecznymi Ziem Zachodnich. (PL ISSN 0081-6752) **2390**
Studia Naturae. Seria A. Wydawnictwa Naukowe. (PL) **1497**
Studia Naturae. Seria B. Wydawnictwa Popularno-Naukowe. (PL ISSN 0551-4193) **1497**
Studia Nauk Politycznych *see* Studia Polityczne **3928**
Studia Neophilologica. (SW ISSN 0039-3274) **2844**
Studia Numismatica et Medailistica. (CS ISSN 0081-6779) **3602**
Studia o Ksiazce. (PL ISSN 0137-3404) **2786**, 4137
Studia Orientalia. (FI ISSN 0039-3282) **3644**
Studia Orientalia Christiana. Collectanea. (IS) **4203**, 2432
Studia Orientalia Christiana. Monographiae. (IS) **4203**, 2432
Studia Orientalia Lundensia. (NE ISSN 0281-4528) **2844**, 3644
Studia Palmyrenskie. (PL ISSN 0081-6787) **286**
Studia Patavina. (IT ISSN 0039-3304) **4203**, 3782
Studia Pedagogicze. (PL ISSN 0081-6795) **1665**
Studia Philologiae Scandinavicae Upsaliensia. (SW ISSN 0081-6809) **2844**
Studia Philologica Jyvaskylaensia. (FI ISSN 0585-5462) **2844**
Studia Philosophiae Religionis. (SW) **3782**, 4203
Studia Philosophica. (SZ) **3782**
Studia Phonetica Posnaniensia. (PL ISSN 0860-2085) **2844**
Studia Phonologica/Onsci Kagaku Kenkyu. (JA ISSN 0300-1067) **2844**
Studia Picena. (IT ISSN 0392-1719) **4276**
Studia Pneumologica et Phtiseologica Cechoslovaca. (CS ISSN 0371-2222) **3367**
Studia Poetica. (HU ISSN 0209-9403) **2964**, 2384, 3006
Studia Pohl. (VC) **3644**
Studia Pohl: Series Maior. (VC) **3644**
Studia Polityczne. (PL) **3928**
Studia Polonijne. (PL) **3988**
Studia Polonistyczne. (PL ISSN 0137-4370) **2844**
Studia Polono-Slavica Orientalia. Acta Litteraria. (PL ISSN 0137-4389) **2964**
Studia Post-Biblica. (NE ISSN 0169-9717) **4203**
Studia Prawnicze. (PL ISSN 0039-3312) **2683**
Studia Prawno-Ekonomiczne. (PL ISSN 0081-6841) **2683**
Studia Psychologica. (CS ISSN 0039-3320) **4047**
Studia Psychologica et Paedagogica. (SW) **1665**, 4047
Studia Psychologiczne. (PL ISSN 0081-685X) **4047**
Studia Romanica et Anglica Zagrabiensia. (CI ISSN 0039-3339) **2845**, 2964
Studia Romanica Upsaliensia. (SW ISSN 0562-3022) **2845**

Studia Rosenthaliana. (NE ISSN 0039-3347) **2024**, 2964
Studia Rossica Posnaniensia. (PL ISSN 0081-6884) **2964**
Studia Scientiae Paedagogicae Upsaliensia see Uppsala Studies in Education **1670**
Studia Scientiarum Mathematicarum Hungarica. (HU ISSN 0081-6906) **3056**
Studia Semiotyczne. (PL ISSN 0137-6608) **2845**
Studia Semitica Neerlandica. (NE ISSN 0081-6914) **4226**
Studia Silesina. (SP) **4203**, 2323
Studia Slaskie/Silesian Studies. (PL ISSN 0039-3355) **2214**
Studia Slavica Academiae Scientiarum Hungaricae. (HU ISSN 0039-3363) **2845**, 2323
Studia Slovenica. (US ISSN 0585-5543) **2390**
Studia Slovenica. Special Series. (US ISSN 0081-6922) **2390**
†Studia Societatis Scientiarum Torunensis. Sectio B. Chemia. (PL ISSN 0082-5530) **5284**
Studia Societatis Scientiarum Torunensis. Sectio C. Geografia et Geologia. (PL ISSN 0082-5549) **2263**, 1582
Studia Societatis Scientiarum Torunensis. Sectio D. Botanica. (PL ISSN 0082-5557) **518**
Studia Societatis Scientiarum Torunensis. Sectio E. Zoologia. (PL ISSN 0082-5565) **592**
Studia Societatis Scientiarum Torunensis. Sectio F. Astronomia. (PL ISSN 0082-5573) **370**
†Studia Societatis Scientiarum Torunensis. Sectio G. Physiologia. (PL ISSN 0082-5581) **5284**
Studia Societatis Scientiarum Torunensis. Sectio H. Medicina. (PL ISSN 0860-9594) **3155**
Studia Socjologiczne. (PL ISSN 0039-3371) **4453**
Studia Spinozana. (GW ISSN 0179-3896) **3782**, 4346
Studia Spoleczno-Ekonomiczne. (PL ISSN 0081-6930) **693**
Studia Staropolskie. (PL ISSN 0081-6949) **2964**
Studia Sumiro-Hungarica. (US ISSN 0585-5578) **250**
Studia Tehologica Lundensia. (SW ISSN 0491-2853) **4203**
Studia Theodisca. (NE ISSN 0081-6957) **2845**
Studia Theologica. (DK ISSN 0039-338X) **4203**
Studia Ubezpieczeniowe. (PL ISSN 0137-9704) **2543**
▼Studia Universitatia "Babes-Bolyai". Psichologia - Pedagogia. (RM) **4047**, 1665
Studia Universitatis "Babes-Bolyai". Biologia. (RM ISSN 0039-3398) **457**
Studia Universitatis "Babes-Bolyai". Chemia. (RM ISSN 0039-3401) **1189**
Studia Universitatis "Babes-Bolyai". Geographia. (RM) **2263**
Studia Universitatis "Babes-Bolyai". Geologia. (RM) **1582**
Studia Universitatis "Babes-Bolyai". Geologia - Geographia see Studia Universitatis "Babes-Bolyai". Geologia **1582**
Studia Universitatis "Babes-Bolyai". Geologia - Geographia see Studia Universitatis "Babes-Bolyai". Geographia **2263**
Studia Universitatis "Babes-Bolyai". Historia. (RM ISSN 0039-3428) **2323**
Studia Universitatis "Babes-Bolyai". Iurisprudentia. (RM ISSN 0578-5464) **2683**
Studia Universitatis "Babes-Bolyai". Mathematica. (RM) **3056**
Studia Universitatis "Babes-Bolyai". Oeconomica. (RM ISSN 0578-5472) **693**
Studia Universitatis "Babes-Bolyai". Philologia. (RM ISSN 0039-3444) **2845**, 2964

Studia Universitatis "Babes-Bolyai". Philosophia. (RM ISSN 0578-5480) **3782**
Studia Universitatis "Babes-Bolyai". Physica. (RM) **3833**
▼Studia Universitatis "Babes-Bolyai". Sociologia - Politologia. (RM) **4453**, 3928
Studia Uralica et Altaica Upsaliensia. (SW ISSN 0081-7015) **2845**
Studia Uralo-Altaica. (US ISSN 0133-4239) **2845**, 2964
Studia z Automatyki. (PL) **1416**
Studia z Dziejow Z S R R i Europy Srodkowej. (PL ISSN 0081-7082) **2390**
Studia z Filologii Polskiej i Slowianskiej. (PL ISSN 0081-7090) **2845**
Studia z Historii Sztuki. (PL ISSN 0081-7104) **345**
Studia z Okresu Oswiecenia. (PL ISSN 0081-7112) **2964**
Studia z Zakresu Budownictwa see Studia z Zakresu Inzynierii **1875**
Studia z Zakresu Inzynierii. (PL ISSN 0137-5393) **1875**
Studias Humanitas. (NE ISSN 0324-7880) **2390**, 4203
Studie o Rukopisech. (CS) **2390**
Studie van de Luchtkwaliteit in Belgie. Zwavel-Rook Meetnet. (BE) **4113**
Studie z Dejin Hornictvi. (CS) **3496**, 2390
Studie z Dejin Techniky. (CS ISSN 0862-3171) **4609**
Studien ueber Asien, Afrika und Lateinamerika. (GW ISSN 0138-5550) **2323**
Studien ueber Wirtschaft- und Systemvergleiche. (US ISSN 0344-824X) **898**
Studien und Berichte. (GW ISSN 0076-5627) **1665**
Studien- und Hochschulfuehrer. (GW) **1717**
Studien und Mitteilungen zur Geschichte des Benediktiner. Ordens und Seiner Zweige. (GW ISSN 0303-4224) **4276**
Studien und Quellen zur Oesterreichischen Zeitgeschichte. (AU) **2390**
Studien und Texte zur Geistesgeschichte des Mittelalters. (NE ISSN 0169-8028) **2390**
Studien und Texte zur Kirchengeschichte und Geschichte. (AU) **4250**
Studien zu den Bogazkoey-Texten. (GW ISSN 0585-5853) **2845**
Studien zu Nichteuropaeischen Rechtstheorien. (GW ISSN 0171-9378) **3644**
Studien zu Politik und Verwaltung. (AU) **2683**, 3928
Studien zum Kleinen Deutschen Sprachatlas. (GW) **2845**
Studien zur Agrarwirtschaft. (GW ISSN 0081-7198) **158**
Studien zur Altaegyptischen Kultur. (GW ISSN 0340-2215) **1280**
Studien zur Altaegyptischen Kultur. Beihefte. (GW) **1280**, 2335
Studien zur Antiken Philosophie. (NE) **3783**
Studien zur Bauwirtschaft. (GW ISSN 0170-5687) **633**
Studien zur Bevoelkerungsoekonomie. (GW ISSN 0721-0086) **693**, 3988
Studien zur Bibliotheksgeschichte. (AU) **2786**
Studien zur Deutschen Kunstgeschichte.(GW ISSN 0081-7228) **345**
Studien zur Deutschen Literatur. (GW ISSN 0081-7236) **2965**
Studien zur Energiewirtschaft. (GW ISSN 0170-7779) **693**, 1796
Studien zur Englischen Philologie, Neue Folge. (GW ISSN 0081-7244) **2845**, 2965
Studien zur Europaeischen Geschichte. (GW ISSN 0081-7252) **2390**
Studien zur Finanzpolitik. (GW ISSN 0081-7279) **800**
Studien zur Franzoesischen Philosophie des Zwanzigsten Jahrhunderts. (GW ISSN 0340-5958) **3783**

Studien zur Germanistik, Anglistik und Komparatistik. (GW ISSN 0340-594X) **2965**
Studien zur Geschichte Asiens, Afrikas und Lateinamerikas. see Studien ueber Asien, Afrika und Lateinamerika **2323**
Studien zur Geschichte der Katholischen Moraltheologie. (GW ISSN 0081-7295) **4276**
Studien zur Geschichte des Neunzehnten Jahrhunderts. (GW ISSN 0081-7309) **2323**
Studien zur Indologie und Iranistik. (GW ISSN 0341-4191) **2342**, 2845
Studien zur Industriewirtschaft. (GW ISSN 0170-5660) **693**
Studien zur Japanologie. (GW ISSN 0585-6094) **2342**
Studien zur Kinderpsychoanalyse. Jahrbuch. (AU ISSN 0255-6715) **4047**
Studien zur Kirchengeschichte Niedersachsens. (GW) **4203**
Studien zur Kulturkunde. (GW ISSN 0170-3544) **250**
Studien zur Literatur der Moderne. (GW ISSN 0340-9023) **2965**
Studien zur Literatur- und Sozialgeschichte Spaniens und Lateinamerikas. (GW ISSN 0340-5990) **2965**, 4453
Studien zur Medizingeschichte des Neunzehnten Jahrhunderts. (GW ISSN 0081-7333) **3155**
Studien zur Modernen Geschichte. (GW ISSN 0178-8310) **2323**
Studien zur Musikgeschichte des Neunzehnten Jahrhunderts. (GW ISSN 0081-7341) **3583**
Studien zur Musikwissenschaft. (GW) **3583**
Studien zur Oesterreichischen Philosophie. (NE ISSN 0167-4102) **3783**
Studien zur Ostasiatischen Schriftkunst. (GW ISSN 0170-3684) **345**, 3644
Studien zur Philosophie des 18. Jahrhunderts. (GW) **3783**
†Studien zur Philosophie und Literatur des Neunzehnten Jahrhunderts. (GW ISSN 0081-735X) **5284**
Studien zur Phonologie, Phonetik und Linguistik des Franzoesischen. see Etudes de Phonologie, Phonetique et Linguistique Descriptive du Francais **2813**
Studien zur Problemgeschichte der Antiken und Mittelalterlichen Philosophie. (NE ISSN 0169-9857) **3783**, 2390
Studien zur Rechts-, Wirtschafts- und Kulturgeschichte. (AU) **2683**, 898
Studien zur Umwelt des Neuen Testaments. (GW) **4203**
Studien zur Verkehrswirtschaft. (GW ISSN 0170-5652) **693**, 4656
Der Studienbeginn. (GW) **1665**
Studienbuecherei. (GW ISSN 0081-7384) **4346**
Studienfuehrer. (GW) **4075**
Studienfuehrer Mathematik. (GW) **3056**, 1717
Studienfuehrer und Personal Verzeichnis. (GW) **1760**
Studienhefte der Paedagogischen Hochschule see Studienhefte Psychologie in Erziehung und Unterricht **1717**
Studienhefte Psychologie in Erziehung und Unterricht. (GW ISSN 0081-7392) **1717**, 4047
Studienkreis zur Erforschung und Vermittlung der Geschichte des Deutschen Widerstands 1933-1945. Informationen. (GW) **2390**
Studienreihe Paedagogische Psychologie. (GW ISSN 0173-0975) **4047**, 1665
Studienstiftung. Jahresbericht. (GW) **1741**, 4422
Studier i Arbetarroerelsens Historia. (SW) **2589**
Studier i Modern Spraakvetenskap/ Stockholm Studies in Modern Philology. (SW) **2845**

Studier i Nordisk Arkeologi/Studies in North European Archaeology. (SW ISSN 0081-7414) **286**
Studier i Politik - Studies in Politics see Goeteborg Studies in Politics **3896**
Studies. (IE ISSN 0039-3495) **4346**, 2515
Studies and Reports in Hydrology Series. (UN ISSN 0081-7449) **1600**
Studies and Reseach in Art History. Series: Theatre, Music, Cinematography. see Studii si Cercetari de Istoria Artei. Seria Teatru, Muzica, Cinematografie **4639**
Studies and Research in Geology. see Studii si Cercetari de Geologie **1582**
Studies for Trade Unionists. (UK ISSN 0307-2444) **994**, 2589
†Studies in Aboriginal Rights. (CN ISSN 0226-3491) **5284**
Studies in Accounting Research. (US ISSN 0586-5050) **756**
Studies in Adult Education see Studies in the Education of Adults **1687**
Studies in Adult Education. (TZ ISSN 0856-0560) **1687**
Studies in African and Afro-American Culture. (US ISSN 0890-4847) **2335**, 2423, 2965, 4453
Studies in African Economic & Social Development. (US) **898**, 4453
Studies in African Education. (US) **1665**
Studies in African Health & Medicine. (US) **3155**
Studies in African History. see Etudes d'Histoire Africaine **2332**
Studies in African Linguistics. (US ISSN 0039-3533) **2845**, 2024
Studies in African Literature. (US) **2965**
Studies in American Drama, 1945 - Present. (US ISSN 0886-7097) **4639**
Studies in American Fiction. (US ISSN 0091-8083) **2965**
Studies in American History. (US) **2323**
Studies in American Humor. (US ISSN 0095-280X) **2885**
Studies in American Indian Literatures. (US ISSN 0730-3238) **2965**, 2024
Studies in American Jewish History. (US ISSN 0081-7511) **2024**, 4226
Studies in American Jewish Literature. (US ISSN 0271-9274) **2025**, 2965
Studies in American Literature. (US) **2965**
Studies in American Negro Life. (US) **2025**
Studies in American Political Development. (US) **3928**
Studies in American Religion. (US) **4203**
Studies in Anabaptist and Mennonite History. (US ISSN 0081-7538) **4288**
Studies in Analytical Chemistry. (NE) **1208**
†Studies in Ancient Art and Archaeology. (US) **5284**
†Studies in Ancient Civilization. (NE) **5284**
Studies in Ancient Medicine. (NE ISSN 0925-1421) **3155**, 2323
Studies in Ancient Oriental Civilization. (US ISSN 0081-7554) **2342**
Studies in Anglesey History. (UK ISSN 0585-6515) **2390**
†Studies in Anthropological Method. (US ISSN 0585-6523) **5284**
Studies in Anthropology and History. (US ISSN 1055-2464) **2323**, 250
Studies in Applied Mathematics. (US ISSN 0022-2526) **3056**, 3833
Studies in Applied Mechanics. (NE) **3845**
†Studies in Applied Regional Science. (US) **5284**
Studies in Arabic Literature. (NE ISSN 0169-9903) **2965**, 2432
Studies in Archaeological Science. (US) **286**

Studies in Art and Religious Interpretation. (US) **345**, **4203**
Studies in Art Education. (US ISSN 0039-3541) **1665**, **345**
Studies in Art of Renaissance and Baroque. *see* Studia dla Sztuka Renesansu i Baroku **345**
Studies in Asian Thought and Religion. (US) **3783**, **4288**
Studies in Astronautics. (NE) **63**
Studies in Automation and Control. (NE) **1416**
Studies in Avian Biology. (US) **567**
Studies in Banking and Finance *see* Journal of Banking and Finance **787**
Studies in Bayesian Econometrics and Statistics. (NE) **898**, **4589**
Studies in Bible and Early Christianity. (US) **4203**
Studies in Bible and Exegesis. (IS) **4204**
Studies in Biblical Greek. (US ISSN 0897-7828) **4204**, **2025**
Studies in Bibliography. (US ISSN 0081-7600) **2795**
Studies in Bibliography and Booklore. (US ISSN 0039-3568) **4142**, **4213**
Studies in Black American Literature. (US ISSN 0738-0755) **2965**, **2025**
Studies in Black Religion in America. (US) **2025**, **4204**
Studies in British & American Literature/Ei-Beibungaku. (JA) **2965**
Studies in British Art. (US) **345**
Studies in British History. (US) **2390**
Studies in British Literature. (US) **2965**
†Studies in British Musicology. (US) **5284**
Studies in Browning and His Circle. (US ISSN 0095-4489) **2965**
Studies in Burke and His Time *see* Eighteenth Century: Theory and Interpretation **2359**
Studies in Business and Society. (US ISSN 0081-7635) **693**
Studies in Calligraphy. *see* Shufa Yanjiu **344**
Studies in Canadian Literature. (CN ISSN 0380-6995) **2965**
Studies in Central and East Asian Religions. (DK ISSN 0904-2431) **4215**, **3644**
Studies in Central and Eastern European Music. (HU) **3583**
Studies in Chinese Chess. *see* Xiangqi Yanjiu **4497**
†Studies in Christian Antiquity. (US) **5284**
Studies in Christian Ethics. (UK ISSN 0953-9468) **3783**, **4204**
Studies in Christian Mission. (NE ISSN 0924-9389) **4204**
Studies in Church and State. (US) **4204**, **3928**
Studies in Cistercian Art and Architecture. (US) **345**, **307**
Studies in Classical Antiquity. (NE ISSN 0167-6679) **1280**
Studies in Classics. (US) **2965**
Studies in Colonial America. (US) **2025**
Studies in Communication. (US) **1343**
Studies in Communications. (US ISSN 0275-7982) **1343**
Studies in Comparative Communism. (UK ISSN 0039-3592) **3928**
Studies in Comparative Education. (US) **1665**
Studies in Comparative International Development. (US ISSN 0039-3606) **4389**
Studies in Comparative Literature (Chapel Hill). (US ISSN 0081-7775) **2965**
Studies in Comparative Literature (Lewiston). (US) **2965**
Studies in Comparative Religion. (UK ISSN 0039-3622) **4204**
Studies in Comparative Religion. (US) **4204**
Studies in Conflict and Terrorism. (US) **3973**
Studies in Conservation. (UK ISSN 0039-3630) **345**, **286**
Studies in Construction Economy. (UK) **4158**, **633**

Studies in Contemporary Continental Philosophy. (US ISSN 0893-6919) **3783**
Studies in Contemporary Economics. (US) **898**
Studies in Contemporary German Social Thought. (US) **3783**
Studies in Contemporary Jewry. (US ISSN 0740-8625) **2025**
Studies in Contemporary Satire. (US ISSN 0163-4143) **2885**
Studies in Crime and Justice *see* Crime and Justice **1512**
Studies in Curriculum Development. (TZ) **1760**
Studies in Cybernetics. (US ISSN 0275-5807) **1443**
Studies in Defense Policy. (US) **3472**, **3928**
Studies in Descriptive Linguistics. (GW ISSN 0171-6794) **2845**
Studies in Design, Education Craft and Technology *see* Design & Technology Teaching **1747**
Studies in Development/Gelisme Dergisi. (TU) **1028**
Studies in Early English History *see* Studies in the Early History of Britain **2324**
Studies in Economic Analysis. (US) **898**
Studies in Economic Growth. (II ISSN 0081-7848) **693**
Studies in Economic History and Policy.(UK) **898**
Studies in Economic Science/Keizai Shushi. (JA) **693**
†Studies in Economics. (UK ISSN 0081-7856) **5284**
Studies in Education *see* Eiunim Bicheinuch **1631**
Studies in Education and Psychology. (SW) **1665**, **4048**
Studies in Education and Teaching Techniques. (II ISSN 0254-0185) **1665**, **1760**
Studies in Educational Administration. (AT) **1731**, **1723**
Studies in Educational Administration and Organization. (IS ISSN 0334-4770) **1732**
Studies in Educational Evaluation. (US ISSN 0191-491X) **1666**, **4048**
Studies in Eighteenth Century Culture. (US) **2515**, **2323**
Studies in Electoral Politics in the Indian States. (II) **3928**
Studies in Electrical and Electronic Engineering. (NE) **1908**
Studies in English Literature/Eibungaku Kenkyu. (JA ISSN 0039-3649) **2965**, **2845**
Studies in English Literature 1500-1900. (US ISSN 0039-3657) **2965**
Studies in Environmental Science. (NE) **1969**
Studies in Epic and Romance Literature. (US) **2984**
Studies in European Politics. (UK) **3928**
Studies in European Thought. (US ISSN 1043-5786) **2390**
Studies in Evangelicalism. (US) **4289**
Studies in Experimental Literature. (US) **2965**
Studies in Family Planning. (US ISSN 0039-3665) **3988**, **4453**
Studies in Federal Taxation. (US) **1107**
Studies in Formative Spirituality. (US ISSN 0193-2748) **4204**, **2515**
Studies in Freedom. (US ISSN 0273-1231) **3928**
Studies in French Civilization. (US) **2390**
Studies in French Literature. (US) **2965**
Studies in French Theatre. (US) **4639**
Studies in Gender and Culture. (US ISSN 0889-3128) **4453**, **3400**, **4860**
Studies in Generative Grammar. (US) **2845**
Studies in Generative Linguistic Analysis. (US ISSN 0081-7961) **2845**
Studies in Geography in Hungary. (HU ISSN 0081-7961) **2263**
▼Studies in Gerard Manley Hopkins. (US ISSN 1043-5751) **3006**

Studies in German Language and Literature. (US) **2965**
†Studies in German Literature. (GW ISSN 0081-797X) **5284**
Studies in German Literature of the 18th and 19th Centuries. (US) **2965**
Studies in German Thought and History.(US) **2025**, **2390**
Studies in Greek and Latin Linguistics. (NE) **2845**
Studies in Greek and Roman Religion. (NE ISSN 0169-9512) **4204**
Studies in Health and Human Services. (US) **3809**, **4422**
Studies in Health and Human Values. (US) **898**
Studies in High Energy Physics Series. (US ISSN 0270-4730) **3833**
Studies in Higher Education. (UK ISSN 0307-5079) **1717**
†Studies in Higher Education in Canada.(CN ISSN 0081-7988) **5284**
Studies in Hispanic American and Latin American Theatre. (US) **4639**, **2025**
Studies in Historical and Political Science. Extra Volumes. (US ISSN 0081-7996) **3928**
▼Studies in Historiography. (US ISSN 1046-526X) **2323**
Studies in History (Newbury Park). (US ISSN 0257-6430) **2342**
Studies in History (Sahibabad). (II ISSN 0258-1698) **2323**
Studies in History and Culture. (US ISSN 0743-2879) **2323**, **2515**
Studies in History and Philosophy of Science. (US ISSN 0039-3681) **4346**, **3783**
Studies in History and Politics/Etudes d'Histoire et de Politique. (US ISSN 0228-6939) **2323**, **3928**
Studies in History and the Social Sciences. *see* Recherches d'Histoire et de Sciences Sociales **2320**
Studies in History of Biology. (US ISSN 0149-6700) **457**
Studies in History of Medicine *see* Studies in History of Medicine and Science **3155**
Studies in History of Medicine and Science. (II ISSN 0970-5562) **3155**
Studies in Hogg and His World. (UK ISSN 0960-6025) **2965**
Studies in Human Rights. (US ISSN 0146-3586) **3973**, **3947**
Studies in Human Society. (NE) **4453**
Studies in Iconography. (US) **345**
Studies in Income and Wealth. (US) **1000**
Studies in Indian Epigraphy/Bharatiya Purabhilekha Patrika. (II) **2845**
Studies in Indian Place Names/ Bharatiya Sthalanama Patrika. (II) **2845**
Studies in Infectious Diseases Research.(US) **3224**
Studies in Information and Behavioral Sciences. *see* Joho Kodo Kagaku Kenkyu **2509**
Studies in Inorganic Chemistry. (NE) **1215**
Studies in International Affairs (Baltimore). (US ISSN 0081-802X) **3928**
Studies in International Affairs (Columbia). (US) **3973**
Studies in International Cultural Relations. *see* Materialien zum Internationalen Kulturaustausch **3965**
Studies in International Economics. (NE) **693**
Studies in International Finance. (US ISSN 0081-8070) **800**
Studies in International Relations. (BE) **3973**
Studies in Islam. (II ISSN 0039-3711) **4220**, **2965**
Studies in Italian Culture: Literature in History. (US ISSN 1043-5794) **2965**, **2025**
Studies in Italian Literature. (US) **2965**
Studies in Jazz Discography *see* Annual Review of Jazz Studies **5136**

Studies in Jazz Research. *see* Beitraege zur Jazzforschung **3541**
Studies in Jewish Education. (IS ISSN 0333-9661) **1666**, **2025**
▼Studies in Josephson Supercomputers. (SI) **1418**
Studies in Judaica & the Holocaust. (US ISSN 0884-6952) **2025**, **2323**, **4226**
Studies in Judaism in Late Antiquity. (NE ISSN 0169-961X) **4226**
Studies in Judaism in Modern Times. (NE ISSN 0169-9660) **4226**
Studies in Labor Market Dynamics *see* Aarhus School of Business. Centre for Labour Economics. Working Papers **970**
Studies in Language. (NE ISSN 0378-4177) **2845**, **3783**
Studies in Language Companion Series. (US ISSN 0165-7763) **2845**, **2965**
Studies in Language Learning. (US) **2845**
Studies in Latin American Popular Culture. (US ISSN 0730-9139) **4453**
†Studies in Latin American Revolution. (US) **5284**
Studies in Law. *see* Faxue Yanjiu **2625**
Studies in Law and Social Change *see* Peace Law Docket **3946**
Studies in Law, Politics, and Society. (US) **2683**, **4453**
Studies in Legal History. (US) **2683**
Studies in Library Management. (UK ISSN 0307-0808) **2786**
Studies in Linguistics and Philosophy. (NE) **4048**, **2845**, **3783**
Studies in Literature and Criticism. (US) **2965**
Studies in Local and Institutional History. (US) **2423**
Studies in Local and Regional History. (UK) **2390**
Studies in Logic and the Foundations of Mathematics. (NE ISSN 0049-237X) **3057**
Studies in Management Science and Systems. (NE) **1028**
Studies in Mao Zedong's Philosophical Thought. *see* Mao Zedong Zhexue Sixiang Yanjiu **3772**
Studies in Marxism. (US) **3928**, **3783**
Studies in Marxist History and Theory. (US) **3928**
Studies in Mathematical and Managerial Economics. (NE ISSN 0081-8194) **1028**, **3057**
Studies in Mathematics (Washington). (US ISSN 0081-8208) **3057**
Studies in Mathematics and Its Applications. (NE) **3057**
Studies in Mathematics Education. (UN) **1723**, **1760**
Studies in Mayan Linguistics. (US ISSN 0733-5776) **250**
Studies in Mechanical Engineering. (NE) **1939**
Studies in Mediaeval Literature. (US) **2965**
Studies in Medical Ethics. (US) **3155**
Studies in Medieval and Reformation Thought. (NE ISSN 0585-6914) **4204**
Studies in Medieval and Renaissance History. (US ISSN 0081-8224) **2390**
Studies in Medieval and Renaissance Teaching. (US) **2965**, **2323**
Studies in Medieval Culture. (US ISSN 0085-6878) **2324**, **2965**
Studies in Medievalism. (US) **2390**
Studies in Mediterranean Archaeology. Monograph Series. (SW ISSN 0081-8232) **286**, **1280**
Studies in Mediterranean Archaeology. Pocket-Book Series. (SW) **286**, **1280**
Studies in Middle Eastern History. (US) **2432**
Studies in Middle Eastern Literatures. (US) **2965**
▼Studies in Modern Art. (US ISSN 1058-997X) **345**
Studies in Modern European History. (US ISSN 0893-6897) **2390**

STUDIES

Studies in Modern European History and Culture. (US ISSN 0098-275X) **2390**
Studies in Modern German Literature. (US ISSN 0888-3904) **2965**
†Studies in Modern Hebrew Literature. (US) **5284**
†Studies in Modern Literature. (US) **5284**
Studies in Modern Philology. (HU) **2845**
Studies in Modern Thermodynamics. (NE ISSN 0166-6061) **1230**
Studies in Monetary Economics. (NE) **800**
Studies in Moral Philosophy. (US ISSN 0899-4897) **3783, 4204**
Studies in Moral, Political, and Legal Philosophy. (US) **5284**
Studies in Museology. (Il ISSN 0081-8259) **3533**
Studies in Music. (AT ISSN 0081-8267) **3583**
Studies in Music. (CN ISSN 0703-3052) **3583**
Studies in Music. (US) **3583**
Studies in Musicology see Studies in Music **3583**
†Studies in Mycenaean Inscriptions and Dialect. (UK ISSN 0081-8275) **5284**
Studies in Mycology. (NE ISSN 0166-0616) **518**
Studies in Natural Language and Linguistic Theory. (NE) **2845**
Studies in Near Eastern Culture and Society. (US ISSN 0742-1168) **2432**
Studies in Neuroscience. (UK) **3384, 3355**
Studies in New England Thought and Literature. (US) **3783, 2965**
Studies in Nineteenth-Century American History. (US) **2324**
Studies in Nonviolence see S I N **3971**
Studies in North European Archaeology. see Studier i Nordisk Arkeologi **286**
Studies in Old Germanic Languages and Literatures. (US ISSN 0899-9872) **2845, 2965**
Studies in Operations Research. (US ISSN 0141-1004) **1400**
Studies in Organic Chemistry Series. (US) **1223**
Studies in Oriental Culture. (US ISSN 0081-8321) **3644, 2342**
Studies in Oriental Religions. (GW ISSN 0340-6792) **4215**
Studies in Philippine Linguistics. (PH ISSN 0116-0516) **2845**
Studies in Philology. (US ISSN 0039-3738) **2846**
Studies in Philosophy. (SW ISSN 1100-4290) **3783**
Studies in Philosophy and Education. (NE ISSN 0039-3746) **1666, 3783**
Studies in Philosophy & the History of Philosophy. (US ISSN 0585-6965) **3783**
Studies in Physical and Theoretical Chemistry. (NE) **1230**
Studies in Physical Anthropology. (PL ISSN 0324-8291) **250**
Studies in Plant Ecology. (SW ISSN 0282-8677) **518**
Studies in Plant Science. (NE) **518**
Studies in Political Economy. (US) **898**
Studies in Political Economy. Socialist Review. (CN ISSN 0707-8552) **3928, 898**
Studies in Popular Culture. (US ISSN 0888-5753) **4453, 1343, 2324**
Studies in Population. (US) **3988**
Studies in Population and Urban Demography. (US ISSN 0147-1104) **3988**
Studies in Pre-Columbian Art and Archaeology. (US ISSN 0585-7023) **286, 345**
Studies in Production and Engineering Economics. (NE) **693, 1085**
▼Studies in Psephology. (Il) **3996, 3938, 4589**
Studies in Puritan American Spirituality.(US ISSN 1048-8553) **4204**
Studies in Rajput History and Culture Series. (Il) **2342**

Studies in Regional Science and Urban Economics. (NE) **885**
Studies in Religion/Sciences Religieuses. (CN ISSN 0008-4298) **4204**
Studies in Religion and Society. (US) **4204**
Studies in Religious Education. (US) **4204, 1666**
Studies in Renaissance Literature. (US) **2965**
Studies in Restoration and Eighteenth-Century Drama. (US) **4639**
Studies in Romance Languages see Studies in Romance Languages & Literatures **2965**
Studies in Romance Languages & Literatures. (US) **2965**
†Studies in Romantic and Modern Literature. (US ISSN 0743-7889) **5284**
Studies in Romanticism. (US ISSN 0039-3762) **2966**
Studies in Russian and East European History. (UK) **2390**
Studies in Science and the Humanities. (US) **2516, 4346**
Studies in Second Language Acquisition.(UK ISSN 0272-2631) **2846**
Studies in Semiotics and Literature. (Il) **2846, 2966**
Studies in Semitic Languages and Linguistics. (NE ISSN 0081-8461) **2846**
Studies in Sexual Politics see Feminist Praxis **4435**
Studies in Short Fiction. (US ISSN 0039-3789) **2966**
Studies in Slavic and General Linguistics. (NE ISSN 0169-0124) **2846**
Studies in Slavic Language and Literature. (US) **2966**
Studies in Slavic Literature and Poetics.(NE ISSN 0169-0175) **2966**
Studies in Social and Economic Demography. (US) **3988**
Studies in Social and Economic History. (BE) **898**
Studies in Social and Political Theory. (US) **3928**
Studies in Social Discontinuity. (US) **4453**
Studies in Social Economics. (US) **693, 4453**
Studies in Social Experimentation. (US) **4453, 4389**
Studies in Social History. (NE) **4389**
†Studies in Social Life. (US ISSN 0081-8518) **5284**
Studies in Social Policy and Welfare. (UK) **4422**
Studies in Social Welfare Policies and Programs. (US ISSN 8755-5360) **4422**
Studies in Society. (AT ISSN 0156-4420) **4453**
Studies in Sociology and Social Anthropology. (Il) **4453**
Studies in South Asian Culture. (NE ISSN 0169-9865) **345**
Studies in Southern Italian and Italian-American Culture/Studi sulla Culture dell'Italia Meridionale e Italo-Americana. (US) **4454, 2025**
Studies in Soviet Thought. (NE ISSN 0039-3797) **3928, 3783**
†Studies in Speculative Fiction. (US) **5284**
Studies in Speleology. (UK ISSN 0585-718X) **1582**
Studies in Sport, Physical Education and Health. (FI) **3809, 4493**
Studies in Statistical Mechanics. (NE ISSN 0081-8542) **3845**
Studies in Surface Science and Catalysis. (NE) **3845, 1213**
Studies in Symbolic Interaction. (US ISSN 0163-2396) **4454**
Studies in Technology. (IS) **4609**
Studies in the Age of Chaucer. (US ISSN 0190-2407) **2966**
٠ Studies in the American Renaissance. (US ISSN 0149-015X) **2966**
Studies in the Developing Countries. (PL ISSN 0860-3359) **4389**

Studies in the Development of Modern Mathematics. (US ISSN 1040-6441) **3057**
Studies in the Early History of Britain. (UK) **2324**
Studies in the Economics of Poultry Farming in Punjab see India. Ministry of Agriculture. Bulletin on Food Statistics **138**
Studies in the Education of Adults. (UK ISSN 0266-0830) **1687**
†Studies in the Fine Arts: Art Patronage.(US) **5284**
†Studies in the Fine Arts: Art Theory. (US) **5284**
†Studies in the Fine Arts: Avant-Garde. (US) **5284**
†Studies in the Fine Arts: Criticism. (US) **5284**
†Studies in the Fine Arts: Iconography. (US) **5284**
†Studies in the Fine Arts: Studies in Baroque Art History. (US) **5284**
†Studies in the Fine Arts: Studies in Photography. (US) **5284**
†Studies in the Fine Arts: Studies in Renaissance Art History. (US) **5284**
Studies in the Foundations, Methodology and Philosophy of Science. (US ISSN 0081-8577) **4346**
Studies in the Geography in Israel. see Michkarim Begeografiyah Shel Eretz Yisrael **2256**
Studies in the Germanic Languages and Literatures. (US ISSN 0081-8593) **2966**
Studies in the Historical Novel. (US) **2966**
Studies in the History and Interpretation of Music. (US) **3583, 2324**
Studies in the History of Art. (US ISSN 0091-7338) **345**
Studies in the History of Cape Town. (SA ISSN 0259-1944) **2335**
Studies in the History of Christian Thought. (NE ISSN 0081-8607) **4204**
Studies in the History of Leiden University. (NE ISSN 0169-8362) **2390**
Studies in the History of Mathematics and Physical Sciences. (US ISSN 0172-570X) **3057, 3833**
Studies in the History of Missions. (US) **4204**
Studies in the History of Modern Science. (NE) **4346**
Studies in the History of Natural Sciences. see Ziran Kexue Shi Yanjiu **4354**
Studies in the History of Philosophy. (US) **3783, 2324**
Studies in the History of Religions see Numen Supplements **4193**
Studies in the History of Science. (US) **4389**
Studies in the History of the Ancient Near East. (NE ISSN 0169-9024) **2432, 1280**
Studies in the Humanities (Indiana). (US ISSN 0039-3800) **2516**
Studies in the Humanities (New York). (US ISSN 0742-6712) **2516**
†Studies in the Learning Sciences. (FR) **5284**
Studies in the Linguistic Sciences. (US) **2846**
Studies in the Literary Imagination. (US ISSN 0039-3819) **2966**
Studies in the National Income and Expenditure of the United Kingdom. (UK ISSN 0081-864X) **1000**
Studies in the National Minority Education. see Minzu Jiaoyu Yanjiu **1648**
†Studies in the Natural Sciences. (US) **5284**
Studies in the Novel. (US ISSN 0039-3827) **2966**
Studies in the Photographic Arts. (US) **3797**.
Studies in the Political Economy of Canada. (CN) **3928, 693**
Studies in the Processing, Marketing and Distribution of Commodities. (UN ISSN 1014-1472) **1054**

Studies in the Psychoanalytic Writings of Ernest Becker. (US) **4048, 3783, 4204**
Studies in the Psychology of Religion. (US) **4204, 4048**
Studies in the Renaissance see Renaissance Quarterly **2953**
Studies in the Romance Languages and Literatures see North Carolina Studies in the Romance Languages and Literatures **2943**
Studies in the Romantic Age. (US ISSN 0897-9243) **2966**
Studies in the Sciences of Language Series. (US) **2846**
Studies in the Social Sciences see West Georgia College Studies in the Social Sciences **4392**
Studies in the Structure of Power: Decision Making in Canada. (CN ISSN 0081-8690) **3928**
Studies in the Theory and Philosophy of Law. (PL ISSN 0239-9997) **2683**
Studies in Theatre Arts. (US) **4639**
Studies in Theoretical Psycholinguistics.(NE) **2846, 4048**
Studies in Transnational Economic Law. (NE) **2729**
Studies in Transnational Legal Policy. (US ISSN 1057-0551) **2729**
Studies in Twentieth-Century American History. (US) **2423**
Studies in Twentieth Century Literature. (US ISSN 0145-7888) **2966**
Studies in U S National Security. (NE) **3472**
Studies in Vermont Geology. (US ISSN 0081-8747) **1582, 1600**
Studies in Wage-Price Policy. (US) **693, 1000**
Studies in Weird Fiction. (US) **3014**
Studies in Welsh History. (UK ISSN 0141-030X) **2390**
Studies in Western Europe see Xi'ou Yanjiu **4392**
Studies in Western History. see Seiyoshigaku **2386**
Studies in Women and Religion. (US) **4204, 4853**
Studies in World Peace. (US) **3973**
Studies in Zambian Society. (ZA) **4454, 2335**
Studies in Zionism. (UK ISSN 0334-1771) **3929, 2025**
Studies - Local History of Northeast China. see Dongbei Difangshi Yanjiu **2337**
Studies of Brain Function. (US ISSN 0172-5742) **3355**
Studies of Broadcasting. (JA ISSN 0585-7325) **1380**
Studies of Classical India. (NE) **3783, 2342**
Studies of Developing Countries. (NE ISSN 0081-8771) **4454**
Studies of Government Finance: Second Series. (US) **1107**
Studies of High Temperature Superconductors. (US) **1213, 3421, 3842**
Studies of Higher Education and Research. (SW ISSN 0283-7692) **1717**
Studies of Israeli Society. (US ISSN 0734-4937) **2025, 4454**
Studies of Japanese Language. see Riyu Xuexi yu Yanjiu **2838**
▼Studies of Nonlinear Phenomena in Life Science. (SI) **575**
Studies of World Literature in English. (US ISSN 1043-8580) **2966, 2846**
Studies on a Dream of Red Mansions. see Hongloumeng Xuekan **2923**
Studies on Asia see School of International Studies. Publications on Asia **2341**
Studies on Asian Topics. (UK ISSN 0142-6028) **3644**
Studies on Chinese Communism. see Chung Kung Yen Chiu **3879**
Studies on Confucius. see Kongzi Yanjiu **3771**
Studies on Current Health Problems. (UK ISSN 0473-8837) **3155, 4113**
Studies on East Asia. (US) **3644**

Studies on Fascism and Hitlerite Crimes. (PL ISSN 0137-1126) **2390**, 3929
Studies on History of Medicine. see Igakushi Kenkyu **3107**
Studies on History - Qing Dynasty. see Qingshi Yanjiu Tongxun **2341**
Studies on Language Acquisition. (US) **2846**
Studies on Modern Chinese History. see Jindai Shi Yanjiu **2339**
Studies on Neotropical Fauna and Environment. (NE ISSN 0165-0521) **592**
Studies on Oriental Music/Toyo Ongaku Kenkyu. (JA ISSN 0039-3851) **3583**
Studies on Religion in Africa. (NE ISSN 0169-9814) **4204**, 250
Studies on Selected Development Problems in Various Countries in the Middle East. (UN ISSN 0085-6908) **935**
Studies on Southeast Asia. (US) **3644**, 2342
▼Studies on Soviet Economic Development. (English translation of: Problemy Prognozirovaniya) (US ISSN 1054-6588) **885**
Studies on the Fauna of Suriname and Other Guyanas. (NE ISSN 0300-5488) **592**
Studies on the Morphology and Systematics of Scale Insects. (US) **538**, 412, 693
Studies on the Neotropical Fauna see Studies on Neotropical Fauna and Environment **592**
Studies on the Shoah. (US ISSN 1054-3120) **2390**
Studies on the Texts of the Desert of Judah. (NE ISSN 0169-9962) **4226**
Studies on Themes and Motifs in Literature. (US) **2966**
Studies on Voltaire and the Eighteenth Century. (UK ISSN 0435-2866) **2966**, 2391
Studies on Women Abstracts. (UK ISSN 0262-5644) **4861**, 23
Studies on World Religion. see Shijie Zongjiao Yanjiu **4201**
Studii Clasice. (RM ISSN 0081-8844) **1280**
Studii de Drept Romanesc. (RM) **2683**
Studii de Hidraulica. (RM) **1600**
Studii de Irigatii Si Desecari. (RM) **4828**
Studii si Articole de Istorie. (RM ISSN 0585-749X) **2391**
Studii si Cercetari de Antropologie. (RM ISSN 0039-3886) **250**
Studii si Cercetari de Biochimie. (RM ISSN 0049-2396) **483**
Studii si Cercetari de Biologie. Seria Biologie Animala. (RM ISSN 0365-5997) **457**
Studii si Cercetari de Biologie. Seria Biologie Vegetala. (RM ISSN 0365-5997) **518**
Studii si Cercetari de Fizica. (RM ISSN 0039-3940) **3833**
Studii si Cercetari de Geofizica. (RM) **1595**
Studii si Cercetari de Geografie. (RM) **2263**
Studii si Cercetari de Geologie/Studies and Research in Geology. (RM) **1582**
Studii si Cercetari de Geologie, Geofizica si Geografie. Geografie see Studii si Cercetari de Geografie **2263**
Studii si Cercetari de Geologie, Geofizica si Geographie. Geofizica see Studii si Cercetari de Geofizica **1595**
Studii si Cercetari de Geologie, Geofizica si Geographie. Geologie see Studii si Cercetari de Geologie **1582**
Studii si Cercetari de Istoria Artei. Seria Arta Plastica. (RM ISSN 0039-3983) **346**, 2324, 3533
Studii si Cercetari de Istoria Artei. Seria Teatru, Muzica, Cinematografie/Studies and Reseach in Art History. Series: Theatre, Music, Cinematography. (RM ISSN 0039-3991) **4639**, 3518, 3583

Studii si Cercetari de Istorie Veche si Arheologie. (RM) **287**
Studii si Cercetari de Mecanica Aplicata.(RM ISSN 0039-4017) **4609**
Studii si Cercetari de Numismatica. (RM ISSN 0081-8887) **2683**
Studii si Cercetari Juridice see Studii de Drept Romanesc **2683**
Studii si Cercetari Lingvistice. (RM ISSN 0039-405X) **2846**
Studii si Cercetari Matematice. (RM ISSN 0039-4068) **3057**
Studii si Materiale de Istorie Medie. (RM ISSN 0567-6312) **2391**
Studii si Materiale de Istorie Moderna. (RM ISSN 0567-6320) **2391**
Studime Filologjike/Etudes Philologiques. (AA ISSN 0563-5780) **3783**
Studime Historike/Etudes Historiques. (AA ISSN 0563-5799) **2324**
Studio. (IT) **374**
Studio. (CI ISSN 0039-4106) **1380**, 3583, 4639
Studio. (AT) **2966**, 4204
Studio Bambini. (AT ISSN 0816-939X) **1294**
†Studio Beauty. (AT) **5284**
Studio Brides. (AT ISSN 1031-9115) **3067**, 1294
Studio Collections. (AT ISSN 0813-4634) **1294**
Studio for Men. (AT ISSN 1031-735X) **1294**
†Studio International. (UK ISSN 0039-4114) **5285**
Studio Legale. (IT) **2683**
Studio Light. (US ISSN 0039-4122) **3797**
Studio Magazine. (CN ISSN 0715-6626) **38**
Studio One. (US) **3006**
Studio Photography. (US) **3797**
Studio Potter. (US ISSN 0091-6641) **357**
Studio Sound & Broadcast Engineering. (UK ISSN 0144-5944) **4462**, 1380
Studio Sound and Broadcasting see Studio Sound & Broadcast Engineering **4462**
Studium. (IT ISSN 0039-4130) **2885**
Das Studium an Muenchner Hochschulen. Lehrbuecher. (GW) **1666**
Studium Biblicum Franciscanum. Analecta. (IS ISSN 0081-8909) **4204**
Studium Biblicum Franciscanum. Collectio Maior. (IS ISSN 0081-8917) **287**, 2432
Studium Biblicum Franciscanum. Collectio Minor. (IS ISSN 0081-8925) **287**, 2432
Studium Biblicum Franciscanum. Liber Annuus. (IS ISSN 0081-8933) **287**, 2432
Studium Biblicum Franciscanum. Museum. (IS) **287**, 2432
†Studium Linguistik. (GW ISSN 0342-8982) **5285**
†Studsvik Technical News. (SW) **5285**
Study. see Xuexi **4392**
Study Abroad/Etudes a l'Etranger/Estudios en el Extranjero. (UN ISSN 0081-895X) **1723**
Study & Exploration. see Xuexi yu Tansuo **4393**
Study and Guidance. see Xuexi yu Fudao **2695**
Study and Play. see Xue yu Wan **1246**
Study Group on Eighteenth-Century Russia. Newsletter. (UK) **2391**, 2966
Study Guide for Elementary Students. see Xiaoxuesheng Xuexi Zhidao **1672**
†Study Guide in Quality Assurance and Utilization Review. (US) **5285**
Study in Ideology and Politics. see Sixiang Zhengzhi Gongzuo Yanjiu **3925**
Study in Nationalities. see Minzu Yanjiu **3641**
†Study in the United Kingdom and Ireland. (US ISSN 0893-0511) **5285**

Study of Chinese History. see Zhongguoshi Yanjiu **2343**
Study of Federal Tax Law. Income Tax Materials, Business Enterprises see Study of Federal Tax Law. Income Tax Volume: Business Enterprises **2683**
Study of Federal Tax Law. Income Tax Volume see Study of Federal Tax Law. Income Tax Volume: Individuals **2683**
Study of Federal Tax Law. Income Tax Volume: Business Enterprises. (US ISSN 0362-2983) **2683**
Study of Federal Tax Law. Income Tax Volume: Individuals. (US) **2683**
Study of Finance & Economics. see Caijing Yanjiu **769**
†Study of Financial Results and Reporting Trends in the Gaming Industry. (US) **5285**
Study of Guizhou Nationalities. see Guizhou Minzu Yanjiu **3637**
Study of Korean Language. see Munhwao Haksup **2830**
Study of Musical Education. see Ongaku Kyoiku Kenkyu **3571**
Study of Nursing Care: Research Project Series. (UK ISSN 0302-1440) **3287**
Study of Tea. see Chagyo Gijutsu Kenkyu **5164**
Study of Time. (US) **370**
Study Peace see L N A C Almanac **5225**
Study - Tibetan Nationalities. see Zhongguo Zangxue **3646**
Study Time. (US) **994**
Studying Adult Life and Work Lessons. (US ISSN 0191-4219) **4250**
Studying Chinese. see Hanyu Xuexi **2816**
Stuekulturer. (DK ISSN 0039-4165) **3714**, 2139
Stufe. (GW) **1266**
Stukadoorspatroon see N A V A S **625**
Das Stukkateur. (GW) **633**
Stumpwork Society Chronicle. (US ISSN 0194-4193) **3592**
Stupeni. (RU ISSN 0321-0642) **1266**
▼Sturza's Medical Investment Letter. (US ISSN 1060-4251) **965**, 3155
Stuttgart. Amtsblatt see Landeshauptstadt Stuttgart. Amtsblatt **4066**
Stuttgarter Arbeiten zur Germanistik. (GW) **2966** ·
Stuttgarter Geographische Studien. (GW ISSN 0343-7906) **2263**
Stuttgarter UniKurier. (GW) **1325**
Stutthof Muzeum. Zeszyty. (PL ISSN 0137-5377) **2391**, 3533
Stuurwiel. (SA ISSN 0039-4203) **4702**
Stvaranje. (YU ISSN 0039-422X) **2885**
Stygologia. (NE ISSN 0169-3662) **1600**
Style. (CN ISSN 0227-4272) **1294**
Style. (HK) **4853**, 1294
Style (DeKalb). (US ISSN 0039-4238) **2966**
Style Auto. (IT ISSN 0039-4254) **4702**
Style Forecast. (US) **1294**, 1288
†Style Magazine. (UK) **5285**
Stylist. (US) **374**
Stylos. (BL) **2966**
Stylus (Brockport). (US ISSN 0039-4289) **1325**
Stylus Literary Report. (US) **2885**, 2025
Su Voz. (CU ISSN 0864-0262) **4250**
Suara Buruh. (MY ISSN 0126-7191) **2589**
Suara N U B E. (National Union of Bank Employees) (MY) **2589**, 800
Suara Sam. (MY ISSN 0127-6409) **1497**, 935, 1969
Sub. (IT) **4530**
Sub-Cellular Biochemistry. (US ISSN 0306-0225) **483**
Sub-Normal Children's Welfare Association. Welfare News see Challenge Advocate **4401**
Sub-Postmaster. (UK ISSN 0039-4335) **1354**

SUCCESS ORIENTATION 6703

Sub-Saharan Africa Report. (US) **885**, 3929
▼Sub-Saharan Monitor. (US ISSN 1018-1520) **3973**, 921
Sub-Stance. (US ISSN 0049-2426) **2966**
Sub-Terrain. (CN) **2966**
Subacqueo. (IT) **1611**
Subaqua. (FR) **4557**
Subaru. see Pleiades **2948**
Subasetha. (CE) **359**
▼Subchapter S Taxation, 3-E. (US) **1107**
Subconsciously Speaking. (US) **3597**, 3671
Subh-i-Adab. (II) **2966**
Subject Collections. (US ISSN 0000-0140) **2795**
Subject Directory of Special Libraries and Information Centers. (US ISSN 0732-927X) **2786**
Subject Guide: Recent and Forthcoming British Books. (UK ISSN 0265-5896) **4142**
Subject Guide to Books in Print. (US ISSN 0000-0159) **412**
Subject Guide to Books in Print on Microfiche. (US) **413**
Subject Guide to Canadian Books in Print. (CN) **413**
Subject Guide to Children's Books in Print. (US ISSN 0000-0167) **413**
Subject Guide to Microform in Print see Guide to Microforms in Print. Subject **401**
Subject Headings for Engineering see S H E **2782**
Subject Index to Articles in Newspapers in Mauritius. (MF) **2579**, 23
†Subject Index to Sources of Comparative International Statistics. (UK) **5285**
Subject Index to Welsh Periodicals see Bibliography of Wales **393**
Subject Matter Index to Public and Private Statues of New Brunswick. (CN) **2700**
Subject Specialists Section Newsletter. (US) **2786**
Subnotes see Waves **1612**
Suboticke Novine. (YU ISSN 0039-436X) **2240**
Subsea Engineering News. (UK ISSN 0266-2205) **3702**, 1939
Subsidia Hagiographica. (BE ISSN 0777-8112) **4204**
Subsidia Mediaevalia. (CN ISSN 0316-0769) **2391**
Subsidia Scientifica Franciscalia. (IT ISSN 0562-4649) **4276**
Subsidie - Info. (BE) **1085**, 1028
Subsidized Government Programs see Government Programs **4406**
Substance Abuse. (US ISSN 0889-7077) **1539**
Substance Abuse Librarians and Information Specialists Directory see S A L I S Directory **2782**
Substance Abuse Librarians and Information Specialists News see S A L I S News **2782**
Substance Abuse Report. (US ISSN 1040-4163) **1539**, 3743
Subterranean Sociology Newsletter. (US ISSN 0039-4394) **4454**, 2885
Subtle Journal of Raw Coinage. (US) **2966**, 2846
Subtropical Plant Bulletin. see Yaredai Zhiwu Tongxun **521**
Subtropical Plant Science. (US) **2139**, 518
Suburban. (CN ISSN 0226-9686) **2179**
Suburban West Business Magazine. (US) **693**
Subversive Agent. (US ISSN 1040-614X) **3006**, 3947
Subway. (IT) **2206**
Suc Khoe/Health. (VN) **4113**
Sucasnist. (US ISSN 0585-8364) **2391**
Success. (CY) **2184**
Success (New York). (US ISSN 0745-2489) **3631**, 4048
†Success (Peterborough). (UK ISSN 0049-2442) **5285**
Success in Fitness Magazine - Billboard.(CN) **3809**
Success Orientation. (US) **1028**

SUCCESSFUL ATTITUDES

Successful Attitudes. (US) **2235**
Successful Dealer. (US ISSN 0161-6080) **4748,** 3023
Successful Estate Planning: Ideas and Methods. (US) **2716**
Successful Farming. (US ISSN 0039-4432) **122**
Successful Hotel Marketer. (US ISSN 1040-600X) **2480,** 1054
Successful Magazine Publishing see MagazineWeek **4132**
†Successful Marketing to Senior Citizens. (US ISSN 8755-321X) **5285**
Successful Meetings. (US ISSN 0148-4052) **1054,** 3394
Successful Meetings Facilities Directory see Successful Meetings Source Book **1154**
Successful Meetings Source Book. (US) **1154**
Successful Nonprofits. (US) **1028**
Successful Payroll Management. (US) **756,** 1107
Successful Print Sales. (US) **4006,** 1054
Successful Selling. (AT ISSN 1030-3928) **1054,** 1118
Successful Slimming. (UK) **3809**
Successful Supervisor. (US) **1029**
Successful Woman see Successful Woman in Business **4853**
Successful Woman in Business. (US) **4853,** 693
SuccessGuide (Year). (US) **2025**
Succulenta. (NE ISSN 0039-4467) **2139**
Such & Find Kraftfahrzeug. (GW) **4702**
Sucht. (GW ISSN 0939-5911) **1539**
Suchtgefahren see Sucht **1539**
Suchtinformation. (GW ISSN 0932-4240) **1540**
Suchtprobleme und Sozialarbeit. (SZ) **1539**
Suchtreport. (GW ISSN 0930-8350) **1539**
Sucrerie Belge. (BE) **194,** 2082
Sucrerie Francaise. (FR ISSN 0039-4491) **2082**
Sud. (FR ISSN 0049-2450) **3006**
Sud Hebdo. (SG) **2170**
Sudan. Department of Statistics. Foreign Trade Statistics. (SJ ISSN 0585-8488) **740,** 4589
Sudan. Department of Statistics. Internal Trade and Other Statistics. (SJ) **740,** 839
Sudan. Department of Statistics. National Income Accounts and Supporting Tables. (SJ) **1000**
Sudan. Department of Statistics. Statistical Yearbook. (SJ) **4589**
Sudan. Economic and Social Research Council. Occasional Paper. (SJ) **4389,** 885
Sudan. Ministry of Finance and National Economy. Annual Budget Speech, Proposals for the General Budget and the Development Budget. (SJ) **4075**
Sudan. Ministry of Finance and National Economy. Economic and Financial Research Section. Economic Survey. (SJ) **885**
Sudan. Ministry of Finance and National Economy. General Budget: Review, Presentation and Analysis. (SJ) **4075**
Sudan. National Council for Research. Economic and Social Research Council. Bibliographies. (SJ) **740,** 4396
Sudan. National Council for Research. Economic and Social Research Council. Bulletin. (SJ) **4389,** 885
Sudan. National Council for Research. Economic and Social Research Council. Research Methods. (SJ) **4389,** 935
Sudan. National Council for Research. Economic and Social Research Council. Research Report. (SJ) **4389,** 885
Sudan. National Council for Research. National Documentation Centre. Library Information Bulletin. (SJ) **2786**
Sudan. National Council for Research. Science Policy and Annual Report. (SJ) **4346**
Sudan. National Planning Commission. Economic Survey see Sudan. Ministry of Finance and National Economy. Economic and Financial Research Section. Economic Survey **885**
Sudan Church Review. (UK) **4204**
Sudan Commercial Bank. Report of the Board of Directors. (SJ) **800**
Sudan Cotton Bulletin. (SJ ISSN 0562-5033) **4623**
Sudan Cotton Review. (SJ ISSN 0562-5068) **194**
Sudan Development Studies Review. (SJ) **935**
Sudan Engineering Society. Journal. (SJ ISSN 0049-2469) **1837**
Sudan Environment. (SJ) **1969**
Sudan Interior Mission Now see S I M Now **4200**
Sudan Journal of Administration and Development. (SJ) **4075**
†Sudan Journal of Development Research. (SJ) **5285**
Sudan Journal of Economic and Social Studies. (SJ) **4389**
Sudan Journal of Food Science and Technology. (SJ) **2082,** 2094
Sudan Law Journal and Reports. (SJ ISSN 0585-8631) **2683**
Sudan Medical Journal. (SJ ISSN 0491-4481) **3155**
Sudan News Agency see S U N A **2218**
Sudan News Agency. Weekly Review/ Wakatlat al-Sudan Lil-Anba. Weekly Review. (SJ) **2170**
Sudan Notes and Records. (SJ) **2432**
Sudan Research Information Bulletin. (SJ ISSN 0453-8129) **2516,** 4346, 4389
Sudan Science Abstracts. (SJ) **4358**
Sudan Silva. (SJ) **2108**
Sudan Society/Al-Mujtama. (SJ ISSN 0562-5130) **250**
Sudan Texts Bulletin. (KU ISSN 0143-6554) **2335**
Sudan Trade Directory. (UK) **885**
Sudan Yearbook of Agricultural Statistics. (SJ) **158**
Sudanese Business. (SJ) **839**
Sudanow. (SJ ISSN 0378-8059) **2432**
Sudebnomeditsinskaya Ekspertiza/ Medico-Legal Expert Testimony. (RU ISSN 0039-4521) **3266**
†Sudene Informa. (Superintendencia do Desenvolvimento do Nordeste) (BL ISSN 0039-453X) **5285**
Sudetendeutscher Erzieherbrief see Erzieherbrief **3956**
Sudha. (II) **2201**
Sudhanidhi. (II) **3155**
Sudhi Sahitya. (II) **3783**
Sudhoffs Archiv. (GW ISSN 0039-4564) **3155,** 4346
Sudhoffs Archiv. Beihefte. (GW ISSN 0341-0773) **3155,** 4346
Sudostroenie. (RU ISSN 0039-4580) **4740**
Suds 'n Stuff. (US) **385**
Suecana Extranea. (SW ISSN 0039-4599) **413,** 2846, 4137
Suecia Hoy see Sweden Now **2218**
Suedafrikanische Exporteure. see South African Exporters **921**
Sueddeutsche Apotheker-Zeitung see Deutsche Apotheker Zeitung **3722**
Sueddeutsche Bauwirtschaft. (GW) **633**
Sueddeutsche Eisen- und Stahl-Berufsgenossenschaft. Mitteilungen. (GW ISSN 0178-0182) **3622,** 2543, 2683
Sueddeutsche Haus- und Wohnwirtschaft. (GW) **2496**
Sueddeutsche Studentenzeitung. (GW) **1325**
Sueddeutscher Molkerei und Kaeserei Adresskalender. (GW ISSN 0724-3235) **204**
Sueddeutscher Verkehrskurier. (GW) **4715**
Suedhessisches Auto Magazin. (GW) **4702**
Suedmaehrische Landschaft. (GW) **2391**
Suedost-Europa. Zeitschrift fuer Gegenwartsforschung. (GW ISSN 0722-480X) **3929**
Suedost-Forschungen. (GW ISSN 0081-9077) **2391**
Suedost-Gesellschaft. Mitteilungen see Suedosteuropa - Mitteilungen **2391**
Suedostasien Aktuell. (GW ISSN 0722-8821) **3929**
Suedostdeutsche. (GW) **2191**
Suedostdeutsche Historische Kommission. Buchreihe. (GW) **2391**
Suedostdeutsche Vierteljahresblaetter. (GW ISSN 0562-5297) **2391**
Suedostdeutsches Archiv. (GW ISSN 0081-9085) **2391,** 2059
Suedostdeutsches Kulturwerk. Veroeffentlichungen. Reihe A: Kultur und Dichtung. (GW) **2391,** 346, 2966
Suedostdeutsches Kulturwerk. Veroeffentlichungen. Reihe B: Wissenschaftliche Arbeiten. (GW) **2391,** 2966
Suedostdeutsches Kulturwerk. Veroeffentlichungen. Reihe C: Erinnerungen und Quellen. (GW) **2391,** 2966
Suedostdeutsches Kulturwerk. Veroeffentlichungen. Reihe D: Kleine Suedostreihe. (GW) **2391,** 2966
Suedostdeutsches Kulturwerk, Munich. Kleine Suedostreihe see Suedostdeutsches Kulturwerk. Veroeffentlichungen. Reihe D: Kleine Suedostreihe **2391**
Suedostdeutsches Kulturwerk, Munich. Schriftenreihen. Reihe A: Kultur und Dichtung see Suedostdeutsches Kulturwerk. Veroeffentlichungen. Reihe A: Kultur und Dichtung **2391**
Suedostdeutsches Kulturwerk, Munich. Schriftenreihen. Reihe B: Wissenschaftliche Arbeiten see Suedostdeutsches Kulturwerk. Veroeffentlichungen. Reihe B: Wissenschaftliche Arbeiten **2391**
Suedostdeutsches Kulturwerk, Munich. Schriftenreihen. Reihe C. Erinnerungen und Quellen see Suedostdeutsches Kulturwerk. Veroeffentlichungen. Reihe C: Erinnerungen und Quellen **2391**
Suedosteuropa - Bibliographie. (GW ISSN 0081-9131) **413**
Suedosteuropa - Jahrbuch. (GW ISSN 0081-914X) **2391**
Suedosteuropa - Mitteilungen. (GW ISSN 0340-174X) **2391**
Suedosteuropa - Studien. (GW ISSN 0081-9166) **2391**
Suedosteuropaeische Arbeiten. (GW) **2391**
Suedtirol in Wort und Bild. (AU ISSN 0039-4629) **2885**
Suedtiroler Landwirt. (IT) **122**
†Suedwestdeutsche Schulblaetter. (GW ISSN 0340-2355) **5285**
Suedwestdeutscher Einzelhandel (Freiburg). (GW) **1360**
Suedwestdeutscher Einzelhandel (Stuttgart). (GW) **4362**
Suedwestfaelische Wirtschaft. (GW ISSN 0039-4637) **823**
Suedwestfunk Journal. (GW) **1360**
Suelchgau. (GW ISSN 0940-4325) **2391,** 287
Suelo y Planta. (SP) **194**
Suesswaren. (GW ISSN 0039-4653) **2090**
Suesswaren Jahrbuch. (GW ISSN 0081-9174) **2082**
Suevica - Beitraege zur Schwabischen Literatur- und Geistesgeschichte. (GW) **2966**
Suffolk Business Directory. (UK ISSN 0269-2716) **1154,** 823
Suffolk County Agricultural News. (US ISSN 0039-467X) **122**
Suffolk County Dental Society. Bulletin see Suffolk Dentistry **3243**
Suffolk County Farm News see Suffolk County Agricultural News **122**
Suffolk County Solar Energy Commission Newsletter. (US) **1812**
Suffolk Dentistry. (US) **3243**
Suffolk Farmer. (UK) **122**
Suffolk Institute of Archaeology and History. Proceedings. (UK ISSN 0262-6004) **287,** 2391
Suffolk Sheep Society Flock Book. (UK) **226**
Suffolk Stud Book. (UK) **4538,** 226
Suffolk Transnational Law Journal. (US ISSN 0886-2648) **2683**
Suffolk University Alumni Bulletin see Suffolk University Magazine **1325**
Suffolk University Law Review. (US ISSN 0039-4696) **2683**
Suffolk University Magazine. (US ISSN 0897-733X) **1325**
Suffrages. (FR) **374,** 376
Sugaku/Mathematics. (JA ISSN 0039-470X) **3057**
Sugaku Expositions. (English translation of: Sugaku) (US ISSN 0898-9583) **3057**
Sugaku Ochikobore Tsushin. (JA ISSN 0912-7569) **5285**
Sugaku Semina/Sugaku Seminar. (JA ISSN 0386-4960) **3057**
Sugaku Seminar. see Sugaku Semina **3057**
Sugakushi Kenkyu/Journal of the History of Mathematics, Japan. (JA ISSN 0386-9555) **3057**
Suganitam. (II) **3057**
Sugar and Health see On Your Mark **3611**
Sugar Bulletin. (US ISSN 0039-4726) **2082**
Sugar Cane. (UK ISSN 0265-7406) **122,** 2082
Sugar Economy. see Zuckerwirtschaft **2084**
Sugar Industry Abstracts. (UK ISSN 0957-5022) **2085,** 23
Sugar Industry Journal Buyer's Guide. (UK) **2082**
Sugar Journal. see Listy Cukrovarnicke **2076**
Sugar Journal. (US ISSN 0039-4734) **2082**
Sugar Milling Research Institute. Annual Report. (SA) **2082,** 194
Sugar Processing Research Conference. Proceedings. (US ISSN 0730-6490) **122**
Sugar Producer. (US ISSN 0199-8498) **122**
Sugar Series. (NE) **2082**
Sugar Technologists' Association of Trinidad and Tobago. Proceedings. (TR ISSN 0302-4555) **2082**
†Sugar Technology Reviews. (NE ISSN 0081-9204) **5285**
Sugar World. (CN ISSN 0229-737X) **2082,** 2589
Sugar y Azucar. (US ISSN 0039-4742) **2082**
Sugar y Azucar Yearbook. (US ISSN 0081-9212) **2082**
Sugarbeet Grower. (US ISSN 0039-4750) **194**
Sugarcane Farmers' Bulletin. (PH) **122,** 2082
Sugarland. (PH ISSN 0039-4777) **2082**
Sugei Pazuru. (JA) **3057,** 2442, 4493
Sugeot Bidinai Misim. (IS) **1107**
Suggested State Legislation. (US ISSN 0070-1157) **4075**
Suggestion Quarterly. (US) **4048**
Sugia. (GW ISSN 0720-0986) **2335,** 2846
Suhakkwa Mulli. (KN) **3833,** 3057
Sui Yuan Wen Hsien. (CH) **2025,** 2342, 3644
Suibi/Random Notes. (CC ISSN 1000-7903) **2967**
Suicide and Life-Threatening Behavior. (US ISSN 0363-0234) **4048,** 3355
Suid-Afrika-Stigting. Beknopte Feitebron see South Africa Foundation. Information Digest (Year) **884**
Suid-Afrika-Stigting Oorsig see South Africa Foundation Review **884**
Suid-Afrikaanse Akademie vir Wetenskap en Kuns. Nuusbrief. (SA ISSN 0039-4807) **4346,** 2967
Suid-Afrikaanse Argiefblad/South African Archives Journal. (SA ISSN 1012-2796) **2786**

Suid-Afrikaanse Biblioteek. Kwartaalblad. see South African Library. Quarterly Bulletin **2785**
Suid-Afrikaanse Bosboutydskrif. see South African Forestry Journal **2108**
Suid Afrikaanse Bouer. see South African Builder **632**
Suid-Afrikaanse Brandweerinstitut Kwartaalblad. see South African Fire Services Institute. Quarterly **2034**
Suid-Afrikaanse Buitelandse Handelsorganisasie Jaarverslag. see S A F T O Annual Report **920**
Suid-Afrikaanse Friesland Joernaal. see South African Friesland Journal **226**
Suid-Afrikaanse Geograaf. see South African Geographer **2263**
Suid-Afrikaanse Gesigkundige. see South African Refractionist **3305**
Suid-Afrikaanse Historiese Joernaal. see South African Historical Journal **2335**
Suid-Afrikaanse Instituut van Internasionale Aangeleenthede. Bibliografiese Reeks. see South African Institute of International Affairs. Bibliographical Series **3938**
Suid-Afrikaanse Jaarboek vir Volkereg. see South African Yearbook of International Law **2729**
Suid-Afrikaanse Kultuurhistoriese Museum. Annale/South African Cultural History Museum. Annals. (SA) **2335**
Suid-Afrikaanse Kultuurhistoriese Museum. Bulletin/South African Cultural History Museum. Bulletin. (SA) **2335**, **250**
Suid-Afrikaanse Kweker. see South African Nurseryman **121**
Suid-Afrikaanse Lapidere Tydskrif. see South African Lapidary Magazine **3496**
Suid-Afrikaanse Mediese Tydskrif. see South African Medical Journal **3154**
Suid-Afrikaanse Museum. Annale. see South African Museum. Annals **457**
Suid-Afrikaanse Musiekonderwyser. see South African Music Teacher **3582**
†Suid-Afrikaanse Oorsig. (SA) **5285**
†Suid-Afrikaanse Regskommissie. Jaarverslag/South African Law Commission. Annual Report. (SA) **5285**
Suid Afrikaanse Rekenaartydskrif. see South African Computer Journal **1400**
Suid-Afrikaanse Reserwebank. Jaarlikse Ekonomiese Verslag. see South African Reserve Bank. Annual Economic Report **884**
Suid-Afrikaanse Reserwebank. Kwartaalblad. see South African Reserve Bank. Quarterly Bulletin **799**
Suid-Afrikaanse Reserwebank. Maandelikse Vrystelling van Geld- en Bankwesestatistiek. see South African Reserve Bank. Monthly Release of Money and Banking Statistics **738**
Suid-Afrikaanse Reserwebank. Verslag van die Gewone Algemene Vergadering. see South African Reserve Bank. Report of the Ordinary General Meeting **799**
Suid-Afrikaanse Statistiese Tydskrif. see South African Statistical Journal **4586**
Suid-Afrikaanse Tesourier. see South African Treasurer **4094**
Suid-Afrikaanse Tipografiese Joernaal. see South African Typographical Journal **2589**
Suid-Afrikaanse Tydskrif vir Apteekwese. see South African Pharmaceutical Journal **3743**
Suid-Afrikaanse Tydskrif vir Bedryfsleiding. see South African Journal of Business Management **1028**
Suid-Afrikaanse Tydskrif vir Chemie. see South African Journal of Chemistry **1188**
Suid-Afrikaanse Tydskrif vir Chirurgie. see South African Journal of Surgery **3384**
Suid-Afrikaanse Tydskrif vir Dierkunde. see South African Journal of Zoology **592**

Suid-Afrikaanse Tydskrif vir Ekonomie. see South African Journal of Economics **692**
Suid-Afrikaanse Tydskrif vir Fisika. see South African Journal of Physics **3831**
Suid-Afrikaanse Tydskrif vir Handelsreg. see South African Mercantile Law Journal **2680**
Suid-Afrikaanse Tydskrif vir Kommunikasieafwykings. see South African Journal of Communication Disorders **3317**
Suid-Afrikaanse Tydskrif vir Landbouvoorligting. see South African Journal of Agricultural Extension **121**
Suid-Afrikaanse Tydskrif vir Landmeetkunde en Kartering. see South African Journal of Surveying and Mapping **1874**
Suid-Afrikaanse Tydskrif vir Musiekwetenskap. see South African Journal of Musicology **3582**
Suid-Afrikaanse Tydskrif vir Natuurnavorsing. see South African Journal of Wildlife Research **1497**
Suid Afrikaanse Tydskrif vir Natuurwetenskap en Tegnologie. (SA ISSN 0254-3486) **4346**
Suid-Afrikaanse Tydskrif vir Navorsing in Sport, Liggaamlike Opvoedkunde en Ontspanning/South African Journal for Research in Sport, Physical Education and Recreation. (SA) **3809**, **2739**, **3373**
Suid Afrikaanse Tydskrif vir Navorsing in Sport - South African Journal for Research in Sport see Suid-Afrikaanse Tydskrif vir Navorsing in Sport, Liggaamlike Opvoedkunde en Ontspanning **3809**
Suid-Afrikaanse Tydskrif vir Opvoedkunde. see South African Journal of Education **1664**
Suid-Afrikaanse Tydskrif vir Plantkunde. see South African Journal of Botany **518**
Suid-Afrikaanse Tydskrif vir Seewetenskap. see South African Journal of Marine Science **2049**
Suid-Afrikaanse Tydskrif vir Serebraalverlamming. see South African Cerebral Palsy Journal **3354**
Suid-Afrikaanse Tydskrif vir Sielkunde. see South African Journal of Psychology **4047**
Suid-Afrikaanse Tydskrif vir Wetenskap. see South African Journal of Science **4345**
Suid-Afrikaanse Unie-Lantern see Maranatha **4285**
Suid-Afrikannse Tydskrif vir Taalkunde. see South African Journal of Linguistics **2842**
Suido Jigyo Nenpo/Annual Statistics of Water Works. (JA) **4835**
Suijun Kihyo Sokuryo Seikahyo. (JA) **1552**
Suiken Kagaku Kenkyujo Nenpo. see Nagoya University. Water Research Institute. Annual Report **4827**
Suikerbietplanter see Betteravier **170**
Suinocultura Industrial. (BL) **226**
Suiri Kagaku/Water Science. (JA ISSN 0039-4858) **4828**, **1497**
Suiro Tsuho. see Japan. Maritime Safety Agency. Hydrographic Department. Notices to Mariners **4730**
Suisan Kai/Fisheries World. (JA ISSN 0039-4866) **2049**
Suisanzoshoku/Aquaculture. (JA ISSN 0371-4217) **2049**
Suizidprophylaxe. (GW ISSN 0173-458X) **3355**, **4422**
Sujaneshu. (BG) **2967**
Sujets se Rapportant a la Sante et la Securite au Travail. see Occupational Health and Safety Topics **3620**
Sujets se Rapportant au Travail. see Labour Topics **987**
Al Sukaria. (SJ) **2082**
Sukh Datta. (II ISSN 0039-4882) **3809**
Sukoyaka Kenpo. (JA) **2544**
Suksa May. (LS) **1666**
Suktara. (II) **1267**
Sukuviesti. (FI ISSN 0357-9492) **2391**, **2165**

Sulco. (US) **122**
Sulfur. (US ISSN 0730-305X) **2967**, **2885**
Sulfur Letters. (US ISSN 0278-6117) **1189**
Sulfur Reports. (US ISSN 0196-1772) **1189**, **1223**
Sulian Wenxue see Sulian Wenxue (Liankan) **2967**
Sulian Wenxue (Liankan)/Russian Literature. (CC) **2967**
Sullivan County Historical Society Newsletter. (US) **2423**
Sulphur. (UK ISSN 0039-4890) **3496**, **1860**
Sulphur in Agriculture. (US ISSN 0160-0680) **122**
Sulphur Institute Journal see Sulphur in Agriculture **122**
Sulphuric Acid and Industry. (JA ISSN 0370-8047) **1189**
Sultan. (II) **2342**
Sultanate of Oman Business Directory (Year). (MK) **1154**
Sultanate of Oman Telephone Directory.(MK) **1154**
Sultanate of Oman Today see Oman Today **2211**
Sulzer Technical Review. (SZ ISSN 0039-4912) **1837**, **1230**, **3023**
Sum and Substance see Corn Belt Library System. Sum and Substance **2753**
▼Sum Monthly News. (US) **756**, **1717**
Suman Saurabh. (II) **1267**
Sumari Bulletin see The (something) **5279**
Sumario Actual de Revistas. (SP ISSN 0210-0592) **413**, **2516**
Sumario de Derechos Humanos see Paz y Justicia: Sumario de Derechos Humanos **3946**
Sumarios Correntes de Periodicos. (BL) **144**, **413**
†Sumarios de Odontologia. (BL ISSN 0039-4947) **5285**
Sumer. (IQ ISSN 0081-9271) **287**
Sumitomo Bulletin of Industrial Health. see Sumitomo Sangyo Eisei **3622**
Sumitomo Corporation. Annual Report. (JA) **921**
Sumitomo Electric Industries Ltd. News see S E I News **1907**
Sumitomo Electric Technical Review. (JA) **1908**
Sumitomo Keikinzoku Giho/Sumitomo Light Metal Technical Reports. (JA ISSN 0039-4963) **3421**
Sumitomo Light Metal Technical Reports. see Sumitomo Keikinzoku Giho **3421**
Sumitomo Sangyo Eisei/Sumitomo Bulletin of Industrial Health. (JA ISSN 0081-928X) **3622**, **3809**
Summa. (AG ISSN 0325-4615) **307**
Summa. (US) **693**
Summa Phytopathologica. (BL ISSN 0100-5405) **518**
Summaries of B F R L Fire Research In-House and Grants (Year). (US) **2035**
Summarios. (AG ISSN 0325-6448) **307**
Summary and Analysis of International Travel in the U.S. (US ISSN 0095-3482) **4787**
Summary Information on Master of Social Work Programs. (US) **1717**, **4422**
Summary Justice S.A. (AT) **1523**
Summary of Agricultural Statistics. see Turkey. Devlet Istatistik Enstitusu. Tarim Istatistikleri Ozeti **125**
Summary of Alaska Legislation. (US) **2683**
Summary of Canadian International Trade. (CN ISSN 0828-1556) **740**
Summary of Congress. (US ISSN 0146-2156) **3929**
Summary of Expenditure Data for Michigan Public Schools. (US ISSN 0094-8268) **1666**
Summary of Insider Transactions. (US) **965**
Summary of Investigations Relating to Reading see Reading Research Quarterly **1658**

Summary of Labor Arbitration Awards. (US ISSN 0039-5005) **994**
Summary of New Laws. (US) **4075**
Summary of Postgraduate Diplomas and Courses in Medicine see Guide to Postgraduate Degrees, Diplomas and Courses in Medicine **1707**
Summary of Public Acts of Interest to Municipal Officials see Summary of New Laws **4075**
Summary of Rate Schedules of Natural Gas Pipeline Companies. (US) **1800**, **3707**, **4589**
Summary of Rate Schedules of Natural Gas Pipeline Companies as Filed with the Federal Energy Regulatory Commission and the National Energy Board of Canada see Summary of Rate Schedules of Natural Gas Pipeline Companies **1800**
†Summary of Recent Decisions and Legislation Relating to the Law of Real Property. (US) **5285**
Summary of Recent Decisions Relating to the Law of Real Property see Summary of Recent Decisions and Legislation Relating to the Law of Real Property **5285**
Summary of State Laws and Regulations Relating to Distilled Spirits. (US ISSN 0081-931X) **385**
Summary of U.S. Export and Import Merchandise Trade see Foreign Trade Reports. U.S. Export and Import Merchandise Trade and Supplement **909**
Summary of White Paper on Science and Technology. (JA) **4609**, **4346**
Summer Assessment (Year). (US) **1908**
Summer Computer Simulation Conference. Proceedings. (US ISSN 0094-7474) **1436**
Summer Employment Directory of the United States. (US ISSN 0081-9352) **1154**, **3631**
Summer Institute in Linguistics. Studies in Descriptive and Applied Linguistics see International Christian University. Language Research Bulletin **2819**
Summer Institute of Linguistics. Australian Aborigines and Islanders Branch. Work Papers. Series A see S I L - A A I B Occasional Papers **2839**
Summer Institute of Linguistics. Australian Aborigines and Islanders Branch. Work Papers. Series B see S I L - A A I B Occasional Papers **2839**
Summer Institute of Linguistics. Language Data. Africa Series. (US ISSN 1040-4406) **2846**
Summer Institute of Linguistics. Language Data. Amerindian Series. (US ISSN 1040-1113) **2846**
Summer Institute of Linguistics. Language Data. Asia-Pacific Series. (US ISSN 1040-4414) **2846**
Summer Institute of Linguistics. Museum of Anthropology Publication see International Museum of Cultures. Publication **242**
Summer Institute of Linguistics. Publications Catalog. (US) **2856**
Summer Institute of Linguistics. Serie Linguistica. (BL ISSN 0102-6526) **2846**
Summer Institute of Linguistics. University of North Dakota Session. Work Papers. (US) **2846**
Summer Institute of Linguistics and The University of Texas at Arlington Publications in Linguistics. (US) **2846**
Summer Institute of Linguistics Bibliography see S I L - A A I B Bibliography **2856**
Summer Institute of Linguistics Occasional Papers see S I L - A A I B Occasional Papers **2839**
Summer Jobs for (Year). (US) **3631**
Summer Study Abroad see Vacation Study Abroad **1724**
Summer Symposium of Operation Research Yokoshu see S S O R Yokoshu **1405**
Summer Texan see Daily Texan **1309**

6706 SUMMER THEATER

Summer Theater Guide see Actor's Complete Summer Theater Guide **5130**
†Summerfield Journal. (US ISSN 0893-9381) **5285**
Summertime. (GW) **2562**, **4557**
Summerville Post. (US) **4095**
▼Summit G C S E Mathematics Review. (UK ISSN 0958-6709) **3057**
Summit: The Mountain Journal. (US ISSN 0039-5056) **4557**
Summons. (US ISSN 0039-5072) **2684**, **1325**
Sumo. see Sumo Wrestling (Tokyo, 1949) **4493**
Sumo World. (JA) **4493**
Sumo Wrestling (Tokyo, 1949)/Sumo. (JA) **4493**
Sumo Wrestling (Tokyo, 1954). (JA) **4493**
The Sun. (II) **2201**
Sun. (JA ISSN 0039-5080) **2208**
Sun. (SA) **4787**
Sun (Boca Raton). (US) **2235**
Sun (Chapel Hill). (US ISSN 0744-9666) **2885**
Sun and Moon Tables for Ghana see Ghana. Meteorological Department. Sun and Moon Tables for Ghana **3435**
Sun Belt Building Journal. (US) **633**
Sun Belt Journal. (US) **693**, **3518**, **4639**
Sun Cities Life see Sun Life **2279**
Sun Coast Architect - Builder. (US ISSN 0192-1703) **633**, **307**
Sun-Diamond Grower. (US) **2082**, **194**
Sun Dog see Sun Dog: The Southeast Review **3006**
Sun Dog: The Southeast Review. (US ISSN 0735-7133) **3006**
†Sun-Eclipse. (US) **5285**
Sun Guide to the Flat. (UK) **4538**, **4493**
Sun Life. (US) **2279**
Sun Living. (CJ) **4787**
Sun Magazine. (US) **3702**
Sun Observer. (US) **1465**
Sun Observer - Europe. (US) **1465**
Sun Reporter. (US) **2025**
Sun Sign Book. (US) **359**
Sun Soccer Annual. (UK) **4513**
Sun Valley Magazine. (US) **2235**
Sun Yat-sen Center for Policy Studies China's Military: P L A in (Year) see China's Military: P L A in (Year) **2337**
Sun Yat-sen Cultural Foundation Bulletin/Chung Shan Hsueh Shu Wen Hua Ch'i K'an. (CH ISSN 0300-3302) **4389**
Sun Yat-sen University. Journal (Social Science Edition). see Zhongshan Daxue Xuebao (Zhexue Shehui Kexue Ban) **4389**
Sunbelt Dairyman. (US ISSN 0039-5145) **204**
Sunbelt Foodservice. (US) **2082**, **2480**
▼Sunbelt Vending and O C S. (US) **2082**
Sunbird. (AT) **567**
Sunceva Energija/Solar Energy. (CI ISSN 0351-2797) **1812**
Suncoast. (US) **2235**
Sunday. (II) **2201**
Sunday. (US ISSN 0039-5161) **4289**
Sunday Digest. (US ISSN 0039-5188) **4204**
Sunday Examiner. (AT) **2172**
Sunday Examiner. (HK) **4204**
Sunday Express. (LB) **2170**
Sunday Express. (UK ISSN 0039-5196) **2195**
Sunday Gleaner. (JM ISSN 0039-520X) **2239**
Sunday Guardian. (TR) **2239**
Sunday Hours. see Kyriatikis Ores **2184**
Sunday Independent. (IE ISSN 0039-5218) **2203**
Sunday Mail. (AT ISSN 0039-5226) **2172**
Sunday Mail. (RH) **2240**
Sunday Mail (English edition). (II) **2201**
Sunday Mail (Hindi edition). (II) **2201**

Sunday Mainichi. (JA ISSN 0039-5234) **2208**
Sunday Mercury. (UK ISSN 0039-5242) **2195**
Sunday Morning Post Magazine. (HK) **2197**
Sunday Nation. (KE) **2170**
Sunday Nation. (MF) **2170**
The Sunday Observer. (II) **2202**
Sunday People. (LB) **2170**
Sunday Post. (PK ISSN 0039-5277) **2213**
Sunday School Adults. (US ISSN 0162-4911) **4250**
Sunday School Counselor. (US ISSN 0039-5285) **4289**
Sunday School Junior Pupil see Bible Searchers **4231**
Sunday School Leadership. (US ISSN 0274-8568) **4250**
Sunday School Lesson Illustrator see Biblical Illustrator **4231**
Sunday School Lessons Simplified see Sunday School Lessons Special Ministries **4250**
Sunday School Lessons Special Ministries. (US ISSN 0748-5360) **4250**
Sunday School Senior Adults. (US ISSN 0585-9328) **4250**
Sunday School Young Adults. (US ISSN 0162-4903) **4250**
Sunday School Youth. (US) **4250**
Sunday School Youth A see Sunday School Youth **4250**
Sunday School Youth Teacher. (US) **4250**
Sunday Standard. (KE) **2208**
Sunday Star. (BG) **2174**
Sunday Star. (NZ) **2212**
Sunday Sun. (AT) **2172**
Sunday Sun. (UK ISSN 0039-5315) **2195**
Sunday Sun Television Magazine (Calgary). (CN) **1380**
Sunday Sun Television Magazine (Edmonton). (CN) **1380**
Sunday Telegraph Business Finance Directory see U K Business Finance Directory (Year) **1156**
Sunday Times. (KE) **2209**
Sunday Times. (CE) **2218**
Sunday Times of Zambia. (ZA) **2240**
The Sunday Visitor. (US) **4276**
Sundhedsbladet. (DK ISSN 0039-5366) **3809**
Sundhedsstyrelsen Vitalstatistik. (DK ISSN 0107-749X) **2471**
Sundog. (US) **3006**
SunExpert. (US) **1465**
Sunflower (Bismarck). (US ISSN 0192-8988) **194**, **2082**
Sunflower (Manhattan). (US ISSN 0039-5382) **3612**
Sunglass Association of America. Newsletter. (US) **1288**, **3305**
Sunjata. (ML) **2170**
Sunjet. (CY ISSN 1011-1727) **4803**
Sunk Island Review. (UK ISSN 0955-9647) **2885**
Sunnhetsbladet. (NO ISSN 0332-7434) **3809**
Sunrise. (US ISSN 0562-6048) **3783**
Sunrise. (UK) **4803**
Sunrust. (US ISSN 0741-0271) **2967**
Sunset. (US ISSN 0039-5404) **2235**, **2449**
Sunshine Artists U S A. (US ISSN 0199-9370) **346**, **1054**
Sunshine Bulletin. (US) **1301**
Sunshine Classroom. (US) **1760**
Sunshine Coast Weekly. (AT) **2172**
Sunshine Magazine. (US ISSN 0039-5412) **2235**
Sunshine State Agricultural Research Report see Florida Agricultural Research **92**
SunSports. (CN) **4493**
Sunstone. (US ISSN 0363-1370) **4289**
Sunt Foernuft. (SW ISSN 0039-5455) **1107**
SunTech Journal. (US ISSN 1046-5456) **1400**, **1796**, **1939**
SunTechnology see SunTech Journal **1400**
Suo. (FI ISSN 0039-5471) **122**, **2108**, **4828**
Suoliao/Plastics. (CC) **3868**

†Suomalainen. (FI ISSN 0039-548X) **5285**
Suomalainen Tiedeakatemia. Vuosikirja. see Academia Scientiarum Fennica. Yearbook **4295**
Suomalais-Ugrilaisen Seuran. Aikakauskirja/Societe Finno-Ougrienne. Journal. (FI ISSN 0355-0214) **250**, **2846**
Suomalais-Ugrilaisen Seuran. Toimituksia. see Societe Finno-Ougrienne. Memoires **249**
Suomen Antropologi/Antropologi i Finland/Finnish Anthropological Society. Journal. (FI ISSN 0355-3930) **250**
Suomen Autolehti. (FI ISSN 0355-2691) **4703**
Suomen Betoniteollisuuden Keskusjarejesto. Julkaisuja/Association of the Concrete Industry of Finland. Publication. (FI) **633**
Suomen Elainlaakarilehti/Finsk Veterinartidskrift. (FI ISSN 0039-5501) **4816**
Suomen Geodeettisen Laitoksen. Julkaisuja/Finnish Geodetic Institute. Publications/Finnische Geodaetische Institut. Veroeffentlichungen. (FI ISSN 0085-6932) **1595**
Suomen Geodeettisen Laitoksen. Tiedonantoja/Finnish Geodetic Institute. Reports. (FI ISSN 0355-1962) **1595**
Suomen Historiallinen Seura. Kasikirjoja.(FI ISSN 0081-9417) **2330**
Suomen Historian Laehteitae/Source Material of Finnish History. (FI ISSN 0081-9425) **2391**
Suomen Invalidi see I T - Invalidityoe **4408**
Suomen Joukkovelkakirjalainat/Finnish Bond Issues/Finlandska Masskuldebrevslaan. (FI ISSN 0781-4437) **965**
Suomen Kalapaikkaopas. (FI) **4557**
Suomen Kalastuslehti. (FI ISSN 0039-5528) **2049**
Suomen Kalatalous. (FI ISSN 0085-6940) **2049**
Suomen Kemistilehti A see Kemia - Kemi **1856**
Suomen Kirjallisuus/Finnish National Bibliography/Finlands Litteratur. (FI ISSN 0355-001X) **413**
Suomen Kunnallislehti. (FI ISSN 0039-5544) **4095**
Suomen Kuvalehti. (FI ISSN 0039-5552) **2186**
Suomen Laakarilehti/Finlands Laekartidning/Finnish Medical Journal. (FI ISSN 0039-5560) **3155**
Suomen Laakintavoimistelija see Fysioterapia **3100**
Suomen Lehdisto/Finlands Press. (FI ISSN 0039-5587) **2575**
Suomen Matkailu - Tourism of Finland see Matkailu **4775**
Suomen Meteorologinen Vuosikiria. Part 1. Ilmastohavainnot see Meteorological Yearbook of Finland. Part 1: Climatological Data **3438**
Suomen Muinaismuistoyhdistyksen Aikakauskirja/Finska Fornminnesfoereningens Tidskrift. (FI ISSN 0355-1822) **287**, **346**
Suomen Museo. (FI ISSN 0355-1806) **287**, **250**, **346**
Suomen Obligaatiorkirja see Suomen Joukkovelkakirjalainat **965**
Suomen Osallistuminen Yhdistyneiden Kansakuntien Toimintaan see Yhdistyneiden Kansakuntien Yleiskokous (Year) **3978**
Suomen Pankki. Julkaisuja. Kasvututkimuksia. (FI ISSN 0355-6050) **1085**
Suomen Pankki. Julkaisuja. Sarja A/Bank of Finland. Publications. Series A/Finlands Bank. Publikationer. Serie A. (FI ISSN 0355-6034) **693**
Suomen Pankki. Julkaisuja. Sarja B/Bank of Finland. Publications. Series B/Finlands Bank. Publikationer. Serie B. (FI ISSN 0357-4776) **693**

Suomen Pankki. Julkaisuja. Sarja C/Bank of Finland. Publications. Series C/Finlands Bank. Publikationer. Serie C. (FI ISSN 0081-9492) **693**
Suomen Pankki. Julkaisuja. Sarja D/Bank of Finland. Publications. Series D/Finlands Bank. Publikationer. Serie D. (FI ISSN 0355-6042) **693**
Suomen Pankki. Taloustieteellinen Tutkimuslaitos. Julkaisuja. Series B see Suomen Pankki. Julkaisuja. Sarja B **693**
Suomen Pankki. Vuosikirja see Bank of Finland. Yearbook **764**
Suomen Sanomalehtien Mikrofilmit/Microfilmed Newspapers of Finland. (FI ISSN 0355-4074) **2579**, **24**, **413**
Suomen Shakki. (FI ISSN 0355-8096) **4493**
Suomen Silta/Suomi Bridge. (FI ISSN 0039-5625) **2025**
Suomen Standardisoimisliitto Catalogue see S F S Catalogue **3448**
Suomen Teollisuusliittoo. Jasenluettelo see Teollisuuden Keskusliitto. Jasenluettelo **1155**
Suomen Tilastollinen Vuosikirja/Statistisk Aarsbok foer Finland/Statistical Yearbook of Finland. (FI ISSN 0081-5063) **4589**
Suomen Tukkudauppiaiden Liitto. Yearbook. (FI) **921**
Suomen Tukkukauppa. (FI) **921**
Suomen Vakuutusvuosikirja/Finnish Insurance Yearbook. (FI ISSN 0356-7826) **2544**
Suomi. (AT) **2025**
Suomi Bridge. see Suomen Silta **2025**
Suomi - Finland U S A. (FI ISSN 0782-8454) **2025**
Suono Stereo Hi-Fi. (IT) **4462**
Suosikki. (FI ISSN 0355-4260) **1267**, **3583**
SupaTimba Technical Review. (UK) **1922**, **2117**, **3655**
Super Automotive Service. (US ISSN 0896-0437) **4703**
Super C G. (JA ISSN 0915-4116) **4703**
Super Chevy. (US ISSN 0146-2628) **4703**
Super Collider News. (US) **3833**
Super Computing. (US) **1400**
Super Cracked. (US) **2885**
Super Ecran. (CN) **1380**
Super Electronics. Jahrbuch. (GW) **1779**
▼Super Fitness Excel. (US) **3809**
Super Ford. (US) **4703**
Super Gaming. (US) **1419**
Super Group Magazine (English Edition). (US ISSN 1043-2418) **1400**
†Super Group Magazine (French Edition). (US) **5285**
Super Knobel Knifflig. (GW ISSN 0138-1687) **1267**, **4493**
Super Marketing. (UK ISSN 0261-4251) **2094**
†Super - Moto Cross. (US) **5285**
Super Mototecnica. (IT) **4521**
Super Pixel. (GR) **1425**
Super Pop. (SP) **1267**
Super Rock. (CL) **3583**
Super Service Station see Super Automotive Service **4703**
†Super Sports. (US ISSN 0039-5684) **5285**
Super Stock & Drag Illustrated. (US ISSN 0039-5692) **4557**, **4703**
▼Super Street Truck. (US) **4703**
Super - T V. (GW) **1380**
Super Television see Camcorder Report **1384**
Super V W. (FR) **4703**
Super Video & Audio. (IT) **1386**, **4462**
Super-8 Journal see Amateurfilm Journal **3503**
†Super 8 Reader. (AT) **5285**
Superannuation & Retirement Benefits in Australia. (AT) **2684**, **994**
Superavit. (AG) **921**
Superba. (IT ISSN 0039-5706) **4493**
SuperBasket. (IT) **4513**
Superbike. (UK ISSN 0262-8457) **4521**
Supercharger. (US) **4703**

Supercomputing and Parallel Processing Today. (US) 1351
Supercomputing Proceedings. (US) 1439
Supercomputing Review. (US) 1439
†Superconductivity. (US ISSN 0897-6279) 5285
†Superconductivity Abstracts. (US ISSN 0959-308X) 5285
Superconductivity Directory. (US) 1154, 1908
Superconductivity: Physics, Chemistry, Technology. (US ISSN 0235-8964) 3833, 1189, 4609
▼Superconductivity Reviews. (US) 1779
†Superconductor Advance. (US) 5285
Superconductor Industry. (US ISSN 1042-4105) 1908
Superconductor Science & Technology. (UK ISSN 0953-2048) 3833, 1189, 1837
Superconductor Week. (US ISSN 0894-7635) 3842
Supercycle. (US ISSN 0162-3923) 4521
Superfund. (US ISSN 0892-2985) 1497, 2684
Superfund Report. (US) 1987
Superfunds. (AT ISSN 0729-3828) 2544
†Supergrowth Technology U S A. (US) 5285
Superintendencia do Desenvolvimento do Nordeste Brazil. S U D E N E. Departamento de Agricultura e Abastecimento see Brazil. S U D E N E. Departamento de Agricultura e Abastecimento 80
Superintendencia do Desenvolvimento do Nordeste Sudene Informa see Sudene Informa 5285
Superintendent of Insurance Annual Report. (CN) 2544, 4158
Superintending for Contractors: How to Bring Jobs in on Time, on Budget. (US) 633
Superintending for the General Contractor see Superintending for Contractors: How to Bring Jobs in on Time, on Budget 633
Superinteressante. (BL) 2175
Superinvestor Hotsheet. (US) 965
Superior California Administration Newsletter see S C A N 5272
Superlattices and Microstructures. (UK ISSN 0749-6036) 1189, 3833
Supermarkeder og Andre Store Dagligvarebutikker (Year). (DK) 1118, 965
Supermarket. (SW ISSN 0039-5781) 1054
Supermarket and Cash & Carry Buyers Guide. (UK) 2094
Supermarket and Retailer. (SA ISSN 0049-2590) 2094
Supermarket Business. (US ISSN 0196-5700) 2094
†Supermarket Circle. (AT) 5285
Supermarket Floral. (US) 2143, 2094
Supermarket News. (US ISSN 0039-5803) 2094
Supermarket News. (AT) 2094
Supermarket Software Directory. (US) 2094
▼Supermarket Strategic Alert. (US ISSN 1053-3648) 2094
Supermarketing. (NZ ISSN 0112-949X) 2094
Supermente. (MX) 3671
Supermercado Moderno. (BL) 1054, 2094
†Supermicro. (US ISSN 0740-4816) 5285
Superstar Wrestler. (US) 4493
Superstereo Audio Magazine. (IT) 4462
Superstore Management International. (UK) 1054
SuperTeen. (US) 1267
SuperTeen's LoudMouth. (US) 1267
Supertrax. (CN) 4557
Supervision. (US ISSN 0039-5854) 994, 1029
Supervisor's Bulletin. (US ISSN 0039-5889) 1029
Supervisor's Bulletin: Office Edition. (US ISSN 0744-3625) 1062

Supervisor's E E O Review see E E O Review 1064
Supervisor's Environmental Alert see Environmental Safety Alert 1953
†Supervisor's Newsletter. (US ISSN 0740-0411) 5285
Supervisor's Production Planner. (US) 1029
Supervisors Quarterly see Teacher Educator 1717
†Supervisor's Safety Clinic. (US ISSN 0194-8717) 5285
Supervisory Management (Lichfield) see Modern Management 1021
Supervisory Management (New York). (US) 1029
Supervisory Sense. (US ISSN 0274-645X) 1029
Supesu Purazuma Kenkyukai. (JA) 3833
Supima Association of America Newsletter. (US) 122
Suplemento Literario de Revolucion y Cultura. (CU) 2885, 2967
Suplementos sobre el Sistema Financiero de Papeles de Economia Espanola. (SP ISSN 0212-5994) 800
Le Supplement. (FR ISSN 0750-1455) 4204
†Supplement Pilze. (GW) 5285
Supplement Umweltanalytik - Umweltschutz see Umwelt Technologie Aktuell 1970
Supplementary Service to European Taxation. (NE ISSN 0039-5927) 1107
▼Supplementary Statement to Statement of Auditing Practice. (AT ISSN 1034-8298) 756
Supplements of Women of Europe. (EI ISSN 1012-1935) 4853
Suppliers Ceramics Book. (IT) 1154, 1166
Suppliers Sanitary - Tableware Book. (IT) 2303, 1166, 2562
Supply and Demand: Educational Personnel in Delaware. (US ISSN 0094-2308) 1666
Supply and Demand for Scientists and Engineers see Technological Marketplace: Supply and Demand for Scientists and Engineers 3631
Supply House Times. (US ISSN 0039-5935) 2303
Supply Line. (US) 2442, 4703
Supply Post. (CN) 2108
Support for Learning. (UK ISSN 0268-2141) 1741
Support for the Learning and Teaching of English Newsletter see S L A T E Newsletter 1759
Supportive Lifestyles News. (US) 3597, 3783
Supreme Court Bulletin. (US ISSN 0199-5030) 2733
Supreme Court Cases. (II ISSN 0039-5951) 2733
Supreme Court Cases (Criminal). (II ISSN 0253-6544) 2714, 2733
Supreme Court Cases (Labour and Services). (II ISSN 0253-6552) 2733
†Supreme Court Cases (Taxation). (II ISSN 0253-6560) 5285
Supreme Court Economic Review. (US ISSN 0736-9921) 2733
Supreme Court Historical Society. Yearbook. (US ISSN 0362-5249) 2733
†Supreme Court Journal. (II) 5285
Supreme Court Law Review. (CN ISSN 0228-0108) 2684
Supreme Court Monthly Review. (PK ISSN 0585-9794) 2733
Supreme Court Notes. (II ISSN 0039-596X) 2733
Supreme Court of Canada Decisions. (CN) 2733
Supreme Court of Canada Decisions. Civil and Criminal see Supreme Court of Canada Decisions 2733
Supreme Court of Canada Reports Service. (CN) 2733
Supreme Court Procedure N S W. (AT) 2733
Supreme Court Review. (US ISSN 0081-9557) 2733

Supremo Tribunal Federal Juriscivel do S T F see Jurisivel do S T F 2641
Al-Suqur. (SU) 63
Sur. (PE) 122
Surah. (IR) 2967
Suraj Mukhi. (PK) 2885
Surat. (PK) 2967
Surchhanda. (II) 3583
Surco Argentina. (US) 122
Surco Latinoamericana. (US) 122
Surco Mexicana. (US) 122
Surete des Installations Nucleaires. Bulletin see Bulletin de la Surete Nucleaire 4098
Surf. (GW) 4557
Surf. (IT) 4557
Surf and Fun. (BE ISSN 0775-8553) 4493
Surf & Ski. (GR) 4493
Surf Report. (US) 4557
Surface. (CN) 2562
Surface. see Oberflaeche 3654
Surface and Coatings Technology. (SZ ISSN 0257-8972) 1209
Surface Coating & Raw Material Directory. (UK ISSN 0268-9766) 1154, 3655
Surface Coatings see Finishing 3653
Surface Coatings Australia. (AT ISSN 0815-709X) 3655
Surface Coatings International. (UK) 3655
Surface Engineering. (UK ISSN 0267-0844) 3421, 1922
Surface Mining Reporter see Mine Regulation Reporter 3488
▼Surface Modification Technology News. (US ISSN 1058-093X) 3833, 1922
†Surface Mount International. (UK ISSN 0959-9517) 5285
Surface Mount Technology. (US) 1908
Surface Mount Technology Today. (US ISSN 0886-618X) 1922
Surface Mount Technology Trends see S M T Trends 3651
▼Surface-Mounted Discretes D.A.T.A. Digest. (US ISSN 1051-7715) 1908
▼Surface-Mounted Integrated Circuits D.A.T.A. Digest. (US ISSN 1051-7707) 1908
Surface Mounting Products and Regulations Microfile (PRISM). (UK) 1837
Surface Science. (NE ISSN 0039-6028) 3833, 1230
Surface Science Letters. (NE) 3839, 24, 3833
Surface Science Reports. (NE ISSN 0167-5729) 3833
▼Surface Science Spectra. (US ISSN 1055-5269) 3833
Surface Structure of Oil Fields. see Youtian Dimian Gongcheng 3704
Surface Technology see Surface and Coatings Technology 1209
Surface Topography. (UK ISSN 0952-5955) 2263
Surface Transportation R & D in Canada. (CN) 4656
Surface Treatment see Surface Treatment Plant and Processes 3421
Surface Treatment Plant and Processes. (UK) 3421, 1860
Surface Treatment Technology Abstracts. (UK ISSN 0950-5199) 3428, 24
Surface Warfare. (US ISSN 0145-1073) 3472
Surface Wave Abstracts. (UK ISSN 0049-2639) 3839, 24
Surfaces (Paris). (FR ISSN 0585-9840) 3655
Surfaces (Paris, 1978). (FR) 3783
Surfactant Science Series. (US ISSN 0081-9603) 1189, 457
Surfboard. (US ISSN 0276-6582) 4493
Surfen. (GW ISSN 0930-9195) 4557
Surfer. (US ISSN 0039-6036) 4557
Surfing. (US ISSN 0194-9314) 4557
Surge International. (II) 2885
Surgelation. (FR ISSN 0049-2647) 2082
Surgeons of Steel. (US) 4703
Surgery. see Zentralorgan Chirurgie 3182

Surgery. see Khirurgiya 3381
Surgery/Geka. (JA ISSN 0016-593X) 3384
Surgery. (US ISSN 0039-6060) 3384
Surgery Alert. (US ISSN 0748-1942) 3384
Surgery and Immunity. (IT ISSN 1120-4834) 3384
Surgery Annual. (US ISSN 0081-9638) 3385
Surgery, Gynecology & Obstetrics. (US ISSN 0039-6087) 3385, 24, 3181
Surgery in Infancy and Childhood. see Zeitschrift fuer Kinderchirurgie 3327
†▼Surgery Report. (US) 5285
Surgical and Radiologic Anatomy. (GW ISSN 0930-312X) 575, 3363, 3385
Surgical Business see Health Industry Today 3103
Surgical Clinics of North America. (US ISSN 0039-6109) 3385
Surgical Endoscopy, Ultrasound and Interventional Techniques. (GW ISSN 0930-2794) 3385
Surgical Forum see Forum on Fundamental Surgical Problems 3378
Surgical Gastroenterology see Digestive Surgery 3378
†Surgical Gastroenterology. (IT) 5285
▼Surgical Laparoscopy and Endoscopy.(US ISSN 1051-7200) 3385, 3270, 3296
Surgical Neurology. (US ISSN 0090-3019) 3385, 3355
▼Surgical Oncology. (UK) 3202
Surgical Practice News. (US ISSN 0273-7655) 3385
Surgical Product Comparison System. (US) 3385
Surgical Products. (US) 3155
Surgical Research Communications. (US ISSN 0882-9233) 3385
Surgical Rounds. (US ISSN 0161-1372) 3385
†Surgical Rounds for Orthopaedics. (US ISSN 0891-1800) 5285
Surgical Team see Journal of Surgical Practice 3381
Surgical Technologist. (US ISSN 0164-4238) 3385
Surgical Trade Buyers Guide see Health Industry Buyers Guide 3103
Surgical Update. (US) 3243
Surgo. (UK ISSN 0039-6125) 3385
Suri Kagaku/Mathematical Sciences. (JA ISSN 0386-2240) 3057
Suri Kaiseki Kenkyujo Dayori. (JA) 3057
Suri Keikaku Shinpojumu Ronbunshu/ Mathematical Programming Symposium, Japan. Proceedings. (JA) 3057, 1432
Surinaams Nieuws Agentschap. Bulletin.(SR) 2217
Surinaamse Landbouw/Surinam Agriculture. (SR ISSN 0039-6133) 122, 227, 2049
Surinam. Advertentieblad. (SR) 39
Surinam. Algemeen Bureau voor de Statistiek. Kwartaal Statistiek van de Industriele Produktie. (SR) 740
Surinam. Centraal Bureau Luchtkartering. Jaarverslag. (SR) 2263, 63
Surinam Agriculture. see Surinaamse Landbouw 122
Suriname. Algemeen Bureau voor de Statistiek. Nationale Rekeningen. (SR) 4589
Suriname Zending see Hernhutter Suriname Zending 4180
Surmach. (UK ISSN 0491-6204) 3472, 2324, 3929
Surplus. (NE ISSN 0921-2981) 2967, 2885, 4853
Surplus Line Reporter. (US) 2544
Surplus Record. (US ISSN 0039-615X) 3025
Surprises. (US) 1267
Surrey and Hants. County Border Times & News see County Border Times 2193
Surrey Archaeological Collections. (UK ISSN 0309-7803) 287
Surrey Archaeological Society. Bulletin. (UK ISSN 0585-9980) 287

Surrey Archaeological Society. Research Volumes. (UK ISSN 0308-342X) 287
Surrey - Delta Magazine. (CN) 1508
Surrey Director. (UK) 693
Surrey Magazine see Surrey - Delta Magazine 1508
Surrey N.F.U. Journal see Central Southern Farmer 83
Surry Scene. (US) 2235
Sursum Corda. (AT ISSN 0039-6184) 4276
Surveillance! (US) 1528
▼Surveillant. (US ISSN 1051-0923) 413, 1528, 3973
Survey. (II) 1029, 4422
Survey see Survey Sarajevo 3929
Survey (La Jolla). (US) 1474, 1837
Survey (Sydney). (AT) 3929
Survey Methodology. (CN ISSN 0714-0045) 4589
Survey of Anesthesiology. (US ISSN 0039-6206) 3181, 24
Survey of Arab Affairs. (IS) 3929
Survey of Arts Administration Training. (US) 346, 4075
Survey of Construction Activities of the Private Sector in Urban Areas of Iran.(IR ISSN 0301-7478) 633
Survey of Current Affairs. (UK ISSN 0039-6214) 3929
Survey of Current Business. (US ISSN 0039-6222) 885
Survey of Dental Practice. (US) 3243
Survey of Economic and Social Conditions in Africa. (UN) 935
Survey of Final Year Accounting Students. (AT) 756, 3631
†Survey of Financial Indicators. (US) 5285
Survey of Food Literature. see Prehledy Potravinarske Literatury 2085
†Survey of Grant-Making Foundations. (US) 5285
Survey of Household Economic Activities (Year). (CE) 885, 158, 4589
Survey of India's Exports. (II ISSN 0537-1120) 823
†Survey of Industrial Purchasing Power.(US) 5285
Survey of International Affairs. (US) 3973
Survey of Israel. Cartographic Papers. (IS) 2263
Survey of Israel. Photogrammetric Papers. (IS) 2263
Survey of Judicial Salaries. (US) 2733
Survey of Local Chambers of Commerce. (US ISSN 0069-2441) 823
Survey of London. (UK ISSN 0081-9751) 346
Survey of London Monograph Series. (UK) 346
Survey of Migration in Bangkok Metropolis. (TH ISSN 0858-0391) 3996
Survey of Operating Performance for Music Dealers. (US) 3583, 4589
Survey of Ophthalmology. (US ISSN 0039-6257) 3181, 24
Survey of Overseas Visitors to Singapore. (SI) 4800, 4787
Survey of Pharmacy Law. (US) 3744, 2684
Survey of Press Freedom in Latin America. (US ISSN 0743-4324) 2575, 2423, 3973
†Survey of Progress in Chemistry. (US ISSN 0081-976X) 5285
Survey of Race Relations in South Africa see Race Relations Survey 3946
†Survey of Research for Sexually Transmitted Diseases. (US) 5285
▼Survey of State Tax Rates and Collections. (US) 1107
†Survey of State Taxation. (US) 5285
Survey of State Travel Offices. (US) 4788
Survey of the Austrian Economy/ Oesterreichs Wirtschaft im Ueberblick. (AU) 839
Survey of Victorian Manufacturing. (AT ISSN 1033-9094) 823, 839
Survey on Graduating Students Abroad. (CY) 1680, 4589
Survey Sarajevo. (BN ISSN 0350-0144) 3929

Surveying. see Maanmittaus 1871
Surveying and Land Information Systems. (US) 2264, 1875
Surveying and Mapping see Surveying and Land Information Systems 2264
Surveying Australia. (AT ISSN 0157-1672) 1875, 3496
Surveying Science in Finland. (FI ISSN 0780-8399) 1875, 1880
Surveying Technician. (UK ISSN 0952-5793) 4158
Surveyor. (MY ISSN 0127-4937) 1582
Surveyor. (UK) 1875
Surveyor. see Celiang Yuan 2244
Surveyor - Public Authority Technology see Surveyor 1875
Surveys and Development Plans of Industry in Israel/Hata'asiyah Be-Yisra. (IS ISSN 0081-9743) 1085
Surveys & Reference Works in Mathematics. (US) 3057
Surveys in Geophysics. (NE ISSN 0169-3298) 1595
Surveys in High Energy Physics. (US ISSN 0142-2413) 3833
Surveys of Applied Economics. (US) 693
▼Surveys on Mathematics for Industry. (AU ISSN 0938-1953) 3057
†Surveys, Polls, Censuses and Forecasts Directory. (US ISSN 0737-545X) 5285
SurView. (US ISSN 0733-8813) 1582
Survival. (UK ISSN 0039-6338) 3973
Survival (London, 1983). (UK) 3947, 250
†Survival Bulletin. (US) 5286
Survival Guide. (US) 1274
Survival International Annual Review. (UK) 3947, 250
Survival International News see Survival (London, 1983) 3947
Survival News Bulletin see Survival Bulletin 5286
Survival News for Cities and Towns see Financing Local Government 1094
Survival Tomorrow. (US ISSN 0273-2017) 4454
Survival Weaponry and Techniques. (UK) 4493
Survive & Win. (US) 828, 1508
Surviving Our Leukemia on Our Own see S O L O 3202
Surviving Together: A Journal on Relations with the Former Soviet Union. (US) 3973
Surviving Together: A Journal on Soviet-American Relations see Surviving Together: A Journal on Relations with the Former Soviet Union 3973
Survivors. (US) 4454
Survivors Outreach Series. (US) 4454
Survivre see Solidaires (Paris) 4421
Surya India. (II) 2202, 2342
Sushama. (II ISSN 0039-6370) 2967
Sushiki Shori Tsushin/Communications for Symbolic and Algebraic Manipulation. (JA ISSN 0288-4046) 3057
Sushmita. (II) 2967, 3518
Susquehanna Alumnus. (US) 1325
Susquehanna Monthly Magazine see Old News 2231
Susquehanna River Basin Commission. Annual Report. (US ISSN 0094-6427) 4828
†Sussex Anthropology. (UK ISSN 0307-823X) 5286
Sussex Business Times. (UK ISSN 0306-2201) 694
Sussex Essays in Anthropology see Sussex Anthropology 5286
†Sussex Genealogical Centre. Occasional Papers. (UK) 5286
Sussex Life. (UK ISSN 0039-6397) 2195
Sussidi Patristici. (IT) 4276
Sustrai. (SP) 2049
Sut Anubis. (UK ISSN 0143-5418) 3671
Sutherland Quarterly. (US) 2165
Sutler. (US) 2165
Sutton Bridge Annual Review. (US ISSN 0309-2968) 158
Sutureline. (US) 3385

Suuri Kasityokerho. (FI ISSN 0355-2098) 3592
Suvremena Metodika Nastave Hrvatskog ili Srpskog Jezika. (CI) 2846
Suvremeni Promet. (CI ISSN 0351-1898) 4677, 4715, 4740
Suzhou Daxue Xuebao (Zhexue Shehui Kexue Ban)/Suzhou University. Journal (Social Science Edition). (CC) 4389, 3783
Suzhou Institute of Medical Sciences. Journal. see Suzhou Yixueyuan Xuebao 3155
Suzhou Institute of Silk Engineering. Journal. see Suzhou Sichou Gongxueyuan Xuebao 4623
Suzhou Sichou Gongxueyuan Xuebao/ Suzhou Institute of Silk Engineering. Journal. (CC ISSN 1000-1999) 4623
Suzhou University. Journal (Social Science Edition). see Suzhou Daxue Xuebao (Zhexue Shehui Kexue Ban) 4389
Suzhou Yixueyuan Xuebao/Suzhou Institute of Medical Sciences. Journal.(CC ISSN 1000-5749) 3155
Suzi Deveraux International Fan Club. (US) 3583, 421, 1301
Suzugamine Joshi Tandai Kenkyu Shuho. Shizen Kagaku/Suzugamine Women's College. Bulletin. Natural Science. (JA ISSN 0389-5025) 4346
Suzugamine Women's College. Bulletin. Natural Science. see Suzugamine Joshi Tandai Kenkyu Shuho. Shizen Kagaku 4346
Sv. Pranciskaus Varpelis/Bell of St. Francis. (US) 4276, 2025
Svampe. (DK ISSN 0106-7451) 518, 2108
Svarochnoe Proizvodstvo. (RU ISSN 0491-6441) 3430
Sveitastjornarmal. (IC) 4095
Svensk Bergs- och Brukstidning. (SW ISSN 0039-6435) 3496
Svensk Bokfoerteckning/Swedish National Bibliography. (SW ISSN 0039-6443) 413
Svensk Bokhandel. (SW ISSN 0039-6451) 4137
Svensk Botanisk Tidskrift. (SW ISSN 0039-646X) 518
Svensk Exegetisk Aarsbok. (SW) 4204
Svensk Export. (SW ISSN 0039-6508) 921
Svensk Faerghandel. (SW ISSN 0039-6516) 3655, 376, 1860
Svensk Farmaceutisk Tidskrift. (SW ISSN 0039-6524) 3744
Svensk Filatelistisk Tidskrift. (SW ISSN 0039-6532) 3758
Svensk Fotboll. (SW) 4513
Svensk Fotografisk Tidskrift see Fotografisk Tidskrift 3791
Svensk Froetidning. (SW ISSN 0346-2099) 194
Svensk Geografisk Aarsbok/Swedish Geographical Yearbook. (SW ISSN 0081-9808) 2264
Svensk Golf. (SW) 4513
Svensk Guldsmeds Tidning see Guldsmedstidningen 2564
Svensk Gymnastik. (SW ISSN 0281-5443) 4493
Svensk Handel see Dagens Industri 658
Svensk Idrott. (SW ISSN 0049-2663) 4493
†Svensk Industritidning. (SW) 5286
Svensk Ishockeymagasin see Hockey 4474
Svensk Jakt. (SW ISSN 0039-6583) 4557
Svensk Juristtidning. (SW ISSN 0039-6591) 2733
Svensk Kyrkomusik (Edition AB for Church Musicians) see Kyrkomusikernas Tidning 3560
Svensk Lantmaeteritidskrift/Swedish Landsurveying Journal. (SW ISSN 0039-6613) 2264
Svensk Leksaksrevy. (SW ISSN 0039-6621) 2282, 2442
Svensk Medicin. (SW ISSN 0284-5342) 3155

Svensk Numismatisk Tidskrift. (SW ISSN 0283-071X) 3602
Svensk Obligationsbok. (SW) 800
Svensk Omnibustidning see Buss - Svensk Omnibustidning 4685
Svensk Papperstidning see Svensk Papperstidning - Nordisk Cellulosa 3666
Svensk Papperstidning - Nordisk Cellulosa. (SW ISSN 0283-6831) 3666
Svensk Pastoral Tidskrift. (SW ISSN 0039-6699) 4204
Svensk Privatradio. (SW) 1360
Svensk Sjoefarts Tidning/Scandinavian Shipping Gazette. (SW ISSN 0039-6702) 4740
Svensk Skidsport. (SW ISSN 0049-2671) 4557
Svensk Skolledartidning see Skolledaren 1663
▼Svensk Tennis/Swedish Tennis. (SW) 4513
Svensk Teologisk Kvartalskrift. (SW ISSN 0039-6761) 4204
Svensk Tidskrift. (SW ISSN 0039-677X) 2885
Svensk Tidskrift foer Musikforskning/ Swedish Journal of Musicology. (SW ISSN 0081-9816) 3583
Svensk Tidskriftsfoerteckning/Current Swedish Periodicals. (SW ISSN 0586-0431) 413
†Svensk Traevaru- och Pappersmassetidning/Swedish Timber and Wood Pulp Journal. (SW ISSN 0039-6796) 5286
Svensk Urmakartidning. (SW) 2566
Svensk Vaegtidning. (SW) 1875
Svensk Varumaerkestidning - Swedish Trademark Journal. Part A (Publications for Opposition). (SW ISSN 0348-324X) 3678
Svensk Varumaerkestidning - Swedish Trademark Journal. Part B (Publications of Registrations). (SW ISSN 0348-3258) 3678
Svensk Varumaerkestidning - Swedish Trademark Journal. Part C (Renewals, Changes of Ownership). (SW ISSN 0348-3266) 3678
Svensk Veckotidning. (SW ISSN 0039-6826) 4204
Svensk Veterinaertidning. (SW ISSN 0346-2250) 4816
Svenska Antavlor. (SW ISSN 0349-1714) 2165
Svenska Arbetsgivarefoereningen Tidningen see S A F - Tidningen 1027
Svenska Arkivsamfundets Skrifterie see Arkiv, Samhaelle och Forskning 2744
Svenska Bankfoereningen. Ekonomiska Meddelanden. (SW ISSN 0345-2719) 885
Svenska Barnboksinstitutet. Skrifter/ Swedish Institute for Children's Books. Studies. (SW ISSN 0347-5387) 1267, 2786
Svenska Bostaeder. Aarsredovisning. see Housing and Urban Planning in Sweden. Annual Report 2488
Svenska Elverksfoereningen see E R A 1886
Svenska Folkskolans Vaenners Kalender.(FI) 2391
Svenska Frisoertidningen. (SW) 374
Svenska Gasfoereningens Maanadsblad see Gasnytt 3687
Svenska Handelsbanken. Annual Report. (SW ISSN 0081-9913) 800
Svenska Handelsbanken. Annual Report and Auditors' Report see Svenska Handelsbanken. Annual Report 800
Svenska Historiska Foereningen. Skrifter. (SW) 2391
Svenska Institutet i Athen. Skrifter. (SW ISSN 0081-9921) 287, 1280
Svenska Institutet i Rom. Skrifter. Acta Series Prima. (SW ISSN 0081-993X) 287, 1280
Svenska Jaernvaegstidningen. (SW) 4715, 994
Svenska Journalen. (SW) 2218
Svenska Kyrkans. (SW) 4204
Svenska Lantbruksproducenternas Centralforbund. Aarsbok. (FI) 123

Svenska Linne-Sallskapet Aarsskrift/ Swedish Linneus Society. Yearbook. (SW ISSN 0375-2038) **518**
Svenska Litteratursaellskapet i Finland. Skrifter. (FI ISSN 0039-6842) **2324, 2846**
Svenska Livsmedelsinstitutet (SIK) Annual Report *see* S I K Annual Report **2081**
Svenska Livsmedelsinstitutet (SIK) Information *see* S I K Information **2081**
Svenska Motor-Magasinet. (SW ISSN 0348-3304) **4703**
Svenska Museer. (SW ISSN 0039-6885) **3533**
Svenska P C World. (SW ISSN 0348-4009) **1474**
Svenska Revisorsamfundet. Revisorn Informerar *see* Revisorn Informerar **755**
Svenska Tidningsartiklar. (SW ISSN 0039-6907) **413**
Svenska Tidskriftsartiklar. (SW ISSN 0039-6915) **413**
Svenska Traeforskningsinstitutet (STFI) Meddelande. Series A *see* S T F I Meddelande. Series A **3666**
Svenska Traeskyddsinstitutet. Meddelanden/Swedish Wood Preservation Institute. Reports. (SW ISSN 0346-7090) **2117**
Svenska Vaegfoereningens Tidskrift *see* Svensk Vaegtidning **1875**
Svenskt Fiske *see* Sportfiskaren **4557**
Svenskt Musikhistoriskt Arkiv. Bulletin. (SW ISSN 0586-0709) **3583**
Svenskt Varumaerkesarkiv/Swedish Trademark Archive. (SW) **3678**
Svenskt Varumaerkeslexikon/Swedish Trade Mark Dictionary. (SW) **3678**
Sverige-Nytt/Swedish Digest. (SW ISSN 0039-6958) **2218**
Sverigekontakt. (SW) **2218**
Sveriges Foerfattarfoerbund. Medlemsfoerteckning/Swedish Writers Association. Membership Roll.(SW) **2967, 421**
Sveriges Jaernvaegar/Railways of Sweden. (SW ISSN 0081-9964) **4715**
Sveriges Landstings Tidskrift *see* Landstingsvaerlden **4089**
Sveriges Lantbruksuniversitet. Institutionen foer Vaextodling. Rapporter och Avhandlingar. (SW) **123**
Sveriges Lantbruksuniversitet. Institutionen foer Virkeslaera. Rapporter. (SW ISSN 0348-4599) **2108**
Sveriges Lantbruksuniversitet. Institutionen foer Virkeslaera. Uppsatser. (SW) **2108**
Sveriges Natur. (SW ISSN 0349-5264) **1497**
Sveriges Riksbank. Foervaltningsberaettelse. (SW ISSN 0347-3198) **800**
Sveriges Riksbank. Kredit- och Valutaoeversikt *see* Sveriges Riksbank. Penning- och Valutapolitik **800**
Sveriges Riksbank. Penning- och Valutapolitik. (SW ISSN 1100-5815) **800**
Sveriges Riksbank. Statistisk Aarsbok/ Sveriges Riksbank - Swedish Central Bank. Statistical Yearbook. (SW ISSN 0348-7342) **800, 740**
Sveriges Riksbank - Swedish Central Bank. Annual Report *see* Sveriges Riksbank. Foervaltningsberaettelse **800**
Sveriges Riksbank - Swedish Central Bank. Quarterly Review *see* Sveriges Riksbank. Penning- och Valutapolitik **800**
Sveriges Riksbank - Swedish Central Bank. Statistical Yearbook. *see* Sveriges Riksbank. Statistisk Aarsbok **800**
Sveriges Skogsvaardsfoerbunds Tidskrift/Swedish Forestry Association. Magazine. (SW ISSN 0371-2907) **2108**
Sveriges Utsaedesfoerenings Tidskrift. (SW ISSN 0039-6990) **194**

Sverkhtverdye Materialy. (KR ISSN 0203-3119) **1215**
Svesos Krastos. (US) **2025**
▼Svet Literatury/World of Literature. (NE) **2967, 2846**
Svet Motoru. (CS ISSN 0039-7016) **4703**
Svet Socialismu. (CS) **3929**
Sveta Cecilija. (CI) **3583**
Svetlosc. (YU ISSN 0488-7557) **2516**
Svetlost. (YU ISSN 0039-7059) **2885**
Svetosavsko Zvonce. (YU) **4289**
Svetotekhnika. (RU ISSN 0039-7067) **1908**
Svetova Literatura. (CS ISSN 0039-7075) **2967**
Svetsaren. (SW ISSN 0039-7083) **3430**
Svetsen. (SW ISSN 0039-7091) **3430**
Sveuciliste u Zagrebu. Fakultet Strojarstva i Brodogradnje. Zbornik Radova. (CI ISSN 0350-3097) **1939, 4740**
Sveuciliste u Zagrebu. Medicinski Fakultet. Radovi/Acta Facultatis Medicae Zagrabiensis. (CI ISSN 0033-8575) **3155**
Sveuciliste u Zagrebu. Prirodoslovno-Matematicki Fakultet. Radovi *see* Geofizika **1589**
Svezia Oggi *see* Sweden Now **2218**
Svijet (Zagreb). (CI ISSN 0039-7113) **2885**
Sviluppo e Organizzazione. (IT ISSN 0391-7045) **1029**
Svineavl og Produktion i Danmark *see* Svineavl og Produktion i Danmark. Aarsberetning (Year) **227**
Svineavl og Produktion i Danmark. Aarsberetning (Year). (DK) **227**
Svineavlsnytt. (NO ISSN 0332-7566) **227**
Svinovodstvo. (RU ISSN 0039-713X) **227**
Svinskoetsel/Pig Farming. (SW ISSN 0346-2471) **227**
Svisa Esperanto Revuo. (SZ) **2846**
Svit/Light. (US ISSN 0039-7156) **4289**
Svithiod Journal. (US ISSN 0300-6212) **2025**
Svitlo/Light. (CN) **4276**
Svivot/Environments. (IS ISSN 0333-6697) **1969**
Svizzera Industriale e Commerciale. (IT) **823**
Svjetlo Rijeci/Light of the Word. (BN) **4276**
Svobodna Skola/Free Thinking School. (US) **2967, 2846**
▼Svobodnyi Kurs. (RU) **2885**
Svyturys. (LI) **2209**
Swadesh. (BG) **2174**
Swamp Gas Journal. (CN ISSN 0707-7106) **63**
Swamp Root. (US ISSN 1045-7682) **2967**
Swank. (US) **3400**
Swansea and West Wales Business World. (UK) **823**
Swansea Geographer. (UK ISSN 0081-9980) **2264**
Swansea Review. (UK) **2967**
Swap Talk *see* Drive! (Pleasant Hill) **4689**
Swara. (KE) **1497**
Swarbica Journal. (PK) **2342, 2786**
Swarthmore College Bulletin. (US ISSN 0888-2126) **1325**
Swashbuckler. (US ISSN 1042-7880) **4493**
Swasth Hind. (II ISSN 0586-1179) **4113**
Swatches. (US) **4623**
Swazi T V Times. (SQ) **1380**
Swaziland. Central Statistical Office. Annual Statistical Bulletin. (SQ ISSN 0586-1357) **4589**
Swaziland. Central Statistical Office. Annual Survey of Swazi Nation Land. (SQ) **4589**
Swaziland. Central Statistical Office. Capital Fund Estimates *see* Swaziland. Ministry of Finance. Capital Fund Estimates **800**

Swaziland. Central Statistical Office. Census of Individual Tenure Farms. (SQ) **123**
Swaziland. Central Statistical Office. Census of Industrial Production *see* Swaziland. Central Statistical Office. Census of Industries **740**
Swaziland. Central Statistical Office. Census of Industries. (SQ) **740, 4589**
Swaziland. Central Statistical Office. Commercial Timber Plantation and Wood Products Statistics *see* Swaziland. Central Statistical Office. Timber Statistics **2113**
Swaziland. Central Statistical Office. Education Statistics. (SQ) **1680, 4589**
Swaziland. Central Statistical Office. Employment and Wages. (SQ) **994**
Swaziland. Central Statistical Office. Recurrent Estimates of Public Expenditure *see* Swaziland. Ministry of Finance. Recurrent Estimates of Public Expenditure **4075**
Swaziland. Central Statistical Office. Timber Statistics. (SQ) **2113, 4589**
Swaziland. Department of Economic Planning and Statistics. Economic Review. (SQ) **886**
Swaziland. Economic Planning Office. Economic Review *see* Swaziland. Department of Economic Planning and Statistics. Economic Review **886**
Swaziland. Geological Survey and Mines Department. Annual Report. (SQ ISSN 0081-9999) **1582**
Swaziland. Geological Survey and Mines Department. Bulletin. (SQ ISSN 0082-0008) **1582**
Swaziland. Ministry of Agriculture. Annual Report. (SQ) **123**
Swaziland. Ministry of Finance. Capital Fund Estimates. (SQ) **800**
Swaziland. Ministry of Finance. Recurrent Estimates of Public Expenditure. (SQ) **4075**
Swaziland National Bibliography. (SQ ISSN 0378-7710) **413, 4142**
Swaziland National Museum. Yearbook *see* Swaziland National Trust Commission. Annual Report **2335**
Swaziland National Trust Commission. Annual Report. (SQ) **2335**
Sweden. Finansdepartmentet. Regeringens Budgetfoerslag. (SW ISSN 0347-7169) **1107**
Sweden. Geological Survey of Sweden. Geomagnetic Publications. *see* Sweden. Sveriges Geologiska Undersoekning. Jordmagnetiska Publikationer **1582**
Sweden. Geological Survey of Sweden. Series C. Memoirs and Notices. *see* Sweden. Sveriges Geologiska Undersoekning. Serie C. Avhandlingar och Uppsatser **1582**
Sweden. Geological Survey of Sweden. Series Ca. Notices in Folio and Quarto. *see* Sweden. Sveriges Geologiska Undersoekning. Serie Ca. Avhandlingar och Uppsatser i Kvarto **1582**
Sweden. Konjunkturinstitutet. Occasional Paper. (SW ISSN 0082-0067) **694**
Sweden. Luftfartsverket. Aarsbok. (SW ISSN 0348-2251) **4667, 4589**
Sweden. Luftfartsverket. Charterstatistik. (SW) **4667, 4589**
Sweden. Luftfartsverket. Flygplatsstatistik. (SW) **4667, 4589**
Sweden. Medicinalvaesendet. Foerfattningssamling *see* Sweden. Socialstyrelsen. Foerfattningssamling: Social **4422**
Sweden. Ministry of Finance. Revised Finance Bill. (SW) **1107**
Sweden. National Board of Health and Welfare. Alcohol Statistics. *see* Sweden. Socialstyrelsen. Alkoholstatistik **388**
Sweden. National Board of Health and Welfare. Authorized Physicians. *see* Sweden. Socialstyrelsen. Legitimerade Laekare **3155**

SWEDEN. STATENS 6709

Sweden. National Environmental Protection Board. Report *see* Sweden. Swedish Environmental Protection Agency. Report **1498**
Sweden. Nationalmusei Skriftserie. (SW) **3533**
Sweden. Nationalmuseum. Skriftserie *see* Sweden. Nationalmusei Skriftserie **3533**
Sweden. Patent- och Registereringsverket. Aarsberaettelse.(SW) **3678**
Sweden. Riksdagen. Foerteckning Oever Riksdagens Ledamoeter. (SW) **3929**
Sweden. Riksdagen. Riksdag *see* Sweden. Riksdagen. Riksdagen Aarsbok **3929**
Sweden. Riksdagen. Riksdagen Aarsbok. (SW) **3929**
Sweden. Riksfoersaekringsverket. Allmaen Foersaekring. (SW ISSN 0082-0075) **2544**
Sweden. Sjukvaardens och Socialvaardens Planerings- och Rationaliseringsinstitut. S P R I Informerar. (SW ISSN 0346-8445) **4113**
Sweden. Sjukvaardens och Socialvaardens Planerings- och Rationaliseringsinstitut. S P R I Litteraturtjaenst. (Sjukvaardens och Socialvaardens Planerings- och Rationaliseringsinstitut) (SW ISSN 0036-1879) **4119, 4427**
Sweden. Sjukvaardens och Socialvaardens Planerings- och Rationaliseringsinstitut. S P R I Rapport. (SW ISSN 0586-1691) **4113**
†Sweden. Sjukvaardens och Socialvaardens Planerings- och Rationaliseringsinstitut. S P R I Raad 7. (SW ISSN 0303-6537) **5286**
Sweden. Socialstyrelsen. Alkoholstatistik/Sweden. National Board of Health and Welfare. Alcohol Statistics. (SW) **388, 385**
Sweden. Socialstyrelsen. Foerfattningssamling: Medical. (SW ISSN 0346-6000) **3155**
Sweden. Socialstyrelsen. Foerfattningssamling: Social. (SW ISSN 0346-6019) **4422**
Sweden. Socialstyrelsen. Legitimerade Laekare/Sweden. National Board of Health and Welfare. Authorized Physicians. (SW ISSN 0345-0171) **3155**
Sweden. Socialstyrelsen. Redovisar *see* Sweden. Socialstyrelsen. S O S - Rapport **4422**
Sweden. Socialstyrelsen. S O S - Rapport. (SW ISSN 1100-2808) **4422**
Sweden. Statens Industriverk. Current Research Projects. (SW) **839, 921**
Sweden. Statens Industriverk. Research Activities *see* Sweden. Statens Industriverk. Current Research Projects **839**
Sweden. Statens Jaernvaegars Centralfoervaltning. Geoteknik och Ingenjoergeologi. Meddelanden *see* Sweden. Statens Jaernvaegars Huvudkontor. Geoteknik och Ingenjoergeologi. Meddelanden **5286**
†Sweden. Statens Jaernvaegars Huvudkontor. Geoteknik och Ingenjoergeologi. Meddelanden. (SW ISSN 0282-2024) **5286**
Sweden. Statens Raad foer Byggnadsforskning. Document. (SW ISSN 0586-6766) **633, 1875, 2496**
Sweden. Statens Raad foer Byggnadsforskning. Fraan Byggnadsforskningen *see* Tidskriften Byggforskning **634**
Sweden. Statens Raad Foer Byggnadsforskning. Rapport. (SW) **633, 1875, 2496**
Sweden. Statens Raad Foer Byggnadsforskning. Summaries. (SW) **633**
Sweden. Statens Raad Foer Byggnadsforskning. Synopses. (SW) **634**

Sweden. Statens Raad foer Byggnadsforskning. Verksamhetsplan.(SW) **634**, 1875, 2496
Sweden. Statens Vaeg- och Trafikinstitut. Verksamhetsberaettelse. (SW ISSN 0282-5996) **4721**
Sweden. Statistiska Centralbyraan. Allmaan Maanadsstatistik/Monthly Digest of Swedish Statistics. (SW ISSN 0039-7253) **4590**
Sweden. Statistiska Centralbyraan. Befolkningsfoeraendringar. (SW ISSN 0082-0156) **3996**
Sweden. Statistiska Centralbyraan. Folkmaengd. (SW) **3996**
Sweden. Statistiska Centralbyraan. Foreign Trade: Import-Export. Distribution by Country - Commodity according to the S I T C. (SW ISSN 0082-0369) **740**
Sweden. Statistiska Centralbyraan. Industri. (SW) **740**
Sweden. Statistiska Centralbyraan. Jordbruksstatistik Aarsbok. (SW ISSN 0082-0199) **144**
Sweden. Statistiska Centralbyraan. Levnadsfoerhaallanden. Rapport. (SW ISSN 0347-7193) **4590**
Sweden. Statistiska Centralbyraan. Living Conditions Reports see Sweden. Statistiska Centralbyraan. Levnadsfoerhaallanden. Rapport **4590**
Sweden. Statistiska Centralbyraan. Loener och Sysselsattninginom Offentlig Sektor. (SW) **740**
Sweden. Statistiska Centralbyraan. Meddelanden i Samordningsfraagor/ Reports on Statistical Co-ordination. (SW ISSN 0082-0229) **4590**
Sweden. Statistiska Centralbyraan. Statistiska Meddelanden. Subgroup Am (Labor Market). (SW ISSN 0082-0237) **740**
Sweden. Statistiska Centralbyraan. Statistiska Meddelanden. Subgroup Bo (Housing and Construction). (SW ISSN 0085-6991) **639**, **4590**
Sweden. Statistiska Centralbyraan. Statistiska Meddelanden. Subgroup Be (Population & Living Conditions). (SW ISSN 0082-0245) **3996**, 2330
Sweden. Statistiska Centralbyraan. Statistiska Meddelanden. Subgroup F (Entreprises). (SW ISSN 0346-606X) **740**
Sweden. Statistiska Centralbyraan. Statistiska Meddelanden. Subgroup HS (Public Health and Medical Care) .(SW ISSN 0346-8992) **4119**, 3181
Sweden. Statistiska Centralbyraan. Statistiska Meddelanden. Subgroup I (Manufacturing). (SW ISSN 0082-027X) **740**
Sweden. Statistiska Centralbyraan. Statistiska Meddelanden. Subgroup J (Agriculture). (SW ISSN 0082-0288) **144**
Sweden. Statistiska Centralbyraan. Statistiska Meddelanden. Subgroup K (Kreditmarknad-Credit Market, Banking and Insurance). (SW ISSN 0346-6078) **740**
Sweden. Statistiska Centralbyraan. Statistiska Meddelanden. Subgroup N (National Accounts and Finance). (SW ISSN 0082-0296) **740**
Sweden. Statistiska Centralbyraan. Statistiska Meddelanden. Subgroup Na (Natural Resources and the Environment). (SW ISSN 0282-3500) **1975**
Sweden. Statistiska Centralbyraan. Statistiska Meddelanden. Subgroup O (Offtentliga Finanser-Public Finances) .(SW ISSN 0282-3497) **740**
Sweden. Statistiska Centralbyraan. Statistiska Meddelanden. Subgroup E (Energy). (SW ISSN 0349-5299) **1800**

Sweden. Statistiska Centralbyraan. Statistiska Meddelanden. Subgroup H (Trade) see Sweden. Statistiska Centralbyraan. Statistiska Meddelanden. Subgroup S E (Service and Trade) **740**
Sweden. Statistiska Centralbyraan. Statistiska Meddelanden. Subgroup Ku. (SW ISSN 0282-3519) **254**
Sweden. Statistiska Centralbyraan. Statistiska Meddelanden. Subgroup P (Prices and Price Indices). (SW ISSN 0082-030X) **740**
Sweden. Statistiska Centralbyraan. Statistiska Meddelanden. Subgroup R (Judicial Statistics. Law and Social Welfare). (SW ISSN 0082-0318) **2700**
Sweden. Statistiska Centralbyraan. Statistiska Meddelanden. Subgroup S E (Service and Trade). (SW ISSN 1100-9373) **740**
Sweden. Statistiska Centralbyraan. Statistiska Meddelanden. Subgroup S (Social Welfare Statistics). (SW ISSN 0082-0326) **4427**
Sweden. Statistiska Centralbyraan. Statistiska Meddelanden. Subgroup T (Transport and Other Forms of Communication). (SW ISSN 0082-0334) **4667**, 1349
Sweden. Statistiska Centralbyraan. Statistiska Meddelanden. Subgroup U (Education and Research). (SW ISSN 0082-0342) **1680**
Sweden. Statistiska Centralbyraan. Urval Skriftseries - Selection Series. (SW ISSN 0082-0350) **4590**
Sweden. Statistiska Centralbyraan. Utbildningsstatistik Aarsbok/ Swedish Educational Statistics Yearbook. (SW ISSN 0348-6397) **1666**
Sweden. Statistiska Centralbyraan. Utrikeshandel. Kvartalsstatistik. (SW ISSN 0039-727X) **4590**
Sweden. Statistiska Centralbyraan. Utrikeshandel. Maanadsstatistik see Statistics Sweden. Quarterly Foreign Trade Statistics S I T C **4589**
Sweden. Statistiska Centralbyraans Bibliotek. Nyfoervaerv. (SW ISSN 0280-7637) **413**
Sweden. Statistiska Centralbyraans Bibliotek. Statistik Fraan Enskilda Laender. (SW ISSN 0280-7610) **413**
Sweden. Sveriges Geologiska Undersoekning. Jordmagnetiska Publikationer/Sweden. Geological Survey of Sweden. Geomagnetic Publications. (SW ISSN 0075-403X) **1582**
Sweden. Sveriges Geologiska Undersoekning. Serie C. Avhandlingar och Uppsatser/Sweden. Geological Survey of Sweden. Series C. Memoirs and Notices. (SW ISSN 0082-0024) **1582**
Sweden. Sveriges Geologiska Undersoekning. Serie Ca. Avhandlingar och Uppsatser i Kvarto/ Sweden. Geological Survey of Sweden. Series Ca. Notices in Folio and Quarto. (SW ISSN 0082-0016) **1582**
Sweden. Swedish Environmental Protection Agency. Report. (SW ISSN 0282-7298) **1498**
Sweden. Televerket. Annual Report see Swedish Telecom. Annual Report **1343**
Sweden & America. (US ISSN 1042-1777) **2025**
Sweden Business Report. (SW ISSN 0348-6508) **965**
Sweden Now. (SW ISSN 0039-7245) **2218**
Sweden Ring Type Stamp Study Unit. Newsletter. (US) **3758**
Sweden Ring Type Study Unit. Newsletter see Sweden Ring Type Stamp Study Unit. Newsletter **3758**
Swedish Agency for Research Cooperation with Developing Countries Report see S A R E C Report **3971**

Swedish Agency for Research Cooperation with Developing Countries Annual Report see S A R E C Annual Report **935**
Swedish American Genealogist. (US ISSN 0275-9314) **2165**
Swedish-American Historical Quarterly. (US ISSN 0730-028X) **2423**
Swedish Archaeology. (SW) **290**
Swedish Book Review. (UK ISSN 0265-8119) **4137**, 3006
Swedish Budget. (SW ISSN 0082-0393) **1107**
Swedish Building Research News. (SW) **634**
Swedish Bus & Coach Magazine. see Buss - Svensk Omnibustidning **4685**
Swedish Canadian. see Canada-Svensken **1995**
Swedish Center of Space Physics. Uppsala Division. Technical Reports. (SW) **3833**
Swedish Dental Journal. (SW ISSN 0347-9994) **3243**
Swedish Digest. see Sverige-Nytt **2218**
Swedish Economy. (English translation of: Konjunkturlaget) (SW ISSN 0039-7296) **694**
Swedish Educational Statistics Yearbook. see Sweden. Statistiska Centralbyraan. Utbildningsstatistik Aarsbok **1666**
Swedish Food Institute. Annual Report see S I K Annual Report **2081**
Swedish Forestry Association. Magazine. see Sveriges Skogsvaardsfoerbunds Tidskrift **2108**
Swedish Geographical Yearbook. see Svensk Geografisk Aarsbok **2264**
Swedish Geotechnical Institute. Report. see Statens Geotekniska Institut. Rapport **1595**
Swedish Institute for Children's Books. Studies. see Svenska Barnboksinstitutet. Skrifter **1267**
Swedish Institute of Space Physics. Annual Report. (SW ISSN 0284-169X) **1595**
†Swedish Institute of Space Physics. Preprint. (SW ISSN 0284-1711) **5286**
Swedish Institute of Space Physics. Scientific Report. (SW ISSN 0284-1703) **1595**
Swedish Institute of Space Physics. Software Report. (SW ISSN 0284-172X) **1595**
Swedish Institute of Space Physics. Technical Report. (SW ISSN 0284-1738) **1595**
Swedish Institute of Space Physics. Uppsala Division. Scientific Reports. (SW) **3833**
Swedish Journal of Agricultural Research. (SW ISSN 0049-2701) **123**
Swedish Journal of Economics see Scandinavian Journal of Economics **690**
Swedish Journal of Musicology. see Svensk Tidskrift foer Musikforskning **3583**
Swedish Landsurveying Journal. see Svensk Lantmaeteritidskrift **2264**
Swedish Linneus Society. Yearbook. see Svenska Linne-Sallskapet Aarsskrift **518**
Swedish National Bibliography. see Svensk Bokfoerteckning **413**
Swedish Natural Science Research Council. Ecological Bulletins see Ecological Research Committee. Ecological Bulletins **1948**
Swedish News. (US) **2218**
Swedish Nuclear News. (SW) **1809**
Swedish Nutrition Foundation. Symposia. (SW ISSN 0082-0415) **3612**
Swedish Press/Nya Svenska Pressen. (CN) **2025**
Swedish Research on Higher Education see Studies of Higher Education and Research **1717**
Swedish Road and Traffic Research Institute. Annual Report see Sweden. Statens Vaeg- och Trafikinstitut. Verksamhetsberaettelse **4721**

Swedish Road Safety Office. Analysis Section Report. (SW ISSN 0281-4447) **4721**
Swedish Steel Manual. (SW) **3421**
Swedish Telecom. Annual Report. (SW) **1343**
Swedish Tennis. see Svensk Tennis **4513**
Swedish Timber and Wood Pulp Journal. see Svensk Traevaru- och Pappersmassetidning **5286**
Swedish Trade Mark Dictionary. see Svenskt Varumaerkeslexikon **3678**
Swedish Trademark Archive. see Svenskt Varumaerkesarkiv **3678**
Swedish University of Agricultural Sciences. Department of Farm Buildings. Special Reports. (SW ISSN 0348-0593) **123**, **634**
Swedish Wood Preservation Institute. Reports. see Svenska Traeskyddsinstitutet. Meddelanden **2117**
Swedish Writers Association. Membership Roll. see Sveriges Foerfattarfoerbund. Medlemsfoerteckning **2967**
Sweeping. (US ISSN 1041-6692) **2035**, 2303
▼Sweepstakes Magazine. (US) **4493**
Sweet Briar Alumnae Magazine. (US) **1326**
Sweet Briar College. Alumnae Magazine see Sweet Briar Alumnae Magazine **1326**
Sweet's Canadian Construction Catalogue File. (CN ISSN 0082-0431) **634**
Sweet's Catalog File for the Civil Engineering & Retrofit Market. (US) **1875**
Sweet's Catalog File for the Electrical Engineering and Retrofit Market. (US) **1908**
Sweet's Contract Interiors File. (US) **2555**
Sweet's General Building and Renovation File. (US) **634**
Sweet's General Building Catalog File see Sweet's General Building and Renovation File **634**
Sweet's Homebuilding and Remodeling File. (US) **634**
Sweet's Industrial Construction and Renovation File. (US) **634**
Sweet's International Construction File. (US) **634**
Sweet's Mechanical Engineering and Retrofit File. (US) **1939**
Swenson Center News. (US ISSN 0895-7126) **2025**
Swiat see Perspektywy **2214**
Swiatowit. (PL ISSN 0082-044X) **287**
Swift Kick. (US ISSN 0277-447X) **2967**
Swift's Directory of Educational Software for the I B M P C. (US) **1481**
Swim see Swimming Times **4494**
Swim Canada. (CN ISSN 0319-0560) **4493**
Swim Fashion Quarterly. (US) **1288**
Swim Magazine. (US ISSN 8755-2027) **4493**
Swim Swim. (US ISSN 0195-6760) **4493**
Swimming. see Youyong **4497**
Swimming and Diving and Water Polo Rulebook. (US) **4493**
Swimming Magazine. (JA) **4493**
Swimming Pool. (UK) **4493**, **634**
Swimming Pool Age and Spa Merchandiser see Swimming Pool - Spa Age **634**
Swimming Pool Age Data and Reference Annual see Swimming Pool - Spa Age Data & Reference Annual **4493**
Swimming Pool and Spa Dealer News. (US) **4493**
Swimming Pool - Spa Age. (US ISSN 0899-1022) **634**, **307**, **4493**
Swimming Pool - Spa Age Data & Reference Annual. (US ISSN 0899-1022) **634**, **4493**
Swimming Pools Today. (US) **4557**, 2442, 3809, 4113
Swimming Technique. (US ISSN 0039-7415) **4493**

Swimming Times. (UK ISSN 0039-7423) **4494**
Swimming World. (US ISSN 0039-7431) **4494**
Swimsuit International. (US) **1294**
Swimwear Illustrated. (US) **1294**
Swimwear U S A. (US) **1294, 1288**
Swindon and Wiltshire Business. (UK) **823**
Swindon Business News. (UK) **694**
Swine Practitioner. (US) **4816**
Swing. (JM) **2239**
Swing Journal. (JA ISSN 0039-744X) **3583**
Swingers Update. (US) **3400, 4853**
Swinging Times. (US) **3400, 4853**
Swingtrend. (GW ISSN 0178-9945) **965**
Swingtrend. (BE) **965**
Swinton Journal. (UK ISSN 0049-271X) **3929**
Swiss American. (US) **2025**
Swiss-American Historical Society. Newsletter *see* Swiss-American Historical Society. Review **2324**
Swiss-American Historical Society. Review. (US) **2324, 3973**
Swiss Bank Corporation. Bulletin *see* Le Mois **874**
Swiss Bank Corporation. Report of the Board of Directors to the Annual General Meeting of Shareholders. (SZ) **800**
Swiss Biographical Index of Prominent Persons/Annuaire Suisse du Monde et des Affaires/Wer ist Wer in der Schweiz und im Fuerstenstum Lichtenstein/Chi e Chi in Svizzera? (SZ) **421**
Swiss Camion. (SZ) **4715**
Swiss Canadian News. (CN ISSN 0049-2728) **2025**
Swiss Chamber of Commerce and Industry in Japan. Newsletter. (JA) **823**
Swiss Economic News *see* SwissBusiness **886**
Swiss Economic Viewpoint. (SZ) **965**
Swiss Export Directory. (SZ) **1154**
Swiss Fairs *see* Switzerland. Center for Trade Fairs **921**
Swiss Financial Year Book. (SZ) **886**
Swiss Hair - Ihr Coiffeur Informiert Sie *see* Hair **373**
Swiss Hair Intern. (SZ) **374**
Swiss Journal/Schweizer Journal. (US ISSN 0039-7474) **2219**
Swiss Journal of Hydrology *see* Aquatic Sciences **1597**
Swiss Journal of Pharmacy. *see* Schweizerische Apotheker-Zeitung 3742
Swiss Mate. (NE) **823**
Swiss Political Science Yearbook. *see* Annuaire Suisse de Science Politique **3873**
Swiss Quality Products. (SZ) **921**
Swiss Review of International Competition Law *see* World Competition **2730**
Swiss Review of World Affairs. (SZ ISSN 0039-7490) **2219**
Swiss Studies in English. *see* Schweizer Anglistische Arbeiten **2840**
Swiss Watch and Jewelry Journal. (SZ ISSN 0039-7520) **2566**
Swissair Gazette. (SZ) **4803**
SwissBusiness. (SZ) **886**
Swissexport. (SZ) **921**
Swissexport Extern. (SZ) **921**
Switching and Transmission *see* Commutation et Transmission **1334**
Switzerland. Bundesamt fuer Industrie, Gewerbe und Arbeit. Volkswirtschaft. (SZ ISSN 0042-8590) **694**
Switzerland. Bundesamt fuer Sozialversicherung. Spezialitaetenliste - Liste des Specialites - Elenco delle Specialita. (SZ ISSN 0082-0504) **3744, 3155**
Switzerland. Bundesamt fuer Statistik. Bilanz der Wohnbevolkerung in den Gemeinden der Schweiz - Bilan Demographique des Communes Suisses. (SZ) **3996, 4590**
†Switzerland. Bundesamt fuer Statistik. Eingefuehrte Motorfahrzeuge - Vehicules a Moteur Importes. (SZ) **5286**

Switzerland. Bundesamt fuer Statistik. Heiraten, Lebendgeborene und Gestorbene in den Gemeinden - Marriages, Naissances et Deces dans les Communes *see* Switzerland. Bundesamt fuer Statistik. Bilanz der Wohnbevolkerung in den Gemeinden der Schweiz - Bilan Demographique des Communes Suisses **3996**
Switzerland. Bundesamt fuer Statistik. In Verkehr Gesetzte Neue Motorfahrzeuge - Vehicles a Moteur Neufs Mis en Circulation. (SZ) **4667**
Switzerland. Bundesamt fuer Statistik. Schuelerinnen, Schueler und Studierende - Eleves et Etudiants. (SZ) **1680, 4590**
Switzerland. Bundesamt fuer Statistik. Schuelerstatistik - Statistique des Eleves *see* Switzerland. Bundesamt fuer Statistik. Schuelerinnen, Schueler und Studierende - Eleves et Etudiants **1680**
Switzerland. Bundesamt fuer Statistik. Strassenverkehrsunfaelle - Accidents de la Circulation Routiere en Suisse. (SZ) **4703**
Switzerland. Center for Trade Fairs. (SZ) **921, 1054**
Switzerland. Commission pour les Questions Conjoncturelles. Etudes Occasionnelles *see* Switzerland. Kommission fuer Konjunkturfragen. Allfaellige Studien **694**
Switzerland. Commission pour les Questions Conjoncturelles. Situation Economique *see* Switzerland. Kommission fuer Konjunkturfragen. Wirtschaftslage **886**
Switzerland. Departement Federal de l'Economie Publique. Vie Economique *see* Switzerland. Bundesamt fuer Industrie, Gewerbe und Arbeit. Volkswirtschaft **694**
Switzerland. Directorate General of Customs. Annual Report. (SZ) **740, 4590**
Switzerland. Directorate General of Customs. Annual Statistics. (SZ ISSN 0081-525X) **740, 4590**
Switzerland. Directorate General of Customs. Monthly Statistics. (SZ ISSN 0049-2183) **740, 4590**
Switzerland. Eidgenoessische Anstalt fuer das Forstliche Versuchswesen. Mitteilungen. (SZ ISSN 0251-4133) **2108**
Switzerland. Kommission fuer Konjunkturfragen. Allfaellige Studien. (SZ) **694**
Switzerland. Kommission fuer Konjunkturfragen. Wirtschaftslage. (SZ) **886**
Switzerland. Schweizerische Anstalt fuer das Forstliche Versuchswesen. Mitteilungen *see* Switzerland. Eidgenoessische Anstalt fuer das Forstliche Versuchswesen. Mitteilungen **2108**
Switzerland. Statistisches Amt. Eingefuehrte Motorfahrzeuge: in Verkehr Gesetzte Neue Motorfahrzeuge *see* Switzerland. Bundesamt fuer Statistik. Eingefuehrte Motorfahrzeuge - Vehicules a Moteur Importes **5286**
†Switzerland Your Partner. (SZ) **5286**
Sword *see* Arthur **1304**
Sword. (UK) **4494**
Sword of Light *see* An Gael **2002**
Sword of the Lord. (US ISSN 0039-7547) **4204**
Swordmaster. (US) **4494**
Der Syburger. (GW) **4521**
Sycamore Leaves. (US) **2165**
Sycamore Review. (US ISSN 1043-1497) **2967, 3006**
Sycamore Tree Newsletter. (US) **1760, 4204**
SyCip, Gorres, Velayo & Co. Group Journal *see* S G V Group Journal **1084**
▸ Sydan. (FI ISSN 0039-7571) **3212**
Sydney Cinema Journal *see* S C J **3517**
Sydney Cityscope. (AT) **4160**
Sydney Cityscope Unit Report. (AT) **4160**

▼Sydney Eats Out. (AT ISSN 1035-7262) **2480**
Sydney Film Festival Programme. (AT) **3518**
Sydney for Kids. (AT ISSN 0727-4327) **1267**
Sydney Gay Guide. (AT ISSN 0155-5936) **2457**
Sydney Jewish News *see* Australian Jewish News (Darlinghurst) **1992**
Sydney Law Review. (AT ISSN 0082-0512) **2684**
Sydney Opera House. Diary. (AT) **3583, 4639**
Sydney Organ Journal. (AT ISSN 0817-2285) **3583**
▼Sydney Residential Auction Market Report. (AT ISSN 1035-4670) **4158**
▼Sydney Residential Auction Market Study. (AT) **4158**
Sydney Residential Auction Market Survey *see* Sydney Residential Auction Market Study **4158**
Sydney Speleological Society. Communications *see* Sydney Speleological Society. Occasional Paper **1582**
Sydney Speleological Society. Journal. (AT) **1582**
Sydney Speleological Society. Occasional Paper. (AT) **1582**
Sydney Studies in English. (AT) **2967**
Sydney to Hobart Yacht Race Programme. (AT) **4530**
Sydney University Speleological Society *see* S U S S **1579**
†Sydney Water Board Journal. (AT ISSN 0039-761X) **5286**
Sydowia: Annales Mycologici. (AU ISSN 0082-0598) **518**
Sydsjaellands Landbrugs-Nyt *see* Nord-Midt- og Vestsjaellands Landbrugs-Nyt **110**
Sydsvenska Ortnamnssaellskapet. Aarsskrift/South Swedish Placename Society. Journal. (SW ISSN 0302-8348) **2846**
Sydthy Aarbog. (DK ISSN 0900-2103) **2391**
Syesis *see* Contributions to Natural Science **1542**
Syesis *see* Contributions to Museum Studies **5172**
Sygdomsmoensteret for Indlagte Patienter. (DK) **2469**
Sygdomsmoensteret ved Somatiske Sygehusafdelinger *see* Sygdomsmoensteret for Indlagte Patienter **2469**
Sygehusklassifikation og Kommunekoder. (DK ISSN 0107-508X) **2469**
Sygehusstatistik. (DK) **2471**
Sygehusvaesenet *see* Sygehusstatistik **2471**
Sygeplejersken. (DK ISSN 0049-3856) **3287**
Sygesikringsstatistik. (DK ISSN 0107-8437) **2547**
Sykepleien *see* Fagtidsskriftet Sykepleien **3278**
Sykepleien *see* Journalen Sykepleien **3281**
Syllabus. (CM) **1666**
Syllabus. (US) **2684, 1760**
Sylloge Nummorum Graecorum. (US ISSN 0271-3993) **3602**
Sylvanian. (US) **1498, 1969, 4557**
Sylvatrop. (PH ISSN 0115-0022) **2108**
†Sylvia Porter's Personal Finance Magazine. (US ISSN 0738-4173) **5286**
Sylwan. (PL ISSN 0039-7660) **2108**
▼Symantec. (US ISSN 1054-3902) **1481**
Symbiosis. (IS ISSN 0334-5114) **457**
Symbol. (GW ISSN 0172-3456) **346**
Symbola and Emblemata. (NE) **346**
Symbolae. Series A. (BE) **2324**
Symbolae. Series B. (BE) **2324**
Symbolae. Series C. Linguistica. (BE) **2846, 1760**
Symbolae. Series D. Literaria. (BE) **2967**
Symbolae Botanicae Upsalienses. (SW ISSN 0082-0644) **518**

SYMPOSIUM 6711

Symbolae Osloenses. (NO ISSN 0039-7679) **1280**
Symbolae Philologorum Posnaniensium.(PL ISSN 0302-7384) **1280**
Symbole. (GW) **1054, 39**
Symbolic Computation. (US) **1423**
Symbolic Interaction. (US) **4389**
Symbolon. (IT) **3783**
†Symbolon. (GW ISSN 0082-0660) **5286**
Symbols of American Libraries. (US ISSN 0095-0874) **2786**
▼Symmetry. (GW) **4346**
Symphony Australia. (AT) **1380**
Symphony Gold Book. (US ISSN 0275-9381) **3583**
Symphony Magazine. (US ISSN 0271-2687) **3583**
Symphony User's Journal. (US ISSN 8750-9415) **1481, 1465, 1474**
Symposia Biologica Hungarica. (HU ISSN 0082-0695) **457**
Symposia Foundation Merieux. (NE) **3155**
Symposia Mathematica. (US ISSN 0082-0725) **3057**
Symposia on Fundamental Cancer Research. Papers. (US ISSN 0082-0733) **3202**
Symposia Otorhinolaryngologica Iugoslavica. (CI ISSN 0586-9145) **3317**
Symposium. (BL ISSN 0039-7695) **2516**
Symposium. (US ISSN 0039-7709) **2967**
Symposium (International) on Combustion. (US ISSN 0082-0784) **1230**
Symposium on Civil Engineering Planning. Proceedings. *see* Doboku Keikakugaku Shinpojumu **1864**
†Symposium on Coal Mine Drainage Research. Papers. (US ISSN 0085-7068) **5286**
Symposium on Computer Applications in Medical Care. Proceedings. (US ISSN 0195-4210) **3226**
Symposium on Computer Arithmetic. Proceedings. (US) **1443, 3057**
Symposium on Engineering Problems of Fusion Research. Proceedings *see* Symposium on Fusion Engineering. Proceedings **1809**
Symposium on Environmental - Problems. Proceedings. *see* Kankyo Mondai Shinpojumu Koen Ronbunshu **1870**
†Symposium on Flames and Industry. Proceedings. (UK) **5286**
Symposium on Foundations of Computer Science. Proceedings. (US ISSN 0272-5428) **1418, 1400, 1416, 1908**
Symposium on Frequency Control. Proceedings. *see* Frequency Control Symposium **1771**
Symposium on Fusion Engineering. Proceedings. (US) **1809, 1908**
Symposium on Hybrid Microelectronics *see* Hybrid Microelectronics Symposium. (Papers) **1771**
Symposium on Incremental Motion Control Systems and Devices. Proceedings. (US ISSN 0092-1661) **3023**
Symposium on Information Display. Digest of Technical Papers *see* S I D International Symposium. Digest of Technical Papers **1836**
†Symposium on Jet Pumps & Ejectors and Gas Lift Techniques. Proceedings. (UK) **5286**
Symposium on Logic in Computer Science. Proceedings. (US) **1439**
†Symposium on Logic Programming Proceedings. (US) **5286**
Symposium on Naval Hydrodynamics. Proceedings. (US ISSN 0082-0849) **3845**
Symposium on Nondestructive Evaluation. (US) **63**
Symposium on Particleboard. Proceedings. (US ISSN 0082-089X) **2117**
Symposium on Private Investments Abroad. (US) **2729, 966**

6712 SYMPOSIUM

Symposium on Reliability in Distributed Software and Database Systems. Proceedings see Symposium on Reliable Distributed Systems. Proceedings **1481**
Symposium on Reliability in Electronics.(HU) **1779**
Symposium on Reliable Distributed Systems. Proceedings. (US) **1481**, 1445
Symposium on Ring Theory. Proceedings. (JA) **3057**
Symposium on Special Ceramics, Stoke-On-Trent, England. Special Ceramics, Proceedings. (UK ISSN 0082-0954) **1166**
†Symposium on Surface Mining and Reclamation (Proceedings). (US) **5286**
Symposium on the Art of Scientific Glassblowing Proceedings. (US ISSN 0569-7468) **1166**, 357
Symposium on Wind Effects on Structures in Japan. Proceedings see Symposium on Wind Engineering. Proceedings **3441**
Symposium on Wind Engineering. Proceedings. (JA) **3441**, 1837
Symposium Series. (US) **2885**
▼Symposuim on Applied Computing. (US) **1401**
Syn og Segn. (NO ISSN 0039-7717) **2885**
Synagogue Council of America Report see S C A Report **2022**
Synagogue Light - Kosher Life. (US) **4226**, 2025
Synapse (Boston). (US) **2885**, 4205
†Synapse (Edinburgh). (UK) **5286**
Synapse (New York). (US) **3355**
Synapse (San Francisco). (US ISSN 0740-2619) **2885**
Synchro. (US ISSN 0746-5726) **4494**
Synchro U S A - News. (US) **4494**
Synchrotron Radiation News. (US ISSN 0894-0886) **3851**
Syncopated Perfs. (US) **3758**
Syndicalisme C F T C. (FR ISSN 0039-775X) **2589**
Syndicalisme Hebdo. (FR) **2589**
Syndicat des Exportateurs et Negociants en Bois de Cote d'Ivoire. Bulletin de Liaison et d'Information. (IV) **2109**, 921
Syndicat des Industries de Materiel Professionnel Electronique et Radioelectrique. Rapport d'Activite. (FR) **1779**, 1360
Syndicat des Industries de Materiel Professionnel Electronique et Radioelectrique Annuaire see S P E R Annuaire **1778**
Syndicat General de la Construction Electrique. Annuaire see Essor de l'Electricite et de l'Electronique **1891**
Syndicat General des Commerces et Industries du Caoutchouc et des Plastiques. Guide see Union des Industries et de la Distribution des Plastiques et du Caoutchouc. Guide **1156**
Syndicat General des Impots. Guide Foncier. (FR) **1107**
Syndicat General des Impots. Guide National de l'Enregistrement et des Domaines see Syndicat General des Impots. Guide Foncier **1107**
Syndicat National de l'Enseignement Superieur Bulletin see S N E S U P Bulletin **1716**
Syndicat National de la Librairie Ancienne et Moderne. Repertoire des Membres. (FR) **4137**
Syndicat National des Architectes d'Interieur. Bulletin. (FR) **307**
Syndicat National des Enseignants. Ecole et Vie see Ecole et Vie **1626**
Syndicate of Lawyers/Nakabat Ul-Muhamin. (JO) **2684**
Syndicated Columnists Contacts (Year). (US) **2575**
Syndicats Vietnamiens. (VN ISSN 0049-2744) **2589**
Syndikale Kamer. (BE) **3155**
Synergatiko Vima/Co-operative Rostrum. (CY) **2184**
Synergy. (SI ISSN 0218-3188) **4346**

Synerjy. (US ISSN 0163-2183) **1796**, 1812, 1812
†Synform. (GW ISSN 0723-3655) **5286**
Synfuels see Clean Coal - Synfuels Letter **1784**
Synfuels Week see Coal & Synfuels Technology **1784**
Synlett. (GW) **1223**, 1230
Synopses of the British Fauna. (NE) **592**
Synopsis. (NO ISSN 0332-656X) **2786**
▼Synopsis (Columbia). (US) **3326**, 3266
Synopsis (Lewiston). (US ISSN 1048-8561) **2967**
Synopsis of Laws Enacted by the State of Maryland see Maryland. State Department of Legislative Reference. Synopsis of Laws Enacted by the State of Maryland **2653**
Synpunkt. (SW ISSN 0039-7849) **346**
Syntarsus. (RH ISSN 1011-7881) **592**
†Syntax. (US ISSN 0273-2696) **5286**
Syntax and Semantics. (US ISSN 0092-4563) **2846**
Syntax Quarterly see S Q **5272**
Syntax ZX80 see Syntax **5286**
Synteza see Ekonomika Prace **4371**
Syntezy. (PL) **3583**
Synthese see Synthesis **1723**
Synthese. (NE ISSN 0039-7857) **3783**, 4346
Synthese Historical Library. (NE ISSN 0082-111X) **3783**
Synthese Language Library see Studies in Linguistics and Philosophy **4048**
Synthese Library. (NE ISSN 0082-1128) **3783**, 4389
Syntheses see Elimu **4371**
Synthesis. (GW ISSN 0039-7881) **1223**, 1230
Synthesis/Composition. (CY) **1288**, 2555
▼Synthesis. (CN ISSN 1180-4734) **1723**
Synthesis. (RM) **2967**
Synthesis (Asheville). (US ISSN 1042-0169) **1717**, 2684
†Synthesis (Bolton). (US ISSN 0279-781X) **5286**
Synthesis (San Pedro) see Green Synthesis (San Pedro) **2967**
Synthesis and Reactivity in Inorganic and Metalorganic Chemistry. (US ISSN 0094-5714) **1230**
Synthetic Communications. (US ISSN 0039-7911) **1223**
Synthetic Metals. (SZ ISSN 0379-6779) **1189**, 3833
Synthetic Methods of Organic Chemistry. (SZ ISSN 0253-200X) **1223**, 1230
Synthetic Organic Chemical Manufacturers Association Newsletter see S O C M A Newsletter **1187**
Synthetic Organic Chemicals, United States Production and Sales. (US ISSN 0082-1144) **1860**
Synthetic Rubber End-use Survey. (US) **4294**
Synthetic Rubber Manual. (US) **4294**
Syokubutsu Bunrui Gakkai Nyusu/Japan Society of Plant Taxonomists. News. (JA) **518**
Syopa/Cancer. (FI ISSN 0356-3081) **3202**
Syovantorjunta - Kampen Mot Kraefta - Against Cancer see Syopa **3202**
Syracuse Business. (US) **839**, 1054, 1118
Syracuse Chemist. (US ISSN 0039-792X) **1189**
Syracuse Health & Fitness. (US) **3809**
Syracuse Jewish Observer. (US) **2025**, 4226
Syracuse Journal of International Law & Commerce. (US ISSN 0093-0709) **2729**, 921
Syracuse Law Review. (US ISSN 0039-7938) **2684**
Syracuse New Times. (US) **2886**
†Syracuse Scholar. (US ISSN 0276-6345) **5286**

Syracuse University. Foreign and Comparative Studies. African Series. (US) **4389**, 2335
Syracuse University. Foreign and Comparative Studies. Latin American Series. (US) **4396**
Syracuse University. Foreign and Comparative Studies. South Asian Series. (US) **4396**
†Syracuse University. Foreign and Comparative Studies. South Asian Special Publications. (US) **5286**
Syracuse University Library Associates Courier. (US) **2516**
Syracuse University Publications in Continuing Education. Landmark and New Horizons Series. (US) **1687**
Syracuse University Publications in Continuing Education. Notes and Essays. (US) **1687**
Syracuse University Publications in Continuing Education. Occasional Papers. (US ISSN 0082-1179) **1687**
†Syracuse Wood Science Series. (US) **5286**
Syria. (FR ISSN 0039-7946) **287**, 346
Syria. Central Bureau of Statistics. Monthly Summary of Foreign Trade see Syria. Central Bureau of Statistics. Summary of Foreign Trade **740**
Syria. Central Bureau of Statistics. Statistical Abstract. (SY ISSN 0081-4725) **4590**
Syria. Central Bureau of Statistics. Summary of Foreign Trade. (SY) **740**
Syrie et Monde Arabe. (SY ISSN 0039-7962) **3973**
Syro-Mesopotamian Studies. (US ISSN 0732-6483) **2432**
▼SysAdmin. (US) **1432**
Sysdata. (SZ) **1401**, 1062, 1349
System. (US ISSN 0346-251X) **1760**, 2846
†System Builder. (US) **5286**
System Development. (US ISSN 0275-6617) **1453**, 1439
System Disturbances (Year). (US) **1908**, 1796
System Dynamics Review. (UK ISSN 0883-7066) **1029**, 4389
System Engineering Theory and Practice. see Xitong Gongcheng Lilun yu Shijian **1440**
System Familie. (GW ISSN 0933-3053) **3355**
System Safety Society. Directory of Consultants. (US) **4113**
Systema Ascomycetum. (UK ISSN 0280-8331) **518**
Systematic and Applied Microbiology. (GW ISSN 0723-2020) **557**
Systematic Biology. (US) **592**
Systematic Botany. (US ISSN 0363-6445) **518**
Systematic Botany Monographs. (US ISSN 0737-8211) **518**
Systematic Entomology. (UK ISSN 0307-6970) **538**
Systematic Parasitology. (NE ISSN 0165-5752) **457**
Systematic Survey of Agricultural Production. see Levantamento Sistematico da Producao Agricola **153**
Systematic Zoology see Systematic Biology **592**
Systeme Communautaire d'Acces a la Documentation Bulletin see S C A D Bulletin **411**
Systeme D. (FR ISSN 0039-8012) **2449**
Systeme D. Cahiers. (FR) **634**
Systeme d'Information sur les Transports de Marchandises: Resultats Generaux, Trafic Interieur et International. (FR ISSN 0181-5334) **921**
Systemes Experts. (FR) **4609**
Systemes Fiscaux Africains see African Tax Systems **1087**
†Systems A I. (US) **5286**
Systems Analysis Modelling Simulation. (GW ISSN 0232-9298) **3057**

Systems and Computers in Japan. (US ISSN 0882-1666) **1439**, 1380, 1416, 1908
Systems and Control Letters. (NE ISSN 0167-6911) **1439**, 1416
Systems and Forecasts. (US) **966**
Systems and Networks Integration. (US) **1439**
Systems and Procedures Exchange Center Kit see S P E C Kit **2782**
▼Systems Building Review. (US) **634**
Systems Development Management. (US ISSN 0735-9985) **1439**
Systems Engineering of Education Series. (US ISSN 0082-1217) **1666**, 1837
Systems Integration see Systems Integration Business **1439**
Systems Integration Business. (US) **1439**, 1465, 1466
Systems Integrator Business see S I Business **1438**
Systems International. (UK ISSN 0305-1668) **1439**
Systems Network Architecture Communications Report see S N A Communications Report **5272**
Systems Network Architecture Perspective see S N A Perspective **1438**
Systems Practice. (US ISSN 0894-9859) **1029**
Systems Research. (NE ISSN 0731-7239) **1837**
Systems Research and Information Science. (US ISSN 0882-3014) **1439**
Systems Research in Psychology. (US ISSN 0891-4451) **4048**
Systems Science. (PL ISSN 0137-1223) **1837**, 3057
Systems Science and Mathematical Sciences. (US ISSN 1000-9590) **3057**, 1416
Systems Software Reports. (US) **1481**
Systems User. (US ISSN 0199-8951) **1439**, 1428
Systems 3X and A S World see Systems 3X - 400 **1465**
Systems 3X - 400. (US ISSN 1055-7768) **1465**
Syukan Baseball. (JA) **4513**
†Syzygy. (UK ISSN 0143-1064) **5286**
Szabad Fold. (HU ISSN 0133-0950) **2198**
Szabad Foldmuves. (CS) **123**, 158
Szabadalmi Kozlony es Vedjegyertesito/Patent and Trade Mark Review. (HU ISSN 0039-8071) **3678**
Szabolcs - Szatmari Szemle. (HU ISSN 0133-2465) **2198**
▼Szachista. (PL) **4494**
†Szachy. (PL ISSN 0137-8198) **5286**
Szamadas. (CN ISSN 0700-5199) **2025**
Szamitastechnika/Computerworld. (HU ISSN 0587-1514) **1401**
Szamitastechnikai Evkonyv see Hungary. Kozponti Statisztikai Hivatal. Szamitastechnikai Statisztikai Zsebkonyv **1404**
Szamitogepes Muszaki Tervezes/Computer-Aided Design. (HU ISSN 0231-3316) **1846**, 1880
Szamvitel es Ugyviteltechnika. (HU ISSN 0039-808X) **756**
Szazadok/Centuries. (HU ISSN 0039-8098) **2324**
Szczecinskie Roczniki Naukowe/Annales Scientrairum Stetinenses. (PL ISSN 0860-2212) **4346**
Szczecinskie Towarzystwo Naukowe. Sprawozdania. (PL ISSN 0082-1241) **4346**
Szczecinskie Towarzystwo Naukowe. Wydzial Nauk Lekarskich. Prace. (PL ISSN 0082-125X) **3155**
Szczecinskie Towarzystwo Naukowe. Wydzial Nauk Przyrodniczo-Rolniczych. Prace. (PL ISSN 0082-1276) **194**
Szemeszet/Ophthalmologica Hungarica. (HU ISSN 0039-8101) **3305**
Szene. (GW ISSN 0039-811X) **4639**
Szene Hamburg. (GW) **2191**
Szene Remscheid. (GW) **4095**

Szene Schweiz/Scene Suisse/Scena Svizzera. (SZ) **4639**
Szep Versek. (HU ISSN 0586-3783) **3006**
Szigma. (HU ISSN 0039-8128) **898, 3057**
Szilikatkemiai Monografiak. (HU ISSN 0082-1306) **1215**
Szinhaz. (HU ISSN 0039-8136) **4639**
Szivarvany. (US ISSN 0270-5508) **2025**
Szkice Legnickie. (PL ISSN 0137-5326) **4346**
Szkice o Kulturze Muzycznej XIX Wieku. Studia i Materialy. (PL ISSN 0239-9148) **3583**
Szklo i Ceramika. (PL ISSN 0039-8144) **1166**
Szkola Glowna Gospodarstwa Wiejskiego. Rozprawy Naukowe i Monografie/Warsaw Agricultural University. Treatises and Monographs. (PL ISSN 0239-8613) **123**
Szkola Specjalna. (PL ISSN 0137-818X) **1741, 2284**
Szkola Zawodowa. (PL ISSN 0137-8171) **1666**
Szocialista Neveles. (CS) **2846,** 1760
Szociologia. (HU ISSN 0133-3461) **4454**
Szociologiai Informacio/Sociological Information. (HU ISSN 0133-2074) **4458**
Szociologiai Tanulmanyok. (HU ISSN 0082-1322) **4454**
Szoleszet es Boraszat *see* Kerteszet es Szoleszet **2133**
Szolotermesztes es Boraszat/Vine-Growing and Viticulture. (HU ISSN 0230-2241) **2139**
Szovet Kereti Kereskedelem/Co-op Trade. (HU) **832**
Szovetkezet/Co-operatives. (HU) **832**
Szovetkezetek Orszagos Szovetsege Szovosz Tajekoztato *see* Szovosz Tajekoztato **832**
Szovetkezeti Hirlap. (HU) **2590,** 346
Szovjetbarat. (CS) **935**
Szovosz Tajekoztato. (Szovetkezetek Orszagos Szovetsege) (HU ISSN 0133-7890) **832**
Szpilki. (PL ISSN 0039-8152) **2886**
Sztuka. (PL ISSN 0324-8232) **346**
T A A Newsletter *see* Sister City News **4094**
T A B. (Technik am Bau) (GW ISSN 0341-2032) **2304,** 307
T A C Attack. (Tactical Air Command) (US ISSN 0494-3880) **63,** 3472
†T A C Bulletin. (Texas Department of Aviation) (US ISSN 0888-1812) **5286**
T A C D A Alert. (The American Civil Defense Association) (US) **1274**
T A C D A Update *see* T A C D A Alert **1274**
T A C D Journal *see* T P G A Journal **1666**
T A C News. (Transportation Association of Canada) (CN) **4656**
T A D *see* Educational Digest **1630**
T A Documents. (Traduction Automatique) (FR ISSN 0066-9776) **2846**
T.A.E. Report. (Technion - Israel Institute of Technology, Department of Aeronautical Engineering) (IS ISSN 0072-9302) **63**
T A F E - Adult Literacy Tutors' Newsletter. (Technical Further Education) (AT) **1687,** 1760
T A G *see* Theoretical and Applied Genetics **547**
T A G *see* I E E E Technical Activities Guide **1896**
T A G *see* The Aquatic Gardener **2122**
T A G *see* American Genealogist **2143**
T A G A Newsletter. (Technical Association of the Graphic Arts) (US) **4006**
T A G A Proceedings. (Technical Association of the Graphic Arts) (US ISSN 0082-2299) **4006**
T A G Brief *see* Forum (New York, 1978) **666**

T A H P E R D Journal. (Texas Association for Health, Physical Education, Recreation and Dance) (US ISSN 0889-0846) **3809**
T A I *see* I E E E International Conference on Tools for A I **1408**
†T A I U S. (Texas A & I University Studies) (US ISSN 0564-7169) **5286**
T.A. Informations. (FR ISSN 0039-8217) **2857**
T A J A. (The Australian Journal of Anthropology) (AT) **250**
†T A M. (FR ISSN 0018-8395) **5286**
T A M Bulletin. (Travelling Art Mail) (NE) **346**
T A M S Journal. (Token and Medal Society) (US ISSN 0039-8233) **3602**
T A P. (Technological Assistance Program) (US) **3014,** 2983
T A P *see* Timing Analysis Projection **4590**
T A P P I Directory *see* Technical Association of the Pulp and Paper Industry. Directory **3666**
T A P P I Journal. (Technical Association of the Pulp and Paper Industry, Inc.) (US ISSN 0734-1415) **3666**
T A P P I Proceedings. (Technical Association of the Pulp and Paper Industry, Inc.) (US ISSN 1046-4166) **3666**
T A P P I Standards and Provisional Methods *see* T A P P I Test Methods **3666**
T A P P I Test Methods. (Technical Association of the Pulp and Paper Industry, Inc.) (US ISSN 1045-618X) **3666**
†T A P Report. (Trend Analysis Program) (US) **5286**
T A Report on Telecom Advertising & Publishing. (US) **39,** 1054, 1380
T A S P O. (Thalacker's Allgemeine Samen- und Pflanzen-Offerte) (GW ISSN 0177-5006) **2139**
T A S P O Gartenkurier. (Thalackers Allgemeiner Samen- und Pflanzen-Offerte) (GW ISSN 0177-6126) **2139**
T A S P O - Magazin. (Thalacker's Allgemeine Samen- und Pflanzen-Offerte) (GW ISSN 0177-5014) **2139**
T A T Journal. (US ISSN 0271-2482) **3783**
T A W T E. (Texas Artists, Writers and Thinkers in Exile) (US) **2967**
T A Z *see* Tageszeitung **3929**
T & A M Report. (Department of Theoretical and Applied Mechanics) (US ISSN 0073-5264) **1922,** 3845
T & C. (Theorie et Critique) (AG) **346**
T & D Canada: The Human Resources Development Journal. (Training & Development) (CN) **1070**
T and D Health and Safety Report *see* Transmission - Distribution Health & Safety Report **3622**
T and E Center Newsletter *see* T & E News **4006**
T & E News. (Technical and Education Center of the Graphic Arts) (US ISSN 0895-6529) **4006**
T & G Record. (Transport and General Workers Union) (UK) **2590**
T B C A Update. (Transportation Brokers Conference of America) (US) **4656**
T.B. Davie Memorial Lecture. (SA ISSN 0082-1330) **2516**
T B G *see* Die Tiefbauberufsgenossenschaft **634**
T B P's Octava. (US) **4853,** 4205
T C *see* Taiwan Computer **1455**
T C. (Terapia del Comportamento) (IT) **3155**
T C A *see* The Canadian Amateur **1355**
T C A Report. (Tissue Culture Association) (US ISSN 0163-772X) **558,** 547, 3202
T C Devlet Yayinlari Bibliyografyasi/Bibliography of Government Publications. (TU) **413**

T.C.I. News *see* Enterprise (Hobart) **815**
T C I News. (Tasmanian Chamber of Industries) (AT) **823**
T C Interface. (US ISSN 0888-3033) **1453**
T C N N Research Bulletin. (Theological College of Northern Nigeria) (NR ISSN 0794-7046) **4205**
T.C.P. *see* The Catholic Pharmacist **3720**
T C Report *see* TeleCommuting Report **5288**
T C S & D Buyer's Guide (Year). (Temperature Controlled Storage & Distribution) (UK) **1154,** 2082
†T D A Timber News. (Timber Development Association (NSW) Ltd.) (AT) **5286**
T D C Magazine *see* Destination Discovery **1372**
T D F Sightlines. (Theatre Development Fund) (US) **4639**
T D M A Today. (Trophy Dealers and Manufacturers Association) (US) **4494**
T.D.O.C. Newsletter *see* T.I.C. Newsletter **994**
T D R. (The Drama Review) (US ISSN 0012-5962) **4639**
†T E A M. (Training and Education for Advanced Manufacturing) (US) **5286**
T E A M Club Newsletter. (Tellington-Jones Equine Awareness Method) (US) **4538**
T E A News. (Tennessee Education Association) (US ISSN 0039-8292) **1666**
T E A Newsletter. (Tucson Education Association) (US ISSN 0039-8306) **1666**
T E & M. (US) **1352**
▼T E & M's Telecom Asia. (Telephone Engineer & Management) (US) **1366**
T E C *see* New Caledonia. Institut Territorial de la Statistique et des Etudes Economiques. Tableaux de l'Economie Caledonienne **731**
T E C. (Transport Environnement Circulation) (FR ISSN 0397-6513) **4721**
T E C Advanced Engineering Information. (Toyo Engineering Corporation) (JA) **1837**
T E C O R *see* The Environmental Contract Opportunity Report **4059**
T E D I Times. (Telecommunications Exchange for the Deaf, Inc.) (US ISSN 0897-9650) **2289,** 1366
T E I *see* Taiwan Electronics Industry **1779**
T E J O - Tutmonde. (Tutmonda Esperantista Junulara Organizo) (NE) **2846,** 1267
T E N C O N (I E E E Region 10 Conference). Proceedings. (US) **1401**
T E News. (Truck Equipment) (US) **4748**
T E P E *see* Teaching Elementary Physical Education **1761**
T E P S A Journal. (Texas Elementary Principals and Supervisors Association) (US ISSN 0300-6433) **1732**
†T.E.S.L.A. Electronics. (CS) **5286**
T E S O L Matters. (Teachers of English to Speakers of Other Languages) (US ISSN 1051-8886) **2847,** 1687, 1760
T E S O L Newsletter *see* T E S O L Matters **2847**
T E S O L Quarterly. (Teachers of English to Speakers of Other Languages) (US ISSN 0039-8322) **2847,** 1666
T E T. (Termeszet es Tarsadalom) (CS) **2886**
T E T (The East Trade). (SP) **921**
T F C Nieuws. (Technisch Film Centrum) (NE ISSN 0039-8330) **3518**
T F I Action. (The Fertilizer Institute) (US) **194**
T F News *see* Texas Trees **2109**
T F Nyhedsbrev *see* Nyhedsbrev **4193**

T L 6713

T F P Newsletter. (American Society for the Defense of Tradition, Family and Property) (US) **4454**
T F R *see* Tidsskrift for Rettsvitenskap **2686**
T G. (Tapicerias Gancedo) (SP ISSN 0210-3761) **346**
T G A - Report. (AU) **1939,** 1416
T.G.I.F. Casting News. (US) **3631,** 3518, 4639
T G M Echo. (Turngemeinde 1861 e.V.) (GW) **4494**
T G N *see* The Giants Newsweekly **4504**
T G - Voices of Today's Generation. (CN ISSN 0843-4557) **1267**
T G W U Record *see* T & G Record **2590**
T.H.E. Journal. (Technological Horizons in Education) (US ISSN 0192-592X) **1691,** 1417
†T H E T A. (Tsimshian, Haida, Eskimo, Tlingit, Aleut) (US) **5286**
T H - Ers Express. (Treasure Hunt) (US ISSN 1053-055X) **2442,** 3496
T H G *see* Target Housewares & Gifts **5287**
T H Kotilaakari. (FI ISSN 0355-1903) **3809**
▼T H R C Newsletter. (Texas Humanities Resource Center) (US) **2516**
T I. (GW ISSN 0176-3660) **2049,** 2139
T.I. (Technical Information for Industry) (SA ISSN 0040-0955) **4610,** 694
T I A C Newsletter. (Tourism Industry Association of Canada) (CN) **4788**
T.I.C. Newsletter. (Teacher Information Center) (US) **994,** 1666
†T I Computing. (US ISSN 0892-2837) **5286**
▼T I D E. (Teri Information Digest on Energy) (II ISSN 0971-085X) **1796,** 1812, 1812
T I D Touristik Kontakt. (GW) **4788**
▼T I E S. (Technology, Innovation and Entrepreneurship for Students) (US ISSN 1041-6587) **4610,** 694
T I F *see* Tidskrift i Fortifikation **1875**
T I G E R Report *see* Tiger Report **5290**
T I M. (XV ISSN 0040-7712) **1267**
T I M *see* Industria Mercato **1930**
T I M I X Buyer's Guide. (US ISSN 0742-678X) **1401**
T I M S - O R S A Meeting Bulletin. (The Institute of Management Sciences) (US ISSN 0161-0295) **4346**
T I M S Studies in the Management Sciences. (NE ISSN 0378-3766) **828**
T I P der Woche. (Trends Infos Praktisches) (GW) **2191**
T I P P C Notes. (T I Personal Programmable Calculator Club) (US) **1474,** 1465
T I P R O Reporter. (Texas Independent Producers & Royalty Owners Association) (US ISSN 0039-8403) **3702**
T I P S Journal *see* The International Permaculture Solutions Journal **442**
T I P S Y *see* The International Permaculture Solutions Journal **442**
T I Personal Programmable Calculator Club Notes *see* T I P P C Notes **1474**
T.I.S. *see* Technologies de l'Information et Societe **4611**
T I S C O Technical Journal. (Tata Iron and Steel Co. Ltd.) (II ISSN 0039-8411) **3421**
T I S: Il Corriere TermoldroSanitario. (IT ISSN 0393-9723) **2304**
T I S T R Research News. (Thailand Institute of Scientific and Technological Research) (TH) **4346,** 4610
T I Z Fachberichte *see* T I Z International **1860**
T I Z International. (GW) **1860,** 3496
T J J *see* Tijdschrift voor Jeugdhulpverlening en Jeugdwerk **1245**
T - J Today. (Traditional Jazz) (US) **3583**
T L C...For Plants. (Tender Loving Care) (CN ISSN 0835-3271) **2139**

T L C Gossip (The Library Club) see The Volunteer Librarian 2790
T L - Teknikeren. (Teknisk Landsforbund) (DK) 4610
T L - Tennessee Librarian see Tennessee Librarian 2787
T M. (Trans Media) (GW) 2886
T M see Technische Mitteilungen fuer Sappeure, Pontoniere und Mineure 3472
T.M. (Tatsachen und Meinungen) (SZ ISSN 0080-7427) 4389
T M. (Travel Management) (JA) 4788
T M A see Tracteurs et Machines Agricoles 164
T M A C Journal see Canadian Treasurer 770
T M A Directory of Cigarette Brands. (Tobacco Merchants Association of the United States, Inc.) (US) 4644
T M A Executive Summary. (Tobacco Merchants Association of the United States, Inc.) (US) 4644
T M A Guide to Tobacco Taxes. (Tobacco Merchants Association of the United States, Inc.) (US) 4644, 2684
T M A International Tobacco Guide. (Tobacco Merchants Association of the United States, Inc.) (US) 4644
T M A Issues Monitor. (Tobacco Merchants Association of the United States, Inc.) (US) 4644
T M A Leaf Bulletin. (Tobacco Merchants Association of the United States, Inc.) (US) 4644
T M A Legislative Bulletin. (Tobacco Merchants Association of the United States, Inc.) (US) 4644, 2684
T M A News. (Treasury Management Association) 800
T M A Tobacco Barometer. (Tobacco Merchants Association of the United States, Inc.) (US) 4644, 1107
T M A Tobacco Barometer: Smoking, Chewing, Snuff. (Tobacco Merchants Association of the United States, Inc.) (US) 4644
T M A Tobacco Trade Barometer. (Tobacco Merchants Association of the United States, Inc.) (US ISSN 0495-6753) 4644
T M A Tobacco Weekly. (Tobacco Merchants Association of the United States, Inc.) (US) 4644, 1107
T M A Trademark Report. (Tobacco Merchants Association of the United States, Inc.) (US) 4645, 3678
T M A World Alert. (Tobacco Merchants Association of the United States, Inc.) (US) 4645
T M A World Consumption & Production. (Tobacco Merchants Association of the United States, Inc.) (US) 4645
T M E see Today's Music Educator 3584
T M H see Target Machinery & Hardware 3023
T M I Bulletin see T M I Focus 1717
T M I Focus. (The Monroe Institute) (US) 1717
T M J Update: A Current Review of Temporomandibular Joint Developments. (US ISSN 0885-9191) 3156
T M P M - Tschermaks Mineralogische und Petrographische Mitteilungen see Mineralogy and Petrology 3489
T M R Travel Marketing Report. (US ISSN 0197-6753) 634
T M S - Letter. (Travel Marketing and Sales Newsletter) (US ISSN 0893-1259) 4788
T M S - Testbroschuere see Test - Info 1326
T M's Singles R S V P. (True Match) (US) 4364
T N C - Aktuellt. (Tekniska Nomenklaturcentralen) (SW ISSN 0039-8438) 2847, 4346, 4610
T N Cs see Transnational Corporations 923
†T N C's Bulletin. (CS) 5286
T N L Research Guide Series see Philippines. National Library. T N L Research Guide Series 409
T N O Building and Construction Research. Annual Report. (NE) 634

T N O Nieuws see T N O Project 4346
T N O Project. (NE) 4346
T N T Magazine. (UK) 2195
T O C S see Transactions on Computer Systems 1439
T O I S see Transactions on Information Systems 828
T O M. (Text on Microfilm) (US) 24, 1680
T O P S News. (Take Off Pounds Sensibly, Inc.) (US) 3809, 3612
†T O P S: The Old Police Station. (UK ISSN 0144-2848) 5286
T P A Messenger. (Texas Press Association) (US) 2575
T P A S Notes. (Tenant Participation Advisory Service) (UK ISSN 0261-197X) 2496
T.P.A. Travelers. (Travelers Protective Association of America) (US ISSN 0039-8454) 4788
T P Annales. (FR ISSN 0039-8462) 4075
T P G A Journal. (Texas Personnel and Guidance Association) (US ISSN 0364-3409) 1666
T P I see Textil Praxis International 4625
T P - Il Giornale della Trasmissione di Potenza. (IT) 1939
T.P.L. News. (Toronto Public Library) (CN ISSN 0039-8470) 2786
▼T P Q: The Tube & Pipe Quarterly. (US ISSN 1051-4120) 3421, 1939
T P R see Tijdschrift voor Privaatrecht 2686
T P S Bulletin. (Thomas Paine Society) (UK) 3929
T P S Nyt see V D L Nyt 4722
T Q. (Teen Quest) (US ISSN 0044-071X) 1267, 4205
The T Q M Magazine. (Total Quality Management) (UK ISSN 0954-478X) 1029
T Q S News. (Tonatiuh-Quinto Sol) (US ISSN 1045-8875) 2967
T R see Tobacco Reporter 4645
T R A C E. (Travaux et Recherches dans les Ameriques du Centre) (MX ISSN 0185-6286) 250, 287, 2025
T R A C E Newsletter see T R A C E S 4205
T R A C E S. (Teachers of Religion and Christian Ethics) (CN ISSN 0704-6421) 4205, 1760
T R A I Report see T S S A Report 694
T R C Current Data News see Thermodynamics at Texas A & M 1231
T R C Spectral Data - Infared. (Thermodynamics Research Center) (US) 1209
T R C Spectral Data - Mass. (US) 1209
T R C Spectral Data - Raman. (US) 1209
T R C Spectral Data - Ultraviolet. (US) 1209
T R C Spectral Data - 1 H Nuclear Magnetic Resonance. (US) 1209
T R C Spectral Data - 13 C Nuclear Magnetic Resonance. (US) 1209
T R C Thermodynamic Tables - Hydrocarbons. (US) 1230
T R C Thermodynamic Tables - Non-Hydrocarbons. (US) 1209, 1230
T.R. Elektronika see Elektronica Revue 1770
†T R I O. (FR) 5286
T R I U M F Annual Report Scientific Activities. (Tri-University Meson Facility) (CN) 3851
T R I U M F Financial and Administrative Annual Report. (Tri-University Meson Facility) (CN) 3851
T R News. (Transportation Research Board) (US ISSN 0738-6826) 4656
T R Report see Travelore Report 4794
T R U K P A C T Info. (Transvaalse Raad vir die Uitvoerende Kunste) (SA) 4639, 3583
T R U Mathematics see S U T Journal of Mathematics 3054

†T R W Series of Software Technology. (NE ISSN 0167-7888) 5286
T S C A - T S C A T S see Toxic Substances Control Act - Test Submission Database 1975
T.S. Eliot Review see Yeats Eliot Review 3009
T S I Journal of Particle Instrumentation. (US) 1939
T S L see Tijdschrift voor Sociaal Wetenschappelijk Onderzoek van de Landbouw 158
T S N News. (IE) 2082
T S P see The Sport Psychologist 4047
T S R Hotline. (Telephone Sales Representative) (US ISSN 8755-4380) 1054, 1366
T S S A Report. (Tackle & Shooting Sports Agents Association) (US) 694, 2049
T S T A Advocate. (Texas State Teachers Association) (US) 1666
T S Today. (Australasian Tuberous Sclerosis Society Inc.) (AT) 3156
▼T-Shirt Business Info Mapping Newsletter. (US ISSN 1053-6493) 1119, 4623
T-Shirt Retailer & Screen Printer. (US) 1288
T Squared Newsletter. (US) 4610, 1837
T T G Asia see Travel Trade Gazette Asia 4793
T T G Europa see Travel Trade Gazette Europa 4793
T T G - U K & Ireland see Travel Trade Gazette U K & Ireland 4793
T T I Q see Tsetse and Trypanosomiasis Information Quarterly 468
T T J Timber Telephone Address Book. (Timber Trade Journal) (UK ISSN 0141-5735) 2117
T T M - Truck en Transport Management. (NE) 4748
T T O S Bulletin. (Toy Train Operating Society) (US) 2282
T T O S Order Board. (Toy Train Operating Society) (US) 2282
T T P see The Tamarind Papers 346
T T P I Trade Gazette. (Tasmanian Trade Protective Institute) (AT ISSN 0011-1716) 839
T T R A Newsletter. (Travel and Tourism Research Association) (US) 4788
T T - Revue. (Transport und Tourismus) (SZ) 4656
T T T see Table Tennis Technical 5287
T T T Interdisciplinair Tijdschrift voor Taal- en Tekstwetenschap. (NE ISSN 0167-4773) 2847
T. Tennis. (JA) 4557
T U see Teknisk Ukeblad 1838
T.U.B.A. Journal. (Tubists Universal Brotherhood Association) (US ISSN 0363-4787) 3583
T.U.B.A. Newsletter see T.U.B.A. Journal 3583
†T.U.B.A. Series. (Tubists Universal Brotherhood Association) (US) 5286
T U C News. (Trades Union Congress of Ghana) (GH) 2590
T U C Newsletter see T U C News 2590
T U C Report see Trades Union Congress. Report 2590
T U G Lines. (Turbo User Group) (US) 1474, 1465
T U Hannover see Uni Hannover 4612
T U I A F P W Information. (Trade Union International of Agricultural, Forestry and Plantation Workers) (RU) 2590, 123, 2109
T U Intern. (Technische Universitaet Berlin) (GW) 1326
T U K Inform. (Tisch und Kueche Informationen) (AU) 1166
T U News. (Tingley's United) (US) 2165
T U S Info. (GW ISSN 0179-0153) 4494
T U S - Turnen und Sport. (GW ISSN 0344-4023) 4494
T U S Vereinsnachrichten. (Turn- und Sportvereinigung Gaarden von 1875 e.V.) (GW) 4494, 1301

T U Sicherheit und Zuverlaessigkeit in Betrieb und Verkehr see T U - Technische Ueberwachung. Sicherheit Zuverlaessigkeit und Umweltschutz in Wirtschaft und Verkehr 3622
T U T. (Textiles et Usages Techniques) (FR) 4623
T U - Technische Ueberwachung. Sicherheit Zuverlaessigkeit und Umweltschutz in Wirtschaft und Verkehr. (GW) 3622
T Ue V Autoreport. (Vereinigung der Technischen Ueberwachungs-Vereine e.V.) (GW) 4703, 1508
T.V. see Science et Culture 4339
T V & Cable Publicity Outlets - Nationwide. (US ISSN 1054-4259) 1380, 39
T V & Entertainment Times. (HK) 1380
T V and Movie Screen. (US ISSN 0041-4492) 3518, 1380
T V Anzeiger. (GW) 1380, 2191
T V Audience Profiles. (AT) 1380
T V Broadcast Data Base. (US) 1349
▼T V Business. (GW) 1380
T V Close Up. (CN) 1381, 4158
T V Collector. (US ISSN 0887-5847) 1381, 2442, 3518
T V Color. (IT) 1381
T V Contigo. (BL) 1381
T V Digest see T V Times (St. Paul) 1381
T V Directory see Professional T V & Radio Media Directory 5262
T V Ekspres. (BE) 1381
T V Engineering Data Base in Order by State. (US) 1349
T V Entertainment see Cable Guide 1370
T V Executive. (US) 1381
T V Facts: Kitchener - Waterloo. (CN) 1381
T V Facts - London. (CN) 1381
T V Film - Tape & Syndication Directory see Backstage T V Film - Tape & Syndication Directory 5145
T V for the Masses. see Dazhong Dianshi 1372
T V Guia. (PO) 1381
T V Guide. (US ISSN 0039-8543) 1381
T V Guide. (CN) 1381
T V Hebdo. (CN ISSN 0039-8551) 1381
T V Hoeren und Sehen. (GW) 1381
T V Host Monthly. (US) 1381
T V Host Weekly. (US) 1381
†T V I. (Television International) (GW ISSN 0934-3180) 1528
T V I Journal see T V I Report 1523
T V I Report. (Terrorism Violence Insurgency) (US ISSN 1041-8474) 1523
T V Junior - il Trenino. (IT) 1267, 1381
T V K 1877 Echo. (Turnverein 1877 e.V. Essen-Kupferdreh) (GW) 4494
T V L U Nuus. see T W A U News 2449
T V Life. (JA) 1381
T V Magazine. (US) 1381
T V Magazine. (CN ISSN 0316-2397) 1381
T V Magazine. (JA) 1381, 1267
▼T V Movie. (GW) 1381
T V News. (US) 1381, 1085
T V News Contacts (Year). (US) 1381
T V News Magazine. (US) 1381
T V P P A News. (Tennessee Valley Public Power Association) (US) 1908
T V Picture Life - Metal Edge. (US) 1381, 3583
T V Plus. (CN) 1381
T V Pro-Log see Network Futures & ProLog 1377
T V Program Investor. (US ISSN 0885-2340) 1381, 966
T V Programm fuer Nobel Hotels. (GW ISSN 0931-5470) 2480
T V R O Technology see Private Cable Plus Wireless Cable 1378
T V Scene (Victoria). (CN) 1381
T V Sorrisi e Canzoni (Rome). (IT ISSN 0041-4522) 1381
†T V Sports. (US) 5286
T V Story. (BE) 4853

TAIWAN ECONOMY 6715

T V Strip. (BE) **1381**
T V Suggestions. (Tidewater Virginia Sanyo Users Group) (US) **1474, 1465**
T V Superstar. (US) **1381**
T V - T S Tapestry. (US ISSN 0884-9749) **4048, 2457**
T V Technology. (US ISSN 0887-1701) **1381**
T V Times. (UK ISSN 0039-8624) **1381**
T V Times (St. Paul). (US) **1381**
T V Today. (US) **1381**
T V Translators Engineering Data Base in Order by State, Channel, Call. (US) **1349**
T V Translators Engineering Data Base in Order by State, City, Channel. (US) **1349**
T V - Veckan och Radio. (FI ISSN 0788-6632) **1381**
T V Week. (AT ISSN 0810-249X) **1381**
T V Week. (HK) **1381**
T V Week Magazine. (CN) **1381**
T V Weekly. (CH) **1382**
T V World. (UK ISSN 0142-7466) **1382**
T V y Novelas. (US) **1382**
T v Z see Tijdschrift voor Ziekenverpleging **3287**
T V Zone. (UK ISSN 0957-3844) **1382, 3014**
T V 3. (GR) **1382**
T W/Convention Industry. (Tagungs-Wirtschaft) (GW ISSN 0342-7951) **3394**
T W A Ambassador. (Trans World Airlines) (US ISSN 0039-8632) **4804**
T W A R O News. (Asian Regional Organisation of the International Textile, Garment and Leather Workers' Federation) (JA) **4623**
T W A U News/T V L U Nuus. (Transvaal Women's Agricultural Union) (SA ISSN 0039-8640) **2449**
T W Dermatologie. (GW) **3250, 376**
T W F. (Oesterreichische Textilreiniger-, Waescher- und Faerberzeitschrift) (AU) **1282**
T W Gynaekologie. (GW ISSN 0935-3208) **3296**
T W I C E. (This Week in Consumer Electronics) (US ISSN 0892-7278) **1779, 1481**
▼T W I Journal. (The Welding Institute) (UK ISSN 0963-6927) **3430**
T W Neurologie - Psychiatrie. (GW ISSN 0935-3224) **3355**
T W Paediatrie. (GW ISSN 0935-3216) **3326**
T W U Express. (Transport Workers Union of America) (US ISSN 0039-8659) **2590, 4656**
T W Veranstaltungsplaner. (GW) **3394**
T Y A Today. (Theatre for Young Audiences) (US) **4639, 1267**
T Y L see Today's Young Life **4250**
T Y S Fund Letter see Graphic Fund Forecaster **948**
†T Z fuer Metallbearbeitung. (GW ISSN 0170-9577) **5287**
Ta Ch'eng. see Panorama Magazine **2878**
Ta Kung Pao. (HK ISSN 0039-8675) **2197**
Ta Ma Ko Yu Chih Sheng. see Sound of Malaysian's Musician **3581**
Taag/Trains. (SW ISSN 0039-8683) **4715**
Taal en Tongval. (BE ISSN 0039-8691) **2847**
Taalgenoot. (SA ISSN 0039-8705) **2847**
Taalkundige. see Linguiste **2826**
Taamuli. (TZ ISSN 0049-2817) **3929**
Taasiot. (IS ISSN 0792-1322) **994, 3023, 3622**
Ta'awun. (IS ISSN 0002-4074) **2590**
Al-Ta'awun Ma'a al Alam al Arabi see Partnerschaft mit der Arabischen Welt **3968**
Tabac. see Tabak **4645**
Tabac et Sante. (FR) **3809, 1539**
Tabak/Tabac. (SZ ISSN 0039-8721) **4645**

Tabak Journal International. (GW ISSN 0039-8748) **4645**
Tabak Plus Benelux. (NE ISSN 0925-7543) **4645, 1029, 1119**
Die Tabak Zeitung. (GW ISSN 0049-2825) **4645**
†Der Tabakpflanzer Oesterreichs. (AU ISSN 0039-8756) **5287**
Tabakverschleisser Oesterreichs see Trafik-Journal **4645**
Tabard. (UK) **2165**
Tabard Talk see Escutcheon **2149**
Tabi ni Deyo. (JA) **4788**
Tabi to Tetsudo. (JA) **4788, 4715**
Tabibak Al-Khass. (UA) **3156**
Tabibok/Your Doctor. (LE) **3156**
Tabla Redonda. (AG) **3007**
Tablas de Mareas: Costas de Cuba see Academia de Ciencias de Cuba. Instituto de Oceanologia. Tablas de Mareas **1601**
Table d'Hote. (CN) **2480, 2082**
Table et Cadeau. (FR ISSN 0039-8780) **2562, 1166, 2282**
Table of International Telex Relations and Traffic. (UN ISSN 0074-9052) **1366**
Table of Sunrise, Sunset, Twilight, Moonrise and Moonset. (PH ISSN 0115-3307) **371**
Table Rock Sentinel. (US ISSN 0732-0523) **2423**
Table Tennis News. (UK ISSN 0039-8799) **4513**
†Table Tennis Technical/Technique Tennis de Table. (CN ISSN 0828-4539) **5287**
Table Tennis Topics. (US ISSN 0887-6576) **4513**
Table Tennis World. see Pingpang Shijie **4509**
Tableau. (CN ISSN 0845-8081) **3533**
Tableau de Bord du Batiment, Genie Civil et Materiaux de Construction. (FR) **634, 1875**
Tableau Economique de la Reunion. (RE ISSN 0994-415X) **886**
Tableaus. (AT ISSN 0313-6744) **1301**
Tableaux de l'Economie Caledonienne see New Caledonia. Institut Territorial de la Statistique et des Etudes Economiques. Tableaux de l'Economie Caledonienne **731**
Tableaux de l'Economie Francaise. (FR ISSN 0039-8802) **886**
Tableaux Economiques de l'Ile-de-France. (FR) **886**
Tableaux Economiques de Midi-Pyrenees. (FR ISSN 0291-8692) **694**
Tableaux Numeriques des Analyses Physico-Chimiques des Eaux du Rhin. see Zahlentafeln der Physikalisch-Chemischen Untersuchungen des Rheinwassers **1980**
Tablelands Advertiser. (AT) **2172**
Tablelender Newspaper. (AT) **2172**
Tables Chronologiques et Alphabetiques du Moniteur Belge. (BE) **2684**
Tables of Redemption Values for U.S. Savings Bonds, Series A-E see Tables of Redemption Values for U.S. Savings Bonds, Series E and Tables of Redemption Values for U.S. Savings Bonds, Series EE **1107**
Tables of Redemption Values for U.S. Savings Bonds, Series E and Tables of Redemption Values for U.S. Savings Bonds, Series EE. (US) **1107**
Tables on Hatchery and Flock Participation in the National Poultry Improvement Plan. (US ISSN 0082-8661) **227**
Tablet. (UK ISSN 0039-8837) **4205, 2886**
Tablet. (US ISSN 0039-8845) **4276**
Tableware International. (UK ISSN 0143-7755) **1166**
Tableware International and Pottery Gazette see Tableware International **1166**
Tableware Reference Book see European Tableware Buyers Guide **355**

Tabona. (SP ISSN 0213-2818) **287, 3783**
Tabor. (XV ISSN 0492-1127) **1244**
Tabortuz. (CS) **1267**
Tabriz University of Medical Sciences. Medical Journal. (IR) **3156**
Tabula Rasa. (GW ISSN 0933-6168) **2886, 2191**
Tacarmi. (IT) **4557**
Taccuino dell'Azionista. (IT ISSN 0082-1446) **966**
Tachydromos. (GR ISSN 0039-8888) **2196**
Tachydromos - Egyptos/Egyptian Post. (UA) **2886, 2025**
Tack 'n Togs Book. (US) **4538**
Tack 'n Togs Merchandising. (US ISSN 0149-3442) **4538**
Tackett Journal. (US ISSN 1052-7753) **2165**
Tackle & Guns. (UK ISSN 0015-3052) **4557**
Tackle & Shooting Sports Agents Association Report see T S S A Report **694**
Tackle Talk. (UK) **2049**
Tackle Test. (US ISSN 1048-9215) **4557**
Tackle Times (Barrington). (US) **4558**
Tackle Times (Washington). (US) **1054**
Tacoma Area Progress see Tacoma - Pierce County Chamber of Commerce Update **823**
Tacoma Facts see Facts **2001**
Tacoma - Pierce County Chamber of Commerce Update. (US) **823**
Tactic. (US ISSN 2296, 1401**
Tactical Air Command Attack see T A C Attack **63**
▼Tactical Technology. (US ISSN 1059-0552) **3472, 63**
Tactual Mapping Newsletter. (AT ISSN 0811-4684) **2264, 1741**
Tadcaster Extra. (UK) **2195**
Al-Tadamun. (UK) **2195**
Tae Kwan Do Times. (US ISSN 0741-028X) **4494**
Taegliche Andachten. (US ISSN 0273-8562) **4250**
Taegliche Praxis. (GW ISSN 0494-464X) **3156**
Taeglicher Hafenbericht. (GW) **4740**
Taeglicher Hafenbericht. Jahresausgabe.(GW) **4740**
Taeglicher Wetterbericht see Europaeischer Wetterbericht **3435**
Taegu Chamber of Commerce and Industry. Monthly. (KO) **823**
Taehan Cheykhoe. Cheyuk Chongso. (KO) **4494**
Taehan Kanho. see Korean Nurse **3281**
Taehan Misaengmul Hakhoe Chi/ Journal of the Korean Society for Microbiology. (KO ISSN 0253-3162) **558**
Taehan P'ibu Kwahakhoe Chi see Korean Journal of Dermatology **3248**
Taehan Saengli Hakhoe Chi see Korean Journal of Physiology **573**
Taehan Sin'gyong Chongsin Uihak Hoeji see Korean Neuropsychiatric Association. Journal **3344**
Taehan Uihak Hyophoe Chi see Korean Medical Association. Journal **3120**
Taehan Yangnihak Chapchi. see Korean Journal of Pharmacology **3733**
Taekwondo Aktuell. (GW) **4494**
Taekwondo World. (US ISSN 1043-1047) **4494**
Taenk/Think. (DK) **1508**
Taetigkeitsbericht des Verkehrs Arbeitsinspektorates fuer das Jahr (Year). (AU) **4667**
†Tafnit. (IS) **5287**
Taft Corporate Giving Directory see Corporate Giving Directory **4403**
Taft Foundation Reporter. (US ISSN 0730-6237) **4422**
†Taft Nonprofit Executive. (US ISSN 0882-5521) **5287**
Tag. (GW) **2191**
Tag des Herrn. (GW ISSN 0492-1283) **4276**
Tag fuer Tag. (GW) **4006**
Tagastan see Augustinian Heritage **4256**
Tageblatt. (LU) **3929, 4389**

Tageszeitung. (GW ISSN 0931-9085) **3929, 1969**
Tageszeitung fuer Brauerei see Brauerei-Forum **379**
Taglit. (IS ISSN 0334-9527) **4610**
Tagore International. (II) **2967**
Tagungs-Wirtschaft see T W **3394**
Taheke. (ER ISSN 0134-2266) **1267**
Tahiti Beach Press. (FP ISSN 1157-349X) **4788**
Tahiti Sun Press. (FP) **4788**
At-Tahrir. (UA) **2186**
T'ai Chi. (US ISSN 0730-1049) **3644, 3809**
Tai Sheng/Voice of Taiwan. (CC) **2025, 2219, 2886**
T'ai-wan Chiao Yu/Taiwan Education Review. (CH) **1666**
Tai-wan Sheng Chiao T'ung T'ung Chi Nien Pao. see Taiwan Annual Statistical Report of Transportation **4667**
Tai-wan Sheng Ho-tso Chin-k'u. Annual Report. see Cooperative Bank of Taiwan. Annual Report **773**
Tai-wan Tang Yeh Yen Chiu So Nien Pao. see Taiwan Sugar Research Institute. Annual Report **194**
T'ai-wan Wen Hsien/Reports on Historiographical Studies of Taiwan. (CH) **2342**
T'ai-wan Wen I. see Taiwan Literature **2967**
Taide. (FI ISSN 0039-8977) **346, 3533**
Taifa Uganda. (UG) **2220**
Taifu Jumapili. (KE) **2209**
Taifu Keirozu see Daily Weather Maps **3434**
Taigang Wenxue Xuankan/Selected Taiwan and Hong Kong Literary Works. (CC) **2967**
Taiheiyo Gakkai Shi. see Pacific Society. Journal **247**
Taiiku no Kagaku/Journal of Health, Physical Education and Recreation. (JA) **1760, 3809**
Taikabutsu/Refractories. (JA ISSN 0039-8993) **3421**
Taikabutsu Overseas/Refractories Overseas. (JA ISSN 0285-0028) **3421**
Taiki Osen Kenkyu. see Japan Society of Air Pollution. Journal **1977**
Tail Ends. (US) **3400**
Tailor and Men's Wear see Menswear Magazine **1286**
Tailspinner. (CN ISSN 0316-2494) **63**
Taipei Hilton. (CH) **2480**
Taipei Hua K'an. see Taipei Pictorial **2219**
Taipei Pictorial/Taipei Hua K'an. (CH ISSN 0039-9051) **2219, 39, 2496**
Taipei Traders Information System. (CH) **1154**
Al-Tairan al-Madani/Civil Aviation. (TS) **63**
Taito. (FI) **357, 3593**
Taiwan see Taiwan Pictorial **2219**
Taiwan Agricultural Information. see Taiwan Nongye Qingkuang **123**
Taiwan Agricultural Research Institute. Annual Report. (CH ISSN 0494-5263) **123**
Taiwan Agricultural Research Institute. Research Summary. (CH) **123, 518**
Taiwan Annual Statistical Report of Transportation/Tai-wan Sheng Chiao T'ung T'ung Chi Nien Pao. (CH) **4667**
Taiwan Australia Business Discussion Papers. (AT ISSN 1032-285X) **921**
Taiwan Bicycles & Parts Buyer's Guide. (CH) **1154**
Taiwan Buyers' Guide. (CH ISSN 0082-1470) **1154**
Taiwan Buyer's Guide: Hardware (Year). (CH) **1154**
Taiwan Communique. (US) **3947, 2342**
Taiwan Computer. (CH) **1455, 1453**
Taiwan Demography Quarterly. (CH) **3996**
Taiwan Economy. (CH ISSN 0255-5697) **886**

Taiwan Education Review. see T'ai-wan Chiao Yu **1666**
Taiwan Electronics Industry. (CH) **1779**, 1054
Taiwan Exporters. (CH) **921**
Taiwan Exports. (CH ISSN 0494-5336) **921**
Taiwan Fisheries Research Institute, Keelung. Bulletin. see Journal of Taiwan Fisheries Research **2045**
Taiwan Furniture. (CH) **2562**
Taiwan Gifts & Housewares. (CH) **1154**, 2566
Taiwan Haixia/Taiwan Strait. (CC ISSN 1000-8160) **1611**
Taiwan I Hsueh Hui Tsa Chih. see Formosan Medical Association. Journal **3099**
Taiwan Industrial Panorama. (CH ISSN 0039-9108) **1085**
Taiwan International Trade. (CH) **922**
Taiwan Jingji see Taiwan Economy **886**
Taiwan Lighting. (CH) **2562**
Taiwan Literature/T'ai-wan Wen I. (CH) **2967**
Taiwan Machinery. (CH) **3023**
Taiwan Nongye Qingkuang/Taiwan Agricultural Information. (CC) **123**
Taiwan Pictorial. (CH) **2219**
Taiwan Provincial Labor Force Survey and Research Institute. Quarterly Report on the Labor Force Survey in Taiwan. (CH) **994**
Taiwan Railway. (CH) **4715**
Taiwan Shengli Bowuguan Jikan see Journal of Taiwan Museum **3526**
T'aiwan Shih-yu Ti-chih. see Petroleum Geology of Taiwan **3698**
Taiwan Sporting Goods Buyer's Guide. (CH) **4494**, 1085, 1288
Taiwan Stationery and Office Products Buyer's Guide. (CH) **1062**, 1085
Taiwan Statistical Data Book. (CH) **740**
Taiwan Strait. see Taiwan Haixia **1611**
Taiwan Study. see Taiwan Yanjiu **4389**
Taiwan Sugar. (CH ISSN 0492-1712) **2082**
Taiwan Sugar Research Institute. Annual Report/Tai-wan Tang Yeh Yen Chiu So Nien Pao. (CH ISSN 0255-5581) **194**
Taiwan Toy Buyer's Guide. (CH) **2282**, 1085
Taiwan Trade Directory see Taipei Traders Information System **1154**
Taiwan Transportation Equipment Guide. (CH) **4656**
Taiwan Yanjiu/Taiwan Study. (US) **4389**, 3929
Taiwan Yellow Pages. (CH ISSN 0379-7910) **1154**
Taiwan Yinhang Jikan see Bank of Taiwan Quarterly **846**
Taiwan Yixuehui Zazhi see Formosan Medical Association. Journal **3099**
Taiwania. (CH ISSN 0372-333X) **518**
Taiyang Neng Xuebao/Acta Energiae Solaris Sinica. (CC ISSN 0254-0096) **1812**
Taiyangneng/Solar Energy. (CC) **1812**
Taiyokei Kagaku Shinpojumu. (JA) **371**
Taiyuan Gongye Daxue Xuebao/Taiyuan Industrial University. Journal. (CC ISSN 1000-1611) **1837**
Taiyuan Industrial University. Journal. see Taiyuan Gongye Daxue Xuebao **1837**
Taj Magazine. (II) **4788**
Al-Takaful. (TS) **994**
Takahe. (NZ ISSN 0114-4138) **2968**, 3007
Takao Museum of Natural History. Science Report. see Tokyo-to Takao Shizen Kagaku Hakubutsukan Kenkyu Hokoku **4348**
Takarajima. (JA) **1267**
Takayama Junior College. Memoirs. see Takayama Tanki Daigaku Kenkyu Kiyo **4346**
Takayama Tanki Daigaku Kenkyu Kiyo/ Takayama Junior College. Memoirs. (JA ISSN 0386-6890) **4346**
†Take Five. (CN ISSN 0821-0160) **5287**
†Take-Home Drinks. (UK ISSN 0956-2710) **5287**
Take It Easy. (FR) **2886**

Take Off. (DK ISSN 0107-1270) **4788**
Take Off Pounds Sensibly, Inc. News see T O P S News **3809**
Take One. (US) **1386**, 3518
Takeda Research Laboratories. Journal. (JA ISSN 0371-5167) **457**, 1189, 3744
Takenaka Gijutsu Kenkyu Hokoku/ Takenaka Technical Research Report. (JA ISSN 0374-4663) **634**
Takenaka Technical Research Report. see Takenaka Gijutsu Kenkyu Hokoku **634**
†Takeover Target Weekly Forecast. (US ISSN 8755-4755) **5287**
Takeover Targets. (US) **694**
Taking Care of O P A Business see Physiotherapy Today **3142**
Taking Shape see Genesis (Garden City) **1312**
Taking Sides: Clashing Views on Controversial Bioethical Issues. (US) **3156**, 3783
Taking Sides: Clashing Views on Controversial Economic Issues. (US) **886**
Taking Sides: Clashing Views on Controversial Educational Issues. (US) **1666**
Taking Sides: Clashing Views on Controversial Environmental Issues. (US) **1969**
Taking Sides: Clashing Views on Controversial Issues in American History. (US) **2423**
▼Taking Sides: Clashing Views on Controversial Issues in Business Ethics and Society. (US) **694**, 3783
Taking Sides: Clashing Views on Controversial Issues in Crime and Criminology. (US) **1523**
▼Taking Sides: Clashing Views on Controversial Issues in Family and Personal Relationships. (US) **4454**
Taking Sides: Clashing Views on Controversial Issues in Human Sexuality. (US) **4048**
▼Taking Sides: Clashing Views on Controversial Issues in Mass Media and Society. (US) **4454**
Taking Sides: Clashing Views on Controversial Issues in World Politics.(US) **3973**
Taking Sides: Clashing Views on Controversial Legal Issues. (US) **2684**
Taking Sides: Clashing Views on Controversial Moral Issues. (US) **4048**
Taking Sides: Clashing Views on Controversial Political Issues. (US) **3929**
Taking Sides: Clashing Views on Controversial Psychological Issues. (US) **4048**
Taking Sides: Clashing Views on Controversial Social Issues. (US) **4454**
Taking Up a Franchise. (UK) **1119**
Tal og Data, Medicin og Sundhedsvaesen/Facts, Medicine and Health Care, Denmark. (DK ISSN 0107-1181) **3744**, 3809
Tal og Data om Medicin see Tal og Data, Medicin og Sundhedsvaesen **3744**
Tala Industrial Relations Bulletin. (PH) **994**
Talanta. (US ISSN 0039-9140) **1209**
Talbotania. (UK ISSN 0141-3589) **2165**
Talbot's Student Planning Book. (US) **1666**
Talbott Tree. (US ISSN 0899-160X) **2165**
†Talent Education Journal. (US ISSN 0889-4175) **5287**
Talent in Action see Billboard's Year-End Awards Issue **3541**
Talent Management. (US) **3518**
TalentEd. (AT ISSN 0815-8150) **1741**
▼Tales from the Crypt. (US) **3014**
Tales of the Paradise Ridge. (US) **2423**
Talespinner see Tailspinner **63**
Taliesin. (UK ISSN 0049-2884) **2886**

Talijanska Privreda Danas. (CI) **694**
Talim. (MU) **1666**
Talim-O-Tarbiat. (PK ISSN 0039-9175) **1267**
Talisman. (US ISSN 0898-8684) **3007**
Talk. (SA) **2217**
Talk. (UK ISSN 0049-2906) **2289**
Talk of the Month. (US ISSN 0743-1384) **3597**, 4048, 4289
†Talkin' Union. (US ISSN 0738-7911) **5287**
Talking Book Topics (Large Print Edition). (US ISSN 0039-9183) **2296**, 2786
†Talking Books, Adult (Large Print Edition). (US ISSN 0082-1519) **5287**
Talking Books in the Public Library Systems of Metropolitan Toronto. (CN ISSN 0380-2973) **2786**, 2296
Talking Electronics. (AT ISSN 0811-3742) **1779**
Talking Leaves. (US ISSN 0894-833X) **1760**, 1969
Talking Machine Review see Talking Machine Review, International **4462**
Talking Machine Review, International. (UK) **4462**, 1343
Talking Points see Headlines (London) **2570**
Talking Sense. (UK) **4422**, 1244
Talking Stick. (US) **2968**, 3007
Talking to the Boss. (US) **694**
Talks and Tales. (US ISSN 0039-9213) **4205**, 1267
Talks of Pope John Paul II see Pro Ecclesia Magazine **4273**
†Tall Timbers Conference on Ecological Animal Control by Habitat Management. Proceedings. (US ISSN 0070-833X) **5287**
Tall Timbers Ecology and Management Conference. Proceedings see Tall Timbers Fire Ecology Conference. Proceedings **2109**
Tall Timbers Fire Ecology Conference. Proceedings. (US) **2109**
Tall Timbers Research Station. Bulletin. (US ISSN 0496-7631) **2109**
Tall Timbers Research Station. Miscellaneous Publication. (US ISSN 0496-764X) **2109**, 1498
Talladega County Historical Association. Newsletter. (US ISSN 0896-3630) **2423**
Talladega Student see Talladega Student Star **1326**
Talladega Student Star. (US) **1326**
Talladegan. (US) **1326**, 2025
Tallahassee Magazine. (US) **2235**
Taller. (NQ ISSN 0039-9221) **2968**
Taller. Literario. (CU) **2886**
Taller de Letras. (CL ISSN 0716-0798) **2968**
Talley...Tally Researcher. (US) **2165**
Tallinna Tehnikaulikool. Algoritmy Ustroistva i Sistemy Tsifrovoi Obrabotki Signalov. (ER) **1443**
Tallinna Tehnikaulikool. Avtomatizatsiya Tekhnologicheskogo Proektirovaniya Protsessov Mekhanicheskoi Obrabotki. (ER ISSN 0868-4375) **1939**
Tallinna Tehnikaulikool. Data Processing, Compiler Writing, Programming. (ER) **1432**
Tallinna Tehnikaulikool. Fizicheskaya Khimiya Soedinenii A2B6 i A4B6. (ER ISSN 0868-4308) **1230**
Tallinna Tehnikaulikool. Gibkie Avtomatizirovannye Proizvodstvennye Sistemy i ikh Elementy dlya Liteinogo Proizvodstva. (ER ISSN 0868-426X) **1909**
Tallinna Tehnikaulikool. Issledovanie Elektromagnitnykh i Elektromashinnykh Ustroistv Upravleniya i Kontrolya Spetsial'nogo Naznacheniya. (ER ISSN 0868-4278) **1909**
Tallinna Tehnikaulikool. Issledovanie Raboty Parogeneratorov Elektrostantsii. (ER) **1909**
Tallinna Tehnikaulikool. Issledovaniya po Prikladnoi Kvantovoi Elektronike. (ER ISSN 0868-4219) **1382**

Tallinna Tehnikaulikool. Metody Stokhasticheskogo Upravleniya Rezhimami Energeticheskikh Sistem. (ER ISSN 0868-4251) **1796**
Tallinna Tehnikaulikool. Modelirovanie i Upravlenie v Sistemakh Tekhnicheskoi Kibernetiki. (ER) **1443**
Tallinna Tehnikaulikool. Neustanovivsheesya Protsessy v Sistemakh Vodosnabzheniya i Vodootvedeniya. (ER ISSN 0868-4103) **4113**
Tallinna Tehnikaulikool. Postroenie Translyatorov, Obrabotka Dannykh, Voprosy Programmirovaniya see Tallinna Tehnikaulikool. Data Processing, Compiler Writing, Programming **1432**
Tallinna Tehnikaulikool. Povyshenie Kachestva Proektirovaniya, Stroitel'stva i Ekspluatatsii Avtodorog i Gorodskikh Ulits. (ER) **4703**
Tallinna Tehnikaulikool. Problemy Raboty Kotelnykh Ustanovok Teplovykh Elektrostantsii. (ER) **2304**
Tallinna Tehnikaulikool. Problemy Razrabotki Mestorozdenii Poleznykh Iskopaemykh Estonii. (ER ISSN 0868-4189) **1231**
Tallinna Tehnikaulikool. Sintez i Primenenie Polikondensatsionnykh Kleev. (ER ISSN 0868-4197) **1860**
Tallinna Tehnikaulikool. Statisticheskie Metody Analiza Effektivnosti Proizvodstva. (ER ISSN 0868-409X) **1085**
Tallinna Tehnikaulikool. Teoriya i Raschet Tonkostennykh i Prostranstvennykh Konstruktsii. (ER ISSN 0868-4138) **634**
Tallinna Tehnikaulikool. Trenie i Iznos v Mashinakh. (RU ISSN 0868-4162) **1939**
Tally-Ho. (US) **3714**
Tallyboard. (CN ISSN 0712-3094) **2109**, 3622
†Talmis Industry Update. (US) **5287**
Taloha. (MG) **3533**, 287, 346
Talouselama. (FI ISSN 0356-5106) **694**
Talyllyn News. (UK ISSN 0300-3272) **4715**
Tam-Tam see Message **1647**
Tam Tam. (IT) **3007**
Tam Ti Delam see Fetes et Festivals **1039**
Tamagawa University. Faculty of Agriculture. Bulletin. (JA ISSN 0082-156X) **123**
Tamaqua. (US) **2886**
The Tamarind Papers. (US ISSN 0276-3397) **346**
Tamarind Technical Papers see The Tamarind Papers **346**
Tamarisk. (US ISSN 0162-1017) **3007**
Tambara. (PH) **250**, 4454
Tambor. (SP ISSN 0049-2922) **2886**
Tamil Arasu. (II ISSN 0039-9280) **2202**
Tamil Ceithi Malar. (II) **1326**
Tamil Chamber of Commerce. Journal. (II) **823**
Tamil Civilization. (II) **2342**, 2025
Tamil Kalai. (II) **2342**, 346, 2847
Tamil Nadu. Department of Statistics. Annual Statistical Abstract. (II ISSN 0082-1578) **4590**
Tamil Nadu. Department of Statistics. Season and Crop Report. (II ISSN 0082-1586) **144**, 194
Tamil Nadu Industrial Development Corporation. Annual Report. (II) **1085**
Tamil Nadu Information. (II ISSN 0039-9310) **4075**
Tamil Nadu Journal of Co-operation. (II ISSN 0377-8002) **832**
Tamil Nadu Labour Journal. (II) **994**
Tamil Nadu Police Journal. (II ISSN 0039-9329) **1523**
Tamil Nadu Tourism Development Corporation. Annual Report. (II) **4788**, 1085
Tamil University. News Bulletin. (II) **1326**

Tamkang Journal: Area Studies. (CH) 3929
Tamkang Journal of Management Sciences see International Journal of Information and Management Sciences 1014
Tamkang Journal of Mathematics. (CH ISSN 0049-2930) 3057
Tamkang Review. (CH ISSN 0049-2949) 2968, 3644
Tammerkoski. (FI) 2391
Tampa Bay. (US) 2235
Tampa Bay Business Journal. (US ISSN 0273-5830) 886
Tampa Bay Business Weekly see Tampa Bay Business Journal 886
Tampa Bay History. (US ISSN 0272-1406) 2424
Tampa Bay Life. (US ISSN 1048-0056) 2236
Tampa Bay Metro Magazine. (US) 2236
†Tampa Bay New Homes. (US) 5287
Tampa Review. (US ISSN 0896-064X) 3007
Tamworth Annual. (US ISSN 0082-1608) 227
Tan. (US) 3809
T'an So/Quest. (US) 2886
Tandanya. (AT) 1498
Tandarra. (AT ISSN 0728-988X) 4422, 1244
Tandheelkundige Vereniging van Suid Afrika. Tydskrif. see Dental Association of South Africa. Journal 3231
Tandlaegebladet/Danish Dental Journal. (DK ISSN 0039-9353) 3243
Tane. (NZ ISSN 0496-8026) 4347
Tanecni Listy. (CS ISSN 0039-937X) 1532
T'ang Studies. (US ISSN 0737-5034) 3644
Tang Tai. see Contemporary 2197
Tanganyika Notes and Records see Tanzania Notes & Records 2219
Tangente. (AU) 3929
Tanglewood. (US) 2236
Taniguchi Symposia on Brain Sciences. (SZ ISSN 1013-2791) 3355, 575
Tank. (UK ISSN 0039-9418) 3472
▼Tank Container World. (UK ISSN 0959-6089) 4740
Tank Talk see FishLines 2041
Tanker Charter Record. (UK ISSN 0958-8787) 3702
Tanker Register. (UK ISSN 0305-179X) 3702, 4740
Tankette. (UK) 2442, 3472
Tankstelle. (GW) 4703
Tankstelle und Garage. (AU) 4703
Tankuang Gongcheng. (CC ISSN 0494-6162) 3496
Tanmiat al-Rafidain/Rafidain Development. (IQ) 4075, 898
Tanmiyah. see Development 1074
▼Tanneck. (US) 3583, 2391
Tanner. (II ISSN 0039-9442) 2738, 4362
Tanner Lectures on Human Values. (US ISSN 0275-7656) 3783
Tanner's Council of America. Newsbreak see Leather Industries of America. Newsbreak 2737
Tanning Trends. (US ISSN 0885-1522) 3809, 1119
Tanoshii Yochien. (JA) 1267
Tanpakushitsu Kakusan Koso/Protein, Nucleic Acid, Enzyme. (JA ISSN 0039-9450) 483
Tansui-ku Suisan Kenkyujo Kenkyu Hokoku. see National Research Institute of Aquaculture. Bulletin 2046
Tansuigyo see Tansuigyo-Hogo 2049
Tansuigyo-Hogo/Freshwater Fish Protection. (JA) 2049
Tansuo see T'an So 2886
Tanta University. Faculty of Literature. Journal. see Jami'at Tanta. Kulliyyat al-Adab. Majallah 2927
Tantalum-Niobium International Study Center. Quarterly Bulletin. (BE) 3421
Tantara. (MG) 2335
Tantsovo Izkustvo/Dance Art. (BU ISSN 0204-8728) 1532
Tanugyi Ujsag see Kozoktatas 1645

Tanulmanyok a Nevelestudomany Korebol. (HU ISSN 0082-1632) 1666
Tany Malagasy. see Terre Malgache 194
Tanz. (GW ISSN 0138-1482) 1532
Tanz und Gymnastik. (SZ) 1532, 4494
TanzAktuell. (GW ISSN 0933-0585) 1532, 4639
Tanzania. Bureau of Standards. Announcer. (TZ ISSN 0856-0374) 3449
Tanzania. Bureau of Standards. Director's Annual Report. (TZ ISSN 0856-2539) 3449
Tanzania. Bureau of Statistics. Directory of Industries. (TZ) 1154
Tanzania. Bureau of Statistics. Employment and Earnings see Tanzania. Bureau of Statistics. Survey of Employment 741
Tanzania. Bureau of Statistics. Migration Statistics. (TZ) 3996
Tanzania. Bureau of Statistics. Quarterly Statistical Bulletin. (TZ ISSN 0039-9469) 4590
Tanzania. Bureau of Statistics. Survey of Employment. (TZ) 741, 994, 4590
Tanzania. Bureau of Statistics. Survey of Industrial Production. (TZ) 741, 4590
Tanzania. Capital Development Authority. Report and Accounts. (TZ) 2496
Tanzania. Central Statistical Bureau. Survey of Industrial Production see Tanzania. Bureau of Statistics. Survey of Industrial Production 741
Tanzania. Mines Division. Review of the Mineral Industry see Review of the Mineral Industry in Tanzania 3494
Tanzania. Ministry of Agriculture and Livestock Development. Bulletin of Crop Statistics. (TZ) 144
Tanzania. Ministry of Agriculture. Bulletin of Crop Statistics see Tanzania. Ministry of Agriculture and Livestock Development. Bulletin of Crop Statistics 144
Tanzania. Ministry of Economic Affairs and Development Planning. Hali Ya Uchumi Wa Taifa - Annual Economic Survey see Tanzania. Planning Commission. Macro Planning Department. Hali Ya Uchumi Wa Taifa - Annual Economic Survey 1085
Tanzania. Ministry of Lands, Housing and Urban Development. Urban Planning Division. Annual Report. (TZ) 2496
Tanzania. Ministry of Planning and Economic Affairs. Hali Ya Uchumi Wa Taifa - Annual Economic Survey see Tanzania. Planning Commission. Macro Planning Department. Hali Ya Uchumi Wa Taifa - Annual Economic Survey 1085
Tanzania. Planning Commission. Macro Planning Department. Hali Ya Uchumi Wa Taifa - Annual Economic Survey. (TZ) 1085
Tanzania Education Journal. (TZ ISSN 0039-9477) 1666
Tanzania High Court Digest see Law Reports of Tanzania 2645
Tanzania Housing Bank. Annual Report and Statement of Accounts/Benki ya Nyumba Tanzania. Ripoti ya Mwaka. (TZ) 800
Tanzania Import and Export Directory. (TZ) 922
Tanzania Industrial Studies and Consulting Organisation. Annual Report and Accounts. (TZ ISSN 0856-2172) 694
Tanzania Investment Bank. Annual Report. (TZ ISSN 0856-2423) 801
Tanzania Journal of Science. (TZ ISSN 0856-1761) 4347
Tanzania Library Service. Occasional Paper. (TZ ISSN 0856-1621) 2786
Tanzania Management Journal see Uongori: Journal of Management Development 1030

Tanzania National Bibliography. (TZ ISSN 0856-003X) 413, 2786
Tanzania News Review. (TZ ISSN 0856-017X) 2219
Tanzania Notes & Records. (TZ ISSN 0039-9485) 2219
Tanzania Railways Corporation. Habari za Reli. (TZ) 4715
Tanzania Rural Development Bank. Annual Report and Accounts see Cooperative and Rural Development Bank. Annual Report and Accounts 773
Tanzania Zamani. (TZ ISSN 0039-9507) 2324
Tanzanian Journalist see Torch 2576
Tanzanian Mathematical Bulletin. (TZ ISSN 0856-065X) 3057, 1760
Tanzanian Studies. (TZ) 2335
Tanzen. (GW ISSN 0724-1062) 1532, 1687
Tanzer Talk. (CN) 4530
Tanzer 22 Newsletter see Tanzer Talk 4530
Taoci Yanjiu/Ceramics Studies Journal. (CC ISSN 1000-9892) 1166
Tap Chi Cong San/Communist Review. (VN) 3929
Tap Chi Tac Pham Van Hoc. (VN) 2968
Tap Chi Van Hoc/Literature Magazine. (VN) 2968
Tap Roots. (US ISSN 0494-6944) 2165
Tapas. (US) 3007
Tape - Disc Business. (US) 413
Tape - Disc Directory (Year). (US) 1386, 3583
Tape Record see Soundings 2296
†Tapestry (Missoula). (US) 5287
Tapia. (TR) 2886
Tapicerias Gancedo see T G 346
TapJoe. (US) 3007
Tapol. (UK) 3973
Tapori. (FR) 1267
Tapori. (US ISSN 0882-5424) 1267
Tapovan Prasad. (II) 4217
Tappezziere in Stoffa. (IT) 2562
Tappi Journal see T A P P I Journal 3666
Taproot. (US ISSN 0887-9257) 2968, 2886, 4639
Taproot Literary Review. (US) 2968
Taptoe. (NE ISSN 0039-9604) 1267
Tar Heel Coast see North Carolina Tarheel Coast 5249
Tar Heel Economist see N C State Economist 155
Tar Heel Junior Historian. (US ISSN 0496-8913) 2424
Tar Heel Libraries. (US ISSN 0193-4309) 2786
Tar Heel Nurse. (US ISSN 0039-9620) 3287
Tar River Poetry. (US ISSN 0039-9639) 3007
†Tarakan Music Letter. (US ISSN 0272-9520) 5287
Taranga. (II) 2202
†Taraxacum. (DK ISSN 0496-8859) 5287
Tarbell's Teacher's Guide. (US ISSN 0082-1713) 4205
Al-Tarbiyyah/Education. (QA) 1666
Al-Tarbiyyah/Education. (TS) 1666
Tarbiz. (IS ISSN 0334-3650) 4226, 287, 2391, 2432
Tarbut. (US) 2025
Tarea. (PE) 1666
Tareas. (PN ISSN 0494-7061) 4389, 2424
Tarex. (FR) 3744
Target. (IT ISSN 0394-9591) 39
Target. (II) 1267
Target. (NE ISSN 0924-1884) 2847
Target. see Lengo 4188
Target. (KE) 4205
Target (Renton) see Friends of Youth Newsletter 1237
Target (Wayne). (US) 2886
Target (Wheeling). (US) 1085
Target (Woodside). (US) 1054
Target an AIM 65 Newsletter. (US) 1465
Target Arson: Update. (US) 2544
Target Electronics Industry see Taiwan Electronics Industry 1779
Target Electronics Industry Computer see Taiwan Computer 1455

Target Financial Service. (HK) 801
Target Gun. (UK ISSN 0143-8751) 4494
†Target Housewares & Gifts. (CH) 5287
Target Intelligence Report. (HK) 801
Target Machinery & Hardware. (CH) 3023
Target Marketing. (US ISSN 0889-5333) 1055, 39
Target Organ Toxicology Series. (US) 1983, 3744
Targumic and Cognate Studies. Newsletter. (CN ISSN 0704-5905) 4226
Tarheel Banker. (US ISSN 0039-9663) 801
Tarheel Coast see North Carolina Tarheel Coast 5249
Tarheel Wheels. (US ISSN 0039-968X) 4748
Tarif Media. (FR ISSN 0038-9579) 39
Tarif Pieces Detachees. (FR) 4656
†Tarif- und Verkehrs-Anzeiger. (GW ISSN 0492-2700) 5287
Tariff Brief see Industry Review 912
Tariff Insight see Industry Review 912
Tariff Schedules of the United States Annotated. (US ISSN 0082-173X) 1107
Tarih Dergisi. (TU) 2391
Tarina see Sinamina 4853
Tarjuman al-Hadith. (PK) 4220
Tark. (NP) 2211
Tarlac College of Technology. Annual Report of the President. (PH) 1717
Tarokalok. (BG) 2174
Tarot Network News. (US) 3597, 2059, 3783, 4048
Tarsadalmi Szemle. (HU ISSN 0039-971X) 4454
Tarsadalomkutatas. (HU ISSN 0231-2522) 2684, 694
Tarsadalomtudomanyi Kozlemenyek. (HU ISSN 0133-0381) 4389
The Tartan. (US ISSN 0890-3107) 1717
Tartan Book Sales Catalog. (US) 4138
Tas Tots. (AT) 1267, 4853
Taschenbuch der Auktionspreise Alten Buecher. (GW) 413
Taschenbuch der Fernmelde-Praxis see Taschenbuch der Telekom Praxis 1343
Taschenbuch der Giesserei-Praxis. (GW ISSN 0082-1772) 3421
Taschenbuch der Pflanzenarztes. (GW ISSN 0082-1799) 194
Taschenbuch der Post- und Fernmelde-Verwaltung see Verwaltungsjahrbuch fuer die Deutsche Bundespost 1367
Taschenbuch der Telekom Praxis. (GW) 1343
Taschenbuch der Textilen Raumausstattung. (GW) 4623
Taschenbuch der Werbung see Deutscher Werbekalender 30
Taschenbuch des Metallhandels. (GW) 3421
Taschenbuch des Oeffentlichen Lebens. (GW ISSN 0082-1829) 4075, 413
Taschenbuch des Textileinzelhandels. (GW ISSN 0082-1837) 4623
Taschenbuch fuer Agrarjournalisten. (GW ISSN 0082-1845) 123, 2575
Taschenbuch fuer die Bekleidungs-Industrie see Bekleidungs-Industrie (Year). Jahrbuch 1283
Taschenbuch fuer die Textil-Industrie. (GW ISSN 0082-1896) 4623
Taschenbuch fuer Kriminalisten. (GW ISSN 0082-1934) 1523
Taschenbuch fuer Lackierbetriebe (Year). (GW ISSN 0340-8167) 3655
†Taschenbuch fuer Liturgie Kirchenmusik und Musikerziehung. (GW ISSN 0344-1407) 5287
Taschenbuch fuer Liturgie und Kirchenmusik see Taschenbuch fuer Liturgie Kirchenmusik und Musikerziehung 5287
Taschenbuch Geschichte. (GW ISSN 0082-1950) 2324

6718 TASCHENBUECHER

Taschenbuecher zur Musikwissenschaft.(GW ISSN 0082-1969) **3584**
Taschenfachbuch der Kraftfahrzeugbetriebe. (GW) **4703**
Taschenstatistik (Year). (SZ) **4590**
Al-Tashkil. (TS) **346**
Task Force on Environmental Cancer and Heart and Lung Disease. Annual Report to Congress. (US ISSN 0164-0968) **1983**, 3202, 3212, 3367
Tasmania. Department of Agriculture. Annual Report see Tasmania. Department of Primary Industry. Annual Report **123**
Tasmania. Department of Agriculture. Insect Pest Survey see Tasmania. Department of Primary Industry. Insect Pest Survey **5287**
Tasmania. Department of Education and the Arts. Gazette see Spectrum **1665**
Tasmania. Department of Mines. Geological Survey Bulletins see Tasmania. Department of Resources and Energy. Division of Mines and Mineral Resources. Geological Survey Bulletins **1582**
Tasmania. Department of Primary Industry. Annual Report. (AT) **123**
†Tasmania. Department of Primary Industry. Insect Pest Survey. (AT) **5287**
Tasmania. Department of Resources and Energy. Division of Mines and Mineral Resources. Geological Survey Bulletins. (AT) **1582**
Tasmania. Department of the Treasury. Budget Papers. (AT) **1107**
Tasmania. Department of the Treasury. Consolidated Revenue Fund see Tasmania. Department of the Treasury. Budget Papers **1107**
Tasmania. Hobart Regional Water Board. Annual Report. (AT) **1969**
Tasmania. Metropolitan Water Board. Report. see Tasmania. Hobart Regional Water Board. Annual Report **1969**
Tasmanian Ancestry. (AT ISSN 0159-0677) **2165**
Tasmanian Baptist Advance. (AT) **4250**
Tasmanian Building Journal. (AT) **634**
Tasmanian Chamber of Industries News see T C I News **823**
Tasmanian Chess Magazine. (AT) **4494**, 1419
Tasmanian Conservationist. (AT) **1498**, 1969
Tasmanian Development Authority Annual Report. (AT ISSN 0817-6418) **694**
Tasmanian Eudcation Gazette see Spectrum **1665**
Tasmanian Fisheries Research. (AT ISSN 0049-3015) **2049**
Tasmanian Fruitgrower & Farmer. (AT ISSN 0039-9787) **2139**
Tasmanian Government Gazette. (AT ISSN 0039-9795) **4075**
Tasmanian Historical Research Association. Papers and Proceedings.(AT ISSN 0039-9809) **2345**
†Tasmanian Hydatid Disease Newsletter. (AT) **5287**
Tasmanian Manufacturers Directory. (AT) **1154**
Tasmanian Motor News see Motor News **4696**
Tasmanian Naturalist. (AT ISSN 0819-6826) **457**, 1969
Tasmanian Numismatist. (AT ISSN 0817-4075) **3602**
Tasmanian Pocket Yearbook. (AT ISSN 0314-1640) **4590**
Tasmanian Reports. (AT ISSN 0085-7106) **2684**
Tasmanian Teacher see Teacher **2590**
Tasmanian Trade Protective Institute Trade Gazette see T T P I Trade Gazette **839**
Tasmanian Tramp. (AT ISSN 0157-2938) **4558**
Tasmanian Transport Bulletin see Tasmanian Transport Statistics **4667**

Tasmanian Transport Statistics. (AT) **4667**, 4656
Tasmanian Travelways. (AT) **4788**
Tasmanian University Law Review see University of Tasmania Law Review **2690**
Tass News and Journal see M S F Journal **2586**
Tassels and Tails. (US) **3714**
Taste. see Yevse **2084**
Taste of Scotland see Taste of Scotland Guide (Year) **4788**
Taste of Scotland Guide (Year). (UK) **4788**
Tasten Welt see Keyboard World **3560**
Tasten Welt. (SZ) **3584**
Taswiq Al-Ziraiy. see Agricultural Marketing **146**
Tata Institute Lecture Notes see Tata Institute Lectures on Mathematics **3057**
Tata Institute Lectures on Mathematics. (US) **3057**
Tata Institute of Fundamental Research. Lectures on Mathematics and Physics. Mathematics see Tata Institute Lectures on Mathematics **3057**
Tata Institute of Fundamental Research. Lectures on Mathematics and Physics. Physics see Tata Institute Lectures on Mathematics **3057**
Tata Institute Studies in Mathematics. (US) **3058**
Tata Iron and Steel Co. Ltd. Technical Journal see T I S C O Technical Journal **3421**
Tate and Lyle's Sugar Industry Abstracts see Sugar Industry Abstracts **2085**
Tate Trails. (US) **2165**, 2424
Tater News. (US) **194**
Tatler. (UK) **2195**
Tatra Eagle. see Tatrzanski Orzel **2026**
Tatrzanski Orzel/Tatra Eagle. (US ISSN 0039-9914) **2026**, 2059
Tatsachen und Meinungen see T.M **4389**
Tatsachen und Zahlen aus der Kraftverkehrswirtschaft. (GW ISSN 0083-548X) **4703**
Tattersall's Club Magazine. (AT) **1301**
I Tatti Studies. (IT ISSN 0393-5949) **2391**
Tattoo. (US) **346**, 2236
†Tattoo Advocate. (US ISSN 0896-8063) **5287**
†Tattoo Historian. (US) **5287**
Tattoo Review. (US ISSN 1047-1499) **346**
Tattootime. (US) **346**
Tauch-Brille. (GW) **4494**
Tauchen. (GW) **4494**, 457, 3797
Taurus (Winchester). (US) **966**
Taurus and Optimum Trades see Taurus (Winchester) **966**
Tavaraleimalehti see Finland. Patentti-ja Rekisterihallitus. Tavaramerkkilehti **3675**
Taverna di Auerbach. (IT ISSN 0394-3518) **3007**
A Tavola. (IT) **2449**
Tawagoto. (US ISSN 1047-4250) **4289**
Tawhid. (UA) **2186**, 4220
Al-Tawzi/Distribution. (TS) **3702**
Tax Accounting. (US) **756**, 1107
Tax Action Coordinator. (US) **1107**
Tax Administration Review. (AG) **1107**
Tax Administrators News. (US ISSN 0039-9949) **1107**
Tax Adviser. (US ISSN 0039-9957) **1107**
†Tax Alert for Management. (US ISSN 0196-8882) **5287**
Tax & Business Adviser. (US) **756**, 801, 1029, 1107
Tax & Insurance Letter. (UK) **1107**
Tax Aspects of Buying and Selling Corporate Businesses. (US) **1107**
Tax - Benefit Position of Production Workers. (FR) **1107**
Tax Briefs. (US) **1107**
Tax Burden on Tobacco. (US ISSN 0563-6191) **4646**, 1107, 4590
Tax Case Analysis. (UK ISSN 0262-7639) **1107**
Tax Case Report. (UK) **1107**
Tax Court. (US) **1107**
Tax Court Decisions. (US) **1108**

Tax Court Reports. (US ISSN 0162-1815) **1108**
Tax Executive. (US ISSN 0040-0025) **1108**
Tax-Exempt News see NonProfit Insights **1022**
Tax-Exempt Organizations. (US) **1108**
Tax Facts on Life Insurance see Tax Facts 1 **2544**
Tax Facts 1. (US) **2544**
Tax Facts 2. (US) **966**
Tax Features. (US ISSN 0883-1335) **1108**
Tax File. (UK) **756**, 1108
Tax, Financial and Estate Planning for the Owner of a Closely-Held Corporation see Closely Held Corporation: Tax, Financial and Estate Planning **1091**
Tax Foundation. Federal Tax Burden by State. (US) **1108**
Tax Foundation. Memorandum on the Allocation of the Federal Tax Burden and Federal Grants-in-Aid by State see Tax Foundation. Federal Tax Burden by State **1108**
Tax Fraud and Evasion (Supplement). (US) **1108**
Tax Guide. see Dalil al-Dara'ib **1092**
Tax Guide. (US ISSN 0361-5871) **1108**
Tax Haven Reporter Newsletter. (BF) **1108**, 966
Tax Haven Review see Tax Planning International Review **1109**
Tax Havens of the World. (BF) **1108**, 966
Tax Hotline. (US) **1108**, 756
Tax Ideas. (US) **1108**
Tax Insight. (US) **801**, 1108
†Tax Law Anthology. (US ISSN 0892-4430) **5287**
†Tax Law Locator. (US) **5287**
Tax Law Review. (US ISSN 0040-0041) **1108**, 2684
Tax Lawyer. (US ISSN 0040-005X) **2684**
Tax Management Compensation Planning. (US) **1108**
Tax Management Compensation Planning Journal. (US ISSN 0747-8607) **1029**
Tax Management Estates, Gifts and Trusts. (US) **1108**
Tax Management Estates, Gifts and Trusts Journal. (US ISSN 0886-3547) **966**
Tax Management Estates, Gifts and Trusts Reference Files. (US) **1108**
Tax Management Executive Compensation see Tax Management Compensation Planning **1108**
Tax Management Financial Planning. (US ISSN 8756-1360) **1108**
Tax Management Financial Planning Journal. (US ISSN 8756-1360) **801**
Tax Management Foreign Income Portfolios. (US) **1108**
▼Tax Management I R S Practice & Policy Bulletin. (US) **1108**
▼Tax Management I R S Practice and Policy Series. (US) **1108**
Tax Management International Forum. (UK ISSN 0143-7941) **1108**
Tax Management International Journal. (US ISSN 0090-4600) **1108**
Tax Management International Portfolios. (UK) **1108**, 922
Tax Management Memorandum. (US ISSN 0148-8295) **1109**
Tax Management Primary Sources. (US ISSN 0738-5285) **1109**
Tax Management Real Estate. (US) **4158**
Tax Management Real Estate Journal. (US ISSN 8755-0628) **4158**
Tax Management Tax Practice Series. (US ISSN 1044-7261) **1109**
Tax Management U S Income. (US) **1109**
Tax Management Washington Tax Review. (US ISSN 0887-2562) **1109**
Tax Management Weekly Report. (US ISSN 0884-6057) **1109**
Tax Memo. (CN) **1109**
Tax News Service. (NE ISSN 0040-0076) **1109**

Tax Notes. (US ISSN 0270-5494) **1109**, 2684
Tax Notes - Digest Bulletin see Index - Digest Bulletin **1097**
Tax Notes Microfiche Data Base. (US ISSN 0730-8604) **1109**
Tax Outlook. (US) **756**
▼Tax Penalties. (US ISSN 1055-2456) **1109**
▼Tax Penalties and Interest Handbook.(US) **1109**
Tax Planner and Business Scan see Tax & Business Adviser **756**
Tax Planner - Scan see Tax & Business Adviser **756**
Tax Planning. (II) **1109**
†Tax Planning. (US ISSN 0040-0084) **5287**
Tax Planning for Corporate Acquisitions.(US) **1109**, 2712
Tax Planning Ideas. (US ISSN 0040-0092) **1109**
Tax Planning International Review. (UK ISSN 0309-7900) **1109**
Tax Planning Review see C C H Tax . Planning Review **1089**
Tax Policy and the Economy. (US ISSN 0892-8649) **1109**
Tax Practice Deskbook (Supplement). (US) **1109**
Tax Practitioner's Diary. (UK ISSN 0269-3720) **1109**
†Tax Preparers Liability Service. (US) **5287**
Tax Principles to Remember. (CN ISSN 0227-1265) **1109**
Tax Profile. (CN ISSN 0827-3677) **1109**
Tax Shelter Investment Review see Limited Partnership Investment Review **1100**
†Tax Shelter Litigation Report. (US) **5287**
Tax Shelter Monitor. (US) **966**
Tax Sheltered Investments Handbook see Investment Limited Partnerships Handbook **951**
Tax Strategies for Separations and Divorce see Divorce Tax Planning Strategies **1092**
Tax Times. (II ISSN 0040-0122) **1109**
Tax Transactions Library. (US) **1109**
Tax Treaties (Chicago). (US) **1109**
Tax Treaties (Englewood Cliffs). (US) **1109**
Tax Treaties Data Base on C D - R O M.(NE) **1109**
Tax Treatment of Transfer Pricing. (NE) **1110**
Tax-Vyapar. (II) **1110**
†Tax Year in Review. (US) **5287**
Taxa Droske Tidende see Dansk Taxi Tidende **4689**
Taxation. (PK ISSN 0040-0157) **1110**
Taxation. (UK ISSN 0040-0149) **1110**
Taxation. (II) **1110**
Taxation and Investment in the Caribbean. (NE) **1110**, 966
Taxation and Investment in the People's Republic of China. (NE) **1110**, 966
†Taxation Digest. Journal. (US) **5287**
Taxation for Accountants. (US ISSN 0040-0165) **1110**, 756
Taxation for Lawyers. (US ISSN 0161-178X) **1110**, 2684
Taxation in Australia. (AT ISSN 0494-8343) **1110**
Taxation in Latin America. (NE) **1110**
Taxation Law Reports. (II) **1110**
Taxation of Closely Held Corporations (Supplement) see Taxation of the Closely Held Corporation (Supplement) **1110**
Taxation of Corporate Liquidations. (US) **1110**
Taxation of Employees. (SA) **1110**
▼Taxation of Mergers and Acquisitions.(US) **1110**, 694
Taxation of the Closely Held Corporation (Supplement). (US) **1110**
Taxation Practitioner. (UK) **1110**
Taxation Precedents, Procedures and Elections. (AT) **1110**
Taxation Record Journal. (AT ISSN 0040-0173) **1110**

Taxation Research. see Shuiwu Yanjiu 1105
Taxation Structure of Pakistan. (PK) 1110
Taxation Tables. (AT ISSN 0082-2175) 1110
Taxes. (US ISSN 0040-0181) 1110
Taxes and Investment in Asia and the Pacific. (NE) 1110
Taxes and Investment in Canada and the U S A. (NE) 1110, 966
Taxes and Investment in the Middle East. (NE) 1110
Taxes on Parade. (US ISSN 0162-3486) 1110
Taxi. (UK ISSN 0049-304X) 4656
Taxi. (NO) 4656
Taxi. (AT) 4656
†Taxi. (US) 5287
Taxi & Livery Management. (US) 4656
†Taxi Drivers Compendium. (UK) 5287
Taxi News. (AT) 4656
Taxi News. (CN) 4656
†Taxi News Digest. (US ISSN 0040-0211) 5287
Taxi Talk. (SA) 4703
Taxidermy Review. (US) 592
Taxinews. (UK ISSN 0040-0254) 4656
Taxitrafiken. (SW ISSN 0040-022X) 4656
Taxletter. (CN ISSN 0821-3704) 1110
Taxon. (GW ISSN 0040-0262) 518
Taxpayer. (AT ISSN 0040-0289) 1110
Taxpayer. (SA ISSN 0040-0270) 1110
Taxpayers' Bulletin see Taxpayer 1110
Tayarut be-Yisrael. see Israel Tourist Statistics 4799
Tayarut v'Sherutei ha-Araha. see Statistics of Travel and Tourism 4800
Taylor. (US) 1717
Taylor Quarterly (Alexandria). (US ISSN 0735-9144) 2165
Taylor Quarterly (El Paso). (US) 2165
Taylor Talk. (US ISSN 0492-3901) 2576, 1666
Taylor University Magazine see Taylor 1717
Taylor's Encyclopedia of Government Officials. Federal and State. (US ISSN 0082-2183) 1782, 3929, 4075
Tbilisskii Universitet. Institut Prikladnoi Matematiki. Seminar. Dokladi. (GS ISSN 0320-9512) 3058
Tchahert/Torch. (LE ISSN 0040-0297) 4289
Tchebec. (CN) 567
Te Puna Matauranga. (NZ ISSN 0114-1090) 2786
Te Reo. (NZ ISSN 0494-8440) 2847
Te-ve Guia. (PR ISSN 0040-0327) 1382
Tea. see Chaye 2063
Tea. (KE) 2082
Tea Abstracts. see Chaye Wenzhai 2084
Tea and Coffee Trade Journal. (US ISSN 0040-0343) 2082
Tea Directory. (II) 385
Tea Journal. (II) 2082
Tea Research Association. Advisory Bulletin. (II) 385
Tea Research Association. Memorandum. (II) 385, 194
Tea Research Association. Occasional Scientific Papers. (II) 385, 194
Tea Research Association. Tocklai Experimental Station. Scientific Annual Report. (II ISSN 0564-6723) 386, 194
Tea Research Foundation. Annual Report see Tea Research Foundation of Kenya. Annual Report 2083
Tea Research Foundation. Annual Report. (MW) 2083
Tea Research Foundation. Quarterly Newsletter. (MW) 123
Tea Research Foundation of Central Africa. Annual Report see Tea Research Foundation. Annual Report 2083

Tea Research Foundation of Central Africa. Quarterly Newsletter see Tea Research Foundation. Quarterly Newsletter 123
Tea Research Foundation of Kenya. Annual Report. (KE) 2083
Tea Talk. (US) 2083
Teach. (US ISSN 8755-8769) 4205
Teach-in see Hospital Update 2465
Teacher. see Ucitelj 1269
Teacher. see Laeraren 1645
Teacher. see Opettaja 1652
Teacher. (MM ISSN 0040-0416) 1666
Teacher. (US ISSN 1046-6193) 1760
The Teacher. (GR) 1760
Teacher. (AT) 2590, 1666
†Teacher. (UK ISSN 0040-0408) 5287
Teacher (Armdale). (CN ISSN 0382-408X) 1732
Teacher (Vancouver). (CN ISSN 0841-9574) 1666
Teacher and Librarian. (AT ISSN 0049-3090) 2786, 1666
Teacher Education. (II ISSN 0379-3400) 1666
Teacher Education and Special Education. (US) 1741, 1760
Teacher Education in Uganda see Makerere University. Faculty of Education. Handbook 1711
Teacher Education Quarterly. (US ISSN 0737-5328) 1761
Teacher Educator. (US) 1717, 1761
Teacher Feedback see Education (Sydney) 1627
†Teacher in Commerce. (UK) 5287
Teacher Information Center Newsletter see T.I.C. Newsletter 994
Teacher Rights Newsletter. (US) 1666, 2684
Teacher Supply and Demand in Florida. (US) 1666
Teacher Supply - Demand. (US) 1732, 3631
Teacher Training Profile see Profile (Wheaton) 1686
Teacher Update. (US ISSN 0194-2859) 1761
Teachers & Writers Magazine. (US ISSN 0146-3381) 1761, 2968
Teachers College Record. (US ISSN 0161-4681) 1667
Teacher's Court. (US) 4513, 1761
Teachers' Forum. (NR) 1667
Teachers' Forum. (RH) 1717
Teachers Guide to Media and Methods see Media & Methods 1754
Teachers' Guide to Overseas Teaching. (US) 1723, 1717, 3631, 4788
Teachers Guild of New South Wales. Proceedings. (AT) 1667
Teacher's Interaction. (US) 1667, 4250
Teachers' Message. see Yememhiran Melkt 1672
Teachers' Money Matters. (CN) 801, 1732
Teachers' Monthly see Teachers' Forum 1667
Teachers of English to Speakers of Other Languages Matters see T E S O L Matters 2847
Teachers of English to Speakers of Other Languages Quarterly see T E S O L Quarterly 2847
Teachers of History in the Universities and Polytechnics of the United Kingdom. (UK ISSN 0268-6732) 1667
Teachers of History in the Universities of the United Kingdom see Teachers of History in the Universities and Polytechnics of the United Kingdom 1667
Teachers of Religion and Christian Ethics see T R A C E S 4205
Teachers of the World see Educadores del Mundo 1627
Teachers of the World. (GW ISSN 0863-0070) 1667, 2590
Teacher's Tax Guide. (AT ISSN 0728-554X) 1110, 756, 1667
†Teacher's Time. (UK) 5287
Teachers Travel Gazette. (US) 4788, 1667

Teacher's Voice see Voice (East Lansing) 1671
Teachers World see Junior Education 1644
Teacher's World. (BG ISSN 0040-0521) 1667
Teaching and Computers. (US ISSN 0738-6087) 1417, 1667, 1691
Teaching and Learning in Medicine. (US ISSN 1040-1334) 3156, 1667
Teaching and Learning: The Journal of Natural Inquiry. (US ISSN 0887-9486) 1761, 1717
Teaching and Research. see Jiaoxue yu Yanjiu 1752
Teaching & Teacher Education. (US ISSN 0742-051X) 1761
Teaching & Training. (UK ISSN 0040-0572) 1741
Teaching and Training in Geriatric Medicine. (SZ ISSN 1011-3738) 2279
Teaching at a Distance see Open Learning 1714
Teaching Chinese in Elementary School. see Xiaoxue Yuwen Jiaoshi 2852
Teaching Earth Sciences. (UK) 1582, 1761
Teaching Economics. (US) 1761, 1000
Teaching Electronics and Computing see Computers in Education 1689
▼Teaching Elementary Physical Education. (US ISSN 1045-4853) 1761, 1244, 3809
Teaching English. (UK ISSN 0305-7755) 1761
Teaching English for Specific Purposes Journal. (PH ISSN 0116-8037) 2847, 1761
Teaching English in the Two-Year College. (US ISSN 0098-6291) 1761
Teaching English to Deaf and Second Language Students. (US) 1741, 2289, 2847
Teaching Exceptional Children. (US ISSN 0040-0599) 1741
Teaching for Learning. (US) 1667
†Teaching Genealogy. (US ISSN 0899-5397) 5287
Teaching Geography. (UK ISSN 0305-8018) 2264, 1667
Teaching Georgia Government. (US) 4075, 1761
Teaching Gifted Children. (US) 1741
Teaching History. (AT ISSN 0040-0602) 1761, 2324
Teaching History. (UK ISSN 0040-0610) 1761, 2324
Teaching History: A Journal of Methods.(US ISSN 0730-1383) 1761, 2324
Teaching K-8. (US) 1761
Teaching Librarian. (CN) 2786
Teaching Mathematics and Its Applications. (UK) 3058
Teaching of English. (AT ISSN 0049-3147) 1761
Teaching of History. (UK ISSN 0073-2605) 1761, 2324
Teaching of Psychology. (US ISSN 0098-6283) 4048, 1761
Teaching Opportunities Overseas - Bulletin. (US ISSN 0889-8839) 1667, 3631
Teaching Philosophy. (US ISSN 0145-5788) 3783, 1761
†Teaching Pictures for Bible Searchers. (US ISSN 0040-0645) 5287
Teaching Political Science see Perspectives on Political Science 3915
Teaching Professor. (US) 1717
Teaching Progress see Milwaukee Public Schools Staff Bulletin 1729
Teaching Public Administration. (UK ISSN 0144-7394) 1761, 4075
Teaching Science. (UK ISSN 0263-6107) 4347, 1667
Teaching Sociology. (US ISSN 0092-055X) 4454, 1761
Teaching Statistics. (UK ISSN 0141-982X) 1680, 4590
Teaching Thinking & Problem Solving Newsletter. (US ISSN 0887-0217) 4048, 1667
Teaching Today. (CN ISSN 0827-3049) 1761

▼Teaching Tolerance. (US) 1742
Teaching Under 5's. (UK) 4205
Teaching 5-7's see Learning Together with 5-7's 4187
Teaching 7-10's see Learning Together with 7-11's 4187
Teaching 10-13's see Learning Together with 11-14's 4187
Team. (II ISSN 0040-0696) 1085
Team and Trail. (US) 3714
Team Baseball Card Checklist see The Sport Americana Team Baseball Card Checklist 2442
Team Football and Basketball Card Checklist see The Sport Americana Team Football and Basketball Card Checklist 2442
Team Horizons. (US ISSN 0163-3422) 4205
Team Licensing Business. (US) 4494, 2684
Team Line-Up. (US) 4494
Team Marketing Report. (US) 1055
Team of Advocates for Special Kids Newsletter. (US) 2284, 1267, 1742
▼Team Rehab Report. (US) 3156
Tears. (UK) 1717
Teashi no Fujiyuuna Kodomotachi/Crippled Children. (JA ISSN 0040-0734) 3156
Teater for Boern og Unge see Boerneteateravisen 4630
Teaterbladet. (DK ISSN 0900-0119) 4639
Teatern. (SW ISSN 0040-0750) 4639
Teaterraadets Indstilling. (DK ISSN 0107-248X) 4639
Teaterseminar. (DK ISSN 0109-3363) 4639
Teatr. (PL ISSN 0040-0769) 4639
Teatr. (RU ISSN 0040-0777) 4639
Teatral'naya Zhizn' (RU ISSN 0040-0785) 4639
Teatro. (AG ISSN 0040-0793) 4639
Teatro. (IT) 4639
Teatro. Studi e Testi. (IT) 4639
Teatro Archivio. (IT) 4643
Teatro C E L C I T. (AG) 4640
Teatro e Storia. (IT ISSN 1120-9569) 4640, 2391, 3584
Teatro Festival. (IT) 4640
Teatro: Teoria y Practica see Teatro C E L C I T 4640
Teatrul see Teatrulazi 4640
Teatrulazi. (RM) 4640
Teatur. (BU ISSN 0204-6253) 4640
Tebb-o Daru. (IR) 3156
Tebiwa. (US) 250
Tebiwa Miscellaneous Papers see Tebiwa 250
The Tech. (US ISSN 0148-9607) 1326
Tech Air see Aerospace 43
Tech Bits see Kodak Tech Bits 3792
Tech Collegian. (US) 1326
Tech-Embal. (FR) 3652
Tech - Europe. (BE) 1352
Tech Exec see 3X - 400 Information Management 5309
Tech Log. (UK) 63
Tech Minnesota. (US) 1837
Tech Roundup see Forms Tech Reference Series 1058
Tech Sample. (US) 3156
Tech Specialist see Windows - D O S Developer's Journal 1432
Tech Teacher see Federation News (Abbotsford) 1633
Tech Topics. (US) 1326
Tech Transfer. (US) 1796
Tech Transfer Report. (US) 1796
TechAgra News. (US) 165
TechComp Review. (US) 1029
†Techknowledge. (US) 5287
Techline. (US ISSN 0896-3215) 1382
Techmart Letter. (US) 1465
Techne. (IT) 3007
Technica. (BE) 2566
Technica. (SZ ISSN 0040-0866) 3023
Technical see Urban Abstracts 4083
Technical Acoustics. see Shengxue Jishu 3860
Technical Aid to the Disabled Journal. (AT ISSN 0725-2919) 2284, 1922

TECHNICAL ANALYSIS

Technical Analysis of Currencies. (UK ISSN 0959-2288) **801**

Technical Analysis of Stocks & Commodities. (US ISSN 0738-3355) **966**

Technical and Commercial Message. (NR) **1837**, 123

Technical and Further Education Australian Journal of T A F E Research and Development see Australian Journal of T A F E Research and Development **1617**

Technical and Further Education Teacher's Association Australian T A F E Teacher see Australian T A F E Teacher **1744**

Technical & Skilled Trade Personnel Report. (US) **1029**, 994

▼Technical & Skills Training. (US ISSN 1047-8388) **1070**

Technical Association of Graphic Arts of Japan. Bulletin see Japanese Society of Printing Science and Technology. Bulletin **4002**

Technical Association of Graphic Arts of Japan. Bulletin (Overseas Edition) see Japanese Society of Printing Science and Technology. Bulletin (Overseas Edition) **4002**

Technical Association of Malaysia. Journal see Malaysian Technologist **4603**

Technical Association of the Graphic Arts Newsletter see T A G A Newsletter **4006**

Technical Association of the Graphic Arts Proceedings see T A G A Proceedings **4006**

Technical Association of the Pulp and Paper Industry. Coating Conference. Proceedings (Year). (US ISSN 1047-305X) **3666**

Technical Association of the Pulp and Paper Industry. Corrugated Containers Conference. Proceedings (Year) see Corrugated Containers Conference (Year) **3648**

Technical Association of the Pulp and Paper Industry. Directory. (US ISSN 0734-1415) **3666**

Technical Association of the Pulp and Paper Industry. Engineering Conference Proceedings (Year). (US ISSN 0271-9959) **3667**

Technical Association of the Pulp and Paper Industry. Environmental Conference Proceedings (Year). (US ISSN 1058-0905) **1969**

Technical Association of the Pulp and Paper Industry. Finishing and Converting Conference. Proceedings (Year). (US ISSN 1050-4265) **3667**

Technical Association of the Pulp and Paper Industry. International Process and Materials Quality Evaluation Proceedings (Year) see Technical Association of the Pulp and Paper Industry. International Process & Product Quality Conference Proceedings (Year) **3667**

Technical Association of the Pulp and Paper Industry. International Process & Product Quality Conference Proceedings (Year). (US ISSN 1046-4166) **3667**

Technical Association of the Pulp and Paper Industry. Nonwood Plant Fiber Pulping Progress Report. (US) **3667**

Technical Association of the Pulp and Paper Industry. Nonwovens Conference. Proceedings (Year). (US) **3667**

Technical Association of the Pulp and Paper Industry. Paper Finishing and Converting Conference. Proceedings (Year) see Technical Association of the Pulp and Paper Industry. Finishing and Converting Conference. Proceedings (Year) **3667**

Technical Association of the Pulp and Paper Industry. Papermakers Conference Proceedings (Year). (US ISSN 0197-5153) **3667**

Technical Association of the Pulp and Paper Industry. Polymers, Laminations & Coatings Conference. Proceedings (Year). (US ISSN 1047-3033) **3667**

Technical Association of the Pulp and Paper Industry. Process Control Conference. Proceedings (Year). (US) **3667**

Technical Association of the Pulp and Paper Industry. Pulping Conference Proceedings (Year). (US ISSN 0275-0899) **3667**

Technical Association of the Pulp and Paper Industry, Inc. Journal see T A P P I Journal **3666**

Technical Association of the Pulp and Paper Industry, Inc. Proceedings see T A P P I Proceedings **3666**

Technical Association of the Pulp and Paper Industry, Inc. Test Methods see T A P P I Test Methods **3666**

Technical Brief. (US ISSN 1053-8860) **4640**

Technical Budget Representations. (UK) **801**

Technical Bulletin - Department of Natural Resources (Madison) see Wisconsin. Department of Natural Resources. Technical Bulletin **1501**

Technical Ceramics Bulletin see Technical Ceramics International **1837**

Technical Ceramics International. (UK) **1837**, 1166

Technical Choice. see Techniki Eklogi **1909**

†Technical Co-operation. (UK ISSN 0040-0904) **5287**

Technical Communication. (US ISSN 0049-3155) **1343**, 2576, 4006

Technical Communication Quarterly. (US) **1761**

Technical Computing. (US) **1401**

Technical Conference on Artifical Insemination and Reproduction. (US) **204**, 227

Technical Conference Proceedings - Irrigation Association see Irrigation Association. Technical Conference Proceedings **181**

Technical Data Series. see Kisho-Cho Kansoku Gijutsu Shiryo **3438**

Technical Diagnostics and Nondestructive Testing. (English translation of: Tekhnicheskaya Diagnostika i Nerazrushayushchii Kontrol') (UK) **3430**

Technical Diagnostics and Nondestructive Testing in Welding see Technical Diagnostics and Nondestructive Testing **3430**

Technical Economic Digest. see Muszaki-Gazdasagi Magazin **729**

Technical Education Abstracts. (UK ISSN 0040-0920) **1680**, 24, 1846, 4615

Technical Education News. (US ISSN 0146-0137) **1761**

Technical Export News. (UK ISSN 0140-4474) **1029**

†Technical Film Cards - International Selection. (HU ISSN 0138-9157) **5287**

Technical Further Education Adult Literacy Tutors' Newsletter see T A F E - Adult Literacy Tutors' Newsletter **1687**

Technical Guide Book of Screen Printing. (US) **4006**

Technical Highlights from Overseas see Kaigai Gijutsu Hairaito **4602**

†Technical Information. (GW) **5287**

Technical Information Digest. (II) **3496**

Technical Information for Industry see T.I **4610**

Technical Journal. see Teknik Dergi **1875**

Technical Journal of the University of Dacca's Ahsanullah Engineering College see Bangladesh University of Engineering and Technology, Dhaka. Technical Journal **1815**

Technical News. see Technicke Noviny **4610**

Technical Papers for the Bible Translator. (US ISSN 0260-0935) **2847**, 4205

Technical Papers in Hydrology Series. (UN ISSN 0082-2310) **1600**

Technical Papers - U.S. Department of Commerce, Bureau of the Census see U.S. Bureau of the Census. Technical Papers **4591**

†Technical Photography. (US ISSN 0040-0971) **5287**

Technical Product Update. (DK ISSN 0900-3762) **1455**

Technical Report of Kirin. (JA) **386**

Technical Research Centre of Finland. Publications see V T T Publications **4350**

Technical Review. Middle East. (UK ISSN 0267-5307) **4610**, 694

Technical Service Data (Automotive) see Technical Service Data (Cars) **4703**

Technical Service Data (Cars). (UK) **4703**

Technical Service Data (Heavy Commercial Vehicles). (UK) **4703**

Technical Service Data (Light Commercial Vehicles). (UK) **4703**

Technical Services Quarterly. (US ISSN 0731-7131) **2787**

Technical Session on Cane Sugar Refining Research. Proceedings see Sugar Processing Research Conference. Proceedings **122**

Technical Soaring. (US) **63**

Technical Stock Advisory Service. (US) **966**

Technical Study - U.S. Civil Service Commission. Personnel Research and Development Center see U.S. Civil Service Commission. Personnel Research and Development Center. Technical Study **5295**

Technical Support. (US ISSN 1052-2581) **1432**

▼Technical Textiles International. (UK ISSN 0964-5993) **4624**, 3868

Technical, Trade & Business School Data Handbook. (US) **1697**

Technical Trends. (US ISSN 0889-9525) **966**

Technical Trends. (GW) **4610**

Technical University Librarian. see Muszaki Egyetemi Konyvtaros **2774**

Technical University of Denmark. Acoustics Laboratory Report. (DK ISSN 0105-3027) **3860**

Technical University of Denmark. Institute of Mathematical Statistics and Operations Research. Research Reports. (DK ISSN 0107-3826) **4590**, 3058

Technical University of Denmark. Institute of Roads, Transport and Town Planning. Paper. see Danmarks Tekniske Hoejskole. Institutet for Veje, Trafik og Byplan. Notat **4718**

Technical University of Denmark. Institute of Roads, Transport and Town Planning. Papers and Reports. (DK ISSN 0105-5119) **4721**

Technical University of Denmark. Institute of Roads, Transport and Town Planning. Report. (DK) **4721**, 2496

▼Technical University of Kosice. Transactions. (UK ISSN 0960-6076) **4347**

Technical Writing Teacher see Technical Communication Quarterly **1761**

Technicalities. (US ISSN 0272-0884) **2787**

Technicar see Car **4686**

Technicien du Film et de la Video. (FR) **3518**, 1386

Technicka Knihovna see I'91 **2765**

Technicka Praca/Engineering. (CS ISSN 0040-1056) **1837**

Technicke Noviny/Technical News. (CS) **4610**

Technicky Tydenik. (CS ISSN 0040-1064) **4610**, 2590

Techniek in de Gezondheidszorg. (NE ISSN 0169-622X) **3156**

Technik am Bau see T A B **2304**

Technik aus Finnland. (FI ISSN 0359-7008) **922**

Technik Heute. (GW) **4610**

Technik Report. (AU) **1939**

Technik und Gesellschaft. (GW) **4610**, 4454

Technik Wlokienniczy see Przeglad Wlokienniczy plus Technik Wlokienniczy **4622**

Technika. (HU ISSN 0040-1110) **413**

Technika Chronika/Annales Techniques.(GR ISSN 0040-4764) **4347**, 4610

Technika i Gospodarka Morska. (PL ISSN 0040-1137) **4740**, 2049

Technika Lotnicza i Astronautyczna. (PL ISSN 0040-1145) **63**

Technika Motoryzacyjna see Auto-Technika Motoryzacyjna **4594**

Technika Poszukiwan Geologicznych see Technika Poszukiwan Geologicznych, Geosynoptyka i Goetermia **1582**

Technika Poszukiwan Geologicznych, Geosynoptyka i Goetermia/Exploration Technology, Geosynoptics and Geothermal Energy. (PL) **1582**, 1595, 3496

Techniki Eklogi/Technical Choice. (GR) **1909**

Technikon Forum. (SA) **1717**

†Technikus. (GW ISSN 0497-0594) **5287**

Technine Kibernetika/Tekhnicheskaya Kibernetika. (LI) **1443**

Technion - Israel Institute of Technology. Abstracts of Research Theses. (IS ISSN 0792-7355) **1680**, 1717

Technion - Israel Institute of Technology. Faculty of Agricultural Engineering. Publications. (IS ISSN 0333-5879) **123**

Technion - Israel Institute of Technology. President's Report. (IS) **4610**

Technion - Israel Institute of Technology. Research Reports. (IS ISSN 0792-0776) **634**

Technion - Israel Institute of Technology Report see T.A.E. Report **63**

Technion Magazine. (IS ISSN 0792-3244) **4610**

Technique. (US) **1326**

Technique. see Teknika **3496**

Technique & Management see Technisch Management **1837**

Technique Chaussure. (FR ISSN 0040-1196) **4362**

Technique du Roulement - Technique Industrielle. (GW ISSN 0934-926X) **1926**

Technique du Roulemont see Technique du Roulement - Technique Industrielle **1926**

Technique et Biologie. (FR ISSN 0766-5725) **3263**, 457

Technique Moderne. (FR ISSN 0040-1250) **4610**

Technique of Self-Defense. see Bo Ji **4466**

Technique Tennis de Table. see Table Tennis Technical **5287**

Techniques and Applications in Organic Synthesis Series. (US ISSN 0082-2418) **1223**, 1231

Techniques and Instrumentation in Analytical Chemistry. (NE) **1209**

Techniques d'Aujourd'Hui. (FR ISSN 0082-2469) **4610**

Techniques de Presse see Newspaper Techniques **4002**

Techniques Economiques see Tertiaire **898**

Techniques et Architecture. (FR) **307**

Techniques et Developpement see Actuel Developpement **925**

Techniques et Equipments de Production. (FR) **3421**

▼Techniques Forestieres. (FR) **2109**, 2117

Techniques Hospitalieres, Medico-Sociales et Sanitaires. (FR ISSN 0040-1374) **2469**, 4113

Techniques in Marine Environmental Sciences. (DK ISSN 0903-2606) **1969**, 1189

Techniques in Orthopaedics. (US ISSN 0885-9698) **3311**

▼Techniques in Protein Chemistry. (US) **1223**

†Techniques in Pure and Applied Microbiology. (US ISSN 0082-2515) **5287**

Techniques Industrielles see Technologie **1761**

Techniques Industrielles du Japon. (JA) 4610
Techniques of Chemistry. (US ISSN 0082-2531) 1189, 3263
Techniques of Measurement in Medicine Series. (UK) 3263
Techniques of Physics. (US) 3833
Techniere of Refrigeration and Air Conditioning see Refrigeration 2302
Techniques Orthopediques. (FR ISSN 0397-3999) 3312
Techniques - Sciences - Methodes. Genie Urbain Rural. (FR ISSN 0299-7258) 4095, 4113, 4828
Technisch Film Centrum Nieuws see T F C Nieuws 3518
Technisch Fysische Dienst T N O - T H. Jaarverslag. (NE) 3833
Technisch Management. (BE ISSN 0774-4056) 1837
†Technisch-Oekonomische Information der Zivilen Luchtfahrt. (GW) 5288
†Technische Beitraege zur Archaeologie.(GW ISSN 0067-4974) 5288
†Technische Hochschule Carl Schorlemmer Leuna-Merseburg. Wissenschaftliche Zeitschrift. (GW ISSN 0323-5270) 5288
†Technische Hochschule Ilmenau. Wissenschaftliche Zeitschrift. (GW ISSN 0043-6917) 5288
Technische Hochschule Karl-Marx-Stadt. Wissenschaftliche Schriftenreihe. (GW) 1909
Technische Hochschule Karl-Marx-Stadt. Wissenschaftliche Zeitschrift. (GW ISSN 0372-7610) 1837
Technische Hochschule Wien. Dissertationen see Technische Universitaet Wien. Dissertationen 1837
Technische Hogeschool Eindhoven. Onderafdeling der Wiskunde en Informatica. E U T Reports - W S K see Technische Universiteit Eindhoven. Faculteit der Wiskunde en Informatica. E U T Reports - W S K 3058
Technische Hogeschool te Delft. Bibliotheek. Aanwinsten see Technische Universiteit te Delft. Bibliotheek. Aanwinsten 4358
Technische Hogeschool te Delft. Bibliotheek. Lijst van Lopende Tijdschriftabonnementen see Technische Universiteit te Delft. Bibliotheek. Lijst van Lopende Tijdschriftabonnementen 1837
†Technische Information Armaturen. (GW ISSN 0040-1420) 5288
Technische Kulturdenkmale. (GW ISSN 0344-9068) 307
Technische Mechanik. (GW ISSN 0232-3869) 1837, 3845
Technische Mitteilungen. (GW ISSN 0040-1439) 3421
Technische Mitteilungen fuer Sappeure, Pontoniere und Mineure. (SZ) 3472, 1875
Technische Mitteilungen Krupp. (GW ISSN 0494-9390) 4610, 1939, 3421
Technische Physik in Einzeldarstellungen. (US ISSN 0082-2590) 3833
Technische Revue. (NE) 4610
Technische Revue. (GW) 4610, 3023
Technische Rundschau. (SZ ISSN 0040-148X) 4610
Technische Universitaet Berlin. Institut fuer Sozialoekonomie der Agrarentwicklung. Jahresbericht see Technische Universitaet Berlin. Institut fuer Sozialoekonomie der Agrarentwicklung. Schriftenreihe des Fachbereichs 158
Technische Universitaet Berlin. Institut fuer Sozialoekonomie der Agrarentwicklung. Schriftenreihe des Fachbereichs. (GW ISSN 0177-6673) 158, 123
Technische Universitaet Berlin Intern see T U Intern 1326
Technische Universitaet Braunschweig. Berichtsband. Forschung see Technische Universitaet Braunschweig. Forschungsbericht 1717

Technische Universitaet Braunschweig. Forschungsbericht. (GW) 1717
Technische Universitaet Braunschweig. Pharmaziegeschichtlichen Seminar. Veroeffentlichungen see Braunschweiger Veroeffentlichungen zur Geschichte der Pharmazie und Naturwissenschaften 3719
Technische Universitaet Braunschweig. Universitaetsbibliothek. Veroeffentlichungen. (GW) 1717, 2787
Technische Universitaet Clausthal. Mitteilungsblatt. (GW ISSN 0040-1501) 3496
Technische Universitaet Dresden. Wissenschaftliche Zeitschrift. (GW ISSN 0043-6925) 4610
Technische Universitaet Hannover. Astronomischer Station. (Veroeffentlichungen) see Universitaet Hannover. Astronomischen Station. (Veroeffentlichungen) 370
Technische Universitaet Hannover. Franzius - Institut fuer Wasserbau und Kuesteningenieurwesen. Mitteilungen see Franzius - Institut fuer Wasserbau und Kuesteningenierurwesen. Mitteilungen 1923
Technische Universitaet Hannover. Institut fuer Siedlungswasserwirtschaft. Veroeffentlichungen see Universitaet Hannover. Institut fuer Siedlungswasserwirtschaft. Veroeffentlichungen 4829
Technische Universitaet Hannover. Institut fuer Statik. Mitteilungen see Universitaet Hannover. Institut fuer Statik. Mitteilungen 1923
Technische Universitaet Hannover. Lehrstuhl fuer Stahlbau. Schriftenreihe see Universitaet Hannover. Institut fuer Stahlbau. Schriftenreihe 1922
Technische Universitaet Muenchen. Institut fuer Wirtschaftslehre des Gartenbaues. Forschungsberichte zur Oekonomie in Gartenbau. (GW) 2139
Technische Universitaet Muenchen. Jahrbuch. (GW ISSN 0077-2089) 4610, 1717
Technische Universitaet Otto von Guericke. Wissenschaftliche Zeitschrift. (GW ISSN 0863-0925) 4610
Technische Universitaet Wien. Dissertationen. (AU ISSN 0259-0697) 1837
Technische Universitaet Wien. Institut fuer Eisenbahnwesen. Arbeiten. (AU) 4715
Technische Universitaet Wien. Institut fuer Eisenbahnwesen, Spezialbahnen und Verkehrswirtschaft. Arbeiten see Technische Universitaet Wien. Institut fuer Eisenbahnwesen. Arbeiten 4715
Technische Universiteit Eindhoven. Faculteit der Wiskunde en Informatica. E U T Reports - W S K. (NE) 3058
Technische Universiteit te Delft. Bibliotheek. Aanwinsten. (NE) 4358, 24
Technische Universiteit te Delft. Bibliotheek. Lijst van Lopende Tijdschriftabonnementen. (NE) 1837
Technische Vereinigung der Grosskraftwerksbetreiber e.V. Kraftwerkstechnik, see V G B Kraftwerkstechnik 1910
Technischen Hochschule Zwickau. Wissenschaftliche Zeitschrift. (GW ISSN 0323-6927) 4347
Technischer Handel. (GW ISSN 0040-1552) 4610
Technisches Messen - A T M see Technisches Messen - T M 2525
Technisches Messen - T M. (GW ISSN 0171-8096) 2525
Technisches Textil Forum. (GW) 4624
Technivisie/Tecnopole. (BE ISSN 0771-4025) 1939, 694, 1410
Techno Japan. (JA) 1085
Techno-Loisirs. (FR) 4494

†Techno-Tip. (GW ISSN 0341-5570) 5288
Technobrief. (SA ISSN 1017-4966) 4347
Technocracy. Information Briefs. (US) 4347
Technocracy Digest. (US ISSN 0040-1587) 4390
Technocrat see Techno Japan 1085
Technologia. (BE ISSN 0771-6826) 4610, 4347
Technological Assistance Program see T A P 3014
Technological Forecasting and Social Change. (US ISSN 0040-1625) 4610, 4454
Technological Horizons in Education Journal see T.H.E. Journal 1691
Technological Marketplace: Supply and Demand for Scientists and Engineers.(US) 3631
Technological Society of Starch. Journal see Japanese Society of Starch Science. Journal 2074
Technologie. (FR ISSN 0768-9454) 1761
Technologie Chimiche. (IT ISSN 0392-3452) 1860
Technologie Manager see Technologie und Management 4611
Technologie-Nachrichten - Management-Informationen. (GW ISSN 0344-9696) 1029, 4610
Technologie-Nachrichten - Programm-Informationen. (GW ISSN 0344-9750) 4611
Technologie und Management. (GW ISSN 0932-2558) 4611, 1029
Technologies. (CN) 1352
Technologies. (IS ISSN 0333-9521) 4611
Technologies. (FR) 4611
Technologies de l'Information et Societe.(CN) 4611
Technologies et Formations. (FR) 4611
Technologist. (US) 4611
Technology Alert. (US ISSN 1054-4267) 4611
Technology Alert and Technology Alert Database Reports see Technology Alert 4611
Technology Analysis & Strategic Management. (UK ISSN 0953-7325) 4611, 1029
Technology and Conservation. (US ISSN 0146-1214) 346, 307
Technology and Culture. (US ISSN 0040-165X) 4611, 2324
▼Technology and Disability. (US ISSN 1055-4181) 2284, 1742
Technology and Learning. (US ISSN 1053-6728) 1691, 1417
†Technology and Learning. (US ISSN 0890-7889) 5288
Technology and People see Information Technology and People 2798
Technology and Science of Informatics. (UK ISSN 0264-7419) 1401
Technology Book Guide see Bibliographic Guide to Technology 392
Technology Design Education. (AT ISSN 1034-6902) 1761
Technology Education Activity Forum. (US) 1761, 694
Technology Focus Newsletter. (CN) 3496
Technology for Anesthesia. (US ISSN 8756-8578) 3192
Technology for Cardiology. (US ISSN 8756-8586) 3212
Technology for Critical Care Nurses. (US ISSN 1055-9620) 3287
Technology for Emergency Care Nurses.(US) 3287
Technology for Emergency Medicine see Technology for Emergency Care Nurses 3287
Technology for Imaging & Radiology. (US ISSN 0892-7340) 3363
Technology for Laboratory Medicine. (US ISSN 0892-7332) 3156
Technology for Materials Management. (US ISSN 8756-8608) 3156
Technology for Nursing see Technology for Critical Care Nurses 3287
Technology for Respiratory Therapy. (US ISSN 8756-8616) 3367

Technology for Surgery. (US ISSN 8756-8624) 3385
Technology Forecasts & Technology Surveys. (US) 4611
†Technology Graduate. (UK) 5288
Technology Highlight. see Kaigai Gijutsu Hairaito 4602
Technology in Society. (US ISSN 0160-791X) 4454
Technology, Innovation and Entrepreneurship for Students see T I E S 4610
Technology Ireland. (IE ISSN 0040-1676) 4611
Technology Management Action. (US ISSN 0886-103X) 922
Technology N Y Newsletter see Technology N Y Report 4611
Technology N Y Report. (US ISSN 1058-2282) 4611
Technology of Meters and Instruments. see Yibiao Jishu 2525
†Technology on Campus. (US) 5288
†Technology Reimbursement Reports: The Beige Sheet. (US ISSN 0882-2611) 5288
Technology Resource Guide. (US) 1154, 4611
Technology Review. (IT) 1837
Technology Review. (US ISSN 0040-1692) 4347, 4611
Technology Survey see Technology Update (Cleveland) 4611
Technology Teacher. (US ISSN 0746-3537) 4611, 1667
Technology Today. (US) 4347
Technology Today. (CN ISSN 0712-9467) 4611
Technology Transfer Action see Technology Management Action 922
Technology Transfer Directory. (US) 1154, 2787
Technology Transfer Society. International Symposium Proceedings. (US) 1029, 922, 4611
Technology Trends Newsletter see Semiconductor Economics Report 5275
Technology Update (Cleveland). (US ISSN 0732-5533) 4611
Technology Update (Palo Alto). (US ISSN 0896-8586) 2296
Technology Watch. (US) 1423, 352
Technomark Register. Contract Research Organisations. (UK) 3156, 3744
Technometrics. (US ISSN 0040-1706) 1838
Technonet Asia Newsletter and Digest. (SI ISSN 0217-247X) 935
Technopolis. (JA) 1909
Technopress Bau Magazin. (AU) 634
Technos. (US ISSN 1060-5649) 1691, 1382, 1761
Technotes see TechNotes - dBASE IV 1432
Technotes see TechNotes - Framework III 1432
TechNotes - dBASE IV. (US ISSN 1047-1367) 1432, 1481
TechNotes - Framework III. (US ISSN 1047-1375) 1432, 1481
TechNotes - Graphics. (US ISSN 1047-1383) 1423
TechNotes - Word Publishing. (US ISSN 1047-1391) 1481
TechnoTrend. (LH) 966
Technova. (HK) 4611, 634, 2083
Technovation. (UK ISSN 0166-4972) 4611
Techpak. (US ISSN 0892-7146) 3652
Techquad. (AT) 694
▼TechScan Newsletter. (US ISSN 1054-979X) 828, 1352
TechTrends. (US ISSN 8756-3894) 1762, 1691, 3518
Techumim. (IS ISSN 0333-6883) 4226, 4611
Tecnica. (PO ISSN 0040-1714) 1838
Tecnica Calzaturiera. (IT) 4362
Tecnica Ceramica. (SP ISSN 0211-7290) 1166
Tecnica de la Regulacion y Mando Automatico see Automatica e Instrumentacion 1411

TECNICA

Tecnica de los Rodamientos see Tecnica de los Rodamientos - Tecnica Industrial **1926**
Tecnica de los Rodamientos - Tecnica Industrial. (GW ISSN 0934-9278) **1926**
Tecnica del Calzado. (SP) **4362**
Tecnica del Frio y del Calor. (AG ISSN 0040-1730) **2304**
Tecnica del Punto see Revista Tecnica de la Industria de Generos de Punto **1287**
Tecnica dell'Automobile. (IT) **4703**
Tecnica della Scuola. (IT) **1732**
Tecnica e Industria. (AG ISSN 0040-1781) **4611, 1838, 3023**
Tecnica e Invencion. (SP ISSN 0040-179X) **3678**
Tecnica e Ricostruzione. (IT ISSN 0040-1803) **634**
Tecnica en Agricultura y Ganaderia. (MX) **194, 227**
Tecnica Grafica. (CU) **4006**
Tecnica Grafica. Suplemento. (CU) **4006**
Tecnica Molitoria. (IT ISSN 0040-1862) **208, 2083**
Tecnica Ospedaliera. (IT ISSN 0392-4831) **2469**
Tecnica Pecuaria en Mexico. (MX ISSN 0040-1889) **227**
†Tecnica Pesquera. (MX ISSN 0304-2499) **5288**
Tecnica Popular. (CU ISSN 0138-8800) **3845**
Tecnica Professionale. (IT) **4715**
Tecnica Sanitaria. (IT ISSN 0040-1897) **4113**
Tecnica Textil Internacional. (SP ISSN 0040-1900) **4624**
Tecnica Topografica. (SP ISSN 0210-282X) **1838**
Tecnicas de Laboratorio. (SP ISSN 0371-5728) **3263**
Tecniche dell'Automazione e Robotica. (IT ISSN 0040-1927) **1416, 1410**
Tecniche dell'Imballaggio. (IT) **3652**
Tecnicouro. (BL ISSN 0101-1138) **2738**
Tecno Hotel. (SP) **2480**
†Tecno Show. (IT ISSN 0393-8204) **5288**
Tecno 2000. (SP ISSN 0213-7488) **4611, 3023**
Tecnologia Alimentaria. (AG ISSN 0040-1943) **2083**
Tecnologia de Alimentos. (MX ISSN 0564-6758) **2083**
Tecnologia del Agua. (SP ISSN 0211-8173) **4828**
Tecnologia del Plastico. (US ISSN 0120-7644) **3868**
Tecnologia della Deformazione. (IT) **3024, 1939, 3421**
Tecnologia en Marcha. (CR ISSN 0379-3982) **4611**
Tecnologia Militar. (GW) **3472**
Tecnologia Quimica. (CU ISSN 0253-9276) **1189**
Tecnologica. (EC ISSN 0257-1749) **4611**
Tecnologie dei Servizi Pubblici. (IT) **4075**
Tecnologie del Filo. (IT ISSN 0392-7954) **3421**
Tecnologie Elettriche. (IT ISSN 0390-6698) **1909**
Tecnologie Elettriche International. (IT ISSN 0392-3460) **1909**
Tecnologie Meccaniche. (IT ISSN 0391-1683) **3422, 1939**
Tecnologie Meccaniche International. (IT ISSN 0392-3487) **1940**
Tecnologie Tessili. (IT ISSN 0394-5413) **4624**
Tecnometal. (PO) **3422**
Tecnorest. (IT) **2480**
El Tecolote. (US) **2026**
Tectonics. (US ISSN 0278-7407) **1595**
Tectonophysics. (NE ISSN 0040-1951) **1595**
Ted Aktiv. (GW) **1267**
Teddy. (GW ISSN 0342-7161) **1267**
Teddy Bear and Friends. (US ISSN 0745-7189) **2442**
Teddy Bear Review. (US ISSN 0890-4162) **2442**
Teddy Tribune. (US) **2442**
Teden Bozje Besede. (XV) **4276**
Tednik. (XV ISSN 0040-1978) **2886**
Teeline. (UK) **1762, 898**
Teen. (US ISSN 0040-2001) **1267**
Teen and Twenty. (NR) **1267**
†Teen Bag. (US ISSN 0731-9991) **5288**
Teen Beat. (US) **1267, 3584**
Teen Generation see T G - Voices of Today's Generation **1267**
Teen Idol Mania. (US) **1267**
Teen Machine. (US) **1267**
†Teen Pin-Ups. (US ISSN 0040-201X) **5288**
Teen Power (1979). (US) **1267, 4205**
Teen Quest see T Q **1267**
Teen Scene. (US) **1267**
Teen-Search. (UK ISSN 0142-5943) **4205, 1762**
Teen Set. (US ISSN 1058-9856) **1267**
Teen Time see SpiritQuest **5282**
Teen Time (Large Print Edition). (US) **1267, 2296, 4250**
Teen Times. (US) **1267, 2449**
†Teenage. (US ISSN 1042-7953) **5288**
▼Teenage Mutant Ninja Turtles Magazine. (US) **1267**
Teenager International. (MX) **1268**
†Teens Today. (US) **5288**
Teens Today (Kansas City). (US) **1268**
Tees and Hartlepool Ports. (UK ISSN 0265-1181) **4740, 1154**
▼Tees Valley Writer. (UK ISSN 0959-7808) **2576**
Teeswater Sheep Breeders' Association. Annual Flock Book. (UK) **227**
Tegen de Tuberculose. (NE ISSN 0040-2125) **3367**
Tegenwoordig. (NE ISSN 0040-2133) **4205**
Tegl. (DK ISSN 0040-2141) **634, 307**
Tegniek. (SA) **694**
Tehnicka Fizika/Journal of Engineering Physics. (YU ISSN 0350-0594) **3833, 1838**
Tehnicke Novine. (YU) **1245, 4611**
Tehnika. (YU ISSN 0350-2597) **1838, 1809**
Tehnium. (RM) **4347, 2442**
Tehnologija Mesa/Meat Technology. (YU ISSN 0494-9846) **227, 2083, 4113**
Teho A. (FI ISSN 0355-0567) **123, 2109**
Teho B. (FI ISSN 0355-2527) **2449**
Tehuda/Resonance. (IS) **3833**
Tehy. (FI ISSN 0358-4038) **3287**
Teilhard Review and Journal of Cosmic Convergence. (UK) **4205, 3783**
Teilhard Review and Journal of Creative Evolution see Teilhard Review and Journal of Cosmic Convergence **4205**
Teilhardian Studies. see Etudes Teilhardiennes **4176**
Teilzahlungswirtschaft see F L F **1093**
Teiresias. (CN ISSN 0381-9361) **1280**
Teka Komisji Historii Sztuki see Towarzystwo Naukowe w Toruniu. Komisja Historii Sztuki. Teka **347**
Tekawennake. (CN ISSN 0300-3159) **2026**
▼Tekeli - li! Journal of Terror. (US) **3014**
Tekens van Die Tye. see Signs of the Times **5277**
Tekhniceska Misal. (BU ISSN 0040-2168) **1838**
Tekhnicheskaya Diagnostika i Nerazrushayushchii Kontrol' (KR) **4347**
Tekhnicheskaya Elektrodinamika. (KR ISSN 0204-3599) **1909**
Tekhnicheskaya Estetika. (RU ISSN 0040-2230) **346**
Tekhnicheskaya Kibernetika. see Technine Kibernetika **1443**
Tekhnicheskii Progress i Effektivnost' Proizvodstva. (KR ISSN 0233-9897) **1085**
Tekhnika Kino i Televideniya. (RU ISSN 0040-2249) **1382, 3518**
Tekhnika Molodezhi. (RU ISSN 0040-2257) **4611, 1268**
Tekhnika v Sel'skom Khozyaistve. (RU ISSN 0131-7105) **164, 3024**
Teki Historyczne. (UK ISSN 0085-4956) **2391**
Tekko Rodo Eisei/Journal of Labor Hygiene in Iron and Steel Industry. (JA ISSN 0040-2273) **3422**
Tekniikan Maailma. (FI ISSN 0355-4287) **4612**
Tekniikka see Tekniikka & Talous **4612**
Tekniikka & Talous/Ingenjoersnytt. (FI ISSN 0785-997X) **4612**
▼Teknik Dergi/Technical Journal. (TU) **1875**
Teknik i Jordskog see Lantmannen **105**
Teknik og Miljoe see Energy - Teknik & Miljoe **5186**
Teknik-Samfund. (DK ISSN 0108-3562) **4612**
Teknik ve Uygulama. (TU) **1940**
Teknika/Technique. (AA) **3496**
†Teknikk og Miljoe. (NO ISSN 0332-5938) **5288**
Teknil foer Alla. (SW) **2442**
Teknisk Landsforbund Teknikeren see T L - Teknikeren **4610**
Teknisk Nyt. (DK ISSN 0040-232X) **1838**
Teknisk Nyts Leverandoerregister. (DK) **1838**
Teknisk Skoletidende see D T L - Nyt **1624**
Teknisk Tidskrift see Ny Teknik **1832**
Teknisk Ukeblad. (NO) **1838**
Teknisk Ukeblad Data see Datatid **1394**
Tekniska Nomenklaturcentralen Aktuellt see T N C - Aktuellt **2847**
Tekniskt Forum see Forum foer Ekonomi och Teknik **1076**
Teknologi. (MY) **4612, 1909**
Teknologi og Effektivitet. (DK ISSN 0107-3761) **4612**
Teksi. (FI ISSN 0355-7898) **4624, 1294**
Tekster fra I M F U F A. (Institut for Studiet af Matematik og Fysik Samt Deres Funktioner i Undervisning Forskning og Anvendelse) (DK ISSN 0106-6242) **3058, 3833**
Tekstiilikauppias see Teksi **4624**
Tekstiililehti. (FI ISSN 0040-2370) **4624**
Tekstiiliopettaja/Textillaren. (FI ISSN 0355-8991) **2449, 1667**
Tekstil. (CI ISSN 0492-5882) **4624**
Tekstil ve Makina see Tekstil ve Muhendis **4624**
Tekstil ve Muhendis. (TU) **4624**
Tekstilec. (XV ISSN 0351-3386) **4624, 4347**
Tekstilforum. (NO) **4624, 1294**
Tekstilna Industrija. (YU ISSN 0040-2389) **4624**
Tekstilna Promishlenost. (BU) **4624**
Tekstil'naya Promyshlennost' (RU ISSN 0040-2397) **4624**
Teksty see Teksty Drugie **2968**
Teksty Drugie. (PL ISSN 0867-0633) **2968**
Tektonika i Stratigrafiya. (KR ISSN 0375-7773) **1582**
Tel Aviv Journal of Archaeology. (IS ISSN 0334-4355) **287, 3644**
Tel Aviv Review. (IS ISSN 0792-1683) **2968**
Tel Aviv University. David Horowitz Institute for the Research of Developing Countries. Annual Report.(IS) **3973**
Tel Aviv University. David Horowitz Institute for the Research of Developing Countries. Research Reports and Papers. (IS) **3973**
Tel Aviv University. Faculty of the Humanities and Social Sciences. Yidion. (IS) **2516, 4422**
Tel Aviv University. Institut fuer Deutsche Geschichte. Jahrbuch. (IS) **2391**
Tel Aviv University. Law Review/Iyunei Mishpat. (IS) **2684**
†Tel Aviv University. Ph.D. Degrees and Abstracts. (IS) **5288**
Tel Aviv University. Wiener Library. Bibliography of New Acquisitions. (IS) **413**
Tel Aviv - Yafo. Center for Economic and Social Research. Research and Surveys Series/Tel Aviv - Yafo. Ha-Merkaz le-Mekhkar Kalkali ve-Khevrati. Mekhkarim ve-Sekarim. (IS ISSN 0792-0601) **4454**
Tel Aviv - Yafo. Center for Economic and Social Research. Statistical Yearbook. (IS ISSN 0792-0598) **4458**
Tel Aviv - Yafo. Ha-Merkaz le-Mekhkar Kalkali ve-Khevrati. Mekhkarim ve-Sekarim. see Tel Aviv - Yafo. Center for Economic and Social Research. Research and Surveys Series **4454**
Tel Aviver Jahrbuch fuer Deutsche Geschichte. (GW ISSN 0932-8408) **2391**
Tel-Com D V und Orga-Brief. (GW) **1062, 828, 1343**
Tel Quel. (FR ISSN 0040-2419) **4347, 3783**
Telcom-Brief see Tel-Com D V und Orga-Brief **1062**
Telcom Highlights International. (US) **1382**
Telcom Report International. (GW ISSN 0344-4880) **1343**
Tele (English Edition). (SW ISSN 0495-0127) **1343**
Tele (Swedish Edition). (SW ISSN 0040-2427) **1343**
Tele-Achat. (FR) **1909**
Tele-Africa Revue/Revue Tele-Africa. (GW) **2335**
Tele-Communications Association. Technical Bulletin. (US) **1343**
Tele Horaire (Montreal). (CN) **1382**
Tele Horaire (Quebec). (CN) **1382**
Tele - Magazine. (FR) **1382**
Tele-Magazine le Soleil. (CN) **1382**
Tele - Poche. (FR) **1382**
Tele Presse. (CN ISSN 0049-3252) **1382**
Tele-Satellit. (GW ISSN 0931-4733) **1382, 694**
†Tele-Scope. (US) **5288**
Tele-Scope Magazine - T.V. World - Satellite Dish Guide. (CN) **1382**
▼Tele-Service News. (US) **1366**
Tele Tjenesten. (NO) **2590, 1343**
Tele Viewing. (US) **1382**
Tele 7 Jours. (FR) **1382**
Tele 7 Jours Reunion. (RE) **1382**
▼Telecom. (IT) **1366**
Telecom Australia. Annual Report. (AT) **1343**
Telecom Bulletin see Clarkson, Tetrault Regulatory Reporter - Telecom **1333**
Telecom Calendar. (US ISSN 1057-6002) **1343**
Telecom Competition and Strategy see U S Telecommunications **1367**
Telecom Connections. (US) **1366, 413**
Telecom - Eye - Bee - Em. (US ISSN 0888-7292) **1343, 1352, 1401, 1433, 1465, 1474**
Telecom Gear. (US) **1366**
Telecom - I B M see Telecom - Eye - Bee - Em **1343**
Telecom Insider. (US ISSN 0742-6445) **1343**
†Telecom Manager. (US) **5288**
Telecom Market Letter. (US) **1366, 1055**
Telecom Markets. (UK ISSN 0267-1484) **1085, 1366**
Telecom Outlook. (US ISSN 1045-6562) **1055, 1366, 1447**
Telecom Report. (GW ISSN 0344-4724) **1366**
Telecom Report. (IE ISSN 0332-0197) **1366, 1447**
Telecom Resources. (US) **1366**
Telecom Strategy Letter. (US) **1366**
Telecom Today. (UK) **1366, 1352**
Telecommagazine. (NE) **1447, 1366**
†Telecommanager. (US) **5288**
Telecomms Abstracts. (UK ISSN 0957-4611) **1405**
Telecomms Profile see Telecomms Abstracts **1405**
†Telecommunicatie. (NE ISSN 0030-8382) **5288**

Telecommunication Authority of Singapore. Singapore Telecom Annual Report. (SI) **1366**
Telecommunication Authority of Singapore. Telecoms Annual Report *see* Telecommunication Authority of Singapore. Singapore Telecom Annual Report **1366**
Telecommunication Journal. (UN ISSN 0497-137X) **1343**
Telecommunication Journal of Australia.(AT ISSN 0040-2486) **1343**
Telecommunication Products Plus Technology *see* Networking Management **1447**
Telecommunication Statistics *see* Yearbook of Common Carrier Telecommunication Statistics **1346**
▼Telecommunication Systems. (SZ ISSN 1018-4864) **1366**
Telecommunication Technology. *see* Dianxin Jishu **1362**
Telecommunications. (FR) **1344**
Telecommunications. (AT) **1344, 1352**
Telecommunications. (Il ISSN 0497-1388) **1366**
Telecommunications (New York). (US) **1344**
Telecommunications (Norwood). (US ISSN 0040-2494) **1344**
†Telecommunications Abstracts. (US ISSN 0882-1429) **5288**
†Telecommunications Abstracts Annual. (US ISSN 0000-1252) **5288**
Telecommunications Alert. (US ISSN 0742-5384) **1349, 24**
Telecommunications and Radio Engineering. (English translation of: Elektrosvyaz i Radiotekhnika) (US ISSN 0040-2508) **1344, 1360**
†Telecommunications Counselor. (US ISSN 0735-388X) **5288**
Telecommunications Directory. (US ISSN 1055-8454) **1344, 1154, 1401, 4612**
Telecommunications Engineering. *see* Sdelovaci Technika **1365**
Telecommunications Exchange for the Deaf, Inc. Times *see* T E D I Times **2289**
†Telecommunications Fiche. (US) **5288**
Telecommunications Index *see* Telecommunications Abstracts Annual **5288**
Telecommunications Policy. (UK ISSN 0308-5961) **1344**
Telecommunications Product Review and C P E Strategies. (US) **1344**
Telecommunications Regulatory Monitor. (US) **1366, 2684**
▼Telecommunications Reporter. (AT) **1366, 2684**
Telecommunications Reports. (US ISSN 0163-9854) **1344**
Telecommunications Reports International. (US) **1344**
Telecommunications Science. *see* Dianxin Kexue **1334**
Telecommunications Sourcebook. (US ISSN 0730-9872) **1366**
Telecommunications Strategies. (AT) **1382, 1352, 1366**
†Telecommunications Surveys & Forecasts. (US) **5288**
Telecommunications Systems and Services Directory *see* Telecommunications Directory **1344**
Telecommunications Week. (US) **1344**
Telecommunications World. (US) **1366**
Telecommunicator. (US) **1366**
†TeleCommuting Report. (US) **5288**
Telecommuting Review: The Gordon Report. (US ISSN 8756-7431) **1070, 1401**
Telecoms International. (FR ISSN 0987-4119) **1344**
Telecoms Technical Quarterly. (CH ISSN 0258-0284) **1366**
Telecomunicazioni. (IT) **1344**
Teleconference Magazine. (US) **1762**
Teleconferencing Resources Directory *see* Video Register and Teleconferencing Resources Directory **1158**
Teleconnect. (US) **1366**
Telecran. (LU) **1382**

Telefax International. International Telefax Directory *see* J & W Telefax International. International Facsimile Directory **1363**
Telefilm Canada Annual Report. (CN) **3518**
Telefilm International Magazine *see* Television International Magazine **1383**
Teleflorist *see* Flowers **2142**
†Telegen Abstracts. (US ISSN 0000-118X) **5288**
†Telegen Abstracts Annual. (US) **5288**
†Telegen Fiche. (US) **5288**
Telegen Reporter *see* Telegen Abstracts **5288**
Telegen Reporter Annual *see* Telegen Abstracts Annual **5288**
Telegraph. (UK ISSN 0040-2575) **4740**
Telegraph Magazine. (UK) **2195**
Telegraph Sunday Magazine *see* Telegraph Magazine **2195**
Teleguia. (US) **1382**
†Teleguide. (CN ISSN 0049-3295) **5288**
Telejazz (Year). (SZ) **3584**
Telekom Praxis. (GW) **1909**
Telekommunikatie Visie. (NE) **1344**
Telekomunikace. (CS ISSN 0040-2591) **1367**
Telekomunikacije. (YU ISSN 0040-2605) **1367**
†Teleks. (YU ISSN 0350-7564) **5288**
Telektronikk. (NO ISSN 0085-7130) **1344**
Telem Utalmia. (IS) **4227**
Telema. (ZR) **4205**
Telemanagement. (CN) **1367**
Telemarketer. (US ISSN 8750-9067) **1055, 922, 1029, 1119**
Telemarketing. (US ISSN 0730-6156) **1344**
†Telemarketing Management. (US) **5288**
Telemarketing Update. (US ISSN 0736-167X) **1344, 1055**
†Telematica. (IT) **5288**
Telematics and Informatics. (US ISSN 0736-5853) **1344**
Telemedium. (US) **1382**
Telemim. (IS) **832**
Telenorma Nachrichten. (GW ISSN 0495-0216) **1367**
Telephone. *see* Puhelin **1365**
Telephone Angles *see* 411 Newsletter **1368**
Telephone Cost and Call Management *see* Telecommunications World **1366**
Telephone Echo *see* M T S Echo **1364**
Telephone Engineer and Management. (US ISSN 0040-263X) **1367**
Telephone Engineer & Management Directory. (US ISSN 0082-2655) **1367**
Telephone Engineer & Management Telecom Asia *see* T E & M's Telecom Asia **1366**
Telephone News. (US ISSN 0271-5430) **1367**
Telephone Organization of Thailand. Annual Report. (TH) **1367, 39**
Telephone Pioneer. (US) **1301, 4422**
Telephone Sales Excellence *see* Professional Telephone Selling **1050**
Telephone Sales Representative Hotline *see* T S R Hotline **1054**
Telephone Selling Report. (US ISSN 0882-1461) **1055, 1367**
Telephone Statistics *see* United States Telephone Association. Annual Statistical Volume **1367**
Telephony. (US ISSN 0040-2656) **1367**
Telephony's Directory & Buyers Guide for the Telecommunications Industry. (US) **1367**
Telephony's Directory & Buyer's Guide for the Telephone Industry *see* Telephony's Directory & Buyers Guide for the Telecommunications Industry **1367**
Telepiu' (IT) **1382**
Teleprograma. (SP ISSN 0040-2672) **1382**
Telepublishing Report. (US ISSN 0894-9581) **4138, 1367**

Telepulestudomanyi Kozlemenyek. (HU ISSN 0040-2680) **2497**
Telerama. (FR ISSN 0040-2699) **1382, 3518**
Telerate Bank Register (Year). (UK) **801**
Teleroman. (CN) **1382**
Telescacco Nuovo. (IT) **4494**
▼Telescope. (FR ISSN 1164-5679) **1762, 1382**
Telescope (Detroit). (US ISSN 0040-2702) **2424**
Telescope (Downsview). (CN) **1326**
Telescope (Tokyo). (JA) **307**
Telescope: Drama of the Skies *see* Sky and Telescope **369**
†Telescope Making. (US ISSN 0190-5570) **5288**
†Telescope Making Techniques. (US) **5288**
TeleServices Report *see* Information & Interactive Services Report **4143**
Telesis (Ottawa). (CN ISSN 0040-2710) **1367**
Telesis (Washington) *see* Crit **297**
Telesna Vychova Mladeze. (CS ISSN 0040-2729) **1762**
TeleSpan. (US ISSN 0743-2283) **1447, 1344, 1352**
TeleSpan's Business T V. (US ISSN 0896-3142) **694, 1382**
Telettra Review *see* Rivista Telettra Review (English Edition) **1379**
Televai Telegram *see* Security News (Los Angeles) **799**
Television (London, 1927). (UK ISSN 0308-454X) **1382**
Television (London, 1934). (UK ISSN 0032-647X) **1382**
Television Age *see* Television - Radio Age **1383**
Television and Cable Factbook. (US ISSN 0732-8648) **1382**
Television and Children *see* Television & Families **1382**
Television & Families. (US) **1382, 1245**
Television and Video Production *see* Television Producer **1383**
Television, Audio & Appliance Dealer. (US) **1382, 1055, 1779**
Television Broadcast. (US) **1383**
Television - Broadcast Communications *see* Television Broadcast **1383**
Television Contacts (Year). (US) **1383**
Television Digest with Consumer Electronics. (US ISSN 0497-1515) **1383, 1779**
▼Television Directors Guide. (US) **1154, 1383**
Television Index. (US ISSN 0739-5531) **1383**
Television International *see* T V I **5286**
Television International Magazine. (US) **1383**
Television Mail *see* Broadcast **1369**
Television Monthly. *see* Dianshi Yuekan **1372**
†Television Network Movies. (US) **5288**
Television News Index and Abstracts. (US ISSN 0085-7157) **1349, 1383**
Television Producer. (UK) **1383**
Television Quarterly. (US ISSN 0040-2796) **1383**
Television - Radio Age. (US ISSN 0040-277X) **1383, 1360**
Television Sponsors Directory. (US ISSN 0049-3317) **1154, 1383**
Television Sponsors Product Cross-Reference Directory *see* Television Sponsors Directory **1154**
†Television: the New Era. (UK) **5288**
Television Writers Guide. (US) **1154, 1383**
TeleVizier. (NE ISSN 0049-3325) **1383**
Televiziia. Radio. (BU ISSN 0205-1281) **1383, 1360**
Telewoman. (US) **2968, 2457, 4853**
Telex and Teletex International. International Telex and Teletex Directory *see* J & W Telex International. International Telex and Teletex Directory **1363**

TEMM POETRY 6723

Telex Danmark/Annuaire des Abonnes Telex du Danemark. (DK ISSN 0109-8071) **1367**
Telex und Travel International *see* J & W Travel International **1363**
Telexbog Danmark *see* Telex Danmark **1367**
Telford Business Directory. (UK ISSN 0957-1116) **1154**
Telhan Patrika/Oilseeds Journal. (Il ISSN 0040-2818) **1223, 123**
Telicom. (US) **3784, 2968**
Teljan Tanhuvilta. (FI) **2392**
Tell. (AT ISSN 1030-8768) **1268**
Tell. (US) **3758**
Teller Vision. (US ISSN 0895-1039) **801**
Teller's Marketing Bulletin *see* Bank Teller's Report **765**
Tellington-Jones Equine Awareness Method Club Newsletter *see* T E A M Club Newsletter **4538**
Telluride Newsletter. (US) **1326**
Tellus. Series A: Dynamic Meteorology and Oceanography. (DK ISSN 0280-6495) **1595**
Tellus. Series B: Chemical and Physical Meteorology. (DK ISSN 0280-6509) **1596**
Telma. (GW ISSN 0340-4927) **123, 519**
Telocator. (US) **1383, 1367**
Telocator. Bulletin. (US) **1344**
Telonde *see* Thomson Magazine **1447**
Telopea. (AT ISSN 0312-9764) **519**
Telos. (US ISSN 0090-6514) **3784**
Telovychovny Pracovnik. (CS ISSN 0040-2850) **1762, 4494**
Tels Press. (JA) **2968**
Telugu Akademi Language Monograph Series. (Il) **2847**
Tema. (CN ISSN 0381-9582) **2847, 1762**
Tema Celeste International *see* Tema Celeste Italia **346**
Tema Celeste Italia. (IT) **346**
†Temadokumentacios Kiadvanyok/Thematical Reviews. (HU ISSN 0521-4602) **5288**
Temas. (US ISSN 0040-2869) **2026**
Temas. (CU) **2184**
Temas Actuales en Ginecologia y Obstetricia *see* Ginecologia y Obstetricia Temas Actuales **3292**
Temas Actuales en Medicina General *see* Clinicas de Atencion Primaria de Norteamerica **3320**
Temas Americanistas. (SP) **2424, 4454**
Temas de Historia del Derecho. (SP) **2684**
Temas de Historia y Politica Contemporaneas. (SP) **2392**
Temas de Orientacion Agropecuaria. (CK ISSN 0049-3333) **123**
Temas de Poblacion. (PY) **3988, 4113**
Temas Economicos. (VE ISSN 0495-0615) **694**
Temas Laborales. (SP ISSN 0213-0750) **994**
Temas Medicos *see* Temas de Poblacion **3988**
Temas N T *see* Biblioteca N T **2504**
Temas Nacionales. (MX) **3929**
Temas Sobre la Profesionalizacion Militar en la Republica Dominicana. (DR) **3473**
Temas Sociales. (CR ISSN 0492-6471) **4422**
Temas Sociales. (BO ISSN 0040-2915) **4454**
Temat - Wynalazczosc i Racjonalizacja *see* Nowator **1082**
Temblor. (US ISSN 0883-1599) **3007**
Teme. (YU) **4454, 3784, 3929**
Temel ve Uygulamali Bilmler Dergisi. *see* Journal of Pure and Applied Sciences **4318**
Temenos (Turku). (FI ISSN 0497-1817) **4205**
Temi di Predicazione - Omelie. (IT) **4205**
Temi Romana. (IT ISSN 0495-0658) **2684**
Temi - Tendenze Moda Italia. (IT) **1294**
Temm Poetry Magazine. (US) **3007**

Temoignage Chretien. (FR ISSN 0244-1462) 2886, 4205
Temoignage Chretien de la Reunion. (RE) 4276
†Temperance Advocate. (AT) 5288
Temperature Controlled Storage & Distribution. (UK) 2083
Temperature Controlled Storage & Distribution Buyer's Guide (Year) see T C S & D Buyer's Guide (Year) 1154
Temperature Controlled Storage and Distribution International see Frigoworld 2071
Temperature: Its Measurement and Control in Science and Industry. (US ISSN 0091-9322) 3842
Tempest Anthology. (US) 3007
Tempest Poetry Journal see Tempest Anthology 3007
Temple Apothecary. (US ISSN 0040-2958) 3744
Temple David Bulletin. (SA ISSN 0040-2966) 4227
Temple David Review see Temple David Bulletin 4227
Temple Law Quarterly see Temple Law Review 2684
Temple Law Review. (US ISSN 0899-8086) 2684
Tempo. (IO ISSN 0126-4273) 2202
Tempo. (MZ) 2211
Tempo. (PO ISSN 0049-335X) 2214
Tempo. (IT) 2968
Tempo. (YU ISSN 0040-3024) 4494
†Tempo. (CN) 5288
Tempo (Hamburg). (GW) 2191
Tempo (Hanau). (GW) 346
Tempo (London, 1939). (UK ISSN 0040-2982) 3584
Tempo (London, 1947). (UK) 2196
Tempo (New York). (US ISSN 0040-3008) 1326
Tempo Australia. (AT) 4788
Tempo Economico. (IT ISSN 0040-3040) 1029
Tempo Medico. (IT ISSN 0492-6749) 3156
Tempo Nuovo. (IT) 2886
Tempo Pollino. (IT) 2206
Tempo Presente. (IT) 2886
Tempo Social. (BL ISSN 0103-2070) 4454
Temporary Culture. (US ISSN 1055-7644) 2886, 2968, 3007, 3014
Temporary Occupations and Employment see Jobs in the 'Gap' Year 3629
Temps de Vivre see Le Belle Age 2270
Temps Libre. (CN ISSN 0823-5708) 4788
Temps Micro. (FR ISSN 0762-7203) 1465, 1474
Temps Modernes. (FR ISSN 0040-3075) 2886
Le Temps Strategique. (SZ) 4390
Tempus. (AT) 250
Ten.8 International Photography Magazine see Ten.8 Photo Paperback 3797
Ten.8 Photo Paperback. (UK) 3797
The Ten Directions. (US) 4289
Tenant/Inquilino. (US ISSN 0040-3083) 2497
Tenant Communications see Telephone News 1367
Tenant Participation Advisory Service Notes see T P A S Notes 2496
Tenants' News. (US) 2497
†Tenaz Talks Teatro. (US) 5288
Tendances des Marches des Capitaux see Financial Market Trends 780
Tendances Sociales Canadiennes see Canadian Social Trends 4567
Tendencia. (BL) 1085
Tendencias Economicas: Legislacion Economicas Argentina/Business Trends: Argentine Economic Legislation. (AG) 694, 2684
Tendenz. (AU) 2173
Tendenze della Occupazione. (IT) 994, 886
Tender Loving Care For Plants see T L C...For Plants 2139
Tenderloin Times. (US) 2026
Tenders see Tenders Australia 1085
Tenders Australia. (AT ISSN 0812-2288) 1085

Tendril. (US ISSN 0197-890X) 3007
Ta Tene/Truth. (CX) 2170
Tenggara see Malay Literature 2936
▼Tenis. (CS) 4513
Tenji Mainichi. (JA) 2208
Tenki. (JA ISSN 0546-0921) 3441
Tenmon Gaido/Guide to Astronomy. (JA ISSN 0288-1977) 370
Tenmon Geppo/Astronomical Herald. (JA ISSN 0374-2466) 370
†Tenneco. (US ISSN 0040-3121) 5288
Tennessee. Department of Safety. Annual Report. (US ISSN 0095-1994) 4721
Tennessee. Higher Education Commission. Biennial Report. (US) 1717
Tennessee. Labor Market Information Directory. (US) 994, 741
Tennessee. State Board for Vocational Education. Information Series. (US ISSN 0093-9889) 1742
Tennessee. The Labor Market Report. (US) 995, 741
Tennessee Academy of Science. Journal.(US ISSN 0040-313X) 4347
Tennessee Agent. (US) 2544
Tennessee Agricultural Experiment Station. Bulletin. (US ISSN 0040 3148) 123
Tennessee Alumnus. (US ISSN 0040-3156) 1326
Tennessee Ancestors. (US ISSN 0882-0635) 2165
Tennessee Annual Average Labor Force Estimates see Labor Force and Nonagricultural Employment Estimates 726
Tennessee Annual Average Work Force Estimates see Labor Force and Nonagricultural Employment Estimates 726
Tennessee Anthropological Association. Miscellaneous Paper. (US) 250
Tennessee Anthropological Association. Newsletter. (US) 250
Tennessee Anthropologist. (US ISSN 0892-7979) 250
Tennessee Archaeological Society Newsletter. (US) 287
Tennessee Archaeologist. (US ISSN 0040-3180) 287
Tennessee Architect. (US) 307
Tennessee Arts Report. (US) 346
Tennessee Attorneys Directory and Buyers Guide. (US) 2684
Tennessee Attorneys Memo see Tennessee Attorneys Memo, Permanent Edition 2684
Tennessee Attorneys Memo, Permanent Edition. (US) 2684
Tennessee Banker. (US ISSN 0040-3199) 801
†Tennessee Bankruptcy Service. (US) 5288
Tennessee Bar Journal. (US ISSN 0497-2325) 2684
Tennessee Broadcaster. (US) 1383
Tennessee Business and Economic Review see Tennessee's Business 1119
Tennessee Business and Industry Review. (US) 694
Tennessee Civilian Work Force Estimates see Labor Force and Nonagricultural Employment Estimates 726
Tennessee Conservationist. (US ISSN 0040-3202) 1498, 4558
Tennessee Cooperative Economic Insect Survey Report see Tennessee Economic Pest Report 519
Tennessee County News. (US) 2424
Tennessee Dental Association. Journal. (US ISSN 0040-3385) 3243
Tennessee Directory of Manufacturers see Tennessee Manufacturers Directory 1155
Tennessee Economic Pest Report. (US) 519, 194
Tennessee Education. (US ISSN 0739-0408) 1667
Tennessee Education Association News see T E A News 1666
Tennessee Employment Law. (US) 2684, 995

Tennessee Employment Law Update. (US ISSN 0886-8557) 995, 2684, 4075
Tennessee Environmental Law Letter. (US ISSN 1042-3168) 2684, 1969
Tennessee Environmental Report see Protect 1966
Tennessee Family Law Letter. (US ISSN 0890-5355) 2718
Tennessee Farm and Home Science. (US ISSN 0040-3229) 123
Tennessee Farm Bureau News. (US ISSN 0162-2617) 123
Tennessee Farmer. (US ISSN 0040-3245) 123
Tennessee Farmer's Exchange see Farmers' Exchange (Fayetteville) 91
Tennessee Farmers Fastline see Farmers Fastline: Tennessee Edition 162
Tennessee Folklore Society Bulletin. (US ISSN 0040-3253) 2059
Tennessee Genealogical Magazine, "Ansearchin'" News. (US) 2165
Tennessee Government Officials Directory. (US) 4095
Tennessee Historical Quarterly. (US ISSN 0040-3261) 2424
Tennessee Home Builder. (US) 634
†Tennessee Illustrated. (US) 5288
Tennessee Journal. (US ISSN 0194-1240) 4075
Tennessee Journal of Health, Physical Education, Recreation and Dance. (US) 3809
†Tennessee Judicial Newsletter. (US) 5288
Tennessee Law Enforcement Bulletin. (US) 1523
Tennessee Law Enforcement Journal. (US ISSN 0040-327X) 1523
▼Tennessee Law Office Desk Book. (US) 2684
Tennessee Law Review. (US ISSN 0040-3288) 2684
Tennessee Lawyer see Tennessee Bar Journal 2684
Tennessee Librarian. (US ISSN 0162-1564) 2787
Tennessee Life Insurance News see Lifetimes 2537
Tennessee Magazine. (US ISSN 0492-746X) 2236
Tennessee Manufacturers Directory. (US ISSN 0360-5477) 1155
Tennessee Medical Association. Journal.(US ISSN 0040-3318) 3156
Tennessee Medico-Legal Reporter. (US) 2684, 3156
Tennessee Musician. (US ISSN 0040-3334) 3584, 1667
Tennessee Native Plant Society Newsletter. (US) 1498
Tennessee Nurses Association. Bulletin. (US ISSN 0040-3342) 3287
Tennessee Organic Grower. (US) 194
Tennessee Parent - Teacher Bulletin. (US) 1667
Tennessee Pharmacist. (US ISSN 1047-0166) 3744
Tennessee Press. (US) 2576
Tennessee Professional Engineer. (US) 1838
Tennessee Public Library Statistics. (US ISSN 0363-7158) 2795, 4590
Tennessee Public Works. (US) 4095
Tennessee Queries. (US ISSN 0898-5472) 2165
Tennessee Real Estate Law Letter. (US) 2716
Tennessee Realtor. (US ISSN 0274-9491) 4158
Tennessee Restauranteur. (US) 2480
Tennessee School Board Bulletin. (US ISSN 0049-3406) 1732
Tennessee School Boards Journal. (US) 1667, 1732
Tennessee Single Life. (US) 4364
Tennessee Sportsman. (US ISSN 0161-3871) 4558
Tennessee State Dental Association. Journal see Tennessee Dental Association. Journal 3243
Tennessee Statistical Abstract. (US ISSN 0082-2760) 4590
Tennessee Studies in Literature. (US ISSN 0497-2384) 2968

Tennessee Tax Guide. (US ISSN 0742-0757) 1110
Tennessee Tax Review. (US ISSN 1044-0798) 1110
Tennessee Teacher. (US ISSN 0040-3407) 1667
†Tennessee Tech Journal. (US ISSN 0082-2779) 5289
Tennessee Town and City. (US ISSN 0040-3415) 4095
Tennessee Travel Guide. (US) 4788
Tennessee Trucker see Fastline for Tennessee Truckers 4744
Tennessee Trucking News. (US) 4748
Tennessee Valley Authority. Annual Report. (US ISSN 0363-101X) 1498
Tennessee Valley Authority. Division of Land and Forest Resources. Technical Note see Tennessee Valley Authority. Division of Land Resources. Technical Note 1498
Tennessee Valley Authority. Division of Land Resources. Technical Note. (US) 1498
†Tennessee Valley Authority. Technical Monographs. (US ISSN 0082-2809) 5289
†Tennessee Valley Authority. Technical Reports. (US ISSN 0082-2817) 5289
Tennessee Valley Public Power Association News see T V P P A News 1908
Tennessee Valley's Hometown Press. (US) 2236
Tennessee Visitor Guide. (US) 4788
Tennessee Warbler. (US) 567
Tennessee Wildlife. (US ISSN 0886-1269) 592
Tennessee Williams Literary Journal. (US) 2968
†Tennessee Williams Newsletter. (US) 5289
Tennessee's Business. (US) 1119, 886
Tennis see Deutsche Tennis Zeitung 4502
Tennis. (US ISSN 0040-3423) 4513
Tennis. (IT) 4513
Tennis Australia see Australian Tennis Magazine 4499
Tennis Avisen. (DK ISSN 0900-7105) 4513
Tennis - Badminton - Squash Guide see N A G W S Guide. Tennis 5241
Tennis Buyers Guide. (US) 4513
Tennis et Golf see Golf Europeen 4505
Tennis Great Britain see L T A Handbook 4507
Tennis Industry. (US ISSN 0191-5851) 4513
Tennis Italiano. (IT ISSN 0393-0890) 4513
Tennis-Jahrbuch. (GW) 4513
Tennis Journal. (JA) 4513
Tennis Magazine. (JA) 4513
Tennis Magazine. (FR) 4513
Tennis Magazine. (UK ISSN 0262-9224) 4513
Tennis Midwest. (US) 4513
Tennis News of Florida. (US) 4513
Tennis Northeast. (US) 4513
Tennis South. (US) 4513
Tennis Ticinese. (SZ) 4513
†Tennis Tidningen. (SW ISSN 0040-3431) 5289
†Tennis U.S.A. (US ISSN 0040-3466) 5289
▼Tennis U S T A. (US) 4513
Tennis Week. (US ISSN 0194-9098) 4513
Tennis West. (US) 4513
Tennis World. (UK ISSN 0040-3474) 4513
Tennismaailma. (FI) 4513
TennisPro. (US) 4513, 1762, 3373
Tennisrevue see Special Sports 4489
Tennista. (IT) 4513
Tennyson Research Bulletin. (UK ISSN 0082-2841) 2968
Tennyson Society, Lincoln, England. Monographs. (UK ISSN 0082-285X) 2968
Tennyson Society, Lincoln, England. Occasional Papers. (UK ISSN 0307-3572) 2968

Tennyson Society, Lincoln, England. Report. (UK ISSN 0082-2868) **2968**
Tenor. (It) **2968**
Tenpercent. (US) **2457**, 4853
Tenqqara. (MY) **2968**
Tenrikyo. (JA ISSN 0040-3482) **4205**
Tensai Kenkyu Hokoku Hokan. *see* Bulletin of Sugar Beet Research. Supplement **171**
Tenside Surfactants Detergents. (GW ISSN 0932-3414) **1231**
Tensor. (JA ISSN 0040-3504) **3058**, **4612**
Tenth Times. (US) **3243**
Tentmaker's Journal. (US ISSN 0272-6939) **4205**
Tentoonstellingsagenda *see* Tentoonstellingsboekje **3533**
Tentoonstellingsboekje. (NE ISSN 0920-7430) **3533**
Teocomunicacao. (BL ISSN 0103-314X) **4276**
Teoiric. (IE) **3929**
Teollisuuden Keskusliitto. Jasenluettelo/Finlands Industrifoerbund. Medlemsfoerteckning/Confederation of Finnish Industries. List of Members. (FI) **1155**
Teollisuus *see* Teollisuusviikko **1085**
Teollisuusviikko/Industrial Week. (FI ISSN 0358-7673) **1085**
Teologia. (HU ISSN 0133-1779) **4276**
Teologia Espiritual. (SP ISSN 0495-1549) **4205**
Teologia y Catequesis. (SP ISSN 0212-1964) **4205**
Teologia y Vida. (CL ISSN 0049-3449) **4276**
Teologinen Aikakauskirja/Teologisk Tidskrift. (FI ISSN 0040-3555) **4205**
Teologisk Tidskrift. *see* Teologinen Aikakauskirja **4205**
Teologiske Fakultet. Bladet *see* Arken **4163**
Teoloski Pogledi. (YU) **4205**
Teorema. (SP ISSN 0210-1602) **3784**
Teorema Italia. (IT) **995**
†Teoresi. (IT ISSN 0040-3563) **5289**
Teoreticheskaya i Eksperimental'naya Khimiya. (KR ISSN 0497-2627) **1189**
Teoreticheskie Osnovy Khimicheskoi Tekhnologii. (RU ISSN 0040-3571) **1189**, **1838**
Teoria. (IT) **3784**
Teoria al Dia. (AG) **4494**
Teoria Literaria: Texto y Teoria. (NE ISSN 0921-2523) **2886**, **2968**
Teoria Politica. (IT) **3929**
†Teoria y Practica de Precios. (CU ISSN 0138-6212) **5289**
†Teorie a Praxe Telesne Vychovy. (CS ISSN 0040-358X) **5289**
Teorie e Oggetti. (IT ISSN 0392-2154) **3929**
Teorie Rozvoje Vedy *see* Teorie Vedy **4347**
Teorie Vedy/Theory of Science. (CS ISSN 1210-0250) **4347**, **1029**, **4612**
Teorija in Praksa. (XV ISSN 0040-3598) **3929**
Teoriya Funktsii, Funktsional'nyi Analiz i ikh Prilozheniya. (KR ISSN 0321-4427) **3058**
Teoriya Funktsii Kompleksnogo Peremennogo i Kraevye Zadachi. (RU) **3058**
Teoriya i Praktika Fizicheskoi Kul'tury. (RU ISSN 0040-3601) **1762**
Teoriya Mekhanizmov i Mashin. (KR ISSN 0321-4419) **3846**, **1940**
Teoriya Sluchainykh Protsessov. (KR ISSN 0321-3900) **3058**
Teoriya Veroyatnostei i ee Primenenie. (RU ISSN 0040-361X) **3058**
Teorja. (YU ISSN 0351-2274) **3784**
Teoros. (CN ISSN 0712-8657) **4788**
†Teosofo. (Spanish edition of: Theosophist) (AG) **5289**
Teploenergetika. (RU ISSN 0040-3636) **1940**, **1909**
Teplofizika. *see* Silumine Fizika **3841**

Teplofizika Vysokikh Temperatur. (RU ISSN 0040-3644) **3833**
Teploprovodnost' i Diffuziya. (LV) **3842**
Tequ Jingji/Special Zone Economy. (CC) **694**
Tequ Wenxue. (CC) **2968**
Tequesta. (US ISSN 0363-3705) **2424**
Teramo. (IT ISSN 0040-3652) **4788**
Terapevticheskii Arkhiv/Therapeutic Archives. (RU ISSN 0040-3660) **3156**
Terapia del Comportamento *see* T C **3155**
Terapia Familiare. (IT) **4048**, **1667**, **3156**
Terapia Moderna. (English edition: Modern Treatment) (IT ISSN 0040-3695) **3156**
Terapia Oggi. (IT) **3156**
Terassi. (FI ISSN 0789-6093) **2186**
Teratogenesis, Carcinogenesis, and Mutagenesis. (US ISSN 0270-3211) **3156**
Teratology. (US ISSN 0040-3709) **457**, **1983**, **3156**
Terbitan Bersiri Kini Malaysia (Bukan Kerajaan). *see* Current Malaysian Serials (Non-Government) **398**
†Tercer Rostro. (AG) **5289**
Teresa de Jesus. (SP) **4277**
Teresianum. (VC ISSN 0392-4556) **4277**
Terezinske Listy. (CS) **2392**
Teri Information Digest on Energy *see* T I D E **1796**
Termeszet es Tarsadalom *see* T E T **2886**
Termeszet Vilaga. (HU ISSN 0040-3717) **4347**
Termica *see* Knafaim **58**
Terminal Care Index *see* Palliative Care Index **3180**
Terminal-Nyt *see* V D L Nyt **4722**
Termination of Employment. (US) **1070**, **2684**
Termino. (US) **2968**
Terminogramme. (CN ISSN 0225-3194) **2847**
†Terminological Information. (EI) **5289**
Terminologie. (CN) **2847**
Terminologie et Traduction. (EI) **2847**
Terminology Update. *see* Actualite Terminologique **2801**
Termite Abstracts. (UK ISSN 0144-5995) **468**, **24**
Termotecnica. (IT ISSN 0040-3725) **2304**
Termotehnika. (YU ISSN 0350-218X) **1796**
Terra. (IT) **123**
Terra. (SP) **123**
Terra. (FI ISSN 0040-3741) **2264**
Terra. (US ISSN 0040-3733) **3533**, **250**, **2424**
Terra Abstracts. (UK ISSN 0954-4887) **1552**
Terra Ameriga. (IT ISSN 0040-375X) **251**, **287**
Terra Cognita *see* Terra Abstracts **1552**
Terra e Sole. (IT ISSN 0040-3768) **123**
Terra e Vita. (IT ISSN 0040-3776) **123**
Terra et Aqua. (NE ISSN 0376-6411) **4740**, **1611**, **1875**
Terra Grischuna - Graubuenden. (SZ ISSN 1011-5196) **1969**, **2264**, **4788**
Terra Nova. (UK ISSN 0954-4879) **1548**
Terra Nova. (US ISSN 1056-8018) **3973**
Terra Plana. (SZ) **4788**, **346**
Terra Poetica. (US) **3007**
Terra Santa. (IS ISSN 0040-3784) **4205**, **287**, **2432**
Terra Una. (US) **4205**
Terrae Incognitae. (US ISSN 0082-2884) **2324**
Terrap Times. (US) **4048**
Terrazzo. (US) **346**, **307**
Terrazzo Topics. (US ISSN 0040-3806) **634**
Terrazzo Trends *see* Terrazzo Topics **634**
Terre. (FR ISSN 0040-3814) **3929**

Terre Africaine. (CX ISSN 0049-3473) **3929**
Terre Dauphinoise. (FR) **123**
Terre de Chez Nous. (CN ISSN 0040-3830) **124**
Terre et Vie *see* Revue d'Ecologie: La Terre et la Vie **1967**
Terre Information. (FR) **3473**
Terre Lorraine. (FR) **2968**, **346**
Terre Magazine. (FR) **3473**
Terre Malgache/Tany Malagasy. (MG ISSN 0563-1637) **194**
Terre Sainte *see* Terra Santa **4205**
Terrebonne Life Lines. (US ISSN 0735-2794) **2165**
Terrell Trails. (US ISSN 0884-2108) **2165**
Terres Lointaines. (FR ISSN 0492-7958) **1268**
Terrier Type. (US ISSN 0199-6495) **3714**
Territoires *see* Cahiers Territoires **2608**
Territoires - Correspondance Municipale.(FR ISSN 0223-5951) **4095**, **2497**
Territorial Herald. (US) **3597**
▼Territorial Sea Journal. (US) **2735**
▼Territories. (UK) **3015**
Il Territorio. (IT) **2206**
Terror Australis: The Australian Horror & Fantasy Magazine. (AT ISSN 1031-3001) **3015**
Terrorism (Bristol) *see* Studies in Conflict and Terrorism **3973**
Terrorism (Minneapolis). (US ISSN 0278-663X) **1523**
Terrorism: An Annual Survey *see* Terrorism (Minneapolis) **1523**
Terrorism and Political Violence. (UK ISSN 0954-6553) **3929**, **3473**
Terrorism Violence Insurgency Report *see* T V I Report **1523**
Terry Family Historian. (US) **2165**
Tertiaire. (FR ISSN 0987-710X) **898**
†Tertiary Research. (NE ISSN 0308-9649) **5289**
†Tertiary Research Special Papers. (NE) **5289**
Terugblik 40-45. (NE ISSN 0920-3958) **2392**
Terveydenhoitolehti *see* T H Kotilaakari **3809**
Terveys. (FI ISSN 0040-3911) **3809**
Terveys 2000. (FI ISSN 0782-3789) **4113**
Terza Pagina. (IT) **2886**
Terzo Mondo/Third World. (IT ISSN 0040-392X) **4390**
Terzo Occhio. (IT ISSN 0390-0355) **346**
Tesinsko. (CS ISSN 0139-7605) **2392**, **3929**
Tesoro Eucaristico. (IT ISSN 0040-3938) **4277**
Tessilcasa Tex Home *see* Tex Home **2555**
Tessuto Collezioni. (IT) **4624**
Test. (GW ISSN 0040-3946) **1508**
Test. (UK) **2525**
Test *see* Scienza Duemila **4342**
Test Achats Magazine. (BE) **1508**
Test & Measurement World. (US ISSN 0744-1657) **1909**, **1418**
Test & Measurement World Buyer's Guide. (US ISSN 0744-1657) **1909**, **1418**, **2525**, **3449**
†Test & Measurement World Market Outlook. (US) **5289**
Test-Cadmat *see* Test **2525**
Test Engineering & Management. (US ISSN 0193-4120) **63**, **1838**, **3846**
Test-Index. (GW ISSN 0171-4163) **1509**
Test - Info. (GW) **1326**, **1667**
Test Jahrbuch (Year). (GW) **1508**
Test- og Undervisningsmaterialer *see* Undervisningsmaterialer til Begynder- og Grundundervisning **1742**
Test Photographers in New York City. (US) **3797**
Testata: il Finanziere. (IT) **1110**
Testata: Rivista della Guardia di Finanza. (IT) **1111**
Testi della Cultura Italiana. (IT) **2206**
Testi e Studi Umanistici. (IT) **2968**
†Testi Medievali di Interesse Dantesco. (IT) **5289**

TEXAS. RAILROAD 6725

Testimoni. (IT) **4277**
Testimoni nel Mondo. (IT) **4205**
Testimonia Siciliae Antiqua. (IT ISSN 0452-2907) **287**, **2324**
Testimonial Privileges. (US) **2685**
Testimonianze. (IT ISSN 0040-3989) **2886**, **4205**
Il Testimonio. (IT) **4205**
Testimonios (en Historieta). (PE) **2424**
Testimonios Violentos. (VE) **3929**
Testimony Magazine. (UK) **4289**
Testing and Control Digest *see* Metallography & Testing Digest **3414**
A Testnevelesi Foiskola Kozlemenyei. (HU ISSN 0230-3337) **4494**
Tests in Print. (US ISSN 0361-025X) **4048**, **1762**
To Tetarto. (GR) **2196**, **346**
Teton. (US ISSN 0049-3481) **4558**
Tetradi Obshchestvennogo Zdravookhranenia *see* Public Health Papers **4110**
Tetrahedron. (US ISSN 0040-4020) **1224**
▼Tetrahedron: Asymmetry. (US ISSN 0957-4166) **1224**, **1215**
†Tetrahedron Computer Methodology. (US ISSN 0898-5529) **5289**
Tetrahedron Letters. (US ISSN 0040-4039) **1224**
Tetsu-to-Hagane. (JA ISSN 0021-1575) **3422**
Tetsudo Pikutoriaru/Railway Pictorial. (JA ISSN 0040-4047) **4715**
Tetsudo Sharyoto Seisan Dotai Tokei Geppo/Monthly Survey on Current Rolling Stock Production. (JA) **4667**
Tetsudo Sharyoto Seisan Dotai Tokei Nenpo/Annual Survey on Current Rolling Stock Production. (JA) **4667**
Teubner-Archiv zur Mathematik. (GW ISSN 0233-0962) **3058**
Teubner-Texte zur Mathematik. (GW ISSN 0138-502X) **3058**
Teubner-Texte zur Physik. (GW ISSN 0233-0911) **3833**
†Teufah. (IS) **5289**
Tev Fema. (TG) **4853**
Teva Va-Aretz. (IS ISSN 0563-2153) **1498**, **1969**
Teviskes Ziburiai/Lights of Homeland. (CN) **2026**
Tevyne. (US ISSN 0040-4071) **2026**
Tevzemes Avize. (LV) **2886**
Tex *see* Hebdo-Tex **1281**
Tex Home. (IT) **2555**
Tex: Mitteilungen Rund Ums Technikum. (GW ISSN 0720-1303) **1326**
Tex-Textilis. (BE) **4624**
Texan Veteran News. (US) **3473**
Texarkana U S A Quarterly. (US ISSN 0741-6105) **2165**
Texas. Department of Corrections. Research and Development Division. Research Report. (US ISSN 0095-1900) **1523**
Texas. Department of Health. Annual Report. (US) **4113**
Texas. Department of Health Resources. Biennial Report *see* Texas. Department of Health. Annual Report **4113**
Texas. Department of Water Resources. Library. Bulletin *see* Texas. Water Commission. Library. Bulletin **4828**
Texas. Department of Water Resources. Report *see* Texas. Water Development Board. Report **4828**
Texas. Department on Aging. Annual Report. (US) **4422**
†Texas. Industrial Commission. Annual Report. (US ISSN 0361-2597) **5289**
Texas. Natural Resources Information System. Newsletter. (US) **1969**, **1498**, **1568**
Texas. Railroad Commission. Oil and Gas Division. Annual Report. (US) **3702**
Texas. Railroad Commission. Oil and Gas Division. Crude Oil and Gas Nominations. (US) **3702**
Texas. Railroad Commission. Oil and Gas Division. Crude Oil Nominations and Purchases. (US) **3702**

6726 TEXAS. RAILROAD

Texas. Railroad Commission. Oil and Gas Division. Gas Monthly Proration Schedule see Texas. Railroad Commission. Oil and Gas Division. Prorated Gas Fields - Monthly Schedule 3702
Texas. Railroad Commission. Oil and Gas Division. Gas Proration Schedule.(US) 3702
Texas. Railroad Commission. Oil and Gas Division. Oil Proration Schedule. (US) 3702
Texas. Railroad Commission. Oil and Gas Division. Prorated Gas Fields - Monthly Schedule. (US) 3702
Texas. Railroad Commission. Oil and Gas Division. Recapitulation of Crude Oil Nominations and Purchases by Company see Texas. Railroad Commission. Oil and Gas Division. Crude Oil and Gas Nominations 3702
Texas. Railroad Commission. Oil and Gas Division. Summary of Crude Oil Nominations and Purchases by District see Texas. Railroad Commission. Oil and Gas Division. Crude Oil Nominations and Purchases 3702
Texas. Water Commission. Library. Bulletin. (US) 4828
Texas. Water Development Board. Report. (US) 4828
Texas A & I University Studies see T A I U S 5286
†Texas A & M Business Forum. (US) 5289
Texas A & M University. College of Geosciences. Contributions in Oceanography. (US ISSN 0069-9640) 1611
Texas A & M University Library Notes. (US ISSN 0040-4136) 2787
Texas Agenda. (US) 4075, 694, 3929
Texas Aggie. (US) 1326
Texas Agriculture. (US) 124
Texas Agriculture Weekly see Texas Agriculture 124
Texas Alcalde. (US) 1326
Texas Almanac see Texas Almanac and State Industrial Guide 2424
Texas Almanac and State Industrial Guide. (US) 2424
Texas Annual of Electronics Research. (US) 1779
Texas Archeological Society. Bulletin. (US ISSN 0082-2930) 287
Texas Archeological Society. Special Publication. (US ISSN 0495-2944) 287
Texas Archeology. (US ISSN 0082-2949) 287
Texas Architect. (US ISSN 0040-4179) 307
Texas Artists, Writers and Thinkers in Exile see T A W T E 2967
Texas Association for Health, Physical Education, Recreation and Dance Journal see T A H P E R D Journal 3809
Texas Bankers Record see Texas Banking 801
Texas Banking. (US) 801
Texas Banking Red Book. (US) 801
Texas Bar Journal. (US ISSN 0040-4187) 2685
Texas Beverage News. (US) 386
Texas Bicyclist. (US) 4521
Texas Bill of Rights. (US) 3947
Texas Blue Book of Life Insurance Statistics. (US ISSN 0739-4691) 2547, 4590
Texas Books in Review. (US ISSN 0739-3202) 413
Texas Brangus. (US) 227
Texas Builder. (US) 634
Texas Builders and Contractors Directory. (US) 1155, 634
Texas Business Review. (US ISSN 0040-4209) 694
Texas Child Care. (US ISSN 1049-9466) 1245
Texas Child Care Quarterly see Texas Child Care 1245
Texas Child Migrant Program. Annual Report. (US) 1667
Texas Civil Engineer. (US) 1875
Texas Co-Op Power. (US) 832

Texas Coach. (US ISSN 0040-4241) 4494
Texas College and University System. Coordinating Board. C B Policy Paper see Texas Higher Education Coordinating Board. C B Policy Paper 1717
†Texas College Student. (US) 5289
Texas Commercial Collections. (US) 2685
Texas Computing see Computer Currents (Dallas) 1423
Texas Concho Register see West Texas Angelus 4279
Texas Condominium Law Manual. (US) 2716
Texas Construction Law Manual. (US) 2716
Texas Contractor. (US ISSN 0192-9216) 634
Texas Coordinating Board. Texas College and University System. C B Study Paper see Texas Higher Education Coordinating Board. C B Study Paper 1717
Texas Corporation Law. (US) 2712
Texas D O. (US) 3156
Texas Dental Assistants Association. Bulletin. (US) 3243
Texas Dental Assistants Association. Newsletter see Texas Dental Assistants Association. Bulletin 3243
Texas Dental Journal. (US ISSN 0040-4284) 3243
Texas Department of Aviation Bulletin see T A C Bulletin 5286
†Texas Department of Commerce. Tourism Division. Newsletter. (US) 5289
Texas Department on Aging. Biennial Report see Texas. Department on Aging. Annual Report 4422
†Texas Desktop News. (US) 5289
Texas Director. (US) 2120
Texas Drunk Driving Law. (US) 2685
Texas Economic Forecast. (US ISSN 0748-0008) 886
Texas Economic Indicators. (US ISSN 0896-0453) 886
Texas Elementary Principals and Supervisors Association Journal see T E P S A Journal 1732
Texas Employment Law Letter. (US ISSN 1046-9214) 2685, 995
Texas Energy. (US) 1796, 1582, 3496
Texas Energy and Mineral Resources see Texas Energy 1796
Texas Energy Reporter. (US) 1796
▼Texas Environmental Law Letter. (US) 2685, 1969
Texas Evidence Reporter. (US ISSN 0266-0814) 2685
Texas F F A Magazine. (US ISSN 0040-4330) 124, 1268
Texas Fact Book. (US) 741
Texas Facts. (US ISSN 0899-7349) 1782
Texas Farm and Ranch News. (US ISSN 0049-3511) 194, 227
Texas Farmer-Stockman. (US ISSN 0279-165X) 194
Texas Finance Report. (US) 801
Texas Fish & Game. (US) 4558
Texas Fisherman see Texas Fish & Game 4558
Texas Folklore Society. Publications. (US ISSN 0082-3023) 2059
Texas Food and Service News see Food & Service 2474
Texas Food Merchant. (US ISSN 0040-4322) 2094
Texas Football Magazine. (US) 4513
Texas Foreclosure: Law and Practice. (US) 2712, 2716
†Texas Forestry Papers. (US ISSN 0082-304X) 5289
Texas Future Farmer see Texas F F A Magazine 124
Texas Gardener. (US ISSN 0744-0987) 2139
Texas Government Newsletter. (US ISSN 0164-9221) 3929, 4075
Texas Health Law Reporter. (US ISSN 0266-0806) 2685, 3156
Texas Heart Institute Journal. (US ISSN 0730-2347) 3212

Texas Higher Education Coordinating Board. Annual Status Report and Statistical Report. (US) 1717
Texas Higher Education Coordinating Board. C B Annual Report and Statistical Supplement see Texas Higher Education Coordinating Board. Annual Status Report and Statistical Report 1717
Texas Higher Education Coordinating Board. C B Policy Paper. (US) 1717
Texas Higher Education Coordinating Board. C B Study Paper. (US) 1717
Texas Highways. (US ISSN 0040-4349) 4788
Texas Historian. (US ISSN 0022-6602) 2424
Texas Horticulturist. (US) 2139
Texas Hospital Law. (US) 2685, 2469
Texas Hospitals see Health Texas 2462
Texas Humanities Resource Center Newsletter see T H R C Newsletter 2516
Texas Independent Producers & Royalty Owners Association Reporter see T I P R O Reporter 3702
Texas Industrial Expansion. (US ISSN 0040-4365) 1085
Texas Industrial Production Index. (US) 1085
Texas Instruments Engineering Journal see Texas Instruments Technical Journal 1838
Texas Instruments Technical Journal. (US ISSN 0893-7877) 1838
Texas Insurance Law Journal. (US) 2685, 2544
Texas Insurance Law Reporter see Texas Insurance Law Journal 2685
Texas Insuror. (US) 2544
Texas International Law Journal. (US ISSN 0163-7479) 2729
Texas Jewish Post. (US ISSN 0040-439X) 2026
Texas Journal. (US) 2304
Texas Journal of Chiropractic. (US) 3216
Texas Journal of Corrections. (US) 1523
Texas Journal of Political Studies. (US ISSN 0191-0930) 3930
Texas Journal of Science. (US ISSN 0040-4403) 4347
▼Texas Journal of Women and the Law. (US ISSN 1058-5427) 2685, 4853
Texas L P - Gas News. (US ISSN 0040-4454) 3702
Texas Labor Market Review. (US) 995, 886
Texas Law of Oil and Gas. (US) 2685, 3702
Texas Law Review. (US ISSN 0040-4411) 2685
Texas Lawman. (US ISSN 0040-442X) 1523
Texas Lawyer. (US ISSN 0267-8306) 2685
†Texas League Savings Account. (US ISSN 0882-0384) 5289
Texas Legion News see Texas Legion Times 1301
Texas Legion Times. (US) 1301
Texas Libraries. (US ISSN 0040-4438) 2787
Texas Library Journal. (US ISSN 0040-4446) 2787
Texas Limitations Manual. (US) 2685
†Texas List of Scientific and Technical Serial Publications. (US) 5289
Texas Litigator's Handbook. (US) 2685
Texas Livestock Statistics. (US ISSN 0091-1550) 144
†Texas Lodging Industry. (US) 5289
Texas Lone Star. (US ISSN 0749-9310) 1732
Texas - Louisiana Trucker. (US) 4748
Texas Manufacturers Register. (US ISSN 0743-1163) 1155
Texas Medicine. (US ISSN 0040-4470) 3156
Texas Memorial Museum. Bulletin. (US ISSN 0082-3074) 3534
Texas Memorial Museum. Conservation Notes. (US) 3534

Texas Memorial Museum. Miscellaneous Papers. (US ISSN 0082-3082) 3534
Texas Memorial Museum. Museum Notes. (US) 3534
Texas Memorial Museum. Speleological Monographs. (US) 1582, 3534
Texas Methodist - United Methodist Reporter see United Methodist Reporter 4251
Texas Migrant Program. Annual Report see Texas Child Migrant Program. Annual Report 1667
Texas Monthly. (US ISSN 0148-7736) 2236
Texas Municipal Zoning Law. (US) 2716, 2497
Texas Music Educator see Southwestern Musician Combined with The Texas Music Educator 3582
Texas Native Plant Society News. (US) 2139
Texas Natural Resources Reporter. (US ISSN 0197-2340) 4829, 1796, 2685, 3702
Texas Neighbors. (US) 124
Texas Notary Law Primer. (US) 2685
Texas Nursing. (US ISSN 0095-036X) 3287
Texas Observer. (US ISSN 0040-4519) 3930
Texas Oil and Gas Law Journal. (US ISSN 0950-3285) 2685
Texas Oil Jobber see Texas Oil Marketer 3702
Texas Oil Marketer. (US ISSN 0896-8969) 3702
Texas Optometric Association. Journal see Texas Optometry 3305
Texas Optometry. (US ISSN 0738-7644) 3305
Texas Ornithological Society. Bulletin. (US ISSN 0040-4543) 567
Texas Outdoor Guide Magazine. (US) 4558
Texas Outlook. (US ISSN 0040-4551) 1732
Texas P T A Communicator see P T A Communicator 1730
†Texas Papers in Foreign Language Education. (US) 5289
Texas Parks and Wildlife Magazine. (US ISSN 0040-4586) 1498
Texas Pecan Press see Pecan Press 187
Texas People and Places. (US) 4788
Texas Personal Injury Law. (US) 2685
Texas Personal Injury Law Reporter. (US ISSN 0264-4770) 2685
Texas Personnel and Guidance Association Journal see T P G A Journal 1666
Texas Petroleum Industry. (US) 3702, 1155
Texas Pharmacy. (US ISSN 0362-7926) 3744
The Texas Philatelist. (US ISSN 0893-2670) 3758
Texas Pollution Report. (US) 1979
Texas Press Association Messenger see T P A Messenger 2575
Texas Press Messenger see T P A Messenger 2575
Texas Printer. (US) 4006
Texas Probate Code Manual. (US) 2685
Texas Product Liability Law. (US) 2685
Texas Professional Engineer. (US ISSN 0040-4632) 1838
Texas Public Employee. (US ISSN 0040-4640) 4075
Texas Public Library Statistics. (US ISSN 0082-3120) 2795
Texas Public Utility News. (US ISSN 0744-7981) 1796, 1809, 2685, 3702
†Texas Real Estate. (US ISSN 0884-7827) 5289
Texas Real Estate Law Reporter. (US ISSN 0267-8896) 2685, 4158
Texas Realtor. (US) 4158
Texas Register. (US ISSN 0362-4781) 2685
Texas Residential Landlord - Tenant Law. (US) 2716
Texas Review. (US ISSN 0885-2685) 2968

Texas Rules of Appellate Procedure. (US) **2733**
Texas Rules of Civil Procedure. (US) **2704**
Texas School Board Journal see Texas Lone Star **1732**
Texas School Directory. (US ISSN 0363-4566) **1697**
Texas School Law Bulletin. (US) **1732,** **2685**
Texas Small Grains Statistics. (US ISSN 0091-4673) **144**
Texas Sourcebook (No.). (US) **4006,** **346**
Texas Southern University Law Review see Thurgood Marshall Law Review **2685**
†Texas Special Libraries Directory. (US ISSN 0082-3163) **5289**
Texas Speech Communication Journal. (US ISSN 0363-8782) **1344,** **2847**
Texas Sportsman. (US) **4558**
Texas State Directory. (US ISSN 0363-7530) **4075**
Texas State Teachers Association Advocate see T S T A Advocate **1666**
Texas Studies in Literature and Language. (US ISSN 0040-4691) **2968,** 2847
Texas Study of Secondary Education Research Bulletin. (US ISSN 0040-4705) **1667**
Texas Surplus Line Reporter. (US) **2544**
The Texas Surveyor. (US) **4788**
Texas Tech Law Review. (US ISSN 0564-6197) **2685**
Texas Tech University. Graduate Studies. (US ISSN 0082-3198) **2516,** 457, 1717, 3784
Texas Tech University. Interdepartmental Committee on Comparative Literature. Proceedings of the Comparative Literature Symposium see Texas Tech University. Interdepartmental Committee on Comparative Literature. Studies in Comparative Literature **2968**
Texas Tech University. Interdepartmental Committee on Comparative Literature. Studies in Comparative Literature. (US ISSN 0899-2193) **2968**
Texas Tech University. Museum. Occasional Papers. (US ISSN 0149-175X) **457**
Texas Tech University. Museum. Special Publications. (US ISSN 0149-1768) **457,** 3534
Texas Techsan. (US ISSN 0040-4721) **1326**
Texas Tennis. (US) **4513**
†Texas Textile Maintenance Reporter. (US) **5289**
Texas Thoroughbred. (US ISSN 0164-6168) **4538**
Texas Times. (US) **2236**
▼Texas Tour and Meeting Guide. (US) **4788**
Texas TourBook see Tourbook: Texas **4790**
Texas Town & City. (US ISSN 0040-473X) **4075**
Texas Trade and Professional Associations and Other Selected Organizations. (US) **1155**
Texas Transportation Researcher. (US ISSN 0040-4748) **4657**
Texas Traveler. (US) **2968**
Texas Trees. (US ISSN 1047-7667) **2109**
Texas Tribune. (US) **3930**
Texas Truck Trader - Louisiana Trucker - Oklahoma Trucker see Texas - Louisiana Trucker **4748**
Texas Veterinary Medical Journal. (US ISSN 0040-4756) **4816**
Texas Vital Statistics. (US ISSN 0495-257X) **3996**
Texas Water Resources. (US) **4829**
▼Texas Water Utilities Journal. (US ISSN 1051-709X) **4829,** 4113
Texas Weekly. (US ISSN 0890-5924) **4075,** 3930
Texas Woman's News. (US) **4853**

Texas Woman's University. School of Library and Information Studies. Alumnae Newsletter. (US) **1326,** 2787
Texas Woman's University. School of Library Science. Alumnae Newsletter see Texas Woman's University. School of Library and Information Studies. Alumnae Newsletter **1326**
Texbel. (BE) **4624,** 1294
Texincon. (II ISSN 0970-5686) **4624**
Texinform. (SA) **1155,** 4624
Texinform Bulletin see Texinform Monthly Bulletin **4624**
Texinform Monthly Bulletin. (SA) **4624**
Texnews. (SA ISSN 0036-1003) **4624**
Texpress. (NE ISSN 0040-4772) **4624**
TexReport. (SA) **4624**
Texscope (New York) see Texscope: U S A Textile Industry Overview **4624**
Texscope: U S A Textile Industry Overview. (US ISSN 0092-3540) **4624**
Text. (SW ISSN 0345-0112) **413**
Text. (GW ISSN 0165-4888) **2516,** 2847, 2968, 4454
Text (New York). (US ISSN 0736-3974) **2968**
Text Management Journal see E D M S Journal **1444**
Text on Microfilm see T O M **24**
Text Technology. (US) **2576**
Text und Kontext. (GW ISSN 0933-4769) **2968**
Text und Kritik. (GW ISSN 0040-5329) **2969**
Textausgaben zur Fruehen Sozialistischen Literatur in Deutschland. (GW ISSN 0081-3257) **2969**
Textautomation see B T S **1057**
▼Textbook Letter. (US) **1762,** 1667
†Textbook News. (US ISSN 0733-8228) **5289**
Textcontext. (GW ISSN 0179-6844) **2847**
Texte. (CN ISSN 0715-8920) **2969**
Texte des Spaeten Mittelalters und der Fruehen Neuzeit. (GW) **2969**
Texte et l'Idee. (FR ISSN 0981-1907) **2969,** 2847
Texte und Studien zum Antiken Judentum. (GW ISSN 0721-8753) **4227**
Texte und Untersuchungen zur Geschichte der Altchristlichen Literatur. (GW ISSN 0082-3589) **4205**
Texten und Schreiben. (GW) **2969**
Textes d'Interet General. (FR) **2685**
Textes Litteraires Francais. (SZ) **2969**
Textielhistorische Bijdragen. (NE) **4624**
Textielverzorging. (NE) **1282**
TextielVisie. (NE) **4624**
Textil/Textile. (CS ISSN 0040-4829) **4624**
Textil. (VE) **4624**
Textil. (DK ISSN 0040-4837) **4624**
Textil-Bekleidung. (GW) **4624**
†Textil- es Textilruhazati Ipari Szakirodalmi Tajekoztato/Abstract Journal for Textile and Clothing Industry. (HU ISSN 0209-9578) **5289**
Textil-Industrie und ihre Helfer. (GW ISSN 0082-3627) **4625**
Textil Magazine. (SW ISSN 0284-6152) **4625,** 1288
Textil Mitteilungen. (GW ISSN 0342-2224) **4625**
Textil-Praxis see Textil Praxis International **4625**
Textil Praxis International. (GW ISSN 0040-4853) **4625**
Textil-Revue. (SZ ISSN 0040-4861) **4625,** 1294
Textil Stunde. (GW) **3593**
Textil Vestido. (MX) **1288**
Textil-Wirtschaft. (GW ISSN 0040-487X) **4625**
Textilarbeit und Unterricht. (GW ISSN 0342-7358) **1294,** 1667
Textilbranschen see Textil Magazine **4625**
Textile. see Textil **4624**
Textile Abstract. see Fangzhi Wenzhai **4628**

Textile and Apparel Index of Australasia.(AT) **4628**
Textile and Apparel Index of Australia see Textile and Apparel Index of Australasia **4628**
Textile and Apparel Manufacturer see Australian Apparel Manufacturer **4616**
Textile and Engineering Directory for India and Pakistan see Worrall's Textile & Engineering Directory **1160**
Textile and Fibre Programme. Division of Processing and Chemical Manufacturing Technology. Annual Report see South Africa. Division of Textile Technology. Annual Report **4623**
Textile Artists' Newsletter. (US) **4625**
Textile Asia. (HK ISSN 0049-3554) **4625**
Textile Asia Index. (HK) **4625**
Textile Association (India). Journal. (II ISSN 0368-4636) **4625**
Textile Business Outlook. (US ISSN 0739-0491) **4625,** 1029
Textile Chemist and Colorist. (US ISSN 0040-490X) **4625,** 1282
Textile Dyer and Printer. (II ISSN 0040-4926) **4625**
Textile-Fibre Forum. (AT ISSN 0818-6308) **4625,** 357
Textile Financial Outlook. (US) **4625,** 1055
Textile Forecast. (UK) **4625**
Textile Hi-Lights. (US) **4625**
Textile Horizons. (UK ISSN 0260-6518) **4625**
Textile India see Textile India Progress **4625**
Textile India Progress. (II) **4625**
Textile Industries Buyers Guide for Southern Africa. (SA) **4625**
Textile Industries Dyegest Southern Africa. (SA ISSN 0254-0533) **4625**
Textile Industries Southern Africa see Textile Industries Dyegest Southern Africa **4625**
Textile Industry & Trade Journal. (II ISSN 0040-4993) **4625**
†Textile Industry in O E C D Countries. (FR ISSN 0474-6023) **5289**
Textile Industry Technical Conference (Publication). (US ISSN 0094-9884) **4625**
Textile Information Condensed see Texincon **4624**
Textile Institute. Annual Conference. (UK) **4625**
Textile Institute. Journal. (UK ISSN 0040-5000) **4625**
Textile Machinery. (II ISSN 0040-5035) **4625**
Textile Machinery Society of Japan. Journal. (JA ISSN 0040-5043) **4625,** 3024
Textile Magazine. (II ISSN 0040-5078) **4626**
Textile Manufacturing. (US) **4626**
Textile Month. (UK ISSN 0040-5116) **4626**
Textile Museum Bulletin. (US) **3534,** 4626
Textile Museum Journal. (US ISSN 0083-7407) **4626,** 346, 357
Textile Museum Newsletter see Textile Museum Bulletin **3534**
Textile Network News. (US) **4626**
Textile News. (II ISSN 0040-5124) **4626**
Textile Newsletter. (US) **3622,** 4626
Textile Organon see Fiber Organon **4618**
Textile Outlook International. (UK ISSN 0268-4764) **4626**
Textile Pricing Outlook. (US ISSN 0739-4144) **4626,** 1055
Textile Progress. (UK ISSN 0040-5167) **4626**
Textile Recorder Annual and Machinery Review see International Textile Machinery **5218**
Textile Red Book see American Textile Directory **4616**
Textile Rental. (US ISSN 0195-0118) **1282**
Textile Research Journal. (US ISSN 0040-5175) **4626**

Textile Review. see Sen-i Kogyo Zasshi **4623**
Textile Review. (GR) **4626**
Textile Science and Technology. (NE) **4626**
Textile Technology Digest. (US ISSN 0040-5191) **4628,** 24
Textile Technology Digest: Abstract Alert. (US) **4628,** 24
▼Textile Technology Digest: Selected Information. (US) **4628,** 24
Textile Times International. (UK) **4626**
Textile Trends. (II ISSN 0040-5205) **4626**
†Textile Worker. (UK) **5289**
Textile World. (US ISSN 0040-5213) **4626**
Textiles Anciens see Centre International d'Etude des Textiles Anciens. Bulletin **4617**
Textiles et Usages Techniques see T U T **4623**
Textiles: Latin American Industrial Report. (US) **4626**
Textiles of Ireland and Linen Trade Circular see Textile Times International **4626**
Textiles Panamericanos. (US ISSN 0040-5140) **4626**
Textiles para el Hogar. (SP ISSN 0211-7975) **4626**
Textiles Suisses. (SZ ISSN 0040-5248) **4626**
Textiles Suisses: Interieur. (SZ ISSN 0082-3708) **4626**
Textilforum. (GW) **4626,** 357
Textilia. (NE ISSN 0040-5264) **4626**
†Textilia Journaal. (NE) **5289**
Textilkunst. (GW ISSN 0934-3342) **4626**
Textillaren. see Tekstiiliopettaja **2449**
Textiltechnik. (GW ISSN 0323-3804) **4626**
Texto e Contexto. (PO ISSN 0120-5455) **2847**
Texts and Monographs in Computer Science. (US ISSN 0172-603X) **1401**
Texts and Monographs in Economics and Mathematical Systems. (US) **898,** 3058
Texts and Monographs in Physics. (US ISSN 0172-5998) **3834**
Texts and Studies in Religion. (US) **4205**
Texts from Cuneiform Sources. (US ISSN 0082-3759) **2324**
Textual Practice. (UK ISSN 0950-236X) **2969**
Textures. (US) **2026,** 4853
Textures and Microstructures. (US ISSN 0730-3300) **1582,** 1838
Textus. (IS ISSN 0082-3767) **4205**
Textus et Studia Historica Carmelitana. (IT ISSN 0394-7793) **4277,** 2324
†Textus Minores. (NE ISSN 0169-8273) **5289**
Textus Patristici et Liturgici. (GW ISSN 0082-3775) **4205**
Teza. (BR) **1268**
Tezhong Boli/Special Glass. (CC) **1215**
Tezukayama College. Journal. Natural Science. see Tezukayama Tanki Daigaku Kiyo. Shizen Kagaku Hen **4347**
Tezukayama Tanki Daigaku Kiyo. Shizen Kagaku Hen/Tezukayama College. Journal. Natural Science. (JA ISSN 0286-5092) **4347**
Thackeray Newsletter. (US) **2969**
Thai Abstracts, Series A. Science and Technology. (TH ISSN 0125-0000) **4358,** 24, 4615
Thai-American Business. (TH ISSN 0125-0191) **823**
Thai Builders Directory. (TH) **1155,** 634
Thai Chamber of Commerce. Handbook (Year). (TH) **823**
Thai Chamber of Commerce. Journal. (TH) **823**
Thai - Chinese Chamber of Commerce. News. (TH) **823**
Thai Economic Review. (TH) **694**
Thai Industrial Directory. (TH ISSN 0857-1155) **1155**
Thai Journal of Agricultural Science. (TH ISSN 0049-3589) **124**

Thai Journal of Development Administration. (TH ISSN 0040-5353) **4075**, 1085
Thai Journal of Public Administration *see* Thai Journal of Development Administration **4075**
Thai Pharmaceutical Directory. (TH) **1155, 3744**
Thai Philately. (US ISSN 0198-7992) **3758**
Thailand. Division of Agricultural Chemistry. Report on Fertilizer Experiments and Soil Fertility Research. (TH ISSN 0085-7246) **194**
Thailand. Ministry of Foreign Affairs. Foreign Affairs Newsletter. (TH ISSN 0125-6459) **3973**
Thailand. Ministry of Foreign Affairs. News Bulletin *see* Thailand. Ministry of Foreign Affairs. Foreign Affairs Newsletter **3973**
Thailand. National Statistical Office. Annotated Statistical Bibliography. (TH ISSN 0857-9164) **413, 4590**
Thailand. National Statistical Office. Annual Report. (TH ISSN 0858-2696) **4590**
Thailand. National Statistical Office. Quarterly Bulletin of Statistics. (TH ISSN 0857-9482) **4590**
†Thailand. National Statistical Office. Report of Industrial Survey in Northeast Region/Thailand. Samnakngan Sathiti Haeng Chat. (TH) **5289**
Thailand. National Statistical Office. Research Paper. (TH) **4590**
Thailand. Samnakngan Sathiti Haeng Chat. *see* Thailand. National Statistical Office. Report of Industrial Survey in Northeast Region **5289**
Thailand Airline Timetable. (TH ISSN 0125-1090) **4677**
Thailand Business. (TH ISSN 0125-0981) **694**
Thailand Company Information (Year). (TH ISSN 0857-7277) **839, 1155**
Thailand: Economic Conditions In And Outlook For. (TH) **886**
Thailand Industrial Buyer's Guide. (TH ISSN 0857-2984) **1155**
Thailand Institute of Scientific and Technological Research Research News *see* T I S T R Research News **4346**
Thailand Investment Bulletin. (TH) **886**
Thailand National Directory. (TH) **2342**
Thailand Standard Industrial Classification. (TH) **995**
Thailand Trade Index. (TH) **922**
Thailand's Budget in Brief. (TH) **1111**
Thailand's Foreign Trade Statistics. (TH) **741**
Thalacker's Allgemeine Samen- und Pflanzen-Offerte *see* T A S P O **2139**
Thalacker's Allgemeine Samen- und Pflanzen-Offerte Magazin *see* T A S P O - Magazin **2139**
Thalackers Allgemeiner Samen- und Pflanzen-Offerte Gartenkurier *see* T A S P O Gartenkurier **2139**
Thalassas. (SP ISSN 0212-5919) **457, 1582, 1611**
Thalassia Jugoslavica. (CI) **457**
Thalassia Salentina. (IT) **519, 592, 4829**
Thalia. (CN ISSN 0706-5604) **2969**
Thames & Chiltern Industrial & Business News. (UK) **839**
Thames Book. (UK ISSN 0082-3805) **4788**, 2264, 4530
Thames-Chiltern Chamber of Commerce & Industry Directory. (UK) **1155, 823**
Thames Essays. (UK) **922**
Thames Gazette *see* Bucks Advertiser **2193**
Thames Valley Business. (UK) **823**
Thames Valley Life Style. (UK) **2196**
Thamesman Publications. Occasional Papers. (UK) **1029**
Thanatology Abstracts. (US) **4052, 24, 4048**
Thanatology Librarian. (US) **4048**
Thanatos. (US) **2120**

Thandi. (SA) **4853**
Thanet Extra. (UK) **2196**
Thapar's Indian Industrial Directory and Import and Export Directory of the World. (II) **1155**
Thaqafa wa Fann/Culture and Art. (TS) **346**
Al-Thaqafah al-Arabiyyah. (LY) **2209**
Thaqafat *see* Al-Ma'arif **3640**
Tharunee. (CE) **4853**
Tharunka. (AT) **1326**
▼That's My Baby. (US) **1245**
That's Yugoslavia. (GW ISSN 0179-3063) **3930**, 694, 2026, 2392
Al Thawrah Al Shaabiyah. (SJ) **2170**
Thawrah al-Ziraia/Agricultural Revolution Review. (SY) **124**
The-A-KiKi. (US ISSN 0091-1607) **2165**
The American Civil Defense Association Alert *see* T A C D A Alert **1274**
The Australian Journal of Anthropology *see* T A J A **250**
The Bureau of National Affairs, Inc. Administrative Practice Manual *see* B N A Administrative Practice Manual **2603**
The Drama Review *see* T D R **4639**
The Fertilizer Institute Action *see* T F I Action **194**
The Institute of Management Sciences Meeting Bulletin *see* T I M S - O R S A Meeting Bulletin **4346**
The Monroe Institute Focus *see* T M I Focus **1717**
The Original Writers Entrepreneurial Research Service Towers Club U S A Newsletter *see* Towers Club U S A Newsletter **4138**
The Second 2000 *see* Britain's Top 10,000 Privately Owned Companies **1124**
The Thao Van Hoa/Sports and Culture. (VN) **4494**
The Thao Viet-Nam/Viet-Nam Sports. (VN) **4494**
The Welding Institute Journal *see* T W I Journal **3430**
The-Yama-To-Keikoku/Mountain and Valley. (JA) **4558**
Theater (New Haven). (US ISSN 0161-0775) **4640**
Theater der Zeit. (GW ISSN 0040-5418) **4640**
Theater Heute. (SZ ISSN 0040-5507) **4640**, 1532, 3584
Theater in Graz. (AU) **4640**, 3584
▼Theater of Blood. (US) **3007**
Theater-Rundschau. (GW ISSN 0040-5442) **4640**
Theater Telegramm. (GW) **4640**
†Theater Three. (US ISSN 1052-0511) **5289**
Theater Week. (US ISSN 0896-1956) **4640**
Theater-Zytig *see* Theaterzytig **4640**
Theatermagazin. (GW) **4640**
Theaternachrichten *see* Theater in Graz **4640**
Theaterpaedagogik. (GW ISSN 0175-5889) **4640**
Theaterpaedagogische Bibliothek. (GW) **4640**
Theaterwork. (US ISSN 0735-1895) **4640**
TheaterZeitSchrift. (GW ISSN 0723-1172) **4640**, 2886
Theaterzytig. (SZ ISSN 0378-6935) **4640**
Theatre. *see* San Khau **4637**
Theatre (New York). (US) **4640**
Theatre Acteurs *see* Acteurs **4629**
Theatre and Cinema. *see* Xiju yu Dianying **350**
†Theatre and Dramatic Studies. (US) **5289**
Theatre & Events Guide. (US) **4640**
Theatre Annual. (US ISSN 0082-3821) **4640**
Theatre Art. *see* Xiju Yishu **4642**
Theatre Arts. *see* Xiju Yishu **4642**
Theatre Classics. (US) **4640**
Theatre Crafts. (US ISSN 0040-5469) **4640**
Theatre Crafts International. (US) **4640**
Theatre d'Aujourd'hui. (FR) **4640**
Theatre Design and Technology. (US ISSN 0040-5477) **4640**

Theatre Development Fund Sightlines *see* T D F Sightlines **4639**
Theatre Directory. (US ISSN 0271-3136) **4640**
Theatre Directory of the Bay Area (Year). (US ISSN 0737-0172) **4640**
†Theatre en Europe. (FR) **5289**
Theatre en Pologne/Theatre in Poland. (PL ISSN 0040-5493) **4640**
Theatre Enfance et Jeunesse. (FR ISSN 0049-3597) **4641**, 1268
Theatre et Animation. (FR ISSN 0398-0049) **4641**
Theatre for Young Audiences Today *see* T Y A Today **4639**
Theatre Francais de la Renaissance. (IT) **4641**
Theatre Guide - Theatre Gids *see* T R U K P A C T Info **4639**
Theatre History in Canada/Histoire du Theatre au Canada. (CN ISSN 0226-5761) **4641**
Theatre History Studies. (US ISSN 0733-2033) **4641**
Theatre in Poland. *see* Theatre en Pologne **4640**
Theatre Information Bulletin. (US ISSN 0040-5515) **4641**
Theatre Ireland. (UK ISSN 0263-6344) **4641**
Theatre Journal (Baltimore). (US ISSN 0192-2882) **4641**, 1667
The Theatre Listing. (CN) **4641**
Theatre Notebook. (UK ISSN 0040-5523) **4641**
Theatre Organ. (US ISSN 0040-5531) **3584**
Theatre Organ Review. (UK ISSN 0040-5558) **3584**, 4641
†Theatre Papers. (UK ISSN 0309-8036) **5289**
▼Theatre Patron. (US) **4641**
Theatre Profiles. (US ISSN 0361-7947) **4641**
Theatre Public. (FR ISSN 0335-2927) **4641**
Theatre Record. (UK ISSN 0962-1792) **4641**, 2576
Theatre Research *see* Theatre Research International **4641**
Theatre Research International. (UK ISSN 0307-8833) **4641**
†Theatre Student Series. (US ISSN 0082-3848) **5289**
Theatre Studies. (US ISSN 0362-0964) **4641**
Theatre Survey. (US ISSN 0040-5574) **4641**
†Theatre Times. (US ISSN 0732-300X) **5289**
▼Theatre Topics. (US ISSN 1054-8378) **4641**
Theatre World. (US ISSN 0082-3856) **4641**
Theatrephile. (UK ISSN 0265-2609) **4641**
Theatron. (IT ISSN 0040-5604) **4641**
Theatrum. (CN) **4641**
Theilheimer's Synthetic Methods of Organic Chemistry *see* Synthetic Methods of Organic Chemistry **1223**
Their World. (US) **1245, 1742, 3326**
Theleme. (CI) **1687**
Them Days. (CN ISSN 0381-6109) **2059, 251, 2424**
Thema. (AU) **694**
Thema. (US ISSN 1041-4851) **3007**
Thema. (GW) **4641**
Thema - Das Theatermagazin. (GW) **4641**
Thema Null *see* Blaue Feder **4430**
Themata. (SP) **1667, 3784**
Themata. (DK ISSN 0107-2676) **2392**
Themata Chorou & Technon. *see* Design & Art in Greece **298**
Thematic Catalogue Series. (US) **3584**
Thematic Poetry Quarterly. (US) **3007**
▼Thematic Studies in Second Language Learning and Acquisition. (US) **2847**
Thematical Reviews. *see* Temadokumentacios Kiadvanyok **5288**
†Thematische Information Philosophie. (GW ISSN 0138-2144) **5289**

Themelios. (UK ISSN 0307-8388) **4205**
▼Themenhefte Gemeindearbeit. (GW ISSN 0937-8766) **4205**
Themenzentrierte Interaktion. (GW ISSN 0934-5272) **4048**
Themes Canadiens. *see* Canadian Issues **2504**
Themes in Drama. (UK ISSN 0263-676X) **4641**
Themis *see* Revue Juridique Themis **2732**
Themis *see* Thesmophoria **4289**
Then and Now *see* Black Powder Times **4466**
Theochem *see* Journal of Molecular Structure: Theochem **1181**
Theodolite *see* McMaster Journal of Theology **4189**
Theodor-Storm-Gesellschaft. Schriften. (GW ISSN 0082-3880) **2969**
Theodore Roosevelt Association Journal.(US ISSN 0161-8423) **421, 2424**
Theokratia: Jahrbuch des Institutum Judaicum Delitzschianum. (NE ISSN 0169-8370) **4227**
Theologia. (GR ISSN 0049-3635) **4289**
Theologia Evangelica. (SA ISSN 0255-8858) **4205**
Theologia Reformata. (NE ISSN 0040-5612) **4250**
Theologia 21. (US ISSN 0362-0085) **4205, 3784**
Theologiai Szemle. (HU ISSN 0133-7599) **4206**
Theologica Xaveriana. (CK ISSN 0120-3649) **4277**
Theological and Religious Bibliographies. (UK) **4213**, 24
Theological and Religious Index *see* Theological and Religious Bibliographies **4213**
Theological Book Review. (UK ISSN 0954-2191) **4206**
Theological College of Northern Nigeria Research Bulletin *see* T C N N Research Bulletin **4205**
Theological Education. (US ISSN 0040-5620) **4206**, 1667
Theological Educator. (US ISSN 0198-6856) **4206**
Theological News. (KO ISSN 0260-3705) **4206**
Theological Studies. (US ISSN 0040-5639) **4206**
Theological Times. (UK ISSN 0049-3651) **2296, 4206**
Theologie der Gegenwart. (GW ISSN 0342-1457) **4206, 2392**
Theologie und Dienst. (GW) **4206**
Theologie und Glaube. (GW ISSN 0049-366X) **4277**
Theologie und Philosophie. (GW ISSN 0040-5655) **4206, 3784**
Theologisch-Praktische Quartalschrift. (AU ISSN 0040-5663) **4206**
Theologische Beitraege. (GW ISSN 0342-2372) **4206**
Theologische Dissertationen. (SZ ISSN 0082-3902) **4206**
Theologische Literaturzeitung. (GW ISSN 0040-5671) **4206**
Theologische Quartalschrift. (GW ISSN 0342-1430) **4277**
Theologische Revue. (GW ISSN 0040-568X) **4277**
Theologische Rundschau. (GW ISSN 0040-5698) **4206**
Theologische Zeitschrift. (SZ ISSN 0040-5701) **4206**
Theology. (UK ISSN 0040-571X) **4206**
Theology/Sharia. (JO) **4220**
Theology Digest. (US ISSN 0040-5728) **4206**
Theology Today. (US ISSN 0040-5736) **4206**
Theoretica Chimica Acta. (GW ISSN 0040-5744) **1189**
Theoretical and Applied Climatology. (US ISSN 0177-798X) **3441**
Theoretical and Applied Fracture Mechanics. (NE ISSN 0167-8442) **3846**
Theoretical and Applied Genetics. (GW ISSN 0040-5752) **547**

Theoretical and Computational Fluid Dynamics. (US ISSN 0935-4964) **3846**
Theoretical and Experimental Biology. (US ISSN 0082-3945) **457**
Theoretical and Experimental Chemistry. (English translation of: Teoreticheskaya i Eksperimental'naya Khimiya) (US ISSN 0040-5760) **1189**
Theoretical and Mathematical Physics. (English translation of: Teoreticheskaya; Matematicheskaya Fizika) (US ISSN 0040-5779) **3834, 3058**
Theoretical Chemical Engineering Abstracts. (UK ISSN 0040-5787) **1846, 24**
Theoretical Chemistry. (US ISSN 0082-3961) **1189**
†Theoretical Chemistry. (UK ISSN 0305-9995) **5289**
†Theoretical Chemistry: Advances and Perspectives. (US ISSN 0361-0551) **5289**
Theoretical Computer Science. (NE ISSN 0304-3975) **1482, 1457**
Theoretical Cybernetics Abstracts see Cybernetics Abstracts **1404**
Theoretical Foundations of Chemical Engineering. (English Edition of: Teoreticheskie Osnovy Khimicheskoi Tekhnologii) (US ISSN 0040-5795) **1860**
Theoretical Issues in Cognitive Science. (US) **4048**
Theoretical Linguistics. (GW ISSN 0301-4428) **2847**
Theoretical Medicine. (NE ISSN 0167-9902) **3156, 3784**
Theoretical Parapsychology. (US ISSN 0894-2528) **4048**
Theoretical Physics Seminar in Trondheim. (NO) **3834**
Theoretical Population Biology. (US ISSN 0040-5809) **458, 3988, 4454**
Theoretical Studies in Literature and Art. see Wenyi Lilun Yanjiu **2975**
Theoretical Studies in Second Language Acquisition. (US ISSN 1051-6670) **2847**
Theoretical Surgery. (GW ISSN 0179-8669) **3385**
Theoria. (SA ISSN 0040-5817) **2516, 4390**
Theoria. (SW ISSN 0040-5825) **3784, 4048**
Theorie de la Production. (FR ISSN 0082-3988) **694**
Theorie et Critique see T & C **346**
Theorie und Praxis. (GW ISSN 0323-5297) **1062, 1667**
Theorie und Praxis der Sozialen Arbeit. (GW) **4422**
Theorie und Praxis der Sozialpaedagogik. (GW ISSN 0342-7145) **1245, 4206**
Theorien der Psychologie. (US) **4048**
Theory and Decision. (NE ISSN 0040-5833) **4390, 3784**
Theory and Decision Library. (NE) **4390, 3784**
Theory and Modernization. see Lilun yu Xiandaihui **4379**
Theory and Practice. (US ISSN 0741-6156) **3584**
Theory and Practice of Scientific Information. see Tudomanyos Tajekoztatas Elmelete es Gyakorlata **5293**
▼Theory & Psychology. (UK ISSN 0959-3543) **4048**
Theory and Research see Theory and Research in Social Education **4390**
Theory and Research in Behavioral Pediatrics. (US) **4048, 3326**
Theory and Research in Social Education. (US ISSN 0093-3104) **4390, 1762**
Theory and Society. (NE ISSN 0304-2421) **4454**
Theory, Computational Science & Computing. (UK ISSN 0265-1831) **1401**
Theory Culture & Society. (UK ISSN 0263-2764) **4454, 2516**
Theory Into Practice. (US ISSN 0040-5841) **1667**

Theory of History. see Shixue Lilun **2322**
Theory of Probability and Its Applications. (English translation of: Teoriya Veroyatnostei i ee Primeneniya) (US ISSN 0040-585X) **3058**
Theory of Probability and Mathematical Statistics. (English translation of: Teoriya Veroyatnostei i Matematicheskaya Statistika) (US ISSN 0094-9000) **3058**
Theory of Science. see Teorie Vedy **4347**
Theosofia. (NE ISSN 0040-5868) **3784, 4206**
Theosofisch Forum. (NE) **3784**
†Theosophical History. (UK ISSN 0951-497X) **5290**
Theosophical Journal. (UK ISSN 0040-5876) **3784, 4206**
Theosophical Movement. (II ISSN 0040-5884) **3784**
Theosophie Heute. (GW ISSN 0177-8005) **4206**
Theosophist. (II ISSN 0040-5892) **3784, 4206**
Theosophy. (US ISSN 0040-5906) **3784**
Theosophy in Australia. (AT ISSN 0049-3694) **4206**
Theosophy in New Zealand. (NZ ISSN 0049-3708) **4289**
†Therapaeia. (US) **5290**
Therapeutic Archives. see Terapevticheskii Arkhiv **3156**
Therapeutic Drug Monitoring. (US ISSN 0163-4356) **3744**
Therapeutic Recreation Journal. (US ISSN 0040-5914) **3809, 4494**
Therapeutikon. (GW ISSN 0935-3194) **3156**
Therapeutiques Naturelles. (FR ISSN 0396-7107) **3157**
Therapeutische Umschau. (SZ ISSN 0040-5930) **3744**
Therapia Hungarica. (HU ISSN 0040-5949) **3157**
Therapie. (FR ISSN 0040-5957) **3157**
Therapie der Gegenwart. (GW ISSN 0040-5965) **3157**
Therapie Familiale. (SZ ISSN 0250-4952) **3355**
Therapiewoche. (GW ISSN 0040-5973) **3157**
Therapy Dogs International. Mini-Newsletter. (US) **3714, 231**
Therapy Weekly. (UK ISSN 0308-7808) **2469, 4422**
Theriaca. (DK ISSN 0082-4003) **3744**
Theriogenology. (US ISSN 0093-691X) **4816**
Thermal Analysis Abstracts see Thermal Analysis Reviews & Abstracts **1202**
Thermal Analysis Review see Thermal Analysis Reviews & Abstracts **1202**
Thermal Analysis Reviews & Abstracts. (UK ISSN 0956-2265) **1202, 1231**
Thermal Engineering. (English translation of: Teploenergetika) (UK ISSN 0040-6015) **1940**
Thermiek. (NE ISSN 0040-6023) **63**
Thermo- and Fluid Dynamics. see Waerme- und Stoffuebertragung **3842**
Thermo Med. (GW ISSN 0934-8395) **3157**
Thermochimica Acta. (NE ISSN 0040-6031) **1231**
Thermodynamics at Texas A & M. (US) **1231, 1860, 3842**
Thermodynamics Research Center. Data Project. Selected Values of Properties of Chemical Compounds. Category A. Tables of Selected Values of Physical and Thermodynamic Properties of Chemical Compounds see T R C Thermodynamic Tables - Non-Hydrocarbons **1209**
Thermodynamics Research Center. Data Project. Selected Values of Properties of Chemical Compounds. Category C. Selected Ultraviolet Spectral Data see T R C Spectral Data - Ultraviolet **1209**

Thermodynamics Research Center. Hydrocarbon Project. Selected Values of Properties of Hydrocarbons and Related Compounds. Category B: Selected Infared Spectral Data see T R C Spectral Data - Infared **1209**
Thermodynamics Research Center. Hydrocarbon Project. Selected Values of Properties of Hydrocarbons and Related Compounds. Category C: Selected Ultraviolet Spectral Data see T R C Spectral Data - Ultraviolet **1209**
Thermodynamics Research Center. Hydrocarbon Project. Selected Values of Properties of Hydrocarbons and Related Compounds. Category D: Selected Raman Spectral Data see T R C Spectral Data - Raman **1209**
Thermodynamics Research Center. Hydrocarbon Project. Selected Values of Properties of Hydrocarbons and Related Compounds. Category E: Selected Mass Spectral Data see T R C Spectral Data - Mass **1209**
Thermodynamics Research Center. Hydrocarbon Project. Selected Values of Properties of Hydrocarbons and Related Compounds. Category F: Selected Nuclear Magnetic Resonance Data see T R C Spectral Data - 1 H Nuclear Magnetic Resonance **1209**
Thermodynamics Research Center. Hydrocarbon Project. Selected Values of Properties of Hydrocarbons and Related Compounds. Category G: Selected 13-C Nuclear Magnetic Resonance Spectral Data see T R C Spectral Data - 13 C Nuclear Magnetic Resonance **1209**
Thermodynamics Research Center. Hydrocarbons Project. Selected Values of Properties of Hydrocarbons and Related Compounds. Category A: Tables of Selected Values of Physical and Thermodynamic Properties of Hydrocarbons see T R C Thermodynamic Tables - Hydrocarbons **1230**
Thermodynamics Research Center. International Data Series. Selected Data on Mixtures. Series A. Thermodynamic Properties on Non-reacting Binary Systems of Organic Substances see International Data Series. Selected Data on Mixtures. Series A. Thermodynamic Properties of Non-reacting Binary Systems of Organic Substances **1226**
Thermodynamics Research Center Spectral Data - Infared see T R C Spectral Data - Infared **1209**
Thermology. (US ISSN 0882-3758) **575, 3355, 3363**
Thermophysics. see Silumine Fizika **3841**
Thermophysics and Electronics Newsletter. (US ISSN 0194-6455) **3842, 1909**
Thesaurismata. (IT ISSN 0082-4097) **2324**
Thesaurus. (CK ISSN 0040-604X) **2847**
Thesaurus - American Petroleum Institute see American Petroleum Institute. Central Abstracting & Information Services. Thesaurus **3704**
Thesaurus of E R I C Descriptors. (Educational Resources Information Center) (US ISSN 1051-2993) **1667, 2787**
Theses and Other Publications of the University of Copenhagen. (DK ISSN 0900-2278) **413**
Theses Canadiennes. see Canadian Theses **396**
Thesis Abstracts. (II ISSN 0379-3990) **144, 24, 2520**
Thesmophoria. (US) **4289, 4853**
Theta. (UK ISSN 0953-0738) **3058**
Theta. (NE) **4289**
Theta. (Carrollton). (US ISSN 0040-6066) **3671**
Theta (New York). (US ISSN 0040-6074) **4206**
Theta Market Reports. (US) **3157, 1055**

Thieu Nien Tien Phong/Young Pioneers.(VN) **1268**
Thikana see Saptahika Thikana **3924**
Thin Films Science and Technology. (NE) **3834, 1189**
Thin-Layer Chromatography Abstracts. (UK ISSN 0049-3763) **1202, 24**
Thin Solid Films. (SZ ISSN 0040-6090) **3834, 1838**
Thin-Walled Structures. (UK ISSN 0263-8231) **1940**
Things of Science. (US) **4347, 1762**
Things to Come. (US) **3015**
Think. see Taenk **1508**
▼Think. (US ISSN 1055-9272) **1667**
Think, Inc. (US) **1268, 1667**
Think On. (US) **2165**
Thinking. (US ISSN 0190-3330) **3784, 1762**
Thinking about Faenza. see Pensare Faenza **2879**
†Thinking Families. (US) **5290**
Thinking Mission. (UK ISSN 0143-8514) **4206, 4250**
Third Branch. (US ISSN 0040-6120) **2733**
Third Century Methodism. (US) **4250**
Third Degree. (AT ISSN 0816-5157) **2886**
Third Degree (Exeter). (UK) **1326**
Third Degree (New York). (US ISSN 0040-6139) **2986, 2969**
Third Degree (Regina). (CN ISSN 0843-7092) **1326**
Third Eye. (US) **3007**
Third Force Psychology see Social Behavior and Personality **4047**
Third Half. (UK) **2969**
Third Indicator. (US) **2787**
Third Lung Review. (US) **3007**
Third Opinion. (AT ISSN 1030-5467) **1810**
Third Party Bulletin. (US) **1055, 3744**
Third Party Rx. (US) **3744**
Third Rail. (US ISSN 0741-5958) **2886**
Third Reich Study Group Bulletin. (US) **1354, 2392**
†Third Republic/Troisieme Republique. (US) **5290**
Third Sector see Third Sector Fortnight and Inform **4422**
Third Sector Fortnight and Inform. (UK) **4422**
Third Way (London, 1977). (UK ISSN 0309-3492) **4250**
Third Way (London, 1980) see Third Way - Beyond Capitalism and Communism **3930**
Third Way - Beyond Capitalism and Communism. (UK ISSN 0959-5031) **3930**
†Third Woman. (US ISSN 0889-0722) **5290**
Third World. see Terzo Mondo **4390**
†Third World Affairs. (UK ISSN 0267-2499) **5290**
Third World Development. (UK) **935**
Third World Economics. (MY ISSN 0128-4134) **694**
Third World First see Heritage (Lagos, 1984) **2004**
▼Third World in Perspective. (US ISSN 0885-2200) **3930, 3973**
Third World International see Thirdworld **935**
Third World Legal Studies (Year). (US ISSN 0895-5018) **2729, 935**
▼Third World Libraries. (US ISSN 1052-3049) **2787, 935**
Third World Planning Review. (UK ISSN 0142-7849) **935, 4075**
Third World Quarterly. (UK ISSN 0143-6597) **935**
Third World Resources. (US ISSN 8755-8831) **935, 1723**
Third World without Superpowers: Collected Documents of the Group of 77. (US ISSN 1046-2066) **3973, 2729**
Third World without Superpowers: Collected Documents of the Non-Aligned Countries. (US ISSN 1046-2074) **3973, 2729**
Third World Woman's Gay-zette. (US) **2457, 4853**

6730 THIRDWORLD

Thirdworld. (PK) 935
Thirteen (Portlandville). (US ISSN 0747-9727) 3007
Thirteenth District Dental Society. Bulletin see Thirtieth District Dental Society, Fresno, California. Bulletin 3243
Thirteenth Moon see 13th Moon 2980
Thirtieth District Dental Society, Fresno, California. Bulletin. (US) 3243
This and That. (US) 1268, 3007
This Caring Business. (UK ISSN 0268-4047) 4422
This England. (UK ISSN 0040-6171) 4788
This is Alaska. (US) 2236
This is Bahrain and What's On. (BA) 2173
This is Botswana. (BS) 4788, 2170
This is Bristol and Bath. (UK) 2196
This Is Ecuador. (EC) 4788
▼This Is Indianapolis. (US) 4788
This is London. (UK ISSN 0040-6198) 4788
This is Malawi. (MW ISSN 0563-4784) 886
This is Mexico. (MX) 4788
This is N E C (Year). (Nippon Electric Company) (JA ISSN 0910-3732) 1344
This is Newcastle and the Hunter Region. (AT ISSN 0726-4690) 2172
This is Qatar. (QA) 4789
▼This is Vietnam. (HK) 694, 4789
This Magazine. (CN ISSN 0381-3746) 3930
This Month in Korea. (KO) 3973
This Month in Mississippi. (US) 2457
This Month in Telecommunications. (US) 1367
This Month in Your Library see Spotlight on Your Library 2786
This People. (US ISSN 0273-6527) 4289
This Week see This Week in Western North Carolina 4789
This Week Big Island. (US) 4789
This Week in Adelaide. (AT) 4789
This Week in Berne. see Berner Wochen Bulletin 4754
This Week in Brisbane. (AT) 4789
†This Week in Cairns. (AT) 5290
This Week in Canberra. (AT) 4789
This Week in Chicago see Key Magazine. This Week in Chicago 4774
This Week in Consumer Electronics see T W I C E 1779
This Week in Court. (US) 2733
This Week in Darwin. (AT) 4789
This Week in Melbourne. (AT) 4789
This Week in Perth. (AT) 4789
This Week in Sydney. (AT) 4789
This Week in Tasmania. (AT) 4789
This Week in Texas. (US) 2457, 3947
This Week in the Piedmont Triad. (US) 4789
This Week in the Poconos. (US) 4789, 2480
This Week in Washington. (US ISSN 0743-2437) 4422, 4075
This Week in Western North Carolina. (US) 4789
This Week in Wood County Schools see Clipboard 1621
This Week Kauai. (US) 4789
This Week Maui. (US) 4789
This Week Oahu. (US) 4789
This Week Singapore. (SI) 4789
Thisweek. (NR ISSN 0794-4810) 2212
Thomas. (NE ISSN 0049-3805) 1762, 4277
Thomas Callander Memorial Lectures. (UK ISSN 0265-4601) 2324
Thomas Cook Airport Links see Thomas Cook Airports Guide Europe 4657
Thomas Cook Airports Guide Europe. (UK ISSN 0266-9404) 4657
†Thomas Cook Berlin Transit. (UK) 5290
Thomas Cook European Timetable. (UK ISSN 0952-620X) 4657
Thomas Cook International Timetable see Thomas Cook Overseas Timetable 4657

Thomas Cook Overseas Timetable. (UK ISSN 0144-7475) 4657
†Thomas Cook Railpass Guide. (UK) 5290
Thomas Food Industry Register. (US) 2083
Thomas Grocery Register see Thomas Food Industry Register 2083
†Thomas Hardy Annual. (US) 5290
Thomas Hardy Journal. (UK ISSN 0268-5418) 2969
Thomas Hardy Society. Review see Thomas Hardy Journal 2969
Thomas Hardy Year Book. (UI ISSN 0082-416X) 2969
Thomas Mann Gesellschaft. Blaetter. (SZ ISSN 0082-4186) 2969
Thomas Paine Society Bulletin see T P S Bulletin 3929
Thomas Register of American Manufacturers see Thomas Register of American Manufacturers and Thomas Register Catalog File 1055
Thomas Register of American Manufacturers and Thomas Register Catalog File. (US ISSN 0362-7721) 1055, 1155
Thomas Say Foundation Monographs. (US ISSN 1040-239X) 538, 124, 413, 4347
Thomas Wolfe Newsletter see Thomas Wolfe Review 2969
Thomas Wolfe Review. (US ISSN 0276-5683) 2969
Thomas Wolfe Society. Proceedings. (US) 2969
Thomas Wolfe Society. Summer Report and Membership List see Thomas Wolfe Society. Proceedings 2969
Thomasian Law Update. (PH) 2685
Thomist. (US ISSN 0040-6325) 4277, 3784
Thom's Commercial Directory. (IE ISSN 0082-4224) 1155
Thom's Dublin & County Street Directory. (IE) 2264, 1875
Thomson Credit Union Directory. (US) 801
Thomson Magazine. (FR) 1447
Thomson's Construction Australia. (AT) 634
Thomson's Liquor Guide. (AT ISSN 0313-0568) 1508, 386
Thomson's Print Production Directory. (AT ISSN 1033-6885) 4138
Thoracic and Cardiovascular Surgeon. (GW ISSN 0171-6425) 3385
Thorax. (UK ISSN 0040-6376) 3157
†Thoreau Quarterly. (US ISSN 0730-868X) 5290
Thoreau Society Bulletin. (US ISSN 0040-6406) 2969
Thoresby Society, Leeds, England. Publications. (UK ISSN 0082-4232) 2324
Thorikos. (BE ISSN 0775-3411) 287
Thorn. (CN) 1326
Thorndike Encyclopedia of Banking and Financial Tables (Supplement). (US) 801
Thorndyke File. (US ISSN 0145-5575) 2984, 2969
Thornhill Month. (CN) 1508
Thorny Trail. (US ISSN 0094-0844) 2165
Thoroton Society of Nottinghamshire. Transactions. (UK ISSN 0309-9210) 287, 2392
Thoroughbred and Classic Cars. (UK) 4703
Thoroughbred & Harness Racing Action.(US) 4538
Thoroughbred Breeders' Handbook. (AT ISSN 0311-8347) 4538
Thoroughbred of California. (US ISSN 0049-3821) 4538
Thoroughbred Racing Associations. Directory and Record Book. (US ISSN 0082-4240) 4538
†Thoroughbred Record. (US) 5290
Thoroughbred Times. (US ISSN 0887-2244) 4538
Thorvaldsens Museum. Meddelelser. (DK ISSN 0085-7262) 3534, 346
Thought. see Shiso 2515
Thought. (US ISSN 0040-6457) 4277, 3784

Thought & Action. (US ISSN 0748-8475) 1717
Thought and Words. see Ssu yu Yen 2515
Thought Starters for Management. (US) 1029
Thoughtline. (US) 3784
Thoughts. see Misli 4285
Thoughts for All Seasons. (US ISSN 0886-6481) 2969, 3784
Thraco-Dacica. (RM) 2392, 251, 287
Thrasher Magazine. (US ISSN 0889-0692) 4494, 1268
Threads. (US) 3593
Threatened Birds of Africa and Related Islands. (UK) 567
Three Counties Farming Review. (UK) 124
Three Crowns. (UK ISSN 0040-652X) 2196
Three - Fives Review see III - Vs Review 1773
Three Hundred Thirty-Eight News. (US ISSN 0040-6546) 2590, 2094
Three Minutes a Day. (US) 4206
Three Rivers Chronicle. (US) 2424, 2165
Three Rivers Poetry Journal. (US ISSN 0362-4846) 3007
Threepenny Review. (US ISSN 0275-1410) 2969
Threshing Floor. (UK ISSN 0260-4892) 4206
Threshold. (US ISSN 0736-1149) 307, 346
Threshold. (UK ISSN 0040-6562) 2969
Thresholds. (US) 3784
Thresholds in Education. (US ISSN 0196-9641) 1667
Thresholds in Secondary Education see Thresholds in Education 1667
Thrift Accountant. (US) 756, 801
Thrift Attorney see Banking Attorney 2603
Thrift Financial Report. (US) 886
Thrift Focus see Sixth District Focus 799
Thrift Regulator. (US) 801
Throb. (SA ISSN 0040-6589) 1838
Thrombosis and Haemostasis. (GW ISSN 0340-6245) 3212
Thrombosis Research. (US ISSN 0049-3848) 3212
▼Thrombotic and Haemorrhagic Disorders. (AU ISSN 0934-9669) 3212
Thronateeska Heritage Foundation. Newsletter. (US) 2424
†Through Casa Guidi Windows. (US) 5290
Through the Ages see Stone Through the Ages 5283
†Through the Looking Glass. (US) 5290
Thrower. (UK) 4558
Thru the Garden Gate. (US ISSN 0040-6619) 2139
Thrum's All About Hawaii. (US) 4789
Thruput see Integrated Networks Update 5215
Thrust (Gaithersburg) see Quantum (Gaithersburg) 3013
Thrust (Sacramento). (US ISSN 0145-2061) 1667
▼Thueringer Zahnaerzteblatt. (GW ISSN 0939-5687) 3243
Thuglak. (II) 2202
Thunder. (GY ISSN 0040-6635) 3930
Thunder & Honey. (US) 2886
Thunder Bay Business. (CN) 1119
†Thunder Bay Camping Guide. (CN ISSN 0380-6197) 5290
Thunder Bay Car & Truck News. (CN) 4703
Thunder Bay Destinations see Thunder Bay Life 4789
Thunder Bay Guest. (CN) 4789
Thunder Bay Guide. (CN) 1383
Thunder Bay Historical Museum Society. Papers and Records. (CN ISSN 0082-4283) 2424
Thunder Bay Life. (CN) 4789
Thunder Bay Magazine. (CN ISSN 0823-6542) 2179
Thunder Bay Real Estate News. (CN) 4158

Thunder from Heaven. (US) 3473, 1301
Thunderbolt see The Truth at Last 3948
Thunderer. (UK) 1326
▼Thuong Mai/Commerce. (VN) 839
Thurgauische Museum. Mitteilungen. (SZ) 3534
Thurgood Marshall Law Review. (US) 2685
Thuringen-Bibliographie. (GW ISSN 0232-3907) 2330
Thursday see Entertainment Guide 1373
Thwe - Thauk Magazine. (BR) 2969
Thymus. (NE ISSN 0165-6090) 3189
†Thymus. (UK ISSN 0266-6618) 5290
Thymus Update. (US ISSN 0896-341X) 3189
Thyras Vold. (DK) 2185
Thyristor D.A.T.A. Book see Thyristor D.A.T.A. Digest 1909
Thyristor D.A.T.A. Digest. (US ISSN 1040-0222) 1909
▼Thyroid. (US ISSN 1050-7256) 3256
†Thyroid Disorders. (UK ISSN 0226-6628) 5290
Thyroid Hormones. (UK ISSN 0142-8349) 3256, 3157
Thyssen Edelstahl Technische Berichte. (GW ISSN 0724-7265) 3422
Thyssen Edelstahlwerke. Mitteilungsblatt. (GW) 4612
Thyssen Technische Berichte. (GW ISSN 0340-5060) 3422
Ti Saluto, Fratello! (IT ISSN 0040-6686) 4206
Tian Feng. (CC) 4250
Tian Nan. (CC) 2969
Tian Wai Tian/Sky Outside Sky. (US) 3518, 4641
Tiancai Tangye/Beet Sugar Industries. (CC ISSN 1000-6451) 124
Tianchi. (CC) 2969
Tianfu Xinlun. (CC) 4390
Tianjin Broadcasting and T V Weekly. (CC) 1383
Tianjin Daxue Xuebao/Tianjin University. Journal. (CC ISSN 0493-2137) 4347
Tianjin Education. see Tianjin Jiaoyu 1667
Tianjin Fangzhi Gongxueyuan Xuebao/ Tianjin Institute of Textile Science and Technology. Journal. (CC ISSN 1000-1557) 4626
Tianjin Gesheng/Songs of Tianjin. (CC) 3584
Tianjin Institute of Light Industry. Journal. see Tianjin Qing Gongye Xueyuan Xuebao 1909
Tianjin Institute of Textile Science and Technology. Journal. see Tianjin Fangzhi Gongxueyuan Xuebao 4626
Tianjin Jiaoyu/Tianjin Education. (CC ISSN 0493-2099) 1667
Tianjin Jiyou/Tianjin Philately. (CC) 3758
Tianjin Pharmacy. see Tianjin Yiyao 3744
Tianjin Philately. see Tianjin Jiyou 3758
Tianjin Qing Gongye Xueyuan Xuebao/ Tianjin Institute of Light Industry. Journal. (CC ISSN 1001-456X) 1909
Tianjin University. Journal. see Tianjin Daxue Xuebao 4347
Tianjin Yiyao/Tianjin Pharmacy. (CC ISSN 0253-9896) 3744
Tianjing/Track & Field. (CC ISSN 1000-3509) 4558
Tianran Chanwu Yanjiu yu Kaifa/Natural Product Research and Development. (CC ISSN 1001-6880) 1189
Tianranqi Gongye/Natural Gas Industry.(CC ISSN 1000-0976) 3702, 1582, 3496
Tianti Wuli Xuebao/Acta Astrophysica Sinica. (CC ISSN 0253-2379) 370, 3834
Tianwen Aihaozhe/Amateur Astronomer.(CC) 370
Tianwen Xuebao/Acta Astronomica Sinica. (CC ISSN 0001-5245) 370

Tianwenxue Jinzhan/Progress in Astronomy. (CC ISSN 1000-8349) **370**
The Tibet Journal. (II ISSN 0970-5368) **3644**
Tibet Society. Journal. (US ISSN 0735-1364) **3644**, **2342**
Tibet Society Bulletin. (US ISSN 0883-7732) **2026**, **4789**
Tibet Society Newsletter see Tibet Society Bulletin **2026**
Tibet und Buddhismus. (GW ISSN 0938-3506) **4215**
Tibetan and Indo-Tibetan Studies. (GW ISSN 0935-7505) **3644**
Tibetan Art Studies. see Xizang Yishu Yanjiu **350**
Tibetan Buddhism. see Xizang Fojiao **4216**
Tibetan Bulletin. (II ISSN 0254-9808) **4216**
Tibetan Culture. see Xueyu Wenhua **3645**
Tibetan Education. see Xizang Jiaoyu **1672**
Tibetan Literature. see Xizang Wenxue **2978**
Tibetan Medicine. (II ISSN 0970-1257) **3157**
Tibetan Review. (II ISSN 0040-6708) **3930**
Tibetan Studies. see Xizang Yanjiu **3645**
Tibia. (GW ISSN 0176-6511) **3584**
Tibiscus. Seria Arta. (RM) **346**
Tibiscus. Seria Etnografie. (RM) **251**
Tibiscus. Seria Istorie. (RM) **2392**
Tibiscus. Seria Stiintele Naturii. (RM) **4347**
Ticao/Gymnastics. (CC ISSN 1000-3444) **4495**
Ticker. (US) **1326**
Ticket. (GW) **3473**, **2191**, **4789**
Ticket. (SZ) **4789**
Tico Times. (CR) **2180**
Tid og Syn. (DK) **2566**, **3305**
Tidal Gravity Corrections. (NE ISSN 0257-4284) **1596**
Tidbits. (US) **1668**, **2686**
Tiddly Dyke. (UK ISSN 0144-2708) **4715**
Tide. (US) **1498**, **1969**, **2686**, **4558**
Tide. see Ushio **2208**
Tiden. (SW ISSN 0040-6759) **3930**
Tidepool. (CN ISSN 0824-7579) **3007**
Tidevandstabeller for Danmark. (DK ISSN 0106-8334) **4829**
Tidevandstabeller for Faeroerne. (DK ISSN 0106-8342) **1611**
Tidevandstabeller for Groenland. (DK ISSN 0107-0398) **1611**
Tidewater Virginia Sanyo Users Group Suggestions see T V Suggestions **1474**
†Tidewater Virginian. (US) **5290**
Tidings see Akim Review **1733**
Tidings. (CN) **4558**, **2179**, **4095**, **4495**
Tidings (Boston). (US) **1969**, **1498**
Tidings (Los Angeles). (US ISSN 0040-6791) **4277**
Tidningen Foeretagarna. (SW) **1119**
†Tidnings Nytt. (SW ISSN 0040-6805) **5290**
Tidningsteknik. (SW ISSN 0347-4135) **4006**, **2576**
Tidskrift foer Barnmorskor. see Katilolehti **3294**
Tidskrift foer Dokumentation/Nordic Journal of Documentation. (SW ISSN 0040-6872) **2787**
Tidskrift foer Kriminalvaard. (SW ISSN 0040-6821) **1523**
Tidskrift foer Kustartilleriet. (SW ISSN 0040-683X) **3473**
Tidskrift foer Raettssociologi. (SW ISSN 0281-2584) **2686**, **4454**
Tidskrift foer Schack. (SW ISSN 0040-6848) **4495**
Tidskrift foer Yngre Laekare. (SW) **995**, **2469**, **3157**
Tidskrift foer Yrkesutbildning. (SW ISSN 0040-6856) **1668**
Tidskrift for Antropologi see Tidsskriftet Antropologi **251**

Tidskrift for Praktiska Ungdomsskolor see Tidskrift foer Yrkesutbildning **1668**
Tidskrift for Sygeplejeforskning. (DK ISSN 0900-3002) **3287**
Tidskrift i Fortifikation. (SW ISSN 0040-6937) **1875**, **3473**
Tidskrift i Sjovasendet. (SW ISSN 0040-6945) **3473**
Tidskriften Byggforskning. (SW) **634**, **1875**, **2497**
Tidskriften Heimdal. (SW ISSN 0040-6988) **3930**
Tidskriften Laboratoriet. (SW ISSN 0345-696X) **3263**
Tidsskrift for Biavl. (DK ISSN 0900-0801) **124**
Tidsskrift for Dansk Faareavl. (DK) **227**
Tidsskrift for Danske Sygehuse. (DK ISSN 0040-702X) **2469**
Tidsskrift for det Norske Utskiftningsvesen see Kart og Plan **2255**
Tidsskrift for Epilepsi see Epilepsi **3336**
Tidsskrift for Faareavl see Tidsskrift for Dansk Faareavl **227**
Tidsskrift for Groenlands Retsvaesen. (DK ISSN 0040-6880) **2686**
Tidsskrift for Hermetikkindustri see Naeringsmiddelindustrien **2078**
Tidsskrift for Kaninavl. (DK ISSN 0900-3401) **227**, **3714**
Tidsskrift for Kortboelge Radio see OZ **1357**
Tidsskrift for Landoekonomi. (DK ISSN 0040-7119) **124**
Tidsskrift for Planteavl/Danish Journal of Plant and Soil Science. (DK ISSN 0040-7135) **519**
Tidsskrift for Racefjerkrae. (DK) **227**
Tidsskrift for Rettsvitenskap. (NO ISSN 0040-7143) **2686**
Tidsskrift for Revisjon og Regnskapsvesen see Revisjon og Regnskap **755**
Tidsskrift for Samfunnsforskning. (NO ISSN 0040-716X) **4390**
Tidsskrift for Skatteret. (DK ISSN 0109-2383) **1111**
Tidsskrift for Sukkersyge. (DK ISSN 0040-7194) **4250**
Tidsskrift for Teologi og Kirke. (NO ISSN 0040-7194) **4250**
Tidsskrift for Tunghoere see Hoerelsen **2287**
Tidsskriftet Antropologi. (DK) **251**
Tidsskriftet den Hoegre Skolen see Skoleforum **1716**
†Tidsskriftet Ny Tid og Vi. (DK ISSN 0040-7224) **5290**
Tidsskriftsindeks for Skolebiblioteker. (DK ISSN 0105-4090) **413**, **1668**
Tie. (US ISSN 0040-7232) **4250**
Tie ja Liikenne. (FI ISSN 0355-7855) **1875**, **4721**
Tie Lines. (US) **1288**, **1055**, **1085**
Tiedao Jianzhu/Railway Construction. (CC) **4715**
Tiedao Xuebao/China Railway Society. Journal. (CC) **4715**
Tiedao Yunshu yu Jingji/Railway Transportation and Economics. (CC) **4715**
Tiedao Zhishi/Railway Knowledge. (CC ISSN 1000-0372) **4716**
Tiede ja Ase. (FI ISSN 0358-8882) **2392**
Tiede 2000. (FI ISSN 0358-1039) **4347**
Tiefbau, Ingenieurbau, Strassenbau. (GW ISSN 0340-5079) **1875**
Die Tiefbauberufsgenossenschaft. (GW ISSN 0340-952X) **634**
Tiempo. (MX ISSN 0040-7275) **2210**
Tiempo Actual. (CR) **2180**
Tiempo de Cine. (AG ISSN 0040-7283) **3518**
Tiempo de Viajar. (SP) **4789**
Tiempo Latino. (US) **2026**
Tiempo y Espacio. (VE) **2424**, **1717**
Tiempos de Ciencia. (MX ISSN 0186-5730) **4347**
Tiempos Medicos. (SP ISSN 0210-9999) **3157**
Tien Phong/Vanguard. (VN) **1268**, **3930**

Tienda de Recambios y Accesorios. (SP) **4703**
Tiendas de Drogueria & Perfumeria. (SP) **377**
Tienerkompas. (SA) **4206**
Das Tier. (SZ ISSN 0040-7291) **592**
Tier und Naturfotografie see Fotografie Draussen **3791**
Tieraerztliche Praxis. (GW ISSN 0303-6286) **4816**
Tieraerztliche Umschau. (GW ISSN 0049-3864) **4816**
Tiered Rate Watch see Rate Watch **796**
Tierfreund see Schweizer Tierschutz **231**
Tierfreund. (GW ISSN 0342-3018) **1268**, **592**, **1969**
Tiergarten Tip. (GW) **39**
Tierra. (SP) **124**
Tierra Nueva. (CK) **4454**, **4206**
Tierra Santa see Terra Santa **4205**
Tierra y Sociedad. (PE) **124**
Tierras de Leon. (SP ISSN 0495-5773) **2218**
Tiers Monde. (FR ISSN 0040-7356) **935**
Tiers Monde Ingenierie. (FR) **1838**
Tierwelt Deutschlands. (GW ISSN 0082-4305) **592**
Tierzucht see Neue Landwirtschaft **109**
Der Tierzuechter. (GW ISSN 0040-7364) **227**
Tiesa. (US ISSN 0040-7372) **2026**
Tietokone. (FI ISSN 0359-4947) **1474**
▼Tietoverkko. (FI ISSN 0788-6381) **1428**
Tiewelt. (SZ) **567**, **4495**
Tigai Xinxi/Economic Reform News. (CC) **1000**
The Tiger. (US) **1326**
Tiger Lily Magazine. (CN) **3007**
†Tiger Report. (Timely Investments Get Excellent Results) (US ISSN 0149-5887) **5290**
Tiger Tales. (US) **4703**
Tigermaedchen. (GW) **1268**
Tight Lines. (US) **4495**, **2442**
†Tightrope. (AT ISSN 1031-8283) **5290**
▼Tightwad Gazette. (US) **1508**
Tiili. (FI ISSN 0040-7402) **634**
Tiiliteollisuus see Tiili **634**
Al-Tijarah. (TS) **823**
Al-Tijarah (Dammam). (SU) **694**
Al-Tijarah (Jeddah). (SU) **823**
Al-Tijarah (Mecca). (SU) **694**
Tijdingen. (BE) **4138**
Tijdschrift der Belgische Posterijen. see Revue des Postes Belges **1354**
Tijdschrift der Openbare Werken van Belgie see Annales des Travaux Publics de Belgique **1861**
Tijdschrift Landinrichting. (NE) **194**, **4721**, **4829**
Tijdschrift voor Agologie. (NE ISSN 0168-8626) **4454**
Tijdschrift voor Alcohol, Drugs en Andere Psychotrope Stoffen. see Journal of Alcohol, Drugs and other Psychotropic Substances **1537**
Tijdschrift voor Arbitrage. (NE ISSN 0167-1359) **2686**
Tijdschrift voor Bejaarden-, Kraam- en Ziekenverzorging see Tijdschrift voor Verzorgenden **3287**
Tijdschrift voor Belgisch Handelsrecht. see Revue de Droit Commercial Belge **2674**
Tijdschrift voor Bestuurswetenschappen en Publiekrecht. (BE ISSN 0040-7437) **2686**
Tijdschrift voor Criminologie. (NE ISSN 0165-182X) **1523**
Tijdschrift voor de Geschiedenis der Geneeskunde, Natuurwetenschappen, Wiskunde en Techniek see Gewina **4311**
Tijdschrift voor de Politie. (NE ISSN 0165-0122) **1523**
Tijdschrift voor de Studie van de Verlichting see Tijdschrift voor de Studie van de Verlichting en van het Vrije Denken **2969**

Tijdschrift voor de Studie van de Verlichting en van het Vrije Denken/ Review for the Study of Enlightenment and Free-Thinking. (BE ISSN 0774-1847) **2969**
Tijdschrift voor Diergeneeskunde/ Netherlands Journal of Veterinary Science. (NE ISSN 0040-7453) **4816**
Tijdschrift voor Economie see Tijdschrift voor Economie en Management **695**
Tijdschrift voor Economie en Management. (BE ISSN 0772-7674) **695**
Tijdschrift voor Economische en Sociale Geografie/Netherlands Journal of Economic and Social Geography. (NE ISSN 0040-747X) **2264**, **4390**
Tijdschrift voor Entomologie. (NE ISSN 0040-7496) **538**
Tijdschrift voor Filosofie. (BE ISSN 0040-750X) **3784**
Tijdschrift voor Geneeskunde. (BE ISSN 0005-8440) **3157**
Tijdschrift voor Gerontologie en Geriatrie. (NE) **2279**
Tijdschrift voor Geschiedenis. (NE ISSN 0040-7518) **2324**
†Tijdschrift voor Gezondheid en Politiek.(NE ISSN 0167-8647) **5290**
Tijdschrift voor het Ouderenwerk in Nederland en Vlaenderen see Senior **2278**
Tijdschrift voor Jeugdhulpverlening see Tijdschrift voor Jeugdhulpverlening en Jeugdwerk **1245**
Tijdschrift voor Jeugdhulpverlening en Jeugdwerk. (NE) **1245**
Tijdschrift voor Kindergeneeskunde. (NE) **3326**
Tijdschrift voor Marketing. (NE ISSN 0165-1439) **1055**
Tijdschrift voor Nederlandse Taal- en Letterkunde. (NE ISSN 0040-7550) **2969**, **2847**
Tijdschrift voor Ontwikkelingssamenwerken see Noord - Zuid Cahier **4444**
Tijdschrift voor Oppervlaktetechnieken en Corrosiebestrijding. (NE ISSN 0923-1722) **3422**
Tijdschrift voor Opvoedkunde see Pedagogisch Tijdschrift **1654**
Tijdschrift voor Orthopedagogiek. (NE) **1762**
Tijdschrift voor Oude Muziek. (NE ISSN 0920-0649) **3584**
Tijdschrift voor Privaatrecht. (BE ISSN 0082-4313) **2686**
Tijdschrift voor Psychiatrie. (NE ISSN 0303-7339) **3355**
Tijdschrift voor Rechtsgeschiedenis/ Revue d'Histoire du Droit/Legal History Review. (NE ISSN 0040-7585) **2686**, **2324**
Tijdschrift voor Revalidatiewetenschappen/Journal of Rehabilitation Sciences. (NE ISSN 0923-0211) **1742**
Tijdschrift voor Sociaal Recht. see Revue de Droit Social **2674**
Tijdschrift voor Sociaal Wetenschappelijk Onderzoek van de Landbouw. (NE ISSN 0921-481X) **158**, **4390**
Tijdschrift voor Sociale Geneeskunde see Tijdschrift voor Sociale Gezondheidszorg **3157**
Tijdschrift voor Sociale Geschiedenis. (NE) **3930**
Tijdschrift voor Sociale Gezondheidszorg. (NE ISSN 0920-0517) **3157**, **4113**
Tijdschrift voor Sociale Wetenschappen. (BE ISSN 0040-7615) **4454**
Tijdschrift voor Taalbeheersing. (NE) **2848**
Tijdschrift voor Theaterwetenschap. (NE ISSN 0167-5516) **4641**
Tijdschrift voor Theologie. (NE ISSN 0168-9959) **4277**, **4250**
Tijdschrift voor Vervoerswetenschap/ Journal for Transport Science. (NE ISSN 0040-7623) **4657**
Tijdschrift voor Verzorgenden. (NE) **3287**
Tijdschrift voor Zeegeschiedenis. (NE ISSN 0167-9988) **4740**

6732 TIJDSCHRIFT

Tijdschrift voor Ziekenverpleging. (NE) **3287**
Tijdspiegel. (BE ISSN 0040-764X) **2886**
Tijjarat al Sharq al Aussat. *see* Middle East Trade **917**
Tikalia. (GT) **124**
▼Tikhviiskaya Ploshchad' (RU) **3930**
Tikker. (NE ISSN 0165-0890) **1268**
Tikkun Magazine. (US ISSN 0887-9982) **2026**, 4454
Tikshoret. (IS) **1352**
Tikvah. (US) **2026**
Tilastokeskus. Pankit *see* Finland. Tilastokeskus. Rahoitus **716**
Tilastokeskus. Tulonjakotilasto *see* Finland. Tilastokeskus. Tulot ja Kulutus **717**
Tilastollisia Kuukaustitietoja Helsingista *see* Helsingin Kaupungin Tilastokeskuksen Neljannesvuosikatsaus **4573**
Tilastotiedotus P A *see* Finland. Tilastokeskus. Tilastotiedotus. Palkat Loner **716**
Tilastotiedotus YR *see* Finland. Tilastokeskus. Tilastotiedotus. Yritykset Foretag **4571**
Tile & Brick International. (GW ISSN 0938-9806) **1166**
Tile and Decorative Surfaces. (US ISSN 0192-9550) **634**, 1166
Tile Book. (IT) **1155**, 1166
Tile Book (Year). (IT) **1155**, 1166
Tile News. (US) **1166**, 635, 2555
Tile World. (US) **1166**
Till Rors (Med Segel och Motor) *see* Paa Kryss och till Rors **4527**
Till Tjaenst. (Evangeliska Fosterlands-Stiftelsen) (SW ISSN 0349-2559) **1668**
Tillidsrepraesentant Information Socialpaedagogernes Landsforbund. T R Information *see* Socialpaedagogernes Landsforbund. T R Information **1664**
Tillman Survey. (US) **966**
Tim *see* Maky **1259**
Tim Bell's Alaska Travel Guide. (US ISSN 1054-5034) **4789**
Tim Kelley's Fishing Guide *see* Colorado Hunting, Fishing & Outdoor Guide **4544**
†Timah Malaysia/Malaysian Tin. (MY ISSN 0126-5547) **5290**
Timarit Idnadarmanna. (IC) **995**
Timarit Um Islenzka Grasafraedi. *see* Acta Botanica Islandica **492**
Timber and Plywood *see* Timber Trades Journal and Wood Processing **2117**
Timber Development Association (NSW) Ltd. Timber News *see* T D A Timber News **5286**
Timber Development Association of India. Journal. (II ISSN 0040-7755) **2117**
Timber Equipment Trader. (US) **2117**
Timber Framing. (US) **635**, 307
Timber Grower. (UK ISSN 0040-7763) **2109**
Timber Harvesting. (US ISSN 0160-6433) **2117**
Timber Mart-North. (US) **2117**
Timber Mart-South. (US ISSN 0194-5955) **2117**
Timber of Canada *see* Canadian Forest Industries **2113**
Timber Processing. (US) **2117**
The Timber Producer. (US) **2109**
Timber Supply Review *see* Quarterly Timber Statistics **2112**
Timber Trade Journal Timber Telephone Address Book *see* T T J Timber Telephone Address Book **2117**
Timber Trades Journal. Annual Special Issue. (UK ISSN 0082-4364) **2117**
Timber Trades Journal and Saw Mill Advertiser *see* Timber Trades Journal and Wood Processing **2117**
Timber Trades Journal and Wood Processing. (UK ISSN 0262-6071) **2117**, 3024
Timber Trades Journal and Woodworking Machinery *see* Timber Trades Journal and Wood Processing **2117**
Timber Trails. (US) **2166**
Timber-West. (US) **2118**

Timberlines. (CN ISSN 0833-0689) **2109**
Timberman *see* Australian Timberman **2113**
†Timbuktu. (US ISSN 0896-3878) **5290**
Time. (US ISSN 0040-781X) **2236**
▼Time and Society. (UK ISSN 0961-463X) **4455**
Time & Tide. (II ISSN 0040-7836) **3518**
†Time and Tide. (UK ISSN 0040-7828) **5290**
Time Charters. (UK) **4740**, 2686
Time for Business. (UK) **695**
Time Management Letter. (AT) **1029**
Time New Zealand. (NZ) **2212**
Time of Change: Handbook on Women Workers. (US) **995**
Time of Singing. (US) **4207**, 3007
Time Out. (UK ISSN 0049-3910) **4789**
Time-Sharing Homes & Holidays *see* Homes Overseas **4150**
Time Top Management. (US) **1029**
†Timecraft. (UK ISSN 0260-5988) **5290**
Timeform *see* Timeform Black Book **4538**
Timeform Black Book. (UK) **4538**
Timekeeper. (US) **2166**
Timeless Fellowship. (II ISSN 0563-5489) **2787**
Timeless Insights *see* Closer Walk **4171**
Timeline. (US ISSN 0748-9579) **2424**, 287, 346
Timely Disclosure. (CN ISSN 0838-5769) **801**, 886, 966
Timely Investments Get Excellent Results Tiger Report *see* Tiger Report **5290**
Timely Tips Magazine. (US) **801**
†Timepiece Register. (UK) **5290**
Times (Bethlehem). (US) **2497**, 635
Times and Challenge. (US ISSN 0040-7879) **1326**
Times and Chimes *see* Times and Challenge **1326**
Times Business Directory of Singapore. (SI ISSN 0217-6009) **1155**
Times Educational Supplement. (UK ISSN 0040-7887) **1668**
Times Enterprise. *see* Shih Tai Chi Yeh **1084**
Times - Foothills Entertainment *see* Surry Scene **2235**
Times Gone By *see* Journal of San Diego History **2411**
Times Guide to Computers. (SI) **1155**
Times Guide to the House of Commons.(UK ISSN 0082-4399) **3930**
Times Higher Education Supplement. (UK ISSN 0049-3929) **1717**
Times: in harness. (US ISSN 1046-9974) **4538**
Times Index. (UK) **2579**, 24
Times International. (NR) **2212**
Times Journal of Manila (International Edition) *see* Manila Journal **2213**
▼Times Law Reports. (UK ISSN 0958-0441) **2686**
Times Literary Supplement. (UK ISSN 0040-7895) **2969**, 4138
Times Observer. (US) **2236**
The Times of Acadiana. (US) **2236**
Times of Malta. (AT) **2026**
Times of Malta and Australia *see* Times of Malta **2026**
Times of Oman. (MK) **2211**
Times of Papua New Guinea. (PP) **2213**
Times of Restoration. (US ISSN 0740-9680) **4207**
The Times of the Americas. (US ISSN 0040-7917) **2180**
Times Review. (US) **4277**
Times Trade and Industrial Directory. (NR) **1155**
Times 1000. (UK ISSN 0082-4429) **1085**
Timesharing Law Reporter. (US ISSN 0738-6923) **2686**, 4158
Timestream. (AT) **3007**
Timewatch. (AT) **1070**, 1085, 1119
Timing. (US) **966**
Timing Analysis Projection. (US) **4590**, 1070

Timire an Chroi Naofa. (IE) **4277**, 2203
Timiryazevskaya Sel'skokhozyaistvennaya Akademiya. Izvestiya. (RU ISSN 0021-342X) **124**
Timken Magazine. (US) **3024**
Timmerfabrikant. (NE ISSN 0040-7933) **640**
Timp Liber. (RM) **347**, 2969
Tin and Its Uses. (UK ISSN 0040-7941) **3422**
Tin Canner. (US) **3758**
Tin International. (US ISSN 0040-795X) **3422**, 3652
Tin Printer and Box Maker *see* Tin International **3422**
Tin Production and Investment. (UK) **3422**
Tin Statistics. (UK) **3428**
Tin Type. (US) **2443**
Tin Wreath. (US) **3007**
Tina. (GW) **2449**, 4853
Tinctoria (Milan). (IT ISSN 0040-7984) **4627**, 1282
Ting og Sager fra Odsherred *see* Alle Tiders Odsherred **2347**
Tingley's United News *see* T U News **2165**
Tinkle. (II) **1268**
Tinney-Green(e) Family Organization Newsletter. (US) **2166**
Tinney-Green(e) Family Organization Quarterly *see* Tinney-Green(e) Family Organization Newsletter **2166**
Tinnitus Today. (American Tinnitus Association) (US ISSN 0897-6368) **3317**, 2289, 4422
Tinplate World. (UK ISSN 1010-609X) **3422**
Tinsae. (ET) **4289**
Tiny Toon Adventures Magazine. (US) **1268**
Tip. (NE) **2449**, 2083
Tip. (SZ ISSN 0040-8018) **4495**
Tip. (CS) **4495**, 4513
Tipografia. (GR ISSN 0257-4292) **4006**
Tippah County Historical and Genealogical Society. News and Journal. (US ISSN 8755-9854) **2424**
Tipperary Star. (IE ISSN 0040-8034) **2203**
Tips. (US ISSN 0049-3937) **3473**
†Tips & Techniques. (US) **5290**
Tips and Topics. (CN) **4716**
Tips for Principals *see* N A S S P Tips for Principals **1729**
Tips fuer die Gastroenterologische Praxis. (GW ISSN 0303-6294) **3270**
Tipsico Bulletin. (US) **3602**
Tipularia. (US) **519**
Tiradores. (SP) **4558**
Tire and Rim Association. Standards Year Book. (US ISSN 0082-4496) **4294**
Tire Business. (US) **4294**, 4703
Tire Dealers Survey *see* N T D R A Dealer News **4292**
Tire Review. (US ISSN 0040-8085) **4703**, 4294
Tiro. (GW) **2848**, 1762
Der Tiroler. (GW) **2392**, 2026, 3973
Tiroler Chronist. (AU) **2392**
Tiroler Geschichtsquellen. (AU) **2392**
Tiroler Heimat. (AU ISSN 1013-8919) **2392**
Tiroler Heimatblaetter. (AU ISSN 0040-8115) **2392**, 347, 2059
Tiroler Landesarchiv. Veroeffentlichungen. (AU) **2392**
Tiroler Landesmuseum Ferdinandeum, Innsbruck. Veroeffentlichungen. (AU ISSN 0379-0231) **3534**
Tiroler Ortschroniken *see* Ortschroniken **2379**
Tiryns. (GW ISSN 0082-450X) **287**, 1280
Tisch und Kueche *see* T U K Inform **1166**
Tisch und Kueche Informationen Inform *see* T U K Inform **1166**
Der Tischler. (AU ISSN 0040-8131) **640**
Tischtennis Lehre. (GW ISSN 0938-1910) **4513**

Tischtennis-Schau. (AU ISSN 0040-814X) **4513**
Tiscia. (HU ISSN 0563-587X) **458**
▼Tisglow. (II ISSN 0970-9703) **1969**, 1975
Tissue & Cell. (UK ISSN 0040-8166) **527**
Tissue Antigens. (DK ISSN 0001-2815) **3157**, 458
Tissue Culture. (US ISSN 0142-8810) **527**, 3263
Tissue Culture Association. Monograph Series. (US) **558**, 547, 3202
Tissue Culture Association. Proceedings.(US) **558**, 547, 3202
Tissue Culture Association Report *see* T C A Report **558**
Tissue Reactions. (SZ ISSN 0250-0868) **527**
Tiszataj. (HU ISSN 0133-1167) **2392**
Titanic. (GW) **2886**
Titanic Commutator. (US ISSN 0040-8182) **4740**, 2324
Titanium Development Association. (Year) Buyer's Guide *see* Guide to Products and Services of Member Companies **3407**
Titanium Digest. (US) **3422**
Title and Registration Book. (US) **4703**, 2686
Title News. (US ISSN 0040-8190) **2547**, 24, 4160
▼Titles. (US) **4138**
Titles of Dissertationa and Theses Completed in Home Economics *see* Home Economics Research Journal **2447**
Titles Office Practice. (AT) **2686**
Tito. (GW) **2848**, 1762
Titogradska Tribina. (YU ISSN 0040-8204) **2240**
Tiyu Aihaozhe/Sports Lovers. (CC) **4495**
Tiyu Bolan. (CC) **4495**
Tiyu Huabao/Sports Pictorial. (US) **4495**
Tiyu Kexue/Sports Science. (CC ISSN 1000-677X) **4495**
Tjaenstemaennens Central Organisation. Aarsrapport *see* Aaret som Gaatt **970**
Tjenestemannsbladet. (NO) **4075**
Tjustbygden. (SW ISSN 0349-764X) **287**, 347
Tlalocan. (MX ISSN 0040-8239) **251**
Tnuat Aliyah. (SA) **2026**
To Aftokinito. (CY) **4703**
To Dragma. (US) **1301**
†To Focus on Unreached Peoples (Year). (US) **5290**
To Know Wallony. *see* Connaitre la Wallonie **2357**
To Manage and To Understand. *see* Gerer et Comprendre **3484**
To the Source - El Ha'ayin *see* Sources of Contemporary Jewish Thought **2884**
▼To Us. (US) **4853**, 3400
To Your Health! (US) **3809**, 3597
Toad Hiway. (US) **3007**
TOAR *see* The Original Art Report **339**
Toastmaster. (US ISSN 0040-8263) **1344**, 39
Tobacco. (UK ISSN 0040-8271) **4645**
Tobacco Abstracts. (US ISSN 0040-8298) **4646**, 24
Tobacco and New Products World. (US) **4645**
Tobacco Associates. Annual Report. (US ISSN 0082-4593) **4645**
▼Tobacco Control: An International Journal. (UK ISSN 0964-4563) **4645**
Tobacco Export Promotion Council. Annual Report and Accounts. (II) **922**
†Tobacco-Free Young America Reporter.(US) **5290**
Tobacco Industry Litigation Reporter. (US ISSN 0887-7831) **2686**, 4645
Tobacco International. (US ISSN 0049-3945) **4645**
Tobacco International Weekly *see* Tobacco International **4645**
Tobacco Journal. (AT) **4645**

Tobacco: Latin American Industrial Report. (US) 4645, 839
Tobacco Merchants Association of the United States, Inc. Directory of Cigarette Brands see T M A Directory of Cigarette Brands 4644
Tobacco Merchants Association of the United States, Inc. Executive Summary see T M A Executive Summary 4644
Tobacco Merchants Association of the United States, Inc. Guide to Tobacco Taxes see T M A Guide to Tobacco Taxes 4644
Tobacco Merchants Association of the United States, Inc. International Tobacco Guide see T M A International Tobacco Guide 4644
Tobacco Merchants Association of the United States, Inc. Issues Monitor see T M A Issues Monitor 4644
Tobacco Merchants Association of the United States, Inc. Leaf Bulletin see T M A Leaf Bulletin 4644
Tobacco Merchants Association of the United States, Inc. Legislative Bulletin see T M A Legislative Bulletin 4644
Tobacco Merchants Association of the United States, Inc. Tobacco Barometer see T M A Tobacco Barometer 4644
Tobacco Merchants Association of the United States, Inc. Tobacco Barometer: Smoking, Chewing, Snuff see T M A Tobacco Barometer: Smoking, Chewing, Snuff 4644
Tobacco Merchants Association of the United States, Inc. Tobacco Trade Barometer see T M A Tobacco Trade Barometer 4644
Tobacco Merchants Association of the United States, Inc. Tobacco Weekly see T M A Tobacco Weekly 4644
Tobacco Merchants Association of the United States, Inc. Trademark Report see T M A Trademark Report 4645
Tobacco Merchants Association of the United States, Inc. World Alert see T M A World Alert 4645
Tobacco Merchants Association of the United States, Inc. World Consumption & Production see T M A World Consumption & Production 4645
Tobacco News. (Il) 4645
†Tobacco Observer. (US) 5290
Tobacco Reporter. (US) 4645
†Tobacco Reprint Series. (US) 5290
Tobacco Research. (Il ISSN 0379-055X) 4645
Tobacco Science Yearbook. (US ISSN 0082-4623) 4645
Tobacco Stocks. (US ISSN 0360-439X) 4645
Tobacco Stocks Report. T O B see Tobacco Stocks 4645
Tobacco Trade Directory and Diary. (UK) 4645
Tobacco Trade Marketing Directory see Tobacco Trade Directory and Diary 4645
†Tobacco Update. (US) 5290
Tobacco World Illustrated. (US) 4645
Tobacconist. see Tobakshandlaren 4645
Tobakk - Frukt - Sjokolade. (NO ISSN 0049-3961) 4645, 2083
Tobakshandlaren/Tobacconist. (SW ISSN 0346-2765) 4645
Toccata. (UK) 3584
Tocher. (UK ISSN 0049-397X) 2059
Tochigi-ken no Jinko/Population in Tochigi Prefecture. (JA) 3988
Tochigi-kenritsu Hakubutsukan Kenkyu Hokokusho/Tochigi Prefectural Museum. Memoirs. (JA ISSN 0910-4100) 4347, 3534
Tochigi Prefectural Dairy Experimental Institute. Bulletin. (JA ISSN 0289-3096) 124, 204
Tochigi Prefectural Museum. Memoirs. see Tochigi-kenritsu Hakubutsukan Kenkyu Hokokusho 4347
Today. see Jintian 2182
Today. see Danas 2863
Today (Kent). (UK ISSN 0040-8360) 1268, 1326, 4455
Today (Lawson). (AT ISSN 1030-0295) 4250, 1268

Today (Mona Vale). (AT) 1969
Today (New Malden) see Alpha (New Malden) 4228
Today and Tomorrow see Newsbreak (San Francisco) 1319
Today in Africa. (KE) 4207
Today in Medicine. (US) 3157
Today in Mississippi. (US ISSN 1052-2433) 1909, 124
Today Literary Magazine/Jintian. (SW) 2969
Today Whitworth College see Whitworth Today 1330
Today's Arizona Woman. (US) 4853
Today's Astrologer see American Federation of Astrologers Bulletin 358
Today's Black Father. (US) 1245, 2026
Today's Bride. (CN) 3067
Today's C P A. (US ISSN 0889-4337) 757
Today's Catholic (Fort Wayne). (US ISSN 0891-1533) 4277
Today's Catholic (San Antonio). (US ISSN 0745-3612) 4277
Today's Catholic Teacher. (US ISSN 0040-8441) 1668, 4277
Today's Challenge. (NR ISSN 0189-0557) 4250
Today's Chemist. (US ISSN 0896-7067) 1189
Today's Chicago Woman. (US) 4853
†Today's Child Leaflets. (AT) 5290
Today's Chiropractic. (US ISSN 0091-2360) 3216
Today's Christian Woman. (US ISSN 0163-1799) 4207, 4853
Today's Coach. (US) 4495
Today's Computers & Software. (US) 1465, 1481
Today's Dads. (US) 2718, 3400
Today's Delinquent. (US ISSN 0733-6551) 1523, 1245
Today's Distributor. (US ISSN 0898-5561) 1055
Today's Education - Educational Support Edition see N E A Today: Educational Support Edition 1729
Today's Education: Higher Education Edition see Thought & Action 1717
†Today's Executive. (US) 5290
Today's F D A. (Florida Dental Association) (US ISSN 1048-5317) 3243
Today's Facility Manager. (US) 2555, 307
▼Today's Family. (US ISSN 1055-3169) 1245
Today's Family Home Plans. (US ISSN 1059-5252) 307, 2555
Today's Farmer. (US) 124
Today's Fireman. (US) 2035
Today's Furniture Design see Furniture - Today's Manufacturing - Today 5197
Today's Guide see Guide Patrol 1255
Today's Horse. (UK) 4538
Today's Insurance Woman. (US ISSN 0892-4414) 2544, 4853
Today's Investor. (US) 966
Today's Lawyer. (US) 2686, 757
Today's Life. see Jinri Shenghuo 2182
Today's Life Sciences. (AT) 4347
▼Today's Lifestyles. (US) 4854
Today's Living. (HK) 2555
Today's Living see Better Nutrition for Today's Living 3603
Today's Music Educator. (US) 3584, 1762
Today's Nursing Home see McKnight's Long Term Care News 2276
Today's O R Nurse. (US ISSN 0194-5181) 3287
Today's Office see Office Technology Management 5251
Today's Parent. (CN) 1245
Today's Parish. (US ISSN 0040-8549) 4207
Today's Policeman. (US) 1523
Today's Refinery. (US ISSN 1048-0935) 3702
Today's Seniors. (CN) 2279
Today's Single. (US) 4364, 4207
Today's Supervisor. (US ISSN 0734-3302) 3622
Today's Times. (CN) 2279
Today's Topic see Today (Kent) 1268

Today's Young Life. (AT ISSN 1030-0309) 4250, 1268
Toddlers' Intelligence World. see You'er Zhili Shijie 1246
Toddlers' Pictorial. see You'er Huabao 1271
Todotransporte. (SP) 4657
Toej - Skandinavian Fashion. (DK) 1294
Toeleveren en Uitbesteden. (NE) 3024
Toestand in de Wereld see Dat Was de Toestand in de Wereld 2309
Toga Calabrese. (IT ISSN 0040-8654) 2686
Toget see Modeltoget 2439
Together (London, 1956). (UK ISSN 0307-5982) 4250
▼Together (London, 1990). (UK ISSN 0958-2800) 4250
Together (Los Angeles). (US) 4854
Together: Calavo Newsletter see Calavo Newsletter 172
Togo. Direction de la Meteorologie Nationale. Resume Annuel du Temps.(TG) 3441
Togo. Direction de la Meteorologie Nationale. Resume Mensuel du Temps. (TG) 3441
Togo. Direction de la Statistique. Bulletin Mensuel de Statistique. (TG) 4590
Togo. Ministry of Economy and Finance. Bulletin de Statistiques. (TG) 741, 4590
Togo Dialogue. (TG) 2170
Toho Gakuho/Dongfang Xuebao. (JA ISSN 0304-2448) 3058
Toho Igakkai Zasshi. see Toho University Medical Society. Journal 3157
Toho University Medical Society. Journal/Toho Igakkai Zasshi. (JA ISSN 0040-8670) 3157
Tohogaku/Eastern Studies. (JA ISSN 0495-7199) 3644
Tohokai. (JA ISSN 0386-426X) 4216
Tohoku Archives of Orthopaedic Surgery and Traumatology. (JA) 3312
Tohoku Daigaku Iden Seitai Kenkyu Senta. (JA ISSN 0915-5228) 458
Tohoku Daigaku Kenkyujo Hokoku. A-shu: Butsurigaku, Kagaku, Yakingaku. see Tohoku University. Science Reports of the Research Institutes. Series A: Physics, Chemistry, and Metallurgy 3834
Tohoku Daigaku Kenkyujo Hokoku, C-shu, Igaku. see Tohoku University. Science Reports of the Research Institutes. Series C: Medicine 3157
Tohoku Daigaku Kogaku Hokoku. see Tohoku University. Faculty of Engineering. Technology Reports 5290
Tohoku Daigaku Kogakubu Zairyo Kyodo Kenkyu Shisetsu Hokoku. see Tohoku University. Research Institute for Strength and Fracture of Materials. Reports 1922
†Tohoku Daigaku Nogaku Kenkyujo Hokoku/Tohoku University. Institute for Agricultural Research. Bulletin. (JA ISSN 0040-8697) 5290
Tohoku Daigaku Rigakubu Chishitsugaku Koseibutsugaku Kyoshitsu Kenkyu Hobun Hokoku/Tohoku University. Faculty of Science. Institute of Geology and Paleontology. Contributions. (JA ISSN 0082-4658) 1582, 3661
Tohoku Daigaku Senko Seiren Kenkyujo Iho/Tohoku University. Research Institute of Mineral Dressing and Metallurgy. Bulletin. (JA ISSN 0040-876X) 3422, 3496
Tohoku Electric Power Co., Inc. Annual Report (Year). (JA) 1909
Tohoku Gakuin University Review. (JA ISSN 0385-406X) 2969, 2848
Tohoku Geophysical Journal. (JA ISSN 0040-8794) 1596
Tohoku - Hokuriku Sugaku Kyoiku Kisoteki Kenkyu Hokoku. (JA ISSN 0913-221X) 3058, 1762
Tohoku Igaku Zasshi. see Tohoku Medical Journal 3157

TOHOKU UNIVERSITY 6733

Tohoku Institute of Technology. Memoirs. Series 1. Science and Engineering. see Tohoku Kogyo Daigaku Kiyo, 1. Rikogaku Hen 1838
Tohoku Institute of Technology. Memoirs. Series 2: Humanities and Social Science. (JA ISSN 0285-3825) 2516
Tohoku Journal of Agricultural Research. (JA ISSN 0040-8719) 194, 1189
Tohoku Journal of Experimental Medicine. (JA ISSN 0040-8727) 3263
Tohoku Kogyo Daigaku Kiyo, 1. Rikogaku Hen/Tohoku Institute of Technology. Memoirs. Series 1. Science and Engineering. (JA ISSN 0285-3817) 1838
Tohoku-ku Suisan Kenkyujo Kenkyu Hokoku. see Tohoku Regional Fisheries Research Laboratory. Bulletin 2049
Tohoku Mathematical Journal/Tohoku Sugaku Zasshi. (JA ISSN 0040-8735) 3058
Tohoku Medical Journal/Tohoku Igaku Zasshi. (JA ISSN 0040-8700) 3157
Tohoku National Agricultural Experiment Station. Bulletin. see Tohoku Nogyo Shikenjo Kenkyu Hokoku 124
Tohoku National Agricultural Experiment Station. Miscellaneous Publication. see Tohoku Nogyo Shikenjo Kenkyu Shiryo 124
Tohoku no Shizen/Nature of Tohoku. (JA ISSN 0910-7177) 4347
Tohoku Nogyo Shikenjo Kenkyu Hokoku/Tohoku National Agricultural Experiment Station. Bulletin. (JA ISSN 0495-7318) 124
Tohoku Nogyo Shikenjo Kenkyu Shiryo/Tohoku National Agricultural Experiment Station. Miscellaneous Publication. (JA ISSN 0387-172X) 124
Tohoku Nogyo Shikenjo Kenkyu Sokuho see Tohoku Nogyo Shikenjo Kenkyu Shiryo 124
Tohoku Psychologica Folia. (JA ISSN 0040-8743) 4048
Tohoku Regional Fisheries Research Laboratory. Bulletin/Tohoku-ku Suisan Kenkyujo Kenkyu Hokoku. (JA ISSN 0049-402X) 2049
Tohoku Sugaku Zasshi. see Tohoku Mathematical Journal 3058
†Tohoku University. Faculty of Engineering. Technology Reports/Tohoku Daigaku Kogaku Hokoku. (JA ISSN 0040-8816) 5290
Tohoku University. Faculty of Science. Institute of Geology and Paleontology. Contributions. see Tohoku Daigaku Rigakubu Chishitsugaku Koseibutsugaku Kyoshitsu Kenkyu Hobun Hokoku 1582
Tohoku University. Faculty of Science. Institute of Geology and Paleontology. Science Reports. Second Series. (JA ISSN 0082-464X) 1582, 3661
Tohoku University. Institute for Agricultural Research. Bulletin. see Tohoku Daigaku Nogaku Kenkyujo Hokoku 5290
Tohoku University. Institute of Genetic Ecology. Newsletter. (JA) 458
Tohoku University. Research Institute for Strength and Fracture of Materials. Reports/Tohoku Daigaku Kogakubu Zairyo Kyodo Kenkyu Shisetsu Hokoku. (JA ISSN 0563-6590) 1922
Tohoku University. Research Institute of Electrical Communication. Technical Report. (JA) 1344
Tohoku University. Research Institute of Mineral Dressing and Metallurgy. Bulletin. see Tohoku Daigaku Senko Seiren Kenkyujo Iho 3422

6734 TOHOKU UNIVERSITY

Tohoku University. Science Reports of the Research Institutes. Series A: Physics, Chemistry, and Metallurgy/ Tohoku Daigaku Kenkyujo Hokoku. A-shu: Butsurigaku, Kagaku, Yakingaku.(JA ISSN 0040-8808) **3834**, 1189, 3422

Tohoku University. Science Reports of the Research Institutes. Series C: Medicine/Tohoku Daigaku Kenkyujo Hokoku, C-shu, Igaku. (JA ISSN 0371-2761) **3157**

Tohoku University. Science Reports. Series 8: Physics and Astronomy. (JA ISSN 0388-5607) **3834**, 370, 1189

Toike Oike. (CN ISSN 0049-4038) **1838**

Toilers of the Deep. (UK ISSN 0040-8824) **4207**

Toiletries, Fragrances and Skin Care: The Rose Sheet. (US ISSN 0279-1110) **377**, 2686, 3250

Tok Tok Bilong Haus Buk. (PP ISSN 0310-463X) **2787**

Tokai Daigaku Kiyo. Bungakubu/Tokai University. Faculty of Letters. Bulletin.(JA ISSN 0563-6760) **2970**, 4390

Tokai Daigaku Kiyo. Gaikokugo Kyoiku Senta/Tokai University. Foreign Language Center. Bulletin. (JA ISSN 0389-3081) **2848**

Tokai Journal of Experimental and Clinical Medicine. (JA ISSN 0385-0005) **3157**

Tokai Monthly Economic Letter. (JA) **886**

Tokai Regional Fisheries Research Laboratory (Report) see Chuo Suisan Kenkyujo Kenkyu Hokoku **2038**

Tokai University. Faculty of Letters. Bulletin. see Tokai Daigaku Kiyo. Bungakubu **2970**

Tokai University. Faculty of Literature. Bulletin see Tokai Daigaku Kiyo. Bungakubu **2970**

Tokai University. Faculty of Science. Proceedings. (JA ISSN 0563-6795) **4348**

Tokai University. Foreign Language Center. Bulletin. see Tokai Daigaku Kiyo. Gaikokugo Kyoiku Senta **2848**

Tokei. (JA ISSN 0285-7677) **4590**, 3058

Tokei Suri/Proceedings of the Institute of Statistical Mathematics. (JA ISSN 0912-6112) **3063**

Tokei Suri Kenkyujo Kenkyu Ripoto/ Japan. Institute of Statistical Mathematics. Research Reports, General Series. (JA) **3058**, 4590

Token and Medal Society Journal see T A M S Journal **3602**

Token Bijutsu/Journal of Japanese Fine Arts Swords. (JA ISSN 0911-4041) **347**, 3534, 3644

Token Perspectives Newsletter. (US ISSN 0886-2362) **1428**, 1465, 1474

Toko-Ginecologia Practica. (SP ISSN 0040-8867) **3296**

Tokovi. (YU) **2392**

Toktokkie (English Edition). (SA ISSN 0256-0437) **1268**, 1498

Tokushima Daigaku Gakugei Kiyo/ Tokushima University. Journal of Gakugei. (JA ISSN 0495-7601) **2516**

Tokushima Daigaku Kyoyobu Kiyo. Shizen Kagaku/University of Tokushima. College of General Education. Journal of Science. (JA ISSN 0563-6981) **4348**

Tokushima Journal of Experimental Medicine. (JA ISSN 0040-8875) **3263**

Tokushima-ken Shizen Hogo Kyokai Chosa Hokoku. (JA) **1498**

Tokushima University. Journal of Gakugei. see Tokushima Daigaku Gakugei Kiyo **2516**

Tokyo Art Directors Annual/A D C Nenkan. (JA) **39**, 4006

Tokyo Astronomical Bulletin see National Astronomical Bulletin **5242**

Tokyo Astronomical Observatory. Report see National Astronomical Observatory. Report **367**

Tokyo Astronomical Observatory. Reprints see National Astronomical Observatory. Reprints **367**

Tokyo Book Development Centre. Newsletter see Asian - Pacific Book Development **4120**

†Tokyo Business Month. (US ISSN 1047-0530) **5290**

Tokyo Business Today. (JA ISSN 0911-7008) **695**

Tokyo City Guide Tour Companion. (JA) **4789**

Tokyo College of Domestic Science. Bulletin see Tokyo Kasei Daigaku Kenkyu Kiyo **2449**

Tokyo College of Economics. Journal - Tokyo Keidai Gakkai-Shi see Tokyo Keizai University. Journal **695**

Tokyo Daigaku Jishin Kenkyujo Iho. see University of Tokyo. Earthquake Research Institute. Bulletin **1596**

Tokyo Daigaku Kaiyo Kenkyujo. see University of Tokyo. Ocean Research Institute. Bulletin **1612**

Tokyo Daigaku Kogakubu. Denki Kogaku, Denshi Kogaku Iho/ University of Tokyo. Electrical and Electronic Engineering Departments. Bulletin. (JA ISSN 0563-7929) **1909**, 1345

Tokyo Daigaku Kogakubu Kiyo B. See University of Tokyo. Faculty of Engineering. Journal: Series B **1839**

Tokyo Daigaku Kyoyogakubu Shizen Kagaku Kiyo. see University of Tokyo. College of Arts and Sciences. Scientific Papers **4350**

Tokyo Daigaku Rigakubu Kiyo, Dai-1-rui A, Sugaku. see University of Tokyo. Faculty of Science. Journal. Section 1A: Mathematics **3061**

Tokyo Daigaku Rigakubu Kiyo, Dai-2-rui, Chishitsugaku, Kobutsugaku, Chirigaku, Chikyu Wakusei Butsurigaku. see University of Tokyo. Faculty of Science. Journal. Section 2: Geology, Mineralogy, Geography, Earth and Planetary Physics **1549**

Tokyo Daigaku Rigakubu Kiyo, Dai-3-rui, Shokubutsugaku. see University of Tokyo. Faculty of Science. Journal. Section 3: Botany **520**

Tokyo Daigaku Rigakubu Kiyo, Dai-4-rui, Dobutsugaku. see University of Tokyo. Faculty of Science. Journal. Section 4: Zoology **5298**

Tokyo Daigaku Rigakubu Kiyo, Dai-5-rui, Jinruigaku. see University of Tokyo. Faculty of Science. Journal. Section 5: Anthropology **252**

Tokyo Daigaku Seisan Gijutsu Kenkyujo Hokoku/University of Tokyo. Institute of Industrial Science. Report. (JA ISSN 0040-9006) **4612**

Tokyo Daigaku Sogo Kenkyu Shiryokan Gyoseikishu/University of Tokyo. University Museum. Collected Reprints. (JA ISSN 0910-4828) **4348**, 3534

Tokyo Daigaku Sogo Kenkyu Shiryokan Kenkyu Hokoku. see University of Tokyo. University Museum. Bulletin **4350**

Tokyo Denki Daigaku Rikogakubu Kiyo. see Tokyo Denki University. Faculty of Science and Engineering. Research Activities **1909**

Tokyo Denki University. Faculty of Engineering. General Education. Research Reports. (JA ISSN 0288-5530) **1838**, 1909, 1940

Tokyo Denki University. Faculty of Engineering. Research Reports. (JA ISSN 0389-617X) **1838**, 1909, 1940

Tokyo Denki University. Faculty of Science and Engineering. Research Activities/Tokyo Denki Daigaku Rikogakubu Kiyo. (JA ISSN 0388-1989) **1909**, 1838

Tokyo Dental College. Bulletin/Tokyo Shika Daigaku Obun Kiyo. (JA ISSN 0040-8891) **3243**

Tokyo Dental College Society Journal. see Shika Gakuho **3242**

Tokyo Financial Review. (JA) **801**

Tokyo Gakugei Daigaku Kiyo/Tokyo Gakugei University. Bulletin. (JA ISSN 0371-6813) **4348**, 483

Tokyo Gakugei University. Bulletin. see Tokyo Gakugei Daigaku Kiyo **4348**

Tokyo Ika Daigaku Zasshi. see Tokyo Medical College. Journal **3157**

Tokyo Ika Shika Daigaku Kiyo. see Tokyo Medical and Dental University. Bulletin **3157**

▼Tokyo Industry. (JA) **4095**, 886, 995

Tokyo Institute of Technology. Research Laboratory of Resources Utilization. Report/Shigen Kagaku Kenkyujo. (JA ISSN 0495-8055) **4612**

Tokyo Joshi Daigaku Kiyo. Ronshu. Kagaku Bumon Hokoku/Tokyo Woman's Christian University. Science Reports. (JA ISSN 0386-4006) **4348**

Tokyo Joshi Ika Daigaku Zasshi/Tokyo Women's Medical College. Journal. (JA ISSN 0040-9022) **3157**

Tokyo Journal. (JA) **4789**

Tokyo Journal of Mathematics. (JA ISSN 0387-3870) **3058**

Tokyo Journal of Psychoanalysis. see Seishin Bunseki **5275**

Tokyo Kasei Daigaku Kenkyu Kiyo/ Tokyo Kasei University. Bulletin. (JA) **2449**

Tokyo Kasei University. Bulletin. see Tokyo Kasei Daigaku Kenkyu Kiyo **2449**

Tokyo Keizai University. Journal. (JA ISSN 0493-4091) **695**

Tokyo Kogyo Daigaku Kodai Mathematical Journal see Kodai Mathematical Journal **3042**

Tokyo Medical and Dental University. Bulletin/Tokyo Ika Shika Daigaku Kiyo. (JA ISSN 0040-8921) **3157**, 3243

Tokyo Medical and Dental University. Institute for Medical and Dental Engineering. Reports/Iyo Kizai Kenkyujo Hokoku. (JA ISSN 0082-4739) **3157**, 3243

Tokyo Medical College. Journal/Tokyo Ika Daigaku Zasshi. (JA ISSN 0040-8905) **3157**

Tokyo Metropolitan Agricultural Experiment Station, Itsukaichi Office. Forestry Experimental Bulletin/Ringyo Shiken Kenkyu Hokoku. (JA ISSN 0082-4720) **2109**

†Tokyo Metropolitan Government. Fuchu Rehabilitation School. Annual Report.(JA) **5290**

Tokyo Metropolitan Institute of Neurosciences. Annual Report. see Tokyo-to Shinkei Kagaku Sogo Kenkyujo Nenpo **3355**

Tokyo Metropolitan News. (JA) **4095**

Tokyo Metropolitan Research Laboratory of Public Health. Annual Report. see Tokyo-toritsu Eisei Kenkyujo Kenkyu Nenpo **3157**

Tokyo Metropolitan University. Annual Report of Research on the Ogasawara (Bonin) Islands. see Ogasawara Kenkyu Nenpo **4331**

Tokyo Metropolitan University. Department of Geography. Geographical Reports/Tokyo-toritsu Daigaku Chirigaku Hokoku. (JA ISSN 0386-8710) **2264**

Tokyo Metropolitan University. Faculty of Technology. Memoirs/Tokyo-toritsu Daigaku Kogakubu Hokoku. (JA ISSN 0082-4747) **4612**

Tokyo Municipal News see Tokyo Metropolitan News **4095**

Tokyo no Ikebana. (JA) **357**, 2143, 2555

Tokyo Noko Daigaku Nenpo. see Tokyo University of Agriculture and Technology. Annual Report **194**

Tokyo Rika Daigaku Kenkyu Ronbunshu/Science University of Tokyo. Collected Papers. (JA ISSN 0918-0753) **4348**

Tokyo Shika Daigaku Obun Kiyo. see Tokyo Dental College. Bulletin **3243**

Tokyo Shosen Daigaku Kenkyu Hokoku. Shizen Kagaku/Tokyo University of Mercantile Marine. Journal. Natural Sciences. (JA ISSN 0493-4474) **4348**, 4740

Tokyo Suisan Daigaku Kenkyu Hokoku. see Tokyo University of Fisheries. Journal **2049**

Tokyo Suisan Daigaku Ronshu. see Tokyo University of Fisheries. Report **2049**

Tokyo Suisan Daigaku Tokubetsu Kenkyu Hokoku. see Tokyo University of Fisheries Journal. Special Edition **5290**

Tokyo Tanabe Quarterly. (JA) **3744**

▼Tokyo Time Out. (JA) **2208**

Tokyo-to no Shizen. (JA ISSN 0288-2329) **4348**

Tokyo-to Shiken Kenkyu Kikan no Kenkyu Keikaku. (JA) **4095**, 4348, 4612

Tokyo-to Shinkei Kagaku Sogo Kenkyujo Nenpo/Tokyo Metropolitan Institute of Neurosciences. Annual Report. (JA) **3355**

Tokyo-to Takao Shizen Kagaku Hakubutsukan Kenkyu Hokoku/ Takao Museum of Natural History. Science Report. (JA ISSN 0286-8768) **4348**, 3534

Tokyo Today. (JA) **2208**

Tokyo-toritsu Daigaku Chirigaku Hokoku. see Tokyo Metropolitan University. Department of Geography. Geographical Reports **2264**

Tokyo-toritsu Daigaku Kogakubu Hokoku. see Tokyo Metropolitan University. Faculty of Technology. Memoirs **4612**

Tokyo-toritsu Eisei Kenkyujo Kenkyu Nenpo/Tokyo Metropolitan Research Laboratory of Public Health. Annual Report. (JA ISSN 0082-4771) **3157**, 4113

Tokyo-toritsu Koka Tanki Daigaku Kenkyu Hokoku/Metropolitan College of Technology, Tokyo. Memoirs. (JA) **4612**

Tokyo University of Agriculture and Technology. Annual Report/Tokyo Noko Daigaku Nenpo. (JA ISSN 0563-8313) **194**

Tokyo University of Fisheries. Journal/ Tokyo Suisan Daigaku Kenkyu Hokoku. (JA ISSN 0040-9014) **2049**

Tokyo University of Fisheries. Report/ Tokyo Suisan Daigaku Ronshu. (JA ISSN 0563-8372) **2049**, 4348

Tokyo University of Fisheries. Transactions. (JA ISSN 0388-0966) **2049**

†Tokyo University of Fisheries Journal. Special Edition/Tokyo Suisan Daigaku Tokubetsu Kenkyu Hokoku. (JA ISSN 0082-4836) **5290**

Tokyo University of Foreign Studies. Summary see Area and Culture Studies **1700**

Tokyo University of Mercantile Marine. Journal. Natural Sciences. see Tokyo Shosen Daigaku Kenkyu Hokoku. Shizen Kagaku **4348**

Tokyo Woman's Christian University. Science Reports. see Tokyo Joshi Daigaku Kiyo. Ronshu. Kagaku Bumon Hokoku **4348**

Tokyo Women's Medical College. Journal. see Tokyo Joshi Ika Daigaku Zasshi **3157**

Tole World. (US ISSN 0199-4514) **347**, 3655

Toledanos. Anales. (SP) **2392**

Toledo Business Journal. (US) **695**

Toledo Business News see Chamber Insider **811**

Toledo City Journal. (US ISSN 0040-9065) **4095**

Toledo Jewish News. (US ISSN 0040-9081) **2026**

Toledo Medicine. (US) **3157**

Toledo Metropolitan. (US) **2236**

Toledot. (US ISSN 0146-9568) **2166**, 2026

▼Tolerances Variations and Pre-Existing Site Conditions for the Wall and Ceiling Industries. (US) **635**

Toll-Free Digest. (US) **1155**, 1367

Toll Gate Journal. (UK) **3007**

Tolle Family Exchange. (US) **2166**

Tolley's Capital Gains Tax (Year). (UK) **1111**

Tolley's Capital Transfer Tax see Tolley's Inheritance Tax (Year) 1111
Tolley's Corporation Tax (Year). (UK) 1111
Tolley's Income Tax (Year). (UK ISSN 0305-8921) 1111
Tolley's Inheritance Tax (Year). (UK) 1111
Tolley's Practical Tax Newsletter. (UK ISSN 0143-294X) 1111
Tolley's Tax Data (Year). (UK ISSN 0262-4583) 1111
Tolley's Tax Tables (Year). (UK ISSN 0307-6687) 1111
Tolley's Taxation in the Republic of Ireland (Year). (UK) 1111, 2729
Tollways. (US) 4721
Tolnai Konyvtaros. (HU ISSN 0133-8358) 2787
†Tolpolski's Chronicle. (UK ISSN 0040-9103) 5290
Tolstoy Foundation News. (US) 4422
Tolvmansbladet see Erhvervs-Jordbruget 88
†Tom og Jerry. (DK) 5290
Tom Purser's B D G World. (US) 4495
Tom Thumb. (IS ISSN 0040-912X) 1268
Tomato Genetics Cooperative Report. (US) 547, 519
The Tombstone. (US ISSN 0893-7664) 2166
Tombstone Epitaph National Edition see National Tombstone Epitaph 2415
Tome. (US ISSN 1050-0421) 3015, 2970
Tomis. (RM) 2215
Tomodachi. (AT) 922
Tomorrow. see Ming Ri 2182
Tomorrow see Studies in Comparative Religion 4204
Tomorrow: Mamaroneck, Harrison, Rye.(US) 2236
Tomorrow: New Rochelle, Pelham, Larchmont. (US) 2236
Tomorrow Through Research see Technology Today 4347
Tomorrow's Business Leader. (US) 3631
▼Tomskie Pravoslavnye Vedomosti. (RU) 4289
Ton - Report. (GW) 4462, 3584
Tonatiuh-Quinto Sol News see T Q S News 2967
Toneel Teatraal. (NE ISSN 0040-9170) 4642
Tonfallet. (SW ISSN 0346-329X) 3584
Tong-Tong see Moesson 3965
Tonga. Minister of Health. Report. (TO ISSN 0082-4895) 4113
Tonggye Suchup. see Korea Statistical Korea 5224
Tongji Medical University. Journal. (CC ISSN 0257-716X) 3158
Tongji Yanjiu/Statistics Research. (CC ISSN 0496-4225) 4590
Tongji Yike Daxue Xuebao see Tongji Medical University. Journal 3158
Tongmul Hakhoe Chi see Korean Journal of Zoology 587
Tongso Yongu. see Journal of East and West Studies 3901
Tongsu Gequ/Popular Songs. (CC) 3584
Tongxin Jishu yu Fazhan/Communication Technology and Development. (CC ISSN 1001-540X) 1360
Tongyi Luntan/United Tribune. (CC) 4390
Tonic. (UK ISSN 0260-7425) 3584, 421
Tonmeister Informationen. (GW) 4462
Tonto Trails see Gila Heritage 2153
Tonus Dentaire. (FR ISSN 0242-6862) 3243
Tonyobyo. see Japan Diabetes Society. Journal 3254
Too Much - University College Hospital Magazine. (UK) 2469, 3158
Took. (US) 2886, 2970
Tool. (GW ISSN 0934-9871) 1401
Tool and Alloy Steels. (II ISSN 0377-9408) 3422, 1838
Tool and Die Institute Purchasing Guide see Tooling and Manufacturing Association. Purchasing Guide 1155

Tool and Die Magazine see Manufacturing & Management Magazine 3412
Toolbox. (GW ISSN 0935-8315) 1432
Tooling and Machining see Precision Toolmaker 3417
Tooling and Manufacturing Association. Purchasing Guide. (US) 1155
Tooling & Production. (US ISSN 0040-9243) 3024
Tools. (DK ISSN 0900-3347) 347
†Tools and Hardware. (GW ISSN 0179-5341) 5290
Tools & Hardware: Latin American Industrial Report. (US) 643
Tools and Tillage. (DK ISSN 0563-8887) 124, 2324
Toorts. (NE) 1687
Toowoomba and Golden West Visitors' Guide. (AT ISSN 0725-5365) 4789
Toowoomba Industrial Profile. (AT) 886, 1119
Toowoomba - Queensland's Growth Centre. (AT) 1086, 2083, 4789
Top. (BE ISSN 0773-1051) 1268
Top (Benningen). (GW) 1268, 2443
Top (Wuppertal). (GW) 1268
Top Agrar. (AU) 124
Top Agrar: Ausgabe B. (GW ISSN 0936-8302) 124
Top Agrar: Ausgabe R. (GW ISSN 0936-8310) 124
Top Agrar: Ausgabe S. (GW ISSN 0936-8329) 124
Top Agrar: Ausgabe S - R. (GW ISSN 0342-2399) 124
Top Blacks in Law Enforcement see Blacks in Law Enforcement 1510
Top Business. (GW) 1029
Top Car Magazine. (UK) 4703
Top Companies. (SA ISSN 0563-8895) 1086
Top Companies in the South West (Year) see Regional Directory of Key Business Prospects - South West 1151
▼Top Dogs. (AT) 3714
Top Drawer. (US) 643
Top Echecs. (FR ISSN 0990-1930) 4495
Top Executive Compensation. (US) 1029, 1070
†Top Farmer Intelligence. (US ISSN 0730-6318) 5290
Top Farmer Market Insight see Brock Report 148
Top Hair. (GW) 374
Top Magazine. (IT) 2206
Top Management Abstracts. (UK ISSN 0049-4100) 741, 24
†Top Management Digest. (UK ISSN 0953-5187) 5290
Top Management Remuneration Review. (AT) 1070
Top Medizin. (GW ISSN 0931-9522) 3158
Top of the Week see Tackle Times (Barrington) 4558
Top Producer. (US) 124
Top Secret see Geheim 3958
Top Security see International Security Review 1526
Top Shelf (Madison). (US ISSN 0749-2022) 386
Top Shelf (Ridgefield). (US ISSN 1040-0885) 386
Top Stories. (US) 2970
†Top Tens and Trivia of Rock and Roll and Rhythm and Blues. Annual Supplement. (US) 5290
Top Video. (IT) 1386
Top 1,500 Companies see Trinet Directory of Leading U S Companies: Top 1,500 695
Top 1,500 Private Companies see Trinet Directory of Leading U S Companies: Top 1,500 Private 695
Top 2,000 Directories and Annuals: A Guide to the Major Titles Used in British Libraries see Top 3,000 Directories and Annuals: A Guide to the Major Titles Used in British Libraries 2787
Top 3,000 Directories and Annuals: A Guide to the Major Titles Used in British Libraries. (UK ISSN 0268-9928) 2787

▼Top 10. (KO) 3584
Top 100 Data Processing Almanac see Yardstick 1062
Top 500 R D T & E Contractors. (US ISSN 1040-9025) 3473
TopCart see Topografia y Cartografia 4006
Topeka Genealogical Society Quarterly. (US ISSN 0734-8495) 2166
TopHealth. (US) 3622
▼TopHealth en Espanol. (US) 3622
Topic. (AU) 1268
Topic. (UK ISSN 0953-895X) 1668
Topic (Washington). (US ISSN 0049-4127) 2516, 4390
Topic Klex - Das Junge Magazin. (AU) 1268
†Topical Issues. (UK ISSN 0268-2494) 5291
†Topical New Issues. (US ISSN 0090-7286) 5291
Topical Stamp Handbooks. (US ISSN 0049-4135) 3758
Topical Time. (US ISSN 0040-9332) 3758
Topical Times Football Book. (UK) 4513
Topical Woman. (US) 3758
Topicator. (US ISSN 0040-9340) 41, 24, 741
Topics (Belfast). (UK) 204
Topics (Boston). (US ISSN 0040-9367) 1367
Topics (Cambridge). (UK ISSN 0262-2548) 995, 1070
Topics for the Month see Topics (Belfast) 204
Topics in Antibiotic Chemistry. (UK) 483
Topics in Applied Physics. (US ISSN 0303-4216) 3834, 1838
Topics in Atmospheric and Oceanographic Sciences. (US) 1611, 3441
†Topics in Bioelectrochemistry and Bioenergetics. (US) 5291
Topics in Boundary Elements Research. (US) 1838
Topics in Chemical Engineering. (UK ISSN 0277-5883) 1860
Topics in Clinical Nutrition. (US ISSN 0883-5691) 3612
Topics in Computer Mathematics. (UK ISSN 0275-5815) 3066
Topics in Current Chemistry. (US ISSN 0340-1022) 1189
Topics in Current Physics. (US ISSN 0342-6793) 3834
Topics in Early Childhood Special Education. (US ISSN 0271-1214) 1742, 1245
Topics in Emergency Medicine. (US ISSN 0164-2340) 3158
Topics in Energy. (US) 1796
Topics in Environmental Health. (NE) 458, 1969
Topics in Enzyme and Fermentation Biotechnology. (UK ISSN 0140-0835) 491
Topics in f-Element Chemistry. (NE) 1215
Topics in Gastroenterology. (US) 3270
Topics in Geobiology. (US) 1583, 458
Topics in Geriatric Rehabilitation. (US ISSN 0882-7524) 2279, 1742
Topics in Health Care Financing. (US ISSN 0095-3814) 2469
Topics in Health Care Materiel Management see Hospital Materiel Management Quarterly 2465
Topics in Health Record Management. (US ISSN 0270-5230) 2469
Topics in Hospital Pharmacy Management. (US ISSN 0271-1206) 3744
Topics in Infectious Diseases. (US ISSN 0171-2160) 3224
Topics in Information Systems. (US) 1447
Topics in Inorganic and General Chemistry. (NE ISSN 0082-495X) 1215, 1189
Topics in Language Disorders. (US ISSN 0271-8294) 1742, 2289
Topics in Magnetic Resonance Imaging.(US ISSN 0899-3459) 3158, 3834

Topics in Molecular Pharmacology. (NE) 3744
Topics in Pain Management. (US ISSN 0882-5645) 3158
Topics in Pediatrics. (US) 3327
Topics in Philosophy. (US) 3784
Topics in Photosynthesis. (NE) 458
Topics in Physical Chemistry. (GW) 1231
Topics in Physical Organometallic Chemistry. (UK) 1231
Topics in Religion: A Bibliographic Series. (US) 4213
Topics in Sociolinguistics. (US) 2848
Topics in Stereochemistry. (US ISSN 0082-500X) 1190
Topics in Total Compensation. (US ISSN 0888-6032) 1070
Topics in Veterinary Medicine. (US) 4816
Topics of Laser Applications see Journal of Laser Applications 3854
Topique - Revue Freudienne. (FR ISSN 0040-9375) 3355, 4048
Topix. (GW) 1401
Topline. (US) 39, 1055
Topmobil. (GW) 4558
Topografia y Cartografia. (SP ISSN 0212-9280) 4006
Topoi. (NE ISSN 0167-7411) 4048, 3784
Topolino. (IT) 1268
Topology. (US ISSN 0040-9383) 3058
Topology and Its Applications. (NE ISSN 0166-8641) 3058
Topology Proceedings. (US ISSN 0146-4124) 3058
Toposcope. (SA) 2335
▼Topps. (US) 4514
Tops. (US ISSN 0563-9093) 2109
Top's Cars. (FR) 4703
Tops News. (US) 3809
Topsy Turvy-Patas Arribas. (US) 2886
Tora ha ku Libelela. (SA) 4289
Tora Ya Tebelo. (SA ISSN 0040-9391) 4289
Torah Education. (IS) 4227
Torakku Yuso Joho. (JA) 4716, 4748
Toranjisuta Gijutsu/Audio & Electronics.(JA ISSN 0040-9413) 1779
Torax. (UY ISSN 0049-4143) 3367
Toray Industries. Annual Report. (JA) 4627
Toray Kagaku Shinkokai Jigyo Hokokusho/Toray Science Foundation. Annual Report. (JA) 4348
Toray Kagaku Shinkokai Kagaku Koenkai Kiroku. (JA) 4348
Toray Rika Kyoikusho Jusho Sakuhinshu. (JA) 4348
Toray Science Foundation. Annual Report. see Toray Kagaku Shinkokai Jigyo Hokokusho 4348
Torch. (LB) 2335
Torch. (TZ) 2576
Torch. see Al-Mash'al 3691
Torch. see Tchahert 4289
Torch (Chicago). (US ISSN 0040-9448) 1301
Torch (Fullerton). (US) 1326
The Torch (Hallaton). (UK) 2296
Torch (London). (UK) 3473
Torch (Sequin). (US) 1326
Torch (Washington). (US) 3534
Torch of Victory see Victorious 3932
Torch Runner. (CN ISSN 0316-2931) 4250, 1245, 1723, 3400
Torch: U.S. (US ISSN 0493-5284) 1280
Torchbearer. (US) 3389
Il Torchio Artistico e Letterario. (IT) 347, 2970, 4455
Torchlight. (US) 4227, 3400
Tordenskjold. (DK ISSN 0904-8987) 2970
Het Torentje. (NE ISSN 0018-1129) 4075
Torfyanaya Promyshlennost' (RU ISSN 0040-9472) 2304
Torgos. (IS ISSN 0333-7383) 567
Torgovaya Gazeta. (RU) 839
Tori see Japanese Journal of Ornithology 564
Torino Motori see Motori 4697
▼Toriyn Medeelel/State Information. (MP) 4075

TORNADOES

Tornadoes and Storms. (UK) 3441
Tornionlaakson Vuosikirja. (FI) 2392
†Toronto. (CN) 5291
Toronto Airport Business Directory. (CN) 4677
Toronto Business Age. (CN) 695
Toronto Business Magazine. (CN ISSN 0831-4160) 1119
Toronto Computes. (CN) 1401
Toronto Construction News. (CN) 635
▼Toronto Events Planner. (CN) 2179
Toronto Field Naturalist. (CN ISSN 0820-683X) 458, 1498
Toronto Film Society. Publication. (CN) 3518
Toronto Historical Board. Year Book. (CN ISSN 0226-7209) 2424
Toronto Humane Society. Society News see Animal Talk 230
Toronto International Auto Show Program. (CN ISSN 0704-7339) 4704
Toronto Jewish Press. (CN ISSN 0049-4186) 2026
Toronto Journal of Theology. (CN ISSN 0826-9831) 4207
Toronto Legal Directory. (CN) 1155, 2686
Toronto Life. (CN ISSN 0049-4194) 2179
Toronto Life Design and Decor Guide see Toronto Life Homes 2555
Toronto Life Epicure. (CN) 2480, 2083
Toronto Life Fashion Magazine. (CN) 1294
Toronto Life Gourmet Guide see Toronto Life Epicure 2480
Toronto Life Homes. (CN) 2555, 2562
Toronto Life Restaurant and Gourmet Guide see Toronto Life Epicure 2480
Toronto Mediaeval Latin Texts. (CN ISSN 0082-5050) 2970, 2392
Toronto Medieval Bibliographies. (CN ISSN 0082-5042) 2330
Toronto Office Guide. (CN ISSN 0835-0663) 4348, 4612
Toronto Old English Series. (CN) 2970, 2848
Toronto Public Library News see T.P.L. News 2786
Toronto Railway Club. Official Proceedings. (CN ISSN 0040-9553) 4716
†Toronto Semitic Texts and Studies. (CN ISSN 0082-5123) 5291
Toronto South Asian Review. (CN ISSN 0714-3508) 2886, 2970
Toronto Stock Exchange Daily Record. (CN ISSN 0705-2170) 966
Toronto Stock Exchange Fact Book see As a Matter of Fact 938
Toronto Stock Exchange Review. (CN ISSN 0049-4216) 966
Toronto Stockwatch. (CN) 966
Toronto Studies in Religion. (US ISSN 8756-7385) 4207
Toronto Studies in Theology. (US) 4207
Toronto Symphony Magazine. (CN) 3584
Toronto Systems Letter. (CN) 1455, 1465
Toronto Teen see Smash Magazine 3580
Toronto Tonight. (CN) 2179
Toronto Vegetarian Association. Newsletter see Lifelines (Toronto) 3805
Torontoer Zeitung. (CN ISSN 0049-4240) 2026
Torpet. (CN ISSN 0821-1809) 1474, 1465
Torquay Natural History Society. Transactions and Proceedings. (UK ISSN 0082-5344) 4348
Torquay Pottery Collectors Society. Magazine. (UK ISSN 0951-6751) 357
Torquay Pottery Collectors Society. Newsletter see Torquay Pottery Collectors Society. Magazine 357
La Torre. (PR ISSN 0040-9588) 2848, 2970
Torre. (IT) 2886
Torre Davidica. (IT ISSN 0040-960X) 4207

Torre de los Panoramas. (UY) 3007
Torre de Papel. (AG) 2970
Torreia. (CU ISSN 0563-9425) 592
Torrens System in N.S.W. (AT) 2686, 4158
Torrens Valley Historical Journal. (AT) 2345
Torrent. see Ben Liu 2898
Torrey Botanical Club. Bulletin. (US ISSN 0040-9618) 519
†Torry Research Station, Aberdeen, Scotland. Annual Report. (UK ISSN 0082-5352) 5291
Torso. (US ISSN 0733-5865) 3400, 2457
Tort & Insurance Law Journal. (US ISSN 0885-856X) 2686
▼Tort Law and Personal Injury Practice (Rhode Island). (US) 2686
Tort Trends Newsletter. (US) 2686
Tortenelmi Szemle/Historical Review. (HU ISSN 0040-9634) 2324
Tortoise. (NR) 1969, 1268
Torts see B A R - B R I Bar Review. Torts 1510
Toscana Qui. (IT) 4789
Toshi Keizai. see Investment Economics 951
Toshi Kenkyu Hokoku/Report on Urban Research. (JA) 2497
Toshi Mondai/Municipal Problems. (JA) 4095
Toshi Sodan. see Investment Advice 950
Tosho. see Books and Essays 4123
Toshokan Gakkai Nenpo. see Japan Society of Library Science. Annals 2765
Toshokan Kenkyu Sirizu/N.D.L. Library Science Series. (JA ISSN 0454-1960) 2787
Toshokan Kyoryoku Tsushin/Library Cooperation News. (JA) 2787
Toshokan Nenkan. see Library Yearbook 2771
Toshokan Zasshi. see Library Journal 2770
Tosoguan Hak. (KO) 2787
Tosoh Kenkyu Hokoku. see Journal of Tosoh Research 1856
Tosomaeup Census Bogo Seo. see Korea (Republic). National Bureau of Statistics. Wholesale and Retail Trade Census Report 5224
Tot Onafhanklijkheid. see Towards Independence 2290
Total Compensation Report. (US) 4095
Total Creative Plunge see Samizdat 3005
Total Health. (US) 3612, 4048
Total Quality Control. see Hinshitsu Kanri 1011
▼Total Quality Environmental Management. (US ISSN 1055-7571) 1969
▼Total Quality Management. (UK ISSN 0954-4127) 1029
Total Quality Management Magazine see The T Q M Magazine 1029
Totalisator Agency Board. Annual Report. (NZ) 4075
Totally Gospel. (US ISSN 0884-738X) 3584, 4207
Totem. (US ISSN 0040-9723) 1498
Totem. (BL) 2886
Toth-Maatian Review. (US) 3834
Totline (Chapel Hill) see Highway Safety Directions 4719
Totline (Everett) see Totline Newsletter 1245
Totline Newsletter. (US) 1245
†Totok: Handbuch der Geschichte der Philosophie. (GW) 5291
Totto. (FI) 2392
Tottori Daigaku Kyoikugakubu Kenkyu Hokoku. Shizen Kagaku/Tottori University. Faculty of Education. Journal: Natural Science. (JA ISSN 0371-5965) 4348
Tottori Daigaku Nogakubu Fuzoku Enshurin Hokoku/Tottori University Forests. Research Bulletin. (JA ISSN 0082-5379) 2109
Tottori-kenritsu Hakubutsukan Kenkyu Hokoku/Tottori Prefectural Museum. Bulletin. (JA ISSN 0287-1688) 4348, 3534

Tottori Prefectural Museum. Bulletin. see Tottori-kenritsu Hakubutsukan Kenkyu Hokoku 4348
Tottori University. Faculty of Agriculture. Journal. (JA ISSN 0082-5360) 124
Tottori University. Faculty of Education. Journal: Natural Science. see Tottori Daigaku Kyoikugakubu Kenkyu Hokoku. Shizen Kagaku 4348
Tottori University Forests. Bulletin see Tottori Daigaku Nogakubu Fuzoku Enshurin Hokoku 2109
Tottori University Forests. Research Bulletin. see Tottori Daigaku Nogakubu Fuzoku Enshurin Hokoku 2109
†Touch of Class. (US) 5291
Touche Ross & Company. Tax Newsletter. (UK ISSN 0261-8664) 1111
Touchstone (Chicago). (US) 4277, 3930
Touchstone (Houston). (US) 3007, 2886
Touchstone (Nashville). (US) 2516
Touchstone Magazine. (US) 4348
Touk Touk. (GW) 2191
T'oung Pao. (NE ISSN 0082-5433) 3645
T'oung Pao. Monographies. (NE ISSN 0169-832X) 3645
Tour & Travel Marketplace. (US) 4789
Tour and Travel News. (US) 4789
Tour Companion. (JA) 4789
Tour de Feu see Nouvelle Tour de Feu 2999
Tour de l'Orle d'Or see Societe des Sciences Historiques et Naturelles de Semur en Auxois et des Fouilles d'Alesia. Bulletin 2387
Tour Hebdo. (CN) 4789
Tour Organizers' Handbook/Guide du Directeur de Tournees de Spectacles.(CN) 4789
Tour Trade. (US) 4789
Tourarts. (CN) 1155, 4642, 4790
Tourbook: Alabama, Louisiana, Mississippi. (US ISSN 0361-4948) 4790
Tourbook: Arizona, New Mexico. (US ISSN 0362-3599) 4790
Tourbook: Arkansas, Kansas, Missouri, Oklahoma. (US) 4790
Tourbook: Atlantic Provinces and Quebec. (US ISSN 0363-1788) 4790
Tourbook: California, Nevada. (US) 4790
Tourbook: Colorado, Utah. (US ISSN 0362-9821) 4790
Tourbook: Connecticut, Massachusetts, Rhode Island. (US) 4790
Tourbook: Florida. (US ISSN 0516-9674) 4790
Tourbook: Georgia, North Carolina, South Carolina. (US ISSN 0361-4956) 4790
Tourbook: Hawaii. (US) 4790
Tourbook: Idaho, Montana, Wyoming. (US ISSN 0363-2695) 4790
Tourbook: Illinois, Indiana, Ohio. (US) 4790
Tourbook: Kentucky, Tennessee. (US ISSN 0361-4964) 4790
Tourbook: Maine, New Hampshire, Vermont. (US) 4790
Tourbook: Michigan, Wisconsin. (US) 4790
Tourbook: Mid-Atlantic. (US ISSN 0364-0086) 4790
Tourbook: New Jersey, Pennsylvania. (US) 4790
Tourbook: New York. (US ISSN 0363-1540) 4790
Tourbook: North Central. (US) 4790
Tourbook: Ontario. (US) 4790
Tourbook: Oregon, Washington. (US) 4790
Tourbook: Texas. (US) 4790
Tourbook: Western Canada and Alaska. (US ISSN 0362-3602) 4790
Touren-Fahrer. (GW ISSN 0933-4440) 4521, 1508
Touring. (CN) 4704, 4113, 4790
Touring. (SZ ISSN 0040-9758) 4790, 4704
Touring. (FR) 4790

▼Touring America. (US ISSN 1055-6850) 4790
Touring and Travel see Preferred Traveller 5261
Touring Artists Directory of the Performing Arts in Canada see Tourarts 1155
Touring Club Magazine. (BE) 4790, 4704
Touring from Salisbury see Salisbury 4785
Touring Giovani. (IT) 1268, 4790
Touring M. (CN) 4790
Touring Nyt. (DK ISSN 0106-1925) 4521
Touring with Towser. (US ISSN 0082-5441) 3714
Tourism. see Matkailu 4775
Tourism. see Luyou 4775
Tourism and Travel Management. (AT) 4790, 1029
Tourism and Wildlife. (II) 4790, 1498
Tourism Chronicle. see Touristika Chronika 4791
Tourism in Arkansas. Activity Report see Arkansas Travel and Tourism Report 4752
Tourism in the British Virgin Islands. (VB) 4800
The Tourism Industry. (UK) 4790
Tourism Industry Association of Canada Newsletter see T I A C Newsletter 4788
Tourism Industry of Puerto Rico. Selected Statistics. (PR) 4801
Tourism Management. (UK ISSN 0261-5177) 4790
Tourism Recreation Research. (II ISSN 0250-8281) 4791
Tourism Room Revenues. (CN) 4801
Tourisme. (FR ISSN 0751-6657) 4791
Tourisme en Suisse. see Tourismus in der Schweiz 4801
Tourisme Plus, le Journal des Voyages. (CN ISSN 0836-205X) 4791
Tourisme Suisse en Chiffres. see Schweizer Tourismus in Zahlen 4800
Tourismus in der Schweiz/Tourisme en Suisse. (SZ) 4801
Tourispress Italia. (IT ISSN 0394-8536) 4791, 2480, 3394, 4657
†Der Tourist. (GW ISSN 0138-3973) 5291
Tourist Attractions and Parks. (US) 4791, 1029
Tourist auf Reisen. (GW ISSN 0936-3637) 4791
†Tourist Guide/Guide Touristique. (CN) 5291
Tourist Guide Book of Ontario. (CN) 4791
Tourist Magazine. (IT) 4558, 4791
Tourist Park Guide. (AT) 4791
Tourist Review. see Zeitschrift fuer Fremdenverkehr 4798
Tourist Weekly see Key to Cayman 4774
Touristes Suisses a l'Etranger. see Reiseverkehr der Schweizer im Ausland 4800
†Touristic Analysis Review. (FR ISSN 0767-2659) 5291
Touristik Aktuell. (GW ISSN 0049-4283) 4791
Touristik R.E.P.O.R.T. (GW ISSN 0173-606X) 4791
Touristika Chronika/Tourism Chronicle. (CY) 4791
Tournament Chess. (UK ISSN 0276-7090) 4495
Tournament Fisherman. (AT) 4558
Touro Law Review. (US ISSN 8756-7326) 2686
Tours! (US) 4791
Tours and Excursions see Coachmart 4757
Tours & Resorts. (US ISSN 0890-2852) 4791
Tours and Visits Directory. (US ISSN 0278-467X) 4791
Tours on Motorcoach. (CN) 4791
Tous les Ouvrages - Toute la Broderie. (FR ISSN 0183-4738) 3593
Tout le Tricot. (FR ISSN 0183-3901) 3593

Tout le Tricot - Le Crochet et le Tricot d'Art see Crochet d'Art **3590**
Tout le Tricot - Tricot d'Art. (FR ISSN 0183-3928) **3593**
Tout Lyon. (FR) **2686**
Tout-Rouen. (FR ISSN 0040-9839) **2188**
Tout Terrain Magazine. (FR) **4704**
▼De Toute Beaute. (CN) **374**
Toute l'Alimentation. (FR ISSN 0758-5055) **2083**
Toute la Boisson. International. (FR ISSN 0082-5484) **386**
Toute la Broderie - Point de Croix. (FR ISSN 0183-3944) **3593**
Toutes les Nouvelles de l'Hotellerie et du Tourisme. (FR ISSN 0150-7540) **2480**, **4791**
Touzi Guanli yu Yanjiu/Investment Management and Study. (CC) **966**
Touzi Yanjiu/Investment Research. (US) **966**
Touzi yu Jianshe/Investment and Construction. (CC) **966**
▼Tovarishch. (RU) **3930**
Tow-Age. (US) **4748**
Tow-Line see Tow-Age **4748**
Tow Times. (US) **4748**, **4721**
Toward Freedom. see I Laisve **2005**
Toward Freedom. (US ISSN 0040-9898) **3973**
Toward the 21st Century. (US) **3988**
Towards Continuing Education. (Il) **1687**
Towards Independence/Tot Onafhanklijkheid. (SA) **2290**
Towards Wholeness. (UK) **4289**
Towarne Avtomobilov in Motorjev Skozi T A M see Skozi T A M **1939**
Towarzystwo Literackie im. A. Mickiewicza. Biblioteka. (PL ISSN 0067-7787) **2970**
Towarzystwo Naukowe w Toruniu. Fontes. (PL ISSN 0082-5506) **2392**, **2324**
Towarzystwo Naukowe w Toruniu. Komisja Historii Sztuki. Teka. (PL ISSN 0082-5514) **347**
Towarzystwo Naukowe w Toruniu. Prace Archeologiczne. (PL) **287**
Towarzystwo Naukowe w Toruniu. Prace Popularnonaukowe. (PL ISSN 0079-4805) **4348**
Towarzystwo Naukowe w Toruniu. Roczniki. (PL ISSN 0082-5522) **2324**
Towarzystwo Naukowe w Toruniu. Sprawozdania. (PL ISSN 0371-375X) **4348**
Tower. (US) **1326**
Tower. (CN ISSN 0495-9701) **3007**
Towers. (US ISSN 0040-9928) **2296**
Towers Club U S A Newsletter. (The Original Writers Entrepreneurial Research Service) (US ISSN 0193-4953) **4138**
Towing News. (US) **1838**, **4657**
Towline. (CN) **63**
Town and Country. (US ISSN 0040-9952) **2236**
Town and Country Farmer. (AT ISSN 0814-4540) **124**, **2109**, **2139**
†Town and Country Librarian. (CN ISSN 0382-0912) **5291**
Town and Country Planning. (UK ISSN 0040-9960) **2497**
Town and Country Planning Association. Annual Report. (UK ISSN 0308-082X) **2497**
Town & Country Planning Association. Planning Bulletin. (UK ISSN 0495-9728) **2497**
Town and Country Planning Summer School: Report of Proceedings. (UK ISSN 0078-2114) **2497**
Town & Village. (US ISSN 0040-9979) **2236**
Town Crier. (US ISSN 0748-5883) **4095**, **4094**
Town Planning and Local Government Guide. (AT ISSN 0040-9995) **4095**, **2497**
Town Planning Law and Practice. (AT) **2716**
Town Planning Review. (UK ISSN 0041-0020) **2497**
Towne Crier (Toms River). (US) **2279**
▼The Towne Crier (West Orange). (US) **2236**

Townsend Newsletter. (US) **2166**
Townsfolk. (US) **2236**
Townsman. (CN) **2179**
Townsville Advertiser see Twin Cities Advertiser **2172**
Townswoman. (UK) **1301**
Towpaths. (US ISSN 0890-7129) **2424**, **4740**
Towson State Journal of International Affairs. (US ISSN 0041-0063) **3974**
†Tox-Tips. (US ISSN 0146-1559) **5291**
Toxic Chemicals Litigation Reporter. (US ISSN 0737-8513) **2686**, **4113**
Toxic Materials News. (US ISSN 0093-5891) **1987**
Toxic Materials Transport see HazMat Transport **1985**
Toxic Substances Control Act - Test Submission Database. (US) **1975**, **1983**
Toxic Substances Journal. (US ISSN 0199-3178) **1987**, **1983**
Toxic Tort Litigation. (US) **2686**, **1987**
Toxic Torts. (US) **4113**, **1987**, **2544**
Toxicity Assessment see Environmental Toxicology and Water Quality **1981**
Toxicologic Pathology. (US ISSN 0192-6233) **1983**, **3158**
Toxicological and Environmental Chemistry. (US ISSN 0277-2248) **1983**, **1190**, **3744**
†Toxicological European Research. (FR ISSN 0249-6402) **5291**
Toxicology. (IE ISSN 0300-483X) **1983**, **3744**
Toxicology Abstracts. (US ISSN 0140-5365) **3748**, **24**, **1983**
Toxicology and Applied Pharmacology. (US ISSN 0041-008X) **1983**, **3744**
Toxicology in Vitro. (US ISSN 0887-2333) **1983**, **483**, **3158**, **3744**
Toxicology Letters. (NE ISSN 0378-4274) **1983**, **3744**
▼Toxicology Methods. (US ISSN 1051-7235) **1983**, **3744**
Toxicomanias. (AG) **1539**
Toxicon. (US ISSN 0041-0101) **3744**, **519**, **1983**, **3158**
Toxics Law Reporter. (US ISSN 0887-7394) **1987**, **2686**
†Toxins. (UK ISSN 0142-8535) **5291**
†Toxoplasmosis. (UK ISSN 0142-8829) **5291**
Toy and Decoration Fair Directory. (CN ISSN 0317-9443) **1155**, **2282**, **2555**
Toy & Hobby Retailer. (SA) **1055**, **2443**
▼Toy & Hobby Retailer. (AT ISSN 1035-9176) **2282**, **2443**
Toy & Hobby World. (US ISSN 0041-011X) **2282**, **2443**
Toy & Hobby World Latin America. (US) **2282**, **2443**
Toy Book. (US) **2282**, **2443**
Toy Car. (US) **2443**
Toy Directory. (UK) **2282**
Toy Farmer. (US ISSN 0894-5055) **2282**
Toy Fayre Earls Court Newspaper see Toy Trader Daily News (Earls Court) **839**
Toy Fayre Harrogate Newspaper see Toy Trader Daily News (Harrogate) **840**
Toy Report. (CN) **2282**
Toy Shop. (US ISSN 0898-5650) **2443**, **2282**
Toy Trade News. (US) **2282**, **2443**
Toy Trader. (UK ISSN 0041-0136) **2282**, **2443**
Toy Trader Daily News (Earls Court). (UK) **839**, **2282**
Toy Trader Daily News (Harrogate). (UK) **840**, **2282**
Toy Trader Year Book see Toy Directory **2282**
Toy Train Operating Society Bulletin see T T O S Bulletin **2282**
Toy Train Operating Society Order Board see T T O S Order Board **2282**
Toy Trucker and Contractor. (US ISSN 1052-2187) **2282**

Toyama Daigaku Kyoikugakubu Kiyo, B. Rikakei/Toyama University. Faculty of Education. Memoirs, B. Natural Science. (JA ISSN 0285-9610) **4348**
Toyama Daigaku Kyoyobu Kiyo. Shizen Kagaku Hen/Toyama University. College of Liberal Arts. Journal: Natural Sciences. (JA ISSN 0385-812X) **4348**
Toyama-ken Eisei Tokei Nenpo/Toyama Prefecture. Annual Report of Public Health. (JA) **4119**, **4113**
Toyama-ken Shizenhogo Kyoukaiho. (JA) **1498**
Toyama Mercantile Marine College. Journal. see Toyama Shosen Koto Senmon Gakko Kenkyu Shuroku **4740**
Toyama Prefecture. Annual Report of Public Health. see Toyama-ken Eisei Tokei Nenpo **4119**
Toyama Science and Technical Documents. see Kagaku Gijutsu Bunken Toyama **4614**
Toyama Science Museum. Bulletin. see Toyama-shi Kagaku Bunka Senta Kenkyu Hokoku **4348**
Toyama-shi Kagaku Bunka Senta Kenkyu Hokoku/Toyama Science Museum. Bulletin. (JA ISSN 0387-9089) **4348**
Toyama Shosen Koto Senmon Gakko Kenkyu Shuroku/Toyama Mercantile Marine College. Journal. (JA) **4740**
Toyama to Shizen. (JA) **3534**, **4348**
Toyama University. College of Liberal Arts. Journal: Natural Sciences. see Toyama Daigaku Kyoyobu Kiyo. Shizen Kagaku Hen **4348**
Toyama University. Faculty of Education. Memoirs, B. Natural Science. see Toyama Daigaku Kyoikugakubu Kiyo, B. Rikakei **4348**
Toyama University. Mathematics Journal. (JA ISSN 0916-6009) **3058**
Toyama University. Mathematics Reports see Toyama University. Mathematics Journal **3058**
▼Toybox Magazine. (US) **2282**
Toyo Daigaku Kiyo. Kyoyo Katei Hen. Shizen Kagaku/Toyo University. Journal. General Education. Natural Science. (JA ISSN 0372-0330) **4348**
Toyo Engineering Corporation. Annual Report. (JA) **1838**
Toyo Engineering Corporation Advanced Engineering Information see T E C Advanced Engineering Information **1837**
Toyo Keizai. Statistics Monthly. (JA) **4590**
Toyo Ongaku Kenkyu. see Studies on Oriental Music **3583**
Toyo Soda Manufacturing Company. Scientific Report see Journal of Tosoh Research **1856**
Toyo Tsushinki Giho. see Toyo's Technical Bulletin **1345**
Toyo University. Journal. General Education. Natural Science. see Toyo Daigaku Kiyo. Kyoyo Katei Hen. Shizen Kagaku **4348**
Toyoda Kenkyu Hokoku/Toyoda Physical and Chemical Research Institute. Reports. (JA ISSN 0372-039X) **3834**, **1190**
Toyoda Koki Giho. see Toyoda Machine Works Technical Review **3024**
Toyoda Machine Works Technical Review/Toyoda Koki Giho. (JA) **3024**
Toyoda Physical and Chemical Research Institute. Reports. see Toyoda Kenkyu Hokoku **3834**
Toyoda Technical Review see Toyoda Machine Works Technical Review **3024**
Toyo's Technical Bulletin/Toyo Tsushinki Giho. (JA ISSN 0386-7587) **1345**
Toyota and Automotive Electronic. (JA) **4704**
▼Toyota and Automotive Safety. (JA) **4704**
▼Toyota and the Environment. (JA) **4704**, **1969**

▼Toyota Engine Technology. (JA) **4704**
Toyota Foundation Occasional Report. (JA ISSN 0285-9033) **2970**
Toyota in Brief see Automobile Industry - Japan and Toyota **4682**
Toyota Motor Corporation. Annual Report. (JA) **4704**
Toys & Games. (CN ISSN 0381-9930) **2282**, **2443**
Toys International see Toys International and Toy Buyer **2283**
Toys International and the Retailer see Toys International and Toy Buyer **2283**
Toys International and Toy Buyer. (UK ISSN 0260-4760) **2283**, **2443**
Tozsde Kurir/Hungarian Stock Market Courier. (HU) **966**
Tra Noi. (IT) **1326**
Trabajadores. (CU) **995**
Trabajo. (DR ISSN 0564-0334) **995**
Trabajo. (CK) **995**
Trabajo en Israel see Labour in Israel **2586**
Trabajo Politico. (CU) **3930**
Trabajo Social see Revista Trabajo Social **4418**
Trabajos de Arqueologia Navarra. (SP ISSN 0211-5174) **287**
Trabajos de Geologia. (SP ISSN 0474-9588) **1583**
Trabajos de Prehistoria. Nueva Serie. (SP ISSN 0082-5638) **287**
Trabajos Monograficos sobre la Independencia de Norteamerica. (SP) **2424**
Trabajos Realizados por el Comite Juridico Interamericano Durante el Periodo Ordinario de Sesiones see Work Accomplished by the Inter-American Juridical Committee during its Meeting **2695**
Trabalho. (AO ISSN 0564-0342) **995**
Trabalhos de Antropologia e Etnologia. (PO ISSN 0304-243X) **251**
Trabalhos em Linguistica Aplicada. (BL ISSN 0103-1813) **2848**
TRAC see Trends in Analytical Chemistry **1209**
†Trac: Global Yearbook of Issues, Events, and Discoveries in Telecommunications, Robotics, Artificial Intelligence, C A D - C A M. (US) **5291**
Trace Analysis. (US ISSN 0275-844X) **4113**
†Trace Elements. (UK ISSN 0268-1463) **5291**
Trace Elements in Medicine. (GW ISSN 0174-7371) **3158**
Trace Substances in Environmental Health. (US ISSN 0361-5162) **1984**, **1969**, **4113**
Tracer see Private Investigator's Connection **1521**
Tracers. (US) **3363**
Traces. (FR ISSN 0041-0276) **3007**
Traces (Glasgow). (US ISSN 0882-2158) **2166**, **2424**
Traces (Jackson). (US) **1301**, **1498**, **1970**, **4558**
Traces in the Sand. (US) **2166**
Traces of Indiana and Midwestern History. (US ISSN 1040-788X) **2424**, **2166**
Trachtenzeitung see Deutsche Trachtenzeitung **2053**
Trachtler. (AU) **4791**
Tracings. (US) **2166**
Track & Field. see Tianjing **4558**
Track and Field Case Book. (US) **4558**
Track & Field Journal. (CN ISSN 0226-2630) **4495**
Track & Field News. (US ISSN 0041-0284) **4558**
Track and Field Officials Manual. (US) **4558**
Track and Field Quarterly Review. (US ISSN 0041-0292) **4558**
Track and Field Rulebook. (US) **4558**
Track Newsletter. (US ISSN 0041-0306) **4558**
Track Technique: Official Technical Publication. (US ISSN 0742-3918) **4558**
Track Yearbook. (US) **4716**
Tracker. (US ISSN 0041-0330) **3584**
Tracks. (AT) **4558**

6738 TRACKS

†Tracks (Chicago). (US) 5291
Tracks and Traces. (US) 2166
Trackside. (US) 4495
Tract Messenger. (US ISSN 0041-0357) 2296, 4250
Tractatenblad van het Koninkrijk der Nederlanden. (NE ISSN 0023-3412) 3974
Tractebel. Annual Report. (BE ISSN 0774-3998) 1838, 1909
†Tractebel News. (BE) 5291
Tracteurs et Machines Agricoles. (FR ISSN 0754-121X) 164
Tractionel News see Tractebel News 5291
Tractor & Farm Machinery Trader. (UK ISSN 0262-8090) 164
Tractor Digest. (US) 164, 4748
Tractrix. (NE) 4348, 2324, 3158
Tracy see Judy and Tracy 1239
Trade (New York) see Fabricnews 4618
Trade-A-Boat. (AT) 4740
Trade-A-Plane. (US ISSN 0041-0365) 63
Trade Action Monitoring System. (US) 840, 922
Trade and Commerce. (CN ISSN 0049-4321) 840
▼Trade & Culture. (US) 922
Trade and Development Report. (UN ISSN 0255-4607) 922, 935
Trade and Industry. (PK ISSN 0041-0373) 695
Trade and Industry/Majallat al-Tijara wal-Sina'a. (TS) 823
Trade and Industry in Ireland see Boardroom 648
Trade & Industry Index. (US) 741
Trade and Industry of Curacao. Monthly Publication see Curacao Trade and Industry Association. Newsletter 858
Trade and Industry of Japan see Focus Japan 908
Trade and Professional Associations in California. (US) 1155
Trade and Technical Careers and Training see Career Education That Works for America 1692
Trade and Technical Review. (GW ISSN 0232-5780) 922
Trade Associations and Professional Bodies of the United Kingdom. (UK ISSN 0082-5689) 1155
Trade Chronicle. (PK ISSN 0041-0411) 1086
Trade Commerce & Industry Weekly Bulletin. (II) 840
Trade Digest see World Fairs Guide 1056
Trade Directories of the World. (US ISSN 0564-0482) 1155
Trade Directory (Year) see Malta Trade Directory (Year) 1145
Trade Directory and Guide Book to Ethiopia. (ET ISSN 0564-0490) 1155, 823
Trade Directory for Denmark. see Udenrigs Handelskalenderen for Danmark 1156
Trade Directory of Seychelles. (SE) 1155
Trade Facilitation see E D I World 5183
▼Trade Fairs in Japan (Year). (JA) 3394
Trade Finance & Banker International. (UK) 801, 922
Trade Focus. (ET) 823
Trade in Natural Resource-Products. (UN) 922, 3496
Trade Information Bulletin. (NE) 823
Trade Intelligence Bulletin. (II) 922
Trade Journal Recap. (US) 1055, 2886
†Trade Law Topics. (CN ISSN 0827-5513) 5291
Trade Leads. (US) 922
Trade-Links Journal. (IE) 922
▼Trade Marketing. (IT) 1055
Trade Marks Journal/Journal des Marques de Commerce. (CN ISSN 0041-0438) 3678
Trade Marks Journal. (UK ISSN 0041-0446) 3678
Trade Marks Journal. (IS ISSN 0334-2425) 3678
Trade Media. (CH) 1155

†Trade Monitor. (CN ISSN 0836-0820) 5291
Trade Names Dictionary see Brands and Their Companies 3673
Trade Names Dictionary: Company Index see Companies and Their Brands 1127
†Trade of China. (CH ISSN 0082-5778) 5291
Trade of the Maltese Islands see Malta Trade Statistics 917
Trade Only see Soundings Trade Only 4529
Trade Opportunities in Taiwan. (CH) 922
Trade Opportunity. (CH) 823, 1155
Trade Pages. (CH) 922
Trade Policy Review. (UN ISSN 1014-7411) 922
†Trade Post. (PH ISSN 0115-2394) 5291
Trade Practices Commission Bulletin. (AT ISSN 0818-044X) 695
Trade Practices Law. (AT) 2686, 695
Trade Regulation Reports. (US ISSN 0572-9912) 840
Trade Shows & Exhibits Schedule. (US) 695, 3394
Trade Statistics. (IE ISSN 0790-9381) 741
Trade Statistics of Ireland see Trade Statistics 741
Trade Times. (JA ISSN 0493-6779) 3024, 922
Trade Trax. (US) 4854, 995
Trade Union Courier. (US ISSN 0041-0497) 2590
Trade Union Handbook. (US ISSN 1053-7007) 2590
Trade Union International of Agricultural, Forestry and Plantation Workers Information see T U I A F P W Information 2590
Trade Union News. (SW) 2590
Trade Union News from the European Community. (EI) 995
Trade Union Press see Flashes from the Trade Unions 2583
Trade Union Record. (II ISSN 0041-0535) 2590
Trade Union Studies Journal. (UK ISSN 0144-7106) 2590
Trade Unionism in Spain. see Sindicalismo en Espana 2589
Trade Unions in India. (II ISSN 0445-6289) 2590
Trade Unions International of Chemical, Oil and Allied Workers. Information Bulletin. (HU) 2590, 823
Trade Unions International of Chemical, Oil and Allied Workers. International Trade Conference. Documents. (HU ISSN 0084-1544) 2590
Trade Unions International of Workers in Commerce. Bulletin. (CS ISSN 0049-433X) 2590, 840
Trade Unions International of Workers in Commerce. News. (CS) 2590, 840
Trade Unions International of Workers of the Building, Wood and Building Materials Industries Bulletin see U I T B B Bulletin 2590
Trade Ways. (KE) 922
Trade Weekly. (CH) 922
Trade-Weighted Value of the Dollar. (US) 922
Trade Winds. (CH) 922
†Trade Winds. (US) 5291
Trade Winds, Channel B see International Trade Winds 913
Trade Winds Monthly. (CH ISSN 0259-9880) 922
Trade Winners. (CH) 1401, 1455, 1909
Trade with Greece. (GR ISSN 0041-0543) 823
Trade with Italy. (US ISSN 0041-0551) 823
▼Trade Yellow Pages (Year). (CH) 1156
Tradefinance Asia. (HK) 695
Tradelink - S M A Annual Directory (Year). (SI ISSN 0217-7447) 1156
Trademark Law Handbook. (US ISSN 0731-5813) 2686, 2729

Trademark Register of the United States. (US ISSN 0082-5786) 3678
Trademark Reporter. (US ISSN 0041-056X) 3678
Trader. (UK) 1055
Traders Magazine. (US ISSN 0894-7295) 801, 966
Trader's Option. (US) 966
Traders Post. (CN) 840
Trader's World Magazine. (US) 966
Trades and Services Newsletter. (US) 3622
Trades Union Congress. Report. (UK) 2590
Trades Union Congress of Ghana News see T U C News 2590
Tradescope. (JA ISSN 0285-3809) 1156, 24
TradeShow & Convention Guide. (US) 4791, 695
Tradeshow and Exhibit Manager. (US ISSN 0893-2662) 1029
Tradeshow and Exhibit Manager Buyers Guide see Tradeshow Directory 1156
Tradeshow Directory. (US ISSN 0893-2662) 1156, 39, 3394, 4791
†Tradeshow Marketing Journal. (US) 5291
▼Tradeshow Report International. (GW) 922
Tradeshow Week. (US) 39, 1055
Tradeshow Week Data Book. (US ISSN 0000-1023) 1055
Tradeshow Week Data Book - International Edition. (US) 1055
Tradeswomen. (US ISSN 0739-344X) 4854, 995
TradeWind Magazine. (US) 4791
Tradewinds. (US) 4558, 1086, 2283
Tradimus see Nursing Standard 3284
▼Trading Cards. (US) 2443, 4514
Trading Cycles. (US) 966
Trading Law. (UK ISSN 0262-9240) 2686
Trading Law Reports. (UK ISSN 0268-9510) 2686
Trading Post (Greenville). (US ISSN 0041-0586) 2443, 3473
†Trading Post (New Orleans). (US) 5291
Trading Standards Review. (UK ISSN 0953-8704) 1055
Trading Systems Technology. (US ISSN 0892-5542) 805
Tradisjon. (NO ISSN 0332-5997) 2059
Traditio. (US ISSN 0362-1529) 2392, 2516
Tradition (New York). (US ISSN 0041-0608) 4227, 3784
Tradition (Walnut). (US) 3584
Tradition et Progres. (FR) 4277
Traditional Building. (US ISSN 0898-0284) 635
Traditional Chinese Architecture and Gardens. see Gujian Yuanlin Jishu 300
Traditional Chinese Medicinal Research. see Zhongyi Yanjiu 3165
Traditional Dwellings and Settlements Review. (US ISSN 1050-2092) 307, 2497
Traditional Home. (US) 2555
Traditional Jazz Today see T - J Today 3583
Traditional Kent Buildings. (UK ISSN 0260-4116) 308, 635
Traditional Medical Systems. (II) 3158
Traditional Music. (UK ISSN 0306-7440) 3584
The Traditional MusicLine. (US ISSN 1059-5953) 3584
Traditional Quilter. (US ISSN 1050-0073) 3593
Traditional Quiltworks. (US ISSN 1050-4435) 3593
Traditiones. (XV ISSN 0352-0447) 251, 2059
Traditionsverbandes Ehemaliger Schutz- und Ueberseetruppen. Mitteilungsblatt. (GW) 2392
Trado: Asian - African Directory of Exporters, Importers and Manufacturers. (II ISSN 0082-5824) 1156

Traduction Automatique see T.A. Informations 2857
Traduction Automatique Documents see T A Documents 2846
Traductions Hebraiques des Evangiles. (BE) 4207
Traduire. (FR ISSN 0395-773X) 2848
Trae Nyt. (DK ISSN 0041-0624) 640
Trae Nyts Leverandoerregister. (DK) 640, 2118
Trae och Byggvaruhandlaren see Bygg & Traevaruhandeln 607
Trae og Industri/Danish Wood Industry. (DK ISSN 0105-8738) 2118
Traedgaardsnytt. (FI ISSN 0049-4356) 2140
Traeindustrien see Trae og Industri 2118
Traeindustrin/Woodworking Industry. (SW ISSN 0346-2846) 640
Traelast-Tidende. (DK) 2118
Traethodydd. (UK) 2970
Trafalgar House News. (UK ISSN 0956-4462) 635, 1875, 4740
Traffic. (MW) 4657
Traffic Audit Bureau. Annual Report. (US) 4721, 39
Traffic Audit Bureau. Newsletter. (US) 4721, 39
Traffic Control Manual for Work on Roadways. (CN) 4721
Traffic Engineering & Control. (UK ISSN 0041-0683) 4721
Traffic Law Reports. (US ISSN 0893-3030) 4704, 2687
Traffic Laws Commentary. (US ISSN 0082-5859) 4721
Traffic Management. (US ISSN 0041-0691) 4657, 1055
Traffic Manager. (US ISSN 0041-0705) 4721
Traffic Report of the St. Lawrence Seaway. (US ISSN 0082-5867) 4740
Traffic Safety (Chicago). (US ISSN 0041-0721) 4721
Traffic Safety (Washington). (US) 4721
Traffic Safety Series. (US) 4721, 2544
Traffic Trends see Maryland. State Highway Administration. Traffic Trends 4719
Traffic World. (US ISSN 0041-073X) 4657
Trafico. (PE) 4791
Trafik. (GW ISSN 0177-1361) 2886
Trafik-Journal. (AU) 4645
Trafikanalyse see Stopinterviewanalyse 4721
Trafikoekonomiske Enhedspriser. (DK ISSN 0106-1852) 4721, 695
Tragaluz. (HO) 2970
Trail and Landscape. (CN ISSN 0041-0748) 1498
Trail and Timberline. (US ISSN 0041-0756) 4558, 1498
Trail Blazer's Almanac see Trail Blazer's Almanac and Pioneer Guide Book 4558
Trail Blazer's Almanac and Pioneer Guide Book. (US) 4558
Trail Breakers. (US ISSN 0362-0344) 2166, 2424
Trail Riders Fellowship Bulletin. (UK) 4521
Trail Riders of the Canadian Rockies Newsletter. (CN) 4538
Trail Talk. (US) 4558
Trail Tracer. (US ISSN 0740-4999) 2166
Trail Walker. (US ISSN 0749-1352) 4558, 1498
Trailblazer. (US) 4791
Trailer. (DK ISSN 0108-6758) 4558
Trailer Boats. (US ISSN 0300-6557) 4530
Trailer-Body Builders. (US ISSN 0041-0772) 4748
Trailer Life. (US ISSN 0041-0780) 4558, 4657
Trailer Life Campground and R V Services Directory. (US) 4558, 4791
†Trailer Life's Recreational Vehicle Buyers Guide. (US) 5291

Trailer Life's Recreational Vehicle Campground and Services Directory. (US) **1156**, **4558**, **4791**
Trailerboats and Fisherman. (AT) **4558**
Trailers Towing & 4WD. (AT) **4530**
Trailfinder. (UK) **4791**
Trails. (CN) **2166**
Trails-a-Way. (US) **4558**, **4791**
†Trails to Churchill County. (US ISSN 8756-7075) **5291**
Train Collectors Quarterly. (US ISSN 0041-0829) **2443**, **4716**
Train Dispatcher. (US ISSN 0041-0837) **2590**, **4716**
Train Rider Magazine. (US ISSN 0896-4424) **4716**
Train Rider Monthly see Train Rider Magazine **4716**
▼Trainers' Forum. (US ISSN 1050-527X) **1070**, **995**
Trainer's Workshop. (US ISSN 0888-5893) **1030**
Trainer's Yearbook see Training Directory (Year) **1668**
Training. (US ISSN 0095-5892) **1030**, **1070**, **1762**
Training Aids Digest. (US ISSN 0889-5732) **1523**
Training and Development see Indian Journal of Training & Development **1066**
Training & Development. (US ISSN 1055-9760) **1070**, **995**
Training and Development Alert. (US ISSN 0192-0596) **741**
Training & Development Canada: The Human Resources Development Journal see T & D Canada: The Human Resources Development Journal **1070**
Training and Development in Australia. (AT ISSN 0310-4664) **995**
Training and Development Organizations Directory. (US) **1030**
Training and Education see Personnel, Training and Education **2779**
Training and Education for Advanced Manufacturing see T E A M **5286**
Training and Management Development Methods. (UK ISSN 0951-3507) **1030**
Training Digest. (UK) **995**, **1030**
Training Directors' Forum Newsletter. (US) **1668**, **1030**
Training Directory (Year). (UK) **1668**
Training, Electronics, C 4 I see Defense & Aerospace Electronics **3456**
Training for Agriculture see Training for Agriculture and Rural Development **1687**
Training for Agriculture and Rural Development. (UN ISSN 0251-1495) **1687**, **124**
Training in Business and Industry see Training **1030**
Training Officer. (UK ISSN 0041-090X) **1070**
Training Resources see A S T D Buyers Guide and Consultants Directory **1120**
†Training Resources Tourism, Hospitality, Recreation. (CN ISSN 0712-7456) **5291**
Training Today. (US) **1668**, **3631**
†Training Today. (UK) **5291**
Training Trends. (US) **1687**
Trainmaster. (US ISSN 0041-0926) **4716**, **2324**
Trains. see Taagg **4715**
Trains. (US ISSN 0041-0934) **4716**
†Trains Illustrated. (US ISSN 0899-7217) **5291**
Trainsheet. (US ISSN 0041-0845) **4716**
Trait-d'Union see Immuno-analyse et Biologie Specialisee **441**
Trait-d'Union. (CN) **1326**
Traitement du Signal. (FR ISSN 0765-0019) **3834**, **3058**
Traitement Thermique/Heat Treatment. (FR ISSN 0041-0950) **3422**
Trajecta. (NE) **4277**, **2392**
†Trajekt. (GW) **5291**
†Trakcja i Wagony. (PL ISSN 0137-2963) **5291**
Trakehner Hefte. (GW ISSN 0720-9150) **4538**
Traktoeren. (SW ISSN 0041-0969) **2480**

Traktor Aktuell. (AU ISSN 0041-0985) **165**
Traktor- og Landbrugsbladet. (DK ISSN 0041-0977) **165**, **3024**
Tramoya. (MX) **4642**
Trampolinturnen. (GW) **4495**
Tramway Museum Society. Journal. (UK ISSN 0049-4372) **4657**
Tranciatura Stampaggio see Tecnologia della Deformazione **3024**
TraNet. (US ISSN 0739-0971) **4612**
Trans - Form - Acao. (BL ISSN 0101-3173) **3784**
Trans Media see T M **2886**
▼Trans-Missouri Art View. (US) **3007**
Trans-Ocean. (GW) **4530**
Trans Tasman. (NZ ISSN 0049-4380) **840**
Trans World Airlines Ambassador see T W A Ambassador **4804**
Transaction. (FR) **4006**
TransAction. (CN ISSN 0714-8100) **4251**, **4657**
Transactional Analysis Journal. (US ISSN 0362-1537) **4049**, **3355**
Transactions of the American Fisheries Society see American Fisheries Society. Transactions **2036**
Transactions of the Charles S. Pierce Society see Charles S. Peirce Society. Transactions **3763**
Transactions of the Monumental Brass Society. (UK ISSN 0143-1250) **288**, **3422**
Transactions of the North American Manufacturing Research Conference. Proceedings. (US) **1838**
Transactions on Computer Systems. (US ISSN 0734-2071) **1439**
Transactions on Information Systems. (US) **828**
Transactions on Office Information Systems see Transactions on Information Systems **828**
Transactions S A E S T. (Society for Advancement of Electrochemical Science and Technology) (II ISSN 0036-0678) **1213**
Transafrica Forum. (US ISSN 0730-8876) **2170**
TransAfrica Forum Issues Briefs. (US ISSN 0730-188X) **2170**
Transafrica Historical Papers. (KE) **2335**
Transafrican Journal of History. (KE ISSN 0041-106X) **2324**, **2026**
Transatlantic Perspectives. (US ISSN 0192-477X) **3974**
TransAtlantik. (GW) **2191**
Transborder Data Flow News see Integrated Service Digital Network **1427**
Transcend. (US) **2026**
†Transcript. (US) **5291**
†Transcription Regulation. (UK ISSN 0952-0376) **5291**
Transcultural Psychiatric Research Review. (CN ISSN 0041-1108) **3355**, **251**
Transdex see Transdex Index **2579**
Transdex Index. (US ISSN 0041-1116) **2579**
Transducer Technology. (UK) **1909**
▼Transearch. (NZ ISSN 1170-7321) **4721**
Transender. (US) **4049**
Transfer. (GW ISSN 0178-4099) **4612**
Transfer Credit Practices of Designated Educational Institutions. (US ISSN 0194-0988) **1668**
Transformacion. (MX ISSN 0041-1124) **1086**
Transformation. (UK ISSN 0265-3788) **4207**
Transformation Times. (US) **3597**, **3216**, **3671**, **4207**
▼Transformations. (US ISSN 1052-5017) **4455**
Transformers Notebook. (US) **1539**, **3597**, **3784**
Transfusion. (US ISSN 0041-1132) **3212**
Transfusion see Revue Francaise de Transfusion et Immuno-Hematologie **3273**
▼Transfusion Medicine. (UK ISSN 0958-7578) **3274**

Transfusion Medicine Reviews. (US ISSN 0887-7963) **3274**
Transfusion Science. (US ISSN 0955-3886) **3274**
Transfusion Today. (FR ISSN 1015-3276) **3274**
▼Transgenic Research. (UK ISSN 0962-8819) **547**
Transient. (US) **2970**
Transilvania. (RM) **2392**, **4455**
Transistor D.A.T.A. Digest. (US ISSN 1040-0230) **1909**
Transistor Gijutsu. (JA) **1909**
Transit see Train Dispatcher **2590**
Transit Australia. (AT ISSN 0818-5204) **4716**
Transit Courier. (GW) **922**
Transit of Chi Epsilon. (US ISSN 0041-1167) **1326**
Transit Postmark Collector. (US ISSN 0041-1175) **3758**
Transit Times (Atlanta). (US) **4716**, **4657**
Transit - Times (Oakland). (US ISSN 0049-4410) **4657**
Transit Topics see C U T A - A C T U Forum **4717**
Transition. (GY ISSN 1012-8263) **4390**
Transition. (CN ISSN 0049-4429) **4455**
†Transition (Cincinnati). (US ISSN 0747-5020) **5291**
Transition (New York). (US) **2887**
Transition (Year). (US) **4422**
Transition Metal Chemistry. (UK ISSN 0340-4285) **3422**
Transition News. (US) **4422**
Transition Summary. (US) **1742**, **2284**
Transitions. (US) **1326**
Transitions see Transitions Abroad **1723**
Transitions Abroad. (US ISSN 0276-4717) **1723**
Transitions in Mental Retardation. (US) **4049**
TransitPulse. (US ISSN 0748-7347) **4657**
Transizione. (IT) **3930**, **3974**, **4422**, **4612**
Transkei Government Gazette Index. (SA ISSN 0257-5418) **4082**, **24**
Transkei Liberal News see Reality **2881**
Transkei Official Gazette see Transkei Government Gazette Index **4082**
Translated Law Literature. see Faxue Yicong **2625**
Translated Literature on Seismology and Geology. see Dizhen Dizhi Yicong **1588**
Translated Tables of Contents of Current Foreign Fisheries, Oceanographic, and Atmospheric Publications. (US) **468**, **24**, **1552**, **3444**
Translation. see Anuvad **2803**
Translation (New York, 1972). (US ISSN 0093-9307) **2970**, **2848**
Translation (New York, 1977). (US) **2848**
Translation and Textlinguistics. Occasional Papers see Journal of Translation and Textlinguistics **2821**
Translation Review. (US ISSN 0737-4836) **2848**, **4138**
Translation Series in Mathematics and Engineering. (US) **3059**, **1838**
Translation Services Directory. (US) **2856**
Translations: A Quarterly of Foreign Literature. see Yilin **2979**
Translations Index. (US ISSN 0278-4238) **3428**
Translations of Mathematical Monographs. (US ISSN 0065-9282) **3059**
Translations on Latin America see Latin America Report **872**
Translations on Mongolia see Mongolia Report **874**
Translations on Near East and North Africa see Near East - South Asia Report **875**
Translations on North Korea see Korean Affairs Report **871**
Translations on Subsaharan Africa see Sub-Saharan Africa Report **885**

TRANSPORT 6739

Translations on U S S R Military Affairs see U S S R Report: Military Affairs **3473**
Translations on U S S R Political and Sociological Affairs see U S S R Report: Political and Sociological Affairs **3931**
Translations - Safety Codes and Guides see Uebersetzungen - Kerntechnische Regeln **1810**
Translatoeren. (DK ISSN 0041-1264) **2848**
Translators' Notes see Zhongguo Fanyi **2854**
Translog. (US ISSN 0041-1639) **4722**, **3473**
Transmission. (UK ISSN 0144-9311) **2059**, **2026**
Transmission and Distribution. (US ISSN 0041-1280) **1909**, **1838**
▼Transmission & Distribution International. (US ISSN 1050-8686) **1909**, **1838**
Transmission and Distribution Specifiers & Buyers Guide. (US) **1909**
Transmission Digest. (US ISSN 0277-8300) **4704**
Transmission - Distribution see Electric Light and Power **1887**
Transmission - Distribution Health & Safety Report. (US ISSN 0737-5743) **3622**, **1910**, **1970**, **4113**
Transmitter. (CN) **1345**
Transmitter. (US) **1383**
Transmitters, Receptors & Synapses. (UK ISSN 0143-4241) **3744**, **3355**
Transnational. (GW ISSN 0344-9823) **3974**
Transnational Associations/Associations Transnationales. (BE ISSN 0250-4928) **3974**
Transnational Corporations. (UN) **923**
Transnational Corporations and Transborder Data Flows. (NE) **828**
Transnational Data and Communications Report. (NE ISSN 0892-399X) **1424**
▼Transnational Law & Contemporary Problems. (US ISSN 1058-1006) **2687**
Transnational Perspectives. (SZ ISSN 0252-9505) **3974**
Transnet Annual Report (Year). (SA) **4657**
Transpacific. (US ISSN 0892-5747) **2026**
†Transparent. (AU ISSN 0041-1302) **5291**
Transpatent. (GW ISSN 0041-1310) **3678**
Transplant International. (GW ISSN 0934-0874) **3158**
Transplantation. (US ISSN 0041-1337) **3385**, **3189**
Transplantation and Clinical Immunology see Symposia Foundation Merieux **3155**
†Transplantation Immunology. (UK ISSN 0142-8446) **5291**
†Transplantation - Implantation Today. (CN) **5291**
Transplantation Proceedings. (US ISSN 0041-1345) **3385**, **527**, **3263**, **3744**
†Transplantation Today. (US ISSN 0074-3984) **5291**
†Transpo. (CN ISSN 0706-3962) **5291**
†Transpo News. (US) **5291**
Transponder. (US) **1383**
Transpor. (MX) **4657**
Transport. see Doprava **4649**
Transport. (II ISSN 0041-137X) **4657**
TransPort. (EC ISSN 1018-2179) **4657**, **4791**
Transport. (LU) **4657**
†Transport (Aarlig). (DK ISSN 0108-8157) **5291**
Transport (Fredensborg) see Transport - Magasinet (Fredensborg) **4658**
Transport (London). (UK ISSN 0144-3453) **4657**
Transport - Action. (CN ISSN 0227-3020) **4657**
†Transport Aktuell. (AU) **5291**
Transport and Communications. (II ISSN 0041-1388) **4657**, **1345**

6740 TRANSPORT

Transport and Communications Bulletin for Asia and the Far East *see* Transport & Communications Bulletin for Asia & the Pacific **4657**
Transport & Communications Bulletin for Asia & the Pacific. (UN ISSN 0252-4392) **4657**, 1345
Transport and Communications Indicators. (AT ISSN 1033-9752) **4667**
Transport and General Workers Union Record *see* T & G Record **2590**
Transport and Handling in the Pulp and Paper Industry. (II) **3667**
Transport and Road Digest/Vervoer- en Padoorsig. (SA ISSN 0379-4792) **4722**
Transport and Road Research *see* Transport and Road Research Laboratory. Research Reports **4722**
Transport and Road Research Laboratory. Research Reports. (UK) **4722**, 1875
Transport and Tourism Journal. (II ISSN 0300-449X) **4657**, 4791
†Transport & Traffic/Vervoer & Verkeer.(SA) **5291**
Transport-De-Regulation Report. (US) **4657**, 2687
Transport-Dienst *see* Transport-Dienst & Wirtschaftscorrespondent **4740**
Transport-Dienst & Wirtschaftscorrespondent. (GW) **4740**
Transport Echo. (BE ISSN 0009-6083) **4657**
Transport Electronic News. (CN) **4748**
Transport en Opslag. (NE) **4657**
Transport en Toerisme. *see* Transport et Tourisme **4791**
Transport Engineer. (UK ISSN 0020-3122) **4658**
Transport Engineer's Handbook. (UK) **4658**
Transport Environment Circulation *see* T E C **4721**
Transport et Tourisme/Transport en Toerisme. (BE ISSN 0041-1442) **4791**
Transport Fleet News. (US) **4748**
Transport, Foerder- und Lagertechnik. (SZ) **4658**, 3652
Transport History. (UK ISSN 0041-1469) **4658**, 2324
Transport i Dag. (SW) **4658**
Transport in Porous Media. (NE ISSN 0169-3913) **1190**, 3834
Transport Indicators *see* Transport and Communications Indicators **4667**
Transport Industry and Trade Annual. (II) **4658**
Transport Industry and Trade Journal *see* Transport Industry and Trade Annual **4658**
Transport-Journalen. (SW ISSN 0348-3118) **4716**
Transport - Magasinet (Fredensborg). (DK) **4658**
Transport Management. (UK) **4658**
Transport Management. (SA) **4658**
Transport Manager's and Operator's Handbook. (UK) **4658**
Transport Manager's Handbook *see* Transport Manager's and Operator's Handbook **4658**
Transport Manager's Handbook *see* Transport Manager's Handbook and Trucker's Guide **4748**
Transport Manager's Handbook and Trucker's Guide. (SA) **4748**
Transport Managers Journal. (UK) **4658**
Transport Maritime: Etudes et Statistiques. (FR) **4667**, 4740
†Transport Marketing. (UK ISSN 0951-3531) **5291**
Transport Museums. (PL ISSN 0137-4435) **4658**
Transport News. (UK) **4658**
Transport News Digest. (UK ISSN 0306-2252) **4658**
Transport News of New Zealand. (NZ ISSN 0110-6236) **4658**
Transport News of Tennessee *see* Tennessee Trucking News **4748**
Transport-Nytt. (SW ISSN 0041-1523) **4740**, 4704
Transport och Hantering. (SW ISSN 0346-2773) **4658**

Transport of Goods by Road in Great Britain. (UK) **4748**
Transport Operator. (UK ISSN 0267-8411) **4748**
Transport Public. (FR ISSN 0397-474X) **4658**
Transport Review. (UK) **4716**
Transport Reviews. (UK ISSN 0144-1647) **4658**
Transport Rundschau. (SZ ISSN 0255-6871) **4748**
Transport Salaried Staff Journal. (UK ISSN 0041-1531) **995**, 4658
Transport Statistics Great Britain. (UK) **4667**, 4722
Transport Teknik Scandinavia *see* Transport i Dag **4658**
Transport Theory and Statistical Physics. (US ISSN 0041-1450) **3834**
Transport Ticket Society. Journal. (UK) **4658**
Transport Topics. (US ISSN 0041-1558) **4748**
†Transport Training. (UK) **5291**
Transport und Lager *see* Euro Transport Journal **5188**
Transport und Lagertechnik *see* Transport, Foerder- und Lagertechnik **4658**
Transport und Tourismus Revue *see* T T - Revue **4656**
Transport Workers of the World. (HU) **2590**, 4658
Transport Workers Union. Triennial Report. (MY) **4658**
Transport Workers Union of America Express *see* T W U Express **2590**
Transport 2000 and Intermodal World. (US) **4658**, 3652
Transport 2000 Canada. News Bulletin.(CN) **4716**
Transportarbetaren/Transportworker. (SW ISSN 0492-004X) **4658**
Transportation. (NE ISSN 0049-4488) **4658**
†Transportation (Baltimore). (US) **5292**
Transportation. Current Literature. (US ISSN 0091-1410) **4667**, 413
▼Transportation (Sacramento). (US) **4658**
Transportation (Springfield). (US) **3839**
Transportation Accident Briefs. (US) **4667**
Transportation Accident Briefs. Aviation.(US) **4668**
Transportation Accident Briefs. Highways. (US) **4668**
Transportation Accident Briefs. Marine. (US) **4668**
Transportation Accident Briefs. Pipeline.(US) **3707**, 4668
Transportation Accident Briefs. Railroads. (US) **4668**
Transportation Accident Reports. (US) **4668**
Transportation Accident Reports. Highway. (US) **4668**
Transportation Accident Reports. Marine. (US) **4668**
Transportation Accident Reports. Pipeline. (US) **3707**, 4668
Transportation Accident Reports. Railroads. (US) **468**
Transportation & Distribution. (US ISSN 0895-8548) **4658**, 4740
†Transportation & Distribution Presidential Issue. (US) **5292**
Transportation and Products Legal Directory. (US ISSN 0092-6175) **2687**
Transportation and Tariff News. *see* Prepravni a Tarifni Vestnik **4655**
Transportation Association of Canada News *see* T A C News **4656**
Transportation Brokers Conference of America Update *see* T B C A Update **4656**
Transportation Builder. (US ISSN 1043-4054) **4722**, 1875
Transportation Business *see* Cargo Express **4648**
Transportation Consumer. (US) **4658**
Transportation Energy Research. (US ISSN 0885-8330) **1800**, 4668
Transportation Engineer *see* Lifting & Transportation International **4745**

Transportation Engineering *see* I T E Journal **4719**
Transportation Executive Update. (US ISSN 0897-8077) **4748**, 1030
Transportation Improvement Program. (US) **4722**
Transportation in America. (US ISSN 0889-0889) **4658**
Transportation Journal. (US ISSN 0041-1612) **4659**, 4722
Transportation: Latin American Industrial Report. (US) **4659**, 840
Transportation Law and Legislation *see* Transportrecht **4659**
Transportation Law Institute Papers and Proceedings. (US) **2687**, 4748
Transportation Law Journal. (US ISSN 0049-450X) **2687**
Transportation Planning and Technology. (US ISSN 0308-1060) **4659**, 4455
Transportation Practitioners Journal. (US ISSN 8756-9302) **2687**, 840
Transportation Quarterly. (US ISSN 0278-9434) **4659**
Transportation R and D in Canada *see* Surface Transportation R & D in Canada **4656**
Transportation Research. Part A: General. (US ISSN 0191-2607) **4659**
Transportation Research. Part B: Methodological. (US ISSN 0191-2615) **4659**
Transportation Research Board. Bibliography *see* National Research Council. Transportation Research Board. Bibliography **4654**
Transportation Research Board Special Report. (US ISSN 0360-859X) **4722**, 1875
Transportation Research Circular. (US ISSN 0097-8515) **4659**
Transportation Research Record. (US ISSN 0361-1981) **4722**, 1875
Transportation Safety Law Practice Manual. (US) **2687**, 4659
Transportation Safety Recommendations. (US) **4113**, 4659
Transportation Safety Special Reports. (US) **4113**, 3622
Transportation Science. (US ISSN 0041-1655) **4659**
Transportation Statistics in the United States. (US ISSN 0082-5956) **4668**, 840
Transportation Studies. (UK ISSN 0278-3819) **4659**
Transportation System Motorists Information Report *see* Quarterly Transportation Activity Report **4720**
Transportation Telephone Tickler. (US ISSN 0447-9181) **1156**, 4659
Transportation Topics. (US) **4722**
Transportation Topics for Consumers *see* Transportation Consumer **4658**
Transportation U S A. (US ISSN 0094-9922) **4659**
Transporte Automotor. (UY) **4704**
Transporte y Vias de Comunicacion. (CU) **4659**
Transportes. (CU ISSN 0496-1021) **4659**
Transportes y Turismo. (MX) **4791**
Transporteur. (CN ISSN 0229-4362) **4251**, 4659
Transportforum-Kollektivtrafikk. (NO) **4659**
TransportMarkt. (GW ISSN 0176-358X) **4659**
Transportnoe Stroitel'stvo. (RU ISSN 0041-1701) **4716**
Transportnyt. (DK ISSN 0109-128X) **4740**
Transportoekonomisk Instituut. Aarsberetning. (NO) **4716**
†Transportraadet Rapport. (SW ISSN 0280-1183) **5292**
Transportrecht. (GW ISSN 0174-559X) **4659**
Transportroutier. (BE) **4716**
Transports. (FR ISSN 0564-1373) **4659**
Transports Actualites. (FR) **4659**
Transports Publics. *see* Oeffentliche Verkehr **4666**

Transports Routiers de Marchandises Effectues par des Transporteurs Etrangers sur le Territoire Francais. (FR) **4668**
Transports Urbains. (FR ISSN 0397-6521) **4659**
Transportworker. *see* Transportarbetaren **4658**
Transputer and Occam Engineering Series. (NE ISSN 0925-4986) **1418**
Transrotas - Travel & Cargo Business Guide. (BL) **4659**
Transsexual Voice. (US) **2457**
▼Transtalk. (SA) **4659**
Transtelel: Transmissions, Telecommunications, Electronique en France. (FR ISSN 0082-5980) **1367**
Transvaal. Education Department. Education Bulletin/Transvaal. Onderwysdepartement. Onderwysbulletin. (SA) **1668**
Transvaal. Education Department. Educational News Flashes/Transvaal. Onderwysdepartment. Onderwysnuusflitse. (SA ISSN 0013-1830) **1668**
Transvaal. Onderwysdepartement. Onderwysbulletin. *see* Transvaal. Education Department. Education Bulletin **1668**
Transvaal. Onderwysdepartment. Onderwysnuusflitse. *see* Transvaal. Education Department. Educational News Flashes **1668**
Transvaal Educational News. (SA ISSN 0041-1728) **1668**
Transvaal Gardener. (SA ISSN 0041-1744) **2140**
Transvaal Golfer *see* Golfer **4506**
Transvaal Museum. Annale. *see* Transvaal Museum. Annals **4348**
Transvaal Museum. Annals/Transvaal Museum. Annale. (SA ISSN 0041-1752) **4348**
Transvaal Museum. Bulletin. (SA ISSN 0496-1102) **3534**
Transvaal Museum. Monographs. (SA ISSN 0255-0172) **3534**
Transvaal Rugby. (SA) **4514**
Transvaal Women's Agricultural Union News *see* T W A U News **2449**
Transvaalse Raad vir die Uitvoerende Kunste Info *see* T R U K P A C T Info **4639**
Transworld Advertising Agency Network. Conference. Transcript. (US) **39**
Transworld Advertising Agency Network. Newsletter. (US) **39**
Transworld Identity Series. (US ISSN 0890-1562) **251**
Transworld Skateboarding. (US ISSN 0748-7401) **4559**
Transworld Snowboarding. (US ISSN 1046-4611) **4559**
Tranvia. (GW ISSN 0930-0724) **2218**, 2214
Trap & Field. (US ISSN 0041-1760) **4559**
Trapananda. (CL) **2424**, 1583, 2264
Trapani Nuova *see* Terza Pagina **2886**
Trapezikos/Bank Employee. (CY) **695**
Trapper. (CN) **2738**
Trapper and Predator Caller. (US ISSN 8750-233X) **4559**
La Trasfusione del Sangue. (IT ISSN 0041-1787) **3274**
Trasmissione Dati e Telecomunicazioni *see* L A N e Telecomunicazioni **1351**
Trasmissioni di Potenza. (IT) **1940**
Trasporti. (IT) **4659**
Trasporti e Trazione. (IT) **4659**
Trasporti Industriali *see* Trasporti Industriali e Movimentazione **4660**
Trasporti Industriali e Movimentazione. (IT) **4660**
†Trasporti Mare Territorio. (IT) **5292**
†Trasporti Pubblici. (IT ISSN 0041-1817) **5292**
Trasumenus. (IT) **2206**
Trattamenti e Finitura - Superfici *see* Trattamenti e Finiture **3655**
Trattamenti e Finiture. (IT) **3655**, 3422
Trattati di Architettura. (IT ISSN 0082-6006) **308**

Trauma & Emergency Medicine. (SA) 3312, 3158
Trauma Quarterly. (US ISSN 0743-6637) 3312
Traumboot Real. (GW) 4530
Travail. see Labour 986
Travail. see Puna 2588
Travail, Capital et Societe. see Labour, Capital and Society 4378
Travail et Emploi. (FR ISSN 0224-4365) 995
Travail et Maitrise (Edition Chimie) see Maitrise (Edition Chimie) 1067
Travail et Maitrise (Edition Generale) see Maitrise (Edition Generale) 1067
Travail et Maitrise (Edition Siderurgie) see Maitrise (Edition Siderurgie) 1067
Travail et Maitrise (Edition Techniciens). (FR) 1070
Travail et Methodes. (FR ISSN 0041-185X) 1030
Travail et Sante. (CN) 3622
Travail et Securite. (FR ISSN 0373-1944) 3622
Travail Humain. (FR ISSN 0041-1868) 4049, 995, 4455
Travailleur/Worker. (CM) 2590
Travailleur. (MF) 3930
Travailleur de Guinee. (GV) 2590
Travailleur du Livre. (BE ISSN 0041-1876) 4138
Travailleur Social. see Social Worker 4420
Travailleurs. (FR ISSN 0754-281X) 3930
Travaux. (FR ISSN 0041-1906) 1875
Travaux Agricoles de France. (FR) 124
Travaux d'Histoire Ethico-Politique. (SZ ISSN 0082-6073) 2324
Travaux d'Humanisme et Renaissance. (SZ ISSN 0082-6081) 2392, 347
Travaux de Chimie Alimentaire et d'Hygiene. see Mitteilungen aus der Gebiete der Lebensmitteluntersuchung und Hygiene 3609
Travaux de Didactique du Francaise Langue Etrangere. (FR ISSN 0765-1635) 2848
Travaux de Droit, d'Economique de Sociologie et de Sciences Politiques. (SZ ISSN 0082-6022) 4390
Travaux de l'Institute de Linguistique de Lund. (SW ISSN 0347-2558) 2848, 1668
Travaux de la Faculte de Philosphie et Lettres U C L see Universite Catholique de Louvain. Faculte de Philosophie et Lettres. Travaux 2517
Travaux de Linguistique. (BE ISSN 0082-6049) 2848
Travaux de Linguistique et de Litterature. (FR ISSN 0082-6057) 2848, 2970
Travaux de Linguistique Japonaise. (FR) 2848
Travaux du Centre de Recherche sur le Proche Orient et la Grece Antiques see Universite des Sciences Humaines de Strasbourg. Centre de Recherche sur le Proche Orient et la Grece Antiques. Travaux 1280
Travaux du Groupe de Recherches et d'Etudes Semitiques Anciennes. (GW ISSN 0938-0051) 3645
Travaux du Museum d'Histoire Naturelle "Grigore Antipa". (RM) 458, 592
Travaux en Cours. (FR) 3059
Travaux et Documents de Geographie Tropicale see Espaces Tropicaux 2247
Travaux et Recherches dans les Ameriques du Centre see T R A C E 250
Travaux Publics et Batiment du Midi. (FR ISSN 0751-5944) 1875
†Travaux sur les Pecheries du Quebec. (CN ISSN 0082-609X) 5292
Travel a la Carte. (CN ISSN 0836-7353) 4791
Travel Agency. (UK ISSN 0041-1981) 4791
Travel Agency. (MY) 4791

Travel Agency Communications Reports - Eastern Edition see Travel Agency Reference & Profile Directory 4791
Travel Agency Communications Reports - North American Edition see Travel Agency Reference & Profile Directory 4791
Travel Agency Communications Reports - Western Edition see Travel Agency Reference & Profile Directory 4791
Travel Agency Reference & Profile Directory. (US) 4791
Travel Agent. (US ISSN 0041-199X) 4791
Travel Agent Domestic Tour Manual see Travel Agent Magazine 4791
Travel Agent Magazine. (US) 4791
Travel Agents Guide to Europe. (CN) 4792
Travel & Leisure. (US ISSN 0041-2007) 4792, 2739
Travel and Tourism - Abstracting, Bibliographies, Statistics. (IS) 4801, 4792
Travel & Tourism Analyst. (UK ISSN 0269-3755) 4792
Travel & Tourism Executive Report. (US) 4792
Travel & Tourism Index. (US ISSN 1040-8142) 4801, 24
Travel & Tourism News International. (BA) 4792
Travel and Tourism Research Association. Proceedings of the Annual Conference. (US ISSN 0276-8968) 4792
Travel and Tourism Research Association Newsletter see T T R A Newsletter 4788
Travel and Traffic Medicine International see Travel Medicine International 4793
†Travel Asia Pacific. (UK) 5292
Travel Australia. (AT) 4792
Travel Business Analyst. (HK ISSN 1011-7768) 4792, 886
†Travel Business Report. (US) 5292
Travel Check. (BE) 4792
Travel China Newsletter. (CN ISSN 0834-258X) 4792
Travel Collector. (US ISSN 1040-0001) 4792, 2443
▼Travel Counselor. (US) 4792
Travel Courier. (CN ISSN 1182-9699) 4792
Travel Diary. (GW) 4792
Travel Directory. (HK ISSN 0256-4203) 4792
Travel Directory (Year). (SI ISSN 0218-236X) 4792
Travel Europe. (CN) 4792
Travel Exchange. (CN) 4792
Travel Executives of New Zealand. (NZ) 1156
Travel Expense Management. (US ISSN 0272-569X) 1070
Travel G.B.I. (UK) 4792
Travel Guide, S.A. (SA) 4792
Travel Guide to Europe. (US) 4792
Travel Guide to the Caribbean. (US) 4792
Travel - Holiday. (US) 4792
Travel in Greece. (GR) 4792
Travel in Shandong. see Shandong Luyou 4786
Travel Industry Personnel Directory. (US ISSN 0082-6146) 1156, 4792
Travel Industry World Yearbook. (US ISSN 0738-9515) 4801, 4792
Travel Journalist/Journaliste de Tourisme. (BE ISSN 0771-937X) 4792, 2576
Travel Life. (US) 4792
Travel-log. (CN ISSN 0713-2840) 4801
Travel Magazine. (LE) 4792
Travel Management see T M 4788
Travel Management Daily. (US ISSN 0041-2015) 4792
Travel Management International. (UK ISSN 0952-0899) 4792
Travel Management Newsletter. (US) 4792
Travel Marketing and Agency Management Guidelines. (US ISSN 0275-3545) 4793
Travel Marketing and Sales Newsletter Letter see T M S - Letter 4788

▼Travel Medicine Advisor. (US) 3158, 4793
Travel Medicine International. (UK) 4793, 3355
Travel New England. (US) 4793
Travel News see Travel Weekly 4793
Travel News. (US) 4793
Travel News Asia. (HK ISSN 0252-9629) 4793, 2481
Travel News from Western Australia see Holiday Western Australia. Travel News 4770
Travel on Saskatchewan Highways. (CN ISSN 0581-8079) 4722
Travel Outlook Forum Proceedings see Outlook for Travel and Tourism 4781
Travel People. (US) 4793
†Travel Photo Source Book. (US) 5292
Travel Planner. (US) 4793, 3394
Travel Printout. (US) 4793
Travel Publishing News see Romantic Traveling 4785
▼Travel Review. (US ISSN 1053-1998) 4793
Travel Scoop. (CN ISSN 0822-9228) 4793
Travel Smart. (US ISSN 0741-5826) 4793
†Travel Smart for Business. (US ISSN 0741-5818) 5292
Travel Smarter see Paul Edwards' Travel Confidential 4782
Travel Times. (SA ISSN 0041-204X) 4793
Travel Times. (JA) 4793
Travel Tips. (US) 4793
Travel Trade. (US ISSN 0041-2066) 4793
Travel Trade. (AT) 4793
Travel Trade Canada. (CN) 4793
Travel Trade Directory. (UK ISSN 0041-2074) 1156, 4793
Travel Trade Directory, U K and Ireland.(UK ISSN 0082-7932) 1156, 4793
Travel Trade Gazette Asia. (SI) 4793
Travel Trade Gazette Europa. (UK) 4793, 2481
Travel Trade Gazette U K & Ireland. (UK) 4793
Travel Trade Journal. (KO) 4793
Travel Trade News Edition. (US) 4793
Travel Trade Repertory. see Repertoire des Voyages 4784
Travel Trade Reporter - Asia. (TH) 4793
Travel Trade Yearbook. (US) 4793
Travel Trends in the United States and Canada. (US) 4793
Travel Tribune. (GW) 4793
†Travel Utah. (US) 5292
Travel Value Report. (SA) 4793
Travel Weekly. (US ISSN 0041-2082) 4793
Travel Weekly's World Travel Directory. (US) 1156, 4793
Travel World see Travel Value Report 4793
Travel World News. (US) 4793
Travel Writer. (US) 2576, 4793
▼Travel 50 & Beyond. (US ISSN 1049-6211) 4793, 2279
Travel 800 see 800 & FAX Travel Directory 1160
TravelAge Caribbean. (US) 4793
TravelAge East. (US ISSN 0041-2104) 4793
TravelAge Europe. (US) 4794
TravelAge Mid-America. (US) 4794
TravelAge Southeast see TravelAge East 4793
TravelAge West. (US ISSN 0041-1973) 4794
Travelaid Guide to Greece see Guide to Greece 5202
†Travelday. (US) 5292
TravLeisure. (AT) 4794
Traveler & Conventioneer. (US) 4794, 2026
Travelers Guide to Mexico. (MX) 4794
Travelers Protective Association of America Travelers see T.P.A. Travelers 4788
Travelgram see Travel Times 4793
Traveling. see Viajando 4795
Traveling Exhibition Information Service. Newsletter. (US ISSN 0733-463X) 3534

TREASURY TODAY 6741

Traveling Healthy. (US) 3809
Traveller. (CN) 4794, 4559
Traveller. (UK ISSN 0262-2726) 4794
Travellers. see Luxingjia 4775
†Traveller's Friend. (SA) 5292
Traveller's Guide to Central and Southern Africa. (UK ISSN 0144-7661) 4794
Traveller's Guide to East Africa and the Indian Ocean. (UK ISSN 0144-7653) 4794
Travellers Guide to Mexico. (MX) 4794
Traveller's Guide to North Africa. (UK ISSN 0144-7637) 4794
Traveller's Guide to the Middle East. (UK ISSN 0140-1319) 4794
Traveller's Guide to West Africa. (UK ISSN 0144-7645) 4794
†Travelling. (GR) 5292
Travelling Art Mail Bulletin see T A M Bulletin 346
Travelling Magazine/Lu Hsing Tsa Chih.(HK) 4794
†Travelling on Business. (CN) 5292
Travelling Scope. see Luyou Tiandi 4775
Travelodge and Viscount Hotels North American Travel Directory. (US) 1156, 4794
Travelodge - Forte Viscount Hotels Travel Directory see Travelodge and Viscount Hotels North American Travel Directory 1156
Travelog. (US) 4794
Travelore Report. (US ISSN 0270-2398) 4794
Travelsavelife. (CN) 4794
Traveltrade Visa Guide. (AT) 923
Travelware. (US) 2738
Travelware Resources Directory. (US) 1156, 2738
Travelweek. (AT) 4794
†Travelweek Blue Book. (AT) 5292
Travelweek Bulletin. (CN) 4794
Travelweek Hotel, Motel Directory see Travelweek Hotel, Motel Index 5292
†Travelweek Hotel, Motel Index. (AT ISSN 0813-4790) 5292
Travelwriter Marketletter. (US ISSN 0738-9094) 2576, 1055, 4794
Traverse. (AT ISSN 0726-125X) 1875
†Traverses. (FR ISSN 0336-9730) 5292
Traverso. (US ISSN 1041-7494) 3584
†Travesia. (PE) 5292
TravLtips. (US ISSN 0162-9816) 4794, 4740
TravLtips Freighter Bulletin see TravLtips 4794
Travsport for Fagfolk. (DK ISSN 0109-2308) 4538
Trax Dance Music Guide. (US) 3584
Tray Full of Lab Mice Publications. (US) 3007
Tre og Moebler. (NO) 2562, 2555
Treasure. (UK ISSN 0041-2139) 1268
Treasure. (US ISSN 0049-4593) 2443
Treasure Chest. (US ISSN 0897-814X) 259
Treasure Coast Illustrated. (US) 2236
Treasure Found. (US) 2443
Treasure Hunt Ers Express see T H - Ers Express 2442
Treasure Hunters Newspaper see T H - Ers Express 2442
Treasure Hunting. (UK ISSN 0140-4539) 2443
Treasure Hunting Research Bulletin. (US ISSN 0897-6511) 2443
Treasure Search - Found see Treasure Found 2443
Treasure State Lines. (US ISSN 1060-0337) 2166
Treasure World see Lost Treasure 2438
▼Treasury. (US) 801, 2544
Treasury. (UK) 4207
Treasury Management Association News see T M A News 800
Treasury Manager. (US ISSN 0896-2987) 801
▼Treasury Today. (UK ISSN 0961-5261) 695

6742 TREATISE

†Treatise on Analytical Chemistry. Part 1: Theory and Practice of Analytical Chemistry. (US ISSN 0082-6243) **5292**
†Treatise on Analytical Chemistry. Part 2: Analytical Chemistry of the Elements; Analytical Chemistry of Inorganic and Organic Compounds. (US ISSN 0082-6251) **5292**
†Treatise on Analytical Chemistry. Part 3: Analytical Chemistry in Industry. (US ISSN 0082-626X) **5292**
Treatise on Materials Science & Technology. (US) **1922**, **4612**
Treatises and Documents. see Razprave in Gradivo **2020**
▼Treatment. (UK) **3158**
Treatment in Clinical Medicine. (US) **3158**
Treatment Issues. (US) **3224**, **2687**
Treaty Council News. (US) **2026**
Treballs del Museu de Zoologia. (SP) **592**
†Tree. (US) **5292**
▼Tree Care Industry. (US) **2109**
Tree City U S A Bulletin. (US) **1498**
Tree Farmer. (US) **2109**
Tree Nut Authority. Report. (MW) **194**
Tree Physiology. (CN ISSN 0829-318X) **519**, **558**, **2109**
Tree - Ring Bulletin. (US ISSN 0041-2198) **519**
Tree Shaker. (US ISSN 0893-2069) **2166**
Tree Talks. (US ISSN 0041-2201) **2166**
Tree Tips see Northbound **2105**
Tree Tracers. (US ISSN 0162-1440) **2166**
Trees. (GW ISSN 0931-1890) **519**, **2109**
Trees. (UK ISSN 0041-221X) **1498**
Trees and Natural Resources. (AT ISSN 0814-4680) **1498**
Trees and Victoria's Resources see Trees and Natural Resources **1498**
Trees in South Africa/Bome in Suid-Afrika. (SA ISSN 0041-2236) **2140**, **2109**
Treesearcher. (US) **2166**
†Treetop Panorama. (US ISSN 0894-3044) **5292**
Treewell. (US ISSN 0085-7378) **3007**
Treeworker. (US) **2109**, **519**
Treffpunkt see German Teaching **2816**
†Treffpunkt. (GW) **5292**
Treffpunkt Film. (GW) **3518**
Treffpunkt Jugendpresse. (GW) **2576**, **1268**
Treffpunkt Senioren. (GW) **2279**
Le Trefile. (GW ISSN 0374-2261) **1910**, **1838**, **3024**
Trefle/Kim. (SZ) **1268**
Trefoil. (US ISSN 0041-2244) **4854**
Treforedlingindustriens Landsforening. Aarsoversikt. see Norwegian Pulp and Paper Association. Annual Review **3663**
Trefpunt. (NE) **4422**
Trekker see Trekkerskrant **4794**
Trekkerskrant. (BE) **4794**
Treklang. (DK ISSN 0109-0003) **1245**
Trellis. (CN ISSN 0380-1470) **2140**
†Trellis (San Marino). (US) **5292**
Trellis Singles Magazine. (US) **4364**
Tremplin. (BE ISSN 0041-2279) **1268**
Trend. (AU ISSN 0049-4623) **695**
Trend. (GW) **2192**
Trend. (UK) **2296**
Trend. (II) **2970**
Trend Aktuell. (GW ISSN 0178-0727) **695**
Trend in Engineering. (US ISSN 0041-2317) **1838**
Trend Monitor see Trend Monitor Reports **2787**
Trend Monitor Reports. (UK) **2787**
Trend of Business in the Lodging Industry see National Trend of Business in the Lodging Industry **5244**
Trend Setter. (US) **4704**
Trendex. (AT) **966**
†Trending. (US) **5292**
Trendletter see Trendletter Megatrends Aktuell **695**

Trendletter Megatrends Aktuell. (GW ISSN 0935-5596) **695**
Trendline Current Market Perspectives. (US) **966**
Trendline Daily Action Stock Charts (Monthly). (US) **966**
Trendline Daily Action Stock Charts (Weekly). (US) **966**
Trendline O T C Chart Manual. (Over-the-Counter) (US) **966**
Trends. (BE) **695**
Trends. (GW) **886**
Trends (Alexandria). (US) **1498**, **4559**
Trends (Liberty). (US) **3631**
Trends (Washington). (US) **801**
Trends (Washington, 1969). (US) **4113**
†Trends & Forecasts. (US) **5292**
Trends and Perspectives of the Brazilian Economy. (BL) **1086**
†Trends & Projections Bulletins. (US) **5292**
Trends & Techniques in the Contemporary Dental Laboratory. (US) **3243**
Trends: Consumer Attitudes and the Supermarket Update. (US ISSN 0278-6346) **2094**
Trends in Adjusting. (US ISSN 0041-2384) **2544**
Trends in Analytical Chemistry. (NE ISSN 0165-9936) **1209**
Trends in Biochemical Sciences. (UK ISSN 0376-5067) **483**
Trends in Biotechnology. (UK ISSN 0167-9430) **491**, **483**
▼Trends in Cardiovascular Medicine. (US ISSN 1050-1738) **3212**
▼Trends in Cell Biology. (UK ISSN 0962-8924) **527**, **547**
Trends in College Media. (US) **2576**, **1668**
Trends in Communications Policy. (US ISSN 0894-6795) **1367**, **4075**
Trends in Communications Regulation see Trends in Communications Policy **1367**
Trends in Communist Media see U.S. Foreign Broadcast Information Service. Trends **3976**
Trends in Computing. (US) **1401**
Trends in Ecology and Evolution. (UK ISSN 0169-5347) **519**, **547**, **592**, **3661**
Trends in Employment and Wages. (US) **886**, **995**
Trends in End-Use Markets for Plastics see End-Use Markets for Plastics **3868**
Trends in Endocrinology and Metabolism. (US ISSN 1043-2760) **3256**
▼Trends in Food Science and Technology. (UK ISSN 0924-2244) **2083**, **3612**
Trends in Futures. (US) **967**
Trends in Genetics. (UK ISSN 0168-9479) **547**, **3158**
Trends in Glycoscience and Glycotechnology. (JA ISSN 0915-7352) **1224**
Trends in Health and Health Services see Contemporary Health Issues **5172**
Trends in High School Media. (US) **2576**, **1668**
Trends in Housing. (US ISSN 0300-6026) **2497**, **3947**
Trends in Journal Subscriptions. (UK) **4138**
Trends in Management - Stockholder Relations see Georgeson Report **947**
Trends in Mutual Fund Activities. (US) **967**
Trends in Neurosciences. (UK ISSN 0166-2236) **3355**
Trends in Pathology. see Berichte Pathologie **3166**
Trends in Pharmacological Sciences. (UK ISSN 0165-604X) **3744**, **1984**
Trends in Southeast Asia. (SI ISSN 0082-6316) **3974**
Trends in Technology. (PH ISSN 0115-2157) **4612**
Trends in Telecommunications. (NE ISSN 0920-2706) **1367**

Trends in the Law Library Management and Technology. (US) **2705**, **2799**
Trends in the Texas Economy see Texas Economic Forecast **886**
Trends in Transport. (NE) **4660**
Trends in World Economy. (HU ISSN 0133-7769) **695**
Trends Infos Praktisches Woche see T I P der Woche **2191**
Trends Magazine. (CN) **695**
Trends Magazine. (American Animal Hospital Association) (US ISSN 0883-1696) **4816**
Trends - Tendances. (BE) **695**
▼Trends, Tips and Tax. (AT) **1030**, **1111**
Trends Update. (US ISSN 0731-5589) **4138**
Trener. (CS) **4495**
Treni Oggi. (IT ISSN 0392-4602) **4716**, **2324**, **2443**
Trent Law Journal see Nottingham Law Journal **2662**
Trent Papers in Education. (UK ISSN 0260-1729) **1668**
Trente Jours. (SZ) **2219**
Trentino. (IT) **1970**, **886**, **4075**
Trenton Junior College. Newsletter see College Voice (Trenton) **1308**
Treoir. (IE ISSN 0790-004X) **3584**
Tres Continentes. (PO) **2516**
Trespass to Try Title. (US) **2687**, **4158**
Trester Compleat Option Report. (US) **967**
Tretzevents. (SP) **1268**
Treubia. (IO ISSN 0082-6340) **592**
Trevithick Society. Occasional Publication. (UK) **4612**
Trgovinski Glasnik. (YU ISSN 0041-2457) **923**
Tri-City Genealogical Society. Bulletin. (US ISSN 0496-1803) **2166**
Tri-City Labor Review. (US) **995**
Tri-County Lutheran. (US) **4251**
Tri-Ology Technical Report. (US ISSN 0041-2481) **124**
Tri-Son News. (US) **3584**
Tri-State Bluegrass Association Band and Festival Guide. (US) **3584**
Tri-State Food News. (US ISSN 0041-249X) **2094**
Tri-State Livestock News. (US) **227**
Tri-State Neighbor. (US) **124**
Tri-State Packet. (US ISSN 0740-896X) **2166**
Tri-State Real Estate Journal. (US) **4158**
Tri-State Singles Connection. (US) **4364**
Tri-University Meson Facility Annual Report Scientific Activities see T R I U M F Annual Report Scientific Activities **3851**
Tri-University Meson Facility Financial and Administrative Annual Report see T R I U M F Financial and Administrative Annual Report **3851**
Tria. (SP ISSN 0210-5616) **124**
Triad (Farmington). (US) **3216**
Triad (Wooster). (US ISSN 0041-2511) **3584**, **1668**
Triad Business. (US) **695**
Triad Style. (US) **2236**
Triage! see Doctors for Disaster Preparedness Newsletter **3094**
Trial. (US ISSN 0041-2538) **2733**
Trial Advocate Quarterly. (US ISSN 0743-412X) **2733**
Trial Communication Skills. (US) **2733**
Trial Diplomacy Journal. (US ISSN 0160-7308) **2733**
Trial Judges News. (US) **2733**
Trial Lawyer's Guide. (US ISSN 0041-2546) **2733**
Trial Lawyers Marketing Briefs. (US) **2733**
Trial Lawyers Quarterly. (US ISSN 0041-2554) **2733**
Trial Style. (US) **2236**
Trialog. (GW ISSN 0724-6234) **2497**, **308**
Trialogue. (US ISSN 0275-5351) **3974**
Trials and Motocross News. (UK) **4521**
▼Trials Digest. (US) **2733**
Triangle. (SZ ISSN 0041-2597) **3158**
Triangle. (UK) **4794**, **1268**
Triangle (Dayton). (US) **1326**

Triangle (Lakeland). (US ISSN 0041-2570) **194**
Triangle (Marion). (US) **1326**
Triangle Business Journal. (US ISSN 0891-0022) **695**
Triangle of Mu Phi Epsilon. (US ISSN 0041-2600) **3584**
Triangle Papers. (US) **3974**
Triangle Pointer. (US ISSN 0041-2619) **4794**
Trias. (NE) **1498**
Triathlete. (US ISSN 0898-3410) **4495**
Triathlon Magazin. (GW) **3809**
Triathlon Sports Magazine. (AT) **4495**
Triathlon Times. (US) **4495**
Triathlon Today. (US) **4559**
Triathlon und Sportwissenschaft. (GW ISSN 0931-3850) **4559**
Tribal Arts Review see EthnoArts Index **352**
Tribal Religions. (II) **4289**
Tribal Research and Development Institute. Bulletin. (II ISSN 0564-2159) **251**
Tribe. (US) **3007**, **2457**
Tribhuvan University. Natural History Museum. Journal. (NP) **519**
Tribina. (XN ISSN 0041-266X) **2887**
Tribolium Information Bulletin. (US ISSN 0082-6391) **538**
Tribologie und Schmierungstechnik. (GW ISSN 0724-3472) **1860**, **1224**
Tribologija u Industriji. (YU) **1940**
Tribologist. (JA ISSN 0915-1168) **1940**, **3024**
†Tribologist. International Edition. (JA) **5292**
▼Tribology & Corrosion Abstracts. (UK ISSN 0962-7189) **1846**, **24**
Tribology International. (UK ISSN 0301-679X) **1940**
†Tribology News. (US) **5292**
Tribology Series. (NE) **1940**
Tribos - Tribology Abstracts. (UK ISSN 0041-2694) **1846**, **24**, **4615**
Tribritta. (II ISSN 0041-2708) **2887**
Tribuene. (GW ISSN 0041-2716) **4227**
Tribuna. (RM) **2215**
†Tribuna Alema. (GW ISSN 0170-8058) **5292**
Tribuna Alemana. (GW ISSN 0041-2732) **2192**
Tribuna Cooperativa. (SP ISSN 0210-7295) **832**
Tribuna del Collezionista. (IT ISSN 0393-7534) **3758**, **3602**
Tribuna dell'Irpinia. (IT) **695**, **2206**, **4095**, **4495**
Tribuna e Gazetarit. (AA) **2576**
Tribuna Economica. (IT) **741**
Tribuna Economica. (RM) **886**
Tribuna Farmaceutica. (BL ISSN 0049-4631) **3744**
Tribuna Informatica. (SP) **1401**
Tribuna International de los Derechos del Nino see International Children's Rights Monitor **3943**
Tribuna Italiana. (CN ISSN 0049-464X) **2026**
Tribuna Medica. (SP ISSN 0212-7512) **3158**
Tribuna Medica. (CK) **3158**
Tribuna Medica. (MX) **3158**
Tribuna Medica. (PE) **3158**
Tribuna Medica. (VE) **3158**
Tribuna Medica for Central America, Panama and the Dominican Republic. (CK) **3158**
Tribuna Medica Hospitales. (SP) **2470**, **2687**
Tribuna Musical. (AG ISSN 0041-2767) **3584**
Tribuna Obrera. see Workers Tribune **5306**
Tribuna Postale see Tribuna Postale e delle Telecomunicazioni **1345**
Tribuna Postale e delle Telecomunicazioni. (IT) **1345**
Tribuna Roja. (CK) **3930**
Tribuna Romaniei see Curierul Romanesc **2863**
Tribuna Scolii. (RM) **1668**
▼Tribuna Sporturilor. (RM) **4495**
†Tribuna Tedesca. (GW ISSN 0344-9033) **5292**
Tribunal. (SP) **2687**

Tribunal de Commerce, Paris. Annuaire.(FR ISSN 0071-9129) **2687**
Tribunal de Justica do Estado do Rio Grande do Sul. Revista de Jurisprudencia. (BL ISSN 0041-2805) **2687**
Tribunal Federal de Recursos. Revista see Revista Trimestral de Jurisprudencia **2673**
Tribunal Supremo Popular. Boletin. (CU) **2687**
Tribunali Amministrativi Regionali. (IT) **2687**
TribunAmCham. (MX) **823**
Tribune. see To Vima **2196**
Tribune. (UK ISSN 0041-2821) **2590**, **3930**
Tribune. (TR) **3930**
Tribune. (US ISSN 0738-9779) **4854**, **3974**
†Tribune. (AT) **5292**
▼Tribune Business Weekly. (US) **695**
Tribune D'Allemagne. (GW ISSN 0344-9041) **2192**
Tribune d'Eau. (BE) **4829**
Tribune de L'Assurance. (FR ISSN 0395-9406) **2544**
Tribune de l'Esperanto see Esperanto - Lingvo Internacia **2812**
Tribune de l'Orgue. (SZ) **3584**
Tribune des Mineurs. (FR) **3496**
Tribune Gaulliste. (FR) **3930**
Tribune Graphologique. (FR ISSN 0041-2864) **4049**
Tribune Internationale. (FR) **3930**
Tribune Internationale des Droits de l'Enfant see International Children's Rights Monitor **3943**
Tribune Libre. (FR ISSN 0041-2872) **923**
Tribune of Folk Literature. see Minjian Wenxue Luntan **2057**
Tribune Psychique. (FR ISSN 0049-4666) **3671**
Tribuno del Pueblo see People's Tribune **3914**
Tribus. (GW ISSN 0082-6413) **251**, **347**
Tributary. (UK) **1326**
Tributary. (US) **2970**
Tribute Goes to the Movies. (CN ISSN 0826-1210) **3518**
Tribute to Oman. (MK) **2211**
Trickster. (GW ISSN 0723-5119) **251**, **2059**
Tricolor. (VE ISSN 0041-2902) **1268**, **1668**
Tricontinental Magazine see Revista Tricontinental **3971**
Tricot Prestige. (FR ISSN 0241-0702) **3593**, **1294**
Tricot - Selection. (FR) **2188**
Tricots Chics. (FR) **3593**, **1295**
▼Tricycle. (US ISSN 1055-484X) **4216**, **347**, **2236**, **2970**
Trident. (UK ISSN 0049-4690) **4741**
Trident of Delta Delta Delta. (US) **1326**
Trident - Visnyk. (US) **3758**, **3602**
Trierer Forum. (GW) **4207**
Trierer Grabungen und Forschungen. (GW ISSN 0082-643X) **288**
Trierer Psychologische Berichte. (GW) **4049**
Trierer Theologische Zeitschrift. (GW ISSN 0041-2945) **4207**
Trierer Zeitschrift fuer Geschichte und Kunst des Trierer Landes und seiner Nachbargebiete. (GW ISSN 0041-2953) **288**, **347**, **3602**
Trieste Economica. (IT) **695**
Trieste Notes in Physics. (US) **3834**
Trigger. (JA) **4612**
Trigon. (DK ISSN 0108-2450) **359**
Trigon. (AT) **3059**, **1762**
Trikon see Trikone **2457**
Trikone. (US ISSN 1042-735X) **2457**
Trilobite News. (NO ISSN 0085-7386) **3661**
Trilogia. (CL ISSN 0716-0356) **2516**
Trilogy. (US) **4559**, **4794**
Trim-a-Tree Business. (US) **2283**
Trimestre. (IT) **2887**
Trimestre Economico. (MX ISSN 0041-3011) **695**
Trinaesti Maj. (YU ISSN 0041-302X) **3930**

Trinet Directory of Leading U S Companies: Second 1,500. (US) **695**
Trinet Directory of Leading U S Companies: Top 1,500. (US) **695**
Trinet Directory of Leading U S Companies: Top 1,500 Private. (US) **695**
Trinidad and Tobago. Central Statistical Office. Agricultural Report. (TR) **144**
Trinidad and Tobago. Central Statistical Office. Annual Statistical Digest. (TR ISSN 0082-6502) **4590**
Trinidad and Tobago. Central Statistical Office. Business Surveys. (TR) **741**, **4590**
Trinidad and Tobago. Central Statistical Office. Conference of Commonwealth Caribbean Government Statistician. Report. (TR) **1405**
Trinidad and Tobago. Central Statistical Office. Continuous Sample Survey of Population. (TR ISSN 0564-2612) **3996**
Trinidad and Tobago. Central Statistical Office. Economic Indicators. (TR) **741**
Trinidad and Tobago. Central Statistical Office. Estimated Internal Migration. Bulletin. (TR) **3996**
Trinidad and Tobago. Central Statistical Office. Financial Statistics. (TR ISSN 0082-6529) **741**
Trinidad and Tobago. Central Statistical Office. International Travel Report. (TR ISSN 0082-6537) **4801**
Trinidad and Tobago. Central Statistical Office. Labour Force by Sex. (TR) **741**
Trinidad and Tobago. Central Statistical Office. Monthly Travel see Trinidad and Tobago. Central Statistical Office. Quarterly Travel **4801**
Trinidad and Tobago. Central Statistical Office. Overseas Trade. Annual Report. (TR ISSN 0082-6545) **741**
Trinidad and Tobago. Central Statistical Office. Overseas Trade. Bi-Monthly Report. (TR ISSN 0030-7505) **741**
Trinidad and Tobago. Central Statistical Office. Pocket Digest. (TR) **4590**
Trinidad and Tobago. Central Statistical Office. Population and Vital Statistics; Report. (TR ISSN 0082-6553) **3996**
Trinidad and Tobago. Central Statistical Office. Quarterly Economic Report. (TR ISSN 0041-3046) **741**
Trinidad and Tobago. Central Statistical Office. Quarterly Travel. (TR) **4801**, **4590**
Trinidad and Tobago. Central Statistical Office. Staff Papers. (TR) **4590**
Trinidad and Tobago. Ministry of Energy and Natural Resources. Monthly Bulletin see Trinidad and Tobago. Ministry of Energy. Monthly Bulletin **3702**
Trinidad and Tobago. Ministry of Energy. Annual Report. (TR) **3702**
Trinidad and Tobago. Ministry of Energy. Monthly Bulletin. (TR) **3702**
Trinidad and Tobago Gazette. (TR) **4075**
Trinidad and Tobago National Bibliography. (TR) **413**
Trinidad and Tobago Review. (TR) **2239**
Trinidad and Tobago Trade Directory. (UK ISSN 0082-657X) **1156**
Trinidad Carnival. (TR) **2059**
Trinidad Naturalist see Naturalist **4327**
Trinidad Philatelic Society Bulletin see Philatelic Society of T & T Bulletin **3756**
Trinitarian Bible Society. Annual Report see Trinitarian Bible Society. Quarterly Record **4207**
Trinitarian Bible Society. Quarterly Record. (UK ISSN 0049-4712) **4207**
Trinitonian. (US) **1326**
Trinity College. Friends of the Library. Newsletter. (IE ISSN 0790-388X) **2787**
Trinity College Journal. (PH) **1717**

Trinity Journal. (US ISSN 0360-3032) **4207**
Trinity Magazine. (UK) **3584**
Trinity News. (IE ISSN 0041-3062) **1327**
Trinity Occasional Papers. (AT ISSN 0811-2304) **4251**
Trinity Report (Ellendale). (US) **1327**
Trinity Review. (US) **3784**, **4251**
Trinity Tidings see Trinity Report (Ellendale) **1327**
Trinity Tripod. (US) **1327**
Trio see Total Health **3612**
Triolo. (FR) **1268**
Triological Society. Transactions see American Laryngological, Rhinological and Otological Society Transactions **5134**
Triomphe see Triomphe Saint-Cyr **3473**
Triomphe Saint-Cyr. (FR ISSN 0036-2794) **3473**
Trip Out. (UK) **4794**
†Triperie Francaise. (FR) **5292**
†Triple A. (AT) **5292**
·Triple I. (SI) **695**
The Tripod. (US) **3441**
†Trips (Columbus). (US) **5292**
TriQuarterly. (US ISSN 0041-3097) **2887**
Trisomy 21. (US ISSN 0737-5174) **3327**, **547**
Tristania. (US ISSN 0360-3385) **2970**, **2059**
Triticale Abstracts see Wheat, Barley and Triticale Abstracts **145**
Triton see Diver **4471**
Tritsch - Tratsch. (UK) **3585**
†Triumph. (US ISSN 0041-3127) **5292**
Triveni. (II ISSN 0041-3135) **2970**, **347**, **2342**
Trivia. (US ISSN 0736-928X) **2887**, **4854**
Trivia Dispatch. (US) **2236**
Trivium. (UK) **2970**, **347**
La Trobe Sociology Papers. (AT) **4455**
La Trobe University Library News. (AT) **2787**
Trochilus. (GW ISSN 0722-0537) **567**
Troedler- und Antiquitaetenmagazin see Troedler- und Magazin Sammeln **259**
Troedler- und Magazin Sammeln. (GW) **259**
Trofeo. (SP) **4559**, **1498**
Trofima & Pota/Food & Beverages. (UK) **386**, **2083**
†Trois. (US) **5292**
Troisdorfer Jahresheft. (GW) **2392**
Troisieme Civilisation. (FR ISSN 0049-4739) **4216**
Troisieme Republique. see Third Republic **5290**
Trolley Fare. (US) **3534**, **4716**
Trolley Wire. (AT ISSN 0155-1264) **4660**
Trolleybus Magazine. (UK ISSN 0266-7452) **4660**
Trombosi e Aterosclerosi. (IT) **3212**
†Trommel. (GW ISSN 0323-8709) **5292**
Trompie see Student **1716**
Trons Segrar. (SW ISSN 0041-3178) **4207**
Trooper. (US ISSN 0564-3287) **1523**
Tropenlandwirt. (GW ISSN 0041-3186) **125**, **2109**
Tropenmedizin und Parasitologie see Tropical Medicine and Parasitology **3224**
Trophoblast Research. (US ISSN 0891-9925) **3297**
Trophy Dealer see T D M A Today **4494**
Trophy Dealers and Manufacturers Association Today see T D M A Today **4494**
Tropic Oceanology. see Redai Haiyang **1610**
Tropical Abstracts see Abstracts on Tropical Agriculture **132**
Tropical Agriculture. (UK ISSN 0041-3216) **125**
Tropical Agriculture Research Series. (JA ISSN 0388-9386) **125**
Tropical Agriculturist. (CE ISSN 0041-3224) **125**

TRUCK 6743

Tropical and Geographical Medicine. (NE ISSN 0041-3232) **3158**
†Tropical Animal Production. (MX) **5292**
Tropical Atmosphere. see Redai Qixiang **3440**
Tropical Bands Survey. (DK ISSN 0106-1968) **1360**
Tropical Dental Journal. see Odonto-Stomatologie Tropicale **3239**
Tropical Diseases Bulletin. (UK ISSN 0041-3240) **3181**
†Tropical Diseases Research Series. (SZ) **5292**
Tropical Doctor. (UK ISSN 0049-4755) **3224**
Tropical Ecology. (II ISSN 0564-3295) **519**
Tropical Fish Hobbyist. (US ISSN 0041-3259) **2443**, **2049**
Tropical Geography. see Redai Dili **2260**
†Tropical Grain Legume Bulletin. (NR ISSN 0304-5765) **5292**
Tropical Grasslands. (AT ISSN 0049-4763) **194**
Tropical Journal of Obstetrics and Gynaecology. (NR ISSN 0189-5117) **3297**, **3158**
Tropical Medicine/Nettai Igaku. (JA ISSN 0041-3267) **3224**
Tropical Medicine and Hygiene News. (US ISSN 0041-3275) **3224**
Tropical Medicine and Parasitology. (GW ISSN 0177-2392) **3224**, **558**
Tropical Oil Seeds. (UK ISSN 0961-351X) **144**, **24**
Tropical Oil Seeds Abstracts see Tropical Oil Seeds **144**
Tropical Pastures Program Annual Report see Informe Anual del Programa de Pastos Tropicales **97**
Tropical Pest Management. (UK ISSN 0143-6147) **195**, **4113**
Tropical Pesticides Research Institute. Annual Report. (TZ ISSN 0082-6642) **195**
Tropical Science. (UK ISSN 0041-3291) **125**
Tropical Science Center, Costa Rica. Occasional Paper. (CR ISSN 0069-2107) **4348**
Tropical Stored Products Information see Tropical Science **125**
Tropical Zoology. (IT ISSN 0394-6975) **592**
Tropico. (HO) **2180**
Tropische und Subtropische Pflanzenwelt. (GW ISSN 0302-9417) **519**
TropMed Seminars on Tropical Medicine. Proceedings. (TH) **3224**
Tropolitan. (US) **1327**
Tros-Kompas. (NE ISSN 0041-3321) **1383**
Trot. (CN ISSN 0704-0733) **4538**
Trottatore. (IT) **4538**
Der Trotter. (GW) **4794**
Trotting and Pacing Guide. (US ISSN 0083-3509) **4538**
Trotto Sportsman. (IT) **4538**
Trotwaer. (NE ISSN 0041-3348) **2970**
Trotzdem. (AU ISSN 0041-3356) **3930**, **1268**
Trouble and Strife. (UK) **4860**
†Troubled Company Investor. (US) **5292**
†Troup County, Georgia and Her People. (US) **5292**
Trout. (US ISSN 0041-3364) **1498**, **2049**
Trout and Salmon. (UK ISSN 0041-3372) **4559**
Trout Fisherman. (UK) **4559**
Trouvailles. (FR) **347**, **259**
†Trowel. (US) **5292**
Trowel and Sword. (AT ISSN 0813-796X) **4207**
Trubus. (IO ISSN 0126-0057) **125**
Truck. (UK) **4748**
Truck and Bus Builder. (UK ISSN 0263-6263) **4748**, **1940**
Truck & Bus, South Africa. (SA ISSN 0258-9281) **4748**
Truck and Bus Transportation. (AT ISSN 0041-3380) **4748**, **4660**
Truck & Commerce. (US) **4748**

TRUCK

Truck & Driver see Truck **4748**
Truck & Off-Highway Industries. (US) **4748**, 1838
Truck & Trailer. (CN) **4748**
Truck & Van Prices - Buyer's Guide Reports. (US ISSN 1050-7272) **4704**, 1055
Truck Australia. (AT) **1875**
Truck Blue Book Lease Guide. (US ISSN 8756-4041) **4748**
Truck Data Book. (CN ISSN 0564-3392) **4749**
Truck Driver's Handbook. (UK) **4704**
Truck Equipment News see T E News **4748**
Truck Facts. (US) **4749**
Truck Fleet. (CN) **4749**
Truck Identification Book. (US ISSN 0889-3888) **4749**
Truck Insider Newsletter see Car Dealer Insider Newsletter **4686**
Truck Modell. (GW) **2443**
Truck News. (US) **4749**
Truck News. (CN ISSN 0712-2683) **4749**
Truck Paper. (US) **4749**
Truck Parts & Service. (US ISSN 0895-3856) **4749**
Truck Prices see Price Guide Presents **4700**
Truck Sales & Leasing Magazine. (US) **4749**, 1055
Truck Trader see Truck Trader - Centerline **4749**
Truck Trader - Centerline. (US ISSN 1047-4366) **4749**, 1055
Truck Treff. (GW) **2443**
Truck Trends. (US ISSN 0049-478X) **4749**
▼Truck West. (CN) **4749**
Truck World & Western Trucking News. (CN) **4749**
Truckers Digest. (US) **4749**
Trucker's News. (US) **4749**
Truckers - U S A. (US) **4749**
Truckin' (US) **4749**
Truckin' Life. (AT ISSN 0155-9648) **4749**
Trucking Canada see Independent Trucker **5211**
†Trucking Digest. (US) **5292**
Trucking Permit & Tax Bulletin. (US) **4749**
Trucking Permit Guide. (US) **4749**
Trucking Safety Guide. (US) **4749**
†Trucking - South. (US) **5292**
Trucks. (US ISSN 0884-8947) **4749**
Truckstop World. (US ISSN 0894-962X) **1119**, 4749
Trudbenik. (XN ISSN 0041-3437) **2590**
Trudov Invalid. (XN ISSN 0041-3445) **2544**, 4422
True Astrology Forecast. (US) **359**
True Confessions. (US ISSN 0041-3488) **2986**
True Detective. (US ISSN 0041-350X) **2986**
True Experience. (US ISSN 0199-0012) **2986**
†True Imaging. (US) **5292**
True Love. (US ISSN 0041-3550) **2984**
True Love. (KE) **2985**
True Love and Family. (SA) **4854**, 2026
True Match. (US) **2236**
True Match Singles R S V P see T M's Singles R S V P **4364**
True Monthly see Loving **2984**
True Police Cases. (US) **1523**, 2970
True Romance. (US ISSN 0199-0020) **2985**, 4854
True Romances. (UK) **2985**
True Seed Exchange see Seed Savers Exchange **2138**
True Story. (UK) **2985**
True Story. (US ISSN 0195-3117) **2985**
True West. (US ISSN 0041-3615) **2424**
Trufax Directory and Consumer Guide see Better Business Bureau of Metropolitan Toronto. Directory & Consumer Guide **1502**
Truly Fine. (US) **2970**
Truly Fine Press see Truly Fine **2970**
Truly Portable. (US) **1465**
Trumpet. (CN) **1245**

†Trumpet. (US) **5292**
Trumpeter. (US ISSN 0148-673X) **3758**
Trumpeter Swan Society Newsletter. (US ISSN 0742-2792) **567**, 1498
Trumpeting News see International Partners in Prayer Trumpeting News **4183**
†Trump's. (US ISSN 0278-1263) **5292**
Truppendienst. (AU ISSN 0041-3658) **3473**
Truppenpraxis. (GW ISSN 0041-3666) **3473**
Trust. (CN ISSN 0381-9612) **1742**
Trust. (GW) **3585**
Trust Department Administration and Operations. (US) **2687**
Trust Law and Practice see Trust Law International **2687**
Trust Law International. (UK) **2687**
Trust Letter. (US) **801**
†Trust Marketing Resource Newsletter. (US) **5293**
Trust News see Money Management Letter **955**
Trustee. (US ISSN 0041-3674) **2470**
†Trustee. (CN) **5293**
Trustee Quarterly. (US ISSN 0271-9746) **1718**, 1732
Trusts see B A R - B R I Bar Review. Trusts **1072**
Trusts and Estates. (US ISSN 0041-3682) **967**, 1111, 2687
Truth. see Ta Tene **2170**
The Truth. (NR ISSN 0331-5975) **4220**
Truth (Mogadore). (US ISSN 0041-3690) **1302**, 2236
The Truth at Last. (US) **3948**
Truth Consciousness Journal see Light of Consciousness **4188**
Truth in Action. (US) **3784**
Truth-in-Lending Manual (Supplement). (US) **801**
Truth Journal. (US) **3597**, 3784
Truth of Life. (US) **3784**
Truth on Fire see Hallelujah **4283**
Truth Seeker. (US ISSN 0041-3712) **3784**
Trux. (UK) **4749**
Truxbook. (CN) **4749**
Truxpress. (CN) **4749**
Try Us. (US) **1156**, 2026
Trybuna Spoldzielcza. (PL ISSN 0041-3720) **832**
Trziste, Novac, Kapital. (YU) **1055**
Trziste Stoke i Stochih Proizoda. (YU ISSN 0041-3755) **144**
Tsa'Aszi. (US) **2026**, 2059
Tschechoslowakische Film see Czechoslovak Film **3507**
Tschechoslowakische Motorrevue see Czechoslovak Motor Review **5176**
Tschechoslowakische Oekumenische Nachrichten. see Czechoslovak Ecumenical News **5176**
Tschechoslowakische Wirtschaftsrundschau. (CS) **886**
Tschechoslowakische Wirtschaftsrundschau see Czechoslovak Economic Digest **5176**
Tschechoslowakisches Leben see Czechoslovak Life **2184**
Tseluloza i Khartiia. (BU) **1860**, 3868
Tsement. (RU ISSN 0041-4867) **635**
Tsentral'nyi Nauchno-Issledovatel'skii Institut Geodezii, Aeros"emki i Kartografii. Trudy. (RU) **2264**
▼Tserkov' i Spasenie. (RU) **4289**
Tsetse and Trypanosomiasis Information Quarterly. (UK ISSN 0142-193X) **468**, 24, 144
Tshiingamo. (SA ISSN 0258-9052) **4289**
Tsimshian, Haida, Eskimo, Tlingit, Aleut see T H E T A **5286**
Tsitologiya/Cytology. (RU ISSN 0041-3771) **527**
Tsitologiya i Genetika. (KR ISSN 0564-3783) **547**
Tsog/Spark. (MP) **2970**
▼Tsogang! (SA) **4289**
Tsoha! (SA) **4289**
Tsopano News. (ZA ISSN 0041-378X) **2240**

Tsuchi to Kiso. see Soil Mechanics and Foundation Engineering **1874**
Tsuda Review. (JA ISSN 0496-3547) **2970**
Tsukuba Journal of Mathematics. (JA ISSN 0387-4982) **3059**
Tsunami Newsletter. (US ISSN 0259-3637) **4348**
Tsushin Kogyo. see Communication Industries **1362**
Tsushin Sogo Kenkyujo Kiho/Communications Research Laboratory. Review. (JA ISSN 0914-9279) **1383**
Tsushinsogo Kenkyujo Eibun Ronbunshu. see Communications Research Laboratory. Journal **1371**
Tsvetnye Metally. (RU ISSN 0041-4891) **3422**
Tsvetovodstvo. (RU ISSN 0041-4905) **2140**
Tu. (PN ISSN 0746-9691) **4854**
Tu Cher Wen Cher Reader's Digest (Chinese Edition). (HK ISSN 0041-3836) **2197**
Tu-Mu Gongcheng Xuebao/China Civil Engineering Journal. (CC) **1875**
Tuam Herald and Western Advertiser. (IE) **2203**
Tuan Tin Tuc/News Weekly. (VN) **2238**
Tuarascail. (IE ISSN 0790-9136) **1668**
Tuatara. (NZ ISSN 0041-3860) **4349**, 458
Tuba. (UK ISSN 0269-4824) **2887**
†Tube. (US) **5293**
Tube International. (UK ISSN 0263-6794) **3422**
Tube Topics. (US ISSN 0300-6190) **1055**
Tubercle see Tubercle and Lung Disease **3367**
Tubercle and Lung Disease. (UK ISSN 0962-8479) **3367**
Tuberculosis. see Kekkaku **3365**
Tuberculosis, Leprosy and Cancer. (JA) **3224**, 3202, 3367
Tuberkulosearzt see Pneumologie **3366**
Tuberkulozis es Tudobetegsegek see Pneumonologia Hungarica **3366**
Tuberous Sclerosis Resources. (US) **3158**
Tubists Universal Brotherhood Association Journal see T.U.B.A. Journal **3583**
Tubists Universal Brotherhood Association Series see T.U.B.A. Series **5286**
Tubular Structures. (UK ISSN 0041-3909) **635**
Tucker Park Press see Baron **1304**
†Tuckers of America. (US) **5293**
Tucson Business Journal. (US) **695**
Tucson Connection see Singles' Paper **4363**
Tucson Education Association Newsletter see T E A Newsletter **1666**
Tucson Lifestyle Magazine. (US) **2236**
Tucson Weekly. (US ISSN 0742-0692) **2887**
Tucumcari Literary Review. (US) **2970**
Tudo e Historia. (BL) **2424**
Tudomany. (Hungarian translation of: Scientific American) (HU ISSN 0237-322X) **4349**, 4612
Tudomanyos es Muszaki Tajekoztatas/Scientific and Technical Information. (HU ISSN 0041-3917) **2796**, 24
Tudomanyos Szocializmus. see Acta Universitatis Szegediensis de Attila Jozsef Nominatae. Sectio Scientiae Socialismi **3869**
†Tudomanyos Tajekoztatas Elmelete es Gyakorlata/Theory and Practice of Scientific Information. (HU ISSN 0373-5354) **5293**
Tudomanyszervezesi Fuzetek. (HU ISSN 0082-6707) **4349**
Tuduv-Studie. Reihe Geschichtswissenschaften. (GW) **2324**
Tuduv-Studie. Reihe Kommunikationswissenschaften. (GW) **1345**
Tuduv-Studie. Reihe Kulturwissenschaften. (GW) **2026**

Tuduv-Studie. Reihe Politikwissenschaften. (GW) **3930**, 3974
Tuduv-Studie. Reihe Religionswissenschaften. (GW) **4207**
Tuduv-Studie. Reihe Sprach- und Literaturwissenschaften. (GW) **2848**
Tuduv-Studie. Reihen Kunstgeschichte. (GW) **347**
Tuduv-Studien. Reihe Bayern Privat. (GW) **421**
Tuduv-Studien. Reihe Sozialwissenschaften. (GW) **4390**
†Tuebinger Aegyptologische Beitraege. (GW) **5293**
Tuebinger Blaetter. (GW ISSN 0930-3642) **1327**, 4794
Tuebinger Geographische Studien. (GW ISSN 0564-4232) **2264**
Tuebinger Rechtswissenschaftliche Abhandlungen. (GW ISSN 0082-6731) **2687**
Tuexenia. (GW ISSN 0722-494X) **4455**
▼Tuff Stuff. (US) **2443**
▼Tuff Stuff Jr. (US) **1268**, 2443
Tufts Kinsmen. (US ISSN 0149-2438) **2166**
Tufts Medical Alumni Bulletin see Tufts Medicine **1327**
Tufts Medicine. (US) **1327**
Tufts University Diet and Nutrition Letter. (US) **3612**
Tug World Newsletter. (UK) **4741**
Tuijin Jishu/Journal of Propulsion Technology. (CC ISSN 1001-4055) **63**
Tuin en Landschap. (NE) **2143**
Tuinbouw Leven see Tuinbouw Visie **2140**
Tuinbouw Visie. (BE) **2140**, 125
Tuinbouwcijfers. (NE ISSN 0440-0771) **2141**
Tuinderij. (NE ISSN 0041-3984) **125**, 2143
Tuinier. see Gardener **5198**
Tuition, Entertainment, News, Views. (UK) **347**, 3585, 4642
Tulane Civil Law Forum. (US) **2704**
Tulane Law Review. (US ISSN 0041-3992) **2687**
Tulane Maritime Law Journal. (US ISSN 1048-3748) **2735**
Tulane Medicine. (US) **3158**, 1327
Tulane Medicine: Faculty and Alumni see Tulane Medicine **3158**
Tulane Studies in Geology and Paleontology. (US ISSN 0041-4018) **1583**, 3661
Tulane Studies in Political Science. (US ISSN 0082-6774) **3930**
Tulane Studies in Zoology see Tulane Studies in Zoology and Botany **592**
Tulane Studies in Zoology and Botany. (US ISSN 0082-6782) **592**, 519
Tulane Tax Institute. (US ISSN 0564-4402) **1111**
Tulanian. (US ISSN 0041-4026) **1327**
Tulimuld. (SW ISSN 0041-4034) **2887**
Tulosuunta. (FI ISSN 0359-9108) **801**
†Tulsa. (US ISSN 0041-4042) **5293**
Tulsa Annals. (US ISSN 0564-4437) **2166**
Tulsa Business Chronicle. (US ISSN 0745-5747) **695**
Tulsa County Medical Society. Bulletin see Tulsa Medicine **3158**
Tulsa Jewish Review. (US) **2026**
Tulsa Law Journal. (US ISSN 0041-4050) **2687**
Tulsa Lawyer. (US ISSN 0041-4069) **2687**
Tulsa Medicine. (US) **3158**
Tulsa People. (US) **2236**
Tulsa Studies in Women's Literature. (US ISSN 0732-7730) **2970**, 4860
Tulsa Women. (US) **4854**
Tulungan sa Kaunlaran/Wall News. (PH) **840**
Tumbuh. (MY) **158**
Tumor Biology. (SZ ISSN 1010-4283) **3202**, 483

Tumor Research: Experimental and Clinical/Gan Kenkyu, Jikken to Rinsho. (JA ISSN 0041-4093) **3202**
Tumordiagnostik & Therapie. (GW ISSN 0722-219X) **3202**
Tumori. (IT ISSN 0041-4352) **3202**
Tumour Marker Update. (UK ISSN 0955-5102) **3202**, 3181
Tumu Shuili see Journal of Civil and Hydraulic Engineering **1869**
Tuna and Billfish Assessment Programme Technical Report. (NL ISSN 1018-0974) **2050**
Tundra Times. (US ISSN 0049-4801) **2026**
†Tune in the World with Ham Radio Kit.(US) **5293**
Tune Monthly Magazine. (SI) **1295**
Tune Up see Philadelphia Folksong Society Newsletter **3574**
Tung Board. Annual Report see Tree Nut Authority. Report **194**
Tungsram Technical Review. see Tungsram Technische Mitteilungen **1910**
Tungsram Technische Mitteilungen/ Tungsram Technical Review. (HU ISSN 0041-4107) **1910**
Tungsten Statistics. (UN ISSN 0049-4828) **3428**, 4590
Tungusica. (GW ISSN 0344-5542) **3645**
Tunisia. Institut National de la Statistique. Bulletin Mensuel de Statistique. (TI ISSN 0041-4115) **4590**
Tunisia. Institut National Scientifique et Technique d'Oceanographie et de Peche. Bulletin. (TI ISSN 0579-7926) **1611**, 2050
Tunisia. Ministere des Travaux Publics et de l'Habitat. Travaux Publics et Habitat see Revue Tunisienne de l'Equipement **1873**
Tunisia. Ministere du Plan. Budget Economique. (TI ISSN 0082-6820) **1111**
Tunisia. Office des Ports Nationaux. Bulletin Annuel des Statistiques. (TI) **4668**, 4741
Tunisia. Office des Ports Nationaux. Bulletin Trimestriel. (TI) **4741**
Tunisia. Office des Ports Nationaux. Trafic Maritime see Tunisia. Office des Ports Nationaux. Bulletin Annuel des Statistiques **4668**
Tunisie Economique. (TI ISSN 0041-4123) **823**
La Tunisie Medicale. (TI ISSN 0041-4131) **3158**
Tunnel. (GW ISSN 0722-6241) **1875**
Tunneling Technology Newsletter. (US ISSN 0095-2664) **1875**
Tunnelling and Underground Space Technology. (US ISSN 0886-7798) **1839**
Tunnelling Directory. (UK) **1875**, 1839
Tunnels & Tunnelling. (UK ISSN 0041-414X) **1875**
Tuo Ling/Camel Bells. (US) **2970**
Turang/Pedology. (CC ISSN 0564-3910) **1548**, 195
Turang Feiliao/Soil Fertilizer. (CC) **195**
Turang Quan. see Pedosphere **1547**
Turang Xue Jinzhan/Advances in Pedology. (CC ISSN 0254-010X) **1549**, 195
Turang Xuebao/Acta Pedologica Sinica. (CC ISSN 0564-3929) **1549**
Turath al-Sha'bi. (IQ ISSN 0002-4082) **2059**
Turath wa Funun/Heritage and Arts. (TS) **2059**
Turbine Engine Overhaul. (US) **3473**, 63
†Turbine Intelligence. (US) **5293**
Turbo & High Tech Performance. (US) **4704**
Turbo Technix. (US ISSN 0893-827X) **1432**
Turbo User Group Lines see T U G Lines **1474**
Turbomachinery Catalog and Workbook see Turbomachinery International Handbook **1940**
Turbomachinery International. (US ISSN 0149-4147) **1940**

Turbomachinery International Handbook. (US ISSN 0748-0903) **1940**
Turbomachinery Maintenance Newsletter. (US) **3024**
Turbomachinery Symposium. Proceedings. (US) **3024**
Turbulence. (PL ISSN 0860-7222) **3441**
Turcica; Revue d'Etudes Turques. (BE ISSN 0082-6847) **2848**
Turcologica. (GW ISSN 0177-4743) **3645**
Turf. (US) **2140**
Turf Aktuell see Turf Sport **4539**
Turf & Recreation. (CN) **2140**
▼Turf Central. (US) **2140**
The Turf Directory. (UK) **4538**
Turf Management. (UK ISSN 0262-0669) **2140**
Turf Monthly. (AT ISSN 0726-8254) **4538**
Turf News. (US ISSN 0899-417X) **195**, 2140
Turf Sport. (AU) **4539**
▼Turf West. (US) **2140**
Turicum. (SZ) **2219**
Turing Institute Abstracts in Artificial Intelligence. (UK ISSN 0269-8862) **1405**, 24
Turisguia. (PN) **4794**
Turismo d'Affari. (IT) **4794**
Turismo d'Italia. (IT) **4794**
Turismo Gradese. (IT) **4794**
Turismo in Italia see Italia Turistica **4773**
Turismo Veneto. (IT) **4794**
Turispress. (BL) **4795**
Turist see Mir Puteshestvii **4778**
Turist. (SW ISSN 0041-4190) **4795**
Turist- og Rutebilbladet. (DK ISSN 0901-3032) **4704**, 4795
†Turista. (CS ISSN 0496-4845) **5293**
Turistfoerer. (DK ISSN 0108-8734) **4795**
Turistfoererforeningen. Medlemliste see Turistfoerer **4795**
Turisticke Novine. (YU ISSN 0041-4204) **4795**
Turistika a Horolezectvi see Turista **5293**
Turizmus. (HU) **4795**
Turk Dili. (TU ISSN 0041-4220) **2970**, 2848
Turk Etnografya Dergisi. see Turkish Review of Ethnography **4455**
Turk Mikrobiyologi Cemiyeti Dergisi. (TU ISSN 0258-2171) **558**
Turk Tarih-Arkeologya ve Etnografya Dergisi see Turkish Review of Ethnography **4455**
Turk Tarih Kurumu. Belgeler. (TU ISSN 0041-4247) **2432**, 3645
Turk Tarih Kurumu. Belleten. (TU ISSN 0041-4255) **2432**, 3645
Turk Tip Dernegi Dergisi. (TU) **3158**
Turkey. Devlet Istatistik Enstusu. Aylik Istatistik Bulteni/Monthly Bulletin of Statistics. (TU ISSN 0041-4263) **4590**
Turkey. Devlet Istatistik Enstusu. Dis Ticaret Yillik Istatistiki/Annual Foreign Trade Statistics/Statistique Annuelle du Commerce Exterieur. (TU ISSN 0082-6901) **741**
Turkey. Devlet Istatistik Enstusu. Milli Egitim Istatistikleri: Ogretim Yili Basi. (TU) **1680**, 4590
Turkey. Devlet Istatistik Enstusu. Tarim Istatistikleri Ozeti/Summary of Agricultural Statistics. (TU ISSN 0082-6928) **125**
Turkey. Devlet Istatistik Enstusu. Tarimsal Yapi ve Uretim/Agricultural Structure and Production. (TU ISSN 0082-6936) **125**
Turkey. Devlet Planama Teskilati. Yili Programi Ucuncu Bes Yil/Annual Program of the Five Year Development Plan. (TU ISSN 0082-6944) **1086**
Turkey. Monthly Economic Letter. (TU) **696**, 886
▼Turkey & Turkey Hunting. (US) **4559**
Turkey Briefing. (UK ISSN 0960-3069) **3948**, 3974
Turkey Call. (US) **567**, 1498

Turkey: Hotels - Camping. (TU) **2481**
Turkey Hunter. (US ISSN 8750-0205) **4559**
Turkey Port and Shipping Handbook (Year). (UK ISSN 0265-8194) **4741**, 1156
Turkey Tracks. (US) **2424**, 2059
Turkey World. (US ISSN 0041-4271) **227**
Turkeys. (UK) **227**
Turkish Atomic Energy Authority. Technical Journal see Turkish Journal of Nuclear Sciences **1810**
Turkish Cypriot Chamber of Commerce. Economy. (TU) **823**
▼Turkish Defence & Aerospace Update.(TU) **3473**, 63
Turkish Electricity Authority. Annual Report. (TU) **1910**
Turkish Forestry, Land Irrigation, Agriculture and Agricultural Industry Workers' Union. Tarim-is/Turkiye Orman, Topraksu, Tarim ve Tarim Sanayii Iscileri Sendikasi. Tarim-is. (TU) **2109**
Turkish Journal of Nuclear Sciences. (TU) **1810**
Turkish Journal of Pediatrics. (TU ISSN 0041-4301) **3327**
Turkish Journal of Population Studies/ Nufusbilim Dergisi. (TU) **3988**
Turkish Journal of Sports Medicine. see Spor Hekimligi Dergisi **3384**
Turkish Medical Association. Journal - Turk Tip Cemiyeti Mecmuasi see Turk Tip Dernegi Dergisi **3158**
Turkish National Bibliography/Turkiye Bibliyografyasi. (TU ISSN 0041-4328) **414**
Turkish Review of Ethnography/Turk Etnografya Dergisi. (TU ISSN 0082-6898) **4455**
Turkish Shipping see Seatrade Turkish Shipping Guide **5275**
Turkish Studies Association Bulletin. (US ISSN 0275-6048) **2432**
Turkish Treasures. (TU) **347**, 4795
Turkiyat Mecmuasi. (TU ISSN 0085-7432) **2432**, 2516
Turkiye Bibliyografyasi. see Turkish National Bibliography **414**
Turkiye Cumhuriyet Merkez Bankasi. Aylik Bulten/Central Bank of the Republic of Turkey. Quarterly Bulletin.(TU ISSN 0041-4336) **802**
Turkiye Is Bankasi. Review of Economic Conditions. (TU ISSN 0034-6500) **886**
Turkiye Istatistik Cep Yilligi. see Statistical Pocket Book of Turkey **4587**
Turkiye Istatistik Yilligi/Statistical Yearbook of Turkey. (TU ISSN 0082-691X) **4590**
Turkiye Makaleler Bibliyografyasi. see Bibliography of Articles in Turkish Periodicals **393**
Turkiye Muhendislik Haberleri. (TU ISSN 0049-4852) **1875**
Turkiye Orman, Topraksu, Tarim ve Tarim Sanayii Iscileri Sendikasi. Tarim-is. see Turkish Forestry, Land Irrigation, Agriculture and Agricultural Industry Workers' Union. Tarim-is **2109**
Turkiye Petrol Kimya, Lastik Iscileeri Sendikasi. Magazine. (TU) **4294**, 1860, 3702
Turkiye Sinai Kalkinma Bankasi. Annual Report. (TU) **802**
Turkluk Bilgisi Arastirmalari. see Journal of Turkish Studies **2430**
Turkologischer Anzeiger/Turkology Annual. (AU) **3647**, 3645
Turkology Annual. see Turkologischer Anzeiger **3647**
Turmberg-Rundschau see Durlach am Wochenende **2188**
Turmschreiber Kalender. (GW ISSN 0723-8177) **2970**
Turn-of-the-Century Women. (US ISSN 8756-1697) **4854**, 2970
Turn-On Letters. (US) **3400**
Turn-Ons. (US) **3400**
Turn- und Sportvereiniging Gaarden von 1875 e.V. Vereinsnachrichten see T U S Vereinsnachrichten **4494**
Turnaround Letter. (US) **967**

Turnarounds & Workouts. (US ISSN 0889-1699) **2687**
▼Turnarounds & Workouts - Europe. (US) **2729**
▼Turnarounds & Workouts - Supplement. (US) **2687**
▼Turnarounds & Workouts - Survey. (US) **2687**
Turnberry. (US) **347**
Turnbull Library Record. (NZ ISSN 0110-1625) **2346**, 2787
Turner Studies. (UK ISSN 0260-597X) **347**
Der Turnermusiker. (GW) **3585**
Turner's Syndrome News. (CN) **4836**
Turngemeinde 1861 e.V. Echo see T G M Echo **4494**
Turning Points. (US) **967**
Turning Wheels. (US) **259**, 2443, 4704
Turnstile. (US ISSN 0896-5951) **2970**, 3007
Turnverein 1877 e.V. Essen-Kupferdreh 1877 Echo see T V K 1877 Echo **4494**
Turrialba. (CR ISSN 0041-4360) **125**
Turtle. (US ISSN 0191-3654) **1268**
Turtle (Niagara Falls) see Turtle Quarterly Magazine **2026**
Turtle Quarterly Magazine. (US ISSN 0896-2022) **2026**, 347, 3585
Turtle Soup. (US) **2481**
Turtledove. see Grlica **3553**
Turun Historiallinen Arkisto. (FI ISSN 0085-7440) **2392**
Turun Historiallisen Yhdistyksen Julkaisuja see Turun Historiallinen Arkisto **2392**
Turun Yliopisto. Julkaisuja. Sarja A. I. Astronomica - Chemica - Physica - Mathematica. (FI ISSN 0082-7002) **4349**
Turun Yliopisto. Julkaisuja. Sarja A. II. Biologica - Geographica - Geologica. (FI ISSN 0082-6979) **458**, 1583, 2264
Turun Yliopisto. Julkaisuja. Sarja B. Humaniora. (FI ISSN 0082-6987) **2516**
Turun Yliopisto. Julkaisuja. Sarja C. Scripta Lingua Fennica Edita. (FI ISSN 0082-6995) **2516**
Turun Yliopisto. Julkaisuja. Sarja D. Medica - Odontologica. (FI ISSN 0355-9483) **3158**
Turun Yliopisto. Kirjasto. Julkaisuja. (FI ISSN 0082-7010) **2787**
†Turun Yliopisto. Klassillisen Filologian Laitos. Opera Ex Instituto Philologiae Classicae Universitatis Turkuensis Edita. (FI ISSN 0082-7029) **5293**
Turun Yliopisto. Psykologian Laitos. Reports see University of Turku. Psychological Research Reports **4049**
Turun Yliopisto. Psykologian Laitos. Reports see Turun Yliopisto. Psykologian Tutkimuksia **4049**
Turun Yliopisto. Psykologian Tutkimuksia. (FI ISSN 0356-8741) **4049**
†Turun Ylioppilas. (FI) **5293**
Tuscan Scene. (IT) **2887**
Tuscia. (IT ISSN 0390-4555) **2059**, 288, 347
Tushu Qingbao Gongzuo/Library and Information Service. (CC ISSN 0252-3116) **2787**
Tushu Qingbao Zhishi/Book Information Knowledge. (CC) **2787**
Tushuguan Gongzuo yu Yanjiu. (CC) **2787**
Tushuguan Jie/Library Circle. (CC) **2787**
Tushuguan Xuekan/Library Journal. (CC) **2787**
Tushuguan Yuan/Librarians. (CC) **2787**
Tushuguanxue Tongxun/Bulletin of Library Science. (CC ISSN 0494-1225) **2787**
Tushuguanxue yu Zixun Kexue. see Journal of Library & Information Science **2766**
Tussen de Rails. (NE ISSN 0041-4379) **4795**, 4716
Tutmonda Esperantista Junulara Organizo Tutmonde see T E J O - Tutmonde **2846**

6746 TUTOR

Tutor & Textbook - Elementary Piping & Drumming. (UK) **3585**
Tutora. Memoria y Balance General. (AG) **2544**
▼Tutorial Monographs in Artificial Intelligence. (US) **1411**
▼Tutorial Monographs in Cognitive Science. (US) **4049**
Tutti. (FR ISSN 0222-3074) **3585**
Tutti al Bar. (IT) **2481**, 386
Tutti Fotografi. (IT ISSN 0041-4395) **3797**
Tutti Fruitti. (US) **1268**
Tutti Frutti. (IT) **3585**
▼Tuttitalia. (UK ISSN 0957-1752) **2848**, 1668
†Tutto Casalinghi & Ferramento. (IT) **5293**
†Tutto Musica. (IT) **5293**
Tutto Musica e Spettacolo. (IT) **3585**
Tutto Strumenti. (IT) **3585**, 4462
Tuttochimica. (IT) **1190**
Tuttociclismo. (IT) **4521**
Tuttodolce. (IT) **2090**
Tuttogiovani Notizie. (IT) **1268**, 1245
Tuttolibri. (IT) **4138**
Tuttomoto. (IT) **4521**
Tuttorally. (IT) **4521**
Tuttoscuola. (IT) **1668**
Tuttosport. (IT ISSN 0041-4441) **4495**
Tuttotrasporti. (IT) **4749**
Tuttoturismo. (IT) **4795**
Tuttovideo. (IT) **1386**
Tuttoville. (IT ISSN 0041-445X) **2562**, 2555
Tutzinger Blaetter. (GW ISSN 0930-732X) **4251**
Tutzinger Studien. (GW) **3930**
Tuulilasi. (FI ISSN 0041-4468) **4704**
Tuvalu Hi-Spots see Maneapa **3754**
Tuzolto. (CS) **2035**
TV and Film Literature. see Dianshi Dianying Wenxue **3507**
Tvaersnitt. (SW ISSN 0348-7997) **2516**
Tvaettnytt see Rent **1282**
Tvai. (IS ISSN 0041-4549) **308**, 2497
Tvorchestvo. (RU ISSN 0041-4565) **347**
Twainian. (US ISSN 0041-4573) **2970**
Twee N. (NE ISSN 0041-4581) **2544**
Tweed. (AT) **2970**, 3007
Tweede Ronde. (NE ISSN 0166-1868) **2970**
Tweetalige Losbladige Wetboeken. (BE) **2687**
Tweewieler. (NE ISSN 0165-1943) **4521**
Twelfth Farm Credit District. Director Digest. (US) **125**, 696
Twelve Step Rag. (US) **1539**
Twentieth Century see Anales de la Literatura Espanola Contemporanea **2894**
Twentieth - Century American Jewish Writers. (US ISSN 0897-7844) **2970**, 2026
Twentieth Century and Peace. (RU ISSN 0320-7986) **3974**
▼Twentieth Century British History. (UK ISSN 0955-2359) **2392**
Twentieth Century Fund. Bulletin see Twentieth Century Fund. Newsletter **3974**
Twentieth Century Fund. Newsletter. (US) **3974**, 802, 4455
†Twentieth Century Legal Philosophy Series. (US ISSN 0082-7088) **5293**
Twentieth - Century Literary Criticism. (US ISSN 0276-8178) **2971**
Twentieth Century Literature. (US ISSN 0041-462X) **2971**
▼XXIst Century. (US) **2971**, 347
Twenty-four. (US) **1383**
Twenty Four Hours. (AT) **1383**
The Twig. (US) **1327**
†Twigs Magazine. (US ISSN 0891-3706) **5293**
Twin Cities. (US ISSN 0164-6532) **2236**
Twin Cities Advertiser. (AT) **2172**
Twin Cities Club Index. (US) **1302**
Twin Cities Computer User see Computer User (Minneapolis) **1392**

Twin Cities Courier. (US ISSN 0300-6603) **2026**
Twin Cities Gaze. (US) **2457**, 3400, 4113, 4854
Twin Plant News. (US) **923**
Twins. (US ISSN 0890-3077) **1245**, 4854
Twirling. (IT) **4495**
Twisted. (US) **3015**, 2971
Two and a Bud. (II ISSN 0496-6201) **386**, 2083
Two Rivers. (UK ISSN 0041-4670) **2971**
Two - Sixteen Magazine see Advanced Computing Magazine **1458**
Two Thirds. (CN) **158**, 4612
Two Wheels. (AT ISSN 0041-4700) **4521**
Twoje Dziecko. (PL) **4854**, 1245
Tworczosc. (PL ISSN 0041-4727) **2887**
Tydenik Rozhlas. (CS) **1360**
Tydskrif vir die Suid-Afrikaanse Reg/Journal of South African Law. (SA ISSN 0257-7747) **2687**
Tydskrif vir Geesteswetenskappe. (SA ISSN 0041-4751) **2516**
Tydskrif vir Hededaagse Romeins-Hollandse Reg/Journal of Contemporary Roman Dutch Law. (SA) **2687**
Tydskrif vir Letterkunde. (SA ISSN 0041-476X) **2887**
Tydskrif vir Literatuurwetenskap. see Journal of Literary Studies **2928**
Tydskrif vir Rasse - Aangeleenthede/Journal of Racial Affairs. (SA ISSN 0041-4794) **4455**
Tydskrif vir Regswetenskap. see Journal for Juridical Science **2638**
Tydskrif vir Skoonlug/Clean Air Journal.(SA ISSN 0379-4709) **1979**, 3441
Tydskrif vir Taalonderrig. (SA ISSN 0259-9570) **1668**
Tydskrif vir Volkskunde en Volkstaal. (SA ISSN 0049-4933) **2059**
Tydskryf vir Studies in Ekonomie en Ekonometrie. see Journal for Studies in Economics and Econometrics **896**
Tygodnik Demokratyczny. (PL) **3930**
Tygodnik Powszechny. (PL ISSN 0041-4808) **2214**
Tygodnik Solidarnosc/Solidarity Weekly. (PL ISSN 0208-8045) **886**, 935, 2590, 3948
▼Tygodnik Wspolczesny. (PL) **2887**
Tyler Junior College News. (US) **1327**
Tyler Review. (US) **2687**
Tyndale Bulletin. (UK ISSN 0082-7118) **4207**
The Tyndall Report. (US) **1383**, 2576, 3930
Tyo - Terveys - Turvallisuus/Work - Health - Safety. (FI ISSN 0041-4816) **3622**
Type & Press. (US ISSN 1042-105X) **4138**
Type Reporter. (US ISSN 8756-4963) **4049**
Typeline. (US) **1062**
Typesetters of Charleston. (US) **4006**
TypeWorld. (US ISSN 0194-4851) **4006**
Typex Magazine. (FR) **125**
Typografia. (CS) **4006**
Typografische Monatsblaetter. (SZ ISSN 0041-4840) **4006**
Typographer. (US ISSN 0279-0327) **4006**
Typographical Journal. (US ISSN 0041-4832) **2590**
Typography. (US ISSN 0275-6870) **4006**
Typological Studies in Language. (US ISSN 0167-7373) **2848**
Typologie des Sources du Moyen Age Occidental. (BE) **2392**
Le Typonyme. (CN) **2848**
Tyre and Rim Association of Australia Standards Manual. (AT) **4294**, 4704
Tyre Samachar. (II) **4704**
Tyres and Accessories. (UK ISSN 0041-4859) **4294**
▼Tyrganskii Vestnik. (RU) **2215**
†Tyro Magazine. (CN ISSN 0829-7010) **5293**
Tyst. (UK) **4251**

Tzeilum Miktzoei/Professional Photography. (IS) **3797**
Tzivos HaShem Children's Newsletter. (US) **1269**, 4227
Tzufit see Torgos **567**
U A B Visual Arts Gallery. Selections from the Permanent Selection. (University of Alabama at Birmingham) (US) **3534**
U A B Visual Arts Gallery Papers. (University of Alabama at Birmingham) (US) **3534**
U A C T A. (United Against Cruelty to Animals) (US) **232**
U A E Air Force Magazine. see Al-Quwwat al-Jawwiyyah **3469**
U A F I W Bulletin see Bulgarian Federation of Agricultural Workers' Independent Unions. Bulletin **2581**
U A M R Newsletter. (United Association Manufacturers' Representatives) (US) **696**
U A P Newsletter. (Universal Availability of Publications) (UK ISSN 0264-2441) **2788**
U A S Extension Series. (University of Agricultural Sciences, Bangalore) (II ISSN 0067-3471) **125**
U A S Miscellaneous Series. (University of Agricultural Sciences, Bangalore) (II ISSN 0067-348X) **125**
U - A S T A - Info. (GW) **1327**
U - A S T A - Info fuer Erstsemester. (GW) **1327**
U A W Ammo. (United Automobile, Aerospace, and Agricultural Implement Workers of America) (US) **2590**
U A W Washington Report. (US ISSN 0041-4980) **2590**
U & B Graphic Guide see United & Babson Graphic Guide **967**
U & C see Unificazione e Certificazione **898**
U & I c. (Upper and Lower Case) (US ISSN 0362-6245) **4006**
U B A H Revue. (Union des Associations de Fabricants de Parties Detachees Horlogeres) (SZ) **2566**
U B C I M Occasional Paper. (GW ISSN 1012-327X) **2788**, 414
U B C Library News. (University of British Columbia) (CN ISSN 0382-0661) **2788**
U B C Planning Papers. (University of British Columbia) (CN) **2497**
†U B S Business Facts and Figures. (Union Bank of Switzerland) (SZ ISSN 0007-6740) **5293**
U B S Publications on Business, Banking and Monetary Problems. (Union Bank of Switzerland) (SZ) **802**
U C A N S S. Bulletin Juridique. (Union des Caisses Nationales de Securite Sociale) (FR) **2687**, 2544
U C A R Newsletter. (University Corporation for Atmospheric Research) (US) **3441**
U C A T News and Views. (University of California, Davis) (US) **4612**, 1970
U C A T T Journal see Viewpoint (London) **640**
U C B Investor's Handbook. (Uganda Commercial Bank) (UG) **967**, 802
U C C C Technical Update. (University of Cincinnati Computing Center) (US) **1691**
†U C Clip Sheet. (University of California) (US ISSN 0745-3213) **5293**
U C Davis Law Review. (US ISSN 0197-4564) **2687**
U C Davis Magazine. (US) **1327**, 1718
U C E A Review. (University Council for Educational Administration) (US ISSN 0734-5798) **1732**
U C Electronics News see E E C S - E R L News **1886**
U C Guide (Year). (Unemployment Compensation) (US) **2712**, 995
U C L A. Occasional Papers in Linguistics. (US) **2848**
U C L A Business Forecast for California. (University of California, Los Angeles) (US) **696**

U C L A Business Forecast for the Nation and California see U C L A Business Forecast for California **696**
U C L A Business Forecast for the Nation and California see U C L A National Business Forecast **696**
U C L A Forum in Medical Sciences. (University of California, Los Angeles) (US ISSN 0082-7134) **3158**
U C L A Historical Journal. (University of California, Los Angeles) (US ISSN 0276-864X) **2324**
U C L A Journal of Dance Ethnology. (US ISSN 0884-3198) **1532**
U C L A Journal of Environmental Law and Policy. (University of California, Los Angeles) (US ISSN 0733-401X) **2687**
U C L A Latin American Center. Special Studies Series. (University of California, Los Angeles) (US) **2424**
U C L A Law Review. (University of California, Los Angeles) (US ISSN 0041-5650) **2687**
U C L A Magazine. (University of California, Los Angeles) (US) **2236**, 1327
U C L A National Business Forecast. (University of California, Los Angeles) (US) **696**
U C L A Symposium on Molecular Biology Proceedings. (University of California, Los Angeles) (US) **527**
U C L A Symposium Series on Molecular and Cellular Biology. (University of California, Los Angeles) (US ISSN 0735-9543) **458**
U C M P Quarterly. (US ISSN 0276-7570) **3181**
U C O Communicator see Co-Op Communicator **829**
U C O Cornerstone see Co-Op Cornerstone **829**
U.C. Review. (CN ISSN 0226-3440) **2971**, 3007
U C S F Magazine. (University of California, San Francisco) (US) **3159**
U C S J Quarterly Report. (Union of Councils for Soviet Jews) (US) **2026**
U - Choose: A Guide to Canadian Universities. (CN ISSN 0706-4713) **1697**
U - Choose: A Guide to Homes for Seniors in Canada (Eastern - Atlantic Province Edition). (CN ISSN 0835-6386) **4158**
U - Choose: A Guide to Homes for Seniors in Canada (Ontario Edition). (CN ISSN 0835-6378) **4159**
U - Choose: A Guide to Homes for Seniors in Canada (Western Edition). (CN ISSN 0835-6394) **4159**
U D I Datagram. (Utility Data Institute, Inc.) (US) **1802**
U D I Utility Datapak. (Utility Data Institute, Inc.) (US) **1802**
▼U D I Who's Who at Electric Power Plants. (Utility Data Institute, Inc.) (US) **1802**
U D M see Upholstery Design & Manufacturing **2562**
U D Review see Urban Design and Preservation Quarterly **2788**
U D T Newsletter/Bulletin de l'U D T. (CN ISSN 1010-9501) **2788**
U - das Technische Umweltmagazin see Umweltmagazin **1970**
U E A Action. (Utah Education Association) (US ISSN 0042-1413) **1668**
U E A Papers in Linguistics. (University of East Anglia) (UK) **2848**
U E Business Review. (University of the East) (PH ISSN 0042-0158) **1030**
U E C A Publication see E C A Publication **1864**
▼U E F A Flash. (Union of European Football Associations) (SZ) **4514**
U E - Hi-Fi Vision see Hi-Fi Vision **4460**
U E News see U E News Magazine **2590**
U E News. (United Electrical, Radio & Machine Workers of America) (US ISSN 0041-5065) **2590**
U E News Magazine. (United Electrical Radio and Machine Workers of Canada) (CN) **2590**, 1910

U E R - Revue Technique see E B U Technical Review 1335
U F A C (Year). (Upholstered Furniture Action Council) (US) 2035, 2562
U F A C Volunteer. (Upholstered Furniture Action Council) (US) 2035, 2562
U F A - Revue. (SZ) 125
U F A W Annual Report and Accounts. (Universities Federation for Animal Welfare) (UK ISSN 0263-4600) 232
U F A W News-Sheet. (Universities Federation for Animal Welfare) (UK ISSN 0566-8700) 232
U.F.C.V. (Union Francaise des Centres de Vacances) (FR) 995
U F C W Action. (United Food and Commercial Workers International Union) (US ISSN 0195-0363) 2590
†U F F. (Utusan Filem dan Feshen) (MY) 5293
U F I T A. (SZ ISSN 0003-9454) 2688
U F M G. Escola de Biblioteconomia. Revista. (Universidade Federal de Minas Gerais) (BL ISSN 0100-0829) 2788
†U F O Annual. (Unidentified Flying Objects) (US ISSN 0162-8046) 5293
U F O Encounter. (AT) 63
†U F O Forskning. (DK ISSN 0109-2596) 5293
U F O I C Newsletter. (Unidentified Flying Objects Investigation Centre) (AT) 64
U F O Magazine. (US) 64
†U F O - Nachrichten. (GW ISSN 0041-5081) 5293
U F O News see Aerospace U F O News 44
U F O Newsclipping Service. (US) 64
U F O - Nyt. (DK ISSN 0049-4976) 64
U F O Ohio Newsletter. (US) 64
U F O Times. (UK) 64
U F O Vision. (DK ISSN 0902-2341) 64
U F Ology. (US) 64
U: For University and College Students see World Christian 4210
U G R A Mitteilungen. (SZ) 4006
†U H Stamp Digest. (Urch, Harris & Co. Ltd.) (UK ISSN 0142-7954) 5293
U I A Information see U I A Newsletter 308
†U I A - International Architect. (Union Internationale des Architectes) (UK) 5293
U I A Journal of Architectural Theory and Criticism. (Union Internationale des Architectes) (US) 308
U.I.A.M.S. Bulletin Trimestriel. (International Union for Moral and Social Action) (GW ISSN 0579-5621) 4422
U.I.A.M.S. Informations. (International Union for Moral and Social Action) (GW ISSN 0041-5103) 3930, 3784, 4455
U I A Newsletter. (Union Internationale des Architectes) (FR) 308
U I C C Calendar of International Meetings on Cancer see U I C C International Calendar of Meetings on Cancer 3394
U I C C International Calendar of Meetings on Cancer. (International Union Against Cancer) (SZ) 3394, 3202
U I C C International Directory of Cancer Institutes and Organizations. (International Union Against Cancer) (SZ) 3202
†U I C C Magazine. (SZ) 5293
†U I C C Technical Report Series. (International Union Against Cancer) (SZ ISSN 0074-9222) 5293
U I E Case Studies. (Unesco Institute for Education) (UN) 1668
U I E Monographs. (Unesco Institute for Education) (UN) 1668
U I E S P Bulletin de Liaison. see I U S S P Newsletter 3983
U I E S P Documents de l'Union. see I U S S P Papers 3983

U I E Studies on Functional Illiteracy in Industrialized Countries. (Unesco Institute for Education) (UN) 1687
U I E Studies on Post-Literacy and Continuing Education. (Unesco Institute for Education) (UN) 1687
U I S Bulletin. (Union Internationale de Speleologie) (AU) 1583
U I T B B Bulletin. (Trade Unions International of Workers of the Building, Wood and Building Materials Industries) (FI) 2590, 635
U I T B B Information see U I T B B Bulletin 2590
U I T Journal see Telecommunication Journal 1343
U I T Journal. (Union International de Tir) (GW) 4495
U I T - Magazine. (BE) 4795, 4704
U I T P Biblio-Express. (International Union of Public Transport) (BE) 4668, 24
U I T P Biblio-Index see U I T P Biblio-Express 4668
U I T P Revue see Public Transport International 4655
U J Q. (Uncle Jam Quarterly) (US) 2887, 4795
U K see Universiteitskrant Groningen 1328
U K Alcohol Alert. (UK) 1539, 4455
U K & U S A. (US ISSN 0893-2107) 823
U K Book Report see The Euromonitor Book Report (Year) 4127
U K Business Finance Directory (Year). (UK) 1156, 802
U K C I S Newsletter see Royal Society of Chemistry. Database Newsletter 5271
U K Centre for Economic and Environmental Development Bulletin. (UK ISSN 0268-7402) 1970
U K Christian Handbook (Year). (Missions Advanced Research & Communications Center) (UK) 4213
U K Current Awareness Bulletin see Selected Current Awareness Bulletin 1540
U K H S Bulletin see Hovercraft Bulletin 54
U K Holiday Guide. (UK) 4795
U K I R T Newsletter see J C M T - U K I R T Newsletter 366
U K I R T Report. (United Kingdom Infrared Telescope) (UK ISSN 0260-9983) 370
U K Industrial Trade Names. (UK) 1156
U K Information Industry - Financial Survey (Year). (UK) 1156, 840
†U K Initial Teaching Alphabet Federation Newsletter. (UK) 5293
U K Iron and Steel Industry. Annual Statistics. (UK ISSN 0952-5505) 3428
U K Magazine. (US ISSN 8750-1082) 2196
▼U K O L N Newsletter. (U K Office for Library Networking) (UK ISSN 0963-7354) 2788
U K Office for Library Networking Newsletter see U K O L N Newsletter 2788
U K Pesticide Guide. (UK ISSN 0952-7788) 195, 2140
U K Plant Hire Guide see Contract Journal (1979) 614
†U K Plastics News. (UK) 5293
U K Press Gazette. (UK ISSN 0041-5170) 2576
▼U K Special Education Directory. (UK) 1742
U K Special Learning Needs Directory see U K Special Education Directory 1742
U K Trade Names see U K Industrial Trade Names 1156
U K Upstream Petroleum Database. (UK) 3702
U K Z - Unsere Kleine Zeitung see U K Z - Zeitschrift Von und Fuer Lesben 2457
U K Z - Zeitschrift Von und Fuer Lesben.(GW) 2457, 2887
U K's 10000 Largest Companies. (UK) 802
U L C News. (Universal Life Church) (US) 4289

U L L I C O Bulletin. (Union Labor Life Insurance Co.) (US ISSN 0041-5189) 2544, 2590
U L M Mag see Ailes Magazine 45
U L Science and Technology Magazine. (University of Liberia) (LB) 4349
U L Science Magazine see U L Science and Technology Magazine 4349
U M A P Journal. (Undergraduate Mathematics Applications Project) (US ISSN 0197-3622) 3059
U M A Students Law Journal. (University of Malawi) (MW) 2688, 2729
†U M E Connexion. (United Ministries in Education) (US) 5293
U M I's Southeastern Basketball Handbook. (US) 4514
U M K C Law Review. (University of Missouri, Kansas City) (US ISSN 0047-7575) 2688
U M Profiles see Montanan 1318
U M T R I Research Review. (University of Michigan, Transportation Research Institute) (US ISSN 0739-7100) 4704, 4741, 4749
U N A F. Bulletin de Liaison see Realites Familiales 4417
†U N A I C C Boletin. (Union Nacional de Arquitectos e Ingenieros de la Construccion de Cuba) (CU) 5293
U N A M Directorio de Bibliotecas. (Universidad Nacional Autonoma de Mexico) (MX) 2788
U N A U L A. (Universidad Autonoma Latinoamericana) (CK) 2887
U N C H S Habitat News. (United Nations Centre for Human Settlements) (UN ISSN 0255-271X) 2497, 3974
U N C Notizie. (Unione Nazionale Consumatori) (IT) 1508
U N C R D Bulletin. (United Nations Centre for Regional Development) (UN) 936
U N C R D Newsletter. (United Nations Centre for Regional Development) (UN ISSN 0379-0347) 936
U N C T A D Bulletin. (United Nations Conference on Trade and Development) (UN ISSN 0259-3181) 923, 936
U N C T A D Commodity Yearbook. (United Nations Conference on Trade and Development) (UN ISSN 1012-0793) 741, 4590
U N C T A D Guide to Publications see Guide to U N C T A D Publications 719
U N C T A D Monthly Bulletin see U N C T A D Bulletin 923
U N C T A D Review. (United Nations Conference on Trade and Development) (UN) 923, 936
U N Chronicle. (UN ISSN 0251-7329) 3974, 3394
U N D O C: Current Index. (United Nations Documents) (UN ISSN 0250-5584) 3938, 24
U N D P Business Bulletin see Development Business 928
U N E Bulletin see U N E Convocation Bulletin & Alumni News 1718
U N E Convocation Bulletin & Alumni News. (University of New England) (AT ISSN 0156-1006) 1718
U N E P Feature see United Nations Environment Programme. Feature 1970
U N E P Information. (United Nations Environment Programme) (UN) 1970
U N E P News see Our Planet 1965
U N E P Regional Seas Reports and Studies. (United Nations Environment Programme) (UN) 1611
U N H C R see Refugees 3970
†U N I C E F Information Bulletin. (United Nations Childrens Fund) (UN ISSN 0049-4984) 5293
†U N I C E F News. (United Nations Childrens Fund) (UN ISSN 0041-5340) 5293
U N I C E F Policy Review Series. (United Nations Childrens Fund) (UN ISSN 1013-3194) 4422, 1245

U N I C E M Annuaire Officiel. (Union Nationale des Industries de Carrieres et Materiaux de Construction) (FR) 635
U N I D I R Newsletter/Lettre de L'U N I D I R. (United Nations Institute for Disarmament Research) (UN ISSN 1012-4934) 3974, 2729, 3473
U N I D O Newsletter. (United Nations Industrial Development Organization) (UN ISSN 0049-5387) 936
U N I S A English Studies. (University of South Africa) (SA ISSN 0041-5359) 2971
U N I S A Psychologia. (SA ISSN 0256-8896) 4049
U N I S I S T Boletin de Informacion. (UN ISSN 0304-0062) 2788
U N I S I S T Newsletter. (Unesco Programme of International Cooperation in Scientific and Technological Information) (UN ISSN 0300-2519) 2788
U N I S I S T Newsletter - General Information Programme. (UN ISSN 0379-2218) 2788
U N Monthly Chronicle see U N Chronicle 3974
U N R I S D News. (UN ISSN 1014-8361) 4390
U N Reform Campaigner. (US) 3974
U N Studies. (UN) 3974
U N U C I. (Unione Nazionale Ufficiali in Congedo d'Italia) (IT ISSN 0041-5375) 3473
U N V News. (United Nations Volunteers Programme) (UN) 936
U N V Newsletter see U N V News 936
U of L. (University of Louisville) (US) 1327
U P A A Newsletter. (University Photographers' Association of America) (US) 3797
U P A D I Bulletin see Pan American Federation of Engineering Societies. Bulletin 1833
U P C Plumbing Code see Uniform Plumbing Code 2304
U P E C. (Union de Periodistas de Cuba) (CU) 4138
U P E N. (University of Port Elizabeth Newspaper) (SA ISSN 0041-5405) 1327
U P F Newsletter. (United Parkinson Foundation) (US) 3355
U P Informations. (Universite de Paix) (BE) 3974
U P Irrigation Research Institute. General Annual Report. (Il ISSN 0080-4045) 4829
U P Irrigation Research Institute. Technical Memorandum. (Il ISSN 0080-4053) 4829
U P Newsletter. (PK) 1327
U P Research Monitor. (University of the Philippines) (PH) 4358, 2520, 2520, 2520, 4396
U P S S A see University of Pennsylvania Studies on South Asia 5298
U P Thesis and Dissertation Abstracts. (University of the Philippines) (PH) 1680, 2520, 4358
U Q A M. Hebdo see U Q A M. Journal 1327
U Q A M. Journal. (University of Quebec at Montreal) (CN) 1327
U R A M Newsletter. (CN ISSN 0315-3002) 3784
U R O B A Messenger. (United Russian Orthodox Brotherhood of America) (US) 4289
U R P E Newsletter. (Union for Radical Political Economics) (US) 696, 3930
U R S I Information Bulletin. (International Union of Radio Science) (BE ISSN 0041-543X) 1360
U R S S Embajada. Boletin de Informacion. (MX) 3974
U S A. (US ISSN 0890-8648) 2497
U S A Amateur Boxing Federation. Media Guide. (US) 4495
U S A Amateur Boxing Federation. Official Rules. (US) 4495

6748   U S A

The U S A and Canada (Year). (UK ISSN 0956-0904) **3930, 886**
U S A B A Agenda. (United States Association for Blind Athletes) (US) **4495, 2296**
U S A C News. (United States Auto Club) (US) **4495**
U S A: Economics, Politics, Ideology see U S S R Report: U S A: Economics, Politics, Ideology **887**
U S A F Fighter Weapons Review. (U.S. Air Force) (US) **3473**
U S A for Business Travelers. (US) **4795, 696**
U S A Gymnastics. (US ISSN 0748-6006) **4495**
U S A Hockey. (US) **4495**
U S A Hockey. Rule Book. (US) **4495**
U S A N and the U S P Dictionary of Drug Names. (United States Adopted Names) (US ISSN 0090-6816) **3744**
U S A Oil Industry Directory. (US ISSN 0082-8599) **3702**
U S A Oilfield Service, Supply, and Manufacturers Directory. (US) **3702**
U S A Outdoors. (US) **4559**
U S A Record. (Uniformed Sanitationmen's Association) (US ISSN 0041-5464) **2590**
U S A Rice Council. Newsletter see Rice Council Review **191**
U S A Singles News see Christian Singles News **4362**
U S A Textile Industry Overview see Texscope: U S A Textile Industry Overview **4624**
U S A Today. (US ISSN 0161-7389) **3930**
▼U S A Today Baseball Weekly. (US) **4514**
U S A Today Index. (US ISSN 0893-2409) **2579, 24**
▼U S A Trade Opportunities. (DK) **923, 936**
U S A Volleyball. (US) **4514**
U S A Weekend. (US) **2236**
U S A 23 Milliones. (US ISSN 0734-5054) **2026**
U S Air Magazine. (US) **4804**
▼U S and Foreign Diplomatic Contacts.(US ISSN 1052-5238) **1156, 3939, 3974**
U S and the Developing World: Agenda for Action see U S and World Development: Agenda **936**
U S and World Development: Agenda. (US) **936**
U S Art. (US ISSN 0899-1782) **347**
U S Association Executive. (US ISSN 0740-2678) **1030**
U S Association for the Club of Rome Newsletter. (US) **3974, 1498**
U S Aviation Reports. (US ISSN 0886-4217) **4677**
U S B E News. (Universal Serials and Book Exchange) (US ISSN 0364-5215) **2788, 4138**
U S B L Nytt. (Ungdomen Selvbyggerlag) (NO) **635, 1762**
U S B W A Tip-Off. (United States Basketball Writers Association) (US ISSN 0041-5472) **4514, 2576**
U S Baha'i Report. (US) **4289**
The U S Beer Market: Impact Databank Review and Forecast. (US) **386**
U S - Belgium Trade Directory see Belgian - American Chamber of Commerce in the United States. Directory **1072**
U S Black Register. (US ISSN 1058-2428) **1839, 2026**
U S Builder Report. (US) **635**
U S C Annual Distinguished Lecture Series Monographs in Special Education and Rehabilitation. (University of Southern California) (US ISSN 0070-6736) **1742**
U S C Engineer. (University of Southern California) (US) **1839**
U S C I D Newsletter. (United States Committee on Irrigation and Drainage) (US) **4829**
U S C O L D Newsletter. (U S Committee on Large Dams) (US ISSN 0041-5480) **4829**
U S C S Log. (Universal Ship Cancellation Society Log) (US ISSN 0279-6139) **3759**

U S C Trojan Family. (University of Southern California) (US ISSN 8750-7927) **1327**
U S Callbook see North American Callbook **1357**
†U S - Canadian Range Management. (US) **5293**
U S Cancellation Club News. (US) **3759**
U S Catholic. (US ISSN 0041-7548) **4277**
U S Census Report see American Marketplace **3979**
U S China Business Review see China Business Review **903**
U S - China Review. (US) **3974**
U S Coal Plant Statistics. (US) **1910, 1796**
U S Committee on Large Dams Annual U S C O L D Lecture see Annual U S C O L D Lecture **1861**
U S Committee on Large Dams Newsletter see U S C O L D Newsletter **4829**
U S Cost Forecasting Service Long-Term Review see D R I - McGraw-Hill Cost and Price Review: U S Long-Range Focus **859**
U S Cost Forecasting Service Near-Term Review see D R I - McGraw-Hill Cost and Price Review: U S Short-Range Focus **859**
U S Croquet Gazette. (US) **4514**
U S Crude Oil, Natural Gas, and Natural Gas Liquids. (US) **3703**
U S Custom House Guide. (US ISSN 0070-2250) **923**
U S D A W Today. (Union of Shop Distributive and Allied Workers) (UK) **2591**
†U S Directory of Marine Scientists. (US) **5293**
The U S Distilled Spirits Market: Impact Databank Review and Forecast. (US) **386**
U S E B Zpravy. (Ustav Systematicke a Ekologicke Biologie) (CS ISSN 0862-9609) **592**
U S E T News. (United States Equestrian Team) (US) **4539**
†U S Economy Lodging Industry. (US) **5293**
U S Electronic Industry Directory. (US ISSN 1047-5583) **1156, 1910**
U S Environmental Laws. (US) **1970, 2688**
U S Excise Tax Guide. (US ISSN 0083-0534) **1111**
U S F A Rule Book: U S & International Rules. (United States Fencing Association, Inc.) (US) **4495**
U S F B Informations. (Union Suisse des Fabricants de Boites de Montres) (SZ) **2566**
†U S F L Guide and Register. (United States Football League) (US ISSN 0742-4299) **5293**
U S F View see University of San Francisco. Alumni Association. Alumnus **1328**
U S Farm News. (US ISSN 0041-7637) **125**
U S Fire Sprinkler Reporter. (US ISSN 0889-6038) **2035**
▼U S Foreign Student Magazine. (US) **1723**
U S G A Green Section Record. (United States Golf Association) (US ISSN 0041-5502) **4514**
U S Glass, Metal & Glazing. (US ISSN 0041-7661) **635, 1166**
U S Healthcare see Healthcare Informatics **3225**
U S I A Economic Analysis of North American Ski Areas see Economic Analysis of North American Ski Areas **4545**
U S I Journal. (United Service Institution of India) (II ISSN 0041-770X) **3473**
U S I M see Upravlyayushchie Sistemy i Mashiny **1440**
U S I News (United States Industrial Chemicals Co.) see Quantum (Cincinnati) **5265**
U S I T T Newsletter see Sightlines (New York) **4638**
U S I U News see Envoy (San Diego) **1311**

▼U S Immigration. (US ISSN 1055-8276) **2688**
U S Industrial Directory. (US) **1156**
▼U S Industrial Export Directory. (US) **923, 1156**
U S Industry Review see D R I - McGraw-Hill U S Markets Review: Industry Focus **1074**
U S Information Moscow see Information Moscow, Western Edition **5213**
U S International Trade Laws. (US) **2729, 923**
U S Investing for Internationals. (US) **967**
U S J. (Uniformed Services Journal) (US) **3473**
†U S - Japan Economic Agenda. (US) **5293**
†U S - Japan Outlook. (US ISSN 0091-407X) **5293**
U S - Japan Relations see U S - Third World Policy Perspectives **2324**
†U S Journal of Drug and Alcohol Dependence. (US ISSN 0148-8619) **5293**
U S Kids. (US ISSN 0895-9471) **1269**
†U S - Korea Society. Economic Newsletter. (US) **5293**
U S L History Series. (University of Southwestern Louisiana) (US) **2324**
U S Labor and Employment Law. (US) **995, 2688**
†U S Lodging Industry. (US ISSN 0361-2198) **5293**
U S M A Newsletter see Metric Today **3447**
U S M A R C Monitor. (University of Southern Mindanao Agricultural Research Center) (PH) **125**
U S M Alumni News. (University of Southern Mississippi) (US) **1327**
U S Machine Tool Directory. (US) **1940**
†U S Market for California Varietal Wine: Impact Databank Review and Forecast. (US ISSN 1044-8780) **5293**
U S Markets Review. (US) **886**
U S Markets Review: Metropolitan Focus. (US) **886**
U S Master Tax Guide. (US ISSN 0083-1700) **1111**
U S Mayor. (US ISSN 1049-2119) **4095**
U S Medical Directory. (US ISSN 0091-8393) **3159**
U S Medicine. (US ISSN 0191-6246) **3159**
†U S - Mexico Report. (US ISSN 0885-176X) **5293**
U S National Student Association. Momentum see U S Student Association. Legislative Update **1718**
U S Naval Academy Alumni Association. Register of Alumni. (US) **1327**
U S Naval Institute. Proceedings. (US ISSN 0041-798X) **3473**
U S News and Notes see News & Notes (Chicago) **3382**
U S News & World Report. (US ISSN 0041-5537) **2236, 3930**
†The U S Non-Alcoholic Beverage Market: Impact Databank Review and Forecast. (US ISSN 1044-8772) **5293**
U S Nuclear Plant Statistics. (US) **1810, 1796, 1910**
U S O Annual Report. (United Service Organizations, Inc.) (US ISSN 0082-8556) **4422**
U S Oil Week. (US ISSN 0502-9767) **3703, 2688**
U S Open Magazine. (US) **4514**
U S Outdoor Drama. (US) **4642**
U S Parish. (US) **4277**
U S Pharmacist. (US ISSN 0148-4818) **3744**
U S Piper. (US ISSN 0041-8048) **3422**
U S Progressive Periodicals Directory see Progressive Periodicals Directory **4142**
U S Progressive Periodicals Update see Progressive Periodicals Directory Update **409**

U S - R & D. (US ISSN 0436-2225) **4349**
U S Rail News. (US ISSN 0275-3758) **4716**
U S Real Estate Register. (US) **4159, 39, 696, 4138**
†U S Real Estate Week. (US) **5294**
▼U S Roller Skating. (US ISSN 1044-0801) **4495**
U S S A News. (United States Sports Academy) (US) **4495, 2236**
U S S Constitution Museum. News and Notes see Constitution Chronicle **3454**
U S S E A Update. (U S Space Education Association) (US ISSN 0741-4587) **64**
U S S Henrico A P A -45 Reunion Association. Newsletter. (US) **3473**
U S S R Academy of Sciences. Transactions (Doklady). Earth Science Sections. (English translation of: Doklady Akademii Nauk S.S.S.R.) (US ISSN 0891-5571) **1549**
U.S.S.R Academy of Sciences. Far Eastern Branch. Bulletin. see Akademiya Nauk S.S.S.R. Dal'nevostochnoe Otdelenie. Vestnik **4397**
▼U S S R & Central and Eastern European Legal Materials. (US) **2729, 923**
U S S R and Eastern Europe Scientific Abstracts: Chemistry see U S S R Report: Chemistry **1203**
U S S R and Eastern Europe Scientific Abstracts: Cybernetics, Computers, and Automation Technology see U S S R Report: Cybernetics, Computers, and Automation Technology **1405**
U S S R and Eastern Europe Scientific Abstracts: Electronics and Electrical Engineering see U S S R Report: Electronics and Electrical Engineering **1910**
U S S R and Eastern Europe Scientific Abstracts: Engineering and Equipment see U S S R Report: Engineering and Equipment **1847**
U S S R and Eastern Europe Scientific Abstracts: Physics and Mathematics see U S S R Report: Physics and Mathematics **3063**
U S S R Calendar of Events. (US) **3930**
U S S R Computational Mathematics and Mathematical Physics. (English translation of: Zhurnal Vychislitel'noi Matematiki i Matematicheskoi Fiziki) (US ISSN 0041-5553) **3059, 3834**
U S S R Documents. (US) **3931**
U S S R Facts & Figures Annual. (US ISSN 0148-7760) **3939, 4591**
U S S R Overview. (IS) **3931**
U S S R Report: Chemistry. (US) **1203, 24**
U S S R Report: Cybernetics, Computers, and Automation Technology. (US) **1405, 24**
U S S R Report: Earth Sciences. (US) **1549**
U S S R Report: Economic Affairs see U S S R Report: National Economy **696**
U S S R Report: Electronics and Electrical Engineering. (US) **1910, 1779**
U S S R Report: Engineering and Equipment. (US) **1847, 24**
U S S R Report: Geophysics, Astronomy, and Space see U S S R Report: Space **1552**
U S S R Report: Kommunist. (US) **3931**
U S S R Report: Life Sciences. (US) **3159, 4049, 4455**
U S S R Report: Life Sciences, Biomedical and Behavioral Sciences see U S S R Report: Life Sciences **3159**
U S S R Report: Machine Tools and Metal - Working Equipment. (US) **3024, 3422**
U S S R Report: Materials Science. (US) **1847, 24, 3428**
U S S R Report: Materials Science and Metallurgy see U S S R Report: Materials Science **1847**

U S S R Report: Military Affairs. (US) **3473**
U S S R Report: National Economy. (US) **696, 886**
U S S R Report: Physics and Mathematics. (US) **3063, 24**
U S S R Report: Political and Sociological Affairs. (US) **3931, 4455**
U S S R Report: Problems of the Far East. (US) **3974, 886, 3931**
U S S R Report: Science and Technology Policy. (US) **4349, 4612**
U S S R Report: Space. (US) **1552, 24, 371**
U S S R Report: Space Biology and Aerospace Medicine. (English translation of: Kosmicheskaya Biologiya i Aviakosmicheskaya Meditsina) (US) **3159, 64**
U S S R Report: Translations from "Kommunist" see U S S R Report: Kommunist **3931**
U S S R Report: U S A: Economics, Politics, Ideology. (English translation of Russian: S Sh A: Ekonomika, Politika, Ideologiya) (US) **887, 3931**
U S S R Report: World Economy and International Relations. (US) **696, 3974**
U S S R Serial Reports: Aviation and Cosmonautics. (US) **3974, 64**
U S S R Serial Reports: Economic Affairs. (US) **3974, 696**
U S S R Serial Reports: Foreign Military Review. (US) **3974, 3473**
U S S R Serial Reports: International Affairs. (US) **3974**
U S S R Serial Reports: Military History Journal. (US) **3974, 3473**
U S S R Serial Reports: Sociological Studies. (US) **3974, 4455**
†U S S R Technology Update. (US ISSN 0892-497X) **5294**
U S S R Today. (US) **3931**
U S S Reports. (United Seamen's Service) (US) **4741**
U S S St. Louis Hubble Bubble. (US) **3473, 4741**
U S Sailing Directory. (US) **4530**
U S Savings and Loan Directory see U S Savings Institutions Directory **1156**
U S Savings Institutions Directory. (US) **1156, 802**
U S Scanner News. (US) **1360**
U S Sci-Tech. (US) **483, 4612**
▼U S Senior Open Magazine. (US) **4514**
U S Ski News see Recreational Skier **4554**
U S Ski Writers Association Newsletter. (US) **2576, 4559**
U S Space Education Association Update see U S S E A Update **64**
U S Sports. (US) **4495, 2026**
U S Statistics. (US ISSN 0888-7926) **4591**
U S Steam Electric Plants: Five Year Production Costs. (US) **1910, 1796**
U S Student Association. Legislative Update. (US) **1718**
U S Student Association. News Update see U S Student Association. Legislative Update **1718**
U S Supreme Court Bulletin. (US) **2733**
U S Survey of Business Expectations. (US) **1086**
U S Swimming News. (US ISSN 0883-0347) **4496, 3809**
U S Symposium on Rock Mechanics. Proceedings. (US ISSN 0586-3031) **3496**
U S T A College Tennis Guide. (United States Tennis Association) (US) **4496**
U S T A Sires and Dams. (United States Trotting Association) (US) **4539**
U S T A Year Book. (United States Trotting Association) (US ISSN 0083-3517) **4539**
†U S Table Tennis News. (US) **5294**
U S Tax Week. (US ISSN 0041-8129) **1111**
U S Taxation of International Operations. (US) **1111**

U S Team Spotlight. (US) **2289, 4496**
†U S Telecom Digest. (US) **5294**
U S Telecommunications. (US) **1367, 1055**
U S - Third World Policy Perspectives. (US) **2324, 3974**
U S U Staff News. (Utah State University) (US ISSN 0041-5561) **1327**
U S Water News. (US ISSN 0749-1980) **4829**
The U S Wine Market: Impact Databank Review and Forecast. (US) **386**
U S Woman Engineer. (US ISSN 0272-7838) **1839, 4854**
U S Y R U Directory see U S Sailing Directory **4530**
U S Y S A National Directory. (United States Youth Soccer Association, Inc.) (US) **4514, 1269**
U S Y S A Network. (United States Youth Soccer Association, Inc.) (US) **4514, 1245, 1269**
U S 1. (US) **2236**
U S 1 Worksheets. (US ISSN 0362-7012) **2971, 3007**
U T see Eksport **906**
U T. (CI ISSN 0041-557X) **4795, 2481**
†U T A C Bulletin de Documentation. (FR) **5294**
U T A French Airlines: Distance. (FR) **4804**
U T D Today. (United Teachers of Dade) (US) **1668**
U T I A S Report see University of Toronto. Institute for Aerospace Studies. Report **64**
U T I A S Technical Note see University of Toronto. Institute for Aerospace Studies. Technical Note **64**
U T O News. (FR) **4095**
U.T.S.A. Annual. (Union of Teachers' Associations of South Africa) (SA) **1732**
U: The National College Newspaper. (US) **1718**
U U M N Notes. (Unitarian Universalist Musician's Network) (US) **3585, 4251**
U U W F Federation Newsletter. (Unitarian Universalist Women's Federation) (US) **4854, 4251**
U U W F Journal. (US) **4854, 4251**
†U.V. Spectrometry Group. Bulletin. (Ultra Violet) (UK ISSN 0144-2317) **5294**
U Vejviser. (DK ISSN 0106-3014) **936**
U W I P A Newsletter. (University of the West Indies Publishers' Association) (JM) **4138**
U W I Students' Law Review. (University of the West Indies) (BB) **2688**
U W L A Law Review. (US ISSN 0899-7446) **2688**
U W M Post. (University of Wisconsin-Milwaukee) (US) **1327**
Uburezi, Ubuhanga n'Umuco. see Education, Science et Culture **1629**
Ubyssey. (CN) **1327**
Uccelli d'Italia. (IT ISSN 0393-1218) **567**
Ucitelj/Teacher. (YU ISSN 0352-2253) **1269, 1691, 1762**
Ucitel'ske Noviny. (CS) **1668**
Ucitelske Vzdelani. (CS) **2392, 1762**
†Uddannelse Institutioner over Grundskoleniveau. (DK ISSN 0107-1629) **5294**
Uddannelse og Erhverv Katalog. (DK ISSN 0900-3479) **3520**
Uddannelsesnoeglen. (DK ISSN 0107-3435) **1687**
Uddannelshistorie. Selskabet for Dansk Skolehistorie. Aarbog. (DK) **1668**
Uddelerbladet. (DK ISSN 0109-1328) **832**
Ude og Hjemme. (DK ISSN 0041-5669) **2185**
Udenlandsk Litteratur i Danske Folkebiblioteker. (DK) **2983**
Udenlandsk Litteratur i Danske Folkebiblioteker. Skoenlitteratur see Udenlandsk Litteratur i Danske Folkebiblioteker **2983**
Udenrigs. (DK ISSN 0903-7845) **3975**

Udenrigs Handelskalenderen for Danmark/Trade Directory for Denmark/Daenischer Handelskalender/Annuaire de l'Exportation du Danemark/Anuario de la Exportacion de Dinamarca. (DK ISSN 0532-1360) **1156**
Udenrigshandelen Fordelt paa Varer og Lande. (DK ISSN 0109-5420) **741**
Udenrigsministeriets Tidsskrift see Eksport **906**
Udenrigspolitiske Skrifter. (DK ISSN 0041-5693) **3975**
Udkast. (DK ISSN 0105-2691) **4049**
Udruzenje Pravoslavnog Svestenstva S.F.R. Jugoslavije. Glavni Savez. Vesnik. (YU ISSN 0042-4552) **4217**
Udumbara. (US) **4216**
Udvikling Danmark og u-Landene. (DK) **3975**
Udviklingstendenserne paa de Langvarigt Uddannedes Arbejdsmarked. (DK ISSN 0108-7886) **1668**
Udyog Banihya Patrika. (NP) **823**
Udyogen Ka Varshika Sarvekshana. see India. Central Statistical Organization. Annual Survey of Industries **721**
Ue Z H - Report. (GW) **1910**
Ueben & Musizieren. (GW) **3585**
Ueber Berg und Tal. (GW) **4075, 2516, 4722**
Ueber Buecher. (GW) **4138**
Ueberblick. (GW ISSN 0343-0553) **3975, 4207**
†Uebergaenge. (GW) **5294**
Uebersee-Museum, Bremen. Veroeffentlichungen. Reihe A: Naturwissenschaften. (GW ISSN 0068-0885) **4349**
Uebersee-Museum, Bremen. Veroeffentlichungen. Reihe C: Geographie. (GW) **2264**
Uebersee-Museum, Bremen. Veroeffentlichungen. Reihe D: Voelkerkundliche Monographien. (GW ISSN 0341-9274) **251**
Uebersee-Museum, Bremen. Veroeffentlichungen. Reihe E: Human-Oekologie. (GW ISSN 0170-2416) **4455**
Uebersee-Museum, Bremen. Veroeffentlichungen. Reihe F: Bremer Afrika-Archiv. (GW ISSN 0344-4317) **2335**
Uebersee-Museum, Bremen. Veroeffentlichungen. Reihe G: Bremer Suedpazifik-Archiv. (GW ISSN 0342-6610) **2346**
Uebersee-Post - Europa-Post/Overseas-Post Trade Journal. (GW ISSN 0030-7475) **923**
Uebersee Rundschau. (GW ISSN 0041-5707) **923**
Uebersetzungen Auslaendischer Arbeiten zur Antiken Sklaverei. (GW ISSN 0170-348X) **2324**
Uebersetzungen - Kerntechnische Regeln. (GW) **1810, 4113**
Uebersichten zur Tierernaehrung. (GW) **125**
Der Uebungsleiter. (GW ISSN 0342-8419) **1491, 1762**
Ufficio Centrale per l'Emigrazione Italiana, Bollettino see Servizio Migranti **3925**
Ufficio Intercantonale di Controllo dei Medicamenti. Bollettino Mensile. see Interkantonale Kontrollstelle fuer Heilmittel. Monatsbericht **3109**
L'Ufficio Tecnico. (IT) **4075, 635**
Uganda. Forestry Department. Annual Report. (UG ISSN 0082-7177) **2109**
Uganda. Forestry Department. Technical Notes. (UG ISSN 0082-7193) **2109**
Uganda. Forestry Department. Timber Leaflet. (UG) **2118**
†Uganda. Game Department. Annual Report. (UG) **5294**
Uganda. Geological Survey and Mines Department. Annual Report see Records of Geological Survey and Mines **1578**

UKIYO-E ART   6749

Uganda. Ministry of Planning and Economic Development. Statistics Division. Enumeration of Employees. (UG ISSN 0082-724X) **741, 995**
Uganda. Ministry of Planning and Economic Development. Statistics Division. Monthly Trade Bulletin. (UG) **741**
Uganda. Ministry of Planning and Economic Development. Statistics Division. Quarterly Economic and Statistical Bulletin. (UG ISSN 0041-5758) **741**
†Uganda. Public Libraries Board. Accession List. (UG) **5294**
Uganda Association of University Women. Bulletin. (UG) **4854**
Uganda Commercial Bank. Annual Report. (UG) **802**
Uganda Commercial Bank. Quarterly Economic Review. (UG) **802**
Uganda Commercial Bank Investor's Handbook see U C B Investor's Handbook **967**
Uganda Estimates of Development Expenditures. (UG) **1086**
Uganda Freshwater Fisheries Research Organization. Annual Report. (UG) **2050**
Uganda Journal. (UG ISSN 0041-574X) **2335, 2887**
Uganda Newsletter. (US) **3931**
Uganda Schools Newsletter. (UG ISSN 0049-5026) **1668**
Ugemagasinet Soendag. (DK) **2185**
Ugeskrift for Jordbrug see Jord og Viden **101**
Ugeskrift for Laeger. (DK ISSN 0041-5782) **3159**
Ugeskrift for Retsvaesen. (DK) **2688, 757**
Ugol'. (RU ISSN 0041-5790) **3496**
Ugol' Ukrainy. (KR ISSN 0041-5804) **3496**
Ugostiteljstvo i Turizam see U T **4795**
Uhandisi. (TZ ISSN 0856-3152) **1839**
Uhli/Coal. (CS ISSN 0041-5812) **3497**
Uhren Juwelen. (AU ISSN 0041-5839) **2566**
Uhren - Juwelen - Schmuck. (GW) **2566**
Uhren Rundschau see Precision **2524**
Uhren und Schmuck see Gold und Silber - Uhren und Schmuck **2564**
Uhren und Schmuck Journel. (GW) **2566**
Uhrenfachgeschaeft/Magasin d'Horlogerie Specialise. (SZ ISSN 0049-5042) **2566**
†Uhrmacher - Jahrbuch fuer Handwerk und Handel. (GW ISSN 0082-7290) **5294**
Uirusu. see Virus **558**
Uit de Pluimveepers see Pluimvee Documentatie **142**
Uit Europoortkringen. (NE ISSN 0041-588X) **4741, 1190, 3703**
Uitgelezen. (NE ISSN 0041-591X) **4396, 24, 4358**
Uitkomsten van de Belgische Zeevisserij. (BE) **2050**
Uitlotings-Archief. (NE ISSN 0041-5936) **967**
Uitvaartwezen. (NE) **4716**
Uitzicht. (NE ISSN 0041-5944) **4251**
Uj Elet. (HU ISSN 0133-1353) **2026**
Uj Elet see Erdeyi Figyelo **2215**
Uj Ember. (HU) **4207**
Uj Ifjusag. (CS) **1269**
Uj Iras. (HU ISSN 0041-5952) **2971**
Uj Konyvek. (HU ISSN 0049-5069) **414**
Uj Magyar Hirek/New Hungarian News. (HU ISSN 0133-090X) **2198**
Uj Magyar Nepkoltesi Gyujtemeny. (HU ISSN 0082-7312) **3007, 2059**
Uj Periodikumok. (HU ISSN 0864-8786) **414**
Uj Technika. (HU) **4612**
Uj Tukor. (HU) **4390**
†Ujena Fashion. (US) **5294**
†Ujena Girl. (US) **5294**
UK Kompass Buyers Guides see Kompass Industrial Sections **1142**
†Ukens Nytt. (NO) **5294**
Ukiyo-E Art/Ukiyo Geijutsu. (JA ISSN 0041-5979) **347**

6750 UKIYOE GEIJUTSU

Ukiyoe Geijutsu. *see* Ukiyo-e Art **347**
Ukraina. (KR ISSN 0041-6088) **2220**
Ukraine. (KR) **2220**
▼Ukraine Update. (US) **887**, 967
Ukrainian Academy of Arts and Sciences in the U S. Annals. (US ISSN 0503-1001) **2027**
Ukrainian Archives. *see* Naukove Tovarystvo Imeni Shevchenka. Ukrains'kyi Arkhiv **2016**
Ukrainian Art Digest/Notatky z Mystetstba. (US ISSN 0550-0850) **347**, 2027
Ukrainian Biochemical Journal. *see* Ukrain'skyi Biokhimichnyi Zhurnal **483**
Ukrainian Biochemistry. (English translation of: Ukrain'skyi Biokhimichnyi Zhurnal) (US) **1190**
Ukrainian Canadian Congress. Bulletin. (CN) **2027**
Ukrainian Cultural and Educational Centre. Visti - News. (CN ISSN 0824-5991) **3534**
Ukrainian Echo. *see* Homin Ukrainy **2005**
Ukrainian Engineering News. *see* Visti Ukrayins'kykh Inzheneriv **1840**
Ukrainian Historian. *see* Ukrains'kyi Istoryk **2325**
Ukrainian Journal of Physics. (UK ISSN 0960-6068) **3834**
Ukrainian Literary Library. *see* Naukove Tovarystvo Imeni Shevchenka. Ukrainska Literaturna Biblioteka **2941**
Ukrainian Mathematical Journal. (English translation of: Ukrainskii Matematicheskii Zhurnal) (US ISSN 0041-5995) **3059**
Ukrainian Medical Association of North America. Journal. (US ISSN 0041-607X) **3159**
Ukrainian National Word/Ukrainske Narodne Slovo. (US) **2027**
Ukrainian News/Ukrainski Visti. (CN ISSN 0041-6002) **2027**
Ukrainian Orthodox Word. English Edition. (US ISSN 0147-1015) **4289**
Ukrainian Philatelist. (US ISSN 0198-6252) **3759**, 3602
Ukrainian Quarterly. (US ISSN 0041-6010) **3931**, 2324
Ukrainian Review. (UK ISSN 0041-6029) **2027**, 3931
Ukrainian Thought. (UK) **2027**
Ukrainian Voice/Ukrainsky Holos. (CN ISSN 0041-6037) **2027**
Ukrainian Weekly. (US ISSN 0273-9348) **2027**
Ukrains'ka Mova i Literatura v Shkoli. (KR ISSN 0041-6096) **2848**, 1762
Ukrains'ke Literaturoznavstvo. (KR) **2971**
Ukrainske Narodne Slovo. *see* Ukrainian National Word **2027**
Ukrains'ke Slov'ianoznavstvo *see* Problemy Slov'iyanoznavstva **2381**
Ukrainski Visti. *see* Ukrainian News **2027**
Ukrainskii Biokhimicheskii Zhurnal. *see* Ukrain'skyi Biokhimichnyi Zhurnal **483**
Ukrainskii Fizicheskii Zhurnal. (KR ISSN 0503-1265) **3834**
Ukrainskii Khimicheskii Zhurnal. (KR ISSN 0041-6045) **1190**
Ukrainskii Matematicheskii Zhurnal/ Ukrains'kyi Matematychnyi Zhurnal. (KR ISSN 0041-6053) **3059**
Ukrainsky Holos. *see* Ukrainian Voice **2027**
Ukrain'skyi Biokhimichnyi Zhurnal/ Ukrainian Biochemical Journal/ Ukrainskii Biokhimicheskii Zhurnal. (KR ISSN 0201-8470) **483**
Ukrain'skyi Botanichnyi Zhurnal. (KR ISSN 0372-4123) **519**
Ukrains'kyi Filatelist *see* Ukrainian Philatelist **3759**
Ukrains'kyi Istorychnyi Zhurnal. (KR ISSN 0130-5247) **2325**
Ukrains'kyi Istoryk/Ukrainian Historian. (US ISSN 0041-6061) **2325**
Ukrains'kyi Matematychnyi Zhurnal. *see* Ukrainskii Matematicheskii Zhurnal **3059**
▼Ukranian Business Report. (US) **840**, 802, 2688
Ukulima Wa Kisasa/Modern Farming. (TZ ISSN 0041-6150) **125**
Ulisse 2000. (IT) **2206**
Ulkopolitiikka/Finnish Journal of Foreign Affairs/Utrikespolitik. (FI ISSN 0501-0659) **3975**
Ulm und Oberschwaben. (GW ISSN 0342-2364) **2392**, 347
Ulrich's and Irregular Serials and Annuals on Microfiche *see* Ulrich's on Microfiche **414**
Ulrich's International Periodicals Directory. (US ISSN 0000-0175) **414**, 4142
†Ulrich's News. (US ISSN 0000-1163) **5294**
Ulrich's on Microfiche. (US) **414**, 4142
Ulrich's Plus. (US) **414**, 4142
Ulrich's Update. (US ISSN 0000-1074) **414**, 4142
Ulricks Strikkeideer. (DK ISSN 0901-1056) **3593**
Ulster Bride. (UK) **3067**, 4854
Ulster Builder and Allied Trades Journal.(UK) **635**
Ulster Business Journal. (UK) **696**
Ulster County Gazette. (US) **2424**
Ulster County, New York Agricultural News. (US) **125**
Ulster Editions and Monographs. (UK ISSN 0954-3392) **2971**, 2392
Ulster Farmer. (UK) **125**
Ulster Folklife. (UK ISSN 0082-7347) **2059**
Ulster Food Trader. (UK) **2083**, 386
Ulster Grocer. (UK) **2094**
Ulster Journal of Archaeology. (UK ISSN 0082-7355) **288**
Ulster Licensed Trade News *see* Licensed and Catering News **383**
Ulster Link *see* Irish Link **2155**
Ulster Medical Journal. (UK ISSN 0041-6193) **3159**
Ulster Motorist. (UK ISSN 0041-6207) **4704**
Ulster Nation. (UK) **3931**
Ulster Place-Name Society. Bulletin. (UK ISSN 0953-461X) **2848**
Ulster Request. (US) **840**, 1119
Ulster Tatler. (UK ISSN 0049-5107) **2196**
Ulster Year Book. (UK ISSN 0082-7371) **2392**
L'Ultima Crociata. (IT) **2392**
Ultima Moda. (MX ISSN 0041-6223) **1295**
Ultimate Early Childhood Music Resource. (US) **3585**
Ultimate Issues. (US ISSN 0888-3440) **4227**, 3975
Ultimate Reality and Meaning. (CN ISSN 0709-549X) **3784**, 4207
Ultimo (Kiel). (GW) **2192**, 3597
Ultimo (Muenster). (GW) **2887**, 3518, 3585
Ultimo Buscadero. (IT) **3585**
Ultimo Reino. (AG ISSN 0326-9779) **3007**
†Ultra Magazine. (US) **5294**
Ultra Product Focus. (US) **2525**
Ultra Truck. (US) **4749**
Ultra Violet Spectrometry Group. Bulletin *see* U.V. Spectrometry Group. Bulletin **5294**
Ultragarsas/Ultrasound. (LI ISSN 0369-6367) **3860**
Ultralight Aircraft. (US) **64**
Ultralight Flying. (US) **64**, 4559
Ultramicroscopy. (NE ISSN 0304-3991) **561**
Ultrapure Water. (US ISSN 0747-8291) **4829**
Ultrarunning. (US ISSN 0744-3609) **4559**
Ultraschall in der Medizin. (GW ISSN 0172-4614) **3159**
Ultraschall in Klinik und Praxis. (GW ISSN 0930-8040) **3159**
Ultrasonic Imaging. (US ISSN 0161-7346) **3159**, 3834
Ultrasonica. (IT ISSN 0393-7801) **3297**
Ultrasonics. (UK ISSN 0041-624X) **3860**
Ultrasonics Symposium. Proceedings. (US ISSN 0090-5607) **3860**, 1839
Ultrasound. *see* Ultragarsas **3860**
Ultrasound Annual. (US ISSN 0888-8264) **3363**
Ultrasound in Medicine & Biology. (US ISSN 0301-5629) **458**, 3159, 3860
▼Ultrasound in Obstetrics & Gynecology. (UK ISSN 0960-7692) **3297**
Ultrasound Quarterly. (US ISSN 0894-8771) **3363**
Ultrastructural Pathology. (US ISSN 0191-3123) **527**, 561, 3202, 3263
Ultreya. (US ISSN 0041-6258) **4289**
Ulum wa Funun - Dirasat wa Buhuth. *see* Science and Arts - Research Studies **4338**
Ulupungu Iwa kwa Kalinda. (SA) **4289**
Ulysses International. (FR ISSN 1143-3914) **2027**, 2971
Umafrika. (SA ISSN 0041-6274) **4207**
Haumah. (IS ISSN 0503-146X) **2204**
Umana Avventura. (IT) **347**, 4349
Umanita. (IT) **3931**
Umbrella. (US ISSN 0160-0699) **347**, 2788
Umbruch. (GW) **347**, 2887, 2971
Umeaa Studies in Politics and Public Administration. (SW) **4076**, 3931
Umeaa Studies in the Humanities. (SW ISSN 0345-0155) **2516**
Umeni/Arts. (CS ISSN 0049-5123) **347**
Umetnost. (YU ISSN 0041-6320) **347**
Umfeld. (AU ISSN 1015-8529) **3931**
†Umform Produkte. (GW) **5294**
Umformtechnik. (GW ISSN 0300-3167) **3422**, 3024, 3868
Umfrage und Analyse. (GW) **39**
Umi/Sea. (JA) **2971**
Umi to Anzen. (JA ISSN 0912-7437) **1611**, 1970
Umjetnost i Dijete. (CI ISSN 0503-1575) **1245**
Umjetnost Rijeci/Word Art. (CI) **2971**
Umma. (TZ ISSN 0011-6696) **2971**
Al-Ummal. (UA) **2591**
Umoja. (US) **2027**
Umoja Sasa News Journal *see* U S Black Engineer **1839**
†Umphako Wabashumayeli. (SA) **5294**
†Umphaphamisi. (SA) **5294**
Umpqua Trapper. (US ISSN 0041-6339) **2424**
Umsatzsteuer-Rundschau. (GW ISSN 0341-8669) **1111**
Umsatzsteuer- und Verkehrsteuer-Recht. (GW) **1111**
†Umschau, das Wissenschafts Magazin. (GW ISSN 0722-8562) **5294**
Umsebenzi. (SA) **3931**
Umthombo Wamandla. (SA ISSN 0378-4134) **4251**
Umuhinzi - Mworozi. (RW) **125**
†Umus. (IT) **5294**
Umwelt. (GW ISSN 0041-6355) **1979**, 1970
Umwelt Aktuell. (AU) **1970**
Umwelt Technologie Aktuell. (GW) **1970**, 1498
Umwelt und Energie. (GW ISSN 0173-8720) **1796**
Umwelt und Technik. (GW) **967**, 1970
Umweltbundesamt. Jahresbericht. (GW) **1970**
Umweltmagazin. (GW ISSN 0341-1206) **1970**
Umweltmedizin. (GW ISSN 0932-2892) **1975**
Umweltschutz. (AU ISSN 0049-5131) **4113**, 1970
Umweltschutz Gesundheitstechnik *see* Umwelttechnik **1970**
Umwelttechnik. (SZ) **1970**
Umwelttechnik Berlin. (GW) **1970**
†Un Pays, un Marche. (SZ) **5294**
Una Voce Korrespondenz. (GW ISSN 0724-2778) **4277**
Unabashed Librarian. (US ISSN 0049-514X) **2788**
Unabhaengige Bauernstimme. (GW ISSN 0934-4632) **125**, 1508
Unabhaengige Brandschutzzeitschrift. (GW ISSN 0500-6260) **2035**
Unarius Light Magazine. (US) **3597**, 3784
Unausforschlicher Reichtum. (GW ISSN 0041-6444) **4207**
Unavicoltura. (IT) **227**
▼Unbridled Lust! (US) **3007**
Uncaptive Minds. (US ISSN 0897-9669) **3948**
†Uncensored Poland News Bulletin. (UK ISSN 0264-6501) **5294**
Uncensored Swinger. (US) **3400**, 4854
Uncharted. (US) **347**
Uncinetto Selezione. (IT) **3593**
Unclaimed Property Law and Reporting Forms. (US) **2688**
Unclassified. (US) **2688**, 1528
Uncle Jam *see* U J Q **2887**
Uncle Jam Quarterly *see* U J Q **2887**
Uncle Sam. (US ISSN 0279-0815) **2887**
†Uncommon Reader. (US) **5294**
†Unconventional Petroleum. (US ISSN 0741-7721) **5294**
Uncoverings. (US ISSN 0277-0628) **4854**, 3593, 4627
Uncut. (US) **3400**, 2457
Und-oder-nor. (US) **1940**, 1910
Und-oder-Nor und Steuerungstechnik *see* Und-oder-nor **1940**
Unda - U S A Newsletter. (US) **1383**, 4277
Under Construction. (US ISSN 0740-4409) **2166**
Under Paraplyen. (DK ISSN 0906-1592) **1245**
Under Svensk Flagg. (SW) **4741**
Under the Runyon Tree. (US) **2166**
Under the Same Sun/Sous un Meme Soleil. (CN) **936**
Under 5. (UK ISSN 0307-9929) **1245**
Undercar Digest. (US) **4704**
Undercar Digest Short Line Newsletter. (US) **4704**
Undercurrent. (US ISSN 0192-0871) **4496**
▼Undercurrents. (US) **1611**
Undercurrents *see* Resurgence **3922**
Undercut. (UK ISSN 0267-8497) **3518**
†Undergraduate Forum. (US) **5294**
Undergraduate Mathematics Applications Project Journal *see* U M A P Journal **3059**
Undergraduate Texts in Mathematics. (US ISSN 0172-6056) **3059**
Underground. (UK ISSN 0269-4670) **1875**
Underground. (CN) **2887**
Underground Forest *see* Underground Forest - Selva Subterranea **2887**
Underground Forest - Selva Subterranea. (US ISSN 1045-3660) **2887**
Underground Lamp Post. (US ISSN 0049-5174) **259**
Underground Surrealist Magazine. (US) **2887**
Underpass. (CN ISSN 0838-6749) **3007**
Undersea Biomedical Research. (US ISSN 0093-5387) **3159**
Undersoegelse over Apotekernes Driftsforhold. (DK ISSN 0108-948X) **3745**
Understanding Japan. (JA ISSN 0041-6576) **2208**, 1668
Understanding Mutual Funds: Your No-Nonsense Everyday Guide. (CN) **967**
Understanding People. (US) **4049**, 3355
Undervisning og Velferd/Education and Welfare. (NO ISSN 0041-6584) **3473**, 4422
Undervisningsmaterialer til Begynder- og Specialundervisning. (DK ISSN 0107-377X) **1742**
Underwater and Hyperbaric Medicine: Abstracts from the Literature. (US) **1552**
Underwater Letter. (US ISSN 0041-6592) **3473**

Underwater Magazine. (US) **1055**, **4741**
Underwater Medicine: Abstracts from the Literature *see* Underwater and Hyperbaric Medicine: Abstracts from the Literature **1552**
Underwater Naturalist. (US ISSN 0041-6606) **1611**
Underwater Reporter *see* Visability **1612**
Underwater System Design *see* International Underwater System Design **1606**
Underwater Technology. (UK) **1611**, **4612**
Underwater U S A. (US ISSN 0749-1794) **4496**, **1611**
Underwood Publications. Issues. (AT) **1970**
Underwriters' Handbook. (US) **2544**
Underwriters Laboratories. Annual Product Directories. (US) **3449**
Underwriters Laboratories. Annual Product Directories. Semi-Annual Supplement *see* Underwriters Laboratories. Annual Product Directories **3449**
Underwriters' Report. (US ISSN 0041-6622) **2544**
Underwriting Results: The Blue Chart *see* Blue Chart Report **2528**
Undesniy Ediyn Dzasag/National Economy. (MP) **840**
Undesniy Soyolyn Dzam/Road of National Culture. (MP) **347**
Undugu Bulletin. (KE) **1668**, **4390**
Undzer Veg. (CN ISSN 0382-0610) **2027**
Une Semaine de Paris-Pariscope. (FR ISSN 0049-5190) **4795**
Une Ville, Un Pays. (FR ISSN 1159-0769) **2392**, **2059**, **4455**
Unemployment Compensation Guide (Year) *see* U C Guide (Year) **2712**
Unemployment Insurance Reports with Social Security. (US) **2544**, **995**
Unemployment Monthly Bulletin. (EI ISSN 0252-9920) **995**
Unesco. A L S E D Newsletter (Anthropology and Language Science in Educational Development) *see* F I P L V World News **1633**
Unesco. Centro de Documentacion Cultural, Havana. Informaciones Trimestrales. (UN ISSN 0049-5204) **2516**
Unesco. Comision Nacional Cubana. Boletin. (UN) **2516**
Unesco. Field Science Office for Latin America. Boletin *see* Unesco. Regional Office for Science and Technology for Latin America and the Caribbean. Boletin **4612**
Unesco. Principal Regional Office for Asia and Pacific. Abstract Bibliography Series on Population Education. (UN) **1680**
Unesco. Principal Regional Office for Asia and the Pacific. Bulletin. (UN) **1669**
Unesco. Records of the General Conference. Proceedings. (UN ISSN 0082-7509) **3975**
Unesco. Records of the General Conference. Resolutions. (UN ISSN 0082-7517) **3975**, **1723**
Unesco. Regional Office for Education in Asia and the Pacific. Abstract Bibliography Series on Population Education *see* Unesco. Principal Regional Office for Asia and Pacific. Abstract Bibliography Series on Population Education **1680**
Unesco. Regional Office for Education in Asia and the Pacific. Bulletin *see* Unesco. Principal Regional Office for Asia and the Pacific. Bulletin **1669**
Unesco. Regional Office for Science and Technology for Africa. Bulletin. (UN ISSN 0503-4434) **4349**
Unesco. Regional Office for Science and Technology for Latin America and the Caribbean. Boletin. (UN) **4612**
Unesco. Report of the Director-General on the Activities of the Organization. (UN ISSN 0082-7525) **3975**, **1723**

Unesco. Scientific Maps and Atlases and Other Related Publications. (UN) **414**
Unesco. Statistics on Science and Technology/Statistiques Relatives aux Science et a la Technologie/Estadisticas Relativas a la Ciencia y a la Tecnologia. (UN) **4358**, **741**
Unesco. Studies on Books and Reading.(UN) **4138**, **1669**
Unesco Asia Bunka News Bulletin. (JA) **2208**
Unesco Australia. (UN) **936**, **1723**
Unesco Bibliographical Handbooks *see* Documentation, Libraries and Archives: Bibliographies and Reference Works **2793**
Unesco Courier *see* Courier (Paris) **3954**
Unesco Institute for Education Case Studies *see* U I E Case Studies **1668**
Unesco Institute for Education Monographs *see* U I E Monographs **1668**
Unesco Institute for Education Studies on Functional Illiteracy in Industrialized Countries *see* U I E Studies on Functional Illiteracy in Industrialized Countries **1687**
Unesco Institute for Education Studies on Post-Literacy and Continuing Education *see* U I E Studies on Post-Literacy and Continuing Education **1687**
Unesco List of Documents and Publications. (UN) **1680**
Unesco Philippines. (UN ISSN 0041-5294) **1669**
Unesco Programme of International Cooperation in Scientific and Technological Information Newsletter *see* U N I S I S T Newsletter **2788**
Unesco Reports in Marine Science. (UN) **458**
Unesco Review *see* Unesco Australia **936**
Unesco Source Books on Curricula and Methods. (UN ISSN 0502-9554) **1762**
Unesco Statistical Reports and Studies. (UN ISSN 0082-7533) **4591**
Unesco Statistical Yearbook. (UN ISSN 0082-7541) **4591**
Unesco Yearbook on Peace and Conflict Studies. (US ISSN 0250-779X) **3975**
The Unexplained. (US) **3597**, **3671**
Der Unfallchirurg. (GW ISSN 0177-5537) **3312**, **3373**, **3622**
Unfallchirurgie. (GW ISSN 0340-2649) **3312**
Unfallheilkunde *see* Der Unfallchirurg **3312**
Unfallschirm. (GW) **4627**
Unfinished Furniture Industry. (US ISSN 0199-8714) **2562**
Ung og Fri. (DK ISSN 0905-1503) **2887**
Unga Diktara. (SW) **2971**
Unga Oernar *see* Oern Bladet **1261**
Ungarische Akademie der Wissenschaften. Archaelogisches Institut. Mitteilungen *see* Antaeus **262**
Ungarische Jahrbuecher *see* Ural-Altaische Jahrbuecher **2393**
Ungarland *see* Hungarian Digest **2198**
Ungarn *see* Magyarorszag **4578**
†Ungarn - Jahrbuch. (GW ISSN 0082-755X) **5294**
Ungdom og Idraet. (DK) **4496**
Ungdomen Selvbyggerlag Nytt *see* U S B L Nytt **635**
Ungdomskalender. (DK ISSN 0107-7783) **1269**
†Ungdomsskolen i Tal. (DK ISSN 0108-2426) **5294**
Ungdomsuddannelser. (DK ISSN 0900-1395) **1669**
Unge Laeser Om. (DK ISSN 0108-6952) **1248**
Unge Paedagoger. (DK) **1669**
Uni Berufswahl-Magazin *see* Uni Perspektiven fuer Beruf und Arbeitsmarkt **3631**
Uni-Forum. (GW) **1327**
Uni Hannover. (GW ISSN 0171-2268) **4612**

Uni Journal. (GW ISSN 0179-9088) **1327**
Uni Perspektiven fuer Beruf und Arbeitsmarkt. (GW) **3631**, **1718**
Uni-Press. (AU) **1669**
Uni Report. (GW ISSN 0179-7182) **4349**, **4612**
Uni Ulm Intern. (GW ISSN 0176-036X) **1327**
Uniao dos Escritores Angolanos. Boletim *see* Lavra & Oficina **2510**
Unibeam. (SI) **4159**
Uniciencia. (CR ISSN 1011-0275) **4349**
Unicorn. (AT ISSN 0311-4775) **1669**, **1718**
†Unicorn (Baltimore). (US) **5294**
Unicorn (Northridge). (US) **3671**
Unicorn German Series. (US) **3008**
Unicum. (GW ISSN 0939-4826) **1327**
Unidad. (PN) **3931**
Unidentified Flying Objects Annual *see* U F O Annual **5293**
Unidentified Flying Objects Investigation Centre Newsletter *see* U F O I C Newsletter **64**
Unidroit Yearbook *see* Uniform Law Review **2729**
Die Unie. (SA ISSN 0259-5591) **1669**
Unifarma. (SP) **3745**
Unificacion. (MX) **4716**, **2591**
Unification/Edinenie. (AT) **2027**
Unification Policy Quarterly. (KO) **3931**
Unificazione e Certificazione. (IT ISSN 0394-9605) **898**, **1086**
Unified List of United States Companies Doing Business in South Africa and Namibia. (US) **923**
Uniform Building Code *see* International Conference of Building Officials. Uniform Building Code **621**
Uniform Commercial Code Law Journal *see* Quinn's Uniform Commercial Code Law Journal **2700**
Uniform Commercial Code Law Letter. (US ISSN 0503-1966) **840**, **2688**
Uniform Commercial Code Reporting Service. (US) **2688**
Uniform Crime Report for the State of Michigan. (US ISSN 0360-9146) **1525**
Uniform Crime Reports for the United States. (US ISSN 0082-7592) **1523**
Uniform Law Cases *see* Uniform Law Review **2729**
Uniform Law Review. (US) **2729**
Uniform Manufacturers Exchange. Newsletter. (US) **1288**
Uniform Plumbing Code. (US) **2304**
Uniformed Sanitationmen's Association Record *see* U S A Record **2590**
Uniformed Services Academy of Family Physicians Newsletter. (US) **3159**
Uniformed Services Almanac. (US ISSN 0503-1982) **3473**
Uniformed Services Journal *see* U S J **3473**
Uniforms and Accessories Review. (US ISSN 0041-6738) **1295**
Uniforum Monthly. (US) **1401**, **39**
Unigram.X. (US ISSN 0952-3359) **1481**, **828**
Unijournal. (GW) **1327**
Unilag Communication Review. (NR) **1345**
Unilit. (II ISSN 0041-6762) **2971**, **3015**
Uninews. (US) **1466**
Uninterruptable Power Supply Systems Directory *see* European Gen - Set Directory **1892**
L'Union. (US) **1302**
Union. *see* Jednota **2008**
Union. (GO) **2170**
Union. (CU ISSN 0041-6770) **2971**
Union. (GW) **3931**, **696**
Union. (MQ) **3931**
Union Academique Internationale. Compte Rendu de la Session Annuelle du Comite. (BE ISSN 0074-9346) **2516**
Union Agriculture. (FR ISSN 0041-6819) **125**

UNION HERALD 6751

Union Bancaria Hispano Marroqui. Assemblee Generale Ordinaire des Actionnaires. Rapport. (MR) **802**
Union Bank of Finland. Annual Report. (FI ISSN 0355-0133) **802**
Union Bank of Switzerland Business Facts and Figures *see* U B S Business Facts and Figures **5293**
Union Bank of Switzerland Publications on Business, Banking and Monetary Problems *see* U B S Publications on Business, Banking and Monetary Problems **802**
Union Catalog of Medical Periodicals *see* U C M P Quarterly **3181**
Union Catalogue of Foreign Literature in Swedish Research Libraries. *see* Accessionskatalog over Utlaendsk Litteratur i Svenska Forskningsbibliotek **388**
†Union Catalogue of Theses and Dissertations of the South African Universities. (SA ISSN 0079-4325) **5294**
Union College. (US) **1718**
Union de Periodistas de Cuba *see* U P E C **4138**
Union Democracy in Action *see* Union Democracy Review **2591**
Union Democracy Review. (US) **2591**, **995**, **3931**
Union Departementale des Syndicats d'Entrepreneurs et d'Artisans du Batiment et des Travaux Publics de la Haute-Garonne. Officiel du Batiment. (FR) **635**
Union des Association Francaises de Relations Publiques. Annuaire. (FR ISSN 0066-9253) **39**
Union des Associations de Fabricants de Parties Detachees Horlogeres Revue *see* U B A H Revue **2566**
Union des Aveugles de Guerre. Bulletin Mensuel. (FR ISSN 0041-6843) **2296**, **3473**
Union des Caisses Nationales de Securite Sociale Bulletin Juridique *see* U C A N S S. Bulletin Juridique **2687**
Union des Cantons de l'Est. (CN) **2179**
Union des Chambres de Commerce et Etablissenents Gestionnaires d'Aeroport. Statistics on Airport Traffic. (FR) **4668**
Union des Industries et de la Distribution des Plastiques et du Caoutchouc. Guide. (FR) **1156**, **3868**, **4294**
Union des Professions Immobilieres de Belgique. Bulletin Mensule - Maandblad. (BE) **4159**
Union des Superieures Majeurs de France. Annuaire. (FR ISSN 0396-2393) **4207**
Union Douaniere et Economique de l'Afrique Centrale. Bulletin des Statistiques Generales *see* Division d'Aide et de Cooperation Francaise. Bulletin Trimestriel de Statistique **713**
Union Economique. (MG) **1669**
Union Europeenne du Commerce de Gros en Fruits et Legumes. Information Bulletin. (BE) **126**
Union Farmer. (CN ISSN 0041-6878) **126**
Union for Radical Political Economics Newsletter *see* U R P E Newsletter **696**
Union Francaise des Centres de Vacances *see* U.F.C.V **995**
Union Genealogique du Centre. Informations Genealogiques *see* Union Genealogique du Centre. Informations Genealogiques du Centre **2166**
Union Genealogique du Centre. Informations Genealogiques du Centre. (FR) **2166**
Union Geodesique et Geophysique Internationale. Chronique *see* I U G G Chronicle **1590**
Union Handbook. (UK) **1718**, **2196**
Union Helvetia. (SZ) **2481**
Union Herald. (MY ISSN 0049-528X) **2591**, **126**

Union Industrial Uruguaya. Guia de Socios y de Productos see Products of Uruguay **1083**
Union Internacional de Estudiantes. El Secretariado Informa see International Union of Students. Secretariat Reports **3900**
Union Internacional de Telecomunicaciones. Biblioteca Central. Lista de Adquisiciones Recientes. see International Telecommunication Union. Central Library. List of Recent Acquisitions **1348**
Union Internacional de Telecomunicaciones. Biblioteca Central. Lista de Publicaciones Anuales. see International Telecommunication Union. Central Library. List of Annuals **1348**
Union International de Telcommunicaciones. Biblioteca Central. Lista de Revistas. see International Telecommunication Union. Central Library. List of Periodicals **1348**
Union International de Tir Journal see U I T Journal **4495**
Union Internationale Contre le Cancer. Manuel. see International Union Against Cancer. Manual **5218**
Union Internationale de Speleologie Bulletin see U I S Bulletin **1583**
Union Internationale des Architectes International Architect see U I A - International Architect **5293**
Union Internationale des Architectes Journal of Architectural Theory and Criticism see U I A Journal of Architectural Theory and Criticism **308**
Union Internationale des Architectes Newsletter see U I A Newsletter **308**
Union Internationale des Associations d'Alpinisme. Bulletin. see International Union of Alpine Associations. Bulletin **4772**
Union Internationale des Etudiants. Secretariat au Fil du Mois see International Union of Students. Secretariat Reports **3900**
Union Internationale des Telecommunications. Bibliotheque Centrale. Liste des Acquisitions Recentes. see International Telecommunication Union. Central Library. List of Recent Acquisitions **1348**
Union Internationale des Telecommunications. Bibliotheque Centrale. Liste des Periodique. see International Telecommunication Union. Central Library. List of Periodicals **1348**
Union Internationale des Telecommunications. Bibliotheque Centrale. Listes des Publications Annuelles. see International Telecommunication Union. Central Library. List of Annuals **1348**
Union Internationale des Transports Publics. Rapports Techniques des Congres Internationaux see International Union of Public Transport. Technical Reports of the Congresses **4651**
Union Internationales des Industries Graphiques de Reproduction. Congress Summaries see Europro. Congress Summaries **3999**
Union Jack. (US) **2027**
Union Labor in California. (US) **2592, 4591**
Union Labor Journal. (US) **2591**
Union Labor Life Insurance Co. Bulletin see U L L I C O Bulletin **2544**
Union Labor News. (US ISSN 0041-6924) **2591**
Union Labor Report. (US ISSN 0091-5459) **995, 2591, 2688**
Union Labor Report Weekly Newsletter. (US ISSN 0190-5260) **995, 2591**
Union Labor Report's - On The Line. (US ISSN 0731-0307) **995, 2591**
Union Leader see In Transit **2584**
†Union List of Legislative Histories. (US) **5294**

Union List of Scientific and Technical Periodicals in Zambia. (ZA) **414, 4349, 4612**
Union List of Scientific Serials in Canadian Libraries/Catalogue Collectif des Publications Scientifiques dans les Bibliotheques Canadiennes. (CN ISSN 0082-7657) **4358**
Union List of Serials in Israel Libraries. (IS ISSN 0082-7665) **4358, 414**
Union Matematica Argentina. Revista. (AG ISSN 0041-6932) **3059, 3834**
Union Matters. (CN) **2591**
Union Medicale Balkanique. Archives. (RM ISSN 0041-6940) **3159**
Union Medicale du Canada. (CN ISSN 0041-6959) **3159**
Union Mondiale des Organisations Syndicales sur Bases Economique et Sociale Liberales. Conferences: Rapport. (SZ ISSN 0503-2334) **2591**
Union Nacional de Arquitectos e Ingenieros de la Construccion de Cuba Boletin see U N A I C C Boletin **5293**
Union Nationale de l'Enseignement Agricole Prive. Annuaire. (FR ISSN 0082-7711) **126, 1669**
Union Nationale des Entrepreneurs Platriers, Staffeurs et Stucateurs. Bulletin. (FR) **635**
Union Nationale des Industries de Carrieres et Materiaux de Construction Annuaire Officiel see U N I C E M Annuaire Officiel **635**
Union Nationale du Commerce de Gros en Fruits et Legumes. Bulletin. (BE) **126**
Union News see Leeds Student **1316**
Union of American Hebrew Congregations. State of Our Union. (US ISSN 0363-3810) **4227**
Union of Bulgarian Composers. News Bulletin. (BU) **3585**
Union of Councils for Soviet Jews Quarterly Report see U C S J Quarterly Report **2026**
Union of European Football Associations. Bulletin. (SZ ISSN 0501-1590) **4514**
Union of European Football Associations. Handbook of U E F A. (SZ ISSN 0570-2070) **4514**
Union of European Football Associations Flash see U E F A Flash **4514**
†Union of European Pedopsychiatrists. Proceedings. (US) **5294**
Union of Forestry and Timber Industry Workers. Bulletin. (BU) **2109**
Union of International Associations. Documents see Collection of Documents for the Study of International Non-Governmental Relations **2720**
Union of Japanese Scientists and Engineers. Reports of Statistical Application Research. (JA ISSN 0034-4842) **3059**
†Union of Nova Scotia Municipalities. Proceedings of the Annual Convention. (CN ISSN 0082-7762) **5294**
Union of Shop Distributive and Allied Workers Today see U S D A W Today **2591**
Union of Teachers' Associations of South Africa Annual see U.T.S.A. Annual **1732**
Union of Yugoslav Composers' Organizations. Bulletin see Savez Organizacija Kompozitora Jugoslavije. Bilten **3579**
Union of Yugoslav Youth. Newsletter. (YU) **1245**
Union Postale. (UN ISSN 0041-7009) **1354**
Union Postale Universelle. Actes. (UN) **1354**
Union Postale Universelle. Statistique des Services Postaux. (UN ISSN 0085-7602) **1354**
Union Recorder. (AT ISSN 0041-7017) **1327**
Union Seminary Quarterly Review. (US ISSN 0041-7025) **4207**
▼Union Shop Bluff. (CN) **3008**

Union Signal. (US ISSN 0041-7033) **1539, 4455**
Union Sociale. (FR ISSN 0041-7041) **4422**
Union Sportive Metropolitaine des Transports Annee Sportive U.S.M.T. see Annee Sportive U.S.M.T **4464**
Union Suisse des Fabricants de Boites de Montres Informations see U S F B Informations **2566**
Union Technique de l'Automobile du Motocycle et du Cycle. Bulletin Mensuel de Documentation see U T A C Bulletin de Documentation **5294**
Union-Tribune Index of San Diego Business Activity. (US ISSN 0041-7068) **887**
†Unioncamere. (IT) **5294**
L'Unione dei Segretari. (IT) **2591**
Unione Italiana del Lavoro Voce della V I L see La Voce della U I L **2591**
Unione Matematica Italiana. Bollettino. (IT ISSN 0041-7084) **3059**
Unione Nazionale Consumatori Notizie see U N C Notizie **1508**
Unione Nazionale Ufficiali in Congedo d'Italia see U N U C I **3473**
Unione Regionale Camere di Commercio dell'Emilia-Romagna. Statistiche Regionali. (IT) **4591**
Unionews. (UK) **1327**
Unionist. see Al Ittihadi **2169**
Unionist. (US ISSN 0041-7092) **2591, 4422**
UniPress. (GW ISSN 0937-6496) **1718**
†Unique (Bridgeview). (US) **5294**
Unique (Denville). (US ISSN 0736-4083) **1465**
Unique (Lawrence). (US) **1466**
Unique & Exotic Travel Reporter. (US) **4795**
Unique Homes. (US) **4159**
Unir. (FR ISSN 0985-1798) **2188**
Unir Cine Media. (SG ISSN 0253-5858) **1345**
Unir Cinema. (SG ISSN 0253-195X) **3518**
Unir: Echo de Saint Louis. (SG ISSN 0253-584X) **2971, 347, 3518**
UniReview. (US) **1466**
▼Unirod. (US) **2971, 347**

Uniscope. (CN ISSN 1181-8409) **1327**
Unisphere. (US ISSN 0279-1579) **1466**
Unispiegel. (GW) **1327, 1718**
Unispiegel Aktuell see Unispiegel **1327**
Unisurv G see Australian Journal of Geodesy, Photogrammetry & Surveying **2243**
Unisys World. (US ISSN 0892-2845) **1465, 828, 1455, 1481**
Unisys World - Europe. (US ISSN 0895-0334) **1424**
Unisys World Software Directory see Unisys World **1465**
Unit Investment Trusts Service Manuals.(US) **967**
Unit Investment Trusts Weekly Reports.(US) **967**
Unit Scheme and Conservation Order Outlines. (CN) **1498**
Unit Trust Yearbook. (UK ISSN 0503-2628) **802**
Unita. (IT) **3931**
Unita Proletaria. (IT) **3931**
Unitarian. (UK ISSN 0049-531X) **4251**
Unitarian and Free Christian Churches. Handbook and Directory of the General Assembly. (UK) **4251**
Unitarian and Free Christian Churches. Yearbook of the General Assembly see Unitarian and Free Christian Churches. Handbook and Directory of the General Assembly **4251**
Unitarian Historical Society, London. Transactions. (UK ISSN 0082-7800) **4251, 2392**
Unitarian Pioneer. (AT) **4207**
Unitarian Quest. (AT) **4207**
Unitarian Universalist Christian. (US ISSN 0362-0492) **4251**
Unitarian Universalist Directory. (US ISSN 0082-7827) **4251**

Unitarian Universalist Historical Society. Proceedings. (US) **4251**
Unitarian Universalist Musician's Network Notes see U U M N Notes **3585**
Unitarian Universalist Women's Federation Federation Newsletter see U U W F Federation Newsletter **4854**
Unitarian Universalist World see World (Boston) **4253**
▼Unitario. (GW) **2848**
Unitarische Blaetter. (GW ISSN 0932-0180) **4207**
Unitas. (FI ISSN 0041-7130) **887**
Unitas. (PH ISSN 0041-7149) **2516**
Unitas/Lien Ho Wen Hsueh. (CH) **2887**
Unitas Fratrum. (GW) **2392, 4277**
L'Unite. (CN) **1327**
†Unite. (FR) **5294**
Unite Africaine. (SG) **3931**
Unite de Programmation du Ministere. Bulletin de Conjoncture. (HT) **887, 802**
Unite des Chretiens. (FR) **4207**
Unite Stenographique. (FR ISSN 0041-7157) **1062**
United see Vis a Vis **4804**
United Against Cruelty to Animals see U A C T A **232**
United & Babson Graphic Guide. (US) **967**
United & Babson Investment Report. (US) **967**
United Arab Emirates. Al-Masraf al-Markazi. Al-Mulhiq al-Ihsa'i/United Arab Emirates. Central Bank. Statistical Supplement. (TS) **741**
United Arab Emirates. Al-Masraf al-Markazi. Al-Nashrah al-Iqtisadiyyah/United Arab Emirates. Central Bank. Economic Bulletin. (TS) **802**
United Arab Emirates. Al-Masraf al-Markazi. Al-Taqrir al-Sanawi/United Arab Emirates. Central Bank. Annual Report. (TS) **1111**
United Arab Emirates. Al-Qiyadah al-Aamah lil-Quwwat al-Musallihah. Majallah al-Tibbiyyah/United Arab Emirates. General Command for the Armed Forces. Medical Journal. (TS) **3159, 3473**
United Arab Emirates. Business Directory. (TS) **1156**
United Arab Emirates. Central Bank. Annual Report. see United Arab Emirates. Al-Masraf al-Markazi. Al-Taqrir al-Sanawi **1111**
United Arab Emirates. Central Bank. Economic Bulletin. see United Arab Emirates. Al-Masraf al-Markazi. Al-Nashrah al-Iqtisadiyyah **802**
United Arab Emirates. Central Bank. Publication see United Arab Emirates. Al-Masraf al-Markazi. Al-Nashrah al-Iqtisadiyyah **802**
United Arab Emirates. Central Bank. Statistical Supplement. see United Arab Emirates. Al-Masraf al-Markazi. Al-Mulhiq al-Ihsa'i **741**
United Arab Emirates. Da'irat al-Mushtariat. Al-Kitab al-Ihsa'i al-Sanawi/United Arab Emirates. Purchasing Department. Statistical Yearbook. (TS) **4082**
United Arab Emirates. General Command for the Armed Forces. Medical Journal. see United Arab Emirates. Al-Qiyadah al-Aamah lil-Quwwat al-Musallihah. Majallah al-Tibbiyyah **3159**
United Arab Emirates. Ministry of Education. Annual Report. see United Arab Emirates. Wizarat al-Tarbiyyah wal-Ta'lim. Al-Taqrir al-Sanawi **1732**
United Arab Emirates. Ministry of Health. Preventive Medicine Department. Annual Report. see United Arab Emirates. Wizarat al-Sihhah. Idarat al-Tibb al-Waqa'i. Al-Taqrir al-Sanawi **4114**
United Arab Emirates. Ministry of Health. Statistical Yearbook. see United Arab Emirates. Wizarat al-Sihhah. Al-Kitab al-Ihsa'i al-Sanawi **3181**

UNITED NATIONS 6753

United Arab Emirates. Ministry of Public Works and Housing. News Bulletin see Nashrat Al-Iskan wal-Ashghal **4067**

United Arab Emirates. Official Gazette. see Al-Jaridah al-Rasmiyyah li-Dawlat al-Imarat al-Arabiyyah al-Muttahidah **4065**

United Arab Emirates. Purchasing Department. Statistical Yearbook. see United Arab Emirates. Da'irat al-Mushtariat. Al-Kitab al-Ihsa'i al-Sanawi **4082**

United Arab Emirates. Wizarat al-Sihhah. Al-Kitab al-Ihsa'i al-Sanawi/ United Arab Emirates. Ministry of Health. Statistical Yearbook. (TS) **3181, 4119, 4591**

United Arab Emirates. Wizarat al-Sihhah. Idarat al-Tibb al-Waqa'i. Al-Taqrir al-Sanawi/United Arab Emirates. Ministry of Health. Preventive Medicine Department. Annual Report. (TS) **4114**

United Arab Emirates. Wizarat al-Tarbiyyah wal-Ta'lim. Al-Taqrir al-Sanawi/United Arab Emirates. Ministry of Education. Annual Report.(TS) **1732**

United Arab Emirates University. Faculty of Arts. Journal. see Jami'at al-Imarat al-Arabiyyah al-Muttahidah. Kulliyyat al-Aadaab. Majallah **2509**

United Arab Emirates University. Faculty of Science. Journal/Jami'at al-Imarat al-Arabiyyah al-Muttahidah. Kulliyyat al-Ulum. Majallah. (TS) **4349**

United Arab Emirates University. Journal. see Jami'at al-Imarat al-Arabiyyah al-Muttahidah. Majallah **2509**

United Arab Republic Journal of Geology. (UA) **1583**

United Association Journal. (US ISSN 0041-7181) **2591**

United Association Manufacturers' Representatives Newsletter see U A M R Newsletter **696**

United Automobile, Aerospace, and Agricultural Implement Workers of America Ammo see U A W Ammo **2590**

United Bank Limited. Economic Journal.(PK) **887**

United Baptist Convention of the Atlantic Provinces. Yearbook. (CN ISSN 0082-7843) **4251**

United Bible Societies. Bulletin. (UK ISSN 0041-719X) **4207**

United Brethren. (US) **4251**

United Business and Investment Report see United & Babson Investment Report **967**

United Caprine News. (US ISSN 0164-9353) **227**

United Church News. (US ISSN 0882-7214) **4251**

United Church Observer. (CN ISSN 0041-7238) **4251**

United Church of Canada. General Council. Record of Proceedings. (CN ISSN 0082-7878) **4251**

United Church of Canada. Year Book see United Church of Canada. Year Book and Directory **4251**

United Church of Canada. Year Book and Directory. (CN) **4251**

United Church of Christ. Pension Boards (Annual Report). (US ISSN 0360-9782) **4289, 2544**

United Community Planning Corporation. Report. (US) **4422**

United Dairy Industry Association. Annual Report. (US) **204**

United Electrical, Radio & Machine Workers of America News see U E News **2590**

United Electrical Radio and Machine Workers of Canada News Magazine see U E News Magazine **2590**

United Evangelical see E.C. Doors and Windows **4236**

United Evangelical Action. (US ISSN 0041-7270) **4251**

†United Flathead Racers Association Newsletter. (US) **5294**

United Food and Commercial Workers International Union Action see U F C W Action **2590**

United for Service. (US) **4422**

United Free Church of Scotland. Handbook. (UK ISSN 0082-7908) **4251**

United Grand Lodge of New South Wales Freemason see N.S.W. Freemason **1299**

United Graphic Guide see United & Babson Graphic Guide **967**

United Kingdom Atomic Energy Authority. Annual Report. (UK ISSN 0082-7940) **1810, 1839**

United Kingdom Atomic Energy Authority. List of Publications Available to the Public. (UK ISSN 0041-7289) **414, 4349**

United Kingdom Atomic Energy Authority Times see A E A Times **1803**

United Kingdom - Commonwealth of Nations - Directory of Governments. (US) **1156, 3931, 3975**

United Kingdom Freedom Bulletin. (US ISSN 0954-075X) **3975**

United Kingdom Infrared Telescope Newsletter see J C M T - U K I R T Newsletter **366**

United Kingdom Infrared Telescope Report see U K I R T Report **370**

United Kingdom Mineral Statistics see United Kingdom Minerals Yearbook **3497**

United Kingdom Minerals Yearbook. (UK ISSN 0957-4697) **3497**

United Kingdom Offshore Legislation Guide. (UK) **2688, 3703**

†United Kingdom Research on Geodesy.(UK) **5294**

United Kingdom Temperance Alliance. Alliance News see U K Alcohol Alert **1539**

United Kingdom - Tin in Tinplate. (UK) **3422**

United Knitwear Manufacturers League. Bulletin. (US) **1288**

United Lumbee Nation Times. (US) **2027**

United Lutheran. (US ISSN 0041-7300) **4251**

United Malays National Organisation. Annual Report. (MY) **3931**

United Malays National Organisation. Penvata see United Malays National Organisation. Annual Report **3931**

United Methodist Board of Higher Education and Ministry. Quarterly Review. (US ISSN 0270-9287) **4208**

United Methodist Christian Advocate. (US ISSN 8750-7668) **4251**

†United Methodist Church. Curriculum Plans. (US ISSN 0160-0885) **5294**

United Methodist Church. General Minutes of the Annual Conferences. (US ISSN 0503-3551) **4251**

United Methodist Church (United States) Division of Education. Adult Planbook see Adult Planbook **5130**

United Methodist Reporter. (US) **4251**

United Mine Workers Journal. (US ISSN 0041-7327) **2591, 3497**

United Ministries in Education Connexion see U M E Connexion **5293**

United Mutual Fund Selector. (US ISSN 0740-557X) **741, 967, 4591**

United Nations. Conference on Trade and Development. Trade and Development Board. Official Records. (UN ISSN 0503-4108) **936**

United Nations. Conference on Trade and Development. Trade and Development Board. Official Records. Supplements. (UN) **3975**

United Nations. Dag Hammarskjold Library. Current Bibliographical Information. (UN ISSN 0041-7343) **3939, 414**

United Nations. Department of International Economic and Social Affairs. Natural Resources - Water Series see United Nations. Economic and Social Commission for Asia and the Pacific. Natural Resources - Water Series **4829**

United Nations. Department of International Economic and Social Affairs. Statistical Office. Construction Statistic Yearbook. (UN ISSN 0257-9073) **639, 4591**

United Nations. Development Programme. Compendium of Approved Projects. (UN) **936**

United Nations. Disarmament Commission. Yearbook see United Nations Disarmament Yearbook **3473**

United Nations. Division of Narcotic Drugs. Information Letter. (UN ISSN 0085-7491) **1539**

United Nations. Economic and Social Commission for Asia and the Pacific. Asian Population Studies Series. (UN ISSN 0066-8451) **3988**

United Nations. Economic and Social Commission for Asia and the Pacific. Development Papers. (UN) **1498**

United Nations. Economic and Social Commission for Asia and the Pacific. Mineral Resources Development Series. (UN ISSN 0082-8114) **3497**

United Nations. Economic and Social Commission for Asia and the Pacific. Natural Resources - Water Series. (UN) **4829**

United Nations. Economic and Social Commission for Asia and the Pacific. Water Resources Development Series see United Nations. Economic and Social Commission for Asia and the Pacific. Water Resources Series **4829**

United Nations. Economic and Social Commission for Asia and the Pacific. Water Resources Series. (UN) **4829**

United Nations. Economic and Social Council. Annexes. (UN) **696, 4390**

United Nations. Economic and Social Council. Index to Proceedings. (UN ISSN 0082-8084) **3939**

United Nations. Economic and Social Council. Official Records. (UN ISSN 0082-8092) **3975, 887**

United Nations. Economic Commission for Africa. Proposals for Programme Budget. (UN) **696, 936**

United Nations. Economic Commission for Asia and the Far East. Sample Surveys in the ECAFE Region. see Sample Surveys in the ESCAP Region **737**

United Nations. Economic Commission for Asia and the Pacific. Energy Resources Development Series. (UN) **1796**

United Nations. Economic Commission for Europe. Information. (UN ISSN 0253-0090) **696**

United Nations. Economic Commission for Europe. Statistical Journal. (NE ISSN 0167-8000) **1030**

United Nations. General Assembly. Annexes. (UN) **696, 3931**

United Nations. General Assembly. Index to Proceedings. (UN ISSN 0082-8157) **3939**

United Nations. General Assembly. Official Records. (UN) **696, 3931**

United Nations. General Assembly. Provisional Records. (UN) **696, 3931**

United Nations. International Law Commission Yearbook. (UN ISSN 0082-8289) **2729**

United Nations. International Narcotics Control Board. Annual Report see International Narcotics Control Board. Report for (Year) **3730**

United Nations. International Narcotics Control Board. Comparative Statement of Estimates and Statistics on Narcotics Drugs Furnished by Governments in Accordance with the International Treaties see Narcotic Drugs: Estimated World Requirements for (Year) **3811**

United Nations. International Narcotics Control Board. Comparative Statement of Estimates and Statistics on Narcotic Drugs for (Year) see Narcotic Drugs: Estimated World Requirements for (Year) **3811**

United Nations. International Narcotics Control Board. Statistics on Narcotic Drugs Furnished by Governments in Accordance with the International Treaties see Narcotic Drugs: Estimated World Requirements for (Year) **3811**

United Nations. International Narcotics Control Board. Statistics on Narcotics Drugs for (Year) see Narcotic Drugs: Estimated World Requirements for (Year) **3811**

United Nations. Multilateral Treaties Deposited with the Secretary-General.(UN ISSN 0255-724X) **2729**

United Nations. National Accounts Statistics. Analysis of Main Aggregates. (UN ISSN 0259-3017) **741, 4591**

United Nations. National Accounts Statistics. Government Accounts and Tables. (UN ISSN 0259-3009) **742, 4591**

United Nations. National Accounts Statistics. Main Aggregates and Detailed Tables. (UN ISSN 0259-3025) **742, 4591**

United Nations. Population and Vital Statistics Report. (UN ISSN 0041-7416) **3996**

United Nations. Regional Centre for Demographic Training and Research in Latin America. Serie A/Centro Latinoamericano de Demografia. Serie A. (UN ISSN 0503-3934) **3988**

United Nations. Regional Centre for Demographic Training and Research in Latin America. Serie C/Centro Latinoamericano de Demografia. Serie C. (UN ISSN 0503-3942) **3988**

United Nations. Regional Centre for Demographic Training and Research in Latin America. Serie D/Centro Latinoamericano de Demografia. Serie D. (UN ISSN 0503-3950) **3988**

United Nations. Regional Centre for Demographic Training and Research in Latin America. Serie E/Centro Latinoamericano de Demografia. Serie E. (UN) **3988**

United Nations. Security Council. Index to Proceedings. (UN ISSN 0082-8408) **3939**

United Nations. Security Council. Official Records. (UN ISSN 0082-8416) **3975**

United Nations. Security Council. Official Records. Supplement. (UN ISSN 0257-067X) **3975**

United Nations. Statistical Yearbook. (UN ISSN 0082-8459) **4591**

United Nations. Trade and Development Board. Official Records see United Nations. Conference on Trade and Development. Trade and Development Board. Official Records **936**

United Nations. Treaty Series. (UN ISSN 0379-8267) **2729**

United Nations. Treaty Series. Cumulative Index. (UN ISSN 0252-5321) **2701, 2729**

United Nations. Trusteeship Council. Index to Proceedings. (UN ISSN 0082-8491) **3939**

United Nations. Trusteeship Council. Ofcial Records. Verbatim Records of Plenary Meetings. (UN) **3975, 696**

United Nations. Trusteeship Council. Official Records. (UN ISSN 0082-8505) **3975**

United Nations. Trusteeship Council. Official Records. Annexes - Sessional Fascicle. (UN) **3975, 696**

United Nations. Trusteeship Council. Official Records. Resolutions. (UN) **3975, 696**

United Nations. Trusteeship Council. Official Records. Supplements. (UN ISSN 0082-8513) **3975**

United Nations. Yearbook. (UN ISSN 0082-8521) **3975**

6754 UNITED NATIONS

United Nations. Yearbook of International Trade Statistics *see* International Trade Statistics Yearbook **723**

United Nations and Related Agencies Handbook *see* United Nations Handbook **3975**

United Nations Association in Canada. Quarterly Bulletin. (CN) **3975,** 1723, 2729

United Nations Association of the Republic of China News Letter. (CH) **3975,** 3931

United Nations Centre for Human Settlements Habitat News *see* U N C H S Habitat News **2497**

United Nations Centre for Regional Development Bulletin *see* U N C R D Bulletin **936**

United Nations Centre for Regional Development Newsletter *see* U N C R D Newsletter **936**

United Nations Children's Fund. Programme Division. Conference Reports Series. (UN ISSN 1013-3186) **4422,** 1245

United Nations Childrens Fund. Programme Division. Staff Working Papers Series. (UN ISSN 1013-3178) **4422,** 1245

United Nations Childrens Fund Information Bulletin *see* U N I C E F Information Bulletin **5293**

United Nations Childrens Fund News *see* U N I C E F News **5293**

United Nations Childrens Fund Policy Review Series *see* U N I C E F Policy Review Series **4422**

United Nations Chronicle. *see* Lianheguo Jishi **3964**

United Nations Commission on International Trade Law. Report on the Work of Its Session. (UN) **2729**

United Nations Commission on International Trade Law. Yearbook. (UN ISSN 0251-4265) **2729,** 923

United Nations Conference on the Standardization of Geographical Names. Report of the Conference. (UN) **2264**

United Nations Conference on Trade and Development Bulletin *see* U N C T A D Bulletin **923**

United Nations Conference on Trade and Development Commodity Yearbook *see* U N C T A D Commodity Yearbook **741**

United Nations Conference on Trade and Development: Proceedings. (UN) **923,** 936

United Nations Conference on Trade and Development Review *see* U N C T A D Review **923**

United Nations Congress on the Prevention of Crime and the Treatment of Offenders. Report. (UN ISSN 0082-8025) **1523**

United Nations Crime and Justice Research Institute. Publication. (UN) **1523**

United Nations Disarmament Yearbook. (UN ISSN 0252-5607) **3473,** 1810, 3931

United Nations Documents and Publications. (US) **414**

United Nations Documents and Publications. Checklist *see* United Nations Documents and Publications **414**

United Nations Documents Current Index *see* U N D O C: Current Index **3938**

United Nations Economic and Social Commission for Asia and the Pacific. Social Development Division. Social Work Education and Development. (UN ISSN 0252-452X) **4422,** 1762

United Nations Economic and Social Commission for Asia and the Pacific. Social Development Division. Social Work Training and Teaching Materials Newsletter *see* United Nations Economic and Social Commission for Asia and the Pacific. Social Development Division. Social Work Education and Development **4422**

United Nations Economic and Social Commission for Asia and the Pacific. Statistical Newsletter. (UN ISSN 0252-3647) **742**

United Nations Economic and Social Commission for Asia and the Pacific Energy News *see* E S C A P Energy News **1785**

United Nations Economic and Social Council. Disarmament Study Series. (UN) **3473,** 1810, 3931

United Nations Economic and Social Council. Official Records. Supplements and Special Supplements. (UN) **696,** 4390

United Nations Economic and Social Council. Resolutions and Decisions. (UN ISSN 0251-9410) **696,** 4390

United Nations Economic and Social Council. Summary Records of Plenary Meetings. (UN) **696,** 4390

United Nations Economic Commission for Africa. Annual Report. (UN) **936**

United Nations Economic Commission for Africa. Statistical Newsletter. (UN) **742**

United Nations Economic Commission for Europe. Annual Bulletin of General Energy Statistics for Europe *see* Annual Bulletin of General Energy Statistics for Europe **1797**

United Nations Economic Commission for Europe. Occasional Studies. (UN) **887**

United Nations Environment Programme. Evaluation Report (Year). (UN) **1970**

United Nations Environment Programme. Feature. (UN) **1970**

United Nations Environment Programme. Governing Council. Report on the Work of its Session. (UN) **1970**

United Nations Environment Programme. The State of the Environment; Report of the Executive Director. (UN) **1970**

United Nations Environment Programme Information *see* U N E P Information **1970**

United Nations Environment Programme Regional Seas Reports and Studies *see* U N E P Regional Seas Reports and Studies **1611**

United Nations General Assembly: Report of the Australian Delegation. (AT) **3975**

United Nations Handbook. (NZ ISSN 0110-1951) **3975**

†United Nations Industrial Development Organization. Development and Transfer of Technology Series. (UN ISSN 0250-801X) **5294**

United Nations Industrial Development Organization Industrial Development Abstracts *see* Industrial Development Abstracts **722**

United Nations Industrial Development Organization Newsletter *see* U N I D O Newsletter **936**

United Nations Institute for Disarmament Research Newsletter *see* U N I D I R Newsletter **3974**

†United Nations Institute for Namibia. Occasional Papers. (UN) **5294**

†United Nations Institute for Namibia. Prospectus. (UN) **5294**

United Nations Issues Conference. Report. (US ISSN 0743-9180) **3975**

United Nations Juridical Yearbook. (UN ISSN 0082-8297) **2730**

United Nations Library. Monthly Bibliography. Part 1: Books, Official Documents, Serials. (UN ISSN 0251-6616) **3939,** 414

United Nations Library. Monthly Bibliography. Part 2: Selected Articles. (UN ISSN 0251-6624) **3939,** 414

United Nations of the Next Decade Conference. Report. (US ISSN 0748-433X) **3975**

United Nations Population Fund. Annual Review of Population Law. (UN) **3988,** 2688

United Nations Publications *see* New United Nations Publications **3910**

United Nations Regional Cartographic Conference for Asia and the Far East. Proceedings of the Conference and Technical Papers *see* United Nations Regional Cartographic Conference for Asia and the Pacific. Report of the Conference **2264**

United Nations Regional Cartographic Conference for Asia and the Pacific. Report of the Conference. (UN) **2264**

United Nations Regional Cartographic Conference for the Americas. Report of the Conference. (UN) **2264**

United Nations Report *see* International Advertiser **33**

United Nations Research Institute for Social Development. Research Notes *see* U N R I S D News **4390**

United Nations Resolutions. Series 1. Resolutions Adopted by the General Assembly. (US ISSN 0886-6686) **2730**

United Nations Resolutions. Series 2. Resolutions and Decisions of the Security Council. (US ISSN 0898-2929) **2730**

United Nations Review. (UN ISSN 0817-9751) **3975,** 2730

United Nations Social Defence Research Institute. Publication *see* United Nations Crime and Justice Research Institute. Publication **1523**

United Nations Statistical Office. Monthly Bulletin of Statistics. (UN ISSN 0041-7432) **4591**

United Nations University. Work in Progress. (UN ISSN 0259-4285) **936,** 1970

United Nations Volunteers Programme News *see* U N V News **936**

United Nations Weekly Report. (US) **3975,** 923, 936

United Nations World. *see* Eine Welt der Vereinten Nationen **5303**

United Neighborhood Centers of America. News & Round Table. (US) **4422**

United Newsletter *see* Unity: United Newsletter **2457**

United Parents Association of New York City Newsletter. (US) **1669**

United Parkinson Foundation Newsletter *see* U P F Newsletter **3355**

United Planting Association of Malaysia. Annual Report. (MY ISSN 0304-8349) **158**

United Presbyterian Church in the United States of America. Minutes of the General Assembly. (US ISSN 0082-8548) **4251**

United Reformed Church History Society. Journal. (UK ISSN 0049-5433) **4251**

United Reformed Church in the United Kingdom. United Reformed Church Year Book. (UK) **4251**

United Reformed Church Pocket Diary. (UK) **4252**

United Reformed Church, Yorkshire Province, Provincial Handbook. (UK) **4252**

United Retirement Bulletin. (US) **2279,** 2544

United Rubber Worker. (US ISSN 0162-3869) **2591,** 4294

United Russian Orthodox Brotherhood of America Messenger *see* U R O B A Messenger **4289**

United Schools International. Documents of the Biennial Conference. (II ISSN 0503-4663) **2688**

United Schools Organisation of India. Annual Report. (II) **1669**

United Seamen's Service Reports *see* U S S Reports **4741**

United Senior Citizens of Ontario. Bulletin *see* Voice of United Senior Citizens of Ontario **2280**

United Service Institution of India Journal *see* U S I Journal **3473**

United Service Organizations, Inc. Annual Report *see* U S O Annual Report **4422**

United Society for the Propagation of the Gospel. Annual Report - Review *see* United Society for the Propagation of the Gospel. Yearbook **4208**

▼United Society for the Propagation of the Gospel. Issues. (UK ISSN 0958-2789) **4252**

▼United Society for the Propagation of the Gospel. Newsbrief. (UK ISSN 0958-2770) **4252**

United Society for the Propagation of the Gospel. Quarterly Intercession Paper *see* Encounter (London, 1990) **4176**

United Society for the Propagation of the Gospel. Yearbook. (UK) **4208**

United Society of Artists. Publication. (UK) **347**

U.S. A I P *see* U.S. Aeronautical Information Publication **64**

U.S. Administrative Office of the United States Courts. Report on Applications for Orders Authorizing or Approving the Interception of Wire or Oral Communications. (US ISSN 0097-7977) **2733,** 1345

†U.S. Advisory Council on Historic Preservation. Report. (US ISSN 0098-4035) **5294**

U.S. Aeronautical Information Publication. (US) **64**

U.S. Agency for International Development. Congressional Presentation, Fiscal Year *see* U.S. International Development Cooperation Agency. Congressional Presentation, Fiscal Year **936**

†U.S. Agency for International Development. Proposed Foreign Aid Program, Summary Presentation to Congress. (US ISSN 0082-8637) **5294**

U.S. Agency for International Development Highlights *see* A.I.D. Highlights **925**

U.S. Agency for International Development Research and Development Abstracts *see* A I D Research and Development Abstracts **701**

U.S. Agricultural Marketing Service. Annual Report on Tobacco Statistics. (US) **4646**

U.S. Agricultural Marketing Service. Dairy and Poultry Market Statistics *see* Poultry Market Statistics **142**

U.S. Agricultural Marketing Service. Dairy Division. Federal Milk Order Market Statistics. (US ISSN 0498-2002) **204,** 158

U.S. Agricultural Research Service. A R S - N C. (Agricultural Research Service, North Central Region) (US ISSN 0092-1785) **126**

U.S. Agricultural Research Service. Animal Science Research Division. Tables on Hatchery and Flock Participation in the National Turkey Improvement Plan *see* Tables on Hatchery and Flock Participation in the National Poultry Improvement Plan **227**

U.S. Air Force. School of Aerospace Medicine. Standard Technical Report Series. (US) **3159**

U.S. Air Force Cambridge Research Laboratories. A F C R L (Series) *see* U.S. Air Force Geophysics Laboratory. A F G L (Series) **3474**

U.S. Air Force Fighter Weapons Review *see* U S A F Fighter Weapons Review **3473**

U.S. Air Force Geophysics Laboratory. A F G L (Series). (US) **3474,** 1596

U.S. Airborne Exports and General Imports *see* Foreign Trade Reports. U.S. Airborne Exports and General Imports **5195**

U.S. Arms Control and Disarmament Agency. Annual Report to Congress. (US ISSN 0082-8769) **3474,** 2735

U.S. Army. Corps of Engineers. Detroit District. Monthly Bulletin of Lake Levels for the Great Lakes. (US) **1925**

†U.S. Army Infantry School. History; Annual Supplement. (US) **5294**

U.S. Army Infantry School Quarterly *see* Infantry **3460**

U.S. Army Medical Research Institute of Infectious Diseases. Annual Progress Report. (US) **3224**

Title

U.S. Army Natick Laboratories. Activities Report *see* Research & Development Associates for Military Food and Packaging Systems. Activities Report **3469**

U.S. Brookhaven National Laboratory, Upton, N.Y. Brookhaven Highlights *see* Brookhaven Highlights **1804**

U.S. Bureau of Alcohol, Tobacco and Firearms. Explosives Incidents. (US ISSN 0273-5032) **1523**

U.S. Bureau of Domestic and International Business Administration. Overseas Business Reports. (US ISSN 0082-9846) **923**

U.S. Bureau of International Commerce. Trade Lists *see* U.S. Department of Commerce. Trade Lists **923**

U.S. Bureau of Labor Statistics. Area Wage Surveys. (US) **742**

U.S. Bureau of Labor Statistics. Bulletins. (US ISSN 0082-9021) **742, 995**

U.S. Bureau of Labor Statistics. C P I Detailed Report. (US ISSN 0095-926X) **1000**

U.S. Bureau of Labor Statistics. Current Wage Developments. (US ISSN 0011-3972) **742, 995**

U.S. Bureau of Labor Statistics. Employee Benefits in Medium and Large Firms. (US) **742, 995**

U.S. Bureau of Labor Statistics. Employment and Earnings. (US ISSN 0013-6840) **742, 995**

U.S. Bureau of Labor Statistics. Employment and Earnings: States and Areas. (US) **742, 996**

U.S. Bureau of Labor Statistics. Employment Situation. (US ISSN 0364-491X) **742, 996, 4591**

U.S. Bureau of Labor Statistics. Handbook of Labor Statistics. (US ISSN 0082-9056) **742**

U.S. Bureau of Labor Statistics. Industry Wage Surveys. (US ISSN 0082-9064) **742, 996**

U.S. Bureau of Labor Statistics. Major Programs. (US) **742**

U.S. Bureau of Labor Statistics. Monthly Labor Review. (US ISSN 0098-1818) **742, 996**

U.S. Bureau of Labor Statistics. National Survey of Professional, Administrative, Technical and Clerical Pay. (US ISSN 0501-7041) **742**

U.S. Bureau of Labor Statistics. Occupational Outlook Handbook. (US) **3632, 742**

U.S. Bureau of Labor Statistics. Occupational Outlook Quarterly. (US ISSN 0029-7968) **996**

U.S. Bureau of Labor Statistics. Productivity Measures for Selected Industries. (US) **742**

U.S. Bureau of Labor Statistics. Southwest Statistical Summary. (US) **742**

U.S. Bureau of Land Management. Public Land Statistics. (US ISSN 0082-9110) **4082**

U.S. Bureau of Mines. Bulletin. (US ISSN 0082-9129) **3497**

U.S. Bureau of Mines. Commodity Data Summaries *see* U.S. Bureau of Mines. Mineral Commodity Summaries **3497**

U.S. Bureau of Mines. Information Circular. (US) **3497**

U.S. Bureau of Mines. Mineral Commodity Summaries. (US ISSN 0160-5151) **3497**

U.S. Bureau of Mines. Mineral Industry Surveys. (US ISSN 0498-7845) **3502**

U.S. Bureau of Mines. Minerals Yearbook. (US ISSN 0076-8952) **3497**

U.S. Bureau of Mines. Report of Investigations. (US) **3497**

U.S. Bureau of Outdoor Recreation. Recreation Grants-in-Aid Manual *see* Land and Water Conservation Fund Grants Manual **1490**

†U.S. Bureau of Radiological Health. Research Grants Program. (US ISSN 0093-5654) **5294**

U.S. Bureau of Reclamation. Annual Report. (US) **1498, 4829**

†U.S. Bureau of Reclamation. Denver Office. Research Reports. (US) **5295**

U.S. Bureau of Reclamation. Engineering and Research Center. Research Reports *see* U.S. Bureau of Reclamation. Denver Office. Research Reports **5295**

U.S. Bureau of Reclamation. Engineering Monograph. (US) **1925, 4829**

U.S. Bureau of the Census. Annual Survey of Manufactures. (US ISSN 0082-9307) **742, 1086**

U.S. Bureau of the Census. Bunker Fuels *see* Foreign Trade Reports. Bunker Fuels **5195**

U.S. Bureau of the Census. Census and You. (US) **4591**

U.S. Bureau of the Census. Census Catalog and Guide. (US) **3996, 4082**

U.S. Bureau of the Census. Census of Agriculture. (US ISSN 0082-9315) **126**

U.S. Bureau of the Census. Census of Construction Industries. (US ISSN 0082-934X) **635**

U.S. Bureau of the Census. Census of Governments. (US ISSN 0082-9358) **4083**

U.S. Bureau of the Census. Census of Housing. (US ISSN 0082-9366) **2500**

U.S. Bureau of the Census. Census of Manufactures. (US ISSN 0082-9374) **742, 1086**

U.S. Bureau of the Census. Census of Mineral Industries. (US ISSN 0082-9382) **3497**

U.S. Bureau of the Census. Census of Population. (US ISSN 0082-9390) **3996**

U.S. Bureau of the Census. Census of Retail Trade. (US) **742**

U.S. Bureau of the Census. Census of Retail Trade, Wholesale Trade and Selected Service Industries *see* U.S. Bureau of the Census. Census of Retail Trade **742**

U.S. Bureau of the Census. Census of Service Industries. (US) **742**

U.S. Bureau of the Census. Census of Transportation. (US ISSN 0082-9404) **4660**

U.S. Bureau of the Census. Census of Wholesale Trade. (US) **742**

U.S. Bureau of the Census. City Employment *see* Current Governments Reports: City Employment **712**

U.S. Bureau of the Census. City Government Finances *see* Current Governments Reports: City Government Finances **1092**

U.S. Bureau of the Census. Congressional Districts. (US) **3939**

U.S. Bureau of the Census. Consumer Income *see* Current Population Reports: Population Characteristics, Special Studies, Consumer Income **998**

U.S. Bureau of the Census. County and City Data Book. (US ISSN 0082-9455) **4591**

U.S. Bureau of the Census. County Business Patterns. (US ISSN 0082-9463) **742**

U.S. Bureau of the Census. County Government Finances *see* Current Governments Reports: County Government Finances **1092**

U.S. Bureau of the Census. Current Business Reports *see* Current Business Reports **859**

U.S. Bureau of the Census. Current Construction Reports *see* Current Construction Reports **614**

U.S. Bureau of the Census. Current Governments Reports *see* Current Governments Reports **4058**

U.S. Bureau of the Census. Current Housing Reports *see* Current Housing Reports **2486**

U.S. Bureau of the Census. Current Industrial Reports *see* Current Industrial Reports **1074**

U.S. Bureau of the Census. Current Population Reports *see* Current Population Reports **3980**

U.S. Bureau of the Census. Data User News *see* U.S. Bureau of the Census. Census and You **4591**

U.S. Bureau of the Census. Finances of Employee Retirement Systems of State and Local Governments *see* Current Governments Reports: Finances of Employee Retirement Systems of State and Local Governments **1092**

U.S. Bureau of the Census. Finances of Selected Public Employee Retirement Systems *see* Current Governments Reports: Finances of Selected Public Employee Retirement Systems **1092**

U.S. Bureau of the Census. Governmental Finances *see* Current Governments Reports: Government Finances **1092**

U.S. Bureau of the Census. Guide to Foreign Trade Statistics. (US ISSN 0565-0933) **742, 923**

U.S. Bureau of the Census. Household and Family Characteristics *see* Current Population Reports: Population Characteristics. Household and Family Characteristics **3980**

U.S. Bureau of the Census. Housing Characteristics *see* Current Housing Reports: Housing Characteristics **2486**

U.S. Bureau of the Census. Housing Starts *see* Current Construction Reports: Housing Starts **2486**

U.S. Bureau of the Census. Housing Vacancies *see* Current Housing Reports: Housing Vacancies **2486**

U.S. Bureau of the Census. Marital Status and Living Arrangements *see* Current Population Reports: Population Characteristics. Marital Status and Living Arrangements **3980**

U.S. Bureau of the Census. Market Absorption of Apartments *see* Current Housing Reports: Market Absorption of Apartments **2486**

U.S. Bureau of the Census. Monthly Retail Trade *see* Current Business Reports: Monthly Retail Trade, Sales and Inventories **712**

U.S. Bureau of the Census. Monthly Wholesale Trade *see* Current Business Reports: Monthly Wholesale Trade: Sales and Inventories **835**

U.S. Bureau of the Census. New One Family Homes Sold and for Sale *see* Current Construction Reports: New One-Family Houses Sold and for Sale **2486**

U.S. Bureau of the Census. Population Characteristics *see* Current Population Reports: Population Characteristics **3980**

U.S. Bureau of the Census. Population Estimates and Projections *see* Current Population Reports: Population Estimates and Projections **3981**

U.S. Bureau of the Census. Public Employment *see* Current Governments Reports: Public Employment **976**

U.S. Bureau of the Census. School Enrollment: Social and Economic Characteristics of Students *see* Current Population Reports: Population Characteristics. School Enrollment: Social and Economic Characteristics of Students **3981**

U.S. Bureau of the Census. Social and Economic Characteristics of the Black Population *see* Current Population Reports: Population Characteristics. Social and Economic Characteristics of the Black Population **5175**

U.S. Bureau of the Census. State and Metropolitan Area Data Book. (US ISSN 0276-6566) **4591**

U.S. Bureau of the Census. State Government Finances *see* Current Governments Reports: State Government Finances **712**

U.S. Bureau of the Census. Technical Papers. (US ISSN 0082-9544) **4591**

U.S. Bureau of the Census. Value of New Construction Put in Place *see* Current Construction Reports: Value of New Construction Put in Place **615**

U.S. Bureau of the Census. Vessel Entrances and Clearances *see* Foreign Trade Reports. Vessel Entrances and Clearances **5195**

U.S. Bureau of the Census. Working Papers. (US ISSN 0082-9552) **4591**

U.S. Center for Population Research. Inventory of Federal Population Research *see* U.S. Interagency Committee on Population Research. Inventory and Analysis of Federal Population Research **3988**

U.S. Centers for Disease Control. Abortion Surveillance Report. (US) **598**

U.S. Centers for Disease Control. Abortion Surveillance. Annual Summary. (US) **598, 4114**

U.S. Centers for Disease Control. Brucellosis Surveillance: Annual Summary. (US ISSN 0090-1156) **4114**

U.S. Centers for Disease Control. Congenital Malformations Surveillance. (US ISSN 0092-5594) **468**

U.S. Centers for Disease Control. Diphtheria Surveillance Report. (US) **3224, 4114**

U.S. Centers for Disease Control. Family Planning Services: Annual Summary. (US ISSN 0094-4424) **598**

U.S. Centers for Disease Control. Foodborne & Waterborne Disease Outbreaks. Annual Summary. (US ISSN 0098-6623) **4114**

U.S. Centers for Disease Control. Leprosy Surveillance Report. (US) **3224, 4114**

U.S. Centers for Disease Control. Listeriosis Surveillance Report. (US) **3224, 4114**

U.S. Centers for Disease Control. Malaria Surveillance Report. (US ISSN 0501-8390) **3224, 4114**

U.S. Centers for Disease Control. Morbidity and Mortality Weekly Report. (US ISSN 0149-2195) **4114, 3988**

†U.S. Centers for Disease Control. Neurotropic Viral Diseases Surveillance: Aseptic Meningitis. (US) **5295**

†U.S. Centers for Disease Control. Neurotropic Viral Diseases Surveillance: Encephalitis. (US) **5295**

†U.S. Centers for Disease Control. Neurotropic Viral Diseases Surveillance: Enterovirus. (US) **5295**

U.S. Centers for Disease Control. Neurotropic Viral Diseases Surveillance: Poliomyelitis. (US) **3355**

U.S. Centers for Disease Control. Salmonella Surveillance. Annual Summary. (US) **4114**

U.S. Centers for Disease Control. Tuberculosis in the United States *see* U.S. Centers for Disease Control. Tuberculosis Statistics in the United States **3368**

U.S. Centers for Disease Control. Tuberculosis Statistics in the United States. (US) **3368**

U.S. Central Intelligence Agency. Appearances of Soviet Leaders. (US) **3975**

U.S. Chamber Watch on Small Business Legislation & Regulation. (US ISSN 0734-4074) **2688, 1119**

†U.S. Civil Service Commission. (US) **5295**

†U.S. Civil Service Commission. Annual Report. (US ISSN 0190-9797) **5295**

6756 U.S. CIVIL

†U.S. Civil Service Commission. Bureau of Personnel Management Evaluation. Evaluation Methods Series. (US ISSN 0361-6797) **5295**
†U.S. Civil Service Commission. Personnel Research and Development Center. Technical Study.(US ISSN 0093-366X) **5295**
U.S. Coast Guard. Environmental Protection Newsletter. (US) **1970**
U.S. Coast Guard. Merchant Marine Council. Proceedings *see* U.S. Coast Guard Marine Safety Council. Proceedings **4741**
U.S. Coast Guard Boating Statistics *see* Boating Statistics **4498**
U.S. Coast Guard Marine Safety Council. Proceedings. (US ISSN 0364-0981) **4741**, 3474
U.S. Coast Guard Technical Report *see* C G O U Technical Report **1602**
U.S. Coastal Engineering Research Center Cular *see* The C E R Cular **1602**
U.S. Commission on Civil Rights. Clearinghouse Publications. (US ISSN 0082-9641) **3948**
U.S. Community Services Administration. Annual Report. (US ISSN 0190-373X) **4422**
U.S. Community Services Administration. Federal Outlays in Summary. (US ISSN 0091-3553) **1111**
†U.S. Congress. Congressional Directory. (US) **5295**
U.S. Congress. Congressional Record. (US ISSN 0363-7239) **3931**
U.S. Congress. Environmental and Energy Study Institute. Weekly Bulletin. (US) **1970**
U.S. Congress. Environmental and Energy Study Institute. Weekly Bulletin *see* U.S. Congress. Environmental and Energy Study Institute. Weekly Bulletin **1970**
U.S. Congress: Mental Health. (US) **3355**
U.S. Congress: Mental Health, Mental Retardation *see* U.S. Congress: Mental Health **3355**
U.S. Copyright Office. Annual Report of the Register of Copyrights. (US ISSN 0090-2845) **3679**
U.S. Copyright Office. Catalog of Copyright Entries. Fourth Series. Part 1: Nondramatic Literary Works. (US ISSN 0163-7290) **3680**
U.S. Copyright Office. Catalog of Copyright Entries. Fourth Series. Part 2: Serials and Periodicals. (US ISSN 0163-7304) **3680**
U.S. Copyright Office. Catalog of Copyright Entries. Fourth Series. Part 3: Performing Arts. (US ISSN 0163-7312) **3680**
U.S. Copyright Office. Catalog of Copyright Entries. Fourth Series. Part 4: Motion Pictures and Filmstrips. (US ISSN 0163-7320) **3520**, 3680
U.S. Copyright Office. Catalog of Copyright Entries. Fourth Series. Part 5: Visual Arts Excluding Maps. (US ISSN 0163-7339) **352**, 3680, 3798
U.S. Copyright Office. Catalog of Copyright Entries. Fourth Series. Part 6: Maps. (US ISSN 0163-7347) **2268**, 3680
U.S. Copyright Office. Catalog of Copyright Entries. Fourth Series. Part 7: Sound Recordings. (US ISSN 0163-7355) **3680**, 4462
U.S. Copyright Office. Catalog of Copyright Entries. Fourth Series. Part 8: Renewals. (US ISSN 0163-7363) **3680**
U.S. Council for Energy Awareness. Info.(US) **1810**, 1796
U.S. Crop Reporting Board. Agricultural Prices. (US ISSN 0002-1601) **158**
U.S. Crop Reporting Board. Cattle and Calves on Feed *see* U.S. Crop Reporting Board. Cattle on Feed **227**
U.S. Crop Reporting Board. Cattle on Feed. (US ISSN 0364-202X) **227**
U.S. Crop Reporting Board. Crop Production. (US ISSN 0363-8561) **195**
U.S. Crop Reporting Board. Reports. (US) **144**
U.S. Defense Logistics Agency. D O D Hazardous Materials Information System: Hazardous Item Listing. (US) **4114**
U.S. Department of Agriculture. Agricultural Cooperative Service. Cooperative Information Report Series. (US) **126**
U.S. Department of Agriculture. Agricultural Economic Reports. (US ISSN 0083-0445) **158**
U.S. Department of Agriculture. Agricultural Economics Research *see* Journal of Agricultural Economics Research **153**
U.S. Department of Agriculture. Agricultural Finance Outlook and Situation *see* U.S. Department of Agriculture. Agricultural Income and Finance Situation and Outlook **158**
U.S. Department of Agriculture. Agricultural Income and Finance Outlook and Situation *see* U.S. Department of Agriculture. Agricultural Income and Finance Situation and Outlook **158**
U.S. Department of Agriculture. Agricultural Income and Finance Situation and Outlook. (US) **158**
U.S. Department of Agriculture. Agricultural Outlook. (US ISSN 0099-1066) **158**
U.S. Department of Agriculture. Agricultural Statistics. (US ISSN 0082-9714) **144**
U.S. Department of Agriculture. Agriculture Handbook. (US ISSN 0065-4612) **126**
U.S. Department of Agriculture. Agriculture Information Bulletin. (US ISSN 0065-4639) **126**
U.S. Department of Agriculture. Animal and Plant Health Inspection Service. Cooperative State-Federal Brucellosis Eradication Program: Statistical Tables. (US) **144**
U.S. Department of Agriculture. Animal and Plant Health Inspection Service. Cooperative State-Federal Bovine Tuberculosis Eradication Program: Statistical Tables. (US) **144**
U.S. Department of Agriculture. Animal and Plant Health Inspection Service. Reported Arthropod-Borne Encephalitides in Horses and Other Equidae. (US) **4816**
U.S. Department of Agriculture. Animal Science Research Branch. Hatcheries and Dealers Participating in the National Improvement Plan *see* Hatcheries and Dealers Participating in the National Poultry Improvement Plan **217**
U.S. Department of Agriculture. Cotton and Wool Outlook and Situation *see* U.S. Department of Agriculture. Cotton and Wool Situation and Outlook **158**
U.S. Department of Agriculture. Cotton and Wool Situation and Outlook. (US) **158**
U.S. Department of Agriculture. Dairy Outlook and Situation *see* U.S. Department of Agriculture. Dairy Situation and Outlook **204**
U.S. Department of Agriculture. Dairy Situation and Outlook. (US) **204**
U.S. Department of Agriculture. Economic Research Service. Agricultural Economics Report *see* U.S. Department of Agriculture. Agricultural Economic Reports **158**
U.S. Department of Agriculture. Economic Research Service. Farm Income Situation *see* U.S. Department of Agriculture. Agricultural Outlook **158**
U.S. Department of Agriculture. Economic Research Service. National Food Situation *see* National Food Review **155**
U.S. Department of Agriculture. Economics Management Staff. Sugar and Sweetener Report *see* U.S. Department of Agriculture. Sugar and Sweetener Situation and Outlook **159**
U.S. Department of Agriculture. Farmer Cooperative Service. Information (Series) *see* U.S. Department of Agriculture. Agricultural Cooperative Service. Cooperative Information Report Series **126**
U.S. Department of Agriculture. Fats and Oils Situation *see* U.S. Department of Agriculture. Oil Crops Situation and Outlook Report **158**
U.S. Department of Agriculture. Feed Outlook and Situation *see* U.S. Department of Agriculture. Feed Situation and Outlook **208**
U.S. Department of Agriculture. Feed Situation *see* U.S. Department of Agriculture. Feed Situation and Outlook **208**
U.S. Department of Agriculture. Feed Situation and Outlook. (US) **208**
U.S. Department of Agriculture. Fruit and Tree Nuts Situation and Outlook Report. (US ISSN 1051-7901) **195**
U.S. Department of Agriculture. Fruit Situation and Outlook Report *see* U.S. Department of Agriculture. Fruit and Tree Nuts Situation and Outlook Report **195**
U.S. Department of Agriculture. Home and Garden Bulletin. (US ISSN 0073-3075) **2140**
U.S. Department of Agriculture. Home Economics Research Report. (US ISSN 0073-3113) **2450**
U.S. Department of Agriculture. Livestock and Poultry Outlook and Situation *see* U.S. Department of Agriculture. Livestock and Poultry Situation and Outlook **227**
U.S. Department of Agriculture. Livestock and Poultry Situation and Outlook. (US) **227**, 158
U.S. Department of Agriculture. Livestock and Poultry Situation *see* U.S. Department of Agriculture. Livestock and Poultry Situation and Outlook **227**
U.S. Department of Agriculture. Marketing Research Report. (US ISSN 0082-9781) **158**
U.S. Department of Agriculture. Oil Crops Outlook and Situation *see* U.S. Department of Agriculture. Oil Crops Situation and Outlook Report **158**
U.S. Department of Agriculture. Oil Crops Situation and Outlook Report. (US) **158**
U.S. Department of Agriculture. Production Research Reports. (US ISSN 0082-979X) **158**
U.S. Department of Agriculture. Report of the Secretary of Agriculture. (US ISSN 0082-9803) **126**
U.S. Department of Agriculture. Rice Outlook and Situation *see* U.S. Department of Agriculture. Rice Situation and Outlook Report **208**
U.S. Department of Agriculture. Rice Situation and Outlook Report. (US) **208**
U.S. Department of Agriculture. Sugar and Sweetener Outlook and Situation *see* U.S. Department of Agriculture. Sugar and Sweetener Situation and Outlook **159**
U.S. Department of Agriculture. Sugar and Sweetener Situation and Outlook.(US) **159**, 2083
U.S. Department of Agriculture. Technical Bulletin. (US ISSN 0082-9811) **126**
U.S. Department of Agriculture. Tobacco Outlook and Situation Report *see* U.S. Department of Agriculture. Tobacco Situation and Outlook Report **159**
U.S. Department of Agriculture. Tobacco Situation and Outlook Report. (US) **159**, 4645
U.S. Department of Agriculture. Vegetable and Specialty Crop Situation and Outlook. (US) **159**
U.S. Department of Agriculture. Vegetable Outlook and Situation *see* U.S. Department of Agriculture. Vegetable and Specialty Crop Situation and Outlook **159**
U.S. Department of Agriculture. Wheat Outlook and Situation *see* U.S. Department of Agriculture. Wheat Situation and Outlook **159**
U.S. Department of Agriculture. Wheat Situation and Outlook. (US ISSN 0895-1454) **159**, 208
U.S. Department of Agriculture. Yearbook of Agriculture. (US ISSN 0084-3628) **126**
†U.S. Department of Commerce. Consumer Goods and Services Division. Franchise Opportunities Handbook. (US) **5295**
U.S. Department of Commerce. Latin American - Caribbean Business Department Center. Bulletin. (US) **936**
U.S. Department of Commerce. National Oceanic and Atmospheric Administration. Oceanographic Monthly Summary. (US) **1611**
†U.S. Department of Commerce. Publications Catalog. (US ISSN 0277-7207) **5295**
U.S. Department of Commerce. Trade Lists. (US) **923**
U.S. Department of Defense. Defense Department Report. (US ISSN 0091-6919) **4076**
U.S. Department of Defense. Defense Program and Defense Budget. (US ISSN 0082-9862) **3474**
U.S. Department of Defense. Index of Specifications and Standards. (US ISSN 0363-8464) **3449**, 3474
U.S. Department of Defense. Report of Secretary of Defense to the Congress. (US ISSN 0098-3888) **3474**
U.S. Department of Education. National Center for Education Statistics. Academic Libraries. (US) **1680**, 1718
U.S. Department of Education. National Center for Education Statistics. Completions in Institutions of Higher Education. (US) **1680**, 1718
U.S. Department of Education. National Center for Education Statistics. Digest of Education Statistics. (US) **1680**
U.S. Department of Education. National Center for Education Statistics. Earned Degrees Conferred *see* U.S. Department of Education. National Center for Education Statistics. Completions in Institutions of Higher Education **1680**
U.S. Department of Education. National Center for Education Statistics. Fall Enrollment in Higher Education. (US ISSN 0362-5036) **1680**, 1718
U.S. Department of Education. National Center for Education Statistics. Library Statistics of Colleges and Universities *see* U.S. Department of Education. National Center for Education Statistics. Academic Libraries **1680**
U.S. Department of Education. National Center for Education Statistics. Public Elementary and Secondary State Aggregate Data, by State. (US) **1680**, 4591
U.S. Department of Education. National Center for Education Statistics. State Higher Education Profiles. (US) **1681**, 1718
U.S. Department of Education. Opportunities for Teachers Abroad. (US) **1724**
U.S. Department of Energy. Annual Report to Congress on the Automotive Technology Development Program. (US ISSN 0270-756X) **4704**
†U.S. Department of Energy. D.O.E. Patents Available for Licensing. (US) **5295**
U.S. Department of Energy. Patents Available for Leasing *see* U.S. Department of Energy. D.O.E. Patents Available for Licensing **5295**

Title

U.S. FOOD 6757

U.S. Department of Energy. Strategic Petroleum Reserve Office. Annual Report. (US) **3703**
U.S. Department of Energy Reports. (US) **1796**
U.S. Department of Energy This Month see D O E This Month **1785**
†U.S. Department of Health and Human Services. Annual Report to the Congress of the United States on Services Provided to Handicapped Children in Project Head Start. (US) **5295**
†U.S. Department of Health, Education, and Welfare. Catalog of H E W Assistance Providing Financial Support and Service to States, Communities, Organizations, Individuals. (US ISSN 0082-9889) **5295**
†U.S. Department of Health, Education and Welfare. Health, Education and Welfare Trends. (US ISSN 0082-9897) **5295**
U.S. Department of Housing and Urban Development. Annual Report. (US ISSN 0565-2820) **2497**
†U.S. Department of Housing and Urban Development. Interim Guide for Environment Assessment. (US) **5295**
†U.S. Department of Housing and Urban Development. Statistical Yearbook. (US ISSN 0147-7870) **5295**
U.S. Department of Housing and Urban Development Newsletter see H U D Newsletter **5202**
U.S. Department of Justice. Annual Report of the Attorney General of the United States. (US ISSN 0082-9943) **2688**
U.S. Department of Justice. National Institute of Justice. Document Retrieval Index see N C J R S Document Retrieval Index **1518**
U.S. Department of Justice. Office of Legal Counsel. Opinions. (US) **2688**
U.S. Department of Justice. Opinions of Attorney General. (US ISSN 0082-9951) **2688**
U.S. Department of Labor. Employee Retirement Income Security Act. Report to Congress. (US ISSN 0271-1567) **996**, **2544**
U.S. Department of Labor. Employment and Training Administration. Area Trends in Employment and Unemployment. (US ISSN 0004-0916) **996**
†U.S. Department of State. African Series. (US ISSN 0083-0003) **5295**
†U.S. Department of State. Bulletin. (US ISSN 0041-7610) **5295**
U.S. Department of State. Bureau of Public Affairs. Current Policy see Dispatch (Washington) **3955**
U.S. Department of State. Commercial Policy Series. (US ISSN 0083-002X) **923**
†U.S. Department of State. Department and Foreign Service Series. (US ISSN 0083-0038) **5295**
U.S. Department of State. Diplomatic List. (US ISSN 0012-3099) **3976**
†U.S. Department of State. East Asian and Pacific Series. (US ISSN 0083-0054) **5295**
U.S. Department of State. Economic Cooperation Series. (US ISSN 0083-0062) **936**
†U.S. Department of State. European and British Commonwealth Series. (US ISSN 0083-0070) **5295**
†U.S. Department of State. General Foreign Policy Series. (US ISSN 0083-0097) **5295**
†U.S. Department of State. Inter-American Series. (US ISSN 0083-0143) **5295**
†U.S. Department of State. International Information and Cultural Series. (US ISSN 0083-0119) **5295**
†U.S. Department of State. International Organization and Conference Series. (US ISSN 0083-0127) **5295**
†U.S. Department of State. International Organization Series. (US ISSN 0083-0135) **5295**

U.S. Department of State. Key Officers of Foreign Service Posts. (US ISSN 0023-0790) **3976**
U.S. Department of State. Library. Commercial Library Program. Publications List. (US) **2796**, 414, 3939
†U.S. Department of State. Near East and South Asian Series. (US) **5295**
U.S. Department of State. Newsletter see State (Washington) **3972**
U.S. Department of State. Office of the Geographer. Geographic Notes. (US ISSN 0083-016X) **2264**, 3931
U.S. Department of State. Treaties and Other International Acts Series. (US ISSN 0083-0186) **2730**
U.S. Department of State. Treaties in Force. (US ISSN 0083-0194) **2730**
U.S. Department of the Interior. Decisions of the Department of the Interior. (US ISSN 0011-7331) **4076**, 2688
U.S. Department of Transportation. Bibliographic Lists. (US ISSN 0083-0380) **4668**, 414
U.S. Department of Transportation. Fiscal Year Budget in Brief. (US ISSN 0092-3117) **4660**
U.S. Department of Transportation. Highway Safety Stewardship Report. (US ISSN 0277-2310) **4722**
U.S. Department of Transportation. National Transportation Statistics. Annual. (US) **1801**, 4591
U.S. Department of Transportation. Office of University Research. Awards to Academic Institutions by the Department of Transportation. (US ISSN 0099-2267) **4660**
U.S. Department of Veterans Affairs. Summary of Medical Programs. (US) **3159**
U.S. Director of Selective Service. Semiannual Report. (US) **3474**
U.S. Earth Science Information Center. Newsletter. (US) **2264**
U.S. Energy Information Administration. Annual Report to Congress. (US ISSN 0161-5807) **1796**
U.S. Energy Information Administration. Monthly Petroleum Statistics Report see Petroleum Supply Monthly **3699**
U.S. Energy Information Administration. Quarterly Coal Report. (US) **1796**, 3497
U.S. Energy Information Administration. Short-Term Energy Outlook. (US) **1796**
U.S. Energy Information Administration. U S Crude Oil, Natural Gas, and Natural Gas Liquids see U S Crude Oil, Natural Gas, and Natural Gas Liquids **3703**
U.S. Energy Information Administration. Weekly Petroleum Status Report. (US) **3703**
U.S. Environmental Protection Agency. Clean Water: Report to Congress. (US ISSN 0092-9433) **1498**
U.S. Environmental Protection Agency. Journal Holdings Report. (US) **1975**, 414
U.S. Environmental Protection Agency. Office of Research and Development. Program Guide. (US) **1970**
U.S. Environmental Protection Agency. Pesticides Enforcement Division. Notices of Judgement under Federal Insecticide, Fungicide, and Rodenticide Act. (US ISSN 0083-0518) **195**
U.S. Environmental Protection Agency Journal see E P A Journal **1947**
U.S. Equal Employment Opportunity Commission. Annual Report. (US ISSN 0083-0526) **996**, 3948
U.S. Equal Employment Opportunity Commission Compliance Manual (Weekly) see E E O C Compliance Manual (Weekly) **5183**
U.S. Federal Aviation Administration. National Aviation System: Challenges of the Decade Ahead see U.S. Federal Aviation Administration. National Aviation System: Development and Capital Needs **4677**

U.S. Federal Aviation Administration. National Aviation System: Development and Capital Needs. (US) **4677**
U.S. Federal Aviation Administration. National Aviation System Policy Summary see U.S. Federal Aviation Administration. National Aviation System: Development and Capital Needs **4677**
U.S. Federal Aviation Administration. Systems Research and Development. Report FAA-RD. (US) **67**
U.S. Federal Aviation Administration Overview of the F A A Engineering & Development Programs see Overview of the F A A Engineering & Development Programs **60**
U.S. Federal Bureau of Investigation. Bomb Summary. (US ISSN 0360-3245) **1524**
U.S. Federal Bureau of Investigation Law Enforcement Bulletin see F B I Law Enforcement Bulletin **1514**
U.S. Federal Communications Commission. I N F Bulletins. (US ISSN 0083-0607) **1345**
U.S. Federal Deposit Insurance Corporation. Annual Report. (US ISSN 0083-0658) **2544**, 802
U.S. Federal Deposit Insurance Corporation. Bank Operating Statistics. (US ISSN 0083-0666) **742**
U.S. Federal Deposit Insurance Corporation. Changes Among Operating Banks and Branches. (US ISSN 0083-0674) **802**
U.S. Federal Deposit Insurance Corporation. Federal Deposit Insurance Act, Rules and Regulations, and Related Laws see F D I C Enforcement Decisions **778**
U.S. Federal Deposit Insurance Corporation. News Releases. (US) **802**
U.S. Federal Deposit Insurance Corporation. Operating Banking Offices. (US) **802**
U.S. Federal Deposit Insurance Corporation. Operating Bank Offices see U.S. Federal Deposit Insurance Corporation. Operating Banking Offices **802**
U.S. Federal Deposit Insurance Corporation. Trust Assets of Banks and Trust Companies. (US ISSN 0278-5692) **802**
U.S. Federal Deposit Insurance Corporation. Trust Assets of Insured Commercial Banks see U.S. Federal Deposit Insurance Corporation. Trust Assets of Banks and Trust Companies **802**
U.S. Federal Deposit Insurance Corporation Enforcement Decisions see F D I C Enforcement Decisions **778**
U.S. Federal Election Commission. Annual Report. (US) **3931**
†U.S. Federal Fire Council. Federal Fire Experience for Fiscal Year. (US ISSN 0083-0682) **5295**
†U.S. Federal Fire Council. Minutes of Annual Meeting. (US ISSN 0083-0690) **5295**
†U.S. Federal Fire Council. Recommended Practices. (US ISSN 0083-0704) **5295**
U.S. Federal Highway Administration. Federally Coordinated Program of Highway Research and Development.(US ISSN 0361-4204) **4722**
U.S. Federal Highway Administration. Highway and Urban Mass Transportation. (US) **4660**
U.S. Federal Highway Administration. Highway Planning Technical Reports.(US ISSN 0073-2184) **1875**
U.S. Federal Highway Administration. Highway Statistics. (US) **4668**
U.S. Federal Highway Administration. Monthly Motor Gasoline Reported by States. (US ISSN 0196-0806) **3707**, 1801, 4591

U.S. Federal Home Loan Bank Board. Report. (US ISSN 0083-0720) **802**, 4159
U.S. Federal Home Loan Bank Board. Research Paper see Office of Thrift Supervision **794**
U.S. Federal Home Loan Bank Board. Trends in the Savings and Loan Field.(US ISSN 0083-0747) **802**, 4159
U.S. Federal Housing Administration. F H A Homes. (US ISSN 0091-4932) **2497**
U.S. Federal Maritime Commission. Annual Report. (US ISSN 0083-0755) **4741**
U.S. Federal Mediation and Conciliation Service. Annual Report. (US ISSN 0083-0771) **996**
†U.S. Federal Power Commission. Annual Report. (US ISSN 0083-078X) **5295**
U.S. Federal Railroad Administration. Office of Safety. Accident Bulletin see U.S. Federal Railroad Administration. Office of Safety. Accident - Incident Bulletin **4716**
U.S. Federal Railroad Administration. Office of Safety. Accident - Incident Bulletin. (US ISSN 0163-4674) **4716**
U.S. Federal Register. (Microfiche Edition). (US ISSN 0042-1219) **2688**
U.S. Federal Reserve System. Annual Report. (US ISSN 0083-0887) **802**
U.S. Federal Reserve System. Annual Statistical Digest. (US) **802**, 743
U.S. Federal Reserve System. Selected Interest and Exchange Rates. Weekly Series of Charts. (US) **802**
U.S. Federal Trade Commission. Annual Report. (US ISSN 0083-0917) **840**
U.S. Federal Trade Commission. Court Decisions Pertaining to the Federal Trade Commission. (US) **840**, 2688
U.S. Federal Trade Commission. Federal Trade Commission Decisions, Findings, Orders and Stipulations. (US ISSN 0083-0925) **840**, 2688
†U.S. Federal Trade Commission. Quarterly Financial Report for Manufacturing, Mining and Trade Corporations. (US ISSN 0098-681X) **5295**
U.S. Federal Trade Commission. Statutes and Court Decisions Pertaining to the Federal Trade Commission. Supplements see U.S. Federal Trade Commission. Court Decisions Pertaining to the Federal Trade Commission **840**
U.S. Fish and Wildlife Service. Investigations in Fish Control. (US ISSN 0565-0704) **2050**
U.S. Fish and Wildlife Service. National Survey of Hunting, Fishing and Wildlife-Associated Recreation. (US) **4499**, 4559, 4591
U.S. Fish and Wildlife Service. Research Reports. (US ISSN 0083-0941) **2050**, 1498
U.S. Fish and Wildlife Service. Selected List of Federal Laws and Treaties Relating to Sport Fish and Wildlife. (US ISSN 0093-4631) **2688**, 1498
U.S. Fish and Wildlife Service. Wildlife Leaflets. (US ISSN 0084-0165) **1498**
U.S. Food and Drug Administration. National Drug Code Directory. (US ISSN 0077-4235) **3745**
U.S. Food and Drug Administration. Compliance Policy Guidance. Manual see F D A Compliance Policy Guidance. Manual **2066**
U.S. Food and Drug Administration Consumer see F D A Consumer **1504**
U.S. Food and Drug Administration Enforcement Report see F D A Enforcement Report **1514**
U.S. Food and Drug Administration Medical Bulletin see F D A Medical Bulletin **3725**

6758 U.S. FOOD

U.S. Food and Nutrition Service. Food and Nutrition Programs. (US ISSN 0360-4594) **3614**

U.S. Food Safety and Inspection Service. Technical Information. Meat and Poultry Inspection Program. (US) **2083**

U.S. Food Safety and Quality Service. Issuances of the Meat and Poultry Inspection Program. (US) **227**

U.S. Foreign Agricultural Service. Food and Agricultural Export Directory. (US ISSN 0083-0976) **159, 923**

U.S. Foreign Agricultural Trade Statistical Report. Calendar Year. (US) **144, 743**

U.S. Foreign Agricultural Trade Statistical Report. Fiscal Year. (US) **144, 743**

U.S. Foreign Broadcast Information Service. Daily Reports: Latin America.(US) **3931**

U.S. Foreign Broadcast Information Service. Daily Reports: Near East & South Asia. (US) **3931**

U.S. Foreign Broadcast Information Service. Daily Reports: People's Republic of China. (US) **3931**

U.S. Foreign Broadcast Information Service. Daily Reports: South Asia see U.S. Foreign Broadcast Information Service. Daily Reports: Near East & South Asia **3931**

U.S. Foreign Broadcast Information Service. Daily Reports: Sub-Saharan Africa. (US) **3931**

U.S. Foreign Broadcast Information Service. Daily Reports: Soviet Union. (US ISSN 0565-5560) **3931**

U.S. Foreign Broadcast Information Service. Daily Reports (FBIS). (US) **3931**

U.S. Foreign Broadcast Information Service. Daily Reports: Western Europe. (US ISSN 0271-0269) **3932**

U.S. Foreign Broadcast Information Service. Trends. (US) **3976**

U.S. Forest Service. General Technical Report I N T. (Intermountain Research Station) (US ISSN 0092-9654) **2109**

U.S. Forest Service. General Technical Report N C. (US) **2109**

U.S. Forest Service. General Technical Report N E. (Northeastern Forest Experiment Station) (US ISSN 0083-2480) **2109**

U.S. Forest Service. Intermountain Forest and Range Experiment Station. Recent Reports. see U.S. Forest Service. Intermountain Research Station. Recent Reports **2109**

U.S. Forest Service. Intermountain Research Station. Recent Reports. (US) **2109**

U.S. Forest Service. North Central Forest Experiment Station. List of Publications. (US) **2113**

U.S. Forest Service. Pacific Southwest Forest and Range Experiment Station. General Technical Report P S W. (US ISSN 0196-2094) **2109**

U.S. Forest Service. Research Note I N T. (US) **2109**

U.S. Forest Service. Research Note N C.(US ISSN 0361-2449) **2109**

U.S. Forest Service. Research Note R M. (Rocky Mountain Forest and Range Experiment Station) (US ISSN 0502-4994) **2109**

U.S. Forest Service. Research Paper I N T. (US) **2109**

U.S. Forest Service. Research Paper N C. (US ISSN 0565-8721) **2110**

U.S. Forest Service. Research Paper R M. (Rocky Mountain Forest and Range Experiment Station) (US ISSN 0502-5001) **2110**

U.S. Forest Service. Resource Bulletin I N T. (US) **2110**

U.S. Forest Service. Resource Bulletin N C. (US ISSN 0565-873X) **2110**

U.S. Forest Service. Resource Bulletin P N W. (Pacific Northwest Research Station) (US) **2110**

U.S. Forest Service. Southern Forest Experiment Station. Research Accomplished see U.S. Forest Service. Southern Forest Experiment Station. Recent Publications **2110**

U.S. Forest Service. Southern Forest Experiment Station. Recent Publications. (US) **2110**

U.S. General Accounting Office. Monthly List of G A O Reports. (US ISSN 0364-8265) **4083**

U.S. General Accounting Office. Office of the General Counsel. Digests of Unpublished Decisions of the Comptroller General of the United States. (US ISSN 0145-1502) **4076**

U.S. General Accounting Office Documents see G A O Documents **751**

U.S. General Accounting Office Review see G A O Review **4061**

U.S. General Services Administration. Catalog of Federal Domestic Assistance. (US) **4076**

U.S. General Services Administration. Management Report. (US ISSN 0091-6242) **4423**

U.S. Geological Survey. Board on Geographic Names. Decisions of Geographic Names in the United States. (US ISSN 0363-6828) **2264**

†U.S. Government Films for Public Educational Use. (US ISSN 0083-1166) **5295**

U.S. Hydrographic Conference. Biennial Meeting. Proceedings. (US ISSN 0276-4849) **1611**

U.S. Immigration and Naturalization Service see I and N Reporter **3982**

U.S. Immigration and Naturalization Service. Administrative Decisions Under Immigration and Nationality Laws. (US ISSN 0083-1220) **3988**

U.S. Immigration and Naturalization Service. Administrative Decisions Under Immigration and Nationality Laws. Interim Decisions of the Department of Justice. (US ISSN 0083-1239) **3988**

U.S. Immigration and Naturalization Service. Annual Report. (US ISSN 0083-1247) **3988**

U.S. Industrial College of the Armed Forces. Monographs. R Series. (US ISSN 0083-1328) **3474**

U.S. Industrial Outlook (Year). (US) **1086**

U.S. Institute of Tropical Forestry. Annual Letter. (PR) **2110**

U.S. Interagency Committee on Population Research. Inventory and Analysis of Federal Population Research. (US) **3988**

U.S. Internal Revenue Service. Annual Report. (US ISSN 0083-1476) **1111**

U.S. Internal Revenue Service. Tax Guide for Small Business. (US ISSN 0083-1484) **1111, 1119**

U.S. International Development Cooperation Agency. Congressional Presentation, Fiscal Year. (US ISSN 0276-6469) **936**

U.S. International Trade Commission. Annual Report. (US) **923**

U.S. International Trade Commission. Operation of the Trade Agreements Program. (US ISSN 0083-3444) **923**

U.S. International Trade Commission. Quarterly Report to the Congress and the East-West Foreign Trade Board on Trade Between the United States and the Nonmarket Economy Countries. (US ISSN 0098-910X) **923**

U.S. Interstate Commerce Commission. Annual Report. (US ISSN 0083-1514) **840**

†U.S. Interstate Commerce Commission. Interstate Commerce Acts Annotated.(US ISSN 0083-1522) **5295**

U.S. Interstate Commerce Commission. Interstate Commerce Commission Reports. Decisions of the Interstate Commerce Commission of the United States. (US ISSN 0083-1530) **840**

†U.S. Labor - Management Services Administration. Decisions and Reports on Rulings of the Assistant Secretary of Labor for Labor - Management Relations. (US ISSN 0091-2646) **5295**

U.S. Library of Congress. Accessions List: Brazil see U.S. Library of Congress. Accessions List: Brazil and Uruguay **414**

U.S. Library of Congress. Accessions List: Brazil and Uruguay. Annual List of Serials. (US ISSN 1042-1734) **414**

U.S. Library of Congress. Accessions List: Brazil and Uruguay. (US ISSN 1041-1763) **414**

U.S. Library of Congress. Accessions List: Brazil. Annual List of Serials see U.S. Library of Congress. Accessions List: Brazil and Uruguay. Annual List of Serials **414**

U.S. Library of Congress. Accessions List: Eastern Africa. (US ISSN 0090-371X) **414**

U.S. Library of Congress. Accessions List: Indonesia, Malaysia, Singapore and Brunei see U.S. Library of Congress. Accessions List: Southeast Asia **415**

U.S. Library of Congress. Accessions List: Middle East. (US ISSN 0041-7769) **414**

U.S. Library of Congress. Accessions List: South Asia. (US ISSN 0271-6445) **414**

U.S. Library of Congress. Accessions List: Southeast Asia. (US ISSN 0096-2341) **415**

U.S. Library of Congress. Annual Report of the Librarian of Congress. (US ISSN 0083-1565) **2788**

U.S. Library of Congress. Cataloging Service see U.S. Library of Congress. Cataloging Service Bulletin **2788**

U.S. Library of Congress. Cataloging Service Bulletin. (US ISSN 0160-8029) **2788**

U.S. Library of Congress. Congressional Research Service. Digest of Public General Bills and Resolutions. (US) **2688, 4076**

U.S. Library of Congress. Information Bulletin. (US ISSN 0041-7904) **2788**

U.S. Library of Congress. L.C. Classification - Additions and Changes. (US ISSN 0041-7912) **2788**

U.S. Library of Congress. Library of Congress Publications in Print. (US ISSN 0083-1603) **2796**

U.S. Library of Congress. Manuscript Division. Acquisitions. (US ISSN 0275-9616) **4138**

U.S. Library of Congress. Manuscript Division. Registers of Papers. (US ISSN 0083-1611) **2325**

U.S. Library of Congress. Monthly Checklist of State Publications. (US ISSN 0027-0288) **4083**

U.S. Library of Congress. National Library for the Blind and Physically Handicapped. News see U.S. Library of Congress. National Library Service for the Blind and Physically Handicapped. News **2296**

U.S. Library of Congress. National Library Service for the Blind and Physically Handicapped. News. (US) **2296, 2788, 3159**

U.S. Library of Congress. Newspapers Received Currently. (US) **2576**

U.S. Library of Congress Catalog - Music and Phonorecords see Music, Books on Music and Sound Recordings **3589**

U.S. Library of Congress Folk Archive Finding Aid see L C Folk Archive Finding Aid **2767**

U.S. Library of Congress Folk Archive Reference Aid see L C Folk Archive Reference Aid **2767**

U.S. Library of Congress Science Tracer Bullet see L C Science Tracer Bullet **4356**

†U.S. M A Library Bulletin. (U.S. Military Academy Library) (US) **5295**

U.S. Maritime Administration. Annual Report see M A R A D (Year) **4732**

U.S. Maritime Administration Year) see M A R A D (Year) **4732**

U.S. Merchandise Trade: Exports, General Imports, and Imports for Consumption - Standard International Trade Classification Revision 3 - Commodity by Country. (US ISSN 1057-9680) **923**

U.S. Military Academy Library Library Bulletin see U.S. M A Library Bulletin **5295**

U.S. Mine Safety and Health Administration. Informational Report. (US) **3497**

U.S. Mining Enforcement and Safety Administration. Informational Report see U.S. Mine Safety and Health Administration. Informational Report **3497**

U.S. National Aeronautics and Space Administration. Research and Technology Operating Plan (RTOP) Summary. (US) **64, 4612**

U.S. National Aeronautics and Space Administration. Technical Memorandum. (US ISSN 0499-9320) **64**

U.S. National Aeronautics and Space Administration. Technical Notes. (US ISSN 0077-3131) **64**

U.S. National Aeronautics and Space Administration. Technical Reports. (US ISSN 0077-314X) **64**

U.S. National Aeronautics and Space Administration. Technical Translations. (US ISSN 0077-3158) **64**

U.S. National Aeronautics and Space Administration Facts see N A S A Facts **59**

U.S. National Aeronautics and Space Administration Magazine see N A S A Magazine **59**

U.S. National Aeronautics and Space Administration Patent Abstracts Bibliography: A Continuing Bibliography. Section 1. Abstracts see N A S A Patent Abstracts Bibliography: A Continuing Bibliography. Section 1. Abstracts **3680**

U.S. National Aeronautics and Space Administration Patent Abstracts Bibliography: A Continuing Bibliography. Section 2. Indexes see N A S A Patent Abstracts Bibliography: A Continuing Bibliography. Section 2. Indexes **3680**

U.S. National Aeronautics and Space Administration Report to Educators see N A S A Report to Educators **59**

U.S. National Arthritis Advisory Board. Annual Report see Advisory Board for Arthritis and Musculoskeletal and Skin Diseases. Annual Report **3368**

U.S. National Bureau of Standards. Building Science Series see N I S T Building Science Series **625**

U.S. National Bureau of Standards. Federal Information Processing Standards see Federal Information Processing Standards Publication **3446**

U.S. National Bureau of Standards. Journal of Research see National Institute of Standards and Technology. Journal of Research **3448**

†U.S. National Bureau of Standards. Journal of Research. Section C: Engineering and Instrumentation. (US ISSN 0022-4316) **5295**

U.S. National Bureau of Standards. Monograph see N I S T Monograph **3447**

U.S. National Bureau of Standards. National Standard Reference Data Series see N S R D S - N B S: National Standard Reference Data Series **3447**

U.S. National Bureau of Standards. Technical Notes see N I S T Technical Notes 3447
U.S. National Cartographic Information Center. Newsletter see U.S. Earth Science Information Center. Newsletter 2264
U.S. National Center for Education Statistics. Digest of Educational Statistics see U.S. Department of Education. National Center for Education Statistics. Digest of Education Statistics 1680
U.S. National Center for Education Statistics. Financial Statistics of Institutions of Higher Education see U.S. Department of Education. National Center for Education Statistics. State Higher Education Profiles 1681
U.S. National Center for Education Statistics. Revenues and Expenditures for Public Elementary and Secondary Education see U.S. Department of Education. National Center for Education Statistics. Public Elementary and Secondary State Aggregate Data, by State 1680
U.S. National Center for Health Care Statistics. Vital and Health Statistics. Series 12. Data from the Institutional Population Surveys see U.S. National Center for Health Statistics. Vital and Health Statistics. Series 13. Data on Health Resources Utilization 4114
U.S. National Center for Health Statistics. Advance Data from Vital and Health Statistics. (US) 4114
U.S. National Center for Health Statistics. Catalog of Publications. (US ISSN 0278-4912) 4119, 24, 3996
U.S. National Center for Health Statistics. Current Listing and Topical Index to the Vital and Health Statistics Series see U.S. National Center for Health Statistics. Catalog of Publications 4119
U.S. National Center for Health Statistics. Monthly Vital Statistics Report. (US ISSN 0364-0396) 3996
U.S. National Center for Health Statistics. Vital and Health Statistics. Series 1. Programs and Collection Procedures. (US ISSN 0083-2014) 4119, 3996
U.S. National Center for Health Statistics. Vital and Health Statistics. Series 2. Data Evaluation and Methods Research. (US ISSN 0083-2057) 4119, 3996
U.S. National Center for Health Statistics. Vital and Health Statistics. Series 3. Analytical Studies. (US ISSN 0083-2065) 4119, 3996
U.S. National Center for Health Statistics. Vital and Health Statistics. Series 4. Documents and Committee Report. (US ISSN 0083-2073) 4119, 3996
U.S. National Center for Health Statistics. Vital and Health Statistics. Series 10. Data from the Health Interview Survey. (US ISSN 0083-1972) 4114
U.S. National Center for Health Statistics. Vital and Health Statistics. Series 11. Data from the Health and Nutrition Examination Survey. (US) 4114
U.S. National Center for Health Statistics. Vital and Health Statistics. Series 11. Data from the Health Examination Survey see U.S. National Center for Health Statistics. Vital and Health Statistics. Series 11. Data from the Health and Nutrition Examination Survey 4114
U.S. National Center for Health Statistics. Vital and Health Statistics. Series 13. Data on Health Resources Utilization. (US) 4114, 2470
U.S. National Center for Health Statistics. Vital and Health Statistics. Series 14. Data on Health Resources. (US) 4114

U.S. National Center for Health Statistics. Vital and Health Statistics. Series 20. Data on Mortality. (US ISSN 0083-2022) 4119, 3996
U.S. National Center for Health Statistics. Vital and Health Statistics. Series 21. Data on Natality, Marriage, and Divorce. (US ISSN 0083-2030) 4119, 3067, 3996
U.S. National Center for Health Statistics. Vital and Health Statistics. Series 22. Data on Natality and Mortality Surveys see U.S. National Center for Health Statistics. Vital and Health Statistics. Series 20. Data on Mortality 4119
U.S. National Center for Health Statistics. Vital and Health Statistics. Series 22. Data on Natality and Mortality Surveys see U.S. National Center for Health Statistics. Vital and Health Statistics. Series 21. Data on Natality, Marriage, and Divorce 4119
U.S. National Center for Health Statistics. Vital and Health Statistics. Series 23: Data from the National Survey of Family Growth. (US) 3996
U.S. National Center for Social Statistics. Fair Hearings in Public Assistance. (US) 4423
U.S. National Commission for Employment Policy. Annual Report. (US) 996
U.S. National Commission for Manpower Policy. Annual Report to the President and the Congress see U.S. National Commission for Employment Policy. Annual Report 996
U.S. National Commission on Libraries and Information Science News see N C L I S News 5241
U.S. National Communicable Disease Center. Morbidity and Mortality see U.S. Centers for Disease Control. Morbidity and Mortality Weekly Report 4114
U.S. National Credit Union Administration. Annual Report. (US) 802, 832
U.S. National Earthquake Information Service. Preliminary Determination of Epicenters, Monthly Listing. (US ISSN 0364-7072) 1596
U.S. National Endowment for the Arts. Annual Report. (US ISSN 0083-2103) 347
U.S. National Highway Traffic Safety Administration. Motor Vehicle Safety Defect Recall Campaigns. (US ISSN 0565-7717) 4704
†U.S. National Institute of Neurological Diseases and Stroke. N I N D S Research Profiles: Summary of Research. (US ISSN 0083-2162) 5296
U.S. National Institute of Standards and Technology Building Science Series see N I S T Building Science Series 625
U.S. National Institute of Standards and Technology Handbook see N I S T Handbook 3447
U.S. National Institute of Standards and Technology Monograph see N I S T Monograph 3447
U.S. National Institute of Standards and Technology Special Publication see N I S T Special Publication 3447
U.S. National Institute of Standards and Technology Technical Note see N I S T Technical Note 3447
U.S. National Institute on Drug Abuse. Research Issues. (US) 1539
U.S. National Institute on Drug Abuse. Research Monograph Series. (US) 1539
U.S. National Institute on Drug Abuse. Statistical Series D. Client Oriented Data Acquisition Process. Quarterly Report see U.S. National Institute on Drug Abuse. Statistical Series D. Data from the Client Oriented Data Acquisition Process. Quarterly Report. Provisional Data 3812

U.S. National Institute on Drug Abuse. Statistical Series D. Data from the Client Oriented Data Acquisition Process. Quarterly Report. Provisional Data. (US ISSN 0161-603X) 3812, 4591
U.S. National Institutes of Health. Division of Research Resources. Program Highlights see U.S. National Institutes of Health. National Center for Research Resources. Program Highlights 3181
U.S. National Institutes of Health. National Center for Research Resources. Program Highlights. (US) 3181, 3263
U.S. National Labor Relations Board. Annual Report. (US ISSN 0083-2200) 996
U.S. National Labor Relations Board. Court Decisions Relating to the National Labor Relations Act. (US ISSN 0083-2219) 996
U.S. National Labor Relations Board. Office of the General Counsel. Quarterly Report. (US) 996
U.S. National Labor Relations Board. Weekly Summary of the National Labor Relations Board Cases. (US) 996
U.S. National Labor Relations Board Case Handling Manual see N L R B Case Handling Manual 2656
U.S. National Library of Medicine. Annual Report see National Library of Medicine. Programs and Services 2775
U.S. National Marine Fisheries Service. Grant-in-Aid for Fisheries: Program Activities. (US ISSN 0094-7008) 2050
U.S. National Marine Fisheries Service. Imports and Exports of Fishery Products. Annual Summary. (US) 2050
U.S. National Marine Fisheries Service. Special Scientific Report: Fisheries see U.S. National Marine Fisheries Service. Technical Report 2050
U.S. National Marine Fisheries Service. Technical Report. (US) 2050
U.S. National Mediation Board. Annual Report. (US ISSN 0083-2286) 996
U.S. National Mediation Board. (Reports of Emergency Boards). (US ISSN 0083-2278) 996
U.S. National Oceanic and Atmospheric Administration. Annual Climate Diagnostic Workshop. Proceedings. (US) 3441
U.S. National Oceanic and Atmospheric Administration. Engineering Support Office. Technical Memorandum. (US) 1611
U.S. National Oceanic and Atmospheric Administration. Interdepartmental Committee for Meteorological Services and Supporting Research. National Hurricane Operations Plan. (US ISSN 0092-2056) 3441
U.S. National Oceanic and Atmospheric Administration. Manned Undersea Science and Technology Program; Report. (US ISSN 0092-8917) 1839, 1611
†U.S. National Oceanic and Atmospheric Administration. National Climatic Center. Marine Climatological Summaries. (US ISSN 0091-8512) 5296
U.S. National Oceanic and Atmospheric Administration. Report to the Congress on Ocean Pollution, Overfishing, and Offshore Development. (US ISSN 0098-4922) 1979, 1970
U.S. National Oceanic and Atmospheric Administration. Test and Evaluation Laboratory. Technical Bulletin see U.S. National Oceanic and Atmospheric Administration. Technical Bulletin 1611

U.S. National Oceanic and Atmospheric Administration. Test and Evaluation Office. Technical Memorandum see U.S. National Oceanic and Atmospheric Administration. Engineering Support Office. Technical Memorandum 1611
U.S. National Oceanic and Atmospheric Administration. Technical Bulletin. (US) 1611
U.S. National Oceanic and Atmospheric Administration National Weather Service. Climate Analysis Center. Monthly and Seasonal Weather Outlook see N O A A National Weather Service. Climate Analysis Center. Monthly and Seasonal Weather Outlook 3439
U.S. National Oceanographic Data Center. Key to Oceanographic Records Documentation. (US ISSN 0091-9500) 1611
U.S. National Park Service. Annual Report to Congress on the Federal Archeological Program see U.S. National Park Service. Federal Archeology: the Current Program 288
U.S. National Park Service. Archaeological Research Series see Publications in Archaeology 1495
U.S. National Park Service. Federal Archeology: the Current Program. (US) 288, 4076
U.S. National Park Service. Historical Handbook Series. (US ISSN 0083-2316) 4795
U.S. National Park Service. Public Use of the National Park System: Calendar Year Report. (US ISSN 0361-9737) 1499
U.S. National Park Service. Public Use of the National Park System: Fiscal Year Report. (US ISSN 0093-3074) 1499
U.S. National Park Service. Research Reports by Service Personnel. (US) 4559
U.S. National Science Foundation. Federal Funds for Research Development. (US) 4349
U.S. National Science Foundation. Federal Funds for Research, Development, and other Scientific Activities see U.S. National Science Foundation. Federal Funds for Research Development 4349
U.S. National Science Foundation. Fiscal Year Awards. (US) 4349
U.S. National Science Foundation. Graduate Science Education Student Support and Postdoctorals see U.S. National Science Foundation. Selected Data on Students and Postdoctorals in Science & Engineering 1718
U.S. National Science Foundation. Grants and Awards see U.S. National Science Foundation. Fiscal Year Awards 4349
U.S. National Science Foundation. Guide to Programs. (US) 1732, 4349
U.S. National Science Foundation. Research and Development in Industry. (US ISSN 0083-2383) 4612
U.S. National Science Foundation. Selected Data on Students and Postdoctorals in Science & Engineering. (US ISSN 0094-7881) 1718
U.S. National Science Foundation Bulletin see N S F Bulletin 4325
U.S. National Technical Information Service Alerts: Administration and Management see N T I S Alerts: Administration and Management 4081
U.S. National Technical Information Service Alerts: Communication see N T I S Alerts: Communication 1349
U.S. National Technical Information Service Bibliographic Data Base see N T I S Bibliographic Data Base 4143
U.S. National Technical Information Service Digest see N T I S Digest 2775

6760 U.S. NATIONAL

U.S. National Technical Information Service NewsLine see N T I S NewsLine 2775

U.S. National Technical Information Service Tech Notes see N T I S Tech Notes 4604

U.S. National Technical Information Service Title Index see N T I S Title Index 4615

U.S. National Toxicology Program. Annual Report on Carcinogens. (US ISSN 0272-2836) 3202, 1984

U.S. National Transportation Safety Board. Aircraft Accident Reports. (US) 4677

†U.S. National Transportation Safety Board. Listing of Aircraft Accidents-Incidents by Make and Model, U.S. Civil Aviation. (US ISSN 0360-3954) 5296

U.S. National Weather Service. Oceanographic Monthly Summary see U.S. Department of Commerce. National Oceanic and Atmospheric Administration. Oceanographic Monthly Summary 1611

†U.S. Naval Observatory. Astronomical Papers Prepared for Use of American Ephemeris and Nautical Almanac. (US ISSN 0083-243X) 5296

†U.S. Naval Observatory. Publications. Second Series. (US ISSN 0083-2448) 5296

U.S. Navy Medical Newsletter see Navy Medicine 3134

U.S. Nuclear Regulatory Commission. Annual Occupational Radiation Exposure Report see U.S. Nuclear Regulatory Commission. Occupational Radiation at Commercial Nuclear Power Reactors and Other Facilities. Annual Report 3622

U.S. Nuclear Regulatory Commission. Construction Status Report of Nuclear Power Plants. (US) 1810, 1839

U.S. Nuclear Regulatory Commission. Information Report on State Legislation. (US) 1810, 2688

U.S. Nuclear Regulatory Commission. Occupational Radiation at Commercial Nuclear Power Reactors and Other Facilities. Annual Report. (US) 3622

U.S. Nuclear Regulatory Commission. Occupational Radiation Exposure. Annual Report see U.S. Nuclear Regulatory Commission. Occupational Radiation at Commercial Nuclear Power Reactors and Other Facilities. Annual Report 3622

U.S. Nuclear Regulatory Commission. Operating Units Status Report. (US) 1810, 1839

U.S. Nuclear Regulatory Commission. Power Reactor Events. (US) 1810

U.S. Nuclear Regulatory Commission. Program Summary Report. (US) 1810

U.S. Nuclear Regulatory Commission. Publications. (US) 1810

U.S. Nuclear Regulatory Commission. Report to Congress on Abnormal Occurrences. (US) 1810, 1796

U.S. Nuclear Regulatory Commission. Water Reactor Safety Research Information Meeting. Proceedings. (US) 1810

U.S. Nuclear Regulatory Commission. Weekly Information Report. (US) 1810, 1796

U.S. Occupational Safety and Health Review Commission. Administrative Law Judge and Commission Decisions. (US ISSN 0094-7776) 3622, 2688

U.S. Office of Economic Opportunity. Annual Report see U.S. Community Services Administration. Annual Report 4422

U.S. Office of Economic Opportunity. Catalog of Federal Domestic Assistance see U.S. General Services Administration. Catalog of Federal Domestic Assistance 4076

U.S. Office of Economic Opportunity. Federal Outlays in Summary see U.S. Community Services Administration. Federal Outlays in Summary 1111

†U.S. Office of Education. Accredited Higher Institutions. (US ISSN 0083-2618) 5296

†U.S. Office of Education. Guide to Organized Occupational Curriculums in Higher Education. (US ISSN 0083-2715) 5296

†U.S. Office of Education. International Teacher Development Program. Annual Report to Bureau of Education and Cultural Affairs, Department of State. (US ISSN 0083-2723) 5296

†U.S. Office of Education. Public School Finance Program. (US ISSN 0083-2774) 5296

†U.S. Office of Education. Residence and Migration of College Students, Analytic Report. (US ISSN 0083-2790) 5296

†U.S. Office of Education. Studies in Comparative Education. Education in (Country). (US ISSN 0083-2855) 5296

†U.S. Office of Education. Title VII: New Educational Media News and Reports. (US ISSN 0083-288X) 5296

U.S. Office of Management and Budget. Catalog of Federal Domestic Assistance see U.S. General Services Administration. Catalog of Federal Domestic Assistance 4076

U.S. Office of Management and Budget. Special Analysis: Budget of the United States Government. (US ISSN 0362-9163) 1111

U.S. Office of Naval Research. Annual Task Summary: Contract Research Program. (US ISSN 0500-1951) 3474

†U.S. Office of Saline Water. Desalting Plants Inventory Report. (US ISSN 0083-2901) 5296

†U.S. Office of Saline Water. Saline Water Conversion Report. (US ISSN 0083-291X) 5296

U.S. Office of Technology Assessment Annual Report to the Congress. (US ISSN 0095-2109) 4076

U.S. Office of the Comptroller of the Currency. Quarterly Journal. (US) 802

U.S. Office of the Federal Register. Federal Register. see Federal Register 2625

U.S. Office of the Federal Register. Weekly Compilation of Presidential Documents. (US ISSN 0511-4187) 4076, 3932

U.S. Patent and Trademark Office. Annual Report of the Commissioner of Patents. (US ISSN 0083-3002) 3679

U.S. Patent and Trademark Office. Classification Bulletins. (US ISSN 0083-3010) 3679

U.S. Patent Office. Index of Patents Issued from the United States Patent Office see Index of Patents Issued from the United States Patent and Trademark Office 3679

U.S. Patent Office. Official Gazette see Official Gazette of the United States Patent and Trademark Office. Patents 3677

U.S. Patent Office. Official Gazette see Official Gazette of the United States Patent and Trademark Office. Trademarks Supplements 3677

U.S. Peace Corps. Annual Report. (US ISSN 0083-3088) 3976

U.S. Postal Service. Revenue and Cost Analysis Report. (US) 1354

U.S. Railroad Retirement Board. Annual Report. (US ISSN 0891-8066) 996

U.S. Railroad Retirement Board. Monthly Benefit Statistics. (US ISSN 0364-7129) 996

†U.S. Renewal Assistance Administration. Technical Guides. (US ISSN 0083-3134) 5296

†U.S. Renewal Assistance Administration. Urban Renewal Project Characteristics. (US ISSN 0083-3142) 5296

†U.S. Renewal Assistance Administration. Urban Renewal Service Bulletins. (US ISSN 0083-3150) 5296

U.S. Rural Electrification Administration. Annual Statistical Report. Rural Electrification Borrowers. (US ISSN 0083-3177) 1910

U.S. Rural Electrification Administration. Annual Statistical Report. Rural Telephone Borrowers. (US) 1367

U.S. Rural Electrification Administration. Annual Statistical Report. Rural Telephone Program see U.S. Rural Electrification Administration. Annual Statistical Report. Rural Telephone Borrowers 1367

U.S. Rural Electrification Administration. Report of the Administrator of the Rural Electrification Administration. (US ISSN 0083-3193) 1910

U.S. Saint Lawrence Seaway Development Corporation. Annual Report. (US ISSN 0083-3207) 4741

U.S. Securities and Exchange Commission. Annual Report. (US ISSN 0083-3215) 967

U.S. Securities and Exchange Commission. Decisions and Reports. (US ISSN 0083-3223) 967

U.S. Securities and Exchange Commission. Judicial Decisions. (US ISSN 0083-3231) 967

U.S. Securities and Exchange Commission. Official Summary of Security Transactions and Holdings. (US ISSN 0364-2267) 967

U.S. Securities and Exchange Commission Docket see S E C Docket 962

U.S. Securities and Exchange Commission News Digest see S E C News Digest 962

U.S. Small Business Administration. Annual Report. (US ISSN 0083-3274) 1119

U.S. Small Business Administration. Office of the Inspector General. Semi-Annual Report. (US) 1119

U.S. Small Business Administration. S B I C Digest. (US ISSN 0149-2500) 1119

†U.S. Social Security Administration. O R S I P Notes. (US ISSN 0566-0327) 5296

U.S. Soil Conservation Service. Annual Report. (US) 4829

U.S. Soil Conservation Service. National Engineering Handbook. (US ISSN 0083-3304) 195

U.S. Soil Conservation Service. Soil Survey Investigation Reports. (US ISSN 0083-3320) 195

U.S. Soil Conservation Service. Technical Publications. (US ISSN 0083-3339) 195

U.S. Tariff Commission. Annual Report see U.S. International Trade Commission. Annual Report 923

U.S. Trade with Puerto Rico and U.S. Possessions see Foreign Trade Reports. U.S. Trade with Puerto Rico and U.S. Possessions 909

U.S. Treasury Department. Bureau of Government Financial Operations. Monthly Statement of Receipts and Outlays of the United States Government see U.S. Treasury Department. Financial Management Service. Monthly Treasury Statement of Receipts and Outlays of the United States Government 802

U.S. Treasury Department. Bureau of Government Financial Operations. Monthly Treasury Statement of Receipts and Outlays of the United States Government see U.S. Treasury Department. Financial Management Service. Monthly Treasury Statement of Receipts and Outlays of the United States Government 802

†U.S. Treasury Department. Bureau of Government Financial Operations. Report on Foreign Currencies Held by the U.S. Government. (US ISSN 0098-3896) 5296

U.S. Treasury Department. Bureau of Government Financial Operations. Treasury Combined Statement of Receipts, Expenditures and Balances of the United States see U.S. Treasury Department. Financial Management Service. United States Government Annual Report and Appendix 1111

U.S. Treasury Department. Bureau of the Mint. Annual Report of the Director of the Mint see U.S. Treasury Department. United States Mint. Annual Report of the Director of the Mint 802

U.S. Treasury Department. Combined Statement of Receipts, Expenditures and Balances of the United States see U.S. Treasury Department. Financial Management Service. United States Government Annual Report and Appendix 1111

U.S. Treasury Department. Financial Management Service. Monthly Treasury Statement of Receipts and Outlays of the United States Government. (US) 802

U.S. Treasury Department. Financial Management Service. United States Government Annual Report and Appendix. (US) 1111

U.S. Treasury Department. Treasury Bulletin. (US ISSN 0041-2155) 802

U.S. Treasury Department. United States Mint. Annual Report of the Director of the Mint. (US) 802

U.S. Urban Initiatives Anti-Crime Program. Annual Report to Congress. (US ISSN 0272-8974) 1524

U.S. Veterans Administration. Annual Report. (US ISSN 0083-3533) 3474, 2544

U.S. Veterans Administration. Medical Research Program. (US ISSN 0083-355X) 3159

U.S. Veterans Administration. Summary of Medical Programs see U.S. Department of Veterans Affairs. Summary of Medical Programs 3159

U.S. Water and Power Resources Service. Annual Report see U.S. Bureau of Reclamation. Annual Report 1498

U.S. Water and Power Resources Service. Engineering Monograph see U.S. Bureau of Reclamation. Engineering Monograph 1925

U.S. Waterborne Exports and General Imports see Foreign Trade Reports. U.S. Waterborne Exports and General Imports 909

U.S. Women's Open Magazine. (US) 4514

United States (Year). (US) 4795

United States Adopted Names Dictionary of Drug Names see U S A N and the U S P Dictionary of Drug Names 3744

United States Air Force Medical Service Digest. (US ISSN 0041-7491) 3159

United States Air Forces Europe Yearbook. (UK ISSN 0956-2826) 3474

United States Animal Health Association. Proceedings of the Annual Meeting. (US ISSN 0082-8750) 4816

United States Anti-Apartheid Newsletter.(US) 3948

United States Army Aviation Digest. (US ISSN 0004-2471) 64, 3474

United States Association for Blind Athletes Agenda see U S A B A Agenda 4495

United States Auto Club News see U S A C News 4495

United States Banker. (US ISSN 0148-8848) 967, 802

United States Basketball Writers Association Tip-Off see U S B W A Tip-Off **4514**
United States Board on Books for Young People. Newsletter. (US) **4138, 2788**
United States Catholic Mission Council. Handbook see Mission Handbook **4269**
United States Committee on Irrigation and Drainage Newsletter see U S C I D Newsletter **4829**
United States Conference of Mayors. Annual Meeting. (US) **4095**
United States Conference of Mayors. Projects and Services. (US) **4096**
United States: Cotton Quality Reports for Ginnings. (US ISSN 0041-7580) **159, 4627**
United States Council for International Business. Newsletter. (US) **823**
United States Cross-Country and Distance Running Coaches Association. Proceedings see United States Cross-Country Coaches Association. Annual Business Meeting. Minutes **4496**
United States Cross-Country Coaches Association. Annual Business Meeting. Minutes. (US) **4496**
United States Cross-Country Coaches Association. Proceedings see United States Cross-Country Coaches Association. Annual Business Meeting. Minutes **4496**
United States Distribution Journal. (US) **4645, 2090**
United States Distribution Journal Supplier Directory. (US) **4645, 2090**
United States Dressage Federation Bulletin. (US) **4539**
United States Equestrian Team News see U S E T News **4539**
United States Fencing Association, Inc. Rule Book: U S & International Rules see U S F A Rule Book: U S & International Rules **4495**
United States Football League Guide and Register see U S F L Guide and Register **5293**
United States Foreign Policy. (US ISSN 0270-370X) **3932**
United States - German Economic Yearbook (Year). (US) **923**
United States Golf Association Green Section Record see U S G A Green Section Record **4514**
United States Government Manual. (US ISSN 0092-1904) **4076, 3932**
United States in the World: Foreign Perspectives. (US) **3976**
United States Independent Telephone Association. Annual Statistical Volume see United States Telephone Association. Annual Statistical Volume **1367**
United States Independent Telephone Association. Holding Company Report see United States Telephone Association. Holding Company Report **1367**
United States International Treaties Today see Current Treaty Index **2698**
†United States International Treaties Today. (US) **5296**
United States Investor - Eastern Banker see United States Banker **967**
United States - Israel Binational Science Foundation. Annual Report. (IS) **4349**
United States - Italy Trade Directory. (US ISSN 0502-5842) **1156, 823**
United States Judicial Reporter. (US ISSN 0094-2553) **2733**
United States Law Week. (US ISSN 0148-8139) **2688**
United States Law Week Summary and Analysis. (US ISSN 0190-5252) **2688**
United States Lawn Tennis Association. Yearbook see United States Tennis Association. Yearbook **4514**
United States League of Savings Institutions. Membership Bulletin. (US) **802**

United States Livestock Sanitary Association. Proceedings see United States Animal Health Association. Proceedings of the Annual Meeting **4816**
United States - Mexico Border Health Association. News - Noticias. (US) **4114**
United States of America - Tin in Tinplate. (UK) **3422**
United States Participation in the United Nations. (US ISSN 0083-0208) **3976**
United States Patents Quarterly. (US ISSN 0041-803X) **3679**
United States Pharmacopeia - National Formulary. (US ISSN 0195-7996) **3745**
United States Pilots Association Bulletin.(US) **64**
United States Pilots Association Newsletter. (US) **64**
United States Political Science Documents. (US) **3932**
United States Polo Association. Yearbook. (US ISSN 0083-3118) **4514**
United States Population Data Sheet. (US ISSN 0896-4416) **3988**
United States Postage Stamps see Postal Service Guide to U S Stamps **3757**
United States Postal Card Catalog. (US ISSN 0276-7244) **2443**
United States Space Foundation. National Space Symposium Proceedings Reports. (US) **64**
United States Space Foundation. National Space Symposium Reports see United States Space Foundation. National Space Symposium Proceedings Reports **64**
United States Specialist. (US ISSN 0164-923X) **3759**
United States Sports Academy News see U S S A News **4495**
United States Squash Racquets Association. Official Year Book. (US ISSN 0083-3398) **4514**
United States Stamp Catalogue. (UK ISSN 0142-9949) **3759**
United States Statutes at Large. (US ISSN 0083-3401) **2688**
United States Tax Court Reports. (US ISSN 0040-0017) **1111, 2688**
United States Telephone Association. Annual Statistical Volume. (US) **1367**
United States Telephone Association. Holding Company Report. (US) **1367**
United States Tennis Association. Yearbook. (US) **4514**
United States Tennis Association College Tennis Guide see U S T A College Tennis Guide **4496**
United States Trade Fair. (US ISSN 0742-3675) **1055**
United States Trade Show Times. (US) **4006**
United States Treaties and Other International Agreements. (US ISSN 0083-3487) **2730**
United States Trotting Association Sires and Dams see U S T A Sires and Dams **4539**
United States Trotting Association Year Book see U S T A Year Book **4539**
United States Volleyball Association. Official Volleyball Guide see United States Volleyball Association. Official Volleyball Rule Book **4514**
United States Volleyball Association. Official Volleyball Rule Book. (US) **4514**
United States Youth Soccer Association, Inc. National Directory see U S Y S A National Directory **4514**
United States Youth Soccer Association, Inc. Network see U S Y S A Network **4514**
United Steelworkers of America. Information. (CN ISSN 0566-0963) **2591, 3422**
United Synagogue Review. (US ISSN 0041-8153) **4227**
United Teacher see New York Teacher **2587**

United Teachers of Dade Today see U T D Today **1668**
United Tribune. see Tongyi Luntan **4390**
United Way see Unitedland **4159**
United Way of America. Information Center. Digest of Selected Reports. (US) **4427, 24**
United Way of Canada. Directory of Members. (CN) **4423**
Unitedland. (US) **4159**
United's Voice. (US) **4704**
Uniter. (CN ISSN 0041-817X) **1327**
The Uniter. (US) **1367**
Uniterra see Our Planet **1965**
†Unites Petrochimiques dans les Pays de l'O P E C et de l'O P A E P/ Petrochemical Units in the O P E C and O A P E C Countries. (FR ISSN 0396-2644) **5296**
Unitholder see Money Management and Unitholder **955**
Units. (US) **2497, 2688**
Unity. (CN) **2027**
Unity. (UK) **2591**
†Unity (Oakland). (US ISSN 0740-4603) **5296**
Unity (Unity Village). (US ISSN 0162-3567) **4289**
Unity Daily Word see Daily Word **2292**
Unity-in-Diversity Centers Bulletin see Spectrum Magazine (Los Angeles) **3596**
Unity of Nationalities. see Minzu Tuanjie **2014**
Unity: United Newsletter. (US) **2457, 3394**
Unity with Nature Newsletter see BeFriending Creation **4164**
†UniverCity. (US) **5296**
Univeristatea din Timisoara. Facultatea de Stiinte ale Naturii. Seminarul de Mecanica see Universitatea din Timisoara. Facultatea de Matematica. Seminarul de Mecanica **3060**
Univeritaet Karlsruhe Forschungsberichte see W B K Forschungsberichte **1840**
Univers de la France et des Pays Francophones. (FR) **2392**
Univers Historique. (FR ISSN 0083-3673) **4349, 2325**
Universal Availability of Publications Newsletter see U A P Newsletter **2788**
Universal Black Writer. (US) **2027, 2971**
Universal Business Directories. Adelaide Business to Business Directory. (AT) **1157**
Universal Business Directories. Brisbane Business to Business Directory. (AT) **1157**
Universal Business Directories. Melbourne Business to Business Directory. (AT) **1157**
Universal Business Directories. New South Wales. Central West Business to Business Directory. (AT) **1157**
Universal Business Directories. New South Wales. Hunter Region Business to Business Directory. (AT) **1157**
Universal Business Directories. New South Wales. Illawarra Region Business to Business Directory. (AT) **1157**
Universal Business Directories. New South Wales. New England Region Business to Business Directory. (AT) **1157**
Universal Business Directories. New South Wales. North Coast Region Business to Business Directory. (AT) **1157**
Universal Business Directories. New South Wales. Riverina Region Business to Business Directory. (AT) **1157**
Universal Business Directories. New South Wales. South Eastern Region Business to Business Directory. (AT) **1157**
Universal Business Directories. Northern Territory Business to Business Directory. (AT) **1157**
Universal Business Directories. Papua New Guinea Business to Business Directory. (AT) **1157**

Universal Business Directories. Perth Business to Business Directory. (AT) **1157**
Universal Business Directories. Queensland. Bundaberg Business to Business Directory. (AT) **1157**
Universal Business Directories. Queensland. Cairns Business to Business Directory. (AT) **1157**
Universal Business Directories. Queensland. Gladstone Business to Business Directory. (AT) **1157**
Universal Business Directories. Queensland. Gympie Business to Business Directory. (AT) **1157**
Universal Business Directories. Queensland. Mackay Business to Business Directory. (AT) **1157**
Universal Business Directories. Queensland. Maryborough Business to Business Directory. (AT) **1157**
Universal Business Directories. Queensland. Redcliffe Business to Business Directory. (AT) **1157**
Universal Business Directories. Queensland. Rockhampton Business to Business Directory. (AT) **1157**
Universal Business Directories. Queensland. Sunshine Coast Business to Business Directory. (AT) **1157**
Universal Business Directories. Queensland. Toowoomba Business to Business Directory. (AT) **1157**
Universal Business Directories. Queensland. Townsville Business to Business Directory. (AT) **1157**
Universal Business Directories. South Australia Business to Business Directory. (AT) **1157**
Universal Business Directories. Sydney Business to Business Directory. (AT) **1157**
Universal Business Directories. Tasmania Business to Business Directory. (AT) **1157**
Universal Business Directories. Victoria. Ballarat Business to Business Directory. (AT) **1157**
Universal Business Directories. Victoria. Bendigo Business to Business Directory. (AT) **1157**
Universal Business Directories. Victoria. Geelong Business to Business Directory. (AT) **1157**
Universal Business Directories. Victoria. Goulburn Valley Business to Business Directory. (AT) **1157**
Universal Business Directories. Victoria. Latrobe Valley Business to Business Directory. (AT) **1157**
Universal Business Directories. Victoria. North East Victoria Business to Business Directory. (AT) **1157**
Universal Business Directories. Victoria. Sunraysia-Mallee Business to Business Directories. (AT) **1157**
Universal Business Directories. Victoria. West District Business to Business Directory. (AT) **1157**
Universal Business Directories. Victoria. Wimmera Business to Business Directory. (AT) **1157**
Universal Business Directories, Adelaide Business and Street Directory see Universal Business Directories. Adelaide Business to Business Directory **1157**
Universal Business Directories, Perth and Fremantle and Suburbs Business and Trade Directory see Universal Business Directories. Perth Business to Business Directory **1157**
Universal Business Directories, Sydney and Suburban Business and Street Directory see Universal Business Directories. Sydney Business to Business Directory **1157**
Universal Business Directories, Tasmania Business and Street Directory see Universal Business Directories. Tasmania Business to Business Directory **1157**
Universal Directory - Conferences - Exhibitions - Functions. (AT) **3394, 1030**
Universal Door/P'u Men. (CH) **4216**
Universal Esperanto Association. Kongresa Libro see Kongresa Libro **3393**

6762 UNIVERSAL LIFE

Universal Life Church News *see* U L C News **4289**
Universal Message. (PK) **4221**
Universal Military Abstracts. (II ISSN 0970-3403) **3477**
Universal Postal Union. Documents du Congres *see* Union Postale Universelle. Actes **1354**
Universal Postal Union Collectors. Publication. (US) **3759**
Universal Reference System: Political Science, Government, and Public Policy Series. Annual Supplement *see* Political Science Abstracts **3938**
Universal Serials and Book Exchange News *see* U S B E News **2788**
Universal Ship Cancellation Society Log Log *see* U S C S Log **3759**
Universale Religion. (GW) **4208**
Universalian. (US) **3671**
Universalist. (II ISSN 0041-8218) **3784**
Universalist. (UK ISSN 0267-6648) **4289**
Universe. (AT ISSN 0049-5506) **370**
Universe. (UK ISSN 0041-8226) **4277**
Universe. *see* Vesmir **4351**
Universe. *see* Wszechswiat **4352**
Universe in a Classroom. (US ISSN 0890-6866) **370, 1669**
Universidad. (CR) **1327**
Universidad Automona de San Luis Potosi. Instituto de Geologia y Metalurgia. Folleto Tecnico *see* Universidad Autonoma de San Luis Potosi. Instituto de Geologia. Folleto Tecnico **1583**
Universidad Autonoma de Centro America. Acta Academica. (CR) **1327**
Universidad Autonoma de Nuevo Leon. Centro de Investigaciones Economicas. Boletin Bimestral. (MX ISSN 0041-8498) **696**
Universidad Autonoma de San Luis Potosi. Instituto de Geologia. Folleto Tecnico. (MX ISSN 0581-5207) **1583, 3422**
Universidad Autonoma de Santo Domingo. Biblioteca Central. Boletin de Adquisiciones. (DR ISSN 0041-8277) **415**
Universidad Autonoma de Santo Domingo. Direccion de Investigaciones. D I C Boletin. (DR) **4349**
Universidad Autonoma de Yucatan. Revista. (MX ISSN 0186-7180) **2516**
Universidad Autonoma Latinoamericana *see* U N A U L A **2887**
Universidad Autonome de Santo Domingo. Comision para el Desarrollo y Reforma Universitarios. (DR) **1718**
Universidad Boliviana Juan Misael Saracho. Informe de Labores. (BO) **1718**
Universidad Boliviana Mayor de San Simon. Instituto de Estudios Sociales y Economicos. Revista. (BO ISSN 0041-8617) **696**
Universidad Catolica de Chile. Facultad de Teologia. Anales. (CL ISSN 0069-3596) **4277**
Universidad Catolica de Chile. Instituto de Planificacion del Desarrollo Urbano. Documentos de Trabajo *see* Pontificia Universidad Catolica de Chile. Instituto de Estudios Urbanos. Documentos de Trabajo **2494**
Universidad Catolica del Tachira. Pagina Cultural e Informativa. (VE) **2516**
Universidad Catolica Nuestra Senora de la Asuncion. Centro de Estudios Antropologicos. Suplemento Antropologico. (PY ISSN 0378-9896) **251**
Universidad Central de Venezuela. Centro de Estudios del Desarrollo. Cuadernos del C E N D E S. (VE ISSN 1012-2508) **4455**

Universidad Central de Venezuela. Consejo de Desarrollo Cientifico y Humanistico. Bibliografia de Humanidades y Ciencias Sociales y Bibliografia de Ciencia y Tecnologia del Profesorado. (VE ISSN 0083-5439) **1718**
Universidad Central de Venezuela. Consejo de Desarrollo Cientifico y Humanistico. Catalogo *see* Universidad Central de Venezuela. Consejo de Desarrollo Cientifico y Humanistico. Bibliografia de Humanidades y Ciencias Sociales y Bibliografia de Ciencia y Tecnologia del Profesorado **1718**
Universidad Central de Venezuela. Facultad de Agronomia. Revista. (VE ISSN 0041-8285) **126**
Universidad Central de Venezuela. Facultad de Agronomia. Revista Alcance. (VE) **126**
Universidad Central de Venezuela. Facultad de Ciencias Juridicas y Politicas. Revista. (VE) **2688**
Universidad Central de Venezuela. Facultad de Ciencias Veterinarias. Revista. (VE) **4816**
Universidad Central de Venezuela. Facultad de Derecho. Revista *see* Universidad Central de Venezuela. Facultad de Ciencias Juridicas y Politicas. Revista **2688**
Universidad Central de Venezuela. Facultad de Farmacia. Revista. (VE ISSN 0041-8307) **3745**
Universidad Central de Venezuela. Instituto de Ciencias Penales y Criminologicas. Anuario. (VE ISSN 0507-570X) **1524**
Universidad Central del Ecuador. Biblioteca General. Bibliografia Ecuatoriana. (EC) **415**
Universidad Central del Ecuador. Instituto de Derecho Comparado. Boletin. (EC) **2689**
Universidad Central del Ecuador. Instituto de Estudios Administrativos. Boletin. (EC) **1030**
Universidad Central del Ecuador. Instituto de Investigaciones Economicas. Boletin Economia. (EC) **887**
Universidad Complutense de Madrid. Departamento de Botanica y Fisiologia Vegetal. Trabajos *see* Botanica Complutensis **497**
Universidad Complutense de Madrid. Revista. (SP) **2971, 3784**
Universidad de Antioquia. Asociacion de Profesionales de la Educacion. Estudios Educativos. (CK) **1669**
Universidad de Antioquia. Departamento de Antropologia. Boletin de Antropologia. (CK ISSN 0120-2510) **251**
Universidad de Antioquia. Departamento de Historia. Coleccion Papeles de Trabajo. (CK) **2516**
Universidad de Antioquia. Departamento de Humanidades. Coleccion Papeles de Trabajo *see* Universidad de Antioquia. Departamento de Historia. Coleccion Papeles de Trabajo **2516**
Universidad de Antioquia. Facultad de Ciencias Economicas. Administracion de Empresas. Tecnologia Administrativa. (CK ISSN 0120-0933) **696**
Universidad de Antioquia. Instituto de Antropologia. Boletin de Antropologia *see* Universidad de Antioquia. Departamento de Antropologia. Boletin de Antropologia **251**
Universidad de Antioquia. Revista. (CK ISSN 0120-2367) **2517**
Universidad de Barcelona. Facultad de Farmacia. Memoria. (SP ISSN 0067-4176) **3745**
Universidad de Barcelona. Facultad de Filologia. Anuario *see* Anuario de Filologia **2803**
Universidad de Barcelona. Instituto de Arqueologia y Prehistoria. Publicaciones Eventuales. (SP ISSN 0067-4184) **288**

Universidad de Bogota Jorge Tadeo Lozano. Museo del Mar. Boletin *see* Ecotropica. Ecosistemas Tropicales. Boletin **1604**
Universidad de Bogota Jorge Tadeo Lozano. Museo del Mar. Informe. (CK) **458**
Universidad de Buenos Aires. Catedra de Patologia y Clinica de la Tuberculosis. Anales. (AG) **3368**
Universidad de Buenos Aires. Instituto de Historia Antigua Oriental. Revista. (AG ISSN 0325-1209) **2432**
Universidad de Buenos Aires. Instituto de Historia Antiguo Oriental. Coleccion Estudios. (AG) **2432**
Universidad de Caldas. Facultad de Filosofia. Revista. (CK ISSN 0120-1492) **3785**
Universidad de Chile. Biblioteca. Instituto de Economia. Boletin *see* Universidad de Chile. Facultad de Ciencias Economicas y Adinistrativas. Biblioteca. Lista de Memorias y Libros Seleccionados **743**
Universidad de Chile. Boletin. (CL ISSN 0041-8374) **2887**
Universidad de Chile. Departamento de Astronomia. Publicaciones. (CL ISSN 0069-3553) **370**
Universidad de Chile. Departamento de Geologia. Serie Comunicaciones. (CL ISSN 0069-357X) **1549**
Universidad de Chile. Facultad de Ciencias Economicas y Adinistrativas. Biblioteca. Lista de Memorias y Libros Seleccionados. (CL) **743**
Universidad de Chile. Facultad de Ciencias Economicas y Administrativas. Desarrollo. (CL) **696**
Universidad de Cuenca. Anales. (EC ISSN 0041-8390) **2887**
Universidad de Granada. Boletin. (SP) **1718**
Universidad de Granada. Catedra Francisco Suarez. Anales. (SP ISSN 0008-7750) **3785**
Universidad de Granada. Coleccion Monografica. (SP ISSN 0072-5382) **2517**
Universidad de Granada. Cuadernos de Arte. (SP) **347**
Universidad de Guadalajara. Instituto de Astronomia y Meteorologia. Informacion. (MX ISSN 0041-8404) **370, 3441**
Universidad de Guadalajara. Instituto de Botanica. Boletin Informativo. (MX) **519**
Universidad de Guayaquil. Escuela de Diplomacia. Revista. (CL) **3976**
Universidad de Guayaquil. Facultad de Ciencias Medicas. Revista. (EC ISSN 0041-8412) **3159**
Universidad de la Habana. Departamento de Actividades Culturales. Revista. (CU ISSN 0041-8420) **2184**
Universidad de la Habana. Direccion de Extension Universitaria. Revista. (CU) **1718**
Universidad de la Habana. Direccion de Informacion Cientifica y Tecnica. Investigacion Operacional. (CU ISSN 0257-4306) **3059**
Universidad de la Habana. Escuela de Matematica. Investigacion Operacional. (CU) **3059**
Universidad de La Laguna. Anuarios. (SP ISSN 0212-8047) **2848**
Universidad de La Laguna. Coleccion Estudios de Historia. (SP) **2393**
Universidad de la Laguna. Facultad de Ciencias. Anales. (SP ISSN 0075-7721) **4349**
Universidad de la Laguna. Facultad de Derecho. Anales. (SP ISSN 0075-773X) **2689**
Universidad de la Republica. Facultad de Agronomia. Boletin. (UY) **126**
Universidad de la Republica. Facultad de Ciencias Economicas y Administracion. Instituto de Estadistica. Indice de Precios al Consumidor. (UY ISSN 0041-8439) **4591**
Universidad de la Republica. Facultad de Ciencias Economicas y de Administracion. Revista. (UY) **696**

Universidad de la Republica. Facultad de Humanidades y Ciencias. Revista. Serie Ciencias *see* Universidad de la Republica. Facultad de Humanidades y Ciencias. Revista. Serie Ciencias Biologicas **458**
Universidad de la Republica. Facultad de Humanidades y Ciencias. Revista. Serie Ciencias Antropologicas. (UY ISSN 0250-6564) **251**
Universidad de la Republica. Facultad de Humanidades y Ciencias. Revista. Serie Ciencias Biologicas. (UY ISSN 0250-653X) **458**
Universidad de la Republica. Facultad de Humanidades y Ciencias. Revista. Serie Ciencias de la Tierra. (UY ISSN 0250-6521) **1549**
Universidad de la Republica. Facultad de Humanidades y Ciencias. Revista. Serie Ciencias Exactas. (UY) **3059**
Universidad de la Republica. Facultad de Humanidades y Ciencias. Revista. Serie Filosofia. (UY) **3785**
Universidad de la Republica. Facultad de Humanidades y Ciencias. Revista. Serie Historia. (UY) **2424**
Universidad de la Republica. Facultad de Humanidades y Ciencias. Revista. Serie Linguistica. (UY ISSN 0250-6548) **2848**
Universidad de la Republica. Facultad de Humanidades y Ciencias. Revista. Serie Letras. (UY ISSN 0250-6556) **2971**
Universidad de la Republica. Facultad de Humanidades y Ciencias. Revista. Serie Musicologia. (UY) **3585**
Universidad de la Republica. Facultad de Ingenieria. Boletin. (UY ISSN 0366-0109) **1839**
Universidad de la Republica. Facultad de Odontologia. Anales. (UY ISSN 0083-4785) **3243**
Universidad de la Republica. Hospital de Clinicas. Informe Estatistico. (UY ISSN 0041-8455) **2471**
Universidad de la Republica. Instituto de Administracion. Boletin. (UY) **1030**
Universidad de la Republica. Instituto de Administracion. Cuaderno. (UY ISSN 0077-1287) **1030**
Universidad de los Andes. Cuadernos de Filosofia y Letras. (CK ISSN 0120-0992) **3008**
Universidad de los Andes. Cuadernos de Letras *see* Universidad de los Andes. Cuadernos de Filosofia y Letras **3008**
Universidad de los Andes. Escuela de Letras. Anuario. (VE) **2971**
Universidad de los Andes. Facultad de Ciencias Juridicas y Politicas. Anuario. (VE) **2689, 3932**
Universidad de Los Andes. Facultad de Derecho. Anuario. (VE ISSN 0076-6550) **2689**
Universidad de Los Andes. Facultad de Derecho. Revista *see* Universidad de Los Andes. Facultad de Derecho. Anuario **2689**
Universidad de Los Andes. Facultad de Odontologia. Revista. (VE) **3243**
Universidad de Los Andes. Instituto de Geografia y Conservacion de Recursos Naturales. Cuadernos Geograficos. (VE ISSN 0076-6569) **2264**
Universidad de Los Andes. Instituto de Investigaciones Literarias. Serie Bibliografico *see* Universidad de Los Andes. Instituto de Investigaciones Literarias. Serie Ensayo y Critica Literaria **415**
Universidad de Los Andes. Instituto de Investigaciones Literarias. Serie Ensayo y Critica Literaria. (VE) **415**
†Universidad de Los Andes. Vicerrectorado Academico. Servicios Bibliotecarios de Ciencias Forestales y Servicios Bibliotecarios de Geografia. Obras Ingresadas. (VE) **5296**

Universidad de Los Andes. Vicerrectorado Academico. Servicios Bibliotecarios de Geografia. Obras Ingresadas *see* Universidad de Los Andes. Vicerrectorado Academico. Servicios Bibliotecarios de Ciencias Forestales y Servicios Bibliotecarios de Geografia. Obras Ingresadas **5296**

Universidad de Madrid. Seminario de Metafisica. Anales. (SP ISSN 0580-8650) **3785**

Universidad de Medellin. Facultad de Ciencias Administrativas. Revista. (CK ISSN 0465-4773) **4076, 1030**

Universidad de Medellin. Revista. (CK ISSN 0120-5692) **1718**

Universidad de Murcia. Anales de Biologia. (SP) **458**

Universidad de Murcia. Anales de Biologia. Seccion Biologia Ambiental. (SP ISSN 0213-4004) **458, 1970**

Universidad de Murcia. Anales de Biologia. Seccion Biologia Animal. (SP ISSN 0213-3997) **593**

Universidad de Murcia. Anales de Biologia. Seccion Biologia General *see* Universidad de Murcia. Anales de Biologia. Seccion Biologia Molecular y Microbiana **458**

Universidad de Murcia. Anales de Biologia. Seccion Biologia Molecular y Microbiana. (SP) **458**

Universidad de Murcia. Anales de Biologia. Seccion Biologia Vegetal. (SP ISSN 0213-5450) **519**

†Universidad de Murcia. Anales de Biologia. Seccion Especial. (SP ISSN 0213-3938) **5296**

Universidad de Murcia. Anales de Ciencias. (SP ISSN 0213-5469) **4349**

†Universidad de Murcia. Anales de Derecho. (SP ISSN 0210-539X) **5296**

Universidad de Murcia. Anales de Filologia Francesa. (SP ISSN 0213-2958) **3785**

Universidad de Murcia. Anales de Filologia Hispanica. (SP ISSN 0213-4365) **3785**

Universidad de Murcia. Anales de Filosofia. (SP ISSN 0212-9698) **3785**

†Universidad de Murcia. Anales de Filosofia y Ciencias de la Educacion. (SP) **5296**

Universidad de Murcia. Anales de Historia Contemporanea. (SP ISSN 0212-6559) **2393**

†Universidad de Murcia. Anales de Letras. (SP) **5296**

Universidad de Murcia. Anales de Pedagogia. (SP ISSN 0212-8322) **1669**

Universidad de Murcia. Anales de Prehistoria y Arqueologia. (SP) **2393, 288**

Universidad de Murcia. Anales de Psicologia. (SP ISSN 0212-9728) **4049**

Universidad de Murcia. Catedra de Teatro. Cuadernos. (SP) **4642**

Universidad de Murcia. Cuadernos de Filologia Inglesa. (SP ISSN 0213-5485) **3785**

Universidad de Murcia. Departamento de Derecho Politico. Publicaciones. Serie Monografias. (SP) **2689**

Universidad de Murcia. Departamento de Geografia. Papeles *see* Universidad de Murcia. Papeles de Geografia **2264**

†Universidad de Murcia. Didactica Geografica. (SP ISSN 0210-492X) **5296**

Universidad de Murcia. Estudios Romanicos. (SP ISSN 0210-4911) **2848, 2971**

Universidad de Murcia. Imafronte. Departamento de Historia del Arte. (SP ISSN 0213-392X) **347, 2393**

Universidad de Murcia. Miscelanea Medieval Murciana. (SP ISSN 0210-4903) **2393**

Universidad de Murcia. Monteagudo. (SP ISSN 0580-6712) **308**

Universidad de Murcia. Papeles de Geografia. (SP ISSN 0213-1781) **2264**

Universidad de Navarra. Coleccion Bibliografia. (SP) **415**

Universidad de Navarra. Coleccion I.L.C.E. (SP) **2849**

Universidad de Navarra. Coleccion Manuales de Derecho. (SP) **2689**

Universidad de Navarra. Departamento de Literatura Espanola. Coleccion Publicaciones. (SP) **2971**

Universidad de Navarra. Documentos Medievales. (SP) **2393**

Universidad de Navarra. Escuela de Arquitectura. Coleccion de Arquitectura. (SP ISSN 0078-8732) **308**

Universidad de Navarra. Escuela de Arquitectura. Manuales: Arquitectura *see* Universidad de Navarra. Escuela de Arquitectura. Coleccion de Arquitectura **308**

Universidad de Navarra. Escuela de Bibliotecarias. Coleccion Bibliotecarias. (SP ISSN 0078-8740) **2788**

Universidad de Navarra. Escuela de Bibliotecarias. Manuales: Bibliotecarias *see* Universidad de Navarra. Escuela de Bibliotecarias. Coleccion Bibliotecarias **2788**

Universidad de Navarra. Facultad de Ciencias de la Educacion. Coleccion. (SP) **1669**

Universidad de Navarra. Facultad de Ciencias de la Informacion. Coleccion de Trabajo. (SP) **2576**

Universidad de Navarra. Facultad de Ciencias de la Informacion. Manuales: Periodismo. (SP ISSN 0078-8783) **2576**

Universidad de Navarra. Facultad de Derecho Canonico. Manuales: Derecho Canonico. (SP ISSN 0078-8759) **4208**

Universidad de Navarra. Instituto de Ciencias de la Educacion. Coleccion I C E *see* Universidad de Navarra. Facultad de Ciencias de la Educacion. Coleccion **1669**

Universidad de Navarra. Instituto de Estudios Superiores de la Empresas. Coleccion I E S E. Serie A C *see* Coleccion la Empresa y Su Entorno. Serie A C **1005**

Universidad de Navarra. Instituto de Estudios Superiores de la Empresa. Coleccion I E S E. Serie L *see* Coleccion la Empresa y Su Entorno. Serie L **1005**

Universidad de Navarra. Manuales: Derecho Notarial Espanol *see* Universidad de Navarra. Coleccion Manuales de Derecho **2689**

†Universidad de Navarra. Publicaciones de Biologia. (SP) **5296**

Universidad de Oriente. Instituto Oceanografico Biblioteca. Boletin Bibliografico. (VE ISSN 0590-3343) **1552**

Universidad de Oriente. Instituto Oceanografico. Boletin. (VE ISSN 0020-417X) **1611**

Universidad de Oriente. Instituto Oceanografico. Cuadernos Oceanograficos. (VE ISSN 0590-3351) **1611**

Universidad de Oviedo. Centro de Estudios del Siglo XVIII. Boletin. (SP) **2393**

Universidad de Oviedo. Departamento de Prehistoria y Arqueologia. Publicaciones. (SP) **288**

Universidad de Oviedo. Facultad de Medicina. Archivos. (SP ISSN 0210-5527) **3159**

Universidad de Oviedo. Revista de Biologia. (SP ISSN 0212-8977) **458**

Universidad de Panama. Centro de Investigacion Juridica. Anuario. (PN) **2733**

Universidad de Panama. Centro de Investigacion Juridica. Boletin de Informacion Juridica. (PN) **2733**

Universidad de Panama. Centro de Investigacion Juridica. Jurisprudencia Constitutional. (PN) **2706**

Universidad de Panama. Centro de Investigacion Juridica. Legislacion Panamena. Indices Cronologicos y Analitico de Leyes (o Decretos Ejecutivos). (PN) **2734**

Universidad de Panama. Departamento de Bibliotecologia. Boletin. (PN) **2788**

Universidad de Panama. Escuela de Bibliotecologia. Boletin *see* Universidad de Panama. Departamento de Bibliotecologia. Boletin **2788**

Universidad de Panama. Facultad de Administracion Publica y Comercio. Revista. (PN) **4076**

Universidad de Panama. Facultad de Derecho y Ciencias Politicas. Cuadernos. (PN) **2689, 3976**

Universidad de Puerto Rico. Centro de Investigaciones Sociales. Informe Anual. (PR) **4455**

Universidad de Puerto Rico. Escuela de Arquitectura. Boletin Informativo *see* Dearquictectura **298**

Universidad de Puerto Rico. Escuela de Derecho. Revista Juridica *see* Universidad de Puerto Rico. Revista Juridica **2734**

Universidad de Puerto Rico. Revista Juridica. (PR) **2734**

Universidad de San Carlos. Facultad de Ingeneria. Escuela Regional de Ingenieria Sanitaria. Carta Periodica. (GT) **4114**

Universidad de San Carlos. Revista. (GT) **347, 2971, 4390**

Universidad de San Carlos Anual. (GT) **2517**

Universidad de San Carlos de Guatemala. Facultad de Medicina Veterinaria y Zootecnia Revista. (GT) **4816**

Universidad de Sevilla. Coleccion de Bolsillo. (SP) **2971**

Universidad de Sevilla. Instituto de Desarrollo Regional. Ediciones. (SP) **887**

Universidad de Sevilla. Instituto Garcia Oviedo. Cuadernos. (SP) **696**

Universidad de Sevilla. Instituto Garcia Oviedo. Publicaciones. (SP ISSN 0582-8929) **2689, 1030, 4076**

Universidad de Sevilla. Seminario de Antropologia Americana. Publicaciones. (SP ISSN 0080-9101) **251**

Universidad de Sevilla. Serie: Arquitectura. (SP) **308**

Universidad de Sevilla. Serie: Bellas Artes. (SP) **347**

Universidad de Sevilla. Serie: Biblioteca Universitaria. (SP) **415**

Universidad de Sevilla. Serie: Ciencias. (SP) **4349**

Universidad de Sevilla. Serie: Ciencias Economicas y Empresariales. (SP) **696**

Universidad de Sevilla. Serie: Derecho. (SP) **2689**

Universidad de Sevilla. Serie: Farmacia. (SP) **3745**

Universidad de Sevilla. Serie: Filosofia y Letras. (SP) **3785, 2517**

Universidad de Sevilla. Serie: Ingenieria. (SP) **1839**

Universidad de Sevilla. Serie: Instituto de Ciencias de la Educacion. (SP) **1669**

Universidad de Sevilla. Serie: Medicina. (SP) **3159**

Universidad de Sevilla. Serie: Testimonio Universitario. (SP) **415, 1669**

Universidad de Uruguay. Departamento de Literatura Iberoamericana Publicaciones. (UY ISSN 0077-1252) **2971**

Universidad de Uruguay. Facultad de Agronomia. Boletin. (UY ISSN 0077-1260) **126**

Universidad de Valencia. Catedra de Derecho del Trabajo. Cuadernos. (SP) **2689**

Universidad de Yucatan. Revista *see* Universidad Autonoma de Yucatan. Revista **2516**

Universidad de Zulia. Facultadad de Ingeniria. Revista Tecnica. (VE ISSN 0254-0770) **1839**

†Universidad del Valle. Departamento de Biliotecas. Boletin de Adquisiciones. (CK) **5296**

Universidad del Valle Biblioteca. Publicaciones *see* Universidad del Valle. Departamento de Biliotecas. Boletin de Adquisiciones **5296**

Universidad del Zulia. Facultad de Derecho. Revista. (VE) **2689**

Universidad del Zulia. Facultad de Medicina. Revista. (VE ISSN 0542-6375) **3159**

Universidad del Zulia. Revista. (VE) **2517**

Universidad del Zulia. Revistas. (VE ISSN 0041-8811) **458, 3159**

Universidad Externado de Colombia. Revista *see* Externado **2624**

Universidad Hispalense. Anales. Serie: Ciencias *see* Universidad de Sevilla. Serie: Ciencias **4349**

Universidad Industrial de Santander. Boletin de Geologia. (CK ISSN 0120-0283) **1583**

Universidad Industrial de Santander. Revista - Humanidades. (CK ISSN 0120-095X) **2517**

Universidad Industrial de Santander. Revista - Investigaciones. (CK ISSN 0120-0852) **1839, 2517, 3159**

Universidad Industrial de Santander. Revista - Medicina *see* Universidad Industrial de Santander. Revista - Salud **3160**

Universidad Industrial de Santander. Revista - Salud. (CK ISSN 0121-0807) **3160, 4114**

Universidad Interamericana de Puerto Rico. Departamento de Ciencias Sociales. Revista Anales. (PR) **4390**

Universidad Interamericana de Puerto Rico. Recinto de San German. Revista de Ciencias Sociales e Historia. Anales. (PR) **4390, 2325**

Universidad Internacional Menendez Pelayo. Publicaciones. (SP ISSN 0080-6145) **1718**

Universidad Javeriana. Facultad de Teologia. Coleccion Profesores. (CK) **4208**

Universidad Nacional. Centro de Estudios Generales. Cuaderno de Estudio. (CR) **2517**

Universidad Nacional Agraria. Taller de Estudios Andinos. Serie Andes Centrales. (PE) **195**

Universidad Nacional Autonoma de Honduras. Instituto de Investigaciones Economicas y Sociales. Boletin. (HO) **4390**

Universidad Nacional Autonoma de Mexico. Anuario de Geografia. (MX ISSN 0185-1322) **2264**

Universidad Nacional Autonoma de Mexico. Centro de Documentacion Legislativa Universitaria. Cuadernos. (MX) **1718**

Universidad Nacional Autonoma de Mexico. Centro de Estudios Clasicos. Cuadernos. (MX) **1280**

Universidad Nacional Autonoma de Mexico. Centro de Estudios Mayas. Cuadernos. (MX ISSN 0076-7166) **2424**

Universidad Nacional Autonoma de Mexico. Facultad de Derecho de Mexico. Revista. (MX) **2689**

Universidad Nacional Autonoma de Mexico. Instituto de Biologia. Anales *see* Universidad Nacional Autonoma de Mexico. Instituto de Biologia. Anales: Serie Botanica **519**

Universidad Nacional Autonoma de Mexico. Instituto de Biologia. Anales *see* Universidad Nacional Autonoma de Mexico. Instituto de Biologia. Anales: Serie Zoologia **593**

Universidad Nacional Autonoma de Mexico. Instituto de Biologia. Anales: Serie Botanica. (MX ISSN 0374-5511) **519**

Universidad Nacional Autonoma de Mexico. Instituto de Biologia. Anales: Serie Zoologia. (MX ISSN 0368-8720) **593**

UNIVERSIDAD NACIONAL

Universidad Nacional Autonoma de Mexico. Instituto de Geofisica. Boletin Sismologico. (MX) **1596**

Universidad Nacional Autonoma de Mexico. Instituto de Geofisica. Datos Geofisicos a Tablas de Prediccion de Mareas, Puertos del Golfo de Mexico y Mar Caribe. (MX) **1600**

Universidad Nacional Autonoma de Mexico. Instituto de Geofisica. Datos Geofisicos a Tablas de Prediccion de Mareas, Puertos del Oceano Pacifico.(MX) **1601**

Universidad Nacional Autonoma de Mexico. Instituto de Geofisica. Monografias. (MX ISSN 0076-7204) **1596**

Universidad Nacional Autonoma de Mexico. Instituto de Geografia. Anuario de Geografia *see* Universidad Nacional Autonoma de Mexico. Anuario de Geografia **2264**

Universidad Nacional Autonoma de Mexico. Instituto de Geografia. Boletin *see* Investigaciones Geograficas **2254**

Universidad Nacional Autonoma de Mexico. Instituto de Geologia. Revista. (MX ISSN 0185-0962) **1583**

Universidad Nacional Autonoma de Mexico. Instituto de Investigaciones Antropologicas. Cuadernos Serie Antropologica *see* Universidad Nacional Autonoma de Mexico. Instituto de Investigaciones Antropologicas. Serie Antropologica **251**

Universidad Nacional Autonoma de Mexico. Instituto de Investigaciones Antropologicas. Serie Antropologica. (MX ISSN 0076-7298) **251**

Universidad Nacional Autonoma de Mexico. Instituto de Investigaciones Bibliograficas. Boletin. (MX ISSN 0006-1719) **415**

Universidad Nacional Autonoma de Mexico. Instituto de Investigaciones Bibliografica. Instrumenta Bibliographica. (MX ISSN 0185-0067) **2788**

Universidad Nacional Autonoma de Mexico. Instituto de Investigaciones Esteticas. Anales. (MX ISSN 0185-1276) **348**

Universidad Nacional Autonoma de Mexico. Instituto de Investigaciones Esteticas. Monografias de Arte. (MX ISSN 0185-1799) **348**

Universidad Nacional Autonoma de Mexico. Instituto de Investigaciones Esteticas. Monografias. Serie Mayor. (MX ISSN 0188-0861) **2517**

Universidad Nacional Autonoma de Mexico. Instituto de Investigaciones Filosoficas. Cuadernos. (MX ISSN 0185-2558) **3785**, **2849**

Universidad Nacional Autonoma de Mexico. Instituto de Investigaciones Historicas. Cuadernos Serie Documental. (MX ISSN 0076-7271) **2424**

Universidad Nacional Autonoma de Mexico. Instituto de Investigaciones Historicas. Serie Bibliografica. (MX ISSN 0076-7301) **2424**

Universidad Nacional Autonoma de Mexico. Instituto de Investigaciones Historicas. Serie Documental. (MX ISSN 0076-731X) **2424**

Universidad Nacional Autonoma de Mexico. Instituto de Investigaciones Historicas. Serie de Culturas Mesoamericanas. (MX ISSN 0076-7328) **2424**

Universidad Nacional Autonoma de Mexico. Instituto de Investigaciones Historicas. Serie de Cultura Nahuatl. Estudios de Cultura Nahuatl. (MX ISSN 0071-1675) **2425**

Universidad Nacional Autonoma de Mexico. Instituto de Investigaciones Historicas. Serie de Cultura Nahuatl. Fuentes. (MX ISSN 0076-7212) **2425**

Universidad Nacional Autonoma de Mexico. Instituto de Investigaciones Historicas. Serie de Cultura Nahuatl. Monografias. (MX ISSN 0076-7344) **2425**

Universidad Nacional Autonoma de Mexico. Instituto de Investigaciones Historicas. Serie de Historia General. (MX ISSN 0076-7352) **2425**

Universidad Nacional Autonoma de Mexico. Instituto de Investigaciones Historicas. Serie de Historia Novohispana *see* Estudios de Historia Novohispana **2405**

Universidad Nacional Autonoma de Mexico. Instituto de Investigaciones Historicas. Serie de Historiadores y Cronistas. (MX ISSN 0076-7387) **2425**

Universidad Nacional Autonoma de Mexico. Instituto de Investigaciones Juridicas. Boletin *see* Boletin Mexicano de Derecho Comparado **2605**

Universidad Nacional Autonoma de Mexico. Instituto de Investigaciones Juridicas. Cuadernos. (US ISSN 0187-0203) **2734**

Universidad Nacional Autonoma de Mexico. Instituto de Matematicas. Anales. (MX ISSN 0185-0644) **3059**

Universidad Nacional Autonoma de Mexico. Instituto de Matematicas. Monografias. (MX ISSN 0187-4780) **3059**

Universidad Nacional Autonoma de Mexico. Revista. (MX ISSN 0026-1750) **1669**

Universidad Nacional Autonoma de Mexico. Seminario de Investigaciones Bibliotecologica. Publicaciones. Serie B. Bibliografia. (MX ISSN 0076-7468) **415**

Universidad Nacional Autonoma de Mexico Directorio de Bibliotecas *see* U N A M Directorio de Bibliotecas **2788**

†Universidad Nacional Autonoma de Mexico, Facultad de Medicina. Revista. (MX) **5296**

Universidad Nacional de Agraria. Taller de Estudios Andinos. Serie Costa Central. (PE) **195**

Universidad Nacional de Asuncion. Escuela de Bibliotecologia. Informaciones. (PY) **2788**

Universidad Nacional de Asuncion. Instituto de Ciencias. Memoria. (PY) **4349**

Universidad Nacional de Colombia. Centro de Estudios Folkloricos. Monografias. (CK ISSN 0067-9534) **2059**, **3585**

Universidad Nacional de Colombia. Direccion de Divulgacion Cultural. Revista. (CK ISSN 0502-949X) **4390**

Universidad Nacional de Colombia. Facultad de Arquitectura. Revista. (CK ISSN 0120-2669) **308**

Universidad Nacional de Colombia. Facultad de Medicina. Revista. (CK ISSN 0120-0011) **3160**

Universidad Nacional de Colombia. Revista. (CK ISSN 0121-0890) **2517**

Universidad Nacional de Cordoba. Facultad de Ciencias Medicas. Revista. (AG ISSN 0014-6722) **3160**

Universidad Nacional de Cordoba. Facultad de Odontologia. Revista. (AG ISSN 0325-1071) **3243**

†Universidad Nacional de Cuyo. Biblioteca Central. Boletin Bibliografico. (AG ISSN 0076-6399) **5296**

†Universidad Nacional de Cuyo. Biblioteca Central. Cuadernos de la Biblioteca. (AG ISSN 0076-6402) **5296**

Universidad Nacional de Cuyo. Facultad de Ciencias Economicas. Revista. (AG ISSN 0041-8668) **696**

Universidad Nacional de la Plata. Facultad de Agronomia. Revista. (AG ISSN 0041-8676) **126**

Universidad Nacional de la Plata. Instituto de la Produccion. Serie Contribuciones. (AG ISSN 0457-1673) **1086**

Universidad Nacional de la Plata. Revista. (AG ISSN 0041-8625) **2517**

Universidad Nacional de Tucuman. Facultad de Filosofia y Letras. Cuadernos de Humanitas. (AG ISSN 0564-4070) **2517**

Universidad Nacional de Tucuman. Instituto de Ingenieria Electrica. Revista. (AG ISSN 0082-6693) **1910**

Universidad Nacional del Centro del Peru. Anales Cientificos. (PE) **1718**

Universidad Nacional del Centro del Peru. Cuadernos Universitarios. Serie: Estudios Andinos del Centro. (PE) **251**

Universidad Nacional del Litoral. Facultad de Ciencias de la Administracion. Revista. (AG) **4076**

Universidad Nacional del Litoral. Facultad de Ciencias Economicas Comerciales y Politicas. (AG) **696**

Universidad Nacional del Litoral. Facultad de Ingenieria Quimica. Revista. (AG ISSN 0376-0456) **1860**

†Universidad Nacional del Zulia. Facultad de Humanidades y Educacion. Conferencias y Coloquios. (VE ISSN 0076-4345) **5296**

Universidad Nacional Federico Villareal. Departamento de Ciencias Historico Sociales. Publicaciones. (PE) **2425**

Universidad Nacional Federico Villareal. Facultad de Derecho. Revista. (PE) **2689**

Universidad Nacional Mayor de San Marcos. Departamento de Sociologia. Revista. (PE) **4455**

Universidad Nacional Mayor de San Marcos. Facultad de Ciencias Economicas y Comerciales. Revista. (PE) **696**

Universidad Nacional Mayor de San Marcos. Facultad de Farmacia y Bioquimica. Revista. (PE) **3745**, **483**

Universidad Nacional Mayor de San Marcos. Instituto de Biologia Andina. Archivos *see* Archivos de Biologia Andina **429**

Universidad Nacional Mayor de San Marcos. Seminario de Historia Rural Andina. Seminario Arqueologico. (PE) **288**

Universidad Pedagogica y Tecnologica de Colombia. Centro de Estudios Economicos. Apuntes del C E N E S. (CK ISSN 0120-3053) **696**

Universidad Peruana Cayetano Heredia. Boletin. (PE) **1718**

Universidad Pontificia Comillas de Madrid. Publicaciones. Serie 1: Estudios. (SP) **4208**, **3785**

Universidad Tecnica del Estado. Revista.(CL) **4390**

Universidad Tecnologica del Choco. Revista. (CK) **4612**, **1718**

Universidad Tecnologica del Magdalena.(CK) **1327**

Universidad Veracruzana. Centro de Investigaciones Linguistico-Literarias. Texto-Critico. (MX ISSN 0185-0830) **2849**, **2971**

Universidad y Cooperativismo. (CK) **887**

Universidade Catolica de Goias. Gabinete de Arqueologia. Anuario de Divulgacao Cientifica. (BL) **288**

Universidade de Coimbra. Faculdade de Farmacia. Edicao Didactica e Edicao Cientifica *see* Universidade de Coimbra. Faculdade de Farmacia. Boletim **3745**

Universidade de Coimbra. Arquivo. Boletim. (PO) **2788**

Universidade de Coimbra. Faculdade de Direito. Boletim de Ciencias Economicas. (PO) **696**

Universidade de Coimbra. Faculdade de Farmacia. Boletim. (PO ISSN 0378-9608) **3745**

Universidade de Lisboa. Faculdade de Ciencias. Instituto Botanico. Artigo de Divulgacao. (PO ISSN 0066-8079) **4349**

Universidade de Lisboa. Faculdade de Direito. Revista. (PO) **2689**

Universidade de Lisboa. Faculdade de Letras. Revista. (PO) **2971**, **2887**

Universidade de Sao Paulo. Centro de Estudos Portugueses. Boletim Informativo. (BL) **2849**

Universidade de Sao Paulo. Departamento de Botanica. Boletim de Botanica. (BL ISSN 0302-2439) **519**

Universidade de Sao Paulo. Departamento de Historia. Boletim. (BL) **2425**

Universidade de Sao Paulo. Escola de Enfermagem. Revista. (BL ISSN 0080-6234) **3287**

Universidade de Sao Paulo. Faculdade de Ciencias Economicas e Administrativas. Biblioteca. Boletim *see* Universidade de Sao Paulo. Faculdade de Economia e Administracao. Biblioteca. Boletim **415**

Universidade de Sao Paulo. Faculdade de Direito. Revista. (BL ISSN 0080-6250) **2689**

Universidade de Sao Paulo. Faculdade de Economia e Administracao. Biblioteca. Boletim. (BL) **415**

Universidade de Sao Paulo. Faculdade de Educacao. Revista. (BL ISSN 0102-2555) **1669**

Universidade de Sao Paulo. Hospital das Clinicas. Revista. (BL ISSN 0041-8781) **3160**, **2470**

Universidade de Sao Paulo. Instituto Astronomico e Geofisico. Anuario Astronomico. (BL) **370**

Universidade de Sao Paulo. Instituto de Estudos Brasileiros. Revista. (BL ISSN 0020-3874) **2264**, **251**, **2059**, **4455**

Universidade de Sao Paulo. Instituto de Pesquisas Economicas. Estatisticas Basicas do Setor Agricola no Brasil. (BL) **144**, **126**

Universidade de Sao Paulo. Instituto de Pesquisas Economicas. Trabalho para Discussao. *see* Universidade de Sao Paulo. Instituto de Pesquisas Economicas. Trabalho para Discussao Interna **696**

Universidade de Sao Paulo. Instituto de Pesquisas Economicas. Trabalho para Discussao Interna. (BL) **696**

Universidade de Sao Paulo. Instituto Oceanografico. Boletim. (BL ISSN 0373-5524) **1612**

Universidade de Sao Paulo. Instituto Oceanografico. Publicacao Especial. (BL ISSN 0100-5146) **1612**

Universidade de Sao Paulo. Instituto Oceanografico. Relatorio de Cruzeiros. (BL ISSN 0100-5197) **1612**

Universidade de Sao Paulo. Instituto Oceanografico. Relatorio Interno. (BL ISSN 0100-5243) **1612**

Universidade de Sao Paulo. Museu de Arte Contemporanea. Boletim Informativo. (BL ISSN 0041-8803) **3534**

Universidade de Sao Paulo. Museu Paulista. Anais. (BL ISSN 0080-6374) **2425**

Universidade de Sao Paulo. Museu Paulista. Colecao. Serie de Arqueologia. (BL) **288**

Universidade de Sao Paulo. Museu Paulista. Colecao. Serie de Etnologia.(BL) **251**

Universidade de Sao Paulo. Museu Paulista. Colecao. Serie de Geografia.(BL) **2264**

Universidade de Sao Paulo. Museu Paulista. Colecao. Serie de Historia. (BL) **2425**

Universidade de Sao Paulo. Museu Paulista. Colecao. Serie de Mobiliario.(BL) **3534**, **2562**

Universidade de Sao Paulo. Museu Paulista. Colecao. Serie de Numismatica. (BL) **3602**

Universidade de Sao Paulo. Museu Paulista. Revista. (BL ISSN 0080-6390) **251**
Universidade de Sao Paulo. Revista de Farmacia e Bioquimica. (BL ISSN 0370-4726) **3745**
Universidade de Sao Paulo. Revista de Odontologia. (BL) **3244**
Universidade de Sao Paulo Boletim I G - U S P. Publicacao Especial *see* Boletim I G - U S P. Publicacao Especial **1541**
Universidade de Sao Paulo Boletim I G - U S P. Serie Cientifica *see* Boletim I G - U S P. Serie Cientifica **1541**
Universidade de Sao Paulo Boletim I G - U S P. Serie Didatica *see* Boletim I G - U S P. Serie Didatica **1541**
Universidade de Uberlandia. Faculdade de Direito. Revista *see* Universidade Federal de Uberlandia. Curso de Direito. Revista **2689**
Universidade do Amazonas. Centro de Pesquisas Socio-Economicas. Boletim Tecnico Informativo. (BL) **4390**
Universidade do Estado do Rio de Janeiro Boletim U E R J *see* Boletim U E R J **1618**
Universidade do Parana. Departamento de Historia. Boletim *see* Universidade do Parana. Setor de Ciencias Humanas, Letras e Artes. Departamento de Historia. Boletim **2325**
Universidade do Parana. Setor de Ciencias Humanas, Letras e Artes. Departamento de Historia. Boletim. (BL) **2325**
Universidade do Recife. Faculdade de Odontologia. Anais *see* Universidade Federal de Pernambuco. Faculdade de Odontologia. Anais **3244**
Universidade do Recife. Instituto Oceanografico. Trabalhos *see* Universidade Federal de Pernambuco. Departamento de Oceanografia. Centro de Tecnologia. Trabalhos Oceanograficos **458**
Universidade Estadual de Campinas. Faculdade de Engenharia de Alimentos e Enpenhoria Agricola. Informativo Annual *see* Universidade Estadual de Campinas. Faculdade de Tecnologia de Alimentos. Informativo Annual **3612**
Universidade Estadual de Campinas. Faculdade de Tecnologia de Alimentos. Informativo Annual. (BL) **3612**
†Universidade Estadual Paulista. Departamento de Educacao. Boletim. (BL) **5296**
Universidade Estadual Paulista. Revista de Odontologia. (BL ISSN 0101-1774) **3244**
Universidade Estadual Paulista Arte U N E S P *see* Arte U N E S P **315**
Universidade Federal de Goias. Publicacao. (BL) **1718**
Universidade Federal de Minas Gerais. Corpo Discente. Revista Literaria. (BL ISSN 0079-9327) **2971**
Universidade Federal de Minas Gerais. Curso de Odontologia. Arquivos do Centro de Estudos. (BL ISSN 0004-2838) **3244**
†Universidade Federal de Minas Gerais. Escola de Engenharia. Revista. (BL ISSN 0041-8838) **5296**
†Universidade Federal de Minas Gerais. Faculdade de Medicina. Anais. (BL ISSN 0301-7729) **5296**
Universidade Federal de Minas Gerais Escola de Biblioteconomia. Revista *see* U F M G. Escola de Biblioteconomia. Revista **2788**
Universidade Federal de Pernambuco. Anuario Estatistico. (BL) **1732**
Universidade Federal de Pernambuco. Departamento de Geologia. Serie B. Estudos e Pesquisas. (BL) **1549**
Universidade Federal de Pernambuco. Departamento de Oceanografia. Centro de Tecnologia. Trabalhos Oceanograficos. (BL ISSN 0374-0412) **458**
Universidade Federal de Pernambuco. Faculdade de Odontologia. Anais. (BL) **3244**
Universidade Federal de Pernambuco. Instituto de Antibioticos. Revista. (BL ISSN 0080-0228) **3745**
Universidade Federal de Pernambuco. Instituto de Geosciencias. Serie B: Estudos e Pesquisas *see* Universidade Federal de Pernambuco. Departamento de Geologia. Serie B. Estudos e Pesquisas **1549**
Universidade Federal de Pernambuco. Instituto Oceanografico. Trabalhos *see* Universidade Federal de Pernambuco. Departamento de Oceanografia. Centro de Tecnologia. Trabalhos Oceanograficos **458**
Universidade Federal de Pernambuco. Jornal. (BL) **1718**
Universidade Federal de Pernambuco. Relatorio des Attividades Universitarias. (BL) **1718**
Universidade Federal de Santa Catarina. Museu de Antropologia. Anais. (BL ISSN 0581-6076) **251**
Universidade Federal de Santa Maria. Centro de Ciencias Rurais. Revista. (BL ISSN 0085-5901) **126**
Universidade Federal de Santa Maria. Faculdade de Farmacia e Bioquimica. Revista. (BL ISSN 0041-8846) **3745**
Universidade Federal de Uberlandia. Curso de Direito. Revista. (BL ISSN 0102-1397) **2689**
Universidade Federal do Ceara. Centro de Ciencias da Saude. Revista de Medicina/Federal University of Ceara School of Medicine. Journal of Medicine. (BL ISSN 0100-1302) **3160**
Universidade Federal do Ceara. Centro de Tecnologia. Boletim Trimestral. (BL) **4612**
Universidade Federal do Ceara. Departamento de Ciencias Sociais e Filosofia. Documentos. (BL ISSN 0041-8870) **4390**
Universidade Federal do Ceara. Escola de Agronomia. Departamento de Fitotecnia. Relatoria Tecnico. (BL ISSN 0084-8646) **126**
Universidade Federal do Para. Relatorio Anual. (BL) **1718**
†Universidade Federal do Parana. Centro de Estudos Portugueses. Arquivos. (BL ISSN 0101-0352) **5297**
Universidade Federal do Parana. Departamento de Botanica. Boletim *see* Acta Biologica Paranaense **425**
Universidade Federal do Rio de Janeiro. Faculdade de Odontologia. Anais. (BL ISSN 0041-8919) **3244**
Universidade Federal do Rio de Janeiro. Instituto de Matematica. Estudos e Comunicacoes. (BL) **3059**
Universidade Federal do Rio de Janeiro. Instituto de Matematica. Memorias de Matematica. (BL) **3063**, 4591
Universidade Federal do Rio de Janeiro. Instituto de Matematica. Textos de Metodos Matematicos. (BL) **3059**
Universidade Federal do Rio Grande do Norte. Centro de Biociencias. Departamento de Oceanografia e Limnologia. Boletim. (BL ISSN 0100-7068) **1601**
Universidade Federal do Rio Grande do Norte. Departamento de Geologia. Boletim. (BL ISSN 0101-5400) **1583**
†Universidade Federal do Rio Grande do Sul. Faculdade de Agronomia. Boletim Tecnico. (BL) **5297**
†Universidade Federal do Rio Grande do Sul. Faculdade de Medicina. Anais.(BL ISSN 0085-042X) **5297**
Universidade Federal do Rio Grande do Sul. Faculdade de Odontologia. Revista *see* Faculdade de Odontologia de Porto Alegre. Revista **3233**
†Universidade Federal do Rio Grande do Sul. Gabinete de Pesquisa de Historia. Boletim. (BL) **5297**
Universidade Federal do Rio Grande do Sul. Instituto de Biociencias. Boletim. (BL ISSN 0102-597X) **4349**
Universidade Federal do Rio Grande do Sul. Instituto de Geociencias. Pesquisas. (BL) **1549**
Universidades. (MX ISSN 0041-8935) **1669**
Universita Cattolica. Istituto di Storia Antica. Ricerche. (IT ISSN 0393-1412) **1280**
Universita Cattolica del Sacro Cuore. Facolta di Agraria. Annali. (IT ISSN 0540-049X) **126**
†Universita Cattolica del Sacro Cuore, Milan. Saggi e Ricerche. Serie Terza. Scienze Psicologiche. (IT ISSN 0076-874X) **5297**
Universita degli Studi di Bari. Centro Studi Bizantini. Corsi di Studi. (IT) **2325**
Universita degli Studi di Bari. Facolta di Agraria. Annali. (IT ISSN 0365-0502) **126**
Universita degli Studi di Cagliari. Facolta di Lettere - Filosofia. Annali. (IT) **2517**
Universita degli Studi di Cagliari. Facolta di Magistero. Annali. (IT) **2517**
Universita degli Studi di Cagliari. Istituto di Storia Medioevale. Publicazioni. (IT ISSN 0068-4805) **2325**
†Universita degli Studi di Cagliari. Istituto Scienze Economiche. Studi di Economia. (IT) **5297**
Universita degli Studi di Cagliari. Seminario della Facolta di Scienza. Rendiconti. (IT ISSN 0041-8951) **4349**
Universita degli Studi di Catania. Istituto di Storia delle Tradizioni Popolari. Studi e Testi. (IT ISSN 0069-1186) **2059**
Universita degli Studi di Ferrara. Dipartimento di Scienze Geologiche e Paleontologiche. Annali. Sezione: Scienze della Terra. (IT) **1583**
Universita degli Studi di Ferrara. Istituto di Geologia. Annali. Sezione 15. Paleontologia Umana e Paletnologia. (IT) **3661**
Universita degli Studi di Ferrara. Istituto di Geologia, Paleontologia e Paleontologia Umana. Annali. Sezione 15. Paleontologia Umana e Paleontologia *see* Universita degli Studi di Ferrara. Istituto di Geologia. Annali. Sezione 15. Paleontologia Umana e Paletnologia **3661**
Universita degli Studi di Ferrara. Istituto di Geologia, Paleontologia e Paleontologia Umana. Pubblicazioni *see* Universita degli Studi di Ferrara. Istituto di Geologia. Pubblicazioni **1583**
Universita degli Studi di Ferrara. Istituto di Geologia. Pubblicazioni. (IT) **1583**, 3661
Universita degli Studi di Ferrara. Istituto di Mineralogia. Annali. Nuova Serie. Sezione: Scienze della Terra. (IT) **3497**
Universita degli Studi di Firenze. Istituto di Composizione Architettonica. Quaderni *see* Studi e Documenti di Architettura **307**
Universita degli Studi di Firenze. Istituto di Filosofia. Annali *see* Universita di Firenze. Dipartimento di Filosofia. Annali **3785**
Universita degli Studi di Firenze. Istituto di Statistica. Documentazione. (IT ISSN 0041-896X) **2500**
Universita degli Studi di Genova. Bollettino dei Musei e degli Istituti Biologici. (IT ISSN 0085-0950) **458**
Universita degli Studi di Genova. Facolta di Giurisprudenza. Annali. (IT ISSN 0435-3048) **2689**
Universita degli Studi di Genova. Fondazione Nobile Agostino Poggi (Pubblicazione). (IT) **2325**
Universita degli Studi di Genova. Istituto di Filologia Classica e Medievale. Pubblicazioni. (IT ISSN 0072-0852) **2849**, 1280
Universita degli Studi di Genova. Istituto di Geologia. Atti. (IT ISSN 0041-8978) **1583**
Universita degli Studi di Genova. Istituto di Medievistica. Collana. Storica di Fonti e Studi. (IT) **2393**
Universita degli Studi di Genova. Istituto di Paleografia e Storia Medievale. Collana. Storica di Fonti e Studi *see* Universita degli Studi di Genova. Istituto di Medievistica. Collana. Storica di Fonti e Studi **2393**
Universita degli Studi di Genova. Istituto di Progettazione Architettonica. Quaderno. (IT) **308**
Universita degli Studi di Lecce. Bollettino di Storia della Filosofia. (IT ISSN 0390-0614) **3785**
Universita degli Studi di Macerata. Facolta di Lettere e Filosofia. Annali. (IT ISSN 0076-1818) **288**, 1280, 2325, 2849
Universita degli Studi di Milano. Annuario. (IT) **1718**
Universita degli Studi di Modena. Seminario Matematico e Fisico. Atti. (IT ISSN 0041-8986) **3059**, 3834
Universita degli Studi di Napoli. Facolta di Scienze Agrarie. Annali. (IT ISSN 0365-799X) **126**
Universita degli Studi di Padova. Centro per la Storia della Tradizione Artistotelica nel Veneto. Saggi e Testi.(IT ISSN 0078-771X) **2393**
Universita degli Studi di Padova. Facolta di Lettere e Filosofia. Opuscoli Accademici. (IT ISSN 0078-7728) **2971**, 3785
Universita degli Studi di Padova. Facolta di Lettere e Filosofia. Pubblicazioni. (IT ISSN 0078-7736) **2971**, 3785
Universita degli Studi di Padova. Facolta di Scienze Statistiche, Demografiche ed Attuariali. Serie Estratti. (IT) **3996**
Universita degli Studi di Padova. Facolta di Scienze Statistiche, Demografiche ed Attuariali. Serie Pubblicazioni. (IT) **3996**
Universita degli Studi di Padova. Istituto di Storia Antica. Pubblicazioni. (IT ISSN 0078-7744) **2325**
Universita degli Studi di Padova. Istituto per la Storia. Contributi. (IT ISSN 0078-7752) **1718**
Universita degli Studi di Padova. Istituto per la Storia. Quaderni. (IT ISSN 0078-7760) **1718**
Universita degli Studi di Padova. Scuola di Perfezionamento in Filosofia. Pubblicazioni. (IT ISSN 0078-7779) **3785**
Universita degli Studi di Parma. Centro Studi e Archivio della Comunicazione. Archivi del Progretto - Collana. (IT) **1345**
Universita degli Studi di Parma. Centro Studi e Archivio della Comunicazione. Cataloghi. (IT) **1345**
Universita degli Studi di Parma. Facolta di Economia e Commercio. Studi e Ricerche. (IT) **696**
Universita degli Studi di Parma. Istituto di Storia dell'Arte. Cataloghi. (IT) **348**, 2555, 3518
Universita degli Studi di Parma. Rivista di Matematica. (IT ISSN 0035-6298) **3059**
Universita degli Studi di Pavia. Istituto Botanico. Atti. (IT ISSN 0079-0265) **519**
Universita degli Studi di Perugia. Facolta di Medicina e Chirurgia. Annali. (IT ISSN 0014-648X) **3385**
Universita degli Studi di Roma. Seminario di Archeologia e Storia dell'Arte Greca e Romana. Studi Miscellanei. (IT ISSN 0557-3122) **348**
Universita degli Studi di Roma "La Sapienza". Dipartamento di Economia Pubblica. Studi e Ricerche. (IT) **696**
Universita degli Studi di Siena. Facolta di Lettere e Filosofia. Annali. (IT) **2971**, 3785
Universita degli Studi di Trieste. Dipartimento di Scienze Matematiche. Rendiconti. (IT) **3059**

Title

6766 UNIVERSITA

Universita degli Studi di Trieste. Facolta di Scienze Politiche. Pubblicazioni. (IT) **3932**

Universita degli Studi di Trieste. Istituto di Matematica. Rendi Conti. *see* Universita degli Studi di Trieste. Dipartimento di Scienze Matematiche. Rendiconti **3059**

Universita degli Studi di Trieste. Istituto di Pedagogia. Quaderni. (IT ISSN 0082-6480) **1669**

Universita degli Studi di Trieste. Istituto di Ricerche Economico Agrarie. Pubblicazione. (IT) **159**

Universita degli Studi di Trieste. Istituto di Storia dell'Arte (Pubblicazioni). (IT ISSN 0564-2477) **348**

Universita degli Studi in Italia. Annuario.(IT ISSN 0392-8411) **1697**

Universita di Cagliari. Facolta di Lettere - Filosofia e Magistero. Annali *see* Universita degli Studi di Cagliari. Facolta di Lettere - Filosofia. Annali **2517**

Universita di Cagliari. Facolta di Lettere - Filosofia e Magistero. Annali *see* Universita degli Studi di Cagliari. Facolta di Lettere - Filosofia. Annali **2517**

Universita di Firenze. Dipartimento di Filosofia. Annali. (IT ISSN 0394-5073) **3785**

Universita di Messina. Facolta di Magistero. Nuovi Annali. (IT) **2517**, **3785**

Universita di Modena. Seminario Matematico e Fisico. Atti *see* Universita degli Studi di Modena. Seminario Matematico e Fisico. Atti **3059**

Universita di Napoli. Facolta di Lettere e Filosofia. Annali. (IT) **2325**, **2971**, **3785**

Universita di Padova. Seminario Matematico. Rendiconti. (IT ISSN 0041-8994) **3059**

Universita di Sassari. Facolta di Giurisprudenza. Pubblicazioni. Serie Economica. (IT) **697**

▼Universita di Siena. Dipartimento di Filosofia. Pubblicazioni. (IT) **3785**

Universita di Torino. Facolta di Agraria. Annali *see* Universita di Torino. Facolta di Scienze Agrarie. Annali **126**

Universita di Torino. Facolta di Scienze Agrarie. Annali. (IT) **126**

Universita e Istituti di Studio e Ricerca in Italia. Annuario D E A. (IT ISSN 0393-6368) **2206**

Universita e Politecnico di Torino. Seminario Matematico. Rendiconti. (IT ISSN 0373-1243) **3059**

Universita Karlova. Acta Universitatis Carolinae. Philosophica et Historica. (CS ISSN 0567-8293) **2393**, **3932**

Universita Karlova. Fakulta Vseobecneho Lekarstvi. Pobocka v Hradci Kralove. Sbornik Vedeckych Praci. (CS ISSN 0049-5514) **3160**

Universita Karlova. Fakulta Vseobecneho Lekarstvi. Pobocka v Hradci Kralove. Sbornik Vedeckych Praci: Supplementum. (CS ISSN 0049-5522) **3160**

Universita Karlova. Pedagogicky Fakulta. Sbornik. Historie. (CS ISSN 0556-1183) **2393**

Universita Palackeho. Filosoficka Fakulta. Slavica. (CS) **2971**

Universita Palackeho. Pedagogicka Fakulta. Sbornik Praci: Rusky Jazyk a Literatura. (CS) **2849**, **2971**

Universita Palackeho Olomouc. Pedagogicka Fakulta. Sbornik Praci. Historie. (CS) **2393**

Universitaet Aalborg. Arbeitspapiere des Instituts fuer Sprache und Interkulturelle Studien *see* Aalborg Universitetscenter. Institut for Sprog og Internationale Kulturstudier. Arbeijdspapirer **2800**

Universitaet Augsburg. Personen- und Studienverzeichnis. (GW ISSN 0938-2569) **1327**

Universitaet Bonn. Institut fuer Kommunikationsforschung und Phonetik. Forschungsberichte. (GW ISSN 0341-3136) **1345**

Universitaet Bonn. Institut fuer Oekonometrie und Operations Research. Neuanschaffungslisten. (GW) **743**

Universitaet Bonn. Seminar fuer Orientalische Kunstgeschichte. Veroeffentlichungen. Reihe A. Nimruz. (GW) **288**

Universitaet Bonn. Seminar fuer Orientalische Kunstgeschichte. Veroeffentlichungen. Reihe B. Antiquitates Orientales. (GW) **348**

Universitaet Bremen - Schwerpunkt Geographie. Materialien und Manuskripte. (GW ISSN 0720-9746) **2264**

Universitaet des Saarlandes. Geographisches Institut. Arbeiten. (GW ISSN 0563-1491) **2265**

Universitaet des Saarlandes. Jahresbibliographie. (GW ISSN 0080-5173) **415**

Universitaet Duesseldorf. Jahrbuch. (GW ISSN 0070-7457) **1718**

Universitaet Erlangen - Nuernberg. Vorlesungsverzeichnis. (GW ISSN 0931-0746) **1327**

Universitaet Frankfurt. Seminar fuer Voelkerkunde. Arbeiten. (GW ISSN 0170-3099) **251**

Universitaet Frankfurt. Wissenschaftliche Gesellschaft. Sitzungsberichte. (GW ISSN 0512-1523) **4349**

Universitaet Frankfurt am Main. Ostasiatischen Seminars. Veroeffentlichungen *see* Johann-Wolfgang-Goethe-Universitaet, Frankfurt. Ostasiatische Seminar. Veroeffentlichungen. Reihe B: Ostasienkunde **5221**

Universitaet fuer Bodenkultur in Wien. Dissertationen. (AU ISSN 0256-4246) **126**, **2110**

Universitaet-Gesamthochschule Duisburg. Universitaets-Report. (GW ISSN 0722-8481) **1669**

Universitaet Giessen. Ergebnisse Landwirtschaftlicher Forschung. (GW ISSN 0075-4609) **126**

†Universitaet Giessen. Mathematisches Institut. Vorlesungen. (GW) **5297**

Universitaet Goettingen. Jahresbericht *see* Universitaet Goettingen. Jahresforschungsbericht **1718**

Universitaet Goettingen. Jahresforschungsbericht. (GW) **1718**

Universitaet Hamburg. Geologisch-Palaeontologisches Institut. Mitteilungen. (GW ISSN 0072-1115) **1583**, **3661**

Universitaet Hamburg. Institut fuer Internationale Angelegenheiten. Veroeffentlichungen. (GW ISSN 0341-3233) **3976**

Universitaet Hamburg. Institut fuer Internationale Angelegenheiten. Werkhefte. (GW ISSN 0341-3241) **2730**, **3976**

Universitaet Hamburg. Mathematisches Seminar. Abhandlungen. (GW ISSN 0025-5858) **3060**

Universitaet Hamburg. Seminar fuer Allgemeine Betriebswirtschaftlehre. Schriftenreihe. (GW) **697**

Universitaet Hamburg. Studien zur Angewandte Wirtschaftsforschung und Oekonometrie. (GW) **697**

Universitaet Hamburg. Zentrum fuer Meereskunde- und Klimaforschung. Berichte *see* Zentrum fuer Meeres- und Klimaforschung. Berichte **1612**

Universitaet Hannover. Astronomische Station. (Veroeffentlichungen). (GW) **370**

Universitaet Hannover. Institut fuer Siedlungswasserwirtschaft. Veroeffentlichungen. (GW) **4829**

Universitaet Hannover. Institut fuer Stahlbau. Schriftenreihe. (GW) **1922**

Universitaet Hannover. Institut fuer Statik. Mitteilungen. (GW) **1923**

Universitaet Heidelberg. Suedasien-Institut. Schriftenreihe. (GW ISSN 0440-601X) **2342**

Universitaet Hohenheim. Amtliche Mitteilungen. (GW) **1718**, **4076**

Universitaet Hohenheim Forschungsbericht. (GW ISSN 0344-0915) **4358**, **743**

Universitaet Innsbruck. Alpenkundliche Studien. (AU) **1583**

Universitaet Innsbruck. Alpin-Biologische Studien. (AU) **458**

Universitaet Innsbruck. Finanzwissenschaftliche Studien. (AU) **802**

Universitaet Innsbruck. Kunstgeschichtliche Studien. (AU) **348**

Universitaet Innsbruck. Mathematische Studien. (AU) **3060**

Universitaet Innsbruck. Medizinische Fakultaet. Arbeiten. (AU ISSN 0579-7772) **3160**

Universitaet Innsbruck. Theologische Fakultaet. Studien und Arbeiten. (AU ISSN 0579-7780) **4208**

Universitaet Kiel. Agrarwissenschaftliche Fakultaet. Schriftenreihe. (GW) **127**

Universitaet Kiel. Geographisches Institut. Schriften. (GW ISSN 0723-9874) **2265**

Universitaet Kiel. Geologisch-Palaeontologisches Institut. Berichte - Reports. (GW ISSN 0175-9302) **1583**

Universitaet Muenchen. Geophysikalisches Observatorium, Fuerstenfeldbruck. Veroeffentlichungen. Serie A. (GW ISSN 0343-7493) **1596**

Universitaet Muenchen. Geophysikalisches Observatorium, Fuerstenfeldbruck. Veroeffentlichungen. Serie B. (GW ISSN 0077-2100) **1596**

Universitaet Muenchen. Wirtschaftsgeographisches Institut. "W G I"-Berichte zur Regionalforschung. (GW ISSN 0077-2127) **2265**

Universitaet Muenster. Institut fuer Verkehrswissenschaft. Beitraege. (GW) **4722**

Universitaet Passau. Vorlesungsverzeichnis. (GW) **1328**

Universitaet Salzburg. Dissertationen. (AU ISSN 0259-0700) **4349**

Universitaet Stuttgart. Institut fuer Geologie und Palaeontologie Arbeiten Neue Folge. (GW ISSN 0585-7856) **1549**, **3661**

Universitaet Stuttgart. Institut fuer Steuerungstechnik der Werkzeugmaschinen und Fertigungseinrichtungen. i S W Berichte. (US ISSN 0085-6916) **3024**, **1940**

Universitaet Wien. Dissertationen. (AU ISSN 0379-1424) **4349**

Universitaet zu Koeln. Geologisches Institut. Sonderveroeffentlichungen. (GW ISSN 0069-5874) **1583**

Universitaet zu Koeln. Institut fuer Geophysik und Meteorologie. Mitteilungen. (GW ISSN 0069-5882) **1596**, **3441**

Universitaet zu Koeln. Institut fuer Handelsforschung. Beitraege zur Dokumentation der Betriebswirtschaftlichen Situation im Gross- und Einzelhandel. (GW) **887**

Universitaet zu Koeln. Institut fuer Handelsforschung. Mitteilungen. (GW ISSN 0531-030X) **840**

Universitaet zu Koeln. Institut fuer Handelsforschung. Sonderhefte. (GW ISSN 0531-0318) **697**

Universitaet Zu Koeln. Jahrbuch. (GW ISSN 0069-5890) **1718**

Universitaet zu Koeln. Kunsthistorisches Institut. Abteilung Asien. Publikationen. (GW ISSN 0170-3692) **348**, **2342**

Universitaet Zuerich. Institut fuer Betriebswirtschaftliche Forschung. Schriftenreihe. (SZ) **1030**

Universitaets- und Landesbibliothek Sachsen-Anhalt. Arbeiten. (GW ISSN 0438-4415) **2788**

Universitaetsbibliothek Giessen. Berichte und Arbeiten. (GW ISSN 0072-4483) **2788**

Universitaetsbibliothek Giessen. Kurzberichte aus den Papyrus-Sammlungen. (GW ISSN 0072-4491) **2325**, **1280**, **3645**

Universitaetsfuehrer. (GW ISSN 0179-7514) **1718**

Universitaetszeitung das Deutsche Hochschulmagazin *see* Deutsche Universitaets-Zeitung **1704**

Universitario. (DR ISSN 0041-9044) **1669**

Universitarios. (MX ISSN 0185-4143) **1718**

Universitas. (GH ISSN 0049-5530) **1718**

Universitas. (US ISSN 0146-9061) **1718**

Universitas. (IT ISSN 0393-2702) **1718**

Universitas. (BL ISSN 0041-9052) **2517**

Universitas. (CH ISSN 1015-8383) **2517**

Universitas. (CK ISSN 0041-9060) **2734**

Universitas (English Edition). (GW ISSN 0341-0129) **2971**, **348**, **4349**

Universitas (German Edition). (GW ISSN 0041-9079) **2972**, **348**, **4349**

Universitas (Spanish Edition). (GW ISSN 0341-0102) **2972**, **348**, **4349**

Universitas Comeniana. Acta Facultatis Pharmaceuticae. (CS ISSN 0041-9087) **3745**

Universitas Comeniana: Acta Facultatis Iuridicae. (CS) **2689**

Universitas Medica. (CK ISSN 0041-9095) **3160**

Universitas 2000. (VE) **1719**

Universitat de Barcelona. Biblioteca. (SP ISSN 0214-6541) **415**, **2788**

Universitat de Barcelona. Biblioteca. Memoria Anual. (SP) **2788**

Universitat Istanbul. Forstlichen Fakultaet. Zeitschrift. *see* Istanbul Universitesi. Orman Fakultesi. Dergisi **2103**

Universitatae din Timisoara. Facultatae de Stiinte ale Naturii. Seminarul de Ecuatii Functionale. (RM) **3060**

Universitatea din Timisoara. Facultatae de Stiinte Ale Naturii. Seminarul de Operatori Liniari si Analiza Armonica. (RM) **3060**

Universitatea "Al. I. Cuza" din Iasi. Analele Stiintifice. Geologie - Geografie. (RM ISSN 0379-7902) **1583**

Universitatea "Al. I. Cuza" din Iasi. Analele Stiintifice. Sectiunea 3b: Filozofie. (RM ISSN 0379-7856) **3785**

Universitatea "Al. I. Cuza" din Iasi. Analele Stiintifice. Sectiunea 2b: Geologie *see* Universitatea "Al. I. Cuza" din Iasi. Analele Stiintifice. Geologie - Geografie **1583**

Universitatea "Al. I. Cuza" din Iasi. Analele Stiintifice. Sectiunea 3e: Lingvistica. (RM ISSN 0379-7880) **2849**

Universitatea "Al. I. Cuza" din Iasi. Analele Stiintifice. Sectiunea 3f: Literatura. (RM ISSN 0379-7899) **2972**

Universitatea "Al. I. Cuza" din Iasi. Analele Stiintifice. Sectiunea 1a: Matematica. (RM ISSN 0041-9109) **3060**

Universitatea "Al. I. Cuza" din Iasi. Analele Stiintifice. Sectiunea 3c: Stiinte Economice. (RM ISSN 0379-7864) **697**

Universitatea "Al. I. Cuza" din Iasi. Analele Stiintifice. Sectiunea 3b: Stiinte Filozofice *see* Universitatea "Al. I. Cuza" din Iasi. Analele Stiintifice. Sectiunea 3b: Filozofie **3785**

Universitatea "Al. I. Cuza" din Iasi. Analele Stiintifice. Sectiunea 3d: Stiinte Juridice. (RM ISSN 0379-7872) **2689**

UNIVERSITE 6767

Universitatea "Al. I. Cuza" din Iasi. Analele Stiintifice. Sectiunea 1b: Fizica. (RM ISSN 0041-9141) **3834**
Universitatea "Al. I. Cuza" din Iasi. Analele Stiintifice. Sectiunea 2a: Biologie. (RM ISSN 0041-9133) **459**
Universitatea "Al. I. Cuza" din Iasi. Analele Stiintifice. Sectiunea 3a: Istorie. (RM ISSN 0041-9125) **2325**
Universitatea Bucuresti. Analele. Filologie. (RM) **2849**
Universitatea Bucuresti. Analele. Filozofie. Istorie. Drept. (RM) **3785,** 2393, 2689
Universitatea Bucuresti. Analele. Stiintele Naturii. (RM) **4349**
Universitatea din Brasov. Buletinul. Seria B. Economia Forestiera *see* Universitatea Transilvania din Brasov. Buletinul. Seria B. Economia Forestiera **2110**
Universitatea din Brasov. Buletinul. Seria C. Matematica, Fizica, Chimie *see* Universitatea Transilvania din Brasov. Buletinul. Seria C. Matematica, Fizica, Chimie **3060**
Universitatea din Craiova. Anale. Seria: Biologie, Agronomie, Horticultura. (RM) **459,** 127
Universitatea din Craiova. Anale. Seria: Matematica, Fizica-Chimie. (RM) **3060,** 1190, 3834
Universitatea din Craiova. Analele: Seria Istorie, Geografie, Filologie. (RM) **2517**
Universitatea din Timisoara. Analele. Stiinte Filologice. (RM ISSN 0082-4461) **2849**
Universitatea din Timisoara. Analele. Stiinte Fizice. (RM) **3834,** 1190
Universitatea din Timisoara. Facultatea de Matematica. Analele: Stiinte Matematice. (RM) **3060**
Universitatea din Timisoara. Facultatea de Matematica. Lucrarile Seminarului de Geometrie si Topologie. (RM) **3060**
Universitatea din Timisoara. Facultatea de Matematica. Seminarul de Mecanica. (RM) **3060**
Universitatea din Timisoara. Facultatea de Matematica. Seminarul de Teoria Structurilor. (RM) **3060**
Universitatea din Timisoara. Facultatea de Stiinte ale Naturii. Analele: Stiinte Matematice *see* Universitatea din Timisoara. Facultatea de Matematica. Analele: Stiinte Matematice **3060**
Universitatea din Timisoara. Facultatea de Stiinte ale Naturii. Lucrarile Seminarului de Geometrie si Topologie *see* Universitatea din Timisoara. Facultatea de Matematica. Lucrarile Seminarului de Geometrie si Topologie **3060**
Universitatea din Timisoara. Facultatea de Stiinte ale Naturii. Seminarul de Teoria Functiilor si Matematici Aplicate. A: Spatii Metrice Probabiliste *see* Universitatea din Timisoara. Facultatea de Stiinte ale Naturii. Seminarul de Teoria Probabilitatilor si Aplicatii **3060**
Universitatea din Timisoara. Facultatea de Stiinte ale Naturii. Seminarul de Teoria Functiilor si Matematici Aplicate. B: Analiza Numerica *see* Universitatea din Timisoara. Sectia Matematica Informatica. Seminarul de Informatica si Analiza Numerica **3060**
Universitatea din Timisoara. Facultatea de Stiinte ale Naturii. Seminarul de Teoria Probabilitatilor si Aplicatii. (RM) **3060**
Universitatea din Timisoara. Facultatea de Stiinte ale Naturii. Seminarul de Teoria Probabilitatilor si Aplicatii *see* Universitatea din Timisoara. Facultatea de Stiinte ale Naturii. Seminarul de Teoria Probabilitatilor si Aplicatii **3060**
Universitatea din Timisoara. Facultatea de Stiinte ale Naturii. Seminarul de Teoria Structurilor *see* Universitatea din Timisoara. Facultatea de Matematica. Seminarul de Teoria Structurilor **3060**
Universitatea din Timisoara. Sectia Matematica Informatica. Seminarul de Informatica si Analiza Numerica. (RM) **3060**
Universitatea Tehnica Petrosani. Lucrari Stiintifice. (RM ISSN 1220-5079) **1583**
Universitatea Transilvania din Brasov. Buletinul. Seria A. Mecanica Aplicata. Electrotehnica si Electronica. Constructia de Masini si Tehnologia Prelucrarii Metalelor. (RM) **1940**
Universitatea Transilvania din Brasov. Buletinul. Seria B. Economia Forestiera. (RM) **2110**
Universitatea Transilvania din Brasov. Buletinul. Seria C. Matematica, Fizica, Chimie. (RM) **3060,** 459, 3834
Universitatis Debreceniensis de Ludovico Kossuth Nominatae. Instituti Philologiae Slavicae. Annales. Slavica.(HU ISSN 0583-5356) **2849**
L'Universite. (AE) **1719**
Universite Catholique de Louvain. Centre d'Etudes Politiques. Working Group "American Foreign Policy." Cahier. (BE ISSN 0076-1206) **3976,** 2425
Universite Catholique de Louvain. Centre International de Dialectologie Generale. Travaux. (BE ISSN 0577-1765) **2849**
Universite Catholique de Louvain. Departement d'Archelogie et d'Histoire de l'Art. Documents de Travail. (BE) **348,** 288
Universite Catholique de Louvain. Departement d'Archeologie et d'Histoire de l'Art. Publications. (BE) **288**
Universite Catholique de Louvain. Ecole des Sciences Politiques et Sociales. Collection. (BE ISSN 0076-1214) **4390**
Universite Catholique de Louvain. Faculte de Philosophie et Lettres. Travaux. (BE ISSN 0076-1222) **2517,** 2325, 2849, 2972
Universite Catholique de Louvain. Faculte de Theologie et de Droit Canonique. Collection des Dissertations Presentees pour l'Obtention du Grade de Maitre a la Faculte de Theologie Ou a la Faculte de Droit Canonique. (BE) **4277**
Universite Catholique de Louvain. Faculte de Theologie et de Droit Canonique. Travaux de Doctorat en Theologie et en Droit Canonique. Nouvelle Serie. (BE ISSN 0076-1230) **4277**
Universite Catholique de Louvain. Institut de Mathematique Pure et Appliquee. Rapport. *see* Universite Catholique de Louvain. Institut de Mathematique. Rapport de Mathematique **3060**
Universite Catholique de Louvain. Institut de Mathematique. Rapport de Mathematique. (BE) **3060**
Universite Catholique de Louvain. Institut des Langues Vivantes. Cahiers. (BE ISSN 0076-1249) **2849**
Universite Catholique de Louvain. Institut Orientaliste. Publications. (BE ISSN 0076-1265) **2342,** 3645
Universite Catholique de Louvain. Institut Superieur de Philosophie. Cours Publies. (BE ISSN 0076-1273) **3785**
Universite Catholique de Louvain. Recueil de Travaux d'Histoire et de Philologie. (BE ISSN 0076-1311) **2849**
Universite Claude Bernard. Departement de Mathematiques. Publications. (FR ISSN 0076-1656) **3060**
Universite d'Abidjan. Annales. Serie F: Ethnosociologie *see* Universite Nationale de Cote d'Ivoire. Annales. Serie F: Ethnosociologie **251**
Universite d'Abidjan. Annales. Serie G: Geographie *see* Universite Nationale de Cote d'Ivoire. Annales. Serie G: Geographie **2265**
Universite d'Aix-Marseille I. Centre d'Etudes des Societes Mediterraneennes. Cahiers. (FR ISSN 0065-4949) **4390**
Universite d'Aix-Marseille I. Centre d'Etudes et de Recherches Helleniques. Publications. (FR ISSN 0065-4981) **2972**
Universite d'Aix-Marseille I. Institut d'Histoire des Pays d'Outre-Mer. Etudes et Documents. (FR ISSN 0065-5007) **2393**
Universite d'Aix-Marseille 3. Centre des Hautes Etudes Touristiques. Collection "Essais". (FR ISSN 0395-8086) **4795**
Universite d'Aix-Marseille 3. Centre des Hautes Etudes Touristiques. Etudes et Memoires. (FR ISSN 0065-4965) **4795**
Universite d'Alger. Observatoire Astronomique. Annales *see* Observatoire Astronomique d'Alger. Annales **367**
Universite d'Alger. Publications Scientifiques. Serie A: Mathematiques. (AE ISSN 0002-5321) **3060**
Universite d'Alger. Publications Scientifiques. Serie B: Sciences Physiques. (AE ISSN 0002-533X) **4350**
Universite d'Ankara. Faculte des Sciences. Communications. Serie C. Biologie. (TU ISSN 0256-7865) **459,** 519, 593
Universite d'Ankara. Faculte des Sciences. Communications. Serie C1. Geologie. (TU ISSN 0253-1216) **1583**
Universite d'Istanbul. Faculte Forestiere. Revue. *see* Istanbul Universitesi. Orman Fakultesi. Dergisi **2103**
Universite d'Odense. Etudes Romanes. (DK ISSN 0107-7392) **2849,** 2972
Universite d'Ottawa. Alumni and Development. Anciens Alumni Ottawa. *see* University of Ottawa. Alumni and Development. Alumni News **1328**
Universite d'Ottawa. Etudes Ukrainiennes. *see* University of Ottawa. Ukrainian Studies **2393**
Universite d'Ottawa. Publications Medievales. *see* University of Ottawa. Medieval Texts and Studies **2325**
†Universite d'Ottawa. Revue/University of Ottawa Quarterly. (CN ISSN 0041-9206) **5297**
Universite de Besancon. Annales Litteraires *see* Recherches en Linguistique Etrangere **2837**
Universite de Besancon. Centre de Documentation et de Bibliographie Philosophiques. Travaux. (FR) **3785**
Universite de Bordeaux II. Cahiers Ethnologiques. (FR ISSN 0249-5635) **4455,** 251, 2027
Universite de Bordeaux III. Centre de Recherches sur l'Amerique Anglophone. Annales. (FR ISSN 0399-0443) **2972**
Universite de Brazzaville. Annales *see* Universite Marien Ngouabi. Annales **1719**
Universite de Bretagne Occidentale. Guide de l'Etudiant. (FR) **1669**
Universite de Bruxelles. Revue. (BE ISSN 0770-0962) **2517**
Universite de Clermont-Ferrand I. Faculte de Droit et de Science Politique. Annales. (FR) **2689**
†Universite de Clermont-Ferrand II. Annales Scientifiques. Serie Biologie Animale. (FR ISSN 0069-4681) **5297**
†Universite de Clermont-Ferrand II. Annales Scientifiques. Serie Biologie Vegetale. (FR ISSN 0069-469X) **5297**
†Universite de Clermont-Ferrand II. Annales Scientifiques. Serie Chemie. (FR ISSN 0069-4703) **5297**
†Universite de Clermont-Ferrand II. Annales Scientifiques. Serie Geologie et Mineralogie. (FR ISSN 0069-4711) **5297**
Universite de Clermont-Ferrand II. Annales Scientifiques. Serie Mathematique. (FR ISSN 0069-472X) **3060**
†Universite de Clermont-Ferrand II. Annales Scientifiques. Serie Physiologie Animale. (FR ISSN 0069-4746) **5297**
†Universite de Clermont-Ferrand II. Annales Scientifiques. Serie Physique.(FR ISSN 0069-4738) **5297**
Universite de Clermont-Ferrand II. Annales Scientifiques. Serie Probabilites et Applications. (FR) **3060**
Universite de Copenhague. Institut du Moyen-Age Grec et Latin. Cahiers. (DK ISSN 0591-0358) **2393**
Universite de Dakar. Faculte des Lettres et Sciences Humaines. Annales. (FR) **2972,** 4390
Universite de Droit, Economie et de Sciences Sociales de Paris. Travaux du Seminaire de Recherches sur les Faits Electoraux de Monsieur le Professeur Robert Villers. (FR) **2689,** 4390
Universite de Fribourg. Historische Schriften. (SZ) **2393**
Universite de Geneve. Department d'Histoire Economique. Bulletin. (SZ) **1719**
Universite de Geneve. Section d'Histoire. Documents. (SZ ISSN 0072-0836) **2393**
Universite de Grenoble. Institut de Phonetique. Manuels. Serie A *see* Universite de Grenoble III. Institut de Phonetique. Travaux. Serie A: Manuals **2849**
Universite de Grenoble III. Institut de Phonetique. Bulletin. (FR) **2849**
Universite de Grenoble III. Institut de Phonetique. Travaux. Serie A: Manuals. (FR) **2849**
Universite de Grenoble III. Institut de Phonetique. Travaux. Serie B: Etudes Linguistiques. (FR ISSN 0085-1272) **2849**
Universite de l'Etat a Gand. Service de Linguistique Francaise. Travaux de Linguistique *see* Travaux de Linguistique **2848**
†Universite de la Reunion. Cahier. (RE ISSN 0337-6176) **5297**
Universite de Lausanne. Faculte des Lettres. Publications. (SZ ISSN 0041-915X) **2972**
Universite de Liege. Faculte de Philosophie et Lettres. Publications. (BE) **2517**
Universite de Liege. Faculte des Sciences Appliquees. Collection des Publications. (BE ISSN 0075-9333) **4612**
Universite de Lille III. Lexique. (FR ISSN 0756-7138) **2849**
Universite de Lubumbashi. Centre de Linguistique Theorique et Appliquee Africanistique. (ZR) **2849**
Universite de Lubumbashi. Centre de Linguistique Theorique et Appliquee. Bulletin de Liaison, Enseignment des Langues. (ZR) **2849**
Universite de Lubumbashi. Centre de Linguistique Theorique et Appliquee. Linguistique et Sciences Humaines. Bulletin d'Information. (ZR) **2849**
Universite de Lyon III. Faculte de Droit. Annales *see* Universite Jean Moulin. Annales **2689**
Universite de Madagascar. Etablissement d'Enseignement Superieur des Sciences. Annales: Serie Sciences de la Nature et Mathematiques. (MG) **4350,** 3060
Universite de Madagascar. Musee d'Art et d'Archeologie. Travaux et Documents. (MG) **348,** 288
Universite de Moncton. Revue. (CN ISSN 0316-6368) **2179**
Universite de Montreal. Faculte de Medecine Veterinaire. Annuaire. (CN ISSN 0383-8455) **4816**

Title

Universite de Nancy II. Centre de Recherches et d'Applications Pedagogiques en Langues. Melanges.(FR ISSN 0077-2712) **1762**, 2849
Universite de Nantes. Centre de Recherches sur l'Histoire de la France Atlantique. Enquetes et Documents *see* Universite de Nantes. Centre de Recherches sur l'Histoire du Monde Atlantique. Enquetes et Documents **2393**
Universite de Nantes. Centre de Recherches sur l'Histoire du Monde Atlantique. Enquetes et Documents. (FR ISSN 0983-2424) **2393**
Universite de Neuchatel. Annales. (SZ) **1719**
Universite de Neuchatel. Centre d'Hydrogeologie. Bulletin. (SZ ISSN 0724-7087) **1601**
Universite de Neuchatel. Faculte des Lettres. Recueil de Travaux. (SZ ISSN 0077-7633) **2972**
Universite de Neuchatel. Seminaire de Geometrie. Publications. Serie 1. Courtes Publications *see* Centre de Recherches en Mathematiques Pures. P 1 **3032**
Universite de Neuchatel. Seminaire de Geometrie. Publications. Serie 2. Monographies *see* Centre de Recherches en Mathematiques Pures. Publications. Serie 2. Monographies **3032**
Universite de Paix Informations *see* U P Informations **3974**
Universite de Paris VI (Pierre et Marie Curie). Institut de Statistique. Publications. (FR ISSN 0041-9184) **3063**
Universite de Paris VII. Groupe de Linguistique Japonaise. Travaux *see* Travaux de Linguistique Japonaise **2848**
Universite de Poitiers. Centre d'Etudes Superieures de Civilisation Medievale. Publications. (FR ISSN 0079-256X) **2325**, 348, 2972
Universite de Provence. Centre d'Aix. Cahiers d'Etudes Germaniques. (FR ISSN 0751-4239) **2517**
Universite de Reims. Institut de Geographie. Travaux. (FR ISSN 0048-7163) **2265**
Universite de Saint Etienne. Centre Jean Palerne. Memoires. (FR ISSN 0223-9469) **2517**
Universite de Sherbrooke. Department de Geographie. Bulletin de Recherche. (CN ISSN 0710-0868) **2265**, 1549
Universite de Sherbrooke. I R E C U S. Cahiers de la Cooperation. (Institut de Recherche et d'Enseignement pour les Cooperatives) (CN) **832**
Universite de Sherbrooke. I R E C U S. Dossiers sur les Cooperatives. (Institut de Recherche et d'Enseignement pour les Cooperatives) (CN) **832**
Universite de Sherbrooke. I R E C U S. Essais. (Institut de Recherche et d'Enseignement pour les Cooperatives) (CN) **832**
Universite de Sherbrooke. Revue de Droit. (CN ISSN 0317-9656) **2689**
Universite de Skopje. Faculte des Sciences Economique. Annuaire. *see* Univerzitet vo Skoplje. Ekonomskiot Fakultet. Godisnik **698**
Universite de Sofia. Faculte d'Histoire. Annuaire. *see* Sofiiski Universitet. Istoricheski Fakultet. Godishnik **2323**
Universite de Sofia. Faculte de Philosophie. Annuaire. *see* Sofiiski Universitet. Filosofski Fakultet. Godisnik **2388**
Universite de Sofia. Faculte des Lettres Classiques et Modernes. Annuaire. *see* Sofiiski Universitet. Fakultet po Klasiceski i Novi Filologii. Godisnik **2842**
Universite de Sofia. Faculte des Mathematiques et de Mecanique. Annuaire. *see* Sofiiski Universitet. Fakultet po Matematika i Mekhanika. Godishnik **3055**
Universite de Strasbourg. Institut d'Etudes Latino-Americaines. Travaux *see* Recherches Iberiques et Cinematographiques **2952**
Universite de Strasbourg II. Centre de Philologie et Litteratures Romanes. Actes et Colloques. (FR ISSN 0081-5918) **2849**, 2972
Universite de Strasbourg II. Institut de Phonetique. Travaux. (FR ISSN 0081-5934) **2849**, 2517, 2972
Universite de Tehran. Faculte des Lettres et des Sciences Humaines. Revue. (IR ISSN 0041-9192) **2517**
Universite de Toulouse. Faculte des Sciences. Annales *see* Universite Paul Sabatier. Faculte des Sciences. Annales **3060**
†Universite de Toulouse II (le Mirail). Institut d'Art Prehistorique. Travaux. (FR ISSN 0563-9794) **5297**
Universite de Toulouse - Le Mirail. Papiers. (FR ISSN 0988-5986) **697**
Universite de Tunis. Ecole Normale Superieure. Section A: Lettres et Sciences Humaines. Serie 1: Langue et Litterature. (TI) **2972**, 2849
Universite de Yaounde. Faculte de Droit et des Sciences Economiques. Economie Generale. (CM) **898**
Universite de Yaounde. Faculte des Sciences. Annales. (CM ISSN 0566-201X) **4350**
Universite des Sciences Humaines de Strasbourg. Centre de Recherche sur le Proche Orient et la Grece Antiques. Travaux. (NE ISSN 0167-7551) **1280**
Universite des Sciences Sociales de Toulouse. Annales. (FR ISSN 0563-9727) **4390**
Universite du Quebec (Province). Rapport Annuel. (CN) **1719**
Universite Jean Moulin. Annales. (FR) **2689**
Universite Laval. Archives de Folklore. (CN ISSN 0085-5243) **2059**
†Universite Laval. Centre d'Etudes Nordiques. Travaux and Documents. (CN ISSN 0079-8347) **5297**
†Universite Laval. Centre de Recherches sur les Atomes et les Molecules. Rapport Annuel. (CN) **5297**
Universite Laval. Departement d'Exploitation et Utilisation des Bois. Note de Recherches. (CN ISSN 0079-8355) **2118**
Universite Laval. Departement d'Exploitation et Utilisation des Bois. Note Technique. (CN ISSN 0079-8363) **2118**
Universite Laval. Les Cahiers d'Histoire. (CN) **2325**
Universite Libre de Bruxelles. Centre d'Etudes de Recherche Operationnelle. Cahiers/Operations Research, Statistics and Applied Mathematics. (BE ISSN 0008-9737) **1401**
Universite Libre de Bruxelles. Faculte de Philosophie et Lettres. Travaux. (BE) **2517**
Universite Libre de Bruxelles. Groupe d'Etude du Dix-Huitieme Siecle. Etudes sur le Dix-Huitieme Siecle. (BE) **2393**
†Universite Libre de Bruxelles. Institut de Philologie et d'Histoire Orientales et Slaves. Annuaire. (BE) **5297**
Universite Libre de Bruxelles. Institut de Philosophie. Annales. (FR ISSN 0771-4963) **3785**
Universite Libre de Bruxelles. Institut de Sociologie. Annee Sociale. (BE ISSN 0066-2380) **4455**
Universite Libre de Bruxelles. Institut de Sociologie. Revue. (BE ISSN 0770-1055) **4455**
Universite Libre de Bruxelles. Institut pour l'Etude de la Renaissance et de l'Humanisme. Colloques. (BE) **2393**
▼Universite Libre de Bruxelles. Revue de Droit. (BE) **2689**
Universite Marien Ngouabi. Annales. (CF) **1719**
Universite Nationale de Cote d'Ivoire. Annales. Serie F: Ethnosociologie. (IV) **251**, 4455
Universite Nationale de Cote d'Ivoire. Annales. Serie G: Geographie. (IV) **2265**
Universite Nationale du Zaire, Kinshasa. Faculte de Droit. Annales. (ZR) **2689**
Universite Nationale du Zaire, Kinshasa. Institut de Recherches Economiques et Sociales. Document du Mois. (ZR) **4076**
Universite Nationale du Zaire, Kinshasa. Institut de Recherches Economiques et Sociales. Lettre Mensuelle. (ZR) **697**
Universite Nationale du Zaire, Lubumbashi. Centre de Linguistique Theorique et Appliquee Africanistique *see* Universite de Lubumbashi. Centre de Linguistique Theorique et Appliquee Africanistique **2849**
Universite Nationale du Zaire, Lubumbashi. Centre de Linguistique Theorique et Appliquee. Linguistique et Sciences Humaines. Bulletin d'Information *see* Universite de Lubumbashi. Centre de Linguistique Theorique et Appliquee. Linguistique et Sciences Humaines. Bulletin d'Information **2849**
Universite Paul Sabatier. Faculte des Sciences. Annales. (FR) **3060**
Universite Saint-Joseph. Faculte des Lettres et des Sciences Humaines. Recherches. Serie A: Langue Arabe et Pensee Islamique. (LE) **4221**, 2849
Universite Saint Joseph. Faculte des Lettres et des Sciences Humaines. Recherches. Serie B: Orient Chretien. (LE) **3645**, 4208
Universite Scientifique et Medicale de Grenoble. Institut Fourier. Annales. (FR ISSN 0373-0956) **3060**
Universite Syndicaliste. (FR ISSN 0751-5839) **1719**
Universiteit van Amsterdam. Fysisch Geografisch en Bodemkundig Laboratorium. Publikaties. (NE ISSN 0066-1317) **2265**
Universiteit van Amsterdam. Instituut voor Algemene Taalwetenschap. Publikaties. (NE) **2849**
†Universiteit van Amsterdam. Mathematisch Instituut. Report. (NE) **5297**
Universiteit van Amsterdam. Zoologisch Museum. Bulletin. (NE ISSN 0066-1325) **593**
Universiteit van Port Elizabeth. Instituut vir Beplanningsnavorsing. Feitestuk Reeks. *see* University of Port Elizabeth. Institute for Planning Research. Fact Paper Series **887**
Universiteit van Port Elizabeth. Instituut vir Beplanningsnavorsing. Inligtingsbulletin Reeks. *see* University of Port Elizabeth. Institute for Planning Research. Information Bulletin Series **887**
Universiteit van Port Elizabeth. Instituut vir Beplanningsnavorsing. Jaarverslag. *see* University of Port Elizabeth. Institute for Planning Research. Annual Report **1000**
†Universiteit van Pretoria. Biblioteekdiens. Verslagreeks. (SA ISSN 0379-7104) **5297**
Universiteit van Pretoria. Jaarverslag. *see* University of Pretoria. Annual Report **1328**
Universiteitskrant Groningen. (NE) **1328**
Universites. (CN ISSN 0226-7454) **1719**
Universitet i Oslo. Pedagogisk Forskningsinstitutt. Rapport. (NO ISSN 0800-6113) **1669**
Universitet i Trondheim. Norges Tekniske Hoegskole. Vassdrags-og Havnelaboratoriet. Meddelelse *see* Norwegian Hydrotechnical Laboratory. Bulletin **1924**
Universitetet i Oslo. Slavisk-Baltisk Avdeling. Meddelelser. (NO ISSN 0803-2505) **2849**, 2972
Universitetet i Oslo. Slavisk-Baltisk Institutt. Meddelelser *see* Universitetet i Oslo. Slavisk-Baltisk Avdeling. Meddelelser **2849**
Universitetet i Trondheim. Biblioteket. Avdeling B. Rapport *see* Universitetsbiblioteket i Trondheim. Rapport **2788**
Universitetet i Trondheim. Norges Tekniske Hoegskole. Institutt for Uorganisk Kjemi. Avhandling. (NO) **1215**
Universitetet i Trondheim. Vitenskapsmuseet. Rapport. Botanisk Serie. (NO ISSN 0802-2992) **519**
Universitetet Statistiske Institut. Computer Programmes. (DK ISSN 0107-9352) **1432**
Universitetets Statistiske Institut. Research Report. (DK ISSN 0105-9645) **4591**
Universitets Oldsaksamling. Aarbok. (NO ISSN 0333-130X) **288**, 2393
Universitetsavisen. (DK) **1719**
Universitetsbiblioteket i Trondheim. Rapport. (NO ISSN 0802-2836) **2788**
Universitetslaeraren. (SW) **1669**, 2591
Universitetslaereren. Beskrivelse. (DK ISSN 0902-2619) **1719**
Universitexts. (US ISSN 0172-5939) **3060**, 1839, 3834
Universiti Kebangsaan Malaysia. Lapuran Tahunan - Annual Report. (MY) **1669**
Universiti Malaya. Fakulti Kejuruteraan. Jernal. *see* University of Malaya. Faculty of Engineering. Journal **1839**
Universities Art Association of Canada. Journal/Association d'Art des Universites du Canada. Journal. (CN ISSN 0315-940X) **348**
Universities Federation for Animal Welfare Annual Report and Accounts *see* U F A W Annual Report and Accounts **232**
Universities Federation for Animal Welfare News-Sheet *see* U F A W News-Sheet **232**
Universities Handbook. (II) **1697**, 1719
Universities Quarterly: Culture, Education and Society *see* Higher Education Quarterly **1708**
Universities Telephone Directory (Year)/ Bottin Telephonique des Universites (year). (CN ISSN 0847-3536) **1719**
University *see* Montanan **1318**
†University (Bristol). (UK ISSN 0265-4512) **5297**
University (Philippines). (PH ISSN 0042-0360) **1328**
University Affairs/Affaires Universitaires.(CN ISSN 0041-9257) **1719**
University Alumni Report. (US) **1328**
University Bookman. (US ISSN 0041-9265) **4138**, 1719
University Bristol Calendar. (UK) **1719**
University Chemistry. *see* Daxue Huaxue **1176**
University College Cork Calendar. (IE) **1719**
University College Hospital Magazine *see* Too Much - University College Hospital Magazine **2469**
University College Literary Review *see* U.C. Review **2971**
University College London. Institute of Archaeology. Bulletin. (UK) **288**
University College London. Institute of Archaeology. Occasional Publication. (UK) **288**
University College London Calendar. (UK ISSN 0953-8364) **1719**
University College of Swaziland. Agricultural Research Division. Annual Report. (SQ) **127**
University Computing. (UK ISSN 0265-4385) **1401**, 1691
University Computing and Information Services Newsletter. (CN ISSN 0829-5425) **1401**
University Computing Systems Dispatch.(CN ISSN 0840-6235) **1401**

Title

University Corporation for Atmospheric Research Newsletter see U C A R Newsletter 3441
University Council for Educational Administration Review see U C E A Review 1732
University du Benin. Annales. Serie Science. (TG) 459
University E. Kardelja in Ljubljana. Biotechnical Faculty. Research Reports see University in Ljubljana. Biotechnical Faculty. Research Reports 195
University Education in Nigeria. (NR) 1719
University Film and Video Association. Journal see Journal of Film and Video 3512
University Film Study Center. Newsletter. (US) 3518
University Film Video Association Digest of the U F V A see Digest of the U F V A 3507
University Folklore Association. Collectanea. (US) 2059
University Folklore Association. Folklore Papers see University Folklore Association. Collectanea 2059
University Geographer. (NR ISSN 0083-3975) 2265
University - Government - Industry Microelectronics Symposium. Proceedings. (US ISSN 0195-9751) 1779
University in Ljubljana. Biotechnical Faculty. Research Reports. (XV) 195
†University Journal. (US) 5297
University Library Expenditure Statistics.(UK ISSN 0268-3539) 2796
†University Medical. (US ISSN 0042-014X) 5297
University Merchant see University Messenger 2236
University Messenger. (US) 2236
University News. (Il) 1719
University of Aberdeen. African Studies Group. Bulletin. (UK ISSN 0001-3196) 2335, 2027
University of Aberdeen. African Studies Group. Occasional Publications. (UK) 2335, 2027
†University of Aberdeen. Department of Forestry. Economic Survey of Private Forestry. (UK ISSN 0065-0277) 5297
University of Aberdeen Review. (UK ISSN 0001-320X) 2887
University of Addis Ababa. Institute of Ethiopian Studies. Ethiopian Publications see Ethiopian Publications: Books, Pamphlets, Annuals and Periodical Articles 400
University of Adelaide. Graduates Union. Monthly Newsletter and Gazette see Lumen 1316
University of Agricultural Sciences, Bangalore. Annual Report. (Il ISSN 0067-3455) 127
University of Agricultural Sciences, Bangalore. Collaborative Series. (Il) 127
University of Agricultural Sciences, Bangalore. Current Research. (Il) 127
University of Agricultural Sciences, Bangalore. Educational Series. (Il) 127
University of Agricultural Sciences, Bangalore. Information Series. (Il) 127
University of Agricultural Sciences, Bangalore. Research Monograph Series. (Il) 127
University of Agricultural Sciences, Bangalore. Research Review Series. (Il) 127
University of Agricultural Sciences, Bangalore. Technical Information Series. (Il) 127
University of Agricultural Sciences, Bangalore. Technical Series. (Il) 127
University of Agricultural Sciences, Bangalore. U A S Textbook Series. (Il) 127
University of Agricultural Sciences, Bangalore Extension Series see U A S Extension Series 125
University of Agricultural Sciences, Bangalore Miscellaneous Series see U A S Miscellaneous Series 125
University of Alabama at Birmingham Visual Arts Gallery. Selections from the Permanent Selection see U A B Visual Arts Gallery. Selections from the Permanent Selection 3534
University of Alabama at Birmingham Visual Arts Gallery Papers see U A B Visual Arts Gallery Papers 3534
University of Alaska. Anthropological Papers. (US ISSN 0041-9354) 251
University of Alaska. Biological Papers. (US ISSN 0568-8604) 459
University of Alaska. Biological Papers. Special Reports see University of Alaska. Biological Papers 459
†University of Alaska. Cooperative Extension Service. Local Government Hi-Lites. (US) 5297
University of Alaska. Geophysical Institute. Report Series. (US ISSN 0041-9362) 1596, 3441
University of Alaska. Institute of Marine Science. Occasional Publication. (US ISSN 0084-6147) 459
University of Alaska. Institute of Marine Science. Technical Report. (US ISSN 0065-5929) 459
University of Alaska. Institute of Northern Engineering. (US) 4829
University of Alaska. Institute of Social and Economic Research. Research Summary. (US) 4455, 697
University of Alaska. Institute of Water Resources-Engineering Experiment Station. Annual Report see University of Alaska. Institute of Northern Engineering 4829
University of Alaska Museum. Annual Report. (US ISSN 0093-7436) 3534
†University of Alberta. Agriculture and Forestry Bulletin. (CN ISSN 0705-3983) 5297
University of Alberta. Centre for Criminological Research. Discussion Papers. (CN ISSN 0824-5134) 1524
University of Alberta. Department of Animal Science. Annual Feeders' Day Report. (CN ISSN 0084-618X) 227
University of Alberta. Department of Computing Science. Publication see University of Alberta. Department of Computing Science. Technical Reports 1401
University of Alberta. Department of Computing Science. Technical Reports. (CN ISSN 0316-4683) 1401
University of Alberta. Department of Rural Economy. Bulletin. (CN) 159
University of Alberta. Department of Rural Economy. Project Reports. (CN) 159
University of Alberta. Department of Rural Economy. Staff Papers. (CN) 159
University of Alberta. Nuclear Research Centre. Progress Report. (CN) 1810
University of Alberta. Studies in Geography. Monographs. (CN) 2265
University of Allahabad. Education Department. Researches and Studies.(Il ISSN 0084-621X) 1669
University of Arkansas. Arkansas Institute for Economic Advancement. Annual Report for the Vice Chancellor and Provost. (A I E A) (US) 1086
University of Arkansas. Lecture Notes in the Mathematical Sciences. (US) 3060
University of Arkansas at Little Rock Law Journal. (US ISSN 0162-8372) 2689
University of Auckland. Department of Geography. Occasional Papers see University of Auckland. Department of Geography. Occasional Publication 2265
University of Auckland. Department of Geography. Occasional Publication. (NZ ISSN 0112-1545) 2265
University of Auckland. Department of Mathematics and Statistics. Report Series. (NZ ISSN 0110-4152) 3060
University of Auckland. Department of Sociology. Papers in Comparative Sociology. (NZ) 4455
†University of Auckland. Fine Arts Library Bulletin. (NZ ISSN 0041-9400) 5297
University of Auckland. Library. Bibliographical Bulletin. (NZ ISSN 0067-0499) 415
University of Auckland Gazette see University of Auckland News 1328
University of Auckland Historical Society. Annual. (NZ ISSN 0067-0480) 2346
University of Auckland News. (NZ) 1328
University of Azarabadegan. Faculty of Letters and Humanities. Publication - Danegash-e Azarabadegan. Daneshkade-ye Adabiyyat va 'Olume Ensani. Nashriyeh - Universite d'Azarabadegan. Faculte des Lettres et Sciences Humaines. Revue see University of Tabriz. Faculty of Human and Social Sciences. Publication 2518
University of Baghdad. College of Science. Bulletin see Iraqi Journal of Science 4316
University of Baghdad. Faculty of Medicine. Journal. (IQ ISSN 0041-9419) 3160
University of Baltimore Law Review. (US ISSN 0091-5440) 2689
University of Bath. Centre for Bibliographic Management. Newsletter. (UK) 2788
University of Bath. Centre for Catalogue Research. Newsletter see University of Bath. Centre for Bibliographic Management. Newsletter 2788
University of Belgrade. Faculty of Sciences. Department of Astronomy. Publications. (YU ISSN 0350-3283) 370
University of Benin. Library. Annual Report. (NR) 2788
University of Bergen. Department of Applied Mathematics. Report. (NO ISSN 0084-778X) 3060
†University of Bergen. Institute of Psychology. Psychological Report Series. (NO ISSN 0333-4325) 5297
University of Bergen. Institute of Psychology. Report see University of Bergen. Institute of Psychology. Psychological Report Series 5297
University of Birmingham. Centre for Urban and Regional Studies. Occasional Papers. (UK ISSN 0067-8953) 2497, 4455
University of Birmingham. Centre for Urban and Regional Studies. Research Memorandum. (UK ISSN 0306-4034) 2497, 4455
University of Birmingham. Centre for Urban and Regional Studies. Urban and Regional Studies. (UK ISSN 0067-8961) 2497, 4455
University of Birmingham. Centre for Urban and Regional Studies. Working Paper. (UK) 2497, 4455
University of Birmingham. Institute of Occupational Health. Bulletin. (UK) 3622
University of Bombay. Journal. (Il ISSN 0304-2286) 4391
University of Botswana, Lesotho and Swaziland. Agricultural Research Division. Annual Report see University College of Swaziland. Agricultural Research Division. Annual Report 127
University of Bridgeport Law Review. (US) 2689, 3932
University of Bristol. Newsletter. (UK ISSN 0143-1951) 1328
University of British Columbia. Center for Continuing Education. Monographs on Comparative and Area Studies in Adult Education. (CN) 1687
University of British Columbia. Center for Continuing Education. Occasional Papers in Continuing Education. (CN ISSN 0068-1695) 1687
University of British Columbia. Department of Civil Engineering. Soil Mechanics Series. (CN ISSN 0068-1709) 1876
†University of British Columbia. Department of Civil Engineering. Water Resources Research Series. (CN) 5297
University of British Columbia. Department of Economics. Discussion Paper. (CN) 697
University of British Columbia. Department of Geological Sciences. Report. (CN) 1583
University of British Columbia. Department of Geophysics and Astronomy. Annual Report. (CN ISSN 0068-1725) 1596, 370
University of British Columbia. Faculty of Forestry. Research and Publications see University of British Columbia. Faculty of Forestry. Research Review 5297
†University of British Columbia. Faculty of Forestry. Research Review. (CN) 5297
University of British Columbia Alumni U B C Chronicle see Alumni U B C Chronicle 1303
University of British Columbia Law Review. (CN ISSN 0068-1849) 2689
University of British Columbia Library News see U B C Library News 2788
University of British Columbia, Physics Society. Journal. (CN) 3834, 370
University of British Columbia Planning Papers see U B C Planning Papers 2497
University of Cairo. Faculty of Medicine. Gazette see University of Cairo. Faculty of Medicine. Medical Journal 3160
University of Cairo. Faculty of Medicine. Medical Journal. (UA ISSN 0045-3803) 3160
University of Cairo. Herbarium. Publications. (UA ISSN 0068-5313) 519
University of Calcutta. Business Studies.(Il) 697
University of Calcutta. Centre of Advanced Study in Ancient Indian History and Culture. Lectures. (Il ISSN 0068-5380) 2342
University of Calcutta. Centre of Advanced Study in Ancient Indian History and Culture. Proceedings of Seminars. (Il ISSN 0068-5399) 2342
University of Calcutta. Department of English. Bulletin see University of Calcutta. Department of English. Journal 2972
University of Calcutta. Department of English. Journal. (Il) 2972
†University of Calcutta. Department of Philosophy. Journal. (Il) 5297
University of Calcutta. Department of Sociology. Journal. (Il) 4455
University of Calcutta. University College of Medicine. Bulletin. (Il ISSN 0008-0705) 3160
University of Calgary. Archaeological Association. Archaeological Conference. Proceedings. (CN) 288, 1970
University of Calgary. Archaeological Association. Paleo-Environmental Workshop. Proceedings see University of Calgary. Archaeological Association. Archaeological Conference. Proceedings 288
University of Calgary. Department of Civil Engineering Research Report. (CN) 1876
University of Calgary. Department of Mathematics and Statistics. Research Papers. (CN) 3060

University of Calgary Gazette. (CN ISSN 0300-4333) **1328**
University of California. Center for South and Southeast Asia Studies. Occasional Papers. (US ISSN 0068-600X) **2342**
University of California. Center for South and Southeast Asia Studies. Research Monograph Series. (US ISSN 0068-6018) **2342**
University of California. Institute of Governmental Studies Library. Accessions List. (US ISSN 0041-9443) **4076**
University of California. Lawrence Berkeley Laboratory. Biology and Medicine Division. Annual Report. (US ISSN 0272-9075) **483,** 3160
University of California. Seismographic Stations. Bulletin. (US ISSN 0041-946X) **1596**
University of California, Berkeley. Academic Computing Newsletter. (US) **1401**
University of California, Berkeley. Archaeological Research Facility. Contributions. (US ISSN 0068-5933) **288**
University of California, Berkeley. Campus Statistics. (US) **1719**
University of California, Berkeley. Center for Real Estate and Urban Economics. Research Report *see* University of California, Berkeley. Center for Real Estate and Urban Economics. Working Paper **4159**
University of California, Berkeley. Center for Real Estate and Urban Economics. Reprint Series. (US ISSN 0068-5968) **4159**
University of California, Berkeley. Center for Real Estate and Urban Economics. Working Paper. (US) **4159**
University of California, Berkeley. Center for Slavic & East European Studies. Newsletter. (US) **2393**
University of California, Berkeley. Computing Services Newsletter *see* University of California, Berkeley. Academic Computing Newsletter **1401**
University of California, Berkeley. Institute of International Studies. Policy Papers in International Affairs.(US ISSN 0731-6321) **3976**
University of California, Berkeley. Institute of International Studies. Research Series. (US ISSN 0068-6093) **3932,** 898, 4455
University of California, Berkeley. Institute of Transportation Studies. Library References. (US ISSN 0068-6115) **4660**
University of California, Berkeley. Library School Library. Selected Additions to the Library School Library Collection. (US ISSN 0037-1300) **2796**
University of California, Berkeley. Office of Institutional Research. Campus Statistics *see* University of California, Berkeley. Campus Statistics **1719**
University of California, Berkeley. Wellness Letter. (US ISSN 0748-9234) **3809,** 3612
University of California Clip Sheet *see* U C Clip Sheet **5293**
University of California, Davis. Game Bird Workshop. Proceedings. (US) **567**
University of California, Davis. Water Resources Center. Contributions. (US ISSN 0068-6301) **4829**
University of California, Davis News and Views *see* U C A T News and Views **4612**
University of California, Los Angeles. Center for Medieval and Renaissance Studies. Contributions. (US ISSN 0068-6239) **2325**
University of California, Los Angeles. Center for Medieval and Renaissance Studies. Publications. (US ISSN 0068-6220) **2325**
University of California, Los Angeles. Center for the Study of Comparative Folklore and Mythology. Publications.(US ISSN 0068-6247) **2059**
University of California, Los Angeles. Fowler Museum of Cultural History. Occasional Papers. (US) **3534,** 348
University of California, Los Angeles. Institute of Archaeology. Archaeological Survey. Special Monograph Series *see* University of California, Los Angeles. Institute of Archaeology. Monograph Series **288**
University of California, Los Angeles. Institute of Archaeology. Monograph Series. (US) **288**
†University of California, Los Angeles. Institute of Archaeology. Occasional Papers. (US) **5297**
University of California, Los Angeles. Institute of Industrial Relations. Monograph and Research Series. (US ISSN 0739-439X) **996**
University of California, Los Angeles. Institute of Industrial Relations. Monograph Series *see* University of California, Los Angeles. Institute of Industrial Relations. Monograph and Research Series **996**
University of California, Los Angeles. James S. Coleman African Studies Center. Newsletter. (US) **2335,** 2170
University of California, Los Angeles. Latin American Center. Latin American Studies Series. (US ISSN 0075-8132) **2425**
University of California, Los Angeles. Latin American Center. Reference Series. (US ISSN 0068-6263) **2425**
University of California, Los Angeles. Museum of Cultural History. Occasional Papers *see* University of California, Los Angeles. Fowler Museum of Cultural History. Occasional Papers **3534**
University of California, Los Angeles Business Forecast for California *see* U C L A Business Forecast for California **696**
University of California, Los Angeles Forum in Medical Sciences *see* U C L A Forum in Medical Sciences **3158**
University of California, Los Angeles Historical Journal *see* U C L A Historical Journal **2324**
University of California, Los Angeles Journal of Environmental Law and Policy *see* U C L A Journal of Environmental Law and Policy **2687**
University of California, Los Angeles Latin American Center. Special Studies Series *see* U C L A Latin American Center. Special Studies Series **2424**
University of California, Los Angeles Law Review *see* U C L A Law Review **2687**
University of California, Los Angeles Magazine *see* U C L A Magazine **2236**
University of California, Los Angeles National Business Forecast *see* U C L A National Business Forecast **696**
University of California, Los Angeles Symposium on Molecular Biology Proceedings *see* U C L A Symposium on Molecular Biology Proceedings **527**
University of California, Los Angeles Symposium Series on Molecular and Cellular Biology *see* U C L A Symposium Series on Molecular and Cellular Biology **458**
University of California Publications. Anthropological Records. (US ISSN 0068-6336) **251**
University of California Publications. Classical Studies. (US ISSN 0068-6344) **1280**
University of California Publications. Folklore & Mythology Studies. (US) **2059**
University of California Publications. Folklore Studies *see* University of California Publications. Folklore & Mythology Studies **2059**
University of California Publications. Near Eastern Studies. (US ISSN 0068-6514) **2343**
University of California Publications in Anthropology. (US ISSN 0068-6379) **251**
University of California Publications in Botany. (US ISSN 0068-6395) **520**
University of California Publications in Entomology. (US ISSN 0068-6417) **538**
University of California Publications in Geography. (US ISSN 0068-6441) **2265**
University of California Publications in Geological Sciences. (US ISSN 0068-645X) **1549**
University of California Publications in Linguistics. (US ISSN 0068-6484) **2849**
University of California Publications in Modern Philology. (US ISSN 0068-6492) **2849**
University of California Publications in Zoology. (US ISSN 0068-6506) **593**
University of California, San Francisco Magazine *see* U C S F Magazine **3159**
University of California, Santa Cruz. Center for Marine Studies. Special Publication *see* University of California, Santa Cruz. Institute for Marine Sciences. Special Publication **1612**
University of California, Santa Cruz. Institute for Marine Sciences. Special Publication. (US) **1612**
University of California U C News Clip Sheet *see* U C Clip Sheet **5293**
University of Canterbury. Department of Psychology and Sociology. Research Projects. (NZ ISSN 0069-3774) **4049,** 4455
University of Cape Town. Centre for African Studies. Communications. (SA) **2335**
University of Cape Town. Department of Geology. Precambrian Research Unit. Annual Report. (SA ISSN 0250-216X) **1583**
University of Cape Town. Department of Geology. Precambrian Research Unit. Bulletin. (SA) **1583**
University of Cape Town. Department of Gynaecology. Annual Report *see* University of Cape Town. Department of Obstetrics and Gynaecology. Annual Report **3297**
University of Cape Town. Department of Obstetrics and Gynaecology. Annual Report. (SA) **3297**
University of Cape Town. Libraries. Statistical Report. (SA ISSN 0576-6885) **2796**
University of Cape Town. Research Report. (SA) **1719**
University of Chicago. Department of Geography. Research Papers. *see* University of Chicago. Geography Research Papers **2265**
University of Chicago. Geography Research Papers. (US) **2265**
University of Chicago. Pritzker School of Medicine. Alumni Association. Bulletin *see* University of Chicago. Pritzker School of Medicine. Alumni Association. Magazine **1328**
University of Chicago. Pritzker School of Medicine. Alumni Association. Magazine. (US) **1328,** 3160
University of Chicago Law Review. (US ISSN 0041-9494) **2689**
University of Chicago Legal Forum. (US) **2689**
University of Chicago Magazine. (US ISSN 0041-9508) **1328**
University of Chicago Oriental Institute. Publications. (US ISSN 0069-3367) **2343**
University of Chicago Record. (US ISSN 0362-4706) **1719,** 1328
University of Chicago Studies in Anthropology. Series in Social, Cultural, and Linguistic Anthropology.(US) **251**
University of Chicago Studies in Library Science. (US ISSN 0069-3375) **2788**
University of Cincinnati Computing Center Technical Update *see* U C C C Technical Update **1691**
University of Cincinnati Law Review *see* Cincinnati Law Review **2612**
University of Cincinnati Studies in Historical and Contemporary Europe. (US ISSN 0888-3882) **2393,** 2972
University of Cochin. Department of Marine Sciences. Bulletin. (II) **1612**
University of Colorado. Institute of Arctic and Alpine Research. Occasional Papers. (US ISSN 0069-6145) **4350,** 459, 1549, 2265
University of Colorado Law Review. (US ISSN 0041-9516) **2689**
University of Connecticut. Center for Real Estate and Urban Economic Studies. Annual Report. (US) **4159**
University of Connecticut. Center for Real Estate and Urban Economic Studies. General Series. (US ISSN 0069-9047) **4159**
University of Connecticut. Institute of Water Resources. Report Series. (US ISSN 0069-9063) **4829**
University of Connecticut. Institute of Water Resources. Wetlands Conference. Proceedings. (US) **4829**
University of Copenhagen. Department of Physical Oceanography. Report. (DK) **1612**
University of Copenhagen. Institute of Mathematical Statistics. Annual Report. (DK) **3060**
University of Copenhagen. Institute of Phonetics. Annual Report. (DK ISSN 0589-6681) **2849**
University of Copenhagen. Institute of Physical Oceanography. Report *see* University of Copenhagen. Department of Physical Oceanography. Report **1612**
University of Copenhagen. Physics Laboratory. Report. (DK ISSN 0106-7222) **3834**
University of Dallas. University News. (US) **1328**
University of Dar es Salaam. Botany Department. Departmental Herbarium Publications. (TZ) **520**
University of Dar es Salaam. Bureau of Resource Assessment and Land Use Planning. Annual Report. (TZ ISSN 0084-960X) **1970,** 3988
University of Dar es Salaam. Bureau of Resource Assessment and Land Use Planning. Research Paper. (TZ ISSN 0084-9626) **1970,** 3988
University of Dar es Salaam. Bureau of Resource Assessment and Land Use Planning. Research Report. (TZ ISSN 0084-9634) **1970,** 3988
University of Dar es Salaam. Economic Research Bureau. Occasional Paper. (TZ) **697**
University of Dar es Salaam. Economic Research Bureau. Papers. (TZ ISSN 0418-3746) **697**
University of Dar es Salaam. Faculty of Agriculture, Forestry and Veterinary Science. Annual Record of Research. (TZ) **127,** 2110, 4816
University of Dar es Salaam. Theatre Arts Department. Annual Report. (TZ) **4642**
University of Dar es Salaam. University Science Journal *see* Tanzania Journal of Science **4347**
University of Dayton. School of Education. Abstracts of Research Projects. (US ISSN 0070-3044) **1681,** 24, 1719
University of Dayton. School of Education. Workshop Proceedings. (US ISSN 0070-3052) **4278**
University of Dayton Law Review. (US ISSN 0162-9174) **2690**
University of Dayton Review. (US ISSN 0041-9524) **2887,** 4208

Title

UNIVERSITY   6771

University of Delaware. College of Agricultural Sciences. Longwood Graduate Program Seminars *see* Longwood Graduate Program Seminars **509**
University of Delaware. Disaster Research Center. Dissertations. (US) **4114, 1274, 1970**
University of Delaware. Disaster Research Center. Final Project Reports. (US) **4114, 1274, 1970**
University of Delaware. Disaster Research Center. Miscellaneous Reports. (US) **4114, 1274, 1970**
University of Delaware. Disaster Research Center. Preliminary Papers. (US) **4114, 1274, 1970**
University of Delaware. Disaster Research Center. Report Series. (US) **4114, 1274, 1970**
University of Delhi. Department of Sanskrit. Journal *see* Indological Studies **2925**
University of Denver Alumni News *see* University of Denver News **1328**
University of Denver News. (US) **1328, 3932**
University of Detroit Journal of Urban Law *see* University of Detroit Law Review **2690**
University of Detroit Law Review. (US) **2690**
University of Dhaka. Department of Law. Journal. (BG) **2690**
University of Dhaka. Institute of Statistical Research and Training. Bulletin *see* Journal of Statistical Research **4576**
University of Dundee Students Association Handbook. (UK) **1719**
University of Durban-Westville. Bulletin for Academic Staff. (SA ISSN 0256-7423) **1719**
University of Durban-Westville. Institute for Social and Economic Research. Annual Report. (SA ISSN 0377-8533) **4391**
University of Durham. Centre for Middle Eastern and Islamic Studies. Occasional Papers Series. (UK ISSN 0307-0654) **3645, 415**
University of East Anglia. Climatic Research Unit. Research Publication.(UK) **3441**
University of East Anglia Papers in Linguistics *see* U E A Papers in Linguistics **2848**
University of Eastern Philippines. Research Center. Report. (PH ISSN 0070-8259) **1669**
University of Edinburgh. Department of Archaeology. Occasional Papers. (UK ISSN 0144-3313) **288**
University of Edinburgh Journal. (UK ISSN 0041-9567) **1328**
†University of Electro-Communications. Research Institute for Communication Sciences. Annual Report/Denki Tsushin Daigaku Denki Tsushin Kenkyu Shisetsu Nenpo. (JA) **5297**
University of Engineering and Technology. Research Bulletin. (PK) **1876**
†University of Esfahan. Faculty of Medicine. Library Bulletin/Daneshgah-e Esfahan. Daneshkade-Ye Pezeshki. Nashriye-Ye Ketabkhaneh. (IR) **5297**
University of Ferdowsi. Faculty of Letters and Humanities. Journal *see* Mashhad University. Faculty of Letters and Humanities. Journal **2937**
University of Ferdowsi. Faculty of Medicine. Letters/Daneshgah-e Ferdowsi. Daneshkade-Ye Pazeshki. Nameh. (IR) **3160**
University of Ferdowsi. Faculty of Theology and Islamic Studies. Publication/Daneshgah-e Ferdowsi. Daneshkade-Ye Elahiyat Va Ma'aref-e Eslami. Nashriyeh. (IR) **4221**
University of Florida. Bureau of Economic and Business Research. Population Studies. (US ISSN 0071-6030) **3988**

†University of Florida. Center for Gerontology. Research Series. (US) **5297**
†University of Florida. Center for Gerontology. Studies and Programs. (US ISSN 0071-6103) **5297**
University of Florida. Department of Accounting. Accounting Series. (US ISSN 0071-6065) **757**
University of Florida. Food and Resource Economics Department. Economic Information Report. (US) **159**
University of Florida. Food and Resource Economics Department. Economics Report *see* University of Florida. Food and Resource Economics Department. Economic Information Report **159**
University of Florida. School of Forest Resources & Conservation. Cooperative Forest Genetics Research Program. Progress Report.(US) **2110, 547**
University of Florida. School of Forestry. Cooperative Forest Genetics Research Program. Progress Report *see* University of Florida. School of Forest Resources & Conservation. Cooperative Forest Genetics Research Program. Progress Report **2110**
University of Florida Law Review *see* Florida Law Review **2627**
University of Florida Monographs. Humanities. (US ISSN 0071-6189) **2517**
University of Florida Monographs. Social Sciences. (US ISSN 0071-6197) **4391**
University of Georgia. Agricultural Experiment Stations. Annual Report *see* Impact (Athens) **96**
University of Georgia. Agricultural Experiment Stations. Southern Cooperative Series Bulletin. (US) **195**
University of Georgia. Alumni News. (US) **1328**
University of Georgia. College of Agriculture Experiment Stations. Bulletin. (US ISSN 0072-1271) **127**
University of Georgia. College of Agriculture Experiment Stations. Research Reports. (US ISSN 0072-128X) **127**
University of Georgia. Institute of Ecology. Annual Report. (US ISSN 0094-9205) **1970**
†University of Ghana. Department of Library and Archival Studies. Occasional Papers. (GH) **5297**
University of Ghana. Department of Sociology. Current Research Report Series. (GH) **4455**
University of Ghana. Institute of African Studies. Collected Language Notes. (GH) **2850**
University of Ghana. Institute of African Studies. Local Studies Series. (GH ISSN 0533-8646) **251**
University of Ghana. Institute of African Studies. Research Review. (GH ISSN 0020-2703) **2887**
University of Ghana. Institute of Statistical, Social and Economic Research. Discussion Papers. (GH) **4391, 697, 4591**
University of Ghana. Institute of Statistical, Social and Economic Research. Technical Publication Series. (GH) **743**
University of Ghana. Institute of Statistical, Social and Economic Research. Technical Research Monographs *see* University of Ghana. Institute of Statistical, Social and Economic Research. Technical Publication Series **743**
University of Ghana Law Journal. (GH ISSN 0041-9605) **2690**
University of Glasgow. Institute of Latin American Studies. Occasional Papers.(UK ISSN 0305-8646) **3932**

University of Guelph. Department of Land Resource Science. Progress Report. (CN ISSN 0085-1329) **195**
University of Guelph Library. Collection Update. (CN ISSN 0226-3300) **2789, 415**
University of Hartford Studies in Literature. (US ISSN 0196-2280) **2972**
University of Hawaii. Computing Center. Newsletter. (US) **1401**
University of Hawaii. Industrial Relations Center. Occasional Publications. (US ISSN 0073-1226) **996**
†University of Hawaii. Sea Grant College Program. Sea Grant Quarterly. (US ISSN 0199-137X) **5298**
University of Hawaii. Water Resources Research Center. Annual Report. (US) **4829**
University of Hawaii. Water Resources Research Center. Collected Reprints. (US ISSN 0073-1293) **4829**
University of Hawaii. Water Resources Research Center. Project Bulletin. (US) **4829**
University of Hawaii. Water Resources Research Center. Rain Water Cistern Systems. (US) **4829**
University of Hawaii. Water Resources Research Center. Technical Report. (US ISSN 0073-1307) **4829**
University of Hawaii. Water Resources Research Center. Workshop Series. (US) **4829**
University of Hawaii Law Review. (US) **2690**
University of Helsinki. Department of Co-operative Studies. Publications. (FI ISSN 0356-1364) **832**
University of Helsinki. Department of Education. Research Bulletin. (FI ISSN 0073-179X) **1669**
University of Hong Kong. Centre of Asian Studies. Bibliographies and Research Guides. (HK ISSN 0441-1900) **3647**
University of Hong Kong. Centre of Asian Studies. Occasional Papers and Monographs. (HK ISSN 0378-2689) **3645, 4391**
University of Hull. Department of Geography. Miscellaneous Series in Geography *see* University of Hull. School of Geography and Earth Resources. Miscellaneous Series in Geography **2265**
University of Hull. School of Geography and Earth Resources. Miscellaneous Series in Geography. (UK) **2265**
University of Ibadan. Department of Linguistics and Nigerian Languages. Research Notes. (NR ISSN 0041-9613) **2850**
University of Ibadan. Institute of Education. Annual Report. (NR) **1669**
University of Ibadan. Institute of Education. Occasional Publications. (NR ISSN 0073-4314) **1669**
University of Ibadan. Library. Annual Report. (NR ISSN 0073-4322) **2789**
University of Ibadan. Library. Library Record. (NR ISSN 0046-8436) **2789, 4138**
University of Ibadan. Student Affairs Office. Student Handbook of Information on University Policies and Practices. (NR) **1719**
University of Idaho. Forest, Wildlife and Range Experiment Station, Moscow. Station Bulletin. (US ISSN 0073-4586) **1499, 2110**
University of Idaho. Forest, Wildlife and Range Experiment Station, Moscow. Station Note. (US ISSN 0073-4594) **1499, 2110**
University of Idaho. Water Resources Research Institute. Annual Report. (US ISSN 0073-4616) **4829**
University of Idaho Anthropological Monographs. (US) **251**
University of Ife. Faculty of Agriculture. Annual Research Report *see* Ife Journal of Agriculture **96**
University of Ife. Faculty of Arts. Lecture Series. (NR) **2517**

University of Ife. Faculty of Law. Law Report *see* Obafemi Awolowo University. Faculty of Law. Law Report **2662**
University of Ife Law Report *see* Obafemi Awolowo University. Faculty of Law. Law Report **2662**
University of Illinois. Department of Linguistics. Working Papers *see* Studies in the Linguistic Sciences **2846**
University of Illinois. Institute of Government and Public Affairs. Working Papers. (US) **4096**
University of Illinois. Small Homes Council. Building Research Council. Council Notes. (US) **635**
University of Illinois. Small Homes Council. Building Research Council. Research Report. (US ISSN 0073-540X) **635**
University of Illinois. Small Homes Council. Building Research Council. Technical Notes. (US ISSN 0073-5426) **635**
University of Illinois at Urbana-Champaign. Agricultural Experiment Station. Research Progress. (US) **127**
University of Illinois at Urbana-Champaign. Center for International Education and Research in Accounting. Monographs. (US ISSN 0073-5191) **757**
University of Illinois at Urbana-Champaign. Clinic on Library Applications of Data Processing. Proceedings. (US ISSN 0069-4789) **2789**
University of Illinois at Urbana-Champaign. Department of Agricultural Economics. Agricultural Finance Program Report. (US ISSN 0073-5213) **159**
University of Illinois at Urbana-Champaign. Department of Agricultural Economics. Landlord and Tenant Shares *see* University of Illinois at Urbana-Champaign. Department of Agricultural Economics. Lease Shares and Farm Returns **159**
University of Illinois at Urbana-Champaign. Department of Agricultural Economics. Lease Shares and Farm Returns. (US) **159**
†University of Illinois at Urbana-Champaign. Department of Agricultural Economics. Research Report. (US ISSN 0073-523X) **5298**
University of Illinois at Urbana-Champaign. Department of Art. Newsletter *see* University of Illinois at Urbana-Champaign. School of Art and Design. Newsletter **348**
†University of Illinois at Urbana-Champaign. Engineering Experiment Station. Bulletin. (US ISSN 0073-5272) **5298**
University of Illinois at Urbana-Champaign. Engineering Experiment Station. Summary of Engineering Research. (US ISSN 0073-5280) **1839**
University of Illinois at Urbana-Champaign. Graduate School of Library and Information Science. Allerton Park Institute. Papers. (US) **2789**
†University of Illinois at Urbana-Champaign. Graduate School of Library and Information Science. Downs Fund Publications Series. (US) **5298**
University of Illinois at Urbana-Champaign. Graduate School of Library and Information Science. Monograph Series. (US) **2789**
University of Illinois at Urbana-Champaign. Graduate School of Library and Information Science. Occasional Papers. (US ISSN 0276-1769) **2789**

UNIVERSITY

University of Illinois at Urbana-Champaign. Graduate School of Library Science. Allerton Park Institute. Papers *see* University of Illinois at Urbana-Champaign. Graduate School of Library and Information Science. Allerton Park Institute. Papers **2789**

University of Illinois at Urbana-Champaign. Graduate School of Library Science. Monograph Series. *see* University of Illinois at Urbana-Champaign. Graduate School of Library and Information Science. Monograph Series **2789**

University of Illinois at Urbana-Champaign. Graduate School of Library Science. Occasional Papers. *see* University of Illinois at Urbana-Champaign. Graduate School of Library and Information Science. Occasional Papers **2789**

University of Illinois at Urbana-Champaign. Institute of Labor and Industrial Relations. Reprint Series. (US ISSN 0073-5353) **996**

University of Illinois at Urbana-Champaign. School of Art and Design. Newsletter. (US) **348**

University of Illinois at Urbana-Champaign. Water Resources Center. Annual Report. (US ISSN 0073-5434) **4829**

University of Illinois at Urbana-Champaign. Water Resources Center. Research Report. (US ISSN 0073-5442) **4829**

University of Illinois at Urbana-Champaign. Water Resources Center. Special Reports. (US) **4829**

University of Illinois Law Review. (US ISSN 0276-9948) **2690**

University of Iowa. Libraries. Newsletter.(US ISSN 0047-1402) **2789**

University of Iowa. School of Library and Information Science. Newsletter. (US) **2789**

University of Istanbul. Faculty of Forestry. Review. *see* Istanbul Universitesi. Orman Fakultesi. Dergisi **2103**

University of Istanbul. Faculty of Veterinary Medicine. Journal. (TU) **4817**

University of Jyvaskyla. Department of Physics. Preprints. (FI) **3834**

University of Kansas. Center for East Asian Studies. International Studies: East Asian Series. Reference Series. (US ISSN 0070-8070) **2343, 3785**

University of Kansas. Center for East Asian Studies. International Studies: East Asian Series. Research Series. (US ISSN 0070-8062) **2343, 3785**

University of Kansas. Department of Anthropology. Publications in Anthropology. (US ISSN 0085-2457) **252**

University of Kansas. Museum of Art. Register *see* Spencer Museum of Art. Register **345**

University of Kansas. Museum of Natural History. Miscellaneous Publications. (US ISSN 0075-5028) **459, 4350**

University of Kansas. Museum of Natural History. Monographs. (US ISSN 0085-2465) **459, 4350**

University of Kansas. Museum of Natural History. Occasional Papers. (US ISSN 0091-7958) **4350**

University of Kansas. Museum of Natural History. Public Education Series. (US) **459, 4350**

University of Kansas. Museum of Natural History. Special Publications. (US) **459, 4350**

University of Kansas. Paleontological Contributions. Articles *see* University of Kansas. Paleontological Contributions. New Series **3661**

University of Kansas. Paleontological Contributions. Monographs *see* University of Kansas. Paleontological Contributions. New Series **3661**

University of Kansas. Paleontological Contributions. New Series. (US ISSN 1046-8390) **3661**

University of Kansas. Paleontological Contributions. Papers. *see* University of Kansas. Paleontological Contributions. New Series **3661**

University of Kansas Humanistic Studies. (US ISSN 0085-2473) **2517**

University of Kansas Law Review. (US ISSN 0083-4025) **2690**

University of Kansas Libraries. Library Series. (US ISSN 0075-5001) **2789**

University of Kansas Publications in Anthropology *see* University of Kansas. Department of Anthropology. Publications in Anthropology **252**

University of Kansas Science Bulletin. (US ISSN 0022-8850) **459**

University of Kashmir. Annual Report. (II) **1719**

University of Kentucky. Center for Business and Economic Research. Review & Perspective. (US) **887**

University of Kentucky Art Museum Newsletter. (US) **3534, 348**

University of Kentucky Libraries. Occasional Papers. (US ISSN 0743-8915) **2789**

University of Kentucky Research Foundation. Annual Report *see* Odyssey (Lexington) **1713**

University of Kerala. Department of Tamil. Research Papers. (II) **2850, 2972**

University of Khartoum. Development Studies and Research Centre. Discussion Papers. (SJ) **936, 4391**

University of Khartoum. Development Studies and Research Centre. Monograph Series. (SJ) **936**

University of Khartoum. Development Studies and Research Centre. Occasional Papers. (SJ) **936**

University of Khartoum. Hydrobiological Research Unit. Annual Report. (SJ) **459**

University of Khartoum. Library Bulletin.(SJ) **2789**

University of Kuwait. Journal (Science). (KU ISSN 0376-4818) **4350**

University of Lagos. Human Resources Research Unit. Monograph. (NR) **3988, 4455**

University of Lagos. Humanities Series. (NR ISSN 0075-7675) **2517**

University of Lagos. Inaugural Lecture Series. (NR ISSN 0075-7659) **2517**

University of Lagos. Library. Annual Report. (NR ISSN 0075-7705) **2789**

University of Lagos. Scientific Monograph Series. (NR ISSN 0075-7713) **4350**

University of Lausanne. Departement des Langues et des Sciences du Langage. Cahiers. (SZ ISSN 0256-1565) **2850**

University of Leeds Review. (UK ISSN 0041-9737) **1719**

University of Leiden. Kamerlingh Onnes Laboratory. Communications. (NE ISSN 0022-8141) **3839**

University of Liberia. A.M. Dogliotti College of Medicine. Annual Report of the Dean. (LB) **3160**

University of Liberia Science and Technology Magazine *see* U L Science and Technology Magazine **4349**

University of Liverpool Calendar. (UK ISSN 0305-9227) **1719**

University of Liverpool Post Graduate Prospectus. (UK) **1719, 1697**

University of Liverpool Prospectus. (UK ISSN 0268-2362) **1719, 1697**

University of London. Contemporary China Institute. Research Notes and Studies. (UK ISSN 0308-6119) **3645, 4391**

University of London. Institute of Archaeology. Bulletin *see* University College London. Institute of Archaeology. Bulletin **288**

University of London. Institute of Archaeology. Occasional Publication *see* University College London. Institute of Archaeology. Occasional Publication **288**

University of London. Institute of Classical Studies. Bulletin. (UK ISSN 0076-0730) **1280**

University of London. Institute of Classical Studies. Bulletin Supplement. (UK ISSN 0076-0749) **1280**

University of London. Institute of Commonwealth Studies. Annual Report. (UK ISSN 0076-0781) **4391**

University of London. Institute of Commonwealth Studies. Collected Seminar Papers. (UK ISSN 0076-0773) **4391**

University of London. Institute of Germanic Studies. Bithell Memorial Lectures. (UK ISSN 0144-9850) **2972**

University of London. Institute of Germanic Studies. Bithell Series of Dissertations. (UK ISSN 0266-7932) **2972**

University of London. Institute of Germanic Studies. Library Publications. (UK ISSN 0076-0803) **2972**

University of London. Institute of Germanic Studies. Publications. (UK ISSN 0076-0811) **2972**

University of London. Institute of Germanic Studies. Research in Germanic Studies. (UK ISSN 0260-5929) **415**

University of London. Institute of Historical Research. Bulletin *see* Historical Research **2312**

University of London. Institute of Latin American Studies. Monographs. (UK ISSN 0076-0846) **2425**

University of London. Institute of Latin American Studies. Occasional Papers *see* University of London. Institute of Latin American Studies. Research Papers **2425**

University of London. Institute of Latin American Studies. Research Papers. (UK ISSN 0957-7947) **2425**

University of London. Royal Postgraduate Medical School. Annual Report. (UK ISSN 0076-0854) **3160**

University of London. School of Oriental and African Studies. Bulletin. (UK ISSN 0041-977X) **2517**

University of London. School of Slavonic and East European Studies. Library. Bibliographical Guides. (UK ISSN 0140-7260) **415, 2789**

†University of London King's College. Department of Geography. Occasional Paper. (UK ISSN 0309-2178) **5298**

University of Louisville *see* U of L **1327**

University of Louisville. Library Review *see* Library Review **2771**

University of Lund. Archeological Institute. Papers. Yearbook/Meddelande fraan Lunds Universitet Historiska Museum. (SW) **288**

University of Lund. Faculty of Odontology. Annual Publications *see* University of Lund. School of Dentistry. Faculty of Odontology. Annual Publications **3244**

University of Lund. School of Dentistry. Faculty of Odontology. Annual Publications. (SW ISSN 0076-3438) **3244**

University of Madras. Archaeological Series. (II ISSN 0076-2202) **288**

University of Madras. Endowment Lectures. (II ISSN 0076-2210) **1719**

University of Madras. Historical Series. (II ISSN 0076-2229) **2343**

University of Madras. Kannada Series. (II ISSN 0076-2237) **2850**

University of Madras. Malayalam Series.(II ISSN 0076-2245) **2850**

University of Madras. Philosophical Series. (II ISSN 0076-2253) **3785**

University of Madras. Sanskrit Series. (II ISSN 0076-2261) **2850**

University of Madras. Tamil Series. (II ISSN 0076-227X) **2850**

University of Madras. Telugu Series. (II ISSN 0076-2288) **2850**

University of Madras. Urdu Series. (II ISSN 0076-2296) **2850**

University of Malawi. Centre for Extension Studies. Annual Report. (MW) **1719**

University of Malawi. Library. Bulletin. (MW) **2789**

University of Malawi Libraries. Report to the Senate on the University Libraries. (MW ISSN 0085-3038) **2789**

University of Malawi Students Law Journal *see* U M A Students Law Journal **2688**

University of Malaya. Chinese Language Society. Journal. *see* Pan T'ai Hsueh Pao **2833**

University of Malaya. Department of Engineering. Journal *see* University of Malaya. Faculty of Engineering. Journal **1839**

University of Malaya. Faculty of Engineering. Journal/Universiti Malaya. Fakulti Kejuruteraan. Jernal. (MY) **1839**

University of Malta. Annual Report. (MM) **1719**

University of Malta. Gazette. (MM) **1719**

University of Malta. International Ocean Institute. Occasional Papers *see* International Ocean Institute. Occasional Papers **1606**

University of Manchester. Department of Computer Science. Technical Report Series. (UK) **1439**

University of Manila Law Gazette. (PH ISSN 0041-9796) **2690**

University of Manitoba. Center for Transportation Studies. Occasional Paper. *see* University of Manitoba. Transport Institute. Occasional Paper **4660**

University of Manitoba. Faculty of Agriculture. Annual Progress Review: Agricultural Research, Teaching and Extension. (CN) **127**

University of Manitoba. Faculty of Agriculture. Progress Report on Agricultural Research and Experimentation *see* University of Manitoba. Faculty of Agriculture. Annual Progress Review: Agricultural Research, Teaching and Extension **127**

University of Manitoba. Transport Institute. Occasional Paper. (CN) **4660**

University of Manitoba Alumni Journal. (CN ISSN 0706-9847) **1328**

University of Manitoba Anthropology Papers. (CN ISSN 0227-0072) **252, 288, 2850**

University of Maryland. College of Library and Information Services. Student Contribution Series. (US ISSN 0076-4841) **2789**

University of Maryland. Medical Alumni Association. Bulletin. (US) **1328**

University of Massachusetts. Department of Anthropology. Research Reports. (US ISSN 0076-5066) **252**

University of Mauritius. Annual Report. (MF) **1719**

University of Mauritius. Journal. (MF) **1328**

University of Melbourne. Department of Electrical Engineering. Research Report. (AT ISSN 0085-3259) **1910**

University of Melbourne. Gazette. (AT ISSN 0085-3275) **1719**

†University of Miami. Center for Theoretical Studies. Quarterly Bulletin.(US) **5298**

University of Miami, Coral Gables. Law Center. Annual Institute on Estate Planning. (US ISSN 0537-9768) **2716**

University of Miami Law Review. (US ISSN 0041-9818) **2690**

University of Michigan. Center for Continuing Education of Women Newsletter *see* Cornerstone (Ann Arbor) **1704**
University of Michigan. Division of Research Development and Administration. Research News. (US ISSN 0041-9842) **1720, 2517, 4350**
University of Michigan. Herbarium. Contributions. (US ISSN 0091-1860) **520**
University of Michigan. Museum of Anthropology. Anthropological Papers. (US ISSN 0076-8367) **252**
University of Michigan. Museum of Anthropology. Memoirs. (US ISSN 0076-8375) **252**
University of Michigan. Museum of Anthropology. Technical Reports. (US) **252**
University of Michigan. Museum of Art. Bulletin *see* University of Michigan. Museums of Art and Archaeology. Bulletin **3534**
University of Michigan. Museum of Paleontology. Contributions. (US ISSN 0041-9834) **3661**
University of Michigan. Museum of Paleontology. Papers on Paleontology. (US ISSN 0148-3838) **3661**
University of Michigan. Museum of Zoology. Miscellaneous Publications. (US ISSN 0076-8405) **593**
University of Michigan. Museum of Zoology. Occasional Papers. (US ISSN 0076-8413) **593**
▼University of Michigan. Museum of Zoology. Special Publications. (US ISSN 1053-6477) **593**
University of Michigan. Museums of Art and Archaeology. Bulletin. (US ISSN 0270-1642) **3534**
University of Michigan. Population Studies Center. Report. (US) **3989**
University of Michigan. School of Dentistry. Alumni Bulletin. (US ISSN 0076-843X) **3244**
University of Michigan. U - M Computing News *see* Information Technology Digest **1396**
University of Michigan Journal of Law Reform. (US ISSN 0033-1546) **2690**
University of Michigan Research Review *see* U M T R I Research Review **4704**
University of Minnesota. Center for Natural Resource Policy and Management. Working Papers. (US) **4830, 1499, 2110**
University of Minnesota. Center for Research in Human Learning. Report and Fellowship Offerings *see* University of Minnesota. Center for Research in Learning, Perception & Cognition. Report and Fellowship Offerings **1669**
University of Minnesota. Center for Research in Learning, Perception & Cognition. Report and Fellowship Offerings. (US) **1669**
University of Minnesota. Center for Youth Development and Research. Center Quarterly Focus. (US) **4455**
University of Mississippi. Studies in English. New Series *see* University of Mississippi Studies in English **2972**
University of Mississippi Studies in English. (US ISSN 0278-310X) **2972**
University of Missouri, Columbia. Library Series. (US) **2789**
University of Missouri, Columbia. Museum of Anthropology. Miscellaneous Publications in Anthropology. (US) **252**
University of Missouri, Columbia. Museum of Anthropology. Museum Briefs. (US ISSN 0362-1235) **252**
University of Missouri, Columbia. Veterinary Medical Diagnostic Laboratory. Annual Report. (US ISSN 0076-9711) **4817**
University of Missouri - Kansas City. Friends of the Library. Publication Series. (US) **2789**

University of Missouri, Kansas City Law Review *see* U M K C Law Review **2688**
University of Missouri Monographs in Anthropology. (US) **252, 288, 2425**
†University of Missouri Studies. (US ISSN 0076-9703) **5298**
University of Montana. Forest and Conservation Experiment Station, Missoula. Bulletin *see* University of Montana. Forest and Conservation Experiment Station, Missoula. Miscellaneous Publications **2110**
University of Montana. Forest and Conservation Experiment Station, Missoula. Miscellaneous Publications.(US) **2110**
University of Montana. Forest and Conservation Experiment Station, Missoula. Research Notes. (US ISSN 0077-1163) **2110**
University of Nairobi. Institute for Development Studies. Discussion Papers. (KE ISSN 0547-1788) **2335, 887**
University of Nairobi. Institute for Development Studies. Occasional Paper. (KE) **936, 1086**
University of Nairobi. Institute for Development Studies. Research and Publications. (KE) **4391**
University of Nairobi. Institute for Development Studies. Working Papers. (KE) **2335, 887**
University of Natal. Centre for Applied Social Research. Annual Report *see* University of Natal. Centre for Social and Development Studies. Annual Report **4391**
University of Natal. Centre for Social and Development Studies. Annual Report. (SA) **4391**
†University of Natal. Low-Income Housing Series. (SA) **5298**
†University of Natal. Monograph Series. (SA) **5298**
†University of Natal. Occasional Papers.(SA) **5298**
University of Nebraska. School of Journalism. Depth Report. (US ISSN 0077-6378) **2576**
University of Nebraska. Water Center. Annual Report of Activities. (US) **4830**
University of Nebraska Studies. New Series. (US ISSN 0077-6386) **2517**
University of Nevada. Basque Studies Program Newsletter. (US ISSN 1047-2932) **2027, 2393**
University of Nevada. Bureau of Business and Economic Research. Research Report. (US ISSN 0077-7943) **697**
University of Nevada. Desert Research Institute. Technical Report. (US ISSN 0897-6376) **4350**
University of Nevada. Seismological Laboratory. Bulletin. (US ISSN 0092-4288) **1596**
University of New Brunswick Law Journal. (CN ISSN 0836-6632) **2690**
University of New England. Animal Genetics and Breeding Unit. Occasional Report. (AT ISSN 0726-8416) **593, 547**
University of New England. Annual Report. (AT ISSN 0375-4588) **1720**
University of New England. Centre for Water Policy Research. Occasional Papers (No.). (AT ISSN 1030-4134) **4830**
University of New England. Computer Centre Annual Report. (AT ISSN 0814-9674) **1401**
University of New England. Computer Centre Handbook. (AT ISSN 0814-9682) **1401**
University of New England. Computer Centre Newsletter. (AT ISSN 0814-9690) **1401**
University of New England. Department of Accounting & Financial Management. Working Papers. (AT ISSN 0814-9372) **757, 802, 1030, 1119**

†University of New England. Department of Administrative, Higher and Adult Education Studies. Centre News. (AT) **5298**
University of New England. Department of Agricultural Economics and Business Management. Agricultural Economics Miscellaneous Publication (No.). (AT ISSN 0313-3788) **159**
University of New England. Department of Agricultural Economics and Business Management. Dairy Economics Research Report (No.). (AT ISSN 1032-9552) **204**
University of New England. Department of Agricultural Economics and Business Management. Farm Management Report. (AT ISSN 0156-0913) **159**
†University of New England. Department of Agricultural Economics and Business Management. Wool Economics Research Reports (No.). (AT ISSN 1036-4161) **5298**
University of New England. Department of Econometrics. Working Papers in Econometrics and Applied Statistics. (AT ISSN 0157-0188) **743, 4591**
University of New England. Department of Geography and Planning. Monograph Series (No.). (AT ISSN 0312-8741) **2265**
University of New England. Department of Geography and Planning. Research Series in Applied Geography. (AT ISSN 0066-7714) **2265**
University of New England. Faculty of Agricultural Economics. Farm Management Report *see* University of New England. Department of Agricultural Economics and Business Management. Farm Management Report **159**
University of New England. Faculty of Economic Studies. Occasional Papers in Economic Development (No.). (AT ISSN 0816-5041) **697**
University of New England. Information Office Specialists List. (AT ISSN 0158-0604) **1720**
University of New England. Management Forum. (AT ISSN 0311-9300) **1030, 1119**
University of New England Convocation Bulletin & Alumni News *see* U N E Convocation Bulletin & Alumni News **1718**
University of New England Library Publications. (AT ISSN 0814-9704) **415**
University of New Mexico. C I R T Newsletter. (Computer & Information Resources & Technology) (US) **1401**
University of New Mexico. C S I S Newsletter *see* University of New Mexico. C I R T Newsletter **1401**
University of New Mexico. Division of Government Research. Monograph Series. (US ISSN 0194-2670) **4076**
University of New Mexico. Institute of Meteoritics. Special Publication. (US ISSN 0085-3968) **370**
University of New Mexico. Latin American Institute. Research Paper Series. (US) **4391, 2027**
University of New Mexico. Office of Research Administration. Research Notes. (US) **1720**
University of New Mexico Art Museum. Bulletin. (US ISSN 0077-8583) **3534**
University of New South Wales. Centre for Applied Economic Research. Paper. (AT ISSN 0314-853X) **898**
University of New South Wales. Faculty Handbooks: Applied Science. (AY ISSN 0811-7586) **1839**
University of New South Wales. Faculty Handbooks: Architecture. (AT ISSN 0811-7594) **308**
University of New South Wales. Faculty Handbooks: Arts. (AT ISSN 0811-7608) **348**
University of New South Wales. Faculty Handbooks: Commerce. (AT ISSN 0811-7616) **840**

University of New South Wales. Faculty Handbooks: Engineering. (AT ISSN 0811-7624) **1839**
University of New South Wales. Faculty Handbooks: Law. (AT ISSN 0811-7632) **2690**
University of New South Wales. Faculty Handbooks: Medicine. (AT ISSN 0312-6137) **3160**
University of New South Wales. Faculty Handbooks: Professional Studies. (AT) **3631**
University of New South Wales. Faculty Handbooks: Sciences. (AT ISSN 0811-7640) **4350**
University of New South Wales. Library. Annual Report. (AT ISSN 0313-427X) **2789**
University of New South Wales. Library. Staff Papers. (AT) **2789**
University of New South Wales. School of Civil Engineering. U N I C I V Reports. Series I. (AT ISSN 0077-8796) **1876**
University of New South Wales. School of Civil Engineering. U N I C I V Reports. Series R. (AT ISSN 0077-880X) **1876**
University of New South Wales. Water Reference Library. Current Awareness List *see* University of New South Wales. Water Research Library. Water Information Update **4835**
University of New South Wales. Water Research Laboratory, Manly Vale. Laboratory Research Reports. (AT ISSN 0077-8818) **4830**
University of New South Wales. Water Research Library. Water Information Update. (AT) **4835**
University of New South Wales, Kensington. Research and Publications. (AT ISSN 0548-6831) **1720**
University of New South Wales Law Journal. (AT ISSN 0313-0096) **2690**
University of Newcastle. Board of Environmental Studies. Research Papers. (AT) **1970**
University of Newcastle. Department of Electrical and Computer Engineering. Technical Report EE. (AT) **1910, 1418**
University of Newcastle. Department of Electrical Engineering. Technical Report EE *see* University of Newcastle. Department of Electrical and Computer Engineering. Technical Report EE **1910**
University of Newcastle-Upon-Tyne. Computing Laboratory. Technical Report Series. (UK) **1401**
University of Newcastle-Upon-Tyne. Department of Geography. Research Series. (UK ISSN 0078-026X) **2265**
University of Nigeria. Annual Report. (NR ISSN 0331-1686) **1720**
University of North Carolina. Sea Grant College Newsletter *see* Coastwatch **1603**
University of North Carolina, Chapel Hill. Institute for Research in Social Science. Technical Papers. (US) **4391**
University of North Carolina, Chapel Hill. Institute for Research in Social Science. Working Papers in Methodology. (US) **4391**
University of North Carolina, Chapel Hill. Institute of Statistics. Mimeo Series. (US ISSN 0078-1495) **4591**
University of North Dakota. Alumni Review. (US ISSN 0895-5409) **1328**
University of North Dakota. Institute for Ecological Studies. Research Report. (US) **1970**
University of North Sumatra. Bulletin/ Majalah Universitas Sumatera Utara. (IO) **1720**
University of Northern Colorado. Museum of Anthropology. Occasional Publications in Anthropology. Archaeology Series. (US ISSN 0085-1221) **288**

University of Northern Colorado. Museum of Anthropology. Occasional Publications in Anthropology. Ethnology Series. (US ISSN 0085-1205) **252**

University of Northern Colorado. Museum of Anthropology. Occasional Publications in Anthropology. Linguistics Series. (US ISSN 0085-123X) **2850**

University of Northern Colorado. Museum of Anthropology. Occasional Publications in Anthropology. Miscellaneous Series. (US ISSN 0085-1213) **252**

University of Notre Dame. Department of Mathematics. Mathematical Lectures. (US ISSN 0076-5341) **3060**

University of Notre Dame. Department of Theology. Liturgical Studies. (US ISSN 0076-003X) **4278**

†University of Notre Dame. Department of Theology. Studies in Christian Democracy. (US ISSN 0081-7708) **5298**

University of Notre Dame. Studies in the Philosophy of Religion. (US) **4208,** 3785

University of Nottingham. Department of Adult Education. Bulletin of Local History, East Midlands Region. (UK ISSN 0141-0008) **2393**

University of Occupational and Environmental Health. Journal. (JA ISSN 0387-821X) **3622,** 3160, 4114

University of Oklahoma. Archaeological Research and Management Center. Project Report Series. (US ISSN 0160-3078) **288**

University of Oklahoma. Archaeological Research and Management Center. Research Series. (US ISSN 0160-3086) **288**

University of Oregon Anthropological Papers. (US ISSN 0078-6071) **252**

University of Osaka Prefecture. Bulletin. Series A: Engineering and Natural Sciences/Osaka-furitsu Daigaku Kiyo, A. Kogaku, Shizen Kagaku. (JA ISSN 0474-7844) **1839,** 4350

University of Osaka Prefecture. Bulletin. Series B: Agriculture and Biology/ Osaka-furitsu Daigaku Kiyo, B. Nogaku, Seibutsugaku. (JA ISSN 0474-7852) **127,** 459

University of Osaka Prefecture. Bulletin. Series D: Economics, Business Administration and Law/Osaka-furitsu Daigaku Kiyo, D. Keizaigaku, Keieigaku, Hogaku. (JA) **697,** 840, 2690

University of Osaka Prefecture. Bulletin. Series D: Sciences of Economy, Commerce and Law *see* University of Osaka Prefecture. Bulletin. Series D: Economics, Business Administration and Law **697**

University of Osaka Prefecture. Research Institute for Advanced Science and Technology. Annual Report/Osaka-furitsu-Daigaku Fuzokukenkyusho Nenpo. (JA ISSN 0917-1630) **1971,** 3835

University of Ottawa. Alumni and Development. Alumni News/ Universite d'Ottawa. Alumni and Development. Anciens Alumni Ottawa.(CN ISSN 0832-7424) **1328**

University of Ottawa. Cahiers d'Histoire. (CN) **2325**

University of Ottawa. Department of Geography and Regional Planning. Notes de Recherches - Research Notes *see* University of Ottawa. Department of Geography. Notes de Recherche - Research Notes **2265**

University of Ottawa. Department of Geography. Notes de Recherche - Research Notes. (CN) **2265**

University of Ottawa. Medieval Texts and Studies/Universite d'Ottawa. Publications Medievales. (CN) **2325**

University of Ottawa. Ukrainian Studies/ Universite d'Ottawa. Etudes Ukrainiennes. (CN) **2393**

University of Ottawa Quarterly. *see* Universite d'Ottawa. Revue **5297**

University of Oxford. School of Geography. Research Papers. (UK ISSN 0305-8190) **2265**

University of Papua New Guinea. Department of Geography. Occasional Papers in Geography. (PP) **2265**

University of Papua New Guinea. Department of Physics. Technical Paper. (PP ISSN 0085-4735) **3835**

University of Pennsylvania. Department of City and Regional Planning. Research Reports Series. (US) **2497**

University of Pennsylvania. Wharton School of Finance and Commerce. Industrial Research Unit Studies *see* Major Industrial Research Unit Studies **1080**

University of Pennsylvania. Wharton School of Finance and Commerce. Labor Relations and Public Policy Series. Reports *see* Labor Relations and Public Policy Series **986**

University of Pennsylvania. Wharton School of Finance and Commerce. Studies in Quantitative Economics. (US ISSN 0081-8437) **697**

University of Pennsylvania Journal of International Business Law. (US ISSN 0891-9895) **2730**

University of Pennsylvania Law Review. (US ISSN 0041-9907) **2690**

†University of Pennsylvania Studies on South Asia. (US ISSN 0169-0361) **5298**

University of Petroleum, China. Journal (Natural Science Edition). *see* Shiyou Daxue Xuebao (Ziran Kexue Ban) **3701**

University of Pittsburgh Law Review. (US ISSN 0041-9915) **2690**

University of Poona. Centre of Advanced Study in Sanskrit. Doctoral Theses and Other Sanskrit & Prakrit Publications. (II) **2850,** 4216

University of Poona. Centre of Advanced Study in Sanskrit. Publications. (II ISSN 0079-3809) **2850**

University of Poona. Centre of Advanced Study in Sanskrit. Sanskrit and Prakrit Studies. (II) **2850**

†University of Poona Science and Technology. Journal. (II ISSN 0551-4932) **5298**

University of Port Elizabeth. Institute for Planning Research. Annual Report/ Universiteit van Port Elizabeth. Instituut vir Beplanningsnavorsing. Jaarverslag. (SA) **1000**

University of Port Elizabeth. Institute for Planning Research. Fact Paper Series/Universiteit van Port Elizabeth. Instituut vir Beplanningsnavorsing. Feitestuk Reeks. (SA) **887**

University of Port Elizabeth. Institute for Planning Research. Information Bulletin Series/Universiteit van Port Elizabeth. Instituut vir Beplanningsnavorsing. Inligtingsbulletin Reeks. (SA) **887**

University of Port Elizabeth. Publications. Bibliographies. (SA) **2517**

University of Port Elizabeth. Publications. General Series. (SA ISSN 0079-3957) **2517**

University of Port Elizabeth. Publications. Inaugural and Emeritus Addresses. (SA ISSN 0085-5022) **2518**

University of Port Elizabeth. Publications. Research Papers. (SA ISSN 0079-3965) **2518**

University of Port Elizabeth. Publications. Symposia, Seminars, and Lectures. (SA) **2518**

University of Port Elizabeth Newspaper *see* U P E N **1327**

University of Portland Review. (US ISSN 0041-9923) **4350,** 2518

University of Pretoria. Annual Report/ Universiteit van Pretoria. Jaarverslag.(SA ISSN 0259-1871) **1328**

University of Pretoria. Institute for Strategic Studies. Bulletin. (SA) **1274**

University of Puerto Rico. Agricultural Experiment Station. Bulletin. (PR ISSN 0163-8238) **127**

University of Puerto Rico. Journal of Agriculture. (PR ISSN 0041-994X) **127**

University of Puget Sound Law Review. (US ISSN 0161-0708) **2690**

University of Qatar. Annual Statistical Report for the School Year. *see* Jami'at Qatar. Al-Taqrir al-Ihsa'i al-Sanawi lil-Aam al-Jami'i **1677**

University of Quebec at Montreal Journal *see* U Q A M. Journal **1327**

University of Queensland. Calendar *see* University of Queensland. Calendar. Volume 1. The University **1328**

University of Queensland. Calendar *see* University of Queensland. Calendar. Volume 2. Student Handbook: Metropolitan Campuses **1720**

University of Queensland. Calendar *see* University of Queensland. Calendar. Volume 3. Gatton College Handbook **1720**

University of Queensland. Calendar. Volume 1. The University. (AT) **1328**

University of Queensland. Calendar. Volume 2. Student Handbook: Metropolitan Campuses. (AT) **1720**

University of Queensland. Calendar. Volume 3. Gatton College Handbook.(AT) **1720,** 1328

University of Queensland. Higher Degree Handbook *see* University of Queensland. Calendar. Volume 2. Student Handbook: Metropolitan Campuses **1720**

University of Queensland. Student Handbook *see* University of Queensland. Calendar. Volume 2. Student Handbook: Metropolitan Campuses **1720**

University of Queensland. Undergraduate Degree Handbook *see* University of Queensland. Calendar. Volume 2. Student Handbook: Metropolitan Campuses **1720**

University of Queensland Law Journal. (AT ISSN 0083-4041) **2690**

University of Rajasthan. South Asian Studies Centre. Annual Report. (II) **3645**

University of Rajasthan. Studies in Sanskrit and Hindi. (II ISSN 0448-1712) **2972,** 2850

University of Reading. Department of Agricultural Economics & Management. Development Studies. (UK) **159**

University of Reading. Department of Agricultural Economics & Management. Farm Business Data. (UK ISSN 0557-6911) **159**

University of Reading. Department of Agricultural Economics & Management. Food Economics Studies. (UK) **159,** 2083

University of Reading. Department of Agricultural Economics & Management. Miscellaneous Studies. (UK ISSN 0486-0845) **159**

†University of Rhode Island. Graduate School of Oceanography. Collected Reprints. (US) **5298**

†University of Rhode Island. Graduate School of Oceanography. Marine Technical Reports. (US) **5298**

University of Rhode Island. Library. Library Letter. (US) **2789**

University of Rhode Island. Water Resources Center. Annual Report. (US) **4830**

University of Richmond Law Review. (US ISSN 0566-2389) **2690**

University of Riyadh. Central Library. Accession List. (SU) **2796**

University of Rochester. School of Medicine and Dentistry. Edward G. Miner Library. Bulletin. (US) **2789,** 3160

University of Rochester Library Bulletin. (US ISSN 0041-9974) **2789**

University of St. Andrews. Library. Current Serials. (UK ISSN 0143-0009) **415**

University of St. Thomas Magazine. (US) **1328,** 4208

University of Salahaddin. College of Agriculture. Scientific Journal "ZANCO". (IQ) **127,** 2083, 2110, 4645

University of San Carlos. Series A: Humanities *see* San Carlos Publications. Series A: Humanities **2514**

University of San Carlos. University Bulletin. (PH ISSN 0041-9990) **1328**

University of San Francisco. Alumni Association. Alumnus. (US) **1328**

University of San Francisco Law Review.(US ISSN 0042-0018) **2690**

University of Santo Tomas. Faculty of Civil Law. Law Review. (PH ISSN 0047-5734) **2704**

University of Santo Tomas. Graduate School. Journal of Graduate Research. (PH ISSN 0047-5742) **4391,** 459, 2518

University of Santo Tomas Journal of Graduate Research *see* University of Santo Tomas. Graduate School. Journal of Graduate Research **4391**

†University of Saskatchewan. Library. Notable Works and Collections. (CN ISSN 0380-9676) **5298**

University of Saugar. Botanical Society. Bulletin. (II) **520**

University of Sheffield. Diary of Events. (UK) **1328**

University of Sheffield. Newsletter. (UK) **1328**

University of Sheffield. Newsletter Diary *see* University of Sheffield. Diary of Events **1328**

University of Sheffield. Newsletter Diary *see* University of Sheffield. Newsletter **1328**

University of Sierra Leone. Fourah Bay College. Philosophical Society. Journal. (SL) **3785**

University of Sind. Research Journal. Arts Series: Humanities and Social Sciences. (PK ISSN 0080-9616) **2518**

University of Sind. Research Journal. Science Series. (PK ISSN 0080-9624) **4350**

University of Singapore. Faculty of Engineering. Journal *see* Engineering Journal of Singapore **1820**

University of Singapore. History Society. Journal. (SI ISSN 0217-913X) **2343**

University of South Africa English Studies *see* U N I S A English Studies **2971**

University of South Carolina. Belle W. Baruch Library in Marine Science and Coastal Research. Collected Papers. (US) **1612**

†University of South Carolina. Bureau of Business and Economic Research. Occasional Studies. (US) **5298**

University of South Carolina. Institute of Archeology and Anthropology. Annual Report. (US) **288,** 252

University of South Carolina. Institute of International Studies. Essay Series. (US ISSN 0085-6452) **3976**

University of South Florida. International Biomedical Symposia Series. (US) **459,** 3160

University of South Florida Language Quarterly *see* Language Quarterly **2824**

†University of Southampton. Library. Automation Project Report. (UK ISSN 0081-2935) **5298**

University of Southern California. Law Center. Bibliography Series. (US) **2701**

†University of Southern California. School of Social Work. Social Work Papers. (US ISSN 0272-9016) **5298**

Title

UNIVERSITY 6775

University of Southern California Annual Distinguished Lecture Series Monographs in Special Education and Rehabilitation *see* U S C Annual Distinguished Lecture Series Monographs in Special Education and Rehabilitation **1742**
University of Southern California Engineer *see* U S C Engineer **1839**
University of Southern California Trojan Family *see* U S C Trojan Family **1327**
University of Southern Mindanao Agricultural Research Center Monitor *see* U S M A R C Monitor **125**
University of Southern Mississippi Alumni News *see* U S M Alumni News **1327**
University of Southwestern Louisiana History Series *see* U S L History Series **2324**
University of Stellenbosch. Bureau for Economic Research. Building and Construction. (SA ISSN 0586-4941) **635**
University of Stellenbosch. Bureau for Economic Research. Consumer Survey *see* University of Stellenbosch. Bureau for Economic Research. Trade and Commerce **1055**
University of Stellenbosch. Bureau for Economic Research. Economic Prospects. (SA ISSN 0259-4862) **697**
University of Stellenbosch. Bureau for Economic Research. Manufacturing Survey. (SA ISSN 0258-9338) **697**
University of Stellenbosch. Bureau for Economic Research. Opinion Survey *see* University of Stellenbosch. Bureau for Economic Research. Manufacturing Survey **697**
University of Stellenbosch. Bureau for Economic Research. Trade and Commerce. (SA ISSN 0258-9311) **1055**
University of Stellenbosch. Bureau for Economic Research. Trends. (SA ISSN 0379-6191) **840**
University of Stockholm. Institute of Linguistics. Monographs. (SW) **2850**
University of Strathclyde. Department of Architecture & Building Science. Research Bulletin. (UK ISSN 0143-7283) **308,** 635
University of Strathclyde. Fraser of Allander Institute for Research on the Scottish Economy. Quarterly Economic Commentary. (UK ISSN 0306-7866) **697**
University of Strathclyde, Fraser of Allander Institute for Research on the Scottish Economy. Research Monograph. (UK ISSN 0306-7408) **697**
University of Sussex. Centre for Continuing Education. Occasional Paper. (UK ISSN 0306-1108) **2325,** 1687
University of Sydney. Archives Record. (AT ISSN 0310-4729) **2346**
University of Sydney. Basser Department of Computer Science. Technical Report. (AT ISSN 0082-0547) **1401**
University of Sydney. Department of Agricultural Economics. Mimeographed Report. *see* University of Sydney. Department of Agricultural Economics. Research Report **159**
University of Sydney. Department of Agricultural Economics. Research Report. (AT ISSN 0817-8771) **159**
University of Sydney. Department of Economics. Information and Research Monograph. (AT) **697**
†University of Sydney. Economics Society. Economic Review. (AT ISSN 0085-7025) **5298**
University of Sydney. Faculty of Economics. Information and Research Monograph *see* University of Sydney. Department of Economics. Information and Research Monograph **697**
University of Sydney. Gazette. (AT ISSN 0042-0107) **1328**
University of Sydney. Institute of Criminology. Proceedings *see* Current Issues in Criminal Justice **1513**
†University of Sydney. Postgraduate Committee in Medicine. Bulletin. (AT ISSN 0042-0115) **5298**
University of Tabriz. Faculty of Human and Social Sciences. Publication/ Daneshgah-e Tabriz. Daneshkade-ye Ulume Ensani va Ijtima'i. Nashriyeh. (IR) **2518**
University of Tasmania. Centre for Environmental Studies. Project Report. (AT ISSN 0811-580X) **1499**
University of Tasmania. Centre for Environmental Studies. Working Papers. (AT ISSN 0313-5780) **1499,** 1796, 1971
University of Tasmania. Environmental Studies. Occasional Paper. (AT ISSN 0810-4395) **1971**
University of Tasmania Law Review. (AT ISSN 0082-2108) **2690**
University of Technology. Sydney Calendar. (AT ISSN 1030-5947) **4612**
University of Technology, Sydney. Annual Report. (AT ISSN 1031-8690) **1720**
▼University of Technology, Sydney. Faculty of Business Handbook. (AT ISSN 1036-0646) **1720**
▼University of Technology, Sydney. Faculty of Design Architecture and Building Handbook. (AT ISSN 1036-0654) **308,** 1762
▼University of Technology, Sydney. Faculty of Education Handbook. (AT ISSN 1036-0662) **1762**
▼University of Technology, Sydney. Faculty of Engineering Handbook. (AT ISSN 1036-0670) **1839,** 1762
▼University of Technology, Sydney. Faculty of Law & Legal Practice Handbook. (AT ISSN 1036-0689) **2690,** 1910
▼University of Technology, Sydney. Faculty of Mathematical & Computing Sciences Handbook. (AT ISSN 1036-0697) **3060,** 1762
▼University of Technology, Sydney. Faculty of Nursing Handbook. (AT ISSN 1036-0700) **3287,** 1762
▼University of Technology, Sydney. Faculty of Science Handbook. (AT ISSN 1036-0719) **4350,** 1762
▼University of Technology, Sydney. Faculty of Social Sciences Handbook. (AT ISSN 1036-0727) **4391,** 1762
University of Technology, Sydney. General Information of Postgraduate Studies. (AT ISSN 1031-8720) **1762**
University of Technology, Sydney. Research and Consultancy Report. (AT) **4612,** 697, 1345, 4350
University of Technology, Sydney. Research Report *see* University of Technology, Sydney. Research and Consultancy Report **4612**
University of Technology, Sydney. Undergraduate Studies Guide. (AT) **1762**
University of Teheran. Agricultural College Publication *see* Iranian Journal of Agricultural Sciences **100**
University of Teheran. Central Library. Library Bulletin/Daneshgah-e Tehran. Ketabkhane-Ye Markazi. Nashriye-Ye Ketabkhaneh. (IR ISSN 0497-1000) **2789**
University of Teheran. Faculty of Education. Journal of Education - Daneshgah-e Tehran. Daneshkade-ye 'Olum-e Tarbiyati. Nashriyeh *see* Olum-e Tarbiati **1652**
University of Teheran. Faculty of Letters and Humanities. Bulletin of Iranian Studies/Daneshgah-e Tehran. Daneshkade-Ye Adabiyat va 'olum-e Ensani. Majalle-Ye Iranshenasi. (IR) **2432**
University of Teheran. Faculty of Medicine. Library Bulletin/Daneshgah-e Tehran. Daneshkade-Ye Pezeshki. Nashriye-Ye Ketabkhaneh. (IR) **2789,** 3160
University of Teheran. Faculty of Science. Quarterly Bulletin. (IR ISSN 0042-0131) **4350**
†University of Teheran. Faculty of Veterinary Medicine. Journal. (IR ISSN 0042-0123) **5298**
†University of Teheran. Faculty of Veterinary Medicine. Library Bulletin/ Daneshgah-e Tehran. Daneshkade-Ye Dam'ezeshki. Nashriye-Ye Ketabkhaneh. (IR) **5298**
University of Teheran. School of Pharmacy. Journal/Daneshgah-e Teheran. Daneshkade-Ye Darusazi. Majalleh. (IR) **3745**
University of Tennessee. Department of Anthropology. Report of Investigations. (US) **288,** 252
University of Texas. Bureau of Economic Geology. Guidebook *see* University of Texas at Austin. Bureau of Economic Geology. Guidebook **1584**
University of Texas. M.D. Anderson Cancer Center. Cancer Bulletin. (US) **3203**
University of Texas at Austin. Bureau of Economic Geology. Annual Report. (US ISSN 0082-3287) **1583**
University of Texas at Austin. Bureau of Economic Geology. Geological Circular. (US ISSN 0082-3309) **1583**
University of Texas at Austin. Bureau of Economic Geology. Guidebook. (US ISSN 0363-4132) **1584**
University of Texas at Austin. Bureau of Economic Geology. Mineral Resource Circulars. (US ISSN 0082-3333) **1584,** 3497
University of Texas at Austin. Bureau of Economic Geology. Report of Investigations. (US ISSN 0082-335X) **1584**
University of Texas at Austin. Bureau of Economic Geology. Special Publications. (US) **1584**
University of Texas at Austin. Center for Research in Water Resources. Symposium Series *see* University of Texas at Austin. Center for Research in Water Resources. Water Resources Symposium Series **4830**
University of Texas at Austin. Center for Research in Water Resources. Technical Report Series. (US) **4830**
University of Texas at Austin. Center for Research in Water Resources. Water Resources Symposium Series. (US) **4830**
University of Texas at Austin. General Libraries. Library Bulletin. (US ISSN 0277-450X) **2789**
University of Texas at Austin. General Libraries. Newsletter. (US ISSN 0362-854X) **2789**
University of Texas at Austin. Graduate School of Library and Information Science. Alumni News. (US) **2789,** 1328
University of Texas, Austin. Bureau of Business Research. Publications. (US ISSN 0495-2634) **697**
University of Texas, Austin. Bureau of Business Research. Research Monograph Series. (US) **697**
University of Texas, Austin. Lyndon B. Johnson School of Public Affairs. Policy Research Project Report *see* University of Texas, Austin. Lyndon B. Johnson School of Public Affairs. Policy Research Project Report Series **3932**
University of Texas, Austin. Lyndon B. Johnson School of Public Affairs. Policy Research Project Report Series. (US) **3932**
University of Texas, Austin. Lyndon B. Johnson School of Public Affairs. Seminar Research Report *see* University of Texas, Austin. Lyndon B. Johnson School of Public Affairs. Policy Research Project Report Series **3932**
University of Texas, Austin. Lyndon B. Johnson School of Public Affairs. Working Paper Series. (US) **4076**
University of Texas, Austin. Tarlton Law Library. Legal Bibliography Series. (US ISSN 0085-7092) **2701**
University of Texas Lifetime Health Letter. (US) **3809,** 3612
University of Texas Medical Branch Newsletter and Alumni Bulletin *see* University Medical **5297**
†University of Texas Publications in Astronomy. (US ISSN 0276-1106) **5298**
University of Texas Studies in Contemporary Spanish-American Fiction. (US) **2972**
University of the East Business Review *see* U E Business Review **1030**
University of the North. Communique. (SA ISSN 0378-5335) **1669,** 2850, 2972
University of the Orange Free State. Institute for Contemporary History. Annual Report. (SA) **2335**
University of the Philippines. Asian Center. Monograph Series. (PH ISSN 0079-9238) **2343**
University of the Philippines. College of Medicine. Proceedings *see* Acta Medica Philippina **3070**
University of the Philippines. College of Public Administration. Local Government Studies. (PH) **4096**
University of the Philippines. College of Public Administration. Public Administration Occasional Papers and Special Studies Series. (PH) **4076**
University of the Philippines. College of Public Administration. Public Administration Special Studies Series *see* University of the Philippines. College of Public Administration. Public Administration Occasional Papers and Special Studies Series **4076**
University of the Philippines. College of Public Administration. (Publication) *see* Philippine Journal of Public Administration **4070**
University of the Philippines. Institute of Library Science. Newsletter. (PH ISSN 0300-3612) **2789**
University of the Philippines at Los Banos. Agrarian Reform Institute. Occasional Papers. (PH) **127**
†University of the Philippines at Los Banos. College of Forestry. Conservation Circular. (PH ISSN 0115-1266) **5298**
University of the Philippines at Los Banos. Rodent Research Center. Annual Report *see* N C P C Annual Report **185**
University of the Philippines Gazette. (PH) **1669**
University of the Philippines Research Monitor *see* U P Research Monitor **4358**
University of the Philippines Thesis and Dissertation Abstracts *see* U P Thesis and Dissertation Abstracts **1680**
University of the Punjab. Arabic and Persian Society. Journal. (PK ISSN 0079-8029) **2343**
University of the Punjab. Department of Mathematics. Journal *see* Punjab University Journal of Mathematics **3051**
University of the Punjab. Department of Zoology. Bulletin. New Series *see* Punjab University Journal of Zoology **591**
University of the Punjab. Institute of Geology. Geological Bulletin. (PK) **1584**
University of the Punjab. Journal of Research: Humanities. (PK ISSN 0555-7666) **2518**
University of the Ryukyus. College of Agriculture. Science Bulletin/Ryukyu Daigaku Nogakubu Gakujutsu Hokoku. (JA ISSN 0370-4246) **127**
University of the Ryukyus. College of Science. Bulletin/Ryukyu Daigaku Rigakubu Kiyo. (JA ISSN 0286-9640) **3061**
University of the South Pacific. Library. Pacific Collection. Accession List *see* South Pacific Bibliography **412**
University of the South Pacific. Publications. (FJ ISSN 1011-5129) **415**

Title

University of the West Indies. Annual Report on Cocoa Research. (TR) **195**

University of the West Indies. Institute of Social and Economic Research. Occasional Bibliography Series. (JM) **4396**

University of the West Indies. Institute of Social and Economic Research. Working Papers. (JM) **4455, 697**

University of the West Indies. Vice-Chancellor's Report. (JM) **1720**

University of the West Indies Publishers' Association Newsletter see U W I P A Newsletter **4138**

University of the West Indies Students' Law Review see U W I Students' Law Review **2688**

University of the West Indies, Trinidad. Institute of Social & Economic Research. Occasional Papers: General Series. (TR) **4391**

University of the West Indies, Trinidad. Institute of Social & Economic Research. Occasional Papers: Human Resources Series. (TR) **996**

University of the Witwatersrand. African Studies Institute. Seminar Papers. (SA) **2335**

University of the Witwatersrand, Johannesburg. Library. Africana Series. (SA) **2789**

University of the Witwatersrand, Johannesburg. Library. Annual Report of the University Librarian. (SA ISSN 0075-3807) **2789**

University of the Witwatersrand, Johannesburg. Library. Archival Series. (SA) **2789**

University of the Witwatersrand, Johannesburg. Library. Bibliographical Series. (SA) **415**

University of the Witwatersrand, Johannesburg. Library. Occasional Publications. (SA) **2789**

University of Tokushima. College of General Education. Journal of Science. see Tokushima Daigaku Kyoyobu Kiyo. Shizen Kagaku **4348**

University of Tokushima. Faculty of Engineering. Bulletin. (JA ISSN 0040-8883) **1839**

University of Tokushima. Faculty of Integrated Arts and Sciences. Natural Science Research. see Shizen Kagaku Kenkyu (Tokushima) **4343**

University of Tokyo. College of Arts and Sciences. Scientific Papers/Tokyo Daigaku Kyoyogakubu Shizen Kagaku Kiyo. (JA ISSN 0289-7520) **4350**

University of Tokyo. College of General Education. Scientific Papers see University of Tokyo. College of Arts and Sciences. Scientific Papers **4350**

University of Tokyo. Department of Astronomy. Contributions. (JA ISSN 0563-8038) **370**

University of Tokyo. Department of Geography. Bulletin. (JA ISSN 0082-478X) **2265**

University of Tokyo. Earthquake Research Institute. Bulletin/Tokyo Daigaku Jishin Kenkyujo Iho. (JA ISSN 0040-8972) **1596**

University of Tokyo. Earthquake Research Institute. Special Bulletin. (JA ISSN 0915-0862) **1596**

University of Tokyo. Electrical and Electronic Engineering Departments. Bulletin. see Tokyo Daigaku Kogakubu. Denki Kogaku, Denshi Kogaku Iho **1909**

University of Tokyo. Faculty of Engineering. Journal: Series B/Tokyo Daigaku Kogakubu Kiyo B. (JA ISSN 0563-7937) **1839**

University of Tokyo. Faculty of Science. Journal. Section 1A: Mathematics/Tokyo Daigaku Rigakubu Kiyo, Dai-1-rui A, Sugaku. (JA ISSN 0040-8980) **3061, 370, 1190, 3835**

University of Tokyo. Faculty of Science. Journal. Section 2: Geology, Mineralogy, Geography, Earth and Planetary Physics/Tokyo Daigaku Rigakubu Kiyo, Dai-2-rui, Chishitsugaku, Kobutsugaku, Chirigaku, Chikyu Wakusei Butsurigaku. (JA) **1549**

University of Tokyo. Faculty of Science. Journal. Section 2: Geology, Mineralogy, Geography, Geophysics see University of Tokyo. Faculty of Science. Journal. Section 2: Geology, Mineralogy, Geography, Earth and Planetary Physics **1549**

University of Tokyo. Faculty of Science. Journal. Section 3: Botany/Tokyo Daigaku Rigakubu Kiyo, Dai-3-rui, Shokubutsugaku. (JA ISSN 0368-2196) **520**

†University of Tokyo. Faculty of Science. Journal. Section 4: Zoology/Tokyo Daigaku Rigakubu Kiyo, Dai-4-rui, Dobutsugaku. (JA ISSN 0368-220X) **5298**

University of Tokyo. Faculty of Science. Journal. Section 5: Anthropology/Tokyo Daigaku Rigakubu Kiyo, Dai-5-rui, Jinruigaku. (JA ISSN 0373-4722) **252**

University of Tokyo. Institute for Nuclear Study. Annual Report. (JA) **3851**

University of Tokyo. Institute for Nuclear Study. INS-J. (JA ISSN 0495-7814) **3851**

University of Tokyo. Institute for Nuclear Study. INS-PH. (JA) **3851**

University of Tokyo. Institute for Nuclear Study. INS-PT. (JA ISSN 0563-7848) **3851**

University of Tokyo. Institute for Nuclear Study. INS-TCH. (JA) **3851**

University of Tokyo. Institute for Nuclear Study. INS-TEC. (JA) **3851**

University of Tokyo. Institute for Nuclear Study. INS-TH. (JA ISSN 0563-7872) **3851**

University of Tokyo. Institute for Nuclear Study. INS-TL. (JA ISSN 0563-7880) **3851**

University of Tokyo. Institute for Nuclear Study. INS-TS. (JA) **3851**

University of Tokyo. Institute for Nuclear Study. Report. (JA ISSN 0495-7822) **3851**

University of Tokyo. Institute for Solid State Physics. Technical Report. Series A. (JA ISSN 0082-4798) **3835**

University of Tokyo. Institute for Solid State Physics. Technical Report. Series B. (JA ISSN 0082-4801) **3835**

University of Tokyo. Institute of Applied Microbiology. Reports. (JA ISSN 0082-481X) **468, 558**

University of Tokyo. Institute of Industrial Science. Report. see Tokyo Daigaku Seisan Gijutsu Kenkyujo Hokoku **4612**

University of Tokyo. Institute of Social Science. Annals. (JA ISSN 0563-8054) **4391**

University of Tokyo. Institute of Space and Aeronautical Science. Report. (JA ISSN 0372-1418) **64**

University of Tokyo. Ocean Research Institute. Bulletin/Tokyo Daigaku Kaiyo Kenkyujo. (JA ISSN 0564-6898) **1612**

University of Tokyo. University Museum. Bulletin/Tokyo Daigaku Sogo Kenkyu Shiryokan Kenkyu Hokoku. (JA) **4350**

University of Tokyo. University Museum. Collected Reprints. see Tokyo Daigaku Sogo Kenkyu Shiryokan Gyosekishu **4348**

University of Toledo. Business Research Center. Bibliographies. (US) **415, 697**

University of Toledo. Business Research Center. Miscellaneous Papers. (US) **697**

University of Toledo. Business Research Center. Newsletter. (US) **697**

University of Toledo. Business Research Center. Studies in Financial Institutions. (US) **802**

University of Toledo. Business Research Center. Studies in International Business. (US) **697, 923**

University of Toledo. Business Research Center. Working Papers. (US) **1030**

University of Toledo. Business Research Center. Working Papers in Operations Analysis see University of Toledo. Business Research Center. Working Papers **1030**

University of Toledo Law Review. (US ISSN 0042-0190) **2690**

University of Toronto. Centre of Criminology Library. Acquisitions List.(CN ISSN 0701-0524) **1525, 415**

University of Toronto. Computer Systems Research Group. Technical Reports see University of Toronto. Computer Systems Research Institute. Technical Reports **1439**

University of Toronto. Computer Systems Research Institute. Technical Reports. (CN ISSN 0834-1648) **1439**

†University of Toronto. Department of Electrical Engineering. Research Report. (CN ISSN 0082-514X) **5298**

University of Toronto. Department of Geography. Discussion Paper Series. (CN ISSN 0317-9893) **2265**

University of Toronto. Department of Mechanical Engineering. Technical Publication Series. (CN ISSN 0082-5182) **1940**

University of Toronto. Faculty of Forestry. Research Report. (CN) **2110, 459, 1549**

University of Toronto. Faculty of Law. Review. (CN ISSN 0381-1638) **2690**

University of Toronto. Institute for Aerospace Studies. Annual Progress Report. (CN ISSN 0082-5239) **64**

University of Toronto. Institute for Aerospace Studies. Report. (CN ISSN 0082-5255) **64**

University of Toronto. Institute for Aerospace Studies. Review. (CN ISSN 0082-5247) **64**

University of Toronto. Institute for Aerospace Studies. Technical Note. (CN ISSN 0082-5263) **64**

University of Toronto. Institute for Policy Analysis. Annual Report. (CN) **697**

University of Toronto. Institute for Policy Analysis. Working Paper Series. (CN ISSN 0829-4909) **697**

University of Toronto Alumni Magazine see University of Toronto Magazine **1328**

University of Toronto Bulletin. (CN) **1328**

University of Toronto Dental Journal. (CN ISSN 0843-5812) **3244**

University of Toronto Law Journal. (CN ISSN 0042-0220) **2691**

University of Toronto Magazine. (CN ISSN 0840-562X) **1328**

University of Toronto Medical Journal. (CN ISSN 0042-0239) **3160**

University of Toronto Quarterly. (CN ISSN 0042-0247) **2518**

University of Toronto Romance Series. (CN ISSN 0082-5336) **2972, 2850**

University of Toronto Undergraduate Dental Journal. (CN ISSN 0042-0255) **3244**

University of Toronto - York University. Joint Program in Transportation. Annual Report. (CN ISSN 0318-1251) **4660**

University of Tulsa. Department of English. Monograph Series see University of Tulsa. Monograph Series **2972**

University of Tulsa. Monograph Series. (US) **2972**

University of Turku. Psychological Research Reports. (FI ISSN 0359-0216) **4049**

University of Utah. Microwave Device and Physical Electronics Laboratory Quarterly Report. (US ISSN 0026-2870) **1779**

University of Utah Anthropological Papers. (US ISSN 0083-4947) **252**

University of Vaasa. Proceedings. Discussion Papers. (FI ISSN 0358-870X) **898**

University of Vaasa. Proceedings. Research Papers. see Vaasan Yliopisto. Julkaisuja. Tutkimuksia **899**

University of Vaasa. Proceedings. Teaching Aid Series. see Vaasan Korkeakoulu. Julkaisuja. Opetusmonisteita **899**

▼University of Virginia. Center for Public Service. Reports. (US) **3989**

University of Virginia. Declaration. (US) **1328**

University of Virginia Alumni News. (US ISSN 0195-8798) **1328**

University of Virginia News Letter. (US ISSN 0042-0271) **4076**

University of Waikato. Antarctic Research Unit. Report. (NZ ISSN 0110-2192) **1584, 459, 520, 558**

University of Warsaw. Department of Economy. Economic Paper. (PL ISSN 0860-5742) **697**

†University of Warwick Business Information Service. Occasional Review. (UK) **5298**

University of Warwick Library. Occasional Publications. (UK) **2790, 2325**

†University of Washington. Academic Computing Services. Newsletter. (US ISSN 0744-8821) **5298**

†University of Washington Medicine. (US ISSN 0094-2006) **5298**

†University of Washington Publications in Fisheries. (US ISSN 0085-7939) **5298**

University of Washington Publications on Asia see School of International Studies. Publications on Asia **2341**

University of Waterloo. Department of Geography. Occasional Papers. (CN) **2265**

University of Waterloo. Department of Geography. Publication Series. (CN) **2265, 1499**

University of Waterloo. Department of Geology. Working Papers Series see University of Waterloo. School of Urban and Regional Planning. Working Papers Series **1971**

University of Waterloo. Gazette. (CN ISSN 0042-031X) **1669**

University of Waterloo. School of Urban and Regional Planning. Working Papers Series. (CN) **1971, 2497**

University of Waterloo. Solid Mechanics Division. Papers. (CN ISSN 0317-7130) **1923**

University of Waterloo. Solid Mechanics Division. Reports. (CN ISSN 0317-7114) **1923**

University of Waterloo. Solid Mechanics Division. Studies Series. (CN ISSN 0318-3122) **1923**

University of Waterloo. Solid Mechanics Division. Technical Notes see University of Waterloo. Solid Mechanics Division. Reports **1923**

University of Waterloo Bibliography Series. (CN ISSN 0829-948X) **2796**

University of Waterloo Biology Series. (CN ISSN 0317-3348) **459**

University of Waterloo Courier. (CN ISSN 0227-2199) **1329**

†University of Western Australia. Asian Studies Centre. Monographs. (AT ISSN 1032-9684) **5298**

†University of Western Australia. Centre for East Asian Studies. Occasional Papers. (AT ISSN 0313-9581) **5298**

†University of Western Australia. Centre for South and Southeast Asian Studies. Research Papers. (AT ISSN 0155-0179) **5298**

University of Western Australia. Department of Music. Music Monograph. (AT) **3585**

University of Western Australia Law Review. (AT ISSN 0042-0328) **2691**

University of Western Ontario. Alumni
Gazette. (CN ISSN 0042-0344)
1329
University of Western Ontario. D.B.
Weldon Library. Library Bulletin. (CN
ISSN 0076-0595) 2790
University of Western Ontario. Gazette.
(CN) 1329
University of Western Ontario Medical
Journal. (CN ISSN 0042-0336)
3160
University of Western Ontario Series in
Philosophy of Science. (NE) 3785,
4350
University of Windsor. Newsline. (CN)
1329
University of Windsor Review. (CN
ISSN 0042-0352) 2887
University of Wisconsin. Bureau of
Business Research and Service.
Monographs see Wisconsin Business
Monographs 700
University of Wisconsin, Madison.
Applied Population Laboratory.
Population Notes. (US ISSN 0084-
0734) 3989
University of Wisconsin, Madison.
Applied Population Laboratory.
Population Series. (US ISSN 0084-
0742) 3989
University of Wisconsin, Madison.
Applied Population Laboratory.
Technical Series. (US) 3989
University of Wisconsin, Madison.
Engineering Experiment Station.
Annual Report. (US ISSN 0193-
9629) 3441
University of Wisconsin, Madison.
Institute for Research on Poverty.
Discussion Paper Series. (US) 4391
University of Wisconsin, Madison.
Institute for Research on Poverty.
Monograph Series. (US) 4391
University of Wisconsin, Madison.
Institute for Research on Poverty.
Reprint Series. (US ISSN 0084-
0769) 4391
University of Wisconsin, Madison.
Institute for Research on Poverty.
Special Report Series. (US) 4391
University of Wisconsin-Milwaukee.
Center for Latin America. Discussion
Paper Series. (US ISSN 0084-
0831) 2425
University of Wisconsin-Milwaukee.
Center for Latin America. Essay
Series. (US ISSN 0084-084X)
2425
University of Wisconsin-Milwaukee. Field
Station Bulletin. (US) 459, 1549
University of Wisconsin-Milwaukee Post
see U W M Post 1327
University of Witwatersrand,
Johannesburg. School of Mechanical
Engineering. Research Reports. (SA)
1940
University of Wollongong. Annual
Report. (AT ISSN 0313-6906)
1329
University of Wollongong. Calendar see
University of Wollongong.
Postgraduate Calendar 1329
University of Wollongong. Faculties
Sector Postgraduate Handbook see
University of Wollongong.
Postgraduate Calendar 1329
†University of Wollongong. Legislation.
(AT ISSN 0726-4844) 5298
University of Wollongong. Postgraduate
Calendar. (AT) 1329
University of Wollongong. Postgraduate
Handbook see University of
Wollongong. Postgraduate Calendar
1329
University of Wollongong. Research
Report. (AT ISSN 1032-0741)
1329
University of Wollongong.
Undergraduate Calendar. (AT) 1329
University of Wollongong.
Undergraduate Handbook see
University of Wollongong.
Undergraduate Calendar 1329
University of Wyoming. Contributions to
Geology. (US ISSN 0010-7980)
1584, 3661
†University of Wyoming American
Studies Conference. Proceedings.
(US) 5298

University of York. Centre for Southern
African Studies. Collected Papers.
(UK) 2335
University of York. Institute of Advanced
Architectural Studies. Research
Papers. (UK ISSN 0306-0624)
308
University of Zambia. Centre for
Continuing Education. Report of the
Annual Resident Tutors' Conference.
(ZA) 1687
University of Zambia. Centre for
Continuing Education. Report of the
Annual Staff Conference see
University of Zambia. Centre for
Continuing Education. Report of the
Annual Resident Tutors' Conference
1687
University of Zambia. School of
Humanities and Social Sciences.
Annual Report. (ZA) 1720
University Photographers' Association of
America Newsletter see U P A A
Newsletter 3797
University Press Book News. (US ISSN
1040-8991) 415, 4138
†University Publishing. (US ISSN
0191-4146) 5299
University Report see University Alumni
Report 1328
University Research in Business and
Economics: a Bibliography of (Year)
Publications. (US ISSN 0738-3215)
743
University Science and Technology. see
Daxue Keji 4306
University Scope. (US) 1329
University Series in Modern
Engineering.(US) 1839
University Star. (US) 1329
University Student. see Daxuesheng
1704
University Studies in Medieval and
Renaissance Literature. (US ISSN
0749-4149) 2325, 2972
University Studies on European
Integration. see Etudes Universitaires
sur l'Integration Europeenne 3956
University Times (Charlotte). (US)
1329
University Times (Los Angeles). (US)
1329
University Urban Programs. (US)
1720, 4076
Universo. (MX) 370
L'Universo. (IT ISSN 0042-0409)
2265
Univerza E. Kardelja v Ljubljani.
Biotehnicki Fakultet. Zbornik see
Univerza v Ljubljani. Veterinarska
Fakulteta. Zbornik 4817
Univerza Edvarda Kardelja v Ljubljani.
Filozofska Fakulteta. Oddelek za
Geografijo. Dela see Univerza v
Ljubljani. Filozofska Fakulteta.
Oddelek za Geografijo. Dela 2265
Univerza v Ljubljani. Filozofska
Fakulteta. Oddelek za Geografijo.
Dela. (XV) 2265, 1971
Univerza v Ljubljani. Veterinarska
Fakulteta. Zbornik. (XV) 4817
Univerzita J.E. Purkyne. Filozoficka
Fakulta. Sbornik Praci. A: Rada
Jazykovedna see Masarykova
Univerzita. Filozoficka Fakulta.
Sbornik Praci. A: Rada Jazykovedna
2828
Univerzita J.E. Purkyne. Filozoficka
Fakulta. Sbornik Praci. B: Rada
Filozoficka see Masarykova
Univerzita. Filozoficka Fakulta.
Sbornik Praci. B: Rada Filozoficka
3772
Univerzita J.E. Purkyne. Filozoficka
Fakulta. Sbornik Praci. C: Rada
Historicka see Masarykova
Univerzita. Filozoficka Fakulta.
Sbornik Praci. C: Rada Historicka
2374
Univerzita J.E. Purkyne. Filozoficka
Fakulta. Sbornik Praci. D: Rada
Literarnevedna see Masarykova
Univerzita. Filozoficka Fakulta.
Sbornik Praci. D: Rada
Literarnevedna 2937

Univerzita J.E. Purkyne. Filozoficka
Fakulta. Sbornik Praci. E: Rada
Archeologicko-Klasicka see
Masarykova Univerzita. Filozoficka
Fakulta. Sbornik Praci. E: Rada
Archeologicko-Klasicka 278
Univerzita J.E. Purkyne. Filozoficka
Fakulta. Sbornik Praci. F: Rada
Umenovedna see Masarykova
Univerzita. Filozoficka Fakulta.
Sbornik Praci. F: Rada Umenovedna
335
Univerzita J.E. Purkyne. Filozoficka
Fakulta. Sbornik Praci. G: Rada
Socialnevedna see Masarykova
Univerzita. Filozoficka Fakulta.
Sbornik Praci. G: Rada
Socialnevedna 897
Univerzita J.E. Purkyne. Filozoficka
Fakulta. Sbornik Praci. H: Rada
Hudebnevedna see Masarykova
Univerzita. Filozoficka Fakulta.
Sbornik Praci. H: Rada
Hudebnevedna 3562
Univerzita J.E. Purkyne. Filozoficka
Fakulta. Sbornik Praci. I: Rada
Pedagogicka - Psychologicka see
Masarykova Univerzita. Filozoficka
Fakulta. Sbornik Praci. I: Rada
Pedagogicka - Psychologicka 4035
Univerzita J.E. Purkyne. Filozoficka
Fakulta. Sbornik Praci. K: Rada
Germanisticko - Anglisticka see
Masarykova Univerzita. Filozoficka
Fakulta. Sbornik Praci. K: Rada
Germanisticko - Anglisticka 2828
Univerzita J.E. Purkyne. Filozoficka
Fakulta. Sbornik Praci. L: Rada
Romanisticka see Masarykova
Univerzita. Filozoficka Fakulta.
Sbornik Praci. L: Rada Romanisticka
2828
Univerzita Komenskeho. Filozoficka
Fakulta. Zbornik: Ethnologia Slavica.
(CS ISSN 0083-4106) 2059
Univerzita Komenskeho. Filozoficka
Fakulta. Zbornik: Graecolatina et
Orientalia. (CS ISSN 0083-4114)
1280, 3645, 3785
Univerzita Komenskeho. Filozoficka
Fakulta. Zbornik: Historica. (CS ISSN
0083-4122) 2325
Univerzita Komenskeho. Filozoficka
Fakulta. Zbornik: Informatika. (CS)
2790
†Univerzita Komenskeho. Filozoficka
Fakulta. Zbornik: Marxizmus-
Leninizmus. (CS) 5299
Univerzita Komenskeho. Filozoficka
Fakulta. Zbornik: Musaica. (CS ISSN
0083-4130) 348, 288, 3585
Univerzita Komenskeho. Filozoficka
Fakulta. Zbornik: Paedagogica. (CS
ISSN 0083-4165) 1670
Univerzita Komenskeho. Filozoficka
Fakulta. Zbornik: Philologica. (CS
ISSN 0083-4173) 2850, 2972
Univerzita Komenskeho. Filozoficka
Fakulta. Zbornik: Philosophica. (CS
ISSN 0083-4181) 3785
Univerzita Komenskeho. Filozoficka
Fakulta. Zbornik: Psychologica. (CS
ISSN 0083-419X) 4049
Univerzita Komenskeho. Filozoficka
Fakulta. Zbornik: Zurnalistika. (CS
ISSN 0083-422X) 2576
Univerzita Komenskeho. Pedagogicka
Fakulta. Katedra Specialnej
Pedagogiky. Zbornik. Paedagogica
Specialis. (CS) 1742
Univerzita Komenskeho. Pedagogicka
Fakulta v Trnave. Prirodne Vedy:
Biologia-Genetika. (CS) 547
Univerzita Komenskeho. Ustav
Marxismu-Leninizmu. Zbornik: Dejiny
Rogotnickeho Hnutia see Univerzita
Komenskeho. Filozoficka Fakulta.
Zbornik: Historica 2325
Univerzita Komenskeho. Ustav
Marxizmu-Leninizmu. Zbornik:
Politicka Ekonomia. (CS) 898, 887
Univerzita Komenskeho. Ustav
Marxizmu-Leninizmu. Zbornik:
Vedecky Komunizmus. (CS) 4391
Univerzita Komenskeho Trnave.
Pedagogicka Fakulta. Zbornik.
Spolocenske Vedy. Historia. (CS
ISSN 0139-5548) 2393

Univerzita Komenskeho v Bratislave so
Sidlom v Trnva. Pedagogicka Fakulta.
Zbornik see Univerzita Komenskeho
Trnave. Pedagogicke Fakulta.
Zbornik. Spolocenske Vedy. Historia
2393
Univerzita Komeskeho. Oddelenie
Liecebnej a Specialnej Pedagogiky.
Zbornik. Paedagogica Specialis see
Univerzita Komenskeho. Pedagogicka
Fakulta. Katedra Specialnej
Pedagogiky. Zbornik. Paedagogica
Specialis 1742
Univerzita Komenskeho. Ustav Marxismu-
Leninizmu. Zbornik: Marxistiska
Filozofia see Univerzita Komenskeho.
Filozoficka Fakulta. Zbornik:
Philosophica 3785
Univerzita P.J. Safariny. Ustav Mrxizmu-
Leninizmus. Zbornik: Marxizmus-
Leninizmus see Univerzita Pavla
Jozefa Safarika. Ustav Marxizmu-
Leninizmu. Zbornik Prac Ucitelov
5299
Univerzita Palackeho. Pedagogicka
Fakulta. Sbornik Praci: Cesky Jazyk a
Literatura. (CS) 2850, 2972
†Univerzita Pavla Jozefa Safarika. Ustav
Marxizmu-Leninizmu. Zbornik Prac
Ucitelov. (CS) 5299
Univerzitet Danas. (BN ISSN 0042-
0425) 1670
Univerzitet Svetozar Markovic u
Kragujevcu. Prirodno-Matematicki
Fakultet. Zbornik Radova/Faculty of
Science, Kragujevac. Collection of
Scientific Papers. (YU ISSN 0351-
6962) 4350
Univerzitet u Beogradu. Institut za
Botaniku i Botanicke Baste. Glasnik.
(YU) 520
Univerzitet u Novom Sadu. Prirodno-
Matematicki Fakultet. Zbornik
Radova. Serija za Matematiku. (YU
ISSN 0352-0900) 3061
Univerzitet u Sarajevu. Doktorske
Disertacije. Rezimei. (BN) 1681
Univerzitet u Sarajevu. Poljoprivredni
Fakultet. Radovi. (BN ISSN 0033-
8583) 127
Univerzitet u Zagrebu. Pravni Fakultet.
Zbornik. (CI ISSN 0350-2058)
2691, 898, 4455
Univerzitet vo Skoplje. Ekonomskiot
Fakultet. Godisnik/Universite de
Skopje. Faculte des Sciences
Economique. Annuaire. (XN) 698
Univesitatea din Brasov. Buletinul. Seria
A. Mecanica Aplicata. Constructii de
Masini. Electrotehnica see
Universitatea Transilvania din Brasov.
Buletinul. Seria A. Mecanica Aplicata.
Electrotehnica si Electronica.
Constructia de Masini si Tehnologia
Prelucrarii Metalelor 1940
Uniwersytet Gdanski. Wydzial Biologii,
Geografii i Oceanologii. Zeszyty
Naukowe. Biologia. (PL) 459
Uniwersytet Gdanski. Wydzial Biologii,
Geografii i Oceanologii. Zeszyty
Naukowe. Geografia. (PL) 2265
Uniwersytet Gdanski. Wydzial Biologii,
Geografii i Oceanologii. Zeszyty
Naukowe. Oceanografia. (PL) 1612
Uniwersytet Gdanski. Wydzial Biologii i
Nauk o Ziemi. Zeszyty Naukowe.
Biologia see Uniwersytet Gdanski.
Wydzial Biologii, Geografii i
Oceanologii. Zeszyty Naukowe.
Biologia 459
Uniwersytet Gdanski. Wydzial Biologii i
Nauk o Ziemi. Zeszyty Naukowe.
Geografia see Uniwersytet Gdanski.
Wydzial Biologii, Geografii i
Oceanologii. Zeszyty Naukowe.
Geografia 2265
Uniwersytet Gdanski. Wydzial Biologii i
Nauk o Ziemi. Zeszyty Naukowe.
Oceanografia see Uniwersytet
Gdanski. Wydzial Biologii, Geografii i
Oceanologii. Zeszyty Naukowe.
Oceanografia 1612
Uniwersytet Gdanski. Wydzial Ekonomiki
Produkcji. Zeszyty Naukowe.
Cybernetyka Ekonomiczna i
Informatyka. (PL ISSN 0208-4805)
1443

UNIWERSYTET GDANSKI

Uniwersytet Gdanski. Wydzial Ekonomiki Produkcji. Zeszyty Naukowe. Ekonomika i Organizacja Turystyki i Uslug. (PL) **4795**, 1086

Uniwersytet Gdanski. Wydzial Ekonomiki Produkcji. Zeszyty Naukowe. Finanse i Rachunek Ekonomiczny. (PL) **1086**

Uniwersytet Gdanski. Wydzial Ekonomiki Produkcji. Zeszyty Naukowe. Organizacja Pracy i Zarzadzanie. (PL ISSN 0208-4791) **1030**

Uniwersytet Gdanski. Wydzial Ekonomiki Produkcji. Zeszyty Naukowe. Zagadnienia Ekonomiki Przemyslu. (PL ISSN 0208-4783) **1086**

Uniwersytet Gdanski. Wydzial Ekonomiki Produkcji. Zeszyty Naukowe. Zagadnienia Finansowe see Uniwersytet Gdanski. Wydzial Ekonomiki Produkcji. Zeszyty Naukowe. Finanse i Rachunek Ekonomiczny **1086**

Uniwersytet Gdanski. Wydzial Ekonomiki Transportu. Zeszyty Naukowe. Ekonomika Handlu Zagranicznego. Prace i Materialy see Uniwersytet Gdanski. Wydzial Ekonomiki Transportu. Zeszyty Naukowe. Instytut Ekonomiki Handlu Zagranicznego. Prace i Materialy **923**

Uniwersytet Gdanski. Wydzial Ekonomiki Transportu. Zeszyty Naukowe. Ekonomika Transportu Ladowego. (PL ISSN 0208-4821) **4660**

Uniwersytet Gdanski. Wydzial Ekonomiki Transportu. Zeszyty Naukowe. Ekonomika Transportu Morskiego. (PL ISSN 0208-483X) **4741**

Uniwersytet Gdanski. Wydzial Ekonomiki Transportu. Zeszyty Naukowe. Instytut Ekonomiki Handlu Zagranicznego. Prace i Materialy. (PL) **923**

Uniwersytet Gdanski. Wydzial Ekonomiki Transportu. Zeszyty Naukowe. Instytut Ekonomii Politycznej. Prace i Materialy. (PL ISSN 0208-4813) **698**

Uniwersytet Gdanski. Wydzial Humanistyczny. Zeszyty Naukowe. Filologia Angielska. (PL ISSN 0208-5240) **2850**

Uniwersytet Gdanski. Wydzial Humanistyczny. Zeszyty Naukowe. Filologia Polska. Prace Jezykoznawcze. (PL ISSN 0302-2315) **2850**

Uniwersytet Gdanski. Wydzial Humanistyczny. Zeszyty Naukowe. Filologia Rosyjska. (PL ISSN 0208-4678) **2850**

Uniwersytet Gdanski. Wydzial Humanistyczny. Zeszyty Naukowe. Filozofia i Socjologia. (PL ISSN 0072-0453) **3785**

Uniwersytet Gdanski. Wydzial Humanistyczny. Zeszyty Naukowe. Historia. (PL ISSN 0072-0461) **2393**

Uniwersytet Gdanski. Wydzial Humanistyczny. Zeszyty Naukowe. Nauki Polityczne. (PL ISSN 0208-4732) **3932**

Uniwersytet Gdanski. Wydzial Humanistyczny. Zeszyty Naukowe. Pedagogika, Historia Wychowania. (PL ISSN 0072-047X) **1670**

Uniwersytet Gdanski. Wydzial Humanistyczny. Zeszyty Naukowe. Prace Historyczno-Literackie. (PL ISSN 0072-0488) **2972**, 2325

Uniwersytet Gdanski. Wydzial Humanistyczny. Zeszyty Naukowe. Psychologia. (PL ISSN 0208-4562) **4049**

Uniwersytet Gdanski. Wydzial Humanistyczny. Zeszyty Naukowe. Slawistyka. (PL ISSN 0208-4740) **2518**

Uniwersytet Gdanski. Wydzial Humanistyczny. Zeszyty Naukowe. Studia Scandinavica. (PL ISSN 0138-063X) **2850**

Uniwersytet Gdanski. Wydzial Humanystyczny. Zeszyty Naukowe. Studium Praktycznej Nauki Jezykow Obcych. (PL ISSN 0324-8895) **2850**, 1762

Uniwersytet Gdanski. Wydzial Matematyki, Fizyki i Chemii. Zeszyty Naukowe. Matematyka. (PL ISSN 0072-0402) **3061**

Uniwersytet Gdanski. Wydzial Matematyki, Fizyki i Chemii. Zeszyty Naukowe. Problemy Dydaktyki Fizyki.(PL ISSN 0208-4872) **3835**, 1762

Uniwersytet Gdanski. Wydzial Prawa i Administracji. Zeszyty Naukowe. Prawo. (PL ISSN 0208-4910) **2691**

Uniwersytet Gdanski. Wydzial Prawa i Administracji. Zeszyty Naukowe. Prace Instytutu Administracji i Zarzadzania see Uniwersytet Gdanski. Wydzial Prawa i Administracji. Zeszyty Naukowe. Prace z Zakresu Administracji i Zarzadzania **2691**

Uniwersytet Gdanski. Wydzial Prawa i Administracji. Zeszyty Naukowe. Prace z Zakresu Administracji i Zarzadzania. (PL) **2691**

Uniwersytet Gdanski. Wydzial Prawa i Administracji. Zeszyty Naukowe. Studia Iuridica Maritima. (PL ISSN 0860-374X) **2735**

Uniwersytet Gdanski. Wydzial Prawa i Administracji. Zeszyty Naukowe. Studia Prawno-Ustrojowe. (PL ISSN 0860-3731) **2691**

Uniwersytet Gdanski. Zeszyty Naukowe. Rozprawy i Monografie. (PL) **4350**

Uniwersytet Gdanski. Zeszyty Naukowe Studium Jezykow Obcych see Uniwersytet Gdanski. Wydzial Humanystyczny. Zeszyty Naukowe. Studium Praktycznej Nauki Jezykow Obcych **2850**

Uniwersytet im. Adama Mickiewicza w Poznaniu. Wydzial Biologii i Nauk of Ziemi. Prace. Seria Geologia see Geologia **1562**

Uniwersytet im. Adama Mickiewicza w Poznaniu. Wydzial Biologii i Nauk o Ziemi. Seria Antropologia see Antropologia **235**

Uniwersytet im. Adama Mickiewicza w Poznaniu. Wydzial Biologii i Nauk o Ziemi. Seria Biologia see Biologia **431**

Uniwersytet im. Adama Mickiewicza w Poznaniu. Wydzial Biologii i Nauk o Ziemi. Seria Zoologia see Zoologia **594**

Uniwersytet im. Adama Mickiewicza w Poznaniu. Wydzial Biologii i Nauk o Ziemi. Zeszyty Naukowe. Seria Geografia see Geografia **2249**

Uniwersytet im. Adama Mickiewicza w Poznaniu. Wydzial Filologiczny. Seria Filologia Angielska see Filologia Angielska **2814**

Uniwersytet im. Adama Mickiewicza w Poznaniu. Wydzial Filologiczny. Seria Filologia Klasyczna see Filologia Klasyczna **2814**

Uniwersytet im. Adama Mickiewicza w Poznaniu. Wydzial Filozoficzno-Historyczny. Prace. Seria Archeologia see Archeologia (Poznan) **264**

Uniwersytet im. Adama Mickiewicza w Poznaniu. Wydzial Filozoficzno-Historyczny. Prace. Seria Filozofia-Logika see Filozofia-Logika **3767**

Uniwersytet im. Adama Mickiewicza w Poznaniu. Wydzial Filozoficzno-Historyczny. Seria Etnografia see Etnografia **2054**

Uniwersytet im. Adama Mickiewicza w Poznaniu. Wydzial Historyczny. Prace. Seria Psychologia-Pedagogika see Psychologia-Pedagogika **4040**

Uniwersytet im. Adama Mickiewicza w Poznaniu. Wydzial Matematyki, Fizyki i Chemii. Prace. Seria Akustyka see Akustyka **3858**

Uniwersytet im. Adama Mickiewicza w Poznaniu. Wydzial Matematyki, Fizyki i Chemii. Seria Astronomia see Astronomia **361**

Uniwersytet im. Adama Mickiewicza w Poznaniu. Wydzial Matematyki, Fizyki i Chemii. Seria Chemia see Chemia **1172**

Uniwersytet im. Adama Mickiewicza w Poznaniu. Wydzial Matematyki, Fizyki i Chemii. Seria Fizyka see Fizyka **3818**

Uniwersytet im. Adama Mickiewicza w Poznaniu. Wydzial Prawa. Prace see Prawo **2667**

Uniwersytet im. Adama Mickiewicza w Poznaniu. Zeszyty Naukowe. Seria Historia Sztuki see Historia Sztuki **328**

Uniwersytet Jagiellonski. Zeszyty Naukowe. Acta Matematica. (PL) **3061**

Uniwersytet Jagiellonski. Zeszyty Naukowe. Prace Archeologiczne. (PL ISSN 0083-4300) **288**

Uniwersytet Jagiellonski. Zeszyty Naukowe. Prace Botaniczne. (PL ISSN 0302-8585) **520**

Uniwersytet Jagiellonski. Zeszyty Naukowe. Prace Chemiczne. (PL ISSN 0083-4319) **1190**

Uniwersytet Jagiellonski. Zeszyty Naukowe. Prace Etnograficzne. (PL ISSN 0083-4327) **252**

Uniwersytet Jagiellonski. Zeszyty Naukowe. Prace Fizyczne. (PL ISSN 0083-4335) **3835**

Uniwersytet Jagiellonski. Zeszyty Naukowe. Prace Geograficzne. (PL ISSN 0083-4343) **2266**

Uniwersytet Jagiellonski. Zeszyty Naukowe. Prace Historyczne. (PL ISSN 0083-4351) **2393**

Uniwersytet Jagiellonski. Zeszyty Naukowe. Prace Historycznoliterackie. (PL ISSN 0083-436X) **2972**

Uniwersytet Jagiellonski. Zeszyty Naukowe. Prace Jezykoznawcze. (PL ISSN 0083-4378) **2850**

Uniwersytet Jagiellonski. Zeszyty Naukowe. Prace Prawnicze. (PL ISSN 0083-4394) **2691**

Uniwersytet Jagiellonski. Zeszyty Naukowe. Prace Psychologiczno-Pedagogiczne. (PL ISSN 0083-4408) **4049**, 1670

Uniwersytet Jagiellonski. Zeszyty Naukowe. Prace z Biologii Molekularnej. (PL ISSN 0137-2351) **459**

Uniwersytet Jagiellonski. Zeszyty Naukowe. Prace z Historii Sztuki. (PL ISSN 0083-4424) **348**

Uniwersytet Jagiellonski. Zeszyty Naukowe. Prace z Nauk Politycznych. (PL ISSN 0137-2378) **3932**

Uniwersytet Jagiellonski. Zeszyty Naukowe. Prace Zoologiczne. (PL ISSN 0083-4416) **593**

Uniwersytet Jagiellonski, Krakow. Zeszyty Naukowe. Prace z Logiki see Reports on Mathematical Logic **3778**

Uniwersytet Lodzki. Prace. (PL ISSN 0076-034X) **2518**

Uniwersytet Lodzki. Zeszyty Naukowe. Seria 1: Nauki Humanistyczno-Spoleczne see Acta Universitatis Lodziensis: Folia Philosophica **3760**

Uniwersytet Lodzki. Zeszyty Naukowe. Seria 2: Nauki Matematyczno-Przyrodnicze see Acta Universitatis Lodziensis: Folia Biochimica et Biophysica **470**

Uniwersytet Mikolaja Kopernika, Torun. Nauki Humanistyczno-Spoleczne. Archeologia see Acta Universitatis Nicolai Copernici. Archeologia **260**

Uniwersytet Mikolaja Kopernika, Torun. Nauki Humanistyczno-Spoleczne. Filozofia see Acta Universitatis Nicolai Copernici. Filozofia **3760**

Uniwersytet Mikolaja Kopernika, Torun. Nauki Humanistyczno-Spoleczne. Filologia Polska see Acta Universitatis Nicolai Copernici. Filologia Polska **2801**

Uniwersytet Mikolaja Kopernika, Torun. Nauki Humanistyczno-Spoleczne. Historia see Acta Universitatis Nicolai Copernici. Historia **2347**

Uniwersytet Mikolaja Kopernika, Torun. Nauki Humanistyczno-Spoleczne. Prawo see Acta Universitatis Nicolai Copernici. Prawo **2594**

Uniwersytet Mikolaja Kopernika, Torun. Nauki Humanistyczno-Spoleczne. Socjologia see Acta Universitatis Nicolai Copernici. Socjologia Wychowania **1614**

Uniwersytet Mikolaja Kopernika, Torun. Nauki Matematyczno-Przyrodnicze. Biologia see Acta Universitatis Nicolai Copernici. Biologia **426**

Uniwersytet Slaski w Katowicach. Prace Matematyczne see Uniwersytet Slaski w Katowicach. Prace Naukowe. Annales Mathematicae Silesianae **3061**

Uniwersytet Slaski w Katowicach. Prace Naukowe. Acta Biologica Silesiana. (PL ISSN 0860-2441) **459**

Uniwersytet Slaski w Katowicach. Prace Naukowe. Annales Mathematicae Silesianae. (PL) **3061**

Uniwersytet Slaski w Katowicach. Prace Naukowe. Fizyka i Chemia Metali. (PL ISSN 0208-578X) **3422**

Uniwersytet Slaski w Katowicach. Prace Naukowe. Fotointerpretacja w Geografii. (PL ISSN 0071-8076) **2266**

Uniwersytet Slaski w Katowicach. Prace Naukowe. Geographia: Studia et Dissertationes. (PL ISSN 0208-5054) **2266**

Uniwersytet Slaski w Katowicach. Prace Naukowe. Geologia. (PL ISSN 0208-5534) **1584**

Uniwersytet Slaski w Katowicach. Prace Naukowe. Historia i Wspolczesnosc. (PL ISSN 0137-3277) **2325**

Uniwersytet Slaski w Katowicach. Prace Naukowe. Jezyk Artystyczny. (PL ISSN 0209-3731) **2850**

Uniwersytet Slaski w Katowicach. Prace Naukowe. Kras i Speleologia. (PL ISSN 0137-5482) **1584**

Uniwersytet Slaski w Katowicach. Prace Naukowe. Neophilologica. (PL ISSN 0208-5550) **2850**

Uniwersytet Slaski w Katowicach. Prace Naukowe. Pedagogika Pracy Kulturalno-Oswiatowej. (PL ISSN 0208-5526) **1670**

Uniwersytet Slaski w Katowicach. Prace Naukowe. Prace Historycznoliterackie. (PL ISSN 0208-5453) **2973**

Uniwersytet Slaski w Katowicach. Prace Naukowe. Prace Jezykoznawcze. (PL ISSN 0208-5445) **2851**

Uniwersytet Slaski w Katowicach. Prace Naukowe. Prace Pedagogiczne. (PL ISSN 0208-5429) **1670**

Uniwersytet Slaski w Katowicach. Prace Naukowe. Prace Wydzialu Techniki. (PL ISSN 0208-5402) **1839**

Uniwersytet Slaski w Katowicach. Prace Naukowe. Prace z Nauk Spolecznych. Folia Philosophica. (PL ISSN 0208-5437) **3785**

Uniwersytet Slaski w Katowicach. Prace Naukowe. Problemy Prawa Przewozowego. (PL ISSN 0208-5518) **2691**, 4660

Uniwersytet Slaski w Katowicach. Prace Naukowe. Problemy Prawne Gornictwa. (PL ISSN 0208-5488) **2691**, 3497

Uniwersytet Slaski w Katowicach. Prace Naukowe. Problemy Prawne Handlu Zagranicznego. (PL ISSN 0208-5496) **2691**, 923

Uniwersytet Slaski w Katowicach. Prace Naukowe. Psychologiczne Problemy Funkcjonowania Czlowieka w Sytuacji Pracy. (PL ISSN 0208-5569) **4049**

Uniwersytet Slaski w Katowicach. Prace Naukowe. Rusycystyczne Studia Literaturoznawcze. (PL ISSN 0208-5038) **2973**

Uniwersytet Slaski w Katowicach. Prace Naukowe. Studia Iuridica Silesiana. (PL ISSN 0208-502X) **2691**, 2706

Uniwersytet Slaski w Katowicach. Prace Naukowe. Z Problematyki Prawa Pracy i Polityki Socjalnej. (PL ISSN 0208-5003) **2691**, **3932**, **4455**
Uniwersytet Slaski w Katowicach. Prace Naukowe. Z Teorii i Praktyki Dydaktycznej Jezyka Polskiego. (PL ISSN 0208-5011) **2851**, **1670**
Uniwersytet Slaski w Katowicach. Prace Nukowe. Problemy Prawa Karnego. (PL ISSN 0208-5577) **2714**
Uniwersytet Warszawski. Instytut Archeologii. Studia Archeologiczne see Uniwersytet Warszawski. Instytut Archeologii. Studia i Materialy Archeologiczne **289**
Uniwersytet Warszawski. Instytut Archeologii. Studia i Materialy Archeologiczne. (PL ISSN 0208-4600) **289**
Uniwersytet Warszawski. Instytut Nauk Politycznych. Zeszyty Naukowe. (PL ISSN 0137-5822) **3932**
Uniwersytet Warszawski. Wydzial Geografii i Studiow Regionalnych. Prace i Studia Geograficzne. (PL ISSN 0208-4589) **2266**
Uniwersytet Warszawski. Wydzial Geologii. Biuletyn Geologiczny. (PL ISSN 0067-9003) **1584**
Uniwersytet Warszawski. Wydzial Nauk Ekonomicznych. Ekonomia. (PL ISSN 0137-3056) **698**
Uniwersytet Wroclawski. Instytut Geograficzny. Prace. Seria A: Geografia Fizyczna. (PL) **2266**
Uniwersytet Wroclawski. Instytut Geograficzny. Prace. Seria B: Geografia Spoleczna i Ekonomiczna. (PL ISSN 0137-1088) **2266**
Uniwersytet Wroclawski. Prace Pedagogiczne i Psychologia see Acta Universitatis Wratislaviensis. Prace Pedagogiczne **1614**
UNIX in the Office. (US ISSN 0887-3054) **1439**
Unix International Gazette. (US) **1481**
Unix Journal see Unix Software Journal **1481**
UNIX - Mail. (GW ISSN 0176-8654) **1481**
UNIX Review. (US ISSN 0742-3136) **1432**, **1439**
Unix Software Journal. (US) **1481**
UNIX Today. (US) **1440**, **1465**
UNIX Video Quarterly. (US) **1402**
UNIX World. (US ISSN 0739-5922) **1455**
Unknown. (US ISSN 1042-7899) **3671**
Unlisted Drugs. (US ISSN 0042-0441) **3745**
Unlisted Drugs Index - Guide. (US ISSN 8755-7142) **3745**
Unlisted Market Guide see Market Guide Over-the-Counter Stock Edition **955**
Unmanned Systems. (US ISSN 0892-4023) **3474**, **1411**
Unmarried Parents Today. (US) **4423**, **2691**
†Unmask. (US) **5299**
Unmuzzled Ox. (US ISSN 0049-5557) **3008**, **2887**
Unnatkrishi/Progress in Agriculture. (II ISSN 0566-2540) **127**
Unpublished and Unnumbered Treaties Index see United States International Treaties Today **5296**
Unscheduled Events. (US ISSN 0042-0468) **4455**, **4114**
Unschoolers Network. (US ISSN 1057-1043) **1762**, **1245**
Unsearchable Riches. (US ISSN 0042-0476) **4208**
Unser Arbeitsbrief. (GW) **1245**
Unser Betrieb. (GW ISSN 0343-8198) **3497**
Unser Bocholt. (GW) **2192**
Unser Bremerhaven. (GW) **3932**
Unser Dorfblaettchen. (GW) **3932**
Unser Land (Berlin). (GW) **128**
Unser Land (Passau). (GW) **128**
Unser Milchvieh. (GW) **204**
Unser Neustadt. (AU ISSN 0042-0484) **1499**, **1971**, **2325**
Unser Niederland. (GW) **2393**
Unser Oberschlesien. (GW) **2393**
Unser Pferd. (GW) **4539**

Unser Pommern see Pommern **340**
Unser Schaffen. (AU ISSN 0042-0492) **2296**
Unser Tsait. (US ISSN 0042-0506) **2887**
Unser Wald. (GW) **2110**
Unser Wanderbote. (GW) **4496**, **4521**
Unsere Alte Liebe. (GW) **4530**
Unsere Archive. (GW) **2325**
Unsere Heimat. (GW ISSN 0937-1508) **2192**
Unsere Heimat (Vienna). (AU ISSN 0502-6938) **2393**
Unsere Heimat (Wohlen). (SZ) **2393**
▼Unsere Illustrierte. (GW) **2192**
†Unsere Jagd. (GW ISSN 0566-2621) **5299**
Unsere Jugend. (GW ISSN 0342-5258) **1245**
Unsere Kunstdenkmaeler/Nos Monuments d'Art et d'Histoire/I Nostri Monumenti Storici. (SZ ISSN 0566-263X) **308**, **2393**
Unsere Sammlung see Katholische Oeffentliche Buecherei **2766**
Unsere Stadt. (GW) **3932**
Unsere Windhunde. (GW) **3714**
Unsere Wirtschaft. (GW ISSN 0042-0549) **823**
Unsere Zeitung see Presse und Sprache **2574**
†Unsin. (IT) **5299**
†Unspeakable Visions of the Individual. (US ISSN 0049-559X) **5299**
Unter der Dorflinde im Odenwald. (GW) **2192**
Unter Uns. (GW) **2296**, **4854**
Unterhaltungskunst see Journal fuer Unterhaltungskunst **4634**
Der Untermieter. (GW) **1670**
Unternehmer. (GW) **1030**
Unternehmer. (AU ISSN 0042-0581) **4114**
Die Unternehmerin. (GW) **698**
Die Unternehmung. (SZ ISSN 0042-059X) **1030**
Unternehmung und Unternehmungsfuehrung. (SZ ISSN 0083-4548) **1030**
Unternehmungsfuehrung im Gewerbe see Chef-Magazin fuer Klein- und Mittelbetriebe **1073**
Unterricht Biologie. (GW) **459**, **1762**
Unterrichtsblaetter fuer die Bundeswehrverwaltung. (GW ISSN 0042-0611) **4076**
Unterrichtspraxis. (US ISSN 0042-062X) **2851**
Unterrichtswissenschaft. (GW ISSN 0340-4099) **1670**
▼Unterschiede. (GW ISSN 0939-5474) **4854**, **1670**
Die Unterstufe. (GW ISSN 0042-0638) **1670**
Untersuchungen zur Deutschen Literaturgeschichte. (GW ISSN 0083-4564) **2973**
Untersuchungen zur Sprach- und Literaturgeschichte der Romanischen Voelker. (GW ISSN 0083-4580) **2851**
Unterwegs (Leverkusen). (GW) **1269**
Unterwegs (Munich). (GW ISSN 0930-1313) **4208**
Untitled. (US ISSN 0163-7916) **3798**
Unuci. (IT) **3474**
Uomini & Business. (IT) **698**
Uomini e Idee. (IT ISSN 0042-0646) **2973**, **348**, **4049**
Uomini e Libri. (IT ISSN 0042-0654) **2887**
Uomo & Cultura. (IT) **252**
Uomo Citta Territorio. (IT) **2206**
Uomo Collezioni. (IT) **1295**
Uomo Harper's Bazaar. (IT) **1295**
Uomo Mare. (IT ISSN 1120-7752) **4496**
Uomo Vogue. (IT ISSN 1120-7760) **1295**
Uongori: Journal of Management Development. (TZ ISSN 0856-1435) **1030**
Uongozi. (TZ) **1030**
Uoorkomen. (NE) **3622**
Up Here. (CN ISSN 0828-4253) **4795**, **2179**
Up-To-Date see Milton Chronicles **2414**

Up-to-Date Civil Reference see Dhaka Law Reports: Civil Digest **2618**
Up-to-Date Price Magazine. (US) **1055**
Up with People News. (US) **4208**
Upbeat. (SA ISSN 0257-8697) **1269**
Upbeat. Lexington Philharmonic Society Newsletter. (US) **3585**
Upchurch Bulletin. (US) **2166**
Update see Maine. Arts Commission. Newsletter **2511**
Update. (UK ISSN 0301-5718) **3160**
Update. (HK) **3160**
Update. (SA ISSN 0258-929X) **3160**
▼Update. (SP) **3160**
†Update. (AT) **5299**
Update (Aarhus) see Areopagus **4163**
†Update (Alexandria). (US ISSN 0162-945X) **5299**
Update (Bridgetown). (BB) **2790**
†Update (Columbia, 1971). (US) **5299**
Update (Gainesville). (US) **3244**
Update (LaCrosse). (US) **823**
†Update (Lansing). (US) **5299**
Update (Louisville). (US) **823**
Update (Massapequa). (US) **2236**
Update (Reston). (US) **3585**, **1762**
Update (Rexdale). (CN) **4749**
Update (Rochester). (US) **1508**
Update (Santa Clara). (US) **1779**
Update (Washington). (US ISSN 0160-9203) **2296**, **2790**
Update (Washington, 1985). (US) **887**, **1055**
Update C S L. (Connecticut State Library) (US) **2790**
Update Central America. (US) **3976**
†Update: Dental Edition. (US) **5299**
†Update in Critical Care Medicine. (CN) **5299**
Update in Intensive Care and Emergency Medicine. (US) **3160**
Update Newsletter. (US) **802**
Update On Computer Audit, Control and Security see Computer Audit Update **1433**
Update on Guatemala. (US) **3932**, **2425**
Update on Law-Related Education. (US ISSN 0147-8648) **2691**, **1762**
Update Postgraduate Centre Series. (UK) **3160**
Update Tahiti see Tahiti Sun Press **4788**
Update: The Executive's Purchasing Advisor. (US) **1062**, **1402**
Update U S S R. (US ISSN 0884-6227) **3976**
Update: Waste Disposal, Recycling, Resource Recovery. (US) **4114**
Updating School Board Policies. (US) **1732**
Upfront. (UK) **4423**
Upholstered Furniture Action Council Volunteer see U F A C Volunteer **2035**
Upholstered Furniture Action Council Year) see U F A C (Year) **2035**
†Upholstering Today. (US ISSN 0744-138X) **5299**
Upholstery Design & Manufacturing. (US) **2562**
Upholstery Manufacturing see Upholstery Design & Manufacturing **2562**
Uplift. (II ISSN 0377-6352) **4423**
Upokul. (BG) **2266**
Upper and Lower Case see U & l c **4006**
Upper Case. (US) **2544**
Upper Gastrointestinal Tumors--Diagnosis, Treatment see I C R D B Cancergram: Upper Gastrointestinal Tumors - Diagnosis, Treatment **3175**
Upper India Motorist. (II) **4704**
Upper Midwest Council. (Reports). (US) **887**
Upper Midwest Economic Study. Progress Report see Upper Midwest Council. (Reports) **887**
Upper Midwest Economic Study. Technical Paper see Upper Midwest Council. (Reports) **887**
Upper Midwest Economic Study. Urban Report see Upper Midwest Council. (Reports) **887**
Upper Midwest Report. (US) **823**

Upper Room. (US ISSN 0042-0735) **4252**, **2296**
▼Upper Silesian Museum in Bytom. Annals. Entomology. (PL ISSN 0867-1966) **538**
Upper Snake River Valley Historical Quarterly see Snake River Echoes **2422**
†Upper South Carolina Genealogy & History. (US) **5299**
Upper Triad. (US) **3785**
Upper Volta. Direction de l'Hydraulique et de l'Equipement Rural. Service I.R.H. Rapport d'Activites see Burkina Faso. Direction de l'Hydraulique et de l'Equipement Rural. Service I.R.H. Rapport d'Activites **4822**
Upper Volta. Direction des Eaux et Forets et de la Conservation des Sols. Rapport Annuel. see Burkina Faso. Direction des Eaux et Forets et de la Conservation des Sols. Rapport Annuel **2096**
Upper Volta. Institut National de la Statistique et de la Demographie. Bulletin Annuaire d'Information Statistique et Economique see Burkina Faso. Institut National de la Statistique et de la Demographie. Bulletin Annuaire d'Information Statistique et Economique **707**
Upper Volta. Service des Statistiques Agricoles. Annuaire see Burkina Faso. Service des Statistiques Agricoles. Annuaire **81**
Uppsala Ionospheric Observatory. Scientific Reports see Swedish Institute of Space Physics. Uppsala Division. Scientific Reports **3833**
Uppsala Ionospheric Observatory. Technical Reports see Swedish Center of Space Physics. Uppsala Division. Technical Reports **3833**
Uppsala Journal of Medical Sciences. (SW ISSN 0300-9734) **3161**
Uppsala Studies in Cultural Anthropology. (SW ISSN 0348-5099) **252**
Uppsala Studies in Economic History. (SW ISSN 0346-6493) **898**
Uppsala Studies in Education. (SW ISSN 0347-1314) **1670**
Uppsala Universitet. Geological Institution. Bulletin. (SW) **1584**
Uppsala University. Department of Sociology. Research Reports. (SW ISSN 0502-7527) **4455**
Upravlyayushchie Sistemy i Mashiny. (KR ISSN 0130-5395) **1440**, **1443**
Upright Ostrich. (US) **1119**, **128**
Upriver - Downriver. (US) **1971**
†Upshaw Family Journal. (US ISSN 0098-8960) **5299**
Upside. (US ISSN 1052-0341) **967**
UPstate Magazine. (US ISSN 0889-9991) **2236**, **348**, **4795**
Upstate New York Directory of Manufacturers. (US) **1157**
Upstream see New Contrast **2942**
Upstream. (US) **3008**, **2887**
Uptime. (US) **1474**
Uptime Lifestyles. (US) **1474**
†Upton Sinclair Quarterly. (US ISSN 0197-8381) **5299**
Uptown. (US) **2027**
Uptown Magazine. (CN) **2179**
UpTrend. (CN) **967**, **698**
Upward see Event **4238**
Upwellings. (US ISSN 0886-2664) **4830**, **1499**, **1971**, **2050**
L'Uquoi. (CN) **1329**
Ur. (UK ISSN 0143-1366) **2027**
†Ur- und Fruehzeit. (GW ISSN 0170-5725) **5299**
Uradni Vestnik Obcin Ormoz in Ptuj. (XV ISSN 0042-0778) **4096**
Ural-Altaic Yearbook. see Ural-Altaische Jahrbuecher **2393**
Ural-Altaische Jahrbuecher/Ural-Altaic Yearbook. (US ISSN 0042-0786) **2393**
Ural-Altaische Jahrbuecher. Neue Folge. (GW ISSN 0174-0652) **2851**
Uralic and Altaic Series see Indiana University. Research Institute for Inner Asian Studies. Uralic and Altaic Series **2818**
Urania. (PL ISSN 0042-0794) **371**

URANIA

Urania. (IT) **2985**
†Urania. (GW ISSN 0049-562X) **5299**
†Urania Universum. (GW) **5299**
Uranium: Resources, Production and Demand/Uranium: Ressources, Production et Demande. (FR) **3423**, 1810
Uranium: Ressources, Production et Demande. see Uranium: Resources, Production and Demand **3423**
Urban Abstracts. (UK) **4083**, 24, 1975
Urban Abstracts Series 1: Policy see Urban Abstracts **4083**
Urban Academic Librarian. (US ISSN 0276-9298) **2790**
Urban Affairs Abstracts. (US ISSN 0300-6859) **4083**, 24
Urban Affairs Annual Reviews. (US ISSN 0083-4688) **2497**
Urban Affairs Association Communication. (US) **2497**, 4391
Urban Affairs Quarterly. (US ISSN 0042-0816) **2497**, 4391
Urban Analysis and Public Management see Journal of Urban Analysis and Public Management **2490**
Urban and Regional Research in Denmark see Oversigt over By- og Regionforskning **5254**
†Urban and Regional Research in Denmark. (DK ISSN 0105-9459) **5299**
Urban and Rural Construction. see Chengxiang Jianshe **2485**
Urban and Rural Planning Thought. (IL ISSN 0042-0824) **308**, 4076
Urban and Social Change Review. (US ISSN 0042-0832) **4423**, 2497
Urban Anthropology and Studies of Cultural Systems and World Economic Development. (US ISSN 0894-6019) **252**, 936, 4455
Urban Business Magazine. (US) **698**
Urban Data Service Report see Baseline Data Report **4084**
Urban Design and Preservation Quarterly. (US) **2498**, 308
Urban Development Corporation. Annual Report. (JM) **2498**
Urban Development Information Service.(UK) **2498**
Urban Edge. (UN) **936**
Urban Education. (US ISSN 0042-0859) **1670**
Urban Finance. see Chengshi Jinrong **772**
Urban Forest. (CN ISSN 0048-1858) **2110**
Urban Forests. (US ISSN 1052-2484) **2110**
Urban Forests Forum see Urban Forests **2110**
▼Urban Forum. (SA ISSN 1015-3802) **2498**
Urban Foundation. Annual Review. (SA) **2498**
Urban Foundation. Progress Report see Urban Foundation. Annual Review **2498**
Urban Futures Idea Exchange see Urban Outlook **2498**
Urban Geography. (US ISSN 0272-3638) **2498**, 2266
Urban Georgia see Georgia's Cities **4088**
Urban Growth Indicators and Residential Activity Permit Report see Shelby County Urban Development Report **2496**
Urban History Review/Revue d'Histoire Urbaine. (CN ISSN 0703-0428) **2425**
Urban History Yearbook. (UK ISSN 0306-0845) **2394**, 4391
Urban India. (II) **2498**
†Urban Insights Monograph Series. (US ISSN 0736-6272) **5299**
Urban Institute. Annual Report. (US ISSN 0092-7481) **698**, 4391
Urban Institute. Policy and Research Report. (US ISSN 0741-8485) **698**, 4391
Urban Institute Report see Urban Institute. Annual Report **698**
Urban Issues. (AT) **2498**
Urban Issues. see Chengshi Wenti **4368**

Urban Land. (US ISSN 0042-0891) **2498**
Urban Land Institute Project Reference File. (US) **2498**, 4159
Urban Lawyer. (US ISSN 0042-0905) **2691**, 4076
Urban League News. (US) **3948**
Urban League of Greater New York. Annual Report see New York Urban League. Annual Report **4415**
Urban League Review. (US ISSN 0147-1740) **2027**, 3948, 4455
Urban Libraries Exchange. (US) **2790**
Urban Life see Journal of Contemporary Ethnography **4440**
Urban Mass Transportation Abstracts. (US ISSN 0090-8223) **4668**, 24
Urban Observers see Eyepiece **364**
Urban Outlook. (US ISSN 0732-8265) **2498**
Urban Perspectives. (KE ISSN 1052-729X) **2498**
Urban Policy & Research. (AT ISSN 0811-1146) **2498**
Urban Profile. (US ISSN 1049-9695) **2027**
Urban Psychiatry. Journal. (US) **3355**, 4455
Urban Reform and Development. see Chengshi Gaige yu Fazhan **2485**
Urban Research Review. (US ISSN 0732-7277) **4391**
†Urban Resources. (US ISSN 0741-1308) **5299**
The Urban Review. (US ISSN 0042-0972) **1670**, 4456
Urban, State, and Local Law Newsletter. (US ISSN 0195-7686) **4096**, 2691
Urban Studies. (UK ISSN 0042-0980) **2498**, 4456
Urban Studies. see Chengshi Yanjiu **4368**
Urban Studies Yearbook. (AT) **2498**
Urban Transport. see Varosi Kozlekedes **4716**
Urban Transport News. (US) **4660**
Urban Transportation Abstracts. (US ISSN 0734-0648) **4668**
Urban Transportation Monitor. (US ISSN 1040-4880) **4660**
Urban Wildlife. (UK ISSN 0951-6425) **1499**
Urban Wildlife Manager's Notebook. (US ISSN 0882-584X) **459**, 3869
Urban Wildlife News. (US ISSN 0882-5858) **459**, 1499, 1971
Urban Wildlife News. (UK ISSN 0268-2664) **1499**
Urbane Gorilla. (UK ISSN 0142-128X) **3008**
Urbanisme. (FR ISSN 0042-1014) **2498**
Urbanizacion, Migraciones y Cambios en la Sociedad Peruana. (PE) **252**, 4456
†Urbanology. (AT ISSN 0310-5601) **5299**
Urbanus see Urbanus - Raizirr **2973**
Urbanus - Raizirr. (US) **2973**, 348, 3008
Urbapress. (FR) **635**
Urbe. (IT ISSN 0042-1030) **2887**
Urch, Harris & Co. Ltd. Stamp Digest see U H Stamp Digest **5293**
Urdon. see Jordan **2208**
†Al Urdun. (US ISSN 0198-635X) **5299**
Ure & Optik. (DK) **2566**
Uremia Investigation see Renal Failure **3389**
Urethane Abstracts. (US ISSN 0149-1342) **3868**
Urethane Plastics and Products. (US ISSN 0049-5700) **3868**, 1860
Urethanes Technology. (UK ISSN 0265-637X) **4294**
Urgences Medicales. (FR ISSN 0923-2524) **3161**
Urgent Action Bulletin. (UK) **3948**, 252
Urgentis Chirurgiae Commentaria see Journal of Emergency Surgery and Intensive Care **3380**
Urja. (II ISSN 0378-9535) **1797**, 1910, 3703
▼Urja Oil and Gas International. (II ISSN 0971-2038) **3703**

Urner Barry's Price-Current. (US) **2083**, 227
Urner Barry's Price Current (West Coast Edition). (US) **2083**, 227
Uro-Gram. (US) **3390**
▼Uro-Imaging. (GW ISSN 0938-8184) **3390**
Urob - Udelej si Sam. (CS) **4612**
Uroboros. (US ISSN 0146-8510) **3008**
▼Urodinamica, Neurourology, Urodynamics and Continence. (IT ISSN 1120-5989) **3390**
Der Urologe. Section A. (GW ISSN 0340-2592) **3390**
Der Urologe. Section B. (GW) **3390**
Urologe-Ausgabe B see Der Urologe. Section B **3390**
Urologia. (IT ISSN 0042-112X) **3390**
Urologia Internationalis. (SZ ISSN 0042-1138) **3390**
Urologic Clinics of North America. (US ISSN 0094-0143) **3390**
Urologic Nursing. (US) **3390**, 3287
Urologic Radiology. (US ISSN 0171-1091) **3390**, 3363
Urological Research. (GW ISSN 0300-5623) **3390**
Urologie Poster. (GW ISSN 0936-9732) **3390**
Urologische Onkologie. (GW) **3390**, 3203
Urologiya i Nefrologiya/Urology and Nephrology. (RU ISSN 0042-1154) **3390**
Urology. (US ISSN 0090-4295) **3390**
Urology. (IT ISSN 0391-5603) **3390**
Urology and Nephrology see International Urology and Nephrology **3388**
Urology and Nephrology. see Urologiya i Nefrologiya **3390**
Urology Annual. (US ISSN 0889-6283) **3390**
Urology Times. (US ISSN 0093-9722) **3390**
Urspring Nachrichten. (GW ISSN 0936-8299) **1670**
Al-Urubah/Arabism. (QA) **2211**
Uruguay. (UY) **823**
Uruguay. Administracion Nacional de Telecomunicaciones. Memoria Anual. (UY) **1345**
Uruguay. Consejo de Estado. Diario de Sessiones. (UY) **4076**
Uruguay. Consejo de Salud Publica. Boletin see Boletin de Salud Publica **4098**
Uruguay. Direccion General de Comercio Exterior. Estadisticas de Comercio Exterior. (UY) **924**
Uruguay. Direccion General de Estadistica y Censos. Estadisticas Vitales. (UY) **3996**
Uruguay. Direccion General de Estadistica y Censos. Indice del Costo de la Construccion. (UY) **639**
Uruguay. Direccion General de Estadistica y Censos. Indice Medio de Salarios. (UY) **743**, 4591
Uruguay. Instituto Nacional de Carnes. Anuario Estadistico de Faena y Exportacion. (UY ISSN 0797-132X) **227**
Uruguay. Instituto Nacional de Carnes. Departamento de Exportaciones. Exportacion de Carnes, Estadisticas see Uruguay. Instituto Nacional de Carnes. Anuario Estadistico de Faena y Exportacion **227**
Uruguay. Instituto Nacional de Carnes. Departamento de Exportaciones. Anuario see Uruguay. Instituto Nacional de Carnes. Anuario Estadistico de Faena y Exportacion **227**
Uruguay. Ministerio de Agricultura y Pesca. Precios de Productos e Insumos Agropecuarios. (UY) **159**, 2050
Uruguay. Poder Legislativo. Biblioteca. Anales Parlamentarios. (UY) **4076**
Uruguay. Servicio de Hidrografia. Avisos a los Navegantes see Uruguay. Servicio de Oceanografia e Hidrografia. Avisos a los Navegantes **1612**

Uruguay. Servicio de Oceanografia e Hidrografia. Avisos a los Navegantes.(UY) **1612**
Uruguay. Unidad Asesora de Promocion Industrial. Memoria de Actividades. (UY) **1797**
Uruguay Economico. (UY) **887**
Uruguay Filatelico. (UY ISSN 0042-1189) **3759**
Uruguay Philatelist. (US) **3759**
Uruguay Sintesis Economica. (UY) **887**
Uruk-Warka: Abhandlungen der Deutschen Orient-Gesellschaft see Deutsche Orient-Gesellschaft. Abhandlung **270**
Urunana. (RW) **4208**
Urval. (IC ISSN 0042-1197) **2198**
Urzica see Moftul Roman **2875**
Us (New York, 1977). (US ISSN 0147-510X) **2236**
Us Wurk. (NE ISSN 0042-1235) **2851**, 2973
US 1 Worksheets see U S 1 Worksheets **2971**
Usage et Perception des Services Grand Public. (FR) **802**
Usahaluan. (MY ISSN 0126-8937) **1086**
Al-Usbu' al-Siyasi. (LY) **2209**
Al-Usbu' al-Thaqafi. (LY) **2209**
Use of English. (UK ISSN 0042-1243) **1670**
Used Boat Price Guide. (US) **4530**
Used Book Price Guide see Mandeville's Used Book Price Guide **4132**
Used Car Dealer. (US) **4704**
▼Used Car Merchandising. (US) **4704**
Used Car Prices - Buyer's Guide Reports. (US ISSN 1050-5415) **4704**, 1055
Used Cars Insider. (US) **4704**, 1055
Used Cars Today see Used Cars Insider **4704**
Used Computer Guide. (US ISSN 0742-6089) **1424**, 1465, 1474
Used Equipment Directory. (US ISSN 1045-3954) **3024**
User Magazin. (GW) **1474**, 1465
Ushaw Magazine. (UK ISSN 0308-6305) **4278**
Ushio/Tide. (JA) **2208**
Usine/Bedrijf Industrial Digest. (BE) **1086**
Usine Nouvelle. (FR ISSN 0042-126X) **4612**, 3024
†Using Personal Computers in Nonprofit Agencies. (US ISSN 0742-9789) **5299**
Uspehi na Moleculiarnata Biologia/ Advances in Molecular Biology. (BU ISSN 0205-0625) **459**
Uspekhi Fizicheskikh Nauk. (RU ISSN 0042-1294) **3835**
Uspekhi Foroniki. (RU) **3858**
Uspekhi Khimii. (RU ISSN 0042-1308) **1190**
Uspekhi Matematicheskikh Nauk. (RU ISSN 0042-1316) **3061**
Uspekhi Sovremennoi Biologii. (RU ISSN 0042-1324) **459**
Al-Usrah. (MK) **2211**
Ustav Vedeckotechnickych Informaci pro Zemedelstvi Genetika a Slechteni see Genetika a Slechteni **543**
Ustredna Sprava Muzei a Galerii. Vyrocne Spravy o Cinnosti Slovenskych Muzei see Vyrocne Spravy o Cinnosti Slovenskych Muzei a Galerii **3535**
Ustredni Sprava Spoju. Vestnik see Federalni Ministerstvo Spoju. Vestnik **1336**
Ustredni Ustav Geologicky. Rozpravy. (CS) **3661**
Ustredni Ustav Geologicky. Vestnik/ Geological Survey. Bulletin. (CS ISSN 0042-4730) **1584**
Ut de Smidte fan de Fryske Akademy. (NE ISSN 0042-1367) **4138**, 2790
Ut i All Verden. (NO) **4252**
Utafiti. (TZ) **2973**, 4391
Utah. Division of Administrative Rules. Utah State Bulletin. (US ISSN 0882-4738) **4076**
Utah. Geological and Mineral Survey. Bulletin see Utah Geological Survey. Bulletin **1584**

Utah. Geological and Mineral Survey. Special Studies see Utah Geological Survey. Special Studies 1584
Utah. Geological and Mineral Survey. Survey Notes see Utah Geological Survey. Survey Notes 1584
Utah. Juvenile Court. Annual Report. (US ISSN 0566-4152) 1245
Utah. State Office of Education. Annual Report of the State Superintendent of Public Instruction. (US ISSN 0094-8314) 1732
Utah. State Office of Education. Opinions of the Utah State Superintendent of Public Instruction. (US ISSN 0093-0040) 1732
Utah Agricultural Statistics. (US) 144
†Utah Beverage Analyst. (US) 5299
Utah Cattleman. (US ISSN 0042-1375) 227
Utah Centennial Series. (US ISSN 0887-3771) 2425
Utah Construction Report. (US ISSN 0042-1383) 635
Utah Directory of Business and Industry.(US ISSN 8755-2841) 1158
Utah Economic and Business Review. (US ISSN 0042-1405) 698
Utah Education Association Action see U E A Action 1668
Utah Farmer-Stockman. (US ISSN 1041-1666) 128
Utah Foundation. Research Report and Research Briefs. (US) 698
Utah Genealogical Association. Genealogical Journal. (US ISSN 0146-2229) 2166
Utah Genealogical Association. Newsletter. (US) 2166
Utah Genealogical Association. Annual Guidebook. (US ISSN 0083-484X) 1584
Utah Geological Survey. Bulletin. (US) 1584, 3497
Utah Geological Survey. Special Studies.(US) 1584, 3497
Utah Geological Survey. Survey Notes. (US) 1584, 3497
Utah Golf. (US) 4514
Utah Historical Quarterly. (US ISSN 0042-143X) 2425
Utah Holiday. (US ISSN 0739-2311) 2237
Utah Labor Market Report. (US) 887
Utah Law Review. (US ISSN 0042-1448) 2691
Utah Library - News. (US) 2790
Utah Marriage and Divorce Annual Report. (US) 3996, 3067, 4591
Utah Notary Law Primer. (US) 2691
Utah Nurses Association Pro Re Nata see Pro Re Nata 3285
Utah P T A Bulletin see Sound-off 1664
Utah Public School Directory. (US) 1697
Utah Public School System see Utah. State Office of Education. Annual Report of the State Superintendent of Public Instruction 1732
Utah State Digest. (US ISSN 0884-6421) 4096
Utah State Historical Society Newsletter.(US ISSN 0042-1529) 2425
Utah State University Staff News see U S U Staff News 1327
Utah Statistical Abstract. (US ISSN 0278-3770) 743, 4591
Utah Studies in Literature and Linguistics. (US ISSN 0171-726X) 2973, 2851
Utah Vital Statistics Annual Report. (US ISSN 0500-7720) 3996
Utama Kheti Bari. (II) 128
Utamaduni. (KE) 2209
Utan. (JA ISSN 0287-2900) 4350
Ute Bulletin. (US) 2027
Ute-Magasinet. (SW ISSN 0281-2932) 4559
Ute och Hemma. (SW ISSN 0042-1553) 4423
Utemiljoe. (NO ISSN 0333-1555) 2140
Utenrikspolitiske Skrifter/Norwegian Foreign Policy Studies. (NO) 3976
Utensil. (IT ISSN 0392-6567) 3024

†Uterus. (UK ISSN 0268-1455) 5299
Uthon/Platform. (II ISSN 0042-157X) 2973
Utilitas. (UK ISSN 0953-8208) 1302
Utilities Industry Litigation Reporter. (US ISSN 1053-0258) 2691
Utilities Law Reports. (US ISSN 0162-1718) 4076
▼Utilities Policy. (UK ISSN 0957-1787) 1910
Utility Analyst. (US) 967
Utility and Telephone Fleets. (US) 1367, 1383
▼Utility Construction and Maintenance. (US) 635
Utility Cost Forecasting Service Review see D R I - McGraw-Hill Cost and Price Review: Utility Focus 859
Utility Data Institute, Inc. Datagram see U D I Datagram 1802
Utility Data Institute, Inc. Utility Datapak see U D I Utility Datapak 1802
Utility Data Institute, Inc. Who's Who at Electric Power Plants see U D I Who's Who at Electric Power Plants 1802
Utility Environment Report. (US) 1910
Utility Fleet Management. (US) 4749, 1910
Utility Reporter: Fuels Energy & Power. (US ISSN 0890-2984) 1797, 3703
Utility Spotlight. (US) 1802
Utility Supervision. (US ISSN 0883-8402) 1030
Utilizacion de la Capacidad Productiva Regional see Boletin de Coyuntura y Estadistica del Pais Vasco 808
Utlaendska Nyfoervaerv till Stoerre Svenska Folkbibliotek. (SW ISSN 0347-6820) 415
Utmost. (US ISSN 0199-3658) 2237, 1329
Utne Reader. (US ISSN 8750-0256) 2888
Utopia 2. (US) 3597, 832, 3785, 4208
Utopie. (FR) 4456
Utpadakta. (II) 1070
Utrecht Micropaleontological Bulletins. (NE ISSN 0083-4963) 3661
Utrecht Publications in Comparative Literature. (US ISSN 0167-8175) 2888
Utrecht Studies in Air and Space Law. (NE) 2691, 64, 2730
Utrikespolitik. see Ulkopolitiikka 3975
Utsaba. (BG) 3008
Utsikt. (SW ISSN 0346-3788) 2888
Utsukushii-Kimono/Beautiful Kimono. (JA) 1295, 4627
Utsunomiya Daigaku Kyoikugakubu Kiyo. Dai-2-bu/Utsunomiya University. Faculty of Education. Bulletin. Section 2. (JA ISSN 0385-2415) 4350
Utsunomiya Daigaku Kyoyobu Kenkyu Hokoku. Dai-2-bu/Utsunomiya University. Faculty of General Education. Bulletin. Section 2. (JA ISSN 0286-6293) 4350
Utsunomiya University. Faculty of Education. Bulletin. Section 2. see Utsunomiya Daigaku Kyoikugakubu Kiyo. Dai-2-bu 4350
Utsunomiya University. Faculty of General Education. Bulletin. Section 2. see Utsunomiya Daigaku Kyoyobu Kenkyu Hokoku. Dai-2-bu 4350
Uttar Bharat Bhoogol Patrika. (II ISSN 0042-1618) 2266
Uttar Pradesh. (II ISSN 0303-5395) 2202
Uttar Pradesh. State Planning Institute. Quarterly Bulletin of Statistics. (II ISSN 0042-1626) 4591
Uttar Pradesh, India. Scientific Research Committee Monograph Series. (II ISSN 0083-5013) 4350
Uttar Pradesh Journal of Zoology. (II ISSN 0256-971X) 593, 538, 575
Uttarakhanda Bharati. (II) 2343
Utunk. (RM) 2973
Utusam Filem dan Feshen. (MY) 3518
Utusan Filem dan Feshen see U F F 5293
Utusan Radio dan T V. (MY) 1360, 1383

Utusan Sarawak. (MY) 2210
Utvikling. (NO) 936
Uudistuva Konttori. (FI ISSN 0355-9912) 1062
†Uusi Elektroniikka. (FI) 5299
Uusi Nainen. (FI ISSN 0500-8476) 4854
Uw Koninkrijk Kome: Zendingsblad. (NE ISSN 0042-1650) 4208, 4252
Uzbek Tili Va Adabieti. (UZ) 2973
Uzbekskii Biologicheskii Zhurnal. (UZ ISSN 0042-1685) 459
Uzbekskii Geologicheskii Zhurnal. (UZ ISSN 0042-1693) 1584
Uzbekskii Khimicheskii Zhurnal. (UZ ISSN 0042-1707) 1190
V. (US ISSN 1041-1402) 1386
V A C C Journal see Motor Industry Journal 4696
V A C News see Indian Vacuum Society. Bulletin 3820
V A H P E R D Journal. (Virginia Association for Health, Physical Education and Dance) (US ISSN 0739-4586) 3809, 4496
V A M Mededelingen. (N.V. Vuilafvoer Maatschappij) (NE ISSN 0042-1715) 1971
V A Medical Center Directory. (US) 2470, 3161
V A N and Resale Carrier Guide see Planning Guide 3. Value-Added Networks and Data Private Line. Telecommunications Rates and Services 1365
V A Practitioner. (US ISSN 0883-5721) 3161
V A R Business. (Value Added Resellers) (US) 840
V A R D S Report. (US) 2544, 967
V A R Industry Products. (Value Added Resellers) (US) 1465
V.A.S.Kh.N. see Vestnik Sel'skokhozyaistvennoi Nauki 128
†V A S L A. (Special Libraries Association, Virginia Chapter) (US ISSN 0042-1723) 5299
V A S Newsletter. (Vermont Archaeological Society, Inc.) (US ISSN 1043-1918) 289
†V A T - C H A T. (Victorian Affiliated Teachers Federation) (AT) 5299
V A T F Newsletter. (Victorian Affiliated Teachers Federation) (AT) 1670
V A T Guide and Casebook. (Value Added Tax) (UK) 1111
V A T Intelligence. (Value Added Tax) (UK ISSN 0263-9947) 1111
V A T Journal see V A T - C H A T 5299
V A X Professional. (US ISSN 8750-9628) 1402
V A X - R S T S Professional see V A X Professional 1402
V B A Bode. (Cooperatieve Vereniging Verenigde Bloemenveilingen Aalsmeer) (NE) 832
V B O Meddelingen see F E B Bulletin 1075
V B R A Directory of Members see V B R A Industry Yearbook 5299
†V B R A Industry Yearbook. (Vehicle Builders and Repairers Association (VBRA)) (UK) 5299
V C A Kennel Gazette. (Victorian Canine Association Inc.) (AT) 3714
V C C Voice see Voice 1329
V.C.F. Newsletter. (Veterinary Christian Fellowship) (UK ISSN 0268-2877) 4817, 4208
V C H Kurier. (GW) 2481
V.C.O.T. see Veterinary and Comparative Orthopaedics and Traumatology 4817
V C R and Film Catalog. (US) 3518
V C R Letter. (US ISSN 8755-9927) 1386
V C S Newsletter. (Vestal Central School District) (US) 1670
V C U Magazine. (Virginia Commonwealth University) (US) 1329
V D C - Nachrichten. (Verband Deutscher Chemo Techniker und Chemisch - Technischer Association) (GW) 824

V D E W die Oeffentliche Elektrizitaetsversorgung. (Vereinigung Deutscher Elektrizitaetswerke e.V.) (GW ISSN 0505-2904) 1910
V D F Die Fuehrungskraft see Die Fuehrungskraft 3483
V D G S A News. (Viola da Gamba Society of America, Inc.) (US ISSN 0506-306X) 3585
V D I. Informationsdienst Regelungstechnik. (GW) 1847, 24
V D I - Berichte. (Verein Deutscher Ingenieure) (GW ISSN 0083-5560) 1839
†V D I - Forschungshefte. (Verein Deutscher Ingenieure) (GW ISSN 0042-174X) 5299
V D I Informationsdienst. Blechbearbeitung. (GW ISSN 0170-9526) 3423
V D I Informationsdienst. Drahtherstellung u. Drahterzeugnisse. (Verein Deutscher Ingenieure) (GW ISSN 0720-4612) 1847, 1940, 3024
V D I Informationsdienst. Elektrisch Abtragende Fertigungsverfahren. (GW ISSN 0170-9569) 3423, 1910
V D I Informationsdienst. Kaltmassivumformung. (GW ISSN 0170-9550) 3423, 1923
V D I Informationsdienst. Mechanische Verbindungstechnik. (GW ISSN 0720-9886) 1940
V D I Informationsdienst. Neue Fertigungsverfahren. (GW ISSN 0720-9878) 3423
V D I Informationsdienst. Schmieden und Pressen. (GW ISSN 0171-3647) 3423
V D I Informationsdienst. Strangpressen von Metallen. (GW ISSN 0721-7242) 3423
V D I - Nachrichten. (GW ISSN 0042-1758) 1839
V D I - Z. (GW ISSN 0042-1766) 1840
V D: Japanese Journal of Venereal Diseases see S T D: Japanese Journal of the Sexually Transmitted Diseases 3249
V D K - Mitteilungen Sozialpolitische Fachzeitschrift see Sozialrecht & Praxis 4421
V D L - Journal. (Verband Deutscher Akademiker fuer Landwirtschaft, Ernaehrung und Landespflege e.V.) (GW) 128
V D L - Nachrichten see V D L - Journal 128
V D L Nyt. (Vejdatalaboratoriet) (DK ISSN 0108-0385) 4722
V D S M - Informationsdienst. (Internationaler Verband der Stadt-, Sport- und Mehrzwerkhallen) (GW) 3394, 3809
V D T A News. (Vacuum Dealers Trade Association) (US) 1055, 2562
V D T A Phone Directory and Product Guide. (Vacuum Dealers Trade Association) (US) 1056, 2562
V D T News. (Video Display Terminal) (US ISSN 0742-938X) 4114, 1402
V E A News. (Virginia Education Association) (US ISSN 0042-1790) 1670
V E A Today see Vermont - N E A Today 1670
V E L K D - Information. (Vereinigte Evangelisch-Lutherische Kirche Deutschlands) (GW) 4252
V E News see The Canadian Amateur 1355
V E S Newsletter. (Voluntary Euthanasia Society) (UK) 4456
V E 6. (CN ISSN 0049-5778) 1360
V-Eight Times. (US) 259
V F A Jahrbuch. (Vereinigung Freischaffender Architeckten) (GW) 308
V F A Profil. (Vereinigung Freischaffender Architekten) (GW) 308
V F D B Zeitschrift see V F D B: Zeitschrift fuer Forschung und Technik im Brandschutz 1860

V F D B: Zeitschrift fuer Forschung und Technik im Brandschutz. (Vereinigung zur Foerderung des Deutschen Brandschutzes e.V.) (GW ISSN 0042-1804) **1860, 4114**

V F W Auxiliary. (Veterans of Foreign Wars of the United States) (US ISSN 0199-865X) **1302**

V F W Magazine. (Veterans of Foreign Wars of the United States) (US ISSN 0042-1820) **3474**

V F Z. (Vieh und Fleisch Handelszeitung) (GW) **227**

V G A Nachrichten. (Bundesverband der Geschaeftsstellenleiter der Assekuranz) (GW ISSN 0170-9690) **2544**

V G B Kraftwerkstechnik, (Technische Vereinigung der Grosskraftwerksbetreiber e.V.) (GW ISSN 0372-5715) **1910**

V G B Mitteilungen see V G B Kraftwerkstechnik **1910**

V-G Quartalshefte. (Versuchsgrubengesellschaft mbH) (GW) **3497**

V G S Newsletter. (Virginia Genealogical Society) (US) **2166**

V G Vendogiocattoli. (IT ISSN 0391-7290) **2283**

V. Graefes Archiv fuer Klinische und Experimentelle Ophthalmologie. see Graefe's Archive for Clinical and Experimental Ophthalmology **3301**

V H F Communications. (UK ISSN 0177-7513) **1345**

V I A Magazin. (Verband der Initiativgruppen in der Auslaenderarbeit e.V.) (GW) **3948, 3989**

V I A Update see I S A Update **1350**

V I C A Journal see V I C A Journal **1687**

V I C A Journal. (Vocational Industrial Clubs of America, Inc.) (US ISSN 1044-0151) **1687**

V I E R Bulletin. (Victorian Institute of Educational Research) (AT ISSN 0049-6154) **1670**

V I N A Quarterly. (Virgin Islands Nurses Association) (VI ISSN 0049-6464) **3287**

†V I Newspapers - Substantive Index. (US ISSN 0748-4976) **5299**

†V I P. (US) **5299**

V I P Address Book. (US ISSN 1043-0261) **421**

V I P Address Book Updates. (US) **421**

V I P Traveler. (US) **1056, 39**

V I R Playback see M E R P Memo **3123**

†V I T A News. (Volunteers in Technical Assistance) (US ISSN 0882-0937) **5299**

V I T Informationstechnik. (GW ISSN 0936-0700) **1062**

†V K G - Nachrichten. (Verband der Kraftfahrzeugteile- und Zweiradgrosshaendler e.V.) (GW ISSN 0177-9761) **5299**

V L B see Verzeichnis Lieferbarer Buecher **415**

V L S. (Voice Literary Supplement) (US ISSN 0887-8633) **2973, 3008**

V L S I Systems Design see High Performance Systems **5204**

†V - Line News. (AT ISSN 0814-7078) **5299**

V M A Engineering Newsletter. (Vanderplaats, Miura & Associates, Inc.) (US) **1880, 1423**

V M & S D. (Visual Merchandising & Store Design) (US ISSN 0745-4295) **39**

V M E-bus. (GW ISSN 0931-5101) **1455, 1481**

V M E Bus Systems. (US ISSN 0884-1357) **1440**

†V M E News. (US ISSN 1040-970X) **5299**

V - M I C Conference see International I E E E V L S I Mutilevel Interconnection Conference. Proceedings **1900**

V M International. (SZ) **1056**

V Mire Knig. (RU ISSN 0042-188X) **2790, 4138**

V Mire Muzyki. (RU) **3585**

V Mire Nauki. (Russian translation of: Scientific American) (RU ISSN 0208-0621) **4350**

V N A B Newsletter. (Visiting Nurse Association of Brooklyn) (US) **3287**

V N A Newsletter see V N A B Newsletter **3287**

V O H D see Verzeichnis der Orientalischen Handschriften in Deutschland **3645**

V O H D Supplementbaende see Verzeichnis der Orientalischen Handschriften in Deutschland. Supplementbaende **3645**

V O N Canada Annual Report (Year). (CN) **3287**

V O N Canada Report. (CN) **3287**

V O P - Fachzeitschrift fuer die Oeffentliche Verwaltung. (Verwaltungsfuehrung - Organisation - Personal) (GW ISSN 0170-7140) **4076**

V O Realites. (SZ) **2591**

V O, Vie Ouvriere. (CN ISSN 0849-035X) **2179, 2888**

V O W: Voice of Women. (ZA) **4854, 3948**

V O Y A see Voice of Youth Advocates **1245**

V og S Priser see V og S Priser. Anlaeg **1056**

V og S Priser. Anlaeg. (DK) **1056, 635**

V og S Priser. Bygningsdele. (DK ISSN 0108-0229) **635**

V og S Priser. Husbygning. (DK ISSN 0105-4201) **1056, 635**

V P N see Veterinary Product News **4819**

V R. (Video Registrare) (IT) **1386, 2443, 3518**

V R B - Informatie. (Vereniging van Religieus - Wetenschappelijke Bibliothecarissen) (BE ISSN 0777-6306) **2790, 4208, 4350**

V R - Express. (FI ISSN 0358-7711) **4795, 4716**

V R F Info. (Verband des Radio-, Fernseh-, und Elektro-Fachhandels und Gewerbes Oesterreichs) (AU) **1383, 1360, 1779**

V S. (IT) **2851**

V S B A Newsletter see From the Board Room **1635**

V S D. (Vendredi Samedi Dimanche) (FR) **2188**

V S D A Reports. (Video Software Dealers Association) (US) **1386, 1481**

V S D - Mitteilungen. (Verband der Schweizer Druckindustrie) (SZ) **4006**

V S F - Bulletin. (SZ) **4006**

V S I G - Mitteilungen/Informations V S I G. (Vereinigung des Schweizerischen Import- und Grosshandels) (SZ) **924**

V S P Bulletin see Vereinigung Schweizerischer Petroleum-Geologen und -Ingenieure. Bulletin **3703**

V S R Kommunikation see Forum **3895**

†V S T A Guide to Victorian State Secondary Schools. (Victorian Secondary Teachers Association) (AT) **5299**

V S T A News. (Victorian Secondary Teachers' Association) (AT) **1762, 1697, 1732**

V S T Revue see T T - Revue **4656**

V T see V T X **5299**

V T F-Post. (GW ISSN 0174-3538) **3671**

V T I Annual Report. (Statens Vaeg- och Trafikinstitut) (SW ISSN 0283-7021) **4722**

V T I Meddelande. (Statens Vaeg- och Trafikinstitut) (SW ISSN 0347-6049) **4722**

V T I Rapport. (Statens Vaeg- och Trafikinstitut) (SW ISSN 0347-6030) **4722**

†V T I Topics. (Vaeg och Trafik Institutet) (SW ISSN 0280-896X) **5299**

V T T Julkaisuja/V T T Publikationer. (FI ISSN 1235-0613) **4613**

V T T Meddelanden. see V T T Tiedotteita **4613**

V T T Publications. (Valtion Teknillinen Tutkimuskeskus) (FI ISSN 1235-0621) **4350**

V T T Publikationer. see V T T Julkaisuja **4613**

V T T Research Notes. see V T T Tiedotteita **4613**

V T T Symposium. (Valtion Teknillinen Tutkimuskeskus) (FI ISSN 0357-9387) **4613**

V T T Tiedotteita/V T T Meddelanden/V T T Research Notes. (FI ISSN 1235-0605) **4613**

V T U Journal see Federation News (Abbotsford) **1633**

†V T X. (SZ) **5299**

†V - The Style of the City. (CN) **5299**

V V see VigneVini **195**

V V P Magazine see Verzekerings Magazine V V P **2545**

V V S. (DK ISSN 0042-1944) **2304**

V V S - Forum. (SW ISSN 0346-4644) **2304**

V V S Installatoeren see Dansk V V S **2298**

V V W C A Newsletter. (Vintage Volkswagen Club of America) (US) **259**

V W A. (SZ ISSN 0259-6512) **2973, 3008**

V W and Porsche Etc see European Car **4690**

V W-Autogramm. (GW) **996, 4722**

V W Autoist. (US) **4704**

V W D Aussenhandelsdienst see Aussenhandelsdienst **938**

V W D-Aussenwirtschaft see Aussenhandelsdienst **938**

V W D - Bauwirtschaft. (Vereinigte Wirtschaftsdienste GmbH) (GW) **967, 635**

V W D-Chemie see V W D - Chemie: Kautschuk **967**

V W D - Chemie: Kautschuk. (Vereinigte Wirtschaftsdienste GmbH) (GW) **967, 1190**

V W D - Elektro. (Vereinigte Wirtschaftsdienste GmbH) (GW) **967, 1910**

V W D - Energie. (Vereinigte Wirtschaftsdienste GmbH) (GW) **967, 1797**

V W D - Europa. (Vereinigte Wirtschaftsdienste GmbH) (GW) **967, 924**

V W D-Finanz see V W D - Finanz- und Wirtschaftsspiegel **967**

V W D - Finanz- und Wirtschaftsspiegel. (Vereinigte Wirtschaftsdienste GmbH) (GW) **967, 802**

V W D - Finanz- und Wirtschaftsspiegel see V W D - Finanz- und Wirtschaftsspiegel **967**

V W D - Getraenke. (Vereinigte Wirtschaftsdienste GmbH) (GW) **968, 386**

V W D - Getreide und Futtermittel. (Vereinigte Wirtschaftsdienste GmbH) (GW) **968, 208**

V W D-Haeute, Leder, Rauchwaren see V W D - Haeute und Leder **968**

V W D - Haeute und Leder. (Vereinigte Wirtschaftsdienste GmbH) (GW) **968, 2738**

V W D-Hart- und Bastfasern see V W D - Landwirtschaft und Ernaehrung **968**

V W D-Informationen see Nachrichten fuer Aussenhandel **957**

V W D-Kaffee, Kakao, Tee, Gewuerze see V W D - Kaffee, Kakao, Tee, Suesswaren **968**

V W D - Kaffee, Kakao, Tee, Suesswaren. (Vereinigte Wirtschaftsdienste GmbH) (GW) **968, 2083**

V W D - Landwirtschaft und Ernaehrung. (Vereinigte Wirtschaftsdienste GmbH) (GW) **968, 4627**

V W D - Maschinen. (Vereinigte Wirtschaftsdienste GmbH) (GW) **968, 2525**

V W D-Maschinenbau see V W D - Maschinen **968**

V W D - Montan. (Vereinigte Wirtschaftsdienste GmbH) (GW) **968, 3497**

V W D - Nachrichten fuer Aussenhandel see Nachrichten fuer Aussenhandel **957**

V W D - NE-Metalle. (Vereinigte Wirtschaftsdienste GmbH) (GW) **968, 3423**

V W D - Oele und Fette. (Vereinigte Wirtschaftsdienste GmbH) (GW) **968, 3703**

V W D - Stahl. (Vereinigte Wirtschaftsdienste GmbH) (GW) **968, 3423**

V W D - Textil. (Vereinigte Wirtschaftsdienste GmbH) (GW) **968, 4627**

V W D - Textil-Bekleidung see V W D - Textil **968**

V W D - Vieh und Fleisch. (Vereinigte Wirtschaftsdienste GmbH) (GW) **968, 227**

V W D - Zucker. (Vereinigte Wirtschaftsdienste GmbH) (GW) **968, 2083**

V W Motoring. (UK ISSN 0953-6167) **4704**

V W Trends. (US) **4705**

V W Z. (Verkehrswirtschaftliche Zahlen) (GW ISSN 0083-5021) **4722**

V X I Journal. (US) **2525**

V Z L U Zpravodaj. (Vyzkumny a Zkusebni Letecky Ustav) (CS ISSN 0044-5355) **64, 3441**

Va-Nytt. (SW ISSN 0042-1995) **1975, 24, 4835**

VA-W VA Queries see Virginia, West Virginia Queries **2167**

Vaabenhistorisk Tidsskrift. (DK ISSN 0506-337X) **259**

Vaabenhistoriske Aarboeger. (DK ISSN 0108-707X) **259**

Vaapen see Vaapenjournalen **4496**

Vaapenjournalen. (NO ISSN 0800-6016) **4496**

Vaar Bostad/Our Dwelling. (SW ISSN 0042-2002) **2498**

Vaar Faagelvaerld. (SW ISSN 0042-2649) **567**

Vaar Fana. (SW ISSN 0042-2010) **4208**

Vaar Foeda. (SW ISSN 0042-2657) **3612**

Vaar Foeda. Supplement. (SW ISSN 0346-7341) **3612**

Vaar Naering. (SW ISSN 0042-2681) **3612**

Vaar Ponny. (SW ISSN 0346-4687) **4539**

Vaara Paelsdjur/Our Furred Animals. (SW ISSN 0042-2703) **2738**

Vaard i Norden. (NO ISSN 0107-4083) **3287**

Vaardfacket. (SW) **3161**

Vaare Veger/Road Engineering. (NO ISSN 0376-7272) **1876**

Vaart Blad. (NO) **832**

Vaart Foersvar. (SW ISSN 0042-2800) **3474, 3976**

Vaart Vern. (NO ISSN 0042-2037) **3474**

Vaasan Korkeakoulu. Julkaisuja. Opetusmonisteita/University of Vaasa. Proceedings. Teaching Aid Series. (FI ISSN 0788-6659) **899**

Vaasan Korkeakoulu. Julkaisuja. Opetusmonisteita see Vaasan Korkeakoulu. Julkaisuja. Opetusmonisteita **899**

Vaasan Korkeakoulu. Julkaisuja. Tutkimuksia see Vaasan Yliopisto. Julkaisuja. Tutkimuksia **899**

Vaasan Yliopisto. Julkaisuja. Tutkimuksia/University of Vaasa. Proceedings. Research Papers. (FI ISSN 0788-6667) **899**

Vaba Eestlane/Free Estonia. (CN) **2027**

Vacances see Bertrand Vacances **4145**

Vacances Actives, Vacances Hiver. (FR) **2481**

Vacare Deo. (IT ISSN 0394-7807) **4278, 2325**

Vacation Overseas see Ideal Traveller **4771**

Vacation Reviews. (US) **4795**

Vacation Study Abroad. (US) **1724**

Vacation Week. (US) **4795**

Vacations. (US ISSN 0894-9093) **4795**

Vacature. (NE ISSN 0042-2053) **1670, 3631**

Vaccination Certificate Requirements and Health Advice for International Travel *see* International Travel and Health: Vaccination Requirements and Health Advice **4105**
Vaccination Certificate Requirements for International Travel *see* International Travel and Health: Vaccination Requirements and Health Advice **4105**
Vaccination Certificate Requirements for International Travel and Health Advice to Travellers *see* International Travel and Health: Vaccination Requirements and Health Advice **4105**
Vaccinations. *see* Immunizations **3175**
Vaccine. (UK ISSN 0264-410X) **3189**
Vaccines (Year). (US) **3189**
Vacher's European Companion. (UK ISSN 0958-0336) **3932**
Vachers Parliamentary Companion. (UK ISSN 0958-0328) **4076**
Vacunaciones. *see* Immunizations **3175**
Vacuum. *see* Zhenkong **1911**
Vacuum. (US ISSN 0042-207X) **3839**, 24, 1847
Vacuum Dealers Trade Association News *see* V D T A News **1055**
Vacuum Dealers Trade Association Phone Directory and Product Guide *see* V D T A Phone Directory and Product Guide **1056**
Vadehavsrapport. (DK ISSN 0109-2472) **2266**
Vademecum Bursatil. (PE) **968**
Vademecum Deutscher Lehr- und Forschungsstaetten. Staetten der Forschung. (GW ISSN 0083-5080) **4350**, 4613
Vademecum voor het Verzekeringswezen. (NE) **2544**
Vaeg och Trafik Institutet Topics *see* V T I Topics **5299**
Vaeg- och Vattenbyggaren. (SW ISSN 0042-2177) **1876**
Vaegmaestaren. (SW) **4660**
Vael & Ve. (SW) **4114**, 4423
Vaer og Klima. (NO) **3442**
Vaeret *see* Vaer og Klima **3442**
Vaerksteds Nyt *see* Produktions Nyt **3022**
Vaerldshorisont. (SW ISSN 0042-2134) **3932**
Vaerldspolitikens Dagsfragor. (SW ISSN 0042-2754) **3976**
Vaern om Danmark. (DK ISSN 0109-7172) **3474**
Vaernskontakt. (DK ISSN 0109-0100) **1274**
Vaesterbottens Norra Fornminnesfoerening. Skelleftea Museum. Meddelande. (SW) **2394**
Vaestgoetalitteratur. (SW ISSN 0042-2150) **415**
Vaestoentutkimuksen Vuosikirja. *see* Yearbook of Population Research in Finland **3989**
Vaextekologiska Studier *see* Studies in Plant Ecology **518**
Vaextskydds - Kuriren. (Swedish translation of: Pflanzenschutz Kurier) (SW ISSN 0346-4997) **195**
Vaextskyddsnotiser. (SW ISSN 0042-2169) **520**
Vaextskyddsrapporter. (SW ISSN 0347-3236) **520**
Vagabond Chapbook. (US) **3008**
Vagabondages. (FR ISSN 0153-9620) **3008**
Vahid. (IR) **2973**
Vaibhav. (II) **824**
Vaikunth Mehta National Institute of Cooperative Management. Publications. (II ISSN 0083-5102) **1030**, 832
Vaikunthbhai Mehta Smarak Trust. Centre for Studies in Decentralised Industries. Documentation Bulletin. (II) **743**
Vail Magazine. (US) **2237**
Vail Valley Magazine. (US) **2237**
Vaillant. *see* Fatosi **1254**
Vaillante Afrique. (IV) **3932**
Vajra Bodhi Sea. (US ISSN 0507-6986) **4216**, 3785
Vajradhatu Sun *see* Shambhala Sun **4215**

Vakantiebesteding van de Nederlandse Bevolking *see* Netherlands. Centraal Bureau voor de Statistiek. Vakantieonderzoek **4800**
Vakblad Mix. (NE) **643**, 2501
Vakblad Mix voor de Ijzerwaren en Doe-het-Zelf Handel *see* Vakblad Mix **643**
Vakblad voor de Bloemisterij. (NE ISSN 0042-2223) **2143**
Vakblad voor de Groothandel in Aardappelen, Groenten en Fruit *see* Vakblad voor de Handel in Aardappelen, Groenten en Fruit **2094**
Vakblad voor de Handel in Aardappelen, Groenten en Fruit. (NE) **2094**
Vakblad voor Textielreiniging *see* Textielverzorging **1282**
De Vakhandel. (NE) **643**
Vakuum in der Praxis. (GW ISSN 0934-9758) **3835**, 1840
Vakuum-Technik *see* Vakuum in der Praxis **3835**
Vakuumist. (XV ISSN 0351-9716) **3835**
Vakuutussanomat. (FI ISSN 0355-7294) **2544**
Valasan Pathet Lao. (LS) **3932**
Valdres Historielag. Aarbok. (NO ISSN 0800-0999) **2394**
Valencia Filatelica. (SP) **3759**
Valencia - Fruits. (SP) **159**
Valencia Port. (SP) **4741**, 4830
Valenciennes. (FR ISSN 0760-5641) **2973**
Valentine Museum. News. (US) **3534**
Valenza Gioielli. (IT) **2566**
Valeurs Actuelles. (FR ISSN 0049-5794) **2188**
Validated Engineering Data Index. (UK) **1847**, 24
Valiseesti. (SW ISSN 0049-5808) **2027**
Valitut Palat/Reader's Digest (Finnish edition). (FI ISSN 0042-2290) **2186**
Vallalatszervezesi es Ipargazdasagi Szakirodalmi Tajekoztato/Industrial Management Abstracts. (HU ISSN 0231-0759) **743**, 24
Valle Santa di Rieti. (IT ISSN 0042-2304) **4278**
Valley Business Perspectives. (US ISSN 0886-6597) **887**
Valley Commerce *see* Roanoke Regional Chamber of Commerce. Agenda **822**
Valley Forge. (US ISSN 0889-0935) **1329**
Valley Forge Journal. (US ISSN 0734-5712) **2425**
Valley Gazette. (US) **2425**
Valley Genealogist. (US ISSN 1046-042X) **2166**
Valley Journal. (US) **2425**
Valley Magazine (Granada Hills). (US) **2237**
Valley Magazine (Hailey). (US) **2237**
Valley Magazine (Selinsgrove). (US ISSN 1046-0454) **2237**
Valley Motorist. (US) **4705**
Valley National Eagle *see* The Eagle (Phoenix) **776**
Valley Newsletter. (US) **1499**
Valley Quarterly. (US) **2166**
Valley: The Magazine for Eastern Ontario. (CN) **2179**
Valley Trader. (US) **2237**
▼Valley Viewpoint Magazine. (US) **2237**
Valley Voice. (US) **2237**
Valley Women's Voice. (US) **4854**, 2457
Valmennus & Kunto. (FI) **3809**
Valokuva. (FI ISSN 0355-1466) **3798**
Valokuvauksen Vuosikirja/Finnish Photographic Yearbook/Finsk Fotografisk Arsbok. (FI ISSN 0356-8075) **3798**
Valori Umani. (IT ISSN 0300-3175) **2888**
Valosag. (HU ISSN 0324-7228) **4456**
Valparaiso University Law Review. (US ISSN 0042-2363) **2691**
Valsalva. (IT ISSN 0042-2371) **3317**
Valstieciu Laikrastis. (LI) **128**

Valtion Teknillinen Tutkimuskeskus. Tiedotteita *see* V T T Tiedotteita **4613**
Valtion Teknillinen Tutkimuskeskus. Tutkimuksia *see* V T T Julkaisuja **4613**
Valtion Teknillinen Tutkimuskeskus Publications *see* V T T Publications **4350**
Valtion Teknillinen Tutkimuskeskus Symposium *see* V T T Symposium **4613**
Valtionyhtiot. (FI ISSN 0356-8091) **1086**
Valuation Journal *see* ViewPoint (Milwaukee) **698**
Valuation Magazine. (US ISSN 0042-238X) **4159**, 348, 968, 2544
Value. (JM) **1508**
Value Added Resellers Business *see* V A R Business **840**
Value Added Resellers Industry Products *see* V A R Industry Products **1465**
Value Added Tax Guide and Casebook *see* V A T Guide and Casebook **1111**
Value Added Tax Intelligence *see* V A T Intelligence **1111**
Value Engineering and Management Digest - Defense Contract Guide. (US ISSN 0275-4371) **1030**, 1840
Value Line Investment Survey. (US ISSN 0042-2401) **968**
†Value Line New Issues Service. (US) **5299**
Value Line O-T-C Special Situations Service. (US) **968**
Value Line Option and Convertible Survey *see* Value Line Options **968**
Value Line Options. (US) **968**
Value Retail News. (US) **1056**
Valuer *see* Valuer and Land Economist **4159**
Valuer. (UK ISSN 0042-2428) **4159**
Valuer and Land Economist. (AT) **4159**
Values. *see* Arachim **3873**
†Values and Measures of the World. (SZ) **5299**
▼ValuTrac. (US) **968**
Valve Magazine. (US) **3024**, 698
Valve News. (US ISSN 0887-5073) **2304**, 1860, 1940, 3024
Vampire Journal. (US) **3015**, 2973
Van & Truck Digest. (US ISSN 1043-4879) **4705**
Van Bedrijfsuitkomsten tot Financiele Positie. (NE ISSN 0921-4135) **128**, 159
Van Buren County Historical Society Newsletter. (US) **2425**
Van Conversion Blue Book. (US ISSN 0884-7231) **4705**, 2443
Van Digest *see* Van & Truck Digest **4705**
Van et le Camping-Car *see* Camping-Car **4648**
Van Hoa Nghe Thuat/Culture and Arts. (VN) **348**
Van Horen Zeggen. (NE ISSN 0166-5677) **2289**
Van Life and Family Trucking *see* MotorHome **4550**
Van Nghe/Arts and Letters. (VN) **2973**
Van Nghe Quan Doi/Army Literature and Arts. (VN) **2973**
Van Nghe Tien Phong. (US) **2027**
Van Taal Tot Taal. (NE ISSN 0165-9030) **2851**, 1670
Van Vechten Report. (US) **1056**, 1367
Vancouver Airport Business Directory. (CN) **4677**
Vancouver & District Dental Society Program. (CN) **3244**
Vancouver Art Gallery. Annual Report. (CN ISSN 0083-5161) **3534**
Vancouver Board of Trade. Annual Report. (CN ISSN 0083-517X) **840**
Vancouver Board of Trade Roster and Purchasers' Guide. (CN) **824**
Vancouver Buy and Sell Press. (CN) **1056**
Vancouver Child. (CN) **1245**, 1269
Vancouver Community College Voice *see* Voice **1329**

Vancouver Downtown Young Men's Christian Association Weekly News (Vancouver, BC) *see* Y M C A Weekly News (Vancouver, BC) **3811**
Vancouver Free Press *see* Georgia Straight **2177**
Vancouver Gastronomic. (CN ISSN 0706-5302) **2481**
Vancouver Island Regional Library Newsletter. (CN ISSN 0380-1691) **2790**
Vancouver Magazine. (CN ISSN 0380-9552) **2739**, 1269
Vancouver Neurological Centre. Annual Reports. (CN ISSN 0083-5196) **3355**
Vancouver Numismatic Society. News Bulletin. (CN ISSN 0049-5824) **3602**
Vancouver Opera Journal *see* Tempo **5288**
Vancouver Port Handbook. (UK ISSN 0264-5661) **4741**, 1158
Vancouver Stock Exchange. Annual Report. (CN ISSN 0083-520X) **968**
Vancouver Stock Exchange Review. (CN ISSN 0049-5832) **968**
Vancouver Stockwatch. (CN) **968**
Vancouver Venture Magazine. (CN) **1056**
Vancouver Visitor News. (CN) **4795**
Vand og Miljoe. (DK ISSN 0109-4130) **1971**
Vandaar. (NE) **4252**
Vandance. (CN ISSN 0705-8063) **1532**
▼Vandeloecht's Fiction Magazine. (US) **2973**
Vanderbilt Hustler. (US ISSN 0042-2517) **1329**
Vanderbilt Journal of Transnational Law.(US ISSN 0090-2594) **2730**
Vanderbilt Law Review. (US ISSN 0042-2533) **2691**
Vanderbilt Magazine. (US) **1329**
Vanderbilt Rubber Handbook. (US ISSN 0083-5218) **4294**
†Vanderbilt University. Abstracts of Theses. (US) **5299**
Vanderbilt University. Department of Environmental and Water Resources Engineering. Technical Reports. (US ISSN 0093-6332) **1971**, 4830
Vanderbilt University Publications in Anthropology. (US) **252**
Vanderplaats, Miura & Associates, Inc. Engineering Newsletter *see* V M A Engineering Newsletter **1880**
†Vanderpool Newsletter. (US) **5300**
Vandoma. (PO) **4456**
Vandteknik. (DK ISSN 0106-3677) **4830**
Vanessa. (GW) **1269**
Vanessas Zeitgeist. (GW ISSN 0934-8786) **1269**
Vanfoerebladet *see* Handicap - Nyt **4407**
Vanfoeres Jul *see* Julehaeftet, Vanfoeres Jul **4411**
Vangnet. (NE ISSN 0921-2574) **3363**
Vanguard. *see* Tien Phong **1268**
Vanguard (Columbia). (US ISSN 0892-6433) **2498**
Vanguard (La Habra). (US) **2083**
Vanguard (Milwaukee). (US ISSN 0042-2568) **4252**
Vanguard (Mobile). (US) **1329**
†Vanguard (Orlando). (US) **5300**
Vanguard (San Francisco) *see* Young Ideas **1246**
†Vanguard (Vancouver). (CN ISSN 0315-5226) **5300**
Vanidades Continental. (US ISSN 0505-0146) **2210**
Vanished Children's Alliance Newsletter. (US) **1245**, 4423
Vanishing Cab. (US) **2888**
Vanita. (IT) **374**
Vanita Jyoti. (II) **4854**
Vanitha. (II) **4854**
Vanitha Vitti. (CE) **4854**
†Vanity. (IT) **5300**
Vanity Fair *see* Honey **2194**
Vanity Fair. (US ISSN 0733-8899) **2888**
Vanning Now. (US) **4660**
Vantage. (US) **2279**

Vantage Conference Report see Report of a Vantage Conference 3970
Vantage Point. (KO) 3932, 887
†Vantage Point. (American Council for the Arts) (US ISSN 0748-6723) 5300
Vantage Point: Issues in American Arts see Vantage Point 5300
Vantage Report see Physician Executive Review 1024
Vanuatu. Geological Survey. Reports. (NN ISSN 0077-8443) 1584
Vanuatu. National Planning and Statistics Office. Census of Population (Year). Base Tables see Vanuatu. Statistics Offices. Census of Population (Year). Basic Tables 3996
Vanuatu. National Planning and Statistics Office. Consumer Prices Indexes see Vanuatu. Statistics Office. Consumer Prices Indexes 1509
Vanuatu. National Planning and Statistics Office. Manpower and Employment Survey. Final Results see Vanuatu. Statistics Office. Manpower and Employment Surveys 743
Vanuatu. National Planning and Statistics Office. Monetary and Banking Statistics see Vanuatu. Statistics Office. Monetary and Bankng Statistics 743
Vanuatu. National Planning and Statistics Office. Overseas Migration see Vanuatu. Statistics Office. Overseas Migration 3996
Vanuatu. National Planning and Statistics Office. Overseas Trade see Vanuatu. Statistics Office. Overseas Trade 743
Vanuatu. National Planning and Statistics Office. Statistical Indicators see Vanuatu. Statistics Office. Statistical Indicators 743
Vanuatu. Statistics Office. Consumer Prices Indexes. (NN) 1509
Vanuatu. Statistics Office. Manpower and Employment Surveys. (NN) 743, 996
Vanuatu. Statistics Office. Monetary and Bankng Statistics. (NN) 743, 802
Vanuatu. Statistics Office. National Accounts of Vanuatu. (NN) 743, 757
Vanuatu. Statistics Office. Overseas Migration. (NN) 3996
Vanuatu. Statistics Office. Overseas Trade. (NN) 743, 924
Vanuatu. Statistics Office. Report of the Agricultural Census. (NN) 144
Vanuatu. Statistics Office. Report on Smallholder Agriculture Survey. (NN) 144
Vanuatu. Statistics Office. Second National Development Pland. (NN) 743
Vanuatu. Statistics Office. Statistical Indicators. (NN) 743, 887
Vanuatu. Statistics Offices. Census of Population (Year). Basic Tables. (NN) 3996
Vanuatu in Facts and Figures. (NN) 4801, 4795
Vanuatu in Figures see Vanuatu in Facts and Figures 4801
Vanyajati. (II ISSN 0042-2622) 252
Vaovao. (MG) 4076
Vaovao F J K M. (MG) 4208
Vapaa Sana/Free Press. (CN) 2027
Vapor Trail's Boating News & International Yachting & Cruiser and Manufacturers Report. (US) 4530
El Vaquero. (US) 1329
Varazdinske Vijesti. (CI ISSN 0042-2711) 2888
Varbergs Museum. Aarsbok. (SW ISSN 0083-5536) 3534
Varehandelsstatistikk see Norway. Statistisk Sentralbyraa. Varehandelsstatistikk 732
Varen. (BE) 4530
Varendra Research Museum. Journal. (BG) 3534, 3645
Variedades. (VE) 4854
Varieties of English around the World. (US ISSN 0172-7362) 2851
Variety. (US ISSN 0042-2738) 4642, 3518

†Variety International Motion Picture Marketplace. (US) 5300
Variety Show. see Qu Yi 4637
†Variety's Complete Home Video Directory. (US ISSN 0000-1015) 5300
†Variety's Complete Home Video Directory. Adult Supplement. (US ISSN 0000-1007) 5300
Variety's Directory of Major U S Show Business Awards. (US) 4642, 415
Variety's Film Reviews. (US) 3519
Variety's Video Directory Plus. (US) 3519, 1386
Variety's Who's Who in Show Business. (US) 415, 4642
Varkens. (NE) 228
Varkenshouderij. (NE) 228
Varlik. (TU ISSN 0042-2762) 2973, 3008
Varme og Sanitets Nyt. (DK ISSN 0042-2770) 2304
Varme og Sanitets Nyt. Leverandoerregister. (DK) 2304
†Varmeforsyningsplanlaegning: Status. (DK ISSN 0108-4615) 5300
Varnado Genealogist. (US) 2166
Varosi Kozlekedes/Urban Transport. (HU ISSN 0133-0314) 4716, 4722
Varsavska Posta see Warsaw Post 5302
†Varshank. (II) 5300
Varsity. (CN ISSN 0042-2789) 1329
Varsity. (SA ISSN 0042-2797) 1329
Varsity Focus. (KE) 1329
Varsity Student Handbook. (CN ISSN 0229-9119) 1329
Varsoi Posta see Warsaw Post 5302
Varstvo Narave/Nature Conservation. (XV ISSN 0506-4252) 1499
Varstvo Spomenikov/Monument Conservation. (XV ISSN 0350-9494) 2394
VARTA - Fuehrer. (GW) 2481, 4795
VARTA - Fuehrer durch Deutschland, Westlicher Teil und Berlin see VARTA - Fuehrer 2481
Vartiaisten Viesti see Sukuviesti 2391
Vas Megyei Konyvtarak Ertesitoje. (HU ISSN 0133-7351) 2790
Vasa. (SZ ISSN 0301-1526) 3212
Vasama. (FI ISSN 0049-5883) 2591, 1910
Vasanta. (MF) 3645, 2335
Vasarnapi Hirek. (HU ISSN 0237-384X) 2198
▼Vascular Medicine Review. (UK ISSN 0954-2582) 3212
Vascular Surgery. (US ISSN 0042-2835) 3385, 3212
Vasculum. (UK ISSN 0049-5891) 4351
Vashudha. (NP) 3932
Vasi Szemle. (HU ISSN 0505-0332) 2394
Vaspitanje i Obrazovanje. (YU ISSN 0350-1094) 1670
Vassar Quarterly. (US ISSN 0042-2851) 1329
Vassar Views. (US) 1329
Vasudha Monthly. (NP ISSN 0042-2878) 2211
Vasuti Kozlekedesi Szakirodalmi Tajekoztato/Railway Transportation Abstracts. (HU ISSN 0231-0767) 4668
▼Vatan. (RU ISSN 0868-7196) 2343, 2394
Vatican Notes. (US) 3759
Vatican Observatory Publications. (VC ISSN 0083-5293) 371
Vatican Voices and Notable Papal Quotes. (US) 4278
Vatra. (RM) 2888
Vatrechni Bolesti. (BU ISSN 0506-2772) 3256, 3270, 3274, 3370
Vatten/Water. (SW ISSN 0042-2886) 4830, 1499, 1971
Vaucluse Agricole. (FR) 128
Vauhdin Maailma. (FI ISSN 0355-4295) 4705
▼Vault of Horror. (US) 3015
Vayu Aerospace Review. (II) 64
Vayu Mandal. (II ISSN 0970-1397) 3442
Vayuyan. (II) 4677
Vcelar. (CS) 128

Vcelarstvi. (CS ISSN 0042-2924) 128
Vcielka. (CS) 1269
Vea. (CL) 2180
Vea. (CK) 2183
Vea. (CU) 4795
Veac Nou see Mapamond 5232
Veale Heritage. (US) 2166
Veba Wohnen Magazin. (GW) 2498
▼Vecinos del Valle. (US) 2027
Vecinos Mundiales en Accion see World Neighbors in Action 3977
Veckan med Radio och T V see T V - Veckan och Radio 1381
Veckans Affaerer. (SW ISSN 0506-4406) 1086
Vector. (SA ISSN 0256-7008) 1910
Vector. (UK ISSN 0505-0448) 3015, 2973
Vector. (CN ISSN 0382-0718) 3061
Vector Buyers Guide see Pulse Buyers Guide 1906
Veda a Tachnika Mlodezi see Veda, Technika a My 1269
Veda, Technika a My/Science, Technology and We. (CS) 1269, 4351, 4613
Vedanta Kesari. (II ISSN 0042-2983) 3786, 4049
Vedecke Prace Ceskoslovenske Akademie Zemedelskych Ved z Dejin Zemedelstvi a Lesnictvi see Zemedelske Muzeum. Vedecke Prace 131
Vedere see Vedere-International 3305
Vedere Contact International. (IT ISSN 0392-0453) 3305
Vedere-International. (IT ISSN 0302-6256) 3305
Vedic Globe. (NP ISSN 0887-2023) 4391
Vedic Light. (II ISSN 0377-6530) 3786
Vedroerende Udviklingen i de Europaeiske Faellesskaber. Beretning.(DK ISSN 0107-2013) 698
Veehouden Nu. (NE) 228
Veehouderij. (NE) 228
Veepraktijk. (NE) 228
Veeteelt. (NE ISSN 0168-7565) 228
Veevoeding see Veehouden Nu 228
Der Veg. (IS) 3932
Vegan. (UK ISSN 0307-4811) 3612, 232
Vegetable and Ornamental Crops Research Station. Bulletin. Series B. (JA ISSN 0386-250X) 128
Vegetables. see Shucai 192
Vegetables and Specialties Situation and Outlook Report. (US) 195, 887
Vegetables Newsletter see Vegetables Specialist 2140
Vegetables Specialist. (CN) 2140
Vegetal see Jardineries Vegetal 2132
Vegetarian see Vegetarian Living 3810
Vegetarian Astrologer. (US) 359, 3612
Vegetarian Courier. (US ISSN 0049-5905) 3809
Vegetarian Handbook. (UK) 3612, 2481, 4795
Vegetarian Health Science see Health Science 3803
Vegetarian Journal. (US ISSN 0885-7636) 3612, 1508, 2083
Vegetarian Living. (UK) 3810
Vegetarian Times. (US ISSN 0164-8497) 3810, 3612
Vegetarian Voice. (US ISSN 0271-1591) 3612, 3810
Vegetarian World see Vegetarian Times 3810
Der Vegetarier. (GW ISSN 0178-9104) 3613
Vegetarisk Tidsskrift. (DK ISSN 0109-8861) 3613
Vegetatio. (NE ISSN 0042-3106) 520
†Die Vegetation Ungarischer Landschaften. (HU ISSN 0083-5323) 5300
Vegetative Resources. see Rastitel'nye Resursy 516
Vegyipari Szakirodalmi Tajekoztato/ Chemical Engineering Abstracts. (HU ISSN 0231-0775) 1203, 24, 1190, 1860

Vehicle Builders and Repairers Association. Directory of Members and Buyers Guide see Vehicle Builders & Repairers Association. Industry Yearbook 5300
†Vehicle Builders & Repairers Association. Industry Yearbook. (UK) 5300
Vehicle Builders and Repairers Association (VBRA) Industry Yearbook see V B R A Industry Yearbook 5299
Vehicle Leasing Today. (US) 4705, 698
Vehicle Sizes and Weights Manual. (US) 4749
Vehicle System Dynamics. (NE ISSN 0042-3114) 4660
Vehicule des Conducteurs Proprietaires.(CN ISSN 0838-5610) 4749
Vehicules a Moteur Importes. see Eingefuehrte Motorfahrzeuge 4663
Vehicules a Moteur, Partie 1, Charges Fiscales et Reglementation. see Canada. Statistics Canada. Motor Vehicle, Part 1, Rates and Regulations 5160
Vehicules a Moteur, Partie 4, Recettes. see Canada. Statistics Canada. Motor Vehicle, Part 4, Revenues 5160
Veiledende Liste for Barne og Ungdomslitteratur. Utvalg av Boker Utkommet. (NO) 1269
Veilig Vliegen. (NE ISSN 0042-3122) 64, 3474
Veiligheidsbestuur. see Safety Management 3621
Veiligheidsjaarboek see Arbo Jaarboek 3614
Veinte Siglos see XX Siglos 2327
Veja. (BL ISSN 0042-3165) 2175
Vejdatalaboratoriet. Rapport. (DK ISSN 0107-0614) 4722
Vejdatalaboratoriet Nyt see V D L Nyt 4722
Vejle amts Aarbog. (DK) 2394
Vejtransporten i Tal og Tekst. (DK ISSN 0083-5358) 4705
Vejviser for Maskinindustrien. (DK) 3024
Vek 20 i Mir see Twentieth Century and Peace 3974
Vekove. (BU ISSN 0324-0967) 2394, 3932
La Vela. (CN) 4530
Vela e Motor see Mar: Vela e Motor 4526
Vela e Motore. (IT ISSN 0042-3181) 4530
Velay Magazine. (FR) 2188
Veld see Veld & Flora 520
Veld & Flora. (SA ISSN 0042-3203) 520
Veliger. (US ISSN 0042-3211) 593
Velikogoricki List. (CI ISSN 0042-322X) 2888
Velki. (II ISSN 0042-3238) 2443
Velo Mag. (CN ISSN 1180-1360) 4521
Velo Magazine. (FR) 4521
Velocidad. (AG ISSN 0049-5913) 4705
VeloNews. (US ISSN 0161-1798) 4521
Veltro. (IT ISSN 0042-3254) 2888
Veluws Kerkblad. (NE ISSN 0042-3262) 4208
Velvet Light Trap. (US ISSN 0149-1830) 3519
Venadam Bibliotheekgids see Nederlandse Bibliotheek- en Documenatiegids 2776
VenAmCham's Executive Newcomers Guide see Living in Venezuela 4774
Vend see Vending Times 1056
Ven'd'Est. (CN ISSN 0831-4039) 2179
Vending. (IT) 1056
Vending Times. (US ISSN 0042-3327) 1056
Vendogiocattoli see V G Vendogiocattoli 2283
Vendor Catalog Services Index. (US) 1158, 1840
Vendor Product Comparison (Design Engineering). (US) 1056, 1158
Vendre Aujourd'hui. (FR) 1056

Vendredi. (FR ISSN 0995-0583) **3932**
Vendredi Samedi Dimanche see V S D **2188**
Vendsyssel Aarbog. (DK ISSN 0085-7645) **2394**
†Vendsyssel Historiske Museum. (DK ISSN 0108-867X) **5300**
Vendsyssel Nu og Da. (DK ISSN 0105-2608) **2394**
Vene. (FI ISSN 0042-3343) **4530**
Veneficus. (NO ISSN 0042-3351) **3745**
Venemaailma. (FI) **4530**
Venereal Diseases in Canada see Sexually Transmitted Diseases in Canada **3249**
Venetica. (IT) **2394**
†Veneto Notizie. (IT) **5300**
Venezie e l'Italia see Italia Turistica **4773**
Venezie Francescane. (IT) **348**
Venezuela. (UK ISSN 0144-4751) **4795**
Venezuela. Archivo General de la Nacion. Boletin. (VE ISSN 0042-3378) **2425**
Venezuela. Congreso de la Republica. Archivo Historico. Boletin. (VE) **2425**
Venezuela. Departamento de Investigaciones Educacionales. Seccion de Estadistica. Estadisticas Educacionales. (VE) **1670**
Venezuela. Hospital Central de la Fuerzas Armadas. Boletin Medico. (VE) **3161**
Venezuela. Ministerio de Agricultura y Cria. Boletin de Precios de Productos Agropecuarios. (VE) **144**
Venezuela. Ministerio de Agricultura y Cria. Direccion de Economia y Estadistica Agropecuaria. Division de Estadistica. Plan de Trabajo. (VE ISSN 0085-7653) **144**
Venezuela. Ministerio de Agricultura y Cria. Direccion de Economia y Estadistica Agropecuaria. Anuario Estadistico Agropecuario. (VE ISSN 0083-5366) **128**
Venezuela. Ministerio de Agricultura y Cria. Direccion de Planificacion y Estadistica. Estadisticas Agropecuarias de las Entidades Federales. (VE) **144**
Venezuela. Ministerio de Agricultura y Cria. Division de Estadistica. Encuesta Avicola Nacional. (VE) **228**
Venezuela. Ministerio de Agricultura y Cria. Division de Estadistica. Encuesta de Ganado Porcino. (VE) **228**
Venezuela. Ministerio de Energia y Minas. Anuario Estadistico Minero. (VE) **3502**
Venezuela. Ministerio de Energia y Minas. Apendice Estadistico. (VE) **1801, 3502, 4591**
Venezuela. Ministerio de Energia y Minas. Boletin de Geologia. (VE ISSN 0006-6281) **1584**
Venezuela. Ministerio de Energia y Minas. Carta Semanal. (VE) **3497, 3703**
Venezuela. Ministerio de Energia y Minas. Informations. (VE) **3497, 3703**
Venezuela. Ministerio de Energia y Minas. Memoria y Cuenta. (VE) **3497, 3703**
Venezuela. Ministerio de Energia y Minas. Petroleo y Otros Datos Estadisticos. (VE) **3707**
Venezuela. Ministerio de Energia y Minas. Quarterly Bulletin. (VE) **3497, 3703**
Venezuela. Ministerio de Hacienda. Boletin Estadistico. (VE) **2500, 4591**
Venezuela. Ministerio de Hacienda. Cuenta General de Ingresos y Gastos Publicos, Bienes Nacionales, Inclusive Materias: Ingresos y Gastos. (VE) **1000**
Venezuela. Ministerio de Hacienda. Memoria. (VE) **4076, 802, 2498**
Venezuela. Ministerio de Sanidad y Asistencia Social. Memoria y Cuenta. (VE) **4423**
Venezuela. Ministerio de Energia y Minas. Memoria. (VE) **1801, 3502**

Venezuela. Oficina Central de Estadistica e Informatica. Coyuntura Economica. (VE) **743**
Venezuela. Oficina Central de Estadistica e Informatica. Encuesta Cualitativa. (VE) **743**
Venezuela. Oficina Central de Estadistica e Informatica. Memoria y Cuenta. (VE) **698**
Venezuela. Oficina Central de Estadistica e Informatico. Anuario Estadistico. (VE) **743**
Venezuela Estadistica e Informatica. (VE) **743**
Venezuela Grafica. (VE) **2238**
Venezuela Odontologia. (VE ISSN 0042-3424) **3244**
Venezuelan - American Chamber of Commerce and Industry. Yearbook and Membership Directory. (VE) **824**
Venezuelan Automotive Guide. see Guia Automotriz de Venezuela **4692**
Venezuelan Petroleum Industry. Statistical Data see Venezuela. Ministerio de Energia y Minas. Petroleo y Otros Datos Estadisticos **3707**
Venga Il Tuo Regno. (IT) **4278**
Venga Que le Cuento. (AG) **2973**
†Vengerskaja Literatura po Bibliotekovedeniju i Informatike. (HU ISSN 0133-7319) **5300**
Vengerski Statisticheski Spravochnik see Magyar Statisztikai Zsebkonyv **4578**
Vengerskii Stroitel'nyi Byulleten' see Hungarian Building Bulletin **5207**
Vengria v Godu see Magyarorszag **4578**
Venice (Year). (US) **4795**
Venite Adoremus. (IT ISSN 0393-9901) **4278**
Venster van die Overberg. (SA) **2217**
Vent - Art. (BE ISSN 0042-3440) **348, 2973**
Ventana. (US ISSN 0042-3459) **4252**
Ventilation du Trafic Commercial. (FR) **4668**
Vento del Sud. (IT) **2027, 3932, 3976**
Ventura County Historical Society Quarterly. (US ISSN 0042-3491) **2425**
Ventura Magazine. (US) **2237**
Ventura Professional. (US) **4138**
Venture. (PK ISSN 0042-3483) **2851, 2973**
†Venture (New York). (US ISSN 0191-3530) **5300**
Venture Capital see Coup **657**
Venture Capital Journal. (US) **968, 1119**
Venture Capital Report. (UK ISSN 0265-6248) **1119, 968**
Venture Capital Report Guide to Venture Capital in Europe. (UK) **1119**
Venture Forth. (CN ISSN 0315-2235) **1670**
Venture Inward. (US ISSN 0748-3406) **3597, 3671, 4208**
Venture Japan. (US) **924, 968**
†Venture Link. (CN) **5300**
Venture - Product Digest. (US) **968**
Venturi. (SA ISSN 0042-3572) **1329, 1840**
†Venue. (US) **5300**
Venue Magazine. (UK) **4642, 348**
Venus. (US) **4854**
Venus: Japanese Journal of Malacology/ Kairuigaku Zasshi. (JA ISSN 0042-3580) **593**
Ver Poets Voices. (UK) **3008**
Vera Lex. (US ISSN 0893-4851) **3786, 2425**
Veranda. (US ISSN 1040-8150) **2555**
Veranstaltungskalender. (GW) **1697**
Verantwoord Levensverkeer. (NE ISSN 0028-999X) **1539**
Verba. (SP ISSN 0210-377X) **2851**
Verba Seniorum. (IT ISSN 0391-8564) **4208, 1280**
Verbaende, Behoerden, Organisationen der Wirtschaft. (GW ISSN 0085-7661) **887**

Verband Angestellter Akademiker und Leitender Angestellter der Chemischen Industrie. Info. (GW) **824**
Verband Baugewerblicher Unternehmer Hessen. Mitteilungsblatt. (GW) **1876**
Verband der Automobilindustrie. Jahresbericht. (GW) **4705**
Verband der Automobilindustrie. Taetigkeitsbericht see Verband der Automobilindustrie. Jahresbericht **4705**
Verband der Deutscher-Amerikanischen Clubs e.V. Gazette. (GW) **1302**
Verband der Initiativgruppen in der Auslaenderarbeit e.V. Magazin see V I A Magazin **3948**
†Verband der Juedische Gemeinden in der D.D.R. Nachrichtenblatt. (GW) **5300**
Verband der Kraftfahrzeugteile- und Zweiradgrosshaendler e.V. Nachrichten see V K G - Nachrichten **5299**
Verband der Schweizer Druckindustrie Mitteilungen see V S D - Mitteilungen **4006**
Verband der Versicherungsunternehmungen Oesterreichs. Bericht ueber das Geschaeftsjahr see Verband der Versicherungsunternehmungen Oesterreichs. Geschaeftsbericht **4423**
Verband der Versicherungsunternehmungen Oesterreichs. Geschaeftsbericht. (AU) **4423**
Verband des Radio-, Fernseh-, und Elektro-Fachhandels und Gewerbes Oesterreichs Info see V R F Info **1383**
Verband des Wurttembergischen Verkehrsgewerbes. Sueddeutscher Verkehrsurier. (GW) **4716**
Verband Deutscher Akademiker fuer Landwirtschaft, Ernaehrung und Landespflege e.V. Journal see V D L - Journal **128**
Verband Deutscher Biologen. Mitteilungen see Biologie Heute **432**
Verband Deutscher Chemo Techniker und Chemisch - Technischer Association Nachrichten see V D C - Nachrichten **824**
Verband fuer Schiffbau und Meerestechnik. Jahresbericht. (GW) **4741**
Verband Schweizer Regionalbanken. Monitor. (SZ) **803**
Verband Schweizerischer Regionalbanken und Sparkassen. Monitor see Verband Schweizer Regionalbanken. Monitor **803**
Verbandsgemeinde Edenkoben. Amtsblatt. (GW) **4096**
Verbatim. (US ISSN 0162-0932) **2851**
†Verbindungstechnik. (GW ISSN 0049-5921) **5300**
Verbindungstechnik in der Elektronik. (GW ISSN 0935-4441) **1910**
Verbond van Belgische Ondernemingen. Jaarlyks Verslag. see Federation des Entreprises de Belgique. Rapport Annuel **1075**
Verbondsnieuws voor de Belgische Sierteelt. (BE) **2110, 2140, 2143**
Verbrauche Aktuell. (GW) **1508**
Verbraucher Politische Korrespondenz. (GW ISSN 0042-3653) **1508**
Verbraucher Rundschau. (GW ISSN 0042-3661) **1508**
Verbraucher Telegramm. (GW) **1508**
Verbraucher und Recht. (GW) **4159, 2691**
Verbreitungsdaten der Schweizer Presse. (SZ) **39, 4138**
Verbum. (US ISSN 0889-4507) **352, 1475**
Verbum. (NE ISSN 0166-6002) **1762, 4278**
Verbum. (FR ISSN 0182-5887) **2851**
Verbum. (GW ISSN 0042-3696) **4289**
Verbundfahrplan. (GW) **4660**
Verbundfahrplan U - S. (GW) **4716**
Verdad y Vida. (SP ISSN 0042-3718) **3786**

VEREIN   6785

Verdauungskrankheiten. (GW ISSN 0174-738X) **3161**
Verde. Boletin. (SP ISSN 0213-8980) **228**
Verde Olivo. (CU ISSN 0506-6913) **2888**
Verde Yerba. (SP) **3008**
Verden og Vi. (NO) **3932**
Verden og Vi see F.N. Orientering **3957**
Verden Rundt. (DK ISSN 0109-0062) **4208**
Verdeta. (IT) **1288, 1269**
Verdi. (IT ISSN 0042-3734) **3585, 2325**
Verdi Newsletter. (US ISSN 0160-2667) **3585, 421**
Verdict Reports see Verdict Review **2692**
Verdict Review. (US) **2692**
Verdicts, Settlements & Tactics. (US) **2692**
Vereeniging Nederlandsch Historisch Scheepvaart Museum te Amsterdam. Jaarverslag. (NE ISSN 0922-1891) **4741, 2325**
Vereeniging tot Uitgaaf van de Bronnen van het Oud-Vaderlandse Recht. Werken. (NE) **2325, 2692**
Verein der am Rohkakaohandel Beteiligten Firmen. Geschaftsbericht. (GW) **2083**
Verein der Freunde Carnuntums. Mitteilungen. (AU ISSN 0042-3750) **289**
Verein Deutscher Ingenieure. Informationsdienst. Instandhaltung. (GW ISSN 0724-1976) **1847, 24, 1940, 3024**
Verein Deutscher Ingenieure Berichte see V D I - Berichte **1839**
Verein Deutscher Ingenieure Forschungshefte see V D I - Forschungshefte **5299**
Verein Deutscher Ingenieure Informationsdienst. Drahtherstellung u. Drahterzeugnisse see V D I Informationsdienst. Drahtherstellung u. Drahterzeugnisse **1847**
Verein Deutscher Kohlenimporteure. Jahresbericht. (GW) **3497**
Verein Deutscher Zementwerke. Forschungsinstitut der Zementindustrie. Taetigkeitsbericht. (GW ISSN 0507-6714) **635**
Verein fuer die Geschichte Berlins. Mitteilungen. (GW) **2394, 4096**
Verein fuer Geschichte der Deutschen in den Sudetenlaendern. Jahrbuch see Bohemia: Zeitschrift fuer Geschichte und Kultur der Bohemischen Laender **2353**
Verein fuer Geschichte der Stadt Nuernberg. Mitteilungen. (GW ISSN 0083-5579) **2394**
Verein fuer Geschichte der Stadt Wien. Jahrbuch. (AU) **2394**
Verein fuer Geschichte des Bodensees und seiner Umgebung. Schriften. (GW ISSN 0342-2070) **2394**
Verein fuer Hamburgische Geschichte. Zeitschrift. (GW ISSN 0083-5587) **2394**
Verein fuer Heimatkunde im Landkreis Birkenfeld und der Heimatfreunde Oberstein. Mitteilungen. (GW ISSN 0341-6992) **2394**
†Verein fuer Krebsforschung. Mitteilungen. (SZ ISSN 0042-3777) **5300**
Verein fuer Luebeckische Geschichte und Altertumskunde. Zeitschrift. (GW ISSN 0083-5609) **2394**
Verein fuer Niederdeutsche Sprachforschung. Korrespondenzblatt.(GW ISSN 0342-0752) **2851**
Verein fuer Niedersaechsisches Volkstum. Bremer Heimatbund. Mitteilungen. (GW) **2027**
Verein fuer Niedersaechsisches Volkstum. Mitteilungen see Verein fuer Niedersaechsisches Volkstum. Bremer Heimatbund. Mitteilungen **2027**
Verein fuer Niedersaechsisches Volkstum e.V. Bremen. Mitteilungen. (GW) **2394**

VEREIN

Verein fuer Vaterlaendische Naturkunde in Wuerttemberg. Jahresheft see Gesellschaft fuer Naturkunde in Wuerttemberg. Jahreshefte **440**
Verein fuer Volkskunde in Wien. Sonderschriften. (AU) **2059**, 252, 348
Verein fuer Wasser-, Boden- und Lufthygiene. Schriftenreihe. (GW ISSN 0300-8665) **1499**, 1971
Verein Hamburger Exporteure. Rundschreibendienst fuer Mitgliedsunternehmen. (GW) **924**
Verein Oberpfaelzisches Bauernmuseum. Mitteilungen. (GW) **128**, 2059
Verein zum Schutz der Bergwelt. Jahrbuch. (GW) **1499**
Verein zur Foerderung eines Deutschen Forschungsnetzes Mitteilungen see D F N Mitteilungen **1446**
Verein zur Foerderung Katholisch-Sozialer Bildungswerke Inform see A K S B - Inform **1681**
Vereinigte Evangelisch-Lutherische Kirche Deutschlands Information see V E L K D - Information **4252**
Vereinigte Wirtschaftsdienste GmbH Bauwirtschaft see V W D - Bauwirtschaft **967**
Vereinigte Wirtschaftsdienste GmbH Chemie: Kautschuk see V W D - Chemie: Kautschuk **967**
Vereinigte Wirtschaftsdienste GmbH Elektro see V W D - Elektro **967**
Vereinigte Wirtschaftsdienste GmbH Energie see V W D - Energie **967**
Vereinigte Wirtschaftsdienste GmbH Europa see V W D - Europa **967**
Vereinigte Wirtschaftsdienste GmbH Finanz- und Wirtschaftsspiegel see V W D - Finanz- und Wirtschaftsspiegel **967**
Vereinigte Wirtschaftsdienste GmbH Getraenke see V W D - Getraenke **968**
Vereinigte Wirtschaftsdienste GmbH Getreide und Futtermittel see V W D - Getreide und Futtermittel **968**
Vereinigte Wirtschaftsdienste GmbH Haeute und Leder see V W D - Haeute und Leder **968**
Vereinigte Wirtschaftsdienste GmbH Kaffee, Kakao, Tee, Suesswaren see V W D - Kaffee, Kakao, Tee, Suesswaren **968**
Vereinigte Wirtschaftsdienste GmbH Landwirtschaft und Ernaehrung see V W D - Landwirtschaft und Ernaehrung **968**
Vereinigte Wirtschaftsdienste GmbH Maschinen see V W D - Maschinen **968**
Vereinigte Wirtschaftsdienste GmbH Montan see V W D - Montan **968**
Vereinigte Wirtschaftsdienste GmbH NE-Metalle see V W D - NE-Metalle **968**
Vereinigte Wirtschaftsdienste GmbH Oele und Fette see V W D - Oele und Fette **968**
Vereinigte Wirtschaftsdienste GmbH Stahl see V W D - Stahl **968**
Vereinigte Wirtschaftsdienste GmbH Textil see V W D - Textil **968**
Vereinigte Wirtschaftsdienste GmbH Vieh und Fleisch see V W D - Vieh und Fleisch **968**
Vereinigte Wirtschaftsdienste GmbH Zucker see V W D - Zucker **968**
Vereinigung der Technischen Ueberwachungs-Vereine e.V. Ue V Autoreport see T Ue V Autoreport **4703**
Vereinigung des Schweizerischen Import- und Grosshandels Mitteilungen see V S I G - Mitteilungen **924**
Vereinigung Deutscher Elektrizitaetswerke e.V. Oeffentliche Elektrizitaetsversorgung see V D E W die Oeffentliche Elektrizitaetsversorgung **1910**
Vereinigung Freischaffender Architeckten Jahrbuch see V F A Jahrbuch **308**
Vereinigung Freischaffender Architekten Profil see V F A Profil **308**
Vereinigung Oesterreichischer Bibliothekare. Mitteilungen. (AU ISSN 0042-3793) **2790**

Vereinigung Schweizerischer Petroleum-Geologen und -Ingenieure. Bulletin/ Association Suisse des Geologues et Ingenieurs du Petrole. Bulletin. (Vereinigung Schweizerischer Petroleum-Geologen und -Ingenieure) (SZ ISSN 0042-1901) **3703**, 1584
Vereinigung Schweizerischer Petroleum-Geologen und -Ingenieure Vereinigung Schweizerischer Petroleum-Geologen und -Ingenieure. Bulletin see Vereinigung Schweizerischer Petroleum-Geologen und -Ingenieure. Bulletin **3703**
Vereinigung Schweizerischer Strassenfachleute. Forschungsberichte. (SZ) **4722**
Vereinigung Schweizerischer Strassenfachleute. Versuchsberichte see Vereinigung Schweizerischer Strassenfachleute. Forschungsberichte **4722**
Vereinigung von Afrikanisten in Deutschland. Schriften. (GW ISSN 0341-275X) **2335**
Vereinigung zur Foerderung des Deutschen Brandschutzes e.V. Zeitschrift fuer Forschung und Technik im Brandschutz see V F D B: Zeitschrift fuer Forschung und Technik im Brandschutz **1860**
Vereins Praxis. (GW) **1302**, 4496
Vereinsbank Kundendienst. (GW) **803**, 887, 936
Vereinsmitteilungen. (GW) **2296**
Vereinte Nationen. (GW ISSN 0042-384X) **3976**
Verena. (GW) **3593**
Verenigde Nederlandse Uitgeversbedrijven. Annual Report. (NE) **4138**
Vereniging Dierenambulance Rotterdam Geluiden see D A R - Geluiden **231**
Vereniging Koninklijke Nederlandsche Heide Maatschappij. Heidemijtijdschrift. (NE) **128**, 1971
Vereniging Koninklijke Nederlandsche Heide Maatschappij. Tijdschrift see Vereniging Koninklijke Nederlandsche Heide Maatschappij. Heidemijtijdschrift **128**
Vereniging tot Uitgave der Bronnen van het oud Vaderlandsche Recht. Verslagen en Mededelingen see Stichting tot Uitgaaf der Bronnen van het oud-Vaderlaandse Recht. 2 Series: Werken, en Verslagen en Mededelingen **2389**
Vereniging van Religieus - Wetenschappelijke Bibliothecarissen Informatie see V R B - Informatie **2790**
Vereniging voor Nederlandse Muziekgeschiedenis. Tijdschrift. (NE ISSN 0042-3871) **3585**
Vereniging voor Oppervlaktetechnieken van Materialen. Documentatieservice.(NE) **3428**, 24
Vereniging voor Oppervlaktetechnieken van Metalen. Documentatieservice see Vereniging voor Oppervlaktetechnieken van Materialen. Documentatieservice **3428**
Verfahrenstechnik. (GW) **1840**
Verfahrenstechnische Berichte/Chemical and Process Engineering Abstracts. (GW ISSN 0042-3890) **1847**, 24
Verfassung und Recht in Uebersee. (GW ISSN 0506-7286) **2692**
Verfassung und Verfassungswirklichkeit.(GW ISSN 0083-5676) **3932**, 2692
Verfkroniek. (NE ISSN 0042-3904) **3655**
Vergel. (SP ISSN 0210-8089) **128**, 1499
Vergilian Society Newsletter see Augustan Age **1275**
Vergilius. (US ISSN 0506-7294) **1280**
Vergleichende Paedagogik/Comparative Education. (GW ISSN 0042-3920) **1670**
▼Verhaltenstherapie. (SZ ISSN 1016-6262) **3355**

Verhaltenstherapie und Psychosoziale Praxis. (GW ISSN 0721-7234) **4049**, 4391
Verhandlungen des Deutschen Geographentages. (GW ISSN 0083-5684) **2266**
Verhuetet Unfaelle. (GW ISSN 0042-3939) **3667**
Verifiche. (IT ISSN 0391-4186) **3786**
Verifiche e Proposte. (IT) **2518**
Veritas. (AG ISSN 0042-3947) **887**
Veritas see Veritas Forum **1876**
Veritas. (BL ISSN 0042-3955) **2175**
Veritas. (CI ISSN 0352-5708) **4278**
Veritas Forum. (NO) **1876**
Verkauf und Marketing see V M International **1056**
Verkaufsleiter Service. (GW ISSN 0178-5893) **1030**
Verkeerde Krant see Itch **2454**
Verkeerskunde. (NE) **4722**
Verkeersrecht. (NE ISSN 0042-398X) **2692**, 4722
Verkehr. (AU) **4722**
Verkehr in Afrika see Dampf und Reise **4708**
Verkehr und Technik. (GW ISSN 0340-4536) **4722**
Verkehrs Rundschau. (GW) **4660**, 4722
Verkehrsblatt. (GW ISSN 0042-4013) **4722**
Verkehrsdienst. (GW) **4722**
Verkehrsgeschichtliche Blaetter. (GW ISSN 0232-9042) **4716**, 2325, 4722
Verkehrsgewerbe. (GW) **4716**
Verkehrsgewerbe fuer Niedersachsen und Bremen. (GW) **4716**
Das Verkehrsgewerbe Westfalen-Lippe. (GW) **4660**
†Verkehrsmedizin und ihre Grenzgebiete. (GW ISSN 0042-4021) **5300**
Verkehrspsychologischer Informationsdienst. (AU ISSN 0042-4048) **4723**, 4114
Verkehrsrechtliche Mitteilungen. (GW) **4660**, 2692
Verkehrstechnik in der Schweiz. (SZ) **4668**
Verkehrsunfall see Verkehrsunfall und Fahrzeugtechnik **4705**
Verkehrsunfall und Fahrzeugtechnik. (GW) **4705**
VerkehrsWirtschaft. (GW ISSN 0723-6689) **4660**
Verkehrswirtschaftliche Zahlen see V W Z **4722**
Verkhovnyi Sovet S.S.S.R. Vedomosti. (RU ISSN 0042-3017) **3932**
▼Verkhovnyi Sud S.S.S.R. Vestnik. (RU) **2692**
Verko. (SW ISSN 0283-4669) **1940**
Verksamheten vid Kvismare Faagelstation see Faaglar i Kvismaren **563**
Verkstaederna. (SW ISSN 0042-4056) **3024**, 1940
Verkuendigung und Forschung. (GW ISSN 0342-2410) **4208**
Vermessungs-Informationen see Journal for Photogrammetrists & Surveyors **1869**
Der Vermessungsingenieur. (GW ISSN 0042-4099) **1876**, 2266
Vermessungstechnik. (GW ISSN 0042-4102) **1876**
Vermessungstechnische Rundschau (VR) see Vermessungswesen und Raumordnung (VR) **1876**
Vermessungswesen und Raumordnung (VR). (GW ISSN 0340-5141) **1876**, 2266
Vermieter und Gast. (GW) **2481**
Vermissa Herald. (US ISSN 0042-4129) **2986**
Vermont. Agricultural Experiment Station, Burlington. Miscellaneous Publications Series see Vermont. Agricultural Experiment Station, Burlington. Research Report **128**
Vermont. Agricultural Experiment Station, Burlington. Research Report.(US ISSN 0083-5706) **128**
Vermont. Agricultural Experiment Station, Burlington. Station Bulletin Series. (US ISSN 0083-5714) **128**

Vermont. Agricultural Experiment Station, Burlington. Station Pamphlet Series. (US ISSN 0083-5722) **128**
Vermont. Agricultural Experiment Station, Burlington. Technical Notes. (US) **128**
Vermont. Commissioner of Banking and Insurance. Annual Reports of the Bank Commissioner see Vermont. Commissioner of Banking Insurance and Securities. Annual Report of the Bank Commissioner **803**
Vermont. Commissioner of Banking Insurance and Securities. Annual Report of the Bank Commissioner. (US) **803**
Vermont Academy of Arts and Sciences. Student Symposium and Annual Conference. Occasional Papers. (US) **1720**
Vermont Archaeological Society, Inc. Newsletter see V A S Newsletter **289**
Vermont Bar Journal and Law Digest. (US) **2692**, 4076
Vermont Beverage Journal. (US) **386**
Vermont Business. (US) **698**
Vermont Business Phone Book & Manufacturers Directory. (US) **1158**
Vermont Buyer's Guide. (US) **1158**
Vermont Catholic Tribune. (US ISSN 0042-4145) **4278**
Vermont Court Rules Annotated. (US) **2734**
Vermont Cynic. (US) **2237**, 1329
Vermont Directory of Manufacturers see Vermont Buyer's Guide **1158**
Vermont Division of Geology and Mineral Resources. Bulletin. (US) **1584**
Vermont Division of Geology and Mineral Resources. Economic Geology. (US) **1584**, 1596
Vermont Division of Geology and Mineral Resources. Environmental Geology. (US) **1584**, 1601
Vermont Division of Geology and Mineral Resources. Special Bulletin. (US) **1585**
Vermont Education Directory. (US) **1670**, 1697
Vermont Fish and Wildlife Regulations. (US) **2692**, 4559
Vermont Geological Survey. Bulletin see Vermont Division of Geology and Mineral Resources. Bulletin **1584**
Vermont Geological Survey. Economic Geology see Vermont Division of Geology and Mineral Resources. Economic Geology **1584**
Vermont Geological Survey. Evironmental Geology see Vermont Division of Geology and Mineral Resources. Environmental Geology **1584**
Vermont Geological Survey. Special Bulletin see Vermont Division of Geology and Mineral Resources. Special Bulletin **1585**
Vermont Geological Survey. Special Publication. (US) **1585**, 1601
Vermont Geological Survey. Special Publications see Vermont Geological Survey. Special Publication **1585**
Vermont Historical Society News and Notes see Vermont History News **2425**
Vermont History. (US ISSN 0042-4161) **2425**
Vermont History News. (US) **2425**
Vermont Industrial Development Authority. Annual Report. (US ISSN 0363-2067) **1086**
Vermont Labor Force see Vermont Labor Market **996**
Vermont Labor Market. (US) **996**
Vermont Life. (US ISSN 0042-417X) **2237**
Vermont Magazine. (US) **2237**
Vermont Manufacturing Directory. (US) **1158**
Vermont - N E A Today. (US) **1670**
Vermont Parent and Child Magazine. (US) **1245**
Vermont Philatelist. (US) **3759**
Vermont Real Estate Guide. (US) **4159**, 39
Vermont Registered Nurse. (US) **3287**
Vermont Reports. (US) **2692**

Vermont Rules of Evidence. (US) **2692**
Vermont Science Newsletter. (US) **128**
Vermont Sports Today. (US) **4496**
Vermont State Medical Society. Newsletter see Vermont State Medical Society. Reporter **3161**
Vermont State Medical Society. Reporter. (US) **3161**
Vermont Statutes Annotated. (US) **2692**
Vermont Vacation. (US) **4795**
†Vermont Woman. (US ISSN 0895-2329) **5300**
Vermont Year Book. (US ISSN 0083-5781) **2425**
†Vermouth. (UK) **5300**
Vero Dialogo. (IT ISSN 0042-420X) **1524**
Veroeffentlichungen aus der Pathologie.(GW ISSN 0340-241X) **3161**
Veroeffentlichungen der Astronomischen Institut der Universitaet Bonn. (GW ISSN 0340-9821) **371**
Veroeffentlichungen des Max-Reger-Institutes. (GW ISSN 0543-1735) **3585**
Veroeffentlichungen fuer Naturschutz und Landschatspflege in Baden-Wuerttemberg. (GW ISSN 0342-684X) **1499**, 1971
Veroeffentlichungen zur Geschichte des Glases und der Glashuetter in Deutschland. (GW ISSN 0170-3447) **1167**
Veroeffentlichungen zur Musikforschung. (GW) **3585**
Veroeffentlichungen zur Verfassungsgeschichte von Baden-Wuerttemberg seit 1945. (GW) **2692**, 2394
Veroeffentlichungen zur Volkskunde und Kulturgeschichte. (GW ISSN 0138-3167) **2059**
Verona Fedele. (IT ISSN 0042-4242) **4278**
Verona Missions see Comboni Missions **4261**
Veronica. (NE) **1383**, 1360, 3519, 3585
Verpackung. (GW ISSN 0042-4269) **3652**
Die Verpackung. (SZ ISSN 0042-4277) **3652**
Verpackungs Berater. (GW ISSN 0042-4293) **3652**
Verpackungs-Rundschau. (GW ISSN 0042-4307) **3652**
Verpakken. (NE ISSN 0042-4315) **3652**
Verpleegkunde. (NE ISSN 0920-3273) **3287**, 1762
Verpleegkundig Historische Cahiers. (NE ISSN 0168-9924) **3288**
Verpleegkundig Historische Monografieen. (NE ISSN 0168-9975) **3288**
Verpleegnuus. see Nursing News **3284**
Verre Actualites. (FR) **1167**
Verre Naasten Naderbij see Culturen **238**
Vers Demain. (CN ISSN 0042-434X) **4208**
Der Versandhausberater. (GW ISSN 0049-5999) **1056**
Versants. (SZ) **2973**
Verschollene und Vergessene. (GW ISSN 0170-3633) **2973**
Verse. (US ISSN 0268-3830) **2973**, 3008
Verses. see Ci Kan **3545**
Versicherungs Betriebswirt. (GW) **2544**
Versicherungs Jahrbuch. (GW) **2544**
Versicherungsbetriebe. (GW ISSN 0344-6379) **2544**
Versicherungskaufmann. (GW ISSN 0049-6006) **2544**
Versicherungsmedizin. (GW ISSN 0933-4548) **3161**
Versicherungsrecht. (GW) **2544**
Versicherungsvermittlung. (GW ISSN 0049-6014) **2545**
Versicherungswirtschaft. (GW ISSN 0042-4358) **2545**
▼Version 90. (US) **2888**
▼Versiya. (RU) **3474**, 4076
Verslunarskyrslur - External Trade/External Trade Statistics. (IC) **4591**

Verso e Reverso. (BL ISSN 0103-1414) **2518**, 1345
Verso l'Azzurro. (IT ISSN 0042-4374) **4278**
Versorgungsbeamte see Die Versorgungsverwaltung **4423**
Die Versorgungsverwaltung. (GW) **4423**
Versorgungswirtschaft. (GW ISSN 0042-4382) **1910**, 4830
Verstaendliche Wissenschaft. (US ISSN 0083-5846) **4351**
Verstandig Ouderschap see Sekstant **4448**
Versuchsgrubengesellschaft mbH Quartalshefte see V-G Quartalshefte **3497**
Versuchsstation fuer das Gaerungsgewerbe in Wien. Mitteilungen see Oesterreichisches Getraenke Institut. Mitteilungen **384**
Versuchstierkunde. (GW ISSN 0300-1016) **3263**, 593
Vertebrata Palasiatica. see Gujizhui Dongwu Xuebao **3657**
Vertebrate Pest Conference. Proceedings. (US ISSN 0507-6773) **195**
Vertebratologicke Zpravy see U S E B Zpravy **592**
Vertegenwoordiger. (NE ISSN 0042-4412) **4138**
Vertex. (SP ISSN 0042-4420) **4559**
†Vertica. (US ISSN 0360-5450) **5300**
Vertical Distribution of Ozone from Ozonosonde Observation. see Wyniki Pomiarow Pionowego Rozkladu Ozonu w Atmosferze **3444**
Vertical File Index. (US ISSN 0042-4439) **24**
Vertice. (PO ISSN 0042-4447) **2888**
Vertiflite. (US ISSN 0042-4455) **64**
Vertragssystem see Wirtschaftsrecht **2695**
Vertrauliche Mitteilungen aus Politik, Wirtschaft und Geldanlage. (GW) **698**
Vertretungen der Bundesrepublik Deutschland im Ausland. (GW) **698**
Vertriebene Bauer. (GW) **128**
Verve. (US) **3008**
Vervoer & Verkeer. see Transport & Traffic **5291**
Vervoer- en Padoorsig. see Transport and Road Digest **4722**
Die Verwaltung. (GW ISSN 0042-4498) **4076**
Die Verwaltung der Stadt Wien. (AU) **4077**
Verwaltungsarchiv. (GW ISSN 0042-4501) **2692**, 4077
Verwaltungsbericht (Year). (GW) **3622**
Verwaltungstuehrung - Organisation - Personal Fachzeitschrift fuer die Oeffentliche Verwaltung see V O P - Fachzeitschrift fuer die Oeffentliche Verwaltung **4076**
Verwaltungsjahrbuch fuer die Deutsche Bundespost. (GW ISSN 0939-4400) **1367**
Verwaltungspraxis see Baden - Wuerttembergische Verwaltungspraxis **4054**
Verwaltungsrundschau. (GW ISSN 0342-5592) **2692**
Der Verwaltungswirt. (GW ISSN 0174-6162) **2692**, 1354
Verwarming en Ventilatie. (NE ISSN 0042-451X) **2304**
Very Large Scale Integration Advances in V L S I and Computer Systems see Advances in V L S I and Computer Systems **5131**
Very Occasional Papers. (US) **2790**
Verzameling van Middelnederlandse Bijbelteksten see Corpus Sacrae Scripturae Neerlandicae Medii Aevii **2908**
Verzeichnis der Konsularischen Vertretungen in Oesterreich. (AU) **3976**
Verzeichnis der Orientalischen Handschriften in Deutschland. (GW ISSN 0506-7936) **3645**
Verzeichnis der Orientalischen Handschriften in Deutschland. Supplementbaende. (GW ISSN 0506-7944) **3645**

Verzeichnis Lieferbarer Buecher/German Books in Print. (GW ISSN 0067-8899) **415**
Verzeichnis Rheinland-Pfaelzischer Recht- und Verwaltungsvorschriften. (GW) **2692**, 4077
Verzeichnis von Jubilaeumsschriften der Graphischen Industrie. see Directory of Company Histories of the Book Industries **4007**
Verzekerings-Archief. (NE ISSN 0042-4528) **2545**
Verzekerings Magazine V V P. (NE) **2545**
Verzekeringsnieuws. (BE) **2545**
Verzlunartidindi. (IC) **1056**
Vesak. (AT ISSN 1036-4471) **4216**
Veseli Svet. (YU ISSN 0042-4536) **2973**
Veselka. see Rainbow (Jersey City) **1263**
Veselka. (CS) **1269**, 1245
Veselye Kartinki. (RU ISSN 0320-8044) **1269**
Vesitalous. (FI ISSN 0505-3838) **4830**, 195, 1925
Veska see Schweizer Spital-Veska **2469**
Vesmir/Universe. (CS ISSN 0042-4544) **4351**
Vesnik. (YU ISSN 0351-6245) **803**
Vesnik Drustva Matematicara i Fizicara SR Srbije see Matematicki Vesnik **3044**
Vessel Inventory Report. (US) **4741**
Vestdijkkroniek. (NE) **2973**
Vestes see Australian Universities' Review **1700**
Vesteuropa Frimaerkekatalog see A F A Vesteuropa Frimaerkekatalog **3748**
Vestfynsk Hjemstavn. (DK ISSN 0108-6391) **2394**
Vestigia Bibliae. (SZ) **4208**
Vestirama. (SP) **1288**
Vestire see Vestire Uomo **1295**
Vestire Uomo. (IT) **1295**
Vestlandsk Landbruk. (NO) **128**
Vestnik. (XV ISSN 0042-4587) **2888**
Vestnik A C. (XV) **4705**
Vestnik Arkhivov Armenii. see Banber Hayastani Arkhivneri **2351**
Vestnik Dermatologii i Venerologii/Annals of Dermatology and Venereology. (RU ISSN 0042-4609) **3250**
Vestnik Drevnei Istorii/Journal of Ancient History. (RU ISSN 0042-4617) **2325**, 1280, 3645
Vestnik Khirurgii im. I.I. Grekova/I.I. Grekov Annals of Surgery. (RU ISSN 0042-4625) **3385**
Vestnik Koroskih Partizanov. (XV ISSN 0350-7130) **2394**
Vestnik Leningrad University: Mathematics. (US ISSN 0146-924X) **3061**
Vestnik Mashinostroeniya. (RU ISSN 0042-4633) **1923**
Vestnik Oftal'mologii/Annals of Ophthalmology. (RU ISSN 0042-465X) **3305**
Vestnik Otorinolaringologii/Annals of Otorhinolaryngology. (RU ISSN 0042-4668) **3317**
Vestnik Rentgenologii i Radiologii/Annals of Roentgenology and Radiology. (RU ISSN 0042-4676) **3363**
Vestnik Sel'skokhozyaistvennoi Nauki. (RU ISSN 0376-0073) **128**
Vestnik Sel'skokhozyaistvennoi Nauki Kazakhstana. (KZ ISSN 0042-4684) **128**
Vestnik Statistiki. (RU ISSN 0042-4692) **4591**
Vestnik Svyazi. (RU ISSN 0042-4706) **1345**
Vestnik Vysshei Shkoly. (RU ISSN 0042-4757) **1720**
Vestnik Zoologii/Zoological Record. (KR ISSN 0084-5604) **593**
Vesuv see Il Vesuvio **348**
Il Vesuvio. (IT ISSN 0393-6147) **348**, 2973
Veter Stranstvii. (RU) **2973**
Vetera Christianorum. (IT) **289**, 348, 1280, 4208
Veteran. (GW) **259**, 4705
Veteran. (US ISSN 0042-4765) **3474**

VETERINARY INSTITUTE 6787

Veteran Athlete. (AT) **4559**
Veteran Belge. (BE) **3474**
Veteran Car. (UK ISSN 0042-4781) **4705**, 2790
Veteranfly Klubben. (DK ISSN 0109-8330) **64**
Veterans Affairs in Wisconsin. (US) **3474**
Veteran's Observer. (US) **3474**
Veterans of Foreign Wars of the United States Auxiliary see V F W Auxiliary **1302**
Veterans of Foreign Wars of the United States Magazine see V F W Magazine **3474**
Veterans of the Vietnam War. (US) **3474**
Veteran's View. (US) **3474**
Veterans' Voices. (US ISSN 0504-0779) **2973**
Veterantics. (SA ISSN 0042-4811) **259**, 4705
Veterinaer-Medizinische Nachrichten. (GW ISSN 0083-5862) **4817**
Veterinaria. (SP) **4817**
Veterinaria. (BN ISSN 0372-6827) **4817**
Veterinaria Argentina. (AG ISSN 0326-4629) **4817**
Veterinaria e Zootecnia. (BL ISSN 0102-5716) **4817**, 228
Veterinaria Mexico. (MX ISSN 0301-5092) **4817**
Veterinaria Tropical. (VE) **4817**
Veterinarian. see Dier - En - Arts **4809**
Veterinarian Magazine. (CN ISSN 0849-5009) **4817**
Veterinarius. (CN) **4817**
Veterinariya. (RU ISSN 0042-4846) **4817**
Veterinarni Medicina/Veterinary Medicine. (CS ISSN 0375-8427) **4817**
Veterinarno-Medicinski Nauki see Abstracts of Bulgarian Scientific Literature. Agriculture and Forestry. Veterinary Medicine **131**
Veterinarski Arhiv. (CI ISSN 0372-5480) **4817**, 593
Veterinarski Glasnik. (YU ISSN 0350-2457) **4817**
Veterinary and Comparative Orthopaedics and Traumatology. (GW ISSN 0932-0814) **4817**, 3312
Veterinary and Human Toxicology. (US ISSN 0145-6296) **1984**, 3745, 4817
Veterinary Annual. (UK ISSN 0083-5870) **4817**
▼Veterinary Biotechnology Newsletter. (FR ISSN 1018-533X) **4817**, 491
Veterinary Bulletin. (UK ISSN 0042-4854) **4820**, 24
Veterinary Christian Fellowship Newsletter see V.C.F. Newsletter **4817**
Veterinary Clinical Pathology. (US) **4817**
Veterinary Clinics of North America see Veterinary Clinics of North America: Small Animal Practice **4818**
Veterinary Clinics of North America: Equine Practice. (US ISSN 0749-0739) **4818**
Veterinary Clinics of North America: Food Animal Practice. (US ISSN 0749-0720) **4818**
Veterinary Clinics of North America: Small Animal Practice. (US ISSN 0195-5616) **4818**
Veterinary Dentistry see Journal of Veterinary Dentistry **4811**
Veterinary Dermatology. (US) **4818**, 3250
Veterinary Drug Registration Newsletter.(FR ISSN 1010-3538) **4818**
Veterinary Economics. (US ISSN 0042-4862) **4818**
Veterinary Focus. (CN) **4818**
Veterinary Forum. (US) **4818**
Veterinary History. (UK ISSN 0301-6943) **4818**
Veterinary Immunology and Immunopathology. (NE ISSN 0165-2427) **4818**, 3189
Veterinary Institute, Pulawy. Bulletin. (PL ISSN 0042-4870) **4818**

6788 VETERINARY MANAGEMENT

†Veterinary Management Update. (US) **5300**
Veterinary Medical Review. (US) **4818**
Veterinary Medicine. see Veterinarni Medicina **4817**
Veterinary Medicine. (US ISSN 8750-7943) **4818**
Veterinary Medicine Guidance Manual. (US) **4114, 2692, 4818**
†Veterinary Medicine Report. (US ISSN 0895-7703) **5300**
Veterinary Microbiology. (NE ISSN 0378-1135) **4818, 558**
Veterinary Parasitology. (NE ISSN 0304-4017) **4818**
Veterinary Pathology. (US ISSN 0300-9858) **4818**
Veterinary Practice. (UK ISSN 0042-4897) **4818**
Veterinary Practice Staff. (US ISSN 1047-8639) **4819**
Veterinary Prescribers Index. (AT ISSN 0157-3136) **4819**
Veterinary Product News. (US) **4819**
Veterinary Quarterly. (NE ISSN 0165-2176) **4819**
Veterinary Radiology see Veterinary Radiology & Ultrasound **4819**
Veterinary Radiology & Ultrasound. (US ISSN 1058-8183) **4819**
Veterinary Record. (UK ISSN 0042-4900) **4819**
Veterinary Research Communications. (NE ISSN 0165-7380) **4819**
Veterinary Science Communications see Veterinary Research Communications **4819**
Veterinary Scope see Veterinary Medical Review **4818**
Veterinary Surgeons in New Zealand. (NZ) **4819**
Veterinary Surgery. (US ISSN 0161-3499) **4819**
Veterinary Technician. (US ISSN 8750-8990) **4819**
Veterinary Times. (UK) **4819**
Veterinary Update. (IE) **4819**
Veterinary Update Clinical Abstract Service. (US) **4820**
Veteris see Athletics Today **4465**
Vetir. (FR) **4627**
Vetrnik see Pionyr **1263**
Vetro Informazione. (IT ISSN 0392-8241) **1167**
Vets' News. (US) **3474**
Vets' Newsletter see Vets' News **3474**
La Vetta d'Italia. (IT) **421, 2027, 2692, 3932**
Vette. (US ISSN 0199-7890) **4705**
Vetus Testamentum. (NE ISSN 0042-4935) **4208**
Vetus Testamentum. Supplements. (NE ISSN 0083-5889) **4208**
†Vetus Testamentum Coptice. (GW) **5300**
Vexillum. (CN ISSN 0316-2508) **1280**
Vezetok Lapja/Bulletin of Hungarian Scout Leaders and Parents. (US) **1302, 1269**
Vi. (SW) **2218**
Vi Bilaegare. (SW) **4705, 4496**
Vi Foeraeldrar. (SW) **1245**
Vi Menn. (NO ISSN 0042-4951) **3400**
Vi och Vaar Landsbygd. (SW) **128**
Vi Unge. (DK) **1269**
Via. (US ISSN 0506-8347) **308**
Via! (IT) **4705, 4795**
Via. (SA ISSN 0042-4978) **4723, 1876**
Via Datch. (DK ISSN 0903-9821) **1742**
†Via Domitia. (FR ISSN 0563-9786) **5300**
Via Emilia. (IT) **2206**
Via Libera. (IT ISSN 0042-4986) **3932**
†Via Libre. (BO) **5300**
Via Magazine. (CN) **4795**
Via Migliore. (IT ISSN 0042-4994) **1269**
Via Port of New York see Via Port of New York - New Jersey **4741**
Via Port of New York - New Jersey. (US) **4741**
Via Satellite. (US ISSN 1041-0643) **1345**
Via Stellaris. (US) **371**

Viaggi Intorno Alla Tavola. (IT) **2450**
Viaggiando in Autostrade. (IT) **4795**
Viajando/Traveling. (US) **4795**
Viaje Bem. (BL) **4795**
Viale Ciro Menotti. (US) **4705**
†Vialidad. (AG ISSN 0042-5028) **5300**
Viandas Tropicales. Boletin de Resenas. (CU) **195**
Viandes et Produits Carnes. (FR ISSN 0241-0389) **228**
Viata Armatei. (RM ISSN 1018-0400) **3474**
Viata Capitalei. (RM) **348, 2973**
Viata Cooperatiei Mestesugaresti. (RM) **357**
Viata Medicala - Cadre Medii. (RM) **3288**
Viata Medicala - Pentru Cadre Superioare see Viata Medicala - Pentru Medici **3161**
Viata Medicala - Pentru Medici. (RM) **3161**
Viata Militara see Viata Armatei **3474**
Viata Romineasca. (RM ISSN 0042-5052) **2973**
Viator. (US ISSN 0083-5897) **2325**
Viborg Stifts Aarbog. (DK ISSN 0107-8925) **2394**
Vibrant Life (Hagerstown). (US ISSN 0749-3509) **3810, 3613**
Vibration. (US ISSN 0049-6073) **2028**
Vibration and Shock. see Zhendong yu Chongji **3846**
†Vibration Engineering. (US ISSN 0883-9506) **5300**
Vibration Institute. Annual Meeting Proceedings. (US) **1923**
Vibrational Spectra and Structure. (NE ISSN 0090-1911) **1231**
▼Vibrational Spectroscopy. (NE ISSN 0924-2031) **1190**
Vibrations. (CN ISSN 0227-6755) **2289**
Vibrations. (US) **2790**
Vic-Nic News. (US) **1475, 1465**
Vice-Chancellor's Annual Report. (UK ISSN 0305-8654) **1720**
Vice Versa Magazine. (CN ISSN 0821-6827) **2973, 348, 3585**
Vicenza Economica. (IT) **824**
Vicenzaoro Magazine. (IT) **2566**
Vichiana. (IT ISSN 0042-5079) **2888**
Vicino Oriente. (IT) **2432, 289**
Vick Family Newsletter. (US) **2166**
Vickers Voice. (US ISSN 0042-5087) **3703**
Victimology. (US ISSN 0361-5170) **4456**
▼Victims of Violence Report. (CN ISSN 1180-0453) **2714, 1524, 4456**
Victor. (UK) **1269**
†Victor Valley Magazine. (US ISSN 0738-8586) **5300**
Victoria. (US ISSN 1040-6883) **2237**
Victoria. Department of Planning and Construction. Annual Report. Housing and Construction Victoria see Victoria. Department of Planning and Housing. Annual Report. Housing and Construction Victoria **2498**
Victoria. Department of Planning and Housing. Annual Report. Housing and Construction Victoria. (AT) **2498**
Victoria. Health Department. Annual Report. (AT ISSN 1030-0873) **2470**
Victoria. Hospitals and Charities Commission. Annual Report see Victoria. Health Department. Annual Report **2470**
Victoria. Office of the Commissioner for Equal Opportunity and the Victorian Equal Opportunity Board. Annual Report see Victoria. Office of the Commissioner for Equal Opportunity. Annual Report **3948**
Victoria. Office of the Commissioner for Equal Opportunity. Annual Report. (AT ISSN 1036-9538) **3948**
Victoria. State Film Centre. New Films and Videotapes see Victoria. State Film Centre. Video Catalogue **3519**
Victoria. State Film Centre. Video Catalogue. (AT ISSN 1036-1839) **3519, 1386**
Victoria A - Z. (AT) **4795**

▼Victoria and Tasmania Stamp Duties. (AT) **1111**
Victoria and Vancouver Island Visitor. (CN) **2179**
Victoria, Australia. Department of Conservation, Forests and Lands. Bulletin see Victoria, Australia. Department of Conservation, Forests and Lands. Lands and Forests Bulletin **2110**
Victoria, Australia. Department of Conservation, Forests and Lands. Lands and Forests Bulletin. (AT) **2110**
Victoria, Australia. Directory of Government Departments and Authorities see Victorian Government Directory **4077**
†Victoria, Australia. Education Department. Curriculum and Research Branch. Research Reports. (AT ISSN 0085-7726) **5300**
Victoria, Australia. Geological Survey. Bulletin. (AT ISSN 0085-7750) **1585**
Victoria, Australia. Geological Survey. Memoirs. (AT ISSN 0085-7769) **1585**
Victoria, Australia. Geological Survey. Reports. (AT ISSN 0810-6959) **1585**
†Victoria, Australia. State Electricity Commission. Science Report. (AT) **5300**
Victoria, Australia. Statutory Rules. (AT ISSN 0506-8509) **2692**
Victoria Boulevard. (CN) **348**
Victoria Clipper. (CN) **4795**
Victoria Court Practice. (AT) **2734**
Victoria Government Gazette. (AT ISSN 0042-5095) **4077**
Victoria League for Commonwealth Friendship. Annual Report. (UK ISSN 0083-601X) **4423**
Victoria Magazine. (CN ISSN 0845-9770) **1508**
Victoria Today. (CN) **2179**
Victoria University of Wellington. Awards Handbook. (NZ ISSN 0083-6036) **1670**
Victoria University of Wellington. Decision Research Centre. Working Paper Series. (NZ) **757**
Victoria University of Wellington Law Review. (NZ ISSN 0042-5117) **2692**
Victoria University of Wellington Zoology Publications. (NZ ISSN 0375-5363) **593**
Victorian. (US) **348**
Victorian. (UI ISSN 0042-5125) **1329**
Victorian Accident Compensation Practice Guide. (AT) **2692, 996**
Victorian Administrative Law. (AT) **2692, 4077**
Victorian Administrative Reports see Victorian Administrative Law **2692**
Victorian Affiliated Teachers Federation see V A T - C H A T **5299**
Victorian Affiliated Teachers Federation Newsletter see V A T F Newsletter **1670**
Victorian Arts Centre Magazine see Stages **4639**
Victorian Baptist Witness. (AT ISSN 0726-4097) **4252**
Victorian Bar Council. Annual Report. (AT) **2692**
Victorian Bar News. (AT ISSN 0159-3285) **2692, 2346**
Victorian Canine Association Gazette Dogs. (AT) **3714**
Victorian Canine Association Inc. Kennel Gazette see V C A Kennel Gazette **3714**
Victorian Canine Association Journal. (AT) **3714**
Victorian Computer Bulletin see A C S Victorian Bulletin **1388**
†Victorian Consultative Committee on Social Development. Annual Review. (AT ISSN 0727-5803) **5300**
Victorian Conveyancing Law and Practice. (AT) **2692**
Victorian Farmer. (AT) **128**
Victorian Farmer's Federation Newsletter see Victorian Farmer **128**

Victorian Fiction Research Guides. (AT ISSN 0158-3921) **2983, 415**
Victorian Government Directory. (AT ISSN 0158-1589) **4077**
Victorian Government Publications. (AT ISSN 0313-2463) **416**
Victorian Historical Journal. (AT ISSN 1030-7710) **2326, 2394**
Victorian Homes. (US ISSN 0744-415X) **2555, 640**
Victorian Humanist. (AT) **1687**
Victorian Institute of Educational Research Bulletin see V I E R Bulletin **1670**
Victorian Municipal Directory. (AT ISSN 0049-6170) **4096**
Victorian Naturalist. (AT ISSN 0042-5184) **4351**
Victorian Newsletter. (US ISSN 0042-5192) **2973**
Victorian Parents Council Newsletter. (AT) **1670**
Victorian Periodicals Newsletter see Victorian Periodicals Review **2576**
Victorian Periodicals Review. (US ISSN 0709-4698) **2576, 2973**
Victorian Pocket Yearbook see Australia. Bureau of Statistics. Victorian Office. Summary of Statistics (Year) **4563**
Victorian Poetry. (US ISSN 0042-5206) **3008**
Victorian Public Libraries. Annual Survey. (AT ISSN 1035-4832) **2796**
Victorian Rail Ways see V - Line News **5299**
Victorian Real Estate Journal. (AT) **4159**
Victorian Reports. (AT ISSN 0042-5214) **2692**
Victorian Review. (CN ISSN 0848-1512) **2973**
Victorian Road Transport Association. Annual Report. (AT) **4660**
Victorian Sampler. (US) **2237**
Victorian Scout see Scout Magazine **1244**
Victorian Secondary Teachers Association Guide to Victorian State Secondary Schools see V S T A Guide to Victorian State Secondary Schools **5299**
Victorian Secondary Teachers' Association News see V S T A News **1762**
Victorian Society. Annual. (UK ISSN 0083-6079) **308**
Victorian Society in America. Bulletin see Victorian **348**
Victorian Statutes - Annotations. (AT ISSN 0816-9799) **2692**
Victorian Statutes Cumulative Supplement. (AT ISSN 0314-5204) **2692**
Victorian Studies. (US ISSN 0042-5222) **2518, 4391**
Victorian Studies Association of Western Canada. Newsletter see Victorian Review **2973**
Victorian Tasmanian Retail Directory. (AT ISSN 0812-2970) **1158, 1508**
†Victorian Teacher. (AT) **5300**
†Victorian Update. (AT) **5300**
Victorian Workers Compensation Practice Guide see Victorian Accident Compensation Practice Guide **2692**
Victoria's Business Report. (CN) **1119**
Victoria's Monday Magazine. (CN) **2179**
Victorious. (CH ISSN 0582-9860) **3932**
Victory. (US) **4496**
Victory Music Review. (US) **3585**
†Vid sem Fljugum. (IC) **5300**
Vida Apicola. (SP ISSN 0213-1005) **2090**
Vida Checoslovaca see Czechoslovak Life **2184**
Vida das Artes. (BL) **348**
Vida Domestica. (BL) **2555**
Vida Economica. (PO) **698**
†Vida Escolar. (SP ISSN 0506-872X) **5300**
Vida Feliz. (AG) **3810**
▼Vida Hispanica. (UK ISSN 0308-4957) **2851, 1670**
Vida Holistica. see Holistic Life **3214**

Vida Infantil. (BL) **1269**
Vida Italiana. (IT ISSN 0042-7292) **4795**
Vida Juvenil. (BL) **1269**
Vida Local. Boletin de Informacion *see* Autonomia Local **4084**
Vida Nueva. (SP ISSN 0505-4605) **4278**
Vida Pastoral. (BL ISSN 0507-7184) **4208**
Vida Religiosa. (SP ISSN 0211-9749) **4278**
Vida Rural/Rural Life. (VE) **128**
Vida Silvestre. (SP ISSN 0210-3605) **1971**
Vida Silvestre. (AG) **2171**
Vida Sovietica. (PO) **2215**
Vidar *see* Gymnastik **4474**
Vide. (FR ISSN 0042-5281) **3835**, **1840**
Video. (GW) **1386**
†Video. Vaered at Se. (DK ISSN 0109-7717) **5300**
Video Actualite. (FR) **1386**
Video Aktiv. (GW) **1386**, **3519**
†Video & Audio Marketing. (AT ISSN 0814-2769) **5300**
Video and Cinema *see* What's on Video and Cinema **1388**
Video & Music Business. (AT ISSN 1033-4831) **1056**, **1386**, **3585**
Video - Audio - Revue. (SZ) **1386**
Video Business *see* Video & Music Business **1056**
Video Business. (UK) **1386**
Video Business. (US ISSN 0279-571X) **1386**, **1158**
Video Business. (BL) **1386**, **698**
Video Camera. (UK) **3798**, **1386**
Video Choice. (US) **1386**
Video Digest. (US ISSN 1054-5433) **1386**
Video Digital ViDi Aktuell *see* ViDi Aktuell **1388**
Video Display Terminal News *see* V D T News **4114**
▼Video Distributor's Directory (Year). (US) **1158**, **1386**
▼Video Duplication Directory. (US) **1158**, **1386**
Video Event. (US) **1386**
Video Extra. (US) **1386**
Video Forecaster. (US) **1386**
†Video Games. (US) **5300**
Video Games and Computer Entertainment. (US ISSN 1059-2938) **1419**, **1386**, **1475**
Video Gesamtkatalog B V V. (GW ISSN 0177-0942) **1386**
Video Guide. (CN ISSN 0228-6726) **1386**, **348**
Video Industry Statistical Report. (US) **1349**, **1386**
Video Innovations. (CN) **1386**
Video Insider. (US) **1386**
Video International. (AT) **1386**
Video Journal of Color Flow Imaging. (US ISSN 1052-2182) **3363**, **3297**
Video Journal of Echocardiography. (US ISSN 1052-2174) **3212**
Video Letter. (US ISSN 1058-8515) **1387**
Video Librarian. (US ISSN 0887-6851) **2790**, **1387**
Video Magazin. (GW ISSN 0723-0818) **1387**
Video Magazine. (US ISSN 1044-7288) **1387**
Video Magazine. (IT) **1387**, **3519**
Video Maker. (UK) **1387**
Video Management *see* A V Video **1384**
Video Marketing News. (US) **1056**, **1387**
Video Marketing Newsletter *see* Video Marketing News **1056**
†Video Marketing Surveys and Forecasts. (US ISSN 0740-4247) **5300**
Video Marketplace *see* Movie Marketplace **3514**
Video Monitor *see* Social Science Monitor **5278**
Video Movies *see* Video Times (Skokie) **5301**
Video Networks. (US ISSN 0738-7563) **1387**

Video News International. (US ISSN 1044-6354) **1387**
Video Out Distribution Catalogue. (CN) **1387**
Video plus Film. (CS) **1387**, **3519**
Video Pratique. (FR) **1387**
Video-Presse. (CN ISSN 0315-3975) **1387**
▼Video Professional. (GW ISSN 0940-5925) **1387**
†Video Prophiles. (US) **5300**
▼Video Rating Guide for Libraries. (US ISSN 1045-3393) **2790**, **1387**
Video Register and Teleconferencing Resources Directory. (US ISSN 0190-3705) **1158**, **1387**
Video Registrare *see* V R **1386**
Video Reserved Collection. (US) **1387**, **3400**, **4854**
Video Retailer Showcase. (US) **1387**
†Video Review (New York). (US ISSN 0196-8793) **5301**
Video Shopper (Fraser) *see* Movie Collectors World **1385**
▼Video Shopper (New York). (US) **1387**, **1910**
Video Software Dealers Association Reports *see* V S D A Reports **1386**
Video Source Book. (US ISSN 0277-3317) **1387**
Video Specialist. (US) **1387**
Video Specialist Newsletter. (US) **1387**
Video Store Magazine. (US) **1387**
Video Swapper *see* Movie Collectors World **1385**
Video Systems. (US ISSN 0361-0942) **1387**
Video Technology News. (US ISSN 1040-2772) **1387**
Video Times. (US) **1387**
†Video Times (Skokie). (US) **5301**
Video Today. (UK ISSN 0144-6010) **1387**
†Video Trade. (CN) **5301**
†Video Trade News. (US) **5301**
Video Viewing. (US) **1387**
Video Voice. (US) **1387**
▼Video Watchdog. (US) **1387**
Video Week. (US ISSN 0196-5905) **1387**
Video Week. (UK) **1387**
Video Week. (AT ISSN 0729-1167) **1387**
†Video World. (UK) **5301**
†Video-X. (AT) **5301**
Videodisc Monitor *see* Multimedia and Videodisc Monitor **1438**
†Videodisc Newsletter. (UK ISSN 0264-6358) **5301**
Videodisque. (FR) **1387**
Videofashion Monthly. (US) **1295**, **1387**
Videofilmen. (GW ISSN 0176-3156) **1388**
Videographic. (UK ISSN 0958-5125) **1388**
Videography. (US ISSN 0363-1001) **1388**, **1465**, **1691**
Videoinfo *see* O M N I **1385**
Videolog. (US ISSN 0746-7680) **1388**
Videolog Reporter. (US) **1388**
Videomaker. (US ISSN 0889-4973) **1388**
Videomania. (CN ISSN 0711-7914) **1388**, **1269**
Videopro. (US ISSN 0746-3286) **1388**, **1086**
Videos for Business and Training. (US ISSN 1043-9579) **1388**, **1762**
Videoscan Database for IBM Compatible Computers *see* P C Videolog **1351**
Videostar *see* Le Fotoguide **1385**
†Videotapes Source Book. (GR) **5301**
Videotex. (FR ISSN 0247-4352) **1388**
Videotex International. (FR) **1388**
Videotex Notes *see* Information Technology Notes **2763**
VideoWoche. (GW) **1388**
†Videoworld. (AT ISSN 0729-1957) **5301**
†Videoworld Buyer's Guide Annual. (AT ISSN 0729-1965) **5301**
Videozine. (US) **1388**
Videregaaende Opplaering. (NO ISSN 0332-5814) **1670**
ViDi Aktuell. (Video Digital) (GW) **1388**

Vidura. (II ISSN 0042-5303) **2202**, **1345**
Vidurava. (CE) **4351**
Vidya *see* Oriente e Occidente **2512**
Vidya. (II ISSN 0505-4753) **4351**
Vidya Bharathi. (II) **2518**, **4391**
Vidya Karya. (IO) **1720**
Vidyajyoti Journal of Theological Reflection. (II ISSN 0970-1079) **4278**
Vidyodaya *see* Viyodaya Journal of Science **4351**
Vidyodaya *see* Vidyodaya Journal of Social Science **4391**
Vidyodaya Journal of Social Science. (CE) **4391**
Vie. (FR) **2188**
La Vie au Bureau. (BE) **1062**
Vie Catholique du Berry. (FR ISSN 0042-5362) **4278**
La Vie Claire. (FR) **3810**
Vie Collective. (FR ISSN 0042-5370) **4423**
Vie Communale et Departementale. (FR ISSN 0042-5400) **4077**
Vie Consacree. (BE ISSN 0771-6842) **4208**
Vie de la Douane. (FR ISSN 0042-5419) **1111**
Vie de la Recherche Scientifique. (FR ISSN 0042-5427) **4351**, **2591**
Vie del Mondo. (IT) **4796**
Vie des Affaires. (FR ISSN 0083-6095) **1031**, **4077**
Vie des Arts. (CN ISSN 0042-5435) **348**
Vie des Betes *see* 30 Millions d'Amis - La Vie des Betes **595**
Vie des Collectivites Ouvrieres *see* Revue des Comites d'Entreprise **992**
La Vie des Science. (FR ISSN 0762-0969) **4351**
Vie du Rail. (FR ISSN 0042-5478) **4716**
Vie e Trasporti. (IT ISSN 0393-8077) **4660**
Vie Economique. (MR ISSN 0505-4885) **803**
Vie en Plein Air. (CN) **4559**
Vie et Camping. (CN) **4559**
Vie et Milieu. (FR ISSN 0240-8759) **460**
Vie et Sante. (FR ISSN 0042-5524) **3810**, **3613**
Vie Feminine. (BE) **4854**
Vie Francaise. (FR) **840**
†Vie Francaise. (CN ISSN 0382-0262) **5301**
Vie Judiciaire. (FR ISSN 0042-5567) **2734**
Vie Mancelle. (FR) **4796**, **1971**
Vie Medicale. (FR ISSN 0042-5583) **3161**
Vie Musicale en France Sous les Rois Bourbons. Serie 1: Etudes. (FR ISSN 0083-6109) **3585**
Vie Musicale en France Sous les Rois Bourbons. Serie 2: Recherches sur la Musique Francaise Classique. (FR ISSN 0080-0139) **3585**
Vie Numismatique. (BE) **3602**
Vie Oblate. (CN ISSN 0318-9392) **4278**
Vie Ouvriere *see* V O, Vie Ouvriere **2179**
Vie Ouvriere. (FR ISSN 0399-1164) **2591**
Vie Pedagogique. (CN ISSN 0707-2511) **1762**
Vie Professionnelle/Beroepsleven. (BE ISSN 0773-0004) **2090**
Vie Quotidienne en U.R.S.S. Prise sur le Vif. *see* Sovetskie Ljudi Segodnja **2962**
Vie Sociale. (FR ISSN 0042-5605) **4456**
Vie Spirituelle. (FR ISSN 0042-5613) **4278**
Vie Tchecoslovaque *see* Czechoslovak Life **2184**
Vie Theresienne. (FR ISSN 0042-5621) **4278**
Vie Touristique. (MR) **4796**
Vieh und Fleisch *see* V F Z **227**
Vieh und Fleisch Handelszeitung *see* V F Z **227**
Viehhandel *see* Oesterreichische Fleischer-Zeitung **222**

Vieilles Maisons Francaises. (FR ISSN 0049-6316) **308**
Vienna. Statistisches Amt der Stadt Wien. Statistische Mitteilungen. (AU) **4591**
Vienna Circle Collection. (NE) **421**, **2394**
Viennese Heritage/Wiener Erbe. (US ISSN 0169-1724) **2973**, **2851**
Viennese Slavonic Yearbook. *see* Wiener Slavistisches Jahrbuch **2852**
Vientin Bibliographic Service. (AG) **4142**
Vienybe. (US) **2028**
Vieques Times. (PR) **2215**
Die Vier im Schweizerischen Wirtschaftsleben. (SZ) **698**
Viers-Veirs Quarterly Newsletter. (US) **2166**
Vierte Internationale. (GW ISSN 0259-5818) **3932**, **2394**
Vierteljaehrliches Namensverzeichnis zum Patentblatt. (GW) **3679**
Vierteljahresberichte - Probleme der Entwicklungslaender *see* Vierteljahresberichte - Probleme der Internationalen Zusammenarbeit **3976**
Vierteljahresberichte - Probleme der Internationalen Zusammenarbeit. (GW) **3976**, **936**
Vierteljahreshefte fuer Media- und Werbewirkung. (GW) **39**
Vierteljahreshefte fuer Mediaplanung *see* Vierteljahreshefte fuer Media- und Werbewirkung **39**
Vierteljahresschrift fuer Heilpaedagogik und ihre Nachbargebiete. (SZ ISSN 0017-9655) **1742**, **4049**
Vierteljahresschrift fuer Sozialrecht. (GW ISSN 0301-2999) **2692**, **2545**
Vierteljahrschrift fuer Sozial- und Wirtschaftsgeschichte. (GW ISSN 0340-8728) **4391**, **899**, **2326**
Vierteljahrschrift fuer Sozial- und Wirtschaftsgeschichte. Beihefte. (GW ISSN 0341-0846) **4391**, **899**, **2326**
Vierteljahrsheftes fuer Zeitgeschichte. (GW ISSN 0042-5702) **2326**
Vierundzwanzigstenjahrsschrift der Internationalen Maultrommelvirtuoseng ssenschaft. (US) **3585**
Viet-Nam Sports. *see* The Thao Viet-Nam **4494**
Vietnam. (VN ISSN 0042-5710) **2238**
Vietnam. (US ISSN 1046-4638) **3474**, **2425**
Vietnam Courier. (VN) **2238**
Vietnam Digest. (AT ISSN 0049-6340) **3932**
Vietnam Generation. (US ISSN 1042-7597) **3474**
Vietnam Hebdo. (VN) **2238**
Vietnam Pictorial. (VN) **2238**
Vietnam Social Science. (VN) **4391**
†Vietnam Veteran. (US) **5301**
Vietnam War Newsletter. (US) **3474**
Vietnam Weekly. (VN) **2238**
Vietnam Youth. (VN ISSN 0049-6375) **1269**, **2238**
Vietnamese Catholic. *see* Nguoi Cong Giao Viet-Nam **4271**
Vietnamese Studies. (VN ISSN 0085-7823) **2343**, **3645**, **4392**
Vietnamese Women. *see* Phu Nu Viet-Nam **4851**
Il Vieusseux. (IT) **2888**
Vieux Marly. (FR ISSN 0988-1808) **2394**
View (Detroit). (US) **348**
View (Seattle). (US) **3810**
View from the University of San Francisco *see* University of San Francisco. Alumni Association. Alumnus **1328**
View World *see* Women's View **4857**
Viewbox. (US) **3363**
†Viewdata - Videotex Report. (US) **5301**
Viewfinder. (UK ISSN 0952-4444) **1763**, **3519**
ViewFinder Journal of Focal Point Gallery. (US) **3798**, **348**
Viewpoint. (PK) **2213**
†Viewpoint (Atlanta). (US) **5301**

Viewpoint (Columbus) see Artspace (Columbus) 317
Viewpoint (London). (UK ISSN 0042-5842) 640
Viewpoint (London, 1965). (UK ISSN 0042-5834) 3932
ViewPoint (Milwaukee). (US) 698
†Viewpoint (New York). (US) 5301
†Viewpoint (Tel Aviv). (IS) 5301
Viewpoint Aquarius. (UK) 3671
Viewpoint; Minority Outlook on Current Issues see Fact Sheets on Institutional Racism 3942
Viewpoint Sweden. (US) 2218
Viewpoints see Applied Marketing Research 1033
Viewpoints see Humanist Viewpoints 2508
Viewpoints. (CN ISSN 0042-5818) 3933
†Viewpoints in Business and Office Education. (US) 5301
Views. (JA) 1269
Views. see Pogledi (Kragujevac) 2879
Views (Boston). (US ISSN 0743-8044) 3798
Views (Silver Spring). (US) 2289
Views & News see Views on Education - News of Episcopal Colleges 1720
Views and News. (US) 4716
Views & Reviews (New York, 1937). (US ISSN 0042-5915) 39
Views & Reviews (New York, 1988). (US ISSN 1040-662X) 1687, 4138
Views on Education - News of Episcopal Colleges. (US) 1720, 1329, 1724, 4208
†ViewText (Potomac). (US ISSN 0275-0686) 5301
Vif see Le Vif - L'Express 2175
Le Vif - L'Express. (BE) 2175
Vigencia. (AG ISSN 0042-594X) 2518
Vigil/Ha-Mishmar. (US) 2028, 3976
Vigil. (UK ISSN 0954-0881) 4138
Vigilance. (UK ISSN 0042-5958) 1840
Vigilancia Epidemiologica see Vigilancia Epidemiologica de la Rabia para las Americas 4819
Vigilancia Epidemiologica de la Rabia para las Americas. (UN) 4819, 4115
†Vigilancia Epidemiologica de las Encefalitis en las Americas. (UN) 5301
Vigile Urbano. (IT ISSN 0394-8285) 1524
Vigilia. (HU ISSN 0042-6024) 4278, 2973
Vigiliae Christianae. (NE ISSN 0042-6032) 4208
Vigiliae Christianae. Supplement. (NE ISSN 0920-623X) 4208
Vigilo. (BE) 3474
Vignana Bharathi. (II ISSN 0377-8487) 4351, 4613
Vigneron Champenois. (FR ISSN 0049-643X) 195, 386
Vignes & Raisins. (FR ISSN 0042-6040) 195
VigneVini. (IT ISSN 0390-0479) 195, 386
Vigyan Pragati. (II ISSN 0042-6075) 4351
Vigyan Shikshak. see Science Teacher 4340
Viitorul Social see Sociologie Romaneasca 4452
Vijesti Muzealaca i Konzervatora Hrvatske. (CI ISSN 0042-6083) 3534
Het Vijfde Zegel. (NE) 2120
Vijnanevedi see K A P T Union Patrika 1644
Vikalpa. (II ISSN 0256-0909) 1031
Vikan. (IC ISSN 0042-6105) 2198
Vikas: Nepal Journal of Development. (NP) 1086
Viking. (NO) 289
Viking. (US ISSN 0095-5744) 1720
Viking. (CN ISSN 0049-6448) 4796
Viking (Northfield) see Viking 1720
The Viking Collection. (DK) 2394
The Viking Press. (US) 1329
Viking Society for Northern Research. Saga Book. (UK ISSN 0305-9219) 2394

Viking Tourist Guide. (CN) 4796
Viking Watch see A S W Log 42
Vikingur. (IC) 2050
Vikram. (II ISSN 0042-6121) 4351
Vikram Research Guide. (II) 4396, 24
Vikrant. (II ISSN 0042-613X) 3474
Vikrant's Defence Diary. (II) 3474
Vilagossag. (HU ISSN 0505-5849) 2394
Vilagtortenet. (HU ISSN 0083-6265) 2326
Villa de Madrid. (SP ISSN 0042-6164) 2498
▼Villa Vigoni. Jahrbuch. (GW ISSN 0938-863X) 3976
Villa Wina. (TH) 4642
Village. (HU) 2498
Village and Town Construction. see Cunzhen Jianshe 297
Village Crier. (US) 2280
Village Idiot. (US) 2973
Village Voice. (US ISSN 0042-6180) 2888
Villager (Bronxville). (US ISSN 0042-6199) 2237
Villager (New York). (US ISSN 0042-6202) 2237
Villages Magazine. (US) 2237
Villamossag. (HU ISSN 0042-6210) 1910
Villanova Engineer. (US) 1840
Villanova Law Review. (US ISSN 0042-6229) 2692
Ville de Paris see Paris le Journal 627
Ville-Giardini. (IT ISSN 0042-6237) 308
Villmarksliv. (NO) 4559
Viltis. (US ISSN 0042-6253) 2059, 1532
Vim & Vigor. (US) 3810
To Vima/Tribune. (GR) 2196
Vinatorul si Pescarul Roman. (RM) 4559
Vinaver Studies in French. (UK ISSN 0264-5564) 2973
Vinculos. (CR ISSN 0304-3703) 252
Vinculum. (AT ISSN 0157-759X) 3061, 1763
Vind - Nyt see D M I News 4726
Vindicacion Feminista see Poder y Libertad 4851
Vinduet. (NO ISSN 0042-6288) 2974
Vine. (UK ISSN 0305-5728) 2799
Vine-Growing and Viticulture. see Szolotermesztes es Boraszat 2139
Vineyard. (US) 4290
Vineyard and Winery Management. (US ISSN 1047-4951) 195, 386
Vineyard View. (US) 386
†Ving. (US) 5301
Vingtieme Siecle et la Paix see Twentieth Century and Peace 3974
Vingtieme Siecle Federaliste. (FR) 3976
Vingtieme Siecle: Revue d'Histoire. (FR ISSN 0294-1759) 2394
Vini d'Italia. (IT ISSN 0042-630X) 386
Vinifera Wine Growers Journal. (US ISSN 0095-3563) 386
Vino. (IT) 386
Vinograd Gospodnji. (YU ISSN 0353-1783) 4290, 2394
Vinohrad. (CS ISSN 0042-6326) 2140, 2083
Vins & Vignes. (CN) 386
Vins d'Alsace. (FR ISSN 0042-6334) 386, 195
Vintage. (US) 386, 2450
Vintage Aircraft Magazine. (UK) 64
Vintage Airplane. (US ISSN 0091-6943) 65, 259
▼Vintage Fashions. (US) 1295, 2566
Vintage Ford. (US ISSN 0042-6350) 259
Vintage Jazz Mart. (UK ISSN 0042-6369) 3585
Vintage Motor Cycle. (UK) 4521
Vintage Motor Cycle Club Magazine see Vintage Motor Cycle 4521
Vintage Northwest. (US) 2974
Vintage Record Mart. (UK) 4462, 3585
Vintage Roadscene. (UK) 4723, 2394
Vintage Tractor. (UK) 165, 259
Vintage Triumph. (US ISSN 0147-9695) 4705

Vintage Volkswagen Club of America Newsletter see V V W C A Newsletter 259
†Vintage '45. (US ISSN 0742-1494) 5301
Vintners World. (IE) 386
Vinyls and Polymers. see Enbi to Porima 1218
Viola d'Amore Society of America. Newsletter. (US) 3585, 1302
Viola da Gamba Society of America. Journal. (US ISSN 0507-0252) 3586
Viola da Gamba Society of America, Inc. News see V D G S A News 3585
†Violations of Human Rights in Soviet Occupied Lithuania. (US ISSN 0360-7453) 5301
Violence and Victims. (US ISSN 0886-6708) 4049, 1524, 4456
Violexchange. (US ISSN 0892-5437) 3586
Violin Society of America. Journal. (US ISSN 0148-6845) 3585
Viomichaniki Epitheorissis/Industrial Review. (GR ISSN 0042-6415) 1086
Virages. (FR) 4705
Viral Immunology. (US ISSN 0882-8245) 3189
Viral Immunology see I C R D B Cancergram: Viral Immunology 5209
Virchows Archiv. Abt. B. Zellpathologie-Cell Pathology see Virchows Archiv. Section B: Cell Pathology 527
Virchows Archiv. Section A: Pathological Anatomy and Histology. see Virchows Archiv. Section A: Pathological Anatomy and Histopathology 460
Virchows Archiv. Section A: Pathological Anatomy and Histopathology. (GW ISSN 0174-7398) 460, 3161
Virchows Archiv. Section B: Cell Pathology. (GW ISSN 0340-6075) 527, 3161
Virgats. (AT ISSN 1030-7699) 2028, 3394
Virgats-Teataja see Virgats 2028
Virgil Society. Proceedings. (UK ISSN 0083-629X) 1280
Virgin Islands (U.S.) Bureau of Labor Statistics. Labor Market Review. (VI) 996
Virgin Islands (U.S.) Bureau of Libraries, Museums and Archaeological Services. Occasional Paper Series see Virgin Islands (U.S.) Division of Libraries, Museums and Archaeological Services. Occasional Paper Series 2426
Virgin Islands (U.S.) Department of Commerce. Economic Review see Virgin Islands (U.S.) Department of Commerce. Quarterly Economic Review 887
Virgin Islands (U.S.) Department of Commerce. Quarterly Economic Review. (VI) 887
Virgin Islands (U.S.) Department of Labor. Annual Report. Fiscal Year. (VI) 996
Virgin Islands (U.S.) Division of Libraries, Museums and Archaeological Services. Occasional Paper Series. (VI) 2426
Virgin Islands Archaeological Society. Journal. (VI ISSN 0363-1168) 289
Virgin Islands Business Journal. (VI) 887
Virgin Islands Code Annotated. (US) 2692
Virgin Islands Nurses Association Quarterly see V I N A Quarterly 3287
Virgin Islands of the United States Blue Book. (VI) 4077
Virgin Islands Playground. (VI) 4796
Virgin Islands Port Authority. Annual Report. (VI) 4741
Virgin Islands Port Authority Directory. (VI) 4741
Virgin Islands Register. (US ISSN 0092-1270) 4077
Virgin Meat. (US) 3008

Virginia. Criminal Justice Officers Training and Standards Commission. Biennial Report see Virginia. Criminal Justice Services Commission. Annual Report 5301
†Virginia. Criminal Justice Services Commission. Annual Report. (US) 5301
Virginia. Department of Agriculture and Consumer Services. Bulletin. (US ISSN 0042-6482) 128
Virginia. Division of Mineral Resources. Publications. (US) 3497, 1585
Virginia. Employment Commission. Annual Planning Report. (US) 996
Virginia. Employment Commission. Annual Report. (US) 996
Virginia. Employment Commission. Annual Rural Manpower Report. (US) 996
Virginia. Employment Commission. Labor Market Review. (US) 996
Virginia. Employment Commission. Labor Market Trends see Virginia. Employment Commission. Labor Market Review 996
†Virginia. State Water Control Board. Annual Report. (US ISSN 0095-1978) 5301
Virginia. State Water Control Board. Basic Data Bulletin. (US) 4830
Virginia. State Water Control Board. Information Bulletin. (US) 4830
Virginia. State Water Control Board. Planning Bulletin. (US) 4830
Virginia. Water Resources Research Center. Bulletin. (US) 4830
Virginia. Water Resources Research Center. Water News. (US) 4830
Virginia Accountant see Disclosures 750
Virginia Advocate see Virginia United Methodist Advocate 4252
Virginia Agricultural Economics. (US ISSN 0042-6466) 159
Virginia Appalachian Notes. (US ISSN 0739-3482) 2166
Virginia Association for Health, Physical Education and Dance Journal see V A H P E R D Journal 3809
Virginia Association of Plumbing - Heating - Cooling Contractors Virginia P H C Image see Virginia P H C Image 2304
Virginia Baptist Register. (US ISSN 0083-6311) 4252
The Virginia Bar Association Journal. (US ISSN 0360-3857) 2693
Virginia Bar News see Virginia Lawyer 2693
Virginia Builder. (US) 635
Virginia Business. (US ISSN 0888-1340) 698
Virginia Business Report. (US ISSN 0363-3551) 698
Virginia Cattleman. (US) 228
Virginia Cavalcade. (US ISSN 0042-6474) 2426
Virginia Churchman see Virginia Episcopalian 4252
Virginia Commonwealth University Magazine see V C U Magazine 1329
Virginia Condominium Law. (US) 2693, 4159
Virginia Country. (US ISSN 0734-6603) 2237
Virginia Dental Association. Bulletin see Virginia Dental Journal 3244
Virginia Dental Journal. (US ISSN 0049-6472) 3244
Virginia Department of Highways and Transportation Bulletin see Virginia Department of Transportation Bulletin 4723
Virginia Department of Transportation Bulletin. (US) 4723
Virginia Economic Indicators. (US ISSN 0042-6490) 887
Virginia Education Association News see V E A News 1670
Virginia Educational Directory. (US ISSN 0083-6354) 1671
Virginia Employment Law Letter. (US ISSN 1042-461X) 2693, 996
Virginia Engineer. (US ISSN 0504-4251) 1840
Virginia English Bulletin. (US ISSN 0504-426X) 1763

Virginia Environmental Law Journal. (US ISSN 1045-5183) **2693**, 1499
Virginia Episcopalian. (US) **4252**
Virginia Extension. (US) **4613**
▼Virginia Facts. (US ISSN 1054-8351) **1782**
▼Virginia Family Law. (US) **2718**
Virginia Farm Bureau News. (US) **128**
Virginia Forests. (US ISSN 0740-011X) **2110**
Virginia Gazette. (US ISSN 0049-6480) **2426**
Virginia Genealogical Society Newsletter *see* V G S Newsletter **2166**
Virginia Genealogist. (US ISSN 0300-645X) **2166**
Virginia Geographer. (US ISSN 0042-6512) **2266**
Virginia Historical Society. Documents. (US ISSN 0083-6389) **2426**
Virginia Historical Society. Historical Notes. (US) **2426**
Virginia Historical Society. Occasional Bulletin *see* Virginia Historical Society. Historical Notes **2426**
Virginia Horse *see* Virginia Horse Council News **4539**
Virginia Horse Council News. (US) **4539**, 228
Virginia Housing. (US) **2498**
†Virginia Housing Network. (US) **5301**
Virginia Independent. (US) **2426**
Virginia Industrial Directory. (US) **1158**, 3497
Virginia Institute of Marine Science. Contributions. (US) **1612**
Virginia Institute of Marine Science. Marine Resource Bulletin *see* Marine Resource Bulletin **2045**
Virginia Institute of Marine Science, Gloucester Point. Educational Series. (US ISSN 0083-6427) **460**
Virginia Institute of Marine Science, Gloucester Point. Marine Resources Advisory Series. (US ISSN 0083-6435) **460**
Virginia Institute of Marine Science, Gloucester Point. Special Report in Applied Marine Science and Ocean Engineering. (US) **1612**
Virginia Institute of Marine Science, Gloucester Point. Special Scientific Report. (US ISSN 0083-6443) **460**
Virginia Journal of International Law. (US ISSN 0042-6571) **2730**
Virginia Journal of Natural Resources Law *see* Virginia Environmental Law Journal **2693**
Virginia Law Review. (US ISSN 0042-6601) **2693**
Virginia Law Weekly. (US ISSN 0042-661X) **2693**
Virginia Lawyer. (US) **2693**
Virginia Lawyer Register *see* Virginia Lawyer **2693**
Virginia Lawyer's Weekly. (US) **2693**
†Virginia Legal Studies. (US) **5301**
Virginia Legionnaire. (US) **1302**
Virginia Librarian. (US) **2790**
Virginia Librarian Newsletter *see* Virginia Librarian **2790**
Virginia Magazine of History and Biography. (US ISSN 0042-6636) **2426**, 421
Virginia Maritimer. (US) **4741**
Virginia Mason Clinic Bulletin. (US) **3161**
Virginia Medical *see* Virginia Medical Quarterly **3161**
Virginia Medical Quarterly. (US ISSN 1052-4231) **3161**
†Virginia Military Institute, Lexington. Publications, Theses, and Dissertations of the Staff and Faculty.(US ISSN 0083-6451) **5301**
Virginia Minerals. (US ISSN 0042-6652) **3497**
Virginia Museum Bulletin *see* Virginia Museum of Fine Arts Bulletin **3535**
Virginia Museum of Fine Arts Bulletin. (US ISSN 0363-3519) **3535**
Virginia Native Plant Society. Bulletin. (US) **2140**
Virginia Nurse. (US ISSN 0270-7780) **3288**
Virginia Nurse Quarterly *see* Virginia Nurse **3288**

†Virginia Outdoors. (US) **5301**
Virginia Outdoors Plan (Year). (US) **4559**
Virginia P H C Image. (Virginia Association of Plumbing - Heating - Cooling Contractors) (US) **2304**
Virginia P T A Bulletin. (US ISSN 0042-6709) **1671**
Virginia Pharmacist. (US ISSN 0042-6717) **3745**
Virginia Philatelic Forum. (US) **3759**
Virginia Polytechnic Institute and State University. College of Agriculture and Life Sciences. Information Series *see* Virginia Polytechnic Institute and State University. Virginia Agricultural Experiment Station. Information Series **129**
Virginia Polytechnic Institute and State University. Department of Entomology. Occasional Papers. (US) **538**
Virginia Polytechnic Institute and State University. Department of Geological Sciences. Geological Guidebooks. (US ISSN 0507-1259) **1585**
Virginia Polytechnic Institute and State University. Extension News. (US ISSN 0042-6725) **128**, 2450
Virginia Polytechnic Institute and State University. Research Division. Bulletin *see* Virginia Polytechnic Institute and State University. Virginia Agricultural Experiment Station. Bulletin **128**
Virginia Polytechnic Institute and State University. Sardo Pallet and Container Research Laboratory. Laboratory Report. (US) **2118**, 635
Virginia Polytechnic Institute and State University. Virginia Agricultural Experiment Station. Bulletin. (US ISSN 0096-6088) **128**
Virginia Polytechnic Institute and State University. Virginia Agricultural Experiment Station. Information Series. (US) **129**
Virginia Polytechnic Institute and State University. Wood Research and Wood Construction Laboratory. Special Report *see* Virginia Polytechnic Institute and State University. Sardo Pallet and Container Research Laboratory. Laboratory Report **2118**
Virginia Ports and Shipping Handbook. (UK ISSN 0266-7274) **1158**, 4741
Virginia Poultryman. (US ISSN 0042-6733) **228**
Virginia Probate Law. (US) **2693**
Virginia Publisher and Printer *see* Virginia's Press **2576**
Virginia Quarterly Review. (US ISSN 0042-675X) **2888**
†Virginia Researcher. (US ISSN 0049-6499) **5301**
▼Virginia Residential Landlord and Tenant Law. (US) **2693**, 4159
Virginia Review. (US) **4096**
†Virginia Road Builder. (US ISSN 0161-6730) **5301**
Virginia School Boards Association Newsletter. (US ISSN 0042-6776) **1732**
Virginia Social Science Journal. (US ISSN 0507-1305) **4392**
Virginia State Bar. Young Lawyers Conference. Newsletter *see* Docket Call (Richmond) **2620**
Virginia State Publications in Print. (US ISSN 0507-102X) **416**
Virginia Tax Review. (US) **1111**
Virginia Tech Collegiate Times. (US) **1329**
Virginia Tidewater Genealogy. (US) **2167**
Virginia Town & City. (US ISSN 0042-6784) **4096**
Virginia United Methodist Advocate. (US) **4252**
Virginia, West Virginia Queries. (US ISSN 0890-9423) **2167**
Virginia Wildflower Preservation Society. Bulletin *see* Virginia Native Plant Society. Bulletin **2140**
Virginia Wildlife. (US ISSN 0042-6792) **1499**, 4559
Virginia Wildlife Federation. Federation Record. (US) **1499**, 1971, 4559

Virginia Woolf Miscellany. (US) **2974**
†Virginiair. (US) **5301**
Virginia's Common Wealth *see* Virginia Outdoors Plan (Year) **4559**
Virginia's Health. (US) **4115**
Virginia's Industry of Agriculture. Report to the Governor *see* Report on Virginia's Industry of Agriculture **116**
Virginia's Local Economies: Accomack-Northampton, P D No. 22 (Eastern Shore Area). (US) **840**
Virginia's Local Economies: Bristol M S A. (US) **840**
Virginia's Local Economies: Central Shenandoah, P D No. 6 (Shenandoah Valley Area). (US) **840**
Virginia's Local Economies: Central Virginia, P D No. 11 (Lynchburg Area). (US) **840**
Virginia's Local Economies: Charlottesville M S A. (US) **840**
Virginia's Local Economies: Crater, P D No. 19 (Petersburg Area). (US) **840**
Virginia's Local Economies: Cumberland Plateau, P D No. 2 (Tazewell Area). (US) **840**
Virginia's Local Economies: Danville M S A. (US) **841**
Virginia's Local Economies: Fifth, P D No. 5 (Roanoke Area). (US) **841**
Virginia's Local Economies: Lenowisco, P D No. 1 (Norton Area). (US) **841**
Virginia's Local Economies: Lord Fairfax, P D No. 7 (Winchester Area). (US) **841**
Virginia's Local Economies: Lynchburg M S A. (US) **841**
Virginia's Local Economies: Middle Peninsula, P D No. 18. (US) **841**
Virginia's Local Economies: Mount Rogers, P D No. 3 (Bristol - Galax Area). (US) **841**
Virginia's Local Economies: New River Valley, P D No. 4 (Blacksburg - Redford Area). (US) **841**
Virginia's Local Economies: Norfolk - Newport News - Virginia Beach M S A. (US) **841**
Virginia's Local Economies: Northern Neck, P D No. 17. (US) **841**
Virginia's Local Economies: Northern Virginia M S A. (US) **841**
Virginia's Local Economies: Northern Virginia, P D No. 8. (US) **841**
Virginia's Local Economies: Peninsula, P D No. 21 (Newport News - Hampton Area). (US) **841**
Virginia's Local Economies: Piedmont, P D No. 14 (Farmville Area). (US) **841**
Virginia's Local Economies: Radco, P D No. 16 (Fredericksburg Area). (US) **841**
Virginia's Local Economies: Rappahanock - Rapidan, P D No. 9 (Culpeper Area). (US) **841**
Virginia's Local Economies: Richmond - Petersburg M S A. (US) **841**
Virginia's Local Economies: Richmond Regional, P D No. 15. (US) **841**
Virginia's Local Economies: Roanoke M S A. (US) **841**
Virginia's Local Economies: Southeastern Virginia, P D No. 20 (Norfolk - Virginia Beach Area). (US) **841**
Virginia's Local Economies: Southside, P D No. 13 (South Boston Area). (US) **841**
Virginia's Local Economies: Thomas Jefferson, P D No. 10 (Charlottesville Area). (US) **841**
Virginia's Local Economies: West Piedmont, P D No. 12 (Danville Area). (US) **841**
Virginia's Press. (US ISSN 0887-5227) **2576**
†Virginia's Supply of Public School Instructional Personnel. (US ISSN 0083-6575) **5301**
Virginie. (MF) **4854**
Virittaajaa. (FI ISSN 0042-6806) **2851**, 2974
Virksomheden ved Sygehuse. (DK ISSN 0903-8086) **2471**
Virksomheds Nyt. (DK ISSN 0106-1666) **4660**
Virksomheds Nyts. (DK) **4660**

VISION RESOURCE 6791

Virologica Sinica. *see* Bingduxue Zazhi **550**
Virology. (US ISSN 0042-6822) **558**, 3224
Virology Abstracts *see* Virology and A I D S Abstracts **3181**
Virology and A I D S Abstracts. (US ISSN 0896-5919) **3181**, 24, 468
Virology Monographs/Virusforschung in Einzeldarstellungen. (US ISSN 0083-6591) **558**, 3224
▼Virtual Reality Report. (US ISSN 1052-6242) **1436**, 1419, 1443
Virtue. (US ISSN 0164-7288) **4854**, 4208
†Virtuous Woman. (US) **5301**
Virus/Uirusu. (JA ISSN 0042-6857) **558**, 3224
Virus Genes. (US ISSN 0920-8569) **558**, 547
Virus Research. (NE ISSN 0168-1702) **558**
Virus Studies in Humans and Other Primates *see* I C R D B Cancergram: Virus Studies in Humans and Other Primates **5209**
Virusforschung in Einzeldarstellungen. *see* Virology Monographs **558**
Vis a Vis. (US) **4804**
Visability. (US) **1612**, 4496
Visage. (CN) **374**
Visages du Vingtieme Siecle. (FR ISSN 0151-3605) **2518**, 348
Visao. (BL ISSN 0042-6873) **2175**
Viscous Processing - Handling. (US) **1840**
†Viscous Products. (US) **5301**
Vishva Jyoti. (II ISSN 0505-7523) **3786**
Vishva Samskrtam. (II) **2974**
Vishva Vicharamala. (II) **3645**, 2343
Vishveshvaranand Indological Journal. (II ISSN 0507-1410) **2518**
Vishveshvaranand Indological Paper Series. (II ISSN 0083-6613) **2343**
Vishveshvaranand Indological Series. (II ISSN 0083-6621) **2851**, 2343
Vishveshvaranand Vedic Research Institute. Research and General Publications. (II) **3645**, 2343
Vishwakarma. (II ISSN 0042-6881) **1840**, 4613
†Visibilities. (US ISSN 0892-7375) **5301**
Visibility. (US) **4559**
Visible. (US) **2280**
Visible Language. (US ISSN 0022-2224) **1345**, 1671, 2518, 2851
Visible Religion. (NE ISSN 0169-5606) **4208**
▼Visic. (JA) **1419**
Visie. (NE) **4252**, 1383
Visier. (GW ISSN 0138-1601) **4559**
Visindafelag Islendinga. Rit/Icelandic Scientific Society. Occasional Papers. (IC ISSN 0376-2599) **4351**
Visio. (FI ISSN 0780-4199) **1763**, 1383
▼Vision. (CN ISSN 1183-7780) **996**
Vision. (MX) **2888**
Vision. (AT) **4252**
Vision (Costa Mesa). (US) **4209**
†Vision (Grand Rapids). (US) **5301**
Vision (Milwaukee). (US) **4278**, 4423
Vision (New York). (US) **2210**
Vision (Sheffield). (UK ISSN 0142-8543) **3305**
Vision (Stamford). (US) **1971**, 1499
†Vision & (IT) **5301**
Vision Boliviana. (BO) **2175**
Vision Care Assistant. (US) **3305**
Vision for America's Future *see* State of America's Children (Year) **4421**
Vision Hispano Americana. (CN) **2028**
Vision Interface Conference Proceedings - Compte Rendu. (CN ISSN 0843-803X) **1429**
Vision Letter. (US ISSN 0042-6962) **3933**
Vision Magazine. (PH ISSN 0042-692X) **348**, 308
Vision Monday. (US ISSN 0891-1770) **3305**, 1056
Vision On. (UK) **3008**
Vision Quarterly. (US) **3305**
Vision Research. (US ISSN 0042-6989) **3305**
Vision Resource List. (US) **2296**

VISION RESOURCE

Vision Resource Update. (US) **2296**
†Vision & Technik. (GW) **5301**
†Vision Views. (US) **5301**
Visionary. (US) **3305**, 2296, 3810
Visionary Company: A Magazine of the Twenties. (US) **348**, 2974
Visione see L'Oroptero **3304**
Visions see Visions International **3008**
Visions (Agoura Hills). (US) **3671**, 3786
Visions (Beaverton). (US ISSN 1051-8711) **4351**, 4613
Visions (Chula Vista). (US) **3305**
Visions (Kansas City). (US) **2028**, 1720
Visions (Lincolnshire). (US) **374**
Visions (Miami). (US) **3597**
Visions (Nashua). (US) **3810**
Visions (Overland Park). (US) **1367**
Visions (St. Louis). (US) **1329**
Visions: An Art Quarterly. (US) **348**
Visions International. (US) **3008**
†Visit California with Fyfe Robertson. (UK ISSN 0260-910X) **5301**
Visit U S A Guide. (US) **4796**
Visiting Nurse Association of Brooklyn Newsletter see V N A B Newsletter **3287**
Visitor. (JM) **4796**, 2481
Visitor Behavior. (US ISSN 0892-4996) **4049**, 3535, 4796
▼Visitors Choice. (CN) **4796**
Visitors' Guide to Mexico see Guis de Viajes **4770**
Visitor's Magazine. (CN ISSN 0839-1335) **4796**
▼Visitor's Pocket Guide to St. Louis. (US) **4796**
Visnyk/Herald. (US ISSN 0042-7004) **2888**
Visnyk. see Herald **4283**
Visnyk Sil's'kogospodar'skoi Nauki. (RU ISSN 0042-7020) **129**
Visserij in Cijfers. (NE ISSN 0921-4283) **2052**
Visserijblad. (BE ISSN 0776-6912) **2050**
Visserijnieuws. (NE) **2050**
Vissha Geodeziia. (BU ISSN 0324-1114) **1585**
Vista. (CN ISSN 0382-0289) **2450**
Vista. (Norman Mackenzie Art Gallery) (CN ISSN 0712-9238) **3535**
Vista see InterDependent **3960**
Vista see Vista U S A **4796**
Vista Magazine. (US) **4796**
Vista Magazine Miami Metro Guide see Vista Magazine **4796**
Vista R A P see R A P **4446**
Vista (U S A). (US) **4796**, 2237, 2443
Vistas. (US) **3535**
Vistas in Astronomy. (US ISSN 0083-6656) **371**
Vistas in Plant Sciences. (II ISSN 0378-9454) **520**
Vistazo. (EC ISSN 0042-7128) **2185**
Visti Iz Sarseliu. (FR ISSN 0083-6672) **4392**
Visti Ukrayins'kykh Inzheneriv/Ukrainian Engineering News. (US ISSN 0042-7136) **1840**
Visto. (IT) **2206**
Visual Anthropology. (US ISSN 0894-9468) **252**
Visual Arts see N E A Grantmaking Programs: Visual Arts **337**
Visual Arts Research. (US ISSN 0736-0770) **1763**, 348
Visual Computer. (GW ISSN 0178-2789) **1423**
Visual Literacy Newsletter. (US) **1763**
Visual Media. (CN ISSN 0840-4313) **3519**
Visual Merchandising & Store Design see V M & S D **39**
Visual Neuroscience. (UK ISSN 0952-5238) **3355**, 3305
Visual Resources. (US ISSN 0197-3762) **349**, 3535, 3798
Visual Resources Association Bulletin. (US) **349**, 2790
Visualeiten see T F C Nieuws **3518**
Visualita. (IT) **349**
Visuelt. (DK ISSN 0108-5220) **1447**
Visva. (CE) **4351**, 349
Visva - Bharati Journal of Philosophy. (II ISSN 0042-7187) **3786**

Visva - Bharati Patrika. (II ISSN 0042-7179) **2974**
Visva - Bharati Quarterly. (II ISSN 0042-7195) **2888**
Viswa Rachana. (II ISSN 0042-7209) **2974**, 349
Viswa Sahiti see Viswa Rachana **2974**
Viswasilpi. (II ISSN 0042-7217) **635**, 308
Vita Cattolica. (IT ISSN 0042-7233) **4278**
Vita Cecoslovacca see Czechoslovak Life **2184**
Vita Consacrata. (IT ISSN 0042-7330) **4209**
Vita dell'Infanzia. (IT ISSN 0042-7241) **1671**, 1269, 4049
Vita e Pensiero. (IT ISSN 0042-725X) **2888**
Vita e Salute. (IT ISSN 0042-7268) **3810**
Vita Evangelica. (CN ISSN 0507-1690) **4209**
Vita Fratrum. (GW) **4278**
Vita Giuseppina. (IT ISSN 0042-7276) **4278**, 1671
Vita in Campagna. (IT) **2140**
La Vita in Cristo e nella Chiesa. (IT ISSN 0042-7284) **4209**
Vita Italiana. (CN) **2028**
Vita Latina. (FR ISSN 0042-7306) **2851**
Vita Lions. (IT) **1302**
Vita Nuova. (IT) **4351**, 3597, 4049
Vita Ospedaliera. (IT ISSN 0391-1470) **2470**, 3161
Vita Pastorale. (IT) **4209**
Vita Scolastica. (IT ISSN 0042-7349) **1671**
Vita Sindacale Bergamasca. (IT ISSN 0042-7357) **2591**
Vita Sociale. (IT ISSN 0042-7365) **4278**, 2518, 4392
Vita Trentina. (IT) **2207**
Vitae. (SA ISSN 0259-0026) **2545**
Vitae Scholasticae. (US ISSN 0735-1909) **421**, 1671
Vital. (GW) **3810**
Vital Christianity. (US ISSN 0042-7381) **4290**
Vital Force. (US) **3786**
Vital Gesundheit, Freizeit, Lebensfreude see Vital **3810**
Vital Issues. (US ISSN 0042-739X) **3933**, 2028, 4392
Vital Margin see Michigan Today **1317**
Vital Signs (Fresno). (US) **3161**
Vital Signs (Oklahoma). (US) **3810**
Vital Signs Pharmacy Services Newsletter. (US ISSN 0739-9588) **3745**, 3288
Vital Speeches of the Day. (US ISSN 0042-742X) **2576**
Vital Statistics, Idaho see Idaho. Department of Health and Welfare. Annual Summary of Vital Statistics **4117**
Vital Statistics Japan see Japan. Ministry of Health and Welfare. Statistics and Information Department. Vital Statistics **4576**
Vital Statistics of Iowa. (US ISSN 0161-8695) **3996**, 4591
Vital Statistics of the Province of British Columbia see Selected Vital Statistics and Health Statistics Indicators. Annual Report **3995**
Vital Statistics of the United States. (US ISSN 0083-6710) **4119**, 3996
Vitality. (IT) **3613**
Vitality. (US) **3810**
Vitality Magazine. (CN ISSN 1180-0291) **3810**, 3161, 3613
†Vitamin D. (UK ISSN 0143-120X) **5301**
Vitamin Supplement. (CN) **3745**
Vitamine, Mineralstoffe, Spurenelemente. (GW ISSN 0930-4827) **3745**
Vitamins and Hormones: Advances in Research and Applications. (US ISSN 0083-6729) **3745**, 3161
▼Vitas. (RU) **3161**
VitaSana. (CN) **3613**, 3810
Vitchyzna. (KR ISSN 0042-7470) **2888**
Vitezna Kridla. (CS ISSN 0042-7497) **3474**, 65
Viti see Cultivar **86**

Viticultura Enologia Profesional. (SP) **195**
Vitis. (GW ISSN 0042-7500) **388**, 24
Vitis - V E A see Vitis - Viticulture and Enology Abstracts **144**
Vitis - Viticulture and Enology Abstracts.(GW ISSN 0175-8292) **144**, 24
Vititechnique see Cultivar **86**
Vitreous Enameller. (UK ISSN 0042-7519) **1167**
Vitriini. (FI ISSN 0357-749X) **2481**
Vittorio Baccelli Magazine. (IT) **4456**
Viva. (SZ) **2888**, 3933
Viva. (NE) **4854**
Viva. (KE) **4854**
Viva (Bellingham). (US) **2280**
Viva (Lima). (PE) **4854**
Viva Africa. (TZ) **887**
Vivant Univers. (BE ISSN 0042-7527) **3976**, 4392
Vivante Afrique see Vivant Univers **3976**
Vivarium. (NE ISSN 0042-7543) **2326**, 3976
Vivarium, Darmstadts Tiergarten. (GW) **593**
Vivat Hussar. (FR) **3474**
Vive la Difference. (UK ISSN 0260-3993) **4456**, 1687, 3400, 4854
Vivekananda Kendra Patrika. (II) **2518**
Vivekananda Vedanta Society of Chicago. Bulletins. (US) **4217**
Vivere - Guarire. (IT) **3613**
Vivi. (JA) **4854**
Vivienda/Dwelling. (AG) **308**
Vivienda. (SP ISSN 0042-756X) **2498**
Vivilcinema. (IT) **3519**
Vivir. (SP ISSN 0042-7578) **3810**
Vivliographika. (GR) **2790**
Vivliothiki Ghoneon. (GR ISSN 0042-7594) **1671**, 1245
Vivre. (FR) **3203**
Vivre Autrement. (SG ISSN 0850-8194) **1508**
Vivre en Harmonie. (FR ISSN 0042-7608) **3613**
Vivre le Cinema. (FR) **3519**
Vivres-Voeding see Federation Belge des Enterprises de Distribution. Courrier Hebdomadaire **2067**
Viyodaya Journal of Science. (CE) **4351**
Vizgazdalkodas see Magyar Vizgazdalkodas **1924**
▼Vizions. (US ISSN 1053-6256) **1345**
Vizugyi Kozlemenyek. (HU ISSN 0042-7616) **1940**
Vjesnik Bibliotekara Hrvatske. (CI ISSN 0507-1925) **2790**
Vjesnik Historijskog Arhiva Rijeka see Historijski Arhiv Rijeka. Vjesnik **2366**
Vjesnik I N A - Naftaplin. (CI) **3703**
Vjesnik Medicinskih Sestara i Medicinskih Tehnicara Hrvatske. (CI ISSN 0352-3721) **3288**
Vjesnik Nadbiskupije Splitsko-Makarske.(CI ISSN 0042-7659) **4209**
Vjesnik Rada. (CI ISSN 0042-7632) **996**
†Vjesnik Radnika Sumarstva - Slavonske Pozege. (YU) **5301**
Vjesnik za Arheologiju i Historiju Dalmatinsku. (CI) **289**, 1167
Vlaams Diergeneeskundig Tijdschrift/Flemish Veterinary Journal. (BE ISSN 0303-9021) **4819**
Vlaamse Filmpjes. (BE ISSN 0773-1027) **1269**
Vlaamse Gids. (BE ISSN 0042-7675) **2888**, 3786
Vlaamse Stam. (BE) **2167**
Vlaanderen. (BE ISSN 0042-7683) **349**, 2974, 3586, 4642
Vlastivedne Muzeum v Olomouci. Zpravy. (CS) **2394**, 3933
Vlastivedny Casopis Pamiatky a Muzea.(CS) **2394**, 3933
Vlastivedny Sbornik Okresu Novy Jicin. (CS ISSN 0139-9462) **2394**
Vlastivedny Sbornik Podbrdska. (CS) **2394**

Vlastivedny Vestnik Moravsky. (CS ISSN 0323-2581) **2394**, 289
Vlastivedny Zbornik Povazia. (CS) **2394**, 289
Vlees en Vleeswaren see Misset's Vlees en Vleeswaren **2077**
Vleesdistributie en Vleestechnologie. (NE ISSN 0042-7691) **2083**
Vlieende Springbok. see Flying Springbok **4802**
Vliegende Hollander. (NE ISSN 0042-7705) **65**
Vliegtuigencyclopedie see Nederlandse Vliegtuigencyclopedie **59**
Vliegtuigparade. (NE) **65**
Vliesstoff Nonwoven International. (GW ISSN 0935-6347) **4627**
VMEbus Systems see V M E Bus Systems **1440**
Vneshnyaya Torgovlya see Foreign Trade **908**
Vnitrni Lekarstvi. (CS ISSN 0042-773X) **3161**
†Vocabulaire des Imprimes Administratifs. (CN) **5301**
Vocal Majority see Washington Equal Times **4855**
Vocation see Vie Catholique du Berry **4278**
▼Vocation - The Who's Who of Human Resources. (NZ) **1158**, 1670
Vocational and Technical Audiovisuals: A Teacher's Sourcebook. (National Information Center for Educational Media) (US) **1697**, 1763
Vocational Aspects of Education. (UK ISSN 0305-7879) **1687**
Vocational Education and Training Database. (AT ISSN 1034-0815) **1681**
Vocational Education Evaluation Report see Connecticut. State Council on Vocational-Technical Education. Vocational Education Evaluation Report **1623**
Vocational Education Journal. (US ISSN 0884-8009) **1687**
Vocational Industrial Clubs of America, Inc. Journal see V I C A Journal **1687**
Vocational Rehabilitation Review. (US) **1742**
Vocational Training. (GW) **3631**, 1763
Vocational Training Council. Annual Report. (HK) **1688**
Vocational Training Information Bulletin.(EI) **3631**
Vocational Training News. (HK) **1688**
Vocational Training News. (US) **3631**, 1763
Voce. (IT ISSN 0042-7780) **4209**
Voce Bruzia. (IT ISSN 0042-7802) **2888**
Voce d'Italia. (UA) **2028**
Voce d'Italia in Canada see Voce degli Italo Canadesi **2028**
Voce degli Italiani. (UK ISSN 0042-7810) **2028**
Voce degli Italo Canadesi. (CN) **2028**
Voce dei Berici. (IT) **4278**
La Voce del Tabaccaio. (IT ISSN 0042-7829) **4645**
†Voce dell'Africa. (IT ISSN 0049-6626) **5301**
Voce dell'Emigrante. (IT ISSN 0394-8153) **2028**, 2059, 3933, 4423
Voce della Campania. (IT) **3933**
Voce della Fiera. (IT ISSN 0042-7837) **1056**
Voce della Madonna delle Grazie. (IT ISSN 0042-7845) **4278**
Voce della Regione. (IT) **2207**
La Voce della U I L (Unione Italiana del Lavoro) (IT) **2591**
Voce di Fiume. (IT) **2326**, 2059, 2974, 3989
Voce di Monasterolo. (IT) **4077**
Voce Italiana. see Italian Voice **2007**
Voce Italiana. see Italian Voice **2007**
La Voce Libera. (IT) **2207**
Voce Nuova see Voce della Regione **2207**
Voce Serafica della Sardegna. (IT) **4278**, 1671, 2028
VocEd see Vocational Education Journal **1687**
Vocero Informativo. (PR) **1671**

Voces de Telefonos de Mexico. (MX) 1367
Voci Amiche. (IT) 4278
Voci del Nostro Tempo. (IT) 2974, 1840
Voci della Rotaia. (IT) 4716
Voci Fraterne. (IT ISSN 0042-7888) 4209
Voco see Voix de la Classe Ouvriere 2591
Vodni Hospodarstvi. Serie A/Water Management. Series A. (CS) 1925, 1601, 4830
Vodni Hospodarstvi. Serie B/Water Management. Series B. (CS) 4830, 1601, 1925
Vodni Problemi. (BU ISSN 0204-8248) 4830, 1925
†Vodni Sporty. (CS ISSN 0139-6765) 5301
Vodnye Resursy. (RU ISSN 0321-0596) 4830
Vodohospodarsky Casopis/Water System Periodical. (CS ISSN 0042-790X) 4830
Vodosnabzhenie i Sanitarnaya Tekhnika.(RU ISSN 0042-7918) 4115, 4830
Voeding. (NE ISSN 0042-7926) 3613
Voedingsblad. (BE ISSN 0011-0434) 2083
Voedingsmiddelentechnologie. (NE ISSN 0042-7934) 2083
Voegel der Heimat see Ornis 566
Voeikov Main Geophysical Observatory. Leningrad. Results of Ground Observations of Atmospheric Electricity. The World Network. Additional Issue. (RU ISSN 0065-0099) 1596
Voeikov Main Geophysical Observatory, Leningrad. Results of Ground Observations of Atmospheric Electricity. The World Network. (RU ISSN 0136-4863) 1596
Die Voelker Rufen. (GW ISSN 0933-6117) 4252
Voelkerkundliche Abhandlungen. (GW ISSN 0073-0270) 252
Voelkerkundliche Veroeffentlichungen. (AU) 252
Voennaya Mysl' (RU) 3474
Voenno Istoricheski Sbornik. (BU ISSN 0204-4080) 2394, 3474
Voenno-Istoricheskii Zhurnal. (RU ISSN 0042-9058) 3474, 2326
Voenno-Meditsinskii Zhurnal. (RU ISSN 0047-7397) 3161
Voennye Znaniya/Military Review. (RU ISSN 0042-9074) 3474
Voennyi Vestnik. (RU ISSN 0042-9066) 3474
Voetbal International. (NE ISSN 0042-7977) 4514
Voetbal Totaal. (Koninklijke Nederlandsche Voetbalbond) (NE) 4514
Voetnoot see Neem Mijnou 1650
Voetplaat. see Footplate 2583
Vogel und Umwelt. (GW ISSN 0173-0266) 567, 1499
Vogeljaar. (NE ISSN 0042-7985) 567
Vogelkundliche Berichte aus Niedersachsen. (GW ISSN 0340-403X) 567, 593, 1971
Vogelkundliche Hefte Edertal. (GW ISSN 0178-0239) 568
Vogelwarte. (GW ISSN 0049-6650) 568
Die Vogelwelt. (GW ISSN 0042-7993) 568
Vognmanden. (DK) 4796
Vogue. (US ISSN 0042-8000) 1295, 2237
Vogue. (FR) 2188, 1295
Vogue Australia. (AT ISSN 0042-8019) 1295, 374
Vogue Bambini. (IT ISSN 1120-7787) 1295, 1245
†Vogue Beauty & Health Guide. (US ISSN 0161-2190) 5301
†Vogue Bellezza. (IT) 5301
Vogue Decoration. (FR) 2555, 2562
Vogue Entertaining Guide. (AT ISSN 0727-6745) 2172
Vogue Espana. (SP) 4854

Vogue Gioiello. (IT ISSN 1120-7817) 2566
Vogue Hommes. (FR ISSN 0750-3725) 1295
Vogue Italia. (IT ISSN 0042-8027) 1295, 374
Vogue Knitting. (US) 3593
Vogue Living. (AT ISSN 0042-8035) 2562
Vogue Patterns. (US ISSN 0095-2788) 1295
†Vogue Patterns (Athens). (GR) 5301
Vogue Pelle. (IT ISSN 1120-7795) 1295, 2738
†Vogue Pellicce. (IT) 5301
†Vogue Sport. (FR ISSN 0757-0090) 5301
Vogue Sposa. (IT ISSN 1120-7809) 3067, 1295
Voi Hyvin. (FI) 3810
Voice. (Vancouver Community College) (CN ISSN 0822-7896) 1329
Voice see Hearing Health 2287
Voice see Full Gospel Business Men's Voice 4283
Voice (Albany). (US) 1720
The Voice (District of Colombia). (US) 635
Voice (East Lansing). (US ISSN 0883-573X) 1671
Voice (Grandville). (US ISSN 0049-6669) 4290
Voice (Newark). (US ISSN 0277-2272) 4252
Voice (Sioux Center). (US) 1329
Voice. Southeastern Community College. South. (US) 1329
Voice Coil. (US) 1383
Voice for Education. (US) 1671
Voice for the Defense. (US ISSN 0364-2232) 2693, 1524
Voice Foundation. Newsletter. (US) 3368
†Voice from Jerusalem. (IS) 5301
Voice from the North. (BG) 2174
†Voice in the Wilderness. (US) 5302
Voice Literary Supplement see V L S 2973
Voice Networking Systems. (US) 1429
Voice of African Workers. (GH) 2591
Voice of Ahinsa. (II ISSN 0042-8086) 4216
Voice of Buddhism. (MY ISSN 0042-8094) 4216
Voice of Chorus America. (US) 3586
Voice of Cooperation/Sawt ul-Ta'wun. (JO) 833
Voice of Egypt see Arab World 3950
Voice of Guatemalan Women. (US) 4855, 1245
Voice of Islam. (PK ISSN 0042-8132) 4221
Voice of Islam. (UG) 4221
Voice of Jordanian Labourers/Sawt Ummal al-Urdon. (JO) 2591
Voice of Judaism. (US) 4227
Voice of Liberty. (US ISSN 0042-8159) 4209
Voice of Local 399. (US) 2591
Voice of Mauritians see Mauritian International 3906
Voice of Methodism. (UK ISSN 0042-8167) 4252
Voice of Missions. (US ISSN 0042-8175) 4252
Voice of Naprapathy. (US) 3216
Voice of Nature. (IO) 1971
Voice of North Carolina School Boards Association. (US ISSN 0744-4583) 1732
Voice of Orthodoxy. (AT) 4217
Voice of P S E A see Voice for Education 1671
Voice of Portugal. see Voz de Portugal 2214
Voice of Prophecy News. (US) 4252, 1383
Voice of S O M A F C O. (Solomon Mahlangu Freedom College) (ZA) 2240
Voice of Samanvaya. (II) 4290
Voice of Silence Newsletter. (IT) 2289, 4423
Voice of Sudan. see Sawt Al Sudan 2170
Voice of Taiwan. see Tai Sheng 2025
Voice of the Arab World. (UK) 2186, 2170

Voice of the Black Community. (US ISSN 0042-8183) 3948
Voice of the British Hospitality Association. (UK) 2481
Voice of the Chinese. see Huaren zhi Sheng 2182
Voice of the Church. see Holas Crakvy 4216
Voice of the Diabetic. (US ISSN 1041-8490) 2296, 1742, 3305, 4423
†Voice of the Elgin Farmer. (CN) 5302
Voice of the Essex Farmer. (CN) 129
Voice of the Gospel. see Phoni Tou Evangeliou 4195
Voice of the Holy Land/Sawt el-Ard el-Mukaddash. (JO) 4278
†Voice of the Huron Farmer. (CN) 5302
Voice of the Kent Farmer. (CN) 129
Voice of the Lambton Farmer. (CN) 129
Voice of the Martyrs. (US) 4209
Voice of the Middlesex Farmer. (CN) 129
Voice of the Movement. see Kol ha-T'nuah 2011
Voice of the Nation. see Sawt Al Ummah 2170
Voice of the Nazarene. (US ISSN 0042-8213) 4290
†Voice of the Oxford Farmer. (CN) 5302
Voice of the Pharmacist. (US) 3745
Voice of the Southwest. (US) 4278
Voice of the Tennessee Walking Horse. (US ISSN 0505-8813) 4539
Voice of the Unions. (UK) 996, 2591, 3933
Voice of the Vaad. (CN) 4227
Voice of the 2nd December Youths. see Siang Khong Gnaovason Song Thanva 1265
Voice of United Senior Citizens of Ontario. (CN ISSN 0382-0068) 2280
†Voice of Universarius. (US ISSN 0744-7884) 5302
Voice of Walden. (US) 1499
Voice of Washington Music Educators. (US ISSN 0147-4367) 3586
Voice of Working Women. (US) 698, 4855
Voice of Youth. (US ISSN 0042-8256) 1269
Voice of Youth Advocates. (US ISSN 0160-4201) 1245, 2790
Voice of Z-39 see Information Standards Quarterly 4130
Voice Processing. (US ISSN 0884-6685) 1345, 1436
Voice Processing Magazine. (US) 1345
Voice Technology News. (US ISSN 1045-1498) 1367
VoiceNews. (US ISSN 0886-2087) 1352, 1367, 1411, 1455
Voicepower Review. (CN) 1367
Voices. (CN ISSN 0838-7176) 997, 2591
▼Voices. (AT ISSN 1036-1561) 2888
Voices. (US ISSN 0042-8272) 4049
Voices from the Attic. (US) 4860
Voices in Education. (US) 1671
†Voices in the Wilderness. (US) 5302
Voices International. (US ISSN 0042-8280) 3008
Voices - Israel. (IS ISSN 0333-676X) 3008
▼Voices of Mexico. (US) 2266
Voices of the Wildcats. (US) 1329
Voices of Youth. (US ISSN 0889-2865) 1269, 1697, 1720
Voicespondent. (US ISSN 0042-8299) 4462
Voici. (FR) 4855
Voies de la Creation Theatrale. (FR) 4642
Voies Publiques, Longueur et Financement. see Canada. Statistics Canada. Road and Street Length and Financing 5160
De Voil. (UK) 1112
Voila Quebec. (CN) 1508
Voila - Renault Revue. (GW) 4705, 4496
†Voile Magazine. (FR) 5302
Voiles et Voiliers. (FR ISSN 0751-5405) 4530

VOLKSKUNDE 6793

▼Voir Ailleurs. (CN) 4796
Voisins Mondiaux en Action see World Neighbors in Action 3977
Voix Bielarusienne. see Bielaruski Holas 1993
Voix d'Afrique. (IV) 2170
Voix d'Afrique. (FR ISSN 0293-9932) 4209
Voix de France. (FR) 4423
Voix de l'Islam. (MF) 4221
Voix de l'Union. (BE) 2591
Voix de la Classe Ouvriere. (CF) 2591
†Voix de la Coiffure Francaise. (FR) 5302
Voix de la Jeunesse. see Zeri i Rinise 1272
Voix des Cultures. (FR) 129
La Voix des Jeunes. (BE ISSN 0504-6556) 1269
Voix des Parents. (FR ISSN 0049-6693) 1671
La Voix des Prairies. (US ISSN 0743-1848) 2167, 2426
Voix du Cheminot Ancien Combattant. (FR) 3475
Voix du Nord. (FR) 2188
Voix du Retraite. (FR ISSN 0049-6707) 2280
Voix du Silence see Voice of Silence Newsletter 2289
Voix et Images. (CN ISSN 0318-9201) 2974
Voix et Visages. (FR ISSN 0042-8396) 2394
Voix Ouvriere see V O Realites 2591
Voix Sepharade. (CN ISSN 0704-5352) 2028
Vojenske Zdravotnicke Listy. (CS ISSN 0372-7025) 3161, 3745
Vojni Glasnik. (YU ISSN 0042-840X) 3475
Vojni Muzej, Belgrade. Vesnik/Military Museum, Belgrade. Bulletin. (YU ISSN 0067-5660) 3475
Vojno Delo. (YU ISSN 0042-8426) 3475
Vojnoistorijski Glasnik. (YU ISSN 0042-8442) 3475
Vojnosanitetski Pregled/Military Medical and Pharmaceutical Review. (YU ISSN 0042-8450) 3161, 3745
Vojnotehnicki Glasnik. (YU ISSN 0042-8469) 3475
Vokrug Sveta. (RU ISSN 0321-0669) 2266
Voksenuddannelse. (DK ISSN 0107-8135) 1688
Vol. No. Magazine. (US) 3008
Vol Libre. see Free Flight 53
Volante. (US) 1329
Volare. (IT) 65
Volcano Review. (US) 2974
Volcanology & Seismology. (English translation of: Vulkanologiya i Seiomologia) (US ISSN 0742-0463) 1596
Die Voliere. (GW ISSN 0344-9270) 568, 2443
Volk auf dem Weg. (GW ISSN 0042-8337) 3976
Volk und Kultur see Jugend und Kultur 332
Volk und Recht see Plaedoyer 2666
Volksarmee. (GW ISSN 0505-9259) 3475
Volksbote. (IT) 3933
Volkscultuur. (NE ISSN 0169-5614) 2059
Volksdans. (NE) 2059, 1532
Volksfreund. see Ami du Peuple 2186
Volksgesundheit. (GW ISSN 0042-8493) 3810
Volkshandel. (SA) 698, 803
Volkshilfe Aktuell. (AU) 4423
Volkshochschule. (GW) 1671
Volkshochschule Flensburg. Arbeitsplan. (GW) 1688
Volkshochschule im Westen see Volkshochschule 1671
Volkskuendlichen Kommission fuer Westfalen. Schriften. (GW) 2059
Volkskunde, Driemaandelijks Tijdschrift voor de Studie van het Volksleven. (BE ISSN 0042-8523) 2060
Volkskunde in Niedersachsen. (GW ISSN 0176-1196) 2394
Volkskunde in Oesterreich. (AU ISSN 0042-8531) 2060

Volkskundig Bulletin. (NE ISSN 0166-0667) 252, 2060, 2395
Volkskundliche Studien. (AU) 2060
†Volkskunst. (GW) 5302
Volksleben. (GW) 2326
Volksmacht. (BE ISSN 0042-854X) 2591
Volksmaerchen. (GW ISSN 0232-3702) 2060
Volkstem. (SA) 3933
Volkstum der Schweiz. (GW ISSN 0083-6877) 2060
Volkswagen. (US) 4705
Volkswagen Audi Car. (UK ISSN 0956-9294) 4705
Volkswagen's World see Volkswagen 4705
Volkswirt. (AU) 968
Vollegrond see Groenten en Fruit - Vakdeel Vollegrondsgroenten 2129
Volleybal. (NE ISSN 0167-0247) 4514
▼Volleyball. (US) 4514
Volleyball Case Book. (US) 4514
Volleyball Monthly. (US) 4514
Volleyball Rulebook. (US) 4514
Volleyball U S A see Inside U S A Volleyball 4506
Volnet Electronic Newsmagazine. (US) 4423
Vologodskaya Biblioteka im. Babushkina. Literatura o Vologodskoi Oblasti. (RU) 416
Volonta. (IT ISSN 0392-5013) 3933
Volonte du Commerce, de l'Industrie et des Prestataires de Services. (FR) 841, 1086
Volonte du Commerce et de l'Industrie see Volonte du Commerce, de l'Industrie et des Prestataires de Services 841
Volta Review. (US ISSN 0042-8639) 2289, 1742
Volume Reversal Survey. (US ISSN 8755-3406) 968, 899
Volume 2 see Reisen in Deutschland: Zimmerkatalog 4784
Volund. (NO ISSN 0048-2277) 3535
Voluntad Hidraulica. (CU ISSN 0505-9461) 1925, 4830
Voluntary Action see N C V O News 4413
Voluntary Action Leadership. (US ISSN 0149-6492) 4423
Voluntary Agencies Directory. (UK) 4423
Voluntary Euthanasia Society Newsletter see V E S Newsletter 4456
Voluntary Housing. (UK) 2498
Voluntary Organisations see Voluntary Agencies Directory 4423
Voluntary Organisations News see Scope (Belfast) 4419
Voluntaryist. (US) 3933
▼Voluntas. (UK ISSN 0957-8765) 4456
Volunteer. (IS ISSN 0042-8671) 2028
†Volunteer (New York, 1961). (US) 5302
Volunteer! (Newton, 1944). (US) 4423
Volunteer (White Plains). (US) 4423, 1742, 2289, 2296
Volunteer Choir. (US) 3586
Volunteer Fire Chief see Fire Chief 2032
Volunteer Firefighter see Fire Chief 2032
Volunteer in Education see Partners in Education 1654
Volunteer Leader. (US ISSN 0005-1861) 2470, 4423
The Volunteer Librarian. (US) 2790
Volunteering. (US ISSN 0275-3030) 4423
Volunteerism. (US ISSN 0000-1325) 4423
Volunteers. (US) 4252, 4423
Volunteers in Technical Assistance News see V I T A News 5299
Volunteers' Voice for Community Safety and Health. (US) 4115
Volunteers Who Produce Books. (US ISSN 0193-113X) 2296
Vom Wasser. (GW ISSN 0083-6915) 4830, 1190
Von. (AU) 1295
Von B bis Y. (GW) 1245

Von Deutschland Nach Amerika. (GW ISSN 0173-1955) 4392
Von Karman Institute for Fluid Dynamics. Lecture Series. (BE ISSN 0377-8312) 65, 1925
Von Mann zu Mann. (GW) 4456
Voodoo Child. (US) 3586, 421
Voor. (IS) 129
Voor U. see Pour Vous 1906
Vooraziatisch-Egyptisch Genootschap "Ex Oriente Lux". Jaarbericht. (NE ISSN 0075-2118) 2343, 3645
Vooraziatisch-Egyptisch Genootschap "Ex Oriente Lux". Mededelingen en Verhandelingen. (NE) 2343, 3645
Die Voorligter. (SA ISSN 0042-8728) 4252
Voorzetten. (NE) 2974, 2851
Voprosy Bibliografii. (RU) 416
Voprosy Ekonomiki. (RU ISSN 0042-8736) 698
Voprosy Ekonomiki Narodnogo Khozyaistva Murmanskoi Oblasti see Voprosy Razvitiya Proizvoditel'nykh Sil Murmanskoi Oblasti - Apatity 698
†Voprosy Ekonomiki Sel'skogo Khozyaistva Dal'nego Vostoka. (UR) 5302
Voprosy Elektroniki Tverdogo Tela. (RU) 1910
Voprosy Filosofii. (RU ISSN 0042-8744) 3786
Voprosy Fiziki Tverdogo Tela. (RU ISSN 0301-6919) 3835
Voprosy Geografii. (RU) 2266
Voprosy Gidrodinamiki i Teploobmena v Kriogennykh Sistemakh. (KR) 3842, 3846
Voprosy Ikhtiologii. (RU ISSN 0042-8752) 593
Voprosy Inzhenernoi Geologii i Gruntovedeniya. (RU) 1941
Voprosy Istorii. (RU ISSN 0042-8779) 2326
Voprosy Istorii Estestvoznanya i Tekhniki. (RU ISSN 0205-9606) 4351, 2395
Voprosy Istorii K.P.S.S. (RU ISSN 0320-8907) 3933, 2395
Voprosy Khimii i Khimicheskoi Tekhnologii. (KR ISSN 0321-4095) 1231
Voprosy Kritiki Burzhuaznoi Politiki i Ideologii. Sbornik Nauchnykh Trudov. (LV) 3933
Voprosy Kurortologii, Fizioterapii i Lechebnoi Fizicheskoi Kul'tury/Problems of Health Resorts, Physiotherapy and Exercise Therapy. (RU ISSN 0042-8787) 3161
Voprosy Literatury. (RU ISSN 0042-8795) 2974
Voprosy Meditsinskoi Khimii/Problems of Medical Chemistry. (RU ISSN 0042-8809) 483
Voprosy Neirokhirurgii/Journal of Neurosurgical Problems. (RU ISSN 0042-8817) 3386, 3355
Voprosy Okhrany Materinstva i Detstva/Problems of Motherhood and Childhood Protection. (RU ISSN 0042-8825) 3288
Voprosy Onkologii/Problems in Oncology. (RU ISSN 0507-3758) 3203
Voprosy Pitaniya/Problems of Nutrition.(RU ISSN 0042-8833) 3613
Voprosy Psikhologii. (RU ISSN 0042-8841) 4049
Voprosy Radiobiologii i Biologicheskogo Deistviya Tsitostaticheskikh Preparatov. (RU) 3363, 460
Voprosy Razvitiya Proizvoditel'nykh Sil Murmanskoi Oblasti - Apatity. (RU) 698
Voprosy Russkogo Yazykoznaniya. (RU) 2851
Voprosy Teatra. (RU ISSN 0507-3952) 4642
Voprosy Teorii Razrabotki Mestorozhdenii Poleznykh Iskopaemykh. (RU) 1840
Voprosy Teorii Sistem Avtomaticheskogo Upravleniya. (RU) 1416, 1440

Voprosy Uchebno-vospitatel'noi Raboty v Samodeyatel'nykh Kollektivakh. (RU) 3586
Voprosy Virusologii/Problems of Virology. (RU ISSN 0507-4088) 558
Voprosy Yazykoznaniya. (RU ISSN 0042-8868) 2851
Vor Tru/Our Faith. (US) 4290
Voran. (GW) 3703
Voran Aktuell see Voran 3703
Vorarlberger Landesmuseumsverein. Jahrbuch. (AU ISSN 1011-8748) 2395
Vorderasiatische Schriftdenkmaler der Staatlichen Mussen zu Berlin. (GW ISSN 0138-4449) 3645
†Vore Kunstnere. (DK ISSN 0107-136X) 5302
Vorgaenge. (GW ISSN 0507-4150) 3933
Vorming. (NE) 1671
Vorreformationsgeschichtliche Forschungen. (GW ISSN 0083-6923) 4209
Vorschau. (AU) 635
Vorschau Hannover see Hannover Vorschau 2868
Vorschau-Monats-Tabelle see Messe- und Kongress-Vorschau 3393
Vorschau-Tabelle see Messe- und Kongress-Vorschau 3393
Vorteilhafte Geldanlagen. (GW ISSN 0172-2530) 803, 887, 968
Vortex. (US) 1190
Vortraege aus der Praktischen Chirurgie see Praktische Chirurgie 3382
Vorwaerts/Forward. (CN) 2028, 3933
Vorwaerts. (AU ISSN 0042-8930) 2591, 3667
Vorwaerts. (GW ISSN 0042-8949) 3933
Vorwerk Nachrichten. (GW) 1910
Vos Enfants. (FR) 1245
Vosotras. (AG) 4855
Vospitanie Shkol'nikov. (RU ISSN 0042-8957) 1763
Vote and Survey. (US) 3933, 887, 4423
Voting Rights Networker. (US) 3948
Votre Beaute. (FR ISSN 0042-8965) 374
Votre Cave. (FR) 386
Votre Maison. (FR ISSN 0042-8973) 2555
Votre Ordinateur/Your Computer. (BE) 1402
Votre Succes. (CN ISSN 0843-6665) 1119, 698
Vous. (CN) 4855
†Vous. (SZ) 5302
Vox see Y Seren 2883
Vox. (AT) 3586
Vox Benedictina. (CN ISSN 0715-8726) 4209
Vox Evangelica. (UK ISSN 0263-6786) 4209
Vox: Hebdomadaire Militaire. (BE) 3475
Vox Latina. (GW ISSN 0172-5300) 2974, 1688
▼Vox Magazine. (US ISSN 1052-8814) 2888, 3008
†Vox Mediaevalis. (US) 5302
Vox: Militair Weekblad see Vox: Hebdomadaire Militaire 3475
Vox Pop Newsletter. (US ISSN 0896-8934) 1671
Vox Reformata. (AT ISSN 0728-0912) 4252
Vox Romanica. (GW ISSN 0042-899X) 2851, 2974
Vox Sanguinis. (SZ ISSN 0042-9007) 3189, 3212
Voxair. (CN ISSN 0300-3213) 3475
Voyage en Chine see China Tourism 4757
Voyage en Groupe. see Group Travel 4769
Voyager (Pensacola). (US) 1329
Voyager International. (US ISSN 1040-8541) 4796, 2481
Voyages Internationaux et Sante. Vaccinations Exigees et Conseils d'Hygiene see International Travel and Health: Vaccination Requirements and Health Advice 4105

Voyages to the Inland Sea. (US ISSN 0095-5388) 3008
Voyageur. (CN) 2179
Voyageur Magazine. (CN) 4796
Voyageur Trail News. (CN) 4559
La Voz (Cupertino). (US) 1330
La Voz (Seattle). (US) 2028
Voz de la Construccion. (VE) 635
Voz de los Lituanos en la Argentina. see Argentinos Lietuviu Balsas 1992
A Voz de Portugal. (CN) 2028
Voz de Portugal/Voice of Portugal. (US) 2214
Voz do Operario. (PO) 2888
Voz do Povo. (CV) 4796
Voz Informativa. (MX) 3671
Voz Proletaria. (CK) 2183
Voz Summary. (US) 2180
Vozhatyi see Stupeni 1266
Vraag & Aanbod. (BE) 1086
Vrachebnoe Delo. (KR ISSN 0049-6804) 3161
Vrede. (NE) 3976
Vrelo Zivota. (BN) 4209
▼Vremya. (RU) 2591
Vriend. (NE ISSN 0042-9139) 2289, 1269
Vriend van Oud en Jong. (NE ISSN 0042-9155) 4209
Vrije Beroepen. (BE) 924
Vrije Fries. (NE) 2395, 2851
Vrije Universiteit. Canada. Cahier. (NE) 2266
Vrije Universiteit. Faculteit der Economische Wetenschappen en Econometrie. Research Memorandum. (NE) 899
Vrishchik. (II ISSN 0042-9198) 349, 2974
Vritta Vidya. (II) 2576
Vrouw en Wereld. (BE) 4855
Vrouwenstudies Utrecht. (NE) 4855
Vrystaatse Biblioteke. see Free State Libraries 2758
Vrystaatse Onderwysnuus. see Free State Educational News 1634
Vsemirnaya Meteorologicheskaya Organizatsiya. Komissiya po Atmosfernym Naukam. Okonchatel'nyi Sokrashchennyi Otchet (No.) Sessii. see World Meteorological Organization. Commission for Atmospheric Sciences. Abridged Final Report of the (No.) Session 3443
Vsemirnaya Meteorologicheskaya Organizatsiya. Komissiya po Aviatsionnoi Meteorologii. Okonchatel'nyi Sokrashchennyi Otchet (No.) Sessii see World Meteorological Organization. Commission for Aeronautical Meteorology. Abridged Final Report of the (No.) Session 3442
Vsemirnaya Meteorologicheskaya Organizatsiya. Komissiya po Gidrologii. Okonchatel'nyi Sokrashchennyi Otchet (No.) Sessii see World Meteorological Organization. Commission for Hydrology. Abridged Final Report of the (No.) Session 3443
Vsemirnaya Meteorologicheskaya Organizatsiya. Komissiya po Morskoi Meteorologii. Okonchatel'nyi Sokrashchennyi Otchet (No.) Sessii see World Meteorological Organization. Commission for Marine Meteorology. Abridged Final Report of the (No.) Session 3443
Vsemirnaya Meteorologicheskaya Organizatsiya. Komissiya po Priboram i Metodam Nablyudenii. Okonchatel'nyi Sokrashchennyi Otchet (No.) Sessii see World Meteorlogical Organization. Commission for Instruments and Methods of Observation. Abridged Final Report of the (No.) Session 3442
Vsemirnaya Meteorologicheskaya Organizatsiya. Komissiya po Spetsial'nym Primeneniyam Meteorologii i Klimatologii. Okonchatel'nyi Sokrashchennyi Otchet (No.) Sessii see World Meteorological Organization. Commission for Special Applications of Meteorology and Climatology. Abridged Final Report of the (No.) Session 5307

Vsemirnaya Meteorologicheskaya Organizatsiya. Komissya po Osnovnym Sistemam. Okonchatel'nyi Sokrashchennyi Otchet (No.) Sessii see World Meteorological Organization. Commission for Basic Systems. Abridged Final Report of the (No.) Session **3443**

Vsemirnaya Meteorologicheskaya Organizatsiya. Kongress. Sokrashchennyi Otchet s Rezolyutsiyami see World Meteorological Organization. Congress. Abridged Report with Resolutions **3443**

Vsemirnaya Meteorologicheskaya Organizatsiya. Regional'naya Assotsiatsiya II (Aziya). Okonchatel'nyi Sokrashchennyi Otchet (No.) Sessii see World Meteorological Organization. Regional Association II (Asia). Abridged Final Report of the (No.) Session **3443**

Vsemirnaya Meteorologicheskaya Organizatsiya. Regional'naya Assotsiatsiya VI (Evropa). Okonchatel'nyi Sokrashchennyi Otchet (No.) Sessii see World Meteorological Organization. Regional Association VI (Europe). Abridged Final Report of the (No.) Session **3443**

Vsemirnaya Meteorologicheskaya Organizatsiya. Sessiya Ispolnitel'nogo Soveta. Sokrashchennyi Otchet s Rezolyutsiyami see World Meteorological Organization. Executive Council Session. Abridged Final Reports with Resolutions **3443**

Vsemirnaya Meteorologicheskaya Organizatsiya Komissya po Sel'skokhozyaistvennoi Meteorologii. Okonchatel'nyi Sokrashchennyi Otchet (No.) Sessii see World Meteorological Organization. Commission for Agricultural Meteorology. Abridged Final Report of the (No.) Session **3443**

Vsemirnoe Profsoyuznoe Dvizhenie. (RU ISSN 0042-9236) **2591**

Vsesoyuznoe Geograficheskoe Obshchestvo. Izvestiya. (RU ISSN 0373-353X) **2266**

Vsesoyuznoe Mineralogicheskoe Obshchestvo. Zapiski. (RU ISSN 0044-1805) **1585**

Vsesoyuznyi Institut Nauchno-Tekhnicheskoi Informatsii. Deponirovannye Nauchnye Raboty. (RU ISSN 0135-0617) **4358**, **4615**

Vsesoyuznyi Institut Nauchno-Tekhnicheskoi Informatsii. Deponirovannye Rukopisi see Vsesoyuznyi Institut Nauchno-Tekhnicheskoi Informatsii. Deponirovannye Nauchnye Raboty **4358**

Vsesoyuznyi Nauchno-Issledovatel'skii Institut Morskogo Rybnogo Khozyaistva i Okeanografii (V N I R O). Trudy. (RU) **1612**

Vsesoyuznyi Nauchno-Issledovatel'skii Institut Transportnogo Stroitel'stva. Trudy. (RU) **4660**

Vsesoyuznyi Nauchno-Issledovatel'skii Institut Vagonostroeniya. Trudy. (RU) **4716**

Vsesoyuznyi Nauchno-Issledovatel'skii Institut Zernovogo Khozyaistva. Trudy. (RU) **195**

Vsesoyuznyi Nauchno-Issledovatel'skii Institut Zheleznodorozhnogo Transporta. Vestnik. (RU ISSN 0042-4749) **4716**

Vsesvit. (KR ISSN 0320-8370) **2888**

Vsezoyuznaya Akademiya Sel'skokhozyaistvennykh Nauk im. V.I. Lenina. Doklady. (RU ISSN 0042-9244) **129**

▼Vskhody. (RU) **2888**

Vspomogatel'nye Istoricheskie Distsipliny. (RU) **2395**, 421

Vstrechi. (US ISSN 0888-5257) **3008**

Vu - Text Newsline. (US) **1445**

Vue. (US) **349**

Vuelta. (MX) **2974**

Vukani! (SA) **4290**

Vulcan see Vigilance **1840**

Vulkanen: Ren L A V A. (Lokalhistoriske Arkiver i Vestsjaeliands Amt) (DK ISSN 0108-691X) **2395**

Vulkaniseur - Jahrbuch see Service - Jahrbuch **4294**

Vulture News. (SA) **568**, 1499

Vuoriteollisus/Bergshanteringen. (FI ISSN 0042-9317) **3497**, 3423

VXIbus Newsletter. (US) **1910**

Vyapar (Gujarati Edition). (II ISSN 0042-9325) **698**

Vyapar (Hindi Edition). (II) **698**

Vyapari-Mitra. (II) **1112**

Vyavasaya Keralam. (II) **841**, 1086

Vyber. (CS) **2576**

†Vyberova Anotovana Bibliografie Studijnich Materialu. (CS) **5302**

Vyberova Bibliografia Muzeologickej Literatury. (CS) **3536**, 416

Vychovavatel. (CS) **1671**, 4049

Vykhodiat iz Pechati see Soon to Appear **412**

Vynalezy see Vynalezy a Zlepsovaci Navrhy **3679**

Vynalezy a Zlepsovaci Navrhy/Inventions and Improvement Suggestions. (CS) **3679**

Vyrocne Spravy o Cinnosti Slovenskych Muzei a Galerii. (CS) **3535**

Vyskumny Ustav Lesneho Hospodarstva vo Zvolene. Lesnicke Studie. (CS) **2110**, 460

Vyskumny Ustav Luk a Pasienkov v Banskej Bystrici. Vedecke Prace. (CS) **129**, 195

Vyskumny Ustav Rastinnej Vyroby v Piestanoch. Vedecke Prace. (CS) **129**, 460

Vyskumny Ustav Zivocisnej Vyroby v Nitre. Vedecke Prace/Research Institute of Animal Production at Nitra. Scientific Works. (CS) **129**, 232

Vysoka Skola Banska. Sbornik Vedeckych Praci: Rada Hutnicka/Institute of Mining and Metallurgy. Transactions: Metallurgical Series. (CS ISSN 0042-3726) **3423**

Vysoka Skola Banska. Sbornik Vedeckych Praci: Rada Strojni. (CS) **1840**

Vysoka Skola Lesnicka a Drevarska vo Zvolene. Lesnicka Fakulta. Zbornik Vedeckych Prac. see Acta Facultatis Forestalis, Zvolen **2095**

Vysoka Skola Zemedelska. Information Bulletin. (CS ISSN 0231-9128) **144**

Vysoka Skola Zemedelska. Library and Documentation Bulletin see Vysoka Skola Zemedelska. Information Bulletin **144**

Vysoke Skoly Banske. Sbornik Vedeckych Praci: Rada Hornicka-Geologicka. (CS) **1585**, 1596, 1971

Vysoke Tatry. (CS) **2185**, 4796

Vysokomolekulyarnye Soedineniya. (RU ISSN 0042-9368) **1231**

Vysokomolekulyarnye Soedineniya. Kratkie Soobshcheniya. (RU) **1231**

Vystavba a Architektura. (CS ISSN 0042-9376) **308**, 2498

Vytis/Knight. (US ISSN 0042-9384) **1302**

Vytvarnictvo, Fotografia, Film. (CS ISSN 0042-9392) **349**, 3519, 3798

Vytvarny Zivot. (CS) **349**

Vyziva/Nutrition. (CS) **3613**

Vyziva a Zdravie/Nutrition and Health. (CS ISSN 0042-9406) **3613**

Vyziva Lidu see Vyziva **3613**

Vyzkumny a Zkusebni Letecky Ustav Zpravodaj see V Z L U Zpravodaj **64**

Vyzkumny Ustav Rybarsky a Hydrobiologicky. Bulletin. (CS ISSN 0007-389X) **2050**

Vyzkumny Ustav Spoju. Sbornik Praci. (CS) **4719**

Vyzkumy v Cechach. (CS) **289**, 2395

▼Vyzov. (RU ISSN 0868-9520) **3948**, 1528

Vyzvol'nyi Shlyakh/Liberation Path. (UK ISSN 0042-9422) **2888**

Vznik a Vyvoj Prumyslovych Oblasti see Prumyslove Oblasti **992**

W. (US) **1295**

W A A see Agricultural Aviation **44**

W A A C C S Motor Industry (Western Australian Automobile Chamber of Commerce) see Motor Trade Association of Western Australia. Journal **4696**

W.A. Business World see Business News **902**

W A D E Exchange. (World Association of Document Examiners) (US) **1524**, 2693

W A E M A Bulletin see W A E M A Wrapup **5302**

†W A E M A Wrapup. (Western and English Manufacturers Association) (US) **5302**

W A M M Newsletter. (Women Against Military Madness) (US) **4855**, 3475

W.A. Meat Worker. (AT) **2591**, 2083

W A N A T C A Yearbook see West Australian Nut and Tree Crop Association Yearbook **196**

W A N D Bulletin. (Women's Action for Nuclear Disarmament) (US) **4855**, 1499

W A News. (Washington Affiliate, Inc.) (US) **3161**

W A P D A News. (Water and Power Development Authority) (PK) **4830**

W A R see World Accounting Report **757**

W.A.S. Newsletter. (World Archaeological Society) (US ISSN 0738-8063) **289**

W A T Acronyms and Initialisms in Australian Library and Information Science see Australian Libraries: The Essential Directory **2746**

W A T C O M News. (Waterloo Computing) (CN) **1455**, 1465, 1475

W.A. Teachers' Journal see Western Teacher **1672**

W A W Newsletter. (William Alanson White Psychoanalytic Institute) (US ISSN 0042-9511) **4049**

W A Y Forum. (World Assembly of Youth) (DK ISSN 0049-8033) **1269**

W & J Magazine. (Washington & Jefferson College) (US ISSN 8750-8133) **1671**

W and J News see W & J Magazine **1671**

W & L Magazine. (Washington and Lee University) (US ISSN 0042-952X) **1330**

W & M/Continuing Education and Media. (Weiterbildung und Medien) (GW ISSN 0170-866X) **1688**, 1383

W & V. (Werben und Verkaufen) (GW ISSN 0042-9538) **39**

†W B. (Waldenbooks) (US) **5302**

W B F O. (Wohnbauforschung in Oesterreich) (AU ISSN 0042-9562) **2498**

W B K see W B K Forschungsberichte **1840**

W B K Forschungsberichte. (Univeritaet Karlsruhe, Institut fuer Werkzeugmaschinen und Betriebstechnik) (US) **1840**

W B K Journal see D M T Journal **3482**

W C C I Forum. (World Council for Curriculum and Instruction) (US ISSN 0116-5461) **1724**

W C I see Western Commerce & Industry Magazine **841**

W.C.J. Meredith Memorial Lectures. (CN ISSN 0509-5166) **2693**

W C J O see Workers' Compensation Journal of Ohio **4077**

W C N Commercial News. (US ISSN 0047-5068) **924**

W C O T P Biennial Report. (World Confederation of Organizations of the Teaching Profession) (SZ) **1732**, 1671

W C O T P Report see W C O T P Biennial Report **1732**

W C P S Quarterly. (Women's Caucus for Political Science) (US) **3933**, 4855

W C R L A Newsletter see C R L A Newsletter **1682**

†W C R P Report. (World Conference on Religion and Peace) (US) **5302**

W C W Magazine. (US) **4496**

†W D. (Warehouse Distribution) (US ISSN 0042-9589) **5302**

W D C Period. (Washington, DC) (US) **2237**

W D L News. (Workers Defense League, Inc.) (US) **997**, 3948

W E A Legend. (Wilderness Education Association) (US) **1499**

W E A News. (Workers' Educational Association) (UK) **1671**

†W E A Southern District Journal. (Worker's Educational Association) (UK ISSN 0141-0660) **5302**

†W E M A Bezugsquellenverzeichnis. (GW ISSN 0171-5038) **5302**

W E P Z A Newsletter. (World Export Processing Zones Association) (US ISSN 0887-9990) **924**, 1086

W E R A Brochure. (Western - English Retailers of America) (US) **1288**, 1056

†W E R A Business Newsletter. (Western - English Retailers of America) (US) **5302**

W E R A Special Newsletter. (Western - English Retailers of America) (US) **1288**, 1056

W E S A Newsletter. (Wisconsin Electronic Sales and Service Association) (US) **1119**, 1779

W E S Authors' and Publishers' Service Newsletter. (Watman Educational Services) (US) **1671**, 2518, 4138

W E S Bulletin see W E S Authors' and Publishers' Service Newsletter **1671**

W E T A Magazine. (US) **1383**

†W E X I T A Exec. (Women Executives International Tourism Association) (US) **5302**

W Europe see W **1295**

W F C D Communicator. (Western Fertilizer & Chemical Dealers Association) (CN) **129**

W F D Y News. (World Federation of Democratic Youth) (HU ISSN 0049-8076) **1269**, 3933

W F L N Philadelphia Guide see W F L N Philadelphia Guide to Events and Places **5302**

†W F L N Philadelphia Guide to Events and Places. (US) **5302**

W F S Quarterly. (Women in the Fire Service) (US) **2035**, 4855

W F T - Werkstoff-Forschung Und - Technik. (US) **1840**

W G A Geschaeftsbericht. (Wirtschaftsvereinigung Gross- und Aussenhandel) (GW ISSN 0042-966X) **924**

†W G & L Tax News. (Warren, Gorham & Lamont Inc.) (US) **5302**

W G O - Monatshefte fuer Osteuropaeisches Recht. (GW ISSN 0042-9678) **2693**

W H. (Wider Horizons) (UK) **2290**

†W.H.A.T. (What's Here and There) (AT ISSN 1030-6196) **5302**

W H M I S Compliance Manual. (Workplace Hazardous Materials Information Systems) (CN) **3623**

W H O AIDS Series. (World Health Organization) (UN ISSN 1011-5773) **3224**

W H O Drug Information. (World Health Organization) (UN ISSN 1010-9609) **4115**, 3745

W H O Offset Publications. (World Health Organization) (UN) **4119**, 4115

W H O Technical Report Series. (World Health Organization) (UN ISSN 0512-3054) **3161**, 4115

W H O's News. (Washington Homeschool Organization) (US) **1671**

W I C C E Newsletter see Women's Information Updates **4857**

W I C H E Reports. (Western Interstate Commission for Higher Education) (US ISSN 0511-7666) **1720**

W I D Bulletin. (Women and International Development Program) (US) **3948**, 936, 4855

W I D Forum. (Women and International Development Program) (US ISSN 0888-7772) **3948**, 936, 4855

W I D News. (Western Institute for the Deaf) (CN ISSN 0049-7436) **2289**

W I D Newsletter see W I D Bulletin **3948**
W I D Working Papers see Working Papers on Women in International Development **936**
W I K. (GW ISSN 0177-5251) **1524, 803**
W I N B A see Nail & Beauty Trends **373**
W I N News. (Women's International Network) (US ISSN 0145-7985) **4860**
W.I.N.O. Newsletter. (Wine Investigation for Novices and Oenophiles) (US) **386, 2443**
W I T S: I. (Wisconsin Introductions to Scandinavia) (US ISSN 0742-7018) **2028**
W I T S: II. (Wisconsin Introductions to Scandinavia) (US ISSN 0742-7026) **2028**
W I - Wohnungswirtschaftliche Informationen. (GW ISSN 0179-7948) **4159**
W I Z O Review. (Women's International Zionist Organization) (IS ISSN 0042-9732) **4855**
W J R see Washington Journalism Review **2576**
W K S B. (GW) **2304**
W L A Newsletter. (Wisconsin Library Association) (US ISSN 0043-6518) **2790**
W L A Selecta. (Wissenschaftlicher Literatur Anzeiger) (GW ISSN 0177-5928) **4358**
W L B see Wasser, Luft und Boden **1979**
W L D F News. (Women's Legal Defense Fund) (US ISSN 0736-9433) **2693, 4855**
W L W Journal. (Women Library Workers) (US ISSN 0272-1996) **2790, 4855**
W M A - Nouncements. (Women Marines Association) (UI) **3475, 4855**
W M Allgemeine Verlosungstabelle. (Wertpapier-Mitteilungen) (GW ISSN 0342-6874) **803**
W M D A Membership Directory and Buyers Guide. (US) **640, 1158**
W M O Bulletin. (World Meteorological Organization) (UN ISSN 0042-9767) **3442**
W M Teil I: Sammelliste mit Opposition Belegte Wertpapiere. (GW) **803**
W M Teil II: Nachrichten Ueber Deutsche Festverzinsliche Werte. (GW ISSN 0342-6939) **803**
W M Teil IIa: Neuemissionen - Schnelldienst. (GW) **803**
W M Teil IIb: Sammelliste Gekuendigter und Verloster Wertpapiere. (Wertpapier-Mitteilungen) (GW ISSN 0170-5458) **803**
W M Teil III: Nachrichten Ueber Deutsche Aktien, Anteile, Genussscheine, Kuxe. (Wertpapier-Mitteilungen) (GW ISSN 0342-6955) **803**
W M Teil IV: Zeitschrift fuer Wirtschafts- und Bankrecht. (GW) **2693, 803**
W M Teil Va: Nachrichten Ueber Auslaendische Aktien und Aktienaehnliche Werte. (GW ISSN 0342-6998) **803**
W M Teil Vb: Nachrichten Ueber Auslaendische Festverzinsliche Wertpapiere. (Wertpapier Mitteilungen) (GW ISSN 0342-6882) **803**
W M: Wertpapierberatung. (GW ISSN 0342-6882) **803**
W N C Business Journal. (Western North Carolina) (US) **698**
W N N R Publikasies. see C S I R Publications **5157**
W N P S Newsletter. (Wyoming Native Plant Society) (US) **520, 2140**
W N Y F. (With New York Firefighters) (US ISSN 0042-9775) **2035, 4115**
†W O H R C News. (Women's Occupational Health Resource Center) (US ISSN 0741-5796) **5302**
W O J see Women's Outdoor Journal **4560**

W O Jeepster Newsletter. (Willys Overland Jeepster Club) (US) **4705**
W O S News see Quarternote **3575**
W P A Journal. (World Pheasant Association) (UK) **568**
W P A News. (World Pheasant Association) (UK) **568**
W P A S Museletter. (Washington Performing Arts Society) (US ISSN 0092-4113) **3586, 1532**
W P C Information Center for the Americas and the Caribbean see C I A C **3877**
W P I Journal. (US ISSN 0148-6128) **1840**
W P M Newsletter (World Presbyterian Missions) see Network (Atlanta) **4191**
W P N R. (Weekblad voor Privaatrecht, Notariaat en Registratie) (NE ISSN 0165-8476) **2693**
W P S Professional Handbook Series. (US ISSN 0083-8977) **4049**
W P W Decor see Home Decor **3653**
W R A P. (UK) **3623**
W R C Progress Reports. (Welding Research Council) (US) **3430**
W R E E - View see W R E E - View of Women **3948**
W R E E - View of Women. (Women for Racial and Economic Equality) (US ISSN 0892-3116) **3948, 4855**
W R I Journal. (Welding Research Institute) (II ISSN 0970-4477) **3430, 1923**
W R I Keywords see W R I Journal **3430**
W R I Newsletter see Peace News **3914**
W R I Newsletter. (Western Review Institute) (US) **3933**
W R P see Wettbewerb in Recht und Praxis **2694**
W R R I News. (Water Resources Research Institute) (US ISSN 0549-799X) **4830**
W R R I News Report. (Water Resources Research Institute) (US ISSN 0044-9970) **4830**
W S D A News. (Washington State Dental Association) (US ISSN 0042-983X) **3244**
W S G A Checkout. (Wine and Spirits Guild of America) (US) **386, 1056**
W S G A Newsletter see W S G A Checkout **386**
W S G Discussion Papers. (Institut fuer Wirtschafts- und Sozialgeographie) (AU) **2266**
W S I Mitteilungen. (Wirtschafts- und Sozialwissenschaftliches Institut) (GW ISSN 0342-300X) **4392, 698, 2591**
W S S A Grapevine. (Wine and Spirits Shippers Association) (US) **386, 924, 4660**
W S T Knitting Technik see Knitting Technique **4621**
†W S V - Aktuell. (Wuerttemburgischer Schwimmverband) (GW) **5302**
W T I see World Translation Index **4358**
W T I A Technical Notes. (Welding Technology Institute of Australia) (AT) **3430**
W T - Werkstattstechnik. (GW ISSN 0340-4544) **4613, 3024**
W U B see Was Uns Betrifft **3948**
W U F A. (Writers Union of Free Afghanistan) (PK) **2888**
W U U A Newsletter. (World Union for a Universal Alphabet) (US ISSN 0734-3116) **1345**
W V A Lifeline see W V A Views & Visions **1688**
W V A Views & Visions. (Wisconsin Vocational Association) (US) **1688**
W V School Journal see West Virginia School Journal **1671**
W W D see Women's Wear Daily **1288**
†W W F & C F Letter. (World Wildlife Fund) (US) **5302**
W W F Magazine. (World Wrestling Federation) (US) **4496**
W W F News. (World Wide Fund for Nature) (UK) **1499, 1971**
W W F Transparent. (Westdeutsche Rundfunkwerbung GmbH) (GW) **1360**

W W F Wrestling Spotlight. (World Wrestling Federation) (US) **4496**
W W S - World Ports see W W S - World Wide Shipping **4741**
W W S - World Wide Shipping. (US) **4741**
W W T - Weiterbildung in Wirtschaft und Technik. (GW) **698, 1688**
W.W. 1 Aero. (World War 1 Aeroplanes, Inc.) (US ISSN 0736-198X) **65, 2326**
W Wintern. (GW) **2481**
W Z B Forschung. (Wissenschafts Zentrum Berlin fuer Sozialforschung) (GW ISSN 0932-3481) **4396**
W Z B - Mitteilungen. (Wissenschaftszentrum Berlin fuer Sozialforschung) (GW ISSN 0174-3120) **4392, 3933**
Die Waage. (GW ISSN 0017-4874) **2192**
Wabul. (NQ) **4209**
Die Wachenburg. (GW ISSN 0935-0659) **1330**
Wacht te Kooi. (NE ISSN 0042-9902) **2212**
Wackenberger Echo. (GW) **2498, 1245**
▼The Wacky World of Peafowl Report. (US ISSN 1056-6759) **228**
The Waco Messenger. (US) **4209**
Waconda Roots and Branches. (US ISSN 8755-2167) **2167**
Wade World. (US ISSN 0898-5421) **2167**
Waegen und Dosieren. (GW ISSN 0342-5916) **1402**
Die Waehrungen der Welt. (GW) **743, 803, 4592**
Waeller Heimat. (GW ISSN 0931-2889) **2192**
Waelzlagertechnik - Industrietechnik. (GW ISSN 0934-8875) **1926**
Waerme- und Stoffuebertragung/ Thermo- and Fluid Dynamics. (GW ISSN 0042-9929) **3842, 3846**
Waermetechnik. (GW ISSN 0720-3438) **2304, 3703**
Waescherei- und Reinigungs-Praxis. (GW ISSN 0042-9937) **1282**
Das Waffen-Arsenal. (GW) **3475**
†Waffen- und Kostumkunde. (GW ISSN 0042-9945) **5302**
Wage. (GW) **2888**
Wage-Price Law & Economics Review. (US ISSN 0361-6665) **1000, 698**
▼Wage Settlements Bulletin/Bulletin des Reglements Salariaux. (CN) **997**
Wage Statistics. see Norway. Statistisk Sentralbyraa. Loennsstatistikk **731**
Wages and Benefits. (US) **1732**
Wages and Hours see B N A Policy and Practice Series. Wages and Hours **973**
Wages and Salaries. see Finland. Tilastokeskus. Tilastotiedotus. Palkat Loner **716**
Wages and Total Labour Costs for Workers: International Survey. (SW ISSN 0280-4743) **997**
Wagga Wagga and District Historical Society. Journal. (AT ISSN 0085-7858) **2346**
Waggoner. (UK ISSN 0042-9961) **3475**
Wagner. (UK) **3586, 421**
Wagner Latin American Newsletter. (US) **2426, 3933**
Wagner News. (UK ISSN 0261-3468) **3586, 421**
Wagon Review see Modern Railways **4711**
Wagoner Journal. (US) **2167**
Die Wagtoring. (SA) **4290**
Al-Wahdah. (TS) **2211**
Wahre Geschichten. (GW) **2985**
Die Wahrheit. (AU ISSN 0042-9996) **3933**
Al-Wa'i. (TS) **1269, 1302**
Al-Wa'i al-Tullabi. (TS) **1330**
Waifarers. (UK ISSN 0143-9138) **232**
Waigani Seminar. Papers. (PP ISSN 0085-7866) **2346**
Waiguo Jiaoyu Dongtai/Foreign Education Development. (CC) **1671**

Waiguo Jiaoyu Ziliao/Foreign Education Material. (CC) **1671**
Waiguo Wenti Yanjiu. (CC) **4392**
Waiguo Wenxue/Foreign Literature. (US) **2974**
Waiguo Wenxue Yanjiu/Foreign Literature Studies. (CC ISSN 1001-2885) **2974**
Waiguoyu/Journal of Foreign Language.(CC) **2851**
Waikiki News. (US) **4796, 2237**
Waixiang Jingji. (CC) **698**
Waiyu Dianhua Jiaoxue/Audio-Visual Teaching of Foreign Languages. (CC ISSN 1001-5795) **1763**
Waiyu Jiaoxue yu Yanjiu/Foreign Language Teaching & Research. (CC) **2851, 1763**
Waiyu Xuekan/Journal of Foreign Languages. (CC ISSN 1000-0100) **2851**
Wajibu. (KE ISSN 1016-9717) **2209**
Wakatlat al-Sudan Lil-Anba. Weekly Review. see Sudan News Agency. Weekly Review **2170**
Wakayama Daigaku Kyoikugakubu Kiyo. Shizen Kagaku/Wakayama University. Faculty of Education. Bulletin: Natural Science. (JA ISSN 0511-0831) **4351**
Wakayama Economic Review. (JA) **1031, 899**
Wakayama Igaku. see Wakayama Medicine **3162**
Wakayama-ken Kisho Geppo. see Wakayama Prefecture. Monthly Report of Meteorology **3442**
Wakayama-ken Kisho Nenpo. see Wakayama Prefecture. Annual Report of Meteorology **3442**
Wakayama Medical Reports. (JA ISSN 0511-084X) **3162**
Wakayama Medicine/Wakayama Igaku. (JA ISSN 0043-0013) **3162**
Wakayama Prefecture. Annual Report of Meteorology/Wakayama-ken Kisho Nenpo. (JA) **3442**
Wakayama Prefecture. Monthly Report of Meteorology/Wakayama-ken Kisho Geppo. (JA ISSN 0043-0021) **3442**
Wakayama University. Faculty of Education. Bulletin: Natural Science. see Wakayama Daigaku Kyoikugakubu Kiyo. Shizen Kagaku **4351**
Wake County Genalogical Society Newsletter see Wake Treasures **2167**
Wake Forest Law Review. (US ISSN 0043-003X) **2693**
Wake Forest University School of Law. Continuing Legal Education. Annual Review, North Carolina. (US) **2693**
Wake-Robin. (US) **4351**
Wake Treasures. (US ISSN 1055-7857) **2167**
Wake-up! (Ayrshire). (UK) **4209**
Wake Up (London). (UK) **4423**
Wakefield Court Rolls Series. (UK) **2395**
Waksman Foundation of Japan. Report. (JA ISSN 0509-5832) **3745**
Walbauernverband Nordrhein-Westfalen. Mitteilungsblatt. (GW) **2110**
Der Wald. (GW ISSN 0863-4807) **2110**
Wald und Holz. (SZ) **2118**
Die Waldarbeit. (GW ISSN 0043-0048) **2110**
Waldeckischer Landeskalender. (GW) **2395**
Waldenbooks see W B **5302**
Walden's A B C Guide and Paper Production Yearbook. (US ISSN 0083-7024) **3667**
Walden's Fiber & Board Report. (US) **3667**
Walden's Paper Report. (US) **3667**
Waldviertel. (AU) **2395**
Wales. (UK ISSN 0043-0056) **2889**
†Wales. National Library. Handlist of Manuscripts in the National Library of Wales. (UK ISSN 0065-0293) **5302**
Wales Best Holidays. (UK) **4796**
Wales Business Directory (Cardiff). (UK) **1158**

Wales Business Directory (Solihull). (UK) 1158, 824
Walford's Guide to Reference Material. (UK) 416
Walia. (ET ISSN 0083-7059) 1499
Walk. (UK ISSN 0144-2694) 4723, 4115
†Walk. (AT) 5302
Walk Away. (US ISSN 1059-6216) 4456, 4209
The Walker. (AT) 4559
†Walker - Ames Lectures. (US) 5302
Walker Footprints. (US ISSN 1056-7321) 2167
Walkerana. (US ISSN 1053-637X) 593
Walker's Estimating & Construction Journal. (US) 636
Walker's Manual of Western Corporations. (US ISSN 0894-153X) 968
Walker's Old Moore's Almanac. (UK ISSN 0083-7067) 1782
Walking and Sinning. (US) 3008
Walking Horse Report. (US) 4539
Walking! Journal. (US ISSN 0739-4497) 4559, 3810
Walking Magazine. (US ISSN 1042-2102) 3810
Walking-Stick Notes. (US) 357, 259, 2060, 2443
†Walking Tours of San Juan & Restaurant Menu Guide. (PR) 5302
WalkWays. (US) 3810, 4496
Wall News. see Tulungan sa Kaunlaran 840
The Wall Paper. (US ISSN 0273-6837) 2555
Wall Street and U S Business News. (US) 968
Wall Street Computer Review. (US) 806
Wall Street Digest. (US) 803, 887, 968
Wall Street Generalist. (US) 968
Wall Street Journal (Eastern Edition). (US ISSN 0099-9660) 803
Wall Street Journal (Midwest Edition). (US ISSN 0163-089X) 803
Wall Street Journal (Southwest Edition). (US ISSN 0193-225X) 803
Wall Street Journal (Western Edition). (US ISSN 0193-2241) 803
Wall Street Journal - Europe. (BE ISSN 0921-9986) 803
Wall Street Journal Guide to Business Travel: Europe. (US) 4796
Wall Street Journal Guide to Business Travel: Pacific Rim. (US) 4796
Wall Street Journal Guide to Business Travel: U S A & Canada. (US) 4796
Wall Street Journal Index. (US ISSN 0083-7075) 803, 968
Wall Street Letter. (US) 968
Wall Street Research Reports. (US) 968
Wall Street Review of Books see Business Library Review 769
Wall Street Transcript. (US ISSN 0043-0102) 968
Wallace Stevens Journal. (US ISSN 0148-7132) 3008
Wallaces Farmer. (US ISSN 0043-0129) 129
†Wallcovering Industry News. (US) 5302
Wallcoverings Letter. (US) 2555
Wallcoverings Magazine see Wallcoverings, Windows & Interior Fashion 3667
Wallcoverings, Windows & Interior Fashion. (US ISSN 1055-4394) 3667, 2555
Wallenberg Papers on International Finance. (US ISSN 0888-2819) 924
Walleye. (US) 4559
†Walling Review. (AT) 5302
Wallis. (SZ) 4796
Wallonie. (BE ISSN 0379-3753) 887
Wallpaper Reproduction News. (US) 2555
Wallraf-Richartz-Jahrbuch; Westdeutsches Jahrbuch fuer Kunstgeschichte. Neue Folge. (GW) 349

Wallraf-Richartz-Jahrbuch; Westdeutsches Jahrbuch fuer Kunstgeschichte see Wallraf-Richartz-Jahrbuch; Westdeutsches Jahrbuch fuer Kunstgeschichte. Neue Folge 349
Walls & Ceilings. (US ISSN 0043-0161) 636
Walneck's Classic Cycle Trader. (US) 4521
Walsall Chamber of Commerce & Industry Directory. (UK) 1158, 824
Walt Disney World (Year). (US) 4796
Walt Disney's Donald Duck. (GW) 1269
Walt Disney's Donald Duck Fun Annual. (UK) 1269
Walt Disney's Lustiges Taschenbuch. (GW) 1269
Walt Disney's Mickey Mouse Club Annual. (UK) 1269
Walt Disney's Mickey Mouse Magazine. (US) 1269
Walt Disney's Micky Maus. (GW) 1269
Walt Disney's Winnie the Pooh Annual. (UK) 1270
Walt Whitman Quarterly Review. (US ISSN 0737-0679) 2974
Walt Whitman Review see Walt Whitman Quarterly Review 2974
Walter and Andree de Nottbeck Foundation Scientific Reports. (FI ISSN 0358-6758) 558, 483
Walter Lynwood Fleming Lectures in Southern History. (US ISSN 0083-7121) 2426
Walter Roth Museum of Anthropology. Journal. (GY ISSN 0256-4653) 252
Walter Roth Museum of Archaeology and Anthropology. Journal see Walter Roth Museum of Anthropology. Journal 252
Walter W.S. Cook Alumni Lecture. (US ISSN 0083-7148) 349
Walters Art Gallery Bulletin. (US ISSN 0043-0188) 349, 3535
Walthari. (GW ISSN 0930-0279) 2974
Wampiurs Wars. (PL) 3015
Wanasan. (TH ISSN 0043-0196) 2110
Wanbli Ho/Eagle's Voice. (US) 2028, 2974
Wanderer. (US) 4209, 3786
Wandering Volhynians. (CN) 2028
Wandering Wolfs. (US ISSN 0887-3860) 2167
Wandermagazin. (GW ISSN 0178-1677) 4559
Wandsbeker Wochenblatt. (GW) 1295, 39
Wang in the News. (US ISSN 0896-2111) 1424, 1475
Wanhuatong Lianhuan Huabao/Kaleidoscope. (CC) 1270
Wanita. (MY) 1295
Wanpi Wawa/Naughty Baby. (CC ISSN 1003-4013) 1270
Wanted. (US) 3400
Wantok. (PP) 2213
Want's Federal - State Court Directory (Year). (US ISSN 0742-1095) 1158, 2734
Wapkrant. (NE) 3586
Waqai al-Iraqiya. (IQ) 2693
Waqa'i Dawlat al-Imarat/Emirates Events. (TS) 2432, 3645
War and Literature. see Krieg und Literatur 2372
War and Society. (AT ISSN 0729-2473) 2326, 2426, 3475
War Communiques. (TZ ISSN 0043-020X) 3933, 3475
War Cover Club Bulletin. (US) 3759
War Cry. (AT) 4209, 4290
War Cry. (UK ISSN 0043-0226) 4252
War Cry. (CN ISSN 0043-0218) 4290
War Cry. (NR ISSN 0049-688X) 4290
War Cry. (NZ ISSN 0043-0242) 4290, 2212
War Cry/Strydkreet. (SA ISSN 0043-0250) 4290
War Cry. (SI ISSN 0049-6898) 4290
War Cry. (US ISSN 0043-0234) 4290

†War In the Air. (UK) 5302
War, Literature, and the Arts. (US ISSN 1046-6967) 2974
†War on Want News. (UK) 5302
War - Peace Report see International Interactions 3961
†War Resister. (US) 5302
War - Whoop. (US) 1330
Warasarn Prachakornsatr. see Journal of Demography 3984
Warburg Institute. Oxford-Warburg Studies. (UK) 2518
Warburg Institute. Studies. (UK ISSN 0083-7199) 2518
Warburg Institute. Surveys see Warburg Institute. Surveys and Texts 2518
Warburg Institute. Surveys and Texts. (UK ISSN 0266-1772) 2518
Ward Foundation News. (US) 3535
Ward - Phillips Lectures in English Language and Literature. (US ISSN 0083-7210) 2974
†Ward's Auto Dealer. (US) 5302
Ward's Auto World. (US ISSN 0043-0315) 4705
Ward's Automotive International. (US) 4705
Ward's Automotive Reports. (US) 4705
Ward's Automotive Yearbook. (US ISSN 0083-7229) 4668, 4705
†Ward's Business Directory of Major International Companies. (US ISSN 0882-8016) 5302
Ward's Business Directory of U S Private and Public Companies. (US ISSN 1048-8707) 1158
Ward's Business Directory of U S Private and Public Companies. Vol.1; Over 11.5 Million Dollars in Sales see Ward's Business Directory of U S Private and Public Companies 1158
Ward's Business Directory of U S Private and Public Companies. Vol.2; From .5 to 11.5 Million Dollars see Ward's Business Directory of U S Private and Public Companies 1158
Ward's Business Directory of U S Private and Public Companies. Vol.3; Ranked by Sales within Industry see Ward's Business Directory of U S Private and Public Companies 1158
Ward's Engine Update see Ward's Engine Update and Vehicle Technology 4705
Ward's Engine Update and Vehicle Technology. (US) 4705
Ward's Quarterly see Ward's Auto World 4705
Ward's Who's Who Among U.S. Motor Vehicle Manufacturers. (US) 4705
Ware Quarterly. (US) 2167
Warehouse Distribution see W D 5302
Warehouse Journal. (US) 1330
Warehousing Supervisor's Bulletin. (US ISSN 0744-8864) 1031
Warempel see Splinter 1266
Warenzeichen- und Musterblatt. (GW ISSN 0323-5394) 3679
Warenzeichenblatt. Teil 1: Angemeldete Zeichen. (GW ISSN 0043-0331) 3679
Warenzeichenblatt. Teil 2: Eingetragene Zeichen. (GW ISSN 0043-034X) 3679
Warfare. (UK ISSN 0308-0676) 3475
Warfield's. (US) 888
Wargamer. (US) 2443, 3475
Warlord. (UK) 1270
Warm Line. (US) 4290
Warp & Weft. (US) 4627, 2443
Warp Four. (US) 3015
Warragul Gazette. (AT) 2172
Warren County Genealogical Society Quarterly see Heir Lines 2154
Warren County Magazine see Skylander Magazine 5277
Warren County Reflections. (US) 2426
Warren Family Historian. (US ISSN 0739-4942) 2167
Warren, Gorham & Lamont Inc. Tax News see W G & L Tax News 5302
Warrior. (UK ISSN 0049-6901) 1270, 4209
Warrior. (CN ISSN 0707-8056) 3475
Warrior. (II) 4796

Warsaw Agricultural University. S G G W - A R. Annals. Horticulture see Warsaw Agricultural University. S G G W. Annals. Horticulture 2140
Warsaw Agricultural University. S G G W. Annals. Agricultural Economics and Rural Sociology. (PL) 160, 4456
Warsaw Agricultural University. S G G W. Annals. Agriculture. (PL) 129
Warsaw Agricultural University. S G G W. Annals. Animal Science. (PL) 228
Warsaw Agricultural University. S G G W. Annals. Food Technology and Nutrition. (PL) 2083, 3613
Warsaw Agricultural University. S G G W. Annals. Forestry and Wood Technology. (PL) 2118
Warsaw Agricultural University. S G G W. Annals. Horticulture. (PL) 2140
Warsaw Agricultural University. S G G W. Annals. Land Reclamation. (PL) 196
Warsaw Agricultural University. S G G W. Annals. Veterinary Medicine. (PL) 4819
Warsaw Agricultural University. Treatises and Monographs. see Szkola Glowna Gospodarstwa Wiejskiego. Rozprawy Naukowe i Monografie 123
†Warsaw Newsletter. (PL) 5302
†Warsaw Post. (PL) 5302
Warsaw Voice. (PL ISSN 0860-7591) 3976, 698
Warschauer Post see Warsaw Post 5302
Warship. (UK ISSN 0142-6222) 3475
Warship International. (US ISSN 0043-0374) 3475, 4741
Warships of the World. see Weyers Flottentaschenbuch 3475
Warta Demografi. (IO ISSN 0125-9679) 3989
Warta Dinas Kesehatan. (IO) 4115
Warta Ekonomi Maritim Review for Entrepreneurs. (IO ISSN 0125-9229) 4741
Warta Geologi. (MY) 1585
Warta Konsumen. (IO) 1508
Warta Nuklear Malaysia/Nuclear Bulletin of Malaysia. (MY ISSN 0127-6948) 1810
Wartturm. (GW ISSN 0723-7553) 2395
Warunki Srodowiskowe Polskiej Strefy Poludniowego Baltyku - Materialy Oddzialu Morskiego see Instytut Meteorologii i Gospodarki Wodnej. Oddzial Morski w Gdyni. Materialy. Warunki Srodowiskowe Polskiej Strefy Poludniowego Baltyku 1606
Warwick Business School Research Papers. (UK) 699
†Warwick Economic Research Papers. (UK ISSN 0083-7350) 5302
Warwick Papers in Management see Warwick Business School Research Papers 699
Warwickshire and Worcestershire Life. (UK ISSN 0043-0390) 2196
Warwickshire Farmer. (UK) 129
Wary Canary. (US ISSN 0899-1405) 1971, 3162, 4115
Was Kostet der Geschaeftswagen? see Autokosten und Steuern Aktuell 4682
Was Lefft. (GW) 2889
Was Tun. (GW ISSN 0043-0404) 3933
Was und Wie? (GW ISSN 0341-7158) 4209
Was Uns Betrifft. (GW ISSN 0936-6520) 3948, 2518, 4252
Wascana Review. (CN ISSN 0043-0412) 2974, 2889
Waseda Architectural News. (JA) 308
Waseda Architecture. (JA) 308
Waseda Bungaku. (JA) 2974
Waseda Business and Economic Studies. (JA) 699
Waseda Commercial Review. see Waseda Shogaku 841

WASEDA DAIGAKU

Waseda Daigaku Daigakuin Rikogaku Kenkyu Iho/Waseda University. Graduate School of Science and Engineering. Synopses of Science and Engineering Papers. (JA ISSN 0507-9683) **1847, 4358, 4615**

Waseda Daigaku Kyoikugakubu Gakujutsu Kenkyu. Seibutsugaku, Chigaku Hen/Waseda University. School of Education. Scientific Researches: Biology, Geology. (JA) **460,** 1549

Waseda Daigaku Kyoikugakubu Gakujutsu Kenkyu. Sugaku Hen/ Waseda University. School of Education. Scientific Researches: Mathematics. (JA ISSN 0913-0195) **3061**

Waseda Daigaku Rikogaku Kenkyujo Hokoku/Waseda University. Science and Engineering Research Laboratory. Bulletin. (JA ISSN 0372-7181) **4351,** 1840

Waseda Journal of Political Science and Economics. see Waseda Seiji Keizaigaku Zasshi **3933**

Waseda Political Studies. (JA ISSN 0511-196X) **3933**

Waseda Seiji Keizaigaku Zasshi/Waseda Journal of Political Science and Economics. (JA ISSN 0287-7007) **3933,** 699

Waseda Shogaku/Waseda Commercial Review. (JA ISSN 0387-3404) **841**

Waseda University. Graduate School of Science and Engineering. Synopses of Science and Engineering Papers. see Waseda Daigaku Daigakuin Rikogaku Kenkyu Iho **1847**

Waseda University. Report of Castings Research Laboratory see Waseda University. Report of Materials Science and Technology **3423**

Waseda University. Report of Materials Science and Technology. (JA) **3423**

Waseda University. School of Education. Scientific Researches: Biology, Geology. see Waseda Daigaku Kyoikugakubu Gakujutsu Kenkyu. Seibutsugaku, Chigaku Hen **460**

Waseda University. School of Education. Scientific Researches: Mathematics. see Waseda Daigaku Kyoikugakubu Gakujutsu Kenkyu. Sugaku Hen **3061**

Waseda University. Science and Engineering Research Laboratory. Bulletin. see Waseda Daigaku Rikogaku Kenkyujo Hokoku **4351**

Waseda University. Science and Engineering Research Laboratory. Report. (JA ISSN 0285-4333) **4351,** 1840

Washburn Law Journal. (US ISSN 0043-0420) **2693**

Washington. Employment Security Department. Annual Demographic Information. (US) **3631**

Washington (Marietta). (US ISSN 1047-6628) **2167**

Washington (Seattle). (US ISSN 0743-2941) **2237**

Washington (State). Attorney General's Office. Charitable Trust Directory. (US) **4423**

Washington (State). Department of Fisheries. Annual Report. (US) **2050**

Washington (State). Department of Natural Resources. Annual Fire Statistics. (US) **2113,** 2035, 4592

Washington (State). Department of Natural Resources. Division of Geology and Earth Resources. Bulletin. (US) **1585,** 3497

Washington (State). Department of Natural Resources. Division of Geology and Earth Resources. Information Circular. (US ISSN 0147-1783) **3497,** 1585

Washington (State). Department of Natural Resources. Division of Geology and Earth Resources. Reports of Investigations. (US) **1585**

Washington (State). Department of Revenue. Forest Tax Annual Report see Washington (State). Department of Revenue. Forest Tax Division. Forest Tax Annual Report **1112**

Washington (State). Department of Revenue. Forest Tax Division. Forest Tax Annual Report. (US) **1112,** 2110

Washington (State). Department of Revenue. Research and Information Division. Comparative State-Local Taxes see Washington (State). Department of Revenue. Research Section. Comparative State - Local Taxes **1112**

Washington (State). Department of Revenue. Research Section. Comparative State - Local Taxes. (US) **1112**

Washington (State). Department of Revenue. Research Section. Property Tax Statistics. (US) **1112**

Washington (State) Department of Social and Health Services. Income Maintenance, Community Social Services and Medical Assistance. (US) **4423,** 4115

Washington (State). Division of Geology and Earth Resources. Report of Investigations. (US) **1585**

Washington (State). Division of Vocational Rehabilitation. State Facilities Development Plan. (US) **1742**

†Washington. State Health Plan. (US) **5302**

Washington (State). Joint Board of Legislative Ethics. Annual Report. (US) **4077**

Washington (State) Legislature. Pictorial Directory. (US ISSN 0091-8253) **4077**

Washington (State) Office of Financial Management Forecasting. Population Trends. (US) **3989**

Washington (State) Office of Financial Management, Policy Analysis and Forecasting. Population Trends see Washington (State) Office of Financial Management Forecasting. Population Trends **3989**

Washington (State) Office of Program Planning and Fiscal Management. Population and Enrollment Section. Population Trends see Washington (State) Office of Financial Management Forecasting. Population Trends **3989**

Washington (State). Vocational Rehabilitation Services Division. State Facilities Development Plan see Washington (State). Division of Vocational Rehabilitation. State Facilities Development Plan **1742**

†Washington. Utilities and Transportation Commission. Railroad-Highway Grade Crossing Accidents. Summary and Analysis. (US) **5302**

Washington (Year). (US ISSN 0083-7393) **416**

Washington Academy of Sciences. Journal. (US ISSN 0043-0439) **4351**

†Washington Accountant. (US) **5302**

Washington Action Report see N R P A Washington Action Report **5242**

Washington Action Reporter. (US) **3475**

Washington Actions on Health see Health Care Competition Week **2462**

▼Washington Administrative Law Practice Manual. (US) **4077,** 2693

Washington Afro-American. (US ISSN 0043-0447) **2028**

Washington Agricultural Record. (US ISSN 0195-0673) **129**

Washington Agricultural Statistics. (US ISSN 0095-4330) **144**

Washington-Alaska Pharmacist see Washington Pharmacist **3745**

Washington Alumnus see Columns (Seattle) **1308**

Washington & Jefferson College Magazine see W & J Magazine **1671**

Washington & Lee Law Review. (US ISSN 0043-0463) **2693**

Washington and Lee University Magazine see W & L Magazine **1330**

Washington Atomic Energy Report. (US) **1810,** 1797, 1840

Washington Atomic Energy Report and Guideletter see Washington Atomic Energy Report **1810**

†Washington Beverage Analyst. (US) **5302**

Washington Blade. (US ISSN 0278-9892) **2457**

Washington Bond & Money Market Report. (US) **969**

Washington Buddhist. (US) **4216**

Washington Bulletin see Washington Social Legislation Bulletin **4423**

Washington Business Journal. (US ISSN 0737-3147) **699**

Washington C E O. (US ISSN 1048-4981) **1031,** 1000

Washington Cattleman. (US) **228**

Washington Counseletter. (US) **3631**

Washington County Education News. (US ISSN 0043-051X) **1671**

Washington Crossing Card Collectors Club Newsletter. (US ISSN 0885-9027) **2443**

Washington, D.C. Visitor's Guide. (US) **4796**

Washington, DC Period see W D C Period **2237**

Washington Diocese. (US ISSN 0043-0544) **4252,** 4423

Washington Drug and Device Letter see Washington Drug Letter (Washington, 1979) **3745**

Washington Drug Letter (Washington, 1979). (US ISSN 0194-1291) **3745,** 1086

Washington Drug Review see Drugs & Drug Abuse Education. Newsletter **1536**

Washington Education Directory. (US) **1671**

Washington Entertainment Magazine. (US) **4796**

Washington Environmental Protection Report. (US ISSN 0014-9136) **1971,** 4077

Washington Equal Times. (US) **4855**

Washington Facts. (US ISSN 1044-9078) **1782**

Washington Farmer-Stockman see Pacific Farmer-Stockman **113**

Washington Federal Science Newsletter. (US ISSN 0740-0535) **4351**

Washington Feedline. (US) **208,** 228

Washington Fishing Holes. (US) **4559**

Washington Flyer Magazine. (US ISSN 1046-3089) **4796**

Washington Food Dealer Magazine. (US ISSN 0043-0560) **2094**

†Washington Formletter. (US) **5302**

Washington Geologic Newsletter see Washington Geology **1585**

Washington Geology. (US ISSN 1058-2134) **1585**

Washington Grange News see Grange News **94**

Washington Guardianship Law. (US) **2693**

†Washington Health Costs Letter. (US ISSN 0277-8548) **5303**

Washington Health Record. (US ISSN 0164-1514) **3162**

Washington Historical Quarterly see Pacific Northwest Quarterly **2418**

Washington History. (US ISSN 1042-9719) **2426**

▼Washington Home & Garden. (US) **2555,** 2140

Washington Homeschool Organization News see W H O's News **1671**

Washington Industry and Association News. (US) **4006**

Washington Information Directory (Year). (US ISSN 0887-8064) **3933**

Washington Inquirer. (US) **3933**

Washington International. (US ISSN 1051-0257) **4796**

Washington International Arts Letter. (US ISSN 0043-0609) **349,** 2518

Washington International Business Report. (US ISSN 0049-691X) **924**

Washington Jewish Singles Newsletter. (US) **4364**

Washington Journal. (US ISSN 1045-5566) **4077,** 699

Washington Journalism Review. (US ISSN 0741-8876) **2576**

Washington Labor Market. (US) **997**

Washington Land Use and Environmental Practice. (US) **2693,** 1499, 1971

Washington Law Review. (US ISSN 0043-0617) **2693**

Washington Lawyer. (US) **2693**

Washington Letter of Oceanography. (US) **1612**

Washington Letter on Puerto Rico. (US) **3933,** 2266

Washington Living. (US) **2028**

Washington Manufacturers Register. (US ISSN 0148-5687) **1158**

Washington Memo. (US) **4252**

Washington Monthly. (US ISSN 0043-0633) **3933,** 2889

Washington Morning Line. (US) **39**

Washington Motorist see Motorist (Seattle) **4778**

Washington Music Educator see Voice of Washington Music Educators **3586**

Washington Native Plant Society. Occasional Papers. (US) **520,** 2140

Washington Newsletter see National Farmers Union Washington Newsletter **108**

Washington Newspaper. (US ISSN 0043-0684) **2576**

Washington Notary Law Primer. (US) **2694**

Washington Notes. (US) **803**

Washington Nurse. (US) **3288**

Washington Opera Magazine. (US) **3586,** 4642

Washington Papers. (US ISSN 0278-937X) **3976**

Washington Peace Center. Newsletter see Washington Peace Letter **3933**

Washington Peace Letter. (US ISSN 1050-2823) **3933**

Washington Performing Arts Society Museletter see W P A S Museletter **3586**

Washington Pharmacist. (US) **3745**

Washington Post Book World see Book World **4122**

Washington Post: National Weekly Edition. (US) **3933**

†Washington Property Law Reporter. (US) **5303**

Washington Quarterly. (US ISSN 0163-660X) **3976**

Washington Real Estate News. (US) **4159**

Washington Recreation and Park Association. Bulletin see Washington Recreation and Park Association. Syllabus **1499**

Washington Recreation and Park Association. Syllabus. (US) **1499,** 4077

Washington Regardie's Business see Regardie's **687**

Washington Regulatory Report. (US ISSN 1042-0142) **4077,** 699

Washington Remote Sensing Letter. (US ISSN 0739-6538) **65**

Washington Report (St. Petersburg). (US) **3933**

Washington Report (Washington, 1960) see Government Report **32**

Washington Report (Washington, 1974) see Handgun Control. Semi-Annual Progress Report **2631**

Washington Report on Africa. (US ISSN 0733-8104) **3933,** 888

Washington Report on Health Legislation and Regulation see Health Legislation and Regulation **3103**

Washington Report on Medicine and Health see McGraw-Hill's Washington Report on Medicine and Health **3123**

Washington Report on Middle East Affairs. (US ISSN 8755-4917) **3976**

Washington Report on the Hemisphere. (US ISSN 0275-5599) **3976,** 888

Washington Representatives. (US ISSN 0192-060X) **4077**

Washington Research Council.
Notebook. (US) **4077**
Washington Researchers' the
Information Report *see* Information
Report **403**
Washington Review. (US ISSN 0163-
903X) **349**
Washington Review of Strategic and
International Studies *see* Washington
Quarterly **3976**
Washington Science Trends *see* Science
Trends **4341**
Washington Social Legislation Bulletin.
(US ISSN 0149-2578) **4423**
Washington Spectator. (US ISSN 0887-
428X) **3934**
Washington Spectator - Between the
Lines *see* Washington Spectator
3934
Washington Square News. (US) **1330**
Washington State Dental Association
News *see* W S D A News **3244**
Washington State Department of
Revenue. Quarterly Business Review.
(US) **699**
Washington State Energy Office. Biennial
Energy Report. (US) **1797**
Washington State Energy Office
Dispatch. (US) **1797**, **3703**
Washington State Energy Office Energy
Access. (US) **1797**
Washington State Entomological Society
Proceedings. (US ISSN 0043-0773)
538
Washington State Environmental Policy
Act. (US) **2694**, 1971
Washington State Health Data Book.
(US) **4077**, **4115**
Washington State Library News. (US
ISSN 0278-4858) **2790**
Washington State Patrol. Annual
Report. (US) **1524**, **2694**
Washington State Research Council
Report *see* Washington Research
Council. Notebook **4077**
Washington State School Directors
Association Newsletter *see* Signal
(Olympia) **1731**
Washington State University. Daily
Evergreen. (US) **2576**, **4138**
Washington State University.
Mathematics Notes. (US ISSN
0043-082X) **3061**
Washington Stylist & Salon. (US) **374**
Washington Summary. (US ISSN
0886-0807) **2701**, **3939**
Washington Tariff & Trade Letter. (US
ISSN 0276-8275) **2730**, 924
Washington Tax Decisions. (US) **1112**
Washington Tax Reporter. (US) **1112**
Washington Tax Review *see* Tax
Management Washington Tax Review
1109
Washington Technology. (US) **4613**
Washington Telecom Directory. (US)
1368, **1158**
Washington Trooper. (US ISSN 0883-
5799) **1524**, **2694**
Washington University Alumni News.
(US) **1330**
Washington University Journal of Urban
& Contemporary Law *see* Journal of
Urban & Contemporary Law **2640**
Washington University Law Quarterly.
(US ISSN 0043-0862) **2694**
Washington University Magazine. (US
ISSN 0162-7570) **1330**
Washington View. (US ISSN 1042-
4229) **2028**
Washington Want Ads *see* Now Hiring
3630
Washington Weekly Report
(Washington). (US) **936**
Washingtonian. (US ISSN 0043-0897)
2237
Washington's Hill Rag. (US) **2237**
Washout Review. (US) **3008**
Wasmann Journal of Biology. (US ISSN
0043-0927) **460**
Wasser - Abwasser - G W F. (GW)
4831
Wasser, Energie, Luft/Eau, Energie, Air.
(SZ) **4831**, **1797**
Wasser - Kalender. (GW ISSN 0511-
3520) **4831**
Wasser, Luft und Betrieb *see* Wasser,
Luft und Boden **1979**
Wasser, Luft und Boden. (GW ISSN
0938-8303) **1979**, 1971, **4831**

Wasser Magazin. (GW) **4831**
Wasser und Abwasser in Forschung und
Praxis. (GW ISSN 0512-5030)
4831
Wasser und Boden. (GW ISSN 0043-
0951) **4831**
Wasserrecht und Wasserwirtschaft. (GW
ISSN 0508-1254) **4831**, **2694**
Wasserski Magazin. (GW) **4530**,
4796
Das Wassertriebwerk. (GW ISSN 0509-
8858) **1797**, **4831**
Wasserwirtschaft. (GW ISSN 0043-
0978) **4831**
Wasserwirtschaft - Wassertechnik (W W
T). (GW ISSN 0043-0986) **4831**
Wasserwirtschaftliche Mitteilungen. (AU
ISSN 0043-0994) **4831**
Waste Age. (US ISSN 0043-1001)
1987
Waste Business International *see* Waste
Business West **1987**
▼Waste Business West. (CN ISSN
1185-4731) **1987**
Waste Disposal and Pollution Control
see From the State Capitals. Waste
Disposal and Pollution Control **1984**
Waste Disposal and Water Management
in Australia. (AT ISSN 0311-3558)
1987, **4831**
Waste Dynamics of New England. (US)
1987
Waste Information Digests. (US ISSN
1050-3153) **1988**, 416, 1975
Waste Management and Research. (UK
ISSN 0734-242X) **1988**
Waste Management Information Bulletin
see Waste Management Today
1975
Waste Management: Nuclear, Chemical,
Biological, Municipal. (US ISSN
0956-053X) **1988**, 1190, 1810
Waste Management Research
Abstracts. (UN ISSN 0083-761X)
4119
Waste Management Today. (UK ISSN
0954-495X) **1975**, 24, 1988
Waste Management Today. News
Journal. (UK ISSN 0953-0975)
1988
Waste Minimization & Recycling
Report.(US ISSN 0890-5509)
1988, 1860, 1971, 2694
Waste Paper *see* Cycle (New York,
1970) **1984**
Waste Recovery Report. (US ISSN
0889-0072) **1840**
Waste Tech News. (US) **1988**
Waste-to-Energy Report *see* Integrated
Waste Management **1985**
Waste Treatment Technology News.
(US) **1988**
Wasteline. (US) **1988**, 1499, 2694
Wastes Management. (UK) **4115**
Wastewater Technology Centre
Newsletter/Centre Technique des
Eaux Usees. Bulletin. (CN ISSN
0829-352X) **4831**, 1979
Wastewater Works News. (US ISSN
0043-1028) **4831**, 1979
Wat Kan Ons Opvoer/What Can We
Stage. (SA ISSN 0043-1036)
4642
Watakushitachi no Shizen/Nature. (JA
ISSN 0910-6987) **568**, **1499**
Watan. (MY) **2210**
Watan al Riyadi. (LE) **4496**
Watan Weekend. (UK) **2028**
Watani. (UA) **4209**, **2028**
Al Watani Al Ittihadi/National Unionist.
(SJ) **2170**
Watashi No Akachan/My Baby. (JA)
1245
Watashi no Heya/My Room. (JA)
2555, **2562**
Watashi no Kenko/My Health. (JA)
3810
Watashitachi no Shizenshi/Natural
History. (JA ISSN 0389-6951)
4351
Watauga Association of Genealogists.
Upper East Tennessee. Bulletin. (US
ISSN 0091-8857) **2167**
Watch and Clock Review. (US ISSN
0279-6198) **2566**
Watch Over Essex. (UK) **1499**
Watching and Waiting. (UK) **4252**
Watchmaker, Jeweller & Silversmith.
(UK ISSN 0043-1079) **2566**

Watchtower. (US ISSN 0043-1087)
4290
▼Watchwords G C S E English Review.
(UK ISSN 0960-877X) **2851**,
1763
Water. *see* Vatten **4830**
Water *see* Water Bulletin **4831**
Water. (AT ISSN 0310-0367) **4831**
Water. (SA) **4831**
Water Activities Trade Report. (US)
4831
Water, Air and Soil Pollution. (NE ISSN
0049-6979) **1979**, 1971
Water and Irrigation Review. (IS ISSN
0334-5807) **4831**
Water and Mineral Development *see*
Australian Drilling **4822**
Water & Pollution Control. (CN) **4831**,
1979
Water & Pollution Control. Directory
and Buyers' Guide. (CN) **4831**
Water and Pollution Control. Directory
and Handbook *see* Water & Pollution
Control. Directory and Buyers' Guide
4831
Water and Power Development
Authority News *see* W A P D A News
4830
Water and Power Development
Consultancy Services. Annual Report
and Statement of Accounts. (II)
4831
Water and the Environment. (AT)
4831
Water and Waste Treatment. (UK ISSN
0043-1133) **4831**, 1988
Water & Waste Treatment: Latin
American Industrial Report. (US)
1876, **888**
Water and Wastes Digest. (US ISSN
0043-1141) **4115**, **4831**
Water Bulletin. (UK ISSN 0262-9909)
4831
Water Center News *see* Aqua Terra
4822
Water Conditioning *see* Water
Conditioning and Purification **4831**
Water Conditioning and Purification.
(US ISSN 0746-4029) **4831**
Water Desalination Report. (US ISSN
0043-1206) **4831**
Water - Engineering and Management.
(US ISSN 0273-2238) **4832**,
1988
Water Environment & Technology. (US
ISSN 1044-9493) **1971**, **4832**
Water Farming Journal. (US ISSN
1051-0583) **4832**, 129, 2083
Water Fittings and Materials Directory.
(UK) **2304**
Water Flying. (US ISSN 0733-1754)
65, **4677**
Water Flying Annual. (US ISSN 0193-
4198) **65**, **4677**
Water Garden Journal. (US) **2140**
Water Impacts. (US) **4832**
Water International. (US ISSN 0250-
8060) **4832**
†Water International/Agua. (SP) **5303**
Water Investment Newsletter. (US)
969, **4832**
Water Japan. (JA) **4832**
Water Journal *see* Sensus Water Journal
4828
Water Law Newsletter. (US ISSN 0043-
1249) **2694**, **4832**
Water Lily Journal *see* Water Garden
Journal **2140**
Water Management. Series A. *see* Vodni
Hospodarstvi. Serie A **1925**
Water Management. Series B. *see* Vodni
Hospodarstvi. Serie B **4830**
Water News. (GH ISSN 0043-1265)
4832
Water News/Nouvelles de l'Eau. (CN)
4832
Water Newsletter. (US ISSN 0043-
1273) **4832**, 1499, 1979
Water Pollution: A Series of
Monographs. (US) **4832**, 1979
Water Pollution Control. (US ISSN
0194-0147) **1979**, **4832**
†Water Pollution Control. (UK ISSN
0043-129X) **5303**
Water Pollution Control Federation.
Journal *see* Water Pollution Control
Federation. Research Journal **1979**

WATER SUPPLY 6799

Water Pollution Control Federation.
Research Journal. (US) **1979**,
4832
Water Pollution Control Federation
Conference. Abstracts of Technical
Papers. (US) **1975**, 24, 1979
Water Pollution Research Journal of
Canada. (CN ISSN 0197-9140)
1979, **4832**
†Water Quality Control Digest. (US)
5303
Water Quality Data for Ontario Streams
& Lakes. (CN ISSN 0383-5472)
4832, 1979
Water Quality International. (UK ISSN
0892-211X) **1980**, **1876**, **4832**
Water Research. (US ISSN 0043-
1354) **4832**
Water Research Centre. Annual Report
see Water Research Centre. Annual
Review **4832**
Water Research Centre. Annual
Review.(UK) **4832**, **1980**
Water Research Foundation of Australia.
Annual Report. (AT) **4832**
Water Research Foundation of Australia.
Bulletin *see* Water Research
Foundation of Australia. Research
Report **4832**
Water Research Foundation of Australia.
Newsletter *see* Water and the
Environment **4831**
Water Research Foundation of Australia.
Research Report. (AT ISSN 0085-
8021) **4832**
Water Research in Australia *see* Water
Research in Australia: Current
Projects **4832**
Water Research in Australia: Current
Projects. (AT) **4832**
Water Resources. (English translation
of: Vodnye Resursy) (US ISSN
0097-8078) **4832**, 1601
Water Resources and Hydropower
Engineering. *see* Shuili Shuidian Jishu
1925
Water Resources Association of the
Delaware River Basin. Alerting
Bulletin. (US) **4832**
Water Resources Association of the
Delaware River Basin. Newsletter.
(US) **4832**
Water Resources Bulletin. (US ISSN
0043-1370) **4832**
Water Resources Development in North
Carolina (Year). (US) **4832**
Water Resources Journal. (UN ISSN
0377-8053) **4833**, **1499**
Water Resources Management. (NE
ISSN 0920-4741) **4833**
Water Resources Monographs. (US)
4833
Water Resources Report Series. (US)
4833
Water Resources Research. (US ISSN
0043-1397) **4833**, 1601
Water Resources Summary. (US ISSN
0518-6374) **4833**, 1601
†Water Rights. (US) **5303**
Water Row Review. (US ISSN 1041-
5874) **2974**, **3008**
Water S.A. (SA ISSN 0378-4738)
4833
Water Safety Journal. (US) **4496**
Water Science. *see* Suiri Kagaku **4828**
Water Science and Technology. (US
ISSN 0273-1223) **4833**, 1980
Water Scooter. (US ISSN 0899-9775)
4530
▼Water Scooter Business. (US) **4530**
Water Services. (UK ISSN 0301-7028)
4833, **1876**
Water Services Handbook *see* Water
Services Year Book **1925**
Water Services Year Book. (UK) **1925**
Water Sewage and Effluent. (SA ISSN
0257-8700) **4115**, 1988, 4833
Water Ski. (US) **4559**
Water Skier. (US ISSN 0049-7002)
4559, **4530**
Water Skier & Powercraft. (UK) **4559**,
4530
Water Supply. (UK ISSN 0735-1917)
4833
Water Supply and Wastewater Disposal -
International Almanac. (NE ISSN
0169-2577) **4833**
†Water Supply Outlook for Montana.
(US) **5303**

6800 WATER SUPPLY

†Water Supply Outlook for Oregon. (US) 5303
Water Supply Outlook for the Western United States. (US) 4833
Water Supply Outlook for Washington. (US) 4833
Water System Periodical. see Vodohospodarsky Casopis 4830
Water Technology. (US) 4833, 1980
Water Tower see C B I News 3403
Water Transport Statistics of India. (II) 4668, 4741
Water Transportation Management. see Shuiyun Guanli 4739
Water Treatment. (CC ISSN 0921-2639) 4833
Water Well Journal. (US ISSN 0043-1443) 4833
Water, Woods & Wildlife. (US ISSN 0161-3561) 520, 1499, 2110
Waterborne Commerce of the United States. (US ISSN 0083-7725) 4741
Waterbury Chess Club Bulletin. (US ISSN 0894-0606) 4496
Watercraft Dealer. (US) 4530
Watercraft Philately. (US) 3759
Waterford Chamber of Commerce. News Letter. (IE) 824
Waterford News & Star. (IE) 2889
Waterfowl. (UK) 568, 1499
†Waterfowler's World. (US) 5303
Waterfront News. (US ISSN 8756-0038) 4530, 4796
Waterfront World. (US ISSN 0733-0677) 2498, 1971
Waterkampioen. (NE ISSN 0043-1451) 4530
Waterlines. (UK ISSN 0262-8104) 4115
Waterloo Campus see Laurier Campus 1316
Waterloo Computing News see W A T C O M News 1455
Waterloo Historical Society. Annual Volume. (CN) 2426
Waterloo Historical Society. Report see Waterloo Historical Society. Annual Volume 2426
Waterloo Region Visitor's Guide see Visitor's Magazine 4796
Watermarks. (US ISSN 0894-511X) 4833
Waters. (CN ISSN 0383-2031) 2050
Waterschapsbelangen. (NE ISSN 0043-1486) 4833
†Watersport Trade News. (UK) 5303
†Watersports News. (US) 5303
Waterway Guide - Great Lakes. (US) 4530
Waterway Guide - Mid-Atlantic. (US) 4530
Waterway Guide - Northern. (US) 4530
Waterway Guide - Southern. (US) 4530
Waterways. (US ISSN 0197-4777) 3008
Waterways. (UK) 4530
Waterways Journal. (US ISSN 0043-1524) 4741
Waterways World. (UK ISSN 0309-1422) 4741
Waterworld News. (US ISSN 0747-9735) 4833
Watford and District Industrial History Society. Journal. (UK ISSN 0307-5281) 2395
Watford and District Industrial History Society Bulletin see Watford and District Industrial History Society. Journal 2395
Watford Business Directory. (UK ISSN 0957-1124) 1158
Al-Watha'iq al-Filastiniyyah/Palestinian Documents. (TS) 2432, 3645
Watha'iq Dawlat al-Imarat/Emirates Documents. (TS) 2432, 3645
Al-Watha'iq wal-Makhtutat. (LY) 2432, 2335
Wathen Family Newsletter. (US) 2167
Wathen Family Organization Newsletter see Wathen Family Newsletter 2167
Al-Wathiqa. (BA) 2432, 3645
Watman Educational Services Authors' and Publishers' Service Newsletter see W E S Authors' and Publishers' Service Newsletter 1671

Watoto Magazine see Sparkle Magazine 1266
Watsonia. (UK ISSN 0043-1532) 520
Watt. (IT) 1910
Wattenmeer International. (GW) 1499
Watt's On. (UK) 1330
Wave Motion. (NE ISSN 0165-2125) 3835
Wavelength (New Orleans). (US ISSN 0741-2460) 3586
Wavelength (Newport Beach). (US) 2545
Waves. (US ISSN 1055-0348) 1612
▼Waves in Random Media. (UK ISSN 0959-7174) 3835
Wavriensia. (BE ISSN 0043-1567) 2395
Wawa Huabao/Picture Stories for Children. (CC) 1270
Wawatay News. (CN) 2028
Way. (JA) 3244
Way. (UK ISSN 0043-1575) 4278
Way-Catholic Viewpoints see Way of St. Francis 4278
The Way Fourth. (US) 4290
Way of Life. (UK ISSN 0043-1605) 4290
Way of St. Francis. (US) 4278, 2889
Way to Victory. see Schlach Peremohy 2022
Way - Ukrainian Catholic Bi-Weekly. (US) 4278, 2028
Waybill. (US ISSN 0897-7577) 4717
Waymark. (UK) 4252
Wayn-E-Gram Magazine. (US) 165, 208
Wayne Engineer. (US ISSN 0049-7037) 1840
Wayne Law Review. (US ISSN 0043-1621) 2694
Wayne State Magazine. (US) 1330
Wayne State University Alumni News. (US ISSN 0043-163X) 1330
Wayne State University Law School. Comparative Criminal Law Project. Publications Series. (US) 1524
Ways & Means. (US ISSN 0193-4716) 4077
Ways to a Successful Composition. see Zuowen Chenggong zhi Lu 1673
Waysider. (AT) 4560, 1499
Waystation for the S F Writer. (US) 4138
We and the World. see My i Svit 5241
We Are the Weird. (US) 3008
We Love Science. see Women Ai Kexue 1271
We Magazine (Hazelwood). (US) 2094
We Magazine (Santa Cruz). (US) 3008
We Proceeded On. (US ISSN 0275-6706) 2426
We Remember Dean International. (US) 4642, 1302
We Remember Dean International Newsletter see We Remember Dean International 4642
We Represent in Israel and Abroad. (IS ISSN 0302-5489) 924
†We the People. (US) 5303
We the People of North Carolina see North Carolina Magazine 838
Weal. (CN) 1330
Wealth and Welfare of Andhra Pradesh Series see Social Sciences Research Series 4388
Wear. (SZ ISSN 0043-1648) 1941
Wear Magazine. (US) 1056
Wearable Wonders. (US) 1295, 357
Weather. (UK ISSN 0043-1656) 3442
Weather Almanac. (US ISSN 0731-5627) 3442
Weather and Climate. (NZ ISSN 0111-5499) 3442
Weather & Climate Report. (US) 3442
Weather and Forecasting. (US ISSN 0882-8156) 3442, 1601, 4592
Weather Guide Calendar see Minnesota Weather Guide Calendar 3439
Weather Service Bulletin. (JA) 3442
†Weather Update. (US) 5303
Weather Vane. (US ISSN 0043-1664) 3288
Weatherbee Round-Up. (US) 2167
Weatherguide see Minnesota Weather Guide Calendar 3439
Weatherly Family Quarterly. (US) 2167
Weatherwise. (US ISSN 0043-1672) 3442

Weavers. (US ISSN 1042-7643) 3593
Weavers Journal see Journal for Weavers, Spinners & Dyers 4621
Weavings. (US ISSN 0890-6491) 4209
The Web. (AT) 1671
Web see Calendher 5158
Webb Society Quarterly Journal. (UK ISSN 0043-1680) 371
Webber's. (AT) 3008
Webe Mit. (GW ISSN 0043-1699) 4627
Weber Studies see Weber Studies: An Interdisciplinary Humanities Journal 2518
Weber Studies: An Interdisciplinary Humanities Journal. (US ISSN 0891-8899) 2518
Die Webereizeitung. (GW) 2192, 349, 3586
Weber's Fund Advisor. (US) 969
Webster Review. (US ISSN 0363-1230) 2974
Webster's Wagon Wheel. (US) 2167
Wechselwirkung. (GW ISSN 0172-1623) 4613, 4351
Wecker (Hamburg). (GW) 1270
Wedding and Home. (UK ISSN 0307-6474) 3067, 2450
Wedding Bells Magazine. (CN ISSN 0829-5654) 4855
Wedding Pages. (CN) 4855, 1295
The Wedding Photographer. (US) 3798
Wedding Photographers International see The Wedding Photographer 3798
Wedvlugduif. see Racing Pigeon 4484
†Wee Wisdom. (US ISSN 0043-1710) 5303
†Wee Wisdom (Braille Edition). (US) 5303
Weed Abstracts. (UK ISSN 0043-1729) 144, 24
Weed Control Manual and Herbicide Guide. (US ISSN 0511-411X) 196, 2140
Weed Research. (UK ISSN 0043-1737) 196
Weed Research. (JA ISSN 0372-798X) 520, 538
Weed Science. (US ISSN 0043-1745) 196
Weed Science Society of America. Abstracts. (US) 145, 25
The Week. (II) 2889
Week End. (TS) 2220
Weekblad voor Bloembollencultuur see Bloembollencultuur 2123
Weekblad voor Privaatrecht, Notariaat en Registratie see W P N R 2693
Weekday Homily Helps. (US) 4279
†Weekend. (UK ISSN 0043-1818) 5303
†Weekend (Year) in Koeln - in Cologne. (GW) 5303
†Weekend Book of Jokes. (UK) 5303
†Weekend Gardener. (US ISSN 1042-9972) 5303
Weekend Gardener Journal see Weekend Gardener 5303
Weekend Property Home Finder. (SA) 4159, 636
Weekend Star. (JM) 2239
Weekend Viaggi. (IT) 4796
Weekend Woodworking Projects. (US) 2501
Weekly Abstract Newsletter: Problem-Solving Information for State and Local Governments see Abstract Newsletter: Problem-Solving Information for State and Local Governments 4078
Weekly Abstract Newsletter: Urban and Regional Technology and Development see Abstract Newsletter: Urban and Regional Technology and Development 2499
Weekly al-Fatah. (PK) 3934
Weekly Analysis of Ecuadorian Issues. (EC ISSN 0252-2659) 888
Weekly Asahi. see Shukan Asahi 2208
Weekly Asahi Encyclopedia. see Shukan Asahi Hyakka 591
Weekly Bank Clearings see Business Forecasts 5155
Weekly Bible Reader. (US) 4209, 1270

Weekly Book Newsletter. (AT) 4138
Weekly Bulletin. (HU ISSN 0024-8495) 2198
Weekly Bulletin of Ireland see Ireland Today 5219
Weekly Bulletin of Statistics. see Norway. Statistisk Sentralbyraa. Statistisk Ukehefte 4582
Weekly Business Failures. (US) 888
†Weekly Business Starts. (US) 5303
▼Weekly Cable Action Update. (US) 1383
Weekly Chosun. (KO) 2209
Weekly Coal Production. (US) 1797, 3497
Weekly Collegian. (US) 1330
Weekly Commercial News and Shipping Guide. (US) 4741
Weekly Congressional Monitor. (US) 3934
Weekly Cotton Trade Report. (US) 160, 969
Weekly-Courier see Weekly Southern Courier 2172
Weekly Criminal Bulletin. (CN ISSN 0703-1319) 2714
Weekly Diamond. see Shukan Daiyamondo 691
Weekly Digest of Civil Procedure (2nd Series). (CN ISSN 0827-4266) 2704
Weekly Digest of Family Law. (CN ISSN 0713-7907) 2719
Weekly Drug News see Japanese Weekly on Pharmacy and Chemistry 3730
Weekly Energy Report see Energy Daily 1787
Weekly Epidemiological Record. (UN ISSN 0049-8114) 4115, 3224
Weekly Executive Update (W E U) see American Chamber of Commerce of the Philippines. Weekly Executive Update 807
Weekly Exploration Service see Petroleum Services. Weekly Service 3698
Weekly Federal Employees News Digest see Federal Employees' News Digest 4060
Weekly for the Masses/Shukan Taishu. (JA) 2208
Weekly Hankook. (KO) 2209
Weekly Hotel & Restaurant. (JA) 2481
Weekly Insiders Dairy & Egg Letter. (US ISSN 0270-4153) 2083, 204
Weekly Insiders Poultry Report. (US ISSN 0160-4872) 2083, 228
Weekly Insiders Turkey Letter. (US ISSN 0160-4910) 2083, 228
Weekly Law Digest. (UK ISSN 0264-3723) 2694
Weekly Law Reports. (UK ISSN 0019-3518) 2694
Weekly Livestock Reporter. (US ISSN 0043-1842) 228
Weekly Market Bulletin. (US ISSN 0043-1850) 160
Weekly News Update on Nicaragua and the Americas. (US) 2180
Weekly Novels/Shukan Shosetsu. (JA) 2985
Weekly Observer. (LE) 1056
Weekly Petroleum Argus. (UK ISSN 0268-7844) 3703, 1056
Weekly Petroleum Status Report see U.S. Energy Information Administration. Weekly Petroleum Status Report 3703
Weekly Pharmacy Reports: The Green Sheet. (US ISSN 0043-1893) 3745, 888
Weekly Post. see Shukan Post 2208
Weekly Probes. (NR ISSN 0795-896X) 3934, 4456
Weekly Propane Newsletter. (US) 3703
Weekly Rates Update: At Call Deposits. (AT ISSN 1032-9439) 803
▼Weekly Rates Update: Continuing Credit. (AT ISSN 1035-0780) 803
Weekly Rates Update: Term Deposits. (AT ISSN 1032-9447) 803
▼Weekly Rates Update: Term Loans. (AT ISSN 1035-0799) 803
Weekly Reader. Summer Edition A. Grade K see Weekly Reader. Summer Edition A. Pre K - Grade 1 1270

Weekly Reader. Summer Edition A. Pre K - Grade 1. (US) **1270**, 1671
Weekly Reader. Summer Edition B. Grades 1-2 see Weekly Reader. Summer Edition B. Grades 2-6 **1270**
Weekly Reader. Summer Edition B. Grades 2-6. (US) **1270**, 1671
†Weekly Reader. Summer Edition C. Grades 3-5. (US ISSN 0899-6121) **5303**
Weekly Reader, Edition K. (US ISSN 0890-3166) **1270**
Weekly Reader, Edition 1. (US ISSN 0890-3220) **1270**, 1763
Weekly Reader, Edition 2. (US ISSN 0890-3212) **1270**, 1763
Weekly Reader, Edition 3. (US ISSN 0890-3204) **1270**, 1763
Weekly Reader, Edition 4. (US) **1270**, 1763
Weekly Reader, Edition 5. (US) **1270**, 1763
Weekly Reader Eye see Weekly Reader, Edition 5 **1270**
Weekly Reader Funday see Weekly Reader, Pre-K Edition **1270**
Weekly Reader News Hunt see Weekly Reader, Edition 2 **1270**
Weekly Reader News Patrol see Weekly Reader, Edition 3 **1270**
Weekly Reader, Pre-K Edition. (US ISSN 0890-3174) **1270**, 1763
Weekly Reader, Senior Edition. (US ISSN 0890-3239) **1270**, 1763
Weekly Reader Surprise see Weekly Reader, Edition K **1270**
†Weekly Record. (US ISSN 0094-257X) **5303**
Weekly Retrospect. (US) **2237**
Weekly Review. (KE) **2209**, 699
Weekly Review. (UK) **4077**, 3934
Weekly Review of Collective Bargaining. (US) **997**, 4677
Weekly Review of the Market. (US) **969**
Weekly: Seattle's Newsmagazine see Seattle Weekly **2234**
Weekly Southern Courier. (AT) **2172**
Weekly Statistical Fishery Report see N M F S Fisheries Market News Report **2051**
Weekly Statistical Release. (NZ) **743**, 803
Weekly Stock Charts - Canadian and U S Industrial Companies. (CN ISSN 0830-1972) **969**
Weekly Stock Charts - Canadian Resource Companies. (CN ISSN 0829-3139) **969**
Weekly Summary of N L R B Cases see U.S. National Labor Relations Board. Weekly Summary of the National Labor Relations Board Cases **996**
▼Weekly Television Action Update. (US) **1383**
Weekly Times. (AT ISSN 0043-194X) **129**
Weekly Times Melbourne Sheep and Woolcraft Show. (AT) **357**
Weekly Track Topics. (US) **4539**
Weekly Treasury Decisions see Customs Bulletin **1092**
Weekly Well Activity Report. (CN) **3703**
Weekly World News. (US ISSN 0199-574X) **2237**
Wees Veilig Tuis. see Be Safe at Home **5146**
Weg der Partei. (GW) **3934**
Weg und Wahrheit see Evangelische Kirchenzeitung **4237**
Weg und Ziel. (AU ISSN 0043-2024) **3934**
Weg und Ziel. (GW) **4209**
Wege... see Wege Magazin **3597**
Wege Magazin. (GW) **3597**
†Wege Vor- und Frühgeschichtlicher Forschung. (GW) **5303**
Wege zum Menschen. (GW ISSN 0043-2040) **4209**
Wege zur Sozialversicherung. (GW ISSN 0043-2059) **4424**
Wegen. (NE ISSN 0043-2067) **1876**, 4723
Weggefaehrte. (GW) **4209**
Wegwijs - U B O T en Route. (BE) **4717**

Wehr und Wirtschaft see Wehrtechnik, Vereinigt mit Wehr und Wirtschaft **65**
Wehrausbildung. (GW) **3475**
Wehrkunde see Europaeische Wehrkunde **3457**
Wehrmedizin und Wehrpharmazie. (GW) **3162**, 3475, 3745
Wehrmedizinische Mitteilungen see Wehrmedizinische Monatsschrift **3162**
Wehrmedizinische Monatsschrift. (GW ISSN 0043-2156) **3162**
Wehrtechnik, Vereinigt mit Wehr und Wirtschaft. (GW) **65**, 3475
Wehrwissenschaftliche Berichte see Bernard und Graefe Aktuell **3453**
Wehrwissenschaftliche Rundschau see Europaeische Sicherheit **3457**
Wei Jisuanji Xinxi/Information on Microcomputers. (CC) **1465**
Weibo Xuebao/Journal of Microwave. (CC) **1779**
Weighing & Measurement. (US ISSN 0095-537X) **3449**
Weighing & Measuring Directory. (UK) **1840**, 2525, 3449
Weight Control see Rx Weight Control **3612**
Weight Engineering. (US) **65**
Weight Watchers Magazine. (US ISSN 0043-2180) **3613**, 3810
Weight Watchers Magazine. (UK) **3810**, 4855
Weightlifting U S A. (US) **3810**, 4496
Der Weihenstephaner. (GW ISSN 0171-5089) **386**
Weile Haizi/For the Children. (CC ISSN 1000-4319) **1246**
Weilheimer Heimatblaetter. (GW ISSN 0173-7007) **2395**
Weimaraner see Weimaraner Magazine **3714**
Weimaraner Magazine. (US ISSN 0162-315X) **3714**
Weimarer Beitraege. (AU ISSN 0043-2199) **2974**
Weimarer Monographien zur Ur- und Fruehgeschichte. (GW ISSN 0232-265X) **289**, 252
Weinberg und Keller. (GW ISSN 0508-2404) **386**
Weinig Info. (GW) **640**
Weinjahr see Marketing Jahrbuch Wein **383**
Weinwirtschaft Anbau. (GW) **386**
Weinwirtschaft - German Wine Review see Weinwirtschaft - Markt **386**
Weinwirtschaft - Markt. (GW ISSN 0723-1350) **386**
Weinwirtschaft Technik. (GW ISSN 0723-1369) **386**
Die Weinwissenschaft. (GW ISSN 0375-8818) **387**
Weiqi/Game of Go. (CC) **4496**
Weiqi Tiandi. (CC) **4496**
Weir Bulletin. (UK) **1840**
Weird Tales. (US ISSN 0898-5073) **3015**
Weirdbook. (US ISSN 8755-7452) **3015**
Weirdo. (US) **2889**
Weisheng Dulixue Zazhi. (CC) **3162**
Weishengwu Xue Zazhi/Journal of Microbiology. (CC) **558**
Weishengwu Xuebao/Acta Microbiologica Sinica. (CC ISSN 0001-6209) **558**
Weishengwuxue Tongbao/Bulletin of Microbiology. (CC ISSN 0253-2654) **558**
Weiss - Blaetter. (GW) **2974**
Weiss - Blaue Rundschau. (GW ISSN 0043-2202) **3934**, 2060
Weissblech Reflexionen see Reflexionen **3418**
Weissbuch zur Sicherheit der Bundesrepublik Deutschland und zur Lage der Bundeswehr. (GW) **3475**
Weisses Minarett. (GW) **4221**, 2974
Weite Welt. (GW) **4209**, 1270
Weiterbildung. (GW ISSN 0935-3097) **1688**
Weiterbildung und Medien see W & M **1688**
Weiti Gushengwu Xuebao/Acta Micropalaeontologica Sinica. (CC ISSN 1000-0674) **559**
Weixing Xiaoshuo Xuankan. (CC) **2974**

Weizhongbing Jijiu Yixue. (CC) **3162**
Weizmann Institute of Science. Research. (IS ISSN 0334-1151) **4351**
Weizmann Institute of Science, Rehovot, Israel. Scientific Activities. (IS ISSN 0083-7849) **4351**, 4613
Welara Journal. (US) **4539**
Welcare. (AT ISSN 0310-6969) **4424**
Welcome. see Odini **4271**
Welcome Back Student Guide. (CN) **1330**
Welcome Home. (US ISSN 8750-9563) **4855**, 1246
Welcome Homeowner. (US) **4159**
Welcome to Cyprus. (CY ISSN 0044-0698) **4796**
Welcome to Czechoslovakia. (CS ISSN 0043-2210) **4796**
Welcome to Lebanon & the Middle East.(LE) **4796**
†Welcome to London. (UK ISSN 0262-9941) **5303**
Welcome to Planet Earth. (US) **359**, 3597
Welcome to Sri Lanka see Sri Lanka Accommodation Guide **4787**
Weldalert. (UK) **3428**, 25, 3430
Welder. (UK ISSN 0043-2237) **3430**
Welding. see Hanjie **3429**
Welding. see Zvaranie **3431**
Welding Abstracts. (US ISSN 0952-0287) **3428**, 25, 3430
Welding & Fabricating Canada. (CN) **3430**
Welding and Fabricating Data Book. (US ISSN 0278-7067) **3430**
Welding and Metal Fabrication. (UK ISSN 0043-2245) **3431**
Welding - Brazing - Soldering Digest. (US) **3431**
Welding Data Book see Welding and Fabricating Data Book **3430**
Welding Design and Fabrication. (US ISSN 0043-2253) **3431**
Welding Distributor. (US ISSN 0192-7671) **3431**
Welding in the World/Soudage dans le Monde. (UK ISSN 0043-2288) **3431**
Welding Innovation Quarterly. (US) **3431**
Welding Institute Research Bulletin. (UK) **3431**
Welding International. (UK ISSN 0950-7116) **3431**
Welding Journal. (US ISSN 0043-2296) **3431**
Welding Quarterly see What's New in Welding **3431**
Welding Research Abroad. (US ISSN 0043-2318) **3431**
Welding Research Council Bulletin. (US ISSN 0043-2326) **3431**
Welding Research Council Progress Reports see W R C Progress Reports **3430**
Welding Research Council Yearbook. (US) **3431**
Welding Research News. (US) **3431**
Welding Review see Welding Review International **3431**
Welding Review International. (UK) **3431**
Welding Technology Institute of Australia. Bulletin. (AT) **3431**
Welding Technology Institute of Australia Technical Notes see W T I A Technical Notes **3430**
Welfare and Social Services Journal see Welfare Journal **4424**
Welfare Journal. (UK) **4424**
Welfare Rights Bulletin. (UK ISSN 0263-2098) **4424**
Welfarer. (AT) **2028**, 4424
†Well Aware. (US) **5303**
Well Connected. (US) **4833**, 1971
Well-read Youth. see Qingnian Bolan **1263**
Well Servicing. (US) **3703**
Wella Aktiengesellschaft. Report. (GW) **699**, 1190, 1671, 3394
Wellcome Unit for the History of Medicine. Research Publications. (UK ISSN 0143-7984) **3162**, 416
Welldoer. (UK ISSN 0043-2407) **4424**
Wellesley College Friends of Art Newsletter. (US) **3535**

†Wellesley Papers. (CN) **5303**
Wellington Regional Employers Association Newsletter. (NZ) **997**
Wellness Center Management see Optimal Health **5253**
Wellness Media: An Audiovisual Sourcebook. (National Information Center for Educational Media) (US) **3812**, 25
The Wellness Newsletter. (US ISSN 0740-8498) **3810**, 3613
Wellness Notes. (US) **3613**
Wellness Perspectives: Research, Theory and Practice. (US) **3810**, 4456
†Wells Fargo Bank Business Review. (US ISSN 0043-2415) **5303**
Wellsian. (UK ISSN 0263-1776) **2974**
†Wellsiana. (UK) **5303**
Wellsprings. (US ISSN 0887-011X) **4227**
Wels, Stadt. Amtsblatt. (AU ISSN 0003-2247) **4096**
Welsh Amateur Swimming Association. Handbook. (UK) **4496**
Welsh Business Contact. (UK) **824**
Welsh Churchman. (UK) **4209**
Welsh Economic Trends. (UK ISSN 0262-8309) **743**
Welsh Farmer/Y Tir. (UK ISSN 0040-8050) **129**
Welsh History Review. (UK ISSN 0043-2431) **2326**
Welsh Hospital Waiting List Bulletin. (UK ISSN 0266-0776) **2470**, 2471
Welsh Journal of Education. (UK ISSN 0957-297X) **1671**, 2851
Welsh Medical Gazette. (UK) **3162**
Welsh Music/Cerddoriaeth Cymru. (UK ISSN 0043-244X) **3586**
Welsh Nation. (UK ISSN 0043-2458) **3934**
Welsh Pony and Cob Society Journal. (UK) **4539**
Welsh Soils Discussion Group. Report. (UK ISSN 0083-7938) **196**
Welsh Springer. (NE) **3714**
Welsh Studies. (US) **2028**
†Welsh Studies in Education Series/Ysgrifam ar Addysg. (UK ISSN 0083-7946) **5303**
Welt Agni see Welt Spirale und Agni Yoga **3597**
Welt am Oberrhein see Baden - Wuerttemberg **4753**
Welt Der Frau. (AU) **1295**
Welt der Luftschiffe. (GW) **65**
Die Welt der Slaven. (GW ISSN 0043-2520) **2974**, 2851
†Eine Welt der Vereinten Nationen/United Nations World. (AU ISSN 0013-2640) **5303**
Die Welt des Islams/World of Islam. (NE ISSN 0043-2539) **3645**
Welt des Kindes. (GW) **4279**, 1246
Die Welt des Orients. (GW ISSN 0340-6229) **2326**
Welt Spirale und Agni Yoga. (AU) **3597**
Welt-Strassen-Statistik see World Road Statistics **4669**
Weltbild. (GW ISSN 0049-7126) **2192**
Die Weltbuehne. (GW ISSN 0043-2598) **2889**
Welter. (US) **2889**
Weltgeschehen. (GW ISSN 0049-7134) **3977**
†Weltgewerkschaftsbewegung. (GW ISSN 0043-2601) **5303**
Welthandel/World Trade. (GW ISSN 0720-3683) **924**
Welthandels Informationen - Europa Technik see World Trade Information **925**
Weltkonjunkturdienst. (GW ISSN 0342-6335) **924**
Weltkunst. (GW ISSN 0043-261X) **260**, 349
Weltmarkt. (GW ISSN 0935-1582) **924**
Die Weltmission. (GW ISSN 0723-6204) **4252**
Weltraum Philatelie. (GW) **3759**
Weltrundschau. (SZ) **2219**
Weltweit Hoeren. (GW ISSN 0170-1304) **1360**

WELTWEITE HILFE

Weltweite Hilfe. (GW ISSN 0043-2644) **4424**
Die Weltwirtschaft. (GW ISSN 0043-2652) **924**
Weltwirtschaft am Jahreswechsel see Weltwirtschaftslage am Jahreswechsel **2395**
Weltwirtschaftliches Archiv/Review of World Economics. (GW ISSN 0043-2636) **699**
Weltwirtschaftslage am Jahreswechsel. (GW) **2395, 699**
Welzijn see C F O - Magazine **3276**
Welzijnsinfo see Onderwijs & Welzijn - Vakmatig **4415**
Wembley History Society Journal. (UK) **2395**
Wen Bo/Journal of Museums & Archaeology. (CC ISSN 1000-7954) **3535, 289**
Wen Hsueh Chieh. see Literary Taiwan **2933**
Wen Shi Zhe/Journal of Literature, History and Philosophy. (CC ISSN 0511-4721) **2518**
Wenatchee Business Journal. (US) **699**
Wendelin. (GW) **1270**
Wending. (NE ISSN 0043-2695) **2212**
Wenhua Chunqiu. (CC) **3645**
Wenhua Guangchang. (CC) **2183**
Wenhua Jiaoliu/Cultural Exchange. (CC) **1724**
Wenhua Yicong. (CC ISSN 1000-6222) **2974**
Wenhua yu Shenghuo/Culture & Life. (CC) **2183**
Wenhua Yule/Culture & Recreation. (CC ISSN 1000-2928) **2739, 2974**
Wenhui Yuekan/Encounter Monthly. (CC) **2889**
Wenlun Yuekan/Criticism Monthly. (CC) **2889**
Wenner Gren Center International Symposium Series. (UK ISSN 0083-7989) **4351**
Wenner - Gren Foundation for Anthropological Research. Annual Report. (US) **253**
Wenner - Gren Foundation for Anthropological Research. Report see Wenner - Gren Foundation for Anthropological Research. Annual Report **253**
Wenshi Zhishi/Knowledge of Literature and History. (CC) **4392, 2974, 3645**
Wenshizhe see Wen Shi Zhe **2518**
Wensleydale Longwool Sheep Breeders' Association. Flock Book. (UK) **228**
Wentorfer Courier. (GW) **3934**
Wentworth Courier. (AT) **2172**
Wenwu/Cultural Relics. (CC ISSN 0511-4772) **289**
Wenwu Chunqiu. (CC) **289**
Wenwu Tiandi. (CC ISSN 1000-0194) **289, 2343**
Wenxian/Documents. (CC ISSN 1000-0437) **416, 2790**
Wenxue Bao/Literature Press. (CC) **2974**
Wenxue Daguan. (CC) **2975**
Wenxue Gang. (CC) **2975**
Wenxue Pinglun/Literary Review. (CC ISSN 0511-4683) **2975**
Wenxue Pinglunjia/Literary Critics. (CC) **2975**
Wenxue Qingnian/Youth Literature Journal. (CC) **2975**
Wenxue Shaonian/Adolescent Literature.(CC) **2975, 1246**
Wenxue Yichan/Literary Heritage. (CC ISSN 0257-5914) **2975**
Wenxue Ziyou Tan/On Literary Freedom.(CC) **2889**
Wenyi Bao/Literature & Art Gazette. (CC ISSN 0258-8226) **2975, 349**
Wenyi Lilun Yanjiu/Theoretical Studies in Literature and Art. (CC ISSN 0257-0254) **2975**
Wenyi Pinglun/Literary and Art Review. (CC) **2889**
Wenyi Pinglun Jia. (CC) **2889**
Wenyi Pinglun yu Piping/Art Review and Criticism. (CC) **2889**
Wenyi Xuexi/Art Studies. (CC) **349**

Wenyi Yanjiu/Literature and Art Studies.(CC ISSN 0257-5876) **2975, 349**
Wenyi Yuebao see Shanghai Wenxue **2959**
Wenyi Zhengming. (CC) **2889**
Wenzhou Institute of Medical Sciences. Journal. see Wenzhou Yixueyuan Xuebao **3162**
Wenzhou Yixueyuan Xuebao/Wenzhou Institute of Medical Sciences. Journal.(CC ISSN 1000-2138) **3162**
Wer Baut Maschinen see Wer Baut Maschinen und Anlagen **1941**
Wer Baut Maschinen und Anlagen. (GW) **1941**
Wer ist Wer? (GW) **421**
Wer ist Wer in der Schweiz und im Fuerstenstum Lichtenstein? see Swiss Biographical Index of Prominent Persons **421**
Wer Leitet. (GW) **699**
Wer Leitet - Die Fuehrungskraefte der Oesterreichischen Wirtschaft. (GW) **1031**
▼Wer Leitet - die Fuehrungskraefte der Ungarischen Wirtschaft. (GW) **1031**
Wer Liefert Was? (GW) **1158**
Wer Schreibt und Spricht Worueber? see Journalisten - Handbuch **5222**
Wer Schreibt Worueber? Journalisten-Handbuch see Journalisten - Handbuch **5222**
Wer und Was in der Deutschen Fleisch-Fisch- und Feinkost-Industrie. (GW ISSN 0170-7353) **228, 2050**
Wer und Was in der Deutschen Getraenke - Industrie. (GW ISSN 0171-4457) **387**
Wer und Was in der Deutschen Koerperpflege-, Wasch- und Reinigungsmittel-Industrie. (GW ISSN 0171-4341) **377, 1282**
Wer und Was in der Deutschen Pharmazeutischen - Industrie. (GW ISSN 0171-4449) **3745**
Wer und Was in der Deutschen Suesswarenindustrie. (GW) **1158**
†Werbe - Mittel Katalog. (GW) **5303**
Die Werbeagenturen G W A. (GW) **39**
Werbealmanach. (AU) **39**
Werbeartikel - Berater. (GW ISSN 0341-5600) **2283**
Werbeartikel Nachrichten fuer Insider. (GW) **39**
Werbeberater - Ideenservice fuer Erfolgreiche Werbung und Oeffentlichekeitsarbeit. (GW ISSN 0930-4487) **39**
Werbeforschung und Praxis. (GW ISSN 0256-4033) **39**
Werbeforum see Kommunikation **985**
Werbegeschenk - Berater see Werbeartikel - Berater **2283**
Werben und Verkaufen see W & V **39**
Werbung/Publicite. (SZ) **39**
Werbung in Deutschland see Jahrbuch der Werbung **3525**
We're Living in Funny Times. (US ISSN 1045-0491) **2889**
We're Next. (US) **1270**
Wereld en Zending. (NE ISSN 0165-988X) **4209**
De Wereld van het Jonge Kind. (NE ISSN 0165-4772) **1671, 1270**
Wereldbrief. (BE) **3977, 4209**
†Wereldverbond van Bouwvakarbeiders-en Houtbewerkersorganisaties. Bulletin. (NE) **5303**
Wereldwijd. (BE) **4209, 3977**
Werk & Wirken. (GW) **1190**
Werk-Archithese see Werk - Bauen & Wohnen **308**
Werk - Bauen & Wohnen. (SZ) **308**
Werk und Zeit. (GW ISSN 0049-7150) **308, 1971**
Werkbund Material see S W B - Information **306**
Werken und Wohnen. (GW ISSN 0083-8047) **308**
Werkgroep Elites. Bulletin. (NE) **2395**
Werkmeister/Contremaitre. (SZ) **4613**
Werkmeister und Techniche Arbeitsleiter - Contremaitre et Agent de Maitrise see Werkmeister **4613**
Die Werkstatt. (GW) **1532, 4642**

Werkstatt und Betrieb. (GW ISSN 0043-2792) **3024, 1840, 1941, 4613**
Werkstatt 3 - Programm. (GW) **3977**
Werkstattbuecher fuer Betriebsfachleute Konstrukteure und Studenten see Fertigung und Betrieb **1076**
Werkstattschriften zur Sozialpsychiatrie.(GW ISSN 0173-3524) **4049, 3288, 3355**
Werkstoff und Innovation. (GW) **636**
Werkstoffe - Betriebsleitung Technik see Werkstoffe - in der Fertigung **4613**
Werkstoffe - in der Fertigung. (GW) **4613**
Werkstoffe und Korrosion/Materials and Corrosion. (GW ISSN 0043-2822) **3423**
Die Werkstunde. (GW) **1688**
Werkverkehr und Verlader. (GW) **4717**
▼Werkzeug & Formenbau. (GW) **3024**
Werkzeuge. (GW ISSN 0936-8760) **3024**
Werte Unserer Heimat. (GW ISSN 0138-3213) **2395, 2266**
Wertheim Publications in Industrial Relations. (US) **997**
Wertpapier. (GW ISSN 0049-7169) **969**
Wertpapier-Mitteilungen Allgemeine Verlosungstabelle see W M Allgemeine Verlosungstabelle **803**
Wertpapier-Mitteilungen Teil IIb: Sammelliste Gekuendigter und Verloster Wertpapiere see W M Teil IIb: Sammelliste Gekuendigter und Verloster Wertpapiere **803**
Wertpapier-Mitteilungen Teil III: Nachrichten Ueber Deutsche Aktien, Anteile, Genussscheine, Kuxe see W M Teil III: Nachrichten Ueber Deutsche Aktien, Anteile, Genussscheine, Kuxe **803**
Wertpapier Mitteilungen Teil Vb: Nachrichten Ueber Auslaendische Festverzinsliche Wertpapiere see W M Teil Vb: Nachrichten Ueber Auslaendische Festverzinsliche Wertpapiere **803**
Wertpapierbesitzer see Volkswirt **968**
Wertpapierboerse in Stuttgart. Amtliches Kursblatt see Baden - Wuerttembergische Wertpapierboerse zu Stuttgart. Amtliches Kursblatt **939**
WerWasWo? im Taschenbuch. (GW ISSN 0723-8061) **416**
Die Weser. (GW ISSN 0043-2849) **1971, 4742**
Weserlotse. (GW ISSN 0043-2857) **4742**
Weserthal Strombote see Energie und Umwelt **1891**
Wesley Historical Society. Lancashire and Cheshire Branch. Journal. (UK) **4252, 2395**
Wesley Historical Society. Proceedings. (UK ISSN 0043-2873) **4252, 2326**
Wesleyan Advocate. (US ISSN 0043-289X) **4252**
Wesleyan Christian Advocate. (US) **4253**
Wesleyan Poetry Program. (US ISSN 0511-4934) **3008**
Wesleyan Theological Journal. (US ISSN 0092-4245) **4253**
Wesleyan University Alumni Magazine. (US) **1330, 1720**
Wesleyan University Alumnus see Wesleyan University Alumni Magazine **1330**
Wessex Cave Club Journal. (UK) **1585**
Wessex Cave Club Occasional Publication see Wessex Cave Club Journal **1585**
Wessex News. (UK) **2196**
Wessex Studies in Special Education. (UK ISSN 0144-5359) **1742, 1763**
West. see Zapad **2890**
West Africa. (UK ISSN 0043-2962) **3934**
West Africa Annual. (NR ISSN 0083-8144) **2335**
West Africa Rice Development Association. Annual Report. (IV) **196**

†West Africa Rice Development Association. Current Bibliography. (LB) **5303**
West Africa Rice Development Association. Occasional Paper. (IV) **129, 2083**
West African Archaeological Newsletter see West African Journal of Archaeology **289**
†West African Archivist. (SG ISSN 0850-430X) **5303**
West African Farming and Food Processing see African Farming and Food Processing **68**
West African Institute of Social and Economic Research. Annual Report see Nigerian Institute of Social and Economic Research. Annual Report **4381**
West African Journal of Archaeology. (NR ISSN 0083-8160) **289**
West African Journal of Biological and Applied Chemistry. (NR ISSN 0043-2989) **1190, 483**
West African Journal of Education. (NR ISSN 0043-2997) **1671**
West African Journal of Educational and Vocational Measurement. (NR ISSN 0331-0515) **4050**
West African Journal of Modern Languages/Revue Ouest Africaine des Langues Vivantes. (NR ISSN 0331-0531) **2851**
West African Journal of Pharmacology and Drug Research. (NR ISSN 0303-691X) **3745**
West African Journal of Sociology and Political Science. (NR ISSN 0308-4450) **4456, 3934**
West African Religion. (NR ISSN 0083-8187) **4209**
West African Science Association. Journal. (NR ISSN 0043-3020) **4351**
West & East/Chung-Mei Yueh-K'an. (CH ISSN 0043-3047) **3977**
West Asia and Africa. see Xiya Feizhou **4392**
West Australian Nut and Tree Crop Association Yearbook. (AT ISSN 0810-6681) **196, 2083**
West Bend Post. (US) **1056**
West Bend Shoppers Guide see West Bend Post **1056**
West Bengal. (II ISSN 0049-7193) **4077, 3934**
West Bengal. Annual Financial Statement (Budget). (II) **743, 4592**
West Bengal. Bureau of Applied Economics and Statistics. Statistical Handbook. (II ISSN 0511-5493) **743, 4592**
West Bengal. Bureau of Educational and Psychological Research. (II) **1671, 4050**
West Bengal Labour Gazette. (II ISSN 0043-3071) **997**
West Boca Raton Living. (US) **2237**
West Branch. (US ISSN 0149-6441) **3008**
West Central Kentucky Family Research Association. Bulletin. (US) **2167**
West China Journal of Stomatology. see Huaxi Kouqiang Yixue Zazhi **3234**
West China Medical Journal. see Huaxi Yixue **3106**
West China University of Medical Sciences. Journal. see Huaxi Yike Daxue Xuebao **3106**
West Coast Dance see In Dance **1531**
West Coast Environmental Law Research Foundation Newsletter. (CN ISSN 0715-4275) **1971**
West Coast Lifestyle Magazine. (US) **2237**
West Coast Line. (CN) **2975, 2889, 3586**
West Coast Peddler. (US) **260, 349, 2555, 3535**
†West Coast Plays. (US ISSN 0147-4502) **5303**
West Coast Reliability Symposium. (US ISSN 0083-8217) **1031**
West Coast Review see West Coast Line **2975**
West Coast Review of Books see Books - 100 Reviews **4123**
West Coast - Rocky Mountain Druggist see Pharmacy West **3740**

West Coast Sailors. (US ISSN 0273-4699) **4531**
West Coast Studies. (US ISSN 1041-4037) **2426**, 2167
West End. (US ISSN 0049-7223) **3008**
West England Medical Journal. (UK) **3162**
West Europe Report. (US) **888**, 3934
†West European Living Costs. (UK ISSN 0142-646X) **5303**
West European Politics. (UK ISSN 0140-2382) **3934**
West Georgia College Review. (US ISSN 0043-3136) **1330**
West Georgia College Studies in the Social Sciences. (US ISSN 0081-8682) **4392**
West Gippsland Trader. (AT) **2172**
West Hills Review. (US ISSN 0890-9024) **3008**
West Hollywood. (US) **2237**
West Indian Law Journal. (JM ISSN 0253-7370) **2694**
West Indian Medical Journal. (JM ISSN 0043-3144) **3162**
†West Michigan Family. (US) **5303**
West Midlands Arts News Sheet *see* Arts Report **5139**
West Midlands Directory for Trade & Industry. (UK ISSN 0952-8806) **1158**
†West of Scotland Visitor. (UK ISSN 0260-4426) **5303**
West-Ost-Journal. (AU ISSN 0043-2954) **924**
West Pakistan Cooperative Review *see* Punjab Cooperative Union. Review **831**
West Pakistan University of Engineering and Technology. Research Bulletin *see* Pakistan University of Engineering and Technology. Research Bulletin **1833**
West Riding Farmer. (UK) **129**
West Side Spirit. (US) **2237**
West Side Story. (US) **1671**, 1246
West Tennessee Historical Society. Papers. (US ISSN 0361-6215) **2426**
West Texas Angelus. (US) **4279**
West Texas Catholic. (US) **4279**
West Texas Geological Society. Fieldtrip Guidebook. (US) **1585**
West Texas Geological Society. Publications. (US) **1585**
West Texas Historical Association Yearbook. (US) **2426**
West Texas Livestock Weekly *see* Livestock Weekly **221**
West Texas Register *see* West Texas Catholic **4279**
West University Magazine. (US) **2237**
West Virginia. Agricultural and Forestry Experiment Station. Annual Report. (US) **129**, 2110
West Virginia. Agricultural and Forestry Experiment Station. Bulletin. (US) **129**, 2110
West Virginia. Agricultural and Forestry Experiment Station. Circular. (US) **129**, 2110
West Virginia. Agricultural and Forestry Experiment Station. Current Report. (US) **129**, 2110
West Virginia. Agricultural Experiment Station, Morgantown. Current Report *see* West Virginia. Agricultural and Forestry Experiment Station. Current Report **129**
West Virginia. Commission on Aging. Annual Progress Report. (US ISSN 0083-8438) **2280**
West Virginia. Department of Agriculture. Market Bulletin. (US ISSN 0025-3545) **129**
West Virginia. Department of Employment Security. Labor Market Trends *see* West Virginia Economic Summary **997**
West Virginia. Department of Mines. Annual Report *see* West Virginia. Office of Miner's Health, Safety & Training. Report & Digest Directory **3497**

West Virginia. Department of Mines. Directory of Mines *see* West Virginia. Office of Miner's Health, Safety & Training. Report & Digest Directory **3497**
West Virginia. Geological and Economic Survey. Annual Report. (US) **1585**
West Virginia. Human Rights Commission. Report. (US ISSN 0083-8594) **3948**
West Virginia. Legislature. Commission on Special Investigations. Report to the West Virginia Legislature. (US) **4077**
†West Virginia. Mineral Industry Status. (US) **5303**
West Virginia. Office of Miner's Health, Safety & Training. Report & Digest Directory. (US) **3497**
West Virginia Academy of Science. Proceedings. (US) **4352**
West Virginia: An Economic-Statistical Profile. (US) **824**
West Virginia Association of College English Teachers. Bulletin. (US) **2975**
West Virginia Business Index. (US) **699**
West Virginia C.P.A. (US ISSN 0043-3217) **757**
West Virginia Coal Facts. (US ISSN 0091-5513) **3497**
West Virginia Coal Mining Institute. Proceedings. (US ISSN 0083-842X) **3497**
West Virginia Construction News. (US) **636**
West Virginia Dental Journal. (US ISSN 0043-3225) **3244**
West Virginia Economic Summary. (US) **997**
West Virginia Education Directory. (US ISSN 0085-8099) **1671**
West Virginia Employment and Earnings Trends: Annual Summary. (US) **997**
West Virginia Forestry Notes. (US ISSN 0197-1387) **2110**
West Virginia Fourth Estatesman. (US) **2576**
West Virginia Game & Fish. (US) **4560**
West Virginia Geological Survey Newsletter *see* Mountain State Geology **1573**
†West Virginia Hills & Streams. (US) **5303**
West Virginia History. (US ISSN 0043-325X) **2426**
West Virginia - It's You. (US) **4796**
West Virginia Law Review. (US ISSN 0043-3268) **2694**
West Virginia Legionnaire. (US) **3475**
West Virginia Libraries. (US ISSN 0043-3276) **2790**
West Virginia Library Commission. Newsletter. (US) **2790**
West Virginia Manufacturers Register. (US ISSN 0893-2824) **1159**
West Virginia Medical Journal. (US ISSN 0043-3284) **3162**
West Virginia Mineral Industries Directory. (US) **3498**
West Virginia Mineral Producers and Processors Directory *see* West Virginia Mineral Industries Directory **3498**
West Virginia Research League. Statistical Handbook. (US ISSN 0893-4568) **1112**
West Virginia School Journal. (US ISSN 0274-8606) **1671**
West Virginia Tax Calendar. (US) **1112**
West Virginia Transporter. (US) **4749**
West Virginia Union List of Serials. (US ISSN 0512-4743) **416**
West Virginia University Alumni Magazine. (US) **1330**, 1671
West Virginia University Alumni News. (US) **1330**
West Virginia University Alumni Quarterly *see* West Virginia University Alumni Magazine **1330**
WestArt. (US ISSN 0043-3357) **349**
Westchester Bulletin. (US) **3162**
Westchester Commerce. (US ISSN 0888-3459) **824**
Westchester - Connecticut Office Buildings. (US) **4159**
Westchester Country Club News. (US) **1302**

Westchester County Press. (US ISSN 0043-3373) **2237**
Westchester Family. (US ISSN 1043-6774) **1246**, 2450
Westchester Historian. (US ISSN 0049-7266) **2426**
Westchester Law Journal. (US ISSN 0049-7274) **2694**
Westchester Office Buildings *see* Westchester - Connecticut Office Buildings **4159**
Westchester Planning. (US) **4077**
Westchester Planning Newsletter *see* Westchester Planning **4077**
Westchester Realtor. (US ISSN 0043-339X) **4159**
Westchester Spotlight. (US) **2179**
Westcoast Aviator. (CN) **65**
Westcoast Fisherman. (CN) **2050**
Westcoast Hospitality. (CN) **2481**
▼Westcoast Logger. (CN) **2118**
Westcoast Mariner. (CN) **4531**
Westcoast Offshore Guide *see* Danish Offshore Guide and Yearbook **3684**
▼Westcoast Reflections. (CN) **2280**
Westcoast Speculator. (CN) **969**
Westdeutsche Arbeiter-Zeitung *see* K A B **4266**
Westdeutsche Gesellschaft fuer Familienkunde. Mitteilungen. (GW ISSN 0172-1879) **2167**
Westdeutsche Rundfunkwerbung GmbH Transparent *see* W W F Transparent **1360**
Westdeutsche Studentenzeitung. (GW) **1330**
Westdeutscher Tuermer. (GW) **4159**
Westen. (GW ISSN 0179-6100) **2192**
Westerfield's Review. (US) **3008**
Westerheem. (NE ISSN 0166-4301) **289**
Westerly. (AT ISSN 0043-342X) **2975**
Western Agricultural Economics Association. Proceedings *see* Western Journal of Agricultural Economics **160**
Western American Literature. (US ISSN 0043-3462) **2975**
Western & Eastern Treasures. (US ISSN 0890-0876) **2443**
Western and English Fashions *see* Equine Business Journal **4534**
Western & English Manufacturers Association. Market Calendar & Directory. (US) **1159**
Western and English Manufacturers Association Wrapup *see* W A E M A Wrapup **5302**
Western Apparel Industry *see* Apparel Industry Magazine **1283**
Western Art Digest *see* Southwest Art **344**
Western Art News. (US) **349**
†Western Association of Africanists. Newsletter. (US ISSN 0035-7642) **5303**
Western Association of Fish and Wildlife Agencies. Proceedings. (US) **1499**
Western Association of Graduate Schools. Proceedings of the Annual Meeting. (US ISSN 0511-6848) **1720**
Western Association of Map Libraries. Information Bulletin. (US ISSN 0049-7282) **2790**, 2266
Western Association of Map Libraries. Occasional Papers. (US) **2790**
Western Association of State Game and Fish Commissioners. Proceedings *see* Western Association of Fish and Wildlife Agencies. Proceedings **1499**
Western Australia. Chemical Centre. Report of Investigations *see* Western Australia. Chemistry Centre. Report of Investigations **1190**
Western Australia. Chemistry Centre. Report of Investigations. (AT) **1190**
Western Australia. Conservation and Environment Council. Annual Report *see* Western Australia. Environmental Protection Authority. Annual Report **1500**
Western Australia. Department for Community Services. Annual Report. (AT) **4424**

Western Australia. Department for Community Welfare. Annual Report *see* Western Australia. Department for Community Services. Annual Report **4424**
Western Australia. Department of Agriculture. Annual Report. (AT ISSN 0726-9366) **129**
Western Australia. Department of Agriculture. Bulletin. (AT ISSN 0729-0012) **129**
Western Australia. Department of Agriculture. Division of Animal Production. Annual Report. (AT) **228**
Western Australia. Department of Agriculture. Division of Plant Industries. Annual Report. (AT) **196**
Western Australia. Department of Agriculture. Technical Bulletin. (AT ISSN 0083-8675) **129**
Western Australia. Department of Conservation and Environment. Annual Report *see* Western Australia. Environmental Protection Authority. Annual Report **1500**
Western Australia. Department of Conservation and Land Management. Bulletin *see* Western Australia. Department of Conservation and Land Management. Research Bulletin **1500**
Western Australia. Department of Conservation and Land Management. Landscape. (AT ISSN 0815-4465) **1499**
Western Australia. Department of Conservation and Land Management. Research Bulletin. (AT ISSN 1032-8106) **1500**, 460, 1971, 2110
Western Australia. Department of Conservation and Land Management. Technical Report. (AT ISSN 0816-6757) **538**, 1500
Western Australia. Department of Fisheries and Wildlife. Report *see* Western Australia. Fisheries Department. Report **2050**
†Western Australia. Department of Occupational Health, Safety and Welfare. Industrial Accidents. (AT) **5303**
Western Australia. Department of Transport. Annual Report. (AT) **4660**
†Western Australia. Economic and Business Review. (AT) **5303**
Western Australia. Education Department. Education Circular *see* Western Australia. Ministry of Education. Education Circular **1671**
Western Australia. Environmental Protection Authority. Annual Report. (AT) **1500**, 1971
Western Australia. Environmental Protection Council. Annual Report *see* Western Australia. Environmental Protection Authority. Annual Report **1500**
Western Australia. Fisheries Department. Report. (AT) **2050**, 1500
Western Australia. Forest Department. Forest Focus *see* Western Australia. Department of Conservation and Land Management. Landscape **1499**
Western Australia. Geological Survey. Bulletin. (AT ISSN 0085-8137) **1585**
Western Australia. Geological Survey. Mineral Resources Bulletin. (AT ISSN 0510-2014) **3498**
Western Australia. Geological Survey. Report. (AT ISSN 0085-8145) **1585**
Western Australia. Geological Survey. 1: 250,000 Geological Series. Explanatory Notes. (AT) **1585**, 2266
Western Australia. Government Gazette.(AT ISSN 0043-3489) **4077**
Western Australia. Industrial Gazette. (AT) **841**
Western Australia. Law Reform Commission. Annual Report. (AT) **2694**

6804 WESTERN AUSTRALIA

Western Australia. Ministry of Education. Education Circular. (AT) **1671**
Western Australia. Ministry of Education. Education Statistics Bulletin. (AT ISSN 0812-1311) **1681**
Western Australia. Office of Technical and Further Education. Handbook. (AT) **1720**
Western Australia. State Energy Commission. Annual Report. (AT) **1797**
Western Australia. Technical Education Division. Handbook *see* Western Australia. Office of Technical and Further Education. Handbook **1720**
Western Australia: Facts and Figures. (AT) **4592**
Western Australia Law Almanac. (AT ISSN 0085-8161) **2694**
Western Australia Reports. (AT) **2694**
▼Western Australia Stamp Duties. (AT) **1112**
Western Australian Coastal Shipping Commission. Annual Report. (AT) **4742**
Western Australian Economic Review. (AT ISSN 0706-2176) **997**
Western Australian Egg Marketing Board. Newsletter. (AT ISSN 0729-3445) **228**
Western Australian Herbarium. Research Notes *see* Kingia **5224**
Western Australian Hotel, Club and Caterer *see* Restaurant Hotel Club & Caterer **2479**
Western Australian Institute of Technology. Department of Biology. Bulletin *see* Curtin University. School of Biology. Bulletin **436**
Western Australian Institute of Technology. Library. Annual Report *see* Curtin University of Technology. Library. Annual Report **2753**
Western Australian Institute of Technology. Library. Monograph Fiche Catalogue *see* Curtin University of Technology. Library. Monograph Fiche Catalogue **2753**
Western Australian Institute of Technology. Library. Western Library Studies *see* Curtin University of Technology. Library. Western Library Studies **2753**
Western Australian Museum. Records. (AT ISSN 0312-3162) **3535**
Western Australian Museum. Records. Supplement. (AT ISSN 0313-122X) **3535**
Western Australian Museum, Perth. Annual Report. (AT) **3535**
Western Australian Naturalist. (AT) **4352**
Western Australian Naturalist Scientific Journal *see* Western Australian Naturalist **4352**
Western Australian Pocket Yearbook *see* Western Australia: Facts and Figures **4592**
Western Australian Resource Developement Services Directory. (AT ISSN 0816-2271) **1159**
Western Australian Yearbook. (AT ISSN 0083-8772) **2346**, **888**
†Western Autobody. (CN) **5303**
Western Bank Directory. (US ISSN 0272-5371) **803**
†Western Boatman. (US ISSN 0738-8608) **5303**
Western Buddhist. (UK ISSN 0144-9818) **4216**
Western Builder. (US ISSN 0043-3535) **636**
Western Building Design *see* Sun Coast Architect - Builder **633**
Western Business. (US) **699**
Western Canada Alaska Campbook. (US) **4797**
Western Canada and Alaska, Alberta, British Columbia, Manitoba, Saskatchewan, Northwest Territories, Yukon Territory and Alaska TourBook *see* Tourbook: Western Canada and Alaska **4790**
Western Canada Outdoors. (CN) **1500**

Western Canada Water and Sewage Conference. Bulletin *see* Western Canada Water and Waste Water Association. Bulletin **4834**
Western Canada Water and Waste Water Association. Bulletin. (CN) **4834**, 1988
Western Canadian Anthropologist. (CN ISSN 0829-0547) **253**
Western Canadian Lumber Worker. (CN ISSN 0049-7371) **2591**, 2118
Western Canadian Society for Horticulture. Reports of Proceedings of Annual Meeting. (CN ISSN 0083-8810) **2140**
Western Canadian Steam Locomotive Directory. (CN ISSN 0085-8188) **4717**
Western Carolinian. (US) **1330**
Western Catholic Reporter. (CN ISSN 0512-5235) **4279**
Western Caver. (AT) **1585**
Western City. (US ISSN 0279-5337) **4096**
Western Cleaner and Launderer. (US ISSN 0049-741X) **1282**
Western Collector *see* Western World Avon Collectors Marketplace **260**
Western Commerce & Industry. (UK) **824**
Western Commerce & Industry Magazine. (CN ISSN 0043-3624) **841**
Western Concept. (US) **1330**
Western Contractor. (AT ISSN 0814-9488) **3498**, 1549
Western Dental Society. Newsletter *see* Westviews **3244**
Western Dry Kiln Association. Proceedings. (US) **2118**
Western Dry Kiln Clubs. Proceedings *see* Western Dry Kiln Association. Proceedings **2118**
▼Western English World Magazine. (US) **4539**
Western Europe (Year). (UK ISSN 0953-6906) **3934**, 888
Western Europe (Year). (US) **4797**
Western Europe Report *see* West Europe Report **888**
Western European Education *see* European Education **1632**
Western European Specialists Section Newsletter. (US ISSN 0734-4503) **2790**
Western European Studies. *see* Xi'ou Yanjiu **4392**
Western Express. (US ISSN 0510-2332) **3759**
Western Farmer and Grazier. (AT) **129**
Western Fertilizer & Chemical Dealers Association Communicator *see* W F C D Communicator **129**
Western Floors. (US ISSN 0049-7398) **636**
Western Folklore. (US ISSN 0043-373X) **2060**
Western Foodservice. (US) **2083**
Western Forestry Conference. Executive Summaries of Proceedings *see* Western Forestry Conference. Proceedings **2111**
Western Forestry Conference. Proceedings. (US) **2111**
Western Foundation of Vertebrate Zoology. Occasional Papers. (US ISSN 0511-7542) **568**
Western Foundation of Vertebrate Zoology. Proceedings. (US ISSN 0511-7550) **568**
Western Frontier Library. (US ISSN 0083-887X) **2426**
Western Frontiersmen Series. (US ISSN 0083-8888) **2426**
Western Fruit Grower. (US ISSN 0043-3764) **196**, 2140
Western Geographer. (AT ISSN 0313-8860) **2266**
Western Geographical Series. (CN ISSN 0315-2022) **2266**, 1971
Western Grape Report. (US) **1056**, 160, 4717, 4749
Western Grocer Magazine. (CN ISSN 0705-906X) **2094**
Western Grocery News. (US) **2094**
Western Grower and Shipper. (US ISSN 0043-3799) **196**
†Western Hemisphere Nutrition Congress. Proceedings. (US) **5303**

Western Highway Institute. Research Committee. Report. (US ISSN 0083-8918) **1876**
Western Historical Quarterly. (US ISSN 0043-3810) **2426**
Western Hog Journal. (CN ISSN 0225-3488) **228**
Western Horizons. (CN ISSN 0043-3829) **3746**
Western Horse. (US) **4539**
Western Horse. (GW ISSN 0933-9345) **4539**
Western Horseman. (US ISSN 0043-3837) **4539**
Western Humanities Review. (US ISSN 0043-3845) **2975**, 2518
Western Illinois Regional Studies. (US) **2426**, 2975
Western Institute for the Deaf News *see* W I D News **2289**
Western Interstate Commission for Higher Education Reports *see* W I C H E Reports **1720**
†Western Investor. (US ISSN 0147-2410) **5304**
†Western Investor Newsletter. (US ISSN 0886-3768) **5304**
Western Journal of Agricultural Economics. (US ISSN 0162-1912) **160**
Western Journal of Applied Forestry. (US ISSN 0885-6095) **2111**
Western Journal of Black Studies. (US ISSN 0197-4327) **2028**
Western Journal of Communication. (US ISSN 1057-0314) **2852**, 1345, 4642
Western Journal of Medicine. (US ISSN 0093-0415) **3162**
Western Journal of Nursing Research. (US ISSN 0193-9459) **3288**, 2470
Western Journal of Speech Communication *see* Western Journal of Communication **2852**
Western Lands and Waters Series. (US ISSN 0083-8934) **1500**
Western Legal History. (US ISSN 0896-2189) **2694**, 2426
▼Western Links. (US) **4514**, 4797
Western Livestock Journal Weekly. (US) **228**
Western Livestock Reporter. (US) **228**
Western Living. (CN ISSN 0049-7444) **2179**
Western Lumber (Year) Buyers Manual. (US) **2118**, 1056
Western Lumber and Building Materials Merchant *see* Merchant Magazine **2116**
Western Lumber Facts. (US ISSN 0511-7704) **2113**, 2118
Western Magazin. (GW) **2426**
Western Management. (UK) **1031**
Western Maryland Genealogy. (US ISSN 0747-7805) **2167**
Western Massachusetts Commercial News. (US) **841**
†Western Medical News. (CN) **5304**
†Western Merchandiser. (US) **5304**
Western Metalworking Directory. (US) **3024**
Western Micro Market. (US) **1465**
Western Mills Today. (US) **2118**
Western Mining Directory. (US) **3498**
Western Mining News. (US ISSN 0300-662X) **969**, 3498
Western Mobile Home News *see* Western Mobile News **2498**
Western Mobile News. (US ISSN 0043-3942) **2498**
Western Municipal Product News. (CN) **4096**
Western New England Law Review. (US ISSN 0190-6593) **2694**
Western New York Business Directory *see* Greater Buffalo Business Directory **1137**
Western New York Buyer's Guide and Roster *see* Greater Buffalo Business Directory **1137**
Western New York Genealogical Society Journal. (US ISSN 0890-6858) **2167**
Western New York Index. (US ISSN 0884-3279) **25**, 2237
Western New York Magazine. (US ISSN 0149-5070) **824**

Western New York Motorist. (US ISSN 0043-3977) **4705**
Western News. (US) **2028**
Western Nigeria Development Corporation. Industrial Directory *see* Investments and Credit Corporation of Oyo State. Industrial Directory **1140**
Western North Carolina Business Journal *see* W N C Business Journal **698**
Western Oil World. (US) **3703**
Western Ontario Series *see* University of Western Ontario Series in Philosophy of Science **3785**
Western Open (Year). (US) **4514**
Western Outdoor News. (US ISSN 0049-7479) **4560**
Western Outdoors. (US ISSN 0043-4000) **4560**
Western Pacific Orthopaedic Association. Journal. (HK ISSN 0043-4019) **3312**
Western Pacific Stock Exchanges Guide.(AT) **924**
Western Packing News *see* National Packing News **3650**
Western Pennsylvania Bluegrass Committee. Newsletter. (US) **3586**
Western Pennsylvania Genealogical Quarterly *see* Western Pennsylvania Genealogical Society Quarterly **2167**
Western Pennsylvania Genealogical Society Quarterly. (US ISSN 0278-7431) **2167**
Western Pennsylvania Historical Magazine *see* Pittsburgh History **2419**
Western Pennsylvania Motorist. (US) **4705**
Western Petroleum Industry. (US) **3703**, 1159
Western Pharmacology Society. Proceedings. (US ISSN 0083-8969) **3746**
Western Plains Library System Newsletter. (US ISSN 0043-4051) **2790**
Western Planner. (US) **2498**
Western Plastics *see* Plastics **3865**
Western Policies. (NP) **3934**, 3977
Western Polled Hereford Journal. (US) **228**
Western Press. (US) **1330**
Western Producer. (CN ISSN 0043-4094) **130**
Western Prospector *see* American Gold News and Western Prospector **3477**
Western R V Traveler *see* R V West **4783**
Western Railroader. (US) **4717**
Western Railroader and Western Railfan *see* Western Railroader **4717**
Western Real Estate News. (US ISSN 0043-4124) **4159**, 969
Western Recorder. (US ISSN 0043-4132) **4253**
Western Report *see* Alberta Report - Western Report **2176**
Western Report *see* British Columbia Report **2176**
Western Reserve Business Review *see* Business Review **941**
Western Reserve Historical Society, Cleveland. Publications *see* Western Reserve Historical Society News **2426**
Western Reserve Historical Society News. (US ISSN 0882-3154) **2426**
†Western Retail Lumbermen's Directory.(CN) **5304**
Western Retailer. (US ISSN 1044-7768) **165**
Western Review Institute Newsletter *see* W R I Newsletter **3933**
Western Rider. (CN ISSN 0702-9071) **4539**
Western Roofing - Insulation - Siding. (US) **636**
Western Sahara Campaign News. (US ISSN 0895-8491) **3948**, 2335
Western Saltwater Fisherman *see* California Angler **4542**
Western Show News. (US) **2283**
Western Skier. (US) **4560**
Western Snow Conference. Proceedings.(US) **1601**

Western Society for French History. Proceedings of the Annual Meeting. (US ISSN 0099-0329) **2395**
Western Society of Malacologists. Annual Report. (US ISSN 0361-1175) **593**
Western Society of Periodontology. Journal. Periodontal Abstracts. (US ISSN 0048-3389) **3182**, 25, 3244
Western Society of Weed Science. Proceedings. (US ISSN 0091-4487) **520**
Western Society of Weed Science. Research Progress Report. (US ISSN 0090-8142) **520**
Western Sportsman. (CN ISSN 0709-1532) **4560**
Western Stamp Collector see Stamp Collector **3758**
Western State. Estimates Including Budget Speech and Memorandum see Oyo State. Estimates Including Budget Speech and Memorandum **4069**
Western State. Gazette see Oyo State of Nigeria Gazette **4069**
Western State. Ministry of Economic Planning and Community Development. Annual Report see Oyo State. Ministry of Economic Planning and Community Development. Annual Report **1082**
Western State College Top O' the World.(US) **1330**
Western States Jewish History. (US) **2028**, 4227
Western Suburbs Courier. (AT) **2173**
Western Sun. (US) **1330**
Western Sunday Independent. (UK) **2196**
Western Sweden Chamber of Commerce. Membership Directory. (SW) **824**
Western Teacher. (AT) **1672**, 2591
Western Technology & Management. (US) **4613**, 1031
Western Temperance Herald see The Herald **1536**
Western Texan. (US) **1330**
Western Transport. (AT ISSN 0725-8895) **4660**, 4749
Western Transportation Law Seminar Papers and Proceedings see Transportation Law Institute Papers and Proceedings **2687**
Western Treasures see Western & Eastern Treasures **2443**
▼Western Turf Management. (US) **2140**
Western Water. (US) **4834**
Western Weekly Reports. (CN ISSN 0049-7525) **2694**
Western Wildlands. (US ISSN 0363-6690) **1500**
Western Wood Products Association. Export Report. (US ISSN 0730-5176) **2113**, 2118
Western Wood Products Association. Monthly F.O.B. Price Summary, Past Sales. Coast Mills. (US ISSN 0511-8298) **2113**, 2118
Western Wood Products Association. Monthly F.O.B. Price Summary, Past Sales. Inland Mills. (US ISSN 0195-9409) **2113**, 2118
Western Wood Products Association. Quarterly Injury & Illness Incidence Report. (US ISSN 0195-9344) **3624**, 2118
Western Wood Products Association. Statistical Yearbook. (US ISSN 0195-931X) **2113**, 2118
Western World Avon Collectors Marketplace. (US) **260**
Western World Avon Collectors Newsletter see Western World Avon Collectors Marketplace **260**
Western Writers Series. (US) **2889**
Westernlore Ghost Town Series. (US ISSN 0083-9019) **2426**
Westerns & Serials. (US) **3519**, 1383
Westfaelische Forschungen. (GW ISSN 0083-9027) **2395**, 2060
Westfaelische Zeitschrift. (GW ISSN 0083-9043) **2395**
Westfaelisches Museum fuer Naturkunde. Abhandlungen. (GW) **4352**

Westfaelischer Heimatbund. Rundschreiben see Heimatpflege in Westfalen **1957**
Westfalen Tennis. (GW) **4514**
Westfalia Sacra. (GW) **4209**, 2395
Westfield State College. Alumni Chronicle see The Chronicle (Westfield) **1307**
Westie Imprint. (US) **3714**
WestIndian Digest. (UK ISSN 0143-6619) **2028**, 2196
Westmeath Examiner. (IE) **2203**
Westminster. (UK) **824**
Westminster Bank Review see National Westminster Bank Quarterly Review **792**
Westminster Chamber of Commerce Directory. (UK) **824**
Westminster Confidential. (UK) **421**
Westminster Hospital Nurses' League. Publication. (UK) **3288**
Westminster Magazine. (US) **1330**
Westminster Review see Westminster **824**
Westminster Studies in Education. (UK ISSN 0140-6728) **1672**
Westminster Theological Journal. (US ISSN 0043-4388) **4210**
Westminster World see Westminster **824**
Westmorland Historical Society. Newsletter. (CN ISSN 0382-0831) **2426**
†Westpac Banking Corporation. Review. (AT ISSN 0812-3470) **5304**
Der Westpreusse. (GW ISSN 0043-4418) **2192**
Westpreussen - Jahrbuch. (GW ISSN 0511-8484) **2395**
Westricher Heimatblaetter. (GW) **2192**
West's Education Law Reporter. (US) **2694**, 1732
West's Legal Alert for Educators. (US) **2694**, 1732
Westscape. (US) **2140**
Westside Shopper. (US) **39**
Westviews. (US) **3244**
Westward. (US) **2426**
Westward Home. (AT) **2450**
Westways. (US ISSN 0043-4434) **4797**, 4705
Westwind (Los Angeles). (US) **349**, 2975, 3586, 3798
Westwind (Seattle). (US) **1302**, 3015
Westword Entertainment Review. (US) **2237**
Westwords. (UK ISSN 0269-9214) **349**, 3008
Westworld Alberta Magazine. (CN) **4706**, 2179
Westworld Magazine see Going Places Magazine **4691**
Westworld Saskatchewan. (CN) **4706**, 4797
Wetenschap & Samenleving. (NE ISSN 0043-4442) **4352**, 4392
Wetlands. (US ISSN 0277-5212) **4834**, 1971
Wetlands Ecology and Management. (NE ISSN 0923-4861) **4834**, 1971
Wettbewerb in Recht und Praxis. (GW ISSN 0172-049X) **2694**, 699
Wettbewerbe see Wettbewerbe Aktuell **308**
Wettbewerbe Aktuell. (GW) **308**, 2498
Wetter und Leben. (AU ISSN 0043-4450) **3442**
Wetterauer Geschichtsblaetter. (GW ISSN 0508-6213) **2395**
Wetterkarte. (GW ISSN 0936-5818) **3442**
Der Wetterlotse. (GW) **3442**
Wetzel County Genealogical Society. Newsletter. (US) **2167**
Weyerhaeuser News see Weyerhaeuser Today **2118**
Weyerhaeuser Today. (US) **2118**, 3667
Weyerhaeuser World see Weyerhaeuser Today **2118**
Weyers Flottentaschenbuch/Warships of the World. (GW ISSN 0083-9078) **3475**
Weyfarers. (UK ISSN 0307-7276) **3008**
Weyher Wecker. (GW) **3934**

Weymouth Surname Newsletter. (US) **2167**
Whakatane & District Historical Society. Monographs. (NZ ISSN 0110-4004) **2346**
†Whale Center Journal. (US) **5304**
Whale Center Newsletter see Whale Center Journal **5304**
Whale News. (US) **1500**, 460
Whales on Wheels. (US) **4706**
Whales Research Institute, Tokyo, Japan. Scientific Reports see Scientific Report of Cetacean Research **591**
Whalewatcher. (US ISSN 0273-4419) **1500**, 460
Whaling Account. (US) **1612**, 593
†Wharfie. (AT) **5304**
Wharton Market Report. (UK) **828**
What. (CN ISSN 0827-1828) **3008**
†What C B. (Citizens Band) (UK ISSN 0262-8481) **5304**
†What C D? (US) **5304**
†What Camera? (UK) **5304**
What Can We Stage. see Wat Kan Ons Opvoer **4642**
What Car? (UK ISSN 0307-2991) **4706**
▼What do I Read Next? (US ISSN 1052-2212) **416**
What Every Engineer Should Know About Series. (US) **1840**
What Every Veteran Should Know. (US ISSN 0083-9108) **3475**
What Finance. (UK) **803**
What Hi-Fi? (UK ISSN 0309-3336) **4462**
What Investment. (UK ISSN 0263-953X) **969**
What Is to Be Read. (US ISSN 0896-6354) **2975**, 4138
What It Costs to Run an Agency. (US) **1031**
What Micro? (UK ISSN 0264-441X) **1465**, 1481
What Mining Means to Australians. (AT) **3498**
What Mortgage. (UK) **699**
▼What People Are Wearing. (US) **2238**
What Personal Computer? (UK) **1475**
What Research Says to the Teacher Series. (US ISSN 0083-9116) **1763**
What She Wants. (US) **4855**
What They Said. (US ISSN 0512-5804) **3934**
What they Say about Forestry on the Hill see Forestry on the Hill **2100**
What to Buy for Business. (UK) **1056**
What to Buy for Business (US Edition). (US ISSN 0886-6163) **1062**
What to Do about Personnel Problems. (US) **1071**
What to Do in the Norfolk Broads. (UK) **4797**
What Video? (UK ISSN 0260-7530) **1388**
Whatcom County Farm Review. (US) **130**
What's Ahead in Personnel. (US) **1071**
What's Brewing. (UK) **387**
What's Brewing. (US) **387**, 1119
What's Cooking in Congress? (US ISSN 0278-4947) **2975**
†What's Developing in Alaska. (US) **5304**
What's Happening see S A M Management Journal **1027**
What's Happening (Washington). (US) **2694**
What's Happening at Vassar. (US) **1330**
What's Happening for Community Leaders. (US) **4096**
What's Happening on the Chinese Mainland. (CH ISSN 0512-5278) **3934**
What's Here and There see W.H.A.T **5302**
What's Line. (US) **2790**
What's New About London, Jack? (US) **2975**
What's New in Advertising and Marketing. (US ISSN 0043-4558) 42, 743
What's New in Arizona? (US) **888**
What's New in Building. (UK ISSN 0142-9094) **636**

WHEAT GRAINS 6805

†What's New in Building. (SI) **5304**
What's New in Business Information. (UK ISSN 0952-7001) **699**
What's New in Collective Bargaining Negotiations & Contracts. (US ISSN 0190-5244) **997**
What's New in Computing. (AT ISSN 0811-2762) **1402**
What's New in Computing. (SI ISSN 0218-253X) **1402**
What's New in Computing. (UK ISSN 0262-2734) **1425**, 1455, 1481
What's New in Electronics. (AT ISSN 0728-3873) **1779**
What's New in Farming. (UK ISSN 0143-9596) **130**
What's New in Fire and Security. Product Information Cards see Building Fire and Security Design **3615**
What's New in Forest Research. (NZ ISSN 0110-1048) **2111**
What's New in Industry. (UK) **1159**
What's New in Interiors. (UK ISSN 0262-2742) **2555**, 1159
What's New in Laundry & Cleaning. (UK) **1282**
Whats New in Networking see What's New in Computing **1425**
†What's New in Plant Physiology. (US ISSN 0193-0648) **5304**
What's New in Process Engineering. (AT ISSN 0819-5447) **1840**
What's New in Processing. (UK ISSN 0268-523X) **1861**, 2525
What's New in Radio Communications. (AT) **1360**
What's New in Scientific & Laboratory Technology. (AT ISSN 1034-7658) **4613**
What's New in Software see What's New in Computing **1425**
What's New in Welding. (CN) **3431**
What's News in Florida Politics. (US) **3934**
†What's News in Fusion. (US) **5304**
What's On see Family Planning Association of Gambia. Newsletter **596**
What's On. (BE) **2175**
What's On. (KE) **2209**
What's On. (TS) **2220**
What's on & Where to go see What's on in London (London, 1966) **4797**
What's on and Where to Shop in Aberdeen see What's On in Aberdeen **4797**
What's On in Aberdeen. (UK) **4797**
What's on in Aberdeen see What's On in Aberdeen **4797**
What's on in Adelaide and South Australia. (AT) **4797**
What's on in and around Manchester. (UK) **4797**
†What's on in and Around Toowoomba. (AT) **5304**
What's on in Avon. (UK) **4797**
What's On In Barbados. (BB) **2239**
What's on in Calcutta. (II ISSN 0043-4647) **4797**
What's on in East Anglia. (UK) **4797**
What's on in London (London, 1935). (UK ISSN 0043-4671) **4797**, 2481, 4642
What's on in London (London, 1966). (UK) **4797**, 4642
What's On in Manila. (PH) **4797**
What's on in Milan. (IT) **4797**
What's On in Victoria. (AT ISSN 0812-2040) **4797**
What's On Magazine. (CN) **2179**
What's on North West. (UK) **4797**
What's On Scotland see Scotland's What's On **4786**
What's on Video and Cinema. (AT) **1388**, 3519
What's On - Voici Ottawa, Hull see Where Ottawa - Hull **2179**
What's up Niagara. (CN) **2179**
What's Working in Direct Marketing and Fulfillment. (US) **1056**, 4138
Wheat Australia. (AT ISSN 0085-8196) **196**
Wheat Australia International. (AT ISSN 0814-9267) **196**
Wheat, Barley and Triticale Abstracts. (UK ISSN 0265-7880) **145**, 25
Wheat Grains in Oregon. (US) **208**

Wheat Grower. (US ISSN 0882-9691) **208**
Wheat Life. (US ISSN 0043-4701) **196**
▼Wheat Technology. (US) **208**
Wheatbelt Mercury. (AT) **2173**
Wheatgrower. (CN ISSN 0829-4763) **196**, 160
Wheaton Alumni. (US) **1330**
Wheel. (CE ISSN 0049-7541) **4216**
Wheel. (US ISSN 0888-1103) **4706**
Wheel Clicks. (US ISSN 0043-4744) **4717**
The Wheel Extended. (JA ISSN 0049-755X) **4706**
Wheel Fare. (II) **4706**
Wheel of Delta Omicron. (US ISSN 0043-4752) **3586**
Wheel of Dharma. (US) **4216**
Wheel Series. (US) **4290**
Wheeler Report. (US) **4077**
Wheelers R V Resort and Campground Guide: North American Edition. (US) **4797**, 4560
Wheelings. (US) **4706**
Wheels. (A) **4424**
Wheels. (AT ISSN 0043-4779) **4706**
Wheels. (RH) **4706**
Wheels & Tracks. (UK ISSN 0263-7081) **4706**, 3475
Wheels Magazine. (GW) **4706**
Wheels of Time. (US ISSN 0738-565X) **4750**, 260
Where. (TH) **4797**
Where (London, 1975). (UK ISSN 0143-2478) **4797**, 2481
Where (New York). (US) **4797**
†Where America's Large Foundations Make Their Grants. (US ISSN 0083-9167) **5304**
Where Calgary. (CN) **4797**
Where Chicago. (US) **4797**
Where Halifax - Dartmouth. (CN) **2179**
Where New Orleans. (US) **4797**
Where Ottawa - Hull. (CN ISSN 1187-1350) **2179**
Where Rocky Mountains. (CN) **4797**
Where Shall I Go to College to Study Advertising? (US) **1697**, 39
Where the Colleges Rank. (US) **1697**
Where the Trails Cross. (US ISSN 0092-4164) **2167**
Where to Build - Where to Repair. (NO ISSN 0800-1200) **4742**, 1159
Where To Buy see Where to Buy: Chemicals & Chemical Plant (Year) **1056**
Where to Buy, Board or Train a Dog. (US) **3714**
Where to Buy: Chemicals & Chemical Plant (Year). (UK) **1056**, 1190
Where to Buy Hardwood Plywood and Veneer. (US) **640**, 2118
Where to Buy Western Red Cedar Lumber Products. (US) **2118**
†Where to Eat & Entertain - Singapore. (SI) **5304**
Where to Eat - Dorset see Where to Eat in Dorset and South Wiltshire **2481**
Where to Eat in Berkshire. (UK) **2481**, 4797
Where to Eat in Bristol, Bath & Avon. (UK) **2481**, 4797
Where to Eat in Canada. (CN ISSN 0315-3088) **2481**, 4797
Where to Eat in Cardiff and South Wales see Where to Eat in Wales **2482**
Where to Eat in Cardiff, Swansea and South Wales see Where to Eat in Wales **2482**
Where to Eat in Cornwall. (UK) **2481**, 4797
Where to Eat in Devon. (UK) **2481**, 4797
Where to Eat in Devon and Cornwall see Where to Eat in Devon **2481** see Where to Eat in Cornwall **2481**
Where to Eat in Dorset and South Wiltshire. (UK) **2481**, 4797
Where to Eat in Edinburgh, Fife and the Lothians see Where to Eat In Scotland **2481**
Where to Eat in Gloucestershire and the Cotswolds see Where to Eat in Gloucestershire, Oxfordshire and the Cotswolds **2481**

Where to Eat in Gloucestershire, Oxfordshire and the Cotswolds. (UK) **2481**, 4797
Where to Eat in Greater Manchester and Cheshire see Where to Eat in North West England **2481**
Where to Eat in Guernsey see Where to Eat in the Channel Islands **2482**
Where to Eat in Hampshire. (UK) **2481**, 4797
Where to Eat in Hampshire and the New Forest see Where to Eat in Hampshire **2481**
Where to Eat in Ireland. (UK) **2481**
Where to Eat in Kent. (UK) **2481**, 4797
Where to Eat in London see London Restaurant Guide (London, 1990) **2477**
Where to Eat in North West England. (UK) **2481**, 4797
Where to Eat In Scotland. (UK) **2481**
Where to Eat in Somerset. (UK) **2481**, 4797
Where to Eat in Surrey. (UK) **2481**, 4797
Where to Eat in Sussex. (UK) **2481**, 4797
Where to Eat in the Channel Islands. (UK) **2482**, 4797
Where to Eat in Wales. (UK) **2482**, 4797
Where to Fish. (UK) **1159**, 4560
Where to Go in the Thames and Chilterns. (UK) **4797**
Where to Go, What to Do in the South. (UK) **4797**
▼Where to Retire. (US) **2280**
Where to Retire on a Small Income. (US ISSN 0511-8719) **4159**
Where-to-Sell-It Directory. (US) **2443**
Where to Stay in Scotland see Scotland: Hotels and Guest Houses **4786**
Where to Stay in Scotland. Hotels and Guest Houses see Scotland: Hotels and Guest Houses **4786**
Where Toronto. (CN) **4797**
Where Twin Cities. (US) **4798**
Where Vancouver. (CN) **1508**
Where Victoria. (CN ISSN 1182-0705) **1508**
Where, When, How... (PE) **4798**
Where Winnipeg. (CN) **1508**
Wherever. (US ISSN 0889-0781) **4210**
Wherever They Go see America's Spirit **4398**
Whetstone (Barrington). (US ISSN 1055-8659) **2975**, 349
Whetstone (Sierra Vista). (US) **3008**
Which? (UK ISSN 0043-4841) **1508**
Which Camera? (UK ISSN 0263-9106) **3798**
Which Car? (UK) **4706**
Which Compact Disc & Hi-Fi for Pleasure. (UK) **4462**
Which Computer? (UK ISSN 0140-3435) **1402**
Which Course? see School Leaver **1716**
†Which Degree. (UK) **5304**
Which? Hotel Guide. (UK) **2482**
†Which Office System? (UK ISSN 0265-6965) **5304**
▼Which P C? (UK ISSN 0950-317X) **1475**
Which School? (UK ISSN 0952-083X) **1697**
†Which Video? (UK ISSN 0269-9354) **5304**
Which Way. (US) **2975**
Which? Way to Health. (UK ISSN 0957-1728) **3810**, 3162
Which? Wine Monthly. (UK) **387**
Whillans's Tax Tables. (UK ISSN 0260-3926) **1112**
Whip see National Union for Civil and Public Servants. Journal **4068**
Whip. (US) **4539**
Whippet News. (US) **3714**
Whippet Newsletter. (US) **3714**
Whirlpool see Physical Therapy Today **3141**
Whirlwind. (US) **1330**
Whirrakee. (AT) **4352**
Whiskey Island Magazine. (US) **2975**
Whisper on Wall Street. (US) **969**
▼Whispering Palm. (US) **3009**

Whispering Wind. (US ISSN 0300-6565) **2029**
Whispers. (US) **3015**
Whispers Near the Inglenook. (US) **3535**
Whistle Stop. (US ISSN 0363-1028) **2791**, 2326
Whitaker's Almanack. (UK ISSN 0083-9256) **1782**
Whitaker's Book List. (UK ISSN 0953-041X) **4143**
Whitaker's Books in Print. (UK ISSN 0953-0398) **416**
Whitaker's Books of the Month and Books to Come. (UK ISSN 0043-4868) **4138**
†Whitaker's Classified Monthly Book List. (UK ISSN 0263-9432) **5304**
Whitaker's Cumulative Book List see Whitaker's Book List **4143**
White Arms Magazine. (US) **2975**
White Book of Ski Areas. U S and Canada. (US ISSN 0163-9684) **1159**, 4560
White Book of U S Ski Areas see White Book of Ski Areas. U S and Canada **1159**
White Clouds Revue. (US) **3009**
White Collar. (US ISSN 0043-4876) **2591**
White-Collar Crime Reporter. (US) **1524**
White Collar Management see Management Policies & Personnel Law **1019**
White Collar Report see Labor Relations Week **986**
White County Heritage. (US ISSN 0043-4906) **2426**, 2167
White Fathers - White Sisters. (UK ISSN 0262-1061) **4279**
White Horse and Fleur de Lys see Kingsman **3462**
White House Weekly. (US ISSN 0737-9218) **4077**, 3934
†White Light. (US ISSN 0742-8820) **5304**
White Paper of Science and Technology in Japan. see Kagaku Gijutsu Hakusho **4602**
White Paper on International Trade: Japan (Year). (JA) **924**
White Paper on Japanese Economy. (JA) **888**
White Paper on Japan's Forest Industries see Japan's Timber Consuming Industries **2115**
White Paper on Police. (JA) **1524**
†White Ravens. (GW) **5304**
The White Ribbon. (UK ISSN 0043-4973) **1539**, 4456
White Ribbon Bulletin. (AT ISSN 0043-4965) **1539**
White River Valley Historical Quarterly. (US ISSN 0510-372X) **2426**
White Sheet. (US) **3746**
White Sun. (US) **359**
White Tops. (US ISSN 0043-499X) **4642**
White Walls. (US ISSN 0190-9835) **349**
White Wing Messenger. (US ISSN 0043-5007) **4290**
Whiteacre. (AT ISSN 0085-820X) **2694**
White's Tax Exempt Bond Market Ratings. (US) **969**
Whiteshell Echo. (CN ISSN 0043-5015) **4560**, 1500
Whitfield's Utility Letter. (US) **699**
Whitman County Genealogical Society. Newsletter. (US ISSN 0887-6959) **2167**
Whitmark Directory. (US ISSN 0511-8794) **1159**
Whitmark Magazine. (US) **1384**
Whitmark News and Views see Whitmark Magazine **1384**
Whitney Museum of American Art. Bulletin. (US) **3535**
Whittier Newsletter. (US ISSN 0511-8832) **3009**
Whitworth Today. (US) **1330**
Whitworthian. (US) **1330**
Whizzer & Chips. (UK) **1270**
Who Audits America. (US ISSN 0149-0281) **1159**

Who is Who in Government, Politics, Banking and Industry in Latin America. (US) **416**, 421
Who is Who in the Oklahoma Legislature. (US) **4077**
Who Knows: a Guide to Washington Experts. (US) **4352**, 4613
Who Knows About Industries and Markets. (US) **699**, 2791
Who Knows: the Directory of Experts see Who Knows: a Guide to Washington Experts **4352**
Who Makes Machinery and Plants see Wer Baut Maschinen und Anlagen **1941**
Who Owns What in World Banking. (UK) **803**
Who Owns Whom. Australasia and Far East. (UK ISSN 0302-4091) **1159**
Who Owns Whom. Australia and Japan International see Who Owns Whom. Australasia and Far East **1159**
Who Owns Whom. Continental Europe. (UK ISSN 0083-9302) **1031**, 1086
Who Owns Whom. United Kingdom see Who Owns Whom. United Kingdom and Republic of Ireland **1159**
Who Owns Whom. United Kingdom and Republic of Ireland. (UK ISSN 0140-4040) **1159**
Who Owns Whom, North America. (UK ISSN 0083-9310) **1056**
Who Sells Foreign Products in Spain. see Quien Vende en Espana los Productos Extranjeros **1151**
Who Was Who in America. (US) **421**
Who, When & Where of Lincoln County, West Virginia. (US) **2167**
Who Writes What in Life and Health Insurance. (US) **2545**
Whole Again Resource Guide. (US ISSN 0734-9033) **4396**
Whole Arts Directory. (US) **1159**, 349
Whole Chile Pepper see Chile Pepper **2445**
Whole Earth Forecaster. (US) **969**, 359, 3442
Whole Earth Review. (US ISSN 0749-5056) **3597**
Whole Foods. (US ISSN 0193-1504) **2094**
†Whole Gay Catalog. (US ISSN 0890-8028) **5304**
†Whole Life. (US ISSN 0888-2061) **5304**
Whole Life Times. (US ISSN 0279-5590) **3597**, 3613, 3810
Whole Notes. (US) **3009**
The Whole World Oil Directory. (US) **3703**
Wholesale and Retail Trade Statistics. see Norway. Statistisk Sentralbyraa. Varehandelsstatistikk **732**
Wholesale Confectioners' Alliance. Yearbook. (UK) **2090**
Wholesale Drugs Magazine. (US) **3746**
Wholesale Price Index in Iran. (IR) **743**, 1000
Wholesale Price Indexes for Thailand. (TH) **888**
Wholesaler. (US ISSN 0032-1680) **2304**
Wholistic Education. (US) **1672**
Wholistic Living News see Good Life Times **3594**
Whom Newsletter. (US) **2326**, 4855
Who's Drilling. (AT ISSN 0159-1878) **3703**, 1549, 1797
▼Who's Inventing What? (US) **3679**
Who's Mailing What! (US) **1056**
Who's Pegging. (AT ISSN 0817-6353) **3498**
†Who's Succeeding. (CN ISSN 0847-2823) **5304**
▼Who's Where in the American Theatre. (US ISSN 1047-1715) **4642**
Who's Who. (UK ISSN 0083-937X) **421**
Who's Who: A Guide to Federal and Provincial Departments and Agencies, Their Funding Programs and the People Who Head Them see Directory of the Arts **324**
Who's Who Among American High School Students. (US) **1681**, 1246
▼Who's Who Among America's Teachers. (US) **1681**, 416

Who's Who Among Black Americans. (US ISSN 0362-5753) **421**

†Who's Who Among Controllers Today. (US) **5304**

▼Who's Who Among Hispanic Americans. (US ISSN 1052-7354) **421**, 2029

Who's Who Among International Students in American Universities and Colleges. (US ISSN 1043-8289) **1724**

†Who's Who Among Music Students in American High Schools. (US ISSN 0362-3750) **5304**

Who's Who Among Students in American Junior Colleges. (US ISSN 0511-8891) **421**, 1720

Who's Who Among Students in American Universities and Colleges. (US) **421**, 1720

Who's Who Among Students in American Vocational and Technical Schools see Who's Who Among Vocational and Technical Students in America **5304**

†Who's Who Among Vocational and Technical Students in America. (US ISSN 0148-6381) **5304**

Who's Who at the Frankfurt Book Fair. (GW ISSN 0170-7213) **4138**

Who's Who in Alberta Agriculture. (CN) **421**

Who's Who in America. (US ISSN 0083-9396) **421**

Who's Who in American Art. (US ISSN 0000-0191) **421**, 3535

Who's Who in American Law. (US ISSN 0162-7880) **2694**, 421

Who's Who in American Politics. (US ISSN 0000-0205) **421**, 3934

Who's Who in America's Caterers see Who's Who in America's Restaurants **1782**

Who's Who in America's Restaurants. (US ISSN 0743-6122) **1782**, 2482, 4798

Who's Who in Art. (UK) **422**, 349

Who's Who in Art Materials. (US) **349**, 357

Who's Who in Asian and Australasian Politics. (UK) **422**, 3934

†Who's Who in Beer Wholesaling. (US) **5304**

†Who's Who in Biotechnology. (US ISSN 0888-5982) **5304**

Who's Who in Black Dentistry in America. (US) **3244**, 2029

Who's Who in British Columbia Agriculture. (CN) **130**

Who's Who in California. (US ISSN 0511-8948) **422**

Who's Who in Canadian Film and Television (Year). (CN ISSN 0831-6309) **422**, 3519

†Who's Who in Chemistry & Plastics. (US ISSN 0888-5958) **5304**

Who's Who in Chiropractic, International.(US ISSN 0147-8265) **422**

†Who's Who in Civil Engineering, Earth Sciences & Energy. (US ISSN 0888-5966) **5304**

Who's Who in Commonwealth Broadcasting. (UK) **1384**

Who's Who in Community, Technical & Junior Colleges. (US) **1698**

Who's Who in Computing. (CN ISSN 0822-8574) **1402**, 422

†Who's Who in Consulting. (US ISSN 0083-9485) **5304**

Who's Who in Corrugated. (UK) **3667**

Who's Who in Direct Marketing Creative Services. (US ISSN 8755-2671) **1159**, 1056

Who's Who in Direct Selling. (US) **1056**

Who's Who in Electronics see U S Electronic Industry Directory **1156**

†Who's Who in Electronics & Computer Science. (US ISSN 0888-5931) **5304**

Who's Who in Electronics - Midwestern Edition see Who's Who in Electronics Sources - Midwestern Edition **422**

Who's Who in Electronics - Northeastern Edition see Who's Who in Electronics Sources - Northeastern Edition **422**

Who's Who in Electronics Sources - Midwestern Edition. (US) **422**, 1910

Who's Who in Electronics Sources - Northeastern Edition. (US) **422**, 1910

Who's Who in Electronics Sources - Southeastern Edition. (US) **422**, 1910

Who's Who in Electronics Sources - Southwestern Edition. (US) **422**, 1911

Who's Who in Electronics Sources - Western Edition. (US) **422**, 1911

Who's Who in Electronics - Southeastern Edition see Who's Who in Electronics Sources - Southeastern Edition **422**

Who's Who in Electronics - Southwestern Edition see Who's Who in Electronics Sources - Southwestern Edition **422**

Who's Who in Electronics - Western Edition see Who's Who in Electronics Sources - Western Edition **422**

Who's Who in Engineering. (US ISSN 0149-7537) **422**, 1840

Who's Who in Entertainment. (US) **3519**, 3586, 4642

Who's Who in Environmental Engineering. (US) **1971**, 1840

▼Who's Who in European Business. (UK) **422**, 699

▼Who's Who in European Politics. (UK) **422**, 3934

Who's Who in Finance and Banking in Thailand. (TH) **422**, 804

Who's Who in Finance and Industry. (US ISSN 0083-9523) **422**, 699

Who's Who in Finland. see Kuka Kukin On **419**

Who's Who in Floriculture. (US ISSN 0511-8964) **422**, 2143

Who's Who in France/Qui Est Qui en France. (FR ISSN 0083-9531) **422**

Who's Who in Hawaii see Men and Women of Hawaii **420**

Who's Who in Housing Finance see Who's Who in Mortgage Finance **1159**

Who's Who in India (Bombay). (II) **422**

Who's Who in India (Calcutta). (II ISSN 0301-5106) **422**

Who's Who in Indian Engineering and Industry. (II ISSN 0083-9558) **422**, 4613

Who's Who in Indian Relics. (US) **2443**, 289

Who's Who in Indian Science. (II ISSN 0083-9566) **422**, 4352

Who's Who in Industrial Editing see B A I E Membership and Services Directory (Year) **1122**

Who's Who in Insurance. (US ISSN 0083-9574) **2545**

Who's Who in International Banking. (UK) **422**, 804

Who's Who in International Organisations. (UK) **422**

Who's Who in Japan. (UK) **422**

Who's Who in Karate and the Other Martial Arts and Directory of Black Belts. (US) **4496**

Who's Who in Lebanon. (LE ISSN 0083-9612) **422**

†Who's Who in Library and Information Services. (US) **5304**

Who's Who in Live Animal Trade & Transport. (US ISSN 1042-2633) **4660**, 130, 1159, 3714

Who's Who in Mass Communication. (UK) **422**, 1345

†Who's Who in Mechanical Engineering & Materials Science. (US ISSN 0888-594X) **5304**

Who's Who in Mortgage Finance. (UK) **1159**, 804

Who's Who in Pakistan. (PK ISSN 0083-9671) **423**

Who's Who in Paper Distribution. (US) **3667**

†Who's Who in Physics & Optics. (US ISSN 0888-5974) **5304**

Who's Who in Public Relations (International). (US ISSN 0511-9022) **423**, 39

Who's Who in Religion. (US ISSN 0160-3728) **423**, 4210

Who's Who in Risk Management. (US) **2545**

Who's Who in S N A P. (Society of National Association Publishers) (US) **4138**, 423, 1302

Who's Who in Saudi Arabia. (SU) **423**

▼Who's Who in Science and Engineering. (US) **423**, 1840, 4352

Who's Who in South African Politics. (UK) **423**, 3934

Who's Who in Special Libraries. (US ISSN 0278-842X) **2791**

Who's Who in Switzerland. (SZ ISSN 0083-9736) **423**

Who's Who in Technology. (US ISSN 0887-5901) **4352**, 4613

Who's Who in Thailand. (TH) **423**

Who's Who in the Arab World. (LE ISSN 0083-9752) **423**

†Who's Who in the Commonwealth. (UK) **5304**

Who's Who in the East. (US ISSN 0083-9760) **423**

Who's Who in the Egg and Poultry Industries. (US ISSN 0510-4130) **145**, 423

Who's Who in the Emergency & Rescue Services (Year). (UK) **4115**, 2035, 2470

Who's Who in the Fish Industry. (US ISSN 0270-160X) **2050**

Who's Who in the Lodging Industry. (US) **2482**

Who's Who in the Midwest. (US ISSN 0083-9787) **423**

Who's Who in the People's Republic of China. (GW) **423**

Who's Who in the Securities Industry. (US ISSN 0090-418X) **969**

Who's Who in the South and Southwest.(US ISSN 0083-9809) **423**

Who's Who in the Tackle Trade. (UK) **1159**, 2050

Who's Who in the Theatre see Contemporary Theatre, Film & Television **418**

▼Who's Who in the U K Information World. (UK) **2791**, 423

Who's Who in the Wall and Ceiling Industry. (US) **640**, 636

Who's Who in the Water Industry. (UK) **4834**

Who's Who in the West. (US ISSN 0083-9817) **423**

Who's Who in the World. (US ISSN 0083-9825) **423**

Who's Who in Training and Development. (US ISSN 0092-4598) **1031**, 423

Who's Who in U S Writers, Editors and Poets see Who's Who in Writers, Editors & Poets in the United States & Canada **2983**

Who's Who in Western Europe. (UK) **423**

Who's Who in World Agriculture see Agriculture and Veterinary Sciences International Who's Who **72**

Who's Who in World Jewry. (US) **423**, 2029

Who's Who in Writers, Editors & Poets in the United States & Canada. (US ISSN 1049-8621) **2983**, 2579

Who's Who of American Women. (US ISSN 0083-9841) **423**

Who's Who of Australian Visual Art. (UK) **423**, 349

Who's Who of Australian Writers. (UK) **423**, 2576

Who's Who of Colombian-American Business. (CK) **1159**

Who's Who of Emerging Leaders in America. (UK) **424**

Who's Who of Southern Africa Including Mauritius, Namibia, Zimbabwe, Botswana, Swaziland and Neighboring Countries. (SA) **424**

Who's Who of Southern Africa Including Mauritius, South West Africa, Zimbabwe and Neighboring Countries see Who's Who of Southern Africa Including Mauritius, Namibia, Zimbabwe, Botswana, Swaziland and Neighboring Countries **424**

▼Who's Who of Women in World Politics. (UK) **424**, 3934, 4855

†Who's Who on Television. (UK) **5304**

Who's Who on the Screen. (UK) **424**, 3519

Why. (US) **4424**, 3977

Wiadomsci Instytutu Meteorologii i Gospodarki Wodnej see Instytut Meteorologii i Gospodarki Wodnej. Wiadomosci **3436**

Wiadomosci Archeologiczne/Bulletin Archeologique Polonais. (PL ISSN 0043-5082) **289**, 2395

Wiadomosci Botaniczne. (PL ISSN 0043-5090) **520**

Wiadomosci Chemiczne. (PL ISSN 0043-5104) **1190**

Wiadomosci Ekologiczne. (PL ISSN 0013-2969) **460**

Wiadomosci Elektrotechniczne. (PL ISSN 0043-5112) **1779**

Wiadomosci Gornicze. (PL ISSN 0043-5120) **3498**

Wiadomosci Historyczne. (PL ISSN 0511-9162) **2326**

Wiadomosci Hutnicze. (PL ISSN 0043-5139) **3423**

Wiadomosci Instytutu Meteorologii i Gospodarki Wodnej see Instytut Meteorologii i Gospodarki Wodnej. Wiadomosci **3436**

Wiadomosci Lekarskie. (PL ISSN 0043-5147) **3162**

Wiadomosci Melioracyjne. (PL ISSN 0510-4262) **1925**

Wiadomosci Numizmatyczne/ Numismatic News. (PL ISSN 0043-5155) **3602**

Wiadomosci Polskie. see Polish News **2019**

Wiadomosci Produkcyjne: Wlokno, Odziez, Skora. (PL ISSN 0137-8120) **1288**, 2738, 4627

Wiadomosci Sluzby Hydrologicznej i Meteorologicznej see Instytut Meteorologii i Gospodarki Wodnej. Wiadomosci **3436**

Wiadomosci Telekomunikacyjne. (PL ISSN 0043-5198) **1345**, 1368, 1384

Wiadomosci Tytoniowe. (PL ISSN 0508-7104) **130**

Wiadomosci Warsztatowe. (PL ISSN 0043-521X) **3024**

Wiadomosci Zielarskie. (PL) **130**

Wicazo Sa Review. (US ISSN 0749-6427) **2029**, 1720

Wiccan Rede. (NE) **3671**

Wiccan Workshop News. (UK ISSN 0952-522X) **3672**

†Wichita Business. (US) **5304**

Wichita Business Journal. (US) **699**

Wichita Postcard Club News. (US) **2443**

Wichita Singles Newsletter see Wichita Singles Newsletter - Heartland Foundation **4364**

Wichita Singles Newsletter - Heartland Foundation. (US) **4364**

Wichita Women Magazine. (US) **4855**

Wichitan. (US) **1330**

The Wick. (US) **1330**

▼Wicked Mystic. (US) **3009**

Wicken's the Law of Life Insurance in Australia. (AT) **2545**, 2694

Wicklow People. (IE) **2203**

Wide Angle/Kuang Chiao Ching. (HK) **2197**

Wide Angle. (US ISSN 0160-6840) **3519**

Wide Open Magazine. (US) **2889**

Wide Open Magazine of Poetry see Wide Open Magazine **2889**

Wide World of Flying. (US) **65**, 1384

Wide World of Taxidermy see Taxidermy Review **592**

Widener Review. (US ISSN 0882-066X) **2975**

Widening Horizons. (UK ISSN 0049-7614) **4855**

Wider Horizons see W H **2290**

Widersprueche. (GW) **4424**

Widescreen see International Widescreen **3792**

Wideworld G C S E Geography Review. (UK ISSN 0956-5353) **2266**

Widnokregi. (PL ISSN 0043-5244) **2889**

Wie Erreiche Ich Wen? (GW) **4742**, 1159

Wie Geht's Heute? (GW ISSN 0179-3004) **3162**

Wie Levert (Year). (NE ISSN 0922-4718) **1911**

Wie Levert Elektro see Wie Levert (Year) 1911
†Wiederherstellung. (GW) 5304
Wiedza o Muzyce. (PL) 3586
Wiel. (SA ISSN 0257-5426) 4661
Wielands Briefwechsel. (GW) 2975, 3009
De Wielewaal. (BE ISSN 0043-5260) 568
Wien Aktuell see Rendezvous Wien 2173
Wien-Veranstaltungen see Programm Wien 4783
Wiener. (AU) 2173
Wiener Arbeiten zur Deutschen Literatur. (AU ISSN 0083-9906) 2975
Wiener Beitraege zur Englischen Philologie. (AU ISSN 0083-9914) 2852, 2975
Wiener Beitraege zur Geschichte der Neuzeit. (AU) 2395
Wiener Beitraege zur Kulturgeschichte und Linguistik. (AU ISSN 0083-9922) 2852
Wiener Blaetter. (AU) 1330
Wiener Blaetter zur Friedensforschung. (AU) 3977
Wiener Boersekammer. Verordnungsblatt. (AU ISSN 0042-4250) 969
Wiener Boersen-Kurier see Boersen-Kurier 940
Wiener Erbe. see Viennese Heritage 2973
Wiener Forschungen zur Theater und Medienwissenschaft. (AU) 4642
Wiener Freie Wort - W F W see Internationales Freies Wort 3900
Wiener Fuhrwerkerzeitung. (GW) 4717
Wiener Geschichtsblaetter. (AU ISSN 0043-5317) 2395
Wiener Gesellschaft fuer Theaterforschung. Jahrbuch. (AU ISSN 0377-0745) 4642
Wiener - Goethe - Verein. Jahrbuch. (AU ISSN 0250-443X) 2975, 3009
Wiener Institut fuer Internationale Wirtschaftsvergleiche. Forschungsberichte. (AU) 936
Wiener Institut fuer Internationale Wirtschaftsvergleiche. Reprint Serie. (AU) 936
Wiener Jahrbuch fuer Kunstgeschichte. (AU ISSN 0083-9981) 349
Wiener Jahrbuch fuer Philosophie. (AU ISSN 0083-999X) 3786
Wiener Journal. (AU) 2173, 2975
Wiener klinische Wochenschrift. (US ISSN 0043-5325) 3162
Wiener Kulturkreis. Mitteilungen. (AU) 2889
Wiener Kunsthandel. (AU) 3759
Wiener Medizinische Wochenschrift. (AU ISSN 0043-5341) 3162
Wiener Mitteilungen: Wasser, Abwasser, Gewaesser. (AU) 4834
Wiener Musikhochschule. Publikationen.(AU ISSN 0084-0017) 3586
Wiener Neustadt. Amtsblatt der Stadt see Wiener Neustadt. Amtsblatt der Statutarstadt 4096
Wiener Neustadt. Amtsblatt der Statutarstadt. (AU) 4096
Wiener Rechtswissenschaftliche Studien.(AU ISSN 0084-0025) 2694, 2730
Wiener Ringstrasse - Bild Einer Epoche. (GW) 349, 2395
Wiener Romanistische Arbeiten. (AU ISSN 0084-0033) 2852, 2975
Wiener Slavistisches Jahrbuch/Viennese Slavonic Yearbook. (AU ISSN 0084-0041) 2852
Wiener Slawistischer Almanach. (AU ISSN 0258-6819) 2852, 2975
Wiener Studien. Zeitschrift fuer Klassische Philologie und Patristik. (AU ISSN 0084-005X) 2852, 1280
†Wiener Tagebuch. (AU ISSN 0039-8934) 5304
Wiener Tieraerztliche Monatsschrift. (AU ISSN 0043-535X) 4819
Wiener Urania. Mitteilungen. (AU ISSN 0026-6906) 1688
Wiener Voelkerkundliche Mitteilungen. (AU ISSN 0084-0068) 253

Wiener Warenboerse. Amtliches Kursblatt. Holz. (AU ISSN 0003-2166) 969
Wiener Warenboerse. Amtliches Kursblatt. Kolonialwaren. (AU) 969
Wiener Warenboerse. Amtliches Kursblatt. Rohhaeute und Felle, Leder Treibriemen und Technische Lederartikel. (AU ISSN 0003-2174) 969
Wiener Wirtschaft. (AU) 699
†Wiener Wirtschaftsberichte. (AU) 5304
Wiener Zeitschrift fuer die Kunde des Morgenlandes. (AU ISSN 0084-0076) 3645
Wiener Zeitschrift fuer die Kunde Suedasiens und Archiv fuer Indische Philosphie. (AU ISSN 0084-0084) 3786, 2343
Wiener Zeitschrift fuer Innere Medizin und ihre Grenzgebiete. see Acta Medica Austriaca 3070
Wienerin. (AU) 2173, 4855
Wienerwald. (GW) 2482
Wiesbadener Leben. (GW ISSN 0049-7622) 2192, 4798
Wiesenberger Investment Companies Service see Investment Companies 5218
Wigfield Newsletter. (US) 2167
†Wigwag. (US ISSN 1044-310X) 5304
Wijk en Speeltuinvereniging Tarwewijk. Mededelingenblad. (NE ISSN 0039-9736) 1246
Wijsgerig Perspectief op Maatschappij en Wetenschap/Philosophical Perspectives on Society and Science. (NE ISSN 0043-5414) 3786
Wijsgerige Teksten en Studies/Philosophical Texts and Studies. (NE ISSN 0084-0106) 3786
Wilbour Monographs. (US) 2326, 289, 349
Wilbur S. Shepperson Series in History and Humanities. (US) 2426
Wilcox Report see Wilcox Report Newsletter 5304
†Wilcox Report Newsletter. (US) 5304
Wild. (AT ISSN 0726-2809) 4560
Wild About Wilde Newsletter. (US) 2976
Wild Animals. see Yesheng Dongwu 594
Wild Apple Press. (US) 2426
Wild Bird. (US) 3714
Wild Cat. (UK ISSN 0260-7492) 1500
▼Wild Earth. (US ISSN 1055-1166) 1500, 1971
Wild Flower Notes. (US) 520, 1500, 2140
Wild Flower Notes and News see Wild Flower Notes 520
Wild Ranch Review. (US) 1500
Wild Rhodesia see Zimbabwe Wildlife 1501
Wild Rose Quarter Horse Country see Alberta Wild Rose Quarter Horse Journal 4531
Wild Sharkaaah. (CS) 2889
Wild und Hund. (GW ISSN 0043-5422) 4560
Wild West. (US) 3400, 4496
†Wildbiologische Information fuer den Jaeger. (GW) 5304
Wildbird. (US ISSN 0892-5534) 568
Wildcat Special. (US) 2985
Wilderness. (US ISSN 0736-6477) 1500, 1971
Wilderness see Wilderness News 1971
Wilderness Alberta. (CN ISSN 0830-8284) 1500, 1971
Wilderness Education Association Legend see W E A Legend 1499
Wilderness Gazette. (US) 4279
Wilderness Medicine see Wilderness Medicine Letter 3162
Wilderness Medicine Letter. (US) 3162
Wilderness News. (AT) 1971, 2111
Wilderness Record. (US ISSN 0194-3030) 1500
Wildfields. (PK) 1500
Wildfire. (US ISSN 0889-7867) 2029
Wildflower. (CN ISSN 0842-5132) 520
Wildflower. (US) 3009

Wildflower, Journal of the National Wildflower Research Center. (US ISSN 0896-4858) 520
Wildflower, Newsletter of the National Research Center. (US ISSN 0898-8803) 520
Wildfowl. (UK ISSN 0954-6324) 568
Wildfowl. (US ISSN 0886-0637) 4560, 3400
Wildfowl Art Journal. (US) 3535
Wildfowl Carving and Collecting. (US) 2443
Wildhaltung. (GW ISSN 0176-9723) 130
Wildland News. (CN ISSN 0316-3350) 1500
Wildlife Art News. (US ISSN 0746-9640) 349
Wildlife Australia. (AT ISSN 0043-5481) 1500, 593
Wildlife Behavior and Ecology. (US ISSN 0084-0122) 460
Wildlife Conservation. (US ISSN 1048-4949) 593
Wildlife Crusader. (CN ISSN 0043-5457) 4560, 1500
Wildlife Disease Association. Journal see Journal of Wildlife Diseases 4812
Wildlife Disease Review. (US ISSN 0736-6094) 3162, 593, 4819
Wildlife Guardian. (UK) 232
Wildlife Harvest. (US ISSN 0886-3458) 4560
Wildlife in North Carolina. (US ISSN 0043-549X) 1500
Wildlife Journal. (US ISSN 0893-6560) 460, 593, 4819
Wildlife Monographs. (US ISSN 0084-0173) 1500
Wildlife News. (US ISSN 0270-0360) 1500
Wildlife Notes see Florida Fish and Wildlife News 1488
Wildlife Preservation Society of Queensland. Newsletter. (AT) 1500
Wildlife Rehabilitation Today. (US ISSN 1044-2618) 4819, 1500
Wildlife Rescue News. (CN) 232, 460, 4819
Wildlife Research. (AT ISSN 1035-3712) 1500
Wildlife Research News. (AT) 1500
Wildlife Review (Fort Collins). (US ISSN 0043-5511) 1502, 25, 4499
Wildlife Society Bulletin. (US ISSN 0091-7648) 1500, 593
Wildlife Update see International Wildlife (Canadian Edition) 1490
Wildlifer. (US ISSN 0163-6359) 1500
†Wildtiere in Gehegen. (GW ISSN 0930-0856) 5305
Wildtiere - Wildbiologie. (SZ) 593, 1500
Wildwood News. (US) 3810
Wiley Monographs in Chemical Physics. (US) 1231
†Wiley Series in Computing. (US) 5305
Wiley Series in Geotechnical Engineering. (US) 196
†Wiley Series on Systems Engineering and Analysis. (US ISSN 0084-019X) 5305
Wiley World. (US ISSN 0899-1634) 2167
Wilhelm-Foerster-Sternwarte, Berlin. Protokoll der Sitzung der Gruppe Berliner Mondbeobachter see Gruppe Berliner Mondbeobachter. Protokoll der Sitzung 364
Wilhelm Furtwaengler Society of America. Newsletter. (US) 3586, 2395
Wilkinson's Road Traffic Law Bulletin. (UK ISSN 0265-7937) 2694
Will. (JA) 1031
Will/Chuokoron Management Affairs. (JA) 1031
▼Will County Marketing Directory. (US) 1159
Will - Grundy Counties Genealogical Society News. (US ISSN 1042-6884) 2167
Will - Grundy Counties Genealogical Society Quarterly. (US ISSN 8756-6931) 2167

Will to Charity: Charities' Story Book see Will to Charity Group: Charities' Story Book 4424
Will to Charity Group: Charities by Counties and Regions. (UK) 4424
Will to Charity Group: Charities' Story Book. (UK) 4424
Will to Charity Group: Handbook of Charities. (UK) 4424
Willa Cather Pioneer Memorial & Educational Foundation Newsletter. (US) 2976
Willamette Week. (US) 2238
Willdenowia. (GW ISSN 0511-9618) 521
Willem Mengelberg Society. Newsletter. (US ISSN 1051-0788) 3586
†Willett House Quarterly. (US ISSN 0883-9891) 5305
William Alanson White Psychoanalytic Institute Newsletter see W A W Newsletter 4049
William & Mary Law Review. (US ISSN 0043-5589) 2694
William and Mary Quarterly. (US ISSN 0043-5597) 2427, 2167
William and Mary Review. (US ISSN 0043-5600) 2976
William Carlos Williams Review. (US ISSN 0196-6286) 2976
William Hammond Mathers Museum. Occasional Papers and Monographs. (US) 3535
William K. McInally Lecture. (US ISSN 0084-0246) 699
William L. Hutcheson Memorial Forest. Bulletin. (US ISSN 0511-9723) 2111
William Mitchell Law Review. (US ISSN 0270-272X) 2694
William Morris Society. Journal. (UK ISSN 0084-0254) 424
William Petschek National Jewish Family Center. Newsletter. (US) 2029
William Winter Comments. (US ISSN 0274-5852) 3977, 2576
Williams Alumni Review. (US) 1330
Williams Kissin Cousins Newsletter. (US) 2167
Williams of Virginia Letter. (US) 2167
Williams Report. (US) 1071
Williamsburg Business Index. (US) 699
†Williamsburg Craft Series. (US) 5305
Williamsburg Decorative Arts Series. (US) 349, 2427
Williamson County Historical Society Newsletter see Williamson County Historical Society Publication 2427
Williamson County Historical Society Publication. (US) 2427
Willing Water (Denver) see A W W A Mainstream 4821
Willing's Press Guide. (UK ISSN 0000-0213) 416, 424
Williston & Rolls Court Forms. (CN) 2694
Willkommen in der Tschechoslowakei see Welcome to Czechoslovakia 4796
Willmore City see McWinners Magazine 2936
Willow Springs. (US ISSN 0739-1277) 2976
†Willowdale Month. (CN) 5305
Wills see B A R - B R I Bar Review. Wills 2715
Wills, Probate & Administration Service N S W. (AT) 2716
▼Wills, Trusts and Gifts - Rhode Island.(US) 2716
Willys Overland Jeepster Club Jeepster Newsletter see W O Jeepster Newsletter 4705
Wilmington Journal. (US ISSN 0049-7649) 2238
Wilmington Society of the Fine Arts. Report see Delaware Art Museum. Annual Report 5178
Wilmington Trust Briefings. (US) 804
Wilson and Wilson's Comprehensive Analytical Chemistry see Comprehensive Analytical Chemistry 1205
Wilson Bulletin. (US ISSN 0043-5643) 568
Wilson Library Bulletin. (US ISSN 0043-5651) 2791
Wilson Museum Bulletin. (US) 2427

Wilson of Virginia Letter. (US) **2167**
Wilson Quarterly. (US ISSN 0363-3276) **2889**
†Wilsonlines. (US) **5305**
Wilton Yearbook of Baking and Cake Decorating. (US) **2090, 2450**
Wiltshire Archaeological and Natural History Magazine (1982) (UK) **289, 4352**
Wiltshire Archaeological and Natural History Society. Annual Bulletin *see* Wiltshire Archaeological and Natural History Society. Annual Report (Year) **289**
Wiltshire Archaeological and Natural History Society. Annual Report (Year). (UK) **289, 4352**
Wiltshire Archaeological Magazine *see* Wiltshire Archaeological and Natural History Magazine (1982) **289**
Wiltshire Family History Society. Journal.(UK ISSN 0260-7174) **2167**
Wiltshire Farmer. (UK ISSN 0043-566X) **130**
Wiltshire Natural History Magazine *see* Wiltshire Archaeological and Natural History Magazine (1982) **289**
†Wimpel. (NE ISSN 0043-5678) **5305**
Win (Van Nuys). (US ISSN 1047-854X) **4496**
†Win the Lottery Today. (US) **5305**
Winckelmann Pelzmarket. (GW) **2738, 1288**
Winckelmann Sales Report. (GW) **1288, 2738**
Wind. (US ISSN 0361-2481) **2976**
Wind and Water Mills. (UK ISSN 0260-504X) **1812**
Wind Bell. (US ISSN 0043-5708) **4216**
†Wind Chimes. (US) **5305**
Wind - Energie Jahrbuch. (GW ISSN 0720-3926) **1812**
Wind Energy Abstracts. (US ISSN 0277-2140) **1801, 1812**
Wind Energy News. (US ISSN 0886-2818) **1812**
Wind Energy Report. (US ISSN 0162-8623) **1813**
Wind Energy Technology. (US) **1801, 1813**
Wind Engineering. (UK ISSN 0309-524X) **1813**
Wind Engineering Abstracts. (UK ISSN 0263-0915) **1801, 1813**
Wind Farm Project Report. (US ISSN 0891-6403) **1813**
Wind River Rendezvous. (US) **4279, 2029**
†Wind Rose. (US ISSN 0049-7657) **5305**
Wind Surf. (US ISSN 0279-9359) **4560**
Windesheimer Rundschau. (GW) **3934**
Windfall. (US ISSN 0893-3375) **3009**
Windham Phoenix. (US ISSN 0888-0832) **2976, 349**
Windhorse Review. (CN ISSN 0847-1762) **3009**
Windhound. (US) **3714**
Winding Up. (UK) **757, 1119**
Windkraft Journal. (GW) **1813**
Windless Orchard. (US ISSN 0043-5716) **3009**
The Windmill (Ontario Edition). (CN) **2029**
Windmill Herald: Central East Canada. (CN) **2029**
Windmill Herald: Western Edition. (CN) **2029**
Windmolen. (NE) **1500**
Window. (GW) **1481**
Window *see* Junkanoo **4241**
Window (New York). (US) **2470**
Window (Omaha). (US) **1330**
Window and Wall Decorating Ideas *see* Better Homes and Gardens Window & Wall Ideas **2549**
Window & Wall Ideas. (US) **2555**
Window Fashions. (US ISSN 0886-9669) **2562**
Window Industries. (UK) **1167, 636**
Window of Knowledge. *see* Zhishi Chuang **4353**
Window on Asia. (PH) **888**

▼Window on Canadian Tax. (CN) **1112**
Window on the World. *see* Shijie zhi Chuang **2183**
▼Windows (Manhasset). (US) **1402**
Windows (San Francisco) *see* P C World **1473**
Windows and OS2 Magazine *see* Windows (Manhasset) **1402**
▼Windows - D O S Developer's Journal. (US) **1432, 1475**
Windows Journal. (US) **1402**
▼Windows Tech Journal. (US) **1402**
Windows Watcher. (US) **1432**
Windows World. (AT) **1475**
Windplayer. (US ISSN 0895-1527) **3586**
Windpower Monthly. (DK ISSN 0109-7318) **1813**
Windrider *see* Windsurfing **4560**
Winds. (JA) **4804**
Winds from the South. *see* Nan Feng Chuang **2182**
Winds of Change. (US ISSN 0888-8612) **2029, 699, 3631**
WindScript. (CN ISSN 0822-2363) **2976, 349**
Windsor Business Life. (CN) **699**
Windsor Sportsmen's News. (CN ISSN 0049-7681) **4560**
Windsor This Month. (CN ISSN 0318-2460) **4798, 2180**
Windsor Yearbook of Access to Justice/ Recueil Annuel de Windsor d'Acces a la Justice. (CN ISSN 0710-0841) **2695**
Windspeaker. (CN) **2029**
Windsport. (CN ISSN 0826-5003) **4531**
Windsurf. (UK) **4531**
Windsurf and Boardsailing *see* Windsurf **4531**
Windsurf Italia. (IT) **4531**
Windsurfing. (US) **4560**
▼Windsurfing California. (US) **4531**
Windwatch. (US) **1501**
Windy City Bowling News. (US) **4514**
Windy City Sports. (US) **4496**
Windy City Times. (US) **2457**
Wine. (UK) **387**
Wine Advocate. (US) **387**
Wine and Dine *see* Wining & Dining **2482**
Wine and Food *see* House & Garden (London) **2552**
Wine & Food Almanac of the Pacific Northwest. (US) **387**
Wine & Food Companion. (US) **2084, 2450**
Wine & Spirit. (UK) **387**
Wine and Spirit Chronicle *see* International Bottler and Packer **382**
Wine and Spirit International Year Book.(UK) **387, 924**
Wine and Spirit Trade International Year Book *see* Wine and Spirit International Year Book **387**
Wine & Spirits. (US ISSN 0890-0299) **387**
Wine and Spirits Buying Guide *see* Wine & Spirits **387**
Wine and Spirits Guild of America Checkout *see* W S G A Checkout **386**
Wine and Spirits Industry Marketing. (US) **387**
Wine and Spirits Shippers Association Grapevine *see* W S S A Grapevine **386**
Wine Country. (US ISSN 0278-047X) **387**
Wine Country Guide to California. (US) **387**
Wine East. (US ISSN 0892-662X) **387**
Wine Enthusiast. (US) **387**
Wine Farmer. *see* Wynboer **196**
Wine Investigation for Novices and Oenophiles Newsletter *see* W.I.N.O. Newsletter **386**
Wine Investor: Buyers' Guide. (US ISSN 0889-9681) **387**
Wine Investor: Executive Edition. (US ISSN 0889-4256) **387**
Wine Marketing Handbook *see* Jobson's Wine Marketing Handbook **382**
Wine News. (US) **387**
Wine on Line. (US) **387**

The Wine Report. (NZ) **387**
Wine Spectator. (US ISSN 0193-497X) **387**
Wine Spectator Wine Maps *see* Wine Country Guide to California **387**
Wine Tidings. (CN ISSN 0228-6157) **387**
Wine Times *see* Wine Enthusiast **387**
Wine Trader. (US) **387, 2443**
Winepress. (UK) **2084**
†Wines, Alcohol and Spirits of the Common Market. Yearbook. (BE) **5305**
Wines and Vines. (US ISSN 0043-583X) **387, 196**
Wines and Vines - Annual Directory of the Wine Industry *see* Wines and Vines: Directory of the Wine Industry in North America **387**
Wines and Vines: Directory of the Wine Industry in North America. (US) **387**
Winesburg Eagle. (US ISSN 0147-3166) **2976, 424**
Winestate. (AT) **387, 4798**
Wing. (JA ISSN 0910-7800) **65**
Wing & Shot. (US) **4560**
Wing Newsletter. (JA ISSN 0388-1032) **65**
Wing Weekly *see* Wing **65**
Winged Chariot. (US) **3597, 359**
Winged Foot. (US ISSN 0043-5856) **3810, 4496**
Winged Head. (US ISSN 0043-5864) **1302**
Winged Mercury Missive. (US) **4456, 3597**
Wingrove. (UK) **3810**
Wings *see* New Zealand Wings **59**
Wings. (AT ISSN 0043-5880) **65**
Wings *see* Wake Up (London) **4423**
Wings. (CN) **4677**
Wings (Granada Hills). (US) **65**
Wings (Portland). (US) **538**
Wings & Hooves. (US) **228**
Wings Club. Bulletin. (US) **65**
Wings Magazine of Canada *see* Wings **4677**
Wings of Aloha. (US) **4677, 4798**
Wings of Gold. (US ISSN 0274-7405) **65, 3475**
Wings of Gold. (MY ISSN 0126-5393) **4804**
Wings of the Motherland. *see* Kryl'ya Rodiny **58**
Wings Over Africa *see* World Airnews **65**
Wings West. (US ISSN 1049-7781) **4678, 65, 4798**
Wingspan. (US) **1330**
Wingspan: Journal of the Male Spirit. (US) **3400, 3597, 4050**
Wingspread Randolph A F B. (US) **3475, 65**
Wining & Dining. (UK ISSN 0261-3956) **2482, 2450**
Winkler Prins Encyclopedisch Jaarboek. (NE) **2395**
Winner. *see* Al-Faez **3397**
Winner (Hagerstown). (US ISSN 0043-5937) **1539**
Winners Magazine *see* McWinners Magazine **2936**
Winnie. (FR) **1270**
Winning! (Bixby). (US) **2443**
Winning at Video & Computer Games. (UK) **1419, 1388**
Winning at Video Games *see* Winning at Video & Computer Games **1419**
Winning Bicycle Racing Illustrated *see* Winning Bicycling Illustrated **4521**
Winning Bicycling Illustrated. (US) **4521**
Winning Points. (US) **4514**
Winning Sweepstakes Newsletter. (US ISSN 0738-0143) **2443**
Winnipeg Industrial - Commercial Real Estate Guide. (CN) **4159**
Winslow Homer: An Annual. (US ISSN 0890-7714) **349**
Winston Cup Illustrated. (US ISSN 0744-4869) **4496**
Winston-Salem Magazine. (US) **2238**
Winston's Travel Deluxe. (US) **4798**
Winter Cities. (CN ISSN 0838-4096) **2180**
Winter Cities News *see* Winter Cities **2180**
†Winter Living. (US ISSN 1045-8069) **5305**

WIRTSCHAFT HEUTE 6809

Winter Simulation Conference. Proceedings. (US) **1436, 1440, 1443, 1911**
†Winterfare. (US) **5305**
Wintergreen. (CN) **2890, 416**
Winterhuder Wochenblatt. (GW) **1295, 39**
Winter's Crimes. (UK) **2986**
Winterthur Conference Report *see* Winterthur Portfolio: A Journal of American Material Culture **3535**
Winterthur Portfolio: A Journal of American Material Culture. (US ISSN 0084-0416) **3535**
Der Winzer. (AU ISSN 0043-5953) **196**
Winzer Kurier *see* Weinwirtschaft Anbau **386**
Wir. (GW) **1270, 1672**
Wir. (GW) **4798**
Wir. (Cologne). (GW) **2545**
Wir Bei Der Stadt. (GW) **4096**
Wir Eltern. (SZ) **1246**
Wir Frauen. (GW ISSN 0178-6083) **4855**
Wir Herbergs Freunde *see* Jugendherbergswerk **1240**
Wir Lehrlinge. (AU) **1271**
Wir Selbst. (GW ISSN 0175-9485) **3934, 2395**
Wir und Unsere Welt *see* Wir Lehrlinge **1271**
Wir vom Konsum. (AU ISSN 0508-8445) **1508**
Wir von Maingas. (GW) **1797**
Wir Walser. (SZ) **2060**
†Wira Scan. (UK) **5305**
Wire. (GW ISSN 0043-5996) **3423**
The Wire. (UK ISSN 0952-0686) **3586**
†Wire. (US) **5305**
Wire and Cable Panorama *see* Draht und Kabel Panorama **3405**
Wire Industry. (UK ISSN 0043-6011) **3423**
Wire Industry News. (US) **3423**
Wire Industry Yearbook. (UK ISSN 0084-0424) **3423**
Wire Journal International. (US ISSN 0277-4275) **1911**
Wire Journal International Directory Catalog *see* Wire Journal International Reference Guide **1911**
Wire Journal International Reference Guide. (US ISSN 0277-4275) **1911**
Wire Rope News and Sling Technology. (US ISSN 0740-1809) **3652, 3423**
Wire Technology International. (US ISSN 0745-7510) **1345, 1911**
Wire Technology Newsletter *see* Wire Technology International **1345**
Wire World International *see* Wireworld **3423**
Wired Librarian's Newsletter. (US ISSN 0884-593X) **2799**
▼Wireless Cellular. (US ISSN 1058-6717) **1345**
Wireless - P C N *see* Wireless - Personal Communication Networks **1352**
▼Wireless - Personal Communication Networks. (US ISSN 1058-6725) **1352**
Wireless Pioneer *see* Sparks (Santa Rosa) **5281**
▼Wireless - Satellite and Broadcasting. (US ISSN 1058-6695) **1345**
▼Wireless - Spectrum Management. (US ISSN 1058-6709) **1345**
▼Wireless Telecommunication. (US ISSN 1057-5391) **1345**
Wires *see* On - Line (New York) **5252**
Wireworld. (GW ISSN 0934-5906) **3423**
Wirkendes Wort. (GW ISSN 0043-6089) **2852, 1672**
Wirkerei - und Strickerei - Technik. (GW ISSN 0043-6097) **4627**
Die Wirtschaft. (GW ISSN 0232-4768) **699**
Die Wirtschaft. (GW) **824**
Wirtschaft am Bayerischen Untermain. (GW ISSN 0173-329X) **824**
Die Wirtschaft Chiles. (CL) **824**
▼Wirtschaft fuer den Arzt. (GW) **3162**
Wirtschaft Heute. (AU) **804**

WIRTSCHAFT

Wirtschaft im Raum Hanau Kinzigtal. (GW) **824**
Wirtschaft im Suedwesten (Freiburg). (GW ISSN 0936-5885) **699**
Wirtschaft im Suedwesten (Villingen). (GW ISSN 0936-5885) **824**
Wirtschaft in Bremen. (GW) **824**
Wirtschaft in Ostwuerttemberg. (GW) **824**
Wirtschaft in Suedostwestfalen. (GW) **824**
Wirtschaft - Neckar - Alb. (GW) **824**
Wirtschaft Nordhessen. (GW) **824**
Wirtschaft und Berufs - Erziehung. (GW ISSN 0341-339X) **3631**
Wirtschaft und Boerse. (GW ISSN 0510-5366) **888**, **969**
Wirtschaft und Energie. (SZ) **1508**
Wirtschaft und Erziehung. (GW ISSN 0174-6170) **899**, **1672**
Wirtschaft und Gesellschaft. (AU) **699**
Wirtschaft und Gesellschaft im Beruf. (GW) **1763**, **699**
Wirtschaft und Gesellschaft im Unterricht *see* Wirtschaft und Gesellschaft im Beruf **1763**
Wirtschaft und Kammer. (GW) **824**
Wirtschaft und Recht. (SZ ISSN 0043-6135) **699**, **2695**
Wirtschaft und Technik im Transport *see* Foerdertechnik **4650**
Wirtschaft und Verkehr im Bayerischen Dreilaendereck. (GW) **841**
Wirtschaft und Verkehr Nordrhein-Westfalens in Zahlen. (GW) **4592**
Wirtschaft und Wettbewerb. (GW ISSN 0043-6151) **1086**, **1056**, **2695**
Wirtschaft und Wissen *see* Angestellten Magazin **2580**
Wirtschaft Zwischen Nord- und Ostsee. (GW ISSN 0049-7703) **824**
Wirtschaftliche Lage in der Bundesrepublik Deutschland. (GW ISSN 0433-7484) **888**
Der Wirtschaftsredakteur. (GW ISSN 0177-3518) **699**
Wirtschafts Kompass. (GW) **699**
Wirtschafts - Kurier Hannover und Muenchen. (GW) **699**
Wirtschafts - Nachrichten. (GW) **699**
†Wirtschafts- und Gesellschaftspolitische Grundinformationen. (GW) **5305**
Wirtschafts und Steuer Hefte. (GW ISSN 0722-3358) **699**
Wirtschaftsanalysen. (GW) **888**
Wirtschaftsberichte *see* Trends **886**
Wirtschaftsblaetter *see* B F G: Wirtschaftsblaetter **844**
Wirtschaftsdienst. (GW ISSN 0043-6275) **699**
Das Wirtschaftseigene Futter. (GW ISSN 0049-7711) **196**
Wirtschaftsinformatik. (GW ISSN 0937-6429) **1453**
Wirtschaftskonjunktur. (GW ISSN 0043-6283) **700**
Wirtschaftspolitische Blaetter. (AU ISSN 0043-6291) **824**
Wirtschaftspolitische Chronik *see* Zeitschrift fuer Wirtschaftspolitik **701**
Wirtschaftspolitische Studien. (US ISSN 0172-5963) **899**
Wirtschaftspruefkammer. Mitteilungen. (GW ISSN 0936-5117) **757**
Die Wirtschaftspruefung. (GW ISSN 0340-9031) **757**
Wirtschaftsrecht. (GW) **2695**
Wirtschaftsreport Siegen-Olpe-Wittgenstein. (GW) **700**
Wirtschaftsrevue *see* Bilanz **847**
Wirtschaftsrundschau. (AU) **824**
Wirtschaftsrundschau Italia - Oesterreich. (AU) **824**
Wirtschaftsschutz *see* Wirtschaftsschutz und Sicherheitstechnik **1524**
Wirtschaftsschutz und Sicherheitstechnik. (GW) **1524**, **1528**
Wirtschaftsspiegel. (GW) **700**
Wirtschaftsspiegel/Reflets de l'Economie. (SZ) **743**
Das Wirtschaftsstudium - W I S U. (GW) **1672**
†Wirtschaftsuniversitaet Wien. Dissertationen. (AU ISSN 0259-0719) **5305**
Wirtschaftsvereinigung Gross- und Aussenhandel Geschaeftsbericht *see* W G A Geschaeftsbericht **924**
†Wirtschaftswissenschaft. (GW ISSN 0043-633X) **5305**
Wirtschaftswissenschaftliche und Wirtschaftsrechtliche Untersuchungen. (GW ISSN 0083-7113) **700**, **2695**
Wirtschaftszahl. (AU ISSN 0510-5609) **743**
Wirtschaftszeitung fuer Handwerk und Gewerbe *see* Deutsche Handwerks Zeitung **976**
Wirtschaftwissenschaftliches Studium (WIST). (GW ISSN 0340-1650) **700**
Wisconsin. (US) **2238**
Wisconsin. Commissioner of Securities. Annual Report *see* Wisconsin. Commissioner of Securities. Biennial Report **969**
Wisconsin. Commissioner of Securities. Biennial Report. (US) **969**
Wisconsin. Department of Administration. Annual Fiscal Report. (US ISSN 0085-8226) **4077**
Wisconsin. Department of Natural Resources. Annual Water Quality Report to Congress. (US ISSN 0362-5354) **4834**, **1971**, **4115**
Wisconsin. Department of Natural Resources. Technical Bulletin. (US ISSN 0084-0564) **1501**
Wisconsin. Department of Transportation. Automatic Traffic Recorder Data *see* Wisconsin Traffic Data - Automatic Traffic Recorder **4668**
Wisconsin. Department of Transportation. Division of Planning and Budget. Highway Mileage Data. (US ISSN 0084-0572) **4668**, **4723**
Wisconsin. Department of Transportation. Division of Planning. Highway Traffic. (US ISSN 0084-0580) **4668**
Wisconsin. Department of Veterans Affairs. Biennial Report. (US) **3477**
Wisconsin. Division of Corrections. Bureau of Planning, Development and Research. Releases from Juvenile Institutions *see* Wisconsin. Division of Corrections. Office of Information Management. Releases from Juvenile Institutions **1525**
Wisconsin. Division of Corrections. Office of Information Management. Admissions to Juvenile Institutions. (US) **1525**, **4592**
Wisconsin. Division of Corrections. Office of Information Management. Releases from Juvenile Institutions. (US) **1525**
Wisconsin. Division of Highways. System Planning Section. Highway Traffic in Wisconsin Cities *see* Wisconsin. Department of Transportation. Division of Planning. Highway Traffic **4668**
Wisconsin. Educational Communications Board. Biennial Report. (US ISSN 0361-2120) **1672**
Wisconsin. Employment Relations Commission. Reporter. (US ISSN 0097-9171) **997**
Wisconsin. Geological and Natural History Survey. Bulletin. (US) **1585**
Wisconsin. Geological and Natural History Survey. Field Trip Guide Books. (US) **1585**
Wisconsin. Geological and Natural History Survey. Geoscience Educational Series. (US) **1585**
Wisconsin. Geological and Natural History Survey. Geoscience Information Series *see* Wisconsin. Geological and Natural History Survey. Geoscience Educational Series **1585**
Wisconsin. Geological and Natural History Survey. Information Circulars.(US ISSN 0512-0640) **1585**
Wisconsin. Geological and Natural History Survey. Programs and Activities. (US) **1585**
Wisconsin. Geological and Natural History Survey. Special Report. (US ISSN 0512-0659) **1586**
Wisconsin. State Elections Board. Biennial Report. (US) **4077**
Wisconsin A I D S Update. (US) **3224**
Wisconsin Academy Review. (US ISSN 0512-1175) **349**, **2976**
Wisconsin Agriculturist. (US ISSN 0043-6356) **130**
Wisconsin Alumni *see* On Wisconsin Magazine **1320**
Wisconsin Archeologist. (US ISSN 0043-6364) **289**
Wisconsin Architect. (US) **308**
Wisconsin Auto Valuation Guide. (US ISSN 0736-7988) **4706**
Wisconsin Bar Bulletin *see* Wisconsin Lawyer **2695**
Wisconsin Beverage Journal. (US ISSN 0043-6399) **387**
Wisconsin Blue Book. (US) **4077**
Wisconsin Bookwatch. (US) **416**
Wisconsin Business Monographs. (US ISSN 0084-0513) **700**
Wisconsin C P A. (US ISSN 0043-6402) **757**
Wisconsin China Series. (US ISSN 0084-053X) **2343**, **3645**
Wisconsin Commerce Studies *see* Wisconsin Economy Studies **700**
†Wisconsin Council of Teachers of English. Service Bulletin Series. (US) **5305**
Wisconsin Counties. (US ISSN 0749-6818) **4096**
Wisconsin County Lands. (US) **4159**
Wisconsin Crime and Arrests (Year). (US) **1524**
Wisconsin Deer Report. (US) **4560**
Wisconsin Dental Association. Journal. (US ISSN 0091-4185) **3244**
Wisconsin Economy Studies. (US ISSN 0084-0599) **700**
Wisconsin Electronic Sales and Service Association Newsletter *see* W E S A Newsletter **1119**
Wisconsin Engineer. (US ISSN 0043-6453) **1840**
Wisconsin English Journal. (US ISSN 0512-1213) **1763**, **2976**
Wisconsin Environmental Decade. (US) **1501**, **1971**
▼Wisconsin Facts. (US ISSN 1046-8331) **1782**
Wisconsin Farmers Fastline *see* Farmers Fastline: Wisconsin Edition **5191**
Wisconsin Fire Journal. (US) **2035**
Wisconsin Golf. (US) **4515**
Wisconsin Golf Directory. (US) **1159**, **4515**
Wisconsin Grocer. (US) **2084**
†Wisconsin Health Care Report. (US) **5305**
Wisconsin Highway Traffic *see* Wisconsin. Department of Transportation. Division of Planning. Highway Traffic **4668**
Wisconsin Insurance *see* Wisconsin Insuror **2545**
Wisconsin Insuror. (US) **2545**
Wisconsin International Law Journal. (US ISSN 0743-7951) **2730**
Wisconsin Introductions to Scandinavia *see* W I T S: I **2028**
Wisconsin Introductions to Scandinavia II *see* W I T S: II **2028**
Wisconsin Issues. (US) **4077**
Wisconsin Jewish Chronicle. (US ISSN 0043-6488) **2029**
Wisconsin Land Information Newsletter. (US) **1880**
Wisconsin Law Review. (US ISSN 0043-650X) **2695**
Wisconsin Lawyer. (US) **2695**
Wisconsin Legislative Council Rules Clearinghouse. Annual Report. (US) **2695**
Wisconsin Library Association. President's Newsletter *see* W L A Newsletter **2790**
Wisconsin Library Association Newsletter *see* W L A Newsletter **2790**
Wisconsin Library Service Record. (US ISSN 0361-2848) **2791**
Wisconsin Magazine of History. (US ISSN 0043-6534) **2427**
Wisconsin Manufacturers Register. (US ISSN 0738-0070) **1159**
Wisconsin Master Plumber *see* Wisconsin P-H-C Contractor **2304**
Wisconsin Medical Journal. (US ISSN 0043-6542) **3162**
Wisconsin Misdemeanors and Moving Traffic Violations. (US) **2695**
Wisconsin Natural Resources. (US ISSN 0736-2277) **1501**, **4560**
Wisconsin Optometric Association. Journal. (US) **3305**
Wisconsin Outdoor Journal. (US ISSN 0893-5769) **4560**
Wisconsin P-H-C Contractor. (US) **2304**
Wisconsin Painters and Sculptors. Newsletter *see* Art in Wisconsin **314**
Wisconsin Parent Teacher. (US) **1732**
Wisconsin Pharmacist. (US ISSN 0043-6585) **3746**
Wisconsin Population Projections. (US ISSN 0091-5254) **3989**
Wisconsin Preservation: National Register of Historic Places. Newsletter. (US ISSN 0276-4156) **2427**
Wisconsin Professional Engineer. (US ISSN 0043-6615) **1840**
Wisconsin Public Documents. (US ISSN 0364-507X) **4083**
Wisconsin Public - Private School Directory. (US) **1698**
Wisconsin Public School Directory *see* Wisconsin Public - Private School Directory **1698**
Wisconsin R E C News. (US) **2238**, **165**, **1911**
Wisconsin Restaurateur. (US ISSN 0274-7472) **2482**
Wisconsin Review. (US ISSN 0043-6631) **3009**
Wisconsin School Board News *see* Wisconsin School News **1732**
Wisconsin School Musician. (US ISSN 0043-6658) **3586**, **1763**
Wisconsin School News. (US) **1732**
Wisconsin Securities Bulletin. (US) **969**
Wisconsin Services Directory. (US) **1159**
Wisconsin Sheriff and Deputy. (US) **1524**
Wisconsin Silent Sports *see* Silent Sports **4488**
Wisconsin Small Business Counselor. (US) **1119**
Wisconsin Snowmobile News. (US) **4560**
Wisconsin Sociologist. (US ISSN 0043-6666) **4456**
Wisconsin South Asian Area Center News Report. (US) **1331**
Wisconsin Sportsman. (US ISSN 0361-9451) **4560**
Wisconsin State Dental Society. Journal *see* Wisconsin Dental Association. Journal **3244**
Wisconsin State Farmer. (US) **130**
Wisconsin State Genealogical Society Newsletter. (US) **2168**
Wisconsin Studies in Contemporary Literature *see* Contemporary Literature **2908**
Wisconsin Taxpayer. (US) **4077**, **1112**
Wisconsin Traffic Data - A T R *see* Wisconsin Traffic Data - Automatic Traffic Recorder **4668**
Wisconsin Traffic Data - Automatic Traffic Recorder. (US ISSN 0098-0323) **4668**
Wisconsin Trails. (US ISSN 0095-4314) **2238**
†Wisconsin Travel and Recreation Guide. (US) **5305**
Wisconsin Vocational Association Views & Visions *see* W V A Views & Visions **1688**
Wisconsin West Magazine. (US) **2427**, **2060**, **4798**
Wisconsin Woman. (US) **4855**
Wisconsin Women's Law Journal. (US ISSN 1052-3421) **2695**, **4855**
Wisconsin's Health *see* Health in Wisconsin **4103**
Wisden Cricket Monthly. (UK ISSN 0263-9041) **4515**
Wisdom. *see* Kinaadman **3640**
Wisdom of Persia. (IR) **2432**

The Wise Woman. (US ISSN 0883-119X) **4855**, 3672
Wishing Well. (US) **2458**, 4855
▼Wissenschaft in den Medien. (GW ISSN 0938-6300) **2576**, 4352
Wissenschaft in der U.D.S.S.R. *see* Nauka v S.S.S.R **4329**
Wissenschaft und Gegenwart. Geisteswissenschaftliche Reihe. (GW ISSN 0175-6486) **3786**
Wissenschaft und Gegenwart. Juristische Reihe. (GW) **2695**
Wissenschaft und Gesellschaft. (GW ISSN 0138-5755) **4456**
Wissenschaft und Praxis in Kirche und Gesellschaft *see* Pastoraltheologie - Monatsschrift fuer Wissenschaft und Praxis in Kirche und Gesellschaft **4194**
†Wissenschaft und Umwelt. (GW ISSN 0170-6977) **5305**
Wissenschaftliche Alpenvereinshefte. (GW ISSN 0084-0912) **2266**
†Wissenschaftliche Blaetter zu Problemen des Blinden- und Sehschwachenwesens. (GW) **5305**
Wissenschaftliche Gesellschaft fuer Luft- und Raumfahrt. Jahrbuecher *see* D G L R Jahrbuecher **50**
Wissenschaftliche Gesellschaft fuer Personenstandswesen und Verwandte Gebiete. Schriftenreihe. Neue Folge. (GW ISSN 0084-0939) **2695**
Wissenschaftliche Kommission des Theodor-Koerner-Stiftungsfonds und des Leopold-Kunschak-Preises zur Erforschung der Oesterreichischen Geschichte der Jahre 1918 bis 1938. Veroeffentlichungen *see* Wissenschaftliche Kommission zur Erforschung der Geschichte der Republik Oesterreich. Veroeffentlichungen **2395**
Wissenschaftliche Kommission zur Erforschung der Geschichte der Republik Oesterreich. Veroeffentlichungen. (AU) **2395**
†Wissenschaftliche Mitteilungen. (GW ISSN 0323-3499) **5305**
Wissenschaftliche Mitteilungen des Bosnisch-Herzegowinischen Landesmuseums. Archaeologie. (BN) **289**
Wissenschaftliche Mitteilungen des Bosnisch-Herzegowinischen Landesmuseums. Naturwissenschaft. (BN ISSN 0350-0012) **4352**
Wissenschaftliche Paperbacks. (GW ISSN 0170-3579) **899**, 4456
Wissenschaftliche Taschenbuecher. Reihe Biologie. (GW ISSN 0084-0963) **460**
Wissenschaftliche Taschenbuecher. Reihe Chemie. (GW ISSN 0084-0971) **1190**
Wissenschaftliche Taschenbuecher. Reihe Mathematik - Physik. (GW ISSN 0084-098X) **3061**, 3835
Wissenschaftliche Taschenbuecher. Reihe Texte und Studien. (GW ISSN 0138-127X) **3835**
Wissenschaftliche Untersuchungen zum Neuen Testament. (GW ISSN 0512-1604) **4210**
Wissenschaftliche Vereinigung der Augenoptiker. Fachvortraege der Jahrestagungen *see* Wissenschaftliche Vereinigung fuer Augenoptik und Optometrie. Fachvortraege des W V A O Jahreskongresses **3305**
Wissenschaftliche Vereinigung fuer Augenoptik und Optometrie. Fachvortraege des W V A O Jahreskongresses. (GW) **3305**
Wissenschaftlicher Dienst fuer Ostmitteleuropa *see* Dokumentation Ostmitteleuropa **4370**
Wissenschaftlicher Literatur Anzeiger Selecta *see* W L A Selecta **4358**
Wissenschaftlicher Literaturanzeiger. (GW ISSN 0341-8723) **4143**, 4358
Wissenschafts Zentrum Berlin fuer Sozialforschung Forschung *see* W Z B Forschung **4396**
Wissenschaftsmagazin. (GW ISSN 0720-9991) **4352**

Wissenschaftspolitik *see* Politique de la Science **4334**
Wissenschaftsrecht, Wissenschaftsverwaltung, Wissenschaftsfoerderung. (GW ISSN 0043-6976) **2695**
Wissenschaftszentrum Berlin fuer Sozialforschung Mitteilungen *see* W Z B - Mitteilungen **4392**
†Wistar Symposium Series. (US ISSN 0271-9347) **5305**
†Wistra. (GW ISSN 0721-6890) **5305**
Witchcraft Digest. (US ISSN 0085-8250) **3672**
Witchcraft - Paganism Directory. (US) **3672**
Witches International Craft Associates. W I C A Newsletter. (US ISSN 0049-7754) **3672**, 3597
With. (JA) **4855**
With New York Firefighters *see* W N Y F **2035**
With One Voice *see* National Mirror **1340**
Within and Beyond. (US ISSN 0898-5839) **3597**
Within Our Gates *see* Open House **1241**
Without Halos. (US ISSN 1052-3162) **3009**
Without Prejudice. (CN ISSN 0833-1278) **2545**
Witness *see* Aware **4164**
Witness (Detroit). (US ISSN 0197-8896) **4253**
The Witness (Dubuque). (US ISSN 0745-0427) **4279**
Witness (Farmington Hills). (US ISSN 0891-1371) **3009**, 2889
Wits Journal of Librarianship and Information Science. (SA) **2791**
▼Wittenberg Review. (US ISSN 1050-7035) **2976**
Wittenberg Review of Literature and Art.(US) **2976**, 349
Wittenburg Door *see* The Door **4236**
Witterung in Oesterreich. Monatsuebersicht. (AU ISSN 0043-7077) **3442**
Witterung in Uebersee. (GW ISSN 0043-7085) **3442**
Wittgenstein. (GW ISSN 0043-7093) **2395**, 2060, 2266
WittyWorld. (US ISSN 0892-9807) **349**
Wivenhoe Park Review. (UK ISSN 0043-7107) **3009**
WiWi-Press. (GW) **1331**, 700
Wo Geht's Lang? (GW) **1720**
Woche in Australien. (AT ISSN 0043-7123) **2029**
Wochen Rundschau. (AU) **2173**
Wochenblatt fuer Kaiserslautern. (GW) **2192**
Wochenblatt fuer Landau. (GW) **2192**
Wochenblatt fuer Ludwigshafen. (GW) **2192**
Wochenblatt fuer Mannheim. (GW) **2192**
Wochenblatt fuer Neustadt. (GW) **2192**
Wochenblatt fuer Papierfabrikation. (GW ISSN 0043-7131) **3667**
Wochenblatt fuer Speyer. (GW) **2192**
Wochenend. (GW) **2192**
Wochenpresse. (AU) **2173**
Wochenschau fuer Politische Erziehung, Sozial- und Gemeinschaftskunde. Ausgabe fuer Sekundarstufe I. (GW ISSN 0342-8990) **4392**, 2326
Wochenschau fuer Politische Erziehung, Sozial- und Gemeinschaftskunde. Ausgabe fuer Sekundarstufe II. (GW ISSN 0342-8974) **4392**, 2326
Woerkshop. (GW) **39**
Wohl Report on End User Computing *see* Amy D. Wohl's Trends Letter **1467**
Der Wohlfahrtsdienst. (AU) **4456**, 2889
Wohnbaden. (GW ISSN 0178-2509) **2562**
Wohnbauforschung in Oesterreich *see* W B F O **2498**
Wohnbautaetigkeit in der Schweiz/ Construction de Logements en Suisse. (SZ) **639**
Wohneigentum. (SZ) **4159**

Das Wohnen. (SZ) **636**
†Wohnen. (GW ISSN 0138-2810) **5305**
†Wohnen im Gruenen. (GW ISSN 0138-2764) **5305**
Wohnen Plus. (AU) **2499**, 636
Wohnen und Siedeln *see* Wohnen Plus **2499**
Wohnen-Zeitschrift fuer das Wohnungswesen in Bayern. (GW) **1112**
Wohnidee. (GW) **2556**
Wohnmagazin. (GW) **2562**
Wohnmedizin. (GW ISSN 0342-5967) **4115**
Wohnung & Gesundheit. (GW) **308**, 460, 1971, 3162
Wohnungsaktiengesellschaft Linz Daheim bei der W A G *see* Daheim bei der W A G **2486**
Der Wohnungseigentuemer. (GW ISSN 0344-8738) **636**, 2695, 4159
Wohnungseigentum. (GW ISSN 0043-7166) **636**
Wohnungswirtschaft. (GW ISSN 0179-745X) **2499**
Wohnungswirtschaft und Mietrecht. (GW) **2695**, 2499
Wojsko Ludowe. (PL) **3475**
Wojsko Ludowe *see* Wojsko Ludowe **3475**
Wojskowy Przeglad Historyczny. (PL ISSN 0043-7182) **3475**, 2326
Wolf Park News. (US) **593**
Wolf Sanctuary Newsletter *see* Wolf Sanctuary Review **1501**
Wolf Sanctuary Review. (US) **1501**
Wolfenbuetteler Barock - Nachrichten. (GW ISSN 0340-6318) **2889**
Wolfenbuetteler Bibliotheks - Informationen. (GW ISSN 0931-4032) **2326**, 2791, 2976, 3394
▼Wolfenbuetteler Mittelalter Studien. (GW ISSN 0937-5724) **2395**
Wolfenbuetteler Notizen zur Buchgeschichte. (GW ISSN 0341-2253) **4138**
Wolfenbuetteler Renaissance Mitteilungen. (GW ISSN 0342-4340) **2395**, 2976
Wolfenbuetteler Studien zur Aufklaerung. Schriftenreihe. (GW) **2326**, 2976
Wolfenbuetteler Abhandlungen zur Renaissanceforschung. (GW ISSN 0724-956X) **2395**
Wolfenbuetteler Arbeiten zur Barockforschung. (GW ISSN 0724-472X) **2395**
Wolfenbuetteler Beitraege. (GW ISSN 0300-2012) **2791**
Wolfenbuetteler Forschungen. (GW ISSN 0724-9594) **2395**
Wolfenbuetteler Schriften zur Geschichte des Buchwesens. (GW ISSN 0724-9586) **4006**
Wolfe's Version. (US) **3934**, 700
Wolff's Guide to the London Metal Exchange. (US ISSN 0144-5960) **3423**, 1056
Wolfman Report on the Photographic Industry in the United States. (US ISSN 0084-103X) **3798**
Wolfpacker. (US) **4496**
Wolgan Konsol Mulka. *see* Construction Material Prices **613**
Wolgan Mot. (KO) **1295**
Wolkenridder. (NE ISSN 0043-7212) **4798**, 4678
Wolnosc i Lud. (PL ISSN 0137-3471) **2395**, 3934
Wolnuus/Wool News. (SA ISSN 0259-0182) **4627**
Wolverhampton Polytechnic Students' Union Handbook. (UK) **1331**
Wolverine. (US ISSN 1048-9940) **4496**
Woman. (UK ISSN 0043-7220) **4855**
The Woman. (CH) **4855**
†Woman. (US ISSN 0043-7239) **5305**
Woman A B C Magazine. (CH) **4855**
Woman Activist. (US ISSN 0049-7770) **3948**, 4855
Woman Alive. (UK ISSN 0962-2152) **4210**
Woman & Co. (US) **4855**
Woman and Home. (UK) **4855**

WOMAN'S NATIONAL 6811

Woman Boutique. (JA) **1295**
Woman Bowler. (US ISSN 0043-7255) **4515**, 4855
†Woman C P A. (US ISSN 0043-7271) **5305**
Woman Engineer. (UK ISSN 0043-7298) **1840**, 4855
Woman Engineer. (US ISSN 0887-2120) **1840**, 4855
Woman Entrepreneur. (US) **4855**
Woman in History. (US ISSN 0195-9743) **4855**, 2326
Woman of Mystery. (US ISSN 1042-1491) **2976**, 4860
Woman of Power. (US ISSN 0743-2356) **4855**, 349, 2976
Woman Poet. (US ISSN 0195-6183) **3009**, 4855
Womanews. (US) **4855**
Woman's Advocate *see* Woman's Weal **5305**
Woman's Affair. (SI) **4855**
Woman's Art Journal. (US ISSN 0270-7993) **350**, 4855
Woman's Building. Calendar. (US) **350**
Woman's Building Newsletter *see* Woman's Building. Calendar **350**
Woman's Day. (US ISSN 0043-7336) **2450**
Woman's Day. (AT ISSN 0043-7328) **4856**
Woman's Day (Year) Guide to Your Body, Your Health *see* Jenny Craig's Your Body, Your Health **3804**
Woman's Day Beautiful Brides. (US) **4856**
Woman's Day Best Ideas for Christmas. (US) **2283**
Woman's Day Christmas Crafts. (US) **3593**
Woman's Day Christmas Traditions. (US) **3593**
†Woman's Day Country Decorating. (US) **5305**
†Woman's Day Dessert Lover's Cookbook. (US) **5305**
Woman's Day Family Holiday Favorites *see* Woman's Day Family Traditions **2450**
Woman's Day Family Traditions. (US) **2450**
Woman's Day Gardening & Outdoor Living Ideas. (US) **2140**
Woman's Day Great Holiday Baking. (US) **2450**
Woman's Day Guide to Your Body Your Health. (US) **374**
Woman's Day Holiday Craft and Granny Square *see* Woman's Day Christmas Crafts **3593**
Woman's Day Home Decorating Ideas. (US ISSN 0361-638X) **2556**, 2562
Woman's Day Home Improvements. (US) **2556**
†Woman's Day House Plants. (US) **5305**
▼Woman's Day Kitchen & Bath New Product Ideas. (US) **2562**, 2556
Woman's Day Kitchens and Baths. (US) **2556**
Woman's Day Light Meals in Minutes. (US) **2450**
Woman's Day Make Yourself Beautiful and Healthy *see* Woman's Day Guide to Your Body Your Health **374**
Woman's Day Mother - Child. (US) **1246**, 3327, 3810
Woman's Day Simply Delicious Meals in Minutes *see* Woman's Day Light Meals in Minutes **2450**
Woman's Day Your Child's Health *see* Woman's Day Mother - Child **1246**
Woman's Day 101 Sweater and Craft Ideas *see* Woman's Day Christmas Traditions **3593**
Woman's Day 101 Ways to Lose Weight and Stay Healthy. (US) **3613**, 3811
†Woman's Enterprise. (US ISSN 0898-6126) **5305**
Woman's Era. (II) **4856**
Woman's Health Adviser. (US) **3162**, 4856
Woman's Journal. (UK ISSN 0043-7344) **4856**, 2450
Woman's Mirror. (KE) **4856**
Woman's National Farm & Garden Magazine. (US) **4856**

WOMAN'S NATIONAL

Woman's National Magazine see Woman's National Farm & Garden Magazine **4856**
Woman's Newspaper. (US) **4856**
Woman's Own. (UK ISSN 0043-7360) **4856**
Woman's Own Holiday Reading. (UK) **4856**
Woman's Realm. (UK ISSN 0043-7387) **4856**
Woman's Touch. (US ISSN 0190-4620) **4290, 4856**
Woman's Value. (SA) **4856**
Woman's Voice. see Sawt al-Mar'ah **4852**
Woman's Voice. (BB) **4856**
Woman's Voice. (US) **4856**
Woman's Way. (IE) **4856**
Woman's Way Weekly see Woman's Way **4856**
†Woman's Weal. (US) **5305**
Woman's Weekly. (UK ISSN 0043-7417) **4856**
Woman's World see Woman's Day **4856**
Woman's World. (US) **4856**
Woman's World. (NR ISSN 0331-4162) **4856**
Woman's World. see Zhinochyi Svit **4858**
†Woman's World. (UK) **5305**
Womansense. (US) **804**
Womanspeak. (AT) **4860**
Womanswear Resources. (UK ISSN 0958-5389) **1288**
†Wombat. (US ISSN 0279-361X) **5305**
Women. see Funu **4843**
Women/Yeo Sung. (KO) **4856**
†Women. (US) **5305**
▼Women: A Cultural Review. (UK ISSN 0957-4042) **4856**
Women Against Military Madness Newsletter see W A M M Newsletter **4855**
Women Against Rape Newsletter. (US) **4856, 4424**
Women Ai Kexue/We Love Science. (CC ISSN 0510-7148) **1271, 4352**
Women and Appropriate Technologies. (AT) **4615, 4858, 4860**
Women & Clothes. see Kvinner og Klaer **4846**
Women & Criminal Justice. (US ISSN 0897-4454) **2714, 4860**
Women and Environments. (CN ISSN 0229-480X) **4860, 1971, 4856**
Women & Guns. (US ISSN 1045-7704) **4496, 2695, 4856**
Women & Health. (US ISSN 0363-0242) **4836**
Women & Health Roundtable Reports. (US ISSN 0272-0515) **4836, 3811, 4856**
Women and International Development Annual. (US ISSN 1045-893X) **936, 4856**
Women and Language. (US ISSN 8755-4550) **2852, 4860**
Women & Literature. (US ISSN 0147-1759) **2976, 4860**
Women and Minorities in Science and Engineering. (US) **1840, 2029, 4352, 4856**
Women & Performance: A Journal of Feminist Theory. (US ISSN 0740-770X) **4642, 4856**
Women & Politics. (US ISSN 0195-7732) **3934, 4860**
Women and Politics (Westport). (US) **3934, 4856**
Women and Revolution. (US) **4856**
Women & Therapy. (US ISSN 0270-3149) **4050, 4836, 4860**
Women and Work. (AT) **997, 4856**
Women and Work (Newbury Park). (US ISSN 0882-0910) **997, 4856**
Women and Work (Washington). (US) **997, 4856**
Women Artist Newsletter see Women Artists News **350**
Women Artists News. (US ISSN 0149-7081) **350, 4856**
†Women at Work. (UN ISSN 0378-4770) **5305**
Women Directors of the Top 1000 Corporations. (US) **1031, 4856**

Women Executives International Tourism Association Exec see W E X I T A Exec **5302**
Women for Racial and Economic Equality View of Women see W R E E - View of Women **3948**
Women in a Changing World. (SZ) **4210, 4856**
Women in Action. (PH) **4856**
Women in B H I. (UK ISSN 0957-1663) **4861, 25, 2520, 2520, 2520**
Women in Broadcast Technology Directory. (US) **1345, 4856**
Women in Business. (US ISSN 0043-7441) **700, 4856**
Women in Context. (US) **4836, 4856**
Women in Context: Development and Stresses see Women in Context **4836**
Women in Culture and Society. (US) **4856, 4456**
Women in Libraries. (US) **2791, 4856**
Women in Management Review. (UK ISSN 0267-4602) **1031, 4856**
Women in Mining National Quarterly. (US) **3498, 4856**
Women in the Arts. (US) **350, 4856**
Women in the Arts Bulletin - Newsletter see Women in the Arts Newsletter **350**
Women in the Arts Newsletter. (US) **350, 4856**
Women in the Fire Service Quarterly see W F S Quarterly **2035**
Women Lawyers Journal. (US ISSN 0043-7468) **2695**
Women Library Workers Journal see W L W Journal **2790**
Women Marines Association Nouncements see W M A - Nouncements **3475**
Women of China. (CC) **4856**
Women of Europe see Supplements of Women of Europe **4853**
†Women of the Whole World. (GW ISSN 0043-7476) **5305**
Women of Vietnam. (VN ISSN 0512-1825) **4856**
Women on Wine Chapter Flyer. (US) **387, 4856**
Women on Wine National News. (US) **387, 4856**
Women Outdoors. (US) **4560, 4856**
Women Scope: Surveys of Women see Marketing to Women **1047**
†Women Strike for Peace. (US ISSN 0042-9864) **5305**
Women Strike for Peace. Legislative Alert. (US) **3948, 3977, 4856**
Women Studies Abstracts. (US ISSN 0049-7835) **4861, 25**
†Women Talking, Women Listening. (US) **5305**
Women Today. (US ISSN 0043-7506) **4856**
Women Unlimited. (US) **4857**
Women with Wheels. (US ISSN 1043-979X) **4706, 4857**
Women Writers of Italy. (US ISSN 1056-4535) **2976, 4857**
Women Writing Newsletter. (US) **2976, 4860**
WomeNews. (US) **4857**
Women's Accessories Buyers - New York Metropolitan Area. (US) **1288**
Women's Action for Nuclear Disarmament Bulletin see W A N D Bulletin **4855**
Women's Affairs. see Funu Gongzuo **4843**
Women's American O R T Reporter see The Reporter (New York) **4417**
Women's and Children's Clothing Industries see Canada. Statistics Canada. Clothing Industries **1288**
†Women's Annual. (US ISSN 0276-7988) **5305**
Womens Athletics see Athletics Weekly **4465**
Women's Caucus for Art. Honor Awards Catalogue. (US) **350, 4857**
Women's Caucus for Art. National Update. (US ISSN 1052-4959) **350, 4857**
Women's Caucus for Political Science Quarterly see W C P S Quarterly **3933**

Women's Circle. (US ISSN 0509-089X) **4857**
Women's Circle Counted Cross-Stitch see Cross-Stitch Plus **3590**
Women's Circle Country Needlecraft see Quick & Easy Crafts **3592**
Women's Circle Crochet. (US ISSN 0279-1978) **3593**
Women's Circle Home Cooking see Home Cooking **4844**
Women's Clubs Magazine. (IE) **4857, 1302**
Women's Coaching Clinic see Coaching Clinic **4502**
Women's Collection Newsletter. (US) **4857**
Women's Concerns Report. (US) **4857, 4210**
Women's Education/Education des Femmes. (CN ISSN 0714-9786) **4857, 1688**
Women's Electoral Lobby. National Bulletin see Ink W E L **4845**
Women's Electoral Lobby (South Australian) Newsletter. (AT ISSN 0310-9062) **4424, 4857**
Women's Electoral Lobby A.C.T. Ink W E L see Ink W E L **4845**
Women's Fastpitch World. (US ISSN 0899-5508) **4515**
Women's Friend. see Fujin no Tomo **1684**
Women's Friend. see Funu zhi You **4843**
Women's Graphic. see Fujin Gaho **2446**
Women's Graphic Beauty/Fujingaho Beauty. (JA) **374**
†Women's Health & Fitness News. (US) **5305**
▼Women's Health Issues. (US ISSN 1049-3867) **4836, 4857**
Women's Health Nursing Scan see N A C O G's Women's Health Nursing Scan **3178**
Women's History Network News. (US) **4857, 2427**
Women's History Resource Catalog. (US) **2427, 4857**
▼Women's History Review. (UK ISSN 0961-2025) **2395, 4857**
Women's Household. (US ISSN 0510-7385) **4857, 2450**
Women's Household Crochet. (US ISSN 0745-0575) **3593**
Women's Information Updates. (SZ) **4857, 2791**
Women's International League for Peace and Freedom. Program and Legislative Action. (US) **3934**
Women's International Network News see W I N News **4860**
Women's International Zionist Organization Review see W I Z O Review **4855**
Women's Intimate Apparel Buyers. (US ISSN 0043-7549) **1288**
Women's League Outlook. (US ISSN 0043-7557) **4227, 4857**
Women's Legal Defense Fund News see W L D F News **2693**
Women's Legal Education and Action Fund Lines see L E A F Lines **2642**
Women's Literature. see Nuzi Wenxue **2944**
Women's, Misses & Jr. Ready to Wear Buyers. (US) **1288**
Women's, Misses & Jr. Sportswear Buyers. (US) **1288**
Women's Music Plus. (US) **3586, 4857**
Women's Network. (US) **4857, 2458, 3586**
†Women's Network/Reseau Femmes. (CN) **5305**
Women's Network - Women in Music see Women's Network **4857**
Women's News. (NL ISSN 1017-3900) **4857**
Women's News. (US) **4857**
Women's Newsletter see Antisexism Newsletter **4837**
Women's Newsletter see Women's News **4857**
Women's Occupational Health Resource Center News see W O H R C News **5302**
Women's Organizations: A National Directory. (US) **4857**

Women's Organizations: A New York City Directory. (US) **4857**
Women's Organizations & Leaders Directory. (US ISSN 0092-6639) **4857**
Women's Outdoor Journal. (US) **4560, 4857**
Women's Pages Arizona see Women's Yellow Pages Arizona **1159**
Women's Physique World. (US) **4836**
Women's Political Times. (US ISSN 0195-1688) **3934, 4857**
Women's Public Opinion/Fujin Koron. (JA) **4857**
†Women's Quarterly Review. (US ISSN 0882-1135) **5305**
Women's Record. (US) **4857**
▼Women's Recovery Network. (US) **1540**
Women's Resource & Action Center. Newsletter. (US) **4857**
Women's Review of Books. (US ISSN 0738-1433) **2889, 4860**
Women's Rights to Women Leaders. (US) **4857**
Women's Sports and Fitness. (US ISSN 8750-653X) **4496, 4836, 4857**
†Women's Squash Rackets Association. Handbook. (UK) **5305**
Women's Studies (Champaign). (US) **4860**
Women's Studies (Lewiston). (US) **4860**
Women's Studies (New York). (US ISSN 0049-7878) **4861**
Women's Studies in Communication. (US ISSN 0749-1409) **4861**
▼Women's Studies Index (Year). (US ISSN 1058-6369) **4861, 25**
Women's Studies International Forum. (US ISSN 0277-5395) **4861**
Women's Studies Quarterly. (US ISSN 0732-1562) **4861**
†Women's Travel Connections. (US ISSN 0882-8458) **5305**
Women's Traveller. (US ISSN 1055-1905) **4798, 2458, 4857**
Women's View. (AT) **4857**
Women's Wear Daily. (US) **1288**
Women's Weekly. (KO) **4857**
Women's World. see Nuzi Shijie **4850**
Women's World. (US ISSN 0043-759X) **4857, 2029**
Women's World. (SZ) **4861**
Women's Yellow Pages. (US) **1159, 4857**
Women's Yellow Pages Arizona. (US) **1159, 4857**
Women's Zionist Council of South Africa. News and Views see Women's Zionist Organization of South Africa. News and Views **3934**
Women's Zionist Organization of South Africa. News and Views. (SA) **3934, 2029, 4227**
WomenWise. (US ISSN 0890-9695) **4836, 3297, 3811, 4857**
Womyn's Press. (US ISSN 0049-786X) **4857**
Wonder. (US) **3015**
▼Wonder: Observing & Confronting the Enigmas that Surround Us. (US ISSN 1057-2821) **4352, 4613**
Wonder Time. (US) **1271, 4253**
Wonderful West Virginia. (US ISSN 0030-7157) **1501, 2050, 4560**
Wonderscience. (US) **1271, 1190**
▼Wonen en Milieu - Vakmatig. (NE ISSN 0924-9826) **2499, 1971, 4096**
Wood. (US ISSN 0743-894X) **357**
Wood. see Drevo **639**
Wood see Timber Trades Journal and Wood Processing **2117**
Wood/Bois. (CN ISSN 1183-6652) **2118**
Wood & Equipment News. (UK ISSN 0043-7646) **640**
Wood and Fiber Science. (US ISSN 0735-6161) **2118**
Wood & Wood Products. (US ISSN 0043-7662) **2118**
Wood & Wood Products Reference Buying Guide. (US) **2118**
Wood & Wood Products Reference Data - Buying Guide see Wood & Wood Products Reference Buying Guide **2118**

Wood Based Panels International. (UK ISSN 0144-7238) **2118**, 3024
Wood Digest. (US ISSN 0746-1089) **2562**
Wood Duck. (CN ISSN 0049-7886) **4352**
Wood Finisher. (US) **640**, 2118
Wood Finishing Quarterly. (US) **640**
Wood Industries of New Mexico. (US) **2118**
Wood Information. *see* Drevarske Informacie **2112**
Wood Leader. (CN) **2118**, 1086
Wood Machinery Manufacturers of America. Buyer's Guide and Directory. (US) **2118**, 3024
Wood Machining News. (US) **640**
Wood 'n Energy *see* Hearth & Home **1790**
Wood Post *see* Wood **2118**
Wood Products Design Focus. (US) **2118**
Wood Products: International Trade and Foreign Markets. (US) **160**, 924, 1056, 2118
Wood Research. *see* Drevarsky Vyskum **2114**
Wood Research/Mokuzai Kenkyu. (JA ISSN 0049-7916) **2118**
Wood Science and Technology. (GW ISSN 0043-7719) **2118**
Wood Southern Africa. (SA ISSN 0256-7172) **2111**, 2119
Wood - Woods Family Magazine. (US ISSN 0091-6706) **2168**
†Woodall's Campground Directory. Arizona, New Mexico Edition. (US) **5305**
†Woodall's Campground Directory. Arkansas, Missouri Edition. (US ISSN 0163-5328) **5306**
†Woodall's Campground Directory. California, Nevada, Mexico Edition. (US) **5306**
†Woodall's Campground Directory. Colorado Edition. (US ISSN 0163-5344) **5306**
†Woodall's Campground Directory. Delaware, Maryland, Virginia, District of Columbia Edition. (US) **5306**
Woodall's Campground Directory. Eastern Edition. (US ISSN 0162-7406) **1159**, 4560
†Woodall's Campground Directory. Florida Edition. (US) **5306**
†Woodall's Campground Directory. Idaho, Oregon, Washington, British Columbia Edition. (US) **5306**
†Woodall's Campground Directory. Illinois, Indiana Edition. (US ISSN 0163-2485) **5306**
†Woodall's Campground Directory. Kentucky, Tennessee Edition. (US ISSN 0163-5336) **5306**
†Woodall's Campground Directory. Michigan Edition. (US ISSN 0163-0121) **5306**
†Woodall's Campground Directory. Minnesota, Wisconsin Edition. (US) **5306**
†Woodall's Campground Directory. New England States Edition. (US ISSN 0163-0083) **5306**
†Woodall's Campground Directory. New Jersey, Ohio, Pennsylvania Editions. (US) **5306**
†Woodall's Campground Directory. New York Edition. (US) **5306**
Woodall's Campground Directory. North American Edition. (US) **1159**, 4560
†Woodall's Campground Directory. North Carolina, South Carolina Edition. (US ISSN 0163-5352) **5306**
†Woodall's Campground Directory. Ontario Edition. (US ISSN 0163-240X) **5306**
†Woodall's Campground Directory. Texas, Mexico Edition. (US) **5306**
Woodall's Campground Directory. Western Edition. (US ISSN 0162-7414) **1159**, 4560
Woodall's R V Buyer's Guide. (US) **4661**
†Woodall's Senior Exchange. (US ISSN 0163-4321) **5306**
Woodall's Tent Camping Guide. (US) **1159**, 4560

Woodall's Campground Directory *see* Woodall's Campground Directory. Western Edition **1159**
Woodall's Campground Directory *see* Woodall's Campground Directory. Eastern Edition **1159**
Woodall's Campground Directory. Florida Campgrounds Edition *see* Woodall's Campground Directory. Florida Edition **5306**
Woodall's Campground Directory. North American - Canadian Edition *see* Woodall's Campground Directory. North American Edition **1159**
Woodall's Campground Management *see* Campground Management **4542**
Woodall's Tenting Directory *see* Woodall's Tent Camping Guide **1159**
The Woodbook. (US) **641**
Woodbridge Lectures, Columbia University. (US) **3786**
▼Woodcrafts. (US) **350**, 641
Wooden Bell. (US) **4424**
WoodenBoat. (US ISSN 0095-067X) **4531**
Woodheat Woodstove Directory *see* Winter Living **5305**
Woodland Report. (US ISSN 0279-9812) **2111**
The Woodlands Forum. (US) **3934**
Woodmen of the World Magazine. (US ISSN 0043-7751) **2545**
Woodpecker. *see* Zhuomuniao **2980**
†Woodrider. (US) **5306**
Woodrow Wilson Birthplace Newsletter. (US) **3535**, 2427
Woodrow Wilson International Center for Scholars. Annual Report. (US ISSN 0092-4261) **1724**
Woodrow Wilson National Fellowship Foundation. Annual Report. (US ISSN 0084-1145) **1720**
Woodrow Wilson National Fellowship Foundation. Newsletter. (US ISSN 0084-1137) **1720**
Woods Hole Folk Music Society Newsletter. (US) **1532**
Woodshop News. (US ISSN 0894-5403) **641**
Woodsman *see* Woodsman Newsletter **2111**
Woodsman Newsletter. (UG) **2111**
Woodsmith. (US ISSN 0164-4114) **641**
†Woodsmith Sourcebook. (US) **5306**
Woodstock Series. (US ISSN 0891-9585) **3586**
▼Woodturning. (UK) **641**
Woodwork. (US) **2501**
Woodworker. (UK ISSN 0043-776X) **641**
Woodworker/Houtwerker. (SA) **641**
Woodworker. (US) **2591**, 641
Woodworker Annual *see* Woodworker **641**
Woodworker Projects & Techniques. (US) **2443**
Woodworker's Journal. (US ISSN 0199-1892) **2501**, 641
Woodworking. (UK) **641**
Woodworking. (CN ISSN 0838-4185) **641**, 2119
Woodworking Crafts *see* Woodworking **641**
Woodworking Industry. *see* Traeindustrin **641**
†Woodworking Industry - Buyers' Guide. (UK) **5306**
Woodworking International *see* Woodworking **641**
Woodworking International. (GW ISSN 0177-7114) **2119**, 3667
Woodworking Plans, Projects and Designs *see* Woodworking **641**
Woodworking Review. (GW) **2111**
Woodworking Today. (UK) **641**
†Wool. (NZ) **5306**
Wool and Woolens of India. (II ISSN 0043-7808) **4627**
Wool & Woollen. (II) **4627**
Wool Gathering *see* Elizabeth Zimmermann's Wool Gathering **3591**
Wool Market News. (AT) **4627**
Wool News. (II ISSN 0043-7824) **4627**
Wool News. *see* Wolnuus **4627**

Wool Quarterly. (UK) **4627**, 1056
Wool Record. (UK) **4627**
Wool Record and Textile World *see* Wool Record **4627**
Wool Record Weekly Market Report. (UK) **4627**
Wool Research Organisation of New Zealand. Special Publications. (NZ ISSN 0112-2754) **4627**
Wool Research Organisation of New Zealand Communications. (NZ ISSN 0112-2908) **4627**
Wool Research Organisation of New Zealand Reports. (NZ ISSN 0112-2851) **4627**
Wool Review. (AT ISSN 0084-1218) **4627**
Wool Sack. (US ISSN 0043-7840) **4627**
Wool Science Review. (UK ISSN 0043-7859) **4627**
Wool Technology and Sheep Breeding. (AT ISSN 0043-7875) **228**, 4627
Woolgrower. (AT) **4627**
Woolhope Naturalists' Field Club, Herefordshire. Transactions. (UK ISSN 0084-1226) **289**, 460
Woollens & Worsteds of India. (II ISSN 0043-7883) **4627**
Woolner Indological Series. (II ISSN 0084-1242) **3786**, 2976
Woonwapark, Kamper and Voetslaangids vir Suider-Afrika. *see* Caravan Park, Camping & Backpacking Guide to Southern Africa **4543**
Woord en Dienst. (NE) **4210**
Woord en Gebaar. (NE) **2290**
Wooster. (US) **1331**
Wooster Alumni Magazine *see* Wooster **1331**
Wooster Review. (US) **2976**
Worcester and Hereford Business. (UK) **824**
Worcester Medicine. (US) **3162**
Worcester Polytechnic Institute. Journal *see* W P I Journal **1840**
Worcester Polytechnic Institute - Studies in Science, Technology and Culture. (US ISSN 0897-926X) **4352**, 4613
Worcester Public Library Staff Newsletter. (US) **2791**
Worcester Review. (US ISSN 8756-5277) **3009**
Worcestershire Archaeological Newsletter *see* Worcestershire Archaeology and Local History Newsletter **289**
Worcestershire Archaeological Society. Transactions. (UK ISSN 0143-2389) **289**
Worcestershire Archaeology and Local History Newsletter. (UK ISSN 0143-4659) **289**
Worcestershire Farmer & Record. (UK) **130**
Worcestershire Record *see* Worcestershire Farmer & Record **130**
Worcestershire Recusant. (UK) **4279**, 2395
Word. (II ISSN 0043-7948) **1345**
The Word. (US) **1779**
Word *see* Library Pointes **2770**
Word. (US ISSN 0043-7956) **2852**
The Word. (US ISSN 0740-6754) **3597**
The Word Among Us. (US ISSN 0742-4639) **4279**
Word and Deed. (US) **3224**, 4210
Word & Image. (UK ISSN 0266-6286) **2889**
†Word & Image. (US) **5306**
†Word & Information Processing. (UK) **5306**
Word & Spirit. (US ISSN 0193-9211) **4279**
Word and Way. (US ISSN 0049-7959) **4253**
Word & Witness. (US) **4253**
Word & World. (US ISSN 0275-5270) **4253**
Word and Writing. *see* Slovo a Slovesnost **2841**
Word Art. *see* Umjetnost Rijeci **2971**
Word at Work. (UK) **4253**
Word for Word. (US ISSN 0896-7717) **1481**, 1482

Word from Washington. (US ISSN 0738-8012) **1742**
Word in Action. (UK) **4210**
Word in Life. (AT ISSN 0155-6894) **4279**, 4290
Word in Season. (US) **4210**
Word of Mouth (San Antonio). (US ISSN 1048-3950) **1742**
Word of Mouth (San Francisco). (US) **3244**
Word of Salvation. (AT ISSN 0813-7951) **4210**
Word on... (US) **1732**, 2695
Word on Guard. *see* Slovo na Storozhi **2842**
Word One. (US) **4210**
Word Processing News *see* Observer (Aptos) **1060**
†Word Processing News. (US) **5306**
Word Processing Quality Clinic. (US ISSN 0895-0628) **1062**
Word Progress. (US) **2705**, 1481
Word Up! (US) **3586**, 1271
Word Ways. (US ISSN 0043-7980) **2852**
Word Wrap. (US) **4138**, 1345, 2976
▼WordPerfect for Windows. (US) **1482**, 1481
▼WordPerfect for Windows Magazine. (US) **1482**, 1481
WordPerfect Magazine. (US ISSN 1042-5152) **828**
WordPerfect Report. (US ISSN 1053-9638) **828**
Words of L I F E. (Living in Freedom Eternally, Inc.) (US) **4210**
Words of Wisdom. (US ISSN 0258-0276) **2029**, 2060, 2238, 4798
†Words of Women. (US) **5306**
Words on Cassette (Year). (US) **416**
Words on Tape *see* Words on Cassette (Year) **416**
Wordstar Scroll. (US ISSN 0890-524X) **1482**
Wordsworth Circle. (US ISSN 0043-8006) **2976**
Wordwatching. (US ISSN 0731-9290) **2852**
▼Work (Reading). (US ISSN 1051-9815) **3623**
Work Accomplished by the Inter-American Juridical Committee during its Meeting. (US ISSN 0074-0837) **2695**
Work and Occupations. (US ISSN 0730-8884) **4456**, 4050
Work and Patrol Boat World *see* Work Boat World **4742**
Work and People. (AT ISSN 0312-455X) **1071**
Work and Stress. (UK ISSN 0267-8373) **4050**, 1071, 3623
†Work-At-Home Report. (US) **5306**
Work-at-Home Sourcebook. (US) **3631**, 1119, 2450
Work Boat World. (AT) **4742**
Work Dynamics. (US ISSN 0884-9420) **1031**, 1071, 1345
Work, Employment & Society. (UK ISSN 0950-0170) **4456**
Work - Environment - Health *see* Scandinavian Journal of Work, Environment & Health **3622**
Work - Health - Safety. *see* Tyo - Terveys - Turvallisuus **3622**
Work in America. (US ISSN 0892-5488) **997**, 1031
Work in Progress. (SA) **3948**, 2591, 4456
†Work Life Review. (US) **5306**
†Work of the European Parliament. (LU) **5306**
Work Programs. (US) **3631**, 3162
Work Related Abstracts. (US ISSN 0273-3234) **743**, 25
†Work Stoppages in New York State. (US) **5306**
Work Study. (UK ISSN 0043-8022) **1031**
Work Study and Management Services *see* Management Services **1020**
Work Study and O and M Abstracts *see* Management Services & Production Abstracts **728**
Work Times. (US ISSN 0736-9166) **888**, 997, 1071, 3631

WORK-YEARS

Work-Years and Personnel Costs. Executive Branch of the United States Government see Federal Civilian Work Force Statistics. Work Years and Personnel Costs. Executive Branch, United States Government **715**
Workamper News. (US ISSN 0895-3678) **3631, 4798**
Workbasket. (US ISSN 0162-9123) **3593**
Workbench. (US ISSN 0043-8057) **2501**
WorkBoat. (US ISSN 0043-8014) **4742, 4531**
▼Workboat Directory. (US) **4742**
Workboat International. (UK) **4742**
Workbook. (US ISSN 0195-4636) **1975, 2890**
Worker. see Travailleur **2590**
Worker Writer. (UK ISSN 0143-2745) **2889**
Workers. see Kulloja **2585**
Workers' Advocate. (US ISSN 0276-363X) **3934, 997**
Workers' Advocate Supplement. (US ISSN 0882-6366) **3934**
Workers' Challenge. (ZA) **997, 4279**
Worker's Compensation see Worker's Compensation Law Bulletin **997**
Workers' Compensation Journal of Ohio.(US ISSN 0886-9162) **4077, 2695**
Worker's Compensation Law Bulletin. (US ISSN 0748-7878) **997**
Workers' Compensation Law Reporter. (US) **2545, 3623**
Worker's Compensation Law Review. (US) **2545, 2695**
Workers' Compensation Laws of California. (US ISSN 0748-4135) **2695, 997, 2545**
Workers Compensation N S W. (AT) **997, 2695**
Workers Defense Bulletin see W D L News **997**
Workers Defense League, Inc. News see W D L News **997**
Worker's Democracy. (US) **3935, 2591**
Workers Education Association. Women's Studies Newsletter. (UK ISSN 0260-6127) **4857**
Workers Education Journal. (II) **1688, 997**
Workers' Educational Association News see W E A News **1671**
Worker's Educational Association Southern District Journal see W E A Southern District Journal **5302**
Worker's Herald. see Ergatiko Vima **979**
Workers Life. (IE) **3935**
Workers Time. (JM) **3935**
†Workers Tribune/Tribuna Obrera. (US) **5306**
Workers Vanguard. (US) **3935**
Worker's Voice. see Ergatiki Phoni **979**
Worker's Voice. see Sawt Al Ummal **2589**
Workers Voice. (ZA) **2592**
Workers Weekly see Tribune **5292**
†Workers Weekly. (UK) **5306**
Workers World. (US ISSN 0043-809X) **3935**
Workforce. (AT) **997**
Working Abroad (London). (UK) **997, 4798**
Working Abroad (London, 1977). (UK) **804**
Working at Home. (US) **1119, 4857**
The Working Border Collie. (US) **3714, 228**
Working Class. (II ISSN 0377-6611) **2592**
Working Class Hero. (US) **1302**
Working Class Opposition/Oposicion Obrera. (US) **3935**
Working Classics. (US ISSN 0886-8484) **2889**
Working Conditions in British Columbia Industry see British Columbia. Ministry of Labour and Consumer Services. Negotiated Working Conditions **974**
Working Country see Delmarva Country **86**
Working Craftsman see Crafts Report **354**

Working Environment. see Arbeidsomstandigheden **3614**
Working Environment. (SW) **4115**
Working for Yourself. (UK) **997**
Working Guide to the Tennessee Business Corporation Act. (US) **2695**
Working Holidays (Year). (UK) **4798**
Working Journalist. (II) **2576**
Working Kelpie Council. National Stud Book. (AT ISSN 0312-3480) **232**
Working Life in Sweden see Viewpoint Sweden **2218**
Working Moms and Dads. (US) **1246**
Working Mother (New York). (US ISSN 0278-193X) **4857, 2450**
Working on Wife Abuse see Battered Women's Directory **4838**
Working Papers in African Studies. (US) **4392, 2335**
Working Papers in Applied Linguistics see Ohio University. Working Papers in Linguistics and Language Teaching **2832**
Working Papers in Business. (US) **744**
Working Papers in Irish Studies. (US ISSN 0732-2674) **2029**
Working Papers on Caribbean Society. Series A: New Perspectives in Theory and Analysis. (TR) **4456**
Working Papers on Caribbean Society. Series C: Research Findings. (TR) **4456**
Working Papers on Women in International Development. (US ISSN 0888-5354) **936, 130, 4456, 4857**
Working Parents. (US) **2450, 1246**
Working - Party Reports. (BE) **3977, 888**
Working Press of the Nation. (US ISSN 0084-1323) **2576**
Working Smart. (US ISSN 0749-6532) **1031**
†Working Symposium on Oceanographic Data Systems. Proceedings. (US) **5306**
Working Title. (CN) **2976**
Working Together. (US) **1071**
Working Together for a Greater Yakima see Chamber Update **811**
Working Together Nationally. (AT) **4210**
Working Woman. (US ISSN 0145-5761) **4858**
Worklife Report. (CN ISSN 0834-292X) **997, 1071, 3623**
Workmen's Circle Call. (US ISSN 0043-8111) **2029**
Workmens' Compensation Law Review see Worker's Compensation Law Review **2545**
Workmen's Compensation Reporter see British Columbia. Workers' Compensation Board. Workers' Compensation Reporter **2528**
WORKout. (GW) **1475**
†WorkOut. (US) **5306**
Workplace. (AT ISSN 1036-5117) **2592**
Workplace Democracy. (US ISSN 0738-6044) **997, 1031**
Workplace Hazardous Materials Information Systems Compliance Manual see W H M I S Compliance Manual **3623**
Workplace Health and Safety Manual. (AT) **3623**
Workplace Health Safety and Liability Report see Occupational Health & Safety Letter **3619**
Workplace in the Community. (US) **4424**
▼Workplace Trends. (US ISSN 1047-4447) **1071**
Workprint. (CN) **833**
Works. (UK ISSN 0954-3902) **3015**
Works and Days. (US ISSN 0886-2060) **2976, 2518**
Works and Housing Bulletin. see Nashrat Al-Iskan wal-Ashghal **4067**
Works by Japanese Composers (Year). (JA) **3586**
Works Management. (UK ISSN 0374-4795) **1031**
†Works News. (NZ) **5306**
Workshop. (US ISSN 0895-4372) **1402**

Workshop Equipment News see O E M Newsletter **163**
†Workshop Masters. (UK) **5306**
Workshop Notes Washington, D.C. Textile Museum see Textile Museum Journal **4626**
Workshop on Color Aerial Photography in the Plant Sciences. Proceedings. (US ISSN 0197-3444) **3798**
†Workshop on Computer Architecture for Pattern Analysis and Machine Intelligence. (US) **5306**
Workshop on Software Testing. Proceedings see Workshop on Software Testing, Verification, and Analysis. Proceedings **5306**
†Workshop on Software Testing, Verification, and Analysis. Proceedings. (US) **5306**
Worksop Trader. (UK) **2196**
Workstation. (US) **1424**
Workstation Magazine. (US ISSN 0896-212X) **1402, 1455**
▼Workstation News. (US) **828**
Workstations (International). (US) **1429**
Workstations & Servers. (US) **1352**
World. see Sekai **3924**
World (Boston). (US) **4253**
The World (New York). (US ISSN 0043-8154) **3009**
World Accounting Report. (UK) **757**
World Acrobatics. (AT) **4496**
World Adventure Trip Catalogue see A Y H Discovery Tours **4750**
World Advertising Expenditures. (US ISSN 0568-0301) **39**
World Advertising Review. (UK) **40**
World Aerospace Technology. (UK ISSN 0959-0846) **65**
World Affairs. (NZ ISSN 0043-8189) **3935**
World Affairs. see Shijie Zhishi **3972**
World Affairs. (US ISSN 0043-8200) **3977**
World Affairs Pictorial. see Shijie Zhishi Huabao **2183**
World Affairs Report. (US ISSN 0090-7103) **3977**
World Affairs Review. (UK) **969**
World Agenda see Agenda World **4751**
World Agricultural Economics and Rural Sociology Abstracts. (UK ISSN 0043-8219) **145, 25, 4458**
World Agricultural Regional Supplement: Africa and the Middle East see World Agriculture Regional Supplement: Middle East and North Africa **160**
World Agricultural Situation. (US ISSN 0084-1358) **160**
World Agricultural Supply and Demand Estimates. (US ISSN 0162-5586) **160**
World Agriculture. see Shijie Nongye **119**
World Agriculture, Forestry and Fisheries. see Sekai no Norinsuisan **119**
World Agriculture - I F A P News. (FR) **130**
World Agriculture Regional Supplement: East Asia see World Agriculture Regional Supplement: East Asia and Oceania **160**
World Agriculture Regional Supplement: East Asia and Oceania. (US) **160**
World Agriculture Regional Supplement: Eastern Europe. (US) **160**
World Agriculture Regional Supplement: Latin America see World Agriculture Regional Supplement: Western Hemisphere **160**
World Agriculture Regional Supplement: Middle East and North Africa. (US) **160**
World Agriculture Regional Supplement: South Asia. (US) **160**
World Agriculture Regional Supplement: Southeast Asia. (US) **160**
World Agriculture Regional Supplement: Soviet Union see World Agriculture Regional Supplement: U S S R **160**
World Agriculture Regional Supplement: Subsaharan Africa. (US) **160**
World Agriculture Regional Supplement: U S S R. (US) **160**
World Agriculture Regional Supplement: Western Europe. (US) **160**

World Agriculture Regional Supplement: Western Hemisphere. (US) **160**
World Air Transport Statistics. (SZ ISSN 0084-1366) **4668, 4678**
World Airline Cooperation Review. (CN) **4678**
World Airline Fleets Handbook see Air-Britain Airline Fleets **4669**
World Airline Fleets Monthly see World Airline Fleets News **4678**
World Airline Fleets News. (UK ISSN 0951-8673) **4678**
▼World Airline News. (US) **4678**
World Airline Record. (US ISSN 0084-1374) **4678**
World Airline Record Newsletter see Airline Newsletter **4670**
World Airnews. (SA ISSN 0261-2399) **65**
World Airshow News. (US ISSN 0888-5265) **65**
World Alliance of Y M C A's Directory. (SZ ISSN 0513-6032) **1302, 1246**
World Almanac and Book of Facts. (US ISSN 0084-1382) **1782**
World Almanac Consumer Information Series. (US) **1508**
World Almanac Guide to Pro Hockey. (US ISSN 0095-7240) **4497**
World Aluminium. (US ISSN 0951-2233) **3423**
World Aluminium Databook see World Aluminium **3423**
World Aluminum Abstracts. (US ISSN 0002-6697) **3429, 25**
World Amateur Golf Council. Record Book. (US) **4515**
The World & I. (US ISSN 0887-9346) **2238**
World and United States Aviation and Space Records. (US) **65**
World Animal Health. (FR ISSN 1017-3102) **4819**
World Animal Science. (NE) **593, 4819**
World Aquaculture. (US ISSN 0735-0147) **1612**
†World Aquaculture Society. Proceedings. (US) **5306**
†World Aquaculture Society. Special Publications. (US) **5306**
World Arab Trade. (TS) **924**
▼World Arbitration & Mediation Report.(UK ISSN 0960-0949) **2695, 997**
World Archaeological Society. Special Publication. (US) **289**
World Archaeological Society Newsletter see W.A.S. Newsletter **289**
World Archaeology. (UK ISSN 0043-8243) **289**
World Architecture. (UK ISSN 0956-9758) **308**
World Architecture Herald. see Shijie Jianzhu Daobao **306**
World Armaments and Disarmament: S I P R I Yearbook see S I P R I Yearbook: World Armaments and Disarmament **3971**
World Armored Vehicle Inventory & Forecast. (US ISSN 1040-2888) **3475**
World Aromatics and Derivatives. (US) **1190**
World Around You. (US ISSN 0199-8293) **2290**
World Around You. Teacher's Edition. (US) **2290**
World Art. see Shijie Meishu **343**
World Assembly of Youth Forum see W A Y Forum **1269**
World Association for Christian Communication. Journal see Media Development **1376**
World Association for Educational Research. Communicationes see Communicationes **1622**
World Association for Educational Research. Congress Reports. (BE) **1672**
World Association of Document Examiners Exchange see W A D E Exchange **1524**
The World At Large. (US) **2238, 2296**
World Auto Forecast Report. (US) **4706**
World Automotive Market. (US) **4706**

World Aviation Directory. (US ISSN 0043-826X) 65
World Badminton. (UK ISSN 0255-4429) 4497
World Bank. Abstracts of Current Studies. (UN ISSN 0253-9535) 744
World Bank. Annual Report. (UN ISSN 0252-2942) 937
World Bank. Monthly Operational Summary. (UN ISSN 0379-8674) 937
World Bank. Publications Update. (UN) 937
▼The World Bank and the Environment.(US ISSN 1014-8132) 924, 1971
World Bank Atlas. (UN ISSN 0512-2457) 937
World Bank Catalog. Accession List see World Bank. Publications Update 937
World Bank Economic Review. (UN ISSN 0258-6770) 888
World Bank Publications. Index see World Bank. Publications Update 937
World Bank Research News. (UN) 937
World Bank Research Observer. (UN ISSN 0257-3032) 804
World Bank Research Program see World Bank. Abstracts of Current Studies 744
World Banking Abstracts. (UK ISSN 0265-9484) 804, 744
World Baseball. (US ISSN 1040-5216) 4515
World Beer Review. (US) 387
World Bibliography of Bibliographies of Bibliographies. (AT) 416
World Bibliography of Social Security/ Bibliographie Universelle de Securite Sociale. (SZ ISSN 0006-1476) 744, 416
World Biolicensing Report. (US ISSN 0883-5527) 470, 3163
World Birdwatch. (UK) 568, 1501
World Book Health and Medical Annual. (US ISSN 0890-4480) 1782, 3163, 3811
†World Book Industry. (UK) 5306
World Book Year Book. (US ISSN 0084-1439) 1782
World Books. see Shijie Tushu 4137
World Bowhunters. (US) 4560
World Bowls Magazine. (UK ISSN 0043-8278) 4515
World Boxing. (US) 4497
World Broadcast News. (US) 1384
World Buiatrics Congress. (BE) 4819, 228
World Bulk Fleet. (NO ISSN 0801-5007) 4742
World Bulk Trades. (NO ISSN 0801-4086) 4742
World Bureau of Metal Statistics. Annual Report. (UK) 3429
World Business Opportunities - Consultants News. (II) 924
World Calendar. (US ISSN 0263-7987) 3394, 3423
World Call see Disciple (St. Louis) 4174
World Cartography. (UN ISSN 0084-1471) 2266
World Cement. (UK ISSN 0263-6050) 636
World Cement Directory. (BE) 636
World Cement Technology see World Cement 636
World Ceramic Abstracts. (UK ISSN 0957-8897) 1167, 25
World Ceramics & Refractories. (UK ISSN 0959-6127) 1167
World Chamber of Commerce Directory.(US ISSN 1048-2849) 824
World Children. see Shijie Ertong 1244
World Choral Census. (US) 3586
World Christian. (US ISSN 0743-2399) 4210
World Christian News. (NE) 4279
World Chronology Series. (US ISSN 0886-4276) 2326, 3935
World Cinema. (UK ISSN 0269-2600) 3519
World Citizen News. (US) 2730, 3977

▼World Class Entertainment. (US) 4858
†World Climate Change Report. (UK ISSN 0957-9370) 5306
World Coal see World Mining Equipment 3498
World Coal Letter see International Coal Letter 1799
World Coal Trade see International Coal 3485
World Coffee & Tea. (US ISSN 0043-8340) 2084, 924
World Cogeneration. (US) 1797, 1911
World Coin News. (US ISSN 0145-9090) 3602
World Collections News. (IT) 3602, 3759
World Collectors Annuary. (NE ISSN 0084-1498) 350
World Commerce Annual. (II ISSN 0084-1501) 924
World Commodity Forecasts. (UK) 700
World Commodity Outlook. (UK) 924, 969
World Communication. (US ISSN 0882-4088) 1345
World Communique. (SZ) 1246
World Competition. (SZ ISSN 1011-4548) 2730
World Confederation of Labour. Information Bulletin see Labor Press and Information 2585
World Confederation of Organizations of the Teaching Profession Biennial Report see W C O T P Biennial Report 1732
World Conference on Animal Production. Proceedings. (UY ISSN 0084-1552) 228
World Conference on Religion and Peace Report see W C R P Report 5302
World Conference on Tin. Proceedings. (UK) 3423
World Congress in Public Park Administration. Programme see Congress in Park and Recreation Administration. Programme 3391
World Congress in Public Park Administration. Reports see Congress in Park and Recreation Administration. Reports 4544
World Congress of Psychiatry. Proceedings. (AU ISSN 0084-1609) 3356
World Congress of the Deaf. Lectures and Papers see World Congress of the W F D. Proceedings 2290
World Congress of the Deaf. Proceedings. (IT ISSN 0510-8292) 2290
World Congress of the W F D. Proceedings. (World Federation of the Deaf) (IT) 2290
World Congress on Fertility and Sterility. Proceedings. (IE ISSN 0084-1641) 460
World Congress on the Prevention of Occupational Accidents and Diseases. Proceedings. (SZ ISSN 0084-165X) 3623
World Construction see International Construction 1868
World Consumer. (NE) 1508
World Copper Databook. (US ISSN 0950-2262) 3498
World Copper Survey see World Copper Databook 3498
World Cotton Markets Review. (PK) 4627
World Cotton Situation. (US) 196, 160
World Council for Curriculum and Instruction Forum see W C C I Forum 1724
World Council for Gifted and Talented Children. Yearbook. (US) 1742, 4050
World Council of Churches. Faith and Order Papers see Faith and Order Papers 4177
World Council of Churches. General Assembly. Assembly - Reports. (SZ ISSN 0084-1676) 4210
World Council of Churches. Minutes and Reports of the Central Committee Meeting. (SZ ISSN 0084-1684) 4210

World Council of Churches. Office of Education. Education Newsletter. (SZ) 4210
World Council of Churches Background Information see C C I A Background Information 4167
World Council of Comparative Education Societies. Newsletter/Conseil Mondial des Societes d'Education Comparee. Bulletin d'Information. (UK) 1672
World Council of Credit Unions. Statistical Report & Directory. (US) 804, 744
World Council of Credit Unions. Technical Reporter. (US) 804
World Council of Enterostomal Therapists Journal. (AT ISSN 0819-4610) 3270
World Council of Indigenous Peoples. Newsletter. (CN) 3948, 253
World Council of Service Clubs. Minutes of the General Meeting. (NZ) 4424
World Council of Young Men's Service Clubs. Minutes of the General Meeting see World Council of Service Clubs. Minutes of the General Meeting 4424
World Country Reports Service. (US) 3935
World Cultural Guides. (US) 4798, 308, 350
World Currency Yearbook. (US ISSN 0743-5363) 804
World C4 Hydrocarbons and Derivatives. (US) 1190
World Data Center A for Glaciology (Snow and Ice). New Accessions List. (US) 1552
World Debt Tables. (UN ISSN 0253-2859) 937
World Development. (US ISSN 0305-750X) 937
World Development Report. (US ISSN 0163-5085) 937
World Directory of Environmental Organizations. (US ISSN 0092-0908) 1501, 1972
World Directory of Fertilizer Manufacturers. (UK) 196
World Directory of Fertilizer Products. (UK) 196
World Directory of Human Rights Teaching and Research. (UN) 1159, 1672, 3948
World Directory of Liner Shipping Agents. (UK ISSN 0951-5879) 1160, 924, 4742
World Directory of Mathematicians. (US ISSN 0512-2740) 3061
World Directory of Multinational Enterprises. (UK) 1160
World Directory of Peace Research and Training Institutions. (UN) 3977
World Directory of Social Science Institutions. (UN) 4396, 25
World Directory of Stock Exchanges. (UK) 969
World Directory of Teaching and Research Institutions in International Law. (UN) 2730, 1672
†World Directory of Travel Agencies. (FR ISSN 0070-6515) 5306
World Dredging and Marine Construction see World Dredging - Mining & Construction 1876
World Dredging - Mining & Construction. (US ISSN 1045-0343) 1876
World Drink Report see World Food & Drink Report 2084
World Drug Market Manual. (UK) 3746
World Eagle. (US ISSN 0193-7871) 4392, 1763, 2266
World Economic Herald. see Shijie Jingji Daobao 5276
†World Economic History. (US) 5306
†World Economic Monitor. (US ISSN 0896-2545) 5306
World Economic Outlook. (US ISSN 0256-6877) 888
World Economic Review. (US) 937, 3935
World Economic Service. (BE) 700
World Economic Survey. (UN ISSN 0084-1714) 888
World Economics Translations. see Shijie Jingji Yicong 691

WORLD FERTILITY 6815

The World Economy. (UK ISSN 0378-5920) 700, 924
World Economy Monthly. see Shijie Jingji 1000
World Economy Research. see Shijie Jingji Yanjiu 1000
World Economy Survey. see Pregled Svetske Privrede 879
†World Education Reports. (US ISSN 0300-7006) 5306
World Electronic Developments. (US ISSN 0740-3585) 1779
World Electronics Companies File. (UK ISSN 0951-5747) 1160, 1779
World Energy and Nuclear Directory (Year). (UK) 1797, 1810
World Energy Conference. Directory of Energy Information Centres in the World. (FR) 1160, 1797
World Energy Conference. Plenary Conferences. Transactions. (FR ISSN 0084-1722) 1797
World Energy Conference. Survey of Energy Resources. (UK ISSN 0084-1730) 1797
World Energy Directory see World Energy and Nuclear Directory (Year) 1797
†World Energy Survey. (US) 5307
World Englishes. (US ISSN 0883-2919) 2852, 1672
World Epidemiology Review see Worldwide Report: Epidemiology 4115
World Ethylene and Derivatives. (US) 1190
World Executive's Digest. (PH ISSN 0115-4842) 1031
World Export Processing Zones Association Newsletter see W E P Z A Newsletter 924
World Factbook. (US ISSN 0277-1527) 3977
World Fairs Guide. (II) 1056
World Faiths Encounter. (US) 4210
World Faiths Insight see World Faiths Encounter 4210
World Farmers' Times. (FR) 130
World Farming Agrimanagement see Agribusiness Worldwide 146
World Federalist see Transnational Perspectives 3974
World Federalist Newsletter. (US) 3977
World Federation. (II ISSN 0043-8448) 3977
World Federation for Mental Health. Newsletter. (US) 4050, 4115
World Federation of Democratic Youth News see W F D Y News 1269
World Federation of Health Agencies for the Advancement of Voluntary Surgical Contraception. Communique.(US) 598
World Federation of Teachers' Unions. Information Letter. (GW ISSN 0020-8884) 1672, 2592
World Federation of the Deaf World Congress of the W F D. Proceedings see World Congress of the W F D. Proceedings 2290
World Feedstocks. (US) 1190
World Fellowship of Buddhists. Book Series. (TH ISSN 0084-1781) 4216
World Fellowship of Buddhists. Review. (TH ISSN 0043-8464) 4216
World Fence News. (US) 4497
†World Fertility Survey. Annual Reports. (NE) 5307
World Fertility Survey. Basic Documentation. (NE) 3989
World Fertility Survey. Country Reports. (NE) 3989
World Fertility Survey. Occasional Papers. (NE) 3989
World Fertility Survey. Progress Reports see World Fertility Survey. Annual Reports 5307
World Fertility Survey. Scientific Reports. (NE) 3989
World Fertility Survey. Summaries see World Fertility Survey. Summaries of Country Reports 3989
World Fertility Survey. Summaries of Country Reports. (NE) 3989
World Fertility Survey. Technical Bulletins. (NE) 3989

World Fertilizer Atlas. (UK ISSN 0512-2953) **196**
World Films. *see* Shijie Dianying **3517**
World Finance Herald. *see* Guoji Jinrong Daokan **783**
World Fine Art. (US) **350, 260, 969**
World Fishing. (UK ISSN 0043-8480) **2050**
World Focus. (II) **3935**
World Food & Drink Report. (US ISSN 0885-7946) **2084, 387**
†World Food Problems. (UN ISSN 0084-179X) **5307**
†World Food Production Conference Summary Report. (US) **5307**
World Food Programme Journal. (UN ISSN 1010-9099) **3613**
World Food Programme News *see* World Food Programme Journal **3613**
World Food Programme Report. (UN) **2084**
▼World Food Regulation Review. (UK ISSN 0963-4894) **2084, 2695**
World Food Report *see* World Food Programme Report **2084**
World Food Report *see* World Food & Drink Report **2084**
World Food Trade and U.S. Agriculture. (US ISSN 0733-2378) **160**
World Footwear. (US) **4362**
†World Forestry Congress. Proceedings.(SP ISSN 0084-1811) **5307**
World Freight. (UK ISSN 0046-5046) **4742**
World Friends. (KO) **2443**
World Futures. (US ISSN 0260-4027) **3786**
World Gaming Report. (US) **4497**
▼World Gas Intelligence. (US) **3703**
World Gastronomy. (UK) **388, 2084**
World Geophysical News. (US ISSN 1053-9859) **3703**
World Gift Review Monthly Newsletter. (US ISSN 0049-8106) **1057, 2283**
World Goodwill Commentary. (US) **3977**
World Goodwill Newsletter. (US ISSN 0818-4984) **4424**
World Government Journal *see* World Peace Journal **3977**
World Grain. (US) **208**
World Grain Statistics Yearbook. (UK) **145**
World Guide to Abbreviations of Organizations. (US) **2791**
World Guide to Covered Bridges. (US) **2427, 1501**
World Guide to Fertilizer Processes and Plant Suppliers *see* N.P.K.S. Processes and Plant Suppliers. World Directory **185**
World Guide to Libraries. *see* Internationales Bibliotheks-Handbuch **2764**
World Guide to Trade Associations. *see* Internationales Verzeichnis der Wirtschaftsverbaende **1140**
World Health/Sante du Monde. (UN ISSN 0043-8502) **4115**
World Health Forum. (UN ISSN 0251-2432) **3163**
World Health Organization. Bulletin. (UN ISSN 0042-9686) **3163**
World Health Organization. Handbook of Resolutions and Decisions of the World Health Assembly and the Executive Board. (UN) **4115**
World Health Organization. Monograph Series. (UN ISSN 0512-3038) **4115**
World Health Organization. Public Health Papers *see* Public Health Papers **4110**
World Health Organization. Regional Office for Africa. Report of the Regional Committee. (UN) **4115**
World Health Organization. Regional Office for Africa. Report of the Regional Committee. Minutes of the Plenary Session *see* World Health Organization. Regional Office for Africa. Report of the Regional Committee **4115**

World Health Organization. Regional Office for Africa. Report of the Regional Director. (UN ISSN 0510-8837) **4115**
World Health Organization. Regional Office for the Eastern Mediterranean. Annual Report of the Regional Director. (UN) **4115**
World Health Organization. Regional Office for the Eastern Mediterranean. Biennial Report of Regional Director *see* World Health Organization. Regional Office for the Eastern Mediterranean. Annual Report of the Regional Director **4115**
World Health Organization. Regional Office for the Western Pacific. Annual Report of the Regional Director to the Regional Committee for the Western Pacific. (UN ISSN 0512-4921) **4115**
World Health Organization. Work of W H O. (UN ISSN 0085-8285) **4115**
World Health Organization. World Health Assembly and the Executive Board. Handbook of Resolutions and Decisions. *see* World Health Organization. Handbook of Resolutions and Decisions of the World Health Assembly and the Executive Board **4115**
World Health Organization A I D S Technical Bulletin. (UN ISSN 1013-0845) **3182**
World Health Organization AIDS Series *see* W H O AIDS Series **3224**
World Health Organization Drug Information *see* W H O Drug Information **4115**
World Health Organization Offset Publications *see* W H O Offset Publications **4119**
World Health Organization Technical Report Series *see* W H O Technical Report Series **3161**
World Health Statistics Annual. (UN ISSN 0250-3794) **4119**
World Health Statistics Quarterly/ Rapport Trimestriel de Sanitares Mondiales. (UN ISSN 0379-8070) **4119**
World Health Statistics Report *see* World Health Statistics Quarterly **4119**
World Helicopter Inventory & Forecast. (US) **3475, 65**
World Highways. (UK ISSN 0043-8529) **4723**
World History. *see* Shijie Lishi **2322**
World Hockey. (UK) **4497**
World Holiday and Time Guide. (US) **4798**
World Hospitals. (UK ISSN 0512-3135) **2470**
World Hotel and Convention Directory. (JA) **2482, 4798**
World Hotel Index. (JA) **2482**
World Humor and Irony Movement Serials Yearbook *see* Humor **4374**
World in (Year). (UK) **700**
World Index of Social Science Institutions *see* World Directory of Social Science Institutions **4396**
World Industrial Reporter. (US ISSN 0043-8561) **3024**
World Industrial Safety and Hygiene Development. *see* Shijie Laodong Anquan Weisheng Dongtai **3622**
World Industry. (CH) **700**
World Informo. (II ISSN 0043-857X) **3977**
World Insurance Report. (UK) **2545**
World Intellectual Property Report. (UK ISSN 0952-7613) **3679**
World Inventions. *see* Shijie Faming **4342**
World Jewelogue (Year). (HK) **2566, 1160**
World Journal. (CN) **2029**
World Journal of Microbiology and Biotechnology. (UK ISSN 0959-3993) **559, 491**
World Journal of Psychosynthesis. (US ISSN 0043-860X) **3356**
World Journal of Surgery. (US ISSN 0364-2313) **3386**
World Journal of Urology. (US ISSN 0724-4983) **3390**
World Jurist. (US) **2730**

World L N G - Gas Contracts. (US) **2730, 3703**
World Labour Report. (UN ISSN 0255-5514) **997**
World Leasing Yearbook. (UK ISSN 0264-0732) **969, 888**
World Leather. (US ISSN 0894-3087) **2738**
†World Leatherlogue (Year). (HK) **5307**
World Leisure and Recreation. (CN) **2739, 4456, 4497, 4798**
World Leisure Review *see* World Leisure and Recreation **2739**
▼World Letter. (US) **3009**
World Link. (UK) **700**
World Link. (SZ ISSN 1016-359X) **1000, 3977**
World List of Family Planning Agencies. (UK ISSN 0535-1774) **598**
World List of Social Science Periodicals. (UN ISSN 0084-1870) **4396**
World List of Universities, Other Institutions of Higher Education and University Organizations. (UK ISSN 0084-1889) **1698**
World Literature. *see* Shijie Wenxue **2959**
World Literature Today. (US ISSN 0196-3570) **2976**
World Literature Written in English. (CN) **2976**
World Lithuanian Roman Catholic Directory. (US ISSN 4279, 2266
World Livestock Industry. *see* Sekai no Chikusan **225**
World M & A Network. (UK ISSN 1046-4778) **700**
World Machinery *see* Machinery World **3020**
World Magazine. (UK ISSN 0951-2195) **4798, 1501, 2266**
World Mariculture Society. Journal *see* World Aquaculture **1612**
World Market. *see* Mercado Mundial **917**
World Market for Bovine Meat *see* International Markets for Meat **219**
World Market for Dairy Products. (UN ISSN 0259-8213) **130**
World Markets Service *see* Global Trends **947**
World Marxist Review. (UK ISSN 0266-867X) **3935**
†World Marxist Review. (CN ISSN 0043-8642) **5307**
World Medical Journal. (GW ISSN 0049-8122) **3163**
†World Medicine. (UK ISSN 0043-8669) **5307**
World Meetings: Medicine. (US ISSN 0161-2875) **3394, 3163**
World Meetings: Outside United States and Canada. (US ISSN 0043-8677) **3394**
World Meetings: Social & Behavioral Sciences, Human Services and Management. (US ISSN 0194-6161) **3394, 1031, 1672, 4392**
World Meetings: United States and Canada. (US ISSN 0043-8693) **3394**
World Metal Statistics. (UK ISSN 0043-8758) **3429**
World Metal Statistics. Yearbook. (UK) **3423, 3429**
World Meteorological Association. Commission for Instruments and Methods of Observation. Abridged Final Report of the (No.) Session. (UN ISSN 0251-8783) **3442**
World Meteorological Association. Technical Commissions Abridged Final Reports *see* World Meteorological Organization. Abridged Final Reports of Sessions of Technical Commissions **3442**
World Meteorological Congress. Proceedings. (UN ISSN 0084-1935) **3442**
World Meteorological Organization. Abridged Final Reports of Sessions of Technical Commissions. (UN) **3442**
World Meteorological Organization. Annual Reports. (UN ISSN 0084-1994) **3442**
World Meteorological Organization. Basic Documents. (UN) **3442**

World Meteorological Organization. Basic Documents and Official Reports *see* World Meteorological Organization. Basic Documents **3442**
World Meteorological Organization. Commission for Aeronautical Meteorology. Abridged Final Report of the (No.) Session. (UN ISSN 0510-906X) **3442, 4678**
World Meteorological Organization. Commission for Agricultural Meteorology. Abridged Final Report of the (No.) Session. (UN ISSN 0510-9078) **3443, 130**
World Meteorological Organization. Commission for Atmospheric Sciences. Abridged Final Report of the (No.) Session. (UN ISSN 0250-9172) **3443**
World Meteorological Organization. Commission for Basic Systems. Abridged Final Report of the (No.) Session. (UN ISSN 0251-8953) **3443**
World Meteorological Organization. Commission for Hydrology. Abridged Final Report of the (No.) Session. (UN ISSN 0251-8775) **3443, 1612**
World Meteorological Organization. Commission for Marine Meteorology. Abridged Final Report of the (No.) Session. (UN ISSN 1011-3207) **3443, 4742**
†World Meteorological Organization. Commission for Special Applications of Meteorology and Climatology. Abridged Final Report of the (No.) Session. (UN ISSN 0251-8945) **5307**
World Meteorological Organization. Congress. Abridged Report with Resolutions. (UN ISSN 0084-1927) **3443**
World Meteorological Organization. Executive Committee Reports. Abridged Final Reports with Resolutions *see* World Meteorological Organization. Executive Council Session. Abridged Final Reports with Resolutions **3443**
World Meteorological Organization. Executive Council Session. Abridged Final Reports with Resolutions. (UN ISSN 1011-3231) **3443**
World Meteorological Organization. Regional Association I (Africa). Abridged Final Report of the (No.) Session. (UN ISSN 0510-9124) **3443**
World Meteorological Organization. Regional Association II (Asia). Abridged Final Report of the (No.) Session. (UN ISSN 0509-3007) **3443**
World Meteorological Organization. Regional Association III (South America). Abridged Final Report of the (No.) Session. (UN ISSN 0510-9132) **3443**
World Meteorological Organization. Regional Association IV (North America and Central America). Abridged Final Report of the (No.) Session. (UN ISSN 0250-9121) **3443**
World Meteorological Organization. Regional Association V (South West Pacific). Abridged Final Report of the (No.) Session. (UN ISSN 0250-9040) **3443**
World Meteorological Organization. Regional Association VI (Europe). Abridged Final Report of the (No.) Session. (UN ISSN 0509-3015) **3443**
World Meteorological Organization. Reports on Marine Science Affairs. (UN ISSN 0084-2001) **1612**
World Meteorological Organization. Special Environmental Reports. (UN) **1972, 3443**
World Meteorological Organization. Technical Notes. (UN ISSN 0084-201X) **3443**
World Meteorological Organization. Weather Reporting. Volume A: Observing Stations. (UN ISSN 0250-9393) **3443**

World Meteorological Organization. Weather Reporting. Volume B: Data Processing. (UN ISSN 0250-9407) 3443

World Meteorological Organization. Weather Reporting. Volume C: Transmissions. (UN ISSN 0250-9415) 3444

World Meteorological Organization. Weather Reporting. Volume D: Information for Shipping. (UN ISSN 0250-9423) 3444

World Meteorological Organization Bulletin *see* W M O Bulletin 3442

World Methanol and Derivatives. (US) 1190

World Methodist Historical Society. Historical Bulletin. (US) 4253

World Methodist Historical Society. News Bulletin *see* World Methodist Historical Society. Historical Bulletin 4253

World Military Aircraft Inventory & Forecast. (US ISSN 1040-2896) 3475, 65

World Military and Social Expenditures. (US ISSN 0363-4795) 1112

World Military Avionics Inventory & Forecast. (US ISSN 1040-290X) 3475

World Military Expenditures *see* World Military Expenditures and Arms Transfers 3476

World Military Expenditures and Arms Transfers. (US ISSN 0897-4667) 3476

World Military Expenditures and Related Data *see* World Military Expenditures and Arms Transfers 3476

World Mine Production of Gold. (US) 3498

World Mineral Statistics. (UK) 3502, 4592

World Mining *see* World Mining Equipment 3498

World Mining Congress. Report. (PL) 3498

World Mining Equipment. (US ISSN 0746-729X) 3498

World Missiles Inventory & Forecast. (US ISSN 1040-2918) 3476

†World Mission. (US) 5307

World Mission Journal (Baptist Men's Edition) *see* Mission Today 4244

World Mission Partners. (AT ISSN 1033-2243) 4210

World Missionary Press News. (US) 4210

World Missions Update. (AT ISSN 0158-6262) 4290

World Monitor. (US ISSN 0897-9472) 924

World Motor Vehicle Data. (US ISSN 0085-8307) 4706

World Movement of Mothers. Reports of Meetings. (FR ISSN 0084-2044) 4424

World Music Connections. (US ISSN 1049-0140) 3586

World Muslim Conference. Proceedings.(PK ISSN 0084-2052) 4221

World Muslim Gazetteer. (PK ISSN 0084-2060) 4221

World National Oil Company Statutes. (US) 2730, 3703

World Neighbors in Action. (US) 3977

World News Digest. (SU) 3935, 2029, 3948

World News Digest. (US ISSN 1042-1572) 3977, 937

World Newsmap of the Week *see* World Newsmap of the Week - Headline Focus 2266

World Newsmap of the Week - Headline Focus. (US) 2266, 3977

World Non-Ferrous Metal Statistics *see* World Metal Statistics 3429

World Notes on Antibiotics. *see* Guowai Yiyao (Kangshengsu Fence) 3727

World Notes on Herbal Medicine. *see* Guowai Yiyao - Zhiwuyao Fence 3727

World Nuclear Directory *see* World Energy and Nuclear Directory (Year) 1797

World Nuclear Performance. (US ISSN 0891-4435) 1810

World O R T Union. Yearbook. (Organization for Rehabilitation through Training) (UK) 1742

The World of A S P. (American Self-Protection Association) (US) 4497, 3811

World of Art. (IS) 350

World of Beef *see* Alberta Beef 209

World of Beer. (IT) 388

World of Birds Wildlife Sanctuary C.C., South Africa. Newsletter. (SA) 1501

World of Chabad. (CN) 2029

World of Culture. *see* Kayhan Farhangi 2870

World of Engineering. *see* Alam al-Handasah 1813

World of English. *see* Yingyu Shijie 2853

World of Faith. *see* Shinanggye 4201

The World of Interiors. (UK ISSN 0264-083X) 2556

World of Irish Nursing. (IE) 3288

World of Islam. *see* Die Welt des Islams 3645

World of Labour. *see* Monde du Travail 989

World of Learning. (UK ISSN 0084-2117) 1698

World of Light. *see* Guang de Shijie 3852

World of Literature. *see* Svet Literatury 2967

The World of Music. (GW ISSN 0043-8774) 3587

World of Novels. *see* Xiaoshuo Jie 2977

World of Poetry. (US) 3009

World of Politics. (US ISSN 0094-2316) 3935

World of Religion. *see* Kayhan Andishe 4219

World of Seeds. *see* Zhongzi Shijie 197

World of Shaker *see* Shaker Messenger 2023

World of Soul. *see* Kosmos Tis Psychis 3670

World of Sport. (GW) 4497

World of Sport. *see* Yertontsiyn Sport 4497

World of Tennis. *see* Cosmos tou Tennis 4502

World of Tennis. (UK) 4515

World of the Creation. *see* Sozo no Sekai 1969

▼World of Tourism/Alam al-Siyaha. (BA) 4798

World of Wheels. (CN ISSN 0824-5487) 4706

World of Winners. (US ISSN 1041-3529) 424, 2427

World of Work Report *see* Work in America 997

World Oil. (US ISSN 0043-8790) 3703

World Oil Trade. (UK ISSN 0950-1029) 3703, 924

World Opinion Update. (US ISSN 0193-3329) 3977

World Order. (US ISSN 0043-8804) 4290, 3786

World Ordnance Inventory & Forecast. (US) 3476

World Outlook. (US ISSN 0895-7452) 3977

World Outlook *see* New World Outlook 4192

World Outlook. (UK) 4253

World Parish. (US ISSN 0043-8839) 4253

World Patent Information. (US ISSN 0172-2190) 3679

World Peace. (NR ISSN 0300-225X) 3977

World Peace Journal. (CE) 3977

World Peace News. (US ISSN 0049-8130) 3977

World Peacemakers Quarterly. (US) 3935

World Perspectives. (US ISSN 1058-1022) 3977

World Petroleum Trends. (UK) 3703

World Pharmaceutical Directory. (US ISSN 0276-2277) 3746, 1160

▼World Pharmaceutical Standards Review. (UK) 3746

World Pheasant Association Journal *see* W P A Journal 568

World Pheasant Association News *see* W P A News 568

World Pipelines. (UK) 3703

World Plant *see* Plant World 628

World Ploughing Contest. Official Handbook. (UK) 165

World Policy Guide. (UK) 2545

World Policy Journal. (US ISSN 0740-2775) 3977

World Politics (Baltimore). (US ISSN 0043-8871) 3978

World Population Data Sheet. (US ISSN 0085-8315) 3989

World Port Construction & Ocean Technology. (UK) 4742, 1840

World Ports and Harbours Abstracts. (UK ISSN 0264-0775) 4668, 25

World Postal Stationery - New Issue Report. (US) 3759

†World Poultry. (UK) 5307

World Precious Metals Databook. (US) 3423

World Precious Metals Survey *see* World Precious Metals Databook 3423

World Press Freedom Review. (UK) 2577

World Press Review. (US ISSN 0195-8895) 2889, 2976

World Progress. (US ISSN 0043-8901) 2238

†World Property. (UK) 5307

World Propylene and Derivatives. (US) 1190

World Publishing Monitor. (US ISSN 0960-653X) 1406, 25, 4144

World Pulse *see* Pulse (Wheaton) 4196

World Pumpkin Confederation. Journal. (US) 2140

World Pumpkin Confederation. Newsletter *see* World Pumpkin Confederation. Journal 2140

World Pumps. (UK ISSN 0262-1762) 1941

World Rabbit Science Association. Newsletter. (IT) 3714

World Radio T V Handbook. (US ISSN 0144-7750) 1360, 1384

World Rainforest Report. (US) 1972, 1501

World Record Game Fishes. (US ISSN 0194-3340) 2050, 4560

World Refugee Survey. (US ISSN 0197-5439) 4424

World Refugee Survey Report *see* World Refugee Survey 4424

World Report on Technical Advancement. (Il ISSN 0043-8944) 4615, 25

World Resource Review. (US ISSN 1042-8011) 1972, 1501, 4077

World Review. (AT) 3978

World Review of Nutrition and Dietetics.(SZ ISSN 0084-2230) 3613

World Right-to-Die Newsletter. (CN ISSN 0742-535X) 3163

World Risk Analysis Reports. (US) 924, 969

World Road Statistics. (SZ ISSN 0444-1419) 4669

World Rubber Statistics Handbook. (UK) 4295

World S F Newsletter. (US ISSN 0735-3995) 3015

World Satellite Directory. (US) 1160

▼World Scanner Report. (US ISSN 1061-9240) 1360, 2501

World Science and Technology. *see* Shijie Kexue Jishu 4342

World Science, Technology and Economy. *see* Khoa Hoc Ky Thuat Kinh Te The Gioi 4320

World Scout Bureau Report *see* World Scout Organization Report 1246

World Scout Organization Report. (SZ) 1246

World Scouting News/Bulletin du Scoutisme Mondial. (SZ) 1246

World Scouting Newsletter *see* World Scouting News 1246

World Ships on Order *see* Newbuildings 4734

World Shrimp Farming. (US ISSN 1047-5672) 2050

World Smoking & Health. (US ISSN 0161-7672) 3811

World Soccer. (UK ISSN 0043-9037) 4515

World Spaceflight News. (US ISSN 0737-8548) 65

World Sports Cars. (UK) 4706

World Stainless Steel Statistics. (UK ISSN 0141-0806) 3429, 924

World Stamps. (UK ISSN 0043-9061) 3759

World Status Map *see* Pinkerton World Status Map 4782

World Steel & Materials Fachberichte. (GW ISSN 0934-5965) 3423

World Steel in Figures (Year). (BE) 3429

World Student News. (CS ISSN 0014-2255) 1672

World Studies Journal *see* Annual Review of Global Education 1615

World Sugar History Newsletter. (UK) 2326, 2084

World Sugar Journal. (UK) 196

World Sugar News/Kaigai Sato Joho. (JA ISSN 0049-8149) 196, 2084

World Surface Coating Abstracts. (UK ISSN 0043-9088) 3656, 25

World Survey of Phosphate Deposits. (UK) 196

World Survey of Sulphur Resources. (UK) 196

World Tanker Fleet Review. (UK ISSN 0049-8157) 4742

World Tax Series. (US) 1112

World Technology. (US) 4613, 3679

World Telecom Databook (Year). (UK) 1346

World Telecom Factbook *see* World Telecom Databook (Year) 1346

World Telecommunications. *see* Shijie Dianxin 1342

†World Tennis. (US ISSN 0043-910X) 5307

World Textile Abstracts. (UK ISSN 0043-9118) 4628, 25

World Time Catalogue (Year). (HK) 2566, 1160

World - Tin in Tinplate. (UK) 3423

World Tin Mining Operations, Exploration and Developments. (UK) 3424

A World to Win. (UK ISSN 0269-9141) 3935

World Tobacco. (UK ISSN 0043-9126) 4645

World Tobacco Directory. (UK ISSN 0084-2273) 4646

World Today. (US ISSN 0043-9134) 3978

World Today Series: Africa. (US ISSN 0084-2281) 2335

World Today Series: Canada. (US ISSN 0883-8135) 2427

World Today Series: East Asia and the Western Pacific. (US) 2343

World Today Series: Far East and Southwest Pacific *see* World Today Series: East Asia and the Western Pacific 2343

World Today Series: Latin America. (US ISSN 0092-4148) 2427

World Today Series: Middle East and South Asia. (US ISSN 0084-2311) 2343

World Today Series: Soviet Union and Eastern Europe. (US ISSN 0090-3868) 2396

World Today Series: Western Europe. (US ISSN 0084-2338) 2396

World Tourism Statistics *see* Yearbook of Tourism Statistics 4801

World Trade. (Il ISSN 0043-9142) 924

World Trade. *see* Welthandel 924

World Trade. (US ISSN 1054-8637) 924

World Trade Annual. (US ISSN 0512-3739) 924

World Trade Annual Supplement. (US ISSN 0512-3747) 924

World Trade Center of Nigeria. Newsletter. (NR) 824

World Trade Center Orlando. Meeting Notice. (US) 924

World Trade Centers Association. Directory. (US) 1160

World Trade Directory *see* Import - Export Directory 911

†World Trade Index. (UK) 5307

World Trade Information. (GW) 925

World Trade Materials. (SZ ISSN 1013-4514) 925

†World Trade Report. (US ISSN 0884-495X) 5307

6818 WORLD TRADE

World Trade - Stainless, High Speed & Other Alloy Steel. (UK ISSN 0952-5742) **3429**
World Trade Steel. (UK ISSN 0952-5734) **3429**
†World Trade Union Movement. (CS ISSN 0306-4824) **5307**
World Traders. (JA ISSN 0388-1865) **925**
World Translation Index. (NE ISSN 0259-8264) **4358**, 25
World Transport Data/Statistiques Mondiales de Transport. (SZ ISSN 0302-7902) **4669**
World Travel Directory see Travel Weekly's World Travel Directory **1156**
World Traveling. (US ISSN 0163-1780) **4798**
World Treaty Index. (US) **3978**
World Tribune. (US ISSN 0049-8165) **4216**, 3786
World Tunnelling. (UK ISSN 0956-8700) **1876**
World Union. (II ISSN 0043-9185) **3978**, 4456
World Union for a Universal Alphabet Newsletter see W U U A Newsletter **1345**
World Union for the Safeguard of Youth. Bulletin. (FR ISSN 0379-3338) **1246**, 4424
World Union for the Safeguard of Youth. Conference Proceedings. (FR) **4424**
World Union of Jewish Studies. (IS ISSN 0333-9068) **2029**
World Union of Organizations for the Safeguard of Youth see World Union for the Safeguard of Youth. Conference Proceedings **4424**
World Veterinary Congress. Proceedings. (SP ISSN 0084-2443) **4820**
World Vision. see Shijie Bolan **2183**
World Vision. (US ISSN 0043-9215) **4424**, 3978
World War II. (US ISSN 0898-4204) **2427**, 3476
World War 1 Aeroplanes see W.W. 1 Aero **65**
World War 1 Aeroplanes, Inc. Aero see W.W. 1 Aero **65**
World Wastes Specification Catalog see Management of World Wastes **1985**
World Watch. (US ISSN 0896-0615) **1972**, 4456
World Water. (UK ISSN 0140-9050) **4834**
World Weather Watch Planning Reports.(UN ISSN 0084-2451) **3444**
World Week. (US) **888**
World Wheat Statistics see World Grain Statistics Yearbook **145**
World Who's Who of Women. (UK) **4858**, 424
World-Wide Bibliography on Parliaments. (SZ) **4083**
World Wide Fund for Nature News see W W F News **1499**
World - Wide Missionary Crusader. (US) **4210**
World Wide Printer. (GW ISSN 0147-4804) **4006**
World Wide Shipping Guide. (US ISSN 0162-0088) **4742**
World Wildlife Fund Letter see W W F & C F Letter **5302**
World Wildlife News see W W F News **1499**
World Wood. (US ISSN 0043-9258) **2119**, 2111
World Wrestling Federation Magazine see W W F Magazine **4496**
World Wrestling Federation Wrestling Spotlight see W W F Wrestling Spotlight **4496**
World Wrought Copper Statistics. (UK ISSN 0266-7347) **3429**, 4592
World Yearbook of Education. (UK ISSN 0084-2508) **1672**
World Yearbook of Fifth Generation Computing Research and Development see World Yearbook of New Generation Computing Research and Development **5307**
†World Yearbook of New Generation Computing Research and Development. (UK) **5307**

World Yearbook of Robotics and C I M Research and Development. (UK) **1411**
World Yearbook of Robotics Research and Development see World Yearbook of Robotics and C I M Research and Development **1411**
World Youth/Jeunesse du Monde/Juventud del Mundo. (HU ISSN 0043-9274) **1271**, 3935
World Zionist Organization. General Council. Addresses, Debates, Resolutions. (IS ISSN 0084-2516) **3935**, 4227
World Zionist Organization. Zionist Congress. see Kongres ha-Tsiyoni. Hahlatot **3903**
World Zionist Organization Press Service see World Zionist Press Service **3935**
World Zionist Press Service. (IS) **3935**
Worldcasts: Product Edition. (US ISSN 0163-6723) **744**, 25
Worldcasts: Regional Edition. (US ISSN 0163-6731) **744**, 25
Worldlit. (CN ISSN 0820-6686) **1672**, 1688
Worldorama. (US) **4210**
The WorldPaper. (US) **3978**
Worldradio. (US) **1360**
World's Children. (UK ISSN 0043-9290) **1246**
World's Fair. (UK ISSN 0043-9304) **1057**
World's Fair. (US ISSN 0273-480X) **2238**
†World's Greatest Love Stories. (US ISSN 0738-095X) **5307**
World's Poultry Science Association. Proceedings of World's Poultry Congress. (US) **228**
World's Poultry Science Journal. (UK ISSN 0043-9339) **229**
World's Wisdom Series. (II) **3786**, 4210
World's Woman's Christian Temperance Union. Triennial Report. (CN) **1540**, 4424
Worldscope Industrial Company Profiles see Disclosure - Worldscope Company Profiles **944**
Worldview. (CN ISSN 0713-3391) **4253**
WorldView Magazine. (US) **937**, 1724, 3978
Worldwatch Papers. (US) **1972**, 4456
†Worldwide Art Catalogue Bulletin. (US ISSN 0043-9363) **5307**
Worldwide Biotech. (US) **491**, 3746
Worldwide Challenge. (US ISSN 0746-9241) **4210**
Worldwide Chamber of Commerce Directory see World Chamber of Commerce Directory **824**
▼Worldwide Databases. (US) **1445**
Worldwide Directory of East Indians see How to Start Your Own Business with 2000 to 5000 Dollars **1115**
Worldwide Directory of Film and Video Festivals and Events. (US) **3519**, 1388
Worldwide Exhibition Directory see International Trade Fairs and Exhibitions Directory **817**
Worldwide Financial Regulations. (US) **925**, 2730
Worldwide Government Directory. (US ISSN 0894-1521) **4078**, 1160
Worldwide Investment News. (US) **804**, 925, 969
Worldwide Marketing Opportunities Digest. (UK ISSN 0309-4960) **1057**
WorldWide News. (NE) **2545**
Worldwide News. (US) **4253**
Worldwide Offshore Rigfinder see Offshore Rig Report **3695**
Worldwide Petrochemical Directory. (US ISSN 0084-2583) **3704**
Worldwide Printer see World Wide Printer **4006**
†Worldwide Projects. (US ISSN 0091-4800) **5307**
Worldwide Refining and Gas Processing Directory. (US ISSN 0277-0962) **3704**
Worldwide Register of Adult Education. (US ISSN 0084-2486) **1688**

Worldwide Report: Arms Control. (US) **3978**, 3476
Worldwide Report: Epidemiology. (US) **4115**
Worldwide Report: Nuclear Development and Proliferation see Worldwide Report: Nuclear Developments **3476**
Worldwide Report: Nuclear Developments. (US) **3476**, 1810
Worldwide Report: Telecommunications.(US) **1346**
Worldwide Report: Telecommunications Policy. Research and Development see Worldwide Report: Telecommunications **1346**
Worldwide Rubber Statistics. (US) **4295**
Worldwide Tanker Nominal Freight Scale see New Worldwide Tanker Nominal Freight Scale **4734**
Worldwide Telecom. (US) **1368**
▼Worldwide Travel Information Contact Book. (US ISSN 1051-6247) **4798**
†Worldwide Travel Planner. (US) **5307**
Worldwide Uranium Producer Profiles. (US) **1810**
Worldwide Videotex Update. (US ISSN 0731-7891) **1402**, 1352, 1388
Worldwind. (CN ISSN 0707-2279) **1271**, 4210
†Wormald Journal. (AT) **5307**
Der Wormsgau. (GW ISSN 0084-2613) **2396**
Wormsloe Foundation. Publications. (US ISSN 0084-2621) **2427**
Wormwood Review. (US ISSN 0043-9401) **3009**, 2889
Woroni. (AT) **2889**
Worrall's Textile & Engineering Directory. (II) **1160**
Worry-Free Investing. (US) **969**
Worship. (US ISSN 0043-941X) **4210**
Worship and Preaching. (UK ISSN 0032-7107) **4253**
Wort in der Welt see Die Weltmission **4252**
Wort und Antwort. (GW ISSN 0342-6378) **4279**, 1672
Wort und Weg. (GW ISSN 0043-9444) **4253**
Worth. (US) **969**
Wortmuehle. (AU) **2173**
†Wot. (CN ISSN 0709-4035) **5307**
Wotanin - Wowapi. (US) **2029**
Wounds. (US ISSN 1044-7946) **3163**
Wow! (US ISSN 0897-4721) **1271**
WPCorp Report see WordPerfect Report **828**
Wprost. (PL ISSN 0209-1747) **2214**
Wrangler. (US ISSN 0512-4077) **2427**
Wrangler's Roost. (UK ISSN 0043-9452) **3519**
Wrecking & Salvage Journal. (US ISSN 0043-9460) **636**
The Wrestler. (US) **4497**
Wrestling. see Brydning **4467**
Wrestling All Stars Heroes and Villains. (US) **4497**
Wrestling Eye. (US) **4497**
Wrestling Fury. (US) **4497**
Wrestling Manual and Case Book. (US) **4497**
The Wrestling News. (US ISSN 0891-0707) **4497**
Wrestling Officials Manual see Wrestling Manual and Case Book **4497**
Wrestling Ringside. (US ISSN 0743-2720) **4497**
Wrestling Rulebook. (US) **4497**
Wrestling Scene. (US) **4497**
Wrestling U.S.A. Magazine. (US ISSN 0199-6258) **4497**
Wrestling U S A. (US) **4497**
Wrestling World. (US) **4497**
Wrestling's Main Event. (US ISSN 0278-9612) **4497**
Wright Family Workbook. (US) **2168**
Wright Investment Advice and Analysis. (US) **969**
Wright's Banker's Service see Wright Investment Advice and Analysis **969**
Writ. (CN ISSN 0316-3768) **2976**
†Write Age. (US ISSN 0892-9955) **5307**
Write in There. (US) **1271**

▼Write Now! (US) **3009**
Writer (Boston). (US ISSN 0043-9517) **2577**
Writer (Penzance). (UK ISSN 0260-2776) **2976**
Writers Alliance Newsletter see Keystrokes **4130**
Writers' and Artists' Yearbook. (UK ISSN 0084-2664) **4139**
Writers' and Photographers' Marketing Guide; Directory of Australian and New Zealand Literary and Photo Markets. (AT ISSN 0084-2680) **4139**, 3798
Writers' and Poets' Yearbook. (UK) **2976**, 3009
†Writers & Their Work. (US) **5307**
†Writers' Bar-B-Q. (US) **5307**
Writers' Bloc. (US) **3009**
Writers Connection. (US ISSN 0749-2014) **4139**, 2577
Writer's Digest. (US ISSN 0043-9525) **2577**
Writers Directory. (US ISSN 0084-2699) **424**, 416
Writers Forum. (US ISSN 0960-2992) **2976**
Writers Gazette. (US) **2976**
Writer's Gazette Newsletter see Writers Gazette **2976**
Writers' Guidelines Magazine. (US ISSN 1053-1793) **2577**
Writers Guild of America, East. Newsletter. (US) **2976**, 3519
Writers Guild of America, West. Journal.(US ISSN 1055-1948) **2977**, 2577
Writers Guild of America, West. Newsletter see Writers Guild of America, West. Journal **2977**
Writer's Handbook. (US ISSN 0084-2710) **4139**
The Writer's Haven Litmag. (US) **2977**
†Writers-in-Waiting Newsletter. (US) **5307**
†Writer's Info. (US) **5307**
Writers Ink. (US) **4139**, 2977
Writers' Journal (N. St. Paul). (US ISSN 0891-8759) **2977**, 2577, 4139
Writer's Lifeline. (CN) **4139**
Writer's Market. (US ISSN 0084-2729) **4139**
Writer's N W. (US ISSN 0895-898X) **4139**, 1481
Writers News. (UK ISSN 0957-3577) **2977**, 2577, 2889
Writers News Manitoba see Prairie Fire **2950**
Writer's Nook News. (US ISSN 0890-9504) **2577**
Writer's Northwest Handbook. (US ISSN 0896-7946) **4139**
Writer's Northwest Newsletter see Writer's N W **4139**
Writer's Notebook Press. Report see The Report (Eugene) **3013**
Writers of Wales. (US ISSN 0141-5050) **2977**
Writers' Own Magazine. (UK ISSN 0267-1360) **2977**, 3009
Writer's Review see Writer (Penzance) **2976**
Writers Union of Free Afghanistan see W U F A **2888**
Writer's Voice. (US) **3009**
†Writers West. (US ISSN 0741-9821) **5307**
Writers Workshop Literary Reader. (II) **2977**
Writers Workshop Miscellany see Miscellany **2939**
Writers' World. (AT ISSN 0043-9576) **2577**, 2977
Writer's Yearbook. (US ISSN 0084-2737) **4139**
Writing. see Xie Zuo **2577**
Writing. (CN ISSN 0706-1889) **2977**, 3009
Writing (Northbrook). (US ISSN 0194-5475) **2977**, 1672, 2577
Writing (San Francisco). (US ISSN 0084-2745) **2977**
Writing About Women: Feminist Literary Studies. (US ISSN 1053-7937) **2977**, 4858
Writing Center Journal. (US ISSN 0889-6143) **1672**
▼Writing Concepts. (US ISSN 1050-4788) **2577**

Writing Instructor. (US ISSN 0277-7789) **2977**
Writing Magazine *see* Writers News **2977**
Writing Research. (US) **2977**
▼Writing Right. (US) **4139**, 2852
†Writing Teacher (Orono). (US) **5307**
Writing Teacher (San Antonio). (US ISSN 0894-5837) **2977**, 1672
†Writings on American History. (US) **5307**
Written Communication. (US ISSN 0741-0883) **1346**, 2977
Written Communication Annual. (US ISSN 0883-9298) **1346**
The Written Word. (US) **1688**
Wroclawski Rocznik Ekonomiczny. (PL ISSN 0084-2974) **700**
Wroclawskie Towarzystwo Naukowe. Komisja Historii Sztuki. Rozprawy. (PL ISSN 0084-2982) **350**
Wroclawskie Towarzystwo Naukowe. Komisja Jezykowa. Rozprawy. (PL ISSN 0084-2990) **2852**
Wroclawskie Towarzystwo Naukowe. Prace. Seria A. Humanistyka. (PL ISSN 0084-3016) **2518**
Wroclawskie Towarzystwo Naukowe. Prace. Seria B. Nauki Scisle. (PL ISSN 0084-3024) **4352**
Wroclawskie Towarzystwo Naukowe. Sprawozdania. Seria A. (PL ISSN 0371-4756) **4352**
Wrongful Discharge Case Law Reporter *see* Wrongful Discharge Report **2695**
Wrongful Discharge Report. (US ISSN 1053-0274) **2695**
Wspolczesna Publicystyka Polska. (PL) **3587**
Wspolczesnosc *see* Literatura **2934**
Wspolpraca *see* Politechnika Wroclawska. Osrodek Badan Prognostycznych. Prace Naukowe. Wspolpraca **5260**
Wszechswiat/Universe. (PL ISSN 0043-9592) **4352**
Wudao/Dancing. (CC ISSN 0512-4204) **1532**
Wudao Luncong/Forum of Dancing. (US) **1532**
Wudao Yishu/Art of Dancing. (CC) **1532**
Wuerttembergisch Franken. (GW ISSN 0084-3067) **2396**
Wuerttembergische Bau-Berufsgenossenschaft. Mitteilungen. (GW ISSN 0172-2514) **636**
Wuerttembergische Blaetter fuer Kirchenmusik. (GW ISSN 0177-6487) **3587**
Wuerttemburgischer Schwimmverband Aktuell *see* W S V - Aktuell **5302**
Wuerzburg-Heute. (GW ISSN 0043-9614) **2889**
Wuerzburger Dioezesangeschichtsblaetter. (GW) **2396**
Wuerzburger Geographische Arbeiten. (GW ISSN 0510-9833) **2266**
Wuerzburger Geographische Manuskript. (GW ISSN 0931-8623) **2266**
Wuerzburger Jahrbuecher fuer die Altertumswissenschaft. (GW) **2852**, 1280
Wuestenrot-Heim *see* Wuestenrot Magazin **804**
Wuestenrot - Journal. (GW) **997**
Wuestenrot Magazin. (AU) **804**
Wugnet Journal *see* Windows Journal **1402**
Wuhan Daxue Xuebao (Shehui Kexue Ban)/Wuhan University. Journal (Social Science Edition). (CC ISSN 1000-5374) **4392**
Wuhan Daxue Xuebao (Ziran Kexue Ban)/Wuhan University. Journal (Natural Science Edition). (CC ISSN 0253-9888) **4352**
Wuhan Daxue Ziran Kexue Xuebao *see* Wuhan Daxue Xuebao (Ziran Kexue Ban) **4352**
Wuhan Institute of Grain Industry. Journal. *see* Wuhan Liangshi Gongye Xueyuan Xuebao **208**
Wuhan Liangshi Gongye Xueyuan Xuebao/Wuhan Institute of Grain Industry. Journal. (CC) **208**, 483

Wuhan University. Journal (Natural Science Edition). *see* Wuhan Daxue Xuebao (Ziran Kexue Ban) **4352**
Wuhan University. Journal (Social Science Edition). *see* Wuhan Daxue Xuebao (Shehui Kexue Ban) **4392**
Wuhun/Soul of Martial Arts. (CC) **4497**
Wuji Cailiao Xuebao/Journal of Inorganic Materials. (CC ISSN 1000-324X) **1215**
Wujia Tongji Yuebao *see* Commodity Price Statistics Monthly **711**
Wujin Keji. (CC ISSN 1001-1587) **3424**
Wuli/Physics. (CC ISSN 0379-4148) **3835**
Wuli Jiaoxue/Physics Teaching. (CC ISSN 0509-4003) **3835**, 1763
Wuli Shiyan/Physics Experiments. (CC) **3835**
Wuli Tongbao/Physics Bulletin. (CC ISSN 0509-4038) **3835**
Wuli Xuebao/Acta Physica Sinica. (CC ISSN 1000-3290) **3835**
Wulin/Martial Arts. (CC ISSN 1000-7318) **4497**
Wunder & Maerchen. *see* Merveilles & Contes **2056**
Wunderblock. (GW ISSN 0344-8274) **4050**
Wupperbruecke. (GW) **2192**
Wuppertaler Schriftenreihe Literatur. (GW ISSN 0341-2172) **2977**
Wurttembergische Bau-Berufsgenossenschaft. Jahresbericht. (GW) **636**, 833
Wurzel. (GW) **1271**
Wushu Jianshen/Health Through Martial Arts. (CC) **4497**, 3811
Wutai Mountain Studies. *see* Wutaishan Yanjiu **2326**
Wutaishan Yanjiu/Wutai Mountain Studies. (CC) **2326**
Wutan Huatan Yicong. (CC) **1549**
Wutan yu Huatan. (CC ISSN 1000-8918) **3498**
Wuxiandian/Radio. (CC) **1360**
Wuxiandian Gongcheng/Radio Engineering. (CC) **1360**
Wuxiandian Tongxin Jishu/Radio Communication Technology. (CC) **1360**
Wuxiandian yu Dianshi/Radio and Television. (CC) **1384**, 1360
Wuyi Kexue/Wuyi Science. (CC) **460**
Wuyi Science. *see* Wuyi Kexue **460**
Wychowanie Fizyczne i Higiena Szkolna.(PL ISSN 0510-9868) **1763**, 3811
Wychowanie Fizyczne i Sport. Studia i Materialy. (PL ISSN 0043-9630) **1763**, 3811
Wychowanie Muzyczne w Szkole. (PL ISSN 0512-4255) **3587**, 1672
Wychowanie Obywatelskie *see* Spoleczenstwo Otwarte **4389**
Wychowanie Techniczne w Szkole. (PL ISSN 0510-9884) **1840**, 1672
Wychowanie w Przedszkolu. (PL ISSN 0137-8082) **1672**
Wydzial Filologiczno-Filozoficzny. Prace. (PL ISSN 0208-497X) **3786**, 350
Wye College (University of London). Agrarian Development Unit. Occasional Paper. (UK) **160**
Wye College (University of London). Department of Agricultural Economics. Farm Business Unit. Occasional Paper. (UK) **160**, 196
Wye College (University of London). School of Rural Economics and Related Studies. Farm Business Unit. Occasional Paper *see* Wye College (University of London). Department of Agricultural Economics. Farm Business Unit. Occasional Paper **160**
Wykamol Preserver. (UK) **641**
Wynboer/Wine Farmer. (SA ISSN 0043-9657) **196**
Wyniki Pomiarow Hydrometrycznych *see* Rocznik Hydrometryczny **1600**
Wyniki Pomiarow Pionowego Rozkladu Ozonu w Atmosferze/Vertical Distribution of Ozone from Ozonosonde Observation. (PL) **3444**
Wyoming. (US ISSN 0884-2930) **2977**

†Wyoming. Characteristics of Recordable Occupational Injuries and Illnesses (Year). (US) **5307**
Wyoming. Department of Education. Education Directory. (US) **1672**
Wyoming. Department of Environmental Quality. Annual Report. (US ISSN 0099-1279) **1972**
Wyoming. Department of Health and Social Services. Annual Report *see* Wyoming. Department of Health. Annual Report **4115**
Wyoming. Department of Health. Annual Report. (US) **4115**
Wyoming. Department of Revenue and Taxation. Annual Report. (US ISSN 0094-9019) **1112**
Wyoming. Division of Planning, Evaluation and Information Services. Statistical Report Series. (US ISSN 0093-5530) **4592**
Wyoming. Division of Public Assistance and Social Services. Quarterly Statistical Report. (US) **4424**
Wyoming. Employment Security Commission. Annual Report. (US) **997**
Wyoming. Employment Security Commission. Research and Analysis Section. Labor Force Trends *see* Wyoming Labor Force Trends **997**
Wyoming. State of Wyoming Annual Report. (US ISSN 0094-3924) **4078**
Wyoming. Water Quality Division. State - E P A Agreement. (US) **4834**, 1980
Wyoming. Water Quality Division. Wyoming State Plan *see* Wyoming. Water Quality Division. State - E P A Agreement **4834**
Wyoming Agriculture. (US) **130**
Wyoming Annual Planning Report. (US) **997**
Wyoming Archaeologist. (US ISSN 0043-9665) **289**
†Wyoming Beverage Analyst. (US ISSN 0043-9673) **5307**
Wyoming Data Handbook. (US) **4078**
Wyoming Directory of Manufacturing and Mining. (US) **1160**
Wyoming Education News. (US ISSN 0043-9681) **1672**
Wyoming Educator. (US ISSN 0043-969X) **1672**
Wyoming Geo-Notes. (US) **1586**
Wyoming History News. (US ISSN 0043-972X) **2427**
Wyoming Labor Force Trends. (US ISSN 0512-4409) **997**
Wyoming Landowner Newsletter. (US) **1501**
†Wyoming Library Roundup. (US ISSN 0043-9738) **5307**
Wyoming Mineral Yearbook. (US ISSN 0096-9842) **1586**
Wyoming Native Plant Society Newsletter *see* W N P S Newsletter **520**
Wyoming Nurse. (US) **3288**
Wyoming Physicians Newsletter. (US) **3163**
Wyoming Rural Electric News. (US ISSN 0043-9770) **998**, 1911
Wyoming Sierran. (US) **1501**, 1972, 4560
Wyoming Stockman Farmer. (US ISSN 0043-9800) **229**
Wyoming Trucker. (US ISSN 0511-0440) **4723**
Wyoming Valley Motorist *see* Valley Motorist **4705**
Wyoming Wildlife. (US ISSN 0043-9819) **1501**, 593
Wyoming Wool Grower. (US ISSN 0043-9827) **229**
Wythe County Historical Review. (US) **2427**
Wyzer. (NE) **4290**, 1271
Wyzsza Szkola Ekonomiczna. Zeszyty Naukowe *see* Akademia Ekonomiczna, Krakow. Zeszyty Naukowe **644**
Wyzsza Szkola Ekonomiczna, Krakow. Zeszyty Naukowe. Seria Specjalna: Monografie *see* Akademia Ekonomiczna, Krakow. Zeszyty Naukowe. Seria Specjalna: Monografie **644**

WYZSZA SZKOLA 6819

Wyzsza Szkola Ekonomiczna we Wroclawiu. Prace Naukowe *see* Akademia Ekonomiczna we Wroclawiu. Prace Naukowe **644**
Wyzsza Szkola Morska. Zeszyty Naukowe. (PL) **4742**
Wyzsza Szkola Pedagogiczna im. Komisji Edukacji Narodowej w Krakowie. Prace Monograficzne/Ecole Normale Superieure a Cracovie. Etudes Monographiques. (PL ISSN 0239-6025) **2518**
Wyzsza Szkola Pedagogiczna im. Komisji Edukacji Narodowej w Krakowie. Problemy Studiow Nauczycielskich. (PL ISSN 0239-6769) **1672**
Wyzsza Szkola Pedagogiczna im. Komisji Edukacji Narodowej w Krakowie. Rocznik Naukowo-Dydaktyczny. Prace Bibliotekoznawcze. (PL) **2791**
Wyzsza Szkola Pedagogiczna im. Komisji Edukacji Narodowej w Krakowie. Roczni Naukowo-Dydaktyczny. Prace Ekonomiczno-Spoleczne. (PL ISSN 0239-7951) **700**, 1763
Wyzsza Szkola Pedagogiczna im. Komisji Edukacji Narodowej w Krakowie. Rocznik Naukowo-Dydaktyczny. Prace Fizjologiczne. (PL ISSN 0860-9063) **575**
Wyzsza Szkola Pedagogiczna im. Komisji Edukacji Narodowej w Krakowie. Rocznik Naukowo-Dydaktyczny. Prace Filozoficzne. (PL) **3786**, 1763
Wyzsza Szkola Pedagogiczna im. Komisji Edukacji Narodowej w Krakowie. Rocznik Naukowo-Dydaktyczny. Prace Fizyczne. (PL ISSN 0867-3594) **3786**, 1763
Wyzsza Szkola Pedagogiczna im. Komisji Edukacji Narodowej w Krakowie. Rocznik Nukowo-Dydaktyczny. Prace Geograficzne. (PL ISSN 0239-796X) **2266**, 1763
Wyzsza Szkola Pedagogiczna im. Komisji Edukacji Narodowej w Krakowie. Rocznik Naukowo-Dydaktyczny. Prace Historyczne. (PL ISSN 0137-5873) **2326**, 1763
Wyzsza Szkola Pedagogiczna im. Komisji Edukacji Narodowej w Krakowie. Rocznik Naukowo-Dydaktyczny. Prace Historycznoliterackie. (PL) **2977**, 1763
Wyzsza Szkola Pedagogiczna im. Komisji Edukacji Narodowej w Krakowie. Rocznik Naukowo-Dydaktyczny. Prace Jezykoznawcze. (PL ISSN 0860-5629) **2852**
Wyzsza Szkola Pedagogiczna im. Komisji Edukacji Narodowej w Krakowie. Rocznik Naukowo-Dydaktyczny. Prace Matematyczne. (PL ISSN 0239-7978) **3061**, 1763
Wyzsza Szkola Pedagogiczna im. Komisji Edukacji Narodowej w Krakowie. Rocznik Naukowo-Dydaktyczny. Prace Pedagogiczne. (PL ISSN 0239-2356) **1672**
Wyzsza Szkola Pedagogiczna im. Komisji Edukacji Narodowej w Krakowie. Rocznik Naukowo-Dydaktyczny. Prace Psychologiczne. (PL) **4050**, 1763
Wyzsza Szkola Pedagogiczna im. Komisji Edukacji Narodowej w Krakowie. Rocznik Naukowo-Dydaktyczny. Prace Romanistyczne. (PL ISSN 0239-6556) **2852**, 1763, 2977
Wyzsza Szkola Pedagogiczna im. Komisji Edukacji Narodowej w Krakowie. Rocznik Naukowo-Dydaktyczny. Prace Rusycystyczne. (PL ISSN 0239-7986) **2977**, 2852
Wyzsza Szkola Pedagogiczna im. Komisji Edukacji Narodowej w Krakowie. Rocznik Naukowo-Dydaktyczny. Prace Techniczne. (PL ISSN 0860-276X) **4613**, 1763

Wyzsza Szkola Pedagogiczna im. Komisji Edukacji Narodowej w Krakowie. Rocznik Naukowo-Dydaktyczny. Prace Zoologiczne. (PL ISSN 0239-7994) **594**

Wyzsza Szkola Pedagogiczna im. Komisji Edukacji Narodowej w Krakowie. Rocznik Naukowo-Dydaktyczny. Prace z Dydaktyki Biologii. (PL) **460**, 1763

Wyzsza Szkola Pedagogiczna im. Komisji Edukacji Narodowej w Krakowie. Rocznik Naukowo-Dydaktyczny. Prace z Dydaktyki Literatury i Jezyka Polskiego. (PL ISSN 0239-6025) **2852**, 1763, 2977

Wyzsza Szkola Pedagogiczna im. Komisji Edukacji Narodowej w Krakowie. Rocznik Naukowo-Dydaktyczny. Prace z Dydaktyki Matematyki. (PL) **3061**, 1763

Wyzsza Szkola Pedagogiczna im. Komisji Edukacji Narodowej w Krakowie. Rocznik Naukowo-Dydaktyczny. Prace z Historii Oswiaty i Wychowania. (PL ISSN 0860-1046) **1672**

Wyzsza Szkola Pedagogiczna im. Komisji Edukacji Narodowej w Krakowie. Rocznik Naukowo-Dydaktyczny. Prace z Rachunku Prawdopodobienstwa i Jego Dydaktyki. (PL ISSN 0860-6994) **3061**, 1763

Wyzsza Szkola Pedagogiczna im. Komisji Edukacji Narodowej w Krakowie. Rocznik Naukowo-Dydaktyczny. Prace z Wychowania Plastycznego. (PL ISSN 0860-9071) **350**, 1763

Wyzsza Szkola Pedagogiczna, Opole. Zeszyty Naukowe. Seria A. Chemia. (PL ISSN 0324-9034) **1190**

Wyzsza Szkola Pedagogiczna, Opole. Zeszyty Naukowe. Seria A. Dydaktyka. (PL ISSN 0324-8968) **1763**

Wyzsza Szkola Pedagogiczna, Opole. Zeszyty Naukowe. Seria A. Ekonomia.(PL ISSN 0474-2966) **888**

Wyzsza Szkola Pedagogiczna, Opole. Zeszyty Naukowe. Seria A. Filogia Angielska. (PL ISSN 0860-2328) **2852**, 2889

Wyzsza Szkola Pedagogiczna, Opole. Zeszyty Naukowe. Seria A. Filologia Polska. (PL ISSN 0324-9050) **2977**

Wyzsza Szkola Pedagogiczna, Opole. Zeszyty Naukowe. Seria A. Filologia Rosyjska. (PL ISSN 0474-2974) **2977**, 2852

Wyzsza Szkola Pedagogiczna, Opole. Zeszyty Naukowe. Seria A. Fizyka. (PL ISSN 0078-5385) **3835**

Wyzsza Szkola Pedagogiczna, Opole. Zeszyty Naukowe. Seria A. Historia. (PL ISSN 0078-5393) **2396**

Wyzsza Szkola Pedagogiczna, Opole. Zeszyty Naukowe. Seria A. Historia Literatury see Wyzsza Szkola Pedagogiczna, Opole. Zeszyty Naukowe. Seria A. Filologia Polska **2977**

Wyzsza Szkola Pedagogiczna, Opole. Zeszyty Naukowe. Seria A. Jezykoznawstwo. (PL ISSN 0078-5423) **2852**

Wyzsza Szkola Pedagogiczna, Opole. Zeszyty Naukowe. Seria A. Matematyka. (PL ISSN 0078-5431) **3061**

Wyzsza Szkola Pedagogiczna, Opole. Zeszyty Naukowe. Seria A. Nauki Spoleczno-Polityczne. (PL ISSN 0239-670X) **4392**

Wyzsza Szkola Pedagogiczna, Opole. Zeszyty Naukowe. Seria A. Nauki Techniczne. (PL ISSN 0324-8992) **1840**

Wyzsza Szkola Pedagogiczna, Opole. Zeszyty Naukowe. Seria A. Pedagogika. (PL ISSN 0474-2982) **1763**

Wyzsza Szkola Pedagogiczna, Opole. Zeszyty Naukowe. Seria A. Psychologia. (PL ISSN 0208-9564) **4050**

Wyzsza Szkola Pedagogiczna, Opole. Zeszyty Naukowe. Seria B. Studia i Monografie. (PL ISSN 0078-544X) **2519**

▼X Book. (GW) **1423**
X-Calibre. (UK) **3009**
X I B. (US) **2977**
X I I I Magazine. (EI ISSN 1017-6950) **1346**
▼The X Journal. (US) **1402**
X Letters. (US) **3400**, 4858
X R S - X-Ray Spectrometry. (UK ISSN 0049-8246) **3858**
X-Ray Diffraction Abstracts. (UK ISSN 0309-5312) **3839**
X-Ray Fluorescence Spectrometry Abstracts. (UK ISSN 0043-9851) **1203**, 25
▼X-Ray Optics. (US) **3858**
X Ref - (Year) see Drug Trade Name Cross Reference List **5182**
X S. (US) **2238**
Xalman. (US) **2977**, 350
Xaloc. (MX ISSN 0043-986X) **2889**
Xanadu. (US ISSN 0146-0463) **3009**
Xareli. (SG) **3935**
Xaverian Missions Newsletter. (US) **4279**
Xaverian Weekly. (CN ISSN 0043-9886) **1331**
Xavier Review. (US ISSN 0887-6681) **2977**, 2519
†Xavier University. Museum and Archives Publications. (PH ISSN 0084-3229) **5307**
Xenobiotica. (UK ISSN 0049-8254) **483**
▼Xenophilia. (US) **2985**, 3009
▼Xenos. (UK) **3015**
Xenozoic Tales. (US) **2985**
Xerolage. (US) **3009**
Xerotic Ephemera. (US) **3009**, 4139
Xerox Disclosure Journal. (US ISSN 0361-4190) **3679**, 3798
Xi Psi Phi Quarterly. (US ISSN 0049-8262) **3244**
Xiamen Daxue Xuebao (Zhexue Shehui Kexue Ban)/Xiamen University. Journal. (Philosophy and Social Sciences Edition). (CC ISSN 0438-0460) **4392**
Xiamen Daxue Xuebao (Ziran Kexue Ban)/Xiamen University. Journal (Natural Science Edition)/Acta Scientiarum Universitatis Amoiensis. (CC ISSN 0438-0479) **4352**
Xiamen Institute of Aquatic Products. Journal. see Xiamen Shuichan Xueyuan Xuebao **2050**
Xiamen Literature. see Xiamen Wenxue **2977**
Xiamen Shuichan Xueyuan Xuebao/Xiamen Institute of Aquatic Products. Journal. (CC) **2050**
Xiamen University. Journal (Natural Science Edition). see Xiamen Daxue Xuebao (Ziran Kexue Ban) **4352**
Xiamen University. Journal. (Philosophy and Social Sciences Edition). see Xiamen Daxue Xuebao (Zhexue Shehui Kexue Ban) **4392**
Xiamen Wenxue/Xiamen Literature. (CC) **2977**
Xi'an Institute of Physical Education. Journal. see Xi'an Tiyu Xueyuan Xuebao **3811**
Xi'an Tiyu Xueyuan Xuebao/Xi'an Institute of Physical Education. Journal. (CC ISSN 1001-747X) **3811**
Xiandai Dizhi/Modern Geology. (CC ISSN 1000-8527) **1586**
Xiandai Faxue/Modern Law Science. (CC ISSN 1001-2397) **2695**
Xiandai Funu/Modern Women. (CC) **4858**
Xiandai Fuzhuang/Modern Clothes. (CC) **1295**
Xiandai Guoji Guanxi/Modern International Relations. (CC ISSN 1000-6192) **3978**
Xiandai Huabao/Modern Pictorial. (CC) **2183**
Xiandai Jiating/Modern Family. (CC ISSN 1000-4300) **2450**, 1246

Xiandai Lingdao/Modern Leader. (CC ISSN 1000-4513) **3935**
Xiandai Minhang/Modern Civil Aviation. (CC) **65**
Xiandai Qiche. see China Automotive Journal **4688**
Xiandai Qiye Daokan/Modern Enterprise Herald. (CC) **1031**
Xiandai Qiyejia/Modern Entrepreneurs. (CC ISSN 1001-6546) **700**
Xiandai Riben Jingji/Contemporary Japanese Economics. (CC ISSN 1000-355X) **700**
Xiandai Shenghuo Yongpin/Modern Daily Necessities. (CC) **1508**, 2283, 2450, 2562
Xiandai Sheying/Modern Photography. (CC) **3798**
Xiandai Tongxin/Communications Today. (CC ISSN 1000-6559) **1354**
Xiandai Wuli Zhishi/Modern Physics. (CC ISSN 1001-0610) **3835**
Xiandai Yuye Xinxi/Modern Fisheries Information. (CC) **2050**
Xiandai Zhongguo see China Today **2181**
Xiandai Zhuangshi/Modern Decoration. (CC) **2556**
Xiandai Zuojia see Sichuan Wenxue **2960**
Xiandaihua/Modernization. (CC ISSN 1001-5396) **4613**, 4352
Xiang Qi/Chinese Chess. (US) **4497**
†Xiang Qi. (GW ISSN 0934-5418) **5307**
Xianggang Fengqing/Hong Kong Customs. (CC) **4456**
Xianggang Huli Zazhi see Hong Kong Nursing Journal **3279**
Xiangjian Xiaolu. (CH ISSN 1015-8367) **130**
Xiangjiao Gongye/China Rubber Industry. (CC ISSN 1000-890X) **4294**
Xiangqi Yanjiu/Studies in Chinese Chess. (CC ISSN 1002-1906) **4497**
Xiangtan Kuangye Xueyuan Xuebao/Journal of Xiangtan Mining Institute. (CC ISSN 1000-9930) **3498**
▼Xiao Huoju/Little Torches. (CC) **1271**
Xiao Mihou/Little Macaque. (CC) **1271**
Xiao Pengyou/Little Friends. (CC) **1271**
Xiao Xi Liu/Brook. (CC) **1271**
Xiao Xiaoshuo Xuankan. (CC) **2977**
Xiao Xingxing/Little Star. (CC) **1271**
Xiao Xuesheng/Elementary School Pupils. (CC) **1246**
Xiaofei Zhinan/Consumption Guide. (CC) **1509**
Xiaoshuo/Short Stories. (CC) **2977**
Xiaoshuo Jia/Novelists. (CC) **2977**
Xiaoshuo Jie/World of Novels. (CC) **2977**, 1271
Xiaoshuo Lin. (CC) **2978**
Xiaoshuo Pinglun/Short Story Reviews. (CC ISSN 1004-2164) **2978**
Xiaoshuo Tiandi. (CC) **2978**
Xiaoshuo Xuankan/Selected Short Stories. (CC ISSN 0257-5604) **2978**
Xiaoshuo Yuebao/Short Stories Monthly.(CC ISSN 0257-9413) **2978**
Xiaoxing Neiranji. (CC) **1941**
Xiaoxing Weixing Jisuanji Xitong/Microcomputer Systems. (CC) **1466**
Xiaoxue Keji/Elementary School Science and Technology. (CC) **4352**, 1271
Xiaoxue Shidai/Elementary School Years. (CC) **1271**
Xiaoxue Shuxue Jiaoshi/Arithmetic Teacher. (CC) **3061**, 1763
Xiaoxue Yuwen Jiaoshi/Teaching Chinese in Elementary School. (CC) **2852**, 1763
Xiaoxue Yuwen Jiaoxue/Elementary School Chinese Teaching. (CC) **1763**, 2852
Xiaoxuesheng Xuexi Zhidao/Study Guide for Elementary Students. (CC) **1672**
Xiaoxuesheng Yuwen Xuexi/Chinese Studies for Pupils. (CC) **2852**, 1271

Xibao Shengwuxue Zazhi. (CC ISSN 0253-9977) **527**
Xibao Yanjiu. see Cell Research **5163**
Xibei Daxue Xuebao. Shehui Kexue Ban/Northwest University. Journal. Social Sciences Edition. (CC ISSN 1000-2731) **4392**
Xibei Minzu Yanjiu/Northwest Minorities Studies. (CC ISSN 1001-5558) **3645**, 253, 2029
Xibei Shi-Di/Historical and Geographical Review of Northwest China. (CC ISSN 1000-4076) **2343**, 2266
Xie Zuo/Writing. (CC) **2577**, 2978
Xihondzo Xo Rindza. (SA ISSN 0258-9079) **4290**
Xijiang Yue. (CC) **2978**
Xiju/Drama. (CC) **4642**
Xiju Wenxue/Drama Literature. (CC) **2978**, 4642
Xiju Yishu/Theatre Arts. (CC ISSN 0257-943X) **4642**
Xiju Yishu/Theatre Art. (CC) **4642**
Xiju yu Dianying/Theatre and Cinema. (CC ISSN 1003-2681) **350**, 3519
Xin Jinrong/New Finance. (CC) **804**
Xin Liaozhai. (CC) **2978**
Xin Meishu/New Fine Art. (CC) **350**
Xin Qingnian/New Youth. (CC) **1246**
Xin Shiji/New Century. (CC) **700**
Xin Shixue Tongxun see Shixue Yuekan **2322**
Xin Tang - New China see Xinya **2852**
Xin Tiyu/New Sports. (CC ISSN 0441-3679) **4497**
Xin Wenhua Shiliao/Historical Records of the New Culture. (CC) **2343**, 4456
Xin Wenxue Shiliao/Historical Materials of New Literature. (CC ISSN 0257-5647) **2978**, 2326
Xin Yixue/New Medical Science. (CC) **3163**
Xinan Luyou/Southwest Tourism. (CC) **4798**
Xinan Minzu Xueyuan Xuebao (Zhexue Shehui Kexue Ban)/Southwest Institute of Nationalities. Journal (Philosophy, Social Science Edition). (CC) **4392**
Xinan Minzu Xueyuan Xuebao (Zhexue Shehui Kexue Ban)/Southwest China Nationalities College. Journal. (Social Science Edition). (CC) **4392**
Xinan Shifan Daxue Xuebao (Shehui Kexue Ban)/Southwest Normal University. Journal (Social Science Edition). (CC ISSN 1000-2677) **4392**
Xinan Shifan Daxue Xuebao (Ziran Kexue Ban)/Southwest Normal University. Journal (Natural Science Edition). (CC ISSN 1000-5471) **4352**
Xincun. (CC) **130**, 888
Xing Huo/Spark. (CC) **2978**
Xingfu/Happiness. (CC) **4858**
Xingxing Shikan/Star Poetry Journal. (CC) **3009**
Xinhua Monthly Report. see Xinhua Yuebao **2183**
Xinhua Wenzhai. (CC ISSN 1001-6651) **2183**
Xinhua Yuebao/Xinhua Monthly Report.(CC ISSN 1001-666X) **2183**
Xinjiang Huabao/Xinjiang Pictorial. (CC) **2183**
Xinjiang Pictorial. see Xinjiang Huabao **2183**
Xinjiang Shehui Kexue/Social Science in Xinjiang. (CC ISSN 1000-4262) **4392**
Xinli Kexue Tongxun/Information on Psychological Sciences. (CC ISSN 1000-6648) **4050**
Xinli Xuebao/Acta Psychologica Sinica. (CC ISSN 0439-755X) **4050**
Xinsheng Erke Zazhi/Journal of Pediatrics for the New-born. (CC) **3327**
Xinwen Bao/Business News. (CC) **700**
Xinwen Jizhe/Journalists. (CC) **2577**
Xinwen Xuekan. (CC) **2577**
Xinwen Yanjiu Ziliao/Journalism Research Materials. (CC) **2577**
Xinwen yu Chengcai. (CC) **2577**

Xinwen yu Xiezuo/Journalism and Writing. (CC) **2577**
Xinwen Zhanxian. (CC ISSN 0257-5930) **2577**
Xinwenjie/Press Circles. (CC) **2577**
Xinxi Huabao/Information Pictorial. (CC) **2183**
Xinxi Shijie/Information World. (CC ISSN 1001-0297) **2791**
Xinxi Xitong Gongcheng/Information System Engineering. (CC ISSN 1001-2362) **1346**
Xinxi yu Kongzhi/Information and Control. (CC) **1416**
Xinxueguanbingxue Jinzhan/Advances in Cardiovascular Disease. (CC) **3212**
Xinya. (US) **2852**
Xinyao yu Linchuang/New Drugs and Clinical Remedies. (CC ISSN 1000-3843) **3746**
Xinyuan. (CC) **2978**
Xinzhongyi/New Journal of Traditional Chinese Medicine. (CC ISSN 0256-7415) **3163**, **3746**
Xi'ou Yanjiu/Western European Studies. (CC ISSN 1000-3576) **4392**, **1000**, **2519**
Xitong Gongcheng Lilun yu Shijian/System Engineering Theory and Practice. (CC) **1440**
Xitong Gongcheng Xuebao/Journal of System Engineering. (CC) **1840**
Xitong Gongcheng yu Dianzi Jishu. see Journal of Systems Engineering and Electronics **57**
Xitong Kexue yu Shuxue. (CC ISSN 1000-0577) **1440**, **3061**
Xiuci Xuexi/Rhetoric Study. (CC ISSN 1000-3584) **2978**, **1763**
Xiwang/Hope. (CC) **4392**
Xiya Feizhou/West Asia and Africa. (CC) **4392**
Xiyou Jinshu see Rare Metals **3418**
Xizang Fojiao/Tibetan Buddhism. (CC) **4216**
Xizang Jiaoyu/Tibetan Education. (CC) **1672**
Xizang Wenxue/Tibetan Literature. (CC) **2978**, **3645**
Xizang Yanjiu/Tibetan Studies. (CC ISSN 1000-0003) **3645**, **253**
Xizang Yishu/Tibetan Art Studies.(CC) **350**
Xizquil. (US) **2890**
Xolo see Los Perros del Mundo **3712**
Xpo see Shrieking Violet **1324**
Xpress. (AT ISSN 0817-4628) **350**, **1295**, **4642**
Xtra! (CN ISSN 0829-3384) **2458**, **4798**
Xtras. (US) **2978**
Xuanchuan Shouce/Propaganda Handbook. (CC) **4392**
Xuanmei Jishu/Coal Selecting Techniques. (CC ISSN 1001-3571) **3498**, **2267**
Xue Hai. (CC) **4392**
Xue Hanyu/Learning Chinese. (CC) **2853**, **1763**
Xue yu Wan/Study and Play. (CC) **1246**
Xueke Jiaoyu. (CC) **1672**
Xueqian Jiaoyu/Preschool Education. (CC ISSN 0439-7843) **1672**
Xueshu Luntan. (CC ISSN 0438-1033) **4392**
Xueshu Yanjiu/Academic Research. (CC ISSN 1000-7326) **4392**
Xueshu Yuekan/Academic Monthly. (CC ISSN 0439-8041) **3704**, **899**, **4392**
Xuewei yu Yanjiusheng Jiaoyu/Academic Degrees and Graduate Education. (CC ISSN 1001-960X) **1720**
Xuexi/Study. (US) **4392**, **1763**
Xuexi yu Fudao/Study and Guidance. (CC) **2695**
Xuexi yu Tansuo/Study & Exploration. (CC) **4393**, **3704**
Xuyu Yanjiu. (CC) **3935**
Xueyu Wenhua/Tibetan Culture. (CC ISSN 1003-7942) **3645**
Xumu Shouyi Xuebao/Acta Veterinaria et Zootechnica Sinica. (CC ISSN 0366-6964) **4820**, **229**

Xuzhou Institute of Medical Sciences. Journal. see Xuzhou Yixueyuan Xuebao **3163**
Xuzhou Yixueyuan Xuebao/Xuzhou Institute of Medical Sciences. Journal.(CC ISSN 1000-2065) **3163**
Y A B A Framework. (US) **4515**, **1271**
Y A B A World see Y A B A Framework **4515**
Y A M see Young Authors Magazine **1271**
Y A M see Vision (Grand Rapids) **5301**
Y A R N. (Your Auckland Railway News) (NZ ISSN 0044-023X) **4717**
Y Canada see Y Triangle **1302**
Y E R Monograph Series. (Yeats Eliot Review) (CN ISSN 0704-5697) **2978**
Y E S International Entomology Resource Guide. (Young Entomologists' Society, Inc.) (US) **538**
Y E S Quarterly. (Young Entomologists' Society, Inc.) (US ISSN 0884-6677) **539**
Y F C Newsrelease. (Geelong Youth for Christ) (AT) **4253**, **1271**
Y H A Hostel Yarn see Hostel Travel **4771**
Y H A Hostels in Australia. (Australian Youth Hostels Association Incorporated) (AT) **4798**
Y M. (Young and Modern) (US ISSN 0888-5842) **1271**
Y M C A Review. (Young Men's Christian Association) (KE) **2209**
Y M C A Weekly News (Vancouver, BC). (Vancouver Downtown Young Men's Christian Association) (CN) **3811**, **3613**, **4497**
Y M C A World Communique see World Communique **1246**
Y M C A Yearbook and Official Roster. (Young Men's Christian Association) (US ISSN 0084-4292) **4424**
Y M I. (US) **4279**, **1271**, **1331**
†Y O! (Yes Osho!) (US) **5307**
Y S L Magazine see Search (London, 1924) **1265**
Y Tir. see Welsh Farmer **129**
Y Tir and Welsh Farmer see Welsh Farmer **129**
Y Triangle. (CN ISSN 0838-6536) **1302**, **1246**
†Y V. (Yhteisvoimin) (FI ISSN 0355-9378) **5307**
Y W C A Interchange. (Young Women's Christian Association of the United States of America) (US) **1302**
Ya'ad. (IS ISSN 0792-2337) **3935**, **2592**
Yachad. (IS) **833**
Yacht. (GW ISSN 0043-9932) **4531**
†Yacht. (US ISSN 0748-805X) **5307**
Yacht Digest. (IT) **4531**
Yacht Racing and Cruising see Sailing World **4529**
Yachting see Yachting News **4531**
Yachting. (US ISSN 0043-9940) **4531**
Yachting a Voile see Voile Magazine **5302**
Yachting Italiano. (IT) **4531**
Yachting Italiano-Atomare see Yachting Italiano **4531**
Yachting Life. (UK) **4531**
Yachting Monthly. (UK ISSN 0043-9983) **4531**
Yachting News. (SZ) **4531**
Yachting Sud - Sur l'Eau. (BE) **4531**
Yachting World. (UK ISSN 0043-9991) **4531**
Yachting Year Book of Northern California. (US ISSN 0094-8136) **4531**
†Yachting's Boat Buyers Guide. (US) **5307**
Yachtrevue. (AU) **4531**
Yachts and Yachting. (UK ISSN 0044-0000) **4531**
Yachtsman's Guide to the Bahamas. (US) **4531**, **4798**
Yachtsman's Guide to the Caribbean. (US ISSN 0084-3261) **4531**

Yachtsman's Guide to the Great Lakes. (US ISSN 0084-327X) **4531**
Yachtsman's Guide to the Greater Antilles see Yachtsman's Guide to the Virgin Islands & Puerto Rico **4531**
Yachtsman's Guide to the Virgin Islands & Puerto Rico. (US ISSN 0735-9020) **4531**
Yad l'Achim Wall Calendar. (IS ISSN 0333-7596) **4227**
Yad Lakore/Reader's Aid. (IS ISSN 0334-200X) **2791**
Yad Vashem Studies. (US) **4227**
Yadam & Silhwa. (KO) **2985**
Yadernaya Fizika. (RU ISSN 0044-0027) **3851**
Yadian yu Shengguang. (CC) **1911**
Yadoriga/Lepidopterological Society of Japan. Journal. (JA ISSN 0513-417X) **539**
Yaghma. (IR) **2978**
Yagl-Ambu. (PP) **4393**, **2519**
Yakhak Hoeji. see Pharmaceutical Society of Korea. Journal **3738**
Yakima Nation Review. (US ISSN 0199-3046) **2029**
Yakkoso Tsuchitorimochi no Tomo. (JA) **521**
Yakkyoku. see Practical Pharmacy **3740**
Yakkyoku No Tomo. see Pharmacy Companion **3739**
Yakugaku Toshokan. see Pharmaceutical Library Bulletin **2779**
Yakugaku Zasshi. see Pharmaceutical Society of Japan. Journal **3738**
Yakugyo Shinbun. see Japanese Weekly on Pharmacy and Chemistry **3730**
Yakuzaigaku. see Journal of Pharmaceutical Science and Technology **3732**
Yakyo-to/Baseball Fans. (JA) **4515**
Yale Alumni Magazine. (US ISSN 0044-0051) **1331**
Yale Classical Studies. (UK ISSN 0084-330X) **1280**
Yale College Series. (US ISSN 0084-3318) **2519**
Yale Daily News. (US ISSN 0890-2240) **1331**
Yale Fastbacks. (US ISSN 0084-3326) **4393**
Yale Forest School News. (US ISSN 0148-5741) **2111**
Yale French Studies. (US ISSN 0044-0078) **2978**, **2890**
†Yale Germanic Studies. (US ISSN 0084-3334) **5307**
Yale Historical Publications. (US ISSN 0084-3350) **2326**
Yale Journal of Biology and Medicine. (US ISSN 0044-0086) **3163**, **460**
Yale Journal of Criticism. (UK ISSN 0893-5378) **2978**
Yale Journal of International Law. (US ISSN 0889-7743) **2730**
Yale Journal of Law and Feminism. (US ISSN 1043-9366) **2695**, **4861**, **4861**
Yale Journal of Law & the Humanities. (US ISSN 1041-6374) **2519**, **2695**, **2978**
Yale Journal on Regulation. (US ISSN 0741-9457) **2695**, **4078**
Yale Judaica Series. (US ISSN 0084-3369) **4227**
Yale Language Series. (US) **2853**
Yale Law & Policy Review. (US) **2695**
Yale Law Journal. (US ISSN 0044-0094) **2696**
Yale Literary Magazine. (US ISSN 0148-4605) **2978**
Yale Near Eastern Researches. (US ISSN 0084-3385) **2432**
Yale Oriental Series. Babylonian Texts. (US) **2432**
Yale Publications in the History of Art. (US ISSN 0084-3415) **350**, **308**
Yale Review. (US ISSN 0044-0124) **2890**
†Yale Romanic Studies. Second Series. (US ISSN 0084-3423) **5307**
†Yale Russian and East European Studies. (US ISSN 0084-3431) **5307**
Yale Scene; University Series. (US ISSN 0084-344X) **1720**

YAMAGUCHI-KEN 6821

Yale Scientific. (US ISSN 0091-0287) **4352**
Yale Scientific Magazine see Yale Scientific **4352**
Yale Series in Economic History. (US) **899**
Yale Series of Younger Poets. (US ISSN 0084-3458) **3009**
Yale Southeast Asia Studies. Monograph Series. (US ISSN 0513-4501) **3646**, **4393**
Yale Studies in English. (US ISSN 0084-3482) **2978**
Yale University. Bulletin. (US) **1720**
Yale University. Department of Anthropology. Publications in Anthropology. (US) **253**
Yale University. Economic Growth Center. Annual Report. (US) **700**
Yale University. Economic Growth Center. Center Discussion Paper. (US) **888**
Yale University. School of Forestry and Environmental Studies. Bulletin. (US) **2111**
Yale University. School of Forestry. Bulletin see Yale University. School of Forestry and Environmental Studies. Bulletin **2111**
Yale University Art Gallery Bulletin. (US ISSN 0084-3539) **3535**
Yale University Library Gazette. (US ISSN 0044-0175) **2791**
Yale Vernacular. (US) **2890**
Yale Western Americana Series. (US ISSN 0084-3563) **2427**
Yalkut. (IS) **4627**
Yalkut Lemachshava Sotzialistit. (IS ISSN 0334-1003) **3935**
Yalu River. see Yalujiang **2978**
Yalujiang/Yalu River. (CC ISSN 1003-4099) **2978**
Yama to Hakubutsukan/Mountain and Museum. (JA) **3535**, **4352**
Yamada Conference. Proceedings. (JA) **4352**
Yamada Kagaku Shinko Zaidan Jigyo Hokokusho/Yamada Science Foundation Annual Report. (JA) **4352**
Yamada Science Foundation Annual Report. see Yamada Kagaku Shinko Zaidan Jigyo Hokokusho **4352**
Yamada Science Foundation News. see Zaidan Nyusu **4353**
Yamagata Daigaku Kiyo/Yamagata University. Bulletin. (JA ISSN 0085-834X) **2519**
Yamagata University. Bulletin. see Yamagata Daigaku Kiyo **2519**
Yamaguchi Daigaku Igakubu Kiyo. see Yamaguchi University. School of Medicine. Bulletin **3163**
Yamaguchi Daigaku Kyoikugakubu Kenkyu Ronso. Dai-2-bu. Shizen Kagaku/Yamaguchi University. Faculty of Education. Bulletin, Part 2.(JA ISSN 0513-1693) **4352**
Yamaguchi Daigaku Kyoyobu Kiyo. Shizen Kagaku Hen/Yamaguchi University. Faculty of Liberal Arts. Journal: Natural Science. (JA ISSN 0387-4087) **4352**
Yamaguchi Joshi Daigaku Kenkyu Hokoku. Dai-2-bu. Shizen Kagaku/Yamaguchi Women's University. Bulletin. Section 2, Natural Science. (JA ISSN 0385-2946) **4352**
Yamaguchi-ken Eisei Kenkyujo Gyoseki Hokoku see Yamaguchi-ken Eisei Kogai Kenkyu Senta Gyoseki Hokoku **4116**
Yamaguchi-ken Eisei Kenkyujo Nenpo see Yamaguchi-ken Eisei Kogai Kenkyu Senta Nenpo **4119**
Yamaguchi-ken Eisei Kogai Kenkyu Senta Gyoseki Hokoku. (JA ISSN 0915-0498) **4116**, **1972**, **3163**
Yamaguchi-ken Eisei Kogai Kenkyu Senta Nenpo. (JA ISSN 0915-048X) **4119**, **4592**
Yamaguchi-ken Kogai Senta Nenpo see Yamaguchi-ken Eisei Kogai Kenkyu Senta Nenpo **4119**
Yamaguchi-ken no Shizen. (JA ISSN 0288-4240) **4352**

Yamaguchi-kenritsu Yamaguchi Hakubutsukan Kenkyu Hokoku/Yamaguchi Prefectural Yamaguchi Museum. Bulletin. (JA ISSN 0288-4232) **4353**, **3535**

Yamaguchi Prefectural Yamaguchi Museum. Bulletin. *see* Yamaguchi-kenritsu Yamaguchi Hakubutsukan Kenkyu Hokoku **4353**

Yamaguchi University. Faculty of Agriculture. Bulletin. (JA ISSN 0513-1715) **130**

Yamaguchi University. Faculty of Education. Bulletin, Part 2. *see* Yamaguchi Daigaku Kyoikugakubu Kenkyu Ronso. Dai-2-bu. Shizen Kagaku **4352**

Yamaguchi University. Faculty of Engineering. Technology Reports. (JA) **4613**

Yamaguchi University. Faculty of Liberal Arts. Journal: Natural Science. *see* Yamaguchi Daigaku Kyoyobu Kiyo. Shizen Kagaku Hen **4352**

Yamaguchi University. School of Medicine. Bulletin/Yamaguchi Daigaku Igakubu Kiyo. (JA ISSN 0513-1812) **3163**

Yamaguchi Women's University. Bulletin. Section 2, Natural Science. *see* Yamaguchi Joshi Daigaku Kenkyu Hokoku. Dai-2-bu. Shizen Kagaku **4352**

Al-Yamamah. (SU) **2216**
Yamamoto Forecast. (US) **969**
Yaman al-Jadiyd. (YE) **2890**
Yamanashi Daigaku Kyoikugakubu Kenkyu Hokoku. Dai-2-bunsatsu, Shizen Kagakukei/Yamanashi University. Faculty of Liberal Arts & Education. Memoirs. Part 2: Mathematics & Natural Sciences. (JA ISSN 0385-8766) **4353**

Yamanashi University. Faculty of Liberal Arts & Education. Memoirs. Part 2: Mathematics & Natural Sciences. *see* Yamanashi Daigaku Kyoikugakubu Kenkyu Hokoku. Dai-2-bunsatsu, Shizen Kagakukei **4353**

Yamashina Chorui Kenkyujo Kenkyu Hokoku. *see* Yamashina Institute for Ornithology. Journal **568**

Yamashina Institute for Ornithology. Journal/Yamashina Chorui Kenkyujo Kenkyu Hokoku. (JA) **568**

Yan Du/Ancient Capital. (US) **2343**
Yan Du/Capital of Yan. (CC) **4393**
Yan He/Yan River. (CC ISSN 1001-6104) **2978**
Yan River. *see* Yan He **2978**
Yan - Zhao Xiangyin. (CC) **3935**
Yana. (GW) **4216**
Yanbian Funu/Yanbian Women. (CC) **4858**
Yanbian Women. *see* Yanbian Funu **4858**
Yandi Bing/Ocular Fundus. (CC ISSN 1001-4071) **3305**
Yang Guan. (CC ISSN 1003-7527) **3646**
Yangtz Literature and Art. *see* Changjiang Wenyi **2904**
Yangtze Literature. *see* Changjiang (Duozhong Wenxue) Congkan **2904**
Yangtze River Scientific Research Institute. Journal. *see* Changjiang Kexueyuan Yuanbao **1923**
Yanhuang Zisun/Descendants of the Emperors. (US) **2183**
Yanjiu Baogao - Guoli Taiwan Daxue Lixueyuan Dizhuexi Xi *see* Acta Geologica Taiwanica **1553**
Yanke Xuebao. *see* Eye Science **3300**
Yankee. (US ISSN 0044-0191) **2238**
Yankee Food Service. (US ISSN 0195-2552) **2482**, **2084**
Yankee Homes. (US) **4159**
Yankee Horsetrader. (US ISSN 0192-5210) **4539**
Yankee Ingenuity. (US) **1402**
Yankee Magazine's Travel Guide to New England and its Neighbors *see* Yankee Magazine's Travel Guide to New England, New York & Eastern Canada **4798**
Yankee Magazine's Travel Guide to New England, New York & Eastern Canada. (US ISSN 1055-226X) **4798**

Yankee Oilman. (US ISSN 0044-0205) **3704**
Yankee Woodlot. (US) **2111**
Yankuang Ceshi. (CC ISSN 0254-5357) **1586**
Yanshi Lixue yu Gongcheng Xuebao/Journal of Rock Mechanics and Engineering. (CC ISSN 1000-6915) **3846**, **1941**
Yanshi Xuebao/Acta Petrologica Sinica. (CC ISSN 1000-0569) **1586**
Yantai Daxue Xuebao/Yantai University. Journal. (CC) **2519**, **4353**
Yantai Daxue Xuebao (Shehui Kexue Ban)/Yantai University. Journal (Social Science Edition). (CC) **4393**
Yantai University. Journal. *see* Yantai Daxue Xuebao **2519**
Yantai University. Journal (Social Science Edition). *see* Yantai Daxue Xuebao (Shehui Kexue Ban) **4393**
Yantu Gongcheng Xuebao. (CC ISSN 1000-4548) **1876**
Yantu Lixue/Rock and Soil Mechanics. (CC ISSN 1000-7598) **3846**
Yaogan Xinxi/Remote Sensing Information. (CC ISSN 1000-3177) **2267**
Yaowu Fenxi Zazhi/Journal of Pharmacologic Analysis. (CC ISSN 0254-1793) **3746**
Yaowu yu Ren/Medicine and Men. (CC) **3746**
Yaoxue Tongbao/Chinese Pharmaceutical Bulletin. (CC) **3746**
Yaoxue Xuebao/Acta Pharmaceutica Sinica. (CC) **3746**
Yapi. (TU) **309**, **350**, **636**
Yapi ve Kredi Bankasi. Annual Report. (TU) **804**
Yaqeen International. (PK ISSN 0044-0213) **4221**, **3646**
Yaqza. (KU) **888**
Yarborough Family Magazine. (US) **2168**
Yarchon Chesev. (IS) **700**
†Yarchon Yisraeli Lemachshevai P C Vetoamim. (IS) **5307**
Yard and Garden. (US ISSN 0896-6834) **2140**
Yard and Garden Product News *see* Yard and Garden **2140**
Yardbird Reader. (US) **2978**
Yardstick. (US) **1062**
Yardstick. (CN) **2119**
Yardsticks for Costing. (CN) **309**
Yaredai Zhiwu Tongxun/Subtropical Plant Bulletin. (CC) **521**
Yarmouk University. Institute of Archaeology and Anthropology. Series. (GW ISSN 0932-3201) **3646**
†Yarn Market News. (US ISSN 0882-7982) **5307**
Yarnspinner. (US) **2978**, **1672**
Yarrow. (US) **3009**
Yarruga *see* Curio **1309**
Yasmine. (FR) **1295**
Yatai Jingji/Economy of Asia and Pacific Rim. (CC ISSN 1000-6052) **700**
Yate y Motonautica. (SP ISSN 0210-0320) **4531**
Yatinataki. (BO) **2853**
Yatri. (II ISSN 0049-8289) **4798**
Yaxkin. (HO) **253**, **289**, **2427**
Yazhou Zhoukan. (HK ISSN 1015-5015) **2197**, **2343**
Yazin. (GW) **2978**
Y'bird *see* Yardbird Reader **2978**
Ye Olde Bastards Bulletin. (US) **424**, **253**, **998**, **3935**
Ye Olde Dutch Mill. (US) **1302**, **2029**
(Year) Annual Index: Photofact, Computerfact, V C R Fact, Radio, T V & Selected Original Manufacturer's Service Data. (US) **1384**
Year-End Regulatory Review. (US ISSN 0275-276X) **1031**
Year-End Tax Planning Guide. (US) **757**
Year in Hematology *see* Contemporary Hematology - Oncology **3271**
Year in Immunology. (SZ ISSN 0256-2308) **3189**
(Year) Peace Calendar. (US) **3009**, **3948**
Year-Rounder. (US) **1732**

▼(Year) State Fiscal Prospects. (US) **1112**
Yearbook and Church Directory of the Orthodox Church in America *see* Orthodox Church in America. Yearbook and Church Directory **4286**
Yearbook and Directory of Members and Separation Technology *see* Directory of Membrane & High Tech Separations (Year) **4596**
Yearbook and Directory of Osteopathic Physicians *see* A O A Yearbook and Directory of Osteopathic Physicians **3213**
Yearbook and Philatelic Societies' Directory. (UK ISSN 0260-1265) **3759**
Yearbook Commercial Arbitration. (NE) **2730**
Yearbook for Jewish Communities and Organizations *see* Jewish World **2009**
Yearbook for Traditional Music. (US ISSN 0740-1558) **3587**, **2060**
Yearbook in Women's Policy Studies *see* Sage Yearbooks in Women's Policy Studies **4852**
Yearbook Maritime Law. (NE) **2696**, **2735**
Yearbook of Adult Continuing Education.(UK ISSN 0265-1726) **1688**, **1681**
Yearbook of Adult Education *see* Yearbook of Adult Continuing Education **1688**
Year Book of Agricultural Co-Operation *see* Year Book of Co-Operative Enterprise **160**
Yearbook of Agricultural Statistics of Bangladesh. (BG) **130**
Yearbook of Agriculture *see* U.S. Department of Agriculture. Yearbook of Agriculture **126**
Yearbook of American and Canadian Churches. (US ISSN 0084-3644) **4210**
Yearbook of American Lutheran Church *see* Evangelical Lutheran Church in America (Year) **4237**
Year Book of Anesthesia. (US ISSN 0084-3652) **3192**
Year Book of Cancer *see* Year Book of Oncology **3203**
Year Book of Cardiology. (US ISSN 0145-4145) **3212**
Year Book of Chess. (UK) **4497**
Year Book of Co-Operative Enterprise. (UK ISSN 0952-5556) **160**, **833**, **1057**
Yearbook of Common Carrier Telecommunication Statistics/Annuaire Statistique des Telecommunications du Secteur Public. (UN) **1346**
Yearbook of Comparative and General Literature. (US ISSN 0084-3695) **2978**
Year Book of Critical Care Medicine. (US ISSN 0734-3299) **3163**
Yearbook of Danish Medical History. *see* Dansk Medicinhistorisk Aarbog **3093**
Year Book of Dentistry. (US ISSN 0084-3717) **3244**
▼Year Book of Dermatologic Surgery. (US ISSN 1059-0587) **3250**, **3386**
Year Book of Dermatology. (US ISSN 0093-3619) **3250**
Year Book of Diagnostic Radiology. (US ISSN 0098-1672) **3363**
Year Book of Digestive Diseases. (US ISSN 0739-5930) **3270**
Year Book of Drug Therapy. (US ISSN 0084-3733) **3746**
Yearbook of Educational Law. (US ISSN 1049-0264) **2696**, **1672**
Year Book of Emergency Medicine. (US ISSN 0271-7964) **3312**
Year Book of Endocrinology. (US ISSN 0084-3741) **3256**
Yearbook of English Studies. (UK ISSN 0306-2473) **2519**, **2978**
Yearbook of European Law. (UK ISSN 0266-7223) **2730**
Yearbook of European Studies/Annuaire d'Etudes Europeennes. (NE) **3978**, **2696**, **2978**

Yearbook of Experts, Authorities & Spokespersons. (US) **1384**
Year Book of Family Practice. (US ISSN 0147-1996) **3163**
Yearbook of Finnish Foreign Policy. (FI ISSN 0355-0079) **3978**
Yearbook of Fishery Statistics *see* F A O Fisheries Series **2039**
Yearbook of Forest Products/Annuaire des Produits Forestiers/Anuario de Productos Forestales. (UN ISSN 0084-3768) **2119**
Yearbook of Forest Statistics. *see* Metsatilastollinen Vuosikirja **2104**
Year Book of Geriatrics and Gerontology. (US ISSN 0894-2757) **2280**
Yearbook of German - American Studies. (US) **2978**
Yearbook of Greek Press. (GR) **2577**
Year Book of Hand Surgery. (US) **3386**, **3163**, **3312**
▼Year Book of Health Care Management. (US ISSN 1050-995X) **2470**
Year Book of Hematology. (US ISSN 0882-5998) **3274**
Year Book of Infectious Diseases. (US ISSN 0743-9261) **3224**
Yearbook of Interdisciplinary Studies in the Fine Arts. (US ISSN 1048-860X) **350**, **2978**, **4642**
Yearbook of International Commodity Statistics *see* U N C T A D Commodity Yearbook **741**
Yearbook of International Congress Proceedings. (BE ISSN 0084-3806) **3978**
Yearbook of International Organizations/Annuaire des Organisations Internationales. (GW ISSN 0084-3814) **3978**
Yearbook of Israel Ports Statistics/Shenaton Statisti: Le Nemlei Israel. (IS ISSN 0084-3830) **744**, **925**
Yearbook of Italian Studies. (IT) **2396**
Yearbook of Jehovah's Witnesses *see* Jehovah's Witnesses Yearbook **4284**
Year Book of Labour Statistics. (UN ISSN 0084-3857) **744**
Yearbook of Law Computers and Technology. (UK ISSN 0269-3712) **2705**, **2696**
Yearbook of Maryland Legislators. (US) **3935**, **2696**, **4078**
Year Book of Medicine. (US ISSN 0084-3873) **3163**
Yearbook of National Account Statistics *see* United Nations. National Accounts Statistics. Analysis of Main Aggregates **741**
Yearbook of National Account Statistics *see* United Nations. National Accounts Statistics. Government Accounts and Tables **742**
Yearbook of National Account Statistics *see* United Nations. National Accounts Statistics. Main Aggregates and Detailed Tables **742**
▼Year Book of Nephrology. (US) **3390**
Year Book of Neurology & Neurosurgery. (US ISSN 0513-5117) **3356**, **3386**
▼Year Book of Neuroradiology. (US) **3363**, **3356**
Yearbook of New York State Charitable Organizations. (US) **4424**
Yearbook of Nordic Statistics. *see* Nordisk Statistisk Aarsbok **4581**
Year Book of Nuclear Medicine. (US ISSN 0084-3903) **3363**
Year Book of Obstetrics and Gynecology. (US ISSN 0084-3911) **3297**
▼Year Book of Occupational Medicine. (US ISSN 0899-8035) **3163**
Year Book of Oncology. (US ISSN 1040-1741) **3203**
Year Book of Ophthalmology. (US ISSN 0084-392X) **3306**
Year Book of Orthopedics. (US ISSN 0276-1092) **3312**
Year Book of Orthopedics, Traumatic and Plastic Surgery *see* Year Book of Orthopedics **3312**
Year Book of Otolaryngology - Head and Neck Surgery. (US ISSN 1041-892X) **3317**

Year Book of Pathology and Clinical Pathology. (US ISSN 0084-3946) **3163**
Year Book of Pediatrics. (US ISSN 0084-3954) **3327**
Year Book of Perinatal - Neonatal Medicine. (US ISSN 1044-4890) **3327**
Yearbook of Physical Anthropology. (US ISSN 0096-848X) **253**
Year Book of Plastic and Reconstructive Surgery see Year Book of Plastic, Reconstructive, and Aesthetic Surgery **3386**
Year Book of Plastic, Reconstructive, and Aesthetic Surgery. (US ISSN 1040-175X) **3386**
Year Book of Podiatric Medicine and Surgery. (US ISSN 0742-194X) **3312, 3386**
Yearbook of Population Research in Finland/Vaestoentutkimuksen Vuosikirja. (FI ISSN 0506-3590) **3989**
Year Book of Psychiatry and Applied Mental Health. (US ISSN 0084-3970) **3356**
Year Book of Pulmonary Disease. (US ISSN 8756-3452) **3368**
Yearbook of Pulp and Paper Statistics. see Kami Parupu Tokei Nenpo **3663**
†Year Book of Rehabilitation. (US ISSN 8756-3460) **5307**
Yearbook of Religious Zionism. (IS) **4227**
Yearbook of Romanian Studies. (US ISSN 0149-7219) **2978, 2396**
Yearbook of Scandinavian Shipowners. see Skandinaviske Skipsrederier **4739**
Yearbook of School Law see Yearbook of Educational Law **2696**
Yearbook of Science and the Future. (US ISSN 0096-3291) **4353**
Yearbook of Selected Osteopathic Papers see American Academy of Osteopathy Yearbook **3213**
Yearbook of Social Policy in Britain see Social Policy Review **4387**
†Yearbook of South Australian Crafts (Year). (AT ISSN 0818-917X) **5307**
†Year Book of Speech, Language and Hearing. (US ISSN 1050-219X) **5308**
Year Book of Sports Medicine. (US ISSN 0162-0908) **3373**
Yearbook of Substance Use and Abuse. (US ISSN 0273-3722) **1540**
Year Book of Surgery. (US ISSN 0090-3671) **3386**
Yearbook of Symbolic Anthropology. (CN) **253**
Yearbook of Technical and Further Education see Directory of Technical and Further Education **1132**
Yearbook of the American Baptist Churches in the U S A see American Baptist Churches in the U S A Yearbook **4228**
Yearbook of the Commonwealth. (UK ISSN 0084-4047) **2396**
Yearbook of the European Communities and of the Other European Organizations. (BE ISSN 0771-7962) **3978**
Year-Book of the Lebanese Joint-Stock Companies/Annuaire des Societes Libanaises Par Action. (LE ISSN 0075-8361) **969**
Year-Book of the Lebanese Limited Liability Companies/Annuaire des Societes Libanaises a Responsibilite Limitee. (LE) **970**
Yearbook of the Literary Museum. see Petofi Irodalmi Muzeum Evkonyve **2948**
Yearbook of the United Nations see United Nations. Yearbook **3975**
Yearbook of Tidal Records. see Choi Nenpo **1603**
Yearbook of Tourism Statistics. (SP) **4801**
▼Year Book of Transplantation. (US) **3386**
▼Year Book of Ultrasound. (US ISSN 1050-4443) **3363, 3163, 3860**

Year Book of Urology. (US ISSN 0084-4071) **3390**
Year Book of Vascular Surgery. (US ISSN 0749-4041) **3163, 3212**
Yearbook of Women's Studies. (US ISSN 1048-8626) **4858**
†Yearbook of Works re Appalachia. (US) **5308**
Yearbook of World Electronics Data Vol. 1: West Europe. (UK) **1779**
Yearbook of World Electronics Data Vol. 2: America, Japan, Asia-Pacific. (UK ISSN 0954-0172) **1779**
Yearbook of World Energy Statistics see Energy Statistics Yearbook **1799**
Yearbook of Yugoslav Theaters. see Godisnjak Jugoslovenskih Pozorista **4633**
Yearbook on Corporate Mergers, Joint Ventures and Corporate Policy see Merger Yearbook: Domestic Edition **679**
Yearbook on Human Rights. (UN ISSN 0084-4098) **3948, 2519**
†Yearbook on International Communist Affairs. (US ISSN 0084-4101) **5308**
Yearbook on Jute. (UK ISSN 0084-411X) **4627**
†Yearbook on Socialist Legal Systems. (US ISSN 0887-9117) **5308**
Yearbook - Supreme Court Historical Society see Supreme Court Historical Society. Yearbook **2733**
Yearly All India Civil Digest. (II) **2704**
Yearly All India Criminal Digest. (II ISSN 0377-6719) **1524**
†Yearly Digest. (II) **5308**
†Yearly Digest of Criminal Cases. (II ISSN 0513-2088) **5308**
Yearly Supreme Court Digest. (II) **2734**
Years Ahead. (US) **4116, 4834**
†Year's Best Fantasy Stories. (US) **5308**
Year's Best Horror Stories. (US) **3015**
Year's Best Science Fiction. (US) **3015**
Year's Work in Comic Indexing. (US ISSN 0733-2793) **2796, 352**
Year's Work in English Studies. (US ISSN 0084-4144) **2978**
Year's Work in Modern Language Studies. (UK ISSN 0084-4152) **2856, 2983**
Yeast. (UK ISSN 0749-503X) **491, 388, 483, 559**
Yeats. (US ISSN 0742-6224) **2979**
Yeats Eliot Review. (CN ISSN 0704-5700) **3009, 2979**
Yeats Eliot Review Monograph Series see Y E R Monograph Series **2978**
Yeda. (IS) **3704**
Yeda-Am. (IS) **2060**
Yeda Lemeida. (IS ISSN 0333-5666) **1112, 700**
Yedies Fun Yivo. see Yivo News **2519**
Yedinaya Tserkov. see One Church **4286**
Yedion see S S D A Newsletter **4385**
†Yediot Hamaskirut. (IS) **5308**
Yediot Keren Kayemit Leyisrael. (IS) **2111, 1501**
Yeh Ko. see Evensongs **2865**
Yejin Nengyuan. (CC ISSN 1001-1617) **3424**
Yejin Shebei/Metallurgical Equipment. (CC ISSN 1001-1269) **3424**
Yell County Historical & Genealogical Association. (US) **2168**
Yellow Book News. (US) **2120**
Yellow Book of Funeral Directors. (US) **1160, 2120**
Yellow Jacket. (US) **1331**
Yellow Mountain. see Huang Shan **2252**
Yellow Page Model Directory. (US) **3400, 2238**
▼Yellow Pages. (US) **3009**
Yellow Pages & Directory Report. (US) **40, 1160**
▼Yellow Pages Industry Sourcebook. (US) **1160**
▼Yellow Pages Moscow. (US) **1160**
Yellow River. see Huang He **2923**
Yellow Sheet Report. (US) **4078, 3935**
Yellow Silk. (US ISSN 0736-9212) **2979, 3009**

Yellowed Pages. (US ISSN 1050-7361) **2168, 2427**
Yellowjacket. (US ISSN 0277-9668) **2168**
Yellowknife Tonight. (CN) **1384**
Yellowknifer. (CN) **2180**
The Yellowstone Desktop Publishing Letter. (US) **4144, 1465**
▼The Yellowstone Windows Letter. (US) **1465, 1475**
Yememhiran Dimts. (ET ISSN 0044-0310) **1672**
Yememhiran Melkt/Teachers' Message. (ET ISSN 0044-0329) **1672**
Yeo Sung. see Women **4856**
Yeon-Gu Weolbo. (KO ISSN 0044-0345) **1672**
Yerevan Banber. Hasarakakan Gitut'yunner. Hamalsarani. (AI) **2519**
▼Yertontsiyn Sport/World of Sport. (MP) **4497**
Yerusholaimer Almanakh. (IS ISSN 0334-9594) **2979**
Yes see Chien d'Or **2905**
Yes. (UK ISSN 0951-726X) **4210**
Yes Osho! see Y O **5307**
Yes You Can. (CN) **636**
Yesheng Dongwu/Wild Animals. (CC ISSN 1000-0127) **594**
Yeshiva University. Annual Report. (US) **1720**
Yeshiva University Sephardic Bulletin. (US) **2029, 4227**
Yesterday and Today. see Gister en Vandag **2311**
Yesterday and Today. see Demb Ak Tey **2910**
Yesterday and Today in Lawrence County. (US) **2427**
▼Yesterday Today in New Jersey. (US) **2427**
Yesterday's Magazette. (US) **2979**
Yesteryear. (US) **260**
Yesteryear Heritage see Industrial Heritage Magazine **3485**
Yesteryears. (US ISSN 0044-037X) **2427, 2168**
Yet Another Small Magazine. (US ISSN 0278-9442) **2890, 3009**
Yeti. (NP) **4798**
Yevanhelskyj Ranok/Evangelical Morning. (US ISSN 0044-0388) **4253**
Yevse/Taste. (GR ISSN 1105-2414) **2084**
Yezarietu Ethiopia. (ET) **2186**
Ygia k Omorfia/Health and Beauty. (GR) **3811, 1295**
Yhdistyneiden Kansakuntien Yleiskokous (Year). (FI ISSN 0781-2442) **3978**
Yhteishyva. (FI ISSN 0044-0396) **833**
Yhteisvoimin see Y V **5307**
Yi Wen see Shijie Wenxue **2959**
Yi Xing. see First Line **2993**
Yibiao Jishu/Technology of Meters and Instruments. (CC) **2525**
Yichuan/Hereditas. (CC ISSN 0253-9772) **547**
Yichuan Xuebao/Acta Genetica Sinica. (CC ISSN 0379-4172) **548**
Yichuan yu Jibing/Heredity and Disease.(CC) **3163**
Der Yid. (US ISSN 0044-040X) **4227**
Yiddish. (US) **2979, 2029**
Yiddish Language. see Yidishe Shprakh **2853**
†Yiddish Literary and Linguistic Periodicals and Miscellanies. (IS) **5308**
Yiddish Welt. (IS) **2029**
Yiddish Zeitung. (IS) **2204**
Yiddishe Heim/Jewish Home. (US ISSN 0044-0418) **4227**
Yiddishe Kultur. (US ISSN 0044-0426) **2029**
Yiddisher Kemfer. (US ISSN 0044-0434) **2029**
Yidion. (IS ISSN 0334-0554) **1501**
Yidiot Hamercaz Ledemografia. (IS) **3989**
Yidiot Letzalam. (IS) **2798**
Yidishe Shprakh/Yiddish Language. (US ISSN 0044-0442) **2853**
Yilin/Translations: A Quarterly of Foreign Literature. (CC ISSN 1001-1897) **2979**

YLIOPPILASAINEITA 6823

Yin Ran/Printing and Dyeing. (CC ISSN 1000-4017) **4627**
Yindu Journal. see Yindu Xuekan **2343**
Yindu Xuekan/Yindu Journal. (CC ISSN 1001-0238) **2343**
Yingchun Hua. (CC) **350**
Yinger Huabao/Infant Pictorial. (CC) **1271, 1246**
Yingju Xinzuo/New Film and Play Scripts. (CC) **2979, 3519, 4642**
Yingju Yishu/Art of Film and Drama. (CC) **3519, 350**
Yingshi Wenxue/Film and Television Literature. (CC) **2979, 3519**
Yingxiang Jishu. (CC ISSN 1001-0270) **3798**
Yingxiang Yixue/Medical Imaging. (CC ISSN 1001-6384) **3363**
Yingyang Xuebao/Journal of Nutrition. (CC ISSN 0512-7955) **3613**
Yingyong Jiguang/Applied Lasers. (CC ISSN 1000-372X) **3858**
Yingyong Kexue Xuebao/Journal of Applied Sciences. (CC ISSN 0255-8297) **4353**
Yingyong Qixiang Xueta. (CC ISSN 1001-7313) **3444**
Yingyong Shengtai Xuebao/Journal of Applied Ecology. (CC) **1972**
Yingyong Shengxue/Applied Acoustics. (CC ISSN 1000-310X) **3860, 4462**
Yingyong Shuxue/Applied Mathematics. (CC) **3061**
Yingyong Shuxue Xuebao. (CC ISSN 0254-3079) **3061**
Yingyong Shuxue yu Lixue/Applied Mathematics and Mechanics. (CC ISSN 1000-0887) **3061, 3846**
Yingyu Shijie/World of English. (CC) **2853**
Yingyu Xuexi/English Language Learning. (CC) **2853**
Yingyu Zixue/English Self-Study. (CC) **2853**
Yinjin yu Zixun/Importing and Consulting. (CC) **970, 925**
Yinmu Neiwai/Around Film. (CC) **3519**
Yinnan Sumla Shi Laika. see Yunnan Huabao **2183**
Yinshua Zazhi/Printing Magazine. (CC) **4006**
Yinxiang Shijie/Audio-Visual World. (CC) **3587**
Yinyue Aihaozhe/Music Lover. (CC) **3587**
Yinyue Chuangzuo/Musical Creation. (US) **3587**
Yinyue Shenghuo/Music Life. (CC ISSN 0512-7920) **3587**
Yinyue Shijie/Music World. (CC) **3587**
Yinyue Tansuo/Explorations in Music. (CC) **3587**
Yinyue Tiandi/Music World. (CC) **3587**
Yinyue Yanjiu/Music Research. (CC) **3587**
Yinyue Yishu/Art of Music. (CC ISSN 1000-4270) **3587**
▼Yippy Yi Yea Magazine. (US) **4539**
Yipster Times see Overthrow **2878**
Yirnar Awha Lirshatad. see Yunnan Huabao **2183**
Yishu Baijia. (CC) **350**
Yishu - Shenghuo/Art - Life. (CC) **357, 2556**
Yishu Shijie/Art World. (CC) **350**
Yishu yu Shidai. (CC) **350**
Yishujia see Artist **316**
Yishujia/Artist. (CC) **350, 2979**
†Yisrael-Am ve-Eretz/Israel - People and Land. (IS ISSN 0334-1798) **5308**
Yivo Annual. (US) **4393, 2029**
Yivo Annual of Jewish Social Science see Yivo Annual **4393**
Yivo Bleter/Yivo Pages. (US ISSN 0084-4217) **4393**
Yivo News/Yedies Fun Yivo. (US) **2519, 4393**
Yivo Pages. see Yivo Bleter **4393**
Yixue Lilun yu Shijian/Medical Theory and Practice. (CC ISSN 1001-7585) **3163**
Yixue Wenzhai/Medical Abstracts. (CC) **3182**
Yiyao Gongcheng Sheji. (CC) **3746**
Yiyao Gongye see Zhongguo Yiyao Gongye Zazhi **3746**
Ylioppilasaineita. (FI ISSN 0355-1784) **1698**

Yllkat/Etoiles. (AA) **1271**
Ymoda. (SP) **4858**
Yo! Magazine. (US) **3587**, 1271
Yo-Yo Times. (US ISSN 0897-7704) **1271**
Yobo Igaku/Health Services Journal. (JA ISSN 0285-0877) **3163**
Yobo Jiho/Accident Prevention Journal. (JA ISSN 0910-4208) **2035**
Yod. (FR) **4227**, 2029
Yodelings. (US) **4139**
Yoder Family History Research Newsletter see Yoder Research **5308**
†Yoder Research. (US) **5308**
Yoga. (DK ISSN 0044-0485) **3786**, 4290
Yoga and Total Health. (II ISSN 0970-1737) **3786**, 3811, 4353
Yoga International. (US ISSN 1055-7911) **3597**, 3786, 4050
Yoga Journal. (US ISSN 0191-0965) **3597**, 3811
Yoga Life. (CN) **3786**, 3811
Yoga - Mimamsa. (II ISSN 0044-0507) **3786**
Yogasana Alaya Vijayam. (II) **4221**
Yogoslavia. Savazni Zavod za Statistiku. Indeks. (YU ISSN 0019-3585) **4592**
Yogyo Kyokai Shi see Seramikkusu Kyokai Shi **1166**
Yojana. (II ISSN 0044-0515) **4078**
Yoji-No-Shido. see Guidance of Infants **1636**
The Yoke. (JA ISSN 0289-551X) **1346**
Yokohama City Institute of Health. Annual Report. (JA ISSN 0912-2826) **4116**
Yokohama City University. Bulletin: Natural Science. see Yokohama-shiritsu Daigaku Ronso. Shizen Kagaku Keiretsu **4353**
Yokohama City University. Journal. Series of Natural Science. see Yokohama-shiritsu Daigaku Kiyo. Shizen Kagaku Hen **4353**
Yokohama Kokuritsu Daigaku Jinbun Kiyo Dai-1-rui, Tetsugaku, Shakai Kagaku/Yokohama National University. Humanities, Section 1: Philosophy and Social Sciences. (JA ISSN 0513-5621) **4393**, 3786
Yokohama Kokuritsu Daigaku Kogakubu Kiyo. see Yokohama National University. Faculty of Engineering. Bulletin **1841**
Yokohama Kokuritsu Daigaku Kyoiku Kiyo. see Yokohama National University. Educational Sciences **1673**
Yokohama Kokuritsu Daigaku Rika Kiyo. Dai-2-rui. Seibutsugaku, Chigaku. see Yokohama National University. Science Reports. Section 2: Biological and Geological Sciences **460**
Yokohama Kokuritsu Daigaku Rika Kiyo, Dai-1-rui, Sugaku, Butsurigaku, Kagaku. see Yokohama National University. Science Reports. Section 1: Mathematics, Physics, Chemistry **4353**
Yokohama Mathematical Journal. (JA ISSN 0044-0523) **3061**
Yokohama Medical Bulletin. (JA ISSN 0044-0531) **3163**
Yokohama Medical Journal. (JA ISSN 0372-7726) **3163**, 460, 3746, 4116
Yokohama National University. Educational Sciences/Yokohama Kokuritsu Daigaku Kyoiku Kiyo. (JA ISSN 0513-5656) **1673**
Yokohama National University. Faculty of Engineering. Bulletin/Yokohama Kokuritsu Daigaku Kogakubu Kiyo. (JA ISSN 0513-2592) **1841**
Yokohama National University. Humanities, Section 1: Philosophy and Social Sciences. see Yokohama Kokuritsu Daigaku Jinbun Kiyo Dai-1-rui, Tetsugaku, Shakai Kagaku **4393**
Yokohama National University. Science Reports. Section 1: Mathematics, Physics, Chemistry/Yokohama Kokuritsu Daigaku Rika Kiyo, Dai-1-rui, Sugaku, Butsurigaku, Kagaku. (JA ISSN 0085-8366) **4353**
Yokohama National University. Science Reports. Section 2: Biological and Geological Sciences/Yokohama Kokuritsu Daigaku Rika Kiyo. Dai-2-rui. Seibutsugaku, Chigaku. (JA) **460**
Yokohama National University. Science Reports. Section 2: Biological Sciences see Yokohama National University. Science Reports. Section 2: Biological and Geological Sciences **460**
Yokohama Plant Protection News/Yokohama Shokubutsu Boeki Nyusu. (JA ISSN 0049-8335) **196**
†Yokohama Port Activities. (JA) **5308**
Yokohama Port News. (JA) **4742**
Yokohama-shiritsu Daigaku Kiyo. Shizen Kagaku Hen/Yokohama City University. Journal. Series of Natural Science. (JA ISSN 0913-9664) **4353**
Yokohama-shiritsu Daigaku Ronso. Shizen Kagaku Keiretsu/Yokohama City University. Bulletin: Natural Science. (JA) **4353**
Yokohama Shokubutsu Boeki Nyusu. see Yokohama Plant Protection News **196**
Yokosuka City Museum. Annual Report. see Yokosuka-shi Hakubutsukanpo **3535**
Yokosuka City Museum. Miscellaneous Report. see Yokosuka-shi Hakubutsukan Shiryoshu **4353**
Yokosuka City Museum. Science Report. see Yokosuka-shi Hakubutsukan Kenkyu Hokoku. Shizen Kagaku **4353**
Yokosuka-shi Hakubutsukan Kenkyu Hokoku. Shizen Kagaku/Yokosuka City Museum. Science Report. (JA ISSN 0513-2622) **4353**, 3535
Yokosuka-shi Hakubutsukan Shiryoshu/Yokosuka City Museum. Miscellaneous Report. (JA ISSN 0386-4286) **4353**, 3535
Yokosuka-shi Hakubutsukanpo/Yokosuka City Museum. Annual Report. (JA ISSN 0385-8472) **3535**, 4353
Yokufukai Chosa Kenkyu Kiyo/Yokufukai Geriatric Journal. (JA) **2280**
Yokufukai Geriatric Journal. see Yokufukai Chosa Kenkyu Kiyo **2280**
Yom Hashishi. (IS) **4227**
Yonago Acta Medica. (JA ISSN 0513-5710) **3163**
Yonago Igaku Zasshi. see Yonago Medical Association. Journal **3164**
Yonago Medical Association. Journal/Yonago Igaku Zasshi. (JA ISSN 0044-0558) **3164**
Ha-Yonah/Dove. (US) **2029**, 2458
Yong Executive Hong Kong see Executive Hong Kong **1009**
Yonsei Business Review. see Sanop Kwa Kyongyong **690**
Yonsei Journal of Medical Science. (KO) **3164**
Yonsei Medical Journal. (KO ISSN 0513-5796) **3164**
Yonsei Reports on Tropical Medicine. (KO) **3224**
York County Farmer. (UK) **130**
York Gazette. (CN ISSN 0827-522X) **1331**
York Georgian Society. Annual Report. (UK) **309**
York Journal of Convocation. (UK ISSN 0085-8374) **4210**
York Pioneer. (CN ISSN 0513-2711) **2427**
York Region Business Journal. (CN ISSN 1183-2231) **700**
York - What's on. (UK) **2196**
Yorker Palatine Newsletter. (US) **3989**, 2029, 2168
Yorkie Express. (US) **3714**
Yorkshire Archaeological Journal. (UK ISSN 0084-4276) **289**
Yorkshire Archaeological Society Parish Register Series. (UK) **2168**
Yorkshire Archaeological Society Record Series. (UK) **2396**
Yorkshire Artscene. (UK ISSN 0951-9084) **350**
Yorkshire Auto Trader. (UK ISSN 0958-4013) **4706**
Yorkshire Dialect Society. Summer Bulletin. (UK ISSN 0513-2762) **2853**
Yorkshire Dialect Society Transactions. (UK) **2853**
Yorkshire Journal. (US ISSN 0044-0612) **229**
Yorkshire Librarian see Yorkshire Library News **2791**
Yorkshire Library News. (UK ISSN 0307-2509) **2791**
Yorkshire Life. (UK ISSN 0044-0620) **2196**
Yorkshire Miner. (UK) **3498**, 2592
Yorkshire Motor Trade see Yorkshire Auto Trader **4706**
Yorkshire Ridings Magazine. (UK ISSN 0044-0639) **2196**
Yorkshire Terrier Journal. (GW ISSN 0343-2963) **3714**
Yorkshire Topic. (UK) **2196**
Yoruba. (NR) **2853**, 2335, 2979
Yosetsu Gakkaishi. see Japan Welding Society. Journal **3429**
Yoshi Ryutsu Tokei Geppo see Monthly Statistics of Paper Distribution **3668**
Yoshida Foundation for Science and Technology. News. see Yoshida Kagaku Gijutsu Zaidan Nyusu **4613**
Yoshida Kagaku Gijutsu Zaidan Nyusu/Yoshida Foundation for Science and Technology. News. (JA ISSN 0388-8738) **4613**, 4353
Yoshoku. see Fish Culture **2040**
Yosong Dong-A. (KO) **4858**
You and the Law. (US) **1119**, 2696
You and Your Business. (US) **1119**
You and Your Camera. (US) **3798**
†You and Your Health. (US) **5308**
You Are Welcome Sir, to Cyprus see Welcome to Cyprus **4796**
You - Living With Verve. (CN) **374**, 1295
You Magazine. (AT) **1271**
†You Magazine. (US) **5308**
You Sheng. (CC) **3978**
You - Verve see You - Living With Verve **374**
You'er Huabao/Toddlers' Pictorial. (CC) **1271**
You'er Zhili Shijie/Toddlers' Intelligence World. (CC) **1246**, 1742
Youji Huaxue/Organic Chemistry. (CC ISSN 0253-2786) **1224**
Youjiao Tongxun see Xueqian Jiaoyu **1672**
Young Academic see Lantern **1645**
Young Adult Bible Study. (US ISSN 0162-4814) **4253**
Young Adults in Training see Baptist Young Adults **4230**
Young Age. (II ISSN 0049-8351) **4456**, 3935
Young Ambassador see T Q **1267**
Young American. (US) **1271**
Young & Alive (Large Print Edition). (US) **2297**, 1271
Young and Modern see Y M **1271**
Young Audio Now. (JA) **3587**
Young Authors Magazine. (US ISSN 0741-7594) **1271**
Young Buddhist. (SI) **4216**
Young Children. (US ISSN 0044-0728) **1764**, 1246
Young Cinema and Theatre/Jeune Cinema et Theatre. (CS) **3519**, 4642
Young Citizen. (IE ISSN 0044-0736) **1271**, 1673
Young Communist see Rebel Youth **3921**
Young Companion. (CN) **4290**
Young Crusader. (US ISSN 0162-9808) **1540**, 1271
Young East. (JA ISSN 0386-4251) **3646**, 4216
Young Entomologists' Society, Inc. International Entomology Resource Guide see Y E S International Entomology Resource Guide **538**
Young Entomologists' Society, Inc. Quarterly see Y E S Quarterly **539**
▼Young Executive. (US) **3400**, 700
†Young Executives Society. (US) **5308**
Young Fabian Pamphlet. (UK ISSN 0513-5982) **3935**
Young Fashions. (US) **1295**, 1246
▼Young Gay - Lesbian Life. (US) **2458**
Young Generation. (HK) **374**
Young Generation. see Qingnian Yidai **1263**
Young Generation. (SI ISSN 0129-6639) **1271**
Young Generation. (SI) **1271**
Young Girl. see Shao Nu **1265**
Young Girl Magazine. (HK) **374**
Young Guitar. (JA) **3587**
Young Ideas. (US) **1246**
Young Ideas. (SA ISSN 0044-0787) **4290**, 1246
Young India. (UK ISSN 0958-4234) **3978**
Young Inventor. see Dzaluu Dzohion Buteegch **4308**
Young Israel Viewpoint. (US ISSN 0044-0809) **4227**
Young Judaean. (US ISSN 0044-0817) **2029**, 1271
Young Lady see Frau **4843**
Young Liberal News see Free Radical **3895**
Young Men's Christian Association Review see Y M C A Review **2209**
Young Men's Christian Association Yearbook and Official Roster see Y M C A Yearbook and Official Roster **4424**
Young Men's Institute. Institute Journal. (US ISSN 0020-2673) **4210**
Young Miss see Y M **1271**
Young Musician. (UK) **3587**
Young Musicians. (US ISSN 0044-0841) **3587**
Young Offenders Service. (CN) **2696**, 1246
Young Parents. (SI) **1246**
Young People. see Nianqingren **1261**
Young People Now. (UK ISSN 0956-2842) **4424**
Young Pioneers. see Thieu Nien Tien Phong **1268**
Young Singaporean see Young Generation **1271**
Young Socialist. (US ISSN 0360-0157) **3935**, 2890
Young Soldier. (UK ISSN 0044-0906) **1271**, 4253
Young Soldier. (AT ISSN 0300-3264) **4290**, 1271
Young Ukraine. see Moloda Ukraina **1260**
Young Warrior see Warrior **1270**
Young Women's Christian Association of the United States of America. National Board. Annual Report. (US) **1302**
Young Women's Christian Association of the United States of America Interchange see Y W C A Interchange **1302**
Young Worker see Dynamic **3891**
Young Worker see Rebel Youth **3921**
Young World see Child Life **1251**
Young Writers. see Qingnian Zuojia **2951**
Young Writers. see Qingnian Wenxuejia **2951**
Young's World on Wheels Newsletter. (US) **1062**
Your (Year) Guide to Social Security Benefits. (US) **4424**, 700
Your Auckland Railway News see Y A R N **4717**
Your Australian Garden. (AT ISSN 0085-8382) **2140**
Your Big Backyard. (US) **1271**, 4353
Your Big Sites List: Camping and Caravanning Club Sites List. (UK) **4560**
Your Business and the Law see Management Policies & Personnel Law **1019**
Your Car Magazine see Top Car Magazine **4703**
Your Child. (US ISSN 0044-1007) **1673**, 2029, 4227
Your Classic. (UK ISSN 0957-6525) **4706**, 260

Your Clipping Analyst see Burrelle's Clipping Analyst **29**
†Your Commodore. (UK ISSN 0269-8277) **5308**
Your Computer. (UK ISSN 0263-0885) **1402**
Your Computer. see Votre Ordinateur **1402**
Your Computer. (AT ISSN 0725-3931) **1475**
†Your Computer Career. (US) **5308**
Your Consultant. (US) **1190**, 1861
Your Doctor. see Tabibok **3156**
Your Edmundite Missions News Letter. (US ISSN 0044-1015) **4210**
Your Family. (SA) **4858**
†Your Family. (US) **5308**
Your First Baby. (UK) **1246**, 3327
†Your Friendly Fascist. (AT) **5308**
Your Garden. (AT ISSN 0044-1031) **2140**
Your Hair. (UK) **374**
Your Health. (CN ISSN 0044-104X) **3368**
Your Health. (US) **3613**
Your Health & Fitness. (US) **3811**
Your Health & Safety. (US) **3811**
†Your Highway Department, Arkansas. (US ISSN 0094-9914) **5306**
Your Home. (US) **2499**, 636
▼Your Home. (NZ ISSN 1170-3229) **2556**
Your Horse. (UK) **4539**
Your Illinois F F A. (US) **130**
Your Investments: How to Increase Your Capital and Income see Dun & Bradstreet's Guide to Your Investments **944**
Your Library. (US) **2791**
Your Life and Health see Vibrant Life (Hagerstown) **3810**
Your Model Railway see Model Railways **2439**
Your Money see Financial Post **780**
Your Money. (US) **1509**, 970
Your Money Weekly. (AT) **970**
Your Oklahoma Dental Association. Journal see Oklahoma Dental Association Journal **3239**
Your Personal Astrology Magazine. (US ISSN 0044-1082) **359**
Your Personal Best Newsletter. (US) **3811**
†Your Pet Parade. (US) **5308**
†Your Pharmacy. (AT ISSN 0817-2455) **5308**
Your Place in the Country: A Guide to Camping and Caravanning Club Sites. (UK) **4560**
▼Your Prom. (US) **1272**, 1246
Your Public Schools see Education News **1629**
Your Region. (US) **4096**, 2499
Your Region in Action see Your Region **4096**
Your School and the Law. (US ISSN 0094-0399) **1732**
Your Schools. (US ISSN 0044-1112) **1732**
†Your Stars. (UK ISSN 0267-4610) **5308**
Your Times Express. (US) **2890**
Your Tomorrow. (UK) **4290**
Your Union see P S A C Union Update **2587**
Your Union Local 480 U S W A. (CN) **2592**
Your United Nations. (UN ISSN 0084-4322) **2326**, 3978
Your Window Into the Future. (US) **970**
Your Wisconsin Government. (US) **4078**
Yourdon Report. (US) **1440**
Yours. (UK) **2196**
Youse Jinshu/Chinese Journal of Nonferrous Metal. (CC ISSN 1001-0211) **3424**
Youth. (ZA) **1272**
Youth. see Qingchun **2951**
Youth (Year). (US) **1272**
†Youth Affairs in Australia. (AT ISSN 0814-4125) **5308**
Youth Alive. (US ISSN 0196-0938) **4253**, 1272
Youth Aliyah Review. (UK ISSN 0044-1155) **2029**, 1246
Youth and Health. see Qingchun yu Jiankang **3807**

Youth and Nation. (US ISSN 0044-1171) **3935**
Youth and Policy. (UK ISSN 0262-9798) **1246**, 1524, 4424
Youth & Society. (US ISSN 0044-118X) **1246**, 3935, 4456
Youth Clubs. (UK) **1246**
The Youth Disciple. (US ISSN 0196-0946) **4253**, 1272
Youth Exchange News. (UK ISSN 0144-7327) **1724**
Youth Exploration. see Qingnian Tansuo **1243**
Youth Focus see Transcend **2026**
Youth Hostels Association (England and Wales) Accommodation Guide. (UK) **4798**
Youth Hostels Association (England and Wales) Guide see Youth Hostels Association (England and Wales) Accommodation Guide **4798**
Youth Hostels Association (England and Wales) Handbook see Youth Hostels Association (England and Wales) Accommodation Guide **4798**
Youth in Action. (US ISSN 0162-4784) **4253**
Youth in Action Teacher. (US ISSN 0162-4792) **4253**
Youth in Discovery. (US ISSN 0162-4776) **4253**
Youth in Discovery Teacher. (US ISSN 0162-4768) **4253**
Youth in Society see Young People Now **4424**
Youth Law News. (US ISSN 0882-8520) **2696**, 1246, 4424
Youth Leadership. (US ISSN 0162-4709) **4253**
Youth Life see Union of Yugoslav Youth. Newsletter **1245**
Youth Life. (II) **1272**
Youth Literature. see Qingnian Wenxue **2951**
Youth Literature Journal. see Wenxue Qingnian **2975**
Youth Markets Alert. (US ISSN 1041-7516) **1509**, 1246
Youth Ministry Quarterly (New Hampton). (US ISSN 1054-7126) **4210**, 1246
Youth Ministry Quarterly (St. Louis). (US) **1272**, 4253
Youth Mirror. (MF ISSN 0049-8459) **1272**, 4221
Youth Mission for the Immaculata International Newsletter see Y M I **4279**
Youth Monthly. see Qingnian Yuekan **1263**
Youth Newsletter. (SZ) **4210**
†Youth of the 21. (FR ISSN 0254-9662) **5308**
Youth Policy. (US ISSN 8756-0909) **1246**, 4078
Youth Policy Network see Youth Policy Today **5308**
†Youth Policy Today. (CN) **5308**
Youth Record. (US ISSN 1047-7144) **1246**, 4078
Youth Review. (II ISSN 0044-1260) **1272**
Youth Service Survey. (US) **1246**, 4424
Youth - Serving Organizations Directory.(US ISSN 0196-9668) **4424**
Youth Soccer News. (US) **4515**
Youth Teacher see Sunday School Youth Teacher **4250**
Youth Theatre Journal. (US ISSN 0892-9092) **4642**, 1272, 1764
Youth Update. (US) **4279**
Youth View. (US) **1246**
Youthful Years. see Qingchun Suiyue **1263**
Youthlink. (NL ISSN 0294-7579) **1272**
Youth's Instructor see Insight (Hagerstown) **4240**
Youtian Dimian Gongcheng/Surface Structure of Oil Fields. (CC ISSN 1001-697X) **3704**
Youyong/Swimming. (CC ISSN 1000-3495) **4497**
Yritystalous. (FI ISSN 0358-4208) **1031**
Yrke. (NO ISSN 0049-8475) **1764**

Yrke och Framtid. (SW ISSN 0513-6261) **3631**
Yrkesbil. (NO) **4750**, 1941
Ysgrifam ar Addysg. see Welsh Studies in Education Series **5303**
Ysgrifau Diwinyddol. (UK ISSN 0143-0092) **4210**
Yskornuus. see Iscor News **3410**
Yu Novosti. (YU) **2240**
Yu Shih Wen I. (CH) **2979**
Yuanlin. (CC) **2140**
Yuanyi Xuebao/Acta Horticulturae Sinica. (CC ISSN 0513-353X) **2141**
Yuanzihe Wuli. (CC ISSN 0253-3790) **3851**
Yuanzineng Kexue Jishu/Science and Technology of Nuclear Energy. (CC ISSN 1000-6931) **1810**
Yuanzineng Nongye Yingyong/ Applications of Atomic Energy in Agriculture. (CC ISSN 0253-3596) **1810**, 130
Yuba - Sutter Philatelic Society. Newsletter. (US) **3759**
Yuca Boletin Informativo. (CK ISSN 0120-1824) **130**
Yucaipa Valley Family Finders Quarterly.(US) **2168**
Yuedu yu Xiezuo/Reading and Writing. (CC) **2979**
Yuefu Xin Sheng. (CC ISSN 1001-5736) **3587**
Yugntruf. (US) **2029**, 2979
†Yugoslav Chemical Papers. (YU ISSN 0351-0085) **5308**
Yugoslav Export - Import Directory. (YU ISSN 0084-4349) **1160**, 925
Yugoslav Facts and Views. (US ISSN 0427-8968) **3978**, 888
Yugoslav Gynecology and Perinatology. (CI ISSN 0352-5562) **3297**
Yugoslav Information Bulletin. (YU ISSN 0350-9508) **3935**
▼Yugoslav Journal of Operations Research. (YU ISSN 0354-0243) **1402**, 1031, 3061
Yugoslav Law/Droit Yougoslave. (YU ISSN 0350-2252) **2696**
Yugoslav Life. (YU ISSN 0044-1333) **2240**
Yugoslav Serbo-Croatian-English Contrastive Project. Series B: Studies.(CI) **2853**
Yugoslav Survey. (English translation of: Jugoslovenski Pregled) (YU ISSN 0044-1341) **2240**
Yugoslav Tourist News. see Jugoslawische Touristenzeitung **4773**
Yugoslav Trade Unions. (YU ISSN 0044-135X) **2592**
Yugoslavia. Federal Secretariat for Foreign Affairs. Diplomatic List. (YU) **3978**
Yugoslavia. Savazni Zavod za Statistiku. Demografska Statistika. (YU ISSN 0084-4357) **3997**, 3989
Yugoslavia. Savezni Zavod za Statistiku. Anketa O Ostvarivanju Prava Radnika Iz Radnog Odnosa. (YU) **744**
Yugoslavia. Savezni Zavod za Statistiku. Anketa O Porodicnim Budzetima Radnickih Domacinstava. (YU) **744**
Yugoslavia. Savezni Zavod za Statistiku. Industrijske Organizacije. (YU) **744**
Yugoslavia. Savezni Zavod za Statistiku. Komunalni Fondovi u Gradskim Naseljima. (YU) **4083**
Yugoslavia. Savezni Zavod za Statistiku. Metodoloske Studije, Rasprave i Dokumentacija. (YU ISSN 0351-0603) **4592**
Yugoslavia. Savezni Zavod za Statistiku. Metodoloski Materijali. (YU ISSN 0513-6547) **4592**
Yugoslavia. Savezni Zavod za Statistiku. Osnovna i Srednje. (YU) **1681**
Yugoslavia. Savezni Zavod za Statistiku. Radne Organizacije Prema Visini Najnjezeg i Najviseg Neto Licnog Dohotka. (YU) **4592**
Yugoslavia. Savezni Zavod za Statistiku. Samoupravljanje u Privredi. (YU) **744**
Yugoslavia. Savezni Zavod za Statistiku. Samoupravljanje u Ustanovama Drustvenih Sluzbi. (YU) **744**

Yugoslavia. Savezni Zavod za Statistiku. Saobracaj i Veze. (YU ISSN 0513-0794) **4669**
Yugoslavia. Savezni Zavod za Statistiku. Statisticka Revija. (YU ISSN 0039-0534) **4592**
Yugoslavia. Savezni Zavod za Statistiku. Statisticki Bilten. (YU ISSN 0084-4365) **4592**
Yugoslavia. Savezni Zavod za Statistiku. Studije, Analize i Prikazi. (YU ISSN 0513-6555) **4592**
Yugoslavia. Savezni Zavod za Statistiku. Turizam. (YU) **4801**
Yugoslavia. Savezni Zavod za Statistiku. Ucenici u Privredi. (YU ISSN 0513-0832) **1681**
Yugoslavia. Savezni Zavod za Statistiku. Vitalna Statistika see Yugoslavia. Savazni Zavod za Statistiku. Demografska Statistika **3997**
Yugoslavia. Savezni Zavod za Statistiku. Zaposleno Osoblje. (YU ISSN 0513-0883) **744**
Yugoslavia. Savezni Zavod za Statistiku. Zaposleno Osoblje i Neto Licni Dohoci po Grupama Delatnosti. (YU) **744**
Yugoslavia. Savezni Zavod za Statistiku. Zaposlenost. (YU ISSN 0513-0891) **744**
Yugoslavia Echo. (XV) **925**
Yugoslavia: Hotel and Tourist Directory. (YU) **2482**
Yugoslavskie Profsoyuzy. (YU ISSN 0022-6041) **2592**
Yugoslovenska Investiciona Banka. Annual Report see Investbanka. Annual Report **787**
Yuhang Xuebao/Journal of Spaceflight. (CC ISSN 1000-1328) **65**
Yuhua/Rain Flower. (CC ISSN 0512-9664) **2979**
Yuin. (JA) **2791**
Yuitnat Huaqboq. see Yunnan Huabao **2183**
Yuk Long T V Weekly. (HK) **1384**
Yukagaku. (JA) **1861**, 1190
Yukijirushi Nyugyo Kenkyujo Hokoku. see Snow Brand Milk Products Company. Research Laboratory. Reports **203**
†Yukon Bibliography Update. (CN) **5308**
Yukon News. (CN ISSN 0044-1376) **2180**
▼Yukon Reader. (CN) **2427**
Yule Log. (US ISSN 0843-7394) **3759**
Yunak. (CN ISSN 0044-1384) **1272**
Yunnan Daxue Xuebao (Shehui Kexue Ban) - Yunnan University. Journal (Social Sciences) see Sixiang Zhanxian **4386**
Yunnan Huabao/Yinnan Sumla Shi Laika/Yuitnat Huaqboq/Yirnar Awha Lirshatad/Lai Rang Ying Nang. (CC) **2183**
Yunnan Institute of Nationalities. Journal. see Yunnan Minzu Xueyuan Xuebao **3646**
Yunnan Journal of Traditional Chinese Medicine. see Yunnan Zhongyi Zazhi **3164**
Yunnan Minzu Xueyuan Xuebao/Yunnan Institute of Nationalities. Journal. (CC ISSN 1001-8913) **3646**, 253, 4456
Yunnan Shehui Kexue/Social Science in Yunnan. (CC ISSN 1000-8691) **4393**
Yunnan Zhiwu Yanjiu/Acta Botanica Yunnanica. (CC ISSN 0253-2700) **521**
Yunnan Zhongyi Zazhi/Yunnan Journal of Traditional Chinese Medicine. (CC ISSN 0255-2914) **3164**, 3746
Yunost'. (RU ISSN 0021-3233) **2890**
Yunyi Khudozhnik. (RU ISSN 0205-5767) **1272**, 350
Yunyi Naturalist. (RU ISSN 0205-5767) **1272**, 460
Yunyi Tekhnik. (RU ISSN 0131-1417) **1272**, 1841
Yuridika. (IO ISSN 0215-840X) **2696**
Yushu. (JA) **3759**
Yuva Bharati. (II ISSN 0302-6981) **1272**, 2979
Yuva Kavi. (II ISSN 0970-0978) **3009**

Yuvak. (II ISSN 0044-1414) **4211**
Yuval. (IS ISSN 0084-439X) **3587**
Yuvdarhsan. (II) **2202**
Yuwen Jianshe/Chinese Language Construction. (CC) **2853**
Yuwen Jiaoxue Tongxun/Bulletin of Chinese Language Teaching. (CC) **2853**, 1764
Yuwen Xuexi/Chinese Language Learning. (CC) **2853**
Yuwen Yanjiu/Chinese Language Research. (CC ISSN 1000-2979) **2853**
Yuwen Yuekan. (CC) **2853**
Yuyan Jiaoxue yu Yanjiu/Language Teaching & Studies. (CC ISSN 0257-9448) **2853**, 1764
Yuyan Wenzi Xue. (CC ISSN 1001-3261) **2853**
Yuye Jixie Yiqi. (CC ISSN 1001-2451) **3024**, 2050
Z. (ZA ISSN 0044-1422) **2240**
Z - A *see* Zuid - Afrika **3936**
Z A Information. (Zentralarchiv fuer Empirische Sozialforschung) (GW ISSN 0723-5607) **4456**
Z A K *see* Zeitschrift fuer Schweizerische Archaeologie und Kunstgeschichte **290**
Z A M M *see* Zeitschrift fuer Angewandte Mathematik und Mechanik **3062**
Z A M P *see* Zeitschrift fuer Angewandte Mathematik und Physik **3062**
Z A R *see* Zeitschrift fuer Auslaenderrecht und Auslaenderpolitik **2696**
Z.A.S.E. Bulletin *see* Science Education in Zambia **1662**
Z B S Review. (Bureau of Standards) (ZA) **1086**
Z Badan nad Polskimi Ksiegozbiorami Historycznymi. (PL ISSN 0137-5172) **2791**
Z D. (Zeitschriftendienst) (GW ISSN 0417-2957) **416**
Z D F Jahrbuch. (Zweites Deutsches Fernsehen) (GW) **1384**
Z Dejin Geodezie a Kartografie. (CS) **1549**
Z Dziejow Form Artystycznych w Literaturze Polskiej. (PL ISSN 0084-4411) **2979**
Z Dziejow Muzyki Polskiej. (PL ISSN 0084-442X) **3587**
†Z Dziejow Stosunkow Polsko-Radzieckich i Rozwoju Wspolnoty Panstw Socjalistycznych. (PL ISSN 0137-6381) **5308**
Z F A. (Zeitschrift fuer Arbeitsrecht) (GW ISSN 0342-328X) **998**, 2696
Z F A *see* Z F A mit Kartei der Praktischen Medizin **3164**
Z F A mit Kartei der Praktischen Medizin. (Zeitschrift fuer Allgemeinmedizin) (GW ISSN 0341-9835) **3164**
Z f B. (Zeitschrift fuer Betriebswirtschaft) (GW ISSN 0044-2372) **1031**
Z F B F. (Zeitschrift fuer Betriebswirtschaftliche Forschung) (GW) **1031**
†Z F I - Mitteilungen. (Zentralinstitut fuer Isotopen- und Strahlenforschung) (GW ISSN 0323-8776) **5308**
Z F L - Internationale Zeitschrift fuer Lebensmittel-Technik, Marketing, Verpackung und Analytik. (GW) **2084**
Z F L - Internationale Zeitschrift fuer Lebensmittel-Technologie und - Verfahrenstechnik *see* Z F L - Internationale Zeitschrift fuer Lebensmittel-Technik, Marketing, Verpackung und Analytik **2084**
Z F N Seminarprogramm. (Zahnaerztliches Fortbildungszentrum Niedersachsen) (GW) **3244**
Z F O *see* Zeitschrift Fuehrung und Organisation **1031**
Z F S *see* Zeitschrift fuer Schadensrecht **2697**
Z Filmtidsskrift. (NO) **3519**
Z G A Bibliographic Series. (Zambia Geographical Association) (ZA ISSN 0250-8125) **2268**, 416

Z G A Magazine *see* Zambian Geographical Journal **2267**
Z G A Occasional Studies. (Zambia Geographical Association) (ZA ISSN 0250-8109) **2267**
Z G A Occasional Studies and Special Publications *see* Z G A Occasional Studies **2267**
Z G A Regional Handbook *see* Zambia Geographical Association. Regional Handbook **2267**
Z G A School Supplement. (ZA ISSN 0250-8117) **2267**
Z I International. (GW ISSN 0341-0552) **1876**
Z I S Mitteilungen *see* Z I S - Report **5308**
†Z I S - Report. (Zentralinstitut fuer Schweisstechnik der DDR) (GW ISSN 0863-2162) **5308**
Z K G: Ausgabe A. (Zement - Kalk - Gips International) (GW ISSN 0722-4397) **636**
Z K G: Ausgabe B/Cement - Lime - Gypsum. Edition B. (Zement - Kalk - Gips International) (GW ISSN 0722-4400) **1876**, 1861
Z L R - Zeitschrift fuer das Gesamte Lebensmittelrecht. (GW ISSN 0342-3476) **2696**, 2084
Z M P Bilanz Getreide-Futtermittel. (GW ISSN 0170-7809) **208**
Z M P D. Kwartalny Biuletyn Informacyjny. (PL ISSN 0514-809X) **4750**
Z Magazine. (US ISSN 1056-5507) **3935**, 4858
Z Minulosti a Pritomnosti Turca. (CS) **2396**
†Z Miscellaneous. (US ISSN 0892-9696) **5308**
Z N C C Newsletter. (Zimbabwe National Chamber of Commerce) (RH) **824**
Z N C C Trade Directory. (Zimbabwe National Chamber of Commerce) (RH) **824**
Z O R - Methods and Models of Operations Research. (GW) **1402**, 3061
Z O R - Zeitschrift fuer Operations Research *see* Z O R - Methods and Models of Operations Research **1402**
▼Z O V. (Zeitschrift fuer Offene Vermoegensfragen) (GW) **2499**
Z Otchlani Wiekow. (PL ISSN 0044-1481) **289**
Z P A. (Zeitschrift fuer Praktische Augenheilkunde) (GW ISSN 0173-2595) **3306**
Z P F - Photogrammetrie und Fernerkundung. (GW) **2267**
Z P F - Zeitschrift fuer das Post- und Fernmeldewesen *see* Z P T **5308**
Z P G National Reporter *see* Z P G Reporter **3989**
Z P G Reporter. (Zero Population Growth, Inc.) (US ISSN 0199-0071) **3989**
†Z P T. (Zeitschrift fuer das Post- und Telekommunikation) (GW) **5308**
Z Pola Walki. (PL ISSN 0044-149X) **998**
Z S Magazin *see* Bevoelkerungsschutz-Magazin **1273**
Z T (Ziekenhuistechniek) *see* Infomedica **3260**
Z U M A - Nachrichten. (GW ISSN 0721-8516) **4456**, 4050, 4592
Z V E I Electro Electronics Buyers' Guide *see* Z V E I Elektro und Elektronik - Einkaufsfuehrer **1880**
Z V E I Elektro-Einkaufsfuehrer *see* Z V E I Elektro und Elektronik - Einkaufsfuehrer **1880**
Z V E I Elektro und Elektronik - Einkaufsfuehrer. (GW ISSN 0044-1686) **1880**, 1911
Z V E I Guia de Equipos Electricos et Electronicos *see* Z V E I Elektro und Elektronik - Einkaufsfuehrer **1880**
Z V E I Guide de l'Equipement Electrique et Electronique *see* Z V E I Elektro und Elektronik - Einkaufsfuehrer **1880**
Z V Informationen. (GW) **208**
Z V S - Info. (Zentralstelle fuer die Vergabe von Studienplaetzen) (GW) **1331**, 1721

†Z V S - Kurzinfo. (Zentralstelle fuer die Vergabe von Studienplaetzen) (GW) **5308**
Z V und Z V (Zeitungsverleger und Zeitschriftenverleger) *see* Copy **5172**
Z W F - C I M. (Zeitschrift fuer Wirtschaftliche Fertigung und Automatisierung) (GW ISSN 0044-3743) **3025**, 1841, 1941, 4613
Z W R. (Zahnaerztliche Welt Rundschau) (GW ISSN 0044-166X) **3244**
Z W R - Zahnaerztliche Welt, Zahnaerztliche Rundschau *see* Z W R **3244**
Z X *see* D B 2 and S Q L - D S Users Bulletin **1468**
†Z X Computing. (UK) **5308**
Za Casopis: Kovcezic. (YU ISSN 0454-4617) **2853**, 2979, 2983
Za i Przeciw. (PL ISSN 0044-1538) **2214**
Za Kadry *see* Dennitsa **1310**
Za Rubezhom. (RU ISSN 0044-1554) **3978**
†Zaaier. (NE ISSN 0044-1562) **5308**
Zabrana Skod. (CS ISSN 0044-1708) **2545**
Zabs Review. (ZA) **3449**
Zack. (LU ISSN 1016-2399) **1272**
Zadarska Revija. (CI ISSN 0044-1589) **2890**
Zadok Centre. Series No.1. (AT ISSN 0156-7470) **4211**, 4456
Zadok Centre. Series No.2. (AT ISSN 0156-7489) **4211**, 4456
Zadok Centre Reading Guides. (AT ISSN 0156-7500) **4211**, 4456
Zadok Perspectives. (AT ISSN 0810-9796) **4211**, 4456
Zagadnienia Ekonomiki Rolnej. (PL ISSN 0044-1600) **160**
Zagadnienia Eksploatacji Maszyn/Exploitation Problems of Machines. (PL ISSN 0084-4454) **1941**
Zagadnienia Informacji Naukowej. (PL ISSN 0324-8194) **2791**, 4353
Zagadnienia Naukoznawstwa. (PL ISSN 0044-1619) **4353**
Zagadnienia Rodzajow Literackich/Problemes des Genres Litteraires. (PL ISSN 0084-4446) **2979**
Zagle. (PL) **4531**
Zagmag. (II) **1272**
Al-Zahf al-Akhdar. (LY) **2209**
Zahir. (US ISSN 0049-8505) **3009**
Zahlen zur Wirtschaftlichen Entwicklung der Bundesrepublik Deutschland. (GW) **700**
Zahlentafeln der Physikalisch-Chemischen Untersuchungen des Rheinwassers/Tableaux Numeriques des Analyses Physico-Chimiques des Eaux du Rhin. (GW ISSN 0173-6507) 1980, 4834
Zahlungsbilanz der Schweiz. (SZ) **1112**
Zahn- Mund- und Kieferheilkunde. (GW ISSN 0303-6464) **3244**
Zahnaerzteblatt Baden-Wuerttemberg. (GW ISSN 0340-3017) **3244**
Zahnaerzteblatt Sachsen. (GW ISSN 0938-8486) **3244**
Zahnaerztliche Mitteilungen. (GW ISSN 0341-8995) **3244**
Zahnaerztliche Praxis. (GW ISSN 0044-1651) **3245**
Zahnaerztliche Welt Rundschau *see* Z W R **3244**
Zahnaerztlicher Anzeiger. (GW ISSN 0027-3198) **3245**
Zahnaerztliches Fortbildungszentrum Niedersachsen Seminarprogramm *see* Z F N Seminarprogramm **3244**
Zahntechnik. (SZ ISSN 0044-1686) **3245**
†Zahntechnik. (GW ISSN 0513-7926) **5308**
Zahradkar. (CS) **2141**
Zahradnicke Listy *see* Zahradnictvo **2141**
Zahradnictvi/Horticulture. (CS) **2141**
Zahradnictvo. (CS) **2141**
Zahranicne Periodika v C S F R. (CS) **416**
Zahranicni Obchod. (CS) **925**
Zahrat al-Khalij. (TS) **4858**

Zaidan Hojin Toyo Bunko. *see* Oriental Library. Research Department. Memoirs **2340**
Zaidan Nyusu/Yamada Science Foundation News. (JA ISSN 0912-2354) **4353**
Zaire. Assemblee Nationale. Compte Rendu Analytique *see* Zaire. Conseil Legislatif National. Compte Rendu Analytique **2696**
Zaire. Conseil Legislatif National. Compte Rendu Analytique. (ZR) **2696**
Zaire. Direction Generale des Finances. Bulletin des Finances. (ZR) **1112**
Zaire. Institut National de la Statistique. Bulletin Trimestriel des Statistiques Generales. (ZR) **4592**
Zaire - Afrique. (ZR ISSN 0049-8513) **3935**
Zaire Business. (ZR) **888**
Zaire Informatique. (ZR) **2335**
†Zaire Monthly. (BE) **5308**
Zairyo Kenkyu Rengo Koenkai Ronbunshu. *see* Japan Congress on Materials Research. Proceedings **1918**
Zairyo to Kankyo. (JA ISSN 0917-0480) **3424**, 1213
Zajednicar. (US) **2029**
Zaji yu Moshu/Acrobatics and Magic. (CC) **2444**, 4497
Zakenauto. (NE) **4706**
Zakenreis/Business Travel. (NE) **4798**, 2482, 4678
Zakenreisnieuws. (NE) **700**
Zakladni a Rekreacni Telesna Vychova *see* Pohyb a My **4483**
Zalai Gyujtemeny. (HU ISSN 0133-5499) **2396**, 289, 2060
†Zalai Tukor. (HU ISSN 0200-5344) **5308**
Zalioji Lietuva. (LI) **1972**
†Zaliv. (IT) **5308**
Zamana. (MF) **2029**
Zambezia: A Journal of Social Studies in Southern and Central Africa *see* Zambezia: The Journal of the University of Zimbabwe **4393**
Zambezia: The Journal of the University of Zimbabwe. (RH ISSN 0379-0622) **4393**
Zambia. Central Statistical Office. Agricultural and Pastoral Production (Commercial and Non-Commercial). (ZA) **145**
Zambia. Central Statistical Office. Agricultural and Pastoral Production (Commercial Farms). (ZA) **145**, 4592
Zambia. Central Statistical Office. Agricultural and Pastoral Production (Non-Commercial). (ZA) **145**, 4592
Zambia. Central Statistical Office. Agricultural and Pastoral Production *see* Zambia. Central Statistical Office. Agricultural and Pastoral Production (Commercial and Non-Commercial) **145**
Zambia. Central Statistical Office. Agricultural and Pastoral Production *see* Zambia. Central Statistical Office. Agricultural and Pastoral Production (Non-Commercial) **145**
Zambia. Central Statistical Office. Agricultural and Pastoral Production *see* Zambia. Central Statistical Office. Agricultural and Pastoral Production (Commercial Farms) **145**
Zambia. Central Statistical Office. Annual Statement of External Trade. (ZA ISSN 0084-4489) **744**
Zambia. Central Statistical Office. Balance of Payments Statistics. (ZA) **744**
Zambia. Central Statistical Office. Consumer Price Statistics. (ZA) **744**, 4592
Zambia. Central Statistical Office. Employment and Earnings. (ZA ISSN 0084-4500) **744**
Zambia. Central Statistical Office. Financial Statistics of Government Sector (Economic and Functional Analysis). (ZA) **4083**
Zambia. Central Statistical Office. Financial Statistics of Public Corporations. (ZA ISSN 0084-4519) **744**

Zambia. Central Statistical Office. Fisheries Statistics (Natural Waters). (ZA ISSN 0514-8731) **2052**
Zambia. Central Statistical Office. Government Sector Accounts (Economic and Functional Analysis) *see* Zambia. Central Statistical Office. Financial Statistics of Government Sector (Economic and Functional Analysis) **4083**
Zambia. Central Statistical Office. Industry Monographs. (ZA) **700**
Zambia. Central Statistical Office. Manpower Survey. (ZA) **744**
Zambia. Central Statistical Office. Migration Statistics. (ZA ISSN 0084-4543) **3997**
Zambia. Central Statistical Office. Migration Statistics: Immigrants and Visitors *see* Zambia. Central Statistical Office. Migration Statistics **3997**
Zambia. Central Statistical Office. Monthly Digest of Statistics. (ZA ISSN 0027-0377) **4592**
Zambia. Central Statistical Office. National Accounts. (ZA) **1112, 4078**
Zambia. Central Statistical Office. Quarterly Agricultural Statistical Bulletin. (ZA) **145, 4592**
Zambia. Central Statistical Office. Registered Births, Marriages and Deaths (Vital Statistics) *see* Zambia. Central Statistical Office. Vital Statistics **3997**
Zambia. Central Statistical Office. Statistical Year Book. (ZA ISSN 0084-4551) **4592**
Zambia. Central Statistical Office. Transport Statistics. (ZA ISSN 0514-5392) **4669**
Zambia. Central Statistical Office. Vital Statistics. (ZA ISSN 0084-456X) **3997, 4592**
Zambia. Commission for Investigations. Annual Report. (ZA) **4078**
Zambia. Commission for the Preservation of Natural and Historical Monuments and Relics. Annual Report. (ZA ISSN 0084-4586) **1501**
Zambia. Department of Agriculture. Research and Specialist Services. Annual Report. (ZA) **197, 130**
Zambia. Department of Civil Aviation. Annual Report. (ZA) **4678**
Zambia. Department of Community Development. Report *see* Zambia. Department of Social Development. Report **4424**
Zambia. Department of Cooperatives. Annual Report *see* Zambia. Ministry of Cooperatives. Annual Report **833**
Zambia. Department of Customs and Excise. Annual Report of the Controller of Customs and Excise. (ZA) **1112**
Zambia. Department of Fisheries. Annual Report. (ZA) **2050**
Zambia. Department of Forestry. Report. (ZA ISSN 0084-4616) **2111**
Zambia. Department of Labour. Report. (ZA ISSN 0084-4632) **998**
Zambia. Department of Legal Aid. Annual Report. (ZA) **2696**
Zambia. Department of Social Development. Report. (ZA) **4424**
Zambia. Department of Social Development. Social Welfare Research Monographs. (ZA) **4425**
Zambia. Department of Social Welfare. Report *see* Zambia. Department of Social Development. Report **4424**
Zambia. Department of Social Welfare. Social Welfare Research Monographs *see* Zambia. Department of Social Development. Social Welfare Research Monographs **4425**
Zambia. Department of Taxes. Annual Report of the Commissioner of Taxes. (ZA ISSN 0084-4675) **1112**
Zambia. Department of the Administrator-General and Official Receiver. Report. (ZA ISSN 0084-4683) **1112**

Zambia. Department of Veterinary and Tsetse Control Services. Annual Report. (ZA) **4820**
Zambia. Department of Water Affairs. Report. (ZA ISSN 0084-4705) **4834**
Zambia. Educational and Occupational Assessment Service. Annual Report. (ZA ISSN 0514-5457) **3631**
Zambia. Geological Survey. Annual Reports. (ZA ISSN 0084-473X) **1586**
Zambia. Geological Survey. Economic Reports. (ZA ISSN 0084-4748) **1586**
Zambia. Geological Survey. Occasional Papers. (ZA ISSN 0084-4756) **1586**
Zambia. Geological Survey. Reports. (ZA ISSN 0084-4764) **1586**
Zambia. Geological Survey. Technical Reports. (ZA) **1586**
Zambia. High Court. Law Directory and Legal Calendar. (ZA) **2696**
Zambia. Immigration Department. Report. (ZA ISSN 0084-4802) **3989**
Zambia. Information Services. Annual Report. (ZA ISSN 0084-4810) **2335**
Zambia. Meteorological Department. Totals of Monthly and Annual Rainfall. (ZA ISSN 0302-5047) **3444**
Zambia. Ministry of Agricultural and Water Development. Quarterly Agricultural Statistical Bulletin *see* Zambia. Ministry of Agriculture, Food and Fisheries. Annual Agricultural Statistical Bulletin **145**
Zambia. Ministry of Agriculture and Water Development. Land Use Branch. Soil Survey Report. (ZA) **197**
Zambia. Ministry of Agriculture, Food and Fisheries. Annual Agricultural Statistical Bulletin. (ZA) **145**
Zambia. Ministry of Cooperatives. Annual Report. (ZA) **833**
Zambia. Ministry of Decentralisation. District Councils Revenue and Capital Estimates. (ZA) **700**
Zambia. Ministry of Development and National Guidance. Annual Report *see* Zambia. Ministry of Planning and Finance. Annual Report **1086**
Zambia. Ministry of Education. Annual Report. (ZA ISSN 0084-487X) **1673**
Zambia. Ministry of Finance. Annual Report *see* Zambia. Ministry of Planning and Finance. Annual Report **1086**
Zambia. Ministry of Lands and Agriculture. Land Use Branch. Soil Survey Report *see* Zambia. Ministry of Agriculture and Water Development. Land Use Branch. Soil Survey Report **197**
Zambia. Ministry of Legal Affairs. Annual Report. (ZA) **700, 2791**
Zambia. Ministry of Planning and Finance. Annual Report. (ZA) **1086**
Zambia. Ministry of Youth and Sport. Department of Youth Development. Annual Report. (ZA) **1246, 4497**
Zambia. Ministry of Youth and Sport. Report. (ZA) **4497**
Zambia. National Commission for Development Planning. Economic Report. (ZA) **888**
Zambia. National Council for Scientific Research. Annual Report. (ZA ISSN 0084-4950) **4353**
Zambia. National Council for Scientific Research. N C S R Bibliography. (ZA) **4358, 416**
Zambia. National Food and Nutrition Commission. Annual Report. (ZA ISSN 0084-4969) **2084, 3613**
Zambia. National Museums Board. Occasional Paper Series *see* Livingstone Museum. Research Notes **2333**
Zambia. National Museums Board. Report. (ZA ISSN 0084-4977) **3535**

Zambia. Natural Resources Advisory Board. Annual Report *see* Zambia. Natural Resources Department. Annual Report **1501**
Zambia. Natural Resources Department. Annual Report. (ZA) **1501**
Zambia. Office of the Auditor-General. Report of the Auditor-General. (ZA ISSN 0084-4497) **1112**
Zambia. Pneumoconiosis Medical and Research Bureau and Pneumoconiosis Compensation Board. Annual Reports. (ZA ISSN 0084-5000) **3368**
Zambia. Posts and Telecommunications Corporation. Annual Report. (ZA) **1354**
Zambia. Prisons Department. Report. (ZA ISSN 0084-4659) **1524**
Zambia. Public Service Commission. Report. (ZA ISSN 0084-5035) **4425**
Zambia. Sports Directorate. Report *see* Zambia. Ministry of Youth and Sport. Report **4497**
Zambia. Survey Department. Report. (ZA ISSN 0084-5078) **2267**
Zambia. Teaching Service Commission. Annual Report. (ZA ISSN 0084-5086) **1673**
Zambia Consolidated Copper Mines Ltd. Annual Report and Accounts. (ZA) **3498, 3424**
Zambia Daily Mail. (ZA) **2240**
Zambia Educational Journal. (ZA) **1673**
Zambia Educational Review. (ZA ISSN 0255-0695) **1673**
Zambia Electricity Supply Corporation. Annual Report. (ZA) **1911**
Zambia Geographical Association. Conference Handbook *see* Zambia Geographical Association. Regional Handbook **2267**
Zambia Geographical Association. Occasional Newsletter. (ZA) **2267**
Zambia Geographical Association. Regional Handbook. (ZA ISSN 0250-8133) **2267**
Zambia Geographical Association Bibliographic Series *see* Z G A Bibliographic Series **2268**
Zambia Geographical Association Occasional Studies *see* Z G A Occasional Studies **2267**
Zambia Industrial and Mining Corporation. Annual Report. (ZA) **3498**
Zambia Journal *see* Zambia Museums Journal **253**
Zambia Journal of Science and Technology. (ZA ISSN 0378-8857) **4353, 4613**
Zambia Law Journal. (ZA) **2696**
Zambia Law Reports. (ZA) **2696**
Zambia Library Association. Journal. (ZA ISSN 0049-853X) **2791**
Zambia Library Association. Newsletter. (ZA) **2791**
Zambia Mining Yearbook. (ZA ISSN 0076-9010) **3498**
Zambia Museums Journal. (ZA) **253, 2853**
Zambia Museums Journal. (ZA) **3535**
Zambia Nurse. (ZA) **3288**
Zambia Science Abstracts. (ZA) **4358, 25**
Zambia State Insurance Corporation. Report and Accounts. (ZA) **2545**
Zambian Climatological Summary; Surface and Upper Air Data. (ZA) **3444**
Zambian Engineer. (ZA) **1841**
Zambian Geographical Journal. (ZA ISSN 0250-5657) **2267**
Zambian Ornithological Society. Newsletter. (ZA ISSN 0378-4533) **568**
Zambian Ornithological Society Occasional Papers. (ZA) **568**
Zambian Papers. (ZA ISSN 0084-5124) **2335**
Zambian Standards Reporter *see* Zabs Review **3449**
Zan-e Ruz. (IR) **4858**
Zandera. (GW) **2141**
Zango/Forum. (ZA) **2240, 2890**
Zaochuan Jishu. (CC ISSN 1000-3878) **4742**

ZBORNIK RADOVA 6827

Zapad/West. (CN ISSN 0226-3068) **2890, 2029**
Zapadne Slovensko. (CS) **2396**
Zapiski. *see* Association of Russian - American Scholars in the U S A. Transactions **1992**
Zapiski Historyczne. (PL ISSN 0044-1791) **2326**
Zapiski Mladych. (CS) **1272**
Zaposleni po Obcinah. (XV) **998**
Zapowiedzi Wydawnicze. (PL ISSN 0044-1813) **416**
Zaraat. (PK) **130**
Zaranie Slaskie. (PL ISSN 0044-183X) **2396**
Zariya Veterinarian. (NR) **4820**
Zarja/Dawn. (US ISSN 0044-1848) **2029, 4858**
Zashchita Metallov. (RU ISSN 0044-1856) **3424**
Zashchita Rastenii. (RU ISSN 0044-1864) **197**
Zashchitnye Pokrytiya na Metallakh. (KR ISSN 0130-1519) **3424**
Zasshi Kiji Sakuin. Jinbun Shakai Hen/ Japanese Periodicals Index. Humanities and Social Science Section. (JA ISSN 0021-5341) **2520, 25, 4396**
Zasshi Kiji Sakuin. Kagaku Gijutsu Hen. *see* Japanese Periodicals Index. Science and Technology **4356**
Zasshi Shinbun Sokatarogu/Periodicals in Print in Japan. (JA ISSN 0387-7000) **416**
Zastita. (XN ISSN 0044-1872) **3935**
Zastita od Pozara/Firefighting Protection. (YU ISSN 0351-9783) **2035, 1274**
Zastita Rada. (YU ISSN 0044-1880) **3623**
Zastosowania Matematyki/Applicationes Mathematicae. (PL ISSN 0044-1899) **3062, 3066**
Zauberkunst. (GW ISSN 0138-1539) **350**
ZauberZeit. (GW ISSN 0930-0007) **3015**
Zav-Zav. (IS) **1272**
Zavarivanje. (CI ISSN 0044-1902) **3431**
Zavod za Hrvatski Jezik. Rasprave. (CI) **2853**
Zavod za Hrvatsku Povijest. Radovi. (CI ISSN 0351-2142) **2396**
Zavod za Jezik. Rasprave *see* Zavod za Hrvatski Jezik. Rasprave **2853**
Zavod za Knjizevnost i Teatrologiju. Kronika. (CI) **2890**
Zavod za Mentalno Zdravlje. Anali *see* Psihijatrija Danas **3350**
Zavod za Zdravstvenu Zastitu S R Srbije. Glasnik. (YU ISSN 0409-0314) **4116**
Zavodskaya Laboratoriya. (RU ISSN 0044-1910) **1209, 3062, 3263**
Zawen Jie. (CC) **2890**
Zayray. (AF) **2853, 2979**
Zbior Dokumentow/Recueil de Documents. (PL ISSN 0044-1929) **3978**
Zbornik Istorije Knjizevnosti/Recueil des Travaux de l'Histoire de la Litterature.(YU ISSN 0084-5183) **2979**
Zbornik Istrazivackih Radova iz Oblasti Materijala i Konstrukcija u Gradjevinarstvu. (BN ISSN 0353-4146) **1876, 636**
Zbornik Obcine Grosuplje. (XV ISSN 0350-8498) **2890**
Zbornik Objavljenih Radova Saradnika Instituta. (YU ISSN 0351-4595) **1911, 1880, 1925**
Zbornik Pedagogickej Fakulty v Presove U P J S v Kosiciach. Prirodne Vedy. (CS) **2267**
Zbornik Pravnog Fakulteta u Zagrebu *see* Univerzitet u Zagrebu. Pravni Fakultet. Zbornik **2691**
Zbornik Radova Muzeja Rudarstva i Metalurgije Bor. (YU ISSN 0351-7160) **290, 3424, 3498**
Zbornik Radova Prirodno-Matematickog Fakulteta Kragujevac *see* Univerzitet Svetozar Markovic u Kragujevcu. Prirodno-Matematicki Fakultet. Zbornik Radova **4350**

ZBORNIK VEDECKYCH

Zbornik Vedeckych Prac Drevarskej Fakulty Vysokej Skoly Lesnickej a Drevarsej vo Zvolene. (CS) **2111**
Zbornik za Drustvene Nauke. (YU ISSN 0044-1937) **4393**
Zbornik za Istoriju. (YU) **2396**
Zbornik za Istoriju, Jezik i Knjizevnost Srpskog Naroda. Fontes Rerum Slavorum Meridionalium. (YU ISSN 0084-5191) **2396**
Zbornik za Istoriju, Jezik i Knjizevnost Srpskog Naroda. Spomenici na Srpskom Jeziku. (YU ISSN 0084-5205) **2979**
Zbornik za Istoriju, Jezik i Knjizevnost Srpskog Naroda. Spomenici na Tudjim Jezicima. (YU ISSN 0084-5213) **2396**
Zbornik za Istoriju Skolstva i Prosvete. (YU ISSN 0514-6151) **1673**
Zbornik za Slavistiku/Review of Slavic Studies. (YU ISSN 0350-0470) **2853**
Zbornik Zagrebacke Slavisticke Skole. (CI) **2853**
Zbornik Zastite Spomenika Kulture/Recueil des Travaux sur la Protection des Monuments Historiques. (YU ISSN 0514-616X) **350**
Zdorov'e. (RU ISSN 0044-1945) **4116**
Zdravie. (CS ISSN 0044-1953) **3811**
Zdravie Ludu see Zdravie **3811**
Zdravookhranenie Belorussii. (BW ISSN 0044-1961) **4116**
Zdravookhranenie Rossiiskoi Federatsii/Public Health of the Russian Federation. (RU ISSN 0044-197X) **4116**
Zdravotni Technika a Vzduchotechnika/Sanitary and Air Technics. (CS ISSN 0044-1988) **2304**
†Zdravotnicka Dokumentace. (CS ISSN 0139-6587) **5308**
Zdravotnicka Pracovnice. (CS ISSN 0049-8572) **4116**
Zdravotnicke Noviny. (CS ISSN 0044-1996) **4116**
Zdravstveni Obzornik. (XV ISSN 0350-9516) **3288**
Zdravstveni Vestnik/Journal of Slovenia Medical Society. (XV ISSN 0350-0063) **3164**
Zdrowie i Trzezwosc. (PL ISSN 0513-8809) **1540**
Zdrowie Publiczne. (PL ISSN 0044-2011) **4116**
Ze Skarbca Kultury. (PL ISSN 0084-5221) **2519**
Ze Zivota SSSR. (CS) **2216**
Zeal. (US ISSN 0514-2482) **4279**
Zealandia see New Zealandia **4271**
Zebra's Voice. (BS) **3535**
Zee. (BE) **4717**
Zeewezen. (NE ISSN 0165-8182) **4742**
Zeffiro Italia see La Griffe **373**
Zehan. (PK) **4050**
Zeichen. (GW) **4253**, 2326, 3948
Zeichen der Zeit. (GW ISSN 0044-2038) **4253**
Zeichnen Fachzeitschrift fuer Alle Bereiche Technischen Zeichens see Zeichnen Fachzeitschrift fuer Konstruieren und Gestalten **309**
Zeichnen Fachzeitschrift fuer Konstruieren und Gestalten. (GW ISSN 0932-7509) **309**, 636, 1880
Zeichnen und Gestalt. (SZ) **350**
Zeilberg-Echo. (GW) **4096**
Zeimu Tokei Kara Mita Hojin Kigyo no Jittai. (JA) **1112**
Zeina. (SU) **4858**
†Zeirei Forum. (US) **5308**
Zeiss Information. (GW ISSN 0044-2054) **3858**
Zeiss Markt - Mode - Meinungen. (GW) **3306**
Zeit. (CN) **2029**
Die Zeit. (GW ISSN 0044-2070) **2192**
Die Zeit im Buch. (AU ISSN 0044-2089) **4139**, 2890
Zeit- und Kulturarchiv see Internationales Handbuch - Zeitarchiv **2314**
†Zeit und Kunst. (AU) **5308**
Das Zeitbild. (GW) **2192**

ZeitBild. (SZ ISSN 0044-2100) **3978**
Zeitgenoessisches Musikschaffen in der Deutschen Demokratischen Republik. Urauffuehrungen. (GW ISSN 0232-9387) **3587**
Zeitgeschichte. (AU) **2326**
Zeitlupe. (GW ISSN 0342-5851) **3948**, 3989
†Zeitraum. (GW) **5308**
Zeitschrift des Bernischen Juristenvereins. (SZ ISSN 0044-2127) **2696**
Zeitschrift Fuehrung und Organisation. (GW ISSN 0722-7485) **1031**, 1062
Zeitschrift fuer Acker- und Pflanzenbau. see Journal of Agronomy and Crop Science **183**
Zeitschrift fuer Aegyptische Sprache und Altertumskunde. (GW ISSN 0044-216X) **3646**, 2853
Zeitschrift fuer Aerztliche Fortbildung. (GW ISSN 0044-2178) **3164**
Zeitschrift fuer Aesthetik und Allgemeine Kunstwissenschaft. (GW ISSN 0044-2186) **3786**, 350
Zeitschrift fuer Agrargeschichte und Agrarsoziologie. (GW ISSN 0044-2194) **130**, 4456
Zeitschrift fuer Allgemeine Mikrobiologie see Journal of Basic Microbiology **554**
Zeitschrift fuer Allgemeine Wissenschaftstheorie. see Journal for General Philosophy of Science **4317**
Zeitschrift fuer Allgemeinmedizin Kartei der Praktischen Medizin see Z F A mit Kartei der Praktischen Medizin **3164**
†Zeitschrift fuer Alternsforschung. (GW ISSN 0044-2224) **5308**
Zeitschrift fuer Althebraistik. (GW ISSN 0932-4461) **2853**
Zeitschrift fuer Analysis und Ihre Anwendungen. (GW ISSN 0232-2064) **3062**
Zeitschrift fuer Angewandte Entomologie. see Journal of Applied Entomology **534**
Zeitschrift fuer Angewandte Geologie. (GW ISSN 0044-2259) **1586**
Zeitschrift fuer Angewandte Ichthyologie. see Journal of Applied Ichthyology **585**
Zeitschrift fuer Angewandte Mathematik und Mechanik. (GW ISSN 0044-2267) **3062**
Zeitschrift fuer Angewandte Mathematik und Physik/Journal of Applied Mathematics and Physics/Journal de Mathematiques et de Physique Appliquees. (SZ ISSN 0044-2275) **3062**, 3835
Zeitschrift fuer Angewandte Psychologie see Zeitschrift fuer Psychologie **4050**
Zeitschrift fuer Angewandte Zoologie. (GW ISSN 0044-2291) **594**
Zeitschrift fuer Anglistik und Amerikanistik. (GW ISSN 0044-2305) **2979**, 2853
Zeitschrift fuer Anorganische und Allgemeine Chemie. (GW ISSN 0044-2313) **1191**
Zeitschrift fuer Arabische Linguistik/Journal of Arabic Linguistics/Journal de Linguistique Arabe. (GW ISSN 0170-026X) **2853**, 2979
Zeitschrift fuer Arbeits- und Organisationspsychologie. (GW ISSN 0932-4089) **4050**
Zeitschrift fuer Arbeitsrecht see Z F A **998**
Zeitschrift fuer Arbeitsrecht und Sozialrecht. (AU ISSN 0044-2321) **2696**, 998
Zeitschrift fuer Arbeitswissenschaft. (GW ISSN 0340-2444) **998**
Zeitschrift fuer Archaeologie. (GW ISSN 0044-233X) **290**
Zeitschrift fuer Archaeologie des Mittelalters. (GW ISSN 0340-0824) **290**
Zeitschrift fuer Assyriologie und Vorderasiatische Archaeologie. (GW ISSN 0084-5299) **290**
Zeitschrift fuer Auslaenderrecht und Auslaenderpolitik. (GW ISSN 0721-5746) **2696**, 3935

Zeitschrift fuer Auslaendische Landwirtschaft/Quarterly Journal of International Agriculture/Journal Trimestriel d'Agriculture Internationale. (GW ISSN 0049-8599) **130**
Zeitschrift fuer Auslaendisches Oeffentliches Recht und Voelkerrecht. (GW ISSN 0044-2348) **2730**
Zeitschrift fuer Auslaendisches und Internationales Arbeits- und Sozialrecht. (GW ISSN 0930-861X) **2696**, 998
Zeitschrift fuer Balkanologie. (GW ISSN 0044-2356) **2396**, 2432
Zeitschrift fuer Bankrecht und Bankwirtschaft. (GW ISSN 0936-2800) **804**
Zeitschrift fuer Bayerische Kirchengeschichte. (GW ISSN 0342-4316) **4253**
Zeitschrift fuer Bayerische Landesgeschichte. (GW ISSN 0044-2364) **2326**
Zeitschrift fuer Beamtenrecht. (GW ISSN 0514-2571) **2696**, 4078
Zeitschrift fuer Bergrecht. (GW) **2696**
Zeitschrift fuer Berufs- und Wirtschaftspaedagogik. (GW ISSN 0172-2875) **1764**
Zeitschrift fuer Berufs- und Wirtschaftspaedagogik. Beihefte. (GW ISSN 0174-0830) **1764**
Zeitschrift fuer Betriebswirtschaft see Z f B **1031**
Zeitschrift fuer Betriebswirtschaftliche Forschung see Z F B F **1031**
Zeitschrift fuer Bevoelkerungswissenschaft: Demographie. (GW ISSN 0340-2398) **3989**
Zeitschrift fuer Bewaesserungswirtschaft. (GW ISSN 0049-8602) **197**
Zeitschrift fuer Bibliothekswesen und Bibliographie. (GW ISSN 0044-2380) **2791**
Zeitschrift fuer Bibliothekswesen und Bibliographie. Sonderhefte. (GW ISSN 0514-6364) **2791**
Zeitschrift fuer Bienenforschung see Apidologie **528**
Zeitschrift fuer Binnenschiffahrt und Wasserstrassen. (GW ISSN 0930-7370) **4742**
Zeitschrift fuer Celtische Philologie. (GW ISSN 0084-5302) **2853**, 2979
Zeitschrift fuer Chemotherapie. (GW ISSN 0722-5067) **3363**
Zeitschrift fuer das Fuersorgewesen. (GW) **4425**
Zeitschrift fuer das Gemeinnuetzige Wohnungswesen in Bayern see Wohnen-Zeitschrift fuer das Wohnungswesen in Bayern **1112**
Zeitschrift fuer das Gesamte Familienrecht. (GW ISSN 0044-2410) **2696**
Zeitschrift fuer das Gesamte Genossenschaftswesen. (GW ISSN 0044-2429) **4393**
Zeitschrift fuer das Gesamte Handelsrecht und Wirtschaftsrecht. (GW ISSN 0044-2437) **2696**
Zeitschrift fuer das Gesamte Kreditwesen. (GW ISSN 0340-8485) **804**
Zeitschrift fuer das Notariat in Baden-Wuerttemberg. (GW) **2696**
Zeitschrift fuer das Post- und Telekommunikation see Z P T **5308**
Zeitschrift fuer den Erdkundeunterricht. (GW ISSN 0044-2461) **2267**
Zeitschrift fuer den Internationalen Eisenbahnverkehr. (SZ) **4717**
Zeitschrift fuer den Lastenausgleich. (GW ISSN 0044-247X) **2696**
Zeitschrift fuer Deutsche Philologie. (GW ISSN 0044-2496) **2853**
Zeitschrift fuer Deutsches Altertum und Deutsche Literatur. (GW ISSN 0044-2518) **2853**
Zeitschrift fuer Deutsches und Internationales Baurecht. (GW ISSN 0170-0413) **3948**
Zeitschrift fuer Dialektologie und Linguistik. (GW ISSN 0044-1449) **2853**

Zeitschrift fuer Dialektologie und Linguistik. Beihefte. (GW ISSN 0341-0838) **2853**
Zeitschrift fuer Didaktik der Philosophie. (GW) **3786**, 1764
Zeitschrift fuer die Alttestamentliche Wissenschaft. (GW ISSN 0044-2526) **4211**
†Zeitschrift fuer die Binnenfischerei der DDR. (GW ISSN 0373-689X) **5308**
Zeitschrift fuer die Gesamte Experimentelle Medizin Einschliesslich Experimenteller Chirurgie see Research in Experimental Medicine **3263**
†Zeitschrift fuer die Gesamte Hygiene und Ihre Grenzgebiete. (GW ISSN 0049-8610) **5308**
Zeitschrift fuer die Gesamte Innere Medizin und Ihre Grenzgebiete. (GW ISSN 0044-2542) **3164**
Zeitschrift fuer die Gesamte Strafrechtswissenschaft. (GW ISSN 0084-5310) **2696**
Zeitschrift fuer die Gesamte Versicherungswissenschaft. (GW ISSN 0044-2585) **2545**
Zeitschrift fuer die Geschichte des Oberrheins. (GW ISSN 0044-2607) **2396**
Zeitschrift fuer die Geschichte und Altertumskunde Ermlands. (GW ISSN 0342-3344) **2396**
Zeitschrift fuer die Neutestamentliche Wissenschaft und die Kunde der Aelteren Kirche. (GW ISSN 0044-2615) **4211**
Zeitschrift fuer die Zuckerindustrie see Zuckerindustrie **2086**
Zeitschrift fuer Differentielle und Diagnostische Psychologie. (SZ ISSN 0170-1789) **4050**
Zeitschrift fuer Eigenheimfreunde see Domus Magazin **944**
Zeitschrift fuer Energiewirtschaft. (GW ISSN 0343-5377) **1797**, 888
Zeitschrift fuer Entwicklungspaedagogik. (GW ISSN 0175-0488) **4393**, 1673
Zeitschrift fuer Entwicklungspsychologie und Paedagogische Psychologie. (GW ISSN 0049-8637) **4050**, 1673
Zeitschrift fuer Ernaehrungswissenschaft/Journal of Nutritional Sciences/Journal des Sciences de la Nutrition. (GW ISSN 0044-264X) **3613**
Zeitschrift fuer Ethnologie. (GW ISSN 0044-2666) **253**
Zeitschrift fuer Evangelische Ethik. (GW ISSN 0044-2674) **4211**
Zeitschrift fuer Evangelische Rundfunk- und Fernseharbeit Medium see Medium **1376**
Zeitschrift fuer Evangelisches Kirchenrecht. (GW ISSN 0044-2690) **4253**, 2696
†Zeitschrift fuer Experimentelle Chirurgie. (GW ISSN 0232-7295) **5308**
Zeitschrift fuer Experimentelle und Angewandte Psychologie. (GW ISSN 0044-2712) **4050**
▼Zeitschrift fuer Fischkunde. (GW ISSN 0939-6330) **594**
Zeitschrift fuer Flugwissenschaften und Weltraumforschung. (GW ISSN 0342-068X) **65**
Zeitschrift fuer Franzoesische Sprache und Literatur. (GW ISSN 0044-2747) **2854**
Zeitschrift fuer Franzoesische Sprache und Literatur. Beihefte. Neue Folge. (GW ISSN 0341-0811) **2854**
Zeitschrift fuer Fremdenverkehr/Revue de Tourisme/Tourist Review. (SZ ISSN 0044-2755) **4798**
†Zeitschrift fuer Freunde der Stenografie - die Neuwacht. (GW) **5308**
Zeitschrift fuer Ganzheitliche Tiermedizin. (GW) **4820**
Zeitschrift fuer Ganzheitsforschung. (AU ISSN 0044-2763) **3787**, 4457
Zeitschrift fuer Gastroenterologie. (GW ISSN 0044-2771) **3270**
Zeitschrift fuer Geburtshilfe und Gynaekologie see Zeitschrift fuer Geburtshilfe und Perinatologie **3297**

Zeitschrift fuer Geburtshilfe und Perinatologie. (GW ISSN 0300-967X) **3297**
Zeitschrift fuer Geologische Wissenschaften. (GW ISSN 0303-4534) **1586**
Zeitschrift fuer Geomorphologie/Annals of Geomorphology/Annales de Geomorphologie. (GW ISSN 0372-8854) **1586**, 2267
Zeitschrift fuer Geomorphologie, Supplementbaende/Annals of Geomorphology, Supplement Volumes/Annales de Geomorphologie, Supplements. (GW) **2267**, 1586
Zeitschrift fuer Geriatrie. (GW ISSN 0938-3808) **2280**
Zeitschrift fuer Germanistik. (GW ISSN 0323-7982) **2979**
Zeitschrift fuer Germanistische Linguistik. (GW ISSN 0301-3294) **2854**
Zeitschrift fuer Gerontologie. (GW ISSN 0044-281X) **2280**
Zeitschrift fuer Gerontopsychologie und Psychiatrie. (SZ ISSN 1011-6877) **2280**, 3356
Zeitschrift fuer Geschichte der Arabisch-Islamischen Wissenschaften. (GW ISSN 0179-4639) **3646**, 4353
Zeitschrift fuer Geschichtswissenschaft. (GW ISSN 0044-2828) **2327**
Zeitschrift fuer Gesetzgebung. (GW ISSN 0179-4051) **2696**
Zeitschrift fuer Gletscherkunde und Glazialgeologie. (AU ISSN 0044-2836) **1586**
Zeitschrift fuer Gottesdienst und Predigt. (GW) **4211**
Zeitschrift fuer Haut- und Geschlechtskrankheiten see Zeitschrift fuer Hautkrankheiten H und G **3250**
Zeitschrift fuer Hautkrankheiten H und G. (GW ISSN 0301-0481) **3250**
Zeitschrift fuer Heereskunde. (GW ISSN 0044-2852) **3476**
Zeitschrift fuer Heilpaedagogik. (GW) **1742**
Zeitschrift fuer Herz, Thorax- und Gefaesschirurgie. (GW ISSN 0930-9225) **3386**, 3213
Zeitschrift fuer Historische Forschung. (GW ISSN 0340-0174) **2396**
Zeitschrift fuer Hohenzollerische Geschichte. (GW ISSN 0514-8561) **2396**
Zeitschrift fuer Individualpsychologie. (GW ISSN 0342-393X) **4050**
Zeitschrift fuer Internationale Erziehungs- und Sozialwissenschaftliche Forschung. (GW ISSN 0930-9381) **4393**
Zeitschrift fuer Jagdwissenschaft. (GW ISSN 0044-2887) **4497**
Zeitschrift fuer Kardiologie. (GW ISSN 0300-5860) **3213**
Zeitschrift fuer Katholische Theologie. (AU ISSN 0044-2895) **4279**, 3787
Zeitschrift fuer Kinder- und Jugendpsychiatrie. (SZ ISSN 0301-6811) **3356**
Zeitschrift fuer Kinderchirurgie/Surgery in Infancy and Childhood. (GW ISSN 0174-3082) **3327**, 3386
Zeitschrift fuer Kinderchirurgie und Grenzgebiete see Zeitschrift fuer Kinderchirurgie **3327**
Zeitschrift fuer Kirchengeschichte. (GW ISSN 0044-2925) **4211**
Zeitschrift fuer Klassische Homoeopathie. (GW ISSN 0935-0853) **3216**
Zeitschrift fuer Klinische Chemie und Klinische Biochemie see European Journal of Clinical Chemistry and Clinical Biochemistry **476**
Zeitschrift fuer Klinische Psychologie - Forschung und Praxis. (GW ISSN 0084-5345) **4050**
Zeitschrift fuer Klinische Psychologie und Psychotherapie. (GW ISSN 0300-869X) **3356**, 4050
Zeitschrift fuer Krankenpflege - Revue Suisse des Infirmieres see Krankenpflege **3281**

Zeitschrift fuer Kristallographie. (GW ISSN 0044-2968) **1211**
ZeitSchrift fuer Kultur Politik Kirche. (SZ) **4211**
Zeitschrift fuer Kulturaustausch. (GW ISSN 0044-2976) **3978**
Zeitschrift fuer Kulturtechnik und Flurbereinigung see Zeitschrift fuer Kulturtechnik und Landentwicklung **1876**
Zeitschrift fuer Kulturtechnik und Landentwicklung/Journal of Rural Engineering and Development. (GW ISSN 0934-666X) **1876**, 197
Zeitschrift fuer Kunstgeschichte. (GW ISSN 0044-2992) **351**, 2327
Zeitschrift fuer Kunstwissenschaft see Deutscher Verein fuer Kunstwissenschaft. Zeitschrift **324**
Zeitschrift fuer Laermbekaempfung. (GW ISSN 0174-1098) **3860**, 4116
Zeitschrift fuer Lateinamerika Wien. (AU ISSN 0049-8645) **2427**, 3935
Zeitschrift fuer Lebensmittel-Untersuchung und -Forschung. (GW ISSN 0044-3026) **2086**, 25
Zeitschrift fuer Literaturwissenschaft und Linguistik LiLi see LiLi **2825**
Zeitschrift fuer Literaturwissenschaft und Linguistik LiLi. Beihefte see LiLi. Beihefte **2825**
Zeitschrift fuer Logistik. (GW ISSN 0173-8062) **1031**
Zeitschrift fuer Luft- und Weltraumrecht.(GW ISSN 0340-8329) **2731**
Zeitschrift fuer Luftrecht und Weltraumrechtsfragen see Zeitschrift fuer Luft- und Weltraumrecht **2731**
Zeitschrift fuer Lymphologie. (GW ISSN 0343-8554) **3189**
Zeitschrift fuer Markt, Meinungs- und Zukunftsforschung. (GW ISSN 0044-3042) **1057**
Zeitschrift fuer Markt- und Meinungsforschung see Zeitschrift fuer Markt, Meinungs- und Zukunftsforschung **1057**
Zeitschrift fuer Mathematische Logik und Grundlagen der Mathematik. Zeitschrift. (GW ISSN 0044-3050) **3062**
†Zeitschrift fuer Medizinische Laboratoriumsdiagnostik. (GW ISSN 0323-5637) **5308**
Zeitschrift fuer Medizinische Labortechnik see Zeitschrift fuer Medizinische Laboratoriumsdiagnostik **5308**
Zeitschrift fuer Medizinische Mikrobiologie und Immunologie see Medical Microbiology and Immunology **3188**
Zeitschrift fuer Menschenkunde. Zentralblatt fuer Schriftpsychologie und Schriftvergleichung. (AU) **4050**
Zeitschrift fuer Menschenkunde und Zentralblatt fuer Graphologie see Zeitschrift fuer Menschenkunde. Zentralblatt fuer Schriftpsychologie und Schriftvergleichung **4050**
Zeitschrift fuer Menschenkunde und Zentralblatt fuer Graphologie, Ausdruckswissenschaft und Charakterkunde see Zeitschrift fuer Menschenkunde. Zentralblatt fuer Schriftpsychologie und Schriftvergleichung **4050**
Zeitschrift fuer Metallkunde. (GW ISSN 0044-3093) **3424**
Zeitschrift fuer Meteorologie. (GW ISSN 0084-5361) **3444**
Zeitschrift fuer Miet- und Raumrecht. (GW ISSN 0340-7497) **4159**, 2696
Zeitschrift fuer Mikroskopisch-Anatomische Forschung. (GW ISSN 0044-3107) **460**, 561
Zeitschrift fuer Militaermedizin. (GW ISSN 0514-8782) **3164**
Zeitschrift fuer Mission. (GW ISSN 0342-9423) **4211**
Zeitschrift fuer Missionswissenschaft und Religionswissenschaft. (GW ISSN 0044-3123) **4211**
Zeitschrift fuer Morphologie und Anthropologie. (GW ISSN 0044-314X) **253**, 460

Zeitschrift fuer Mundartforschung see Zeitschrift fuer Dialektologie und Linguistik **2853**
Zeitschrift fuer Musikpaedagogik. (GW) **3587**, 1764
Zeitschrift fuer Naturforschung. Section A: Physical Sciences. (GW ISSN 0932-0784) **3836**, 371, 1231
Zeitschrift fuer Naturforschung. Section B: Chemical Sciences. (GW ISSN 0932-0776) **1215**, 1224
Zeitschrift fuer Naturforschung. Section B: Inorganic and Organic Chemistry see Zeitschrift fuer Naturforschung. Section B: Chemical Sciences **1215**
Zeitschrift fuer Naturforschung. Section C: Biosciences. (GW ISSN 0341-0382) **460**
Zeitschrift fuer Naturheilkunde. (GW ISSN 0044-3182) **3811**
Zeitschrift fuer Neuere Rechtsgeschichte. (AU ISSN 0250-6459) **2696**
Zeitschrift fuer Neurologie. see Journal of Neurology **3342**
Zeitschrift fuer Oeffentliche Fuersorge. (SZ ISSN 0044-3204) **4425**
Zeitschrift fuer Oeffentliche und Gemeinwirtschaftliche Unternehmen. (GW ISSN 0344-9777) **4078**, 833
▼Zeitschrift fuer Oekologie und Naturschutz. (GW ISSN 0940-5178) **1972**, 1501
Zeitschrift fuer Offene Vermoegensfragen see Z O V **2499**
Zeitschrift fuer Orgelbau. see Organ Building Periodical **3572**
Zeitschrift fuer Orthopaedie und Ihre Grenzgebiete. (GW ISSN 0044-3220) **3312**
Zeitschrift fuer Ostforschung. (GW ISSN 0044-3239) **2396**, 899, 4393
Zeitschrift fuer Ostkirchliche Kunst Hermeneia. (GW ISSN 0930-6897) **351**
Zeitschrift fuer Paedagogik. (GW ISSN 0044-3247) **1673**
Zeitschrift fuer Paedagogische Psychologie. (SZ ISSN 1010-0652) **4050**
Zeitschrift fuer Papyrologie und Epigraphik. (GW ISSN 0084-5388) **290**
Zeitschrift fuer Parapsychologie und Grenzgebiete der Psychologie. (GW ISSN 0028-3479) **3672**
Zeitschrift fuer Parasitenkunde see Parasitology Research **3222**
Zeitschrift fuer Parlamentsfragen. (GW ISSN 0340-1758) **3935**, 4078
†Zeitschrift fuer Personenzentrierte Psychologie und Psychotherapie. (GW ISSN 0723-1237) **5309**
Zeitschrift fuer Pflanzenernaehrung und Bodenkunde/Journal of Plant Nutrition and Soil Science. (GW ISSN 0044-3263) **468**, 25, 145
Zeitschrift fuer Pflanzenkrankheiten und Pflanzenschutz. (GW ISSN 0044-3271) **521**, 539
Zeitschrift fuer Pflanzenzuechtung. see Plant Breeding **514**
Zeitschrift fuer Philosophische Forschung. (GW ISSN 0044-3301) **3787**
Zeitschrift fuer Philosophische Forschung. Beihefte. (GW ISSN 0514-2733) **3787**
Zeitschrift fuer Phonetik, Sprachwissenschaft und Kommunikationsforschung. (GW ISSN 0044-331X) **2854**
Zeitschrift fuer Physik. Section A: Atomic and Nuclei see Zeitschrift fuer Physik. Section A. Atomic Nuclei **3851**
Zeitschrift fuer Physik. Section A. Atomic Nuclei. (GW ISSN 0930-1151) **3851**, 3836
Zeitschrift fuer Physik. Section B: Condensed Matter. (GW ISSN 0722-3277) **3836**
Zeitschrift fuer Physik. Section C: Particles and Fields. (GW ISSN 0170-9739) **3836**
Zeitschrift fuer Physik. Section D: Atoms, Molecules and Clusters. (GW ISSN 0178-7683) **3836**

ZEITSCHRIFT 6829

Zeitschrift fuer Physikalische Chemie. (GW ISSN 0044-3336) **1231**
Zeitschrift fuer Physikalische Medizin, Balneologie und Medizinische Klimatologie. (GW ISSN 0720-9762) **3164**
Zeitschrift fuer Physiotherapie see Physikalische Medizin Rehabilitationsmedizin Kurortmedizin **3142**
Zeitschrift fuer Phytotherapie. (GW ISSN 0722-348X) **521**
▼Zeitschrift fuer Planung/Journal of Planning. (GW ISSN 0936-8787) **701**
Zeitschrift fuer Plastische Chirurgie see Handchirurgie - Mikrochirurgie - Plastische Chirurgie **3379**
Zeitschrift fuer Politik. (GW ISSN 0044-3360) **3935**
Zeitschrift fuer Praeventivmedizin see Sozial- und Praeventivmedizin **3154**
Zeitschrift fuer Praktische Augenheilkunde see Z P A **3306**
Zeitschrift fuer Psycho-Somatische Medizin see Zeitschrift fuer Psychosomatische Medizin und Psychoanalyse **3356**
Zeitschrift fuer Psychologie. (GW ISSN 0044-3409) **4050**
Zeitschrift fuer Psychosomatische Medizin und Psychoanalyse. (GW ISSN 0340-5613) **3356**
Zeitschrift fuer Psychosomatische Medizin und Psychoanalyse. Beihefte. (GW ISSN 0085-8412) **3356**, 4050
Zeitschrift fuer Radiaesthesie see Zeitschrift fuer Radiaesthesie und Harmoniefindung **3597**
Zeitschrift fuer Radiaesthesie und Harmoniefindung. (GW) **3597**, 3672
Zeitschrift fuer Rechtsmedizin - Journal of Legal Medicine see International Journal of Legal Medicine **3265**
Zeitschrift fuer Rechtspolitik. (GW ISSN 0514-6496) **2696**
Zeitschrift fuer Rechtssoziologie. (GW ISSN 0174-0202) **4457**, 2696
Zeitschrift fuer Rechtsvergleichung see Zeitschrift fuer Rechtsvergleichung, Internationales Privatrecht und Europarecht **2696**
Zeitschrift fuer Rechtsvergleichung, Internationales Privatrecht und Europarecht. (AU) **2696**
Zeitschrift fuer Religions- und Geistesgeschichte/Journal of Religious and Intellectual History. (NE ISSN 0044-3441) **4211**
Zeitschrift fuer Religions- und Geistesgeschichte. Beihefte. (NE ISSN 0514-650X) **4211**
Zeitschrift fuer Religionspaedagogik see Religion Heute: Supplement **1658**
Zeitschrift fuer Rheumaforschung see Zeitschrift fuer Rheumatologie **3370**
Zeitschrift fuer Rheumatologie. (GW ISSN 0340-1855) **3370**
Zeitschrift fuer Romanische Philologie. (GW ISSN 0049-8661) **2854**, 2979
Zeitschrift fuer Romanische Philologie. Beihefte. (GW ISSN 0084-5396) **2854**, 2979
Zeitschrift fuer Saeugetierkunde. (GW ISSN 0044-3468) **594**
Zeitschrift fuer Schadensrecht. (GW ISSN 0173-0568) **2697**
Zeitschrift fuer Schulgesundheitspflege see Aerztliche Jugendkunde **3318**
Zeitschrift fuer Schweizerische Archaeologie und Kunstgeschichte/Revue Suisse d'Art et d'Archeologie. (SZ ISSN 0044-3476) **290**, 351
Zeitschrift fuer Schweizerische Kirchengeschichte/Revue d'Histoire Ecclesiastique Suisse. (SZ ISSN 0044-3484) **4211**
Zeitschrift fuer Schweizerisches Recht/Revue de Droit Suisse. (SZ ISSN 0254-945X) **2697**
Zeitschrift fuer Semiotik. (GW ISSN 0170-6241) **3787**, 1346, 2854
Zeitschrift fuer Sexualforschung. (GW ISSN 0932-8114) **3164**, 4050

6830 ZEITSCHRIFT

Zeitschrift fuer Siebenbuergische Landeskunde. (GW ISSN 0344-3418) **2267**, 2396
Zeitschrift fuer Slavische Philologie. (GW ISSN 0044-3492) **2854**
Zeitschrift fuer Slawistik. (GW ISSN 0044-3506) **2854**
Zeitschrift fuer Sozialisationsforschung und Erziehungssoziologie. (GW ISSN 0720-4361) **4457**
Zeitschrift fuer Sozialpsychologie. (SZ ISSN 0049-867X) **4050**, 4457
Zeitschrift fuer Sozialreform. (GW ISSN 0514-2776) **3936**, 4425
Zeitschrift fuer Soziologie. (GW ISSN 0340-1804) **4457**
Zeitschrift fuer Sprachwissenschaft. (GW ISSN 0721-9067) **2854**
Zeitschrift fuer Stadtgeschichte, Stadtsoziologie und Denkmalpflege see Die Alte Stadt **2483**
Zeitschrift fuer Stomatologie. (AU ISSN 0175-7784) **3245**
Zeitschrift fuer Strafvollzug und Straffaelligenhilfe. (GW ISSN 0342-3514) **1524**, 2697
Zeitschrift fuer Systemische Therapie. (GW ISSN 0723-9505) **4050**
Zeitschrift fuer Theologie und Kirche. (GW ISSN 0513-9147) **4253**
Zeitschrift fuer Tierphysiologie, Tierernaehrung und Futtermittelkunde. see Journal of Animal Physiology and Animal Nutrition **585**
Zeitschrift fuer Tierpsychologie see Ethology **582**
Zeitschrift fuer Tierzuechtung und Zuechtungsbiologie. see Journal of Animal Breeding and Genetics **219**
Zeitschrift fuer Transaktionsanalyse in Theorie und Praxis. (GW ISSN 0176-9855) **4050**
Zeitschrift fuer Transplantationsmedizin.(GW ISSN 0935-1965) **3386**
Zeitschrift fuer Tropenmedizin und Parasitologie see Tropical Medicine and Parasitology **3224**
Zeitschrift fuer Tuerkeistudien. (GW ISSN 0934-0696) **3646**, 2432
Zeitschrift fuer Umweltpolitik. (GW ISSN 0343-7167) **1972**, 4393
Zeitschrift fuer Unfallchirurgie und Versicherungsmedizin. (SZ) **3164**
Zeitschrift fuer Unfallchirurgie, Versicherungsmedizin und Berufskrankheiten see Zeitschrift fuer Unfallchirurgie und Versicherungsmedizin **3164**
Zeitschrift fuer Unternehmens- und Gesellschaftsrecht. (GW ISSN 0340-2479) **2697**
Zeitschrift fuer Unternehmensgeschichte. (GW ISSN 0342-2852) **1087**
Zeitschrift fuer Unternehmensgeschichte. Beihefte. (GW ISSN 0342-3956) **899**
Zeitschrift fuer Urheber- und Medienrecht. (GW) **2697**, 1384, 3519
Zeitschrift fuer Urologie und Nephrologie see Aktuelle Urologie **3387**
†Zeitschrift fuer Vegetationstechnik. (GW ISSN 0170-5261) **5309**
Zeitschrift fuer Vergleichende Rechtswissenschaft. (GW ISSN 0044-3638) **2731**
Zeitschrift fuer Vergleichende Sprachforschung see Historische Sprachforschung **2817**
Zeitschrift fuer Verkehrserziehung. (GW ISSN 0341-2334) **4723**, 1673
Zeitschrift fuer Verkehrsrecht. (AU ISSN 0044-3662) **2697**
Zeitschrift fuer Verkehrssicherheit. (GW ISSN 0044-3654) **4723**
Zeitschrift fuer Verkehrswissenschaft. (GW ISSN 0044-3670) **4353**
Zeitschrift fuer Vermessungswesen. (GW ISSN 0340-4560) **1876**, 2267
Zeitschrift fuer Versicherungswesen. (GW) **2545**
Zeitschrift fuer Versuchstierkunde. see Journal of Experimental Animal Science **3260**
Zeitschrift fuer Verwaltung. (AU) **4078**
Zeitschrift fuer Volkskunde. (GW ISSN 0044-3700) **2060**, 253, 290
Zeitschrift fuer Wahrscheinlichkeitstheorie und Verwandte Gebiete see Probability Theory and Related Fields **3051**
Zeitschrift fuer Wasser- und Abwasserforschung/Journal for Water and Waste Water Research. (GW ISSN 0044-3727) **4834**, 4116
Zeitschrift fuer Wasserrecht. (GW ISSN 0722-8910) **4834**, 2697
Zeitschrift fuer Werkstofftechnik see Materialwissenschaft und Werkstofftechnik **3413**
Zeitschrift fuer Wirtschaftliche Fertigung und Automatisierung see Z W F - C I M **3025**
Zeitschrift fuer Wirtschafts- und Sozialwissenschaften. (GW ISSN 0342-1783) **701**, 4457
Zeitschrift fuer Wirtschaftsgeographie. (GW ISSN 0044-3751) **2267**
Zeitschrift fuer Wirtschaftspolitik. (GW ISSN 0721-3808) **701**
Zeitschrift fuer Wirtschaftsrecht - Z I P. (GW ISSN 0723-9416) **2697**, 804, 841
Zeitschrift fuer Wuerttembergische Landesgeschichte. (GW ISSN 0044-3786) **2396**
Zeitschrift fuer Zahnaerztliche Implantologie. (GW) **3245**
Zeitschrift fuer Zivilprozess. (GW ISSN 0342-3468) **2697**
Zeitschrift fuer Zoelle und Verbrauchsteuern. (GW ISSN 0342-3484) **1112**
Zeitschrift fuer Zoologische Systematik und Evolutionsforschung. (GW ISSN 0044-3808) **594**
Zeitschrift fur Verbraucherpolitik see Journal of Consumer Policy **1505**
Zeitschrift Interne Revision. (GW ISSN 0044-3816) **757**
Zeitschriften - Datenbank (Z D B). (GW ISSN 0171-8922) **2791**
Zeitschriften- und Buecherschau "Stahl und Eisen" see Literaturschau "Stahl und Eisen" **3412**
Zeitschriftenbibliographie Gerontologie. (GW ISSN 0721-1872) **2280**, 416, 4427
Zeitschriftendienst see Z D **416**
Zeitschriftendienst Musik. (GW ISSN 0044-3824) **416**
Zeitschrifteninhaltsdienst Theologie. (GW ISSN 0340-8361) **4211**
†Zeitschriftenschau Keramik. (GW ISSN 0138-2233) **5309**
Zeitschrift fuer Astrophysik see Astronomy and Astrophysics **362**
Zeitungs - Dokumentation Bildungswesen. (GW ISSN 0177-9419) **1247**, 1673
Zeitungs - Index. (GW ISSN 0340-0107) **2579**, 25, 2192
Zeitungstechnik see Newspaper Techniques **4002**
Zeleznicni Technika. (CS ISSN 0513-9295) **4717**
†Zelfbestuur. (NE ISSN 0169-7471) **5309**
Zelfkazer. (NE) **204**
Zelfzwichter. (NE) **1501**
Zellstoff und Papier. (GW ISSN 0044-3867) **3667**
Zelluloid. (GW ISSN 0724-7656) **3519**
Zelte Planen Markisen see Technisches Textil Forum **4624**
Zeltgruss. (GW) **4253**
Zemaljski Muzej Bosne i Hercegovine. Glasnik. Arheologija. (BN ISSN 0581-7501) **290**
Zemaljski Muzej Bosne i Hercegovine. Glasnik. Etnologija. (BN ISSN 0581-751X) **2060**, 253
Zemaljski Muzej Bosne i Hercegovine. Glasnik. Prirodne Nauke. (BN ISSN 0581-7528) **4353**
Zemedelska Ekonomika/Agricultural Economy. (CS ISSN 0139-570X) **160**
Zemedelska Informatika/Information Sciences for Agriculture. (CS ISSN 0862-2086) **2791**, 130
Zemedelska Literatura. (CS ISSN 0862-2264) **145**, 416
Zemedelska Technika/Agricultural Technology. (CS ISSN 0044-3883) **130**, 165
Zemedelske Aktuality ze Sveta see Zemedelske - Polnohospodarske Aktuality **131**
Zemedelske Muzeum. Vedecke Prace/Museum of Agriculture. Scientifical Works. (CS ISSN 0375-4855) **131**, 2396
Zemedelske - Polnohospodarske Aktuality. (CS) **131**
Zemedelsky a Lesni Zamestnanec see Socialisticky Zemedelec **120**
Zement - Kalk - Gips International Ausgabe A see Z K G: Ausgabe A **636**
Zement - Kalk - Gips International Ausgabe B see Z K G: Ausgabe B **1876**
Zement - Taschenbuch. (GW ISSN 0514-2938) **1877**
Zement und Beton. (AU) **636**
Zemia. (BU) **2592**, 2084
Zemledelie. (RU ISSN 0044-3913) **131**
†Zemlja Sovjeta. (YU ISSN 0044-3921) **5309**
Zemljiste i Biljka see Acta Biologica Iugoslavica. Serija A: Zemljiste i Biljka **425**
Zemlya i Vselennaya. (RU ISSN 0044-3948) **371**
Zen. (GW ISSN 0921-5174) **4290**
Zen Bow see Zen Bow Newsletter **3787**
Zen Bow Newsletter. (US) **3787**
Zen Extra. (GW) **4216**
Zen Notes. (US) **4290**
Zena. (CI ISSN 0513-9481) **4858**
Zenchu Farm News. (JA) **833**
Zendingsblad see Uw Koninkrijk Kome: Zendingsblad **4208**
Zenit. (NE ISSN 0165-0211) **371**
Zenit. (SW ISSN 0044-3980) **3936**
Zenit. (CS) **4353**, 4613
Zenith. see Cenit **2861**
Zenit Pionierov see Zenit **4353**
Zenken Janaru. see Zenken Journal **636**
Zenken Journal/Zenken Janaru. (JA ISSN 0044-4006) **636**
Zenos. (UK) **3009**
Zensen Monthly Journal. (JA) **4627**
Zensen Newspaper. (JA) **4627**
Zentai Fuzetek. (YU) **2396**
Zentralasiatische Studien. (GW ISSN 0514-857X) **2343**
Zentralausschuss der Werbewirtschaft Service. (GW) **40**
Zentralblatt der Bulgarischen Wissenschaftliche Literatur. Geschichte, Archaeologie und Ethnographie see Abstracts of Bulgarian Scientific Literature. History, Archaeology and Ethnography **2346**
Zentralblatt fuer Allgemeine Pathologie und Pathologische Anatomie see Zentralblatt fuer Pathologie **3164**
Zentralblatt fuer Arbeitsmedizin, Arbeitsschutz und Prophylaxe. (GW ISSN 0340-7047) **3623**
Zentralblatt fuer Arbeitsmedizin und Arbeitsschutz see Zentralblatt fuer Arbeitsmedizin, Arbeitsschutz und Prophylaxe **3623**
Zentralblatt fuer Bakteriologie. (GW ISSN 0934-8840) **3224**, 559
Zentralblatt fuer Bakteriologie, Mikrobiologie und Hygiene see Systematic and Applied Microbiology **557**
Zentralblatt fuer Bakteriologie, Mikrobiologie und Hygiene. Abstracts.(GW ISSN 0177-3100) **468**, 416
Zentralblatt fuer Bakteriologie, Parasitenkunde, Infektionskrankheiten und Hygiene. Series B: Krankenhaushygiene - Praeventive Medizin - Betriebshygiene see Zentralblatt fuer Hygiene und Umweltmedizin **4116**
Zentralblatt fuer Bakteriologie, Parasitenkunde, Infektionskrankheiten und Hygiene see Zentralblatt fuer Bakteriologie, Mikrobiologie und Hygiene. Abstracts **468**
Zentralblatt fuer Bakteriologie, Parasitenkunde, Infektionskrankheiten und Hygiene. Series A: Medizinische Mikrobiologie und Parasitologie see Zentralblatt fuer Bakteriologie **3224**
Zentralblatt fuer Bakteriologie, Parasitenkunde, Infektionskrankheiten und Hygiene: Zweite Abteilung - Naturwissenschaft see Zentralblatt fuer Mikrobiologie **559**
Zentralblatt fuer Bibliothekswesen see Zeitschrift fuer Bibliothekswesen und Bibliographie **2791**
Zentralblatt fuer Chirurgie. (GW ISSN 0044-409X) **3386**
Zentralblatt fuer Didaktik der Mathematik. (GW ISSN 0044-4103) **3062**, 1764, 3066
Zentralblatt fuer die Gesamte Neurologie und Psychiatrie see Zentralblatt Neurologie - Psychiatrie **3182**
Zentralblatt fuer die Gesamte Radiologie see Zentralblatt Radiologie **3182**
Zentralblatt fuer Geologie und Palaeontologie. Teil I: Allgemeine, Angewandte, Regionale und Historische Geologie. (GW ISSN 0340-5109) **1552**, 25
Zentralblatt fuer Geologie und Palaeontologie. Teil II: Palaeontologie.(GW ISSN 0044-4189) **3661**, 25
Zentralblatt fuer Gynaekologie. (GW ISSN 0044-4197) **3297**
Zentralblatt fuer Gynaekologie und Geburtshilfe see Zentralblatt fuer Gynaekologie **3297**
Zentralblatt fuer Hygiene und Umweltmedizin. (GW ISSN 0934-8859) **4116**
Zentralblatt fuer Industriebau see Industriebau **620**
Zentralblatt fuer Jugendrecht. (GW ISSN 0176-6449) **1247**, 2697, 4425
Zentralblatt fuer Mathematik und ihre Grenzgebiete/Mathematics Abstracts.(GW ISSN 0044-4235) **3063**, 25
Zentralblatt fuer Mikrobiologie. (GW ISSN 0232-4393) **559**, 131, 1972
Zentralblatt fuer Mineralogie. Teil I: Kristallographie, Mineralogie. (GW ISSN 0514-7115) **3502**, 25
Zentralblatt fuer Mineralogie. Teil II: Petrographie, Technische Mineralogie, Geochemie und Lagerstaettenkunde. (GW ISSN 0514-7123) **3502**, 25, 1552
Zentralblatt fuer Neurochirurgie. (GW ISSN 0044-4251) **3356**, 3386
Zentralblatt fuer Pathologie. (GW ISSN 0863-4106) **3164**, 460
†Zentralblatt fuer Pharmazie, Pharmakotherapie und Laboratoriumsdiagnostik. (GW ISSN 0049-8696) **5309**
Zentralblatt fuer Phlebologie see Vasa **3212**
Zentralblatt fuer Sozialversicherung, Sozialhilfe und Versorgung. (GW ISSN 0044-4278) **3936**, 2697
Zentralblatt fuer Veterinaermedizin. Series A see Journal of Veterinary Medicine. Series A **4812**
Zentralblatt fuer Veterinaermedizin. Series B see Journal of Veterinary Medicine. Series B **4812**
Zentralblatt fuer Veterinaermedizin. Series C. see Anatomia, Histologia, Embryologia. Series C **4805**
Zentralblatt Hals-, Nasen- und Ohrenheilkunde, Plastische Chirurgie an Kopf und Hals/Oto-Rhino-Laryngology, Plastic Surgery of Head and Neck. (GW ISSN 0340-5214) **3182**, 25

Zentralblatt Haut- und Geschlechtskrankheiten/Dermatology, Venerology, Andrology. (GW ISSN 0343-3048) **3182**, 25
†Zentralblatt Innere Medizin/Internal Medicine. (GW ISSN 0931-4695) **5309**
Zentralblatt Kinderheilkunde/Pediatrics. (GW ISSN 0722-8953) **3182**, 25
Zentralblatt Neurologie - Psychiatrie/Neurology - Psychiatry. (GW ISSN 0722-3064) **3182**, 25
Zentralblatt Ophthalmologie/Ophthalmology. (GW ISSN 0722-9933) **3182**, 25
Zentralblatt Radiologie/Radiology. (GW ISSN 0722-3072) **3182**, 25
Zentralblatt Rechtsmedizin/Legal Medicine. (GW ISSN 0722-3056) **3182**, 25
Zentraler Bewerberanzeiger Markt und Chance. (GW ISSN 0177-3836) **4425**, 3631
†Zentralinstitut fuer Bibliothekswesen. Mitteilungen und Materialien. (GW ISSN 0433-6933) **5309**
Zentralinstitut fuer Kunstgeschichte. Jahrbuch. (GW ISSN 0177-8978) **351**
Zentralinstitut fuer Schweisstechnik der DDR Report see Z I S - Report **5308**
Zentralinstitut fuer Versuchstierzucht. Jahresbericht. (GW ISSN 0174-2795) **460**, 3164, 4820
Zentralinstituts fuer Alte Geschichte und Archaeologie. Veroeffentlichungen. (GW ISSN 0138-3914) **2327**, 290, 2979
Zentralkomitee der Deutschen Katholiken. Mitteilungen. (GW) **4279**
Zentralmarkt. (GW) **925**
Zentralorgan Chirurgie/Surgery. (GW ISSN 0722-6985) **3182**, 25
Zentralsparkasse der Gemeinde Wien. Information see Informationen aus der Wirtschaft **784**
Zentralstelle fuer die Vergabe von Studienplaetzen Info see Z V S - Info **1331**
Zentralstelle fuer die Vergabe von Studienplaetzen Kurzinfo see Z V S - Kurzinfo **5308**
Zentralverband der Deutschen Geographen. Rundbrief. (GW) **2267**
Zentralverband der Landwirtschaftlichen Arbeitgeber in Niederoesterreich, Burgenland und Wien. Mitteilungen. (AU) **131**
Zentralverband fuer Logopaedie. Forum der Mitglieder. (GW ISSN 0932-0547) **3164**
Zentrum fuer Meeres- und Klimaforschung. Berichte. (GW ISSN 0936-949X) **1612**
Zentrumsnachrichten see Tibet und Buddhismus **4216**
Zeolites. (US ISSN 0144-2449) **1209**
Zerb. (UK ISSN 0261-1686) **1384**, 1911
Zeri i Popullit. (AA) **3936**
Zeri i Rinise/Voix de la Jeunesse. (AA) **1272**
Zeri i Rinise. (YU ISSN 0514-7352) **2240**
Zernovoe Khozyaistvo. (RU ISSN 0372-9893) **197**
Zero Hour. (US) **2890**, 1524
▼Zero Hour. (UK) **3015**
Zero One. (UK ISSN 0044-4340) **2196**
Zero Population Growth, Inc. Reporter see Z P G Reporter **3989**
Zero to Three. (US ISSN 0736-8038) **1247**, 4425
Zero - Un Informatique see Zero - Un References **4078**
Zero - Un References. (FR ISSN 0398-1169) **4078**
†Zerosei. (IT) **5309**
Zerouno - Espansione. (IT) **1402**
†Zeroventi. (IT) **5309**
Zerowork. (US) **5309**
Zeszyty "Argumentow". (PL ISSN 0514-342X) **3936**
Zeszyty Gliwickie. (PL ISSN 0514-3446) **2396**, 290

Zeszyty Historyczne. (FR ISSN 0044-4391) **2327**
Zeszyty Literackie. (FR ISSN 0751-0357) **2979**
Zeszyty Prasoznawcze. (PL ISSN 0555-0025) **4139**
†Zeszyty Problemowe Gornictwa. (PL ISSN 0044-4383) **5309**
Zeszyty Problemowe Postepow Nauk Rolniczych. (PL ISSN 0084-5477) **131**
Zeszyty Teoretyczno-Polityczne see Prezentacje **4445**
Zeta. (VE) **2890**
Zeta. (UY) **4457**
Zeta Magazine see Z Magazine **3935**
Zetetic Scholar. (US ISSN 0741-6229) **3672**
Zeus. (GW ISSN 0172-9357) **1681**, 417
Zgoda. (US) **2030**
Zgodovinski Casopis. (XV ISSN 0350-5774) **2396**, 290, 2030
Zhanghui Xiaoshuo. (CC) **2979**
Zhanjiang Literature. see Zhanjiang Wenxue **2979**
Zhanjiang Wenxue/Zhanjiang Literature.(CC) **2979**
Zhaoxiangji/Cameras. (CC) **3798**
Zhejiang Agricultural Science. see Zhejiang Nongye Kexue **131**
Zhejiang Daxue Xuebao (Ziran Kexue Ban)/Zhejiang University. Journal (Natural Science Edition). (CC) **4353**
Zhejiang Economics. see Zhejiang Jingji **701**
Zhejiang Forestry. see Zhejiang Linye **2111**
Zhejiang Gongxueyuan Xuebao/Zhejiang Institute of Engineering. Journal. (CC ISSN 1000-209X) **1841**
Zhejiang Institute of Engineering. Journal. see Zhejiang Gongxueyuan Xuebao **1841**
Zhejiang Institute of Forestry. Journal. see Zhejiang Linxueyuan Xuebao **2111**
Zhejiang Jingji/Zhejiang Economics. (CC) **701**
Zhejiang Journal of Traditional Chinese Medicine. see Zhejiang Zhongyi Zazhi **3164**
Zhejiang Linxueyuan Xuebao/Zhejiang Institute of Forestry. Journal. (CC ISSN 1000-5692) **2111**
Zhejiang Linye/Zhejiang Forestry. (CC) **2111**
Zhejiang Linye Keji. (CC ISSN 1001-3776) **2111**
Zhejiang Nongye Daxue Xuebao/Zhejiang University of Agriculture. Journal. (CC ISSN 1000-2111) **131**
Zhejiang Nongye Kexue/Zhejiang Agricultural Science. (CC ISSN 0528-9017) **131**
Zhejiang Normal University. Journal (Social Science Edition). see Zhejiang Shifan Daxue Xuebao (Shehui Kexue Ban) **4393**
Zhejiang Shifan Daxue Xuebao (Shehui Kexue Ban)/Zhejiang Normal University. Journal (Social Science Edition). (CC ISSN 1001-5035) **4393**
Zhejiang Sichou Gongxueyuan Xuebao. (CC ISSN 1000-2103) **4627**
Zhejiang Traditional Chinese Medical College. Journal. see Zhejiang Zhongyi Xueyuan Xuebao **3164**
Zhejiang University. Journal (Natural Science Edition). see Zhejiang Daxue Xuebao (Ziran Kexue Ban) **4353**
Zhejiang University of Agriculture. Journal. see Zhejiang Nongye Daxue Xuebao **131**
Zhejiang Zhongyi Xueyuan Xuebao/Zhejiang Traditional Chinese Medical College. Journal. (CC) **3164**, 3746
Zhejiang Zhongyi Zazhi/Zhejiang Journal of Traditional Chinese Medicine. (CC ISSN 0411-8421) **3164**, 3746
Zheleznodorozhnyi Transport. (RU ISSN 0044-4448) **4717**
Zhendong yu Chongji/Vibration and Shock. (CC ISSN 1000-3835) **3846**

Zhengfa Luntan/Political Science & Law Tribune. (CC ISSN 1000-0208) **2697**, 3936
Zhengming. (CC) **4393**
Zhengzhi Jiaoyu/Political Education. (CC) **1673**, 3936
Zhengzhi yu Falu/Politics and Law. (CC) **2697**, 3936
Zhengzhixue Yanjiu/Political Science Research. (CC ISSN 1000-3355) **3936**
Zhengzhou Daxue Xuebao (Shehui Kexue Ban)/Zhengzhou University. Journal (Social Science Edition). (CC) **4393**
Zhengzhou Daxue Xuebao (Ziran Kexue Ban)/Zhengzhou University. Journal (Natural Science Edition). (CC ISSN 1001-8212) **4353**
Zhengzhou Gongxueyuan Xuebao/Zhengzhou Institute of Engineering. Journal. (CC ISSN 1000-517X) **1841**
Zhengzhou Institute of Engineering. Journal. see Zhengzhou Gongxueyuan Xuebao **1841**
Zhengzhou University. Journal (Natural Science Edition). see Zhengzhou Daxue Xuebao (Ziran Kexue Ban) **4353**
Zhengzhou University. Journal (Social Science Edition). see Zhengzhou Daxue Xuebao (Shehui Kexue Ban) **4393**
Zhenjiang Chuanbo Xueyuan Xuebao. (CC ISSN 1000-5765) **4742**
Zhenjun Xuebao/Acta Mycologica Sinica.(CC ISSN 0256-1883) **521**, 559
Zhenkong/Vacuum. (CC) **1911**
▼Zhenshchina: Vek XX. (RU) **4858**
Zhenshchiny Mira. (RU ISSN 0044-4456) **4858**
Zhexue Dongtai. (CC) **3787**
Zhexue Luncong. (CC) **3787**
Zhexue Yanjiu/Philosophy Studies. (CC) **3787**, 4216
Zhexue yu Wenhua Yuekan see Universitas **2517**
Zhexue Yuanli. (CC ISSN 1001-2710) **3787**
Zhi he Zaozhi/Paper and Paper Manufacturing. (CC ISSN 1001-6309) **3667**
Zhili/Intelligence. (CC ISSN 1001-1730) **2183**
Zhiliang Guanli/Quality Control. (CC) **1087**
Zhilishchnoe i Kommunal'noe Khozyaistvo. (RU ISSN 0044-4464) **1087**, 636
Zhilishchnoe Stroitel'stvo. (RU ISSN 0044-4472) **636**
Zhinochyi Svit/Woman's World. (CN ISSN 0513-9856) **4858**
Zhishan. (CC) **2979**
Zhishi Chuang/Window of Knowledge. (CC) **4353**
Zhishi Jiushi Liliang/Knowledge is Power. (CC) **4353**
Zhishi Wenku. (CC) **2183**
Zhishi yu Shenghuo/Knowledge and Life. (CC) **2183**
Zhivotnovodstvo see Zootekhniia **229**
Zhiwu Baohu/Plant Protection. (CC ISSN 0529-1542) **521**, 2141
Zhiwu Baohu Xuebao/Acta Phytophylactica Sinica. (CC) **521**
Zhiwu Bingli Xuebao/Acta Phytopathologica Sinica. (CC ISSN 0412-0914) **521**
Zhiwu Fenlei Xuebao/Acta Phytotaxonomica Sinica. (CC ISSN 0529-1526) **521**
Zhiwu Shengli Xuebao/Acta Phytophysiologica Sinica. (CC ISSN 0257-4829) **521**, 575
Zhiwu Shenglixue Tongxun/Plant Physiology Communications. (CC ISSN 0412-0922) **521**, 575
Zhiwu Shengtai Xuebao yu Dizhiwuxue Xuebao. (CC) **521**
Zhiwu Shengtaixue yu Dizhiwuxue Xuebao/Acta Phytoecologica et Geobotanica Sinica. (CC ISSN 1000-0011) **521**, 1972
Zhiwu Xuebao/Acta Botanica Sinica. (CC ISSN 0577-7496) **521**

ZHONGGUO DUIWAI 6831

Zhiwu Zazhi/Plants. (CC ISSN 1000-0631) **521**
Zhiwuxue Tongbao/Botanical Bulletin. (CC) **521**
Zhiye Yixue/Occupational Medicine. (CC) **3164**
Zhiye yu Jiankang/Occupation and Health. (CC ISSN 1004-1257) **4116**
Zhiyin/Bosom Friend. (CC ISSN 1000-4157) **4858**
Zhong Cao Yao/Chinese Herbal Medicine. (CC) **3746**, 3164
Zhong Cheng Yao/Chinese Traditional Patent Medicine. (CC ISSN 1001-1528) **3746**
Zhong Gong Dangshi Yanjiu/Journal of Chinese Communist Party History. (CC) **3936**, 2343
Zhong Lao Nian Baojian. (CC) **3811**
Zhong Wai Shuzhai. (CC) **2979**
Zhong-Xiyi Jiehe Zazhi/Chinese Journal of Integrated Traditional and Western Medicine. (CC ISSN 0254-9034) **3164**
Zhonggang Jibao see China Steel Technical Report **3404**
Zhonggong Dangshi/History of the Chinese Communist Party. (CC) **3936**, 2327
Zhonggong Yanjiu see Chung Kung Yen Chiu **3879**
Zhongguo Aizheng Yanjiu. see Chinese Journal of Cancer Research **3196**
Zhongguo Baodao. see El Popola Cinio **2181**
Zhongguo Baoxian/Insurance in China. (CC ISSN 1001-4489) **2545**
Zhongguo Baozhuang/China Packaging.(US) **3652**
Zhongguo Bingli Shengli Zazhi/Chinese Journal of Pathology and Physiology.(CC ISSN 1000-4718) **3164**
Zhongguo Bowuguan/Chinese Museums. (CC) **3535**
Zhongguo Canjiren/Chinese Handicapped. (CC) **2285**
Zhongguo Chaoxianzu Jiaoyu/Korean Chinese Education. (CC) **1673**, 2030
Zhongguo Chaye/Chinese Tea. (CC) **2084**
Zhongguo Chuban Nianjian/China Publishing Yearbook. (CC ISSN 1001-8859) **4139**
Zhongguo Chuji Weisheng Baojian/Chinese Primary Health Care. (CC ISSN 1001-568X) **3164**
Zhongguo Chukou Shangpin Jiaoyihui Tekan. see Special Issues for Chinese Export Commodities Fair **1054**
Zhongguo Cuoliao Xiangjiao. see China Plastic and Rubber Journal **3862**
Zhongguo Dalu see Mainland China Monthly **2182**
Zhongguo Dalu Yanjiu see Chung-Kuo Ta-Lu Yen-Chiu **3880**
Zhongguo Daojiao/Chinese Taoism. (CC) **4216**
Zhongguo Dianda Jiaoyu/Chinese Broadcasting University Education. (CC) **1688**
Zhongguo Dianti/Chinese Elevator. (CC ISSN 1001-7151) **636**, 1941
Zhongguo Dianxin Jianshe. see China Telecommunication Construction **1362**
Zhongguo Dianying Nianjian/China Film Yearbook. (CC) **3520**, 3519
Zhongguo Diaoyu/Angling in China. (CC ISSN 1000-3487) **4560**
Zhongguo Difangbing Fangzhi Zazhi/Chinese Journal of Endemic Disease Prevention and Treatment. (CC ISSN 1001-1889) **3164**
Zhongguo Dili Kexue. see Chinese Geographical Science **1557**
Zhongguo Dizhen/Chinese Seismology. (CC ISSN 1001-4683) **1596**
Zhongguo Dizhi/Chinese Geology. (CC ISSN 1000-3657) **1586**
Zhongguo Dizhi Wenzhai. (CC) **1552**, 3502
Zhongguo Duiwai Jingji Maoyi Nianjian see Almanac of China's Foreign Economic Relations and Trade **926**
Zhongguo Duiwai Maoyi see China's Foreign Trade **904**

Zhongguo E Yu Jiaoxue/Chinese Journal of Russian Teaching. (CC) **2854**
Zhongguo Ertong/Chinese Children. (CC ISSN 0412-4154) **1272**, 1247
Zhongguo Ertong Fazhan/Chinese Child Development. (CC) **1247**
Zhongguo Falu Nianjian/China Law Yearbook. (CC) **2697**
Zhongguo Fangdi Xinxi/China Real Estate News. (CC) **4159**
Zhongguo Fangdichan/Chinese Real Estate. (CC) **4159**
Zhongguo Fangzhi/Chinese Textile. (CC ISSN 0529-6013) **4627**
Zhongguo Fangzhi Bao/China's Textiles.(US) **4628**
Zhongguo Fangzhi Daxue Xuebao. (CC ISSN 1000-1476) **4628**
Zhongguo Fanyi/Chinese Translators Journal. (CC ISSN 1000-873X) **2854**
Zhongguo Faxue/Jurisprudence in China. (CC) **2697**
Zhongguo Fayixue Zazhi/Chinese Journal of Forensic Sciences. (CC ISSN 1001-5728) **3266**
Zhongguo Fazhi. *see* China Textile **4617**
Zhongguo Funu *see* Women of China **4856**
Zhongguo Funu Jiankang/China Women's Health. (CC) **3297**, 4116
Zhongguo Fuyou Baojian/Chinese Women and Children's Health. (CC) **3297**
Zhongguo Fuzhuang/Chinese Fashions. (US) **1295**
Zhongguo Gangchangbing Zazhi. (CC ISSN 1000-1174) **3270**
Zhongguo Gangkou/Chinese Harbor. (CC) **4742**
Zhongguo Gaodeng Jiaoyu/Higher Education in China. (CC ISSN 1002-4417) **1721**
Zhongguo Geshui Paishui/China Water & Wastewater. (CC ISSN 1000-4602) **1877**
Zhongguo Gongcheng Xuekan *see* Chinese Institute of Engineers. Journal **1816**
Zhongguo Gongchengshi/Chinese Engineers. (CC) **1841**
Zhongguo Gonggong Weisheng/China's Public Health. (CC ISSN 1001-0580) **4116**
Zhongguo Gonggong Weisheng Xuebao/Chinese Journal of Public Health. (CC ISSN 1001-0572) **4116**
Zhongguo Gonglu Xuebao/China Road Journal. (CC ISSN 1001-7372) **4723**
Zhongguo Gongshang/Chinese Industry & Commerce. (CC) **841**
Zhongguo Gongye Jingji Yanjiu/China Industrial Economics Research. (CC ISSN 1002-5928) **1000**
Zhongguo Gongyun Xueyuan Xuebao/Chinese Institute of Labor Movement. Journal. (CC) **2592**
Zhongguo Guangbo Yingshi/Chinese Radio, Film and Television. (CC) **1361**, 1384, 3519
Zhongguo Guanggao/China Advertising.(CC) **40**
Zhongguo Guanggao Bao/China's Advertising Journal. (CC) **40**, 1057
Zhongguo Guangxue yu Yingyong Guangxue Wenzhai/Chinese Optics and Applied Optics Abstracts. (CC) **3839**, 25, 3858
Zhongguo Guoshu/China's Fruit Trees. (CC ISSN 1000-8047) **131**
Zhongguo Gushi/Chinese Stories. (CC ISSN 1002-7564) **2979**
Zhongguo Haiguan/China Customs. (CC ISSN 1001-0637) **925**
Zhongguo Haishang Youqi (Dizhi). (CC) **3704**
Zhongguo Haishang Youqi (Gongcheng). (CC ISSN 1001-7682) **3704**
Zhongguo Haiyang Pingtai. (CC ISSN 1001-4500) **3704**
Zhongguo Haiyuan/Chinese Seamen. (CC) **4742**
Zhongguo Haiyun/Maritime China. (HK ISSN 0258-3240) **4742**
Zhongguo Hanghai/Chinese Navigation. (CC ISSN 1000-4653) **4742**

Zhongguo Hangkong Wenzhai *see* China Aerospace Abstracts **50**
Zhongguo Hangkong Xinxi. *see* China Aero Information **49**
Zhongguo Hangtian/Aerospace China. (CC ISSN 1002-7742) **66**
Zhongguo Hua/Chinese Painting. (US) **351**
Zhongguo Huahui Bao/Chinese Journal of Flowers. (CC) **2141**
Zhongguo Huahui Penjing/Chinese Flowers - Potted Landscape. (US) **2141**
Zhongguo Huaxue. (CC) **1191**
Zhongguo Huaxue Gongcheng Xuehui Huizhi *see* Chinese Institute of Chemical Engineers. Journal **1852**
Zhongguo Jianzhu. *see* Chinese Architecture **296**
Zhongguo Jiaotong Nianjian/China Communications and Transportation Yearbook. (CC) **1346**, 4661
Zhongguo Jiaoyu Bao/Chinese Journal of Education. (US) **1673**
Zhongguo Jiaoyu Xuekan/Journal of Chinese Education. (CC) **1673**
Zhongguo Jiguang/Laser Sinica. (CC ISSN 0258-7025) **3858**
Zhongguo Jihua Guanli/Chinese Journal of Planned Management. (CC) **701**
Zhongguo Jijiu Yixue/Chinese First Aid Medical Science. (CC) **3164**
Zhongguo Jingji Nianjian/Alamanc of China's Economy. (CC ISSN 1002-5766) **1673**
Zhongguo Jingji Tizhi Gaige/China's Economic Structure Reform. (CC ISSN 1002-865X) **1000**
Zhongguo Jingji Wenti. (CC ISSN 1000-4181) **1000**
Zhongguo Jingji Xinwen/China Economic News. (CC ISSN 1000-9094) **888**, 1000
Zhongguo Jingjishi Yanjiu/Chinese Economic History Research. (CC) **899**
Zhongguo Jinrong/China Finance. (CC ISSN 0578-1485) **804**
Zhongguo Jinrong Nianjian/China Finance Year Book. (CC ISSN 1001-5841) **804**
Zhongguo Jinshu Kexue Jishu Zazhi. *see* Chinese Journal of Metallurgy **3404**
Zhongguo Jishengchongxue yu Jishengchongbing Zazhi/Chinese Journal of Parasitology and Parasitosis. (CC ISSN 1000-7423) **559**
Zhongguo Jizhe/Chinese Journalist. (CC) **2577**
Zhongguo Kangfu Yixue Zazhi/Chinese Journal of Recovery. (CC) **3164**
Zhongguo Kangshengsu Zazhi/Chinese Journal of Antibiotics. (CC ISSN 1001-8689) **3746**
Zhongguo Ke-Ji Shiliao/China Historical Materials of Science and Technology. (CC) **4353**, 4613
Zhongguo Keji Chanye/Chinese Scientific and Technological Industry. (CC) **1031**
Zhongguo Keji Qikan Yanjiu/Chinese Science and Technology Periodicals Research. (CC) **4139**
Zhongguo Keji Shiliao/Historical Material of Chinese Science and Technology. (CC ISSN 1000-0798) **4353**, 4613
Zhongguo Keji Zhengce yu Guanli/Chinese Policy and Administration of Science and Technology. (CC) **4078**
Zhongguo Kexue A. (CC ISSN 1000-3126) **4353**
Zhongguo Kexue B. (CC ISSN 1000-3134) **4353**
Zhongguo Kexue Bao/China's Science. (US) **4353**
Zhongguo Kexue Jijin/National Natural Science Foundation of China. Bulletin.(CC ISSN 1000-8217) **4354**
Zhongguo Kexue Jishu Daxue Xuebao/China University of Science and Technology. Journal. (CC ISSN 0253-2778) **4354**, 4613
Zhongguo Kexue Wenzhai A *see* Chinese Science Abstracts. Part A **4355**

Zhongguo Kexue Wenzhai B *see* Chinese Science Abstracts. Part B **4355**
†Zhongguo Kexueyuan Daqi Wulisuo Nianbao. (CC ISSN 0217-9725) **5309**
Zhongguo Kexueyuan Yuankan. (CC ISSN 1000-3045) **4354**
Zhongguo Kongjian Kexue Jishu/Chinese Journal of Space Science and Technology. (CC ISSN 1000-758X) **66**
Zhongguo Laodong Kexue/Labor Science of China. (CC ISSN 1000-6230) **998**
Zhongguo Laodong Kexue. (CC) **998**
Zhongguo Laonian/Elderly Chinese. (CC) **2280**
Zhongguo Laonian Bao/China's Elderly Daily. (US) **2280**
Zhongguo Lianhuanhua/Chinese Picture Stories. (CC) **351**
Zhongguo - Liaodong Bandao Guoji Jiaoliu/China - Liaodong Peninsula International Exchange. (CC) **3978**
Zhongguo Linye/Forestry in China. (CC ISSN 1000-0623) **2111**
Zhongguo Linye Jiaoyu/China Forestry Education. (CC) **2111**
Zhongguo Lushi/Chinese Lawyers. (US) **2697**
Zhongguo Luyou *see* China Tourism **4757**
Zhongguo Mafeng Zazhi/Chinese Journal of Leprosy. (CC ISSN 1000-629X) **3164**
Zhongguo Manhua/China Cartoons. (CC) **351**
Zhongguo Meijie Shengwuxue ji Kongzhi Zazhi. (CC) **3189**
Zhongguo Mianyixue Zazhi/Chinese Journal of Immunology. (CC) **3189**
Zhongguo Minban Keji Shiye/Chinese Privately-Owned Science and Technology Enterprises. (CC) **841**
Zhongguo Minhang/C A A C Inflight Magazine. (CC) **4678**
Zhongguo Minhang Bao/Civil Aviation Administration of China. Journal. (CC ISSN 1002-2079) **4798**, 4678
Zhongguo Minhang Xueyuan Xuebao/Civil Aviation Institute of China. Journal. (CC ISSN 1001-5000) **66**
Zhongguo Minzheng. (CC) **3936**
Zhongguo Minzu Jiaoyu/Nationality Education of China. (CC ISSN 1002-5952) **1673**
Zhongguo Mucai/Chinese Lumber. (CC) **2119**
Zhongguo Nianjian. (CC ISSN 1000-9647) **2183**, 4592
Zhongguo Nong-Shi/Agricultural History of China. (CC ISSN 1000-4459) **131**, 2327
Zhongguo Nongcun Jingji/Chinese Rural Economics. (CC) **160**, 888
Zhongguo Nongcun Jinrong/China Rural Finance. (CC) **804**, 131
Zhongguo Nongcun Yixue/Medical Science in Rural China. (CC) **3164**
Zhongguo Nongye Huaxue Huizhi *see* Chinese Agricultural Chemical Society. Journal **173**
Zhongguo Nongye Kexue/Chinese Agricultural Sciences. (CC ISSN 0578-1752) **131**, 229
Zhongguo Nongye Qixiang/Chinese Agricultural Meteorology. (CC ISSN 1000-6362) **3444**, 131
Zhongguo Nongye Wenzhai - Nongye Gongcheng/Chinese Agriculture Abstracts - Agricultural Engineering. (CC) **145**, 25
Zhongguo Nongye Wenzhai - Shuichan/Chinese Agriculture Abstracts - Aquatic Products. (CC) **2052**
Zhongguo Paiqiu/China's Volleyball. (CC) **4515**
Zhongguo Pengren/Chinese Cookery. (CC ISSN 1000-1115) **2450**
Zhongguo Qianbi/China Numismatics. (CC) **3602**
Zhongguo Qigong. (CC ISSN 1000-8268) **3811**
Zhongguo Qinggongye Jingji/Chinese Light Industry Economics. (CC) **841**
Zhongguo Qinggongye Nianjian/China Light Industry Yearbook. (CC) **701**

Zhongguo Qingnian/Chinese Youth. (CC) **1272**, 2183, 2979, 3787
Zhongguo Qingnian Bao/Chinese Youth Daily. (CC) **1272**, 2979
Zhongguo Qingnian Yanjiu/Chinese Youth Study. (CC) **1247**, 4393
Zhongguo Qingyun/Chinese Youth Movement. (CC) **3936**
Zhongguo Qiyejia/Chinese Entrepreneurs. (CC) **1119**
Zhongguo Rencai/Chinese Talent. (CC) **1071**
Zhongguo Renkou Kexue *see* Chinese Journal of Population Science **3980**
Zhongguo Renmin Daxue Xuebao/China People's University. Journal. (CC ISSN 1000-5420) **4393**
Zhongguo Renmin Zhengzhi Xieshang Huiyi Renmin Zhengxie Bao *see* Renmin Zhengxie Bao **4072**
Zhongguo Renshi/Chinese Human Affairs. (CC) **1071**
Zhongguo Renshi Guanli/Chinese Personnel Management. (CC) **1071**
Zhongguo Renshou Gonghuanbing Zazhi. (CC) **559**, 4820
Zhongguo Rupin Gongye/China Dairy Industry. (CC ISSN 1001-2230) **204**
Zhongguo Shamo/Chinese Desert. (CC ISSN 1000-694X) **1549**
Zhongguo Shangye Nianjian/Almanac of China's Commerce. (CC ISSN 1002-591X) **841**
Zhongguo Shaonian Bao/Chinese Pioneers. (US) **1272**
Zhongguo Shaoshang Chuangshang Zazhi/Chinese Journal of Burns and Wounds. (CC) **3250**
Zhongguo Shaoshu Minzu. (CC ISSN 1001-0882) **3646**, 2030, 4393
Zhongguo Shebei Guanli/Chinese Equipment Management. (CC ISSN 1001-5876) **1032**
Zhongguo Shehui Jingjishi Yanjiu/Journal of Chinese Social and Economic History. (CC ISSN 1000-422X) **2343**, 899, 3646, 4393
Zhongguo Shehui Kexue *see* Social Sciences in China **4388**
Zhongguo Shehui Kexue Wenxian Tilu/Chinese Social Science Documentations Index. (CC) **4396**, 417
Zhongguo Shehui Kexueyuan Yanjiushengyuan Xuebao/Chinese Academy of Social Sciences. Graduate School. Journal. (CC ISSN 1000-2952) **4393**
Zhongguo Shenglixue Zazhi *see* Chinese Journal of Physiology **570**
Zhongguo Shengwuxue Wenzhai/Chinese Biological Abstracts. (CC ISSN 1001-1900) **468**, 3189
Zhongguo Shenji/Auditing in China. (CC ISSN 1002-5049) **757**
Zhongguo Sheying/Chinese Photography. (CC) **3798**
Zhongguo Shipin/Chinese Food. (US) **2450**, 2482
Zhongguo Shipin Bao/China's Food News. (US) **2084**, 2450
Zhongguo Shiyou Huabao/China Oil Pictorial. (CC) **3704**
Zhongguo Shizhuang/Fashion in China. (CC) **1295**
Zhongguo Shouyi Zazhi/Chinese Journal of Veterinary Medicine. (CC) **4820**
Zhongguo Shucai/Chinese Vegetables. (CC ISSN 1000-6346) **197**
Zhongguo Shufa/Chinese Calligraphy. (US) **351**
Zhongguo Shuhua/Chinese Calligraphy and Painting. (CC) **351**
Zhongguo Shuichan/Chinese Aquatic Products. (CC) **2050**
Zhongguo Shuidao Kexue/China Rice Science. (CC ISSN 1001-7216) **208**
Zhongguo Shuitu Baochi. (CC ISSN 1000-0941) **197**
Zhongguo Shuiwu/China's Taxation. (CC) **1112**
Zhongguo Shuxue Wenzhai/Chinese Mathematics Abstracts. (CC ISSN 1001-1919) **3063**, 25
Zhongguo Taoci/Chinese Ceramics. (CC) **1167**

Zhongguo Tiancai/Chinese Beets. (CC ISSN 1001-4187) **131**
Zhongguo Tiaoweipin/Chinese Spices. (CC ISSN 1000-9973) **2084**
Zhongguo Tiedao Kexue/China Railway Science. (CC ISSN 1001-4632) **4717**
Zhongguo Tielu/China Railroad. (CC ISSN 1001-683X) **4717**
Zhongguo Tiyu. see China Sports **4469**
Zhongguo Tiyu Bao/China's Sports News. (US) **4497**
Zhongguo Tongji/China Statistics. (CC ISSN 1002-4557) **4592**
Zhongguo Tongji Nianjian see China Statistical Yearbook **4568**
Zhongguo Tushu Pinglun/Chinese Book Reviews. (CC) **4139**, **2979**
Zhongguo Tushuguan Xuehui Huiwu Tongxun see Library Association of China. Newsletter **2769**
Zhongguo Weisheng Huakan/China Health Pictorial. (CC) **4116**
Zhongguo Wenfang Sibao/Chinese Four Treasures of the Study. (CC) **1062**
Zhongguo Wenhua Bao/China Culture Newspaper. (US) **2183**
Zhongguo Wenwu Bao/China's Cultural Relics News. (US) **290**, **2343**
Zhongguo Wuji Fenxi Huaxue Wenzhai/Chinese Inorganic Analytical Chemistry Abstracts. (CC) **1203**, 25, 1215
Zhongguo Wuli Kuaibao. see Chinese Physics Letters **3816**
Zhongguo Wuli Wenzhai/Chinese Physics Abstracts. (CC ISSN 1000-8802) **3839**, 25
Zhongguo Wuzi Jingji/Chinese Commodity Economics. (CC) **701**
Zhongguo Xiandai, Dangdai Wenxue Yanjiu. (CC ISSN 1001-2907) **2979**
Zhongguo Xiandai Shi/Chinese Contemporary History. (CC ISSN 1001-2672) **2343**
Zhongguo Xiangcun Yisheng/Chinese Rural Doctors. (CC) **3164**
Zhongguo Xiangzhen Qiye/China's Township Enterprises. (CC) **1119**
Zhongguo Xiaoduxue Zazhi/Chinese Journal of Disinfection. (CC ISSN 1001-7658) **3164**
Zhongguo Xiaofang/Fire Fighting in China. (CC ISSN 1000-1107) **2035**
Zhongguo Xiaofeizhe Bao. (US) **1509**
Zhongguo Xibu Wenxue. (CC ISSN 1000-8896) **2979**, **3009**
Zhongguo Xiju/China's Theater. (CC) **4642**
Zhongguo Xingzheng Guanli/Chinese Administration Management. (CC) **4078**
Zhongguo Xinli Weisheng Zazhi/Chinese Mental Health Journal. (CC ISSN 1000-6729) **4051**
Zhongguo Xitu Xuebao see Journal of Rare Earths **3411**
Zhongguo Xiuchuan/China Shiprepair. (CC ISSN 1001-8328) **4742**
Zhongguo Xizang. (CC ISSN 1002-9591) **2183**, **4393**
Zhongguo Xumu Zazhi/Chinese Journal of Animal Science. (CC ISSN 0258-7033) **4820**
Zhongguo Yangfeng/Chinese Apiculture.(CC ISSN 0412-4367) **131**
Zhongguo Yanrong/Karst in China. (CC ISSN 1001-4810) **1586**
Zhongguo Yaofang. (CC ISSN 1001-0408) **3746**
Zhongguo Yaoli Xuebao/Acta Pharmacologica Sinica. (CC ISSN 0253-9756) **3746**
Zhongguo Yaolixue Tongbao/Chinese Bulletin of Pharmacology. (CC ISSN 1001-1978) **3746**
Zhongguo Yaolixue yu Dulixue Zazhi. (CC) **3746**
Zhongguo Yaoxue Wenzhai/Chinese Pharmaceutical Abstracts. (CC ISSN 1003-3521) **3748**, 25
Zhongguo Yaoxue Zazhi/Chinese Pharmaceutical Journal. (CC) **3746**

Zhongguo Yingyong Shenglixue Zazhi/Chinese Journal of Applied Physiology. (CC ISSN 1000-6834) **575**
Zhongguo Yinmu. see China Screen **3505**
Zhongguo Yinyue/Chinese Music. (US) **3587**
Zhongguo Yinyuexue/Musicology in China. (CC) **3587**
Zhongguo Yishu/Chinese Art. (CC) **351**
Zhongguo Yixue Kexueyuan Xuebao/Acta Academiae Medicinae Sinica. (CC ISSN 1000-503X) **3165**
Zhongguo Yixue Wenzhai (Erkexue)/China Medical Abstracts (Pediatrics). (CC) **3182**, 25, 3327
Zhongguo Yixue Wenzhai (Jihua Shengyu, Fuchan Kexue)/China Medical Abstracts (Birth Control and Gynecology). (CC ISSN 1001-1315) **3182**, 25, 3297
Zhongguo Yixue Wenzhai (Kouqiang Yixue)/China Medical Abstracts (Stomatology). (CC) **3182**, 25, 3245
Zhongguo Yixue Wenzhai (Neike Xue). (CC ISSN 1001-4136) **3182**, 25
Zhongguo Yixue Yingxiang Jishu/Chinese Medical Photography Technology. (CC) **3363**
Zhongguo Yiyao/Journal of Chinese Pharmacy. (CC) **3746**
Zhongguo Yiyao Gongye Zazhi/Chinese Journal of Pharmaceutical Industry. (CC ISSN 1001-8255) **3746**
Zhongguo Yiyao Xuebao/Journal of Chinese Pharmacology. (CC ISSN 1000-4971) **3746**
Zhongguo Yiyuan Guanli/Chinese Hospital Management. (CC ISSN 1001-5329) **2470**
Zhongguo Youhua/China Oil Painting. (CC) **351**
Zhongguo Youzheng/China Postal Affairs. (CC) **1354**
Zhongguo yu Feizhou. see China and Africa **3953**
Zhongguo Yundong Yixue Zazhi/Chinese Journal of Sports Medical Science. (CC ISSN 1000-6710) **3373**
Zhongguo Yuwen. (CC ISSN 0578-1949) **2854**
Zhongguo Zangxue/Study - Tibetan Nationalities. (US) **3646**, 253, 2030
Zhongguo Zaozhi/Chinese Journal of Paper Manufacturing. (CC ISSN 0254-508X) **3667**
Zhongguo Zhenjiu/Chinese Acupuncture and Moxibustion. (CC) **3165**
Zhongguo Zhexueshi Yanjiu. (CC) **3787**, **4216**
Zhongguo zhi Chun see China Spring **3940**
Zhongguo zhi You/Friends of China. (CC) **3978**
Zhongguo Zhongliu Linchuang/Chinese Journal of Clinical Oncology. (CC ISSN 1000-8179) **3203**
Zhongguo Zhongyi Gushangke Zazhi. (CC) **3216**
Zhongguo Zhuanli Bao/Patent Review of China. (US) **3679**
Zhongguo Zixingche/Chinese Bicycles. (CC ISSN 1000-999X) **4521**, 4613
Zhongguo Zuojia. (CC) **2980**, 424
Zhongguo Zuzhibie Renmingbu. see China Directory **3953**
Zhongguoshi Yanjiu/Study of Chinese History. (CC) **2343**
Zhongguoxue Daobao/Sinological Pioneer. (CC) **3646**
Zhonghua Chuanranbing Zazhi/Chinese Journal of Infectious Diseases. (CC ISSN 1000-6680) **3165**
Zhonghua Erke Zazhi/Chinese Journal of Pediatrics. (CC) **3327**
Zhonghua Ernu/Children of China. (CC) **1247**
Zhonghua Fu-Chanke Zazhi/Chinese Journal of Obstetrics and Gynecology.(CC) **3297**
Zhonghua Gongshang Shibao/China's Industry News. (US) **888**
Zhonghua Guke Zazhi/Chinese Journal of Orthopedics. (CC) **3312**

Zhonghua Laonian Yixue Zazhi/Chinese Journal of Geriatrics. (CC ISSN 0254-9026) **2280**
Zhonghua Liliao Zazhi/Chinese Journal of Physical Therapy. (CC ISSN 0254-1408) **3165**
Zhonghua Liuxingbingxue Zazhi/Chinese Journal of Epidemiology. (CC) **3165**
Zhonghua Mazuixue Zazhi/Chinese Journal of Anaesthesiology. (CC) **3192**
Zhonghua Minguo Chuban Tushumulu see Chinese National Bibliography **2793**
Zhonghua Minguo Qikan Lunwen Suoyin see Index to Chinese Periodicals **14**
Zhonghua Minguo Xiao'erke Yixuehui Zazhi see Acta Paediatrica Sinica **3317**
Zhonghua Neifenmi Daixie Zazhi/Chinese Journal of Endocrinology and Metabolism. (CC ISSN 1000-6699) **3256**, **3297**
Zhonghua Neike Zazhi/Chinese Journal of Internal Medicine. (CC) **3165**
Zhonghua Nongye Yanjiu see Journal of Agricultural Research of China **101**
Zhonghua Renmin Gongheguo. Quanguo Renda Changweihui Gongbao/China, People's Republic. National People's Congress. Standing Committee. Bulletin. (US) **4078**
Zhonghua Renmin Gongheguo. Zuigao Renmin Jianchayuan Gongbao/China, People's Republic. Supreme People's Procurate Post. (US) **4078**, **2697**
Zhonghua Renmin Gongheguo Guowuyuan Gongbao/China, People's Republic. State Council. Bulletin. (US) **4078**
Zhonghua Renmin Gongheguo Zuigao Renmin Fayuan Gongbao/China, People's Republic. People's Supreme Court. Bulletin. (US) **2697**
Zhonghua Shenjing-Jingshenke Zazhi/Chinese Journal of Neurology and Psychology. (CC) **3356**
Zhonghua Shenjing Waike Zazhi/Chinese Journal of Neurosurgery. (CC ISSN 1001-2346) **3356**, 3203, 3386
Zhonghua Waike Zazhi/Chinese Journal of Surgery. (CC) **3386**
Zhonghua Weishengwuxue he Mianyixue Zazhi/Chinese Journal of Microbiology and Immunology. (CC) **3189**
Zhonghua Wuli Yixue Zazhi/Chinese Journal of Physical Medicine. (CC ISSN 0254-1424) **3165**, **3836**
Zhonghua Wushu/Chinese Martial Arts. (CC ISSN 1000-3525) **4497**
Zhonghua Xiaohua Zazhi/Chinese Journal of Gastroenterology. (CC ISSN 0254-1432) **3270**
Zhonghua Xin-Xueguanbing Zazhi/Chinese Journal of Cardiology. (CC) **3213**
Zhonghua Xueyexue Zazhi/Chinese Journal of Hematology. (CC ISSN 0253-2727) **3274**
Zhonghua Yingcai. (CC) **2183**
Zhonghua Yishi Zazhi/Chinese Journal of Medical History. (CC) **3165**
Zhonghua Yixue Zazhi see Chinese Medical Journal **3087**
Zhonghua Yixue Zazhi Yingwen Ban. see Chinese Medical Journal **3087**
Zhonghua Yufang Yixue Zazhi/Chinese Journal of Preventive Medicine. (CC) **3165**
Zhonghua Zhengxing Shaoshang Waike Zazhi/Chinese Journal of Plastic Surgery and Burns. (CC ISSN 1000-7806) **3386**
Zhonghua Zhongliu Zazhi/Chinese Journal of Oncology. (CC) **3203**
Zhongji Yikan. (CC ISSN 0529-5548) **3811**
Zhongnan Caijing Daxue Xuebao/Central-South University of Finance and Economics. Journal. (CC ISSN 1003-5230) **899**, 804
Zhongnan Kuangye Xueyuan Xuebao/Central-South Institute of Mining and Metallurgy. Journal. (CC ISSN 0253-4347) **3498**, 1841, 3424

Zhongnan Minzu Xueyuan Xuebao (Shehui Kexue Ban)/South-Central College for Nationalities. Journal (Social Science Edition). (CC ISSN 1000-5439) **4393**, 2343, 3704, 4425
Zhongnan Zhengfa Xueyuan Xuebao. (CC ISSN 1000-5234) **2697**
Zhongpian Xiaoshuo/Novelette. (CC) **2980**
Zhongpian Xiaoshuo Xuankan/Selected Novelle. (CC) **2980**
Zhongri Youhao Yiyuan Xuebao/Sino-Japanese Friendship Hospital. Journal. (CC ISSN 1001-0025) **3165**
Zhongshan. (CC) **2980**
Zhongshan Daxue Shehui Kexue Xuebao see Zhongshan Daxue Xuebao (Zhexue Shehui Kexue Ban) **4393**
Zhongshan Daxue Xuebao (Zhexue Shehui Kexue Ban)/Sun Yat-sen University. Journal (Social Science Edition). (CC ISSN 1000-9639) **4393**
Zhongshan Daxue Xuebao (Ziran Kexue Ban)/Acta Scientiarum Naturalium Universitatis Sunyatseni. (CC ISSN 0253-4088) **4354**
Zhongwai Dianshi/Chinese & World T V.(CC) **1384**
Zhongwai Funu Wenzhai. (CC) **4858**
Zhongwai Fuzhuang/Chinese & Foreign Garments. (CC) **1295**
Zhongwai Gushi/Chinese and Foreign Stories. (CC) **2980**
Zhongwai Gushi Chuanqi. (CC) **2985**, 2980
Zhongwai Jishu Qingbao/Chinese and Foreign Technology Information. (CC) **4354**, 4613
Zhongwai Shaonian. (CC) **1247**
Zhongwai Tonghua Huakan/Chinese and Foreign Fairy Tales Pictorial. (CC) **1272**
Zhongwai Wenxue/Chinese and Foreign Literature. (CC) **2980**
Zhongwai Zazhi see Kaleidoscope **2870**
Zhongwen Falu Lunwen Suoyin see Index to Chinese Legal Periodicals **2699**
Zhongwen Xinxi/Chinese Information Processing. (CC ISSN 1003-9082) **2791**
Zhongwen Zixiu/Chinese Self-Study. (CC ISSN 1000-7245) **2854**, 1673
Zhongwen Zixue Zhidao/Guide to Teaching Yourself Chinese. (CC) **2854**, 1673
Zhongxiaoxue Guanli/Administration of Elementary and High School. (CC) **1732**
Zhongxiaoxue Yingyu Jiaoxue yu Yanjiu/English Teaching and Research for Elementary and Secondary Schools. (CC) **2854**, 1673
Zhongxiyi Jiehe Yanke Zazhi. (CC) **3306**
Zhongxue Jiaoyu/Secondary School Education. (CC ISSN 0412-3921) **1673**
Zhongxue Keji/Middle School Science & Technology. (CC) **1673**, **4354**
Zhongxue Yuwen/Middle School Chinese. (CC ISSN 1000-419X) **2854**
Zhongxue Yuwen Jiaoxue/Language Teaching in Middle School. (US ISSN 1001-280X) **2854**, 1764
Zhongxuesheng/Middle School Student. (CC) **1673**
Zhongxuesheng Kexue Jiaoyu/Middle-School Student Science Education. (CC) **1673**
Zhongxuesheng Shu-Li-Hua (Gaozhong Ban). (CC ISSN 1001-6953) **1764**, 1191, 3062, 3836
Zhongxuesheng Shuxue/Mathematics for Middle School Students. (CC) **3062**, 1272
Zhongxuesheng Wuli Yuandi/Physics for Middle School Students. (CC) **3836**, 1764
Zhongyang Minzu Xueyuan Xuebao/Central Institute of Nationalities. Journal. (CC ISSN 1000-8667) **2030**

Zhongyang Xiju Xueyuan Xuebao see Xiju **4642**
Zhongyang Yanjiuyuan Zhiwuxue Huikan see Academia Sinica. Botanical Bulletin **491**
Zhongyang Yinyue Xueyuan Xuebao/Central Conservatory of Music. Journal. (CC ISSN 1001-9871) **3587**
Zhongyao Tongbao/Chinese Medicine Bulletin. (CC) **3746**, 3165
Zhongyao Yaoli yu Linchuang/Pharmacology and Clinics of Chinese Materia Medica. (CC ISSN 1001-859X) **3746**
Zhongyi Yanjiu/Traditional Chinese Medicinal Research. (CC ISSN 1001-6910) **3165**
Zhongyi Zazhi/Journal of Traditional Chinese Medicine. (CC) **3165**, 3746
Zhongyi Zhenggu. (CC) **3312**
Zhongyuan Wenwu/Relics of Central China. (CC) **290**, 2343
Zhongzhou Chengshi Yanjiu. (CC) **2499**
Zhongzhou Jingu/Zhongzhou Today & Yesterday. (CC) **2267**
Zhongzhou Today & Yesterday. see Zhongzhou Jingu **2267**
Zhongzhou Xuekan. (CC) **4393**
Zhongzi Shijie/World of Seeds. (CC ISSN 1000-8071) **197**
Zhovten' see Dzvin **2864**
Zhu Ji see Footprint **1311**
Zhuangshi/Decoration. (US) **351**
Zhuanji Wenxue/Biographical Literature.(CC) **2980**
Zhugong (Gaoxiong) see Chukung **3404**
Zhuiqiu/Pursuit. (CC) **2183**
Zhuomuniao/Woodpecker. (CC) **2980**
Zhurnal Analiticheskoi Khimii. (RU ISSN 0044-4502) **1210**
Zhurnal Eksperimental'noi i Klinicheskoi Meditsiny. (AI ISSN 0013-3310) **3165**, 3263
Zhurnal Eksperimental'noi i Teoreticheskoi Fiziki. (RU ISSN 0044-4510) **3836**
Zhurnal Evolyutsionnoi Biokhimii i Fiziologii. (RU ISSN 0044-4529) **483**, 575
Zhurnal Fizicheskoi Khimii. (RU ISSN 0044-4537) **1231**
Zhurnal Gigieny, Epidemiologii, Mikrobiologii i Immunologii see Journal of Hygiene, Epidemiology, Microbiology and Immunology **3116**
Zhurnal Mikrobiologii, Epidemiologii i Immunobiologii/Journal of Microbiology, Epidemiology and Immunobiology. (RU ISSN 0372-9311) **559**, 3165, 4116
Zhurnal Mod. (RU ISSN 0321-1576) **1295**
Zhurnal Nauchnoi i Prikladnoi Fotografii i Kinematografii. (RU ISSN 0044-4561) **3798**, 3519
Zhurnal Neorganicheskoi Khimii. (RU ISSN 0044-457X) **1215**
Zhurnal Nevropatologii i Psikhiatrii im. S.S. Korsakova/Journal of Neuropathology and Psychiatry. S.S. Korsakov. (RU ISSN 0044-4588) **3356**
Zhurnal Obshchei Biologii. (RU ISSN 0044-4596) **460**
Zhurnal Obshchei Khimii. (RU ISSN 0044-460X) **1191**
Zhurnal Prikladnoi Khimii. (RU ISSN 0044-4618) **1861**, 1191
Zhurnal Prikladnoi Mekhaniki i Tekhnicheskoi Fiziki. (RU ISSN 0044-4626) **1941**, 3846
Zhurnal Strukturnoi Khimii. (RU ISSN 0044-4634) **1231**
Zhurnal Tekhnicheskoi Fiziki. (RU ISSN 0044-4642) **3836**
Zhurnal Ushnykh, Nosovykh i Gorlovykh Boleznei. (RU ISSN 0044-4650) **3317**
Zhurnal Vychislitel'noi Matematiki i Matematicheskoi Fiziki. (English translation: U S S R Computational Mathematics and Mathematical Physics) (RU ISSN 0044-4669) **3062**, 3836

Zhurnal Vysshei Nervnoi Deyatel'nosti. (RU ISSN 0044-4677) **575**, 3356
Zhurnalist. (RU ISSN 0022-5568) **2577**
Zhyttia i Shkola. see Life & School **2012**
Zi Xue/Self-Teaching. (US) **1688**, 1764
Zibaldone. (DK ISSN 0108-2795) **2185**
†Zidis. (GW) **5309**
Zidis-Information see Zidis **5309**
Zidonghua Xuebao/Acta Automatica Sinica. (CC ISSN 0254-4156) **1416**, 1411
Zidonghua Yibiao. (CC ISSN 1000-0380) **2525**, 1416
Zie Magazine. (BE) **1384**
Ziegeleitechnisches Jahrbuch. (GW ISSN 0084-5485) **1877**
Ziegelindustrie see Z I International **1876**
Ziekenhuis. (NE ISSN 0044-4715) **2470**
Zielony Sztandar. (PL) **3936**
Zielsprache Deutsch. (GW ISSN 0341-5864) **2854**, 1724
Zielsprache Englisch. (GW ISSN 0342-6173) **2854**, 1688
Zielsprache Franzoesisch. (GW ISSN 0342-6203) **2854**
Zielsprache Russisch. (GW ISSN 0173-9522) **2854**
Ziemie Zachodnie. Studia i Materialy. (PL ISSN 0084-5507) **2396**
Zien Magazine see Blind **5151**
Die Zigarre. (GW) **3936**
Zika. (IS) **3476**
Zillions. (US ISSN 1050-8163) **1272**, 1509
Zimanim. (IS) **2327**
Zimbabwe. Agricultural and Rural Development Authority. Annual Report and Accounts. (RH) **131**
Zimbabwe. Central Statistical Office. Agricultural Production in European Areas: Livestock. National and Provincial Totals see Zimbabwe. Central Statistical Office. Large Scale Agricultural Units **161**
Zimbabwe. Central Statistical Office. Agricultural Production in Purchase Lands: National and Provincial Totals.(RH) **197**
Zimbabwe. Central Statistical Office. Agricultural Production in Tribal Trust Land Irrigation Schemes and Tilcor Estates. (RH) **131**
Zimbabwe. Central Statistical Office. Census of Production. (RH) **744**, 4592
Zimbabwe. Central Statistical Office. Census of Registered Deciduous Fruit Growers. (RH) **2141**, 145
Zimbabwe. Central Statistical Office. Crop Production of Large-Scale Commercial Agricultural Units. (RH) **197**
Zimbabwe. Central Statistical Office. Income Tax Statistics. (RH) **744**, 1112, 4592
Zimbabwe. Central Statistical Office. Large Scale Agricultural Units. (RH) **161**
Zimbabwe. Central Statistical Office. Monthly Digest of Statistics. (RH ISSN 0556-8706) **4592**
Zimbabwe. Central Statistical Office. Monthly Migration and Tourist Statistics. (RH) **4801**, 3997
Zimbabwe. Central Statistical Office. Quarterly Digest of Statistics. (RH) **4592**
Zimbabwe. Central Statistical Office. Quarterly Poultry Census. (RH) **145**, 4592
Zimbabwe. Central Statistical Office. Statement of External Trade. (RH) **925**
Zimbabwe. Coffee Research Institute. Annual Report. Part 2. Nyanga Experimental Station. (RH) **197**
Zimbabwe. Cotton Research Institute. Annual Report. (RH) **197**
†Zimbabwe. Department of Meteorological Services. Rainfall Report. (RH ISSN 0085-5693) **5309**

Zimbabwe. Department of Meteorological Services. Report of the Director. (RH ISSN 0085-5707) **3444**
Zimbabwe. Estimates of Expenditure. (RH) **1112**
Zimbabwe. Ministry of Agriculture. Division of Livestock and Pastures. Annual Report. (RH) **229**
Zimbabwe. Ministry of Agriculture. Seed Services. Annual Report. (RH) **197**
Zimbabwe. Ministry of Education. African Education Report. (RH ISSN 0080-2859) **1673**
Zimbabwe. Ministry of Energy and Water Resources and Development. Hydrological Summaries. (RH) **1925**, 1586
Zimbabwe. Ministry of Finance. Financial Statement. (RH) **1112**
Zimbabwe. Ministry of Lands and Natural Resources. Report of the Secretary for Lands and Natural Resources. (RH) **1501**, 3498
Zimbabwe. Ministry of Water Resources and Development. Hydrological Summaries see Zimbabwe. Ministry of Energy and Water Resources and Development. Hydrological Summaries **1925**
Zimbabwe. National Archives. Annual Report. (RH ISSN 0301-4347) **2335**
Zimbabwe. National Archives. Occasional Papers. (RH ISSN 0035-4716) **2336**
Zimbabwe. Registrar of Insurance. Report. (RH ISSN 0556-8692) **2547**
Zimbabwe. Tobacco Research Board. Annual Report and Accounts. (RH) **4646**
Zimbabwe: A Field for Investment. (RH) **888**
Zimbabwe Agricultural Journal. (RH) **131**
Zimbabwe Banking Corporation. Group Annual Report. (RH) **804**
Zimbabwe Engineer see Mining and Engineering **3490**
Zimbabwe Government Gazette. (RH) **4078**
Zimbabwe in Brief. (RH) **2240**
Zimbabwe in Figures. (RH) **888**
†Zimbabwe Insight. (RH) **5309**
Zimbabwe Journal of Agricultural Research. (RH) **131**
Zimbabwe Law Review. (RH) **2697**
Zimbabwe Librarian. (RH) **2791**
Zimbabwe National Bibliography. (RH) **417**
Zimbabwe National Chamber of Commerce Directory. (RH) **1160**, 825
Zimbabwe National Chamber of Commerce Newsletter see Z N C C Newsletter **824**
Zimbabwe National Chamber of Commerce Trade Directory see Z N C C Trade Directory **824**
Zimbabwe Research Index. (RH) **4358**, 25
Zimbabwe Science News. (RH) **4354**
Zimbabwe Scientific Association. Transaction. (RH) **4354**
Zimbabwe Stamp Catalogue. (RH) **3759**
Zimbabwe Tobacco Today. (RH) **4646**, 131
Zimbabwe Veterinary Journal. (RH) **4820**
Zimbabwe Wildlife. (RH) **1501**
Zimbabwea. (RH ISSN 0250-3018) **2336**
Zimbabwean History. (RH) **2336**
Zimmerkatalog see Reisen in Deutschland: Zimmerkatalog **4784**
Der Zimmermann. (GW ISSN 0342-6521) **641**
Zinatne un Tekhnika. see Nauka i Tekhnika **4328**
Zinbvn. (JA) **2519**
Zinc Abstracts see Zincscan **3429**
Zinc Today. (AT ISSN 0158-7765) **3424**
Zincscan. (UK ISSN 0950-1592) **3429**, 25
Zingiber. (US) **2141**

Zingsheim Times. (US ISSN 0887-3046) **2168**
Zion. (IS ISSN 0044-4758) **2030**, 2327, 4227
Zionist Literature. (IS ISSN 0044-4774) **4143**, 3939, 4213
Zionist Record and S.A. Jewish Chronicle. (SA ISSN 0044-4782) **2030**
†Zionist Year Book. (UK ISSN 0084-5531) **5309**
Zions Freund. (SA ISSN 0028-3568) **4211**
Zip. (UK ISSN 0260-7654) **3009**
Zip - Area Code Directory. (US) **1354**, 1368
Zip Me News. (US) **3759**
Zipper. (UK) **3400**, 2458
Al-Zira'a fil-Alam al-Arabi/Agriculture in the Arab World. (BA) **131**
Zira'at Fi El-Urdon. see Agriculture in Jordan **72**
Ziraim. (IS) **1272**
Ziran Bianzhengfa Tongxun/Journal of Dialectics of Nature. (CC) **4354**, 4613
Ziran Kexue Jinzhan see Progress in Natural Science **4334**
Ziran Kexue Shi Yanjiu/Studies in the History of Natural Sciences. (CC ISSN 1000-0224) **4354**
Ziran yu Ren/Nature and Man. (CC) **2327**
Ziran Zazhi/Nature Journal. (CC ISSN 0253-9608) **4354**
Ziran Ziyuan/Natural Resources. (CC ISSN 1000-0038) **1501**, 1972
Ziran Ziyuan Xuebao/Journal of Natural Resources. (CC ISSN 1000-3037) **1549**
Zise. (DK ISSN 0105-8355) **925**
Zisin. see Seismological Society of Japan. Journal **1594**
Zito Hleb. (YU ISSN 0351-0999) **208**
Zittleiana. (GW ISSN 0373-9627) **3661**, 1586
Ziva. (CS ISSN 0044-4812) **461**, 521, 594
Zivilcourage. (GW) **3978**
Zivildienst. (GW ISSN 0177-1965) **4078**
Zivilschutz Aktuell. (AU) **1274**
Zivilverteidigung see Notfallvorsorge und Zivile Verteidigung **1273**
Zivocisna Vyroba/Animal Production. (CS ISSN 0044-4847) **229**
Zivot i Skola. (CI ISSN 0044-4855) **1673**
Zivot i Zdravije. (CI ISSN 0350-7335) **3165**, 4116
Zivotne Prostredie. (CS ISSN 0044-4863) **1972**
Zivotnovadni Nauki. (BU ISSN 0514-7441) **229**
Ziyou Zhongguo zhi Gongye see Industry of Free China **671**
Ziyuan yu Kaifa/Resource Development and Conservation. (CC ISSN 1001-3822) **1501**
Zlaty Maj. (CS ISSN 0044-4871) **1272**, 2980
Zlodzenia Polskiej Strefy Przybrzeznej - Materialy Oddzialu Morskiego see Instytut Meteorologii i Gospodarki Wodnej. Oddzial Morski w Gdyni. Materialy. Zlodzenie Polskiej Strefy Przybrzeznej **1606**
Znaci Vremena. (CI ISSN 0353-0434) **4211**
Znak. (PL ISSN 0044-488X) **4211**, 3787
Znamya. (RU ISSN 0044-4898) **2890**
Zo ha-Derekh. (IS) **3936**
Zobozdravstveni Vestnik. (XV ISSN 0044-4928) **3245**
Zodchestvo. (RU) **309**
Zodiac (English Edition). (US ISSN 0394-9249) **309**
Zodiac (Italian Edition). (IT ISSN 0044-4936) **309**
Zodiaque. (FR ISSN 0044-4952) **351**
Zoll - Rundschau/Revue des Douanes/Rivista delle Dogane. (SZ) **1112**
Zolnierz Polski. (PL ISSN 0044-4979) **3476**
Zona Franca. (VE) **2980**
Zondagsmis. (NE ISSN 0044-5002) **4211**

Zondervan Pastor's Annual. (US ISSN 0084-5558) **4211**
Zone (New York). (US ISSN 0887-0411) **2980**, 351, 2519, 2890
†Zone (Waverly). (US ISSN 0882-1658) **5309**
Zone Environmental Engineering in Ireland *see* Irish Heating and Ventilating News **2301**
Zone 3. (US ISSN 0888-000X) **3009**
Zoneterapi og Sundhed. (DK ISSN 0107-6663) **4116**
Zongheng. (CC) **2343**
Zongjiaoxue Yanjiu/Religion Research. (CC) **4211**
Zoning and Planning Law Report. (US ISSN 0161-8113) **2499**
Zoning Bulletin. (US ISSN 0514-7905) **2697**
Zoning Digest *see* Land Use Law and Zoning Digest **4151**
†Zoning Law Anthology. (US ISSN 0193-757X) **5309**
Zoning News. (US) **2499**, 309, 1972, 4159
Zonnekind. (BE ISSN 0772-7402) **1272**
Zonneland. (BE ISSN 0049-8750) **1272**
Zonnestraal. (BE ISSN 0772-9898) **1272**
Zontian. (US ISSN 0279-3229) **4858**
Zoo Antwerpen *see* Zoo Anvers **594**
Zoo Anvers. (BE ISSN 0044-5029) **594**, 1501
Zoo Biology. (US ISSN 0733-3188) **594**
Zoo Life. (US ISSN 1046-4565) **594**, 1501
Zoo Magazine (Edinburgh). (UK) **594**
Zoo - Nachrichten. (GW) **594**, 3535
Zoobooks. (US ISSN 0737-9005) **594**, 1272
Zooespresso. (IT) **594**
Der Zoofreund. (GW) **594**
ZooGoer. (US ISSN 0163-416X) **594**
Zoologia *see* Acta Biologica Paranaense **425**
Zoologia. (PL ISSN 0554-8136) **594**
Zoologica. (GW ISSN 0044-5088) **594**
Zoologica Baetica. (SP) **594**
Zoologica Poloniae. (PL ISSN 0044-510X) **594**
Zoologica Scripta. (UK ISSN 0300-3256) **594**
Zoological Parks & Aquariums in the Americas. (US) **594**
Zoological Proceedings. *see* Allattani Kozlemenyek **576**
Zoological Record. (US ISSN 0144-3607) **468**
Zoological Record. *see* Vestnik Zoologii **593**
Zoological Science. (JA ISSN 0289-0003) **594**
Zoological Society, Calcutta. Proceedings. (II ISSN 0373-5893) **594**
Zoological Society of India. Journal. (II ISSN 0049-8769) **594**
Zoological Society of London. Journal of Zoology. Series A *see* Journal of Zoology **586**
Zoological Society of London. Journal of Zoology. Series B *see* Journal of Zoology **586**
Zoological Society of London. Symposia.(US ISSN 0084-5612) **595**
Zoological Society of South Africa Newsletter *see* Aardvark **575**
Zoological Study. *see* Dongwuxue Yanjiu **581**
Zoological Survey of India. Bulletin. (II ISSN 0255-9587) **595**
Zoological Survey of India. Memoirs. (II ISSN 0379-3540) **595**
Zoological Survey of India. News. (II) **595**
Zoologicheskii Zhurnal. (RU ISSN 0044-5134) **595**
Zoologicka Zahrada v Praze. Vyrocni Zprava *see* Gazella. Annual Report and Scientific Articles **583**
Zoologisch - Botanische Gesellschaft, Vienna. Abhandlungen. (AU ISSN 0084-5639) **522**, 595

Zoologisch - Botanische Gesellschaft, Vienna. Verhandlungen. (AU ISSN 0084-5647) **522**, 595
Zoologische Beitraege. (GW ISSN 0044-5150) **595**
Der Zoologische Garten. (GW ISSN 0044-5169) **595**
Zoologische Jahrbuecher. Abteilung fuer Allgemeine Zoologie und Physiologie der Tiere. (GW ISSN 0044-5185) **595**, 575
Zoologische Jahrbuecher. Abteilung fuer Anatomie und Ontogenie der Tiere. (GW ISSN 0044-5177) **595**
Zoologische Jahrbuecher. Abteilung fuer Systematik, Oekologie und Geographie der Tiere. (GW ISSN 0044-5193) **595**
Zoologischen Staatssammlung Muenchen. Veroeffentlichungen. *see* Spixiana **592**
Zoologischer Anzeiger. (GW ISSN 0044-5231) **595**
Zoologisches Museum Hamburg. Entomologische Mitteilungen. (GW ISSN 0044-5223) **595**
†Zoology of Iceland. (DK ISSN 0084-5655) **5309**
Zoom (Italian Edition). (IT ISSN 0393-4330) **3798**
Zoom (U S Edition). (US) **3798**
Zooming In. (US) **3519**
Zoomorphology. (GW ISSN 0720-213X) **461**, 595
Zoonooz. (US ISSN 0044-5282) **595**
Zoophysiology. (US ISSN 0720-1842) **461**
Zoophysiology and Ecology *see* Zoophysiology **461**
Zoos and Aquariums in the Americas *see* Zoological Parks & Aquariums in the Americas **594**
Zoosletter. (US) **595**
Zootecnica e Nutrizione Animale. (IT ISSN 0390-0487) **229**
Zootekhniia. (RU) **229**
Zora Neale Hurston Forum. (US) **2980**
Zornicka. (CS) **1272**
Zouxiang Shijie. (CC ISSN 1001-2370) **4393**
▼Zov. (RU) **232**
Zpravy Ceskoslovenske Spolecnosti Archeologicke *see* Ceska Archeologicka Spolecnost. Zpravy **269**
Zpravy Geografickeho Ustavu CSAV *see* Ceskoslovenska Akademie Ved. Geograficky Ustav, Brno. Zpravy **2245**
Zrodla do Dziejow Bydgoszczy. (PL ISSN 0084-568X) **2396**
Zrodla Pamietnikarsko-Literackie do Dziejow Muzyki Polskiej. (PL) **3587**
Zshurnalist. (IS) **2577**, 2030, 3936
Zu Ji *see* Footprint **1311**
Zuanjing Ye yu Wanjing Ye. (CC ISSN 1001-5620) **3704**
Zuchtbuch fuer Deutsche Schaeferhunde. (GW) **3714**
Zuchthygiene *see* Reproduction in Domestic Animals **4815**
Zuchtwahl und Besamung. (GW) **229**
Zucker *see* Zuckerindustrie **2086**
Zucker- und Suesswaren Wirtschaft. (GW ISSN 0373-0204) **2090**
Zuckerindustrie. (GW ISSN 0344-8657) **2086**, 25
Die Zuckerruebe. (GW ISSN 0044-5398) **197**
Zuckerwirtschaft/Sugar Economy/ Economie Sucriere. (GW) **2084**
Zuckerwirtschaftliches Taschenbuch *see* Zuckerwirtschaft **2084**
Zuechter *see* Theoretical and Applied Genetics **547**
Zuechtungskunde. (GW ISSN 0044-5401) **229**
Zuercher Archaeologische Hefte. (SZ) **290**
Zuercher Boerse. Jahresbericht. (SZ) **970**
Zuerl's Adressbuch der Deutschen Luft- und Raumfahrt. (GW ISSN 0065-2024) **66**
Zugaku Kenkyu/Journal of Graphic Science of Japan. (JA ISSN 0387-5512) **351**, 3062, 4006
Zuhause. (GW) **2556**, 2562

Zuid - Afrika. (NE ISSN 0044-5428) **3936**, 2890
Zuidelijk Afrika Niews *see* Anti Apartheidskrant **2331**
Zuidhollands Landschap. (NE) **4354**
Zuivelkoerier. (NE) **204**
Zuivelnieuws. (NE ISSN 0044-5436) **204**
Zuivelzicht. (NE ISSN 0165-8573) **204**
Zukunft. (AU ISSN 0044-5452) **2890**
Zukunft. (US ISSN 0044-5460) **2890**, 2030
Zukunftsforschung. (SZ) **4393**, 2499
Zulassungsarbeit. (GW) **1673**
Zulieferer und Maschinenausruester von A - Z. (GW) **636**
Zulqarnain. (Il ISSN 0044-5479) **3936**
Zululand Chamber of Commerce and Industry. News. (SA) **825**
Zum Nachdenken. (GW ISSN 0044-5487) **3936**
Zum Thema. (GW) **4211**
Zum Weitergeben. (GW ISSN 0936-7136) **4253**
Zumaque. (VE) **3704**, 1861
Zumberacke Novine. (CI) **2030**, 2060, 2444
Zunzun. (CU) **2184**
Zuojia. (CC) **2980**
Zuopin. (CC ISSN 0494-1101) **2980**
Zuopin yu Zhengming. (CC) **2980**
Zuowen Chenggong zhi Lu/Ways to a Successful Composition. (CC ISSN 1001-571X) **1673**, 2980
Zuowu Pinzhong Ziyuan. (CC) **197**
Zuowu Xuebao/Acta Agronomica Sinica.(CC ISSN 0496-3490) **197**
Zuowu Zazhi. (CC ISSN 1001-7283) **131**
Zupfmusik Magazin. (GW ISSN 0176-0971) **3587**
Zuqiu Shijie/Football World. (CC ISSN 1000-3517) **4515**
Zur Debatte. (GW ISSN 0179-6658) **4279**, 3787
Zur Geschichte der Pharmazie *see* Geschichte der Pharmazie **3727**
Zur Lage der Schweiz. (SZ ISSN 0084-5809) **2396**
Zur Politik und Zeitgeschichte. (GW ISSN 0514-8294) **2327**, 3936
Zur Zeit. (GW ISSN 0342-6904) **4279**
Zusammen. (GW ISSN 0721-4626) **1272**
Zusammensetzung der Lebensmittel, Naehrwert Tabellen. *see* Food Composition and Nutrition Tables **3605**
Zusammenstellung Studieneinfuehrender Schriften. (GW) **1673**
Zuversicht und Staerke. (GW ISSN 0722-3234) **4253**
▼Zuzu Petal Quarterly. (US) **2980**
Zvaranie/Welding. (CS ISSN 0044-5525) **3431**
Zvezda. (YU) **841**
Zvezda. (RU ISSN 0039-7105) **2890**, 2980, 3009
Zvornik Radova Etnografskog Instituta *see* Srpska Akademija Nauka i Umetnosti. Etnografski Institut. Zbornik Radova **249**
Zvuk. (YU ISSN 0044-555X) **3587**
Zwart en Wit. (NE) **351**
Zwaanse-Rook Meetnet *see* Studie van de Luchtkwaliteit in Belgie. Zwavel-Rook Meetnet **4113**
Zweig Forecast. (US) **970**
Zweig Performance Ratings Report. (US) **970**
Zweites Deutsches Fernsehen Jahrbuch *see* Z D F Jahrbuch **1384**
Zweiwochen Dienst. (GW) **1688**
Zweiwochendienst Frauen und Politik. (GW) **4858**
Zwiazkowiec/Alliancer. (CN) **2030**
Zwiebel. (GW) **4139**
Zwischen Eider und Wiedau. (GW ISSN 0514-8413) **2060**, 2396
Zwischen Hausmannsturm und Walbecker Warte. (NE) **2397**
Zwischen Orient und Okzident. (GW ISSN 0934-6155) **2980**
Zwischen Vogelsberg und Spessart. (GW) **2192**

Zwischenschritte. (GW ISSN 0724-3766) **4051**, 1673, 3165, 4393
Zycie Gospodarcze. (PL) **701**, 131, 1972
Zycie i Mysl/Life and Thought. (PL ISSN 0044-5584) **3787**
Zycie i Zdrowie. (PL) **4116**
Zycie Literackie. (PL ISSN 0591-2369) **2890**
Zycie Szkoly. (PL ISSN 0137-7310) **1673**
†Zycie Szkoly Wyzszej. (PL ISSN 0591-2377) **5309**
Zydowski Instytut Historyczny w Polsce. Biuletyn. (PL ISSN 0006-4033) **2030**, 2397
Zygon. (US ISSN 0591-2385) **4211**
†Zygos (1982). (GR ISSN 0252-8150) **5309**
Zyma. (GW ISSN 0937-7549) **351**
†Zymergy. (CN ISSN 0835-0264) **5309**
Zymurgy. (US ISSN 0196-5921) **388**
Zywienie Czlowieka. (PL) **3613**
Zywienie Czlowieka *see* Zywienie Czlowieka **3613**
Zyzzyva. (US ISSN 8756-5633) **2980**, 351
Zzap. (GW) **1673**
01 - Informatique. (FR) **1453**
01 - Informatique Hebdo. (FR) **1453**
1 x 1 Ihr Partner. (GW) **131**, 3394
▼1,000 Worldwide Newspapers. (US ISSN 1052-5335) **417**
1 - 1 Journal. (US ISSN) **3588**
1 - 1 Quarterly *see* 1 - 1 Journal **3588**
▼1-2-3 for Macintosh Report. (US) **1481**
▼1-2-3 for Windows Report. (US) **1481**
1-2-3 User's Journal. (US ISSN 0891-5121) **1481**
2 A M Magazine. (US ISSN 0886-8743) **2985**
2 C Caravan Camping Camper *see* 2 C Plein Air **4560**
2 C Plein Air. (IT) **4560**, 4798
Les 2 Ecrans. (AE) **1384**
2 Hype. (US) **1272**
2 M B S - F M Stereo F M Radio Program Guide. (AT ISSN 0313-0797) **3588**
2 Trochi/2 Wheels. (GR ISSN 1105-1299) **4521**
2 Wheels. *see* 2 Trochi **4521**
2 x 4. (CN ISSN 0824-0868) **2119**
2D: Drama, Dance. (UK ISSN 0261-6939) **4642**, 1532
3 & 4 Wheel Action. (US) **4706**, 4521
†3-D Education. (UK ISSN 0943-612X) **5309**
3 D Film Gids *see* Catalogus Films en Video **3504**
3 L Llama Magazine *see* Llamas Magazine **587**
3 R - International. (GW) **3704**
3 Tech. (US) **1455**
†3 - Wheeling. (US ISSN 0196-5549) **5309**
3-2-1 Contact. (US) **1273**, 4354
3D. (UK) **1423**
3d World Magazine. (AT) **2173**
†3X - 400 Information Management. (US) **5309**
4 Taxis. (FR ISSN 0181-687X) **351**, 4798
4 times 4 Italia. (IT) **2207**
4 Trochi/4 Wheels. (GR ISSN 1105-1280) **4706**
4 Trochoi Test/4 Wheels Test. (GR ISSN 1105-1329) **4706**
4-W D Action *see* 4-W D Sport Utility **4706**
4-W D Sport Utility. (US) **4706**
4 Wheels. *see* 4 Trochi **4706**
4 Wheels Test. *see* 4 Trochoi Test **4706**
4-3 Fachzeitschrift zu Kriegsdienstverweigerung, Wehrdienst und Zivildienst. (GW) **3948**
4H-Journalen *see* Kloeverbladet **1258**
4H - Klubben. (NO ISSN 0800-6032) **1273**
▼4th Media Journal. (US) **40**
4x4. (UK ISSN 0267-4629) **4706**

5 AM. (US) 3010
†5 Great Romances. (US ISSN 0738-0941) 5309
7-Day Rate Update. (UK) 2545
7 Days see Changes (London, 1990) 3879
†7 Days. (US ISSN 1041-4355) 5309
7 Jours. (CN) 2180
7 Tage. (GW ISSN 0037-461X) 2192
7-1-71 Affair Catalog - Handbook. (US) 3759
7-1-71 Affair Newsletter. (US) 3759
†7th Angel. (US) 5309
8 Days see Radio & T V Times 1358
9 to 5 Newsletter. (US) 998, 4858
†9-1-1 Hotline to Contemporary Culture. (US) 5309
9-1-1 Magazine. (US) 2238
9-1-1 Reports see 9-1-1 Hotline to Contemporary Culture 5309
9N - 2N - 8N Newsletter. (US ISSN 0896-5641) 165, 260, 3025
†10. (CN ISSN 0828-1890) 5309
10 Best Censored Stories. (US) 2577
11 X 13 - Broadside. (US) 3010
11 - Zeitschrift fuer Internationale Fussball-Geschichte und -Statistik see Fussball-Weltzeitschrift 4504
11th Circuit Law Letter. (US ISSN 0892-7308) 2697
13th Moon. (US ISSN 0094-3320) 2980, 4858
The 13th Street Journal. (US) 351, 357, 1167, 3535
15 Dias en Costa Rica. (CR) 3936
15th and 16th Century Sculpture in Italy see Courtauld Institute Illustration Archives. Archive 2 323

16 de Abril. (CU ISSN 0257-7402) 3811
16 Magazine. (US ISSN 0270-899X) 1273
17. (GW) 4211, 1273
18 Karati Gold & Fashion. (IT) 2566
19. (UK ISSN 0262-1126) 4858
19th Century Music. (US ISSN 0148-2076) 3588
020 see Zeroventi 5309
20 Ans. (FR) 4858, 1295
20 de Mayo Spanish Newspaper. (US) 2030
20 Jahrhundert und der Frieden see Twentieth Century and Peace 3974
▼XX Siglos. (SP ISSN 1130-3948) 2327
20-20. (UK) 2196
20-20. (US ISSN 0192-1304) 3306
20 - 20. (CN) 4515
20-20 Europe. (US) 3306
20th Century. see Siglo XX 2960
20th Century Christian. (US ISSN 0162-6418) 4211
21st Century Christian see Alpha (New Malden) 4228
24 Hours. (AT) 1384
24 Hours. (US ISSN 1047-451X) 2238
24 Images. (CN ISSN 0707-9389) 3519
27 East. (US) 2238
27 rue Jacob. (FR) 2980
30 Millions d'Amis - La Vie des Betes. (FR) 595
32E Events. (US) 2592
33 Metal Producing. (US ISSN 0149-1210) 3424
35MM Photography see Photography 3795
39 - 45 Magazine. (FR) 3476, 2327
40 Minutes. (II) 1062
43rd Infantry Division Veterans Association. Bulletin. (US) 3476
48 Degrees North. (US) 4531
50 e Piu. (IT) 2280
50 Millions de Consommateurs. (FR ISSN 0339-1531) 1509
50 Plus see New Choices 2277
50 Plus. (CN) 2280
50 State Legislative Review. (US ISSN 0164-0356) 3936, 4078
64. (RU) 4497

64er. (GW) 1402
68 Micro Journal. (US ISSN 0194-5025) 1466, 1475
73 Amateur Radio Magazine see 73 Amateur Radio Today 1361
73 Amateur Radio Today. (US ISSN 1052-2522) 1361
80-User Digest see Northern Bytes 1463
84. (AG) 3936
90 see Social Practice 4387
100 Cose. (IT) 4858
100 European Banks see Leading European Banks 789
100 Highest Yields. (US ISSN 0885-4777) 804
100 Idees. (FR) 4858
100 Livelihood Occupations. (NP) 3631, 937
†100 Top Licensed Properties. (US) 5309
100A1. (UK ISSN 0266-8971) 4742
108 Review. (US) 351
112 - Magazin der Feuerwehr. (GW ISSN 0724-7443) 2035
128 News. (US) 701
132 Expres. (SP) 1087
200 Groupes Francais d'Afrique Noire. (FR) 4457
†225 - Portfolio. (US) 5309
356 Registry. (US) 4706, 2444
370 - 390 Data Base Management see Data Base Management 1444
401 (K) News. (US) 40
411 Newsletter. (US) 1368
500 Premiers Entreprises Publiques Algeriennes. (FR) 701
501(C)(3) Monthly Letter. (US ISSN 0897-5736) 4425
505 Great Britain. (UK) 4531
516 Magazine. (US) 2238
630 News. (US) 4678
750 Bulletin. (UK ISSN 0306-6312) 4706
800 & FAX Travel Directory. (US) 1160, 4798
976 Cities Plus. (US) 1057

1001 Decorating Ideas see Select Homes 306
†1001 Home Ideas. (US ISSN 0278-0844) 5309
1040 Preparation. (US) 1112
1066 Tidsskrift for Historisk Forskning.(DK ISSN 0106-0627) 2397, 3978
†1199 News. (US ISSN 0012-6535) 5309
1745 Association and National Military History Society. Quarterly Notes see Jacobete 2370
1766. (US) 1331
1814 Union News. (US) 2592
1860 Settler. (SA ISSN 0013-2578) 2890
1869 Times. (US ISSN 0363-6542) 3759
The 1992 M & A Monthly. (US ISSN 1044-2960) 701
1992 Single Market Communications Review. (UK ISSN 0955-9760) 1368, 1447
1992: The External Impact of European Unification see Eurowatch 3957
1999. (GW ISSN 0930-9977) 2890
†2000. (US) 5309
2000 A D. (UK) 1273
2000 Days Out in Britain. (UK) 4798
2000 Places to Visit in Britain see 2000 Days Out in Britain 4798
2001. (II) 2202
2029 Magazin. (GW) 3798, 351, 1295, 1532
2600. (US ISSN 0749-3851) 1424, 1346
3000 Largest Companies in Finland (Year). (FI ISSN 0786-5546) 1160
†3000 Punti. (IT) 5309
5001 Hard to Find Publishers. (UK) 4139
▼6100 Building Gift Market News. (US) 2283
6800er S T - Magazin see S T - Magazin 1419
8000 Plus. (UK) 1402